2025
LexisNexis®
Corporate Affiliations™

Content Operations:
Director-News & Business Content Operations & Metadata: Tammy Bair
Manager-Corporate Affiliations & Entity Management: Elizabeth A. Powers
Lead Content Analysts: Eric Eelman, Kevin Gaven

Production:
Senior Production Specialist: Joseph C. Stewart

Reed Elsevier Philippines-Corporate Affiliations Iloilo Team:
Operations Manager: Timothy J. Vilches
Operations Supervisor: Kristel Faye B. De la Cruz
Product Lead: Raquel G. Gajardo

2025

LexisNexis®
Corporate Affiliations™

Master Index
U.S. PUBLIC • U.S. PRIVATE • INTERNATIONAL

Volume I

QUESTIONS ABOUT THIS PUBLICATION?

For CONTENT questions concerning this publication, please call:
Content Operations Department at (800) 340-3244
FAX (908) 790-5405

For CUSTOMER SERVICE ASSISTANCE concerning shipments, billing or other matters, please call:
Customer Service at (800) 340-3244, press 3

For SALES ASSISTANCE, please call:
The Sales Department at (800) 340-3244, press 2

No part of this publication may be reproduced or transmitted in any form or by any means sorted in any information storage and retrieval system without prior written permission of LexisNexis, Content Operations, 9443 Springboro Pike, Miamisburg, OH 45342.

Library of Congress Catalog Card Number: 67-22770

Master Index Volume 1, ISBN: 979-8-3417-0459-6

Corporate Affiliations 8-Volume Library, ISBN: 979-8-3417-0458-9

©2025 LexisNexis Group.

All Rights Reserved

LexisNexis, the knowledge burst logo and Corporate Affiliations are trademarks of Reed Elsevier Properties Inc., used under license.

The LexisNexis Group has used its best efforts in collecting and preparing material for inclusion in *Corporate Affiliations*™ but does not assume, and hereby disclaims, any liability to any person for any loss or damage caused by errors or omissions in *Corporate Affiliations* whether such errors or omissions result from negligence, accident or any other cause.

Corporate Affiliations

Content Operations
9443 Springboro Pike
Miamisburg, OH 45342

www.lexisnexis.com

ISBN 979-8-3417-0459-6

9 798341 704596

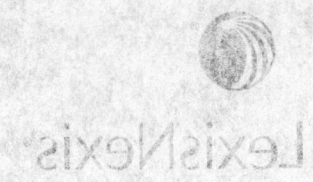

CONTENTS

Preface vii
How To Use *Corporate Affiliations* ix
Master Index of Company Names 1

CONTENTS

Preface vii
How To Use Corporate Affiliations ix
Master Index of Company Names 1

PREFACE

CORPORATE AFFILIATIONS

Corporate Affiliations is a logically organized business reference tool that covers major public and private businesses in the United States and throughout the world. The principle of organization for the set is geographical (by parent company) and hierarchical (by company reportage). Subsidiaries of a parent company, no matter where they are located, will be found in the same volume as the ultimate parent.

Entry criteria for the set are flexible. Generally speaking, domestic companies must demonstrate revenue in excess of $10 million, a work force in excess of 100 persons, or be traded on a major stock exchange. Non-U.S. based companies must demonstrate revenues in excess of $10 million.

SET ORGANIZATION AND CONTENT

A brief outline of the volumes and their components follows. Please note that every volume in the set, including this one, has a customized 'How-to-Use' guide for the benefit of the researcher. These include extensive listing and referencing examples that go into great detail.

Master Index, Volume I
Company Name Index

Master Index, Volume II
N.A.I.C.S. Index

U.S. Public Companies A-Z, Volume III
Public Company Listings

U.S. Private Companies A-J, Volume IV
Private Company Listings

U.S. Private Companies K-Z, Volume V
Private Company Listings

International Public and Private Companies A-F, Volume VI
International Company Listings

International Public and Private Companies G-O, Volume VII
International Company Listings

International Public and Private Companies P-Z, Volume VIII
International Company Listings

CUMULATIVE ENTRY STATISTICS FOR THIS EDITION

These statistics show the sum of entry listings across all the volumes. Individual statistics are provided in each volume.

Ultimate parent companies 133,466
U.S. located sub companies 186,355
Non-U.S. located sub companies 180,962
Total entry units listed **500,783**

Outside service firms: 70,337

COMPILATION

Corporate Affiliations is compiled and updated from information supplied by the companies themselves, business publications, internet research and annual reports.

RELATED SERVICES

For information on the corporateaffiliations.com web site, please call (800) 340-3244.

Mailing lists compiled from information contained in *Corporate Affiliations* may be ordered from:
R. Michael Patterson, Inside Sales Representative
DM2 Decision Maker
2000 Clearwater Drive, Oak Brook, IL
Tel: (630) 288-8348
E-mail: robert.patterson@dm2decisionmaker.com

Electronic database tapes of the directory in raw data format are available for licensing. For electronic database tapes or alliance opportunities, please contact:
LexisNexis, Corporate Affiliations
9443 Springboro Pike, Miamisburg, OH 45342
Tel: (800) 285-3947
E-mail: information@lexisnexis.com

Companies who wish to add or correct their listings can send information to:
LexisNexis, Corporate Affiliations Content Operations
9443 Springboro Pike
Miamisburg, OH 45342
Tel: (937) 865-6800

In addition to keeping the information in our directories as up to date as possible, we are constantly trying to improve their design and add useful new features. Any comments or suggestions in this regard can be directed to the Managers of Operations at the above address.

HOW TO USE
CORPORATE AFFILIATIONS

Corporate Affiliations contains useful information about firms whose ultimate parent companies, both public and private, are located in the United States and abroad. Entries include information on financials, personnel, outside service firms, and subsidiaries with an emphasis on hierarchy and reportage.

This user guide is divided into three parts:

Part A, 'How to Locate a Company' gives referencing instructions and samples of indexes. It demonstrates many useful methods for getting the information you need from this volume and from the *Corporate Affiliations* set at large.

Part B, 'Sample Entries' shows the various data elements and listing style of companies in *Corporate Affiliations*.

Part C, 'Understanding Levels of Reportage' demonstrates how company reportage structures are simply and clearly presented throughout *Corporate Affiliations*.

PART A: HOW TO LOCATE A COMPANY

1. **If you know the name of the company, but do not know its nationality or ownership status:**

    Look in the 'Master Index of Company Names' located in volume I. This index will direct you to the correct volume of the set (i.e. Public, Private or International) and the correct page listing therein.

    > **ALLING AND CORY COMPANY**; *U.S. Private*, pg. 37
    > ALLING-LANDER—See Regal-Beloit Corporation; *U.S. Public*, pg. 1429
    > ALLINSURE—See GIB Group; *Int'l*, pg. 511
    > **ALLIS-CHALMERS CORPORATION**; *U.S. Public*, pg. 58

2. **If you do know a parent company's nationality and ownership status:**

    You can turn directly to the company listings in the appropriate volume, all of which are alphabetized by the name of the parent company.

3. **If you know the name of a subsidiary or division:**

    You can turn to the 'Master Index of Company Names' located in volume I. The subsidiary entry will also show you the name of its ultimate parent and the volume and page of its listing.

    > JHK & ASSOCIATES, INC.—See Science Applications
    >   International Corp.; *U.S. Private*, pg. 986
    > JIB GROUP PLC—See Jardine Matheson Holdings Limited; *Int'l*, pg. 711

JII/SALES PROMOTION ASSOCIATES, INC.—See Jordan
Industries, Inc.; *U.S. Private*, pg. 604
JIT-STAL AB—See Rautaruukki Oy; *Int'l*, pg. 1036
JJC SPECIALIST CORP.—See The Quick & Reilly Group
Inc.; *U.S. Public*, pg. 1397

4. **If you cannot find the company's name in the indexes:**

   It may mean that the company has been acquired or changed its name. To confirm this, try looking in the 'Mergers and Acquisitions' section at the front of the appropriate volume.

   Sample of Mergers Section

   Friendly Ice Cream Corp.—acquired by Hershey Foods Corp.
   Frigitronics, Inc.—acquired by Revlon, Inc.
   Frontier Oil Corporation—acquired by Wainoco Oil Corporation
   Furr Cafeterias, Inc.—acquired by K Mart Corp.
   GAC Corp.—name changed to Avatar Holdings, Inc.

5. **To locate companies in a given line of business:**

   Use the 'N.A.I.C.S. (North American Industrial Classification System) Master Index' located in volume II. This index interfiles data from all six volumes of Corporate Affiliations, arranging companies by particular products and services according to their primary N.A.I.C.S. code. The index is preceded by two helpful compendia: one sorts the codes alphabetically by the name of the product or service, the other numerically by the code itself.

   Sample of Alpha Compendium of N.A.I.C.S. Codes

Description	N.A.I.C.S.
Administration of Conservation Programs	924120
Administration of Education Programs	923110

   Sample of Numeric Compendium of N.A.I.C.S. Codes

Code	Description
111150	Corn Farming
111160	Rice Farming
111191	Oilseed and Grain Combination Farming

Both parent and sub companies are covered in this index; parent companies are printed in bold type, sub companies in regular typeface, followed by the name of its ultimate parent. A samples of the N.A.I.C.S. Master Index is shown here:

337211 — WOOD OFFICE FURNITURE MANUFACTURING

ABCO—Jami, Inc.; *Int'l*, pg. 586
ANDERSON HICKEY, INC.—Haworth, Inc.; *U.S. Public*, pg. 516
BELVEDERE COMPANY—Smith Investment Company; *Int'l*, pg. 1019
BRAYTON INTERNATIONAL INC.—Steelcase Inc.; *U.S. Public*, pg. 1048
BRODART COMPANY; *U.S. Private*, pg. 172
COMMUNITY—Jasper Seating Co., Inc.; *U.S. Private*, pg. 589
CRAMER INC.; *U.S. Public*, pg. 288
EAC CORPORATION; *Int'l*, pg. 357

PART B: BASIC COMPONENTS OF A PUBLIC COMPANY LISTING

Following is an example of a typical parent company listing with tags to some of its basic components.

STANDARD MEDICAL GROUP ─────────── **Company Name**
560 River Rd ──────────────────── **Company Address**
Richmond, VA 23219
Tel: 804-223-3289   DE ──── **Telecommunications Data & State of Incorporation**
Fax: 804-555-8334
Web Site: www.smg.com ─────────── **Electronic Address**
Year Founded: 1967
SMG—(NYSE) ───────────────── **Ticker Symbol & Stock Exchange Data**
Rev.: $32,000,000 ──────────────── **Financial Data**
Assets: $48,000,000
Liabilities: $32,000,000
Net Worth: $16,000,000
Earnings: ($4,500,000)
Emp: 620 ──────────────────── **Number of Employees, Including Subsidiaries**
Fiscal Year End: 12/31/24
Research Technology; ─────────────── **Business Description**
Medical Products Mfr
N.A.I.C.S.: 325411 ──────────────── **North American Industry Classification Code**
John R. Callahan (*Chm*) ───────────── **Key Personnel**
Cynthia I. Jenkins (*Pres & CEO*)
William E. Kirkpatrick (*Exec VP*)
Albert N. Hackett (*VP-Res & Dev*)
Lawrence Woods (*VP-Sls*)

Following each parent company listing are the entries for each of that company's divisions, subsidiaries, affiliates, joint ventures, units etc. Though companies vary widely in their usage of these terms, some of the more common company designations can be defined as follows:

Affiliate	A chartered business owned by the company at less than 50%.
Division	An internal unit of a company, not incorporated.
Joint Venture	A business in which two or more companies share responsibility and ownership.
Subsidiary	A chartered business owned by the company at 50% or more.

PART C: UNDERSTANDING LEVELS OF REPORTAGE

Each sub-unit of the company will have a number in parentheses to the right of the company name. This number represents the level of reportage for that particular company. Any company with a level (1) reports directly to the parent company. Level (2) companies report to the level (1) company immediately above them. Level (3) companies report to the level (2) company immediately above them, etc.

Subsidiaries:

Brock Corporation   (1) ——————— **Reports to the Parent Company**
6060 Wall St   **(Standard Medical Group from**
Hartford, CT 06103   **previous example)**
Tel: 203-251-6526   (100%) ——————— **Percentage of Ownership**
Sales Range: $25-49.9 Million
Emp: 98
Pharmaceuticals Mfr
N.A.I.C.S.: 325412
J.M. McAleer *(Pres)*

Subsidiary:

Clark Technology   (2) ——————— **Reports to Level 1 Company Above**
601 Pulaski St   **(Brock Corporation)**
Jackson, MS 39215
Tel: 601-848-4626   (100%)
CT—(NYSE)
Sutures Mfr & Other Surgical Products
N.A.I.C.S.: 339113
Steven Colaccino *(Pres)*

Branch:

Clark Technology   (3) ——————— **Reports to Level 2 Company Above**
52 Main St   **(Clark Technology)**
Wayne, NJ 07435
Tel: 201-662-7654
Sutures Mfr
N.A.I.C.S.: 339113

Non-U.S. Subsidiary:

Merieux Pharmaceuticals   (1) ——————— **Subsidiary Not Located in the U.S.**
1421 rue Gourbet, 75755   **Reports to the Parent Company**
Paris, Cedex 15, France   **(Standard Medical Group)**
Tel: 42 73 10 08   (100%)
Rev.: $1,500,000
Emp: 118
Pharmaceuticals Mfr
N.A.I.C.S.: 325412
G. Bidaud *(Pres)*

Request For Additional Companies Not Now Listed

Corporate Affiliations
The LexisNexis Publishing Group
9443 Springboro Pike, Miamisburg, OH 45342
Tel: 937-865-6800

AS A CURRENT SUBSCRIBER to *Corporate Affiliations*, are there companies not currently listed in the directory that you would like to see included? If so, please fill out the following and return to the above address via mail or fax.

Please type or print all information and return completed form.

_____
Company or Institution Name

_____
Address

_____ _____ _____
City   State/ Country   Zip/ Postal Code

_____ _____
Phone   Fax

_____
Company or Institution Name

_____
Address

_____ _____ _____
City   State/ Country   Zip/ Postal Code

_____ _____
Phone   Fax

COMPANY NAME INDEX

0

000 ELME MESSER K—See Messer Group GmbH; *Int'l*, pg. 4842
000 WIDEX—See EQT AB; *Int'l*, pg. 2480
0014 PTY. LTD.—See Aware Super Pty Ltd; *Int'l*, pg. 752
0014 PTY. LTD.—See Macquarie Group Limited; *Int'l*, pg. 4629
010017 TELECOM GMBH—See 3U Holding AG; *Int'l*, pg. 10
010090 GMBH—See q.beyond AG; *Int'l*, pg. 6131
01024 TELEFONDIENSTE GMBH—See freenet AG; *Int'l*, pg. 2770
01050.COM GMBH—See freenet AG; *Int'l*, pg. 2770
01 COMMUNIQUE LABORATORY INC.; *Int'l*, pg. 1
024 PHARMA, INC.; *U.S. Private*, pg. 1
029 GROUP SE; *Int'l*, pg. 1
066 059 809 PTY LIMITED—See BSA Limited; *Int'l*, pg. 1201
0800 REVERSE LIMITED—See BBG Communications, Inc.; *U.S. Private*, pg. 498
0867893 B.C. LTD.—See ONEnergy Inc.; *Int'l*, pg. 5576
09WOMEN CO., LTD.; *Int'l*, pg. 1

1

1000 ISLAND RV CENTRE; *Int'l*, pg. 1
1000MERCIS S.A.; *Int'l*, pg. 1
1001 BRICKELL BAY DRIVE, LLC—See Apartment Investment and Management Company; *U.S. Public*, pg. 143
100 FEDERAL SUBSIDIARY REIT LLC—See Boston Properties, Inc.; *U.S. Public*, pg. 372
101013121 SASKATCHEWAN LTD; *Int'l*, pg. 1
101059035 SASKATCHEWAN LTD.; *Int'l*, pg. 1
101069101 SASKATCHEWAN LTD.—See Crown Investments Corporation of Saskatchewan; *Int'l*, pg. 1857
1010DATA, INC.—See Symphony Innovation, LLC; *U.S. Private*, pg. 3899
1010 PRINTING (UK) LIMITED—See Lion Rock Group Ltd; *Int'l*, pg. 4519
10/13 COMMUNICATIONS LLC; *U.S. Private*, pg. 2
10-15 ASSOCIATES, INC.—See TA Associates, Inc.; *U.S. Private*, pg. 3919
101 HUDSON LEASING ASSOCIATES—See Veris Residential, Inc.; *U.S. Public*, pg. 2281
101, INC.—See TEGNA Inc.; *U.S. Public*, pg. 1989
101 LIVESTOCK MARKET INC.; *U.S. Private*, pg. 2
101 MOBILITY, LLC; *U.S. Private*, pg. 2
101 PIPE & CASING INC.; *U.S. Private*, pg. 2
101 STUDIO LIMITED—See SUN HING VISION GROUP HOLDINGS LIMITED; *Int'l*, pg. 7304
101 VERMONT AUTO GROUP, LLC; *U.S. Private*, pg. 2
101 VERTICAL FABRICATION, INC.—See 101 Pipe & Casing Inc.; *U.S. Private*, pg. 2
101 VERTICAL FABRICATION INC.—See 101 Pipe & Casing Inc.; *U.S. Private*, pg. 2
101 VERTICAL FABRICATION, MANUFACTURING FACILITY—See 101 Pipe & Casing Inc.; *U.S. Private*, pg. 2
101WAREHOUSE PTY. LTD.—See Silk Logistics Holdings Limited; *Int'l*, pg. 6921
10-20 SERVICES INC.—See Mission Ready Solutions Inc.; *Int'l*, pg. 4921
102.4 WISH FM LIMITED—See News Corporation; *U.S. Public*, pg. 1520
1026128 ALBERTA LTD—See ITT Inc.; *U.S. Public*, pg. 1177
1028918 ONTARIO INC; *Int'l*, pg. 1
1031 SOLUTIONS, LLC—See First American Financial Corporation; *U.S. Public*, pg. 835
1035312 ONTARIO LIMITED; *Int'l*, pg. 1
1042735 ONTARIO INC; *Int'l*, pg. 1
104.6 RTL—See Bertelsmann SE & Co. KGaA; *Int'l*, pg. 993

104 CORPORATION; *Int'l*, pg. 1
1053038 ONTARIO LIMITED—See AutoCanada Inc.; *Int'l*, pg. 726
1053038 ONTARIO LIMITED; *Int'l*, pg. 1
1060038 ONTARIO LTD; *Int'l*, pg. 1
1075 PEACHTREE, LLC—See MetLife, Inc.; *U.S. Public*, pg. 1429
1091 MEDIA—See JDS Capital Management, Inc.; *U.S. Private*, pg. 2196
1092072 ONTARIO INC; *Int'l*, pg. 1
1099 PRO, INC.—See HgCapital Trust plc; *Int'l*, pg. 3377
10 DAY PARTS, INC.—See BlackBern Partners LLC; *U.S. Private*, pg. 573
10 DAY PARTS, INC.—See Lee Equity Partners LLC; *U.S. Private*, pg. 2412
10G LLC—See Caterpillar, Inc.; *U.S. Public*, pg. 449
THE 10 GROUP LIMITED—See Cromwell Property Group; *Int'l*, pg. 1854
10PEARLS LLC; *U.S. Private*, pg. 2
10STAR CINEMAS SDN. BHD.—See MAA Group Berhad; *Int'l*, pg. 4618
10TH MAGNITUDE INC.—See Pamlico Capital Management, L.P.; *U.S. Private*, pg. 3083
10X CAPITAL VENTURE ACQUISITION CORP. III; *U.S. Public*, pg. 1
10X CAPITAL VENTURE ACQUISITION CORP. II; *U.S. Public*, pg. 1
10X CAPITAL VENTURE ACQUISITION CORP.; *U.S. Public*, pg. 1
10X GENOMICS, INC.; *U.S. Public*, pg. 1
10X INNOVATION GMBH & CO. KG—See Melitta Unternehmensgruppe Bentz KG; *Int'l*, pg. 4810
1100 HOLDINGS LLC; *U.S. Private*, pg. 2
1101489 ONTARIO LTD; *Int'l*, pg. 2
1104816 ONTARIO LIMITED—See Custom Truck One Source, Inc.; *U.S. Public*, pg. 612
1105 MEDIA GOVERNMENT INFORMATION GROUP—See Alta Communications, Inc.; *U.S. Private*, pg. 203
1105 MEDIA GOVERNMENT INFORMATION GROUP—See Nautic Partners, LLC; *U.S. Private*, pg. 2868
1105 MEDIA, INC.—See Alta Communications, Inc.; *U.S. Private*, pg. 203
1105 MEDIA, INC.—See Nautic Partners, LLC; *U.S. Private*, pg. 2868
110 CONSULTING; *U.S. Private*, pg. 2
111, INC.; *Int'l*, pg. 2
11:24 DESIGN ADVERTISING, INC.; *U.S. Private*, pg. 2
1.12 ACQUISITION CORP.; *U.S. Public*, pg. 1
1133571 ALBERTA LTD; *Int'l*, pg. 2
11336 NEWFOUNDLAND INC; *Int'l*, pg. 2
11400, INC.—See Clark Associates, Inc.; *U.S. Private*, pg. 912
1166709 ONTARIO INC; *Int'l*, pg. 2
1170880 ONTARIO LIMITED; *Int'l*, pg. 2
1185 DESIGN; *U.S. Private*, pg. 2
11880 INTERNET SERVICES AG—See united vertical media GmbH; *Int'l*, pg. 8073
11880 SOLUTIONS AG—See united vertical media GmbH; *Int'l*, pg. 8073
118 HOLDINGS INC.—See Cosco Capital, Inc.; *Int'l*, pg. 1809
1191557 ONTARIO CORP.—See Thunder Gold Corp.; *Int'l*, pg. 7722
1&1 AG—See United Internet AG; *Int'l*, pg. 8068
11 BIT STUDIOS SA; *Int'l*, pg. 1
11 EAST 68TH STREET LLC—See Vornado Realty Trust; *U.S. Public*, pg. 2309
11 FREUNDE VERLAG GMBH & CO. KG—See Bertelsmann SE & Co. KGaA; *Int'l*, pg. 993
1&1 INTERNET DEVELOPMENT SRL—See United Internet AG; *Int'l*, pg. 8068
1&1 INTERNET LTD—See United Internet AG; *Int'l*, pg. 8069

1&1 INTERNET (PHILIPPINES) INC.—See United Internet AG; *Int'l*, pg. 8068
1&1 INTERNET SARL—See United Internet AG; *Int'l*, pg. 8069
1&1 INTERNET SE—See United Internet AG; *Int'l*, pg. 8068
1&1 IONOS CLOUD INC.—See United Internet AG; *Int'l*, pg. 8069
1&1 MAIL & MEDIA GMBH—See United Internet AG; *Int'l*, pg. 8069
11. MART A.D.; *Int'l*, pg. 1
11 PLC—See NIPCO Plc; *Int'l*, pg. 5309
11STREET CO., LTD.—See SK Telecom Co., Ltd.; *Int'l*, pg. 6975
1&1 TELECOMMUNICATION SE—See United Internet AG; *Int'l*, pg. 8068
11TH HOUR BUSINESS CENTERS, LLC; *U.S. Private*, pg. 2
1&1 VERSATEL GMBH—See United Internet AG; *Int'l*, pg. 8069
1200 BROADWAY, LLC—See UDR, Inc.; *U.S. Public*, pg. 2218
1201 LOUISIANA CO. L.P.—See Brookfield Corporation; *Int'l*, pg. 1186
1211863 ONTARIO INC.; *Int'l*, pg. 2
12 & 12, INC.—See Grand Lake Mental Health Center, Inc.; *U.S. Private*, pg. 1753
121 FINANCIAL CREDIT UNION—See VyStar Credit Union; *U.S. Private*, pg. 4417
121 FINANCIAL CREDIT UNION; *U.S. Private*, pg. 2
121 INFLIGHT CATERING LLC—See The Emirates Group; *Int'l*, pg. 7639
1220 EXHIBITS, INC.; *U.S. Private*, pg. 2
123DENTIST, INC.—See Peloton Capital Management, Inc.; *Int'l*, pg. 5783
123ERFASST.DE GMBH—See Nemetschek SE; *Int'l*, pg. 5193
123 EXTERIORS, INC.; *U.S. Private*, pg. 2
123 FAHRSCHULE RHEIN-SIEG GMBH—See 123fahrschule SE; *Int'l*, pg. 2
123FAHRSCHULE SE; *Int'l*, pg. 2
123GREETINGS.COM, INC.—See IntraSoft Technologies Limited; *Int'l*, pg. 3769
123 HOME CARE SERVICES, LLC; *U.S. Private*, pg. 2
123 MISSION LLC—See Sumitomo Corporation; *Int'l*, pg. 7273
123 MONEY LIMITED—See Intact Financial Corporation; *Int'l*, pg. 3726
123 MONEY LIMITED—See Tryg A/S; *Int'l*, pg. 7946
123PRINT, INC.—See Taylor Corporation; *U.S. Private*, pg. 3938
123-REG LIMITED—See KKR & Co. Inc.; *U.S. Public*, pg. 1252
123-REG LIMITED—See Silver Lake Group, LLC; *U.S. Private*, pg. 3657
123-REG LIMITED—See TCMI, Inc.; *U.S. Private*, pg. 3943
1249270 ONTARIO INC; *Int'l*, pg. 2
1260261 ONTARIO INC; *Int'l*, pg. 2
1283465 ONTARIO INC.—See Swisher Hygiene Inc.; *U.S. Private*, pg. 3894
128 AUTO GROUP; *U.S. Private*, pg. 2
128 FORD, INC.; *U.S. Private*, pg. 3
12902 SOUTH 301 HIGHWAY, LLC—See CubeSmart; *U.S. Public*, pg. 603
129157 CANADA INC; *Int'l*, pg. 2
1295908 B.C. LTD.; *Int'l*, pg. 2
12 INTERACTIVE, LLC; *U.S. Private*, pg. 2
12 POINTS CONSULTING CORP.—See Renodis, Inc.; *U.S. Private*, pg. 3399
12 RETECH CORPORATION; *U.S. Public*, pg. 1
12 YARD PRODUCTIONS LIMITED—See ITV plc; *Int'l*, pg. 3844
1300 HOME LOAN HOLDINGS PTY LTD—See BNK Banking Corporation Limited; *Int'l*, pg. 1079

12 RETECH CORPORATION — CORPORATE AFFILIATIONS

Company Index

1300 SMILES LIMITED—See BGH Capital Pty Ltd; *Int'l*, pg. 1007
1300 SMILES LIMITED—See Ontario Teachers' Pension Plan; *Int'l*, pg. 5585
1300 SMILES LIMITED; *Int'l*, pg. 2
1306043 B.C. LTD.—See Torr Metals Inc.; *Int'l*, pg. 7830
131448 CANADA INC; *Int'l*, pg. 2
1315 CAPITAL LLC; *U.S. Private*, pg. 3
1323785 ALBERTA LTD.—See First Canadian Management Corporation; *Int'l*, pg. 2682
1325 AVENUE OF THE AMERICAS, L.P.—See Paramount Group Inc.; *U.S. Public*, pg. 1637
1369 CONSTRUCTION JOINT STOCK COMPANY; *Int'l*, pg. 2
138 STUDENT LIVING JAMAICA LIMITED; *Int'l*, pg. 2
1399 INTERNET TECHNOLOGY APPLICATION GROUP, INC.; *Int'l*, pg. 2
139 ENTERPRISES LIMITED—See Central Wealth Group Holdings Limited; *Int'l*, pg. 1410
13CABS INNOVATIONS PTY. LTD.—See ComfortDelGro Corporation Limited; *Int'l*, pg. 1712
13I CAPITAL CORPORATION; *U.S. Private*, pg. 3
13TEN LIMITED—See Citipost Group; *Int'l*, pg. 1622
13TH & MARKET PROPERTIES LLC—See UDR, Inc.; *U.S. Public*, pg. 2218
140 BBDO—See Omnicom Group Inc.; *U.S. Public*, pg. 1573
1414 DEGREES LIMITED; *Int'l*, pg. 2
141 CAPITAL, INC.; *U.S. Public*, pg. 2
142258 CANADA INC; *Int'l*, pg. 2
147766 CANADA INC; *Int'l*, pg. 2
14FORTY LIMITED—See Compass Group PLC; *Int'l*, pg. 1750
1500 ROCKVILLE PIKE LLC—See Saul Centers, Inc.; *U.S. Public*, pg. 1842
1501 BROADWAY RESTAURANT CORP.—See TPG Capital, L.P.; *U.S. Public*, pg. 2167
1507953 ONTARIO INC.; *Int'l*, pg. 2
150 MAIN STREET, L.L.C.—See Veris Residential, Inc.; *U.S. Public*, pg. 2281
1512804 ONTARIO INC; *Int'l*, pg. 2
151 PRODUCTS LTD.; *Int'l*, pg. 2
1520 GROUP OF COMPANIES; *Int'l*, pg. 2
1520 SIGNAL LTD.—See 1520 Group of Companies; *Int'l*, pg. 2
15384150 CANADA INC.—See BBTV Holdings Inc.; *Int'l*, pg. 921
154TH STREET MEDICAL PLAZA, INC.—See Humana, Inc.; *U.S. Public*, pg. 1069
159 SOLUTIONS, INC.—See IQVIA Holdings Inc.; *U.S. Public*, pg. 1168
15 EDISON ROAD, LLC—See Welltower Inc.; *U.S. Public*, pg. 2347
15SQUARED LIMITED—See Inflexion Private Equity Partners LLP; *Int'l*, pg. 3689
1600 SMITH CO. LLC—See Brookfield Corporation; *Int'l*, pg. 1186
1611 SUMMIT, INC.—See Apax Partners LLP; *Int'l*, pg. 505
1620 CENTRAL LLC—See Highlands REIT, Inc.; *U.S. Private*, pg. 1940
166606 CANADA INC; *Int'l*, pg. 2
16TH STREET PARTNERS, LLC—See Starwood Property Trust, Inc.; *U.S. Public*, pg. 1939
17402 HIDDEN VALLEY LLC—See Vail Resorts, Inc.; *U.S. Public*, pg. 2271
1740 BROADWAY ASSOCIATES L.P.—See Vornado Realty Trust; *U.S. Public*, pg. 2310
174 POWER GLOBAL CORPORATION—See Hanwha Group; *Int'l*, pg. 3264
1798, LLC—See Knox Lane LP; *U.S. Private*, pg. 2324
17 EDUCATION & TECHNOLOGY GROUP INC.; *Int'l*, pg. 2
17 JUIN MEDIA SA—See Television Francaise 1 S.A.; *Int'l*, pg. 7542
17LIVE GROUP LIMITED; *Int'l*, pg. 3
17TH STREET ALD MANAGEMENT CORP.—See Force-Field Energy Inc.; *U.S. Public*, pg. 1563
1-800 CONTACTS, INC.—See AEA Investors LP; *U.S. Private*, pg. 113
1800ENDOSCOPE.COM, LLC; *U.S. Private*, pg. 3
1-800-FLOWERS.COM FRANCHISE CO., INC.—See 1-800-FLOWERS.COM, Inc.; *U.S. Public*, pg. 1
1-800-FLOWERS.COM, INC.; *U.S. Public*, pg. 1
1-800-FLOWERS RETAIL, INC.—See 1-800-FLOWERS.COM, Inc.; *U.S. Public*, pg. 1
1-800-FLOWERS TEAM SERVICES, INC.—See 1-800-FLOWERS.COM, Inc.; *U.S. Public*, pg. 1
1-800 NY BULBS, LIMITED—See Tarsier Ltd.; *U.S. Public*, pg. 1982
1-800-PACK-RAT, LLC; *U.S. Private*, pg. 1
1-800-PACK-RAT, LLC—See Waste Management, Inc.; *U.S. Public*, pg. 2330
1-800-RADIATOR & A/C—See Roark Capital Group Inc.; *U.S. Private*, pg. 3454
1.800.VENDING, INC.; *U.S. Public*, pg. 2
1-800 WE ANSWER, INC.; *U.S. Private*, pg. 1
180/AMSTERDAM; *Int'l*, pg. 3
180 DEGREE CAPITAL CORP.; *U.S. Public*, pg. 2
180 LIFE SCIENCES CORP.; *U.S. Public*, pg. 2

180 LOS ANGELES—See 180/Amsterdam; *Int'l*, pg. 3
180 MEDICAL, INC.—See Avista Capital Partners, L.P.; *U.S. Private*, pg. 408
180 MEDICAL, INC.—See Nordic Capital AB; *Int'l*, pg. 5420
180S, LLC; *U.S. Private*, pg. 3
1812 BREWING COMPANY, INC.; *U.S. Public*, pg. 2
1822 CORPUS IMMOBILIEN-VERMITTLUNG GMBH—See Frankfurter Sparkasse; *Int'l*, pg. 2761
1822DIREKT GESELLSCHAFT DER FRANKFURTER SPARKASSE MBH—See Helaba Landesbank Hessen-Thuringen; *Int'l*, pg. 3327
1822 DIREKT—See Frankfurter Sparkasse; *Int'l*, pg. 2761
1832 ASSET MANAGEMENT L.P.—See The Bank of Nova Scotia; *Int'l*, pg. 7616
1834 INVESTMENT ADVISORS CO.—See Old National Bancorp; *U.S. Public*, pg. 1566
1834 INVESTMENTS LIMITED; *Int'l*, pg. 3
1844 RESOURCES INC.; *Int'l*, pg. 3
1847 HOLDINGS LLC; *U.S. Public*, pg. 2
1855 CAPITAL PARTNERS, LLC; *U.S. Private*, pg. 3
1859 HISTORIC HOTELS, LTD.—See Gal-Tex Hotel Corporation; *U.S. Private*, pg. 1635
1864 BANCORP, INC; *U.S. Private*, pg. 3
1867 WESTERN FINANCIAL CORPORATION; *U.S. Public*, pg. 2
1871—See Chicagoland Entrepreneurial Center; *U.S. Private*, pg. 879
1880 BANK—See Delmarva Bancshares, Inc.; *U.S. Private*, pg. 1197
1880 NUMMEROPPLYSNING AS—See Eniro Group AB; *Int'l*, pg. 2439
1888 MILLS, LLC - DISTRIBUTION FACILITY—See 1888 Mills, LLC; *U.S. Private*, pg. 3
1888 MILLS, LLC - GRIFFIN MILL—See 1888 Mills, LLC; *U.S. Private*, pg. 3
1888 MILLS, LLC; *U.S. Private*, pg. 3
1-888-OHIOCOMP, INC.; *U.S. Private*, pg. 1
1895 BANCORP OF WISCONSIN, INC.; *U.S. Public*, pg. 2
1897 SERVICES CORPORATION—See BNP Paribas SA; *Int'l*, pg. 1087
18 FEET & RISING LIMITED; *Int'l*, pg. 3
18 MONTROSE RETAIL LIMITED—See Frasers Group plc; *Int'l*, pg. 2765
18TH PLACE HEALTH HOLDINGS LLC—See CareTrust REIT, Inc.; *U.S. Public*, pg. 435
1901 GROUP, LLC—See Leidos Holdings, Inc.; *U.S. Public*, pg. 1304
1901 PARTNERS MANAGEMENT, LP; *U.S. Private*, pg. 3
1911 GOLD CORPORATION; *Int'l*, pg. 3
1919 INVESTMENT COUNSEL, LLC—See Stifel Financial Corp.; *U.S. Public*, pg. 1949
1933 INDUSTRIES INC.; *Int'l*, pg. 3
1957 & CO. (HOSPITALITY) LIMITED; *Int'l*, pg. 3
19 ENTERTAINMENT LIMITED—See Apollo Global Management, Inc.; *U.S. Public*, pg. 148
1 ALLIANCE GEOMATICS, LLC—See GI Manager L.P.; *U.S. Private*, pg. 1691
1 A PHARMA GMBH—See Novartis AG; *Int'l*, pg. 5455
1API GMBH—See Team Internet Group plc; *Int'l*, pg. 7500
1BG LLC; *U.S. Private*, pg. 3
1-CALL STAFFING LLC; *U.S. Private*, pg. 1
1CM INC.; *Int'l*, pg. 3
#1 COCHRAN, INC.; *U.S. Private*, pg. 1
1 DIAMOND, LLC—See Quanta Services, Inc.; *U.S. Public*, pg. 1750
1FORM ONLINE PTY LTD—See News Corporation; *U.S. Public*, pg. 1518
1. K+S VERWALTUNGS GMBH & CO. ERWERBS KG—See K+S Aktiengesellschaft; *Int'l*, pg. 4039
1. K+S VERWALTUNGS GMBH—See K+S Aktiengesellschaft; *Int'l*, pg. 4039
1LIFE HEALTHCARE, INC.—See Amazon.com, Inc.; *U.S. Public*, pg. 90
1LIFE HEALTHCARE, INC.; *U.S. Public*, pg. 2
1LINK TECHNOLOGY, LLC; *U.S. Private*, pg. 3
1NKEMIA IUCT GROUP, S.A.; *Int'l*, pg. 3
1 ON 1 PHYSICAL THERAPY, LLC—See U.S. Physical Therapy, Inc.; *U.S. Public*, pg. 2213
1PM INDUSTRIES, INC.; *U.S. Public*, pg. 3
1PM PLC; *Int'l*, pg. 3
1 PRIORITY ENVIRONMENTAL SERVICES, LLC—See Earth Services & Abatement, Inc.; *U.S. Private*, pg. 1314
1SHARPE ACQUISITION CORP.; *U.S. Private*, pg. 3
1 SOURCE BUSINESS SOLUTIONS, LLC—See PCF Insurance Services of The West, LLC; *U.S. Private*, pg. 3120
1 SOURCE CONSULTING, INC.; *U.S. Private*, pg. 1
1SPATIAL AUSTRALIA PTY LIMITED—See 1Spatial Plc; *Int'l*, pg. 3
1SPATIAL FRANCE SAS—See 1Spatial Plc; *Int'l*, pg. 3
1SPATIAL GROUP LIMITED—See 1Spatial Plc; *Int'l*, pg. 3
1SPATIAL HOLDINGS LIMITED—See 1Spatial Plc; *Int'l*, pg. 3
1SPATIAL INC.—See 1Spatial Plc; *Int'l*, pg. 3
1SPATIAL PLC; *Int'l*, pg. 3
1ST AMERICAN CARD SERVICE; *U.S. Private*, pg. 3

1ST AMERICAN SYSTEMS AND SERVICES, LLC; *U.S. Private*, pg. 3
1ST AMERICAN SYSTEMS AND SERVICES—See 1st American Systems And Services, LLC; *U.S. Private*, pg. 3
1ST AVENUE PHARMACY, INC.—See UnitedHealth Group Incorporated; *U.S. Public*, pg. 2238
1ST BANK—See Glacier Bancorp, Inc.; *U.S. Public*, pg. 938
1ST CAPITAL BANK; *U.S. Private*, pg. 3
1ST CENTURY BANK—See Midland Financial Co.; *U.S. Private*, pg. 2715
1ST CHOICE AEROSPACE, INC.—See VSE Corporation; *U.S. Public*, pg. 2312
1ST CHOICE FACILITIES SERVICES CORP.; *U.S. Private*, pg. 4
1ST CHOICE PROPERTY MANAGEMENT & DEVELOPMENT COMPANY, LLC—See 1st Choice Facilities Services Corp.; *U.S. Private*, pg. 4
1ST CLASS PACKAGING LTD—See Sequana SA; *Int'l*, pg. 6719
1ST CLASS REAL ESTATE LLC; *U.S. Private*, pg. 4
1ST COLONIAL COMMUNITY BANK; *U.S. Public*, pg. 2
1ST CONSTITUTION BANCORP—See Provident Financial Services, Inc.; *U.S. Public*, pg. 1730
1ST CONSTITUTION BANCORP; *U.S. Public*, pg. 2
1ST CONSTITUTION BANK—See Provident Financial Services, Inc.; *U.S. Public*, pg. 1730
1ST C.O.R.P. SERVICES; *U.S. Private*, pg. 3
1ST DETECT CORPORATION—See Astrotech Corporation; *U.S. Public*, pg. 218
1STDIBS.COM, INC.; *U.S. Public*, pg. 3
1ST FARM CREDIT SERVICES, ACA; *U.S. Private*, pg. 4
1ST FEDERAL SAVINGS BANK OF SC, INC.; *U.S. Private*, pg. 4
1ST FINANCIAL BANK USA; *U.S. Private*, pg. 4
1ST FRANKLIN FINANCIAL CORPORATION; *U.S. Private*, pg. 4
1ST & FRESH, LLC—See Aramark; *U.S. Public*, pg. 176
1ST GROUP LIMITED; *Int'l*, pg. 3
1ST GUARD CORPORATION—See Biglari Holdings Inc.; *U.S. Public*, pg. 331
1ST INSULATION PARTNERS LIMITED—See Carillion plc; *Int'l*, pg. 1330
1ST INTERACTIVE DESIGN LIMITED—See RB Global, Inc.; *Int'l*, pg. 6226
1ST IN VIDEO-MUSIC WORLD, INC.; *U.S. Private*, pg. 4
1ST KNIGHT REALTY, LLC; *U.S. Private*, pg. 4
1ST MERCHANT FUNDING, LLC; *U.S. Private*, pg. 4
1ST MIDAMERICA CREDIT UNION; *U.S. Private*, pg. 4
1ST NORTHERN CALIFORNIA CREDIT UNION; *U.S. Private*, pg. 4
1ST NRG CORP.; *U.S. Public*, pg. 2
1-STOP TRANSLATION USA, LLC.; *U.S. Private*, pg. 1
1ST RED AG; *Int'l*, pg. 3
1ST RESOURCE CREDIT UNION—See Legacy Community Federal Credit Union; *U.S. Private*, pg. 2416
1ST SECURITY BANK OF WASHINGTON—See FS Bancorp, Inc.; *U.S. Public*, pg. 888
1ST SOURCE BANK—See 1st Source Corporation; *U.S. Public*, pg. 2
1ST SOURCE CAPITAL CORPORATION—See 1st Source Corporation; *U.S. Public*, pg. 3
1ST SOURCE CORPORATION INVESTMENT ADVISORS, INC.—See 1st Source Corporation; *U.S. Public*, pg. 3
1ST SOURCE CORPORATION; *U.S. Public*, pg. 2
1ST SOURCE INSURANCE, INC.—See 1st Source Corporation; *U.S. Public*, pg. 3
1ST SOURCE LEASING, INC.—See 1st Source Corporation; *U.S. Public*, pg. 3
1ST SOURCE SERVALL INC.; *U.S. Private*, pg. 4
1ST STOP INC.; *U.S. Private*, pg. 4
1ST SUMMIT BANCORP JOHNSTOWN, INC.; *U.S. Public*, pg. 3
1ST SUMMIT BANK—See 1st Summit Bancorp Johnstown, Inc.; *U.S. Public*, pg. 3
1SUMMIT GLOBAL PTE LTD—See Wong Fong Industries Limited; *Int'l*, pg. 8447
1SYNC INC.; *U.S. Private*, pg. 4
1TOUCH MARKETING; *U.S. Private*, pg. 4
1WORLDSYNC, INC.—See Battery Ventures, L.P.; *U.S. Private*, pg. 488

2

2000 SOFT INC.—See QXO, Inc.; *U.S. Public*, pg. 1758
2001 SIXTH LLC—See Digital Realty Trust, Inc.; *U.S. Public*, pg. 663
2002 PERLINDUSTRIA, S.L.U.—See RPM International Inc.; *U.S. Public*, pg. 1816
2008788 ONTARIO LTD.—See Martinrea International, Inc.; *Int'l*, pg. 4704
200 EAST 87TH STREET COMPANY, LLC—See Equitable Holdings, Inc.; *U.S. Public*, pg. 788
2020 BULKERS LTD.; *Int'l*, pg. 4
2020 EXHIBITS, INC.; *U.S. Private*, pg. 5
2020 EXHIBITS, INC.; *U.S. Private*, pg. 5
20/20 FORESIGHT EXECUTIVE SEARCH LLC; *U.S. Private*, pg. 4

COMPANY NAME INDEX 2X1 HOLDING CAPE MIDIA SHIPYARD

Company Index

20/20 GLOBAL, INC.; *U.S. Public*, pg. 3
20.20 LIMITED—See Writtle Holdings Limited; *Int'l*, pg. 8495
2020 LIVERPOOL LIMITED—See Kier Group plc; *Int'l*, pg. 4159
20:20 MSL—See Publicis Groupe S.A.; *Int'l*, pg. 6102
20:20 MSL—See Publicis Groupe S.A.; *Int'l*, pg. 6102
20:20 MSL—See Publicis Groupe S.A.; *Int'l*, pg. 6102
20:20 MSL—See Publicis Groupe S.A.; *Int'l*, pg. 6102
20:20 MSL—See Publicis Groupe S.A.; *Int'l*, pg. 6102
20 20 OPTICS PVT LTD—See EssilorLuxottica SA; *Int'l*, pg. 2512
20/20 RESEARCH INC.—See Schlesinger Group; *U.S. Private*, pg. 3565
20230930-DK-BUTTERFLY-1, INC.; *U.S. Private*, pg. 5
2029861 ONTARIO LTD.—See Skyline International Development Inc.; *Int'l*, pg. 6994
206INC.; *U.S. Private*, pg. 5
209 ENTERPRISES—See Haines & Kibblehouse Inc.; *U.S. Private*, pg. 1840
20 LAMBOURNE LLC—See UDR, Inc.; *U.S. Public*, pg. 2218
20 MCC PRIVATE LIMITED—See 20 Microns Limited; *Int'l*, pg. 4
20 MICRONS LIMITED; *Int'l*, pg. 3
20 MICRONS NANO MINERALS LTD—See 20 Microns Limited; *Int'l*, pg. 4
20 MINUTEN AG—See TX Group AG; *Int'l*, pg. 7991
20 MINUTES SA—See TX Group AG; *Int'l*, pg. 7991
20 MINUTOS ESPANA S.L.—See Henneo Media, SA; *Int'l*, pg. 3354
THE 20 MSP GROUP LLC; *U.S. Private*, pg. 3980
20 PINE STREET LLC—See Africa Israel Investments Ltd.; *Int'l*, pg. 189
20 VIC MANAGEMENT INC.; *Int'l*, pg. 4
2100 XENON GROUP LLC—See Callodine Acquisition Corporation; *U.S. Public*, pg. 424
2-10 HOME BUYERS WARRANTY CORP.; *U.S. Private*, pg. 4
215 HOLDING CO.; *U.S. Private*, pg. 5
21 CENTRALE PARTNERS SA—See 21 Investimenti Societa' di Gestione del Risparmio S.p.A.; *Int'l*, pg. 4
21 CLUB INC.—See LVMH Moet Hennessy Louis Vuitton SE; *Int'l*, pg. 4591
21C MUSEUM HOTELS LLC—See Accor S.A.; *Int'l*, pg. 91
21 GRAMS AB—See Unifiedpost Group SA; *Int'l*, pg. 8043
21 GRAMS AS—See Unifiedpost Group SA; *Int'l*, pg. 8043
21 INVESTIMENTI SOCIETA' DI GESTIONE DEL RISPARMIO S.P.A.; *Int'l*, pg. 4
21 LADY CO., LTD.; *Int'l*, pg. 4
21 PARTNERS S.P.A.—See 21 Investimenti Societa' di Gestione del Risparmio S.p.A.; *Int'l*, pg. 4
21ST AMENDMENT INC.; *U.S. Private*, pg. 5
21ST CENTURY BIOCHEMICALS; *U.S. Private*, pg. 5
21ST CENTURY COOPERATIVE CO.; *U.S. Private*, pg. 5
21ST CENTURY FOOD AND PACKAGING LTD—See Mohammed Enterprises Tanzania Limited; *Int'l*, pg. 5018
21ST CENTURY INSURANCE GROUP—See Zurich Insurance Group Limited; *Int'l*, pg. 8698
21ST CENTURY ONCOLOGY HOLDINGS, INC.—See Vestar Capital Partners, LLC; *U.S. Private*, pg. 4371
21ST CENTURY ONCOLOGY, INC.—See Vestar Capital Partners, LLC; *U.S. Private*, pg. 4371
21ST CENTURY PARKS INC.; *U.S. Private*, pg. 5
21ST CENTURY SYSTEMS, INC.; *U.S. Private*, pg. 5
21ST CENTURY TEXTILES LTD—See Mohammed Enterprises Tanzania Limited; *Int'l*, pg. 5018
21ST C SCANDINAVIA AB—See Journeo plc; *Int'l*, pg. 4003
21ST MORTGAGE CORPORATION; *U.S. Private*, pg. 5
21VIANET GROUP LIMITED—See Tsinghua Holdings Co., Ltd.; *Int'l*, pg. 7951
220 LABORATORIES INC.—See The Pritzker Group - Chicago, LLC; *U.S. Private*, pg. 4099
2-20 RECORDS MANAGEMENT, LLC—See Windjammer Capital Investors, LLC; *U.S. Private*, pg. 4538
2-20 RECORDS MANAGEMENT, LLC; *U.S. Private*, pg. 4
225 UNLIMITED INCORPORATED; *U.S. Private*, pg. 5
2267166 ALBERTA LTD.—See Newstar Capital; *Int'l*, pg. 5238
22ND & BURN INC.—See Acreage Holdings, Inc.; *U.S. Public*, pg. 36
22ND CENTURY GROUP, INC.; *U.S. Public*, pg. 3
22ND CENTURY LIMITED, LLC—See 22nd Century Group, Inc.; *U.S. Public*, pg. 3
22ND CENTURY TECHNOLOGIES, INC.; *U.S. Private*, pg. 5
22SQUARED, INC.; *U.S. Private*, pg. 5
22SQUARED - TAMPA—See 22squared, Inc.; *U.S. Private*, pg. 6
2350 HARPER HOUSE, L.L.C.—See Starwood Real Estate Income Trust, Inc.; *U.S. Private*, pg. 3789
235 HOLDINGS LTD.; *Int'l*, pg. 4
2390 GRAHAM PARK, L.L.C.—See Starwood Real Estate Income Trust, Inc.; *U.S. Private*, pg. 3789
23ANDME HOLDING CO.; *U.S. Public*, pg. 3
23ANDME, INC.—See 23andMe Holding Co.; *U.S. Public*, pg. 3
23ANDME, INC.; *U.S. Public*, pg. 3
23RD GROUP LLC; *U.S. Private*, pg. 6
23RED LIMITED—See Capgemini SE; *Int'l*, pg. 1303
23RED LIMITED; *Int'l*, pg. 4
241 PIZZA (2006) LTD.—See Chairman's Brands Corporation; *Int'l*, pg. 1437
2435386 ONTARIO INC.—See Mountain Province Diamonds Inc.; *Int'l*, pg. 5057
24/7 CUSTOMER INC.; *U.S. Private*, pg. 6
24/7 CUSTOMER PHILIPPINES INC.—See 24/7 Customer Inc.; *U.S. Private*, pg. 6
24/7 CUSTOMER PVT. LTD.—See 24/7 Customer Inc.; *U.S. Private*, pg. 6
24-7 ENTERTAINMENT APS—See Ceconomy AG; *Int'l*, pg. 1373
24/7 EXPRESS LOGISTICS, INC.; *U.S. Private*, pg. 6
24-7 INTOUCH, INC.—See Ontario Teachers' Pension Plan; *Int'l*, pg. 5585
24/7 REAL MEDIA FRANCE SARL—See WPP plc; *Int'l*, pg. 8491
24/7 REAL MEDIA, INC.—See WPP plc; *Int'l*, pg. 8491
24/7 REAL MEDIA—See WPP plc; *Int'l*, pg. 8491
24/7 REAL MEDIA—See WPP plc; *Int'l*, pg. 8491
24/7 REAL MEDIA—See WPP plc; *Int'l*, pg. 8491
24/7 REAL MEDIA—See WPP plc; *Int'l*, pg. 8491
24/7 REAL MEDIA—See WPP plc; *Int'l*, pg. 8491
24/7 REAL MEDIA—See WPP plc; *Int'l*, pg. 8491
24/7 REAL MEDIA SOUTH KOREA—See WPP plc; *Int'l*, pg. 8491
24/7 REAL MEDIA UK LTD.—See WPP plc; *Int'l*, pg. 8491
24/7 TECHNOLOGY INC.—See Incline MGMT Corp.; *U.S. Private*, pg. 2054
24HOLDINGS INC.; *U.S. Private*, pg. 6
24 HOUR COMPANY; *U.S. Private*, pg. 6
24 HOUR FITNESS USA, INC.—See AEA Investors LP; *U.S. Private*, pg. 113
24 HOUR FITNESS USA, INC.—See Ontario Teachers' Pension Plan; *Int'l*, pg. 5587
24HR HOMECARE; *U.S. Private*, pg. 6
24 IANUARIE S.A.; *Int'l*, pg. 4
24I MEDIA USA LLC—See Afierian plc; *Int'l*, pg. 185
24 KITCHEN MEDYA HIZMETLERI ANONIM SIRKETI—See The Walt Disney Company; *U.S. Public*, pg. 2140
24KITCHEN TELEVISION B.V.—See The Walt Disney Company; *U.S. Public*, pg. 2140
24 LIGNE LLC—See Constellation Brands, Inc.; *U.S. Public*, pg. 570
24 MOBILE ADVERTISING SOLUTIONS AB; *Int'l*, pg. 4
24+ NV—See KBC Group NV; *Int'l*, pg. 4106
24 SEVEN, LLC; *U.S. Private*, pg. 6
24 SHOPPING CO., LTD.—See C.P. All Public Company Limited; *Int'l*, pg. 1243
24VIP LOGISTICS SERVICES D.O.O.—See Osterreichische Post AG; *Int'l*, pg. 5653
250 HIGH STREET, L.L.C.—See Starwood Real Estate Income Trust, Inc.; *U.S. Private*, pg. 3789
250OK INC.—See Silversmith Management, L.P.; *U.S. Private*, pg. 3664
262695 HOLDINGS LIMITED—See The Equitable Life Insurance Company of Canada; *Int'l*, pg. 7640
2639-1862 QUEBEC, INC.; *Int'l*, pg. 4
26 CALIFORNIA BAZAR INC.; *U.S. Private*, pg. 6
26 CAPITAL ACQUISITION CORP.; *U.S. Public*, pg. 3
26NORTH BDC, INC.; *U.S. Private*, pg. 6
2700 EMPIRE, LLC—See Hovnanian Enterprises, Inc.; *U.S. Public*, pg. 1056
2701 S. CONGRESS AVENUE, LLC—See CubeSmart; *U.S. Public*, pg. 603
2768691 CANADA, INC.—See Otsuka Holdings Co., Ltd.; *Int'l*, pg. 5658
2825 FOUR MILE ROAD LLC—See WEC Energy Group, Inc.; *U.S. Public*, pg. 2342
284 FUEL SUPPLY, LLC—See Iowa 80 Group, Inc.; *U.S. Private*, pg. 2134
284 PARTNERS LLC—See Ankura Consulting Group, LLC; *U.S. Private*, pg. 284
28 VILLAGES PTY LTD.—See Compass Group PLC; *Int'l*, pg. 1750
2/90 SIGN SYSTEMS INC.; *U.S. Private*, pg. 4
2929 ENTERTAINMENT LP; *U.S. Private*, pg. 6
2929 PRODUCTIONS LLC—See 2929 Entertainment LP; *U.S. Private*, pg. 6
29METALS LIMITED; *Int'l*, pg. 4
29 PRIME; *U.S. Private*, pg. 6
2ADVANCED STUDIOS, LLC.; *U.S. Private*, pg. 6
2CHECKOUT.COM, INC.—See British Columbia Investment Management Corp.; *Int'l*, pg. 1170
2CHECKOUT.COM, INC.—See Francisco Partners Management, LP; *U.S. Private*, pg. 1592
2CONNECT BV; *Int'l*, pg. 4
2CRSI CORPORATION—See 2Crsi SA; *Int'l*, pg. 4
2CRSI ME FZE—See 2Crsi SA; *Int'l*, pg. 4
2CRSI SA; *Int'l*, pg. 4
2CRSI UK LTD.—See 2Crsi SA; *Int'l*, pg. 4
2CUREX AB; *Int'l*, pg. 4
2CUREX GMBH—See 2cureX AB; *Int'l*, pg. 4
2CV INC—See Arsenal Capital Management LP; *U.S. Private*, pg. 337
2CV LIMITED—See Arsenal Capital Management LP; *U.S. Private*, pg. 337
2D3 INC.—See Oxford Metrics plc; *Int'l*, pg. 5675
2D3 LIMITED—See Oxford Metrics plc; *Int'l*, pg. 5675
2DFACTO, INC.—See Dai Nippon Printing Co., Ltd.; *Int'l*, pg. 1914
2D FLUIDICS PTY LTD—See First Graphene Limited; *Int'l*, pg. 2684
2E CREATIVE, INC.; *U.S. Private*, pg. 6
2ERGO AUSTRALIA PTY. LTD.—See Gomeeki Pty Ltd.; *Int'l*, pg. 3037
2FA, INC.—See Identity Automation, LP; *U.S. Private*, pg. 2037
2G CENERGY POWER SYSTEMS TECHNOLOGIES INC.—See 2G Energy AG; *Int'l*, pg. 5
2.GC, INC.; *U.S. Private*, pg. 4
2G DRIVES GMBH—See 2G Energy AG; *Int'l*, pg. 5
2G ENERGIE SAS—See 2G Energy AG; *Int'l*, pg. 5
2G ENERGY AG; *Int'l*, pg. 4
2G ENERGY CORP.—See 2G Energy AG; *Int'l*, pg. 5
2G ENERGY INC.—See 2G Energy AG; *Int'l*, pg. 5
2G ENERGY LTD.—See 2G Energy AG; *Int'l*, pg. 5
2GEN NET; *Int'l*, pg. 5
2 GETTHERE B.V.—See ZF Friedrichshafen AG; *Int'l*, pg. 8640
2G ITALIA S.R.L.—See 2G Energy AG; *Int'l*, pg. 5
2GM CORPORATION; *U.S. Private*, pg. 6
2GO EXPRESS, INC.—See SM Investments Corporation; *Int'l*, pg. 6998
2GO GROUP INC.—See SM Investments Corporation; *Int'l*, pg. 6998
2GO TRAVEL, INC.—See SM Investments Corporation; *Int'l*, pg. 6998
2G POLSKA SP. Z O.O.—See 2G Energy AG; *Int'l*, pg. 5
2G RENTAL GMBH—See 2G Energy AG; *Int'l*, pg. 5
2G SOLUTIONS OF COGENERATION S.L.—See 2G Energy AG; *Int'l*, pg. 5
2G STATION FOR AFRICA GMBH—See 2G Energy AG; *Int'l*, pg. 5
2G STATION LLC—See 2G Energy AG; *Int'l*, pg. 5
2G STATION TUNISIE SARL—See 2G Energy AG; *Int'l*, pg. 5
2HB SOFTWARE DESIGNS, INC.; *U.S. Private*, pg. 6
2 H ENERGY S.A.S.—See CNH Industrial N.V.; *Int'l*, pg. 1674
2H OFFSHORE ENGINEERING LTD.—See Buckthorn Partners LLP; *Int'l*, pg. 1210
2H OFFSHORE ENGINEERING LTD.—See OEP Capital Advisors, L.P.; *U.S. Private*, pg. 2997
2H RESOURCES PTY LIMITED—See Buru Energy Limited; *Int'l*, pg. 1227
2INVEST AG; *Int'l*, pg. 5
2IS INC.; *U.S. Private*, pg. 7
2JR PIZZA ENTERPRISES, LLC; *U.S. Private*, pg. 7
2J SUPPLY INC.; *U.S. Private*, pg. 7
2K CZECH, S.R.O.—See Take-Two Interactive Software, Inc.; *U.S. Public*, pg. 1979
2K GAMES, INC.—See Take-Two Interactive Software, Inc.; *U.S. Public*, pg. 1979
2K GAMES WEST—See Take-Two Interactive Software, Inc.; *U.S. Public*, pg. 1979
2K PLAY, INC.—See Take-Two Interactive Software, Inc.; *U.S. Public*, pg. 1979
2-K PURCHASING CENTRE INC; *Int'l*, pg. 3
2KS CLOUD SERVICES GMBH; *Int'l*, pg. 5
2K VEGAS, INC.—See Take-Two Interactive Software, Inc.; *U.S. Public*, pg. 1979
2M2 GROUP AB—See Storskogen Group AB; *Int'l*, pg. 7227
2M COMPANY INC.—See Franklin Electric Co., Inc.; *U.S. Public*, pg. 878
2MORO SAS—See Sopra Steria Group S.A.; *Int'l*, pg. 7109
2M-TEK, INC.—See Parker Wellbore Company; *U.S. Public*, pg. 1650
2M TOOL COMPANY, INC.; *U.S. Private*, pg. 7
2ND CITY RESOURCING LIMITED—See Empresaria Group Plc; *Int'l*, pg. 2388
2ND STORY SOFTWARE, INC.—See Genstar Capital, LLC; *U.S. Private*, pg. 1676
2ND SWING; *U.S. Private*, pg. 7
2ND WIND EXERCISE EQUIPMENT; *U.S. Private*, pg. 7
2ND WIND HEATING & AIR CONDITIONING, INC.—See NearU Services; *U.S. Private*, pg. 2877
2PI SOLUTIONS; *U.S. Private*, pg. 7
2 PLACES AT 1 TIME, INC.—See Accor S.A.; *Int'l*, pg. 92
2SEVENTY BIO, INC.; *U.S. Public*, pg. 3
2 SISTERS FOOD GROUP LIMITED—See Boparan Holdings Limited; *Int'l*, pg. 1111
2S METAL PUBLIC COMPANY LIMITED; *Int'l*, pg. 5
2TRG INC; *U.S. Private*, pg. 7
2U, INC.; *U.S. Public*, pg. 3
2VALORISE N.V.; *Int'l*, pg. 5
2WAYTRAFFIC MOBILE—See Sony Group Corporation; *Int'l*, pg. 7105
2WAYTRAFFIC N.V.—See Sony Group Corporation; *Int'l*, pg. 7105
2WHEELBIKES.COM; *U.S. Private*, pg. 7
2X1 HOLDING CAPE MIDIA SHIPYARD; *Int'l*, pg. 5

3

3001, INC.—See Northrop Grumman Corporation; *U.S. Public*, pg. 1540
300 BROADWAY, LLC—See Ryman Hospitality Properties, Inc.; *U.S. Public*, pg. 1829
300 MAIN STREET REALTY, LLC—See United Natural Foods, Inc.; *U.S. Public*, pg. 2231
302 ENLISA S.A.—See Energoprojekt Holding a.d.; *Int'l*, pg. 2421
3030 PARK HEALTH SYSTEMS INC.; *U.S. Public*, pg. 7
303 MULLENLOWE—See The Interpublic Group of Companies, Inc.; *U.S. Public*, pg. 2089
303 MULLENLOWE - SYDNEY—See The Interpublic Group of Companies, Inc.; *U.S. Public*, pg. 2090
305 DEGREES LLC; *U.S. Private*, pg. 7
30 BENCOOLEN PTE. LTD.—See Oriental Holdings Berhad; *Int'l*, pg. 5624
30DC, INC.; *U.S. Public*, pg. 3
30DC, INC.; *U.S. Private*, pg. 7
30 SECONDSTOFLY (THAILAND) CO., LTD.—See Global Business Travel Group, Inc.; *U.S. Public*, pg. 940
317298 SASKATCHEWAN LTD.—See Weyerhaeuser Company; *U.S. Public*, pg. 2365
319 BRAGG STUDENT HOUSING AUBURN AL LLC—See Greystar Real Estate Partners, LLC; *U.S. Private*, pg. 1785
31-W INSULATION CO. INC.; *U.S. Private*, pg. 7
32ND STREET 99 CENTS CORP.; *U.S. Private*, pg. 8
32ND STREET SURGERY CENTER, LLC—See KKR & Co. Inc.; *U.S. Public*, pg. 1244
32 NORTH CORP.—See Berkshire Partners LLC; *U.S. Private*, pg. 535
330542 BC LTD; *Int'l*, pg. 6
333D LTD.; *Int'l*, pg. 6
3385434 CANADA INC.—See Hyatt Hotels Corporation; *U.S. Public*, pg. 1076
33ACROSS INC.; *U.S. Private*, pg. 8
33 SOUTH 6TH STREET LLC—See Brookfield Corporation; *Int'l*, pg. 1186
3463192 CANADA INC.; *Int'l*, pg. 6
34 DEGREES AGENCY—See King James Group Company; *Int'l*, pg. 4169
3535 N. HALL STREET, LLC—See Welltower Inc.; *U.S. Public*, pg. 2347
360 BLUE, LLC—See Natural Retreats US LLC; *U.S. Private*, pg. 2867
360 CAPITAL GROUP LIMITED—See Centuria Capital Limited; *Int'l*, pg. 1416
360 CAPITAL INVESTMENT MANAGEMENT LIMITED—See Centuria Capital Limited; *Int'l*, pg. 1416
360 CAPITAL MORTGAGE REIT; *Int'l*, pg. 6
360 CAPITAL REIT—See Centuria Capital Limited; *Int'l*, pg. 1416
360CONNECT S.A.—See Vodafone Group Plc; *Int'l*, pg. 8284
360 DIGITECH, INC.; *Int'l*, pg. 6
360 ENTERPRISES LLC; *U.S. Private*, pg. 8
360 FINANCE, INC.; *Int'l*, pg. 6
360 FINANCE PTY LTD—See Eagers Automotive Limited; *Int'l*, pg. 2263
360 GROUP; *U.S. Private*, pg. 8
360 IMAGING INC.—See Seaman Paper Company of Massachusetts Inc.; *U.S. Private*, pg. 3585
360 INC.; *U.S. Private*, pg. 8
360INSIGHTS.COM CANADA, INC.; *Int'l*, pg. 6
360 LUDASHI HOLDINGS LIMITED; *Int'l*, pg. 6
360 MARKETING COMMUNICATIONS & CONTACTS—See The Interpublic Group of Companies, Inc.; *U.S. Public*, pg. 2092
360 MED CARE PTY. LTD.—See Enovis Corporation; *U.S. Public*, pg. 770
360 MORTGAGE GROUP, LLC; *U.S. Private*, pg. 8
360 ONE WAM LIMITED; *Int'l*, pg. 6
360PARTNERS, LP; *U.S. Private*, pg. 8
360 PSG, INC.; *U.S. Private*, pg. 8
360 PUBLIC RELATIONS LLC; *U.S. Private*, pg. 8
360 RESIDENCES, L.P.—See Essex Property Trust, Inc.; *U.S. Public*, pg. 795
360SCIENCE, INC.—See Bridge Growth Partners, LLC; *U.S. Private*, pg. 648
360SCIENCE LTD.—See Bridge Growth Partners, LLC; *U.S. Private*, pg. 648
360SCIENCE LTD.; *U.S. Private*, pg. 8
360T ASIA PACIFIC PTE. LTD.—See Deutsche Borse AG; *Int'l*, pg. 2063
360 TRADING NETWORKS INC—See Deutsche Borse AG; *Int'l*, pg. 2063
360 TRADING NETWORKS LLC—See Deutsche Borse AG; *Int'l*, pg. 2063
360TRAINING.COM, INC.; *U.S. Private*, pg. 8
360 TREASURY SYSTEMS AG—See Deutsche Borse AG; *Int'l*, pg. 2063
3617581 CANADA INC; *Int'l*, pg. 7
361 CAPITAL LLC—See Hamilton Lane Incorporated; *U.S. Public*, pg. 982
361 DEGREES INTERNATIONAL LIMITED; *Int'l*, pg. 6
361 EUROPE B.V.—See 361 Degrees International Limited; *Int'l*, pg. 7

361 USA, INC—See 361 Degrees International Limited; *Int'l*, pg. 7
365 HEALTHCARE LIMITED—See Bunzl plc; *Int'l*, pg. 1216
365 HF; *Int'l*, pg. 7
365 MEDIA, INC.—See Mobius Knowledge Services Pvt. Ltd.; *Int'l*, pg. 5012
365 OPERATING COMPANY LLC; *U.S. Private*, pg. 8
365 SERVICES LLC—See Stonecourt Capital LP; *U.S. Private*, pg. 3828
36KR HOLDINGS INC.; *Int'l*, pg. 7
374WATER, INC.; *U.S. Public*, pg. 3
3770818 CANADA INC; *Int'l*, pg. 7
37 BAKING HOLDINGS, LLC; *U.S. Private*, pg. 8
37 CAPITAL INC.; *Int'l*, pg. 7
37TH AVE MARKET INC.—See Bogopa Enterprises Inc.; *U.S. Private*, pg. 609
3811 BELL MEDICAL PROPERTIES, LLC—See Universal Health Realty Income Trust; *U.S. Public*, pg. 2255
3965546 CANADA INC; *Int'l*, pg. 7
399 FREMONT LLC—See UDR, Inc.; *U.S. Public*, pg. 2218
39 NORTH CAPITAL LLC—See Eastbridge Group; *Int'l*, pg. 2271
3A-BESTGROUP JSC; *Int'l*, pg. 7
3AC CO., LTD.; *Int'l*, pg. 7
3A COMPOSITES ASIA PACIFIC PTE. LTD.—See Schweiter Technologies AG; *Int'l*, pg. 6645
3A COMPOSITES (CHINA) LTD.—See Schweiter Technologies AG; *Int'l*, pg. 6645
3A COMPOSITES GERMANY GMBH—See Schweiter Technologies AG; *Int'l*, pg. 6645
3A COMPOSITES GMBH—See Schweiter Technologies AG; *Int'l*, pg. 6645
3A COMPOSITES GMBH—See Schweiter Technologies AG; *Int'l*, pg. 6645
3A COMPOSITES HOLDING AG—See Schweiter Technologies AG; *Int'l*, pg. 6645
3A COMPOSITES INDIA PTE. LTD.—See Schweiter Technologies AG; *Int'l*, pg. 6645
3A COMPOSITES INTERNATIONAL AG—See Schweiter Technologies AG; *Int'l*, pg. 6645
3A COMPOSITES MOBILITY AG—See Schweiter Technologies AG; *Int'l*, pg. 6645
3A COMPOSITES MOBILITY SA—See Schweiter Technologies AG; *Int'l*, pg. 6645
3A COMPOSITES USA INC.—See Schweiter Technologies AG; *Int'l*, pg. 6645
3A HEALTH CARE S.R.L.—See OMRON Corporation; *Int'l*, pg. 5564
3ALITY TECHNICA; *U.S. Private*, pg. 8
3A MCOM SRL—See HEXPOL AB; *Int'l*, pg. 3372
3AM TECHNOLOGIES, INC.; *Int'l*, pg. 7
3ANGLE EPCM V.O.F.—See Fluor Corporation; *U.S. Public*, pg. 857
3B BLACKBIO BIOTECH INDIA LIMITED—See Kilpest India Limited; *Int'l*, pg. 4162
3BETONY LTD.—See Bain Capital, LP; *U.S. Private*, pg. 438
3B-FIBREGLASS A/S—See The Braj Binani Group; *Int'l*, pg. 7627
3B-FIBREGLASS SPRL—See The Braj Binani Group; *Int'l*, pg. 7627
3 BIRDS MARKETING LLC—See Digital Air Strike Inc.; *U.S. Private*, pg. 1229
3BL MEDIA LLC; *U.S. Private*, pg. 8
3B MEDICAL, INC.; *U.S. Private*, pg. 8
3 BOYS ENTERPRISES LLC; *U.S. Private*, pg. 7
3 BRIDGE SOLUTIONS LLC; *U.S. Private*, pg. 7
3B SCIENTIFIC GMBH—See J.H. Whitney & Co., LLC; *U.S. Private*, pg. 2166
3BUMI OLEO SDN BHD—See Melewar Industrial Group Berhad; *Int'l*, pg. 4808
3C ASSET MANAGEMENT LTD.—See Sampo plc; *Int'l*, pg. 6507
3C-CARBON GROUP AG; *Int'l*, pg. 7
3C CONSULTANTS LTD.—See Aquila Services Group PLC; *Int'l*, pg. 528
3 C DEUTSCHLAND GMBH—See Bertelsmann SE & Co. KGaA; *Int'l*, pg. 989
3CEMS GROUP - FREMONT BRANCH—See FIC Global, INC; *Int'l*, pg. 2653
3CINTERACTIVE CORP.; *U.S. Private*, pg. 9
3CLOUD, LLC—See Gryphon Investors, LLC; *U.S. Private*, pg. 1798
3CNERGY LIMITED; *Int'l*, pg. 7
3C! PACKAGING COMPANY—See Essentra plc; *Int'l*, pg. 2510
3C SOFTWARE INC.; *U.S. Private*, pg. 8
3C TECHNOLOGY AS—See TowerBrook Capital Partners, L.P.; *U.S. Private*, pg. 4194
3C TEST LIMITED—See I Squared Capital Advisors (US) LLC; *U.S. Private*, pg. 2021
3C TEST LIMITED—See TDR Capital LLP; *Int'l*, pg. 7490
3C TOULOUSE SAS—See Sonepar S.A.; *Int'l*, pg. 7090
3 DAY BLINDS LLC; *U.S. Private*, pg. 7
3 D BODY WORKS, INC.; *U.S. Private*, pg. 7
3DCART SHOPPING CARTS; *U.S. Private*, pg. 9

3DCONNEXION GMBH—See Logitech International S.A.; *U.S. Public*, pg. 1341
3DCONNEXION INC.—See Logitech International S.A.; *U.S. Public*, pg. 1341
3D CORPORATE SOLUTIONS, LLC; *U.S. Public*, pg. 9
3D DOMINIQUE DECLERCQ DISTRIBUTION—See FAYAT SAS; *Int'l*, pg. 2624
3DEGREES GROUP, INC.; *U.S. Private*, pg. 9
3D ENERGI LIMITED; *Int'l*, pg. 7
3DENT TECHNOLOGY, LLC—See Ocean Power Technologies, Inc.; *U.S. Public*, pg. 1562
3-D ENVIRONMENTAL SERVICES CORP.; *U.S. Private*, pg. 7
3D EUROPEAN HOLDINGS LTD.—See 3D Systems Corporation; *U.S. Public*, pg. 4
3D EXHIBITS, INC.—See Freeman Decorating Co.; *U.S. Private*, pg. 1605
3D EXHIBITS, INC.; *U.S. Private*, pg. 8
3D FUTURE VISION II, INC.; *U.S. Private*, pg. 9
3D GLASS SOLUTIONS, INC.—See Nagase & Co., Ltd.; *Int'l*, pg. 5126
3D-ID, LLC—See LogicMark, Inc.; *U.S. Public*, pg. 1340
3DIEMME SRL—See Zimmer Biomet Holdings, Inc.; *U.S. Public*, pg. 2405
3D INCORPORATED—See Denso Corporation; *Int'l*, pg. 2028
3DING CONSULTING S.R.L.—See Prismi S.p.A.; *Int'l*, pg. 5982
3D LABS INC., LTD.—See Creative Technology Ltd.; *Int'l*, pg. 1833
3DLABS—See Creative Technology Ltd.; *Int'l*, pg. 1833
3D LASER SYSTEME GMBH—See Trimble, Inc.; *U.S. Public*, pg. 2190
3D LINE RESEARCH AND DEVELOPMENT S.R.L.—See Elekta AB; *Int'l*, pg. 2355
3-D MATRIX ASIA PTE. LTD.—See 3-D Matrix, Ltd.; *Int'l*, pg. 6
3-D MATRIX (BEIJING) BIOTECHNOLOGY CO., LTD.—See 3-D Matrix, Ltd.; *Int'l*, pg. 6
3-D MATRIX EMEA B.V.—See 3-D Matrix, Ltd.; *Int'l*, pg. 6
3-D MATRIX EUROPE SAS—See 3-D Matrix, Ltd.; *Int'l*, pg. 6
3-D MATRIX, INC.—See 3-D Matrix, Ltd.; *Int'l*, pg. 6
3-D MATRIX, LTD.; *Int'l*, pg. 6
3-D MATRIX MEDICAL TECHNOLOGY, LTD.—See 3-D Matrix, Ltd.; *Int'l*, pg. 6
3-D MATRIX MEDICAL TECHNOLOGY PTY LTD—See 3-D Matrix, Ltd.; *Int'l*, pg. 6
3-D MATRIX UK LTD.—See 3-D Matrix, Ltd.; *Int'l*, pg. 6
3DM DIGITAL MANUFACTURING LTD.; *Int'l*, pg. 7
3D MEDICINES INC.; *Int'l*, pg. 7
3D PIONEER SYSTEMS, INC.; *U.S. Public*, pg. 4
3D PLASTICS, INC.—See Quantum Plastics, Inc.; *U.S. Private*, pg. 3323
3D PLM SOFTWARE SOLUTIONS LIMITED—See Dassault Systemes S.A.; *Int'l*, pg. 1974
3D PLUS SAS—See HEICO Corporation; *U.S. Public*, pg. 1020
3D PLUS U.S.A., INC.—See HEICO Corporation; *U.S. Public*, pg. 1020
3D-P—See Epiroc AB; *Int'l*, pg. 2463
3D-P—See Epiroc AB; *Int'l*, pg. 2463
3D REALMS ENTERTAINMENT APS—See Embracer Group AB; *Int'l*, pg. 2375
3D RESOURCES LIMITED; *Int'l*, pg. 7
3D-SHAPE GMBH—See Atlas Copco AB; *Int'l*, pg. 682
3DSHOPPING.COM INC.; *U.S. Public*, pg. 4
3D SOLAR LLC; *U.S. Private*, pg. 7
3D SYSTEMS ASIA-PACIFIC PTY LTD—See 3D Systems Corporation; *U.S. Public*, pg. 4
3D SYSTEMS - BURLINGTON—See 3D Systems Corporation; *U.S. Public*, pg. 4
3D SYSTEMS CORPORATION; *U.S. Public*, pg. 4
3D SYSTEMS EUROPE LTD.—See 3D Systems Corporation; *U.S. Public*, pg. 4
3D SYSTEMS FRANCE SARL—See 3D Systems Corporation; *U.S. Public*, pg. 4
3D SYSTEMS GMBH—See 3D Systems Corporation; *U.S. Public*, pg. 4
3D SYSTEMS, INC.—See 3D Systems Corporation; *U.S. Public*, pg. 4
3D SYSTEMS INDUSTRIA E COMERCIO LTDA.—See 3D Systems Corporation; *U.S. Public*, pg. 4
3D SYSTEMS ITALIA S.R.L.—See 3D Systems Corporation; *U.S. Public*, pg. 4
3D SYSTEMS JAPAN K.K.—See 3D Systems Corporation; *U.S. Public*, pg. 4
3D SYSTEMS KOREA, INC.—See 3D Systems Corporation; *U.S. Public*, pg. 4
3D SYSTEMS S.A.—See 3D Systems Corporation; *U.S. Public*, pg. 4
3D SYSTEMS SOFTWARE GMBH—See Battery Ventures, L.P.; *U.S. Private*, pg. 488
3D SYSTEMS SOFTWARE SRL—See 3D Systems Corporation; *U.S. Public*, pg. 4
3 D&V—See Fast Undercar Inc.; *U.S. Public*, pg. 1482
3DX INDUSTRIES, INC.; *U.S. Public*, pg. 4
3DX-RAY LTD.—See Image Scan Holdings plc; *Int'l*, pg. 3618

COMPANY NAME INDEX

3E COMPANY ENVIROMENTAL, ECOLOGICAL & ENGINEERING—See Verisk Analytics, Inc.; *U.S. Public*, pg. 2282
3E (CYPRUS) LIMITED—See Coca-Cola HBC AG; *Int'l*, pg. 1685
3E TECHNOLOGIES INTERNATIONAL INC.—See Advent International Corporation; *U.S. Private*, pg. 100
3 FEET MEDIA; *U.S. Private*, pg. 7
3F FILIPPI SPA; *Int'l*, pg. 7
3FORCES INC.; *U.S. Private*, pg. 9
3FORM LLC—See Armstrong World Industries, Inc.; *U.S. Public*, pg. 193
3G CAPITAL INC.; *U.S. Private*, pg. 9
3G CAPITAL MANAGEMENT LLC; *U.S. Private*, pg. 11
3G CAPITAL PARTNERS L.P.; *U.S. Private*, pg. 11
3G GRAPHIC SOLUTIONS; *U.S. Private*, pg. 13
3GNS SP. Z O.O.—See Iliad S.A.; *Int'l*, pg. 3614
3GTMS, INC.—See Sumeru Equity Partners LLC; *U.S. Private*, pg. 3852
3G YATIRIM VE GAYRIMENKUL TICARET A.S—See Autoliv, Inc.; *Int'l*, pg. 728
3I ASIA PACIFIC LTD—See 3i Group plc; *Int'l*, pg. 8
3I ASIA PACIFIC PLC—See 3i Group plc; *Int'l*, pg. 8
3I BENELUX B.V.—See 3i Group plc; *Int'l*, pg. 7
3I CORPORATION—See 3i Group plc; *Int'l*, pg. 8
3I DEUTSCHLAND GESELLSCHAFT FUR INDUSTRIE-BETEILIGUNGEN MBH—See 3i Group plc; *Int'l*, pg. 8
3I EUROPE PLC, BENELUX—See 3i Group plc; *Int'l*, pg. 8
3I EUROPE PLC—See 3i Group plc; *Int'l*, pg. 8
3I EUROPE PLC—See 3i Group plc; *Int'l*, pg. 8
3I FRANCE SAS—See 3i Group plc; *Int'l*, pg. 8
3I GESTION S.A.—See 3i Group plc; *Int'l*, pg. 8
3I GROUP PLC; *Int'l*, pg. 7
3I HONG KONG—See 3i Group plc; *Int'l*, pg. 8
3I INDIA PRIVATE LIMITED—See 3i Group plc; *Int'l*, pg. 8
3I INFRASTRUCTURE PLC—See 3i Group plc; *Int'l*, pg. 8
3I INVESTMENTS PLC—See 3i Group plc; *Int'l*, pg. 8
3I NETHERLANDS B.V.—See 3i Group plc; *Int'l*, pg. 8
3I NORDIC PLC—See 3i Group plc; *Int'l*, pg. 8
3 INTERACTIVE; *U.S. Private*, pg. 7
3I PEOPLE, INC.; *U.S. Private*, pg. 13
3I PLC—See 3i Group plc; *Int'l*, pg. 8
3I PLC—See 3i Group plc; *Int'l*, pg. 8
3I SGR—See 3i Group plc; *Int'l*, pg. 8
3I SWEDEN—See 3i Group plc; *Int'l*, pg. 8
3I SWITZERLAND LIMITED—See 3i Group plc; *Int'l*, pg. 8
3 K'S ENGINEERING COMPANY LIMITED—See MBH Corporation Plc; *Int'l*, pg. 4752
3. K+S VERWALTUNGS GMBH & CO. ERWERBS KG—See K+S Aktiengesellschaft; *Int'l*, pg. 4039
3 KV GMBH—See HPI AG; *Int'l*, pg. 3500
3L ENTRANCE, INC.—See Apaman Co., Ltd.; *Int'l*, pg. 500
3L LOCACOES E SERVICOS S.A.—See Metalfrio Solutions S.A.; *Int'l*, pg. 4846
3L SRL—See M.J. Maillis S.A.; *Int'l*, pg. 4615
3M ABRASIVE SYSTEMS DIVISION—See 3M Company; *U.S. Public*, pg. 5
3M ABRASIVE SYSTEMS—See 3M Company; *U.S. Public*, pg. 5
3. MAJ BRODOGRADILISTE D.D.; *Int'l*, pg. 6
3M A/S—See 3M Company; *U.S. Public*, pg. 8
3M A/S—See 3M Company; *U.S. Public*, pg. 5
3M AUSTRALIA PTY. LTD.—See 3M Company; *U.S. Public*, pg. 5
3M AUTOMOTIVE AFTERMARKET DIVISION—See 3M Company; *U.S. Public*, pg. 5
3M BELGIUM N.V./S.A.—See 3M Company; *U.S. Public*, pg. 5
3M BRICOLAGE AND BATIMENT—See 3M Company; *U.S. Public*, pg. 5
3M CANADA COMPANY—See 3M Company; *U.S. Public*, pg. 5
3M CANADA COMPANY—See 3M Company; *U.S. Public*, pg. 5
3M CHILE S.A.—See 3M Company; *U.S. Public*, pg. 5
3M CHINA LIMITED—See 3M Company; *U.S. Public*, pg. 5
3M COLOMBIA S.A.—See 3M Company; *U.S. Public*, pg. 5
3M COMPANY - CONOVER PLANT—See 3M Company; *U.S. Public*, pg. 5
3M COMPANY - MONTROSE—See 3M Company; *U.S. Public*, pg. 5
3M COMPANY - ROYERSFORD—See 3M Company; *U.S. Public*, pg. 5
3M COMPANY - SANTA CRUZ—See 3M Company; *U.S. Public*, pg. 5
3M COMPANY; *U.S. Public*, pg. 4
3M COSTA RICA, S.A.—See 3M Company; *U.S. Public*, pg. 5
3M CZECH REPUBLIC—See 3M Company; *U.S. Public*, pg. 5
3M DEUTSCHLAND GMBH - SEPARATION AND PURIFICATION SCIENCES DIVISION—See 3M Company; *U.S. Public*, pg. 5
3M DEUTSCHLAND GMBH—See 3M Company; *U.S. Public*, pg. 5
3M DOMINICANA S.A.—See 3M Company; *U.S. Public*, pg. 5
3M (EAST) AG—See 3M Company; *U.S. Public*, pg. 5
3M ECC EUROPA B.V.—See 3M Company; *U.S. Public*, pg. 5
3M ECUADOR C.A.—See 3M Company; *U.S. Public*, pg. 5
3M EGYPT LTD.—See 3M Company; *U.S. Public*, pg. 5
3M EMEA, GMBH—See 3M Company; *U.S. Public*, pg. 5
3M ESPANA S.A.—See 3M Company; *U.S. Public*, pg. 5
3M ESPE—See Solventum Corporation; *U.S. Public*, pg. 1901
3M FALL PROTECTION BUSINESS—See 3M Company; *U.S. Public*, pg. 5
3M FINANCIAL MANAGEMENT COMPANY—See 3M Company; *U.S. Public*, pg. 6
3M FRANCE S.A.S.—See 3M Company; *U.S. Public*, pg. 6
3M GUATEMALA, S.A.—See 3M Company; *U.S. Public*, pg. 6
3M GULF LTD.—See 3M Company; *U.S. Public*, pg. 6
3M HEALTHCARE GERMANY GMBH—See 3M Company; *U.S. Public*, pg. 6
3M HEALTH CARE LIMITED—See Solventum Corporation; *U.S. Public*, pg. 1901
3M HEALTH CARE LTD.—See Solventum Corporation; *U.S. Public*, pg. 1901
3M HEALTH CARE—See Solventum Corporation; *U.S. Public*, pg. 1901
3M HEALTH INFORMATION SYSTEMS—See Solventum Corporation; *U.S. Public*, pg. 1901
3M HEALTH INFO SYSTEMS CONSULTING SERVICES—See Solventum Corporation; *U.S. Public*, pg. 1901
3M HONG KONG LIMITED—See 3M Company; *U.S. Public*, pg. 6
3M HUNGARIA KFT.—See 3M Company; *U.S. Public*, pg. 6
3M IMTEC CORPORATION—See Solventum Corporation; *U.S. Public*, pg. 1901
3M INDIA LTD.—See 3M Company; *U.S. Public*, pg. 6
3M INDUSTRIAL ADHESIVES & TAPES DIVISION—See 3M Company; *U.S. Public*, pg. 6
3M INNOVATION SINGAPORE PTE LTD—See 3M Company; *U.S. Public*, pg. 6
3M INNOVATION SINGAPORE PTE LTD.—See 3M Company; *U.S. Public*, pg. 6
3M INNOVATIVE PROPERTIES COMPANY—See 3M Company; *U.S. Public*, pg. 6
3M INTERAMERICA, INC.—See 3M Company; *U.S. Public*, pg. 6
3M INTERAMERICA, INC.—See 3M Company; *U.S. Public*, pg. 6
3M INTERAMERICA, INC. (TRINIDAD & TOBAGO DIV.)—See 3M Company; *U.S. Public*, pg. 6
3M IRELAND LTD.—See 3M Company; *U.S. Public*, pg. 6
3M ITALIA S.P.A.—See 3M Company; *U.S. Public*, pg. 6
3M ITALIA SRL—See 3M Company; *U.S. Public*, pg. 6
3M JAPAN HOLDINGS COMPANY—See 3M Company; *U.S. Public*, pg. 6
3M JAPAN PRODUCTS LIMITED—See 3M Company; *U.S. Public*, pg. 6
3M KENYA LTD.—See 3M Company; *U.S. Public*, pg. 6
3M KOREA LTD.—See 3M Company; *U.S. Public*, pg. 6
3M MANUFACTURERA VENEZUELA S.A.—See 3M Company; *U.S. Public*, pg. 6
3M MEXICO S.A. DE C.V.—See 3M Company; *U.S. Public*, pg. 6
3M NEDERLAND B.V.—See 3M Company; *U.S. Public*, pg. 6
3M NEW ZEALAND LTD.—See 3M Company; *U.S. Public*, pg. 6
3M NORGE A/S—See 3M Company; *U.S. Public*, pg. 6
3M NORTHALLERTON—See 3M Company; *U.S. Public*, pg. 7
3M OESTERREICH GES MBH—See 3M Company; *U.S. Public*, pg. 6
3M PAKISTAN (PVT) LTD.—See 3M Company; *U.S. Public*, pg. 6
3M PANAMA S.A.—See 3M Company; *U.S. Public*, pg. 6
3M PERU S.A.—See 3M Company; *U.S. Public*, pg. 6
3M PHILIPPINES—See 3M Company; *U.S. Public*, pg. 6
3M POLAND SP. Z.O.O.—See 3M Company; *U.S. Public*, pg. 6
3M PORTUGAL, LDA—See 3M Company; *U.S. Public*, pg. 7
3M PRECISION GRINDING GMBH—See 3M Company; *U.S. Public*, pg. 7
3M PUERTO RICO, INC.—See 3M Company; *U.S. Public*, pg. 7
3M PURIFICATION INC.—See 3M Company; *U.S. Public*, pg. 7
3M PURIFICATION PTY. LIMITED—See 3M Company; *U.S. Public*, pg. 7
3M REAL ESTATE GMBH & CO. KG—See 3M Company; *U.S. Public*, pg. 7
3M ROMANIA S.R.L.—See 3M Company; *U.S. Public*, pg. 7
3M RUSSIA—See 3M Company; *U.S. Public*, pg. 7
3M SANAYI VE TICARET AS—See 3M Company; *U.S. Public*, pg. 7
3M (SCHWEITZ) GMBH—See 3M Company; *U.S. Public*, pg. 5

3S NETWORK INC.

3M SECURITY PRINTING AND SYSTEMS LTD.—See 3M Company; *U.S. Public*, pg. 7
3M SINGAPORE PTE. LTD.—See 3M Company; *U.S. Public*, pg. 7
3M SOUTH AFRICA (PTY.) LTD.—See 3M Company; *U.S. Public*, pg. 7
3M (SUISSE) SA—See 3M Company; *U.S. Public*, pg. 5
3M SVENSKA AB—See 3M Company; *U.S. Public*, pg. 7
3M TAIWAN LIMITED—See 3M Company; *U.S. Public*, pg. 7
3M TECHNOLOGIES PRIVATE LIMITED—See 3M Company; *U.S. Public*, pg. 7
3M THAILAND LIMITED—See 3M Company; *U.S. Public*, pg. 7
3M TOUCH SYSTEMS, INC.—See 3M Company; *U.S. Public*, pg. 7
3M TOUCH SYSTEMS, INC.—See 3M Company; *U.S. Public*, pg. 7
3MT (THAILAND) CO., LTD.—See MURO CORPORATION; *Int'l*, pg. 5099
3M UK HOLDINGS LIMITED—See 3M Company; *U.S. Public*, pg. 7
3M UNITED KINGDOM, PLC—See 3M Company; *U.S. Public*, pg. 7
3M UNITEK CORPORATION—See Solventum Corporation; *U.S. Public*, pg. 1901
3M URUGUAY SA—See 3M Company; *U.S. Public*, pg. 7
3MV BANCORP, INC.; *U.S. Private*, pg. 13
3MV ENERGY CORP.; *Int'l*, pg. 9
3NINE AB—See Grimaldi Industri AB; *Int'l*, pg. 3085
3NINE USA INC.—See Grimaldi Industri AB; *Int'l*, pg. 3085
3NORTH; *U.S. Private*, pg. 13
3ONEDATA CO., LTD.; *Int'l*, pg. 9
3 PAGEN HANDELSGESELLSCHAFT MBH—See Damartex SA; *Int'l*, pg. 1955
3 PAGEN VERSAND UND HANDELSGESELLSCHAFT MBH—See Damartex SA; *Int'l*, pg. 1955
3PAR INC.—See Hewlett Packard Enterprise Company; *U.S. Public*, pg. 1030
3P CORP.—See Dentsu Group Inc.; *Int'l*, pg. 2034
3PEAK, INC.; *Int'l*, pg. 9
3P FRIGOGLASS ROMANIA SRL—See Frigoglass S.A.I.C.; *Int'l*, pg. 2792
3P GMBH—See Burelle S.A.; *Int'l*, pg. 1222
3PHASE ELEVATOR CORP; *U.S. Private*, pg. 13
3 PHOENIX, INC.—See Advent International Corporation; *U.S. Private*, pg. 100
3PILLAR GLOBAL, INC.; *U.S. Private*, pg. 14
3P LAND HOLDINGS LIMITED; *Int'l*, pg. 9
3PLAY MEDIA, INC.—See Riverside Partners, LLC; *U.S. Private*, pg. 3445
3P LEARNING LIMITED; *Int'l*, pg. 9
3P MANUFACTURING, INC.—See Highland Capital Management, L.P.; *U.S. Private*, pg. 1938
3POINTS, LLC—See Southfield Capital Advisors, LLC; *U.S. Private*, pg. 3736
3P- PRODUCTOS PLASTICOS PERFORMANTES SA—See Burelle S.A.; *Int'l*, pg. 1222
3PS, INC.—See McCoy Global Inc.; *Int'l*, pg. 4757
3P SPA—See Burelle S.A.; *Int'l*, pg. 1222
3Q CO., LTD.—See EDION Corporation; *Int'l*, pg. 2310
3Q DIGITAL, INC.; *U.S. Private*, pg. 14
3Q HOLDINGS LIMITED; *Int'l*, pg. 9
3Q MAHUMA CONCRETE (PTY) LTD.—See PPC Ltd.; *Int'l*, pg. 5950
3-RD CO., LTD.—See GMM Grammy Public Company Limited; *Int'l*, pg. 3012
3RD STREET GROUP LTD.; *Int'l*, pg. 7
3 RIVERS CAPITAL, LLC; *U.S. Private*, pg. 7
3RIVERS FEDERAL CREDIT UNION; *U.S. Private*, pg. 14
3 RIVERS MATERIALS INC—See Cumberland Materials; *U.S. Private*, pg. 1122
3 RIVERS TELEPHONE COOPERATIVE; *U.S. Private*, pg. 7
3R LIMITED—See Anderson Group Limited; *Int'l*, pg. 450
3SBIO INC.; *Int'l*, pg. 9
3S ENGINEERING—See Sierra Nevada Corporation; *U.S. Private*, pg. 3647
3SERVICES FACTORY S.A.—See PCC SE; *Int'l*, pg. 5766
3 SHARE INC.—See Publicis Groupe S.A.; *Int'l*, pg. 6097
3 SIGMA CORP.—See Brixey & Meyer, Inc.; *U.S. Private*, pg. 658
3SI HOLDING, SASU—See Otto GmbH & Co. KG; *Int'l*, pg. 5662
3S INCORPORATED—See APi Group Corporation; *Int'l*, pg. 513
3SI SECURITY SYSTEMS, INC.—See Stirling Square Capital Partners LLP; *Int'l*, pg. 7216
3SIXTY GROUP LLC; *U.S. Private*, pg. 14
3 SIXTYMEDIA LTD.—See ITV plc; *Int'l*, pg. 3844
3 SIXTY RISK SOLUTIONS LTD.; *Int'l*, pg. 5
3 SIXTY SECURE CORP; *Int'l*, pg. 5
3S KOREA CO., LTD.; *Int'l*, pg. 9
3S NETWORK INC.; *U.S. Private*, pg. 14
3S PHOTONICS S.A.S - MARCOUSSIS—See Eurazeo SE; *Int'l*, pg. 2527
3S PHOTONICS S.A.S.—See Eurazeo SE; *Int'l*, pg. 2527
3SP TECHNOLOGIES S.A.S.—See O-Net Technologies (Group) Limited; *Int'l*, pg. 5502

3S NETWORK INC.

CORPORATE AFFILIATIONS

3S SOLVAY SHARED SERVICES-SOCIEDADE DE SERVICOS PARTILHADOS UNIPESSOAL LDA—See Solvay S.A.; *Int'l*, pg. 7077
3 STEP IT AS—See 3 Step It Group Oy; *Int'l*, pg. 6
3 STEP IT AS—See 3 Step It Group Oy; *Int'l*, pg. 6
3 STEP IT GROUP OY; *Int'l*, pg. 5
3 STEP IT (HONG KONG) LIMITED—See 3 Step It Group Oy; *Int'l*, pg. 6
3 STEP IT, INC.—See 3 Step It Group Oy; *Int'l*, pg. 6
3 STEP IT MALAYSIA SDN. BHD.—See 3 Step It Group Oy; *Int'l*, pg. 6
3 STEP IT OU—See 3 Step It Group Oy; *Int'l*, pg. 6
3 STEP IT OY—See 3 Step It Group Oy; *Int'l*, pg. 6
3 STEP IT SINGAPORE PTE LTD.—See 3 Step It Group Oy; *Int'l*, pg. 6
3 STEP IT SWEDEN AB—See 3 Step It Group Oy; *Int'l*, pg. 6
3 STEP IT UAB—See 3 Step It Group Oy; *Int'l*, pg. 6
3 STEP IT (UK) LIMITED—See 3 Step It Group Oy; *Int'l*, pg. 6
3-STJERNET A/S—See Atria Plc; *Int'l*, pg. 693
3 STORY SOFTWARE LLC—See Hays Plc; *Int'l*, pg. 3293
3S/TRACERE—See Cegedim S.A.; *Int'l*, pg. 1390
3 SUISSES INTERNATIONAL S.A.—See Otto GmbH & Co. KG; *Int'l*, pg. 5662
3TAILER, LLC; *U.S. Private*, pg. 14
3T SYSTEMS, INC.; *U.S. Private*, pg. 14
3U ENERGY AG—See 3U Holding AG; *Int'l*, pg. 10
3U ENERGY PE GMBH—See 3U Holding AG; *Int'l*, pg. 10
3U HOLDING AG; *Int'l*, pg. 10
3U TELECOM GMBH—See 3U Holding AG; *Int'l*, pg. 10
3V COMPANY; *U.S. Private*, pg. 14
3-V FASTENER CO, INC—See Stanley Black & Decker, Inc.; *U.S. Public*, pg. 1931
3VR SECURITY, INC.—See Identiv, Inc.; *U.S. Public*, pg. 1089
3WIRE GROUP INC—See Berkshire Hathaway Inc.; *U.S. Public*, pg. 308
3WM UGANDA LIMITED—See Envipro Holdings Inc.; *Int'l*, pg. 2454
3W POWER S.A.; *Int'l*, pg. 10
3W POWER S.P.A.—See 3W Power S.A.; *Int'l*, pg. 10
3XLOGIC FLORIDA, LLC—See Stanley Black & Decker, Inc.; *U.S. Public*, pg. 1931
3XLOGIC, INC.—See Stanley Black & Decker, Inc.; *U.S. Public*, pg. 1931
3XLOGIC INDIANA, LLC—See Stanley Black & Decker, Inc.; *U.S. Public*, pg. 1931
3Y POWER TECHNOLOGY (TAIWAN) INC.—See FSP Technology Inc.; *Int'l*, pg. 2800
3 ZIVLJENJSKA ZAVAROVALNICA VITA D.D.—See Pozavarovalnica Sava, d.d.; *Int'l*, pg. 5949

4

401 AUTO DEALERS EXCHANGE; *Int'l*, pg. 11
401-DIXIE NISSAN; *Int'l*, pg. 11
401KEXCHANGE.COM INC.; *U.S. Private*, pg. 14
4077491 CANADA INC; *Int'l*, pg. 11
407 INTERNATIONAL INC.—See Ontario Municipal Employees Retirement System; *Int'l*, pg. 5583
40/86 ADVISORS, INC.—See CNO Financial Group, Inc.; *U.S. Public*, pg. 519
40SEVEN LTD—See IDEX Corp; *U.S. Public*, pg. 1089
410613 ONTARIO LIMITED—See Northampton Group Inc.; *Int'l*, pg. 5442
THE 410 BRIDGE; *U.S. Private*, pg. 3980
412688 B.C. LTD.—See Esstra Industries Inc.; *Int'l*, pg. 2517
413554 ONTARIO LIMITED; *Int'l*, pg. 11
THE 41ST PARAMETER, INC.—See Experian plc; *Int'l*, pg. 2587
420 PROPERTY MANAGEMENT LLC; *U.S. Public*, pg. 9
4211 BELLAIRE BLVD., LLC—See CubeSmart; *U.S. Public*, pg. 603
4236009 MANITOBA LTD—See AutoCanada Inc.; *Int'l*, pg. 726
4236009 MANITOBA LTD; *Int'l*, pg. 11
424 CAPITAL, LLC; *U.S. Private*, pg. 15
429149 B.C. LTD; *Int'l*, pg. 11
42 DEGREES—See Publicis Groupe S.A.; *Int'l*, pg. 6111
42WEST LLC—See Dolphin Entertainment, Inc.; *U.S. Public*, pg. 673
4370 FOUNTAIN HILLS DRIVE NE, LLC—See CubeSmart; *U.S. Public*, pg. 603
440 FORD LINCOLN LAVAL—See Ford Motor Company; *U.S. Public*, pg. 865
44 BLUE PRODUCTIONS, INC.—See ProSiebenSat.1 Media SE; *Int'l*, pg. 5999
44 BUSINESS CAPITAL—See Berkshire Hills Bancorp, Inc.; *U.S. Public*, pg. 320
450477 ONTARIO LTD; *Int'l*, pg. 11
451 GROUP, LLC; *U.S. Private*, pg. 15
451 RESEARCH, LLC—See S&P Global Inc.; *U.S. Public*, pg. 1830
463 COMMUNICATIONS, LLC—See Next 15 Group plc; *Int'l*, pg. 5245
'47 BRAND, LLC; *U.S. Private*, pg. 1

47CLUB INC.—See Dentsu Group Inc.; *Int'l*, pg. 2034
482 JOINT STOCK COMPANY; *Int'l*, pg. 11
48FORTY SOLUTIONS, LLC—See Audax Group, Limited Partnership; *U.S. Private*, pg. 386
48NORTH CANNABIS CORP.—See Tilray Brands, Inc.; *Int'l*, pg. 7748
49ER COMMUNICATIONS; *U.S. Private*, pg. 15
49 NORTH RESOURCES INC.; *Int'l*, pg. 11
49'S LIMITED—See Entain PLC; *Int'l*, pg. 2449
4AIM SICAF SPA; *Int'l*, pg. 11
4B AFRICA ELEVATOR COMPONENTS (PTY) LIMITED—See Braime Group Plc; *Int'l*, pg. 1136
4BASEBIO PLC; *Int'l*, pg. 11
4BASEBIO S.L.U—See 2invest AG; *Int'l*, pg. 5
4B ASIA PACIFIC COMPANY LIMITED—See Braime Group Plc; *Int'l*, pg. 1136
4B BRAIME (CHANGZHOU) INDUSTRIAL CONTROL EQUIPMENT COMPANY LIMITED—See Braime Group Plc; *Int'l*, pg. 1136
4B BRAIME COMPONENTS LIMITED—See Braime Group Plc; *Int'l*, pg. 1136
4B ELEVATOR COMPONENTS LIMITED—See Braime Group Plc; *Int'l*, pg. 1136
4BIOFUELS S.A.—See 2Valorise N.V.; *Int'l*, pg. 5
4BIO MEDICAMENTOS S.A.—See Raia Drogasil S.A.; *Int'l*, pg. 6182
4BRANDS REPLY GMBH & CO, KG—See Reply S.p.A.; *Int'l*, pg. 6290
4 BUSINESS LIMITED—See OCRA (Isle of Man) Limited; *Int'l*, pg. 5520
4BY4 INC.; *Int'l*, pg. 11
4CABLE TV INTERNATIONAL, INC.; *U.S. Public*, pg. 9
4CARE GMBH—See EssilorLuxottica SA; *Int'l*, pg. 2515
4CAST INC.—See Malam-Team Ltd.; *Int'l*, pg. 4659
4CAST LTD.—See Malam-Team Ltd.; *Int'l*, pg. 4659
4C FOODS CORPORATION; *U.S. Private*, pg. 15
4C GROUP AB; *Int'l*, pg. 11
4CITE MARKETING, LLC—See Dentsu Group Inc.; *Int'l*, pg. 2036
4CLICKS SOLUTIONS, LLC—See Fortive Corporation; *U.S. Public*, pg. 872
4C OFFSHORE LTD.—See TGS ASA; *Int'l*, pg. 7587
4 CORNERS CUSTOM HOMES; *U.S. Private*, pg. 14
4CORNERS HOMES; *U.S. Private*, pg. 15
4CS HOLDINGS CO., LTD.; *Int'l*, pg. 11
4C STRATEGIES AB—See 4C Group AB; *Int'l*, pg. 11
4DDDD CORPORATION—See Gaseteria Oil Corp.; *U.S. Private*, pg. 1648
4DMEDICAL LIMITED; *Int'l*, pg. 11
4DMED, LTD.; *Int'l*, pg. 11
4D MOLECULAR THERAPEUTICS, INC.; *U.S. Public*, pg. 9
4D PHARMA PLC; *Int'l*, pg. 11
4DS MEMORY LIMITED; *Int'l*, pg. 11
4DSP LLC—See AMETEK, Inc.; *U.S. Public*, pg. 119
4D TECHNOLOGY CORPORATION—See Onto Innovation Inc.; *U.S. Public*, pg. 1605
4FINANCE HOLDING S.A.; *Int'l*, pg. 11
4 FORCES GROUP LLC; *U.S. Private*, pg. 14
4 FREE AG—See NSI Asset AG; *Int'l*, pg. 5477
4FRONT CREDIT UNION; *U.S. Private*, pg. 15
4FRONT ENGINEERED SOLUTIONS, INC.—See ASSA ABLOY AB; *Int'l*, pg. 633
4FRONT ENGINEERED SOLUTIONS - MUSKEGO—See ASSA ABLOY AB; *Int'l*, pg. 633
4FRONT SERVICES LIMITED—See NCR Voyix Corporation.; *U.S. Public*, pg. 1501
4FRONT VENTURES CORP.; *U.S. Public*, pg. 9
4FUN MEDIA S.A.; *Int'l*, pg. 12
4G ENTERPRISES, INC.; *U.S. Private*, pg. 15
4 GLOBAL PLC; *Int'l*, pg. 10
4-H TRANSPORTATION CO. INC.; *U.S. Private*, pg. 14
4IG NYRT.; *Int'l*, pg. 12
4IMPRINT GROUP PLC; *Int'l*, pg. 12
4IMPRINT INC.—See 4imprint Group plc; *Int'l*, pg. 12
4INFO, INC.—See Novacap Management Inc.; *Int'l*, pg. 5453
4IP MANAGEMENT AG; *Int'l*, pg. 12
4IT, INC.—See Court Square Capital Partners, L.P.; *U.S. Private*, pg. 1070
4. JULI A.D.; *Int'l*, pg. 10
4KIDZ INC.; *U.S. Private*, pg. 15
4K INVEST INTERNATIONAL; *Int'l*, pg. 12
4K S.R.L.—See CompuGroup Medical SE & Co. KGaA; *Int'l*, pg. 1755
4LIFE RESEARCH LC; *U.S. Private*, pg. 15
4M BUILDING SOLUTIONS, INC.—See O2 Investment Partners, LLC; *U.S. Private*, pg. 2982
4M METALS, INC.—See Industrial Opportunity Partners, LLC; *U.S. Private*, pg. 2067
4MOTIONS GMBH—See RWE AG; *Int'l*, pg. 6433
4M; *Int'l*, pg. 12
4M SYSTEMS INC.—See Perfect Holding SA; *Int'l*, pg. 5798
4M SYSTEMS LTD—See Perfect Holding SA; *Int'l*, pg. 5798
4M SYSTEMS SA—See Perfect Holding SA; *Int'l*, pg. 5798
4 OFFICE AUTOMATION LTD.; *Int'l*, pg. 10
4OVER, INC.; *U.S. Private*, pg. 15

4REFUEL CANADA LP—See Finning International Inc.; *Int'l*, pg. 2676
4R ENERGY CORPORATION—See Nissan Motor Co., Ltd.; *Int'l*, pg. 5367
4 RIVERS EQUIPMENT LLC; *U.S. Private*, pg. 14
4SC AG; *Int'l*, pg. 12
4 SCIENCE S.R.L.—See Itway S.p.A.; *Int'l*, pg. 3845
4 SEASONS CAR WASH—See Splash Car Wash, Inc.; *U.S. Private*, pg. 3759
4. SEPTEMBAR A.D.; *Int'l*, pg. 11
4 SERVICE S.R.L.—See TESMEC S.p.A.; *Int'l*, pg. 7572
4SIGHT HOLDINGS LTD.; *Int'l*, pg. 12
4SL CONSULTING LIMITED—See Databarracks Limited; *Int'l*, pg. 1977
4 STAR ELECTRONICS, INC.; *U.S. Private*, pg. 14
4SUBSEA AS—See Subsea 7 S.A.; *Int'l*, pg. 7248
4SURE.COM, INC.—See The ODP Corporation; *U.S. Public*, pg. 2117
4 SWEET BRIAR ROAD LIMITED—See ANSA McAL Limited; *Int'l*, pg. 476
4-TELL INC.—See Scaleworks, Inc.; *U.S. Private*, pg. 3561
4TH STREET HOLDINGS LLC—See CareTrust REIT, Inc.; *U.S. Public*, pg. 435
4TITUDE LTD.—See Azenta, Inc.; *U.S. Public*, pg. 257
4U APPLICATIONS, INC—See FUJISOFT INCORPORATED; *Int'l*, pg. 2830
4 VILLY INC.; *U.S. Private*, pg. 14
4WALL ENTERTAINMENT, INC. - ORANGE COUNTY—See 4Wall Entertainment, Inc.; *U.S. Private*, pg. 15
4WALL ENTERTAINMENT, INC.; *U.S. Private*, pg. 15
4 WALLS, INC.; *U.S. Private*, pg. 15
4WARRANTY CORPORATION—See Tiptree Inc.; *U.S. Public*, pg. 2159
4 WAY SUSPENSION PRODUCTS PTY. LTD.—See Eastern Polymer Group Public Company Limited; *Int'l*, pg. 2273
4WHEELS SERVICE + LOGISTIK GMBH—See CAPCELLENCE Mittelstandspartner GmbH; *Int'l*, pg. 1302

5

500.COM LIMITED; *Int'l*, pg. 12
500 GROUP INC.—See Boxabl Inc.; *U.S. Private*, pg. 626
500 MILDRED AVENUE PRIMOS, LLC—See CubeSmart; *U.S. Public*, pg. 603
500VOLT INC; *Int'l*, pg. 12
5:01 ACQUISITION CORP.; *U.S. Public*, pg. 9
THE 501 ALLIANCE; *U.S. Private*, pg. 3980
502386 ALBERTA LTD; *Int'l*, pg. 12
505DESIGN CHARLOTTE, INC.—See Cooper Carry, Inc; *U.S. Private*, pg. 1041
505 GAMES GMBH—See Digital Bros SpA; *Int'l*, pg. 2120
505 GAMES LTD—See Digital Bros SpA; *Int'l*, pg. 2120
505 GAMES S.R.L—See Digital Bros SpA; *Int'l*, pg. 2120
50 BEALE STREET LLC—See Paramount Group Inc.; *U.S. Public*, pg. 1637
50HERTZ OFFSHORE GMBH—See Elia Group SA; *Int'l*, pg. 2360
50HERTZ TRANSMISSION GMBH—See Elia Group SA; *Int'l*, pg. 2360
50 SOUTH CAPITAL ADVISORS, LLC—See Northern Trust Corporation; *U.S. Public*, pg. 1538
511220 N.B. INC.—See Immersion Corporation; *U.S. Public*, pg. 1112
5.11 ACQUISITION CORP.—See Compass Diversified Holdings; *U.S. Public*, pg. 559
5.11, INC.—See Compass Diversified Holdings; *U.S. Public*, pg. 560
5.11 INTERNATIONAL A.B.—See Compass Diversified Holdings; *U.S. Public*, pg. 559
5.11 SOURCING, LIMITED—See Compass Diversified Holdings; *U.S. Public*, pg. 559
518 PROPERTY MANAGEMENT AND LEASING, LLC—See State Automobile Mutual Insurance Company; *U.S. Private*, pg. 3791
51 CREDIT CARD INC.; *Int'l*, pg. 12
51JOB, INC.; *Int'l*, pg. 12
51TALK ONLINE EDUCATION GROUP; *Int'l*, pg. 12
520 BROADWAY PARALLEL REIT LLC—See Vornado Realty Trust; *U.S. Public*, pg. 2310
524 PARTICIPACOES S.A.; *Int'l*, pg. 12
525 MADE IN AMERICA INC.; *U.S. Private*, pg. 16
52 ALDERLEY ROAD LLP—See HCA Healthcare, Inc.; *U.S. Public*, pg. 990
52 WEEKS ENTERTAINMENT LIMITED; *Int'l*, pg. 12
545 LLC—See Kellanova; *U.S. Public*, pg. 1218
54 LOMBARD STREET INVESTMENTS LIMITED—See Barclays PLC; *Int'l*, pg. 859
54TH STREET MEDICAL PLAZA, INC.—See Humana, Inc.; *U.S. Public*, pg. 1069
555 1290 HOLDINGS LLC—See Vornado Realty Trust; *U.S. Public*, pg. 2310
55 NORTH MINING, INC.; *Int'l*, pg. 13
55 NORTH MINING, INC.; *Int'l*, pg. 13
55 WEST 17TH STREET PARTNERS LLC.—See Toll Brothers, Inc.; *U.S. Public*, pg. 2161
561870 ONTARIO LTD; *Int'l*, pg. 13

COMPANY NAME INDEX

565 CONSTRUCTION JOINT STOCK COMPANY; *Int'l*, pg. 13
5700 WASHINGTON AVENUE, LLC—See CubeSmart; *U.S. Public*, pg. 603
5715 BURNET ROAD, LLC—See CubeSmart; *U.S. Public*, pg. 603
577 INVESTMENT CORPORATION; *Int'l*, pg. 13
58.COM INC.; *Int'l*, pg. 13
591182 ONTARIO LIMITED; *Int'l*, pg. 13
591226 SASKATCHEWAN LTD; *Int'l*, pg. 13
595242 BC LTD; *Int'l*, pg. 13
598755 B.C. LTD; *Int'l*, pg. 13
59 CLUB ASIA CO., LTD.—See U City Public Company Limited; *Int'l*, pg. 7996
5 ALARM FIRE & SAFETY EQUIPMENT, LLC—See Rotunda Capital Partners LLC; *U.S. Private*, pg. 3488
5AM SOLUTIONS INC.; *U.S. Private*, pg. 16
5AM VENTURE MANAGEMENT, LLC; *U.S. Private*, pg. 16
5BARZ INTERNATIONAL INC.; *U.S. Private*, pg. 16
5B INVESTMENTS, INC.; *U.S. Private*, pg. 16
5 B'S INC.; *U.S. Private*, pg. 15
5BY5, LLC; *U.S. Private*, pg. 15
5C INVESTMENTS, LLC—See Campbell Soup Company; *U.S. Public*, pg. 427
5 DEVELOPMENT CORP.; *U.S. Private*, pg. 15
5D MARKETING LLC—See Plains GP Holdings, L.P.; *U.S. Public*, pg. 1697
5-D SYSTEMS, INC.—See Kratos Defense & Security Solutions, Inc.; *U.S. Public*, pg. 1276
5E ADVANCED MATERIALS, INC.; *U.S. Public*, pg. 9
5FLOW GMBH—See Matthews International Corporation; *U.S. Public*, pg. 1399
5G EDGE ACQUISITION CORP.; *U.S. Public*, pg. 9
5G NETWORK OPERATIONS PTY., LTD.—See 5G Networks Limited; *Int'l*, pg. 13
5G NETWORKS HOLDINGS PTY. LTD.—See 5G Networks Limited; *Int'l*, pg. 13
5G NETWORKS LIMITED; *Int'l*, pg. 13
515J HOLDING GROUP CO., LTD.; *Int'l*, pg. 13
5J OILFIELD SERVICES, LLC—See SMG Industries Inc.; *U.S. Public*, pg. 1896
5K YUZEY TEKNOLOJILERI A.S.—See Gentas AS; *Int'l*, pg. 2928
5LINX ENTERPRISES, INC.; *U.S. Private*, pg. 16
5METACOM; *U.S. Private*, pg. 16
5N PLUS ASIA LIMITED—See 5N Plus Inc.; *Int'l*, pg. 13
5N PLUS BELGIUM SA—See 5N Plus Inc.; *Int'l*, pg. 13
5N PLUS INC.; *Int'l*, pg. 13
5N PLUS LUBECK GMBH—See 5N Plus Inc.; *Int'l*, pg. 13
5N PLUS UK LIMITED—See 5N Plus Inc.; *Int'l*, pg. 13
5N PLUS WISCONSIN INC—See 5N Plus Inc.; *Int'l*, pg. 13
5N PV GMBH—See 5N Plus Inc.; *Int'l*, pg. 13
5. OKTOBAR A.D.; *Int'l*, pg. 12
5PAISA CAPITAL LTD.; *Int'l*, pg. 13
5 STAR BUILDING PRODUCTS LLC—See Installed Building Products, Inc.; *U.S. Public*, pg. 1131
5 STAR HOTEL LAUNDRY, INC; *U.S. Private*, pg. 16
5-STAR REFRIGERATION & AIR CONDITIONING, INC.; *U.S. Private*, pg. 16
5 STAR ROOFING & RESTORATION LLC; *U.S. Private*, pg. 16
5 STAR TERMITE & PEST CONTROL, INC.—See Arrow Exterminators Inc.; *U.S. Private*, pg. 335
5 SUR 5 S.A.—See Tofane Global SAS; *Int'l*, pg. 7774
5TH GEAR ADVERTISING; *U.S. Private*, pg. 16
5TH GEAR TECHNOLOGIES CONCEPTS, INC.; *U.S. Private*, pg. 16
5TH KIND, INC—See Sohonet Limited; *Int'l*, pg. 7060
5TH PLANET GAMES A/S; *Int'l*, pg. 14
5V INC.; *Int'l*, pg. 14
5W PUBLIC RELATIONS; *U.S. Private*, pg. 16
5W PUBLIC RELATIONS—See 5W Public Relations; *U.S. Private*, pg. 16

6

600956 ONTARIO LTD; *Int'l*, pg. 14
600 GOODALE, L.L.C.—See Starwood Real Estate Income Trust, Inc.; *U.S. Public*, pg. 3789
THE 600 GROUP (OVERSEAS) LIMITED—See The 600 Group PLC; *Int'l*, pg. 7609
THE 600 GROUP PLC; *Int'l*, pg. 7609
600 INTERNATIONAL LTD—See The 600 Group PLC; *Int'l*, pg. 7609
600 LB GORILLAS INC; *U.S. Private*, pg. 16
600 MACHINERY INTERNATIONAL LTD—See The 600 Group PLC; *Int'l*, pg. 7609
600 MACHINE TOOLS NEW SOUTH WALES—See The 600 Group PLC; *Int'l*, pg. 7609
600 MACHINE TOOLS NEW ZEALAND—See The 600 Group PLC; *Int'l*, pg. 7609
600 MACHINE TOOLS PTY LTD—See The 600 Group PLC; *Int'l*, pg. 7609
600 MACHINE TOOLS QUEENSLAND—See The 600 Group PLC; *Int'l*, pg. 7609
600 MACHINE TOOLS—See The 600 Group PLC; *Int'l*, pg. 7609
600 MACHINE TOOLS VICTORIA—See The 600 Group PLC; *Int'l*, pg. 7609
600 RACING INC.—See Sonic Financial Corporation; *U.S. Private*, pg. 3713
600SA HOLDINGS (PTY) LTD.—See enX Group Limited; *Int'l*, pg. 2456
600SA MACHINE TOOLS (PTY.) LTD.—See Quaser Machine Tools, Inc.; *U.S. Public*, pg. 6156
THE 600 UK LTD.—See The 600 Group PLC; *Int'l*, pg. 7609
602390 ONTARIO LIMITED; *Int'l*, pg. 14
605 STUDIOS, LLC—See Broadridge Financial Solutions, Inc.; *U.S. Public*, pg. 391
60 DEGREES PHARMACEUTICALS, INC.; *U.S. Public*, pg. 9
60 PLUS ASSOCIATION; *U.S. Private*, pg. 16
610 SAWDUST ROAD, LLC—See CubeSmart; *U.S. Public*, pg. 603
615315 SASKATCHEWAN LTD; *Int'l*, pg. 14
61 SOUTHWARK STREET LTD—See Helical Plc; *Int'l*, pg. 3329
62NORD AS—See Flakk Holding AS; *Int'l*, pg. 2697
63 MOONS TECHNOLOGIES LIMITED; *Int'l*, pg. 14
650 MADISON OWNER LLC—See Vornado Realty Trust; *U.S. Public*, pg. 2310
655 WEST BROADWAY, LLC—See MetLife, Inc.; *U.S. Public*, pg. 1429
65PLUS S.R.L.—See Gruppo MutuiOnline S.p.A; *Int'l*, pg. 3140
668824 ALBERTA LTD; *Int'l*, pg. 14
669069 ALBERTA LTD; *Int'l*, pg. 14
66DEGREES INC.—See Sunstone Partners Management LLC; *U.S. Private*, pg. 3873
66 RESOURCES CORP.; *Int'l*, pg. 14
695 ATLANTIC AVENUE COMPANY, LLC—See The Plymouth Rock Co.; *U.S. Private*, pg. 4097
6CONNEX CHINA—See Dura Software Series A Qof LLC; *U.S. Private*, pg. 1292
6CONNEX INC.—See Dura Software Series A Qof LLC; *U.S. Private*, pg. 1292
6DEGREES INTEGRATED COMMUNICATIONS CORP.—See Stagwell, Inc.; *U.S. Public*, pg. 1925
6D GLOBAL TECHNOLOGIES, INC.; *U.S. Public*, pg. 9
6FUSION USA, INC.; *U.S. Private*, pg. 16
6GWORLD, INC.—See InterDigital, Inc.; *U.S. Public*, pg. 1143
6K SYSTEMS, INC.; *U.S. Private*, pg. 16
6 SWEET BRIAR ROAD LIMITED—See ANSA McAL Limited; *Int'l*, pg. 476
6TH & K LTD. PARTNERSHIP; *U.S. Private*, pg. 16
6TH WAVE INNOVATIONS CORP.—See Sixth Wave Innovations Inc.; *Int'l*, pg. 6968

7

7000 SET MEAL SAS—See Compass Group PLC; *Int'l*, pg. 1750
THE 707 COMPANY—See Safeguard Chemical Corporation; *U.S. Private*, pg. 3524
70 CC, LLC—See Howard Hughes Holdings Inc.; *U.S. Public*, pg. 1060
711 AIR CORP.—See Allen Holding Inc.; *U.S. Private*, pg. 179
714607 ONTARIO LTD.; *Int'l*, pg. 14
720 DEGREES OY—See Investment AB Latour; *Int'l*, pg. 3780
723926 ONTARIO LIMITED; *Int'l*, pg. 14
727 COMMUNICATIONS, INC.; *U.S. Public*, pg. 9
72ANDSUNNY PARTNERS LLC—See Stagwell, Inc.; *U.S. Public*, pg. 1925
72ANDSUNNY—See Stagwell, Inc.; *U.S. Public*, pg. 1925
7324375 CANADA INC.—See Swisher Hygiene Inc.; *U.S. Private*, pg. 3894
733907 ONTARIO LTD; *Int'l*, pg. 14
734758 ONTARIO LIMITED; *Int'l*, pg. 14
777 PARTNERS LLC; *U.S. Private*, pg. 17
THE 77 BANK, LTD.; *Int'l*, pg. 7609
THE 77 BANK LTD. - TREASURY ADMINISTRATION & INTERNATIONAL DIVISION—See The 77 Bank, Ltd.; *Int'l*, pg. 7609
77 BUSINESS SERVICES CO., LTD.—See The 77 Bank, Ltd.; *Int'l*, pg. 7609
THE 77 CARD CO., LTD.—See The 77 Bank, Ltd.; *Int'l*, pg. 7610
77 COMPUTER SERVICES CO., LTD.—See The 77 Bank, Ltd.; *Int'l*, pg. 7609
77 LEASE CO., LTD.—See The 77 Bank, Ltd.; *Int'l*, pg. 7609
77 SHIN-YO HOSYO CO., LTD.—See The 77 Bank, Ltd.; *Int'l*, pg. 7609
786 INVESTMENTS LIMITED; *Int'l*, pg. 14
79NORTH, INC.—See Miata Metals Corp.; *Int'l*, pg. 4873
79NORTH, INC.; *Int'l*, pg. 15
79 RESOURCES LTD.; *Int'l*, pg. 15
7 ACQUISITION CORPORATION; *U.S. Public*, pg. 9
7AC TECHNOLOGIES INC.—See Emerson Electric Co.; *U.S. Public*, pg. 740
7 C'S MANUFACTURING, INC.; *U.S. Private*, pg. 16
7C SOLARPARKEN AG; *Int'l*, pg. 15
7C SOLARPARKEN BELGIUM B.V.—See 7C Solarparken AG; *Int'l*, pg. 15
7C SOLARPARKEN NV—See 7C Solarparken AG; *Int'l*, pg. 15
7DAYS GROUP GMBH & CO. KG; *Int'l*, pg. 15
7DAYS MEDIA SERVICES GMBH—See 7Days Group GmbH & Co. KG; *Int'l*, pg. 15
7DELTA, INC.—See The Carlyle Group Inc.; *U.S. Private*, pg. 2048
7DIGITAL GROUP PLC—See Songtradr, Inc.; *U.S. Private*, pg. 3713
7DIGITAL GROUP PLC; *U.S. Private*, pg. 17
7DREAM.COM CO., LTD.—See Seven & i Holdings Co., Ltd.; *Int'l*, pg. 6730
7-ELEVEN CANADA, INC.—See Seven & i Holdings Co., Ltd.; *Int'l*, pg. 6731
7-ELEVEN, INC.—See Seven & i Holdings Co., Ltd.; *Int'l*, pg. 6731
7-ELEVEN MALAYSIA HOLDINGS BERHAD; *Int'l*, pg. 14
7-ELEVEN STORES PTY. LTD.; *Int'l*, pg. 14
7FC LLP; *Int'l*, pg. 15
7 FOR ALL MANKIND—See GMM Capital LLC; *U.S. Private*, pg. 1722
7GC & CO. HOLDINGS INC.; *U.S. Public*, pg. 9
7G DISTRIBUTING, LLC; *U.S. Private*, pg. 17
7IM INVESTMENT & RETIREMENT SOLUTIONS LTD.—See Caledonia Investments plc; *Int'l*, pg. 1262
7. JULI A.D.; *Int'l*, pg. 14
7. JULI MAJKE JEVROSIME 47-49 A.D.; *Int'l*, pg. 14
7LAYERS S.R.L.—See Swisscom AG; *Int'l*, pg. 7373
7NR RETAIL LIMITED; *Int'l*, pg. 15
7PIXEL S.R.L.—See Gruppo MutuiOnline S.p.A; *Int'l*, pg. 3140
7ROAD.COM LIMITED—See SOHU.com Ltd.; *Int'l*, pg. 7060
7ROAD HOLDINGS LIMITED; *Int'l*, pg. 15
7SAFE LIMITED—See The Carlyle Group Inc.; *U.S. Private*, pg. 2051
7SEAS ENTERTAINMENT LIMITED; *Int'l*, pg. 15
7SUMMITS, LLC—See International Business Machines Corporation; *U.S. Public*, pg. 1145
7-TECHNOLOGIE A/S—See Schneider Electric SE; *Int'l*, pg. 6625
7TH AVENUE SHOWCASE LTD—See The New York Look Inc.; *U.S. Private*, pg. 4083
7THSENSE DESIGN LIMITED; *Int'l*, pg. 15
7 WEST 34TH STREET LLC—See Vornado Realty Trust; *U.S. Public*, pg. 2310

8

800 SUPER HOLDINGS LIMITED—See Keppel Corporation Limited; *Int'l*, pg. 4130
801 POLARIS HOLDINGS, L.L.C.—See Starwood Real Estate Income Trust, Inc.; *U.S. Private*, pg. 3790
80/20 INC.; *U.S. Private*, pg. 17
808 RENEWABLE ENERGY CORP.; *U.S. Public*, pg. 9
80 ON THE COMMONS, L.L.C.—See Starwood Real Estate Income Trust, Inc.; *U.S. Private*, pg. 3789
80STEES.COM INC.; *U.S. Private*, pg. 17
80 WESTCLIFF (PTY) LTD.—See LVMH Moet Hennessy Louis Vuitton SE; *Int'l*, pg. 4590
8121 INSURANCE MANAGEMENT, INC.—See Clayton, Dubilier & Rice, LLC; *U.S. Private*, pg. 927
8121 INSURANCE MANAGEMENT, INC.—See Mubadala Investment Company PJSC; *Int'l*, pg. 5076
8121 INSURANCE MANAGEMENT, INC.—See Stone Point Capital LLC; *U.S. Private*, pg. 3825
84.51 LLC—See The Kroger Co.; *U.S. Public*, pg. 2107
845453 ONTARIO LTD; *Int'l*, pg. 15
84 COMPONENTS COMPANY—See 84 Lumber Company; *U.S. Private*, pg. 17
84 FINANCIAL L.P.—See 84 Lumber Company; *U.S. Private*, pg. 17
84 LUMBER COMPANY - CHARLOTTE TRUSS PLANT—See 84 Lumber Company; *U.S. Private*, pg. 17
84 LUMBER COMPANY - COAL CENTER TRUSS PLANT—See 84 Lumber Company; *U.S. Private*, pg. 17
84 LUMBER COMPANY - MT AIRY TRUSS PLANT—See 84 Lumber Company; *U.S. Private*, pg. 17
84 LUMBER COMPANY; *U.S. Private*, pg. 17
850 THORN ST INC—See Thomson Properties Inc.; *U.S. Private*, pg. 4162
866229 ONTARIO INC.; *Int'l*, pg. 15
888 MEDIA CO., LTD.—See BTS Group Holdings Public Company Limited; *Int'l*, pg. 1205
88 ENERGY LIMITED; *Int'l*, pg. 15
890 5TH AVENUE PARTNERS, INC.; *U.S. Public*, pg. 10
89419 BC LTD; *Int'l*, pg. 15
898984 ONTARIO INC; *Int'l*, pg. 15
8990 HOLDINGS, INC.; *Int'l*, pg. 15
8990 HOUSING DEVELOPMENT CORP.—See 8990 Holdings, Inc.; *Int'l*, pg. 15
89BIO, INC.; *U.S. Public*, pg. 10
8BALL MUSIC B.V.—See Bertelsmann SE & Co. KGaA; *Int'l*, pg. 989
8COMMON LIMITED; *Int'l*, pg. 16

8I ACQUISITION 2 CORP.
CORPORATE AFFILIATIONS

8I ACQUISITION 2 CORP.; *Int'l*, pg. 15
8I ENTERPRISES ACQUISITION CORP; *Int'l*, pg. 16
8I HOLDINGS LIMITED; *Int'l*, pg. 16
8 IN 1 PET PRODUCTS GMBH—See Spectrum Brands Holdings, Inc.; *U.S. Public*, pg. 1916
8IP EMERGING COMPANIES LIMITED; *Int'l*, pg. 15
8K MILES SOFTWARE SERVICES LTD; *Int'l*, pg. 15
8. NOVEMBAR A.D.; *Int'l*, pg. 15
8TELECOM INTERNATIONAL HOLDINGS CO. LTD.; *Int'l*, pg. 16
8TH AVENUE FOOD & PROVISIONS, INC.—See Post Holdings, Inc.; *U.S. Public*, pg. 1703
8TH LIGHT, INC.; *U.S. Private*, pg. 17
8VIC HOLDINGS LIMITED; *Int'l*, pg. 16
8VIC JOOY MEDIA SDN. BHD.—See 8VI Holdings Limited; *Int'l*, pg. 16
8VIC MALAYSIA SDN. BHD.—See 8VI Holdings Limited; *Int'l*, pg. 16
8VI HOLDINGS LIMITED; *Int'l*, pg. 16
8WORKS LTD.—See Marsh & McLennan Companies, Inc.; *U.S. Public*, pg. 1374
8X8, INC.; *U.S. Public*, pg. 10
8X8 INTERNATIONAL PTY LTD.—See 8x8, Inc.; *U.S. Public*, pg. 10
8X8 INTERNATIONAL SRL—See 8x8, Inc.; *U.S. Public*, pg. 10
8X8 UK LIMITED—See 8x8, Inc.; *U.S. Public*, pg. 10

9

9008 GROUP INC.; *U.S. Private*, pg. 17
901D, LLC—See Curtiss-Wright Corporation; *U.S. Public*, pg. 611
9039-7571 QUEBEC INC; *Int'l*, pg. 16
9083-7436 QUEBEC INC; *Int'l*, pg. 16
908 DEVELOPMENT GROUP; *U.S. Private*, pg. 17
908 DEVICES INC.; *U.S. Public*, pg. 10
909 PRODUCTION—See Vivehdi SE; *Int'l*, pg. 8275
90 DEGREES NORTH, INC.—See Transition Evergreen; *Int'l*, pg. 7900
90OCTANE, LLC; *U.S. Private*, pg. 17
9101-9091 QUEBEC INC.; *Int'l*, pg. 16
9108-9458 QUEBEC INC.—See Welltower Inc.; *U.S. Public*, pg. 2347
9&10 NEWS; *U.S. Private*, pg. 17
9116-4509 QUEBEC INC.; *Int'l*, pg. 16
9119-6832 QUEBEC INC.; *Int'l*, pg. 16
911 HELP NOW, LLC—See Global Technologies, Ltd.; *U.S. Public*, pg. 945
9164-4187 QUEBEC INC.; *Int'l*, pg. 16
9183-7252 QUEBEC INC.—See Parker Hannifin Corporation; *U.S. Public*, pg. 1640
919 MARKETING COMPANY—See Greens Farms Capital LLC; *U.S. Private*, pg. 1779
919 MARKETING COMPANY—See Landon Capital Partners, LLC; *U.S. Private*, pg. 2386
919 MARKETING COMPANY; *U.S. Private*, pg. 17
9274-5322 QUEBEC INC.—See Viavi Solutions Inc.; *U.S. Public*, pg. 2295
92 ENERGY LIMITED—See ATI IA Energy Corp.; *Int'l*, pg. 669
92 ENERGY LIMITED; *Int'l*, pg. 16
93.3 LA RAZA KRZZ FM—See Spanish Broadcasting System Inc.; *U.S. Public*, pg. 1914
93 OCTANE; *U.S. Private*, pg. 17
941-2401 HEATING LIMITED; *Int'l*, pg. 16
942599 ONTARIO LIMITED; *Int'l*, pg. 16
944 MEDIA, LLC; *U.S. Private*, pg. 17
94 COUNTRY WKKJ—See iHeartMedia, Inc.; *U.S. Public*, pg. 1096
957447 ALBERTA LTD; *Int'l*, pg. 16
966850 ONTARIO INC; *Int'l*, pg. 16
970207 ONTARIO LIMITED; *Int'l*, pg. 16
979094 ALBERTA LTD; *Int'l*, pg. 16
982874 ONTARIO LTD; *Int'l*, pg. 16
9850-333 CANADA INC.—See Fagerhult Group AB; *Int'l*, pg. 2601
98.7 FM—See Window to the World Communications, Inc.; *U.S. Public*, pg. 4538
98.7 WFGR—See Brookfield Corporation; *Int'l*, pg. 1183
988883 ONTARIO INC; *Int'l*, pg. 16
9938982 CANADA INC.—See Fairfax Financial Holdings Limited; *Int'l*, pg. 2605
9938982 CANADA INC.—See Power Corporation of Canada; *Int'l*, pg. 5944
9994165 CANADA INC.—See Extendicare Inc.; *Int'l*, pg. 2591
999 DESIGN GROUP LTD.—See Matthews International Corporation; *U.S. Public*, pg. 1400
99 ACQUISITION GROUP INC.; *U.S. Public*, pg. 10
99 CENTS ONLY STORES LLC—See Ares Management Corporation; *U.S. Public*, pg. 187
99 CENTS ONLY STORES LLC—See Canada Pension Plan Investment Board; *U.S. Private*, pg. 1278
99DESIGNS INC.—See Cimpress plc; *Int'l*, pg. 1609
99 ICHIBA CO., LTD.—See G-7 HOLDINGS Inc.; *Int'l*, pg. 2862
99 LOYALTY LIMITED; *Int'l*, pg. 16

99 PRO MEDIA GMBH—See Bertelsmann SE & Co. KGaA; *Int'l*, pg. 989
99 RESTAURANTS, LLC—See Fidelity National Financial, Inc.; *U.S. Public*, pg. 830
9-BLOCK CO., LTD.—See EAT&HOLDINGS Co.,Ltd; *Int'l*, pg. 2277
9 CAPITAL CORP.; *Int'l*, pg. 16
9DIGIT CO., LTD.—See POSCO Holdings Inc.; *Int'l*, pg. 5937
9F INC.; *Int'l*, pg. 16
9FRUITSMEDIA, INC.—See Transcosmos Inc.; *Int'l*, pg. 7898
9GAUGE PARTNERS, LLC—See Element 78 LLC; *U.S. Private*, pg. 1357
9G ELEVATOR PTE. LTD.—See Otis Worldwide Corporation; *U.S. Public*, pg. 1622
9G PRODUCTS, INC.—See Compass Diversified Holdings; *U.S. Public*, pg. 559
9 METERS BIOPHARMA, INC.; *U.S. Public*, pg. 10
9R CANARY SDN. BHD.—See 9R Limited; *Int'l*, pg. 17
9REN GROUP—See First Reserve Management, L.P.; *U.S. Private*, pg. 1525
9R LEISURE SDN. BHD.—See 9R Limited; *Int'l*, pg. 17
9R LIMITED; *Int'l*, pg. 17
9R MANAGEMENT SDN. BHD.—See 9R Limited; *Int'l*, pg. 17
9SLIDES, INC.—See KKR & Co. Inc.; *U.S. Public*, pg. 1254
9 SQUARED INC.—See LaNetro Zed S.A.; *Int'l*, pg. 4408

A

A10 CENTER WILDAU GMBH—See Deutsche EuroShop AG; *Int'l*, pg. 2065
A10 CLINICAL SOLUTIONS, INC.; *U.S. Private*, pg. 29
A10 NETWORKS INC.—See A10 Networks, Inc.; *U.S. Public*, pg. 12
A10 NETWORKS, INC.—See A10 Networks, Inc.; *U.S. Public*, pg. 12
A10 NETWORKS, INC.; *U.S. Public*, pg. 12
A10 NETWORKS MALAYSIA SDN. BHD.—See A10 Networks, Inc.; *U.S. Public*, pg. 12
A1A AIRPORT & LIMOUSINE SERVICE; *U.S. Private*, pg. 29
A-1 ACID LIMITED; *Int'l*, pg. 19
A-1 A-LECTRICIAN INC.; *U.S. Private*, pg. 21
A1A TRANSPORTATION, INC.—See Mobico Group PLC; *Int'l*, pg. 5008
A1 BANK AG—See America Movil, S.A.B. de C.V.; *Int'l*, pg. 421
A1 BULGARIA EAD—See America Movil, S.A.B. de C.V.; *Int'l*, pg. 421
A1 CAPITAL YATIRIM MENKUL DEGERLER A.S.; *Int'l*, pg. 28
A1-CBISS LIMITED—See Diploma PLC; *Int'l*, pg. 2128
A-1 CHEMICAL, INC.—See Inland Supply Co., Inc.; *U.S. Private*, pg. 2079
A-1 CONTRACT STAFFING, LLC; *U.S. Private*, pg. 21
A1C PARTNERS, LLC; *U.S. Private*, pg. 29
A-1 DISPOSAL SERVICE, INC.—See Watts Trucking Service, Inc.; *U.S. Private*, pg. 4456
A-1 DOOR AND BUILDING SOLUTIONS INC.; *U.S. Private*, pg. 21
A1 ELEKTRO AG—See BKW AG; *Int'l*, pg. 1054
A1-ENVIROSCIENCES GMBH—See Diploma PLC; *Int'l*, pg. 2129
A1-ENVIROSCIENCES LIMITED—See Diploma PLC; *Int'l*, pg. 2129
A-1 EXCAVATING, INC.; *U.S. Private*, pg. 21
A-1 EXPRESS DELIVERY SERVICE, INC.; *U.S. Private*, pg. 21
A-1 FIBER GLASS, INC.; *U.S. Private*, pg. 21
A-1 FLORIDA SOD, INC.; *U.S. Private*, pg. 21
A-1 FREEMAN MOVING & STORAGE INC.; *U.S. Private*, pg. 21
A1 GARAGE DOOR SERVICES LLC; *U.S. Private*, pg. 29
A1 GROUP, INC.; *U.S. Private*, pg. 29
A-1 HEATING & AIR CONDITIONING, INC.; *U.S. Private*, pg. 21
A-1 HOSPITALITY PRODUCTS INC.; *U.S. Private*, pg. 21
A1 HRVATSKA D.O.O.—See America Movil, S.A.B. de C.V.; *Int'l*, pg. 421
A-1 INTERNATIONAL, INC.; *U.S. Private*, pg. 21
A1 INVESTMENTS & RESOURCES LTD.; *U.S. Private*, pg. 29
A-1 LIMOUSINE INC.; *U.S. Private*, pg. 21
A-1 MACHINING COMPANY—See Lionheart Ventures; *U.S. Private*, pg. 2464
A1 METAL RECYCLING LTD.—See Madison Dearborn Partners, LLC; *U.S. Private*, pg. 2541
A1 OUTDOOR—See The Interpublic Group of Companies, Inc.; *U.S. Public*, pg. 2097
A-1 PLATING INC.; *U.S. Private*, pg. 21
A1 POOL PARTS; *U.S. Private*, pg. 29
A1 PRINTER REPAIR & SUPPLIES, INC.—See Restored Digital Solutions, LLC; *U.S. Private*, pg. 3410
A-1 ROOF TRUSSES, LLC—See Builders FirstSource, Inc.; *U.S. Public*, pg. 409
A1 SERVICES (MANCHESTER) LIMITED—See Heidelberg Materials AG; *Int'l*, pg. 3308

A-1 STRIPING INC.—See Warburg Pincus LLC; *U.S. Private*, pg. 4439
A1 TELEKOM AUSTRIA AG—See America Movil, S.A.B. de C.V.; *Int'l*, pg. 421
A-1 TEMPS INC.; *U.S. Private*, pg. 21
A-1 TOOL CORPORATION—See Triangle Tool Corporation; *U.S. Private*, pg. 4226
A-1 TOYOTA; *U.S. Private*, pg. 21
A-1 TRUCK PARTS—See Auto-Wares, LLC; *U.S. Private*, pg. 398
A24 FILMS LLC; *U.S. Private*, pg. 29
A-27 SA—See Emmi AG; *Int'l*, pg. 2384
A2A AMBIENTE S.P.A.—See A2A S.p.A.; *Int'l*, pg. 29
A2A CALORE & SERVIZI S.R.L.—See A2A S.p.A.; *Int'l*, pg. 29
A2A CICLO IDRICO S.P.A.—See A2A S.p.A.; *Int'l*, pg. 29
A2A ENERGIA S.P.A.—See A2A S.p.A.; *Int'l*, pg. 29
A2A ENERGIEFUTURE S.P.A.—See A2A S.p.A.; *Int'l*, pg. 29
A2A GENCOGAS S.P.A.—See A2A S.p.A.; *Int'l*, pg. 29
A2A LOGISTICA S.P.A.—See A2A S.p.A.; *Int'l*, pg. 29
A2A MONTENEGRO D.O.O.—See A2A S.p.A.; *Int'l*, pg. 29
A2A RETI GAS S.P.A.—See A2A S.p.A.; *Int'l*, pg. 29
A2A SMART CITY S.P.A.—See A2A S.p.A.; *Int'l*, pg. 29
A2A S.P.A.; *Int'l*, pg. 29
A2A TRADING S.R.L.—See A2A S.p.A.; *Int'l*, pg. 29
A2B AUSTRALIA LIMITED—See ComfortDelGro Corporation Limited; *Int'l*, pg. 1712
A2C AIR COST CONTROL SAS—See HEICO Corporation; *U.S. Public*, pg. 1019
A 2 CUSTOMER CARE SP. Z O.O.—See Atende S.A.; *Int'l*, pg. 668
A2EP—See Roche Ltd., Consulting Group; *Int'l*, pg. 6376
A2E VENTURE CATALYSTS LIMITED; *Int'l*, pg. 30
A2 HEALTHCARE CORPORATION—See ITOCHU Corporation; *Int'l*, pg. 3834
A2 HEALTHCARE CORPORATION—See Nippon Telegraph & Telephone Corporation; *Int'l*, pg. 5350
A2IA SAS—See Mitek Systems, Inc.; *U.S. Public*, pg. 1452
A2I SA—See Airesis S.A.; *Int'l*, pg. 247
A2K TECHNOLOGIES LIMITED—See Schneider Electric SE; *Int'l*, pg. 6624
A2K TECHNOLOGIES PTY. LTD.—See Schneider Electric SE; *Int'l*, pg. 6624
A2L TECHNOLOGIES, INC.; *U.S. Private*, pg. 29
A2MEDIA CORPORATION—See Link & Motivation Inc.; *Int'l*, pg. 4513
A2MICILE EUROPE SA; *Int'l*, pg. 30
THE A2 MILK COMPANY LIMITED; *Int'l*, pg. 7610
A2M INDUSTRIES, SAS—See I Squared Capital Advisors (US) LLC; *U.S. Private*, pg. 2021
A2M INDUSTRIES, SAS—See TDR Capital LLP; *Int'l*, pg. 7490
A2Z ENVIRONMENTAL GROUP, LLC; *U.S. Private*, pg.
A2Z FIELD SERVICES; *U.S. Private*, pg. 29
A2Z, INC.; *U.S. Private*, pg. 29
A2Z INFRA ENGINEERING LIMITED; *Int'l*, pg. 30
A2Z INFRASERVICES LANKA PRIVATE LIMITED—See A2Z Infra Engineering Limited; *Int'l*, pg. 30
A2Z INFRASERVICES PRIVATE LIMITED—See A2Z Infra Engineering Limited; *Int'l*, pg. 30
A2Z INFRASTRUCTURE LIMITED—See A2Z Infra Engineering Limited; *Int'l*, pg. 30
A2Z POWERCOM LIMITED—See A2Z Infra Engineering Limited; *Int'l*, pg. 30
A2Z POWERTECH LIMITED—See A2Z Infra Engineering Limited; *Int'l*, pg. 30
A2Z SMART TECHNOLOGIES CORP.; *Int'l*, pg. 30
A3 ALLMANNA IT-OCH TELEKOMAKTI; *Int'l*, pg. 30
A3A STRATEGY CONSULTING GMBH—See adesso SE; *Int'l*, pg. 144
A3 COMMUNICATIONS INC.—See Platinum Equity, LLC; *U.S. Private*, pg. 3208
A3 DISTRIB SAS—See Brookfield Corporation; *Int'l*, pg. 1176
A3 DISTRIB SAS—See Elliott Management Corporation; *U.S. Private*, pg. 1369
A3GEO, INC.—See OceanSound Partners, LP; *U.S. Private*, pg. 2991
A3 GLOBAL, LLC; *U.S. Private*, pg. 29
A3 MULTIMEDIA S.L.U.—See Atresmedia Corporacion de Medios de Comunicacion, S.A.; *Int'l*, pg. 693
A3 PRIVATE AB; *Int'l*, pg. 30
A3 WATER SOLUTIONS GMBH—See EnviTec Biogas AG; *Int'l*, pg. 2455
A4 BUSINESS SOLUTIONS GMBH—See Osterreichische Post AG; *Int'l*, pg. 5653
A4E LTD.—See Staffline Group PLC; *Int'l*, pg. 7162
A4F-ALGAE FOR FUTURE SA; *Int'l*, pg. 30
A8 NEW MEDIA GROUP LTD.; *Int'l*, pg. 30
A9.COM, INC.—See Amazon.com, Inc.; *U.S. Public*, pg. 91
A.A.A. AG ALLGEMEINE ANLAGEVERWALTUNG; *Int'l*, pg. 22
AAA AIRCRAFT SUPPLY, LLC—See The Boeing Company; *U.S. Public*, pg. 2040
AAA ALLIED GROUP, INC—See The American Automobile Association, Inc.; *U.S. Private*, pg. 3985

COMPANY NAME INDEX

AAA ALLIED INSURANCE SERVICES, INC.—See The American Automobile Association, Inc.; *U.S. Private*, pg. 3985
AAA AUTO CLUB SOUTH—See The American Automobile Association, Inc.; *U.S. Private*, pg. 3985
AAA AUTO INTERNATIONAL A.S.—See Abris Capital Partners Sp. z o.o.; *Int'l*, pg. 69
AAA AVIATION PRIVATE LIMITED—See Delta Corp Ltd.; *Int'l*, pg. 2016
AAAA WORLD IMPORT EXPORT; *U.S. Private*, pg. 30
AAA BUSINESS SUPPLIES LIMITED PARTNERSHIP; *U.S. Private*, pg. 30
AAA CLUB ALLIANCE INC.—See The American Automobile Association, Inc.; *U.S. Private*, pg. 3985
AAA COOPER TRANSPORTATION, INC.—See Knight-Swift Transportation Holdings Inc.; *U.S. Public*, pg. 1269
AA ADVANCE AIR, INC.; *U.S. Private*, pg. 29
AAA FIRE SAFETY & ALARM INC.—See Pye-Barker Fire & Safety, LLC; *U.S. Private*, pg. 3309
AAA FLAG & BANNER MANUFACTURING CO., INC.; *U.S. Private*, pg. 30
AAA GALVANIZING - CHELSEA, INC.—See AZZ, Inc.; *U.S. Public*, pg. 258
AAA GALVANIZING - DIXON, INC.—See AZZ, Inc.; *U.S. Public*, pg. 258
AAA GALVANIZING - HAMILTON, INC.—See AZZ, Inc.; *U.S. Public*, pg. 258
AAA GALVANIZING - JOLIET, INC.—See AZZ, Inc.; *U.S. Public*, pg. 258
AAA GALVANIZING - PEORIA, INC.—See AZZ, Inc.; *U.S. Public*, pg. 258
AAA GALVANIZING - WINSTED, INC.—See AZZ, Inc.; *U.S. Public*, pg. 258
AAA HOME HEALTH INC.—See UnitedHealth Group Incorporated; *U.S. Public*, pg. 2243
AAA INVESTMENT CO.—See The American Automobile Association, Inc.; *U.S. Private*, pg. 3985
AA ALARMS, INC.—See Stanley Black & Decker, Inc.; *U.S. Public*, pg. 1931
AAA LIFE INSURANCE COMPANY—See The American Automobile Association, Inc.; *U.S. Private*, pg. 3985
AAA LTD.—See Sword Group SE; *Int'l*, pg. 7375
AAA MID-ATLANTIC INC.—See The American Automobile Association, Inc.; *U.S. Private*, pg. 3985
A.A. ANDERSON COMPANY INCORPORATED; *U.S. Private*, pg. 24
AAA NORTHERN CALIFORNIA, NEVADA & UTAH—See The American Automobile Association, Inc.; *U.S. Private*, pg. 3985
AAA NORTHWEST OHIO—See The American Automobile Association, Inc.; *U.S. Private*, pg. 3985
AAA REFRIGERATION SERVICE INC; *U.S. Private*, pg. 30
AAA SALES & ENGINEERING, INC. - ANGOLA—See Industrial Opportunity Partners, LLC; *U.S. Private*, pg. 2067
AAA SALES & ENGINEERING INC.—See Industrial Opportunity Partners, LLC; *U.S. Private*, pg. 2067
AA ASIA LIMITED—See Walgreens Boots Alliance, Inc.; *U.S. Public*, pg. 2321
AAA SUNDRIES INC.; *U.S. Private*, pg. 30
AAA TECHNOLOGIES LIMITED; *Int'l*, pg. 30
AAA TRANSPORTATION GROUP LTD.; *U.S. Private*, pg. 30
A&A AUTO PARTS STORES, INC.—See LKQ Corporation; *U.S. Public*, pg. 1334
AAA VALLEY GRAVEL, LLC—See Ahtna, Inc.; *U.S. Private*, pg. 131
AAAZA, INC.—See Admerasia, Inc.; *U.S. Private*, pg. 80
AABAKUS, INC.—See New Mountain Capital, LLC; *U.S. Private*, pg. 2901
AABAR INVESTMENT PJSC—See Mubadala Investment Company PJSC; *Int'l*, pg. 5074
AABAR PROPERTIES LLC—See Mubadala Investment Company PJSC; *Int'l*, pg. 5074
AABBITT ADHESIVES INC.; *U.S. Private*, pg. 30
AABHARAN JEWELLERY LLC—See NMC Health PLC; *Int'l*, pg. 5392
AABHARAN JEWELLERY LLC—See NMC Health PLC; *Int'l*, pg. 5392
AAB HOLDINGS PTY LIMITED; *Int'l*, pg. 30
AABR; *U.S. Private*, pg. 30
AAC ACOUSTIC TECHNOLOGIES (SHENZHEN) CO., LTD.—See AAC Technologies Holdings Inc.; *Int'l*, pg. 31
AAC ACOUSTIC TECHNOLOGIES—See AAC Technologies Holdings Inc.; *Int'l*, pg. 31
AAC ACOUSTIC TECHNOLOGIES SWEDEN AB—See AAC Technologies Holdings Inc.; *Int'l*, pg. 31
A.A. CASEY CO.; *U.S. Private*, pg. 24
AA CATER TRUCK MANUFACTURING COMPANY, INC.; *U.S. Private*, pg. 29
AAC CAPITAL BENELUX—See AAC Capital Partners Holding B.V.; *Int'l*, pg. 30
AAC CAPITAL PARTNERS HOLDING B.V.; *Int'l*, pg. 30
AAC CLYDE SPACE AB; *Int'l*, pg. 31
AAC CONTRACTING INC.; *U.S. Private*, pg. 30

AAC DALLAS OUTPATIENT CENTER, LLC—See AAC Holdings, Inc.; *U.S. Private*, pg. 30
AAC ENTERPRISES LLC; *U.S. Private*, pg. 30
AACER FLOORING LLC; *U.S. Private*, pg. 31
AAC GLOBAL AB—See Groupe BPCE; *Int'l*, pg. 3095
AAC GLOBAL DENMARK—See Groupe BPCE; *Int'l*, pg. 3095
AAC GLOBAL OY—See Groupe BPCE; *Int'l*, pg. 3095
AAC GROUP HOLDING CORP.—See Fenway Partners, LLC; *U.S. Private*, pg. 1495
AA CHARTER BROKERAGE LLC—See Macquarie Group Limited; *Int'l*, pg. 4627
AAC HOLDINGS, INC.; *U.S. Private*, pg. 30
AAC LAS VEGAS OUTPATIENT CENTER, LLC—See AAC Holdings, Inc.; *U.S. Private*, pg. 30
AAC MICROTECH (CHANGZHOU) CO., LTD.—See AAC Technologies Holdings Inc.; *Int'l*, pg. 31
AAC NORDIC ADVISORY AB—See AAC Capital Partners Holding B.V.; *Int'l*, pg. 30
AACOA EXTRUSIONS, INC.—See Tredegar Corporation; *U.S. Public*, pg. 2186
A & A CONTRACT CUSTOMS BROKERS LTD.; *Int'l*, pg. 17
AAC SAATCHI & SAATCHI—See Publicis Groupe S.A.; *Int'l*, pg. 6107
AAC STRUCTURAL FOAM LTD.—See Madison Dearborn Partners, LLC; *U.S. Private*, pg. 2541
AAC TECHNOLOGIES HOLDINGS INC.; *Int'l*, pg. 31
AACTION MOVERS; *U.S. Private*, pg. 31
A-ACTIVE TERMITE & PEST CONTROL COMPANY; *U.S. Private*, pg. 22
AAC WIRELESS TECHNOLOGIES AB—See AAC Technologies Holdings Inc.; *Int'l*, pg. 31
AADG, INC.—See ASSA ABLOY AB; *Int'l*, pg. 636
AADHAAR VENTURES INDIA LIMITED; *Int'l*, pg. 31
AADI AUSTRALIA PTY LTD—See Bapcor Limited; *Int'l*, pg. 857
AADI BIOSCIENCE, INC.; *U.S. Public*, pg. 12
AADI INDUSTRIES LTD.; *Int'l*, pg. 31
AADLEN BROTHERS AUTO WRECKING; *U.S. Private*, pg. 31
A&A ELECTRICAL DISTRIBUTORS LTD.—See Dewhurst Group plc; *Int'l*, pg. 2091
AA ELECTRIC INC.; *U.S. Private*, pg. 29
AA ELECTRIC SE INC.—See AA Electric Inc.; *U.S. Private*, pg. 29
AAEON ELECTRONICS, INC.—See ASUSTeK Computer Inc.; *Int'l*, pg. 663
AAEON ELECTRONICS—See ASUSTeK Computer Inc.; *Int'l*, pg. 663
AAEON TECHNOLOGY (EUROPE) B.V.—See ASUSTeK Computer Inc.; *Int'l*, pg. 663
AAEON TECHNOLOGY GMBH—See ASUSTeK Computer Inc.; *Int'l*, pg. 663
AAEON TECHNOLOGY INC.—See ASUSTeK Computer Inc.; *Int'l*, pg. 663
AAEON TECHNOLOGY SINGAPORE PTE LTD—See ASUSTeK Computer Inc.; *Int'l*, pg. 663
AAEON TECHNOLOGY (SUZHOU) INC.—See ASUSTeK Computer Inc.; *Int'l*, pg. 663
A&A EXPRESS, LLC—See Roadrunner Transportation Systems, Inc.; *U.S. Public*, pg. 1802
AAFA OF MISSISSIPPI, INC.—See Grupo Salinas, S.A. de C.V.; *Int'l*, pg. 3135
AAFCPAS, INC.; *U.S. Private*, pg. 31
AAF INTERNATIONAL B.V.—See Daikin Industries, Ltd.; *Int'l*, pg. 1936
AAF-LUFTTECHNIK GMBH—See Daikin Industries, Ltd.; *Int'l*, pg. 1932
AAGAARD FERTILITETSKLINIK APS—See Virtus Health Limited; *Int'l*, pg. 8248
AAGAM CAPITAL LIMITED; *Int'l*, pg. 31
THE AAGARD GROUP, LLC; *U.S. Private*, pg. 3980
AA GASKETS PTY LTD—See Amotiv Limited; *Int'l*, pg. 431
AAGE HEMPEL GROUP—See Grupo Arbulu S.L.; *Int'l*, pg. 3120
A AGENCIA BRASILEIRA DE PROMOCAO DE EXPORTACOES E INVESTIMENTOS; *Int'l*, pg. 17
AAG ENERGY HOLDINGS LTD.—See Xinjiang Xintai Natural Gas Co., Ltd.; *Int'l*, pg. 8532
AAGES DEVCO SERVICES S.A.—See Abengoa S.A.; *Int'l*, pg. 59
AAGES DEVCO SERVICES S.A.—See Algonquin Power & Utilities Corp.; *U.S. Public*, pg. 319
AAGES S.A.; *Int'l*, pg. 31
A&A GLOBAL INDUSTRIES INC.; *U.S. Private*, pg. 19
A.AGRATI S.P.A.; *Int'l*, pg. 23
A.A.G. STUCCHI ASIA PACIFIC LTD.—See A.A.G. STUCCHI s.r.l.; *Int'l*, pg. 22
A.A.G. STUCCHI NORTH AMERICA, INC.—See A.A.G. STUCCHI s.r.l.; *Int'l*, pg. 22
A.A.G. STUCCHI SHANGHAI LTD.—See A.A.G. STUCCHI s.r.l.; *Int'l*, pg. 22
A.A.G. STUCCHI S.R.L.; *Int'l*, pg. 22
AAH PHARMACEUTICALS LTD.—See McKesson Corporation; *U.S. Public*, pg. 1408
AAI AEROSONDE PTY LTD—See Textron Inc.; *U.S. Public*, pg. 2029

AAI ARCHITECTS, P.C.—See Adamson Associates Architects; *Int'l*, pg. 124
A&A IBARAKI CORPORATION—See A&A Material Corporation; *Int'l*, pg. 18
AAIC, INC.; *U.S. Private*, pg. 31
AAI CORP. - AUTOMATED TEST EQUIPMENT—See Textron Inc.; *U.S. Public*, pg. 2029
AAI CORPORATION—See Textron Inc.; *U.S. Public*, pg. 2029
AAI INSURANCE LTD.—See Suncorp Group Limited; *Int'l*, pg. 7311
AAIMCONTROLS, INC.—See Danfoss A/S; *Int'l*, pg. 1960
AA IMPORTING; *U.S. Private*, pg. 29
AA INDUSTRIAL BELTING (SHANGHAI) CO., LTD.; *Int'l*, pg. 30
AAI SERVICES CORPORATION—See Textron Inc.; *U.S. Public*, pg. 2029
AAJ CAPITAL 2 CORP.; *Int'l*, pg. 31
A & A JEWELRY TOOLS FINDINGS; *U.S. Private*, pg. 17
AAJ TECHNOLOGIES, INC.; *U.S. Private*, pg. 31
AAK AB; *Int'l*, pg. 31
AAKASH CHEMICALS & DYESTUFFS, INC.—See CenterOak Partners LLC; *U.S. Private*, pg. 816
AAKASH EXPLORATION SERVICES LIMITED; *Int'l*, pg. 32
AAK AUST. PTY. LTD.—See AAK AB; *Int'l*, pg. 31
AAK AUST. PTY LTD.—See AAK AB; *Int'l*, pg. 31
AAK AUSTRALIA PTY LTD.—See AAK AB; *Int'l*, pg. 31
AAK BD FOODS LTD.—See AAK AB; *Int'l*, pg. 31
AAK BELGIUM N.V.—See AAK AB; *Int'l*, pg. 31
AAK BF SARL—See AAK AB; *Int'l*, pg. 31
AAK BURKINA FASO SARL—See AAK AB; *Int'l*, pg. 31
AAK CANADA LTD.—See AAK AB; *Int'l*, pg. 31
AAK CHINA LTD.—See AAK AB; *Int'l*, pg. 31
AAK COLOMBIA S.A.S.—See AAK AB; *Int'l*, pg. 31
AAK COTE D'IVOIRE SASU—See AAK AB; *Int'l*, pg. 31
AAK CZECH REPUBLIC SPOL.S.R.O.—See AAK AB; *Int'l*, pg. 31
AAK CZECH REPUBLIC S.R.O.—See AAK AB; *Int'l*, pg. 31
AAK DALBY AB—See AAK AB; *Int'l*, pg. 32
AAK DENMARK A/S—See AAK AB; *Int'l*, pg. 32
AAK DO BRASIL INDUSTRIA E COMERCIA DE OLEOS VEGETAIS LTDA.—See AAK AB; *Int'l*, pg. 32
AAK DO BRASIL INDUSTRIA E COMERCIO DE OLEOS VEGETAIS LTDA.—See AAK AB; *Int'l*, pg. 32
AAK GERMANY GMBH—See AAK AB; *Int'l*, pg. 32
AAK HAVNEN A/S—See AAK AB; *Int'l*, pg. 32
AAK KAMANI PVT. LTD.—See AAK AB; *Int'l*, pg. 32
AAK MALAYSIA SDN. BHD.—See AAK AB; *Int'l*, pg. 32
AAK MALI SARL—See AAK AB; *Int'l*, pg. 32
AAK MEXICO, S.A. DE C.V.—See AAK AB; *Int'l*, pg. 32
AAK MIYOSHI JAPAN CO. LTD.—See AAK AB; *Int'l*, pg. 32
AAK NETHERLANDS BV—See AAK AB; *Int'l*, pg. 32
AAK NETHERLANDS BV—See AAK AB; *Int'l*, pg. 32
AAK NORWAY AS—See AAK AB; *Int'l*, pg. 32
AAK OOO—See AAK AB; *Int'l*, pg. 32
AAK POLAND SP. Z O. O.—See AAK AB; *Int'l*, pg. 32
AAK ROTTERDAM BV—See AAK AB; *Int'l*, pg. 32
AAK SG PTE. LTD.—See AAK AB; *Int'l*, pg. 32
AAK SINGAPORE PTE. LTD.—See AAK AB; *Int'l*, pg. 32
AAK SWEDEN AB—See AAK AB; *Int'l*, pg. 32
AAK TURKEY GIDA SANAYI VE TICARET LIMITED SIRKETI—See AAK AB; *Int'l*, pg. 32
AAK TURKEY GIDA SANAY VE TICARET LIMITED—See AAK AB; *Int'l*, pg. 32
AAK (UK) LIMITED—See AAK AB; *Int'l*, pg. 31
AAK (UK) LIMITED—See AAK AB; *Int'l*, pg. 31
AAK USA K1/K2 LLC—See AAK AB; *Int'l*, pg. 32
AAK USA RICHMOND CORP.—See AAK AB; *Int'l*, pg. 32
AALBERS TOOL & MOLD INC.; *U.S. Private*, pg. 32
AALBERTS INTEGRATED PIPING SYSTEMS APAC INC.—See Aalberts N.V.; *Int'l*, pg. 33
AALBERTS INTEGRATED PIPING SYSTEMS B.V.—See Aalberts N.V.; *Int'l*, pg. 33
AALBERTS N.V.; *Int'l*, pg. 33
AALBERTS SURFACE TECHNOLOGIES GMBH—See Aalberts N.V.; *Int'l*, pg. 33
AALBERTS SURFACE TREATMENT TAMWORTH LIMITED—See Aalberts N.V.; *Int'l*, pg. 33
AALBORG BOLDSPILKLUB A/S; *Int'l*, pg. 36
AALBORG CEMENT COMPANY INC.—See Cementir Holding N.V.; *Int'l*, pg. 1397
AALBORG INDUSTRIES D.O.O.—See Alfa Laval AB; *Int'l*, pg. 308
AALBORG INDUSTRIES LTDA—See Alfa Laval AB; *Int'l*, pg. 308
AALBORG PORTLAND (ANQING) CO., LTD.—See Cementir Holding N.V.; *Int'l*, pg. 1397
AALBORG PORTLAND A/S—See Cementir Holding N.V.; *Int'l*, pg. 1397
AALBORG PORTLAND BELGIUM SA—See Cementir Holding N.V.; *Int'l*, pg. 1397
AALBORG PORTLAND FRANCE SAS—See Cementir Holding N.V.; *Int'l*, pg. 1397
AALBORG PORTLAND HOLDING A/S—See Cementir Holding N.V.; *Int'l*, pg. 1397

AALBORG PORTLAND ISLANDI EHF—See Cementir Holding N.V.; *Int'l*, pg. 1397
AALBORG PORTLAND MALAYSIA SDN BHD—See Cementir Holding N.V.; *Int'l*, pg. 1397
AALBORG PORTLAND OOO—See Cementir Holding N.V.; *Int'l*, pg. 1397
AALBORG PORTLAND POLSKA SP.Z.O.O—See Cementir Holding N.V.; *Int'l*, pg. 1397
AALBORG PORTLAND US INC.—See Cementir Holding N.V.; *Int'l*, pg. 1397
AALBORG STEVEDORE COMPANY A/S—See Royal Arctic Line A/S; *Int'l*, pg. 6409
AALBORG WHITE ITALIA SRL—See Cementir Holding N.V.; *Int'l*, pg. 1397
AALCO FORWARDING INC.; *U.S. Private*, pg. 31
AALCO METALS LTD.—See Henley Management Company; *U.S. Private*, pg. 1916
AALF'S MANUFACTURING INC.—See Ropa Siete Leguas SA de CV; *Int'l*, pg. 6398
AALLIED DIE CASTING MANUFACTURING, INC.—See RCM Industries, Inc.; *U.S. Private*, pg. 3362
AALLIED DIE CASTING MANUFACTURING, INC.—See RCM Industries, Inc.; *U.S. Private*, pg. 3362
AALLON GROUP OY; *Int'l*, pg. 36
A&A LOGISTICS, LLC—See Roadrunner Transportation Systems, Inc.; *U.S. Public*, pg. 1802
AALP, INC. - ATLANTA—See AALP, Inc.; *U.S. Private*, pg. 31
AALP, INC. - CHICAGO—See AALP, Inc.; *U.S. Private*, pg. 31
AALP, INC. - CLEVELAND—See AALP, Inc.; *U.S. Private*, pg. 31
AALP, INC. - DENVER—See AALP, Inc.; *U.S. Private*, pg. 31
AALP, INC. - DETROIT—See AALP, Inc.; *U.S. Private*, pg. 31
AALP, INC. - KANSAS CITY—See AALP, Inc.; *U.S. Private*, pg. 31
AALP, INC. - LOS ANGELES—See AALP, Inc.; *U.S. Private*, pg. 31
AALP, INC. - MIAMI—See AALP, Inc.; *U.S. Private*, pg. 31
AALP, INC. - NEW YORK—See AALP, Inc.; *U.S. Private*, pg. 31
AALP, INC. - PHILADELPHIA—See AALP, Inc.; *U.S. Private*, pg. 31
AALP, INC. - PHOENIX—See AALP, Inc.; *U.S. Private*, pg. 32
AALP, INC. - SAN DIEGO—See AALP, Inc.; *U.S. Private*, pg. 32
AALP, INC. - SAN FRANCISCO—See AALP, Inc.; *U.S. Private*, pg. 32
AALP, INC. - SEATTLE—See AALP, Inc.; *U.S. Private*, pg. 32
AALP, INC.; *U.S. Private*, pg. 31
AALP, INC. - ST. LOUIS—See AALP, Inc.; *U.S. Private*, pg. 32
AALP, INC. - WASHINGTON, D.C.—See AALP, Inc.; *U.S. Private*, pg. 32
AAL REALTY CORP.—See The Great Atlantic & Pacific Tea Company, Inc.; *U.S. Private*, pg. 4038
A&A MACHINE & FABRICATION, LLC.; *U.S. Private*, pg. 19
A&A MACHINERY MOVING, INC.—See Olympus Partners; *U.S. Private*, pg. 3013
AAM ADVISORY PTE. LTD.—See Quilter plc; *Int'l*, pg. 6162
AAMAL CEMENT INDUSTRIES W.L.L.—See Aamal Company Q.S.C.; *Int'l*, pg. 36
AAMAL COMPANY Q.S.C.; *Int'l*, pg. 36
AAMAL READYMIX—See Aamal Company Q.S.C.; *Int'l*, pg. 36
AAMAL SERVICES W.L.L.—See Aamal Company Q.S.C.; *Int'l*, pg. 36
AAMAL TRAVEL & TOURISM W.L.L.—See Aamal Company Q.S.C.; *Int'l*, pg. 36
A&A MATERIAL CORPORATION; *Int'l*, pg. 18
AAMCO TRANSMISSIONS, INC.—See Ares Management Corporation; *U.S. Public*, pg. 187
AAM DO BRASIL LTDA.—See American Axle & Manufacturing Holdings, Inc.; *U.S. Public*, pg. 96
AA MEAT SHOP SDN. BHD.—See MKH Berhad; *Int'l*, pg. 5002
AA MEDICAL STORE, INC.—See Shore Capital Partners, LLC; *U.S. Private*, pg. 3641
A AMERICA INC.; *U.S. Private*, pg. 18
AA METALS, INC; *U.S. Private*, pg. 29
AAM GERMANY GMBH—See American Axle & Manufacturing Holdings, Inc.; *U.S. Public*, pg. 96
AAM INTERNATIONAL HOLDINGS, INC.—See American Axle & Manufacturing Holdings, Inc.; *U.S. Public*, pg. 96
AAM PANTNAGAR AXLE PRIVATE LIMITED—See American Axle & Manufacturing Holdings, Inc.; *U.S. Public*, pg. 96
A&D COMPANY, LIMITED; *Int'l*, pg. 18
A&D MAINTENANCE LEASING & REPAIRS, INC.; *U.S. Public*, pg. 10
AAMP OF FLORIDA, INC.; *U.S. Private*, pg. 32

AAM POLAND SP. Z O. O.—See American Axle & Manufacturing Holdings, Inc.; *U.S. Public*, pg. 96
A&P CONSULTING TRANSPORTATION ENGINEERS, CORP.; *U.S. Private*, pg. 20
A&W (MALAYSIA) SDN BHD; *Int'l*, pg. 19
A&W REVENUE ROYALTIES INCOME FUND; *Int'l*, pg. 19
AAMRA TECHNOLOGIES LIMITED; *Int'l*, pg. 36
AANANDA LAKSHMI SPINNING MILLS LIMITED; *Int'l*, pg. 36
AANCHAL ISPAT LTD.; *Int'l*, pg. 36
AANDERAA DATA INSTRUMENTS AS—See Xylem Inc.; *U.S. Public*, pg. 2395
AANDERAA DATA INSTRUMENTS INC.—See Xylem Inc.; *U.S. Public*, pg. 2395
AANNEMINGEN VAN WELLEN—See Ackermans & van Haaren NV; *Int'l*, pg. 104
AANNEMINGSMAATSCHAPPIJ MARKUS B.V.—See HAL Trust N.V.; *Int'l*, pg. 3224
AON, INC.; *U.S. Public*, pg. 12
A&A OSAKA CORPORATION—See A&A Material Corporation; *Int'l*, pg. 18
AAPICO AGUEDA, S.A.—See AAPICO Hitech plc; *Int'l*, pg. 37
AAPICO AMATA CO., LTD.—See AAPICO Hitech plc; *Int'l*, pg. 37
AAPICO ELECTRONICS COMPANY LIMITED—See AAPICO Hitech plc; *Int'l*, pg. 37
AAPICO ENGINEERING COMPANY LIMITED—See AAPICO Hitech plc; *Int'l*, pg. 37
AAPICO ENGINEERING SDN. BHD.—See AAPICO Hitech plc; *Int'l*, pg. 37
AAPICO FORGING PLC—See AAPICO Hitech plc; *Int'l*, pg. 37
AAPICO FORGING PUBLIC CO., LTD.—See AAPICO Hitech plc; *Int'l*, pg. 37
AAPICO HITECH AUTOMATION COMPANY LIMITED—See AAPICO Hitech plc; *Int'l*, pg. 37
AAPICO HITECH PARTS CO., LTD—See AAPICO Hitech plc; *Int'l*, pg. 37
AAPICO HITECH PLC - PLUAKDAENG FACTORY—See AAPICO Hitech plc; *Int'l*, pg. 37
AAPICO HITECH PLC; *Int'l*, pg. 36
AAPICO HITECH TOOLING CO., LTD.—See AAPICO Hitech plc; *Int'l*, pg. 37
AAPICO INVESTMENT PTE. LTD.—See AAPICO Hitech plc; *Int'l*, pg. 37
AAPICO ITS COMPANY LIMITED—See AAPICO Hitech plc; *Int'l*, pg. 37
AAPICO LEMTECH (THAILAND) COMPANY LIMITED—See AAPICO Hitech plc; *Int'l*, pg. 37
AAPICO MAIA, S.A.—See AAPICO Hitech plc; *Int'l*, pg. 37
AAPICO MITSUIKE (THAILAND) COMPANY LIMITED—See AAPICO Hitech plc; *Int'l*, pg. 37
AAPICO PLASTICS PUBLIC CO., LTD.—See AAPICO Hitech plc; *Int'l*, pg. 37
AAPICO PRECISION COMPANY LIMITED—See AAPICO Hitech plc; *Int'l*, pg. 37
AAPICO SHANGHAI CO., LTD.—See AAPICO Hitech plc; *Int'l*, pg. 37
AAPICO STRUCTURAL PRODUCTS CO., LTD.—See AAPICO Hitech plc; *Int'l*, pg. 37
AAPICO TRAINING CENTER COMPANY LIMITED—See AAPICO Hitech plc; *Int'l*, pg. 37
AAPICO VENTURE COMPANY LIMITED—See AAPICO Hitech plc; *Int'l*, pg. 37
AAP IMPLANTATE AG; *Int'l*, pg. 36
AAP, INC.; *Int'l*, pg. 36
AA PLC—See TowerBrook Capital Partners, L.P.; *U.S. Private*, pg. 4194
AA PLC—See Warburg Pincus LLC; *U.S. Private*, pg. 4436
AAP LEHRERFACHVERLAGE GMBH—See Ernst Klett AG; *Int'l*, pg. 2495
AA PLUS TRADELINK LIMITED; *Int'l*, pg. 30
AAP METALS, LLC—See Triple-S Steel Holdings Inc.; *U.S. Private*, pg. 4237
AAP METALS, LLC—See The Home Depot, Inc.; *U.S. Public*, pg. 2089
AAPT LIMITED—See CK Hutchison Holdings Limited; *Int'l*, pg. 1638
AAPT LIMITED—See Vodafone Group Plc; *Int'l*, pg. 8285
A.A. PULP MILL 2 COMPANY LIMITED—See Double A (1991) Public Company Limited; *Int'l*, pg. 2180
AAP WINDOWS LTD; *Int'l*, pg. 36
AAR AIRCRAFT COMPONENT SERVICES - AMSTERDAM—See AAR Corp.; *U.S. Public*, pg. 13
AAR AIRCRAFT COMPONENT SERVICES - LONDON—See AAR Corp.; *U.S. Public*, pg. 13
AAR AIRCRAFT COMPONENT SERVICES - NEW YORK—See AAR Corp.; *U.S. Public*, pg. 13
AAR AIRCRAFT & ENGINE SALES & LEASING—See AAR Corp.; *U.S. Public*, pg. 12
AAR AIRCRAFT SERVICES, INC.—See AAR Corp.; *U.S. Public*, pg. 13
AAR AIRCRAFT SERVICES - MIAMI—See AAR Corp.; *U.S. Public*, pg. 13
AAR AIRCRAFT SERVICES - OKLAHOMA—See AAR Corp.; *U.S. Public*, pg. 13
AAR AIRCRAFT TURBINE CENTER—See AAR Corp.; *U.S. Public*, pg. 13

AAR AIRLIFT GROUP, INC.—See AAR Corp.; *U.S. Public*, pg. 13
AAR ALLEN ASSET MANAGEMENT—See AAR Corp.; *U.S. Public*, pg. 13
AARAMBHA MICROFINANCE BITTIYA SANSTHA LIMITED; *Int'l*, pg. 37
AAR COMMERCIAL COMPANY LTD.; *Int'l*, pg. 37
AAR CORP. - AVIATION SUPPLY CHAIN—See AAR Corp.; *U.S. Public*, pg. 13
AAR CORP.; *U.S. Public*, pg. 12
AAR DEFENSE SYSTEMS & LOGISTICS—See AAR Corp.; *U.S. Public*, pg. 13
AARDVARK EVENT LOGISTICS, INC.; *U.S. Private*, pg. 32
AARDVARK SWIM & SPORT, INC.; *U.S. Private*, pg. 32
AARDWOLF PESTKARE (SINGAPORE) PTE. LTD.—See Rollins, Inc.; *U.S. Public*, pg. 1808
A&A READY MIXED CONCRETE INC.; *U.S. Private*, pg. 19
AAREAL BANK AG—See Advent International Corporation; *U.S. Private*, pg. 96
AAREAL BANK AG—See Centerbridge Partners, L.P.; *U.S. Private*, pg. 812
AAREAL BANK AG—See Advent International Corporation; *U.S. Private*, pg. 96
AAREAL BANK AG—See Centerbridge Partners, L.P.; *U.S. Private*, pg. 812
AAREAL BANK ASIA LIMITED—See Advent International Corporation; *U.S. Private*, pg. 96
AAREAL BANK ASIA LIMITED—See Centerbridge Partners, L.P.; *U.S. Private*, pg. 812
AAREAL BANK CAPITAL FUNDING TRUST—See Advent International Corporation; *U.S. Private*, pg. 96
AAREAL BANK CAPITAL FUNDING TRUST—See Centerbridge Partners, L.P.; *U.S. Private*, pg. 812
AAREAL CAPITAL CORPORATION—See Advent International Corporation; *U.S. Private*, pg. 96
AAREAL CAPITAL CORPORATION—See Centerbridge Partners, L.P.; *U.S. Private*, pg. 812
AAREAL ESTATE AG—See Advent International Corporation; *U.S. Private*, pg. 96
AAREAL ESTATE AG—See Centerbridge Partners, L.P.; *U.S. Private*, pg. 812
AAREAL-FINANCIAL SERVICE, SPOL. S R.O.—See Advent International Corporation; *U.S. Private*, pg. 96
AAREAL-FINANCIAL SERVICE, SPOL. S R.O.—See Centerbridge Partners, L.P.; *U.S. Private*, pg. 812
AAREAL FIRST FINANCIAL SOLUTIONS AG—See Advent International Corporation; *U.S. Private*, pg. 96
AAREAL FIRST FINANCIAL SOLUTIONS AG—See Centerbridge Partners, L.P.; *U.S. Private*, pg. 812
AAREAL GESELLSCHAFT FUR BETEILIGUNGEN UND GRUNDBESITZ DRITTE MBH & CO. KG—See Advent International Corporation; *U.S. Private*, pg. 96
AAREAL GESELLSCHAFT FUR BETEILIGUNGEN UND GRUNDBESITZ DRITTE MBH & CO. KG—See Centerbridge Partners, L.P.; *U.S. Private*, pg. 812
AAREAL GESELLSCHAFT FUR BETEILIGUNGEN UND GRUNDBESITZ ERSTE MBH & CO. KG—See Advent International Corporation; *U.S. Private*, pg. 96
AAREAL GESELLSCHAFT FUR BETEILIGUNGEN UND GRUNDBESITZ ERSTE MBH & CO. KG—See Centerbridge Partners, L.P.; *U.S. Private*, pg. 812
AAREAL IT BETEILIGUNGEN GMBH—See Advent International Corporation; *U.S. Private*, pg. 96
AAREAL IT BETEILIGUNGEN GMBH—See Centerbridge Partners, L.P.; *U.S. Private*, pg. 812
AAREAL VALUATION GMBH—See Advent International Corporation; *U.S. Private*, pg. 96
AAREAL VALUATION GMBH—See Centerbridge Partners, L.P.; *U.S. Private*, pg. 812
AARE ENERGIE AG—See Alpiq Holding AG; *Int'l*, pg. 372
AAREN SCIENTIFIC INC.—See Carl-Zeiss-Stiftung; *Int'l*, pg. 1334
AAREON AG—See Advent International Corporation; *U.S. Private*, pg. 96
AAREON AG—See Centerbridge Partners, L.P.; *U.S. Private*, pg. 812
AAREON DEUTSCHLAND GMBH—See Advent International Corporation; *U.S. Private*, pg. 96
AAREON DEUTSCHLAND GMBH—See Centerbridge Partners, L.P.; *U.S. Private*, pg. 812
AAREON FINLAND OY—See Advent International Corporation; *U.S. Private*, pg. 96
AAREON FINLAND OY—See Centerbridge Partners, L.P.; *U.S. Private*, pg. 812
AAREON FRANCE S.A.S.—See Advent International Corporation; *U.S. Private*, pg. 96
AAREON FRANCE S.A.S.—See Centerbridge Partners, L.P.; *U.S. Private*, pg. 812
AAREON NEDERLAND B.V.—See Advent International Corporation; *U.S. Private*, pg. 96
AAREON NEDERLAND B.V.—See Centerbridge Partners, L.P.; *U.S. Private*, pg. 812
AAREON NORGE AS—See Advent International Corporation; *U.S. Private*, pg. 96
AAREON NORGE AS—See Centerbridge Partners, L.P.; *U.S. Private*, pg. 812

COMPANY NAME INDEX

AAREON SOFTWARE HANDELSGESELLSCHAFT MBH—See Advent International Corporation; *U.S. Private*, pg. 96
AAREON SOFTWARE HANDELSGESELLSCHAFT MBH—See Centerbridge Partners, L.P.; *U.S. Private*, pg. 812
AAREON SVERIGE AB—See Advent International Corporation; *U.S. Private*, pg. 96
AAREON SVERIGE AB—See Centerbridge Partners, L.P.; *U.S. Private*, pg. 812
AAREON UK LTD.—See Advent International Corporation; *U.S. Private*, pg. 96
AAREON UK LTD.—See Centerbridge Partners, L.P.; *U.S. Private*, pg. 812
AAREON WODIS GMBH—See Advent International Corporation; *U.S. Private*, pg. 96
AAREON WODIS GMBH—See Centerbridge Partners, L.P.; *U.S. Private*, pg. 812
AAREY DRUGS & PHARMACEUTICALS LTD.; *Int'l*, pg. 37
ARGAUER ZEITUNG AG—See BT Holding AG; *Int'l*, pg. 1204
AARGUS PLASTICS, INC.—See Alpha Industries, Inc.; *U.S. Private*, pg. 197
AARHUS 3 A/S—See AAK AB; *Int'l*, pg. 32
AARHUSGEOSOFTWARE APS—See Bentley Systems, Inc.; *U.S. Public*, pg. 296
AARHUSKARLSHAMN BALTIC HOLDING AB—See AAK AB; *Int'l*, pg. 32
AARHUSKARLSHAMN BALTIC LTD.—See AAK AB; *Int'l*, pg. 32
AARHUSKARLSHAMN CANADA LTD.—See AAK AB; *Int'l*, pg. 32
AARHUSKARLSHAMN DO BRASIL DESENVOLVIMENTO DE NEGOSIOS LTDA.—See AAK AB; *Int'l*, pg. 32
AARHUSKARLSHAMN GHANA LTD.—See AAK AB; *Int'l*, pg. 32
AARHUSKARLSHAMN LATIN AMERICA S.A.—See AAK AB; *Int'l*, pg. 32
AARHUSKARLSHAMN MEXICO, S.A. DE C.V.—See AAK AB; *Int'l*, pg. 32
AARHUSKARLSHAMN NORWAY AS—See AAK AB; *Int'l*, pg. 32
AARHUSKARLSHAMN POLAND SP.Z O.O.—See AAK AB; *Int'l*, pg. 32
AARHUSKARLSHAMN RU OOO—See AAK AB; *Int'l*, pg. 32
AARHUSKARLSHAMN SWEDEN AB—See AAK AB; *Int'l*, pg. 32
AARHUSKARLSHAMN UK LTD. - AAK FOODS—See AAK AB; *Int'l*, pg. 31
AARHUS MALAYSIA SDN. BHD.—See AAK AB; *Int'l*, pg. 32
AAR INTERNATIONAL (FRANCE) S.A.R.L.—See AAR Corp.; *U.S. Public*, pg. 13
AARKI, LLC—See Skillz Inc.; *U.S. Public*, pg. 1892
AAR LANDING GEAR LLC—See AAR Corp.; *U.S. Public*, pg. 13
AARNAV FASHIONS LIMITED; *Int'l*, pg. 37
A. ARNOLD MOVING COMPANY, INC. - INDIANAPOLIS DIVISION—See A. Arnold Moving Company, Inc.; *U.S. Private*, pg. 22
A. ARNOLD MOVING COMPANY, INC.; *U.S. Private*, pg. 22
A. ARNOLD OF KANSAS CITY, LLC—See A. Arnold Moving Company, Inc.; *U.S. Private*, pg. 22
AAR OF NORTH CAROLINA INC.; *U.S. Private*, pg. 32
AARO KOHONEN OY—See Sweco AB; *Int'l*, pg. 7363
AARON BROTHERS, INC.—See Apollo Global Management, Inc.; *U.S. Public*, pg. 164
AARON CARLSON CORPORATION; *U.S. Private*, pg. 32
AARON & COMPANY INC.; *U.S. Private*, pg. 32
AARON CONCRETE CONTRACTORS LP—See Heidelberg Materials AG; *Int'l*, pg. 3313
AARON CTP DENTAL SURGERY PTE LTD—See OUE Limited; *Int'l*, pg. 5665
AARON DENTALCARE PTE LTD—See OUE Limited; *Int'l*, pg. 5665
AARON EQUIPMENT COMPANY; *U.S. Private*, pg. 32
AARON FERER & SONS CO.; *U.S. Private*, pg. 32
AARON GROUP OF COMPANIES; *U.S. Private*, pg. 32
AARON INDUSTRIES LTD.; *Int'l*, pg. 37
AARON INVESTMENTS INC.; *U.S. Private*, pg. 32
AARON KITCHEN & BATH DESIGN GALLERY—See Aaron & Company Inc.; *U.S. Private*, pg. 32
AARON OIL COMPANY, LLC—See Grupo Tradebe Medioambiente S.L.; *Int'l*, pg. 3138
AARON'S COMPANY, INC.; *U.S. Public*, pg. 13
AARON SEOW INTERNATIONAL PTE LTD—See OUE Limited; *Int'l*, pg. 5665
AARON'S SALES & LEASE OWNERSHIP—See Aaron's Company, Inc.; *U.S. Public*, pg. 13
AARON THOMAS CO. INC.; *U.S. Private*, pg. 32
AARP PUBLICATIONS—See AARP; *U.S. Private*, pg. 33
AARP; *U.S. Private*, pg. 32
AARQUE GRAPHICS NZ LTD—See Hancock & Gore Ltd.; *Int'l*, pg. 3242
AARQUE GROUP LIMITED—See Japan Pulp and Paper Company Limited; *Int'l*, pg. 3903

AARROW, INC.; *U.S. Private*, pg. 33
AARSAND & COMPANY, INC.; *U.S. Private*, pg. 33
AAR SHYAM INDIA INVESTMENT COMPANY LIMITED; *Int'l*, pg. 37
AARSLEFF BALTIC SIA LLC—See Per Aarsleff Holding A/S; *Int'l*, pg. 5795
AARSLEFF BIZ SP. Z O.O.—See Per Aarsleff Holding A/S; *Int'l*, pg. 5795
AARSLEFF GROUND ENGINEERING LIMITED—See Per Aarsleff Holding A/S; *Int'l*, pg. 5795
AARSLEFF GRUNDBAU GMBH—See Per Aarsleff Holding A/S; *Int'l*, pg. 5795
AARSLEFF GRUNDLAGGNINGS AB—See Per Aarsleff Holding A/S; *Int'l*, pg. 5795
AARSLEFF HULIN S.R.O.—See Per Aarsleff Holding A/S; *Int'l*, pg. 5795
AARSLEFF LEIDINGRENOVATIE B.V.—See Per Aarsleff Holding A/S; *Int'l*, pg. 5795
AARSLEFF RAIL A/S—See Per Aarsleff Holding A/S; *Int'l*, pg. 5795
AARSLEFF RORTEKNIK AB—See Per Aarsleff Holding A/S; *Int'l*, pg. 5795
AARSLEFF SPEZIALTIEFBAU GMBH—See Per Aarsleff Holding A/S; *Int'l*, pg. 5795
AARSLEFF SRL—See Per Aarsleff Holding A/S; *Int'l*, pg. 5795
AAR SUPPLY CHAIN, INC.—See AAR Corp.; *U.S. Public*, pg. 13
AARTECH SOLONICS LIMITED; *Int'l*, pg. 37
AARTI DRUGS LTD.; *Int'l*, pg. 38
AARTI HEALTHCARE LTD.—See Aarti Industries Ltd.; *Int'l*, pg. 38
AARTI INDUSTRIES LTD. - AARTI CRAMS DIVISION—See Aarti Industries Ltd.; *Int'l*, pg. 38
AARTI INDUSTRIES LTD.; *Int'l*, pg. 38
AARTI SURFACTANTS LIMITED; *Int'l*, pg. 38
AARTSENFRUIT ASIA LTD.—See Aartsenfruit Holding B.V.; *Int'l*, pg. 38
AARTSENFRUIT BREDA B.V.—See Aartsenfruit Holding B.V.; *Int'l*, pg. 38
AARTSENFRUIT HOLDING B.V.; *Int'l*, pg. 38
AARTSENFRUIT N.V.—See Aartsenfruit Holding B.V.; *Int'l*, pg. 38
AARTSENFRUIT VENLO B.V.—See Aartsenfruit Holding B.V.; *Int'l*, pg. 38
AARVEE DENIMS & EXPORTS LTD.; *Int'l*, pg. 38
AARVI ENCON FZE—See Aarvi Encon Ltd.; *Int'l*, pg. 38
AARVI ENCON LTD.; *Int'l*, pg. 38
AARVI ENGINEERING & CONSULTANTS PRIVATE LIMITED—See Aarvi Encon Ltd.; *Int'l*, pg. 38
AAS CATERING CO., LTD.—See Gourmet Kineya Co., Ltd.; *Int'l*, pg. 3044
AASEBY INDUSTRIAL MACHINING, LLC—See Gremada Industries Inc.; *U.S. Private*, pg. 1783
AASEN SPAREBANK; *Int'l*, pg. 38
AASGARD SUMMIT MANAGEMENT SERVICES INC.—See Lovell Minnick Partners LLC; *U.S. Private*, pg. 2502
AAS GJENSIDIGE BALTIC—See Gjensidige Forsikring ASA; *Int'l*, pg. 2982
AASHKA HOSPITALS LTD.; *Int'l*, pg. 38
AASKI TECHNOLOGY, INC.; *U.S. Private*, pg. 33
AASSET GERMANY GMBH—See TKH Group N.V.; *Int'l*, pg. 7763
AASSET SECURITY INTERNATIONAL SAS—See TKH Group N.V.; *Int'l*, pg. 7763
AASSET SECURITY ITALIA SPA.—See TKH Group N.V.; *Int'l*, pg. 7763
AASSET SECURITY LTD.—See TKH Group N.V.; *Int'l*, pg. 7763
AASTAMANGALAM FINANCE LIMITED; *Int'l*, pg. 38
AASTOCKS.COM LTD.—See Shanghai DZH Limited; *Int'l*, pg. 6765
AASTRA TELECOM EUROPE A/S—See Searchlight Capital Partners, L.P.; *U.S. Private*, pg. 3588
AASYS GROUP, INC.; *U.S. Private*, pg. 33
AAS ZURICH LATVIA LTD.—See Zurich Insurance Group Limited; *Int'l*, pg. 8697
AAT ALBER ANTRIEBSTECHNIK GMBH—See Investment AB Latour; *Int'l*, pg. 3780
A&A TANK TRUCK, INC.—See Gibson Energy Inc.; *Int'l*, pg. 2963
AAT ASTON GMBH—See Komax Holding AG; *Int'l*, pg. 4240
AAT CARRIERS, INC.—See Covenant Logistics Group, Inc.; *U.S. Public*, pg. 588
AATCO LLC—See Badr Investment Group LLC; *Int'l*, pg. 796
AATECH S.P.A.; *Int'l*, pg. 38
AATEST AG—See PHM Group Holding Oyj; *Int'l*, pg. 5848
AATLANTIDE SAS—See PAO Severstal; *Int'l*, pg. 5731
AAT MEDICAL LIMITED—See Neurotech International Limited; *Int'l*, pg. 5220
AAT PORT KEMBLA PTY. LTD.—See Qube Holdings Limited; *Int'l*, pg. 6157
AATRIX SOFTWARE, INC.—See HgCapital Trust plc; *Int'l*, pg. 3377
AA TRUCK RENTING CORPORATION; *U.S. Private*, pg. 30

A&A UNDERWRITING SERVICES INC.—See Aon plc; *Int'l*, pg. 488
AAVALAR CONSULTING, INC.; *U.S. Private*, pg. 33
AAVAS FINANCIERS LTD.; *Int'l*, pg. 38
AAVA WHISTLER HOTEL LTD—See TA Enterprise Berhad; *Int'l*, pg. 7399
AAVID ALLCAST, LLC—See The Goldman Sachs Group, Inc.; *U.S. Public*, pg. 2080
AAVID CHINA—See The Goldman Sachs Group, Inc.; *U.S. Public*, pg. 2080
AAVID INDIA—See The Goldman Sachs Group, Inc.; *U.S. Public*, pg. 2080
AAVID NIAGARA LLC—See The Goldman Sachs Group, Inc.; *U.S. Public*, pg. 2080
AAVID—See The Goldman Sachs Group, Inc.; *U.S. Public*, pg. 2080
AAVID THERMALLOY S.R.L.—See The Goldman Sachs Group, Inc.; *U.S. Public*, pg. 2080
AAVIN, LLC; *U.S. Private*, pg. 33
AAVOIP (EXPRESS)—See Odyssey Telecommunications, Inc.; *U.S. Private*, pg. 2996
AA WHEEL & TRUCK SUPPLY INC.; *U.S. Private*, pg. 30
A&A WINDOW PRODUCTS INC.; *U.S. Private*, pg. 19
AA WORLD CLASS CORP.; *U.S. Private*, pg. 30
A'AYAN LEASING AND INVESTMENT COMPANY KSCC; *Int'l*, pg. 19
A'AYAN REAL ESTATE COMPANY K.S.C.C.—See A'ayan Leasing and Investment Company KSCC; *Int'l*, pg. 19
AAYUSH FOOD & HERBS LTD.; *Int'l*, pg. 38
AAZ-PHARMA B.V.—See Nestle S.A.; *Int'l*, pg. 5206
ABAAD REAL ESTATE COMPANY B.S.C.—See Bahrain Islamic Bank; *Int'l*, pg. 800
ABABA BOLT; *U.S. Private*, pg. 33
ABAC AIR COMPRESSORS S.A PTY LTD.—See Atlas Copco AB; *Int'l*, pg. 677
ABAC AMERICAN IMC INC—See Atlas Copco AB; *Int'l*, pg. 677
ABAC ARIA COMPRESSA S.P.A—See Atlas Copco AB; *Int'l*, pg. 677
ABACAST, INC.; *U.S. Private*, pg. 33
ABAC CATALUNYA S.L.—See Atlas Copco AB; *Int'l*, pg. 677
ABAC DMS AIR COMPRESSORS PTE LTD—See Atlas Copco AB; *Int'l*, pg. 677
ABAC FRANCE S.A.S.—See Atlas Copco AB; *Int'l*, pg. 677
AB ACHEMA—See Koncernas Achemos Grupe; *Int'l*, pg. 4246
ABA CHEMICALS CORPORATION; *Int'l*, pg. 47
ABA CHEMICALS (SHANGHAI) LIMITED—See ABA Chemicals Corporation; *Int'l*, pg. 47
ABACI AS—See TowerBrook Capital Partners, L.P.; *U.S. Private*, pg. 4194
ABACO ENERGY TECHNOLOGIES LLC—See Riverstone Holdings LLC; *U.S. Private*, pg. 3447
ABACO INSURANCE BROKERS LIMITED—See PSC Insurance Group Limited; *Int'l*, pg. 6015
ABACO MOBILE INC.; *U.S. Private*, pg. 33
ABACORE CAPITAL HOLDINGS, INC.; *Int'l*, pg. 47
ABACO SYSTEMS INC.—See AMETEK, Inc.; *U.S. Public*, pg. 119
ABACO SYSTEMS LIMITED—See AMETEK, Inc.; *U.S. Public*, pg. 119
ABAC UK LTD—See Atlas Copco AB; *Int'l*, pg. 677
ABACUS 24-7 LLC; *U.S. Private*, pg. 33
ABACUS CAPITAL GROUP LLC—See Affiliated Managers Group, Inc.; *U.S. Public*, pg. 53
ABACUS CORPORATION; *U.S. Private*, pg. 33
ABACUS DATA SYSTEMS, INC.—See Thomas H. Lee Partners, L.P.; *U.S. Private*, pg. 4155
ABACUS DISTRIBUTION SYSTEMS (MALAYSIA) SDN. BHD.—See Khazanah Nasional Berhad; *Int'l*, pg. 4153
ABACUS DISTRIBUTION SYSTEMS TAIWAN LTD.—See China Airlines Ltd.; *Int'l*, pg. 1481
ABACUS DX PTY LIMITED—See Diploma PLC; *Int'l*, pg. 2128
ABACUS (FINANCIAL CONSULTANTS) LIMITED—See ClearDebt Group Plc; *Int'l*, pg. 1656
ABACUS FUNDS MANAGEMENT LIMITED—See Abacus Group, LLC; *Int'l*, pg. 47
ABACUS GROUP, LLC—See WestView Capital Partners, L.P.; *U.S. Private*, pg. 4501
ABACUS GROUP, LLC; *Int'l*, pg. 47
ABACUS GROUP LLC; *U.S. Private*, pg. 33
ABACUS INSURANCE LIMITED—See Steinhoff International Holdings N.V.; *Int'l*, pg. 7194
ABACUS LIFE, INC.; *U.S. Public*, pg. 13
ABACUS MINING & EXPLORATION CORPORATION; *Int'l*, pg. 47
ABACUS PLANNING GROUP, INC.; *U.S. Private*, pg. 34
ABACUS PLUMBING COMPANY; *U.S. Private*, pg. 34
ABACUS SOFTWARE LIMITED—See Vista Equity Partners, LLC; *U.S. Private*, pg. 4398
ABACUS SOLUTIONS GROUP LLC (ASG); *U.S. Private*, pg. 34
ABACUS SOLUTIONS LLC—See American Pacific Group, LLC; *U.S. Private*, pg. 242
ABACUS TECHNOLOGY CORP.; *U.S. Private*, pg. 34
ABACUS (UK) LTD.—See Publicis Groupe S.A.; *Int'l*, pg. 6099

ABACUS WEALTH PARTNERS, LLC

CORPORATE AFFILIATIONS

ABACUS WEALTH PARTNERS, LLC; *U.S. Private*, pg. 34
ABADGARAN IRAN TOURISM AND WELFARE COMPLEXES (PUBLIC LIMITED COMPANY); *Int'l*, pg. 47
ABADIA RETUERTA S.A.—See Novartis AG; *Int'l*, pg. 5455
ABADI CANGGIH SDN. BHD.—See Minho (M) Berhad; *Int'l*, pg. 4909
AB AGRI LTD—See The Garfield Weston Foundation; *Int'l*, pg. 7647
ABA INDUSTRY INC.—See Wonderful Hi-Tech Co., Ltd.; *Int'l*, pg. 8446
ABA INSURANCE SERVICES INC.—See American Financial Group, Inc.; *U.S. Public*, pg. 102
ABAJIAN MOTOR SALES; *U.S. Private*, pg. 34
ABAKAN INC.; *U.S. Private*, pg. 34
ABALANCE CORPORATION LTD.; *Int'l*, pg. 48
ABALAT S.A. DE C.V.—See HORIBA Ltd; *Int'l*, pg. 3474
AB AMBER GRID; *Int'l*, pg. 39
ABA MORIAH CORPORATION; *U.S. Private*, pg. 33
ABANCA CORPORACION BANCARIA, SA; *Int'l*, pg. 48
ABANDONED CHILDREN'S FUND; *U.S. Private*, pg. 34
ABAN ENERGIES LIMITED—See Aban Offshore Limited; *Int'l*, pg. 48
ABANKA VIPA D.D.—See OTP Bank Plc; *Int'l*, pg. 5657
ABAN OFFSHORE LIMITED; *Int'l*, pg. 48
ABANO HEALTHCARE GROUP LIMITED—See BGH Capital Pty Ltd; *Int'l*, pg. 1007
ABANO HEALTHCARE GROUP LIMITED—See Ontario Teachers' Pension Plan; *Int'l*, pg. 5585
ABANS ELECTRICALS PLC; *Int'l*, pg. 48
ABANS ENTERPRISES LIMITED; *Int'l*, pg. 48
ABANS FINANCE PLC; *Int'l*, pg. 48
ABANS HOLDINGS LIMITED; *Int'l*, pg. 48
ABAN SINGAPORE PTE. LTD.—See Aban Offshore Limited; *Int'l*, pg. 48
ABAP BETEILIGUNGS HOLDING GMBH—See PORR AG; *Int'l*, pg. 5922
ABA-PGT INC.; *U.S. Private*, pg. 33
ABAPOR - COMERCIO E INDUSTRIA DE CARNES, S.A.—See SODIM, SGPS, SA; *Int'l*, pg. 7049
AB ARCHYVU SISTEMOS—See Iron Mountain Incorporated; *U.S. Public*, pg. 1171
AB ARCHYVU SISTEMOS—See Iron Mountain Incorporated; *U.S. Public*, pg. 1171
AB ARCHYVU SISTEMOS—See Iron Mountain Incorporated; *U.S. Public*, pg. 1171
ABA RESOURCES PTY. LTD.; *Int'l*, pg. 47
ABARIS HOLDINGS LIMITED—See Sanderson Design Group PLC; *Int'l*, pg. 6525
ABARTA INC.; *U.S. Private*, pg. 34
A BASIC CONCEPTS AND DESIGNS PTY. LTD.—See Samvardhana Motherson International Limited; *Int'l*, pg. 6516
ABASTECEDORA DE ALIMENTOS DE MEXICO, S.A. DE C.V.—See Grupo LALA S.A. de C.V.; *Int'l*, pg. 3131
ABASTECEDORA DE COMBUSTIBLES S.A.—See AntarChile S.A.; *Int'l*, pg. 481
ABA STEPHENSON & BROOK—See Anchin, Block & Anchin LLP; *U.S. Private*, pg. 272
ABATE AS INDUSTRIES LTD.; *Int'l*, pg. 48
ABATEL AB—See Addtech AB; *Int'l*, pg. 131
ABATIX CORP., *U.S. Private*, pg. 34
ABATTIS BIOCEUTICALS CORPORATION; *Int'l*, pg. 48
ABATTOIR SA/NV; *Int'l*, pg. 48
ABAXBANK SPA—See Credito Emiliano S.p.A.; *Int'l*, pg. 1836
ABAX INVESTMENTS PROPRIETARY LIMITED—See Affiliated Managers Group, Inc.; *U.S. Public*, pg. 53
ABAXIS EUROPE GMBH—See Zoetis, Inc.; *U.S. Public*, pg. 2409
ABAXIS HOLDING GMBH—See Zoetis, Inc.; *U.S. Public*, pg. 2409
ABAXIS, INC.—See Zoetis, Inc.; *U.S. Public*, pg. 2409
ABAXIS UK LIMITED—See Zoetis, Inc.; *U.S. Public*, pg. 2409
ABAXX TECHNOLOGIES INC.; *Int'l*, pg. 48
AB AZUCARERA IBERIA, S.L.—See The Garfield Weston Foundation; *Int'l*, pg. 7647
ABB AB—See ABB Ltd.; *Int'l*, pg. 49
ABB AG—See ABB Ltd.; *Int'l*, pg. 50
ABB AS—See ABB Ltd.; *Int'l*, pg. 50
ABBA HITECH (SHANGHAI) CO., LTD.—See SKF AB; *Int'l*, pg. 6982
ABBA HOME HEALTH, L.P.—See Encompass Health Corporation; *U.S. Public*, pg. 754
ABBAKUS GMBH & CO. KG—See Bilfinger SE; *Int'l*, pg. 1024
ABB ALGERIA SPA—See ABB Ltd.; *Int'l*, pg. 50
ABBA MARKETING SDN. BHD.—See Asia File Corporation Bhd.; *Int'l*, pg. 612
ABBA MEDIX CORP.—See Canada House Wellness Group Inc.; *Int'l*, pg. 1278
AB BANAN-KOMPANIET—See Dole plc; *Int'l*, pg. 2157
AB BANK LIMITED; *Int'l*, pg. 39
ABBAR & ZAINY DAIKIN AIRCONDITIONING COMPANY LTD.—See Daikin Industries, Ltd.; *Int'l*, pg. 1932
ABB ASEA BROWN BOVERI LTD.—See ABB Ltd.; *Int'l*, pg. 50
ABB AS—See ABB Ltd.; *Int'l*, pg. 50
ABB A/S—See ABB Ltd.; *Int'l*, pg. 49

ABB A/S—See ABB Ltd.; *Int'l*, pg. 49
ABBA STAFFING & CONSULTING SERVICES; *U.S. Private*, pg. 34
ABBA TECHNOLOGIES INC.; *U.S. Private*, pg. 34
ABB AUSTRALIA PTY LIMITED—See ABB Ltd.; *Int'l*, pg. 49
ABB AUTOMATION CO. LTD.—See ABB Ltd.; *Int'l*, pg. 54
ABB AUTOMATION E.C.—See ABB Ltd.; *Int'l*, pg. 50
ABB AUTOMATION EOOD—See ABB Ltd.; *Int'l*, pg. 50
ABB AUTOMATION GMBH—See ABB Ltd.; *Int'l*, pg. 50
ABB AUTOMATION PRODUCTS GMBH—See ABB Ltd.; *Int'l*, pg. 50
ABB AUTOMATION TECHNOLOGIES AB—See ABB Ltd.; *Int'l*, pg. 49
ABB AVANGARD AD—See ABB Ltd.; *Int'l*, pg. 50
ABB BAILEY BEIJING ENGINEERING CO. LTD.—See ABB Ltd.; *Int'l*, pg. 49
ABB BAILEY JAPAN LIMITED—See ABB Ltd.; *Int'l*, pg. 52
ABB BEIJING DRIVE SYSTEMS CO. LTD.—See ABB Ltd.; *Int'l*, pg. 49
ABB BEIJING SWITCHGEAR LIMITED—See ABB Ltd.; *Int'l*, pg. 50
ABB BETEILIGUNGS- UND VERWALTUNGSGES. MBH—See ABB Ltd.; *Int'l*, pg. 50
ABB BULGARIA EOOD—See ABB Ltd.; *Int'l*, pg. 50
ABB BUSINESS SERVICES GMBH—See ABB Ltd.; *Int'l*, pg. 50
ABB BUSINESS SERVICES SP. Z O.O.—See ABB Ltd.; *Int'l*, pg. 50
ABB B.V.—See ABB Ltd.; *Int'l*, pg. 50
ABB CALOR EMAG MITTELSPANNUNG GMBH—See ABB Ltd.; *Int'l*, pg. 50
ABB (CHINA) INVESTMENT LIMITED—See ABB Ltd.; pg. 49
ABB (CHINA) LTD.—See ABB Ltd.; *Int'l*, pg. 49
ABB CONCISE INC.—See ABB/Con-Cise Optical Group LLC; *U.S. Private*, pg. 34
ABB/CON-CISE OPTICAL GROUP LLC; *U.S. Private*, pg. 34
ABB CONTRACTING COMPANY LTD.—See ABB Ltd.; *Int'l*, pg. 54
ABB D.O.O.—See ABB Ltd.; *Int'l*, pg. 55
ABB D.O.O., ZAGREB—See ABB Ltd.; *Int'l*, pg. 55
ABB ECUADOR S.A.—See ABB Ltd.; *Int'l*, pg. 50
ABB ELECTRICAL INDUSTRIES LTD.—See ABB Ltd.; *Int'l*, pg. 54
ABB ELECTRICAL MACHINES LTD.—See ABB Ltd.; *Int'l*, pg. 49
ABB ELEKTRIK SANAYI A.S.—See ABB Ltd.; *Int'l*, pg. 51
ABB ELETRIFICACAO LTDA.—See ABB Ltd.; *Int'l*, pg. 50
ABBELL ASSOCIATES, LLC; *U.S. Private*, pg. 34
ABB E-MOBILITY B.V.—See ABB Ltd.; *Int'l*, pg. 50
ABB ENERGY AUTOMATION S.P.A.—See ABB Ltd.; *Int'l*, pg. 51
ABB ENGINEERING (SHANGHAI) LTD.—See ABB Ltd.; *Int'l*, pg. 49
ABB ENGINEERING TECHNOLOGIES CO. (KSCC)—See ABB Ltd.; *Int'l*, pg. 50
ABB ENGINEERING TRADING AND SERVICE LTD.—See ABB Ltd.; *Int'l*, pg. 50
ABB ENTRELEC SP. Z.O.O.—See ABB Ltd.; *Int'l*, pg. 55
AB BERNSTEIN ISRAEL LTD.—See Equitable Holdings, Inc.; *U.S. Public*, pg. 788
AB BEST MATIC—See Ingersoll Rand Inc.; *U.S. Public*, pg. 1120
AB BEVERAGE CO., INC.; *U.S. Private*, pg. 33
ABBEY CAPITAL LIMITED; *Int'l*, pg. 56
ABBEY CAPITAL (US) LLC—See Abbey Capital Limited; *Int'l*, pg. 56
ABBEY CARPET CO., INC.; *U.S. Private*, pg. 34
ABBEY COMMUNICATIONS (NETHERLANDS) B.V.—See Mediahuis Partners NV; *Int'l*, pg. 4772
ABBEY COMMUNICATIONS (NETHERLANDS) B.V.—See VP Exploitatie N.V.; *Int'l*, pg. 8311
ABBEYCREST THAILAND LTD.—See Brown & Newirth Ltd.; *Int'l*, pg. 1198
ABBEY DEVELOPMENTS LIMITED—See Gallagher Holdings Ltd.; *Int'l*, pg. 2873
ABBEY FORGED PRODUCTS LIMITED; *Int'l*, pg. 56
ABBEY GROUP LIMITED—See Gallagher Holdings Ltd.; *Int'l*, pg. 2873
ABBEY HOLDINGS LIMITED—See Gallagher Holdings Ltd.; *Int'l*, pg. 2873
ABBEY HR SERVICES—See Markel Group Inc.; *U.S. Public*, pg. 1367
ABBEY INVESTMENTS LIMITED—See Gallagher Holdings Ltd.; *Int'l*, pg. 2873
ABBEY LEGAL PROTECTION LIMITED—See Markel Group Inc.; *U.S. Public*, pg. 1367
ABBEY LIFE ASSURANCE COMPANY LIMITED—See Phoenix Group Holdings PLC; *Int'l*, pg. 5851
ABBEY METAL FINISHING COMPANY LIMITED—See Camellia Plc; *Int'l*, pg. 1270
ABBEY MORTGAGE BANK PLC; *Int'l*, pg. 56
ABBEY PLC—See Gallagher Holdings Ltd.; *Int'l*, pg. 2873
ABBEY PROTECTION GROUP LIMITED—See Markel Group Inc.; *U.S. Public*, pg. 1367
ABBEY PROTECTION PLC—See Markel Group Inc.; *U.S. Public*, pg. 1367

ABBEYPURE PTE LTD—See PT Wintermar Offshore Marine Tbk; *Int'l*, pg. 6083
ABBEY ROAD GROUP LAND DEVELOPMENT SERVICES COMPANY—See Abbey Road Group LLC; *U.S. Private*, pg. 34
ABBEY ROAD GROUP LLC; *U.S. Private*, pg. 34
ABBEY ROAD STUDIOS LTD.—See Universal Music Group N.V.; *Int'l*, pg. 8081
ABBEY, S.R.O.—See Gallagher Holdings Ltd.; *Int'l*, pg. 2873
ABBEY TAX & CONSULTANCY SERVICES LIMITED—See Markel Group Inc.; *U.S. Public*, pg. 1367
ABBEY WOOD AGENCIES LIMITED—See James Latham Plc; *Int'l*, pg. 3877
ABB FRANCE SAS—See ABB Ltd.; *Int'l*, pg. 51
ABB FZ-LLC—See ABB Ltd.; *Int'l*, pg. 50
ABB GENERATORS LTD.—See ABB Ltd.; *Int'l*, pg. 49
ABB GLOBAL MARKETING FZ LLC—See ABB Ltd.; *Int'l*, pg. 51
ABB GROUP HOLDINGS PTY. LTD.—See ABB Ltd.; *Int'l*, pg. 51
ABB GROUP INVESTMENT MANAGEMENT PTY. LTD.—See ABB Ltd.; *Int'l*, pg. 50
ABB HEFEI TRANSFORMER CO. LTD.—See ABB Ltd.; *Int'l*, pg. 49
ABB HIGH VOLTAGE SWITCHGEAR (XIAMEN) COMPANY LTD.—See ABB Ltd.; *Int'l*, pg. 49
ABB HOLDING A.S.—See ABB Ltd.; *Int'l*, pg. 51
ABB HOLDINGS BV—See ABB Ltd.; *Int'l*, pg. 50
ABB HOLDINGS LIMITED—See ABB Ltd.; *Int'l*, pg. 53
ABB HOLDINGS PTE. LTD.—See ABB Ltd.; *Int'l*, pg. 51
ABB HOLDINGS (PTY) LTD.—See ABB Ltd.; *Int'l*, pg. 55
ABB HOLDINGS SDN. BHD.—See ABB Ltd.; *Int'l*, pg. 53
ABB (HONG KONG) LTD.—See ABB Ltd.; *Int'l*, pg. 49
ABB IMMOBILIEN AG—See ABB Ltd.; *Int'l*, pg. 54
ABB INC. - ANALYTICAL & ADVANCED SOLUTIONS—See ABB Ltd.; *Int'l*, pg. 51
ABB INC. - AUTOMATION TECHNOLOGIES DRIVES & MOTORS—See ABB Ltd.; *Int'l*, pg. 51
ABB INC. - AUTOMATION TECHNOLOGIES INSTRUMENTATION PRODUCTS—See ABB Ltd.; *Int'l*, pg. 51
ABB INC. - AUTOMATION TECHNOLOGIES—See ABB Ltd.; *Int'l*, pg. 51
ABB INC. - POWER SYSTEMS—See ABB Ltd.; *Int'l*, pg. 51
ABB INC. - POWER TECHNOLOGIES COMPONENTS FACTORY—See ABB Ltd.; *Int'l*, pg. 51
ABB INC. - POWER TECHNOLOGIES MEDIUM VOLTAGE—See ABB Ltd.; *Int'l*, pg. 51
ABB INC.—See ABB Ltd.; *Int'l*, pg. 51
ABB INC.—See ABB Ltd.; *Int'l*, pg. 51
ABB INC.—See ABB Ltd.; *Int'l*, pg. 51
ABB INC.—See ABB Ltd.; *Int'l*, pg. 51
ABB INC.—See ABB Ltd.; *Int'l*, pg. 51
ABB INC.—See ABB Ltd.; *Int'l*, pg. 51
ABB INC. - SSAC—See ABB Ltd.; *Int'l*, pg. 51
ABB INC. - TURBOCHARGING—See ABB Ltd.; *Int'l*, pg. 51
ABB INDIA LTD.—See ABB Ltd.; *Int'l*, pg. 52
ABB INDUSTRIAL SOLUTIONS (BIELSKO-BIALA) SP. Z O.O.—See ABB Ltd.; *Int'l*, pg. 52
ABB INDUSTRIAL SOLUTIONS (KLODZKO) SP.Z O.O.—See ABB Ltd.; *Int'l*, pg. 52
ABB INDUSTRIES LLC—See ABB Ltd.; *Int'l*, pg. 51
ABB INDUSTRIES (L.L.C.)—See ABB Ltd.; *Int'l*, pg. 51
ABB INFORMATION SYSTEMS LTD.—See ABB Ltd.; *Int'l*, pg. 52
ABB INSTALLATION PRODUCTS INC.—See ABB Ltd.; *Int'l*, pg. 52
ABB INSURANCE BROKERS LTD—See ABB Ltd.; *Int'l*, pg. 54
ABB INSURANCE LIMITED—See ABB Ltd.; *Int'l*, pg. 52
ABB INTERNATIONAL FINANCE LIMITED—See ABB Ltd.; *Int'l*, pg. 52
ABB INTERNATIONAL MARKETING LTD.—See ABB Ltd.; *Int'l*, pg. 50
ABB INTERNATIONAL MARKETING LTD.—See ABB Ltd.; *Int'l*, pg. 53
ABB INVESTMENTS (PTY.) LTD.—See ABB Ltd.; *Int'l*, pg. 52
AB BIOFUTURE—See MG Baltic UAB; *Int'l*, pg. 4871
AB-BIOTICS S.A.; *Int'l*, pg. 47
ABBISKO CAYMAN LIMITED; *Int'l*, pg. 56
ABBISKO THERAPEUTICS CO., LTD.—See Abbisko Cayman Limited; *Int'l*, pg. 56
ABB K.K.—See ABB Ltd.; *Int'l*, pg. 52
ABB LIMITED—See ABB Ltd.; *Int'l*, pg. 53
ABB LIMITED—See ABB Ltd.; *Int'l*, pg. 51
ABB LIMITED—See ABB Ltd.; *Int'l*, pg. 53
ABB LLC—See ABB Ltd.; *Int'l*, pg. 53
ABB LOGISTICS CENTER EUROPE GMBH—See ABB Ltd.; *Int'l*, pg. 50
ABB LTDA.—See ABB Ltd.; *Int'l*, pg. 53
ABB LTD.—See ABB Ltd.; *Int'l*, pg. 55
ABB LTD.—See ABB Ltd.; *Int'l*, pg. 53
ABB LTD.—See ABB Ltd.; *Int'l*, pg. 53
ABB LTD.—See ABB Ltd.; *Int'l*, pg. 53
ABB LTD.—See ABB Ltd.; *Int'l*, pg. 53
ABB LTD.—See ABB Ltd.; *Int'l*, pg. 53
ABB LTD.—See ABB Ltd.; *Int'l*, pg. 53

COMPANY NAME INDEX

ABB LTD.—See ABB Ltd.; *Int'l*, pg. 53
ABB LTD.—See ABB Ltd.; *Int'l*, pg. 53
ABB LTD.—See ABB Ltd.; *Int'l*, pg. 53
ABB LTD.—See ABB Ltd.; *Int'l*, pg. 53
ABB LTD.—See ABB Ltd.; *Int'l*, pg. 53
ABB LTD.—See ABB Ltd.; *Int'l*, pg. 53
ABB LTD.—See ABB Ltd.; *Int'l*, pg. 53
ABB LTD.; *Int'l*, pg. 49
ABB LTD.—See ABB Ltd.; *Int'l*, pg. 53
ABB LTD. - STONEHOUSE—See ABB Ltd.; *Int'l*, pg. 53
ABB LV INSTALLATION MATERIALS CO. LTD.—See ABB Ltd.; *Int'l*, pg. 49
ABB MAGHREB SERVICES S.A.—See ABB Ltd.; *Int'l*, pg. 53
ABB MALAYSIA SDN BHD.—See ABB Ltd.; *Int'l*, pg. 53
ABB MANAGEMENT SERVICES LTD.—See ABB Ltd.; *Int'l*, pg. 53
ABB MANUFACTURING SDN. BHD.—See ABB Ltd.; *Int'l*, pg. 53
ABB MEXICO S.A. DE C.V—See ABB Ltd.; *Int'l*, pg. 53
ABB MOTORS AND MECHANICAL INC.—See ABB Ltd.; *Int'l*, pg. 51
ABB NEAR EAST TRADING LTD.—See ABB Ltd.; *Int'l*, pg. 53
ABBNG LIMITED—See ABB Ltd.; *Int'l*, pg. 53
ABB NG LTD—See ABB Ltd.; *Int'l*, pg. 53
ABB NORDEN HOLDING AB—See ABB Ltd.; *Int'l*, pg. 53
AB BORAS RORINSTALLATIONER—See Instalco AB; *Int'l*, pg. 3721
ABBOT GROUP LIMITED—See Pamplona Capital Management LLP; *Int'l*, pg. 5711
ABBOTSFORD CHRYSLER DODGE JEEP RAM LTD.; *Int'l*, pg. 57
ABBOTSINCH TYRES & EXHAUSTS LTD.—See Sumitomo Rubber Industries, Ltd.; *Int'l*, pg. 7298
ABBOTT AG-DIAGNOSTICS—See Abbott Laboratories; *U.S. Public*, pg. 14
ABBOTT AG-NUTRITIONALS—See Abbott Laboratories; *U.S. Public*, pg. 17
ABBOTT AG—See Abbott Laboratories; *U.S. Public*, pg. 14
ABBOTT AG—See Abbott Laboratories; *U.S. Public*, pg. 14
ABBOTT AMBULANCE, INC.—See KKR & Co. Inc.; *U.S. Public*, pg. 1251
ABBOTT ANALYTICAL LIMITED—See Neogen Corporation; *U.S. Public*, pg. 1505
ABBOTT ARZNEIMITTEL GMBH—See Abbott Laboratories; *U.S. Public*, pg. 17
ABBOTT AUSTRALASIA PTY. LTD.—See Abbott Laboratories; *U.S. Public*, pg. 14
ABBOTT AUTOMATION SOLUTIONS GMBH—See Abbott Laboratories; *U.S. Public*, pg. 14
ABBOTT BIOLOGICALS BV—See Abbott Laboratories; *U.S. Public*, pg. 14
ABBOTT BIOTECHNOLOGY DEUTSCHLAND GMBH—See Abbott Laboratories; *U.S. Public*, pg. 15
ABBOTT B.V.—See Abbott Laboratories; *U.S. Public*, pg. 14
ABBOTT CAPITAL INDIA LIMITED—See Abbott Laboratories; *U.S. Public*, pg. 14
ABBOTT CIENTIFICA, S.A.—See Abbott Laboratories; *U.S. Public*, pg. 14
ABBOTT DEUTSCHLAND GMBH—See Abbott Laboratories; *U.S. Public*, pg. 15
ABBOTT DIABETES CARE B.V.—See Abbott Laboratories; *U.S. Public*, pg. 14
ABBOTT DIABETES CARE, INC.—See Abbott Laboratories; *U.S. Public*, pg. 14
ABBOTT DIABETES CARE LIMITED—See Abbott Laboratories; *U.S. Public*, pg. 14
ABBOTT DIABETES CARE—See Abbott Laboratories; *U.S. Public*, pg. 14
ABBOTT DIAGNOSTICOS RAPIDOS S.A.—See Abbott Laboratories; *U.S. Public*, pg. 14
ABBOTT DIAGNOSTICS GMBH—See Abbott Laboratories; *U.S. Public*, pg. 14
ABBOTT DIAGNOSTICS KOREA, INC.—See Abbott Laboratories; *U.S. Public*, pg. 14
ABBOTT DIAGNOSTICS MEDICAL CO., LTD.—See Abbott Laboratories; *U.S. Public*, pg. 14
ABBOTT DIAGNOSTICS SCARBOROUGH, INC.—See Abbott Laboratories; *U.S. Public*, pg. 14
ABBOTT DIAGNOSTICS—See Abbott Laboratories; *U.S. Public*, pg. 14
ABBOTT DIAGNOSTICS—See Abbott Laboratories; *U.S. Public*, pg. 14
ABBOTT DIAGNOSTICS TECHNOLOGIES AS—See Abbott Laboratories; *U.S. Public*, pg. 14
ABBOTT EQUITY HOLDINGS LTD.—See Abbott Laboratories; *U.S. Public*, pg. 16
ABBOTT-ESTABLISHED PRODUCTS DIVISION—See Abbott Laboratories; *U.S. Public*, pg. 17
ABBOTT FINANCE B.V.—See Abbott Laboratories; *U.S. Public*, pg. 14
ABBOTT FRANCE S.A.—See Abbott Laboratories; *U.S. Public*, pg. 15
ABBOTT GESELLSCHAFT M.B.H.—See Abbott Laboratories; *U.S. Public*, pg. 15
ABBOTT GMBH & CO. KG - PHARMACEUTICAL DIVISION—See Abbott Laboratories; *U.S. Public*, pg. 15
ABBOTT GMBH & CO. KG—See Abbott Laboratories; *U.S. Public*, pg. 15
ABBOTT HEALTHCARE B.V.—See Abbott Laboratories; *U.S. Public*, pg. 14
ABBOTT HEALTHCARE CONNECTIONS LIMITED—See Abbott Laboratories; *U.S. Public*, pg. 15
ABBOTT HEALTHCARE CONNECTIONS LIMITED—See Abbott Laboratories; *U.S. Public*, pg. 18
ABBOTT HEALTHCARE COSTA RICA, S.A.—See Abbott Laboratories; *U.S. Public*, pg. 15
ABBOTT HEALTHCARE PRIVATE LIMITED—See Abbott Laboratories; *U.S. Public*, pg. 17
ABBOTT HEALTHCARE PRODUCTS B.V.—See Abbott Laboratories; *U.S. Public*, pg. 17
ABBOTT HEALTHCARE PRODUCTS LTD.—See Abbott Laboratories; *U.S. Public*, pg. 16
ABBOTT HEALTHCARE VIETNAM COMPANY LIMITED—See Abbott Laboratories; *U.S. Public*, pg. 15
ABBOTT HEMATOLOGY- DIAGNOSTICS DIVISION—See Abbott Laboratories; *U.S. Public*, pg. 14
ABBOTT HOLDING GMBH—See Abbott Laboratories; *U.S. Public*, pg. 15
ABBOTT HOLDINGS B.V.—See Abbott Laboratories; *U.S. Public*, pg. 15
ABBOTT INDIA LIMITED—See Abbott Laboratories; *U.S. Public*, pg. 15
ABBOTT INDUSTRIES INC.; *U.S. Private*, pg. 35
ABBOTT INFORMATICS ASIA PACIFIC LIMITED—See Abbott Laboratories; *U.S. Public*, pg. 15
ABBOTT INFORMATICS AUSTRALIA PTY LIMITED—See Abbott Laboratories; *U.S. Public*, pg. 15
ABBOTT INFORMATICS CORPORATION—See Abbott Laboratories; *U.S. Public*, pg. 15
ABBOTT INFORMATICS EUROPE LIMITED—See Abbott Laboratories; *U.S. Public*, pg. 15
ABBOTT INFORMATICS EUROPE LIMITED—See Abbott Laboratories; *U.S. Public*, pg. 20
ABBOTT INFORMATICS FRANCE—See Abbott Laboratories; *U.S. Public*, pg. 15
ABBOTT INFORMATICS GERMANY GMBH—See Abbott Laboratories; *U.S. Public*, pg. 15
ABBOTT INFORMATICS NETHERLANDS B.V.—See Abbott Laboratories; *U.S. Public*, pg. 15
ABBOTT INFORMATICS SINGAPORE PTE. LIMITED—See Abbott Laboratories; *U.S. Public*, pg. 15
ABBOTT INFORMATICS SPAIN, S.A.—See Abbott Laboratories; *U.S. Public*, pg. 15
ABBOTT INFORMATICS TECHNOLOGIES LTD—See Abbott Laboratories; *U.S. Public*, pg. 15
ABBOTT INTERNATIONAL LLC—See Abbott Laboratories; *U.S. Public*, pg. 15
ABBOTT INVESTMENTS LIMITED—See Abbott Laboratories; *U.S. Public*, pg. 16
ABBOTT IRELAND LIMITED—See Abbott Laboratories; *U.S. Public*, pg. 15
ABBOTT IRELAND—See Abbott Laboratories; *U.S. Public*, pg. 15
ABBOTT JAPAN CO., LTD.—See Abbott Laboratories; *U.S. Public*, pg. 15
ABBOTT KOREA LIMITED—See Abbott Laboratories; *U.S. Public*, pg. 15
ABBOTT LABORATORIES ARGENTINA, S.A.—See Abbott Laboratories; *U.S. Public*, pg. 15
ABBOTT LABORATORIES A/S—See Abbott Laboratories; *U.S. Public*, pg. 15
ABBOTT LABORATORIES BALTICS—See Abbott Laboratories; *U.S. Public*, pg. 15
ABBOTT LABORATORIES B.V.—See Abbott Laboratories; *U.S. Public*, pg. 15
ABBOTT LABORATORIES, C.A.—See Abbott Laboratories; *U.S. Public*, pg. 16
ABBOTT LABORATORIES DE CHILE LIMITADA—See Abbott Laboratories; *U.S. Public*, pg. 16
ABBOTT LABORATORIES DE COLOMBIA, S.A.—See Abbott Laboratories; *U.S. Public*, pg. 16
ABBOTT LABORATORIES DE MEXICO S.A. DE C.V.—See Abbott Laboratories; *U.S. Public*, pg. 16
ABBOTT LABORATORIES D.O.O. HRK—See Abbott Laboratories; *U.S. Public*, pg. 16
ABBOTT LABORATORIES D.O.O.—See Abbott Laboratories; *U.S. Public*, pg. 16
ABBOTT LABORATORIES DRUZBA ZA FARMACIJO IN DIAGNOSTIKO D.O.O.—See Abbott Laboratories; *U.S. Public*, pg. 16
ABBOTT LABORATORIES EMPLOYEES CREDIT UNION; *U.S. Private*, pg. 35
ABBOTT LABORATORIES FINANCE B.V.—See Abbott Laboratories; *U.S. Public*, pg. 15
ABBOTT LABORATORIES GMBH—See Abbott Laboratories; *U.S. Public*, pg. 15
ABBOTT LABORATORIES (HELLAS) S.A.—See Abbott Laboratories; *U.S. Public*, pg. 15
ABBOTT LABORATORIES INC; *U.S. Private*, pg. 35
ABBOTT LABORATORIES INTERNATIONAL CO.—See Abbott Laboratories; *U.S. Public*, pg. 15
ABBOTT LABORATORIES, LIMITADA—See Abbott Laboratories; *U.S. Public*, pg. 16

ABBOTT LABORATORIES

ABBOTT LABORATORIES LIMITED - DIAGNOSTIC DIVISION—See Abbott Laboratories; *U.S. Public*, pg. 16
ABBOTT LABORATORIES, LIMITED—See Abbott Laboratories; *U.S. Public*, pg. 16
ABBOTT LABORATORIES LIMITED—See Abbott Laboratories; *U.S. Public*, pg. 16
ABBOTT LABORATORIES LIMITED—See Abbott Laboratories; *U.S. Public*, pg. 16
ABBOTT LABORATORIES LIMITED—See Abbott Laboratories; *U.S. Public*, pg. 16
ABBOTT LABORATORIES (MALAYSIA) SDN. BHD.—See Abbott Laboratories; *U.S. Public*, pg. 15
ABBOTT LABORATORIES (N.Z.) LTD.—See Abbott Laboratories; *U.S. Public*, pg. 15
ABBOTT LABORATORIES PACIFIC LTD.—See Abbott Laboratories; *U.S. Public*, pg. 16
ABBOTT LABORATORIES (PAKISTAN) LIMITED—See Abbott Laboratories; *U.S. Public*, pg. 15
ABBOTT LABORATORIES PHARMACEUTICALS (PR) LTD.—See Abbott Laboratories; *U.S. Public*, pg. 17
ABBOTT LABORATORIES (PHILIPPINES)—See Abbott Laboratories; *U.S. Public*, pg. 15
ABBOTT LABORATORIES POLAND SP Z.O.O.—See Abbott Laboratories; *U.S. Public*, pg. 16
ABBOTT LABORATORIES (PUERTO RICO) INCORPORATED—See Abbott Laboratories; *U.S. Public*, pg. 15
ABBOTT LABORATORIES, S.A.—See Abbott Laboratories; *U.S. Public*, pg. 16
ABBOTT LABORATORIES (SINGAPORE) PRIVATE LIMITED—See Abbott Laboratories; *U.S. Public*, pg. 15
ABBOTT LABORATORIES SLOVAKIA S.R.O.—See Abbott Laboratories; *U.S. Public*, pg. 16
ABBOTT LABORATORIES; *U.S. Public*, pg. 14
ABBOTT LABORATORIES SOUTH AFRICA (PROPRIETARY) LIMITED—See Abbott Laboratories; *U.S. Public*, pg. 16
ABBOTT LABORATORIES S.R.O.—See Abbott Laboratories; *U.S. Public*, pg. 16
ABBOTT LABORATORIES TAIWAN—See Abbott Laboratories; *U.S. Public*, pg. 16
ABBOTT LABORATORIES TRADING (SHANGHAI) CO., LTD.—See Abbott Laboratories; *U.S. Public*, pg. 16
ABBOTT LABORATORIES TRUSTEE COMPANY LIMITED—See Abbott Laboratories; *U.S. Public*, pg. 16
ABBOTT LABORATORIES URUGUAY S.A.—See Abbott Laboratories; *U.S. Public*, pg. 16
ABBOTT LABORATORIOS DEL ECUADOR CIA. LTDA.—See Abbott Laboratories; *U.S. Public*, pg. 16
ABBOTT LABORATORIOS DO BRASIL LTDA—See Abbott Laboratories; *U.S. Public*, pg. 16
ABBOTT LABORATORIOS, LIMITADA—See Abbott Laboratories; *U.S. Public*, pg. 16
ABBOTT LABORATORIOS S.A.—See Abbott Laboratories; *U.S. Public*, pg. 16
ABBOTT LABORATORIOS, S.A.—See Abbott Laboratories; *U.S. Public*, pg. 16
ABBOTT LABORATUARLARI ITHALAT IHRACAT VE TECARET LIMITED SIRKETI—See Abbott Laboratories; *U.S. Public*, pg. 16
ABBOTT LABORATUARLARI ITHALAT IHRACAT VE TICARET LIMITED SIRKETI—See Abbott Laboratories; *U.S. Public*, pg. 16
ABBOTT LOGISTICS B.V.—See Abbott Laboratories; *U.S. Public*, pg. 14
ABBOTT MANAGEMENT GMBH—See Abbott Laboratories; *U.S. Public*, pg. 15
ABBOTT MANUFACTURING SINGAPORE PRIVATE LIMITED—See Abbott Laboratories; *U.S. Public*, pg. 16
ABBOTT MEAD VICKERS BBDO—See Omnicom Group Inc.; *U.S. Public*, pg. 1573
ABBOTT MEAD VICKERS GROUP LIMITED—See Omnicom Group Inc.; *U.S. Public*, pg. 1573
ABBOTT MEDICAL AUSTRALIA PTY. LTD.—See Abbott Laboratories; *U.S. Public*, pg. 16
ABBOTT MEDICAL AUSTRIA GES.M.B.H.—See Abbott Laboratories; *U.S. Public*, pg. 16
ABBOTT MEDICAL CANADA CO.—See Abbott Laboratories; *U.S. Public*, pg. 16
ABBOTT MEDICAL DANMARK AS—See Abbott Laboratories; *U.S. Public*, pg. 17
ABBOTT MEDICAL DEVICES TRADING (SHANGHAI) CO., LTD.—See Abbott Laboratories; *U.S. Public*, pg. 17
ABBOTT MEDICAL ESPANA, S.A.—See Abbott Laboratories; *U.S. Public*, pg. 17
ABBOTT MEDICAL ESTONIA OU—See Abbott Laboratories; *U.S. Public*, pg. 17
ABBOTT MEDICAL FRANCE SAS—See Abbott Laboratories; *U.S. Public*, pg. 17
ABBOTT MEDICAL GMBH—See Abbott Laboratories; *U.S. Public*, pg. 17
ABBOTT MEDICAL ITALIA S.P.A.—See Abbott Laboratories; *U.S. Public*, pg. 17
ABBOTT MEDICAL LABORATORIES LTD—See Abbott Laboratories; *U.S. Public*, pg. 17
ABBOTT MEDICAL (MALAYSIA) SDN. BHD.—See Abbott Laboratories; *U.S. Public*, pg. 16

ABBOTT LABORATORIES

ABBOTT MEDICAL NEDERLAND B.V.—See Abbott Laboratories; *U.S. Public*, pg. 17
ABBOTT MEDICAL (PORTUGAL) DISTRIBUICAO DE PRODUTOS MEDICOS LDA—See Abbott Laboratories; *U.S. Public*, pg. 16
ABBOTT MEDICAL (SCHWEIZ) AG—See Abbott Laboratories; *U.S. Public*, pg. 16
ABBOTT MEDICAL SPOLKA Z OGRANICZONA ODPOWIEDZIALNOSCIA—See Abbott Laboratories; *U.S. Public*, pg. 17
ABBOTT MEDICAL SWEDEN AB—See Abbott Laboratories; *U.S. Public*, pg. 17
ABBOTT & MILLS INC.; *U.S. Private*, pg. 34
ABBOTT MOLECULAR INC.—See Abbott Laboratories; *U.S. Public*, pg. 14
ABBOTT NEDERLAND C.V.—See Abbott Laboratories; *U.S. Public*, pg. 14
ABBOTT NORGE AS—See Abbott Laboratories; *U.S. Public*, pg. 17
ABBOTT-NORTHWESTERN MEDICAL BUILDING PHARMACY INC.—See Allina Health System, Inc.; *U.S. Private*, pg. 192
ABBOTT NUTRITION LIMITED—See Abbott Laboratories; *U.S. Public*, pg. 17
ABBOTT NUTRITION—See Abbott Laboratories; *U.S. Public*, pg. 17
ABBOTT NUTRITION—See Abbott Laboratories; *U.S. Public*, pg. 17
ABBOTT NUTRITION—See Abbott Laboratories; *U.S. Public*, pg. 17
ABBOTT OY—See Abbott Laboratories; *U.S. Public*, pg. 17
ABBOTT PATHOLOGY PTY LTD—See Healius Limited; *Int'l*, pg. 3302
ABBOTT PHARMACEUTICAL CORPORATION—See Abbott Laboratories; *U.S. Public*, pg. 17
ABBOTT POINT OF CARE CANADA LTD.—See Abbott Laboratories; *U.S. Public*, pg. 14
ABBOTT POINT OF CARE, INC.—See Abbott Laboratories; *U.S. Public*, pg. 14
ABBOTT POINT OF CARE INTERNATIONAL—See Abbott Laboratories; *U.S. Public*, pg. 14
ABBOTT PRODUCTS AG—See Abbott Laboratories; *U.S. Public*, pg. 17
ABBOTT PRODUCTS OPERATIONS AG—See Abbott Laboratories; *U.S. Public*, pg. 17
ABBOTT PRODUCTS ROMANIA S.R.L.—See Abbott Laboratories; *U.S. Public*, pg. 17
ABBOTT PRODUTOS OTICOS LTDA.—See Abbott Laboratories; *U.S. Public*, pg. 17
ABBOTT RAPID DIAGNOSTICS AB—See Abbott Laboratories; *U.S. Public*, pg. 17
ABBOTT RAPID DIAGNOSTICS ARGENTINA S.A.—See Abbott Laboratories; *U.S. Public*, pg. 17
ABBOTT RAPID DIAGNOSTICS AS—See Abbott Laboratories; *U.S. Public*, pg. 17
ABBOTT RAPID DIAGNOSTICS AUSTRIA GMBH—See Abbott Laboratories; *U.S. Public*, pg. 17
ABBOTT RAPID DIAGNOSTICS BV—See Abbott Laboratories; *U.S. Public*, pg. 18
ABBOTT RAPID DIAGNOSTICS GERMANY GMBH—See Abbott Laboratories; *U.S. Public*, pg. 17
ABBOTT RAPID DIAGNOSTICS HEALTHCARE, S.L.—See Abbott Laboratories; *U.S. Public*, pg. 17
ABBOTT RAPID DIAGNOSTICS HEALTH CORP.—See Abbott Laboratories; *U.S. Public*, pg. 17
ABBOTT RAPID DIAGNOSTICS INFORMATICS, INC.—See Abbott Laboratories; *U.S. Public*, pg. 18
ABBOTT RAPID DIAGNOSTICS JENA GMBH—See Abbott Laboratories; *U.S. Public*, pg. 17
ABBOTT RAPID DIAGNOSTICS LDA—See Abbott Laboratories; *U.S. Public*, pg. 17
ABBOTT RAPID DIAGNOSTICS LIMITED—See Abbott Laboratories; *U.S. Public*, pg. 18
ABBOTT RAPID DIAGNOSTICS MEDICAL—See Abbott Laboratories; *U.S. Public*, pg. 18
ABBOTT RAPID DIAGNOSTICS OY AB—See Abbott Laboratories; *U.S. Public*, pg. 17
ABBOTT RAPID DIAGNOSTICS (PTY) LTD.—See Abbott Laboratories; *U.S. Public*, pg. 17
ABBOTT RAPID DIAGNOSTICS PTY. LTD.—See Abbott Laboratories; *U.S. Public*, pg. 17
ABBOTT RAPID DIAGNOSTICS S.A.S—See Abbott Laboratories; *U.S. Public*, pg. 17
ABBOTT RAPID DIAGNOSTICS SCHWEIZ GMBH—See Abbott Laboratories; *U.S. Public*, pg. 17
ABBOTT RAPID DIAGNOSTICS—See Abbott Laboratories; *U.S. Public*, pg. 17
ABBOTT RAPID DIAGNOSTICS S.R.L.—See Abbott Laboratories; *U.S. Public*, pg. 17
ABBOTT RAPID DIAGNOSTICS ULC—See Abbott Laboratories; *U.S. Public*, pg. 18
ABBOTT RAPID DX INTERNATIONAL LIMITED—See Abbott Laboratories; *U.S. Public*, pg. 17
ABBOTT RAPID DX NORTH AMERICA, LLC—See Abbott Laboratories; *U.S. Public*, pg. 18
ABBOTT RUBBER COMPANY, INC.; *U.S. Private*, pg. 35
ABBOTT SA/NV - DIAGNOSTICS DIVISION—See Abbott Laboratories; *U.S. Public*, pg. 18
ABBOTT SA/NV—See Abbott Laboratories; *U.S. Public*, pg. 18
ABBOTT S.A.—See Abbott Laboratories; *U.S. Public*, pg. 18
ABBOTT SAUDI ARABIA FOR TRADING—See Abbott Laboratories; *U.S. Public*, pg. 18
ABBOTT SAUDI ARABIA TRADING COMPANY—See Abbott Laboratories; *U.S. Public*, pg. 18
ABBOTT SCANDINAVIA A.B.—See Abbott Laboratories; *U.S. Public*, pg. 18
ABBOTT (SHANGHAI) DIAGNOSTICS SALES CO., LTD.—See Abbott Laboratories; *U.S. Public*, pg. 14
ABBOTT S.R.L.—See Abbott Laboratories; *U.S. Public*, pg. 18
ABBOTT STAFFING GROUP—See The Eastridge Group, Inc.; *U.S. Private*, pg. 4024
ABBOTT TOXICOLOGY LIMITED—See Abbott Laboratories; *U.S. Public*, pg. 18
ABBOTT TOXICOLOGY LIMITED—See Abbott Laboratories; *U.S. Public*, pg. 18
ABBOTT TOXICOLOGY LIMITED—See Abbott Laboratories; *U.S. Public*, pg. 18
ABBOTT TRUECARE PHARMA PRIVATE LIMITED—See Abbott Laboratories; *U.S. Public*, pg. 18
ABBOTT (UK) FINANCE LIMITED—See Abbott Laboratories; *U.S. Public*, pg. 16
ABBOTT (UK) HOLDINGS LIMITED—See Abbott Laboratories; *U.S. Public*, pg. 16
ABBOTT VASCULAR DEUTSCHLAND GMBH—See Abbott Laboratories; *U.S. Public*, pg. 18
ABBOTT VASCULAR DEUTSCHLAND GMBH—See Abbott Laboratories; *U.S. Public*, pg. 18
ABBOTT VASCULAR DEVICES (2) LIMITED—See Abbott Laboratories; *U.S. Public*, pg. 14
ABBOTT VASCULAR DEVICES HOLLAND B.V.—See Abbott Laboratories; *U.S. Public*, pg. 14
ABBOTT VASCULAR DEVICES IRELAND LIMITED—See Abbott Laboratories; *U.S. Public*, pg. 14
ABBOTT VASCULAR DEVICES LIMITED—See Abbott Laboratories; *U.S. Public*, pg. 14
ABBOTT VASCULAR INC.—See Abbott Laboratories; *U.S. Public*, pg. 18
ABBOTT VASCULAR INSTRUMENTS DEUTSCHLAND GMBH—See Abbott Laboratories; *U.S. Public*, pg. 18
ABBOTT VASCULAR INTERNATIONAL BVBA—See Abbott Laboratories; *U.S. Public*, pg. 18
ABBOTT VASCULAR JAPAN CO., LTD.—See Abbott Laboratories; *U.S. Public*, pg. 18
ABBOTT VASCULAR JAPAN CO., LTD—See Abbott Laboratories; *U.S. Public*, pg. 18
ABBOTT VASCULAR NETHERLANDS B.V.—See Abbott Laboratories; *U.S. Public*, pg. 18
ABBOT WALK (CHATTERIS) RESIDENTS MANAGEMENT COMPANY LIMITED—See Persimmon plc; *Int'l*, pg. 5815
A.B. BOYD CO.—See The Goldman Sachs Group, Inc.; *U.S. Public*, pg. 2080
ABB OY—See ABB Ltd.; *Int'l*, pg. 53
ABB POWER AND AUTOMATION SYSTEMS LTD.—See ABB Ltd.; *Int'l*, pg. 55
ABB POWER TECHNOLOGIES AB—See ABB Ltd.; *Int'l*, pg. 49
ABB POWER TECHNOLOGIES AB—See ABB Ltd.; *Int'l*, pg. 49
ABB (PRIVATE) LTD.—See ABB Ltd.; *Int'l*, pg. 49
ABB PTE. LTD.—See ABB Ltd.; *Int'l*, pg. 53
ABB (PTY) LTD.—See ABB Ltd.; *Int'l*, pg. 53
AB BRASIL INDUSTRIA E COMERCIO DE ALIMENTOS LTDA—See The Garfield Weston Foundation; *Int'l*, pg. 7648
AB BROADCAST—See Groupe AB S.A.; *Int'l*, pg. 3091
ABB ROBOTICS AB—See ABB Ltd.; *Int'l*, pg. 49
ABB ROBOTICS AB—See ABB Ltd.; *Int'l*, pg. 49
ABB ROBOTICS—See ABB Ltd.; *Int'l*, pg. 49
ABB ROMANIA—See ABB Ltd.; *Int'l*, pg. 53
ABB SACE LIMITADA—See ABB Ltd.; *Int'l*, pg. 53
ABB SACE S.P.A.—See ABB Ltd.; *Int'l*, pg. 54
ABB SACE S.P.A.—See ABB Ltd.; *Int'l*, pg. 54
ABB S.A. DE CV—See ABB Ltd.; *Int'l*, pg. 54
ABB S.A./N.V.—See ABB Ltd.; *Int'l*, pg. 54
ABB S.A.—See ABB Ltd.; *Int'l*, pg. 54
ABB S.A.—See ABB Ltd.; *Int'l*, pg. 53
ABB S.A.—See ABB Ltd.; *Int'l*, pg. 54
ABB S.A.—See ABB Ltd.; *Int'l*, pg. 54
ABB S.A.—See ABB Ltd.; *Int'l*, pg. 53
ABB S.A.—See ABB Ltd.; *Int'l*, pg. 54
ABB S.A.—See ABB Ltd.; *Int'l*, pg. 53
ABB SAUDI ARABIA—See ABB Ltd.; *Int'l*, pg. 54
ABB SCHWEIZ AG—See ABB Ltd.; *Int'l*, pg. 54
ABB SCHWEIZ HOLDING AG—See ABB Ltd.; *Int'l*, pg. 54
ABB SECHERON LTD.—See ABB Ltd.; *Int'l*, pg. 54
ABB SERVICE CO. LTD.—See ABB Ltd.; *Int'l*, pg. 54
ABB SERVICE GMBH—See ABB Ltd.; *Int'l*, pg. 50
ABB SHANGHAI MOTORS CO. LTD.—See ABB Ltd.; *Int'l*, pg. 49
ABB SHANGHAI TRANSFORMER CO. LTD.—See ABB Ltd.; *Int'l*, pg. 49
ABB SIA—See ABB Ltd.; *Int'l*, pg. 54

CORPORATE AFFILIATIONS

ABB SIFANG POWER SYSTEM CO., LTD.—See Beijing Sifang Automation Co., Ltd.; *Int'l*, pg. 957
ABB SISTEMAS INDUSTRIALES AB—See ABB Ltd.; *Int'l*, pg. 55
ABB SOUTH AFRICA (PTY) LTD.—See ABB Ltd.; *Int'l*, pg. 55
ABB S.P.A.—See ABB Ltd.; *Int'l*, pg. 54
ABB SP. Z O.O.—See ABB Ltd.; *Int'l*, pg. 55
ABB S.R.O.—See ABB Ltd.; *Int'l*, pg. 55
ABB S.R.O.—See ABB Ltd.; *Int'l*, pg. 55
ABB STOTZ-KONTAKT GMBH—See ABB Ltd.; *Int'l*, pg. 50
ABB STOTZ-KONTAKT S.A.—See ABB Ltd.; *Int'l*, pg. 56
ABB STOTZ-KONTAKT/STRIEBEL & JOHN VERTRIEBSGMBH—See ABB Ltd.; *Int'l*, pg. 50
ABB STRIEBEL & JOHN GMBH—See ABB Ltd.; *Int'l*, pg. 50
ABB STRIEBEL & JOHN GMBH—See ABB Ltd.; *Int'l*, pg. 55
ABB SUSA INC.—See ABB Ltd.; *Int'l*, pg. 52
ABB SWITZERLAND LTD - CMC LOW VOLTAGE PRODUCTS—See ABB Ltd.; *Int'l*, pg. 54
ABB SWITZERLAND LTD - CORPORATE RESEARCH—See ABB Ltd.; *Int'l*, pg. 54
ABB SWITZERLAND LTD - DRIVES—See ABB Ltd.; *Int'l*, pg. 54
ABB SWITZERLAND LTD - HIGH VOLTAGE PRODUCTS—See ABB Ltd.; *Int'l*, pg. 54
ABB SWITZERLAND LTD - MANUFACTURING & ROBOTICS—See ABB Ltd.; *Int'l*, pg. 54
ABB SWITZERLAND LTD., MICAFIL—See ABB Ltd.; *Int'l*, pg. 54
ABB SWITZERLAND LTD - MINERALS & PRINTING—See ABB Ltd.; *Int'l*, pg. 54
ABB SWITZERLAND LTD - NORMELEC—See ABB Ltd.; *Int'l*, pg. 54
ABB SWITZERLAND LTD - POWER ELECTRONICS—See ABB Ltd.; *Int'l*, pg. 54
ABB SWITZERLAND LTD - POWER SYSTEMS—See ABB Ltd.; *Int'l*, pg. 54
ABB SWITZERLAND LTD - SEMICONDUCTORS—See ABB Ltd.; *Int'l*, pg. 54
ABB TECHNOLOGIES LTD.—See ABB Ltd.; *Int'l*, pg. 55
ABB TECHNOLOGIES S.A.—See ABB Ltd.; *Int'l*, pg. 55
ABB TECHNOLOGIES W.L.L.—See ABB Ltd.; *Int'l*, pg. 55
ABB TIANJIN SWITCHGEAR CO., LTD.—See ABB Ltd.; *Int'l*, pg. 49
ABB TRAINING CENTER GMBH & CO. KG—See ABB Ltd.; *Int'l*, pg. 50
ABB TRANSFORMERS S.A.E.—See ABB Ltd.; *Int'l*, pg. 55
ABB TRANSMISSION & DISTRIBUTION LTD.—See ABB Ltd.; *Int'l*, pg. 51
ABB TURBO SYSTEMS HOLDING LTD.—See ABB Ltd.; *Int'l*, pg. 54
ABB TURBO SYSTEMS (HONG KONG) LIMITED—See ABB Ltd.; *Int'l*, pg. 49
ABB TURBO SYSTEMS LTD—See ABB Ltd.; *Int'l*, pg. 54
ABB UAB—See ABB Ltd.; *Int'l*, pg. 55
AB BUILDERS GROUP LTD.; *Int'l*, pg. 39
ABB VERWALTUNGS AG—See ABB Ltd.; *Int'l*, pg. 55
ABBVIE AB—See AbbVie Inc.; *U.S. Public*, pg. 21
ABBVIE AG—See AbbVie Inc.; *U.S. Public*, pg. 21
ABBVIE A/S; *Int'l*, pg. 57
ABBVIE AS—See AbbVie Inc.; *U.S. Public*, pg. 21
ABBVIE BIOFARMACEVTSKA DRUZBA D.O.O.—See AbVie Inc.; *U.S. Public*, pg. 21
ABBVIE BIOPHARMACEUTICALS LTD.—See AbbVie Inc.; *U.S. Public*, pg. 21
ABBVIE BIORESEARCH CENTER INC.—See AbbVie Inc.; *U.S. Public*, pg. 21
ABBVIE BIOTECHNOLOGY GMBH—See AbbVie Inc.; *U.S. Public*, pg. 21
ABBVIE BIOTECH VENTURES INC.—See AbbVie Inc.; *U.S. Public*, pg. 21
ABBVIE BIOTHERAPEUTICS INC.—See AbbVie Inc.; *U.S. Public*, pg. 21
ABBVIE B.V.—See AbbVie Inc.; *U.S. Public*, pg. 21
ABBVIE CORPORATION—See AbbVie Inc.; *U.S. Public*, pg. 21
ABBVIE DEUTSCHLAND GMBH & CO. KG—See AbbVie Inc.; *U.S. Public*, pg. 21
ABBVIE D.O.O.—See AbbVie Inc.; *U.S. Public*, pg. 22
ABBVIE ENDOCRINOLOGY INC.—See AbbVie Inc.; *U.S. Public*, pg. 21
ABBVIE FARMACEUTICA, S.L.U.—See AbbVie Inc.; *U.S. Public*, pg. 21
ABBVIE FARMACEUTICOS, S.A. DE C.V.—See AbbVie Inc.; *U.S. Public*, pg. 21
ABBVIE GK—See AbbVie Inc.; *U.S. Public*, pg. 21
ABBVIE GMBH—See AbbVie Inc.; *U.S. Public*, pg. 21
ABBVIE HEALTHCARE INDIA PRIVATE LIMITED—See AbbVie Inc.; *U.S. Public*, pg. 21
ABBVIE INC.; *U.S. Public*, pg. 21
ABBVIE INVESTMENT KFT.—See AbbVie Inc.; *U.S. Public*, pg. 21
ABBVIE IRELAND LIMITED—See AbbVie Inc.; *U.S. Public*, pg. 21
ABBVIE IRELAND NL B.V.—See AbbVie Inc.; *U.S. Public*, pg. 21
ABBVIE KFT.—See AbbVie Inc.; *U.S. Public*, pg. 21

COMPANY NAME INDEX

ABBVIE, L.DA—See AbbVie Inc.; *U.S. Public*, pg. 22
ABBVIE LIMITED—See AbbVie Inc.; *U.S. Public*, pg. 21
ABBVIE LIMITED—See AbbVie Inc.; *U.S. Public*, pg. 21
ABBVIE LIMITED—See AbbVie Inc.; *U.S. Public*, pg. 21
ABBVIE LTD.—See AbbVie Inc.; *U.S. Public*, pg. 21
ABBVIE LTD—See AbbVie Inc.; *U.S. Public*, pg. 21
ABBVIE LTD—See AbbVie Inc.; *U.S. Public*, pg. 21
ABBVIE OY—See AbbVie Inc.; *U.S. Public*, pg. 22
ABBVIE POLSKA SP. Z O.O.—See AbbVie Inc.; *U.S. Public*, pg. 22
ABBVIE PRODUCTOS FARMACEUTICOS LIMITADA—See AbbVie Inc.; *U.S. Public*, pg. 22
ABBVIE PROMOCAO, L.DA—See AbbVie Inc.; *U.S. Public*, pg. 22
ABBVIE PTE. LTD.—See AbbVie Inc.; *U.S. Public*, pg. 22
ABBVIE PTY LTD—See AbbVie Inc.; *U.S. Public*, pg. 22
ABBVIE REAL ESTATE MANAGEMENT GMBH—See AbbVie Inc.; *U.S. Public*, pg. 21
ABBVIE SARL—See AbbVie Inc.; *U.S. Public*, pg. 22
ABBVIE S.A.—See AbbVie Inc.; *U.S. Public*, pg. 22
ABBVIE SA—See AbbVie Inc.; *U.S. Public*, pg. 22
ABBVIE S.A.—See AbbVie Inc.; *U.S. Public*, pg. 22
ABBVIE S.A.—See AbbVie Inc.; *U.S. Public*, pg. 22
ABBVIE SDN. BHD.—See AbbVie Inc.; *U.S. Public*, pg. 22
ABBVIE SPAIN, S.L.—See AbbVie Inc.; *U.S. Public*, pg. 22
ABBVIE SP. Z O.O.—See AbbVie Inc.; *U.S. Public*, pg. 22
ABBVIE, S.R.L.—See AbbVie Inc.; *U.S. Public*, pg. 22
ABBVIE, S.R.O.—See AbbVie Inc.; *U.S. Public*, pg. 22
ABBVIE S.R.O.—See AbbVie Inc.; *U.S. Public*, pg. 22
ABBVIE TIBBI ILACLAR SANAYI VE TICARET LIMITED SIRKETI—See AbbVie Inc.; *U.S. Public*, pg. 22
ABBVIE TIBBI LIACLAR SANAYI VE TICARET LIMITED SIRKETI—See AbbVie Inc.; *U.S. Public*, pg. 22
ABB VIETNAM—See ABB Ltd.; *Int'l*, pg. 55
ABB WIRTSCHAFTSBETRIEBE GMBH—See ABB Ltd.; *Int'l*, pg. 50
ABB XIAMEN ELECTRICAL CONTROLGEAR CO. LTD.—See ABB Ltd.; *Int'l*, pg. 49
ABB XIAMEN LOW VOLTAGE EQUIPMENT CO. LTD.—See ABB Ltd.; *Int'l*, pg. 49
ABB XIAMEN SWITCHGEAR CO. LTD.—See ABB Ltd.; *Int'l*, pg. 55
ABB XI'AN POWER CAPACITOR COMPANY LIMITED—See ABB Ltd.; *Int'l*, pg. 49
ABB XINHUI LOW VOLTAGE SWITCHGEAR CO. LTD.—See ABB Ltd.; *Int'l*, pg. 55
ABBYLAND FOODS, INC.; *U.S. Private*, pg. 35
ABBYLAND PORK PACK—See Abbyland Foods, Inc.; *U.S. Private*, pg. 35
ABBYLAND TRUCKING, INC.—See Abbyland Foods, Inc.; *U.S. Private*, pg. 35
ABBYS INC.; *U.S. Private*, pg. 35
ABBYSON LIVING; *U.S. Private*, pg. 35
ABB ZHONGSHAN TRANSFORMER COMPANY LTD.—See ABB Ltd.; *Int'l*, pg. 49
ABC AGENCY NETWORK, INC.—See The Allstate Corporation; *U.S. Public*, pg. 2033
ABC AGENCY NETWORK OF TEXAS, LLC—See The Allstate Corporation; *U.S. Public*, pg. 2033
ABCAM AUSTRALIA PTY. LIMITED—See Danaher Corporation; *U.S. Public*, pg. 623
ABC/AMEGA INC.—See Trivest Partners, LP; *U.S. Private*, pg. 4240
ABCAM (HONG KONG) LIMITED—See Danaher Corporation; *U.S. Public*, pg. 623
ABCAM KK—See Danaher Corporation; *U.S. Public*, pg. 624
ABCAM LIMITED—See Danaher Corporation; *U.S. Public*, pg. 623
ABCAM SINGAPORE PTE. LIMITED—See Danaher Corporation; *U.S. Public*, pg. 624
ABCANN GERMANY GMBH—See MediPharm Labs Corp.; *Int'l*, pg. 4779
ABCANN MEDICINALS INC.—See MediPharm Labs Corp.; *Int'l*, pg. 4779
ABC ANSAI RURAL BANK LIMITED LIABILITY COMPANY—See Agricultural Bank of China Limited; *Int'l*, pg. 216
ABC APPLIANCE INC.; *U.S. Private*, pg. 35
ABC ARBITRAGE ASSET MANAGEMENT—See ABC Arbitrage S.A.; *Int'l*, pg. 57
ABC ARBITRAGE S.A.; *Int'l*, pg. 57
AB CARL A CARLSON CHARKUTERIER—See Atria Plc; *Int'l*, pg. 694
AB CARLSSON & MOLLER—See Indutrade AB; *Int'l*, pg. 3677
AB CARTER INC.; *U.S. Private*, pg. 33
AB CARVAL INVESTORS, L.P.—See Equitable Holdings, Inc.; *U.S. Public*, pg. 788
ABC ASSICURA S.P.A.—See Societa Cattolica di Assicurazione-Societa Cooperativa; *Int'l*, pg. 7033
ABC AUTOMOTIVE, INC.; *U.S. Private*, pg. 35
ABC AUTO PARTS LTD.; *U.S. Private*, pg. 35
ABC AUTOS, INC.; *U.S. Private*, pg. 35
ABC BAKERY SUPPLIES & EQUIPMENT, INC.; *U.S. Private*, pg. 35
ABC BEARINGS LIMITED—See The Timken Company; *U.S. Public*, pg. 2133

ABC BROADCAST OPERATIONS & ENGINEERING—See The Walt Disney Company; *U.S. Public*, pg. 2137
ABC BUS COMPANIES, INC.; *U.S. Private*, pg. 35
ABC CABINETRY—See Bain Capital, LP; *U.S. Private*, pg. 450
ABC CABLE NETWORKS GROUP—See The Walt Disney Company; *U.S. Public*, pg. 2137
ABC-CA FUND MANAGEMENT CO., LTD.—See Agricultural Bank of China Limited; *Int'l*, pg. 217
ABC CARPET & HOME INC.; *U.S. Private*, pg. 35
ABC CLEARING LTD—See Viel & Compagnie SA; *Int'l*, pg. 8192
ABC-CLIO; *U.S. Private*, pg. 36
ABC COMPANIES INC.—See ABC Bus Companies, Inc.; *U.S. Private*, pg. 35
ABC COMPOUNDING COMPANY, INC.; *U.S. Private*, pg. 35
ABC CONTRACT SERVICES LTD.—See HFBG Holding B.V.; *Int'l*, pg. 3374
ABC COSTRUZIONI SRL—See Argo Finanziaria S.p.A.; *Int'l*, pg. 562
ABC DESIGN GMBH—See Invision AG; *Int'l*, pg. 3789
ABC DEVELOPMENT CORPORATION—See Asahi Broadcasting Group Holdings Corporation; *Int'l*, pg. 592
ABC DISPOSAL SERVICE, INC.; *U.S. Private*, pg. 35
ABC DISTRIBUTION AND RETAIL SOLUTIONS GMBH—See Electronic Arts Inc.; *U.S. Public*, pg. 723
ABCELEC—See FAYAT SAS; *Int'l*, pg. 2624
ABC ELECTRIC CORP.—See Bain Capital, LP; *U.S. Private*, pg. 432
ABCELLERA BIOLOGICS INC.; *Int'l*, pg. 57
AB CERBO; *Int'l*, pg. 39
AB CERNELLE—See Dermapharm Holding SE; *Int'l*, pg. 2043
ABC FACTORS A.E.—See Alpha Services and Holdings S.A.; *Int'l*, pg. 369
ABC FAMILY WORLDWIDE, INC.—See The Walt Disney Company; *U.S. Public*, pg. 2137
ABCFINANCE GMBH—See Wilh. Werhahn KG; *Int'l*, pg. 8410
ABC FINANCIAL LEASING CO., LTD.—See Agricultural Bank of China Limited; *Int'l*, pg. 216
ABC FINANCIAL SERVICES, INC.—See Thoma Bravo, L.P.; *U.S. Private*, pg. 4145
ABC FINANCIAL SERVICES—See ABC Bus Companies, Inc.; *U.S. Private*, pg. 35
ABC FINE WINES & SPIRITS; *U.S. Private*, pg. 35
ABC FIRE EXTINGUISHER CO. INC.—See BlackRock, Inc.; *U.S. Public*, pg. 346
ABC FRONTIER HOLDINGS, INC.—See Asahi Broadcasting Group Holdings Corporation; *Int'l*, pg. 592
ABC FULFILLMENT LLC—See Hub Group, Inc.; *U.S. Public*, pg. 1066
ABC GAS (INTERNATIONAL) LTD.; *Int'l*, pg. 57
ABCHECK S.R.O.; *Int'l*, pg. 57
ABCHIMIE—See KKR & Co. Inc.; *U.S. Public*, pg. 1242
ABC HOLDINGS LIMITED—See Atlas Mara Limited; *Int'l*, pg. 686
ABC HOME & COMMERCIAL SERVICES; *U.S. Private*, pg. 35
ABC HOME MEDICAL SUPPLY, INC.; *U.S. Private*, pg. 36
ABC HORIZON PTE. LTD.—See Asahi Broadcasting Group Holdings Corporation; *Int'l*, pg. 592
ABC HUBEI HANCHUAN RURAL BANK LIMITED LIABILITY COMPANY—See Agricultural Bank of China Limited; *Int'l*, pg. 217
ABC IMAGING LLC; *U.S. Private*, pg. 36
ABC INC.; *U.S. Private*, pg. 36
ABC, INC.—See The Walt Disney Company; *U.S. Public*, pg. 2137
ABC, INC.—See The Walt Disney Company; *U.S. Public*, pg. 2137
ABC INDIA LTD.; *Int'l*, pg. 57
ABC INDUSTRIES INC.—See Branford Castle, Inc.; *U.S. Private*, pg. 639
AB CINEMAS NY, INC.—See AB International Group Corp.; *U.S. Public*, pg. 13
ABC INTERNATIONAL BANK PLC—See Arab Banking Corporation B.S.C.; *Int'l*, pg. 529
ABC INTERNATIONAL HOLDINGS LIMITED—See Agricultural Bank of China Limited; *Int'l*, pg. 217
ABC ISLAMIC BANK EC—See Arab Banking Corporation B.S.C.; *Int'l*, pg. 529
ABC KIMYA SANAYI VE DIS TICARET ANONIM SIRKETI—See Sika AG; *Int'l*, pg. 6914
ABC LIBRA CO., LTD.—See Asahi Broadcasting Group Holdings Corporation; *Int'l*, pg. 592
ABCLON, INC.; *Int'l*, pg. 57
A.B. CLOSING CORPORATION; *U.S. Private*, pg. 24
ABC-MART, INC.; *Int'l*, pg. 57
ABC-MART KOREA, INC.—See ABC-Mart, Inc.; *Int'l*, pg. 57
ABC MEDIA COMMUNICATIONS—See Asahi Broadcasting Group Holdings Corporation; *Int'l*, pg. 592
ABC MEDICAL, LLC—See AdaptHealth Corp.; *U.S. Public*, pg. 38
ABC MOTORS COMPANY LIMITED; *Int'l*, pg. 57
ABC MOVING & STORAGE INC.; *U.S. Private*, pg. 36
ABC MTS INC.—See IMV CORPORATION; *Int'l*, pg. 3638

ABC SECURITY SERVICE, INC.

ABC MULTIACTIVE LIMITED; *Int'l*, pg. 57
ABC NA KOLACH SP. Z O.O.—See Eurocash S.A.; *Int'l*, pg. 2533
ABC NATIONAL TELEVISION SALES, INC.—See The Walt Disney Company; *U.S. Public*, pg. 2137
ABC NEWS HOLDING COMPANY, INC.—See The Walt Disney Company; *U.S. Public*, pg. 2137
ABC NEWS, INC.—See The Walt Disney Company; *U.S. Public*, pg. 2137
ABC NEWS INTERCONTINENTAL, INC.—See The Walt Disney Company; *U.S. Public*, pg. 2137
ABC NEWS & SPORTS—See The Walt Disney Company; *U.S. Public*, pg. 2137
ABC NURSERY INC; *U.S. Private*, pg. 36
ABCO ADVISORY SERVICES INDIA PRIVATE LIMITED—See UnitedHealth Group Incorporated; *U.S. Public*, pg. 2248
ABCO AUTOMATION, INC.; *U.S. Private*, pg. 36
ABCO BUILDERS, INC.—See C.P. Richards Construction Co., Inc.; *U.S. Private*, pg. 708
ABCO BUILDING CORPORATION—See Selzer-Ornst Construction Company LLC; *U.S. Private*, pg. 3603
ABCO ELECTRONICS CO., LTD. - ABCO SHENYANG PLANT—See ABCO Electronics Co., Ltd.; *Int'l*, pg. 57
ABCO ELECTRONICS CO., LTD. - ABCO WEIHAI PLANT—See ABCO Electronics Co., Ltd.; *Int'l*, pg. 57
ABCO ELECTRONICS CO., LTD. - ABCO YANTAI PLANT—See ABCO Electronics Co., Ltd.; *Int'l*, pg. 57
ABCO ELECTRONICS CO., LTD.; *Int'l*, pg. 57
ABCO ELECTRONICS VINA CO., LTD.—See ABCO Electronics Co., Ltd.; *Int'l*, pg. 57
ABCO ENERGY, INC.; *U.S. Public*, pg. 24
ABCO ENGINEERING CORP.—See Ei Companies; *U.S. Private*, pg. 1346
ABCO FIRE PROTECTION, INC.; *U.S. Private*, pg. 36
ABCO FIRE PROTECTION, INC.—See Align Capital Partners, LLC; *U.S. Private*, pg. 167
ABCO HUNGARY KFT—See ABCO Electronics Co., Ltd.; *Int'l*, pg. 57
ABCO INDIA PRIVATE LIMITED—See UnitedHealth Group Incorporated; *U.S. Public*, pg. 2238
ABCO KOVEX LIMITED—See Bunzl plc; *Int'l*, pg. 1217
ABCO KOVEX (UK) LIMITED—See Bunzl plc; *Int'l*, pg. 1217
A.B. COLEMAN MORTUARY, INC.—See Service Corporation International; *U.S. Public*, pg. 1869
ABCOM COMPUTER RENTAL, INC.; *U.S. Private*, pg. 36
AB&COMPANY CO., LTD.; *Int'l*, pg. 47
AB CONNECTORS LIMITED—See TT Electronics plc; *Int'l*, pg. 7958
ABCO OFFICE FURNITURE—See JSJ Corporation; *U.S. Private*, pg. 2241
ABCO REFRIGERATION SUPPLY CORP.; *U.S. Private*, pg. 36
ABCORP USA—See American Banknote Corporation; *U.S. Private*, pg. 224
ABC ORTHODONTICS SA; *Int'l*, pg. 57
ABCO SLOVAKIA SRO—See ABCO Electronics Co., Ltd.; *Int'l*, pg. 57
ABCO SUPPLY, LLC—See Leonard Green & Partners, L.P.; *U.S. Private*, pg. 2428
ABCO SYSTEMS LLC; *U.S. Private*, pg. 36
ABCO TECH CO., LTD.—See ABCO Electronics Co., Ltd.; *Int'l*, pg. 57
A B COTSPIN INDIA LIMITED; *Int'l*, pg. 17
ABCOURT MINES INC.; *Int'l*, pg. 57
ABCO WELDING & INDUSTRIAL SUPPLIES INC.; *U.S. Private*, pg. 36
ABC OWNED TELEVISION STATIONS—See The Walt Disney Company; *U.S. Public*, pg. 2138
ABC PACKAGING MACHINE CORPORATION; *U.S. Private*, pg. 36
ABC PAVING CO. INC.—See New Enterprise Stone & Lime Co., Inc.; *U.S. Private*, pg. 2895
ABC PAVING COMPANY; *U.S. Private*, pg. 36
AB+C PHILADELPHIA LLC—See Aloysius, Butler & Clark Associates, Inc.; *U.S. Private*, pg. 196
ABC PHONES OF NORTH CAROLINA, INC.; *U.S. Private*, pg. 36
ABC POLYMER INDUSTRIES, LLC; *U.S. Private*, pg. 36
ABC PRECAST & READY MIX LTD.—See Penney Group; *Int'l*, pg. 5787
ABC PRINTING CO.—See Greater Georgia Printers, Inc.; *U.S. Private*, pg. 1769
A. B. C. RECYCLING LTD; *Int'l*, pg. 21
ABC REFRIGERATION & AIR CONDITIONING, INC.—See Ares Management Corporation; *U.S. Public*, pg. 189
ABC S.A.—See Arab Banking Corporation B.S.C.; *Int'l*, pg. 529
ABCS CO., LTD.—See Country Group Development Public Company Limited; *Int'l*, pg. 1818
ABC SECURITY SERVICE, INC.; *U.S. Private*, pg. 36
ABC SNICKERIER I HINDAS AB—See Ratos AB; *Int'l*, pg. 6220
ABC SOFTWARE GMBH—See Electronic Arts Inc.; *U.S. Public*, pg. 723
ABC SPORTS, INC.—See The Walt Disney Company; *U.S. Public*, pg. 2138
ABC SP. Z O.O.—See Eurocash S.A.; *Int'l*, pg. 2533

ABC STONE, INC.

CORPORATE AFFILIATIONS

ABC STONE, INC.; *U.S. Private*, pg. 36
ABC STORES; *U.S. Private*, pg. 36
ABC SUPERABRASIVES—See Compagnie de Saint-Gobain SA; *Int'l*, pg. 1730
ABC SUPPLY CO. INC.; *U.S. Private*, pg. 36
ABC TARGET, LLC; *U.S. Private*, pg. 36
ABC TECHNOLOGIES HOLDINGS INC.—See Apollo Global Management, Inc.; *U.S. Public*, pg. 146
ABC TECHNOLOGIES INC.—See Cerberus Capital Management, L.P.; *U.S. Private*, pg. 835
ABC TELEVISION & APPLIANCE RENTAL; *U.S. Private*, pg. 36
ABC TELEVISION NETWORK GROUP—See The Walt Disney Company; *U.S. Public*, pg. 2137
ABC TRANSPORT PLC; *Int'l*, pg. 57
ABCUR AB—See ADVANZ PHARMA Corp. Limited; *Int'l*, pg. 166
ABDA INSURANCE; *Int'l*, pg. 58
ABDALLAH INCORPORATED; *U.S. Private*, pg. 37
A.B. DATA, LTD.; *U.S. Private*, pg. 24
A.B. DATA, LTD. - WASHINGTON, D.C.—See A.B. Data, Ltd.; *U.S. Private*, pg. 24
AB DFDS SEAWAYS—See DFDS A/S; *Int'l*, pg. 2094
ABDI COMPANY JSC; *Int'l*, pg. 58
ABD INSURANCE & FINANCIAL SERVICES, INC.; *U.S. Private*, pg. 37
ABD INSURANCE & FINANCIAL SERVICES INC. - WALNUT CREEK—See ABD Insurance & Financial Services, Inc.; *U.S. Private*, pg. 37
ABDO INVESTMENTS, INC.; *U.S. Private*, pg. 37
AB DRITTE FLUGZEUGVERMIETUNGS GMBH—See Air Berlin PLC & Co. Luftverkehrs KG; *Int'l*, pg. 236
ABDS D. D.—See KD Group dd; *Int'l*, pg. 4110
ABDUL AALI AL AJMI CO. LTD.; *Int'l*, pg. 58
ABDULAZIZ & MANSOUR IBRAHIM ALBABTIN COMPANY; *Int'l*, pg. 58
ABDULLA AHMED NASS CONTRACTING COMPANY WLL—See Abdulla Ahmed Nass Group WLL; *Int'l*, pg. 58
ABDULLA AHMED NASS GROUP WLL; *Int'l*, pg. 58
ABDULLA FOUAD CORPORATION LTD.—See Abdulla Fouad Holding Co.; *Int'l*, pg. 58
ABDULLA FOUAD HOLDING CO.; *Int'l*, pg. 58
ABDULLA FOUAD IMPALLOY LTD. CO.—See Abdulla Fouad Holding Co.; *Int'l*, pg. 58
ABDULLA FOUAD INFORMATION TECHNOLOGY CO. LTD.—See Abdulla Fouad Holding Co.; *Int'l*, pg. 58
ABDULLA FOUAD MEDICAL SUPPLIES DIVISION—See Abdulla Fouad Holding Co.; *Int'l*, pg. 59
ABDULLA FOUAD-SUPPLY & SERVICES DIVISION—See Abdulla Fouad Holding Co.; *Int'l*, pg. 59
ABDULLA FOUAD-TESTRADE DIVISION—See Abdulla Fouad Holding Co.; *Int'l*, pg. 59
ABDULLAH ABDUL MOHSIN AL-KHODARI SONS COMPANY; *Int'l*, pg. 59
ABDULLAH AL-OTHAIM INVESTMENT & REAL ESTATE DEVELOPMENT COMPANY—See Al-Othaim Holding Company; *Int'l*, pg. 288
ABDULLAH AL OTHAIM MARKET CO.—See Abdullah Al-Othaim Markets Company; *Int'l*, pg. 59
ABDULLAH AL-OTHAIM MARKETS COMPANY; *Int'l*, pg. 59
ABDULLAH A M AL-KHODARI SONS CO JSC; *Int'l*, pg. 59
ABDULLA HASHIM GASES & EQUIPMENT CO. LIMITED—See Air Products & Chemicals, Inc.; *U.S. Public*, pg. 64
ABDULLAH HASHIM INDUSTRIAL GASES & EQUIPMENT CO. LTD.; *Int'l*, pg. 59
ABDULLAH & SAID M.O. BINZAGR COMPANY—See Binzagr Company; *Int'l*, pg. 1035
ABDULLAH SHAH GHAZI SUGAR MILLS LIMITED; *Int'l*, pg. 59
ABDULLAH SUGAR MILLS LIMITED—See Haseeb Waqas Group of Companies; *Int'l*, pg. 3282
ABDULLA NASS & PARTNERS CO. LTD.—See Abdulla Ahmed Nass Group WLL; *Int'l*, pg. 58
ABDUL LATIF JAMEEL GROUP OF COMPANIES; *Int'l*, pg. 58
ABDUL MOHSEN AL-HOKAIR GROUP FOR TOURISM AND DEVELOPMENT COMPANY; *Int'l*, pg. 58
ABDUL MOHSIN BADER AL KHORAFI EST. CO. FOR GEN. TRADING & CONTRACTING WLL—See Aiphone Co., Ltd.; *Int'l*, pg. 235
AB DYNAMICS EUROPE GMBH—See AB Dynamics plc; *Int'l*, pg. 39
AB DYNAMICS GK—See AB Dynamics plc; *Int'l*, pg. 39
AB DYNAMICS INC.—See AB Dynamics plc; *Int'l*, pg. 39
AB DYNAMICS PLC; *Int'l*, pg. 39
ABEBOOKS INC.—See Amazon.com, Inc.; *U.S. Public*, pg. 90
ABEC EXHIBITIONS & CONFERENCES PVT. LTD.—See Providence Equity Partners L.L.C.; *U.S. Private*, pg. 3292
ABEC EXHIBITIONS & CONFERENCES PVT. LTD.—See Searchlight Capital Partners, L.P.; *U.S. Private*, pg. 3587
ABEDNEGO ENVIRONMENTAL SERVICES, LLC—See Ecolab Inc.; *U.S. Public*, pg. 715

AB EFFECTENBETEILIGUNGEN AG; *Int'l*, pg. 39
ABE FRANCE SARL—See Outokumpu Oyj; *Int'l*, pg. 5667
ABE IRON WORKS LTD.—See Shikoku Electric Power Co., Incorporated; *Int'l*, pg. 6830
ABEKA EL & KRAFTANLAGGNINGAR AB—See Bravida Holding AB; *Int'l*, pg. 1142
ABEKAS, INC.—See Ross Video Limited; *Int'l*, pg. 6401
ABEKAWA KAIHATSU CO., LTD—See Taiheiyo Cement Corporation; *Int'l*, pg. 7411
A. BELANGER, LTEE.; *Int'l*, pg. 21
ABEL BUILDING SOLUTIONS—See ANSA McAl Limited; *Int'l*, pg. 477
ABEL CHEVROLET PONTIAC BUICK; *U.S. Private*, pg. 37
ABELCONN LLC; *U.S. Private*, pg. 37
ABEL CONSTRUCTION CO. INC.; *U.S. Private*, pg. 37
ABEL CONSTRUCTION COMPANY; *U.S. Private*, pg. 37
AB ELECTROLUX; *Int'l*, pg. 39
ABELEI, INC—See T. Hasegawa Co. Ltd.; *Int'l*, pg. 7396
AB ELEKTRONIK GMBH—See TT Electronics plc; *Int'l*, pg. 7958
AB ELEKTRONIK SACHSEN GMBH—See TT Electronics plc; *Int'l*, pg. 7958
ABEL EQUIPOS, S.A.—See Hillenbrand, Inc.; *U.S. Public*, pg. 1036
ABEL GMBH—See Hillenbrand, Inc.; *U.S. Public*, pg. 1035
ABELKO INNOVATION AB—See Indutrade AB; *Int'l*, pg. 3677
ABELL CORPORATION; *U.S. Private*, pg. 37
ABELLIO GMBH—See NV Nederlandse Spoorwegen; *Int'l*, pg. 5497
ABELLIO GREATER ANGLIA LTD—See NV Nederlandse Spoorwegen; *Int'l*, pg. 5497
ABELLIO LONDON & ABELLIO SURREY—See NV Nederlandse Spoorwegen; *Int'l*, pg. 5497
ABELLIO LONDON LIMITED—See NV Nederlandse Spoorwegen; *Int'l*, pg. 5497
ABELLIO—See NV Nederlandse Spoorwegen; *Int'l*, pg. 5497
ABELLIO TRANSPORT HOLDINGS LTD—See NV Nederlandse Spoorwegen; *Int'l*, pg. 5497
ABEL OIL CO. INC.; *U.S. Private*, pg. 37
ABEL PUMPS, L.P.—See IDEX Corp; *U.S. Public*, pg. 1089
ABEL SOLUTIONS, INC.; *U.S. Private*, pg. 37
ABELSONTAYLOR, INC.; *U.S. Private*, pg. 37
ABELSON-TAYLOR, INC.—See AbelsonTaylor, Inc.; *U.S. Private*, pg. 37
ABEL UNLIMITED INC.; *U.S. Private*, pg. 37
ABEL WOMACK INTEGRATED HANDLING SOLUTIONS; *U.S. Private*, pg. 37
ABEMAPRODUCTION, INC.—See TV Asahi Holdings Corporation; *Int'l*, pg. 7986
ABE MATERIALS - EASTON—See Haines & Kibblehouse Inc.; *U.S. Private*, pg. 1840
A-B EMBLEMS AND CAPS—See Conrad Industries, Inc.; *U.S. Private*, pg. 1019
ABEMEC B.V.—See BayWa AG; *Int'l*, pg. 915
ABENAKI WATER COMPANY—See New England Services Company; *U.S. Public*, pg. 1511
A BENBOW HOLDING INC.; *U.S. Private*, pg. 17
ABENEX CAPITAL S.A.; *Int'l*, pg. 59
ABENGOA BIOENERGY CORP.—See Abengoa S.A.; *Int'l*, pg. 59
ABENGOA BIOENERGY INC.—See Abengoa S.A.; *Int'l*, pg. 59
ABENGOA S.A.; *Int'l*, pg. 59
ABEN MINERALS LTD; *Int'l*, pg. 59
A&B ENTERPRISES INC.; *U.S. Private*, pg. 19
AB ENZYMES GMBH—See The Garfield Weston Foundation; *Int'l*, pg. 7648
ABEONA THERAPEUTICS INC.; *U.S. Public*, pg. 24
ABEO SAS; *Int'l*, pg. 59
AB EQUIPMENT LIMITED—See Maui Capital Ltd.; *Int'l*, pg. 4731
ABERA BIOSCIENCE AB; *Int'l*, pg. 60
ABERCROMBIE & FITCH CO.; *U.S. Public*, pg. 24
ABERCROMBIE & FITCH EUROPE SA—See Abercrombie & Fitch Co.; *U.S. Public*, pg. 25
ABERCROMBIE & FITCH HOLDING CORP.—See Abercrombie & Fitch Co.; *U.S. Public*, pg. 25
ABERCROMBIE & FITCH TRADING CO.—See Abercrombie & Fitch Co.; *U.S. Public*, pg. 25
ABERCROMBIE & KENT USA, LLC; *U.S. Private*, pg. 37
ABERCROMBIE OIL COMPANY INCORPORATED; *U.S. Private*, pg. 37
ABERCROMBIE TEXTILES, LLC—See W.R. Berkley Corporation; *U.S. Public*, pg. 2316
ABERCROSS HOLDINGS LTD.; *Int'l*, pg. 60
ABERDEEN ADVISORS INC.; *U.S. Private*, pg. 38
ABERDEEN AIRPORT LTD.—See Ferrovial S.A.; *Int'l*, pg. 2644
ABERDEEN ASSET MANAGEMENT COMPANY LIMITED—See abrdn PLC; *Int'l*, pg. 68
ABERDEEN ASSET MANAGEMENT FINLAND OY—See abrdn PLC; *Int'l*, pg. 68
ABERDEEN ASSET MANAGEMENT PLC—See abrdn PLC; *Int'l*, pg. 68

ABERDEEN ASSET MANAGERS LTD.—See abrdn PLC; *Int'l*, pg. 68
ABERDEEN ASSET MANAGERS LTD.—See abrdn PLC; *Int'l*, pg. 68
ABERDEEN CAPITAL MANAGEMENT LLC—See abrdn PLC; *Int'l*, pg. 68
ABERDEEN CHRYSLER CENTER INC.; *U.S. Private*, pg. 38
ABERDEEN DIALYSIS, LLC—See DaVita Inc.; *U.S. Public*, pg. 635
ABERDEEN DO BRASIL GESTAO DE RECURSOS LTD.—See abrdn PLC; *Int'l*, pg. 68
ABERDEEN DYNAMICS SUPPLY INC.; *U.S. Private*, pg. 38
ABERDEEN EMERGING MARKETS EQUITY INCOME, INC.; *Int'l*, pg. 60
ABERDEEN EMERGING MARKETS INVESTMENT CO. LTD.; *Int'l*, pg. 60
ABERDEEN FUND MANAGEMENT LIMITED—See Giordano International Limited; *Int'l*, pg. 2977
ABERDEEN GLOBAL INCOME FUND, INC.; *U.S. Public*, pg. 25
ABERDEEN GLOBAL SERVICES S.A.—See abrdn PLC; *Int'l*, pg. 68
ABERDEEN GLOBAL STATE STREET BANK LUXEMBOURG S.A—See abrdn PLC; *Int'l*, pg. 68
THE ABERDEEN GROUP, LLC—See Ziff Davis, Inc.; *U.S. Public*, pg. 2404
ABERDEEN HOTEL LTD. PARTNERSHIP; *U.S. Private*, pg. 38
ABERDEEN INTERNATIONAL INC.; *Int'l*, pg. 60
ABERDEEN INVESTMENT MANAGEMENT K.K.—See abrdn PLC; *Int'l*, pg. 68
ABERDEEN MANUFACTURING CORPORATION—See CHF Industries, Inc.; *U.S. Private*, pg. 876
ABERDEEN MARKET INTELLIGENCE U.S., LLC—See Ziff Davis, Inc.; *U.S. Public*, pg. 2404
ABERDEEN MINI STORAGE, L.L.C.—See National Storage Affiliates Trust; *U.S. Public*, pg. 1497
ABERDEEN NEWS COMPANY—See Gannett Co., Inc.; *U.S. Public*, pg. 901
ABERDEEN PROPERTY INVESTORS FRANCE SAS—See abrdn PLC; *Int'l*, pg. 68
ABERDEEN PROPERTY INVESTORS SWEDEN AB—See abrdn PLC; *Int'l*, pg. 68
ABERDEEN PROPERTY INVESTORS THE NETHERLANDS B.V.—See abrdn PLC; *Int'l*, pg. 68
ABERDEEN RESTAURANT ENTERPRISES LIMITED—See Melco International Development, Ltd.; *Int'l*, pg. 4808
ABERDEEN ROAD COMPANY; *U.S. Private*, pg. 38
ABERDEEN STANDARD ASSET MANAGEMENT (SHANGHAI) CO., LTD.—See abrdn PLC; *Int'l*, pg. 68
ABERDEEN STANDARD ASSET MANAGEMENT (THAILAND) LIMITED—See abrdn PLC; *Int'l*, pg. 68
ABERDEEN STANDARD EUROPEAN LOGISTICS INCOME PLC; *Int'l*, pg. 60
ABERDEEN STANDARD FUND MANAGERS LIMITED—See abrdn PLC; *Int'l*, pg. 68
ABERDEEN STANDARD INVESTMENTS (CANADA) LIMITED—See abrdn PLC; *Int'l*, pg. 68
ABERDEEN STANDARD INVESTMENTS CO. LTD.—See abrdn PLC; *Int'l*, pg. 68
ABERDEEN STANDARD INVESTMENTS DEUTSCHLAND AG—See abrdn PLC; *Int'l*, pg. 68
ABERDEEN STANDARD INVESTMENTS (HONG KONG) LIMITED—See abrdn PLC; *Int'l*, pg. 68
ABERDEEN STANDARD INVESTMENTS INC.—See abrdn PLC; *Int'l*, pg. 68
ABERDEEN STANDARD INVESTMENTS LUXEMBOURG S.A.—See abrdn PLC; *Int'l*, pg. 68
ABERDEEN STANDARD INVESTMENTS SWEDEN AB—See abrdn PLC; *Int'l*, pg. 68
ABERDEEN STANDARD INVESTMENTS (SWITZERLAND) AG—See abrdn PLC; *Int'l*, pg. 68
ABERDEEN STANDARD INVESTMENTS TAIWAN LIMITED—See abrdn PLC; *Int'l*, pg. 68
ABERDEEN STANDARD ISLAMIC INVESTMENTS (MALAYSIA) SDN. BHD.—See abrdn PLC; *Int'l*, pg. 68
ABERDEEN UNIT TRUST MANAGERS LTD.—See abrdn PLC; *Int'l*, pg. 68
ABERDEEN VETS4PETS LIMITED—See Pets at Home Group Plc; *Int'l*, pg. 5833
ABER ELECTRONICS LIMITED—See Creo Medical Group PLC; *Int'l*, pg. 1838
ABERFORTH PARTNERS LLP; *Int'l*, pg. 60
ABERFORTH SMALLER COMPANIES TRUST PLC; *Int'l*, pg. 60
ABERFORTH SPLIT LEVEL INCOME TRUST PLC; *Int'l*, pg. 60
ABERGELLI POWER LIMITED—See Drax Group plc; *Int'l*, pg. 2200
ABERLE GMBH—See Korber AG; *Int'l*, pg. 4281
ABERLE LOGISTICS GMBH—See Korber AG; *Int'l*, pg. 4281
ABERLE SOFTWARE GMBH—See Korber AG; *Int'l*, pg. 4281
THE ABERNATHY MACGREGOR GROUP, INC. - LOS ANGELES—See Vivendi SE; *Int'l*, pg. 8267

COMPANY NAME INDEX

AB ERNST HJ RYDAHL BROMSBANDFABRIK—See OEM International AB; *Int'l*, pg. 5528
ABERS GARAGE INC.; *U.S. Private*, pg. 38
ABERSON B.V.—See Wienerberger AG; *Int'l*, pg. 8404
AB ERSTE FLUGZEUGVERMIETUNGS GMBH—See Air Berlin PLC & Co. Luftverkehrs KG; *Int'l*, pg. 236
ABERTIS AIRPORTS S.A.—See ACS, Actividades de Construccion y Servicios, S.A.; *Int'l*, pg. 112
ABERTIS INFRAESTRUCTURAS, S.A.—See ACS, Actividades de Construccion y Servicios, S.A.; *Int'l*, pg. 112
ABERTIS LOGISTICA CHILE—See ACS, Actividades de Construccion y Servicios, S.A.; *Int'l*, pg. 112
ABERTIS LOGISTICA, S.A.—See ACS, Actividades de Construccion y Servicios, S.A.; *Int'l*, pg. 112
ABES TECHNOSEAL—See Hudaco Industries Limited; *Int'l*, pg. 3521
ABETECH, INC.; *U.S. Private*, pg. 38
ABETONG AB—See Heidelberg Materials AG; *Int'l*, pg. 3315
ABETONG AB—See Heidelberg Materials AG; *Int'l*, pg. 3315
ABETONG TEKNIK AB—See Heidelberg Materials AG; *Int'l*, pg. 3315
ABETRANS LOGISTICS LTD.; *Int'l*, pg. 60
A BETTERWAY RENT-A-CAR INC.; *U.S. Private*, pg. 18
A BETTER WAY THERAPY LLC—See UnitedHealth Group Incorporated; *U.S. Public*, pg. 2238
ABEX DISPLAY SYSTEMS; *U.S. Private*, pg. 38
ABEXTRA, INC.—See Huseby, LLC; *U.S. Private*, pg. 2013
ABFALLWIRTSCHAFTSZENTRUM MOSTVIERTEL GMBH—See Fomento de Construcciones y Contratas, S.A.; *Int'l*, pg. 2722
ABFAR COMPANY (PUBLIC JOINT STOCK); *Int'l*, pg. 60
AB FARESTA GRUS—See Peab AB; *Int'l*, pg. 5771
ABFB INC.; *U.S. Private*, pg. 38
ABF DATA SYSTEMS INC.; *U.S. Private*, pg. 38
AB FERROLEGERINGAR—See Nordic Elements AB; *Int'l*, pg. 5421
ABF FREIGHT SYSTEM (B.C.), LTD.—See ArcBest Corporation; *U.S. Public*, pg. 180
ABF FREIGHT SYSTEM CANADA, LTD.—See ArcBest Corporation; *U.S. Public*, pg. 180
ABF FREIGHT SYSTEM, INC.—See ArcBest Corporation; *U.S. Public*, pg. 180
ABF GLOBAL SUPPLY CHAIN, INC.—See ArcBest Corporation; *U.S. Public*, pg. 180
ABF LOGISTICS II, INC.—See ArcBest Corporation; *U.S. Public*, pg. 180
ABF LOGISTICS, INC.—See ArcBest Corporation; *U.S. Public*, pg. 180
AB FOOD & BEVERAGES AUSTRALIA PTY LTD.—See The Garfield Weston Foundation; *Int'l*, pg. 7648
AB FOOD & BEVERAGES PHILIPPINES, INC.—See The Garfield Weston Foundation; *Int'l*, pg. 7648
AB FOOD & BEVERAGES (THAILAND) LIMITED—See The Garfield Weston Foundation; *Int'l*, pg. 7648
AB FORTUM VARME HOLDING SAMAGT MED STOCKHOLMS STAD—See Fortum Oyj; *Int'l*, pg. 2741
AB FORTUM VARME SAMAGT MED STOCKHOLMS STAD—See Fortum Oyj; *Int'l*, pg. 2741
ABG ALLGEMEINE BAUMASCHINEN-GESELLSCHAFT MBH—See AB Volvo; *Int'l*, pg. 43
ABG CAULKING CONTRACTORS INC.; *U.S. Private*, pg. 38
AB GERMA—See ADDvise Group AB; *Int'l*, pg. 136
ABG-FRANCE E.U.R.L—See Ingersoll Rand Inc.; *U.S. Public*, pg. 1120
AB GF SWEDENBORG—See Christian Berner Tech Trade AB; *Int'l*, pg. 1586
ABG-IBERICA—See Ingersoll Rand Inc.; *U.S. Public*, pg. 1120
ABG SUNDAL COLLIER AB—See ABG Sundal Collier Holding ASA; *Int'l*, pg. 60
ABG SUNDAL COLLIER ASSET MANAGEMENT AS—See ABG Sundal Collier Holding ASA; *Int'l*, pg. 60
ABG SUNDAL COLLIER FORVALTNING AS—See ABG Sundal Collier Holding ASA; *Int'l*, pg. 60
ABG SUNDAL COLLIER HOLDING ASA; *Int'l*, pg. 60
ABG SUNDAL COLLIER INC.—See ABG Sundal Collier Holding ASA; *Int'l*, pg. 60
ABG SUNDAL COLLIER LTD.—See ABG Sundal Collier Holding ASA; *Int'l*, pg. 60
ABG SUNDAL COLLIER NORGE ASA—See ABG Sundal Collier Holding ASA; *Int'l*, pg. 60
AB GUSTAF KAHR—See Vestar Capital Partners, LLC; *U.S. Private*, pg. 4372
AB HANDEL OCH INDUSTRI—See Svenska Handelsbanken AB; *Int'l*, pg. 7358
AB HANGO ELEKTRISKA - HANGON SAHKO OY—See Bravida Holding AB; *Int'l*, pg. 1142
AB HANGO ELEKTRISKA—See Bravida Holding AB; *Int'l*, pg. 1142
ABHE & SVOBODA, INC.; *U.S. Private*, pg. 38
ABH FINANCIAL LIMITED—See ABH Holdings S.A.; *Int'l*, pg. 60
ABH HOLDINGS S.A.; *Int'l*, pg. 60
ABH HOLDINGS S.A.—See Alfa Group; *Int'l*, pg. 308

ABHI-CROCKETT, INC.—See Matson, Inc.; *U.S. Public*, pg. 1398
ABHIJIT TRADING COMPANY LTD.; *Int'l*, pg. 60
ABHINAV CAPITAL SERVICES LIMITED; *Int'l*, pg. 60
ABHINAV LEASING & FINANCE LIMITED; *Int'l*, pg. 60
ABHISHEK CORPORATION LTD.—See Mohite Industries Limited; *Int'l*, pg. 5019
ABHISHEK FINLEASE LIMITED; *Int'l*, pg. 61
ABHISHEK INFRAVENTURES LIMITED; *Int'l*, pg. 61
ABHISHEK INTEGRATIONS LIMITED; *Int'l*, pg. 61
A & B HOMECARE SOLUTIONS, LLC—See Encompass Health Corporation; *U.S. Public*, pg. 754
AB HOORS PLAT—See AB Electrolux; *Int'l*, pg. 39
ABHOTEL CO., LTD.; *Int'l*, pg. 61
ABH STROMSCHIENEN GMBH—See Addtech AB; *Int'l*, pg. 131
AB HUSKVARNA ELEKTROLYTPOLERING—See Outokumpu Oyj; *Int'l*, pg. 5668
A. BIANCHINI INGENIERO S.A.—See Societa Esercizi Commerciali Industriali; *Int'l*, pg. 7034
ABI ASIA—See Ruder Finn Group, Inc.; *U.S. Private*, pg. 3501
ABIBOW RECYCLING LLC—See PT Sinar Mas Group; *Int'l*, pg. 6073
ABIC BIOLOGICAL LABORATORIES LTD.—See Phibro Animal Health Corporation; *U.S. Public*, pg. 1685
ABICO GROUP; *Int'l*, pg. 61
ABICO HOLDINGS PUBLIC COMPANY LIMITED; *Int'l*, pg. 61
ABI COMPANIES, INC.; *U.S. Private*, pg. 38
ABICO NETCOM CO., LTD.; *Int'l*, pg. 61
ABIDE THERAPEUTICS, INC.—See Lundbeckfonden; *Int'l*, pg. 4582
ABI EUROPE—See Ruder Finn Group, Inc.; *U.S. Private*, pg. 3501
A&B II, LLC—See Alexander & Baldwin, Inc.; *U.S. Public*, pg. 75
ABILA, INC.—See Insight Venture Management, LLC; *U.S. Private*, pg. 2088
ABILENE AERO INC.; *U.S. Private*, pg. 38
THE ABILENE EYE ASC, L.P.—See KKR & Co. Inc.; *U.S. Public*, pg. 1247
ABILENE MACHINE INC.; *U.S. Private*, pg. 38
ABILENE MOTOR EXPRESS, LLC—See Knight-Swift Transportation Holdings Inc.; *U.S. Public*, pg. 1269
ABILENE NUCLEAR, LLC—See Cardinal Health, Inc.; *U.S. Public*, pg. 433
ABILENE OIL & GAS LIMITED; *Int'l*, pg. 61
ABILENE REPORTER-NEWS, LLC—See Gannett Co., Inc.; *U.S. Public*, pg. 898
ABILIA D.O.O.—See Adris Grupa d.d.; *Int'l*, pg. 153
ABILIO SERVICER CO., LTD.—See Sumitomo Mitsui Financial Group, Inc.; *Int'l*, pg. 7294
ABILIS, INC.; *U.S. Private*, pg. 38
ABILIS SYSTEMS LLC—See ALi Corporation; *Int'l*, pg. 320
ABILIS SYSTEMS SARL—See ALi Corporation; *Int'l*, pg. 320
ABILITAS HOSPITALITY CO., LTD.—See XYMAX Corporation; *Int'l*, pg. 8542
ABILITY BEYOND DISABILITY; *U.S. Private*, pg. 38
ABILITY CENTER—See Investor AB; *Int'l*, pg. 3787
ABILITY COMMERCE, INC.; *U.S. Private*, pg. 38
ABILITY CONNECTION TEXAS; *U.S. Private*, pg. 38
ABILITY DESIGN, LTD.—See SoftBank Group Corp.; *Int'l*, pg. 7051
ABILITY ENTERPRISE CO., LTD—See Abico Group; *Int'l*, pg. 61
ABILITYFIRST; *U.S. Private*, pg. 38
ABILITY HEALTH SERVICES & REHABILITATION, L.P.—See U.S. Physical Therapy, Inc.; *U.S. Public*, pg. 2213
ABILITY INC.; *Int'l*, pg. 61
ABILITY INTERNATIONAL CO., LTD.—See Abico Group; *Int'l*, pg. 61
ABILITY LIFTS LTD.—See Investment AB Latour; *Int'l*, pg. 3780
ABILITY NETWORK INC.—See Inovalon Holdings, Inc.; *U.S. Public*, pg. 1128
ABILITY OPTO-ELECTRONICS TECHNOLOGY CO., LTD.; *Int'l*, pg. 61
A. BILLITZ S.R.L.—See Coeclerici S.p.A.; *Int'l*, pg. 1688
ABI MARKETING PUBLIC RELATIONS—See Ruder Finn Group, Inc.; *U.S. Private*, pg. 3501
AB INBEV AFRICA B.V.—See Anheuser-Busch InBev SA/NV; *Int'l*, pg. 464
AB - INBEV FRANCE S.A.S.—See Anheuser-Busch InBev SA/NV; *Int'l*, pg. 464
AB INBEV UK LIMITED—See Anheuser-Busch InBev SA/NV; *Int'l*, pg. 464
A&B INC.—See Alexander & Baldwin, Inc.; *U.S. Public*, pg. 75
AB INDUSTRIVARDEN; *Int'l*, pg. 41
A B INFRABUILD LIMITED; *Int'l*, pg. 17
ABINGDON FLOORING LIMITED—See Victoria Plc; *Int'l*, pg. 8188
ABINGDON FURNITURE GALLERY LIMITED; *Int'l*, pg. 61
ABINGDON HEALTH PLC; *Int'l*, pg. 61
ABINGDON HEARING CARE—See Alpaca Audiology; *U.S. Private*, pg. 196

ABLEGROUP BERHAD

A&B INGREDIENTS, INC.; *U.S. Private*, pg. 19
ABINGTON BANK—See Hometown Financial Group, Inc.; *U.S. Private*, pg. 1975
ABINGTON GROUP INC.; *U.S. Private*, pg. 38
ABINGTON MARINER—See Gannett Co., Inc.; *U.S. Public*, pg. 901
ABINGTON RESOURCES LTD.; *Int'l*, pg. 61
ABINGWORTH LLP; *Int'l*, pg. 61
A&B INSURANCE AND FINANCIAL, LLC—See Genstar Capital, LLC; *U.S. Private*, pg. 1674
A & B INSURANCE & REINSURANCE S.R.L.—See Assiteca SpA; *Int'l*, pg. 648
AB INTERNATIONAL FINANCE LTD—See AB Bank Limited; *Int'l*, pg. 39
AB INTERNATIONAL GROUP CORP.; *U.S. Public*, pg. 13
AB INTER RAO LIETUVA—See JSC INTER RAO UES; *Int'l*, pg. 4009
AB INVESTOR GROUP FINANCE—See Investor AB; *Int'l*, pg. 3785
ABIO MARKETING SDN. BHD.—See Apex Healthcare Berhad; *Int'l*, pg. 511
ABIOMED EUROPE—See Johnson & Johnson; *U.S. Public*, pg. 1193
ABIOMED, INC.—See Johnson & Johnson; *U.S. Public*, pg. 1193
ABIOMED R&D, INC.—See Johnson & Johnson; *U.S. Public*, pg. 1193
ABION, INC.; *Int'l*, pg. 61
ABIONYX PHARMA SA; *Int'l*, pg. 61
ABI ORTHOTIC/PROSTHETIC LABORATORIES, LTD.—See Patient Square Capital, L.P.; *U.S. Private*, pg. 3107
ABIP, PC; *U.S. Private*, pg. 38
ABIRAMI FINANCIAL SERVICES INDIA LTD.; *Int'l*, pg. 62
ABIRD HOLDING BV; *Int'l*, pg. 62
ABI RESEARCH SINGAPORE—See Allied Business Intelligence, Inc.; *U.S. Private*, pg. 185
ABI RESEARCH SWITZERLAND—See Allied Business Intelligence, Inc.; *U.S. Private*, pg. 185
ABI RESEARCH UK—See Allied Business Intelligence, Inc.; *U.S. Private*, pg. 185
ABI SAB GROUP HOLDING LIMITED—See Anheuser-Busch InBev SA/NV; *Int'l*, pg. 464
ABIS GMBH—See Deutsche Post AG; *Int'l*, pg. 2071
AB&I; *U.S. Private*, pg. 33
ABIST CO., LTD.; *Int'l*, pg. 62
ABITA BREWING CO.; *U.S. Private*, pg. 39
ABITALIA, INC.—See American Biltrite Inc.; *U.S. Public*, pg. 97
ABITARE IN S.P.A.; *Int'l*, pg. 62
ABITEC CORPORATION—See The Garfield Weston Foundation; *Int'l*, pg. 7648
ABITIBI MINING CORP.; *Int'l*, pg. 62
ABITIBI ROYALTIES INC.—See Gold Royalty Corp.; *Int'l*, pg. 3026
ABITS GROUP INC.; *Int'l*, pg. 62
ABIVAX SA; *Int'l*, pg. 62
ABIX SERVICE S.L.U.—See Inmobiliaria Colonial SOCIMI SA; *Int'l*, pg. 3706
ABJ ENGINEERING & CONTRACTING CO. (KSC)—See Mohammed Abdulmohsin Al-Kharafi & Sons WLL; *Int'l*, pg. 5018
AB JOURMONTOR—See Securitas AB; *Int'l*, pg. 6675
AB KAROSSERITILLBEHOR—See Axel Johnson Gruppen AB; *Int'l*, pg. 763
ABK AS—See NIBE Industrier AB; *Int'l*, pg. 5259
ABK BETRIEBGESELLSCHAFT DER AKITIENBRAUEREI KAUFBEUREN GMBH—See Rok Stars PLC; *Int'l*, pg. 6388
ABK-CONCRETE PLANT LLP—See Build Investments Group JSC; *Int'l*, pg. 1212
ABKO CO., LTD.; *Int'l*, pg. 62
ABK-QVILLER AS—See NIBE Industrier AB; *Int'l*, pg. 5259
ABLAK HOLDINGS, LLC; *U.S. Private*, pg. 39
ABLATION FRONTIERS L.L.C.—See Medtronic plc; *Int'l*, pg. 4788
ABLAZE EXPORT PVT. LTD.—See Level Biotechnology, Inc.; *Int'l*, pg. 4470
ABL BIO, INC.; *Int'l*, pg. 62
ABL DIAGNOSTICS S.A.—See Advanced Biological Laboratories (ABL) S.A.; *Int'l*, pg. 157
ABLE2 ENHANCING POTENTIAL; *U.S. Private*, pg. 39
ABLE AEROSPACE SERVICES, INC.—See Textron Inc.; *U.S. Public*, pg. 2028
ABLE ANALYTICS CO., LTD.—See Green Cross WellBeing Corp.; *Int'l*, pg. 3070
ABLE BRANDS CO.; *U.S. Public*, pg. 25
ABLE C&C CO., LTD.; *Int'l*, pg. 62
ABLECO FINANCE, LLC—See Cerberus Capital Management, L.P.; *U.S. Private*, pg. 835
ABLE DISTRIBUTING CO. INC.—See Blackfriars Corp.; *U.S. Private*, pg. 575
ABLE ENGINEERING HOLDINGS LIMITED; *Int'l*, pg. 62
ABLE EQUIPMENT RENTAL, INC.; *U.S. Private*, pg. 39
ABLE FREIGHT SERVICES INC.; *U.S. Private*, pg. 39
ABLE GLOBAL BERHAD; *Int'l*, pg. 62
ABLEGROUP BERHAD; *Int'l*, pg. 63
ABLE HEALTH LLC—See Health Catalyst, Inc.; *U.S. Public*, pg. 1014

ABLEGROUP BERHAD

ABLE HOME HEALTH, INC.—See UnitedHealth Group Incorporated; *U.S. Public*, pg. 2243
ABLE INFORMATION TECHNOLOGIES, INC.; *U.S. Private*, pg. 39
ABLE INFORMATION TECHNOLOGIES, INC.—See Able Information Technologies, Inc.; *U.S. Private*, pg. 39
ABLE INSURANCE SERVICES LIMITED—See Admiral Group plc; *Int'l*, pg. 151
AB LEISURE EXPONENT, INC.—See Leisure & Resorts World Corporation; *Int'l*, pg. 4447
ABLE MACHINERY MOVERS, INC.; *U.S. Private*, pg. 39
ABLE MANUFACTURING AND ASSEMBLY LLC; *U.S. Private*, pg. 39
ABLEMEX, S.A. DE C.V.—See SigmaTron International, Inc.; *U.S. Public*, pg. 1877
ABLE MOTORS CO., LTD.—See AAPICO Hitech plc; *Int'l*, pg. 37
ABLENET, INC.; *U.S. Private*, pg. 39
ABLE NEW ENERGY CO., LTD—See Ultralife Corporation; *U.S. Public*, pg. 2224
ABLE & PARTNERS CO., LTD.; *Int'l*, pg. 62
ABLE PROFIT (HONG KONG) LIMITED—See Grand Peace Group Holdings Limited; *Int'l*, pg. 3056
ABLEREX CORPORATION—See Ablerex Electronics Co., Ltd.; *Int'l*, pg. 63
ABLEREX ELECTRONICS (BEIJING) CO., LTD.—See Ablerex Electronics Co., Ltd.; *Int'l*, pg. 63
ABLEREX ELECTRONICS CO., LTD.; *Int'l*, pg. 63
ABLEREX ELECTRONICS ITALY S.R.L.—See Ablerex Electronics Co., Ltd.; *Int'l*, pg. 63
ABLEREX ELECTRONICS (S) PTE. LTD.—See Ablerex Electronics Co., Ltd.; *Int'l*, pg. 63
ABLEREX ELECTRONICS (SUZHOU) CO., LTD.—See Ablerex Electronics Co., Ltd.; *Int'l*, pg. 63
ABLEREX ELECTRONICS (THAILAND) CO., LTD.—See Ablerex Electronics Co., Ltd.; *Int'l*, pg. 63
ABLEREX LATAM CORPORATION—See Ablerex Electronics Co., Ltd.; *Int'l*, pg. 63
ABLE ROLLING STEEL DOOR, INC.—See On-Point Group, LLC; *U.S. Private*, pg. 3018
ABLE SALES COMPANY, INC.; *U.S. Private*, pg. 39
ABLE SANOH INDUSTRIES (1996) CO., LTD.—See Sanoh Industrial Co., Ltd.; *Int'l*, pg. 6552
ABLESTIK MALAYSIA—See Henkel AG & Co. KGaA; *Int'l*, pg. 3353
ABLESTIK (SHANGHAI) LTD.—See Henkel AG & Co. KGaA; *Int'l*, pg. 3348
AB LESTO—See UAB Ignitis grupe; *Int'l*, pg. 7998
ABLETON AG; *Int'l*, pg. 63
ABLE TRANSPORTE DE CARGA S. DE R.L. DE C.V.—See Able Freight Services Inc.; *U.S. Private*, pg. 39
ABLEVETS LLC—See Oracle Corporation; *U.S. Public*, pg. 1610
ABLE WASTE MANAGEMENT LTD.—See Hills Waste Solutions Limited; *Int'l*, pg. 3393
ABL EXCHANGE LLC—See Alexander & Baldwin, Inc.; *U.S. Public*, pg. 75
ABL GROUP ASA; *Int'l*, pg. 62
ABLIC EUROPE GMBH—See Minebea Mitsumi Inc.; *Int'l*, pg. 4902
ABLIC HONG KONG LIMITED—See Minebea Mitsumi Inc.; *Int'l*, pg. 4902
ABLIC INC.—See Minebea Mitsumi Inc.; *Int'l*, pg. 4902
ABLIC KOREA INC.—See Minebea Mitsumi Inc.; *Int'l*, pg. 4902
ABLIC SHENZHEN INC.—See Minebea Mitsumi Inc.; *Int'l*, pg. 4902
ABLIC TAIWAN INC.—See Minebea Mitsumi Inc.; *Int'l*, pg. 4902
ABLIC U.S.A. INC.—See Minebea Mitsumi Inc.; *Int'l*, pg. 4902
AB LINDEX—See Stockmann plc; *Int'l*, pg. 7220
ABLIVA AB; *Int'l*, pg. 63
AB LKI KALDMAN OY; *Int'l*, pg. 41
AB LK PRECISION PARTS—See XANO Industri AB; *Int'l*, pg. 8519
ABL MANAGEMENT INC.; *U.S. Private*, pg. 39
ABLON GROUP LIMITED; *Int'l*, pg. 63
ABLON KFT.—See Ablon Group Limited; *Int'l*, pg. 63
ABLON SP. Z O.O.—See Ablon Group Limited; *Int'l*, pg. 63
ABLON S.R.L.—See Ablon Group Limited; *Int'l*, pg. 63
ABLON S.R.O.—See Ablon Group Limited; *Int'l*, pg. 63
ABLOY CANADA INC.—See ASSA ABLOY AB; *Int'l*, pg. 637
ABLOY HIGH SECURITY LOCKS PRIVATE LTD.—See ASSA ABLOY AB; *Int'l*, pg. 637
ABLOY MUL-T-LOCK MEXICO S.A. DE C.V.—See ASSA ABLOY AB; *Int'l*, pg. 637
ABLOY OY—See ASSA ABLOY AB; *Int'l*, pg. 637
ABLOY SECURITY INC.—See ASSA ABLOY AB; *Int'l*, pg. 636
ABLOY UK LTD—See ASSA ABLOY AB; *Int'l*, pg. 636
ABLOY UK LTD—See ASSA ABLOY AB; *Int'l*, pg. 636
ABL-TECHNIC BOGENSBERGER GES.M.B.H.—See Rubicon Partners Limited; *Int'l*, pg. 6422
ABL-TECHNIC BOGENSBERGER GES.M.B.H.—See Vision Capital, LLP; *Int'l*, pg. 8251
ABL-TECHNIC ENTLACKUNG GMBH—See Rubicon Partners Limited; *Int'l*, pg. 6422
ABL-TECHNIC ENTLACKUNG GMBH—See Vision Capital, LLP; *Int'l*, pg. 8251
ABLYNX N.V.—See Sanofi; *Int'l*, pg. 6547
ABLY RESOURCES LTD.—See J&J Denholm Ltd.; *Int'l*, pg. 3853
ABM AMRO COMMERCIAL FINANCE N.V.—See ABN AMRO Group N.V.; *Int'l*, pg. 63
AB MARKARYDS METALLARMATUR—See Rettig Group Ltd.; *Int'l*, pg. 6310
AB MAURI AUSTRALIA LTD.—See The Garfield Weston Foundation; *Int'l*, pg. 7648
AB MAURI BRAZIL—See The Garfield Weston Foundation; *Int'l*, pg. 7648
AB MAURI FOOD, S.A.—See The Garfield Weston Foundation; *Int'l*, pg. 7648
AB MAURI INDIA (PRIVATE) LIMITED—See The Garfield Weston Foundation; *Int'l*, pg. 7648
AB MAURI ITALY S.P.A.—See The Garfield Weston Foundation; *Int'l*, pg. 7648
AB MAURI MALAYSIA SDN. BHD.—See The Garfield Weston Foundation; *Int'l*, pg. 7648
AB MAURI PORTUGAL, SA—See The Garfield Weston Foundation; *Int'l*, pg. 7648
AB MAURI (UK) LIMITED—See The Garfield Weston Foundation; *Int'l*, pg. 7648
AB MAURI (UK) LTD. - IRELAND OFFICE—See The Garfield Weston Foundation; *Int'l*, pg. 7648
ABM BUILDING SERVICES, LLC—See ABM Industries, Inc.; *U.S. Public*, pg. 25
ABM BUILDING SOLUTIONS, LLC—See ABM Industries, Inc.; *U.S. Public*, pg. 25
ABM DATA SYSTEMS LTD.—See WiseTech Global Limited; *Int'l*, pg. 8436
ABM ELECTRICAL & LIGHTING SERVICES, LLC—See ABM Industries, Inc.; *U.S. Public*, pg. 25
ABM ELECTRICAL & LIGHTING SOLUTIONS, INC.—See ABM Industries, Inc.; *U.S. Public*, pg. 25
ABM ELECTRICAL POWER SERVICES, LLC—See ABM Industries, Inc.; *U.S. Public*, pg. 25
ABM ELECTRICAL POWER SOLUTIONS, LLC—See ABM Industries, Inc.; *U.S. Public*, pg. 25
ABM ENERGIE CONSEIL SAS—See ENGIE SA; *Int'l*, pg. 2428
ABM FACILITY SERVICES, INC.—See ABM Industries, Inc.; *U.S. Public*, pg. 25
ABM FACILITY SERVICES—See ABM Industries, Inc.; *U.S. Public*, pg. 25
ABM FACILITY SOLUTIONS GROUP, LLC—See ABM Industries, Inc.; *U.S. Public*, pg. 25
ABM FACILITY SOLUTIONS GROUP, LLC—See ABM Industries, Inc.; *U.S. Public*, pg. 25
ABM FRANCHISING GROUP, LLC—See ABM Industries, Inc.; *U.S. Public*, pg. 25
ABM FUJIYA BERHAD; *Int'l*, pg. 63
ABM GLOBAL SOLUTIONS, INC.—See PLDT Inc.; *Int'l*, pg. 5895
ABM GROUP UK LIMITED—See ABM Industries, Inc.; *U.S. Public*, pg. 26
ABM HEALTHCARE SUPPORT SERVICES, INC.—See ABM Industries, Inc.; *U.S. Public*, pg. 25
AB MIKROELEKTRONIK GMBH—See KYOCERA Corporation; *Int'l*, pg. 4358
ABM INDUSTRIES, INC.; *U.S. Public*, pg. 25
ABM INTERNATIONAL LIMITED; *Int'l*, pg. 63
ABM JANITORIAL SERVICES COMPANY, LTD.—See ABM Industries, Inc.; *U.S. Public*, pg. 26
ABM JANITORIAL SERVICES - HAWAIIAN REGION—See ABM Industries, Inc.; *U.S. Public*, pg. 25
ABM JANITORIAL SERVICES, INC.—See ABM Industries, Inc.; *U.S. Public*, pg. 25
ABM JANITORIAL SERVICES - MID-ATLANTIC REGION—See ABM Industries, Inc.; *U.S. Public*, pg. 25
ABM JANITORIAL SERVICES - MIDWEST REGION—See ABM Industries, Inc.; *U.S. Public*, pg. 25
ABM JANITORIAL SERVICES - NATIONAL ACCOUNTS—See ABM Industries, Inc.; *U.S. Public*, pg. 25
ABM JANITORIAL SERVICES - NORTH CENTRAL REGION—See ABM Industries, Inc.; *U.S. Public*, pg. 25
ABM JANITORIAL SERVICES - NORTHERN CALIFORNIA REGION—See ABM Industries, Inc.; *U.S. Public*, pg. 25
ABM JANITORIAL SERVICES - NORTHWEST MOUNTAIN REGION—See ABM Industries, Inc.; *U.S. Public*, pg. 26
ABM JANITORIAL SERVICES - NORTHWEST PACIFIC REGION—See ABM Industries, Inc.; *U.S. Public*, pg. 26
ABM JANITORIAL SERVICES - SOUTH CENTRAL REGION—See ABM Industries, Inc.; *U.S. Public*, pg. 26
ABM JANITORIAL SERVICES - SOUTHEAST REGION—See ABM Industries, Inc.; *U.S. Public*, pg. 26

CORPORATE AFFILIATIONS

ABM JANITORIAL SERVICES - WEST CENTRAL & WEST PACIFIC REGION—See ABM Industries, Inc.; *U.S. Public*, pg. 26
ABM KNOWLEDGEWARE LTD; *Int'l*, pg. 63
ABM KUPRAL KFT.—See Wieland-Werke AG; *Int'l*, pg. 8402
ABM ONSITE SERVICES, INC.—See ABM Industries, Inc.; *U.S. Public*, pg. 25
AB MONSTERAS METALL; *Int'l*, pg. 41
ABM PARKING SERVICES, INC.—See ABM Industries, Inc.; *U.S. Public*, pg. 26
ABM PARKING SERVICES, INC.—See ABM Industries, Inc.; *U.S. Public*, pg. 26
ABM REXEL—See Rexel, S.A.; *Int'l*, pg. 6316
ABNA FEED (LIAONING) CO., LTD—See The Garfield Weston Foundation; *Int'l*, pg. 7648
ABN AMRO BANK BRUSSELS—See ABN AMRO Group N.V.; *Int'l*, pg. 64
ABN AMRO BANK (LUXEMBOURG) S.A.—See BNP Paribas SA; *Int'l*, pg. 1084
ABN AMRO BANK N.V.—See ABN AMRO Group N.V.; *Int'l*, pg. 63
ABN AMRO CLEARING CHICAGO LLC—See ABN AMRO Group N.V.; *Int'l*, pg. 64
ABN AMRO CLEARING HONG KONG LTD.—See ABN AMRO Group N.V.; *Int'l*, pg. 64
ABN AMRO CLEARING LONDON LTD.—See ABN AMRO Group N.V.; *Int'l*, pg. 65
ABN AMRO CLEARING SINGAPORE PTE LTD—See ABN AMRO Group N.V.; *Int'l*, pg. 64
ABN AMRO CLEARING SYDNEY NOMINEES PTY. LTD.—See ABN AMRO Group N.V.; *Int'l*, pg. 65
ABN AMRO CLEARING SYDNEY PTY—See ABN AMRO Group N.V.; *Int'l*, pg. 64
ABN AMRO CLEARING TOKYO LTD—See ABN AMRO Group N.V.; *Int'l*, pg. 64
ABN AMRO COMMERCIAL FINANCE GMBH—See ABN AMRO Group N.V.; *Int'l*, pg. 64
ABN AMRO COMMERCIAL FINANCE S.A.—See ABN AMRO Group N.V.; *Int'l*, pg. 64
ABN AMRO COMMERCIAL FINANCE (UK) LTD—See ABN AMRO Group N.V.; *Int'l*, pg. 64
ABN AMRO GROENBANK B.V.—See ABN AMRO Group N.V.; *Int'l*, pg. 64
ABN AMRO GROUP N.V.; *Int'l*, pg. 63
ABN AMRO (GUERNSEY) LIMITED—See ABN AMRO Group N.V.; *Int'l*, pg. 64
ABN AMRO HYPOTHEKEN GROEP B.V.—See ABN AMRO Group N.V.; *Int'l*, pg. 64
ABN AMRO INVESTMENT SOLUTIONS S.A.—See ABN AMRO Group N.V.; *Int'l*, pg. 65
ABN AMRO LEASE N.V.—See ABN AMRO Group N.V.; *Int'l*, pg. 64
ABN AMRO MEESPIERSON—See ABN AMRO Group N.V.; *Int'l*, pg. 64
ABN AMRO PARTICIPATIES—See ABN AMRO Group N.V.; *Int'l*, pg. 64
ABN AMRO VERZEKERINGEN B.V.—See ABN AMRO Group N.V.; *Int'l*, pg. 65
ABN AMRO VERZEKERINGEN B.V.—See NN Group N.V.; *Int'l*, pg. 5393
AB NASDAQ OMX VILNIUS—See Nasdaq, Inc.; *U.S. Public*, pg. 1491
ABNA (SHANGHAI) FEED CO., LTD—See The Garfield Weston Foundation; *Int'l*, pg. 7648
ABN ASSURANTIE HOLDING B.V.—See ABN AMRO Group N.V.; *Int'l*, pg. 65
AB NAUJOJI RUTA—See Koncernas Achemos Grupe; *Int'l*, pg. 4246
ABNIEH GOSTAR KARAFARIN CO.—See Karafarin Bank; *Int'l*, pg. 4078
A B N INTERCORP LIMITED; *Int'l*, pg. 17
ABN INTERNATIONAL DIAMOND DIVISION—See ABN AMRO Group N.V.; *Int'l*, pg. 65
AB NORCLEAN—See Nederman Holding AB; *Int'l*, pg. 5188
AB NORDIC SUGAR KEDAINIAI—See Nordzucker AG; *Int'l*, pg. 5426
ABNOTE AUSTRALASIA PTY. LTD.—See American Banknote Corporation; *U.S. Private*, pg. 224
ABNOTE NORTH AMERICA—See American Banknote Corporation; *U.S. Private*, pg. 224
ABNOTE NORTH AMERICA—See American Banknote Corporation; *U.S. Private*, pg. 224
ABNOTE NZ LTD—See American Banknote Corporation; *U.S. Private*, pg. 224
ABNOVA GMBH—See Abnova (Taiwan) Corporation; *Int'l*, pg. 65
ABNOVA (TAIWAN) CORPORATION; *Int'l*, pg. 65
ABOALARM GMBH—See Mountain Alliance AG; *Int'l*, pg. 5057
ABOARD PUBLISHING, INC.—See Chatham Asset Management, LLC; *U.S. Private*, pg. 866
ABOCOM SYSTEMS, INC. - MIAO-LIH HSUAN FACTORY—See AboCom Systems, Inc.; *Int'l*, pg. 66
ABOCOM SYSTEMS, INC.; *Int'l*, pg. 66
ABODA, INC.—See Westbridge Capital Ltd.; *Int'l*, pg. 8387
ABODE HOME PRODUCTS LTD.—See Norcros plc; *Int'l*, pg. 5415

COMPANY NAME INDEX

ABODEINAUTO GMBH—See Baloise Holding AG; *Int'l*, pg. 810
ABO ERG—See ABO-Group NV/SA; *Int'l*, pg. 66
ABO FARM S.A.; *Int'l*, pg. 65
ABOFFS INC.; *U.S. Private*, pg. 39
ABO GEOMET BV—See ABO-Group NV/SA; *Int'l*, pg. 66
ABO-GROUP NV/SA; *Int'l*, pg. 66
ABO GRUNDSTUCKSVERWALTUNGSGESELLSCHAFT MBH—See DZ BANK AG Deutsche Zentral-Genossenschaftsbank; *Int'l*, pg. 2243
ABOINGO SERVICES—See Aquiline Capital Partners LLC; *U.S. Private*, pg. 304
ABOITIZ EQUITY VENTURES, INC.; *Int'l*, pg. 66
ABOITIZLAND, INC.—See Aboitiz Equity Ventures, Inc.; *Int'l*, pg. 66
ABOITIZ POWER CORPORATION—See Aboitiz Equity Ventures, Inc.; *Int'l*, pg. 66
ABOL SOFTWARE, INC.—See Thoma Bravo, L.P.; *U.S. Private*, pg. 4153
ABO-MILIEUCONSULT BV—See ABO-Group NV/SA; *Int'l*, pg. 66
ABO MIX S.A.; *Int'l*, pg. 65
ABO MLLIEUCONSULT BV—See ABO-Group NV/SA; *Int'l*, pg. 66
ABON BIOPHARM (HANGZHOU) CO., LTD.—See Abbott Laboratories; *U.S. Public*, pg. 18
ABONMAX CO., LTD; *Int'l*, pg. 67
ABO NV—See ABO-Group NV/SA; *Int'l*, pg. 66
AB ORLEN BALTICS RETAIL—See Orlen S.A.; *Int'l*, pg. 5640
AB ORLEN LIETUVA—See Orlen S.A.; *Int'l*, pg. 5640
ABO SUPPLY S.A.—See VINCI S.A.; *Int'l*, pg. 8217
ABOUNDBIO—See Galapagos N.V.; *Int'l*, pg. 2870
ABOUND SOLAR, INC.—See United Power Inc.; *U.S. Private*, pg. 4295
ABOUTBAGS NV—See Samsonite International S.A.; *Int'l*, pg. 6509
ABOUTGOLF EUROPE LTD.—See AboutGolf Ltd.; *U.S. Private*, pg. 39
ABOUTGOLF LTD.; *U.S. Private*, pg. 39
ABOUT HEALTH LIMITED—See Totally Plc; *Int'l*, pg. 7844
ABOUT, INC.—See IAC Inc.; *U.S. Public*, pg. 1081
ABOUT TIME INC.; *U.S. Private*, pg. 39
ABOUT YOU HOLDING SE; *Int'l*, pg. 67
ABOVE FOOD CORP.—See Above Food Ingredients Inc.; *Int'l*, pg. 67
ABOVE FOOD INGREDIENTS INC.; *Int'l*, pg. 67
ABOV SEMICONDUCTOR CO., LTD.; *Int'l*, pg. 67
ABO WIND AG; *Int'l*, pg. 65
ABO WIND BELGIUM SPRL—See ABO Wind AG; *Int'l*, pg. 65
ABO WIND BETRIEBS GMBH—See ABO Wind AG; *Int'l*, pg. 65
ABO WIND BULGARIA EOOD—See ABO Wind AG; *Int'l*, pg. 65
ABO WIND ENERGIAS RENOVABLES S.A.—See ABO Wind AG; *Int'l*, pg. 66
ABO WIND ESPANA S.A.U.—See ABO Wind AG; *Int'l*, pg. 66
ABO WIND IRELAND LTD.—See ABO Wind AG; *Int'l*, pg. 66
ABO WIND MEZZANINE GMBH & CO. KG—See ABO Wind AG; *Int'l*, pg. 66
ABO WIND OY—See ABO Wind AG; *Int'l*, pg. 66
ABO WIND SARL—See ABO Wind AG; *Int'l*, pg. 66
ABO WIND UK LTD.—See ABO Wind AG; *Int'l*, pg. 66
A-BOY PLUMBING & ELECTRICAL SUPPLY; *U.S. Private*, pg. 22
AB PAREX BANKAS—See AS Reverta; *Int'l*, pg. 591
ABP AYR—See GIC Pte. Ltd.; *Int'l*, pg. 2964
ABP AYR—See M&G Group Limited; *Int'l*, pg. 4612
ABP AYR—See Ontario Municipal Employees Retirement System; *Int'l*, pg. 5583
ABP AYR—See The Goldman Sachs Group, Inc.; *U.S. Public*, pg. 2076
ABP BARROW—See GIC Pte. Ltd.; *Int'l*, pg. 2964
ABP BARROW—See M&G Group Limited; *Int'l*, pg. 4612
ABP BARROW—See Ontario Municipal Employees Retirement System; *Int'l*, pg. 5583
ABP BARROW—See The Goldman Sachs Group, Inc.; *U.S. Public*, pg. 2076
ABP CARDIFF—See GIC Pte. Ltd.; *Int'l*, pg. 2964
ABP CARDIFF—See M&G Group Limited; *Int'l*, pg. 4612
ABP CARDIFF—See Ontario Municipal Employees Retirement System; *Int'l*, pg. 5583
ABP CARDIFF—See The Goldman Sachs Group, Inc.; *U.S. Public*, pg. 2076
ABP FLEETWOOD—See GIC Pte. Ltd.; *Int'l*, pg. 2964
ABP FLEETWOOD—See M&G Group Limited; *Int'l*, pg. 4612
ABP FLEETWOOD—See Ontario Municipal Employees Retirement System; *Int'l*, pg. 5583
ABP FLEETWOOD—See The Goldman Sachs Group, Inc.; *U.S. Public*, pg. 2076
ABP GARSTON—See GIC Pte. Ltd.; *Int'l*, pg. 2964
ABP GARSTON—See M&G Group Limited; *Int'l*, pg. 4612
ABP GARSTON—See Ontario Municipal Employees Retirement System; *Int'l*, pg. 5583

ABP GARSTON—See The Goldman Sachs Group, Inc.; *U.S. Public*, pg. 2076
ABP GOOLE—See GIC Pte. Ltd.; *Int'l*, pg. 2964
ABP GOOLE—See M&G Group Limited; *Int'l*, pg. 4612
ABP GOOLE—See Ontario Municipal Employees Retirement System; *Int'l*, pg. 5583
ABP GOOLE—See The Goldman Sachs Group, Inc.; *U.S. Public*, pg. 2076
AB PH. NEDERMAN & CO.—See Nederman Holding AB; *Int'l*, pg. 5188
ABP HULL—See GIC Pte. Ltd.; *Int'l*, pg. 2964
ABP HULL—See M&G Group Limited; *Int'l*, pg. 4612
ABP HULL—See Ontario Municipal Employees Retirement System; *Int'l*, pg. 5583
ABP HULL—See The Goldman Sachs Group, Inc.; *U.S. Public*, pg. 2076
ABP INDUCTION L.C; *U.S. Public*, pg. 39
ABP IPSWICH—See GIC Pte. Ltd.; *Int'l*, pg. 2964
ABP IPSWICH—See M&G Group Limited; *Int'l*, pg. 4612
ABP IPSWICH—See Ontario Municipal Employees Retirement System; *Int'l*, pg. 5583
ABP IPSWICH—See The Goldman Sachs Group, Inc.; *U.S. Public*, pg. 2076
AB P.J. JONSSON OCH SONER—See Valmet Oyj; *Int'l*, pg. 8118
ABP KAKAAKO COMMERCE 1 LLC—See Alexander & Baldwin, Inc.; *U.S. Public*, pg. 75
ABP PLYMOUTH—See GIC Pte. Ltd.; *Int'l*, pg. 2964
ABP PLYMOUTH—See M&G Group Limited; *Int'l*, pg. 4612
ABP PLYMOUTH—See Ontario Municipal Employees Retirement System; *Int'l*, pg. 5583
ABP PLYMOUTH—See The Goldman Sachs Group, Inc.; *U.S. Public*, pg. 2076
AB PRECISION (POOLE) LIMITED—See HWH Investments Limited; *Int'l*, pg. 3543
AB PREMIA KPC—See PRFoods AS; *Int'l*, pg. 5968
AB PREVIA—See Lundbeckfonden; *Int'l*, pg. 4579
AB PRIVATE CREDIT INVESTORS CORPORATION; *U.S. Private*, pg. 33
ABPRO BIO CO., LTD.; *Int'l*, pg. 67
A&B PROCESS SYSTEM CORP.; *U.S. Private*, pg. 19
A & B PROCESS SYSTEMS CORP.—See John Bean Technologies Corporation; *U.S. Public*, pg. 1191
ABPRO CORPORATION—See Abpro Holdings, Inc.; *U.S. Public*, pg. 26
ABPRO HOLDINGS, INC.; *U.S. Public*, pg. 26
A&B PROPERTIES, INC.—See Alexander & Baldwin, Inc.; *U.S. Public*, pg. 75
ABQ HEALTH PARTNERS ENDOSCOPY CENTER, LLC—See DaVita Inc.; *U.S. Public*, pg. 635
AB "CITADELE" BANKAS—See Ripplewood Holdings LLC; *U.S. Private*, pg. 3439
ABRAAJ CAPITAL LIMITED; *Int'l*, pg. 67
ABRA AUTO BODY & GLASS LP—See Hellman & Friedman LLC; *U.S. Private*, pg. 1907
ABRA AUTOMOTIVE SYSTEMS LP—See Hellman & Friedman LLC; *U.S. Private*, pg. 1907
ABR ABFALL BEHANDLUNG UND RECYCLING GMBH—See STRABAG SE; *Int'l*, pg. 7229
ABRACADABRA RESTORATION, INC.—See Kustom US, Inc.; *U.S. Private*, pg. 2358
ABRACON LLC—See Genstar Capital, LLC; *U.S. Private*, pg. 1673
ABRA DEVELOPMENT SDN. BHD.—See Talam Transform Berhad; *Int'l*, pg. 7443
ABRA FRANCHISE SERVICES LP—See Hellman & Friedman LLC; *U.S. Private*, pg. 1907
ABRAHAM CHEVROLET-MIAMI, INC.—See AutoNation, Inc.; *U.S. Public*, pg. 232
ABRAHAM CHEVROLET-MIAMI, INC.—See AutoNation, Inc.; *U.S. Public*, pg. 232
ABRAHAM GMBH—See Coop-Gruppe Genossenschaft; *Int'l*, pg. 1789
ABRAJ ENERGY SERVICES LLC—See OQ S.A.O.C.; *Int'l*, pg. 5607
ABRAKADOODLE INC.; *U.S. Private*, pg. 39
ABRA MINING & INDUSTRIAL CORPORATION; *Int'l*, pg. 67
ABRA MINING LIMITED—See Hunan Nonferrous Metals Corporation Ltd.; *Int'l*, pg. 3533
ABRAM INTERSTATE INSURANCE SERVICES, INC.—See Arthur J. Gallagher & Co.; *U.S. Public*, pg. 202
ABRAMS AIRBORNE MANUFACTURING, INC.; *U.S. Private*, pg. 39
ABRAMS CAPITAL, LLC; *U.S. Private*, pg. 40
ABRAMS CAPITAL MANAGEMENT, LLC—See Abrams Capital, LLC; *U.S. Private*, pg. 40
ABRAMS & COMPANY PUBLISHERS, INC.—See Learning Trends, LLC; *U.S. Private*, pg. 2408
ABRAMS INTERNATIONAL LLP; *U.S. Private*, pg. 40
ABRA S.A.—See Steinhoff International Holdings N.V.; *Int'l*, pg. 7195
ABRASERVICE BELGIUM SA—See Jacquet Metal Service SA; *Int'l*, pg. 3866
ABRASERVICE CZECH S.R.O.—See Jacquet Metal Service SA; *Int'l*, pg. 3866
ABRASERVICE DEUTSCHLAND GMBH—See SSAB AB; *Int'l*, pg. 7153

ABRASERVICE HOLDING SAS—See SSAB AB; *Int'l*, pg. 7153
ABRASERVICE LYON SAS—See SSAB AB; *Int'l*, pg. 7153
ABRASERVICE NEDERLAND BV—See SSAB AB; *Int'l*, pg. 7153
ABRASERVICE PORTUGAL LDA—See Jacquet Metal Service SA; *Int'l*, pg. 3866
ABRASERVICE UK LIMITED—See SSAB AB; *Int'l*, pg. 7153
ABRASILVER RESOURCE CORP.; *Int'l*, pg. 67
ABRASIVE PRODUCTS & EQUIPMENT, LLC—See Ridgemont Partners Management LLC; *U.S. Private*, pg. 3432
ABRASIVE TECHNOLOGY INCORPORATED; *U.S. Private*, pg. 40
ABRASIVE-TOOL CORPORATION; *U.S. Private*, pg. 40
ABRAU-DURSO AO; *Int'l*, pg. 67
ABRAXAS PETROLEUM CORPORATION; *U.S. Public*, pg. 26
ABRAZO MEDICAL GROUP URGENT CARE, LLC—See Tenet Healthcare Corporation; *U.S. Public*, pg. 2014
ABRDN ASIA FOCUS PLC; *Int'l*, pg. 68
ABRDN ASIA LIMITED—See abrdn PLC; *Int'l*, pg. 68
ABRDN AUSTRALIA LTD.—See abrdn PLC; *Int'l*, pg. 68
ABRDN GLOBAL DYNAMIC DIVIDEND FUND; *U.S. Public*, pg. 26
ABRDN GLOBAL PREMIER PROPERTIES FUND; *U.S. Public*, pg. 26
ABRDN GOLD ETF TRUST; *U.S. Public*, pg. 26
ABRDN HEALTHCARE OPPORTUNITIES FUND; *U.S. Public*, pg. 26
ABRDN INCOME CREDIT STRATEGIES FUND; *U.S. Public*, pg. 26
ABRDN JAPAN EQUITY FUND INC.; *U.S. Public*, pg. 26
ABRDN LIFE SCIENCES INVESTORS; *U.S. Public*, pg. 26
ABRDN NATIONAL MUNICIPAL INCOME FUND; *U.S. Public*, pg. 27
ABRDN NEW INDIA INVESTMENT TRUST PLC; *Int'l*, pg. 68
ABRDN PLC; *Int'l*, pg. 68
ABRDN SILVER ETF TRUST; *U.S. Public*, pg. 27
ABRDN TOTAL DYNAMIC DIVIDEND FUND; *U.S. Public*, pg. 27
ABRDN UK SMALLER COMPANIES GROWTH TRUST PLC; *Int'l*, pg. 69
ABRDN WORLD HEALTHCARE FUND; *U.S. Public*, pg. 27
ABREOS BIOSCIENCES, INC.; *U.S. Private*, pg. 40
AB RENRONIK—See Carl Bennet AB; *Int'l*, pg. 1331
ABR FINANCIAL B.V.—See PJSC IC RUSS-INVEST; *Int'l*, pg. 5880
ABRH, LLC—See Cannae Holdings, Inc.; *U.S. Public*, pg. 429
ABR HOLDINGS, LTD.; *Int'l*, pg. 67
ABRI CREDIT UNION; *U.S. Private*, pg. 40
A. BRIGHT IDEA; *U.S. Private*, pg. 22
A. BRIGHT IDEA—See A. Bright Idea; *U.S. Private*, pg. 22
ABRIL ABOGADOS SLU; *Int'l*, pg. 69
ABRIMIX (PTY) LTD.—See LifeQuest World Corp.; *U.S. Public*, pg. 1313
AB RINCO ULTRASONICS SVERIGE—See Crest Group Inc.; *U.S. Private*, pg. 1096
ABRISA TECHNOLOGIES—See The Graham Group, Inc.; *U.S. Private*, pg. 4036
ABRIS CAPITAL PARTNERS SP. Z O.O.; *Int'l*, pg. 69
ABRISUD SAS—See Andera Partners SCA; *Int'l*, pg. 449
A BRITE COMPANY; *U.S. Private*, pg. 18
ABRO DISTRIBUTION SERVICE LLC—See ABRO Industries, Inc.; *U.S. Private*, pg. 40
ABRO INDUSTRIES, INC.; *U.S. Private*, pg. 40
A BROWN COMPANY, INC.; *Int'l*, pg. 17
A. BROWN-OLMSTEAD ASSOCIATES; *U.S. Private*, pg. 22
ABRUZZOENERGIA S.P.A.—See A2A S.p.A.; *Int'l*, pg. 29
ABR WHOLESALERS INC.; *U.S. Private*, pg. 39
ABRY PARTNERS, LLC; *U.S. Private*, pg. 40
ABSA ASSET MANAGEMENT (PROPRIETARY) LIMITED—See Sanlam Limited; *Int'l*, pg. 6545
ABSA BANK LIMITED—See Absa Group Limited; *Int'l*, pg. 69
ABSA BANK MOZAMBIQUE, SA—See Absa Group Limited; *Int'l*, pg. 69
ABSA CAPITAL REPRESENTATIVE OFFICE NIGERIA LIMITED—See Absa Group Limited; *Int'l*, pg. 69
ABSA FINANCIAL CORP.; *Int'l*, pg. 69
ABSA FINANCIAL SERVICES AFRICA HOLDINGS PROPRIETARY LIMITED—See Absa Group Limited; *Int'l*, pg. 69
ABSA FINANCIAL SERVICES LIMITED—See Absa Group Limited; *Int'l*, pg. 69
ABSA FUND MANAGERS LIMITED—See Sanlam Limited; *Int'l*, pg. 6545
AB SAGAX; *Int'l*, pg. 41
ABSA GROUP LIMITED; *Int'l*, pg. 69
ABSA IDIRECT LIMITED—See Absa Group Limited; *Int'l*, pg. 69

ABSA GROUP LIMITED

ABSA INSURANCE AND FINANCIAL ADVISERS PROPRIETARY LIMITED—See Absa Group Limited; *Int'l*, pg. 69
ABSA INSURANCE COMPANY LIMITED—See Absa Group Limited; *Int'l*, pg. 69
ABSAL COMPANY; *Int'l*, pg. 69
ABSA LIFE LIMITED—See Absa Group Limited; *Int'l*, pg. 69
ABSALOKA COAL, LLC—See Westmoreland Coal Company; *U.S. Private*, pg. 4500
ABSA MANX INSURANCE COMPANY LIMITED—See Absa Group Limited; *Int'l*, pg. 69
AB SANDVIK CONSTRUCTION SEGMENT—See Sandvik AB; *Int'l*, pg. 6532
AB SANDVIK COROMANT—See Sandvik AB; *Int'l*, pg. 6533
AB SANDVIK MATERIALS TECHNOLOGY—See Sandvik AB; *Int'l*, pg. 6528
AB SANDVIK SERVICE—See Sandvik AB; *Int'l*, pg. 6528
AB SANDVIK VASTBERGA SERVICE—See Sandvik AB; *Int'l*, pg. 6528
ABSA PORTFOLIO MANAGERS PROPRIETARY LIMITED—See Absa Group Limited; *Int'l*, pg. 69
ABSAR & ELIAS ENTERPRISE LTD.—See Intraco Refueling Staton Ltd.; *Int'l*, pg. 3767
ABS ARGENTINA S.A.—See Genus Plc; *Int'l*, pg. 2930
AB S.A.; *Int'l*, pg. 41
ABSA TRUST LIMITED—See Absa Group Limited; *Int'l*, pg. 69
ABSA VEHICLE MANAGEMENT PROPRIETARY LIMITED—See Absa Group Limited; *Int'l*, pg. 69
ABSA VEHICLE MANAGEMENT SOLUTIONS PROPRIETARY LIMITED—See Absa Group Limited; *Int'l*, pg. 69
ABSA WEALTH & INVESTMENT MANAGEMENT—See Absa Group Limited; *Int'l*, pg. 69
AB SCA FINANS—See Svenska Cellulosa Aktiebolaget SCA; *Int'l*, pg. 7356
ABS CAPITAL PARTNERS, L.P.; *U.S. Private*, pg. 43
ABS-CBN AUSTRALIA PTY LTD—See Lopez, Inc.; *Int'l*, pg. 4556
ABS-CBN CORPORATION—See Lopez, Inc.; *Int'l*, pg. 4556
ABS-CBN FILM PRODUCTIONS INC.—See Lopez, Inc.; *Int'l*, pg. 4556
ABS-CBN FOUNDATION, INC.—See Lopez, Inc.; *Int'l*, pg. 4556
ABS-CBN HOLDINGS CORPORATION—See Lopez, Inc.; *Int'l*, pg. 4556
ABS-CBN INTERNATIONAL—See Lopez, Inc.; *Int'l*, pg. 4556
ABS CENTRE METALLURGIQUE SARL—See Danieli & C. Officine Meccaniche S.p.A.; *Int'l*, pg. 1962
ABS CHILE LIMITADA—See Genus Plc; *Int'l*, pg. 2930
ABSCI CORP.; *U.S. Public*, pg. 27
AB SCIENCE SA; *Int'l*, pg. 41
AB SCIEX GERMANY GMBH—See Danaher Corporation; *U.S. Public*, pg. 623
AB SCIEX KK—See Danaher Corporation; *U.S. Public*, pg. 623
AB SCIEX LLC—See Danaher Corporation; *U.S. Public*, pg. 623
AB SCIEX LP—See Danaher Corporation; *U.S. Public*, pg. 623
AB SCIEX NETHERLANDS B.V.—See Danaher Corporation; *U.S. Public*, pg. 623
ABS COASTAL INSULATING COMPANY, LLC—See Installed Building Products, Inc.; *U.S. Public*, pg. 1132
ABSCO LTD. CORP.; *U.S. Private*, pg. 44
ABS COMPUTER TECHNOLOGIES INC.—See Newegg Commerce, Inc.; *Int'l*, pg. 5234
ABS CONSULTING LTD.—See American Bureau of Shipping; *U.S. Private*, pg. 225
ABSECON BANCORP; *U.S. Public*, pg. 27
AB SECURITIES LIMITED—See AB Bank Limited; *Int'l*, pg. 39
ABSENCE.IO GMBH—See Grupa Pracuj S.A.; *Int'l*, pg. 3117
ABSEN INC.—See Shenzhen Absen Optoelectronic Company Limited; *Int'l*, pg. 6804
ABSENTYS, LLC—See The Carlyle Group Inc.; *U.S. Public*, pg. 2053
ABS EUROPE LTD.—See American Bureau of Shipping; *U.S. Private*, pg. 225
ABSG CONSULTING DE VENEZUELA, C.A.—See American Bureau of Shipping; *U.S. Private*, pg. 226
ABSG CONSULTING INC.—See American Bureau of Shipping; *U.S. Private*, pg. 225
ABSG CONSULTING INC.—See American Bureau of Shipping; *U.S. Private*, pg. 225
ABSG CONSULTING - IRVINE—See American Bureau of Shipping; *U.S. Private*, pg. 225
ABSG CONSULTING - KNOXVILLE—See American Bureau of Shipping; *U.S. Private*, pg. 225
ABSG CONSULTING - LAKEWOOD—See American Bureau of Shipping; *U.S. Private*, pg. 225
ABSG CONSULTING - MIDDLE EAST—See American Bureau of Shipping; *U.S. Private*, pg. 225
ABSG CONSULTING - ROCKVILLE—See American Bureau of Shipping; *U.S. Private*, pg. 225
ABSG CONSULTING - SAINT LOUIS—See American Bureau of Shipping; *U.S. Private*, pg. 225
ABSG CONSULTING - SALT LAKE CITY—See American Bureau of Shipping; *U.S. Private*, pg. 225
ABSG CONSULTING - SAN ANTONIO—See American Bureau of Shipping; *U.S. Private*, pg. 225
ABSG CONSULTING - TAIWAN—See American Bureau of Shipping; *U.S. Private*, pg. 225
ABSG CONSULTING - WILMINGTON—See American Bureau of Shipping; *U.S. Private*, pg. 225
ABS GLOBAL (CANADA) INC.—See Genus Plc; *Int'l*, pg. 2930
ABS GLOBAL—See Genus Plc; *Int'l*, pg. 2930
ABS GROUP OF COMPANIES, INC.—See American Bureau of Shipping; *U.S. Private*, pg. 225
ABS GROUP SERVICES DE MEXICO, S.A. DE C.V.—See American Bureau of Shipping; *U.S. Private*, pg. 225
ABS GROUP SERVICES DO BRASIL LTDA.—See American Bureau of Shipping; *U.S. Private*, pg. 225
ABSHER CONSTRUCTION COMPANY; *U.S. Private*, pg. 44
AB SIGFRID STENBERG—See J2L Holding AB; *Int'l*, pg. 3859
ABS INFOLINK INC.—See American Bureau of Shipping; *U.S. Private*, pg. 225
ABS INSULATING COMPANY, INC.—See Installed Building Products, Inc.; *U.S. Public*, pg. 1132
ABS ITALIA S.R.L.—See Genus Plc; *Int'l*, pg. 2930
AB SKANDINAVISK SPAENDBETONG—See VINCI S.A.; *Int'l*, pg. 8231
ABS LINCS SC, INC.—See Universal Health Services, Inc.; *U.S. Public*, pg. 2255
ABS LINCS VA, INC.—See Universal Health Services, Inc.; *U.S. Public*, pg. 2255
ABSL POWER SOLUTIONS LTD.—See EnerSys; *U.S. Public*, pg. 767
ABS MANUFACTURING & DISTRIBUTING LIMITED; *Int'l*, pg. 69
ABS MARITIME SERVICES - HELLAS—See American Bureau of Shipping; *U.S. Private*, pg. 225
ABS MATERIALS, INC.—See AQUANEX, Servicio Domiciliario del Agua de EXTREMADURA SA; *Int'l*, pg. 527
ABS MEXICO S.A. DE C.V.—See Genus Plc; *Int'l*, pg. 2930
ABS NAUTICAL SYSTEMS ASIA PACIFIC—See American Bureau of Shipping; *U.S. Private*, pg. 225
ABS NAUTICAL SYSTEMS CHILE—See American Bureau of Shipping; *U.S. Private*, pg. 225
ABS NAUTICAL SYSTEMS LLC—See American Bureau of Shipping; *U.S. Private*, pg. 225
ABS NAUTICAL SYSTEMS MALAYSIA—See American Bureau of Shipping; *U.S. Private*, pg. 225
ABSOCOLD CORPORATION; *U.S. Private*, pg. 44
ABSOLENT AIR CARE GROUP AB; *Int'l*, pg. 69
ABSOLENT (BEIJING) CO., LTD.—See Absolent Air Care Group AB; *Int'l*, pg. 70
ABSOLENT FILTERMIST INDIA PRIVATE LTD.—See Absolent Air Care Group AB; *Int'l*, pg. 70
ABSOLENT GMBH—See Absolent Air Care Group AB; *Int'l*, pg. 70
ABSOLENT INC.—See Absolent Air Care Group AB; *Int'l*, pg. 70
ABSOLENT JAPAN LTD.—See Absolent Air Care Group AB; *Int'l*, pg. 70
ABSOLENT SAS—See Absolent Air Care Group AB; *Int'l*, pg. 70
ABSOLENT S.R.L.—See Absolent Air Care Group AB; *Int'l*, pg. 70
ABSOLICON SOLAR COLLECTOR AB; *Int'l*, pg. 70
ABSOLUT BANK OAO; *Int'l*, pg. 70
ABSOLUT CAPITAL MANAGEMENT HOLDING LTD; *Int'l*, pg. 70
THE ABSOLUT COMPANY SA—See Pernod Ricard S.A.; *Int'l*, pg. 5811
ABSOLUTDATA RESEARCH & ANALYTICS (P) LTD.; *U.S. Private*, pg. 44
ABSOLUTE ASSEMBLY CO., LTD.—See Energy Absolute Public Company Limited; *Int'l*, pg. 2422
ABSOLUTE AVIATION SERVICES, LLC—See HEICO Corporation; *U.S. Public*, pg. 1021
ABSOLUTE BATHROOMS LIMITED—See Grafton Group plc; *Int'l*, pg. 3050
ABSOLUTE CAPITAL MANAGEMENT LLC; *U.S. Private*, pg. 44
ABSOLUTE CLEAN ENERGY PUBLIC COMPANY LIMITED; *Int'l*, pg. 70
ABSOLUTE COATINGS, INC.—See Huron Capital Partners LLC; *U.S. Private*, pg. 2011
ABSOLUTE CONCRETE, INC.; *U.S. Private*, pg. 44
ABSOLUTE CONSULTING, INC.—See GSE Systems, Inc.; *U.S. Public*, pg. 973
ABSOLUTE DENTAL GROUP, LLC; *U.S. Private*, pg. 44
ABSOLUTE DESIGN SERVICES CO., LTD.—See U City Public Company Limited; *Int'l*, pg. 7996
ABSOLUTE EQUITY PERFORMANCE FUND LIMITED—See WAM Leaders Limited; *Int'l*, pg. 8337
ABSOLUTE HAITIAN CORPORATION—See Haitian International Holdings Ltd.; *Int'l*, pg. 3217
ABSOLUTE HEALTH & FITNESS, INC.; *U.S. Public*, pg. 27
ABSOLUTE INSURANCE BROKERS LIMITED—See PSC Insurance Group Limited; *Int'l*, pg. 6015
ABSOLUTE IT SOLUTIONS, LLC; *U.S. Private*, pg. 44
ABSOLUTE IT SOLUTIONS, SRL—See Absolute IT Solutions, LLC; *U.S. Private*, pg. 44
ABSOLUTELY OUTDOORS; *U.S. Private*, pg. 44
ABSOLUTE MACHINE TOOL INC.; *U.S. Private*, pg. 44
ABSOLUTE MEDIA INC.; *U.S. Private*, pg. 44
ABSOLUTE MOBILITY CENTER—See Edwards Capital, LLC; *U.S. Private*, pg. 1342
ABSOLUTE PROTECTIVE SYSTEMS, INC.—See The Carlyle Group Inc.; *U.S. Public*, pg. 2053
ABSOLUTE RADIO LTD.—See Heinrich Bauer Verlag KG; *Int'l*, pg. 3324
ABSOLUTE RETURN CAPITAL, LLC—See Bain Capital, LP; *U.S. Private*, pg. 428
ABSOLUTE SOFTWARE CORPORATION—See Crosspoint Capital Partners LP; *U.S. Private*, pg. 1107
ABSOLUTE SOFTWARE EMEA LIMITED—See Crosspoint Capital Partners LP; *U.S. Private*, pg. 1107
ABSOLUTE SOFTWARE, INC.—See Crosspoint Capital Partners LP; *U.S. Private*, pg. 1107
ABSOLUTE TOTAL CARE, INC—See Centene Corporation; *U.S. Public*, pg. 467
ABSOLUTE WINDOW & SHUTTER, INC.; *U.S. Private*, pg. 44
THE ABSOLUT SPIRITS COMPANY INC.—See Pernod Ricard S.A.; *Int'l*, pg. 5811
ABSON INDUSTRIES LIMITED; *Int'l*, pg. 70
ABSOPURE WATER COMPANY INC.; *U.S. Private*, pg. 44
ABSORBENT, INK.; *U.S. Private*, pg. 44
ABSORB SOFTWARE INC.—See Welsh, Carson, Anderson & Stowe; *U.S. Private*, pg. 4479
ABSORBTECH, LLC—See Industrial Towel & Uniform; *U.S. Private*, pg. 2068
ABSORPTION SYSTEMS LLC—See Pharmaron Beijing Co., Ltd.; *Int'l*, pg. 5841
ABSOTHERM FACILITY MANAGEMENT PVT. LIMITED—See OCS Group Limited; *Int'l*, pg. 5521
ABS PACIFIC—See American Bureau of Shipping; *U.S. Private*, pg. 226
ABS PECPLAN LTDA.—See Genus Plc; *Int'l*, pg. 2930
AB SPINTAB—See Swedbank AB; *Int'l*, pg. 7364
ABS PUMPS AS—See Sulzer AG; *Int'l*, pg. 7257
ABS SISAK DOO—See Danieli & C. Officine Meccaniche S.p.A.; *Int'l*, pg. 1962
ABS SPA—See Danieli & C. Officine Meccaniche S.p.A.; *Int'l*, pg. 1962
AB STAFFING SOLUTIONS, LLC; *U.S. Private*, pg. 33
ABS TECHNOLOGY S.P.A.—See Sesa S.p.A.; *Int'l*, pg. 6728
ABSTRACT DISPLAYS, INC.; *U.S. Private*, pg. 44
ABSTRACTERS' INFORMATION SERVICE, INC.—See First American Financial Corporation; *U.S. Public*, pg. 835
AB SVAFO—See Studsvik AB; *Int'l*, pg. 7244
AB SVENSKA WAVIN—See Bharti Enterprises Limited; *Int'l*, pg. 1012
AB SVENSK EXPORTKREDIT; *Int'l*, pg. 41
AB SVENSK HANDELSTIDNING JUSTITIA—See Ratos AB; *Int'l*, pg. 6215
AB SVYTURYS—See Carlsberg A/S; *Int'l*, pg. 1339
ABSYS CYBORG SAS—See Keyrus SA; *Int'l*, pg. 4146
ABT ASSOCIATES INC.; *U.S. Private*, pg. 44
ABT ASSOCIATES INC.—See Abt Associates Inc.; *U.S. Private*, pg. 45
AB TEBECO—See Beijer Alma AB; *Int'l*, pg. 942
ABTECH HOLDINGS, INC.; *U.S. Private*, pg. 45
ABTECH INDUSTRIES, INC.—See ABTECH HOLDINGS, INC.; *U.S. Private*, pg. 45
ABTECH SYSTEMS, INC.—See Abtech Technologies, Inc.; *U.S. Private*, pg. 45
ABTECH TECHNOLOGIES, INC.; *U.S. Private*, pg. 45
ABTEK (BIOLOGICALS) LTD.—See Neogen Corporation; *U.S. Public*, pg. 1505
ABT ELECTRONICS, INC.; *U.S. Private*, pg. 45
ABTERRA LTD.; *Int'l*, pg. 70
ABTERRA MACAO COMMERCIAL OFFSHORE LIMITED—See Abterra Ltd.; *Int'l*, pg. 70
AB TEST LIMITED—See TT Electronics plc; *Int'l*, pg. 7958
AB TETRA PAK—See Tetra Laval International S.A.; *Int'l*, pg. 7577
ABTEX BEVERAGE LTD; *U.S. Private*, pg. 45
ABTEX LLC—See The Malish Corp.; *U.S. Private*, pg. 4074
ABTEY PRODUCTIONS; *Int'l*, pg. 70
ABT GLOBAL INC.—See Abt Associates Inc.; *U.S. Private*, pg. 45
AB THAI FOUNDRY SUPPLIERS CO., LTD.—See Huettenes-Albertus Chemische Werke GmbH; *Int'l*, pg. 3522
ABT HOLDING COMPANY—See Healios K.K.; *Int'l*, pg. 3302

COMPANY NAME INDEX

ACADIA MALIBU, INC.

AB TINGSTAD RORINSTALLATION—See Instalco AB; *Int'l*, pg. 3721
ABT JTA PTY LTD.—See Abt Associates Inc.; *U.S. Private*, pg. 45
AB&T NATIONAL BANK—See Community Capital Bancshares, Inc.; *U.S. Public*, pg. 550
AB TRACTION—See Duroc AB; *Int'l*, pg. 2229
ABTRE, INC.—See American Biltrite Inc.; *U.S. Public*, pg. 97
ABT SPORTSLINE GMBH; *Int'l*, pg. 70
ABT SRBI, INC.—See Abt Associates Inc.; *U.S. Private*, pg. 45
ABU AB—See Sycamore Partners Management, LP; *U.S. Private*, pg. 3896
ABU DHABI AIRCRAFT TECHNOLOGIES LLC—See Mubadala Investment Company PJSC; *Int'l*, pg. 5075
ABU DHABI AVIATION; *Int'l*, pg. 70
ABU DHABI COMMERCIAL BANK PJSC; *Int'l*, pg. 70
ABU DHABI COMMERCIAL BANK—See Abu Dhabi Commercial Bank PJSC; *Int'l*, pg. 71
ABU DHABI COMMERCIAL ENGINEERING SERVICES LLC—See Abu Dhabi Commercial Bank PJSC; *Int'l*, pg. 71
ABU DHABI COMPANY ONSHORE OIL OPERATIONS—See Abu Dhabi National Oil Company; *Int'l*, pg. 72
ABU DHABI DEVELOPMENTAL HOLDING COMPANY PJSC; *Int'l*, pg. 71
ABU DHABI DISTRIBUTION COMPANY—See Abu Dhabi Water & Electricity Authority; *Int'l*, pg. 73
ABU DHABI FINANCE PJSC—See Mubadala Investment Company PJSC; *Int'l*, pg. 5075
ABU DHABI FINANCIAL GROUP, LLC—See SHUAA Capital psc; *Int'l*, pg. 6868
ABU DHABI FUTURE ENERGY COMPANY PJSC—See Mubadala Investment Company PJSC; *Int'l*, pg. 5075
ABU DHABI GAS DEVELOPMENT CO. LTD.—See Abu Dhabi National Oil Company; *Int'l*, pg. 72
ABU DHABI GAS INDUSTRIES LIMITED—See Abu Dhabi National Oil Company; *Int'l*, pg. 72
ABU DHABI GAS LIQUEFACTION LIMITED—See Abu Dhabi National Oil Company; *Int'l*, pg. 72
ABU DHABI GROUP; *Int'l*, pg. 71
ABU DHABI INVESTMENT AUTHORITY; *Int'l*, pg. 71
ABU DHABI INVESTMENT COMPANY; *Int'l*, pg. 72
ABU DHABI ISLAMIC BANK-EGYPT; *Int'l*, pg. 72
ABU DHABI ISLAMIC BANK PJSC; *Int'l*, pg. 72
ABU DHABI LAND GENERAL CONTRACTING LLC—See International Holdings Company PJSC; *Int'l*, pg. 3750
ABU DHABI MARINE DREDGING COMPANY S.P.C.—See National Marine Dredging Company PJSC; *Int'l*, pg. 5161
ABU DHABI MARINE OPERATING COMPANY—See Abu Dhabi National Oil Company; *Int'l*, pg. 72
ABU DHABI MEDIA; *Int'l*, pg. 72
ABU DHABI NATIONAL COMPANY FOR BUILDING MATERIAL; *Int'l*, pg. 72
ABU DHABI NATIONAL ENERGY COMPANY PJSC—See Abu Dhabi Water & Electricity Authority; *Int'l*, pg. 73
ABU DHABI NATIONAL HOTELS PJSC; *Int'l*, pg. 72
ABU DHABI NATIONAL INSURANCE COMPANY; *Int'l*, pg. 72
ABU DHABI NATIONAL ISLAMIC FINANCE PVT. JSC—See First Abu Dhabi Bank P.J.S.C.; *Int'l*, pg. 2681
ABU DHABI NATIONAL LEASING LLC—See First Abu Dhabi Bank P.J.S.C.; *Int'l*, pg. 2681
ABU DHABI NATIONAL OIL COMPANY FOR DISTRIBUTION—See Abu Dhabi National Oil Company; *Int'l*, pg. 73
ABU DHABI NATIONAL OIL COMPANY; *Int'l*, pg. 72
ABU DHABI NATIONAL PROPERTIES PRJC—See First Abu Dhabi Bank P.J.S.C.; *Int'l*, pg. 2681
ABU DHABI NATIONAL TAKAFUL CO. P.S.C.; *Int'l*, pg. 73
ABU DHABI NATIONAL TANKER COMPANY—See Abu Dhabi National Oil Company; *Int'l*, pg. 73
ABU DHABI OIL CO., LTD.—See ENEOS Holdings, Inc.; *Int'l*, pg. 2415
ABU DHABI OIL REFINING COMPANY—See Abu Dhabi National Oil Company; *Int'l*, pg. 73
ABU DHABI PETROLEUM PORTS OPERATING COMPANY—See Abu Dhabi National Oil Company; *Int'l*, pg. 73
ABU DHABI POLYMERS CO. LTD.—See Abu Dhabi National Oil Company; *Int'l*, pg. 73
ABU DHABI PORTS COMPANY PJSC—See Abu Dhabi Developmental Holding Company PJSC; *Int'l*, pg. 71
ABU DHABI SECURITIES EXCHANGE; *Int'l*, pg. 73
ABU DHABI SHIP BUILDING PJSC; *Int'l*, pg. 73
ABU DHABI TRANSMISSION & DESPATCH COMPANY—See Abu Dhabi Water & Electricity Authority; *Int'l*, pg. 73
ABU DHABI UNITED HOSPITALITY - SOLE PROPRIETORSHIP LLC—See Alpha Dhabi Holding PJSC; *Int'l*, pg. 367
ABU DHABI WATER & ELECTRICITY AUTHORITY; *Int'l*, pg. 73
ABU GOSCH Y COMPANIA LIMITADA—See SMU S.A.; *Int'l*, pg. 7017

A-BUILD EGYPT LTD.—See Orascom Construction PLC; *Int'l*, pg. 5613
ABUNDANCE INTERNATIONAL LTD.; *Int'l*, pg. 74
ABUNDANTE LIMITED; *Int'l*, pg. 74
ABUNDANT PRODUCE LIMITED; *Int'l*, pg. 74
ABUNDANT TREE CARE SERVICES LLC—See Apax Partners LLP; *Int'l*, pg. 505
ABU-PLAST GMBH—See Aliaxis S.A./N.V.; *Int'l*, pg. 323
ABU QIR FERTILIZERS AND CHEMICAL INDUSTRIES CO.; *Int'l*, pg. 74
ABURAHI AGRORESEARCH CO.,LTD.—See Shionogi & Co., Ltd.; *Int'l*, pg. 6851
ABURAHI LABORATORIES—See Shionogi & Co., Ltd.; *Int'l*, pg. 6851
ABURAIHAN PHARMACEUTICAL COMPANY; *Int'l*, pg. 74
ABUS LEVAGE FRANCE S.A.S.; *Int'l*, pg. 74
ABUTMENT DIRECT INC—See Straumann Holding AG; *Int'l*, pg. 7237
A&B VALVE & PIPING SYSTEMS, LLC; *U.S. Private*, pg. 19
ABVC BIOPHARMA, INC.; *U.S. Public*, pg. 27
ABV CONSULTING, INC.; *Int'l*, pg. 74
AB VENDELS GRUSTAG—See Peab AB; *Int'l*, pg. 5771
ABVENT S.A.—See Nemetschek SE; *Int'l*, pg. 5193
AB VENTUS-NAFTA—See Orlen S.A.; *Int'l*, pg. 5640
ABVI AYMOND BRUNEL VEHICULES INDUSTRIEL; *Int'l*, pg. 74
AB VICKERS LIMITED—See Lallemand, Inc.; *Int'l*, pg. 4399
AB VIERTE FLUGZEUGVERMIETUNGS GMBH—See Air Berlin PLC & Co. Luftverkehrs KG; *Int'l*, pg. 236
AB VILNIAUS VINGIS; *Int'l*, pg. 74
AB VOLVO PENTA ITALIA S.P.A.—See AB Volvo; *Int'l*, pg. 42
AB VOLVO PENTA—See AB Volvo; *Int'l*, pg. 42
AB VOLVO; *Int'l*, pg. 42
AB VOLVO - VOLVO DE MEXICO AUTOBUSES DIVISION—See AB Volvo; *Int'l*, pg. 42
ABW ABBRUCH BODEN- UND WASSERREINIGUNGSGESELLSCHAFT M.B.H.—See PORR AG; *Int'l*, pg. 5922
A&B WAIANAE LLC—See Alexander & Baldwin, Inc.; *U.S. Public*, pg. 341
ABWASSERGESELLSCHAFT GELSENKIRCHEN MBH—See Gelsenwasser AG; *Int'l*, pg. 2913
A & B WELDING, INC.—See Precision Tank & Equip Co.; *U.S. Private*, pg. 3247
AB WERBA—See Saab AB; *Int'l*, pg. 6459
AB WIDEX—See EQT AB; *Int'l*, pg. 2480
AB WILH. BECKER—See Lincengruppen AB; *Int'l*, pg. 4510
A&B WIPER SUPPLY INC.; *U.S. Private*, pg. 19
ABX ADVANCED BIOCHEMICAL COMPOUNDS, GMBH—See Otsuka Holdings Co., Ltd.; *Int'l*, pg. 5659
ABX AIR, INC.—See Air Transport Services Group, Inc.; *U.S. Public*, pg. 67
ABX GROUP LIMITED; *Int'l*, pg. 74
ABYAAR REAL ESTATE DEVELOPMENT COMPANY K.S.C.C.; *Int'l*, pg. 74
ABYARA PLANEJAMENTO IMOBILIARIO S.A.—See PDG Realty S.A. Empreendimentos e Participacoes; *Int'l*, pg. 5770
AB YIT KAUSTA—See YIT Corporation; *Int'l*, pg. 8586
ABYO TM S.L.—See MAHLE GmbH; *Int'l*, pg. 4648
ABYSS GROUP INC; *U.S. Private*, pg. 45
ABZENA PLC—See Welsh, Carson, Anderson & Stowe; *U.S. Private*, pg. 4479
ABZU GOLD LTD.; *Int'l*, pg. 74
AB ZWEITE FLUGZEUGVERMIETUNGS GMBH—See Air Berlin PLC & Co. Luftverkehrs KG; *Int'l*, pg. 236
AC6 METROLOGIA, S.L.—See I Squared Capital Advisors (US) LLC; *U.S. Private*, pg. 2021
AC6 METROLOGIA, S.L.—See TDR Capital LLP; *Int'l*, pg. 7490
ACACIA CAPITAL NL LLC; *U.S. Private*, pg. 46
ACACIA CAPITAL PARTNERS LIMITED; *Int'l*, pg. 74
ACACIA COMMUNICATIONS (CANADA) LIMITED—See Cisco Systems, Inc.; *U.S. Public*, pg. 497
ACACIA COMMUNICATIONS, INC.—See Cisco Systems, Inc.; *U.S. Public*, pg. 497
ACACIA DIVERSIFIED HOLDINGS, INC.; *U.S. Public*, pg. 27
ACACIA FINANCIAL GROUP, INC.; *U.S. Private*, pg. 46
ACACIA INVERSION S.G.I.I.C., S.A.U.; *Int'l*, pg. 75
ACACIA LIFE INSURANCE COMPANY—See Ameritas Mutual Holding Company; *U.S. Private*, pg. 261
ACACIA MINING PLC—See Barrick Gold Corporation; *Int'l*, pg. 869
ACACIA PARTNERS LLC; *U.S. Private*, pg. 46
ACACIA PHARMA GROUP PLC—See Eagle Pharmaceuticals, Inc.; *U.S. Public*, pg. 703
ACACIA PHARMA INC—See Eagle Pharmaceuticals, Inc.; *U.S. Public*, pg. 703
ACACIA RESEARCH CORPORATION; *U.S. Public*, pg. 27
ACACIA RESEARCH GROUP, LLC—See Acacia Research Corporation; *U.S. Public*, pg. 27
ACACIA TRAINING LTD.—See MBH Corporation Plc; *Int'l*, pg. 4752

ACACIA WEALTH ADVISORS, LLC.—See HighTower Holding LLC; *U.S. Private*, pg. 1941
ACA CORP.; *U.S. Private*, pg. 46
ACADEMEDIA AB; *Int'l*, pg. 75
ACADEMEDIA EDUCATION GMBH—See AcadeMedia AB; *Int'l*, pg. 75
ACADEMEDIA GMBH—See AcadeMedia AB; *Int'l*, pg. 75
ACADEMIA LTD.—See Strive Capital LLP; *Int'l*, pg. 7241
ACADEMIC ASSESSMENT SERVICES PTY. LTD.—See Janison Education Group Limited; *Int'l*, pg. 3879
ACADEMICS LIMITED—See Servoca Plc; *Int'l*, pg. 6726
ACADEMIC SOFTWARE BV—See Signpost NV; *Int'l*, pg. 6912
ACADEMIC SUPERSTORE, LP—See Snorrason Holdings ehf; *Int'l*, pg. 7028
ACADEMIC TRAVEL ABROAD, INC.; *U.S. Private*, pg. 46
ACADEMICWORKS, LLC—See Blackbaud, Inc.; *U.S. Public*, pg. 341
ACADEMIE ACCOR SA—See Accor S.A.; *Int'l*, pg. 91
ACADEMIES AUSTRALASIA COLLEGE PTE. LIMITED—See Academies Australasia Group Limited; *Int'l*, pg. 77
ACADEMIES AUSTRALASIA GROUP LIMITED; *Int'l*, pg. 77
ACADEMIES AUSTRALASIA HAIR & BEAUTY PTY LIMITED—See Academies Australasia Group Limited; *Int'l*, pg. 77
ACADEMIES AUSTRALASIA INSTITUTE PTY. LIMITED—See Academies Australasia Group Limited; *Int'l*, pg. 77
ACADEMIES AUSTRALASIA (MANAGEMENT) PTY LIMITED—See Academies Australasia Group Limited; *Int'l*, pg. 77
ACADEMIES AUSTRALASIA POLYTECHNIC PTY LIMITED—See Academies Australasia Group Limited; *Int'l*, pg. 77
ACADEMIES AUSTRALASIA PTY LIMITED—See Academies Australasia Group Limited; *Int'l*, pg. 77
ACADEMI LLC—See Apollo Global Management, Inc.; *U.S. Public*, pg. 150
ACADEMIXDIRECT INC.; *U.S. Private*, pg. 46
ACADEMY 1 SPORTS LTD.—See MBH Corporation Plc; *Int'l*, pg. 4752
ACADEMY21 LIMITED—See Inspired Education Holdings Limited; *Int'l*, pg. 3720
ACADEMY BANK, N.A.—See Dickinson Financial Corporation; *U.S. Private*, pg. 1227
ACADEMY BRUSHWARE PRODUCTS PROPRIETARY LIMITED—See The Bidvest Group Limited; *Int'l*, pg. 7621
ACADEMY BUS LLC; *U.S. Private*, pg. 46
ACADEMY COMMUNICATIONS INC.; *U.S. Private*, pg. 46
ACADEMY CORPORATION—See Materion Corporation; *U.S. Public*, pg. 1396
ACADEMY DU VIN CO., LTD.—See Digital Garage, Inc.; *Int'l*, pg. 2121
ACADEMY FOR URBAN SCHOOL LEADERSHIP; *U.S. Private*, pg. 46
ACADEMYHEALTH; *U.S. Private*, pg. 46
ACADEMY HOTEL, LLC—See Silver Lake Group, LLC; *U.S. Private*, pg. 3654
ACADEMY, LTD.—See Academy Sports and Outdoors, Inc.; *U.S. Public*, pg. 27
ACADEMY MORTGAGE CORPORATION; *U.S. Private*, pg. 46
ACADEMY NURSING HOME, INC.—See Welltower Inc.; *U.S. Public*, pg. 2347
ACADEMY OF ENGLISH PTY. LIMITED—See Academies Australasia Group Limited; *Int'l*, pg. 77
ACADEMY OF ENVIRONMENTAL PLANNING & DESIGN, CO., LTD.; *Int'l*, pg. 77
ACADEMY OF GENERAL DENTISTRY; *U.S. Private*, pg. 46
ACADEMY OF INFORMATION TECHNOLOGY PTY LTD—See iCollege Limited; *Int'l*, pg. 3582
ACADEMY OF MOTION PICTURE ARTS & SCIENCES; *U.S. Private*, pg. 46
ACADEMY OF NURSING (M) SDN BHD—See Berjaya Corporation Berhad; *Int'l*, pg. 982
THE ACADEMY OF RADIO BROADCASTING, INC.; *U.S. Private*, pg. 3980
THE ACADEMY OF RADIO & TV—See The Academy of Radio Broadcasting, Inc.; *U.S. Private*, pg. 3981
ACADEMY PRESS PLC.; *Int'l*, pg. 77
ACADEMY SOLUTIONS GROUP, LLC.; *U.S. Private*, pg. 46
THE ACADEMY; *Int'l*, pg. 7610
ACADEMY SPORTS AND OUTDOORS, INC.; *U.S. Public*, pg. 27
ACADIA AUTO GROUP INC.; *U.S. Private*, pg. 46
ACADIA HEALTHCARE COMPANY, INC.; *U.S. Public*, pg. 27
ACADIA INSURANCE COMPANY—See W.R. Berkley Corporation; *U.S. Public*, pg. 2318
ACADIA MALIBU, INC.; *U.S. Private*, pg. 46
ACADIA MONTANA, INC.—See Acadia Healthcare Company, Inc.; *U.S. Public*, pg. 27
ACADIANA ADDICTION CENTER, LLC—See Acadia Healthcare Company, Inc.; *U.S. Public*, pg. 27

ACADIA MALIBU, INC.
CORPORATE AFFILIATIONS

ACADIANA BEARING CO—See Purvis Bearing Service Ltd.; *U.S. Private*, pg. 3307
ACADIANA BOTTLING CO. INC.; *U.S. Private*, pg. 47
ACADIANA COMPUTER SYSTEMS INC; *U.S. Private*, pg. 47
ACADIANA DODGE, INC.; *U.S. Private*, pg. 47
ACADIAN AMBULANCE SERVICE INC; *U.S. Private*, pg. 47
ACADIAN ASSET MANAGEMENT LLC—See BrightSphere Investment Group Inc.; *U.S. Public*, pg. 383
ACADIAN ASSET MANAGEMENT (SINGAPORE) PTE. LTD.—See BrightSphere Investment Group Inc.; *U.S. Public*, pg. 383
ACADIANA SYMPHONY ASSOCIATION; *U.S. Private*, pg. 47
ACADIAN ENERGY, LLC; *U.S. Private*, pg. 47
ACADIAN GAS, LLC—See Enterprise Products Partners L.P.; *U.S. Public*, pg. 778
ACADIAN GAS PIPELINE SYSTEM—See Enterprise Products Partners L.P.; *U.S. Public*, pg. 778
ACADIAN HOMECARE, LLC—See UnitedHealth Group Incorporated; *U.S. Public*, pg. 2243
ACADIAN HOMECARE OF NEW IBERIA, LLC—See UnitedHealth Group Incorporated; *U.S. Public*, pg. 2243
ACADIAN PHYSICAL THERAPY SERVICES, LLC—See UnitedHealth Group Incorporated; *U.S. Public*, pg. 2243
ACADIAN TIMBER CORP.; *Int'l*, pg. 77
ACADIA PHARMACEUTICALS INC.; *U.S. Public*, pg. 31
ACADIA REALTY TRUST; *U.S. Public*, pg. 31
ACADIASOFT, INC.; *U.S. Private*, pg. 47
ACADIASOFT (UK) LTD.—See AcadiaSoft, Inc.; *U.S. Private*, pg. 47
ACADIA TECHNOLOGY GROUP; *U.S. Private*, pg. 47
ACADIA TRUST, N.A.—See Camden National Corporation; *U.S. Public*, pg. 426
ACADIA WHOLESALE & TOBACCO COMPANY, INC.; *U.S. Private*, pg. 47
ACADIA - YFCS HOLDINGS, INC.—See Acadia Healthcare Company, Inc.; *U.S. Public*, pg. 27
AC ADVERTISING; *U.S. Private*, pg. 45
A.C. ADVISORY, INC.—See Public Financial Management, Inc.; *U.S. Private*, pg. 3299
AC&A ENTERPRISES LLC—See AE Industrial Partners, LP; *U.S. Private*, pg. 111
ACA FINANCIAL GUARANTY CORPORATION—See Manifold Capital Corp.; *U.S. Private*, pg. 2564
ACAI ASSOCIATES; *U.S. Private*, pg. 47
ACAL AUSTRALIA PTY. LTD.—See discoverIE Group plc; *Int'l*, pg. 2132
ACAL BFI BELGIUM NV/SA—See discoverIE Group plc; *Int'l*, pg. 2132
ACAL BFI DENMARK—See discoverIE Group plc; *Int'l*, pg. 2132
ACAL BFI FRANCE SAS—See discoverIE Group plc; *Int'l*, pg. 2132
ACAL BFI GERMANY GMBH—See discoverIE Group plc; *Int'l*, pg. 2132
ACAL BFI GERMANY GMBH—See discoverIE Group plc; *Int'l*, pg. 2132
ACAL BFI GERMANY GMBH—See discoverIE Group plc; *Int'l*, pg. 2132
ACAL BFI IBERIA SLU—See discoverIE Group plc; *Int'l*, pg. 2132
ACAL BFI ITALY S.R.L—See discoverIE Group plc; *Int'l*, pg. 2132
ACAL BFI ITALY SR—See discoverIE Group plc; *Int'l*, pg. 2132
ACAL BFI NETHERLANDS BV—See discoverIE Group plc; *Int'l*, pg. 2132
ACAL BFI NETHERLANDS BV—See discoverIE Group plc; *Int'l*, pg. 2133
ACAL BFI NORDIC AB—See discoverIE Group plc; *Int'l*, pg. 2133
ACAL BFI NORDIC AB—See discoverIE Group plc; *Int'l*, pg. 2133
ACAL BFI UK LTD.—See discoverIE Group plc; *Int'l*, pg. 2132
ACAL BFI UK LTD.—See discoverIE Group plc; *Int'l*, pg. 2132
ACAL CONTROLS LTD.—See discoverIE Group plc; *Int'l*, pg. 2132
ACAL EUROPE HOLDING BV—See discoverIE Group plc; *Int'l*, pg. 2132
ACAL MANAGEMENT SERVICES LTD.—See discoverIE Group plc; *Int'l*, pg. 2133
ACAL NEDERLAND BV—See discoverIE Group plc; *Int'l*, pg. 2133
ACAMBIS RESEARCH LTD.—See Sanofi; *Int'l*, pg. 6548
ACAMPORA TRAVEL S.R.L.—See TUI AG; *Int'l*, pg. 7963
ACAMS (AUSTRALIA) PTY. LTD.—See Wendel S.A.; *Int'l*, pg. 8376
ACAMS CONSULTING (BEIJING) CO.—See Wendel S.A.; *Int'l*, pg. 8376
ACAMS FRANCE SAS—See Wendel S.A.; *Int'l*, pg. 8376
ACAMS (HK) LTD.—See Wendel S.A.; *Int'l*, pg. 8376
ACAMS JAPAN K.K.—See Wendel S.A.; *Int'l*, pg. 8376
ACAMS MEXICO, S. DE R.L. DE C.V.—See Wendel S.A.; *Int'l*, pg. 8376

ACAMS (PANAMA) S. DE R.I.—See Wendel S.A.; *Int'l*, pg. 8376
ACAMS (SINGAPORE) PTE. LTD.—See Wendel S.A.; *Int'l*, pg. 8376
ACAMS (TAIWAN) LIMITED—See Wendel S.A.; *Int'l*, pg. 8376
ACAMS (UK) LTD.—See Wendel S.A.; *Int'l*, pg. 8376
AC ANALYTICAL CONTROLS B.V.—See Roper Technologies, Inc.; *U.S. Public*, pg. 1810
ACANDO AB; *Int'l*, pg. 77
ACANDO AS—See Acando AB; *Int'l*, pg. 77
ACANDO BUSINESS INTELLIGENCE AB—See Acando AB; *Int'l*, pg. 77
ACANDO CONSULTING AB—See Acando AB; *Int'l*, pg. 77
ACANDO DENMARK A/S—See Acando AB; *Int'l*, pg. 78
ACANDO INCENTIVE AB—See Acando AB; *Int'l*, pg. 78
ACANDO LTD—See Acando AB; *Int'l*, pg. 78
ACANDO MANAGEMENT CONSULTING AB—See Acando AB; *Int'l*, pg. 78
ACANDO SVERIGE AB—See Acando AB; *Int'l*, pg. 78
AC ANTENNAS A/S—See Lagercrantz Group AB; *Int'l*, pg. 4393
ACANTHE DEVELOPPEMENT SA; *Int'l*, pg. 78
ACA PARTNERS PTE LTD.; *Int'l*, pg. 74
ACAP ASSET MANAGEMENT COMPANY LIMITED—See Asia Capital Public Company Limited; *Int'l*, pg. 610
A-CAP ENERGY LIMITED; *Int'l*, pg. 19
ACAP (MALAYSIA) SDN. BHD.—See Asia Capital Public Company Limited; *Int'l*, pg. 610
A-CAP RESOURCES BOTSWANA (PTY.) LTD.—See Lotus Resources Limited; *Int'l*, pg. 4561
ACARIAHEALTH, INC.—See Centene Corporation; *U.S. Public*, pg. 468
ACARIAHEALTH PHARMACY #11, INC.—See Centene Corporation; *U.S. Public*, pg. 467
ACARIAHEALTH PHARMACY #12, INC.—See Centene Corporation; *U.S. Public*, pg. 467
ACARIAHEALTH PHARMACY #13, INC.—See Centene Corporation; *U.S. Public*, pg. 467
ACARIX AB; *Int'l*, pg. 78
ACARIX USA INC.—See Acarix AB; *Int'l*, pg. 78
ACARLAR DIS TICARET VE MAKINA SANAYI A S.—See Haulotte Group SA; *Int'l*, pg. 3285
ACASA GROUP BVBA; *Int'l*, pg. 78
ACA SALUD—See Asociacion de Cooperativas Argentinas C.L.; *Int'l*, pg. 628
ACAST AB; *Int'l*, pg. 78
ACASTA ENTERPRISES, INC.; *Int'l*, pg. 78
ACASTI PHARMA INC.—See Neptune Wellness Solutions, Inc.; *Int'l*, pg. 5200
AC AUSTRO CAR HANDELSGESELLSCHAFT MBH & CO.—See Stellantis N.V.; *Int'l*, pg. 7196
AC-B AIR TRAFFIC CONTROL & BUSINESS SYSTEMS GMBH—See Indra Sistemas, S.A.; *Int'l*, pg. 3659
ACB AMERICAN INC.; *U.S. Private*, pg. 47
ACB CAPITAL MANAGEMENT COMPANY LIMITED—See Asia Commercial Bank; *Int'l*, pg. 611
ACBEL ELECTRONIC (DONG GUAN) CO., LTD.—See AcBel Polytech Inc.; *Int'l*, pg. 78
ACBEL ELECTRONIC (WUHAN) CO., LTD.—See AcBel Polytech Inc.; *Int'l*, pg. 78
ACBEL POLYTECH INC.; *Int'l*, pg. 78
ACBEL POLYTECH JAPAN INC.—See AcBel Polytech Inc.; *Int'l*, pg. 78
ACBEL POLYTECH (MALAYSIA) SDN. BHD.—See AcBel Polytech Inc.; *Int'l*, pg. 78
ACBEL POLYTECH (PHILIPPINES) INC.—See AcBel Polytech Inc.; *Int'l*, pg. 78
ACBEL POLYTECH (UK) CO. LTD.—See AcBel Polytech Inc.; *Int'l*, pg. 78
ACBEL (USA) POLYTECH INC.—See AcBel Polytech Inc.; *Int'l*, pg. 78
A&C BLACK PUBLISHERS LTD.—See Bloomsbury Publishing Plc; *Int'l*, pg. 1065
ACBZ IMPORTACAO E COMERCIO LTDA.—See ASUSTeK Computer Inc.; *Int'l*, pg. 663
ACCA INTERNATIONAL CO., LTD.—See Daiwa House Industry Co., Ltd.; *Int'l*, pg. 1947
ACC AVIATION LTD.; *Int'l*, pg. 78
ACC BUSINESS—See AT&T Inc.; *U.S. Public*, pg. 218
AC&C COMPANIES, INC.—See Brance Krachy Company, Inc.; *U.S. Private*, pg. 635
ACC COMPRESSORS SPA—See Guangzhou Wanbao Group Co., Ltd.; *Int'l*, pg. 3168
ACC CONCRETE LIMITED—See ACC Limited; *Int'l*, pg. 78
ACC CONSTRUCTION COMPANY, INC.; *U.S. Private*, pg. 47
ACC DISTRIBUTORS, INC.; *U.S. Private*, pg. 47
ACCEDERE LIMITED; *Int'l*, pg. 79
ACCEDO GROUP LTD.; *Int'l*, pg. 79
ACCEL AB—See Littelfuse, Inc.; *U.S. Public*, pg. 1326
ACCELA INC.; *U.S. Private*, pg. 49
ACCELA INC.—See Berkshire Partners LLC; *U.S. Private*, pg. 534
ACCELALPHA INC.—See Century Park Capital Partners, LLC; *U.S. Private*, pg. 833
ACCEL DISTRIBUCION, S. A. DE C. V.—See Accel, S.A.B. de C.V.; *Int'l*, pg. 79

ACCEL ELEKTRONIKA UAB—See Littelfuse, Inc.; *U.S. Public*, pg. 1326
ACCEL ENTERTAINMENT, INC.; *U.S. Public*, pg. 31
ACCEL ENTERTAINMENT, LLC—See Accel Entertainment, Inc.; *U.S. Public*, pg. 31
ACCELER8 VENTURES PLC; *Int'l*, pg. 79
ACCELERA INNOVATIONS, INC.; *U.S. Public*, pg. 32
ACCELERA SOLUTIONS, INC.; *U.S. Private*, pg. 49
ACCELERATE ACQUISITION CORP.; *U.S. Public*, pg. 32
ACCELERATEBS INDIA LIMITED; *Int'l*, pg. 80
ACCELERATE COMMERCE GMBH—See Ceconomy AG; *Int'l*, pg. 1373
ACCELERATED ARTIFICIAL LIFT SYSTEMS, LLC—See Dover Corporation; *U.S. Public*, pg. 678
ACCELERATED BENEFITS—See Caisse de Depot et Placement du Quebec; *Int'l*, pg. 1256
ACCELERATED BENEFITS—See KKR & Co., Inc.; *U.S. Public*, pg. 1264
ACCELERATED CARE PLUS CORP.—See Patient Square Capital, L.P.; *U.S. Private*, pg. 3106
ACCELERATED CHRISTIAN EDUCATION INC.; *U.S. Private*, pg. 49
ACCELERATED CLAIMS INC.; *U.S. Private*, pg. 49
ACCELERATED COMPANIES, LLC—See Dover Corporation; *U.S. Public*, pg. 678
ACCELERATED CONCEPTS, INC.—See Digi International Inc.; *U.S. Public*, pg. 662
ACCELERATED CONCEPTS PTY. LTD.—See Digi International Inc.; *U.S. Public*, pg. 662
ACCELERATED CONNECTIONS INC.—See GTT Communications, Inc.; *U.S. Public*, pg. 1807
ACCELERATED DESIGNS, INC.—See EMA Design Automation, Inc.; *U.S. Private*, pg. 1377
ACCELERATED ENROLLMENT SOLUTIONS, INC.—See Thermo Fisher Scientific Inc.; *U.S. Public*, pg. 2150
ACCELERATED GENETICS—See Select Sires Inc.; *U.S. Private*, pg. 3601
ACCELERATE DIAGNOSTICS, INC.; *U.S. Public*, pg. 32
ACCELERATED INTERNATIONAL FORWARDERS LLC.; *U.S. Private*, pg. 49
ACCELERATED PHARMA, INC.; *U.S. Public*, pg. 49
ACCELERATED PRODUCTION SYSTEMS, INC.—See Dover Corporation; *U.S. Public*, pg. 678
ACCELERATED PRODUCTION SYSTEMS LIMITED—See Dover Corporation; *U.S. Public*, pg. 678
ACCELERATED SYSTEMS, INC.; *Int'l*, pg. 80
ACCELERATED TECHNOLOGIES HOLDING CORP.; *U.S. Public*, pg. 32
ACCELERATED WASTE SOLUTIONS, LLC; *U.S. Private*, pg. 49
ACCELERATE PROPERTY FUND LTD.; *Int'l*, pg. 80
ACCELERATE RESOURCES LIMITED; *Int'l*, pg. 80
ACCELERATE SOLAR LLC; *U.S. Private*, pg. 49
ACCELERATION COMMUNITY OF COMPANIES; *U.S. Private*, pg. 49
ACCELERATION PARTNERS LLC—See Mountaingate Capital Management, L.P.; *U.S. Private*, pg. 2801
ACCELERO CAPITAL HOLDINGS SARL; *Int'l*, pg. 80
ACCELERO HEALTH PARTNERS, LLC—See Zimmer Biomet Holdings, Inc.; *U.S. Public*, pg. 2405
ACCELERON PHARMA INC.—See Merck & Co., Inc.; *U.S. Public*, pg. 1415
ACCELEWARE LTD.; *Int'l*, pg. 80
ACCEL GROUP HOLDINGS LIMITED; *Int'l*, pg. 79
THE ACCEL GROUP LLC; *U.S. Private*, pg. 3981
ACCELINK DENMARK A/S—See Accelink Technologies Co., Ltd.; *Int'l*, pg. 80
ACCELINK TECHNOLOGIES CO., LTD.; *Int'l*, pg. 80
ACCELINK TECHNOLOGIES EUROPE GMBH—See Accelink Technologies Co., Ltd.; *Int'l*, pg. 80
ACCEL INNOVATIONS LIMITED—See Accel Group Holdings Limited; *Int'l*, pg. 79
ACCEL-KKR COMPANY LLC—See Accel Partners L.P.; *U.S. Private*, pg. 47
ACCEL-KKR COMPANY LLC—See KKR & Co. Inc.; *U.S. Public*, pg. 1237
ACCELLACARE ESPANA S.L.—See ICON plc; *Int'l*, pg. 3583
ACCELLACARE OF BRISTOL, LLC—See ICON plc; *Int'l*, pg. 3583
ACCELLACARE OF CHARLESTON, LLC—See ICON plc; *Int'l*, pg. 3583
ACCELLACARE OF CHARLOTTE, LLC—See ICON plc; *Int'l*, pg. 3584
ACCELLACARE OF HICKORY, LLC—See ICON plc; *Int'l*, pg. 3584
ACCELLACARE OF RALEIGH, LLC—See ICON plc; *Int'l*, pg. 3584
ACCELLACARE OF ROCKY MOUNT, LLC—See ICON plc; *Int'l*, pg. 3584
ACCELLACARE OF SALISBURY, LLC—See ICON plc; *Int'l*, pg. 3584
ACCELLACARE OF WILMINGTON, LLC—See ICON plc; *Int'l*, pg. 3584
ACCELLACARE OF WINSTON-SALEM, LLC—See ICON plc; *Int'l*, pg. 3584
ACCELLACARE SOUTH AFRICA (PTY.) LTD.—See ICON plc; *Int'l*, pg. 3583
ACCELLACARE US INC.—See ICON plc; *Int'l*, pg. 3583

COMPANY NAME INDEX

ACCELLA POLYURETHANE SYSTEMS, LLC—See Carlisle Companies Incorporated; *U.S. Public*, pg. 436
ACCELL ASIA LTD.—See Accell Group N.V.; *Int'l*, pg. 80
ACCELL BISIKLET SANAYI VE TICARET A.S.—See Accell Group N.V.; *Int'l*, pg. 80
ACCELL DUITSLAND B.V.—See Accell Group N.V.; *Int'l*, pg. 80
ACCELLECARE ESPANA S.L.—See ICON plc; *Int'l*, pg. 3584
ACCELLECARE OF RALEIGH, LLC—See ICON plc; *Int'l*, pg. 3584
ACCELLECARE OF WILMINGTON, LLC—See ICON plc; *Int'l*, pg. 3584
ACCELLECARE SOUTH AFRICA (PTY) LTD.—See ICON plc; *Int'l*, pg. 3584
ACCELL GERMANY GMBH—See Accell Group N.V.; *Int'l*, pg. 80
ACCELL GROUP N.V.; *Int'l*, pg. 80
ACCELL HUNLAND KFT—See Accell Group N.V.; *Int'l*, pg. 80
ACCEL LIMITED; *Int'l*, pg. 79
ACCELLION, INC., *U.S. Private*, pg. 49
ACCEL LIQUID GELS, INC.; *U.S. Private*, pg. 47
ACCELL IT B.V.—See Accell Group N.V.; *Int'l*, pg. 80
ACCELL IT SERVICES B.V.—See Accell Group N.V.; *Int'l*, pg. 80
ACCELL NEDERLAND B.V.—See Accell Group N.V.; *Int'l*, pg. 80
ACCELL NORTH AMERICA, INC.—See Regent, L.P.; *U.S. Private*, pg. 3387
ACCEL LOGISTICA S.A. DE C.V.—See Accel, S.A.B. de C.V.; *Int'l*, pg. 79
ACCELLOS, INC.; *U.S. Private*, pg. 50
ACCELL PROPERTY MANAGEMENT INC.—See Seabreeze Management Company, Inc.; *U.S. Private*, pg. 3583
ACCELL SUISSE AG—See Accell Group N.V.; *Int'l*, pg. 80
ACCEL MEDIA VENTURES LTD.—See Accel Limited; *Int'l*, pg. 79
ACCELMED PARTNERS II MANAGEMENT, LLC; *U.S. Private*, pg. 50
ACCELOGIX LLC—See Black Lake Capital, LLC; *U.S. Private*, pg. 572
ACCELON CAPITAL LLC; *U.S. Private*, pg. 50
ACCELONIX B.V.—See Accelonix Limited; *Int'l*, pg. 81
ACCELONIX IBERICA S.L.—See Accelonix Limited; *Int'l*, pg. 81
ACCELONIX LIMITED; *Int'l*, pg. 81
ACCELONIX SARL—See Accelonix Limited; *Int'l*, pg. 81
ACCELOPS, INC.—See Fortinet, Inc.; *U.S. Public*, pg. 869
ACCEL PARTNERS L.P.; *U.S. Private*, pg. 47
ACCEL PROTECTION & TECHNOLOGIES, LLC.—See American Integration Contractors, LLC; *U.S. Private*, pg. 238
ACCELRYS, INC.—See Dassault Systemes S.A.; *Int'l*, pg. 1974
ACCELRYS K.K.—See Dassault Systemes S.A.; *Int'l*, pg. 1974
ACCELRYS LIMITED—See Dassault Systemes S.A.; *Int'l*, pg. 1974
ACCELRYS SARL—See Dassault Systemes S.A.; *Int'l*, pg. 1974
ACCELRYS SOFTWARE INCORPORATED—See Dassault Systemes S.A.; *Int'l*, pg. 1974
ACCEL, S.A.B. DE C.V.; *Int'l*, pg. 79
ACCEL SERVICIOS, S. A. DE C. V.—See Accel, S.A.B. de C.V.; *Int'l*, pg. 79
ACCEL SOLUTIONS LTD.; *Int'l*, pg. 79
ACCELSTAR PACIFIC LIMITED—See China Oil & Gas Group Limited; *Int'l*, pg. 1538
ACCELYA HOLDING WORLD SL—See Vista Equity Partners, LLC; *U.S. Private*, pg. 4394
ACCELYA SOLUTIONS INDIA LIMITED—See Warburg Pincus LLC; *U.S. Private*, pg. 4436
ACCENT ANNEX ENTERPRISES INC.; *U.S. Private*, pg. 50
ACCENT BUSINESS SERVICES, INC.—See Univerus Software, Inc.; *Int'l*, pg. 8083
ACCENTCARE, INC.—See Advent International Corporation; *U.S. Private*, pg. 97
ACCENT COMPUTER SOLUTIONS, INC.—See VC3, Inc.; *U.S. Private*, pg. 4349
ACCENT ENERGY GROUP, LLC—See ACI Capital Co. LLC; *U.S. Private*, pg. 59
ACCENT EQUITY PARTNERS AB; *Int'l*, pg. 81
A C CENTER, INC.; *U.S. Private*, pg. 18
ACCENT FURNITURE, INC.—See The Bedroom Store; *U.S. Private*, pg. 3992
ACCENT GRAPHIC S.L.—See Fluidra SA; *Int'l*, pg. 2713
ACCENT GROUP LIMITED; *Int'l*, pg. 81
ACCENTHEALTH LLC—See Catterton Management Company, LLC; *U.S. Private*, pg. 794
ACCENTIA TECHNOLOGIES - COCHIN UNIT—See Accentia Technologies Limited; *Int'l*, pg. 81
ACCENTIA TECHNOLOGIES LIMITED; *Int'l*, pg. 81
ACCENTIA TECHNOLOGIES LTD. - TRIVANDRUM UNIT—See Accentia Technologies Limited; *Int'l*, pg. 82
ACCENT INTERMEDIA, LLC—See Cuentas Inc.; *U.S. Public*, pg. 604
ACCENTIS SA/NV; *Int'l*, pg. 82
ACCENTIV BRESIL MIMETICA—See Edenred S.A.; *Int'l*, pg. 2307
ACCENTIV' KADEOS S.A.S.—See Edenred S.A.; *Int'l*, pg. 2307
ACCENTIV' SERVICOS TECNOLOGICA DA INFORMACAO S/A—See Edenred S.A.; *Int'l*, pg. 2307
ACCENTIV SHANGHAI COMPANY—See Edenred S.A.; *Int'l*, pg. 2307
ACCENTMARKETING—See The Interpublic Group of Companies, Inc.; *U.S. Public*, pg. 2090
ACCENTMARKETING—See The Interpublic Group of Companies, Inc.; *U.S. Public*, pg. 2090
ACCENT MEDIA PRODUCTIONS, INC.; *U.S. Private*, pg. 50
ACCENT MICROCELL LTD.; *Int'l*, pg. 81
ACCENT PLASTICS INC.—See Syntech Development & Manufacturing, Inc.; *U.S. Private*, pg. 3904
ACCENT RESOURCES N.L.; *Int'l*, pg. 81
ACCENTRO REAL ESTATE AG—See Vestigo Capital Advisors LLP; *Int'l*, pg. 8178
ACCENT TELECOM UK LIMITED—See CloudCoCo Group plc; *Int'l*, pg. 1662
ACCENTUATE LIMITED; *Int'l*, pg. 82
ACCENTURE 2, INC.—See Accenture plc; *Int'l*, pg. 85
ACCENTURE A.B.—See Accenture plc; *Int'l*, pg. 82
ACCENTURE AG—See Accenture plc; *Int'l*, pg. 82
ACCENTURE ARGENTINA—See Accenture plc; *Int'l*, pg. 82
ACCENTURE A/S—See Accenture plc; *Int'l*, pg. 82
ACCENTURE A/S—See Accenture plc; *Int'l*, pg. 82
ACCENTURE AUSTRALIA LTD.—See Accenture plc; *Int'l*, pg. 82
ACCENTURE AUSTRALIA—See Accenture plc; *Int'l*, pg. 82
ACCENTURE AUSTRIA—See Accenture plc; *Int'l*, pg. 82
ACCENTURE AUTOMACAO E TI INDUSTRIAL LTDA—See Accenture plc; *Int'l*, pg. 82
ACCENTURE BELGIUM—See Accenture plc; *Int'l*, pg. 82
ACCENTURE (BOTSWANA) (PTY) LTD.—See Accenture plc; *Int'l*, pg. 82
ACCENTURE BPM IS YONETIMI LIMITED SIRKETI—See Accenture plc; *Int'l*, pg. 82
ACCENTURE BPM S.A.—See Accenture plc; *Int'l*, pg. 82
ACCENTURE BRANCH HOLDINGS B.V.—See Accenture plc; *Int'l*, pg. 82
ACCENTURE BRAZIL—See Accenture plc; *Int'l*, pg. 82
ACCENTURE BULGARIA EOOD—See Accenture plc; *Int'l*, pg. 82
ACCENTURE BUSINESS FOR UTILITIES INC.—See Accenture plc; *Int'l*, pg. 82
ACCENTURE BUSINESS SERVICES OF BRITISH COLUMBIA LIMITED PARTNERSHIP—See Accenture plc; *Int'l*, pg. 82
ACCENTURE BV—See Accenture plc; *Int'l*, pg. 82
ACCENTURE CANADA HOLDINGS INC.—See Accenture plc; *Int'l*, pg. 83
ACCENTURE CANADA—See Accenture plc; *Int'l*, pg. 83
ACCENTURE CAPITAL INC.—See Accenture plc; *Int'l*, pg. 85
ACCENTURE C.A.—See Accenture plc; *Int'l*, pg. 82
ACCENTURE CENTRAL EUROPE B.V.—See Accenture plc; *Int'l*, pg. 83
ACCENTURE CENTRAL EUROPE B. V.—See Accenture plc; *Int'l*, pg. 83
ACCENTURE CHILE ASESORIAS Y SERVICIOS LTDA.—See Accenture plc; *Int'l*, pg. 83
ACCENTURE (CHINA) CO., LTD. - SHANGHAI—See Accenture plc; *Int'l*, pg. 82
ACCENTURE (CHINA) CO., LTD.—See Accenture plc; *Int'l*, pg. 82
ACCENTURE COLOMBIA—See Accenture plc; *Int'l*, pg. 83
ACCENTURE CO LTD.—See Accenture plc; *Int'l*, pg. 83
ACCENTURE CO. LTD. (TAIWAN)—See Accenture plc; *Int'l*, pg. 83
ACCENTURE COMPANY LTD.—See Accenture plc; *Int'l*, pg. 83
ACCENTURE CONSULTORES DE GESTAO S.A.—See Accenture plc; *Int'l*, pg. 83
ACCENTURE DANISMANLIK LIMITED SIRKETI—See Accenture plc; *Int'l*, pg. 83
ACCENTURE DENMARK HOLDINGS A/S—See Accenture plc; *Int'l*, pg. 83
ACCENTURE DENMARK—See Accenture plc; *Int'l*, pg. 83
ACCENTURE DIENSTLEISTUNGEN GMBH—See Accenture plc; *Int'l*, pg. 33
ACCENTURE DO BRASIL LTDA—See Accenture plc; *Int'l*, pg. 85
ACCENTURE EUROPEAN SERVICE CENTRE LTD.—See Accenture plc; *Int'l*, pg. 83
ACCENTURE FEDERAL SERVICES LLC—See Accenture plc; *Int'l*, pg. 85
ACCENTURE FINANCE AND ACCOUNTING BPO SERVICES SPA—See Accenture plc; *Int'l*, pg. 83
ACCENTURE FINANCIAL CORPORATION—See Accenture plc; *Int'l*, pg. 35
ACCENTURE GLOBAL SERVICES LTD.—See Accenture plc; *Int'l*, pg. 83
ACCENTURE GMBH—See Accenture plc; *Int'l*, pg. 83

ACCENTURE PLC

ACCENTURE GMBH—See Accenture plc; *Int'l*, pg. 83
ACCENTURE HEALTHCARE PROCESSING INC.—See Accenture plc; *Int'l*, pg. 83
ACCENTURE HOLDING GMBH & CO. KG—See Accenture plc; *Int'l*, pg. 83
ACCENTURE HOLDINGS B.V.—See Accenture plc; *Int'l*, pg. 83
ACCENTURE HOLDINGS FRANCE SAS—See Accenture plc; *Int'l*, pg. 84
ACCENTURE HOLDINGS (IBERIA) S.L.—See Accenture plc; *Int'l*, pg. 83
ACCENTURE HOLDINGS PLC—See Accenture plc; *Int'l*, pg. 82
ACCENTURE HUMAN CAPITAL MGMT. SOL. S.L.—See Accenture plc; *Int'l*, pg. 83
ACCENTURE INC.—See Accenture plc; *Int'l*, pg. 83
ACCENTURE INC.—See Accenture plc; *Int'l*, pg. 83
ACCENTURE, INC.—See Accenture plc; *Int'l*, pg. 85
ACCENTURE INDIA PRIVATE LTD.—See Accenture plc; *Int'l*, pg. 83
ACCENTURE INTERNATIONAL CAPITAL SCA—See Accenture plc; *Int'l*, pg. 83
ACCENTURE INTERNATIONAL SARL—See Accenture plc; *Int'l*, pg. 83
ACCENTURE (IRELAND)—See Accenture plc; *Int'l*, pg. 82
ACCENTURE JAPAN LTD.—See Accenture plc; *Int'l*, pg. 83
ACCENTURE (KOREA) LTD.—See Accenture plc; *Int'l*, pg. 82
ACCENTURE LLC—See Accenture plc; *Int'l*, pg. 85
ACCENTURE LTDA—See Accenture plc; *Int'l*, pg. 83
ACCENTURE LTD. NIGERIA—See Accenture plc; *Int'l*, pg. 83
ACCENTURE LTD.—See Accenture plc; *Int'l*, pg. 83
ACCENTURE MANAGEMENT GMBH—See Accenture plc; *Int'l*, pg. 83
ACCENTURE MAURITIUS LTD.—See Accenture plc; *Int'l*, pg. 83
ACCENTURE (MAURITIUS) ONSHORE LTD.—See Accenture plc; *Int'l*, pg. 83
ACCENTURE MIDDLE EAST B.V.—See Accenture plc; *Int'l*, pg. 83
ACCENTURE NV SA—See Accenture plc; *Int'l*, pg. 83
ACCENTURE NZ LIMITED—See Accenture plc; *Int'l*, pg. 86
ACCENTURE OOO—See Accenture plc; *Int'l*, pg. 83
ACCENTURE OUTSOURCING SERVICES S.A.—See Accenture plc; *Int'l*, pg. 83
ACCENTURE OY—See Accenture plc; *Int'l*, pg. 83
ACCENTURE PARTICIPATIONS BV—See Accenture plc; *Int'l*, pg. 83
ACCENTURE PLC; *Int'l*, pg. 82
ACCENTURE PTE. LTD.—See Accenture plc; *Int'l*, pg. 84
ACCENTURE SARL—See Accenture plc; *Int'l*, pg. 84
ACCENTURE S.A.—See Accenture plc; *Int'l*, pg. 84
ACCENTURE SAS—See Accenture plc; *Int'l*, pg. 84
ACCENTURE SAUDI ARABIA LTD.—See Accenture plc; *Int'l*, pg. 86
ACCENTURE S.C.—See Accenture plc; *Int'l*, pg. 84
ACCENTURE SDN. BHD.—See Accenture plc; *Int'l*, pg. 84
ACCENTURE SERVICE CENTER SRL—See Accenture plc; *Int'l*, pg. 84
ACCENTURE SERVICE CENTRE MOROCCO SA—See Accenture plc; *Int'l*, pg. 84
ACCENTURE SERVICES AG—See Accenture plc; *Int'l*, pg. 84
ACCENTURE SERVICES GMBH—See Accenture plc; *Int'l*, pg. 84
ACCENTURE SERVICES (MAURITIUS) LTD.—See Accenture plc; *Int'l*, pg. 84
ACCENTURE SERVICES OY—See Accenture plc; *Int'l*, pg. 84
ACCENTURE SERVICES PRIVATE LTD.—See Accenture plc; *Int'l*, pg. 84
ACCENTURE SERVICES (SOUTH AFRICA) PTY LTD.—See Accenture plc; *Int'l*, pg. 84
ACCENTURE SERVICES SP. Z.O.O.—See Accenture plc; *Int'l*, pg. 84
ACCENTURE SERVICES S.R.L.—See Accenture plc; *Int'l*, pg. 84
ACCENTURE SERVICES S.R.O—See Accenture plc; *Int'l*, pg. 84
ACCENTURE SERVICES S.R.O.—See Accenture plc; *Int'l*, pg. 84
ACCENTURE, S.L.—See Accenture plc; *Int'l*, pg. 86
ACCENTURE SOLUTIONS CO. LTD.—See Accenture plc; *Int'l*, pg. 84
ACCENTURE SOLUTIONS PRIVATE LIMITED—See Accenture plc; *Int'l*, pg. 86
ACCENTURE SOLUTIONS SDN BHD—See Accenture plc; *Int'l*, pg. 84
ACCENTURE (SOUTH AFRICA) PTY. LTD.—See Accenture plc; *Int'l*, pg. 82
ACCENTURE SPA—See Accenture plc; *Int'l*, pg. 84
ACCENTURE SP. Z.O.O.—See Accenture plc; *Int'l*, pg. 84
ACCENTURE SRL—See Accenture plc; *Int'l*, pg. 86
ACCENTURE S.R.O.—See Accenture plc; *Int'l*, pg. 85
ACCENTURE TANACSADO KORLATOLT FELELOSSEGU TARSASAG KFT—See Accenture plc; *Int'l*, pg. 84

ACCENTURE PLC

ACCENTURE TECHNOLGY SOLUTIONS (THAILAND) LTD.—See Accenture plc; *Int'l*, pg. 84
ACCENTURE TECHNOLOGY SERVICES LTDA.—See Accenture plc; *Int'l*, pg. 84
ACCENTURE TECHNOLOGY SOLUTIONS A/S—See Accenture plc; *Int'l*, pg. 84
ACCENTURE TECHNOLOGY SOLUTIONS (ATS) NV—See Accenture plc; *Int'l*, pg. 82
ACCENTURE TECHNOLOGY SOLUTIONS BV—See Accenture plc; *Int'l*, pg. 84
ACCENTURE TECHNOLOGY SOLUTIONS-CANADA, INC.—See Accenture plc; *Int'l*, pg. 85
ACCENTURE TECHNOLOGY SOLUTIONS (DALIAN) CO LTD.—See Accenture plc; *Int'l*, pg. 84
ACCENTURE TECHNOLOGY SOLUTIONS GMBH—See Accenture plc; *Int'l*, pg. 84
ACCENTURE TECHNOLOGY SOLUTIONS GMBH—See Accenture plc; *Int'l*, pg. 84
ACCENTURE TECHNOLOGY SOLUTIONS (HK) CO. LTD.—See Accenture plc; *Int'l*, pg. 84
ACCENTURE TECHNOLOGY SOLUTIONS LTD.—See Accenture plc; *Int'l*, pg. 84
ACCENTURE TECHNOLOGY SOLUTIONS OY—See Accenture plc; *Int'l*, pg. 84
ACCENTURE TECHNOLOGY SOLUTIONS PTE LTD.—See Accenture plc; *Int'l*, pg. 84
ACCENTURE TECHNOLOGY SOLUTIONS PTY LTD.—See Accenture plc; *Int'l*, pg. 84
ACCENTURE TECHNOLOGY SOLUTIONS S.A.—See Accenture plc; *Int'l*, pg. 84
ACCENTURE TECHNOLOGY SOLUTIONS SAS—See Accenture plc; *Int'l*, pg. 84
ACCENTURE TECHNOLOGY SOLUTIONS S.C.—See Accenture plc; *Int'l*, pg. 84
ACCENTURE TECHNOLOGY SOLUTIONS SDN BHD—See Accenture plc; *Int'l*, pg. 85
ACCENTURE TECHNOLOGY SOLUTIONS-SLOVAKIA S.R.O.—See Accenture plc; *Int'l*, pg. 85
ACCENTURE TECHNOLOGY SOLUTIONS-SOLUCOES INFORMATICAS INTEGRADOS, S.A.—See Accenture plc, pg. 85
ACCENTURE TECHNOLOGY SOLUTIONS SRL—See Accenture plc; *Int'l*, pg. 84
ACCENTURE TECHNOLOGY SOLUTIONS S.R.O.—See Accenture plc; *Int'l*, pg. 85
ACCENTURE TECHNOLOGY VENTURES BV—See Accenture plc; *Int'l*, pg. 85
ACCENTURE TECHNOLOGY VENTURES S.P.R.L.—See Accenture plc; *Int'l*, pg. 85
ACCENTURE TURKEY—See Accenture plc; *Int'l*, pg. 85
ACCENTURE (UK) LTD.—See Accenture plc; *Int'l*, pg. 82
ACCENTUS INC.—See Microsoft Corporation; *U.S. Public*, pg. 1442
ACCENTUS MEDICAL PLC—See Coller Capital Ltd.; *Int'l*, pg. 1699
ACCENT WINDOWS INC.; *U.S. Private*, pg. 50
ACCENT WIRE; *U.S. Private*, pg. 50
ACCEO SOLUTIONS, INC. - QUEBEC—See Constellation Software Inc.; *Int'l*, pg. 1773
ACCEO SOLUTIONS, INC.—See Constellation Software Inc.; *Int'l*, pg. 1773
ACCEPTANCE CAPITAL MORTGAGE CORPORATION—See Complete Financial Solutions, Inc.; *U.S. Public*, pg. 561
ACCEPTANCE INSURANCE AGENCY OF TENNESSEE, INC.—See Stone Point Capital LLC; *U.S. Private*, pg. 3818
ACCEPTANCE LOAN CO. INC.—See First US Bancshares, Inc.; *U.S. Public*, pg. 848
ACCEPTANCE LOAN COMPANY, INC.—See First US Bancshares, Inc.; *U.S. Public*, pg. 848
ACCERTIFY, INC.—See Accel Partners L.P.; *U.S. Private*, pg. 47
ACCERTIFY, INC.—See KKR & Co. Inc.; *U.S. Public*, pg. 5746
ACCES INDUSTRIE SA—See Parquest Capital SAS; *Int'l*, pg. 5746
ACCESS 2 HEALTH CARE PHYSICIANS, LLC—See HCA Healthcare, Inc.; *U.S. Public*, pg. 990
ACCESS ADVERTISING, LLC; *U.S. Private*, pg. 50
ACCESS AP TAIWAN CO., LTD.—See Access Co., Ltd.; *Int'l*, pg. 88
ACCESS AUSTRALASIA SDN. BHD.—See AusGroup Limited; *Int'l*, pg. 716
ACCESS BANK (D.R. CONGO) SARL—See Access Corporation; *Int'l*, pg. 88
ACCESS BANK (GAMBIA) LIMITED—See Access Corporation; *Int'l*, pg. 88
ACCESS BANK (GHANA) LIMITED—See Access Corporation; *Int'l*, pg. 88
ACCESS BANK (RWANDA) LIMITED—See Access Corporation; *Int'l*, pg. 88
ACCESS BANK (SIERRA LEONE) LIMITED—See Access Corporation; *Int'l*, pg. 88
ACCESS BANK—See 3MV Bancorp, Inc.; *U.S. Private*, pg. 13
ACCESS BANK (UK) LIMITED—See Access Corporation; *Int'l*, pg. 88

ACCESS BANK (ZAMBIA) LIMITED—See Access Corporation; *Int'l*, pg. 88
ACCESS (BEIJING) CO., LTD.—See Access Co., Ltd.; *Int'l*, pg. 88
ACCESS BIO, INC.; *U.S. Public*, pg. 32
ACCESS BUSINESS GROUP LLC—See Alticor Inc.; *U.S. Private*, pg. 208
ACCESS BUSINESS GROUP—See Alticor Inc.; *U.S. Private*, pg. 208
ACCESS CABLE COMPANY—See The Furukawa Electric Co., Ltd.; *Int'l*, pg. 7644
ACCESS CAPITAL, INC.; *U.S. Private*, pg. 50
ACCESS CAPITAL PARTNERS SA; *Int'l*, pg. 88
ACCESS CAPITAL SERVICES, INC; *U.S. Private*, pg. 50
ACCESS CASH GENERAL PARTNERSHIP—See Morgan Stanley; *U.S. Public*, pg. 1474
ACCESS CATALOG COMPANY LLC—See Centrio Group LLC; *U.S. Private*, pg. 830
ACCESS CLOSURE, INC.—See Cardinal Health, Inc.; *U.S. Public*, pg. 433
ACCESS CO., LTD.; *Int'l*, pg. 88
ACCESS COMMERCIAL INVESTORS 4 PLC; *Int'l*, pg. 88
ACCESS COMMUNICATIONS LLC—See Monitor Clipper Partners, LLC; *U.S. Private*, pg. 2770
ACCESS COMMUNITY HEALTH LIMITED—See Green Cross Health Limited; *Int'l*, pg. 3070
ACCESS CONSTRUCTIONS PTY LTD—See Charter Hall Limited; *Int'l*, pg. 1454
ACCESS CONTROL SYSTEMS, LLC—See Brixey & Meyer, Inc.; *U.S. Private*, pg. 658
ACCESS CONTROL TECHNOLOGIES, INC.—See Clearlake Capital Group, L.P.; *U.S. Private*, pg. 935
ACCESS CORPORATION; *Int'l*, pg. 88
ACCESS DATA CONSULTING CORPORATION—See GEE Group Inc.; *U.S. Public*, pg. 909
ACCESS DATA CORP.—See Broadridge Financial Solutions, Inc.; *U.S. Public*, pg. 391
ACCESSDATA GROUP, LLC—See Leeds Equity Partners, LLC; *U.S. Private*, pg. 2414
ACCESS DESIGN & ENGINEERING LIMITED—See Hill & Smith PLC; *Int'l*, pg. 3391
ACCESS DESTINATION SERVICES - CHICAGO—See ACCESS Destination Services; *U.S. Private*, pg. 50
ACCESS DESTINATION SERVICES - LAFAYETTE—See ACCESS Destination Services; *U.S. Private*, pg. 50
ACCESS DESTINATION SERVICES; *U.S. Private*, pg. 50
ACCESS DESTINATION SERVICES—See ACCESS Destination Services; *U.S. Private*, pg. 50
ACCESS DESTINATION SERVICES—See ACCESS Destination Services; *U.S. Private*, pg. 50
ACCESS DESTINATION SERVICES—See ACCESS Destination Services; *U.S. Private*, pg. 50
ACCESS DESTINATION SERVICES—See ACCESS Destination Services; *U.S. Private*, pg. 50
ACCESS DESTINATION SERVICES—See ACCESS Destination Services; *U.S. Private*, pg. 50
ACCESS DESTINATION SERVICES—See ACCESS Destination Services; *U.S. Private*, pg. 50
ACCESS DESTINATION SERVICES—See ACCESS Destination Services; *U.S. Private*, pg. 50
ACCESS DESTINATION SERVICES—See ACCESS Destination Services; *U.S. Private*, pg. 50
ACCESS DIRECT SYSTEMS, INC.; *U.S. Private*, pg. 50
ACCESS DISPLAY GROUP INC.; *U.S. Private*, pg. 51
ACCESS EAST INC; *U.S. Private*, pg. 51
ACCESS EMANATE COMMUNICATIONS—See Omnicom Group Inc.; *U.S. Public*, pg. 1586
ACCESS EUROPE GMBH—See Access Co., Ltd.; *Int'l*, pg. 88
ACCESS EVENT NETWORK, INC.—See MicroTek; *U.S. Private*, pg. 2704
ACCESS GAMES INC.—See Kaga Electronics Co., Ltd.; *Int'l*, pg. 4048
ACCESS GENETICS, LLC; *U.S. Private*, pg. 51
ACCESS GROUP HOLDINGS CO., LTD.; *Int'l*, pg. 89
ACCESS GROUP INC.; *U.S. Private*, pg. 51
ACCESS HEALTH CARE, LLC; *U.S. Private*, pg. 51
ACCESS HEALTH CARE PHYSICIANS, LLC—See HCA Healthcare, Inc.; *U.S. Public*, pg. 990
ACCESS HOSPICE, LLC—See UnitedHealth Group Incorporated; *U.S. Public*, pg. 2243
ACCESSIBLE ACCESSORIES LTD.—See Quorum Information Technologies Inc.; *Int'l*, pg. 6166
ACCESSIBLE PRODUCTS COMPANY - TECHLITE INSULATION DIVISION—See The Zippertubing Company; *U.S. Private*, pg. 4140
ACCESSIBLE SPACE INC; *U.S. Private*, pg. 53
ACCESSIBLE SYSTEMS, INC.; *U.S. Private*, pg. 53
ACCESS INDUSTRIES, INC.; *U.S. Private*, pg. 51
ACCESS INFORMATION INFORMATION MANAGEMENT SHARED SERVICES LLC—See Berkshire Partners LLC; *U.S. Private*, pg. 534
ACCESS INSURANCE COMPANY; *U.S. Private*, pg. 52
ACCESS INTELLIGENCE, LLC—See Veronis Suhler Stevenson Partners LLC; *U.S. Private*, pg. 4368
ACCESS INTELLIGENCE MEDIA & COMMUNICATIONS LTD.—See Pulsar Group; *U.S. Private*, pg. 6116
ACCESS INTERNATIONAL EDUCATION LTD.; *Int'l*, pg. 89
ACCESS INTERNATIONAL PROJECTS (PVT) LTD.—See Daikin Industries, Ltd.; *Int'l*, pg. 1932

CORPORATE AFFILIATIONS

ACCESSITE SAS—See Nexity SA; *Int'l*, pg. 5244
ACCESS KELLYOCG GMBH—See Kelly Services, Inc.; *U.S. Public*, pg. 1219
ACCESSKENYA GROUP LIMITED—See Nippon Telegraph & Telephone Corporation; *Int'l*, pg. 5340
ACCESS LASER (SHENZHEN) CO., LTD.—See TRUMPF SE + Co. KG; *Int'l*, pg. 7942
ACCESS LEO BURNETT—See Publicis Groupe S.A.; *Int'l*, pg. 6100
ACCESS LTD.—See AIDA Engineering, Ltd.; *Int'l*, pg. 231
ACCESS MAIL PROCESSING SERVICES, INC.; *U.S. Private*, pg. 52
ACCESS MECHANISM L.L.C.—See Minebea Mitsumi Inc.; *Int'l*, pg. 4902
ACCESS MEDIA 3, INC.; *U.S. Private*, pg. 52
ACCESS MEDIQUIP, LLC—See Water Street Healthcare Partners, LLC; *U.S. Private*, pg. 4452
ACCESS MLP OPERATING, L.L.C.—See The Williams Companies, Inc.; *U.S. Public*, pg. 2143
ACCESS ONCOLOGY INC.—See Akebia Therapeutics, Inc.; *U.S. Public*, pg. 69
ACCESSORIES MARKETING, INC.—See Illinois Tool Works Inc.; *U.S. Public*, pg. 1101
ACCESSORY EXCHANGE L.L.C.—See Bag Bazaar Ltd.; *U.S. Private*, pg. 425
ACCESSORY EXPORT, LLC; *U.S. Private*, pg. 53
ACCESSORYGEEKS.COM; *U.S. Private*, pg. 53
ACCESSORY NETWORK GROUP INC.; *U.S. Private*, pg. 53
ACCESSORY PLACE INC.; *U.S. Private*, pg. 53
ACCESSORY TECHNOLOGIES CORPORATION—See HEICO Corporation; *U.S. Public*, pg. 1021
ACCESSO TECHNOLOGY GROUP PLC; *Int'l*, pg. 89
ACCESS OVERHEAD DOOR, INC.; *U.S. Private*, pg. 52
ACCESS PENSION FUND CUSTODIAN LIMITED—See FBN Holdings PLC; *Int'l*, pg. 2627
ACCESS PLANS, INC.—See Aon plc; *Int'l*, pg. 489
ACCESS PLANS USA, INC.—See Aon plc; *Int'l*, pg. 489
ACCESS POINT INC.—See GTT Communications, Inc.; *U.S. Private*, pg. 1808
ACCESS POINT LLC—See Management Recruiters International, Inc.; *U.S. Private*, pg. 2560
ACCESSPOINT—See Brand Innovation Group; *U.S. Private*, pg. 637
ACCESS POINT TECHNOLOGIES, LLC—See Wasatch Advantage Group, LLC; *U.S. Private*, pg. 4445
ACCESS-POWER, INC.; *U.S. Private*, pg. 53
ACCESS PUBLISHING CO. LTD.—See Access Co., Ltd.; *Int'l*, pg. 88
ACCESS QUALITY CARE SERVICES—See Chenega Corporation; *U.S. Private*, pg. 872
ACCESS RESPIRATORY HOME CARE, LLC—See Quipt Home Medical Corp.; *U.S. Public*, pg. 1757
ACCESS SCIENTIFIC, LLC—See ICU Medical, Inc.; *U.S. Public*, pg. 1087
ACCESS SEOUL CO. LTD—See Access Co., Ltd.; *Int'l*, pg. 88
ACCESS SERVICES (HK) LIMITED—See Hargreaves Services plc; *Int'l*, pg. 3275
ACCESS SOLUTIONS BELGIUM B.V.—See Carrier Global Corporation; *U.S. Public*, pg. 440
ACCESS; *U.S. Private*, pg. 50
ACCESS SYSTEMS FRANCE SARL—See Access Co., Ltd.; *Int'l*, pg. 88
ACCESS SYSTEMS INC.—See Computer Sites Inc.; *U.S. Private*, pg. 1005
ACCESS SYSTEMS, INC.; *U.S. Private*, pg. 52
ACCESS SYSTEMS USA, INC.—See Access Co., Ltd.; *Int'l*, pg. 88
ACCESS TAIWAN LAB CO., LTD.—See Access Co., Ltd.; *Int'l*, pg. 88
ACCESS TCA INC.; *U.S. Private*, pg. 52
ACCESS TECHNOLOGY GROUP LIMITED; *Int'l*, pg. 89
ACCESS TECHNOLOGY SOLUTIONS, LC; *U.S. Private*, pg. 53
ACCESS TELEVISION NETWORK; *U.S. Private*, pg. 53
ACCESS (UK) EDUCATION LIMITED—See China Financial Services Holdings Limited; *Int'l*, pg. 1502
ACCESS USA SHIPPING, LLC—See Aramex PJSC; *Int'l*, pg. 535
ACCESS US OIL AND GAS INC.; *U.S. Private*, pg. 53
ACCESS VALUE INVESTORS LLC; *U.S. Private*, pg. 53
THE ACCESS WORKS, INC.—See Fleet Engineers, Inc.; *U.S. Public*, pg. 1541
ACCESS WORLD AG; *Int'l*, pg. 89
ACCESS WORLDWIDE COMMUNICATIONS, INC. - AUGUSTA—See Access Worldwide Communications, Inc.; *U.S. Public*, pg. 32
ACCESS WORLDWIDE COMMUNICATIONS, INC.; *U.S. Public*, pg. 32
ACCESS WORLDWIDE, INC.—See Passport Global Inc.; *U.S. Private*, pg. 3104
ACC GERMANY GMBH—See Guangzhou Wanbao Group Co., Ltd.; *Int'l*, pg. 3168
ACC HOLDING, INC.; *U.S. Private*, pg. 47
ACCIAI DELLA SAAR SPA—See Saarstahl AG; *Int'l*, pg. 6461
ACCIAIERIE DI SICILIA S.P.A.—See Alfa Acciai SpA; *Int'l*, pg. 307

COMPANY NAME INDEX — ACCORD SYNERGY LTD.

ACCIAIERIE VALBRUNA S.P.A. - BOLZANO PLANT—See Acciaierie Valbruna S.p.A.; *Int'l*, pg. 89
ACCIAIERIE VALBRUNA S.P.A.; *Int'l*, pg. 89
ACCIAI SPECIALI TERNI S.P.A.—See ThyssenKrupp AG; *Int'l*, pg. 7729
ACCIDENT EXCHANGE GROUP PLC; *Int'l*, pg. 90
ACCIDENT EXCHANGE LIMITED—See Accident Exchange Group Plc; *Int'l*, pg. 90
ACCIDENT FUND HOLDINGS, INC.—See Blue Cross Blue Shield of Michigan; *U.S. Private*, pg. 587
ACCIDENT FUND INSURANCE COMPANY OF AMERICA; *U.S. Private*, pg. 53
ACCIDENT & HEALTH UNDERWRITING LTD.—See White Mountains Insurance Group, Ltd.; *U.S. Public*, pg. 2368
ACCIDENT REPAIR MANAGEMENT PTY LTD—See AMA Group Limited; *Int'l*, pg. 403
ACCIDENTS HAPPEN ASSISTANCE LIMITED—See WNS (Holdings) Limited; *Int'l*, pg. 8441
ACC INDUSTRIES INCORPORATED; *U.S. Private*, pg. 47
AC&C INTERNATIONAL CO., LTD.; *Int'l*, pg. 74
ACCIONA AGUA, S.A.—See Acciona, S.A.; *Int'l*, pg. 90
ACCIONA AIRPORT SERVICES, S.A.—See Acciona, S.A.; *Int'l*, pg. 90
ACCIONA APARCAMIENTOS, S.L.—See Acciona, S.A.; *Int'l*, pg. 90
ACCIONA CONCESIONES, S.L.—See Acciona, S.A.; *Int'l*, pg. 90
ACCIONA DO BRASIL, LTDA—See Acciona, S.A.; *Int'l*, pg. 90
ACCIONA ENERGIA, S.A.—See Acciona, S.A.; *Int'l*, pg. 90
ACCIONA ENERGY GLOBAL POLAND SP. Z.O.O.—See Acciona, S.A.; *Int'l*, pg. 90
ACCIONA ENERGY USA GLOBAL LLC—See Acciona, S.A.; *Int'l*, pg. 90
ACCIONA FACILITY SERVICES, S.A.—See Acciona, S.A.; *Int'l*, pg. 90
ACCIONA FACILITY SERVICES SUR, S.A.—See Acciona, S.A.; *Int'l*, pg. 90
ACCIONA INFRAESTRUCTURAS, S.A.—See Acciona, S.A.; *Int'l*, pg. 90
ACCIONA INMOBILIARIA, S.L.—See Acciona, S.A.; *Int'l*, pg. 90
ACCIONA LOGISTICA, S.A.—See Acciona, S.A.; *Int'l*, pg. 90
ACCIONA MEDIO AMBIENTE—See Acciona, S.A.; *Int'l*, pg. 90
ACCIONA NIERUCHOMOSCI SP. Z O.O.—See Acciona, S.A.; *Int'l*, pg. 90
ACCIONA, S.A.; *Int'l*, pg. 90
ACCIONA SOLAR, S.A.—See Acciona, S.A.; *Int'l*, pg. 90
ACCIONES Y VALORES BANAMEX, S.A. DE C.V.—See Citigroup Inc.; *U.S. Public*, pg. 504
ACCION LABS US, INC.—See TA Associates, Inc.; *U.S. Private*, pg. 3914
ACCION SOCIAL DE PUERTO RICO, INC.; *U.S. Private*, pg. 53
ACCIPITER HOLDINGS DESIGNATED ACTIVITY COMPANY—See CK Asset Holdings Limited; *Int'l*, pg. 1635
ACCLAIM GAMES, INC.—See The Walt Disney Company; *U.S. Public*, pg. 2139
ACCLAIM INVESTMENT LIMITED—See Tsim Sha Tsui Properties Limited; *Int'l*, pg. 7951
ACCLAIM TECHNICAL SERVICES—See Blue Delta Capital Partners LLC; *U.S. Private*, pg. 588
ACCLARA SOLUTIONS, LLC—See R1 RCM Inc.; *U.S. Public*, pg. 1758
ACCLARENT, INC.—See Integra LifeSciences Holdings Corporation; *U.S. Public*, pg. 1135
ACCLARIS BUSINESS SOLUTIONS PRIVATE LTD—See Willis Towers Watson Public Limited Company; *Int'l*, pg. 8414
ACCLARIS HOLDINGS, INC.—See Willis Towers Watson Public Limited Company; *Int'l*, pg. 8414
ACCLARIS, INC.—See Willis Towers Watson Public Limited Company; *Int'l*, pg. 8414
ACC LICENSEE, LLC—See Sinclair, Inc.; *U.S. Public*, pg. 1885
ACCLIME; *Int'l*, pg. 90
ACC LIMITED - BACHUPALLY PLANT—See ACC Limited; *Int'l*, pg. 78
ACC LIMITED - BARGARH CEMENT WORKS—See ACC Limited; *Int'l*, pg. 78
ACC LIMITED - CHANDA CEMENT WORKS—See ACC Limited; *Int'l*, pg. 78
ACC LIMITED - CHANGODAR PLANT—See ACC Limited; *Int'l*, pg. 78
ACC LIMITED - DAMODHAR CEMENT WORKS—See ACC Limited; *Int'l*, pg. 78
ACC LIMITED - GHAZIABAD CONCRETE PLANT—See ACC Limited; *Int'l*, pg. 78
ACC LIMITED - GREATER NOIDA CONCRETE PLANT—See ACC Limited; *Int'l*, pg. 78
ACC LIMITED - JAIPUR PLANT—See ACC Limited; *Int'l*, pg. 79
ACC LIMITED - JAMUL CEMENT WORKS—See ACC Limited; *Int'l*, pg. 79
ACC LIMITED - KUNDALI PLANT—See ACC Limited; *Int'l*, pg. 79
ACC LIMITED - KYMORE CEMENT WORKS—See ACC Limited; *Int'l*, pg. 79
ACC LIMITED - LAKHERI CEMENT WORKS—See ACC Limited; *Int'l*, pg. 79
ACC LIMITED - LUDHIANA PLANT—See ACC Limited; *Int'l*, pg. 79
ACC LIMITED - MANDOLI PLANT—See ACC Limited; *Int'l*, pg. 79
ACC LIMITED - MOHALI PLANT—See ACC Limited; *Int'l*, pg. 79
ACC LIMITED - PATANCHERU PLANT—See ACC Limited; *Int'l*, pg. 79
ACC LIMITED - RAJARHAT PLANT—See ACC Limited; *Int'l*, pg. 79
ACC LIMITED - RAVIRALA PLANT—See ACC Limited; *Int'l*, pg. 79
ACC LIMITED; *Int'l*, pg. 78
ACC LIMITED - TIKARIA CEMENT GRINDING AND PACKING PLANT—See ACC Limited; *Int'l*, pg. 79
ACC LIMITED - VADODARA FRANCHISEE PLANT—See ACC Limited; *Int'l*, pg. 79
ACC LOAN MANAGEMENT DAC—See Capita plc; *Int'l*, pg. 1308
ACC MINERAL RESOURCES LIMITED—See ACC Limited; *Int'l*, pg. 79
ACCO ASIA LIMITED—See ACCO Brands Corporation; *U.S. Public*, pg. 32
ACCOAT A/S—See SP Group A/S; *Int'l*, pg. 7122
ACCO AUSTRALIA PTY. LTD.—See ACCO Brands Corporation; *U.S. Public*, pg. 32
ACCO BRANDS AUSTRALIA HOLDING PTY LTD—See ACCO Brands Corporation; *U.S. Public*, pg. 32
ACCO BRANDS CANADA INC.—See ACCO Brands Corporation; *U.S. Public*, pg. 32
ACCO BRANDS CORPORATION; *U.S. Public*, pg. 32
ACCO BRANDS ITALIA S.R.L.—See ACCO Brands Corporation; *U.S. Public*, pg. 33
ACCO BRANDS JAPAN K.K.—See ACCO Brands Corporation; *U.S. Public*, pg. 32
ACCO BRANDS NEW ZEALAND LIMITED—See ACCO Brands Corporation; *U.S. Public*, pg. 32
ACCO BRANDS PORTUGUESA LDA—See ACCO Brands Corporation; *U.S. Public*, pg. 32
ACCO ENGINEERED SYSTEMS; *U.S. Private*, pg. 53
ACCO EUROPE LIMITED—See ACCO Brands Corporation; *U.S. Public*, pg. 32
AC COIN & SLOT SERVICE COMPANY; *U.S. Private*, pg. 45
ACCO INTERNATIONAL HOLDINGS, INC.—See ACCO Brands Corporation; *U.S. Public*, pg. 32
ACCOLADE FINLAND OY—See Apollo Global Management, Inc.; *U.S. Public*, pg. 165
ACCOLADE FRANCE SAS—See Apollo Global Management, Inc.; *U.S. Public*, pg. 165
ACCOLADE, INC.; *U.S. Public*, pg. 33
ACCOLADE WINES AUSTRALIA LIMITED—See The Carlyle Group Inc.; *U.S. Public*, pg. 2044
ACCOLADE WINES AUSTRALIA LTD. - BOTANY—See The Carlyle Group Inc.; *U.S. Public*, pg. 2044
ACCOLADE WINES AUSTRALIA LTD. - MOUNT WAVERLEY—See The Carlyle Group Inc.; *U.S. Public*, pg. 2044
ACCOLADE WINES HOLDINGS AUSTRALIA PTY LIMITED—See The Carlyle Group Inc.; *U.S. Public*, pg. 2043
ACCOLADE WINES HOLDINGS EUROPE LIMITED—See The Carlyle Group Inc.; *U.S. Public*, pg. 2044
ACCOLADE WINES JAPAN K.K.—See The Carlyle Group Inc.; *U.S. Public*, pg. 2044
ACCOLADE WINES LIMITED—See The Carlyle Group Inc.; *U.S. Public*, pg. 2044
ACCOLADE WINES NEW ZEALAND LIMITED—See The Carlyle Group Inc.; *U.S. Public*, pg. 2044
ACCOLADE WINES SOUTH AFRICA (PTY) LTD.—See The Carlyle Group Inc.; *U.S. Public*, pg. 2044
ACCOLITE, INC.—See New Mountain Capital, LLC; *U.S. Private*, pg. 2899
ACCOLO, INC.; *U.S. Private*, pg. 53
ACCO MATERIAL HANDLING SOLUTIONS, INC. - NUTTING DIVISION—See KKR & Co. Inc.; *U.S. Public*, pg. 1239
ACCO MATERIAL HANDLING SOLUTIONS, INC.—See KKR & Co. Inc.; *U.S. Public*, pg. 1239
ACCOMMATE CO., LTD.—See NHN Corp.; *Int'l*, pg. 5258
ACCOMMODATION MOLLEN, INC.—See Bain Capital, LP; *U.S. Private*, pg. 440
ACCONEER AB; *Int'l*, pg. 90
ACCOR ACQUISITION COMPANY S.A.; *Int'l*, pg. 90
ACCOR AUSTRIA AG—See Accor S.A.; *Int'l*, pg. 91
ACCOR BRASIL SA—See Accor S.A.; *Int'l*, pg. 91
ACCOR BUSINESS & LEISURE NORTH AMERICA INC.—See Accor S.A.; *Int'l*, pg. 91
ACCOR CANADA INC.—See Accor S.A.; *Int'l*, pg. 91
ACCOR CASINOS—See Accor S.A.; *Int'l*, pg. 91
ACCOR CENTRE DE CONTACTS CLIENTS—See Accor S.A.; *Int'l*, pg. 91
ACCORDANT HEALTH SERVICES, INC.—See CVS Health Corporation; *U.S. Public*, pg. 613
ACCORD CAPX LLC—See Accord Financial Corp.; *Int'l*, pg. 92
ACCORD CUSTOMER CARE SOLUTIONS FZ CO.—See mDR Limited; *Int'l*, pg. 4762
ACCORD CUSTOMER CARE SOLUTIONS (M) SDN BHD—See mDR Limited; *Int'l*, pg. 4761
ACCORD CUSTOMER CARE SOLUTIONS (NSW) PTY. LTD.—See mDR Limited; *Int'l*, pg. 4761
ACCORD CUSTOMER CARE SOLUTIONS (SA) PTY LTD—See mDR Limited; *Int'l*, pg. 4762
ACCORD ENERGY LTD.—See Centrica plc; *Int'l*, pg. 1413
ACCORD FARMA S.A. DE C.V.—See Intas Pharmaceuticals Ltd.; *Int'l*, pg. 3727
ACCORD FINANCE S.A.—See Auchan Holding S.A.; *Int'l*, pg. 699
ACCORD FINANCIAL CORP.; *Int'l*, pg. 92
ACCORD FINANCIAL GROUP INC.; *U.S. Private*, pg. 53
ACCORD FINANCIAL INC.—See Accord Financial Corp.; *Int'l*, pg. 92
ACCORD FINANCIAL, INC.—See Accord Financial Corp.; *Int'l*, pg. 92
ACCORD GMBH—See Intas Pharmaceuticals Ltd.; *Int'l*, pg. 3727
ACCORD GROUP LIMITED; *Int'l*, pg. 93
ACCORD HEALTHCARE AB—See Intas Pharmaceuticals Ltd.; *Int'l*, pg. 3728
ACCORD HEALTHCARE BVBA—See Intas Pharmaceuticals Ltd.; *Int'l*, pg. 3728
ACCORD HEALTHCARE B.V.—See Intas Pharmaceuticals Ltd.; *Int'l*, pg. 3728
ACCORD HEALTHCARE FRANCE SAS—See Intas Pharmaceuticals Ltd.; *Int'l*, pg. 3728
ACCORD HEALTHCARE GMBH—See Intas Pharmaceuticals Ltd.; *Int'l*, pg. 3728
ACCORD HEALTHCARE INC.—See Intas Pharmaceuticals Ltd.; *Int'l*, pg. 3727
ACCORD HEALTHCARE IRELAND, LTD.—See Intas Pharmaceuticals Ltd.; *Int'l*, pg. 3727
ACCORD HEALTHCARE ITALIA S.R.L.—See Intas Pharmaceuticals Ltd.; *Int'l*, pg. 3728
ACCORD HEALTHCARE (KENYA) LTD.—See Intas Pharmaceuticals Ltd.; *Int'l*, pg. 3727
ACCORD HEALTHCARE LTD.—See Intas Pharmaceuticals Ltd.; *Int'l*, pg. 3727
ACCORD HEALTHCARE OU—See Intas Pharmaceuticals Ltd.; *Int'l*, pg. 3728
ACCORD HEALTHCARE OY—See Intas Pharmaceuticals Ltd.; *Int'l*, pg. 3728
ACCORD HEALTHCARE POLSKA SP. Z O.O.—See Intas Pharmaceuticals Ltd.; *Int'l*, pg. 3728
ACCORD HEALTHCARE PTY LTD.—See Intas Pharmaceuticals Ltd.; *Int'l*, pg. 3728
ACCORD HEALTHCARE S.A.C.—See Intas Pharmaceuticals Ltd.; *Int'l*, pg. 3728
ACCORD HEALTHCARE SA—See Intas Pharmaceuticals Ltd.; *Int'l*, pg. 3728
ACCORD HEALTHCARE, S.L.U.—See Intas Pharmaceuticals Ltd.; *Int'l*, pg. 3728
ACCORD HUMAN RESOURCES, INC.—See Virgo Capital; *U.S. Private*, pg. 4388
ACCORDIA GOLF CO., LTD.—See MBK Partners Ltd.; *Int'l*, pg. 4753
ACCORDIA GOLF TRUST; *Int'l*, pg. 93
ACCORDIA LIFE AND ANNUITY COMPANY—See KKR & Co. Inc.; *U.S. Public*, pg. 1251
ACCORD INC.; *U.S. Private*, pg. 53
ACCORD INDUSTRIES LLC; *U.S. Private*, pg. 53
ACCORDION PARTNERS LLC; *U.S. Private*, pg. 53
ACCORD LEASING LLC—See Accord Financial Group Inc.; *U.S. Private*, pg. 53
ACCORD LIFT SERVICES LTD.—See CNIM Constructions Industrielles de la Mediterranee SA; *Int'l*, pg. 1676
ACCORD PHARMACEUTICALS LTD—See Intas Pharmaceuticals Ltd.; *Int'l*, pg. 3728
ACCORD SMALL BUSINESS FINANCE CORP—See Accord Financial Corp.; *Int'l*, pg. 92
ACCORD SYNERGY LTD.; *Int'l*, pg. 93
ACCORD SYSTEM CO., LTD.—See Core Corporation; *Int'l*, pg. 1797
ACCORD WATCH & JEWELLERY (INTERNATIONAL) LIMITED—See Asia Commercial Holdings Limited; *Int'l*, pg. 611
ACCOR GESTION MAROC SA—See Accor S.A.; *Int'l*, pg. 91
ACCOR GMBH—See Accor S.A.; *Int'l*, pg. 91
ACCOR HOSPITALITY ARGENTINA SA—See Accor S.A.; *Int'l*, pg. 91
ACCOR HOSPITALITY GERMANY GMBH—See Accor S.A.; *Int'l*, pg. 91
ACCOR HOSPITALITY NEDERLAND B.V.—See Accor S.A.; *Int'l*, pg. 91
ACCOR HOTELES ESPANA S.A.—See Accor S.A.; *Int'l*, pg. 91
ACCOR HOTELS BELGIUM NV—See Accor S.A.; *Int'l*, pg. 91
ACCOR HOTELS ROMANIA S.R.L.—See Accor S.A.; *Int'l*, pg. 91
ACCOR NORTH AMERICA, INC.—See Accor S.A.; *Int'l*, pg. 91

AC CORPORATION
CORPORATE AFFILIATIONS

AC CORPORATION; *U.S. Private*, pg. 45
ACCOR RESERVATION—See Accor S.A.; *Int'l*, pg. 91
ACCOR S.A.; *Int'l*, pg. 91
ACCOR UK ECONOMY HOTELS LIMITED—See Accor S.A.; *Int'l*, pg. 91
ACCOR (U.K.) LIMITED—See Accor S.A.; *Int'l*, pg. 91
ACCOTEST TECHNOLOGY (MALAYSIA) SDN. BHD.—See Beijing Huafeng Test & Control Technology Co., Ltd.; *Int'l*, pg. 952
ACCO UK LIMITED—See ACCO Brands Corporation; *U.S. Public*, pg. 32
ACCOUNTABILIT, LLC—See WestView Capital Partners, L.P.; *U.S. Private*, pg. 4501
ACCOUNTABILITY OUTSOURCING, INC.; *U.S. Private*, pg. 54
ACCOUNTABLE CARE COALITION OF COMMUNITY HEALTH CENTERS, LLC—See Centene Corporation; *U.S. Public*, pg. 471
ACCOUNTABLE CARE COALITION OF DEKALB, LLC—See Centene Corporation; *U.S. Public*, pg. 471
ACCOUNTABLE CARE COALITION OF SOUTHEAST TEXAS, INC.—See Centene Corporation; *U.S. Public*, pg. 471
THE ACCOUNTABLE CARE ORGANIZATION LTD.—See Evolent Health, Inc.; *U.S. Public*, pg. 804
ACCOUNTABLE HEALTHCARE HOLDINGS CORP.—See Mitsui & Co., Ltd.; *Int'l*, pg. 4973
ACCOUNTABLE HEALTHCARE STAFFING, INC. - PHOENIX—See Mitsui & Co., Ltd.; *Int'l*, pg. 4973
ACCOUNTANTS IN TRANSITION, INC.; *U.S. Private*, pg. 54
ACCOUNTAX CONSULTING LIMITED—See Markel Group Inc.; *U.S. Public*, pg. 1367
ACCOUNT CONTROL TECHNOLOGY HOLDINGS, INC.—See Platinum Equity, LLC; *U.S. Private*, pg. 3209
ACCOUNT CONTROL TECHNOLOGY, INC.—See Platinum Equity, LLC; *U.S. Private*, pg. 3209
ACCOUNTFULLY LLC; *U.S. Private*, pg. 54
ACCOUNTING EQUIPMENT CORP.; *U.S. Private*, pg. 54
ACCOUNTING MANAGEMENT SOLUTIONS, INC.; *U.S. Private*, pg. 54
ACCOUNTING PRINCIPALS INC.—See Adecco Group AG; *Int'l*, pg. 136
ACCOUNTING SYSTEMS, INC.—See Eide Bailly LLP; *U.S. Private*, pg. 1347
ACCOUNTNOW, INC.; *U.S. Private*, pg. 54
ACCOUNTPLAN PTY LIMITED—See Insignia Financial Ltd.; *Int'l*, pg. 3718
ACCOUNT RECOVERY SPECIALISTS, INC. (ARSI); *U.S. Private*, pg. 53
ACCRA BREWERY LIMITED—See Anheuser-Busch InBev SA/NV; *Int'l*, pg. 464
ACCRA CARE; *U.S. Private*, pg. 54
ACCRA-FAB INC.; *U.S. Private*, pg. 54
ACCRA MANUFACTURING, INC.—See Berkshire Hathaway Inc.; *U.S. Public*, pg. 314
ACCRAM INC.; *U.S. Private*, pg. 54
ACCRAPLY CANADA, INC.—See Barry-Wehmiller Companies, Inc.; *U.S. Private*, pg. 481
ACCRAPLY, INC.—See Barry-Wehmiller Companies, Inc.; *U.S. Private*, pg. 481
ACCRAPLY, INC.—See Barry-Wehmiller Companies, Inc.; *U.S. Private*, pg. 481
ACCREATE LIMITED—See Premier Recruitment (International) Unlimited Company; *Int'l*, pg. 5961
ACCREDITED DISTRIBUTORS PTY. LTD.; *Int'l*, pg. 93
ACCREDITED GROUP AGENCY, INC.—See R&Q Insurance Holdings Ltd.; *Int'l*, pg. 6168
ACCREDITED HEALTH SERVICES, INC.—See Blue Wolf Capital Partners LLC; *U.S. Private*, pg. 595
ACCREDITED HOLDING CORPORATION—See R&Q Insurance Holdings Ltd.; *Int'l*, pg. 6168
ACCREDITED HOME ELEVATOR, INC.—See Aldine Capital Partners, Inc.; *U.S. Private*, pg. 159
ACCREDITED HOME ELEVATOR, INC.—See Stoic Holdings LLC; *U.S. Private*, pg. 3816
ACCREDITED INSURANCE HOLDINGS INC.—See R&Q Insurance Holdings Ltd.; *Int'l*, pg. 6168
ACCREDITED SOLUTIONS, INC.; *U.S. Public*, pg. 33
ACCREDITED SURETY AND CASUALTY COMPANY INC.—See R&Q Insurance Holdings Ltd.; *Int'l*, pg. 6168
ACCREDITING COUNCIL FOR INDEPENDENT COLLEGES AND SCHOOLS; *U.S. Private*, pg. 54
ACCREDO CARE NETWORK, INC.—See The Cigna Group; *U.S. Public*, pg. 2062
ACCREDO HEALTH GROUP, INC.—See The Cigna Group; *U.S. Public*, pg. 2062
ACCREDO HEALTH, INCORPORATED—See The Cigna Group; *U.S. Public*, pg. 2062
ACCRELIST A.I. TECH PTE. LTD.—See Accrelist Ltd.; *Int'l*, pg. 93
ACCRELIST CROWDFUNDING PTE. LTD.—See Accrelist Ltd.; *Int'l*, pg. 93
ACCRELIST LTD.; *Int'l*, pg. 93
ACCRELIST MEDICAL AESTHETICS (BM) PTE. LTD.—See Accrelist Ltd.; *Int'l*, pg. 93

ACCRELIST MEDICAL AESTHETICS (CENTRAL-LARKE QUAY) PTE. LTD.—See Accrelist Ltd.; *Int'l*, pg. 93
ACCRELIST MEDICAL AESTHETICS (CM) PTE. LTD.—See Accrelist Ltd.; *Int'l*, pg. 93
ACCRELIST MEDICAL AESTHETICS (LOT1) PTE. LTD.—See Accrelist Ltd.; *Int'l*, pg. 93
ACCRELIST MEDICAL AESTHETICS (ORCHARD CENTRAL) PTE. LTD.—See Accrelist Ltd.; *Int'l*, pg. 93
ACCRELIST MEDICAL AESTHETICS (PENANG) SDN. BHD.—See Accrelist Ltd.; *Int'l*, pg. 93
ACCRELIST MEDICAL AESTHETICS (RAFFLES CITY) PTE. LTD.—See Accrelist Ltd.; *Int'l*, pg. 93
ACCRELIST MEDICAL AESTHETICS (SPC) PTE. LTD.—See Accrelist Ltd.; *Int'l*, pg. 93
ACCRETECH ADAMAS (THAILAND) CO., LTD.—See Tokyo Seimitsu Co., Ltd.; *Int'l*, pg. 7795
ACCRETECH AMERICA INC.—See Tokyo Seimitsu Co., Ltd.; *Int'l*, pg. 7795
ACCRETECH (CHINA) CO., LTD.—See Tokyo Seimitsu Co., Ltd.; *Int'l*, pg. 7795
ACCRETECH CREATE CORP.—See Tokyo Seimitsu Co., Ltd.; *Int'l*, pg. 7795
ACCRETECH (EUROPE) GMBH—See Tokyo Seimitsu Co., Ltd.; *Int'l*, pg. 7795
ACCRETECH FINANCE CO., LTD.—See Tokyo Seimitsu Co., Ltd.; *Int'l*, pg. 7795
ACCRETECH KOREA CO., LTD.—See Tokyo Seimitsu Co., Ltd.; *Int'l*, pg. 7795
ACCRETECH (MALAYSIA) SDN. BHD.—See Tokyo Seimitsu Co., Ltd.; *Int'l*, pg. 7795
ACCRETECH POWERTRO SYSTEM CO., LTD.—See Tokyo Seimitsu Co., Ltd.; *Int'l*, pg. 7795
ACCRETECH SBS INC.—See Tokyo Seimitsu Co., Ltd.; *Int'l*, pg. 7795
ACCRETECH-SBS UK LTD.—See Tokyo Seimitsu Co., Ltd.; *Int'l*, pg. 7795
ACCRETECH (SINGAPORE) PTE. LTD.—See Tokyo Seimitsu Co., Ltd.; *Int'l*, pg. 7795
ACCRETECH TAIWAN CO., LTD.—See Tokyo Seimitsu Co., Ltd.; *Int'l*, pg. 7795
ACCRETECH (THAILAND) CO., LTD.—See Tokyo Seimitsu Co., Ltd.; *Int'l*, pg. 7795
ACCRETECH-TOSEI DO BRASIL LTDA.—See Tokyo Seimitsu Co., Ltd.; *Int'l*, pg. 7795
ACCRETECH-TOSEI HUNGARY KFT.—See Tokyo Seimitsu Co., Ltd.; *Int'l*, pg. 7795
ACCRETECH VIETNAM CO., LTD.—See Tokyo Seimitsu Co., Ltd.; *Int'l*, pg. 7795
ACCRETE, INC.; *Int'l*, pg. 93
ACCRETION ACQUISITION CORP.; *U.S. Public*, pg. 33
ACCRETIVE CO., LTD.—See Fuyo General Lease Co., Ltd.; *Int'l*, pg. 2859
ACCRINGTON VETS4PETS LIMITED—See Pets at Home Group Plc; *Int'l*, pg. 5833
ACCRIVA DIAGNOSTICS, INC.—See Werfen Life Group, S.A.U.; *Int'l*, pg. 8379
ACCROFAB HOLDINGS LIMITED—See Endless LLP; *Int'l*, pg. 2403
ACCROL GROUP HOLDINGS PLC—See SODIM, SGPS, SA; *Int'l*, pg. 7049
ACCROTOOL, INC.; *U.S. Private*, pg. 54
ACCRUENT, LLC—See Fortive Corporation; *U.S. Public*, pg. 870
ACCRUEPARTNERS, INC.; *U.S. Private*, pg. 54
ACCRUIT HOLDINGS LLC—See ABRY Partners, LLC; *U.S. Private*, pg. 42
ACC SILICONES LTD.—See Akoya Capital LLC; *U.S. Private*, pg. 146
ACC SILICONES LTD.—See Century Park Capital Partners, LLC; *U.S. Private*, pg. 833
ACCSYS LLC—See PAR Technology Corporation; *U.S. Public*, pg. 1636
ACCSYS (PROPRIETARY) LIMITED—See Business Connexion Group Limited; *Int'l*, pg. 1228
ACCSYS TECHNOLOGIES PLC; *Int'l*, pg. 93
ACCSYS TECHNOLOGY, INC.—See Hitachi, Ltd.; *Int'l*, pg. 3413
ACCTAX MANAGEMENT CONSULTANCY PRIVATE LIMITED—See Medinex Limited; *Int'l*, pg. 4777
ACCTON TECHNOLOGY CORPORATION; *Int'l*, pg. 93
ACCTON TECHNOLOGY CORP—See Accton Technology Corporation; *Int'l*, pg. 93
ACC TOWER SUB, LLC—See American Tower Corporation; *U.S. Public*, pg. 110
ACCTTWO SHARED SERVICES, LLC; *U.S. Private*, pg. 54
ACCUAIR CONTROL SYSTEMS LLC—See MidOcean Partners, LP; *U.S. Private*, pg. 2716
ACCUBUILT ACQUISITION HOLDINGS INC.; *U.S. Private*, pg. 54
ACCUBUILT INC.—See Accubuilt Acquisition Holdings Inc.; *U.S. Private*, pg. 54
ACCUCAPS INDUSTRIES LIMITED—See Catalent, Inc.; *U.S. Public*, pg. 448
ACCU-CAST INC.—See UCA Group Component Specialty Inc.; *U.S. Private*, pg. 4273
ACCUCODE, INC.; *U.S. Private*, pg. 54
ACCUCOMP, LLC; *U.S. Private*, pg. 54

ACCU COPY OF GREENVILLE, INC.—See Taylor Corporation; *U.S. Private*, pg. 3939
ACCUDATA HOLDINGS, INC.—See Compact Information Systems, Inc.; *U.S. Private*, pg. 998
ACCUDATA TECHNOLOGIES; *U.S. Private*, pg. 54
ACCUDRILL L. L. C.—See Schoeller-Bleckmann Oilfield Equipment AG; *Int'l*, pg. 6637
ACCUDUCT MANUFACTURING INC.; *U.S. Private*, pg. 54
ACCUDYNAMICS LLC—See Halma plc; *Int'l*, pg. 3231
ACCUDYNE INDUSTRIES ASIA PTE. LTD.—See BC Partners LLP; *Int'l*, pg. 922
ACCUDYNE INDUSTRIES ASIA PTE. LTD.—See The Carlyle Group Inc.; *U.S. Public*, pg. 2044
ACCUDYNE INDUSTRIES, LLC—See BC Partners LLP; *Int'l*, pg. 922
ACCUDYNE INDUSTRIES, LLC—See The Carlyle Group Inc.; *U.S. Public*, pg. 2044
ACCUFAS LAB CENTER COMPANY LIMITED—See Intermedical Care & Lab Hospital Public Company Limited; *Int'l*, pg. 3743
ACCUFIX RESEARCH INSTITUTE INC.—See Ansell Limited; *Int'l*, pg. 478
ACCUFLEX INDUSTRIAL HOSE, LTD.—See Kuriyama Holdings Corporation; *Int'l*, pg. 4341
ACCUFLEX INDUSTRIAL HOSE, LTD.—See Kuriyama Holdings Corporation; *Int'l*, pg. 4341
ACCUFORM MANUFACTURING, INC.; *U.S. Private*, pg. 54
ACCUFUND INC.—See i3 Verticals, Inc.; *U.S. Public*, pg. 1081
ACCUGEAR, INC.—See American Axle & Manufacturing Holdings, Inc.; *U.S. Public*, pg. 96
ACCUGENIX, INC.—See Charles River Laboratories International, Inc.; *U.S. Public*, pg. 479
ACCUHEALTH TECHNOLOGIES LLC—See Sunstone Partners Management LLC; *U.S. Private*, pg. 3873
ACCU HOLDING AG; *Int'l*, pg. 94
ACCUITY INC.—See RELX plc; *Int'l*, pg. 6266
ACCU-LUBE MANUFACTURING GMBH—See Illinois Tool Works Inc.; *U.S. Public*, pg. 1101
ACCULYNK, INC.—See Fiserv, Inc.; *U.S. Public*, pg. 850
ACCUMA CORPORATION; *U.S. Private*, pg. 55
ACCUMARK COMMUNICATIONS, INC.—See Stagwell, Inc.; *U.S. Public*, pg. 1925
ACCUMARK PARTNERS INC—See Stagwell, Inc.; *U.S. Public*, pg. 1925
ACCUMED CORPORATION—See Lear Corporation; *U.S. Public*, pg. 1296
ACCUMEN, INC.—See Arsenal Capital Management LP; *U.S. Private*, pg. 337
ACCUMETRIC LLC—See Soudal NV; *Int'l*, pg. 7113
ACCUMETRIC SILICONES PRIVATE LIMITED—See Soudal NV; *Int'l*, pg. 7113
ACCUMETRICS, INC.—See Amphenol Corporation; *U.S. Public*, pg. 130
ACCU-MOLD, LLC—See Pokagon Band of Potawatomi Indians; *U.S. Private*, pg. 3223
ACCUMULI LIMITED—See NCC Group Plc; *Int'l*, pg. 5180
ACCUNET SOLUTIONS—See Red River Computer Co., Inc.; *U.S. Private*, pg. 3375
ACCUPAC, INC.—See Palladium Equity Partners, LLC; *U.S. Private*, pg. 3077
ACCUQUEST HEARING CENTER LLC—See Demant A/S; *Int'l*, pg. 2022
ACCUQUILT, LLC—See WILsquare Capital LLC; *U.S. Private*, pg. 4532
ACCUQUOTE; *U.S. Private*, pg. 55
ACCURACY SAS—See Aon plc; *Int'l*, pg. 488
ACCURACY SHIPPING LIMITED; *Int'l*, pg. 94
ACCURACY SRL—See Aon plc; *Int'l*, pg. 488
ACCURA GROUP LIMITED—See Wright Industries Ltd.; *Int'l*, pg. 8494
ACCURA MACHINERY & MANUFACTURING (TAICANG) CO., LTD.; *Int'l*, pg. 94
ACCURASEA SAS—See Shell plc; *Int'l*, pg. 6794
ACCURA.S.R.L.—See GPI S.p.A.; *Int'l*, pg. 3046
ACCURATE AIR ENGINEERING INCORPORATED—See Atlas Copco AB; *Int'l*, pg. 680
ACCURATE AUTO PARTS, INC.—See Free Flow, Inc.; *U.S. Public*, pg. 884
ACCURATE BACKGROUND, INC.—See Boathouse Capital Management, LLC; *U.S. Private*, pg. 603
ACCURATE BOX COMPANY, INC.; *U.S. Private*, pg. 55
ACCURATE BRAZING CORPORATION—See Aalberts N.V.; *Int'l*, pg. 33
ACCURATE BUSHING COMPANY, INC.; *U.S. Private*, pg. 55
ACCURATE CASTINGS INC.—See Hiler Industries; *U.S. Private*, pg. 1944
ACCURATE CHEMICAL & SCIENTIFIC CORPORATION; *U.S. Private*, pg. 55
ACCURATE COMPONENT SALES - CEDAR RAPIDS—See MSC Industrial Direct Co., Inc.; *U.S. Public*, pg. 1483
ACCURATE COMPONENT SALES, INC.—See MSC Industrial Direct Co., Inc.; *U.S. Public*, pg. 1483
ACCURATE COMPUTER SOLUTIONS, LLC—See The 20 Msp Group LLC; *U.S. Private*, pg. 3980

COMPANY NAME INDEX

ACCURATE ELASTOMER PRODUCTS; *U.S. Private,* pg. 55
ACCURATE ENGINEERING INC.—See Austin Engineering Co. Ltd.; *Int'l,* pg. 718
ACCURATE FORMING LLC; *U.S. Private,* pg. 55
ACCURATE GROUP; *U.S. Private,* pg. 55
ACCURATE HOME CARE, LLC; *U.S. Private,* pg. 55
ACCURATE INC.—See Advanex Inc.; *Int'l,* pg. 163
ACCURATE INSULATION LLC—See Installed Building Products, Inc.; *U.S. Public,* pg. 1132
ACCURATE LUBRICANTS & METALWORKING FLUIDS, INC.; *U.S. Private,* pg. 55
ACCURATE METAL FABRICATING—See Accurate Perforating Company, Inc.; *U.S. Private,* pg. 55
ACCURATE METAL FABRICATORS, LLC; *U.S. Private,* pg. 55
ACCURATE METAL MACHINING CO., LTD.—See Sumitomo Electric Industries, Ltd.; *Int'l,* pg. 7285
ACCURATE METAL MACHINING, INC.—See HEICO Corporation; *U.S. Public,* pg. 1021
ACCURATE MOLDED PLASTICS INC.; *U.S. Private,* pg. 55
ACCURATE MOLD & PLASTICS CORP.—See Diversified Plastics Corporation; *U.S. Private,* pg. 1243
ACCURATE MOLD USA INC.—See Wentworth Technologies Co. Ltd.; *Int'l,* pg. 8377
ACCURATE PAPER HOLDINGS, LLC—See PT Sinar Mas Group; *Int'l,* pg. 6073
ACCURATE PARTITIONS CORP.—See ITR Industries Inc.; *U.S. Private,* pg. 2150
ACCURATE PERFORATING COMPANY, INC.; *U.S. Private,* pg. 55
ACCURATE PLASTICS INC.; *U.S. Private,* pg. 55
ACCURATE POLY SERVICES APS—See Mettler-Toledo International, Inc.; *U.S. Public,* pg. 1432
ACCURATE RX PHARMACY CONSULTING, LLC—See UnitedHealth Group Incorporated; *U.S. Public,* pg. 2247
ACCURATE SURGICAL & SCIENTIFIC INSTRUMENTS CORPORATION—See Accurate Chemical & Scientific Corporation; *U.S. Private,* pg. 55
ACCURAY EUROPE SAS—See Accuray Incorporated; *U.S. Public,* pg. 33
ACCURAY INCORPORATED; *U.S. Public,* pg. 33
ACCURAY JAPAN K.K.—See Accuray Incorporated; *U.S. Public,* pg. 33
ACCURAY SURGICALS LTD.—See Lakson Group of Companies; *Int'l,* pg. 4398
ACCUREC LLC; *U.S. Private,* pg. 55
ACCURENCE, INC.—See Insight Venture Management, LLC; *U.S. Private,* pg. 2089
ACCURENCE, INC.—See Stone Point Capital LLC; *U.S. Private,* pg. 3823
ACCURI CYTOMETERS (EUROPE) LTD.—See Becton, Dickinson & Company; *U.S. Public,* pg. 288
ACCURI CYTOMETERS, INC.—See Becton, Dickinson & Company; *U.S. Public,* pg. 288
ACCURIDE CANADA, INC.—See Crestview Partners, L.P.; *U.S. Private,* pg. 1097
ACCURIDE CORPORATION—See Crestview Partners, L.P.; *U.S. Private,* pg. 1097
ACCURIDE DE MEXICO, S.A. DE C.V.—See Crestview Partners, L.P.; *U.S. Private,* pg. 1098
ACCURIDE ERIE, L.P.—See Crestview Partners, L.P.; *U.S. Private,* pg. 1097
ACCURIDE HENDERSON LIMITED LIABILITY COMPANY—See Crestview Partners, L.P.; *U.S. Private,* pg. 1097
ACCURIDE INTERNATIONAL INC.; *U.S. Private,* pg. 55
ACCURIDE JAPAN CO., LTD.—See Kurogane Kosakusho Ltd.; *Int'l,* pg. 4342
ACCURIDE WHEELS EUROPE & ASIA GMBH—See Crestview Partners, L.P.; *U.S. Private,* pg. 1097
ACCURISK SOLUTIONS LLC—See Ryan Specialty Holdings, Inc.; *U.S. Public,* pg. 1827
ACCURIS NETWORKS LIMITED—See ESW Capital, LLC; *U.S. Private,* pg. 1430
ACCURIS NETWORKS LIMITED—See ESW Capital, LLC; *U.S. Private,* pg. 1431
ACCURIS NETWORKS MALAYSIA SDN. BHD.—See ESW Capital, LLC; *U.S. Private,* pg. 1431
ACCURISTIX HEALTHCARE LOGISTICS INC.—See Andlauer Healthcare Group, Inc.; *Int'l,* pg. 451
ACCURIST WATCHES LTD—See Time Products Ltd.; *Int'l,* pg. 7751
THE ACCURO GROUP, INC.; *U.S. Private,* pg. 3981
ACCURO SOLUTIONS, LLC; *U.S. Private,* pg. 55
ACCURSIA CAPITAL GMBH; *Int'l,* pg. 94
ACCURUS SCIENTIFIC CO., LTD.—See Mi Technovation Berhad; *Int'l,* pg. 4873
ACCUSERVE INC.—See Electrical Test Instrument, LLC; *U.S. Private,* pg. 1353
ACCUSOFT CORPORATION—See Pegasus Imaging Corporation; *U.S. Private,* pg. 3129
ACCUSOFT CORPORATION—See Pegasus Imaging Corporation; *U.S. Private,* pg. 3129
ACCUSONIC TECHNOLOGIES—See IDEX Corp; *U.S. Public,* pg. 1089

ACCU-SORT SYSTEMS, INC.—See Danaher Corporation; *U.S. Private,* pg. 624
ACCUSPEC ELECTRONICS, LLC—See Armstrong Holdings, Inc.; *U.S. Private,* pg. 331
ACCUSTEM SCIENCES, INC.; *Int'l,* pg. 94
AC CUSTOM PUMPS DIVISION—See Xylem Inc.; *U.S. Public,* pg. 2395
ACCUSWEEP SERVICES, INC.—See Warburg Pincus LLC; *U.S. Private,* pg. 4439
ACCU-TECH CORPORATION—See WESCO International, Inc.; *U.S. Public,* pg. 2350
ACCUTECH DATA SUPPLIES INC.; *U.S. Private,* pg. 55
ACCUTECH FILMS, INC.—See Apollo Global Management, Inc.; *U.S. Public,* pg. 154
ACCU TECH PLASTICS, INC.; *U.S. Private,* pg. 54
ACCU-TECH SYSTEMS, LTD.—See Amano Corporation; *Int'l,* pg. 410
ACCU-TEC INC.; *U.S. Private,* pg. 54
ACCUTEMP HEATING-COOLING, INC.—See New Mountain Capital, LLC; *U.S. Private,* pg. 2902
ACCU-TIME SYSTEMS, INC.—See Amano Corporation; *Int'l,* pg. 410
ACCUTITLE LLC; *U.S. Private,* pg. 55
ACCUTOME, INC.—See Halma plc; *Int'l,* pg. 3231
ACCUTRAC CAPITAL SOLUTIONS, INC.—See Global Merchant Fund Corp.; *U.S. Private,* pg. 1716
ACCUTREX PRODUCTS INC.; *U.S. Private,* pg. 55
ACCUTRONICS, LTD.—See Ultralife Corporation; *U.S. Public,* pg. 2224
ACCUTRON, INC.—See Foxtronics EMS; *U.S. Private,* pg. 1585
ACCUTRUST MORTGAGE INC.; *U.S. Private,* pg. 56
ACCU-TUBE CORP.—See Washington Equity Partners L.L.C.; *U.S. Private,* pg. 4447
ACC-U-TUNE—See Icahn Enterprises L.P.; *U.S. Public,* pg. 1083
ACCU-TURN INC.—See Marini Manufacturing, Inc.; *U.S. Private,* pg. 2576
ACCUVAR, INC.—See Datix, Inc.; *U.S. Private,* pg. 1167
ACCUWEATHER, INC.; *U.S. Private,* pg. 56
ACCUWEB, INC.—See SMS Holding GmbH; *Int'l,* pg. 7016
ACCU-WELD, LLC—See H.I.G. Capital, LLC; *U.S. Private,* pg. 1831
ACCUWORX, LLC; *U.S. Private,* pg. 56
ACDC LED LIMITED—See Zumtobel Group AG; *Int'l,* pg. 8606
ACDC METALS LTD.; *Int'l,* pg. 94
A.C. DELLOVADE INC.; *U.S. Private,* pg. 24
AC DESIGNS, INC.—See Gemini Investors LLC; *U.S. Private,* pg. 1658
A.C. DISPENSING EQUIPMENT INC.; *Int'l,* pg. 23
ACD, LLC—See Nikkiso Co., Ltd.; *Int'l,* pg. 5291
ACDOCTOR.COM INC.—See Watsco, Inc.; *U.S. Public,* pg. 2336
AC DOCTOR LLC—See Watsco, Inc.; *U.S. Public,* pg. 2336
ACD SYSTEMS INTERNATIONAL INC.; *Int'l,* pg. 94
ACEA ATO 2 S.P.A.—See ACEA S.p.A.; *Int'l,* pg. 95
ACEA BIOSCIENCES INC.—See Agilent Technologies, Inc.; *U.S. Public,* pg. 60
ACE ACCESSORIES CO., LTD.—See Ting Sin Co., Ltd.; *Int'l,* pg. 7754
ACE ACHIEVE INFOCOM LIMITED; *Int'l,* pg. 94
ACEA DOMINICANA S.A.—See ACEA S.p.A.; *Int'l,* pg. 95
ACE ADVENTURE RESORT; *U.S. Private,* pg. 56
ACEA ENERGIA S.P.A.—See ACEA S.p.A.; *Int'l,* pg. 95
ACE ALUMINUM DISTRIBUTORS, INC.—See Hendricks Holding Company, Inc.; *U.S. Private,* pg. 1915
ACE AMERICAN INSURANCE COMPANY—See Chubb Limited; *Int'l,* pg. 1590
ACEA MOLISE SRL—See ACEA S.p.A.; *Int'l,* pg. 95
ACE ANTENNA CO., LTD.—See Ace Technologies Corp.; *Int'l,* pg. 95
ACE ANTENNA COMPANY INC.—See Ace Technologies Corp.; *Int'l,* pg. 95
ACE ANTENNA INDIA PRIVATE LIMITED—See Ace Technologies Corp.; *Int'l,* pg. 95
ACE APPARATEBAU CONSTRUCTION & ENGINEERING GMBH—See Christof Holding AG; *Int'l,* pg. 1587
ACEARIETI S.R.L.—See ACEA S.p.A.; *Int'l,* pg. 95
ACEA S.P.A.; *Int'l,* pg. 95
ACE ASPHALT OF ARIZONA, INC.—See Huron Capital Partners LLC; *U.S. Private,* pg. 2012
ACE AUTOMATION (TIANJIN) CO. LTD.—See ATS Corporation; *Int'l,* pg. 694
ACEAXIS LTD—See Ace Technologies Corp.; *Int'l,* pg. 95
ACE BATTERY SALES, INC.; *U.S. Private,* pg. 56
ACE BEAUTY CO.—See L'Oreal S.A.; *Int'l,* pg. 4380
ACEBED CO. LTD. - GUANGZHOU FACTORY—See Acebed Co. Ltd.; *Int'l,* pg. 95
ACEBED CO. LTD.; *Int'l,* pg. 95
ACEBED CO. LTD. - YEOJU FACTORY—See Acebed Co. Ltd.; *Int'l,* pg. 95
ACE BED INTERNATIONAL PTE LTD.—See Acebed Co. Ltd.; *Int'l,* pg. 95
ACE-BIZ-SERV INC.—See Nissan Tokyo Sales Holdings Co., Ltd.; *Int'l,* pg. 5370
ACE CAPITAL LTD.—See Nepal Investment Mega Bank Limited; *Int'l,* pg. 5199

ACEMCO INCORPORATED

ACE CAPITAL TITLE REINSURANCE COMPANY—See Chubb Limited; *Int'l,* pg. 1590
ACE CASH EXPRESS, INC.—See JLL Partners, LLC; *U.S. Private,* pg. 2212
ACE CLEARWATER ENTERPRISES; *U.S. Private,* pg. 56
ACE COFFEE BAR, INC.; *U.S. Private,* pg. 56
ACE CONSULTING CO., LTD.—See Tokai Tokyo Financial Holdings, Inc.; *Int'l,* pg. 7781
ACE CONTROLS, INC.—See Triton Advisers Limited; *Int'l,* pg. 7933
ACE CONTROLS INTERNATIONAL - UK—See Triton Advisers Limited; *Int'l,* pg. 7933
ACE CONTROLS JAPAN, LLC—See Triton Advisers Limited; *Int'l,* pg. 7933
ACECO PRECISION MANUFACTURING; *U.S. Private,* pg. 57
ACE COPY SYSTEMS, INC.—See Hon Hai Precision Industry Co., Ltd.; *Int'l,* pg. 3458
ACE CORPORATION HOLDINGS LIMITED—See Berry Global Group, Inc; *U.S. Public,* pg. 320
ACE DORAN BROKERAGE CO—See Ace Doran Hauling & Rigging Company; *U.S. Private,* pg. 56
ACE DORAN HAULING & RIGGING COMPANY; *U.S. Private,* pg. 56
ACE EDUTREND LTD.; *Int'l,* pg. 94
ACEE ELECTRIC PTE. LTD.—See Raffles United Holdings Ltd.; *Int'l,* pg. 6178
ACE ENDICO CORP.; *U.S. Private,* pg. 56
ACE ENGINEERING INC.; *U.S. Private,* pg. 56
ACE ETHANOL LLC; *U.S. Private,* pg. 56
ACE EUROPEAN HOLDINGS LIMITED—See Chubb Limited; *Int'l,* pg. 1590
ACE EXHIBITS, INC.; *U.S. Private,* pg. 56
ACE EXTRUSION SDN. BHD.—See Press Metal Aluminium Holdings Bhd; *Int'l,* pg. 5965
ACE FIANZAS MONTERREY, S.A.—See Chubb Limited; *Int'l,* pg. 1590
ACE FIRE UNDERWRITERS INSURANCE COMPANY—See Chubb Limited; *Int'l,* pg. 1590
ACEGASAPSAMGA S.P.A.—See Hera S.p.A.; *Int'l,* pg. 3356
ACEGAS-APS SPA; *Int'l,* pg. 95
ACE GLASS INCORPORATED; *U.S. Private,* pg. 56
ACE GLOBAL BUSINESS ACQUISITION LIMITED; *Int'l,* pg. 94
ACEGREEN ECO-MATERIAL TECHNOLOGY CO., LTD.—See Acelon Chemicals & Fiber Corporation; *Int'l,* pg. 98
ACE HANDYMAN SERVICES—See Ace Hardware Corporation; *U.S. Private,* pg. 56
ACE HARDWARE BLUE RIDGE LLC; *U.S. Private,* pg. 56
ACE HARDWARE CORPORATION - PAINT DIVISION—See Ace Hardware Corporation; *U.S. Private,* pg. 56
ACE HARDWARE CORPORATION; *U.S. Private,* pg. 56
ACE HARDWARE OF OAK FOREST; *U.S. Private,* pg. 57
ACE HIGHTECH CO., LTD.; *Int'l,* pg. 94
ACE-HI INC.—See The Schafer Company Inc.; *U.S. Private,* pg. 4114
ACEHILL INVESTMENTS PTY. LTD.—See Elders Limited; *Int'l,* pg. 2346
ACE HOME CENTER DE MICHOACAN S.A. DE C.V.—See Ace Hardware Corporation; *U.S. Private,* pg. 56
ACE INA INTERNATIONAL HOLDING, LTD—See Kuok Brothers Sdn. Bhd.; *Int'l,* pg. 4334
ACE INDUSTRIAL MACHINERY CO., LTD.—See Morito Co., Ltd.; *Int'l,* pg. 5048
ACE INDUSTRIES INC.; *U.S. Private,* pg. 57
ACE INFO SOLUTIONS, INC.—See Veritas Capital Fund Management, LLC; *U.S. Private,* pg. 4362
ACE INSURANCE COMPANY OF THE MIDWEST—See Chubb Limited; *Int'l,* pg. 1590
ACE INTEGRATED SOLUTIONS LTD.; *Int'l,* pg. 94
ACE IRON & METAL—See Duggan Industries, Inc.; *U.S. Private,* pg. 1285
ACEITES BORGES PONT, S.A.; *Int'l,* pg. 95
ACE JANITORIAL SUPPLY CO., INC.—See Creative Technologies Corp.; *U.S. Private,* pg. 1090
ACEK DESARROLLO Y GESTION INDUSTRIAL SL; *Int'l,* pg. 96
ACE LEASING BV—See BNP Paribas SA; *Int'l,* pg. 1079
A-C ELECTRIC COMPANY; *U.S. Private,* pg. 22
ACE LIBERTY & STONE PLC; *Int'l,* pg. 94
ACE LITHOGRAPHERS OF MORRIS COUNTY, INC.; *U.S. Private,* pg. 57
ACELITY HOLDINGS, INC.—See 3M Company; *U.S. Public,* pg. 7
ACELITY L.P. INC.; *U.S. Private,* pg. 57
ACELL, INC.—See Integra LifeSciences Holdings Corporation; *U.S. Public,* pg. 1135
ACELON CHEMICALS & FIBER CORPORATION; *Int'l,* pg. 98
ACELYRIN, INC.; *U.S. Public,* pg. 33
ACE MANAGEMENT—See Tikehau Capital Advisors SAS; *Int'l,* pg. 7747
ACE MART RESTAURANT SUPPLY COMPANY INC.; *U.S. Private,* pg. 57
ACEMCO INCORPORATED; *U.S. Private,* pg. 58

ACE MEDIAS TOOLS JSC—See Transition Evergreen; *Int'l*, pg. 7900
ACE MEN ENGG WORKS LIMITED; *Int'l*, pg. 94
ACE METRIX, INC.—See ISpot.tv, Inc.; *U.S. Private*, pg. 2146
ACE MINERS HARDWARE, INC.; *U.S. Private*, pg. 57
ACE MOBILIER URBAIN SA—See Signaux Girod S.A.; *Int'l*, pg. 6910
ACE MOLD (HEFEI) COMPANY LIMITED—See Berry Global Group, Inc; *U.S. Public*, pg. 320
ACE MOLD INDUSTRIAL (SHENZHEN) COMPANY LIMITED—See Berry Global Group, Inc; *U.S. Public*, pg. 320
ACE MOLD (SHANGHAI) COMPANY LIMITED—See Berry Global Group, Inc; *U.S. Public*, pg. 320
ACENATURE BIOTECHNOLOGY CO., LTD.—See Acelon Chemicals & Fiber Corporation; *Int'l*, pg. 98
ACENA UAB—See INVL Technology AB; *Int'l*, pg. 3790
ACEN CORPORATION—See Ayala Corporation; *Int'l*, pg. 773
ACENDA INTEGRATED HEALTH; *U.S. Private*, pg. 58
ACENDEN LIMITED—See Barclays PLC; *Int'l*, pg. 860
ACENDRE PTY. LTD.—See Strattam Capital, LLC; *U.S. Private*, pg. 3837
AC ENERGY HOLDINGS, INC.—See Ayala Corporation; *Int'l*, pg. 773
AC ENERGY, INC.—See Ayala Corporation; *Int'l*, pg. 773
ACE NETWORK ZRT. PLC.—See 4iG Nyrt.; *Int'l*, pg. 12
ACE NEVADA CORP.—See Icahn Enterprises L.P.; *U.S. Public*, pg. 1083
ACENS TECHNOLOGIES, S.L.—See Telefonica, S.A.; *Int'l*, pg. 7535
ACENTA STEEL LIMITED - HOT ROLLED DIVISION—See Acenta Steel Limited; *Int'l*, pg. 98
ACENTA STEEL LIMITED; *Int'l*, pg. 98
AC ENTERTAINMENT, LLC—See Live Nation Entertainment, Inc.; *U.S. Public*, pg. 1328
ACENTIA, LLC—See MAXIMUS, Inc.; *U.S. Public*, pg. 1402
ACENTO ADVERTISING, INC.; *U.S. Private*, pg. 58
ACENTO ADVERTISING—See Acento Advertising, Inc.; *U.S. Private*, pg. 58
ACENTRIX GMBH—See CANCOM SE; *Int'l*, pg. 1288
ACENZIA, INC.—See Novo Integrated Sciences, Inc.; *U.S. Public*, pg. 1549
ACE OF BLADES LLC—See Senske Lawn & Tree Care, Inc.; *U.S. Private*, pg. 3608
ACE OFFICE SOLUTIONS INC.—See Hon Hai Precision Industry Co., Ltd.; *Int'l*, pg. 3458
ACE OHLSSON PTY LIMITED—See Elders Limited; *Int'l*, pg. 2346
ACE PACK CO., LTD.—See Tosoh Corporation; *Int'l*, pg. 7832
ACE PARKING MANAGEMENT INC.; *U.S. Private*, pg. 57
ACE PAVING CO. INC.; *U.S. Private*, pg. 57
ACEP FRANCE; *Int'l*, pg. 98
ACE PILLAR CO., LTD; *Int'l*, pg. 94
ACE PILLAR (S) PTE LTD—See ACE PILLAR Co., Ltd; *Int'l*, pg. 94
ACE PIPE CLEANING, INC.—See Carylon Corporation; *U.S. Private*, pg. 777
ACE PLASTICS (SHENZHEN) COMPANY LIMITED—See Berry Global Group, Inc; *U.S. Public*, pg. 320
ACE PLASTICS (ZHUHAI) COMPANY LIMITED—See Berry Global Group, Inc; *U.S. Public*, pg. 320
ACE PRECISION MACHINING CORP.; *U.S. Private*, pg. 57
ACE PRODUCE LTD.—See Dole plc; *Int'l*, pg. 2157
ACE PRODUCTION TECHNOLOGIES, INC.—See Nordson Corporation; *U.S. Public*, pg. 1532
ACE PROPERTY AND CASUALTY INSURANCE COMPANY—See Chubb Limited; *Int'l*, pg. 1590
A-C EQUIPMENT SERVICES CORP.—See ThyssenKrupp AG; *Int'l*, pg. 7732
ACER AFRICA PTY. LTD.—See Acer Incorporated; *Int'l*, pg. 98
ACERAGEN, INC.; *U.S. Public*, pg. 34
ACER AI CLOUD INC.—See Acer Incorporated; *Int'l*, pg. 98
ACER AMERICA CORPORATION—See Acer Incorporated; *Int'l*, pg. 98
ACER AMERICA CORPORATION—See Acer Incorporated; *Int'l*, pg. 98
ACER AMERICAN HOLDING CORP.—See Acer Incorporated; *Int'l*, pg. 98
ACER ASIA PACIFIC SDN BHD—See Acer Incorporated; *Int'l*, pg. 98
ACER AUSTRIA GMBH—See Acer Incorporated; *Int'l*, pg. 98
ACERBRAG S.A.—See Votorantim S.A.; *Int'l*, pg. 8309
ACER CAPITAL CORPORATION—See Acer Incorporated; *Int'l*, pg. 98
ACER CIS, INC.—See Acer Incorporated; *Int'l*, pg. 98
ACER CLOUD TECHNOLOGY CO.—See Acer Incorporated; *Int'l*, pg. 98
ACER COMPUTEC MEXICO, S.A. DE C.V.—See Acer Incorporated; *Int'l*, pg. 98
ACER COMPUTER AUSTRALIA PTY. LTD.—See Acer Incorporated; *Int'l*, pg. 98

ACER COMPUTER B.V. BENELUX—See Acer Incorporated; *Int'l*, pg. 98
ACER COMPUTER CO., LTD.—See Acer Incorporated; *Int'l*, pg. 98
ACER COMPUTER CZECH AND SLOVAK REPUBLICS—See Acer Incorporated; *Int'l*, pg. 98
ACER COMPUTER (FAR EAST) LIMITED—See Acer Incorporated; *Int'l*, pg. 98
ACER COMPUTER FINLAND OY—See Acer Incorporated; *Int'l*, pg. 98
ACER COMPUTER FRANCE S.A.R.L.—See Acer Incorporated; *Int'l*, pg. 98
ACER COMPUTER GMBH—See Acer Incorporated; *Int'l*, pg. 99
ACER COMPUTER IBERICA, S.A.U.—See Acer Incorporated; *Int'l*, pg. 99
ACER COMPUTER INTERNATIONAL LTD.—See Acer Incorporated; *Int'l*, pg. 99
ACER COMPUTER (M.E.) LTD.—See Acer Incorporated; *Int'l*, pg. 98
ACER COMPUTER NEW ZEALAND LTD.—See Acer Incorporated; *Int'l*, pg. 99
ACER COMPUTER NORWAY A/S—See Acer Incorporated; *Int'l*, pg. 99
ACER COMPUTER POLAND—See Acer Incorporated; *Int'l*, pg. 99
ACER COMPUTER (SHANGHAI) LTD.—See Acer Incorporated; *Int'l*, pg. 98
ACER COMPUTER (SINGAPORE) PTE. LTD.—See Acer Incorporated; *Int'l*, pg. 98
ACER COMPUTER SWEDEN AB—See Acer Incorporated; *Int'l*, pg. 99
ACER COMPUTER (SWITZERLAND) AG—See Acer Incorporated; *Int'l*, pg. 98
ACER CYBER CENTER SERVICES LTD—See Acer Incorporated; *Int'l*, pg. 99
ACER CZECH REPUBLIC S.R.O.—See Acer Incorporated; *Int'l*, pg. 99
ACER DENMARK A/S—See Acer Incorporated; *Int'l*, pg. 99
ACER DO BRASIL LIMITADA—See Acer Incorporated; *Int'l*, pg. 99
ACE RELOCATION SYSTEMS INC.; *U.S. Private*, pg. 57
ACE RENT A CAR, INC.—See Avis Budget Group, Inc.; *U.S. Public*, pg. 248
ACER EUROPE SA—See Acer Incorporated; *Int'l*, pg. 99
ACER EUROPE SERVICES S.R.L.—See Acer Incorporated; *Int'l*, pg. 99
ACEREX S.A.—See Techint S.p.A.; *Int'l*, pg. 7505
ACER FIDUCIARY, INC.—See AutoNation, Inc.; *U.S. Public*, pg. 231
ACER GADGET INC.; *Int'l*, pg. 98
ACERGY FRANCE S.A.—See Subsea 7 S.A.; *Int'l*, pg. 7248
ACER HELLAS LTD—See Acer Incorporated; *Int'l*, pg. 99
ACERIA DE ALAVA S.A.—See Tubacex S.A.; *Int'l*, pg. 7962
ACER INCORPORATED; *Int'l*, pg. 98
ACER INDIA (PVT) LTD.—See Acer Incorporated; *Int'l*, pg. 99
ACER INFORMATION PRODUCTS GROUP—See Acer Incorporated; *Int'l*, pg. 99
ACER INFORMATION SERVICES INTERNATIONAL—See Acer Incorporated; *Int'l*, pg. 99
ACERINOX ARGENTINA, S.A.—See Acerinox, S.A.; *Int'l*, pg. 100
ACERINOX AUSTRALASIA PTY LTD—See Acerinox, S.A.; *Int'l*, pg. 100
ACERINOX BENELUX, S.A./NV—See Acerinox, S.A.; *Int'l*, pg. 100
ACERINOX CHILE, S.A.—See Acerinox, S.A.; *Int'l*, pg. 100
ACERINOX COLOMBIA, S.A.S.—See Acerinox, S.A.; *Int'l*, pg. 100
ACERINOX DEUTSCHLAND GMBH—See Acerinox, S.A.; *Int'l*, pg. 100
ACERINOX DEUTSCHLAND GMBH—See Acerinox, S.A.; *Int'l*, pg. 100
ACERINOX EUROPA, S.A.U—See Acerinox, S.A.; *Int'l*, pg. 100
ACERINOX FRANCE SAS—See Acerinox, S.A.; *Int'l*, pg. 100
ACERINOX ITALIA SRL—See Acerinox, S.A.; *Int'l*, pg. 100
ACERINOX MALAYSIA SDN. BHD.—See Acerinox, S.A.; *Int'l*, pg. 100
ACERINOX METAL SANAYII VE TIKARET L.S.—See Acerinox, S.A.; *Int'l*, pg. 100
ACERINOX NORWAY A.S.—See Acerinox, S.A.; *Int'l*, pg. 100
ACERINOX PACIFIC LTD.—See Acerinox, S.A.; *Int'l*, pg. 100
ACERINOX POLSKA SP.ZO.O.—See Acerinox, S.A.; *Int'l*, pg. 100
ACERINOX RUSSIA, L.L.C.—See Acerinox, S.A.; *Int'l*, pg. 100
ACERINOX, S.A.; *Int'l*, pg. 100
ACERINOX, S.A. - VENEZUELA—See Acerinox, S.A.; *Int'l*, pg. 100
ACERINOX SCANDINAVIA A.B.—See Acerinox, S.A.; *Int'l*, pg. 100

ACERINOX (SCHWEIZ) A.G.—See Acerinox, S.A.; *Int'l*, pg. 100
ACERINOX SEA PTE LTD—See Acerinox, S.A.; *Int'l*, pg. 100
ACERINOX SOUTH EAST ASIA, PTE. LTD.—See Acerinox, S.A.; *Int'l*, pg. 100
ACERINOX UK LTD—See Acerinox, S.A.; *Int'l*, pg. 100
ACER INTERNET SERVICES INC.—See Acer Incorporated; *Int'l*, pg. 99
ACER ITALY S.R.L.—See Acer Incorporated; *Int'l*, pg. 99
ACER JAPAN CORPORATION—See Acer Incorporated; *Int'l*, pg. 99
ACER LATIN AMERICA, INC.—See Acer Incorporated; *Int'l*, pg. 99
ACER MAGYARORSZAG—See Acer Incorporated; *Int'l*, pg. 99
ACEROL COMERCIO E INDUSTRIA DE ACOS INOXIDAVEIS UNIPESSOAL, LTDA.—See Acerinox, S.A.; *Int'l*, pg. 100
ACEROLUX SL; *Int'l*, pg. 101
ACEROS BOEHLER DEL ECUADOR S.A.—See voestalpine AG; *Int'l*, pg. 8287
ACEROS BOEHLER DEL PERU S.A.—See voestalpine AG; *Int'l*, pg. 8291
ACEROS BOEHLER S.A.—See voestalpine AG; *Int'l*, pg. 8291
ACEROS BOEHLER UDDEHOLM S.A.—See voestalpine AG; *Int'l*, pg. 8287
ACEROS BOHLER UDDEHOLM, S.A. DE C.V.—See voestalpine AG; *Int'l*, pg. 8287
ACEROS CALIBRADOS, S.A.—See Tubos Reunidos, S.A.; *Int'l*, pg. 7963
ACEROS CAMESA, S.A. DE C.V.—See ONEX Corporation; *Int'l*, pg. 5580
ACEROS CHAPA INDUSTRIAL S.L.—See BAMESA Aceros; *Int'l*, pg. 813
ACEROS CHAPA INDUSTRIAL, S.L.—See BAMESA Aceros; *Int'l*, pg. 813
ACEROS COX COMERCIAL S.A.—See Metalurgica Gerdau S.A.; *Int'l*, pg. 4849
ACEROS FORTUNA, S.A. DE C.V.—See Carpenter Technology Corporation; *U.S. Public*, pg. 439
ACEROS IMS INT., S.A.—See Jacquet Metal Service SA; *Int'l*, pg. 3866
ACER PHILIPPINES, INC.—See Acer Incorporated; *Int'l*, pg. 99
ACER PROPERTY DEVELOPMENT, INC.—See Acer Incorporated; *Int'l*, pg. 99
ACER SALES & SERVICES SDN. BHD.—See Acer Incorporated; *Int'l*, pg. 99
ACER SERVICE CORPORATION—See Acer Incorporated; *Int'l*, pg. 99
ACER SWEDEN AB—See Acer Incorporated; *Int'l*, pg. 99
ACERTA PHARMA B.V.—See AstraZeneca PLC; *Int'l*, pg. 659
ACER TECHNOLOGIES CORP.—See Acer Incorporated; *Int'l*, pg. 99
ACER TECHNOLOGY, INC.—See Acer Incorporated; *Int'l*, pg. 99
ACERTEC PLC; *Int'l*, pg. 102
ACER THERAPEUTICS, INC.—See Zevra Therapeutics, Inc.; *U.S. Public*, pg. 2403
ACERTYS HEALTHCARE NV—See Gimv NV; *Int'l*, pg. 2976
ACER UK LIMITED—See Acer Incorporated; *Int'l*, pg. 99
ACERUS PHARMACEUTICALS CORPORATION; *Int'l*, pg. 102
ACER VIETNAM CO., LTD.—See Acer Incorporated; *Int'l*, pg. 99
ACE SAATCHI & SAATCHI—See Publicis Groupe S.A.; *Int'l*, pg. 6107
ACES A/C SUPPLY INC.; *U.S. Private*, pg. 58
ACESA-DRIVES S.A. DE C.V.; *Int'l*, pg. 102
ACES DENTAL—See Absolute Dental Group, LLC; *U.S. Private*, pg. 44
ACES DONG GUAN—See Aces Electronic Co., Ltd.; *Int'l*, pg. 70
ACE SECURITIES CO., LTD.—See Tokai Tokyo Financial Holdings, Inc.; *Int'l*, pg. 7781
ACES ELECTRONIC CO., LTD.; *Int'l*, pg. 102
ACE SERVICIOS S.A.—See Chubb Limited; *Int'l*, pg. 1590
A.C.E. (SHANGHAI) TRADING CO. LTD.—See Atlas Converting Equipment Limited; *Int'l*, pg. 676
ACESIAN PARTNERS LIMITED; *Int'l*, pg. 102
ACESITE (PHILS.) HOTEL CORPORATION—See Waterfront Philippines, Incorporated; *Int'l*, pg. 8357
ACE SOFTWARE EXPORTS LTD.; *Int'l*, pg. 95
ACE SOLAR CO., LTD.—See Absolute Clean Energy Public Company Limited; *Int'l*, pg. 70
ACE SOLAR LLC—See ALLETE, Inc.; *U.S. Public*, pg. 79
ACE SOLID WASTE, INC.—See Waste Connections, Inc.; *Int'l*, pg. 8353
ACESO LIFE SCIENCE GROUP LIMITED; *Int'l*, pg. 102
ACES REGIONAL SERVICE CO., LTD.—See Jasmine International Public Company Limited; *Int'l*, pg. 3912
ACESS TAIWAN LAB. CO., LTD.—See Access Co., Ltd.; *Int'l*, pg. 88
ACE STAMPING & MACHINE CO, INC.; *U.S. Private*, pg. 57

COMPANY NAME INDEX

ACE STEEL SUPPLY, INC.—See Commercial Steel Products LLC; *U.S. Private*, pg. 984
ACE SUPPLY CO. INC.; *U.S. Private*, pg. 57
ACE SURGICAL SUPPLY CO., INC.—See Henry Schein, Inc.; *U.S. Public*, pg. 1025
ACE TANK & EQUIPMENT CO.; *U.S. Private*, pg. 57
ACETATE PRODUCTS LTD.—See CVC Capital Partners SICAV-FIS S.A.; *Int'l*, pg. 1886
ACE TECHNOLOGIES CORP.; *Int'l*, pg. 95
ACE TECHNOLOGIES INC.; *U.S. Private*, pg. 57
ACETEC INC.—See Radiall S.A.; *Int'l*, pg. 6173
ACETEK MATERIAL CO., LTD.—See Jinan Acetate Chemical Co., Ltd.; *Int'l*, pg. 3965
ACE TELEPHONE ASSOCIATION; *U.S. Private*, pg. 57
ACE-TEX ENTERPRISES INC.—See Crown Capital Investments LLC; *U.S. Private*, pg. 1110
ACETO AGRICULTURAL CHEMICALS CORP.—See Aceto Corporation; *U.S. Private*, pg. 58
ACETO B.V.—See Aceto Corporation; *U.S. Private*, pg. 58
ACETO CORPORATION; *U.S. Private*, pg. 58
ACETO FINECHEM GMBH—See Aceto Corporation; *U.S. Private*, pg. 58
ACETO FRANCE S.A.S.—See Aceto Corporation; *U.S. Private*, pg. 58
ACETO (HOLDING) B.V.—See Aceto Corporation; *U.S. Private*, pg. 58
ACE TOOL CO.—See Sycamore Partners Management, LP; *U.S. Private*, pg. 3896
ACE TOOL REPAIR, INC.; *U.S. Private*, pg. 57
ACETO PHARMA GMBH—See Aceto Corporation; *U.S. Private*, pg. 58
ACETO PHARMA INDIA PVT. LTD.—See Aceto Corporation; *U.S. Private*, pg. 58
ACETO PTE LTD.—See Aceto Corporation; *U.S. Private*, pg. 58
ACETO (SHANGHAI) LTD.—See Aceto Corporation; *U.S. Private*, pg. 58
ACE UNDERWRITING GROUP; *U.S. Private*, pg. 57
ACE VAN LINES INC.—See Stevens Group, Inc.; *U.S. Private*, pg. 3809
ACEWIN AGRITECK LIMITED; *Int'l*, pg. 102
ACE WINCHES NORGE AS—See Ashtead Technology Holdings Plc; *Int'l*, pg. 609
ACE WINE & CADLE CO. INC.; *U.S. Private*, pg. 57
ACE WORLD WIDE MOVING & STORAGE CO. INC.; *U.S. Private*, pg. 57
ACEZ INSTRUMENTS PHILIPPINES CORPORATION—See Acez Instruments Pte. Ltd.; *Int'l*, pg. 102
ACEZ INSTRUMENTS PTE. LTD.; *Int'l*, pg. 102
ACEZ INSTRUMENTS (SHENZHEN) CO., LTD—See Acez Instruments Pte. Ltd.; *Int'l*, pg. 102
ACEZ SENSING PTE LTD.—See Acez Instruments Pte. Ltd.; *Int'l*, pg. 102
ACF COMPONENTS & FASTENERS; *U.S. Private*, pg. 58
ACF ENVIRONMENTAL; *U.S. Private*, pg. 58
ACF INDUSTRIES LLC; *U.S. Private*, pg. 58
ACF INVESTMENT CORP.—See General Motors Company; *U.S. Private*, pg. 924
ACF MEDICAL SERVICES, INC.—See Encore Capital Group, Inc.; *U.S. Public*, pg. 759
AC-FOLIEN GMBH—See CPH Chemie + Papier Holding AG; *Int'l*, pg. 1824
ACF SOLUTIONS, LLC.—See Attain, LLC; *U.S. Private*, pg. 383
AC FURNITURE CO. INC.; *U.S. Private*, pg. 45
ACG ADVISORS (UK) LLP; *Int'l*, pg. 102
ACG INSURANCE AGENCY, LLC—See The Auto Club Group; *U.S. Private*, pg. 3990
AC GLASS HOLDING B.V.—See Turkiye Sise ve Cam Fabrikalari A.S.; *Int'l*, pg. 7977
A.C.G. PRAHA A.S.—See Raiffeisenlandesbank Oberosterreich Aktiengesellschaft; *Int'l*, pg. 6187
ACGT SDN BHD—See Genting Berhad; *Int'l*, pg. 2928
ACHAL INVESTMENTS LIMITED; *Int'l*, pg. 102
ACHARI VENTURES HOLDINGS CORP. I; *U.S. Public*, pg. 34
A C HATHORNE CO—See Altas Partners LP; *Int'l*, pg. 386
ACHA TRADING CO. INC.; *U.S. Private*, pg. 58
ACHAT-VERRE AFLOX S.A.—See A.A.G. STUCCHI s.r.l.; *Int'l*, pg. 22
ACHATZ SERVICE GMBH—See Bilfinger SE; *Int'l*, pg. 1024
ACH, D.D.; *Int'l*, pg. 102
A-CHECK AMERICA INC.—See Sterling Check Corp.; *U.S. Public*, pg. 1946
ACHEM INDUSTRY AMERICA, INC.—See ACHEM Technology Corporation; *Int'l*, pg. 103
ACHEM OPTO-ELECTRONIC CORPORATION—See Yem Chio Co., Ltd.; *Int'l*, pg. 8577
ACHEM TECHNOLOGY (CHENGDU) CO., LTD.—See Yem Chio Co., Ltd.; *Int'l*, pg. 8577
ACHEM TECHNOLOGY CORPORATION; *Int'l*, pg. 103
ACHEM TECHNOLOGY (DONGGUAN) ADHESIVE PRODUCT CO., LTD.—See Yem Chio Co., Ltd.; *Int'l*, pg. 8577
ACHEM TECHNOLOGY (M) SDN. BHD.—See Yem Chio Co., Ltd.; *Int'l*, pg. 8577

ACHEM TECHNOLOGY (NINGBO) CO., LTD.—See Yem Chio Co., Ltd.; *Int'l*, pg. 8577
ACHEM TECHNOLOGY (SHANGHAI) CO., LTD.—See Yem Chio Co., Ltd.; *Int'l*, pg. 8577
ACHEM TECHNOLOGY (VIET NAM) CO., LTD.—See Yem Chio Co., Ltd.; *Int'l*, pg. 8577
ACHEN-GARDNER CONSTRUCTION, LLC; *U.S. Private*, pg. 58
ACHEN-GARDNER INC. - GDC HOMES—See Achen-Gardner Construction, LLC; *U.S. Private*, pg. 58
ACHERNAR S.A.—See SATO Holdings Corporation; *Int'l*, pg. 6585
ACHERON PORTFOLIO CORP (LUXEMBOURG) SA; *Int'l*, pg. 103
ACHESON COLLOIDEN—See Henkel AG & Co. KGaA; *Int'l*, pg. 3353
ACHESON COLLOIDS COMPANY—See Henkel AG & Co. KGaA; *Int'l*, pg. 3353
ACHESON DO BRASIL IND. E COM LTDA—See Henkel AG & Co. KGaA; *Int'l*, pg. 3353
ACHESON FRANCE S.A.—See Henkel AG & Co. KGaA; *Int'l*, pg. 3353
ACHESON & GLOVER LTD.; *Int'l*, pg. 103
ACHESON INDUSTRIES (EUROPE) LTD.—See Henkel AG & Co. KGaA; *Int'l*, pg. 3353
ACHESON ITALIANA S.R.L.—See Henkel AG & Co. KGaA; *Int'l*, pg. 3353
ACHESON VENTURES, LLC—See Henkel AG & Co. KGaA; *Int'l*, pg. 3352
ACHETER LOUER FR SA—See Adomos SA; *Int'l*, pg. 152
ACH FOAM TECHNOLOGIES, LLC - FOND DULAC—See Atlas Roofing Corp.; *U.S. Private*, pg. 380
ACH FOAM TECHNOLOGIES, LLC - GEORGIA PLANT—See Atlas Roofing Corp.; *U.S. Private*, pg. 380
ACH FOAM TECHNOLOGIES, LLC - NEVADA PLANT—See Atlas Roofing Corp.; *U.S. Private*, pg. 380
ACH FOAM TECHNOLOGIES, LLC—See Atlas Roofing Corp.; *U.S. Private*, pg. 380
ACH FOAM TECHNOLOGIES, LLC—See Atlas Roofing Corp.; *U.S. Private*, pg. 380
ACH FOAM TECHNOLOGIES, LLC—See Atlas Roofing Corp.; *U.S. Private*, pg. 380
ACH FOAM TECHNOLOGIES, LLC - UTAH PLANT—See Atlas Roofing Corp.; *U.S. Private*, pg. 380
ACH FOOD COMPANIES, INC.—See The Garfield Weston Foundation; *Int'l*, pg. 7648
ACH FOODS MEXICO, S.DE R.L.DE C.V.—See The Garfield Weston Foundation; *Int'l*, pg. 7648
ACHIDATEX NAZARETH ELITE (1977) LTD—See DEFENSE INDUSTRIES INTERNATIONAL, INC.; *Int'l*, pg. 2004
ACHIEVA CREDIT UNION; *U.S. Private*, pg. 58
ACHIEVA INSURANCE AGENCY, LLC—See Achieva Credit Union; *U.S. Private*, pg. 58
ACHIEVA INVESTMENTS PTE LTD—See SUTL Enterprise Limited; *Int'l*, pg. 7347
ACHIEVA MEDICAL (SHANGHAI) CO., LTD.—See Peijia Medical Limited; *Int'l*, pg. 5781
ACHIEVA MEDICAL (SUZHOU) CO., LTD.—See Peijia Medical Limited; *Int'l*, pg. 5781
ACHIEVA TECHNOLOGY AUSTRALIA PTY. LTD.—See Serial System Ltd.; *Int'l*, pg. 6722
ACHIEVA TECHNOLOGY PTE LTD—See Serial System Ltd.; *Int'l*, pg. 6722
ACHIEVA TECHNOLOGY SDN. BHD—See Serial System Ltd.; *Int'l*, pg. 6722
ACHIEVE 3000, INC.; *U.S. Private*, pg. 59
ACHIEVEFORUM (UK) LIMITED—See Korn Ferry; *U.S. Public*, pg. 1274
ACHIEVEGLOBAL INC.—See Korn Ferry; *U.S. Public*, pg. 1274
ACHIEVE IT SOLUTIONS, INC.—See VistaVu Solutions Inc.; *Int'l*, pg. 8254
ACHIEVE LIFE SCIENCES, INC.; *Int'l*, pg. 103
ACHIEVEMENT CENTER, INC.; *U.S. Private*, pg. 59
ACHIEVENEXT, LLC; *U.S. Private*, pg. 59
ACHIEVE PARTNERS MANAGEMENT, LLC; *U.S. Private*, pg. 59
ACHIEVE PHYSICAL THERAPY, LIMITED PARTNERSHIP—See U.S. Physical Therapy, Inc.; *U.S. Public*, pg. 2213
ACHIEVERS CORP.—See P2 Capital Partners, LLC; *U.S. Private*, pg. 3061
ACHIEVERS CORP.—See Silver Lake Group, LLC; *U.S. Private*, pg. 3656
ACHIEVERS LLC—See P2 Capital Partners, LLC; *U.S. Private*, pg. 3061
ACHIEVERS LLC—See Silver Lake Group, LLC; *U.S. Private*, pg. 3656
ACHIKO AG; *Int'l*, pg. 103
ACHILLES ADVANCED TECHNOLOGY CO., LTD.—See Achilles Corporation; *Int'l*, pg. 103
ACHILLES & ASSOCIATES PC—See Aon plc; *Int'l*, pg. 495
ACHILLES CORPORATION; *Int'l*, pg. 103
ACHILLES DEVELOPMENT SERVICES AS—See Bridgepoint Group Plc; *Int'l*, pg. 1153

ACHILLES DO BRASIL LTDA—See Bridgepoint Group Plc; *Int'l*, pg. 1154
ACHILLES FIRST POINT ASSESSMENT LIMITED—See Bridgepoint Group Plc; *Int'l*, pg. 1153
ACHILLES GROUP LIMITED—See Bridgepoint Group Plc; *Int'l*, pg. 1153
ACHILLES GUARD, INC.—See HGGC, LLC; *U.S. Private*, pg. 1929
ACHILLES HONG KONG CO., LTD.—See Achilles Corporation; *Int'l*, pg. 103
ACHILLES INFORMATION APS—See Bridgepoint Group Plc; *Int'l*, pg. 1153
ACHILLES INFORMATION (AUSTRALIA) PTY LTD—See Bridgepoint Group Plc; *Int'l*, pg. 1153
ACHILLES INFORMATION CENTRE AS—See Bridgepoint Group Plc; *Int'l*, pg. 1153
ACHILLES INFORMATION GMBH—See Bridgepoint Group Plc; *Int'l*, pg. 1153
ACHILLES INFORMATION HONG KONG LTD—See Bridgepoint Group Plc; *Int'l*, pg. 1153
ACHILLES INFORMATION INC—See Bridgepoint Group Plc; *Int'l*, pg. 1153
ACHILLES INFORMATION (INDIA) PRIVATE LIMITED—See Bridgepoint Group Plc; *Int'l*, pg. 1153
ACHILLES INFORMATION LIMITED—See Bridgepoint Group Plc; *Int'l*, pg. 1153
ACHILLES INFORMATION LIMITED—See Bridgepoint Group Plc; *Int'l*, pg. 1153
ACHILLES INFORMATION SLOVAKIA S.R.O—See Bridgepoint Group Plc; *Int'l*, pg. 1153
ACHILLES PROCUREMENT SERVICES LIMITED—See Bridgepoint Group Plc; *Int'l*, pg. 1153
ACHILLES (SHANGHAI) INTERNATIONAL TRADING CO., LTD.—See Achilles Corporation; *Int'l*, pg. 103
ACHILLES SOUTH EUROPE, S.L.U.—See Bridgepoint Group Plc; *Int'l*, pg. 1154
ACHILLES SOUTH EUROPE S.L.U.—See Bridgepoint Group Plc; *Int'l*, pg. 1154
ACHILLES SOUTH EUROPE S.L.U.—See Bridgepoint Group Plc; *Int'l*, pg. 1154
ACHILLES THERAPEUTICS PLC; *Int'l*, pg. 103
ACHILLES USA, INC.—See Achilles Corporation; *Int'l*, pg. 103
ACHILLES INFORMATION AB—See Bridgepoint Group Plc; *Int'l*, pg. 1154
ACHILLION PHARMACEUTICALS, INC.—See AstraZeneca PLC; *Int'l*, pg. 659
ACHIM IMPORTING COMPANY INC.; *U.S. Private*, pg. 59
ACHIT ALKABY JOINT STOCK COMPANY; *Int'l*, pg. 103
ACHMEA BANK N.V.—See Achmea B.V.; *Int'l*, pg. 103
ACHMEA B.V.; *Int'l*, pg. 103
ACHMEA INTERNE DIENSTEN N.V.—See Achmea B.V.; *Int'l*, pg. 103
ACHMEA PENSIOEN - EN LEVENSVERZEKERINGEN N.V.—See Achmea B.V.; *Int'l*, pg. 103
AC HOLDING CO.; *U.S. Private*, pg. 45
A.C. HORN & COMPANY; *U.S. Private*, pg. 24
A.C. HOUSTON LUMBER COMPANY; *U.S. Private*, pg. 24
ACHP LEVICE A.S.—See Agrofert Holding, a.s.; *Int'l*, pg. 218
ACHP PLC—See Financiere Pinault SCA; *Int'l*, pg. 2668
A. CHRISTENSSEN ENGROS A/S—See Aurelius Equity Opportunities SE & Co. KGaA; *Int'l*, pg. 709
ACH SEEDS INC.—See KWS SAAT SE & Co. KGaA; *Int'l*, pg. 4352
ACHYUT HEALTHCARE LTD.; *Int'l*, pg. 104
ACI - AGENCIA CONTINENTAL DE IMPORTACIONES, S.A.—See Motta-Internacional, S.A.; *Int'l*, pg. 5056
ACI AGROLINKS LTD.—See Advanced Chemical Industries Limited; *Int'l*, pg. 158
ACIAL SAS—See Blackstone Inc.; *U.S. Public*, pg. 348
ACI AUSTRALIA PTY. LTD.—See ACI Worldwide, Inc.; *U.S. Public*, pg. 34
ACIBADEM SAGLIK HIZMETLERI VE TICARET AS—See Khazanah Nasional Berhad; *Int'l*, pg. 4152
ACIBADEM SIGORTA—See Khazanah Nasional Berhad; *Int'l*, pg. 4152
ACI BIOTECH LIMITED—See Advanced Chemical Industries Limited; *Int'l*, pg. 158
ACI BRANDS INC.; *Int'l*, pg. 104
ACI BUILDING SYSTEMS, LLC—See Promus Holdings, LLC; *U.S. Private*, pg. 3284
ACI CAPITAL CO. LLC; *U.S. Private*, pg. 59
ACI CHEMICALS LTD.—See Advanced Chemical Industries Limited; *Int'l*, pg. 158
ACI CINCINNATI—See Amano Corporation; *Int'l*, pg. 410
ACICO INDUSTRIES CO. K.S.C.C.; *Int'l*, pg. 104
ACI CONTROLS INC.; *U.S. Private*, pg. 59
ACIDCHEM (USA) INC—See IOI Corporation Berhad; *Int'l*, pg. 3791
ACI D.D.; *Int'l*, pg. 104
ACI DO BRASIL S.A.—See Corporacion America Airports S.A.; *Int'l*, pg. 1803
ACIDS CO., LTD.—See Dowa Holdings Co., Ltd.; *Int'l*, pg. 2183
ACID SERVICES, LLC—See Basic Energy Services Inc.; *U.S. Public*, pg. 279

ACI D.D.

CORPORATE AFFILIATIONS

ACI EDIBLE OILS LTD.—See Advanced Chemical Industries Limited; *Int'l*, pg. 158
ACI ELEVATION S.A.; *Int'l*, pg. 104
ACIERIES DE PLOERMEL—See AMSTED Industries Incorporated; *U.S. Private*, pg. 267
ACIER LEROUX—See Russel Metals Inc.; *Int'l*, pg. 6430
ACIERNET SA—See Econocom Group SA; *Int'l*, pg. 2297
ACIEROID S.A.—See Bouygues S.A.; *Int'l*, pg. 1121
ACIERTA ASISTENCIA, S.A.—See Helvetia Holding AG; *Int'l*, pg. 3339
ACIETA LLC—See Angeles Equity Partners, LLC; *U.S. Private*, pg. 282
ACI FOODS LIMITED—See Advanced Chemical Industries Limited; *Int'l*, pg. 158
ACI FORMULATIONS LIMITED—See Advanced Chemical Industries Limited; *Int'l*, pg. 158
ACI GLOBAL LIMITED—See ACI Worldwide, Inc.; *U.S. Public*, pg. 34
ACI GLOBAL LIMITED—See ACI Worldwide, Inc.; *U.S. Public*, pg. 34
ACI GROUP; *U.S. Private*, pg. 59
ACIG TECHNOLOGY CORP.—See Identiv, Inc.; *U.S. Public*, pg. 1089
ACI GUANGDONG GLASS COMPANY LTD.—See O-I Glass, Inc.; *U.S. Public*, pg. 1559
ACI HEALTHCARE LTD.—See Advanced Chemical Industries Limited; *Int'l*, pg. 158
ACI HOLDINGS INC.—See Thermo Fisher Scientific Inc.; *U.S. Public*, pg. 2145
ACI INDUSTRIES PTE LTD—See Asian Micro Holdings Ltd.; *Int'l*, pg. 618
ACI INFOCOM LIMITED; *Int'l*, pg. 104
ACI INFOTECH; *U.S. Private*, pg. 59
ACI INTERNATIONAL; *U.S. Private*, pg. 59
ACI LAST MILE NETWORK LLC; *U.S. Private*, pg. 59
ACI LOGISTICS LIMITED—See Advanced Chemical Industries Limited; *Int'l*, pg. 158
ACI MECHANICAL & HVAC SALES; *U.S. Private*, pg. 59
ACI MECHANICAL, INC.—See Comfort Systems USA, Inc.; *U.S. Public*, pg. 543
ACI MERCHANT SYSTEMS, LLC—See NCR Voyix Corporation; *U.S. Public*, pg. 1502
AC IMMUNE SA; *Int'l*, pg. 74
ACI MOTORS LIMITED—See Mitsui & Co., Ltd.; *Int'l*, pg. 4974
AC INC.; *U.S. Private*, pg. 45
ACINDAR INDUSTRIA ARGENTINA DE ACEROS S.A.—See ArcelorMittal S.A.; *Int'l*, pg. 543
ACINO HOLDING AG—See Avista Capital Partners, L.P.; *U.S. Private*, pg. 408
ACINO HOLDING AG—See Nordic Capital AB; *Int'l*, pg. 5419
ACINO PHARMA AG—See Avista Capital Partners, L.P.; *U.S. Private*, pg. 408
ACINO PHARMA AG—See Nordic Capital AB; *Int'l*, pg. 5419
ACI NORTHWEST, INC.; *U.S. Private*, pg. 59
ACINO SUPPLY AG—See Avista Capital Partners, L.P.; *U.S. Private*, pg. 408
ACINO SUPPLY AG—See Nordic Capital AB; *Int'l*, pg. 5419
ACI OPERATIONS NZ LIMITED—See O-I Glass, Inc.; *U.S. Public*, pg. 1559
ACI PURE FLOUR LIMITED—See Advanced Chemical Industries Limited; *Int'l*, pg. 158
ACIRL QUALITY TESTING SERVICES PTY LTD—See ALS Limited; *Int'l*, pg. 377
ACI SALT LIMITED—See Advanced Chemical Industries Limited; *Int'l*, pg. 158
ACIS ARZNEIMITTEL GMBH—See Dermapharm Holding SE; *Int'l*, pg. 2043
ACISELSAN ACIPAYAM SELULOZ SANAYI VE TICARET A.S.—See Verusa Holding A.S.; *Int'l*, pg. 8175
ACISELSAN ACIPAYAM SELULOZ SANAYI VE TICARET—See Verusa Holding A.S.; *Int'l*, pg. 8175
ACIS IMMOBILIEN- UND PROJEKTENTWICKLUNGS GMBH—See UniCredit S.p.A.; *Int'l*, pg. 8033
ACI (SINGAPORE) PTE. LTD.—See ACI Worldwide, Inc.; *U.S. Public*, pg. 34
A.C. ISRAEL ENTERPRISES, INC.; *U.S. Private*, pg. 24
ACIST MEDICAL SYSTEMS, INC.—See Bracco S.p.A.; *Int'l*, pg. 1134
ACI SUPPORT SPECIALISTS, INC.—See Dungarvin, Inc.; *U.S. Private*, pg. 1289
ACI TIANJIN MOULD COMPANY LIMITED—See O-I Glass, Inc.; *U.S. Public*, pg. 1559
ACI WORLDWIDE (ASIA) PTE. LTD.—See ACI Worldwide, Inc.; *U.S. Public*, pg. 34
ACI WORLDWIDE BRASIL LTDA.—See ACI Worldwide, Inc.; *U.S. Public*, pg. 34
ACI WORLDWIDE B.V.—See ACI Worldwide, Inc.; *U.S. Public*, pg. 34
ACI WORLDWIDE CANADA, INC.—See ACI Worldwide, Inc.; *U.S. Public*, pg. 34
ACI WORLDWIDE COLOMBIA S.A.S.—See ACI Worldwide, Inc.; *U.S. Public*, pg. 34
ACI WORLDWIDE CORP. - AUSTIN OFFICE—See ACI Worldwide, Inc.; *U.S. Public*, pg. 34

ACI WORLDWIDE CORP. - CHANTILLY OFFICE—See ACI Worldwide, Inc.; *U.S. Public*, pg. 34
ACI WORLDWIDE CORP. - COLUMBUS OFFICE—See ACI Worldwide, Inc.; *U.S. Public*, pg. 34
ACI WORLDWIDE CORP. - PRINCETON OFFICE—See ACI Worldwide, Inc.; *U.S. Public*, pg. 34
ACI WORLDWIDE CORP.—See ACI Worldwide, Inc.; *U.S. Public*, pg. 34
ACI WORLDWIDE CORP. - WEST HILLS OFFICE—See ACI Worldwide, Inc.; *U.S. Public*, pg. 34
ACI WORLDWIDE DE ARGENTINA S.A.—See ACI Worldwide, Inc.; *U.S. Public*, pg. 35
ACI WORLDWIDE EASTERN EUROPE DEVELOPMENT S.R.L.—See ACI Worldwide, Inc.; *U.S. Public*, pg. 34
ACI WORLDWIDE (EMEA) LIMITED—See ACI Worldwide, Inc.; *U.S. Public*, pg. 34
ACI WORLDWIDE (EPS) AG—See ACI Worldwide, Inc.; *U.S. Public*, pg. 34
ACI WORLDWIDE FRANCE S.A.R.L.—See ACI Worldwide, Inc.; *U.S. Public*, pg. 34
ACI WORLDWIDE (GERMANY) GMBH—See ACI Worldwide, Inc.; *U.S. Public*, pg. 34
ACI WORLDWIDE (HELLAS) EPE—See ACI Worldwide, Inc.; *U.S. Public*, pg. 34
ACI WORLDWIDE, INC.; *U.S. Public*, pg. 34
ACI WORLDWIDE ITALIA S.R.L.—See ACI Worldwide, Inc.; *U.S. Public*, pg. 34
ACI WORLDWIDE (JAPAN) K.K.—See ACI Worldwide, Inc.; *U.S. Public*, pg. 34
ACI WORLDWIDE KOREA YUHAN HOESA—See ACI Worldwide, Inc.; *U.S. Public*, pg. 34
ACI WORLDWIDE MEXICO S.A. DE C.V.—See ACI Worldwide, Inc.; *U.S. Public*, pg. 34
ACI WORLDWIDE (PACIFIC) PTY. LTD.—See ACI Worldwide, Inc.; *U.S. Public*, pg. 34
ACI WORLDWIDE SOLUTIONS PVT. LTD.—See ACI Worldwide, Inc.; *U.S. Public*, pg. 35
ACI WORLDWIDE (THAILAND) LIMITED—See ACI Worldwide, Inc.; *U.S. Public*, pg. 34
ACI WORLDWIDE (UK DEVELOPMENT) LIMITED—See ACI Worldwide, Inc.; *U.S. Public*, pg. 34
ACK CONTROLS INC.—See Chuo Spring Co., Ltd.; *Int'l*, pg. 1599
A.C.K. DEVELOPMENT, INC.; *U.S. Private*, pg. 25
ACKERMAN & CO.; *U.S. Private*, pg. 59
ACKERMAN INVESTMENT COMPANY; *U.S. Private*, pg. 60
ACKERMAN MCQUEEN, INC. - COLORADO SPRINGS—See Ackerman McQueen, Inc.; *U.S. Private*, pg. 60
ACKERMAN MCQUEEN, INC.; *U.S. Private*, pg. 60
ACKERMAN MCQUEEN, INC.—See Ackerman McQueen, Inc.; *U.S. Private*, pg. 60
ACKERMAN MCQUEEN, INC.—See Ackerman McQueen, Inc.; *U.S. Private*, pg. 60
ACKERMAN PR; *U.S. Private*, pg. 60
ACKERMANS PROPRIETARY LIMITED—See Steinhoff International Holdings N.V.; *Int'l*, pg. 7194
ACKERMANS & VAN HAAREN NV; *Int'l*, pg. 104
ACKER MERRALL & CONDIT COMPANY, INC.; *U.S. Private*, pg. 59
ACK FORANKRA SAS—See Axel Johnson Gruppen AB; *Int'l*, pg. 763
A.C. KISSLING, INC.; *U.S. Private*, pg. 24
ACKLANDS-GRAINGER INC.—See W.W. Grainger, Inc.; *U.S. Public*, pg. 2319
ACKLEY BEVERAGE GROUP, LLC; *U.S. Private*, pg. 60
ACKLEY STATE BANK; *U.S. Private*, pg. 60
ACKLEY SWEENEY ADVERTISING; *U.S. Private*, pg. 60
ACKNIT INDUSTRIES LTD.; *Int'l*, pg. 106
ACKRILL MEDIA GROUP—See JPIMedia Holdings Limited; *Int'l*, pg. 4006
ACKRILL NEWSPAPERS LTD—See JPIMedia Holdings Limited; *Int'l*, pg. 4006
ACKROO INC.; *Int'l*, pg. 106
ACKU METAL INDUSTRIES (M) SDN. BHD.—See San Shing Fastech Corp.; *Int'l*, pg. 6521
ACKURAT INDUSTRIPLAST AB—See XANO Industri AB; *Int'l*, pg. 8519
ACL ADVANCED COMMERCE LABS GMBH—See Osterreichische Post AG; *Int'l*, pg. 5653
ACLAIRO PHARMACEUTICAL DEVELOPMENT GROUP, INC.—See Lillo SpA; *Int'l*, pg. 4498
ACL AIRSHOP PTE LTD—See Ranger Aerospace LLC; *U.S. Private*, pg. 3354
ACL AIRSHOP (SHANGHAI) LIMITED—See Ranger Aerospace LLC; *U.S. Private*, pg. 3354
ACLA LTD.—See ARCADIS N.V.; *Int'l*, pg. 541
ACLARA POWER-LINE SYSTEMS INC.—See Hubbell Incorporated; *U.S. Public*, pg. 1067
ACLARA RESOURCES INC.; *Int'l*, pg. 107
ACLARA SOFTWARE—See Hubbell Incorporated; *U.S. Public*, pg. 1067
ACLARA TECHNOLOGIES LLC—See Hubbell Incorporated; *U.S. Public*, pg. 1067
ACLARION, INC.; *U.S. Public*, pg. 35
ACLARIS THERAPEUTICS, INC.; *U.S. Public*, pg. 35
A CLASSIC TIME WATCH COMPANY INC.; *U.S. Private*, pg. 18

ACL CABLES PLC - FACTORY—See ACL Cables PLC; *Int'l*, pg. 106
ACL CABLES PLC; *Int'l*, pg. 106
A CLEAN ENVIRONMENT CO., INC.; *U.S. Private*, pg. 18
A.C. LEGG PACKING COMPANY, INC.; *U.S. Private*, pg. 24
ACLINE HR—See New Mountain Capital, LLC; *U.S. Private*, pg. 2901
ACL INTERNATIONAL LTD.; *Int'l*, pg. 106
ACLIVITI LLC; *U.S. Private*, pg. 60
ACLOCHE - EXECUTIVE SEARCH DIVISION—See Acloche; *U.S. Private*, pg. 60
ACLOCHE; *U.S. Private*, pg. 60
A-C LOGISTICS—See Am-Can Transport Service Inc.; *U.S. Private*, pg. 215
A CLOUD GURU LTD.; *U.S. Private*, pg. 18
ACL PLASTIC PLC; *Int'l*, pg. 107
ACL PTY LTD.—See Navitas Limited; *Int'l*, pg. 5176
ACL SERVICES LTD.—See Insight Venture Management, LLC; *U.S. Private*, pg. 2090
ACMA COMPUTERS INC.; *U.S. Private*, pg. 60
ACMA ENGINEERS PRIVATE LIMITED—See Acma Ltd.; *Int'l*, pg. 107
ACMA GD—See Coesia S.p.A.; *Int'l*, pg. 1690
ACMA LTD.; *Int'l*, pg. 107
A.C. MANUFACTURING LTD.—See Lindab International AB; *Int'l*, pg. 4503
AC MARCA, S.A.; *Int'l*, pg. 74
AC MARTIN PARTNERS, INC.; *U.S. Private*, pg. 45
ACMA SA—See NV Bekaert SA; *Int'l*, pg. 5495
ACMA S.P.A.—See Coesia S.p.A.; *Int'l*, pg. 1689
ACMAT COMPANIES, INC.—See ACMAT Corporation; *U.S. Public*, pg. 35
ACMAT CORPORATION; *U.S. Public*, pg. 35
ACMAT OF TEXAS, INC.—See ACMAT Corporation; *U.S. Public*, pg. 35
ACM BERNSTEIN GMBH—See Equitable Holdings, Inc.; *U.S. Public*, pg. 789
ACMBERNSTEIN GMBH—See Equitable Holdings, Inc.; *U.S. Public*, pg. 789
ACMDC VENTURES, INC. (AVI)—See Atlas Consolidated Mining & Development Corporation; *Int'l*, pg. 676
ACME AEROSPACE, INC.—See TransDigm Group Incorporated; *U.S. Public*, pg. 2181
ACME ARCHITECTURAL PRODUCTS INC.; *U.S. Private*, pg. 60
ACME AUTOMOTIVE—See Coilhose Pneumatics Inc.; *U.S. Private*, pg. 964
ACME BIOSCIENCE, INC.—See Hangzhou Tigermed Consulting Co., Ltd.; *Int'l*, pg. 3250
ACME BRICK COMPANY—See Berkshire Hathaway Inc.; *U.S. Public*, pg. 297
ACME BUILDING MAINTENANCE COMPANY; *U.S. Private*, pg. 60
ACME CONCRETE PAVING INC.; *U.S. Private*, pg. 60
ACME CONSTRUCTION SUPPLY CO. INC.; *U.S. Private*, pg. 60
ACME CRYOGENICS INC.—See Dover Corporation; *U.S. Public*, pg. 678
ACME DELIVERY SERVICE INC.; *U.S. Private*, pg. 60
ACME DIE CASTING CORPORATION; *U.S. Private*, pg. 60
ACME ELECTRIC LLC—See Hubbell Incorporated; *U.S. Public*, pg. 1066
ACME ELECTRIC MOTOR INC.; *U.S. Private*, pg. 60
ACME ELECTRONICS CORPORATION; *Int'l*, pg. 107
ACME ELECTRONICS (GUANGZHOU) CO. LTD.—See Acme Electronics Corporation; *Int'l*, pg. 107
ACME ELECTRONICS (KUNSHAN) CO. LTD.—See Acme Electronics Corporation; *Int'l*, pg. 107
ACME ENGINEERING AND MANUFACTURING CORP.; *U.S. Private*, pg. 60
ACME FARMS, INC.; *U.S. Private*, pg. 60
ACME FERRITE PRODUCTS SDN. BHD.—See Acme Electronics Corporation; *Int'l*, pg. 107
ACME FOOD SALES, INC.; *U.S. Private*, pg. 61
ACME FOUNDRY, INC.; *U.S. Private*, pg. 61
ACME GALVANIZING, INC.—See AZZ, Inc.; *U.S. Public*, pg. 259
ACME-HARDESTY CO.—See Jacob Stern & Sons, Inc.; *U.S. Private*, pg. 2179
ACME HOLDING CO.—See Swarovski & Co.; *Int'l*, pg. 7362
ACME HOLDINGS BERHAD; *Int'l*, pg. 107
ACME HOLDINGS, INC.; *U.S. Private*, pg. 61
ACME INDUSTRIAL COMPANY—See Jergens Inc.; *U.S. Private*, pg. 2201
ACME INDUSTRIAL PIPING, LLC—See Limbach Holdings, Inc.; *U.S. Public*, pg. 1316
ACME INTERNATIONAL HOLDINGS LIMITED; *Int'l*, pg. 107
ACM ELEVATOR CO.—See Otis Worldwide Corporation; *U.S. Public*, pg. 1623
ACME LIFT COMPANY; *U.S. Private*, pg. 61
ACME MANUFACTURING COMPANY INC.; *U.S. Private*, pg. 61
ACME MARKETS, INC.—See Cerberus Capital Management, L.P.; *U.S. Private*, pg. 836

COMPANY NAME INDEX

ACME MATERIALS COMPANY—See WG Block Co.; *U.S. Private*, pg. 4503
ACME-MCCRARY CORPORATION; *U.S. Private*, pg. 61
ACME METAL CAP CO., INC.; *U.S. Private*, pg. 61
ACME MILLS CO. INC.; *U.S. Private*, pg. 61
ACME-MONACO CORPORATION; *U.S. Private*, pg. 61
ACME NISSAN; *U.S. Private*, pg. 61
ACME-OCHS BRICK AND STONE, INC.—See Berkshire Hathaway Inc.; *U.S. Public*, pg. 298
ACME PACKET, INC.—See Oracle Corporation; *U.S. Public*, pg. 1610
ACME PAPER & SUPPLY CO. INC.; *U.S. Private*, pg. 61
ACME PAPER & SUPPLY CO., INC.—See Acme Paper & Supply Co. Inc.; *U.S. Private*, pg. 61
ACME PLASTICS, INC.; *U.S. Private*, pg. 61
ACME PRINTING & PACKAGING PLC; *Int'l*, pg. 107
ACME REFINING SCRAP IRON & METAL COMPANY; *U.S. Private*, pg. 61
ACME REFRIGERATION LTD.—See Pentland Group Limited; *Int'l*, pg. 5792
ACME REFRIGERATION OF BATON ROUGE, LLC—See Watsco, Inc.; *U.S. Public*, pg. 2336
ACME RESOURCES LIMITED; *Int'l*, pg. 107
ACME ROLLING STEEL DOOR CORP.—See DuraServ Corp; *U.S. Private*, pg. 1293
ACME/ROMAC INC.—See Nusser Industries Inc.; *U.S. Private*, pg. 2974
ACME SMOKED FISH CORPORATION; *U.S. Private*, pg. 61
ACME SPONGE COMPANY—See Armaly Sponge Company, Inc.; *U.S. Private*, pg. 330
ACME STEEL DOOR CORP.—See Acme Architectural Products Inc.; *U.S. Private*, pg. 60
ACME TRADING CORPORATION; *U.S. Private*, pg. 61
ACME TRUCK LINE, INC.; *U.S. Private*, pg. 61
ACME UNITED (ASIA PACIFIC) LTD.—See Acme United Corporation; *U.S. Public*, pg. 35
ACME UNITED CORPORATION; *U.S. Public*, pg. 35
ACME UNITED EUROPE GMBH—See Acme United Corporation; *U.S. Public*, pg. 35
ACME UNITED LIMITED—See Acme United Corporation; *U.S. Public*, pg. 35
ACMG, INC.; *U.S. Private*, pg. 62
A.C. MILLER CONCRETE PRODUCTS INC., *U.S. Private*, pg. 24
ACML—See FAYAT SAS; *Int'l*, pg. 2624
ACM MEXICO, S.A. DE C.V.—See Prysmian S.p.A.; *Int'l*, pg. 6010
AC MOBIL D.O.O.—See Honda Motor Co., Ltd.; *Int'l*, pg. 3459
A.C. MOORE ARTS & CRAFTS, INC.—See Sbar's, Inc.; *U.S. Private*, pg. 3559
ACMOS INC.; *Int'l*, pg. 107
ACMOS SOURCING SERVICE INC.—See ACMOS INC.; *Int'l*, pg. 107
ACM PROJEKTENTWICKLUNG GMBH—See SOCRATES Privatstiftung; *Int'l*, pg. 7044
ACM PROPERTY SERVICES, LLC—See Macquarie Group Limited; *Int'l*, pg. 4627
ACM RESEARCH, INC.; *U.S. Public*, pg. 35
ACM RESEARCH (SHANGHAI), INC.—See Acm Research, Inc.; *U.S. Public*, pg. 35
ACM-SERVICE COMPANY LLC—See Chien Wei Precise Technology Co., Ltd.; *Int'l*, pg. 1477
A.C.M.S., INC.—See Waste Connections, Inc.; *Int'l*, pg. 8352
ACM TECHNOLOGIES INC.; *U.S. Private*, pg. 60
A.C.N. 079 010 772 PTY LTD—See Expedia Group, Inc.; *U.S. Public*, pg. 809
ACN 108 719 197 PTY LTD—See Insight Venture Management, LLC; *U.S. Private*, pg. 2088
ACN 108 719 197 PTY LTD—See Stone Point Capital LLC; *U.S. Private*, pg. 3822
A.C.N. 603 303 126 PTY LTD—See Cerberus Capital Management, L.P.; *U.S. Private*, pg. 837
ACNA—See Air France-KLM S.A.; *Int'l*, pg. 237
ACNA—See Air France-KLM S.A.; *Int'l*, pg. 237
ACNB BANK—See ACNB Corporation; *U.S. Public*, pg. 35
ACNB CORPORATION; *U.S. Public*, pg. 35
ACNB INSURANCE SERVICES INC.—See ACNB Corporation; *U.S. Public*, pg. 35
ACNE CORP.—See Acne Studio AB; *Int'l*, pg. 107
A.C. NELSEN ENTERPRISES INC.; *U.S. Private*, pg. 24
ACNE STUDIO AB; *Int'l*, pg. 107
ACN GROUP OF CALIFORNIA, INC.—See UnitedHealth Group Incorporated; *U.S. Public*, pg. 2238
ACNIELSEN AB—See Brookfield Corporation; *Int'l*, pg. 1177
ACNIELSEN AB—See Elliott Management Corporation; *U.S. Private*, pg. 1370
ACNIELSEN ARGENTINA S.A.—See Brookfield Corporation; *Int'l*, pg. 1177
ACNIELSEN ARGENTINA S.A.—See Elliott Management Corporation; *U.S. Private*, pg. 1369
ACNIELSEN CAMEROON SARL—See Brookfield Corporation; *Int'l*, pg. 1177
ACNIELSEN CAMEROON SARL—See Elliott Management Corporation; *U.S. Private*, pg. 1369

A.C. NIELSEN CHILE LIMITADA—See Brookfield Corporation; *Int'l*, pg. 1177
A.C. NIELSEN CHILE LIMITADA—See Elliott Management Corporation; *U.S. Private*, pg. 1369
ACNIELSEN COMPANY (BELGIUM) S.A.—See Brookfield Corporation; *Int'l*, pg. 1177
ACNIELSEN COMPANY (BELGIUM) S.A.—See Elliott Management Corporation; *U.S. Private*, pg. 1370
A.C. NIELSEN COMPANY, LLC—See Brookfield Corporation; *Int'l*, pg. 1176
A.C. NIELSEN COMPANY, LLC—See Elliott Management Corporation; *U.S. Private*, pg. 1369
ACNIELSEN COMPANY LTD.—See Brookfield Corporation; *Int'l*, pg. 1177
ACNIELSEN COMPANY LTD.—See Elliott Management Corporation; *U.S. Private*, pg. 1370
A.C. NIELSEN COMPANY OF CANADA—See Brookfield Corporation; *Int'l*, pg. 1177
A.C. NIELSEN COMPANY OF CANADA—See Elliott Management Corporation; *U.S. Private*, pg. 1369
A.C. NIELSEN COMPANY, S.L.—See Brookfield Corporation; *Int'l*, pg. 1177
A.C. NIELSEN COMPANY, S.L.—See Elliott Management Corporation; *U.S. Private*, pg. 1369
ACNIELSEN CORPORATION JAPAN—See Brookfield Corporation; *Int'l*, pg. 1178
ACNIELSEN CORPORATION JAPAN—See Brookfield Corporation; *Int'l*, pg. 1178
ACNIELSEN CORPORATION JAPAN—See Elliott Management Corporation; *U.S. Private*, pg. 1370
ACNIELSEN CORPORATION JAPAN—See Elliott Management Corporation; *U.S. Private*, pg. 1370
ACNIELSEN CORPORATION—See Brookfield Corporation; *Int'l*, pg. 1176
ACNIELSEN CORPORATION—See Elliott Management Corporation; *U.S. Private*, pg. 1369
AC NIELSEN COTE D'IVOIRE LIMITED—See Brookfield Corporation; *Int'l*, pg. 1177
AC NIELSEN COTE D'IVOIRE LIMITED—See Elliott Management Corporation; *U.S. Private*, pg. 1369
ACNIELSEN CYPRUS LIMITED—See Brookfield Corporation; *Int'l*, pg. 1177
ACNIELSEN CYPRUS LIMITED—See Elliott Management Corporation; *U.S. Private*, pg. 1369
A.C. NIELSEN DE COLOMBIA LTDA.—See Brookfield Corporation; *Int'l*, pg. 1177
A.C. NIELSEN DE COLOMBIA LTDA.—See Elliott Management Corporation; *U.S. Private*, pg. 1369
A.C. NIELSEN DE VENEZUELA, S.A.—See Brookfield Corporation; *Int'l*, pg. 1177
A.C. NIELSEN DE VENEZUELA, S.A.—See Elliott Management Corporation; *U.S. Private*, pg. 1369
A.C. NIELSEN DO BRASIL LTDA.—See Brookfield Corporation; *Int'l*, pg. 1177
A.C. NIELSEN DO BRASIL LTDA.—See Elliott Management Corporation; *U.S. Private*, pg. 1369
ACNIELSEN ECUADOR S.A.—See Brookfield Corporation; *Int'l*, pg. 1177
ACNIELSEN ECUADOR S.A.—See Elliott Management Corporation; *U.S. Private*, pg. 1369
ACNIELSEN EUROPE—See Brookfield Corporation; *Int'l*, pg. 1177
ACNIELSEN EUROPE—See Elliott Management Corporation; *U.S. Private*, pg. 1369
A.C. NIELSEN GESELLSCHAFT M.B.H.—See Brookfield Corporation; *Int'l*, pg. 1177
A.C. NIELSEN GESELLSCHAFT M.B.H.—See Elliott Management Corporation; *U.S. Private*, pg. 1369
ACNIELSEN GHANA LIMITED—See Brookfield Corporation; *Int'l*, pg. 1177
ACNIELSEN GHANA LIMITED—See Elliott Management Corporation; *U.S. Private*, pg. 1369
A.C. NIELSEN GMBH—See Brookfield Corporation; *Int'l*, pg. 1177
A.C. NIELSEN GMBH—See Elliott Management Corporation; *U.S. Private*, pg. 1369
ACNIELSEN GROUP LIMITED—See Brookfield Corporation; *Int'l*, pg. 1178
ACNIELSEN GROUP LIMITED—See Elliott Management Corporation; *U.S. Private*, pg. 1370
ACNIELSEN KAZAKHSTAN LTD.—See Brookfield Corporation; *Int'l*, pg. 1177
ACNIELSEN KAZAKHSTAN LTD.—See Elliott Management Corporation; *U.S. Private*, pg. 1369
ACNIELSEN (KOREA) LTD.—See Brookfield Corporation; *Int'l*, pg. 1178
ACNIELSEN (KOREA) LTD.—See Elliott Management Corporation; *U.S. Private*, pg. 1370
ACNIELSEN LIMITED LIABILITY COMPANY—See Brookfield Corporation; *Int'l*, pg. 1177
ACNIELSEN LIMITED LIABILITY COMPANY—See Elliott Management Corporation; *U.S. Private*, pg. 1369
ACNIELSEN (NEDERLAND) B.V.—See Brookfield Corporation; *Int'l*, pg. 1177
ACNIELSEN (NEDERLAND) B.V.—See Elliott Management Corporation; *U.S. Private*, pg. 1370
ACNIELSEN NIGERIA LIMITED—See Brookfield Corporation; *Int'l*, pg. 1177

ACON INVESTMENTS, LLC

ACNIELSEN NIGERIA LIMITED—See Elliott Management Corporation; *U.S. Private*, pg. 1369
ACNIELSEN NORGE AS—See Brookfield Corporation; *Int'l*, pg. 1177
ACNIELSEN NORGE AS—See Elliott Management Corporation; *U.S. Private*, pg. 1370
ACNIELSEN (N.Z.) LTD.—See Brookfield Corporation; *Int'l*, pg. 1178
ACNIELSEN (N.Z.) LTD.—See Elliott Management Corporation; *U.S. Private*, pg. 1370
A.C. NIELSEN OF IRELAND LIMITED—See Brookfield Corporation; *Int'l*, pg. 1177
A.C. NIELSEN OF IRELAND LIMITED—See Elliott Management Corporation; *U.S. Private*, pg. 1369
ACNIELSEN PAKISTAN (PRIVATE) LIMITED—See Brookfield Corporation; *Int'l*, pg. 1177
ACNIELSEN PAKISTAN (PRIVATE) LIMITED—See Elliott Management Corporation; *U.S. Private*, pg. 1369
A.C. NIELSEN PORTUGAL—See Brookfield Corporation; *Int'l*, pg. 1177
A.C. NIELSEN PORTUGAL—See Elliott Management Corporation; *U.S. Private*, pg. 1369
ACNIELSEN PUERTO RICO INC.—See Brookfield Corporation; *Int'l*, pg. 1177
ACNIELSEN PUERTO RICO INC.—See Elliott Management Corporation; *U.S. Private*, pg. 1369
ACNIELSEN SARL—See Brookfield Corporation; *Int'l*, pg. 1177
ACNIELSEN SARL—See Elliott Management Corporation; *U.S. Private*, pg. 1369
ACNIELSEN S.A.—See Brookfield Corporation; *Int'l*, pg. 1177
ACNIELSEN S.A.—See Brookfield Corporation; *Int'l*, pg. 1177
ACNIELSEN SA—See Brookfield Corporation; *Int'l*, pg. 1178
ACNIELSEN S.A.—See Elliott Management Corporation; *U.S. Private*, pg. 1369
ACNIELSEN S.A.—See Elliott Management Corporation; *U.S. Private*, pg. 1370
ACNIELSEN SA—See Elliott Management Corporation; *U.S. Private*, pg. 1370
A.C. NIELSEN, S. DE RL DE C.V.—See Brookfield Corporation; *Int'l*, pg. 1177
A.C. NIELSEN, S. DE RL DE C.V.—See Elliott Management Corporation; *U.S. Private*, pg. 1369
ACNIELSEN—See Brookfield Corporation; *Int'l*, pg. 1177
ACNIELSEN—See Brookfield Corporation; *Int'l*, pg. 1177
ACNIELSEN—See Elliott Management Corporation; *U.S. Private*, pg. 1369
ACNIELSEN—See Elliott Management Corporation; *U.S. Private*, pg. 1369
ACNIELSEN (TANZANIA) LTD.—See Brookfield Corporation; *Int'l*, pg. 1177
ACNIELSEN (TANZANIA) LTD.—See Elliott Management Corporation; *U.S. Private*, pg. 1369
ACNIELSEN (US), INC.—See Brookfield Corporation; *Int'l*, pg. 1176
ACNIELSEN (US), INC.—See Elliott Management Corporation; *U.S. Private*, pg. 1369
ACN, INC.; *U.S. Private*, pg. 62
ACNOVER, S.L.; *Int'l*, pg. 107
ACN RECYCLING INDUSTRIES LLC—See America Chung Nam Inc.; *U.S. Private*, pg. 220
ACOBAL S.A.S.—See Northern Technologies International Corporation; *U.S. Public*, pg. 1537
ACOEM AB—See ACOEM Group; *Int'l*, pg. 107
ACOEM GROUP; *Int'l*, pg. 107
ACO GROUP BERHAD; *Int'l*, pg. 107
ACO HARDWARE, INC.; *U.S. Private*, pg. 62
ACO HEALTH PARTNERS LLC—See HealthLynked Corp.; *U.S. Public*, pg. 1016
A.C.O. INFORMATICA S.R.L.—See WiseTech Global Limited; *Int'l*, pg. 8436
ACOMA ENERGY, LLC; *U.S. Private*, pg. 62
ACOMAR—See CMA CGM S.A.; *Int'l*, pg. 1666
ACOM CO., LTD.—See Mitsubishi UFJ Financial Group, Inc.; *Int'l*, pg. 4968
ACOM MEDICAL BILLING—See ACOM Solutions Inc.; *U.S. Private*, pg. 62
ACOMMERCE GROUP PUBLIC COMPANY LIMITED; *Int'l*, pg. 108
ACOMMIT AG—See Bechtle AG; *Int'l*, pg. 937
ACOMO INVESTMENTS B.V.—See ACOMO N.V.; *Int'l*, pg. 108
ACOMON AG—See Mitsui Chemicals, Inc.; *Int'l*, pg. 4980
ACOMO N.V.; *Int'l*, pg. 108
ACOM SOLUTIONS INC. -ISERIES AS/400 DIVISION—See ACOM Solutions Inc.; *U.S. Private*, pg. 62
ACOM SOLUTIONS INC.; *U.S. Private*, pg. 62
ACONCAGUA DISTRIBUCIONES SRL—See Sealed Air Corporation; *U.S. Public*, pg. 1852
A CONE ZONE, INC.—See Investcorp Holdings B.S.C.; *Int'l*, pg. 3776
A CONE ZONE, INC.—See Trilantic Capital Management L.P.; *U.S. Private*, pg. 4231
ACON INVESTMENTS, LLC; *U.S. Private*, pg. 62

ACON INVESTMENTS, LLC

A CONTACT ELECTRIC RENTALS, L.P.—See I Squared Capital Advisors (US) LLC; *U.S. Private*, pg. 2021
A CONTACT ELECTRIC RENTALS, L.P.—See TDR Capital LLP; *Int'l*, pg. 7490
ACOPIAN TECHNICAL COMPANY; *U.S. Public*, pg. 63
ACOPIO FACILITY GMBH & CO. KG.—See Covivio; *Int'l*, pg. 1821
ACORDA THERAPEUTICS, INC.; *U.S. Public*, pg. 36
ACORDIS BV—See CVC Capital Partners SICAV-FIS S.A.; *Int'l*, pg. 1886
ACORDY INVEST S.A.; *Int'l*, pg. 108
A-CORE JIANGMEN ELECTRONICS CO., LTD.—See Lingyi iTech (Guangdong) Company; *Int'l*, pg. 4512
ACORIO LLC; *U.S. Private*, pg. 63
ACORIS RESEARCH LIMITED—See Hikal Limited; *Int'l*, pg. 3389
ACORN CAPITAL INVESTMENT FUND LIMITED—See Acorn Capital Limited; *Int'l*, pg. 108
ACORN CAPITAL LIMITED; *Int'l*, pg. 108
ACORN DIRECT MARKETING LIMITED—See Bread Financial Holdings Inc.; *U.S. Public*, pg. 381
ACORN ENERGY, INC.; *U.S. Public*, pg. 36
ACORN ENGINEERING COMPANY, INC.; *U.S. Private*, pg. 63
ACORN ENVIRONMENTAL SYSTEMS LIMITED—See Bord na Mona Plc; *Int'l*, pg. 1113
ACORNE PLC - EXHILARATION—See Inflexion Private Equity Partners LLP; *Int'l*, pg. 3689
ACORN-GENCON PLASTICS—See Acorn Engineering Company, Inc.; *U.S. Private*, pg. 63
ACORN GLOBAL RECRUITMENT LTD.—See Synergie SA; *Int'l*, pg. 7383
ACORN GROWTH COMPANIES, LC; *U.S. Private*, pg. 63
ACORN INCOME CORP.; *Int'l*, pg. 108
ACORN INDUSTRIAL, INC.—See Comfort Systems USA, Inc.; *U.S. Public*, pg. 543
ACORN INDUSTRIAL SERVICES LTD.—See THK CO., LTD.; *Int'l*, pg. 7711
ACORN INTERNATIONAL, INC.; *Int'l*, pg. 108
ACORN INTERNATIONAL NETWORK PTE. LTD.—See Brown & Brown, Inc.; *U.S. Public*, pg. 396
ACORN LEARNING SOLUTIONS LTD.—See Synergie SA; *Int'l*, pg. 7383
ACORN MEDIA GROUP, INC.—See AMC Networks Inc.; *U.S. Public*, pg. 92
ACORN PACKAGING INC.—See Aga Khan Development Network; *Int'l*, pg. 199
ACORN PAPER PRODUCTS COMPANY—See Oak Paper Products Co. Inc.; *U.S. Private*, pg. 2984
ACORN PETROLEUM; *U.S. Private*, pg. 63
ACORN PRODUCTIONS LTD—See AMC Networks Inc.; *U.S. Public*, pg. 92
ACORN PRODUCTS CO. INC.; *U.S. Private*, pg. 63
ACORN RECRUITMENT LTD.—See Synergie SA; *Int'l*, pg. 7383
ACORN ROOFING SUPPLY, CO.—See Leonard Green & Partners, L.P.; *U.S. Private*, pg. 2428
ACORNS ADVISERS, LLC—See Acorns Grow Incorporated; *U.S. Private*, pg. 64
ACORN SERVICES INC.; *U.S. Private*, pg. 64
ACORNS GROW INCORPORATED; *U.S. Private*, pg. 64
ACORNSOFT CO., LTD.—See Namutech Co., Ltd.; *Int'l*, pg. 5137
ACORNS SECURITIES, LLC—See Acorns Grow Incorporated; *U.S. Private*, pg. 64
ACORN (SYNERGIE) UK LTD.—See Synergie SA; *Int'l*, pg. 7383
ACOR & TEREOS IBERIA SA—See Tereos; *Int'l*, pg. 7564
ACOS BOHLER-UDDEHOLM DO BRASIL LTDA.—See voestalpine AG; *Int'l*, pg. 8287
ACO SMARTCARE CO., LTD.—See Compal Electronics, Inc.; *Int'l*, pg. 1746
ACOSTA FOODSERVICE—See Acosta, Inc.; *U.S. Private*, pg. 64
ACOSTA, INC.; *U.S. Private*, pg. 64
ACOSTA MILITARY SALES, LLC—See Acosta, Inc.; *U.S. Private*, pg. 64
ACOSTA SALES & MARKETING CO. - BOSTON/MARLBOROUGH OFFICE—See Acosta, Inc.; *U.S. Private*, pg. 64
ACOSTA SALES & MARKETING COMPANY—See Acosta, Inc.; *U.S. Private*, pg. 64
ACOSTA SALES & MARKETING CO. - PLEASANTON OFFICE—See Acosta, Inc.; *U.S. Private*, pg. 64
ACOTEC SCIENTIFIC HOLDINGS LIMITED; *Int'l*, pg. 108
ACOT GROUP OF COMPANIES; *Int'l*, pg. 108
ACOT PLASTICS (XIAMEN) CO., LTD.—See Acma Ltd.; *Int'l*, pg. 107
ACOT TOOLING XIAMEN LTD.—See Acma Ltd.; *Int'l*, pg. 107
ACOUNS NIGERIA LTD.—See HORIBA Ltd; *Int'l*, pg. 3474
ACOUS CORPORATION—See TOA Corporation; *Int'l*, pg. 7768
ACOUSOFT INFORMATISERING BV; *Int'l*, pg. 108
ACOUSORT AB; *Int'l*, pg. 108
ACOUSTIBLOK INC.; *U.S. Private*, pg. 64
ACOUSTICAL SHEETMETAL INCORPORATED; *U.S. Private*, pg. 64

ACOUSTICAL SPECIALTIES & SUPPLY, INC.; *U.S. Private*, pg. 64
ACOUSTIC ENERGY LIMITED—See Formosa Prosonic Industries Berhad; *Int'l*, pg. 2736
ACOUSTICFAB, LLC—See ITT Inc.; *U.S. Public*, pg. 1177
ACOUSTIC INNOVATIONS INC.; *U.S. Private*, pg. 64
ACOUSTIC, L.P.—See International Business Machines Corporation; *U.S. Public*, pg. 1148
ACOUSTIC METROLOGY LIMITED—See Demant A/S; *Int'l*, pg. 2022
ACOUSTICS BY DESIGN, INC.; *U.S. Private*, pg. 64
ACOUSTIC TECHNOLOGIES, INC.—See Cirrus Logic, Inc.; *U.S. Public*, pg. 496
ACOUSTI ENGINEERING CO. OF FLORIDA—See Ardian SAS; *Int'l*, pg. 554
ACOUSTI ENGINEERING CO.—See Ardian SAS; *Int'l*, pg. 554
ACOUSTIGUIDE ASIA LTD.—See Espro Information Technologies Ltd.; *Int'l*, pg. 2507
ACOUSTIGUIDE GMBH—See Espro Information Technologies Ltd.; *Int'l*, pg. 2507
ACOUSTIGUIDE INC.—See Espro Information Technologies Ltd.; *Int'l*, pg. 2507
ACOUSTIGUIDE JAPAN LTD.—See Espro Information Technologies Ltd.; *Int'l*, pg. 2507
ACOUSTIGUIDE LTD.—See Espro Information Technologies Ltd.; *Int'l*, pg. 2507
ACOUSTIGUIDE OF AUSTRALIA PTY., LTD.—See Espro Information Technologies Ltd.; *Int'l*, pg. 2507
ACOUSTIGUIDE SAS—See Espro Information Technologies Ltd.; *Int'l*, pg. 2507
ACOUSTI INCORPORATED; *U.S. Private*, pg. 64
ACPA TECHNOLOGY CO., LTD.—See Ahoku Electronic Company; *Int'l*, pg. 225
ACP BELGIUM NV—See Air Products & Chemicals, Inc.; *U.S. Public*, pg. 64
ACP GMBH & CO. BETEILIGUNGEN KG—See Allianz SE; *Int'l*, pg. 341
ACP INC.—See Ali Holding S.r.l; *Int'l*, pg. 322
ACP JETS, LLC—See Air Rutter International, LLC; *U.S. Private*, pg. 139
A&C PLASTIC PRODUCTS INC.; *U.S. Private*, pg. 19
A&C PLASTICS, INC.; *U.S. Private*, pg. 19
AC PLASTIQUES USA, LLC—See Nimbus B.V.; *Int'l*, pg. 5296
ACP MAGAZINES PTE. LTD.—See Singapore Press Holdings Ltd.; *Int'l*, pg. 6942
ACP MARKETING, INC.; *Int'l*, pg. 108
ACP MARKETING UK LTD.—See ACP Marketing, Inc.; *Int'l*, pg. 108
ACP MARKETING US INC.—See ACP Marketing, Inc.; *Int'l*, pg. 108
ACP METAL FINISHING PTE LTD—See Grand Venture Technology Limited; *Int'l*, pg. 3057
ACP PHARMA S.A.—See NEUCA S.A.; *Int'l*, pg. 5218
AC PRODUCTS, INC.—See Quaker Chemical Corporation; *U.S. Public*, pg. 1745
AC PRODUCTS, INC.—See AIP, LLC; *U.S. Private*, pg. 133
AC PRO; *U.S. Private*, pg. 45
ACP VERMOGENSVERWALTUNG GMBH & CO. KG NR. 4A—See Allianz SE; *Int'l*, pg. 341
ACP VERMOGENSVERWALTUNG GMBH & CO. KG NR. 4C—See Allianz SE; *Int'l*, pg. 341
ACQUA DI PARMA LLC—See LVMH Moet Hennessy Louis Vuitton SE; *Int'l*, pg. 4590
ACQUA DI PARMA S.R.L.—See LVMH Moet Hennessy Louis Vuitton SE; *Int'l*, pg. 4600
ACQUAENNA S.C.P.A.—See Iren S.p.A.; *Int'l*, pg. 3807
ACQUE DI CALTANISSETTA, S.P.A.—See Fomento de Construcciones y Contratas, S.A.; *Int'l*, pg. 2722
ACQUEDOTTO DI DOMODOSSOLA S.P.A.—See Eni S.p.A.; *Int'l*, pg. 2437
ACQUEDOTTO DI SAVONA S.P.A.—See Eni S.p.A.; *Int'l*, pg. 2437
ACQUE INDUSTRIALI S.R.L.—See ACEA S.p.A.; *Int'l*, pg. 95
ACQUE SERVIZI S.R.L.—See ACEA S.p.A.; *Int'l*, pg. 95
ACQUIA AUSTRALIA—See Vista Equity Partners, LLC; *U.S. Private*, pg. 4394
ACQUIA INC.—See Vista Equity Partners, LLC; *U.S. Private*, pg. 4394
ACQUIA UK—See Vista Equity Partners, LLC; *U.S. Private*, pg. 4394
ACQUI POLO ESPANA SL—See Ralph Lauren Corporation; *U.S. Public*, pg. 1761
ACQUI POLO SAS—See Ralph Lauren Corporation; *U.S. Public*, pg. 1761
ACQUIRE MEDIA 1 UK LIMITED—See Moody's Corporation; *U.S. Public*, pg. 1466
ACQUIRENT, LLC; *U.S. Private*, pg. 64
ACQUIS CONSULTING GROUP, LLC; *U.S. Private*, pg. 65
ACQUISIO INC.—See Siris Capital Group, LLC; *U.S. Private*, pg. 3675
ACQUISITION BELL HOSPITAL, LLC—See Apollo Global Management, Inc.; *U.S. Public*, pg. 154

ACQUISITIONS RESEARCH & LOGISTICS LLC; *U.S. Private*, pg. 65
ACQYRE B.V.—See Fluor Corporation; *U.S. Public*, pg. 857
ACRATHON PRECISION TECHNOLOGIES (DONGGUAN) CO., LTD.—See TDK Corporation; *Int'l*, pg. 7487
ACRATHON PRECISION TECHNOLOGIES (HK) LIMITED—See InnoTek Limited; *Int'l*, pg. 3710
A.C.R. DI REGGIANI ALBERTINO S.P.A.—See Hera S.p.A.; *Int'l*, pg. 3356
ACREAGE HOLDINGS, INC.; *U.S. Public*, pg. 36
ACREDIA VERSICHERUNG AG—See Allianz SE; *Int'l*, pg. 352
ACREE OIL COMPANY; *U.S. Private*, pg. 65
ACRELEC APS—See GLORY Ltd.; *Int'l*, pg. 3009
ACRELEC FINLAND OY—See GLORY Ltd.; *Int'l*, pg. 3009
ACRELEC GMBH—See GLORY Ltd.; *Int'l*, pg. 3009
ACRELEC GROUP BVBA—See GLORY Ltd.; *Int'l*, pg. 3009
ACRELEC GROUP SAS—See GLORY Ltd.; *Int'l*, pg. 3009
ACRELEC INC.—See GLORY Ltd.; *Int'l*, pg. 3009
ACRELEC INFORMATICA GROUP SL—See GLORY Ltd.; *Int'l*, pg. 3009
ACRELEC SWEDEN AB—See GLORY Ltd.; *Int'l*, pg. 3009
ACR ELECTRONICS, INC.—See The Jordan Company, L.P.; *U.S. Private*, pg. 4059
ACRELEC UK LIMITED—See GLORY Ltd.; *Int'l*, pg. 3009
ACRE LIFTS LIMITED—See KONE Oyj; *Int'l*, pg. 4247
ACRE, LLC; *U.S. Private*, pg. 65
ACRES COMMERCIAL REALTY CORP.; *U.S. Public*, pg. 36
ACRES REAL ESTATE SERVICES INC.; *U.S. Private*, pg. 65
ACRESS LTD—See Septeni Holdings Co., Ltd.; *Int'l*, pg. 6718
ACRESVALE INVESTMENT PTE LTD—See Keppel Corporation Limited; *Int'l*, pg. 4130
ACR FAMILY CONSTRUCTION, INC.—See Builders FirstSource, Inc.; *U.S. Public*, pg. 409
ACRI CAPITAL ACQUISITION CORPORATION; *U.S. Public*, pg. 36
ACRILEX INC.; *U.S. Private*, pg. 65
ACRINOVA AB; *Int'l*, pg. 108
ACRISON, INC. - ACRISON INTERNATIONAL DIVISION—See Acrison, Inc.; *U.S. Private*, pg. 65
ACRISON, INC.; *U.S. Private*, pg. 65
ACRISURE, LLC; *U.S. Private*, pg. 65
ACRO AIRCRAFT SEATING LIMITED—See Zhejiang Tiancheng Controls Co., Ltd.; *Int'l*, pg. 8664
ACRO ASSOCIATES EUROPE—See IMI plc; *Int'l*, pg. 3624
ACRO ASSOCIATES, INC.—See IMI plc; *Int'l*, pg. 3624
ACRO AUTOMATION SYSTEMS INC.; *U.S. Private*, pg. 65
ACROBATANT, LLC; *U.S. Private*, pg. 65
ACROBIOSYSTEMS CO., LTD.; *Int'l*, pg. 109
ACRODEA KOREA, INC.—See The Why How Do Company, Inc; *Int'l*, pg. 7701
ACRODEX INC.—See Insight Enterprises, Inc.; *U.S. Public*, pg. 1130
ACRO ENERGY TECHNOLOGIES CORP.; *U.S. Private*, pg. 65
ACROFAX INC.—See Equifax Inc.; *U.S. Public*, pg. 786
ACRO INDUSTRIES INC.; *U.S. Private*, pg. 65
ACROMAS HOLDINGS LTD.—See Charterhouse Capital Partners LLP; *Int'l*, pg. 1454
ACROMAS HOLDINGS LTD.—See CVC Capital Partners SICAV-FIS S.A.; *Int'l*, pg. 1881
ACROMAS HOLDINGS LTD.—See Permira Advisers LLP; *Int'l*, pg. 5802
ACROMAS HOLIDAYS LIMITED—See Charterhouse Capital Partners LLP; *Int'l*, pg. 1454
ACROMAS HOLIDAYS LIMITED—See CVC Capital Partners SICAV-FIS S.A.; *Int'l*, pg. 1882
ACROMAS HOLIDAYS LIMITED—See Permira Advisers LLP; *Int'l*, pg. 5802
ACROMAS SHIPPING LIMITED—See Charterhouse Capital Partners LLP; *Int'l*, pg. 1454
ACROMAS SHIPPING LIMITED—See CVC Capital Partners SICAV-FIS S.A.; *Int'l*, pg. 1882
ACROMAS SHIPPING LIMITED—See Permira Advisers LLP; *Int'l*, pg. 5802
ACROMEC ENGINEERS PTE LTD.; *Int'l*, pg. 109
ACROMETA GROUP LIMITED; *Int'l*, pg. 109
ACRON AG; *Int'l*, pg. 109
ACRONAME INC.—See Valens Semiconductor Ltd.; *Int'l*, pg. 8112
ACRON ARGENTINA S.R.L.—See Public Joint Stock Company Acron; *Int'l*, pg. 6094
ACRON BRASIL LTDA.—See Public Joint Stock Company Acron; *Int'l*, pg. 6094
ACRONET CORPORATION—See ITOCHU Corporation; *Int'l*, pg. 3834
ACRON FRANCE SAS—See Public Joint Stock Company Acron; *Int'l*, pg. 6094
ACRONIS INC.; *U.S. Private*, pg. 65
ACRON SWITZERLAND AG—See Public Joint Stock Company Acron; *Int'l*, pg. 6094

COMPANY NAME INDEX

ACRON USA INC.—See Public Joint Stock Company Acron; *Int'l*, pg. 6094
ACRONYM ASIA PTE. LTD.—See Acronym Media Inc.; *U.S. Private*, pg. 66
ACRONYM EUROPE—See Acronym Media Inc.; *U.S. Private*, pg. 66
ACRONYM MEDIA INC.; *U.S. Private*, pg. 66
ACRONYM MEDIA—See Acronym Media Inc.; *U.S. Private*, pg. 66
ACRO PAINTS LIMITED—See JK Cement Ltd; *Int'l*, pg. 3972
ACRO PHARMACEUTICAL SERVICES LLC—See Premier, Inc.; *U.S. Public*, pg. 1715
ACROPOLIS COMPUTERS, INC.—See IT Solutions Consulting LLC; *U.S. Private*, pg. 2148
ACROPOLIS INFRASTRUCTURE ACQUISITION CORP.; *U.S. Public*, pg. 36
ACROPOLIS TELECOM S.A.; *Int'l*, pg. 109
ACRORAD CO., LTD.—See Siemens Aktiengesellschaft; *Int'l*, pg. 6886
ACRO SERVICE CORP.; *U.S. Private*, pg. 65
ACROS ORGANICS B.V.B.A.—See Thermo Fisher Scientific Inc.; *U.S. Public*, pg. 2145
ACROSS SOLUTIONS, INC.—See System Support, Inc.; *Int'l*, pg. 7390
ACROSS THE POND—See SiteOne Landscape Supply, Inc.; *U.S. Public*, pg. 1888
ACROSS TRANSPORT CO., LTD.—See Onward Holdings Co., Ltd.; *Int'l*, pg. 5592
ACROTECH BIOPHARMA LLC—See Aurobindo Pharma Ltd.; *Int'l*, pg. 712
ACROTECH CO., LTD—See Encourage Technologies Co., Ltd.; *Int'l*, pg. 2402
ACROTEC UK LTD.—See Forsyth Capital Investors LLC; *U.S. Private*, pg. 1573
ACROUD AB; *Int'l*, pg. 109
ACROW INDIA LTD.; *Int'l*, pg. 109
ACROW LIMITED; *Int'l*, pg. 109
ACROW MISR FOR SCAFFOLDING & FORMWORK; *Int'l*, pg. 109
A.C.R. THUKHACHANTHAR CO., LTD.—See Daiki Axis Co., Ltd.; *Int'l*, pg. 1932
ACRUX DDS PTY LTD—See Acrux Limited; *Int'l*, pg. 109
ACRUX LIMITED; *Int'l*, pg. 109
ACRUX PHARMA PTY LTD—See Acrux Limited; *Int'l*, pg. 109
ACRY FAB INC.—See The Vollrath Company LLC; *U.S. Private*, pg. 4132
ACRYLIC DESIGN ASSOCIATES—See Taylor Corporation; *U.S. Private*, pg. 3938
ACRYLON PLASTICS INC.; *Int'l*, pg. 109
ACRY SUNDAY CO., LTD.—See Mitsubishi Chemical Group Corporation; *Int'l*, pg. 4930
ACS, ACTIVIDADES DE CONSTRUCCION Y SERVICIOS, S.A.; *Int'l*, pg. 109
ACS AIRCONTAINER SERVICES GESELLSCHAFT M.B.H—See Deutsche Lufthansa AG; *Int'l*, pg. 2066
AC-SANAFOR—See The Interpublic Group of Companies, Inc.; *U.S. Public*, pg. 2104
AC S.A.; *Int'l*, pg. 74
ACS BUSINESS SUPPLIES LIMITED; *Int'l*, pg. 109
ACS CARSTAR; *U.S. Private*, pg. 66
A.C. SCHULTES, INC.; *U.S. Private*, pg. 24
A.C. SCHULTES OF CAROLINA, INC.—See A.C. Schultes, Inc.; *U.S. Private*, pg. 24
A.C. SCHULTES OF DELAWARE, INC.—See A.C. Schultes, Inc.; *U.S. Private*, pg. 24
A.C. SCHULTES OF FLORIDA, INC.—See A.C. Schultes, Inc.; *U.S. Private*, pg. 24
A.C. SCHULTES OF MARYLAND, INC.—See A.C. Schultes, Inc.; *U.S. Private*, pg. 25
ACS DATALINE, LP—See Black Box Limited; *Int'l*, pg. 1056
ACS DOBFAR SPA; *Int'l*, pg. 109
ACSET INDONUSA CO. LTD.—See PT United Tractors Tbk; *Int'l*, pg. 6080
ACS GROUP, INC.—See Harbour Group Industries, Inc.; *U.S. Private*, pg. 1860
ACSIA PARTNERS LLC—See LTC Global, Inc.; *U.S. Private*, pg. 2509
A.C. SIMMONDS & SONS, INC.; *Int'l*, pg. 23
ACS (INDIA) LIMITED—See Dell Technologies Inc.; *U.S. Public*, pg. 649
ACS INDUSTRIES, INC. - SCRUBBLE PRODUCTS DIVISION—See ACS Industries, Inc.; *U.S. Private*, pg. 66
ACS INDUSTRIES, INC.; *U.S. Private*, pg. 66
ACS INDUSTRIES INC.; *U.S. Private*, pg. 66
ACS INDUSTRIES (SHANGHAI) CO—See ACS Industries, Inc.; *U.S. Private*, pg. 66
ACS INFRASTRUCTURE CANADA, INC.—See ACS, Actividades de Construccion y Servicios, S.A.; *Int'l*, pg. 109
ACS INFRASTRUCTURE DEVELOPMENT, INC.—See ACS, Actividades de Construccion y Servicios, S.A.; *Int'l*, pg. 109
ACS INTEGRATED SYSTEMS, INC.; *U.S. Private*, pg. 66
ACS INTERNACIONAL S.A. DE C.V.—See ACS Industries, Inc.; *U.S. Private*, pg. 66

ACS INTERNACIONAL S. DE R.L. DE C.V.—See ACS Industries, Inc.; *U.S. Private*, pg. 66
ACS INTERNATIONAL RESOURCES INC.; *U.S. Private*, pg. 66
ACS INTERNET, INC.—See ATN International, Inc.; *U.S. Public*, pg. 224
ACS INTERNET, INC.—See Freedom 3 Capital, LLC; *U.S. Private*, pg. 1603
ACSION LIMITED; *Int'l*, pg. 117
ACSIP TECHNOLOGY CORP.; *Int'l*, pg. 117
ACSIS, INC.—See Saints Capital, LLC; *U.S. Private*, pg. 3530
ACSL LTD; *Int'l*, pg. 117
ACS LONG DISTANCE LICENSE SUB, INC.—See ATN International, Inc.; *U.S. Public*, pg. 224
ACS LONG DISTANCE LICENSE SUB, INC.—See Freedom 3 Capital, LLC; *U.S. Private*, pg. 1603
ACSM-AGAM S.P.A.; *Int'l*, pg. 117
ACS MOTION CONTROL LTD.—See Physik Instrumente (PI) GmbH & Co. KG; *Int'l*, pg. 5858
ACS PLYN, S.R.O.—See Arca Capital Slovakia, A.S.; *Int'l*, pg. 539
ACS SERVICES, INC.; *U.S. Private*, pg. 66
ACS, SERVICIOS COMUNICACIONES Y ENERGA, S.L.—See ACS, Actividades de Construccion y Servicios, S.A.; *Int'l*, pg. 109
ACS, SERVICIOS COMUNICACIONES Y ENERGIA, S.L.—See ACS, Actividades de Construccion y Servicios, S.A.; *Int'l*, pg. 110
ACS SERVICIOS Y CONCESIONES, S.L.—See ACS, Actividades de Construccion y Servicios, S.A.; *Int'l*, pg. 109
ACS SLUCHMED SP. Z O.O.—See Demant A/S; *Int'l*, pg. 2022
ACS SOLUTIONS POLAND SP. Z.O.O.—See Conduent Incorporated; *U.S. Public*, pg. 566
ACS SYSTEMS UK LIMITED—See Bechtle AG; *Int'l*, pg. 936
ACSTAR HOLDINGS, INC.—See ACMAT Corporation; *U.S. Public*, pg. 35
ACSTAR INSURANCE COMPANY—See ACMAT Corporation; *U.S. Public*, pg. 35
ACS TECHNOLOGIES LIMITED; *Int'l*, pg. 109
ACS TELEFONIA MOVIL, S.L.—See ACS, Actividades de Construccion y Servicios, S.A.; *Int'l*, pg. 109
ACSUD; *Int'l*, pg. 117
AC SUPPLY COMPANY; *U.S. Private*, pg. 46
ACT 1 PERSONNEL SERVICES; *U.S. Private*, pg. 66
ACTAGRO, LLC—See Nutrien Ltd.; *Int'l*, pg. 5492
ACTA, LLC—See Advanced Core Concepts, LLC; *U.S. Private*, pg. 89
ACT APPRAISAL MANAGEMENT; *U.S. Private*, pg. 66
ACTA PRINT TAMPERE—See Alma Media Corporation; *Int'l*, pg. 362
ACTARIS PTY LTD—See Itron, Inc.; *U.S. Public*, pg. 1175
ACTAS INC.—See BANDAI NAMCO Holdings Inc.; *Int'l*, pg. 828
ACTA S.P.A.; *Int'l*, pg. 117
ACTAVIA LIFE SCIENCES, INC.; *U.S. Public*, pg. 36
ACTAVIS D.O.O. BELGRADE—See Teva Pharmaceutical Industries, Ltd.; *Int'l*, pg. 7579
ACTAVIS GROUP PTC EHF—See Teva Pharmaceutical Industries, Ltd.; *Int'l*, pg. 7579
ACTAVIS IRELAND LTD.—See Intas Pharmaceuticals Ltd.; *Int'l*, pg. 3728
ACTAVIS UK LIMITED—See Intas Pharmaceuticals Ltd.; *Int'l*, pg. 3728
ACTBLUE CO., LTD.; *Int'l*, pg. 117
ACT-B RECYCLING CO., LTD.—See Dowa Holdings Co., Ltd.; *Int'l*, pg. 2182
ACTCALL INC.; *Int'l*, pg. 117
ACTCELERATE INTERNATIONAL GROUP LIMITED; *Int'l*, pg. 117
A.C.&T. CO. INC.; *U.S. Private*, pg. 25
ACTE AS—See Lagercrantz Group AB; *Int'l*, pg. 4393
ACTE AB—See Lagercrantz Group AB; *Int'l*, pg. 4393
ACTECH GMBH—See Materialise NV; *Int'l*, pg. 4727
AC TECHNICAL SYSTEMS LTD.—See Creative Vistas Inc.; *Int'l*, pg. 1833
AC TECHNOLOGY, INC.; *U.S. Private*, pg. 46
ACTECH NORTH AMERICA INC.—See Materialise NV; *Int'l*, pg. 4727
ACT EDUCATION SOLUTIONS (AUSTRALIA) PTY. LIMITED—See ACT Inc.; *U.S. Private*, pg. 66
ACTEGA ARTISTICA S.A.—See SKion GmbH; *Int'l*, pg. 6989
ACTEGA COATINGS-SEALANTS GMBH—See SKion GmbH; *Int'l*, pg. 6989
ACTEGA DO BRASIL TINTAS E VERNIZES LTDA.—See SKion GmbH; *Int'l*, pg. 6989
ACTEGA DS GMBH—See SKion GmbH; *Int'l*, pg. 6986
ACTEGA FOSHAN CO., LTD.—See SKion GmbH; *Int'l*, pg. 6986
ACTEGA GMBH—See SKion GmbH; *Int'l*, pg. 6989
ACTEGA METAL PRINT GMBH—See SKion GmbH; *Int'l*, pg. 6989
ACTEGA RHENACOAT S.A.—See SKion GmbH; *Int'l*, pg. 6986

ACTEOS S.A.

ACTEGA RHENANIA COATINGS GMBH—See SKion GmbH; *Int'l*, pg. 6986
ACTEGA RHENANIA GMBH—See SKion GmbH; *Int'l*, pg. 6989
ACTEGA TERRA GMBH—See SKion GmbH; *Int'l*, pg. 6986
ACTEGA WIT INC.—See SKion GmbH; *Int'l*, pg. 6986
ACTEL ELECTRONIC (DONG GUAN) CO., LTD.—See AcBel Polytech Inc.; *Int'l*, pg. 78
ACTELION CLINICAL RESEARCH, INC.—See Johnson & Johnson; *U.S. Public*, pg. 1194
ACTELION LTD.—See Johnson & Johnson; *U.S. Public*, pg. 1193
ACTELION PHARMACEUTICALS AUSTRALIA PTY. LIMITED—See Johnson & Johnson; *U.S. Public*, pg. 1193
ACTELION PHARMACEUTICALS CANADA, INC.—See Johnson & Johnson; *U.S. Public*, pg. 1193
ACTELION PHARMACEUTICALS DO BRASIL LTDA.—See Johnson & Johnson; *U.S. Public*, pg. 1194
ACTELION PHARMACEUTICALS ESPANA, SL—See Johnson & Johnson; *U.S. Public*, pg. 1193
ACTELION PHARMACEUTICALS FRANCE SAS—See Johnson & Johnson; *U.S. Public*, pg. 1193
ACTELION PHARMACEUTICALS HELLAS SA—See Johnson & Johnson; *U.S. Public*, pg. 1193
ACTELION PHARMACEUTICALS ITALIA SRL—See Johnson & Johnson; *U.S. Public*, pg. 1193
ACTELION PHARMACEUTICALS JAPAN LTD.—See Johnson & Johnson; *U.S. Public*, pg. 1194
ACTELION PHARMACEUTICALS KOREA LTD.—See Johnson & Johnson; *U.S. Public*, pg. 1194
ACTELION PHARMACEUTICALS LTD.—See Johnson & Johnson; *U.S. Public*, pg. 1194
ACTELION PHARMACEUTICALS MEXICO S.A. DE C.V.—See Johnson & Johnson; *U.S. Public*, pg. 1194
ACTELION PHARMACEUTICALS UK LTD.—See Johnson & Johnson; *U.S. Public*, pg. 1194
ACTELION PHARMACEUTICALS US, INC.—See Johnson & Johnson; *U.S. Public*, pg. 1194
ACTELION US HOLDING CO.—See Johnson & Johnson; *U.S. Public*, pg. 1194
ACTELIS NETWORKS, INC.; *U.S. Public*, pg. 36
ACTEL KFT.—See Cyprus Telecommunications Authority; *Int'l*, pg. 1897
ACTEL POWER CO., LTD.—See AcBel Polytech Inc.; *Int'l*, pg. 78
ACTEL S.A.—See P&V Assurances SCRL; *Int'l*, pg. 5681
ACTEMIUM ASAS, S.L.—See VINCI S.A.; *Int'l*, pg. 8211
ACTEMIUM BEA BALKAN—See VINCI S.A.; *Int'l*, pg. 8236
ACTEMIUM BEA GMBH—See VINCI S.A.; *Int'l*, pg. 8211
ACTEMIUM BEA POLSKA SP. Z O.O.—See VINCI S.A.; *Int'l*, pg. 8211
ACTEMIUM BELGIUM SA—See VINCI S.A.; *Int'l*, pg. 8236
ACTEMIUM CEGELEC AUTOMATION CONTROL SYSTEM (BEIJING) LIMITED—See VINCI S.A.; *Int'l*, pg. 8211
ACTEMIUM CEGELEC SERVICES GMBH—See VINCI S.A.; *Int'l*, pg. 8211
ACTEMIUM CONTROLMATIC AG—See VINCI S.A.; *Int'l*, pg. 8236
ACTEMIUM CONTROLMATIC ENNS—See VINCI S.A.; *Int'l*, pg. 8236
ACTEMIUM CONTROLMATIC GMBH—See VINCI S.A.; *Int'l*, pg. 8211
ACTEMIUM ENERGY PROJECTS GMBH—See VINCI S.A.; *Int'l*, pg. 8211
ACTEMIUM FORDERTECHNIK RHEINLAND GMBH—See VINCI S.A.; *Int'l*, pg. 8211
ACTEMIUM H&F GMBH—See VINCI S.A.; *Int'l*, pg. 8212
ACTEMIUM KAPPELHOFF GMBH—See VINCI S.A.; *Int'l*, pg. 8212
ACTEMIUM KASACHSTAN TOO—See VINCI S.A.; *Int'l*, pg. 8236
ACTEMIUM LANGER GMBH—See VINCI S.A.; *Int'l*, pg. 8212
ACTEMIUM LEITEC AG—See VINCI S.A.; *Int'l*, pg. 8212
ACTEMIUM LISBON—See VINCI S.A.; *Int'l*, pg. 8236
ACTEMIUM MECHATRONIC GMBH—See VINCI S.A.; *Int'l*, pg. 8212
ACTEMIUM - NANCY ARS—See VINCI S.A.; *Int'l*, pg. 8236
ACTEMIUM SCHWEIZ AG—See VINCI S.A.; *Int'l*, pg. 8212
ACTEMIUM (SHENYANG) INDUSTRIAL ENGINEERING CO., LTD.—See VINCI S.A.; *Int'l*, pg. 8211
ACTEMIUM—See VINCI S.A.; *Int'l*, pg. 8236
ACTEMIUM UK—See VINCI S.A.; *Int'l*, pg. 8236
ACT ENTERTAINMENT AG—See CTS Eventim AG & Co. KGAA; *Int'l*, pg. 1872
ACTEON GROUP LTD.—See Buckthorn Partners LLP; *Int'l*, pg. 1210
ACTEON GROUP LTD.—See OEP Capital Advisors, L.P.; *Int'l*, pg. 2997
ACTEOS GMBH & CO. KG—See Acteos S.A.; *Int'l*, pg. 117
ACTEOS S.A.; *Int'l*, pg. 117
ACTE OY—See Lagercrantz Group AB; *Int'l*, pg. 4393

ACTERA GROUP STRATEJIK YONETIM HIZMETLERI A.S.

CORPORATE AFFILIATIONS

ACTERA GROUP STRATEJIK YONETIM HIZMETLERI A.S.; *Int'l*, pg. 117
ACTER CO., LTD.; *Int'l*, pg. 117
ACTER TECHNOLOGY CO., LTD.—See Acter Co., Ltd.; *Int'l*, pg. 117
ACTES KYOSAN INC.—See Kyosan Electric Manufacturing Co., Ltd.; *Int'l*, pg. 4365
ACTE SOLUTIONS AB—See Lagercrantz Group AB; *Int'l*, pg. 4393
ACTE SP. Z O.O.—See Lagercrantz Group AB; *Int'l*, pg. 4393
ACTE UK LIMITED—See Lagercrantz Group AB; *Int'l*, pg. 4393
ACT GLOBAL AMERICAS INC.—See Beaulieu International Group NV; *Int'l*, pg. 934
ACTIA 3E S.A.—See Actia Group SA; *Int'l*, pg. 118
ACTIA-AIXIA—See Actia Group SA; *Int'l*, pg. 118
ACTIA AUTOMOTIVE JOINT STOCK COMPANY—See Actia Group SA; *Int'l*, pg. 118
ACTIA CHINA AUTOMOTIVE ELECTRONICS CO., LTD—See Actia Group SA; *Int'l*, pg. 118
ACTIA CHINA CO., LTD.—See Actia Group SA; *Int'l*, pg. 118
ACTIA COLOMIERS SA—See Actia Group SA; *Int'l*, pg. 118
ACTIA CORPORATION—See Actia Group SA; *Int'l*, pg. 118
ACTIA DE MEXICO S.A. DE C.V.—See Actia Group SA; *Int'l*, pg. 118
ACTIA DO BRASIL IND. E COM. LTDA.—See Actia Group SA; *Int'l*, pg. 118
ACTIA DO BRASIL LTDA.—See Actia Group SA; *Int'l*, pg. 118
ACTIA ELECTRONICS, INC.—See Actia Group SA; *Int'l*, pg. 118
ACTIA ENGINEERING SERVICES SA—See Actia Group SA; *Int'l*, pg. 118
ACTIA GROUP SA - ACTIA MULLER (FRANCE) DIVISION—See Actia Group SA; *Int'l*, pg. 118
ACTIA GROUP SA - ACTIA TUNISIE DIVISION—See Actia Group SA; *Int'l*, pg. 118
ACTIA GROUP SA - CIPI ACTIA DIVISION—See Actia Group SA; *Int'l*, pg. 118
ACTIA GROUP SA - COLOMIERS DIVISION—See Actia Group SA; *Int'l*, pg. 118
ACTIA GROUP SA; *Int'l*, pg. 117
ACTIA IME GMBH—See Actia Group SA; *Int'l*, pg. 118
ACTIA INDIA PVT LTD—See Actia Group SA; *Int'l*, pg. 118
ACTIA ITALIA SRL—See Actia Group SA; *Int'l*, pg. 118
ACTIA JAPAN K.K.—See Actia Group SA; *Int'l*, pg. 118
ACTIA MULLER (UK) LTD.—See Actia Group SA; *Int'l*, pg. 118
ACTIANCE EUROPE LIMITED—See K1 Investment Management, LLC; *U.S. Private*, pg. 2252
ACTIANCE, INC.—See K1 Investment Management, LLC; *U.S. Private*, pg. 2252
ACTIANCE INDIA PVT. LTD.—See K1 Investment Management, LLC; *U.S. Private*, pg. 2252
ACTIAN CORPORATION—See HCL Technologies Ltd.; *Int'l*, pg. 3298
ACTIA NEDERLAND BV—See Actia Group SA; *Int'l*, pg. 118
ACTIAN EUROPE LIMITED—See HCL Technologies Ltd.; *Int'l*, pg. 3298
ACTIAN GERMANY GMBH—See HCL Technologies Ltd.; *Int'l*, pg. 3298
ACTIA NORDIC AB—See Actia Group SA; *Int'l*, pg. 118
ACTIA-POLSKA SP. Z O.O.—See Actia Group SA; *Int'l*, pg. 118
ACTIA S.A.—See Actia Group SA; *Int'l*, pg. 118
ACTIA SYSTEMS S.A.U.—See Actia Group SA; *Int'l*, pg. 118
ACTIA TELEMATICS SERVICES SA—See Actia Group SA; *Int'l*, pg. 118
ACTIA TUNISIE SA—See Actia Group SA; *Int'l*, pg. 118
ACTIA (UK) LIMITED—See Actia Group SA; *Int'l*, pg. 118
ACTIA VIDEO BUS, S.A.—See Actia Group SA; *Int'l*, pg. 118
ACTICA OMSORG AB—See Apax Partners LLP; *Int'l*, pg. 502
ACTIC GROUP AB; *Int'l*, pg. 118
ACTI-CHEM A/S—See Indutrade AB; *Int'l*, pg. 3677
ACTICOR BIOTECH SA; *Int'l*, pg. 118
ACTIFIO, INC.—See Alphabet Inc.; *U.S. Public*, pg. 83
ACTIFY LLC—See Hainan Traffic Administration Holding Co., Ltd.; *Int'l*, pg. 3215
ACTIGRAPH, LLC—See ArchiMed SAS; *Int'l*, pg. 548
ACTIGROUP—See DPG Media Group NV; *Int'l*, pg. 2188
ACTIMIZE INC.—See NICE Ltd.; *Int'l*, pg. 5265
ACTIMIZE JAPAN KK—See NICE Ltd.; *Int'l*, pg. 5265
ACTIMIZE UK LIMITED—See NICE Ltd.; *Int'l*, pg. 5265
ACTIMO APS—See The Goldman Sachs Group, Inc.; *U.S. Public*, pg. 2082
ACT INC.; *U.S. Private*, pg. 66
ACT INDUSTRIAL PROCESS SERVICES LLC—See ACS, Actividades de Construccion y Servicios, S.A.; *Int'l*, pg. 111
ACT INFORMATION CONSULTING (SHANGHAI) CO., LTD.—See ACT Inc.; *U.S. Private*, pg. 66

ACTINIUM PHARMACEUTICALS, INC.; *U.S. Public*, pg. 36
ACTINOGEN MEDICAL LIMITED; *Int'l*, pg. 118
ACTINVER S.A. DE C.V.; *Int'l*, pg. 118
ACTION ADVERTISING, INC.—See Gannett Co., Inc.; *U.S. Public*, pg. 896
ACTION AIR SYSTEMS, INC.; *U.S. Private*, pg. 67
ACTION AMBULANCE SERVICE INC.; *U.S. Private*, pg. 67
ACTION ASIA LIMITED; *Int'l*, pg. 119
ACTION ASIA (SHENZHEN) CO., LTD.—See Action Electronics Co., Ltd.; *Int'l*, pg. 119
ACTION BAG COMPANY; *U.S. Private*, pg. 67
ACTION BOLT (PTY.) LTD.—See Wurth Verwaltungsgesellschaft mbH; *Int'l*, pg. 8503
ACTION BOLT & TOOL COMPANY; *U.S. Private*, pg. 67
ACTION BOX COMPANY INC.; *U.S. Private*, pg. 67
ACTION CARRIER; *U.S. Private*, pg. 67
ACTION CARTING ENVIRONMENTAL SERVICES, INC.—See Interstate Waste Services, Inc.; *U.S. Private*, pg. 2126
ACTION CHEVROLET BUICK GMC INC.; *Int'l*, pg. 119
ACTION CLICK CO., LTD.—See Dentsu Group Inc.; *Int'l*, pg. 2034
ACTION COMPANY; *U.S. Private*, pg. 67
ACTION CONSTRUCTION EQUIPMENT LTD.; *Int'l*, pg. 119
ACTION DRILL & BLAST PTY. LTD.—See NRW Holdings Limited; *Int'l*, pg. 5475
ACTION ELECTRIC SALES CO. INC.; *U.S. Private*, pg. 67
ACTION ELECTRONICS, CO., LTD.; *Int'l*, pg. 119
ACTION ENVELOPE & PRINTING CO., INC.; *U.S. Private*, pg. 67
ACTION EQUIPMENT & SCAFFOLD CO. INC.; *U.S. Private*, pg. 67
ACTIONET, INC.; *U.S. Private*, pg. 68
ACTION EUROPE GMBH—See ACTION S.A.; *Int'l*, pg. 119
ACTION FABRICATION & TRUCK EQUIPMENT, INC.—See J.B. Poindexter & Co., Inc.; *U.S. Private*, pg. 2159
ACTION FABRICATORS, INC.—See The Goldman Sachs Group, Inc.; *U.S. Public*, pg. 2080
ACTION FINANCIAL SERVICES (INDIA) LTD.; *Int'l*, pg. 119
ACTION FLOORING; *Int'l*, pg. 119
ACTION FOOD SALES INC.; *U.S. Private*, pg. 67
ACTION FOR BOSTON COMMUNITY DEVELOPMENT, INC.; *U.S. Private*, pg. 67
ACTION FOR BRIDGEPORT COMMUNITY DEVELOPMENT, INC.; *U.S. Private*, pg. 67
ACTION GLOBAL COMMUNICATIONS LTD.—See The Interpublic Group of Companies, Inc.; *U.S. Public*, pg. 2094
ACTION GROUP HOLDINGS COMPANY K.S.C.C.; *Int'l*, pg. 119
ACTION HELLAS—See The Interpublic Group of Companies, Inc.; *U.S. Public*, pg. 2094
ACTION HOTELS PLC—See Action Group Holdings Company K.S.C.C.; *Int'l*, pg. 119
ACTION-HOUSING, INC.; *U.S. Private*, pg. 68
ACTION, INC.; *U.S. Private*, pg. 68
ACTION INC.; *U.S. Private*, pg. 67
ACTION INDUSTRIES (M) SDN. BHD.—See Action Electronics Co., Ltd.; *Int'l*, pg. 119
ACTION INSTRUMENTS—See Schneider Electric SE; *Int'l*, pg. 6627
ACTION INTERNATIONAL MARKETING, INC.; *U.S. Private*, pg. 67
ACTION INVESTMENT GROUP, INC.; *U.S. Private*, pg. 67
ACTION LABOR MANAGEMENT, LLC; *U.S. Private*, pg. 67
ACTION LIFT, INC.; *U.S. Private*, pg. 67
ACTION LINE—See WPP plc; *Int'l*, pg. 8478
ACTION LINE TELEMARKETING BRAZIL—See WPP plc; *Int'l*, pg. 8478
ACTION LOGISTICS (WA) PTY LTD—See CTI Logistics Limited; *Int'l*, pg. 1871
ACTION MANUFACTURING CO.; *U.S. Private*, pg. 67
ACTION MANUFACTURING & SUPPLY, INC.—See Franklin Electric Co., Inc.; *U.S. Public*, pg. 878
ACTION MEDIA, INC.; *U.S. Private*, pg. 67
ACTION NETWORK INC.—See Better Collective A/S; *Int'l*, pg. 1003
ACTION PARTY RENTALS; *U.S. Private*, pg. 67
ACTION PETROLEUM COMPANY LTD.; *U.S. Private*, pg. 67
ACTION PIN SA—See Firmenich International SA; *Int'l*, pg. 2681
ACTION PLUMBING SUPPLY CO.; *U.S. Private*, pg. 67
ACTION PR CYPRUS—See The Interpublic Group of Companies, Inc.; *U.S. Public*, pg. 2094
ACTION PRODUCTS MARKETING CORP.—See Edgewater Services, LLC; *U.S. Private*, pg. 1335
ACTION PRODUCTS MARKETING CORP.—See JZ Capital Partners Limited; *Int'l*, pg. 4037
ACTION RESEARCH CORPORATION—See HEICO Corporation; *U.S. Public*, pg. 1021

ACTION RESOURCES INC.; *U.S. Private*, pg. 67
ACTION S.A.; *Int'l*, pg. 119
ACTIONSPORTGAMES A/S; *Int'l*, pg. 119
ACTION SPORTS MEDIA, INC.; *U.S. Private*, pg. 68
ACTIONS SEMICONDUCTOR CO., LTD.; *Int'l*, pg. 119
ACTION STAINLESS & ALLOYS INC.—See Olympic Steel Inc.; *U.S. Public*, pg. 1570
ACTIONS TECHNOLOGY (HK) COMPANY LIMITED—See Actions Semiconductor Co., Ltd.; *Int'l*, pg. 119
ACTION SUPPLY CO., INC.—See Vulcan Materials Company; *U.S. Public*, pg. 2313
ACTION TARGET, INC.; *U.S. Private*, pg. 68
ACTIONTEC ELECTRONICS, INC.; *U.S. Private*, pg. 68
ACTION TECHNOLOGY BELGIUM—See Genstar Capital, LLC; *U.S. Private*, pg. 1678
ACTION TECHNOLOGY (JIAN) CO., LTD.—See Action Electronics Co., Ltd.; *Int'l*, pg. 119
ACTION TITLE RESEARCH, LLC—See Strattam Capital, LLC; *U.S. Private*, pg. 3837
ACTIONTOP ELECTRONICS (SHENZHEN) CO., LTD.—See Cantronic Systems Inc.; *Int'l*, pg. 1299
ACTION TRANSPORT, INC.—See Heritage Home Group, LLC; *U.S. Private*, pg. 1924
ACTION TRAVEL CENTER, INC.—See ABRY Partners, LLC; *U.S. Private*, pg. 41
ACTIONWEAR SASKATOON INC.; *Int'l*, pg. 119
ACTIO OPTICAL CORP.—See Hoya Corporation; *Int'l*, pg. 3494
ACTIO SOFTWARE CORP.—See Thoma Bravo, L.P.; *U.S. Private*, pg. 4146
ACTIS BSP GERMANY GMBH—See Temenos AG; *Int'l*, pg. 7554
ACTIS LLP - BEIJING OFFICE—See General Atlantic Service Company, L.P.; *U.S. Private*, pg. 1661
ACTIS LLP - MUMBAI OFFICE—See General Atlantic Service Company, L.P.; *U.S. Private*, pg. 1661
ACTIS LLP - SAO PAULO OFFICE—See General Atlantic Service Company, L.P.; *U.S. Private*, pg. 1661
ACTIS LLP—See General Atlantic Service Company, L.P.; *U.S. Private*, pg. 1660
ACTIS MANUFACTURING, LTD. LLC—See Toyota Industries Corporation; *Int'l*, pg. 7868
ACTITO S.A.—See Altor Equity Partners AB; *Int'l*, pg. 395
ACTIV8 DISTRIBUTION LTD.; *Int'l*, pg. 119
ACTIVA CAPITAL S.A.S.; *Int'l*, pg. 119
ACTIVAIDED ORTHOTICS LLC—See Elizur Corp.; *U.S. Private*, pg. 1362
ACTIVA MEDIA (S) PTE. LTD.—See AM Group Holdings Limited; *Int'l*, pg. 402
ACTIVAR CONSTRUCTION PRODUCTS GROUP, INC.—See Activar, Inc.; *U.S. Private*, pg. 68
ACTIVA RESOURCES AG; *Int'l*, pg. 119
ACTIVA RESOURCES, LLC—See Activa Resources AG; *Int'l*, pg. 119
ACTIVA RESOURCES, LLC—See CIC Partners, L.P.; *U.S. Private*, pg. 896
ACTIVAR, INC.; *U.S. Private*, pg. 68
ACTIVAR INDUSTRIAL PRODUCTS GROUP, INC.—See Activar, Inc.; *U.S. Private*, pg. 68
ACTIVAR PLASTIC PRODUCTS GROUP, INC.—See Activar, Inc.; *U.S. Private*, pg. 68
ACTIVAR TECHNICAL PRODUCTS GROUP, INC.—See Activar, Inc.; *U.S. Private*, pg. 68
ACTIVATED HOLDINGS LLC; *U.S. Private*, pg. 68
ACTIVATE INC.; *U.S. Private*, pg. 68
ACTIVATE MARKETING SERVICES, LLC—See Next 15 Group plc; *Int'l*, pg. 5245
ACTIVATE NETWORKS INC.—See Clarivate PLC; *Int'l*, pg. 1649
ACTIVATE PERMANENT CAPITAL CORP.; *U.S. Private*, pg. 68
ACTIVATION GROUP HOLDINGS LIMITED; *Int'l*, pg. 119
ACTIVCARE A/S—See Lundbeckfonden; *Int'l*, pg. 4580
ACTIV CARS GMBH—See Sovereign Speed GmbH; *Int'l*, pg. 7122
ACTIV C.S.A.; *Int'l*, pg. 119
ACTIVE ACQUISITION CORP.—See TFI International Inc.; *Int'l*, pg. 7586
ACTIVE AERO GROUP, INC.—See Roadrunner Transportation Systems, Inc.; *U.S. Public*, pg. 1802
ACTIVE AERO MOTOR CARRIER, LLC—See Roadrunner Transportation Systems, Inc.; *U.S. Public*, pg. 1802
ACTIVE AERO SERVICES, LLC—See Roadrunner Transportation Systems, Inc.; *U.S. Public*, pg. 1802
ACTIVE ANTS BELGIUM BV—See bpost NV/SA; *Int'l*, pg. 1133
ACTIVE ASSISTANCE—See August Equity LLP; *Int'l*, pg. 703
ACTIVE BIOTECH AB; *Int'l*, pg. 120
ACTIVE BRAINS & TRUST CO., LTD.—See Core Corporation; *Int'l*, pg. 1797
ACTIVECAMPAIGN, LLC—See Silversmith Management, L.P.; *U.S. Private*, pg. 3663
ACTIVE CANADA INC.—See TFI International Inc.; *Int'l*, pg. 7586
ACTIVE CAPITAL COMPANY HOLDING BV; *Int'l*, pg. 120
ACTIVE CLOTHING CO., LTD.; *Int'l*, pg. 120
ACTIVE CO., LTD.—See Yamatane Corporation; *Int'l*, pg. 8553

COMPANY NAME INDEX

ACTIVE CONTROL TECHNOLOGY INC.; *Int'l*, pg. 120
ACTIVE DAY INC.—See Audax Group, Limited Partnership; *U.S. Private*, pg. 389
ACTIVE DAY OF RANDALLSTOWN—See Audax Group, Limited Partnership; *U.S. Private*, pg. 389
ACTIVE EDGE SDN BHD—See Fiamma Holdings Berhad; *Int'l*, pg. 2650
ACTIVE ELECTRICAL SUPPLY COMPANY; *U.S. Private*, pg. 69
ACTIVE ENERGY GROUP PLC; *Int'l*, pg. 120
ACTIVE ENERGY LIMITED—See Active Energy Group plc; *Int'l*, pg. 120
ACTIVE EXHAUST CORP.; *Int'l*, pg. 120
ACTIVE FINE CHEMICALS LIMITED; *Int'l*, pg. 120
ACTIVEGEN SA—See T&M Phaedra Public Company Ltd.; *Int'l*, pg. 7395
ACTIVE HEALTHCARE, INC.; *U.S. Private*, pg. 69
ACTIVE HEALTH MANAGEMENT, INC.—See CVS Health Corporation; *U.S. Public*, pg. 614
ACTIVE HEALTH MANAGEMENT, INC.—See CVS Health Corporation; *U.S. Public*, pg. 614
ACTIVE INDUSTRIA DE COSMETICOS S.A.—See Ontex Group N.V.; *Int'l*, pg. 5591
ACTIVE INTEREST MEDIA, INC.; *U.S. Private*, pg. 69
ACTIVE INTERNATIONAL AUSTRALIA PTY LTD.—See Active Media Services, Inc.; *U.S. Private*, pg. 69
ACTIVE INTERNATIONAL CORPORATE TRADING SPAIN S.L.—See Active Media Services, Inc.; *U.S. Private*, pg. 69
ACTIVE INTERNATIONAL DO BRASIL S.A.—See Active Media Services, Inc.; *U.S. Private*, pg. 69
ACTIVE INTERNATIONAL (EUROPE) S.A.R.L.—See Active Media Services, Inc.; *U.S. Private*, pg. 69
ACTIVE INTERNATIONAL GMBH—See Active Media Services, Inc.; *U.S. Private*, pg. 69
ACTIVE INTERNATIONAL INC.—See Active Media Services, Inc.; *U.S. Private*, pg. 69
ACTIVE INTERNATIONAL LLC—See Active Media Services, Inc.; *U.S. Private*, pg. 69
ACTIVE INTERNATIONAL LTD.—See Active Media Services, Inc.; *U.S. Private*, pg. 69
ACTIVE INTERNATIONAL (MEXICO) S.A. DE C.V.—See Active Media Services, Inc.; *U.S. Private*, pg. 69
ACTIVE INTERNATIONAL NORTHERN EUROPE—See Active Media Services, Inc.; *U.S. Private*, pg. 69
ACTIVE INTERNATIONAL POLAND SP. Z O.O.—See Active Media Services, Inc.; *U.S. Private*, pg. 69
ACTIVE INTERNET TECHNOLOGIES, INC.—See Bridge Growth Partners, LLC; *U.S. Private*, pg. 648
ACTIVE KEY GMBH—See Cherry SE; *Int'l*, pg. 1472
ACTIVELOGIX LLC—See Building Controls & Solutions; *U.S. Private*, pg. 682
ACTIVE MEDIA SERVICES CANADA, INC.—See Active Media Services, Inc.; *U.S. Private*, pg. 69
ACTIVE MEDIA SERVICES- CENTRAL EUROPE GROUP—See Active Media Services, Inc.; *U.S. Private*, pg. 69
ACTIVE MEDIA SERVICES, INC.; *U.S. Private*, pg. 69
ACTIVE MINERALS INTERNATIONAL, LLC—See Golden Gate Capital Management II, LLC; *U.S. Private*, pg. 1730
ACTIVE MOTIF-EUROPE—See Active Motif, Inc.; *U.S. Private*, pg. 70
ACTIVE MOTIF, INC.; *U.S. Private*, pg. 70
ACTIVE MOTIF-JAPAN—See Active Motif, Inc.; *U.S. Private*, pg. 70
ACTIVE NETWORK IPICO (US) INC.—See Global Payments Inc.; *U.S. Public*, pg. 943
ACTIVE NETWORK, LLC—See Global Payments Inc.; *U.S. Public*, pg. 943
ACTIVENGAGE, INC.; *U.S. Private*, pg. 70
ACTIVE NUTRITION INTERNATIONAL GMBH—See Post Holdings, Inc.; *U.S. Public*, pg. 1704
ACTIVE OFFICE FINLAND OY—See Wulff-Group Plc; *Int'l*, pg. 8502
ACTIVEOPS LTD.; *Int'l*, pg. 120
ACTIVEOUTDOORS—See Vista Equity Partners, LLC; *U.S. Private*, pg. 4394
ACTIVEPATH SOLUTIONS, INC.—See Broadridge Financial Solutions, Inc.; *U.S. Public*, pg. 391
ACTIVEPATH SOLUTIONS LTD.—See Broadridge Financial Solutions, Inc.; *U.S. Public*, pg. 391
ACTIVEPDF, INC.—See Thoma Bravo, L.P.; *U.S. Private*, pg. 4146
ACTIVE PHARMA CO., LTD.—See Mitani Sangyo Co., Ltd.; *Int'l*, pg. 4924
ACTIVE PHYSICAL THERAPY, LIMITED PARTNERSHIP—See U.S. Physical Therapy, Inc.; *U.S. Public*, pg. 2213
ACTIVE PLUMBING SUPPLY CO; *U.S. Private*, pg. 70
ACTIVEPORT GROUP LIMITED; *Int'l*, pg. 120
ACTIVE POWER (GERMANY) GMBH—See Langley Holdings Plc; *Int'l*, pg. 4410
ACTIVE POWER SOLUTIONS LTD.—See Langley Holdings Plc; *Int'l*, pg. 4410
ACTIVE POWER—See Langley Holdings Plc; *Int'l*, pg. 4410
ACTIVE PRIVATE EQUITY ADVISORY LLP; *Int'l*, pg. 120

ACTIVE QUILTING DIV.—See Rockville Fabrics Corporation; *U.S. Private*, pg. 3467
ACTIVE RETIREMENT COMMUNITY INC.; *U.S. Private*, pg. 70
ACTIVE SALES CO. INC.; *U.S. Private*, pg. 70
ACTIVE SCREW & FASTENER; *U.S. Private*, pg. 70
ACTIVE SMART LIMITED—See PC Partner Group Limited; *Int'l*, pg. 5766
ACTIVE SPORTS, INC.—See Camping World Holdings, Inc.; *U.S. Public*, pg. 427
ACTIVE SPORTS LIFESTYLE USA, LLC; *U.S. Private*, pg. 70
ACTIVESTATE SOFTWARE INC.—See Pender Financial Group Corporation; *Int'l*, pg. 5785
ACTIVESTRATEGY, INC.—See UnitedHealth Group Incorporated; *U.S. Public*, pg. 2248
ACTIVE TRUCK TRANSPORTATION COMPANY LLC—See TFI International Inc.; *Int'l*, pg. 7586
ACTIVE USA INC.—See TFI International Inc.; *Int'l*, pg. 7586
ACTIVEVIDEO NETWORKS, INC.—See CommScope Holding Company, Inc.; *U.S. Public*, pg. 548
ACTIVE VOICES LIMITED—See Comcast Corporation; *U.S. Public*, pg. 537
ACTIVEWORLDS, INC.; *U.S. Private*, pg. 70
ACTIVEX LIMITED; *Int'l*, pg. 120
ACTIV FACTORING AG—See Raiffeisenlandesbank Oberosterreich Aktiengesellschaft; *Int'l*, pg. 6188
ACTIV FINANCIAL SYSTEMS, INC—See ABRY Partners, LLC; *U.S. Private*, pg. 43
ACTIVIA PROPERTIES INC.; *Int'l*, pg. 120
ACTIVIDADES DE SERVICIOS E INSTALACIONES COBRA, S.A.—See ACS, Actividades de Construccion y Servicios, S.A.; *Int'l*, pg. 110
ACTIVIDENTITY AUSTRALIA PTY. LTD.—See ASSA ABLOY AB; *Int'l*, pg. 637
ACTIVIDENTITY CORPORATION—See ASSA ABLOY AB; *Int'l*, pg. 637
ACTIVIDENTITY EUROPE S.A.—See ASSA ABLOY AB; *Int'l*, pg. 637
ACTIVIDENTITY JAPAN K.K.—See ASSA ABLOY AB; *Int'l*, pg. 637
ACTIVIDENTITY UK LTD.—See ASSA ABLOY AB; *Int'l*, pg. 007
ACTIVI DEPLOYMENT SERVICES (PROPRIETARY) LIMITED—See Blue Label Telecoms Limited; *Int'l*, pg. 1068
ACTIVINSTINCT LTD.; *Int'l*, pg. 120
ACTIVIOMICS LIMITED—See Open Orphan plc; *Int'l*, pg. 5596
ACTIVISION BLIZZARD DEUTSCHLAND GMBH—See Microsoft Corporation; *U.S. Public*, pg. 1438
ACTIVISION BLIZZARD, INC.—See Microsoft Corporation; *U.S. Public*, pg. 1438
ACTIVISION BLIZZARD PTY LIMITED—See Microsoft Corporation; *U.S. Public*, pg. 1438
ACTIVISION BLIZZARD UK LIMITED—See Microsoft Corporation; *U.S. Public*, pg. 1438
ACTIVISION PUBLISHING, INC.—See Microsoft Corporation; *U.S. Public*, pg. 1438
ACTIVISION PUBLISHING MINNEAPOLIS, INC—See Microsoft Corporation; *U.S. Public*, pg. 1438
ACTIVIS SAS—See ADLPartner SA; *Int'l*, pg. 151
ACTIVITYREZ, INC.; *U.S. Private*, pg. 70
ACTIVSKEEN SAS—See VINCI S.A.; *Int'l*, pg. 8212
ACTIVSTYLE, INC—See AdaptHealth Corp.; *U.S. Public*, pg. 38
ACTIVU CORPORATION; *U.S. Private*, pg. 70
ACTIVX BIOSCIENCES, INC.—See KYORIN Holdings, Inc.; *Int'l*, pg. 4364
ACTIX LIMITED—See Amdocs Limited; *Int'l*, pg. 419
ACTOM (PTY) LTD.; *Int'l*, pg. 120
ACTON AWKK (OSAKA)—See ACTON International Ltd.; *U.S. Private*, pg. 70
ACTON DIREKT-MARKETING GMBH—See ACTON International Ltd.; *U.S. Private*, pg. 70
ACTON FORD, INC.; *U.S. Private*, pg. 70
ACTON INTERNATIONAL LTD.; *U.S. Private*, pg. 70
ACTON LEATHER CO. INC.; *Int'l*, pg. 121
ACT-ON SOFTWARE, INC.; *U.S. Private*, pg. 66
ACT-ON SOFTWARE INDIA PRIVATE LIMITED—See Act-On Software, Inc.; *U.S. Private*, pg. 66
ACTON TECHNOLOGIES, INC.; *U.S. Private*, pg. 70
ACTON WINS CO. LTD.—See ACTON International Ltd.; *U.S. Private*, pg. 70
THE ACTORS FUND; *U.S. Private*, pg. 3981
ACTOZ SOFT CO. LTD.—See Shanda Interactive Entertainment Limited; *Int'l*, pg. 6751
ACT PIPE & SUPPLY INC.; *U.S. Private*, pg. 66
A C TRAFIK A/S—See Lundbeckfonden; *Int'l*, pg. 4579
ACTREN MANTENIMIENTO FERROVIARIO, S.A.—See Construcciones y Auxiliar de Ferrocarriles S.A.; *Int'l*, pg. 1776
ACTRO CO., LTD.; *Int'l*, pg. 120
ACTROL PARTS HOLDINGS PTY LTD—See Reece Limited; *Int'l*, pg. 6249
ACTRON ENGINEERING, INC.; *U.S. Private*, pg. 70
ACTRON MANUFACTURING, INC.; *U.S. Private*, pg. 70

ACULA TECHNOLOGY CORP.

ACTS 29 CONSULTING, LLC—See CMTA Inc.; *U.S. Private*, pg. 951
ACTS-AVIATION SECURITY, INC.; *U.S. Private*, pg. 70
ACTSOFT, INC.; *U.S. Private*, pg. 70
ACTSOLAR, INC.—See Texas Instruments Incorporated; *U.S. Public*, pg. 2025
ACTS RETIREMENT-LIFE COMMUNITIES, INC.; *U.S. Private*, pg. 70
ACT-T CO., LTD.—See Mitani Sangyo Co., Ltd.; *Int'l*, pg. 4924
ACT TECHNICAL SUPPORT INC.—See Kajima Corporation; *Int'l*, pg. 4053
ACT TEST PANELS, INC.—See Talon LLC; *U.S. Private*, pg. 3927
ACTUA CORPORATION; *U.S. Private*, pg. 71
ACTUAIRES ET ASSOCIES SA—See Swiss Life Holding; *Int'l*, pg. 7368
ACTUAL EXPERIENCE PLC; *Int'l*, pg. 121
ACTUAL FENSTER GMBH; *Int'l*, pg. 121
ACTUAL INVEST HOUSE SRL—See Impact Developer & Contractor S.A.; *Int'l*, pg. 3630
ACTUAL I.T., D.D.—See DBA Group SRL; *Int'l*, pg. 1986
ACTUANT ASIA PTE LTD—See Enerpac Tool Group Corp.; *U.S. Public*, pg. 765
ACTUANT AUSTRALIA LTD.—See Enerpac Tool Group Corp.; *U.S. Public*, pg. 765
ACTUANT CHINA LTD.—See Enerpac Tool Group Corp.; *U.S. Public*, pg. 765
ACTUANT CORPORATION JAPAN—See Enerpac Tool Group Corp.; *U.S. Public*, pg. 765
ACTUANT GMBH—See Enerpac Tool Group Corp.; *U.S. Public*, pg. 765
ACTUANT INDIA PVT. LTD.—See Enerpac Tool Group Corp.; *U.S. Public*, pg. 765
ACTUANT KOREA LTD.—See Enerpac Tool Group Corp.; *U.S. Public*, pg. 765
ACTUANT OPERATIONS UK LTD.—See Enerpac Tool Group Corp.; *U.S. Public*, pg. 765
ACTUARIAL CONSULTANTS, INC.—See CBIZ, Inc.; *U.S. Public*, pg. 456
ACTUARIAL EDUCATION COMPANY LIMITED—See TDR Capital LLP; *Int'l*, pg. 7493
ACTUATE CANADA CORPORATION—See Open Text Corporation; *Int'l*, pg. 5596
ACTUATOR COMPONENTS GMBH & CO. KG—See Eagle Industry Co., Ltd.; *Int'l*, pg. 2265
ACTURIS LTD.; *Int'l*, pg. 121
ACTUS CO., LTD.—See Kokuyo Co., Ltd.; *Int'l*, pg. 4231
ACTUS LEND LEASE—See Lendlease Corporation Limited; *Int'l*, pg. 4451
ACTVILA CORPORATION—See WOWOW, Inc.; *Int'l*, pg. 8460
ACUANT, INC.—See GB Group plc; *Int'l*, pg. 2892
ACUATIVE CORP.; *U.S. Private*, pg. 71
ACUATIVE - RESEARCH & DEVELOPMENT—See Acuative Corp.; *U.S. Private*, pg. 71
ACUATIVE - SERVICE CONTRACT ADMINISTRATION—See Acuative Corp.; *U.S. Private*, pg. 71
ACUCAL, INC.—See Ontario Municipal Employees Retirement System; *Int'l*, pg. 5585
ACUCAREIRA QUATA S.A—See Zilor Energia e Alimentos Ltda.; *Int'l*, pg. 8683
ACUCELA, INC.—See Kubota Pharmaceutical Holdings Co., Ltd.; *Int'l*, pg. 4322
ACUCORT AB; *Int'l*, pg. 121
ACUCOTE INC.—See Fedrigoni SpA; *Int'l*, pg. 2631
ACUFF-ROSE MUSIC PUBLISHING—See Sony Group Corporation; *Int'l*, pg. 7105
ACUFOCUS, INC.—See Bausch Health Companies Inc.; *Int'l*, pg. 895
ACUITYADS INC.; *Int'l*, pg. 121
ACUITY BRANDS, INC.; *U.S. Public*, pg. 36
ACUITY BRANDS LIGHTING CANADA, INC.—See Acuity Brands, Inc.; *U.S. Public*, pg. 37
ACUITY BRANDS LIGHTING, INC.—See Acuity Brands, Inc.; *U.S. Public*, pg. 37
ACUITY BRANDS LIGHTING MEXICO, S. DE R.L. DE C.V.—See Acuity Brands, Inc.; *U.S. Public*, pg. 37
ACUITYCFO, LLC; *U.S. Private*, pg. 71
ACUITY FUNDS LTD—See AGF Management Limited; *Int'l*, pg. 206
ACUITY INC.; *U.S. Private*, pg. 71
ACUITY INVESTMENT MANAGEMENT INC—See AGF Management Limited; *Int'l*, pg. 206
ACUITY KNOWLEDGE PARTNERS COSTA RICA SOCIEDAD ANONIMA—See Equistone Partners Europe Limited; *Int'l*, pg. 2486
ACUITY KNOWLEDGE PARTNERS (UK) LIMITED—See Equistone Partners Europe Limited; *Int'l*, pg. 2486
ACUITY; *U.S. Private*, pg. 71
ACUITY SPATIAL GENOMICS, INC.—See Bruker Corporation; *U.S. Public*, pg. 404
ACUITY SURGICAL DEVICES, LLC; *U.S. Private*, pg. 71
ACULA TECHNOLOGY CORP.; *U.S. Private*, pg. 71
ACUMATICA, INC.—See EQT AB; *Int'l*, pg. 2467
ACUMBAMAIL SL—See Growens S.p.A.; *Int'l*, pg. 3112
ACUMEDIA MANUFACTURERS, INC.—See Neogen Corporation; *U.S. Public*, pg. 1505

ACUMED IBERICA S.L.—See Berkshire Hathaway Inc.; *U.S. Public*, pg. 308
ACUMED LLC—See Berkshire Hathaway Inc.; *U.S. Public*, pg. 308
ACUMED LTD.—See Berkshire Hathaway Inc.; *U.S. Public*, pg. 308
ACUMEN BUILDING ENTERPRISE, INC.; *U.S. Private*, pg. 71
ACUMEN CO., LTD.—See Jasmine International Public Company Limited; *Int'l*, pg. 3912
ACUMEN DETECTION, LLC—See SRC, Inc.; *U.S. Private*, pg. 3767
ACUMEN LEARNING, LLC; *U.S. Private*, pg. 71
ACUMEN, LLC—See Alpine Investors; *U.S. Private*, pg. 201
ACUMEN PHARMACEUTICAL, INC.; *U.S. Public*, pg. 37
ACUMEN RE MANAGEMENT CORPORATION—See Brown & Brown, Inc.; *U.S. Public*, pg. 396
ACUMEN SCIENTIFIC SDN. BHD.—See Merieux NutriSciences Corp.; *U.S. Private*, pg. 2674
ACUMEN SECURITY, LLC—See Intertek Group plc; *Int'l*, pg. 3762
ACUMENT GLOBAL TECHNOLOGIES INC—See Fontana Luigi S.p.A.; *Int'l*, pg. 2726
ACUMENTIS BRISBANE PTY LTD—See Acumentis Group Limited; *Int'l*, pg. 121
ACUMENTIS GOLD COAST PTY LTD—See Acumentis Group Limited; *Int'l*, pg. 121
ACUMENTIS GROUP LIMITED; *Int'l*, pg. 121
ACUMENTIS MELBOURNE PTY LTD—See Acumentis Group Limited; *Int'l*, pg. 121
ACUMENTRICS CORPORATION; *U.S. Private*, pg. 71
ACUMIUM LLC—See Omega Laboratories, Inc.; *U.S. Private*, pg. 3015
ACUMO AB—See Indutrade AB; *Int'l*, pg. 3677
ACUMULADORES INDUSTRIALES ENERSYS SA—See EnerSys; *U.S. Public*, pg. 766
ACUO TECHNOLOGIES (PTY) LIMITED—See Reunert Limited; *Int'l*, pg. 6311
ACUPAC PACKAGING, INC.—See Novacap Management Inc.; *Int'l*, pg. 5454
ACU PHARMA UND CHEMIE GMBH—See BRENNTAG SE; *Int'l*, pg. 1146
ACUPOWDER INTERNATIONAL LLC—See Palladium Equity Partners, LLC; *U.S. Private*, pg. 3078
ACUPOWDER TENNESSEE LLC—See Palladium Equity Partners, LLC; *U.S. Private*, pg. 3078
ACURA OF AUGUSTA; *U.S. Private*, pg. 71
ACURA OF OCEAN; *U.S. Private*, pg. 71
ACURA OF SEATTLE AT SOUTHCENTER—See Michael O'Brien Enterprises, Inc.; *U.S. Private*, pg. 2698
ACURA OF WAPPINGERS FALLS; *U.S. Private*, pg. 71
ACURA PHARMACEUTICALS, INC.—See Galen Partners, L.P.; *U.S. Private*, pg. 1637
ACURA PHARMACEUTICAL TECHNOLOGIES, INC.—See Galen Partners, L.P.; *U.S. Private*, pg. 1637
ACURA SHERWAY—See Chesswood Group Limited; *Int'l*, pg. 1472
ACURE ASSET MANAGEMENT LTD—See Moelis & Company; *U.S. Public*, pg. 1456
ACUREN CORPORATION; *Int'l*, pg. 121
ACUREN GROUP INC.—See Acuren Corporation; *Int'l*, pg. 121
ACUREN INSPECTION, INC. - NORTH REGION—See Acuren Corporation; *Int'l*, pg. 121
ACUREN INSPECTION, INC.—See Acuren Corporation; *Int'l*, pg. 121
ACUREN INSPECTION, INC. - SOUTH REGION—See Acuren Corporation; *Int'l*, pg. 121
ACURIS INTERNATIONAL LIMITED—See ION Investment Group Ltd.; *Int'l*, pg. 3794
ACURITY HEALTH GROUP LIMITED—See Evolution Healthcare Pty. Ltd.; *Int'l*, pg. 2572
ACURUS PTY. LTD.—See Superloop Limited; *Int'l*, pg. 7338
ACURX PHARMACEUTICALS, INC.; *U.S. Public*, pg. 37
ACUSENSUS LIMITED; *Int'l*, pg. 121
ACUSHNET CANADA INC—See FILA Holdings Corporation; *Int'l*, pg. 2662
ACUSHNET COMPANY—See FILA Holdings Corporation; *Int'l*, pg. 2662
ACUSHNET EUROPE LTD—See FILA Holdings Corporation; *Int'l*, pg. 2662
ACUSHNET GMBH—See FILA Holdings Corporation; *Int'l*, pg. 2662
ACUSHNET HOLDINGS CORP.—See FILA Holdings Corporation; *Int'l*, pg. 2662
ACUSHNET KOREA CO., LTD.—See FILA Holdings Corporation; *Int'l*, pg. 2662
ACUSHNET NEDERLAND B.V.—See FILA Holdings Corporation; *Int'l*, pg. 2662
ACUSHNET SVERIGE AB—See FILA Holdings Corporation; *Int'l*, pg. 2662
ACUSIS LLC—See Rare Enterprises Ltd.; *Int'l*, pg. 6211
ACUSPORT CORPORATION; *U.S. Private*, pg. 71
ACUSTICA SP. Z O.O.—See Demant A/S; *Int'l*, pg. 2023
ACUTE BEHAVIORAL HEALTH, LLC—See Petra Capital Partners, LLC; *U.S. Private*, pg. 3161

ACUTECARE TELEMEDICINE, LLC—See Teladoc Health, Inc.; *U.S. Public*, pg. 1992
ACUTECH NETWORK SERVICES INC—See Integritek LLC; *U.S. Private*, pg. 2102
ACUTE KIDS URGENT CARE OF MEDICAL CITY CHILDREN'S HOSPITAL, PLLC—See HCA Healthcare, Inc.; *U.S. Public*, pg. 990
ACUTE REALTY CO., LTD.—See Sena Development Public Company Limited; *Int'l*, pg. 6707
ACUTE TECHNOLOGICAL SERVICES, INC.—See Oil States International, Inc.; *U.S. Public*, pg. 1565
ACUTRONIC SCHWEIZ AG—See Jung Technologies Holding AG; *Int'l*, pg. 4027
ACUTRONIC USA INC.—See Jung Technologies Holding AG; *Int'l*, pg. 4027
ACUTUS MEDICAL, INC.; *U.S. Public*, pg. 37
ACUTUS MEDICAL, N.V.—See Acutus Medical, Inc.; *U.S. Public*, pg. 37
ACUVI AB; *Int'l*, pg. 121
ACV AUCTIONS INC.; *U.S. Public*, pg. 37
ACWA HOLDING CO.; *Int'l*, pg. 121
ACWA POWER BARKA S.A.O.G.—See The AES Corporation; *U.S. Public*, pg. 2030
ACWA POWER COMPANY; *Int'l*, pg. 122
ACWA POWER SASAKURA LTD.—See Sasakura Engineering Co., Ltd.; *Int'l*, pg. 6582
ACW CORP.; *U.S. Private*, pg. 71
ACW-FILM GMBH & CO. KG—See Melitta Unternehmensgruppe Bentz KG; *Int'l*, pg. 4810
ACW GROUP, LLC—See GCP Capital Partners Holdings LLC; *U.S. Private*, pg. 1654
A.C. WHITE TRANSFER & STORAGE CO.; *U.S. Private*, pg. 25
ACW MANAGEMENT CORPORATION; *U.S. Private*, pg. 71
AC WORLD ELECTRONICS LTD.—See Daikin Industries, Ltd.; *Int'l*, pg. 1932
ACX DO BRASIL REPRESENTACOES, LTDA.—See Acerinox, S.A.; *Int'l*, pg. 100
ACX INTERNATIONAL (PTE) LTD—See Hemas Holdings PLC; *Int'l*, pg. 3340
ACXIOM AUSTRALIA PTY LTD—See The Interpublic Group of Companies, Inc.; *U.S. Public*, pg. 2090
ACXIOM CH, INC.—See The Interpublic Group of Companies, Inc.; *U.S. Public*, pg. 2090
ACXIOM DEUTSCHLAND GMBH—See The Interpublic Group of Companies, Inc.; *U.S. Public*, pg. 2090
ACXIOM DIGITAL; *U.S. Private*, pg. 71
ACXIOM FRANCE SAS—See The Interpublic Group of Companies, Inc.; *U.S. Public*, pg. 2090
ACXIOM GLOBAL SERVICE CENTER POLSKA SP.Z.O.O.—See The Interpublic Group of Companies, Inc.; *U.S. Public*, pg. 2090
ACXIOM GOVERNMENT SERVICES, INC.—See The Interpublic Group of Companies, Inc.; *U.S. Public*, pg. 2090
ACXIOM JAPAN K. K.—See The Interpublic Group of Companies, Inc.; *U.S. Public*, pg. 2090
ACXIOM LLC—See The Interpublic Group of Companies, Inc.; *U.S. Public*, pg. 2090
ACXIOM LTD.—See The Interpublic Group of Companies, Inc.; *U.S. Public*, pg. 2090
ACXION FOODSERVICE—See Prospect Hill Growth Partners, L.P.; *U.S. Private*, pg. 3288
ACYCLICA INC.—See Teledyne Technologies Incorporated; *U.S. Public*, pg. 1993
AD1 HOLDINGS LIMITED; *Int'l*, pg. 123
AD 2-ONE; *Int'l*, pg. 122
ADA BELTRAMI COOP; *U.S. Private*, pg. 72
ADA CARBON SOLUTIONS, LLC—See Advanced Emissions Solutions, Inc.; *U.S. Public*, pg. 46
ADAC AUTOVERSICHERUNG AG—See Allianz SE; *Int'l*, pg. 341
ADACEL INC.—See Adacel Technologies Limited; *Int'l*, pg. 123
ADACEL SYSTEMS, INC.—See Adacel Technologies Limited; *Int'l*, pg. 123
ADACEL TECHNOLOGIES LIMITED; *Int'l*, pg. 123
ADACHI FACTORY INC.—See Beauty Garage Inc.; *Int'l*, pg. 935
ADA COCA-COLA BOTTLING COMPANY; *U.S. Private*, pg. 72
ADACOM S.A.—See Ideal Group S.A.; *Int'l*, pg. 3589
ADAC PLASTICS INC.; *U.S. Private*, pg. 72
ADACTO S.R.L.—See Sesa S.p.A.; *Int'l*, pg. 6728
A.D. ADAMS ADVERTISING, INC.; *U.S. Private*, pg. 25
ADAERO PRECISION COMPONENTS LTD.—See Indutrade AB; *Int'l*, pg. 3677
ADA-ES, INC.—See Advanced Emissions Solutions, Inc.; *U.S. Public*, pg. 46
ADA FORD LINCOLN MOTORS; *U.S. Private*, pg. 72
ADAFRUIT INDUSTRIES, LLC; *U.S. Private*, pg. 72
ADAGENE INC.; *Int'l*, pg. 123
AD AGENTS AG—See ad pepper media International NV; *Int'l*, pg. 122
AD AGENTS GMBH—See ad pepper media International NV; *Int'l*, pg. 122
ADAGE TECHNOLOGIES; *U.S. Private*, pg. 72
ADAGIO HEALTH; *U.S. Private*, pg. 72

A. DAIGGER & COMPANY INC.; *U.S. Private*, pg. 23
ADA INTERNATIONAL REAL ESTATE OWNED BY ABU DHABI AVIATION-SOLE PROPRIETORSHIP CO. L.L.C.—See Abu Dhabi Aviation; *Int'l*, pg. 70
ADAIR COUNTY HOSPITAL DISTRICT; *U.S. Private*, pg. 73
ADAIR FEED & GRAIN COMPANY; *U.S. Private*, pg. 73
ADAIR GREENE-MCCANN; *U.S. Private*, pg. 73
ADAIR PRINTING COMPANY; *U.S. Private*, pg. 73
ADAIRS LIMITED; *Int'l*, pg. 123
ADALET—See Berkshire Hathaway Inc.; *U.S. Public*, pg. 299
AD'ALL CO., LTD.—See Unitika Ltd.; *Int'l*, pg. 8074
AD ALLIANCE GMBH—See Bertelsmann SE & Co. KGaA; *Int'l*, pg. 989
ADALTA LIMITED; *Int'l*, pg. 123
ADALTIS SRL—See BATM Advanced Communications Ltd.; *Int'l*, pg. 890
ADAM 360 LTD.—See WPP plc; *Int'l*, pg. 8478
ADAMA AGRICULTURAL SOLUTIONS LTD.—See China National Chemical Corporation; *Int'l*, pg. 1526
ADAMA AGRICULTURAL SOLUTIONS S.R.L.—See China National Chemical Corporation; *Int'l*, pg. 1526
ADAMA AGRICULTURAL SOLUTIONS UK LTD.—See China National Chemical Corporation; *Int'l*, pg. 1526
ADAMA AGRICULTURE ESPANA, S.A.—See China National Chemical Corporation; *Int'l*, pg. 1526
ADAMA ANDINA B.V. SUCURSAL COLOMBIA—See China National Chemical Corporation; *Int'l*, pg. 1526
ADAMA ARGENTINA S.A.—See China National Chemical Corporation; *Int'l*, pg. 1526
ADAMA BRASIL S.A.—See China National Chemical Corporation; *Int'l*, pg. 1526
ADAMA FRANCE S.A.S—See China National Chemical Corporation; *Int'l*, pg. 1526
ADAMA ITALIA S.R.L.—See China National Chemical Corporation; *Int'l*, pg. 1526
ADAMA LTD.—See China National Chemical Corporation; *Int'l*, pg. 1526
ADAMA MAKHTESHIM LTD.—See China National Chemical Corporation; *Int'l*, pg. 1526
ADAMANT DRI PROCESSING & MINERALS GROUP; *Int'l*, pg. 123
ADAMANTEM CAPITAL MANAGEMENT PTY LIMITED; *Int'l*, pg. 123
ADAMANT HOLDING INC.; *Int'l*, pg. 123
ADAMAS INCORPORATION PUBLIC COMPANY LIMITED; *Int'l*, pg. 124
ADAMAS ONE CORP.; *U.S. Public*, pg. 37
ADAMAS PHARMACEUTICALS, INC.—See Supernus Pharmaceuticals, Inc.; *U.S. Public*, pg. 1967
ADAMAS VENTURES, INC.; *Int'l*, pg. 124
ADAMA TECHNOLOGIES CORP.; *U.S. Private*, pg. 73
ADAMATION—See Superior Equipment Solutions; *U.S. Private*, pg. 3878
ADAM AUDIO GMBH—See Focusrite plc; *Int'l*, pg. 2720
ADAM AUDIO USA, INC.—See Focusrite plc; *Int'l*, pg. 2720
ADAMBA IMPORTS INTERNATIONAL; *U.S. Private*, pg. 73
ADAM BANK GROUP, INC.—See The Adam Corporation/Group; *U.S. Private*, pg. 3981
AD AM CO., LTD.—See Nihon Yamamura Glass Co., Ltd.; *Int'l*, pg. 5288
ADAM COMMUNICATIONS; *U.S. Private*, pg. 73
ADAM & COMPANY GROUP PLC—See NatWest Group plc; *Int'l*, pg. 5170
ADAM & COMPANY INTERNATIONAL LIMITED—See NatWest Group plc; *Int'l*, pg. 5170
ADAM & COMPANY INVESTMENT MANAGEMENT LIMITED—See NatWest Group plc; *Int'l*, pg. 5170
THE ADAM CORPORATION/GROUP; *U.S. Private*, pg. 3981
ADAM&CO.; *U.S. Private*, pg. 73
ADAM DEVELOPMENT PROPERTIES, L.P.—See The Adam Corporation/Group; *U.S. Private*, pg. 3981
ADAMECS CYCLE SALES CO. INC.; *U.S. Private*, pg. 73
ADAMERA MINERALS CORP.; *Int'l*, pg. 124
ADAM & EVE/DDB—See Omnicom Group Inc.; *U.S. Public*, pg. 1579
ADAM FINANCIAL ASSOCIATES INC.—See Genstar Capital, LLC; *U.S. Private*, pg. 1677
ADAM FINANCIAL ASSOCIATES INC.—See Keystone Group, L.P.; *U.S. Private*, pg. 2298
ADAM FRIEDMAN ASSOCIATES; *U.S. Private*, pg. 73
THE ADAM GROUP; *U.S. Private*, pg. 3981
ADAM HOUSE; *U.S. Private*, pg. 73
ADA MILLENNIUM CONSULTING-OWNED BY ABU DHABI AVIATION SOLE PROPRIETORSHIP L.L.C.—See Abu Dhabi Aviation; *Int'l*, pg. 70
A.D.A.M., INC.—See Ebix Inc.; *U.S. Public*, pg. 710
ADAMIS CORPORATION—See DMK Pharmaceuticals Corporation; *U.S. Public*, pg. 671
ADAMJEE INSURANCE COMPANY LIMITED; *Int'l*, pg. 124
ADAMJEE INSURANCE COMPANY LIMITED—See Adamjee Insurance Company Limited; *Int'l*, pg. 124
ADAMJEE LIFE ASSURANCE COMPANY LIMITED—See Adamjee Insurance Company Limited; *Int'l*, pg. 124

COMPANY NAME INDEX

ADAM KAEPPEL GMBH—See Dierig Holding AG; *Int'l*, pg. 2115
ADAM OG EVA AS—See Validus AS; *Int'l*, pg. 8116
ADAM OPEL GMBH—See Stellantis N.V.; *Int'l*, pg. 7200
ADAMPAK LIMITED—See Navis Capital Partners Limited; *Int'l*, pg. 5175
ADAMPAK (SUZHOU) CO., LTD.—See Navis Capital Partners Limited; *Int'l*, pg. 5175
ADAMPAK (THAILAND) LTD—See Navis Capital Partners Limited; *Int'l*, pg. 5175
ADAMPOL CZECH REPUBLIC CORPORATION—See Hyundai Glovis Co., Ltd.; *Int'l*, pg. 3556
ADAMPOL S.A. CORPORATION—See Hyundai Glovis Co., Ltd.; *Int'l*, pg. 3556
ADAMPOL SLOVAKIA CORPORATION—See Hyundai Glovis Co., Ltd.; *Int'l*, pg. 3556
ADAM RIESE GMBH—See Wuestenrot & Wuerttembergische AG; *Int'l*, pg. 8499
ADAMS AND REESE LLP; *U.S. Private*, pg. 73
ADAMS AUTOMOTIVE INC.; *U.S. Private*, pg. 73
ADAMS AUTO PARTS, LLC—See Genuine Parts Company; *U.S. Public*, pg. 932
ADAMS BANK & TRUST, CORPORATE OFFICE—See Adbanc, Inc.; *U.S. Private*, pg. 76
ADAMS BEVERAGES, INC.; *U.S. Private*, pg. 73
ADAMS BEVERAGES OF NORTH CAROLINA, LLC—See Adams Beverages, Inc.; *U.S. Private*, pg. 73
ADAMS BOOK CO. INC.; *U.S. Private*, pg. 73
ADAMS BROS. CABINETRY, INC.; *U.S. Private*, pg. 73
ADAMS BROWN, LLC; *U.S. Private*, pg. 73
ADAMS BUICK-GMC TRUCK, INC.; *U.S. Private*, pg. 74
ADAMS-BURCH, LLC—See Warburg Pincus LLC; *U.S. Private*, pg. 4440
ADAMS CAMPBELL COMPANY LTD.; *U.S. Private*, pg. 74
ADAMS-COLUMBIA ELECTRIC COOPERATIVE; *U.S. Private*, pg. 76
ADAMS CONSTRUCTION COMPANY; *U.S. Private*, pg. 74
ADAMS, COOPER & MARKS—See I.C. System, Inc.; *U.S. Private*, pg. 2026
ADAMS COUNTY PHYSICAL THERAPY, LIMITED PARTNERSHIP—See U.S. Physical Therapy, Inc.; *U.S. Public*, pg. 2213
ADAMS DIVERSIFIED EQUITY FUND, INC.; *U.S. Public*, pg. 38
ADAMS ELECTRIC COOPERATIVE; *U.S. Private*, pg. 74
ADAMS ENTERPRISES (1993) LTD; *Int'l*, pg. 124
ADAMS EXTRACT & SPICE LLC; *U.S. Private*, pg. 74
ADAMS FAIRACRE FARMS INC.; *U.S. Private*, pg. 74
ADAMS FOODS LIMITED—See Ornua Co-operative Limited; *Int'l*, pg. 5642
ADAMS GLOBAL COMMUNICATIONS, LLC—See ADDvantage Technologies Group, Inc.; *U.S. Public*, pg. 40
ADAMS GOLF, INC.—See Taylor Made Golf Company, Inc.; *U.S. Private*, pg. 3940
THE ADAMS GROUP INC.; *U.S. Private*, pg. 3981
THE ADAMS GROUP; *U.S. Private*, pg. 3981
ADAMS HOMES OF NORTHWEST FLORIDA INC.; *U.S. Private*, pg. 74
ADAMS INVESTMENT COMPANY; *U.S. Private*, pg. 74
ADAMS JEEP OF MARYLAND; *U.S. Private*, pg. 74
ADAMS KEEGAN, INC.; *U.S. Private*, pg. 74
ADAMS & KNIGHT ADVERTISING/PUBLIC RELATIONS; *U.S. Private*, pg. 73
ADAMS LAND & CATTLE CO.; *U.S. Private*, pg. 74
ADAMS MACHINERY MOVERS, INC.—See Olympus Partners; *U.S. Private*, pg. 3013
ADAMS MAGNETIC PRODUCTS CO.—See High Street Capital Management, Inc.; *U.S. Private*, pg. 1937
ADAMS MCCLURE, LP—See Ennis, Inc.; *U.S. Public*, pg. 768
ADAMS MEDIA CORPORATION—See Tinicum Enterprises, Inc.; *U.S. Private*, pg. 4174
ADAMS MFG CORP.—See BC Partners LLP; *Int'l*, pg. 925
ADAMS MFG. CO.; *U.S. Private*, pg. 74
ADAMS NATURAL RESOURCES FUND, INC.; *U.S. Public*, pg. 38
ADAMSON ASSOCIATES ARCHITECTS; *Int'l*, pg. 124
ADAMSON ASSOCIATES, INC.—See Adamson Associates Architects; *Int'l*, pg. 124
ADAMSON ASSOCIATES (INTERNATIONAL) LIMITED—See Adamson Associates Architects; *Int'l*, pg. 124
ADAMSON CAR & TRUCK RENTAL INC.—See A Betterway Rent-A-Car Inc.; *U.S. Private*, pg. 18
ADAMSON FORD INC.; *U.S. Private*, pg. 76
ADAMS PEST CONTROL PTY LTD—See Rollins, Inc.; *U.S. Public*, pg. 1809
ADAMSPLACE, LLC—See National HealthCare Corporation; *U.S. Public*, pg. 1495
ADAMS PLC; *Int'l*, pg. 124
ADAMS PUBLISHING GROUP, LLC; *U.S. Private*, pg. 74
ADAMS RANCH INC.; *U.S. Private*, pg. 75
ADAMS REMCO INC.; *U.S. Private*, pg. 75
ADAMS RESOURCES & ENERGY, INC.; *U.S. Public*, pg. 38
ADAMS RITE AEROSPACE INC.—See TransDigm Group Incorporated; *U.S. Public*, pg. 2181

ADAMS RITE EUROPE LIMITED—See ASSA ABLOY AB; *Int'l*, pg. 633
ADAMS RITE MANUFACTURING CO.—See ASSA ABLOY AB; *Int'l*, pg. 633
ADAMS ROBINSON ENTERPRISES; *U.S. Private*, pg. 75
ADAMS RURAL ELECTRIC COOPERATIVE INC.; *U.S. Private*, pg. 75
ADAMS & SMITH INC.; *U.S. Private*, pg. 73
ADAMS THERMAL SYSTEMS, INC.; *U.S. Private*, pg. 75
ADAMS TOYOTA LEES SUMMIT; *U.S. Private*, pg. 75
ADAMS TOYOTA; *U.S. Private*, pg. 75
ADAMS TRI CITIES ENTERPRISES; *U.S. Private*, pg. 75
ADAM SUGAR MILLS LIMITED; *Int'l*, pg. 123
ADAMS UNLIMITED; *U.S. Private*, pg. 75
ADAMS USA ATHLETICS INC.; *U.S. Private*, pg. 75
ADAMS VEGETABLE OILS, INC.—See The Adams Group Inc.; *U.S. Private*, pg. 3981
ADAMS WHOLESALE COMPANY; *U.S. Private*, pg. 75
ADAMS WHOLESALE SUPPLY, INC.—See SiteOne Landscape Supply, Inc.; *U.S. Public*, pg. 1888
ADAMS WINE GROUP, LLC; *U.S. Private*, pg. 75
ADAM SYSTEMS—See Karmak Inc.; *U.S. Private*, pg. 2263
ADAMWORKS, LLC—See Odyssey Investment Partners, LLC; *U.S. Private*, pg. 2994
ADANA CEMENT INDUSTRIES INC.—See OYAK Cement Group; *Int'l*, pg. 5677
ADANI AEROSPACE & DEFENCE LIMITED—See Adani Enterprises Limited; *Int'l*, pg. 124
ADANI AGRI FRESH LTD—See Adani Enterprises Limited; *Int'l*, pg. 124
ADANI AGRI LOGISTICS LTD—See Adani Enterprises Limited; *Int'l*, pg. 124
ADANI AIRPORT HOLDINGS LIMITED—See Adani Enterprises Limited; *Int'l*, pg. 124
ADANI BUNKERING PRIVATE LIMITED—See Adani Enterprises Limited; *Int'l*, pg. 124
ADANI ELECTRICITY MUMBAI LIMITED—See Adani Energy Solutions Limited; *Int'l*, pg. 124
ADANI ENERGY SOLUTIONS LIMITED; *Int'l*, pg. 124
ADANI ENTERPRISES LIMITED; *Int'l*, pg. 124
ADANI GAS LTD—See Adani Enterprises Limited; *Int'l*, pg. 124
ADANI GLOBAL FZE—See Adani Enterprises Limited; *Int'l*, pg. 125
ADANI GLOBAL LTD.—See Adani Enterprises Limited; *Int'l*, pg. 125
ADANI GREEN ENERGY LTD.—See Adani Enterprises Limited; *Int'l*, pg. 125
ADANI INFRASTRUCTURE PRIVATE LIMITED—See Adani Enterprises Limited; *Int'l*, pg. 125
ADANI LOGISTICS LTD—See Adani Enterprises Limited; *Int'l*, pg. 125
ADANI PORTS AND SPECIAL ECONOMIC ZONE LIMITED—See Adani Enterprises Limited; *Int'l*, pg. 125
ADANI POWER LIMITED—See Adani Enterprises Limited; *Int'l*, pg. 125
ADANI WELSPUN EXPLORATION LIMITED—See Adani Enterprises Limited; *Int'l*, pg. 125
ADANI WILMAR LTD.; *Int'l*, pg. 125
ADAN LIMITED—See VELJAN DENISON LIMITED; *Int'l*, pg. 8149
ADAPAZARI ELEKTRIK URETIM LIMITED SIRKETI—See Enka Insaat ve Sanayi A.S.; *Int'l*, pg. 2440
ADAPCO, LLC—See EQT AB; *Int'l*, pg. 2469
ADAPTAFLEX LIMITED—See ABB Ltd.; *Int'l*, pg. 52
ADAPTALIA OUTSOURCING SL—See Groupe Crit, S.A.; *Int'l*, pg. 3101
ADAPTAS SOLUTIONS, LLC—See IMI plc; *Int'l*, pg. 3624
ADAPT CORPORATION—See Nemetschek SE; *Int'l*, pg. 5195
ADAPT ENGINEERING GMBH & CO. KG—See TUV NORD AG; *Int'l*, pg. 7981
ADAPTEO OYJ; *Int'l*, pg. 125
ADAPT GROUP LIMITED—See Apollo Global Management, Inc.; *U.S. Public*, pg. 154
ADAPTHEALTH CORP.; *U.S. Public*, pg. 38
ADAPTHEALTH PATIENT CARE SOLUTIONS, INC.—See AdaptHealth Corp.; *U.S. Public*, pg. 38
ADAPTIK CORPORATION—See Sapiens International Corporation N.V.; *Int'l*, pg. 6571
ADAPTIMMUNE THERAPEUTICS PLC; *Int'l*, pg. 125
ADAPT IT AUSTRALASIA (PTY) LTD—See Constellation Software Inc.; *Int'l*, pg. 1775
ADAPT IT BOTSWANA (PTY) LTD—See Constellation Software Inc.; *Int'l*, pg. 1775
ADAPTIT HOLDINGS LIMITED—See Constellation Software Inc.; *Int'l*, pg. 1775
ADAPT IT INTERNATIONAL LIMITED—See Constellation Software Inc.; *Int'l*, pg. 1775
ADAPT IT NIGERIA LIMITED—See Constellation Software Inc.; *Int'l*, pg. 1775
ADAPT IT SOLUTIONS LIMITED—See Constellation Software Inc.; *Int'l*, pg. 1775
ADAPT IT SOLUTIONS PTE LIMITED—See Constellation Software Inc.; *Int'l*, pg. 1775
ADAPTIVE AD SYSTEMS, INC.; *U.S. Public*, pg. 39
ADAPTIVE BIOTECHNOLOGIES CORPORATION; *U.S. Public*, pg. 39

ADATA TECHNOLOGY CO., LTD.

ADAPTIVE COMPUTING ENTERPRISES INC.—See ALA Services LLC; *U.S. Private*, pg. 148
ADAPTIVE CORP.; *U.S. Private*, pg. 76
ADAPTIVE ENERGY LLC—See AE Industrial Partners, LP; *U.S. Private*, pg. 112
ADAPTIVE INSIGHTS CO., LTD.—See Workday, Inc.; *U.S. Public*, pg. 2378
ADAPTIVE INSIGHTS LIMITED—See Workday, Inc.; *U.S. Public*, pg. 2378
ADAPTIVE INSIGHTS LLC—See Workday, Inc.; *U.S. Public*, pg. 2378
ADAPTIVE INSIGHTS, LTD.—See Workday, Inc.; *U.S. Public*, pg. 2378
ADAPTIVE INSIGHTS PTY. LTD.—See Workday, Inc.; *U.S. Public*, pg. 2378
ADAPTIVE MEDIA, INC.—See Adaptive Ad Systems, Inc.; *U.S. Public*, pg. 39
ADAPTIVE MICRO SYSTEMS LLC—See Traffic & Parking Control Co., Inc.; *U.S. Private*, pg. 4203
ADAPTIVEMOBILE SECURITY LTD.—See Enea AB; *Int'l*, pg. 2410
ADAPTIVE NURSING & HEALTHCARE SERVICES, INC.; *U.S. Private*, pg. 76
ADAPTIVE PLASMA TECHNOLOGY CORPORATION; *Int'l*, pg. 125
ADAPTIVE SOLUTIONS, INC.—See Morae Global Corp.; *U.S. Private*, pg. 2781
ADAPTIVE SPORTS USA, INC.; *U.S. Private*, pg. 76
ADAPTIVE SWITCH LABORATORIES, INC.—See Invacare Corporation; *U.S. Private*, pg. 2130
ADAPTIVE TECHNOLOGIES CORP.—See Kennametal Inc.; *U.S. Public*, pg. 1222
ADAPTIVE VISION SPOLKA Z OGRANICZONA ODPOWIEDZIALNOSCIA—See Zebra Technologies Corporation; *U.S. Public*, pg. 2401
ADAPT LASER SYSTEMS, LLC—See Boyne Capital Management, LLC; *U.S. Private*, pg. 628
ADAPTLY, INC.—See Accenture plc; *Int'l*, pg. 86
ADAPTOGENICS HEALTH CORP.; *Int'l*, pg. 125
ADAPT PHARMA INC.—See Emergent BioSolutions Inc.; *U.S. Public*, pg. 739
ADAPT PHARMA OPERATIONS LIMITED—See Emergent BioSolutions Inc.; *U.S. Public*, pg. 739
ADAPTRICITY AG—See LEONI AG; *Int'l*, pg. 4462
ADAPTRONIC PRUEFTECHNIK GMBH—See Metall Zug AG; *Int'l*, pg. 4847
ADAPT SOFTWARE APPLICATIONS, INC.; *U.S. Private*, pg. 76
ADAPT TELEPHONY SERVICES LLC—See TTEC Holdings, Inc.; *U.S. Public*, pg. 2203
ADAQUEST, INC.; *U.S. Private*, pg. 76
ADARA, INC.—See RateGain Travel Technologies Limited; *Int'l*, pg. 6213
AD AREA CO., LTD.—See Dentsu Group Inc.; *Int'l*, pg. 2034
ADARE GROUP LIMITED—See Endless LLP; *Int'l*, pg. 2403
ADARE INTERNATIONAL LIMITED—See HH Global Group Limited; *Int'l*, pg. 3378
ADARE SEC LIMITED - REDDITCH—See Endless LLP; *Int'l*, pg. 2403
ADARE SEC LIMITED—See Endless LLP; *Int'l*, pg. 2403
ADA RESOURCES, INC.—See Adams Resources & Energy, Inc.; *U.S. Public*, pg. 38
ADARSH MERCANTILE LIMITED; *Int'l*, pg. 125
ADARSH PLANT PROTECT LTD.; *Int'l*, pg. 125
THE AD ART COMPANY; *U.S. Private*, pg. 3981
ADA SA—See G7 Entreprises; *Int'l*, pg. 2867
ADASIA COMMUNICATIONS, INC.; *U.S. Private*, pg. 76
ADA S. MCKINLEY COMMUNITY SERVICES, INC.; *U.S. Private*, pg. 72
ADA SOLUTIONS INC.—See Partners Group Holding AG; *Int'l*, pg. 5750
ADASTRA CORPORATION; *Int'l*, pg. 125
ADASTRA HOLDINGS LTD.; *Int'l*, pg. 125
AD ASTRA RECOVERY SERVICES INC.—See CURO Group Holdings Inc.; *U.S. Public*, pg. 611
ADASTRIA ASIA CO., LTD.—See Adastria Co., Ltd.; *Int'l*, pg. 126
ADASTRIA CO., LTD.; *Int'l*, pg. 126
ADASTRIA EAT CREATIONS CO., LTD.—See Adastria Co., Ltd.; *Int'l*, pg. 126
ADASTRIA GENERAL SUPPORT CO., LTD.—See Adastria Co., Ltd.; *Int'l*, pg. 126
ADASTRIA KOREA CO., LTD.—See Adastria Co., Ltd.; *Int'l*, pg. 126
ADASTRIA LOGISTICS CO., LTD.—See Adastria Co., Ltd.; *Int'l*, pg. 126
ADASTRIA TAIWAN CO., LTD.—See Adastria Co., Ltd.; *Int'l*, pg. 126
ADATA ELECTRONICS (SHANGHAI) CO. LTD.—See ADATA Technology Co., Ltd.; *Int'l*, pg. 126
ADATA TECHNOLOGY CO., LTD.; *Int'l*, pg. 126
ADATA TECHNOLOGY (HK) CO. LTD.—See ADATA Technology Co., Ltd.; *Int'l*, pg. 126
ADATA TECHNOLOGY MEXICO SDRL DE CV—See ADATA Technology Co., Ltd.; *Int'l*, pg. 126
ADATA TECHNOLOGY (SUZHOU) CO., LTD.—See ADATA Technology Co., Ltd.; *Int'l*, pg. 126

ADATA TECHNOLOGY CO., LTD.
CORPORATE AFFILIATIONS

Company Index

A&D AUSTRALASIA PTY. LTD.—See A&D Co., Ltd.; *Int'l*, pg. 18
A&D AUTOMATIC GATE & ACCESS; *U.S. Private*, pg. 20
ADAVALE RESOURCES LIMITED; *Int'l*, pg. 126
ADAX S.A.S.—See Lauridsen Group Inc.; *U.S. Private*, pg. 2399
ADAYANA GOVERNMENT GROUP—See Comvest Group Holdings LLC; *U.S. Private*, pg. 1007
ADAYANA INC.—See Comvest Group Holdings LLC; *U.S. Private*, pg. 1007
ADAYANA, INC.—See Comvest Group Holdings LLC; *U.S. Private*, pg. 1007
ADAYANA LEARNING SOLUTIONS PVT LTD—See Comvest Group Holdings LLC; *U.S. Private*, pg. 1007
AD-BAG DISTRIBUTION—See Transcontinental Inc.; *Int'l*, pg. 7897
ADB AIRFIELD SOLUTIONS—See The Carlyle Group Inc.; *U.S. Public*, pg. 2043
ADBANC, INC.; *U.S. Private*, pg. 76
AD-BASE GROUP, INC.; *U.S. Private*, pg. 72
ADB BROADBAND S.P.A.—See Advanced Digital Broadcast Holdings SA; *Int'l*, pg. 158
ADB COMPANIES, INC.—See Warren Equity Partners, LLC; *U.S. Private*, pg. 4443
AD BEL LTD.; *U.S. Private*, pg. 71
ADB INTERESTS, LLC; *U.S. Private*, pg. 76
ADBIOTECH CO., LTD.; *Int'l*, pg. 126
ADBIT'S ADVERTISING & PR; *U.S. Private*, pg. 76
AD BOATS LTD.—See Prevent DEV GmbH; *Int'l*, pg. 5967
ADBODMER AG—See Bellevue Group AG; *Int'l*, pg. 967
AD BOSCH RECANVIS S.L.—See s.a. D'Ieteren n.v.; *Int'l*, pg. 6447
ADBRI LIMITED—See CRH plc; *Int'l*, pg. 1842
ADBRI MASONRY GROUP PTY. LTD.—See CRH plc; *Int'l*, pg. 1842
ADBRI MASONRY PTY. LTD.—See CRH plc; *Int'l*, pg. 1842
ADB SAFEGATE AMERICAS, LLC—See The Carlyle Group Inc.; *U.S. Public*, pg. 2043
ADB SAFEGATE BVBA—See The Carlyle Group Inc.; *U.S. Public*, pg. 2043
ADB SERVICES S.A.—See Advanced Digital Broadcast Holdings SA; *Int'l*, pg. 158
ADB STAGELIGHT S.A.S.U.—See ams AG; *Int'l*, pg. 438
ADC ACQUISITION COMPANY, INC.—See Trelleborg AB; *Int'l*, pg. 7912
ADC ACQUISITION CORP. PJSC; *Int'l*, pg. 126
ADC AFRICAN DEVELOPMENT CORPORATION AG—See Atlas Mara Limited; *Int'l*, pg. 686
ADCAPITAL AG; *Int'l*, pg. 126
ADCAP NETWORK SYSTEMS, INC.; *U.S. Private*, pg. 76
ADCARE CRIMINAL JUSTICE SERVICES, INC.—See AAC Holdings, Inc.; *U.S. Private*, pg. 30
ADCARE HOSPITAL OF WORCESTER, INC.—See AAC Holdings, Inc.; *U.S. Private*, pg. 30
ADCARE RHODE ISLAND, INC.—See AAC Holdings, Inc.; *U.S. Private*, pg. 30
ADCB ASSET MANAGEMENT LIMITED—See Abu Dhabi Commercial Bank PJSC; *Int'l*, pg. 70
ADCB FINANCE (CAYMAN) LIMITED—See Abu Dhabi Commercial Bank PJSC; *Int'l*, pg. 71
ADC BRETAGNE—See FAYAT SAS; *Int'l*, pg. 2624
ADCB SECURITIES LLC—See Abu Dhabi Commercial Bank PJSC; *Int'l*, pg. 71
ADC DOLLS INC.—See Gefinor S.A.; *Int'l*, pg. 2911
ADCELLERANT, LLC; *U.S. Private*, pg. 76
ADCETERA GROUP; *U.S. Private*, pg. 76
ADCHECK PROPRIETARY LIMITED—See Caxton and CTP Publishers and Printers Ltd.; *Int'l*, pg. 1363
ADCHEM CORPORATION—See Berry Global Group, Inc; *U.S. Public*, pg. 320
ADC INTEGRATED SYSTEMS, INC.—See Sole Source Capital LLC; *U.S. Private*, pg. 3708
ADCITYMEDIA AB; *Int'l*, pg. 126
ADCLOUD GMBH—See Deutsche Post AG; *Int'l*, pg. 2071
ADCLOUD OPERATIONS SPAIN S.L.—See Deutsche Post AG; *Int'l*, pg. 2071
ADC L.P.; *U.S. Private*, pg. 76
ADC LTD. NM; *U.S. Private*, pg. 76
AD CLUB 2-SALES OFFICE—See Ad Club; *U.S. Private*, pg. 72
AD CLUB; *U.S. Private*, pg. 71
ADCM ALTUS INVESTMENT MANAGEMENT LIMITED—See SHUAA Capital psc; *Int'l*, pg. 6868
ADC MANUFACTURING—See CRH plc; *Int'l*, pg. 1845
ADC MEDITERRANEE—See FAYAT SAS; *Int'l*, pg. 2624
ADC NORD—See FAYAT SAS; *Int'l*, pg. 2624
ADC NORMANDIE—See FAYAT SAS; *Int'l*, pg. 2624
ADCOCK FINANCIAL GROUP; *U.S. Private*, pg. 76
ADCOCK INGRAM CRITICAL CARE (PTY) LIMITED—See The Bidvest Group Limited; *Int'l*, pg. 7621
ADCOCK INGRAM HEALTHCARE (PTY) LIMITED—See Samara Capital Management Ltd.; *Int'l*, pg. 6501
ADCOCK INGRAM HOLDINGS LIMITED—See The Bidvest Group Limited; *Int'l*, pg. 7621
ADCOCK INGRAM LIMITED—See The Bidvest Group Limited; *Int'l*, pg. 7621
ADCO ELECTRICAL CORP.; *U.S. Private*, pg. 76
ADCO INC.—See Atlan Plastics Inc.; *U.S. Private*, pg. 370

ADCO, INC.—See Mentor Partners LLC; *U.S. Private*, pg. 2667
ADCOLE CORPORATION - AEROSPACE DIVISION—See Artemis Capital Partners Management Co., LLC; *U.S. Private*, pg. 340
ADCOLE CORPORATION—See Artemis Capital Partners Management Co., LLC; *U.S. Private*, pg. 340
ADCOLE CORPORATION—See Artemis Capital Partners Management Co., LLC; *U.S. Private*, pg. 340
ADCOLE FAR EAST LTD.—See Artemis Capital Partners Management Co., LLC; *U.S. Private*, pg. 340
ADCOLE GMBH—See Artemis Capital Partners Management Co., LLC; *U.S. Private*, pg. 340
ADCOLE MARYLAND AEROSPACE, LLC—See Redwire Corporation; *U.S. Public*, pg. 1771
ADCOLONY, INC.—See Digital Turbine, Inc.; *U.S. Public*, pg. 664
A&D CO., LTD.; *Int'l*, pg. 18
ADCOM EXPRESS, INC.—See Radiant Logistics, Inc.; *U.S. Public*, pg. 1759
THE ADCOM GROUP, INC.; *U.S. Private*, pg. 3981
AD-COMM CO., LTD.; *Int'l*, pg. 122
ADCOMM GROUP, INC.; *U.S. Private*, pg. 76
AD-COMM GROUP INC.—See ad-comm Co., Ltd.; *Int'l*, pg. 122
ADCOMM, INC; *U.S. Private*, pg. 76
ADCOMM LIMITED—See The Interpublic Group of Companies, Inc.; *U.S. Public*, pg. 2090
A.D. COMPUTER CORPORATION—See NCR Voyix Corporation.; *U.S. Public*, pg. 1502
ADCON ADMINISTRADORA DE CONVENIOS ODONTO-LOGICOS LTDA.—See Odontoprev S.A.; *Int'l*, pg. 5527
ADCON CAPITAL SERVICES LTD.; *Int'l*, pg. 127
ADCONION GMBH—See Adconion Media Group Ltd.; *Int'l*, pg. 127
ADCONION GMBH—See Adconion Media Group Ltd.; *Int'l*, pg. 127
ADCONION GMBH—See Adconion Media Group Ltd.; *Int'l*, pg. 127
ADCONION MEDIA GROUP LTD.; *Int'l*, pg. 127
ADCONION MEDIA, INC.—See Adconion Media Group Ltd.; *Int'l*, pg. 127
ADCONION MEDIA INC.—See Adconion Media Group Ltd.; *Int'l*, pg. 127
ADCONION S.L.—See Adconion Media Group Ltd.; *Int'l*, pg. 127
AD CONSULTANT GROUP INC.; *U.S. Private*, pg. 72
AD CONTACT AB GAMMETER—See Komax Holding AG; *Int'l*, pg. 4240
ADCONTACT AB—See Komax Holding AG; *Int'l*, pg. 4240
ADCORE, INC.; *Int'l*, pg. 127
ADCORP AUSTRALIA LIMITED; *Int'l*, pg. 127
ADCORP AUSTRALIA (QLD) PTY LTD—See Adcorp Australia Limited; *Int'l*, pg. 127
ADCORP AUSTRALIA (VIC) PTY LTD—See Adcorp Australia Limited; *Int'l*, pg. 127
ADCORP HOLDINGS LIMITED; *Int'l*, pg. 127
ADCORP MANAGEMENT SERVICES (PTY) LIMITED—See Adcorp Holdings Limited; *Int'l*, pg. 127
ADCORP NEW ZEALAND LIMITED—See Adcorp Australia Limited; *Int'l*, pg. 127
ADCORP SIGN SYSTEMS, LLC—See Darrell's Sign Company; *U.S. Private*, pg. 1159
ADCOS GMBH—See Nabtesco Corporation; *Int'l*, pg. 5119
ADCOTRON EMS INC.—See East West Manufacturing, LLC; *U.S. Private*, pg. 1318
ADC RHONE-ALPES—See FAYAT SAS; *Int'l*, pg. 2624
ADCS CLINICS, LLC—See Harvest Partners L.P.; *U.S. Private*, pg. 1876
ADC SUD-OUEST—See FAYAT SAS; *Int'l*, pg. 2624
ADC SURGICENTER, LLC—See HCA Healthcare, Inc.; *U.S. Public*, pg. 990
ADC THE MAP PEOPLE—See Langenscheidt Kommanditgesellschaft; *Int'l*, pg. 4409
ADC THERAPEUTICS SA; *Int'l*, pg. 126
ADCURAM GROUP AG; *Int'l*, pg. 128
ADD3, LLC.; *U.S. Private*, pg. 77
AD DAIKO GIFU INC.—See Hakuhodo DY Holdings Incorporated; *Int'l*, pg. 3220
AD DAIKO NAGOYA INC.—See Hakuhodo DY Holdings Incorporated; *Int'l*, pg. 3220
ADDAR REAL ESTATE SERVICES LLC—See ALDAR Properties PJSC; *Int'l*, pg. 304
ADDCAR SYSTEMS LLC—See UGM Holdings Pty Ltd.; *Int'l*, pg. 8015
ADDCN TECHNOLOGY CO., LTD.; *Int'l*, pg. 128
ADDED VALUE, INC.; *U.S. Private*, pg. 77
ADDENDA CAPITAL INC.—See The Co-operators Group Limited; *Int'l*, pg. 7633
ADDENDA CHEMICAL CORPORATION LIMITED—See Metals and Additives; *U.S. Private*, pg. 2682
ADDENDA CORPORATION—See Metals and Additives; *U.S. Private*, pg. 2682
ADDEN FURNITURE, INC.; *U.S. Private*, pg. 77
ADDENTAX GROUP CORP.; *U.S. Private*, pg. 77
AD DENTSU OSAKA INC.—See Dentsu Group Inc.; *Int'l*, pg. 2034
ADDEPAR, INC.; *U.S. Private*, pg. 77
ADDERACARE AB; *Int'l*, pg. 128

AD DEVICE CO., LTD.—See Kaga Electronics Co., Ltd.; *Int'l*, pg. 4048
AD DEVICE (H.K.) LIMITED—See Kaga Electronics Co., Ltd.; *Int'l*, pg. 4048
AD DEVICE (SHANGHAI) CO., LTD.—See Kaga Electronics Co., Ltd.; *Int'l*, pg. 4048
AD DEVICE (THAILAND) CO., LTD.—See Kaga Electronics Co., Ltd.; *Int'l*, pg. 4048
ADDEV MATERIAL SAS; *Int'l*, pg. 128
ADDEX PHARMA S.A.—See Addex Therapeutics Ltd.; *Int'l*, pg. 128
ADDEX THERAPEUTICS LTD.; *Int'l*, pg. 128
ADDFOR INDUSTRIALE SRL—See Sesa S.p.A.; *Int'l*, pg. 6728
ADD HEALTH MEDIA AB—See Schibsted ASA; *Int'l*, pg. 6616
AD DIALETO AGENCIA DE PUBLICIDADE SA—See Accenture plc; *Int'l*, pg. 82
ADDICKS & KREYE CONTAINER LOGISTIK GMBH & CO—See Addicks & Kreye Holding GmbH; *Int'l*, pg. 128
ADDICKS & KREYE CONTAINER SERVICE GMBH & CO. KG—See A.P. Moller-Maersk A/S; *Int'l*, pg. 26
ADDICKS & KREYE HOLDING GMBH; *Int'l*, pg. 128
ADDICKS & TALLY UNION GMBH & CO—See Addicks & Kreye Holding GmbH; *Int'l*, pg. 128
ADDICTION LABS OF AMERICA, LLC—See AAC Holdings, Inc.; *U.S. Private*, pg. 30
ADDICTION & MENTAL HEALTH SERVICES, LLC—See Lee Equity Partners LLC; *U.S. Private*, pg. 2412
ADDI INDUSTRIES LIMITED; *Int'l*, pg. 128
ADDIKO BANK A.D.—See Addiko Bank AG; *Int'l*, pg. 129
ADDIKO BANK A.D.—See Addiko Bank AG; *Int'l*, pg. 129
ADDIKO BANK A.D.—See Addiko Bank AG; *Int'l*, pg. 129
ADDIKO BANK AG; *Int'l*, pg. 129
ADDIKO BANK D.D.—See Addiko Bank AG; *Int'l*, pg. 129
ADDIKO BANK D.D.—See Addiko Bank AG; *Int'l*, pg. 129
ADDIKO BANK D.D.—See Addiko Bank AG; *Int'l*, pg. 129
ADD INDUSTRY (ZHEJIANG) CORPORATION LIMITED; *Int'l*, pg. 128
ADDIS CRESON; *U.S. Private*, pg. 77
ADDISON CAPITAL PARTNERS; *U.S. Private*, pg. 77
ADDISON CORPORATE MARKETING LTD.—See WPP plc; *Int'l*, pg. 8462
ADDISON FOODS INC.; *U.S. Private*, pg. 77
ADDISON LEE LIMITED—See ComfortDelGro Corporation Limited; *Int'l*, pg. 1712
ADDISONMCKEE INC.—See Albion Investors, LLC; *U.S. Private*, pg. 153
ADDISON PROFESSIONAL FINANCIAL SEARCH LLC—See Odyssey Investment Partners, LLC; *U.S. Private*, pg. 2994
ADDISON SAWS LIMITED; *Int'l*, pg. 129
ADDISON; *U.S. Private*, pg. 77
ADDITECH, INC.; *U.S. Private*, pg. 77
ADDITIONAL SECURITIES LIMITED—See Lloyd's of London; *Int'l*, pg. 4536
ADDITIONELLE—See Reitmans (Canada) Limited; *Int'l*, pg. 6259
ADDITIVE FLIGHT SOLUTIONS PTE. LTD.—See Stratasys Ltd.; *Int'l*, pg. 7235
ADDITIVES AND PETROLEUM PRODUCTS JSC—See Masan Consumer Corp.; *Int'l*, pg. 4719
ADDITIVE SOLUTIONS PTY LTD—See Cinven Limited; *Int'l*, pg. 1611
ADDIVANT FRANCE SAS—See LANXESS AG; *Int'l*, pg. 4415
ADDIVANT USA, LLC—See SK Capital Partners, LP; *U.S. Private*, pg. 3678
ADDLIFE AB; *Int'l*, pg. 129
ADDLOGIX, INC.; *U.S. Private*, pg. 77
ADDMASTER CORPORATION; *U.S. Public*, pg. 40
ADD NEW ENERGY INVESTMENT HOLDINGS GROUP LIMITED; *Int'l*, pg. 129
ADDNODE BALKAN D.O.O.—See Addnode Group AB; *Int'l*, pg. 130
ADDNODE GROUP AB; *Int'l*, pg. 130
ADD NV—See KBC Group NV; *Int'l*, pg. 4106
ADD ONE GMBH & CO. KG—See Deutsche Bank Aktiengesellschaft; *Int'l*, pg. 2055
ADD-ON FACTORY—See Vivendi SE; *Int'l*, pg. 8274
ADDONS, INC.—See COSOL Ltd.; *Int'l*, pg. 1814
ADDORO AB—See Unifiedpost Group SA; *Int'l*, pg. 8043
ADDPHARMA INC.—See Yuhan Corporation; *Int'l*, pg. 8611
ADDPRO AB—See Adelis Equity Partners AB; *Int'l*, pg. 142
AD DRAGAN MARKOVIC; *Int'l*, pg. 122
ADDRESSABLE NETWORKS, INC.; *U.S. Private*, pg. 77
ADDRESSDOCTOR GMBH—See Canada Pension Plan Investment Board; *Int'l*, pg. 1279
ADDRESSDOCTOR GMBH—See Permira Advisers LLP; *Int'l*, pg. 5805
ADDRESSPOINT AB—See PostNord AB; *Int'l*, pg. 5940
ADDRESS SOFTWARE SRL—See Poste Italiane S.p.A.; *Int'l*, pg. 5939
ADD-SHOP ERETAIL LTD.; *Int'l*, pg. 128
ADDSINO CO., LTD.; *Int'l*, pg. 131
ADD SYSTEM CO., LTD.—See TAKASE CORPORATION; *Int'l*, pg. 7435

COMPANY NAME INDEX

ADDTECH AB; *Int'l*, pg. 131
ADDTECH BUSINESS SUPPORT AB—See Addtech AB; *Int'l*, pg. 131
ADDTECH COMPONENTS AB—See Addtech AB; *Int'l*, pg. 131
ADDTECH ENERGY & EQUIPMENT AB—See Addtech AB; *Int'l*, pg. 131
ADDTECH LIFE SCIENCE AB—See Addtech AB; *Int'l*, pg. 131
ADDTECH TRANSMISSION AB—See Addtech AB; *Int'l*, pg. 131
ADDTHIS, INC.—See Oracle Corporation; *U.S. Public*, pg. 1610
ADDTRONICS BUSINESS SYSTEMS, INC.—See ID Group, Inc.; *U.S. Private*, pg. 2034
AD DULAYL INDUSTRIAL PARK & REAL ESTATE CO.; *Int'l*, pg. 122
ADDUS HEALTHCARE (DELAWARE), INC.—See Addus HomeCare Corporation; *U.S. Public*, pg. 40
ADDUS HEALTHCARE (IDAHO), INC.—See Addus HomeCare Corporation; *U.S. Public*, pg. 40
ADDUS HEALTHCARE, INC.—See Addus HomeCare Corporation; *U.S. Public*, pg. 40
ADDUS HEALTHCARE (NEVADA), INC.—See Addus HomeCare Corporation; *U.S. Public*, pg. 40
ADDUS HEALTHCARE (SOUTH CAROLINA), INC.—See Addus HomeCare Corporation; *U.S. Public*, pg. 40
ADDUS HOMECARE CORPORATION; *U.S. Public*, pg. 40
ADD VALUE FUND MANAGEMENT BV—See Svenska Handelsbanken AB; *Int'l*, pg. 7358
ADDVALUE INNOVATION PTE LTD—See Addvalue Technologies Ltd.; *Int'l*, pg. 136
ADDVALUE TECHNOLOGIES LTD.; *Int'l*, pg. 136
ADDVANTAGE TECHNOLOGIES GROUP, INC.; *U.S. Public*, pg. 40
ADDVANTAGE TECHNOLOGIES GROUP OF MISSOURI INC—See Leveling 8, Inc.; *U.S. Private*, pg. 2434
ADDVANTAGE TECHNOLOGIES GROUP OF TEXAS—See Leveling 8, Inc.; *U.S. Private*, pg. 2434
(ADD)VENTURES; *U.S. Private*, pg. 1
ADDVISE GROUP AB; *Int'l*, pg. 136
ADDVISE TILLQUIST AB—See ADDvise Group AB; *Int'l*, pg. 136
ADDX CORPORATION; *U.S. Private*, pg. 77
ADECCO ARGENTINA S.A.—See Adecco Group AG; *Int'l*, pg. 136
ADECCO AUSTRALIA PTY LTD.—See Adecco Group AG; *Int'l*, pg. 136
ADECCO BETEILIGUNGS GMBH—See Adecco Group AG; *Int'l*, pg. 136
ADECCO BULGARIA EOOD—See Adecco Group AG; *Int'l*, pg. 136
ADECCO CALEDONIE SARL—See Adecco Group AG; *Int'l*, pg. 136
ADECCO-COLOMBIA—See Adecco Group AG; *Int'l*, pg. 139
ADECCO COORDINATION CENTER NV—See Adecco Group AG; *Int'l*, pg. 136
ADECCO DENMARK A/S—See Adecco Group AG; *Int'l*, pg. 136
ADECCO DETACHERING BV—See Adecco Group AG; *Int'l*, pg. 136
ADECCO DO BRASIL LTDA.—See Adecco Group AG; *Int'l*, pg. 139
ADECCO EMPLOYMENT SERVICES LIMITED—See Adecco Group AG; *Int'l*, pg. 138
ADECCO FINLAND OY—See Adecco Group AG; *Int'l*, pg. 136
ADECCO FRANCE SASU—See Adecco Group AG; *Int'l*, pg. 137
ADECCO GMBH—See Adecco Group AG; *Int'l*, pg. 137
ADECCO GROUP AG; *Int'l*, pg. 136
ADECCO GROUPE FRANCE—See Adecco Group AG; *Int'l*, pg. 137
ADECCO GROUP NORWAY AS—See Adecco Group AG; *Int'l*, pg. 137
ADECCO HIZMET VE DANISNANLIK A/S—See Adecco Group AG; *Int'l*, pg. 137
ADECCO HOLDING FRANCE SASU—See Adecco Group AG; *Int'l*, pg. 137
ADECCO H.R. D.O.O—See Adecco Group AG; *Int'l*, pg. 137
ADECCO IBERIA SA—See Adecco Group AG; *Int'l*, pg. 137
ADECCO INDIA PRIVATE LIMITED—See Adecco Group AG; *Int'l*, pg. 137
ADECCO INDUSTRIAL PTY LTD—See Adecco Group AG; *Int'l*, pg. 137
ADECCO INTERNATIONAL FINANCIAL SERVICES BV—See Adecco Group AG; *Int'l*, pg. 137
ADECCO IRELAND LTD.—See Adecco Group AG; *Int'l*, pg. 138
ADECCO IRVINE—See Adecco Group AG; *Int'l*, pg. 138
ADECCO ISRAEL STAFFING SERVICES LTD.—See Adecco Group AG; *Int'l*, pg. 137
ADECCO ITALIA S.P.A.—See Adecco Group AG; *Int'l*, pg. 137
ADECCO ITALY SPA—See Adecco Group AG; *Int'l*, pg. 137
ADECCO KFT—See Adecco Group AG; *Int'l*, pg. 137
ADECCO-KUALA LUMPUR—See Adecco Group AG; *Int'l*, pg. 139
ADECCO LTD.—See Adecco Group AG; *Int'l*, pg. 137
ADECCO LUXEMBOURG S.A.—See Adecco Group AG; *Int'l*, pg. 137
ADECCO MANAGEMENT & CONSULTING S.A.—See Adecco Group AG; *Int'l*, pg. 137
ADECCO MEDICAL SASU—See Adecco Group AG; *Int'l*, pg. 137
ADECCO MONACO SAM—See Adecco Group AG; *Int'l*, pg. 137
ADECCO MOROCCO—See Adecco Group AG; *Int'l*, pg. 137
ADECCO NETHERLANDS BEHEER B.V.—See Adecco Group AG; *Int'l*, pg. 137
ADECCO NORGE AS—See Adecco Group AG; *Int'l*, pg. 137
ADECCO OUTSOURCING D.O.O.—See Adecco Group AG; *Int'l*, pg. 137
ADECCO PERSONALDIENSTLEISTUNGEN GMBH—See Adecco Group AG; *Int'l*, pg. 137
ADECCO PERSONEELSDIENSTEN BV—See Adecco Group AG; *Int'l*, pg. 137
ADECCO PERSONNEL CONSULTANTS CO., LTD. TAIWAN—See Adecco Group AG; *Int'l*, pg. 137
ADECCO PERSONNEL LIMITED—See Adecco Group AG; *Int'l*, pg. 136
ADECCO PERSONNEL PTE. LTD.—See Adecco Group AG; *Int'l*, pg. 137
ADECCO PERSONNEL SERVICES S.A.—See Adecco Group AG; *Int'l*, pg. 137
ADECCO PERU S.A.—See Adecco Group AG; *Int'l*, pg. 137
ADECCO PHAHOLYOTHIN—See Adecco Group AG; *Int'l*, pg. 137
ADECCO POLAND SP. Z O.O.—See Adecco Group AG; *Int'l*, pg. 137
ADECCO PUERTO RICO—See Adecco Group AG; *Int'l*, pg. 138
ADECCO RAMA IV RECRUITMENT LTD.—See Adecco Group AG; *Int'l*, pg. 137
ADECCO RECRUITMENT SERVICES—See Adecco Group AG; *Int'l*, pg. 137
ADECCO RECURSOS HUMANOS S.A.—See Adecco Group AG; *Int'l*, pg. 138
ADECCO RECURSOS HUMANOS—See Adecco Group AG; *Int'l*, pg. 138
ADECCO RESSOURCES HUMAINES S.A.—See Adecco Group AG; *Int'l*, pg. 138
ADECCO RESURSE UMANE SRL—See Adecco Group AG; *Int'l*, pg. 138
ADECCO ROMANIA SRL—See Adecco Group AG; *Int'l*, pg. 138
ADECCO-SHANGHAI—See Adecco Group AG; *Int'l*, pg. 139
ADECCO SLOVAKIA, S.R.O—See Adecco Group AG; *Int'l*, pg. 138
ADECCO SPOL. S R.O.—See Adecco Group AG; *Int'l*, pg. 139
ADECCO-STOCKHOLM—See Adecco Group AG; *Int'l*, pg. 139
ADECCO SWEDEN AB—See Adecco Group AG; *Int'l*, pg. 138
ADECCO SZEMELYZETI KOZVETITO KFT—See Adecco Group AG; *Int'l*, pg. 138
ADECCO TT SA—See Adecco Group AG; *Int'l*, pg. 138
ADECCO UK LTD.—See Adecco Group AG; *Int'l*, pg. 138
ADECCO URUGUAY S.A.—See Adecco Group AG; *Int'l*, pg. 139
ADECCO USA, INC.—See Adecco Group AG; *Int'l*, pg. 138
ADECCO-VENEZUELA—See Adecco Group AG; *Int'l*, pg. 139
ADECCO VIETNAM JOINT STOCK COMPANY—See Adecco Group AG; *Int'l*, pg. 139
ADECCO-WANCHAI—See Adecco Group AG; *Int'l*, pg. 139
THE ADEC GROUP; *U.S. Private*, pg. 3981
A-DEC, INC.; *U.S. Private*, pg. 22
ADEC INC.; *U.S. Private*, pg. 77
ADECOAGRO S.A.; *Int'l*, pg. 141
ADECOL INDUSTRIA QUIMICA LTDA.—See H.B. Fuller Company; *U.S. Public*, pg. 977
ADECOM QUIMICA LTDA—See Ecolab Inc.; *U.S. Public*, pg. 712
ADE CORPORATION—See Transition Evergreen; *Int'l*, pg. 7900
ADEC SOLUTIONS USA, INC.—See The ADEC Group; *U.S. Private*, pg. 3981
ADEEDO! DRAIN, PLUMBING, HEATING, AIR, & ELECTRICAL—See Odyssey Investment Partners, LLC; *U.S. Private*, pg. 2995
ADEEM INVESTMENT & WEALTH MANAGEMENT CO., K.S.C.C.—See Efad Real Estate Company; *Int'l*, pg. 2318
ADEEVA NUTRITIONALS CANADA INC.—See The Co-operators Group Limited; *Int'l*, pg. 7634
ADEIA INC.; *U.S. Public*, pg. 40
ADEKA AL GHURAIR ADDITIVES LLC—See Al Ghurair Group; *Int'l*, pg. 277
ADEKA AL OTAIBA MIDDLE EAST LLC—See Adeka Corporation; *Int'l*, pg. 141
ADEKA (ASIA) PTE. LTD.—See Adeka Corporation; *Int'l*, pg. 141
ADEKA BRASIL LTDA.—See Adeka Corporation; *Int'l*, pg. 141
ADEKA CHEMICAL SUPPLY CORPORATION—See Adeka Corporation; *Int'l*, pg. 141
ADEKA (CHINA) CO., LTD.—See Adeka Corporation; *Int'l*, pg. 141
ADEKA CLEAN AID CORPORATION—See Adeka Corporation; *Int'l*, pg. 141
ADEKA CORPORATION; *Int'l*, pg. 141
ADEKA ENGINEERING & CONSTRUCTION CORP.—See Adeka Corporation; *Int'l*, pg. 141
ADEKA EUROPE GMBH—See Adeka Corporation; *Int'l*, pg. 141
ADEKA FINE CHEMICAL (CHANGSHU) CO., LTD.—See Adeka Corporation; *Int'l*, pg. 141
ADEKA FINE CHEMICAL (SHANGHAI) CO., LTD.—See Adeka Corporation; *Int'l*, pg. 141
ADEKA FINE CHEMICAL TAIWAN CORP.—See Adeka Corporation; *Int'l*, pg. 141
ADEKA FINE CHEMICAL (THAILAND) CO., LTD.—See Adeka Corporation; *Int'l*, pg. 141
ADEKA FINE FOODS CORPORATION—See Adeka Corporation; *Int'l*, pg. 141
ADEKA FOODS (ASIA) SDN. BHD.—See Adeka Corporation; *Int'l*, pg. 141
ADEKA FOODS (CHANGSHU) CO., LTD.—See Adeka Corporation; *Int'l*, pg. 141
ADEKA FOODS SALES CORPORATION—See Adeka Corporation; *Int'l*, pg. 141
ADEKA INDIA PVT. LTD.—See Adeka Corporation; *Int'l*, pg. 141
ADEKA KOREA CORPORATION—See Adeka Corporation; *Int'l*, pg. 141
ADEKA LIFE-CREATE CORP.—See Adeka Corporation; *Int'l*, pg. 142
ADEKA LOGISTICS CORP.—See Adeka Corporation; *Int'l*, pg. 142
ADEKA POLYMER ADDITIVES EUROPE SAS—See Adeka Corporation; *Int'l*, pg. 142
ADEKA (SINGAPORE) PTE. LTD.—See Adeka Corporation; *Int'l*, pg. 141
ADEKA USA CORP.—See Adeka Corporation; *Int'l*, pg. 142
ADELAIDE APOTHECARY LLC—See Mayne Pharma Group Limited; *Int'l*, pg. 4745
ADELAIDE BANK LIMITED—See Bendigo & Adelaide Bank Ltd.; *Int'l*, pg. 970
ADELAIDE BRIGHTON CEMENT (FLORIDA) INC.—See CRH plc; *Int'l*, pg. 1842
ADELAIDE BRIGHTON CEMENT LTD.—See CRH plc; *Int'l*, pg. 1842
ADELAIDE CLINIC HOLDINGS PTY LIMITED—See Ramsay Health Care Limited; *Int'l*, pg. 6200
ADELAIDE DIGITAL HEARING SOLUTIONS PTY. LTD.—See Demant A/S; *Int'l*, pg. 2023
ADELAIDE GARDEN SHEDS PTY LIMITED—See Oldfields Holdings Limited; *Int'l*, pg. 5552
ADELAIDE SCAFFOLD SOLUTIONS PTY LIMITED—See Oldfields Holdings Limited; *Int'l*, pg. 5553
ADELANTE LIVE INC.; *U.S. Private*, pg. 77
ADELANTE S.R.L.—See WIIT SpA; *Int'l*, pg. 8408
ADELBROOK, INC.; *U.S. Private*, pg. 77
A-DEL CONSTRUCTION COMPANY, INC.; *U.S. Private*, pg. 22
A&D ELECTRONICS (SHENZHEN) CO., LTD.—See A&D Co., Ltd.; *Int'l*, pg. 18
ADELIS EQUITY PARTNERS AB; *Int'l*, pg. 142
ADEL KALEMCILIK TICARET VE SANAYI A.S.; *Int'l*, pg. 142
ADELL CORPORATION—See Kinderhook Industries, LLC; *U.S. Private*, pg. 2306
ADELL PLASTICS INC.; *U.S. Private*, pg. 77
ADELL SAATCHI & SAATCHI—See Publicis Groupe S.A.; *Int'l*, pg. 6108
ADELL TAIVAS OGILVY—See WPP plc; *Int'l*, pg. 8484
ADELMAN ENTERPRISES, INC.; *U.S. Private*, pg. 77
ADELMAN TRAVEL SYSTEMS, INC.—See BCD Holdings N.V.; *Int'l*, pg. 926
ADELONG GOLD LIMITED; *Int'l*, pg. 142
ADELPHIA LAMP & SHADE INC.; *U.S. Private*, pg. 77
ADELPHIA SEAFOOD INC.; *U.S. Private*, pg. 77
ADELPHI-CARLTON LIMITED—See Cineworld Group plc; *Int'l*, pg. 1610
ADELPHI EDEN HEALTH COMMUNICATIONS—See Omnicom Group Inc.; *U.S. Public*, pg. 1573
ADELPHI ENTERPRISES L.P.; *U.S. Private*, pg. 77
ADELPHI GROUP LIMITED—See Omnicom Group Inc.; *U.S. Public*, pg. 1573
ADELPHI PAPER HANGINGS LLC; *U.S. Private*, pg. 77
ADEL SAATCHI & SAATCHI—See Publicis Groupe S.A.; *Int'l*, pg. 6108
ADELT MECHANICAL WORKS LTD.—See ENGIE SA; *Int'l*, pg. 2430
ADEL WHOLESALERS, INC.; *U.S. Private*, pg. 77

ADELWIGGINS GROUP—See TransDigm Group Incorporated; *U.S. Public*, pg. 2181
ADELYA S.A.S.—See Obiz SA; *Int'l*, pg. 5511
ADEM ALLGEMEINE DIENSTLEISTUNGEN FUR ENGINEERING UND MANAGEMENT GMBH—See BayernLB Holding AG; *Int'l*, pg. 913
ADEMCO 1 GMBH—See Resideo Technologies, Inc.; *U.S. Public*, pg. 1789
ADEMCO 1 LIMITED—See Resideo Technologies, Inc.; *U.S. Public*, pg. 1789
ADEMCO AUSTRIA GMBH—See Resideo Technologies, Inc.; *U.S. Public*, pg. 1789
ADEMCO CZ S.R.O.—See Resideo Technologies, Inc.; *U.S. Public*, pg. 1789
ADEMCO (MALAYSIA) SDN. BHD.—See Industronics Berhad; *Int'l*, pg. 3675
ADEMCO OTOMASYON LIMITED SIRKETI—See Resideo Technologies, Inc.; *U.S. Public*, pg. 1789
ADEMCO (PTY) LTD.—See Resideo Technologies, Inc.; *U.S. Public*, pg. 1789
ADEMCO SUPPLY S.R.L.—See Resideo Technologies, Inc.; *U.S. Public*, pg. 1789
ADENA CORPORATION; *U.S. Private*, pg. 77
ADENA HEALTH SYSTEM; *U.S. Private*, pg. 78
ADEN & ANAIS, INC—See Transom Capital Group, LLC; *U.S. Private*, pg. 4209
ADENA SPRINGS COMPANY—See The Stronach Group Inc.; *Int'l*, pg. 7689
ADEN FRANCE—See FAYAT SAS; *Int'l*, pg. 2624
A&D ENGINEERING, INC.—See A&D Co., Ltd.; *Int'l*, pg. 18
ADENIA PARTNERS LTD; *Int'l*, pg. 142
ADENNA; *U.S. Private*, pg. 78
A+ DENTAL CARE—See Gryphon Investors, LLC; *U.S. Private*, pg. 1799
A+ DENTAL CARE—See Gryphon Investors, LLC; *U.S. Private*, pg. 1799
ADENTATEC GMBH—See Elementis plc; *Int'l*, pg. 2358
A&D ENVIRONMENTAL SERVICES, INC.—See Ross Consolidated Corp.; *U.S. Private*, pg. 3485
ADENZA FRANCE SARL—See Nasdaq, Inc.; *U.S. Public*, pg. 1491
ADENZA HONG KONG CO., LTD.—See Nasdaq, Inc.; *U.S. Public*, pg. 1491
ADENZA LTD.—See Nasdaq, Inc.; *U.S. Public*, pg. 1491
ADENZA SINGAPORE PTE. LTD.—See Nasdaq, Inc.; *U.S. Public*, pg. 1491
ADEO BILISIM DANISMANLIK HIZMETLERI SAN. VE TIC, A.S.—See Arena Bilgisayar Sanayi ve Ticaret A.S.; *Int'l*, pg. 558
A.D.E. OF ARK-LA-TEX, INC.—See OPENLANE, Inc.; *U.S. Public*, pg. 1606
ADEP ASSISTANCE—See L'Air Liquide S.A.; *Int'l*, pg. 4373
ADEPLAST S.R.L.—See Sika AG; *Int'l*, pg. 6914
ADEPT4 MANAGED IT LIMITED—See CloudCoCo Group plc; *Int'l*, pg. 1662
ADEPTIO LLC; *Int'l*, pg. 143
ADEPT MARKETING OUTSOURCED LLC—See Ascentium Corporation; *U.S. Private*, pg. 348
ADEPTO D.O.O.—See INSTITUT IGH d.d.; *Int'l*, pg. 3723
ADEPTPROS INC.; *U.S. Private*, pg. 78
ADEPTRA LIMITED—See Fair Isaac Corporation; *U.S. Public*, pg. 820
ADEPTRA PTY. LTD.—See Fair Isaac Corporation; *U.S. Public*, pg. 820
ADEPT TECHNOLOGY GROUP PLC—See Macquarie Group Limited; *Int'l*, pg. 4630
ADEPTUS HEALTH INC.; *U.S. Private*, pg. 78
ADEPTUS HEALTH LLC—See Adeptus Health Inc.; *U.S. Private*, pg. 78
ADERANS CO., LTD.; *Int'l*, pg. 143
ADERANS FRANCE SAS—See Aderans Co., Ltd.; *Int'l*, pg. 143
ADERANS HAIRGOODS, INC.—See Aderans Co., Ltd.; *Int'l*, pg. 143
ADERANS INC—See Aderans Co., Ltd.; *Int'l*, pg. 143
ADERANS PHILIPPINES, INC.—See Aderans Co., Ltd.; *Int'l*, pg. 143
ADERANS (SHANGHAI) CO., LTD—See Aderans Co., Ltd.; *Int'l*, pg. 143
ADERANS (SHANGHAI) TRADING CO., LTD—See Aderans Co., Ltd.; *Int'l*, pg. 143
ADERANS THAI., LTD. (BURIRAM FACTORY)—See Aderans Co., Ltd.; *Int'l*, pg. 143
ADERANS THAI. LTD.—See Aderans Co., Ltd.; *Int'l*, pg. 143
ADERANT HOLDINGS, INC.—See Roper Technologies, Inc.; *U.S. Public*, pg. 1810
ADERANT LEGAL HOLDINGS (AUS) PTY LTD—See Roper Technologies, Inc.; *U.S. Public*, pg. 1810
ADERANT NORTH AMERICA, INC.—See Roper Technologies, Inc.; *U.S. Public*, pg. 1810
ADERAS, INC.; *U.S. Private*, pg. 78
ADERIA CO., LTD.—See Ishizuka Glass Co., Ltd.; *Int'l*, pg. 3818
ADERIA GLASS (ZHUHAI) CO., LTD.—See Ishizuka Glass Co., Ltd.; *Int'l*, pg. 3818

A+ DERR HEATING & AIR CONDITIONING, LLC; *U.S. Private*, pg. 21
ADESA ARKANSAS, LLC—See OPENLANE, Inc.; *U.S. Public*, pg. 1606
ADESA ATLANTA, LLC—See OPENLANE, Inc.; *U.S. Public*, pg. 1606
ADESA AUCTIONS PITTSBURGH—See OPENLANE, Inc.; *U.S. Public*, pg. 1606
ADESA BELGIUM NV—See OPENLANE, Inc.; *U.S. Public*, pg. 1606
ADESA BIRMINGHAM, LLC—See OPENLANE, Inc.; *U.S. Public*, pg. 1606
ADESA COLORADO, LLC—See OPENLANE, Inc.; *U.S. Public*, pg. 1606
ADESA DES MOINES, LLC—See OPENLANE, Inc.; *U.S. Public*, pg. 1606
ADESA DEUTSCHLAND GMBH—See OPENLANE, Inc.; *U.S. Public*, pg. 1606
ADESA EUROPE NV—See OPENLANE, Inc.; *U.S. Public*, pg. 1606
ADESA FRANCE SAS—See OPENLANE, Inc.; *U.S. Public*, pg. 1606
ADESA-GOLDEN GATE—See OPENLANE, Inc.; *U.S. Public*, pg. 1607
ADESA, INC.—See OPENLANE, Inc.; *U.S. Public*, pg. 1606
ADESA ITALIA S.R.L.—See OPENLANE, Inc.; *U.S. Public*, pg. 1606
ADESA-KANSAS CITY—See OPENLANE, Inc.; *U.S. Public*, pg. 1607
ADESA LANSING, LLC—See OPENLANE, Inc.; *U.S. Public*, pg. 1606
ADESA LEXINGTON, LLC—See OPENLANE, Inc.; *U.S. Public*, pg. 1606
ADESAL TELECOM S.L.—See Cellnex Telecom, S.A.; *Int'l*, pg. 1394
ADESA MEXICO, LLC—See OPENLANE, Inc.; *U.S. Public*, pg. 1606
ADESA MINNESOTA, LLC—See OPENLANE, Inc.; *U.S. Public*, pg. 1606
ADESA NEDERLAND B.V.—See OPENLANE, Inc.; *U.S. Public*, pg. 1606
ADESA NEW JERSEY, LLC—See OPENLANE, Inc.; *U.S. Public*, pg. 1606
ADESA NEW YORK, LLC—See OPENLANE, Inc.; *U.S. Public*, pg. 1606
ADESA OHIO, LLC—See OPENLANE, Inc.; *U.S. Public*, pg. 1606
ADESA OREGON, LLC—See OPENLANE, Inc.; *U.S. Public*, pg. 1606
ADESA PENNSYLVANIA, LLC—See OPENLANE, Inc.; *U.S. Public*, pg. 1606
ADESA PHOENIX, LLC—See OPENLANE, Inc.; *U.S. Public*, pg. 1607
ADESA QUEBEC CORPORATION—See OPENLANE, Inc.; *U.S. Public*, pg. 1607
ADESA REMARKETING SERVICES INC.—See OPENLANE, Inc.; *U.S. Public*, pg. 1607
ADESA SAN DIEGO, LLC—See OPENLANE, Inc.; *U.S. Public*, pg. 1607
ADESA-SEATTLE—See OPENLANE, Inc.; *U.S. Public*, pg. 1607
ADESA SUBASTAS ESPANA, S.L.U.—See OPENLANE, Inc.; *U.S. Public*, pg. 1607
ADESA-TAMPA—See OPENLANE, Inc.; *U.S. Public*, pg. 1607
ADESA US AUCTION, LLC—See Carvana Co.; *U.S. Public*, pg. 445
ADESA WISCONSIN, LLC—See OPENLANE, Inc.; *U.S. Public*, pg. 1607
ADESE ALISVERIS MERKEZLERI TICARET A.S.—See Loras Holding A.S.; *Int'l*, pg. 4557
ADESE PETROL URUNLERI TAS. SAN. TIC. A.S.—See Loras Holding A.S.; *Int'l*, pg. 4557
ADESHWAR MEDITEX LIMITED; *Int'l*, pg. 144
ADES INTERNATIONAL HOLDING PLC; *Int'l*, pg. 144
ADESIS, INC.—See Universal Display Corporation; *U.S. Public*, pg. 2255
ADESITAL SPA—See Mapei SpA; *Int'l*, pg. 4681
ADESSO AS A SERVICE GMBH—See adesso SE; *Int'l*, pg. 144
ADESSO AUSTRIA GMBH—See adesso SE; *Int'l*, pg. 144
ADESSO BENEFIT SOLUTIONS GMBH—See adesso SE; *Int'l*, pg. 144
ADESSO HEALTH SOLUTIONS GMBH—See adesso SE; *Int'l*, pg. 144
ADESSO, INC.; *U.S. Private*, pg. 78
ADESSO INSURANCE SOLUTIONS GMBH—See adesso SE; *Int'l*, pg. 144
ADESSO LAKES GMBH—See adesso SE; *Int'l*, pg. 144
ADESSO MOBILE SOLUTIONS GMBH—See adesso SE; *Int'l*, pg. 144
ADESSO ORANGE AG—See adesso SE; *Int'l*, pg. 144
ADESSO ORANGE AUSTRIA GMBH—See adesso SE; *Int'l*, pg. 144
ADESSO SCHWEIZ AG—See adesso SE; *Int'l*, pg. 144
ADESSO SE; *Int'l*, pg. 144
ADESSO SPAIN CONSULTORIA Y SOLUCIONES TECNOLOGICAS S. L.—See adesso SE; *Int'l*, pg. 144

ADESSO TURKEY BILGI TEKNOLOJILERI LTD. STI.—See adesso SE; *Int'l*, pg. 144
ADESSO U.K. LIMITED—See adesso SE; *Int'l*, pg. 144
ADESTA LLC—See Allied Universal Manager LLC; *U.S. Private*, pg. 188
ADESTO TECHNOLOGIES CORPORATION—See Renesas Electronics Corporation; *Int'l*, pg. 6275
ADE TP—See FAYAT SAS; *Int'l*, pg. 2624
ADEUNIS RF; *Int'l*, pg. 145
A&D EUROPE GMBH—See A&D Co., Ltd.; *Int'l*, pg. 18
ADEUS AKTIENREGISTER-SERVICE GMBH—See Allianz SE; *Int'l*, pg. 343
AD-EVENT K.K.—See ad-comm Co., Ltd.; *Int'l*, pg. 123
ADEVINTA ASA; *Int'l*, pg. 145
ADEXA INC.; *U.S. Private*, pg. 78
ADEX BV—See Aalberts N.V.; *Int'l*, pg. 33
AD EXCELLENCE; *U.S. Private*, pg. 72
ADEX CORPORATION—See High Wire Networks Inc.; *U.S. Public*, pg. 1035
ADEXI A/S—See Elof Hansson AB; *Int'l*, pg. 2368
ADEX MACHINING TECHNOLOGIES, LLC; *U.S. Private*, pg. 78
ADEX MINERALS CORP.—See Adex Mining Inc.; *Int'l*, pg. 145
ADEX MINING INC.; *Int'l*, pg. 145
ADEX SECURITIES, INC.; *Int'l*, pg. 145
ADEXUS S.A.—See Aenza S.A.A.; *Int'l*, pg. 176
ADEX ZONEX PTE. LTD.—See Caterpillar, Inc.; *U.S. Public*, pg. 449
ADFA BLANKET COMPANY—See Al Abdullatif Industrial Investment Company; *Int'l*, pg. 275
ADFACTORS PR PVT. LTD.; *Int'l*, pg. 145
ADFAST CORP.; *Int'l*, pg. 145
ADFERENCE GMBH—See ABOUT YOU Holding SE; *Int'l*, pg. 67
ADFERO GROUP; *U.S. Private*, pg. 79
ADF FOODS LTD.; *Int'l*, pg. 145
ADF GROUP INC.; *Int'l*, pg. 145
ADF INTERNATIONAL INC.—See ADF Group Inc.; *Int'l*, pg. 145
A & D FIRE PROTECTION INC.; *U.S. Private*, pg. 17
AD FIRE PROTECTION SYSTEMS INC.—See RPM International Inc.; *U.S. Public*, pg. 1816
ADFITECH, INC.—See Mortgage Connect, LP; *U.S. Private*, pg. 2791
ADFLEX COMMUNICATIONS INC.—See Bain Capital, LP; *U.S. Private*, pg. 449
ADFLOW NETWORKS, INC.—See Daktronics, Inc.; *U.S. Public*, pg. 620
ADFONIC GMBH—See Adfonic Ltd.; *Int'l*, pg. 145
ADFONIC INC.—See Adfonic Ltd.; *Int'l*, pg. 145
ADFONIC LTD.; *Int'l*, pg. 145
ADFORMATIX, INC.; *Int'l*, pg. 145
ADG APOTHEKEN DIENSTLEISTUNGSGESELLSCHAFT MB—See PHOENIX Pharmahandel GmbH & Co. KG; *Int'l*, pg. 5854
ADGAR CANADA INC.—See ADGAR INVESTMENTS AND DEVELOPMENT LIMITED; *Int'l*, pg. 145
ADGAR INVESTMENTS AND DEVELOPMENT LIMITED; *Int'l*, pg. 145
ADGAR POLAND SP. Z O.O—See ADGAR INVESTMENTS AND DEVELOPMENT LIMITED; *Int'l*, pg. 145
ADGATE MEDIA LLC—See Great Hill Partners, L.P.; *U.S. Private*, pg. 1763
ADGEAR TECHNOLOGIES INC.—See Samsung BioLogics Co., Ltd.; *Int'l*, pg. 6510
ADGERO BIOPHARMACEUTICALS HOLDINGS, INC.—See Kintara Therapeutics, Inc.; *U.S. Public*, pg. 1235
ADGOOROO, LLC—See Adthena Ltd.; *Int'l*, pg. 154
ADGRAPHICS (US), INC.—See Taylor Corporation; *U.S. Private*, pg. 3938
AD GREEN CO., LTD.—See AISIN Corporation; *Int'l*, pg. 251
ADHARSHILA CAPITAL SERVICES LTD.; *Int'l*, pg. 145
ADHBHUT INFRASTRUCTURE LIMITED; *Int'l*, pg. 145
A.D. HEMBROUGH ADVERTISING & MARKETING SERVICES; *U.S. Private*, pg. 25
ADHERA THERAPEUTICS, INC.; *U.S. Public*, pg. 41
ADHEREX GROUP—See Akoya Capital LLC; *U.S. Private*, pg. 146
ADHERIUM LIMITED; *Int'l*, pg. 145
ADHERIUM NORTH AMERICA, INC.—See Adherium Limited; *Int'l*, pg. 145
ADHESION WEALTH ADVISOR SOLUTIONS, INC.—See GTCR LLC; *U.S. Public*, pg. 1802
ADHESIVE APPLICATIONS, INC.; *U.S. Private*, pg. 79
ADHESIVE MATERIALS GROUP—See Distribution Solutions Group, Inc.; *U.S. Public*, pg. 668
ADHESIVE PACKAGING SPECIALTIES, INC.; *U.S. Private*, pg. 79
ADHESIVE RESEARCH, INC.; *U.S. Private*, pg. 79
ADHESIVES RESEARCH PTE LTD.—See Adhesive Research, Inc.; *U.S. Private*, pg. 79
ADHESIVES SPECIALISTS, INC.—See EUKALIN Spezial-Klebstoff Fabrik GmbH; *Int'l*, pg. 2526
ADHESIVES TECHNOLOGY CORP.—See Arsenal Capital Management LP; *U.S. Private*, pg. 339

COMPANY NAME INDEX

ADHESIVE SYSTEMS INC.—See Diversified Chemical Technologies Inc.; *U.S. Private*, pg. 1241
ADHESIVE TECHNOLOGIES INC.; *U.S. Private*, pg. 79
ADHESIVOS DE JALISCO (LEON), S.A. DE C.V.—See Grupo Lamosa S.A. de C.V.; *Int'l*, pg. 3131
ADHESIVOS DE JALISCO, S.A. DE C.V.—See Grupo Lamosa S.A. de C.V.; *Int'l*, pg. 3131
ADHESIVOS PERDURA, S. A. DE C. V.—See Grupo Lamosa S.A. de C.V.; *Int'l*, pg. 3131
ADHESIVOS Y BOQUILLAS INTERCERAMIC, S. DE R.L. DE C.V.—See Internacional de Ceramica, S.A.B. de C.V.; *Int'l*, pg. 3743
ADHESO-GRAPHICS, INC.; *U.S. Private*, pg. 79
ADHESYS MEDICAL GMBH—See Grunenthal GmbH; *Int'l*, pg. 3114
ADHETEC SAS—See Power Corporation of Canada; *Int'l*, pg. 5944
ADHEZION BIOMEDICAL, LLC—See H.B. Fuller Company; *U.S. Public*, pg. 977
ADH HEALTH PRODUCTS, INC.; *U.S. Private*, pg. 79
ADHI MULTIPOWER PTE. LTD.—See PT Adhi Karya (Persero) Tbk; *Int'l*, pg. 6019
ADHIRAJ DISTRIBUTORS LTD.; *Int'l*, pg. 145
ADHORNA PREFABRICACION, SA—See Elecnor, S.A.; *Int'l*, pg. 2347
ADH SOFT SP. Z.O.O.—See Asseco Poland S.A.; *Int'l*, pg. 641
ADHUNIK METALIKS LIMITED—See GFG Alliance Limited; *Int'l*, pg. 2956
ADHUNIK POWER & NATURAL RESOURCES LTD.—See GFG Alliance Limited; *Int'l*, pg. 2956
ADIACENT APAC LIMITED—See Sesa S.p.A.; *Int'l*, pg. 6728
ADIA FRANCE—See Adecco Group AG; *Int'l*, pg. 137
ADIAL PHARMACEUTICALS, INC.; *U.S. Public*, pg. 41
ADI AMERICAN DISTRIBUTORS LLC—See Promus Holdings, LLC; *U.S. Private*, pg. 3283
ADI AMERICAN DISTRIBUTORS LLC—See Stonebridge Partners, LLC; *U.S. Private*, pg. 3827
ADIA NUTRITION, INC.; *U.S. Public*, pg. 41
ADIATOR AB—See Addtech AB; *Int'l*, pg. 131
ADIB (UK) LIMITED—See Abu Dhabi Islamic Bank PJSC; *Int'l*, pg. 72
ADICET BIO, INC.; *U.S. Public*, pg. 41
ADICORA SERVICIOS DE INGENIERIA, S.L.—See Iberdrola, S.A.; *Int'l*, pg. 3570
ADI CORPORATION; *Int'l*, pg. 145
ADIDAS AG; *Int'l*, pg. 145
ADIDAS AMERICA, INC.—See adidas AG; *Int'l*, pg. 146
ADIDAS ARGENTINA S.A.—See adidas AG; *Int'l*, pg. 146
ADIDAS AUSTRALIA PTY. LIMITED—See adidas AG; *Int'l*, pg. 146
ADIDAS AUSTRIA GMBH—See adidas AG; *Int'l*, pg. 146
ADIDAS BALTICS SIA—See adidas AG; *Int'l*, pg. 146
ADIDAS BELGIUM N.V.—See adidas AG; *Int'l*, pg. 146
ADIDAS BENELUX B.V.—See adidas AG; *Int'l*, pg. 146
ADIDAS BETEILIGUNGSGESELLSCHAFT MBH—See adidas AG; *Int'l*, pg. 146
ADIDAS BUDAPEST KFT.—See adidas AG; *Int'l*, pg. 146
ADIDAS BULGARIA EAD—See adidas AG; *Int'l*, pg. 146
ADIDAS CDC IMMOBILIENINVEST GMBH—See adidas AG; *Int'l*, pg. 146
ADIDAS CHILE LTDA.—See adidas AG; *Int'l*, pg. 146
ADIDAS (CHINA) LTD.—See adidas AG; *Int'l*, pg. 146
ADIDAS COLOMBIA LTDA.—See adidas AG; *Int'l*, pg. 146
ADIDAS CROATIA D.O.O.—See adidas AG; *Int'l*, pg. 146
ADIDAS CR S.R.O.—See adidas AG; *Int'l*, pg. 146
ADIDAS (CYPRUS) LIMITED—See adidas AG; *Int'l*, pg. 146
ADIDAS DANMARK A/S—See adidas AG; *Int'l*, pg. 146
ADIDAS DE MEXICO S.A. DE C.V.—See adidas AG; *Int'l*, pg. 147
ADIDAS DO BRASIL LTDA.—See adidas AG; *Int'l*, pg. 147
ADIDAS EMERGING MARKET L.L.C.—See adidas AG; *Int'l*, pg. 146
ADIDAS EMERGING MARKETS FZE—See adidas AG; *Int'l*, pg. 146
ADIDAS ESPANA S.A.—See adidas AG; *Int'l*, pg. 147
ADIDAS ESPANA S.A.U.—See adidas AG; *Int'l*, pg. 147
ADIDAS FINANCE SPAIN S.A.—See adidas AG; *Int'l*, pg. 147
ADIDAS FRANCE S.A.R.L.—See adidas AG; *Int'l*, pg. 147
ADIDAS HELLAS A.E.—See adidas AG; *Int'l*, pg. 147
ADIDAS HONG KONG LTD.—See adidas AG; *Int'l*, pg. 147
ADIDAS INDIA PRIVATE LTD.—See adidas AG; *Int'l*, pg. 147
ADIDAS INDUSTRIAL, S.A. DE C.V.—See adidas AG; *Int'l*, pg. 147
ADIDAS INSURANCE & RISK CONSULTANTS GMBH—See adidas AG; *Int'l*, pg. 147
ADIDAS INTERNATIONAL B.V.—See adidas AG; *Int'l*, pg. 147
ADIDAS INTERNATIONAL FINANCE B.V.—See adidas AG; *Int'l*, pg. 147
ADIDAS INTERNATIONAL MARKETING B.V.—See adidas AG; *Int'l*, pg. 147
ADIDAS INTERNATIONAL TRADING B.V.—See adidas AG; *Int'l*, pg. 147

ADIDAS (IRELAND) LTD.—See adidas AG; *Int'l*, pg. 146
ADIDAS ISRAEL LTD.—See adidas AG; *Int'l*, pg. 147
ADIDAS ITALY S.P.A—See adidas AG; *Int'l*, pg. 147
ADIDAS JAPAN K.K.—See adidas AG; *Int'l*, pg. 147
ADIDAS KOREA LTD.—See adidas AG; *Int'l*, pg. 147
ADIDAS KOREA TECHNICAL SERVICES LTD.—See adidas AG; *Int'l*, pg. 147
ADIDAS LATIN AMERICA, S.A.—See adidas AG; *Int'l*, pg. 147
ADIDAS LEVANT LIMITED—See adidas AG; *Int'l*, pg. 147
ADIDAS (MALAYSIA) SDN. BHD.—See adidas AG; *Int'l*, pg. 146
ADIDAS NEW ZEALAND LIMITED—See adidas AG; *Int'l*, pg. 147
ADIDAS NORGE A/S—See adidas AG; *Int'l*, pg. 147
ADIDAS NORTH AMERICA, INC.—See adidas AG; *Int'l*, pg. 147
ADIDAS POLAND SP. Z. O. O.—See adidas AG; *Int'l*, pg. 147
ADIDAS ROMANIA S.R.L.—See adidas AG; *Int'l*, pg. 147
ADIDAS SARRAGAN FRANCE S.A.R.L.—See adidas AG; *Int'l*, pg. 147
ADIDAS SERBIA D.O.O.—See adidas AG; *Int'l*, pg. 147
ADIDAS SERVICES LIMITED—See adidas AG; *Int'l*, pg. 147
ADIDAS SINGAPORE PTE. LTD.—See adidas AG; *Int'l*, pg. 147
ADIDAS SLOVAKIA S.R.O.—See adidas AG; *Int'l*, pg. 147
ADIDAS SOURCING LIMITED—See adidas AG; *Int'l*, pg. 147
ADIDAS (SOUTH AFRICA) (PTY) LTD.—See adidas AG; *Int'l*, pg. 146
ADIDAS SPOR MALZEMELERI SATIS VE PAZARLAMA A.S.—See adidas AG; *Int'l*, pg. 147
ADIDAS SPORT GMBH—See adidas AG; *Int'l*, pg. 147
ADIDAS SPORTS (CHINA) CO. LTD.—See adidas AG; *Int'l*, pg. 146
ADIDAS SUOMI OY—See adidas AG; *Int'l*, pg. 147
ADIDAS (SUZHOU) CO. LTD.—See adidas AG; *Int'l*, pg. 146
ADIDAS SVERIGE AB—See adidas AG; *Int'l*, pg. 147
ADIDAS TAIWAN LIMITED—See adidas AG; *Int'l*, pg. 147
ADIDAS TEAM, INC.—See adidas AG; *Int'l*, pg. 146
ADIDAS (THAILAND) CO., LTD.—See adidas AG; *Int'l*, pg. 146
ADIDAS TREFOIL TRADING (U.K.) LIMITED—See adidas AG; *Int'l*, pg. 147
ADIDAS TRGOVINA D.O.O.—See adidas AG; *Int'l*, pg. 147
ADIDAS (UK) LTD.—See adidas AG; *Int'l*, pg. 146
ADI ENGINEERING, INC.—See RAD Group; *Int'l*, pg. 6173
ADIEN LIMITED—See Pipehawk Plc; *Int'l*, pg. 5873
ADIENT ARVIND AUTOMOTIVE FABRICS INDIA PRIVATE LIMITED—See Lalbhai Group; *Int'l*, pg. 4398
ADIENT AUTOMOTIVE ARGENTINA S.R.L.—See Adient plc; *Int'l*, pg. 148
ADIENT AUTOMOTIVE ROMANIA S.R.L.—See Adient plc; *Int'l*, pg. 148
ADIENT BELGIUM BVBA—See Adient plc; *Int'l*, pg. 148
ADIENT BOR S.R.O.—See Adient plc; *Int'l*, pg. 148
ADIENT CLANTON INC.—See Adient plc; *Int'l*, pg. 148
ADIENT ELDON INC.—See Adient plc; *Int'l*, pg. 148
ADIENT INDIA PRIVATE LIMITED—See Adient plc; *Int'l*, pg. 148
ADIENT LTD. & CO. KG.—See Adient plc; *Int'l*, pg. 148
ADIENT NOVO MESTO, PROIZVODNJA AVTOMOBILSKIH SEDEZEV, D.O.O.—See Adient plc; *Int'l*, pg. 148
ADIENT PLC; *Int'l*, pg. 148
ADIENT POLAND SP. Z O.O.—See Adient plc; *Int'l*, pg. 148
ADIENT SAARLOUIS LTD. & CO. KG.—See Adient plc; *Int'l*, pg. 148
ADIENT SEATING CANADA LP.—See Adient plc; *Int'l*, pg. 148
ADIENT SEATING INC.—See Adient plc; *Int'l*, pg. 148
ADIENT SOUTH AFRICA (PTY) LTD.—See Adient plc; *Int'l*, pg. 148
ADIENT SWEDEN AB—See Adient plc; *Int'l*, pg. 148
ADIENT (THAILAND) CO., LTD.—See Adient plc; *Int'l*, pg. 148
ADIENT US LLC—See Adient plc; *Int'l*, pg. 148
A. DIETRICH KALTE KLIMA LUFTUNG AG—See BKW AG; *Int'l*, pg. 1054
ADI-GARDINER LIMITED—See Honeywell International Inc.; *U.S. Public*, pg. 1046
ADIG FONDSVERTRIEB GMBH—See Allianz SE; *Int'l*, pg. 341
ADI GLOBAL DISTRIBUTION AB—See Resideo Technologies, Inc.; *U.S. Public*, pg. 1789
ADI GLOBAL DISTRIBUTION—See Honeywell International Inc.; *U.S. Public*, pg. 1049
ADIGO DRIVES AB—See Addtech AB; *Int'l*, pg. 131
ADI GROUP INC.; *Int'l*, pg. 145
ADIKA STYLE LTD.; *Int'l*, pg. 148
ADIL BEY HOLDING A.S.; *Int'l*, pg. 148
ADI, LLC—See Bread Financial Holdings Inc.; *U.S. Public*, pg. 380
ADIL TEXTILE MILLS LIMITED; *Int'l*, pg. 148
ADIM COTE D'AZUR SAS—See VINCI S.A.; *Int'l*, pg. 8234
ADIM EST—See VINCI S.A.; *Int'l*, pg. 8230

ADIM LYON SAS—See VINCI S.A.; *Int'l*, pg. 8234
ADIMMUNE CORPORATION; *Int'l*, pg. 148
ADIM NORD-PICARDIE SAS—See VINCI S.A.; *Int'l*, pg. 8234
ADIM NORMANDIE CENTRE SAS—See VINCI S.A.; *Int'l*, pg. 8234
ADIM NOUVELLE AQUITAINE SAS—See VINCI S.A.; *Int'l*, pg. 8234
ADIM OCCITANIE SAS—See VINCI S.A.; *Int'l*, pg. 8234
ADIM OUEST SAS—See VINCI S.A.; *Int'l*, pg. 8234
ADIM PARIS ILE-DE-FRANCE SAS—See VINCI S.A.; *Int'l*, pg. 8234
ADIM PROVENCE SAS—See VINCI S.A.; *Int'l*, pg. 8234
ADIM SAS—See VINCI S.A.; *Int'l*, pg. 8234
ADINATH BIO-LABS LTD.; *Int'l*, pg. 148
ADINATH EXIM RESOURCES LTD.; *Int'l*, pg. 148
ADINATH TEXTILES LIMITED—See Shreyans Industries Limited; *Int'l*, pg. 6865
ADINC/J. KAPLAN ADVERTISING; *U.S. Private*, pg. 79
ADING AD; *Int'l*, pg. 149
ADING BULGARIA EOOD—See Ading AD; *Int'l*, pg. 149
ADING D.O.O.—See Ading AD; *Int'l*, pg. 149
ADINGO, INC.—See Polaris Capital Group Co., Ltd.; *Int'l*, pg. 5907
ADIN MEDIA(SHANGHAI) CO., LTD.—See Wutong Holding Group Co., Ltd.; *Int'l*, pg. 8514
ADINO ENERGY CORPORATION; *U.S. Private*, pg. 79
A&D INSTRUMENTS INDIA PVT. LTD.—See A&D Co., Ltd.; *Int'l*, pg. 18
A&D INSTRUMENTS LTD.—See A&D Co., Ltd.; *Int'l*, pg. 18
A&D INSTRUMENTS (THAILAND) LIMITED—See A&D Co., Ltd.; *Int'l*, pg. 18
AD INSURANCE POLICY; *Int'l*, pg. 122
ADINTE CO., LTD.—See Vector Inc.; *Int'l*, pg. 8144
AD INVESTMENT MANAGEMENT CO., LTD.—See ITOCHU Corporation; *Int'l*, pg. 3834
ADI PUERTO RICO—See Honeywell International Inc.; *U.S. Public*, pg. 1049
ADIRA ENERGY CORP—See Empower Clinics Inc.; *Int'l*, pg. 2388
ADIRA ENERGY ISRAEL LTD.—See Empower Clinics Inc.; *Int'l*, pg. 2388
ADIR INTERNATIONAL EXPORT LTD.; *U.S. Private*, pg. 79
ADIRONDACK BANKCORP, INC.; *U.S. Private*, pg. 79
ADIRONDACK BANK—See Adirondack Bankcorp, Inc.; *U.S. Private*, pg. 79
ADIRONDACK BEVERAGES—See Polar Beverages; *U.S. Private*, pg. 3223
ADIRONDACK PUBLISHING CO. INC.—See The Nutting Company, Inc.; *U.S. Private*, pg. 4086
ADIRONDACK ROCK CREEK EMERGING MARKETS FUND, LP—See Wells Fargo & Company; *U.S. Public*, pg. 2343
ADIRONDACK SCENIC, INC.; *U.S. Private*, pg. 79
THE ADIRONDACK TRUST COMPANY; *U.S. Public*, pg. 2030
ADISHAKTI LOHA & ISPAT LIMITED; *Int'l*, pg. 149
ADISH CO., LTD.; *Int'l*, pg. 149
ADISH INTERNATIONAL CORPORATION—See Adish Co., Ltd.; *Int'l*, pg. 149
ADISH PLUS CO., LTD.—See Adish Co., Ltd.; *Int'l*, pg. 149
ADISORN SONGKHLA CO., LTD.—See STARK Corporation Public Company Limited; *Int'l*, pg. 7177
ADI—See Honeywell International Inc.; *U.S. Public*, pg. 1049
ADI—See Honeywell International Inc.; *U.S. Public*, pg. 1049
ADISSEO FRANCE S.A.S.—See China National Chemical Corporation; *Int'l*, pg. 1526
ADISTRIBUZIONEGAS S.R.L.—See ACEA S.p.A.; *Int'l*, pg. 95
ADISYN LTD.; *Int'l*, pg. 149
ADI SYSTEMS ASIA PACIFIC LIMITED—See ADI Group Inc.; *Int'l*, pg. 145
ADI SYSTEMS USA INC.—See ADI Group Inc.; *Int'l*, pg. 145
ADIT EDTECH ACQUISITION CORP.—See GRIID Infrastructure Inc.; *U.S. Public*, pg. 969
ADITI CONSULTING LLC; *U.S. Private*, pg. 79
ADITI TECHNOLOGIES PRIVATE LTD.—See Samsung Group; *Int'l*, pg. 6512
ADITRI INDUSTRIES LIMITED; *Int'l*, pg. 149
ADITRO AB—See Nordic Capital AB; *Int'l*, pg. 5419
ADITRO LOGISTICS AB—See Valedo Partners AB; *Int'l*, pg. 8112
ADITXT, INC.; *U.S. Public*, pg. 41
ADITYA BIRLA CAPITAL ADVISORS PRIVATE LIMITED—See The Aditya Birla Group; *Int'l*, pg. 7610
ADITYA BIRLA CAPITAL LTD.; *Int'l*, pg. 149
ADITYA BIRLA CHEMICALS (THAILAND) LTD., EPOXY DIVISION—See The Aditya Birla Group; *Int'l*, pg. 7610
ADITYA BIRLA COMMODITIES BROKING LIMITED—See The Aditya Birla Group; *Int'l*, pg. 7611
ADITYA BIRLA FASHION & RETAIL LIMITED—See The Aditya Birla Group; *Int'l*, pg. 7610

ADITYA BIRLA CAPITAL LTD.

CORPORATE AFFILIATIONS

ADITYA BIRLA FINANCE LIMITED—See The Aditya Birla Group; *Int'l*, pg. 7610
THE ADITYA BIRLA GROUP; *Int'l*, pg. 7610
ADITYA BIRLA MANAGEMENT CORPORATION LIMITED—See The Aditya Birla Group; *Int'l*, pg. 7610
ADITYA BIRLA MONEY LIMITED—See The Aditya Birla Group; *Int'l*, pg. 7610
ADITYA BIRLA MONEY MART LIMITED—See The Aditya Birla Group; *Int'l*, pg. 7611
ADITYA BIRLA NUVO LIMITED—See The Aditya Birla Group; *Int'l*, pg. 7611
ADITYA BIRLA NUVO LTD - JAYA SHREE TEXTILES UNIT—See The Aditya Birla Group; *Int'l*, pg. 7611
ADITYA BIRLA SUN LIFE AMC LTD.; *Int'l*, pg. 149
ADITYA BIRLA TELECOM LIMITED—See Vodafone Idea Limited; *Int'l*, pg. 8286
ADITYA CONSUMER MARKETING LIMITED; *Int'l*, pg. 149
ADITYA FORGE LIMITED; *Int'l*, pg. 149
ADITYA INFOTECH—See Netlink Solutions (India) Limited; *Int'l*, pg. 5214
ADITYA ISPAT LTD.; *Int'l*, pg. 149
ADITYA SPINNERS LTD.; *Int'l*, pg. 149
ADITYA VISION LIMITED; *Int'l*, pg. 149
ADIUVA CAPITAL GMBH; *Int'l*, pg. 149
ADIUVO INVESTMENTS SA; *Int'l*, pg. 150
ADIVIC TECHNOLOGY CO., LTD.—See WPG Holdings Limited; *Int'l*, pg. 8460
ADIXEN VACUUM PRODUCTS SAS—See Dr. Ing. K. Busch GmbH; *Int'l*, pg. 2194
ADIXEN VACUUM TECHNOLOGY KOREA LTD.—See Dr. Ing. K. Busch GmbH; *Int'l*, pg. 2194
ADJACENT PRODUCTIONS, LLC—See British Broadcasting Corporation; *Int'l*, pg. 1168
AD JAVNA SKLADISTA SUBOTICA; *Int'l*, pg. 122
ADJIA TECHNOLOGIES LIMITED; *Int'l*, pg. 150
ADJ INDUSTRIES INC.—See CoorsTek, Inc.; *U.S. Private*, pg. 1043
ADJMI APPAREL GROUP, INC.; *U.S. Private*, pg. 79
ADJUSTABLE CLAMP COMPANY; *U.S. Private*, pg. 79
ADJUSTERS INTERNATIONAL INC.; *U.S. Private*, pg. 79
ADJUST YOUR SET LIMITED—See You & Mr Jones Inc.; *U.S. Private*, pg. 4591
ADJUTORIS CONSEIL S.A.—See Edmond de Rothschild Holding S.A.; *Int'l*, pg. 2312
ADJUVANT HOLDINGS CO., LTD.; *Int'l*, pg. 150
ADJUVANTS UNLIMITED, LLC—See KFM Enterprises, LLC; *U.S. Private*, pg. 2300
ADK AMERICA, INC. - NEW YORK OFFICE—See Bain Capital, LP; *U.S. Private*, pg. 428
ADK AMERICA, INC.—See Bain Capital, LP; *U.S. Private*, pg. 428
ADK EMOTIONS INC.—See Bain Capital, LP; *U.S. Private*, pg. 428
ADK HOLDINGS INC.—See Bain Capital, LP; *U.S. Private*, pg. 428
ADKINS DESIGN VISUAL COMMUNICATIONS LLC; *U.S. Private*, pg. 79
ADKINS ELECTRIC, INC.—See White Wolf Capital LLC; *U.S. Private*, pg. 4510
ADKINS ENERGY LLC; *U.S. Private*, pg. 79
ADKINS, MATCHETT & TOY (HONG KONG) LIMITED—See Wilmington plc; *Int'l*, pg. 8421
ADKINS MATCHETT & TOY LIMITED—See Wilmington plc; *Int'l*, pg. 8422
ADKINS, MATCHETT & TOY LIMITED—See Wilmington plc; *Int'l*, pg. 8421
ADKINS & MATCHETT (UK) LIMITED—See Wilmington plc; *Int'l*, pg. 8421
ADK INTERNATIONAL INC.—See Bain Capital, LP; *U.S. Private*, pg. 428
ADK LUMBER CITY OPERATOR, LLC—See Regional Health Properties, Inc.; *U.S. Public*, pg. 1775
ADKM, INC.; *U.S. Private*, pg. 80
ADKNOWLEDGE, INC.; *U.S. Private*, pg. 80
ADKNOWLEDGE UK LIMITED—See Adknowledge, Inc.; *U.S. Private*, pg. 80
ADK OCEANSIDE OPERATOR, LLC—See Regional Health Properties, Inc.; *U.S. Public*, pg. 1775
A&D KOREA LIMITED—See A&D Co., Ltd.; *Int'l*, pg. 18
ADKORE STAFFING GROUP; *U.S. Private*, pg. 80
ADK POWDER SPRINGS OPERATOR, LLC—See Regional Health Properties, Inc.; *U.S. Public*, pg. 1775
ADLAI NORTYE BIOPHARMA CO., LTD.—See Adlai Nortye Ltd.; *U.S. Public*, pg. 41
ADLAI NORTYE LTD.; *U.S. Public*, pg. 41
ADLAI NORTYE USA INC—See Adlai Nortye Ltd.; *U.S. Public*, pg. 41
ADLAM FILMS—See Bryce Corporation; *U.S. Private*, pg. 674
ADL BIONATUR SOLUTIONS, S.A.—See Wacker Chemie AG; *Int'l*, pg. 8323
ADL BIONATUR SOLUTIONS; *Int'l*, pg. 150
ADL BIOPHARMA S.L.U.—See Wacker Chemie AG; *Int'l*, pg. 8323
ADL DELIVERY; *U.S. Private*, pg. 80
ADLER & ALLAN LIMITED—See Sun Capital Partners, Inc.; *U.S. Private*, pg. 3861
ADLER, CHOMSKI GREY—See WPP plc; *Int'l*, pg. 8469

ADLER GROUP, INC.; *U.S. Private*, pg. 80
ADLER GROUP SA; *Int'l*, pg. 150
ADLER MEDIEQUIP PRIVATE LIMITED—See Smith & Nephew plc; *Int'l*, pg. 7007
ADLER MODEMARKTE AG—See Steilmann Holding AG; *Int'l*, pg. 7193
ADLER PELZER HOLDING GMBH—See Adler Plastic SpA; *Int'l*, pg. 150
THE ADLER PLANETARIUM & ASTRONOMY MUSEUM; *U.S. Private*, pg. 3982
ADLER PLASTIC SPA; *Int'l*, pg. 150
ADLER REAL ESTATE AG—See ADLER Group SA; *Int'l*, pg. 150
ADLER REAL ESTATE HOTEL GMBH—See ADLER Group SA; *Int'l*, pg. 150
ADLER REAL ESTATE PROPERTIES GMBH & CO. KG—See ADLER Group SA; *Int'l*, pg. 150
ADLER SA—See Materials Technologies; *Int'l*, pg. 4727
ADLERSHOFER SARL—See CLS Holdings plc; *Int'l*, pg. 1663
ADLER SOLAR WORKS CO., LTD.—See Japan Investment Adviser Co., Ltd.; *Int'l*, pg. 3898
ADLER TANK RENTALS, LLC—See Kinderhook Industries, LLC; *U.S. Private*, pg. 2306
ADLER WOHNEN SERVICE GMBH—See ADLER Group SA; *Int'l*, pg. 150
ADLETA CORPORATION; *U.S. Private*, pg. 80
ADLEY FORMULATIONS PRIVATE LIMITED—See Beta Drugs Limited; *Int'l*, pg. 1001
A D LIFT TRUCK—See Wolter Group LLC; *U.S. Private*, pg. 4554
ADLINE CHEM LAB LIMITED; *Int'l*, pg. 150
ADLINK CABLE ADVERTISING, LLC.; *U.S. Private*, pg. 80
ADLINK TECHNOLOGY B.V.—See ADLINK Technology, Inc.; *Int'l*, pg. 150
ADLINK TECHNOLOGY (CHINA) CO., LTD.—See ADLINK Technology, Inc.; *Int'l*, pg. 150
ADLINK TECHNOLOGY, INC.; *Int'l*, pg. 150
ADLINK TECHNOLOGY JAPAN CORPORATION—See ADLINK Technology, Inc.; *Int'l*, pg. 150
ADLINK TECHNOLOGY KOREA LTD.—See ADLINK Technology, Inc.; *Int'l*, pg. 150
ADLINK TECHNOLOGY LTD.—See ADLINK Technology, Inc.; *Int'l*, pg. 151
ADLINK TECHNOLOGY SARL—See ADLINK Technology, Inc.; *Int'l*, pg. 151
ADLINK TECHNOLOGY SINGAPORE PTE. LTD.—See ADLINK Technology, Inc.; *Int'l*, pg. 151
ADLON INTELLIGENT SOLUTIONS GMBH; *Int'l*, pg. 151
ADLPARTNER SA; *Int'l*, pg. 151
ADLP ASSURANCES SAS—See ADLPartner SA; *Int'l*, pg. 151
ADL PLC; *Int'l*, pg. 150
ADL SOFTWARE PTY LTD—See Insight Venture Management, LLC; *U.S. Private*, pg. 2088
ADL SOFTWARE PTY LTD—See Stone Point Capital LLC; *U.S. Private*, pg. 3822
A D LUBOW LLC; *U.S. Private*, pg. 25
ADLUCENT, INC.; *U.S. Private*, pg. 80
ADMA BIO CENTERS GEORGIA INC.—See ADMA Biologics, Inc.; *U.S. Public*, pg. 42
ADMA BIOLOGICS, INC.; *U.S. Public*, pg. 42
ADM AGRICULTURE LIMITED—See Archer-Daniels-Midland Company; *U.S. Public*, pg. 181
ADM AGRI-INDUSTRIES COMPANY—See Archer-Daniels-Midland Company; *U.S. Public*, pg. 184
ADM AGRI-INDUSTRIES COMPANY—See Archer-Daniels-Midland Company; *U.S. Public*, pg. 184
ADM AGRI-INDUSTRIES COMPANY—See Archer-Daniels-Midland Company; *U.S. Public*, pg. 184
ADM AGRI-INDUSTRIES COMPANY—See Archer-Daniels-Midland Company; *U.S. Public*, pg. 184
ADM AGRI-INDUSTRIES COMPANY—See Archer-Daniels-Midland Company; *U.S. Public*, pg. 184
ADM AGRI-INDUSTRIES COMPANY—See Archer-Daniels-Midland Company; *U.S. Public*, pg. 184
ADM AGRI-INDUSTRIES COMPANY—See Archer-Daniels-Midland Company; *U.S. Public*, pg. 184
ADM AGRI-INDUSTRIES COMPANY—See Archer-Daniels-Midland Company; *U.S. Public*, pg. 184
ADM AGRI-INDUSTRIES COMPANY—See Archer-Daniels-Midland Company; *U.S. Public*, pg. 184
ADM AGRO IBERICA S.L.U.—See Archer-Daniels-Midland Company; *U.S. Public*, pg. 181
ADM AGRO INDUSTRIES INDIA PRIVATE LIMITED—See Archer-Daniels-Midland Company; *U.S. Public*, pg. 181
ADM AGRO INDUSTRIES KOTA & AKOLA PRIVATE LIMITED—See Archer-Daniels-Midland Company; *U.S. Public*, pg. 181
ADM AGRO INDUSTRIES LATUR & VIZAG PRIVATE LIMITED—See Archer-Daniels-Midland Company; *U.S. Public*, pg. 181
A&D MAINTENANCE LEASING & REPAIRS, INC.—See Custom Truck One Source, Inc.; *U.S. Private*, pg. 612
A.D. MAKEPEACE COMPANY; *U.S. Public*, pg. 12

ADMAK GENERAL CONTRACTING COMPANY W.L.L.—See Mohammed Abdulmohsin Al-Kharafi & Sons WLL; *Int'l*, pg. 5018
ADM ALFRED C. TOEPFER INTERNATIONAL BV—See Archer-Daniels-Midland Company; *U.S. Public*, pg. 184
ADM ALLIANCE NUTRITION, INC.—See Archer-Daniels-Midland Company; *U.S. Public*, pg. 181
ADM ALLIANCE NUTRITION OF PUERTO RICO, LLC—See Archer-Daniels-Midland Company; *U.S. Public*, pg. 181
ADM ALLIANCE NUTRITION—See Archer-Daniels-Midland Company; *U.S. Public*, pg. 181
ADM ALLIANCE NUTRITION—See Archer-Daniels-Midland Company; *U.S. Public*, pg. 181
ADM ALLIANCE NUTRITION—See Archer-Daniels-Midland Company; *U.S. Public*, pg. 181
ADM ALLIANCE NUTRITION—See Archer-Daniels-Midland Company; *U.S. Public*, pg. 181
ADM ALLIANCE NUTRITION—See Archer-Daniels-Midland Company; *U.S. Public*, pg. 181
ADMAN ELECTRIC, INC.; *U.S. Private*, pg. 80
ADM ANIMAL NUTRITION (CAMBODIA) CO., LTD.—See Archer-Daniels-Midland Company; *U.S. Public*, pg. 181
ADM ANTWERP NV—See Archer-Daniels-Midland Company; *U.S. Public*, pg. 181
AD-MANUM FINANCE LTD.; *Int'l*, pg. 123
ADMAP INC. - SALES DIVISION—See Mitsui E&S Holdings Co., Ltd.; *Int'l*, pg. 4984
ADMAP INC.—See Mitsui E&S Holdings Co., Ltd.; *Int'l*, pg. 4984
AD MARCHE S.R.L.—See s.a. D'Ieteren n.v.; *Int'l*, pg. 6447
ADMARK ADVERTISING LIMITED; *Int'l*, pg. 151
ADMARKETPLACE, INC.; *U.S. Private*, pg. 80
THE ADMARK GROUP; *U.S. Private*, pg. 3982
ADMARSH, INC.; *U.S. Private*, pg. 80
ADMAR SUPPLY CO. INC.; *U.S. Private*, pg. 80
ADMARVEL, INC.—See Otello Corporation ASA; *Int'l*, pg. 5656
ADM ASIA-PACIFIC TRADING PTE. LTD.—See Archer-Daniels-Midland Company; *U.S. Public*, pg. 181
ADM AUSTRALIA PTY. LIMITED—See Archer-Daniels-Midland Company; *U.S. Public*, pg. 181
ADM BAZANCOURT SASU—See Archer-Daniels-Midland Company; *U.S. Public*, pg. 181
ADM BENSON INC.—See Archer-Daniels-Midland Company; *U.S. Public*, pg. 181
ADM BENSON-QUINN COMPANY—See Archer-Daniels-Midland Company; *U.S. Public*, pg. 181
ADM BIO-PRODUCTOS, S.A. DE C.V.—See Archer-Daniels-Midland Company; *U.S. Public*, pg. 181
ADM/CHS, LLC—See CHS INC.; *U.S. Public*, pg. 491
ADM CLINTON BIOPROCESSING, INC.—See Archer-Daniels-Midland Company; *U.S. Public*, pg. 181
ADM COLLINGWOOD GRAIN, INC.—See Archer-Daniels-Midland Company; *U.S. Public*, pg. 181
ADM COLLINGWOOD GRAIN INC.—See Archer-Daniels-Midland Company; *U.S. Public*, pg. 181
ADM-COLLINGWOOD GRAIN—See Archer-Daniels-Midland Company; *U.S. Public*, pg. 181
ADM CZERNIN S.A.—See Archer-Daniels-Midland Company; *U.S. Public*, pg. 181
ADM DIRECT POLSKA SP. Z O.O.—See Archer-Daniels-Midland Company; *U.S. Public*, pg. 181
ADM DO BRASIL LTDA—See Archer-Daniels-Midland Company; *U.S. Public*, pg. 184
ADMEA SA; *Int'l*, pg. 151
ADME BIOANALYSES SAS—See Eurofins Scientific S.E.; *Int'l*, pg. 2542
AD-MEDIA K.K—See ad-comm Co., Ltd.; *Int'l*, pg. 123
ADMEDIA—See The Interpublic Group of Companies, Inc.; *U.S. Public*, pg. 2092
ADM EDIBLE BEAN SPECIALTIES, INC.—See Archer-Daniels-Midland Company; *U.S. Public*, pg. 181
ADM EDIBLE BEAN SPECIALTIES, INC.—See Archer-Daniels-Midland Company; *U.S. Public*, pg. 181
ADM EDIBLE BEAN SPECIALTIES, INC.—See Archer-Daniels-Midland Company; *U.S. Public*, pg. 181
ADM EDIBLE BEAN SPECIALTIES, INC.—See Archer-Daniels-Midland Company; *U.S. Public*, pg. 181
AD MEDICAL AB—See Indutrade AB; *Int'l*, pg. 3677
ADMEDUS SARL—See Anteris Technologies Ltd.; *Int'l*, pg. 482
ADMELD INC.—See Alphabet Inc.; *U.S. Public*, pg. 83
ADM ENDEAVORS, INC.; *U.S. Public*, pg. 41
ADM ENERGY PLC; *Int'l*, pg. 151
ADMERA HEALTH, LLC; *U.S. Private*, pg. 80
ADMERASIA, INC.; *U.S. Private*, pg. 80
ADMEREX (SINGAPORE) PTE LIMITED—See CB Australia Limited; *Int'l*, pg. 1364
AD ME TECH CO., LTD.; *Int'l*, pg. 122
ADMET, INC.; *U.S. Private*, pg. 80
ADMET SA; *Int'l*, pg. 151
ADM GERMANY GMBH—See Archer-Daniels-Midland Company; *U.S. Public*, pg. 181
ADM GRAIN CO. - MENDOTA—See Archer-Daniels-Midland Company; *U.S. Public*, pg. 182
ADM GRAIN COMPANY—See Archer-Daniels-Midland Company; *U.S. Public*, pg. 181

COMPANY NAME INDEX

ADM GRAIN COMPANY—See Archer-Daniels-Midland Company; *U.S. Public*, pg. 182
ADM GRAIN CO—See Archer-Daniels-Midland Company; *U.S. Public*, pg. 181
ADM GRAIN CO.—See Archer-Daniels-Midland Company; *U.S. Public*, pg. 181
ADM GRAIN RIVER SYSTEM, INC.—See Archer-Daniels-Midland Company; *U.S. Public*, pg. 182
ADM GRAIN RIVER SYSTEM, INC.—See Archer-Daniels-Midland Company; *U.S. Public*, pg. 182
ADM GRAIN RIVER SYSTEM, INC.—See Archer-Daniels-Midland Company; *U.S. Public*, pg. 182
ADM GRAIN—See Archer-Daniels-Midland Company; *U.S. Public*, pg. 181
ADM-GRAIN—See Archer-Daniels-Midland Company; *U.S. Public*, pg. 182
ADM HAMBURG AKTIENGESELLSCHAFT—See Archer-Daniels-Midland Company; *U.S. Public*, pg. 182
ADM HUNGARY AGRO TRADING LLC—See Archer-Daniels-Midland Company; *U.S. Public*, pg. 182
ADMICOM OYJ; *Int'l*, pg. 151
ADM, INC.—See Kaga Electronics Co., Ltd.; *Int'l*, pg. 4048
ADMINISTER OY; *Int'l*, pg. 151
ADMINISTRACION PORTUARIA INTEGRAL DE AL-CAPULCO, S.A. DE C.V.—See Grupo TMM, S.A.B.; *Int'l*, pg. 3137
ADMINISTRACION Y RECUPERACION DE CARTERA MICHOACAN S. A. DE C. V., SOFOM; E. N. R—See ProCredit Holding AG & Co. KGaA; *Int'l*, pg. 5987
ADMINISTRADORA CLINICA LA COLINA S.A.S.—See UnitedHealth Group Incorporated; *U.S. Public*, pg. 2238
ADMINISTRADORA DE FONDOS DE CESANTIA S.A.—See Grupo de Inversiones Suramericana S.A.; *Int'l*, pg. 3125
ADMINISTRADORA DE FONDOS DE PENSIONES AR-GENTUM S.A.—See Principal Financial Group, Inc.; *U.S. Public*, pg. 1720
ADMINISTRADORA DE FONDOS DE PENSIONES CU-PRUM S.A.—See Principal Financial Group, Inc.; *U.S. Public*, pg. 1720
ADMINISTRADORA DE FONDOS DE PENSIONES PROVIDA S.A.—See MetLife, Inc.; *U.S. Public*, pg. 1429
ADMINISTRADORA DE FONDOS DE PENSIONES Y DE SANTIA PROTECCION SA; *Int'l*, pg. 151
ADMINISTRADORA DE SERVICIOS PARIS LTDA.—See Cencosud S.A.; *Int'l*, pg. 1400
ADMINISTRADORA EVERCORE, S.C.—See Evercore, Inc.; *U.S. Public*, pg. 800
ADMINISTRADORA PICSA, S.A. DE C.V.—See Desarrolladora Homex, S.A. de C.V.; *Int'l*, pg. 2043
ADMINISTRATIVE CONCEPT CORP.; *U.S. Private*, pg. 80
ADMINISTRATIVE RESOURCE OPTIONS, INC.; *U.S. Private*, pg. 80
ADMINISTRATIVE RESOURCES, INC.; *U.S. Private*, pg. 80
ADMINISTRATORS FOR THE PROFESSIONS, INC.; *U.S. Private*, pg. 81
ADMIN NUCOAL; *Int'l*, pg. 151
ADM INTERNATIONAL SARL—See Archer-Daniels-Midland Company; *U.S. Public*, pg. 184
ADM INVESTOR SERVICES INC.—See Archer-Daniels-Midland Company; *U.S. Public*, pg. 182
ADM INVESTOR SERVICES INTERNATIONAL LIMITED—See Archer-Daniels-Midland Company; *U.S. Public*, pg. 182
ADMIRAL AIR EXPRESS INC.—See ALG Admiral Inc; *U.S. Private*, pg. 166
ADMIRAL BEVERAGE CORPORATION; *U.S. Private*, pg. 81
ADMIRAL BUILDING PRODUCTS, INC.; *U.S. Private*, pg. 81
ADMIRAL COVE DEVELOPMENT SDN BHD—See Avillion Berhad; *Int'l*, pg. 743
ADMIRAL D.O.O.—See Novomatic AG; *Int'l*, pg. 5466
ADMIRAL EXPRESS, LLC—See The ODP Corporation; *U.S. Public*, pg. 2117
ADMIRAL FINANCIAL CORP.; *U.S. Private*, pg. 81
ADMIRAL GROUP PLC; *Int'l*, pg. 151
ADMIRAL INDEMNITY COMPANY—See W.R. Berkley Corporation; *U.S. Public*, pg. 2316
ADMIRAL INSURANCE COMPANY—See W.R. Berkley Corporation; *U.S. Public*, pg. 2318
ADMIRAL INSURANCE (GIBRALTAR) LIMITED—See Admiral Group plc; *Int'l*, pg. 151
ADMIRAL INSURANCE GROUP, LLC—See W.R. Berkley Corporation; *U.S. Public*, pg. 2316
ADMIRAL LAW LIMITED—See Admiral Group plc; *Int'l*, pg. 151
ADMIRAL LINEN SERVICE INC.; *U.S. Private*, pg. 81
ADMIRAL MARINA BERHAD—See Avillion Berhad; *Int'l*, pg. 743
ADMIRAL MARINE CONTINENTAL SUPPLIES BV—See Admiral Marine Supplies Limited; *Int'l*, pg. 152
ADMIRAL MARINE SERVICES PVT LTD—See Admiral Marine Supplies Limited; *Int'l*, pg. 152
ADMIRAL MARINE SUPPLIES LIMITED; *Int'l*, pg. 151

ADMIRAL MARINE SUPPLIES LTD—See Admiral Marine Supplies Limited; *Int'l*, pg. 152
ADMIRAL MARINE SUPPLIES LTD—See Admiral Marine Supplies Limited; *Int'l*, pg. 152
ADMIRAL MARINE SUPPLIES PTE LTD—See Admiral Marine Supplies Limited; *Int'l*, pg. 152
ADMIRAL METALS SERVICENTER COMPANY INC.—See BMH Corp.; *U.S. Private*, pg. 600
ADMIRAL NISSAN INC.; *U.S. Private*, pg. 81
ADMIRAL PACKAGING, INC.; *U.S. Private*, pg. 81
ADMIRAL PLAY GMBH—See Novomatic AG; *Int'l*, pg. 5467
ADMIRALS CLUB, INC.—See American Airlines Group Inc.; *U.S. Public*, pg. 95
ADMIRALS COVE ASSOCIATES LTD.; *U.S. Private*, pg. 81
ADMIRAL SECURITY SERVICES—See Red Coats Inc.; *U.S. Private*, pg. 3373
ADMIRAL SECURITY SERVICES—See Red Coats Inc.; *U.S. Private*, pg. 3373
ADMIRAL SECURITY SERVICES—See Red Coats Inc.; *U.S. Private*, pg. 3373
ADMIRAL SECURITY SERVICES—See Red Coats Inc.; *U.S. Private*, pg. 3373
ADMIRAL SPORTS BETTING LTD.—See Novomatic AG; *Int'l*, pg. 5466
ADMIRAL SPORTWETTEN GMBH—See Novomatic AG; *Int'l*, pg. 5466
ADMIRAL STRAND FERIEHUSE APS—See Axel Springer SE; *Int'l*, pg. 766
ADMIRAL TAVERNS LTD.—See C&C Group Plc; *Int'l*, pg. 1238
ADMIRAL TAVERNS LTD.—See Proprium Capital Partners, L.P.; *U.S. Private*, pg. 3286
ADMIRAL TOOL & MANUFACTURING COMPANY INC.; *U.S. Private*, pg. 81
ADMIRAL TRAVEL INTERNATIONAL, INC.; *U.S. Private*, pg. 81
ADMIRALTY ISLAND FISHERIES INC.; *U.S. Private*, pg. 81
ADMIRALTY PARTNERS, INC.; *U.S. Private*, pg. 81
ADMIRALTY RESOURCES NL; *Int'l*, pg. 152
ADMIRAL WINE & LIQUOR CO.; *U.S. Private*, pg. 81
ADMIS HONG KONG LIMITED—See Archer-Daniels-Midland Company; *U.S. Public*, pg. 182
ADMIS SINGAPORE PTE. LIMITED—See Archer-Daniels-Midland Company; *U.S. Public*, pg. 183
AD MISSIONS; *Int'l*, pg. 122
ADM ITALIA S.R.L.—See Archer-Daniels-Midland Company; *U.S. Public*, pg. 182
ADM JAPAN LTD.—See Archer-Daniels-Midland Company; *U.S. Public*, pg. 182
ADM MAINZ GMBH—See Archer-Daniels-Midland Company; *U.S. Public*, pg. 182
ADM MALBORK S.A.—See Archer-Daniels-Midland Company; *U.S. Public*, pg. 182
ADM MILLING COMPANY—See Archer-Daniels-Midland Company; *U.S. Public*, pg. 184
ADM MILLING CO.—See Archer-Daniels-Midland Company; *U.S. Public*, pg. 182
ADM MILLING CO.—See Archer-Daniels-Midland Company; *U.S. Public*, pg. 182
ADM MILLING CO.—See Archer-Daniels-Midland Company; *U.S. Public*, pg. 182
ADM MILLING CO.—See Archer-Daniels-Midland Company; *U.S. Public*, pg. 182
ADM MILLING CO.—See Archer-Daniels-Midland Company; *U.S. Public*, pg. 182
ADM MILLING CO.—See Archer-Daniels-Midland Company; *U.S. Public*, pg. 182
ADM MILLING CO.—See Archer-Daniels-Midland Company; *U.S. Public*, pg. 182
ADM MILLING CO.—See Archer-Daniels-Midland Company; *U.S. Public*, pg. 184
ADM MILLING CO.—See Archer-Daniels-Midland Company; *U.S. Public*, pg. 182
ADM MILLING CO.—See Archer-Daniels-Midland Company; *U.S. Public*, pg. 182
ADM MILLING LIMITED—See Archer-Daniels-Midland Company; *U.S. Public*, pg. 182
ADM MYANMAR COMPANY LIMITED—See Archer-Daniels-Midland Company; *U.S. Public*, pg. 182
ADM NATURAL HEALTH & NUTRITION—See Archer-Daniels-Midland Company; *U.S. Public*, pg. 182
ADM NEW ZEALAND LTD.—See Archer-Daniels-Midland Company; *U.S. Public*, pg. 182
ADM NORTH AMERICAN OILSEED PROCESSING DIVISION—See Archer-Daniels-Midland Company; *U.S. Public*, pg. 182
ADMO, INC.; *U.S. Private*, pg. 81
ADM OLOMOUC S.R.O.—See Archer-Daniels-Midland Company; *U.S. Public*, pg. 182
ADMOOVE SWEDEN AB—See AdUX SA; *Int'l*, pg. 155
ADMORE, INC.—See Ennis, Inc.; *U.S. Public*, pg. 768
ADMORE INVESTMENTS LIMITED—See Hysan Development Company Limited; *Int'l*, pg. 3554
ADMORE WEST—See Ennis, Inc.; *U.S. Public*, pg. 768
A.D. MORGAN CORPORATION; *U.S. Private*, pg. 25

ADOBE INC.

ADMOSPHERE, S.R.O.—See Brookfield Corporation; *Int'l*, pg. 1178
ADMOSPHERE, S.R.O.—See Elliott Management Corporation; *U.S. Private*, pg. 1370
ADMOZART INC.—See Vertoz Advertising Limited; *Int'l*, pg. 8175
ADM PARAGUAY SRL—See Archer-Daniels-Midland Company; *U.S. Public*, pg. 182
ADM PORTUGAL, SA—See Archer-Daniels-Midland Company; *U.S. Public*, pg. 182
ADM PROTEXIN LIMITED—See Archer-Daniels-Midland Company; *U.S. Public*, pg. 182
ADM PURA LIMITED—See Archer-Daniels-Midland Company; *U.S. Public*, pg. 182
ADM RAZGRAD EAD—See Archer-Daniels-Midland Company; *U.S. Public*, pg. 182
ADM ROTHENSEE GMBH & CO. KG—See Archer-Daniels-Midland Company; *U.S. Public*, pg. 182
ADM (SHANGHAI) MANAGEMENT CO., LTD.—See Archer-Daniels-Midland Company; *U.S. Public*, pg. 181
ADM SOUTHERN CELLULOSE—See Archer-Daniels-Midland Company; *U.S. Public*, pg. 182
ADM SPECIALTY INGREDIENTS—See Archer-Daniels-Midland Company; *U.S. Public*, pg. 182
ADM STANLEY—See Archer-Daniels-Midland Company; *U.S. Public*, pg. 182
ADM STF PTE. LTD.—See Archer-Daniels-Midland Company; *U.S. Public*, pg. 182
ADM STF SWITZERLAND SARL—See Archer-Daniels-Midland Company; *U.S. Public*, pg. 182
ADM (THAILAND) LTD.—See Archer-Daniels-Midland Company; *U.S. Public*, pg. 181
ADM TRADING AUSTRALIA PTY. LTD.—See Archer-Daniels-Midland Company; *U.S. Public*, pg. 182
ADM TRONICS UNLIMITED, INC.; *U.S. Public*, pg. 42
ADM TRUCKING COMPANY—See Archer-Daniels-Midland Company; *U.S. Public*, pg. 183
ADM TRUCKING INC.—See Archer-Daniels-Midland Company; *U.S. Public*, pg. 183
ADM VENTURES INC.; *U.S. Private*, pg. 80
ADM VIETNAM CO., LTD.—See Archer-Daniels-Midland Company; *U.S. Public*, pg. 183
ADMV—See Coesia S.p.A.; *Int'l*, pg. 1690
ADM WILD EUROPE GMBH & CO. KG—See Archer-Daniels-Midland Company; *U.S. Public*, pg. 183
ADM WILD NAUEN GMBH—See Archer-Daniels-Midland Company; *U.S. Public*, pg. 183
ADM WILD VALENCIA—See Archer-Daniels-Midland Company; *U.S. Public*, pg. 183
ADMY TECHNOLOGY GROUP, INC.; *U.S. Private*, pg. 81
ADNAMS PLC; *Int'l*, pg. 152
ADNET ADVERTISING AGENCY, INC.; *U.S. Private*, pg. 81
ADNET SYSTEMS, INC.; *U.S. Private*, pg. 81
ADNEXUS, A BRISTOL-MYERS SQUIBB R&D COMPANY—See Bristol-Myers Squibb Company; *U.S. Public*, pg. 384
ADNIC INTERNATIONAL LTD.—See Abu Dhabi National Insurance Company; *Int'l*, pg. 72
AD NIEUWSMEDIA BV—See DPG Media Group NV; *Int'l*, pg. 2188
AD NOBI CO., LTD.—See AISIN Corporation; *Int'l*, pg. 251
ADNOC DISTRIBUTION—See Abu Dhabi National Oil Company; *Int'l*, pg. 72
ADNOC DRILLING COMPANY PJSC—See Abu Dhabi National Oil Company; *Int'l*, pg. 72
ADNOSTIC—See Future plc; *Int'l*, pg. 2857
ADNOVUM INFORMATIK AG—See IHAG Holding AG; *Int'l*, pg. 3603
ADOBE INC.; *U.S. Public*, pg. 42
ADOBE SYSTEMS BENELUX BV—See Adobe Inc.; *U.S. Public*, pg. 42
ADOBE SYSTEMS CANADA—See Adobe Inc.; *U.S. Public*, pg. 42
ADOBE SYSTEMS CO., LTD.—See Adobe Inc.; *U.S. Public*, pg. 42
ADOBE SYSTEMS EUROPE LIMITED.—See Adobe Inc.; *U.S. Public*, pg. 42
ADOBE SYSTEMS FRANCE—See Adobe Inc.; *U.S. Public*, pg. 42
ADOBE SYSTEMS GMBH—See Adobe Inc.; *U.S. Public*, pg. 42
ADOBE SYSTEMS HONG KONG LIMITED—See Adobe Inc.; *U.S. Public*, pg. 42
ADOBE SYSTEMS IBERICA SL—See Adobe Inc.; *U.S. Public*, pg. 42
ADOBE SYSTEMS INCORPORATED - SEATTLE—See Adobe Inc.; *U.S. Public*, pg. 42
ADOBE SYSTEMS INC. - SAN FRANCISCO—See Adobe Inc.; *U.S. Public*, pg. 42
ADOBE SYSTEMS ITALIA SRL—See Adobe Inc.; *U.S. Public*, pg. 42
ADOBE SYSTEMS NORDIC AB—See Adobe Inc.; *U.S. Public*, pg. 42
ADOBE SYSTEMS PTE. LTD.—See Adobe Inc.; *U.S. Public*, pg. 42
ADOBE SYSTEMS PTY. LTD.—See Adobe Inc.; *U.S. Public*, pg. 42

ADOBE INC.
CORPORATE AFFILIATIONS

ADOBE SYSTEMS ROMANIA SRL—See Adobe Inc.; *U.S. Public*, pg. 42
ADOBE SYSTEMS SOFTWARE IRELAND LIMITED—See Adobe Inc.; *U.S. Public*, pg. 42
ADOBE SYSTEMS UK—See Adobe Inc.; *U.S. Public*, pg. 42
ADOBE VENTURES—See Adobe Inc.; *U.S. Public*, pg. 42
ADO BUYING GROUP—See Walman Optical Company; *U.S. Private*, pg. 4432
ADOCIA SAS; *Int'l*, pg. 152
ADOCIM CIMENTO BETON SANAYI VE TICARET A.S.—See Titan Cement Company S.A.; *Int'l*, pg. 7759
A.D.O. GROUP LTD.—See ADLER Group SA; *Int'l*, pg. 150
ADOLF ELLERMANN GMBH—See Georgsmarienhutte Holding GmbH; *Int'l*, pg. 2941
ADOLF MENSCHEL VERBINDUNGSTECHNIK GMBH & CO. KG—See Wurth Verwaltungsgesellschaft mbH; *Int'l*, pg. 8503
ADOLFO DOMINGUEZ, S.A.; *Int'l*, pg. 152
ADOLF SCHUCH GMBH; *Int'l*, pg. 152
THE ADOLFSEN GROUP; *Int'l*, pg. 7612
ADOLFSON & PETERSON, ARIZONA—See Adolfson & Peterson, Inc.; *U.S. Private*, pg. 81
ADOLFSON & PETERSON, COLORADO—See Adolfson & Peterson, Inc.; *U.S. Private*, pg. 81
ADOLFSON & PETERSON, INC.; *U.S. Private*, pg. 81
ADOLFSON & PETERSON, TEXAS—See Adolfson & Peterson, Inc.; *U.S. Private*, pg. 81
ADOLF WURTH GMBH & CO. KG—See Wurth Verwaltungsgesellschaft mbH; *Int'l*, pg. 8503
ADOLPH GASSER INC.; *U.S. Private*, pg. 81
ADOLPH KIEFER & ASSOCIATES, INC.; *U.S. Private*, pg. 81
ADOLPHUS HOTEL—See Crescent Hotels & Resorts; *U.S. Private*, pg. 1094
ADOMATECHS CO., LTD.—See Shin-Etsu Chemical Co. Ltd.; *Int'l*, pg. 6838
ADOMOS SA; *Int'l*, pg. 152
ADONEL CONCRETE; *U.S. Private*, pg. 82
ADONIS CO., LTD.—See Mitani Sangyo Co., Ltd.; *Int'l*, pg. 4924
ADONIS CONSTRUCTION LTD; *Int'l*, pg. 152
ADONIS INSURANCE COMPANY SYRIA S.A.—See Byblos Bank S.A.L.; *Int'l*, pg. 1233
ADONIS INSURANCE & REINSURANCE CO. (ADIR) SAL—See Byblos Bank S.A.L.; *Int'l*, pg. 1233
ADONIS INSURANCE & REINSURANCE SYRIA S.A.—See Byblos Bank S.A.L.; *Int'l*, pg. 1233
ADON PRODUCTION AG; *Int'l*, pg. 152
ADO OPTRONIC CORP.; *Int'l*, pg. 152
ADO PRODUCTS LLC—See TopBuild Corp.; *U.S. Public*, pg. 2163
ADO PROFESSIONAL SOLUTIONS, INC.—See Adecco Group AG; *Int'l*, pg. 136
AD OPT TECHNOLOGIES INC.—See IBS Software Private Limited; *Int'l*, pg. 3577
ADORABLE LINGERIE INC.; *Int'l*, pg. 152
ADORA FERTILITY PTY LTD—See Healius Limited; *Int'l*, pg. 3302
ADORAMA CAMERA INC.; *U.S. Private*, pg. 82
ADORE BEAUTY GROUP LIMITED; *Int'l*, pg. 152
ADORE ME, INC.—See Victoria's Secret & Co.; *U.S. Public*, pg. 2296
ADOR FONTECH LTD.—See Ador Welding Ltd; *Int'l*, pg. 152
ADOR MULTIPRODUCTS LTD.—See Ador Welding Ltd; *Int'l*, pg. 152
ADORN FASHIONS INC.; *U.S. Private*, pg. 82
ADOR POWERTRON LTD.—See Ador Welding Ltd; *Int'l*, pg. 152
ADOR WELDING LTD; *Int'l*, pg. 152
ADOS PAKISTAN LIMITED; *Int'l*, pg. 152
AD PARTNERS INC.; *U.S. Private*, pg. 72
ADP ATLANTIC, LLC—See Automatic Data Processing, Inc.; *U.S. Public*, pg. 230
ADPAY, INC.—See Blackstone Inc.; *U.S. Public*, pg. 348
ADP BELGIUM CVA—See Automatic Data Processing, Inc.; *U.S. Public*, pg. 229
ADP BRASIL LTDA—See Automatic Data Processing, Inc.; *U.S. Public*, pg. 229
ADP BUSINESS SERVICES (SHANGHAI) CO., LTD.—See Automatic Data Processing, Inc.; *U.S. Public*, pg. 229
ADP CANADA CO.—See Automatic Data Processing, Inc.; *U.S. Public*, pg. 230
ADP DEALER SERVICES ITALIA S.R.L.—See Automatic Data Processing, Inc.; *U.S. Public*, pg. 229
ADP D.O.O.—See AD Plastik d.d.; *Int'l*, pg. 122
ADP EMPLOYER SERVICES GMBH—See Automatic Data Processing, Inc.; *U.S. Public*, pg. 229
AD PEPPER MEDIA FRANCE S.A.R.L.—See ad pepper media International NV; *Int'l*, pg. 122
AD PEPPER MEDIA GMBH—See ad pepper media International NV; *Int'l*, pg. 122
AD PEPPER MEDIA INTERNATIONAL NV; *Int'l*, pg. 122
AD PEPPER MEDIA SPAIN S.A.—See ad pepper media International NV; *Int'l*, pg. 122
AD PEPPER MEDIA UK LTD—See ad pepper media International NV; *Int'l*, pg. 122

AD PEPPER MEDIA USA LLC—See ad pepper media International NV; *Int'l*, pg. 122
ADPERIO; *U.S. Private*, pg. 82
ADP EUROPE S.A.—See Automatic Data Processing, Inc.; *U.S. Public*, pg. 230
ADP GAUSELMANN GMBH—See Gauselmann AG; *Int'l*, pg. 2890
ADP GLOBALVIEW B.V.—See Automatic Data Processing, Inc.; *U.S. Public*, pg. 230
ADP GSI FRANCE SAS—See Automatic Data Processing, Inc.; *U.S. Public*, pg. 229
ADP GSI ITALIA SPA—See Automatic Data Processing, Inc.; *U.S. Public*, pg. 230
A&D PHARMA HOLDINGS S.R.L.; *Int'l*, pg. 19
ADPI LIBYA—See Artelia Holding SA; *Int'l*, pg. 581
ADP, INC. - ALPHARETTA (WESTSIDE) OFFICE—See Automatic Data Processing, Inc.; *U.S. Public*, pg. 230
ADP, INC. - ALPHARETTA (WINDWARD) OFFICE—See Automatic Data Processing, Inc.; *U.S. Public*, pg. 230
ADP, INC. - CAMARILLO OFFICE—See Automatic Data Processing, Inc.; *U.S. Public*, pg. 230
ADP, INC.—See Automatic Data Processing, Inc.; *U.S. Public*, pg. 230
ADP INGENIERIE—See Artelia Holding SA; *Int'l*, pg. 581
ADP INTERNATIONAL SERVICES BV—See Automatic Data Processing, Inc.; *U.S. Public*, pg. 230
AD PK SOMBOR HOLDING CO.; *Int'l*, pg. 122
AD PLASTIK D.D.; *Int'l*, pg. 122
AD PLASTIK D.D. - ZAGREB PLANT 1—See AD Plastik d.d.; *Int'l*, pg. 122
AD PLASTIK D.D. - ZAGREB PLANT 2—See AD Plastik d.d.; *Int'l*, pg. 122
AD PLASTIK D.O.O.—See AD Plastik d.d.; *Int'l*, pg. 122
AD PLASTIK TISZA KFT.—See AD Plastik d.d.; *Int'l*, pg. 122
ADPLAY S.R.L.—See Azerion Group N.V.; *Int'l*, pg. 778
ADPLEX INC.; *U.S. Private*, pg. 82
ADP NATIONAL ACCOUNT SERVICES—See Automatic Data Processing, Inc.; *U.S. Public*, pg. 230
ADP NATIONAL ACCOUNT SERVICES—See Automatic Data Processing, Inc.; *U.S. Public*, pg. 230
ADP NEDERLAND B.V.—See Automatic Data Processing, Inc.; *U.S. Public*, pg. 230
ADPOL SP. Z O.O.—See Agora S.A.; *Int'l*, pg. 212
AD PORT OF ADRIA-BAR—See Global Yatirim Holding A.S.; *Int'l*, pg. 3002
ADP PRIVATE LIMITED—See Automatic Data Processing, Inc.; *U.S. Public*, pg. 230
ADPR LTD.; *Int'l*, pg. 152
THE AD PROS GROUP; *U.S. Private*, pg. 3981
ADP SCREENING & SELECTION SERVICES—See Automatic Data Processing, Inc.; *U.S. Public*, pg. 230
ADP SECURITIES INDUSTRY SOFTWARE—See Automatic Data Processing, Inc.; *U.S. Public*, pg. 230
ADP TAX CREDIT SERVICES—See Automatic Data Processing, Inc.; *U.S. Public*, pg. 230
ADP TOTALSOURCE GROUP, INC.—See Automatic Data Processing, Inc.; *U.S. Public*, pg. 230
ADP TOTALSOURCE I, INC.—See Automatic Data Processing, Inc.; *U.S. Public*, pg. 230
ADP TOTALSOURCE—See Automatic Data Processing, Inc.; *U.S. Public*, pg. 230
AD PUTEVI UZICE; *Int'l*, pg. 122
ADR ADVERTISING S.P.A.—See Edizione S.r.l.; *Int'l*, pg. 2312
ADRAL, MATRICERIA Y PUESTA A PUNTO, S.L.—See Acek Desarrollo y Gestion Industrial SL; *Int'l*, pg. 96
ADREACH GROUP (PTY) LIMITED—See Tiso Blackstar Group SE; *Int'l*, pg. 7759
ADREKA ADVERTISING; *U.S. Private*, pg. 82
ADRELEVANCE—See Brookfield Corporation; *Int'l*, pg. 1179
ADRELEVANCE—See Elliott Management Corporation; *U.S. Private*, pg. 1371
ADRENALINA; *U.S. Private*, pg. 82
ADRENALINE, INC.—See NewGround Resources; *U.S. Private*, pg. 2915
ADRENNA PROPERTY GROUP LIMITED; *Int'l*, pg. 152
AD RESULTS; *U.S. Private*, pg. 72
ADREXO SAS; *Int'l*, pg. 152
ADR GROUP; *U.S. Private*, pg. 82
ADRIA AIRWAYS D.D.—See 4K Invest International; *Int'l*, pg. 12
ADRIA BANK AG—See Nova Ljubljanska banka d.d.; *Int'l*, pg. 5451
ADRIACHEM D.D.; *Int'l*, pg. 153
ADRIAFRUIT ITALIA S.R.L.—See Coeclerici S.p.A.; *Int'l*, pg. 1688
ADRIA GAMING VICENZA S.R.L.—See Novomatic AG; *Int'l*, pg. 5466
ADRIAGAS S.R.L.—See INA-Industrija Nafte, d.d.; *Int'l*, pg. 3642
ADRIA INVESTICIJE, D.O.O.—See Luka Koper d.d.; *Int'l*, pg. 4576
ADRIA LEASING SPA—See Societe Generale S.A.; *Int'l*, pg. 7039
ADRIAN EQUIPMENT COMPANY INC.—See Adrian Steel Company Inc.; *U.S. Private*, pg. 82
ADRIANNA PAPELL, LLC; *U.S. Private*, pg. 82

ADRIANO CARE SOCIMI S.A.; *Int'l*, pg. 153
ADRIAN STEEL COMPANY INC.; *U.S. Private*, pg. 82
ADRIAN UPFITTING COMPANY INC.—See Adrian Steel Company Inc.; *U.S. Private*, pg. 82
ADRIAPLIN PODJETJE ZA DISTRIBUCIJO ZEMELJSKEGA PLINA D.O.O.—See Eni S.p.A.; *Int'l*, pg. 2436
ADRIA RESORTS D.O.O.—See Adris Grupa d.d.; *Int'l*, pg. 153
ADRIASOLE, D.O.O.—See Luka Koper d.d.; *Int'l*, pg. 4576
ADRIA TERMINALI, D.O.O.—See Luka Koper d.d.; *Int'l*, pg. 4576
ADRIATICA DE SEGUROS C.A.—See Allianz SE; *Int'l*, pg. 342
ADRIATIC BST TRGOVINA IN STORITVE D.O.O.—See Perrigo Company plc; *Int'l*, pg. 5812
ADRIATIC MEDIA INVESTORS LLC; *U.S. Private*, pg. 82
ADRIATIC METALS PLC; *Int'l*, pg. 153
ADRIATIC OSIGURANJE D.D.; *Int'l*, pg. 153
ADRIATIC SLOVENICA D. D.—See KD Group dd; *Int'l*, pg. 4110
ADRIATIKAGENT INTERNATIONLA SHIPPING AGENCY D.O.O.—See Albert Ballin KG; *Int'l*, pg. 294
ADRIA TOW—See Luka Koper d.d.; *Int'l*, pg. 4576
ADRIA-WIEN PIPELINE GESELLSCHAFT M.B.H.—See OMV Aktiengesellschaft; *Int'l*, pg. 5567
THE ADRIENNE ARSHT CENTER FOR THE PERFORMING ARTS OF MIAMI-DADE COUNTY, INC.; *U.S. Private*, pg. 3982
ADRIENNE DESIGNS INC.; *U.S. Private*, pg. 82
ADRIEN TARGE S.A.S.—See Klockner & Co. SE; *Int'l*, pg. 4201
ADR INFRASTRUTTURE S.P.A.—See Edizione S.r.l.; *Int'l*, pg. 2311
A DRINK TRADE CO., LTD.—See Almedio, Inc.; *Int'l*, pg. 364
ADRIS GRUPA D.D.; *Int'l*, pg. 153
ADRITEC DE LAS AMERICAS S. DE R.L. DE C.V.—See Adritec Group International, E.C.; *Int'l*, pg. 153
ADRITEC EGYPT—See Adritec Group International, E.C.; *Int'l*, pg. 153
ADRITEC EUROPE—See Adritec Group International, E.C.; *Int'l*, pg. 153
ADRITEC GROUP INTERNATIONAL, E.C.; *Int'l*, pg. 153
ADRITEC JORDAN—See Adritec Group International, E.C.; *Int'l*, pg. 153
ADRITEC LEBANON—See Adritec Group International, E.C.; *Int'l*, pg. 153
ADRITEC MAROC—See Adritec Group International, E.C.; *Int'l*, pg. 153
ADRITEC ROMANIA S.L.R—See Adritec Group International, E.C.; *Int'l*, pg. 153
ADRITEC SOUTH AFRICA—See Adritec Group International, E.C.; *Int'l*, pg. 153
ADRITEC TRADING & SERVICES COMPANY—See Adritec Group International, E.C.; *Int'l*, pg. 153
ADRITEC TUNIS—See Adritec Group International, E.C.; *Int'l*, pg. 153
ADRITEC TUNIS—See Societe Commerciale et Industrielle des Produits en Plastique; *Int'l*, pg. 7037
ADRITEC TURKEY—See Adritec Group International, E.C.; *Int'l*, pg. 153
A-DRIVE TECHNOLOGY GMBH; *Int'l*, pg. 19
ADR MOBILITY SRL—See Edizione S.r.l.; *Int'l*, pg. 2312
ADROIT ASSOCIATES INC.; *U.S. Private*, pg. 82
ADROIT INFOTECH PRIVATE LIMITED—See Sphere Global Services Limited; *Int'l*, pg. 7134
ADROIT INSPECTION SERVICES PRIVATE LIMITED—See CarTrade Tech Ltd.; *Int'l*, pg. 1348
ADROIT PRIVATE EQUITY AG—See Swiss Life Holding; *Int'l*, pg. 7368
ADROLL, INC.; *U.S. Private*, pg. 82
ADRONICS/ELROB MANUFACTURING; *U.S. Private*, pg. 82
ADR SALES LTD.—See Tex Holdings Plc; *Int'l*, pg. 7582
ADR TEL S.P.A.—See Edizione S.r.l.; *Int'l*, pg. 2312
ADR TRANSPORTDIENSTEN B.V.—See Synergie SA; *Int'l*, pg. 7383
ADR UITZENDGROEP B.V.—See Synergie SA; *Int'l*, pg. 7383
A&D RUS CO., LTD.—See A&D Co., Ltd.; *Int'l*, pg. 18
ADS2 BRANDS LIMITED—See Ardian SAS; *Int'l*, pg. 555
ADS ALLIANCE DATA SYSTEMS, INC.—See Bread Financial Holdings; *U.S. Public*, pg. 380
ADSCALE GMBH—See Stroer SE & Co. KGaA; *Int'l*, pg. 7242
ADSCALE LABORATORIES LTD.—See Stroer SE & Co. KGaA; *Int'l*, pg. 7242
A&D SCALES CO., LTD.—See A&D Co., Ltd.; *Int'l*, pg. 19
ADS CANADA INC—See Advanced Drainage Systems, Inc.; *U.S. Public*, pg. 46
A.D. SCHINNER CO.—See Bunzl plc; *Int'l*, pg. 1218
ADSCOM CORPORATION—See Adrian Steel Company Inc.; *U.S. Private*, pg. 82
ADS DIAGNOSTICS LIMITED; *Int'l*, pg. 153
ADS DIRECT MEDIA INC.; *U.S. Private*, pg. 82
ADS ENVIRONMENTAL SERVICES—See IDEX Corp; *U.S. Public*, pg. 1089
AD SERVO MIHALJ INZENJERING; *Int'l*, pg. 122

COMPANY NAME INDEX

ADS EUROPE B.V.—See Advanced Drainage Systems, Inc.; *U.S. Public*, pg. 46
ADS GESELLSCHAFT FUR AKTIVE SCHUTZSYSTEME MBH—See Rheinmetall AG; *Int'l*, pg. 6323
ADSG, INC.—See Apollo Global Management, Inc.; *U.S. Public*, pg. 146
ADSHEL (BRAZIL) LTDA—See Clear Channel Outdoor Holdings, Inc.; *U.S. Public*, pg. 511
ADSHEL IRELAND LIMITED—See Clear Channel Outdoor Holdings, Inc.; *U.S. Public*, pg. 511
ADSHEL NEW ZEALAND LTD—See oOh!media Limited; *Int'l*, pg. 5594
ADSHEL STREET FURNITURE PTY LTD—See oOh!media Limited; *Int'l*, pg. 5594
ADS INC.; *Int'l*, pg. 153
ADS, INC.; *U.S. Private*, pg. 82
ADSKYLABS S.A.—See Nayax Ltd.; *Int'l*, pg. 5178
ADS LIMITED—See Publicis Groupe S.A.; *Int'l*, pg. 6100
ADS LLC—See IDEX Corp; *U.S. Public*, pg. 1089
ADS LOGISTICS CO, LLC—See Odyssey Logistics & Technology Corp.; *U.S. Private*, pg. 2996
ADSLOT INC.—See Adslot Ltd.; *Int'l*, pg. 154
ADSLOT LTD.; *Int'l*, pg. 154
ADSLOT UK LIMITED—See Adslot Ltd.; *Int'l*, pg. 154
ADS MARITIME HOLDING PLC; *Int'l*, pg. 153
ADS MEXICANA, S.A DE C.V.—See Advanced Drainage Systems, Inc.; *U.S. Public*, pg. 46
AD-SOL NISSIN CORPORATION; *Int'l*, pg. 123
AD SOLUTIONS S.R.L.—See Altair Engineering, Inc.; *U.S. Public*, pg. 86
ADSOUTH PARTNERS, INC.; *U.S. Private*, pg. 82
ADSPACE INC.—See Septeni Holdings Co., Ltd.; *Int'l*, pg. 6718
ADSPACE NETWORKS, INC.; *U.S. Private*, pg. 83
A&D SPITZ (PTY) LIMITED—See AVI Limited; *Int'l*, pg. 740
ADSPREE MEDIA GMBH—See Verve Group SE; *Int'l*, pg. 8176
ADS R US; *U.S. Private*, pg. 82
ADS SECURITY L.P.—See The Philadelphia Contributionship; *U.S. Private*, pg. 4094
ADS STRUCTURES, INC.—See Advanced Drainage Systems, Inc.; *U.S. Public*, pg. 46
ADS SYSTEM SAFETY CONSULTING, LLC—See DSS Sustainable Solutions Switzerland SA; *Int'l*, pg. 2210
ADSTAFFING.COM; *U.S. Private*, pg. 83
ADS-TEC ENERGY PUBLIC LIMITED COMPANY; *Int'l*, pg. 154
THE AD STORE BRUSSELS—See The Ad Store, Inc.; *U.S. Private*, pg. 3981
THE AD STORE GMBH—See The Ad Store, Inc.; *U.S. Private*, pg. 3981
THE AD STORE, INC.; *U.S. Private*, pg. 3981
THE AD STORE ITALIA—See The Ad Store, Inc.; *U.S. Private*, pg. 3981
THE AD STORE PACIFIQUE—See The Ad Store, Inc.; *U.S. Private*, pg. 3981
THE AD STORE ROMANIA—See The Ad Store, Inc.; *U.S. Private*, pg. 3981
THE AD STORE WASHINGTON—See The Ad Store, Inc.; *U.S. Private*, pg. 3981
ADSTORM—See Precis Marketing; *Int'l*, pg. 5957
ADS/TRANSICOIL CORP.—See TransDigm Group Incorporated; *U.S. Public*, pg. 2182
AD STYLA SP. Z O.O.—See Demant A/S; *Int'l*, pg. 2022
AD-SUCCESS MARKETING; *U.S. Private*, pg. 72
A & D SUPPLY OF OKC, INC.—See American Securities LLC; *U.S. Private*, pg. 248
A.D. SUTTON & SONS; *U.S. Private*, pg. 25
ADS VENTURES, INC.; *U.S. Private*, pg. 82
ADSWIZZ INC.—See Liberty Media Corporation; *U.S. Public*, pg. 1311
ADTAILY SP. Z O.O.—See Agora S.A.; *Int'l*, pg. 212
ADT ALARM MONITORING HONG KONG LTD.—See SECOM Co., Ltd.; *Int'l*, pg. 6670
ADTALEM GLOBAL EDUCATION INC.; *U.S. Public*, pg. 43
ADT COMMERCIAL LLC—See GTCR LLC; *U.S. Private*, pg. 1801
ADT DEUTSCHLAND GMBH—See Johnson Controls International plc; *Int'l*, pg. 3989
ADTEC ELECTROPLATING INC.; *U.S. Private*, pg. 83
ADTEC ENGINEERING CO., LTD.—See Ushio, Inc.; *Int'l*, pg. 8097
ADTEC EUROPE LIMITED—See Adtec Plasma Technology Co., Ltd.; *Int'l*, pg. 154
ADTECH CORPORATION—See NSK Ltd.; *Int'l*, pg. 5478
ADTECHNOLOGY CO., LTD.; *Int'l*, pg. 154
A&D TECHNOLOGY INC.—See A&D Co., Ltd.; *Int'l*, pg. 19
AD TECHNOLOGY LTD.—See Adtec Plasma Technology Co., Ltd.; *Int'l*, pg. 154
A&D TECHNOLOGY TRADING (SHANGHAI) CO., LTD.—See A&D Co., Ltd.; *Int'l*, pg. 19
ADTECH SYSTEMS INC.; *U.S. Private*, pg. 83
ADTEC PLASMA TECHNOLOGY CHINA LTD.—See Adtec Plasma Technology Co., Ltd.; *Int'l*, pg. 154
ADTEC PLASMA TECHNOLOGY CO., LTD.; *Int'l*, pg. 154
ADTEC PLASMA TECHNOLOGY KOREA CO., LTD.—See Adtec Plasma Technology Co., Ltd.; *Int'l*, pg. 154

ADTEC PLASMA TECHNOLOGY TAIWAN LTD.—See Adtec Plasma Technology Co., Ltd.; *Int'l*, pg. 154
ADTEC PLASMA TECHNOLOGY VIETNAM CO., LTD.—See Adtec Plasma Technology Co., Ltd.; *Int'l*, pg. 154
ADTEC TECHNOLOGY, INC.—See Adtec Plasma Technology Co., Ltd.; *Int'l*, pg. 154
ADTEGRITY.COM INTERNATIONAL, INC.; *U.S. Public*, pg. 43
ADTEGRITY.COM; *U.S. Private*, pg. 83
ADTEK FUJI CO., LTD.—See Fuji Corporation; *Int'l*, pg. 2809
ADTEX FUJI CO., LTD.—See Fuji Corporation; *Int'l*, pg. 2809
ADT FIRE AND SECURITY LIMITED—See Johnson Controls International plc; *Int'l*, pg. 3988
ADT FIRE AND SECURITY PLC—See Johnson Controls International plc; *Int'l*, pg. 3988
ADT GROUP SP. Z O.O.—See Johnson Controls International plc; *Int'l*, pg. 3988
ADTHENA LTD.; *Int'l*, pg. 154
ADTHEORENT HOLDING COMPANY, INC.; *U.S. Public*, pg. 43
ADTHEORENT, INC.—See AdTheorent Holding Company, Inc.; *U.S. Public*, pg. 43
ADTHINK MEDIA SA; *Int'l*, pg. 154
ADT HONG KONG LIMITED—See Johnson Controls International plc; *Int'l*, pg. 3988
ADT INC.—See Apollo Global Management, Inc.; *U.S. Public*, pg. 146
ADT INTEGRATED SECURITY SOLUTIONS PTE. LTD.—See SECOM Co., Ltd.; *Int'l*, pg. 6670
ADT INTEGRATED SOLUTIONS, S.A. DE C.V.—See Johnson Controls International plc; *Int'l*, pg. 3989
ADT LLC - CARROLLTON OFFICE—See Apollo Global Management, Inc.; *U.S. Public*, pg. 146
ADT LLC - LOUISVILLE OFFICE—See Apollo Global Management, Inc.; *U.S. Public*, pg. 146
ADT LLC - MELVILLE OFFICE—See Apollo Global Management, Inc.; *U.S. Public*, pg. 146
ADT LLC - NEW YORK OFFICE—See Apollo Global Management, Inc.; *U.S. Public*, pg. 146
ADT LLC - SAN ANTONIO OFFICE—See Apollo Global Management, Inc.; *U.S. Public*, pg. 146
ADT, LLC—See Q-Lab Corp.; *U.S. Public*, pg. 3312
ADT LLC—See Apollo Global Management, Inc.; *U.S. Public*, pg. 146
ADT LLC - TOTOWA OFFICE—See Apollo Global Management, Inc.; *U.S. Public*, pg. 146
ADTOLLO AB—See Addnode Group AB; *Int'l*, pg. 130
ADT PRIVATE SECURITY SERVICES DE MEXICO, S.A. DE C.V.—See Johnson Controls International plc; *Int'l*, pg. 3989
THE ADTRACK CORPORATION; *U.S. Private*, pg. 3982
ADTRACTION GROUP AB; *Int'l*, pg. 154
ADTRAN EUROPE LIMITED—See ADTRAN Holdings, Inc.; *U.S. Public*, pg. 43
ADTRAN HOLDINGS, INC.; *U.S. Public*, pg. 43
ADTRAN, INC.—See ADTRAN Holdings, Inc.; *U.S. Public*, pg. 43
ADTRAN NETWORKS CANADA, INC.—See ADTRAN Holdings, Inc.; *U.S. Public*, pg. 43
ADTRAN NETWORKS HONG KONG LIMITED—See ADTRAN Holdings, Inc.; *U.S. Public*, pg. 43
ADTRAN NETWORKS INDIA PRIVATE LIMITED—See ADTRAN Holdings, Inc.; *U.S. Public*, pg. 43
ADTRAN NETWORKS, PTY. LTD.—See ADTRAN Holdings, Inc.; *U.S. Public*, pg. 44
ADTRAN NETWORKS SE—See ADTRAN Holdings, Inc.; *U.S. Public*, pg. 44
ADTRANS AUSTRALIA PTY LTD—See Eagers Automotive Limited; *Int'l*, pg. 2263
ADTRANS AUTOMOTIVE GROUP PTY. LTD.—See Eagers Automotive Limited; *Int'l*, pg. 2263
ADTRANS CORPORATE PTY. LTD.—See Eagers Automotive Limited; *Int'l*, pg. 2263
ADTRANS GROUP LTD.—See Eagers Automotive Limited; *Int'l*, pg. 2263
ADTRANS HINO PTY LTD—See Eagers Automotive Limited; *Int'l*, pg. 2263
ADTRANS TRUCK CENTRE PTY. LTD.—See Eagers Automotive Limited; *Int'l*, pg. 2263
ADTRANS TRUCKS PTY LTD—See Eagers Automotive Limited; *Int'l*, pg. 2263
THE ADT SECURITY CORPORATION—See Apollo Global Management, Inc.; *U.S. Public*, pg. 146
ADT SECURITY DEUTSCHLAND GMBH—See Johnson Controls International plc; *Int'l*, pg. 3989
ADT SECURITY SERVICES CANADA, INC.—See TELUS CORPORATION; *Int'l*, pg. 7546
ADT SECURITY SERVICES, LLC - AURORA OFFICE—See Apollo Global Management, Inc.; *U.S. Public*, pg. 146
ADT SECURITY SERVICES, S.A.—See Johnson Controls International plc; *Int'l*, pg. 3989
ADT SECURITY SERVICES, S.A.—See Johnson Controls International plc; *Int'l*, pg. 3989
ADT SECURITY SERVICES—See Johnson Controls International plc; *Int'l*, pg. 3989

ADVANCE BOILER & TANK CO.

ADT SERVICE-CENTER GMBH—See Johnson Controls International plc; *Int'l*, pg. 3989
ADT SERVICES (M) SDN BHD.—See Johnson Controls International plc; *Int'l*, pg. 3989
ADT SERVICOS DE MONITORAMENTO LTDA.—See Johnson Controls International plc; *Int'l*, pg. 3989
ADT TRUSTEES LIMITED—See Johnson Controls International plc; *Int'l*, pg. 3986
A. DUCHINI INCORPORATED; *U.S. Private*, pg. 23
A. DUDA & SONS INC.; *U.S. Private*, pg. 23
A. DUIE PYLE INC.; *U.S. Private*, pg. 23
ADULARIA INVERSIONES 2010 S.L.—See Crown Holdings, Inc.; *U.S. Public*, pg. 597
ADULT AND CHILD; *U.S. Private*, pg. 83
ADULT DAY CARE OF AMERICA, INC.—See UnitedHealth Group Incorporated; *U.S. Public*, pg. 2243
ADULT DAY HEALTH, INC.—See Centerbridge Partners, L.P.; *U.S. Private*, pg. 813
ADULT & PEDIATRIC DERMATOLOGY, PC; *U.S. Private*, pg. 83
ADUNIT LTD.—See Swisscom AG; *Int'l*, pg. 7373
ADUNO FINANCE AG—See Aduno Holding AG; *Int'l*, pg. 154
ADUNO HOLDING AG; *Int'l*, pg. 154
ADUNOKAUTION PLC—See Aduno Holding AG; *Int'l*, pg. 154
ADURO BIOTECH, EUROPE B.V.—See Novartis AG; *Int'l*, pg. 5457
ADURO CLEAN TECHNOLOGIES INC.; *Int'l*, pg. 154
A. DURR & CO. AG—See Oettinger IMEX AG; *Int'l*, pg. 5529
A.D. USLUGA; *Int'l*, pg. 23
ADUT S.R.O—See Africa Israel Investments Ltd.; *Int'l*, pg. 189
ADUX BENELUX SPRL—See AdUX SA; *Int'l*, pg. 155
ADUX SA; *Int'l*, pg. 154
ADVADIS S.A.; *Int'l*, pg. 155
ADV ADVANCE SYSTEMS (ASIA) LTD.—See ITOCHU Corporation; *Int'l*, pg. 3838
ADVAITA PROPERTIES PRIVATE LIMITED—See Omaxe Ltd; *Int'l*, pg. 5561
ADVAIT INFRATECH LIMITED; *Int'l*, pg. 155
ADVAL CO., LTD.—See Vision, Inc; *Int'l*, pg. 8253
ADVA-LITE INC.—See Camsing Global, LLC; *U.S. Private*, pg. 732
AD VALOREM RECORDS, INC.—See i3 Verticals, Inc.; *U.S. Public*, pg. 1081
ADVALSO S.P.A.—See TIM S.p.A.; *Int'l*, pg. 7749
ADVAL TECH DO BRASIL INDUSTRIA DE AUTOPECAS LTDA.—See Adval Tech Holding AG; *Int'l*, pg. 155
ADVAL TECH (GRENCHEN) AG—See Adval Tech Holding AG; *Int'l*, pg. 155
ADVAL TECH HOLDING AG; *Int'l*, pg. 155
ADVAL TECH (HUNGARY) KFT.—See Adval Tech Holding AG; *Int'l*, pg. 155
ADVAL TECH (HUNGARY) PLANT 2 KFT.—See Adval Tech Holding AG; *Int'l*, pg. 155
ADVAL TECH MANAGEMENT LTD—See Adval Tech Holding AG; *Int'l*, pg. 155
ADVAL TECH (MEXICO) S.A. DE C. V.—See Adval Tech Holding AG; *Int'l*, pg. 155
ADVAL TECH (SUZHOU) CO. LTD.—See Adval Tech Holding AG; *Int'l*, pg. 155
ADVAL TECH (SWITZERLAND) AG—See Adval Tech Holding AG; *Int'l*, pg. 155
ADVAL TECH US INC.—See Adval Tech Holding AG; *Int'l*, pg. 155
ADVANCE AB—See CompuGroup Medical SE & Co. KGaA; *Int'l*, pg. 1755
ADVANCE ACCEPTANCE CORPORATION—See First Western Bank & Trust; *U.S. Private*, pg. 1530
ADVANCE AGRICENTRE LTD—See The Colonial Motor Company Limited; *Int'l*, pg. 7634
ADVANCE AMERICA, CASH ADVANCE CENTERS, INC.—See Grupo Salinas, S.A. de C.V.; *Int'l*, pg. 3135
ADVANCE AMERICA, CASH ADVANCE CENTERS OF SOUTH CAROLINA, INC.—See Grupo Salinas, S.A. de C.V.; *Int'l*, pg. 3135
ADVANCE AMERICA, CASH ADVANCE CENTERS OF TENNESSEE, INC.—See Grupo Salinas, S.A. de C.V.; *Int'l*, pg. 3135
ADVANCE AMERICA, CASH ADVANCE CENTERS OF VIRGINIA, INC.—See Grupo Salinas, S.A. de C.V.; *Int'l*, pg. 3135
ADVANCE ASSET MANAGEMENT LIMITED—See Marsh & McLennan Companies, Inc.; *U.S. Public*, pg. 1384
ADVANCE AUTO PARTS, INC.; *U.S. Public*, pg. 44
ADVANCE AUTO PARTS—See Advance Auto Parts, Inc.; *U.S. Public*, pg. 44
ADVANCE BAG & PACKAGING CO.; *U.S. Private*, pg. 83
ADVANCE BIOFACTURES CORP.—See Endo International, Inc; *U.S. Public*, pg. 2403
ADVANCE BIOSCIENCE LABORATORIES, INC.—See Institut Merieux; *Int'l*, pg. 3724
ADVANCE BOILERS SDN. BHD.—See CB Industrial Product Holding Berhad; *Int'l*, pg. 1364
ADVANCE BOILER & TANK CO.; *U.S. Private*, pg. 83
ADVANCE BUSINESS CAPITAL LLC—See Triumph Financial, Inc.; *U.S. Public*, pg. 2196

ADVANCE BUSINESS SYSTEMS & SUPPLY COMPANY—See Oval Partners; *U.S. Private*, pg. 3052
ADVANCE CAR TECHNOLOGY COMPANY LIMITED—See Aucnet Inc.; *Int'l*, pg. 699
ADVANCE CO., LTD.—See KOSE Corporation; *Int'l*, pg. 4290
ADVANCE COMMUNICATION CORP.—See Advance Publications, Inc.; *U.S. Private*, pg. 84
ADVANCE COMPUTER SERVICES LTD.—See ACS International Resources Inc.; *U.S. Private*, pg. 66
ADVANCE COMPUTER TECHNOLOGY—See International Turnkey Systems; *Int'l*, pg. 3753
ADVANCECON HOLDINGS BERHAD; *Int'l*, pg. 157
ADVANCE CONTROL SYSTEMS, INC.—See Indra Sistemas, S.A.; *Int'l*, pg. 3659
ADVANCE CREATE CO., LTD.; *Int'l*, pg. 155
ADVANCED ACCELERATOR APPLICATIONS CANADA, INC.—See Novartis AG; *Int'l*, pg. 5455
ADVANCED ACCELERATOR APPLICATIONS GMBH—See Novartis AG; *Int'l*, pg. 5455
ADVANCED ACCELERATOR APPLICATIONS IBERICA S.L.—See Novartis AG; *Int'l*, pg. 5455
ADVANCED ACCELERATOR APPLICATIONS INTERNATIONAL SA—See Novartis AG; *Int'l*, pg. 5455
ADVANCED ACCELERATOR APPLICATIONS ITALY, S.R.L.—See Novartis AG; *Int'l*, pg. 5455
ADVANCED ACCELERATOR APPLICATIONS PORTUGAL LDA.—See Novartis AG; *Int'l*, pg. 5455
ADVANCED ACCELERATOR APPLICATIONS S.A.—See Novartis AG; *Int'l*, pg. 5455
ADVANCED ACCELERATOR APPLICATIONS (UK & IRELAND) LIMITED—See Novartis AG; *Int'l*, pg. 5455
ADVANCED ACCELERATOR APPLICATIONS (UK & IRELAND) LIMITED—See Novartis AG; *Int'l*, pg. 5455
ADVANCED ACCELERATOR APPLICATIONS USA, INC.—See Novartis AG; *Int'l*, pg. 5455
ADVANCED ACOUSTIC CONCEPTS, INC. - COLUMBIA—See Leonardo S.p.A.; *Int'l*, pg. 4458
ADVANCED ACOUSTIC CONCEPTS, INC. - LEMONT FURNACE—See Leonardo S.p.A.; *Int'l*, pg. 4458
ADVANCED ACOUSTIC CONCEPTS, LLC—See Leonardo S.p.A.; *Int'l*, pg. 4458
ADVANCEDADVT LIMITED; *Int'l*, pg. 163
ADVANCED AIRFOIL COMPONENTS LLC—See Siemens Energy AG; *Int'l*, pg. 6902
ADVANCED AMBULATORY SURGICAL CARE, L.P.—See Tenet Healthcare Corporation; *U.S. Public*, pg. 2009
ADVANCED AMERICAN CONSTRUCTION, INC.; *U.S. Private*, pg. 87
ADVANCED ANALOG TECHNOLOGY, INC.; *Int'l*, pg. 157
ADVANCED APPLICATIONS INSTITUTE, INC.; *U.S. Private*, pg. 87
ADVANCED APPLIED ENGINEERING, INC.—See Bowman Consulting Group Ltd.; *U.S. Public*, pg. 376
ADVANCED ARCHITECTURAL PRODUCTS, LLC; *U.S. Private*, pg. 87
ADVANCED AROMATICS, LLC—See Heritage Group; *U.S. Private*, pg. 1923
ADVANCED ASPHALT COMPANY; *U.S. Private*, pg. 87
ADVANCED ASSEMBLY LLC—See Summit Interconnect, Inc.; *U.S. Private*, pg. 3855
ADVANCED AUTOMATED SYSTEMS, INC.—See Huron Capital Partners LLC; *U.S. Private*, pg. 2011
ADVANCED AUTOMATION GROUP, LLC; *U.S. Private*, pg. 87
ADVANCED AUTOMATION INC.—See Doerfer Corporation; *U.S. Private*, pg. 1253
ADVANCED AV, LLC; *U.S. Private*, pg. 88
ADVANCED BANK OF ASIA LIMITED—See National Bank of Canada; *Int'l*, pg. 5152
ADVANCED BARRIER EXTRUSIONS, LLC—See The Graham Group, Inc.; *U.S. Private*, pg. 4036
ADVANCED BATTERY TECHNOLOGIES, INC.; *U.S. Private*, pg. 88
ADVANCED BEAUTY, INC.; *U.S. Private*, pg. 88
ADVANCED BIO-AGRO TECH LIMITED—See Advanced Enzyme Technologies Limited; *Int'l*, pg. 159
ADVANCED BIOCHEMICAL (THAILAND) COMPANY LTD—See Solvay S.A.; *Int'l*, pg. 7077
ADVANCED BIOENERGY, LLC; *U.S. Public*, pg. 46
ADVANCED BIOHEALING, INC.—See Takeda Pharmaceutical Company Limited; *Int'l*, pg. 7438
ADVANCED BIOLOGICAL LABORATORIES (ABL) S.A.; *Int'l*, pg. 157
ADVANCED BIOLOGICS, LLC—See Thompson Street Capital Manager LLC; *U.S. Private*, pg. 4161
ADVANCED BIOMATRIX INC.—See BICO Group AB; *Int'l*, pg. 1019
ADVANCED BIOMEDICAL TECHNOLOGIES, INC.; *U.S. Public*, pg. 46
ADVANCED BIONICS ASIA PACIFIC LTD.—See Sonova Holding AG; *Int'l*, pg. 7100
ADVANCED BIONICS EUROPEAN RESEARCH CENTER GMBH—See Sonova Holding AG; *Int'l*, pg. 7100
ADVANCED BIONICS LLC—See Sonova Holding AG; *Int'l*, pg. 7100
ADVANCED BIONICS SARL—See Sonova Holding AG; *Int'l*, pg. 7100

ADVANCED BIONICS SPAIN, S.R.L.—See Sonova Holding AG; *Int'l*, pg. 7100
ADVANCED BIONICS UK LTD.—See Sonova Holding AG; *Int'l*, pg. 7100
ADVANCED BIOSENSORS, INC.—See NetScientific plc; *Int'l*, pg. 5215
ADVANCED BLOCKCHAIN AG; *Int'l*, pg. 157
ADVANCED BORING & TOOL COMPANY—See Utica Enterprises, Inc.; *U.S. Private*, pg. 4325
ADVANCED BRAIN MONITORING, INC.; *U.S. Private*, pg. 88
ADVANCED BRAKING PTY LTD—See Advanced Braking Technology Ltd.; *Int'l*, pg. 157
ADVANCED BRAKING TECHNOLOGY LTD.; *Int'l*, pg. 157
ADVANCED BROADBAND NETWORK COMPANY LIMITED—See Advanced Info Service Plc; *Int'l*, pg. 159
ADVANCED BUILDING PRODUCTS, INC.—See Leonard Green & Partners, L.P.; *U.S. Private*, pg. 2428
ADVANCED BUSINESS ANALYTICS (M) SDN. BHD.; *Int'l*, pg. 157
ADVANCED BUSINESS EQUIPMENT LIMITED—See Xerox Holdings Corporation; *U.S. Public*, pg. 2386
ADVANCED BUSINESS METHODS INC.; *U.S. Private*, pg. 88
ADVANCED BUSINESS SOFTWARE & SOLUTIONS LTD.; *Int'l*, pg. 157
ADVANCED BUSINESS SOLUTIONS—See Vista Equity Partners, LLC; *U.S. Private*, pg. 4394
ADVANCED C4 SOLUTIONS, INC.—See Hui Huliau; *U.S. Private*, pg. 2004
ADVANCED CABLE COMMUNICATIONS, INC.—See Schurz Communications, Inc.; *U.S. Private*, pg. 3571
ADVANCED CABLE CONNECTION, INC.; *U.S. Private*, pg. 88
ADVANCED CAE, INC.—See Advanced Holdings Ltd.; *Int'l*, pg. 159
ADVANCED CAE LTD.—See Advanced Holdings Ltd.; *Int'l*, pg. 159
ADVANCED CAE (ME) CONTROL SYSTEM L.L.C.—See Advanced Holdings Ltd.; *Int'l*, pg. 159
ADVANCED CAE PTE. LTD.—See Advanced Holdings Ltd.; *Int'l*, pg. 159
ADVANCED CAE SAUDI ARABIA COMPANY LTD.—See Advanced Holdings Ltd.; *Int'l*, pg. 159
ADVANCED CALL CENTER TECHNOLOGIES, LLC; *U.S. Private*, pg. 88
ADVANCED CARE MANAGEMENT, INC.—See Bain Capital, LP; *U.S. Private*, pg. 431
ADVANCED CARE PARTNERS, LLC; *U.S. Private*, pg. 88
ADVANCED CARE PHYSICAL THERAPY MANAGEMENT LLC—See Investcorp Holdings B.S.C.; *Int'l*, pg. 3775
ADVANCED CARE SCRIPS, INC.—See CVS Health Corporation; *U.S. Public*, pg. 616
ADVANCED CARE SCRIPTS, INC.—See CVS Health Corporation; *U.S. Public*, pg. 613
ADVANCED CAST PRODUCTS, INC.—See Gamut Capital Management, L.P.; *U.S. Private*, pg. 1641
ADVANCED CELL DIAGNOSTICS, INC.—See Bio-Techne Corporation; *U.S. Public*, pg. 334
THE ADVANCED CENTER FOR PHYSICAL THERAPY—See Audax Group, Limited Partnership; *U.S. Private*, pg. 389
ADVANCED CENTER FOR SURGERY - VERO BEACH, LLC—See Tenet Healthcare Corporation; *U.S. Public*, pg. 2001
ADVANCED CERAMICS TECHNOLOGY (M) SDN. BHD.—See Crest Group Inc.; *U.S. Private*, pg. 1095
ADVANCED CERAMIC X CORPORATION; *Int'l*, pg. 157
ADVANCED CHEMICAL COMPANY; *U.S. Private*, pg. 88
ADVANCED CHEMICAL CONCEPTS, INC.; *U.S. Private*, pg. 88
ADVANCED CHEMICAL INDUSTRIES LIMITED; *Int'l*, pg. 158
ADVANCED CHEMICAL TRANSPORT, INC.; *U.S. Private*, pg. 88
ADVANCED CHEMTECH—See CreoSalus, Inc.; *U.S. Private*, pg. 1092
ADVANCED CHROMATOGRAPHY TECHNOLOGIES LTD.—See Avantor, Inc.; *U.S. Public*, pg. 241
ADVANCED CIRCUITS, INC.—See IGP Industries, LLC; *U.S. Private*, pg. 2039
ADVANCED CIRCUITS, INC.—See Compass Diversified Holdings; *U.S. Public*, pg. 559
ADVANCED CLEANUP TECHNOLOGIES; *U.S. Private*, pg. 88
ADVANCED CLINICAL SERVICES LLC—See The Advanced Group of Companies; *U.S. Private*, pg. 3982
ADVANCED CLINICAL SERVICES—See The Advanced Group of Companies; *U.S. Private*, pg. 3982
ADVANCED COLLATERAL SOLUTIONS, LLC—See Wells Fargo & Company; *U.S. Public*, pg. 2343
ADVANCED COMFORT SYSTEMS FRANCE, S.A.S.—See Cie Automotive S.A.; *Int'l*, pg. 1603
ADVANCED COMFORT SYSTEMS IBERICA, S.L.U.—See Cie Automotive S.A.; *Int'l*, pg. 1603
ADVANCED COMFORT SYSTEMS ROMANIA, S.R.L.—See Cie Automotive S.A.; *Int'l*, pg. 1603
ADVANCED COMFORT SYSTEMS SHANGHAI CO. LTD.—See Cie Automotive S.A.; *Int'l*, pg. 1604

ADVANCED COMMUNICATIONS SERVICE INC.; *U.S. Private*, pg. 88
ADVANCED COMMUNICATIONS TECHNOLOGY, INC.—See Range Telephone Cooperative Inc.; *U.S. Private*, pg. 3354
ADVANCED COMPOSITE PRODUCTS & TECHNOLOGY, INC.—See Charger Investment Partners LP; *U.S. Private*, pg. 850
ADVANCED COMPOSITES, INC.—See Marubeni Corporation; *Int'l*, pg. 4706
ADVANCED COMPOSITES, INC.—See Mitsui & Co., Ltd.; *Int'l*, pg. 4975
ADVANCED COMPOSITES, INC.—See Mitsui Chemicals, Inc.; *Int'l*, pg. 4982
ADVANCED COMPOSITES MEXICANA S.A. DE C.V.—See Marubeni Corporation; *Int'l*, pg. 4706
ADVANCED COMPOSITES MEXICANA S.A. DE C.V.—See Mitsui & Co., Ltd.; *Int'l*, pg. 4975
ADVANCED COMPOSITES MEXICANA S.A. DE C.V.—See Mitsui Chemicals, Inc.; *Int'l*, pg. 4982
ADVANCED COMPUTER CONCEPTS; *U.S. Private*, pg. 88
ADVANCED COMPUTER SOFTWARE GROUP LIMITED—See Vista Equity Partners, LLC; *U.S. Private*, pg. 4394
ADVANCED COMPUTER SOLUTIONS GROUP LLC—See BAE Systems Applied Intelligence US Corp; *U.S. Private*, pg. 425
ADVANCED CONCEPTS, INC.—See BAE Systems plc; *Int'l*, pg. 797
ADVANCED CONCEPTS & TECHNOLOGIES INTERNATIONAL, LLC - ARLINGTON—See Advanced Concepts & Technologies International, LLC; *U.S. Private*, pg. 88
ADVANCED CONCEPTS & TECHNOLOGIES INTERNATIONAL, LLC; *U.S. Private*, pg. 88
ADVANCED CONNECTION TECHNOLOGY INC.; *Int'l*, pg. 158
ADVANCED CONTACT CENTER CO., LTD.—See Advanced Info Service Plc; *Int'l*, pg. 159
ADVANCED CONTAINER TECHNOLOGIES, INC.; *U.S. Public*, pg. 46
ADVANCED CONTROLS CO., LTD.—See Advanced Holdings Ltd.; *Int'l*, pg. 159
ADVANCED CONTROLS (M) SDN. BHD—See Advanced Holdings Ltd.; *Int'l*, pg. 159
ADVANCED CONTROL SOLUTIONS—See Applied Industrial Technologies, Inc.; *U.S. Public*, pg. 170
ADVANCED CONTROLS PTE. LTD. - BEIJING REPRESENTATIVE OFFICE—See Advanced Holdings Ltd.; *Int'l*, pg. 159
ADVANCED CONTROLS PTE. LTD.—See Advanced Holdings Ltd.; *Int'l*, pg. 159
ADVANCED CONTROL SYSTEMS, INC.—See Indra Sistemas, S.A.; *Int'l*, pg. 3659
ADVANCED CONTROL & SYSTEMS INC.—See CTCI Corporation; *Int'l*, pg. 1870
ADVANCED COOLING TECHNOLOGIES, INC.; *U.S. Private*, pg. 88
ADVANCED COOLING THERAPY, INC.—See Haemonetics Corporation; *U.S. Public*, pg. 979
ADVANCED CORE CONCEPTS, LLC; *U.S. Private*, pg. 88
ADVANCED CORE TECHNOLOGY CO., LTD.—See Aucnet Inc.; *Int'l*, pg. 699
ADVANCED CORRECTIONAL HEALTHCARE; *U.S. Private*, pg. 89
ADVANCED CUTTING SYSTEMS CORP.—See The Weir Group PLC; *Int'l*, pg. 7699
ADVANCED CYBER SECURITY SYSTEMS, LLC—See NEWTEKONE, INC.; *U.S. Public*, pg. 1521
ADVANCED CYBER TECHNOLOGY CO., LTD.—See Premier Technology Public Company Limited; *Int'l*, pg. 5962
ADVANCED DATACOMM SOLUTIONS, INC.; *U.S. Private*, pg. 89
ADVANCED DATA SYSTEMS CORP.; *U.S. Private*, pg. 89
ADVANCED DEPOSITION TECHNOLOGIES, INC.; *U.S. Public*, pg. 46
ADVANCED DESIGN TECHNOLOGY LIMITED—See Ebara Corporation; *Int'l*, pg. 2282
ADVANCED DETECTION SYSTEMS—See Venturedyne, Ltd.; *U.S. Private*, pg. 4358
ADVANCED DIAGNOSTIC GROUP, LLC—See Akumin, Inc.; *U.S. Public*, pg. 69
ADVANCED DIGITAL BROADCAST HOLDINGS SA; *Int'l*, pg. 158
ADVANCED DIGITAL BROADCAST HONG KONG LTD.—See Advanced Digital Broadcast Holdings SA; *Int'l*, pg. 158
ADVANCED DIGITAL BROADCAST INC.—See Advanced Digital Broadcast Holdings SA; *Int'l*, pg. 158
ADVANCED DIGITAL BROADCAST ITALIA S.R.L.—See Advanced Digital Broadcast Holdings SA; *Int'l*, pg. 158
ADVANCED DIGITAL BROADCAST SA—See Advanced Digital Broadcast Holdings SA; *Int'l*, pg. 158
ADVANCED DIGITAL BROADCAST POLSKA SP. Z.O.O.—See Advanced Digital Broadcast Holdings SA; *Int'l*, pg. 158

COMPANY NAME INDEX

ADVANCED DIGITAL BROADCAST S.A.—See Advanced Digital Broadcast Holdings SA; *Int'l*, pg. 158
ADVANCED DIGITAL BROADCAST SPAIN S.L.U.—See Advanced Digital Broadcast Holdings SA; *Int'l*, pg. 158
ADVANCED DIGITAL CHIPS INC.; *U.S. Private*, pg. 89
ADVANCED DIGITAL DATA INC.; *U.S. Private*, pg. 89
ADVANCED DIGITAL DISTRIBUTION COMPANY LIMITED—See Advanced Info Service Plc; *Int'l*, pg. 159
ADVANCED DIGITAL HEALTH MEDICINA PREVENTIVA S.A.; *Int'l*, pg. 158
ADVANCED DIGITAL SERVICES; *U.S. Private*, pg. 89
ADVANCED DIGITAL SOLUTIONS INTERNATIONAL, INC.; *U.S. Private*, pg. 89
ADVANCED DISPOSAL SERVICES BLACKFOOT LANDFILL, INC.—See Waste Management, Inc.; *U.S. Public*, pg. 2330
ADVANCED DISPOSAL SERVICES BLUE RIDGE LANDFILL, INC.—See Waste Management, Inc.; *U.S. Public*, pg. 2330
ADVANCED DISPOSAL SERVICES CEDAR HILL LANDFILL, INC.—See Waste Management, Inc.; *U.S. Public*, pg. 2330
ADVANCED DISPOSAL SERVICES CRANBERRY CREEK LANDFILL, LLC—See Waste Management, Inc.; *U.S. Public*, pg. 2330
ADVANCED DISPOSAL SERVICES CYPRESS ACRES LANDFILL, INC.—See Waste Management, Inc.; *U.S. Public*, pg. 2330
ADVANCED DISPOSAL SERVICES EVERGREEN LANDFILL, INC.—See Waste Management, Inc.; *U.S. Public*, pg. 2330
ADVANCED DISPOSAL SERVICES, INC.—See Waste Management, Inc.; *U.S. Public*, pg. 2330
ADVANCED DISPOSAL SERVICES JACKSON, LLC—See Waste Management, Inc.; *U.S. Public*, pg. 2330
ADVANCED DISPOSAL SERVICES LANCASTER LANDFILL, LLC—See Waste Management, Inc.; *U.S. Public*, pg. 2330
ADVANCED DISPOSAL SERVICES LITHONIA TRANSFER STATION, LLC—See Waste Management, Inc.; *U.S. Public*, pg. 2330
ADVANCED DISPOSAL SERVICES MACON, LLC—See Waste Management, Inc.; *U.S. Public*, pg. 2330
ADVANCED DISPOSAL SERVICES MAPLE HILL LANDFILL, INC.—See Waste Management, Inc.; *U.S. Public*, pg. 2330
ADVANCED DISPOSAL SERVICES MIDDLE GEORGIA, LLC—See Waste Management, Inc.; *U.S. Public*, pg. 2330
ADVANCED DISPOSAL SERVICES MOREHEAD LANDFILL, INC.—See Waste Management, Inc.; *U.S. Public*, pg. 2330
ADVANCED DISPOSAL SERVICES NORTH GEORGIA, LLC—See Waste Management, Inc.; *U.S. Public*, pg. 2330
ADVANCED DISPOSAL SERVICES ORCHARD HILLS LANDFILL, INC.—See Waste Management, Inc.; *U.S. Public*, pg. 2330
ADVANCED DISPOSAL SERVICES SELMA TRANSFER STATION, LLC—See Waste Management, Inc.; *U.S. Public*, pg. 2330
ADVANCED DISPOSAL SERVICES STAR RIDGE LANDFILL, INC.—See Waste Management, Inc.; *U.S. Public*, pg. 2330
ADVANCED DISPOSAL SERVICES VALLEY VIEW LANDFILL, INC.—See Waste Management, Inc.; *U.S. Public*, pg. 2330
ADVANCED DISTRIBUTOR PRODUCTS LLC—See Lennox International Inc.; *U.S. Public*, pg. 1307
ADVANCED DOCUMENT SOLUTIONS, INC.; *U.S. Private*, pg. 89
ADVANCED DRAINAGE SYSTEMS, INC.; *U.S. Public*, pg. 46
ADVANCED DUPLICATION SERVICES INC.; *U.S. Private*, pg. 89
ADVANCED DYNAMICS CORPORATION LTD.; *Int'l*, pg. 158
ADVANCED EDUCATIONAL PRODUCTS, INC.; *U.S. Private*, pg. 89
ADVANCED ELECTRIC SYSTEMS, LLC—See Quanta Services, Inc.; *U.S. Public*, pg. 1750
ADVANCED ELECTROMAGNETICS, INC—See Microwave Vision SA; *Int'l*, pg. 4882
ADVANCED ELECTRONICS COMPANY—See Saudi Arabian Military Industries; *Int'l*, pg. 6589
ADVANCED ELECTRONIC SERVICES, INC.; *U.S. Private*, pg. 89
ADVANCED ELECTRONIC SYSTEMS INTEGRATORS, LLC; *U.S. Private*, pg. 89
ADVANCED ELEMENTS, INC.—See Pelican International Inc.; *Int'l*, pg. 5782
ADVANCED ELEVATOR TECHNOLOGIES, INC.—See KONE Oyj; *Int'l*, pg. 4248
ADVANCED EMISSIONS SOLUTIONS, INC.; *U.S. Public*, pg. 46
ADVANCED ENERGY ECONOMY; *U.S. Private*, pg. 89
ADVANCED ENERGY INDUSTRIES GMBH—See Advanced Energy Industries, Inc.; *U.S. Public*, pg. 47

ADVANCED ENERGY INDUSTRIES, INC., SHANGHAI—See Advanced Energy Industries, Inc.; *U.S. Public*, pg. 47
ADVANCED ENERGY INDUSTRIES, INC.—See Advanced Energy Industries, Inc.; *U.S. Public*, pg. 47
ADVANCED ENERGY INDUSTRIES, INC.; *U.S. Public*, pg. 46
ADVANCED ENERGY INDUSTRIES SDN. BHD.—See Advanced Energy Industries, Inc.; *U.S. Public*, pg. 47
ADVANCED ENERGY INDUSTRIES—See Advanced Energy Industries, Inc.; *U.S. Public*, pg. 47
ADVANCED ENERGY INDUSTRIES UK LTD.—See Advanced Energy Industries, Inc.; *U.S. Public*, pg. 47
ADVANCED ENERGY JAPAN K.K.—See Advanced Energy Industries, Inc.; *U.S. Public*, pg. 47
ADVANCED ENERGY MANAGEMENT LTD.; *Int'l*, pg. 158
ADVANCED ENERGY MINERALS INC.; *Int'l*, pg. 158
ADVANCED ENERGY PROTECTION—See Irex Corporation; *U.S. Private*, pg. 2137
ADVANCED ENERGY RENEWABLES, INC.—See Advanced Energy Industries, Inc.; *U.S. Public*, pg. 47
ADVANCED ENERGY SINGAPORE, PTE. LTD.—See Advanced Energy Industries, Inc.; *U.S. Public*, pg. 47
ADVANCED ENERGY SOLUTIONS LLC—See Irex Corporation; *U.S. Private*, pg. 2137
ADVANCED ENERGY SYSTEMS LIMITED; *Int'l*, pg. 158
ADVANCED ENERGY SYSTEMS, LLC—See Arthur J. Gallagher & Co.; *U.S. Public*, pg. 202
ADVANCED ENERGY TAIWAN, LTD.—See Advanced Energy Industries, Inc.; *U.S. Public*, pg. 47
ADVANCED ENERGY XI'AN CO. LTD.—See Advanced Energy Industries, Inc.; *U.S. Public*, pg. 47
ADVANCED ENGINEERING CONSULTANTS; *U.S. Private*, pg. 89
ADVANCED ENGINEERING HOLDINGS PTE. LTD.—See Advanced Holdings Ltd.; *Int'l*, pg. 159
ADVANCED ENTERPRISES INC.; *U.S. Private*, pg. 89
ADVANCED ENVIRONMENTAL RECYCLING TECHNOLOGIES, INC.—See CRH plc; *Int'l*, pg. 1845
ADVANCED ENVIRONMENTAL TECHNOLOGIES PTE. LTD.—See Advanced Holdings Ltd.; *Int'l*, pg. 159
ADVANCED ENZYMES USA, INC.—See Advanced Enzyme Technologies Limited; *Int'l*, pg. 159
ADVANCED ENZYME TECHNOLOGIES LIMITED; *Int'l*, pg. 158
ADVANCED EQUIPMENT COMPANY; *U.S. Private*, pg. 89
ADVANCE DEVELOPMENT SDN BHD—See Johor Corporation; *Int'l*, pg. 3994
ADVANCED FEDERAL SERVICES; *U.S. Private*, pg. 89
ADVANCED FIBER, LLC—See Installed Building Products, Inc.; *U.S. Public*, pg. 1132
ADVANCED FIBER RESOURCES (HK) LTD.—See Advanced Fiber Resources (Zhuhai) Ltd; *Int'l*, pg. 159
ADVANCED FIBER RESOURCES (ZHUHAI) LTD; *Int'l*, pg. 159
ADVANCED FILTRATION CONCEPTS, INC.—See Komline-Sanderson Corporation; *U.S. Private*, pg. 2342
ADVANCED FILTRATION SYSTEMS, INC.—See Caterpillar, Inc.; *U.S. Public*, pg. 449
ADVANCED FILTRATION SYSTEMS, INC.—See Donaldson Company, Inc.; *U.S. Public*, pg. 675
ADVANCED FINANCIAL INC.—See The Advanced Group of Companies; *U.S. Private*, pg. 3982
ADVANCED FIRE & SECURITY, INC.—See FirstService Corporation; *Int'l*, pg. 2691
ADVANCED FIRE SYSTEMS INC.—See Halma plc; *Int'l*, pg. 3230
ADVANCED FLUID SYSTEMS INC.; *U.S. Private*, pg. 89
ADVANCED FOOD PRODUCTS LLC—See Savencia Fromage & Dairy; *Int'l*, pg. 6597
ADVANCED FOOD PRODUCTS LLC—See Savencia Fromage & Dairy; *Int'l*, pg. 6597
ADVANCED FOOD SYSTEMS, INC.; *U.S. Private*, pg. 89
ADVANCED FOOD TECHNOLOGIES, INC.—See Zoetis, Inc.; *U.S. Public*, pg. 2409
ADVANCED FORMING TECHNOLOGY, INC.—See ARC Group Worldwide, Inc.; *U.S. Public*, pg. 179
ADVANCED FOUNDATIONS SYSTEMS INC.—See VINCI S.A.; *Int'l*, pg. 8231
ADVANCED FRAUD SOLUTIONS; *U.S. Private*, pg. 89
ADVANCED FRESH CONCEPTS CORP.—See Zensho Holdings Co., Ltd.; *Int'l*, pg. 8634
ADVANCED GLASSFIBER YARNS LLC; *U.S. Private*, pg. 89
ADVANCED GOVERNMENT SOLUTIONS, INC.; *U.S. Private*, pg. 90
ADVANCED GRAPHIC PRODUCTS INC.—See Follett Corporation; *U.S. Private*, pg. 1559
ADVANCED GRAPHICS TECHNOLOGIES, INC.—See Rotation Dynamics Corp.; *U.S. Private*, pg. 3486
ADVANCED GREEN ENERGY PTE LTD—See Advanced Holdings Ltd.; *Int'l*, pg. 159
THE ADVANCED GROUP OF COMPANIES; *U.S. Private*, pg. 3982
ADVANCED HANDLING LTD—See Amplex AB; *Int'l*, pg. 434
ADVANCED HEALTH CARE CORPORATION—See Larry H. Miller Group of Companies; *U.S. Private*, pg. 2392

ADVANCED HEALTH & CARE—See Vista Equity Partners, LLC; *U.S. Private*, pg. 4394
ADVANCED HEALTH EDUCATION CENTER, LTD.; *U.S. Private*, pg. 90
ADVANCED HEALTH INTELLIGENCE LTD; *Int'l*, pg. 159
ADVANCED HEALTH MEDIA, LLC—See Arlington Capital Partners LLC; *U.S. Private*, pg. 327
ADVANCED HI-TECH CORPORATION; *U.S. Private*, pg. 90
ADVANCED HOLDINGS LTD.; *Int'l*, pg. 159
ADVANCED HOMECARE HOLDINGS, INC.—See Encompass Health Corporation; *U.S. Public*, pg. 754
ADVANCED HOME CARE INC.—See AdaptHealth Corp.; *U.S. Public*, pg. 38
ADVANCED HOMECARE MANAGEMENT, INC.—See Encompass Health Corporation; *U.S. Public*, pg. 754
ADVANCED HOME CONCEPT DEVELOPMENT CORP.—See ATN Holdings, Inc.; *Int'l*, pg. 687
ADVANCED HORIZONS INC.; *U.S. Private*, pg. 90
ADVANCE DIGITAL, INC.—See Advance Local LLC; *U.S. Private*, pg. 83
ADVANCED IMAGING SOLUTIONS, INC.; *U.S. Private*, pg. 90
ADVANCED IMAGING SOLUTIONS INC.; *U.S. Private*, pg. 90
ADVANCED INDEPENDENT MONITORING LIMITED—See Johnson Controls International plc; *Int'l*, pg. 3989
ADVANCED INDUSTRIAL COATINGS, INC.—See Crawford United Corporation; *U.S. Public*, pg. 592
ADVANCED INDUSTRIAL COMPUTER INC.; *U.S. Private*, pg. 90
ADVANCED INDUSTRIAL DEVICES, INC.; *U.S. Private*, pg. 90
ADVANCED INDUSTRIAL SERVICES, INC.—See Cemtrex, Inc.; *U.S. Public*, pg. 466
ADVANCED INDUSTRIAL SERVICES—See Irex Corporation; *U.S. Private*, pg. 2137
ADVANCED INFORMATION TECHNOLOGY PCL; *Int'l*, pg. 160
ADVANCED INFO SERVICE PLC; *Int'l*, pg. 159
ADVANCED INPUT DEVICES, INC.—See TransDigm Group Incorporated; *U.S. Public*, pg. 2180
ADVANCED INSTRUCTIONAL SYSTEMS, INC.—See Apax Partners LLP; *Int'l*, pg. 502
ADVANCED INSTRUCTIONAL SYSTEMS, INC.—See Apollo Global Management, Inc.; *U.S. Public*, pg. 168
ADVANCED INSTRUCTIONAL SYSTEMS, INC.—See KKR & Co. Inc.; *U.S. Public*, pg. 1256
ADVANCED INSTRUCTIONAL SYSTEMS, INC.—See Searchlight Capital Partners, L.P.; *U.S. Private*, pg. 3587
ADVANCED INSTRUMENTS, LLC—See Investor AB; *Int'l*, pg. 3786
ADVANCED INSURANCE UNDERWRITERS LLC—See Kelso & Company, L.P.; *U.S. Private*, pg. 2279
ADVANCED INTEGRATED MANUFACTURING CORP. LTD.; *Int'l*, pg. 160
ADVANCED INTEGRATION TECHNOLOGY, INC.—See SRA Holdings Inc; *Int'l*, pg. 7147
ADVANCED INTEGRATION TECHNOLOGY, LP; *U.S. Private*, pg. 90
ADVANCED INTERACTIVE SOLUTIONS LTD.—See Advanced Interactive Systems; *U.S. Private*, pg. 90
ADVANCED INTERACTIVE SYSTEMS; *U.S. Private*, pg. 90
ADVANCED INTERCONNECT MANUFACTURING, INC.—See Flotum Inc.; *U.S. Private*, pg. 1551
ADVANCED INTERNATIONAL MULTITECH CO., LTD.; *Int'l*, pg. 160
ADVANCED INTERNET TECHNOLOGIES INC.; *U.S. Private*, pg. 90
ADVANCED INVESTMENTS GROUP; *Int'l*, pg. 160
ADVANCE DISPLAY TECHNOLOGIES, INC.; *U.S. Private*, pg. 83
ADVANCE DISPLAY TECHNOLOGY LIMITED—See Tak Shun Technology Group Limited; *Int'l*, pg. 7428
ADVANCED LABELS N. W.—See Ares Management Corporation; *U.S. Public*, pg. 190
ADVANCED LABELWORX, INC. - ANDERSON—See Advanced Labelworx, Inc.; *U.S. Private*, pg. 90
ADVANCED LABELWORX, INC.; *U.S. Private*, pg. 90
ADVANCED LEARNING CENTERS, INC.; *U.S. Private*, pg. 90
ADVANCED LEISURE TECHNOLOGIES PLC; *Int'l*, pg. 160
ADVANCED LIFE SCIENCE INSTITUTE, INC.—See H.U. Group Holdings, Inc.; *Int'l*, pg. 3196
ADVANCED LIGHTING CONCEPTS, LLC—See Pfingsten Partners, LLC; *U.S. Private*, pg. 3164
ADVANCED LIGHTING TECHNOLOGIES ASIA PTE LTD.—See Saratoga Partners L.P.; *U.S. Private*, pg. 3549
ADVANCED LIGHTING TECHNOLOGIES AUSTRALIA, INC.—See Saratoga Partners L.P.; *U.S. Private*, pg. 3549
ADVANCED LIGHTING TECHNOLOGIES, INC.—See Saratoga Partners L.P.; *U.S. Private*, pg. 3549

47

ADVANCED LEISURE TECHNOLOGIES PLC

CORPORATE AFFILIATIONS

ADVANCED LIQUID FEEDS LIMITED—See W&R Barnett Ltd.; *Int'l*, pg. 8320
ADVANCED LIQUID LOGIC, INC.; *U.S. Private*, pg. 90
ADVANCED LITHIUM ELECTROCHEMISTRY (HK) CO., LIMITED—See Advanced Lithium Electrochemistry (KY) Co., Ltd.; *Int'l*, pg. 160
ADVANCED LITHIUM ELECTROCHEMISTRY (KY) CO., LTD.; *Int'l*, pg. 160
ADVANCED LOGISTICS GROUP S.A.—See Indra Sistemas, S.A.; *Int'l*, pg. 3660
ADVANCED LOGISTICS, LLC.; *U.S. Private*, pg. 90
ADVANCED LOGISTICS LTD.—See Tachibana Eletech Co., Ltd.; *Int'l*, pg. 7402
ADVANCED LOGISTICS SOLUTIONS CO., LTD.—See Toyota Industries Corporation; *Int'l*, pg. 7865
ADVANCED MACHINE & ENGINEERING CO.; *U.S. Private*, pg. 90
ADVANCED MACHINERY COMPANIES; *U.S. Private*, pg. 91
ADVANCED MACHINE & TOOL CORP.; *U.S. Private*, pg. 90
ADVANCED MACHINING & TOOLING, INC.—See Shorehill Capital LLC; *U.S. Private*, pg. 3641
ADVANCED MAGIC CARD CO., LTD.—See Advanced Info Service Plc; *Int'l*, pg. 159
ADVANCED MAGNESIUM TECHNOLOGIES PTY LTD—See Magontec Limited; *Int'l*, pg. 4642
ADVANCED MAGNETIC INTERACTION, AMI S.A.S.U.—See Societe BIC S.A.; *Int'l*, pg. 7036
ADVANCED MAGNETIC MATERIALS (THAILAND) CO., LTD.—See Brookfield Corporation; *Int'l*, pg. 1181
ADVANCED MAINTENANCE; *U.S. Private*, pg. 91
ADVANCED MANAGEMENT TECHNOLOGY, INC.—See Tetra Tech, Inc.; *U.S. Public*, pg. 2022
ADVANCED MANUFACTURING CONTROL SYSTEMS LTD.; *Int'l*, pg. 160
ADVANCED MANUFACTURING CORPORATION PTE. LTD.—See Advanced Integrated Manufacturing Corp. Ltd.; *Int'l*, pg. 160
ADVANCED MANUFACTURING CORP SDN. BHD.—See Advanced Integrated Manufacturing Corp. Ltd.; *Int'l*, pg. 160
ADVANCED MANUFACTURING & DEVELOPMENT, INC.—See Montage Partners, Inc.; *U.S. Private*, pg. 2774
ADVANCED MARINE PRESERVATION, LLC—See Stellex Capital Management LP; *U.S. Private*, pg. 3800
ADVANCED MARKETING GROUP, INC.; *U.S. Private*, pg. 91
ADVANCED MARKETING & PROCESSING, INC.—See Crestview Partners, L.P.; *U.S. Private*, pg. 1098
ADVANCED MARKETING STRATEGIES; *U.S. Private*, pg. 91
ADVANCED MARKETING STRATEGIES—See Advanced Marketing Strategies; *U.S. Private*, pg. 91
ADVANCED MARKETPLACE INC.; *U.S. Private*, pg. 91
ADVANCED MASONRY SYSTEMS LLC; *U.S. Private*, pg. 91
ADVANCED MATERIAL JAPAN CORPORATION—See Alconix Corporation; *Int'l*, pg. 302
ADVANCED MATERIAL TRADING PTE LTD.—See Alconix Corporation; *Int'l*, pg. 302
ADVANCEDMD, INC.—See Global Payments Inc.; *U.S. Public*, pg. 943
ADVANCED M & D SALES INC.; *U.S. Private*, pg. 90
ADVANCED MEASUREMENTS INC.—See First Reserve Management, L.P.; *U.S. Private*, pg. 1525
ADVANCED MEASUREMENT TECHNOLOGY, INC.—See AMETEK, Inc.; *U.S. Public*, pg. 118
ADVANCED MEDIA, INC., *Int'l*, pg. 160
ADVANCED MEDIA TECHNOLOGIES, INC.—See ITOCHU Corporation; *Int'l*, pg. 3838
ADVANCED MEDICAL IMAGING, LLC—See Franciscan Health System; *U.S. Private*, pg. 1587
ADVANCED MEDICAL INSTITUTE INC.; *Int'l*, pg. 161
ADVANCED MEDICAL PERSONNEL SERVICES, INC.—See AMN Healthcare Services, Inc.; *U.S. Public*, pg. 125
ADVANCED MEDICAL PREDICTIVE DEVICES, DIAGNOSTICS AND DISPLAYS, LLC—See Nihon Kohden Corporation; *Int'l*, pg. 5285
ADVANCED MEDICAL SOLUTIONS B.V.—See Advanced Medical Solutions Group plc; *Int'l*, pg. 161
ADVANCED MEDICAL SOLUTIONS GROUP PLC; *Int'l*, pg. 161
ADVANCED MEDICAL SOLUTIONS ISRAEL (SEALANTIS) LIMITED—See Advanced Medical Solutions Group plc; *Int'l*, pg. 161
ADVANCED MEDICAL SOLUTIONS LTD.—See Advanced Medical Solutions Group plc; *Int'l*, pg. 161
ADVANCED MEDICAL SOLUTIONS (PLYMOUTH) LTD.—See Advanced Medical Solutions Group plc; *Int'l*, pg. 161
ADVANCED MEDICAL SOLUTIONS (UK) LTD.—See Advanced Medical Solutions Group plc; *Int'l*, pg. 161
ADVANCED MEDICAL SOLUTIONS (US) INC—See Advanced Medical Solutions Group plc; *Int'l*, pg. 161
ADVANCED MEDICAL SPECIALTIES; *U.S. Private*, pg. 91

ADVANCED MEDICAL SYSTEMS INC.—See ATC Group, Inc.; *U.S. Private*, pg. 365
ADVANCED MEDICAL TRANSPORT OF CENTRAL ILLINOIS; *U.S. Private*, pg. 91
ADVANCED MERGER PARTNERS, INC.; *U.S. Public*, pg. 48
ADVANCED METALS GROUP, LLC; *U.S. Private*, pg. 91
ADVANCED MICRO DEVICES (CHINA) CO. LTD.—See Advanced Micro Devices, Inc.; *U.S. Public*, pg. 48
ADVANCED MICRO DEVICES EXPORT SDN. BHD.—See Advanced Micro Devices, Inc.; *U.S. Public*, pg. 48
ADVANCED MICRO DEVICES GLOBAL SERVICES (M) SDN. BHD.—See Advanced Micro Devices, Inc.; *U.S. Public*, pg. 48
ADVANCED MICRO DEVICES GMBH—See Advanced Micro Devices, Inc.; *U.S. Public*, pg. 48
ADVANCED MICRO DEVICES INC.—See Advanced Micro Devices, Inc.; *U.S. Public*, pg. 48
ADVANCED MICRO DEVICES, INC.; *U.S. Public*, pg. 48
ADVANCED MICRO DEVICES, INC.—See Advanced Micro Devices, Inc.; *U.S. Public*, pg. 48
ADVANCED MICRO DEVICES, INC.—See Advanced Micro Devices, Inc.; *U.S. Public*, pg. 48
ADVANCED MICRO DEVICES, INC.—See Advanced Micro Devices, Inc.; *U.S. Public*, pg. 48
ADVANCED MICRO DEVICES, S.A.—See Advanced Micro Devices, Inc.; *U.S. Public*, pg. 48
ADVANCED MICRO DEVICES (SHANGHAI) CO. LTD.—See Advanced Micro Devices, Inc.; *U.S. Public*, pg. 48
ADVANCED MICRO DEVICES (SINGAPORE) PTE. LTD.—See Advanced Micro Devices, Inc.; *U.S. Public*, pg. 48
ADVANCED MICRO DEVICES SPA—See Advanced Micro Devices, Inc.; *U.S. Public*, pg. 48
ADVANCED MICRO DEVICES (U.K.) LIMITED—See Advanced Micro Devices, Inc.; *U.S. Public*, pg. 48
ADVANCED MICRO - ELECTRONICS, INC.; *U.S. Private*, pg. 91
ADVANCED MICROELECTRONICS, INC.; *U.S. Private*, pg. 91
ADVANCED MICRO-FABRICATION EQUIPMENT, INC.; *Int'l*, pg. 161
ADVANCED MICRO INSTRUMENTS, INC.—See Enpro Inc.; *U.S. Public*, pg. 774
ADVANCED MICRONIC DEVICES LTD.—See Opto Circuits (India) Limited; *Int'l*, pg. 5605
ADVANCED MICRONIC DEVICES LTD.—See Opto Circuits (India) Limited; *Int'l*, pg. 5605
ADVANCED MICROWAVE, INC.—See NeoMagic Corporation; *U.S. Public*, pg. 1506
ADVANCED MOBILITY SYSTEMS OF TEXAS, INC.—See Edwards Capital, LLC; *U.S. Private*, pg. 1342
ADVANCED MOTION SYSTEMS INC.—See Applied Industrial Technologies, Inc.; *U.S. Public*, pg. 170
ADVANCED MP TECHNOLOGY INC.—See Wynnchurch Capital, L.P.; *U.S. Private*, pg. 4576
ADVANCED NANO PRODUCTS CO., LTD. - DAEJEON FACILITY—See Advanced Nano Products Co., Ltd.; *Int'l*, pg. 161
ADVANCED NANO PRODUCTS CO., LTD.; *Int'l*, pg. 161
ADVANCED NETWORK MANAGEMENT, INC.; *U.S. Private*, pg. 91
ADVANCED NETWORK MARKETING, INC.; *U.S. Private*, pg. 91
ADVANCED NETWORK PRODUCTS, INC.—See Wells Fargo & Company; *U.S. Public*, pg. 2344
ADVANCED NETWORK SOLUTIONS; *U.S. Private*, pg. 91
ADVANCED NEW TECHNOLOGIES LTD—See L3Harris Technologies, Inc.; *U.S. Public*, pg. 1280
ADVANCED NUCLEAR FUELS GMBH—See Electricite de France S.A.; *Int'l*, pg. 2351
ADVANCED NUCLEAR—See Irex Corporation; *U.S. Private*, pg. 2137
ADVANCED OFFICE ENVIRONMENTS, INC.; *U.S. Private*, pg. 91
ADVANCED OFFICE SYSTEMS, INC.; *U.S. Private*, pg. 91
ADVANCED ONCOTHERAPY PLC; *Int'l*, pg. 161
ADVANCE DOOR SYSTEMS LTD; *Int'l*, pg. 156
ADVANCED O & P SOLUTIONS, L.L.C.—See Patient Square Capital, L.P.; *U.S. Private*, pg. 3106
ADVANCED OPTICAL COMPONENTS—See Coherent Corp.; *U.S. Public*, pg. 528
ADVANCED OPTOELECTRONIC TECHNOLOGY INC.; *Int'l*, pg. 161
ADVANCED OXYGEN TECHNOLOGIES, INC.; *U.S. Public*, pg. 49
ADVANCED PACKAGING TECHNOLOGY (M) BHD; *Int'l*, pg. 161
ADVANCED PATIENT ADVOCACY LLC—See GrowthCurve Capital LP; *U.S. Private*, pg. 1796
ADVANCED PATIENT ADVOCACY LLC—See Riverside Partners, LLC; *U.S. Private*, pg. 3446
ADVANCED PAVEMENT GROUP CORP.; *U.S. Private*, pg. 91
ADVANCED PEDESTALS, INC.—See Petroflex North America, Ltd.; *U.S. Private*, pg. 3162
ADVANCED PERSONNEL, INC.—See Elwood Staffing Services, Inc.; *U.S. Private*, pg. 1377
ADVANCED PETROCHEMICAL COMPANY; *Int'l*, pg. 161

ADVANCED PHARMACEUTICAL PACKAGING CO.; *Int'l*, pg. 161
ADVANCED PHOTONIX, INC.—See Luna Innovations Incorporated; *U.S. Public*, pg. 1348
ADVANCED PIPES AND CASTS COMPANY W.L.L.—See Aamal Company Q.S.C.; *Int'l*, pg. 36
ADVANCED PLANNING SERVICES, INC.; *U.S. Private*, pg. 92
ADVANCED PLASTICS INCORPORATED; *U.S. Private*, pg. 92
ADVANCED PNEUMATICS CO., INC.—See Hartfiel Automation; *U.S. Private*, pg. 1873
ADVANCED POLYMERS INTERNATIONAL—See H.B. Fuller Company; *U.S. Public*, pg. 978
ADVANCED POLYMER TECHNOLOGY CORPORATION; *U.S. Private*, pg. 92
ADVANCED POWER CONTROL INCORPORATED; *U.S. Private*, pg. 92
ADVANCED POWER ELECTRONICS CORP.; *Int'l*, pg. 161
ADVANCED POWERLINE TECHNOLOGIES, INC.; *U.S. Public*, pg. 49
ADVANCED POWER SOLUTIONS; *U.S. Private*, pg. 92
ADVANCED PRACTICE STRATEGIES, INC.—See Bertelsmann SE & Co. KGaA; *Int'l*, pg. 991
ADVANCED PRECISION INC.—See The Jordan Company, L.P.; *U.S. Private*, pg. 4060
ADVANCED PRESSURE TECHNOLOGY, INC.—See SMC Corporation; *Int'l*, pg. 7003
ADVANCED PRIMARY MINERALS USA CORP—See Morien Resources Corp.; *Int'l*, pg. 5045
ADVANCED PROCESS EQUIPMENT (THAILAND) CO., LTD.—See Advanced Holdings Ltd.; *Int'l*, pg. 159
ADVANCED PRODUCTION & LOADING INC.—See NOV, Inc.; *U.S. Public*, pg. 1543
ADVANCED PRODUCTS CORPORATION PTE LTD—See Venture Corporation Limited; *Int'l*, pg. 8151
ADVANCED PROGRAMMING RESOURCES; *U.S. Private*, pg. 92
ADVANCED PROSTHETICS CENTER, LLC—See Patient Square Capital, L.P.; *U.S. Private*, pg. 3107
ADVANCED PROSTHETICS OF AMERICA, INC.—See Patient Square Capital, L.P.; *U.S. Private*, pg. 3107
ADVANCED PROSTHETICS & ORTHOTICS, L.L.C.—See Patient Square Capital, L.P.; *U.S. Private*, pg. 3106
ADVANCED PROTECTION TECHNOLOGIES, INC.; *U.S. Private*, pg. 92
ADVANCED PROTECTIVE COATINGS INC.; *U.S. Private*, pg. 92
ADVANCED PROTEOME THERAPEUTICS CORPORATION; *U.S. Public*, pg. 49
ADVANCED PSYCHIATRIC GROUP, P.A—See Thurston Group, LLC; *U.S. Private*, pg. 4166
ADVANCED PUBLIC SAFETY, INC.—See TA Associates, Inc.; *U.S. Private*, pg. 3914
ADVANCED QUARTZ MATERIAL (HANGZHOU) CO., LTD.—See Ferrotec Holdings Corporation; *Int'l*, pg. 2643
ADVANCED RADAR CORPORATION—See NDP, LLC; *U.S. Private*, pg. 2876
ADVANCED RADIOLOGY, LLC—See RadNet, Inc.; *U.S. Public*, pg. 1760
ADVANCED RAILWAY SYSTEMS GMBH—See voestalpine AG; *Int'l*, pg. 8289
ADVANCED REFINING TECHNOLOGIES, LLC - CATALYSTS—See Chevron Corporation; *U.S. Public*, pg. 486
ADVANCED REFINING TECHNOLOGIES, LLC—See Chevron Corporation; *U.S. Public*, pg. 486
ADVANCED REGIONAL SURGERY CENTER, LLC—See Tenet Healthcare Corporation; *U.S. Public*, pg. 2001
ADVANCED RELIABILITY TECHNOLOGIES, LLC—See PinnacleART International, LLC; *U.S. Private*, pg. 3186
ADVANCED RESOURCES HOLDINGS PTE. LTD.—See Sound Global Ltd.; *Int'l*, pg. 7114
ADVANCED RESOURCES INC.—See The Advanced Group of Companies; *U.S. Private*, pg. 3982
ADVANCED RESOURCES INC.—See The Advanced Group of Companies; *U.S. Private*, pg. 3982
ADVANCED RESOURCES INC.—See The Advanced Group of Companies; *U.S. Private*, pg. 3982
ADVANCED RESOURCES LLC—See The Advanced Group of Companies; *U.S. Private*, pg. 3982
ADVANCED RESOURCE TECHNOLOGIES, INC.; *U.S. Private*, pg. 92
ADVANCED RESPONSE CONCEPTS CORPORATION—See WidePoint Corporation; *U.S. Public*, pg. 2370
ADVANCED ROOFING INC.; *U.S. Private*, pg. 92
ADVANCED ROOFING & SHEET METAL—See Johns Lyng Group Limited; *Int'l*, pg. 3984
ADVANCE DRUM SERVICE, INC.; *U.S. Private*, pg. 83
ADVANCED SAFETY SYSTEMS INC.—See Littlejohn & Co., LLC; *U.S. Private*, pg. 2471
ADVANCED SCIENTIFICS, INC.—See Thermo Fisher Scientific Inc.; *U.S. Public*, pg. 2145
ADVANCED SEALING & SUPPLY COMPANY, INC.—See LKCM Headwater Investments; *U.S. Private*, pg. 2475

COMPANY NAME INDEX

ADVANCED SEMICONDUCTOR ENGINEERING, INC.—See ASE Technology Holding Co., Ltd.; *Int'l*, pg. 604
ADVANCED SEMICONDUCTOR MANUFACTURING CORPORATION LIMITED; *Int'l*, pg. 162
ADVANCED SENSORS LIMITED—See Roper Technologies, Inc.; *U.S. Public*, pg. 1810
ADVANCED SERVICES, INC.—See Haier Smart Home Co., Ltd.; *Int'l*, pg. 3210
ADVANCED SERVICE SOLUTIONS, INC.—See Lincolnshire Management, Inc.; *U.S. Private*, pg. 2459
ADVANCED SOFTWARE SYSTEMS, INC.; *U.S. Private*, pg. 92
ADVANCED SOFTWARE TALENT, LLC; *U.S. Private*, pg. 92
ADVANCED SOLTECH SWEDEN AB; *Int'l*, pg. 162
ADVANCED SOLUTIONS, INC.—See Rocket Lab USA, Inc.; *U.S. Public*, pg. 1804
ADVANCED SOLUTIONS INTERNATIONAL, INC.; *U.S. Private*, pg. 92
ADVANCED SOLUTIONS INTERNATIONAL INC.; *U.S. Private*, pg. 92
ADVANCED; *U.S. Private*, pg. 87
ADVANCED SPECIALTY CONTRACTORS—See Irex Corporation; *U.S. Private*, pg. 2137
ADVANCED SPINE CENTER OF WISCONSIN, LLC—See Tenet Healthcare Corporation; *U.S. Public*, pg. 2001
ADVANCED SPORTS, INC.; *U.S. Private*, pg. 92
ADVANCED STEEL & CRANE INC.—See EMC Limited; *Int'l*, pg. 2376
ADVANCED STEEL RECOVERY LLC—See Commercial Metals Company; *U.S. Public*, pg. 545
ADVANCED STERILIZATION PRODUCTS, INC.—See Johnson & Johnson; *U.S. Public*, pg. 1195
ADVANCED STIMULATION TECHNOLOGIES INC.; *U.S. Private*, pg. 92
ADVANCED SURGERY CENTER OF BETHESDA, LLC—See Tenet Healthcare Corporation; *U.S. Public*, pg. 2001
ADVANCED SURGERY CENTER OF CLIFTON, LLC—See UnitedHealth Group Incorporated; *U.S. Public*, pg. 2238
ADVANCED SURGERY CENTER OF METAIRIE, LLC—See Tenet Healthcare Corporation; *U.S. Public*, pg. 2001
ADVANCED SURGERY CENTER OF NORTHERN LOUISIANA, LLC—See Tenet Healthcare Corporation; *U.S. Public*, pg. 2001
ADVANCED SURGERY CENTER OF SARASOTA, LLC—See Tenet Healthcare Corporation; *U.S. Public*, pg. 2001
ADVANCED SURGERY CENTER OF TAMPA, LLC—See Tenet Healthcare Corporation; *U.S. Public*, pg. 2001
ADVANCED SURGICAL CARE OF CLEARWATER, LLC—See Tenet Healthcare Corporation; *U.S. Public*, pg. 2001
ADVANCED SURGICAL CARE OF ST LOUIS, LLC—See Tenet Healthcare Corporation; *U.S. Public*, pg. 2001
ADVANCED SURGICAL CONCEPTS, LLC—See Tenet Healthcare Corporation; *U.S. Public*, pg. 2009
ADVANCED SURGICAL HOSPITAL, LLC—See UnitedHealth Group Incorporated; *U.S. Public*, pg. 2238
ADVANCED SYNERGIC PTE. LTD.—See ASM Technologies Limited; *Int'l*, pg. 627
ADVANCED SYSTEM DESIGN INC.; *U.S. Private*, pg. 92
ADVANCED SYSTEMS AUTOMATION LIMITED; *Int'l*, pg. 162
ADVANCED SYSTEMS COMPANY LLC—See ASBISc Enterprises Plc; *Int'l*, pg. 600
ADVANCED SYSTEMS CONCEPTS, INC.—See Redwood Software, Inc.; *U.S. Private*, pg. 3381
ADVANCED SYSTEMS ENGINEERING CORPORATION—See Sterling Investment Partners, L.P.; *U.S. Private*, pg. 3806
ADVANCED SYSTEMS GROUP INC.; *U.S. Private*, pg. 92
ADVANCED SYSTEMS GROUP, LLC; *U.S. Private*, pg. 92
ADVANCED SYSTEMS GROUP—See EMCOR Group, Inc.; *U.S. Public*, pg. 739
ADVANCED SYSTEMS INC.—See Gordon Flesch Company, Inc.; *U.S. Private*, pg. 1743
ADVANCED SYSTEMS PORTABLE RESTROOMS, INC.—See Waste Connections, Inc.; *Int'l*, pg. 8353
ADVANCED SYSTEMS TECHNOLOGY, INC.; *U.S. Private*, pg. 92
ADVANCED TECHNICAL RESOURCES INC.; *U.S. Private*, pg. 93
ADVANCED TECHNICAL SOLUTIONS, INC.; *U.S. Private*, pg. 93
ADVANCED TECHNICAL SOLUTIONS IN SCANDINAVIA AB—See FARO Technologies, Inc.; *U.S. Public*, pg. 823
ADVANCED TECHNICAL SOLUTIONS, LLC; *U.S. Private*, pg. 93
ADVANCED TECHNOLOGIES GROUP, INC.—See Jones Lang LaSalle Incorporated; *U.S. Public*, pg. 1201
ADVANCED TECHNOLOGY COMPANY K.S.C.C.; *Int'l*, pg. 162
ADVANCED TECHNOLOGY CONSULTING SERVICE INC.—See Nagarro SE; *Int'l*, pg. 5126

ADVANCED TECHNOLOGY CORP.—See ATC Group, Inc.; *U.S. Private*, pg. 365
ADVANCED TECHNOLOGY INTERNATIONAL, LLC; *U.S. Private*, pg. 93
ADVANCED TECHNOLOGY INTERNATIONAL—See Analytic Services, Inc.; *U.S. Private*, pg. 271
ADVANCED TECHNOLOGY MACHINING, INC.—See ESCO Technologies, Inc.; *U.S. Public*, pg. 793
ADVANCED TECHNOLOGY & MATERIALS CO., LTD. - AMORPHOUS METAL PRODUCTS DIVISION—See Advanced Technology & Materials Co., Ltd.; *Int'l*, pg. 162
ADVANCED TECHNOLOGY & MATERIALS CO., LTD. - FUNCTIONAL MATERIALS DIVISION—See Advanced Technology & Materials Co., Ltd.; *Int'l*, pg. 162
ADVANCED TECHNOLOGY & MATERIALS CO., LTD. - INTERNATIONAL TRADING DIVISION—See Advanced Technology & Materials Co., Ltd.; *Int'l*, pg. 162
ADVANCED TECHNOLOGY & MATERIALS CO., LTD.; *Int'l*, pg. 162
ADVANCED TECHNOLOGY SERVICES, INC.—See WestView Capital Partners, L.P.; *U.S. Private*, pg. 4501
ADVANCED TECHNOLOGY SOLUTIONS, INC.; *U.S. Private*, pg. 93
ADVANCED TECHNOLOGY & SYSTEMS CO., LTD.; *Int'l*, pg. 162
ADVANCED TELECOM SERVICES; *U.S. Private*, pg. 93
ADVANCED TEL, INC.—See RTC Holdings, L.L.C.; *U.S. Private*, pg. 3498
ADVANCED TEMPERATURE TEST SYSTEMS GMBH—See FormFactor, Inc.; *U.S. Public*, pg. 868
ADVANCED TEMPORARIES, INC.; *U.S. Private*, pg. 93
ADVANCED TEMPORARIES, INC.; *U.S. Private*, pg. 93
ADVANCED TEST CONCEPTS, LLC—See Dr. Ing. K. Busch GmbH; *Int'l*, pg. 2193
ADVANCED TESTING LABORATORY, INC.—See Bureau Veritas S.A.; *Int'l*, pg. 1221
ADVANCED THERMAL SCIENCES CORPORATION—See RTX Corporation; *U.S. Public*, pg. 1822
ADVANCED THERMAL SCIENCES TAIWAN CORP.—See RTX Corporation; *U.S. Public*, pg. 1822
ADVANCED THIN FILMS LLC—See IDEX Corp; *U.S. Public*, pg. 1089
ADVANCED TOOLING TEK (SHANGHAI) CO., LTD.—See voestalpine AG; *Int'l*, pg. 8287
ADVANCED TRANSIT DYNAMICS, INC.—See Enpro Inc.; *U.S. Public*, pg. 775
ADVANCED TRAVEL NURSING—See AMN Healthcare Services, Inc.; *U.S. Public*, pg. 125
ADVANCED TREATMENT SYSTEMS, INC.—See Acadia Healthcare Company, Inc.; *U.S. Public*, pg. 28
ADVANCED TURF TECHNOLOGIES LTD.—See Stanley Black & Decker, Inc.; *U.S. Public*, pg. 1931
ADVANCED UTILITY SYSTEMS CORPORATION—See Constellation Software Inc.; *Int'l*, pg. 1773
ADVANCED VALVE SOLUTIONS B.V.—See Addtech AB; *Int'l*, pg. 131
ADVANCED VALVE TECHNOLOGIES, LLC—See Wind Point Advisors LLC; *U.S. Private*, pg. 4534
ADVANCED VISION RESEARCH, INC.—See Akorn, Inc.; *U.S. Private*, pg. 145
ADVANCED VISION SCIENCE INC.—See Santen Pharmaceutical Co., Ltd.; *Int'l*, pg. 6557
ADVANCED VISION TECHNOLOGY LTD.—See Danaher Corporation; *U.S. Public*, pg. 624
ADVANCED VISUAL SYSTEMS INC.; *U.S. Private*, pg. 93
ADVANCED VITAL ENZYMES PVT. LTD.; *Int'l*, pg. 163
ADVANCED VOICE RECOGNITION SYSTEMS, INC.; *U.S. Public*, pg. 49
ADVANCED WASTE SERVICES OF INDIANA, INC.—See EQT AB; *U.S. Private*, pg. 2473
ADVANCED WATER RECLAMATION (CHENGDU) CO., LTD.—See Sound Global Ltd.; *Int'l*, pg. 7114
ADVANCED WEB TECHNOLOGIES, INC.; *U.S. Private*, pg. 93
ADVANCED WEIGHT LOSS CLINICS; *U.S. Private*, pg. 93
ADVANCED WINDOW, INC.—See Exchange Income Corporation; *Int'l*, pg. 2579
ADVANCED WIRELESS COMMUNICATIONS; *U.S. Private*, pg. 93
ADVANCED WIRELESS NETWORK CO., LTD.—See Advanced Info Service Plc; *Int'l*, pg. 159
ADVANCED WOMEN'S IMAGING PTY. LTD.—See Integral Diagnostics Limited; *Int'l*, pg. 3730
ADVANCED WORKPLACE STRATEGIES, INC.; *U.S. Private*, pg. 93
ADVANCE ELECTRICAL SUPPLY CO.; *U.S. Private*, pg. 83
ADVANCE ENGINEERING COMPANY; *U.S. Private*, pg. 83
ADVANCE ENGINEERING COMPANY—See Advance Engineering Company; *U.S. Private*, pg. 83
ADVANCE EQUITY HOLDING; *Int'l*, pg. 156
ADVANCE E-SERVICE SOLUTIONS, INC.—See Advance Auto Parts, Inc.; *U.S. Public*, pg. 44
ADVANCE FINANCIAL; *U.S. Private*, pg. 83
ADVANCE GOLD CORP.; *Int'l*, pg. 156
THE ADVANCE GROUP; *U.S. Private*, pg. 3982

ADVANCE SYNTEX LIMITED

ADVANCE HYDROCARBON CORPORATION—See COFRA Holding AG; *Int'l*, pg. 1694
ADVANCE INDUSTRIES SDN. BHD.—See Kerjaya Prospek Group Berhad; *Int'l*, pg. 4136
ADVANCE INFORMATION MARKETING BERHAD; *Int'l*, pg. 156
ADVANCE INTELLIGENCE MODERNITY COMPANY LIMITED—See MFEC Public Company Limited; *Int'l*, pg. 4870
ADVANCE INTERNATIONAL FREIGHT SDN. BHD.—See FM Global Logistics Holdings Berhad; *Int'l*, pg. 2717
ADVANCE LATEX PRODUCTS, INC.; *U.S. Private*, pg. 83
ADVANCE LIFESTYLES LIMITED; *Int'l*, pg. 156
ADVANCE LOCAL LLC; *U.S. Private*, pg. 83
ADVANCE LOGISTICS INVESTMENT CORPORATION; *Int'l*, pg. 156
ADVANCE MECHANICAL CONTRACTORS; *U.S. Private*, pg. 83
ADVANCE MECHANICAL SYSTEMS, INC.; *U.S. Private*, pg. 83
ADVANCE MEDICAL HEALTH CARE MANAGEMENT SERVICES CHILE S.A.—See Teladoc Health, Inc.; *U.S. Public*, pg. 1992
ADVANCE MEDICAL HEALTH-CARE MANAGEMENT SERVICES, S.A.—See Teladoc Health, Inc.; *U.S. Public*, pg. 1992
ADVANCE MEDICAL, INC.—See Teladoc Health, Inc.; *U.S. Public*, pg. 1992
ADVANCEMENT PROJECT; *U.S. Private*, pg. 93
ADVANCE METALS LIMITED; *Int'l*, pg. 156
ADVANCE METAL SUBSTRATE TECHNOLOGY SDN. BHD.—See Hexagon Holdings Berhad; *Int'l*, pg. 3370
ADVANCE METERING TECHNOLOGY LIMITED; *Int'l*, pg. 156
ADVANCE MOLD & MANUFACTURING INC.—See Flex Ltd.; *Int'l*, pg. 2703
ADVANCE MOTION CONTROL SYSTEMS PVT LTD—See THK CO., LTD.; *Int'l*, pg. 7711
ADVANCE MULTITECH LTD.; *Int'l*, pg. 156
ADVANCE NOTICE, INC.; *U.S. Private*, pg. 83
ADVANCEONLINE SOLUTIONS, INC.—See 360training.com, Inc.; *U.S. Private*, pg. 8
ADVANCE OPTICAL—See EssilorLuxottica SA; *Int'l*, pg. 2513
ADVANCE PACIFIC HOLDINGS LIMITED—See Tan Chong International Limited; *Int'l*, pg. 7452
ADVANCE PACKAGING CORPORATION; *U.S. Private*, pg. 84
ADVANCE PACKAGING LIMITED—See Alco Holdings Limited; *Int'l*, pg. 301
ADVANCE PAPER BOX COMPANY; *U.S. Private*, pg. 84
ADVANCE PETROCHEMICALS LIMITED - AHMEDABAD WORKS—See Advance Petrochemicals Limited; *Int'l*, pg. 156
ADVANCE PETROCHEMICALS LIMITED; *Int'l*, pg. 156
ADVANCE PETROLEUM DISTRIBUTING CO.; *U.S. Private*, pg. 84
ADVANCE PETROLEUM, INC.—See World Kinect Corporation; *U.S. Public*, pg. 2380
ADVANCE PETROLEUM SERVICES LTD.—See Dabbagh Group Holding Company Ltd.; *Int'l*, pg. 1902
ADVANCEPIERRE FOODS HOLDINGS, INC.—See Tyson Foods, Inc.; *U.S. Public*, pg. 2209
ADVANCEPIERRE FOODS, INC.—See Tyson Foods, Inc.; *U.S. Public*, pg. 2209
ADVANCE PLANNING LIMITED—See Dignity plc; *Int'l*, pg. 2124
ADVANCE POLYBAG INC.; *U.S. Private*, pg. 84
ADVANCE POWER & TRADING GMBH—See Advance Metering Technology Limited; *Int'l*, pg. 156
ADVANCE PREFAB COMPANY LIMITED—See Nawarat Patanakarn Public Company Limited; *Int'l*, pg. 5177
ADVANCE PRODUCTS CORPORATION—See Industrial Innovations, Inc.; *U.S. Private*, pg. 2066
ADVANCE PUBLICATIONS, INC.; *U.S. Private*, pg. 84
ADVANCE PUBLICATIONS—See Advance Publications, Inc.; *U.S. Private*, pg. 84
ADVANCE REALTY GROUP, LLC; *U.S. Private*, pg. 87
ADVANCE RESIDENCE INVESTMENT CORPORATION; *Int'l*, pg. 87
ADVANCERETAIL TECHNOLOGY ASIA SDN BHD—See 3Q Holdings Limited; *Int'l*, pg. 9
ADVANCERETAIL TECHNOLOGY LIMITED—See 3Q Holdings Limited; *Int'l*, pg. 9
ADVANCER GLOBAL LIMITED; *Int'l*, pg. 163
ADVANCE RIKO, INC.—See ULVAC, Inc.; *Int'l*, pg. 8020
ADVANCE RIKO, INC.—See CHINO Corporation; *Int'l*, pg. 1570
ADVANCE ROSS ELECTRONICS CORPORATION—See Chartwell Investments; *U.S. Private*, pg. 859
ADVANCER SMART TECHNOLOGY PTE. LTD.—See Advancer Global Limited; *Int'l*, pg. 163
ADVANCE SALES & MARKETING INC.; *U.S. Private*, pg. 87
ADVANCE STEEL CO.; *U.S. Private*, pg. 87
ADVANCE SYNERGY BERHAD; *Int'l*, pg. 156
ADVANCE SYNERGY REALTY SDN. BHD.—See Advance Synergy Berhad; *Int'l*, pg. 156
ADVANCE SYNTEX LIMITED; *Int'l*, pg. 157

ADVANCE TABCO, INC.—See Kinplex Corp.; *U.S. Private*, pg. 2313
ADVANCE TABCO, INC. - TEXAS—See Kinplex Corp.; *U.S. Private*, pg. 2313
AD-VANCE TALENT SOLUTIONS, INC.; *U.S. Private*, pg. 72
ADVANCE TANK & CONSTRUCTION CO. INC.; *U.S. Private*, pg. 87
ADVANCETC LIMITED; *Int'l*, pg. 163
ADVANCE TECHNOLOGY, INC.—See Comfort Systems USA, Inc.; *U.S. Public*, pg. 543
ADVANCETEC INDUSTRIES INC.; *U.S. Private*, pg. 93
ADVANCETEK ENTERPRISE CO., LTD.; *Int'l*, pg. 163
ADVANCE TERRAFUND REIT; *Int'l*, pg. 157
ADVANCE THERMAL CORP.—See Transco Inc.; *U.S. Private*, pg. 4207
ADVANCE TOOLING CONCEPTS, LLC—See ARC Group Worldwide, Inc.; *U.S. Public*, pg. 179
ADVANCE TRADING INC.; *U.S. Private*, pg. 87
ADVANCE TURNING & MANUFACTURING, INC.; *U.S. Private*, pg. 87
ADVANCE YOUR REACH LLC; *U.S. Private*, pg. 87
ADVANCE ZINTECK LIMITED; *Int'l*, pg. 157
ADVANCIA CORPORATION; *U.S. Private*, pg. 93
ADVANCIAL FEDERAL CREDIT UNION; *U.S. Private*, pg. 93
ADVANCING EYECARE HOLDINGS, INC.—See Atlantic Street Capital Management LLC; *U.S. Private*, pg. 374
ADVANCING NATIVE MISSIONS; *U.S. Private*, pg. 93
ADVANET INC.—See Eurotech S.p.A.; *Int'l*, pg. 2558
ADVANEX AMERICAS, INC.—See Advanex Inc.; *Int'l*, pg. 163
ADVANEX (CHANGZHOU) INC.—See Advanex Inc.; *Int'l*, pg. 163
ADVANEX CZECH REPUBLIC S.R.O.—See Advanex Inc.; *Int'l*, pg. 163
ADVANEX (DALIAN) INC.—See Advanex Inc.; *Int'l*, pg. 163
ADVANEX DE MEXICO S. DE R.L. DE C.V.—See Advanex Inc.; *Int'l*, pg. 163
ADVANEX DEUTSCHLAND GMBH—See Advanex Inc.; *Int'l*, pg. 163
ADVANEX (DONGGUAN) INC.—See Advanex Inc.; *Int'l*, pg. 163
ADVANEX EUROPE LTD—See Advanex Inc.; *Int'l*, pg. 163
ADVANEX EUROPE LTD.—See Advanex Inc.; *Int'l*, pg. 163
ADVANEX (HK) LTD.—See Advanex Inc.; *Int'l*, pg. 163
ADVANEX INC.; *Int'l*, pg. 163
ADVANEX (INDIA) PRIVATE LIMITED—See Advanex Inc.; *Int'l*, pg. 163
ADVANEX PRECISION COMPONENTS (DALIAN) CO., LTD.—See Advanex Inc.; *Int'l*, pg. 163
ADVANEX PRECISION COMPONENTS (DONGGUAN) CO., LTD.—See Advanex Inc.; *Int'l*, pg. 163
ADVANEX (SINGAPORE) PTE. LTD.—See Advanex Inc.; *Int'l*, pg. 163
ADVANEX (THAILAND) LTD.—See Advanex Inc.; *Int'l*, pg. 163
ADVANEX (VIETNAM) LTD.—See Advanex Inc.; *Int'l*, pg. 163
ADVANFACILITIES CO., LTD.—See Advantest Corporation; *Int'l*, pg. 165
AD VAN GELOVEN BV—See McCain Foods Limited; *Int'l*, pg. 4756
ADVAN GROUP CO., LTD.; *Int'l*, pg. 155
ADVANIA HOLDING HF—See Enterprise Investment Fund slhf.; *Int'l*, pg. 2451
ADVANIDE GMBH—See Development Bank of Japan, Inc.; *Int'l*, pg. 2087
ADVANIDE GMBH—See RISA Partners, Inc.; *Int'l*, pg. 6348
ADVANIDE INC.—See Development Bank of Japan, Inc.; *Int'l*, pg. 2087
ADVANIDE INC.—See RISA Partners, Inc.; *Int'l*, pg. 6349
ADVANIDE PTE. LTD.—See Development Bank of Japan, Inc.; *Int'l*, pg. 2087
ADVANIDE PTE. LTD.—See RISA Partners, Inc.; *Int'l*, pg. 6348
ADVANI HOTELS & RESORTS (INDIA) LIMITED; *Int'l*, pg. 164
ADVAN INT'L CORP.—See Barco N.V.; *Int'l*, pg. 863
ADVANIXS CORPORATION—See Advantech Co., Ltd.; *Int'l*, pg. 164
ADVANSA PTY. LTD.; *Int'l*, pg. 164
ADVANSIA AS—See AFRY AB; *Int'l*, pg. 194
ADVANSIX INC.; *U.S. Public*, pg. 49
ADVANSIX'S HOPEWELL FACILITY—See Honeywell International Inc.; *U.S. Public*, pg. 1047
ADVANSOFT DEVELOPMENT CORPORATION—See Advantest Corporation; *Int'l*, pg. 165
ADVANSOFT INTERNATIONAL INC.; *U.S. Private*, pg. 93
ADVANSOR A/S—See Dover Corporation; *U.S. Public*, pg. 678
ADVANSTAR COMMUNICATIONS INC.—See Informa plc; *U.S. Public*, pg. 3694
ADVANTA ENTERPRISES LIMITED—See UPL Limited; *Int'l*, pg. 8088

ADVANTAGE ACADEMY OF MIAMI INC.; *U.S. Private*, pg. 93
AD-VANTAGE ADVERTISING; *U.S. Private*, pg. 72
ADVANTAGE AVIATION TECHNOLOGIES, INC.; *U.S. Private*, pg. 93
ADVANTAGE BARRICADE AND ROADMARKS, LLC—See Kohlberg & Company, LLC; *U.S. Private*, pg. 2337
ADVANTAGE BENEFIT SOLUTIONS; *U.S. Private*, pg. 94
ADVANTAGE BMW CLEAR LAKE—See Group 1 Automotive, Inc.; *U.S. Public*, pg. 970
ADVANTAGE BMW MIDTOWN—See Group 1 Automotive, Inc.; *U.S. Public*, pg. 970
ADVANTAGE BUSINESS MEDIA LLC—See Owner Resource Group, LLC; *U.S. Private*, pg. 3055
ADVANTAGE CAPITAL CORPORATION; *U.S. Private*, pg. 94
ADVANTAGE CAPITAL FUNDS LLC; *U.S. Private*, pg. 94
ADVANTAGECARS.COM, INC.—See Group 1 Automotive, Inc.; *U.S. Public*, pg. 970
ADVANTAGE CHEVROLET OF BOLINGBROOK, INC.—See General Motors Company; *U.S. Public*, pg. 923
ADVANTAGE COMMUNICATIONS GROUP, LLC; *U.S. Private*, pg. 94
ADVANTAGE COMMUNICATIONS, INC.; *Int'l*, pg. 164
ADVANTAGECOM NETWORKS, INC.—See Cloud Equity Group, LLC; *U.S. Private*, pg. 946
THE ADVANTAGE COMPANY; *U.S. Private*, pg. 3982
ADVANTAGE COMP. INC.; *U.S. Private*, pg. 94
ADVANTAGE COMPUTING SYSTEMS INC.; *U.S. Private*, pg. 94
ADVANTAGE CORPORATE COMMUNICATIONS GMBH—See Omnicom Group Inc.; *U.S. Public*, pg. 1583
ADVANTAGE DATA INC.—See Solve Advisors Inc.; *U.S. Private*, pg. 3711
ADVANTAGED CANADIAN HIGH YIELD BOND FUND—See The Bank of Nova Scotia; *Int'l*, pg. 7617
ADVANTAGE DISPOSAL SOLUTIONS, INC.; *U.S. Private*, pg. 94
ADVANTAGE ENERGY LTD.; *Int'l*, pg. 164
ADVANTAGE ENGINEERING INCORPORATED; *U.S. Private*, pg. 94
ADVANTAGE FINANCE LTD.—See S&U PLC; *Int'l*, pg. 6445
ADVANTAGE FIRE SPRINKLER CO., INC.—See FirstService Corporation; *Int'l*, pg. 2691
ADVANTAGE FORWARDERS INC.—See Stevens Group, Inc.; *U.S. Private*, pg. 3809
ADVANTAGE FUNDING CORPORATION; *U.S. Private*, pg. 94
ADVANTAGE FUNDING MANAGEMENT CO., INC.—See Sterling Bancorp; *U.S. Public*, pg. 1946
ADVANTAGE HEALTHCARE, INC.—See Arsenal Capital Management LP; *U.S. Private*, pg. 338
ADVANTAGE HOUSING INC.; *U.S. Private*, pg. 94
ADVANTAGE INC.—See C.S. Wo & Sons Ltd.; *U.S. Private*, pg. 709
ADVANTAGE INDUSTRIAL AUTOMATION INC.—See Graybar Electric Company, Inc.; *U.S. Private*, pg. 1760
ADVANTAGE INSURANCE INC.; *U.S. Private*, pg. 94
ADVANTAGE INVESTMENT PARTNERS A/S—See PATRIZIA SE; *Int'l*, pg. 5758
ADVANTAGE LABEL & PACKAGING, INC.—See UFP Industries, Inc.; *U.S. Public*, pg. 2218
ADVANTAGE LITHIUM CORP.—See Allkem Limited; *Int'l*, pg. 359
ADVANTAGE LOGISTICS - SOUTHEAST—See United Natural Foods, Inc.; *U.S. Public*, pg. 2231
ADVANTAGE LOGISTICS - SOUTHWEST—See United Natural Foods, Inc.; *U.S. Public*, pg. 2231
ADVANTAGE LOGISTICS USA, INC.—See United Natural Foods, Inc.; *U.S. Public*, pg. 2231
ADVANTAGE L.P.; *U.S. Private*, pg. 94
ADVANTAGE MANUFACTURING CORP.—See ASSA ABLOY AB; *Int'l*, pg. 639
ADVANTAGE MARKETING, INC.; *U.S. Private*, pg. 94
ADVANTAGE MEDIA GROUP, INC.; *U.S. Private*, pg. 94
ADVANTAGE MEDIA SERVICES, INC.—See Fort Point Capital, LLC; *U.S. Private*, pg. 1574
ADVANTAGE MEDICAL GROUP, LLC—See Elevance Health, Inc.; *U.S. Public*, pg. 728
ADVANTAGE MEDICAL, INC.—See Ares Management Corporation; *U.S. Public*, pg. 188
ADVANTAGE METALS RECYCLING, LLC—See Nucor Corporation; *U.S. Public*, pg. 1554
AD-VANTAGENET, INC.; *U.S. Private*, pg. 72
ADVANTAGE NURSING SERVICES, INC.; *U.S. Private*, pg. 94
ADVANTAGE ON CALL, LLC—See Cross Country Healthcare, Inc.; *U.S. Public*, pg. 595
ADVANTAGE PARTNERS LLP; *Int'l*, pg. 164
ADVANTAGE PAYROLL SERVICES INC.—See Paychex, Inc.; *U.S. Public*, pg. 1655
ADVANTAGE PERFORMANCE GROUP—See BTS Group AB; *Int'l*, pg. 1205
ADVANTAGE PERSONNEL CONSULTANTS, INC.; *U.S. Private*, pg. 95

ADVANTAGE REHABILITATION CLINICS, INC.—See Select Medical Holdings Corporation; *U.S. Public*, pg. 1857
ADVANTAGE RENT A CAR—See The Catalyst Capital Group Inc.; *Int'l*, pg. 7630
ADVANTAGE RESOURCING AMERICA, INC.—See Recruit Holdings Co., Ltd.; *Int'l*, pg. 6240
ADVANTAGE RISK MANAGEMENT CO.,LTD.; *Int'l*, pg. 164
ADVANTAGE RN, LLC—See Cross Country Healthcare, Inc.; *U.S. Public*, pg. 595
ADVANTAGE SALES & MARKETING, LLC - GRAND RAPIDS—See Leonard Green & Partners, L.P.; *U.S. Private*, pg. 2423
ADVANTAGE SALES & MARKETING, LLC - RENTON—See Leonard Green & Partners, L.P.; *U.S. Private*, pg. 2423
ADVANTAGE SALES & MARKETING, LLC - SCHAUMBURG—See Leonard Green & Partners, L.P.; *U.S. Private*, pg. 2423
ADVANTAGE SALES & MARKETING LLC—See Leonard Green & Partners, L.P.; *U.S. Private*, pg. 2423
ADVANTAGE SALES & MARKETING, LLC; *U.S. Private*, pg. 95
ADVANTAGE SALES & MARKETING, LLC - WOODCLIFF LAKE—See Leonard Green & Partners, L.P.; *U.S. Private*, pg. 2423
ADVANTAGE SALES & MARKETING - SAN ANTONIO—See Leonard Green & Partners, L.P.; *U.S. Private*, pg. 2423
ADVANTAGE SCI; *U.S. Private*, pg. 95
ADVANTAGE SOLUTIONS INC.; *U.S. Public*, pg. 49
ADVANTAGE STAFFING; *U.S. Private*, pg. 95
ADVANTAGE STEEL SERVICE, INC.—See JM Walker LP; *U.S. Private*, pg. 2214
ADVANTAGE SYSTEMS INC.—See NCH Corporation; *U.S. Private*, pg. 2875
ADVANTAGE TANK LINES LLC—See Ontario Municipal Employees Retirement System; *Int'l*, pg. 5584
ADVANTAGE TECHNOLOGIES CONSULTING, INC.; *U.S. Private*, pg. 95
ADVANTAGE TITLE OF FT. BEND, LC—See Stewart Information Services Corporation; *U.S. Public*, pg. 1947
ADVANTAGE TRAILER COMPANY—See Wind Point Advisors LLC; *U.S. Private*, pg. 4533
ADVANTAGE TRANSPORT, INC.—See The Jordan Company, L.P.; *U.S. Private*, pg. 4061
ADVANTAGE TRAVEL LLC; *U.S. Private*, pg. 95
ADVANTAGE WAYPOINT LLC—See Prospect Hill Growth Partners, L.P.; *U.S. Private*, pg. 3288
ADVANTAGE WHEATS PTY LTD—See Corteva, Inc.; *U.S. Public*, pg. 581
ADVANTAGEWON OIL CORP.; *Int'l*, pg. 164
ADVANTAGE Y&R—See WPP plc; *Int'l*, pg. 8491
ADVANTA INSURANCE PARTNERS; *U.S. Private*, pg. 93
ADVANTA MAURITIUS LIMITED—See UPL Limited; *Int'l*, pg. 8088
ADVANTAR LABORATORIES, INC.—See Eurofins Scientific S.E.; *Int'l*, pg. 2548
ADVANTA SEEDS PTY. LTD.—See UPL Limited; *Int'l*, pg. 8088
ADVANTA SEEDS ROMANIA S.R.L.—See UPL Limited; *Int'l*, pg. 8088
ADVANTA SEMILLAS S.A.I.C.—See UPL Limited; *Int'l*, pg. 8088
ADVANTA US, LLC—See UPL Limited; *Int'l*, pg. 8088
ADVANTECH ADVANCED MICROWAVE TECHNOLOGIES INC.; *Int'l*, pg. 164
ADVANTECH AUSTRALIA PTY. LIMITED—See Advantech Co., Ltd.; *Int'l*, pg. 164
ADVANTECH AUTOMATION CORP.—See Advantech Co., Ltd.; *Int'l*, pg. 164
ADVANTECH B&B SMARTWORX S.R.O.—See Advantech Co., Ltd.; *Int'l*, pg. 165
ADVANTECH BRAZIL LTDA.—See Advantech Co., Ltd.; *Int'l*, pg. 164
ADVANTECH CO., LTD.; *Int'l*, pg. 164
ADVANTECH CO. MALAYSIA SDN. BHD.—See Advantech Co., Ltd.; *Int'l*, pg. 164
ADVANTECH CORPORATION—See Advantech Co., Ltd.; *Int'l*, pg. 164
ADVANTECH CORPORATION (THAILAND) CO., LTD.—See Advantech Co., Ltd.; *Int'l*, pg. 164
ADVANTECH CO. SINGAPORE PTE. LTD.—See Advantech Co., Ltd.; *Int'l*, pg. 164
ADVANTECH CZECH S.R.O.—See Advantech Co., Ltd.; *Int'l*, pg. 164
ADVANTECH ELECTRONICS, S.DE R.L.DE C.—See Advantech Co., Ltd.; *Int'l*, pg. 164
ADVANTECH EMBEDDED EPLATFORM GROUP—See Advantech Co., Ltd.; *Int'l*, pg. 164
ADVANTECH EUROPE B.V.—See Advantech Co., Ltd.; *Int'l*, pg. 164
ADVANTECH EUROPE HOLDING B.V—See Advantech Co., Ltd.; *Int'l*, pg. 164
ADVANTECH JAPAN CO., LTD.—See Advantech Co., Ltd.; *Int'l*, pg. 164
ADVANTECH POLAND SP Z O.O.—See Advantech Co., Ltd.; *Int'l*, pg. 164

COMPANY NAME INDEX

ADVANTECH RAISER INDIA PRIVATE LIMITED—See Advantech Co., Ltd.; *Int'l*, pg. 165
ADVANTECH TECHNOLOGIES LTD.; *Int'l*, pg. 165
ADVANTECH TECHNOLOGY (CHINA) COMPANY LTD.—See Advantech Co., Ltd.; *Int'l*, pg. 165
ADVANTECH TURKEY TEKNOLOJI AS—See Advantech Co., Ltd.; *Int'l*, pg. 165
ADVANTECH VIETNAM TECHNOLOGY COMPANY LIMITED—See Advantech Co., Ltd.; *Int'l*, pg. 165
ADVANTECH WIRELESS TECHNOLOGIES (USA) INC.—See Baylin Technologies Inc.; *Int'l*, pg. 914
ADVANT-E CORPORATION; *U.S. Public*, pg. 49
ADVANTEDGE HEALTHCARE SOLUTIONS, INC.; *U.S. Private*, pg. 95
ADVANTEGO CORPORATION; *U.S. Private*, pg. 95
ADVANTEK INC.—See Cornell Capital LLC; *U.S. Private*, pg. 1051
ADVANTEST ACADEMY, KK.—See Advantest Corporation; *Int'l*, pg. 165
ADVANTEST AMERICA INC.—See Advantest Corporation; *Int'l*, pg. 165
ADVANTEST - BOBLINGEN—See Advantest Corporation; *Int'l*, pg. 165
ADVANTEST CANADA, INC.—See Advantest Corporation; *Int'l*, pg. 165
ADVANTEST (CHINA) CO., LTD.—See Advantest Corporation; *Int'l*, pg. 165
ADVANTEST COMPONENT, INC. - SENDAI FACTORY—See Advantest Corporation; *Int'l*, pg. 165
ADVANTEST COMPONENT, INC.—See Advantest Corporation; *Int'l*, pg. 165
ADVANTEST CORPORATION - GUNMA FACTORY 2—See Advantest Corporation; *Int'l*, pg. 166
ADVANTEST CORPORATION - GUNMA FACTORY—See Advantest Corporation; *Int'l*, pg. 165
ADVANTEST CORPORATION; *Int'l*, pg. 165
ADVANTEST-ENGINEERING (MALAYSIA) SDN. BHD.—See Advantest Corporation; *Int'l*, pg. 165
ADVANTEST (EUROPE) GMBH—See Advantest Corporation; *Int'l*, pg. 165
ADVANTEST EUROPE R&D S.A.R.L.—See Advantest Corporation; *Int'l*, pg. 165
ADVANTEST EUROPE SYSTEMS GMBH—See Advantest Corporation; *Int'l*, pg. 165
ADVANTEST FINANCE INC—See Advantest Corporation; *Int'l*, pg. 166
ADVANTEST FRANCE SAS—See Advantest Corporation; *Int'l*, pg. 166
ADVANTEST GREEN CORPORATION—See Advantest Corporation; *Int'l*, pg. 166
ADVANTEST ISRAEL LTD.—See Advantest Corporation; *Int'l*, pg. 166
ADVANTEST ITALIA S.R.L.—See Advantest Corporation; *Int'l*, pg. 166
ADVANTEST KOREA CO., LTD.—See Advantest Corporation; *Int'l*, pg. 166
ADVANTEST KYUSHU SYSTEMS CO., LTD—See Advantest Corporation; *Int'l*, pg. 166
ADVANTEST LABORATORIES LTD—See Advantest Corporation; *Int'l*, pg. 166
ADVANTEST (MALAYSIA) SDN. BHD.—See Advantest Corporation; *Int'l*, pg. 166
ADVANTEST MEDIA SERVICE CORPORATION—See Advantest Corporation; *Int'l*, pg. 166
ADVANTEST (M) SDN. BHD.—See Advantest Corporation; *Int'l*, pg. 165
ADVANTEST PHILIPPINES, INC.—See Advantest Corporation; *Int'l*, pg. 165
ADVANTEST PRE-OWNED SOLUTIONS CO., LTD.—See Advantest Corporation; *Int'l*, pg. 166
ADVANTEST SALES & SUPPORT (M) SDN. BHD.—See Advantest Corporation; *Int'l*, pg. 166
ADVANTEST SHANGHAI CO., LTD.—See Advantest Corporation; *Int'l*, pg. 166
ADVANTEST (SINGAPORE) PTE. LTD.—See Advantest Corporation; *Int'l*, pg. 165
ADVANTEST (SUZHOU) CO., LTD.—See Advantest Corporation; *Int'l*, pg. 165
ADVANTEST SYSTEMS CORPORATION—See Advantest Corporation; *Int'l*, pg. 166
ADVANTEST TAIWAN, INC.—See Advantest Corporation; *Int'l*, pg. 166
ADVANTEST TECHNOLOGY (SHANGHAI) CO., LTD.—See Advantest Corporation; *Int'l*, pg. 166
ADVANTEST TEST SOLUTIONS, INC.—See Advantest Corporation; *Int'l*, pg. 166
ADVANTEST (THAILAND) LTD.—See Advantest Corporation; *Int'l*, pg. 165
ADVANTEST VIETNAM CO., LTD.—See Advantest Corporation; *Int'l*, pg. 166
ADVANTEX DINING CORPORATION—See Advantex Marketing International Inc.; *Int'l*, pg. 166
ADVANTEX MARKETING CORPORATION—See Advantex Marketing International Inc.; *Int'l*, pg. 166
ADVANTEX MARKETING INTERNATIONAL INC.; *Int'l*, pg. 166
ADVANTEX PROFESSIONAL SERVICES—See Kimco Staffing Services Inc.; *U.S. Private*, pg. 2305
ADVANTEX; *U.S. Private*, pg. 95
ADVANTICA; *U.S. Private*, pg. 95
ADVANTICO GMBH—See Compagnie Generale des Etablissements Michelin SCA; *Int'l*, pg. 1741
ADVANTICOM, INC.; *U.S. Private*, pg. 95
ADVANTI RACING USA, LLC—See YHI International Limited; *Int'l*, pg. 8580
ADVANTIS CREDIT LIMITED—See Bain Capital, LP; *U.S. Private*, pg. 433
ADVANTIS CREDIT UNION; *U.S. Private*, pg. 95
ADVANTIS GLOBAL, INC.; *U.S. Private*, pg. 95
ADVANTIS INTASL BANGLADESH (PVT) LTD.—See Hayleys PLC; *Int'l*, pg. 3291
ADVANTIS KUSUHARA SEDATE MYANMAR (PVT) LTD.—See Hayleys PLC; *Int'l*, pg. 3291
ADVANTIS SABANG RAYA LINES PTE. LTD.—See Hayleys PLC; *Int'l*, pg. 3291
ADVANTIVE LLC; *U.S. Private*, pg. 95
ADVANTIX SOLUTIONS GROUP, INC.—See ScanSource, Inc.; *U.S. Public*, pg. 1843
ADVANTIX SYSTEMS; *U.S. Private*, pg. 95
ADVANTOR HOLDING CORPORATION; *U.S. Private*, pg. 95
ADVANTOR SYSTEMS CORPORATION—See V2X, Inc.; *U.S. Public*, pg. 2270
ADVANTUS CAPITAL MANAGEMENT, INC.—See Securian Financial Group, Inc.; *U.S. Private*, pg. 3594
ADVANTUS CORPORATION; *U.S. Private*, pg. 95
ADVANZ FIDELIS IP SDN BHD—See Adamantem Capital Management Pty Limited; *Int'l*, pg. 123
ADVANZIA BANK S.A.—See Kistefos AS; *Int'l*, pg. 4192
ADVANZ PHARMA CORP. LIMITED; *Int'l*, pg. 166
ADVANZ PHARMA CORP.; *Int'l*, pg. 166
ADVA OPTICAL NETWORKING AB—See ADTRAN Holdings, Inc.; *U.S. Public*, pg. 44
ADVA OPTICAL NETWORKING AS—See ADTRAN Holdings, Inc.; *U.S. Public*, pg. 44
ADVA OPTICAL NETWORKING CORP.—See ADTRAN Holdings, Inc.; *U.S. Public*, pg. 44
ADVA OPTICAL NETWORKING HONG KONG, LTD.—See ADTRAN Holdings, Inc.; *U.S. Public*, pg. 44
ADVA OPTICAL NETWORKING (INDIA) PRIVATE LTD.—See ADTRAN Holdings, Inc.; *U.S. Public*, pg. 44
ADVA OPTICAL NETWORKING ISRAEL LTD—See ADTRAN Holdings, Inc.; *U.S. Public*, pg. 44
ADVA OPTICAL NETWORKING LTD.—See ADTRAN Holdings, Inc.; *U.S. Public*, pg. 44
ADVA OPTICAL NETWORKING NORTH AMERICA, INC. - CHATSWORTH—See ADTRAN Holdings, Inc.; *U.S. Public*, pg. 44
ADVA OPTICAL NETWORKING NORTH AMERICA, INC.—See ADTRAN Holdings, Inc.; *U.S. Public*, pg. 44
ADVA OPTICAL NETWORKING NORTH AMERICA, INC.—See ADTRAN Holdings, Inc.; *U.S. Public*, pg. 44
ADVA OPTICAL NETWORKING NORTH AMERICA, INC.—See ADTRAN Holdings, Inc.; *U.S. Public*, pg. 44
ADVA OPTICAL NETWORKING PTY LTD—See ADTRAN Holdings, Inc.; *U.S. Public*, pg. 44
ADVA OPTICAL NETWORKING SERVICOS BRAZIL LTDA.—See ADTRAN Holdings, Inc.; *U.S. Public*, pg. 44
ADVA OPTICAL NETWORKING SE—See ADTRAN Holdings, Inc.; *U.S. Public*, pg. 44
ADVA OPTICAL NETWORKING SE—See ADTRAN Holdings, Inc.; *U.S. Public*, pg. 44
ADVA OPTICAL NETWORKING SE—See ADTRAN Holdings, Inc.; *U.S. Public*, pg. 44
ADVA OPTICAL NETWORKING SE—See ADTRAN Holdings, Inc.; *U.S. Public*, pg. 44
ADVA OPTICAL NETWORKING SE—See ADTRAN Holdings, Inc.; *U.S. Public*, pg. 44
ADVA OPTICAL NETWORKING SE—See ADTRAN Holdings, Inc.; *U.S. Public*, pg. 44
ADVA OPTICAL NETWORKING (SHENZHEN) LTD—See ADTRAN Holdings, Inc.; *U.S. Public*, pg. 44
ADVA OPTICAL NETWORKING SINGAPORE PTE. LTD.—See ADTRAN Holdings, Inc.; *U.S. Public*, pg. 44
ADVA OPTICAL NETWORKING SP. Z.O.O.—See ADTRAN Holdings, Inc.; *U.S. Public*, pg. 44
ADVA OPTICAL NETWORKING TRADING (SHENZHEN) LTD.—See ADTRAN Holdings, Inc.; *U.S. Public*, pg. 44
ADVARIO SINGAPORE CHEMICAL PTE. LTD.—See Marquard & Bahls AG; *Int'l*, pg. 4700
ADVARIO SINGAPORE CHEMICAL PTE. LTD.—See Odfjell SE; *Int'l*, pg. 5526
ADVARRA, INC.—See Genstar Capital, LLC; *U.S. Private*, pg. 1673
ADVAZONE INTERNATIONAL LTD.—See Elitegroup Computer Systems Co., Ltd.; *Int'l*, pg. 2363
ADVECOR, INC.; *U.S. Private*, pg. 95
ADVEN EESTI AS—See AMP Limited; *Int'l*, pg. 432
ADVEN EESTI AS—See M&G Group Limited; *Int'l*, pg. 4612
ADVENICA AB; *Int'l*, pg. 166
ADVENIS; pg. 166
ADVEN OY—See AMP Limited; *Int'l*, pg. 432
ADVEN OY—See M&G Group Limited; *Int'l*, pg. 4612
ADVENS AG—See Alpiq Holding AG; *Int'l*, pg. 372
ADVENTA BERHAD—See Southern Capital Group Pte. Ltd.; *Int'l*, pg. 7118

ADVENTA HEALTH SDN. BHD.—See Southern Capital Group Pte. Ltd.; *Int'l*, pg. 7118
ADVENTA LOWE—See The Interpublic Group of Companies, Inc.; *U.S. Public*, pg. 2090
ADVENT-AWI HOLDINGS INC.; *U.S. Private*, pg. 167
ADVENT CAPITAL (HOLDINGS) PLC—See Fairfax Financial Holdings Limited; *Int'l*, pg. 2605
ADVENT COMPUTER SERVICES LTD.; *Int'l*, pg. 167
ADVENT CONVERTIBLE & INCOME FUND; *U.S. Public*, pg. 49
ADVENT DATA LIMITED—See DCC plc; *Int'l*, pg. 1989
ADVENT DO BRASIL CONSULTORIA E PARTICIPACOES LTDA.—See Advent International Corporation; *U.S. Private*, pg. 97
ADVENTECH, INC.; *U.S. Private*, pg. 108
ADVENT ELECTRIC, INC.; *U.S. Private*, pg. 95
ADVENT ENERGY LIMITED—See MEC Resources Limited; *Int'l*, pg. 4765
ADVENT FINANCIAL SERVICES—See Novation Companies, Inc.; *U.S. Public*, pg. 1548
ADVENT GLOBAL SOLUTIONS, INC.; *U.S. Private*, pg. 95
ADVENTHEALTH HEART OF FLORIDA—See Adventist Health System Sunbelt Healthcare Corporation; *U.S. Private*, pg. 108
ADVENTHEALTH OCALA—See Community Health Systems, Inc.; *U.S. Public*, pg. 550
ADVENT HEALTH PARTNERS, INC.—See Trend Health Partners LLC; *U.S. Private*, pg. 4218
ADVENTHEALTH SURGERY CENTER CELEBRATION, LLC—See Tenet Healthcare Corporation; *U.S. Public*, pg. 2009
ADVENTHEALTH SURGERY CENTER DAVENPORT, LLC—See Tenet Healthcare Corporation; *U.S. Public*, pg. 2001
ADVENTHEALTH SURGERY CENTER MILLS PARK, LLC—See Tenet Healthcare Corporation; *U.S. Public*, pg. 2001
ADVENTHEALTH SURGERY CENTER WELLSWOOD, LLC—See Tenet Healthcare Corporation; *U.S. Public*, pg. 2001
ADVENT INDIA PE ADVISORS PVT. LTD.—See Advent International Corporation; *U.S. Private*, pg. 97
ADVENT INTERNATIONAL ADVISORY S.L.—See Advent International Corporation; *U.S. Private*, pg. 97
ADVENT INTERNATIONAL COLUMBIA S.A.S.—See Advent International Corporation; *U.S. Private*, pg. 97
ADVENT INTERNATIONAL CORPORATION; *U.S. Private*, pg. 95
ADVENT INTERNATIONAL GMBH—See Advent International Corporation; *U.S. Private*, pg. 97
ADVENT INTERNATIONAL PE ADVISORS S.C—See Advent International Corporation; *U.S. Private*, pg. 97
ADVENT INTERNATIONAL PLC—See Advent International Corporation; *U.S. Private*, pg. 97
ADVENT INTERNATIONAL ROMANIA S.R.L.—See Advent International Corporation; *U.S. Private*, pg. 97
ADVENT INTERNATIONAL SAS—See Advent International Corporation; *U.S. Private*, pg. 97
ADVENT INTERNATIONAL (SHANGHAI) CO LTD.—See Advent International Corporation; *U.S. Private*, pg. 97
ADVENT INTERNATIONAL SP. Z.O.O. SP.K—See Advent International Corporation; *U.S. Private*, pg. 97
ADVENT INTERNATIONAL S.R.O—See Advent International Corporation; *U.S. Private*, pg. 97
ADVENTIS HEALTH LIMITED—See Reabold Resources Plc; *Int'l*, pg. 6230
ADVENTIST GLENOAKS HOSPITAL—See Adventist Health System Sunbelt Healthcare Corporation; *U.S. Private*, pg. 109
ADVENTIST HEALTHCARE; *U.S. Private*, pg. 109
ADVENTIST HEALTH CENTRAL VALLEY NETWORK—See Adventist Health System; *U.S. Private*, pg. 108
ADVENTIST HEALTH/HOME CARE & HOSPICE SERVICES - MENDOCINO COUNTY—See Adventist Health System; *U.S. Private*, pg. 108
ADVENTIST HEALTH SYSTEM; *U.S. Private*, pg. 108
ADVENTIST HEALTH SYSTEM SUNBELT HEALTHCARE CORPORATION; *U.S. Private*, pg. 108
ADVENTIST HINSDALE HOSPITAL—See Adventist Health System Sunbelt Healthcare Corporation; *U.S. Private*, pg. 109
ADVENTIST MIDWEST HEALTH—See Adventist Health System Sunbelt Healthcare Corporation; *U.S. Private*, pg. 108
ADVENTIST RISK MANAGEMENT INC.; *U.S. Private*, pg. 109
ADVENTURE MARKETING, INC.; *U.S. Private*, pg. 109
ADVENT, LLC; *U.S. Private*, pg. 108
ADVENT MARKETING INC.—See Advent-AWI Holdings Inc.; *U.S. Private*, pg. 167
ADVENT PHARMA LIMITED; *Int'l*, pg. 167
ADVENT PROCESS ENGINEERING INC.—See Vesuvius plc; *Int'l*, pg. 8178
ADVENT SOFTWARE APS—See SS&C Technologies Holdings, Inc.; *U.S. Public*, pg. 1922
ADVENT SOFTWARE, INC.—See SS&C Technologies Holdings, Inc.; *U.S. Public*, pg. 1922

ADVENT PHARMA LIMITED

ADVENT SOFTWARE (MIDDLE EAST) LIMITED—See SS&C Technologies Holdings, Inc.; *U.S. Public*, pg. 1922
ADVENT SOFTWARE (SINGAPORE) PTE. LTD—See SS&C Technologies Holdings, Inc.; *U.S. Public*, pg. 1922
ADVENT SWITZERLAND AG—See SS&C Technologies Holdings, Inc.; *U.S. Public*, pg. 1922
ADVENT SYSTEMS INC.—See Allied Universal Manager LLC; *U.S. Private*, pg. 191
ADVENT TECHNOLOGIES HOLDINGS, INC.; *U.S. Public*, pg. 49
ADVENTURE 16 INC.; *U.S. Private*, pg. 109
ADVENTURE BOUND ALASKA; *U.S. Private*, pg. 109
ADVENTURE CREDIT UNION; *U.S. Private*, pg. 109
ADVENTURE DESTINATIONS INTERNATIONAL—See Pic Investment Group Inc.; *Int'l*, pg. 5859
ADVENTURE INC.; *Int'l*, pg. 167
ADVENTURE INTERNATIONAL TOURS, INC.—See Transnational Diversified Group of Companies; *Int'l*, pg. 7902
ADVENTURE ISLAND—See United Parks & Resorts Inc.; *U.S. Public*, pg. 2234
ADVENTURE LANDS OF AMERICA, INC.; *U.S. Private*, pg. 109
ADVENTURE LIFE; *U.S. Private*, pg. 109
ADVENTURE LINE PRODUCTIONS S.A—See De Agostini S.p.A.; *Int'l*, pg. 1994
ADVENTURE PROPERTIES INC.; *U.S. Private*, pg. 109
AD VENTURE PUBLIC COMPANY LIMITED—See Advanced Info Service Plc; *Int'l*, pg. 159
ADVENTURES BY DISNEY—See The Walt Disney Company; *U.S. Public*, pg. 2138
ADVENTURES IN ADVERTISING FRANCHISE INC—See The Riverside Company; *U.S. Private*, pg. 4107
AD VENTURES, INC.; *U.S. Private*, pg. 72
ADVENTURES UNLIMITED CANOE RENTAL & SALES, INC.; *U.S. Private*, pg. 109
ADVENTURES WORLDWIDE LIMITED—See TUI AG; *Int'l*, pg. 7964
ADVENTURE TOURS AUSTRALIA GROUP PTY LTD—See TUI AG; *Int'l*, pg. 7963
ADVENTUS HOLDINGS LIMITED; *Int'l*, pg. 167
ADVENTUS MINING CORPORATION—See Silvercorp Metals Inc.; *Int'l*, pg. 6925
ADVENTZ GROUP; *Int'l*, pg. 167
ADVEO GROUP INTERNATIONAL, S.A.; *Int'l*, pg. 167
ADVEO ITALIA S. R. L.—See ADVEO Group International, S.A.; *Int'l*, pg. 167
ADVEQ INVESTMENT MANAGEMENT (BEIJING) CO., LTD.—See Schroders plc; *Int'l*, pg. 6640
ADVEQ MANAGEMENT (DEUTSCHLAND) GMBH—See Schroders plc; *Int'l*, pg. 6640
ADVEQ MANAGEMENT (HONG KONG) LIMITED—See Schroders plc; *Int'l*, pg. 6640
ADVEQ MANAGEMENT (UK) LIMITED—See Schroders plc; *Int'l*, pg. 6640
ADVEQ MANAGEMENT US, INC.—See Schroders plc; *Int'l*, pg. 6640
ADVEQ (SHANGHAI) EQUITY INVESTMENT MANAGEMENT CO., LTD.—See Schroders plc; *Int'l*, pg. 6640
ADVERIO PHARMA GMBH—See Bayer Aktiengesellschaft; *Int'l*, pg. 901
ADVERITAS LIMITED; *Int'l*, pg. 167
ADVERLINE S.A.—See La Poste S.A.; *Int'l*, pg. 4388
ADVERTEX COMMUNICATIONS INC.—See Macy's, Inc.; *U.S. Public*, pg. 1353
ADVERTISEMENT EDI CENTER INC.—See Dentsu Group Inc.; *Int'l*, pg. 2034
ADVERTISE PURPLE, INC.; *U.S. Private*, pg. 109
THE ADVERTISER COMPANY—See Gannett Co., Inc.; *U.S. Public*, pg. 900
ADVERTISERS PRESS INCORPORATED; *U.S. Private*, pg. 109
ADVERTISING AGE—See Crain Communications, Inc.; *U.S. Private*, pg. 1084
ADVERTISING AND PUBLICITY COMPANY SAOC—See Omar Zawawi Establishment LLC; *Int'l*, pg. 5561
ADVERTISING ASSOCIATES, INC.; *U.S. Private*, pg. 109
ADVERTISING ASSOCIATES INTERNATIONAL; *U.S. Private*, pg. 109
ADVERTISING CHECKING BUREAU INCORPORATED; *U.S. Private*, pg. 109
ADVERTISING CONNECTION INC.; *U.S. Private*, pg. 110
ADVERTISING DISTRIBUTORS OF AMERICA INC; *U.S. Private*, pg. 110
ADVERTISING INTERNATIONAL COMPANY LLC—See Omar Zawawi Establishment LLC; *Int'l*, pg. 5561
ADVERTISING SAVANTS, INC.; *U.S. Private*, pg. 110
THE ADVERTISING SPECIALTY INSTITUTE; *U.S. Private*, pg. 3982
ADVERTISING WORKS & PRODUCTION; *U.S. Private*, pg. 110
ADVERTUS D.O.O.—See Avtotehna, d.d.; *Int'l*, pg. 751
ADVERUM BIOTECHNOLOGIES, INC.; *U.S. Public*, pg. 50
THE ADVERTISING GROUP, INC.—See Equitable Holdings, Inc.; *U.S. Public*, pg. 790
ADVESTO GMBH—See OVB Holding AG; *Int'l*, pg. 5670

ADVETIS MEDICAL S.A.S.—See Vimian Group AB; *Int'l*, pg. 8208
AD VETPRODUKT; *Int'l*, pg. 122
ADVFINANCE SP. Z O.O.—See Grupa SMT S.A.; *Int'l*, pg. 3117
ADVFN PLC; *Int'l*, pg. 167
ADVIA CREDIT UNION; *U.S. Private*, pg. 110
ADVICE A/S; *Int'l*, pg. 168
ADVICE ELECTRONICS LTD.—See P-Duke Technology Co., Ltd.; *Int'l*, pg. 5681
ADVICE, INC.; *U.S. Private*, pg. 110
ADVICE INTERACTIVE GROUP LLC; *U.S. Private*, pg. 110
ADVICE MEDIA LLC; *U.S. Private*, pg. 110
ADVICENNE S.A.; *Int'l*, pg. 168
ADVICOM SP. Z O.O.—See Jastrzebska Spolka Weglowa S.A.; *Int'l*, pg. 3913
ADVICS ASIA PACIFIC CO., LTD.—See AISIN Corporation; *Int'l*, pg. 251
ADVICS CO., LTD.—See AISIN Corporation; *Int'l*, pg. 251
ADVICS MANUFACTURING INDIANA, L.L.C.—See AISIN Corporation; *Int'l*, pg. 251
ADVICS MANUFACTURING OHIO, INC.—See AISIN Corporation; *Int'l*, pg. 251
ADVICS NORTH AMERICA, INC.—See AISIN Corporation; *Int'l*, pg. 251
A&D VIETNAM LIMITED—See A&D Co., Ltd.; *Int'l*, pg. 19
ADVIK CAPITAL LTD; *Int'l*, pg. 168
ADVIK LABORATORIES LTD.; *Int'l*, pg. 168
ADVIK OPTOELECTRONICS LIMITED—See Advik Capital Ltd; *Int'l*, pg. 168
ADVILLE/USA; *U.S. Private*, pg. 110
ADVINI POLSKA, SP. Z O.O.—See AdVini S.A.; *Int'l*, pg. 168
ADVINI S.A.; *Int'l*, pg. 168
ADVINUS THERAPEUTICS LTD.—See Tata Sons Limited; *Int'l*, pg. 7468
ADVION, INC.—See Beijing Bohui Innovation Biotechnology Group Co., Ltd.; *Int'l*, pg. 946
ADVISEN LTD.—See Clearlake Capital Group, L.P.; *U.S. Private*, pg. 938
ADVISER INVESTMENT MANAGEMENT INC; *U.S. Private*, pg. 110
ADVISERS CAPITAL MANAGEMENT INC.; *U.S. Private*, pg. 110
ADVISORENGINE INC.—See Franklin Resources, Inc.; *U.S. Public*, pg. 879
ADVISOR GROUP, INC.—See Reverence Capital Partners LLC; *U.S. Private*, pg. 3414
ADVISORS ASSET MANAGEMENT, INC.—See Sun Life Financial Inc.; *Int'l*, pg. 7305
ADVISORS MORTGAGE GROUP, LLC; *U.S. Private*, pg. 110
ADVISOR-SOURCE NEWSPAPERS—See Alden Global Capital LLC; *U.S. Private*, pg. 155
THE ADVISORS RESOURCE, INC—See Bates Group LLC; *U.S. Private*, pg. 486
ADVISORSTREAM LTD.—See Broadridge Financial Solutions, Inc.; *U.S. Public*, pg. 391
THE ADVISORY BOARD COMPANY—See UnitedHealth Group Incorporated; *U.S. Public*, pg. 2248
ADVISORYCLOUD, INC.; *U.S. Private*, pg. 110
ADVISORY RESEARCH, INC.; *U.S. Private*, pg. 110
ADVISORYWORLD—See LPL Financial Holdings Inc.; *U.S. Public*, pg. 1343
ADVITAM BELGIUM—See VINCI S.A.; *Int'l*, pg. 8211
ADVITAM INC—See VINCI S.A.; *Int'l*, pg. 8211
ADVITAM SA—See VINCI S.A.; *Int'l*, pg. 8211
ADVITAM SOLUTIONS INC—See VINCI S.A.; *Int'l*, pg. 8211
ADVITAM SWITZERLAND—See VINCI S.A.; *Int'l*, pg. 8211
ADVITAM TAIWAN - PAA INTERNATIONAL ENG. CORP—See VINCI S.A.; *Int'l*, pg. 8211
ADVIUM CORPORATE FINANCE OY—See eQ Oyj; *Int'l*, pg. 2466
ADVIZE GREY—See WPP plc; *Int'l*, pg. 8469
ADVIZEX TECHNOLOGIES LLC; *U.S. Private*, pg. 110
ADVIZOR SOLUTIONS, INC.—See Allegiance Fundraising LLC; *U.S. Private*, pg. 176
ADVOC8, LLC; *U.S. Private*, pg. 110
ADVOCATE AURORA ENTERPRISES, INC.—See Advocate Health Care Network; *U.S. Private*, pg. 111
ADVOCATE BILLING LLC; *U.S. Private*, pg. 110
ADVOCATE CAPITAL, INC.—See Pinnacle Financial Partners, Inc.; *U.S. Public*, pg. 1692
ADVOCATE CHARITABLE FOUNDATION—See Advocate Health Care Network; *U.S. Private*, pg. 111
ADVOCATE COMMUNICATIONS INC.—See Schurz Communications, Inc.; *U.S. Private*, pg. 3571
ADVOCATE HEALTH CARE NETWORK; *U.S. Private*, pg. 110
ADVOCATE HOME CARE SERVICES; *U.S. Private*, pg. 111
ADVOCATE INSURANCE SERVICES CORP.—See Brown & Brown, Inc.; *U.S. Public*, pg. 396
ADVOCATE MEDIA; *U.S. Private*, pg. 111
ADVOCATE MEDICAL GROUP—See Advocate Health Care Network; *U.S. Private*, pg. 111

CORPORATE AFFILIATIONS

ADVOCATE NETWORKS, INC.—See Accenture plc; *Int'l*, pg. 86
THE ADVOCATE NEWSPAPER PROPRIETARY LIMITED—See Nine Entertainment Co. Holdings Limited; *Int'l*, pg. 5299
ADVOCATE PRINTING & PUBLISHING CO. LTD. - DARTMOUTH PLANT—See Advocate Printing & Publishing Co. Ltd.; *Int'l*, pg. 168
ADVOCATE PRINTING & PUBLISHING CO. LTD.; *Int'l*, pg. 168
ADVOCATE SHERMAN HOSPITAL, L.P.—See Community Health Systems, Inc.; *U.S. Public*, pg. 550
THE ADVOCATE—See Alden Global Capital LLC; *U.S. Private*, pg. 157
THE ADVOCATE—See Gannett Co., Inc.; *U.S. Public*, pg. 900
THE ADVOCATE—See The Hearst Corporation; *U.S. Private*, pg. 4048
ADVOCAT FINANCE, INC.—See Diversicare Healthcare Services, Inc.; *U.S. Public*, pg. 669
ADVOKATFIRMAET PRICEWATERHOUSECOOPERS AS; *Int'l*, pg. 168
ADVOKATFIRMAET SCHJODT AS; *Int'l*, pg. 168
ADV PHARMA ,INC.—See Standard Chem. & Pharm. Co., Ltd.; *Int'l*, pg. 7168
ADVTECH HOUSE—See ADvTECH Limited; *Int'l*, pg. 168
ADVTECH LIMITED; *Int'l*, pg. 168
ADVTECH RESOURCING (PTY) LTD - COMMUNICATE PERSONNEL DIVISION—See ADvTECH Limited; *Int'l*, pg. 168
ADVTECH RESOURCING (PTY) LTD - INSOURCE.ICT DIVISION—See ADvTECH Limited; *Int'l*, pg. 168
ADVTECH RESOURCING (PTY) LTD - IT EDGE DIVISION—See ADvTECH Limited; *Int'l*, pg. 168
ADVTECH RESOURCING (PTY) LTD - NETWORK RECRUITMENT DIVISION—See ADvTECH Limited; *Int'l*, pg. 168
ADVTECH RESOURCING (PTY) LTD - PRO REC RECRUITMENT DIVISION—See ADvTECH Limited; *Int'l*, pg. 168
ADVTECH RESOURCING (PTY) LTD—See ADvTECH Limited; *Int'l*, pg. 168
ADVTECH RESOURCING (PTY) LTD - TECH-PRO PERSONNEL DIVISION—See ADvTECH Limited; *Int'l*, pg. 168
ADW ACOSTA, LLC—See Acosta, Inc.; *U.S. Private*, pg. 64
ADWAYS CHINA CO., LTD.—See Adways Inc.; *Int'l*, pg. 169
ADWAYS FRONTIER INC.—See Adways Inc.; *Int'l*, pg. 169
ADWAYS INC.; *Int'l*, pg. 169
ADWAYS INTERACTIVE, INC.—See Adways Inc.; *Int'l*, pg. 169
ADWAYS KOREA, INC.—See Adways Inc.; *Int'l*, pg. 169
ADWAYS LABS (THAILAND) CO., LTD.—See Adways Inc.; *Int'l*, pg. 169
ADWAYS PHILIPPINES INC.—See Adways Inc.; *Int'l*, pg. 169
ADWAYS TECHNOLOGY CO., JSC.—See Adways Inc.; *Int'l*, pg. 169
ADWAYS VENTURES, INC.—See Adways Inc.; *Int'l*, pg. 169
ADWEEK, LLC—See Shamrock Capital Advisors, LLC; *U.S. Private*, pg. 3624
A&D WEIGHING PTY. LTD.—See A&D Co., Ltd.; *Int'l*, pg. 18
AD WEST END, LLC—See Prologis, Inc.; *U.S. Public*, pg. 1726
ADWEST TECHNOLOGIES, INC.—See CECO Environmental Corp.; *U.S. Public*, pg. 463
A.D. WILLIS COMPANY, INC.; *U.S. Public*, pg. 25
A.D. WINSTON CORPORATION; *U.S. Private*, pg. 25
A.D. WORKS CORPORATION; *Int'l*, pg. 23
A.D.WORKS GROUP CO., LTD.; *Int'l*, pg. 23
AD WORKSHOP; *U.S. Private*, pg. 72
ADWORKS, INC.; *U.S. Private*, pg. 111
ADX ENERGY LIMITED; *Int'l*, pg. 169
ADX ENERGY PANONIA SRL—See ADX Energy Limited; *Int'l*, pg. 169
ADX FIRE PROTECTION, INC.; *U.S. Private*, pg. 111
ADX VIE GMBH—See ADX Energy Limited; *Int'l*, pg. 169
ADYA INC.; *Int'l*, pg. 169
ADYARD ABU DHABI LLC—See Interserve Plc; *Int'l*, pg. 3759
ADYEN AUSTRALIA PTY LIMITED—See Adyen N.V.; *Int'l*, pg. 169
ADYEN CANADA LTD.—See Adyen N.V.; *Int'l*, pg. 169
ADYEN (CHINA) SOFTWARE TECHNOLOGY CO. LTD.—See Adyen N.V.; *Int'l*, pg. 169
ADYEN DO BRAZIL LTDA.—See Adyen N.V.; *Int'l*, pg. 170
ADYEN GMBH—See Adyen N.V.; *Int'l*, pg. 169
ADYEN HONG KONG LIMITED—See Adyen N.V.; *Int'l*, pg. 169
ADYEN IBERIA SLU—See Adyen N.V.; *Int'l*, pg. 169
ADYEN INC.—See Adyen N.V.; *Int'l*, pg. 169
ADYEN INDIA TECH HUB PVT. LTD.—See Adyen N.V.; *Int'l*, pg. 169
ADYEN INTERNATIONAL B.V.—See Adyen N.V.; *Int'l*, pg. 169

COMPANY NAME INDEX

ADYEN JAPAN K.K.—See Adyen N.V.; *Int'l*, pg. 169
ADYEN MEXICO, S.A. DE C.V.—See Adyen N.V.; *Int'l*, pg. 170
ADYEN NORDIC AB—See Adyen N.V.; *Int'l*, pg. 170
ADYEN N.V.; *Int'l*, pg. 169
ADYEN SINGAPORE PTE. LTD.—See Adyen N.V.; *Int'l*, pg. 170
ADYEN UK LIMITED—See Adyen N.V.; *Int'l*, pg. 170
ADYNXX, INC.; *U.S. Public*, pg. 50
ADYTON RESOURCES CORPORATION; *Int'l*, pg. 170
ADZAM INC.; *U.S. Private*, pg. 111
ADZURITE INC.—See Vertoz Advertising Limited; *Int'l*, pg. 8175
ADZURITE SOLUTIONS PRIVATE LIMITED—See Vertoz Advertising Limited; *Int'l*, pg. 8175
AEA-BRIDGES IMPACT CORP.; *Int'l*, pg. 170
AE ADVANCED FUELS, INC.—See Aemetis, Inc.; *U.S. Public*, pg. 52
AEA FEDERAL CREDIT UNION; *U.S. Private*, pg. 112
AEA INTERNATIONAL HOLDINGS PTE. LTD.; *Int'l*, pg. 170
AEA INTERNATIONAL SOS (CAMBODIA) LTD.—See Raffles Medical Group Ltd; *Int'l*, pg. 6177
AEA INVESTORS (ASIA) LIMITED—See AEA Investors LP; *U.S. Private*, pg. 113
AEA INVESTORS (GERMANY) GMBH—See AEA Investors LP; *U.S. Private*, pg. 113
AEA INVESTORS LP; *U.S. Private*, pg. 112
AEA INVESTORS (UK) LIMITED—See AEA Investors LP; *U.S. Private*, pg. 113
AEARO TECHNOLOGIES LLC—See 3M Company; *U.S. Public*, pg. 8
AEAS NETHERLANDS B.V.—See Titan Cement Company S.A.; *Int'l*, pg. 7759
A&E BANGLADESH LTD.—See Platinum Equity, LLC; *U.S. Private*, pg. 3201
A.E. BARNES INSURANCE AGENCY, INC.—See Cross Financial Corporation; *U.S. Private*, pg. 1104
AEBI & CO. AG MASCHINENFABRIK—See Aebi Schmidt Holding AG; *Int'l*, pg. 170
AEB INTERNATIONAL INC.; *U.S. Private*, pg. 116
AEBI SCHMIDT AUSTRIA GMBH—See Aebi Schmidt Holding AG; *Int'l*, pg. 170
AEBI SCHMIDT BELGIUM—See Aebi Schmidt Holding AG; *Int'l*, pg. 170
AEBI SCHMIDT DEUTSCHLAND GMBH—See Aebi Schmidt Holding AG; *Int'l*, pg. 170
AEBI SCHMIDT HOLDING AG; *Int'l*, pg. 170
AEBI SCHMIDT IBERICA S.A.—See Aebi Schmidt Holding AG; *Int'l*, pg. 170
AEBI SCHMIDT INTERNATIONAL AG—See Aebi Schmidt Holding AG; *Int'l*, pg. 170
AEBI SCHMIDT ITALIA S.R.L.—See Aebi Schmidt Holding AG; *Int'l*, pg. 170
AEBI SCHMIDT NEDERLAND BV—See Aebi Schmidt Holding AG; *Int'l*, pg. 170
AEBI SCHMIDT NORGE AS—See Aebi Schmidt Holding AG; *Int'l*, pg. 170
AEBI SCHMIDT POLSKA SP. Z O. O.—See Aebi Schmidt Holding AG; *Int'l*, pg. 170
AEBI SCHMIDT SWEDEN AB—See Aebi Schmidt Holding AG; *Int'l*, pg. 170
AEBI SCHMIDT UK LIMITED—See Aebi Schmidt Holding AG; *Int'l*, pg. 170
AEC BILINGUAL PTE LTD.—See AEC Education plc; *Int'l*, pg. 170
AECC AERO ENGINE CONTROL CO., LTD.; *Int'l*, pg. 171
AECC AERO SCIENCE & TECHNOLOGY CO., LTD.; *Int'l*, pg. 171
AECC AVIATION POWER CO., LTD.; *Int'l*, pg. 171
AEC CHINA LIMITED—See Ookami Limited; *Int'l*, pg. 5594
AEC COLLEGE PTE. LTD.—See AEC Education plc; *Int'l*, pg. 170
AECC SHANGHAI COMMERCIAL AIRCRAFT ENGINE MANUFACTURING CO.; *Int'l*, pg. 171
AECC TOTAL VISION HEALTH PLAN OF TEXAS, INC.—See Centene Corporation; *U.S. Public*, pg. 467
AEC EDUCATION PLC; *Int'l*, pg. 170
AEC EDU GROUP PTE LTD—See AEC Education plc; *Int'l*, pg. 170
AEC ENVIRONMENTAL PTY. LTD.—See WSP Global, Inc.; *Int'l*, pg. 8497
AEC GROUP, INC.; *U.S. Private*, pg. 116
AECI LIMITED; *Int'l*, pg. 171
AEC, INC.—See Harbour Group Industries, Inc.; *U.S. Private*, pg. 1860
AEC INTERNATIONAL S.R.L.—See Allis Electric Co., Ltd.; *Int'l*, pg. 359
AECOM BRASIL LTDA.—See AECOM; *U.S. Public*, pg. 50
AECOM CANADA—See AECOM; *U.S. Public*, pg. 50
AECOM CANADA—See AECOM; *U.S. Public*, pg. 50
AECOM C&E, INC.—See AECOM; *U.S. Public*, pg. 50
AECOM ENVIRONMENT—See AECOM; *U.S. Public*, pg. 50
AECOM ENVIRONMENT—See AECOM; *U.S. Public*, pg. 50
AECOM ENVIRONMENT—See AECOM; *U.S. Public*, pg. 51

AECOM GOVERNMENT SERVICES, INC.—See AECOM; *U.S. Public*, pg. 51
AECOM-LATHAM—See AECOM; *U.S. Public*, pg. 51
AECOM—See AECOM; *U.S. Public*, pg. 50
AECOM—See AECOM; *U.S. Public*, pg. 50
AECOM; *U.S. Public*, pg. 50
AECOM—See AECOM; *U.S. Public*, pg. 50
AECOM—See AECOM; *U.S. Public*, pg. 50
AECOM—See AECOM; *U.S. Public*, pg. 50
AECOM—See AECOM; *U.S. Public*, pg. 50
AECOM—See AECOM; *U.S. Public*, pg. 50
AECOM—See AECOM; *U.S. Public*, pg. 50
AECOM—See AECOM; *U.S. Public*, pg. 50
AECOM—See AECOM; *U.S. Public*, pg. 50
AECOM—See AECOM; *U.S. Public*, pg. 50
AECOM—See AECOM; *U.S. Public*, pg. 50
AECOM—See AECOM; *U.S. Public*, pg. 50
AECOM—See AECOM; *U.S. Public*, pg. 50
AECOM—See AECOM; *U.S. Public*, pg. 50
AECOM—See AECOM; *U.S. Public*, pg. 50
AECOM—See AECOM; *U.S. Public*, pg. 50
AECOM USA, INC.—See AECOM; *U.S. Public*, pg. 50
AECOM VENEZUELA—See AECOM; *U.S. Public*, pg. 51
AECON ATLANTIC INDUSTRIAL INC.—See Aecon Group Inc.; *Int'l*, pg. 172
AECON BUILDINGS—See Aecon Group Inc.; *Int'l*, pg. 172
AECON BUILDINGS—See Aecon Group Inc.; *Int'l*, pg. 172
AECON CONCESSIONS—See Aecon Group Inc.; *Int'l*, pg. 172
AECON CONSTRUCTION GROUP INC.—See Aecon Group Inc.; *Int'l*, pg. 172
AECON CONSTRUCTION MANAGEMENT INC.—See Aecon Group Inc.; *Int'l*, pg. 172
AECON CONSTRUCTION & MATERIALS LTD.—See Aecon Group Inc.; *Int'l*, pg. 172
AECON CONSTRUCTORS—See Aecon Group Inc.; *Int'l*, pg. 172
AECON GROUP INC.; *Int'l*, pg. 172
AECON INDUSTRIAL—See Aecon Group Inc.; *Int'l*, pg. 172
AECON INDUSTRIAL - WESTERN CANADA—See Aecon Group Inc.; *Int'l*, pg. 172
AECON INDUSTRIAL WESTERN INC.—See Aecon Group Inc.; *Int'l*, pg. 172
AECON INFRASTRUCTURE—See Aecon Group Inc.; *Int'l*, pg. 172
AECON MATERIALS ENGINEERING CORP.—See Aecon Group Inc.; *Int'l*, pg. 172
AECON MINING INC.—See Aecon Group Inc.; *Int'l*, pg. 172
AECON TRANSPORTATION WEST LTD.—See Aecon Group Inc.; *Int'l*, pg. 172
AECON UTILITIES—See Aecon Group Inc.; *Int'l*, pg. 172
AECON UTILITY ENGINEERING—See Aecon Group Inc.; *Int'l*, pg. 172
AE CORPORATION (M) SDN. BHD.—See AE Multi Holdings Berhad; *Int'l*, pg. 170
AECO TECHNOLOGY CO., LTD.—See WPG Holdings Limited; *Int'l*, pg. 8460
AEC RESOURCE DEVELOPMENT PTE LTD.—See AEC Education plc; *Int'l*, pg. 170
AEC SAS—See Draegerwerk AG & Co. KGaA; *Int'l*, pg. 2196
AEC SECURITIES PUBLIC COMPANY LIMITED; *Int'l*, pg. 171
AEDAN FINANCIAL CORP.; *U.S. Private*, pg. 116
AEDAS HOMES; *Int'l*, pg. 173
AE DESIGN, INC.—See Lemay Online; *Int'l*, pg. 4448
AEDES SIIQ S.P.A.; *Int'l*, pg. 173
AEDGE GROUP LIMITED; *Int'l*, pg. 173
AEDIAN SA—See Aubay SA; *Int'l*, pg. 698
AEDIFICA INVEST SA—See Aedifica SA; *Int'l*, pg. 173
AEDIFICA SA; *Int'l*, pg. 173
A-E DOOR SALES AND SERVICE, INC.; *U.S. Private*, pg. 22
AEEC LLC; *U.S. Private*, pg. 116
AE&E ENERGY & ENVIRONMENT CONSULTING SHANGHAI CO. LTD.—See A-TEC Industries AG; *Int'l*, pg. 21
AE&E GEOMICROBIAL TECHNOLOGIES, INC.—See New Jcm Group CO., Ltd; *Int'l*, pg. 5226
AE&E I.D.E.A. INDIA PVT. LTD.—See The Dodsal Group; *Int'l*, pg. 7637
AE&E LENTJES PRAHA S.R.O.—See Doosan Corporation; *Int'l*, pg. 2173
AE&E NANJING BOILER CO. LTD.—See A-TEC Industries AG; *Int'l*, pg. 21
AEERIS LIMITED; *Int'l*, pg. 173
AEES, INC.—See Samvardhana Motherson International Limited; *Int'l*, pg. 6517
AEES MANUFACTURERA, S. DE R.L DE C.V—See Samvardhana Motherson International Limited; *Int'l*, pg. 6517
AEE SOLAR, INC.—See Sunrun Inc.; *U.S. Public*, pg. 1965
AEES POWER SYSTEMS LIMITED PARTNERSHIP—See Samvardhana Motherson International Limited; *Int'l*, pg. 6517

AE FARMS, INC.—See Anderson Erickson Dairy Company; *U.S. Private*, pg. 276
AEFFE FRANCE S.A.R.L—See Aeffe SpA; *Int'l*, pg. 173
AEFFE RETAIL S.P.A.—See Aeffe SpA; *Int'l*, pg. 173
AEFFE SPA; *Int'l*, pg. 173
AEFFE USA INC—See Aeffe SpA; *Int'l*, pg. 173
A.E. FINLEY & ASSOCIATES OF TENNESSEE, INC.; *U.S. Private*, pg. 25
AEGA ASA; *Int'l*, pg. 173
AEGATE LTD.—See Ipex Capital, Ltd.; *Int'l*, pg. 3797
AEGEA MEDICAL INC.—See The Cooper Companies, Inc.; *U.S. Public*, pg. 2066
AEGEAN ACE MARITIME COMPANY—See Minerva Bunkering; *Int'l*, pg. 4907
AEGEAN AGENCY (GIBRALTAR) LIMITED—See Minerva Bunkering; *Int'l*, pg. 4907
AEGEAN AIRLINES S.A.; *Int'l*, pg. 173
AEGEAN BUNKERING (C VERDE) LDA—See Minerva Bunkering; *Int'l*, pg. 4907
AEGEAN BUNKERING (GHANA) LTD—See Minerva Bunkering; *Int'l*, pg. 4907
AEGEAN BUNKERING (GIBRALTAR) LIMITED—See Minerva Bunkering; *Int'l*, pg. 4907
AEGEAN BUNKERING (HONG KONG) LIMITED—See Minerva Bunkering; *Int'l*, pg. 4907
AEGEAN BUNKERING (JAM) LTD—See Minerva Bunkering; *Int'l*, pg. 4907
AEGEAN BUNKERING (SINGAPORE) PTE LTD.—See Minerva Bunkering; *Int'l*, pg. 4907
AEGEAN BUNKERING (TRINIDAD) LTD.—See Minerva Bunkering; *Int'l*, pg. 4907
AEGEAN (FUJAIRAH) BUNKERING SA—See Minerva Bunkering; *Int'l*, pg. 4907
AEGEAN MARINE PETROLEUM LLC—See Minerva Bunkering; *Int'l*, pg. 4907
AEGEAN MARITIME PETROLEUM INC.—See Minerva Bunkering; *Int'l*, pg. 4907
AEGEAN MARITIME PETROLEUM NETWORK INC.—See Minerva Bunkering; *Int'l*, pg. 4907
AEGEAN MOTORWAY S.A.—See PATHE Motorway S.A.; *Int'l*, pg. 5756
AEGEAN NORTH-WEST EUROPE—See Minerva Bunkering; *Int'l*, pg. 4907
AEGEAN OIL (USA) LLC—See Minerva Bunkering; *Int'l*, pg. 4907
AEGEAN OSTRIA MARITIME COMPANY—See Minerva Bunkering; *Int'l*, pg. 4907
AEGEAN ROSE MARITIME COMPANY—See Minerva Bunkering; *Int'l*, pg. 4907
AEGEAN SHIP III MARITIME COMPANY—See Minerva Bunkering; *Int'l*, pg. 4907
AEGEAN SHIP VIII MARITIME COMPANY—See Minerva Bunkering; *Int'l*, pg. 4907
AEGEAN SHIP XII MARITIME COMPANY—See Minerva Bunkering; *Int'l*, pg. 4907
AEGEAN TIFFANY MARITIME COMPANY—See Minerva Bunkering; *Int'l*, pg. 4907
AEGEK GROUP; *Int'l*, pg. 173
AEGERION PHARMACEUTICALS, INC.—See Chiesi Farmaceutici SpA; *Int'l*, pg. 1477
AEGERION PHARMACEUTICALS S.A.S.—See Chiesi Farmaceutici SpA; *Int'l*, pg. 1477
AEG HOLDING COMPANY, INC.; *U.S. Private*, pg. 116
AEGION COATING SERVICES, LLC—See Voyager Interests, LLC; *U.S. Private*, pg. 4414
AEGION CORPORATION—See New Mountain Capital, LLC; *U.S. Private*, pg. 2899
AEGION HOLDING COMPANY, LLC—See New Mountain Capital, LLC; *U.S. Private*, pg. 2899
AEGIRBIO AB—See Abreos Biosciences, Inc.; *U.S. Private*, pg. 40
AEGIRBIO AB—See LifeAssays AB; *Int'l*, pg. 4494
AEGIS ANALYTICAL CORPORATION—See Dassault Systemes S.A.; *Int'l*, pg. 1974
AEGIS ASSISTED LIVING PROPERTIES LLC; *U.S. Private*, pg. 116
AEGIS BPO SERVICES AUSTRALIA HOLDINGS PTY. LTD.—See StarTek, Inc.; *U.S. Private*, pg. 3788
AEGIS BUSINESS LTD.—See Century Plyboards (I) Ltd.; *Int'l*, pg. 1419
AEGIS CHEMICAL SOLUTIONS, LLC—See Intervale Capital, LLC; *U.S. Private*, pg. 2127
AEGIS CLEANING & MAINTENANCE SERVICES PTE. LTD.—See SingAsia Holdings Limited; *Int'l*, pg. 6943
AEGIS CORP.—See Lovell Minnick Partners LLC; *U.S. Private*, pg. 2502
AEGIS ENERGY SERVICES, LLC—See Electricite de France S.A.; *Int'l*, pg. 2350
AEGIS ENGINEERING LIMITED—See Kanders & Company, Inc.; *U.S. Private*, pg. 2259
AEGIS FIRE PROTECTION SYSTEMS, LLC.; *U.S. Private*, pg. 116
AEGIS FIRE SYSTEMS, INC.—See Pye-Barker Fire & Safety, LLC; *U.S. Private*, pg. 3309
AEGIS FLOW TECHNOLOGIES—See IDEX Corp; *U.S. Public*, pg. 1089
THE AEGIS GROUP, INC.—See Ontario Teachers' Pension Plan; *Int'l*, pg. 5587

53

AEGIS HEDGING SOLUTIONS, LLC

CORPORATE AFFILIATIONS

AEGIS HEDGING SOLUTIONS, LLC; *U.S. Private,* pg. 116
AEGIS LIGHTWAVE, INC.; *U.S. Private,* pg. 116
AEGIS LIMITED—See MMC Limited; *Int'l,* pg. 5005
AEGIS LINK CORP.—See RichWave Technology Corporation; *Int'l,* pg. 6332
AEGIS LOGISTICS LTD.; *Int'l,* pg. 173
AEGIS METAL FRAMING, LLC—See Berkshire Hathaway Inc.; *U.S. Public,* pg. 312
THE AEGIS MOBILE, LLC; *U.S. Private,* pg. 3982
AEGIS ORTHOPAEDICS PTY. LTD.—See L&K Biomed Co., Ltd.; *Int'l,* pg. 4369
AEGIS PERU S.A.C—See StarTek, Inc.; *U.S. Private,* pg. 3788
AEGIS POWER SYSTEMS, INC.; *U.S. Private,* pg. 116
AEGIS RESOURCE MANAGEMENT PTE. LTD.—See SingAsia Holdings Limited; *Int'l,* pg. 6943
AEGIS SECURITY INSURANCE CO.—See Warburg Pincus LLC; *U.S. Private,* pg. 4438
AEGIS SERVICES LANKA PRIVATE LIMITED—See StarTek, Inc.; *U.S. Private,* pg. 3788
AEGIS SIMULATION TECHNOLOGIES UK, LTD.—See Arlington Capital Partners LLC; *U.S. Private,* pg. 327
AEGIS THERAPIES—See Fillmore Capital Partners, LLC; *U.S. Private,* pg. 1506
AEGIS TOXICOLOGY SCIENCES CORPORATION—See ABRY Partners, LLC; *U.S. Private,* pg. 40
AEGON BANK N.V.—See BAWAG Group AG; *Int'l,* pg. 900
AEGON BELGIUM—See ASR Nederland N.V.; *Int'l,* pg. 632
AEGON CAPPITAL B.V.—See Aegon N.V.; *Int'l,* pg. 174
AEGON COMPANIES OF FLORIDA—See Aegon N.V.; *Int'l,* pg. 174
AEGON DIRECT MARKETING SERVICES, INC.—See Aegon N.V.; *Int'l,* pg. 174
AEGON EMEKLILIK VE HAYAT A.S.—See Aegon N.V.; *Int'l,* pg. 174
AEGON ESPANA S.A.—See Aegon N.V.; *Int'l,* pg. 174
AEGON LEVENSVERZEKERING N.V.—See ASR Nederland N.V.; *Int'l,* pg. 632
AEGON MAGYARORSZAG ALTALANOS BIZTOSITO ZRT.—See Aegon N.V.; *Int'l,* pg. 174
AEGON MAGYARORSZAG BEFEKTETESI ALAPKEZELO ZARTKORUEN MUKODO RESZVENYTARSASAG—See Aegon N.V.; *Int'l,* pg. 175
AEGON NEDERLAND N.V.—See ASR Nederland N.V.; *Int'l,* pg. 632
AEGON N.V.; *Int'l,* pg. 173
AEGON PENSII SOCIETATE DE ADMINISTRARE A FONDURILOR DE PENSII PRIVATE S.A.—See Aegon N.V.; *Int'l,* pg. 175
AEGON POWSZECHNE TOWARZYSTAINE EMERYTAINE SPOLKA AKCYJNA—See Aegon N.V.; *Int'l,* pg. 175
AEGON SCHADEVERZEKERING N.V.—See ASR Nederland N.V.; *Int'l,* pg. 632
AEGON SCOTTISH EQUITABLE PLC—See Aegon N.V.; *Int'l,* pg. 174
AEGON TOWARZYSTWO UBEZPIECZEN NA ZYCIE SPOLKA AKCYJNA—See Aegon N.V.; *Int'l,* pg. 175
AEGON UK PLC—See Aegon N.V.; *Int'l,* pg. 174
AEGON USA, INC.—See Aegon N.V.; *Int'l,* pg. 174
AEGON USA, INC.—See Aegon N.V.; *Int'l,* pg. 174
AEGON USA-INDIVIDUAL DIVISION—See Aegon N.V.; *Int'l,* pg. 174
AEGON USA INVESTMENT MANAGEMENT LLC—See Aegon N.V.; *Int'l,* pg. 174
AEGON USA-MONUMENTAL DIVISION—See Aegon N.V.; *Int'l,* pg. 174
AEGON USA REALTY ADVISORS, LLC—See Aegon N.V.; *Int'l,* pg. 174
AEGON USA-SPECIAL MARKETS GROUP-CONSUMER DIRECT—See Aegon N.V.; *Int'l,* pg. 174
AEG POWER SOLUTIONS ARAM. KFT—See 3W Power S.A.; *Int'l,* pg. 10
AEG POWER SOLUTIONS B.V.—See 3W Power S.A.; *Int'l,* pg. 10
AEG POWER SOLUTIONS CO.—See 3W Power S.A.; *Int'l,* pg. 10
AEG POWER SOLUTIONS (FRANCE) S.A.S—See 3W Power S.A.; *Int'l,* pg. 10
AEG POWER SOLUTIONS GMBH—See 3W Power S.A.; *Int'l,* pg. 10
AEG POWER SOLUTIONS IBERICA SL—See 3W Power S.A.; *Int'l,* pg. 10
AEG POWER SOLUTIONS INC.—See 3W Power S.A.; *Int'l,* pg. 10
AEG POWER SOLUTIONS LTD.—See 3W Power S.A.; *Int'l,* pg. 10
AEG POWER SOLUTIONS MIDDLE EAST—See 3W Power S.A.; *Int'l,* pg. 10
AEG POWER SOLUTIONS (RUSSIA) LLC—See 3W Power S.A.; *Int'l,* pg. 10
AEG POWER SOLUTIONS S.A.S—See 3W Power S.A.; *Int'l,* pg. 10
AEG POWER SOLUTIONS SDN BHD—See 3W Power S.A.; *Int'l,* pg. 10
AEG POWER SOLUTIONS, S.L.—See 3W Power S.A.; *Int'l,* pg. 10

AEG POWER SOLUTIONS SPOL. S.R.O.—See 3W Power S.A.; *Int'l,* pg. 10
AEG POWER SOLUTIONS USA, INC.—See 3W Power S.A.; *Int'l,* pg. 10
AEG PRESENTS LLC—See The Anschutz Corporation; *U.S. Private,* pg. 3986
AE GROUP MATERIALS INC.—See AE Industrial Partners, LP; *U.S. Private,* pg. 111
AEG SOLAR INDIA PVT. LTD.—See Armstrong Energy Global Limited; *Int'l,* pg. 575
AEG WEST, INC.—See Tetra Tech, Inc; *U.S. Public,* pg. 2022
AEHR TEST SYSTEMS GMBH—See Aehr Test Systems; *U.S. Public,* pg. 52
AEHR TEST SYSTEMS JAPAN K.K.—See Aehr Test Systems; *U.S. Public,* pg. 52
AEHR TEST SYSTEMS; *U.S. Public,* pg. 52
AEI CABLES LIMITED—See Paramount Communications Limited; *Int'l,* pg. 5737
A. EICOFF & CO.—See WPP plc; *Int'l,* pg. 8484
AEI COMPOUNDS LIMITED—See Saco Polymers Inc.; *U.S. Private,* pg. 3522
AEI CORE PROPERTY INCOME TRUST, INC.; *U.S. Private,* pg. 117
AEI DRAWBACK SERVICES INC.—See Deutsche Post AG; *Int'l,* pg. 2071
AEI ENGINEERING PTE LTD—See Ascent Bridge Limited; *Int'l,* pg. 602
AEIFOROS BULGARIA S.A.—See Viohalco SA/NV; *Int'l,* pg. 8243
AEIFOROS SA - ALMYROS PLANT—See Viohalco SA/NV; *Int'l,* pg. 8243
AEIFOROS SA—See Viohalco SA/NV; *Int'l,* pg. 8242
AEI INSURANCE GROUP PTY LTD—See AUB Group Limited; *Int'l,* pg. 643
AE INDUSTRIAL PARTNERS, LP; *U.S. Private,* pg. 111
A&E IPLIK SANAYI VE TICARET ANONIM SIRKETI—See The Kroger Co.; *U.S. Public,* pg. 2108
AEI POWER CABLES LIMITED—See Paramount Communications Limited; *Int'l,* pg. 5737
AEI POWER GMBH—See Advanced Energy Industries, Inc.; *U.S. Public,* pg. 47
AEI POWER INDIA PVT. LTD.—See Advanced Energy Industries, Inc.; *U.S. Public,* pg. 47
AEI SERVICES LLC—See Ashmore Group plc; *Int'l,* pg. 608
AEI—See Ashmore Group plc; *Int'l,* pg. 608
AEK BUILD TEC AG—See BKW AG; *Int'l,* pg. 1054
AEK ELEKTRO AG—See BKW AG; *Int'l,* pg. 1054
AEK ENERGIE AG—See BKW AG; *Int'l,* pg. 1054
AE KOREA, LTD.—See Advanced Energy Industries, Inc.; *U.S. Public,* pg. 47
AEK PELLET AG—See BKW AG; *Int'l,* pg. 1054
AEKYUNG CHEMICAL CO., LTD.—See AK Holdings, Inc.; *Int'l,* pg. 259
AEKYUNG HONGKONG CO., LTD—See AK Holdings, Inc.; *Int'l,* pg. 259
AEKYUNG INDUSTRIAL CO., LTD.—See AK Holdings, Inc.; *Int'l,* pg. 259
AEKYUNG (NINGBO) CHEMICAL CO., LTD.—See AK Holdings, Inc.; *Int'l,* pg. 259
AEL DDS LTD—See Taylor Smith Group; *Int'l,* pg. 7478
AEL HOLDCO LIMITED—See AECI Limited; *Int'l,* pg. 171
AELIA CZECH REPUBLIC S.R.O.—See Vivendi SE; *Int'l,* pg. 8275
AELIA RETAIL ESPANA SA—See Vivendi SE; *Int'l,* pg. 8275
AELIA—See Vivendi SE; *Int'l,* pg. 8275
AELIA UK LTD—See Vivendi SE; *Int'l,* pg. 8275
AELIS FARMA SA; *Int'l,* pg. 175
AEL SISTEMAS S.A.—See Elbit Systems Limited; *Int'l,* pg. 2344
AEL TEXTILES LIMITED—See Dar Al-Maal Al-Islami Trust; *Int'l,* pg. 1971
AELUMA, INC.; *U.S. Public,* pg. 52
AEMA GROUPE; *Int'l,* pg. 175
A&E MANUFACTURING COMPANY; *U.S. Private,* pg. 20
AE MATERIALS GROUP, INC. - FLORIDA—See AE Industrial Partners, LP; *U.S. Private,* pg. 111
AEMETIS ADVANCED FUELS KEYES, INC.—See Aemetis, Inc.; *U.S. Public,* pg. 52
AEMETIS, INC.; *U.S. Public,* pg. 52
AEM HOLDINGS LTD.; *Int'l,* pg. 175
AEM (HONGKONG) PTE LTD—See AEM Holdings Ltd.; *Int'l,* pg. 175
AEM, INC.; *U.S. Public,* pg. 117
AEM LIMITED—See AMETEK, Inc.; *U.S. Public,* pg. 116
AEM MICROTRONICS (M) SDN. BHD.—See AEM Holdings Ltd.; *Int'l,* pg. 175
AEM MICROTRONICS (SUZHOU) CO., LTD.—See AEM Holdings Ltd.; *Int'l,* pg. 175
AEMOS SDN BHD; *Int'l,* pg. 175
AEM SERVICE S.R.L.—See A2A S.p.A.; *Int'l,* pg. 29
AEM SINGAPORE PTE. LTD.—See AEM Holdings Ltd.; *Int'l,* pg. 175
AEMS SERVICE COMPANY; *U.S. Private,* pg. 117
AEM (SUZHOU) CO., LTD.—See AEM Holdings Ltd.; *Int'l,* pg. 175
AEMTEC GMBH—See capiton AG; *Int'l,* pg. 1314

AEM TESTECH (SHANGHAI) CO., LTD.—See AEM Holdings Ltd.; *Int'l,* pg. 175
AEM TRADING S.R.L.—See A2A S.p.A.; *Int'l,* pg. 29
AE MULTI HOLDINGS BERHAD; *Int'l,* pg. 170
AEMULUS CORPORATION SDN. BHD. - SAN RAMON BRANCH—See Aemulus Holdings Berhad; *Int'l,* pg. 176
AEMULUS CORPORATION SDN. BHD.—See Aemulus Holdings Berhad; *Int'l,* pg. 175
AEMULUS HOLDINGS BERHAD; *Int'l,* pg. 175
AENA SME, S.A.—See ENAIRE; *Int'l,* pg. 2396
A.E. NATHAN COMPANY INC.; *U.S. Private,* pg. 25
AENEAS COMMUNICATIONS, LLC; *U.S. Private,* pg. 117
A&E NETWORK—See The Hearst Corporation; *U.S. Private,* pg. 4045
A&E NETWORK—See The Walt Disney Company; *U.S. Public,* pg. 2137
A.E. NEW, JR., INC.; *U.S. Private,* pg. 25
AENIX INFORMATIQUE S.A.; *Int'l,* pg. 176
AENOVA HOLDING GMBH—See BC Partners LLP; *Int'l,* pg. 922
AENZA S.A.A.; *Int'l,* pg. 176
AEO FOREIGN HOLD CO LLC—See American Eagle Outfitters, Inc.; *U.S. Public,* pg. 99
AEOLIAN CORPORATION—See Dainichiseika Color & Chemicals Mfg. Co., Ltd.; *Int'l,* pg. 1938
AEOLIKI KANDILIOU SA—See ELLAKTOR S.A.; *Int'l,* pg. 2364
AEOLIKI OLYMPUS EVIA S.A.—See ELLAKTOR S.A.; *Int'l,* pg. 2364
AEOLIKI PARNONOS SA—See ELLAKTOR S.A.; *Int'l,* pg. 2364
AEOLOS LIMITED—See Francoudi & Stephanou Ltd.; *Int'l,* pg. 2761
AEOLUS PHARMACEUTICALS, INC.; *U.S. Public,* pg. 52
AEOLUS TYRE CO., LTD.; *Int'l,* pg. 176
AEON ACQUISITION CORP.; *U.S. Private,* pg. 117
AEON AGRI CREATE CO., LTD.—See AEON Co., Ltd.; *Int'l,* pg. 176
AEON ALLIANZ LIFE INSURANCE CO., LTD.—See AEON Co., Ltd.; *Int'l,* pg. 177
AEON BANK, LTD.—See AEON Co., Ltd.; *Int'l,* pg. 176
AEON BIG (M) SDN. BHD.—See AEON Co., Ltd.; *Int'l,* pg. 176
AEON BIOPHARMA, INC.; *U.S. Public,* pg. 52
AEON BIOPHARMA SUB, INC.—See AEON Biopharma, Inc.; *U.S. Public,* pg. 52
AEON BODY CO., LTD—See AEON Co., Ltd.; *Int'l,* pg. 176
AEON (CAMBODIA) CO., LTD.—See AEON Co., Ltd.; *Int'l,* pg. 177
AEON CINEMAS CO., LTD.—See AEON Co., Ltd.; *Int'l,* pg. 176
AEON CO., LTD.; *Int'l,* pg. 176
AEON CO. (M) BHD.—See AEON Co., Ltd.; *Int'l,* pg. 176
AEON COMPASS CO., LTD.—See AEON Co., Ltd.; *Int'l,* pg. 177
AEON CREDIT SERVICE (ASIA) COMPANY LIMITED—See AEON Financial Service Co., Ltd; *Int'l,* pg. 178
AEON CREDIT SERVICE (M) BERHAD—See AEON Co., Ltd.; *Int'l,* pg. 176
AEON DELIGHT ACADEMY CO., LTD.—See AEON Co., Ltd.; *Int'l,* pg. 176
AEON DELIGHT (CHINA) CO., LTD.—See AEON Co., Ltd.; *Int'l,* pg. 176
AEON DELIGHT CO., LTD.—See AEON Co., Ltd.; *Int'l,* pg. 176
AEON DELIGHT SECURITY CO., LTD.—See AEON Co., Ltd.; *Int'l,* pg. 176
AEON EAHEART CO., LTD.—See AEON Co., Ltd.; *Int'l,* pg. 176
AEON EAST CHINA (SUZHOU) CO., LTD.—See AEON Co., Ltd.; *Int'l,* pg. 176
AEON FANTASY CO., LTD.—See AEON Co., Ltd.; *Int'l,* pg. 177
AEON FINANCIAL SERVICE CO., LTD; *Int'l,* pg. 178
AEON FOOD SUPPLY CO., LTD—See AEON Co., Ltd.; *Int'l,* pg. 176
AEON FOREST CO., LTD—See AEON Co., Ltd.; *Int'l,* pg. 176
AEON GLOBAL HEALTH CORP.; *U.S. Private,* pg. 117
AEON GLOBAL SCM CO., LTD—See AEON Co., Ltd.; *Int'l,* pg. 176
AEON HOKKAIDO CORPORATION—See AEON Co., Ltd.; *Int'l,* pg. 177
AEON HOUSING LOAN SERVICE CO., LTD.—See AEON Co., Ltd.; *Int'l,* pg. 176
AEON INSURANCE SERVICE CO., LTD—See AEON Co., Ltd.; *Int'l,* pg. 176
AEON INTEGRATED BUSINESS SERVICE CO., LTD—See AEON Co., Ltd.; *Int'l,* pg. 176
AEON KYUSHU CO., LTD.—See AEON Co., Ltd.; *Int'l,* pg. 176
AEON LAW PLLC; *U.S. Private,* pg. 117
AEON MALL CO., LTD.—See AEON Co., Ltd.; *Int'l,* pg. 177
AEON METALS LIMITED; *Int'l,* pg. 178
AEON MOTOR CO., LTD.; *Int'l,* pg. 179

COMPANY NAME INDEX

AEON NEXT CO., LTD.—See AEON Co., Ltd.; *Int'l*, pg. 177
AEON PET CO., LTD.—See AEON Co., Ltd.; *Int'l*, pg. 177
AEON PROCARE PRIVATE LIMITED—See Ashapura Minechem Limited; *Int'l*, pg. 606
AEON PRODUCT FINANCE CO., LTD.—See Orient Corporation; *Int'l*, pg. 5621
AEON REIT INVESTMENT CORPORATION; *Int'l*, pg. 179
AEON RETAIL CO., LTD.—See AEON Co., Ltd.; *Int'l*, pg. 177
AEON RYUKYU CO., LTD.—See AEON Co., Ltd.; *Int'l*, pg. 177
AEON SAVEUR CO., LTD.—See AEON Co., Ltd.; *Int'l*, pg. 177
AEON; *U.S. Private*, pg. 117
AEON SOUTH CHINA CO., LTD.—See AEON Co., Ltd.; *Int'l*, pg. 177
AEON STORES (HONG KONG) CO., LIMITED—See AEON Co., Ltd.; *Int'l*, pg. 177
AEON SUPERCENTER CO., LTD.—See AEON Co., Ltd.; *Int'l*, pg. 177
AEON (THAILAND) CO., LTD—See AEON Co., Ltd.; *Int'l*, pg. 176
AEON TOHOKU CO., LTD.—See AEON Co., Ltd.; *Int'l*, pg. 177
AEON TOPVALU CO., LTD.—See AEON Co., Ltd.; *Int'l*, pg. 177
AEON TOPVALU (HONG KONG) CO., LIMITED—See AEON Co., Ltd.; *Int'l*, pg. 177
AEON TOPVALU VIETNAM COMPANY LIMITED—See AEON Co., Ltd.; *Int'l*, pg. 177
AEON TOWN CO., LTD.—See AEON Co., Ltd.; *Int'l*, pg. 177
AEON TOWN CO., LTD.—See AEON Co., Ltd.; *Int'l*, pg. 177
AEONX DIGITAL SOLUTIONS PRIVATE LIMITED—See ASHOK ALCO CHEM LIMITED; *Int'l*, pg. 608
AEOON TECHNOLOGIES GMBH; *Int'l*, pg. 179
AEOREMA COMMUNICATIONS PLC; *Int'l*, pg. 179
AE OUTFITTERS RETAIL CO.—See American Eagle Outfitters, Inc.; *U.S. Public*, pg. 99
AEP ENERGY, INC.—See American Electric Power Company, Inc.; *U.S. Public*, pg. 99
AEP ENERGY PARTNERS, INC.—See American Electric Power Company, Inc.; *U.S. Public*, pg. 99
A.E.P. ENVIRONMENTAL, L.L.C.; *U.S. Private*, pg. 25
A.E. PETSCHE BELGIUM BVBA—See Arrow Electronics, Inc.; *U.S. Public*, pg. 194
A.E. PETSCHE CANADA, INC.—See Arrow Electronics, Inc.; *U.S. Public*, pg. 194
A.E. PETSCHE COMPANY INC.—See Arrow Electronics, Inc.; *U.S. Public*, pg. 194
A.E. PETSCHE SAS—See Arrow Electronics, Inc.; *U.S. Public*, pg. 194
A.E. PETSCHE UK LIMITED—See Arrow Electronics, Inc.; *U.S. Public*, pg. 195
AEP GENERATING COMPANY—See American Electric Power Company, Inc.; *U.S. Public*, pg. 99
AEP GMBH—See Osterreichische Post AG; *Int'l*, pg. 5653
THE AEP GROUP; *U.S. Private*, pg. 3982
AEP INDUSTRIES FINANCE INC.—See Berry Global Group, Inc; *U.S. Public*, pg. 320
AEP NVH OPCO, LLC—See Angeles Equity Partners, LLC; *U.S. Private*, pg. 281
AEP OHIO—See American Electric Power Company, Inc.; *U.S. Public*, pg. 100
AEP PLANUNG UND BERATUNG GESELLSCHAFT MBH—See BKW AG; *Int'l*, pg. 1054
AE PRECISION POWER PRODUCTS PVT. LTD.—See Advanced Energy Industries, Inc.; *U.S. Public*, pg. 47
AEP RIVER TRANSPORTATION—See American Electric Power Company, Inc.; *U.S. Public*, pg. 99
AEPS CORPORATION; *U.S. Private*, pg. 117
A. EPSTEIN & SONS INTERNATIONAL, INC.; *U.S. Private*, pg. 23
AEP TEXAS CENTRAL TRANSITION FUNDING III LLC—See American Electric Power Company, Inc.; *U.S. Public*, pg. 99
AEP TEXAS CENTRAL TRANSITION FUNDING II LLC—See American Electric Power Company, Inc.; *U.S. Public*, pg. 99
AEP TEXAS CENTRAL TRANSITION FUNDING LLC—See American Electric Power Company, Inc.; *U.S. Public*, pg. 99
AEP TEXAS INC.—See American Electric Power Company, Inc.; *U.S. Public*, pg. 99
AEP TRANSMISSION COMPANY, LLC—See American Electric Power Company, Inc.; *U.S. Public*, pg. 99
AEQUI ACQUISITION CORP.; *U.S. Public*, pg. 52
AEQUITAS CAPITAL MANAGEMENT; *U.S. Private*, pg. 117
AEQUITA SE & CO. KGAA; *Int'l*, pg. 179
AEQUITAS GMBH ALLIANZ EQUITY - ALTERNATIVE STRATEGIES—See Allianz SE; *U.S. Public*, pg. 343
AEQUOR TECHNOLOGIES, LLC; *U.S. Private*, pg. 117
AEQUUS BIOPHARMA, INC.—See Swedish Orphan Biovitrum AB; *Int'l*, pg. 7365
AEQUUS PHARMACEUTICALS INC.; *Int'l*, pg. 179

AERA ENERGY LLC—See Aera Energy LLC; *U.S. Private*, pg. 117
AERA ENERGY LLC; *U.S. Private*, pg. 117
AERA KOREA LTD.—See Advanced Energy Industries, Inc.; *U.S. Public*, pg. 47
AER ARANN EXPRESS LTD.; *Int'l*, pg. 179
AERAZUR—See Safran SA; *Int'l*, pg. 6477
AERC ACQUISITION CORPORATION—See Compass Diversified Holdings; *U.S. Public*, pg. 559
AERCAP AVIATION SOLUTIONS—See Cerberus Capital Management, L.P.; *U.S. Private*, pg. 835
AERCAP B.V.—See AerCap Holdings N.V.; *Int'l*, pg. 179
AERCAP DUTCH AIRCRAFT LEASING B.V.—See AerCap Holdings N.V.; *Int'l*, pg. 179
AERCAP FINANCIAL SERVICES (IRELAND) LTD—See AerCap Holdings N.V.; *Int'l*, pg. 179
AERCAP GROUP SERVICES B.V.—See AerCap Holdings N.V.; *Int'l*, pg. 179
AERCAP HOLDINGS N.V.; *Int'l*, pg. 179
AERCAP IRELAND LIMITED—See AerCap Holdings N.V.; *Int'l*, pg. 179
AERCAP IRELAND LTD.—See Cerberus Capital Management, L.P.; *U.S. Private*, pg. 836
AERCAP NETHERLANDS B.V.—See AerCap Holdings N.V.; *Int'l*, pg. 179
AERCAP SINGAPORE PTE. LTD.—See AerCap Holdings N.V.; *Int'l*, pg. 179
AERCAP USA, INC.—See AerCap Holdings N.V.; *Int'l*, pg. 179
AERC ARROWHEAD STATION, INC.—See Brookfield Corporation; *Int'l*, pg. 1175
AERC DORAL WEST, LLC—See Brookfield Corporation; *Int'l*, pg. 1174
AERCO INTERNATIONAL, INC.—See Watts Water Technologies, Inc.; *U.S. Public*, pg. 2337
AERC RECYCLING SOLUTIONS—See Enviri Corporation; *U.S. Public*, pg. 780
AEREX INDUSTRIES, INC.—See Consolidated Water Co. Ltd.; *Int'l*, pg. 1771
AER FABER AS—See Lindab International AB; *Int'l*, pg. 4503
AERFI GROUP LIMITED—See AerCap Holdings N.V.; *Int'l*, pg. 179
AERGO CAPITAL LTD.; *Int'l*, pg. 179
AERIA INC.; *Int'l*, pg. 179
AERIAL ADVERTISING SERVICES; *U.S. Private*, pg. 117
AERIAL BOUQUETS; *U.S. Private*, pg. 117
AERIAL COMPANY INC.—See Sally Beauty Holdings, Inc.; *U.S. Public*, pg. 1838
AERIAL LIGHTING & ELECTRIC INC.—See IES Holdings, Inc.; *U.S. Public*, pg. 1094
AERIAL POWER LINES SDN. BHD.—See Sarawak Cable Berhad; *Int'l*, pg. 6576
AERIAL WORK PLATFORMS, INC.—See Herc Holdings Inc.; *U.S. Public*, pg. 1028
AERIE PHARMACEUTICALS, INC.—See Alcon Inc.; *Int'l*, pg. 302
AERIES ENTERPRISES, LLC; *U.S. Private*, pg. 117
AERIES TECHNOLOGY, INC.; *U.S. Public*, pg. 52
AERION CORPORATION—See Keystone Group, L.P.; *U.S. Private*, pg. 2296
AERIS BIOLOGICAL SYSTEMS PTY LTD—See Aeris Environmental Ltd; *Int'l*, pg. 180
AERIS ENVIRONMENTAL LLC—See Aeris Environmental Ltd; *Int'l*, pg. 180
AERIS ENVIRONMENTAL LTD; *Int'l*, pg. 179
AERIS HYGIENE SERVICES PTY LTD.—See Aeris Environmental Ltd; *Int'l*, pg. 180
AERISON GROUP LIMITED; *Int'l*, pg. 180
AERIS RESOURCES LIMITED; *Int'l*, pg. 180
AERKOMM INC.; *U.S. Public*, pg. 52
AER LINGUS GROUP DAC—See International Consolidated Airlines Group S.A.; *Int'l*, pg. 3745
AER MANUFACTURING, INC.; *U.S. Private*, pg. 117
AERMONT CAPITAL LLP; *Int'l*, pg. 180
AERNNOVA AEROSPACE CORPORATION S.A.—See Torreal, S.A.; *Int'l*, pg. 7830
AERNNOVA AEROSPACE CORPORATION S.A.—See TowerBrook Capital Partners, L.P.; *U.S. Private*, pg. 4194
AEROANTENNA TECHNOLOGY, INC.—See HEICO Corporation; *U.S. Public*, pg. 1020
AERO AVIATION LTD; *Int'l*, pg. 180
AERO BALKAN, D.O.O.—See Aero d.d.; *Int'l*, pg. 180
AEROBIE, INC.—See Spin Master Corp.; *Int'l*, pg. 7136
A.E. ROBINSON OIL CO. INC.; *U.S. Private*, pg. 25
AERO - BOND CORP.—See Rift Valley Equity Partners, LLC; *U.S. Private*, pg. 3435
AEROBOTIX, INC.; *U.S. Private*, pg. 118
AEROCAR B.V.—See Deutsche Post AG; *Int'l*, pg. 2071
AEROCARE HOLDINGS, INC.—See AdaptHealth Corp.; *U.S. Public*, pg. 38
AEROCARE HOME MEDICAL EQUIPMENT, INC.—See AdaptHealth Corp.; *U.S. Public*, pg. 38
AERO-CARE PTY LTD.—See Archer Capital Pty. Ltd.; *Int'l*, pg. 547
AEROCAST, INC.; *U.S. Private*, pg. 118
AEROC INTERNATIONAL AS; *Int'l*, pg. 180

AEROCISION, LLC—See Arlington Capital Partners LLC; *U.S. Private*, pg. 327
AEROC JAMERA AS—See Aeroc International AS; *Int'l*, pg. 180
AEROC JAMERA OY—See Aeroc International AS; *Int'l*, pg. 180
AEROCOM FRANCE S.A.R.L.—See aerocom GmbH & Co.; *Int'l*, pg. 180
AEROCOM GCT S.R.L.—See aerocom GmbH & Co.; *Int'l*, pg. 180
AEROCOM GMBH & CO.; *Int'l*, pg. 180
AEROCOM GMBH & CO.—See aerocom GmbH & Co.; *Int'l*, pg. 180
AERO COMMUNICATIONS, INC.—See Resilience Capital Partners, LLC; *U.S. Private*, pg. 3405
AEROCOM NEUMATICA S. L.—See aerocom GmbH & Co.; *Int'l*, pg. 180
AERO COMPONENTS, LLC—See P4G Capital Management, LLC; *U.S. Private*, pg. 3062
AEROCON, LLC—See Berry Global Group, Inc; *U.S. Public*, pg. 321
AEROCONTROLEX GROUP—See TransDigm Group Incorporated; *U.S. Public*, pg. 2181
AERO CONTROLS INC.; *U.S. Private*, pg. 118
AERO COPY D.O.O.—See Aero d.d.; *Int'l*, pg. 180
AEROCRAFT HEAT TREATING CO., INC.—See Berkshire Hathaway Inc.; *U.S. Public*, pg. 313
AEROCRINE AB—See Niox Group PLC; *Int'l*, pg. 5309
AERO-DATA METAL CRAFTERS, INC.; *U.S. Private*, pg. 118
AERO D.D.; *Int'l*, pg. 180
AERO DESIGN, INC.—See HEICO Corporation; *U.S. Public*, pg. 1019
AERO DESIGN & MANUFACTURING, INC.; *U.S. Private*, pg. 118
AERODROME GROUP LTD.; *Int'l*, pg. 181
AERODROMI REPUBLIKE SRPSKE A.D.; *Int'l*, pg. 181
AERODROM LJUBLJANA, LLC—See Fraport AG; *Int'l*, pg. 2763
AERODROM NIKOLA TESLA A.D.; *Int'l*, pg. 181
AERODYNAMICS, INCORPORATED; *U.S. Private*, pg. 118
AERO DYNAMIEK BV—See IMI plc; *Int'l*, pg. 3624
AERODYNE ALLOYS LLC—See O'Neal Industries, Inc.; *U.S. Private*, pg. 2979
AERODYN ENGINEERING, INC.; *U.S. Private*, pg. 118
AERO-ELECTRIC CONNECTOR INC.; *U.S. Private*, pg. 118
AEROELITE LIMITED—See L3Harris Technologies, Inc.; *U.S. Public*, pg. 1280
AEROEQUITY PARTNERS, LLC; *U.S. Private*, pg. 118
AERO EXCLUSIVE D.O.O.—See Aero d.d.; *Int'l*, pg. 180
AERO EXPRESS DEL ECUADOR TRANSAM CIA LTD.—See Deutsche Post AG; *Int'l*, pg. 2071
AERO EXPRESS DEL ECUADOR (TRANSAM) LTDA.—See Deutsche Post AG; *Int'l*, pg. 2071
AERO FASTENER CO., INC.; *U.S. Private*, pg. 118
AEROFIL INC.—See Absolent Air Care Group AB; *Int'l*, pg. 70
AEROFIL TECHNOLOGY, INC.—See Novacap Management Inc.; *Int'l*, pg. 5454
AEROFIN CORP.—See Ampco-Pittsburgh Corporation; *U.S. Public*, pg. 126
AEROFIT, LLC—See Tinicum Enterprises, Inc.; *U.S. Private*, pg. 4174
AEROFLEX AG—See swisspor Management AG; *Int'l*, pg. 7374
AEROFLEX AVCOMM-RESEARCH & DEVELOPMENT CENTER—See Advent International Corporation; *U.S. Private*, pg. 99
AEROFLEX AVCOMM—See Advent International Corporation; *U.S. Private*, pg. 99
AEROFLEX FINANCE PRIVATE LIMITED—See Sat Industries Ltd.; *Int'l*, pg. 6584
AEROFLEX HOLDING CORP.—See Advent International Corporation; *U.S. Private*, pg. 98
AEROFLEX INCORPORATED—See Advent International Corporation; *U.S. Private*, pg. 99
AEROFLEX INDUSTRIES LIMITED—See Sat Industries Ltd.; *Int'l*, pg. 6584
AEROFLEX IRELAND LIMITED—See Viavi Solutions Inc.; *U.S. Public*, pg. 2295
AEROFLEX LIMITED—See Viavi Solutions Inc.; *U.S. Public*, pg. 2295
AEROFLEX NANJING—See Advent International Corporation; *U.S. Private*, pg. 99
AEROFLEX USA INC.—See Eastern Polymer Group Public Company Limited; *Int'l*, pg. 2273
AEROFLEX WICHITA, INC.—See Viavi Solutions Inc.; *U.S. Public*, pg. 2295
AEROFLOW, INC.; *U.S. Private*, pg. 119
AEROFLUID CO., LTD.—See Hydac International GmbH; *Int'l*, pg. 3544
AEROFOAM METALS, INC.; *Int'l*, pg. 181
AEROFORM—See Air France-KLM S.A.; *Int'l*, pg. 237
AEROFREEZE, INC.—See GEA Group Aktiengesellschaft; *Int'l*, pg. 2897
AERO FULFILLMENT SERVICES CORPORATION; *U.S. Private*, pg. 118

AERO FULFILLMENT SERVICES CORPORATION

CORPORATE AFFILIATIONS

AERO-GLEN INTERNATIONAL, LLC—See HEICO Corporation; *U.S. Public*, pg. 1021

AERO GROUP, INC.—See Furst-McNess Company; *U.S. Private*, pg. 1624

AEROGROUP INTERNATIONAL LLC—See Palladin Consumer Retail Partners, LLC; *U.S. Private*, pg. 3077

AEROGROW INTERNATIONAL, INC.—See The Scotts Miracle-Gro Company; *U.S. Public*, pg. 2127

AEROHIVE NETWORKS EUROPE LTD—See Extreme Networks, Inc.; *U.S. Public*, pg. 813

AEROHIVE NETWORKS, INC.—See Extreme Networks, Inc.; *U.S. Public*, pg. 813

AEROHOMEX, S.A. DE C.V.—See Desarrolladora Homex, S.A. de C.V.; *Int'l*, pg. 2043

AERO INDUSTRIAL TOOL CO., INC.; *U.S. Private*, pg. 118

AEROINFO SYSTEMS, INC.—See The Boeing Company; *U.S. Public*, pg. 2040

AERO-INSTRUMENTS CO., LLC—See TransDigm Group Incorporated; *U.S. Public*, pg. 2181

AERO INVENTORY (CANADA) INC—See Aero Inventory plc; *Int'l*, pg. 180

AERO INVENTORY (HONG KONG) LIMITED—See Aero Inventory plc; *Int'l*, pg. 180

AERO INVENTORY (JAPAN) KK—See Aero Inventory plc; *Int'l*, pg. 180

AERO INVENTORY PLC; *Int'l*, pg. 180

AERO INVENTORY (UK) LIMITED—See Aero Inventory plc; *Int'l*, pg. 180

AERO INVENTORY (USA) INC—See Aero Inventory plc; *Int'l*, pg. 180

AEROJET INTERNATIONAL, INC.—See L3Harris Technologies, Inc.; *U.S. Public*, pg. 1279

AEROJET ORDNANCE TENNESSEE, INC.—See L3Harris Technologies, Inc.; *U.S. Public*, pg. 1279

AEROJET ROCKETDYNE HOLDINGS, INC.—See L3Harris Technologies, Inc.; *U.S. Public*, pg. 1279

AEROJET ROCKETDYNE, INC. - CAMDEN—See L3Harris Technologies, Inc.; *U.S. Public*, pg. 1279

AEROJET ROCKETDYNE, INC. - GAINESVILLE—See L3Harris Technologies, Inc.; *U.S. Public*, pg. 1279

AEROJET ROCKETDYNE, INC.—See L3Harris Technologies, Inc.; *U.S. Public*, pg. 1279

AEROJET ROCKETDYNE OF DE, INC.—See L3Harris Technologies, Inc.; *U.S. Public*, pg. 1279

AEROKLAS ASIA PACIFIC GROUP PTY. LTD.—See Eastern Polymer Group Public Company Limited; *Int'l*, pg. 2273

AEROKLAS AUSTRALIA PTY LTD.—See Eastern Polymer Group Public Company Limited; *Int'l*, pg. 2273

AEROKLAS CO., LTD—See Eastern Polymer Group Public Company Limited; *Int'l*, pg. 2273

AEROKLAS MALAYSIA SDN. BHD.—See Eastern Polymer Group Public Company Limited; *Int'l*, pg. 2273

AEROKLAS (SHANGHAI) CO., LTD.—See Eastern Polymer Group Public Company Limited; *Int'l*, pg. 2273

AEROLAC—See VINCI S.A.; *Int'l*, pg. 8211

AEROLIA S.A.S. - MEAULTE FACILITY—See Airbus SE; *Int'l*, pg. 246

AEROLIA S.A.S. - SAINT-NAZAIRE FACILITY—See Airbus SE; *Int'l*, pg. 246

AEROLIA S.A.S.—See Airbus SE; *Int'l*, pg. 246

AEROLIA S.A.S. - TOULOUSE FACILITY—See Airbus SE; *Int'l*, pg. 246

AEROLINK UGANDA LIMITED—See AirKenya Aviation Ltd.; *Int'l*, pg. 247

AEROLITE EXTRUSION COMPANY, INC.; *U.S. Private*, pg. 119

AEROLITORAL, S.A. DE C.V.—See Grupo Aeromexico, S.A.B. de C.V.; *Int'l*, pg. 3118

AERO LLOYD FLUGREISEN GMBH & CO. LUFTVERKEHRS-KG—See BayernLB Holding AG; *Int'l*, pg. 913

AEROLOG EXPRESS PTE LTD.—See Temasek Holdings (Private) Limited; *Int'l*, pg. 7550

AERO MAINTENANCE GROUP LLC—See Air France-KLM S.A.; *Int'l*, pg. 236

AEROMARITIME AMERICA INC—See Bain Capital, LP; *U.S. Private*, pg. 433

AEROMED GROUP LLC—See Copley Equity Partners,LLC; *U.S. Private*, pg. 1045

AEROMEDICAL COLLECTION SERVICES, INC.; *U.S. Private*, pg. 119

AERO METALS INC.; *U.S. Private*, pg. 118

AEROMETALS INC.; *U.S. Private*, pg. 119

AEROMETREX LIMITED; *Int'l*, pg. 181

AEROMETREX LTD.—See Aerometrex Limited; *Int'l*, pg. 181

AEROMIX SYSTEMS, INC.—See Fluence Corporation Limited; *U.S. Public*, pg. 857

AERO-MODEL INC—See The Zippertubing Company; *U.S. Private*, pg. 4140

AEROMOTIVE, INC.—See The Roadster Shop; *U.S. Private*, pg. 4111

AERONAUTICAL & GENERAL INSTRUMENTS LIMITED—See HWH Investments Limited; *Int'l*, pg. 3543

AERONAUTICS LTD.—See Rafael Advanced Defense Systems Ltd.; *Int'l*, pg. 6177

AERONAVDATA, INC.—See Garmin Ltd.; *Int'l*, pg. 2884

AERONET WORLDWIDE INC.; *U.S. Private*, pg. 119

AERO PAPIROTTI D.O.O.—See Aero d.d.; *Int'l*, pg. 180

AEROPEOPLE LIMITED—See Marshall of Cambridge (Holdings) Limited; *Int'l*, pg. 4702

AEROPHARM GMBH—See Novartis AG; *Int'l*, pg. 5455

AEROPLAN CANADA INC—See Aimia Inc.; *Int'l*, pg. 233

AEROPLEX OF CENTRAL EUROPE LTD.; *Int'l*, pg. 181

AEROPOD SDN BHD—See S P Setia Berhad; *Int'l*, pg. 6443

AEROPORTI DI ROMA S.P.A.—See Edizione S.r.l.; *Int'l*, pg. 2312

AEROPORTO DI GENOVA S.P.A.—See Edizione S.r.l.; *Int'l*, pg. 2311

AEROPORTO GUGLIELMO MARCONI DI BOLOGNA S.P.A.; *Int'l*, pg. 181

AEROPORTS DE MONTREAL; *Int'l*, pg. 181

AEROPORTS DE PARIS S.A.; *Int'l*, pg. 181

AEROPOST COLOMBIA, SAS—See PriceSmart Inc.; *U.S. Public*, pg. 1716

AEROPOST INTERNATIONAL SERVICES, INC.—See PriceSmart Inc.; *U.S. Public*, pg. 1716

AERO PRECISION PRODUCTS, INC.—See Mistequay Group Ltd.; *U.S. Private*, pg. 2749

AERO PRECISION & REPAIR OVERHAUL COMPANY INC.—See Groupe Industriel Marcel Dassault S.A.; *Int'l*, pg. 3105

AEROPRES CORPORATION-SIBLEY PLANT—See Aeropres Corporation; *U.S. Private*, pg. 119

AEROPRES CORPORATION; *U.S. Private*, pg. 119

AERO PRODUCTS INTERNATIONAL, INC.—See Investcorp Holdings B.S.C.; *Int'l*, pg. 3776

AEROPUERTO ACAPULCO S.A. DE C.V.—See Empresas ICA S.A.B. de C.V.; *Int'l*, pg. 2390

AEROPUERTO CHIHUAHUA, S.A. DE C.V.—See Empresas ICA S.A.B. de C.V.; *Int'l*, pg. 2390

AEROPUERTO CIUDAD JUAREZ, S.A. DE C.V.—See Empresas ICA S.A.B. de C.V.; *Int'l*, pg. 2390

AEROPUERTO CULIACAN, S.A. DE C.V.—See Empresas ICA S.A.B. de C.V.; *Int'l*, pg. 2390

AEROPUERTO DE AGUASCALIENTES, S.A. DE C.V.—See Grupo Aeroportuario del Pacifico, S.A.B. de C.V.; *Int'l*, pg. 3118

AEROPUERTO DE COZUMEL S.A. DE C.V.—See Grupo Aeroportuario del Sureste, S.A.B. de C.V.; *Int'l*, pg. 3119

AEROPUERTO DE GUADALAJARA, S.A. DE C.V.—See Grupo Aeroportuario del Pacifico, S.A.B. de C.V.; *Int'l*, pg. 3118

AEROPUERTO DE HERMOSILLO, S.A. DE C.V.—See Grupo Aeroportuario del Pacifico, S.A.B. de C.V.; *Int'l*, pg. 3118

AEROPUERTO DE HUATULCO, S.A. DE C.V.—See Grupo Aeroportuario del Sureste, S.A.B. de C.V.; *Int'l*, pg. 3119

AEROPUERTO DE LA PAZ, S.A. DE C.V.—See Grupo Aeroportuario del Pacifico, S.A.B. de C.V.; *Int'l*, pg. 3118

AEROPUERTO DEL BAJIO, S.A. DE C.V.—See Grupo Aeroportuario del Pacifico, S.A.B. de C.V.; *Int'l*, pg. 3118

AEROPUERTO DE LOS CABOS, S.A. DE C.V.—See Grupo Aeroportuario del Pacifico, S.A.B. de C.V.; *Int'l*, pg. 3118

AEROPUERTO DE LOS MOCHIS, S.A. DE C.V.—See Grupo Aeroportuario del Pacifico, S.A.B. de C.V.; *Int'l*, pg. 3118

AEROPUERTO DE MANZANILLO, S.A. DE C.V.—See Grupo Aeroportuario del Pacifico, S.A.B. de C.V.; *Int'l*, pg. 3118

AEROPUERTO DE MERIDA S.A. DE C.V.—See Grupo Aeroportuario del Sureste, S.A.B. de C.V.; *Int'l*, pg. 3119

AEROPUERTO DE MEXICALI, S.A. DE C.V.—See Grupo Aeroportuario del Pacifico, S.A.B. de C.V.; *Int'l*, pg. 3118

AEROPUERTO DE MORELIA, S.A. DE C.V.—See Grupo Aeroportuario del Pacifico, S.A.B. de C.V.; *Int'l*, pg. 3118

AEROPUERTO DE PUERTO VALLARTA, S.A. DE C.V.—See Grupo Aeroportuario del Pacifico, S.A.B. de C.V.; *Int'l*, pg. 3118

AEROPUERTO DE PUNTA DEL ESTE—See Corporacion America S.A.; *Int'l*, pg. 1803

AEROPUERTO DE SAN JOSE DEL CABO, S.A. DE C.V.—See Grupo Aeroportuario del Pacifico, S.A.B. de C.V.; *Int'l*, pg. 3118

AEROPUERTO DE SAN LUIS POTOSI, S.A. DE C.V.—See Grupo Aeroportuario del Centro Norte, S.A.B. de C.V.; *Int'l*, pg. 3118

AEROPUERTO DE TIJUANA, S.A. DE C.V.—See Grupo Aeroportuario del Pacifico, S.A.B. de C.V.; *Int'l*, pg. 3118

AEROPUERTO DE VERACRUZ S.A. DE C.V.—See Grupo Aeroportuario del Sureste, S.A.B. de C.V.; *Int'l*, pg. 3119

AEROPUERTO DE ZIHUATANEJO, S.A. DE C.V.—See Grupo Aeroportuario del Centro Norte, S.A.B. de C.V.; *Int'l*, pg. 3118

AEROPUERTO DURANGO—See Empresas ICA S.A.B. de C.V.; *Int'l*, pg. 2390

AEROPUERTO INTERNACIONAL DE TOCUMEN S.A.; *Int'l*, pg. 181

AEROPUERTO MAZATLAN, S.A. DE C.V.—See Empresas ICA S.A.B. de C.V.; *Int'l*, pg. 2390

AEROPUERTO MONTERREY—See Empresas ICA S.A.B. de C.V.; *Int'l*, pg. 2390

AEROPUERTO REYNOSA SA DE CV—See Empresas ICA S.A.B. de C.V.; *Int'l*, pg. 2390

AEROPUERTOS ARGENTINA 2000—See Corporacion America S.A.; *Int'l*, pg. 1803

AEROPUERTOS DEL NEUQUEN S.A.—See Corporacion America S.A.; *Int'l*, pg. 1803

AEROPUERTO TAMPICO, S. A. DE C. V.—See Empresas ICA S.A.B. de C.V.; *Int'l*, pg. 2390

AEROPUERTO TORREON S.A. DE C.V.—See Empresas ICA S.A.B. de C.V.; *Int'l*, pg. 2390

AEROPUERTO ZACATECAS, S.A. DE C.V.—See Empresas ICA S.A.B. de C.V.; *Int'l*, pg. 2390

AEROQUEST AIRBORNE—See Geotech Ltd.; *Int'l*, pg. 2941

AEROQUEST INTERNATIONAL LIMITED—See Geotech Ltd.; *Int'l*, pg. 2941

AEROQUEST LIMITED—See Geotech Ltd.; *Int'l*, pg. 2941

AEROQUEST MAPCON LTD.—See Geotech Ltd.; *Int'l*, pg. 2941

AEROQUIP IBERICA S.L.—See Eaton Corporation plc; *Int'l*, pg. 2277

AERO RENTALS SERVICES DIVISION—See Western Energy Services Corp.; *Int'l*, pg. 8388

AEROREPAIR CORP.—See GenNx360 Capital Partners, L.P.; *U.S. Private*, pg. 1672

AEROREPAIR—See GenNx360 Capital Partners, L.P.; *U.S. Private*, pg. 1672

AEROREPUBLICA, S.A.—See Copa Holdings, S.A.; *Int'l*, pg. 1792

AEROSAN AIRPORT SERVICES S.A.—See Quinenco S.A.; *Int'l*, pg. 6163

AEROSCOUT, INC.; *U.S. Private*, pg. 119

AEROSCOUT JAPAN, CO., LTD.—See Stanley Black & Decker, Inc.; *U.S. Public*, pg. 1931

AEROSCOUT LLC—See Stanley Black & Decker, Inc.; *U.S. Public*, pg. 1931

AEROSCOUT LTD.—See Stanley Black & Decker, Inc.; *U.S. Public*, pg. 1931

AEROSCOUT (SINGAPORE) PTE. LTD.—See Stanley Black & Decker, Inc.; *U.S. Public*, pg. 1931

AEROSEAL, LLC; *U.S. Private*, pg. 119

AERO SEKUR S.P.A.—See Hunting Plc; *Int'l*, pg. 3536

AEROSERVICE CONSULTORIA E ENGENHARIA DE PROJETO LTDA—See Caisse des Depots et Consignations; *Int'l*, pg. 1257

AERO SHADE TECHNOLOGIES, INC.; *U.S. Private*, pg. 118

AEROSHARES CHARTER, LLC; *U.S. Private*, pg. 119

AEROSIM, INC.—See Lincolnshire Management, Inc.; *U.S. Private*, pg. 2459

AEROSIM TECHNOLOGIES, INC.—See L3Harris Technologies, Inc.; *U.S. Public*, pg. 1280

AERO SIMULATION, INC.; *U.S. Private*, pg. 118

AERO SNOW REMOVAL, LLC—See Guggenheim Partners, LLC; *U.S. Private*, pg. 1811

AEROSOLUTIONS, LLC; *U.S. Private*, pg. 119

AEROSONIC CORPORATION—See TransDigm Group Incorporated; *U.S. Public*, pg. 2181

AEROSPACE ASSET TRADING, LLC; *U.S. Private*, pg. 119

AEROSPACE CH UAV CO., LTD.; *Int'l*, pg. 181

AEROSPACE CLAIMS MANAGEMENT GROUP, INC.—See Hallmark Financial Services, Inc.; *U.S. Public*, pg. 981

AEROSPACE & COMMERCIAL TECHNOLOGIES, LLC—See HEICO Corporation; *U.S. Public*, pg. 1021

AEROSPACE COMMMUNICATIONS HOLDINGS GROUP CO., LTD.; *Int'l*, pg. 181

AEROSPACE COMPONENT ENGINEERING SERVICES PTE. LIMITED—See Temasek Holdings (Private) Limited; *Int'l*, pg. 7551

THE AEROSPACE CORPORATION; *U.S. Private*, pg. 3982

AEROSPACE DISTRIBUTORS INC.; *U.S. Private*, pg. 119

AEROSPACE DISTRIBUTORS PTE LTD—See Aerospace Distributors Inc.; *U.S. Private*, pg. 119

AEROSPACE DYNAMICS INTERNATIONAL INC.—See Berkshire Hathaway Inc.; *U.S. Public*, pg. 313

AEROSPACE HI-TECH HOLDING GROUP CO., LTD.; *Int'l*, pg. 181

AEROSPACE HOLDINGS, INC.—See Harlow Aerostructures, LLC; *U.S. Private*, pg. 1865

AEROSPACE HOLDINGS, LLC—See Hallmark Financial Services, Inc.; *U.S. Public*, pg. 981

AEROSPACE INDUSTRIAL DEVELOPMENT CORPORATION; *Int'l*, pg. 181

AEROSPACE INSURANCE MANAGERS, INC.—See Hallmark Financial Services, Inc.; *U.S. Public*, pg. 981

AEROSPACE LIGHTING CORPORATION—See RTX Corporation; *U.S. Public*, pg. 1822

COMPANY NAME INDEX

AEROSPACE LUBRICANTS, INC.—See Amsoil Inc.; *U.S. Private*, pg. 267

AEROSPACE METAL COMPOSITES LIMITED—See Materion Corporation; *U.S. Public*, pg. 1395

AEROSPACE PRECISION INC.—See Aerospace Distributors Inc.; *U.S. Private*, pg. 119

AEROSPACE PRODUCTS INTERNATIONAL, INC. - ASIA PACIFIC—See Resilience Capital Partners, LLC; *U.S. Private*, pg. 3405

AEROSPACE PRODUCTS INTERNATIONAL, INC. - CANADA—See Resilience Capital Partners, LLC; *U.S. Private*, pg. 3405

AEROSPACE PRODUCTS INTERNATIONAL, INC.—See Resilience Capital Partners, LLC; *U.S. Private*, pg. 3405

AEROSPACE RESERCH & TRADING, INC.—See Eagle Industry Co., Ltd.; *Int'l*, pg. 2265

AERO-SPACE SOUTHWEST INC.—See Bossard Holding AG; *Int'l*, pg. 1117

AEROSPACE SPECIAL RISK, INC.—See Hallmark Financial Services, Inc.; *U.S. Public*, pg. 981

AEROSPACE SYSTEMS & COMPONENTS INC.—See Great Plains Ventures, Inc.; *U.S. Private*, pg. 1767

AEROSPACE TECHNOLOGIES GROUP, INC.; *U.S. Private*, pg. 119

AEROSPACE TECHNOLOGY OF KOREA, INC.; *Int'l*, pg. 181

AEROSPARES 2000 LIMITED—See Acorn Growth Companies, LC; *U.S. Private*, pg. 63

AEROSPATIALE MATRA ATR—See Airbus SE; *Int'l*, pg. 246

AEROSTAFF AUSTRALIA PTY LIMITED—See Mahindra & Mahindra Limited; *Int'l*, pg. 4645

AEROSTAR AEROSPACE MANUFACTURING, INC.—See Nautic Partners, LLC; *U.S. Private*, pg. 2868

AEROSTAR AIRPORT HOLDINGS, LLC—See Grupo Aeroportuario del Sureste, S.A.B. de C.V.; *Int'l*, pg. 3119

AEROSTAR AIRPORT HOLDINGS, LLC—See Public Sector Pension Investment Board; *Int'l*, pg. 6095

AEROSTAR INTERNATIONAL, INC.—See TCOM, L.P.; *U.S. Private*, pg. 3943

AEROSTAR S.A.; *Int'l*, pg. 181

AEROSTAR SES LLC—See Bristol Bay Native Corporation; *U.S. Private*, pg. 666

AEROSTRUCTURES ACQUISITION, LLC—See AE Industrial Partners, LP; *U.S. Private*, pg. 111

AEROSUN CORPORATION; *Int'l*, pg. 182

AEROSVIT AIRLINES; *Int'l*, pg. 182

AERO SYSTEMS WEST, INC.—See Nippon Kayaku Co., Ltd.; *Int'l*, pg. 5320

AEROTECH CHINA—See Aerotech Inc.; *U.S. Private*, pg. 119

AEROTECH CZECH S.R.O.—See OHB SE; *Int'l*, pg. 5532

AERO TECH DESIGNS CYCLING APPAREL; *U.S. Private*, pg. 118

AEROTECH FRANCE S.A.S.—See OHB SE; *Int'l*, pg. 5532

AEROTECH GMBH—See Aerotech World Trade Corp.; *U.S. Private*, pg. 120

AEROTECH HOLLAND B.V.—See Aerotech World Trade Corp.; *U.S. Private*, pg. 120

AEROTECH INC.; *U.S. Private*, pg. 119

AEROTECH KK—See Aerotech Inc.; *U.S. Private*, pg. 119

AEROTECH LTD—See Aerotech Inc.; *U.S. Private*, pg. 119

AERO TECH MANUFACTURING INC.; *U.S. Private*, pg. 118

AEROTECH TAIWAN—See Aerotech Inc.; *U.S. Private*, pg. 119

AEROTECHTELUB TEST SYSTEMS AB—See Saab AB; *Int'l*, pg. 6460

AEROTECH WORLD TRADE CO., LTD.—See Aerotech World Trade Corp.; *U.S. Private*, pg. 120

AEROTECH WORLD TRADE CORP.; *U.S. Private*, pg. 120

AEROTECH WORLD TRADE LTD.—See Aerotech World Trade Corp.; *U.S. Private*, pg. 120

AEROTECH WORLD TRADE LTD.—See Aerotech World Trade Corp.; *U.S. Private*, pg. 120

AEROTEK, INC.—See Allegis Group, Inc.; *U.S. Private*, pg. 177

AEROTEST OPERATIONS, INC.—See Autoliv, Inc.; *Int'l*, pg. 729

AE ROTOR HOLDING B.V.—See Suzlon Energy Ltd.; *Int'l*, pg. 7353

AERO TRADING COMPANY LIMITED—See TOHTO SUISAN Co., Ltd.; *Int'l*, pg. 7777

AERO TRANSPORTATION PRODUCTS, INC—See Westinghouse Air Brake Technologies Corporation; *U.S. Public*, pg. 2357

AEROTURBINE ASIA PTE LTD—See AerCap Holdings N.V.; *Int'l*, pg. 179

AEROTURBINE EUROPE LIMITED—See AerCap Holdings N.V.; *Int'l*, pg. 179

AEROTURBINE, INC.—See AerCap Holdings N.V.; *Int'l*, pg. 179

AEROVATE THERAPEUTICS, INC.; *U.S. Public*, pg. 52

AEROVENT—See Twin City Fan Companies, Ltd.; *U.S. Private*, pg. 4265

AEROVIAS DEL CONTINENTE AMERICANO S.A.—See Synergy Group; *Int'l*, pg. 7384

AEROVIAS DE MEXICO, S.A. DE C.V.—See Grupo Aeromexico, S.A.B. de C.V.; *Int'l*, pg. 3118

AEROVIAS DE MEXICO, S.A. DE C.V. - USA SALES OFFICE—See Grupo Aeromexico, S.A.B. de C.V.; *Int'l*, pg. 3118

AEROVIRONMENT, INC.; *U.S. Public*, pg. 52

AEROVISION INTERNATIONAL, LLC—See LKQ Corporation; *U.S. Public*, pg. 1333

AEROVOX CORP.—See Buckingham Capital, LLC; *U.S. Private*, pg. 677

AEROWASH AB; *Int'l*, pg. 182

AERO WIN TECHNOLOGY CORPORATION; *Int'l*, pg. 180

AEROWORKS (ASIA) LTD.—See HEICO Corporation; *U.S. Public*, pg. 1019

AEROWORKS EUROPE B.V.—See HEICO Corporation; *U.S. Public*, pg. 1019

AEROX AVIATION OXYGEN SYSTEMS, LLC—See O2 Aero Acquisitions LLC; *U.S. Private*, pg. 2981

AERO ZAGREB D.O.O.—See Aero d.d.; *Int'l*, pg. 180

AERPACE INDUSTRIES LTD.—See Intellivate Capital Ventures Limited; *Int'l*, pg. 3734

A ERP COMPANY LIMITED—See AAPICO Hitech plc; *Int'l*, pg. 37

AERRE S.R.L.—See Edizione S.r.l.; *Int'l*, pg. 2311

AERSALE AVIATION, LTD.—See Leonard Green & Partners, L.P.; *U.S. Private*, pg. 2424

AERSALE CORP; *U.S. Public*, pg. 53

AERSALE HOLDINGS, INC.—See Leonard Green & Partners, L.P.; *U.S. Private*, pg. 2423

AERSALE, INC.—See Leonard Green & Partners, L.P.; *U.S. Private*, pg. 2423

AERSALE SINGAPORE—See Leonard Green & Partners, L.P.; *U.S. Private*, pg. 2424

AER TECHNOLOGIES, INC.; *U.S. Private*, pg. 117

AERTICKET AG; *Int'l*, pg. 182

AER TRE S.P.A.—See InfraVia Capital Partners SAS; *Int'l*, pg. 3699

AE RUBBER SDN. BHD.—See Blackstone Inc.; *U.S. Public*, pg. 354

AERUS ELECTROLUX CANADA—See Aerus LLC; *U.S. Private*, pg. 120

AERUS LLC; *U.S. Private*, pg. 120

AERVA, INC.—See H.I.G. Capital, LLC; *U.S. Private*, pg. 1834

AERVOE INDUSTRIES INCORPORATED; *U.S. Private*, pg. 120

AERWINS INC—See AERWINS Technologies Inc.; *Int'l*, pg. 182

AERWINS TECHNOLOGIES INC.; *Int'l*, pg. 182

AERZTEMEDIKA AG—See Zur Rose Group AG; *Int'l*, pg. 8696

AESA AIR ENGINEERING PRIVATE LIMITED—See Batliboi Ltd.; *Int'l*, pg. 890

AESA AIR ENGINEERING SA—See Batliboi Ltd.; *Int'l*, pg. 890

AES ANDES, INC.—See The AES Corporation; *U.S. Public*, pg. 2030

AES ANDES SA—See The AES Corporation; *U.S. Public*, pg. 2030

AES ASSET ACQUISITION CORPORATION—See Compass Diversified Holdings; *U.S. Public*, pg. 559

AES BALLYLUMFORD LIMITED—See The AES Corporation; *U.S. Public*, pg. 2030

AES BALLYLUMFORD—See The AES Corporation; *U.S. Public*, pg. 2030

AES BRASIL ENERGIA SA; *Int'l*, pg. 182

AES BULGARIA TRADING EOOD—See The AES Corporation; *U.S. Public*, pg. 2030

AES CHENGDU—See The AES Corporation; *U.S. Public*, pg. 2030

AES CHIVOR & CIA S.C.A. E.S.P.—See The AES Corporation; *U.S. Public*, pg. 2030

AES CLEAN TECHNOLOGY INC.; *U.S. Private*, pg. 120

THE AES CORPORATION; *U.S. Public*, pg. 2030

AESCU DATA GESELLSCHAFT FUR DATENVERARBEITUNG MBH—See CompuGroup Medical SE & Co. KGaA; *Int'l*, pg. 1755

AESCUDATA GMBH—See CompuGroup Medical SE & Co. KGaA; *Int'l*, pg. 1755

AESCULAP 98 BT.—See PHOENIX Pharmahandel GmbH & Co. KG; *Int'l*, pg. 5854

AESCULAP AG & CO. KG—See B. Braun Melsungen AG; *Int'l*, pg. 785

AESCULAP CHIFA SP. Z OO.—See B. Braun Melsungen AG; *Int'l*, pg. 785

AESCULAP FLEXIMED GMBH—See B. Braun Melsungen AG; *Int'l*, pg. 785

AESCULAP, INC.—See B. Braun Melsungen AG; *Int'l*, pg. 785

AESCULAPIO S.R.L.—See Garofalo Health Care SpA; *Int'l*, pg. 2886

AESCULAP S.A.—See B. Braun Melsungen AG; *Int'l*, pg. 785

AESCULAP SUHL GMBH—See B. Braun Melsungen AG; *Int'l*, pg. 785

AESP, INC.

A.E.S. DESTRUCTIVE & NON-DESTRUCTIVE TESTING LTD.—See Offshore Oil Engineering Company Limited; *Int'l*, pg. 5530

AES DISTRIBUTED ENERGY, INC.—See The AES Corporation; *U.S. Public*, pg. 2030

AES DPL HOLDINGS, LLC—See The AES Corporation; *U.S. Public*, pg. 2030

AES DRAX POWER FINANCE HOLDINGS LIMITED—See The AES Corporation; *U.S. Public*, pg. 2030

AES DRILLING FLUIDS, LLC—See CES Energy Solutions Corp.; *Int'l*, pg. 1423

A & E SECURITY NV—See Stanley Black & Decker, Inc.; *U.S. Public*, pg. 1931

AES ELECTRICAL, INC.; *U.S. Private*, pg. 120

AES ELSTA BV—See The AES Corporation; *U.S. Public*, pg. 2030

AES ENERJI LIMITED SIRKETI—See The AES Corporation; *U.S. Public*, pg. 2030

AES ENVIRONMENTAL LLC—See Enviri Corporation; *U.S. Public*, pg. 780

AES FAMATEC—See FAYAT SAS; *Int'l*, pg. 2624

A ESFERA DOS LIVROS S.L.U.—See RCS MediaGroup S.p.A.; *Int'l*, pg. 6229

AES GLOBAL HOLDINGS PTE LTD.—See Advanced Energy Industries, Inc.; *U.S. Public*, pg. 47

AES GLOBAL INSURANCE COMPANY—See The AES Corporation; *U.S. Public*, pg. 2030

AES HAMES LLC—See The AES Corporation; *U.S. Public*, pg. 2030

AES HUNTINGTON BEACH, L.L.C.—See The AES Corporation; *U.S. Public*, pg. 2031

AESICA PHARMACEUTICALS LIMITED—See Pharmaron Beijing Co., Ltd.; *Int'l*, pg. 5841

AESI (HK) LIMITED—See Mobicon Group Limited; *Int'l*, pg. 5009

AES INDUSTRIES, INC.—See Lennox International Inc.; *U.S. Public*, pg. 1307

AES (IRELAND) LIMITED—See Bord na Mona Plc; *Int'l*, pg. 1113

AES KALAELOA VENTURE, L.L.C.—See The AES Corporation; *U.S. Public*, pg. 2031

AES KILROOT POWER LIMITED—See The AES Corporation; *U.S. Public*, pg. 2031

AESKU.DIAGNOSTICS GMBH & CO. KG; *Int'l*, pg. 182

AESKULAB HOLDING, A.S.—See Mid Europa Partners LLP; *Int'l*, pg. 4882

AES LAL PIR (PVT) LTD.—See The AES Corporation; *U.S. Public*, pg. 2031

AES LOGISTICS, INC.; *U.S. Private*, pg. 120

AES MERIDA MANAGEMENT SERVICES, S. DE R.L. DE C.V.—See The AES Corporation; *U.S. Public*, pg. 2031

AES MERIDA OPERACIONES SRL DE CV—See The AES Corporation; *U.S. Public*, pg. 2031

A.E. SMITH SERVICE PTY LTD—See Downer EDI Limited; *Int'l*, pg. 2185

A.E. SMITH & SON PROPRIETARY LIMITED—See Downer EDI Limited; *Int'l*, pg. 2185

AESO HOLDING LIMITED; *Int'l*, pg. 182

AES PACIFIC OCEAN HOLDINGS B.V.—See The AES Corporation; *U.S. Public*, pg. 2031

AES PANAMA S.A.—See The AES Corporation; *U.S. Public*, pg. 2031

AES PANAMA, S.R.L.—See The AES Corporation; *U.S. Public*, pg. 2031

AESP, INC.; *U.S. Private*, pg. 120

AES POLAND WIND SP.Z O.O.—See The AES Corporation; *U.S. Public*, pg. 2031

AES PORTLAOISE—See Bord na Mona Plc; *Int'l*, pg. 1113

AES PUERTO RICO, L.P.—See The AES Corporation; *U.S. Public*, pg. 2031

AESPULA TECHNOLOGY INC.—See Alpha Networks Inc.; *Int'l*, pg. 369

AES RED OAK, L.L.C.—See The AES Corporation; *U.S. Public*, pg. 2031

A.E. SRL—See FLY Srl; *Int'l*, pg. 2715

AESSEAL ARGENTINA SA—See AESSEAL Plc; *Int'l*, pg. 182

AESSEAL AUSTRALIA PTY LTD—See AESSEAL Plc; *Int'l*, pg. 182

AESSEAL BENELUX BV—See AESSEAL Plc; *Int'l*, pg. 182

AESSEAL BRASIL LTDA—See AESSEAL Plc; *Int'l*, pg. 182

AESSEAL CANADA INC.—See AESSEAL Plc; *Int'l*, pg. 182

AESSEAL CARIBBEAN LIMITED—See AESSEAL Plc; *Int'l*, pg. 182

AESSEAL CHILE SA—See AESSEAL Plc; *Int'l*, pg. 182

AESSEAL CHINA LTD.—See AESSEAL Plc; *Int'l*, pg. 182

AESSEAL COLOMBIA S.A.—See AESSEAL Plc; *Int'l*, pg. 183

AESSEAL CZECH S.R.O.—See AESSEAL Plc; *Int'l*, pg. 182

AESSEAL DANMARK A/S—See AESSEAL Plc; *Int'l*, pg. 182

AESSEAL DEUTSCHLAND GMBH—See AESSEAL Plc; *Int'l*, pg. 182

AESSEAL FINLAND OY—See AESSEAL Plc; *Int'l*, pg. 182

AESSEAL FRANCE SAS—See AESSEAL Plc; *Int'l*, pg. 182

AESSEAL IBERICA S.L.—See AESSEAL Plc; *Int'l*, pg. 182

AESP, INC. — CORPORATE AFFILIATIONS

AESSEAL INC.—See AESSEAL Plc; *Int'l*, pg. 182
AESSEAL INDIA PRIVATE LIMITED—See AESSEAL Plc; *Int'l*, pg. 182
AESSEAL IRELAND LTD—See AESSEAL Plc; *Int'l*, pg. 183
AESSEAL ITALIA S.R.L.—See AESSEAL Plc; *Int'l*, pg. 182
AESSEAL MEXICO S. DE R.L. DE C.V.—See AESSEAL Plc; *Int'l*, pg. 182
AESSEAL MIDDLE EAST FZE—See AESSEAL Plc; *Int'l*, pg. 182
AESSEAL (M) SDN BHD—See AESSEAL Plc; *Int'l*, pg. 182
AESSEAL NORWAY AS—See AESSEAL Plc; *Int'l*, pg. 182
AESSEAL PLC; *Int'l*, pg. 182
AESSEAL POLSKA SP. Z O.O.—See AESSEAL Plc; *Int'l*, pg. 182
AESSEAL PTY LTD—See AESSEAL Plc; *Int'l*, pg. 182
AESSEAL SAUDI ARABIA CO. LTD.—See AESSEAL Plc; *Int'l*, pg. 182
AESSEAL SIZDIRMAZLIK SISTEMLERI TIC.LTD.STI.—See AESSEAL Plc; *Int'l*, pg. 183
AESSEAL (SWEDEN) AB—See AESSEAL Plc; *Int'l*, pg. 182
AESSEAL TAIWAN CO., LTD—See AESSEAL Plc; *Int'l*, pg. 182
AESSEAL UNIVEDA LDA—See AESSEAL Plc; *Int'l*, pg. 182
AES SERVICES, INC.—See The AES Corporation; *U.S. Public*, pg. 2031
AES SERVICIOS AMERICA S.R. L.—See The AES Corporation; *U.S. Public*, pg. 2031
AES SHADY POINT LLC—See OGE Energy Corp.; *U.S. Public*, pg. 1564
AES SIGORTA ARAC. HIZM. A.S.—See Loras Holding A.S.; *Int'l*, pg. 4557
AES SOLAR ALCUDIA, S.L.—See The AES Corporation; *U.S. Public*, pg. 2031
AES SONEL S.A.—See General Atlantic Service Company, L.P.; *U.S. Private*, pg. 1661
AES SOUTHLAND, LLC—See The AES Corporation; *U.S. Public*, pg. 2031
AES TEG OPERATIONS, S. DE R.L. DE C.V.—See The AES Corporation; *U.S. Public*, pg. 2031
AESTHETIC AND RECONSTRUCTIVE CENTRE PTE. LTD.—See Pacific Healthcare Holdings Ltd.; *Int'l*, pg. 5689
AESTHETIC MEDICAL CENTRE PTE LTD—See Asia-Medic Ltd.; *Int'l*, pg. 616
AESTHETIC MEDICAL INTERNATIONAL HOLDINGS GROUP LIMITED; *Int'l*, pg. 183
AESTHETIC MOBILE LASER SERVICES, INC.—See Sensus Healthcare, Inc.; *U.S. Public*, pg. 1868
AESTHETIC ZECRET (AT-ZE) COMPANY LIMITED—See Winner Group Enterprise Public Company Limited; *Int'l*, pg. 8429
AES-TISZA EROMU KFT—See The AES Corporation; *U.S. Public*, pg. 2031
A&E STORES, INC.; *U.S. Private*, pg. 20
AES TULLAMORE—See Bord na Mona Plc; *Int'l*, pg. 1113
AES URUGUAIANA EMPREENDIMENTOS S.A.—See The AES Corporation; *U.S. Public*, pg. 2031
AES WARRIOR RUN, INC.—See The AES Corporation; *U.S. Public*, pg. 2031
AESYNT HOLDINGS, INC.—See Omnicell, Inc.; *U.S. Public*, pg. 1572
AESYNT, INC.—See Omnicell, Inc.; *U.S. Public*, pg. 1572
AESYS TECHNOLOGIES, LLC; *U.S. Private*, pg. 120
AETC LIMITED—See Berkshire Hathaway Inc.; *U.S. Public*, pg. 314
AETEA INFORMATION TECHNOLOGY INC.—See Great Mill Rock LLC; *U.S. Private*, pg. 1766
A&E TELEVISION NETWORKS, LLC - DETROIT OFFICE—See The Hearst Corporation; *U.S. Private*, pg. 4045
A&E TELEVISION NETWORKS, LLC - DETROIT OFFICE—See The Walt Disney Company; *U.S. Public*, pg. 2137
A&E TELEVISION NETWORKS, LLC—See The Hearst Corporation; *U.S. Private*, pg. 4045
A&E TELEVISION NETWORKS, LLC—See The Walt Disney Company; *U.S. Public*, pg. 2137
AETERNA ZENTARIS GMBH—See COSCIENS Biopharma Inc.; *U.S. Public*, pg. 585
AETHER CATALYST SOLUTIONS, INC.; *Int'l*, pg. 183
AETHERCOMM INC.—See Veritas Capital Fund Management, LLC; *U.S. Private*, pg. 4362
AETHER CONSULTING INC.—See BrainSell Technologies, LLC; *U.S. Private*, pg. 634
AETHER GLOBAL INNOVATIONS CORP.; *Int'l*, pg. 183
AETHER INDUSTRIES LIMITED; *Int'l*, pg. 183
AETHER INVESTMENT PARTNERS, LLC—See Pacific Current Group Limited; *Int'l*, pg. 5688
AETHERIUM ACQUISITION CORP.; *U.S. Public*, pg. 53
AETHERPAL INC.—See Broadcom Inc.; *U.S. Public*, pg. 390
AETHERPAL (INDIA) PRIVATE LIMITED—See Broadcom Inc.; *U.S. Public*, pg. 390
AETHERTEK TECHNOLOGY CO., LTD.; *Int'l*, pg. 183

AETHER WATER SYSTEMS, LLC—See Nephros, Inc.; *U.S. Public*, pg. 1506
AETHLON MEDICAL, INC.; *U.S. Public*, pg. 53
AET HOLDINGS, LLC; *U.S. Private*, pg. 120
AETHON INC.—See Temasek Holdings (Private) Limited; *Int'l*, pg. 7552
AETHON MINERALS CORP.—See AbraSilver Resource Corp.; *Int'l*, pg. 67
AET ITALIA SPA—See Azienda Elettrica Ticinese; *Int'l*, pg. 778
AETNA BEARING COMPANY; *U.S. Private*, pg. 120
AETNA BETTER HEALTH INC.—See CVS Health Corporation; *U.S. Public*, pg. 614
AETNA BETTER HEALTH, INC.—See CVS Health Corporation; *U.S. Public*, pg. 614
AETNA BETTER HEALTH INC.—See CVS Health Corporation; *U.S. Public*, pg. 614
AETNA BETTER HEALTH INC.—See CVS Health Corporation; *U.S. Public*, pg. 614
AETNA BETTER HEALTH INC.—See CVS Health Corporation; *U.S. Public*, pg. 614
AETNA BETTER HEALTH INC.—See CVS Health Corporation; *U.S. Public*, pg. 614
AETNA BETTER HEALTH INC.—See CVS Health Corporation; *U.S. Public*, pg. 614
AETNA BETTER HEALTH INC.—See CVS Health Corporation; *U.S. Public*, pg. 614
AETNA BETTER HEALTH OF CALIFORNIA INC.—See CVS Health Corporation; *U.S. Public*, pg. 614
AETNA BETTER HEALTH OF FLORIDA INC.—See CVS Health Corporation; *U.S. Public*, pg. 614
AETNA BETTER HEALTH OF FLORIDA INC.—See CVS Health Corporation; *U.S. Public*, pg. 613
AETNA BETTER HEALTH OF KANSAS INC.—See CVS Health Corporation; *U.S. Public*, pg. 614
AETNA BETTER HEALTH OF KENTUCKY INSURANCE COMPANY—See CVS Health Corporation; *U.S. Public*, pg. 614
AETNA BETTER HEALTH OF MICHIGAN INC.—See CVS Health Corporation; *U.S. Public*, pg. 614
AETNA BETTER HEALTH OF MICHIGAN INC.—See CVS Health Corporation; *U.S. Public*, pg. 614
AETNA BETTER HEALTH PREMIER PLAN MMAI INC.—See CVS Health Corporation; *U.S. Public*, pg. 613
AETNA BRIDGE COMPANY; *U.S. Private*, pg. 120
AETNA BUILDING MAINTENANCE, INC.; *U.S. Private*, pg. 120
AETNA CAPITAL MANAGEMENT, LLC—See CVS Health Corporation; *U.S. Public*, pg. 614
AETNA CONSTRUCTION CO. INC.—See Aetna Bridge Company; *U.S. Private*, pg. 120
AETNA CONSTRUCTION, INC.—See Oxford Holdings Inc.; *U.S. Private*, pg. 3057
AETNA FELT CORP.—See Industrial Opportunity Partners, LLC; *U.S. Private*, pg. 2067
AETNA FREIGHT LINES, INC.—See Transport Investments, Inc.; *U.S. Private*, pg. 4210
AETNA GLOBAL BENEFITS (ASIA PACIFIC) LIMITED—See CVS Health Corporation; *U.S. Public*, pg. 614
AETNA GLOBAL BENEFITS (EUROPE) LIMITED—See CVS Health Corporation; *U.S. Public*, pg. 614
AETNA GLOBAL BENEFITS LIMITED—See CVS Health Corporation; *U.S. Public*, pg. 614
AETNA GLOBAL BENEFITS (MIDDLE EAST) LLC—See CVS Health Corporation; *U.S. Public*, pg. 613
AETNA GLOBAL BENEFITS (UK) LIMITED—See CVS Health Corporation; *U.S. Public*, pg. 614
AETNA HEALTH HOLDINGS, LLC—See CVS Health Corporation; *U.S. Public*, pg. 614
AETNA HEALTH INC. (CONNECTICUT)—See CVS Health Corporation; *U.S. Public*, pg. 614
AETNA HEALTH INC. (NEW YORK)—See CVS Health Corporation; *U.S. Public*, pg. 614
AETNA HEALTH INC. (PENNSYLVANIA)—See CVS Health Corporation; *U.S. Public*, pg. 614
AETNA HEALTH INC.—See CVS Health Corporation; *U.S. Public*, pg. 614
AETNA HEALTH INC.—See CVS Health Corporation; *U.S. Public*, pg. 614
AETNA HEALTH INSURANCE (THAILAND) PUBLIC COMPANY LIMITED—See CVS Health Corporation; *U.S. Public*, pg. 615
AETNA HEALTH OF CALIFORNIA INC.—See CVS Health Corporation; *U.S. Public*, pg. 614
AETNA HEALTH OF IOWA INC.—See CVS Health Corporation; *U.S. Public*, pg. 614
AETNA HEALTH OF UTAH INC.—See CVS Health Corporation; *U.S. Public*, pg. 614
AETNA HEALTH SERVICES (UK) LIMITED—See CVS Health Corporation; *U.S. Public*, pg. 615
AETNA INC.—See CVS Health Corporation; *U.S. Public*, pg. 614
AETNA INSURANCE COMPANY LIMITED—See CVS Health Corporation; *U.S. Public*, pg. 615
AETNA INSURANCE (SINGAPORE) PTE. LTD.—See CVS Health Corporation; *U.S. Public*, pg. 615
AETNA INTELIHEALTH INC.—See CVS Health Corporation; *U.S. Public*, pg. 615

AETNA MEDICAID ADMINISTRATORS LLC—See CVS Health Corporation; *U.S. Public*, pg. 614
AETNA MULTI-STRATEGY 1099 FUND—See CVS Health Corporation; *U.S. Public*, pg. 615
AETNA PLASTICS CORP.—See Bain Capital, LP; *U.S. Private*, pg. 432
AETNA PLYWOOD, INC.; *U.S. Private*, pg. 120
AETNA REALTY FINANCIAL CORP.—See United States Realty & Investment Company; *U.S. Private*, pg. 4299
AETNA SERVICE CENTER—See CVS Health Corporation; *U.S. Public*, pg. 615
AETNA (SHANGHAI) ENTERPRISE SERVICES CO. LTD.—See CVS Health Corporation; *U.S. Public*, pg. 614
AETNA (SHANGHAI) ENTERPRISE SERVICES CO. LTD.—See CVS Health Corporation; *U.S. Public*, pg. 614
AETNA SPECIALTY PHARMACY, LLC—See CVS Health Corporation; *U.S. Public*, pg. 614
AETNA STUDENT HEALTH AGENCY INC.—See CVS Health Corporation; *U.S. Public*, pg. 614
AETOS CAPITAL REAL ESTATE, LP; *U.S. Private*, pg. 120
AETOS CONSTRUCTION COMPANY—See Giant Eagle, Inc.; *U.S. Private*, pg. 1694
AETOS GROUP, INC.—See Mistras Group, Inc.; *U.S. Public*, pg. 1451
AET SUPER SOLUTIONS PTY LIMITED—See Insignia Financial Ltd.; *Int'l*, pg. 3718
AEVA, INC.—See Aeva Technologies, Inc.; *U.S. Public*, pg. 53
AEV - AMERICAN EMERGENCY VEHICLES—See AIP, LLC; *U.S. Private*, pg. 135
A-EVANGELISTA S.A.—See YPF S.A.; *Int'l*, pg. 8605
AEVA TECHNOLOGIES, INC.; *U.S. Public*, pg. 53
AEV CRH HOLDINGS, INC.—See Aboitiz Equity Ventures, Inc.; *Int'l*, pg. 66
AEV CRH HOLDINGS, INC.—See CRH plc; *Int'l*, pg. 1842
AEVEX AEROSPACE; *U.S. Private*, pg. 120
AEVI CZ S.R.O—See Diebold Nixdorf, Inc.; *U.S. Public*, pg. 659
AEVI GENOMIC MEDICINE, LLC—See Avalo Therapeutics, Inc.; *U.S. Public*, pg. 239
AEVI INTERNATIONAL GMBH—See Diebold Nixdorf, Inc.; *U.S. Public*, pg. 659
AEVIS EUROPA, S.L.—See Banco Santander, S.A.; *Int'l*, pg. 825
AEVIS VICTORIA SA; *Int'l*, pg. 183
AEVITAS, INC.; *Int'l*, pg. 183
AEVITAS SPECIALTY SERVICES CORP.—See Aevitas, Inc.; *Int'l*, pg. 183
AEVI UK LIMITED—See Diebold Nixdorf, Inc.; *U.S. Public*, pg. 659
AEW ASIA LIMITED—See Groupe BPCE; *Int'l*, pg. 3092
AEW ASIA PTE. LTD.—See Groupe BPCE; *Int'l*, pg. 3092
AEW CAPITAL MANAGEMENT, L.P.—See Groupe BPCE; *Int'l*, pg. 3096
AEW CENTRAL EUROPE SP. Z O.O.—See Groupe BPCE; *Int'l*, pg. 3092
AEW CILOGER—See Groupe BPCE; *Int'l*, pg. 3096
A.E. WEASE INC.; *U.S. Private*, pg. 25
AEW EUROPE—See Groupe BPCE; *Int'l*, pg. 3096
AEW GLOBAL LIMITED—See Groupe BPCE; *Int'l*, pg. 3096
AEWIN TECH INC.—See AEWIN Technologies Co., Ltd.; *Int'l*, pg. 183
AEWIN TECHNOLOGIES CO., LTD.; *Int'l*, pg. 183
AEW INVEST GMBH—See Groupe BPCE; *Int'l*, pg. 3092
AE WORKS LTD.; *U.S. Private*, pg. 112
AEW UK REIT PLC; *Int'l*, pg. 183
AEXCEL CORP.; *U.S. Private*, pg. 121
AEXIS FRANCE—See Aexis N.V.; *Int'l*, pg. 183
AEXIS MEDICAL BVBA—See STERIS plc; *Int'l*, pg. 7208
AEXIS NEDERLAND—See Aexis N.V.; *Int'l*, pg. 183
AEXIS N.V.; *Int'l*, pg. 183
AEYE, INC.; *U.S. Public*, pg. 53
AF1 CAPITAL CORP.; *Int'l*, pg. 184
AF ACQUISITION CORP.; *U.S. Public*, pg. 53
AF ADVANSIA AS—See AFRY AB; *Int'l*, pg. 193
AF ADVANSIA NORDVEST AS—See AFRY AB; *Int'l*, pg. 193
AF AERONMOLLIER AS—See AF Gruppen ASA; *Int'l*, pg. 184
AF AEROSPACE LIMITED—See Berkshire Hathaway Inc.; *U.S. Public*, pg. 313
AFAG AUTOMATION TECHNOLOGY (SHANGHAO) CO., LTD.—See Emerson Electric Co.; *U.S. Public*, pg. 740
AFAG GMBH—See Emerson Electric Co.; *U.S. Public*, pg. 740
AFAI SOUTHERN SHIPYARD (PANYU GUANGZHOU) LTD.—See China Shipbuilding Industry Company Limited; *Int'l*, pg. 1551
AFA JCDECAUX AS—See JCDecaux S.A.; *Int'l*, pg. 3920
AFA JCDECAUX ICELAND—See JCDecaux S.A.; *Int'l*, pg. 3920
AFA MASSACHUSETTS, INC.—See Wind Point Advisors LLC; *U.S. Private*, pg. 4535

COMPANY NAME INDEX

AFA PROTECTIVE SYSTEMS, INC. - ALTAMONTE SPRINGS, FLORIDA—See Wind Point Advisors LLC; *U.S. Private*, pg. 4535
AFA PROTECTIVE SYSTEMS, INC. - NATIONAL ACCOUNTS DIVISION—See Wind Point Advisors LLC; *U.S. Private*, pg. 4535
AFA PROTECTIVE SYSTEMS, INC. - NORTHERN NEW JERSEY—See Wind Point Advisors LLC; *U.S. Private*, pg. 4535
AFA PROTECTIVE SYSTEMS, INC.—See Wind Point Advisors LLC; *U.S. Private*, pg. 4535
AFAQ EDUCATIONAL SERVICES COMPANY—See Boubyan Petrochemical Co. KSC; *Int'l*, pg. 1119
AFAQ FOR ENERGY CO. PLC; *Int'l*, pg. 185
AFAQ HOLDING FOR INVESTMENT & REAL ESTATE DEVELOPMENT CO P.L.C.; *Int'l*, pg. 185
AFARAK DOO—See Afarak Group SE; *Int'l*, pg. 185
AFARAK GROUP SE; *Int'l*, pg. 185
AFARAK SOUTH AFRICA (PTY) LTD.—See Afarak Group SE; *Int'l*, pg. 185
AFARAK TRADING LTD.—See Afarak Group SE; *Int'l*, pg. 185
AFAS ERP SOFTWARE B.V.; *Int'l*, pg. 185
AFAS INC.—See BIPROGY Inc.; *Int'l*, pg. 1045
AFA SOUTHEAST, INC.—See Wind Point Advisors LLC; *U.S. Private*, pg. 4535
AF A/S—See AFRY AB; *Int'l*, pg. 194
AF-AUTOMAATIKA OU—See AFRY AB; *Int'l*, pg. 193
AF-AUTOMATIKKA OU—See AFRY AB; *Int'l*, pg. 193
AFBA - THE 5 STAR ASSOCIATION; *U.S. Private*, pg. 121
AFB INTERNATIONAL, INC.—See Incitec Pivot Limited; *Int'l*, pg. 3648
AF BYGG GOTEBORG AB—See AF Gruppen ASA; *Int'l*, pg. 184
AF BYGG SYD AB—See AF Gruppen ASA; *Int'l*, pg. 184
AFC AGRO BIOTECH LIMITED; *Int'l*, pg. 185
AFC AJAX NV; *Int'l*, pg. 185
AFC AQUISITION CORP.; *U.S. Private*, pg. 121
AFC CABLE SYSTEMS, INC.—See Clayton, Dubilier & Rice, LLC; *U.S. Private*, pg. 919
AFC CAPITAL LTD.—See Active Fine Chemicals Limited; *Int'l*, pg. 120
AFC CO., LTD.—See Aohata Corporation; *Int'l*, pg. 487
AFC ENERGY PLC; *Int'l*, pg. 185
AFC GAMMA, INC.; *U.S. Public*, pg. 53
AFC-HD AMS LIFE SCIENCE CO., LTD.; *Int'l*, pg. 185
AFC HEALTH LTD.—See Active Fine Chemicals Limited; *Int'l*, pg. 120
AFC-HOLCROFT LLC; *U.S. Private*, pg. 121
AFC INDUSTRIES, INC.—See Bertram Capital Management, LLC; *U.S. Private*, pg. 539
AFCO ACCEPTANCE CORPORATION—See Truist Financial Corporation; *U.S. Public*, pg. 2201
AFCO CREDIT CORPORATION—See Truist Financial Corporation; *U.S. Public*, pg. 2201
AFCO GLOBAL PORTS LLC—See Aviation Facilities Company, Inc.; *U.S. Private*, pg. 406
AFCO INDUSTRIES, INC.; *U.S. Private*, pg. 121
AF-COLENCO THAILAND LTD.—See AFRY AB; *Int'l*, pg. 193
AFCOM GROUP LIMITED—See The Bidvest Group Limited; *Int'l*, pg. 7621
AFCON HOLDINGS LTD.; *Int'l*, pg. 185
AFCONS INFRASTRUCTURE LIMITED—See Shapoorji Pallonji & Co. Ltd.; *Int'l*, pg. 6788
AF-CONSULT AB—See AFRY AB; *Int'l*, pg. 193
AF-CONSULT CZECH REPUBLIC S.R.O.—See AFRY AB; *Int'l*, pg. 193
AF CONSULT DO BRASIL LTDA.—See AFRY AB; *Int'l*, pg. 193
AF-CONSULT ENERGY DOO—See AFRY AB; *Int'l*, pg. 193
AF-CONSULT GMBH—See AFRY AB; *Int'l*, pg. 193
AF-CONSULT INDIA PVT. LTD.—See AFRY AB; *Int'l*, pg. 193
AF-CONSULT ITALY S.R.L.—See AFRY AB; *Int'l*, pg. 193
AF-CONSULT, LLC—See AFRY AB; *Int'l*, pg. 193
AF-CONSULT LTD.—See AFRY AB; *Int'l*, pg. 194
AF-CONSULT OY—See AFRY AB; *Int'l*, pg. 193
AF-CONSULT SWITZERLAND LTD.—See AFRY AB; *Int'l*, pg. 193
AF-CONSULT (THAILAND) LTD.—See AFRY AB; *Int'l*, pg. 193
AF-CONSULT UAB—See AFRY AB; *Int'l*, pg. 193
AFCO STEEL INC.; *U.S. Private*, pg. 121
AFCO STEEL—See W&W Steel Company Inc.; *U.S. Private*, pg. 4417
AFC STAMPING & PRODUCTION INC.—See F.C. Industries Inc.; *U.S. Private*, pg. 1456
A.F.C. TOOL COMPANY INC.—See F.C. Industries Inc.; *U.S. Private*, pg. 1456
AFCV HOLDINGS, LLC—See Summit Partners, L.P.; *U.S. Private*, pg. 3855
AFCV HOLDINGS, LLC—See TA Associates, Inc.; *U.S. Private*, pg. 3914
AFC WORLDWIDE EXPRESS INC.—See R & L Carriers, Inc.; *U.S. Private*, pg. 3331

AFD CONTRACT FURNITURE, INC.; *U.S. Private*, pg. 121
AF DECOM AS—See AF Gruppen ASA; *Int'l*, pg. 184
AFEED, A.S.—See Agrofert Holding, a.s.; *Int'l*, pg. 218
THE AFE GROUP LTD.—See Ali Holding S.r.l; *Int'l*, pg. 322
AFE INDUSTRIES, INC.; *U.S. Private*, pg. 121
AF ENERGIJA BALTIC UAB—See AF Gruppen ASA; *Int'l*, pg. 184
AF ENERGI & MILJOTEKNIKK AS—See AF Gruppen ASA; *Int'l*, pg. 184
AF ENERGI OG MILJO AS—See AF Gruppen ASA; *Int'l*, pg. 184
AF ENGINEERING AS—See AFRY AB; *Int'l*, pg. 193
AF-ENGINEERING OY—See AFRY AB; *Int'l*, pg. 193
AF-ENGINEERING S.R.O.—See AFRY AB; *Int'l*, pg. 193
A.F. ENTERPRISES LIMITED; *Int'l*, pg. 23
AFENTRA PLC; *Int'l*, pg. 185
AFERIAN PLC; *Int'l*, pg. 185
AF-ESTIVO AS—See AFRY AB; *Int'l*, pg. 193
AFEX INTERNATIONAL (HK) LIMITED—See AMCO United Holding Limited; *Int'l*, pg. 416
AFFCO EUROPE LIMITED—See AFFCO Holdings Limited; *Int'l*, pg. 185
AFFCO HOLDINGS LIMITED HOROTIU PLANT—See AFFCO Holdings Limited; *Int'l*, pg. 185
AFFCO HOLDINGS LIMITED IMLAY PLANT—See AFFCO Holdings Limited; *Int'l*, pg. 185
AFFCO HOLDINGS LIMITED INVERCARGILL PLANT—See AFFCO Holdings Limited; *Int'l*, pg. 186
AFFCO HOLDINGS LIMITED MALVERN PLANT—See AFFCO Holdings Limited; *Int'l*, pg. 186
AFFCO HOLDINGS LIMITED MANAWATU PLANT—See AFFCO Holdings Limited; *Int'l*, pg. 186
AFFCO HOLDINGS LIMITED - MOEREWA PLANT—See AFFCO Holdings Limited; *Int'l*, pg. 185
AFFCO HOLDINGS LIMITED RANGIURU PLANT—See AFFCO Holdings Limited; *Int'l*, pg. 186
AFFCO HOLDINGS LIMITED; *Int'l*, pg. 185
AFFCO HOLDINGS LIMITED WAIROA PLANT—See AFFCO Holdings Limited; *Int'l*, pg. 186
AFFCO HOLDINGS LIMITED WANGANUI PLANT—See AFFCO Holdings Limited; *Int'l*, pg. 186
AFFCO LLC; *U.S. Private*, pg. 121
AFFCO NEW ZEALAND LIMITED—See AFFCO Holdings Limited; *Int'l*, pg. 186
AFFECTO DENMARK A/S—See CGI Inc.; *Int'l*, pg. 1433
AFFECTO NORWAY AS—See CGI Inc.; *Int'l*, pg. 1433
AFFECTO PLC—See CGI Inc.; *Int'l*, pg. 1433
AFFECTO POLAND SP.Z. O.O.—See CGI Inc.; *Int'l*, pg. 1433
AFFECTO SWEDEN AB—See CGI Inc.; *Int'l*, pg. 1433
AFFERENT PHARMACEUTICALS, INC.—See Merck & Co., Inc.; *U.S. Public*, pg. 1415
AFFERO LAB PARTICIPACOES S.A.—See Bertelsmann SE & Co. KGaA; *Int'l*, pg. 989
AFFICHAGE ROMANIA SRL; *Int'l*, pg. 186
AFFIDEA B.V. - OPERATIONS HEADQUARTERS—See B-FLEXION Group Holdings SA; *Int'l*, pg. 785
AFFIDEA B.V.—See B-FLEXION Group Holdings SA; *Int'l*, pg. 785
AFFIDEA GROUP B.V.—See B-FLEXION Group Holdings SA; *Int'l*, pg. 785
AFFILIATED BANK, N.A; *U.S. Public*, pg. 53
AFFILIATED COMPUTER SERVICES GMBH—See Conduent Incorporated; *U.S. Public*, pg. 566
AFFILIATED DISTRIBUTORS INC.; *U.S. Private*, pg. 121
AFFILIATED ENDOSCOPY SERVICES OF CLIFTON, LLC—See KKR & Co. Inc.; *U.S. Public*, pg. 1244
AFFILIATED ENGINEERS, INC.; *U.S. Private*, pg. 121
AFFILIATED FINANCE INC.—See Affiliated Foods, Inc.; *U.S. Private*, pg. 122
AFFILIATED FM INSURANCE COMPANY—See Factory Mutual Insurance Company; *U.S. Private*, pg. 1460
AFFILIATED FOODS, INC.; *U.S. Private*, pg. 121
AFFILIATED FOOD STORES, INC.; *U.S. Private*, pg. 121
AFFILIATED HEALTHCARE SYSTEMS, INC.—See Eastern Maine Healthcare Systems; *U.S. Private*, pg. 1320
AFFILIATED LABORATORY, INC.—See Eastern Maine Healthcare Systems; *U.S. Private*, pg. 1320
AFFILIATED MANAGERS GROUP, INC.; *U.S. Public*, pg. 53
AFFILIATED MANAGERS GROUP LIMITED—See Affiliated Managers Group, Inc.; *U.S. Public*, pg. 53
AFFILIATED MANAGERS GROUP (SWITZERLAND) AG—See Affiliated Managers Group, Inc.; *U.S. Public*, pg. 53
AFFILIATED PUBLISHERS, INC.; *U.S. Private*, pg. 122
AFFILIATED RESOURCES, INC.—See Forest City Trading Group, LLC; *U.S. Private*, pg. 1566
AFFILIATED STEAM EQUIPMENT CO. - INDIANAPOLIS—See Affiliated Steam Equipment Company; *U.S. Private*, pg. 122
AFFILIATED STEAM EQUIPMENT COMPANY; *U.S. Private*, pg. 122
AFFILIATED STEAM EQUIPMENT CO. - WISCONSIN—See Affiliated Steam Equipment Company; *U.S. Private*, pg. 122

AFFINITY, INC.

AFFILIATED WASTEWATER ENVIRONMENTAL SERVICES, LLC—See The Pritzker Group - Chicago, LLC; *U.S. Private*, pg. 4100
AFFILIATEFUTURE INC.—See GlobalData Plc; *Int'l*, pg. 3003
AFFILIATEFUTURE UK—See GlobalData Plc; *Int'l*, pg. 3003
AFFILIATE SALES & MARKETING, INC—See Qurate Retail, Inc.; *U.S. Public*, pg. 1758
AFFILIATE TRACTION—See eBay Inc.; *U.S. Public*, pg. 709
AFFILINET SCHWEIZ GMBH—See Axel Springer SE; *Int'l*, pg. 767
AFFIMED GMBH—See Affimed N.V.; *Int'l*, pg. 186
AFFIMED N.V.; *Int'l*, pg. 186
AFFIMEX CORED WIRE S. DE R.L. DE C.V.—See SKW Stahl-Metallurgie Holding AG; *Int'l*, pg. 6991
AFFINAGE CHAMPAGNE ARDENNES; *Int'l*, pg. 186
AFFINE S.A.; *Int'l*, pg. 186
AFFIN HOLDINGS BERHAD; *Int'l*, pg. 186
AFFIN HWANG ASSET MANAGEMENT BERHAD—See AFFIN Holdings Berhad; *Int'l*, pg. 186
AFFIN HWANG FUTURES SDN. BHD.—See AFFIN Holdings Berhad; *Int'l*, pg. 186
AFFIN HWANG INVESTMENT BANK BERHAD—See AFFIN Holdings Berhad; *Int'l*, pg. 186
AFFINIA HOSPITALITY; *U.S. Private*, pg. 122
AFFINIA THERAPEUTICS INC.; *U.S. Private*, pg. 122
AFFINIPAY, LLC; *U.S. Private*, pg. 122
AFFINISCAPE, INC.—See Insight Venture Management, LLC; *U.S. Private*, pg. 2088
THE AFFINIS GROUP; *U.S. Private*, pg. 3983
AFFINITAS CORPORATION; *U.S. Private*, pg. 122
AFFINITAS GMBH—See Spark Networks SE; *Int'l*, pg. 7126
AFFINITAS MARKETING, INC.—See Affinitas Corporation; *U.S. Private*, pg. 122
AFFINITECH, INC.; *U.S. Private*, pg. 122
AFFINI TECHNOLOGY LTD.—See Team Telecommunications Group Ltd.; *Int'l*, pg. 7500
AFFINITI INTEGRATED SOLUTIONS LTD.—See Macquarie Group Limited; *Int'l*, pg. 4626
AFFINITI LLC; *U.S. Private*, pg. 122
AFFINITIVE LLC—See Project: Worldwide, Inc.; *U.S. Private*, pg. 3280
AFFINITIV, INC.; *U.S. Private*, pg. 122
AFFINITY BANCSHARES, INC.; *U.S. Public*, pg. 56
AFFINITY BANK, NATIONAL ASSOCIATION—See Affinity Bancshares, Inc.; *U.S. Public*, pg. 56
AFFINITY BEAUTY BRANDS; *U.S. Private*, pg. 122
AFFINITY BEVERAGE GROUP, INC.; *U.S. Public*, pg. 57
AFFINITY BUILDING SYSTEMS, LLC—See Vantem Global, Inc.; *U.S. Private*, pg. 4345
AFFINITY CARDIO-THORACIC SPECIALISTS, LLC—See Community Health Systems, Inc.; *U.S. Public*, pg. 551
AFFINITY CARDIOVASCULAR SPECIALISTS, LLC—See Community Health Systems, Inc.; *U.S. Public*, pg. 551
AFFINITY DISPLAY & EXPOSITION; *U.S. Private*, pg. 122
AFFINITY EDUCATION GROUP LIMITED—See Anchorage Capital Partners Pty. Limited; *Int'l*, pg. 448
AFFINITY ELEVATOR COMPANY, LLC—See L Squared Capital Management LP; *U.S. Private*, pg. 2362
AFFINITY ENERGY AND HEALTH LIMITED; *Int'l*, pg. 186
AFFINITY EQUITY PARTNERS (AUSTRALIA) PTY. LTD.—See Affinity Equity Partners (HK) Ltd.; *Int'l*, pg. 186
AFFINITY EQUITY PARTNERS BEIJING LIMITED LIABILITY COMPANY—See Affinity Equity Partners (HK) Ltd.; *Int'l*, pg. 186
AFFINITY EQUITY PARTNERS (HK) LTD.; *Int'l*, pg. 186
AFFINITY EQUITY PARTNERS KOREA LLC—See Affinity Equity Partners (HK) Ltd.; *Int'l*, pg. 186
AFFINITY EQUITY PARTNERS (S) PTE LTD—See Affinity Equity Partners (HK) Ltd.; *Int'l*, pg. 186
AFFINITY EXPRESS, INC.—See Ayala Corporation; *Int'l*, pg. 774
AFFINITY FEDERAL CREDIT UNION; *U.S. Private*, pg. 122
AFFINITY GAMING—See Z Capital Group, LLC; *U.S. Private*, pg. 4595
AFFINITY GOLD CORP.; *U.S. Private*, pg. 123
AFFINITY HEALTH ALLIANCE, INC.—See Christiana Care Health System, Inc.; *U.S. Private*, pg. 891
AFFINITY HEALTH PTY LIMITED—See Ramsay Health Care Limited; *Int'l*, pg. 6199
AFFINITY HEALTH SYSTEMS, LLC—See Community Health Systems, Inc.; *U.S. Public*, pg. 551
AFFINITY HEALTH SYSTEM; *U.S. Private*, pg. 123
AFFINITY HOSPITAL, LLC—See Community Health Systems, Inc.; *U.S. Public*, pg. 551
AFFINITY HOSPITALS HOLDING LIMITED—See Acadia Healthcare Company, Inc.; *U.S. Public*, pg. 28
AFFINITY, INC.; *U.S. Private*, pg. 123
AFFINITY INSURANCE SERVICES, INC.—See Aon plc; *Int'l*, pg. 488
AFFINITY LLC - PENNSYLVANIA OFFICE—See Affiniti LLC; *U.S. Private*, pg. 122
AFFINITY MEDICAL TECHNOLOGIES, LLC—See Koch Industries, Inc.; *U.S. Private*, pg. 2333

AFFINITY METALS CORP.

AFFINITY METALS CORP.; *Int'l*, pg. 186
AFFINITY ORTHOPEDIC SERVICES, LLC—See Community Health Systems, Inc.; *U.S. Public*, pg. 551
AFFINITY PHYSICIAN SERVICES, LLC—See Community Health Systems, Inc.; *U.S. Public*, pg. 551
AFFINITY SPECIAL APPAREL, INC.—See Resilience Capital Partners, LLC; *U.S. Private*, pg. 3405
AFFINITY SPORTS, LLC—See Genstar Capital, LLC; *U.S. Private*, pg. 1678
AFFIN MONEYBROKERS SDN. BHD.—See AFFIN Holdings Berhad; *Int'l*, pg. 186
AFFINNOVA FRANCE SARL—See Brookfield Corporation; *Int'l*, pg. 1178
AFFINNOVA FRANCE SARL—See Elliott Management Corporation; *U.S. Private*, pg. 1370
AFFINNOVA, INC.—See Brookfield Corporation; *Int'l*, pg. 1178
AFFINNOVA, INC.—See Elliott Management Corporation; *U.S. Private*, pg. 1370
AFFINOR GROWERS INC.; *Int'l*, pg. 187
AFFIRMA CAPITAL LIMITED; *Int'l*, pg. 187
AFFIRMA CAPITAL MANAGERS (SINGAPORE) PTE. LTD.—See Affirma Capital Limited; *Int'l*, pg. 187
AFFIRMA CONSULTING; *U.S. Private*, pg. 123
AFFIRMATIVE FINANCE LIMITED; *Int'l*, pg. 188
AFFIRMATIVE INSURANCE COMPANY—See J.C. Flowers & Co. LLC; *U.S. Private*, pg. 2159
AFFIRMATIVE INSURANCE HOLDINGS, INC.—See J.C. Flowers & Co. LLC; *U.S. Private*, pg. 2159
AFFIRMATIVE INVESTMENT MANAGEMENT PARTNERS LTD.—See MetLife, Inc.; *U.S. Public*, pg. 1429
AFFIRMATIVE PREMIUM FINANCE, INC.—See J.C. Flowers & Co. LLC; *U.S. Private*, pg. 2159
AFFIRMATIVE PROPERTY HOLDINGS, INC.—See J.C. Flowers & Co. LLC; *U.S. Private*, pg. 2159
AFFIRMED NETWORKS, INC.; *U.S. Private*, pg. 123
AFFIRM HOLDINGS, INC.; *U.S. Public*, pg. 57
AFFISH B.V.—See Camellia Plc; *Int'l*, pg. 1270
AFFIVAL INC.—See SKW Stahl-Metallurgie Holding AG; *Int'l*, pg. 6991
AFFIVAL KK—See SKW Stahl-Metallurgie Holding AG; *Int'l*, pg. 6991
AFFIVAL KOREA CO. LTD.—See SKW Stahl-Metallurgie Holding AG; *Int'l*, pg. 6991
AFFIVAL S.A.—See SKW Stahl-Metallurgie Holding AG; *Int'l*, pg. 6991
AFFLE (INDIA) LIMITED; *Int'l*, pg. 188
AFFLINK, INC.—See Performance Food Group Company; *U.S. Public*, pg. 1674
AFFLUENCE CORP.; *U.S. Public*, pg. 57
AFFLUENT FOUNDATION HOLDINGS LIMITED; *Int'l*, pg. 188
AFFLUENT INSIGHTS; *U.S. Private*, pg. 123
AFFLUENT MEDICAL SAS; *Int'l*, pg. 188
AFFLUENT PARTNERS HOLDINGS LIMITED; *Int'l*, pg. 188
AFFORDABLE ALARM & MONITORING, INC. (AAMI); *U.S. Private*, pg. 123
AFFORDABLEBUTTONS.COM; *U.S. Private*, pg. 123
AFFORDABLE CARE, INC.—See Berkshire Partners LLC; *U.S. Private*, pg. 534
AFFORDABLE CAR LEASING PTY. LTD.—See Mizuho Leasing Company, Limited; *Int'l*, pg. 4999
AFFORDABLE CARS & FINANCE; *U.S. Private*, pg. 123
AFFORDABLE CONCEPTS, INC.; *U.S. Private*, pg. 123
AFFORDABLE FUNERALS AND CREMATIONS OF AMERICA, INC.—See Security National Financial Corporation; *U.S. Public*, pg. 1856
AFFORDABLE GREAT LOCATIONS; *U.S. Private*, pg. 123
AFFORDABLE INTERIOR SYSTEMS, INC.—See Audax Group, Limited Partnership; *U.S. Private*, pg. 386
AFFORDABLE RENT TO OWN LLC; *U.S. Private*, pg. 123
AFFORDABLE ROBOTIC & AUTOMATION LTD.; *Int'l*, pg. 188
AFFORDABLE SUITES OF AMERICA, INC.—See Goldberg Lindsay & Co., LLC; *U.S. Private*, pg. 1729
AFFYMAX, INC.; *U.S. Public*, pg. 57
AFG BIOSOLUTIONS, INC.; *U.S. Private*, pg. 123
AFG GROUP NIJMEGEN B.V.; *Int'l*, pg. 188
AFG HOLDINGS, INC; *U.S. Private*, pg. 123
AFG HOME LOANS PTY LTD—See Australia Finance Group Ltd; *Int'l*, pg. 720
AFG IMMOBILIEN AG—See Arbonia AG; *Int'l*, pg. 537
AFG IMMOBILIEN AG—See Arbonia AG; *Int'l*, pg. 537
AFG INTERNATIONAL AG—See Arbonia AG; *Int'l*, pg. 537
AFGLOBAL CORPORATION—See First Reserve Management, L.P.; *U.S. Private*, pg. 1525
AF GLOBAL LIMITED—See Aspial Corporation Limited; *Int'l*, pg. 630
AF GLOBAL LIMITED—See Fragrance Group Limited; *Int'l*, pg. 2758
AF GLOENCO INC. - GREENVILLE—See First Reserve Management, L.P.; *U.S. Private*, pg. 1525
AF GLOENCO INC.—See First Reserve Management, L.P.; *U.S. Private*, pg. 1525
AFG MANAGEMENT AG—See Arbonia AG; *Int'l*, pg. 537

AFGRI ANIMAL FEEDS EASTERN CAPE (PTY) LTD.—See AFGRI Limited; *Int'l*, pg. 188
AFGRI ANIMAL FEEDS—See AFGRI Limited; *Int'l*, pg. 188
AFGRI FINANCIAL AND LOGISTICS SERVICES—See AFGRI Limited; *Int'l*, pg. 188
AFGRI LIMITED; *Int'l*, pg. 188
AFGRITECH LIMITED—See AFGRI Limited; *Int'l*, pg. 188
AFGRITECH LIMITED—See Carr's Group PLC; *Int'l*, pg. 1343
AF GRUPPEN ASA; *Int'l*, pg. 183
AF GRUPPEN NORGE AS—See AF Gruppen ASA; *Int'l*, pg. 184
AFG RUS—See Arbonia AG; *Int'l*, pg. 537
AFG SCHWEIZ AG—See Arbonia AG; *Int'l*, pg. 537
AFG SERVICES AG—See Arbonia AG; *Int'l*, pg. 537
AFG WARENDORFER IMMOBILIEN GMBH.—See Arbonia AG; *Int'l*, pg. 537
AF-HANSEN & HENNEBERG A/S—See AFRY AB; *Int'l*, pg. 194
AF HARNOSAND BYGGRETURER AB—See AF Gruppen ASA; *Int'l*, pg. 184
AFH AUSTRALIA PTY. LTD.—See Abercrombie & Fitch Co.; *U.S. Public*, pg. 25
AFH FINANCIAL GROUP PLC—See Edwards Capital, LLC; *U.S. Private*, pg. 1341
AF HOLDING COMPANY; *U.S. Private*, pg. 121
AFH STORES UK LIMITED—See Abercrombie & Fitch Co.; *U.S. Public*, pg. 25
AFICOM; *Int'l*, pg. 189
AFI DEVELOPMENT PLC; *Int'l*, pg. 189
AFI EUROPE BULGARIA EOOD—See Africa Israel Investments Ltd.; *Int'l*, pg. 189
AFI EUROPE B.V.—See Africa Israel Investments Ltd.; *Int'l*, pg. 190
AFI EUROPE CZECH REPUBLIC, S.R.O.—See Africa Israel Investments Ltd.; *Int'l*, pg. 189
AFI EUROPE FINANCING B.V.—See Africa Israel Investments Ltd.; *Int'l*, pg. 190
AFI EUROPE INFRASTRUCTURE B.V.—See Africa Israel Investments Ltd.; *Int'l*, pg. 190
AFI EUROPE (ISRAEL BRANCH) LTD.—See Africa Israel Investments Ltd.; *Int'l*, pg. 189
AFI EUROPE MANAGEMENT SRL—See Africa Israel Investments Ltd.; *Int'l*, pg. 190
AFI EUROPE N.V—See Africa Israel Investments Ltd.; *Int'l*, pg. 190
AFI FLIGHT INSPECTION GMBH—See Advent International Corporation; *U.S. Public*, pg. 98
AFI GERMANY GMBH—See Africa Israel Investments Ltd.; *Int'l*, pg. 190
AFI GERMANY INVESTMENT GMBH—See Africa Israel Investments Ltd.; *Int'l*, pg. 190
AFILIAS, INC.—See Ethos Capital, LLC; *U.S. Private*, pg. 1432
AFI MANAGEMENT SIA—See Africa Israel Investments Ltd.; *Int'l*, pg. 190
AFI MANAGEMENT SP. Z O.O.—See Africa Israel Investments Ltd.; *Int'l*, pg. 190
AFIN BROKER DE ASIGURARE - REASIGURARE S.R.L.—See CNH Industrial N.V.; *Int'l*, pg. 1674
AF INDUSTRIER AS—See AFRY AB; *Int'l*, pg. 194
AF-INDUSTRY AB—See AFRY AB; *Int'l*, pg. 194
AFINE INVESTMENTS LIMITED; *Int'l*, pg. 189
AF INFRASTRUCTURE POLSKA SP. Z O.O.—See AFRY AB; *Int'l*, pg. 193
AF-INGEMANSSON AB—See AFRY AB; *Int'l*, pg. 194
AFINITICA TECHNOLOGIES S.L.—See Arkema S.A.; *Int'l*, pg. 568
A. FINKL & SONS CO.—See Swiss Steel Holding AG; *Int'l*, pg. 7372
AFIN SLOVAKIA S.R.O.—See CNH Industrial N.V.; *Int'l*, pg. 1674
AFIN TECHNOLOGIES, INC.—See Afin Technologies Limited; *Int'l*, pg. 189
AFIN TECHNOLOGIES LIMITED; *Int'l*, pg. 189
AF INTERNATIONAL CORPORATION; *U.S. Private*, pg. 121
AFINUM MANAGEMENT GMBH; *Int'l*, pg. 189
AFI PALACE COTROCENI—See Africa Israel Investments Ltd.; *Int'l*, pg. 189
AFI PARTNERS LLC; *U.S. Private*, pg. 123
AFI PROPERTIES LTD.—See BIG Shopping Centers Ltd.; *Int'l*, pg. 1021
AFIRMA—See The Interpublic Group of Companies, Inc.; *U.S. Public*, pg. 2092
A-FIRST TECHNOLOGY CO., LTD.—See Taiwan Optical Platform Co., Ltd.; *Int'l*, pg. 7422
AFI RUS LLC—See AFI Development PLC; *Int'l*, pg. 189
AFIS, S.A.—See Energizer Holdings, Inc.; *U.S. Public*, pg. 760
AFI TECHNOLOGIES (CHANGAN) LIMITED—See TDK Corporation; *Int'l*, pg. 7487
AFIX TECHNOLOGIES, INC.—See Aware, Inc.; *U.S. Public*, pg. 254
AFKAR HOLDING CO.—See Gulf Investment House K.S.C.P.; *Int'l*, pg. 3181
AFKEM AG; *Int'l*, pg. 189

CORPORATE AFFILIATIONS

AFK LEASING POLSKA S.A.—See Vorwerk & Co. KG; *Int'l*, pg. 8308
AFLAC HEARTFUL SERVICES COMPANY LIMITED—See Aflac Incorporated; *U.S. Public*, pg. 57
AFLAC INCORPORATED; *U.S. Public*, pg. 57
AFLAC INSURANCE SERVICE COMPANY, LTD.—See Aflac Incorporated; *U.S. Public*, pg. 57
AFLAC INTERNATIONAL, INCORPORATED—See Aflac Incorporated; *U.S. Public*, pg. 57
AFLAC JAPAN—See Aflac Incorporated; *U.S. Public*, pg. 57
AFLAC - LEHIGH VALLEY; *U.S. Private*, pg. 123
AFLAC PAYMENT SERVICE COMPANY, LTD.—See Aflac Incorporated; *U.S. Public*, pg. 57
AFLAC PET SMALL-AMOUNT-AND-SHORT-TERM INSURANCE CO., LTD.—See Aflac Incorporated; *U.S. Public*, pg. 57
AF LEGAL GROUP LTD.; *Int'l*, pg. 184
AFLEX HOSE LTD.—See Spirax-Sarco Engineering plc; *Int'l*, pg. 7137
AFL INDUSTRIES, INC.—See RGF Environmental Group; *U.S. Private*, pg. 3420
AFL TELECOMMUNICATIONS EUROPE LTD.—See Fujikura Ltd.; *Int'l*, pg. 2827
AFL TELECOMMUNICATIONS LLC—See Fujikura Ltd.; *Int'l*, pg. 2827
AFL TELECOMMUNICATIONS—See Fujikura Ltd.; *Int'l*, pg. 2827
AFLUENTE GERACAO DE ENERGIA ELETRICA SA—See ContourGlobal Limited; *Int'l*, pg. 1785
AFLUENTE TRANSMISSAO DE ENERGIA ELETRICA S.A.—See Iberdrola, S.A.; *Int'l*, pg. 3573
AFLVELAR EHF.—See Tym Corporation; *Int'l*, pg. 7994
AFM ALUMINIUMFOLIE MERSEBURG GMBH—See Mansfelder Metals Ltd.; *Int'l*, pg. 4676
AFM CAPITAL PARTNERS, INC.; *U.S. Private*, pg. 123
AF-MERCADOS EMI ENERJI MUHENDISLIGI AR-GE KONTROL VE TEST HIZMETLERI LTD. STI.—See AFRY AB; *Int'l*, pg. 193
AF MERCADOS ENERGY MARKETS INTERNATIONAL S.A.—See AFRY AB; *Int'l*, pg. 193
AFM HOLDING CORPORATION—See Compass Diversified Holdings; *U.S. Public*, pg. 559
AFM RECYCLAGE S.A.—See Derichebourg S.A.; *Int'l*, pg. 2041
AFMS LOGISTICS MANAGEMENT GROUP; *U.S. Private*, pg. 123
AFM TRANSPORT S.A.—See Derichebourg S.A.; *Int'l*, pg. 2041
AF MUTUAL HOLDING CO., INC.; *U.S. Private*, pg. 121
AF NORGE AS—See AFRY AB; *Int'l*, pg. 193
AFOGNAK NATIVE CORPORATION; *U.S. Private*, pg. 123
AFONE PARTICIPATIONS SA; *Int'l*, pg. 189
AFONWEN LAUNDRY LIMITED; *Int'l*, pg. 189
AFORA S.A.U.—See Thermo Fisher Scientific Inc.; *U.S. Public*, pg. 2145
AFORD AWARDS LIMITED—See CEPS PLC; *Int'l*, pg. 1420
AFORE BANAMEX, S.A. DE C.V.—See Citigroup Inc.; *U.S. Public*, pg. 501
AFORE INBURSA S.A. DE C.V.—See Grupo Financiero Inbursa, S.A. de C.V.; *Int'l*, pg. 3129
AFORE OY—See AEM Holdings Ltd.; *Int'l*, pg. 175
AFORE SURA S.A. DE C.V.—See Grupo de Inversiones Suramericana S.A.; *Int'l*, pg. 3125
AFORGE DEGROOF FINANCE SA—See Banque Degroof S.A.; *Int'l*, pg. 853
AFOR SDN. BHD.—See Epicentre Holdings Limited; *Int'l*, pg. 2460
AFORTI HOLDING SA; *Int'l*, pg. 189
A.F.P. CAPITAL S.A.—See Grupo de Inversiones Suramericana S.A.; *Int'l*, pg. 3125
AFPD PTE., LTD.—See AUO Corporation; *Int'l*, pg. 706
AFP GENESIS ADMINISTRADORA DE FONDOS Y FIDEICOMISOS S.A.—See MetLife, Inc.; *U.S. Public*, pg. 1429
AFP GMBH—See Agence France-Presse; *Int'l*, pg. 205
AFP HORIZONTE SA—See Banco Bilbao Vizcaya Argentaria, S.A.; *Int'l*, pg. 816
AFP INDUSTRIES, INC.; *U.S. Private*, pg. 124
AFP INTEGRA S.A.—See Grupo de Inversiones Suramericana S.A.; *Int'l*, pg. 3125
AFP-SERVICES SA—See Agence France-Presse; *Int'l*, pg. 205
AFP (SHANGHAI) LIMITED—See Sealed Air Corporation; *U.S. Public*, pg. 1852
AFP TRANSFORMERS, INC.—See United Capital Corp.; *U.S. Public*, pg. 4288
A-FRAKT AB—See Peab AB; *Int'l*, pg. 5771
AFREECATV CO., LTD.; *Int'l*, pg. 189
AFRIBON CAMEROUN S.A.R.L.—See Kerry Group plc; *Int'l*, pg. 4138
AFRIBOOM PROPRIETARY LIMITED—See CSG Holdings Limited; *Int'l*, pg. 1864
AFRICA BROADCASTING UGANDA LIMITED—See Nation Media Group Limited; *Int'l*, pg. 5149
AFRICA CAPITALWORKS HOLDINGS; *Int'l*, pg. 189
AFRICA ENERGY CORP.; *Int'l*, pg. 189

COMPANY NAME INDEX

AFRICA GROWTH CORPORATION; *U.S. Private*, pg. 124
AFRICA HR SOLUTIONS LTD.—See ADvTECH Limited; *Int'l*, pg. 168
AFRICA ISRAEL (EAST EUROPE) INVESTMENTS B.V.—See Africa Israel Investments Ltd.; *Int'l*, pg. 190
AFRICA ISRAEL (FINANCE) 1985 LTD.—See Africa Israel Investments Ltd.; *Int'l*, pg. 190
AFRICA ISRAEL HOTELS LTD.—See Africa Israel Investments Ltd.; *Int'l*, pg. 190
AFRICA ISRAEL INDUSTRIES LTD.—See Africa Israel Investments Ltd.; *Int'l*, pg. 190
AFRICA ISRAEL INTERNATIONAL HOLDINGS LTD.—See Africa Israel Investments Ltd.; *Int'l*, pg. 190
AFRICA ISRAEL INTERNATIONAL PROPERTIES (2002) LTD.—See Africa Israel Investments Ltd.; *Int'l*, pg. 190
AFRICA ISRAEL INVESTMENTS LTD.; *Int'l*, pg. 189
AFRICA ISRAEL PROPERTIES LTD.—See Africa Israel Investments Ltd.; *Int'l*, pg. 190
AFRICA ISRAEL RESIDENCES LTD.—See Africa Israel Investments Ltd.; *Int'l*, pg. 190
AFRICA ISRAEL TRADE & AGENCIES LTD.—See Africa Israel Investments Ltd.; *Int'l*, pg. 190
AFRICAN AGRICULTURE HOLDINGS INC.; *U.S. Public*, pg. 57
AFRICAN AGRICULTURE, INC.—See African Agriculture Holdings Inc.; *U.S. Public*, pg. 57
AFRICAN ALLIANCE INSURANCE PLC; *Int'l*, pg. 191
AFRICAN ASSAY LABORATORIES (TANZANIA) LTD.—See SGS SA; *Int'l*, pg. 6742
AFRICAN BANKING CORPORATION BOTSWANA LIMITED—See Atlas Mara Limited; *Int'l*, pg. 686
AFRICAN BANKING CORPORATION MOZAMBIQUE LIMITED—See Atlas Mara Limited; *Int'l*, pg. 686
AFRICAN BANKING CORPORATION TANZANIA LIMITED—See Atlas Mara Limited; *Int'l*, pg. 686
AFRICAN BANKING CORPORATION ZAMBIA LIMITED—See Atlas Mara Limited; *Int'l*, pg. 686
AFRICAN BANK LIMITED—See Peresec South Africa Proprietary Limited; *Int'l*, pg. 5798
AFRICAN CABLES LTD.—See Reunert Limited; *Int'l*, pg. 6311
AFRICAN COMMERCE DEVELOPING COMPANY (PTY) LIMITED—See The Bidvest Group Limited; *Int'l*, pg. 7621
AFRICAN CONSUMER CARE LTD.—See Dabur India Ltd; *Int'l* pg. 1903
AFRICAN DAWN CAPITAL LIMITED; *Int'l*, pg. 191
AFRICAN DISTILLERS LIMITED—See Delta Corporation Limited; *Int'l*, pg. 2016
AFRICAN EAGLE RESOURCES PLC; *Int'l*, pg. 191
AFRICAN ENERGY METALS INC.; *Int'l*, pg. 191
AFRICAN EQUITY EMPOWERMENT INVESTMTS LIMITED; *Int'l*, pg. 191
AFRICAN EXPERIENCE LIMITED—See Wilderness Holdings Limited; *Int'l*, pg. 8409
AFRICAN EXPLORATION MINING AND FINANCE CORPORATION—See CEF (SOC) Limited; *Int'l*, pg. 1389
AFRICAN EXPLOSIVES (BOTSWANA) LIMITED—See AECI Limited; *Int'l*, pg. 171
AFRICAN EXPLOSIVES HOLDINGS (PTY) LIMITED—See AECI Limited; *Int'l*, pg. 171
AFRICAN EXPLOSIVES LIMITED—See AECI Limited; *Int'l*, pg. 171
AFRICAN EXPLOSIVES (TANZANIA) LIMITED—See AECI Limited; *Int'l*, pg. 171
AFRICAN EXPORT IMPORT BANK LIMITED; *Int'l*, pg. 191
AFRICAN FINE CARBON (PTY) LIMITED—See Glencore plc; *Int'l*, pg. 2990
AFRICAN GOLD ACQUISITION CORPORATION; *U.S. Public*, pg. 57
AFRICAN GOLD B.V.—See Conquest Resources Limited; *Int'l*, pg. 1769
AFRICAN GOLD LTD.; *Int'l*, pg. 191
AFRICAN INFRASTRUCTURE INVESTMENT MANAGERS; *Int'l*, pg. 191
AFRICAN INVESTMENT GROUP S.A.—See Grupa Azoty S.A.; *Int'l*, pg. 3116
THE AFRICAN LAKES CORPORATION PLC; *Int'l*, pg. 7612
AFRI-CAN MARINE MINERALS CORPORATION; *Int'l*, pg. 189
AFRICAN MEDIA ENTERTAINMENT LIMITED; *Int'l*, pg. 192
AFRICAN MEDICAL INVESTMENT PLC; *Int'l*, pg. 192
AFRICAN MINERALS EXPLORATION & DEVELOPMENT SICAR SCA; *Int'l*, pg. 192
AFRICAN MINERAL STANDARDS—See Set Point Group Limited; *Int'l*, pg. 6730
AFRICAN MINING SERVICES (GHANA) PTY LTD.—See Perenti Global Limited; *Int'l*, pg. 5797
AFRICAN & OVERSEAS ENTERPRISES LIMITED; *Int'l*, pg. 191
AFRICAN OXYGEN LIMITED—See Linde plc; *Int'l*, pg. 4506
AFRICAN PAINTS (NIGERIA) PLC.; *Int'l*, pg. 192
AFRICAN PHOENIX INVESTMENTS LTD—See Peresec South Africa Proprietary Limited; *Int'l*, pg. 5798

AFRICAN RAINBOW CAPITAL INVESTMENTS; *Int'l*, pg. 192
AFRICAN RAINBOW MINERALS LIMITED; *Int'l*, pg. 192
AFRICAN REALTY TRUST (PTY) LTD.—See Hanover Acceptances Limited; *Int'l*, pg. 3258
AFRICAN RESONANCE BUSINESS SOLUTIONS PROPRIETARY LIMITED—See Capital Appreciation Ltd.; *Int'l*, pg. 1309
AFRICAN SUN LIMITED; *Int'l*, pg. 192
AFRICAN SUN ZIMBABWE (PRIVATE) LIMITED—See African Sun Limited; *Int'l*, pg. 192
AFRICAN TRAVEL CONCEPT PTY. LTD.—See TUI AG; *Int'l*, pg. 7964
AFRICAN WILDLIFE FOUNDATION; *U.S. Private*, pg. 124
AFRICA OIL CORPORATION; *Int'l*, pg. 190
AFRICA OIL ETHIOPIA B.V.—See Africa Oil Corporation; *Int'l*, pg. 190
AFRICA OIL KENYA B.V.—See Africa Oil Corporation; *Int'l*, pg. 190
AFRICA OIL TURKANA B.V.—See Africa Oil Corporation; *Int'l*, pg. 191
AFRICA OIL UK LIMITED—See Africa Oil Corporation; *Int'l*, pg. 191
AFRICA ONLINE EGYPT LTD.—See The African Lakes Corporation plc; *Int'l*, pg. 7612
AFRICA ONLINE GHANA LIMITED—See The African Lakes Corporation plc; *Int'l*, pg. 7612
AFRICA ONLINE KENYA LIMITED—See The African Lakes Corporation plc; *Int'l*, pg. 7612
AFRICA ONLINE NAMIBIA (PTY) LIMITED—See The African Lakes Corporation plc; *Int'l*, pg. 7612
AFRICA ONLINE SWAZILAND (PTY) LIMITED—See The African Lakes Corporation plc; *Int'l*, pg. 7612
AFRICA ONLINE TANZANIA LIMITED—See The African Lakes Corporation plc; *Int'l*, pg. 7612
AFRICA ONLINE UGANDA LIMITED—See The African Lakes Corporation plc; *Int'l*, pg. 7612
AFRICA ONLINE ZIMBABWE (PVT) LIMITED—See The African Lakes Corporation plc; *Int'l*, pg. 7612
AFRICA PREPAID SERVICES (MOZAMBIQUE) LIMITADA—See Blue Label Telecoms Limited; *Int'l*, pg. 1068
AFRICARE; *U.S. Private*, pg. 124
AFRICA RISK CONSULTING LTD.; *Int'l*, pg. 191
AFRICA SWISS TRADING (MAURITIUS) LIMITED—See DISTRIBUTION AND WAREHOUSING NETWORK LIMITED; *Int'l*, pg. 2136
AFRICA SWISS TRADING (PROPRIETARY) LIMITED—See DISTRIBUTION AND WAREHOUSING NETWORK LIMITED; *Int'l*, pg. 2136
AFRICA SWISS TRADING (ZAMBIA) LIMITED—See DISTRIBUTION AND WAREHOUSING NETWORK LIMITED; *Int'l*, pg. 2136
AFRICA TRUCK ACCIDENT REPAIRS (PTY) LIMITED—See Super Group Limited; *Int'l*, pg. 7334
AFRICA UPSKILL PROPRIETARY LIMITED—See Workforce Holdings Ltd.; *Int'l*, pg. 8455
AFRIC INDUSTRIES SA; *Int'l*, pg. 189
AFRICINVEST; *Int'l*, pg. 192
AFRICO RESOURCES (B.C.) LTD.—See Eurasian Natural Resources Corporation Limited; *Int'l*, pg. 2527
AFRICO RESOURCES LTD.—See Eurasian Natural Resources Corporation Limited; *Int'l*, pg. 2527
AFRIKA4U; *Int'l*, pg. 192
AFRIKA GOLD AG; *Int'l*, pg. 192
AFRILAND FIRST BANK; *Int'l*, pg. 192
AFRIMAT CONCRETE PRODUCTS—See Afrimat Limited; *Int'l*, pg. 192
AFRIMAT LIMITED; *Int'l*, pg. 192
AFRIMAT READYMIX (CAPE) (PTY) LIMITED—See Afrimat Limited; *Int'l*, pg. 192
AFRIMIX READY MIXED CONCRETE (PROPRIETARY) LIMITED - BENONI PLANT—See Group Five Limited; *Int'l*, pg. 3089
AFRIMIX READY MIXED CONCRETE (PROPRIETARY) LIMITED - BLUE HILLS PLANT—See Group Five Limited; *Int'l*, pg. 3089
AFRIMIX READY MIXED CONCRETE (PROPRIETARY) LIMITED—See Group Five Limited; *Int'l*, pg. 3089
AFRINAT PROPRIETARY LIMITED—See AYO Technology Solutions Ltd.; *Int'l*, pg. 775
AFR INSURANCE; *U.S. Private*, pg. 124
AFRIQUE ASCENSEURS—See Schindler Holding AG; *Int'l*, pg. 6618
AFRIQUE ENERGIE CORP.; *Int'l*, pg. 193
AFRIQUE TELECOM SA; *Int'l*, pg. 193
AFRISAM (SOUTH AFRICA) (PTY) LTD.; *Int'l*, pg. 193
AFRISTRAT INVESTMENT HOLDINGS LIMITED; *Int'l*, pg. 193
AFRISUN KZN (PTY) LIMITED—See Sun International Limited; *Int'l*, pg. 7304
AFRITEX LTD—See Mohammed Enterprises Tanzania Limited; *Int'l*, pg. 5018
AFRITOOL (PTY) LTD.—See Honda Motor Co., Ltd.; *Int'l*, pg. 3459
AFR LIMITED—See Carillion plc; *Int'l*, pg. 1330
AFR NUVENTURE RESOURCES INC.; *Int'l*, pg. 189
AFROCENTRIC INVESTMENT CORPORATION LIMITED; *Int'l*, pg. 193

AFTERMARKET AUTO PARTS ALLIANCE, INC.

AFROX LESOTHO (PTY) LIMITED—See Linde plc; *Int'l*, pg. 4506
AFROX MALAWI LIMITED—See Linde plc; *Int'l*, pg. 4506
AFRY AB; *Int'l*, pg. 193
AFRY APS—See AFRY AB; *Int'l*, pg. 194
AFRY AUSTRIA GMBH—See AFRY AB; *Int'l*, pg. 194
AFRY CANADA INC.—See AFRY AB; *Int'l*, pg. 194
AFRY CAPITAL LIMITED—See AFRY AB; *Int'l*, pg. 194
AFRY CZ S.R.O.—See AFRY AB; *Int'l*, pg. 194
AFRY DEUTSCHLAND GMBH—See AFRY AB; *Int'l*, pg. 194
AFRY ENGINEERING INDIA PRIVATE LIMITED—See AFRY AB; *Int'l*, pg. 194
AFRY EROTERV ZRT.—See AFRY AB; *Int'l*, pg. 194
AFRY ESTONIA OU—See AFRY AB; *Int'l*, pg. 194
AFRY FINLAND OY—See AFRY AB; *Int'l*, pg. 194
AFRY INDIA PRIVATE LIMITED—See AFRY AB; *Int'l*, pg. 194
AFRY IRELAND LIMITED—See AFRY AB; *Int'l*, pg. 194
AFRY ITALY S.R.L.—See AFRY AB; *Int'l*, pg. 194
AFRY MALAYSIA SDN. BHD.—See AFRY AB; *Int'l*, pg. 194
AFRY MANAGEMENT CONSULTING AUSTRIA GMBH—See AFRY AB; *Int'l*, pg. 194
AFRY MANAGEMENT CONSULTING INC.—See AFRY AB; *Int'l*, pg. 194
AFRY MANAGEMENT CONSULTING S.R.L.—See AFRY AB; *Int'l*, pg. 194
AFRY (PERU) S.A.C.—See AFRY AB; *Int'l*, pg. 194
AFRY POLAND SP. Z.O.O.—See AFRY AB; *Int'l*, pg. 194
AFRY RUS LLC—See AFRY AB; *Int'l*, pg. 194
AFRY SOLUTIONS SPAIN, S.A.U.—See AFRY AB; *Int'l*, pg. 194
AFRY SOLUTIONS UK LIMITED—See AFRY AB; *Int'l*, pg. 194
AFRY SOUTH-EAST ASIA LTD.—See AFRY AB; *Int'l*, pg. 194
AFRY (THAILAND) LTD.—See AFRY AB; *Int'l*, pg. 194
AFRY USA LLC—See AFRY AB; *Int'l*, pg. 194
AFRY VIETNAM LTD.—See AFRY AB; *Int'l*, pg. 194
AFS ACCEPTANCE LLC—See Credito Real S.A.B. de C.V.; *Int'l*, pg. 1837
AF SANDELLSANDBERG ARKITEKTER AB—See AFRY AB; *Int'l*, pg. 193
AFSCO INC.; *U.S. Private*, pg. 124
AF SERVICES, LLC—See Insight Enterprises, Inc.; *U.S. Public*, pg. 1130
AFS FORECOURT SOLUTIONS PROPRIETARY LIMITED—See Vontier Corporation; *U.S. Public*, pg. 2308
AFS FRANCHISE-SYSTEME GMBH—See BayWa AG; *Int'l*, pg. 915
AFS HEALTHCARE SUPPORT SERVICES—See AFS Janitorial LLC; *U.S. Private*, pg. 124
AFS/IBEX FINANCIAL SERVICES INC. OF CALIFORNIA—See Pathward Financial, Inc.; *U.S. Public*, pg. 1652
AFS/IBEX—See Pathward Financial, Inc.; *U.S. Public*, pg. 1652
AFSI EUROPE S.R.O.—See Caterpillar, Inc.; *U.S. Public*, pg. 449
AFSI EUROPE S.R.O.—See Donaldson Company, Inc.; *U.S. Public*, pg. 675
AFS INSURANCE SERVICES, INC.—See Associated Food Stores, Inc.; *U.S. Private*, pg. 355
AFS IT SERVICES ESTONIA OU—See Bertelsmann SE & Co. KGaA; *Int'l*, pg. 989
AFS JANITORIAL LLC; *U.S. Private*, pg. 124
AFS LOGISTICS, LLC; *U.S. Private*, pg. 124
AF SRL—See Generac Holdings Inc.; *U.S. Public*, pg. 912
AFS SENSUB CORP.—See General Motors Company; *U.S. Public*, pg. 925
AFS TECHNOLOGIES, INC.—See Court Square Capital Partners, L.P.; *U.S. Private*, pg. 1068
AF STEELCASE S.A.—See Steelcase Inc.; *U.S. Public*, pg. 1944
A.F. STERLING HOME BUILDERS LTD. INC.; *U.S. Private*, pg. 25
AF SUPPLY CORP.; *U.S. Private*, pg. 121
AFTAB AUTOMOBILES LIMITED—See Navana Group of Companies; *Int'l*, pg. 5173
AFT AUTOMATION AND CONVEYING SYSTEMS (SHANGHAI) CO. LTD.—See Certina Holding AG; *Int'l*, pg. 1423
AFT AUTOMATION LIMITED—See Certina Holding AG; *Int'l*, pg. 1423
AFT AUTOMATISIERUNGS- UND FORDERTECHNIK GMBH & CO. KG—See Certina Holding AG; *Int'l*, pg. 1423
AFT CORPORATION LIMITED; *Int'l*, pg. 196
AFTENPOSTEN AS—See Schibsted ASA; *Int'l*, pg. 6616
AFTENPOSTEN DISTRIBUSJON AS—See Schibsted ASA; *Int'l*, pg. 6616
AFTERCOLLEGE, INC.—See Jobcase, Inc.; *U.S. Private*, pg. 2217
AFTER HOURS PEDIATRICS, INC.—See Blackstone Inc.; *U.S. Public*, pg. 359
AFTERMARKET AUTO PARTS ALLIANCE, INC.; *U.S. Private*, pg. 124

AFTERMARKET AUTO PARTS ALLIANCE, INC.

CORPORATE AFFILIATIONS

AFTERMARKET CONTROLS CORPORATION—See Superior Capital Partners LLC; *U.S. Private*, pg. 3876
AFTERMARKET CONTROLS HOLDINGS CORP.—See Superior Capital Partners LLC; *U.S. Private*, pg. 3876
THE AFTERMARKET GROUP, INC.—See Invacare Corporation; *U.S. Private*, pg. 2131
AFTERMARKET PARTS INC—See Matt Management Inc.; *U.S. Private*, pg. 2613
AFTER MARKET SOLUTIONS (CE) PTE. LTD.—See mDR Limited; *Int'l*, pg. 4762
AFTERMARKET (UK) LIMITED—See General Motors Company; *U.S. Public*, pg. 927
AFTERMASTER, INC.; *U.S. Public*, pg. 57
AFTERMATH SERVICES LLC—See ABRY Partners, LLC; *U.S. Private*, pg. 40
AFTERMATH SILVER LTD.; *Int'l*, pg. 196
AFTERNEXT HEALTHTECH ACQUISITION CORP.; *U.S. Public*, pg. 57
AFTERPAY HOLDINGS LIMITED—See Block, Inc.; *U.S. Public*, pg. 361
AFTERPAY LIMITED—See Block, Inc.; *U.S. Public*, pg. 361
AFTER SCHOOL MATTERS, INC.; *U.S. Private*, pg. 124
AFTER SIX, LLC—See The Anderson Group, LLC; *U.S. Private*, pg. 3986
AFTER YOU PCL; *Int'l*, pg. 196
AFT EUROPA KFT—See ARC Group Worldwide, Inc.; *U.S. Public*, pg. 179
AFT-FORDERANLAGEN BAUTZEN GMBH & CO. KG—See Certina Holding AG; *Int'l*, pg. 1423
AFT-HUNGARY KFT.—See ARC Group Worldwide, Inc.; *U.S. Public*, pg. 179
AFT KOREA CO. LTD.—See Certina Holding AG; *Int'l*, pg. 1423
AFTON ALPS INC.; *U.S. Private*, pg. 124
AFTONBLADET GRUPPEN—See Schibsted ASA; *Int'l*, pg. 6616
AFTONBLADET HIERTA AB—See Schibsted ASA; *Int'l*, pg. 6616
AFTONBLADET KOLPORTAGE AB—See Schibsted ASA; *Int'l*, pg. 6617
AFTON CHEMICAL ADDITIVES CORPORATION—See Newmarket Corporation; *U.S. Public*, pg. 1516
AFTON CHEMICAL ASIA PTE. LTD.—See Newmarket Corporation; *U.S. Public*, pg. 1516
AFTON CHEMICAL CANADA CORPORATION—See Newmarket Corporation; *U.S. Public*, pg. 1516
AFTON CHEMICAL CORPORATION—See Newmarket Corporation; *U.S. Public*, pg. 1516
AFTON CHEMICAL DE MEXICO S.A. DE C.V.—See Newmarket Corporation; *U.S. Public*, pg. 1516
AFTON CHEMICAL GMBH—See Newmarket Corporation; *U.S. Public*, pg. 1516
AFTON CHEMICAL INDIA PRIVATE LIMITED—See Newmarket Corporation; *U.S. Public*, pg. 1516
AFTON CHEMICAL INTANGIBLES LLC—See Newmarket Corporation; *U.S. Public*, pg. 1516
AFTON CHEMICAL LIMITED—See Newmarket Corporation; *U.S. Public*, pg. 1516
AFTON CHEMICAL S.P.R.L.—See Newmarket Corporation; *U.S. Public*, pg. 1516
AFTON DIALYSIS, LLC—See DaVita Inc.; *U.S. Public*, pg. 635
AFT PHARMACEUTICALS LIMITED; *Int'l*, pg. 196
AFTRON ELECTRONICS—See Al-Futtaim Private Company LLC; *Int'l*, pg. 285
AFVALSTOFFEN TERMINAL MOERDIJK B.V.—See Renewi plc; *Int'l*, pg. 6279
AFVALVERWERKING STAINKOELN B.V.—See Sweco AB; *Int'l*, pg. 7363
A.F.W CO., LTD.; *Int'l*, pg. 23
AF WILLIS BAHRAIN WLL—See Willis Towers Watson Public Limited Company; *Int'l*, pg. 8415
AFX INC.; *U.S. Private*, pg. 124
AFX INDUSTRIES LLC—See Exco Technologies Limited; *Int'l*, pg. 2580
AFYA LIMITED; *Int'l*, pg. 196
AFYON CIMENTO SANAYI TURK A.S.—See Haci Omer Sabanci Holding A.S.; *Int'l*, pg. 3203
AFYREN SA; *Int'l*, pg. 196
AF-ZETA, INC.—See The Zuellig Group Inc.; *Int'l*, pg. 7705
AGA ASSISTANCE AUSTRALIA PTY LTD—See Allianz SE; *Int'l*, pg. 342
AGA ASSISTANCE AUSTRALIA PTY LTD—See Allianz SE; *Int'l*, pg. 341
AGA ASSISTANCE (INDIA) PRIVATE LIMITED—See Allianz SE; *Int'l*, pg. 341
AGABANG & COMPANY; *Int'l*, pg. 199
AG ACQUISITION GROUP, INC.; *U.S. Private*, pg. 124
AGA FINANCIAL GROUP INC.; *Int'l*, pg. 198
AGAIN FASTER LLC; *U.S. Private*, pg. 125
AGAINST THE GRAIN GOURMET LLC—See HumanCo LLC; *U.S. Private*, pg. 2006
AG AJIKAWA CORPORATION; *Int'l*, pg. 196
AGA JOHN ORIENTAL RUGS; *U.S. Private*, pg. 125
AGA KHAN DEVELOPMENT NETWORK; *Int'l*, pg. 198
AGA KHAN FUND FOR ECONOMIC DEVELOPMENT S.A.—See Aga Khan Development Network; *Int'l*, pg. 199

AGALAWATTE PLANTATIONS PLC; *Int'l*, pg. 199
AGA MARVEL (USA)—See The Middleby Corporation; *U.S. Public*, pg. 2114
AGAMATRIX, INC.—See i-SENS Inc.; *Int'l*, pg. 3564
AGAMERICA LENDING LLC—See Land South Holdings, LLC; *U.S. Private*, pg. 2384
AGAMYA CAPITAL LLC; *U.S. Private*, pg. 125
AG ANADOLU GRUBU HOLDING ANONIM SIRKETI; *Int'l*, pg. 197
AG ANADOLU GRUBU HOLDING A.S.; *Int'l*, pg. 196
AGAPE ATP CORPORATION; *Int'l*, pg. 199
AGAPE CARE GROUP—See Ridgemont Partners Management LLC; *U.S. Private*, pg. 3432
AGAPE HEALTHCARE PARTNERS, LP—See CoVerica, Inc.; *U.S. Private*, pg. 1072
AGAPE INSURANCE SERVICES—See Inszone Insurance Services, LLC; *U.S. Private*, pg. 2096
AGAPE LUXURY CORP.; *U.S. Private*, pg. 126
AGAPE PACKAGE MANUFACTURING (SHANGHAI) LTD.—See Alpha and Omega Semiconductor Limited; *Int'l*, pg. 366
AGAPE PHYSICAL THERAPY & SPORTS REHABILITATION, LIMITED PARTNERSHIP—See U.S. Physical Therapy, Inc.; *U.S. Public*, pg. 2213
AGA RANGEMASTER GROUP PLC—See The Middleby Corporation; *U.S. Public*, pg. 2114
AGA RANGEMASTER LIMITED—See The Middleby Corporation; *U.S. Public*, pg. 2114
AGA RAYBURN LTD—See The Middleby Corporation; *U.S. Public*, pg. 2113
AGARIK SAS—See Atos SE; *Int'l*, pg. 691
AGAR SCIENTIFIC LIMITED; *Int'l*, pg. 200
AGARTHA REAL ESTATE SOCIMI, S.A.U.; *Int'l*, pg. 200
AGARWAL INDUSTRIAL CORPORATION LTD.; *Int'l*, pg. 200
A-GAS AMERICAS, INC.—See A-Gas Limited; *Int'l*, pg. 19
A-GAS (AUSTRALIA) PTY LTD—See A-Gas Limited; *Int'l*, pg. 19
A-GAS ELECTRONIC MATERIALS LTD—See A-Gas Limited; *Int'l*, pg. 19
AGA SERVICE COMPANY CORP.—See Allianz SE; *Int'l*, pg. 341
AGA SERVICES (THAILAND) CO., LTD.—See Allianz SE; *Int'l*, pg. 342
A-GAS INTERNATIONAL LTD.—See KKR & Co. Inc.; *U.S. Public*, pg. 1237
A-GAS LIMITED; *Int'l*, pg. 19
A-GAS (SEA) PTE LTD—See A-Gas Limited; *Int'l*, pg. 19
A-GAS (SHANGHAI) CHEMICAL CO. LTD—See A-Gas Limited; *Int'l*, pg. 19
A-GAS (SOUTH AFRICA) (PTY) LTD—See A-Gas Limited; *Int'l*, pg. 19
AGASTA CO., LTD.—See WebCrew Inc.; *Int'l*, pg. 8365
A-GAS (THAILAND) LTD—See A-Gas Limited; *Int'l*, pg. 19
AGATE BAY RESIDENTIAL MORTGAGE SECURITIES LLC—See Two Harbors Investment Corp.; *U.S. Public*, pg. 2207
AGATE CONSTRUCTION COMPANY, INC.—See Johnston Enterprises Inc.; *U.S. Private*, pg. 2230
AGAT EJENDOMME A/S; *Int'l*, pg. 200
AGATE RESOURCES, INC.—See Centene Corporation; *U.S. Public*, pg. 468
AGATOS ENERGIA SRL—See Agatos S.p.A.; *Int'l*, pg. 200
AGATOS S.p.A.; *Int'l*, pg. 200
AGATSUMA BIO POWER CO., LTD.—See ORIX Corporation; *Int'l*, pg. 5633
AGAVE CONSULTANTS LIMITED—See Accenture plc; *Int'l*, pg. 86
AGBA GROUP HOLDING LIMITED; *Int'l*, pg. 200
A&G BANCA PRIVADA S.A.U.—See EFG International AG; *Int'l*, pg. 2319
A.G. BARR PLC; *Int'l*, pg. 23
AGBAR UK LTD.—See Veolia Environnement S.A.; *Int'l*, pg. 8155
AGBAYANI CONSTRUCTION CORP.; *U.S. Private*, pg. 126
AG BELT, INC.—See Genuine Parts Company; *U.S. Public*, pg. 933
AGBEST LLC; *U.S. Private*, pg. 126
AGB NIELSEN MEDIA RESEARCH (THAILAND) LTD.—See Brookfield Corporation; *Int'l*, pg. 1178
AGB NIELSEN MEDIA RESEARCH (THAILAND) LTD.—See Elliott Management Corporation; *U.S. Private*, pg. 1370
AGB NIELSEN, MEDIJSKE RAZISKAVE, D.O.O—See Brookfield Corporation; *Int'l*, pg. 1178
AGB NIELSEN, MEDIJSKE RAZISKAVE, D.O.O.—See Elliott Management Corporation; *U.S. Private*, pg. 1370
AG-BOX CO; *U.S. Private*, pg. 126
AGB STAT IPSOS SAL—See Brookfield Corporation; *Int'l*, pg. 1178
AGB STAT IPSOS SAL—See Elliott Management Corporation; *U.S. Private*, pg. 1370
AGC ACQUISITION LLC—See Loar Group, Inc.; *U.S. Private*, pg. 2477
AGC ADVANCED BUSINESS EXPERTS (THAILAND) LTD.—See AGC Inc.; *Int'l*, pg. 200
AGC ADVANCED ELECTRONICS DISPLAY GLASS (SHENZHEN) CO., LTD.—See AGC Inc.; *Int'l*, pg. 203

AGC AMENITECH CO., LTD.—See AGC Inc.; *Int'l*, pg. 200
AGC AMERICA, INC.—See AGC Inc.; *Int'l*, pg. 200
AG CAPITAL LIMITED—See Allied Group Limited; *Int'l*, pg. 357
AG CAPITAL; *Int'l*, pg. 197
AGCAREERS.COM—See Farms.com Ltd.; *Int'l*, pg. 2620
AGCAROLINA FINANCIAL; *U.S. Private*, pg. 126
AGC ASIA PACIFIC (INDIA) PVT. LTD.—See AGC Inc.; *Int'l*, pg. 203
AGC ASIA PACIFIC PTE., LTD.—See AGC Inc.; *Int'l*, pg. 201
AGC ASIA PACIFIC (VIETNAM) CO., LTD.—See AGC Inc.; *Int'l*, pg. 201
AGC AUSTRALIA PTY LTD—See AusGroup Limited; *Int'l*, pg. 716
AGC AUTOMOTIVE AMERICAS CO.—See AGC Inc.; *Int'l*, pg. 200
AGC AUTOMOTIVE AMERICAS R&D, INC.—See AGC Inc.; *Int'l*, pg. 200
AGC AUTOMOTIVE CALIFORNIA, INC.—See AGC Inc.; *Int'l*, pg. 200
AGC AUTOMOTIVE CANADA, INC.—See AGC Inc.; *Int'l*, pg. 201
AGC AUTOMOTIVE (CHINA) CO., LTD.—See AGC Inc.; *Int'l*, pg. 203
AGC AUTOMOTIVE EUROPE S.A.—See AGC Inc.; *Int'l*, pg. 201
AGC AUTOMOTIVE FOSHAN CO., LTD.—See AGC Inc.; *Int'l*, pg. 201
AGC AUTOMOTIVE GLASS MEXICO S.A. DE C.V.—See AGC Inc.; *Int'l*, pg. 203
AGC AUTOMOTIVE ITALY S.R.L—See AGC Inc.; *Int'l*, pg. 202
AGC AUTOMOTIVE MEXICO S.DE R.L. DE C.V.—See AGC Inc.; *Int'l*, pg. 203
AGC AUTOMOTIVE PHILIPPINES INC.—See AGC Inc.; *Int'l*, pg. 201
AGC AUTOMOTIVE (QINHUANGDAO) INC.—See AGC Inc.; *Int'l*, pg. 201
AGC AUTOMOTIVE—See AGC Inc.; *Int'l*, pg. 200
AGC AUTOMOTIVE (SUZHOU) INC.—See AGC Inc.; *Int'l*, pg. 203
AGC AUTOMOTIVE (THAILAND) CO., LTD.—See AGC Inc.; *Int'l*, pg. 201
AGC AUTOMOTIVE U.K. LTD.—See AGC Inc.; *Int'l*, pg. 202
AGC AUTOMOTIVE WINDOW SYSTEMS CO., LTD.—See AGC Inc.; *Int'l*, pg. 201
AGC BIOLOGICS A/S—See AGC Inc.; *Int'l*, pg. 201
AGC BIOLOGICS GMBH—See AGC Inc.; *Int'l*, pg. 202
AGC BIOLOGICS INC.—See AGC Inc.; *Int'l*, pg. 201
AGC BIOLOGICS S.P.A.—See AGC Inc.; *Int'l*, pg. 201
AGC BOR GLASSWORKS OOO—See AGC Inc.; *Int'l*, pg. 203
AGC CAPITAL, INC.—See AGC Inc.; *Int'l*, pg. 200
AGC CERAMICS CO., LTD.—See AGC Inc.; *Int'l*, pg. 201
AGC CHEMICALS AMERICAS, INC.—See AGC Inc.; *Int'l*, pg. 200
AGC CHEMICALS AMERICAS, INC. - THORNDALE MANUFACTURING PLANT—See AGC Inc.; *Int'l*, pg. 200
AGC CHEMICALS ASIA PACIFIC PTE. LTD.—See AGC Inc.; *Int'l*, pg. 201
AGC CHEMICALS EUROPE, LTD.—See AGC Inc.; *Int'l*, pg. 202
AGC CHEMICALS EUROPE, LTD.—See AGC Inc.; *Int'l*, pg. 202
AGC CHEMICALS (THAILAND) CO., LTD. - PHRAPRADAENG PLANT—See AGC Inc.; *Int'l*, pg. 201
AGC CHEMICALS (THAILAND) CO., LTD. - RAYONG PLANT—See AGC Inc.; *Int'l*, pg. 201
AGC CHEMICALS TRADING (SHANGHAI) CO., LTD.—See AGC Inc.; *Int'l*, pg. 201
AGC CHEMICALS VIETNAM CO., LTD.—See AGC Inc.; *Int'l*, pg. 203
AGC (CHINA) HOLDINGS CO., LTD.—See AGC Inc.; *Int'l*, pg. 200
AGC COAT-TECH CO., LTD.—See AGC Inc.; *Int'l*, pg. 201
AGC DISPLAY GLASS (CHONGQING) INC.—See AGC Inc.; *Int'l*, pg. 203
AGC DISPLAY GLASS (HUIZHOU) CO., LTD.—See AGC Inc.; *Int'l*, pg. 203
AGC DISPLAY GLASS (KUNSHAN) INC.—See AGC Inc.; *Int'l*, pg. 203
AGC DISPLAY GLASS OCHANG CO., LTD.—See AGC Inc.; *Int'l*, pg. 203
AGC DISPLAY GLASS (SHENZHEN) INC.—See AGC Inc.; *Int'l*, pg. 203
AGC DISPLAY GLASS TAIWAN INC.—See AGC Inc.; *Int'l*, pg. 203
AGC DISPLAY GLASS YONEZAWA CO., LTD.—See AGC Inc.; *Int'l*, pg. 201
AGC ELECTRONICS AMERICA, INC.—See AGC Inc.; *Int'l*, pg. 200
AGC ELECTRONICS CO., LTD.—See AGC Inc.; *Int'l*, pg. 201
AGC ELECTRONICS SINGAPORE PTE. LTD.—See AGC Inc.; *Int'l*, pg. 201

COMPANY NAME INDEX

AGC ELECTRONICS TAIWAN INC.—See AGC Inc.; *Int'l*, pg. 203
AGC ENGINEERING CO., LTD.—See AGC Inc.; *Int'l*, pg. 201
AGC EUROPE S.A.—See AGC Inc.; *Int'l*, pg. 201
AGC FABRITECH CO., LTD.—See AGC Inc.; *Int'l*, pg. 202
AGC FINANCE CO., LTD.—See AGC Inc.; *Int'l*, pg. 202
AGC FINE TECHNO KOREA CO., LTD.—See AGC Inc.; *Int'l*, pg. 203
AGC FLAT GLASS ASIA PACIFIC PTE. LTD.—See AGC Inc.; *Int'l*, pg. 202
AGC FLAT GLASS CZECH A.S.—See AGC Inc.; *Int'l*, pg. 202
AGC FLAT GLASS (DALIAN) CO., LTD.—See Shanghai Yaohua Pilkington Glass Group Co., Ltd.; *Int'l*, pg. 6781
AGC FLAT GLASS EUROPE—See AGC Inc.; *Int'l*, pg. 202
AGC FLAT GLASS (HONG KONG) CO., LTD.—See AGC Inc.; *Int'l*, pg. 202
AGC FLAT GLASS IBERICA S.A.—See AGC Inc.; *Int'l*, pg. 202
AGC FLAT GLASS ITALIA S.R.L—See AGC Inc.; *Int'l*, pg. 202
AGC FLAT GLASS NEDERLAND B.V.—See AGC Inc.; *Int'l*, pg. 202
AGC FLAT GLASS NORTH AMERICA, INC. - ABINGDON PLANT—See AGC Inc.; *Int'l*, pg. 201
AGC FLAT GLASS NORTH AMERICA, INC. - AGC-ALVARADO PLANT—See AGC Inc.; *Int'l*, pg. 200
AGC FLAT GLASS NORTH AMERICA, INC. - AGC-BATON ROUGE PLANT—See AGC Inc.; *Int'l*, pg. 200
AGC FLAT GLASS NORTH AMERICA, INC. - AGC-CALGARY PLANT—See AGC Inc.; *Int'l*, pg. 200
AGC FLAT GLASS NORTH AMERICA, INC. - AGC-CARBONDALE PLANT—See AGC Inc.; *Int'l*, pg. 200
AGC FLAT GLASS NORTH AMERICA, INC. - AGC-EDMONTON PLANT—See AGC Inc.; *Int'l*, pg. 200
AGC FLAT GLASS NORTH AMERICA, INC. - AGC-FALL RIVER PLANT—See AGC Inc.; *Int'l*, pg. 200
AGC FLAT GLASS NORTH AMERICA, INC. - AGC-HOUSTON PLANT—See AGC Inc.; *Int'l*, pg. 200
AGC FLAT GLASS NORTH AMERICA, INC. - AGC-JACKSONVILLE PLANT—See AGC Inc.; *Int'l*, pg. 200
AGC FLAT GLASS NORTH AMERICA, INC. - AGC-KNOXVILLE PLANT—See AGC Inc.; *Int'l*, pg. 200
AGC FLAT GLASS NORTH AMERICA, INC. - AGC-ORLOUGAC PLANT—See AGC Inc.; *Int'l*, pg. 200
AGC FLAT GLASS NORTH AMERICA, INC. - AGC-REGINA PLANT—See AGC Inc.; *Int'l*, pg. 201
AGC FLAT GLASS NORTH AMERICA, INC. - AGC-RICHMOND PLANT—See AGC Inc.; *Int'l*, pg. 201
AGC FLAT GLASS NORTH AMERICA, INC. - AGC-SALT LAKE CITY PLANT—See AGC Inc.; *Int'l*, pg. 201
AGC FLAT GLASS NORTH AMERICA, INC. - AGC-SAN ANTONIO PLANT—See AGC Inc.; *Int'l*, pg. 201
AGC FLAT GLASS NORTH AMERICA, INC. - AGC-WINNIPEG PLANT—See AGC Inc.; *Int'l*, pg. 201
AGC FLAT GLASS NORTH AMERICA, INC. - BLUE RIDGE PLANT—See AGC Inc.; *Int'l*, pg. 201
AGC FLAT GLASS NORTH AMERICA, INC. - BOARDMAN PLANT—See AGC Inc.; *Int'l*, pg. 201
AGC FLAT GLASS NORTH AMERICA, INC. - CARBONDALE—See AGC Inc.; *Int'l*, pg. 201
AGC FLAT GLASS NORTH AMERICA, INC. - GREENLAND PLANT—See AGC Inc.; *Int'l*, pg. 201
AGC FLAT GLASS NORTH AMERICA, INC. - MARIETTA—See AGC Inc.; *Int'l*, pg. 201
AGC FLAT GLASS NORTH AMERICA, INC. - QUAKERTOWN PLANT—See AGC Inc.; *Int'l*, pg. 201
AGC FLAT GLASS NORTH AMERICA, INC. - RICHMOND PLANT—See AGC Inc.; *Int'l*, pg. 201
AGC FLAT GLASS NORTH AMERICA, INC.—See AGC Inc.; *Int'l*, pg. 200
AGC FLAT GLASS NORTH AMERICA, INC. - SPRING HILL PLANT—See AGC Inc.; *Int'l*, pg. 201
AGC FLAT GLASS PROTECH (SHENZHEN) CO., LTD.—See AGC Inc.; *Int'l*, pg. 202
AGC FLAT GLASS (SUZHOU) CO., LTD.—See AGC Inc.; *Int'l*, pg. 202
AGC FLAT GLASS (THAILAND) PUBLIC CO., LTD. - CHON BURI FACTORY—See AGC Inc.; *Int'l*, pg. 202
AGC FLAT GLASS (THAILAND) PUBLIC CO., LTD.—See AGC Inc.; *Int'l*, pg. 202
AGC FRANCE S.A.—See AGC Inc.; *Int'l*, pg. 203
AGC GLASS EUROPE SA—See AGC Inc.; *Int'l*, pg. 202
AGC GLASS FRANCE S.A.—See AGC Inc.; *Int'l*, pg. 202
AGC GLASS KENZAI CO., LTD.—See AGC Inc.; *Int'l*, pg. 202
AGC GLASS PRODUCTS CO., LTD—See AGC Inc.; *Int'l*, pg. 202
AGC GLASS UK LTD.—See AGC Inc.; *Int'l*, pg. 203
AGC GREEN-TECH CO., LTD.—See AGC Inc.; *Int'l*, pg. 202
AGC HEAT TRANSFER INC.—See Alfa Laval AB; *Int'l*, pg. 309
AGC HEAT TRANSFER INC. - WESTERN FACTORY—See Alfa Laval AB; *Int'l*, pg. 309
AG-CHEM EUROPE FERTILIZER EQUIPMENT BV—See AGCO Corporation; *U.S. Public*, pg. 58
AGCHOICE FARM CREDIT; *U.S. Private*, pg. 126

AGC INC.; *Int'l*, pg. 200
AGC INDUSTRIES PTY LTD—See AusGroup Limited; *Int'l*, pg. 716
AGC INSURANCE MANAGEMENT CO., LTD.—See AGC Inc.; *Int'l*, pg. 202
AGC LOGISTICS CO., LTD.—See AGC Inc.; *Int'l*, pg. 202
AGC MANUFACTURING SERVICES INC—See Gentor, S.A. de C.V.; *Int'l*, pg. 2929
AGC MATEX CO., LTD.—See AGC Inc.; *Int'l*, pg. 202
AGC MICRO GLASS CO., LTD.—See AGC Inc.; *Int'l*, pg. 202
AGC MICRO GLASS (THAILAND) CO., LTD.—See AGC Inc.; *Int'l*, pg. 202
AGC MIDDLE EAST & AFRICA FZCO—See AGC Inc.; *Int'l*, pg. 203
AGC MINERAL CO., LTD.—See AGC Inc.; *Int'l*, pg. 202
AGC MULTI MATERIAL AMERICA, INC.—See AGC Inc.; *Int'l*, pg. 202
AGC MULTI MATERIAL EUROPE SA—See AGC Inc.; *Int'l*, pg. 202
AGC MULTI MATERIAL SINGAPORE PTE. LTD.—See AGC Inc.; *Int'l*, pg. 202
AGC MULTI MATERIAL (SUZHOU) INC.—See AGC Inc.; *Int'l*, pg. 202
AGC NETWORKS & CYBER SOLUTIONS LIMITED—See Black Box Limited; *Int'l*, pg. 1056
AGC NETWORKS, INC.—See Black Box Limited; *Int'l*, pg. 1058
AGC NETWORKS PTE. LIMITED—See Black Box Limited; *Int'l*, pg. 1056
AGCO AB—See AGCO Corporation; *U.S. Public*, pg. 58
A&G COAL CORPORATION—See Southern Coal Corporation; *U.S. Private*, pg. 3730
AGCO ARGENTINA S.A.—See AGCO Corporation; *U.S. Public*, pg. 58
AGCO A/S—See AGCO Corporation; *U.S. Public*, pg. 58
AGCO AUSTRALIA LTD.—See AGCO Corporation; *U.S. Public*, pg. 58
AGCO AUSTRIA GMBH—See AGCO Corporation; *U.S. Public*, pg. 58
AGCO CANADA LTD.—See AGCO Corporation; *U.S. Public*, pg. 58
AGCO (CHINA) INVESTMENT CO., LTD.—See AGCO Corporation; *U.S. Public*, pg. 58
AGCO CORPORATION-JACKSON OPERATIONS—See AGCO Corporation; *U.S. Public*, pg. 58
AGCO CORPORATION; *U.S. Public*, pg. 58
AGCO DANMARK A/S—See AGCO Corporation; *U.S. Public*, pg. 58
AGCO DEUTSCHLAND GMBH—See AGCO Corporation; *U.S. Public*, pg. 58
AGCO FEUCHT GMBH—See AGCO Corporation; *U.S. Public*, pg. 58
AGCO FEUCHT GMBH—See AGCO Corporation; *U.S. Public*, pg. 58
AGCO FINANCE LLC—See AGCO Corporation; *U.S. Public*, pg. 58
AGCO FUNDING CORPORATION—See AGCO Corporation; *U.S. Public*, pg. 58
AGCO GMBH—See AGCO Corporation; *U.S. Public*, pg. 58
AGCO GSI ASIA SDN BHD—See AGCO Corporation; *U.S. Public*, pg. 58
AGCO HOLDING BV—See AGCO Corporation; *U.S. Public*, pg. 58
AGCO HOLDINGS (SINGAPORE) PTE. LTD—See AGCO Corporation; *U.S. Public*, pg. 58
AGCO IBERIA SA—See AGCO Corporation; *U.S. Public*, pg. 58
AGCO INC.; *U.S. Private*, pg. 126
AGCO INC.; *U.S. Private*, pg. 126
AGCO INTERNATIONAL LTD.—See AGCO Corporation; *U.S. Public*, pg. 58
AGCO LTD—See AGCO Corporation; *U.S. Public*, pg. 58
AGCO MACHINERY LTD—See AGCO Corporation; *U.S. Public*, pg. 58
AGCO MEXICO S DE RL DE CV—See AGCO Corporation; *U.S. Public*, pg. 58
AG CONCEPTS UNLIMITED PTY. LTD.—See Nutrien Ltd.; *Int'l*, pg. 5492
AG CONNECTIONS, LLC—See China National Chemical Corporation; *Int'l*, pg. 1529
AGCO OF SPEARMAN INC.; *U.S. Private*, pg. 126
AGCO POWER OY—See AGCO Corporation; *U.S. Public*, pg. 59
AGCO POWER OY—See AGCO Corporation; *U.S. Public*, pg. 58
AGCO SPZOO—See AGCO Corporation; *U.S. Public*, pg. 59
AGCO SUOMI OY—See AGCO Corporation; *U.S. Public*, pg. 58
AGCOUNTRY FARM CREDIT SERVICES, ACA; *U.S. Private*, pg. 126
AGC PHARMA CHEMICALS EUROPE, S.L.U.—See AGC Inc.; *Int'l*, pg. 203
AGC PLIBRICO CO., LTD.—See AGC Inc.; *Int'l*, pg. 203
AGC POLYCARBONATE CO., LTD.—See AGC Inc.; *Int'l*, pg. 202

AGC POLYMER MATERIAL CO., LTD.—See AGC Inc.; *Int'l*, pg. 202
AGC PRECISION GLASS (SHENZHEN) INC.—See AGC Inc.; *Int'l*, pg. 203
AG CREDIT, ACA; *U.S. Private*, pg. 124
AGC RESEARCH INSTITUTE, INC.—See AGC Inc.; *Int'l*, pg. 202
AG CROWDFUNDING CO., LTD.—See AIFUL Corporation; *Int'l*, pg. 231
AGCS AMERICAS—See Allianz SE; *Int'l*, pg. 341
AGCS ARGENTINA—See Allianz SE; *Int'l*, pg. 341
AGCS AUSTRALIA—See Allianz SE; *Int'l*, pg. 341
AGCS DUBAI—See Allianz SE; *Int'l*, pg. 345
AGC SEIMI CHEMICAL CO., LTD. - KASHIMA PLANT—See AGC Inc.; *Int'l*, pg. 202
AGC SEIMI CHEMICAL CO., LTD.—See AGC Inc.; *Int'l*, pg. 202
AGC SHANGHAI CO., LTD.—See AGC Inc.; *Int'l*, pg. 202
AGCS HONG KONG—See Allianz SE; *Int'l*, pg. 344
AGC SINGAPORE SERVICES PTE. LTD.—See AGC Inc.; *Int'l*, pg. 203
AGC SI-TECH CO., LTD.—See AGC Inc.; *Int'l*, pg. 202
AGCS LEBANON—See Allianz SE; *Int'l*, pg. 341
AGCS MARINE INSURANCE COMPANY—See Allianz SE; *Int'l*, pg. 341
AGCS NORTH AMERICA—See Allianz SE; *Int'l*, pg. 341
AGC SODA CORP.—See AGC Inc.; *Int'l*, pg. 203
AGCS RESSEGUROS BRASIL S.A.—See Allianz SE; *Int'l*, pg. 341
AGCS SINGAPORE—See Allianz SE; *Int'l*, pg. 341
AGCS SOUTH AFRICA LIMITED—See Allianz SE; *Int'l*, pg. 342
AGC SUNSMILE, INC.—See AGC Inc.; *Int'l*, pg. 203
AGC TECHNO GLASS CO., LTD.—See AGC Inc.; *Int'l*, pg. 203
AGC TECHNO GLASS CORPORATION—See AGC Inc.; *Int'l*, pg. 203
AGC TECHNO GLASS (THAILAND) CO., LTD.—See AGC Inc.; *Int'l*, pg. 203
AGC TECHNOLOGY SOLUTIONS CO., LTD.—See AGC Inc.; *Int'l*, pg. 203
AGC TECHNOLOGY SOLUTIONS (KUNSHAN) CO., LTD.—See AGC Inc.; *Int'l*, pg. 203
AGC TECHNOLOGY SOLUTIONS TAIWAN INC.—See AGC Inc.; *Int'l*, pg. 203
AGC TECHNOLOGY SOLUTIONS (THAILAND) CO., LTD.—See AGC Inc.; *Int'l*, pg. 203
AGC VIDROS DO BRASIL LTDA.—See AGC Inc.; *Int'l*, pg. 203
AGC VINYTHAI PUBLIC COMPANY LIMITED—See AGC Inc.; *Int'l*, pg. 203
AGC WAKASA CHEMICALS CO., LTD.—See AGC Inc.; *Int'l*, pg. 203
AGDATA, LP—See Levine Leichtman Capital Partners, LLC; *U.S. Private*, pg. 2435
A.G. DAVIS/AA GAGE; *U.S. Private*, pg. 25
AGD DIAMONDS JSC—See Central Bank of the Russian Federation; *Int'l*, pg. 1405
AG DER DILLINGER HUTTENWERKE; *Int'l*, pg. 197
AGDER ENERGI AS; *Int'l*, pg. 204
AGDER OPS VEGSELSKAP AS—See BBGI Global Infrastructure S.A; *Int'l*, pg. 920
AG DISTRIBUTORS, INC.—See Tennessee Farmers Cooperative; *U.S. Private*, pg. 3967
AGDNA TECHNOLOGIES PTY LTD.—See CNH Industrial N.V.; *Int'l*, pg. 1674
AGD RENOVATIONEN AG—See Investis Holding SA; *Int'l*, pg. 3780
AGEACARE SWITZERLAND S.A.—See Eurofins Scientific S.E.; *Int'l*, pg. 2535
AGEAGLE AERIAL SYSTEMS INC.; *U.S. Public*, pg. 60
AGEAS FRANCE S.A.—See Ageas SA/NV; *Int'l*, pg. 204
AGEAS INSURANCE LIMITED—See Ageas SA/NV; *Int'l*, pg. 205
AGEAS N.V.—See Ageas SA/NV; *Int'l*, pg. 205
AGEAS SA/NV; *Int'l*, pg. 204
AGEAS UK LTD.—See Ageas SA/NV; *Int'l*, pg. 205
AGEATIA TECHNOLOGY CONSULTANCY SERVICES INC.; *U.S. Private*, pg. 126
THE AGE COMPANY LTD.—See Nine Entertainment Co. Holdings Limited; *Int'l*, pg. 5299
AGECREDIT S.R.L.—See Kruk S.A.; *Int'l*, pg. 4308
AGE D'OR EXPANSION SA—See CNP Assurances SA; *Int'l*, pg. 1677
AGEFRED SA—See Veolia Environnement S.A.; *Int'l*, pg. 8157
AGE GROUP LTD; *U.S. Private*, pg. 126
AGEHA INC; *Int'l*, pg. 205
AGE INTERNATIONAL, INC.—See Takara Holdings, Inc.; *Int'l*, pg. 7432
AGEL ENTERPRISES ARGENTINA SRL—See JRjr33, Inc.; *U.S. Private*, pg. 2240
AGEL ENTERPRISES, INC.—See JRjr33, Inc.; *U.S. Private*, pg. 2240
AGEL ENTERPRISES INTERNATIONAL SDN. BHD.—See JRjr33, Inc.; *U.S. Private*, pg. 2240
AGEL ENTERPRISES (MALAYSIA) SDN. BHD.—See JRjr33, Inc.; *U.S. Private*, pg. 2240

AGEL ENTERPRISES PTE. LTD.—See JRjr33, Inc.; *U.S. Private*, pg. 2240
AGEL ENTERPRISES RS LLC—See JRjr33, Inc.; *U.S. Private*, pg. 2240
AGELESS SERVICE CENTER CO., LTD.—See Mitsubishi Gas Chemical Company, Inc.; *Int'l*, pg. 4948
AGELESS (THAILAND) CO., LTD.—See Mitsubishi Gas Chemical Company, Inc.; *Int'l*, pg. 4948
AGEL INTERNATIONAL SRL—See JRjr33, Inc.; *U.S. Private*, pg. 2240
AGELLAN CAPITAL PARTNERS INC.; *Int'l*, pg. 205
AGELLAN COMMERCIAL REAL ESTATE INVESTMENT TRUST—See El-Ad Group, Ltd.; *U.S. Private*, pg. 1349
AGEMAR S.A. DE C.V.-VERACRUZ, VER.—See Grupo TMM, S.A.B.; *Int'l*, pg. 3137
AGENA BIOSCIENCE, INC.—See Mesa Laboratories, Inc.; *U.S. Public*, pg. 1426
AGENA S.A.—See Deutsche Bank Aktiengesellschaft; *Int'l*, pg. 2055
AGENCE 154 S.A.—See Hakuhodo DY Holdings Incorporated; *Int'l*, pg. 3220
AGENCE EURO SERVICES; *Int'l*, pg. 205
AGENCE FRANCE-PRESSE; *Int'l*, pg. 205
AGENCE HAGUENAU POINT P—See Compagnie de Saint-Gobain SA; *Int'l*, pg. 1722
AGENCE MEESTERS; *Int'l*, pg. 205
AGENCE SARADAR D'ASSURANCES SAL—See Bank Audi sal; *Int'l*, pg. 837
AGENCE SCHILLING COMMUNICATION; *Int'l*, pg. 205
AGENCIA COLPISA, S.L.U.—See Vocento, S.A.; *Int'l*, pg. 8283
AGENCIA DE ADUANAS DHL EXPRESS COLOMBIA LTDA.—See Deutsche Post AG; *Int'l*, pg. 2071
AGENCIA DE ADUANAS DHL GLOBAL FORWARDING (COLOMBIA) S.A.—See Deutsche Post AG; *Int'l*, pg. 2071
AGENCIA DE ADUANAS KN COLOMBIA S.A.S.—See Kuehne + Nagel International AG; *Int'l*, pg. 4324
AGENCIA DE VIAGENS E TURISMO GRAND, LIMITADA—See China Travel International Investment Hong Kong Ltd; *Int'l*, pg. 1560
AGENCIA EFE, S.A.; *Int'l*, pg. 205
AGENCIA EFE, S.A.—See Agencia EFE, S.A.; *Int'l*, pg. 205
AGENCIA EFE, S.A.—See Agencia EFE, S.A.; *Int'l*, pg. 205
AGENCIA EFE, S.A.—See Agencia EFE, S.A.; *Int'l*, pg. 205
AGENCIA EFE, S.A.—See Agencia EFE, S.A.; *Int'l*, pg. 205
AGENCIA EFE, S.A.—See Agencia EFE, S.A.; *Int'l*, pg. 205
AGENCIA EFE, S.A.—See Agencia EFE, S.A.; *Int'l*, pg. 205
AGENCIA EFE, S.A.—See Agencia EFE, S.A.; *Int'l*, pg. 205
AGENCIA MARITIMA ARGENPAR S.A.—See Southern Cross Capital Management SA; *Int'l*, pg. 7118
AGENCIA MARITIMA INTERNACIONAL S.A.—See Ultramar Ltda.; *Int'l*, pg. 8018
AGENCIA MARITIMA MEXICANA, S.A. DE C.V.—See Grupo TMM, S.A.B.; *Int'l*, pg. 3137
AGENCIA MARITIMA MEXICANA, S.A. DE C.V.—See Grupo TMM, S.A.B.; *Int'l*, pg. 3137
AGENCIA MARITIMA MEXICANA, S.A. DE C.V.—See Grupo TMM, S.A.B.; *Int'l*, pg. 3137
AGENCIA MARITIMA MEXICANA, S.A. DE C.V.—See Grupo TMM, S.A.B.; *Int'l*, pg. 3137
AGENCIA MARITIMA MEXICANA, S.A. DE C.V.—See Grupo TMM, S.A.B.; *Int'l*, pg. 3137
AGENCIA MARITIMA MEXICANA, S.A. DE C.V.—See Grupo TMM, S.A.B.; *Int'l*, pg. 3137
AGENCIA MARITIMA REMAR S.R.L.—See Albert Ballin KG; *Int'l*, pg. 294
AGENCIA MARITIMA SUDOCEAN SRL—See Ultramar Ltda.; *Int'l*, pg. 8018
AGENCIA NAVIERA EUROPA S.A.—See Albert Ballin KG; *Int'l*, pg. 294
AGENCIAS CONTINENTAL S.A.—See Albert Ballin KG; *Int'l*, pg. 294
AGENCIAS PAN AMERICANAS, S DE R.L. DE C.V.—See Aiphone Co., Ltd.; *Int'l*, pg. 235
AGENCIAS UNIVERSALES SA—See Grupo Empresas Navieras S.A.; *Int'l*, pg. 3128
AGENCIE EFE—See Agencia EFE, S.A.; *Int'l*, pg. 205
AGENCIJA ZA POSEBNI OTPAD D.O.O.—See Hrvatska elektroprivreda d.d.; *Int'l*, pg. 3502
AGENCJA RYNKU ENERGII S.A.—See PGE Polska Grupa Energetyczna S.A.; *Int'l*, pg. 5837
AGENCY212, LLC; *U.S. Private*, pg. 126
AGENCY 33; *U.S. Private*, pg. 126
AGENCY59 RESPONSE—See AGENCY59; *Int'l*, pg. 205
AGENCY59; *Int'l*, pg. 205
AGENCYBLOC—See Resurgens Technology Partners, LLC; *U.S. Private*, pg. 3410
AGENCY.COM—See Omnicom Group Inc.; *U.S. Public*, pg. 1594
AGENCY.COM—See Omnicom Group Inc.; *U.S. Public*, pg. 1594
AGENCY.COM—See Omnicom Group Inc.; *U.S. Public*, pg. 1594

AGENCY EA, LLC; *U.S. Private*, pg. 126
AGENCY FOR COMMUNITY TREATMENT SERVICES, INC.; *U.S. Private*, pg. 126
THE AGENCY GROUP AUSTRALIA LIMITED; *Int'l*, pg. 7612
AGENCY HOLDING COMPANY OF MARYLAND INC.; *U.S. Private*, pg. 126
AGENCY INSURANCE COMPANY OF MARYLAND, INC.—See Agency Holding Company of Maryland Inc.; *U.S. Private*, pg. 126
AGENCY INTERMEDIARIES, INC.—See The Carlyle Group Inc.; *U.S. Public*, pg. 2047
AGENCY MATRIX LLC—See Clearlake Capital Group, L.P.; *U.S. Private*, pg. 938
AGENCYPORT INSURANCE SERVICES, INC.—See Thomas H. Lee Partners, L.P.; *U.S. Private*, pg. 4155
AGENCY REPUBLIC—See Omnicom Group Inc.; *U.S. Public*, pg. 1573
AGENCY SERVICES, INC.—See Agency Holding Company of Maryland Inc.; *U.S. Private*, pg. 126
AGENCY SERVICES INC.—See Agency Holding Company of Maryland Inc.; *U.S. Private*, pg. 126
AGENCY SERVICES OF ARKANSAS, INC.—See Stone Point Capital LLC; *U.S. Private*, pg. 3819
THE AGENCY; *U.S. Private*, pg. 3983
AGENCYTWOFIFTEEN—See The Interpublic Group of Companies, Inc.; *U.S. Public*, pg. 2106
AGENDA CORPORATION; *Int'l*, pg. 205
AGENDA; *U.S. Private*, pg. 126
AGENDA—See Agenda; *U.S. Private*, pg. 127
AGENDIA INC.—See Agendia NV; *Int'l*, pg. 205
AGENDIA NV; *Int'l*, pg. 205
A GEN EVENT AGENCY CO., LTD.—See GMM Grammy Public Company Limited; *Int'l*, pg. 3012
AGENNIX AG; *Int'l*, pg. 205
AGENNIX INCORPORATED—See Agennix AG; *Int'l*, pg. 205
AGENNIX INC. - PRINCETON—See Agennix AG; *Int'l*, pg. 205
AGENSI PEKERJAAN ASIA RECRUIT (JOHOR) SDN. BHD.—See Will Group, Inc.; *Int'l*, pg. 8412
AGENSI PEKERJAAN ASIA RECRUIT (MELAKA) SDN. BHD.—See Will Group, Inc.; *Int'l*, pg. 8412
AGENSI PEKERJAAN ASIA RECRUIT SDN. BHD.—See Will Group, Inc.; *Int'l*, pg. 8412
AGENSI PEKERJAAN GLOBESOFT SERVICES SDN. BHD.—See Nippon Telegraph & Telephone Corporation; *Int'l*, pg. 5340
AGENSI PEKERJAAN KERJAYA SUKSES SDN. BHD.—See Kelly Services, Inc.; *U.S. Public*, pg. 1219
AGENSI PEKERJAAN KORN FERRY SDN. BHD.—See Korn Ferry; *U.S. Public*, pg. 1272
AGENSI PEKERJAAN SELECT APPOINTMENTS MALAYSIA—See Randstad N.V.; *Int'l*, pg. 6201
AGENSI PEKERJAAN TRS MALAYSIA SDN. BHD.—See Fluor Corporation; *U.S. Public*, pg. 857
AGENSYS, INC.—See Astellas Pharma Inc.; *Int'l*, pg. 653
AGENT16; *U.S. Private*, pg. 127
AGENT3 LIMITED—See Next 15 Group plc; *Int'l*, pg. 5245
AGENTA-CONSULTING KFT.—See UNIQA Insurance Group AG; *Int'l*, pg. 8057
AGENT ALLIANCE INSURANCE COMPANY—See The Allstate Corporation; *U.S. Public*, pg. 2033
AGENTA RISIKO- UND FINANZIERUNGSBERATUNG GESELLSCHAFT M.B.H.—See UNIQA Insurance Group AG; *Int'l*, pg. 8057
AGENT COMMERCIAL FRANCE DE GEITH INTERNATIONAL LTD.—See HD Hyundai Infracore Co., Ltd.; *Int'l*, pg. 3300
AGENTCUBED, LLC—See The Allstate Corporation; *U.S. Public*, pg. 2033
AGENTEK, INC.; *U.S. Private*, pg. 127
AGENT ELITE, INC.; *U.S. Private*, pg. 127
AGENT, INC.; *Int'l*, pg. 205
AGENT INFORMATION SOFTWARE, INC.; *U.S. Public*, pg. 60
AGENTIX CORP.; *U.S. Public*, pg. 60
AGENT LINK; *U.S. Private*, pg. 127
AGENTPLUS PTY LTD—See Little Real Estate Pty. Ltd.; *Int'l*, pg. 4528
THE AGENT (PROPERTY EXPERT) CO., LTD.—See Ananda Development Public Company Limited; *Int'l*, pg. 447
AGENT PROVOCATEUR LIMITED—See Four Marketing Ltd.; *Int'l*, pg. 2755
AGENT SUPPORT SERVICES INC.; *U.S. Private*, pg. 127
AGENTUS THERAPEUTICS, INC.—See Agenus Inc.; *U.S. Public*, pg. 60
AGENT X; *U.S. Private*, pg. 127
AGENUS INC.; *U.S. Public*, pg. 60
AGENUS SWITZERLAND INC.—See Agenus Inc.; *U.S. Public*, pg. 60
AG ENVIRONMENTAL PRODUCTS, LLC—See Ag Processing Inc.; *U.S. Private*, pg. 125
AGENZIA1 S.R.L.—See AUTO1 Group SE; *Int'l*, pg. 725
AGENZIA GIORNALISTICA ITALIA SPA—See Eni S.p.A.; *Int'l*, pg. 2436
AGENZIA ITALIA S.P.A.—See Gruppo MutuiOnline S.p.A; *Int'l*, pg. 3140

AGENZIA LA TORRE S.R.L.—See Assicurazioni Generali S.p.A.; *Int'l*, pg. 647
AGENZIA NAZIONALE PER L'ATTRAZIONE DEGLI INVESTIMENTI E LO SVILUPPO D'IMPRESA SPA; *Int'l*, pg. 206
AGEOPTIONS; *U.S. Private*, pg. 127
THE AGE PRINT COMPANY PTY LTD—See Nine Entertainment Co. Holdings Limited; *Int'l*, pg. 5299
AGERATEC AB—See Alfa Laval AB; *Int'l*, pg. 308
AGE REVERSAL, INC.; *U.S. Private*, pg. 126
AGERO, INC.—See The Cross Country Group, LLC; *U.S. Private*, pg. 4017
AGER S.R.L.—See Intercos S.p.A.; *Int'l*, pg. 3739
AGESA HAYAT VE EMEKLILIK AS; *Int'l*, pg. 206
AGESCA NEDERLAND NV—See BNP Paribas SA; *Int'l*, pg. 1090
AGESCA NEDERLAND NV—See Frere-Bourgeois; *Int'l*, pg. 2773
AGES FALKENBERG AB—See AGES Industri AB; *Int'l*, pg. 206
AGES HORLE AB—See AGES Industri AB; *Int'l*, pg. 206
AGES INDUSTRI AB; *Int'l*, pg. 206
AGES KULLTORP AB—See AGES Industri AB; *Int'l*, pg. 206
AGESON BERHAD; *Int'l*, pg. 206
AGESPAN, INC.; *U.S. Private*, pg. 127
AGES SHARED SERVICES AB—See AGES Industri AB; *Int'l*, pg. 206
AGEST, INC.—See Digital Hearts Holdings Co., Ltd.; *Int'l*, pg. 2122
AGES VARNAMO AB—See AGES Industri AB; *Int'l*, pg. 206
AGETEC INC.; *U.S. Private*, pg. 127
AGEVAL SA—See Veolia Environnement S.A.; *Int'l*, pg. 8157
AGEVAL SERVICIO SA—See Veolia Environnement S.A.; *Int'l*, pg. 8157
AGEVAL SERVICIO SA—See Veolia Environnement S.A.; *Int'l*, pg. 8157
AG EXPRESS, INC.; *U.S. Private*, pg. 124
AGF 2X, S.A.—See Allianz SE; *Int'l*, pg. 342
AGFA CORPORATION—See Agfa-Gevaert N.V.; *Int'l*, pg. 208
AGFA DE MEXICO S.A. DE C.V.—See Agfa-Gevaert N.V.; *Int'l*, pg. 207
AGFA FINANCE INC.—See Agfa-Gevaert N.V.; *Int'l*, pg. 207
AGFA FINANCE NV—See Agfa-Gevaert N.V.; *Int'l*, pg. 207
AGFA-GEVAERT AB—See Agfa-Gevaert N.V.; *Int'l*, pg. 208
AGFA-GEVAERT A.E.B.E.—See Agfa-Gevaert N.V.; *Int'l*, pg. 208
AGFA-GEVAERT AG/SA—See Agfa-Gevaert N.V.; *Int'l*, pg. 208
AGFA-GEVAERT ARGENTINA S.A.—See Agfa-Gevaert N.V.; *Int'l*, pg. 208
AGFA-GEVAERT B.V.—See Agfa-Gevaert N.V.; *Int'l*, pg. 208
AGFA-GEVAERT COLOMBIA LTDA.—See Agfa-Gevaert N.V.; *Int'l*, pg. 208
AGFA-GEVAERT DE VENEZUELA S.A.—See Agfa-Gevaert N.V.; *Int'l*, pg. 208
AGFA-GEVAERT DO BRASIL LTDA.—See Agfa-Gevaert N.V.; *Int'l*, pg. 208
AGFA-GEVAERT DO BRASIL LTD.—See Agfa-Gevaert N.V.; *Int'l*, pg. 208
AGFA-GEVAERT HEALTHCARE GMBH—See Agfa-Gevaert N.V.; *Int'l*, pg. 208
AGFA-GEVAERT INTERNATIONAL NV—See Agfa-Gevaert N.V.; *Int'l*, pg. 208
AGFA-GEVAERT INVESTMENT FUND NV—See Agfa-Gevaert N.V.; *Int'l*, pg. 208
AGFA-GEVAERT JAPAN, LTD.—See Agfa-Gevaert N.V.; *Int'l*, pg. 208
AGFA-GEVAERT LIMITED—See Agfa-Gevaert N.V.; *Int'l*, pg. 208
AGFA-GEVAERT LTDA.—See Agfa-Gevaert N.V.; *Int'l*, pg. 208
AGFA-GEVAERT LTD.—See Agfa-Gevaert N.V.; *Int'l*, pg. 208
AGFA-GEVAERT N.V.; *Int'l*, pg. 207
AGFA-GEVAERT S.A.—See Agfa-Gevaert N.V.; *Int'l*, pg. 208
AGFA-GEVAERT S.A.U.—See Agfa-Gevaert N.V.; *Int'l*, pg. 208
AGFA-GEVAERT S.P.A.—See Agfa-Gevaert N.V.; *Int'l*, pg. 208
AGFA GRAPHICS ARGENTINA S.A.—See Agfa-Gevaert N.V.; *Int'l*, pg. 207
AGFA GRAPHICS AUSTRIA GMBH—See Agfa-Gevaert N.V.; *Int'l*, pg. 207
AGFA GRAPHICS GERMANY GMBH & CO. KG—See Agfa-Gevaert N.V.; *Int'l*, pg. 207
AGFA GRAPHICS LTD.—See Agfa-Gevaert N.V.; *Int'l*, pg. 207
AGFA GRAPHICS MIDDLE EAST FZCO—See Agfa-Gevaert N.V.; *Int'l*, pg. 207
AGFA GRAPHICS NV—See Agfa-Gevaert N.V.; *Int'l*, pg. 208

COMPANY NAME INDEX

AGFA GRAPHICS SP. Z.O.O.—See Agfa-Gevaert N.V.; *Int'l*, pg. 207
AGFA GRAPHICS S.R.L.—See Agfa-Gevaert N.V.; *Int'l*, pg. 207
AGFA GRAPHICS SWITZERLAND AG—See Agfa-Gevaert N.V.; *Int'l*, pg. 207
AGFA HEALTHCARE AG—See Agfa-Gevaert N.V.; *Int'l*, pg. 207
AGFA HEALTHCARE ARGENTINA S.A.—See Agfa-Gevaert N.V.; *Int'l*, pg. 207
AGFA HEALTHCARE AUSTRALIA LIMITED—See Agfa-Gevaert N.V.; *Int'l*, pg. 207
AGFA HEALTHCARE BRAZIL IMPORTACAO E SERVICOS LTDA.—See Agfa-Gevaert N.V.; *Int'l*, pg. 207
AGFA HEALTHCARE COLOMBIA LTDA.—See Agfa-Gevaert N.V.; *Int'l*, pg. 207
AGFA HEALTHCARE DENMARK A/S—See Agfa-Gevaert N.V.; *Int'l*, pg. 207
AGFA HEALTHCARE EQUIPMENTS PORTUGAL LDA.—See Agfa-Gevaert N.V.; *Int'l*, pg. 208
AGFA HEALTHCARE FINLAND OY AB—See Agfa-Gevaert N.V.; *Int'l*, pg. 207
AGFA HEALTHCARE FRANCE S.A.—See Agfa-Gevaert N.V.; *Int'l*, pg. 208
AGFA HEALTHCARE GERMANY GMBH—See Ardian SAS; *Int'l*, pg. 555
AGFA HEALTHCARE GMBH—See Ardian SAS; *Int'l*, pg. 555
AGFA HEALTHCARE HONG KONG LTD.—See Agfa-Gevaert N.V.; *Int'l*, pg. 207
AGFA HEALTHCARE HUNGARY KFT.—See Agfa-Gevaert N.V.; *Int'l*, pg. 207
AGFA HEALTHCARE IMAGING AGENTS GMBH—See Agfa-Gevaert N.V.; *Int'l*, pg. 207
AGFA HEALTHCARE INC.—See Agfa-Gevaert N.V.; *Int'l*, pg. 207
AGFA HEALTHCARE INDIA PRIVATE LTD.—See Wartsila Corporation; *Int'l*, pg. 8346
AGFA HEALTHCARE IT UK LIMITED—See Agfa-Gevaert N.V.; *Int'l*, pg. 208
AGFA HEALTHCARE KAZAKHSTAN LLP—See Agfa-Gevaert N.V.; *Int'l*, pg. 208
AGFA HEALTHCARE - KNIGHTSBRIDGE GMBH—See Ardian SAS; *Int'l*, pg. 555
AGFA HEALTHCARE LUXEMBOURG S.A.—See Agfa-Gevaert N.V.; *Int'l*, pg. 207
AGFA HEALTHCARE MEXICO S.A. DE C.V.—See Agfa-Gevaert N.V.; *Int'l*, pg. 208
AGFA HEALTHCARE MIDDLE EAST FZ-LLC—See Agfa-Gevaert N.V.; *Int'l*, pg. 208
AGFA HEALTHCARE NORWAY AS—See Agfa-Gevaert N.V.; *Int'l*, pg. 207
AGFA HEALTHCARE NV—See Agfa-Gevaert N.V.; *Int'l*, pg. 208
AGFA HEALTHCARE SAUDI ARABIA COMPANY LIMITED LLC—See Agfa-Gevaert N.V.; *Int'l*, pg. 208
AGFA HEALTHCARE SHANGHAI LTD.—See Agfa-Gevaert N.V.; *Int'l*, pg. 207
AGFA HEALTHCARE SINGAPORE PTE. LTD.—See Agfa-Gevaert N.V.; *Int'l*, pg. 207
AGFA HEALTHCARE SOUTH AFRICA PTY. LTD.—See Agfa-Gevaert N.V.; *Int'l*, pg. 207
AGFA HEALTHCARE SPAIN, S.A.U.—See Agfa-Gevaert N.V.; *Int'l*, pg. 208
AGFA HEALTHCARE SWEDEN AB—See Agfa-Gevaert N.V.; *Int'l*, pg. 207
AGFA HEALTHCARE UK LIMITED—See Agfa-Gevaert N.V.; *Int'l*, pg. 208
AGFA HEALTHCARE UKRAINE LLC—See Agfa-Gevaert N.V.; *Int'l*, pg. 208
AGFA HEALTHCARE VIETNAM CO. LTD.—See Agfa-Gevaert N.V.; *Int'l*, pg. 208
AGFA IMAGING PRODUCTS (SHENZHEN) CO., LTD.—See Agfa-Gevaert N.V.; *Int'l*, pg. 208
AGFA INDIA PRIVATE LTD.—See Agfa-Gevaert N.V.; *Int'l*, pg. 207
AGFA INDUSTRIES KOREA LTD.—See Agfa-Gevaert N.V.; *Int'l*, pg. 207
AGFA LIMITED—See Agfa-Gevaert N.V.; *Int'l*, pg. 207
AGF ALLIANZ CHILE COMPANIA DE SEGUROS GENERALES S.A.—See Allianz SE; *Int'l*, pg. 342
AGFA MATERIALS CORPORATION—See Agfa-Gevaert N.V.; *Int'l*, pg. 208
AGFA MATERIALS JAPAN LTD.—See Agfa-Gevaert N.V.; *Int'l*, pg. 208
AGFA MATERIALS TAIWAN CO., LTD.—See Agfa-Gevaert N.V.; *Int'l*, pg. 208
AGFARM PTY. LTD.—See Nutrien Ltd.; *Int'l*, pg. 5492
AGFA SINGAPORE PTE. LTD.—See Agfa-Gevaert N.V.; *Int'l*, pg. 207
AGFA SP. Z.O.O.—See Agfa-Gevaert N.V.; *Int'l*, pg. 208
AGF ASSET MANAGEMENT ASIA LTD.—See AGF Management Limited; *Int'l*, pg. 206
AGF A S; *Int'l*, pg. 206
AGF ASSURANCES LUXEMBOURG S.A.—See Allianz SE; *Int'l*, pg. 342
AGF BRASIL SEGUROS SA—See Allianz SE; *Int'l*, pg. 342

AGF BURKINA ASSURANCES—See Allianz SE; *Int'l*, pg. 342
AGF BURKINA ASSURANCES VIE—See Allianz SE; *Int'l*, pg. 342
AGF CAMEROUN ASSURANCES—See Allianz SE; *Int'l*, pg. 342
AGF CAMEROUN ASSURANCES VIE—See Allianz SE; *Int'l*, pg. 342
AGF CAPITAL INVESTISSEMENT 2—See Allianz SE; *Int'l*, pg. 342
AGF CENTRAFRIQUE ASSURANCES—See Allianz SE; *Int'l*, pg. 342
AGF COTE D'IVOIRE ASSURANCES VIE—See Allianz SE; *Int'l*, pg. 342
AGFEED ANIMAL NUTRITION HOLDINGS, INC.—See AgFeed Industries, Inc.; *Int'l*, pg. 209
AGFEED INDUSTRIES, INC.; *Int'l*, pg. 209
A.G. FERRARI FOODS; *U.S. Private*, pg. 25
AGF FUNDS INC.—See AGF Management Limited; *Int'l*, pg. 206
AGFIA LIMITED—See AGF Management Limited; *Int'l*, pg. 206
AG FINANCIAL INVESTMENT TRUST, INC.; *U.S. Private*, pg. 124
AG FINANCIAL PRODUCTS INC.—See Assured Guaranty Ltd.; *Int'l*, pg. 650
AGFINITY, INC.; *U.S. Private*, pg. 127
AGF INTERNATIONAL ADVISORS COMPANY LTD.—See AGF Management Limited; *Int'l*, pg. 206
AGF INTERNATIONAL COMPANY LTD.—See AGF Management Limited; *Int'l*, pg. 206
AGF INVESTMENTS INC.—See AGF Management Limited; *Int'l*, pg. 206
AGFIRST FARM CREDIT BANK—See Federal Farm Credit Banks Funding Corporation; *U.S. Private*, pg. 1487
AG FIRST FARMERS COOPERATIVE; *U.S. Private*, pg. 124
AGF LIFE LUXEMBOURG S.A—See Allianz SE; *Int'l*, pg. 342
AGF MANAGEMENT LIMITED; *Int'l*, pg. 206
AGFM HOLDING CORPORATION; *U.S. Private*, pg. 127
AGF S.A.—See Allianz SE; *Int'l*, pg. 342
AGF SECURITIES (CANADA) LTD.—See AGF Management Limited; *Int'l*, pg. 206
AGF SENEGAL ASSURANCES VIE—See Allianz SE; *Int'l*, pg. 342
AGF SUZUKA CO., LTD.—See Mondelez International, Inc.; *U.S. Public*, pg. 1461
AGGEORGIA FARM CREDIT, ACA; *U.S. Private*, pg. 127
AGGERENERGIE GMBH—See E.ON SE; *Int'l*, pg. 2251
AGGIE GREY'S HOTEL & BUNGALOWS; *Int'l*, pg. 209
AGGLITE OF VIRGINIA INC.—See Eagle Corporation; *U.S. Private*, pg. 1309
AGGLOTAP, S.A.—See CORTICEIRA AMORIM, S.G.P.S., S.A.; *Int'l*, pg. 1807
AGGM AUSTRIAN GAS GRID MANAGEMENT AG—See OMV Aktiengesellschaft; *Int'l*, pg. 5567
AGGORA LIMITED—See Bunzl plc; *Int'l*, pg. 1217
AGGREGATED MICRO POWER HOLDINGS PLC; *Int'l*, pg. 209
AGGREGATE INDUSTRIES HOLDINGS LIMITED—See Holcim Ltd.; *Int'l*, pg. 3446
AGGREGATE INDUSTRIES MANAGEMENT, INC.—See Holcim Ltd.; *Int'l*, pg. 3446
AGGREGATE INDUSTRIES MID-ATLANTIC REGION—See Holcim Ltd.; *Int'l*, pg. 3446
AGGREGATE INDUSTRIES MIDWEST REGION—See Holcim Ltd.; *Int'l*, pg. 3446
AGGREGATE INDUSTRIES NORTHEAST REGION—See Holcim Ltd.; *Int'l*, pg. 3446
AGGREGATE INDUSTRIES - SOUTHWEST REGION—See Holcim Ltd.; *Int'l*, pg. 3446
AGGREGATE INDUSTRIES UK LIMITED—See Holcim Ltd.; *Int'l*, pg. 3446
AGGREGATE INTELLIGENCE, INC.; *U.S. Private*, pg. 127
AGGREGATE PLANT PRODUCTS CO.—See NOV, Inc.; *U.S. Public*, pg. 1543
AGGREGATES USA (AUGUSTA), LLC—See Vulcan Materials Company; *U.S. Public*, pg. 2313
AGGREGATES USA (MACON), LLC—See Vulcan Materials Company; *U.S. Public*, pg. 2313
AGGREGATES USA (SAVANNAH), LLC—See Vulcan Materials Company; *U.S. Public*, pg. 2313
AGGREGATES USA (SPARTA), LLC—See Vulcan Materials Company; *U.S. Public*, pg. 2313
AGGREGATO GLOBAL PTY. LTD.; *Int'l*, pg. 209
AGGREGATO MOBILE PTY. LTD.—See Aggregato Global Pty. Ltd.; *Int'l*, pg. 209
AGGREGATO PREPAID PTY. LTD.—See Aggregato Global Pty. Ltd.; *Int'l*, pg. 209
AGGREKO ANGOLA LDA.—See I Squared Capital Advisors (US) LLC; *U.S. Private*, pg. 2020
AGGREKO ANGOLA LDA.—See TDR Capital LLP; *Int'l*, pg. 7490
AGGREKO CANADA INC.—See I Squared Capital Advisors (US) LLC; *U.S. Private*, pg. 2020

AGGREGATO GLOBAL PTY. LTD.

AGGREKO CANADA INC.—See TDR Capital LLP; *Int'l*, pg. 7490
AGGREKO CHILE LIMITADA—See I Squared Capital Advisors (US) LLC; *U.S. Private*, pg. 2020
AGGREKO CHILE LIMITADA—See TDR Capital LLP; *Int'l*, pg. 7490
AGGREKO DE VENEZUELA C.A.—See I Squared Capital Advisors (US) LLC; *U.S. Private*, pg. 2021
AGGREKO DE VENEZUELA C.A.—See TDR Capital LLP; *Int'l*, pg. 7490
AGGREKO ENERGY RENTAL SOLUTIONS INC.—See I Squared Capital Advisors (US) LLC; *U.S. Private*, pg. 2021
AGGREKO ENERGY RENTAL SOLUTIONS INC.—See TDR Capital LLP; *Int'l*, pg. 7490
AGGREKO ENERGY RENTAL SOUTH AFRICA (PROPRIETARY) LIMITED—See I Squared Capital Advisors (US) LLC; *U.S. Private*, pg. 2021
AGGREKO ENERGY RENTAL SOUTH AFRICA (PROPRIETARY) LIMITED—See TDR Capital LLP; *Int'l*, pg. 7490
AGGREKO ENERGY RENTALS PANAMA SA—See I Squared Capital Advisors (US) LLC; *U.S. Private*, pg. 2021
AGGREKO ENERGY RENTALS PANAMA SA—See TDR Capital LLP; *Int'l*, pg. 7490
AGGREKO EURASIA LLC—See I Squared Capital Advisors (US) LLC; *U.S. Private*, pg. 2021
AGGREKO EURASIA LLC—See TDR Capital LLP; *Int'l*, pg. 7490
AGGREKO FINLAND OY—See I Squared Capital Advisors (US) LLC; *U.S. Private*, pg. 2021
AGGREKO FINLAND OY—See TDR Capital LLP; *Int'l*, pg. 7490
AGGREKO GENERATOR RENTALS (PNG) LIMITED—See I Squared Capital Advisors (US) LLC; *U.S. Private*, pg. 2021
AGGREKO GENERATOR RENTALS (PNG) LIMITED—See TDR Capital LLP; *Int'l*, pg. 7490
AGGREKO HOLDINGS, INC.—See I Squared Capital Advisors (US) LLC; *U.S. Private*, pg. 2021
AGGREKO HOLDINGS, INC.—See TDR Capital LLP; *Int'l*, pg. 7490
AGGREKO HOLDINGS LTD.—See I Squared Capital Advisors (US) LLC; *U.S. Private*, pg. 2021
AGGREKO HOLDINGS LTD.—See TDR Capital LLP; *Int'l*, pg. 7490
AGGREKO IBERIA SA—See I Squared Capital Advisors (US) LLC; *U.S. Private*, pg. 2021
AGGREKO IBERIA SA—See TDR Capital LLP; *Int'l*, pg. 7490
AGGREKO ITALIA S.R.L.—See I Squared Capital Advisors (US) LLC; *U.S. Private*, pg. 2021
AGGREKO ITALIA S.R.L.—See TDR Capital LLP; *Int'l*, pg. 7490
AGGREKO JAPAN LIMITED—See I Squared Capital Advisors (US) LLC; *U.S. Private*, pg. 2021
AGGREKO JAPAN LIMITED—See TDR Capital LLP; *Int'l*, pg. 7490
AGGREKO KENYA ENERGY RENTALS LIMITED—See I Squared Capital Advisors (US) LLC; *U.S. Private*, pg. 2021
AGGREKO KENYA ENERGY RENTALS LIMITED—See TDR Capital LLP; *Int'l*, pg. 7490
AGGREKO, LLC—See I Squared Capital Advisors (US) LLC; *U.S. Private*, pg. 2021
AGGREKO, LLC—See TDR Capital LLP; *Int'l*, pg. 7490
AGGREKO MYANMAR CO. LIMITED—See I Squared Capital Advisors (US) LLC; *U.S. Private*, pg. 2021
AGGREKO MYANMAR CO. LIMITED—See TDR Capital LLP; *Int'l*, pg. 7490
AGGREKO NAMIBIA ENERGY RENTALS (PTY) LTD.—See I Squared Capital Advisors (US) LLC; *U.S. Private*, pg. 2021
AGGREKO NAMIBIA ENERGY RENTALS (PTY) LTD.—See TDR Capital LLP; *Int'l*, pg. 7490
AGGREKO NORWAY AS—See I Squared Capital Advisors (US) LLC; *U.S. Private*, pg. 2021
AGGREKO NORWAY AS—See TDR Capital LLP; *Int'l*, pg. 7490
AGGREKO (NZ) LIMITED—See I Squared Capital Advisors (US) LLC; *U.S. Private*, pg. 2020
AGGREKO (NZ) LIMITED—See TDR Capital LLP; *Int'l*, pg. 7490
AGGREKO PLC—See I Squared Capital Advisors (US) LLC; *U.S. Private*, pg. 2020
AGGREKO PLC—See TDR Capital LLP; *Int'l*, pg. 7490
AGGREKO POLSKA SPOLKA ZORGANICZANA—See I Squared Capital Advisors (US) LLC; *U.S. Private*, pg. 2021
AGGREKO POLSKA SPOLKA ZORGANICZANA—See TDR Capital LLP; *Int'l*, pg. 7490
AGGREKO SOUTH EAST EUROPE S.R.L.—See I Squared Capital Advisors (US) LLC; *U.S. Private*, pg. 2021
AGGREKO SOUTH EAST EUROPE S.R.L.—See TDR Capital LLP; *Int'l*, pg. 7490
AGGREKO SOUTH KOREA LIMITED—See I Squared Capital Advisors (US) LLC; *U.S. Private*, pg. 2021

AGGREKO SOUTH KOREA LIMITED—See TDR Capital LLP; *Int'l*, pg. 7490
AGGREKO (THAILAND) LIMITED—See I Squared Capital Advisors (US) LLC; *U.S. Private*, pg. 2020
AGGREKO (THAILAND) LIMITED—See TDR Capital LLP; *Int'l*, pg. 7490
AGGREKO UK LTD.—See I Squared Capital Advisors (US) LLC; *U.S. Private*, pg. 2021
AGGREKO UK LTD.—See TDR Capital LLP; *Int'l*, pg. 7490
AGGRENE CORPORATION; *U.S. Private*, pg. 127
AGGRESSOR ADVENTURES, LLC; *U.S. Private*, pg. 127
AG/GRO FERTILIZER COMPANY; *U.S. Private*, pg. 125
AG GROWTH INDUSTRIES LIMITED PARTNERSHIP—See Ag Growth International Inc.; *Int'l*, pg. 198
AG GROWTH INTERNATIONAL - EDWARDS GRAIN GUARD DIVISION—See Ag Growth International Inc.; *Int'l*, pg. 198
AG GROWTH INTERNATIONAL INC.; *Int'l*, pg. 198
AG GROWTH INTERNATIONAL - WESTFIELD DIVISION—See Ag Growth International Inc.; *Int'l*, pg. 198
AG GUARANTEE CO., LTD.—See AIFUL Corporation; *Int'l*, pg. 231
AGHEERA GMBH—See Deutsche Post AG; *Int'l*, pg. 2071
AG HILL PARTNERS LLC; *U.S. Private*, pg. 124
AGI AFRICA (PTY) LTD.—See Novomatic AG; *Int'l*, pg. 5466
AGI ALUMINIUM (PTY) LIMITED—See AG Industries Limited; *Int'l*, pg. 198
AGI BRASIL INDUSTRIA E COMERCIO S.A.—See Ag Growth International Inc.; *Int'l*, pg. 198
AGIDENS AG—See Ackermans & van Haaren NV; *Int'l*, pg. 104
AGIDENS INC.—See Ackermans & van Haaren NV; *Int'l*, pg. 104
AGIDENS INTERNATIONAL NV—See Ackermans & van Haaren NV; *Int'l*, pg. 104
AGIE CHARMILLES BV—See Georg Fischer AG; *Int'l*, pg. 2934
AGIE CHARMILLES CHINA (H.K.) LTD.—See Mikron Holding AG; *Int'l*, pg. 4892
AGIE CHARMILLES CHINA (SHANGHAI) LTD—See Georg Fischer AG; *Int'l*, pg. 2934
AGIE CHARMILLES CHINA (SHENZHEN) LTD—See Georg Fischer AG; *Int'l*, pg. 2934
AGIE CHARMILLES CHINA (TIANJIN) LTD—See Georg Fischer AG; *Int'l*, pg. 2934
AGIE CHARMILLES GMBH—See Georg Fischer AG; *Int'l*, pg. 2934
AGIE CHARMILLES HOLDING LIMITED—See Georg Fischer AG; *Int'l*, pg. 2934
AGIE CHARMILLES JAPAN LTD.—See Georg Fischer AG; *Int'l*, pg. 2934
AGIE CHARMILLES KOREA CO LTD—See Georg Fischer AG; *Int'l*, pg. 2934
AGIE CHARMILLES LLC—See Georg Fischer AG; *Int'l*, pg. 2934
AGIE CHARMILLES LTDA—See Georg Fischer AG; *Int'l*, pg. 2934
AGIE CHARMILLES LTD.—See Georg Fischer AG; *Int'l*, pg. 2934
AGIE CHARMILLES LTD.—See Georg Fischer AG; *Int'l*, pg. 2934
AGIE CHARMILLES MACHINE TOOL CO., LTD.—See Georg Fischer AG; *Int'l*, pg. 2934
AGIE CHARMILLES MANAGEMENT SA—See Georg Fischer AG; *Int'l*, pg. 2934
AGIE CHARMILLES NEW TECHNOLOGIES SA—See Georg Fischer AG; *Int'l*, pg. 2934
AGIE CHARMILLES SALES LTD.—See Georg Fischer AG; *Int'l*, pg. 2934
AGIE CHARMILLES S.A.R.L.—See Georg Fischer AG; *Int'l*, pg. 2934
AGIE CHARMILLES SA—See Georg Fischer AG; *Int'l*, pg. 2934
AGIE CHARMILLES SERVICES SA—See Georg Fischer AG; *Int'l*, pg. 2934
AGIE CHARMILLES SOUTH EAST ASIA PTE LTD—See Georg Fischer AG; *Int'l*, pg. 2934
AGIE CHARMILLES S.R.O.—See Georg Fischer AG; *Int'l*, pg. 2934
AGIE LTD—See Georg Fischer AG; *Int'l*, pg. 2934
AGI EMEA S.R.L.—See Ag Growth International Inc.; *Int'l*, pg. 198
AGIE S.P.A.—See Georg Fischer AG; *Int'l*, pg. 2934
AGI GAMING COLOMBIA S.A.S.—See Novomatic AG; *Int'l*, pg. 5466
AGIGA TECH (CHENGDU) LLC—See Infineon Technologies AG; *Int'l*, pg. 3685
AGIGA TECH, INC.—See Infineon Technologies AG; *Int'l*, pg. 3685
AGI GENERAL CONTRACTING; *U.S. Private*, pg. 127
AGI GLASS (PTY) LIMITED—See AG Industries Limited; *Int'l*, pg. 198
AGI GREENPAC LIMITED; *Int'l*, pg. 209
AGI HUNGARIA KFT.—See Novomatic AG; *Int'l*, pg. 5466
AGI INDUSTRIES, INC.; *U.S. Private*, pg. 127
AGI INFRA LTD.; *Int'l*, pg. 209

AGIITO LIMITED—See Capita plc; *Int'l*, pg. 1308
AGILAIRE LLC; *U.S. Private*, pg. 127
AGILA SPECIALTIES POLSKA SP. ZO.O—See Viatris Inc.; *U.S. Public*, pg. 2293
AGILE360, INC.—See Entisys Solutions, Inc.; *U.S. Private*, pg. 1405
AGILEASSETS, INC.; *U.S. Private*, pg. 128
AGILE CAPITAL; *Int'l*, pg. 209
AGILE CONTENT SA; *Int'l*, pg. 209
AGILE DECISIONPOINT CORPORATION; *U.S. Private*, pg. 127
AGILE DEFENSE, INC.—See Enlightenment Capital LLC; *U.S. Private*, pg. 1400
AGILE EDUCATION GROUP—See Agile Group Holdings Limited; *Int'l*, pg. 209
AGILE GLOBAL SOLUTIONS INC.; *U.S. Private*, pg. 127
AGILE GROUP HOLDINGS LIMITED; *Int'l*, pg. 209
AGILE GROWTH CORP.; *U.S. Public*, pg. 60
AGILE INTELLIGENT TECHNOLOGY CO., LTD.—See Suzhou Gold Mantis Construction Decoration Co., Ltd.; *Int'l*, pg. 7349
AGILE MAGNETICS, INC.—See Standex International; *U.S. Public*, pg. 1930
AGILE MALTA HOLDINGS LIMITED—See Aurobindo Pharma Ltd.; *Int'l*, pg. 712
AGILE MEDIA NETWORK, INC.; *Int'l*, pg. 209
AGILENCE, INC.; *U.S. Private*, pg. 128
AGILE NETWORK BUILDERS, LLC—See Macquarie Group Limited; *Int'l*, pg. 4628
AGILENT TECHNOLOGIES AUSTRALIA PTY LTD—See Agilent Technologies, Inc.; *U.S. Public*, pg. 60
AGILENT TECHNOLOGIES BELGIUM S.A./N.V.—See Agilent Technologies, Inc.; *U.S. Public*, pg. 60
AGILENT TECHNOLOGIES BRASIL LTDA.—See Agilent Technologies, Inc.; *U.S. Public*, pg. 60
AGILENT TECHNOLOGIES CANADA INC.—See Agilent Technologies, Inc.; *U.S. Public*, pg. 60
AGILENT TECHNOLOGIES DEUTSCHLAND ALPHA GMBH—See Agilent Technologies, Inc.; *U.S. Public*, pg. 61
AGILENT TECHNOLOGIES DEUTSCHLAND GMBH—See Agilent Technologies, Inc.; *U.S. Public*, pg. 61
AGILENT TECHNOLOGIES DEUTSCHLAND HOLDING GMBH—See Agilent Technologies, Inc.; *U.S. Public*, pg. 60
AGILENT TECHNOLOGIES EUROPE B.V.—See Agilent Technologies, Inc.; *U.S. Public*, pg. 60
AGILENT TECHNOLOGIES FRANCE SAS—See Agilent Technologies, Inc.; *U.S. Public*, pg. 60
AGILENT TECHNOLOGIES, INC.; *U.S. Public*, pg. 60
AGILENT TECHNOLOGIES, INC. - VACUUM PRODUCTS—See Agilent Technologies, Inc.; *U.S. Public*, pg. 61
AGILENT TECHNOLOGIES INTERNATIONAL SARL—See Agilent Technologies, Inc.; *U.S. Public*, pg. 61
AGILENT TECHNOLOGIES IRELAND FINANCE LIMITED—See Agilent Technologies, Inc.; *U.S. Public*, pg. 61
AGILENT TECHNOLOGIES IRELAND LTD.—See Agilent Technologies, Inc.; *U.S. Public*, pg. 61
AGILENT TECHNOLOGIES ITALIA S.P.A.—See Agilent Technologies, Inc.; *U.S. Public*, pg. 61
AGILENT TECHNOLOGIES JAPAN, LTD.—See Agilent Technologies, Inc.; *U.S. Public*, pg. 61
AGILENT TECHNOLOGIES (MALAYSIA) SDN. BHD.—See Agilent Technologies, Inc.; *U.S. Public*, pg. 60
AGILENT TECHNOLOGIES MEXICO, S.DE R.L. DE C.V.—See Agilent Technologies, Inc.; *U.S. Public*, pg. 61
AGILENT TECHNOLOGIES SINGAPORE PTE. LTD.—See Agilent Technologies, Inc.; *U.S. Public*, pg. 61
AGILENT TECHNOLOGIES SINGAPORE VISION OPERATION PTE LTD.—See Agilent Technologies, Inc.; *U.S. Public*, pg. 61
AGILENT TECHNOLOGIES SWEDEN HOLDING AB—See Agilent Technologies, Inc.; *U.S. Public*, pg. 61
AGILENT TECHNOLOGIES TAIWAN LTD.—See Agilent Technologies, Inc.; *U.S. Public*, pg. 61
AGILENT TECHNOLOGIES WORLD TRADE, LTD.—See Agilent Technologies, Inc.; *U.S. Public*, pg. 61
AGILEPATH CORPORATION; *U.S. Private*, pg. 128
AGILE PHARMA (MALTA) LIMITED—See Aurobindo Pharma Ltd.; *Int'l*, pg. 712
AGILE PURSUITS FRANCHISING, INC.—See The Procter & Gamble Company; *U.S. Public*, pg. 2120
AGILE REAL ESTATE CONSTRUCTION MANAGEMENT GROUP CO., LTD.—See Agile Group Holdings Limited; *Int'l*, pg. 209
AGILE RESOURCES, INC.—See GEE Group Inc.; *U.S. Public*, pg. 909
AGILE SPORTS TECHNOLOGIES, INC.; *U.S. Public*, pg. 127
AGILE TECHNOLOGIES, LLC—See Thoma Bravo, L.P.; *U.S. Private*, pg. 4149
AGILE TECHNOLOGY SOLUTIONS, INC.—See Humana, Inc.; *U.S. Public*, pg. 1069
AGILETEK ENGINEERING LIMITED—See Tekmar Group plc; *Int'l*, pg. 7527

AGILE TELECOM SPA—See Growens S.p.A.; *Int'l*, pg. 3112
AGILE THERAPEUTICS, INC.; *U.S. Public*, pg. 60
AGILEX BIOLABS PTY. LTD.—See Healius Limited; *Int'l*, pg. 3302
AGILEX FLAVORS & FRAGRANCES, INC.—See Firmenich International SA; *Int'l*, pg. 2680
AGILIANCE, INC.—See Permira Advisers LLP; *Int'l*, pg. 5807
AGILIS HOLDING COMPANY LLC; *U.S. Private*, pg. 128
AGILITAS PRIVATE EQUITY LLP; *Int'l*, pg. 209
AGILITI HEALTH, INC.—See Thomas H. Lee Partners, L.P.; *U.S. Private*, pg. 4155
AGILITI, INC.—See Thomas H. Lee Partners, L.P.; *U.S. Private*, pg. 4155
AGILITY APPLICATIONS PTY LTD—See HUB24 Limited; *Int'l*, pg. 3516
AGILITY CENTRALIZED RESEARCH SERVICES, INC.—See Koninklijke Philips N.V.; *Int'l*, pg. 4267
AGILITY CLINICAL, INC.—See Precision Medicine Group, Inc.; *U.S. Private*, pg. 3245
AGILITY COMPANY L.L.C.—See Agility; *Int'l*, pg. 209
AGILITY DGS UK LTD.—See Agility; *Int'l*, pg. 209
AGILITY FUEL SOLUTIONS HOLDINGS INC.—See Hexagon Composites ASA; *Int'l*, pg. 3370
AGILITY FUEL SOLUTIONS LLC—See Hexagon Composites ASA; *Int'l*, pg. 3370
AGILITY HEALTH, INC.; *Int'l*, pg. 210
AGILITY HOLDINGS INC.—See Agility; *Int'l*, pg. 209
AGILITY INC.; *Int'l*, pg. 210
AGILITY INTERNATIONAL LOGISTICS PTE. LTD.—See Agility; *Int'l*, pg. 209
AGILITY LOGISTICS CORP.—See Agility; *Int'l*, pg. 210
AGILITY LOGISTICS GMBH—See Agility; *Int'l*, pg. 210
AGILITY LOGISTICS HOLDINGS PTE. LTD.—See Agility; *Int'l*, pg. 210
AGILITY LOGISTICS INTERNATIONAL B.V.—See Agility; *Int'l*, pg. 210
AGILITY LOGISTICS LIMITED—See Agility; *Int'l*, pg. 210
AGILITY LOGISTICS LLC—See Agility; *Int'l*, pg. 210
AGILITY LOGISTICS SARL—See DSV A/S; *Int'l*, pg. 2210
AGILITY MFG, INC.; *U.S. Private*, pg. 128
AGILITY MULTICHANNEL LTD.—See TA Associates, Inc.; *U.S. Private*, pg. 3915
AGILITY PARTNERS PTE. LTD.—See Phillip Capital Pte. Ltd.; *Int'l*, pg. 5846
AGILITY PROJECT LOGISTICS INC.—See Agility; *Int'l*, pg. 210
AGILITY PROJECT LOGISTICS INC.—See Agility; *Int'l*, pg. 210
AGILITY RECOVERY SOLUTIONS, INC.—See New State Capital Partners LLC; *U.S. Private*, pg. 2906
AGILITY RISE CO., LTD.—See MIRAIT ONE Corporation; *Int'l*, pg. 4917
AGILITY; *Int'l*, pg. 209
AGILLIC A/S; *Int'l*, pg. 210
AGILOFT, INC.—See Salesforce, Inc.; *U.S. Public*, pg. 1838
AGILONE INC.—See Vista Equity Partners, LLC; *U.S. Private*, pg. 4394
AGILON HEALTH, INC.; *U.S. Public*, pg. 62
AGILTRON, INC.; *U.S. Private*, pg. 128
AGILUX LABORATORIES, INC.—See Charles River Laboratories International, Inc.; *U.S. Public*, pg. 479
AGILYSYS HK LIMITED—See Agilysys, Inc.; *U.S. Public*, pg. 62
AGILYSYS, INC.; *U.S. Public*, pg. 62
AGILYSYS SINGAPORE PTE. LTD.—See Agilysys, Inc.; *U.S. Public*, pg. 62
AGILYSYS TECHNOLOGIES INDIA PRIVATE LIMITED—See Agilysys, Inc.; *U.S. Public*, pg. 62
AGILYSYS UK LTD.—See Agilysys, Inc.; *U.S. Public*, pg. 62
AGILYX ASA; *U.S. Public*, pg. 62
AGI MANUFACTURING (PTY) LIMITED—See AG Industries Limited; *Int'l*, pg. 198
AGINCOURT AUTOHAUS INC.; *Int'l*, pg. 210
AGINCOURT PRODUCTIONS, INC.—See BCE Inc.; *Int'l*, pg. 927
A & G, INC.—See Gildan Activewear Inc.; *Int'l*, pg. 2973
AG INDUSTRIES, INC.—See AG Ajikawa Corporation; *Int'l*, pg. 196
AG INDUSTRIES LIMITED; *Int'l*, pg. 198
AG INDUSTRIES VIETNAM COMPANY LIMITED—See AG Industries Limited; *Int'l*, pg. 198
AGINGCARE, LLC; *U.S. Private*, pg. 128
AG INSURANCE N.V.—See Ageas SA/NV; *Int'l*, pg. 204
AG INSURANCE SA/NV—See Ageas SA/NV; *Int'l*, pg. 204
AG INTERACTIVE—See Clayton, Dubilier & Rice, LLC; *U.S. Private*, pg. 919
AGIO PAPER & INDUSTRIES LIMITED - BILASPUR MILL—See AGIO PAPER & INDUSTRIES LIMITED; *Int'l*, pg. 210
AGIO PAPER & INDUSTRIES LIMITED; *Int'l*, pg. 210
AGIOS PHARMACEUTICALS INC.; *U.S. Public*, pg. 62
AGIO SYSTEM OCH KOMPETENS I SKANDINAVIEN AB—See Storskogen Group AB; *Int'l*, pg. 7227
AGIP CASPIAN SEA BV—See Eni S.p.A.; *Int'l*, pg. 2436

COMPANY NAME INDEX

AGI PROPERTIES INC.—See Brookfield Reinsurance Ltd.; *Int'l*, pg. 1193
AGIP S.P.A.—See Eni S.p.A.; *Int'l*, pg. 2436
AGI PUBLISHING, INC; *U.S. Private*, pg. 127
AGIS-AGROINDUSTRIJA; *Int'l*, pg. 210
AGI SOLUTIONS INC.—See Ag Growth International Inc.; *Int'l*, pg. 198
AGIS SA—See CJSC Russian Standard Corporation; *Int'l*, pg. 1634
AGI SURETRACK LLC—See Ag Growth International Inc.; *Int'l*, pg. 198
AGIT - AGENCIJA ZA INTEGRALNI TRANSPORT D.O.O.—See HZ Hrvatske Zeljeznice Holding d.o.o.; *Int'l*, pg. 3561
AGITAL HOLDINGS, LLC; *U.S. Private*, pg. 128
AGI TRAFFIC TECHNOLOGY, INC.—See Aecon Group Inc.; *Int'l*, pg. 172
AGI-VR/WESSON INC—See The Jordan Company, L.P.; *U.S. Private*, pg. 4060
AGJUNCTION INC.—See Kubota Corporation; *Int'l*, pg. 4321
AGJUNCTION LLC—See Kubota Corporation; *Int'l*, pg. 4321
AGKNOWLEDGE, LLC—See KCoe Isom, LLP; *U.S. Private*, pg. 2270
AGLAB, INC.—See Astrotech Corporation; *U.S. Public*, pg. 218
AGL ACT RETAIL INVESTMENTS PTY LIMITED—See AGL Energy Limited; *Int'l*, pg. 211
AG LAND CO-OP INC.; *U.S. Private*, pg. 124
AGLAND CO-OP; *U.S. Private*, pg. 128
AGLAND CORP.; *Int'l*, pg. 211
AG-LAND FS, INC.; *U.S. Private*, pg. 125
A.G. LAYNE INC.; *U.S. Private*, pg. 25
AGL CORPORATE SERVICES PTY LIMITED—See AGL Energy Limited; *Int'l*, pg. 211
AGL CORPORATION—See Nippon Steel Corporation; *Int'l*, pg. 5336
A.G. LEE OIL COMPANY INC.; *U.S. Private*, pg. 25
AGL ELECTRICITY (VIC) PTY LIMITED—See AGL Energy Limited; *Int'l*, pg. 211
AGL ENERGY LIMITED; *Int'l*, pg. 210
AGL ENERGY SERVICES PTY LIMITED—See AGL Energy Limited; *Int'l*, pg. 211
AGL HYDRO PARTNERSHIP—See AGL Energy Limited; *Int'l*, pg. 211
AGL LOY YANG PTY LTD—See AGL Energy Limited; *Int'l*, pg. 211
AGL MACQUARIE—See AGL Energy Limited; *Int'l*, pg. 211
AG LOAN SERVICES CORPORATION—See AIFUL Corporation; *Int'l*, pg. 231
AGLOBIS AG—See Mitsui & Co., Ltd.; *Int'l*, pg. 4973
AGLOBIS GMBH—See Chemtrade Logistics Income Fund; *Int'l*, pg. 1464
AGLOMERADOS ALBACETE SA—See Eiffage S.A.; *Int'l*, pg. 2330
AGLOMERADOS LOS SERRANOS SA—See Eiffage S.A.; *Int'l*, pg. 2330
AGL POWER GENERATION PTY LIMITED—See AGL Energy Limited; *Int'l*, pg. 211
AGL SA GENERATION PTY LIMITED—See AGL Energy Limited; *Int'l*, pg. 211
AGL SALES PTY LIMITED—See AGL Energy Limited; *Int'l*, pg. 211
AGL SALES (QUEENSLAND ELECTRICITY) PTY LIMITED—See AGL Energy Limited; *Int'l*, pg. 211
AGLSM SDN. BHD.—See Aptech Limited; *Int'l*, pg. 523
AGL SOUTHERN HYDRO (NSW) PTY LIMITED—See AGL Energy Limited; *Int'l*, pg. 211
AGL SOUTHERN HYDRO PTY LIMITED—See AGL Energy Limited; *Int'l*, pg. 211
AGL TORRENS ISLAND HOLDINGS PTY LIMITED—See AGL Energy Limited; *Int'l*, pg. 211
AGL TORRENS ISLAND PTY LIMITED—See AGL Energy Limited; *Int'l*, pg. 211
AGLUKON SPEZIALDUNGER GMBH & CO. KG; *Int'l*, pg. 211
AGL WELDING SUPPLY CO. INC.; *U.S. Private*, pg. 128
A & G MACHINE, INC.; *U.S. Private*, pg. 17
AGMARK INTERMODAL SYSTEMS, INC.; *U.S. Private*, pg. 128
THE A.G. MAURO COMPANY—See American Securities LLC; *U.S. Private*, pg. 249
AGM AUTOMOTIVE, LLC—See Flex Ltd.; *Int'l*, pg. 2702
AGM BATTERIES LTD—See GS Yuasa Corporation; *Int'l*, pg. 3143
AGM CONTAINER CONTROLS, INC.; *U.S. Private*, pg. 128
AGM D.O.O.—See Zagrebacki holding d.o.o.; *Int'l*, pg. 8620
AG MEDICAL CORPORATION—See AIFUL Corporation; *Int'l*, pg. 231
AG-MEIER INDUSTRIES LLC; *U.S. Private*, pg. 125
AG MELCO ELEVATOR CO. L.L.C.—See Mitsubishi Electric Corporation; *Int'l*, pg. 4943
AGMET METALS INC; *U.S. Private*, pg. 128
AGM GROUP HOLDINGS INC.; *Int'l*, pg. 211
AGM INDIA ADVISORS PRIVATE LIMITED—See Apollo Global Management, Inc.; *U.S. Public*, pg. 146
AGMO CORPORATION—See MFA Incorporated; *U.S. Private*, pg. 2693
AGMO HOLDINGS BERHAD; *Int'l*, pg. 211
AG MORTGAGE INVESTMENT TRUST, INC.—See TPG Capital, L.P.; *U.S. Public*, pg. 2166
AGMS INC.—See Bausch Health Companies Inc.; *Int'l*, pg. 895
AGN AGROINDUSTRIAL, PROJETOS E PARTICIPACOES LTDA.; *Int'l*, pg. 211
AGNC INVESTMENT CORP.; *U.S. Public*, pg. 62
AG NEOVO TECHNOLOGY B.V.—See Associated Industries China, Inc.; *Int'l*, pg. 649
AG NEOVO TECHNOLOGY CORPORATION—See Associated Industries China, Inc.; *Int'l*, pg. 649
AGNES BANKS EQUINE CLINIC PTY. LIMITED—See Apiam Animal Health Limited; *Int'l*, pg. 515
AGNES HUFF COMMUNICATIONS GROUP, LLC.; *U.S. Private*, pg. 128
AGNEW GOLD MINING COMPANY (PTY) LIMITED—See Gold Fields Limited; *Int'l*, pg. 3024
AG NEW MEXICO, FARM CREDIT SERVICES, PCA—See Lone Star AG Credit; *U.S. Private*, pg. 2484
AGNICO-EAGLE FINLAND OY—See Agnico Eagle Mines Limited; *Int'l*, pg. 212
AGNICO EAGLE MEXICO S.A. DE C.V.—See Agnico Eagle Mines Limited; *Int'l*, pg. 211
AGNICO-EAGLE MINES LIMITED-EXPLORATION DIVISION—See Agnico Eagle Mines Limited; *Int'l*, pg. 211
AGNICO-EAGLE MINES LIMITED-LARONDE DIVISION—See Agnico Eagle Mines Limited; *Int'l*, pg. 212
AGNICO-EAGLE MINES LIMITED-MEADOWBANK—See Agnico Eagle Mines Limited; *Int'l*, pg. 212
AGNICO EAGLE MINES LIMITED; *Int'l*, pg. 211
AGNICO-EAGLE MINES MEXICO COOPERATIE U.A.—See Agnico Eagle Mines Limited; *Int'l*, pg. 212
AGNICO-EAGLE MINES SWEDEN COOPERATIE U.A.—See Agnico Eagle Mines Limited; *Int'l*, pg. 212
AGNICO-EAGLE (USA) LIMITED—See Agnico Eagle Mines Limited; *Int'l*, pg. 211
AGNI SYSTEMS LIMITED; *Int'l*, pg. 211
AGNITE EDUCATION LIMITED; *Int'l*, pg. 212
AGNITY GLOBAL, INC.—See mCloud Technologies Corp.; *Int'l*, pg. 4760
AGNIV, INC.—See Clayton, Dubilier & Rice, LLC; *U.S. Private*, pg. 920
AGNIV, INC.—See KKR & Co. Inc.; *U.S. Public*, pg. 1243
AGNOLI, BARBER & BRUNDAGE, INC.—See LJA Engineering, Inc.; *U.S. Private*, pg. 2474
AGNO PHARMA; *U.S. Private*, pg. 128
AGNORA LTD; *Int'l*, pg. 212
AGNOVA TECHNOLOGIES PTY LTD—See American Vanguard Corporation; *U.S. Public*, pg. 111
AGNUS HOLDINGS PVT. LTD.; *Int'l*, pg. 212
AGO AG ENERGIE + ANLAGEN—See HCS Beteiligungsgesellschaft mbH; *Int'l*, pg. 3299
AGO ENERGY (PTY) LTD.—See HCS Beteiligungsgesellschaft mbH; *Int'l*, pg. 3299
AGOGE GLOBAL USA, INC.—See SPARTA COMMERCIAL SERVICES, INC.; *U.S. Public*, pg. 1914
AGOLA MADENCILIK LIMITED SIRKETI—See Liberty Gold Corp.; *Int'l*, pg. 4486
AGOLUX AB—See OEM International AB; *Int'l*, pg. 5528
AGORA A.D.; *Int'l*, pg. 212
AGORA CORRETORA DE TITULOS E VALORES MOBILIARIOS S.A.—See Banco Bradesco S.A.; *Int'l*, pg. 819
AGORA DIGITAL HOLDINGS, INC.; *U.S. Private*, pg. 128
AGORAE INFORMATION CONSULTING (BEIJING) CO., LTD.—See TDCX Inc.; *Int'l*, pg. 7486
AGORA HOLDINGS INC.; *Int'l*, pg. 212
AGORA HOSPITALITY GROUP CO., LTD.; *Int'l*, pg. 212
AGORA, INC.; *U.S. Public*, pg. 62
AGORA LIMITED—See Saudi Arabian Mining Company - Ma'aden; *Int'l*, pg. 6589
AGORA POLIGRAFIA SP. Z O.O—See Agora S.A.; *Int'l*, pg. 212
AGORA S.A.; *Int'l*, pg. 212
AGORA TC SP. Z O.O.—See Agora S.A.; *Int'l*, pg. 212
AGORA TURIZM VE TICARET LTD. STI.—See Messe Munchen GmbH; *Int'l*, pg. 4841
AGOSTINI INSURANCE BROKERS GRENADA LTD—See Aon plc; *Int'l*, pg. 489
AGOSTINI INSURANCE BROKERS LTD—See Aon plc; *Int'l*, pg. 489
AGOSTINI INSURANCE BROKERS ST. LUCIA LTD—See Aon plc; *Int'l*, pg. 489
AGOSTINI MARKETING—See Agostini's Limited; *Int'l*, pg. 213
AGOSTINI'S LIMITED; *Int'l*, pg. 213
AGOSTO, INC.; *U.S. Private*, pg. 128
AGOURON PHARMACEUTICALS, INC.—See Pfizer Inc.; *U.S. Public*, pg. 1679
AG PARTNERS COOPERATIVE INC.; *U.S. Private*, pg. 124
AG PARTNERS CO-OP; *U.S. Private*, pg. 124
AG PARTNERS L.L.C.—See Albert City Elevator, a Cooperative; *U.S. Private*, pg. 152
AGP CORPORATION; *Int'l*, pg. 213

AGRANI INSURANCE COMPANY LIMITED

AG PLUS INC.; *U.S. Private*, pg. 124
AGP MALAGA SOCIMI, S.A.; *Int'l*, pg. 213
AGPOINT AUSTRALIA—See Great Western Corporation Pty. Ltd.; *Int'l*, pg. 3066
AG POWER ENTERPRISE INC.; *U.S. Private*, pg. 125
AG-POWER INC.; *U.S. Private*, pg. 125
AG PROCESSING INC.; *U.S. Private*, pg. 125
AG PRODUCERS CO-OP; *U.S. Private*, pg. 125
AG-PRO, LLC; *U.S. Private*, pg. 125
AGPRO (N.Z.) LTD.—See RPM International Inc.; *U.S. Public*, pg. 1819
AGPROTEIN, INC.—See WH Group Limited; *Int'l*, pg. 8394
A.G. PRUDEN & CIA. S.A.—See KKR & Co. Inc.; *U.S. Public*, pg. 1254
A.G. PRUDEN & CIA. S.A.—See The Goldman Sachs Group, Inc.; *U.S. Public*, pg. 2079
AGRA CEAS CONSULTING LIMITED—See Informa plc; *Int'l*, pg. 3691
AGRACE HOSPICECARE, INC.; *U.S. Private*, pg. 128
AGRA INDUSTRIES, INC.; *U.S. Private*, pg. 128
AGRA INFORMA LTD.—See Informa plc; *Int'l*, pg. 3691
AGRA LIMITED; *Int'l*, pg. 213
AGRALYS SERVICES; *Int'l*, pg. 213
AGRAM D.D.; *Int'l*, pg. 213
AGRAMKOW ASIA PACIFIC PTE. LTD.—See Durr AG; *Int'l*, pg. 2230
AGRAMKOW DO BRASIL LTDA.—See Durr AG; *Int'l*, pg. 2230
AGRAMKOW FLUID SYSTEMS A/S—See Durr AG; *Int'l*, pg. 2230
AGRAM NEKRETNINE D.D.; *Int'l*, pg. 213
AGRA MOAB INCORPORADORA LTDA—See PDG Realty S.A. Empreendimentos e Participacoes; *Int'l*, pg. 5770
AGRANA BETEILIGUNGS-AG; *Int'l*, pg. 213
AGRANA FRUCHT GMBH & CO KG—See AGRANA Beteiligungs-AG; *Int'l*, pg. 213
AGRANA FRUIT ARGENTINA S.A.—See AGRANA Beteiligungs-AG; *Int'l*, pg. 213
AGRANA FRUIT AUSTRALIA PTY. LTD.—See AGRANA Beteiligungs-AG; *Int'l*, pg. 213
AGRANA FRUIT AUSTRIA GMBH—See AGRANA Beteiligungs-AG; *Int'l*, pg. 213
AGRANA FRUIT BRASIL INDUSTRIA, COMERCIO, IMPORTACAO E EXPORTACAO LTDA.—See AGRANA Beteiligungs-AG; *Int'l*, pg. 214
AGRANA FRUIT DACHANG CO. LTD.—See AGRANA Beteiligungs-AG; *Int'l*, pg. 213
AGRANA FRUIT FIJI PTY. LTD.—See AGRANA Beteiligungs-AG; *Int'l*, pg. 213
AGRANA FRUIT FRANCE S.A.—See AGRANA Beteiligungs-AG; *Int'l*, pg. 213
AGRANA FRUIT GERMANY GMBH—See AGRANA Beteiligungs-AG; *Int'l*, pg. 214
AGRANA FRUIT ISTANBUL GIDA SAN VE TIC A.S.—See AGRANA Beteiligungs-AG; *Int'l*, pg. 213
AGRANA FRUIT JAPAN CO., LTD.—See AGRANA Beteiligungs-AG; *Int'l*, pg. 214
AGRANA FRUIT (JIANGSU) COMPANY LIMITED—See AGRANA Beteiligungs-AG; *Int'l*, pg. 214
AGRANA FRUIT KOREA CO. LTD.—See AGRANA Beteiligungs-AG; *Int'l*, pg. 214
AGRANA FRUIT LUKA TOV—See AGRANA Beteiligungs-AG; *Int'l*, pg. 214
AGRANA FRUIT MEXICO SA DE CV—See AGRANA Beteiligungs-AG; *Int'l*, pg. 213
AGRANA FRUIT POLSKA SP Z.O.O.—See AGRANA Beteiligungs-AG; *Int'l*, pg. 213
AGRANA FRUIT S.A.S.—See AGRANA Beteiligungs-AG; *Int'l*, pg. 214
AGRANA FRUIT SERVICES GMBH—See AGRANA Beteiligungs-AG; *Int'l*, pg. 214
AGRANA FRUIT SOUTH AFRICA PTY. LTD..—See AGRANA Beteiligungs-AG; *Int'l*, pg. 213
AGRANA FRUIT UKRAINE TOV—See AGRANA Beteiligungs-AG; *Int'l*, pg. 214
AGRANA FRUIT US, INC.—See AGRANA Beteiligungs-AG; *Int'l*, pg. 213
AGRANA JUICE (XIANYANG) CO., LTD.—See AGRANA Beteiligungs-AG; *Int'l*, pg. 214
AGRANA RESEARCH & INNOVATION CENTER GMBH—See AGRANA Beteiligungs-AG; *Int'l*, pg. 214
AGRANA ROMANIA S.R.L.—See AGRANA Beteiligungs-AG; *Int'l*, pg. 214
AGRANA SALES & MARKETING GMBH—See AGRANA Beteiligungs-AG; *Int'l*, pg. 213
AGRANA STARKE GMBH—See AGRANA Beteiligungs-AG; *Int'l*, pg. 214
AGRANA-STUDEN SERBIA D.O.O.—See Studen & Co. Holding GmbH; *Int'l*, pg. 7244
AGRANA TRADING EOOD—See AGRANA Beteiligungs-AG; *Int'l*, pg. 214
AGRANA ZUCKER GMBH—See AGRANA Beteiligungs-AG; *Int'l*, pg. 214
AGRANI INSURANCE COMPANY LIMITED; *Int'l*, pg. 214
AGRAR CARGO SPEDITION GMBH—See AGRAVIS Raiffeisen AG; *Int'l*, pg. 215
AGRARGESELLSCHAFT ALTJESSNITZ MBH—See KTG Agrar SE; *Int'l*, pg. 4316

AGRAR GMBH KOHLBERG—See KTG Agrar SE; *Int'l*, pg. 4316
AGRAR GMBH LANDWIRTSCHAFTLICHER PRODUKTIONSBETRIEB ALTDOBERN—See KTG Agrar SE; *Int'l*, pg. 4316
AGRARINVEST AG; *Int'l*, pg. 214
AGRARIUS AG; *Int'l*, pg. 214
AGRARPRODUKTENHANDEL GMBH—See BayWa AG; *Int'l*, pg. 915
AGRARTEST GMBH—See Eurofins Scientific S.E.; *Int'l*, pg. 2535
AGR ASIA LIMITED—See Clayton, Dubilier & Rice, LLC; *U.S. Private*, pg. 924
AGRA STAHLHANDELS-GMBH; *Int'l*, pg. 213
AGRAS VIENNA INSURANCE GROUP S.A.—See Vienna Insurance Group AG Wiener Versicherung Gruppe; *Int'l*, pg. 8193
AGRATI GIE—See A.Agrati S.p.A.; *Int'l*, pg. 23
AGRATIO URBAN DESIGN, INC.; *Int'l*, pg. 214
AGRATI VIEUX CONDE S.A.S.—See A.Agrati S.p.A.; *Int'l*, pg. 23
AGR (AUSTRALIA) PTY LTD—See Akastor ASA; *Int'l*, pg. 260
AGRAUXINE S.A. - LOCHES FACTORY—See Compagnie des Levures Lesaffre SA; *Int'l*, pg. 1738
AGRAUXINE S.A. - PLOMELIN FACTORY—See Compagnie des Levures Lesaffre SA; *Int'l*, pg. 1738
AGRAUXINE S.A.—See Compagnie des Levures Lesaffre SA; *Int'l*, pg. 1738
AGRAVIS BAUSTOFFHANDEL GMBH—See AGRAVIS Raiffeisen AG; *Int'l*, pg. 214
AGRAVIS EMS-JADE GMBH—See AGRAVIS Raiffeisen AG; *Int'l*, pg. 214
AGRAVIS KORNHAUS OSTWESTFALEN GMBH—See AGRAVIS Raiffeisen AG; *Int'l*, pg. 214
AGRAVIS MISCHFUTTER EMSLAND GMBH—See AGRAVIS Raiffeisen AG; *Int'l*, pg. 214
AGRAVIS MISCHFUTTER OLDENBURG/OSTFRIESLAND GMBH—See AGRAVIS Raiffeisen AG; *Int'l*, pg. 214
AGRAVIS MISCHFUTTER OSTWESTFALEN-LIPPE GMBH—See AGRAVIS Raiffeisen AG; *Int'l*, pg. 214
AGRAVIS MISCHFUTTER WESTFALEN GMBH—See AGRAVIS Raiffeisen AG; *Int'l*, pg. 214
AGRAVIS NIEDERSACHSEN-SUD GMBH—See AGRAVIS Raiffeisen AG; *Int'l*, pg. 215
AGRAVIS RAIFFEISEN AG - HANNOVER HEAD OFFICE—See AGRAVIS Raiffeisen AG; *Int'l*, pg. 215
AGRAVIS RAIFFEISEN AG; *Int'l*, pg. 214
AGRAVIS TECHNIK BVL GMBH—See AGRAVIS Raiffeisen AG; *Int'l*, pg. 215
AGRAVIS TECHNIK CENTER GMBH—See AGRAVIS Raiffeisen AG; *Int'l*, pg. 215
AGRAVIS TECHNIK HEIDE-ALTMARK GMBH—See AGRAVIS Raiffeisen AG; *Int'l*, pg. 215
AGRAVIS TECHNIK HESSEN-PFALZ GMBH—See AGRAVIS Raiffeisen AG; *Int'l*, pg. 215
AGRAVIS TECHNIK LENNE-LIPPE GMBH—See AGRAVIS Raiffeisen AG; *Int'l*, pg. 215
AGRAVIS TECHNIK MUNSTERLAND-EMS GMBH—See AGRAVIS Raiffeisen AG; *Int'l*, pg. 215
AGRAVIS TECHNIK POLSKA SP. Z O.O.—See AGRAVIS Raiffeisen AG; *Int'l*, pg. 215
AGRAVIS TECHNIK RAIFFEISEN GMBH—See AGRAVIS Raiffeisen AG; *Int'l*, pg. 215
AGRAVIS TECHNIK SACHSEN-ANHALT/BRANDENBURG GMBH—See AGRAVIS Raiffeisen AG; *Int'l*, pg. 215
AGRAVIS TECHNIK SALTENBROCK GMBH—See AGRAVIS Raiffeisen AG; *Int'l*, pg. 215
AGRAVIS VERSICHERUNGSSERVICE GMBH & CO. KG—See AGRAVIS Raiffeisen AG; *Int'l*, pg. 215
AGR BANGKOK LTD—See Clayton, Dubilier & Rice, LLC; *U.S. Private*, pg. 924
AG REAL ESTATE—See Ageas SA/NV; *Int'l*, pg. 204
AGRECOL, LLC; *U.S. Private*, pg. 129
AGREDA BUS, S.L.—See Mobico Group PLC; *Int'l*, pg. 5008
AGREE REALTY CORPORATION; *U.S. Public*, pg. 62
AGREEYA SOLUTIONS LLC; *U.S. Private*, pg. 129
AGREGAT JSC—See Russian Technologies State Corporation; *Int'l*, pg. 6432
AGREGATS STE CLOTILDE INC.—See VINCI S.A.; *Int'l*, pg. 8212
AGRE KOMPRESSOREN GMBH—See Atlas Copco AB; *Int'l*, pg. 679
AGREL DIS TICARET A.S.—See Uzel Makina Sanayi A.S.; *Int'l*, pg. 8103
AGRELIANT GENETICS LLC - LEBANON—See Groupe Limagrain Holding SA; *Int'l*, pg. 3108
AGRELIANT GENETICS LLC - LEBANON—See KWS SAAT SE & Co. KGaA; *Int'l*, pg. 4352
AGRELIANT GENETICS LLC—See Groupe Limagrain Holding SA; *Int'l*, pg. 3108
AGRELIANT GENETICS LLC—See KWS SAAT SE & Co. KGaA; *Int'l*, pg. 4351
AGR ENERGY SERVICES AS—See Akastor ASA; *Int'l*, pg. 260

AGREPOR AGREGADOS - EXTRACCAO DE INERTES S.A.—See Camargo Correa S.A.; *Int'l*, pg. 1267
AG RESERVES INC; *U.S. Private*, pg. 125
AGRESERVES, INC.—See Ag Reserves Inc; *U.S. Private*, pg. 125
AGRES SISTEMAS ELETRONICOS S.A.—See Emak S.p.A.; *Int'l*, pg. 2373
AGRESSO FRANCE S.A.—See UNIT4 N.V.; *Int'l*, pg. 8062
AGRESSO TRAVEL INDUSTRY SOLUTIONS LTD—See UNIT4 N.V.; *Int'l*, pg. 8063
AGRESTA STORMS & O'LEARY P.C.; *U.S. Private*, pg. 129
AGR EUROPE GMBH—See Clayton, Dubilier & Rice, LLC; *U.S. Private*, pg. 924
AGR EUROPE S.R.L.—See Clayton, Dubilier & Rice, LLC; *U.S. Private*, pg. 924
AGREVOLUTION, LLC—See AGCO Corporation; *U.S. Public*, pg. 58
AGREX DNP VIETNAM CO., LTD.—See TIS Inc.; *Int'l*, pg. 7757
AGREX DO BRASIL S.A.—See Mitsubishi Corporation; *Int'l*, pg. 4937
AGREX FINE TECHNO CO., LTD.—See TIS Inc.; *Int'l*, pg. 7757
AGREX, INC.—See TIS Inc.; *Int'l*, pg. 7757
AGREX, INC.—See Mitsubishi Corporation; *Int'l*, pg. 4937
AGREX LIMITED—See ENL Limited; *Int'l*, pg. 2441
AGR GROUP AMERICAS, INC.—See Akastor ASA; *Int'l*, pg. 260
AGR GROUP ASA—See Altor Equity Partners AB; *Int'l*, pg. 394
A.G. RHODES HEALTH & REHAB; *U.S. Private*, pg. 25
AGRIA CORPORATION; *Int'l*, pg. 216
AGRIA CORPORATION—See Agria Corporation; *Int'l*, pg. 216
AGRIA GROUP HOLDING JSC; *Int'l*, pg. 216
AGRIAUTO INDUSTRIES LTD—See House of Habib; *Int'l*, pg. 3491
AGRIAUTO STAMPING COMPANY (PVT.) LTD.—See House of Habib; *Int'l*, pg. 3491
AGRIBANK, FCB—See Federal Farm Credit Banks Funding Corporation; *U.S. Private*, pg. 1487
AGRIBANK SECURITIES JOINT STOCK CORPORATION; *Int'l*, pg. 216
AGRIBBON CORPORATION—See Shikoku Electric Power Co., Incorporated; *Int'l*, pg. 6830
AGRI BEEF CO., INC.; *U.S. Private*, pg. 129
AGRIBIO HOLDING B.V.—See H2 Equity Partners B.V.; *Int'l*, pg. 3199
AGRI BRAND PURINA CANADA INC.—See Cargill, Inc.; *U.S. Private*, pg. 755
AGRIBRANDS PURINA (LANGFANG) FEEDMILL CO., LTD.—See Cargill, Inc.; *U.S. Private*, pg. 754
AGRIBRANDS PURINA (XINJIANG) FEEDMILL CO., LTD.—See Cargill, Inc.; *U.S. Private*, pg. 755
AGRIBRANDS PURINA (ZHENGZHOU) FEEDMILL CO., LTD.—See Cargill, Inc.; *U.S. Private*, pg. 754
AGRI BUSINESS FINANCE, INC.—See Kova Fertilizer Inc.; *U.S. Private*, pg. 2345
AGRICHEM B.V.—See Punjab Chemicals & Crop Protection Limited; *Int'l*, pg. 6120
AGRICHEM HELVETIA GMBH—See Punjab Chemicals & Crop Protection Limited; *Int'l*, pg. 6120
AGRI-CHEM INC.; *U.S. Private*, pg. 129
AGRICO ACQUISITION CORP.—See Kalera Public Limited Company; *U.S. Public*, pg. 1213
AGRICO CANADA LIMITED; *Int'l*, pg. 216
AGRICOLA CERRO PRIETO S.A.; *Int'l*, pg. 216
AGRICOLA GROUP LTD; *Int'l*, pg. 216
AGRICOLA NACIONAL S.A.C.I.; *Int'l*, pg. 216
AGRICOLA NOVA INDEMIL LTDA—See General Mills, Inc.; *U.S. Public*, pg. 921
AGRICOLA PONTE ALTA S.A.—See Cosan S.A.; *Int'l*, pg. 1809
AGRICOLA PROPERTIES LIMITED—See Dairygold Co-Operative Society Ltd; *Int'l*, pg. 1940
AGRICOLA SAN GIORGIO S.P.A.—See Assicurazioni Generali S.p.A.; *Int'l*, pg. 643
AGRICOM LIMITED—See DLF Seeds A/S; *Int'l*, pg. 2141
AGRI COMMODITIES LLC—See Temasek Holdings (Private) Limited; *Int'l*, pg. 7549
AGRICOMPASS INC.—See JFE Holdings, Inc.; *Int'l*, pg. 3934
AGRICOR INC.—See Grain Millers, Inc.; *U.S. Private*, pg. 1751
AGRI CORPORATION—See Kamei Corporation; *Int'l*, pg. 4061
AGRICORTES.COM MAQ. E EQUIP. S.A.—See Tym Corporation; *Int'l*, pg. 7994
AGRICO SALES INC.; *U.S. Private*, pg. 129
AGRI-COVER, INC.; *U.S. Private*, pg. 129
AGRICULTURAL BANK OF CHINA - HONG KONG—See Agricultural Bank of China Limited; *Int'l*, pg. 217
AGRICULTURAL BANK OF CHINA LIMITED; *Int'l*, pg. 216
AGRICULTURAL BANK OF CHINA (MOSCOW) LIMITED; *Int'l*, pg. 216
AGRICULTURAL BANK OF CHINA - SINGAPORE—See Agricultural Bank of China Limited; *Int'l*, pg. 217

AGRICULTURAL BANK OF CHINA - TOKYO—See Agricultural Bank of China Limited; *Int'l*, pg. 217
AGRICULTURAL BANK OF CHINA - UK—See Agricultural Bank of China Limited; *Int'l*, pg. 217
AGRICULTURAL BANK OF GREECE, S.A.—See Piraeus Financial Holdings S.A.; *Int'l*, pg. 5873
AGRICULTURAL CHEMICALS (MALAYSIA) SDN. BHD.—See Adeka Corporation; *Int'l*, pg. 142
AGRICULTURAL COMMODITIES INC.; *U.S. Private*, pg. 129
AGRICULTURAL CREDIT CORPORATION JSC—See National Holding KazAgro JSC; *Int'l*, pg. 5158
AGRICULTURAL DEVELOPMENT BANK LIMITED; *Int'l*, pg. 217
AGRICULTURAL DEVELOPMENT COMPANY LTD.—See Dabbagh Group Holding Company Ltd.; *Int'l*, pg. 1902
AGRICULTURAL ENGINEERING COMPANY FOR INVESTMENTS; *Int'l*, pg. 217
THE AGRICULTURAL & LABOR PROGRAM INC.; *U.S. Private*, pg. 3983
AGRICULTURAL LAND MANAGEMENT LIMITED—See Elders Limited; *Int'l*, pg. 2346
AGRICULTURAL LAND TRUST; *Int'l*, pg. 217
THE AGRICULTURAL MORTGAGE CORPORATION PLC—See Lloyds Banking Group plc; *Int'l*, pg. 4538
AGRICULTURAL PLASTIC INDUSTRIAL COMPANY (APICO)—See Arab Supply & Trading Co.; *Int'l*, pg. 532
AGRICULTURAL PUBLISHERS PTY LIMITED—See Nine Entertainment Co. Holdings Limited; *Int'l*, pg. 5298
AGRICULTURAL SERVICE INC.; *U.S. Private*, pg. 129
AGRICULTURAL SERVICES, INC.—See The Pritzker Group - Chicago, LLC; *U.S. Private*, pg. 4100
AGRICULTURA, TECNOLOGIA, PASION ATP S.A.—See HORIBA Ltd; *Int'l*, pg. 3474
AGRICULTURE MODERN ENGINEERING CO. LLC—See Muscat Overseas Co., L.L.C.; *Int'l*, pg. 5102
AGRICULTURE & NATURAL SOLUTIONS ACQUISITION CORPORATION; *U.S. Public*, pg. 63
AGRICULTURE PRINTING & PACKAGING JOINT STOCK COMPANY; *Int'l*, pg. 217
AGRICULTURE TECHNOLOGY RESEARCH INSTITUTE—See Dongbu Group; *Int'l*, pg. 2165
AGRIDENT GMBH—See Merck & Co., Inc.; *U.S. Public*, pg. 1415
AGRI-DYNAMICS, INC.; *U.S. Public*, pg. 63
AGRI-EDGE DEVELOPMENT, LLC—See Dairy Farmers of America, Inc.; *U.S. Private*, pg. 1145
AGRI-EMPRESA INC.; *U.S. Private*, pg. 129
AGRIEURO CORP.; *Int'l*, pg. 217
AGRIEX AGENCIAMENTOS, AFRETAMENTOS E APOIO MARITIMO LTDA.—See Southern Cross Capital Management SA; *Int'l*, pg. 7118
AGRIEXPORT INDUSTRY LTD.—See Tym Corporation; *Int'l*, pg. 7994
AGRI-FAB INC.—See AF Holding Company; *U.S. Private*, pg. 121
AGRIFAC MACHINERY BV—See Exel Industries SA; *Int'l*, pg. 2582
AGRIFARM INDUSTRIES LLC; *U.S. Private*, pg. 129
AGRI-FEEDS LIMITED—See Agria Corporation; *Int'l*, pg. 216
AGRI-FINTECH HOLDINGS, INC.; *U.S. Public*, pg. 63
AGRIFOCUS LIMITADA—See Element Solutions Inc.; *U.S. Public*, pg. 725
AGRIFOODS INTERNATIONAL COOPERATIVE LTD; *Int'l*, pg. 217
AGRIFOOD TECHNOLOGY PTY LTD.—See Australian Wool Testing Authority Ltd.; *Int'l*, pg. 723
AGRIFORCE GROWING SYSTEMS, LTD.; *Int'l*, pg. 217
AGRIFRESH COMPANY LIMITED—See Agripure Holdings Company Limited; *Int'l*, pg. 218
AGRI FUTURA GMBH—See AGRAVIS Raiffeisen AG; *Int'l*, pg. 215
AGRIFY CORPORATION; *U.S. Public*, pg. 63
AGRI GENERAL INSURANCE COMPANY—See Chubb Limited; *Int'l*, pg. 1592
AGRIGENETICS, INC.—See Corteva, Inc.; *U.S. Public*, pg. 580
AGRIGOLD—See Groupe Limagrain Holding SA; *Int'l*, pg. 3107
AGRIGUARD LLC—See The Garfield Weston Foundation; *Int'l*, pg. 7648
AGRIHOLDING INC.; *U.S. Private*, pg. 129
AGRI-KING INC.; *U.S. Private*, pg. 129
AGRILAND FS, INC.; *U.S. Private*, pg. 129
AGRILEASE BV—See BNP Paribas SA; *Int'l*, pg. 1079
AGRILIANCE, LLC—See CHS INC.; *U.S. Public*, pg. 491
AGRILIANCE, LLC—See Land O'Lakes, Inc.; *U.S. Private*, pg. 2383
AGRILOGIC CONSULTING, LLC—See Apollo Global Management, Inc.; *U.S. Public*, pg. 147
AGRIMA CONSULTANTS INTERNATIONAL LIMITED—See Saurashtra Cement Ltd.; *Int'l*, pg. 6595
AGRIMARINE HOLDINGS INC.—See Dundee Corporation; *Int'l*, pg. 2225
AGRIMARINE INDUSTRIES INC.—See Dundee Corporation; *Int'l*, pg. 2225
AGRI MARKETING INC.; *U.S. Private*, pg. 129

COMPANY NAME INDEX

AGRI-MARK, INC.; *U.S. Private*, pg. 129
AGRIMART CORP.—See Adeka Corporation; *Int'l*, pg. 142
AGRI-MAX FINANCIAL SERVICES, L.P.—See Dairy Farmers of America, Inc.; *U.S. Private*, pg. 1145
AGRIMAX LTD.—See Nufarm Limited; *Int'l*, pg. 5486
AGRIMINCO CORP.; *Int'l*, pg. 217
AGRIMIN LIMITED; *Int'l*, pg. 217
AGRIMONY COMMODITIES LTD; *Int'l*, pg. 217
AGRINATIONAL INSURANCE COMPANY—See Archer-Daniels-Midland Company; *U.S. Public*, pg. 183
AGRINDUSTRIAL S.A.—See UPL Limited; *Int'l*, pg. 8089
AGRI NEGOCE S.A.—See Ameropa AG; *Int'l*, pg. 423
AGRI NORTHWEST—See Ag Reserves Inc; *U.S. Private*, pg. 125
AGRINOS DO BRAZIL FERTILIZANTES BIOLOGICOS LTDA—See American Vanguard Corporation; *U.S. Public*, pg. 111
AGRINOS INDIA PRIVATE LIMITED—See American Vanguard Corporation; *U.S. Public*, pg. 111
AGRINOS UKRAINE LLC—See American Vanguard Corporation; *U.S. Public*, pg. 111
AGR INTERNATIONAL, INC.—See Clayton, Dubilier & Rice, LLC; *U.S. Private*, pg. 924
AGRINURTURE, INC.; *Int'l*, pg. 217
AGRIOS GLOBAL HOLDINGS LTD.; *Int'l*, pg. 217
AGRIPHAR DE COLOMBIA SAS—See Element Solutions Inc.; *U.S. Public*, pg. 725
AGRIPHAR DE COSTA RICA SA—See Element Solutions Inc.; *U.S. Public*, pg. 725
AGRIPHAR HELLAS SA—See Element Solutions Inc.; *U.S. Public*, pg. 725
AGRIPHAR ITALIA SRL—See Element Solutions Inc.; *U.S. Public*, pg. 725
AGRIPHAR SARL—See Element Solutions Inc.; *U.S. Public*, pg. 725
AGRI PHIL CORPORATION—See Calata Corporation; *Int'l*, pg. 1261
AGRIPLAS COMPANY—See Compagnie Financiere et de Participations Roullier SA; *Int'l*, pg. 1740
AGRIPLAST TECH INDIA PRIVATE LIMITED—See Ginegar Plastic Products Ltd.; *Int'l*, pg. 2976
AGRI PLUS S.A.—See WH Group Limited; *Int'l*, pg. 8394
AGRI PLUS SP. Z.O.O.—See WH Group Limited; *Int'l*, pg. 8395
AGRIPOLYANE SA—See Plastika Kritis S.A.; *Int'l*, pg. 5002
AGRI PORT SERVICES, LLC—See Archer-Daniels-Midland Company; *U.S. Public*, pg. 183
AGRIPOWER FRANCE SA; *Int'l*, pg. 217
AGRIPOWER LTD—See Exel Industries SA; *Int'l*, pg. 2582
AGRIPPA LLC—See Pantheon Resources plc; *Int'l*, pg. 5731
AGRI PRODUCERS INC.; *U.S. Private*, pg. 129
AGRI PRODUCTS INC—See The Kroger Co.; *U.S. Public*, pg. 2107
AGRIPURE HOLDINGS COMPANY LIMITED; *Int'l*, pg. 217
AGRISEM INTERNATIONAL SAS—See UNIA Sp. z o.o.; *Int'l*, pg. 8029
AGRI SERVICE INCORPORATED; *U.S. Private*, pg. 129
AGRI-SERVICE, LLC—See AGCO Corporation; *U.S. Public*, pg. 58
AGRI-SERVICES AGENCY, LLC—See Dairy Farmers of America, Inc.; *U.S. Private*, pg. 1145
AGRI SERVICES BRUNSWICK LLC; *U.S. Private*, pg. 129
AGRISOMA BIOSCIENCES INC.—See Calyx Ventures Inc.; *Int'l*, pg. 1266
AGRISTAR, INC.; *U.S. Public*, pg. 63
AGRI STATS, INC.—See Eli Lilly & Company; *U.S. Public*, pg. 731
AGRI-SUPPLY COMPANY INC.—See Direct Distributors Inc.; *U.S. Private*, pg. 1235
AGRI-SYSTEMS; *U.S. Private*, pg. 129
AGRI-TECH, INC. OF OREGON—See Republic Services, Inc.; *U.S. Public*, pg. 1785
AGRI-TECH (INDIA) LIMITED; *Int'l*, pg. 216
AGRITECH LIMITED; *Int'l*, pg. 218
AGRITECH WORLWIDE, INC.; *U.S. Private*, pg. 129
AGRITEK HOLDINGS, INC.; *U.S. Private*, pg. 129
AGRITENX SRL—See Tenax International BV; *Int'l*, pg. 7558
AGRITERRA LTD.; *Int'l*, pg. 218
AGRI-TRADE HOLDINGS LIMITED; *Int'l*, pg. 216
AGRI TRADING FATS & OILS, LLC—See Neste Oyj; *Int'l*, pg. 5201
AGRIUM INC.—See Nutrien Ltd.; *Int'l*, pg. 5492
AGRIUM U.S. INC.—See Nutrien Ltd.; *Int'l*, pg. 5492
AGRI-VALLEY IRRIGATION LLC—See Jain Irrigation Systems Limited; *Int'l*, pg. 3872
AGRIVEST INC.; *U.S. Private*, pg. 129
AGRIVIDA, INC.—See Mitsui & Co., Ltd.; *Int'l*, pg. 4979
AGRIVISION GROUP, LLC; *U.S. Private*, pg. 130
AGRI-WEST INTERNATIONAL INC.; *U.S. Private*, pg. 129
AGRO-100 LTEE; *Int'l*, pg. 218
AGRO100—See Aqua Capital; *Int'l*, pg. 527
AGROALIM DISTRIBUTION S.R.L.—See WH Group Limited; *Int'l*, pg. 8395
AGRO ALLIANZ LIMITED; *Int'l*, pg. 218

AGROBACKA A.D.; *Int'l*, pg. 218
AGROBACKA A.D.; *Int'l*, pg. 218
AGRO BALTIC GMBH—See Nutrien Ltd.; *Int'l*, pg. 5492
AGROBEST (M) SDN. BHD.—See Maruha Nichiro Corporation; *Int'l*, pg. 4711
AGROB IMMOBILIEN AG; *Int'l*, pg. 218
AGROBIONOVA, S.A. DE C.V.—See Pulsar Internacional S.A. de C.V.; *Int'l*, pg. 6116
AGROBIOTHERS LABORATOIRE SAS—See Gimv NV; *Int'l*, pg. 2976
AGRO BIZZ A/S—See Lantmannen ek for; *Int'l*, pg. 4413
AGROBUD BHP S.A.—See Impel S.A.; *Int'l*, pg. 3632
AGRO BULK LTD.—See Livestock Feed Limited; *Int'l*, pg. 4531
AGRO CAPITAL MANAGEMENT CORP.; *U.S. Public*, pg. 63
AGROCERES PIC—See Genus Plc; *Int'l*, pg. 2930
AGROCHEMA EESTI OU—See Koncernas Achemos Grupe; *Int'l*, pg. 4246
AGROCHEM CZLUCHOW SP. Z.O.O.—See Kulczyk Investments S.A.; *Int'l*, pg. 4327
AGROCHEM DOBRE MIASTO SP. Z.O.O.—See Kulczyk Investments S.A.; *Int'l*, pg. 4327
AGRO CHEMICALS INC—See Barbados Shipping & Trading Co. Ltd.; *Int'l*, pg. 858
AGROCHEM PULAWY SP. Z O.O.—See Grupa Azoty S.A.; *Int'l*, pg. 3116
AGRO-CHEREPOVETS, CJSC—See PJSC PhosAgro; *Int'l*, pg. 5883
AGROCULTIVO—See HORIBA Ltd; *Int'l*, pg. 3474
AGRODAN APS—See UPL Limited; *Int'l*, pg. 8088
AGRO DISTRIBUTION, LLC—See CHS INC.; *U.S. Public*, pg. 491
AGRO ENERGY CO., LTD—See Electricity Generating Public Co., Ltd.; *Int'l*, pg. 2352
AGROENERGY INVEST REIT; *Int'l*, pg. 218
AGROENERGY REIT; *Int'l*, pg. 218
AGROETANOL AB—See Lantmannen ek for; *Int'l*, pg. 4413
AGROEXPANSION, S.A.—See Agrosalga, S.L.; *Int'l*, pg. 220
AGROEXPORT PROIZVODNJA I PROMET A.D.; *Int'l*, pg. 218
AGROFERT CHINA CO LTD—See Agrofert Holding, a.s.; *Int'l*, pg. 218
AGROFERT HOLDING, A.S.; *Int'l*, pg. 218
AGROFERT HUNGARIA KFT.—See Agrofert Holding, a.s.; *Int'l*, pg. 218
AGRO FINANCE REIT; *Int'l*, pg. 218
AGROFIRMA NIVA LLC—See OJSC Pava; *Int'l*, pg. 5541
AGROFIX N.V.—See Husqvarna AB; *Int'l*, pg. 3538
AGROFREIGHT SPEDITION CZ S.R.O.—See OBB-Holding AG; *Int'l*, pg. 5509
AGROFRESH COMERCIAL PERU S.A.C.—See Paine Schwartz Partners, LLC; *U.S. Private*, pg. 3075
AGROFRESH INC.—See Paine Schwartz Partners, LLC; *U.S. Private*, pg. 3075
AGROFRESH ITALIA SRL—See Paine Schwartz Partners, LLC; *U.S. Private*, pg. 3075
AGROFRESH POLSKA SP. Z.O.O.—See Paine Schwartz Partners, LLC; *U.S. Private*, pg. 3075
AGROFRESH SOLUTIONS, INC.—See Paine Schwartz Partners, LLC; *U.S. Private*, pg. 3075
AGROFRESH SPAIN, S.L.—See Paine Schwartz Partners, LLC; *U.S. Private*, pg. 3075
AGROGENERATION SA—See NOVAAGRO group; *Int'l*, pg. 5453
AGROGORICA D.D.; *Int'l*, pg. 219
AGROGUACHAL SA; *Int'l*, pg. 219
AGRO HARAPAN LESTARI SDN. BHD—See Carson Cumberbatch PLC; *Int'l*, pg. 1347
AGRO HARAPAN LESTAR (PRIVATE) LIMITED—See Carson Cumberbatch PLC; *Int'l*, pg. 1347
AGROHERCEGOVINA A.D.; *Int'l*, pg. 219
AGROHOLDING STEPPE JSC—See Sistema PJSFC; *Int'l*, pg. 6963
AGROHUARPES - EUROFINS AGROSCIENCES SERVICES S.A.—See Eurofins Scientific S.E.; *Int'l*, pg. 2535
AGROINDUSTRIAL DEL NOROESTE S. DE R.L. DE C.V.; *Int'l*, pg. 219
AGRO INDUSTRIAL EXPORTADORA, S.A. DE C.V.; *Int'l*, pg. 218
AGROINDUSTRIAL LAREDO SAA; *Int'l*, pg. 219
AGROINDUSTRIAS AIB S.A.; *Int'l*, pg. 219
AGROINDUSTRIAS ARRIBA DEL ECUADOR, AGROARRIBA S.A.—See Ecom Agroindustrial Corporation Ltd.; *Int'l*, pg. 2295
AGROINDUSTRIAS DIADEMA ZONA FRANCA HONDURAS SA—See Oettinger IMEX AG; *Int'l*, pg. 5529
AGROINDUSTRIAS UNIDAS DE MEXICO S.A. DE C.V. (AMSA)—See Ecom Agroindustrial Corporation Ltd.; *Int'l*, pg. 2295
AGRO-INDUSTRIE RECHERCHES ET DEVELOPPEMENTS S.A.—See Vivescia; *Int'l*, pg. 8278
AGRO INNOVATION LAB GMBH—See BayWa AG; *Int'l*, pg. 915
AGRO-IRON, INC.; *U.S. Private*, pg. 130
AGRO-KANESHO CO., LTD.—See BayWa AG; *Int'l*, pg. 218

AGRO-K CORP.—See Rovensa SA; *Int'l*, pg. 6407
AGROKOMBINAT A.D.; *Int'l*, pg. 219
AGROKOMBINAT MARIBOR D.D.—See MHP SE; *Int'l*, pg. 4873
AGROKRAJINA A.D.; *Int'l*, pg. 219
AGROLABS, INC.—See Integrated Biopharma, Inc.; *U.S. Public*, pg. 1136
AGROLI GROUP; *Int'l*, pg. 220
AGROLUX NEDERLAND B.V.—See The Scotts Miracle-Gro Company; *U.S. Public*, pg. 2126
AGROMAIS GMBH—See KWS SAAT SE & Co. KGaA; *Int'l*, pg. 4352
AGROMAN SP. Z O.O.—See Polski Holding Nieruchomosci S.A.; *Int'l*, pg. 5912
AGROMEC SA; *Int'l*, pg. 220
AGROMEC SA; *Int'l*, pg. 220
AGROMEC SA; *Int'l*, pg. 220
AGROMEC SA; *Int'l*, pg. 220
AGROMEC TILEAGD SA; *Int'l*, pg. 220
AGROMED AUSTRIA GMBH—See BayWa AG; *Int'l*, pg. 915
AGROMEHANIKA AD; *Int'l*, pg. 220
AGRO MERCHANTS NORTH AMERICA HOLDINGS LLC—See Americold Realty Trust, Inc.; *U.S. Public*, pg. 113
AGROMET ZEHS LUBAN S.A.—See Przedsiebiorstwo Hydrauliki Silowej Hydrotor S.A.; *Int'l*, pg. 6013
AGROMIN INC.; *U.S. Private*, pg. 130
AGROMINO A/S; *Int'l*, pg. 220
AGRONA, A. S.—See Agrofert Holding, a.s.; *Int'l*, pg. 218
AGRONAMIC (PTY) LTD—See Element Solutions Inc.; *U.S. Public*, pg. 725
AGRONET SAS—See Rentokil Initial plc; *Int'l*, pg. 6286
AGRONOMICS LTD.; *Int'l*, pg. 220
AGRO OIL AB—See Lantmannen ek for; *Int'l*, pg. 4413
AGROOPREMA ODZACI A.D.; *Int'l*, pg. 220
AGRO PARI AD—See Industrial Holding Bulgaria AD; *Int'l*, pg. 3672
AGROPECUARIA DE GUISSONA, S. COOP. LTDA.; *Int'l*, pg. 220
AGRO PHOS INDIA LTD.; *Int'l*, pg. 218
AGROPLOD AD; *Int'l*, pg. 220
AGROPODNIK DOMAZLICE A. S.—See Agrofert Holding, a.s.; *Int'l*, pg. 218
AGROPRODUKT A.D.; *Int'l*, pg. 220
AGROPROMCREDIT JSCB; *Int'l*, pg. 220
AGROPROM LLC—See Onexim Group Limited; *Int'l*, pg. 5581
AGRO-PROPERTY KFT.—See BayWa AG; *Int'l*, pg. 915
AGRO PUCALA S.A.A.; *Int'l*, pg. 218
AGROPUR COOPERATIVE - ALLEGRO—See Agropur Cooperative; *Int'l*, pg. 220
AGROPUR COOPERATIVE - CHEESE & INGREDIENTS DIVISION—See Agropur Cooperative; *Int'l*, pg. 220
AGROPUR COOPERATIVE - DIVISION NATREL & FRESH PRODUCTS—See Agropur Cooperative; *Int'l*, pg. 220
AGROPUR COOPERATIVE; *Int'l*, pg. 220
AGROPUR INC. - LITTLE CHUTE (APPLETON) PLANT—See Agropur Cooperative; *Int'l*, pg. 220
AGROPUR INC.—See Agropur Cooperative; *Int'l*, pg. 220
AGROQUALITA S.P.A.—See RINA S.p.A.; *Int'l*, pg. 6342
AGROQUIMICOS Y SEMILLAS DE MX DE CV—See Element Solutions Inc.; *U.S. Public*, pg. 725
AGRO-RYDZYNA SP. Z O.O.—See Dino Polska SA; *Int'l*, pg. 2127
AGROSAAT D.O.O—See BayWa AG; *Int'l*, pg. 915
AGROS A.D.; *Int'l*, pg. 220
AGROSALGA, S.L.; *Int'l*, pg. 220
AGROSAVEZ A.D.; *Int'l*, pg. 220
AGROS DEVELOPMENT COMPANY PROODOS PUBLIC LTD.; *Int'l*, pg. 220
AGROSEME PANONIJA A.D.; *Int'l*, pg. 220
AGROSISTEMA LLC—See Onexim Group Limited; *Int'l*, pg. 5581
AGROSISTEMI S.R.L.—See Sdiptech AB; *Int'l*, pg. 6658
AGROSTULLN GMBH—See ASTRA INDUSTRIAL GROUP COMPANY; *Int'l*, pg. 657
AGROSUPER SA; *Int'l*, pg. 220
AGROTEC A.S.—See Agrofert Holding, a.s.; *Int'l*, pg. 218
AGRO TECH FOODS LTD.—See Conagra Brands, Inc.; *U.S. Public*, pg. 563
AGROTECHIMPEX JOINT STOCK COMPANY; *Int'l*, pg. 221
AGRO TECHNICA LTD.—See Hayleys PLC; *Int'l*, pg. 3292
AGROTECHNIC MORAVIA A.S.—See Agrofert Holding, a.s.; *Int'l*, pg. 218
AGROTON PUBLIC LTD; *Int'l*, pg. 221
AGRO TRADE LATVIJA SIA—See Kesko Corporation; *Int'l*, pg. 4141
A GROUP OF RETAIL ASSETS SWEDEN AB; *Int'l*, pg. 17
AGROVET A.S.; *Int'l*, pg. 221
AGROVISTA B.V.—See Marubeni Corporation; *Int'l*, pg. 4707
AGROVISTA UK LIMITED—See Marubeni Corporation; *Int'l*, pg. 4707
AGROVOJVODINA EXPORT - IMPORT A.D.; *Int'l*, pg. 221
AGROVOJVODINA KOMERCSERVIS AD; *Int'l*, pg. 221

AGROVRSAC A.D.; *Int'l*, pg. 221
AGROW AUSTRALIA PTY LTD—See Nufarm Limited; *Int'l*, pg. 5486
AGROW CORPORATION SDN. BHD.—See OCB Berhad; *Int'l*, pg. 5515
AGROWEALTH CO., LTD.—See Thai Rubber Latex Group Public Company Limited; *Int'l*, pg. 7595
AGROW HEALTHTECH SDN. BHD.—See OCB Berhad; *Int'l*, pg. 5515
AGROZZN, A.S.—See Agrofert Holding, a.s.; *Int'l*, pg. 218
AGRUPACIO ENERGIAS RENOVABLES, S.A.U—See RWE AG; *Int'l*, pg. 6433
AGRUPACION EOLICA, S.L.U.—See EDP - Energias de Portugal, S.A.; *Int'l*, pg. 2314
AGRUPACION GUINOVART OBRAS Y SERVICIOS HISPANIA, S.A.—See Grupo Villar Mir, S.A.U.; *Int'l*, pg. 3138
AGRU PLASTICS CO., LTD.—See Nomura Micro Science Co., Ltd.; *Int'l*, pg. 5412
AG RX, INC.; *U.S. Private*, pg. 125
AGS AUTOMOTIVE SOLUTIONS LLC—See 3 Rivers Capital, LLC; *U.S. Private*, pg. 7
AGS AUTOMOTIVE SYSTEMS - CAMBRIDGE PLANT—See AGS Automotive Systems; *Int'l*, pg. 221
AGS AUTOMOTIVE SYSTEMS, INC. - CAMBRIDGE PLANT—See J2 Management Corporation; *Int'l*, pg. 3859
AGS AUTOMOTIVE SYSTEMS, INC. - OSHAWA PLANT—See J2 Management Corporation; *Int'l*, pg. 3859
AGS AUTOMOTIVE SYSTEMS, INC. - WINDSOR PLANT—See J2 Management Corporation; *Int'l*, pg. 3859
AGS AUTOMOTIVE SYSTEMS - OSHAWA PLANT—See AGS Automotive Systems; *Int'l*, pg. 221
AGS AUTOMOTIVE SYSTEMS; *Int'l*, pg. 221
AGS AUTOMOTIVE SYSTEMS - STERLING HEIGHTS PLANT—See AGS Automotive Systems; *Int'l*, pg. 221
AGS AUTOMOTIVE SYSTEMS - WINDSOR PLANT—See AGS Automotive Systems; *Int'l*, pg. 221
AGS BUSINESS COMPUTER CO., LTD.—See AGS Corporation; *Int'l*, pg. 221
AGS CAPITAL, LLC—See PlayAGS, Inc.; *U.S. Public*, pg. 1697
AG SCIENTIFIC, INC.—See Research Products International Corporation; *U.S. Private*, pg. 3404
AGS CORPORATION; *Int'l*, pg. 221
AGS CUSTOM GRAPHICS, INC.—See Chatham Asset Management, LLC; *U.S. Private*, pg. 862
AGSENSE, LLC—See Valmont Industries, Inc.; *U.S. Public*, pg. 2273
AGS FINANCIAL CORPORATION—See A.G. Spanos Companies; *U.S. Private*, pg. 26
AGS FLEXITALLIC, INC.—See Bridgepoint Group Plc; *Int'l*, pg. 1154
A.G.S. GROEP B.V.—See The Brink's Company; *U.S. Public*, pg. 2041
AG (SHANGHAI) AGRICULTURE TECHNOLOGY CO., LTD.—See Corteva, Inc.; *U.S. Public*, pg. 580
AG SHIP MAINTENANCE CORP.; *U.S. Private*, pg. 125
AGSIN LIMITED—See Zagro Asia Ltd; *Int'l*, pg. 8620
AGS INTEGRATION PTE. LTD.—See Advancer Global Limited; *Int'l*, pg. 163
AGSI; *U.S. Private*, pg. 130
AG SMILE LEASEBACK CORPORATION—See AIFUL Corporation; *Int'l*, pg. 231
AG SOLUTIONS L.L.C.; *U.S. Private*, pg. 125
AGSOURCE COOPERATIVE SERVICES—See Cooperative Resources International Inc.; *U.S. Private*, pg. 1043
AG SOUTH CAROLINA LLC—See Eagle Materials Inc.; *U.S. Public*, pg. 702
A.G. SPANOS COMPANIES; *U.S. Private*, pg. 25
A.G. SPANOS CONSTRUCTION—See A.G. Spanos Companies; *U.S. Private*, pg. 25
A.G. SPANOS DEVELOPMENT—See A.G. Spanos Companies; *U.S. Private*, pg. 26
A.G. SPANOS ENTERPRISES—See A.G. Spanos Companies; *U.S. Private*, pg. 26
A.G. SPANOS MANAGEMENT—See A.G. Spanos Companies; *U.S. Private*, pg. 26
A.G. SPANOS REALTY—See A.G. Spanos Companies; *U.S. Private*, pg. 26
A.G. SPANOS SECURITIES—See A.G. Spanos Companies; *U.S. Private*, pg. 26
AGS PRO SERVICE CO., LTD.—See AGS Corporation; *Int'l*, pg. 221
AG SQUARE, LTD.—See Sega Sammy Holdings, Inc.; *Int'l*, pg. 6680
AGS SA—See Groupe Bruxelles Lambert SA; *Int'l*, pg. 3099
AGS-SECUTRANS B.V.—See The Brink's Company; *U.S. Public*, pg. 2042
AGS SYSTEM ADVISORY CO., LTD.—See AGS Corporation; *Int'l*, pg. 221
AGSTAR PLC; *Int'l*, pg. 221
AG STATES AGENCY, LLC—See CHS INC.; *U.S. Public*, pg. 491
AGSTEN CONSTRUCTION COMPANY; *U.S. Private*, pg. 130

AG STOCK CENTER CORPORATION—See AIFUL Corporation; *Int'l*, pg. 231
AGS TRANSACT TECHNOLOGIES LTD.; *Int'l*, pg. 221
AG SUPERMARKETS INC.—See Associated Grocers of New England, Inc.; *U.S. Private*, pg. 356
AGT ADVANCED COMMUNICATIONS—See TELUS CORPORATION; *Int'l*, pg. 7546
AGTA RECORD AG—See ASSA ABLOY AB; *Int'l*, pg. 638
AGTATEC AG—See ASSA ABLOY AB; *Int'l*, pg. 638
AGTECH GLOBAL INTERNATIONAL, INC.; *U.S. Public*, pg. 63
AGTECH HOLDINGS LIMITED—See Alibaba Group Holding Limited; *Int'l*, pg. 326
AGTECH, LLC—See AGCO Corporation; *U.S. Public*, pg. 58
AGTECH PRODUCTS, INC.—See International Flavors & Fragrances Inc.; *U.S. Public*, pg. 221
AGTEGRA COOPERATIVE; *U.S. Private*, pg. 130
AGT FOOD AND INGREDIENTS INC.; *Int'l*, pg. 221
AGT FOODS AUSTRALIA PTY LTD—See AGT Food and Ingredients Inc.; *Int'l*, pg. 221
AGTHIA GROUP EGYPT LLC—See Agthia Group PJSC; *Int'l*, pg. 221
AGTHIA GROUP PJSC; *Int'l*, pg. 221
AGT MOBILITY INC.—See TELUS CORPORATION; *Int'l*, pg. 7546
AGTRAX TECHNOLOGIES—See Integrated Solutions Group, Inc.; *U.S. Private*, pg. 2101
A.G. TRUCANO, SON & GRANDSONS, INC.—See Maverick Gold LLC; *U.S. Private*, pg. 2616
AG TWIN BROOK BDC, INC.; *U.S. Private*, pg. 125
AGUA DE LA FALDA S.A.—See Rio Tinto plc; *Int'l*, pg. 6346
AGUA DE ORO VENTURES CORPORATION—See Benguet Corporation; *Int'l*, pg. 974
AGUA IMARA ACA PTE LTD—See Statkraft AS; *Int'l*, pg. 7184
AGUA LIBRE MIDSTREAM LLC—See Basic Energy Services Inc.; *U.S. Public*, pg. 279
AGUAS ANDINAS SA—See Veolia Environnement S.A.; *Int'l*, pg. 8155
AGUAS AZUIS CONSTRUCAO NAVAL SPE LTDA.—See ThyssenKrupp AG; *Int'l*, pg. 7723
AGUAS DANONE DE ARGENTINA—See Danone; *Int'l*, pg. 1967
AGUAS DE ANDRADINA S.A.—See Igua Saneamento SA; *Int'l*, pg. 3603
AGUAS DE ANTOFAGASTA S.A.—See Empresas Publicas de Medellin ESP; *Int'l*, pg. 2391
AGUAS DE CASTILHO S.A.—See Igua Saneamento SA; *Int'l*, pg. 3603
AGUAS DECIMA S.A.—See Marubeni Corporation; *Int'l*, pg. 4705
AGUAS DEL VALLE DEL GUADIARO, S.L.—See Sacyr, S.A.; *Int'l*, pg. 6465
AGUAS DE PANAMA S.A—See Sembcorp Industries Ltd.; *Int'l*, pg. 6702
AGUASIN SPA—See Danaher Corporation; *U.S. Public*, pg. 624
AGUAS Y SERVICIOS DE LA COSTA TROPICAL DE GRANADA, A.I.E.—See Fomento de Construcciones y Contratas, S.A.; *Int'l*, pg. 2722
AGUA Y SANEAMIENTOS ARGENTINOS, S.A.; *Int'l*, pg. 222
AGUDATH ISREAL OF AMERICA COMMUNITY SERVICES INC; *U.S. Private*, pg. 130
AGUER HAVELOCK ASSOCIATES, INC.—See Avison Young (Canada) Inc.; *Int'l*, pg. 744
AGUERREBERE S.A.—See Husqvarna AB; *Int'l*, pg. 3538
AGUIA METAIS LTDA—See Aguia Resources Limited; *Int'l*, pg. 222
AGUIA RESOURCES LIMITED; *Int'l*, pg. 222
AGUILA COPPER CORP.; *Int'l*, pg. 222
AGUILAR CHILENA DE EDICIONES, S.A.—See Promotora de Informaciones S.A.; *Int'l*, pg. 5995
AGUNG PODOMORO LAND TBK; *Int'l*, pg. 222
A.G. UNIVERSAL LIMITED; *Int'l*, pg. 24
AGUSTA AEROSPACE SERVICES - A.A.S.—See Leonardo S.p.A.; *Int'l*, pg. 4458
AGUSTA PARK YEOVIL MANAGEMENT COMPANY LIMITED—See Persimmon plc; *Int'l*, pg. 5815
AGUSTAWESTLAND AUSTRALIA PTY. LTD.—See Leonardo S.p.A.; *Int'l*, pg. 4458
AGUSTAWESTLAND DO BRASIL LTDA.—See Leonardo S.p.A.; *Int'l*, pg. 4458
AGUSTAWESTLAND HOLDINGS LIMITED—See Leonardo S.p.A.; *Int'l*, pg. 4458
AGUSTAWESTLAND INC.—See Leonardo S.p.A.; *Int'l*, pg. 4458
AGUSTAWESTLAND INTERNATIONAL LIMITED—See Leonardo S.p.A.; *Int'l*, pg. 4458
AGUSTAWESTLAND LIMITED—See Leonardo S.p.A.; *Int'l*, pg. 4458
AGUSTAWESTLAND LTD. - YEOVIL PLANT—See Leonardo S.p.A.; *Int'l*, pg. 4458
AGUSTAWESTLAND MALAYSIA SDN. BHD.—See Leonardo S.p.A.; *Int'l*, pg. 4458
AGUSTAWESTLAND NORTH AMERICA INC—See Leonardo S.p.A.; *Int'l*, pg. 4458

AGUSTAWESTLAND PHILADELPHIA CORPORATION—See Leonardo S.p.A.; *Int'l*, pg. 4458
AGUSTAWESTLAND PORTUGAL SA—See Leonardo S.p.A.; *Int'l*, pg. 4458
AGUSTAWESTLAND S.P.A.—See Leonardo S.p.A.; *Int'l*, pg. 4457
AGUSTAWESTLAND UK PENSION SCHEME (TRUSTEE) LIMITED—See Leonardo S.p.A.; *Int'l*, pg. 4458
AGVA CORPORATION LIMITED; *Int'l*, pg. 222
AG VALLEY COOPERATIVE NON-STOCK; *U.S. Private*, pg. 125
AGVANTAGE FS, INC.; *U.S. Private*, pg. 130
AGVA SINGAPORE PTE LTD—See AGVA Corporation Limited; *Int'l*, pg. 222
AGVENTURE FEEDS & SEED INC.; *U.S. Private*, pg. 130
AGVENTURES, LLC.; *U.S. Private*, pg. 130
AGV GALVANIZING (M) SDN. BHD.—See AGV Group Limited; *Int'l*, pg. 222
AGV GROUP LIMITED; *Int'l*, pg. 222
AG VIEW FS, INC.; *U.S. Private*, pg. 125
AGV PRODUCTS CORP.; *Int'l*, pg. 222
AGWAY ENERGY SERVICES, LLC—See Suburban Propane Partners, L.P.; *U.S. Public*, pg. 1958
AGWAY SYSTEMS; *U.S. Private*, pg. 130
AGW CAPITAL ADVISORS; *U.S. Private*, pg. 130
AGWE LDA.—See Weber-Ingenieure GmbH; *Int'l*, pg. 8366
AG-WEST DISTRIBUTING COMPANY; *U.S. Private*, pg. 125
AG WURTH EURASIEN—See Wurth Verwaltungsgesellschaft mbH; *Int'l*, pg. 8503
AH4R MANAGEMENT-GA, LLC—See American Homes 4 Rent; *U.S. Public*, pg. 104
AH4R MANAGEMENT-NC, LLC—See American Homes 4 Rent; *U.S. Public*, pg. 104
AH4R MANAGEMENT-TX, LLC—See American Homes 4 Rent; *U.S. Public*, pg. 104
AH4R PROPERTIES, LLC—See American Homes 4 Rent; *U.S. Public*, pg. 104
AHA CO., LTD.; *Int'l*, pg. 222
A.H. ALGOSAIBI & BROS.; *Int'l*, pg. 24
AHANA RENEWABLES, LLC—See ATN International, Inc.; *U.S. Public*, pg. 224
A. HAROLD & ASSOCIATES, LLC; *U.S. Private*, pg. 23
AHASOLAR TECHNOLOGIES LIMITED; *Int'l*, pg. 222
AHA!; *U.S. Private*, pg. 130
AHB DISTRIBUTION SDN. BHD.—See AHB Holdings Berhad; *Int'l*, pg. 222
A.H. BECK FOUNDATION CO. INC.; *U.S. Private*, pg. 26
A.H. BELO CORPORATION; *U.S. Public*, pg. 12
AHB HOLDINGS BERHAD; *Int'l*, pg. 222
AHB TECHNOLOGY SDN. BHD.—See AHB Holdings Berhad; *Int'l*, pg. 222
AHC ADVISORS, INC.—See Mission Wealth Management, LLC; *U.S. Private*, pg. 2748
AHC BENELUX B.V.—See Aalberts N.V.; *Int'l*, pg. 33
AHC B.V.—See Aalberts N.V.; *Int'l*, pg. 33
AHC CALIFORNIA DISPOSITIONS, INC.—See DallasNews Corporation; *U.S. Public*, pg. 621
AHC DIGITAL LLC—See Arthur J. Gallagher & Co.; *U.S. Public*, pg. 206
AHC GROUP, INC.; *Int'l*, pg. 222
AHC INC.; *U.S. Private*, pg. 130
AHC ITALIA S.R.L.—See Aalberts N.V.; *Int'l*, pg. 33
AHC LIMITED; *Int'l*, pg. 222
AHC MEDIA LLC—See Bertelsmann SE & Co. KGaA; *Int'l*, pg. 991
AHC OBERFLACHENTECHNIK GES.M.B.H.—See Aalberts N.V.; *Int'l*, pg. 33
AHC OBERFLACHENTECHNIK GMBH—See Aalberts N.V.; *Int'l*, pg. 33
AHC SOUTHLAND-MELBOURNE, LLC—See Brookdale Senior Living Inc.; *U.S. Public*, pg. 393
AHC SOUTHLAND-ORMOND BEACH, LLC—See Brookdale Senior Living Inc.; *U.S. Public*, pg. 393
AHC SPECIAL COATINGS GMBH—See Aalberts N.V.; *Int'l*, pg. 33
AHC SURFACE TECHNOLOGY S.A.S.—See Aalberts N.V.; *Int'l*, pg. 33
AHC WAREHOUSE & TRADING (SHENZHEN) CO., LTD.—See Audix Corporation; *Int'l*, pg. 702
AHD ASSOCIATES INC.; *U.S. Private*, pg. 130
AHD AUTO-HIFI & -DESIGN GMBH—See Wurth Verwaltungsgesellschaft mbH; *Int'l*, pg. 8503
AHEAD ALL COMPANY LIMITED—See Univentures Public Company Limited; *Int'l*, pg. 8077
AHEADCOM BETEILIGUNGS-GMBH—See Deutsche Bank Aktiengesellschaft; *Int'l*, pg. 2055
A-HEAD FOR PROFITS LLC; *U.S. Private*, pg. 22
AHEAD INC.—See New Wave Group AB; *Int'l*, pg. 5229
AHEAD, LLC—See Berkshire Partners LLC; *U.S. Private*, pg. 534
AHEAD MAGNETICS, INC.; *U.S. Private*, pg. 130
AHEARINGAID.COM LLC; *U.S. Private*, pg. 130
AHEARN & SOPER INC.; *U.S. Private*, pg. 130
AHEARN & SOPER INC.—See Ahearn & Soper Inc.; *Int'l*, pg. 223
AHEARN & SOPER INC.—See Ahearn & Soper Inc.; *Int'l*, pg. 223

COMPANY NAME INDEX

AHEARN & SOPER INC.—See Ahearn & Soper Inc.; *Int'l*, pg. 222
AHEARN & SOPER INC.—See Ahearn & Soper Inc.; *Int'l*, pg. 222
AHEARN & SOPER INC.—See Ahearn & Soper Inc.; *Int'l*, pg. 223
AHEIM CAPITAL GMBH; *Int'l*, pg. 223
THE A.H. EMERY COMPANY; *U.S. Private*, pg. 3980
A.H. ENTERTAINERS INC.; *U.S. Private*, pg. 26
AHERN & ASSOCIATES INC.; *U.S. Private*, pg. 130
AHERN AUSTRALIA PTY. LTD.—See Tanfield Group Plc; *Int'l*, pg. 7457
AHERN AUSTRALIA PTY. LTD.—See Xtreme Manufacturing, LLC; *U.S. Private*, pg. 4583
AHERN DIALYSIS, LLC—See DaVita Inc.; *U.S. Public*, pg. 635
AHERN FIRE PROTECTION—See J.F. Ahern Co.; *U.S. Private*, pg. 2162
AHERN FIRE PROTECTION—See J.F. Ahern Co.; *U.S. Private*, pg. 2162
AHERN FIRE PROTECTION—See J.F. Ahern Co.; *U.S. Private*, pg. 2162
AHERN FIRE PROTECTION—See J.F. Ahern Co.; *U.S. Private*, pg. 2162
AHERN FIRE PROTECTION—See J.F. Ahern Co.; *U.S. Private*, pg. 2162
AHERN RENTALS, INC.—See United Rentals, Inc.; *U.S. Public*, pg. 2235
AHF INDUSTRIES, INC.; *U.S. Private*, pg. 130
AHF, LLC—See Paceline Equity Partners LLC; *U.S. Private*, pg. 3064
AHF PHARMACY - SAN DIEGO—See AIDS Healthcare Foundation; *U.S. Private*, pg. 132
AHG 1 PTY LTD—See Eagers Automotive Limited; *Int'l*, pg. 2263
AHGAR INTERNATIONAL CO.—See Fouad Alghanim & Sons Group of Companies; *Int'l*, pg. 2753
AHG OF NEW YORK, INC.—See The Cigna Group; *U.S. Public*, pg. 2062
A.H. HERMEL CANDY & TOBACCO CO. INC.; *U.S. Private*, pg. 26
AHH HOLDINGS HEALTH CARE PTY LIMITED—See Ramsay Health Care Limited; *Int'l*, pg. 6199
A.H. HOFFMAN, INC.—See Good Earth, Inc.; *U.S. Private*, pg. 1738
AH HOLDINGS HEALTH CARE PTY LIMITED—See Ramsay Health Care Limited; *Int'l*, pg. 6199
AH HOLDINGS, LLC—See Ascension Health Alliance; *U.S. Private*, pg. 346
AHI CARRIER FZC—See Carrier Global Corporation; *U.S. Public*, pg. 440
AHI ELECTRONICS WAREHOUSE (HANG ZHOU) CO., LTD.—See Audix Corporation; *Int'l*, pg. 702
AHI ELECTRONICS WAREHOUSE (SHANGHAI) CO., LTD.—See Audix Corporation; *Int'l*, pg. 702
AHI ELECTRONICS WAREHOUSE (WU JIANG) CO., LTD.—See Audix Corporation; *Int'l*, pg. 702
AHI-HEALTHLINK—See Elevance Health, Inc.; *U.S. Public*, pg. 728
A.H.I. INVESTMENT INC.; *U.S. Private*, pg. 26
AHIMSA INDUSTRIES LIMITED; *Int'l*, pg. 223
AH INDUSTRIES A/S; *Int'l*, pg. 222
AHI ROOFING GYARTO ES KERESKEDELMI KORLATOLT FELELOSSEGU TARASAG—See Fletcher Building Limited; *Int'l*, pg. 2699
AHI ROOFING LIMITED—See Fletcher Building Limited; *Int'l*, pg. 2699
AHI ROOFING (MALAYSIA) SDN BHD—See Fletcher Building Limited; *Int'l*, pg. 2699
AHI SUPPLY INC.; *U.S. Private*, pg. 130
AHJIKAN CO., LTD.; *Int'l*, pg. 223
AHK ASERBAIDSCHAN—See Messe Munchen GmbH; *Int'l*, pg. 4841
AHLADA ENGINEERS LIMITED; *Int'l*, pg. 223
AHLCON PARENTERALS (INDIA) LTD.—See B. Braun Melsungen AG; *Int'l*, pg. 785
AHLCON READY MIX CONCRETE PVT. LTD. - BOMMENHALLI PLANT—See Ahluwalia Contracts (India) Limited; *Int'l*, pg. 225
AHLCON READY MIX CONCRETE PVT. LTD.—See Ahluwalia Contracts (India) Limited; *Int'l*, pg. 225
AHLENS AB—See Axel Johnson Gruppen AB; *Int'l*, pg. 765
AHLERS AG—See WTW-Beteiligungsgesellschaft mbH; *Int'l*, pg. 8499
AHLIA INSURANCE COMPANY (S.A.); *Int'l*, pg. 223
AHLI BANK QPSC; *Int'l*, pg. 223
AHLI BANK S.A.O.G.; *Int'l*, pg. 223
AHLI BROKERAGE COMPANY—See Jordan Ahli Bank; *Int'l*, pg. 3997
AHLI FINTECH COMPANY LTD.—See Jordan Ahli Bank; *Int'l*, pg. 3997
AHLI MICROFINANCE COMPANY—See Jordan Ahli Bank; *Int'l*, pg. 3997
AHLI UNITED BANK B.S.C.—See Kuwait Finance House K.S.C.; *Int'l*, pg. 4344
AHLI UNITED BANK (EGYPT) S.A.E.—See Kuwait Finance House K.S.C.; *Int'l*, pg. 4344
AHLI UNITED BANK K.S.C.P.—See Kuwait Finance House K.S.C.; *Int'l*, pg. 4344
AHLI UNITED BANK (U.K.) PLC—See Kuwait Finance House K.S.C.; *Int'l*, pg. 4344
AHLSELL AB; *Int'l*, pg. 223
AHLSELL APS—See Ahlsell AB; *Int'l*, pg. 223
AHLSELL DANMARK APS—See Ahlsell AB; *Int'l*, pg. 223
AHLSELL NORWAY AS—See Ahlsell AB; *Int'l*, pg. 223
AHLSELL OY—See Ahlsell AB; *Int'l*, pg. 223
AHLSELL SVERIGE AB—See Ahlsell AB; *Int'l*, pg. 223
AHLSTROM ASIA HOLDINGS PTE LTD—See Ahlstrom Capital Oy; *Int'l*, pg. 223
AHLSTROM ASIA HOLDINGS PTE LTD—See Bain Capital, LP; *U.S. Private*, pg. 429
AHLSTROM BRASIL LTDA.—See Ahlstrom Capital Oy; *Int'l*, pg. 224
AHLSTROM BRASIL LTDA.—See Bain Capital, LP; *U.S. Private*, pg. 429
AHLSTROM CAPITAL OY; *Int'l*, pg. 223
AHLSTROM GLASSFIBRE OY - MIKKELI PLANT—See ADCURAM Group AG; *Int'l*, pg. 128
AHLSTROM-MUNKSJO AB—See Ahlstrom Capital Oy; *Int'l*, pg. 224
AHLSTROM-MUNKSJO AB—See Bain Capital, LP; *U.S. Private*, pg. 429
AHLSTROM-MUNKSJO APPRIEU S.A.S—See Ahlstrom Capital Oy; *Int'l*, pg. 224
AHLSTROM-MUNKSJO APPRIEU S.A.S—See Bain Capital, LP; *U.S. Private*, pg. 429
AHLSTROM-MUNKSJO ARCHES S.A.S—See Ahlstrom Capital Oy; *Int'l*, pg. 224
AHLSTROM-MUNKSJO ARCHES S.A.S—See Bain Capital, LP; *U.S. Private*, pg. 429
AHLSTROM-MUNKSJO ASPA BRUK AB—See Ahlstrom Capital Oy; *Int'l*, pg. 224
AHLSTROM-MUNKSJO ASPA BRUK AB—See Bain Capital, LP; *U.S. Private*, pg. 429
AHLSTROM-MUNKSJO BRASIL INDUSTRIA E COMERCIO DE PAPEIS ESPECIAIS LTDA.—See Ahlstrom Capital Oy; *Int'l*, pg. 224
AHLSTROM-MUNKSJO BRASIL INDUSTRIA E COMERCIO DE PAPEIS ESPECIAIS LTDA.—See Bain Capital, LP; *U.S. Private*, pg. 429
AHLSTROM-MUNKSJO BRASIL LTDA.—See Ahlstrom Capital Oy; *Int'l*, pg. 224
AHLSTROM-MUNKSJO BRASIL LTDA.—See Bain Capital, LP; *U.S. Private*, pg. 429
AHLSTROM-MUNKSJO BRIGNOUD SAS—See Ahlstrom Capital Oy; *Int'l*, pg. 224
AHLSTROM-MUNKSJO BRIGNOUD SAS—See Bain Capital, LP; *U.S. Private*, pg. 429
AHLSTROM-MUNKSJO CHIRNSIDE LIMITED - MANCHESTER PLANT—See Ahlstrom Capital Oy; *Int'l*, pg. 224
AHLSTROM-MUNKSJO CHIRNSIDE LIMITED - MANCHESTER PLANT—See Bain Capital, LP; *U.S. Private*, pg. 429
AHLSTROM-MUNKSJO CHIRNSIDE LTD.—See Ahlstrom Capital Oy; *Int'l*, pg. 224
AHLSTROM-MUNKSJO CHIRNSIDE LTD.—See Bain Capital, LP; *U.S. Private*, pg. 429
AHLSTROM-MUNKSJO FALUN AB—See Ahlstrom Capital Oy; *Int'l*, pg. 224
AHLSTROM-MUNKSJO FALUN AB—See Bain Capital, LP; *U.S. Private*, pg. 429
AHLSTROM-MUNKSJO FIBERCOMPOSITES (BINZHOU) LIMITED—See Ahlstrom Capital Oy; *Int'l*, pg. 224
AHLSTROM-MUNKSJO FIBERCOMPOSITES (BINZHOU) LIMITED—See Bain Capital, LP; *U.S. Private*, pg. 429
AHLSTROM MUNKSJO FIBER COMPOSITES INDIA PRIVATE LTD.—See Ahlstrom Capital Oy; *Int'l*, pg. 224
AHLSTROM MUNKSJO FIBER COMPOSITES INDIA PRIVATE LTD.—See Bain Capital, LP; *U.S. Private*, pg. 429
AHLSTROM MUNKSJO FIBER COMPOSITES INDIA PRIVATE LTD.—See Ahlstrom Capital Oy; *Int'l*, pg. 224
AHLSTROM MUNKSJO FIBER COMPOSITES INDIA PRIVATE LTD.—See Bain Capital, LP; *U.S. Private*, pg. 429
AHLSTROM-MUNKSJO FILTRATION LLC - MOUNT HOLLY SPRINGS PLANT—See Ahlstrom Capital Oy; *Int'l*, pg. 224
AHLSTROM-MUNKSJO FILTRATION LLC - MOUNT HOLLY SPRINGS PLANT—See Bain Capital, LP; *U.S. Private*, pg. 429
AHLSTROM-MUNKSJO FILTRATION LLC—See Ahlstrom Capital Oy; *Int'l*, pg. 224
AHLSTROM-MUNKSJO FILTRATION LLC—See Bain Capital, LP; *U.S. Private*, pg. 429
AHLSTROM-MUNKSJO FILTRATION LLC - TAYLORVILLE PLANT—See Ahlstrom Capital Oy; *Int'l*, pg. 224
AHLSTROM-MUNKSJO FILTRATION LLC - TAYLORVILLE PLANT—See Bain Capital, LP; *U.S. Private*, pg. 430
AHLSTROM-MUNKSJO GERMANY GMBH—See Ahlstrom Capital Oy; *Int'l*, pg. 224
AHLSTROM-MUNKSJO GERMANY GMBH—See Bain Capital, LP; *U.S. Private*, pg. 429
AHLSTROM-MUNKSJO GERMANY HOLDING GMBH—See Ahlstrom Capital Oy; *Int'l*, pg. 224

AHLSTROM CAPITAL OY

AHLSTROM-MUNKSJO GERMANY HOLDING GMBH—See Bain Capital, LP; *U.S. Private*, pg. 429
AHLSTROM-MUNKSJO GLASSFIBRE OY—See Ahlstrom Capital Oy; *Int'l*, pg. 224
AHLSTROM-MUNKSJO GLASSFIBRE OY—See Bain Capital, LP; *U.S. Private*, pg. 429
AHLSTROM-MUNKSJO ITALIA S.P.A.—See Ahlstrom Capital Oy; *Int'l*, pg. 224
AHLSTROM-MUNKSJO ITALIA S.P.A.—See Bain Capital, LP; *U.S. Private*, pg. 429
AHLSTROM-MUNKSJO ITALIA S.P.A.—See Ahlstrom Capital Oy; *Int'l*, pg. 224
AHLSTROM-MUNKSJO ITALIA S.P.A.—See Bain Capital, LP; *U.S. Private*, pg. 429
AHLSTROM-MUNKSJO JAPAN INC.—See Ahlstrom Capital Oy; *Int'l*, pg. 224
AHLSTROM-MUNKSJO JAPAN INC.—See Bain Capital, LP; *U.S. Private*, pg. 429
AHLSTROM-MUNKSJO KOREA CO., LTD.—See Ahlstrom Capital Oy; *Int'l*, pg. 223
AHLSTROM-MUNKSJO KOREA CO., LTD.—See Bain Capital, LP; *U.S. Private*, pg. 429
AHLSTROM-MUNKSJO LA GERE S.A.S.—See Ahlstrom Capital Oy; *Int'l*, pg. 224
AHLSTROM-MUNKSJO LA GERE S.A.S.—See Bain Capital, LP; *U.S. Private*, pg. 429
AHLSTROM-MUNKSJO MALMEDY SA—See Ahlstrom Capital Oy; *Int'l*, pg. 224
AHLSTROM-MUNKSJO MALMEDY SA—See Bain Capital, LP; *U.S. Private*, pg. 429
AHLSTROM-MUNKSJO MONTERREY, S. DE R.L. DE C.V.—See Ahlstrom Capital Oy; *Int'l*, pg. 224
AHLSTROM-MUNKSJO MONTERREY, S. DE R.L. DE C.V.—See Bain Capital, LP; *U.S. Private*, pg. 429
AHLSTROM-MUNKSJO NA SPECIALTY SOLUTIONS LLC - NICOLET PLANT—See Ahlstrom Capital Oy; *Int'l*, pg. 224
AHLSTROM-MUNKSJO NA SPECIALTY SOLUTIONS LLC - NICOLET PLANT—See Bain Capital, LP; *U.S. Private*, pg. 430
AHLSTROM-MUNKSJO NA SPECIALTY SOLUTIONS LLC - RHINELANDER MILL—See Ahlstrom Capital Oy; *Int'l*, pg. 224
AHLSTROM-MUNKSJO NA SPECIALTY SOLUTIONS LLC - RHINELANDER MILL—See Bain Capital, LP; *U.S. Private*, pg. 430
AHLSTROM-MUNKSJO NA SPECIALTY SOLUTIONS LLC—See Ahlstrom Capital Oy; *Int'l*, pg. 224
AHLSTROM-MUNKSJO NA SPECIALTY SOLUTIONS LLC—See Bain Capital, LP; *U.S. Private*, pg. 430
AHLSTROM-MUNKSJO NONWOVENS LLC—See Ahlstrom Capital Oy; *Int'l*, pg. 224
AHLSTROM-MUNKSJO NONWOVENS LLC—See Bain Capital, LP; *U.S. Private*, pg. 429
AHLSTROM-MUNKSJO OYJ - CAIEIRAS PLANT—See Ahlstrom Capital Oy; *Int'l*, pg. 224
AHLSTROM-MUNKSJO OYJ - CAIEIRAS PLANT—See Bain Capital, LP; *U.S. Private*, pg. 429
AHLSTROM-MUNKSJO OYJ - JACAREI PLANT—See Ahlstrom Capital Oy; *Int'l*, pg. 224
AHLSTROM-MUNKSJO OYJ - JACAREI PLANT—See Bain Capital, LP; *U.S. Private*, pg. 429
AHLSTROM-MUNKSJO OYJ - LOUVEIRA PLANT—See Ahlstrom Capital Oy; *Int'l*, pg. 224
AHLSTROM-MUNKSJO OYJ - LOUVEIRA PLANT—See Bain Capital, LP; *U.S. Private*, pg. 429
AHLSTROM-MUNKSJO OYJ—See Ahlstrom Capital Oy; *Int'l*, pg. 223
AHLSTROM-MUNKSJO OYJ—See Bain Capital, LP; *U.S. Private*, pg. 429
AHLSTROM-MUNKSJO PAPER GMBH—See Ahlstrom Capital Oy; *Int'l*, pg. 224
AHLSTROM-MUNKSJO PAPER GMBH—See Bain Capital, LP; *U.S. Private*, pg. 429
AHLSTROM-MUNKSJO PAPER INC.—See Ahlstrom Capital Oy; *Int'l*, pg. 224
AHLSTROM-MUNKSJO PAPER INC.—See Bain Capital, LP; *U.S. Private*, pg. 430
AHLSTROM-MUNKSJO PAPER S.A.—See Ahlstrom Capital Oy; *Int'l*, pg. 224
AHLSTROM-MUNKSJO PAPER S.A.—See Bain Capital, LP; *U.S. Private*, pg. 430
AHLSTROM-MUNKSJO PAPER (TAICANG) CO., LTD.—See Ahlstrom Capital Oy; *Int'l*, pg. 223
AHLSTROM-MUNKSJO PAPER (TAICANG) CO., LTD.—See Bain Capital, LP; *U.S. Private*, pg. 429
AHLSTROM-MUNKSJO PAPER TRADING (SHANGHAI) CO., LTD.—See Ahlstrom Capital Oy; *Int'l*, pg. 223
AHLSTROM-MUNKSJO PAPER TRADING (SHANGHAI) CO., LTD.—See Bain Capital, LP; *U.S. Private*, pg. 429
AHLSTROM-MUNKSJO ROTTERSAC S.A.S.—See Ahlstrom Capital Oy; *Int'l*, pg. 224
AHLSTROM-MUNKSJO ROTTERSAC S.A.S.—See Bain Capital, LP; *U.S. Private*, pg. 430
AHLSTROM-MUNKSJO RUS LLC—See Ahlstrom Capital Oy; *Int'l*, pg. 224
AHLSTROM-MUNKSJO RUS LLC—See Bain Capital, LP; *U.S. Private*, pg. 430

AHLSTROM CAPITAL OY

CORPORATE AFFILIATIONS

AHLSTROM-MUNKSJO SPECIALTIES S.A.S. - SAINT SEVERIN PLANT—See Ahlstrom Capital Oy; *Int'l*, pg. 224
AHLSTROM-MUNKSJO SPECIALTIES S.A.S. - SAINT SEVERIN PLANT—See Bain Capital, LP; *U.S. Private*, pg. 430
AHLSTROM-MUNKSJO SPECIALTIES S.A.S.—See Ahlstrom Capital Oy; *Int'l*, pg. 224
AHLSTROM-MUNKSJO SPECIALTIES S.A.S.—See Bain Capital, LP; *U.S. Private*, pg. 430
AHLSTROM-MUNKSJO STALLDALEN AB—See Ahlstrom Capital Oy; *Int'l*, pg. 224
AHLSTROM-MUNKSJO STALLDALEN AB—See Bain Capital, LP; *U.S. Private*, pg. 430
AHLSTROM-MUNKSJO TAMPERE OY—See Ahlstrom Capital Oy; *Int'l*, pg. 225
AHLSTROM-MUNKSJO TAMPERE OY—See Bain Capital, LP; *U.S. Private*, pg. 430
AHLSTROM-MUNKSJO TVER LLC—See Ahlstrom Capital Oy; *Int'l*, pg. 224
AHLSTROM-MUNKSJO TVER LLC—See Bain Capital, LP; *U.S. Private*, pg. 429
AHLSTROM RESEARCH AND SERVICES SA—See Ahlstrom Capital Oy; *Int'l*, pg. 224
AHLSTROM RESEARCH AND SERVICES SA—See Bain Capital, LP; *U.S. Private*, pg. 429
AHLSTROM SALES HELSINKI OY—See Ahlstrom Capital Oy; *Int'l*, pg. 224
AHLSTROM SALES HELSINKI OY—See Bain Capital, LP; *U.S. Private*, pg. 429
AHLSTROM SEOUL CO. LTD—See Ahlstrom Capital Oy; *Int'l*, pg. 223
AHLSTROM SEOUL CO. LTD—See Bain Capital, LP; *U.S. Private*, pg. 429
AHLUWALIA CONTRACTS (INDIA) LIMITED; *Int'l*, pg. 225
AHMAD ALBINALI & TETRA ARABIA COMPANY LTD.—See TETRA Technologies, Inc.; *U.S. Public*, pg. 2024
AHMAD HASSAN TEXTILE MILLS LIMITED; *Int'l*, pg. 225
AHMAD ZAKI RESOURCES BERHAD; *Int'l*, pg. 225
AHMC & AHMC HEALTHCARE INC.; *U.S. Private*, pg. 130
AHMEDABAD STEELCRAFT LTD.; *Int'l*, pg. 225
AHMEDAHLS AB—See Almedahls Oy; *Int'l*, pg. 363
AHMED MANSOOR AL-A'ALI CO.; *Int'l*, pg. 225
AHM ENGINEERING COMPANY LIMITED—See CCT Fortis Holdings Limited; *Int'l*, pg. 1369
AHMET YAR REFRIGERATING INDUSTRY CO.—See Carrier Global Corporation; *U.S. Public*, pg. 441
AHM LIFESTYLES-CREATIVE HOSPITALITY JOINT STOCK COMPANY—See Charoen Pokphand Foods Public Company Limited; *Int'l*, pg. 1451
AHN BIOTECHNOLOGIE GMBH—See Harvard Bioscience, Inc.; *U.S. Public*, pg. 987
AHNEMAN KIRBY LLC—See The Fibersmith Company; *U.S. Private*, pg. 4028
AHN-GOOK PHARMACEUTICAL CO., LTD.; *Int'l*, pg. 225
AHN INTERNATIONAL LLC; *U.S. Private*, pg. 131
AHNLAB, INC.; *Int'l*, pg. 225
AHN TARGET HOLDINGS, LLC—See UnitedHealth Group Incorporated; *U.S. Public*, pg. 2238
AHNTECH, INC.; *U.S. Private*, pg. 131
AHOCHN AG—See BKW AG; *Int'l*, pg. 1054
AHOKU ELECTRONIC COMPANY; *Int'l*, pg. 225
AHOKU TECHLAND ELECTRONICS LTD.—See Ahoku Electronic Company; *Int'l*, pg. 225
AHOLD CZECH REPUBLIC A.S—See Koninklijke Ahold Delhaize N.V.; *Int'l*, pg. 4260
AHOLD FINANCIAL SERVICES, LLC—See Koninklijke Ahold Delhaize N.V.; *Int'l*, pg. 4260
AHOLD INFORMATION SERVICES, INC—See Koninklijke Ahold Delhaize N.V.; *Int'l*, pg. 4260
AHOLD USA, INC.—See Koninklijke Ahold Delhaize N.V.; *Int'l*, pg. 4260
AHORN-GERATE & WERKZEUGE VERTRIEBS GMBH—See Simpson Manufacturing Company, Inc.; *U.S. Public*, pg. 1882
A-HOST CO., LTD.—See Country Group Development Public Company Limited; *Int'l*, pg. 1818
AHP HOLDINGS PTY. LIMITED—See Pfizer Inc.; *U.S. Public*, pg. 1679
AHREN ACQUISITION CORP.; *Int'l*, pg. 225
AHRENS GROUP PTY. LTD.; *Int'l*, pg. 225
AHRESTY CORPORATION - HIGASHIMATSUYAMA PLANT—See Ahresty Corporation; *Int'l*, pg. 225
AHRESTY CORPORATION - KUMAGAYA PLANT—See Ahresty Corporation; *Int'l*, pg. 225
AHRESTY CORPORATION; *Int'l*, pg. 225
AHRESTY DIE MOLD HAMAMATSU CORPORATION—See Ahresty Corporation; *Int'l*, pg. 225
AHRESTY DIE MOLD KUMAMOTO CORPORATION—See Ahresty Corporation; *Int'l*, pg. 225
AHRESTY DIE MOLD TOCHIGI CORPORATION—See Ahresty Corporation; *Int'l*, pg. 225
AHRESTY INDIA PRIVATE LIMITED—See Ahresty Corporation; *Int'l*, pg. 226

AHRESTY KUMAMOTO CORPORATION—See Ahresty Corporation; *Int'l*, pg. 226
AHRESTY MEXICANA, S.A. DE C.V.—See Ahresty Corporation; *Int'l*, pg. 226
AHRESTY PRECISION DIE MOLD (GUANGZHOU) CO., LTD.—See Ahresty Corporation; *Int'l*, pg. 226
AHRESTY PRETECH CORPORATION—See Ahresty Corporation; *Int'l*, pg. 226
AHRESTY TECHNO SERVICE CORPORATION—See Ahresty Corporation; *Int'l*, pg. 226
AHRESTY TOCHIGI CORPORATION—See Ahresty Corporation; *Int'l*, pg. 226
AHRESTY WILMINGTON CORPORATION—See Ahresty Corporation; *Int'l*, pg. 226
AHRESTY YAMAGATA CORPORATION—See Ahresty Corporation; *Int'l*, pg. 226
A.H. RIISE STORES; *U.S. Private*, pg. 26
AHSAY BACKUP SOFTWARE DEVELOPMENT COMPANY LIMITED; *Int'l*, pg. 226
AHSAY SYSTEMS CORPORATION LIMITED—See Ahsay Backup Software Development Company Limited; *Int'l*, pg. 226
A.H. SCHADE INC.; *U.S. Private*, pg. 26
AHS OKLAHOMA HEALTH SYSTEM, LLP—See Ventas, Inc.; *U.S. Public*, pg. 2277
AHS OKLAHOMA HOLDINGS, INC.—See Ventas, Inc.; *U.S. Public*, pg. 2277
A&H SPORTSWEAR CO. INC; *U.S. Private*, pg. 20
A&H STORES INC.; *U.S. Private*, pg. 20
AHT COOLING SYSTEMS GMBH—See Daikin Industries, Ltd.; *Int'l*, pg. 1932
AHTNA CONSTRUCTION & PRIMARY PRODUCTS CORPORATION—See Ahtna Incorporated; *U.S. Private*, pg. 131
AHTNA CONTRACTORS, LLC—See Ahtna Incorporated; *U.S. Private*, pg. 131
AHTNA DESIGN-BUILD, INC.—See Ahtna Incorporated; *U.S. Private*, pg. 131
AHTNA DEVELOPMENT CORPORATION—See Ahtna Incorporated; *U.S. Private*, pg. 131
AHTNA ENGINEERING SERVICES, LLC—See Ahtna Incorporated; *U.S. Private*, pg. 131
AHTNA ENTERPRISES CORPORATION—See Ahtna Incorporated; *U.S. Private*, pg. 131
AHTNA ENVIRONMENTAL, INC.—See Ahtna Incorporated; *U.S. Private*, pg. 131
AHTNA GOVERNMENT SERVICES CORPORATION—See Ahtna Incorporated; *U.S. Private*, pg. 131
AHTNA INCORPORATED; *U.S. Private*, pg. 131
AHTNA, INC.; *U.S. Private*, pg. 131
AHTNA NETIYE', INC.—See Ahtna Incorporated; *U.S. Private*, pg. 131
AHTNA PROFESSIONAL SERVICES, INC.—See Ahtna Incorporated; *U.S. Private*, pg. 131
AHTNA SUPPORT AND TRAINING SERVICES, LLC—See Ahtna Incorporated; *U.S. Private*, pg. 131
AHTNA TECHNICAL SERVICES INC.—See Ahtna Incorporated; *U.S. Private*, pg. 131
AHTNA TECHNOLOGIES, INC.—See Ahtna Incorporated; *U.S. Private*, pg. 131
AH-TRADING GMBH—See BHG Group AB; *Int'l*, pg. 1014
AHT SERVICES, LLC—See World Kinect Corporation; *U.S. Public*, pg. 2380
AHT SYNGAS TECHNOLOGY NV; *Int'l*, pg. 226
AH-VEST LIMITED; *Int'l*, pg. 222
AHWATUKEE FOOTHILLS NEWS—See EOS Publishing, LLC; *U.S. Private*, pg. 1411
AHWAZ PIPE MILLS COMPANY; *Int'l*, pg. 226
AHWAZ ROLLING & PIPE MILLS CO.; *Int'l*, pg. 226
AIA AUSTRALIA LIMITED—See AIA Group Limited; *Int'l*, pg. 227
AIA BHD.—See AIA Group Limited; *Int'l*, pg. 227
AIA CO., LTD. - AIA II PLANT—See Ecoplastic Corporation; *Int'l*, pg. 2299
AIA CO., LTD.—See Ecoplastic Corporation; *Int'l*, pg. 2299
AIA COMPANY, LIMITED—See AIA Group Limited; *Int'l*, pg. 227
AIA CORPORATION; *U.S. Private*, pg. 131
AIADVERTISING, INC.; *U.S. Public*, pg. 63
AIA ENGINEERING LTD.; *Int'l*, pg. 227
AIA EVEREST LIFE COMPANY LIMITED—See AIA Group Limited; *Int'l*, pg. 227
AIA GROUP LIMITED; *Int'l*, pg. 227
AIAI CHILD CARE CO., LTD.—See AIAI Group Corporation; *Int'l*, pg. 227
AIAI GROUP CORPORATION; *Int'l*, pg. 227
AIALA VIDRIO, S.A.U.—See Vidrala S.A.; *Int'l*, pg. 8192
AIA LIFE INSURANCE CO. LTD.—See AIA Group Limited; *Int'l*, pg. 227
AI AND ROBOTICS VENTURES COMPANY LIMITED—See PTT Public Company Limited; *Int'l*, pg. 6092
AIA NEW ZEALAND LIMITED—See AIA Group Limited; *Int'l*, pg. 227
A+I ART AND INFORMATION GMBH & CO. KG—See SPIEGEL-Verlag Rudolf Augstein GmbH & Co.; *Int'l*, pg. 7135
AIA SINGAPORE PRIVATE LIMITED—See AIA Group Limited; *Int'l*, pg. 227

AIAS INVESTMENT PUBLIC LTD.; *Int'l*, pg. 227
AIA (VIETNAM) LIFE INSURANCE COMPANY LIMITED—See AIA Group Limited; *Int'l*, pg. 227
AIB ACQUISITION CORPORATION—See PS International Group Ltd.; *Int'l*, pg. 6014
AI BATNAH HOTELS COMPANY SAOG; *Int'l*, pg. 226
AIB CAPITAL MARKETS PLC—See AIB Group plc; *Int'l*, pg. 228
AIB CORPORATE BANKING LIMITED—See AIB Group plc; *Int'l*, pg. 228
AIB CORPORATE FINANCE LTD.—See AIB Group plc; *Int'l*, pg. 228
AIBEL AS—See Ferd AS; *Int'l*, pg. 2635
AIBEL AS—See Herkules Capital AS; *Int'l*, pg. 3362
AIB FINANCE & LEASING LTD.—See AIB Group plc; *Int'l*, pg. 228
AIB FINANCIAL GROUP; *U.S. Private*, pg. 131
AIB GROUP PLC; *Int'l*, pg. 227
AIB HOLDINGS (NI) LIMITED—See AIB Group plc; *Int'l*, pg. 228
AIB INSURANCE SERVICES LIMITED—See AIB Group plc; *Int'l*, pg. 228
AIB INTERNATIONAL CONSULTANTS LTD.—See AIB Group plc; *Int'l*, pg. 228
AIB INTERNATIONAL FINANCE—See AIB Group plc; *Int'l*, pg. 228
AIBIT CO., LTD.; *Int'l*, pg. 228
AIB MORTGAGE BANK UNLIMITED COMPANY—See AIB Group plc; *Int'l*, pg. 228
A&I BROADWAY REALTY; *U.S. Private*, pg. 20
AIB SECURITIES SERVICES LTD.—See AIB Group plc; *Int'l*, pg. 228
AIB-VINCOTTE BELGIUM VZW; *Int'l*, pg. 228
AICA ADTEK SDN. BHD.—See AICA Kogyo Company, Limited; *Int'l*, pg. 228
AIC-AARTECH SOLONICS PRIVATE LIMITED—See Aartech solonics Limited; *Int'l*, pg. 38
AICA ASIA LAMINATES HOLDING CO., LTD.—See AICA Kogyo Company, Limited; *Int'l*, pg. 228
AICA ASIA PACIFIC HOLDING PTE. LTD.—See AICA Kogyo Company, Limited; *Int'l*, pg. 228
AICA BANGKOK CO., LTD.—See AICA Kogyo Company, Limited; *Int'l*, pg. 228
AICA DONG NAI CO., LTD.—See AICA Kogyo Company, Limited; *Int'l*, pg. 228
AICA HARIMA KOGYO CO., LTD.—See AICA Kogyo Company, Limited; *Int'l*, pg. 228
AICA HATYAI CO., LTD.—See AICA Kogyo Company, Limited; *Int'l*, pg. 228
AICA KOGYO CO., LTD.—See AICA Kogyo Company, Limited; *Int'l*, pg. 228
AICA KOGYO COMPANY, LIMITED; *Int'l*, pg. 228
AICA LAMINATES INDIA PVT. LTD. - RUDRAPUR FACTORY—See AICA Kogyo Company, Limited; *Int'l*, pg. 228
AICA LAMINATES INDIA PVT. LTD.—See AICA Kogyo Company, Limited; *Int'l*, pg. 228
AICA LAMINATES VIETNAM CO., LTD.—See AICA Kogyo Company, Limited; *Int'l*, pg. 228
AICA MALAYSIA SDN. BHD.—See AICA Kogyo Company, Limited; *Int'l*, pg. 228
AIC AMERICA—See Nevada General Insurance Company; *U.S. Private*, pg. 2891
AICA NANJING CO., LTD.—See AICA Kogyo Company, Limited; *Int'l*, pg. 228
AICA NZ LTD.—See AICA Kogyo Company, Limited; *Int'l*, pg. 228
AICA SINGAPORE PTE. LTD.—See AICA Kogyo Company, Limited; *Int'l*, pg. 228
AICA TECH KENZAI CO., LTD.—See AICA Kogyo Company, Limited; *Int'l*, pg. 228
AICA THAI CHEMICAL LTD.—See AICA Kogyo Company, Limited; *Int'l*, pg. 228
AICA TRADING (SHANGHAI) CO., LTD.—See AICA Kogyo Company, Limited; *Int'l*, pg. 228
AIC CORPORATION BERHAD—See Globaltec Formation Berhad; *Int'l*, pg. 3004
AI CHAMPDANY INDUSTRIES LIMITED; *Int'l*, pg. 226
AICHELIN GMBH—See Berndorf AG; *Int'l*, pg. 986
AICHELIN HEAT TREATMENT SYSTEMS (BEIJING) CO., LTD.—See Berndorf AG; *Int'l*, pg. 986
AICHELIN HEAT TREATMENT SYSTEMS INC.—See Berndorf AG; *Int'l*, pg. 986
AICHELIN SERVICE GMBH—See Berndorf AG; *Int'l*, pg. 986
AICHER, DE MARTIN, ZWENG AG—See BKW AG; *Int'l*, pg. 1054
AICHI AUS PTY LTD—See Aichi Corporation; *Int'l*, pg. 229
THE AICHI BANK, LTD.—See Aichi Financial Group Co., Ltd.; *Int'l*, pg. 229
AICHI CERATEC CORPORATION—See Aichi Steel Corporation; *Int'l*, pg. 230
AICHI CORPORATION; *Int'l*, pg. 229
AICHI ELECTRIC CO., LTD.; *Int'l*, pg. 229
AICHI ELECTRIC DEVELOPMENT & ENVIRONMENT DIVISION—See Aichi Electric Co., Ltd.; *Int'l*, pg. 229
AICHI ELECTRIC & ELECTRONIC PRODUCTS DIVISION—See Aichi Electric Co., Ltd.; *Int'l*, pg. 229

COMPANY NAME INDEX

AICHI ELECTRIC POWER PRODUCTS DIVISION—See Aichi Electric Co., Ltd.; *Int'l*, pg. 229
AICHI ELECTRIC WORKS CO., LTD.—See NITTO KOGYO CORPORATION; *Int'l*, pg. 5387
AICHI EUROPE B.V.—See Aichi Corporation; *Int'l*, pg. 229
AICHI EUROPE GMBH—See Aichi Steel Corporation; *Int'l*, pg. 230
AICHI FINANCIAL GROUP CO., LTD.; *Int'l*, pg. 229
AICHI FORGE & GEAR WORKS, LLC—See Aichi Steel Corporation; *Int'l*, pg. 230
AICHI FORGE PHILIPPINES, INC.—See Aichi Steel Corporation; *Int'l*, pg. 230
AICHI FORGE (THAILAND) CO., LTD.—See Aichi Steel Corporation; *Int'l*, pg. 230
AICHI FORGE USA, INC.—See Aichi Steel Corporation; *Int'l*, pg. 230
AICHI FORGING COMPANY OF ASIA, INC.—See Aichi Steel Corporation; *Int'l*, pg. 230
AICHI GIKEN CO., LTD.—See AISIN Corporation; *Int'l*, pg. 252
AICHI INFORMATION SYSTEM CORPORATION—See Aichi Steel Corporation; *Int'l*, pg. 230
AICHI KANZAI KOGYO CORPORATION—See JFE Holdings, Inc.; *Int'l*, pg. 3936
AICHI KINZOKU KOGYO CO., LTD.—See Aichi Electric Co., Ltd.; *Int'l*, pg. 229
AICHI KOKAN INDUSTRIES, LTD.—See Toyota Tsusho Corporation; *Int'l*, pg. 7875
AICHI KOREA CORPORATION—See Aichi Steel Corporation; *Int'l*, pg. 230
AICHI MACHINE INDUSTRY CO., LTD.—See Nissan Motor Co., Ltd.; *Int'l*, pg. 5367
AICHI MAGFINE CZECH S.R.O—See Aichi Steel Corporation; *Int'l*, pg. 230
AICHI MAGFINE TECHNOLOGY (PINGHU) CO., LTD.—See Aichi Steel Corporation; *Int'l*, pg. 230
AICHI NDS CO., LTD.—See COMSYS Holdings Corporation; *Int'l*, pg. 1761
AICHI NIKON CO., LTD.—See Nikon Corporation; *Int'l*, pg. 5292
AICHI NITTO DENKO CORPORATION—See Nitto Denko Corporation; *Int'l*, pg. 5384
AICHI NZ LIMITED—See Aichi Corporation; *Int'l*, pg. 229
AICHI STEEL CORPORATION; *Int'l*, pg. 230
AICHI STEEL LOGISTICS CO., LTD.—See Aichi Steel Corporation; *Int'l*, pg. 230
AICHI TECHNO METAL FUKAUMI CO., LTD.—See Aichi Steel Corporation; *Int'l*, pg. 230
AICHI TELEVISION BROADCASTING CO., LTD.—See Nikkei Inc.; *Int'l*, pg. 5289
AICHI TESAC CORPORATION—See Kobelco Wire Co Ltd; *Int'l*, pg. 4221
AICHI TOKEI DENKI CO., LTD.; *Int'l*, pg. 230
AICHI TOYO INK CO., LTD.—See Toyo Ink SC Holdings Co., Ltd.; *Int'l*, pg. 7853
AICHI USA INC.—See Aichi Steel Corporation; *Int'l*, pg. 230
AICHNER CLODI GGK—See GGK Zurich Werbeagentur AG; *Int'l*, pg. 2957
AIC INGENIEURGESELLSCHAFT FUER BAUPLANUNG CHEMNITZ GMBH—See Hormann Holding GmbH & Co. KG; *Int'l*, pg. 3479
AIC INVESTMENT LTD.—See Maxwell Electronics Ltd.; *Int'l*, pg. 4743
AI CLAIMS SOLUTIONS PLC; *Int'l*, pg. 226
AI CLAIMS SOLUTIONS (UK) LIMITED—See AI Claims Solutions Plc; *Int'l*, pg. 226
AIC MINES LIMITED; *Int'l*, pg. 228
AI COLLABORATIVE, INC.; *U.S. Private*, pg. 131
AI CO., LTD.—See Wacoal Holdings Corp.; *Int'l*, pg. 8325
AI CO., LTD.; *Int'l*, pg. 226
AI CONVERSATION SYSTEMS LTD.; *Int'l*, pg. 226
A & I CORPORATION; *U.S. Private*, pg. 18
AIC RESOURCES LIMITED—See AIC Mines Limited; *Int'l*, pg. 228
AI CROSS, INC.; *Int'l*, pg. 226
AI CUBE INC.—See Yaskawa Electric Corporation; *Int'l*, pg. 8569
AIC VENTURES, LP; *U.S. Private*, pg. 131
AIDA BUSINESS CORP.—See AIDA Engineering, Ltd.; *Int'l*, pg. 230
AIDA CANADA INC.—See AIDA Engineering, Ltd.; *Int'l*, pg. 231
AIDA DO BRASIL COMERCIO DE MAQUINAS LTDA.—See AIDA Engineering, Ltd.; *Int'l*, pg. 230
AIDA ENGINEERING CHINA CO., LTD.—See AIDA Engineering, Ltd.; *Int'l*, pg. 230
AIDA ENGINEERING DE MEXICO, S. DE R. L. DE C.V.—See AIDA Engineering, Ltd.; *Int'l*, pg. 230
AIDA ENGINEERING, LTD.; *Int'l*, pg. 230
AIDA ENGINEERING (M) SDN. BHD.—See AIDA Engineering, Ltd.; *Int'l*, pg. 230
AIDA EUROPE GMBH—See AIDA Engineering, Ltd.; *Int'l*, pg. 231
AIDA GERMANY GMBH—See AIDA Engineering, Ltd.; *Int'l*, pg. 231
AIDA GREATER ASIA PHILIPPINES, INC.—See AIDA Engineering, Ltd.; *Int'l*, pg. 230
AIDA GREATER ASIA PTE. LTD.—See AIDA Engineering, Ltd.; *Int'l*, pg. 231
AIDA HONG KONG, LTD.—See AIDA Engineering, Ltd.; *Int'l*, pg. 230
AIDA INDIA PVT. LTD.—See AIDA Engineering, Ltd.; *Int'l*, pg. 230
AIDALA MUNAI JSC; *Int'l*, pg. 231
AIDA MANUFACTURING (ASIA) SDN. BHD.—See AIDA Engineering, Ltd.; *Int'l*, pg. 230
AIDA MAROC SARL—See AIDA Engineering, Ltd.; *Int'l*, pg. 230
AID-ANALYSE INFORMATIQUE DE DONNEES—See Omnicom Group Inc.; *U.S. Public*, pg. 1592
AIDAN INDUSTRIES, INC.; *U.S. Private*, pg. 131
AIDA PHARMACEUTICALS, INC.; *Int'l*, pg. 231
AIDA PRESSEN GMBH—See AIDA Engineering, Ltd.; *Int'l*, pg. 230
AIDA PRESS MACHINERY SYSTEMS CO., LTD.—See AIDA Engineering, Ltd.; *Int'l*, pg. 231
AIDARADIO GMBH—See Carnival Corporation; *U.S. Public*, pg. 437
AIDA STAMPING TECHNOLOGY (INDIA) PVT LTD.—See AIDA Engineering, Ltd.; *Int'l*, pg. 230
AIDA STAMPING TECHNOLOGY (THAILAND) CO., LTD.—See AIDA Engineering, Ltd.; *Int'l*, pg. 230
AIDA (THAILAND) CO., LTD.—See AIDA Engineering, Ltd.; *Int'l*, pg. 230
AIDA VIETNAM CO., LTD.—See AIDA Engineering, Ltd.; *Int'l*, pg. 230
AIDC USA LLC—See Aerospace Industrial Development Corporation; *Int'l*, pg. 181
AIDEC CORPORATION—See TIS Inc.; *Int'l*, pg. 7758
AIDELLS SAUSAGE COMPANY, INC.—See Tyson Foods, Inc.; *U.S. Public*, pg. 2209
AIDEM VENTURES—See New Delhi Television Limited; *Int'l*, pg. 5222
AIDENT CORPORATION (KL) SDN. BHD—See Navis Capital Partners Limited; *Int'l*, pg. 5175
AIDENT CORPORATION SDN. BHD—See Navis Capital Partners Limited; *Int'l*, pg. 5175
AIDENT CORPORATION (TIANJIN) LTD.—See Navis Capital Partners Limited; *Int'l*, pg. 5175
AIDIAN DENMARK APS—See Axcel Management A/S; *Int'l*, pg. 762
AIDIAN GERMANY GMBH—See Axcel Management A/S; *Int'l*, pg. 762
AIDIAN NORWAY AS—See Axcel Management A/S; *Int'l*, pg. 762
AIDIAN OY—See Axcel Management A/S; *Int'l*, pg. 762
AIDIAN SWEDEN AB—See Axcel Management A/S; *Int'l*, pg. 762
AIDIGONG MATERNAL & CHILD HEALTH LIMITED; *Int'l*, pg. 231
AIDMA MARKETING COMMUNICATION CORPORATION; *Int'l*, pg. 231
AID PARTNERS TECHNOLOGY HOLDINGS LIMITED; *Int'l*, pg. 230
AI DREAM LIFE SUPPORT CO., LTD.—See AISIN Corporation; *Int'l*, pg. 251
AID RESTAURANT, INC.—See Dream Center Foundation, a California Nonprofit Corp.; *U.S. Private*, pg. 1274
AIDS ACTION COMMITTEE OF MA, INC.; *U.S. Private*, pg. 131
AIDS HEALTHCARE FOUNDATION; *U.S. Private*, pg. 131
AIDS RESOURCE CENTER OF WISCONSIN; *U.S. Private*, pg. 132
AIDS UNITED; *U.S. Private*, pg. 132
AIENCE INC.—See Nagase & Co., Ltd.; *Int'l*, pg. 5126
AI ENERGY PUBLIC COMPANY LIMITED; *Int'l*, pg. 226
AI ENGLISH PTY. LTD.—See Retech Technology Co., Limited; *Int'l*, pg. 6306
AIER EYE HOSPITAL GROUP CO., LTD.; *Int'l*, pg. 231
AIEX, INC.—See LIXIL Group Corporation; *Int'l*, pg. 4533
AIFARM LTD.; *Int'l*, pg. 231
AI FINANCIAL INFORMATION UK LIMITED—See Genstar Capital, LLC; *U.S. Private*, pg. 1675
AIFINYO AG; *Int'l*, pg. 231
AI FIRE, LLC—See TruArc Partners, L.P.; *U.S. Private*, pg. 4244
AIFORIA TECHNOLOGIES OYJ; *Int'l*, pg. 231
A.I. FRIEDMAN LP; *U.S. Private*, pg. 26
AIFUL BUSINESS FINANCE CORPORATION—See AIFUL Corporation; *Int'l*, pg. 231
AIFUL CORPORATION; *Int'l*, pg. 231
AIFUL GUARANTEE CO., LTD.—See AIFUL Corporation; *Int'l*, pg. 231
AIFUL PARTNERS CORPORATION—See AIFUL Corporation; *Int'l*, pg. 231
AIFUL STOCK CENTER CORPORATION—See AIFUL Corporation; *Int'l*, pg. 231
AIG AEROSPACE INSURANCE SERVICES, INC.—See American International Group, Inc.; *U.S. Public*, pg. 106
AIGAN CO., LTD.; *Int'l*, pg. 232
AIG APAC HOLDINGS PTE. LTD.—See American International Group, Inc.; *U.S. Public*, pg. 105
AIG ASIA PACIFIC INSURANCE PTE. LTD.—See American International Group, Inc.; *U.S. Public*, pg. 105
AIG ASSET MANAGEMENT (U.S.), LLC—See American International Group, Inc.; *U.S. Public*, pg. 104

AIGLON CAPITAL MANAGEMENT LLC

AIG AUSTRALIA LIMITED—See Steadfast Group Limited; *Int'l*, pg. 7187
AIG CAPITAL CORPORATION—See American International Group, Inc.; *U.S. Public*, pg. 104
AIG CLAIMS, INC.—See American International Group, Inc.; *U.S. Public*, pg. 104
AIG CONSULTANTS, INC.—See American International Group, Inc.; *U.S. Public*, pg. 104
AIG CONSUMER FINANCE GROUP, INC.—See American International Group, Inc.; *U.S. Public*, pg. 104
AIG CREDIT CORP.—See American International Group, Inc.; *U.S. Public*, pg. 104
AIG CYPRUS LIMITED—See American International Group, Inc.; *U.S. Public*, pg. 105
AIG DIRECT INSURANCE SERVICES, INC.; *U.S. Private*, pg. 132
AIG EGYPT INSURANCE COMPANY S.A.E.—See American International Group, Inc.; *U.S. Public*, pg. 105
AIG EUROPE LIMITED—See American International Group, Inc.; *U.S. Public*, pg. 104
AIG EUROPE, SA—See American International Group, Inc.; *U.S. Public*, pg. 104
AIG EUROPE (U.K.) LIMITED—See American International Group, Inc.; *U.S. Public*, pg. 104
AIG FEDERAL SAVINGS BANK—See American International Group, Inc.; *U.S. Public*, pg. 104
AIG FINANCIAL PRODUCTS CORP—See American International Group, Inc.; *U.S. Public*, pg. 104
AIG GENERAL INSURANCE CO., LTD.—See American International Group, Inc.; *U.S. Public*, pg. 104
AIG HOLDINGS, LLC—See Tenet Healthcare Corporation; *U.S. Public*, pg. 2009
AIGIN BUSINESS SERVICE CO., LTD.—See Aichi Financial Group Co., Ltd.; *Int'l*, pg. 229
AIGIN COMPUTER SERVICE CO., LTD.—See Aichi Financial Group Co., Ltd.; *Int'l*, pg. 229
AIGIN DC CARD CO., LTD.—See Aichi Financial Group Co., Ltd.; *Int'l*, pg. 229
AIGIN LEASE CO., LTD.—See Aichi Financial Group Co., Ltd.; *Int'l*, pg. 229
AIG INSURANCE COMPANY CHINA LIMITED—See American International Group, Inc.; *U.S. Public*, pg. 105
AIG INSURANCE COMPANY, JSC—See American International Group, Inc.; *U.S. Public*, pg. 104
AIG INSURANCE COMPANY OF CANADA—See American International Group, Inc.; *U.S. Public*, pg. 104
AIG INSURANCE COMPANY-PUERTO RICO—See American International Group, Inc.; *U.S. Public*, pg. 105
AIG INSURANCE HONG KONG LIMITED—See American International Group, Inc.; *U.S. Public*, pg. 105
AIG INSURANCE LIMITED—See American International Group, Inc.; *U.S. Public*, pg. 105
AIG INSURANCE NEW ZEALAND LIMITED—See American International Group, Inc.; *U.S. Public*, pg. 105
AIG INSURANCE (THAILAND) PUBLIC COMPANY LIMITED—See American International Group, Inc.; *U.S. Public*, pg. 104
AIG INTERNATIONAL INC.—See American International Group, Inc.; *U.S. Public*, pg. 104
AIG INVESTMENTS UK LIMITED—See American International Group, Inc.; *U.S. Public*, pg. 104
AIG ISRAEL INSURANCE COMPANY LIMITED—See American International Group, Inc.; *U.S. Public*, pg. 105
AIG JAPAN HOLDINGS KABUSHIKI KAISHA—See American International Group, Inc.; *U.S. Public*, pg. 104
AIG KENYA INSURANCE COMPANY LIMITED—See American International Group, Inc.; *U.S. Public*, pg. 105
AIG KOREA INC.—See American International Group, Inc.; *U.S. Public*, pg. 105
AIG LEBANON SAL—See American International Group, Inc.; *U.S. Public*, pg. 104
AIGLE, S.A.—See Maus Freres S.A.; *Int'l*, pg. 4732
AIG LIFE INSURANCE COMPANY (SWITZERLAND) LTD.—See American International Group, Inc.; *U.S. Public*, pg. 105
AIG LIFE LIMITED—See American International Group, Inc.; *U.S. Public*, pg. 105
AIG LIFE & RETIREMENT—See American International Group, Inc.; *U.S. Public*, pg. 104
AIG LIFE SOUTH AFRICA LIMITED—See American International Group, Inc.; *U.S. Public*, pg. 105
AIGLON CAPITAL MANAGEMENT LLC; *U.S. Private*, pg. 132
AIG MALAYSIA INSURANCE BERHAD—See American International Group, Inc.; *U.S. Public*, pg. 105
AIG MANAGEMENT FRANCE S.A.—See American International Group, Inc.; *U.S. Public*, pg. 104
AIG MARKETING, INC.—See American International Group, Inc.; *U.S. Public*, pg. 105
AIG MARKETS, INC.—See American International Group, Inc.; *U.S. Public*, pg. 105
AIG MATCHED FUNDING CORP.—See American International Group, Inc.; *U.S. Public*, pg. 104
AIG MEA HOLDINGS LIMITED—See American International Group, Inc.; *U.S. Public*, pg. 105
AIG MEA LIMITED—See American International Group, Inc.; *U.S. Public*, pg. 106

AIGLON CAPITAL MANAGEMENT LLC CORPORATE AFFILIATIONS

AIG-METROPOLITANA CIA DE SEGUROS Y REASE-GUROS S.A.—See American International Group, Inc.; *U.S. Public*, pg. 106
AIGNER PRENSKY MARKETING GROUP; *U.S. Private*, pg. 132
AIG PHILIPPINES INSURANCE, INC.—See American International Group, Inc.; *U.S. Public*, pg. 105
AIG PLANUNGS- UND INGENIEURGESELLSCHAFT MBH—See Robert Bosch GmbH; *Int'l*, pg. 6358
AIG PROPERTY CASUALTY COMPANY—See American International Group, Inc.; *U.S. Public*, pg. 105
AIG PROPERTY CASUALTY INC.—See American International Group, Inc.; *U.S. Public*, pg. 105
AIG PROPERTY CASUALTY INSURANCE AGENCY, INC.—See American International Group, Inc.; *U.S. Public*, pg. 106
AIG PROPERTY CASUALTY INTERNATIONAL, LLC—See American International Group, Inc.; *U.S. Public*, pg. 105
AIG PROPERTY CASUALTY U.S., INC.—See American International Group, Inc.; *U.S. Public*, pg. 106
AIG RESSEGUROS BRASIL S.A.—See American International Group, Inc.; *U.S. Public*, pg. 105
AIG RE-TAKAFUL (L) BERHAD—See American International Group, Inc.; *U.S. Public*, pg. 105
AIG RISK MANAGEMENT, INC.—See American International Group, Inc.; *U.S. Public*, pg. 106
AIG SEGUROS BRASIL S.A.—See American International Group, Inc.; *U.S. Public*, pg. 106
AIG SEGUROS MEXICO, S.A. DE C.V.—See American International Group, Inc.; *U.S. Public*, pg. 106
AIG SHARED SERVICES CORPORATION—See American International Group, Inc.; *U.S. Public*, pg. 106
AIG SOUTH AFRICA LIMITED—See American International Group, Inc.; *U.S. Public*, pg. 106
AIG SPECIALTY INSURANCE COMPANY—See American International Group, Inc.; *U.S. Public*, pg. 106
AIG STAR LIFE INSURANCE CO., LTD.—See Prudential Financial, Inc.; *U.S. Public*, pg. 1733
AIG TAIWAN INSURANCE CO., LTD.—See American International Group, Inc.; *U.S. Public*, pg. 105
AIG TRADING GROUP INC.—See American International Group, Inc.; *U.S. Public*, pg. 106
AIG TRAVEL ASSIST, INC.—See American International Group, Inc.; *U.S. Public*, pg. 106
AIGUES DE VALLIRANA, S.A.—See Fomento de Construcciones y Contratas, S.A.; *Int'l*, pg. 2722
AIGUES MINERALS DE VILAJUIGA, S.A.—See Grifols, S.A.; *Int'l*, pg. 3083
AIG UGANDA LIMITED—See American International Group, Inc.; *U.S. Public*, pg. 106
AIGUILLE ROCK CLIMBING CENTER, INC—See TOCCA Life Holdings, Inc.; *U.S. Public*, pg. 2161
AIG UKRAINE INSURANCE COMPANY PJSC—See American International Group, Inc.; *U.S. Public*, pg. 106
AIG VIETNAM INSURANCE COMPANY LIMITED—See American International Group, Inc.; *U.S. Public*, pg. 105
AI HOLDINGS CORP.; *Int'l*, pg. 227
A.I. HOLDINGS (USA) CORP.—See Africa Israel Investments Ltd.; *Int'l*, pg. 189
AIH TOOL REPAIR CENTER—See Bering Straits Native Corporation; *U.S. Private*, pg. 532
AII CLUBMAN—See American International Industries Company; *U.S. Private*, pg. 238
AIICO CAPITAL LIMITED—See AIICO Insurance PLC; *Int'l*, pg. 232
AIICO INSURANCE PLC; *Int'l*, pg. 232
AIICO MULTISHIELD LIMITED—See AIICO Insurance PLC; *Int'l*, pg. 232
AII DATA PROCESSING LTD.; *Int'l*, pg. 232
AIIMI LTD—See The Rethink Group Limited; *Int'l*, pg. 7678
AI INSIDE, INC.; *Int'l*, pg. 227
AI INTERNATIONAL CORP.; *U.S. Private*, pg. 131
AI INTERNATIONAL, INC.—See Avis Industrial Corporation; *U.S. Private*, pg. 407
AIIR CONSULTING, LLC; *U.S. Private*, pg. 132
AIJJ ENTERPRISES INC.; *U.S. Private*, pg. 132
AI KARAAUYL JSC; *Int'l*, pg. 227
AIKAWA KOGYO CO., LTD.—See Nagase & Co., Ltd.; *Int'l*, pg. 5126
AIK BAACKA TOPOLA A.D.; *Int'l*, pg. 232
AIK BANKA A.D.—See MK Group doo; *Int'l*, pg. 5000
AIKBEE RESOURCES BERHAD; *Int'l*, pg. 232
AIKBEE TIMBERS (SABAH) SDN. BHD.—See Aikbee Resources Berhad; *Int'l*, pg. 232
AIKCHOL HOSPITAL PUBLIC COMPANY LIMITED; *Int'l*, pg. 232
AIKEI FARMS SHAKOTAN CO., LTD.—See Inabata & Co. Ltd.; *Int'l*, pg. 3643
AIKEI FARMS YOICHI CO., LTD.—See Inabata & Co. Ltd.; *Int'l*, pg. 3643
AIKEN ELECTRIC COOPERATIVE INC.; *U.S. Private*, pg. 132
AIKEN REGIONAL MEDICAL CENTERS, LLC—See Universal Health Services, Inc.; *U.S. Public*, pg. 2255
AIKEN STANDARD—See Evening Post Publishing Co.; *U.S. Private*, pg. 1436
AIK FOTBOLL AB; *Int'l*, pg. 232
AIKIDO PHARMA INC.; *U.S. Public*, pg. 63

AIKITEC CO., LTD.—See Honda Motor Co., Ltd.; *Int'l*, pg. 3459
AIKO BEAUTY (SHENZHEN) LIMITED—See Link-Asia International MedTech Group Limited; *Int'l*, pg. 4514
AIKO CORPORATION; *Int'l*, pg. 232
AIKOH ENGINEERING CO., LTD.—See NIHON DENKEI CO., LTD.; *Int'l*, pg. 5284
AIKOKIKI MFG. CO., LTD.—See Aichi Electric Co., Ltd.; *Int'l*, pg. 229
AIKO PRODUCTS LIMITED—See Link-Asia International MedTech Group Limited; *Int'l*, pg. 4514
AIKO SERVICE CO., LTD.—See Aichi Steel Corporation; *Int'l*, pg. 230
AIKYO SANGYO CO., LTD.—See Aisan Industry Co., Ltd.; *Int'l*, pg. 250
AI LABS INC.—See Predictiv AI, Inc.; *Int'l*, pg. 5958
AILE MEDICALE SAS—See Synergie SA; *Int'l*, pg. 7383
AILERON CAPITAL MANAGEMENT, LLC; *U.S. Private*, pg. 132
AILERON THERAPEUTICS, INC.; *U.S. Public*, pg. 63
AILES MARINE, S.A.S.—See Iberdrola, S.A.; *Int'l*, pg. 3570
AIL INDUSTRIES CO., LTD.—See GIBCA Limited; *Int'l*, pg. 2962
AILLERON SA; *Int'l*, pg. 232
AILLEURS EXACTEMENT; *Int'l*, pg. 232
AI LOGISTICS COMPANY LIMITED—See AI Energy Public Company Limited; *Int'l*, pg. 226
AILSEN LIMITED.; *Int'l*, pg. 232
AIM3 VENTURES, INC.; *Int'l*, pg. 232
AIM AEROSPACE AUBURN, INC.—See Sekisui Chemical Co., Ltd.; *Int'l*, pg. 6693
AIM AEROSPACE, INC.—See Sekisui Chemical Co., Ltd.; *Int'l*, pg. 6693
AIM AEROSPACE SUMNER, INC.—See Sekisui Chemical Co., Ltd.; *Int'l*, pg. 6693
AIM AGENCY; *U.S. Private*, pg. 132
AIM-ASSEMBLY IN MOTION GMBH—See MAX Automation SE; *Int'l*, pg. 4733
AIMBRIDGE HOSPITALITY, LLC—See Advent International Corporation; *U.S. Private*, pg. 97
AIM CANADA INC—See Aim International, Inc.; *U.S. Private*, pg. 132
A.I.M. CHEMICAL INDUSTRIES PTE LTD—See AP Oil International Ltd.; *Int'l*, pg. 499
AIMCLEAR BLOG; *U.S. Private*, pg. 133
AIMCO 21 FITZSIMONS, LLC—See Blackstone Inc.; *U.S. Public*, pg. 350
AIMCO 777 SOUTH BROAD, LLC—See Blackstone Inc.; *U.S. Public*, pg. 350
AIMCO ANGELES GP, LLC—See Apartment Investment and Management Company; *U.S. Public*, pg. 143
AIMCO ANTIOCH, L.L.C.—See Apartment Investment and Management Company; *U.S. Public*, pg. 143
AIMCO BENT TREE, LLC—See Blackstone Inc.; *U.S. Public*, pg. 350
AIMCO/BETHESDA GP, L.L.C.—See Apartment Investment and Management Company; *U.S. Public*, pg. 144
AIMCO BROADWAY LOFTS, L.P.—See Blackstone Inc.; *U.S. Public*, pg. 350
AIMCO EQUITY SERVICES, LLC—See Apartment Investment and Management Company; *U.S. Public*, pg. 143
AIMCO ESPLANADE AVENUE APARTMENTS, LLC—See Apartment Investment and Management Company; *U.S. Public*, pg. 143
AIMCO KEY TOWERS, L.P.—See Apartment Investment and Management Company; *U.S. Public*, pg. 143
AIMCO LOCUST ON THE PARK, LLC—See Blackstone Inc.; *U.S. Public*, pg. 350
AIM CO., LTD.—See Kamei Corporation; *Int'l*, pg. 4061
AIMCO MONTEREY GROVE APARTMENTS, LLC—See Blackstone Inc.; *U.S. Public*, pg. 350
AIMCO/NASHUA, L.L.C.—See Blackstone Inc.; *U.S. Public*, pg. 350
AIM CONSULTING GROUP, LLC; *U.S. Private*, pg. 132
AIMCO PARK AND 12TH, LLC—See Apartment Investment and Management Company; *U.S. Public*, pg. 143
AIMCO PESTICIDES LIMITED; *Int'l*, pg. 232
AIMCORE TECHNOLOGY CO., LTD.; *Int'l*, pg. 232
AIMCO SAN MELIA, LLC—See Apartment Investment and Management Company; *U.S. Public*, pg. 143
AIMCO SOUTHSTAR LOFTS, LLC—See Apartment Investment and Management Company; *U.S. Public*, pg. 144
AIMCO WARWICK, L.L.C.—See Apartment Investment and Management Company; *U.S. Public*, pg. 143
AIM CREATE CO., LTD.—See Marui Group Co., Ltd.; *Int'l*, pg. 4713
AIME BELLAVANCE & SONS INCORPORATED; *U.S. Private*, pg. 133
AIMECHATEC LTD.; *Int'l*, pg. 232
AI-MEDIA TECHNOLOGIES LIMITED; *Int'l*, pg. 227
AIMEDIC MMT CO., LTD.—See Bando Chemical Industries, Ltd.; *Int'l*, pg. 830
AIMEE LYNN ACCESSORIES INC.; *U.S. Private*, pg. 133
AIMEI HEALTH TECHNOLOGY CO., LTD.; *U.S. Public*, pg. 63
AIM ELECTRONICS; *U.S. Private*, pg. 132

AIM ENGINEERING & SURVEYING INC.; *U.S. Private*, pg. 132
AIMER CO., LTD.; *Int'l*, pg. 233
AIMERI AMBIENTE SRL—See Biancamano S.p.A.; *Int'l*, pg. 1017
AIME SUPERMAX K.K.—See Supermax Corporation Berhad; *Int'l*, pg. 7339
AI METRIX, INC.—See Kratos Defense & Security Solutions, Inc.; *U.S. Public*, pg. 1276
AIM EXPLORATION INC.; *U.S. Public*, pg. 63
AIMFLEX BERHAD; *Int'l*, pg. 233
AIM GIBRALTAR LTD.—See Aon plc; *Int'l*, pg. 488
AIM HEALTH GROUP INC.—See Imperial Capital Group Ltd.; *Int'l*, pg. 3634
AIM HIGH EQUIPMENT RENTALS, INC.—See Kinderhook Industries, LLC; *U.S. Public*, pg. 2307
AIMHIGH GLOBAL CORP.; *Int'l*, pg. 233
AIMIA ACQUISITION UK LIMITED—See Aimia Inc.; *Int'l*, pg. 233
AIMIA FOODS LIMITED; *Int'l*, pg. 233
AIMIA INC.; *Int'l*, pg. 233
AIMI INC.; *U.S. Private*, pg. 133
AIM IMMUNOTECH INC.; *U.S. Public*, pg. 63
AIM INDUSTRIAL GROWTH FREEHOLD & LEASEHOLD REIT; *Int'l*, pg. 232
AIMING GLOBAL SERVICE, INC.—See Aiming Inc.; *Int'l*, pg. 234
AIMING INC.; *Int'l*, pg. 234
AIM INTERNATIONAL, INC.; *U.S. Private*, pg. 132
AIM LEASING CO.; *U.S. Private*, pg. 132
AIML RESOURCES INC; *Int'l*, pg. 234
AIM MEDIA TEXAS, LLC; *U.S. Private*, pg. 132
AIM METALS, LLC—See Promus Holdings, LLC; *U.S. Private*, pg. 3284
AIM MICRO SYSTEMS GMBH—See MAX Automation SE; *Int'l*, pg. 4733
AIMMUNE THERAPEUTICS, INC.—See Nestle S.A.; *Int'l*, pg. 5205
AIMMUNE THERAPEUTICS UK LIMITED—See Nestle S.A.; *Int'l*, pg. 5206
AIM NEDERLAND B.V.—See Johnson Controls International plc; *Int'l*, pg. 3986
AIMOBILE CO., LTD.—See Inventec Corporation; *Int'l*, pg. 3773
AIMO SOLUTION AB—See Sumitomo Corporation; *Int'l*, pg. 7268
AIM PROCESSING, INC.—See Mcm Capital Partners, LP; *U.S. Private*, pg. 2642
AIM REPLY LTD.—See Reply S.p.A.; *Int'l*, pg. 6290
AIMRITE HOLDINGS CORP.; *U.S. Public*, pg. 63
AIMS APAC REIT; *Int'l*, pg. 234
AIMS DATA CENTRE PTE. LTD.—See TIME dotCom Berhad; *Int'l*, pg. 7750
AIMS DATA CENTRE SDN. BHD.—See TIME dotCom Berhad; *Int'l*, pg. 7750
AIM SERVICES CO., LTD.—See Aramark; *U.S. Public*, pg. 177
AIM SERVICES CO., LTD.—See Mitsui & Co., Ltd.; *Int'l*, pg. 4973
AIM SERVICES, INC.; *U.S. Private*, pg. 133
AIM SERVICES SA—See Sword Group SE; *Int'l*, pg. 7375
AIMS FINANCIAL GROUP; *Int'l*, pg. 234
AIM SMARTER LLC—See Altitude Group plc; *Int'l*, pg. 393
AIMS POLSKA SP. Z O.O.—See WPP plc; *Int'l*, pg. 8478
AIMS PROPERTY SECURITIES FUND; *Int'l*, pg. 234
AIMSUN INC.—See Siemens Aktiengesellschaft; *Int'l*, pg. 6889
AIMSUN LIMITED—See Siemens Aktiengesellschaft; *Int'l*, pg. 6886
AIMSUN PTE LTD.—See Siemens Aktiengesellschaft; *Int'l*, pg. 6886
AIMSUN PTY LTD.—See Siemens Aktiengesellschaft; *Int'l*, pg. 6886
AIMSUN SARL—See Siemens Aktiengesellschaft; *Int'l*, pg. 6886
AIMSUN S.L.—See Siemens Aktiengesellschaft; *Int'l*, pg. 6886
AIM SWEDEN AB—See Aon plc; *Int'l*, pg. 488
AIM SYSTEM PTE. LTD.—See Noble Vici Group, Inc.; *Int'l*, pg. 5398
AIM TRIMARK INVESTMENTS—See Invesco Ltd.; *U.S. Public*, pg. 1161
AIMT TRATERH, S.A.U.—See Aalberts N.V.; *Int'l*, pg. 33
AIM UNDERWRITING LIMITED—See Allianz SE; *Int'l*, pg. 345
AIM U.S.A. INC.—See Aim International, Inc.; *U.S. Private*, pg. 132
AIM VACCINE CO., LTD.; *Int'l*, pg. 232
AIMVALLEY B.V.; *Int'l*, pg. 234
AINA LE'A, INC.; *U.S. Private*, pg. 133
AINAVO HOLDINGS CORPORATION; *Int'l*, pg. 234
AINET SYSTEMS, INC.—See Ship Healthcare Holdings, Inc.; *Int'l*, pg. 6851
A INFRASTRUCTURE LIMITED; *Int'l*, pg. 17
AIN GLOBALCOMM CO., LTD.—See Advanced Info Service Plc; *Int'l*, pg. 159
AIN HOLDINGS INC.; *Int'l*, pg. 234
AINO HEALTH AB; *Int'l*, pg. 234

COMPANY NAME INDEX

AINO HEALTH MANAGEMENT OY—See Aino Health AB; *Int'l*, pg. 234
AINOS, INC.; *U.S. Public*, pg. 64
AIN PLASTICS, INC.—See ThyssenKrupp AG; *Int'l*, pg. 7729
AINS INC.—See Gemspring Capital Management, LLC; *U.S. Private*, pg. 1658
A+ INSULATION OF KANSAS CITY, LLC—See Installed Building Products, Inc.; *U.S. Public*, pg. 1131
A-INSURANCE LTD—See OP Financial Group; *Int'l*, pg. 5595
AINSWORTH GAME TECHNOLOGY INC—See Novomatic AG; *Int'l*, pg. 5466
AINSWORTH GAME TECHNOLOGY LIMITED—See Novomatic AG; *Int'l*, pg. 5466
AINSWORTH, INC.—See GDI Integrated Facility Services Inc.; *Int'l*, pg. 2896
AINSWORTH PET NUTRITION, INC. - AINSWORTH SPECIALTY BRANDS DIVISION—See The J.M. Smucker Company; *U.S. Public*, pg. 2106
AINSWORTH PET NUTRITION, INC.—See The J.M. Smucker Company; *U.S. Public*, pg. 2106
AIN TOKAI INC.—See AIN Holdings Inc.; *Int'l*, pg. 234
AINTREE GROUP FINANCIAL SERVICES PTY LTD—See Prime Financial Group Limited; *Int'l*, pg. 5977
AIO ACQUISITIONS INC.; *U.S. Private*, pg. 133
AIOBIO CO., LTD.; *Int'l*, pg. 234
AIO COMPONENTS COMPANY LIMITED—See WPG Holdings Limited; *Int'l*, pg. 8461
AIOI LIFE INSURANCE CO., LTD.—See MS&AD Insurance Group Holdings, Inc.; *Int'l*, pg. 5065
AIOI NISSAY DOWA EUROPE LIMITED—See MS&AD Insurance Group Holdings, Inc.; *Int'l*, pg. 5065
AIOI NISSAY DOWA INSURANCE COMPANY LTD.—See MS&AD Insurance Group Holdings, Inc.; *Int'l*, pg. 5065
AIOI NISSAY DOWA INSURANCE SERVICES USA CORPORATION—See MS&AD Insurance Group Holdings, Inc.; *Int'l*, pg. 5065
AIOI NISSAY DOWA LIFE INSURANCE OF EUROPE AG—See MS&AD Insurance Group Holdings, Inc.; *Int'l*, pg. 5065
AIOI NISSAY DOWA SERVICES ASIA PTE. LTD.—See MS&AD Insurance Group Holdings, Inc.; *Int'l*, pg. 5065
AIOLOS INC; *Int'l*, pg. 234
AIOLOS MEDICAL A.B.—See L'Air Liquide S.A.; *Int'l*, pg. 4371
AION CO., LTD. - KANTO PLANT—See Soft99 Corporation; *Int'l*, pg. 7050
AION CO., LTD.—See Soft99 Corporation; *Int'l*, pg. 7050
AION SA/NV—See Warburg Pincus LLC; *U.S. Private*, pg. 4436
AION-TECH SOLUTIONS LIMITED; *Int'l*, pg. 234
AION THERAPEUTIC INC.; *Int'l*, pg. 234
AIP/AEROSPACE HOLDINGS, LLC—See AIP, LLC; *U.S. Private*, pg. 133
AIPAX CO., LTD.—See Oji Holdings Corporation; *Int'l*, pg. 5536
AIP FOUNDATION; *Int'l*, pg. 234
AIPHONE CO., LTD.; *Int'l*, pg. 234
AIPHONE COMMUNICATIONS (VIETNAM) CO., LTD.—See Aiphone Co., Ltd.; *Int'l*, pg. 235
AIPHONE CORPORATION—See Aiphone Co., Ltd.; *Int'l*, pg. 235
AIPHONE PTE. LTD.—See Aiphone Co., Ltd.; *Int'l*, pg. 235
AIPHONE PTY LTD.—See Aiphone Co., Ltd.; *Int'l*, pg. 235
AIPHONE S.A.S.—See Aiphone Co., Ltd.; *Int'l*, pg. 235
AIPHONE SHANGHAI CO., LTD.—See Aiphone Co., Ltd.; *Int'l*, pg. 235
AIPHONE UK LIMITED—See Aiphone Co., Ltd.; *Int'l*, pg. 235
AIP INNENPROJEKT GMBH—See MEYER WERFT GmbH; *Int'l*, pg. 4870
AIP, LLC - SAN FRANCISCO—See AIP, LLC; *U.S. Private*, pg. 133
AIP, LLC; *U.S. Private*, pg. 133
AIP LOGISTICS, INC.—See Trimac Transportation Ltd.; *Int'l*, pg. 7923
AI PORTS AND TERMINALS COMPANY LIMITED—See AI Energy Public Company Limited; *Int'l*, pg. 226
AIP SAS—See Sintex Industries, Ltd.; *Int'l*, pg. 6957
AIPS TECHNOLOGY CO., LTD.—See Giant Manufacturing Co., Ltd.; *Int'l*, pg. 2961
AIPTEK INTERNATIONAL GMBH—See AIPTEK International Inc.; *Int'l*, pg. 235
AIPTEK INTERNATIONAL INC.; *Int'l*, pg. 235
AIQI (FUJIAN) SHOES MODEL CO., LTD.—See Jinli Group Holdings Limited; *Int'l*, pg. 3969
AIQ LIMITED; *Int'l*, pg. 236
AIQ SMART CLOTHING INC.—See Tex-Ray Industrial Co., Ltd.; *Int'l*, pg. 7582
AIR2, LLC—See Primoris Services Corporation; *U.S. Public*, pg. 1718
AIR2MP3 GMBH—See freenet AG; *Int'l*, pg. 2770
AIR ADVISORY CO., LTD.—See AIRA Factoring Public Company Limited; *Int'l*, pg. 241
AIRA & AIFUL PUBLIC COMPANY LIMITED—See AIFUL Corporation; *Int'l*, pg. 231
AIRA CAPITAL PUBLIC COMPANY LIMITED; *Int'l*, pg. 241

AIRA FACTORING PUBLIC COMPANY LIMITED; *Int'l*, pg. 241
AIRA LEASING PLC—See AIRA Factoring Public Company Limited; *Int'l*, pg. 241
AIR ALLIANCE GMBH—See DPE Deutsche Private Equity GmbH; *Int'l*, pg. 2187
AIRAM PRESS CO. LTD—See Industrial Machining Services, Inc.; *U.S. Private*, pg. 2067
AIRAN AUSTRALIA PTY LIMITED—See AIRAN Limited; *Int'l*, pg. 241
AIRAN GLOBAL PRIVATE LIMITED—See AIRAN Limited; *Int'l*, pg. 241
AIRAN LIMITED; *Int'l*, pg. 241
AIR ARABIA PJSC; *Int'l*, pg. 236
AIRA SECURITIES PUBLIC COMPANY LIMITED—See AIRA Capital Public Company Limited; *Int'l*, pg. 241
AIRASIA BERHAD—See Capital A Bhd; *Int'l*, pg. 1309
AIRASIA X BERHAD; *Int'l*, pg. 241
AIR ATLANTA ICELANDIC—See Eimskipafelag Islands Hf.; *Int'l*, pg. 2332
AIRBAGS INTERNATIONAL LTD.—See Autoliv, Inc.; *Int'l*, pg. 728
AIR BALTIC CORPORATION AS; *Int'l*, pg. 236
AIRBALTIC TRAINING—See Air Baltic Corporation AS; *Int'l*, pg. 236
AIR BANK A.S.—See PPF Group N.V.; *Int'l*, pg. 5950
AIRBASE SERVICES INC.—See Regent Aerospace Corporation; *U.S. Private*, pg. 3387
AIRBATH GROUP PLC; *Int'l*, pg. 241
AIR BEARING TECHNOLOGY, INC.—See KLA Corporation; *U.S. Public*, pg. 1267
AIR BERLIN GMBH & CO. FUNFTE FLUGZEUGVERMIETUNGS OHG—See Air Berlin PLC & Co. Luftverkehrs KG; *Int'l*, pg. 236
AIR BERLIN LUFTFAHRTTECHNISCHER BETRIEB GMBH—See Air Berlin PLC & Co. Luftverkehrs KG; *Int'l*, pg. 236
AIR BERLIN PLC & CO. LUFTVERKEHRS KG; *Int'l*, pg. 236
AIRBNB, INC.; *U.S. Public*, pg. 68
AIRBORNE ACCESS CORPORATION—See PLDT Inc.; *Int'l*, pg. 5895
AIRBORNE ENGINES LTD.—See M International Inc.; *U.S. Private*, pg. 2523
AIRBORNE IMAGING INC.—See Barr Air Patrol, LLC; *U.S. Private*, pg. 479
AIRBORNE, INC.—See GF Capital Management & Advisors, LLC; *U.S. Private*, pg. 1689
AIRBORNE MAINTENANCE AND ENGINEERING SERVICES, INC.—See Air Transport Services Group, Inc.; *U.S. Public*, pg. 67
AIRBORNE SECURITY & PROTECTION SERVICES, INC.; *U.S. Public*, pg. 68
AIRBORNE—See FIMOPART Group; *Int'l*, pg. 2664
AIRBORNE SYSTEMS FRANCE—See TransDigm Group Incorporated; *U.S. Public*, pg. 2181
AIRBORNE SYSTEMS GROUP LIMITED—See TransDigm Group Incorporated; *U.S. Public*, pg. 2181
AIRBORNE SYSTEMS NORTH AMERICA INC.—See TransDigm Group Incorporated; *U.S. Public*, pg. 2181
AIRBORNE SYSTEMS NORTH AMERICA OF CA INC.—See TransDigm Group Incorporated; *U.S. Public*, pg. 2181
AIRBORNE SYSTEMS NORTH AMERICA OF NJ INC.—See TransDigm Group Incorporated; *U.S. Public*, pg. 2181
AIRBORNE TACTICAL ADVANTAGE COMPANY, LLC—See Textron Inc.; *U.S. Public*, pg. 2028
AIRBORNE WIRELESS NETWORK; *U.S. Private*, pg. 140
AIRBORN INC.—See Koch Industries, Inc.; *U.S. Private*, pg. 2333
AIRBOSS DEFENSE GROUP, LLC—See AirBoss of America Corp.; *Int'l*, pg. 241
AIRBOSS DEFENSE GROUP LTD.—See AirBoss of America Corp.; *Int'l*, pg. 241
AIRBOSS-DEFENSE INC.—See AirBoss of America Corp.; *Int'l*, pg. 241
AIRBOSS-DEFENSE—See AirBoss of America Corp.; *Int'l*, pg. 241
AIRBOSS FLEXIBLE PRODUCTS LLC—See AirBoss of America Corp.; *Int'l*, pg. 241
AIRBOSS OF AMERICA CORP.; *Int'l*, pg. 241
AIRBOSS RUBBER COMPOUNDING (NC) INC.—See AirBoss of America Corp.; *Int'l*, pg. 241
AIRBOSS RUBBER COMPOUNDING—See AirBoss of America Corp.; *Int'l*, pg. 241
AIR BP AMERICAS—See BP plc; *Int'l*, pg. 1125
AIR BP ARGENTINA S.A.—See BP plc; *Int'l*, pg. 1125
AIR BP BRASIL S.A.—See BP plc; *Int'l*, pg. 1125
AIR BP CANADA LIMITED—See BP plc; *Int'l*, pg. 1125
AIR BP CHINA—See BP plc; *Int'l*, pg. 1125
AIR BP EASTERN MEDITERRANIAN LTD—See BP plc; *Int'l*, pg. 1125
AIR BP FINLAND OY—See BP plc; *Int'l*, pg. 1125
AIR BP ITALIA S.P.A.—See BP plc; *Int'l*, pg. 1125
AIR BP LIMITED—See BP plc; *Int'l*, pg. 1125
AIR BP MOSCOW—See BP plc; *Int'l*, pg. 1125
AIR BP NORWAY AS—See BP plc; *Int'l*, pg. 1126
AIR BP PUERTO RICO—See BP plc; *Int'l*, pg. 1125

AIR CARGO ASSOCIATES INC.

AIR BP SALES ROMANIA SRL—See BP plc; *Int'l*, pg. 1125
AIR BP SWEDEN AB—See BP plc; *Int'l*, pg. 1125
AIR BP SWITZERLAND—See BP plc; *Int'l*, pg. 1126
AIR BURKINA SA—See Aga Khan Development Network; *Int'l*, pg. 199
AIRBUS AMERICAS, INC.—See Airbus SE; *Int'l*, pg. 244
AIR BUSAN INC.—See Kumho Asiana Group; *Int'l*, pg. 4330
AIRBUS BANK GMBH—See Airbus SE; *Int'l*, pg. 242
AIRBUS CHINA—See Airbus SE; *Int'l*, pg. 244
AIRBUS CORPORATE JET CENTRE S.A.S.—See Airbus SE; *Int'l*, pg. 244
AIRBUS DEFENCE AND SPACE LIMITED—See Airbus SE; *Int'l*, pg. 245
AIRBUS DEFENCE AND SPACE SAS—See Airbus SE; *Int'l*, pg. 245
AIRBUS DEFENCE & SPACE GMBH - CASSIDIAN DIVISION—See Airbus SE; *Int'l*, pg. 242
AIRBUS DEFENCE & SPACE GMBH—See Airbus SE; *Int'l*, pg. 242
AIRBUS DEFENCE & SPACE LIMITED—See Airbus SE; *Int'l*, pg. 243
AIRBUS DEFENCE & SPACE S.A.—See Airbus SE; *Int'l*, pg. 243
AIRBUS DEFENCE & SPACE SAS—See Airbus SE; *Int'l*, pg. 246
AIRBUS DEUTSCHLAND GMBH—See Airbus SE; *Int'l*, pg. 244
AIRBUS DS OPTRONICS GMBH—See Airbus SE; *Int'l*, pg. 242
AIRBUS DS OPTRONICS (PTY) LTD.—See Airbus SE; *Int'l*, pg. 242
AIRBUS GROUP, INC.—See Airbus SE; *Int'l*, pg. 243
AIRBUS GROUP LIMITED—See Airbus SE; *Int'l*, pg. 243
AIRBUS HELICOPTERS CANADA—See Airbus SE; *Int'l*, pg. 243
AIRBUS HELICOPTERS DEUTSCHLAND GMBH—See Airbus SE; *Int'l*, pg. 243
AIRBUS HELICOPTERS ESPANA, S. A.—See Airbus SE; *Int'l*, pg. 243
AIRBUS HELICOPTERS HOLDING SAS—See Airbus SE; *Int'l*, pg. 243
AIRBUS HELICOPTERS, INC.—See Airbus SE; *Int'l*, pg. 243
AIRBUS HELICOPTERS MALAYSIA SDN BHD—See Airbus SE; *Int'l*, pg. 243
AIRBUS HELICOPTERS ROMANIA SA—See Airbus SE; *Int'l*, pg. 243
AIRBUS HELICOPTERS S.A.S.—See Airbus SE; *Int'l*, pg. 243
AIRBUS HELICOPTERS TRAINING SERVICES—See Airbus SE; *Int'l*, pg. 243
AIR BUSINESS LTD—See An Post LLC; *Int'l*, pg. 443
AIRBUS JAPAN KK—See Airbus SE; *Int'l*, pg. 244
AIRBUS MILITARY NORTH AMERICA—See Airbus SE; *Int'l*, pg. 244
AIRBUS OPERATIONS GMBH—See Airbus SE; *Int'l*, pg. 244
AIRBUS OPERATIONS LTD.—See Airbus SE; *Int'l*, pg. 244
AIRBUS OPERATIONS SAS—See Airbus SE; *Int'l*, pg. 244
AIRBUS OPERATIONS, S.L.—See Airbus SE; *Int'l*, pg. 244
AIRBUS PROSKY S.A.S.—See Airbus SE; *Int'l*, pg. 244
AIRBUS REAL ESTATE PREMIUM AEROTEC NORD GMBH & CO. KG—See Airbus SE; *Int'l*, pg. 244
AIRBUS SAFRAN LAUNCHERS SAS—See Airbus SE; *Int'l*, pg. 245
AIRBUS SAFRAN LAUNCHERS SAS—See Safran SA; *Int'l*, pg. 6472
AIRBUS S.A.S.—See Airbus SE; *Int'l*, pg. 244
AIRBUS SE; *Int'l*, pg. 241
AIRBUS TRANSPORT INTERNATIONAL S.N.C.—See Airbus SE; *Int'l*, pg. 244
AIRBUS UK—See Airbus SE; *Int'l*, pg. 244
THE AIR CANADA CENTRE—See BCE Inc.; *Int'l*, pg. 927
THE AIR CANADA CENTRE—See Rogers Communications Inc.; *Int'l*, pg. 6383
AIR CANADA EXPRESS—See Chorus Aviation Inc.; *Int'l*, pg. 1584
AIR CANADA EXPRESS—See Chorus Aviation Inc.; *Int'l*, pg. 1584
AIR CANADA; *Int'l*, pg. 236
AIRCANO AB—See Instalco AB; *Int'l*, pg. 3721
AIR CAPITAL INSURANCE, LLC—See GTCR LLC; *U.S. Private*, pg. 1802
AIR CARGO ASSOCIATES INC.; *U.S. Private*, pg. 138
AIR CARGO CARRIERS, LLC—See ACC Holding, Inc.; *U.S. Private*, pg. 47
AIR CARGO WORLD MAGAZINE—See Royal Media Group, Inc.; *U.S. Private*, pg. 3492
AIRCASTLE ADVISOR (IRELAND) LIMITED—See Marubeni Corporation; *Int'l*, pg. 4705
AIRCASTLE ADVISOR (IRELAND) LIMITED—See Mizuho Leasing Company, Limited; *Int'l*, pg. 4999
AIRCASTLE ADVISOR LLC—See Marubeni Corporation; *Int'l*, pg. 4705
AIRCASTLE ADVISOR LLC—See Mizuho Leasing Company, Limited; *Int'l*, pg. 4999

AIR CARGO ASSOCIATES INC.
CORPORATE AFFILIATIONS

AIRCASTLE LIMITED—See Marubeni Corporation; *Int'l*, pg. 4705
AIRCASTLE LIMITED—See Mizuho Leasing Company, Limited; *Int'l*, pg. 4999
AIRCASTLE SINGAPORE PTE. LIMITED—See Marubeni Corporation; *Int'l*, pg. 4705
AIRCASTLE SINGAPORE PTE. LIMITED—See Mizuho Leasing Company, Limited; *Int'l*, pg. 4999
AIRCELL BUSINESS AVIATION SERVICES LLC—See Gogo Inc.; *U.S. Public*, pg. 949
AIRCELLE EUROPE SERVICES SAS—See Safran SA; *Int'l*, pg. 6473
AIRCELLE—See Safran SA; *Int'l*, pg. 6473
AIRCEL LIMITED—See Maxis Berhad; *Int'l*, pg. 4742
AIRCERT GMBH—See The British Standards Institution; *Int'l*, pg. 7628
AIR CHANGE INTERNATIONAL LIMITED; *Int'l*, pg. 236
AIR CHANGE PTY LTD—See Air Change International Limited; *Int'l*, pg. 236
AIR CHARTER OF OHIO, INC.—See A.P. Moller-Maersk A/S; *Int'l*, pg. 27
AIR CHARTERS, INC.; *U.S. Private*, pg. 138
AIRCHECK INDIA PVT. LTD.—See iHeartMedia, Inc.; *U.S. Public*, pg. 1095
AIR CHEFS (PTY) LTD.—See South African Airways (Pty) Ltd.; *Int'l*, pg. 7115
AIR CHINA CARGO CO., LTD.—See China National Aviation Holding Company; *Int'l*, pg. 1525
AIR CHINA LTD.—See China National Aviation Holding Company; *Int'l*, pg. 1525
AIR-CITY INC.—See Greenbriar Equity Group, L.P.; *U.S. Private*, pg. 1776
AIRCO INDUSTRIES, INC.—See Firan Technology Group Corporation; *Int'l*, pg. 2678
AIRCO LTD.—See Trane Technologies Plc; *Int'l*, pg. 7892
AIRCO MECHANICAL INC.; *U.S. Private*, pg. 140
AIR COMET GROUP—See Viajes Marsans S.A.; *Int'l*, pg. 8183
AIRCOM INTERNATIONAL LTD.—See TEOCO Corporation; *U.S. Private*, pg. 3969
AIR COMMAND SYSTEMS INTERNATIONAL—See Thales S.A.; *Int'l*, pg. 7601
AIRCOM MANUFACTURING, INC.—See Kimball Electronics, Inc.; *U.S. Public*, pg. 1228
AIR COMM CORPORATION - ADDISON—See Arcline Investment Management LP; *U.S. Private*, pg. 312
AIR COMM CORPORATION—See Arcline Investment Management LP; *U.S. Private*, pg. 312
AIRCOM PACIFIC INC.—See Aerkomm Inc.; *U.S. Public*, pg. 52
AIRCOMPANY SEVERSTAL LTD.—See PAO Severstal; *Int'l*, pg. 5731
AIRCOM PNEUMATIC GMBH—See Fukuda Corporation; *Int'l*, pg. 2839
AIR-COM PNEUMATYKA AUTOMATYKA S.C.—See AIRTEC Pneumatic GmbH; *Int'l*, pg. 249
AIR COMPONENTS & ENGINEERING; *U.S. Private*, pg 138
AIR COMPRESSOR ENGINEERING COMPANY; *U.S. Private*, pg. 138
AIR COMPRESSOR SOLUTIONS; *U.S. Private*, pg. 138
AIRCON AIRFREIGHT CONTAINER MAINTENANCE GMBH—See Deufol SE; *Int'l*, pg. 2048
AIRCONDITIONING DIRECT PTY. LTD.—See Beijer Ref AB; *Int'l*, pg. 943
AIR-CONDITIONING, HEATING, AND REFRIGERATION INSTITUTE; *U.S. Private*, pg. 140
AIRCON GUARDRAILS PRIVATE LIMITED—See Valmont Industries, Inc.; *U.S. Public*, pg. 2273
AIR CONTACT TRANSPORT INC.; *U.S. Private*, pg. 138
AIR-CON TECHNOLOGIES, INC.—See Regal Rexnord Corporation; *U.S. Public*, pg. 1772
AIRCON TEKNIK A/S—See Beijer Ref AB; *Int'l*, pg. 944
AIR CONTROL PRODUCTS INC.; *U.S. Private*, pg. 138
AIR COOLED MOTORS—See Danbury AeroSpace, Inc.; *U.S. Private*, pg. 1152
AIRCO SERVICES, LLC—See Air T, Inc.; *U.S. Public*, pg. 67
AIRCO—See Ingersoll Rand Inc.; *U.S. Public*, pg. 1120
AIR COST CONTROL GERMANY GMBH—See HEICO Corporation; *U.S. Public*, pg. 1019
AIR COST CONTROL PTE. LTD.—See HEICO Corporation; *U.S. Public*, pg. 1019
AIR COST CONTROL US, LLC—See HEICO Corporation; *U.S. Public*, pg. 1019
AIRCRAFT APPLIANCES & EQUIPMENT LIMITED—See J.F. Lehman & Company, Inc.; *U.S. Private*, pg. 2162
AIRCRAFT BELTS, INC.—See Hicks Holdings, LLC; *U.S. Private*, pg. 1934
AIRCRAFT BELTS, INC.—See The Riverside Company; *U.S. Private*, pg. 4108
AIRCRAFT BELTS, INC.—See Weinberg Capital Group, Inc.; *U.S. Private*, pg. 4471
AIRCRAFT BRAKING SYSTEMS CORPORATION—See Parker Hannifin Corporation; *U.S. Public*, pg. 1642
AIRCRAFT CABIN SYSTEMS; *U.S. Private*, pg. 140
AIRCRAFT GEAR CORPORATION; *U.S. Private*, pg. 140
AIRCRAFT INSTRUMENT & RADIO CO.; *U.S. Private*, pg. 140

AIRCRAFT KLIMA-WARME- KALTE-ROHRLEITUNGSBAU GMBH—See E.ON SE; *Int'l*, pg. 2251
AIRCRAFT LEASING & MANAGEMENT LIMITED—See Fuyo General Lease Co., Ltd.; *Int'l*, pg. 2859
AIRCRAFT LOGISTICS PTY. LTD.—See Bristow Group, Inc.; *U.S. Public*, pg. 387
AIRCRAFT MAINTENANCE & ENGINEERING CORP.—See China National Aviation Holding Company; *Int'l*, pg. 1525
AIRCRAFT MAINTENANCE & ENGINEERING CORP.—See Deutsche Lufthansa AG; *Int'l*, pg. 2069
AIRCRAFT MAINTENANCE SUPPORT SERVICES LIMITED—See John Bean Technologies Corporation; *U.S. Public*, pg. 1191
AIRCRAFT MEDICAL LTD.—See Medtronic plc; *Int'l*, pg. 4786
AIRCRAFT PERFORMANCE GROUP, INC.—See Liberty Hall Capital Partners, L.P.; *U.S. Private*, pg. 2444
AIRCRAFT PRECISION PRODUCTS, INC.; *U.S. Private*, pg. 140
AIRCRAFT RESEARCH ASSOCIATION LIMITED—See BAE Systems plc; *Int'l*, pg. 796
AIRCRAFT SERVICE INTERNATIONAL GROUP, INC.—See Agility; *Int'l*, pg. 210
AIRCRAFT SPRUCE & SPECIALTY CO.—See Irwin International, Inc.; *U.S. Private*, pg. 2142
AIRCRAFT SYSTEMS DIVISION, LOS ANGELES—See The Heico Companies, L.L.C.; *U.S. Private*, pg. 4050
AIRCRAFT TECHNICAL PUBLISHERS—See ParkerGale, LLC; *U.S. Private*, pg. 3098
AIRCRAFT TECHNOLOGY, INC.—See HEICO Corporation; *U.S. Public*, pg. 1019
AIR CREEBEC; *Int'l*, pg. 236
AIR CRUISERS COMPANY, LLC—See Safran SA; *Int'l*, pg. 6477
AIRDESK, INC.—See Sierra Wireless, Inc.; *Int'l*, pg. 6904
AIRDEX INTERNATIONAL; *U.S. Private*, pg. 140
AIR DIGITAL SOLUTIONS PTE. LTD.—See Pan-United Corporation Ltd.; *Int'l*, pg. 5716
AIR DIMENSIONS, INC.—See Ingersoll Rand Inc.; *U.S. Public*, pg. 1118
AIR DISPATCH (CLC) SPOLKA Z.O.O.—See The Emirates Group; *Int'l*, pg. 7638
AIR DISTRIBUTION ENTERPRISES, INC.; *U.S. Private*, pg. 138
AIR DOLOMITI S.P.A.—See Deutsche Lufthansa AG; *Int'l*, pg. 2066
AIR DRAULICS ENGINEERING CO.—See Applied Industrial Technologies, Inc.; *U.S. Public*, pg. 170
AIRDRIE CHRYSLER DODGE JEEP; *Int'l*, pg. 247
AIRDROME PRECISION COMPONENTS—See Berkshire Hathaway Inc.; *U.S. Public*, pg. 313
AIR-DRY COMPANY OF AMERICA LLC—See TransDigm Group Incorporated; *U.S. Public*, pg. 2181
AIRDYNE AEROSPACE INC.; *U.S. Private*, pg. 140
AIRDYNE INC.; *U.S. Private*, pg. 141
AIRDYNE R&D INC.—See Airdyne Aerospace Inc.; *U.S. Private*, pg. 141
AIREA PLC; *Int'l*, pg. 247
AIREC ENGINEERING CORPORATION—See Nippon Telegraph & Telephone Corporation; *Int'l*, pg. 5354
AIRECO SUPPLY, INC.; *U.S. Private*, pg. 141
AIREDALE AIR CONDITIONING S.A. PTY LTD—See Modine Manufacturing Company; *U.S. Public*, pg. 1454
AIREDALE GROUP LIMITED—See Modine Manufacturing Company; *U.S. Public*, pg. 1454
AIREDALE NORTH AMERICA, INC.—See Modine Manufacturing Company; *U.S. Public*, pg. 1454
AIREDALE SHEET METAL LIMITED—See Modine Manufacturing Company; *U.S. Public*, pg. 1455
AIREFCO INC.—See Ferguson plc; *Int'l*, pg. 2637
AIREFRESH INDUSTRIES (M) SDN. BHD.—See Ancom Nylex Berhad; *Int'l*, pg. 449
AIREHEALTH, LLC; *U.S. Private*, pg. 141
AIREKO CONSTRUCTION CORP.; *U.S. Private*, pg. 141
AIR ENERGY, INC.; *U.S. Private*, pg. 138
AIRENKA HAVA TASIMACILIGI A.S.—See Enka Insaat ve Sanayi A.S.; *Int'l*, pg. 2440
AIREON LLC—See Iridium Communications Inc.; *U.S. Public*, pg. 1171
AIRE RADIO NETWORK LLC—See Spanish Broadcasting System Inc.; *U.S. Public*, pg. 1914
AIRE SERV LLC—See Harvest Partners L.P.; *U.S. Private*, pg. 1877
AIRESIS S.A.; *Int'l*, pg. 247
AIRES; *U.S. Private*, pg. 141
AIREST CATERING D.O.O.—See InfraVia Capital Partners SAS; *Int'l*, pg. 3699
AIREST GASTRONOMY & RETAIL GMBH—See InfraVia Capital Partners SAS; *Int'l*, pg. 3699
AIREST RUSSIA O.O.O.—See InfraVia Capital Partners SAS; *Int'l*, pg. 3699
AIREST S.R.L.—See InfraVia Capital Partners SAS; *Int'l*, pg. 3699
AIR EVAC EMS, INC.—See KKR & Co. Inc.; *U.S. Public*, pg. 1251
AIREX AG—See Schweiter Technologies AG; *Int'l*, pg. 6645

AIREX INC.; *Int'l*, pg. 247
AIREX INC.—See TCS Holdings Co., Ltd.; *Int'l*, pg. 7485
AIREX, LLC—See Allient Inc.; *U.S. Public*, pg. 80
AIR EXPERTS TODAY CORP.; *U.S. Private*, pg. 138
AIR EXPRESS, INC.—See Konoike Transport Co., Ltd.; *Int'l*, pg. 4274
AIR EXPRESS INTERNATIONAL USA, INC.—See Deutsche Post AG; *Int'l*, pg. 2071
AIREY-THOMPSON COMPANY INC.; *U.S. Private*, pg. 141
AIR FAYRE CA INC.—See Harwood Capital LLP; *Int'l*, pg. 3282
AIR FAYRE USA INC.—See Harwood Capital LLP; *Int'l*, pg. 3282
AIR FILTER SUPPLY, INC.—See Audax Group, Limited Partnership; *U.S. Private*, pg. 389
AIR FILTRATION MANAGEMENT INC.—See Medical Technology Associates, LLC; *U.S. Private*, pg. 2656
AIRFIX—See Phoenix Asset Management Partners Ltd.; *Int'l*, pg. 5849
AIRFLITE INC.—See Toyota Motor Corporation; *Int'l*, pg. 7874
AIRFLITE JAPAN CORP.—See Japan Airlines Co., Ltd.; *Int'l*, pg. 3881
AIR FLOW DESIGNS INC.; *U.S. Private*, pg. 138
AIR FLOW—See Enerphase Industrial Solutions, Inc.; *U.S. Private*, pg. 1396
AIRFOIL PUBLIC RELATIONS; *U.S. Private*, pg. 141
AIRFOIL TECHNOLOGIES INTERNATIONAL SINGAPORE PTE LTD.—See General Electric Company; *U.S. Public*, pg. 918
AIR FORCE ACADEMY; *U.S. Private*, pg. 138
AIR FORCE AID SOCIETY, INC.; *U.S. Private*, pg. 138
THE AIR FORCE ASSOCIATION; *U.S. Private*, pg. 3983
AIR FORCE ONE; *U.S. Private*, pg. 138
AIR FORCE RETIRED OFFICERS COMMUNITY; *U.S. Private*, pg. 138
AIRFORCE S.P.A.—See Elica S.p.A.; *Int'l*, pg. 2360
AIR FRAME STRAIGHTENING; *U.S. Private*, pg. 138
AIR FRANCE C.S. PARTICIPATION—See Air France-KLM S.A.; *Int'l*, pg. 236
AIR FRANCE KLM COMPONENT SERVICES CO. LTD.—See Air France-KLM S.A.; *Int'l*, pg. 236
AIR FRANCE-KLM S.A.; *Int'l*, pg. 236
AIR FRANCE SA—See Air France-KLM S.A.; *Int'l*, pg. 236
AIR FRANCE—See Air France-KLM S.A.; *Int'l*, pg. 236
AIR FRANCE, USA—See Air France-KLM S.A.; *Int'l*, pg. 236
AIR FREIGHT NZ LIMITED—See Freightways Group Limited; *Int'l*, pg. 2771
AIRGAIN, INC.; *U.S. Public*, pg. 68
AIRGARD, INC.—See M+W Group GmbH; *Int'l*, pg. 4613
AIRGAS CANADA INC.—See L'Air Liquide S.A.; *Int'l*, pg. 4372
AIRGAS EAST—See L'Air Liquide S.A.; *Int'l*, pg. 4372
AIRGAS GREAT LAKES—See L'Air Liquide S.A.; *Int'l*, pg. 4372
AIRGAS GULF COAST—See L'Air Liquide S.A.; *Int'l*, pg. 4372
AIRGAS, INC.—See L'Air Liquide S.A.; *Int'l*, pg. 4371
AIRGAS MERCHANT GASES, LLC—See L'Air Liquide S.A.; *Int'l*, pg. 4372
AIRGAS MID-AMERICA—See L'Air Liquide S.A.; *Int'l*, pg. 4372
AIRGAS MID-SOUTH—See L'Air Liquide S.A.; *Int'l*, pg. 4372
AIRGAS NATIONAL WELDERS—See L'Air Liquide S.A.; *Int'l*, pg. 4372
AIRGAS NORTH CENTRAL—See L'Air Liquide S.A.; *Int'l*, pg. 4372
AIRGAS NORTHEAST—See L'Air Liquide S.A.; *Int'l*, pg. 4372
AIRGAS NORTHERN CALIFORNIA & NEVADA—See L'Air Liquide S.A.; *Int'l*, pg. 4372
AIRGAS NORTH PACIFIC—See L'Air Liquide S.A.; *Int'l*, pg. 4372
AIRGAS PRIORITY NITROGEN, LLC—See L'Air Liquide S.A.; *Int'l*, pg. 4372
AIRGAS, S.A. DE C.V.—See L'Air Liquide S.A.; *Int'l*, pg. 4372
AIRGAS SAFETY, INC.—See L'Air Liquide S.A.; *Int'l*, pg. 4372
AIRGAS SOUTHEAST—See L'Air Liquide S.A.; *Int'l*, pg. 4372
AIRGAS SOUTHWEST—See L'Air Liquide S.A.; *Int'l*, pg. 4372
AIRGAS SPECIALTY PRODUCTS, INC.—See L'Air Liquide S.A.; *Int'l*, pg. 4372
AIRGAS WEST—See L'Air Liquide S.A.; *Int'l*, pg. 4372
AIR GENERAL INC.; *U.S. Private*, pg. 138
AIR GENIE AIR CONDITIONING CO.; *U.S. Private*, pg. 138
AIR GEORGIAN LTD—See Georgian International Limited; *Int'l*, pg. 2939
AIRGEST S.P.A.—See Corporacion America S.A.; *Int'l*, pg. 1803
AIR GREENLAND A/S; *Int'l*, pg. 238
AIR GROUND XPRESS, INC.; *U.S. Private*, pg. 138
AIRGUIDE CORPORATION; *U.S. Private*, pg. 141

COMPANY NAME INDEX

AIRLINE TARIFF PUBLISHING COMPANY

AIR GUNSA S.R.L—See ANEST IWATA Corporation; *Int'l*, pg. 458
AIR HARRODS LTD—See Harrods Ltd.; *Int'l*, pg. 3279
AIR & HYDRAULIC EQUIPMENT, INC.; *U.S. Private*, pg. 138
AIR & HYDRAULIC POWER CENTRE—See Baker & Provan Pty. Ltd.; *Int'l*, pg. 805
AIR-HYDRAULIC SYSTEMS INC.—See Applied Industrial Technologies, Inc.; *U.S. Public*, pg. 170
AIR HYDRO POWER INC.; *U.S. Private*, pg. 139
AIR INDIA CHARTERS LTD.—See Air India Limited; *Int'l*, pg. 238
AIR INDIA LIMITED; *Int'l*, pg. 238
AIR INDIA—See Air India Limited; *Int'l*, pg. 238
AIR INDUSTRIES COMPANY—See Berkshire Hathaway Inc.; *U.S. Public*, pg. 314
AIR INDUSTRIES GROUP; *U.S. Public*, pg. 64
AIR INDUSTRIES MACHINING CORPORATION—See Air Industries Group; *U.S. Public*, pg. 64
AIRINMAR HOLDINGS LIMITED—See AAR Corp.; *U.S. Public*, pg. 13
AIRINMAR LTD.—See AAR Corp.; *U.S. Public*, pg. 13
AIR INSTAL B.V.—See CENTROTEC SE; *Int'l*, pg. 1414
AIR INTERNATIONAL (SHANGHAI) CO., LTD—See Unitas Capital Pte. Ltd.; *Int'l*, pg. 8063
AIR INTERNATIONAL THERMAL (AUSTRALIA) PTY LTD.—See Unitas Capital Pte. Ltd.; *Int'l*, pg. 8063
AIR INTERNET SERVICE CO., LTD.—See Aeria Inc.; *Int'l*, pg. 179
AIRIQ, INC.; *Int'l*, pg. 247
AIRIT AIRPORT IT SERVICES HAHN AG—See Fraport AG; *Int'l*, pg. 2764
AIRITE HEATING, AIR CONDITIONING & SHEET METAL, INC.—See ABM Industries, Inc.; *U.S. Public*, pg. 25
AIRIT SERVICES AG—See Fraport AG; *Int'l*, pg. 2764
AIRITSYSTEMS HANNOVER GMBH—See Fraport AG; *Int'l*, pg. 2764
AIRIX TALOTEKNIIKKA OY—See Sweco AB; *Int'l*, pg. 7363
AIR-IX TIETO OY—See Sweco AB; *Int'l*, pg. 7363
AIR JAPAN CO., LTD—See ANA Holdings Inc.; *Int'l*, pg. 444
AIR KEDAH SDN. BHD.—See Taliworks Corporation Berhad; *Int'l*, pg. 7447
AIRKENYA AVIATION LTD.; *Int'l*, pg. 247
AIR KILROE LIMITED—See Bristow Group, Inc.; *U.S. Public*, pg. 387
AIR KING INDUSTRIAL CO., LTD.—See Allis Electric Co., Ltd.; *Int'l*, pg. 359
AIR KING—See Lasko Products, LLC; *U.S. Private*, pg. 2395
AIRKIT S.A.; *Int'l*, pg. 248
AIRLANCO INC.—See Ag Growth International Inc.; *Int'l*, pg. 198
AIRLANE HOTEL & CONFERENCE CENTRE THUNDER BAY—See Clarke Inc.; *Int'l*, pg. 1650
AIR LAUREL, INC.—See Telephone Electronics Corporation; *U.S. Private*, pg. 3961
AIR LEASE CORPORATION; *U.S. Public*, pg. 64
AIR LIFT COMPANY; *U.S. Private*, pg. 139
AIRLINE ACCOUNTING CENTER DE MEXICO S.A. DE C.V.—See Deutsche Lufthansa AG; *Int'l*, pg. 2069
AIRLINE ACCOUNTING CENTER SP. Z O.O—See Deutsche Lufthansa AG; *Int'l*, pg. 2069
AIRLINE ALLIED SERVICES LIMITED—See Air India Limited; *Int'l*, pg. 238
AIRLINE CARGO RESOURCES FZCO—See Expolanka Holdings PLC; *Int'l*, pg. 2589
AIRLINE CONTAINER LEASING, LLC - NEW YORK—See Ranger Aerospace LLC; *U.S. Private*, pg. 3354
AIRLINE CONTAINER LEASING, LLC—See Ranger Aerospace LLC; *U.S. Private*, pg. 3354
AIRLINE HOTEL CO., LTD.—See Pan Pacific International Holdings Corporation; *Int'l*, pg. 5715
AIRLINE HYDRAULICS CORPORATION; *U.S. Private*, pg. 141
AIRLINE PETROLEUM, CO.—See Santarelli & Sons Oil Co., Inc.; *U.S. Private*, pg. 3548
AIRLINE ROTABLES LIMITED—See Temasek Holdings (Private) Limited; *Int'l*, pg. 7551
AIRLINES REPORTING CORPORATION; *U.S. Private*, pg. 141
AIRLINE TARIFF PUBLISHING COMPANY; *U.S. Private*, pg. 141
AIRLINK COMMUNICATIONS PVT. LTD.—See GTPL Hathway Ltd.; *Int'l*, pg. 3151
AIR LINK PTY LIMITED—See REGIONAL EXPRESS HOLDINGS LIMITED; *Int'l*, pg. 6254
AIRLINKS AIRPORT SERVICES LIMITED—See Mobico Group PLC; *Int'l*, pg. 5009
AIRLINK TECHNOLOGY CO., LTD.—See Apollo Global Management, Inc.; *U.S. Public*, pg. 151
AIR LIQUIDE ACETYLENE B.V.—See L'Air Liquide S.A.; *Int'l*, pg. 4370
AIR LIQUIDE ADVANCED MATERIALS, INC.—See L'Air Liquide S.A.; *Int'l*, pg. 4370
AIR LIQUIDE ADVANCED TECHNOLOGIES S.A.—See L'Air Liquide S.A.; *Int'l*, pg. 4370

AIR LIQUIDE ADVANCED TECHNOLOGIES U.S. LLC—See L'Air Liquide S.A.; *Int'l*, pg. 4371
AIR LIQUIDE ALGERIE - SIDAL SPA—See L'Air Liquide S.A.; *Int'l*, pg. 4370
AIR LIQUIDE AL-KHAFRAH INDUSTRIAL GASES LLC—See Abdullah Hashim Industrial Gases & Equipment Co. Ltd.; *Int'l*, pg. 59
AIR LIQUIDE AMERICA CORPORATION—See L'Air Liquide S.A.; *Int'l*, pg. 4370
AIR LIQUIDE AMERICA L.P.—See L'Air Liquide S.A.; *Int'l*, pg. 4371
AIR LIQUIDE AMERICA SPECIALTY GASES LLC—See L'Air Liquide S.A.; *Int'l*, pg. 4371
AIR LIQUIDE ANGOLA LTDA—See L'Air Liquide S.A.; *Int'l*, pg. 4370
AIR LIQUIDE ARABIA LLC—See L'Air Liquide S.A.; *Int'l*, pg. 4370
AIR LIQUIDE ARGENTINA S.A.—See L'Air Liquide S.A.; *Int'l*, pg. 4371
AIR LIQUIDE ASIA - PACIFIC CO., LTD—See L'Air Liquide S.A.; *Int'l*, pg. 4370
AIR LIQUIDE AUSTRALIA LTD.—See L'Air Liquide S.A.; *Int'l*, pg. 4370
AIR LIQUIDE AUSTRIA GMBH—See L'Air Liquide S.A.; *Int'l*, pg. 4370
AIR LIQUIDE (BEIJING) CO., LTD—See L'Air Liquide S.A.; *Int'l*, pg. 4369
AIR LIQUIDE BELGE S.A.—See L'Air Liquide S.A.; *Int'l*, pg. 4370
AIR LIQUIDE BELGIUM S.A.—See L'Air Liquide S.A.; *Int'l*, pg. 4370
AIR LIQUIDE BENELUX S.A.—See L'Air Liquide S.A.; *Int'l*, pg. 4370
AIR LIQUIDE BENIN S.A.—See Adenia Partners Ltd; *Int'l*, pg. 143
AIR LIQUIDE BOTSWANA PROPERIETARY LIMITED—See L'Air Liquide S.A.; *Int'l*, pg. 4370
AIR LIQUIDE BRASIL S.A.—See L'Air Liquide S.A.; *Int'l*, pg. 4371
AIR LIQUIDE BULGARIA EOOD—See L'Air Liquide S.A.; *Int'l*, pg. 4370
AIR LIQUIDE BURKINA FASO S.A.—See Adenia Partners Ltd; *Int'l*, pg. 143
AIR LIQUIDE B.V.—See L'Air Liquide S.A.; *Int'l*, pg. 4370
AIR LIQUIDE CAMEROUN S.A.—See Adenia Partners Ltd; *Int'l*, pg. 143
AIR LIQUIDE CANADA INC.—See L'Air Liquide S.A.; *Int'l*, pg. 4371
AIR LIQUIDE CHANGSHU CO., LTD—See L'Air Liquide S.A.; *Int'l*, pg. 4369
AIR LIQUIDE (CHENGDU) CO., LTD—See L'Air Liquide S.A.; *Int'l*, pg. 4369
AIR LIQUIDE CHILE S.A.—See L'Air Liquide S.A.; *Int'l*, pg. 4371
AIR LIQUIDE CHINA HOLDING CO., LTD—See L'Air Liquide S.A.; *Int'l*, pg. 4369
AIR LIQUIDE COLOMBIA S.A.S—See L'Air Liquide S.A.; *Int'l*, pg. 4370
AIR LIQUIDE CONGO S.A.—See Adenia Partners Ltd; *Int'l*, pg. 143
AIR LIQUIDE COTE D'IVOIRE S.A.—See Adenia Partners Ltd; *Int'l*, pg. 143
AIR LIQUIDE CZ, S.R.O.—See Messer Group GmbH; *Int'l*, pg. 4842
AIR LIQUIDE DALIAN CO., LTD—See L'Air Liquide S.A.; *Int'l*, pg. 4370
AIR LIQUIDE DANMARK A.S.—See L'Air Liquide S.A.; *Int'l*, pg. 4370
AIR LIQUIDE DEUTSCHLAND GMBH—See L'Air Liquide S.A.; *Int'l*, pg. 4370
AIR LIQUIDE DOMINICANA S.A.—See L'Air Liquide S.A.; *Int'l*, pg. 4370
AIR LIQUIDE EGYPTE S.A.E.—See L'Air Liquide S.A.; *Int'l*, pg. 4370
AIR LIQUIDE ELECTRONICS EUROPE—See L'Air Liquide S.A.; *Int'l*, pg. 4370
AIR LIQUIDE ELECTRONICS GMBH—See L'Air Liquide S.A.; *Int'l*, pg. 4370
AIR LIQUIDE ELECTRONICS MATERIALS S.A.—See L'Air Liquide S.A.; *Int'l*, pg. 4371
AIR LIQUIDE ELECTRONICS SYSTEMS ASIA LTD.—See L'Air Liquide S.A.; *Int'l*, pg. 4371
AIR LIQUIDE ELECTRONICS SYSTEMS S.A.—See L'Air Liquide S.A.; *Int'l*, pg. 4371
AIR LIQUIDE ELECTRONICS U.S. LP - CALIFORNIA—See L'Air Liquide S.A.; *Int'l*, pg. 4371
AIR LIQUIDE ELECTRONICS U.S. LP—See L'Air Liquide S.A.; *Int'l*, pg. 4371
AIR LIQUIDE EMIRATES FOR INDUSTRIAL GASES LLC—See L'Air Liquide S.A.; *Int'l*, pg. 4371
AIR LIQUIDE ENGINEERING JAPAN, CO—See L'Air Liquide S.A.; *Int'l*, pg. 4373
AIR LIQUIDE ENGINEERING MIDDLE EAST—See L'Air Liquide S.A.; *Int'l*, pg. 4371
AIR LIQUIDE ENGINEERING—See L'Air Liquide S.A.; *Int'l*, pg. 4371
AIR LIQUIDE ENGINEERING SERVICES ASIA CO., LTD.—See L'Air Liquide S.A.; *Int'l*, pg. 4375

AIR LIQUIDE ENGINEERING SERVICES ASIA (SHANGHAI) COMPANY LTD—See L'Air Liquide S.A.; *Int'l*, pg. 4370
AIR LIQUIDE ESPANA SA—See L'Air Liquide S.A.; *Int'l*, pg. 4371
AIR LIQUIDE FAR EASTERN LTD.—See L'Air Liquide S.A.; *Int'l*, pg. 4371
AIR LIQUIDE FINANCE SA—See L'Air Liquide S.A.; *Int'l*, pg. 4371
AIR LIQUIDE FINLAND OY—See L'Air Liquide S.A.; *Int'l*, pg. 4369
AIR LIQUIDE FORSCHUNG UND ENTWICKLUNG GMBH—See L'Air Liquide S.A.; *Int'l*, pg. 4375
AIR LIQUIDE FRANCE INDUSTRIE S.A.—See L'Air Liquide S.A.; *Int'l*, pg. 4371
AIR LIQUIDE GABOA—See Adenia Partners Ltd; *Int'l*, pg. 143
AIR LIQUIDE GAS A.B.—See L'Air Liquide S.A.; *Int'l*, pg. 4371
AIR LIQUIDE GAZ SAN. VE TIC. A.S.—See L'Air Liquide S.A.; *Int'l*, pg. 4371
AIR LIQUIDE GHANA LTD.—See Adenia Partners Ltd; *Int'l*, pg. 143
AIR LIQUIDE GLOBAL E&C SOLUTIONS CANADA LP—See L'Air Liquide S.A.; *Int'l*, pg. 4371
AIR LIQUIDE GLOBAL E&C SOLUTIONS FRANCE S.A.—See L'Air Liquide S.A.; *Int'l*, pg. 4371
AIR LIQUIDE GLOBAL E&C SOLUTIONS GERMANY GMBH—See L'Air Liquide S.A.; *Int'l*, pg. 4371
AIR LIQUIDE GLOBAL E&C SOLUTIONS JAPAN K.K—See L'Air Liquide S.A.; *Int'l*, pg. 4371
AIR LIQUIDE GLOBAL E&C SOLUTIONS SINGAPORE PTE. LTD.—See L'Air Liquide S.A.; *Int'l*, pg. 4371
AIR LIQUIDE GLOBAL E&C SOLUTIONS US, INC.—See L'Air Liquide S.A.; *Int'l*, pg. 4371
AIR LIQUIDE (GUANGDONG) INDUSTRIAL GAS CO., LTD.—See L'Air Liquide S.A.; *Int'l*, pg. 4369
AIR LIQUIDE HANGZHOU CO., LTD—See L'Air Liquide S.A.; *Int'l*, pg. 4370
AIR LIQUIDE HEALTHCARE AMERICA CORPORATION—See L'Air Liquide S.A.; *Int'l*, pg. 4371
AIR LIQUIDE HEALTHCARE ESPANA SL—See L'Air Liquide S.A.; *Int'l*, pg. 4372
AIR LIQUIDE HEALTHCARE IRELAND LIMITED—See L'Air Liquide S.A.; *Int'l*, pg. 4372
AIR LIQUIDE HEALTHCARE P/L—See L'Air Liquide S.A.; *Int'l*, pg. 4370
AIR LIQUIDE HEALTHCARE—See L'Air Liquide S.A.; *Int'l*, pg. 4370
AIR LIQUIDE HELIUM AMERICA, INC.—See L'Air Liquide S.A.; *Int'l*, pg. 4371
AIR LIQUIDE HELLAS S.A.—See L'Air Liquide S.A.; *Int'l*, pg. 4372
AIR LIQUIDE HOLDING CO., LTD.—See L'Air Liquide S.A.; *Int'l*, pg. 4369
AIR LIQUIDE (HOMECARE) LTD.—See L'Air Liquide S.A.; *Int'l*, pg. 4369
AIR LIQUIDE HYDROGEN ENERGY SA—See L'Air Liquide S.A.; *Int'l*, pg. 4372
AIR LIQUIDE INDIA HOLDING PVT. LTD.—See L'Air Liquide S.A.; *Int'l*, pg. 4372
AIR LIQUIDE INDUSTRIAL U.S. LP—See L'Air Liquide S.A.; *Int'l*, pg. 4371
AIR LIQUIDE INDUSTRIE B.V.—See L'Air Liquide S.A.; *Int'l*, pg. 4372
AIR LIQUIDE INDUSTRIEGASE GMBH & CO. KG—See L'Air Liquide S.A.; *Int'l*, pg. 4372
AIR LIQUIDE INDUSTRIES BELGIUM S.A.—See L'Air Liquide S.A.; *Int'l*, pg. 4372
AIR LIQUIDE INTERNATIONAL S.A.—See L'Air Liquide S.A.; *Int'l*, pg. 4372
AIR LIQUIDE ITALIA SERVICE S.R.L.—See L'Air Liquide S.A.; *Int'l*, pg. 4373
AIR LIQUIDE ITALIA SIEGE—See L'Air Liquide S.A.; *Int'l*, pg. 4369
AIR LIQUIDE ITALIA SRL—See L'Air Liquide S.A.; *Int'l*, pg. 4373
AIR LIQUIDE JAPAN LTD.—See L'Air Liquide S.A.; *Int'l*, pg. 4373
AIR LIQUIDE KOREA CO., LTD.—See L'Air Liquide S.A.; *Int'l*, pg. 4373
AIR LIQUIDE LARGE INDUSTRIES U.S. LP—See L'Air Liquide S.A.; *Int'l*, pg. 4371
AIR LIQUIDE LTD.—See L'Air Liquide S.A.; *Int'l*, pg. 4374
AIR LIQUIDE LUXEMBOURG S.A.—See L'Air Liquide S.A.; *Int'l*, pg. 4373
AIR LIQUIDE MADAGASCAR S.A.—See Adenia Partners Ltd; *Int'l*, pg. 143
AIR LIQUIDE MALAYSIA SDN BHD—See L'Air Liquide S.A.; *Int'l*, pg. 4373
AIR LIQUIDE MALI S.A.—See Adenia Partners Ltd; *Int'l*, pg. 143
AIR LIQUIDE MAROC S.A.—See L'Air Liquide S.A.; *Int'l*, pg. 4373
AIR LIQUIDE MEDICAL GMBH—See L'Air Liquide S.A.; *Int'l*, pg. 4370
AIR LIQUIDE MEDICAL S.A.—See L'Air Liquide S.A.; *Int'l*, pg. 4370

AIRLINE TARIFF PUBLISHING COMPANY — CORPORATE AFFILIATIONS

Company Index

AIR LIQUIDE MEDICAL SYSTEMS S.A.—See L'Air Liquide S.A.; *Int'l*, pg. 4373
AIR LIQUIDE MEDICINAL S.A.—See L'Air Liquide S.A.; *Int'l*, pg. 4373
AIR LIQUIDE MEDICINAL SL—See L'Air Liquide S.A.; *Int'l*, pg. 4373
AIR LIQUIDE MEXICO—See L'Air Liquide S.A.; *Int'l*, pg. 4371
AIR LIQUIDE MIDDLE EAST & NORTH AFRICA FZCO—See L'Air Liquide S.A.; *Int'l*, pg. 4373
AIR LIQUIDE MOZAMBIQUE LDA.—See L'Air Liquide S.A.; *Int'l*, pg. 4373
AIR LIQUIDE MUNAY TECH GASES LLP—See L'Air Liquide S.A.; *Int'l*, pg. 4373
AIR LIQUIDE NAMIBIA PROPRIETARY LTD.—See L'Air Liquide S.A.; *Int'l*, pg. 4373
AIR LIQUIDE NEW ZEALAND LTD.—See L'Air Liquide S.A.; *Int'l*, pg. 4373
AIR LIQUIDE NIGERIA PLC—See L'Air Liquide S.A.; *Int'l*, pg. 4373
AIR LIQUIDE NORWAY AS—See L'Air Liquide S.A.; *Int'l*, pg. 4373
AIR LIQUIDE OFFSHORE AS—See L'Air Liquide S.A.; *Int'l*, pg. 4373
AIR LIQUIDE OOO—See L'Air Liquide S.A.; *Int'l*, pg. 4373
AIR LIQUIDE PANAMA S.A.—See L'Air Liquide S.A.; *Int'l*, pg. 4373
AIR LIQUIDE PHILIPPINES INC. - MAIN PLANT—See L'Air Liquide S.A.; *Int'l*, pg. 4373
AIR LIQUIDE PHILIPPINES INC.—See L'Air Liquide S.A.; *Int'l*, pg. 4373
AIR LIQUIDE POLSKA SP. Z O.O—See L'Air Liquide S.A.; *Int'l*, pg. 4373
AIR LIQUIDE PROCESS & CONSTRUCTION, INC.—See L'Air Liquide S.A.; *Int'l*, pg. 4373
AIR LIQUIDE PROGETTI ITALIA S.P.A—See L'Air Liquide S.A.; *Int'l*, pg. 4373
AIR LIQUIDE PROPRIETARY LTD.—See L'Air Liquide S.A.; *Int'l*, pg. 4373
AIR LIQUIDE (PTY) LIMITED—See L'Air Liquide S.A.; *Int'l*, pg. 4370
AIR LIQUIDE REUNION S.A.—See L'Air Liquide S.A.; *Int'l*, pg. 4373
AIR LIQUIDE ROMANIA S.R.L—See L'Air Liquide S.A.; *Int'l*, pg. 4373
AIR LIQUIDE RUSSIE S.A.—See L'Air Liquide S.A.; *Int'l*, pg. 4373
AIR LIQUIDE SANITA S.P.A—See L'Air Liquide S.A.; *Int'l*, pg. 4373
AIR LIQUIDE SANTE DOMICILE—See L'Air Liquide S.A.; *Int'l*, pg. 4373
AIR LIQUIDE SANTE FRANCE S.A.—See L'Air Liquide S.A.; *Int'l*, pg. 4373
AIR LIQUIDE SANTE (INTERNATIONAL)—See L'Air Liquide S.A.; *Int'l*, pg. 4373
AIR LIQUIDE SANTE SERVICES S.A.—See L'Air Liquide S.A.; *Int'l*, pg. 4374
AIR LIQUIDE SANTE—See L'Air Liquide S.A.; *Int'l*, pg. 4373
AIR LIQUIDE SENEGAL S.A.—See Adenia Partners Ltd; *Int'l*, pg. 143
AIR LIQUIDE SHANGHAI CO., LTD—See L'Air Liquide S.A.; *Int'l*, pg. 4370
AIR LIQUIDE SHANGHAI INTERNATIONAL TRADING CO., LTD—See L'Air Liquide S.A.; *Int'l*, pg. 4370
AIR LIQUIDE SHENYANG TEISAN CO., LTD.—See L'Air Liquide S.A.; *Int'l*, pg. 4370
AIR LIQUIDE SHUAIBA OXYGEN—See L'Air Liquide S.A.; *Int'l*, pg. 4374
AIR LIQUIDE SINGAPORE PTE. LTD.—See L'Air Liquide S.A.; *Int'l*, pg. 4374
AIR LIQUIDE SIVOA—See L'Air Liquide S.A.; *Int'l*, pg. 4374
AIR LIQUIDE SKAGERAK AS—See L'Air Liquide S.A.; *Int'l*, pg. 4374
AIR LIQUIDE SKAGERAK AS—See Statkraft AS; *Int'l*, pg. 7185
AIR LIQUIDE SLOVAKIA, S.R.O.—See Messer Group GmbH; *Int'l*, pg. 4842
AIR LIQUIDE SOHAR INDUSTRIAL GASES LLC—See L'Air Liquide S.A.; *Int'l*, pg. 4374
AIR LIQUIDE SOUTH EAST LTD—See L'Air Liquide S.A.; *Int'l*, pg. 4374
AIR LIQUIDE THAILAND LTD—See L'Air Liquide S.A.; *Int'l*, pg. 4374
AIR LIQUIDE TIANJIN CO., LTD.—See L'Air Liquide S.A.; *Int'l*, pg. 4370
AIR LIQUIDE TOGO S.A.—See Adenia Partners Ltd; *Int'l*, pg. 143
AIR LIQUIDE TRINIDAD AND TOBAGO LTD—See L'Air Liquide S.A.; *Int'l*, pg. 4374
AIR LIQUIDE TUNISIE S.A.—See L'Air Liquide S.A.; *Int'l*, pg. 4369
AIR LIQUIDE UK LTD.—See L'Air Liquide S.A.; *Int'l*, pg. 4374
AIR LIQUIDE UKRAINE S.A.—See L'Air Liquide S.A.; *Int'l*, pg. 4374
AIR LIQUIDE URUGUAY SA—See L'Air Liquide S.A.; *Int'l*, pg. 4371

AIR LIQUIDE USA LLC—See L'Air Liquide S.A.; *Int'l*, pg. 4371
AIR LIQUIDE VIETNAM CO., LTD—See L'Air Liquide S.A.; *Int'l*, pg. 4374
AIR LIQUIDE WELDING CENTRAL EUROPE S.R.O.—See Lincoln Electric Holdings, Inc.; *U.S. Public*, pg. 1316
AIR LIQUIDE WELDING LUXEMBOURG S.A.—See Lincoln Electric Holdings, Inc.; *U.S. Public*, pg. 1316
AIR LIQUIDE WELDING MIDDLE EAST FZE—See Lincoln Electric Holdings, Inc.; *U.S. Public*, pg. 1316
AIR LIQUIDE WELDING POLSKA SPOLKA ZOGRANIC-ZONA ODPOWIEDZIALNOSCIA—See Lincoln Electric Holdings, Inc.; *U.S. Public*, pg. 1317
AIR LIQUIDE WELDING (THAILAND) LTD—See Lincoln Electric Holdings, Inc.; *U.S. Public*, pg. 1316
AIR LIQUIDE (WUHAN) CO., LTD.—See L'Air Liquide S.A.; *Int'l*, pg. 4369
AIR LIQUID HOUPU HYDROGEN EQUIPMENT CO., LTD.—See Houpu Clean Energy Group Co., Ltd; *Int'l*, pg. 3490
AIR & LIQUID SYSTEMS CORPORATION—See Ampco-Pittsburgh Corporation; *U.S. Public*, pg. 126
AIRLITE PLASTICS COMPANY; *U.S. Private*, pg. 141
AIRLITE PLASTICS CO.—See Airlite Plastics Company; *U.S. Private*, pg. 141
AIR-LOCK INCORPORATED—See David Clark Company Incorporated; *U.S. Private*, pg. 1169
AIRLOCK LIMITED—See Publicis Groupe S.A.; *Int'l*, pg. 6100
AIR LOGISTICS CORPORATION; *U.S. Private*, pg. 139
AIR-LOG—See General Electric Company; *U.S. Public*, pg. 918
AIR LOUVERS, INC.—See Activar, Inc.; *U.S. Private*, pg. 68
AIRLUX ELECTRICAL CO., LTD.; *Int'l*, pg. 248
AIR LYNX SAS—See Atos SE; *Int'l*, pg. 690
AIR MACAU CO., LTD.—See China National Aviation Holding Company; *Int'l*, pg. 1525
AIRMAGNET, INC.—See NetScout Systems, Inc.; *U.S. Public*, pg. 1509
AIRMAIL CENTER FRANKFURT GMBH—See Fraport AG; *Int'l*, pg. 2764
AIR MALAWI LIMITED; *Int'l*, pg. 238
AIR MALTA PLC—See Ryanair Holdings PLC; *Int'l*, pg. 6438
AIR MANAGEMENT SUPPLY—See Century Air Conditioning Supply Inc.; *U.S. Private*, pg. 831
AIR MANAGEMENT SYSTEMS INC.; *U.S. Private*, pg. 139
AIR MANAS AIR COMPANY LLC—See ESAS Holding A.S.; *Int'l*, pg. 2501
AIRMAN ASIA SDN. BHD.—See Hokuetsu Industries Co., Ltd.; *Int'l*, pg. 3444
AIRMAN-FUSHENG (SHANGHAI) ELECTROMECHANICAL CO., LTD—See Hokuetsu Industries Co., Ltd.; *Int'l*, pg. 3444
AIRMAN USA CORPORATION—See Hokuetsu Industries Co., Ltd.; *Int'l*, pg. 3444
AIRMAR EMEA EURL—See Amphenol Corporation; *U.S. Public*, pg. 126
AIR MARINE SA; *Int'l*, pg. 238
AIR MARSHALL ISLANDS; *Int'l*, pg. 238
AIRMASTER FAN COMPANY; *U.S. Private*, pg. 141
AIR MASTERS HVAC SERVICES OF NEW ENGLAND, INC.—See Thielsch Engineering, Inc.; *U.S. Private*, pg. 4144
AIRMATE (CAYMAN) INTERNATIONAL CO. LIMITED; *Int'l*, pg. 248
AIRMATE CHINA INTERNATIONAL LIMITED—See Airmate (Cayman) International Co. Limited; *Int'l*, pg. 248
AIRMATE COMPANY; *U.S. Private*, pg. 141
AIRMATE E-COMMERCE (SHENZHEN) CO., LTD.—See Airmate (Cayman) International Co. Limited; *Int'l*, pg. 248
AIRMATE ELECTRICAL APPLIANCES (JIUJIANG) CO., LIMITED—See Airmate (Cayman) International Co. Limited; *Int'l*, pg. 248
AIRMATE INTERNATIONAL HOLDINGS LIMITED—See Airmate (Cayman) International Co. Limited; *Int'l*, pg. 248
AIRMATE LTD—See Air Mauritius Limited; *Int'l*, pg. 238
AIR MAURITIUS LIMITED; *Int'l*, pg. 238
AIR MAURITIUS SOUTH AFRICA (PTY) LIMITED—See Air Mauritius Limited; *Int'l*, pg. 238
AIR MECHANICAL & SERVICE CORP.; *U.S. Private*, pg. 139
AIRMECH WLL—See Mohammed Jalal & Sons WLL; *Int'l*, pg. 5018
AIR MEDICAL LTD.—See KKR & Co. Inc.; *U.S. Public*, pg. 1251
AIR MENZIES INTERNATIONAL (CAPE) PROPRIETARY LTD.—See Agility; *Int'l*, pg. 210
AIR MENZIES INTERNATIONAL (INDIA) PRIVATE LTD.—See Agility; *Int'l*, pg. 210
AIR MENZIES INTERNATIONAL (NZ) LTD.—See Agility; *Int'l*, pg. 210
AIR MENZIES INTERNATIONAL SA PROPRIETARY LTD.—See Agility; *Int'l*, pg. 210
AIR MENZIES INTERNATIONAL—See Agility; *Int'l*, pg. 210

AIR METHODS CORPORATION—See American Securities LLC; *U.S. Private*, pg. 247
AIR MILES MIDDLE EAST—See Aimia Inc.; *Int'l*, pg. 233
AIR MONITOR CORP.—See Harbour Group Industries, Inc.; *U.S. Private*, pg. 1860
AIRMONTE CORPORATION—See Kuriyama Holdings Corporation; *Int'l*, pg. 4341
AIRMOTIVE ENGINEERING CORP.—See Danbury Aerospace, Inc.; *U.S. Private*, pg. 1152
AIRMOVENT LIMITED—See AoFrio Limited; *Int'l*, pg. 487
AIR NAMIBIA (PTY) LTD.; *Int'l*, pg. 238
AIR NELSON LIMITED—See Air New Zealand Limited; *Int'l*, pg. 238
AIRNET GROUP, INC.; *U.S. Private*, pg. 141
AIRNET II, LLC—See H.I.G. Capital, LLC; *U.S. Private*, pg. 1828
AIRNET TECHNOLOGY INC.; *Int'l*, pg. 248
AIR NEW ZEALAND AIRCRAFT HOLDINGS LIMITED—See Air New Zealand Limited; *Int'l*, pg. 239
AIR NEW ZEALAND (AUSTRALIA) PTY LIMITED—See Air New Zealand Limited; *Int'l*, pg. 238
AIR NEW ZEALAND CARGO SERVICES—See Air New Zealand Limited; *Int'l*, pg. 239
AIR NEW ZEALAND ENGINEERING SERVICES—See Air New Zealand Limited; *Int'l*, pg. 239
AIR NEW ZEALAND LIMITED; *Int'l*, pg. 238
AIR NEW ZEALAND LTD. (U.S.A.)—See Air New Zealand Limited; *Int'l*, pg. 239
AIR NEXT CO., LTD.—See ANA Holdings Inc.; *Int'l*, pg. 444
AIR NIGERIA DEVELOPMENT LIMITED; *Int'l*, pg. 239
AIR NIPPON CO., LTD.—See ANA Holdings Inc.; *Int'l*, pg. 444
AIR NOSTRUM LINEAS AEREAS DEL MEDITERRANEO SA—See Nefinsa S.A.; *Int'l*, pg. 5191
AIROBOTICS LTD.—See Ondas Holdings, Inc.; *U.S. Public*, pg. 1602
AIRO CATERING SERVICES EESTI OU—See Deutsche Lufthansa AG; *Int'l*, pg. 2067
AIRO CATERING SERVICES LATVIJA SIA—See Deutsche Lufthansa AG; *Int'l*, pg. 2067
AIRO CATERING SERVICES - UKRAINE—See Deutsche Lufthansa AG; *Int'l*, pg. 2066
AIROHA TECHNOLOGY CORP.—See MediaTek Inc.; *Int'l*, pg. 4773
AIROHA TECHNOLOGY (SUZHOU) LIMITED—See MediaTek Inc.; *Int'l*, pg. 4773
AIROIL FLAREGAS PVT. LTD. - INDRAD WORKS—See Airoil Flaregas Pvt. Ltd.; *Int'l*, pg. 248
AIROIL FLAREGAS PVT. LTD.; *Int'l*, pg. 248
AIRO LAM LIMITED; *Int'l*, pg. 248
AIROLDI BROTHERS INC.; *U.S. Private*, pg. 142
THE AIROLITE COMPANY; *U.S. Private*, pg. 3983
AIRON CORPORATION—See Inspiration Healthcare Group Plc; *Int'l*, pg. 3720
AIR ONE S.P.A.—See Alitalia - Compagnia Aerea Italiana S.p.A.; *Int'l*, pg. 329
AIROOM INCORPORATED; *U.S. Private*, pg. 142
A.I. ROOT CO. - SAN ANTONO FACTORY—See A.I. Root Co.; *U.S. Private*, pg. 26
A.I. ROOT CO.; *U.S. Private*, pg. 26
AIROPS SOFTWARE LIMITED—See Gama Aviation plc; *Int'l*, pg. 2876
AIROTEK (CHENGDU) INC.—See MediaTek Inc.; *Int'l*, pg. 4773
AIROTEK (SHENZHEN) INC.—See MediaTek Inc.; *Int'l*, pg. 4773
AIROX—See Medtronic plc; *Int'l*, pg. 4786
AIR PACIFIC LIMITED; *Int'l*, pg. 239
AIR PARTNER HAVACILIK VE TASIMACILIK LTD.—See Wheels Up Experience Inc.; *U.S. Public*, pg. 2366
AIR PARTNER INC—See Wheels Up Experience Inc.; *U.S. Public*, pg. 2366
AIR PARTNER INTERNATIONAL GMBH—See Wheels Up Experience Inc.; *U.S. Public*, pg. 2366
AIR PARTNER INTERNATIONAL SAS—See Wheels Up Experience Inc.; *U.S. Public*, pg. 2366
AIR PARTNER PLC—See Wheels Up Experience Inc.; *U.S. Public*, pg. 2366
AIR PARTNER SRL—See Wheels Up Experience Inc.; *U.S. Public*, pg. 2366
AIR PARTNER SWITZERLAND AG—See Wheels Up Experience Inc.; *U.S. Public*, pg. 2366
AIR PARTNER TRAVEL CONSULTANTS LTD—See Wheels Up Experience Inc.; *U.S. Public*, pg. 2366
AIRPARTS COMPANY INC.; *U.S. Private*, pg. 142
AIR PARTS & SUPPLY CO.—See VSE Corporation; *U.S. Public*, pg. 2312
AIRPAS AVIATION GMBH—See Sabre Corporation; *U.S. Public*, pg. 1833
AIRPAY (THAILAND) CO., LTD—See Sea Limited; *Int'l*, pg. 6660
AIRPLANES, INC.—See STS Holdings, Inc.; *U.S. Private*, pg. 3842
AIRPLUS AIR TRAVEL CARD VERTRIEBSGESELLSCHAFT MBH—See Deutsche Lufthansa AG; *Int'l*, pg. 2068
AIRPLUS HOLDING GMBH—See Deutsche Lufthansa AG; *Int'l*, pg. 2068

COMPANY NAME INDEX

AIRPLUS INTERNATIONAL, INC.—See Deutsche Lufthansa AG; *Int'l*, pg. 2068
AIRPLUS INTERNATIONAL LIMITED—See Deutsche Lufthansa AG; *Int'l*, pg. 2068
AIRPLUS INTERNATIONAL S.R.L.—See Deutsche Lufthansa AG; *Int'l*, pg. 2068
AIR PLUS PTY LTD—See Reece Limited; *Int'l*, pg. 6249
AIRPLUS, SPOL. S R.O.—See CEZ, a.s.; *Int'l*, pg. 1426
AIRPORT ASSEKURANZ VERMITTLUNGS-GMBH—See Fraport AG; *Int'l*, pg. 2764
AIRPORT AUTHORITY WASHOE COUNTY; *U.S. Private*, pg. 142
AIRPORT CATER SERVICE GMBH—See Fraport AG; *Int'l*, pg. 2764
AIRPORT CITY BELGRADE D.O.O.—See Africa Israel Investments Ltd.; *Int'l*, pg. 190
AIRPORT CITY LTD.—See Equital Ltd.; *Int'l*, pg. 2487
AIRPORT CITY PROPERTY MANAGEMENT D.O.O.—See Africa Israel Investments Ltd.; *Int'l*, pg. 190
AIRPORT CLUB FUR INTERNATIONAL EXECUTIVES GMBH—See K&K Group AG; *Int'l*, pg. 4038
AIRPORT EQUIPMENT RENTALS INC.; *U.S. Private*, pg. 142
AIRPORT FACILITIES CO., LTD.; *Int'l*, pg. 248
AIRPORT FASHION SA—See Vivendi SE; *Int'l*, pg. 8275
AIRPORT FREIGHT FORWARDING CENTRE COMPANY LIMITED—See Sun Hung Kai Properties Limited; *Int'l*, pg. 7304
AIRPORT FUEL SERVICES PTY LTD—See Ampol Limited; *Int'l*, pg. 436
AIRPORT GROUND SERVICE CO., LTD.—See Japan Airlines Co., Ltd.; *Int'l*, pg. 3881
AIRPORT INTERNATIONAL GROUP P.S.C.—See Aeroports de Paris S.A.; *Int'l*, pg. 181
AIRPORT LINK CO. PTY LTD—See CP2 Group Limited; *Int'l*, pg. 1823
AIRPORT LINK CO. PTY LTD—See Westpac Banking Corporation; *Int'l*, pg. 8392
AIRPORT MARINA FORD—See Noarus Auto Group; *U.S. Private*, pg. 2932
AIRPORT MEDICAL SERVICES C.V.—See Air France-KLM S.A.; *Int'l*, pg. 236
AIRPORT MUNICH LOGISTICS AND SERVICES GMBH—See Siemens Aktiengesellschaft; *Int'l*, pg. 6886
AIRPORT RESTAURANTS (1996) LIMITED—See Goddard Enterprises Limited; *Int'l*, pg. 3018
AIRPORT SERVICES DRESDEN GMBH—See Deutsche Lufthansa AG; *Int'l*, pg. 2066
AIRPORT SERVICES FRIEDRICHSHAFEN GMBH—See Deutsche Lufthansa AG; *Int'l*, pg. 2066
AIRPORT SERVICES LEIPZIG GMBH—See Deutsche Lufthansa AG; *Int'l*, pg. 2066
AIRPORT SHUTTLE SERVICES LIMITED—See Brockman Mining Limited; *Int'l*, pg. 1173
AIRPORTS OF THAILAND PUBLIC COMPANY LIMITED; *Int'l*, pg. 248
AIRPORTS VANUATU LTD; *Int'l*, pg. 248
AIRPORT SYSTEMS UTAH-GROUND EQUIPMENT—See Oshkosh Corporation; *U.S. Public*, pg. 1620
AIRPORT TERMINAL SERVICE CO., LTD.—See Konoike Transport Co., Ltd.; *Int'l*, pg. 4274
AIRPORT TERMINAL SERVICES INC.; *U.S. Private*, pg. 142
AIR POWER, INC.; *U.S. Private*, pg. 139
AIR POWER INC.—See Van Bortel Aircraft Inc.; *U.S. Private*, pg. 4339
AIR POWER OF NEBRASKA, INC.—See Atlas Copco AB; *Int'l*, pg. 680
AIR PRECISION SAS—See Advent International Corporation; *U.S. Private*, pg. 99
AIRPRODUCT AG—See Wurth Verwaltungsgesellschaft mbH; *Int'l*, pg. 8503
AIR PRODUCTIONS—See LOV Group Invest SAS; *Int'l*, pg. 4563
AIR PRODUCTS AND CHEMICALS (CHINA) INVESTMENT CO. LTD.—See Air Products & Chemicals, Inc.; *U.S. Public*, pg. 66
AIR PRODUCTS AND CHEMICALS (NANJING) CO., LTD.—See Air Products & Chemicals, Inc.; *U.S. Public*, pg. 66
AIR PRODUCTS AND CHEMICALS (SHANGHAI) CO. LTD.—See Air Products & Chemicals, Inc.; *U.S. Public*, pg. 66
AIR PRODUCTS AND CHEMICALS (SHANGHAI) GASES CO., LTD.—See Air Products & Chemicals, Inc.; *U.S. Public*, pg. 66
AIR PRODUCTS ASIA, INC.—See Air Products & Chemicals, Inc.; *U.S. Public*, pg. 64
AIR PRODUCTS A/S—See Air Products & Chemicals, Inc.; *U.S. Public*, pg. 64
AIR PRODUCTS BRASIL LTDA.—See Air Products & Chemicals, Inc.; *U.S. Public*, pg. 64
AIR PRODUCTS (BR) LIMITED—See Air Products & Chemicals, Inc.; *U.S. Public*, pg. 64
AIR PRODUCTS CANADA LTD.—See Air Products & Chemicals, Inc.; *U.S. Public*, pg. 64
AIR PRODUCTS CANADA LTD.—See Air Products & Chemicals, Inc.; *U.S. Public*, pg. 64
AIR PRODUCTS CANADA LTD.—See Air Products & Chemicals, Inc.; *U.S. Public*, pg. 64
AIR PRODUCTS CANADA LTD.—See Air Products & Chemicals, Inc.; *U.S. Public*, pg. 64
AIR PRODUCTS CANADA LTD.—See Air Products & Chemicals, Inc.; *U.S. Public*, pg. 64
AIR PRODUCTS & CHEMICALS, INC.—See Air Products & Chemicals, Inc.; *U.S. Public*, pg. 64
AIR PRODUCTS & CHEMICALS, INC.; *U.S. Public*, pg. 64
AIR PRODUCTS (CHEMICALS) PUBLIC LIMITED COMPANY—See Air Products & Chemicals, Inc.; *U.S. Public*, pg. 64
AIR PRODUCTS CHILE S. A.—See Air Products & Chemicals, Inc.; *U.S. Public*, pg. 64
AIR PRODUCTS CHINA INC.—See Air Products & Chemicals, Inc.; *U.S. Public*, pg. 64
AIR PRODUCTS GAS O.O.O.—See Air Products & Chemicals, Inc.; *U.S. Public*, pg. 65
AIR PRODUCTS GAZ SANAYI VI TICARET LIMITED—See Air Products & Chemicals, Inc.; *U.S. Public*, pg. 65
AIR PRODUCTS GB LIMITED—See Air Products & Chemicals, Inc.; *U.S. Public*, pg. 65
AIR PRODUCTS GMBH—See Air Products & Chemicals, Inc.; *U.S. Public*, pg. 65
AIR PRODUCTS GMBH—See Air Products & Chemicals, Inc.; *U.S. Public*, pg. 65
AIR PRODUCTS HELIUM, INC.—See Air Products & Chemicals, Inc.; *U.S. Public*, pg. 65
AIR PRODUCTS HOLDINGS B.V.—See Air Products & Chemicals, Inc.; *U.S. Public*, pg. 65
AIR PRODUCTS IBERICA, S.L.—See Air Products & Chemicals, Inc.; *U.S. Public*, pg. 65
AIR PRODUCTS INDUSTRY CO., LTD.—See Mitsubishi Chemical Group Corporation; *Int'l*, pg. 4935
AIR PRODUCTS INTERNATIONAL CORPORATION—See Air Products & Chemicals, Inc.; *U.S. Public*, pg. 65
AIR PRODUCTS INVESTMENTS B.V.—See Air Products & Chemicals, Inc.; *U.S. Public*, pg. 65
AIR PRODUCTS INVESTMENTS ESPANA, S.L.—See Air Products & Chemicals, Inc.; *U.S. Public*, pg. 65
AIR PRODUCTS IRELAND LIMITED—See Air Products & Chemicals, Inc.; *U.S. Public*, pg. 65
AIR PRODUCTS ITALIA—See Air Products & Chemicals, Inc.; *U.S. Public*, pg. 65
AIR PRODUCTS JAPAN K.K.—See Air Products & Chemicals, Inc.; *U.S. Public*, pg. 65
AIR PRODUCTS KOREA, INC.—See Air Products & Chemicals, Inc.; *U.S. Public*, pg. 65
AIR PRODUCTS MALAYSIA SDN BHD—See Air Products & Chemicals, Inc.; *U.S. Public*, pg. 65
AIR PRODUCTS MANAGEMENT S.A.—See Air Products & Chemicals, Inc.; *U.S. Public*, pg. 65
AIR PRODUCTS MANUFACTURING CORPORATION—See Air Products & Chemicals, Inc.; *U.S. Public*, pg. 65
AIR PRODUCTS (MIDDLE EAST) FZE—See Air Products & Chemicals, Inc.; *U.S. Public*, pg. 64
AIR PRODUCTS NEDERLAND B.V.-CHEMICALS DIV—See Air Products & Chemicals, Inc.; *U.S. Public*, pg. 65
AIR PRODUCTS NEDERLAND B.V.—See Air Products & Chemicals, Inc.; *U.S. Public*, pg. 65
AIR PRODUCTS NEDERLAND B.V.—See Air Products & Chemicals, Inc.; *U.S. Public*, pg. 65
AIR PRODUCTS NEDERLAND B.V.—See Air Products & Chemicals, Inc.; *U.S. Public*, pg. 65
AIR PRODUCTS NEDERLAND B.V.—See Air Products & Chemicals, Inc.; *U.S. Public*, pg. 65
AIR PRODUCTS N.V.—See Air Products & Chemicals, Inc.; *U.S. Public*, pg. 65
AIR PRODUCTS N.V.—See Air Products & Chemicals, Inc.; *U.S. Public*, pg. 65
AIR PRODUCTS O.O.O.—See Air Products & Chemicals, Inc.; *U.S. Public*, pg. 65
AIR PRODUCTS PERFORMANCE MANUFACTURING, INC.—See Air Products & Chemicals, Inc.; *U.S. Public*, pg. 65
AIR PRODUCTS PERFORMANCE MATERIALS GMBH—See Air Products & Chemicals, Inc.; *U.S. Public*, pg. 65
AIR PRODUCTS PERU S.A.—See Air Products & Chemicals, Inc.; *U.S. Public*, pg. 65
AIR PRODUCTS PLC—See Air Products & Chemicals, Inc.; *U.S. Public*, pg. 65
AIR PRODUCTS PLC—See Air Products & Chemicals, Inc.; *U.S. Public*, pg. 65
AIR PRODUCTS PLC—See Air Products & Chemicals, Inc.; *U.S. Public*, pg. 65
AIR PRODUCTS SAN FU CO., LTD.—See Air Products & Chemicals, Inc.; *U.S. Public*, pg. 65
AIR PRODUCTS SAN FU GAS CO., LTD.—See Air Products & Chemicals, Inc.; *U.S. Public*, pg. 65
AIR PRODUCTS SAN FU GAS CO., LTD.—See San Fu Chemical Co., Ltd.; *Int'l*, pg. 6520
AIR PRODUCTS S.A.—See Air Products & Chemicals, Inc.; *U.S. Public*, pg. 65
AIR PRODUCTS S.A.—See Air Products & Chemicals, Inc.; *U.S. Public*, pg. 65
AIR PRODUCTS SAS—See Air Products & Chemicals, Inc.; *U.S. Public*, pg. 65
AIR PRODUCTS SCHLUCHTERN GMBH—See Air Products & Chemicals, Inc.; *U.S. Public*, pg. 65
AIR PRODUCTS SERVICES EUROPE, S.A.—See Air Products & Chemicals, Inc.; *U.S. Public*, pg. 65
AIR PRODUCTS SINGAPORE INDUSTRIAL GASES PTE. LTD.—See Air Products & Chemicals, Inc.; *U.S. Public*, pg. 65
AIR PRODUCTS SINGAPORE PTE LTD.—See Air Products & Chemicals, Inc.; *U.S. Public*, pg. 66
AIR PRODUCTS SLOVAKIA S.R.O.—See Air Products & Chemicals, Inc.; *U.S. Public*, pg. 66
AIR PRODUCTS SOUTH AFRICA (PTY) LTD.—See Air Products & Chemicals, Inc.; *U.S. Public*, pg. 66
AIR PRODUCTS SOUTH AFRICA (PTY) LTD.—See Remgro Limited; *Int'l*, pg. 6269
AIR PRODUCTS-SPECIALTY GASES FACILITY—See Air Products & Chemicals, Inc.; *U.S. Public*, pg. 66
AIR PRODUCTS SPOL S.R.O.—See Air Products & Chemicals, Inc.; *U.S. Public*, pg. 66
AIR PRODUCTS SP. Z.O.O.—See Air Products & Chemicals, Inc.; *U.S. Public*, pg. 66
AIR PRODUCTS STB—See Air Products & Chemicals, Inc.; *U.S. Public*, pg. 65
AIR PRODUCTS STB—See Air Products & Chemicals, Inc.; *U.S. Public*, pg. 65
AIR PRODUCTS TAIWAN CO., LTD.—See Air Products & Chemicals, Inc.; *U.S. Public*, pg. 66
AIR PRO HOLDINGS, INC.; *U.S. Private*, pg. 139
AIRPRO INC.—See Comfort Services Inc.; *U.S. Private*, pg. 981
AIR PROS; *U.S. Private*, pg. 139
AIR PROS USA; *U.S. Private*, pg. 139
AIR PURCHASES INCORPORATED; *U.S. Private*, pg. 139
AIR PURCHASES OF NEW HAMPSHIRE—See Ridgemont Partners Management LLC; *U.S. Private*, pg. 3433
AIR QUALITY CONTROL, INC.; *U.S. Private*, pg. 139
AIRRATTLE INC.; *U.S. Private*, pg. 142
AIRREPS HAWAII—See Heide & Cook Mechanical Contractors; *U.S. Private*, pg. 1904
AIR RESCUE AIR CONDITIONING, INC.; *U.S. Private*, pg. 139
AIR-RIDE INC.; *U.S. Private*, pg. 140
AIR RIDE TECHNOLOGIES, INC.—See Fox Factory Holding Corp.; *U.S. Public*, pg. 877
AIR RIDE TECHNOLOGIES LLC; *U.S. Private*, pg. 139
AIR-RITE HEATING & COOLING; *U.S. Private*, pg. 140
AIRROBOT GMBH & CO. KG—See Nordic Unmanned ASA; *Int'l*, pg. 5423
AIRROSTI REHAB CENTERS, LLC; *U.S. Private*, pg. 142
AIR ROVER, INC.—See Guardian Capital Partners, LLC; *U.S. Private*, pg. 1810
AIR ROYALE INTERNATIONAL INC.; *U.S. Private*, pg. 139
AIR RUTTER INTERNATIONAL, LLC; *U.S. Private*, pg. 139
AIR SAFETY EQUIPMENT INC.; *U.S. Private*, pg. 139
AIR SAMPLER DIV.—See The Staplex Company, Inc.; *U.S. Private*, pg. 4121
AIRSAN CORPORATION—See Clover Creek Partners, LLC; *U.S. Private*, pg. 947
AIRSCREW LIMITED—See AMETEK, Inc.; *U.S. Public*, pg. 117
AIRSCULPT TECHNOLOGIES, INC.; *U.S. Public*, pg. 68
AIR-SEA FORWARDERS INC.; *U.S. Private*, pg. 140
AIR SEA WORLDWIDE (CHINA) LTD.—See Yamatane Corporation; *Int'l*, pg. 8553
AIRSEC S.A.S.—See Clariant AG; *Int'l*, pg. 1646
AIRSEP CORPORATION—See Niterra Co., Ltd.; *Int'l*, pg. 5380
AIR SERV CORPORATION—See ABM Industries, Inc.; *U.S. Public*, pg. 26
AIR-SERV GROUP, LLC—See Pamplona Capital Management LLP; *Int'l*, pg. 5711
AIR SERVICE HAWAII; *U.S. Private*, pg. 139
AIR SERVICES INC.—See 1100 Holdings LLC; *U.S. Private*, pg. 2
AIR SEYCHELLES LTD.; *Int'l*, pg. 239
AIRSHIP AI HOLDINGS, INC.; *U.S. Public*, pg. 68
AIRSHIP & BALLOON COMPANY LTD.; *Int'l*, pg. 248
AIRSHIP, LLC—See Trivest Partners, LP; *U.S. Private*, pg. 4241
AIR SHOP B.V.—See Ranger Aerospace LLC; *U.S. Private*, pg. 3354
AIRSIDE MOBILE INC.—See Onfido Ltd; *Int'l*, pg. 5581
AIRSIS, INC.—See Oceaneering International, Inc.; *U.S. Public*, pg. 1562
AIRSOL B.V.—See SOL S.p.A.; *Int'l*, pg. 7067
AIRSOUTH INSURANCE, INC.—See GTCR LLC; *U.S. Private*, pg. 1802
AIRSPAN COMMUNICATIONS LTD.—See Airspan Networks Holdings Inc.; *U.S. Public*, pg. 68

AIRSPAN COMMUNICATIONS (SHANGHAI) CO. LTD.—See Airspan Networks Holdings Inc.; *U.S. Public*, pg. 68
AIRSPAN JAPAN KK (KABUSHIKI KAISHA)—See Airspan Networks Holdings Inc.; *U.S. Public*, pg. 68
AIRSPAN NETWORKS HOLDINGS INC.; *U.S. Public*, pg. 68
AIRSPAN NETWORKS INC.—See Airspan Networks Holdings Inc.; *U.S. Public*, pg. 68
AIRSPAN NETWORKS (ISRAEL) LTD—See Airspan Networks Holdings Inc.; *U.S. Public*, pg. 68
AIRSPAN NETWORKS PTY LTD—See Airspan Networks Holdings Inc.; *U.S. Public*, pg. 68
AIRSPARES—See Airbus SE; *Int'l*, pg. 244
AIRSPEED, LLC—See Mercury Aircraft Inc.; *U.S. Private*, pg. 2670
AIRSPLAT, CO.; *U.S. Private*, pg. 142
AIRSPRUNG FURNITURE LIMITED—See Airsprung Group PLC; *Int'l*, pg. 248
AIRSPRUNG GROUP PLC; *Int'l*, pg. 248
AIRSTREAM, INC.—See Thor Industries, Inc.; *U.S. Public*, pg. 2156
AIR SUNSHINE INC.; *U.S. Private*, pg. 139
AIR-SUR, INC.—See Arthur J. Gallagher & Co.; *U.S. Public*, pg. 202
AIRSYS COMMUNICATIONS TECHNOLOGY LIMITED; *Int'l*, pg. 248
AIR SYSTEM COMPONENTS, INC.—See Canada Pension Plan Investment Board; *Int'l*, pg. 1278
AIR SYSTEMS DISTRIBUTORS LLC—See Watsco, Inc.; *U.S. Public*, pg. 2336
AIR SYSTEMS ENGINEERING, INC.—See Comfort Systems USA, Inc.; *U.S. Public*, pg. 543
AIR SYSTEMS, INC.—See EMCOR Group, Inc.; *U.S. Public*, pg. 736
AIR SYSTEMS SALES INC.; *U.S. Private*, pg. 139
AIR SYSTEM TECHNOLOGY (S) PTE LTD—See Acesian Partners Limited; *Int'l*, pg. 102
AIRT ACADEMY OF INFRARED TRAINING INC.—See Cantronic Systems Inc.; *Int'l*, pg. 1299
AIRTAC (CHINA) CO., LTD.—See Airtac International Group; *Int'l*, pg. 248
AIRTAC CO., LTD.—See Airtac International Group; *Int'l*, pg. 249
AIRTAC (FUJIAN) INTELLIGENT EQUIPMENT CO., LTD.—See Airtac International Group; *Int'l*, pg. 248
AIRTAC INDUSTRIAL CO., LTD.—See Airtac International Group; *Int'l*, pg. 249
AIRTAC INDUSTRIAL (MALAYSIA) SDN. BHD.—See Airtac International Group; *Int'l*, pg. 249
AIRTAC INTERNATIONAL GROUP; *Int'l*, pg. 248
AIRTAC (JIANGSU) AUTOMATION CO., LTD.—See Airtac International Group; *Int'l*, pg. 248
AIRTAC (TIANJIN) INTELLIGENT TECHNOLOGY CO., LTD.—See Airtac International Group; *Int'l*, pg. 248
AIRTAC USA CORPORATION—See Airtac International Group; *Int'l*, pg. 249
AIR TAHITI; *Int'l*, pg. 239
AIRTASKER LIMITED; *Int'l*, pg. 249
AIRTEC FRANCE SARL—See AIRTEC Pneumatic GmbH; *Int'l*, pg. 249
AIRTECH EQUIPMENT PTE. LTD.—See AIRTECH JAPAN, LTD.; *Int'l*, pg. 249
AIRTECH GROUP, INC.—See IDEX Corp.; *U.S. Public*, pg. 1089
AIRTECH INTERNATIONAL INC.; *U.S. Private*, pg. 142
AIRTECH JAPAN, LTD. - CLEAN SUPPLY FACTORY—See AIRTECH JAPAN, LTD.; *Int'l*, pg. 249
AIRTECH JAPAN, LTD. - GUNMA FACTORY—See AIRTECH JAPAN, LTD.; *Int'l*, pg. 249
AIRTECH JAPAN, LTD. - KAZO FACTORY—See AIRTECH JAPAN, LTD.; *Int'l*, pg. 249
AIRTECH JAPAN, LTD. - SOKA FACTORY—See AIRTECH JAPAN, LTD.; *Int'l*, pg. 249
AIRTECH JAPAN, LTD.; *Int'l*, pg. 249
AIR TECHNIQUES, INC.; *U.S. Private*, pg. 139
AIR TECHNIQUES, INC. - WESTERN FACILITY—See Air Techniques, Inc.; *U.S. Private*, pg. 140
AIR TECHNOLOGIES, INC.—See Genstar Capital, LLC; *U.S. Private*, pg. 1678
AIR TECHNOLOGY ENGINES, INC.; *U.S. Private*, pg. 140
AIRTECH SYSTEM CO., LTD.—See AIRTECH JAPAN, LTD.; *Int'l*, pg. 249
AIRTEC LIMITED—See Ingersoll Rand Inc.; *U.S. Public*, pg. 1120
AIRTEC PNEUMATIC C.C.—See AIRTEC Pneumatic GmbH; *Int'l*, pg. 249
AIRTEC PNEUMATIC ENGINEERING BV—See AIRTEC Pneumatic GmbH; *Int'l*, pg. 249
AIRTEC PNEUMATIC GMBH; *Int'l*, pg. 249
AIRTEC PNEUMATICS INC—See AIRTEC Pneumatic GmbH; *Int'l*, pg. 249
AIRTEC PNEUMATICS UK LTD.—See AIRTEC Pneumatic GmbH; *Int'l*, pg. 249
AIRTEC PNEUMATIC SWEDEN AB—See AIRTEC Pneumatic GmbH; *Int'l*, pg. 249
AIRTEL AFRICA PLC; *Int'l*, pg. 249
AIRTEL CONGO RDC S.A.—See Airtel Africa Plc; *Int'l*, pg. 249
AIRTEL GHANA LIMITED—See Bharti Enterprises Limited; *Int'l*, pg. 1012
AIRTEL GHANA LIMITED—See Millicom International Cellular S.A.; *Int'l*, pg. 4896
AIRTEL MALAWI LIMITED—See Bharti Enterprises Limited; *Int'l*, pg. 1012
AIRTEL M COMMERCE SERVICES LIMITED—See Bharti Enterprises Limited; *Int'l*, pg. 1012
AIRTEL MOBILE COMMERCE HOLDINGS B.V.—See Bharti Enterprises Limited; *Int'l*, pg. 1012
AIRTEL MONEY TANZANIA LIMITED—See Airtel Africa Plc; *Int'l*, pg. 249
AIRTEL MONEY TRANSFER LIMITED—See Airtel Africa Plc; *Int'l*, pg. 249
AIRTEL NETWORKS KENYA LIMITED—See Bharti Enterprises Limited; *Int'l*, pg. 1011
AIRTEL NETWORKS LIMITED—See Bharti Enterprises Limited; *Int'l*, pg. 1012
AIRTEL NETWORKS ZAMBIA PLC—See Bharti Enterprises Limited; *Int'l*, pg. 1012
AIRTEL RWANDA LIMITED—See Bharti Enterprises Limited; *Int'l*, pg. 1012
AIRTEL (SEYCHELLES) LIMITED—See Bharti Enterprises Limited; *Int'l*, pg. 1012
AIRTEL TANZANIA LIMITED—See Bharti Enterprises Limited; *Int'l*, pg. 1012
AIRTEL TCHAD S.A.—See Bharti Enterprises Limited; *Int'l*, pg. 1012
AIRTEL UGANDA LIMITED—See Bharti Enterprises Limited; *Int'l*, pg. 1013
AIRTEMP, INC.—See Comfort Systems USA, Inc.; *U.S. Public*, pg. 543
AIR TEMP MECHANICAL SERVICES, INC.—See United Mechanical, Inc.; *U.S. Private*, pg. 4294
AIRTEX MANUFACTURING PARTNERSHIP - CALGARY HEAT TRANSFER PLANT—See Airtex Manufacturing Partnership; *Int'l*, pg. 249
AIRTEX MANUFACTURING PARTNERSHIP - EDMONTON FACTORY—See Airtex Manufacturing Partnership; *Int'l*, pg. 249
AIRTEX MANUFACTURING PARTNERSHIP - NEWMARKET FACTORY—See Airtex Manufacturing Partnership; *Int'l*, pg. 249
AIRTEX MANUFACTURING PARTNERSHIP; *Int'l*, pg. 249
AIRTEX PRODUCTS, LP—See Crowne Group LLC; *U.S. Private*, pg. 1112
AIRTIFICIAL INTELLIGENCE STRUCTURES SA; *Int'l*, pg. 249
AIR TIGER EXPRESS COMPANIES, INC.—See Kawasaki Kisen Kaisha, Ltd.; *Int'l*, pg. 4098
AIRTIGHT NETWORKS, INC.; *U.S. Private*, pg. 142
AIRTIME MANAGEMENT AND PROGRAMMING SDN. BHD.—See Astro All Asia Networks plc; *Int'l*, pg. 662
AIR T, INC.; *U.S. Public*, pg. 67
AIR TINDI LTD.—See Clairvest Group Inc.; *Int'l*, pg. 1641
AIRTISSUE S.R.L.—See Cartiera Lucchese S.p.A.; *Int'l*, pg. 1348
AIRTITE CONTRACTORS INC.—See CDM Investment Group, Inc.; *U.S. Private*, pg. 802
AIR TOOL SERVICE COMPANY—See Shoreview Industries, LLC; *U.S. Private*, pg. 3642
AIR TOTAL INTERNATIONAL SA—See TotalEnergies SE; *Int'l*, pg. 7835
AIRTOUCH SOLAR LTD; *Int'l*, pg. 249
AIR TRADE CENTRE BELGIUM N.V.—See SIG plc; *Int'l*, pg. 6906
AIRTRADE HOLLAND B.V.—See Koninklijke Luchtvaart Maatschappij N.V.; *Int'l*, pg. 4267
AIR-TRAK—See EROAD Limited; *Int'l*, pg. 2496
AIRTRAN AIRWAYS, INC.—See Southwest Airlines Co.; *U.S. Public*, pg. 1913
AIR TRANSAT A T INC—See Transat A.T., Inc.; *Int'l*, pg. 7896
AIR TRANSPORT COMPONENTS, LLC; *U.S. Private*, pg. 140
AIR TRANSPORT, INC.—See Air Transport Investments, Inc.; *U.S. Private*, pg. 4210
AIR TRANSPORT INTERNATIONAL, INC.—See Air Transport Services Group, Inc.; *U.S. Public*, pg. 67
AIR TRANSPORT INTERNATIONAL LIMITED LIABILITY COMPANY—See Air Transport Services Group, Inc.; *U.S. Public*, pg. 67
AIR TRANSPORT INTERNATIONAL, LLC—See Air Transport Services Group, Inc.; *U.S. Public*, pg. 67
AIR-TRANSPORT IT SERVICES, INC.—See Amadeus IT Group, S.A.; *Int'l*, pg. 406
AIR TRANSPORT SERVICES GROUP, INC.; *U.S. Public*, pg. 67
AIR TRAVEL BUREAU PRIVATE LIMITED—See Yatra Online, Inc.; *Int'l*, pg. 8571
AIR TREATMENT CORP.; *U.S. Private*, pg. 140
AIRTREKS; *U.S. Private*, pg. 142
AIRTRICITY ENERGY SUPPLY (NORTHERN IRELAND) LIMITED—See SSE Plc; *Int'l*, pg. 7155
AIRTRICITY LIMITED—See SSE Plc; *Int'l*, pg. 7156
AIRTRIP CORP.; *Int'l*, pg. 250
AIRTROL, INC.; *U.S. Private*, pg. 142
AIRTRONA INTERNATIONAL, INC.; *Int'l*, pg. 250
AIRTRON HOUSTON—See NRG Energy, Inc.; *U.S. Public*, pg. 1549
AIR TROPOLIS EXPRESS (S) PTE. LTD.—See T3EX Global Holdings Corp.; *Int'l*, pg. 7398
AIRUL ENTERPRISES, INC.—See Roark Capital Group, Inc.; *U.S. Private*, pg. 3454
AIR VACUUM AUTOMATION VIETNAM COMPANY LIMITED—See ISDN Holdings Limited; *Int'l*, pg. 3813
AIRVANA, INC.; *U.S. Private*, pg. 142
AIRVANA NETWORKS INDIA PRIVATE LIMITED—See Airvana, Inc.; *U.S. Private*, pg. 142
AIRVANCE GROUP; *Int'l*, pg. 250
AIR VANUATU LTD; *Int'l*, pg. 239
AIR VENT INC.—See Gibraltar Industries, Inc.; *U.S. Public*, pg. 935
AIRWAIR INTERNATIONAL LIMITED—See Permira Advisers LLP; *Int'l*, pg. 5808
AIRWALK COMMUNICATIONS, INC.—See Ubee Interactive, Inc.; *U.S. Private*, pg. 4273
AIRWATCH LLC—See Dell Technologies Inc.; *U.S. Public*, pg. 649
AIR WATER AMERICA INC.—See Air Water Inc.; *Int'l*, pg. 239
AIR WATER ASIA PTE. LTD.—See Air Water Inc.; *Int'l*, pg. 239
AIR WATER BELLPEARL INC.—See Air Water Inc.; *Int'l*, pg. 239
AIR WATER CARBONIC INC.—See Air Water Inc.; *Int'l*, pg. 239
AIR WATER ECOROCA INC.—See Air Water Inc.; *Int'l*, pg. 239
AIR WATER & ENERGIA POWER YAMAGUCHI CORPORATION—See The Chugoku Electric Power Co., Inc.; *Int'l*, pg. 7632
AIR WATER INC. - HOKKAIDO—See Air Water Inc.; *Int'l*, pg. 239
AIR WATER INC. - KASHIMA PLANT—See Air Water Inc.; *Int'l*, pg. 239
AIR WATER INC.; *Int'l*, pg. 239
AIR & WATER, INC.; *U.S. Private*, pg. 138
AIR WATER, INC. - TOKYO—See Air Water Inc.; *Int'l*, pg. 239
AIR WATER INDIA PRIVATE LIMITED—See Air Water Inc.; *Int'l*, pg. 239
AIR WATER LINK INC.—See Air Water Inc.; *Int'l*, pg. 239
AIR WATER MACH (DALIAN) CO., LTD.—See Air Water Inc.; *Int'l*, pg. 239
AIR WATER MACH INC.—See Air Water Inc.; *Int'l*, pg. 239
AIR WATER MACH RUBBER PRODUCTS (FUJIAN) CO., LTD.—See Air Water Inc.; *Int'l*, pg. 239
AIR WATER MATERIALS INC.—See Air Water Inc.; *Int'l*, pg. 239
AIR WATER NV INC.—See Air Water Inc.; *Int'l*, pg. 239
AIR WATER NV (SHANGHAI) CO., LTD.—See Air Water Inc.; *Int'l*, pg. 239
AIR WATER PHILIPPINES, INC.—See Air Water Inc.; *Int'l*, pg. 239
AIR WATER PLANT & ENGINEERING, INC.—See Air Water Inc.; *Int'l*, pg. 239
AIR WATER SAFETY SERVICE INC.—See Air Water Inc.; *Int'l*, pg. 239
AIR WATER & SOIL LABORATORIES, INC.—See Montrose Environmental Group, Inc.; *U.S. Public*, pg. 1466
AIR WATER SOL INC.—See Air Water Inc.; *Int'l*, pg. 239
AIR WATER SOL (SHANGHAI) TRADING CO. LTD.—See Air Water Inc.; *Int'l*, pg. 239
AIR WATER SPECIAL GAS CO., LTD.—See Air Water Inc.; *Int'l*, pg. 239
AIR WATER (THAILAND) CO., LTD.—See Air Water Inc.; *Int'l*, pg. 239
AIR WATER VIETNAM CO., LTD.—See Air Water Inc.; *Int'l*, pg. 239
AIRWAVE SOLUTIONS LIMITED—See Motorola Solutions, Inc.; *U.S. Public*, pg. 1478
AIR-WAY MANUFACTURING COMPANY; *U.S. Private*, pg. 140
AIRWAY MEDIX SA; *Int'l*, pg. 250
AIRWAY OXYGEN, INC.—See AdaptHealth Corp.; *U.S. Public*, pg. 38
AIRWELD INC.; *U.S. Private*, pg. 142
AIR WISCONSIN AIRLINES CORPORATION; *U.S. Private*, pg. 140
AIR WISCONSIN, INC.—See United Airlines Holdings, Inc.; *U.S. Public*, pg. 2228
AIR WIS SERVICES, INC.—See United Airlines Holdings, Inc.; *U.S. Public*, pg. 2228
AIRWORK HOLDINGS LIMITED—See Zhejiang RIFA Digital Precision Machinery Co., Ltd.; *Int'l*, pg. 8662
AIRWORKS LLC—See ATL Partners, LLC; *U.S. Private*, pg. 369
AIR WORLDWIDE CORPORATION—See Verisk Analytics, Inc.; *U.S. Public*, pg. 2282
AIRXCEL, INC.—See Thor Industries, Inc.; *U.S. Public*, pg. 2156
AIRXPANDERS INC.; *U.S. Private*, pg. 142
AIR'ZONA AIRCRAFT SERVICES, INC.—See Air T, Inc.; *U.S. Public*, pg. 67
A.I.S. AG; *Int'l*, pg. 24

COMPANY NAME INDEX

AISAN AUTOPARTES MEXICO, S.A. DE C.V.—See Aisan Industry Co., Ltd.; *Int'l*, pg. 250
AISAN BITRON LOUNY S.R.O.—See Aisan Industry Co., Ltd.; *Int'l*, pg. 250
AISAN COMPUTER SERVICES CORP.—See Aisan Industry Co., Ltd.; *Int'l*, pg. 250
AISAN CORPORATION ASIA PACIFIC LIMITED—See Aisan Industry Co., Ltd.; *Int'l*, pg. 250
AISAN CORPORATION EUROPE S.A.—See Aisan Industry Co., Ltd.; *Int'l*, pg. 250
AISAN CORPORATION GAUANGZHOU CO., LTD—See Aisan Industry Co., Ltd.; *Int'l*, pg. 250
AISAN CORPORATION OF AMERICA, INC.—See Aisan Industry Co., Ltd.; *Int'l*, pg. 250
AISAN (FHOSHAN) AUTO PARTS CO., LTD—See Aisan Industry Co., Ltd.; *Int'l*, pg. 250
AISAN (FOSHAN) AUTO PARTS CO., LTD.—See Aisan Industry Co., Ltd.; *Int'l*, pg. 250
AISAN INDUSTRY CO., LTD - ANJO PLANT—See Aisan Industry Co., Ltd.; *Int'l*, pg. 250
AISAN INDUSTRY CO., LTD.; *Int'l*, pg. 250
AISAN INDUSTRY CO., LTD. - TOYOTA PLANT—See Aisan Industry Co., Ltd.; *Int'l*, pg. 250
AISAN INDUSTRY CZECH S.R.O.—See Aisan Industry Co., Ltd.; *Int'l*, pg. 250
AISAN INDUSTRY FRANCE SA—See Aisan Industry Co., Ltd.; *Int'l*, pg. 250
AISAN INDUSTRY INDIA PVT. LTD.—See Aisan Industry Co., Ltd.; *Int'l*, pg. 250
AISAN INDUSTRY KENTUCKY, LLC—See Aisan Industry Co., Ltd.; *Int'l*, pg. 250
AISAN INDUSTRY LOUNY S.R.O.—See Aisan Industry Co., Ltd.; *Int'l*, pg. 250
AISAN KUMAMOTO CO., LTD.—See Aisan Industry Co., Ltd.; *Int'l*, pg. 250
AISAN SALES INDIA PVT. LTD.—See Aisan Industry Co., Ltd.; *Int'l*, pg. 250
AISAN TECHNOLOGY CO., LTD.; *Int'l*, pg. 251
AISAN (TIANJIN) AUTO PARTS CO., LTD—See Aisan Industry Co., Ltd.; *Int'l*, pg. 250
AIS, CO., LTD.—See Ubicom Holdings, Inc.; *Int'l*, pg. 8003
AIS CONSTRUCTION EQUIPMENT CORP.; *U.S. Private*, pg. 142
AISEI MYANMAR CO., LTD.—See Taisei Corporation; *Int'l*, pg. 7415
AISEI PHARMACY CO., LTD.; *Int'l*, pg. 251
AISEL CORPORATION—See ITFOR Inc.; *Int'l*, pg. 3833
AISHA STEEL MILLS LIMITED; *Int'l*, pg. 251
AISHIDA CO., LTD.; *Int'l*, pg. 251
AISHIDA CO., LTD.; *Int'l*, pg. 251
AISHIN TSUSHO CO., LTD.—See Sac's Bar Holdings Inc.; *Int'l*, pg. 6463
AISIN AI (THAILAND) CO., LTD.—See AISIN Corporation; *Int'l*, pg. 251
AISIN ASIA PACIFIC CO., LTD—See AISIN Corporation; *Int'l*, pg. 251
AISIN ASIA PTE. LTD.—See AISIN Corporation; *Int'l*, pg. 252
AISIN (AUSTRALIA) PTY. LTD.—See AISIN Corporation; *Int'l*, pg. 252
AISIN AUTOMOTIVE CASTING, LLC—See AISIN Corporation; *Int'l*, pg. 252
AISIN AUTOMOTIVE CASTING TENNESSEE, INC.—See AISIN Corporation; *Int'l*, pg. 251
AISIN AW INDUSTRIES CO., LTD.—See AISIN Corporation; *Int'l*, pg. 252
AISIN CANADA, INC—See AISIN Corporation; *Int'l*, pg. 251
AISIN CHEMICAL CO., LTD.—See AISIN Corporation; *Int'l*, pg. 252
AISIN CHEMICAL INDIANA, LLC—See AISIN Corporation; *Int'l*, pg. 252
AISIN CHEMICAL (THAILAND) CO., LTD.—See AISIN Corporation; *Int'l*, pg. 251
AISIN COLLABO CO., LTD—See AISIN Corporation; *Int'l*, pg. 252
AISIN COMCRUISE CO., LTD—See AISIN Corporation; *Int'l*, pg. 252
AISIN CORPORATION - HANDA ELECTRONICS PLANT—See AISIN Corporation; *Int'l*, pg. 251
AISIN CORPORATION - NISHIO ENGINE COMPONENT PLANT—See AISIN Corporation; *Int'l*, pg. 251
AISIN CORPORATION; *Int'l*, pg. 251
AISIN CORPORATION—See Toyota Motor Corporation; *Int'l*, pg. 7870
AISIN DEVELOPMENT CO., LTD.—See AISIN Corporation; *Int'l*, pg. 252
AISIN DRIVETRAIN, INC.—See AISIN Corporation; *Int'l*, pg. 252
AISIN ELECTRONICS ILLINOIS, LLC—See AISIN Corporation; *Int'l*, pg. 252
AISIN ELECTRONICS, INC.—See AISIN Corporation; *Int'l*, pg. 252
AISIN ENGINEERING CO., LTD—See AISIN Corporation; *Int'l*, pg. 252
AISIN EUROPE MANUFACTURING CZECH S.R.O.—See AISIN Corporation; *Int'l*, pg. 251
AISIN EUROPE MANUFACTURING (UK) LTD.—See AISIN Corporation; *Int'l*, pg. 252

AISIN EUROPE S.A.—See AISIN Corporation; *Int'l*, pg. 252
AISIN HOKKAIDO CO., LTD.—See AISIN Corporation; *Int'l*, pg. 252
AISIN HOLDINGS OF AMERICA, INC.—See AISIN Corporation; *Int'l*, pg. 252
AISIN INFOTEX CO., LTD.—See AISIN Corporation; *Int'l*, pg. 252
AISIN KEIKINZOKU CO., LTD.—See AISIN Corporation; *Int'l*, pg. 252
AISIN KIKO CO., LTD.—See AISIN Corporation; *Int'l*, pg. 252
AISIN KYUSHU CASTING CO., LTD—See AISIN Corporation; *Int'l*, pg. 252
AISIN KYUSHU CO., LTD.—See AISIN Corporation; *Int'l*, pg. 252
AISIN LIGHT METALS, LLC—See AISIN Corporation; *Int'l*, pg. 252
AISIN MACHINE TECH CO. LTD.—See AISIN Corporation; *Int'l*, pg. 252
AISIN MAINTENANCE CO., LTD.—See AISIN Corporation; *Int'l*, pg. 252
AISIN METALTECH CO., LTD.—See AISIN Corporation; *Int'l*, pg. 252
AISIN MEXICANA S.A. DE. C.V.—See AISIN Corporation; *Int'l*, pg. 253
AISIN MFG. AGUASCALIENTES, S. A. DE C.V.—See AISIN Corporation; *Int'l*, pg. 252
AISINO CORPORATION; *Int'l*, pg. 254
AISIN OTOMOTIV PARCALARI SANAYI VE TICARET A. S.—See AISIN Corporation; *Int'l*, pg. 252
AISIN SEIKI CO., LTD. - ANJO PLANT—See AISIN Corporation; *Int'l*, pg. 253
AISIN SEIKI CO., LTD. - HANDA PLANT—See AISIN Corporation; *Int'l*, pg. 253
AISIN SEIKI CO., LTD. - KINUURA PLANT—See AISIN Corporation; *Int'l*, pg. 253
AISIN SEIKI CO., LTD. - MACHINERY & EQUIPMENT PLANT—See AISIN Corporation; *Int'l*, pg. 253
AISIN SEIKI CO., LTD. - NISHIO DIE-CASTING PLANT—See AISIN Corporation; *Int'l*, pg. 253
AISIN SEIKI CO., LTD. - OGAWA PLANT—See AISIN Corporation; *Int'l*, pg. 253
AISIN SEIKI CO., LTD. - SHINKAWA PLANT—See AISIN Corporation; *Int'l*, pg. 253
AISIN SEIKI CO., LTD. - SHINTOYO PLANT—See AISIN Corporation; *Int'l*, pg. 253
AISIN SIN'EI CO., LTD.—See AISIN Corporation; *Int'l*, pg. 252
AISIN SINWA CO., LTD.—See AISIN Corporation; *Int'l*, pg. 253
AISIN TAKAOKA CO., LTD.—See AISIN Corporation; *Int'l*, pg. 253
AISIN TECHNICAL CENTER OF AMERICA, INC.—See AISIN Corporation; *Int'l*, pg. 252
AISIN TOHOKU CO., LTD.—See AISIN Corporation; *Int'l*, pg. 253
AISIN USA MANUFACTURING INC.—See AISIN Corporation; *Int'l*, pg. 253
AISIN WORLD CORP. OF AMERICA—See AISIN Corporation; *Int'l*, pg. 253
AISLANTES NACIONALES S.A.—See Henkel AG & Co. KGaA; *Int'l*, pg. 3348
AISLAPOL S.A.—See BASF SE; *Int'l*, pg. 872
AISLE NETWORK PRIVATE LIMITED—See Info Edge India Ltd; *Int'l*, pg. 3689
AISLING CAPITAL LLC; *U.S. Private*, pg. 142
AIS MANAGEMENT LLC—See Mercury General Corporation; *U.S. Public*, pg. 1421
AI SOLAR SDN. BHD.—See Ygl Convergence Berhad; *Int'l*, pg. 8580
A.I.S. RESOURCES LIMITED; *Int'l*, pg. 24
AIT APPLIED INFORMATION TECHNOLOGIES GMBH & CO. KG—See Siemens Aktiengesellschaft; *Int'l*, pg. 6886
AIT-AUSTRIA GMBH—See NIBE Industrier AB; *Int'l*, pg. 5263
AIT BIOSCIENCE LLC—See Ampersand Management LLC; *U.S. Private*, pg. 265
AITC LOGISTICS (VIETNAM) CO., LTD—See AIT Corporation; *Int'l*, pg. 254
AIT CORPORATION; *Int'l*, pg. 254
AI TECHNOLOGY GROUP, INC.; *U.S. Public*, pg. 63
AITECH RUGGED COMPUTER SYSTEMS; *U.S. Private*, pg. 143
AITECH SPACE SYSTEMS INC—See AITECH Rugged Computer Systems; *U.S. Private*, pg. 143
AITEX CORPORATION—See XYMAX Corporation; *Int'l*, pg. 8542
AITHENUTRIGENE CO.; *Int'l*, pg. 254
AIT (HKG) LIMITED—See AIT Corporation; *Int'l*, pg. 254
AIT INTERNATIONAL LOGISTICS (SHANGHAI) CO., LTD.—See AIT Corporation; *Int'l*, pg. 254
AIT INTERNATIONAL LOGISTICS (TAIWAN) CO., LTD.—See AIT Corporation; *Int'l*, pg. 254
AIT JAPAN INC.—See WPG Holdings Limited; *Int'l*, pg. 8460
AITKEN CHEVROLET BUICK GMC; *Int'l*, pg. 254

AITKEN MANUFACTURING INC.—See INNOVATE Corp.; *U.S. Public*, pg. 1125
AITKEN SPENCE CARGO (PVT) LTD.—See Aitken Spence PLC; *Int'l*, pg. 254
AITKEN SPENCE ELEVATORS (PVT) LTD—See Aitken Spence PLC; *Int'l*, pg. 254
AITKEN SPENCE ENGINEERING SOLUTIONS (PVT) LTD.—See Daikin Industries, Ltd.; *Int'l*, pg. 1932
AITKEN SPENCE HOTEL HOLDINGS PLC—See Aitken Spence PLC; *Int'l*, pg. 254
AITKEN SPENCE HOTEL MANAGEMENTS (PVT) LTD.—See Aitken Spence PLC; *Int'l*, pg. 254
AITKEN SPENCE PLC; *Int'l*, pg. 254
AITKEN SPENCE SHIPPING LTD.—See Aitken Spence PLC; *Int'l*, pg. 254
AITKEN SPENCE TECHNOLOGIES (PVT) LTD.—See Aitken Spence PLC; *Int'l*, pg. 254
AITKIN COMMUNITY HOSPITAL; *U.S. Private*, pg. 143
AITO MEDIA OY—See Vivendi SE; *Int'l*, pg. 8271
AI TOPPER & CO; *Int'l*, pg. 227
AITOSA CORPORATION—See Shikoku Electric Power Co., Incorporated; *Int'l*, pg. 6830
A & I TRAVEL SERVICE; *U.S. Private*, pg. 18
AIT SCHWEIZ AG—See NIBE Industrier AB; *Int'l*, pg. 5263
AIT-VARMETEKNIK-SVERIGE AB—See NIBE Industrier AB; *Int'l*, pg. 5259
AIT WORLDWIDE LOGISTICS, INC.; *U.S. Private*, pg. 142
AI UNITED ENGINEERING INC.—See Nittetsu Mining Co., Ltd.; *Int'l*, pg. 5383
AIUTO CO., LTD.—See MCJ Co., Ltd.; *Int'l*, pg. 4759
AIVEBS SPA—See Capgemini SE; *Int'l*, pg. 1303
AIVE BST SPA—See Capgemini SE; *Int'l*, pg. 1303
AIVE SPA—See Capgemini SE; *Int'l*, pg. 1303
AIV GMBH + CO. KG; *Int'l*, pg. 254
AIWA INSURANCE SERVICE CO., LTD.—See Bunka Shutter Co., Ltd.; *Int'l*, pg. 1216
AIXAM LUSITANA SOCIEDAD DE COMERCIALIZACAE DE AUTOMOVEIS, S.A.—See Polaris, Inc.; *U.S. Public*, pg. 1700
AIXAM-MEGA IBERICA, S.L.—See Polaris, Inc.; *U.S. Public*, pg. 1700
AIXAM MEGA ITALIA S.R.L.—See Polaris, Inc.; *U.S. Public*, pg. 1700
AIXAM MEGA NEDERLAND BV—See Polaris, Inc.; *U.S. Public*, pg. 1700
AIXAM MEGA S.A.S.—See Polaris, Inc.; *U.S. Public*, pg. 1700
AIX HOLDINGS, INC.—See The Hanover Insurance Group, Inc.; *U.S. Public*, pg. 2087
AIXIA CORPORATION—See Maruha Nichiro Corporation; *Int'l*, pg. 4711
AIXIAL GMBH—See Alten S.A.; *Int'l*, pg. 389
AIXIAL SAS—See Alten S.A.; *Int'l*, pg. 389
AIXIAL SPRL—See Alten S.A.; *Int'l*, pg. 390
AIXIAL S.R.O.—See Alten S.A.; *Int'l*, pg. 389
AIX, INC.—See The Hanover Insurance Group, Inc.; *U.S. Public*, pg. 2087
AIXIN LIFE INTERNATIONAL, INC.; *Int'l*, pg. 254
AIX SPECIALTY INSURANCE COMPANY—See The Hanover Insurance Group, Inc.; *U.S. Public*, pg. 2087
AIXTRON CHINA LTD.—See Aixtron SE; *Int'l*, pg. 255
AIXTRON INC.—See Aixtron SE; *Int'l*, pg. 255
AIXTRON KK—See Aixtron SE; *Int'l*, pg. 255
AIXTRON KOREA CO. LTD.—See Aixtron SE; *Int'l*, pg. 255
AIXTRON LTD.—See Aixtron SE; *Int'l*, pg. 255
AIXTRON SE; *Int'l*, pg. 254
AIXTRON TAIWAN CO. LTD.—See Aixtron SE; *Int'l*, pg. 255
AIYON TECH. CO., LTD.—See Okada Aiyon Corporation; *Int'l*, pg. 5544
AIZAWA ASSET MANAGEMENT CO., LTD.—See Aizawa Securities Group Co., Ltd.; *Int'l*, pg. 255
AIZAWA INVESTMENTS CO., LTD.—See Aizawa Securities Group Co., Ltd.; *Int'l*, pg. 255
AIZAWA SECURITIES GROUP CO., LTD.; *Int'l*, pg. 255
AIZEN SB (THAILAND) CO., LTD.—See Nippon Steel Corporation; *Int'l*, pg. 5336
AIZU LABORATORY, INC.—See Nihon Enterprise Co., Ltd.; *Int'l*, pg. 5284
AIZU OLYMPUS CO., LTD.—See Olympus Corporation; *Int'l*, pg. 5556
AIZU TAMURA CORPORATION—See Tamura Corporation; *Int'l*, pg. 7451
AIZU WAKAMATSU FACTORY OF KANTOH DIET EGG CO., LTD.—See Kenko Mayonnaise Co., Ltd.; *Int'l*, pg. 4127
AJACCIO AUTOMOBILES; *Int'l*, pg. 255
AJ ADVANCE TECHNOLOGY PUBLIC COMPANY LIMITED; *Int'l*, pg. 255
AJAL MEDICAL SPECIALTY COMPANY LTD.—See Eurofins Scientific S.E.; *Int'l*, pg. 2535
AJANTA PHARMA LIMITED; *Int'l*, pg. 255
AJANTA PHARMA (MAURITIUS) LIMITED—See Ajanta Pharma Limited; *Int'l*, pg. 255
AJANTA PHARMA PHILIPPINES INC.—See Ajanta Pharma Limited; *Int'l*, pg. 255

AJANTA PHARMA LIMITED

AJANTA PHARMA USA INC.—See Ajanta Pharma Limited; *Int'l*, pg. 255
AJANTA SOYA LIMITED; *Int'l*, pg. 255
AJA PHARMA COMPANY—See Saudi Chemical Holding Company; *Int'l*, pg. 6593
A&J ASSETS LLC—See Postal Realty Trust, Inc.; *U.S. Public*, pg. 1704
AJASTO PAPER PRODUCTS LTD—See Schneider Electric SE; *Int'l*, pg. 6625
AJAX BUILDING CORPORATION; *U.S. Private*, pg. 143
AJAX BUSINESS INTERIORS, INC.; *U.S. Private*, pg. 143
AJAX COMB COMPANY—See Antonio's Manufacturing Inc.; *U.S. Private*, pg. 288
AJAX CONSTRUCTION CO., INC.; *U.S. Private*, pg. 143
AJAX DISTRIBUTING CO. INC.; *U.S. Private*, pg. 143
AJAX ELECTRIC CO.; *U.S. Private*, pg. 143
AJAX ENVIRONMENTAL & SAFETY SUPPLY, INC.—See In-Situ, Inc.; *U.S. Private*, pg. 2052
AJAX METAL PROCESSING—See Cold Heading Co.; *U.S. Private*, pg. 965
AJAX PAVING INDUSTRIES, INC. - BALD MOUNTAIN PLANT—See Ajax Paving Industries, Inc.; *U.S. Private*, pg. 143
AJAX PAVING INDUSTRIES, INC. - INKSTER ROAD PLANT—See Ajax Paving Industries, Inc.; *U.S. Private*, pg. 143
AJAX PAVING INDUSTRIES, INC. - LARGO PLANT—See Ajax Paving Industries, Inc.; *U.S. Private*, pg. 143
AJAX PAVING INDUSTRIES, INC. - NEW HAVEN PLANT—See Ajax Paving Industries, Inc.; *U.S. Private*, pg. 143
AJAX PAVING INDUSTRIES, INC. - NOKOMIS PLANT—See Ajax Paving Industries, Inc.; *U.S. Private*, pg. 143
AJAX PAVING INDUSTRIES, INC. - ODESSA PLANT—See Ajax Paving Industries, Inc.; *U.S. Private*, pg. 143
AJAX PAVING INDUSTRIES, INC. - PLANT 5—See Ajax Paving Industries, Inc.; *U.S. Private*, pg. 143
AJAX PAVING INDUSTRIES, INC. - PORT MANATEE PLANT—See Ajax Paving Industries, Inc.; *U.S. Private*, pg. 143
AJAX PAVING INDUSTRIES, INC. - PUNTA GORDA PLANT—See Ajax Paving Industries, Inc.; *U.S. Private*, pg. 143
AJAX PAVING INDUSTRIES, INC.; *U.S. Private*, pg. 143
AJAX PAVING INDUSTRIES INC.—See HHJ Holdings Limited; *U.S. Private*, pg. 1931
AJAX PAVING INDUSTRIES, INC. - TAMPA PLANT—See Ajax Paving Industries, Inc.; *U.S. Private*, pg. 143
AJAX RESOURCES PLC; *Int'l*, pg. 255
AJAX TECHNOLOGY CENTRE PTY LTD.—See Nylex Limited; *Int'l*, pg. 5500
AJAX TOCCO DE MEXICO, S.A. DE C.V.—See Park-Ohio Holdings Corp.; *U.S. Public*, pg. 1639
AJAX TOCCO INTERNATIONAL LTD.—See Park-Ohio Holdings Corp.; *U.S. Public*, pg. 1639
AJAX TOCCO MAGNETHERMIC CANADA LIMITED—See Park-Ohio Holdings Corp.; *U.S. Public*, pg. 1639
AJAX TOCCO MAGNETHERMIC CORPORATION—See Park-Ohio Holdings Corp.; *U.S. Public*, pg. 1639
AJAX TOCCO MAGNETHERMIC CORPORATION—See Park-Ohio Holdings Corp.; *U.S. Public*, pg. 1639
AJAX TOCCO MAGNETHERMIC CORPORATION—See Park-Ohio Holdings Corp.; *U.S. Public*, pg. 1639
AJAX TOCCO MAGNETHERMIC GMBH—See Park-Ohio Holdings Corp.; *U.S. Public*, pg. 1639
AJAX UNION; *U.S. Private*, pg. 143
AJAX-UNITED PATTERNS & MOLDS, INC.—See Francisco Partners Management, LP; *U.S. Private*, pg. 1590
AJAY GLASS & MIRROR COMPANY INCORPORATED; *U.S. Private*, pg. 143
AJAY - SQM CHILE S.A.—See Sociedad Quimica y Minera de Chile S.A.; *Int'l*, pg. 7032
AJ BART INC.; *U.S. Private*, pg. 143
A.J. BAYLISS PETROLEUM ENGINEERS LTD—See Sun Capital Partners, Inc.; *U.S. Private*, pg. 3861
AJ BELL MEDIA LIMITED—See AJ Bell Plc; *Int'l*, pg. 255
AJ BELL PLC.; *Int'l*, pg. 255
AJ BELL SECURITIES LIMITED—See AJ Bell Plc.; *Int'l*, pg. 255
AJ CATAGNUS INC.; *U.S. Private*, pg. 143
AJC FOOD—See AJC International, Inc.; *U.S. Private*, pg. 143
AJC INTERNATIONAL, INC.; *U.S. Private*, pg. 143
AJC INTERNATIONAL, INC.—See AJC International, Inc.; *U.S. Private*, pg. 143
AJCON GLOBAL SERVICES LTD.; *Int'l*, pg. 255
A.J. DANBOISE SON INC.; *U.S. Private*, pg. 26
A.J. DAW PRINTING INK CO; *U.S. Private*, pg. 26
AJ DEMOR & SONS INC.; *U.S. Private*, pg. 143
AJD FOREST PRODUCTS LIMITED PARTNERSHIP—See CMS Energy Corporation; *U.S. Public*, pg. 518
AJD HOLDING CO.; *U.S. Public*, pg. 473
AJ DIANI CONSTRUCTION CO; *U.S. Private*, pg. 143
AJE BEST-ON SDN. BHD.—See Ann Joo Resources Berhad; *Int'l*, pg. 473
AJECOBOND - AL JABER ALUMINIUM COMPOSITE LLC—See Al Jaber Group; *Int'l*, pg. 279

A. J. EDMOND COMPANY—See OceanSound Partners, LP; *U.S. Private*, pg. 2991
A&J ELECTRIC CABLE CORP.; *U.S. Private*, pg. 20
AJEL LTD.; *Int'l*, pg. 255
AJEL TECHNOLOGIES INC—See Ajel Ltd.; *Int'l*, pg. 256
AJ FOREST PRODUCTS LTD.—See E.R. Probyn Ltd.; *Int'l*, pg. 2260
A.J. FORSYTH—See Russel Metals Inc.; *U.S. Public*, pg. 6430
A.J. FUNK & CO. INC.; *U.S. Private*, pg. 26
AJG CAPITAL, INC.—See Arthur J. Gallagher & Co.; *U.S. Public*, pg. 202
AJG FINANCIAL SERVICES, LLC—See Arthur J. Gallagher & Co.; *U.S. Public*, pg. 202
A.J. GREEN SHELL PLC; *Int'l*, pg. 24
AJG TWO PIERCE, INC.—See Arthur J. Gallagher & Co.; *U.S. Public*, pg. 202
AJ HOWARD INDUSTRIAL SUPPLIES LIMITED—See W.W. Grainger, Inc.; *U.S. Public*, pg. 2319
AJIA INNOGROUP HOLDINGS, LTD.; *U.S. Public*, pg. 68
AJIAL REAL ESTATE ENTERTAINMENT COMPANY K.S.C.C.; *Int'l*, pg. 256
AJIGAURA DAIICHI TRAFFIC LTD.—See Daiichi Koutsu Sangyo Co., Ltd.; *Int'l*, pg. 1928
AJIKAWA & SCI METAL TECH CO., LTD.—See SCI Electric Public Company Limited; *Int'l*, pg. 6646
AJILA LTD.—See Swisscom AG; *Int'l*, pg. 7373
AJILLUS INC.; *U.S. Private*, pg. 144
AJILON NORTH AMERICA, LLC—See Adecco Group AG; *Int'l*, pg. 138
AJILON PROFESSIONAL STAFFING LLC—See Adecco Group AG; *Int'l*, pg. 138
AJILON TECHNOLOGY PROFESSIONALS B.V.—See Adecco Group AG; *Int'l*, pg. 140
AJINEXTEK CO., LTD.; *Int'l*, pg. 256
A-JIN INDUSTRY CO.,LTD; *Int'l*, pg. 19
AJ INNUSCREEN GMBH—See Endress+Hauser (International) Holding AG; *Int'l*, pg. 2405
AJINOMOTO ALTHEA, INC—See Ajinomoto Company, Inc.; *Int'l*, pg. 257
AJINOMOTO AMINOSCIENCE LLC—See Ajinomoto Company, Inc.; *Int'l*, pg. 257
AJINOMOTO BAKERY CO., LTD.—See Ajinomoto Company, Inc.; *Int'l*, pg. 257
AJINOMOTO BETAGRO FROZEN FOODS (THAILAND) CO., LTD.—See Ajinomoto Company, Inc.; *Int'l*, pg. 256
AJINOMOTO BETAGRO FROZEN FOODS (THAILAND) CO., LTD.—See Betagro Public Company Limited; *Int'l*, pg. 1002
AJINOMOTO BETAGRO SPECIALTY FOODS (THAILAND) CO., LTD.—See Ajinomoto Company, Inc.; *Int'l*, pg. 256
AJINOMOTO BETAGRO SPECIALTY FOODS (THAILAND) CO., LTD.—See Betagro Public Company Limited; *Int'l*, pg. 1002
AJINOMOTO BIOITALIA S.P.A.—See Ajinomoto Company, Inc.; *Int'l*, pg. 256
AJINOMOTO BIOLATINA INDUSTRIA E COMERCIO LTDA.—See Ajinomoto Company, Inc.; *Int'l*, pg. 256
AJINOMOTO CAMBROOKE, INC.—See Ajinomoto Company, Inc.; *Int'l*, pg. 256
AJINOMOTO (CHINA) CO., LTD.—See Ajinomoto Company, Inc.; *Int'l*, pg. 256
AJINOMOTO CO., (HONG KONG) LTD.—See Ajinomoto Company, Inc.; *Int'l*, pg. 256
AJINOMOTO COMMUNICATIONS CO., INC.—See Ajinomoto Company, Inc.; *Int'l*, pg. 256
AJINOMOTO COMPANY, INC.; *Int'l*, pg. 256
AJINOMOTO CO., (THAILAND) LTD.—See Ajinomoto Company, Inc.; *Int'l*, pg. 256
AJINOMOTO DEL PERU S.A.—See Ajinomoto Company, Inc.; *Int'l*, pg. 256
AJINOMOTO DE MEXICO, S. DE R.L. DE C.V.—See Ajinomoto Company, Inc.; *Int'l*, pg. 257
AJINOMOTO DO BRASIL IND. E COM. DE ALIMENTOS LTDA.—See Ajinomoto Company, Inc.; *Int'l*, pg. 257
AJINOMOTO EURO-ASPARTAME S.A.—See Ajinomoto Company, Inc.; *Int'l*, pg. 256
AJINOMOTO EUROLYSINE S.A.S.—See Ajinomoto Company, Inc.; *Int'l*, pg. 256
AJINOMOTO EUROPE S.A.S.—See Ajinomoto Company, Inc.; *Int'l*, pg. 256
AJINOMOTO FINE-TECHNO CO., INC.—See Ajinomoto Company, Inc.; *Int'l*, pg. 256
AJINOMOTO FOODS EUROPE SAS—See Ajinomoto Company, Inc.; *Int'l*, pg. 256
AJINOMOTO FOODS EUROPE S.A.S—See Ajinomoto Company, Inc.; *Int'l*, pg. 256
AJINOMOTO FOODS NORTH AMERICA, INC.—See Ajinomoto Company, Inc.; *Int'l*, pg. 256
AJINOMOTO FROZEN FOODS CO., INC.—See Ajinomoto Company, Inc.; *Int'l*, pg. 256
AJINOMOTO FROZEN FOODS (THAILAND) CO., LTD.—See Ajinomoto Company, Inc.; *Int'l*, pg. 256
AJINOMOTO GENERAL FOODS, INC.—See Ajinomoto Company, Inc.; *Int'l*, pg. 256
AJINOMOTO GENERAL FOODS, INC.—See Mondelez International, Inc.; *U.S. Public*, pg. 1461
AJINOMOTO-GENETIKA RESEARCH INSTITUTE—See Ajinomoto Company, Inc.; *Int'l*, pg. 257

CORPORATE AFFILIATIONS

AJINOMOTO GENEXINE CO., LTD.—See Ajinomoto Company, Inc.; *Int'l*, pg. 256
AJINOMOTO HEALTH & NUTRITION NORTH AMERICA, INC.—See Ajinomoto Company, Inc.; *Int'l*, pg. 256
AJINOMOTO HEALTHY SUPPLY CO., INC.—See Ajinomoto Company, Inc.; *Int'l*, pg. 256
AJINOMOTO INDIA PRIVATE LIMITED—See Ajinomoto Company, Inc.; *Int'l*, pg. 256
AJINOMOTO INTERAMERICANA INDUSTRIA E COMERCIO LTDA.—See Ajinomoto Company, Inc.; *Int'l*, pg. 256
AJINOMOTO KOHJIN BIO CO., LTD.—See Ajinomoto Company, Inc.; *Int'l*, pg. 257
AJINOMOTO KOREA, INC.—See Ajinomoto Company, Inc.; *Int'l*, pg. 256
AJINOMOTO LOGISTICS CORPORATION—See Ajinomoto Company, Inc.; *Int'l*, pg. 256
AJINOMOTO (MALAYSIA) BERHAD—See Ajinomoto Company, Inc.; *Int'l*, pg. 256
AJINOMOTO NORTH AMERICA, INC.—See Ajinomoto Company, Inc.; *Int'l*, pg. 257
AJINOMOTO PHARMACEUTICALS EUROPE LTD.—See Ajinomoto Company, Inc.; *Int'l*, pg. 257
AJINOMOTO PHILIPPINES CORPORATION—See Ajinomoto Company, Inc.; *Int'l*, pg. 257
AJINOMOTO POLAND SP. Z O.O.—See Ajinomoto Company, Inc.; *Int'l*, pg. 257
AJINOMOTO (SINGAPORE) PTE. LTD.—See Ajinomoto Company, Inc.; *Int'l*, pg. 257
AJINOMOTO TAIWAN INC.—See Ajinomoto Company, Inc.; *Int'l*, pg. 256
AJINOMOTO TRADING, INC.—See Ajinomoto Company, Inc.; *Int'l*, pg. 257
AJINOMOTO TREASURY MANAGEMENT, INC.—See Ajinomoto Company, Inc.; *Int'l*, pg. 257
AJINOMOTO VIETNAM CO., LTD.—See Ajinomoto Company, Inc.; *Int'l*, pg. 257
AJINOMOTO WINDSOR, INC.—See Ajinomoto Company, Inc.; *Int'l*, pg. 257
A & J INSURANCE, INC.—See Seeman Holtz Property & Casualty, LLC; *U.S. Private*, pg. 3598
AJIN USA LLC—See DAEWOO ELECTRONIC COMPONENTS Co Ltd.; *Int'l*, pg. 1910
AJISCO-DNT (NINGBO) PAINT CO.,LTD.—See Dai Nippon Toryo Co., Ltd.; *Int'l*, pg. 1916
AJIS CO., LTD.; *Int'l*, pg. 258
AJISEN CHINA HOLDINGS LTD.; *Int'l*, pg. 258
AJIS HOKKAIDO CO., LTD.—See AJIS Co., Ltd.; *Int'l*, pg. 258
AJIS (HONG KONG) CO., LIMITED—See AJIS Co., Ltd.; *Int'l*, pg. 258
AJIS KYUSHU CO., LTD.—See AJIS Co., Ltd.; *Int'l*, pg. 258
AJIS MALAYSIA SDN BHD.—See AJIS Co., Ltd.; *Int'l*, pg. 258
AJIS MERCHANDISING SERVICE CO., LTD.—See AJIS Co., Ltd.; *Int'l*, pg. 258
AJIS PHILIPPINES, INC.—See AJIS Co., Ltd.; *Int'l*, pg. 258
AJIS RETAIL SUPPORT CO., LTD.—See AJIS Co., Ltd.; *Int'l*, pg. 258
AJIS SHIKOKU CO., LTD.—See AJIS Co., Ltd.; *Int'l*, pg. 258
AJIS (THAILAND) CO., LTD.—See AJIS Co., Ltd.; *Int'l*, pg. 258
AJIS USA, INC.—See AJIS Co., Ltd.; *Int'l*, pg. 258
AJIYA BERHAD; *Int'l*, pg. 258
AJIYA SAFETY GLASS SDN. BHD.—See Ajiya Berhad; *Int'l*, pg. 258
AJIYA STI SDN. BHD.—See Ajiya Berhad; *Int'l*, pg. 258
AJJ BANCORP, INC.; *U.S. Private*, pg. 144
A.J. JERSEY INC.; *U.S. Private*, pg. 26
A.J. JOHNS, INC.; *U.S. Private*, pg. 26
AJKA CRYSTAL GLASS FACTORY LTD.—See Fotex Holding SE; *Int'l*, pg. 2752
AJKA CRYSTAL USA—See Fotex Holding SE; *Int'l*, pg. 2752
AJ LUCAS COAL TECHNOLOGIES PTY LIMITED—See A.J. Lucas Group Limited; *Int'l*, pg. 24
AJ LUCAS DRILLING PTY LIMITED—See A.J. Lucas Group Limited; *Int'l*, pg. 24
A.J. LUCAS GROUP LIMITED; *Int'l*, pg. 24
AJ LUCAS OPERATIONS PTY LIMITED—See A.J. Lucas Group Limited; *Int'l*, pg. 24
AJ LUCAS PLANT & EQUIPMENT PTY LIMITED—See A.J. Lucas Group Limited; *Int'l*, pg. 24
AJ LUCAS TESTING PTY LIMITED—See A.J. Lucas Group Limited; *Int'l*, pg. 24
AJMAN BANK PJSC; *Int'l*, pg. 258
AJ MANUFACTURING INC.; *U.S. Private*, pg. 143
AJMERA REALTY & INFRA INDIA LIMITED; *Int'l*, pg. 258
A.J.M. INTERNATIONAL SPORTS PROMOTIONS LTD.—See Young An Hat Co., Ltd.; *Int'l*, pg. 8602
AJM PACKAGING CORPORATION; *U.S. Private*, pg. 144
AJM TECHNOLOGY (SHANGHAI) CO., LTD.—See Argo Graphics Inc.; *Int'l*, pg. 562
A&J MUCKLOW GROUP PLC—See LondonMetric Property Plc; *Int'l*, pg. 4548
AJ NETWORKS CO LTD; *Int'l*, pg. 255

COMPANY NAME INDEX

AJNH MEDICAL CENTER LLC—See Adeptus Health Inc.; U.S. Private, pg. 78
AJN RESOURCES, INC.; Int'l, pg. 258
AJNS NEW MEDIA GMBH—See Robert Bosch GmbH; Int'l, pg. 6358
AJOCO'91 EXPLORATION CO., LTD.—See Mitsubishi Corporation; Int'l, pg. 4937
AJOCO EXPLORATION CO., LTD.—See Mitsubishi Corporation; Int'l, pg. 4937
A.J. O'NEAL & ASSOCIATES, INC.; U.S. Private, pg. 26
AJOONI BIOTECH LIMITED; Int'l, pg. 258
AJOS A/S—See Hojgaard Holding A/S; Int'l, pg. 3442
A.J. OSTER CARIBE INC—See Wieland-Werke AG; Int'l, pg. 8403
A.J. OSTER FOILS, INC.—See Wieland-Werke AG; Int'l, pg. 8403
A.J. OSTER MEXICO S.A. DE CV—See Wieland-Werke AG; Int'l, pg. 8403
A.J. OSTER WEST—See Wieland-Werke AG; Int'l, pg. 8403
A. J. PERRI, INC.—See Del-Air Heating, Air Conditioning & Refrigeration Corp.; U.S. Private, pg. 1193
A.J. PLAST PUBLIC COMPANY LIMITED; Int'l, pg. 24
AJ POWER LIMITED; Int'l, pg. 255
AJR INFRA AND TOLLING LIMITED—See Gammon India Limited; Int'l, pg. 2879
AJ ROBOSCREEN GMBH—See Endress+Hauser (International) Holding AG; Int'l, pg. 2405
A.J. ROSE MANUFACTURING CO. INC.; U.S. Private, pg. 26
AJS & ASSOCIATES INC.—See Hankscraft Inc.; U.S. Private, pg. 1854
A&J SEABRA SUPERMARKET INC.; U.S. Private, pg. 20
A&J SEABRA SUPERMARKET—See Seabra Group; U.S. Private, pg. 3583
AJS INC.—See TIS Inc.; Int'l, pg. 7757
AJS REALTY GROUP, INC.; U.S. Private, pg. 144
AJ STATIONERS INC.; U.S. Private, pg. 143
AJT ENGINEERING LIMITED—See Camellia Plc; Int'l, pg. 1270
AJU EGL CO., LTD.—See AJU Steel Co., Ltd.; Int'l, pg. 258
AJU IB INVESTMENT CO., LTD.; Int'l, pg. 258
AJU MCM CO., LTD.—See AJU Steel Co., Ltd.; Int'l, pg. 258
A-JUNG ELECTRIC SDN BHD—See Sunrise Shares Holdings Ltd.; Int'l, pg. 7322
AJUNGILAK AS—See Bystronic AG; Int'l, pg. 1236
AJU STEEL CO., LTD.; Int'l, pg. 258
AJWA EDIBLE OIL COMPANY LIMITED—See Ajwa Group for Food Industries Holding Ltd. Co.; Int'l, pg. 258
AJWA FUN WORLD & RESORT LIMITED; Int'l, pg. 258
AJWA GROUP FOR FOOD INDUSTRIES HOLDING LTD. CO.; Int'l, pg. 258
AJWAN GULF REAL ESTATE CO. (K.S.C.C.); Int'l, pg. 259
AJWAN INTERNATIONAL CO. WLL—See Caesars Group; Int'l, pg. 1249
A.J. WELLER CORP.; U.S. Private, pg. 26
AKABIRA PAPER CORPORATION—See Daio Paper Corporation; Int'l, pg. 1939
A.K.A. BRANDS HOLDING CORP.; U.S. Public, pg. 12
AKACHAN HONPO CO., LTD.—See Seven & i Holdings Co., Ltd.; Int'l, pg. 6730
AKAD BILDUNGSGESELLSCHAFT MBH—See Galileo Global Education; Int'l, pg. 2873
AKADEMA, INC.; U.S. Private, pg. 144
AKADEMIA UMIEJETNOSCI EUROCASH SP. Z O.O.—See Eurocash S.A.; Int'l, pg. 2533
AKADEMIBOKHANDELSGRUPPEN AB—See Volati AB; Int'l, pg. 8300
AKADEMIE FUR INTERNATIONALE RECHNUNGSLEGUNG (AKIR) GMBH—See Amadeus Fire AG; Int'l, pg. 405
AKADEMIE FUR INTERNATIONALE RECHNUNGSLEGUNG PROF. DR. LEIBFRIED GMBH—See Amadeus Fire AG; Int'l, pg. 405
AKADEMOS, INC.—See Ingram Industries, Inc.; U.S. Private, pg. 2076
AKADO CO., LTD.—See Renova Group; Int'l, pg. 6285
AKA ENTERPRISE SOLUTIONS, INC.—See HSO Group BV; Int'l, pg. 3507
A.K.A. GOURMET—See Baker Capital Partners, LLC; U.S. Private, pg. 455
AKA GROUP LIMITED; Int'l, pg. 259
AKAHAGI FLANGE CO. LTD.—See Meiwa Corporation; Int'l, pg. 4805
AKAI PROFESSIONAL, L.P.—See inMusic, LLC; U.S. Private, pg. 2080
A.K. AL-MUHAIDIB & SONS GROUP OF COMPANIES; Int'l, pg. 24
AKAL SECURITY, INC.; U.S. Private, pg. 144
AK ALTYNALMAS JSC; Int'l, pg. 259
AKAMAI JAPAN K.K.—See Akamai Technologies, Inc.; U.S. Public, pg. 68
AKAMAI TECHNOLOGIES GMBH—See Akamai Technologies, Inc.; U.S. Public, pg. 68
AKAMAI TECHNOLOGIES HONG KONG LIMITED—See Akamai Technologies, Inc.; U.S. Public, pg. 68

AKAMAI TECHNOLOGIES, INC.; U.S. Public, pg. 68
AKAMAI TECHNOLOGIES INDIA PRIVATE LTD.—See Akamai Technologies, Inc.; U.S. Public, pg. 68
AKAMAI TECHNOLOGIES INTERNATIONAL AG—See Akamai Technologies, Inc.; U.S. Public, pg. 69
AKAMAI TECHNOLOGIES ISRAEL LIMITED—See Akamai Technologies, Inc.; U.S. Public, pg. 68
AKAMAI TECHNOLOGIES LTD.—See Akamai Technologies, Inc.; U.S. Public, pg. 69
AKAMAI TECHNOLOGIES NETHERLANDS B.V.—See Akamai Technologies, Inc.; U.S. Public, pg. 69
AKAMAI TECHNOLOGIES POLAND SP. Z O.O.—See Akamai Technologies, Inc.; U.S. Public, pg. 69
AKAMAI TECHNOLOGIES SARL—See Akamai Technologies, Inc.; U.S. Public, pg. 69
AKAMAI TECHNOLOGIES S.R.I.—See Akamai Technologies, Inc.; U.S. Public, pg. 69
AKA MEDIA INC; U.S. Private, pg. 144
AKAMEX OY—See Indutrade AB; Int'l, pg. 3677
AKANDA CORP.; Int'l, pg. 259
AKANI EGOLI (PTY) LIMITED—See Hosken Consolidated Investments Limited; Int'l, pg. 3485
AKANI MSUNDUZI (PTY) LTD.—See Hosken Consolidated Investments Limited; Int'l, pg. 3485
AKANKSHA POWER & INFRASTRUCTURE LIMITED; Int'l, pg. 259
AKANOVA GMBH—See AcadeMedia AB; Int'l, pg. 75
AKAPP STEMMANN BV—See Westinghouse Air Brake Technologies Corporation; U.S. Public, pg. 2358
AKARA MINING LIMITED—See Kingsgate Consolidated Limited; Int'l, pg. 4174
AKAR AUTO INDUSTRIES LTD.; Int'l, pg. 259
AKARD HOLDINGS LP—See Sci-Roev Texas Partners LP; U.S. Private, pg. 3573
AKARI THERAPEUTICS, PLC; Int'l, pg. 259
AKARSH CONSTRUCTIONS PRIVATE LIMITED—See Marg Ltd; Int'l, pg. 4692
AKARUA LIMITED—See Skeggs Group Limited; Int'l, pg. 6980
AKARUA WINERY—See Skeggs Group Limited; Int'l, pg. 6980
AKARY FOR INDUSTRIES & REAL ESTATE INVESTMENTS PLC; Int'l, pg. 259
AKASAKA DIESELS LIMITED - NAKAMINATO FACTORY—See Akasaka Diesels Limited; Int'l, pg. 260
AKASAKA DIESELS LIMITED; Int'l, pg. 259
AKASAKA DIESELS LIMITED - TOYODA FACTORY—See Akasaka Diesels Limited; Int'l, pg. 260
AKASAKA GRAPHICS ART INC—See TBS Holdings, Inc.; Int'l, pg. 7481
AKASAKA HEAT SUPPLY CO LTD—See TBS Holdings, Inc.; Int'l, pg. 7481
AKASHA CRYSTALS, INC.; U.S. Private, pg. 144
AKASHI-KIKAI INDUSTRY CO., LTD.—See Toyota Motor Corporation; Int'l, pg. 7870
AKASHINA DAIICHI TRAFFIC LTD.—See Daiichi Koutsu Sangyo Co., Ltd.; Int'l, pg. 1928
AKASH INFRA PROJECTS LTD.; Int'l, pg. 260
AKASHI SDN. BHD.—See BRENNTAG SE; Int'l, pg. 1146
AKASHI SHIP MODEL BASIN CO., LTD.—See Kawasaki Heavy Industries, Ltd.; Int'l, pg. 4095
AKASOL AG—See BorgWarner Inc.; U.S. Public, pg. 369
AK ASSET MANAGEMENT—See Akbank T.A.S.; Int'l, pg. 260
AKASTOR ASA; Int'l, pg. 260
AKATEAK SDN. BHD.—See KPS Consortium Berhad; Int'l, pg. 4299
AKATEEMINEN KIRJAKAUPPA—See Bonnier AB; Int'l, pg. 1108
AKATHERM B.V.—See Aliaxis S.A./N.V.; Int'l, pg. 323
AKATHERM FIP GMBH—See Aliaxis S.A./N.V.; Int'l, pg. 323
AKATHERM INTERNATIONAL B.V.—See Aliaxis S.A./N.V.; Int'l, pg. 323
AKATI IMPEX PTE. LTD.—See Dominant Enterprise Berhad; Int'l, pg. 2161
AKATI WOOD (VIETNAM) CO., LTD.—See Dominant Enterprise Berhad; Int'l, pg. 2161
AKATSUKI CORP.; Int'l, pg. 2161
AKATSUKI EAZIMA CO., LTD.; Int'l, pg. 260
AKATSUKI ENTERTAINMENT USA, INC.—See Akatsuki, Inc.; Int'l, pg. 260
AKATSUKI, INC.; Int'l, pg. 260
AKAY FLAVOURS & AROMATICS PVT. LTD.—See Novonesis A/S; Int'l, pg. 5468
AKAZAWA PAPER CO., LTD.—See Japan Pulp and Paper Company Limited; Int'l, pg. 3903
AKA ZRT.—See STRABAG SE; Int'l, pg. 7229
AKBANK AG—See Akbank T.A.S.; Int'l, pg. 261
AKBANK (DUBAI) LIMITED—See Akbank T.A.S.; Int'l, pg. 261
AKBANK INTERNATIONAL N.V.—See Akbank T.A.S.; Int'l, pg. 261
AKBANK T.A.S.; Int'l, pg. 260
AKBAR GROUP; Int'l, pg. 261
AKB AVANGARD OAO; Int'l, pg. 260
AKCANSA CIMENTO SANAYI VE TICARET A.S.—See Haci Omer Sabanci Holding A.S.; Int'l, pg. 3203

AKCANSA CIMENTO SANAYI VE TICARET A.S.—See Heidelberg Materials AG; Int'l, pg. 3308
A.K. CAPITAL SERVICES LTD.; Int'l, pg. 25
AKCEA THERAPEUTICS, INC.—See Ionis Pharmaceuticals, Inc.; U.S. Public, pg. 1166
AKCELERANT ADVISORS LLC—See Akcelerant Holdings LLC; U.S. Private, pg. 144
AKCELERANT HOLDINGS LLC; U.S. Private, pg. 144
AKCENTA DE GMBH—See Raiffeisen Bank International AG; Int'l, pg. 6182
AKCENT MEDIA SP. Z O. O.—See Agora S.A.; Int'l, pg. 212
AKCIONARSKO DRUSTVO ZA REOSIGURANJE GENERALI REOSIGURANJE SRBIJA—See Assicurazioni Generali S.p.A.; Int'l, pg. 643
AKCIONARSKO DRUSTVO ZA UPRAVLJANJE DOBROVOLJNIM PENZIJSKIM FONDOM GENERALI—See Assicurazioni Generali S.p.A.; Int'l, pg. 643
A&K C.N.C. MACHINING, LLC—See Promus Holdings, LLC; U.S. Private, pg. 3284
AK COAL RESOURCES, INC.—See Cleveland-Cliffs, Inc.; U.S. Public, pg. 513
AK COATINGS INC.—See Cleveland-Cliffs, Inc.; U.S. Public, pg. 513
AKD CAPITAL LIMITED; Int'l, pg. 261
AKDEMIR CELIK SANAYI VE TICARET A.S.—See Izmir Demir Celik Sanayi AS; Int'l, pg. 3851
AKD ENGINEERING LIMITED—See Camellia Plc; Int'l, pg. 1270
AKDENIZ FAKTORING A.S.; Int'l, pg. 261
AKDENIZ KIMYA SAN. VE TIC. A.S.—See OYAK Cement Group; Int'l, pg. 5677
AKDENIZ MINERAL KAYNAKLARI A.S—See Grecian Magnesite S.A; Int'l, pg. 3068
AKDENIZ YATIRIM HOLDING AS; Int'l, pg. 261
A&K DIE FRISCHE KUCHE GMBH—See Storskogen Group AB; Int'l, pg. 7227
AKD SA; Int'l, pg. 261
AKD SECURITIES LIMITED—See AKD Capital Limited; Int'l, pg. 261
A.K. DURNIN CHRYSLER JEEP INC; U.S. Private, pg. 26
A&K EARTH MOVERS INC.; U.S. Private, pg. 20
AKEBIA THERAPEUTICS, INC.; U.S. Public, pg. 69
AKEBONO 123 CO., LTD.—See Akebono Brake Industry Co., Ltd.; Int'l, pg. 261
AKEBONO ADVANCED ENGINEERING CO., LTD.—See Akebono Brake Industry Co., Ltd.; Int'l, pg. 261
AKEBONO ADVANCED ENGINEERING (UK) LTD.—See Akebono Brake Industry Co., Ltd.; Int'l, pg. 261
AKEBONO BRAKE ASTRA VIETNAM CO., LTD.—See Akebono Brake Industry Co., Ltd.; Int'l, pg. 261
AKEBONO BRAKE - CLARKSVILLE PLANT—See Akebono Brake Industry Co., Ltd.; Int'l, pg. 261
AKEBONO BRAKE CORPORATION—See Akebono Brake Industry Co., Ltd.; Int'l, pg. 261
AKEBONO BRAKE - ELIZABETHTOWN PLANT—See Akebono Brake Industry Co., Ltd.; Int'l, pg. 261
AKEBONO BRAKE EUROPE N.V.—See Akebono Brake Industry Co., Ltd.; Int'l, pg. 261
AKEBONO BRAKE FUKUSHIMA MANUFACTURING CO., LTD.—See Akebono Brake Industry Co., Ltd.; Int'l, pg. 261
AKEBONO BRAKE INDUSTRY CO., LTD.; Int'l, pg. 261
AKEBONO BRAKE IWATSUKI MANUFACTURING CO., LTD.—See Akebono Brake Industry Co., Ltd.; Int'l, pg. 261
AKEBONO BRAKE MEXICO S.A. DE C.V.—See Akebono Brake Industry Co., Ltd.; Int'l, pg. 261
AKEBONO BRAKE SANYO MANUFACTURING CO., LTD.—See Akebono Brake Industry Co., Ltd.; Int'l, pg. 261
AKEBONO BRAKE SLOVAKIA S.R.O.—See Akebono Brake Industry Co., Ltd.; Int'l, pg. 261
AKEBONO BRAKE (THAILAND) CO., LTD.—See Akebono Brake Industry Co., Ltd.; Int'l, pg. 261
AKEBONO BRAKE YAMAGATA MANUFACTURING CO., LTD.—See Akebono Brake Industry Co., Ltd.; Int'l, pg. 261
AKEBONO COOPERATION (THAILAND) CO., LTD.—See Akebono Brake Industry Co., Ltd.; Int'l, pg. 261
AKEBONO CORPORATION (GUANGZHOU)—See Akebono Brake Industry Co., Ltd.; Int'l, pg. 262
AKEBONO CORPORATION—See Akebono Brake Industry Co., Ltd.; Int'l, pg. 262
AKEBONO CORPORATION (SUZHOU)—See Akebono Brake Industry Co., Ltd.; Int'l, pg. 262
AKEBONO ENGINEERING CO.—See METAWATER Co., Ltd.; Int'l, pg. 4851
AKEBONO EUROPE GMBH—See Akebono Brake Industry Co., Ltd.; Int'l, pg. 262
AKEBONO EUROPE S.A.S (ARRAS)—See Akebono Brake Industry Co., Ltd.; Int'l, pg. 262
AKEBONO EUROPE S.A.S (GONESSE)—See Akebono Brake Industry Co., Ltd.; Int'l, pg. 262
AKEBONO R&D ENGINEERING CENTER—See Akebono Brake Industry Co., Ltd.; Int'l, pg. 261
AKEBONO RESEARCH & DEVELOPMENT CENTRE LTD.—See Akebono Brake Industry Co., Ltd.; Int'l, pg. 262

AKECHI INSULATORS CO LTD—See NGK Insulators, Ltd.; *Int'l*, pg. 5254
AKEEL/SAATCHI & SAATCHI—See Publicis Groupe S.A.; *Int'l*, pg. 6108
AKELA LTD.—See Thermwood Corporation; *U.S. Private*, pg. 4143
AKELA PHARMA, INC.; *U.S. Private*, pg. 144
AKELIUS LAGENHETER AB—See Akelius Residential AB; *Int'l*, pg. 262
AKELIUS RESIDENTIAL AB; *Int'l*, pg. 262
AKEMI BRASIL INDUSTRIA E COMERCIO LTDA.—See AKEMI chemisch technische Spezialfabrik GmbH; *Int'l*, pg. 262
AKEMI CHEMISCH TECHNISCHE SPEZIALFABRIK GMBH; *Int'l*, pg. 262
AKEMI ELECTRIC POWER, LTD.—See Topy Industries, Ltd.; *Int'l*, pg. 7821
AKEMI GAS, LTD.—See Topy Industries, Ltd.; *Int'l*, pg. 7821
AKEMI RECYCLING CENTER, LTD.—See Topy Industries, Ltd.; *Int'l*, pg. 7821
AKEMI TECHNOLOGY INDIA PRIVATE LIMITED—See AKEMI chemisch technische Spezialfabrik GmbH; *Int'l*, pg. 262
AKENERJI ELEKTRIK URETIM A.S.; *Int'l*, pg. 262
AKER ASA; *Int'l*, pg. 262
AKER BIOMARINE ASA—See Aker ASA; *Int'l*, pg. 262
AKER BP ASA; *Int'l*, pg. 262
AKER CAPITAL AS—See Aker ASA; *Int'l*, pg. 262
AKER CARBON CAPTURE ASA; *Int'l*, pg. 262
AKER DRIFT AS—See Swiss Life Holding; *Int'l*, pg. 7368
AKER EGERSUND AS—See Aker Solutions ASA; *Int'l*, pg. 262
AKER EIENDOMSDRIFT AS—See Swiss Life Holding; *Int'l*, pg. 7368
AKER ENGINEERING MALAYSIA SDN BHD—See Aker Solutions ASA; *Int'l*, pg. 262
AKER ENGINEERING & TECHNOLOGY AS—See Aker Solutions ASA; *Int'l*, pg. 262
AKER FLOATING PRODUCTION ASA—See KKR & Co. Inc.; *U.S. Public*, pg. 1262
AKER HORIZONS ASA—See Aker ASA; *Int'l*, pg. 262
AKERHUS TRAKTOR AS—See Lantmannen ek for; *Int'l*, pg. 4414
AKERMAN LLP - DALLAS—See Akerman LLP; *U.S. Private*, pg. 145
AKERMAN LLP - FORT LAUDERDALE—See Akerman LLP; *U.S. Private*, pg. 145
AKERMAN LLP - HOUSTON—See Akerman LLP; *U.S. Private*, pg. 145
AKERMAN LLP - MIAMI—See Akerman LLP; *U.S. Private*, pg. 145
AKERMAN LLP; *U.S. Private*, pg. 144
AKERN S.R.L.—See Pharmanutra S.p.A.; *Int'l*, pg. 5840
AKERO THERAPEUTICS, INC.; *U.S. Public*, pg. 69
AKER SOLUTIONS ASA; *Int'l*, pg. 262
AKER SOLUTIONS DO BRASIL LTDA.—See Aker Solutions ASA; *Int'l*, pg. 262
AKER SOLUTIONS FINLAND OY—See Aker Solutions ASA; *Int'l*, pg. 262
AKER SOLUTIONS INC.—See Aker Solutions ASA; *Int'l*, pg. 262
AKERS PACKAGING SERVICE INC.; *U.S. Private*, pg. 145
AKERSTROMS BJORBO AB—See Verdane Capital Advisors AS; *Int'l*, pg. 8165
AKER SUBSEA AS—See Aker Solutions ASA; *Int'l*, pg. 262
AKERS VALJI RAVNE D.O.O.—See Ampco-Pittsburgh Corporation; *U.S. Public*, pg. 126
AKERUE INDUSTRIES, LLC; *U.S. Private*, pg. 145
AKESOGEN, INC.—See Tempus AI, Inc.; *U.S. Public*, pg. 2000
AKESO, INC.; *Int'l*, pg. 263
AKESO MEDICAL HOLDINGS, LLC—See Kain Capital, LLC; *U.S. Private*, pg. 2254
AKEY—See Cargill, Inc.; *U.S. Private*, pg. 760
AK FAKTORING AS; *Int'l*, pg. 259
AKF BANK GMBH & CO.—See Vorwerk & Co. KG; *Int'l*, pg. 8308
AK FELDFRUCHT GMBH—See KTG Agrar SE; *Int'l*, pg. 4316
AKFEN GAYRIMENKUL YATIRIM ORTAKLIGI A.S.; *Int'l*, pg. 263
AKFEN HOLDING A.S.; *Int'l*, pg. 263
AKFEN INSAAT TURIZM VE TICARET A.S.—See Akfen Holding A.S.; *Int'l*, pg. 263
AKF EQUIPRENT S.A.—See Vorwerk & Co. KG; *Int'l*, pg. 8308
AK FINANSAL KIRALAMA A.S.—See Akbank T.A.S.; *Int'l*, pg. 261
AKF LEASING GMBH & CO.—See Vorwerk & Co. KG; *Int'l*, pg. 8308
AKF SERVICELEASE GMBH—See Vorwerk & Co. KG; *Int'l*, pg. 8308
AKG DO BRASIL—See Autokuhler GmbH & Co. KG; *Int'l*, pg. 727
AKG EXIM LTD.; *Int'l*, pg. 263
AKG FRANCE S.A.S—See Autokuhler GmbH & Co. KG; *Int'l*, pg. 727

AKG INDIA PRIVATE LTD.—See Autokuhler GmbH & Co. KG; *Int'l*, pg. 727
AKG JAPAN LTD.—See Autokuhler GmbH & Co. KG; *Int'l*, pg. 727
AKG KLINIK HOHWALD GMBH—See Asklepios Kliniken GmbH & Co. KGaA; *Int'l*, pg. 622
AKG KLINIK PARCHIM GMBH—See Asklepios Kliniken GmbH & Co. KGaA; *Int'l*, pg. 622
AKG KOREA LTD.—See Autokuhler GmbH & Co. KG; *Int'l*, pg. 727
AKG NORTH AMERICAN OPERATIONS, INC.—See Autokuhler GmbH & Co. KG; *Int'l*, pg. 727
AKG TERMOTEKNIK SISTEMLER SAN. VE TIC. LTD.—See Autokuhler GmbH & Co. KG; *Int'l*, pg. 727
AKG THERMAL SYSTEMS, INC.—See Autokuhler GmbH & Co. KG; *Int'l*, pg. 727
AKG THERMAL SYSTEMS (TAICANG) CO., LTD.—See Autokuhler GmbH & Co. KG; *Int'l*, pg. 727
AKG THERMOTECHNIK GMBH & CO. KG—See Autokuhler GmbH & Co. KG; *Int'l*, pg. 727
AKG UK LIMITED—See Autokuhler GmbH & Co. KG; *Int'l*, pg. 727
AKG VERWALTUNGSGESELLSCHAFT MBH—See Autokuhler GmbH & Co. KG; *Int'l*, pg. 727
AKH COMPANY, INC.; *U.S. Private*, pg. 145
AKHEA CONSORTIUM—See Hera S.p.A.; *Int'l*, pg. 3356
AKHELA S.R.L.—See Angelo Moratti S.A.P.A.; *Int'l*, pg. 460
AK HOLDINGS, INC.; *Int'l*, pg. 259
AKHURST MACHINERY INC.—See Akhurst Machinery Limited; *Int'l*, pg. 263
AKHURST MACHINERY LIMITED; *Int'l*, pg. 263
AK HVAC, INC.—See Marathon HVAC Services, LLC; *U.S. Private*, pg. 2570
AKIBA HOLDINGS CO., LTD.; *Int'l*, pg. 263
AKIBANK PJSC; *Int'l*, pg. 263
A KID'S PLACE OF TAMPA BAY, INC.; *U.S. Private*, pg. 18
AKIEM—See SNCF; *Int'l*, pg. 7025
AKI HABARA ELECTRIC CORPORATION PTE. LTD.—See TT International Limited; *Int'l*, pg. 7959
AKI, INC.; *U.S. Private*, pg. 145
AKI INDIA LIMITED; *Int'l*, pg. 263
AKIKAWA FOODS & FARMS CO., LTD.; *Int'l*, pg. 263
AKILI INC.—See UnitedHealth Group Incorporated; *U.S. Public*, pg. 2252
AKIMA CONSTRUCTION SERVICES, LLC—See Nana Regional Corporation, Inc.; *U.S. Private*, pg. 2832
AKIMA FACILITIES MANAGEMENT, LLC—See Nana Regional Corporation, Inc.; *U.S. Private*, pg. 2832
AKIMA GLOBAL SERVICES, LLC—See Nana Regional Corporation, Inc.; *U.S. Private*, pg. 2832
AKIMA INFRASTRUCTURE SERVICES, LLC—See Nana Regional Corporation, Inc.; *U.S. Private*, pg. 2832
AKIMA INTRA-DATA, LLC—See Nana Regional Corporation, Inc.; *U.S. Private*, pg. 2832
AKIMA, LLC—See Nana Regional Corporation, Inc.; *U.S. Private*, pg. 2832
AKIMA LOGISTICS SERVICES, LLC—See Nana Regional Corporation, Inc.; *U.S. Private*, pg. 2832
AKIMA MANAGEMENT SERVICES LLC; *U.S. Private*, pg. 145
AKIMA TECHNICAL SOLUTIONS, LLC—See Nana Regional Corporation, Inc.; *U.S. Private*, pg. 2832
AKIMEKA LLC—See VSE Corporation; *U.S. Public*, pg. 2313
AKIMOTOSEIKIKOGYO CO., LTD.—See Fuji Seiki Co., Ltd.; *Int'l*, pg. 2817
AKIN COMPLETE FURNITURE; *U.S. Private*, pg. 145
AKINDO SUSHIRO CO., LTD.—See Permira Advisers LLP; *Int'l*, pg. 5803
AKIN FAKTORING HIZMETLERI A.S.; *Int'l*, pg. 263
AKIN GUMP STRAUSS HAUER & FELD LLP; *U.S. Private*, pg. 145
AKINION PHARMACEUTICALS AB—See Karolinska Development AB; *Int'l*, pg. 4084
AKIN TEKSTIL A.S.; *Int'l*, pg. 263
AKIOLIS GROUP S.A.S.—See Tessenderlo Group NV; *Int'l*, pg. 7573
AKIRA CORPORATION PTE. LTD.—See TT International Limited; *Int'l*, pg. 7959
AKIRA ELECTRONICS HONG KONG LIMITED—See TT International Limited; *Int'l*, pg. 7959
AKIRA ENERGY LTD.—See Banpu Public Company Limited; *Int'l*, pg. 851
AKIRA INTERNATIONAL PTE. LTD.—See TT International Limited; *Int'l*, pg. 7959
AKIRA MIDDLE EAST L.L.C—See TT International Limited; *Int'l*, pg. 7960
AKIRA SINGAPORE PTE LTD—See TT International Limited; *Int'l*, pg. 7960
AKIRA WEST AFRICA COMPANY LIMITED—See TT International Limited; *Int'l*, pg. 7960
AKIS GAYRIMENKUL YATIRIM ORTAKLIGI A.S.; *Int'l*, pg. 263
AKISHIMA CHEMICAL INDUSTRIES CO., LTD—See OpenGate Capital Management, LLC; *U.S. Private*, pg. 3030

AKISHIMA LABORATORIES (MITSUI ZOSEN) INC.—See Mitsui E&S Holdings Co., Ltd.; *Int'l*, pg. 4985
THE AKITA BANK, LTD.; *Int'l*, pg. 7612
AKITA DRILLING LTD.; *Int'l*, pg. 263
AKITA DRILLING USA CORP.—See Akita Drilling Ltd.; *Int'l*, pg. 263
AKITA ENGINEERING CO., LTD.—See Dowa Holdings Co., Ltd.; *Int'l*, pg. 2182
AKITA GLULAM CO., LTD.—See JK Holdings Co., Ltd.; *Int'l*, pg. 3972
AKITA INAFUKU CONFECTIONERY CO., LTD—See Yamazaki Baking Co., Ltd.; *Int'l*, pg. 8556
AKITAKENHAKKO KOGYO CO., LTD.—See Oenon Holdings Inc; *Int'l*, pg. 5529
AKITA KUBOTA CORPORATION—See Kubota Corporation; *Int'l*, pg. 4320
AKITA NATURAL GAS PIPELINE CO., LTD.—See Japan Petroleum Exploration Co. Ltd.; *Int'l*, pg. 3900
AKITA NEW URBAN-CENTER BUILDING CO., LTD.—See Sojitz Corporation; *Int'l*, pg. 7061
AKITA OFFSHORE WIND CORPORATION—See Marubeni Corporation; *Int'l*, pg. 4705
AKITA PRIMA FOODS CO., LTD.—See Prima Meat Packers Ltd.; *Int'l*, pg. 5975
AKITA RARE METALS CO., LTD—See Dowa Holdings Co., Ltd.; *Int'l*, pg. 2183
AKITA RECYCLE & FINEPACK CO., LTD.—See Dowa Holdings Co., Ltd.; *Int'l*, pg. 2182
AKITA SHINDENGEN CO., LTD.—See Shindengen Electric Manufacturing Co., Ltd.; *Int'l*, pg. 6841
AKITA SHIZUKI CO., INC.—See Shizuki Electric Company, Inc.; *Int'l*, pg. 6855
AKITA SUMITOMO BAKELITE CO., LTD.—See Sumitomo Bakelite Co., Ltd.; *Int'l*, pg. 7262
AKITA ZINC CO., LTD.—See Dowa Holdings Co., Ltd.; *Int'l*, pg. 2182
AKITA ZINC RECYCLING CO., LTD.—See Dowa Holdings Co., Ltd.; *Int'l*, pg. 2183
AKITA ZINC SOLUTIONS CO., LTD.—See Dowa Holdings Co., Ltd.; *Int'l*, pg. 2182
AKIYAMA CORPORATION AMERICA—See Akiyama International Company Ltd.; *Int'l*, pg. 263
AKIYAMA INTERNATIONAL COMPANY LTD.; *Int'l*, pg. 263
AKIYAMA INTERNATIONAL CORP (USA)—See Akiyama International Company Ltd.; *Int'l*, pg. 263
AKKA BELGIUM SA—See Adecco Group AG; *Int'l*, pg. 139
AKKA BENELUX NV/SA—See Adecco Group AG; *Int'l*, pg. 139
AKKA CONSULTING GMBH—See Adecco Group AG; *Int'l*, pg. 139
AKKA CZECH REPUBLIC S.R.O.—See Adecco Group AG; *Int'l*, pg. 139
AKKA MIDDLE EAST DMCC—See Adecco Group AG; *Int'l*, pg. 139
AKKA TECHNOLOGIES BEIJING LTD.—See Adecco Group AG; *Int'l*, pg. 139
AKKA TECHNOLOGIES SE—See Adecco Group AG; *Int'l*, pg. 139
AKKHIE PRAKARN PUBLIC COMPANY LIMITED; *Int'l*, pg. 263
AKKM CO., LTD.—See AISIN Corporation; *Int'l*, pg. 252
AKKODIS GROUP AG—See Adecco Group AG; *Int'l*, pg. 139
AKKO INVEST NYRT.; *Int'l*, pg. 263
AK KRAUS UND HILLER SCHADLINGSBEKAMPFUNG GMBH—See Ecolab Inc.; *U.S. Public*, pg. 712
AKKUPOJAT OY—See OEM International AB; *Int'l*, pg. 5528
AKLI RESOURCES SDN BHD—See Johor Corporation; *Int'l*, pg. 3994
AKL TELECOMMUNICATIONS GMBH—See TD Synnex Corp; *U.S. Public*, pg. 1985
AKM ASIA PTE LTD—See Fortive Corporation; *U.S. Public*, pg. 870
AK MEDICAL HOLDINGS LIMITED; *Int'l*, pg. 259
AKM ELECTRONICS INDUSTRIAL (PANYU) LTD—See AKM Industrial Company Limited; *Int'l*, pg. 264
AKM ELECTRONICS TECHNOLOGY (SUZHOU) COMPANY LIMITED—See AKM Industrial Company Limited; *Int'l*, pg. 264
AKM ELECTRONIC TECHNOLOGY (SUZHOU) COMPANY LIMITED—See AKM Industrial Company Limited; *Int'l*, pg. 264
AKMERKEZ GAYRIMENKUL YATIRIM ORTAKLIGI A.S.; *Int'l*, pg. 264
AKM INDUSTRIAL COMPANY LIMITED; *Int'l*, pg. 264
AKM LACE AND EMBROTEX PRIVATE LIMITED; *Int'l*, pg. 264
AKM LLC; *U.S. Private*, pg. 145
AKM SEMICONDUCTOR, INC.—See Asahi Kasei Corporation; *Int'l*, pg. 595
AKO ARMATUREN - SEPARATION GMBH—See Axel Johnson Gruppen AB; *Int'l*, pg. 762
AKOBO MINERALS AB; *Int'l*, pg. 261
AKODE ELEKTRONIK PARA VE ODEME HIZMETLERI A.S.—See Akbank T.A.S.; *Int'l*, pg. 261
AKOESTIKON GELUIDSISOLATIE B.V.—See Merford Holding B.V.; *Int'l*, pg. 4834

COMPANY NAME INDEX

AKORA RESOURCES LIMITED; *Int'l*, pg. 264
AKORN AG—See Akorn, Inc.; *U.S. Private*, pg. 146
AKORN, INC.; *U.S. Private*, pg. 145
AKORN (NEW JERSEY), INC.—See Akorn, Inc.; *U.S. Private*, pg. 146
AKORN STRIDES LLC—See Strides Pharma Science Limited; *Int'l*, pg. 7240
AKO STONEWOOD INC.; *Int'l*, pg. 264
AKOUOS, INC.—See Eli Lilly & Company; *U.S. Public*, pg. 731
AKOUSTICA MEDICA M EPE—See Demant A/S; *Int'l*, pg. 2023
AKOUSTIS, INC.—See Akoustis Technologies, Inc.; *U.S. Public*, pg. 69
AKOUSTIS TECHNOLOGIES, INC.; *U.S. Public*, pg. 69
AKOYA BIOSCIENCES, INC.; *U.S. Public*, pg. 69
AKOYA CAPITAL LLC; *U.S. Private*, pg. 146
AKOYA, INC.—See KPIT Technologies Ltd; *Int'l*, pg. 4296
AKPA A.S.—See Koc Holding A.S.; *Int'l*, pg. 4222
AKPA DAYANIKLI TUKETIM LPG VE AKARYAKIT URUNLERI PAZARLAMA A.S.—See Koc Holding A.S.; *Int'l*, pg. 4222
AK PORTFOY YONETIMI A.S.—See Akbank T.A.S.; *Int'l*, pg. 261
AKQA B.V.—See WPP plc; *Int'l*, pg. 8467
AKQA, INC. - NEW YORK—See WPP plc; *Int'l*, pg. 8467
AKQA, INC.—See WPP plc; *Int'l*, pg. 8467
AKQA, INC. - WASHINGTON, DC—See WPP plc; *Int'l*, pg. 8467
AKQA LIMITED—See WPP plc; *Int'l*, pg. 8467
AKQA (SHANGHAI) CO., LTD.—See WPP plc; *Int'l*, pg. 8467
AKQURACY; *U.S. Private*, pg. 146
AKRAB PERKASA SDN BHD—See IJM Corporation Berhad; *Int'l*, pg. 3608
A&K RAILROAD MATERIALS INC. - KANSAS CITY MFG FACILITY—See A&K Railroad Materials Inc.; *U.S. Private*, pg. 20
A&K RAILROAD MATERIALS INC.; *U.S. Private*, pg. 20
AKRA POLYESTER, S.A. DE C.V.—See ALFA, S.A.B. de C.V.; *Int'l*, pg. 313
AKRAYA, INC.; *U.S. Private*, pg. 146
AK RETAIL HOLDINGS LIMITED; *Int'l*, pg. 259
AKR (GUIGANG) TRANSSHIPMENT PORT CO LTD—See PT AKR Corporindo Tbk; *Int'l*, pg. 6020
AKRION SYSTEMS, LLC—See NAURA Technology Group Co., Ltd.; *Int'l*, pg. 5172
AKRITAS S.A.; *Int'l*, pg. 264
AKRITIV TECHNOLOGIES, INC.—See Genpact Limited; *Int'l*, pg. 2926
AKROCHEM CORPORATION; *U.S. Private*, pg. 146
AKRO-MILS—See Myers Industries, Inc.; *U.S. Public*, pg. 1488
AKRON BARBERTON CLUSTER RAILWAY COMPANY, INC.—See The Wheeling Corporation Inc.; *U.S. Private*, pg. 4134
AKRON BEACON JOURNAL—See Gannett Co., Inc.; *U.S. Public*, pg. 904
AKRON BRASS COMPANY—See IDEX Corp.; *U.S. Public*, pg. 1089
THE AKRON COCA-COLA BOTTLING COMPANY—See The Coca-Cola Company; *U.S. Public*, pg. 2065
AKRON FOUNDRY CO.; *U.S. Private*, pg. 146
AKRON GEAR & ENGINEERING INC.—See Forge Industries, Inc.; *U.S. Private*, pg. 1568
AKRON HARDWARE CONSULTANTS, INC.; *U.S. Private*, pg. 146
AKRON NEWS-REPORTER—See Alden Global Capital LLC; *U.S. Private*, pg. 157
AKRON PORCELAIN & PLASTICS CO.; *U.S. Private*, pg. 146
AKRON REBAR CO.; *U.S. Private*, pg. 146
AKRON SERVICES, BRIMFIELD—See Akron Services Inc.; *U.S. Private*, pg. 146
AKRON SERVICES INC.; *U.S. Private*, pg. 146
AKRON SPA—See Hera S.p.A.; *Int'l*, pg. 3356
AKRON TENT & AWNING CO.—See Ohio Awning & Manufacturing Co.; *U.S. Private*, pg. 3003
AKRO SA—See Viohalco SA/NV; *Int'l*, pg. 8243
AKROS PHARMA INC.—See Japan Tobacco Inc.; *Int'l*, pg. 3905
AKROS SILICON, INC.—See Kinetic Technologies, Inc.; *U.S. Private*, pg. 2308
AKROS TRADING CO., LTD.—See Denki Company Limited; *Int'l*, pg. 2027
AKROTEX EXTUSION & RECYCLING INC.—See Akrotex, Inc.; *U.S. Private*, pg. 146
AKROTEX FILMS INC.—See Akrotex, Inc.; *U.S. Private*, pg. 146
AKROTEX, INC.; *U.S. Private*, pg. 146
AKROTEX TRUCKING INC—See Akrotex, Inc.; *U.S. Private*, pg. 146
AKROTEX WAREHOUSING, INC.—See Akrotex, Inc.; *U.S. Private*, pg. 146
AKSA AKRILIK KIMYA SANAYII A.S.; *Int'l*, pg. 264
AKSA EGYPT ACRYLIC FIBER INDUSTRY SAE—See Aksa Akrilik Kimya Sanayii A.S.; *Int'l*, pg. 264
AKSA ENERJI URETIM A.S.; *Int'l*, pg. 264

AKS CORPORATION PUBLIC COMPANY LIMITED; *Int'l*, pg. 264
AKS EAST JAPAN CO., LTD.—See NSK Ltd.; *Int'l*, pg. 5477
AK SECURITIES—See Akbank T.A.S.; *Int'l*, pg. 261
AKSHARCHEM (INDIA) LIMITED; *Int'l*, pg. 264
AKSHAR SPINTEX LIMITED; *Int'l*, pg. 264
AKSHAT CORPORATION—See Persistent Systems Ltd.; *Int'l*, pg. 5818
AKSH OPTIFIBRE LIMITED; *Int'l*, pg. 264
AKSIGORTA A.S.; *Int'l*, pg. 264
AKSO HEALTH GROUP; *Int'l*, pg. 265
AK SPECIALTY VEHICLES B.V.—See Oshkosh Corporation; *U.S. Public*, pg. 1620
A.K. SPINTEX LTD.; *Int'l*, pg. 25
AKS PRECISION BALL EUROPE LTD.—See NSK Ltd.; *Int'l*, pg. 5478
AKS PRECISION BALL (HANGZHOU) CO., LTD.—See NSK Ltd.; *Int'l*, pg. 5478
AKS PRECISION BALL POLSKA SP. Z.O.O.—See NSK Ltd.; *Int'l*, pg. 5478
AKS SALES CO., LTD.—See NSK Ltd.; *Int'l*, pg. 5478
AK STEEL BV—See Cleveland-Cliffs, Inc.; *U.S. Public*, pg. 513
AK STEEL CORP.—See Cleveland-Cliffs, Inc.; *U.S. Public*, pg. 513
AK STEEL GMBH—See Cleveland-Cliffs, Inc.; *U.S. Public*, pg. 513
AK STEEL HOLDING CORPORATION—See Cleveland-Cliffs, Inc.; *U.S. Public*, pg. 513
AK STEEL INTERNATIONAL BV—See Cleveland-Cliffs, Inc.; *U.S. Public*, pg. 513
AK STEEL LIMITED—See Cleveland-Cliffs, Inc.; *U.S. Public*, pg. 513
AK STEEL MERCHANDISING S.A.—See Cleveland-Cliffs, Inc.; *U.S. Public*, pg. 514
AK STEEL NV—See Cleveland-Cliffs, Inc.; *U.S. Public*, pg. 514
AK STEEL S.A.R.L.—See Cleveland-Cliffs, Inc.; *U.S. Public*, pg. 514
AK STEEL SRL—See Cleveland-Cliffs, Inc.; *U.S. Public*, pg. 514
AKSU ENERJI VE TICARET A.S.; *Int'l*, pg. 265
AK SVERIGE AB—See PRA Group, Inc.; *U.S. Public*, pg. 1712
AKT AMERICA, INC.—See Applied Materials, Inc.; *U.S. Public*, pg. 172
AKTA WEB STUDIO; *U.S. Private*, pg. 147
AKTEK GIYIM SAN. VE TIC. A.S.; *Int'l*, pg. 265
AKT ENTERPRISES; *U.S. Private*, pg. 146
AKTIA BANK PLC; *Int'l*, pg. 265
AKTIA FUND MANAGEMENT COMPANY LTD.—See Aktia Bank PLC; *Int'l*, pg. 265
AKTIA LIFE INSURANCE LTD.—See Aktia Bank PLC; *Int'l*, pg. 265
AKTIA WEALTH MANAGEMENT LTD.—See Aktia Bank PLC; *Int'l*, pg. 265
AKTIEBOLAGET NORRKOPING SILVRET 1—See Eurocommercial Properties N.V.; *Int'l*, pg. 2534
AKTIEBOLAGET RORLAGGAREN—See Instalco AB; *Int'l*, pg. 3721
AKTIEBOLAGET SMIDMEK ESLOV—See Peab AB; *Int'l*, pg. 5771
AKTIENGESELLSCHAFT ADOLPH SAURER—See OC Oerlikon Corporation AG; *Int'l*, pg. 5514
AKTIESELSKABET ESAB—See Enovis Corporation; *U.S. Public*, pg. 770
AKTIESELSKABET SCHOUW & Co.; *Int'l*, pg. 265
AKTIESELSKABET TYSSEFALDENE—See Statkraft AS; *Int'l*, pg. 7184
AKTIF BANK SUKUK VARLIK KIRALAMA A.S.; *Int'l*, pg. 267
AKTIFSPED ULUSLARARASI NAKLIYAT VE TIC. LTD. STI—See Hoyer GmbH; *Int'l*, pg. 3498
AKTIF YATIRIM BANKASI A.S.; *Int'l*, pg. 267
AKT II LIMITED—See Tetra Tech, Inc.; *U.S. Public*, pg. 2024
AKTIO CORPORATION—See Aktio Holdings Corporation; *Int'l*, pg. 267
AKTIO HOLDINGS CORPORATION; *Int'l*, pg. 267
AKTIO MALAYSIA SDN BHD—See Aktio Holdings Corporation; *Int'l*, pg. 267
AKTIO PACIFIC PTE. LTD.—See Aktio Holdings Corporation; *Int'l*, pg. 267
AKTIO TAIWAN CO., LTD.—See Aktio Holdings Corporation; *Int'l*, pg. 267
AKTIO THAILAND CO., LTD.—See Aktio Holdings Corporation; *Int'l*, pg. 267
AKTIVE ENERGI ANLAEG A/S—See 2G Energy AG; *Int'l*, pg. 5
AKTIV EIENDOMSMEGLING JAEREN AS—See Sandnes Sparebank; *Int'l*, pg. 6526
AKTIV KAPITAL FINANCIAL SERVICES AS—See PRA Group, Inc.; *U.S. Public*, pg. 1712
AKTIV KAPITAL INVESTMENT AS—See PRA Group, Inc.; *U.S. Public*, pg. 1712
AKTIV PROPERTIES REIT; *Int'l*, pg. 267
AKTOBE METALWARE PLANT JSC; *Int'l*, pg. 267

AKTOBE OIL EQUIPMENT PLANT JSC; *Int'l*, pg. 267
AKTOBE REFINERY LLP; *Int'l*, pg. 267
AKTOBE-TEMIR-VS JSC; *Int'l*, pg. 267
AKTOR BULGARIA SA—See ELLAKTOR S.A.; *Int'l*, pg. 2364
AKTOR CONCESSIONS S.A—See ELLAKTOR S.A.; *Int'l*, pg. 2364
AKTOR FACILITY MANAGEMENT S.A.—See ELLAKTOR S.A.; *Int'l*, pg. 2364
AKTOR KUWAIT WLL—See ELLAKTOR S.A.; *Int'l*, pg. 2364
AKTOROM SRL—See ELLAKTOR S.A.; *Int'l*, pg. 2364
AKTOR S.A.—See ELLAKTOR S.A.; *Int'l*, pg. 2364
AK TUBE LLC—See Cleveland-Cliffs, Inc.; *U.S. Public*, pg. 513
AKUMIN, INC.; *U.S. Public*, pg. 69
AKUMPLAST JSC; *Int'l*, pg. 267
AKUSTICA INC.—See Robert Bosch GmbH; *Int'l*, pg. 6366
AKUVOX (XIAMEN) NETWORKS CO., LTD.—See Fujian Star-net Communication Co.,Ltd; *Int'l*, pg. 2819
AKUWA SOLUTIONS GROUP, INC.; *U.S. Private*, pg. 147
AKVA GROUP ASA—See Egersund Group AS; *Int'l*, pg. 2323
AKVA GROUP CHILE S.A.—See Egersund Group AS; *Int'l*, pg. 2323
AKVA GROUP DENMARK A/S—See Egersund Group AS; *Int'l*, pg. 2323
AKVA GROUP NORTH AMERICA INC.—See Egersund Group AS; *Int'l*, pg. 2323
AKVA GROUP SCOTLAND LTD.—See Egersund Group AS; *Int'l*, pg. 2323
AKVARR INC.—See Futuris Company; *U.S. Public*, pg. 893
AKVA-TEK SDN. BHD.—See Brite-Tech Berhad; *Int'l*, pg. 1165
AKVATERM OY—See NIBE Industrier AB; *Int'l*, pg. 5259
AK VINA CO., LTD.—See AK Holdings, Inc.; *Int'l*, pg. 259
AKWA-WORX PTY. LTD.—See De.mem Limited; *Int'l*, pg. 1997
AKWEL AUTOMOTIVE PUNE INDIA PRIVATE LIMITED—See AKWEL; *Int'l*, pg. 268
AKWEL BURSA TURKEY OTOMOTIVE A.S—See AKWEL; *Int'l*, pg. 268
AKWEL CADILLAC USA INC.—See AKWEL; *Int'l*, pg. 268
AKWEL CHIPPENHAM UK LIMITED—See AKWEL; *Int'l*, pg. 268
AKWEL CHONGQING AUTO PARTS CO, LTD—See AKWEL; *Int'l*, pg. 268
AKWEL CORDOBA ARGENTINA SA—See AKWEL; *Int'l*, pg. 268
AKWEL EL JADIDA MOROCCO SARL—See AKWEL; *Int'l*, pg. 268
AKWEL GEBZE TURKEY OTOMOTIVE SANAYI LIMITED SIRKETI—See AKWEL; *Int'l*, pg. 268
AKWEL GERMANY SERVICES GMBH—See AKWEL; *Int'l*, pg. 268
AKWEL JAPAN SERVICES CO., LTD.—See AKWEL; *Int'l*, pg. 268
AKWEL JUNDIAI BRAZIL LTDA.—See AKWEL; *Int'l*, pg. 268
AKWEL MATEUR TUNISIA SARL—See AKWEL; *Int'l*, pg. 268
AKWEL NINGBO CHINA CO, LTD—See AKWEL; *Int'l*, pg. 268
AKWEL ORIZABA MEXICO S.A. DE C.V.—See AKWEL; *Int'l*, pg. 268
AKWEL PAREDES DE COURA (PORTUGAL) UNIPESSOAL LDA—See AKWEL; *Int'l*, pg. 268
AKWEL RUDNIK CZECH REPUBLIC A.S—See AKWEL; *Int'l*, pg. 268
AKWEL SANT JUST SPAIN S.L.—See AKWEL; *Int'l*, pg. 268
AKWEL; *Int'l*, pg. 267
AKWEL SWEDEN AB—See AKWEL; *Int'l*, pg. 267
AKWEL SWEDEN AB—See AKWEL; *Int'l*, pg. 268
AKWEL TIMISOARA ROMANIA SRL—See AKWEL; *Int'l*, pg. 268
AKWEL TONDELA (PORTUGAL), LDA—See AKWEL; *Int'l*, pg. 268
AKWEL USA INC.—See AKWEL; *Int'l*, pg. 268
AKWEL VANNES FRANCE S.A.S—See AKWEL; *Int'l*, pg. 268
AKWEL VIGO SPAIN S.L.—See AKWEL; *Int'l*, pg. 268
AKWEL WUHAN AUTO PARTS CO., LTD.—See AKWEL; *Int'l*, pg. 267
AKWEN LLC; *U.S. Private*, pg. 147
AKYASAM YONETIM HIZMETLERI A.S.—See Akis Gayrimenkul Yatirim Ortakligi A.S.; *Int'l*, pg. 263
AK YATIRIM MENKUL DEGERLER A.S.—See Akbank T.A.S.; *Int'l*, pg. 261
AK YATIRIM ORTAKLIGI A.S.—See Akbank T.A.S.; *Int'l*, pg. 261
AKYUREK TUKETIM URUNLERI PAZARLAMA DAGITIM VE TICARET AS; *Int'l*, pg. 268
AKZO COATINGS LTDA -TINTAS—See Akzo Nobel N.V.; *Int'l*, pg. 272
AKZO NOBEL AB—See Akzo Nobel N.V.; *Int'l*, pg. 268
AKZO NOBEL AEROSPACE COATINGS GMBH—See Akzo Nobel N.V.; *Int'l*, pg. 268

AKYUREK TUKETIM URUNLERI PAZARLAMA DAGITIM VE TICARET AS

AKZO NOBEL AEROSPACE COATINGS LTD—See Akzo Nobel N.V.; *Int'l*, pg. 268
AKZO NOBEL AEROSPACE COATINGS—See Akzo Nobel N.V.; *Int'l*, pg. 272
AKZO NOBEL ARGENTINA S.A.—See Akzo Nobel N.V.; *Int'l*, pg. 268
AKZO NOBEL ASIA CO., LTD.—See Akzo Nobel N.V.; *Int'l*, pg. 268
AKZONOBEL (ASIA PACIFIC) PTE. LTD.—See Akzo Nobel N.V.; *Int'l*, pg. 273
AKZO NOBEL ASSURANTIE N.V.—See Akzo Nobel N.V.; *Int'l*, pg. 268
AKZO NOBEL (AUSTRALIA) PTY LTD—See Akzo Nobel N.V.; *Int'l*, pg. 268
AKZO NOBEL AUTOMOTIVE AND AEROSPACE COATINGS MEXICO S.A. DE C.V.—See Akzo Nobel N.V.; *Int'l*, pg. 268
AKZO NOBEL BALTICS AS—See Akzo Nobel N.V.; *Int'l*, pg. 268
AKZO NOBEL BALTICS SIA—See Akzo Nobel N.V.; *Int'l*, pg. 268
AKZO NOBEL BALTICS, UAB—See Akzo Nobel N.V.; *Int'l*, pg. 268
AKZO NOBEL BOYA SANAYI VE TICARET AS—See Akzo Nobel N.V.; *Int'l*, pg. 268
AKZO NOBEL BYGGLIM AB—See Akzo Nobel N.V.; *Int'l*, pg. 268
AKZO NOBEL CANADA INC.—See Akzo Nobel N.V.; *Int'l*, pg. 268
AKZO NOBEL CAR REFINISHES AB—See Akzo Nobel N.V.; *Int'l*, pg. 269
AKZO NOBEL CAR REFINISHES AG—See Akzo Nobel N.V.; *Int'l*, pg. 269
AKZO NOBEL CAR REFINISHES A/S—See Akzo Nobel N.V.; *Int'l*, pg. 269
AKZO NOBEL CAR REFINISHES AUSTRALIA PTY LTD—See Akzo Nobel N.V.; *Int'l*, pg. 269
AKZO NOBEL CAR REFINISHES BV—See Akzo Nobel N.V.; *Int'l*, pg. 272
AKZO NOBEL CAR REFINISHES INDIA PVT LTD—See Akzo Nobel N.V.; *Int'l*, pg. 269
AKZO NOBEL CAR REFINISHES (IRELAND) LTD—See Akzo Nobel N.V.; *Int'l*, pg. 269
AKZO NOBEL CAR REFINISHES KOREA CO. LTD—See Akzo Nobel N.V.; *Int'l*, pg. 269
AKZO NOBEL CAR REFINISHES SAS—See Akzo Nobel N.V.; *Int'l*, pg. 269
AKZO NOBEL CAR REFINISHES (SINGAPORE) PTE. LTD.—See Akzo Nobel N.V.; *Int'l*, pg. 269
AKZO NOBEL CAR REFINISHES SL—See Akzo Nobel N.V.; *Int'l*, pg. 269
AKZO NOBEL CAR REFINISHES (SUZHOU) CO. LTD—See Akzo Nobel N.V.; *Int'l*, pg. 269
AKZO NOBEL CELLULOSIC SPECIALTIES INC.—See Akzo Nobel N.V.; *Int'l*, pg. 269
AKZO NOBEL CENTER ENERGIE B.V.—See Akzo Nobel N.V.; *Int'l*, pg. 269
AKZO NOBEL CHANGCHENG COATING (LANGFANG) CO., LTD.—See Akzo Nobel N.V.; *Int'l*, pg. 269
AKZO NOBEL CHANG CHENG COATINGS (GUANGDONG) CO LTD—See Akzo Nobel N.V.; *Int'l*, pg. 269
AKZO NOBEL CHANG CHENG COATINGS (SUZHOU) CO LTD—See Akzo Nobel N.V.; *Int'l*, pg. 269
AKZO NOBEL CHANG CHENG LIMITED—See Akzo Nobel N.V.; *Int'l*, pg. 269
AKZO NOBEL CHEMICAL LTD.—See GIC Pte. Ltd.; *Int'l*, pg. 2967
AKZO NOBEL CHEMICAL LTD.—See The Carlyle Group Inc.; *U.S. Public*, pg. 2050
AKZO NOBEL CHEMICALS LLC—See GIC Pte. Ltd.; *Int'l*, pg. 2967
AKZO NOBEL CHEMICALS LLC—See The Carlyle Group Inc.; *U.S. Public*, pg. 2050
AKZO NOBEL CHEMICALS PTY LTD—See GIC Pte. Ltd.; *Int'l*, pg. 2968
AKZO NOBEL CHEMICALS PTY LTD—See The Carlyle Group Inc.; *U.S. Public*, pg. 2050
AKZO NOBEL CHEMICALS SA DE CV—See GIC Pte. Ltd.; *Int'l*, pg. 2968
AKZO NOBEL CHEMICALS SA DE CV—See The Carlyle Group Inc.; *U.S. Public*, pg. 2051
AKZO NOBEL CHEMICALS S.A.—See GIC Pte. Ltd.; *Int'l*, pg. 2968
AKZO NOBEL CHEMICALS S.A.—See The Carlyle Group Inc.; *U.S. Public*, pg. 2051
AKZO NOBEL (C) HOLDINGS B.V.—See Akzo Nobel N.V.; *Int'l*, pg. 268
AKZO NOBEL COATINGS A.E.—See Akzo Nobel N.V.; *Int'l*, pg. 269
AKZO NOBEL COATINGS AG—See Akzo Nobel N.V.; *Int'l*, pg. 269
AKZO NOBEL COATINGS AS—See Akzo Nobel N.V.; *Int'l*, pg. 269
AKZO NOBEL COATINGS B.V.—See Akzo Nobel N.V.; *Int'l*, pg. 269
AKZO NOBEL COATINGS (DONGGUAN) CO. LTD.—See Akzo Nobel N.V.; *Int'l*, pg. 269
AKZO NOBEL COATINGS GMBH—See Akzo Nobel N.V.; *Int'l*, pg. 269

AKZO NOBEL COATINGS GMBH—See Akzo Nobel N.V.; *Int'l*, pg. 269
AKZO NOBEL COATINGS INC. (KY)—See Akzo Nobel N.V.; *Int'l*, pg. 272
AKZO NOBEL COATINGS INC. (MI)—See Akzo Nobel N.V.; *Int'l*, pg. 272
AKZO NOBEL COATINGS INC.—See Akzo Nobel N.V.; *Int'l*, pg. 272
AKZO NOBEL COATINGS INC.—See Akzo Nobel N.V.; *Int'l*, pg. 272
AKZO NOBEL COATINGS INC.—See Akzo Nobel N.V.; *Int'l*, pg. 272
AKZO NOBEL COATINGS INC.—See Akzo Nobel N.V.; *Int'l*, pg. 272
AKZO NOBEL COATINGS INC.—See Akzo Nobel N.V.; *Int'l*, pg. 272
AKZO NOBEL COATINGS INC.—See Akzo Nobel N.V.; *Int'l*, pg. 272
AKZO NOBEL COATINGS INDIA PRIVATE LTD—See Akzo Nobel N.V.; *Int'l*, pg. 269
AKZO NOBEL COATINGS INTERNATIONAL B.V.—See Akzo Nobel N.V.; *Int'l*, pg. 269
AKZO NOBEL COATINGS (JIAXING) CO. LTD—See Akzo Nobel N.V.; *Int'l*, pg. 269
AKZO NOBEL COATINGS K.K.—See Akzo Nobel N.V.; *Int'l*, pg. 269
AKZO NOBEL COATINGS LTD.—See Akzo Nobel N.V.; *Int'l*, pg. 272
AKZO NOBEL COATINGS OY—See Akzo Nobel N.V.; *Int'l*, pg. 269
AKZO NOBEL COATINGS SA—See Akzo Nobel N.V.; *Int'l*, pg. 272
AKZO NOBEL COATINGS SA—See Akzo Nobel N.V.; *Int'l*, pg. 272
AKZO NOBEL COATINGS, S.L.—See Akzo Nobel N.V.; *Int'l*, pg. 269
AKZO NOBEL COATINGS S.P.A.—See Akzo Nobel N.V.; *Int'l*, pg. 272
AKZO NOBEL COATINGS SP. Z O.O.—See Akzo Nobel N.V.; *Int'l*, pg. 269
AKZO NOBEL COATINGS SRL—See Akzo Nobel N.V.; *Int'l*, pg. 269
AKZO NOBEL COATINGS (TIANJIN) CO., LTD.—See Akzo Nobel N.V.; *Int'l*, pg. 269
AKZO NOBEL COATINGS TRADING LTD—See Akzo Nobel N.V.; *Int'l*, pg. 269
AKZO NOBEL COATINGS VIETNAM LIMITED—See Akzo Nobel N.V.; *Int'l*, pg. 269
AKZONOBEL COATINGS VIETNAM LTD.—See Akzo Nobel N.V.; *Int'l*, pg. 272
AKZO NOBEL COATINGS ZRT—See Akzo Nobel N.V.; *Int'l*, pg. 269
AKZO NOBEL COIL COATINGS SA—See Akzo Nobel N.V.; *Int'l*, pg. 269
AKZO NOBEL CROSS LINKING PEROXIDES (NINGBO) CO. LTD—See Akzo Nobel N.V.; *Int'l*, pg. 269
AKZO NOBEL DECO A/S—See Akzo Nobel N.V.; *Int'l*, pg. 269
AKZO NOBEL DECO GMBH—See Akzo Nobel N.V.; *Int'l*, pg. 269
AKZONOBEL DECO GMBH—See Akzo Nobel N.V.; *Int'l*, pg. 273
AKZO NOBEL DECORATIVE COATINGS A/S—See Akzo Nobel N.V.; *Int'l*, pg. 269
AKZO NOBEL DECORATIVE COATINGS BV—See Akzo Nobel N.V.; *Int'l*, pg. 269
AKZO NOBEL DECORATIVE COATINGS B.V.—See Akzo Nobel N.V.; *Int'l*, pg. 270
AKZO NOBEL DECORATIVE COATINGS B.V.—See Akzo Nobel N.V.; *Int'l*, pg. 270
AKZO NOBEL DECORATIVE COATINGS B.V.—See Akzo Nobel N.V.; *Int'l*, pg. 270
AKZO NOBEL DECORATIVE COATINGS SVERIGE AB—See Akzo Nobel N.V.; *Int'l*, pg. 269
AKZO NOBEL DECORATIVE COATINGS TURKEY B.V.—See Akzo Nobel N.V.; *Int'l*, pg. 269
AKZO NOBEL DECORATIVE INTERNATIONAL—See Akzo Nobel N.V.; *Int'l*, pg. 269
AKZO NOBEL DECORATIVE PAINTS BELGIUM NV—See Akzo Nobel N.V.; *Int'l*, pg. 271
AKZO NOBEL DECORATIVE PAINTS—See Akzo Nobel N.V.; *Int'l*, pg. 269
AKZONOBEL DECORATIVE PAINTS—See Akzo Nobel N.V.; *Int'l*, pg. 270
AKZO NOBEL DECORATIVE PAINTS SP. Z O.O—See Akzo Nobel N.V.; *Int'l*, pg. 271
AKZO NOBEL DECORATIVE PAINTS, USA—See Akzo Nobel N.V.; *Int'l*, pg. 272
AKZO NOBEL DISTRIBUTION LLE DE FRANCE S.A.S.—See Akzo Nobel N.V.; *Int'l*, pg. 271
AKZO NOBEL DISTRIBUTION OUEST S.A.S.—See Akzo Nobel N.V.; *Int'l*, pg. 271
AKZO NOBEL DISTRIBUTION SAS—See Akzo Nobel N.V.; *Int'l*, pg. 271
AKZO NOBEL ENERGIE HENGELO B.V.—See Akzo Nobel N.V.; *Int'l*, pg. 271
AKZO NOBEL ENERGY B.V.—See Akzo Nobel N.V.; *Int'l*, pg. 271

CORPORATE AFFILIATIONS

AKZO NOBEL ENGINEERING & OPERATIONAL SOLUTIONS B.V.—See Akzo Nobel N.V.; *Int'l*, pg. 271
AKZO NOBEL FARBEN BETEILIGUNGS-GMBH—See Akzo Nobel N.V.; *Int'l*, pg. 271
AKZO NOBEL FASER PENSIONSVERWALTUNGS-GMBH—See Akzo Nobel N.V.; *Int'l*, pg. 271
AKZO NOBEL FUNCTIONAL CHEMICALS AB—See GIC Pte. Ltd.; *Int'l*, pg. 2968
AKZO NOBEL FUNCTIONAL CHEMICALS AB—See The Carlyle Group Inc.; *U.S. Public*, pg. 2051
AKZO NOBEL FUNCTIONAL CHEMICALS VERWALTUNGS-GMBH—See GIC Pte. Ltd.; *Int'l*, pg. 2968
AKZO NOBEL FUNCTIONAL CHEMICALS VERWALTUNGS-GMBH—See The Carlyle Group Inc.; *U.S. Public*, pg. 2051
AKZO NOBEL GMBH—See Akzo Nobel N.V.; *Int'l*, pg. 271
AKZO NOBEL HOLDING DUITSLAND B.V.—See Akzo Nobel N.V.; *Int'l*, pg. 271
AKZO NOBEL HOLDING OSTERREICH GMBH—See Akzo Nobel N.V.; *Int'l*, pg. 271
AKZO NOBEL INC.—See Akzo Nobel N.V.; *Int'l*, pg. 271
AKZO NOBEL INDA, S.A. DE C.V.—See Akzo Nobel N.V.; *Int'l*, pg. 271
AKZO NOBEL INDIA LIMITED—See Akzo Nobel N.V.; *Int'l*, pg. 271
AKZONOBEL INDIA LTD.—See Akzo Nobel N.V.; *Int'l*, pg. 273
AKZONOBEL INDIA LTD.—See Akzo Nobel N.V.; *Int'l*, pg. 273
AKZO NOBEL INDUSTRIAL CHEMICALS AB—See GIC Pte. Ltd.; *Int'l*, pg. 2968
AKZO NOBEL INDUSTRIAL CHEMICALS AB—See The Carlyle Group Inc.; *U.S. Public*, pg. 2051
AKZO NOBEL INDUSTRIAL COATINGS AB—See Akzo Nobel N.V.; *Int'l*, pg. 271
AKZO NOBEL INDUSTRIAL COATINGS KOREA LTD.—See Akzo Nobel N.V.; *Int'l*, pg. 273
AKZO NOBEL INDUSTRIAL COATINGS LTD—See Akzo Nobel N.V.; *Int'l*, pg. 271
AKZO NOBEL INDUSTRIAL COATINGS MEXICO SA DE CV—See Akzo Nobel N.V.; *Int'l*, pg. 271
AKZO NOBEL INDUSTRIAL COATINGS SA—See Akzo Nobel N.V.; *Int'l*, pg. 271
AKZO NOBEL INDUSTRIAL COATINGS SDN BHD—See Akzo Nobel N.V.; *Int'l*, pg. 271
AKZO NOBEL INDUSTRIAL COATINGS SP. Z O.O.—See Akzo Nobel N.V.; *Int'l*, pg. 271
AKZO NOBEL INDUSTRIAL FINISHES AB—See Akzo Nobel N.V.; *Int'l*, pg. 270
AKZO NOBEL INDUSTRIAL FINISHES AB—See Nippon Paint Holdings Co., Ltd.; *Int'l*, pg. 5325
AKZO NOBEL INDUSTRIAL FINISHES GMBH—See Akzo Nobel N.V.; *Int'l*, pg. 271
AKZO NOBEL INDUSTRIAL PAINTS, S.L.—See Akzo Nobel N.V.; *Int'l*, pg. 271
AKZO NOBEL INDUSTRIES LIMITED—See Akzo Nobel N.V.; *Int'l*, pg. 271
AKZO NOBEL INSURANCE MANAGEMENT B.V.—See Akzo Nobel N.V.; *Int'l*, pg. 271
AKZO NOBEL KEMIPOL A.S.—See Akzo Nobel N.V.; *Int'l*, pg. 271
AKZO NOBEL LAKOKRASKA LTD—See Akzo Nobel N.V.; *Int'l*, pg. 271
AKZO NOBEL LIMITED—See Akzo Nobel N.V.; *Int'l*, pg. 272
AKZO NOBEL LTDA.—See Akzo Nobel N.V.; *Int'l*, pg. 272
AKZONOBEL LTD.—See Akzo Nobel N.V.; *Int'l*, pg. 270
AKZO NOBEL MANAGEMENT B.V.—See Akzo Nobel N.V.; *Int'l*, pg. 272
AKZO NOBEL NEDERLAND BV—See Akzo Nobel N.V.; *Int'l*, pg. 272
AKZO NOBEL NIPPON PAINT ESPANIA SA—See Akzo Nobel N.V.; *Int'l*, pg. 270
AKZO NOBEL NIPPON PAINT ESPANIA SA—See Nippon Paint Holdings Co., Ltd.; *Int'l*, pg. 5325
AKZO NOBEL NIPPON PAINT GMBH—See Akzo Nobel N.V.; *Int'l*, pg. 270
AKZO NOBEL NIPPON PAINT GMBH—See Nippon Paint Holdings Co., Ltd.; *Int'l*, pg. 5325
AKZO NOBEL NIPPON PAINT LIMITED—See Akzo Nobel N.V.; *Int'l*, pg. 270
AKZO NOBEL NIPPON PAINT LIMITED—See Nippon Paint Holdings Co., Ltd.; *Int'l*, pg. 5325
AKZO NOBEL NIPPON PAINT SRL—See Akzo Nobel N.V.; *Int'l*, pg. 270
AKZO NOBEL NIPPON PAINT SRL—See Nippon Paint Holdings Co., Ltd.; *Int'l*, pg. 5325
AKZO NOBEL N.V.—*Int'l*, pg. 268
AKZO NOBEL PACKAGE COATINGS GMBH—See Akzo Nobel N.V.; *Int'l*, pg. 272
AKZO NOBEL PACKAGING COATINGS LTD—See Akzo Nobel N.V.; *Int'l*, pg. 272
AKZO NOBEL PACKAGING COATINGS S.A.—See Akzo Nobel N.V.; *Int'l*, pg. 272
AKZO NOBEL PACKAGING COATINGS, S.A.S.—See Akzo Nobel N.V.; *Int'l*, pg. 272
AKZONOBEL PAINTS (ASIA PACIFIC) PTE LTD—See Akzo Nobel N.V.; *Int'l*, pg. 270

COMPANY NAME INDEX

AKZO NOBEL PAINTS BELGIUM NV/SA—See Akzo Nobel N.V.; *Int'l*, pg. 270
AKZONOBEL PAINTS ESPANA—See Akzo Nobel N.V.; *Int'l*, pg. 270
AKZO NOBEL PAINTS LLC—See Akzo Nobel N.V.; *Int'l*, pg. 272
AKZO NOBEL PAINTS (PUERTO RICO) INC.—See Akzo Nobel N.V.; *Int'l*, pg. 272
AKZO NOBEL PAINTS (SINGAPORE) PTE LIMITED—See Akzo Nobel N.V.; *Int'l*, pg. 270
AKZONOBEL PAINTS (SINGAPORE) PTE LTD.—See Akzo Nobel N.V.; *Int'l*, pg. 270
AKZONOBEL PAINTS SP. Z O.O.—See Akzo Nobel N.V.; *Int'l*, pg. 270
AKZO NOBEL PAINTS TAIWAN LIMITED—See Akzo Nobel N.V.; *Int'l*, pg. 270
AKZO NOBEL PAINTS (THAILAND) LTD., EKA BANGKOK BRANCH—See Akzo Nobel N.V.; *Int'l*, pg. 270
AKZO NOBEL PAINTS VIETNAM LTD—See Akzo Nobel N.V.; *Int'l*, pg. 270
AKZO NOBEL PAKISTAN LIMITED—See Akzo Nobel N.V.; *Int'l*, pg. 272
AKZO NOBEL PENSIONS GMBH—See Akzo Nobel N.V.; *Int'l*, pg. 272
AKZO NOBEL PERFORMANCE COATINGS—See Akzo Nobel N.V.; *Int'l*, pg. 272
AKZO NOBEL PERU S.A.C.—See Akzo Nobel N.V.; *Int'l*, pg. 272
AKZONOBEL POLSKA SP. ZO.O.—See Akzo Nobel N.V.; *Int'l*, pg. 273
AKZO NOBEL POLYMER CHEMICALS (NINGBO) CO., LTD.—See Akzo Nobel N.V.; *Int'l*, pg. 272
AKZO NOBEL POWDER COATINGS A.E.—See Akzo Nobel N.V.; *Int'l*, pg. 272
AKZO NOBEL POWDER COATINGS B.V.—See Akzo Nobel N.V.; *Int'l*, pg. 272
AKZO NOBEL POWDER COATINGS (CHENGDU) CO., LTD.—See Akzo Nobel N.V.; *Int'l*, pg. 272
AKZO NOBEL POWDER COATINGS FZE—See Akzo Nobel N.V.; *Int'l*, pg. 273
AKZO NOBEL POWDER COATINGS GMBH—See Akzo Nobel N.V.; *Int'l*, pg. 273
AKZO NOBEL POWDER COATINGS GMBH—See Akzo Nobel N.V.; *Int'l*, pg. 273
AKZO NOBEL POWDER COATINGS KOREA CO., LIMITED—See Akzo Nobel N.V.; *Int'l*, pg. 273
AKZO NOBEL POWDER COATINGS (LANGFANG) CO. LTD.—See Akzo Nobel N.V.; *Int'l*, pg. 272
AKZO NOBEL POWDER COATINGS LTD.—See Akzo Nobel N.V.; *Int'l*, pg. 272
AKZO NOBEL POWDER COATINGS (NINGBO) CO., LTD.—See Akzo Nobel N.V.; *Int'l*, pg. 272
AKZO NOBEL POWDER COATINGS SNC—See Akzo Nobel N.V.; *Int'l*, pg. 273
AKZO NOBEL POWDER COATINGS SOUTH AFRICA (PROPRIETARY) LIMITED—See Akzo Nobel N.V.; *Int'l*, pg. 273
AKZO NOBEL POWDER COATINGS (SUZHOU) CO., LTD.—See Akzo Nobel N.V.; *Int'l*, pg. 272
AKZO NOBEL POWDER COATINGS (VIETNAM) CO., LTD.—See Akzo Nobel N.V.; *Int'l*, pg. 272
AKZO NOBEL PROTECTIVE COATINGS (SUZHOU) CO. LTD—See Akzo Nobel N.V.; *Int'l*, pg. 273
AKZO NOBEL PULP AND PERFORMANCE CHEMICALS AB—See GIC Pte. Ltd.; *Int'l*, pg. 2968
AKZO NOBEL PULP AND PERFORMANCE CHEMICALS AB—See The Carlyle Group Inc.; *U.S. Public*, pg. 2051
AKZO NOBEL PULP AND PERFORMANCE CHEMICALS NORWAY AS—See GIC Pte. Ltd.; *Int'l*, pg. 2968
AKZO NOBEL PULP AND PERFORMANCE CHEMICALS NORWAY AS—See The Carlyle Group Inc.; *U.S. Public*, pg. 2051
AKZO NOBEL REPRESENTATIVE OFFICES B.V.—See Akzo Nobel N.V.; *Int'l*, pg. 273
AKZO NOBEL SALT A/S—See GIC Pte. Ltd.; *Int'l*, pg. 2968
AKZO NOBEL SALT A/S—See The Carlyle Group Inc.; *U.S. Public*, pg. 2051
AKZO NOBEL SALT B.V.—See Akzo Nobel N.V.; *Int'l*, pg. 273
AKZONOBEL SA—See Akzo Nobel N.V.; *Int'l*, pg. 270
AKZO NOBEL S.A.S.—See Akzo Nobel N.V.; *Int'l*, pg. 273
AKZONOBEL SDN BHD—See Akzo Nobel N.V.; *Int'l*, pg. 273
AKZO NOBEL (SHANGHAI) CO. LTD.—See Akzo Nobel N.V.; *Int'l*, pg. 268
AKZO NOBEL SINO COATINGS B.V.—See Akzo Nobel N.V.; *Int'l*, pg. 273
AKZONOBEL—See Akzo Nobel N.V.; *Int'l*, pg. 272
AKZONOBEL—See Akzo Nobel N.V.; *Int'l*, pg. 268
AKZONOBEL—See Akzo Nobel N.V.; *Int'l*, pg. 270
AKZONOBEL—See Akzo Nobel N.V.; *Int'l*, pg. 270
AKZONOBEL—See GIC Pte. Ltd.; *Int'l*, pg. 2968
AKZONOBEL—See The Carlyle Group Inc.; *U.S. Public*, pg. 2051
AKZO NOBEL SOURCING B.V.—See Akzo Nobel N.V.; *Int'l*, pg. 273
AKZO NOBEL SURFACE CHEMISTRY AB—See Akzo Nobel N.V.; *Int'l*, pg. 273
AKZO NOBEL SURFACE CHEMISTRY LLC—See GIC Pte. Ltd.; *Int'l*, pg. 2968
AKZO NOBEL SURFACE CHEMISTRY LLC—See The Carlyle Group Inc.; *U.S. Public*, pg. 2050
AKZONOBEL SURFACE CHEMISTRY—See Akzo Nobel N.V.; *Int'l*, pg. 273
AKZO NOBEL SWIRE PAINTS (GUANGZHOU) LIMITED—See Akzo Nobel N.V.; *Int'l*, pg. 273
AKZO NOBEL SWIRE PAINTS LIMITED—See Akzo Nobel N.V.; *Int'l*, pg. 273
AKZO NOBEL TINTAS PARA AUTOMOVEIS LDA—See Akzo Nobel N.V.; *Int'l*, pg. 273
AKZO NOBEL UK LIMITED—See GIC Pte. Ltd.; *Int'l*, pg. 2968
AKZO NOBEL UK LIMITED—See The Carlyle Group Inc.; *U.S. Public*, pg. 2051
AKZO NOBEL UK LTD—See Akzo Nobel N.V.; *Int'l*, pg. 273
AKZO NOBEL WILTON APPLIED RESEARCH GROUP—See Akzo Nobel N.V.; *Int'l*, pg. 273
AKZO NOBEL WOOD COATINGS LTD—See Akzo Nobel N.V.; *Int'l*, pg. 273
AKZO NOBEL WOOD FINISHES AND ADHESIVES—See Akzo Nobel N.V.; *Int'l*, pg. 273
AKZO NOBLE FINANCE UNITED STATES INC—See Akzo Nobel N.V.; *Int'l*, pg. 273
ALABAMA BOLT & SUPPLY, INC.—See Air Hydro Power Inc.; *U.S. Private*, pg. 139
ALABAMA BULK TERMINAL INC.—See Hunt Consolidated, Inc.; *U.S. Private*, pg. 2008
ALABAMA BUREAU OF TOURISM & TRAVEL; *U.S. Private*, pg. 148
ALABAMA CARRIERS, INC.—See Daseke, Inc.; *U.S. Private*, pg. 1161
ALABAMA CATFISH FEEDMILL, LLC.; *U.S. Private*, pg. 148
ALABAMA CONCRETE CO., INC.; *U.S. Private*, pg. 148
ALABAMA CREDIT UNION; *U.S. Private*, pg. 148
ALABAMA DIGESTIVE HEALTH ENDOSCOPY CENTER, L.L.C.—See Tenet Healthcare Corporation; *U.S. Public*, pg. 2007
ALABAMA DUMPSTER SERVICE, LLC—See BC Partners LLP; *Int'l*, pg. 923
ALABAMA ELECTRIC COMPANY INC. OF DOTHAN; *U.S. Private*, pg. 148
ALABAMA FARMERS COOPERATIVE, INC.; *U.S. Private*, pg. 148
ALABAMA FARMERS CO-OP – SOUTHFRESH FARMS DIVISION—See Alabama Farmers Cooperative, Inc.; *U.S. Private*, pg. 148
ALABAMA HAND AND SPORTS MEDICINE, L.L.C.—See Tenet Healthcare Corporation; *U.S. Public*, pg. 2002
ALABAMA HOMECARE OF VESTAVIA HILLS—See UnitedHealth Group Incorporated; *U.S. Public*, pg. 2243
ALABAMA INTERACTIVE, LLC—See Tyler Technologies, Inc.; *U.S. Public*, pg. 2208
ALABAMA INTER-FOREST CORP.; *U.S. Private*, pg. 148
ALABAMA METAL INDUSTRIES CORPORATION—See Gibraltar Industries, Inc.; *U.S. Public*, pg. 935
ALABAMA MOTOR EXPRESS INC.; *U.S. Private*, pg. 148
ALABAMA ONE CREDIT UNION; *U.S. Private*, pg. 148
ALABAMA POWER COMPANY—See The Southern Company; *U.S. Public*, pg. 2130
ALABAMA PUBLIC TELEVISION; *U.S. Private*, pg. 148
ALABAMA REASSURANCE CO. INC.—See Greene Group Inc.; *U.S. Private*, pg. 1776
ALABAMA SPECIALTY PRODUCTS, INC.; *U.S. Private*, pg. 148
ALABAMA & TENNESSEE RIVER RAILWAY, LLC—See The Broe Companies, Inc.; *U.S. Private*, pg. 4001
ALABANG NUMBERS & GAMING CORPORATION—See Leisure & Resorts World Corporation; *Int'l*, pg. 4447
ALABASTINE HOLLAND BV—See Akzo Nobel N.V.; *Int'l*, pg. 270
AL-ABBAS SUGAR MILLS LIMITED - DHABEJI PLANT—See AL-ABBAS SUGAR Mills Limited; *Int'l*, pg. 284
AL-ABBAS SUGAR MILLS LIMITED - MIRWAH PLANT—See AL-ABBAS SUGAR Mills Limited; *Int'l*, pg. 284
AL-ABBAS SUGAR MILLS LIMITED; *Int'l*, pg. 283
A-LAB CORP.—See Gray America Corp.; *U.S. Private*, pg. 1759
AL ABDULLATIF INDUSTRIAL INVESTMENT COMPANY; *Int'l*, pg. 275
AL-ABID SILK MILLS LIMITED; *Int'l*, pg. 284
AL-ABRAJ HOLDING COMPANY KSCC; *Int'l*, pg. 284
A-LABS CAPITAL II CORP.; *Int'l*, pg. 19
ALACARE HOME HEALTH SERVICES, INC.—See Encompass Health Corporation; *U.S. Public*, pg. 754
A LA CARTE CHARTS CORPORATION; *U.S. Private*, pg. 18
ALACER CORP.—See Pfizer Inc.; *U.S. Public*, pg. 1679
ALACER GOLD CORP.—See SSR Mining Inc.; *Int'l*, pg. 7157
ALAC INTERNATIONAL, INC.; *U.S. Private*, pg. 148
A-LACKERING AB—See Ratos AB; *Int'l*, pg. 6220
ALACRA, INC.—See GTCR LLC; *U.S. Private*, pg. 1806
ALACRITY SECURITIES LIMITED; *Int'l*, pg. 289
ALACRITY SOLUTIONS GROUP, INC.; *U.S. Private*, pg. 148
ALADDIN BLOCKCHAIN TECHNOLOGIES; *Int'l*, pg. 289
ALADDIN FOOD MANAGEMENT SERVICES, LLC—See Charterhouse Capital Partners LLP; *Int'l*, pg. 1455
ALADDIN MANUFACTURING OF ALABAMA, LLC—See Mohawk Industries, Inc.; *U.S. Public*, pg. 1457
ALADDIN METAL PRODUCTS INC.—See Dealers Supply Company Inc.; *U.S. Private*, pg. 1182
ALADDIN SEPARATION TECHNOLOGIES, INC.; *U.S. Public*, pg. 70
ALADDIN; *U.S. Private*, pg. 148
ALADDIN STEEL INC.; *U.S. Private*, pg. 148
ALADDIN TEMP-RITE CANADA—See Ali Holding S.r.l; *Int'l*, pg. 320
ALADDIN TEMP-RITE, LLC—See Ali Holding S.r.l; *Int'l*, pg. 320
ALADDIN TEMP-RITE PUERTO RICO—See Ali Holding S.r.l; *Int'l*, pg. 320
AL ADEKHAR REAL ESTATE CO. W.L.L.—See Taleb Group; *Int'l*, pg. 7446
ALADIN GMBH—See Dr. Honle AG; *Int'l*, pg. 2192
ALADIN VERLAG GMBH—See Bonnier AB; *Int'l*, pg. 1108
AL AFRAH AL SHARQIYA GENERAL TRADING AND CONTRACTING COMPANY W.L.L.—See Caesars Group; *Int'l*, pg. 1249
ALAGEN LLC—See General Microsystems, Inc.; *U.S. Private*, pg. 1666
AL-AHLEIA INSURANCE COMPANY S.A.K.—See National Industries Group Holding S.A.K.; *Int'l*, pg. 5159
AL-AHLEIA SWITCHGEAR COMPANY K.S.C.C.; *Int'l*, pg. 284
AL-AHLEIA SWITCHGEAR COMPANY K.S.C.C. - UNIT 4—See Al-Ahleia Switchgear Company K.S.C.C.; *Int'l*, pg. 284
AL-AHLEIA SWITCHGEAR COMPANY K.S.C.C. - UNIT 5—See Al-Ahleia Switchgear Company K.S.C.C.; *Int'l*, pg. 284
AL-AHLEIA SWITCHGEAR COMPANY K.S.C.C. - UNIT 6—See Al-Ahleia Switchgear Company K.S.C.C.; *Int'l*, pg. 284
AL AHLIA ENTERPRISES PLC; *Int'l*, pg. 275
AL AHLIAH TRANSPORT COMPANY; *Int'l*, pg. 275
AL AHLIA INSURANCE COMPANY SAOG—See Intact Financial Corporation; *Int'l*, pg. 3726
AL AHLIA INSURANCE COMPANY SAOG—See Tryg A/S; *Int'l*, pg. 7946
AL-AHLIA INTEGRATED GENERAL TRADING & CONTRACTING CO. W.L.L.—See Fouad Alghanim & Sons Group of Companies; *Int'l*, pg. 2753
AL AHLIA RESTAURANTS CO.—See Adeptio LLC; *Int'l*, pg. 143
AL AHLIA VEGETABLE OIL COMPANY; *Int'l*, pg. 284
AL AHLI BANK OF KUWAIT KSC—See Kuwait Finance House K.S.C.; *Int'l*, pg. 4344
AL-AHLI LEASING COMPANY—See National Bank of Egypt; *Int'l*, pg. 5152
AL AHLI TAKAFUL COMPANY—See Arabian Shield Cooperative Insurance Company; *Int'l*, pg. 533
AL AHLY FOR DEVELOPMENT & INVESTMENT; *Int'l*, pg. 275
AL-AHLYIA FOR AGRICULTURAL PRODUCTION; *Int'l*, pg. 284
AL AHLY MORTGAGE FINANCE CO.—See National Bank of Egypt; *Int'l*, pg. 5152
ALA HOSPITALITY LLC—See Sphere Entertainment Co.; *U.S. Public*, pg. 1918
AL AHRAM BEVERAGES COMPANY S.A.E.—See L'Arche Green N.V.; *Int'l*, pg. 4376
ALAIN AFFLELOU FRANCHISEUR SAS—See Lion Capital LLP; *Int'l*, pg. 4517
AL AIN AHLIA INSURANCE COMPANY; *Int'l*, pg. 275
AL AIN DISTRIBUTION COMPANY—See Abu Dhabi Water & Electricity Authority; *Int'l*, pg. 73
AL AIN FOOD & BEVERAGES PJSC—See Agthia Group PJSC; *Int'l*, pg. 221
ALAIN PINEL REALTORS, INC.—See Compass, Inc.; *U.S. Public*, pg. 561
AL AIR LIQUIDE ESPANA S.A.—See L'Air Liquide S.A.; *Int'l*, pg. 4369
ALAKAI MECHANICAL CORPORATION—See Taisei Oncho Co., Ltd.; *Int'l*, pg. 7416
ALAKARI WINES LTD—See Altia Oyj; *Int'l*, pg. 392
ALAKIERNIA SP.Z.O.O—See Ratos AB; *Int'l*, pg. 6220
AL AKRAM FOR METAL INDUSTRIES LTD. COMPANY—See MAS Economic Group; *Int'l*, pg. 4718
AL ALAM INDUSTRIAL COMPANY LLC—See Hayel Saeed Anam Group of Companies; *Int'l*, pg. 3290
AL-AMAL FINANCIAL INVESTMENT COMPANY; *Int'l*, pg. 284
AL AMAL INDUSTRIES CO. SAOC—See Omar Zawawi Establishment LLC; *Int'l*, pg. 5561
AL AMANA BUILDING MATERIALS CO. L.L.C—See DAMAC Group; *Int'l*, pg. 1955
ALAMANCE CROSSING, LLC—See CBL & Associates Properties, Inc.; *U.S. Public*, pg. 457

ALAMANCE EXTENDED CARE, INC.

ALAMANCE EXTENDED CARE, INC.; *U.S. Private*, pg. 149
ALAMANCE FOODS INC.; *U.S. Private*, pg. 149
AL-AMAN INVESTMENT COMPANY K.S.C.C.; *Int'l*, pg. 284
ALAMBRADOS AUTOMOTRICES, S.A. DE C.V.—See General Motors Company; *U.S. Public*, pg. 923
ALAM CONSTRUCTIONS LTD.—See Alam Group of Companies; *Int'l*, pg. 289
ALAMEDA-CONTRA COSTA TRANSIT DISTRICT; *U.S. Private*, pg. 149
ALAMEDA COUNTY COMMUNITY FOOD BANK; *U.S. Private*, pg. 149
THE ALAMEDA COUNTY FAIR ASSOCIATION; *U.S. Private*, pg. 3983
ALAMEDA COUNTY WATER DISTRICT; *U.S. Private*, pg. 149
ALAMEDA ELECTRICAL DISTRIBUTORS INC.; *U.S. Private*, pg. 149
ALAMEDA JOURNAL—See Alden Global Capital LLC; *U.S. Private*, pg. 155
ALAMEDA JUICE LLC; *U.S. Private*, pg. 149
ALAMEDA MUNICIPAL POWER; *U.S. Private*, pg. 149
ALAMEDA PIPE & SUPPLY CO., INC.—See J.D. Fields & Company Inc.; *U.S. Private*, pg. 2161
ALAMEDA TIMES-STAR—See Alden Global Capital LLC; *U.S. Private*, pg. 155
AL AMEEN INSURANCE COMPANY; *Int'l*, pg. 275
AL AMEEN REAL ESTATE INVESTMENT CO.; *Int'l*, pg. 275
ALAM FOOD INDUSTRIES (M) SDN. BHD.—See Alam Maritim Resources Berhad; *Int'l*, pg. 290
ALAM GROUP OF COMPANIES; *Int'l*, pg. 289
ALAM HIDRO (M) SDN. BHD.—See Alam Maritim Resources Berhad; *Int'l*, pg. 290
ALAM HZEM SDN. BHD.—See Hitachi Zosen Corporation; *Int'l*, pg. 3410
AL-AMIN BROTHERS TRANSPORTATION, LLC.; *U.S. Private*, pg. 148
AL AMIN FOR INVESTMENT P.L.C.; *Int'l*, pg. 275
ALAM MARITIM (M) SDN. BHD.—See Alam Maritim Resources Berhad; *Int'l*, pg. 290
ALAM MARITIM RESOURCES BERHAD; *Int'l*, pg. 289
ALAMO 1; *U.S. Private*, pg. 149
ALAMO AEROSPACE, LP—See Greenwich AeroGroup, Inc.; *U.S. Private*, pg. 1781
ALAMO CARIBE BAKERY DISTRIBUTORS; *U.S. Private*, pg. 149
ALAMO CEMENT COMPANY; *U.S. Private*, pg. 149
ALAMO CITY HARLEY-DAVIDSON; *U.S. Private*, pg. 149
ALAMO CONCRETE PRODUCTS LTD.—See Alamo Cement Company; *U.S. Private*, pg. 149
A LA MODE, INC.—See Insight Venture Management, LLC; *U.S. Private*, pg. 2089
A LA MODE, INC.—See Stone Point Capital LLC; *U.S. Private*, pg. 3823
ALAMO DRAFTHOUSE CINEMAS, LTD.—See Sony Group Corporation; *Int'l*, pg. 7105
ALAMO ENERGY CORP.; *U.S. Private*, pg. 149
ALAMO FOREST PRODUCTS, INC.—See Vaughan & Sons, Inc.; *U.S. Private*, pg. 4348
ALAMO FOREST PRODUCTS; *U.S. Private*, pg. 149
ALAMOGORDO DAILY NEWS—See Gannett Co., Inc.; *U.S. Public*, pg. 899
ALAMOGORDO FINANCIAL CORP.—See AF Mutual Holding Co., Inc.; *U.S. Private*, pg. 121
ALAMO GROUP (EUROPE) LIMITED—See Alamo Group Inc.; *U.S. Public*, pg. 70
ALAMO GROUP (IA) INC.—See Alamo Group Inc.; *U.S. Public*, pg. 71
ALAMO GROUP (IL) INC.—See Alamo Group Inc.; *U.S. Public*, pg. 71
ALAMO GROUP INC.; *U.S. Public*, pg. 70
ALAMO GROUP THE NETHERLANDS B.V.—See Alamo Group Inc.; *U.S. Public*, pg. 71
ALAMO GROUP THE NETHERLANDS MIDDELBURG B.V.—See Alamo Group Inc.; *U.S. Public*, pg. 71
ALAMO GROUP (TX), INC.—See Alamo Group Inc.; *U.S. Public*, pg. 71
ALAMO GULF COAST RAILROAD COMPANY—See Martin Marietta Materials, Inc.; *U.S. Public*, pg. 1389
ALAMO HEIGHTS SURGICARE, L.P.—See Tenet Healthcare Corporation; *U.S. Public*, pg. 2009
ALAMO IRON WORKS - BROWNSVILLE—See Triple-S Steel Holdings Inc.; *U.S. Private*, pg. 4237
ALAMO IRON WORKS, INC.—See Triple-S Steel Holdings Inc.; *U.S. Private*, pg. 4237
ALAMO LUMBER COMPANY—See Vaughan & Sons, Inc.; *U.S. Private*, pg. 4348
ALAMO MANUFACTURING SERVICES (UK) LIMITED—See Alamo Group Inc.; *U.S. Public*, pg. 70
ALAMON TELCO INCORPORATED; *U.S. Private*, pg. 149
ALAMO PHARMA SERVICES, INC.—See JLL Partners, LLC; *U.S. Private*, pg. 2212
ALAMO PHARMA SERVICES, INC.—See Water Street Healthcare Partners, LLC; *U.S. Private*, pg. 4452
ALAMO RENT-A-CAR—See Enterprise Holdings, Inc.; *U.S. Private*, pg. 1403

ALAMOSA DIALYSIS, LLC—See DaVita Inc.; *U.S. Public*, pg. 635
ALAMOSA NEWSPAPERS INC.—See News Media Corporation; *U.S. Private*, pg. 2916
ALAMOS GOLD INC.; *Int'l*, pg. 290
ALAMO TILE CO. INC.; *U.S. Private*, pg. 149
ALAMO TOYOTA INC.; *U.S. Private*, pg. 149
THE ALAMO TRAVEL GROUP, INC.; *U.S. Private*, pg. 3983
ALAMO WORKFORCE DEVELOPMENT, INC.; *U.S. Private*, pg. 149
A LAMP CONCRETE CONTRACTORS, INC.; *U.S. Private*, pg. 18
ALAM SEKITAR ECO-TECHNOLOGY SDN. BHD.—See Progressive Impact Corporation Berhad; *Int'l*, pg. 5991
ALAM SEKITAR MALAYSIA SDN. BHD.—See Progressive Impact Corporation Berhad; *Int'l*, pg. 5991
ALAM SUBSEA PTE. LTD.—See Alam Maritim Resources Berhad; *Int'l*, pg. 290
ALAN ALLMAN ASSOCIATES SA; *Int'l*, pg. 290
ALAN/ANTHONY, INC.; *Int'l*, pg. 150
ALANAR MEYVE VE GIDA URETIM PAZARLAMA SANAYI VE TIC. A.S.—See Tekfen Holding A.S.; *Int'l*, pg. 7526
ALAN BYER AUTO SALES INC.; *U.S. Private*, pg. 149
ALANCO TECHNOLOGIES, INC.; *U.S. Public*, pg. 71
ALANDALE INSURANCE AGENCY INC.; *U.S. Private*, pg. 150
ALANDALUS PROPERTY COMPANY; *Int'l*, pg. 290
ALAN DICK COMMUNICATIONS LTD—See Mutares SE & Co. KGaA; *Int'l*, pg. 5104
ALAND LIMITED—See Golden Resources Development International Limited; *Int'l*, pg. 3031
ALANDSBANKEN ABP; *Int'l*, pg. 290
ALANDSBANKEN ASSET MANAGEMENT AB—See Alandsbanken Abp; *Int'l*, pg. 290
ALANDSBANKEN EQUITIES RESEARCH AB—See Alandsbanken Abp; *Int'l*, pg. 290
ALANDSBANKEN FONDBOLAG AB—See Alandsbanken Abp; *Int'l*, pg. 290
ALANDSBANKEN SVERIGE AB—See Alandsbanken Abp; *Int'l*, pg. 290
ALANGKA-SUKA HOTELS & RESORTS SDN. BHD.—See Advance Synergy Berhad; *Int'l*, pg. 156
ALANG MARINE LTD.; *Int'l*, pg. 290
ALAN GRAY LLC; *U.S. Private*, pg. 149
ALAN HICKINBOTHAM PTY. LTD.; *Int'l*, pg. 290
ALAN JAY AUTOMOTIVE MANAGEMENT, INC.; *U.S. Private*, pg. 149
ALAN JAY AUTOMOTIVE NETWORK; *U.S. Private*, pg. 150
ALAN JAY CHRYSLER JEEP, INC.—See Alan Jay Automotive Management, Inc.; *U.S. Private*, pg. 149
ALAN JAY FORD LINCOLN MERCURY, INC.—See Alan Jay Automotive Management, Inc.; *U.S. Private*, pg. 150
ALAN KAYE INSURANCE AGENCY, INC.—See Aon plc; *Int'l*, pg. 495
ALANKIT CORPORATE SERVICES LIMITED; *Int'l*, pg. 290
ALAN NUTTALL LTD.; *Int'l*, pg. 290
ALANOD-XXENTRIA TECHNOLOGY MATERIALS COMPANY LIMITED—See Xxentria Technology Materials Co., Ltd.; *Int'l*, pg. 8541
ALAN RITCHEY INC.; *U.S. Private*, pg. 150
ALAN SCOTT INDUSTRIES LIMITED; *Int'l*, pg. 290
ALAN SHINTANI INC.; *U.S. Private*, pg. 150
ALANT CORPORATION; *U.S. Private*, pg. 150
ALAN & THOMAS INSURANCE BROKERS LIMITED—See Brown & Brown, Inc.; *U.S. Public*, pg. 396
ALANTRA PARTNERS, SA; *Int'l*, pg. 291
ALANTUM CORP.—See Korea Zinc Company, Ltd.; *Int'l*, pg. 4287
AL ANWAR CERAMIC TILES CO. SAOG; *Int'l*, pg. 275
AL ANWAR HOLDINGS S.A.O.G—See Al Yousef Group; *Int'l*, pg. 283
ALAN WEBB AUTOMOTIVE GROUP; *U.S. Private*, pg. 150
ALAN WEINKRANTZ & COMPANY; *U.S. Private*, pg. 150
THE ALAN WHITE COMPANY INC.; *U.S. Private*, pg. 3983
AL (AP) HOLDING LLC—See Ventas, Inc.; *U.S. Public*, pg. 2277
ALAPIS HOLDING INDUSTRIAL & COMMERCIAL SA; *Int'l*, pg. 291
AL-'AQAR HEALTHCARE REIT; *Int'l*, pg. 283
AL-AQARIYA TRADING INVESTMENT COMPANY; *Int'l*, pg. 284
AL AQEEQ REAL ESTATE DEVELOPMENT COMPANY—See Taiba Investments Company; *Int'l*, pg. 7410
AL ARABIA ELECTRO MECHANICAL L.L.C—See Juma Al Majid Group; *Int'l*, pg. 4025
AL ARABIA FOR OPERATION & MAINTENANCE L.L.C—See Juma Al Majid Group; *Int'l*, pg. 4025
AL ARABI INVESTMENT GROUP CO.—See Arab Bank plc; *Int'l*, pg. 529

CORPORATE AFFILIATIONS

AL ARABI STEEL STRUCTURE MANUFACTURING CO.—See Al-Osais International Holding Company; *Int'l*, pg. 287
ALARA ENGINEERING AB—See Studsvik AB; *Int'l*, pg. 7244
AL-ARAFAH ISLAMI BANK PLC; *Int'l*, pg. 284
ALARA RESOURCES LIMITED; *Int'l*, pg. 291
ALAR ENGINEERING CORPORATION—See SKion GmbH; *Int'l*, pg. 6990
ALARGAN BAHRAIN W.L.L.—See Alargan International Real Estate Co. K.S.C.C.; *Int'l*, pg. 291
ALARGAN INTERNATIONAL REAL ESTATE CO. K.S.C.C.; *Int'l*, pg. 291
ALARGAN TOWEL INVESTMENT COMPANY LLC—See Alargan International Real Estate Co. K.S.C.C.; *Int'l*, pg. 291
AL ARGAN TOWELL INVESTMENT CO.—See W.J. Towell & Co. LLC; *Int'l*, pg. 8322
A LARGE EVIL CORPORATION LTD.—See Funko Inc.; *U.S. Public*, pg. 893
ALARI AUSTRIA GMBH—See Henley Management Company; *U.S. Private*, pg. 1916
ALARIC COMPLIANCE SERVICES LLC—See Genstar Capital, LLC; *U.S. Private*, pg. 1677
ALARIS ANTENNAS PROPRIETARY LIMITED—See Alaris Holdings Limited; *Int'l*, pg. 291
ALARIS EQUITY PARTNERS INCOME TRUST; *Int'l*, pg. 291
ALARIS GROUP, INC.—See Summit Partners, L.P.; *U.S. Private*, pg. 3856
ALARIS HOLDINGS LIMITED; *Int'l*, pg. 291
ALARKO CARRIER SANAYI VE TICARET A.S.—See Alarko Holding A.S.; *Int'l*, pg. 291
ALARKO GAYRIMENKUL YATIRIM ORTAKLIGI AS; *Int'l*, pg. 291
ALARKO HOLDING A.S.; *Int'l*, pg. 291
ALARMAX DISTRIBUTORS INC.; *U.S. Private*, pg. 150
ALARM CENTER, INC.; *U.S. Private*, pg. 150
ALARMCOM AB—See Siemens Aktiengesellschaft; *Int'l*, pg. 6888
ALARMCOM AG—See Siemens Aktiengesellschaft; *Int'l*, pg. 6888
ALARMCOM GMBH—See Siemens Aktiengesellschaft; *Int'l*, pg. 6888
ALARM.COM HOLDINGS, INC.—See ABS Capital Partners, L.P.; *U.S. Private*, pg. 43
ALARM.COM INC.—See ABS Capital Partners, L.P.; *U.S. Private*, pg. 43
ALARMCOM LEPTONICS PTY LTD—See Siemens Aktiengesellschaft; *Int'l*, pg. 6888
ALARM DETECTION SYSTEMS, INC.; *U.S. Private*, pg. 150
ALARMGUARD SECURITY INC.—See Pye-Barker Fire & Safety, LLC; *U.S. Private*, pg. 3309
ALARM LOCK SYSTEMS, INC.—See Napco Security Technologies, Inc.; *U.S. Public*, pg. 1491
ALARM NEW ENGLAND LLC; *U.S. Private*, pg. 150
ALARM SPECIALISTS, INC.—See Pye-Barker Fire & Safety, LLC; *U.S. Private*, pg. 3309
ALARM TEAM, INC.; *U.S. Private*, pg. 150
ALARMTEC AS—See Allied Universal Manager LLC; *U.S. Private*, pg. 188
ALARM TECH SOLUTIONS LLC—See GTCR LLC; *U.S. Private*, pg. 1801
ALARM WEST GROUP D.O.O—See Securitas AB; *Int'l*, pg. 6675
ALARUM TECHNOLOGIES LTD.; *Int'l*, pg. 291
ALA SERVICES LLC; *U.S. Private*, pg. 148
AL ASHER & SONS, INC.; *U.S. Private*, pg. 147
AL ASILAH DESALINATION COMPANY SAOC—See JGC Holdings Corporation; *Int'l*, pg. 3939
ALASKA AIR GROUP, INC.; *U.S. Public*, pg. 71
ALASKA AIRLINES, INC.—See Alaska Air Group, Inc.; *U.S. Public*, pg. 71
ALASKA BASIC INDUSTRIES, INC.—See MDU Resources Group, Inc.; *U.S. Public*, pg. 1409
ALASKA COMMUNICATIONS SYSTEMS GROUP, INC.—See ATN International, Inc.; *U.S. Public*, pg. 224
ALASKA COMMUNICATIONS SYSTEMS GROUP, INC.—See Freedom 3 Capital, LLC; *U.S. Private*, pg. 1603
ALASKA COMMUNICATIONS SYSTEMS HOLDINGS, INC.—See ATN International, Inc.; *U.S. Public*, pg. 224
ALASKA COMMUNICATIONS SYSTEMS HOLDINGS, INC.—See Freedom 3 Capital, LLC; *U.S. Private*, pg. 1603
ALASKA COMMUNITY FOUNDATION; *U.S. Private*, pg. 150
ALASKA COMPREHENSIVE HEALTH INSURANCE ASSOCIATION; *U.S. Private*, pg. 150
ALASKA DENALI TRAVEL—See Viad Corp.; *U.S. Public*, pg. 2291
ALASKA DIGITEL WIRELESS COMMUNICATIONS LLC; *U.S. Private*, pg. 150
ALASKA DISPATCH PUBLISHING LLC; *U.S. Private*, pg. 150
ALASKA DISTRIBUTORS CO.; *U.S. Private*, pg. 150
ALASKA ELECTRIC LIGHT & POWER COMPANY; *U.S. Private*, pg. 150

COMPANY NAME INDEX

ALASKA ENERGY METALS CORPORATION; *Int'l*, pg. 291
ALASKA GROWTH CAPITAL BIDCO, INC.—See Arctic Slope Regional Corporation; *U.S. Private*, pg. 316
ALASKA HIGHWAY NEWS—See Glacier Media Inc.; *Int'l*, pg. 2987
ALASKA HOUSEWARES INC.; *U.S. Private*, pg. 150
ALASKA HOUSING FINANCE CORPORATION; *U.S. Private*, pg. 150
ALASKA HYDRO CORPORATION; *Int'l*, pg. 291
ALASKA INDUSTRIAL HARDWARE INC.—See Bering Straits Native Corporation; *U.S. Private*, pg. 532
ALASKA INSTRUMENT COMPANY, LLC.—See The Aleut Corporation; *U.S. Private*, pg. 3984
ALASKA JOURNAL OF COMMERCE—See Shivers Trading & Operating Company; *U.S. Private*, pg. 3638
ALASKA LOGISTICS, LLC.; *U.S. Private*, pg. 151
ALASKA MARINE LINES, INC.—See Lynden Incorporated; *U.S. Private*, pg. 2521
ALASKA MECHANICAL INC.; *U.S. Private*, pg. 151
ALASKA MILK CORPORATION—See Zuivelcooperatie FrieslandCampina U.A.; *Int'l*, pg. 8694
ALASKA MINING & DIVING SUPPLY, INC., *U.S. Private*, pg. 151
ALASKA NATIONAL CORPORATION; *U.S. Private*, pg. 151
ALASKA NATIONAL INSURANCE COMPANY—See Alaska National Corporation; *U.S. Private*, pg. 151
ALASKA NATIVE INDUSTRIES COOP ASSOCIATION; *U.S. Private*, pg. 151
ALASKAN BREWING COMPANY; *U.S. Private*, pg. 151
ALASKAN COPPER & BRASS COMPANY-PORTLAND—See Alco Investment Co., Inc.; *U.S. Private*, pg. 154
ALASKAN COPPER & BRASS COMPANY-SEATTLE—See Alco Investment Co., Inc.; *U.S. Private*, pg. 154
ALASKAN COPPER & BRASS COMPANY—See Alco Investment Co., Inc.; *U.S. Private*, pg. 153
ALASKAN COPPER & BRASS COMPANY—See Alco Investment Co., Inc.; *U.S. Private*, pg. 154
ALASKAN COPPER WORKS—See Alco Investment Co., Inc.; *U.S. Private*, pg. 154
ALASKAN MARINE LINES, INC.—See Lynden Incorporated; *U.S. Private*, pg. 2521
ALASKA PACIFIC TRADING COMPANY; *U.S. Private*, pg. 151
ALASKA POWER & TELEPHONE COMPANY; *U.S. Public*, pg. 72
ALASKA POWER & TELEPHONE—See Alaska Power & Telephone Company; *U.S. Public*, pg. 72
ALASKA PUBLIC MEDIA, INC.; *U.S. Private*, pg. 151
ALASKA PUMP & SUPPLY, INC.—See DXP Enterprises, Inc.; *U.S. Public*, pg. 697
ALASKA RAILROAD CORPORATION; *U.S. Private*, pg. 151
ALASKA REGIONAL HOSPITAL—See HCA Healthcare, Inc.; *U.S. Public*, pg. 990
ALASKA REGIONAL MEDICAL GROUP, LLC—See HCA Healthcare, Inc.; *U.S. Public*, pg. 990
ALASKA ROAD BORING COMPANY; *U.S. Private*, pg. 151
ALASKA SALES & SERVICE, INC.; *U.S. Private*, pg. 151
ALASKA SPINE CENTER, LLC—See HCA Healthcare, Inc.; *U.S. Public*, pg. 990
ALASKA STAR—See Shivers Trading & Operating Company; *U.S. Private*, pg. 3638
ALASKA STEEL CO.—See Reliance Steel & Aluminum Co.; *U.S. Public*, pg. 1779
ALASKA SURGERY CENTER, INC.—See UnitedHealth Group Incorporated; *U.S. Public*, pg. 2238
ALASKA SURGERY CENTER LIMITED PARTNERSHIP—See HCA Healthcare, Inc.; *U.S. Public*, pg. 990
ALASKA TANKER COMPANY LLC—See Saltchuk Resources Inc.; *U.S. Private*, pg. 3534
ALASKA TRAVEL INDUSTRY ASSOCIATION; *U.S. Private*, pg. 151
ALASKA UNITED FIBER SYSTEM PARTNERSHIP—See Liberty Broadband Corporation; *U.S. Public*, pg. 1310
ALASKA VILLAGE ELECTRIC COOPERATIVE, INC.; *U.S. Private*, pg. 151
ALASKA WASTE-INTERIOR, LLC—See Waste Connections, Inc.; *Int'l*, pg. 8353
ALASKA WASTE-JUNEAU, LLC—See Waste Connections, Inc.; *Int'l*, pg. 8353
ALASKA WASTE-KENAI PENINSULA, LLC—See Waste Connections, Inc.; *Int'l*, pg. 8353
ALASKA WASTE-KETCHIKAN, LLC—See Waste Connections, Inc.; *Int'l*, pg. 8352
ALASKA WASTE-NOME, LLC—See Waste Connections, Inc.; *Int'l*, pg. 8352
ALASKA WASTE-SITKA, LLC—See Waste Connections, Inc.; *Int'l*, pg. 8353
ALASKA WEST EXPRESS, INC.—See Lynden Incorporated; *U.S. Private*, pg. 2521
ALA SPA; *Int'l*, pg. 289
A. LASSONDE, INC.—See Lassonde Industries, Inc.; *Int'l*, pg. 4421

ALASTIN SKINCARE, INC—See Abu Dhabi Investment Authority; *Int'l*, pg. 71
ALASTIN SKINCARE, INC—See EQT Corporation; *U.S. Public*, pg. 785
ALASTIN SKINCARE, INC—See Public Sector Pension Investment Board; *Int'l*, pg. 6095
ALASTREAN CARE HOME ABOYNE—See Balhousie Holdings Limited; *Int'l*, pg. 808
ALATAU ZHARYK COMPANY JSC; *Int'l*, pg. 291
ALATNICA A.D.; *Int'l*, pg. 292
ALATOSCANA SPA—See Corporacion America Airports S.A.; *Int'l*, pg. 1803
AL ATOUN STEEL INDUSTRIES COMPANY—See Kuwait Projects Company (Holding) K.S.C.P.; *Int'l*, pg. 4346
ALAUNOS THERAPEUTICS, INC.; *U.S. Public*, pg. 72
A. LAVIN COMMUNICATIONS—See Public; pg. 23
ALAWWAL BANK—See The Saudi British Bank; *Int'l*, pg. 7680
ALAYA CARE INC.; *Int'l*, pg. 292
ALAY SRL—See Oriflame Cosmetics S.A.; *Int'l*, pg. 5627
AL-AZHAR TEXTILE MILLS LIMITED; *Int'l*, pg. 284
ALAZOR INVERSIONES, S.A.—See Sacyr, S.A.; *Int'l*, pg. 6465
ALBAAD DEUTSCHLAND GMBH—See Albaad Massuot Yitzhak Ltd.; *Int'l*, pg. 293
ALBAAD MASSUOT YITZHAK LTD.; *Int'l*, pg. 293
ALBA ALLGEMEINE VERSICHERUNGS-GESELLSCHAFT—See Allianz SE; *Int'l*, pg. 350
ALBA BAUPROJEKTMANAGEMENT GMBH—See PORR AG; *Int'l*, pg. 5925
AL-BAB CARE OF DAEWOO—See POSCO Holdings Inc.; *Int'l*, pg. 5937
ALBA BERLIN GMBH—See Alba SE; *Int'l*, pg. 292
ALBA BRAUNSCHWEIG GMBH—See Alba SE; *Int'l*, pg. 292
ALBA BROADCASTING CORPORATION LIMITED—See Harvard International Ltd.; *Int'l*, pg. 3280
AL-BABTAIN BODY MANUFACTURING CO.—See Al-Babtain Group; *Int'l*, pg. 284
AL-BABTAIN GROUP; *Int'l*, pg. 284
AL-BABTAIN POWER & TELECOMMUNICATION COMPANY; *Int'l*, pg. 284
ALBA CHINA RECYCLING SOLUTIONS LTD.—See Alba SE; *Int'l*, pg. 292
ALBACORE CONSULTING GROUP PTY LTD.—See Bain Capital, LP; *U.S. Private*, pg. 433
ALBA COTTBUS GMBH—See Alba SE; *Int'l*, pg. 292
AL BADIA FOR GENERAL TRANSPORTATION; *Int'l*, pg. 275
ALBA DOLNY SLASK SP. Z O.O.—See Alba SE; *Int'l*, pg. 292
ALBA EKOPLUS SP. Z O.O.—See Alba SE; *Int'l*, pg. 292
ALBA ELECTRONICS RECYCLING GMBH—See Alba SE; *Int'l*, pg. 292
ALBA EUROPE HOLDING PLC & CO. KG—See Alba SE; *Int'l*, pg. 292
ALBA FERROUS TRADING GMBH—See Alba SE; *Int'l*, pg. 292
ALBA FRUCT SA; *Int'l*, pg. 292
AL-BAGHLI SPONGE MANUFACTURING COMPANY; *Int'l*, pg. 284
ALBA GRUPO MARCH; *Int'l*, pg. 292
AL-BAHA INVESTMENT AND DEVELOPMENT CO.; *Int'l*, pg. 284
ALBAHEALTH, LLC—See Encompass Group LLC; *U.S. Private*, pg. 1390
ALBA HEILBRONN-FRANKEN PLC & CO. KG—See Alba SE; *Int'l*, pg. 292
ALBA INTEGRATED WASTE SOLUTIONS (HONG KONG) LIMITED—See Alba SE; *Int'l*, pg. 292
ALBALACT S.A.—See Groupe Lactalis SA; *Int'l*, pg. 3105
ALBA LOCKING PRODUCTS, LTD—See ASSA ABLOY AB; *Int'l*, pg. 640
ALBA LOGISTIK GMBH—See Alba SE; *Int'l*, pg. 292
ALBALOG S.R.L.—See Sesa S.p.A.; *Int'l*, pg. 6728
ALBA MANUFACTURING INC.; *U.S. Private*, pg. 151
ALBA METALL NORD GMBH—See Alba SE; *Int'l*, pg. 292
ALBA METALL SUD FRANKEN GMBH—See Alba SE; *Int'l*, pg. 292
ALBA METALL SUD RHEIN-MAIN GMBH—See Alba SE; *Int'l*, pg. 292
ALBA MINERAL RESOURCES PLC; *Int'l*, pg. 292
ALBA MODA GMBH—See K - Mail Order GmbH & Co. KG; *Int'l*, pg. 4037
ALBA MPGK SP. Z O.O.—See Alba SE; *Int'l*, pg. 292
ALBA MPO SP. Z O.O.—See Alba SE; *Int'l*, pg. 292
ALBANIA MARKETING SERVICE SH.P.K.—See Teleperformance SE; *Int'l*, pg. 7539
ALBANIAN AIRLINES MAK—See Kharafi National; *Int'l*, pg. 4151
ALBANIAN FERRY TERMINAL OPERATOR SHPK—See FRS GmbH & Co. KG; *Int'l*, pg. 2797
ALBANIA SINOMINE RESOURCE CO. SHPK.—See Sinomine Resource Group Co., Ltd.; *Int'l*, pg. 6953
ALBANI BRYGGERIERNE A/S—See Royal Unibrew A/S; *Int'l*, pg. 6414
ALBA NIEDERSACHSEN-ANHALT GMBH—See Alba SE; *Int'l*, pg. 292

ALBANY TRAVEL UNLIMITED INC.

ALBANI SVERIGE AB—See Royal Unibrew A/S; *Int'l*, pg. 6414
ALBA NORDBADEN GMBH—See Alba SE; *Int'l*, pg. 292
ALBA NORD GMBH—See Alba SE; *Int'l*, pg. 292
ALBAN RENTS, LLC—See Carter Machinery Company, Inc.; *U.S. Private*, pg. 776
ALBAN TIRE CORP.; *U.S. Private*, pg. 151
ALBAN TRACTOR COMPANY INC. - ALBAN MACHINING & HYDRAULICS DIVISION—See Carter Machinery Company, Inc.; *U.S. Private*, pg. 776
ALBAN TRACTOR COMPANY INC. - ALBAN RENTAL SOLUTIONS DIVISION—See Carter Machinery Company, Inc.; *U.S. Private*, pg. 776
ALBAN TRACTOR COMPANY INC.—See Carter Machinery Company, Inc.; *U.S. Private*, pg. 776
ALBANY ADVOCACY RESOURCE CENTER, INC.; *U.S. Private*, pg. 151
ALBANY ASSISTANCE LIMITED—See ZIGUP plc; *Int'l*, pg. 8682
ALBANY BANCORP, INC.; *U.S. Private*, pg. 151
ALBANY BANK & TRUST COMPANY, N.A.; *U.S. Private*, pg. 151
ALBANY CHICAGO COMPANY, LLC—See Shiloh Industries, Inc.; *U.S. Private*, pg. 3636
ALBANY DAY HOSPITAL PTY LTD—See Healius Limited; *Int'l*, pg. 3302
THE ALBANY DEMOCRAT-HERALD—See Lee Enterprises, Incorporated; *U.S. Public*, pg. 1300
ALBANY DOOR SYSTEMS, INC.—See ASSA ABLOY AB; *Int'l*, pg. 634
ALBANY ENGINEERED COMPOSITES, INC.—See Albany International Corp.; *U.S. Public*, pg. 72
ALBANY ENGINEERED COMPOSITES - SALT LAKE CITY—See Albany International Corp.; *U.S. Public*, pg. 72
ALBANY ENVIRONMENTAL SERVICES LTD.—See Rollins, Inc.; *U.S. Public*, pg. 1809
ALBANY FAMILY PRACTICE, LLC—See HCA Healthcare, Inc.; *U.S. Public*, pg. 990
ALBANY FORD INC.; *U.S. Private*, pg. 151
THE ALBANY HERALD PUBLISHING CO.—See Southern Community Newspapers Inc.; *U.S. Private*, pg. 3730
ALBANY INTERNATIONAL AB—See Albany International Corp.; *U.S. Public*, pg. 72
ALBANY INTERNATIONAL CANADA CORP.—See Albany International Corp.; *U.S. Public*, pg. 72
ALBANY INTERNATIONAL CANADA CORP.—See Albany International Corp.; *U.S. Public*, pg. 72
ALBANY INTERNATIONAL CORP.; *U.S. Public*, pg. 72
ALBANY INTERNATIONAL DE MEXICO S.A. DE C.V.—See Albany International Corp.; *U.S. Public*, pg. 72
ALBANY INTERNATIONAL ENGINEERED FABRICS—See Albany International Corp.; *U.S. Public*, pg. 72
ALBANY INTERNATIONAL/ENGINEERED FABRICS—See Albany International Corp.; *U.S. Public*, pg. 72
ALBANY INTERNATIONAL FORMING FABRICS—See Albany International Corp.; *U.S. Public*, pg. 72
ALBANY INTERNATIONAL FRANCE S.A.S.—See Albany International Corp.; *U.S. Public*, pg. 72
ALBANY INTERNATIONAL JAPAN KABUSHIKI KAISHA—See Albany International Corp.; *U.S. Public*, pg. 72
ALBANY INTERNATIONAL LTD.—See Albany International Corp.; *U.S. Public*, pg. 72
ALBANY INTERNATIONAL OY—See Albany International Corp.; *U.S. Public*, pg. 72
ALBANY INTERNATIONAL PTY. LTD.—See Albany International Corp.; *U.S. Public*, pg. 72
ALBANY INTERNATIONAL TECHNIWEAVE, INC.—See Albany International Corp.; *U.S. Public*, pg. 72
ALBANY INTERNATIONAL TECIDOS TECNICOS LTDA.—See Albany International Corp.; *U.S. Public*, pg. 72
ALBANY INVESTMENTS LIMITED—See CK Asset Holdings Limited; *Int'l*, pg. 1635
ALBANY PHYSICAL THERAPY, PC—See Gryphon Investors, LLC; *U.S. Private*, pg. 1799
ALBANY PLANTATION EXPORT COMPANY PTY. LTD.—See Oji Holdings Corporation; *Int'l*, pg. 5536
ALBANY PLANTATION FOREST COMPANY OF AUSTRALIA PTY. LTD.—See Oji Holdings Corporation; *Int'l*, pg. 5536
ALBANY PORT RAILROAD CO.—See CSX Corporation; *U.S. Public*, pg. 602
ALBANY PORT RAILROAD CO.—See Norfolk Southern Corporation; *U.S. Public*, pg. 1535
ALBANY SOLAR LLC—See Enel S.p.A.; *Int'l*, pg. 2411
ALBANY STEEL INC.; *U.S. Private*, pg. 151
ALBANY TIMES UNION—See The Hearst Corporation; *U.S. Private*, pg. 4047
ALBANY TRACTOR CO. - LAWN & GARDEN DIVISION—See Flint Equipment Holdings, Inc.; *U.S. Private*, pg. 1545
ALBANY TRACTOR CO.—See Flint Equipment Holdings, Inc.; *U.S. Private*, pg. 1545
ALBANY TRAVEL UNLIMITED INC.; *U.S. Private*, pg. 152
ALBANY VEHICLE RENTALS LIMITED—See ZIGUP plc; *Int'l*, pg. 8682

ALBA PGK SP. Z O.O.—See Alba SE; *Int'l*, pg. 292
ALBA POLUDNIE POLSKA SP. Z O.O.—See Alba SE; *Int'l*, pg. 292
ALBA POWER LIMITED—See Sulzer Ltd.; *Int'l*, pg. 7256
ALBA PTS SP. Z O.O.—See Alba SE; *Int'l*, pg. 292
ALBA RADIO LIMITED—See Harvard International Ltd.; *Int'l*, pg. 3280
AL BARAKA BANK EGYPT—See Al Baraka Banking Group B.S.C.; *Int'l*, pg. 276
AL BARAKA BANKING GROUP B.S.C.; *Int'l*, pg. 275
AL BARAKA BANK LEBANON SAL—See Al Baraka Banking Group B.S.C.; *Int'l*, pg. 276
AL BARAKA BANK LTD.—See Al Baraka Banking Group B.S.C.; *Int'l*, pg. 276
AL BARAKA BANK (PAKISTAN) LIMITED—See Al Baraka Banking Group B.S.C.; *Int'l*, pg. 276
AL BARAKA BANK SUDAN—See Al Baraka Banking Group B.S.C.; *Int'l*, pg. 276
AL BARAKA BANK SYRIA—See Al Baraka Banking Group B.S.C.; *Int'l*, pg. 276
AL BARAKA BANK TUNISIA—See Al Baraka Banking Group B.S.C.; *Int'l*, pg. 276
AL BARAKA ISLAMIC BANK E.C.—See Al Baraka Banking Group B.S.C.; *Int'l*, pg. 276
ALBARAKA PORTFOY YONETIMI A.S.—See Albaraka Turk Katilim Bankasi A.S.; *Int'l*, pg. 293
ALBARAKA TURKISH FINANCE HOUSE—See Al Baraka Banking Group B.S.C.; *Int'l*, pg. 276
ALBARAKA TURK KATILIM BANKASI A.S.; *Int'l*, pg. 293
ALBARELLA S.P.A.—See Marcegaglia S.p.A.; *Int'l*, pg. 4688
ALBARELL ELECTRIC INC.; *U.S. Private*, pg. 152
ALBAR INDUSTRIES, INC.; *U.S. Private*, pg. 152
ALBA RISING GREEN FUEL (HONG KONG) LTD.—See Alba SE; *Int'l*, pg. 293
ALBA SACHSEN GMBH—See Alba SE; *Int'l*, pg. 293
ALBA SE; *Int'l*, pg. 292
ALBA SUD GMBH & CO. KG—See Alba SE; *Int'l*, pg. 293
ALBA SUPPLY CHAIN MANAGEMENT GMBH—See Alba SE; *Int'l*, pg. 293
ALBA TAV BETRIEBS GMBH—See Alba SE; *Int'l*, pg. 293
AL BATEK FINANCIAL INVESTMENT CO.; *Int'l*, pg. 276
AL BATINAH DEVELOPMENT & INVESTMENT HOLDING CO. SAOG; *Int'l*, pg. 276
AL BATINAH POWER CO SAOG; *Int'l*, pg. 276
AL BATIN BUSINESS CENTRE L.L.C.—See STV Group, Inc.; *U.S. Private*, pg. 3845
ALBA TRAFFIC MANAGEMENT LIMITED—See Breedon Group plc; *Int'l*, pg. 1144
ALBATRANS FRANCE S.A.R.L—See Savino Del Bene S.p.A.; *Int'l*, pg. 6600
ALBATRANS GMBH—See Savino Del Bene S.p.A.; *Int'l*, pg. 6600
ALBATRANS INC—See Savino Del Bene S.p.A.; *Int'l*, pg. 6600
ALBATRANS PTY LTD.—See Savino Del Bene S.p.A.; *Int'l*, pg. 6600
ALBATRANS SPAIN S.L—See Savino Del Bene S.p.A.; *Int'l*, pg. 6600
ALBATRANS SPA—See Savino Del Bene S.p.A.; *Int'l*, pg. 6600
ALBATRANS UK LTD.—See Savino Del Bene S.p.A.; *Int'l*, pg. 6600
ALBATRAOS VERSICHERUNGSDIENSTE GMBH—See Deutsche Lufthansa AG; *Int'l*, pg. 2066
ALBATRON TECHNOLOGY CO., LTD.; *Int'l*, pg. 293
ALBATROS DATENSERVICE GMBH—See Comcast Corporation; *U.S. Public*, pg. 537
ALBATROS LOGISTIC, MAROC, S.A.—See ACS, Actividades de Construccion y Servicios, S.A.; *Int'l*, pg. 110
ALBATROS LOGISTIC, S.A.—See ACS, Actividades de Construccion y Servicios, S.A.; *Int'l*, pg. 110
ALBATROS SERVICE CENTER GMBH—See Deutsche Lufthansa AG; *Int'l*, pg. 2066
ALBAT+WIRSAM SOFTWARE GMBH—See Constellation Software Inc.; *Int'l*, pg. 1773
ALBA UCKERMARK GMBH—See Alba SE; *Int'l*, pg. 293
ALBAUGH INC.; *U.S. Private*, pg. 152
ALBA UTILITY SCRAP SOLUTIONS GMBH—See Alba SE; *Int'l*, pg. 293
ALBAVET LIMITED—See CVS Group Plc; *Int'l*, pg. 1890
ALBA WERTSTOFFMANAGEMENT GMBH—See Alba SE; *Int'l*, pg. 293
ALBA WHEELS UP INTERNATIONAL, INC.—See Southfield Capital Advisors, LLC; *U.S. Private*, pg. 3736
ALBA WHEELS UP INTERNATIONAL, INC.—See Southfield Capital Advisors, LLC; *U.S. Private*, pg. 3736
ALBA WHEELS UP INTERNATIONAL, INC.—See Southfield Capital Advisors, LLC; *U.S. Private*, pg. 3736
ALBA W&H SMART CITY PTE. LTD.—See Alba SE; *Int'l*, pg. 293
ALBA ZENICA D.O.O.—See Alba SE; *Int'l*, pg. 293
ALBAZINO RESOURCES LTD—See Solidcore Resources plc; *Int'l*, pg. 7073
AL BAZZINI COMPANY INCORPORATION; *U.S. Private*, pg. 147
ALBCO SALES INC.; *U.S. Private*, pg. 152
ALBEA BEAUTY HOLDINGS S.A.—See PAI Partners S.A.S.; *Int'l*, pg. 5699

ALBEA BEAUTY SOLUTIONS USA, LLC—See PAI Partners S.A.S.; *Int'l*, pg. 5699
ALBEA S.A.—See PAI Partners S.A.S.; *Int'l*, pg. 5699
ALBECCA INC.—See Berkshire Hathaway Inc.; *U.S. Public*, pg. 298
ALBECK FINANCIAL SERVICE INC.—See Calabrese Consulting, LLC; *U.S. Private*, pg. 715
ALBECO INC.; *U.S. Private*, pg. 152
ALBECOUR INC.—See Investissement Quebec; *Int'l*, pg. 3780
ALBEDO CORPORATION PTE. LTD.—See China Medical (International) Group Limited; *Int'l*, pg. 1518
ALBEDO SDN. BHD.—See China Medical (International) Group Limited; *Int'l*, pg. 1518
ALBE MARKETING SDN. BHD.—See LB Aluminium Berhad; *Int'l*, pg. 4428
ALBEMARLE AMENDMENTS, LLC—See Albemarle Corporation; *U.S. Public*, pg. 73
ALBEMARLE CHEMICALS (SHANGHAI) COMPANY LIMITED—See Albemarle Corporation; *U.S. Public*, pg. 73
ALBEMARLE CHEMICALS SOUTH AFRICA (PTY) LTD.—See Albemarle Corporation; *U.S. Public*, pg. 73
ALBEMARLE CHEMICALS U.K. LIMITED—See Albemarle Corporation; *U.S. Public*, pg. 73
ALBEMARLE CORPORATION; *U.S. Public*, pg. 72
ALBEMARLE CORP. - PENNSYLVANIA—See Albemarle Corporation; *U.S. Public*, pg. 73
ALBEMARLE DEUTSCHLAND GMBH—See Albemarle Corporation; *U.S. Public*, pg. 73
ALBEMARLE EUROPE SPRL—See Albemarle Corporation; *U.S. Public*, pg. 73
ALBEMARLE GERMANY GMBH—See Albemarle Corporation; *U.S. Public*, pg. 73
ALBEMARLE HUNGARY LTD.—See Albemarle Corporation; *U.S. Public*, pg. 73
ALBEMARLE JAPAN CORPORATION—See Albemarle Corporation; *U.S. Public*, pg. 73
ALBEMARLE KOREA CORPORATION—See Albemarle Corporation; *U.S. Public*, pg. 73
ALBEMARLE LIMITADA—See Albemarle Corporation; *U.S. Public*, pg. 73
ALBEMARLE LITHIUM PTY. LTD.—See Albemarle Corporation; *U.S. Public*, pg. 73
ALBEMARLE MANAGEMENT (SHANGHAI) CO., LTD.—See Albemarle Corporation; *U.S. Public*, pg. 73
ALBEMARLE MIDDLE EAST CORPORATION FZE—See Albemarle Corporation; *U.S. Public*, pg. 73
ALBEMARLE SINGAPORE PTE LTD—See Albemarle Corporation; *U.S. Public*, pg. 73
ALBEMARLE SORBENT TECHNOLOGIES—See Albemarle Corporation; *U.S. Public*, pg. 73
ALBEMARLE U.S., INC.—See Albemarle Corporation; *U.S. Public*, pg. 73
ALBE METAL SDN. BHD.—See LB Aluminium Berhad; *Int'l*, pg. 4428
ALBENA TOUR LTD; *Int'l*, pg. 293
ALBEO TECHNOLOGIES INC.; *U.S. Private*, pg. 152
ALBERCO CONSTRUCTION LTD.; *Int'l*, pg. 293
ALBERCO HOLDING B.V.; *Int'l*, pg. 293
ALBER CORP.—See Vertiv Holdings Co; *U.S. Public*, pg. 2288
ALBER GMBH—See Invacare Corporation; *U.S. Private*, pg. 2130
ALBERIC COLON AUTO SALES INC.; *U.S. Private*, pg. 152
ALBERICI CONSTRUCCIONES S.A. DE C.V.—See Alberici Corporation; *U.S. Private*, pg. 152
ALBERICI CONSTRUCTORS, LTD.—See Alberici Corporation; *U.S. Private*, pg. 152
ALBERICI CORPORATION; *U.S. Private*, pg. 152
ALBERICI HEALTHCARE, LLC—See Alberici Corporation; *U.S. Private*, pg. 152
ALBERICI WESTERN CONSTRUCTORS, LTD.—See Alberici Corporation; *U.S. Private*, pg. 152
ALBERN CO.; *U.S. Private*, pg. 152
AL-BERRI UNITED FOOD CO. LTD.—See Al-Osais International Holding Company; *Int'l*, pg. 287
ALBERS MECHANICAL CONTRACTORS, INC.—See The Vollrath Company LLC; *U.S. Private*, pg. 4132
ALBERTA DILUENT TERMINAL LTD.—See Keyera Corporation; *Int'l*, pg. 4146
ALBERTA DISTILLERS LIMITED—See Suntory Holdings Limited; *Int'l*, pg. 7325
ALBERTA ELECTRONIC COMPANY LIMITED—See Pentair plc; *Int'l*, pg. 5790
ALBERTA ENVIROFUELS, INC.—See Keyera Corporation; *Int'l*, pg. 4146
ALBERTA HEALTH SERVICES; *Int'l*, pg. 297
ALBERTA INVESTMENT MANAGEMENT CORPORATION; *Int'l*, pg. 297
ALBERTA NEWSPAPER GROUP INC—See Glacier Media Inc.; *Int'l*, pg. 2987
ALBERTA-PACIFIC FOREST INDUSTRIES INC.—See Hokuetsu Corporation; *Int'l*, pg. 3443
ALBERTA PENSION SERVICES CORPORATION; *Int'l*, pg. 298
ALBERT & ASSOCIATES INC.; *U.S. Private*, pg. 152
ALBERTA TEACHERS RETIREMENT FUND; *Int'l*, pg. 298

ALBERTA TREASURY BRANCHES; *Int'l*, pg. 298
ALBERT BALLIN KG; *Int'l*, pg. 294
ALBERT BERNER DEUTSCHLAND GMBH—See Berner SE; *Int'l*, pg. 988
ALBERT BONNIERS FORLAG AB—See Bonnier AB; *Int'l*, pg. 1108
ALBERT BROS., INC.; *U.S. Private*, pg. 152
ALBERT BROWNE LIMITED—See STERIS plc; *Int'l*, pg. 7210
ALBERT CESKA REPUBLIKA, S.R.O.—See Koninklijke Ahold Delhaize N.V.; *Int'l*, pg. 4260
ALBERT CITY ELEVATOR, A COOPERATIVE; *U.S. Private*, pg. 152
ALBERT C. KOBAYASHI INC.; *U.S. Private*, pg. 152
ALBERT COMPANIES, INC.—See ArcBest Corporation; *U.S. Public*, pg. 180
ALBERT DAVID LTD. - KOLKATTA UNIT—See Albert David Ltd; *Int'l*, pg. 297
ALBERT DAVID LTD; *Int'l*, pg. 297
ALBERT F. AMLING, LLC; *U.S. Private*, pg. 152
ALBERT-FRANKENTHAL GMBH—See Koenig & Bauer AG; *Int'l*, pg. 4226
ALBERT FREI & SONS INC.—See Martin Marietta Materials, Inc.; *U.S. Public*, pg. 1389
ALBERT GREIFENBERG GMBH & CO. KG; *Int'l*, pg. 297
ALBERT HEIJN B.V.—See Koninklijke Ahold Delhaize N.V.; *Int'l*, pg. 4260
ALBERT INC.—See Accenture plc; *Int'l*, pg. 83
ALBERT KAHN ASSOCIATES, INC.; *U.S. Private*, pg. 153
ALBERT KEMPERLE INC.; *U.S. Private*, pg. 153
ALBERT KEMPERLE OF FLORIDA, LLC—See Albert Kemperle Inc.; *U.S. Private*, pg. 153
ALBERT LABS INTERNATIONAL CORP.; *Int'l*, pg. 297
ALBERT M. GREENFIELD & CO., INC.; *U.S. Private*, pg. 153
ALBERT M. HIGLEY COMPANY; *U.S. Private*, pg. 153
ALBERT MOTORS INC.; *U.S. Private*, pg. 153
ALBERT MOVING & STORAGE, INC.; *U.S. Private*, pg. 153
ALBERTO HERNANDEZ REAL ESTATE INC.; *U.S. Private*, pg. 153
ALBERTON ACQUISITION CORPORATION; *Int'l*, pg. 298
ALBERT PASVAHL (GMBH & CO.); *Int'l*, pg. 297
ALBERT SCHEID GMBH—See Deutsche Post AG; *Int'l*, pg. 2071
ALBERT SCHUCK GMBH & CO. KG; *Int'l*, pg. 297
ALBERT SMITH (CHINA) COMPANY LIMITED—See Pico Far East Holdings Limited; *Int'l*, pg. 5860
ALBERT'S NEW ENGLAND—See United Natural Foods, Inc.; *U.S. Public*, pg. 2231
ALBERTSONS COMPANIES, INC.—See Cerberus Capital Management, L.P.; *U.S. Private*, pg. 836
ALBERTSON'S, INC.-OREGON DIVISION—See Cerberus Capital Management, L.P.; *U.S. Private*, pg. 836
ALBERTSON'S, INC.-SOUTHERN CALIFORNIA DIVISION—See Cerberus Capital Management, L.P.; *U.S. Private*, pg. 836
ALBERTSON'S LLC—See Cerberus Capital Management, L.P.; *U.S. Private*, pg. 836
ALBERT'S ORGANICS, INC.—See United Natural Foods, Inc.; *U.S. Public*, pg. 2231
ALBERT'S ORGANICS INC.—See United Natural Foods, Inc.; *U.S. Public*, pg. 2231
ALBERT'S ORGANICS TWIN CITIES—See United Natural Foods, Inc.; *U.S. Public*, pg. 2231
ALBERT SPIESS AG—See Orior AG; *Int'l*, pg. 5633
ALBERT'S TRUCK SERVICE & SUPPLY, INC.—See American Securities LLC; *U.S. Private*, pg. 248
ALBERT TECHNOLOGIES LIMITED; *Int'l*, pg. 297
ALBERT USTER IMPORTS, INC.—See Vestar Capital Partners, LLC; *U.S. Private*, pg. 4372
ALBERT VIEILLE S.A.S.—See Givaudan S.A.; *Int'l*, pg. 2979
ALBERTVILLE QUALITY FOODS, INC.—See Industrias Bachoco S.A.B. de C.V.; *Int'l*, pg. 3673
ALBERT ZIEGLER GMBH—See China International Marine Containers (Group) Co., Ltd.; *Int'l*, pg. 1510
ALBER USA, LLC—See Invacare Corporation; *U.S. Private*, pg. 2130
ALBESS CO., LTD.—See New Japan Chemical Co., Ltd.; *Int'l*, pg. 5225
ALBEST METAL STAMPING, CORP.; *U.S. Private*, pg. 153
ALB-GOLD TEIGWAREN GMBH; *Int'l*, pg. 292
ALBIDON AUSTRALIA PTY LTD—See Jinchuan Group Limited; *Int'l*, pg. 3965
ALBIDON LIMITED—See Jinchuan Group Limited; *Int'l*, pg. 3965
ALBIDON ZAMBIA LIMITED—See Jinchuan Group Limited; *Int'l*, pg. 3965
ALBILAD INVESTMENT COMPANY—See BANK ALBILAD; *Int'l*, pg. 836
AL-BILAD MEDICAL SERVICES CO.; *Int'l*, pg. 284
AL BILAD SECURITIES & INVESTMENT CO.; *Int'l*, pg. 276
ALBI MANUFACTURING—See SK Capital Partners, LP; *U.S. Private*, pg. 3679
ALBINA HEAD START, INC.; *U.S. Private*, pg. 153

COMPANY NAME INDEX

ALBIN COMPONENTS AB—See Storskogen Group AB; *Int'l*, pg. 7227
ALBINGIA SA—See Eurazeo SE; *Int'l*, pg. 2527
ALBINI & PITIGLIANI S.P.A.; *Int'l*, pg. 298
ALBINI & PITIGLIANI SVERIGE AB—See Albini & Pitigliani S.p.A.; *Int'l*, pg. 298
ALBIN PUMP SAS—See Ingersoll Rand Inc.; *U.S. Public*, pg. 1118
ALBIO DATA S.A.—See Biokarpet S.A.; *Int'l*, pg. 1038
ALBIOMA SA—See KKR & Co. Inc.; *U.S. Public*, pg. 1239
ALBION AUTOMOTIVE (HOLDINGS) LIMITED—See American Axle & Manufacturing Holdings, Inc.; *U.S. Public*, pg. 96
ALBION AUTOMOTIVE LIMITED—See American Axle & Manufacturing Holdings, Inc.; *U.S. Public*, pg. 96
ALBION BRAND COMMUNICATIONS, LTD.—See Newton Europe Ltd; *Int'l*, pg. 5239
ALBION CAPITAL; *Int'l*, pg. 299
ALBION CHARLES HOTEL (BMG) PTY LTD—See Woolworths Group Limited; *Int'l*, pg. 8451
ALBION CO., LTD.—See KOSE Corporation; *Int'l*, pg. 4290
ALBION COSMETICS (AMERICA) INC.—See KOSE Corporation; *Int'l*, pg. 4290
ALBION CROWN VCT PLC; *Int'l*, pg. 299
ALBION DEVELOPMENT VCT PLC; *Int'l*, pg. 299
ALBION HOTEL (WA) PTY LTD—See Woolworths Group Limited; *Int'l*, pg. 8451
ALBION INVESTORS, LLC; *U.S. Private*, pg. 153
ALBION LABORATORIES, INC.—See Balchem Corporation; *U.S. Public*, pg. 265
ALBION LAND (BUSHEY MILL) LTD—See Helical Plc; *Int'l*, pg. 3329
ALBION RESOURCES LIMITED; *Int'l*, pg. 299
ALBION RIVER INN, INC.—See Soul Community Planet, Inc.; *U.S. Private*, pg. 3717
ALBION STAFFING SOLUTIONS INC.—See Hoosier Investment LLC; *U.S. Private*, pg. 1978
ALBION TECHNOLOGY & GENERAL VCT PLC; *Int'l*, pg. 299
ALBION VENTURE CAPITAL TRUST PLC; *Int'l*, pg. 299
ALBION VET SURGERY PTY LTD—See National Veterinary Care Ltd; *Int'l*, pg. 5164
ALBION WATER HEATER LIMITED—See Kingspan Group PLC; *Int'l*, pg. 4176
ALBI PROTECTIVE COATINGS—See SK Capital Partners, LP; *U.S. Private*, pg. 6670
ALBIREO AB—See Albireo Pharma, Inc.; *U.S. Public*, pg. 74
ALBIREO ENERGY, LLC—See Huron Capital Partners LLC; *U.S. Private*, pg. 2011
ALBIREO PHARMA, INC.; *U.S. Public*, pg. 74
ALBIS ARZTESERVICE PRODUCT GMBH & CO KG—See CompuGroup Medical SE & Co. KGaA; *Int'l*, pg. 1755
ALBIS CO., LTD.; *Int'l*, pg. 299
ALBIS-ELCON SYSTEM GERMANY GMBH—See UET United Electronic Technology AG; *Int'l*, pg. 8015
ALBIS HITEC LEASING GMBH—See ALBIS Leasing AG; *Int'l*, pg. 299
ALBIS LEASING AG; *Int'l*, pg. 299
ALBIS OPTOELECTRONICS AG; *Int'l*, pg. 299
ALBIS SERVICE GMBH—See ALBIS Leasing AG; *Int'l*, pg. 299
ALBIS TECHNIK AG—See Poenina Holding AG; *Int'l*, pg. 5903
ALBONAIR AUTOMOTIVE TECHNOLOGY CO. LTD.—See Hinduja Group Ltd.; *Int'l*, pg. 3398
ALBONAIR GMBH—See Hinduja Group Ltd.; *Int'l*, pg. 3398
ALBONAIR (INDIA) PRIVATE LIMITED—See Hinduja Group Ltd.; *Int'l*, pg. 3398
ALBORAN S.P.A.—See Banca Mediolanum S.p.A.; *Int'l*, pg. 815
ALBORS & ASSOCIATES, INC.—See Interpreters Unlimited, Inc.; *U.S. Private*, pg. 2123
ALBORZ BULK RAW MATERIALS COMPANY—See Alborz Investment Company; *Int'l*, pg. 299
ALBORZ CABLE COMPANY; *Int'l*, pg. 299
ALBORZ DAROU PHARMACEUTICAL COMPANY; *Int'l*, pg. 299
ALBORZ INSURANCE COMPANY; *Int'l*, pg. 299
ALBORZ INVESTMENT COMPANY; *Int'l*, pg. 299
ALBORZ TURBINE COMPANY—See MAPNA Group; *Int'l*, pg. 4686
ALBOURNE AMERICA LLC—See Albourne Partners Limited; *Int'l*, pg. 299
ALBOURNE PARTNERS (ASIA) LIMITED—See Albourne Partners Limited; *Int'l*, pg. 299
ALBOURNE PARTNERS DEUTSCHLAND AG—See Albourne Partners Limited; *Int'l*, pg. 299
ALBOURNE PARTNERS JAPAN LIMITED—See Albourne Partners Limited; *Int'l*, pg. 299
ALBOURNE PARTNERS LIMITED; *Int'l*, pg. 299
ALBOURNE PARTNERS (SINGAPORE) PTE. LTD.—See Albourne Partners Limited; *Int'l*, pg. 299
ALBRAS - ALUMINIO BRASILEIRO S.A.—See Vale S.A.; *Int'l*, pg. 8111
THE ALBRECHT COMPANIES, INC.; *U.S. Private*, pg. 3983

ALBRECHT KNAUS VERLAG—See Bertelsmann SE & Co. KGaA; *Int'l*, pg. 989
ALBRECHT NURSING AGENCY (PROPRIETARY) LIMITED—See Workforce Holdings Ltd.; *Int'l*, pg. 8455
ALBRIDGE SOLUTIONS, INC.—See The Bank of New York Mellon Corporation; *U.S. Public*, pg. 2038
ALBRIGHT CAPITAL MANAGEMENT LLC; *U.S. Private*, pg. 153
ALBRIGHT & WILSON (AUSTRALIA) LIMITED—See PT Unggul Indah Cahaya Tbk; *Int'l*, pg. 6080
ALBRIGHT & WILSON NEW ZEALAND LTD.—See PT Unggul Indah Cahaya Tbk; *Int'l*, pg. 6080
ALBRITTON FRUIT COMPANY INC.; *U.S. Private*, pg. 153
ALBU & ASSOCIATES, INC.; *U.S. Private*, pg. 153
ALBUFEIRA RETAIL PARK LDA.—See Frey S.A.; *Int'l*, pg. 2791
AL BUHAIRA NATIONAL INSURANCE COMPANY P.S.C.; *Int'l*, pg. 276
ALBUMPRINTER SERVICES B.V.—See Cimpress plc; *Int'l*, pg. 1609
ALBUM TRADING COMPANY LIMITED—See China Rare Earth Resources And Technology Co., Ltd.; *Int'l*, pg. 1545
ALBUQUERQUE ANUSA, LLC—See AutoNation, Inc.; *U.S. Public*, pg. 232
ALBUQUERQUE HARDWOOD LUMBER COMPANY—See Hardwoods Distribution Inc.; *Int'l*, pg. 3273
ALBUQUERQUE HOOTERS, INC.—See Restaurants of America, Inc.; *U.S. Private*, pg. 3408
ALBUQUERQUE NEUROSCIENCE, INC.—See IMA Group Management Company, LLC; *U.S. Private*, pg. 2044
ALBUQUERQUE SUITE HOSPITALITY LLC—See Inn-Suites Hospitality Trust; *U.S. Public*, pg. 1128
ALBURY ASSET RENTALS LTD.—See BNP Paribas SA; *Int'l*, pg. 1079
ALBUS A.D.; *Int'l*, pg. 299
ALCAD A.B.—See TotalEnergies SE; *Int'l*, pg. 7838
ALCAD, D.O.O.—See Impol d.d.; *Int'l*, pg. 3636
ALCAD LIMITED—See Nokia Corporation; *Int'l*, pg. 5404
ALCADON AB—See DistIT AB; *Int'l*, pg. 2136
ALCADON APS—See Alcadon Group AB; *Int'l*, pg. 300
ALCADON A/S—See DistIT AB; *Int'l*, pg. 2136
ALCADON GMBH—See Alcadon Group AB; *Int'l*, pg. 300
ALCADON GROUP AB; *Int'l*, pg. 299
ALOALIDEN O.A., *Int'l*, pg. 000
ALCAL SPECIALTY CONTRACTING, INC.—See Pacific Coast Building Products, Inc.; *U.S. Private*, pg. 3065
ALCAMI CAROLINAS CORPORATION—See Ares Management Corporation; *U.S. Public*, pg. 188
ALCAMPO—See Auchan Holding S.A.; *Int'l*, pg. 699
ALCANA DESTILARIA DE ALCOOL DE NANUQUE S/A—See Infinity Bio-Energy Ltd.; *Int'l*, pg. 3687
ALCANCE—See WPP plc; *Int'l*, pg. 8474
ALCAN ELECTRICAL & ENGINEERING; *U.S. Private*, pg. 153
ALCANNA INC.—See SNDL Inc.; *Int'l*, pg. 7027
ALCAN PACKAGING BAIE D'URFE—See Amcor plc; *Int'l*, pg. 417
ALCAN PACKAGING IZMIR GRAVUR BASKILI KARTON SANAYI VE TICARET AS—See Amcor plc; *Int'l*, pg. 417
ALCAN PACKAGING LAINATE—See Amcor plc; *Int'l*, pg. 417
ALCAN PACKAGING RORSCHACH AG—See Amcor plc; *Int'l*, pg. 417
ALCANTARA GROUP; *Int'l*, pg. 300
ALCANTARA S.P.A.—See Toray Industries, Inc.; *Int'l*, pg. 7822
ALCAN TECHNOLOGY & MANAGEMENT AG—See Amcor plc; *Int'l*, pg. 417
ALCAP COMERCIAL, S.A.—See Prysmian S.p.A.; *Int'l*, pg. 6011
ALCARD INDUSTRIA MECANICA LTDA—See LivaNova PLC; *Int'l*, pg. 4530
ALCASTING LEGUTIANO, S.L.U.—See Cie Automotive S.A.; *Int'l*, pg. 1604
ALCAT CONTRACTING COMPANY—See Zad Holding Company S.A.Q.; *Int'l*, pg. 8619
ALCATEL-LUCENT CZECH S.R.O—See Nokia Corporation; *Int'l*, pg. 5404
ALCATEL-LUCENT EAST AFRICA LIMITED—See Nokia Corporation; *Int'l*, pg. 5404
ALCATEL-LUCENT ENTERPRISE INDONESIA—See Nokia Corporation; *Int'l*, pg. 5404
ALCATEL-LUCENT ENTERPRISE—See Nokia Corporation; *Int'l*, pg. 5404
ALCATEL-LUCENT HOLDING, S.A. DE C.V.—See Nokia Corporation; *Int'l*, pg. 5404
ALCATEL-LUCENT TECHINT S.A—See Techint S.p.A.; *Int'l*, pg. 7503
ALCATEL-LUCENT TELETAS TELEKOMUNIKASYON AS; *Int'l*, pg. 300
ALCATEL-LUCENT UK LIMITED—See Nokia Corporation; *Int'l*, pg. 5404
ALCATEL SUBMARINE NETWORKS S.A.—See Nokia Corporation; *Int'l*, pg. 5404
ALCATRAZ INTERLOCKS B.V.—See Indutrade AB; *Int'l*, pg. 3677

ALCOA CORPORATION

ALCCO CORP.—See The Belknap White Group, LLC.; *U.S. Private*, pg. 3993
ALCEA TECHNOLOGIES INC.; *Int'l*, pg. 300
ALCECAP S.A.S.—See Hanwa Co., Ltd.; *Int'l*, pg. 3261
ALCEDO S.R.L.—See Sumitomo Corporation; *Int'l*, pg. 7268
ALCENTRA CAPITAL CORPORATION—See Crescent Capital BDC, Inc.; *U.S. Public*, pg. 593
ALCENTRA LIMITED—See The Bank of New York Mellon Corporation; *U.S. Public*, pg. 2036
ALCENTRA NY LLC—See Franklin Resources, Inc.; *U.S. Public*, pg. 879
ALCEON GROUP PTY LTD.; *Int'l*, pg. 300
ALCERA (SUZHOU) CO., LTD.—See Almedio, Inc.; *Int'l*, pg. 364
ALCERECO INC.—See Grafoid, Inc.; *Int'l*, pg. 3050
THE ALC GROUP—See Burd & Fletcher Company; *U.S. Private*, pg. 686
THE ALCHEMEE LLC—See Sun Pharmaceutical Industries Ltd.; *Int'l*, pg. 7308
ALCHEMER LLC—See KKR & Co. Inc.; *U.S. Public*, pg. 1239
ALCHEMIA S.A.; *Int'l*, pg. 300
ALCHEMIE EUROPE LTD.—See Aarti Industries Ltd.; *Int'l*, pg. 38
ALCHEMIST AVIATION PVT. LTD.—See Alchemist Ltd; *Int'l*, pg. 300
ALCHEMIST CODES SDN. BHD.—See AIQ Limited; *Int'l*, pg. 236
ALCHEMIST CORPORATION LIMITED; *Int'l*, pg. 300
ALCHEMIST LTD; *Int'l*, pg. 300
ALCHEMIST MEDIA, INC.; *U.S. Private*, pg. 153
ALCHEMIST REALTY LTD.; *Int'l*, pg. 300
ALCHEMY PARTNERS LLP; *Int'l*, pg. 300
ALCHEMY RESOURCES LIMITED; *Int'l*, pg. 300
ALCHEMY SEARCH PARTNERS, INC.—See SOAProjects, Inc.; *U.S. Private*, pg. 3702
ALCHEMY SYSTEMS TRAINING, INC.—See Intertek Group plc; *Int'l*, pg. 3762
ALCHEMY WORX INC.—See SellUp Inc.; *U.S. Private*, pg. 3603
ALCHEMY WORX LIMITED—See SellUp Inc.; *U.S. Private*, pg. 3603
ALCHEMY WORX—See SellUp Inc.; *U.S. Private*, pg. 3603
ALCHERA INC., *Int'l*, pg. 300
ALCHIMIE SA; *Int'l*, pg. 301
ALCHIP INVESTMENT INC.—See Alchip Technologies, Limited; *Int'l*, pg. 301
ALCHIP TECHNOLOGIES, (CHONGQING) INC.—See Alchip Technologies, Limited; *Int'l*, pg. 301
ALCHIP TECHNOLOGIES, (GUANGZHOU) INC.—See Alchip Technologies, Limited; *Int'l*, pg. 301
ALCHIP TECHNOLOGIES, (HEFEI) INC.—See Alchip Technologies, Limited; *Int'l*, pg. 301
ALCHIP TECHNOLOGIES, INC.—See Alchip Technologies, Limited; *Int'l*, pg. 301
ALCHIP TECHNOLOGIES, (JINAN) INC.—See Alchip Technologies, Limited; *Int'l*, pg. 301
ALCHIP TECHNOLOGIES, KK—See Alchip Technologies, Limited; *Int'l*, pg. 301
ALCHIP TECHNOLOGIES, LIMITED; *Int'l*, pg. 301
ALCHIP TECHNOLOGIES, LIMITED—See Alchip Technologies, Limited; *Int'l*, pg. 301
ALCHIP TECHNOLOGIES (SHANGHAI) LIMITED—See Alchip Technologies, Limited; *Int'l*, pg. 301
ALCHIP TECHNOLOGIES, (WUXI) INC.—See Alchip Technologies, Limited; *Int'l*, pg. 301
ALCIDION GROUP LIMITED; *Int'l*, pg. 301
ALCIDION NZ LIMITED—See Alcidion Group Limited; *Int'l*, pg. 301
ALCIDION UK LIMITED—See Alcidion Group Limited; *Int'l*, pg. 301
ALCION GROUP—See Insight Venture Management, LLC; *U.S. Private*, pg. 2091
ALCOA ALUMINIO S.A.—See Alcoa Corporation; *U.S. Public*, pg. 74
ALCOA AUSTRALIAN HOLDINGS PTY. LTD.—See Alcoa Corporation; *U.S. Public*, pg. 74
ALCOA AUSTRALIA ROLLED PRODUCTS—See Kobe Steel, Ltd.; *Int'l*, pg. 4217
ALCOA CANADA LTD.—See Alcoa Corporation; *U.S. Public*, pg. 74
ALCOA CORPORATION; *U.S. Public*, pg. 74
ALCOA HOLDING FRANCE SAS—See Howmet Aerospace Inc.; *U.S. Public*, pg. 1061
ALCOA INESPAL, S.A.—See Alcoa Corporation; *U.S. Public*, pg. 74
ALCOA INTALCO WORKS—See Alcoa Corporation; *U.S. Public*, pg. 74
ALCOA LISTA-NORWAY—See Alcoa Corporation; *U.S. Public*, pg. 74
ALCOA LTD.—See Alcoa Corporation; *U.S. Public*, pg. 74
ALCOA MOSJOEN—See Alcoa Corporation; *U.S. Public*, pg. 74
ALCOA NORWAY ANS—See Alcoa Corporation; *U.S. Public*, pg. 74
ALCOA OF AUSTRALIA LIMITED—See Alcoa Corporation; *U.S. Public*, pg. 74

ALCOA CORPORATION

ALCOA REMEDIATION MANAGEMENT, INC.—See Alcoa Corporation; *U.S. Public*, pg. 74
ALCOA WORLD ALUMINA LLC—See Alcoa Corporation; *U.S. Public*, pg. 74
ALCO CAD-NICKEL CORP.; *U.S. Private*, pg. 153
ALCO CONTROLS SPOL. S.R.O—See Emerson Electric Co.; *U.S. Public*, pg. 745
ALCO CORPORATION; *U.S. Private*, pg. 153
ALCODES INTERNATIONAL LIMITED—See AIQ Limited; *Int'l*, pg. 236
ALCO DIGITAL DEVICES LIMITED—See Alco Holdings Limited; *Int'l*, pg. 301
ALCO DOORS, INC.—See Bain Capital, LP; *U.S. Private*, pg. 450
ALCO ELECTRONICS LIMITED—See Alco Holdings Limited; *Int'l*, pg. 301
ALCO ELECTRONICS (SHENZHEN) LIMITED—See Alco Holdings Limited; *Int'l*, pg. 301
ALCO ENGINEERING, INC.—See Thielsch Engineering, Inc.; *U.S. Private*, pg. 4144
ALCO HELLAS S.A.; *Int'l*, pg. 301
ALCO HIGH-TECH PLASTICS, INC.; *U.S. Private*, pg. 153
ALCOHOL COUNTERMEASURE SYSTEMS CORP.; *Int'l*, pg. 302
ALCO HOLDINGS LIMITED; *Int'l*, pg. 301
ALCOHOL & DRUG RECOVERY CENTERS, INC.; *U.S. Private*, pg. 154
ALCOHOLES Y VINOS, S.A.—See Suntory Holdings Limited; *Int'l*, pg. 7325
ALCOHOL MONITORING SYSTEMS, INC.—See Riverside Partners, LLC; *U.S. Private*, pg. 3445
ALCO INTERNATIONAL LIMITED—See Alco Holdings Limited; *Int'l*, pg. 301
ALCO INVESTMENT CO., INC.; *U.S. Private*, pg. 153
ALCO IRON & METAL CO.; *U.S. Private*, pg. 154
ALCO MANUFACTURING CORPORATION LLC—See MiddleGround Management, LP; *U.S. Public*, pg. 2711
ALCOM ELECTRONICOS DE MEXICO, S.A. DE C.V.—See Alps Alpine Co., Ltd.; *Int'l*, pg. 375
ALCOMET AD; *Int'l*, pg. 302
AL COMPOSITES MATERIALS FZE—See China XD Plastics Company Ltd.; *Int'l*, pg. 1563
A-L COMPRESSED GASES, INC.; *U.S. Private*, pg. 22
AL-COM PRINTING GROUP, INC.; *U.S. Private*, pg. 154
ALCOM SA TIMISOARA; *Int'l*, pg. 302
ALCON BULGARIA EOOD—See Novartis AG; *Int'l*, pg. 5455
ALCON CANADA, INC.—See Novartis AG; *Int'l*, pg. 5455
ALCON (CHINA) OPHTHALMIC PRODUCT CO., LTD.—See Novartis AG; *Int'l*, pg. 5455
ALCON-CUSI S.A.—See Novartis AG; *Int'l*, pg. 5456
ALCON DEUTSCHLAND GMBH—See Novartis AG; *Int'l*, pg. 5455
ALCON DISTRIBUTION CENTER - ELKRIDGE—See Novartis AG; *Int'l*, pg. 5455
ALCON DIVISION OF PHARMACO LTD.—See Novartis AG; *Int'l*, pg. 5455
ALCON ELECTRONICS PVT. LTD.—See HEICO Corporation; *U.S. Public*, pg. 1019
ALCONE MARKETING GROUP—See Omnicom Group Inc.; *U.S. Public*, pg. 1573
ALCONE MARKETING GROUP—See Omnicom Group Inc.; *U.S. Public*, pg. 1573
ALCONEX SPECIALTY PRODUCTS, INC.; *U.S. Private*, pg. 154
ALCON EYECARE (UK) LTD.—See Novartis AG; *Int'l*, pg. 5456
ALCON FARMACEVTIKA LLC—See Novartis AG; *Int'l*, pg. 5456
ALCON HONG KONG, LTD—See Novartis AG; *Int'l*, pg. 5456
ALCON HUNGARIA KFT—See Novartis AG; *Int'l*, pg. 5456
ALCON HUNGARY PHARMACEUTICALS TRADING LTD—See Novartis AG; *Int'l*, pg. 5456
ALCON INC.; *Int'l*, pg. 302
ALCON INDUSTRIES INC.; *U.S. Private*, pg. 154
ALCON ITALIA S.P.A.—See Novartis AG; *Int'l*, pg. 5456
ALCONIX CORPORATION; *Int'l*, pg. 302
ALCONIX EUROPE GMBH—See Alconix Corporation; *Int'l*, pg. 302
ALCONIX HONG KONG CORP.,LTD.—See Alconix Corporation; *Int'l*, pg. 302
ALCONIX KOREA CORPORATION—See Alconix Corporation; *Int'l*, pg. 302
ALCONIX LOGISTICS (THAILAND) LTD.—See Alconix Corporation; *Int'l*, pg. 302
ALCONIX (MALAYSIA) SDN. BHD.—See Alconix Corporation; *Int'l*, pg. 302
ALCONIX MITAKA CORPORATION—See Alconix Corporation; *Int'l*, pg. 302
ALCONIX SANSHIN CORPORATION—See Alconix Corporation; *Int'l*, pg. 302
ALCONIX (SHANGHAI) CORP.—See Alconix Corporation; *Int'l*, pg. 302
ALCONIX (TAIWAN) CORPORATION—See Alconix Corporation; *Int'l*, pg. 302
ALCONIX (THAILAND) LTD.—See Alconix Corporation; *Int'l*, pg. 302

ALCONIX USA, INC.—See Alconix Corporation; *Int'l*, pg. 302
ALCONIX VIETNAM CO., LTD.—See Alconix Corporation; *Int'l*, pg. 302
ALCON JAPAN LTD.—See Novartis AG; *Int'l*, pg. 5456
ALCON KOREA LTD—See Novartis AG; *Int'l*, pg. 5456
ALCON LABORATORIES (AUSTRALIA) PTY. LTD.—See Novartis AG; *Int'l*, pg. 5456
ALCON LABORATORIES HELLAS COMMERCIAL & INDUSTRIAL S.A.—See Novartis AG; *Int'l*, pg. 5456
ALCON LABORATORIES INC.—See Novartis AG; *Int'l*, pg. 5455
ALCON LABORATORIES, INC.—See Novartis AG; *Int'l*, pg. 5456
ALCON LABORATORIES (INDIA) PRIVATE LIMITED—See Novartis AG; *Int'l*, pg. 5456
ALCON LABORATORIES IRELAND LIMITED—See Novartis AG; *Int'l*, pg. 5456
ALCON LABORATORIES (PTY.) LTD.—See Novartis AG; *Int'l*, pg. 5456
ALCON LABORATORIES SDN. BHD.—See Novartis AG; *Int'l*, pg. 5456
ALCON LABORATORIES (THAILAND) LTD—See Novartis AG; *Int'l*, pg. 5456
ALCON LABORATORIES (UK) LTD.—See Novartis AG; *Int'l*, pg. 5456
ALCON LABORATORIOS ARGENTINA S.A.—See Novartis AG; *Int'l*, pg. 5456
ALCON LABORATORIOS CHILE LIMITADA—See Novartis AG; *Int'l*, pg. 5456
ALCON LABORATORIOS DO BRASIL LTDA.—See Novartis AG; *Int'l*, pg. 5456
ALCON LABORATORIOS, S.A. DE C.V.—See Novartis AG; *Int'l*, pg. 5456
ALCON LABORATORIOS URUGUAY, S.A.—See Novartis AG; *Int'l*, pg. 5456
ALCON LABORATUVARLARI TICARET A.S.—See Novartis AG; *Int'l*, pg. 5456
ALCON MECHANICAL, INC.; *U.S. Private*, pg. 154
ALCON NEDERLAND B.V.—See Novartis AG; *Int'l*, pg. 5456
ALCON NORDIC A/S—See Novartis AG; *Int'l*, pg. 5456
ALCON NORGE AS—See Novartis AG; *Int'l*, pg. 5456
ALCON OPHTHALMIKA GMBH—See Alcon Inc.; *Int'l*, pg. 302
ALCONOX, INC.; *U.S. Private*, pg. 154
ALCON PHARMACEUTICALS (CZECH REPUBLIC) S.R.O.—See Novartis AG; *Int'l*, pg. 5456
ALCON PHARMACEUTICALS LTD.—See Novartis AG; *Int'l*, pg. 5456
ALCON PHARMACEUTICALS LTD—See Novartis AG; *Int'l*, pg. 5456
ALCON PHARMACEUTICALS LTD—See Novartis AG; *Int'l*, pg. 5456
ALCON PHARMACEUTICALS TAIWAN LTD—See Novartis AG; *Int'l*, pg. 5456
ALCON PORTUGAL, PRODUTOS E EQUIPAMENTOS OFTALMOLOGICOS, LDA—See Novartis AG; *Int'l*, pg. 5456
ALCON (PUERTO RICO) INC.—See Novartis AG; *Int'l*, pg. 5455
ALCON RESEARCH, LTD.—See Novartis AG; *Int'l*, pg. 5456
ALCON RESEARCH, LTD.—See Novartis AG; *Int'l*, pg. 5456
ALCON RESEARCH, LTD.—See Novartis AG; *Int'l*, pg. 5456
ALCON ROMANIA S.R.L.—See Novartis AG; *Int'l*, pg. 5456
ALCON SWITZERLAND SA—See Novartis AG; *Int'l*, pg. 5456
ALCOP PARKING CORP.; *U.S. Private*, pg. 154
ALC OPERATING, LLC—See TPG Capital, L.P.; *U.S. Public*, pg. 2168
ALCO PLASTIC PRODUCTS LIMITED; *Int'l*, pg. 301
ALCO PLASTICS INC.; *U.S. Private*, pg. 154
ALCO PROPERTIES LIMITED—See Alco Holdings Limited; *Int'l*, pg. 301
ALCOR CORP.—See Wavepoint 3PI Expedite LLC; *U.S. Private*, pg. 4458
ALCO REALTY, INC.—See Clayton, Dubilier & Rice, LLC; *U.S. Private*, pg. 928
ALCORE BRIGANTINE SA—See M.C. Gill Corporation; *U.S. Private*, pg. 2528
ALCORE, INC.—See M.C. Gill Corporation; *U.S. Private*, pg. 2528
ALCORLINK CORP.; *Int'l*, pg. 303
ALCOR MICRO CORPORATION LTD.; *Int'l*, pg. 303
ALCOR MICRO (SHENZHEN) CORPORATION LTD.—See Alcor Micro Corporation Ltd.; *Int'l*, pg. 303
ALCORN FENCE COMPANY; *U.S. Private*, pg. 154
ALCORN MCBRIDE, INC.; *U.S. Private*, pg. 154
ALCORN PETROLEUM & MINERALS CORPORATION—See Cosco Capital, Inc.; *Int'l*, pg. 1809
ALCO ROM TRADE SRL—See ALCO Hellas S.A.; *Int'l*, pg. 301
ALCO SALES & SERVICE CO.; *U.S. Private*, pg. 154

ALCOTEC WIRE CORPORATION—See Enovis Corporation; *U.S. Public*, pg. 770
ALCOTRADE INC.; *U.S. Private*, pg. 154
ALCO TRANSPORTATION INC.; *U.S. Private*, pg. 154
ALCOTT HR; *U.S. Private*, pg. 154
ALCO VALVES GROUP LIMITED—See Graco, Inc.; *U.S. Public*, pg. 952
ALCO VALVES INC.—See Graco, Inc.; *U.S. Public*, pg. 952
ALCO VALVES (US), INC.—See Graco, Inc.; *U.S. Public*, pg. 952
ALCOVA MORTGAGE; *U.S. Private*, pg. 154
ALCO VENTURES INC.; *Int'l*, pg. 301
ALCRO-BECKERS AB—See PPG Industries, Inc.; *U.S. Public*, pg. 1710
ALCUIN CAPITAL PARTNERS LLP; *Int'l*, pg. 303
ALCUMUS HOLDINGS LTD; *Int'l*, pg. 303
ALCURA FRANCE—See Walgreens Boots Alliance, Inc.; *U.S. Public*, pg. 2321
ALCURA HEALTH ESPANA, S.A.—See Walgreens Boots Alliance, Inc.; *U.S. Public*, pg. 2321
ALCURA UK LIMITED—See Walgreens Boots Alliance, Inc.; *U.S. Public*, pg. 2321
ALCUT CO., LTD.—See Sumitomo Corporation; *Int'l*, pg. 7268
ALCYON BV—See Carrefour SA; *Int'l*, pg. 1344
ALCYONIX—See DBAY Advisors Limited; *Int'l*, pg. 1987
A.L.C.Z A.S—See Iron Mountain Incorporated; *U.S. Public*, pg. 1172
ALDACHANIE; *Int'l*, pg. 304
A.L.D. ADVANCED LOGISTICS DEVELOPMENTS LTD.; *Int'l*, pg. 24
ALDAGEN, INC.—See Nuo Therapeutics, Inc.; *U.S. Public*, pg. 1555
ALDAG-HONOLD MECHANICAL, INC.; *U.S. Private*, pg. 154
ALDAMAN FOR INVESTMENTS PLC; *Int'l*, pg. 304
ALDANA & ASSOCIATES PSC LTD.; *U.S. Private*, pg. 155
AL DANUBE BUILDING MATERIALS TRADING CO., LLC; *Int'l*, pg. 276
ALDA OFFICE PROPERTIES, INC.; *U.S. Private*, pg. 154
ALDAR EDUCATION - SOLE PROPRIETORSHIP LLC—See ALDAR Properties PJSC; *Int'l*, pg. 304
ALDARIS JSC—See Carlsberg A/S; *Int'l*, pg. 1339
AL-DAR NATIONAL REAL ESTATE COMPANY K.S.C.C.; *Int'l*, pg. 284
ALDAR PROPERTIES PJSC; *Int'l*, pg. 304
ALDATA SOFTWARE MANAGEMENT INC.—See Valsef Group; *Int'l*, pg. 8122
ALD AUTOLEASING D GMBH—See Societe Generale S.A.; *Int'l*, pg. 7038
ALD AUTOMOTIVE AB—See Societe Generale S.A.; *Int'l*, pg. 7038
ALD AUTOMOTIVE AG—See ALD Automotive; *Int'l*, pg. 303
ALD AUTOMOTIVE ALGERIE SPA—See ALD Automotive; *Int'l*, pg. 303
ALD AUTOMOTIVE A/S—See Societe Generale S.A.; *Int'l*, pg. 7038
ALD AUTOMOTIVE AS—See Societe Generale S.A.; *Int'l*, pg. 7038
ALD AUTOMOTIVE D.O.O.—See ALD Automotive; *Int'l*, pg. 303
ALD AUTOMOTIVE D.O.O. ZA—See ALD Automotive; *Int'l*, pg. 303
ALD AUTOMOTIVE EESTI AS—See ALD Automotive; *Int'l*, pg. 303
ALD AUTOMOTIVE EOOD—See ALD Automotive; *Int'l*, pg. 303
ALD AUTOMOTIVE FUHRPARKMANAGEMENT UND LEASING GMBH—See ALD Automotive; *Int'l*, pg. 303
ALD AUTOMOTIVE GROUP PLC—See Societe Generale S.A.; *Int'l*, pg. 7038
ALD AUTOMOTIVE LIMITADA—See ALD Automotive; *Int'l*, pg. 303
ALD AUTOMOTIVE LIMITED—See Societe Generale S.A.; *Int'l*, pg. 7038
ALD AUTOMOTIVE MAGYARORSZAG AUTOPARK - KEZELO ES FINANSZIROZO KFT—See ALD Automotive; *Int'l*, pg. 303
ALD AUTOMOTIVE OOO—See ALD Automotive; *Int'l*, pg. 303
ALD AUTOMOTIVE OPERATIONAL LEASING DOO—See ALD Automotive; *Int'l*, pg. 303
ALD AUTOMOTIVE PERU S.A.C.—See ALD Automotive; *Int'l*, pg. 303
ALD AUTOMOTIVE POLSKA SP Z O.O.—See ALD Automotive; *Int'l*, pg. 303
ALD AUTOMOTIVE PRIVATE LIMITED—See ALD Automotive; *Int'l*, pg. 303
ALD AUTOMOTIVE S.A. DE C.V.—See ALD Automotive; *Int'l*, pg. 303
ALD AUTOMOTIVE S.A.—See ALD Automotive; *Int'l*, pg. 303
ALD AUTOMOTIVE S.A.—See ALD Automotive; *Int'l*, pg. 303
ALD AUTOMOTIVE S.A.S—See ALD Automotive; *Int'l*, pg. 303

COMPANY NAME INDEX

ALD AUTOMOTIVE S.A.U—See ALD Automotive; *Int'l*, pg. 303
ALD AUTOMOTIVE SIA—See ALD Automotive; *Int'l*, pg. 303
ALD AUTOMOTIVE SLOVAKIA S.R.O—See ALD Automotive; *Int'l*, pg. 303
ALD AUTOMOTIVE; *Int'l*, pg. 303
ALD AUTOMOTIVE SRL—See ALD Automotive; *Int'l*, pg. 303
ALD AUTOMOTIVE SRO—See Societe Generale S.A.; *Int'l*, pg. 7038
ALD AUTOMOTIVE TURIZM TICARET ANONIM SIRKETI—See ALD Automotive; *Int'l*, pg. 303
ALD AUTOMOTIVE UKRAINE LIMITED LIABILITY COMPANY—See ALD Automotive; *Int'l*, pg. 303
AL-DAWAA MEDICAL SERVICES COMPANY; *Int'l*, pg. 284
AL DAWLIYAH FOR HOTELS & MALLS PLC; *Int'l*, pg. 276
ALDEASA CHILE, LTD.—See Avolta AG; *Int'l*, pg. 749
ALDEBARAN ARGENTINA S.A.—See Aldebaran Resources, Inc.; *Int'l*, pg. 304
ALDEBARAN RESOURCES, INC.; *Int'l*, pg. 304
ALDEBRA S.P.A.—See Sesa S.p.A.; *Int'l*, pg. 6728
AL-DEERA HOLDING CO. K.S.C.C.; *Int'l*, pg. 285
ALDELANO PACKAGING CORPORATION; *U.S. Private*, pg. 155
ALDEM CELIK ENDUSTRI SAN. VE TIC. A.S.—See Verusa Holding A.S.; *Int'l*, pg. 8175
ALDEN ENTERPRISES, INC.; *U.S. Private*, pg. 155
ALDEN GLOBAL CAPITAL LLC; *U.S. Private*, pg. 155
ALDEN LEEDS, INC.; *U.S. Private*, pg. 159
ALDEN OPTICAL LABORATORIES, INC.—See Bausch Health Companies Inc.; *Int'l*, pg. 896
ALDEN PADFIELD INC.; *U.S. Private*, pg. 159
ALDEN RESEARCH LABORATORY, INC.—See Round Table Capital Management, LP; *U.S. Private*, pg. 3488
ALDEN ROOFING, INC.—See Restoration Builders Inc.; *U.S. Private*, pg. 3409
THE ALDEN SHOE COMPANY; *U.S. Private*, pg. 3983
ALDEN STATE BANK; *U.S. Private*, pg. 159
ALDEN SYSTEMS, INC.; *U.S. Private*, pg. 159
AL DENTE PASTA COMPANY—See ALB-GOLD Teigwaren GmbH; *Int'l*, pg. 292
ALDERAN RESOURCES LIMITED; *Int'l*, pg. 304
ALDER BIOPHARMACEUTICALS, INC—See Lundbeckfonden; *Int'l*, pg. 4582
ALDERBROOK WINERY—See The Terlato Wine Group; *U.S. Private*, pg. 4126
ALDERFER, INC.; *U.S. Private*, pg. 159
ALDER FUND I AB; *Int'l*, pg. 304
ALDER II AB—See Alder Fund I AB; *Int'l*, pg. 304
ALDERMAN BUILDING COMPANY, INC.; *U.S. Private*, pg. 159
THE ALDERMAN COMPANY; *U.S. Private*, pg. 3983
ALDERMAN'S CHEVROLET, INC.; *U.S. Private*, pg. 159
ALDERMORE BANK PLC—See AnaCap Financial Partners LLP; *Int'l*, pg. 445
ALDERMORE INVOICE FINANCE LIMITED—See AnaCap Financial Partners LLP; *Int'l*, pg. 445
ALDERON IRON ORE CORP.; *Int'l*, pg. 304
ALDER OPTOMECHANICAL CORP.—See Alltek Technology Corporation; *Int'l*, pg. 360
ALDERSON ENTERPRISES INC.; *U.S. Private*, pg. 159
ALDERSON REPORTING CO., INC.—See TrustPoint International, LLC; *U.S. Private*, pg. 4251
ALDER TECHNOLOGY, INC.—See Blue Delta Capital Partners LLC; *U.S. Private*, pg. 588
ALDERWOOD WATER & WASTE WATER DISTRICT; *U.S. Private*, pg. 159
ALDERYS SAS—See Givaudan S.A.; *Int'l*, pg. 2979
ALDES AERAULIQUE SAS; *Int'l*, pg. 304
ALDETEC, INC.—See Greenbriar Equity Group, L.P.; *U.S. Private*, pg. 1775
ALDEVRON, LLC—See Danaher Corporation; *U.S. Public*, pg. 624
ALDEWAN FASTFOOD COMPANY LTD.—See The Al Fadl Group of Companies; *Int'l*, pg. 7612
ALDEYRA THERAPEUTICS, INC.; *U.S. Public*, pg. 74
ALDEZ CONTAINERS, LLC—See Rengo Co., Ltd.; *Int'l*, pg. 6279
ALDHAFRA INSURANCE COMPANY P.S.C; *Int'l*, pg. 304
ALD HOLCROFT VACUUM TECHNOLOGIES CO.—See AMG Critical Materials N.V.; *Int'l*, pg. 425
AL DIA, INC.—See DallasNews Corporation; *U.S. Public*, pg. 621
ALDI EINKAUF SE & CO. OHG; *Int'l*, pg. 304
ALDI FOOD INC.—See Aldi Einkauf SE & Co. oHG; *Int'l*, pg. 304
ALDIGE—See Media 6 SA; *Int'l*, pg. 4770
ALDILA, INC.—See Mitsubishi Chemical Group Corporation; *Int'l*, pg. 4933
ALD INDUSTRIE- UND MONTAGEPARK STAAKEN GMBH—See AMG Critical Materials N.V.; *Int'l*, pg. 425
ALDINE CAPITAL PARTNERS, INC.; *U.S. Private*, pg. 159
ALDINGER COMPANY; *U.S. Private*, pg. 160
ALD INTERNATIONAL SAS & CO. KG—See Societe Generale S.A.; *Int'l*, pg. 7038

ALDIPRESS B.V.—See DPG Media Group NV; *Int'l*, pg. 2188
ALD LEASE FINANZ GMBH—See Societe Generale S.A.; *Int'l*, pg. 7038
ALDOBEC TECHNOLOGIES, S.R.O.—See W.A.G Payment Solutions Plc; *Int'l*, pg. 8321
THE ALDO GROUP INC.; *Int'l*, pg. 7613
ALDON COMPUTER GROUP—See Marlin Equity Partners, LLC; *U.S. Private*, pg. 2583
ALDORA ALUMINUM & GLASS PRODUCTS, INC.; *U.S. Private*, pg. 160
ALDORO RESOURCES LIMITED; *Int'l*, pg. 305
AL-DORRA PETROLEUM SERVICES KSCC; *Int'l*, pg. 285
ALD OWN & OPERATE GMBH—See AMG Critical Materials N.V.; *Int'l*, pg. 425
ALDPRO CORPORATE SERVICES SDN. BHD.—See Aldrich Resources Bhd; *Int'l*, pg. 305
ALDREES PETROLEUM & TRANSPORT SERVICES COMPANY; *Int'l*, pg. 305
ALDRICH CAPITAL PARTNERS, LLC; *U.S. Private*, pg. 160
ALDRICH CHEMICAL CO. LLC—See Merck KGaA; *Int'l*, pg. 4832
ALDRICH CLEAN-TECH EQUIPMENT CORP.—See EVI Industries, Inc.; *U.S. Public*, pg. 803
ALDRICH & ELLIOTT PC; *U.S. Public*, pg. 160
ALDRICH FARMS, LLC; *U.S. Private*, pg. 160
ALDRICH RESOURCES BHD; *Int'l*, pg. 305
THE ALDRIDGE COMPANY - DALLAS OFFICE—See The Aldridge Company; *U.S. Private*, pg. 3983
THE ALDRIDGE COMPANY; *U.S. Private*, pg. 3983
ALDRIDGE CONSTRUCTION, INC.; *U.S. Private*, pg. 160
ALDRIDGE ELECTRIC INC.; *U.S. Private*, pg. 160
ALDRIDGE MINERALS INC.; *Int'l*, pg. 305
ALDRIDGE PHYSICAL THERAPY, LLC—See Audax Group, Limited Partnership; *U.S. Private*, pg. 389
ALDRIDGE TRAFFIC SYSTEMS PTY LTD—See Traffic Technologies Ltd.; *Int'l*, pg. 7889
ALD S.A.—See Societe Generale S.A.; *Int'l*, pg. 7038
ALD SOFTWARE LTD.—See HUB Cyber Security Ltd.; *Int'l*, pg. 3516
ALD THERMAL TREATMENT, INC.—See AMG Critical Materials N.V.; *Int'l*, pg. 425
ALD THERMO TECHNOLOGIES FAR EAST CO., LTD.—See AMG Critical Materials N.V.; *Int'l*, pg. 425
ALD TRATAMIENTOS TERMICOS S.A. DE C.V.—See AMG Critical Materials N.V.; *Int'l*, pg. 425
AL DUCA D'AOSTA SPA; *Int'l*, pg. 276
ALDUS PTY. LTD.; *Int'l*, pg. 305
ALD VACUUM TECHNOLOGIES GMBH—See AMG Critical Materials N.V.; *Int'l*, pg. 425
ALD VACUUM TECHNOLOGIES, INC.—See AMG Critical Materials N.V.; *Int'l*, pg. 425
ALD VACUUMYJE TECHNOLOGII OOO—See AMG Critical Materials N.V.; *Int'l*, pg. 425
ALEADRI-SCHINNI PARTICIPACOES E REPRESENTACOES S.A.; *Int'l*, pg. 305
ALEAFIA HEALTH INC.; *Int'l*, pg. 305
ALEA HEAT & POWER S.R.L.—See CogenInfra SpA; *Int'l*, pg. 1694
ALEA INZENIRING DOO; *Int'l*, pg. 305
ALEA MOBILITA' URBANA S.R.L.—See CogenInfra SpA; *Int'l*, pg. 1694
ALE ARGENTINA S.R.L.—See Nokia Corporation; *Int'l*, pg. 5403
AL EARTHWORX MINING & CIVIL PTY. LIMITED—See MAAS Group Holdings Limited; *Int'l*, pg. 4618
A-LEASING SPA—See Raiffeisen Bank International AG; *Int'l*, pg. 6182
A.L. EASTMOND & SONS INC.; *U.S. Private*, pg. 26
ALEATICA LABS, S.A.—See Industry Super Holdings Pty. Ltd.; *Int'l*, pg. 3676
ALEATICA, S.A.B. DE C.V.—See Industry Super Holdings Pty. Ltd.; *Int'l*, pg. 3675
ALEATOR ENERGY LIMITED; *Int'l*, pg. 305
ALE AUSTRIA GMBH—See Nokia Corporation; *Int'l*, pg. 5403
ALE BRASIL INTERMEDIACAO DE NEGOCIOS LTDA.—See Nokia Corporation; *Int'l*, pg. 5403
ALECOP S. COOP.—See Mondragon Corporation; *Int'l*, pg. 5028
ALECTA PENSIONSFORSAKRING, OMSESIDIGT; *Int'l*, pg. 305
ALECTA REAL ESTATE INVESTMENT, LLC—See Alecta pensionsforsakring, omsesidigt; *Int'l*, pg. 305
ALECTA REAL ESTATE USA, LLC—See Alecta pensionsforsakring, omsesidigt; *Int'l*, pg. 305
ALECTO MINERALS PLC; *Int'l*, pg. 305
ALECTOR, INC.; *U.S. Public*, pg. 74
ALECTRA INC.—See Hydro One Limited; *Int'l*, pg. 3546
ALECTRA LIMITED—See Smiths City Group Limited; *Int'l*, pg. 7009
ALECTRA UTILITIES CORPORATION—See Hydro One Limited; *Int'l*, pg. 3546
ALEDCO, INC.—See DXP Enterprises, Inc.; *U.S. Public*, pg. 697
ALE DEUTSCHLAND GMBH—See Nokia Corporation; *Int'l*, pg. 5403
AL & ED'S CORPORATION; *U.S. Private*, pg. 147

ALENCO WINDOW HOLDING CORP.

ALEEDA INC.; *Int'l*, pg. 305
ALEEES AU PTY. LTD.—See Advanced Lithium Electrochemistry (KY) Co., Ltd.; *Int'l*, pg. 160
ALEEES EU SARL—See Advanced Lithium Electrochemistry (KY) Co., Ltd.; *Int'l*, pg. 160
ALEEES UK, LTD.—See Advanced Lithium Electrochemistry (KY) Co., Ltd.; *Int'l*, pg. 160
ALEFARM BREWING A/S; *Int'l*, pg. 306
ALEF-BANK CJSC JSCB; *Int'l*, pg. 306
ALEF S.A.; *Int'l*, pg. 306
ALEGEUS TECHNOLOGIES, LLC—See Vista Equity Partners, LLC; *U.S. Private*, pg. 4395
ALEGIS REVENUE GROUP LLC—See MEDNAX, Inc.; *U.S. Public*, pg. 1413
ALEGRE PTY LTD—See Assurant, Inc.; *U.S. Public*, pg. 214
ALEGRI INTERNATIONAL AUSTRIA GMBH—See Devoteam SA; *Int'l*, pg. 2089
ALEGRI INTERNATIONAL SERVICE GMBH—See Devoteam SA; *Int'l*, pg. 2089
ALE GROUP HOLDING LIMITED; *Int'l*, pg. 305
A-LEHDET OY; *Int'l*, pg. 20
ALE HOUSE MANAGEMENT, INC.; *U.S. Private*, pg. 160
AL EID FOOD CO; *Int'l*, pg. 276
ALE INDIA PVT. LTD.—See Nokia Corporation; *Int'l*, pg. 5403
ALE INTERNATIONAL AGENCY IN CHILE—See Nokia Corporation; *Int'l*, pg. 5403
ALE INTERNATIONAL BELGIUM—See Nokia Corporation; *Int'l*, pg. 5403
ALE INTERNATIONAL - CZECH REPUBLIC, ODSTEPNY ZAVOD—See Nokia Corporation; *Int'l*, pg. 5403
ALE INTERNATIONAL - FINLAND REPRESENTATION OFFICE—See Nokia Corporation; *Int'l*, pg. 5403
ALE INTERNATIONAL - NORWAY BRANCH—See Nokia Corporation; *Int'l*, pg. 5403
ALE INTERNATIONAL - PORTUGAL—See Nokia Corporation; *Int'l*, pg. 5403
ALE INTERNATIONAL, SAS—See Nokia Corporation; *Int'l*, pg. 5404
ALE INTERNATIONAL—See Nokia Corporation; *Int'l*, pg. 5403
ALEIS PTY LTD—See Merck & Co., Inc.; *U.S. Public*, pg. 1415
ALE ITALIA S.R.L.—See Nokia Corporation; *Int'l*, pg 5404
AL-EKBAL PRINTING & PACKAGING CO.—See Mayr-Melnhof Karton AG; *Int'l*, pg. 4745
ALEKSA SANTIC U RESTRUKTURIRANJU A.D.; *Int'l*, pg. 306
ALEKS CORPORATION—See Platinum Equity, LLC; *U.S. Private*, pg. 3205
ALELION ENERGY SYSTEMS AB; *Int'l*, pg. 306
AL EMAN PRINTING PRESS CO—See HAK Algahtani Group of Companies; *Int'l*, pg. 3219
ALEMBIC GLASS INDUSTRIES LTD.—See Alembic Limited; *Int'l*, pg. 306
ALEMBIC LIMITED; *Int'l*, pg. 306
ALEMBIC PHARMACEUTICALS LIMITED—See Alembic Limited; *Int'l*, pg. 306
ALEMBO B.V.—See Majorel Group Luxembourg S.A.; *Int'l*, pg. 4655
ALEMITE LLC—See SKF AB; *Int'l*, pg. 6985
ALEMPEDRAS - SOCIEDADE DE BRITAS LDA—See Camargo Correa S.A.; *Int'l*, pg. 1267
ALEN AMERICAS INC.—See Industrias Alen S.A. de C.V.; *Int'l*, pg. 3673
ALENCO INC.—See Ovintiv Inc.; *U.S. Public*, pg. 1625
ALENCO WINDOW HOLDING CORP.; *U.S. Private*, pg. 160
ALE NETHERLANDS B.V.—See Nokia Corporation; *Int'l*, pg. 5404
ALENIA AERMACCHI S.P.A.—See Leonardo S.p.A.; *Int'l*, pg. 4458
ALENIA AERONAUTICA S.P.A.—See Leonardo S.p.A.; *Int'l*, pg. 4458
ALENIA NORTH AMERICA, INC.—See Leonardo S.p.A.; *Int'l*, pg. 4458
ALENIA SIA SPA—See Leonardo S.p.A.; *Int'l*, pg. 4458
ALENIA SPAZIO S.P.A.—See Leonardo S.p.A.; *Int'l*, pg. 4458
AL-ENMA'A REAL ESTATE COMPANY K.S.C.C.—See Kuwait Finance House K.S.C.; *Int'l*, pg. 4344
ALENT ALPHA METALS (SHANGHAI) TRADING CO. LTD—See Element Solutions Inc.; *U.S. Public*, pg. 726
ALENT ALPHA METALS (SHENZEN) CO. LTD—See Element Solutions Inc.; *U.S. Public*, pg. 726
ALENTARIS LTD.—See Ireland Blyth Limited; *Int'l*, pg. 3806
ALENT ASSEMBLY SOLUTIONS BRASIL SOLDAS LTDA.—See Element Solutions Inc.; *U.S. Public*, pg. 726
ALENT ENTHONE CHEMISTRY (SHANGHAI) CO. LTD.—See Element Solutions Inc.; *U.S. Public*, pg. 726
ALENTERPRISE MEXICO—See Nokia Corporation; *Int'l*, pg. 5404
ALENT HONG KONG LTD—See Element Solutions Inc.; *U.S. Public*, pg. 726
ALENT ITALIA SRL—See Element Solutions Inc.; *U.S. Public*, pg. 726

ALENCO WINDOW HOLDING CORP.
CORPORATE AFFILIATIONS

ALENT JAPAN COMPANY—See Element Solutions Inc.; *U.S. Public*, pg. 726
AL ENTKAEYA FOR INVESTMENT & REAL ESTATE DEVELOPMENT CO. PLC; *Int'l*, pg. 276
ALEN USA, LLC—See Industrias Alen S.A. de C.V.; *Int'l*, pg. 3673
ALEO SOLAR GMBH—See Sunrise Global Solar Energy Co., Ltd.; *Int'l*, pg. 7321
ALEPH GROUP, INC.; *Int'l*, pg. 306
ALEPH NETWORKS CORPORATION—See Kinden Corporation; *Int'l*, pg. 4165
ALE PROPERTY GROUP—See Charter Hall Limited; *Int'l*, pg. 1454
ALE PROPERTY GROUP—See Host-Plus Pty. Limited; *Int'l*, pg. 3486
AL-EQBAL INVESTMENT CO. (PLC); *Int'l*, pg. 285
ALERA GROUP, INC.—See Genstar Capital, LLC; *U.S. Private*, pg. 1673
ALERE AB—See Abbott Laboratories; *U.S. Public*, pg. 18
ALERE COLOMBIA S.A.—See Abbott Laboratories; *U.S. Public*, pg. 18
ALERE GMBH—See Abbott Laboratories; *U.S. Public*, pg. 18
ALERE GMBH—See Abbott Laboratories; *U.S. Public*, pg. 18
ALERE HEALTH BVBA—See Abbott Laboratories; *U.S. Public*, pg. 18
ALERE HEALTH B.V.—See Abbott Laboratories; *U.S. Public*, pg. 18
ALERE HEALTHCARE CONNECTIONS LIMITED—See Abbott Laboratories; *U.S. Public*, pg. 18
ALERE HEALTHCARE INC.—See Abbott Laboratories; *U.S. Public*, pg. 18
ALERE HEALTHCARE (PTY) LIMITED—See Abbott Laboratories; *U.S. Public*, pg. 18
ALERE HEALTH, LLC—See UnitedHealth Group Incorporated; *U.S. Public*, pg. 2248
ALERE HEALTH SYSTEMS, INC.—See UnitedHealth Group Incorporated; *U.S. Public*, pg. 2248
ALERE HOME MONITORING INC—See Abbott Laboratories; *U.S. Public*, pg. 18
ALERE INC.—See Abbott Laboratories; *U.S. Public*, pg. 18
ALERE MEDICAL CO., LTD.—See Abbott Laboratories; *U.S. Public*, pg. 18
ALERE MEDICAL PRIVATE LIMITED—See Abbott Laboratories; *U.S. Public*, pg. 18
ALERE PHILIPPINES, INC.—See Abbott Laboratories; *U.S. Public*, pg. 18
ALERE SAN DIEGO, INC.—See Abbott Laboratories; *U.S. Public*, pg. 19
ALERE S.A.—See Abbott Laboratories; *U.S. Public*, pg. 18
ALERE SAS—See Abbott Laboratories; *U.S. Public*, pg. 19
ALERE SPAIN, S.L.—See Abbott Laboratories; *U.S. Public*, pg. 19
ALERE S.R.L.—See Abbott Laboratories; *U.S. Public*, pg. 18
ALERE TECHNOLOGIES AS—See Abbott Laboratories; *U.S. Public*, pg. 19
ALERE TECHNOLOGIES GMBH—See Abbott Laboratories; *U.S. Public*, pg. 19
ALERE TOXICOLOGY, INC.—See Abbott Laboratories; *U.S. Public*, pg. 19
ALERE TOXICOLOGY SERVICES, INC.—See Abbott Laboratories; *U.S. Public*, pg. 19
ALERE WELLBEING INC.—See UnitedHealth Group Incorporated; *U.S. Public*, pg. 2248
ALERIO GOLD CORP.; *Int'l*, pg. 306
ALERION CAPITAL GROUP, LLC; *U.S. Private*, pg. 160
ALERION CLEAN POWER S.P.A.; *Int'l*, pg. 306
ALERIS ALUMINIUM VOGT GMBH—See The Aditya Birla Group; *Int'l*, pg. 7611
ALERIS ALUMINUM BITTERFELD GMBH—See The Aditya Birla Group; *Int'l*, pg. 7611
ALERIS ALUMINUM DUFFEL BVBA—See Sankyo Tateyama Inc.; *Int'l*, pg. 6543
ALERIS ALUMINUM KOBLENZ GMBH—See The Aditya Birla Group; *Int'l*, pg. 7611
ALERIS CORPORATION—See The Aditya Birla Group; *Int'l*, pg. 7611
ALERIS INTERNATIONAL, INC.—See The Aditya Birla Group; *Int'l*, pg. 7611
ALERISLIFE INC.; *U.S. Private*, pg. 160
ALERIS ROLLED PRODUCTS, INC.—See The Aditya Birla Group; *Int'l*, pg. 7611
ALERIS ROLLED PRODUCTS NORTH AMERICA—See The Aditya Birla Group; *Int'l*, pg. 7611
ALERIS SPECIALTY PRODUCTS, INC.—See The Aditya Birla Group; *Int'l*, pg. 7611
ALERMAC INVERSIONES, S.A. DE C.V.—See PPG Industries, Inc.; *U.S. Public*, pg. 1707
ALERT AMBULANCE SERVICE, INC.; *U.S. Private*, pg. 162
A-LERT CONSTRUCTION SERVICES INC. - FABRICATION FACILITY—See Centurion Industries Inc.; *U.S. Private*, pg. 831
A-LERT CONSTRUCTION SERVICES INC.—See Centurion Industries Inc.; *U.S. Private*, pg. 831
ALERT ENGINE PARTS (PTY) LIMITED—See Dubai World Corporation; *Int'l*, pg. 2221

ALERTER GROUP LTD.—See Sdiptech AB; *Int'l*, pg. 6658
ALERT FIRE PROTECTION SYSTEMS PRIVATE LIMITED—See Nitin Fire Protection Industries Ltd; *Int'l*, pg. 5381
ALERT HOLDINGS GROUP, INC.; *U.S. Public*, pg. 162
ALERT LOGIC, INC.—See HGGC, LLC; *U.S. Private*, pg. 1929
ALERT MARKETING, INC.—See The Wicks Group of Companies, LLC; *U.S. Private*, pg. 4135
ALERUS FINANCIAL CORPORATION; *U.S. Public*, pg. 74
ALERUS FINANCIAL, NATIONAL ASSOCIATION—See Alerus Financial Corporation; *U.S. Public*, pg. 74
ALES - AIR LIQUIDE ELECTRONICS SYSTEMS—See L'Air Liquide S.A.; *Int'l*, pg. 4371
ALESAYI TRADING CORPORATION; *Int'l*, pg. 306
THE ALESCO GROUP, LLC; *U.S. Private*, pg. 3983
ALESCO RISK MANAGEMENT SERVICES LIMITED—See Arthur J. Gallagher & Co.; *U.S. Public*, pg. 202
ALESCO S.R.L.—See Pharmanutra S.p.A.; *Int'l*, pg. 5840
ALES GROUP COSMETIC GMBH—See Impala SAS; *Int'l*, pg. 3631
ALES GROUPE BENELUX SPRL—See Impala SAS; *Int'l*, pg. 3631
ALES GROUPE CANADA INC—See Impala SAS; *Int'l*, pg. 3631
ALES GROUPE COSMETIC DEUTSCHLAND GMBH—See Impala SAS; *Int'l*, pg. 3631
ALES GROUPE ESPANA S.L.—See Impala SAS; *Int'l*, pg. 3631
ALES GROUPE INDUSTRIES—See Impala SAS; *Int'l*, pg. 3631
ALES GROUPE ITALIA S.P.A.—See Impala SAS; *Int'l*, pg. 3631
ALES GROUPE POLSKA SP. Z O.O.—See Impala SAS; *Int'l*, pg. 3631
ALES GROUPE PORTUGAL LDA—See Impala SAS; *Int'l*, pg. 3631
ALES GROUPE SA—See Impala SAS; *Int'l*, pg. 3631
ALES GROUP INC—See Impala SAS; *Int'l*, pg. 3631
ALES GROUP UK LTD—See Impala SAS; *Int'l*, pg. 3631
ALESIS, L.P.—See inMusic, LLC; *U.S. Private*, pg. 2080
ALE SOLUTIONS, INC.—See Corpay, Inc.; *U.S. Public*, pg. 579
ALESSANDRO ROSSO GROUP S.P.A.; *Int'l*, pg. 306
ALESSANDRO ROSSO INCENTIVE S.R.L.—See Alessandro Rosso Group S.p.A.; *Int'l*, pg. 306
ALESSI BAKERIES, INC.; *U.S. Private*, pg. 162
ALE SWITZERLAND GMBH—See Nokia Corporation; *Int'l*, pg. 5404
ALETSCH AG—See EnBW Energie Baden-Wurttemberg AG; *Int'l*, pg. 2398
ALEUT COMMUNICATIONS SERVICES, LLC—See The Aleut Corporation; *U.S. Private*, pg. 3984
THE ALEUT CORPORATION; *U.S. Private*, pg. 3983
ALEUT GLOBAL SOLUTIONS—See The Aleut Corporation; *U.S. Private*, pg. 3984
ALEUT MANAGEMENT SERVICES—See The Aleut Corporation; *U.S. Private*, pg. 3984
ALEVA NEUROTHERAPEUTICS SA—See BNP Paribas SA; *Int'l*, pg. 1089
ALEVA STORES; *U.S. Private*, pg. 162
ALEXA ENERGY LTD.; *U.S. Private*, pg. 163
ALEXA INTERNET, INC.—See Amazon.com, Inc.; *U.S. Public*, pg. 90
ALEXANDER AUTOMOTIVE GROUP; *U.S. Private*, pg. 163
ALEXANDER AUTOMOTIVE; *U.S. Private*, pg. 163
ALEXANDER & BALDWIN, INC.; *U.S. Public*, pg. 75
ALEXANDER & BALDWIN SUGAR MUSEUM—See Alexander & Baldwin, Inc.; *U.S. Public*, pg. 75
ALEXANDER BARON VON ESSEN WEINHANDELS GMBH—See Hawesko Holding AG; *Int'l*, pg. 3288
ALEXANDER BENEFITS CONSULTING, LLC—See Aon plc; *Int'l*, pg. 495
ALEXANDER BONHILL LIMITED—See HML Holdings plc; *Int'l*, pg. 3432
ALEXANDER BUICK GMC CADILLAC; *U.S. Private*, pg. 163
ALEXANDER BUILDING CONSTRUCTION, CO.; *U.S. Private*, pg. 163
ALEXANDER BUILDING CONSTRUCTION LLC—See Butz Enterprises, Inc.; *U.S. Private*, pg. 698
ALEXANDER CHEMICAL CORPORATION; *U.S. Private*, pg. 163
ALEXANDER CHEVROLET—See Alexander Automotive; *U.S. Private*, pg. 163
ALEXANDER DENNIS (ASIA PACIFIC) LIMITED—See NFI Group Inc.; *Int'l*, pg. 5252
ALEXANDER DENNIS INCORPORATED—See NFI Group Inc.; *Int'l*, pg. 5252
ALEXANDER DENNIS LIMITED—See NFI Group Inc.; *Int'l*, pg. 5252
ALEXANDER DENNIS (MALAYSIA) SDNBHD—See NFI Group Inc.; *Int'l*, pg. 5252
ALEXANDER DENNIS (SINGAPORE) SERVICES PTE LIMITED—See NFI Group Inc.; *Int'l*, pg. 5252
ALEXANDER DOLL COMPANY, INC.—See Kahn-Lucas-Lancaster Inc.; *U.S. Private*, pg. 2254

ALEXANDER FORBES CHANNEL ISLANDS LIMITED—See Alexander Forbes Group Holdings Limited; *Int'l*, pg. 306
ALEXANDER FORBES COMMUNITY TRUST—See Alexander Forbes Group Holdings Limited; *Int'l*, pg. 306
ALEXANDER FORBES COMPENSATION TECHNOLOGIES (PTY) LTD—See Alexander Forbes Group Holdings Limited; *Int'l*, pg. 306
ALEXANDER FORBES CONSULTING ACTUARIES NIGERIA LIMITED—See Alexander Forbes Group Holdings Limited; *Int'l*, pg. 306
ALEXANDER FORBES GROUP HOLDINGS LIMITED; *Int'l*, pg. 306
ALEXANDER FORBES INTERNATIONAL LTD.—See Alexander Forbes Group Holdings Limited; *Int'l*, pg. 307
ALEXANDER FORBES LIMITED—See Alexander Forbes Group Holdings Limited; *Int'l*, pg. 306
ALEXANDER FORD CO. INC.—See Alexander Automotive; *U.S. Private*, pg. 163
ALEXANDER FORD LINCOLN-MERCURY, INC.—See Alexander Automotive Group; *U.S. Private*, pg. 163
ALEXANDER GLOBAL PROMOTIONS, INC.; *U.S. Private*, pg. 163
ALEXANDER KARTEN; *U.S. Private*, pg. 163
ALEXANDER LUMBER CO., INC.; *U.S. Private*, pg. 163
ALEXANDER MACHINE & TOOL COMPANY, INC.—See Behrman Brothers Management Corp.; *U.S. Private*, pg. 515
ALEXANDER MARINE CO., LTD.; *Int'l*, pg. 306
ALEXANDER MCQUEEN AUSTRALIA PTY LTD—See Kering S.A.; *Int'l*, pg. 4133
ALEXANDER MCQUEEN FRANCE SAS—See Kering S.A.; *Int'l*, pg. 4133
ALEXANDER MCQUEEN (HONG KONG) LTD.—See Kering S.A.; *Int'l*, pg. 4133
ALEXANDER MCQUEEN (MACAU) LTD.—See Kering S.A.; *Int'l*, pg. 4133
ALEXANDER MCQUEEN NEW ZEALAND LTD.—See Kering S.A.; *Int'l*, pg. 4133
ALEXANDER MCQUEEN (SINGAPORE) PTE LTD—See Kering S.A.; *Int'l*, pg. 4133
ALEXANDER MCQUEEN (THAILAND) LTD.—See Kering S.A.; *Int'l*, pg. 4133
ALEXANDER MCQUEEN (THE NETHERLANDS) B.V.—See Kering S.A.; *Int'l*, pg. 4133
ALEXANDER MCQUEEN TRADING CANADA INC.—See Kering S.A.; *Int'l*, pg. 4133
ALEXANDER MORTGAGE CORP.; *U.S. Private*, pg. 163
ALEXANDER OIL COMPANY; *U.S. Private*, pg. 164
ALEXANDER-PATTERSON GROUP INC.; *U.S. Private*, pg. 164
ALEXANDER PLASTICS INC.; *U.S. Private*, pg. 164
ALEXANDER PROUDFOOT CANADA—See Management Consulting Group PLC; *Int'l*, pg. 4666
ALEXANDER PROUDFOOT COMPANY—See Management Consulting Group PLC; *Int'l*, pg. 4666
ALEXANDER PROUDFOOT (EUROPE) LIMITED—See Management Consulting Group PLC; *Int'l*, pg. 4666
ALEXANDER PROUDFOOT SOUTH AFRICA—See Management Consulting Group PLC; *Int'l*, pg. 4666
ALEXANDER PROUDFOOT UK—See Management Consulting Group PLC; *Int'l*, pg. 4666
ALEXANDER/RYAN MARINE AND SAFETY LLC—See Court Square Capital Partners, L.P.; *U.S. Private*, pg. 1068
ALEXANDER/RYAN MARINE & SAFETY CO.; *U.S. Private*, pg. 164
ALEXANDER SCHNEIDER LTD.; *Int'l*, pg. 307
ALEXANDER SERVICES, LLC; *U.S. Private*, pg. 164
ALEXANDER'S HOLDINGS, LC; *U.S. Private*, pg. 164
ALEXANDER'S, INC.; *U.S. Public*, pg. 75
ALEXANDER'S, INC.—See Vornado Realty Trust; *U.S. Public*, pg. 2310
ALEXANDER'S MOBILITY SERVICES; *U.S. Private*, pg. 164
ALEXANDER'S MOBILITY SERVICES—See Alexander's Mobility Services; *U.S. Private*, pg. 164
ALEXANDER STAMPS & COIN LTD.; *Int'l*, pg. 307
ALEXANDER TECH CORP.; *Int'l*, pg. 307
ALEXANDER YOUTH NETWORK; *U.S. Private*, pg. 164
ALEXANDRE LIMITED—See Heidelberg Materials AG; *Int'l*, pg. 3308
ALEXANDRA ADVANTAGE WARRANTY COMPANY; *U.S. Public*, pg. 75
ALEXANDRIA AGTECH/CLIMATE INNOVATION ACQUISITION CORP.; *U.S. Private*, pg. 164
ALEXANDRIA BANCORP LTD—See Guardian Capital Group Limited; *Int'l*, pg. 3169
ALEXANDRIA CONTAINER & CARGO HANDLING COMPANY; *Int'l*, pg. 307
ALEXANDRIA EXTRUSION COMPANY INC.; *U.S. Private*, pg. 164
ALEXANDRIA GLOBAL INVESTMENT MANAGEMENT LTD.—See Guardian Capital Group Limited; *Int'l*, pg. 3169
ALEXANDRIA GROUP OYJ; *Int'l*, pg. 307
ALEXANDRIA INTERNATIONAL CONTAINER TERMINALS COMPANY S.A.E.—See CK Hutchison Holdings Limited; *Int'l*, pg. 1636

COMPANY NAME INDEX

ALEXANDRIA MINERAL OILS CO.; *Int'l*, pg. 307
ALEXANDRIA MINERALS CORP.—See O3 Mining Inc.; *Int'l*, pg. 5503
ALEXANDRIA NATIONAL COMPANY FOR FINANCIAL INVESTMENT; *Int'l*, pg. 307
ALEXANDRIA NEWSPAPERS, INC.—See Gannett Co., Inc.; *U.S. Public*, pg. 896
THE ALEXANDRIA OPHTHALMOLOGY ASC, LLC—See KKR & Co. Inc.; *U.S. Public*, pg. 1247
ALEXANDRIA PETERSON CO. INC.; *U.S. Private*, pg. 164
ALEXANDRIA REAL ESTATE EQUITIES, INC.; *U.S. Public*, pg. 75
ALEXANDRIA SPINNING & WEAVING CO.; *Int'l*, pg. 307
ALEXANDRIA TOYOTA; *U.S. Private*, pg. 164
ALEXANDRIA TRUST CORPORATION—See Guardian Capital Group Limited; *Int'l*, pg. 3169
ALEX & ANI LLC; *U.S. Private*, pg. 162
ALEX APPAREL GROUP, INC.—See Independence Capital Partners, LLC; *U.S. Private*, pg. 2057
ALEXA'S ANGELS, INC.; *U.S. Private*, pg. 163
ALEX BEGG & CO—See Lindengruppen AB; *Int'l*, pg. 4510
ALEX C. FERGUSSON, INC.; *U.S. Private*, pg. 162
ALEXCO KENO HILL MINING CORP.—See Hecla Mining Company; *U.S. Public*, pg. 1018
ALEXCO RESOURCE CORP.—See Hecla Mining Company; *U.S. Public*, pg. 1018
ALEXCO RESOURCE US CORP—See Hecla Mining Company; *U.S. Public*, pg. 1019
ALEX & CO.—See Sun Capital Partners, Inc.; *U.S. Private*, pg. 3861
ALEX ENERGY, INC.—See Alpha Natural Resources, Inc.; *U.S. Private*, pg. 199
ALEX E. PARIS CONTRACTING CO., INC.; *U.S. Private*, pg. 162
ALEX FERT CO. - S.A.E.—See Egyptian Kuwaiti Holding; *Int'l*, pg. 2327
ALEX FOOD INC.; *U.S. Private*, pg. 162
ALEX FRASER ASPHALT PTY. LTD.—See Heidelberg Materials AG; *Int'l*, pg. 3308
ALEX FRASER PTY LIMITED - ASPHALT - LAVERTON PLANT—See Heidelberg Materials AG; *Int'l*, pg. 3311
ALEX FRASER PTY LIMITED—See Heidelberg Materials AG; *Int'l*, pg. 3311
ALEXIAN BROTHERS HEALTH SYSTEM, INC.—See Ascension Health Alliance; *U.S. Private*, pg. 346
ALEXION ILAC TICARET LIMITED SIRKETI—See AstraZeneca PLC; *Int'l*, pg. 659
ALEXION PHARMACEUTICALS AUSTRALASIA PTY LTD—See AstraZeneca PLC; *Int'l*, pg. 659
ALEXION PHARMACEUTICALS, INC.—See AstraZeneca PLC; *Int'l*, pg. 659
ALEXION PHARMACEUTICALS (SHANGHAI) COMPANY LIMITED—See AstraZeneca PLC; *Int'l*, pg. 659
ALEXION PHARMA GMBH—See AstraZeneca PLC; *Int'l*, pg. 659
ALEXION PHARMA INTERNATIONAL OPERATIONS UNLIMITED COMPANY—See AstraZeneca PLC; *Int'l*, pg. 659
ALEXION PHARMA INTERNATIONAL SARL—See AstraZeneca PLC; *Int'l*, pg. 659
ALEXION PHARMA INTERNATIONAL TRADING—See AstraZeneca PLC; *Int'l*, pg. 659
ALEXION PHARMA MIDDLE EAST FZ-LLC—See AstraZeneca PLC; *Int'l*, pg. 659
ALEXION PHARMA UK—See AstraZeneca PLC; *Int'l*, pg. 659
ALEXION SERVICES LATIN AMERICA, INC.—See AstraZeneca PLC; *Int'l*, pg. 659
ALEXIS BITTAR, LLC—See Brooks Brothers, Inc.; *U.S. Private*, pg. 664
ALEXIS MANUFACTURING CO.—See Roll & Hill, LLC; *U.S. Private*, pg. 3474
ALEXI TRAINING & CONSULTING COMPANY LIMITED—See Do Day Dream PCL; *Int'l*, pg. 2152
ALEXIUM INC—See Alexium International Group Limited; *Int'l*, pg. 307
ALEXIUM INTERNATIONAL GROUP LIMITED; *Int'l*, pg. 307
ALEX LEE, INC.; *U.S. Private*, pg. 162
ALEX MACINTYRE & ASSOCIATES LTD.; *Int'l*, pg. 306
ALEX - MECHKOV OOD—See Doppelmayr Group; *Int'l*, pg. 2174
ALEX MONTGOMERY MT. WASHINGTON; *U.S. Private*, pg. 163
ALEX N SILL COMPANY—See CNL Strategic Capital Management LLC; *U.S. Private*, pg. 952
ALEXON INTERNATIONAL LIMITED—See Sun Capital Partners, Inc.; *U.S. Private*, pg. 3861
ALEX PANLINE USA, INC.—See Propel Equity Partners, LLC; *U.S. Private*, pg. 3284
ALEX PHARM LTD.; *Int'l*, pg. 306
ALEX R. MASSON INC.; *U.S. Private*, pg. 163
ALEX'S LEMONADE STAND FOUNDATION FOR CHILDHOOD CANCER; *U.S. Private*, pg. 163
ALEXSSA ENTERPRISES LTD.—See River Run Computers, Inc.; *U.S. Private*, pg. 3444

ALEX WHITE & CO (PTY) LTD—See Tadbik Group; *Int'l*, pg. 7404
ALEX WILSON COLDSTREAM LTD.; *Int'l*, pg. 306
ALEXX, INC.; *U.S. Private*, pg. 164
ALEXZA PHARMACEUTICALS, INC.—See Grupo Ferrer Internacional, S.A.; *Int'l*, pg. 3129
AL EZZ DEKHEILA STEEL COMPANY ALEXANDRIA SAE—See Ezz Steel Co. S.A.E.; *Int'l*, pg. 2594
AL EZZ DEKHEILA STEEL CO.—See Ezz Steel Co. S.A.E.; *Int'l*, pg. 2594
AL EZZ FLAT STEEL COMPANY—See Ezz Steel Co. S.A.E.; *Int'l*, pg. 2594
AL EZZ ROLLING MILLS COMPANY—See Ezz Steel Co. S.A.E.; *Int'l*, pg. 2594
ALFA ACCIAI SPA; *Int'l*, pg. 307
ALFA AESAR (CHINA) CHEMICAL CO. LTD.—See Thermo Fisher Scientific Inc.; *U.S. Public*, pg. 2145
ALFA AGENCY—See Alfa Corporation; *U.S. Private*, pg. 164
ALFA AGRICULTURAL SUPPLIES S.A.—See China National Chemical Corporation; *Int'l*, pg. 1526
ALFA ALLIANCE INSURANCE CORP.—See Alfa Corporation; *U.S. Private*, pg. 164
ALFA-BANK JSC—See ABH Holdings S.A.; *Int'l*, pg. 60
ALFA BETA ROTO S.A.—See UniCredit S.p.A.; *Int'l*, pg. 8039
ALFA BETA ROTO S.A.—See UniCredit S.p.A.; *Int'l*, pg. 8039
ALFA-BETA VASSILOPOULOS S.A.—See Koninklijke Ahold Delhaize N.V.; *Int'l*, pg. 4260
ALFABET, INC.; *U.S. Private*, pg. 164
ALFABET S.A.S.—See evoke plc; *Int'l*, pg. 2572
ALFABET SAUDI ARABIA LLC—See Silver Lake Group, LLC; *U.S. Private*, pg. 3658
ALFAB JONKOPING 5 AB—See Alecta pensionsforsakring, omsesidigt; *Int'l*, pg. 305
ALFAB VALUTAN 13 AB—See Alecta pensionsforsakring, omsesidigt; *Int'l*, pg. 305
ALFA CAPITAL LLC—See Alfa Group; *Int'l*, pg. 308
ALFACO POLSKA SP.Z.O.O.—See Carel Industries S.p.A.; *Int'l*, pg. 1324
ALFA CORPORATION; *U.S. Private*, pg. 164
ALFA CORPORATIVO, S.A. DE C.V.—See ALFA, S.A.B. de C.V.; *Int'l*, pg. 313
ALFA CTP SYSTEMS, INC.—See IPA Systems Ltd.; *Int'l*, pg. 3796
ALFA CTP SYSTEMS, INC.—See IPA Systems Ltd.; *Int'l*, pg. 3796
AL FADL BRC (SAUDIA) LTD.—See The Al Fadl Group of Companies; *Int'l*, pg. 7612
THE AL FADL GROUP OF COMPANIES; *Int'l*, pg. 7612
ALFA FINANCE HOLDING AD; *Int'l*, pg. 307
ALFA FINANCIAL CORPORATION—See Alfa Corporation; *U.S. Private*, pg. 164
ALFA FINANCIAL SOFTWARE HOLDINGS PLC; *Int'l*, pg. 308
ALFA FINANCIAL SOFTWARE LIMITED—See Alfa Financial Software Holdings PLC; *Int'l*, pg. 308
ALFA-GIROD KFT.—See Signaux Girod S.A.; *Int'l*, pg. 6910
ALFAGOMMA AMERICA INC.—See Alfagomma S.p.A.; *Int'l*, pg. 315
ALFAGOMMA AUSTRALIA PTY LTD—See Alfagomma S.p.A.; *Int'l*, pg. 315
ALFAGOMMA CANADA, INC.—See Alfagomma S.p.A.; *Int'l*, pg. 315
ALFAGOMMA DO BRASIL LTDA—See Alfagomma S.p.A.; *Int'l*, pg. 315
ALFAGOMMA FRACNE PARIS IDF—See Alfagomma S.p.A.; *Int'l*, pg. 315
ALFAGOMMA GERMANY GMBH—See Alfagomma S.p.A.; *Int'l*, pg. 315
ALFAGOMMA HELLAS S.A.—See Alfagomma S.p.A.; *Int'l*, pg. 315
ALFAGOMMA INTERNATIONAL BV—See Alfagomma S.p.A.; *Int'l*, pg. 315
ALFAGOMMA KOREA CO. LTD.—See Alfagomma S.p.A.; *Int'l*, pg. 315
ALFAGOMMA (NINGBO) CO LTD—See Alfagomma S.p.A.; *Int'l*, pg. 315
ALFAGOMMA PACIFIC PTE LTD—See Alfagomma S.p.A.; *Int'l*, pg. 315
ALFAGOMMA SOUTH AFRICA PTY LTD—See Alfagomma S.p.A.; *Int'l*, pg. 315
ALFAGOMMA S.P.A.; *Int'l*, pg. 315
ALFAGOMMA UK LTD.—See Alfagomma S.p.A.; *Int'l*, pg. 315
ALFA GROUP; *Int'l*, pg. 308
AL FAHED VALUABLE ASSETS IN TRANSIT UNITED CO. LTD.—See Bank of Khartoum; *Int'l*, pg. 845
AL FAHIM GROUP; *Int'l*, pg. 277
ALFA ICA (INDIA) LTD.; *Int'l*, pg. 308
ALFA INSURANCE CORP.—See Alfa Corporation; *U.S. Private*, pg. 164
AL FAISALIAH ELECTRONICS SERVICES—See Al Faisaliah Group; *Int'l*, pg. 277
AL FAISALIAH GROUP; *Int'l*, pg. 277
AL FAISALIAH HOTEL—See Chow Tai Fook Enterprises Limited; *Int'l*, pg. 1585

AL FAISALIAH MEDICAL SYSTEMS—See Al Faisaliah Group; *Int'l*, pg. 277
AL-FAISAL STEEL PRODUCTS COMPANY—See Al-Tuwairqi Group; *Int'l*, pg. 289
AL FAJAR AL ALAMIA COMPANY SAOG; *Int'l*, pg. 277
AL FAJR COFFEE ROASTING & PROCESSING COMPANY—See MAS Economic Group; *Int'l*, pg. 4718
AL FAKHER FOR TOBACCO TRADING & AGENCIES LLC—See Al-Eqbal Investment Co. (PLC); *Int'l*, pg. 285
ALFALAH GHP INVESTMENT MANAGEMENT LIMITED—See Abu Dhabi Group; *Int'l*, pg. 71
ALFALAH INSURANCE COMPANY LIMITED—See Abu Dhabi Group; *Int'l*, pg. 71
ALFALAH SECURITIES (PVT.) LTD.—See Abu Dhabi Group; *Int'l*, pg. 71
ALFA LAVAL AALBORG A/S—See Alfa Laval AB; *Int'l*, pg. 308
ALFA LAVAL AALBORG BV—See Alfa Laval AB; *Int'l*, pg. 308
ALFA LAVAL AALBORG (FPS) PTE LTD—See Alfa Laval AB; *Int'l*, pg. 308
ALFA LAVAL AALBORG INC.—See Alfa Laval AB; *Int'l*, pg. 309
ALFA LAVAL AALBORG INDUSTRIA E COMERCIO LTDA.—See Alfa Laval AB; *Int'l*, pg. 308
ALFA LAVAL AALBORG LTD.—See Alfa Laval AB; *Int'l*, pg. 308
ALFA LAVAL AALBORG NIJMEGEN BV—See Alfa Laval AB; *Int'l*, pg. 308
ALFA LAVAL AALBORG OY—See Alfa Laval AB; *Int'l*, pg. 308
ALFA LAVAL AALBORG PTY LTD—See Alfa Laval AB; *Int'l*, pg. 309
ALFA LAVAL AB; *Int'l*, pg. 308
ALFA LAVAL AEBE—See Alfa Laval AB; *Int'l*, pg. 308
ALFA LAVAL A/O—See Alfa Laval AB; *Int'l*, pg. 308
ALFA LAVAL AUSTRALIA PTY LTD—See Alfa Laval AB; *Int'l*, pg. 309
ALFA-LAVAL BENELUX B.V.—See Alfa Laval AB; *Int'l*, pg. 311
ALFA-LAVAL BENELUX N.V.—See Alfa Laval AB; *Int'l*, pg. 311
ALFA LAVAL (CHINA) LTD.—See Alfa Laval AB; *Int'l*, pg. 308
ALFA LAVAL COPENHAGEN A/S—See Alfa Laval AB; *Int'l*, pg. 309
ALFA LAVAL CORPORATE AB—See Alfa Laval AB; *Int'l*, pg. 309
ALFA LAVAL DIS TICARET LTD STI—See Alfa Laval AB; *Int'l*, pg. 309
ALFA LAVAL D.O.O.—See Alfa Laval AB; *Int'l*, pg. 312
ALFA LAVAL EOOD—See Alfa Laval AB; *Int'l*, pg. 309
ALFA LAVAL EUROPE AB—See Alfa Laval AB; *Int'l*, pg. 309
ALFA LAVAL FINANCE CO LTD—See Alfa Laval AB; *Int'l*, pg. 310
ALFA LAVAL FLOW EQUIPMENT (KUNSHAN) CO LTD—See Alfa Laval AB; *Int'l*, pg. 308
ALFA LAVAL FLOW INC.—See Alfa Laval AB; *Int'l*, pg. 309
ALFA LAVAL FRANCE SAS—See Alfa Laval AB; *Int'l*, pg. 309
ALFA LAVAL GRONINGEN BV—See Alfa Laval AB; *Int'l*, pg. 309
ALFA LAVAL HAIPHONG CO. LTD—See Alfa Laval AB; *Int'l*, pg. 308
ALFA LAVAL HES SA—See Alfa Laval AB; *Int'l*, pg. 309
ALFA LAVAL HOLDING AB—See Alfa Laval AB; *Int'l*, pg. 308
ALFA LAVAL HOLDING BV—See Alfa Laval AB; *Int'l*, pg. 309
ALFA LAVAL HOLDING GMBH—See Alfa Laval AB; *Int'l*, pg. 309
ALFA LAVAL HOLDINGS LTD—See Alfa Laval AB; *Int'l*, pg. 310
ALFA LAVAL IBERIA S.A.—See Alfa Laval AB; *Int'l*, pg. 310
ALFA LAVAL INC. - KENOSHA—See Alfa Laval AB; *Int'l*, pg. 309
ALFA LAVAL INC. - PRODUCT CENTER—See Alfa Laval AB; *Int'l*, pg. 309
ALFA LAVAL INC.—See Alfa Laval AB; *Int'l*, pg. 309
ALFA-LAVAL INC.—See Alfa Laval AB; *Int'l*, pg. 310
ALFA LAVAL, INC.—See Alfa Laval AB; *Int'l*, pg. 309
ALFA LAVAL (INDIA) LTD.—See Alfa Laval AB; *Int'l*, pg. 308
ALFA-LAVAL IRAN CO.—See Alfa Laval AB; *Int'l*, pg. 311
ALFA LAVAL ITALY S.R.L.—See Alfa Laval AB; *Int'l*, pg. 312
ALFA LAVAL (JIANGYIN) MANUFACTURING CO LTD—See Alfa Laval AB; *Int'l*, pg. 308
ALFA LAVAL KFT.—See Alfa Laval AB; *Int'l*, pg. 310
ALFA LAVAL K.K.—See Alfa Laval AB; *Int'l*, pg. 310
ALFA LAVAL KOLDING A/S—See Alfa Laval AB; *Int'l*, pg. 310
ALFA LAVAL KOREA LTD.—See Alfa Laval AB; *Int'l*, pg. 310
ALFA LAVAL KRAKOW SP.Z.O.O.—See Alfa Laval AB; *Int'l*, pg. 310

ALFA LAVAL AB

ALFA LAVAL (KUNSHAN) MANUFACTURING CO LTD—See Alfa Laval AB; *Int'l*, pg. 308
ALFA LAVAL LIMITED—See Alfa Laval AB; *Int'l*, pg. 310
ALFA LAVAL LIMITED—See Alfa Laval AB; *Int'l*, pg. 310
ALFA LAVAL LKM A/S—See Alfa Laval AB; *Int'l*, pg. 310
ALFA LAVAL LTDA—See Alfa Laval AB; *Int'l*, pg. 310
ALFA LAVAL LTD.—See Alfa Laval AB; *Int'l*, pg. 310
ALFA LAVAL LTD.—See Alfa Laval AB; *Int'l*, pg. 310
ALFA LAVAL LUND AB—See Alfa Laval AB; *Int'l*, pg. 310
ALFA LAVAL MAKINE SANAYII VE TICARET LTD STI—See Alfa Laval AB; *Int'l*, pg. 310
ALFA-LAVAL (MALAYSIA) SDN BHD—See Alfa Laval AB; *Int'l*, pg. 311
ALFA LAVAL MIDDLE EAST LTD—See Alfa Laval AB; *Int'l*, pg. 310
ALFA-LAVAL MID EUROPE AG—See Alfa Laval AB; *Int'l*, pg. 309
ALFA LAVAL MID EUROPE GMBH—See Alfa Laval AB; *Int'l*, pg. 309
ALFA LAVAL MID EUROPE GMBH—See Alfa Laval AB; *Int'l*, pg. 309
ALFA LAVAL MOATTI SAS—See Alfa Laval AB; *Int'l*, pg. 309
ALFA LAVAL NAKSKOV A/S—See Alfa Laval AB; *Int'l*, pg. 310
ALFA LAVAL NEDERLAND BV—See Alfa Laval AB; *Int'l*, pg. 310
ALFA LAVAL NEW ZEALAND LTD.—See Alfa Laval AB; *Int'l*, pg. 310
ALFA LAVAL NEW ZEELAND PTY. LTD.—See Alfa Laval AB; *Int'l*, pg. 312
ALFA LAVAL NIAGARA INC.—See Alfa Laval AB; *Int'l*, pg. 312
ALFA LAVAL NIJMEGEN B.V.—See Alfa Laval AB; *Int'l*, pg. 312
ALFA LAVAL NORDIC A/S—See Alfa Laval AB; *Int'l*, pg. 310
ALFA LAVAL NORDICK AB—See Alfa Laval AB; *Int'l*, pg. 310
ALFA LAVAL, NV—See Alfa Laval AB; *Int'l*, pg. 310
ALFA-LAVAL (N.Z.) LTD.—See Alfa Laval AB; *Int'l*, pg. 311
ALFA LAVAL OLMI SPA—See Alfa Laval AB; *Int'l*, pg. 310
ALFA LAVAL OY—See Alfa Laval AB; *Int'l*, pg. 310
ALFA LAVAL PACKINOX—See Alfa Laval AB; *Int'l*, pg. 310
ALFA LAVAL PARMA SRL—See Alfa Laval AB; *Int'l*, pg. 311
ALFA LAVAL PHILIPPINES, INC.—See Alfa Laval AB; *Int'l*, pg. 311
ALFA LAVAL POLSKA SP. ZOO—See Alfa Laval AB; *Int'l*, pg. 311
ALFA LAVAL POLSKA SP. ZOO—See Alfa Laval AB; *Int'l*, pg. 311
ALFA LAVAL (PORTUGAL) LDA—See Alfa Laval AB; *Int'l*, pg. 308
ALFA LAVAL (PTY) LTD—See Alfa Laval AB; *Int'l*, pg. 308
ALFA LAVAL (QINGDAO) CO. LTD—See Alfa Laval AB; *Int'l*, pg. 308
ALFA LAVAL S.A.C.I.—See Alfa Laval AB; *Int'l*, pg. 311
ALFA LAVAL S.A. DE C.V.—See Alfa Laval AB; *Int'l*, pg. 310
ALFA LAVAL S.A.—See Alfa Laval AB; *Int'l*, pg. 311
ALFA LAVAL S.A.—See Alfa Laval AB; *Int'l*, pg. 310
ALFA LAVAL S.A.—See Alfa Laval AB; *Int'l*, pg. 311
ALFA LAVAL S.A.S—See Alfa Laval AB; *Int'l*, pg. 311
ALFA LAVAL (SHANGHAI) TECHNOLOGIES CO LTD—See Alfa Laval AB; *Int'l*, pg. 308
ALFA LAVAL SHARPLES—See Alfa Laval AB; *Int'l*, pg. 309
ALFA LAVAL SIA—See Alfa Laval AB; *Int'l*, pg. 311
ALFA LAVAL SIA—See Alfa Laval AB; *Int'l*, pg. 311
ALFA LAVAL SINGAPORE PTE. LTD.—See Alfa Laval AB; *Int'l*, pg. 311
ALFA LAVAL SLOVAKIA SPOL, S.R.O.—See Alfa Laval AB; *Int'l*, pg. 311
ALFA LAVAL SOUTH EAST EUROPE LTD.—See Alfa Laval AB; *Int'l*, pg. 311
ALFA LAVAL S.P.A.—See Alfa Laval AB; *Int'l*, pg. 311
ALFA LAVAL SPIRAL SAS—See Alfa Laval AB; *Int'l*, pg. 309
ALFA LAVAL SPOL S.R.O.—See Alfa Laval AB; *Int'l*, pg. 311
ALFA LAVAL S.R.L.—See Alfa Laval AB; *Int'l*, pg. 311
ALFA LAVAL (TAICANG) TECHNOLOGIES CO. LTD.—See Alfa Laval AB; *Int'l*, pg. 308
ALFA LAVAL, TAIWAN—See Alfa Laval AB; *Int'l*, pg. 311
ALFA LAVAL TANK EQUIPMENT A/S—See Alfa Laval AB; *Int'l*, pg. 311
ALFA LAVAL TECHNOLOGIES AB—See Alfa Laval AB; *Int'l*, pg. 312
ALFA LAVAL TECHNOLOGIES EQUIPMENT AND SERVICE SOLUTIONS LLC—See Alfa Laval AB; *Int'l*, pg. 312
ALFA LAVAL (THAILAND) LTD.—See Alfa Laval AB; *Int'l*, pg. 308
ALFA LAVAL THERMAL A/S—See Alfa Laval AB; *Int'l*, pg. 311
ALFA LAVAL TREASURY INTERNATIONAL AB—See Alfa Laval AB; *Int'l*, pg. 311
ALFA LAVAL TUMBA AB—See Alfa Laval AB; *Int'l*, pg. 311
ALFA LAVAL UKRAINE—See Alfa Laval AB; *Int'l*, pg. 311

ALFA LAVAL USA INC.—See Alfa Laval AB; *Int'l*, pg. 309
ALFA LAVAL US HOLDING INC.—See Alfa Laval AB; *Int'l*, pg. 309
ALFA LAVAL VANTAA OY—See Alfa Laval AB; *Int'l*, pg. 310
ALFA LAVAL VENEZOLANA S.A.—See Alfa Laval AB; *Int'l*, pg. 311
ALFA LAVAL VICARB SAS—See Alfa Laval AB; *Int'l*, pg. 309
ALFA LAVAL VIETNAM LLC—See Alfa Laval AB; *Int'l*, pg. 311
ALFA LIFE INSURANCE CORPORATION—See Alfa Corporation; *U.S. Private*, pg. 164
ALFALIGHT, INC.—See Gooch & Housego PLC; *Int'l*, pg. 3038
AL FALTAS GROUP FOR CARBONATE & COLORING MATERIAL CO.—See Omya (Schweiz) AG; *Int'l*, pg. 5570
ALFAM HOLDING N.V.—See ABN AMRO Group N.V.; *Int'l*, pg. 65
ALFANAR TRADING CO.; *Int'l*, pg. 315
ALFA NETWORK INC—See Accton Technology Corporation; *Int'l*, pg. 93
ALFANO MOTORCARS, INC.; *U.S. Private*, pg. 164
ALFA PAINTS B.V.—See LKQ Corporation; *U.S. Public*, pg. 1333
ALFA-PLAM A.D.; *Int'l*, pg. 314
ALFAQUEST BV—See IPA Systems Ltd.; *Int'l*, pg. 3796
ALFAQUEST, INC.—See IPA Systems Ltd.; *Int'l*, pg. 3796
AL FARAZDAQ COMPANY W.L.L.—See Aamal Company Q.S.C.; *Int'l*, pg. 36
ALFA REALTY, INC.—See Alfa Corporation; *U.S. Private*, pg. 164
AL-FARIS NATIONAL COMPANY FOR INVESTMENT & EXPORT PLC; *Int'l*, pg. 285
ALFARO BRAKES S.L.U.—See ZF Friedrichshafen AG; *Int'l*, pg. 8640
ALFA ROMEO - FCA ITALY S.P.A.—See Stellantis N.V.; *Int'l*, pg. 7197
ALFA ROMEO INC.—See Stellantis N.V.; *Int'l*, pg. 7198
ALFA ROMEO U.S.A. S.P.A.—See Stellantis N.V.; *Int'l*, pg. 7197
ALFA, S.A.B. DE C.V.; *Int'l*, pg. 312
ALFASAP S.R.L.—See Sesa S.p.A.; *Int'l*, pg. 6728
ALFASIGMA S.P.A.; *Int'l*, pg. 315
ALFA SKO AS—See Katalysator S.A.; *Int'l*, pg. 4089
ALFA SOLUTIONS S.P.A.—See Iren S.p.A.; *Int'l*, pg. 3807
ALFA; *Int'l*, pg. 307
ALFA S.R.L.—See Currys plc; *Int'l*, pg. 1879
ALFASTRAKHOVANIE PLC; *Int'l*, pg. 315
AL FATH TRADING CO. LTD.; *Int'l*, pg. 277
ALFA TRANSFORMERS LTD.; *Int'l*, pg. 312
ALFA VALVOLE S.R.L.—See Interpump Group S.p.A.; *Int'l*, pg. 3755
ALFAVISION OVERSEAS (INDIA) LIMITED; *Int'l*, pg. 315
ALFA WASSERMANN (BEIJING) MARKET RESEARCH & MANAGEMENT CO. LTD.—See Alfa-Wassermann S.p.A.; *Int'l*, pg. 314
ALFA-WASSERMANN B.V.—See Alfa-Wassermann S.p.A.; *Int'l*, pg. 314
ALFA WASSERMANN CZECH S. R. O.—See Alfa-Wassermann S.p.A.; *Int'l*, pg. 314
ALFA WASSERMANN INC.—See Alfa-Wassermann S.p.A.; *Int'l*, pg. 314
ALFA WASSERMANN MAGHREB S.A.R.L.—See Alfa-Wassermann S.p.A.; *Int'l*, pg. 314
ALFA WASSERMANN PHARMA SAS—See Alfa-Wassermann S.p.A.; *Int'l*, pg. 314
ALFA WASSERMANN POLSKA SP.Z O.O.—See Alfa-Wassermann S.p.A.; *Int'l*, pg. 314
ALFA WASSERMANN PRODUTOS FARMACEUTICOS, LDA.—See Alfa-Wassermann S.p.A.; *Int'l*, pg. 314
ALFA WASSERMANN S.A. DE C.V.—See Alfa-Wassermann S.p.A.; *Int'l*, pg. 314
ALFA WASSERMANN S.P.A. - ALANNO MANUFACTURING DIVISION—See Alfa-Wassermann S.p.A.; *Int'l*, pg. 314
ALFA WASSERMANN S.P.A. - MILANO INTERNATIONAL DIVISION—See Alfa-Wassermann S.p.A.; *Int'l*, pg. 314
ALFA-WASSERMANN S.P.A.; *Int'l*, pg. 314
ALFA WASSERMANN SRL—See Alfa-Wassermann S.p.A.; *Int'l*, pg. 314
ALFA WASSERMANN TUNISIE SARL—See Alfa-Wassermann S.p.A.; *Int'l*, pg. 314
ALFA WOOD BULGARIA S.A.; *Int'l*, pg. 312
ALFAX WHOLESALE FURNITURE INC.—See Franz Haniel & Cie. GmbH; *Int'l*, pg. 2763
ALFE HEAT TREATING INC.—See Aalberts N.V.; *Int'l*, pg. 35
ALFEMMINILE.COM S.R.L.—See Television Francaise 1 S.A.; *Int'l*, pg. 7543
ALFEN BELGIE BV—See Alfen N.V.; *Int'l*, pg. 315
ALFEN ELKAMO OY AB—See Alfen N.V.; *Int'l*, pg. 315
ALFEN N.V.; *Int'l*, pg. 315
ALFESCA HF; *Int'l*, pg. 315
ALF HELLAND OLSEN—See REHAU Verwaltungszentrale AG; *Int'l*, pg. 6255
ALFIGEN S.A.—See Otto GmbH & Co. KG; *Int'l*, pg. 5663
ALFI, INC.; *U.S. Public*, pg. 75

CORPORATE AFFILIATIONS

A-L FINANCIAL CORPORATION; *U.S. Private*, pg. 22
ALF INC.—See Toho Holdings Co., Ltd.; *Int'l*, pg. 7776
ALFIO BARDOLLA TRAINING GROUP SPA; *Int'l*, pg. 315
AL FIRDOUS HOLDINGS (P.J.S.C.); *Int'l*, pg. 277
AL FOAH COMPANY LLC—See Agthia Group PJSC; *Int'l*, pg. 221
ALFONS HAAR INCORPORATED—See Alfons Haar Maschinenbau GmbH & Co. KG; *Int'l*, pg. 315
ALFONS HAAR LIMITED—See Alfons Haar Maschinenbau GmbH & Co. KG; *Int'l*, pg. 315
ALFONS HAAR MASCHINENBAU GMBH & CO. KG; *Int'l*, pg. 315
ALFONS HAAR SVENSKA AB—See Alfons Haar Maschinenbau GmbH & Co. KG; *Int'l*, pg. 315
ALFONSINO S.P.A.; *Int'l*, pg. 316
ALFONSO ARCHITECTS, INC. - ITALY OFFICE—See Alfonso Architects, Inc.; *U.S. Private*, pg. 165
ALFONSO ARCHITECTS, INC.; *U.S. Private*, pg. 165
ALFONSO GALLARDO S.A.; *Int'l*, pg. 316
ALFORD BURTON AND COMPANY LIMITED—See Brown & Brown, Inc.; *U.S. Public*, pg. 396
ALFORD MOTORS INC.; *U.S. Private*, pg. 165
ALFORD SAFETY SERVICES, INC.—See Lundbeckfonden; *Int'l*, pg. 4580
ALFORD SERVICES, INC—See Lundbeckfonden; *Int'l*, pg. 4580
ALFOREX SEEDS LLC—See Corteva, Inc.; *U.S. Public*, pg. 580
ALFOREX SEEDS LLC—See Corteva, Inc.; *U.S. Public*, pg. 580
AL FORSAN TADBEER CENTER LLC—See Alpha Dhabi Holding PJSC; *Int'l*, pg. 367
ALFOT TECHNOLOGIES CO., LTD.; *Int'l*, pg. 316
ALFRA RUSSLAND OVERTIME JSC—See Alfred Raith GmbH; *Int'l*, pg. 317
ALFRA UK, LTD.—See Alfred Raith GmbH; *Int'l*, pg. 317
ALFRA USA, LLC—See Alfred Raith GmbH; *Int'l*, pg. 317
ALFREBRO, LLC—See Archer-Daniels-Midland Company; *U.S. Public*, pg. 183
ALFRED A. KNOPF, INC.—See Bertelsmann SE & Co. KGaA; *Int'l*, pg. 990
ALFRED ANGELO, INC.; *U.S. Private*, pg. 165
ALFRED BENESCH & COMPANY - MILWAUKEE—See Alfred Benesch & Company; *U.S. Private*, pg. 165
ALFRED BENESCH & COMPANY—See Alfred Benesch & Company; *U.S. Private*, pg. 165
ALFRED BENESCH & COMPANY—See Alfred Benesch & Company; *U.S. Private*, pg. 165
ALFRED BENESCH & COMPANY—See Alfred Benesch & Company; *U.S. Private*, pg. 165
ALFRED BENESCH & COMPANY—See Alfred Benesch & Company; *U.S. Private*, pg. 165
ALFRED BENESCH & COMPANY—See Alfred Benesch & Company; *U.S. Private*, pg. 165
ALFRED BENESCH & COMPANY—See Alfred Benesch & Company; *U.S. Private*, pg. 165
ALFRED BENESCH & COMPANY—See Alfred Benesch & Company; *U.S. Private*, pg. 165
ALFRED BENESCH & COMPANY—See Alfred Benesch & Company; *U.S. Private*, pg. 165
ALFRED BENESCH & COMPANY—See Alfred Benesch & Company; *U.S. Private*, pg. 165
ALFRED BENESCH & COMPANY—See Alfred Benesch & Company; *U.S. Private*, pg. 165
ALFRED BENESCH & COMPANY—See Alfred Benesch & Company; *U.S. Private*, pg. 165
ALFRED BENESCH & COMPANY; *U.S. Private*, pg. 165
ALFRED BENESCH & COMPANY—See Alfred Benesch & Company; *U.S. Private*, pg. 165
ALFRED BENESCH & COMPANY—See Alfred Benesch & Company; *U.S. Private*, pg. 165
ALFRED BENESCH & COMPANY—See Alfred Benesch & Company; *U.S. Private*, pg. 165
ALFRED BENESCH & COMPANY—See Alfred Benesch & Company; *U.S. Private*, pg. 165
ALFRED BENESCH & COMPANY—See Alfred Benesch & Company; *U.S. Private*, pg. 165
ALFRED BENESCH & COMPANY—See Alfred Benesch & Company; *U.S. Private*, pg. 165
ALFRED BENESCH & COMPANY—See Alfred Benesch & Company; *U.S. Private*, pg. 165
ALFRED BENESCH & COMPANY—See Alfred Benesch & Company; *U.S. Private*, pg. 165
ALFRED BERG ASSET MANAGEMENT AB—See BNP Paribas SA; *Int'l*, pg. 1082
ALFRED BERG FONDER AB—See BNP Paribas SA; *Int'l*, pg. 1082
ALFRED BERG FORVALTNING AS—See BNP Paribas SA; *Int'l*, pg. 1082
ALFRED BERG KAPITALFORVALTNING AB—See BNP Paribas SA; *Int'l*, pg. 1082
ALFRED BERG KAPITALFORVALTNING AS—See BNP Paribas SA; *Int'l*, pg. 1082
ALFRED BERG KAPITALFORVALTNING FINLAND AB—See BNP Paribas SA; *Int'l*, pg. 1082
ALFRED CHEYNE ENGINEERING LIMITED—See Ashtead Technology Holdings Plc; *Int'l*, pg. 609
ALFRED CONHAGEN INCORPORATED; *U.S. Private*, pg. 165

ALFRED DUNHILL LIMITED—See Compagnie Financiere Richemont S.A.; *Int'l*, pg. 1740
ALFRED FUELING SYSTEMS INC.—See Dover Corporation; *U.S. Public*, pg. 678
ALFRED HERBERT (INDIA) LTD.; *Int'l*, pg. 316
ALFRED HERRHAUSEN GESELLSCHAFT - DAS INTERNATIONALE FORUM DER DEUTSCHEN BANK - MBH—See Deutsche Bank Aktiengesellschaft; *Int'l*, pg. 2055
ALFRED KARCHER GES.M.B.H.—See Alfred Karcher GmbH & Co. KG; *Int'l*, pg. 316
ALFRED KARCHER GMBH & CO. KG; *Int'l*, pg. 316
ALFRED KARCHER VERTRIEBS-GMBH—See Alfred Karcher GmbH & Co. KG; *Int'l*, pg. 316
ALFRED MAINZER, INC.—See CBC Group; *U.S. Private*, pg. 797
ALFRED MATTHEWS, INC.; *U.S. Private*, pg. 165
ALFRED MUSIC CO. (UK) LTD.—See Alfred Publishing Company Inc.; *U.S. Private*, pg. 166
ALFRED MUSIC GMBH—See Alfred Publishing Company Inc.; *U.S. Private*, pg. 166
ALFRED MUSIC (S) PTE LTD—See Alfred Publishing Company Inc.; *U.S. Private*, pg. 166
ALFRED NICKLES BAKERY, INC. - LIMA—See Alfred Nickles Bakery, Inc.; *U.S. Private*, pg. 165
ALFRED NICKLES BAKERY, INC.; *U.S. Private*, pg. 165
ALFREDO'S FOREIGN CARS INC.; *U.S. Private*, pg. 166
ALFRED PUBLISHING COMPANY INC.; *U.S. Private*, pg. 165
ALFRED RAITH GMBH; *Int'l*, pg. 317
ALFRED SCHELLENBERG GMBH; *Int'l*, pg. 317
ALFRED STEIN INC.; *U.S. Private*, pg. 166
ALFRED TEVES BRAKE SYSTEMS (PTY) LTD.—See Metair Investments Limited; *Int'l*, pg. 4844
ALFRED THOMAS CONSULTANCY LIMITED—See Restore plc; *Int'l*, pg. 6304
ALFRED TRONSER GMBH; *Int'l*, pg. 317
ALFRED WILLIAMS & COMPANY; *U.S. Private*, pg. 166
ALFRESA CORPORATION—See Alfresa Holdings Corporation; *Int'l*, pg. 317
ALFRESA FINE CHEMICAL CORPORATION—See Alfresa Holdings Corporation; *Int'l*, pg. 317
ALFRESA HEALTHCARE CORPORATION—See Alfresa Holdings Corporation; *Int'l*, pg. 317
ALFRESA HOLDINGS CORPORATION; *Int'l*, pg. 317
ALFRESA MEDICAL SERVICE CORPORATION—See Alfresa Holdings Corporation; *Int'l*, pg. 317
ALFRESA NIKKEN SANGYO CORPORATION—See Alfresa Holdings Corporation; *Int'l*, pg. 317
ALFRESA PHARMA CORPORATION—See Alfresa Holdings Corporation; *Int'l*, pg. 317
ALFRESA SHINOHARA CHEMICALS CORPORATION—See Alfresa Holdings Corporation; *Int'l*, pg. 317
ALFRESA SYSTEM CORPORATION—See Alfresa Holdings Corporation; *Int'l*, pg. 317
ALFRESCO SOFTWARE, INC.—See Thoma Bravo, L.P.; *U.S. Private*, pg. 4148
ALFRESCO SOFTWARE LIMITED—See Thoma Bravo, L.P.; *U.S. Private*, pg. 4148
ALFTA KVALITETSINDUSTRI AB—See Storskogen Group AB; *Int'l*, pg. 7227
AL FUJAIRAH NATIONAL INSURANCE COMPANY (P.S.C.); *Int'l*, pg. 277
AL-FUTTAIM ACE COMPANY L.L.C.—See Al-Futtaim Private Company LLC; *Int'l*, pg. 285
AL-FUTTAIM AUTO & MACHINERY COMPANY LLC—See AB Volvo; *Int'l*, pg. 42
AL-FUTTAIM AUTOMALL—See Al-Futtaim Private Company LLC; *Int'l*, pg. 285
AL FUTTAIM CARILLION—See Carillion plc; *Int'l*, pg. 1330
AL FUTTAIM CARILLION—See KKR & Co. Inc.; *U.S. Public*, pg. 1239
AL-FUTTAIM ELECTRONICS—See Al-Futtaim Private Company LLC; *Int'l*, pg. 285
AL-FUTTAIM ENGINEERING COMPANY LLC—See Al-Futtaim Private Company LLC; *Int'l*, pg. 285
AL-FUTTAIM GROUP REAL ESTATE—See Al-Futtaim Private Company LLC; *Int'l*, pg. 285
AL-FUTTAIM MOTORS COMPANY LLC—See Al-Futtaim Private Company LLC; *Int'l*, pg. 285
AL-FUTTAIM PANATECH COMPANY LLC—See Al-Futtaim Private Company LLC; *Int'l*, pg. 285
AL-FUTTAIM PRIVATE COMPANY LLC; *Int'l*, pg. 285
AL-FUTTAIM TECHNOLOGIES LLC—See Al-Futtaim Private Company LLC; *Int'l*, pg. 285
AL-FUTTAIM TRADING ENTERPRISES COMPANY L.L.C—See Al-Futtaim Private Company LLC; *Int'l*, pg. 285
AL-FUTTAIM TRAVEL—See Al-Futtaim Private Company LLC; *Int'l*, pg. 285
AL-FUTTAIM WATCHES AND JEWELLERY—See Al-Futtaim Private Company LLC; *Int'l*, pg. 285
ALFUTURO SERVIZI ASSICURATIVI S.R.L.—See Assicurazioni Generali S.p.A.; *Int'l*, pg. 643
ALFY, INC.; *U.S. Private*, pg. 166
ALG ADMIRAL INC; *U.S. Private*, pg. 166
ALGAIDA EDITORES SA—See Vivendi SE; *Int'l*, pg. 8271
ALGAI OOO—See JSC Russian Railways; *Int'l*, pg. 4011

ALGAM DRUGS & CHEMICALS CO., LTD.—See HORIBA Ltd; *Int'l*, pg. 3474
ALGAR S.P.A.—See Fuji Corporation; *Int'l*, pg. 2809
ALGAR TELECOM S.A.; *Int'l*, pg. 317
ALGARVE SHOPPING - CENTRO COMERCIAL, SA—See Frey S.A.; *Int'l*, pg. 2791
ALGA S.P.A.—See VINCI S.A.; *Int'l*, pg. 8231
ALGAS-SDI INTERNATIONAL LLC—See Honeywell International Inc.; *U.S. Public*, pg. 1047
AL GASSIM INVESTMENT HOLDING CO.; *Int'l*, pg. 277
ALGATECHNOLOGIES LTD.—See Societe la Biochimie Appliquee SAS; *Int'l*, pg. 7043
ALGECO SAS—See Brookfield Corporation; *Int'l*, pg. 1176
ALGECO SCOTSMAN, INC.—See TDR Capital LLP; *Int'l*, pg. 7490
ALGECO UK LIMITED—See Brookfield Corporation; *Int'l*, pg. 1176
ALGEMENE AANNEMINGEN VAN LAERE NV—See Ackermans & van Haaren NV; *Int'l*, pg. 104
ALGEMENE LEVENSHERVERZEKERING MAATSCHAPPIJ NV—See Swiss Re Ltd.; *Int'l*, pg. 7371
ALGEMENE SPAARBANK VOOR NEDERLAND ASN N.V.—See SNS Bank N.V.; *Int'l*, pg. 7029
ALGEMENE ZEEUWSE VERZEKERING MAATSCHAPPIJ N.V.—See De Goudse N.V.; *Int'l*, pg. 1995
ALGENOL BIOFUELS GERMANY GMBH—See Algenol Biofuels, Inc.; *U.S. Private*, pg. 166
ALGENOL BIOFUELS INC.; *U.S. Private*, pg. 166
A.L. GEORGE INC.; *U.S. Private*, pg. 26
ALGER ASSOCIATES, INC.; *U.S. Private*, pg. 166
ALGER GROUP HOLDINGS, LLC.—See Alger Associates, Inc.; *U.S. Private*, pg. 166
ALGERIE TELECOM SPA; *Int'l*, pg. 318
ALGER MANUFACTURING, LLC; *U.S. Private*, pg. 166
ALGERNON PHARMACEUTICALS, INC.; *Int'l*, pg. 317
AL-GHANAEM INDUSTRIAL COMPANY—See Fouad Alghanim & Sons Group of Companies; *Int'l*, pg. 2753
ALGHANIM GROUP OF SHIPPING & TRANSPORT W.L.L.—See Fouad Alghanim & Sons Group of Companies; *Int'l*, pg. 2753
ALGHANIM INTERNATIONAL FOR RENTAL EQUIPMENT CO. W.L.L—See Fouad Alghanim & Sons Group of Companies; *Int'l*, pg. 2753
AL GHAZAL TRANSPORT CO.—See Abu Dhabi National Hotels PJSC; *Int'l*, pg. 70
AL-GHAZI TRACTORS LIMITED; *Int'l*, pg. 285
AL GHURAIR CONSTRUCTION - ALUMINUM INDIA PRIVATE LIMITED—See Al Ghurair Investment LLC; *Int'l*, pg. 278
AL GHURAIR CONSTRUCTION ALUMINUM QATAR—See Al Ghurair Investment LLC; *Int'l*, pg. 278
AL GHURAIR CONSTRUCTION - FOUNDATIONS LLC—See Al Ghurair Investment LLC; *Int'l*, pg. 278
AL GHURAIR CONSTRUCTION & FOUNDATIONS SAUDI LLC—See Al Ghurair Investment LLC; *Int'l*, pg. 278
AL GHURAIR CONSTRUCTION LLC—See Al Ghurair Investment LLC; *Int'l*, pg. 278
AL GHURAIR CONSTRUCTION - READYMIX LLC—See Al Ghurair Investment LLC; *Int'l*, pg. 278
AL GHURAIR CONSTRUCTION & READYMIX SAUDI LLC—See Al Ghurair Investment LLC; *Int'l*, pg. 278
AL GHURAIR CONSTRUCTION - READYMIX WLL—See Al Ghurair Investment LLC; *Int'l*, pg. 278
AL GHURAIR ENERGY TRADING DMCC—See Al Ghurair Investment LLC; *Int'l*, pg. 278
AL GHURAIR FOODS - ANIMAL NUTRITION LLC—See Al Ghurair Investment LLC; *Int'l*, pg. 278
AL GHURAIR FOODS LLC—See Al Ghurair Investment LLC; *Int'l*, pg. 278
AL GHURAIR GROUP; *Int'l*, pg. 277
AL GHURAIR INVESTMENT LLC; *Int'l*, pg. 278
AL GHURAIR PRINTING AND PUBLISHING LLC—See Al Ghurair Investment LLC; *Int'l*, pg. 278
AL GHURAIR RESOURCES LLC—See Al Ghurair Investment LLC; *Int'l*, pg. 278
AL GHURAIR RETAIL LLC—See Al Ghurair Investment LLC; *Int'l*, pg. 278
ALGIERE CONSTRUCTION SERVICES, INC.; *U.S. Private*, pg. 166
A.L. GILBERT COMPANY; *U.S. Private*, pg. 26
ALGIST BRUGGEMAN S.A.—See Compagnie des Levures Lesaffre SA; *Int'l*, pg. 1738
AL GIZA GENERAL FOR CONTRACTING & REAL ESTATE CO.—See Pioneers Holding Company; *Int'l*, pg. 5872
AL GLOBAL CORPORATION—See Youngevity International Corp.; *U.S. Public*, pg. 2399
ALGOA OFFICE AUTOMATION (PTY) LIMITED—See Reunert Limited; *Int'l*, pg. 6311
ALGODONERA GUARANI S.A.—See Ecom Agroindustrial Corporation Ltd.; *Int'l*, pg. 2296
ALGODONES DEL BAGES, S.A.U.—See PT Sinar Mas Group; *Int'l*, pg. 6073
ALGOE EXECUTIVE—See Algoe; *Int'l*, pg. 318
ALGOE; *Int'l*, pg. 318
ALGOL CHEMICALS AB—See Algol Oy; *Int'l*, pg. 318
ALGOL CHEMICALS APS—See Algol Oy; *Int'l*, pg. 318
ALGOL CHEMICALS AS—See Algol Oy; *Int'l*, pg. 318
ALGOL CHEMICALS OU—See Algol Oy; *Int'l*, pg. 318

ALGOL CHEMICALS SIA—See Algol Oy; *Int'l*, pg. 318
ALGOL DIAGNOSTICS A/S—See Algol Oy; *Int'l*, pg. 318
ALGOLD RESOURCES LTD.—See Aya Gold & Silver Inc.; *Int'l*, pg. 773
ALGOL-EESTI OU—See Algol Oy; *Int'l*, pg. 318
ALGOL OY; *Int'l*, pg. 318
ALGOL TECHNICS OY—See Algol Oy; *Int'l*, pg. 318
ALGOL TECHNIQUES—See Algol Oy; *Int'l*, pg. 318
ALGOLTEK TECHNOLOGY CO., LTD.; *Int'l*, pg. 318
ALGOMA CENTRAL CORPORATION - FRASER MARINE & INDUSTRIAL DIVISION—See Algoma Central Corporation; *Int'l*, pg. 318
ALGOMA CENTRAL CORPORATION; *Int'l*, pg. 318
ALGOMA CENTRAL PROPERTIES, INC.—See Algoma Central Corporation; *Int'l*, pg. 318
ALGOMA HARDWOODS, INC.—See Owens Corning; *U.S. Public*, pg. 1627
ALGOMA INC.; *Int'l*, pg. 318
ALGOMA NET COMPANY—See Gleason Corporation; *U.S. Private*, pg. 1708
ALGOMA POWER INC.—See Fortis Inc.; *Int'l*, pg. 2739
ALGOMA SHIPPING INC.—See Algoma Central Corporation; *Int'l*, pg. 318
ALGOMA STEEL GROUP INC.; *Int'l*, pg. 318
ALGOMA STEEL INC.—See Algoma Steel Group Inc.; *Int'l*, pg. 318
ALGOMA TANKERS—See Algoma Central Corporation; *Int'l*, pg. 318
ALGONQUIN GAS TRANSMISSION, LLC—See Enbridge Inc.; *Int'l*, pg. 2397
ALGONQUIN INDUSTRIES DIVISION—See REA Magnet Wire Company, Inc.; *U.S. Private*, pg. 3365
ALGONQUIN POWER & UTILITIES CORP.; *Int'l*, pg. 318
ALGOOD FOOD COMPANY; *U.S. Private*, pg. 166
ALGOQUANT FINTECH LIMITED; *Int'l*, pg. 319
ALGOREX INC.—See Texas Instruments Incorporated; *U.S. Public*, pg. 2025
ALGORITHMIC IMPLEMENTATIONS, INC.—See Freedom Scientific Inc.; *U.S. Private*, pg. 1604
ALGORITHM MEDIA LIMITED—See Fidelity Bank Plc.; *Int'l*, pg. 2654
ALGOR, S.L.—See Alten S.A.; *Int'l*, pg. 390
ALGOR SRL—See Solutions 30 SE; *Int'l*, pg. 7076
ALGOS FACHKLINIK BAD KLOSTERLAUSNITZ GMBH—See MK-Kliniken AG; *Int'l*, pg. 5001
ALGOWIRE TRADING TECHNOLOGIES PRIVATE LIMITED—See Share India Securities Limited; *Int'l*, pg. 6789
ALGRAM GROUP LTD.—See Olympus Corporation; *Int'l*, pg. 5557
AL GROUP LIMITED; *Int'l*, pg. 278
AL HABTOOR GROUP LLC; *Int'l*, pg. 278
AL HABTOOR LEIGHTON GROUP—See Al Habtoor Group LLC; *Int'l*, pg. 278
AL HABTOOR MOTORS COMPANY LLC—See Al Habtoor Group LLC; *Int'l*, pg. 278
AL-HAJ ENTERPRISES (PRIVATE) LIMITED—See Al-Haj Group of Companies; *Int'l*, pg. 285
AL-HAJ FAW MOTORS PRIVATE LIMITED—See Al-Haj Group of Companies; *Int'l*, pg. 285
AL-HAJ GROUP OF COMPANIES; *Int'l*, pg. 285
AL-HAJ TEXTILE MILLS LIMITED; *Int'l*, pg. 285
AL HAMAD CONTRACTING COMPANY LLC; *Int'l*, pg. 278
AL HAMAD INDUSTRIAL COMPANY LLC—See Al Hamad Contracting Company LLC; *Int'l*, pg. 278
AL-HAMARA'A INSURANCE COMPANY; *Int'l*, pg. 285
AL HAMAS TRADING COMPANY LLC—See Al Hassan Engineering Company S.A.O.G.; *Int'l*, pg. 278
ALHAMBRA CHRYSLER JEEP DODGE; *U.S. Private*, pg. 166
ALHAMBRA LONGMAN S.A.—See Pearson plc; *Int'l*, pg. 5776
ALHAMBRA NISSAN; *U.S. Private*, pg. 166
ALHAMBRA RESOURCES LTD; *Int'l*, pg. 319
AL HAMMADI HOLDING COMPANY; *Int'l*, pg. 278
AL HAMRA CONSTRUCTION COMPANY LLC—See Ras Al Khaimah Ceramics PJSC; *Int'l*, pg. 6211
ALHAMRANI COMPANY FOR INDUSTRY—See Alhamrani Group; *Int'l*, pg. 319
ALHAMRANI COMPANY FOR INVESTMENT IN TRADE LIMITED—See Alhamrani Group; *Int'l*, pg. 319
ALHAMRANI-FUCHS PETROLEUM SAUDI ARABIA LTD.—See Alhamrani Group; *Int'l*, pg. 319
ALHAMRANI-FUCHS PETROLEUM SAUDI ARABIA LTD.—See FUCHS SE; *Int'l*, pg. 2802
ALHAMRANI GROUP; *Int'l*, pg. 319
ALHAMRANI INDUSTRIAL GROUP LTD—See Alhamrani Group; *Int'l*, pg. 319
ALHAMRANI REAL ESTATE DEVELOPMENT COMPANY—See Alhamrani Group; *Int'l*, pg. 319
ALHAMRANI UNITED COMPANY—See Alhamrani Group; *Int'l*, pg. 319
ALHAMRANI UNIVERSAL COMPANY LTD—See Alhamrani Group; *Int'l*, pg. 319
A.L. HANSEN MANUFACTURING CO.; *U.S. Private*, pg. 27
ALHASAWI FACTORIES FOR WATER HEATERS W.L.L.—See Al-Hasawi Industrial Group; *Int'l*, pg. 285

AL-HASAWI INDUSTRIAL GROUP; *Int'l*, pg. 285
AL HASSAN ELECTRICALS LLC—See Al Hassan Engineering Company S.A.O.G.; *Int'l*, pg. 278
AL HASSAN ENGINEERING CO. ABU DHABI LLC—See Al Hassan Engineering Company S.A.O.G.; *Int'l*, pg. 278
AL HASSAN ENGINEERING CO. DUBAI LLC—See Al Hassan Engineering Company S.A.O.G.; *Int'l*, pg. 278
AL HASSAN ENGINEERING COMPANY S.A.O.G.; *Int'l*, pg. 278
AL HASSAN ENGINEERING CO. SAOG—See Al Hassan Engineering Company S.A.O.G.; *Int'l*, pg. 279
AL HASSAN GHAZI IBRAHIM SHAKER; *Int'l*, pg. 279
AL-HASSAN G.I. SHAKER COMPANY; *Int'l*, pg. 286
AL HASSAN LIGHTING & FANS INDUSTRIES LLC—See Al Hassan Engineering Company S.A.O.G.; *Int'l*, pg. 279
AL HASSAN POWER INDUSTRIES—See Al Hassan Engineering Company S.A.O.G.; *Int'l*, pg. 279
AL HASSAN SWITCHGEAR MANUFACTURING—See Al Hassan Engineering Company S.A.O.G.; *Int'l*, pg. 279
AL-HEJAILAN GROUP; *Int'l*, pg. 286
AL HENDRICKSON TOYOTA; *U.S. Private*, pg. 147
ALH GROUP PROPERTY HOLDINGS PTY LTD—See Woolworths Group Limited; *Int'l*, pg. 8451
ALH GROUP PTY. LTD.—See Woolworths Group Limited; *Int'l*, pg. 8451
ALH HOLDINGS, LLC—See Ventas, Inc.; *U.S. Public*, pg. 2277
AL HILAL LIFE B.S.C.—See Kuwait Finance House K.S.C.; *Int'l*, pg. 4344
ALH INC.—See SHIFT, Inc.; *Int'l*, pg. 6828
A&L HOLDING COMPANY INC.; *U.S. Private*, pg. 20
AL HOMAIZI FOODSTUFF CO.—See Kout Food Group K.S.C.C.; *Int'l*, pg. 4293
ALH SYSTEMS LIMITED—See Indutrade AB; *Int'l*, pg. 3677
ALI ABDULLAH AL TAMIMI COMPANY; *Int'l*, pg. 319
ALIA CORP.; *U.S. Private*, pg. 166
ALIADA QUIMICA DE PORTUGAL LTD.—See Kemira Oyj; *Int'l*, pg. 4124
ALIADO FACTORING, S.A.—See Grupo Aliado S.A.; *Int'l*, pg. 3119
ALIADO LEASING, S.A.—See Grupo Aliado S.A.; *Int'l*, pg. 3119
ALIANCA NAVEGACAO E LOGISTICA LTDA.—See A.P. Moller-Maersk A/S; *Int'l*, pg. 26
ALIANCYS AG—See CVC Capital Partners SICAV-FIS S.A.; *Int'l*, pg. 1886
ALIANCYS (CHINA) HOLDING B.V.—See CVC Capital Partners SICAV-FIS S.A.; *Int'l*, pg. 1886
ALIANCYS FRANCE SAS—See CVC Capital Partners SICAV-FIS S.A.; *Int'l*, pg. 1886
ALIANCYS HOLDING INTERNATIONAL B.V.—See CVC Capital Partners SICAV-FIS S.A.; *Int'l*, pg. 1886
ALIANCYS ITALIA S.R.L.—See CVC Capital Partners SICAV-FIS S.A.; *Int'l*, pg. 1886
ALIANDA; *U.S. Private*, pg. 166
ALIANSALUD ENTIDAD PROMOTORA DE SALUD S.A.—See UnitedHealth Group Incorporated; *U.S. Public*, pg. 2238
ALIANSCE MALL E MIDIA LTDA—See Allos SA; *Int'l*, pg. 359
ALIANSCE SHOPPING CENTERS SA—See Allos SA; *Int'l*, pg. 359
ALIANTA INVESTMENTS GROUP SA; *Int'l*, pg. 323
ALIANTE GAMING, LLC—See Boyd Gaming Corporation; *U.S. Public*, pg. 377
ALIANZA EDITORIAL, S.A.—See Vivendi SE; *Int'l*, pg. 8272
ALIANZA HOLDINGS LTD.—See Silver North Resources Ltd.; *Int'l*, pg. 6924
ALIANZA INC.; *U.S. Private*, pg. 167
ALI ASGHAR TEXTILE MILS LTD.; *Int'l*, pg. 320
ALIAXIS HOLDING ITALIA SPA—See Aliaxis S.A./N.V.; *Int'l*, pg. 323
ALIAXIS HOLDINGS UK LTD—See Aliaxis S.A./N.V.; *Int'l*, pg. 323
ALIAXIS NEDERLAND B.V.—See Aliaxis S.A./N.V.; *Int'l*, pg. 323
ALIAXIS S.A./N.V.; *Int'l*, pg. 323
ALIAXIS SERVICES S.A.—See Aliaxis S.A./N.V.; *Int'l*, pg. 323
ALIAXIS—See Aliaxis S.A./N.V.; *Int'l*, pg. 323
ALIAXIS UTILITIES & INDUSTRY AG—See Aliaxis S.A./N.V.; *Int'l*, pg. 323
ALIBABA.COM HONG KONG LIMITED—See Alibaba Group Holding Limited; *Int'l*, pg. 326
ALIBABA.COM, INC.—See Alibaba Group Holding Limited; *Int'l*, pg. 326
ALIBABA.COM JAPAN CO., LTD.—See SoftBank Group Corp.; *Int'l*, pg. 7051
ALIBABA.COM LIMITED—See Alibaba Group Holding Limited; *Int'l*, pg. 326
ALIBABA GROUP HOLDING LIMITED - HANGZHOU OFFICE—See Alibaba Group Holding Limited; *Int'l*, pg. 325
ALIBABA GROUP HOLDING LIMITED; *Int'l*, pg. 325

ALIBABA HEALTH INFORMATION TECHNOLOGY LIMITED; *Int'l*, pg. 326
ALIBABA PICTURES GROUP LTD; *Int'l*, pg. 326
ALIBABA TECHNOLOGY (SHANGHAI) CO., LTD.—See Alibaba Group Holding Limited; *Int'l*, pg. 326
A. LIBENTAL HOLDINGS LTD.; *Int'l*, pg. 21
ALIBERICO, S.L.; *Int'l*, pg. 326
ALI-BIG INDUSTRIA ALIMENTARE S.R.L.—See Coop-Gruppe Genossenschaft; *Int'l*, pg. 1789
ALI BIN ALI ESTABLISHMENT; *Int'l*, pg. 320
ALI BIN ALI & PARTNERS—See Ali Bin Ali Establishment; *Int'l*, pg. 320
ALI BIN ALI TECHNOLOGY SOLUTIONS—See Ali Bin Ali Establishment; *Int'l*, pg. 320
ALIBRE, INC.—See 3D Systems Corporation; *U.S. Public*, pg. 4
ALIBRIS, INC.—See Keystone Group, L.P.; *U.S. Private*, pg. 2296
ALICANTO MINERALS LIMITED; *Int'l*, pg. 326
ALICAT BV—See Halma plc; *Int'l*, pg. 3230
ALICAT SCIENTIFIC, INC.—See Halma plc; *Int'l*, pg. 3231
ALICAT SCIENTIFIC INDIA PRIVATE LIMITED—See Halma plc; *Int'l*, pg. 3230
ALICAT WORKBOATS LIMITED—See HAL Trust N.V.; *Int'l*, pg. 3226
ALICE BBDO—See Omnicom Group Inc.; *U.S. Public*, pg. 1573
ALICE ECHO-NEWS, INC.—See American Consolidated Media LP; *U.S. Private*, pg. 228
ALICE EVENEMENTS; *Int'l*, pg. 327
ALICE MANUFACTURING CO. INC.; *U.S. Private*, pg. 167
ALICE NEUMATICOS DE VENEZUELA, C.A.—See Corimon, C.A.; *Int'l*, pg. 1800
ALICE QUEEN LIMITED; *Int'l*, pg. 327
ALICHAMPI ALICANTE S.L.—See Dole plc; *Int'l*, pg. 2157
ALI (CHINA) CORPORATION—See ALi Corporation; *Int'l*, pg. 320
ALICO-AGRI, LTD.—See Continental Grain Company; *U.S. Private*, pg. 1029
ALICO AIG LIFE UKRAINE—See MetLife, Inc.; *U.S. Public*, pg. 1429
ALICO ASIGURARI ROMANIA S.A—See MetLife, Inc.; *U.S. Public*, pg. 1429
ALICO A.S.—See MetLife, Inc; *U.S. Public*, pg. 1429
ALICO BULGARIA—See MetLife, Inc.; *U.S. Public*, pg. 1429
ALICO CIA DE SEGUROS S.A.—See MetLife, Inc.; *U.S. Public*, pg. 1429
ALICO CITRUS NURSERY, LLC—See Continental Grain Company; *U.S. Private*, pg. 1029
ALICO EGYPT LTD.—See Orascom Construction PLC; *Int'l*, pg. 5612
ALICO FRUIT COMPANY, LLC—See Continental Grain Company; *U.S. Private*, pg. 1029
ALICO, INC.—See Continental Grain Company; *U.S. Private*, pg. 1029
ALICO ITALIA S.P.A.—See MetLife, Inc.; *U.S. Public*, pg. 1429
ALICO LAND DEVELOPMENT, INC.—See Continental Grain Company; *U.S. Private*, pg. 1029
ALI COMENDA S.A.—See Ali Holding S.r.l; *Int'l*, pg. 320
ALICONA CORPORATION—See Bruker Corporation; *U.S. Public*, pg. 404
ALICONA GMBH—See Bruker Corporation; *U.S. Public*, pg. 404
ALICONA IMAGING GMBH—See Bruker Corporation; *U.S. Public*, pg. 404
ALICONA KOREA PCIFIC LTD.—See Bruker Corporation; *U.S. Public*, pg. 404
ALICONA SARL—See Bruker Corporation; *U.S. Public*, pg. 404
ALICONA S.R.L.—See Bruker Corporation; *U.S. Public*, pg. 404
ALICONA UK LIMITED—See Bruker Corporation; *U.S. Public*, pg. 404
ALICON CASTALLOY LIMITED; *Int'l*, pg. 327
ALICORN LIMITED; *Int'l*, pg. 327
ALI CORPORATION; *Int'l*, pg. 320
ALICORP S.A.—See Grupo Romero; *Int'l*, pg. 3134
ALICROS S.P.A.; *Int'l*, pg. 327
AL I/EAST BRUNSWICK SENIOR HOUSING, LLC—See Ventas, Inc.; *U.S. Public*, pg. 2277
ALIEN METALS LTD.; *Int'l*, pg. 327
A LIENOR S.A.,—See Eiffage S.A.; *Int'l*, pg. 2329
ALIEN TECHNOLOGY CORPORATION; *U.S. Private*, pg. 167
ALIENVAULT, INC.—See AT&T Inc.; *U.S. Public*, pg. 219
ALIENWARE LIMITED—See Dell Technologies Inc.; *U.S. Public*, pg. 649
ALIF MANUFACTURING COMPANY LTD.; *Int'l*, pg. 327
ALI FOODSERVICE EQUIPMENT (SHANGHAI) CO., LTD.—See Ali Holding S.r.l; *Int'l*, pg. 320
ALIGHT FINANCIAL SOLUTIONS, LLC—See Alight, Inc.; *U.S. Public*, pg. 75
ALIGHT HEALTH MARKET INSURANCE SOLUTIONS INC.—See Alight, Inc.; *U.S. Public*, pg. 75
ALIGHT, INC.; *U.S. Public*, pg. 75
ALIGHT SOLUTIONS LLC—See Alight, Inc.; *U.S. Public*, pg. 76

ALIGNA AG; *Int'l*, pg. 327
ALIGN AEROSPACE FRANCE SAS—See AVIC International Holdings Limited; *Int'l*, pg. 742
ALIGN AEROSPACE HOLDINGS, INC.—See AVIC International Holdings Limited; *Int'l*, pg. 742
ALIGN AEROSPACE LLC—See AVIC International Holdings Limited; *Int'l*, pg. 742
ALIGN AS—See HitecVision AS; *Int'l*, pg. 3425
ALIGN CAPITAL PARTNERS, LLC; *U.S. Private*, pg. 167
ALIGN COMMUNICATIONS INC.; *U.S. Private*, pg. 167
ALIGN CREDIT UNION; *U.S. Private*, pg. 168
ALIGNED GENETICS, INC.; *Int'l*, pg. 327
ALIGNED TECHNOLOGY SOLUTIONS, LLC—See Teal; *U.S. Private*, pg. 3948
ALIGN FINANCIAL GROUP, LLC; *U.S. Private*, pg. 168
ALIGN GENERAL INSURANCE AGENCY, LLC—See Align Financial Group, LLC; *U.S. Private*, pg. 168
ALIGNMENT HEALTHCARE, INC.; *U.S. Public*, pg. 77
ALIGN PHARMACEUTICALS, LLC—See Cyclacel Pharmaceuticals, Inc.; *U.S. Public*, pg. 617
ALIGN TECHNICAL RESOURCES, LLC; *U.S. Private*, pg. 168
ALIGN TECHNOLOGY, B.V.—See Align Technology, Inc.; *U.S. Public*, pg. 77
ALIGN TECHNOLOGY, INC.; *U.S. Public*, pg. 77
ALIGN TECHNOLOGY SWITZERLAND GMBH—See Align Technology, Inc.; *U.S. Public*, pg. 77
ALIGNVEST AQUISITION II CORP.—See Alignvest Management Corporation; *Int'l*, pg. 327
ALIGNVEST MANAGEMENT CORPORATION; *Int'l*, pg. 327
ALIGN WEALTH MANAGEMENT, LLC—See Hellman & Friedman LLC; *U.S. Private*, pg. 1908
ALIGOS THERAPEUTICS, INC.; *U.S. Public*, pg. 77
ALIG VENTILATION AB—See Lindab International AB; *Int'l*, pg. 4503
ALI HOLDING S.R.L; *Int'l*, pg. 320
ALI (HSINCHU) CORPORATION—See ALi Corporation; *Int'l*, pg. 320
ALI INDUSTRIES, INC.—See RPM International Inc.; *U.S. Public*, pg. 1817
ALIJARAH HOLDING QSC; *Int'l*, pg. 328
ALILA HOTELS & RESORTS PTE. LTD.—See Hyatt Hotels Corporation; *U.S. Public*, pg. 1076
ALIMACH HOLDINGS SDN. BHD.—See Engtex Group Berhad; *Int'l*, pg. 2436
ALIMA-GERBER SA—See Nestle S.A.; *Int'l*, pg. 5208
ALIMAK GROUP AB—See Triton Advisers Limited; *Int'l*, pg. 7928
ALIMAK HEK AB—See Triton Advisers Limited; *Int'l*, pg. 7929
ALIMAK HEK INC.—See Triton Advisers Limited; *Int'l*, pg. 7929
ALIMAK HEK LTD.—See Triton Advisers Limited; *Int'l*, pg. 7929
ALIMAK HEK PTY. LTD.—See Triton Advisers Limited; *Int'l*, pg. 7929
ALIMCO FINANCIAL CORPORATION; *U.S. Private*, pg. 168
AL IMDAD COMPANY—See Invest Bank; *Int'l*, pg. 3775
ALIMED, INC.; *U.S. Private*, pg. 168
ALIMENTA S.A.; *Int'l*, pg. 328
ALIMENTATION COUCHE-TARD INC.; *Int'l*, pg. 328
ALIMENTATION DU FLORIVAL; *Int'l*, pg. 328
ALIMENTOS CARNICOS S.A.S.—See Grupo Nutresa S.A.; *Int'l*, pg. 3133
ALIMENTOS DEL ISTMO, S.A.—See PepsiCo, Inc.; *U.S. Public*, pg. 1668
ALIMENTOS FINOS DE OCCIDENTE, S.A. DE C.V.—See ALFA, S.A.B. de C.V.; *Int'l*, pg. 313
ALIMENTOS HEINZ C.A.—See 3G Capital Inc.; *U.S. Private*, pg. 9
ALIMENTOS HEINZ C.A.—See Berkshire Hathaway Inc.; *U.S. Public*, pg. 317
ALIMENTOS HEINZ DE COSTA RICA S.A.—See 3G Capital Inc.; *U.S. Private*, pg. 9
ALIMENTOS HEINZ DE COSTA RICA S.A.—See Berkshire Hathaway Inc.; *U.S. Public*, pg. 317
ALIMENTOS KERN DE GUATEMALA, S.A.—See Florida Ice and Farm Co. S.A.; *Int'l*, pg. 2707
ALIMENTOS LATINOAMERICANOS VENEZUELA ALV, C.A.—See Arcos Dorados Holdings Inc.; *Int'l*, pg. 550
ALIMENTOS LIQUIDOS INDUSTRIALES—See Able Sales Company, Inc.; *U.S. Private*, pg. 39
ALIMENTOS MARAVILLA S.A.; *Int'l*, pg. 328
ALIMENTS FONTAINE SANTE, INC.; *Int'l*, pg. 328
ALIMENTS KRISPY KERNELS INC; *Int'l*, pg. 328
ALIMENTS ULTIMA INC—See General Mills, Inc.; *U.S. Public*, pg. 921
ALIMERA SCIENCES EUROPE LIMITED—See ANI Pharmaceuticals, Inc.; *U.S. Public*, pg. 137
ALIMERA SCIENCES, INC.—See ANI Pharmaceuticals, Inc.; *U.S. Public*, pg. 137
ALIMERA SCIENCES LIMITED—See ANI Pharmaceuticals, Inc.; *U.S. Public*, pg. 137
ALIMERA SCIENCES OPTHAMOLOGIE GMBH—See ANI Pharmaceuticals, Inc.; *U.S. Public*, pg. 137
ALIMEX ALUMINYUM SAN. VE. TIC. LTD. STI.—See Nordstjernan AB; *Int'l*, pg. 5426

COMPANY NAME INDEX

ALIMPORT DO BRASIL LTDA.—See Leifheit AG; *Int'l*, pg. 4446
ALIMTEC S.A.—See The Murugappa Group, Ltd.; *Int'l*, pg. 7668
AL IMTIAZ INVESTMENT GROUP COMPANY- K.S.C.; *Int'l*, pg. 279
ALINABAL ENGINEERED PRODUCTS—See Alinabal Holdings Corporation; *U.S. Private*, pg. 168
ALINABAL HOLDINGS CORPORATION; *U.S. Private*, pg. 168
ALINABAL INC.—See Alinabal Holdings Corporation; *U.S. Private*, pg. 168
ALINABAL MOTION TRANSFER DEVICES—See Alinabal Holdings Corporation; *U.S. Private*, pg. 168
ALINA HOLDINGS PLC; *Int'l*, pg. 328
ALINAMIN PHARMACEUTICAL CO., LTD.—See Blackstone Inc.; *U.S. Public*, pg. 347
ALINCO INCORPORATED; *Int'l*, pg. 328
ALINCO SCAFFOLDING RENTAL SERVICE CO., LTD.—See Alinco Incorporated; *Int'l*, pg. 329
ALINCO SCAFFOLDING (THAILAND) CO., LTD.—See Alinco Incorporated; *Int'l*, pg. 329
ALINCO (THAILAND) CO., LTD.—See Alinco Incorporated; *Int'l*, pg. 328
ALINDA INVESTMENTS LLC—See Astatine Investment Partners LLC; *U.S. Private*, pg. 360
ALINEAN, INC.—See Boathouse Capital Management, LLC; *U.S. Private*, pg. 603
ALINEA SAS; *Int'l*, pg. 329
ALINEA—See Egmont Fonden; *Int'l*, pg. 2326
ALINES AUTO GROUP; *U.S. Private*, pg. 168
ALINITA UAB—See Panevezio statybos trestas AB; *Int'l*, pg. 5727
ALINK INTERNET, INC.; *Int'l*, pg. 329
ALINMA BANK; *Int'l*, pg. 329
ALINMA INVESTMENT COMPANY—See Alinma Bank; *Int'l*, pg. 329
ALINMA RETAIL REIT FUND; *Int'l*, pg. 329
ALINMA TOKIO MARINE CO.—See Alinma Bank; *Int'l*, pg. 329
ALINMA TOKIO MARINE CO.—See Tokio Marine Holdings, Inc.; *Int'l*, pg. 7783
ALINOX SP.Z.O.O.—See Scope Metals Group Ltd.; *Int'l*, pg. 6650
ALIO GOLD INC.—See Argonaut Gold Inc.; *U.S. Public*, pg. 101
ALIO HEALTH SERVICES INC.—See Calian Group Ltd.; *Int'l*, pg. 1263
ALIO INDUSTRIES, LLC—See Allient Inc.; *U.S. Public*, pg. 80
ALION SCIENCE AND TECHNOLOGY CORPORATION—See Veritas Capital Fund Management, LLC; *U.S. Private*, pg. 4360
ALIONTEK CORPORATION—See Ferrotec Holdings Corporation; *Int'l*, pg. 2642
ALIOR BANK S.A.; *Int'l*, pg. 329
ALIOR LEASING SP. Z O.O.—See Alior Bank S.A.; *Int'l*, pg. 329
ALIOR TFI SA—See Alior Bank S.A.; *Int'l*, pg. 329
ALIOS BIOPHARMA, INC.—See Johnson & Johnson; *U.S. Public*, pg. 1196
ALIPAY CO., LTD.—See Zhejiang Ant Small & Micro Financial Services Group Co., Ltd.; *Int'l*, pg. 8648
ALIPHCOM; *U.S. Private*, pg. 168
ALIPLAST FRANCE RECYCLAGE S.A.S.—See Hera S.p.A.; *Int'l*, pg. 3356
ALIPLAST IBERIA SL—See Hera S.p.A.; *Int'l*, pg. 3356
ALIPLAST SPA—See Hera S.p.A.; *Int'l*, pg. 3356
THE ALIQUIPPA & OHIO RIVER RAILROAD CO.—See Brookfield Infrastructure Partners L.P.; *Int'l*, pg. 1192
THE ALIQUIPPA & OHIO RIVER RAILROAD CO.—See GIC Pte. Ltd.; *Int'l*, pg. 2967
ALIRAN IHSAN RESOURCES BERHAD; *Int'l*, pg. 329
ALIRAN PERKASA SDN. BHD.—See MKH Berhad; *Int'l*, pg. 5002
ALIRM, LLC; *U.S. Private*, pg. 168
A&L IRON AND METAL COMPANY; *U.S. Private*, pg. 20
ALIRON INTERNATIONAL, INC.; *U.S. Private*, pg. 168
ALISECA GMBH—See LANXESS AG; *Int'l*, pg. 4414
ALI (SHANGHAI) CORPORATION—See ALi Corporation; *Int'l*, pg. 320
ALI SOLUTIONS, INC.—See Vector Capital Management, L.P.; *U.S. Private*, pg. 4350
THE ALISON GROUP; *U.S. Private*, pg. 3984
ALISON HAYES; *Int'l*, pg. 329
ALISO VIEJO COUNTRY CLUB—See Apollo Global Management, Inc.; *U.S. Public*, pg. 149
ALI S.P.A.—See Ali Holding S.r.l; *Int'l*, pg. 320
ALI SPECIALTIES; *U.S. Private*, pg. 166
ALISRA FOR EDUCATION & INVESTMENT CO. PLC; *Int'l*, pg. 329
ALISTHE INVESTMENTS PTY LTD; *Int'l*, pg. 329
ALITALIA - COMPAGNIA AEREA ITALIANA S.P.A.; *Int'l*, pg. 329
ALITA RESOURCES LIMITED; *Int'l*, pg. 329
ALITECH INDIA LLP—See ALi Corporation; *Int'l*, pg. 320
ALITE DESIGNS, INC.—See The Travel Hammock Inc.; *U.S. Private*, pg. 4128
ALITER CAPITAL LLP; *Int'l*, pg. 329

ALITHYA CANADA INC.—See Alithya Group, Inc.; *Int'l*, pg. 329
ALITHYA GROUP, INC.; *Int'l*, pg. 329
ALITHYA USA, INC.—See Alithya Group, Inc.; *Int'l*, pg. 329
AL ITTEFAQ STEEL PRODUCTS COMPANY—See Al-Tuwairqi Group; *Int'l*, pg. 289
ALIUD PHARMA GMBH—See Bain Capital, LP; *U.S. Private*, pg. 443
ALIUD PHARMA GMBH—See Cinven Limited; *Int'l*, pg. 1613
ALIUD PHARMA VERWALTUNGS-GMBH—See Bain Capital, LP; *U.S. Private*, pg. 443
ALIUD PHARMA VERWALTUNGS-GMBH—See Cinven Limited; *Int'l*, pg. 1613
ALIVE CO., LTD.—See AB&Company Co., Ltd.; *Int'l*, pg. 47
ALIVE COMPANIES, INC.—See Skybridge Americas, Inc.; *U.S. Private*, pg. 3684
ALIVE COR INC.; *U.S. Private*, pg. 169
ALIVE HOSPICE; *U.S. Private*, pg. 169
ALIVE & KICKIN—See Port City Bakery Inc.; *U.S. Private*, pg. 3230
A-LIVING SERVICES CO., LTD.; *Int'l*, pg. 19
A-LIVING SMART CITY SERVICES CO., LTD.; *Int'l*, pg. 20
ALIVIRA ANIMAL HEALTH LIMITED—See SeQuent Scientific Limited; *Int'l*, pg. 6719
ALIVIRA ITALIA S.R.L.—See SeQuent Scientific Limited; *Int'l*, pg. 6719
ALIVI; *U.S. Private*, pg. 169
ALIXPARTNERS ARGENTINA SRL—See Caisse de Depot et Placement du Quebec; *Int'l*, pg. 1253
ALIXPARTNERS ARGENTINA SRL—See Investcorp Holdings B.S.C.; *Int'l*, pg. 3775
ALIXPARTNERS ARGENTINA SRL—See Public Sector Pension Investment Board; *Int'l*, pg. 6095
ALIXPARTNERS, LLP—See Caisse de Depot et Placement du Quebec; *Int'l*, pg. 1253
ALIXPARTNERS, LLP—See Investcorp Holdings B.S.C.; *Int'l*, pg. 3775
ALIXPARTNERS, LLP—See Public Sector Pension Investment Board; *Int'l*, pg. 6095
ALIXPARTNERS UK LLP—See Caisse de Depot et Placement du Quebec; *Int'l*, pg. 1253
ALIXPARTNERS UK LLP—See Investcorp Holdings B.S.C.; *Int'l*, pg. 3775
ALIXPARTNERS UK LLP—See Public Sector Pension Investment Board; *Int'l*, pg. 6095
ALI ZAID AL-QURAISHI & BROTHERS CO.; *Int'l*, pg. 323
ALI (ZHUHAI) CORPORATION—See ALi Corporation; *Int'l*, pg. 320
ALIZZ ISLAMIC BANK SAOG—See Arab Bank plc; *Int'l*, pg. 529
ALIZZ ISLAMIC BANK SAOG—See Oman International Development & Investment Company SAOG; *Int'l*, pg. 5560
AL JABAL AL AKHDAR CONSERVE COMPANY—See MAS Economic Group; *Int'l*, pg. 4718
AL JABER ALUMINUM EXTRUSION L.L.C.—See Al Jaber Group; *Int'l*, pg. 279
AL JABER BITUMEN LLC—See Al Jaber Group; *Int'l*, pg. 279
AL JABER BUILDING L.L.C.—See Al Jaber Group; *Int'l*, pg. 279
AL JABER CARPENTRY & DECOR L.L.C.—See Al Jaber Group; *Int'l*, pg. 279
AL JABER CATERING SERVICES L.L.C—See Al Jaber Group; *Int'l*, pg. 279
AL JABER CONTRACTING LTD.—See Al Jaber Group; *Int'l*, pg. 279
AL JABER DELTA ENERGY SERVICES & GENERAL CONSTRUCTION—See Al Jaber Group; *Int'l*, pg. 279
AL JABER ENERGY SERVICES—See Al Jaber Group; *Int'l*, pg. 279
AL JABER FUSION-BONDED EPOXY COATING PLANT—See Al Jaber Group; *Int'l*, pg. 279
AL JABER GROUP; *Int'l*, pg. 279
AL JABER HEAVY LIFT—See Al Jaber Group; *Int'l*, pg. 279
AL JABER HEAVY LIFT & TRANSPORT LLC—See Al Jaber Group; *Int'l*, pg. 279
AL JABER HEAVY LIFT & TRANSPORT PTE.LTD—See Al Jaber Group; *Int'l*, pg. 279
AL JABER IRON & STEEL FOUNDRY LLC—See Al Jaber Group; *Int'l*, pg. 279
AL JABER LANDSCAPE LLC—See Al Jaber Group; *Int'l*, pg. 279
AL JABER LEASING SERVICES L.L.C.—See Al Jaber Group; *Int'l*, pg. 279
AL JABER L.E.G.T. ENGINEERING & CONTRACTING L.L.C.—See Investment Corporation of Dubai; *Int'l*, pg. 3784
AL JABER LIGHTING LLC—See Al Jaber Group; *Int'l*, pg. 279
AL JABER & PARTNERS - CONSTRUCTION & ENERGY PROJECTS W.L.L.—See Al Jaber Group; *Int'l*, pg. 279
AL JABER & PARTNERS L.L.C.—See Al Jaber Group; *Int'l*, pg. 280

ALKALOID A.D. SKOPJE

AL JABER PRECISION ENGINEERING ESTABLISHMENT—See Al Jaber Group; *Int'l*, pg. 279
AL JABER PROTECTIVE COATING L.L.C.—See Al Jaber Group; *Int'l*, pg. 279
AL JABER SHIPPING AGENCY & MARINE WORKS LLC—See Al Jaber Group; *Int'l*, pg. 279
AL JABER SIGNS L.L.C.—See Al Jaber Group; *Int'l*, pg. 279
AL JABER STEEL PRODUCTS L.L.C.—See Al Jaber Group; *Int'l*, pg. 279
AL JABER TRADING LLC—See Al Jaber Group; *Int'l*, pg. 279
AL JABER TRAILERS, STEEL AND METAL WORKS ESTABLISHMENT—See Al Jaber Group; *Int'l*, pg. 279
AL JABER TRANSPORT & GENERAL CONTRACTING CO.—See Al Jaber Group; *Int'l*, pg. 280
AL JABER TUNNELING & MECHANICAL WORKS EST—See Al Jaber Group; *Int'l*, pg. 280
AL JAMIL FOR INVESTMENT COMPANY; *Int'l*, pg. 280
AL JAZEERA AMERICA, LLC—See Al-Jazeera Satellite Network; *Int'l*, pg. 286
ALJAZEERA BALKANS D.O.O.—See Al-Jazeera Satellite Network; *Int'l*, pg. 286
AL JAZEERA ENGLISH—See Al-Jazeera Satellite Network; *Int'l*, pg. 286
ALJAZEERAH PHARMACEUTICAL INDUSTRIES LTD.—See Hikma Pharmaceuticals PLC; *Int'l*, pg. 3390
AL JAZEERA MEDIA NETWORK—See Al-Jazeera Satellite Network; *Int'l*, pg. 286
AL-JAZEERA SATELLITE NETWORK; *Int'l*, pg. 286
AL JAZEERA STEEL PRODUCTS COMPANY S.A.O.G.; *Int'l*, pg. 280
AL JAZEERA SUDANESE JORDANIAN BANK; *Int'l*, pg. 280
AL JAZEERA TECHNICAL LABORATORIES COMPANY LLC—See Taleb Group; *Int'l*, pg. 7446
AL-JAZEERA TRADING FZCO.—See Al-Rakaez PLC; *Int'l*, pg. 288
AL-JAZEIRA SERVICES CO. SAOG—See DAMAC Group; *Int'l*, pg. 1955
ALJAZIRA CAPITAL COMPANY—See Bank Aljazira; *Int'l*, pg. 837
AL-JAZIRA MARINE RESOURCES COMPANY LTD.—See Hayel Saeed Anam Group of Companies; *Int'l*, pg. 3290
AL JAZIRA OIL & GAS SERVICES COMPANY EC—See Dabbagh Group Holding Company Ltd.; *Int'l*, pg. 1902
AL JAZIRA TAKAFUL TA'AWUNI COMPANY; *Int'l*, pg. 280
ALJ FINANSMAN A.S.; *Int'l*, pg. 329
AL JIMI MALL LLC—See ALDAR Properties PJSC; *Int'l*, pg. 304
AL J. MUELLER CONSTRUCTION COMPANY; *U.S. Private*, pg. 147
A.L. JOHNSON COMPANY; *U.S. Public*, pg. 12
ALJOMA LUMBER, INC.—See UFP Industries, Inc.; *U.S. Public*, pg. 2218
AL-JOUF AGRICULTURAL DEVELOPMENT COMPANY; *Int'l*, pg. 286
AL JOUF CEMENT COMPANY; *Int'l*, pg. 280
ALJ REGIONAL HOLDINGS, INC.; *U.S. Public*, pg. 77
AL-JUBAIL FERTILIZER CO.(SAMAD)—See Taiwan Fertilizer Co., Ltd.; *Int'l*, pg. 7420
AL-JUBAIL FERTILIZER CO.—See Saudi Basic Industries Corporation; *Int'l*, pg. 6590
AL-JUBAIL PETROCHEMICAL CO.—See Saudi Basic Industries Corporation; *Int'l*, pg. 6590
ALK-ABELLO AG—See Lundbeckfonden; *Int'l*, pg. 4579
ALK - ABELLO ALLERGIE-SERVICE GMBH—See Lundbeckfonden; *Int'l*, pg. 4579
ALK - ABELLO ARZNEIMITTEL GMBH—See Lundbeckfonden; *Int'l*, pg. 4579
ALK-ABELLO A/S—See Lundbeckfonden; *Int'l*, pg. 4579
ALK-ABELLO BV—See Lundbeckfonden; *Int'l*, pg. 4579
ALK-ABELLO B.V.—See Lundbeckfonden; *Int'l*, pg. 4579
ALK-ABELLO GMBH—See Lundbeckfonden; *Int'l*, pg. 4579
ALK-ABELLO, INC.—See Lundbeckfonden; *Int'l*, pg. 4579
ALK-ABELLO LTD.—See Lundbeckfonden; *Int'l*, pg. 4579
ALK-ABELLO NORDIC A/S—See Lundbeckfonden; *Int'l*, pg. 4579
ALK-ABELLO NORDIC A/S—See Lundbeckfonden; *Int'l*, pg. 4579
ALK - ABELLO PHARMACEUTICALS, INC.—See Lundbeckfonden; *Int'l*, pg. 4579
ALK-ABELLO S.A.—See Lundbeckfonden; *Int'l*, pg. 4579
ALK-ABELLO S.P.A.—See Lundbeckfonden; *Int'l*, pg. 4579
ALK-ABELLO SP. Z.O.O.—See Lundbeckfonden; *Int'l*, pg. 4579
ALKA DIAMOND INDUSTRIES LIMITED; *Int'l*, pg. 329
ALKAHEST, INC.—See Grifols, S.A.; *Int'l*, pg. 3084
ALKA INDIA LIMITED; *Int'l*, pg. 330
ALKA-LAB DOO—See Alkaloid A.D. Skopje; *Int'l*, pg. 330
ALKALI METALS LIMITED; *Int'l*, pg. 330
THE ALKALINE WATER COMPANY INC.; *U.S. Public*, pg. 2032
ALKALOIDA CHEMICAL COMPANY ZRT—See Sun Pharmaceutical Industries Ltd.; *Int'l*, pg. 7307
ALKALOID A.D. SKOPJE; *Int'l*, pg. 330

ALKALOID A.D. SKOPJE

ALKALOID BUCHUREST SRL—See Alkaloid A.D. Skopje; *Int'l*, pg. 330
ALKALOID DOO (PODGORICA)—See Alkaloid A.D. Skopje; *Int'l*, pg. 330
ALKALOID DOO (SARAJEVO)—See Alkaloid A.D. Skopje; *Int'l*, pg. 330
ALKALOID D.O.O.—See Alkaloid A.D. Skopje; *Int'l*, pg. 330
ALKALOID DOO (ZAGREB)—See Alkaloid A.D. Skopje; *Int'l*, pg. 330
ALKALOID E.D.O.O—See Alkaloid A.D. Skopje; *Int'l*, pg. 330
ALKALOID-FARM D.O.O.—See Alkaloid A.D. Skopje; *Int'l*, pg. 330
ALKALOID ILAC TLS—See Alkaloid A.D. Skopje; *Int'l*, pg. 330
ALKALOID INT DOO—See Alkaloid A.D. Skopje; *Int'l*, pg. 330
ALKALOID KIEV CO, LTD.—See Alkaloid A.D. Skopje; *Int'l*, pg. 330
ALKALOID KONS DOOEL—See Alkaloid A.D. Skopje; *Int'l*, pg. 330
ALKALOIDPHARMA SA—See Alkaloid A.D. Skopje; *Int'l*, pg. 330
ALKALOID SH.P.K. (TIRANA)—See Alkaloid A.D. Skopje; *Int'l*, pg. 330
ALKALOID USA LLC—See Alkaloid A.D. Skopje; *Int'l*, pg. 330
ALKALOID VELEDROGERIJA DOO—See Alkaloid A.D. Skopje; *Int'l*, pg. 330
ALKAME HOLDINGS, INC.; *U.S. Public*, pg. 78
ALKAME WATER INC.—See Alkame Holdings, Inc.; *U.S. Public*, pg. 78
ALKAMI TECHNOLOGY, INC.; *U.S. Public*, pg. 78
ALKANE ENERGY LIMITED—See 3i Group plc; *Int'l*, pg. 8
ALKANE, INC.; *U.S. Public*, pg. 78
ALKANE RESOURCES LIMITED; *Int'l*, pg. 330
ALKANO CHEMICAL, INC.; *U.S. Private*, pg. 169
ALKAN SAS; *Int'l*, pg. 330
ALKAREEM MACHINERY—See Juki Corporation; *Int'l*, pg. 4022
ALKARGO S COOP—See Mondragon Corporation; *Int'l*, pg. 5028
ALKAR-RAPIDPAK, INC.—See The Middleby Corporation; *U.S. Public*, pg. 2113
ALKAR-RAPIDPAK-MP EQUIPMENT, INC.—See The Middleby Corporation; *U.S. Public*, pg. 2113
ALKAS CONSULTING—See Jones Lang LaSalle Incorporated; *U.S. Public*, pg. 1201
ALKA SECURITIES LIMITED; *Int'l*, pg. 330
AL KATHIRI HOLDING CO; *Int'l*, pg. 280
AL KAWTHAR COMPANY—See BERICAP GmbH & Co. KG; *Int'l*, pg. 980
ALKEME INSURANCE SERVICES, INC.—See GCP Capital Partners Holdings LLC; *U.S. Private*, pg. 1654
ALKEM LABORATORIES LTD.; *Int'l*, pg. 330
ALKEM LABORATORIES (PTY) LIMITED—See Alkem Laboratories Ltd.; *Int'l*, pg. 330
ALKEMY CAPITAL INVESTMENTS PLC; *Int'l*, pg. 331
ALKEMY SPA; *Int'l*, pg. 331
ALKERMES CONTROLLED THERAPEUTICS, INC.—See Alkermes plc; *Int'l*, pg. 331
ALKERMES, INC.—See Alkermes plc; *Int'l*, pg. 331
ALKERMES, INC. - WILMINGTON FACILITY—See Alkermes plc; *Int'l*, pg. 331
ALKERMES PHARMA IRELAND LIMITED—See Alkermes plc; *Int'l*, pg. 331
ALKERMES PLC - ATHLONE FACILITY—See Novo Nordisk Fonden; *Int'l*, pg. 5463
ALKERMES PLC; *Int'l*, pg. 331
ALKERN SAS—See Chequers SA; *Int'l*, pg. 1471
AL-KHAIR GADOON LIMITED; *Int'l*, pg. 286
AL KHALEEJ INVESTMENT P.J.S.C.; *Int'l*, pg. 280
AL KHALEEJ TAKAFUL INSURANCE COMPANY Q.P.S.C.; *Int'l*, pg. 280
ALKHALEEJ TRAINING & EDUCATION COMPANY; *Int'l*, pg. 331
AL KHALIJ COMMERCIAL BANK (AL KHALIJI) Q.S.C.—See Masraf Al Rayan (Q.S.C.); *Int'l*, pg. 4722
AL KHALIJI FRANCE S.A.—See Masraf Al Rayan (Q.S.C.); *Int'l*, pg. 4722
AL KHALILI UNITED ENTERPRISES LLC; *Int'l*, pg. 280
AL KHAZER FOR CONSTRUCTION MATERIALS, REAL ESTATE INVESTMENTS & GENERAL CONTRACTING; *Int'l*, pg. 280
AL KHAZNA INSURANCE COMPANY - ABU DHABI TRAFFIC—See Al Khazna Insurance Company P.S.C.; *Int'l*, pg. 280
AL KHAZNA INSURANCE COMPANY - AL AIN BRANCH—See Al Khazna Insurance Company P.S.C.; *Int'l*, pg. 280
AL KHAZNA INSURANCE COMPANY - AL AIN TRAFFIC—See Al Khazna Insurance Company P.S.C.; *Int'l*, pg. 281
AL KHAZNA INSURANCE COMPANY - AL MUSSAFAH LIGHT VEHICLE—See Al Khazna Insurance Company P.S.C.; *Int'l*, pg. 281
AL KHAZNA INSURANCE COMPANY - AL MUSSAFAH—See Al Khazna Insurance Company P.S.C.; *Int'l*, pg. 281
AL KHAZNA INSURANCE COMPANY - AL WAGAN—See Al Khazna Insurance Company P.S.C.; *Int'l*, pg. 281
AL KHAZNA INSURANCE COMPANY - BEDA ZAYED—See Al Khazna Insurance Company P.S.C.; *Int'l*, pg. 281
AL KHAZNA INSURANCE COMPANY - DUBAI—See Al Khazna Insurance Company P.S.C.; *Int'l*, pg. 281
AL KHAZNA INSURANCE COMPANY P.S.C.; *Int'l*, pg. 280
AL-KHODARI INDUSTRIAL TRADING & SERVICES—See Abdullah Abdul Mohsin Al-Khodari Sons Company; *Int'l*, pg. 59
AL KHOORY BUILDING MATERIALS & TRADING CO.—See Taleb Group; *Int'l*, pg. 7446
AL KHUWAIR DEVELOPMENT & SERVICES CO. SAOC—See Omar Zawawi Establishment LLC; *Int'l*, pg. 5561
ALKI CORPORATION—See Japan Tobacco Inc.; *Int'l*, pg. 3907
ALKIM ALKALI KIMYA A.S.; *Int'l*, pg. 331
ALKIMIA-PACKAGING SA—See The Chemical Society ALKIMIA; *Int'l*, pg. 7631
ALKIM KAGIT SANAYI VE TICARET A.S.; *Int'l*, pg. 331
AL KINDI OF VETERINARY VACCINES CO.; *Int'l*, pg. 281
ALKIS H. HADJIKYRIACOS (FROU FROU BISCUITS) PUBLIC LTD.; *Int'l*, pg. 331
ALKIT PRO-CAMERA INC.; *U.S. Private*, pg. 169
ALK&KOS SH.P.K.—See Alkaloid A.D. Skopje; *Int'l*, pg. 330
ALK & KOS SHPK—See Alkaloid A.D. Skopje; *Int'l*, pg. 330
AL-KO AIR TECHNOLOGY CO. LTD.—See PRIMEPULSE SE; *Int'l*, pg. 5979
AL-KO AUTOMOTIVE PARTS MANUFACTURING (NINGBO) CO. LTD.—See PRIMEPULSE SE; *Int'l*, pg. 5979
ALKO DISTRIBUTORS, INC.; *U.S. Private*, pg. 169
AL-KO ESPANA S.A.U.—See PRIMEPULSE SE; *Int'l*, pg. 5979
AL-KO KFT.—See PRIMEPULSE SE; *Int'l*, pg. 5979
AL-KO KOBER AB—See PRIMEPULSE SE; *Int'l*, pg. 5979
AL-KO KOBER G.M.B.H./S.R.L.—See PRIMEPULSE SE; *Int'l*, pg. 5979
AL-KO KOBER LTD.—See PRIMEPULSE SE; *Int'l*, pg. 5979
AL-KO KOBER SE—See PRIMEPULSE SE; *Int'l*, pg. 5979
AL-KO KOBER SIA—See PRIMEPULSE SE; *Int'l*, pg. 5979
AL-KO KOBER SLOVAKIA SPOL. S.R.O.—See PRIMEPULSE SE; *Int'l*, pg. 5979
AL-KO KOBER SP.Z.O.O.—See PRIMEPULSE SE; *Int'l*, pg. 5979
AL KOOT INSURANCE & REINSURANCE COMPANY P.J.S.C.—See Gulf International Services QSC; *Int'l*, pg. 3181
AL-KO RECORD S.A.—See PRIMEPULSE SE; *Int'l*, pg. 5979
ALKOR PETROO LIMITED—See IVRCL Limited; *Int'l*, pg. 3847
AL-KO S.A.S.—See PRIMEPULSE SE; *Int'l*, pg. 5979
ALKOSIGN LIMITED; *Int'l*, pg. 331
AL-KO TEKNOLOJI VE ARAC LTD. STI.—See PRIMEPULSE SE; *Int'l*, pg. 5979
AL-KO TRAILCO (PTY.) LTD.—See PRIMEPULSE SE; *Int'l*, pg. 5979
AL-KO USA, INC.—See PRIMEPULSE SE; *Int'l*, pg. 5979
AL-KOUT INDUSTRIAL PROJECTS COMPANY K.S.C.C.; *Int'l*, pg. 286
ALK-SCHERAX ARZNEIMITTEL GMBH—See Bayer Aktiengesellschaft; *Int'l*, pg. 904
ALK-SCHERAX ARZNEIMITTEL GMBH—See Lundbeckfonden; *Int'l*, pg. 4580
ALK SLOVAKIA S.R.O.—See Lundbeckfonden; *Int'l*, pg. 4579
ALK SVERIGE AB—See Lundbeckfonden; *Int'l*, pg. 4579
ALK TECHNOLOGIES, INC.—See Trimble, Inc.; *U.S. Public*, pg. 2190
AL KUHAIMI METAL INDUSTRIES LTD.; *Int'l*, pg. 281
ALKU, LLC—See FFL Partners LLC; *U.S. Private*, pg. 1500
ALKURI GLOBAL ACQUISITION CORP.; *U.S. Public*, pg. 78
ALKYL AMINES CHEMICALS LIMITED; *Int'l*, pg. 331
ALL3MEDIA HOLDINGS LTD—See Liberty Global plc; *Int'l*, pg. 4484
ALL3MEDIA HOLDINGS LTD—See Warner Bros. Discovery, Inc.; *U.S. Public*, pg. 2326
ALL3SPORTS, INC.—See C.C. Clark, Inc.; *U.S. Private*, pg. 706
ALL4LABELS GROUP GMBH—See Triton Advisers Limited; *Int'l*, pg. 7929
ALL4LABELS KASSEL GMBH—See Triton Advisers Limited; *Int'l*, pg. 7929
ALL4LABELS SCHEIZ AG—See Triton Advisers Limited; *Int'l*, pg. 7929
ALL4 LLC; *U.S. Private*, pg. 174
ALL ABFALL-LOGISTIK LEIPZIG GMBH—See Alba SE; *Int'l*, pg. 293
ALLABINC DE MEXICO, S.A. DE C.V.—See Zoetis, Inc.; *U.S. Public*, pg. 2409
ALL ABOARD AMERICA! HOLDINGS INC.—See Kelsian Group Limited; *Int'l*, pg. 4121
ALL ABOUT GIFTS & BASKETS; *U.S. Private*, pg. 169
ALL ABOUT, INC.; *Int'l*, pg. 331
ALL ABOUT PACKAGING; *U.S. Private*, pg. 169
ALL ABOUT PEOPLE, INC.; *U.S. Private*, pg. 169
ALL ABOUT STAFFING, INC.—See HCA Healthcare, Inc.; *U.S. Public*, pg. 990
ALLABOUTXPERT (PTY) LIMITED—See Adcorp Holdings Limited; *Int'l*, pg. 127
ALL ACCESS APPAREL INC.; *U.S. Private*, pg. 169
ALL ACCESS COMMUNICATION TECHNOLOGY (SHENZHEN) LIMITED—See China All Access (Holdings) Limited; *Int'l*, pg. 1482
ALL ACCESS MUSIC GROUP, INC.—See iHeartMedia, Inc.; *U.S. Public*, pg. 1095
ALL ACTIVE ASSET CAPITAL LTD.; *Int'l*, pg. 331
ALLAKOS, INC.; *U.S. Public*, pg. 78
ALLAMANDA PRIVATE HOSPITAL PTY. LTD.—See Brookfield Corporation; *Int'l*, pg. 1176
ALL AMERICAN INSURANCE COMPANY—See Central Mutual Insurance Company; *U.S. Private*, pg. 822
ALL AMERICAN-ARKANSAS POLY CORP.—See All American Poly Corp.; *U.S. Private*, pg. 170
ALL AMERICAN ASPHALT; *U.S. Private*, pg. 169
ALL AMERICAN AUTO SALES GROUP; *U.S. Private*, pg. 169
ALL AMERICAN BUILDING PRODUCTS—See Strength Capital Partners, LLC; *U.S. Private*, pg. 3839
ALL-AMERICAN CONTAINERS, LLC—See Clayton, Dubilier & Rice, LLC; *U.S. Private*, pg. 928
ALL AMERICAN CONTAINERS OF GEORGIA, LLC—See Clayton, Dubilier & Rice, LLC; *U.S. Private*, pg. 928
ALL AMERICAN CONTAINERS OF PUERTO RICO, LLC—See Clayton, Dubilier & Rice, LLC; *U.S. Private*, pg. 928
ALL AMERICAN CONTAINERS OF SOUTHERN CALIFORNIA INC.—See Clayton, Dubilier & Rice, LLC; *U.S. Private*, pg. 928
ALL AMERICAN CONTAINERS OF TAMPA, LLC—See Clayton, Dubilier & Rice, LLC; *U.S. Private*, pg. 928
ALL AMERICAN CONTAINERS OF TEXAS INC.—See Clayton, Dubilier & Rice, LLC; *U.S. Private*, pg. 928
ALL AMERICAN CONTAINERS OF THE MIDWEST INC.—See Clayton, Dubilier & Rice, LLC; *U.S. Private*, pg. 928
ALL AMERICAN CONTAINERS OF THE NORTHEAST, LLC—See Clayton, Dubilier & Rice, LLC; *U.S. Private*, pg. 928
ALL AMERICAN CONTAINERS OF THE PACIFIC COAST INC.—See Clayton, Dubilier & Rice, LLC; *U.S. Private*, pg. 928
ALL-AMERICAN CO-OP; *U.S. Private*, pg. 173
ALL-AMERICAN FIRE EQUIPMENT, INC.; *U.S. Private*, pg. 173
ALL AMERICAN FOODS, INC.; *U.S. Private*, pg. 169
ALL AMERICAN FORD, INC.—See All American Auto Sales Group; *U.S. Private*, pg. 169
ALL AMERICAN FORD OF KINGSTON, LLC—See All American Auto Sales Group; *U.S. Private*, pg. 169
ALL AMERICAN GLAMOUR CORP.; *U.S. Private*, pg. 169
ALL AMERICAN GLASS DISTRIBUTORS INC.; *U.S. Private*, pg. 169
ALL AMERICAN HOLDINGS LLC; *U.S. Private*, pg. 169
ALL AMERICAN HOMES, LLC—See Innovative Building Systems LLC; *U.S. Private*, pg. 2082
ALL AMERICAN HOMES OF IOWA, LLC—See Innovative Building Systems LLC; *U.S. Private*, pg. 2082
ALL AMERICAN LABEL & PACKAGING—See Heartwood Partners, LLC; *U.S. Private*, pg. 1901
ALL AMERICAN LENDING GROUP, LLC; *U.S. Private*, pg. 169
ALL AMERICAN MARINE, INC.—See Bryton Marine Group; *Int'l*, pg. 1201
ALL AMERICAN MEAT INC.; *U.S. Private*, pg. 169
ALL AMERICAN MEATS INC.; *U.S. Private*, pg. 169
ALL-AMERICAN MOVING GROUP LLC; *U.S. Private*, pg. 173
ALL AMERICAN POLY CORP. - LAWRENCEVILLE PLANT—See All American Poly Corp.; *U.S. Private*, pg. 170
ALL AMERICAN POLY CORP.; *U.S. Private*, pg. 169
ALL AMERICAN PROPANE, INC.; *U.S. Private*, pg. 170
ALL AMERICAN QUALITY FOODS INC.; *U.S. Private*, pg. 170
ALL-AMERICAN SCAFFOLD, LLC—See Brand Industrial Services, Inc.; *U.S. Private*, pg. 636
ALL AMERICAN SEMICONDUCTOR, LLC; *U.S. Private*, pg. 170
ALL AMERICAN SPORTS CORPORATION—See Fenway Partners, LLC; *U.S. Private*, pg. 1495
ALL AMERICAN SUBARU—See All American Auto Sales Group; *U.S. Private*, pg. 169
ALL AMERICAN SWIM; *U.S. Private*, pg. 170
ALL AMERICA-PHILLIP'S FLOWER SHOPS, INC.; *U.S. Private*, pg. 169
ALLANA BUICK & BERS, INC.; *U.S. Private*, pg. 174

COMPANY NAME INDEX

ALLAN A. MYERS, INC.; *U.S. Private*, pg. 174
ALLANASONS PRIVATE LIMITED; *Int'l*, pg. 333
ALLAN BLOCK CORPORATION; *U.S. Private*, pg. 174
ALLAN BRITEWAY ELECTRICAL CONTRACTORS, INC.; *U.S. Private*, pg. 174
ALLAN BROTHERS LTD.—See Ratos AB; *Int'l*, pg. 6220
THE ALLAN CANDY COMPANY LIMITED—See The Hershey Co.; *U.S. Public*, pg. 2089
ALLAN COMPANY - ROLL DIVISION—See Allan Company; *U.S. Private*, pg. 174
ALLAN COMPANY; *U.S. Private*, pg. 174
ALLAN CRAWFORD ASSOCIATES LIMITED; *Int'l*, pg. 332
ALLAND ET ROBERT; *Int'l*, pg. 333
ALLAN ELECTRIC MFG., LIMITED—See Allan International Holdings Limited; *Int'l*, pg. 332
ALLAN ERIKSSON MARK AB—See Storskogen Group AB; *Int'l*, pg. 7227
ALLANE SE—See Banco Santander, S.A.; *Int'l*, pg. 826
ALLANE SE—See Hyundai Motor Company; *Int'l*, pg. 3559
ALLAN INDUSTRIES INC.; *U.S. Private*, pg. 174
ALLAN INTERNATIONAL HOLDINGS LIMITED; *Int'l*, pg. 332
ALLAN MASKEW (PTY) LTD—See ARGENT INDUSTRIAL LIMITED; *Int'l*, pg. 560
ALLAN MOULD MANUFACTURING LIMITED—See Allan International Holdings Limited; *Int'l*, pg. 332
ALLAN MYERS, INC.; *U.S. Private*, pg. 174
ALLANN BROS. COFFEE, INC.; *U.S. Private*, pg. 174
ALLANNIC FRERES SA; *Int'l*, pg. 333
ALLAN PLASTIC MFG., LIMITED—See Allan International Holdings Limited; *Int'l*, pg. 332
ALLAN REHNSTROM AB—See Addtech AB; *Int'l*, pg. 131
ALLAN R. NELSON ENGINEERING (1997) INC.; *Int'l*, pg. 332
ALLAN S. GOODMAN INCORPORATED; *U.S. Private*, pg. 174
ALLANSON INTERNATIONAL INC.; *Int'l*, pg. 333
ALLANT GROUP, LLC—See Vencap Technologies, LLC; *U.S. Private*, pg. 4356
ALLAN TOOL & MACHINE CO., INC.; *U.S. Private*, pg. 174
ALLAN VIGIL'S FORD; *U.S. Private*, pg. 174
ALLAN WINDOW TECHNOLOGIES LTD.; *Int'l*, pg. 332
ALLA PUBLIC COMPANY LIMITED; *Int'l*, pg. 332
ALLARD NAZARIAN GROUP INC.; *U.S. Private*, pg. 174
ALL AREA PLUMBING, INC.—See ACCO Engineered Systems; *U.S. Private*, pg. 53
ALL AREA ROOFING & WATERPROOFING, INC.; *U.S. Private*, pg. 170
ALLARI SOLUTIONS, INC.; *U.S. Private*, pg. 175
ALLARITY THERAPEUTICS, INC.; *U.S. Public*, pg. 78
ALL AROUND LIGHTING, INC.—See Revolution Lighting Technologies, Inc.; *U.S. Public*, pg. 1793
ALL AROUND PROPERTY PRESERVATION, LLC.; *U.S. Private*, pg. 170
AL LARSON BOAT SHOP, INC.; *U.S. Private*, pg. 147
ALL ARTISTS AGENCY GMBH—See CTS Eventim AG & Co. KGAA; *Int'l*, pg. 1872
ALLATA, LLC; *U.S. Private*, pg. 175
ALLAWASAYA TEXTILE & FINISHING MILLS LTD.; *Int'l*, pg. 333
ALLBANC SPLIT CORP. II—See The Bank of Nova Scotia; *Int'l*, pg. 7617
ALLBANC SPLIT CORP.—See The Bank of Nova Scotia; *Int'l*, pg. 7617
ALL BASES COVERED INC.; *U.S. Private*, pg. 170
ALL BATTERY SALES & SERVICE, INC.—See Mitsubishi Heavy Industries, Ltd.; *Int'l*, pg. 4953
ALLBILDELAR I HUDDINGE AB—See Bilia AB; *Int'l*, pg. 1029
ALLBIRDS, INC.; *U.S. Public*, pg. 78
ALLBODEN AG ALLGEMEINE GRUNDSTUCKS-AKTIENGESELLSCHAFT—See Aroundtown SA; *Int'l*, pg. 578
ALLBOX NV—See KBC Group NV; *Int'l*, pg. 4104
ALLBRIDGE, LLC; *U.S. Private*, pg. 175
ALLBRIGHT INDUSTRIES (M) SDN BHD—See Karyon Industries Berhad; *Int'l*, pg. 4086
ALLBUSINESS.COM, INC.—See Cannae Holdings, Inc.; *U.S. Public*, pg. 429
ALLBUSINESS.COM, INC.—See CC Capital Partners, LLC; *U.S. Private*, pg. 798
ALLBUSINESS.COM, INC.—See Intercontinental Exchange, Inc.; *U.S. Public*, pg. 1141
ALL BY PHONE + NET DIALOGMARKETING & CONSULTING GMBH—See Teleperformance SE; *Int'l*, pg. 7539
ALL CAMPUS LLC; *U.S. Private*, pg. 170
ALLCANES CORP.—See Follett Corporation; *U.S. Private*, pg. 1559
ALLCAP ASSET MANAGEMENT LTD; *Int'l*, pg. 333
ALLCARE CLINICAL ASSOCIATES, PLLC—See Bain Capital, LP; *U.S. Private*, pg. 445
ALLCARE MEDICAL SNJ CORP.—See Quadrant Management, Inc.; *U.S. Private*, pg. 3316
ALLCARE PLUS PHARMACY LLC—See IQVIA Holdings Inc.; *U.S. Public*, pg. 1168
ALLCARGO LOGISTICS LIMITED; *Int'l*, pg. 333

ALLCELLS, LLC.—See Discovery Life Sciences, LLC; *U.S. Private*, pg. 1238
ALLCHECKDEALS INDIA PVT. LTD.—See Info Edge India Ltd; *Int'l*, pg. 3689
ALL CHEMICAL LEASING, INC.; *U.S. Private*, pg. 170
ALL CHEMICAL TRANSPORT—See All Chemical Leasing, Inc.; *U.S. Private*, pg. 170
ALLCHEM INDUSTRIES GROUP; *U.S. Private*, pg. 175
ALLCHEM INDUSTRIES INDUSTRIAL CHEMICALS GROUP—See AllChem Industries Group; *U.S. Private*, pg. 175
ALLCHEM INDUSTRIES PERFORMANCE PRODUCTS—See AllChem Industries Group; *U.S. Private*, pg. 175
ALLCHEM INDUSTRIES PERFORMANCE PRODUCTS—See AllChem Industries Group; *U.S. Private*, pg. 175
ALLCHEM INDUSTRIES PETROLEUM CHEMICALS GROUP—See AllChem Industries Group; *U.S. Private*, pg. 175
ALL CHICAGOLAND MOVING & STORAGE CO.; *U.S. Private*, pg. 170
ALL CHILDREN'S HOSPITAL INC.; *U.S. Private*, pg. 170
ALL-CLAD METALCRAFTERS LLC—See SEB S.A.; *Int'l*, pg. 6667
ALL-CLAD USA, INC.—See SEB S.A.; *Int'l*, pg. 6667
ALL CLOSURES IN, S.A.—See CORTICEIRA AMORIM, S.G.P.S., S.A.; *Int'l*, pg. 1807
ALL COAST, LLC; *U.S. Private*, pg. 170
ALLCOAT TECHNOLOGY, INC.; *U.S. Private*, pg. 175
ALLCO INCORPORATED; *U.S. Private*, pg. 175
ALLCO LTD.; *U.S. Private*, pg. 175
ALL COMMERCIAL FLOORS, INC.; *U.S. Private*, pg. 170
ALLCOMM (H.K.) LIMITED—See Alltronics Holdings Limited; *Int'l*, pg. 361
ALLCOMM WIRELESS, INC.—See Sentinel Capital Partners, L.L.C.; *U.S. Private*, pg. 3609
ALLCOM PRODUCTS LLC—See Oblong, Inc.; *U.S. Public*, pg. 3609
ALLCONNECT, INC.; *U.S. Private*, pg. 175
ALLCONNEX; *U.S. Private*, pg. 175
ALL CONSTRUCTION SERVICES, LLC—See Installed Building Products, Inc.; *U.S. Public*, pg. 1132
ALL CONTROL ENTERPRISES INC.; *U.S. Private*, pg. 170
ALLCOOL REFRIGERANT RECLAIM, LLC—See BC Partners LLP; *Int'l*, pg. 923
ALLCOOL REFRIGERANT RECLAIM, LLC—See EQT AB; *Int'l*, pg. 2482
ALL COPY PRODUCTS LLC; *U.S. Private*, pg. 170
ALLCORE S.P.A.; *Int'l*, pg. 334
ALL COSMOS BIO-TECH HOLDING CORPORATION; *Int'l*, pg. 331
ALL COSMOS INDUSTRIES SDN. BHD.—See All Cosmos Bio-Tech Holding Corporation; *Int'l*, pg. 331
ALL COUNTIES GLASS, INC.—See Patrick Industries, Inc.; *U.S. Public*, pg. 1652
ALL COVERED, INC.—See Konica Minolta, Inc.; *Int'l*, pg. 4258
ALLO SHIYKIVSKE—See Agroton Public Ltd; *Int'l*, pg. 221
ALL CYCLE WASTE, INC.—See Casella Waste Systems, Inc.; *U.S. Public*, pg. 445
ALLDATA LLC—See AutoZone, Inc.; *U.S. Public*, pg. 239
ALLEANZA ASSICURAZIONI S.P.A.—See Assicurazioni Generali S.p.A.; *Int'l*, pg. 643
ALLEANZA HOLDINGS CO., LTD.; *Int'l*, pg. 334
ALLEANZA TORO SERVIZI ASSICURATIVI S.R.L—See Assicurazioni Generali S.p.A.; *Int'l*, pg. 643
ALLEANZA TORO S.P.A.—See Assicurazioni Generali S.p.A.; *Int'l*, pg. 643
ALLEARTH RENEWABLES, INC.; *U.S. Private*, pg. 175
ALLEASING PTY LTD—See CHAMP Private Equity Pty. Ltd.; *Int'l*, pg. 1439
ALLEATO ASSEKURANZMAKLER GMBH—See adesso SE; *Int'l*, pg. 144
ALLEE-CENTER HAMM KG—See Deutsche EuroShop AG; *Int'l*, pg. 2065
A.L. LEE CORP.—See Victory of West Virginia, Inc.; *U.S. Private*, pg. 4379
ALLEGAN GENERAL HOSPITAL; *U.S. Private*, pg. 175
ALLEGANY OPTICAL LLC; *U.S. Private*, pg. 175
ALLEGHANY CAPITAL CORPORATION—See Berkshire Hathaway Inc.; *U.S. Public*, pg. 298
ALLEGHANY CORPORATION—See Berkshire Hathaway Inc.; *U.S. Public*, pg. 298
ALLEGHANY HOSPITALISTS, LLC—See HCA Healthcare, Inc.; *U.S. Public*, pg. 990
ALLEGHANY INSURANCE HOLDINGS LLC—See Berkshire Hathaway Inc.; *U.S. Public*, pg. 298
ALLEGHANY MEMORIAL PARK LLC—See Axar Capital Management L.P.; *U.S. Private*, pg. 411
ALLEGHANY PROPERTIES, LLC—See Berkshire Hathaway Inc.; *U.S. Public*, pg. 298
ALLEGHENY BRADFORD CORPORATION; *U.S. Private*, pg. 175
ALLEGHENY COUNTY LIBRARY ASSOCIATION; *U.S. Private*, pg. 175
ALLEGHENY DIMENSION LLP—See Allegheny Wood Products Inc.; *U.S. Private*, pg. 176

ALLEGIENT LLC

ALLEGHENY & EASTERN RAILROAD, LLC—See Brookfield Infrastructure Partners L.P.; *Int'l*, pg. 1190
ALLEGHENY & EASTERN RAILROAD, LLC—See GIC Pte. Ltd.; *Int'l*, pg. 2965
ALLEGHENY ELECTRIC COOPERATIVE; *U.S. Private*, pg. 176
ALLEGHENY HEALTH NETWORK; *U.S. Private*, pg. 176
ALLEGHENY HIGH LIFT INCORPORATED; *U.S. Private*, pg. 176
ALLEGHENY INSURANCE SERVICE INC.; *U.S. Private*, pg. 176
ALLEGHENY LUDLUM, LLC—See ATI Inc.; *U.S. Public*, pg. 221
ALLEGHENY LUDLUM-VANDERGRIFT—See ATI Inc.; *U.S. Public*, pg. 222
ALLEGHENY LUTHERAN SOCIAL MINISTRIES; *U.S. Private*, pg. 176
ALLEGHENY MILLWORK; *U.S. Private*, pg. 176
ALLEGHENY MINERAL CORPORATION—See The Snyder Group, Inc.; *U.S. Private*, pg. 4119
ALLEGHENY PIPE & SUPPLY CO—See Winsupply, Inc.; *U.S. Private*, pg. 4545
ALLEGHENY PLASTICS, INC. - PERFORMANCE PLASTICS DIVISION—See Allegheny Plastics Inc.; *U.S. Private*, pg. 176
ALLEGHENY PLASTICS INC.; *U.S. Private*, pg. 176
ALLEGHENY PRINTED PLASTICS, LLC—See Allegheny Plastics Inc.; *U.S. Private*, pg. 176
ALLEGHENY RAIL PRODUCTS—See L.B. Foster Company; *U.S. Public*, pg. 1278
ALLEGHENY RAW MATERIALS, LLC—See AMG Resources Corp.; *U.S. Private*, pg. 262
ALLEGHENY RECYCLED PRODUCTS, INC.—See Audax Group, Limited Partnership; *U.S. Private*, pg. 386
ALLEGHENY RODNEY—See ATI Inc.; *U.S. Public*, pg. 221
ALLEGHENY STEEL DISTRIBUTORS, INC.—See Reliance Steel & Aluminum Co.; *U.S. Public*, pg. 1779
ALLEGHENY SURFACE TECHNOLOGY—See Allegheny Bradford Corporation; *U.S. Private*, pg. 175
ALLEGHENY TECHNOLOGIES GMBH—See ATI Inc.; *U.S. Public*, pg. 221
ALLEGHENY TECHNOLOGIES INCORPORATED - SINGAPORE—See ATI Inc.; *U.S. Public*, pg. 222
ALLEGHENY TECHNOLOGIES JAPAN LTD.—See ATI Inc.; *U.S. Public*, pg. 222
ALLEGHENY TECHNOLOGIES KOREA—See ATI Inc.; *U.S. Public*, pg. 222
ALLEGHENY TECHNOLOGIES LIMITED—See ATI Inc.; *U.S. Public*, pg. 222
ALLEGHENY TECHNOLOGIES SAS—See ATI Inc.; *U.S. Public*, pg. 222
ALLEGHENY & WESTERN RAILWAY CO.—See CSX Corporation; *U.S. Public*, pg. 602
ALLEGHENY WOOD PRODUCTS INC.; *U.S. Private*, pg. 176
ALLEGHENY WOOD PRODUCTS PRINCETON—See Allegheny Wood Products Inc.; *U.S. Private*, pg. 176
ALLEGIANCE BANCSHARES, INC.—See Stellar Bancorp, Inc.; *U.S. Public*, pg. 1944
ALLEGIANCE BANK—See Stellar Bancorp, Inc.; *U.S. Public*, pg. 1944
ALLEGIANCE COAL LIMITED; *Int'l*, pg. 334
ALLEGIANCE CREDIT UNION; *U.S. Private*, pg. 176
ALLEGIANCE FIRE & RESCUE—See Allegiance Trucks, LLC; *U.S. Private*, pg. 176
ALLEGIANCE FUNDRAISING LLC; *U.S. Private*, pg. 176
ALLEGIANCE, INC.; *U.S. Private*, pg. 176
ALLEGIANCE MARKETING GROUP LLC—See Allianz SE; *Int'l*, pg. 343
ALLEGIANCE MOBILE HEALTH; *U.S. Private*, pg. 176
ALLEGIANCE TITLE COMPANY—See First Title Abstract & Services, LLC; *U.S. Private*, pg. 1530
ALLEGIANCE TRUCKS, LLC; *U.S. Private*, pg. 176
ALLEGIAN INSURANCE COMPANY—See Tenet Healthcare Corporation; *U.S. Public*, pg. 2014
ALLEGIANT GOLD LTD.; *Int'l*, pg. 334
ALLEGIANT GOLD (U.S.) LTD.—See Allegiant Gold Ltd.; *Int'l*, pg. 334
ALLEGIANT NETWORKS, LLC—See Crexendo, Inc.; *U.S. Public*, pg. 594
ALLEGIANT NONSTOP MICHIGAN, LLC—See Allegiant Travel Company; *U.S. Public*, pg. 78
ALLEGIANT PROFESSIONAL BUSINESS SERVICES, INC.; *U.S. Private*, pg. 176
ALLEGIANT SYSTEMS, INC.—See Allegiant Travel Company; *U.S. Public*, pg. 78
ALLEGIANT TRAVEL COMPANY; *U.S. Public*, pg. 78
ALLEGIENT DEFENSE INC.—See BCS, LLC; *U.S. Private*, pg. 500
ALLEGIENT LLC; *U.S. Private*, pg. 176
ALLEGION A/S—See Allegion Public Limited Company; *Int'l*, pg. 335
ALLEGION (AUSTRALIA) PTY LIMITED—See Allegion Public Limited Company; *Int'l*, pg. 335
ALLEGION B.V.—See Allegion Public Limited Company; *Int'l*, pg. 335
ALLEGION CANADA INC.—See Allegion Public Limited Company; *Int'l*, pg. 335

ALLEGIENT LLC / CORPORATE AFFILIATIONS

ALLEGION EMNIYET VE GUVENLIK SISTEMLERI SANAYI A.S.—See Allegion Public Limited Company; *Int'l*, pg. 335

ALLEGION FU HSING LIMITED—See Allegion Public Limited Company; *Int'l*, pg. 335

ALLEGION INTERNATIONAL AG—See Allegion Public Limited Company; *Int'l*, pg. 335

ALLEGION NV—See Allegion Public Limited Company; *Int'l*, pg. 335

ALLEGION PLC - EUROPE, MIDDLE EAST, INDIA & AFRICA MAIN OFFICE—See Allegion Public Limited Company; *Int'l*, pg. 335

ALLEGION PUBLIC LIMITED COMPANY; *Int'l*, pg. 334

ALLEGION SECURITY TECHNOLOGIES (CHINA) CO., LTD.—See Allegion Public Limited Company; *Int'l*, pg. 335

ALLEGION (UK) LIMITED—See Allegion Public Limited Company; *Int'l*, pg. 335

ALLEGION US HOLDING COMPANY INC.—See Allegion Public Limited Company; *Int'l*, pg. 335

ALLEGION US—See Allegion Public Limited Company; *Int'l*, pg. 335

ALLEGIS CORPORATION; *U.S. Private*, pg. 177

ALLEGIS GROUP GMBH—See Allegis Group, Inc.; *U.S. Private*, pg. 177

ALLEGIS GROUP, INC.; *U.S. Private*, pg. 177

ALLEGIS GROUP LTD.—See Allegis Group, Inc.; *U.S. Private*, pg. 177

ALLEGO B.V.—See Meridiam Infrastructure Partners SAS; *Int'l*, pg. 4835

ALLEGO N.V.—See Meridiam Infrastructure Partners SAS; *Int'l*, pg. 4835

ALLEGRA BRANDS; *U.S. Private*, pg. 177

ALLEGRA NETWORK LLC—See Alliance Franchise Brands LLC; *U.S. Private*, pg. 182

ALLEGRA ORTHOPAEDICS LTD.; *Int'l*, pg. 336

ALLEGRE PUERICULTURE S.A.S.—See Newell Brands Inc.; *U.S. Public*, pg. 1513

ALLEGRO COFFEE CO.—See Amazon.com, Inc.; *U.S. Public*, pg. 91

ALLEGRO CORPORATION; *U.S. Private*, pg. 178

ALLEGRO DEVELOPMENT CORPORATION—See ION Investment Group Ltd.; *Int'l*, pg. 3794

ALLEGRO FUNDS PTY. LTD.; *Int'l*, pg. 336

ALLEGRO LIMITED—See Dole plc; *Int'l*, pg. 2158

ALLEGRO MANUFACTURING, INC.—See American Securities LLC; *U.S. Private*, pg. 247

ALLEGRO MERGER CORP.; *U.S. Private*, pg. 178

ALLEGRO MICROSYSTEMS ARGENTINA, S.A.—See Allegro MicroSystems, Inc.; *U.S. Public*, pg. 78

ALLEGRO MICROSYSTEMS EUROPE LIMITED—See Sanken Electric Co., Ltd.; *Int'l*, pg. 6540

ALLEGRO MICROSYSTEMS FRANCE SAS—See Allegro MicroSystems, Inc.; *U.S. Public*, pg. 78

ALLEGRO MICROSYSTEMS GERMANY GMBH—See Allegro MicroSystems, Inc.; *U.S. Public*, pg. 78

ALLEGRO MICROSYSTEMS, INC.; *U.S. Public*, pg. 78

ALLEGRO MICROSYSTEMS, LLC—See Sanken Electric Co., Ltd.; *Int'l*, pg. 6540

ALLEGRO MICROSYSTEMS MARKETING INDIA PRIVATE LIMITED—See Allegro MicroSystems, Inc.; *U.S. Public*, pg. 78

ALLEGRO MICROSYSTEMS PHILIPPINES, INC.—See Sanken Electric Co., Ltd.; *Int'l*, pg. 6540

ALLEGRO MICROSYSTEMS PHILIPPINES REALTY INC.—See Allegro MicroSystems, Inc.; *U.S. Public*, pg. 78

ALLEGRO SENIOR LIVING, LLC—See Love Real Estate Company; *U.S. Private*, pg. 2501

ALLEGRO (SHANGHAI) MICRO ELECTRONICS COMMERCIAL & TRADING CO., LTD.—See Allegro MicroSystems, Inc.; *U.S. Public*, pg. 78

ALLEGRO WIRELESS CANADA INC.; *Int'l*, pg. 336

ALL EIGHTS (M) SDN BHD—See HORIBA Ltd; *Int'l*, pg. 3474

ALLELIX NEUROSCIENCE, INC.—See Takeda Pharmaceutical Company Limited; *Int'l*, pg. 7438

ALLEN AIRCRAFT PRODUCTS, INC. - AIRCRAFT DIVISION—See Allen Aircraft Products, Inc.; *U.S. Private*, pg. 178

ALLEN AIRCRAFT PRODUCTS, INC.; *U.S. Private*, pg. 178

ALLEN, ALLEN, ALLEN & ALLEN; *U.S. Private*, pg. 180

ALLEN & ALLEN COMPANY; *U.S. Private*, pg. 178

ALLENA PHARMACEUTICALS, INC.; *U.S. Public*, pg. 79

ALLEN ASSOCIATES; *U.S. Private*, pg. 178

ALLEN AUDIO, INC.—See Allen Organ Company; *U.S. Private*, pg. 179

ALLEN-BAILEY TAG & LABEL INC.; *U.S. Private*, pg. 180

ALLEN-BECK INDUSTRIES INC.—See Hickory Springs Manufacturing Company; *U.S. Private*, pg. 1933

ALLEN BETHANY MEDICAL CENTER LLC—See Adeptus Health Inc.; *U.S. Private*, pg. 78

ALLENBUILD LTD.—See Renew Holdings plc; *Int'l*, pg. 6277

ALLEN & CARON INC—See Dresner Corporate Services Inc.; *U.S. Private*, pg. 1276

ALLEN C. EWING & CO.; *U.S. Private*, pg. 178

ALLEN CHRISTIAN BUICK OLDSMOBILE PONTIAC GMC, INC.; *U.S. Private*, pg. 178

ALLEN CODING GMBH—See Illinois Tool Works Inc.; *U.S. Public*, pg. 1101

ALLEN & COMPANY INCORPORATED—See Allen Holding Inc.; *U.S. Private*, pg. 179

THE ALLEN COMPANY INC.; *U.S. Private*, pg. 3984

ALLEN & COMPANY OF FLORIDA, INC.—See LPL Financial Holdings Inc.; *U.S. Public*, pg. 1343

ALLEN CORPORATION OF AMERICA, INC.; *U.S. Private*, pg. 178

ALLEN COUNTY RECYCLERS INC.; *U.S. Private*, pg. 178

ALLEN CREEK HEALTHCARE, INC.—See The Ensign Group, Inc.; *U.S. Public*, pg. 2069

ALLEN DANIEL ASSOCIATES INC.; *U.S. Private*, pg. 178

ALLEN DISTRIBUTION; *U.S. Private*, pg. 178

ALLEN EDMONDS LLC—See Caleres, Inc.; *U.S. Public*, pg. 422

ALLEN ENGINEERING CORPORATION; *U.S. Private*, pg. 178

ALLEN ENTERPRISES, INC.; *U.S. Private*, pg. 178

ALLEN EQUIPMENT, INC.—See American Securities LLC; *U.S. Private*, pg. 247

ALLEN EQUIPMENT, INC.—See Cleaners Closet Inc.; *U.S. Private*, pg. 931

ALLEN EXTRUDERS, LLC—See Sekisui Chemical Co., Ltd.; *Int'l*, pg. 6694

ALLEN FAMILY FOODS, INC.; *U.S. Private*, pg. 178

ALLEN FRANCE SAS—See Illinois Tool Works Inc.; *U.S. Public*, pg. 1101

ALLEN & GERRITSEN, INC.; *U.S. Private*, pg. 178

ALLEN GWYNN CHEVROLET; *U.S. Private*, pg. 179

ALLEN HARIM FOODS LLC—See Harim Holdings Co., Ltd.; *Int'l*, pg. 3275

ALLEN HOLDING INC.; *U.S. Private*, pg. 179

ALLEN & HOSHALL INC - NASHVILLE—See Allen & Hoshall, Inc.; *U.S. Private*, pg. 178

ALLEN & HOSHALL, INC.; *U.S. Private*, pg. 178

ALLEN & HOSHALL—See Allen & Hoshall, Inc.; *U.S. Private*, pg. 178

ALLEN & HOSHALL—See Allen & Hoshall, Inc.; *U.S. Private*, pg. 178

ALLEN INDUSTRIES INC.; *U.S. Private*, pg. 179

ALLEN INSURANCE ASSOCIATES, INC.—See Aon plc; *Int'l*, pg. 489

ALLEN INTEGRATED ASSEMBLIES—See Allen Organ Company; *U.S. Private*, pg. 179

ALLEN INVESTMENTS LIMITED—See Speedy Hire Plc; *Int'l*, pg. 7133

THE ALLEN J. FLOOD COMPANIES, INC.—See Tokio Marine Holdings, Inc.; *Int'l*, pg. 7783

ALLEN-KEITH CONSTRUCTION CO., INC.; *U.S. Private*, pg. 180

ALLEN LANE LIMITED—See Bain Capital, LP; *U.S. Private*, pg. 433

ALLEN L. BENDER, INC.; *U.S. Private*, pg. 179

ALLEN LUMBER COMPANY INC.; *U.S. Private*, pg. 179

ALLEN LUND COMPANY, LLC; *U.S. Private*, pg. 179

ALLEN MATKINS LECK GAMBLE MALLORY & NATSIS LLP; *U.S. Private*, pg. 179

ALLEN MEDIA BROADCASTING EVANSVILLE, INC.—See Entertainment Studios, Inc.; *U.S. Private*, pg. 1405

ALLEN MEDIA BROADCASTING LAFAYETTE, INC.—See Entertainment Studios, Inc.; *U.S. Private*, pg. 1405

ALLEN MEDIA BROADCASTING LLC—See Entertainment Studios, Inc.; *U.S. Private*, pg. 1405

ALLEN MEDICAL SYSTEMS, INC.—See Baxter International Inc.; *U.S. Public*, pg. 282

ALLEN & O'HARA EDUCATION SERVICES, INC.—See Greystar Real Estate Partners, LLC; *U.S. Private*, pg. 1785

ALLEN OIL COMPANY INC.; *U.S. Private*, pg. 179

ALLEN OIL COMPANY OF SYLACAUGA; *U.S. Private*, pg. 179

ALLEN ORGAN COMPANY; *U.S. Private*, pg. 179

ALLEN OVERY SHEARMAN STERLING LLP; *Int'l*, pg. 336

ALLEN PACKAGING CO.—See GenNx360 Capital Partners, L.P.; *U.S. Private*, pg. 1672

ALLEN PRESS INC.; *U.S. Private*, pg. 179

ALLEN PRINTING, INC.; *U.S. Private*, pg. 179

ALLEN SAMUEL CHRYSLER DODGE JEEP; *U.S. Private*, pg. 179

ALLEN SAMUELS AUTO GROUP; *U.S. Private*, pg. 179

ALLEN SAMUELS CHEVROLET OF CORPUS CHRISTI, INC.—See AutoNation, Inc.; *U.S. Public*, pg. 232

ALLEN SAMUELS CHEVROLET OF WACO, INC.—See AutoNation, Inc.; *U.S. Public*, pg. 232

ALLEN SAMUELS CHEVROLET—See Allen Samuels Auto Group; *U.S. Private*, pg. 179

ALLENS ASPHALT PTY LTD—See Seven Group Holdings Limited; *Int'l*, pg. 6732

ALLEN & SHARIFF CORPORATION; *U.S. Private*, pg. 178

ALLEN-SHERMAN-HOFF—See Babcock & Wilcox Enterprises, Inc.; *U.S. Public*, pg. 262

ALLENS OF HASTINGS, INC.; *U.S. Private*, pg. 180

ALLEN'S PHARMASERV, INC.—See Procare LTC Holding LLC; *U.S. Private*, pg. 3271

ALLENS STEEL PRODUCTS INC.; *U.S. Private*, pg. 180

ALLEN SUPER SAVE MARKETS; *U.S. Private*, pg. 179

ALLENSVILLE PLANING MILL INC.; *U.S. Private*, pg. 180

ALLEN SYSTEMS GROUP, INC.; *U.S. Private*, pg. 180

ALLEN SYSTEMS GROUP—See Allen Systems Group, Inc.; *U.S. Private*, pg. 180

ALLENTECH, INC.—See Matrix Service Company; *U.S. Public*, pg. 1397

ALLEN TILLERY CHEVROLET, INC.; *U.S. Private*, pg. 180

ALLENTOWN, INC.—See Aterian Investment Management, L.P.; *U.S. Private*, pg. 366

ALLENTOWN MACK SALES & SERVICE, INC.; *U.S. Private*, pg. 180

ALLEN TURNER HYUNDAI INC.; *U.S. Private*, pg. 180

ALLEN-VANGUARD CORPORATION—See Independence Capital Partners, LLC; *U.S. Public*, pg. 2057

ALLEN-VANGUARD LIMITED—See Independence Capital Partners, LLC; *U.S. Public*, pg. 2057

ALLEN & WEBB INDUSTRIAL SUPPLY; *U.S. Private*, pg. 178

ALL ERECTION & CRANE RENTAL CORP.; *U.S. Private*, pg. 170

ALLERGAN AG—See AbbVie Inc.; *U.S. Public*, pg. 22

ALLERGAN APS—See AbbVie Inc.; *U.S. Public*, pg. 22

ALLERGAN AS—See AbbVie Inc.; *U.S. Public*, pg. 22

ALLERGAN AUSTRALIA (PTY.) LTD.—See AbbVie Inc.; *U.S. Public*, pg. 22

ALLERGAN BIOLOGICS LIMITED—See AbbVie Inc.; *U.S. Public*, pg. 23

ALLERGAN BOTOX LIMITED—See AbbVie Inc.; *U.S. Public*, pg. 22

ALLERGAN B.V.—See AbbVie Inc.; *U.S. Public*, pg. 22

ALLERGAN C.I.S. SARL—See AbbVie Inc.; *U.S. Public*, pg. 22

ALLERGAN COLOMBIA S.A.—See AbbVie Inc.; *U.S. Public*, pg. 22

ALLERGAN CZ, S.R.O.—See AbbVie Inc.; *U.S. Public*, pg. 22

ALLERGAN DEVELOPMENT VENTURES I UK—See AbbVie Inc.; *U.S. Public*, pg. 22

ALLERGAN D.O.O. BEOGRAD—See AbbVie Inc.; *U.S. Public*, pg. 22

ALLERGAN FRANCE S.A.S.—See AbbVie Inc.; *U.S. Public*, pg. 23

ALLERGAN GMBH—See AbbVie Inc.; *U.S. Public*, pg. 22

ALLERGAN HOLDINGS LIMITED—See AbbVie Inc.; *U.S. Public*, pg. 23

ALLERGAN HONG KONG LIMITED—See AbbVie Inc.; *U.S. Public*, pg. 23

ALLERGAN HUNGARY KFT.—See AbbVie Inc.; *U.S. Public*, pg. 22

ALLERGAN INC.—See AbbVie Inc.; *U.S. Public*, pg. 23

ALLERGAN, INC.—See AbbVie Inc.; *U.S. Public*, pg. 22

ALLERGAN INDIA LIMITED—See AbbVie Inc.; *U.S. Public*, pg. 23

ALLERGAN INDUSTRIE S.A.S.—See AbbVie Inc.; *U.S. Public*, pg. 23

ALLERGAN K.K.—See AbbVie Inc.; *U.S. Public*, pg. 23

ALLERGAN KOREA LTD.—See AbbVie Inc.; *U.S. Public*, pg. 23

ALLERGAN LABORATORIOS LTDA.—See AbbVie Inc.; *U.S. Public*, pg. 23

ALLERGAN LIMITED—See AbbVie Inc.; *U.S. Public*, pg. 23

ALLERGAN-LOA S.A.—See AbbVie Inc.; *U.S. Public*, pg. 23

ALLERGAN MIDDLE EAST LIMITED—See AbbVie Inc.; *U.S. Public*, pg. 22

ALLERGAN NEW ZEALAND LIMITED—See AbbVie Inc.; *U.S. Public*, pg. 23

ALLERGAN NORDEN AB—See AbbVie Inc.; *U.S. Public*, pg. 23

ALLERGAN N.V.—See AbbVie Inc.; *U.S. Public*, pg. 23

ALLERGAN PHARMACEUTICALS IRELAND (EUROCENTRE)—See AbbVie Inc.; *U.S. Public*, pg. 23

ALLERGAN PHARMACEUTICALS (IRELAND) LTD., INC.—See AbbVie Inc.; *U.S. Public*, pg. 23

ALLERGAN PHARMACEUTICALS (PROPRIETARY) LIMITED—See AbbVie Inc.; *U.S. Public*, pg. 23

ALLERGAN PHARMA CO.—See AbbVie Inc.; *U.S. Public*, pg. 23

ALLERGAN PLC—See AbbVie Inc.; *U.S. Public*, pg. 22

ALLERGAN PRODUCTOS FARMACEUTICOS LTDA.—See AbbVie Inc.; *U.S. Public*, pg. 22

ALLERGAN PRODUTOS FARMACEUTICOS, LTDA.—See AbbVie Inc.; *U.S. Public*, pg. 23

ALLERGAN S.A. DE C.V.—See AbbVie Inc.; *U.S. Public*, pg. 23

ALLERGAN SAUDI ARABIA LLC—See AbbVie Inc.; *U.S. Public*, pg. 22

ALLERGAN S.A.U.—See AbbVie Inc.; *U.S. Public*, pg. 23

ALLERGAN SCIENTIFIC OFFICE—See AbbVie Inc.; *U.S. Public*, pg. 22

ALLERGAN SINGAPORE PTE. LTD.—See AbbVie Inc.; *U.S. Public*, pg. 23

COMPANY NAME INDEX

ALLERGAN SINGAPORE PTE. LTD.—See AbbVie Inc.; *U.S. Public*, pg. 22
ALLERGAN SINGAPORE PTE. LTD.—See AbbVie Inc.; *U.S. Public*, pg. 22
ALLERGAN SK S.R.O.—See AbbVie Inc.; *U.S. Public*, pg. 22
ALLERGAN S.P.A.—See AbbVie Inc.; *U.S. Public*, pg. 23
ALLERGAN SP. Z.O.O.—See AbbVie Inc.; *U.S. Public*, pg. 22
ALLERGAN SRL—See AbbVie Inc.; *U.S. Public*, pg. 22
ALLERGAN UKRAINE, LLC—See AbbVie Inc.; *U.S. Public*, pg. 22
ALLERGAN USA, INC.—See AbbVie Inc.; *U.S. Public*, pg. 23
ALLERGON AB—See Thermo Fisher Scientific Inc.; *U.S. Public*, pg. 2145
ALLERGOPHARMA (BEIJING) PHARMACEUTICAL TECHNOLOGY CO., LTD.—See Dermapharm Holding SE; *Int'l*, pg. 2043
ALLERGOPHARMA ESPANA S.L.—See Dermapharm Holding SE; *Int'l*, pg. 2043
ALLERGOPHARMA JOACHIM GANZER KG—See Merck KGaA; *Int'l*, pg. 4830
ALLERGOPHARMA VERTRIEBSGES, MBH—See Dermapharm Holding SE; *Int'l*, pg. 2043
ALLERGY & ASTHMA CARE NEW YORK PLLC—See Schweiger Dermatology Group; *U.S. Private*, pg. 3572
ALLERGY LABORATORIES, INC.—See Lundbeckfonden; *Int'l*, pg. 4580
ALLERGY RESEARCH GROUP LLC—See WM Partners LP; *U.S. Private*, pg. 4552
ALLERGY THERAPEUTICS NETHERLANDS BV—See ZQ Capital Management Limited; *Int'l*, pg. 8691
ALLERGY THERAPEUTICS PLC—See ZQ Capital Management Limited; *Int'l*, pg. 8691
ALLER HOLDING A/S; *Int'l*, pg. 336
ALLER MEDIA AB—See Aller Holding A/S; *Int'l*, pg. 336
ALLER MEDIA AS—See Aller Holding A/S; *Int'l*, pg. 336
ALLER MEDIA OY—See Aller Holding A/S; *Int'l*, pg. 336
ALLER-RETOUR; *Int'l*, pg. 336
ALLERS FAMILIE-JOURNAL A/S—See Aller Holding A/S; *Int'l*, pg. 336
ALLERSHAUSEN CARE GMBH—See SOL S.p.A.; *Int'l*, pg. 7067
ALLENTHAL WERKE AG; *Int'l*, pg. 336
ALLERTON SUPPLY CO.; *U.S. Private*, pg. 180
ALLER TRYK A/S—See Aller Holding A/S; *Int'l*, pg. 336
ALLERVIE HEALTH PROFESSIONAL CORPORATION; *U.S. Private*, pg. 180
ALLESCO INDUSTRIES INC.; *U.S. Private*, pg. 180
ALLESON OF ROCHESTER, INC.—See Platinum Equity, LLC; *U.S. Private*, pg. 3207
ALLESSA GMBH—See International Chemical Investors S.E.; *Int'l*, pg. 3744
ALLETE & AFFILIATED COMPANIES RETIREE HEALTH PLAN A; *U.S. Private*, pg. 180
ALLETE CLEAN ENERGY, INC.—See ALLETE, Inc.; *U.S. Public*, pg. 79
ALLETE ENTERPRISES, INC.—See ALLETE, Inc.; *U.S. Public*, pg. 79
ALLETE, INC.; *U.S. Public*, pg. 79
ALLETTI GESTIELLE SGR S.P.A.—See Banco BPM S.p.A.; *Int'l*, pg. 818
ALLEVATO ARCHITECTS INC—See Harrison French & Associates, Ltd.; *U.S. Private*, pg. 1870
ALLEY-CASSETTY BRICK BOWLING GREEN DIVISION—See Alley-Cassetty Companies; *U.S. Private*, pg. 180
ALLEY-CASSETTY BRICK COLUMBIA DIV.—See Alley-Cassetty Companies; *U.S. Private*, pg. 180
ALLEY-CASSETTY BRICK GALLATIN DIV.—See Alley-Cassetty Companies; *U.S. Private*, pg. 180
ALLEY-CASSETTY BRICK MURFREESBORO DIV.—See Alley-Cassetty Companies; *U.S. Private*, pg. 180
ALLEY-CASSETTY BRICK NASHVILLE DIV.—See Alley-Cassetty Companies; *U.S. Private*, pg. 180
ALLEY-CASSETTY COMPANIES - ALLEY-CASSETTY TRUCK CENTER DIVISION—See Alley-Cassetty Companies; *U.S. Private*, pg. 181
ALLEY-CASSETTY COMPANIES; *U.S. Private*, pg. 180
ALLEYCORP; *U.S. Private*, pg. 181
ALLEY THEATRE; *U.S. Private*, pg. 180
ALLEYTON RESOURCE COMPANY, LLC—See Summit Materials, Inc.; *U.S. Public*, pg. 1959
ALL FASHIONS IMPORTS INC.; *U.S. Private*, pg. 170
ALLFAST FASTENING SYSTEMS, LLC—See TriMas Corporation; *U.S. Public*, pg. 2189
ALLFAVOR CIRCUITS (SHENZHEN) CO., LTD.—See Jiangsu Allfavor Intelligent Circuits Technology Co., Ltd.; *Int'l*, pg. 3943
ALLFAX SPECIALTIES INC.; *U.S. Private*, pg. 181
ALLFINANZ VERSICHERUNGS- UND FINANZSERVICE GMBH—See UNIQA Insurance Group AG; *Int'l*, pg. 8057
ALLFIN NV-SA—See Immobel SA; *Int'l*, pg. 3627
ALLFLEX ARGENTIA S.A.—See Merck & Co., Inc.; *U.S. Public*, pg. 1415
ALLFLEX AUSTRALIA PTY LTD—See Merck & Co., Inc.; *U.S. Public*, pg. 1415

ALLFLEX DAN-MARK APS—See Merck & Co., Inc.; *U.S. Public*, pg. 1415
ALLFLEX EUROPE SA—See BC Partners LLP; *Int'l*, pg. 923
ALL FLEX FLEXIBLE CIRUITS, LLC—See Granite Equity Partners LLC; *U.S. Private*, pg. 1755
ALLFLEX GROUP GERMANY GMBH—See Merck & Co., Inc.; *U.S. Public*, pg. 1415
ALLFLEX INDIA PRIVATE LIMITED—See Merck & Co., Inc.; *U.S. Public*, pg. 1415
ALLFLEX INTERNATIONAL DO BRASIL LTDA—See Merck & Co., Inc.; *U.S. Public*, pg. 1415
ALLFLEX NEW ZEALAND LIMITED—See Merck & Co., Inc.; *U.S. Public*, pg. 1415
ALLFLEX POLSKA SP Z O.O.—See Merck & Co., Inc.; *U.S. Public*, pg. 1415
ALLFLEX SCR VOSTOK—See Merck & Co., Inc.; *U.S. Public*, pg. 1415
ALLFLEX UK GROUP—See Merck & Co., Inc.; *U.S. Public*, pg. 1415
ALLFLEX USA, INC.—See BC Partners LLP; *Int'l*, pg. 923
ALL-FLO PUMP COMPANY, LIMITED—See Dover Corporation; *U.S. Public*, pg. 680
ALL FLORIDA ELECTRIC COMPANY INC.; *U.S. Private*, pg. 170
ALL FLORIDA PAPER; *U.S. Private*, pg. 170
ALL FOR ONE GROUP SE—See Unternehmens Invest AG; *Int'l*, pg. 8085
ALL FOR ONE MEDIA CORP.; *U.S. Public*, pg. 78
ALL FOR ONE STEEB AG—See Unternehmens Invest AG; *Int'l*, pg. 8085
ALL FREIGHT SYSTEMS INC.; *U.S. Private*, pg. 171
ALLFUNDS BANK, S.A.—See GIC Pte. Ltd.; *Int'l*, pg. 2964
ALLFUNDS BANK, S.A.—See Hellman & Friedman LLC; *U.S. Private*, pg. 1907
ALLFUNDS GROUP PLC; *Int'l*, pg. 336
ALLGAS INC. OF MONTGOMERY—See Ergon, Inc.; *U.S. Private*, pg. 1418
ALLGAU RESORT GMBH—See Fresenius SE & Co. KGaA; *Int'l*, pg. 2777
ALLGEIER CORE GMBH—See Allgeier SE; *Int'l*, pg. 336
ALLGEIER CYRIS GMBH—See Allgeier SE; *Int'l*, pg. 336
ALLGEIER DMS SOLUTIONS—See Allgeier SE; *Int'l*, pg. 336
ALLGEIER EDUCATION GMBH—See Allgeier SE; *Int'l*, pg. 336
ALLGEIER ENGINEERING GMBH—See Allgeier SE; *Int'l*, pg. 336
ALLGEIER ENTERPRISE SERVICES SE—See Allgeier SE; *Int'l*, pg. 336
ALLGEIER EXPERTS GMBH—See Allgeier SE; *Int'l*, pg. 336
ALLGEIER EXPERTS GO GMBH—See Allgeier SE; *Int'l*, pg. 336
ALLGEIER EXPERTS HOLDING GMBH—See Allgeier SE; *Int'l*, pg. 336
ALLGEIER EXPERTS PRO GMBH—See Allgeier SE; *Int'l*, pg. 336
ALLGEIER EXPERTS SE—See Allgeier SE; *Int'l*, pg. 336
ALLGEIER GRC GMBH—See Allgeier SE; *Int'l*, pg. 337
ALLGEIER INOVAR GMBH—See Allgeier SE; *Int'l*, pg. 337
ALLGEIER IT SERVICES GMBH—See Allgeier SE; *Int'l*, pg. 337
ALLGEIER IT SOLUTIONS AG—See Allgeier SE; *Int'l*, pg. 337
ALLGEIER IT SOLUTIONS GMBH—See Allgeier SE; *Int'l*, pg. 337
ALLGEIER LTD.—See Allgeier SE; *Int'l*, pg. 337
ALLGEIER, MARTIN & ASSOCIATES, INC.; *U.S. Private*, pg. 181
ALLGEIER PUBLIC SE—See Allgeier SE; *Int'l*, pg. 337
ALLGEIER S.A.—See Allgeier SE; *Int'l*, pg. 337
ALLGEIER (SCHWEIZ) AG—See Allgeier SE; *Int'l*, pg. 336
ALLGEIER SECION GMBH—See Allgeier SE; *Int'l*, pg. 337
ALLGEIER SE; *Int'l*, pg. 336
ALLGEMEINE GOLD- UND SILBERSCHEIDEANSTALT AG—See Umicore S.A./N.V.; *Int'l*, pg. 8024
ALLGEMEINE MULTIMEDIA SERVICE GMBH—See Lenovo Group Limited; *Int'l*, pg. 4454
ALLGEMEINE PLAKATGESELLSCHAFT APG—See APG/SGA SA; *Int'l*, pg. 513
ALLGEMEINE RENTENANSTALT PENSIONSKASSE AG—See Wuestenrot & Wuerttembergische AG; *Int'l*, pg. 8499
ALLGEMEINE STRASSENBAU GMBH—See PORR AG; *Int'l*, pg. 5922
ALLGEMEINE SUISSE SA—See Umicore S.A./N.V.; *Int'l*, pg. 8024
ALLGEMEINE VERWALTUNGSGESELLSCHAFT MBH—See M.M. Warburg & Co. KGaA; *Int'l*, pg. 4616
ALLGENS MEDICAL TECHNOLOGY CO., LTD.; *Int'l*, pg. 338
ALLGLASS SYSTEMS INC.; *U.S. Private*, pg. 181
ALLGO EMBEDDED SYSTEMS PVT. LTD.—See Visteon Corporation; *U.S. Public*, pg. 2305
ALLGON AB—See Bure Equity AB; *Int'l*, pg. 1221
ALLGOOD SERVICES, INC.—See Rentokil Initial plc; *Int'l*, pg. 6286

ALLGO SYSTEMS, INC.—See Visteon Corporation; *U.S. Public*, pg. 2305
ALLGREEN PROPERTIES LTD.; *Int'l*, pg. 338
ALLGREEN PROPERTIES (TIANJIN) PTE. LTD.—See Allgreen Properties Ltd.; *Int'l*, pg. 338
ALLGREEN PROPERTIES (VIETNAM) PTE. LTD.—See Allgreen Properties Ltd.; *Int'l*, pg. 338
ALLGREENTECH INTERNATIONAL PLC; *Int'l*, pg. 338
ALLGREEN TIMBER PRODUCTS SDN. BHD.—See Evergreen Fibreboard Berhad; *Int'l*, pg. 2565
ALL-GREEN TURF MANAGEMENT CORP.—See Rahn Contracting, LLC; *U.S. Private*, pg. 3346
ALL HAPPENING LLC; *U.S. Private*, pg. 171
ALL HOMES CORP.—See Green Courte Partners, LLC; *U.S. Private*, pg. 1772
ALL HORIZONS TRAVEL INC.—See Frosch International Travel Inc.; *U.S. Private*, pg. 1616
ALLIANCE 2020, INC.; *U.S. Private*, pg. 181
ALLIANCE ADVISORS LLC; *U.S. Private*, pg. 181
ALLIANCE AIRLINES; *Int'l*, pg. 338
ALLIANCE APPLIANCES AUSTRALIA P/L—See SIETEL LIMITED; *Int'l*, pg. 6904
ALLIANCE AUTOMOTIVE HOLDING LIMITED—See Blackstone Inc.; *U.S. Public*, pg. 359
ALLIANCE AUTO NIGERIA LIMITED—See Toyota Tsusho Corporation; *Int'l*, pg. 7875
ALLIANCE BANCORP; *U.S. Private*, pg. 181
ALLIANCE BANK INC.; *U.S. Private*, pg. 181
ALLIANCE BANK MALAYSIA BHD—See Alliance Financial Group Berhad; *Int'l*, pg. 338
ALLIANCE BANK; *U.S. Private*, pg. 181
ALLIANCE BANK—See Alliance Bancorp; *U.S. Private*, pg. 181
ALLIANCE BENEFIT GROUP CAROLINAS, INC.—See Alliance Benefit Group, LLC; *U.S. Private*, pg. 181
ALLIANCE BENEFIT GROUP, LLC; *U.S. Private*, pg. 181
ALLIANCE BENEFIT GROUP MIDATLANTIC, LLC—See Alliance Benefit Group, LLC; *U.S. Private*, pg. 181
ALLIANCE BENEFIT GROUP OF HOUSTON, INC.—See Alliance Benefit Group, LLC; *U.S. Private*, pg. 181
ALLIANCE BENEFIT GROUP OF ILLINOIS, INC.—See Alliance Benefit Group, LLC; *U.S. Private*, pg. 181
ALLIANCE BENEFIT GROUP OF MICHIGAN, INC.—See Alliance Benefit Group, LLC; *U.S. Private*, pg. 181
ALLIANCEBERNSTEIN (ARGENTINA) S.R.L—See Equitable Holdings, Inc.; *U.S. Public*, pg. 789
ALLIANCEBERNSTEIN ASSET MANAGEMENT (KOREA) LTD.—See Equitable Holdings, Inc.; *U.S. Public*, pg. 789
ALLIANCEBERNSTEIN AUSTRALIA LIMITED—See Equitable Holdings, Inc.; *U.S. Public*, pg. 789
ALLIANCEBERNSTEIN CANADA, INC—See Equitable Holdings, Inc.; *U.S. Public*, pg. 789
ALLIANCEBERNSTEIN (CHILE) SPA—See Equitable Holdings, Inc.; *U.S. Public*, pg. 788
ALLIANCEBERNSTEIN (FRANCE) S.A.S.—See Equitable Holdings, Inc.; *U.S. Public*, pg. 789
ALLIANCEBERNSTEIN GLOBAL DERIVATIVES CORPORATION—See Equitable Holdings, Inc.; *U.S. Public*, pg. 789
ALLIANCEBERNSTEIN GLOBAL HIGH INCOME FUND, INC.; *U.S. Public*, pg. 79
ALLIANCEBERNSTEIN GLOBAL WEALTH MANAGEMENT—See Equitable Holdings, Inc.; *U.S. Public*, pg. 789
ALLIANCEBERNSTEIN HOLDING L.P.—See Equitable Holdings, Inc.; *U.S. Public*, pg. 788
ALLIANCEBERNSTEIN HOLDINGS LIMITED—See Equitable Holdings, Inc.; *U.S. Public*, pg. 789
ALLIANCEBERNSTEIN HONG KONG LIMITED—See Equitable Holdings, Inc.; *U.S. Public*, pg. 789
ALLIANCEBERNSTEIN INSTITUTIONAL INVESTMENTS—See Equitable Holdings, Inc.; *U.S. Public*, pg. 789
ALLIANCEBERNSTEIN INVESTMENT MANAGEMENT AUSTRALIA LIMITED—See Equitable Holdings, Inc.; *U.S. Public*, pg. 789
ALLIANCEBERNSTEIN INVESTMENTS, INC.—See Equitable Holdings, Inc.; *U.S. Public*, pg. 789
ALLIANCEBERNSTEIN INVESTMENTS TAIWAN LIMITED—See Equitable Holdings, Inc.; *U.S. Public*, pg. 789
ALLIANCEBERNSTEIN INVESTOR SERVICES, INC.—See Equitable Holdings, Inc.; *U.S. Public*, pg. 789
ALLIANCEBERNSTEIN JAPAN LTD—See Equitable Holdings, Inc.; *U.S. Public*, pg. 789
ALLIANCEBERNSTEIN LIMITED—See Equitable Holdings, Inc.; *U.S. Public*, pg. 789
ALLIANCEBERNSTEIN LIMITED—See Equitable Holdings, Inc.; *U.S. Public*, pg. 789
ALLIANCEBERNSTEIN L.P.—See Equitable Holdings, Inc.; *U.S. Public*, pg. 789
ALLIANCEBERNSTEIN (LUXEMBOURG) S.A.—See Equitable Holdings, Inc.; *U.S. Public*, pg. 789
ALLIANCEBERNSTEIN NATIONAL MUNICIPAL INCOME FUND, INC.; *U.S. Public*, pg. 79
ALLIANCEBERNSTEIN SERVICES LIMITED—See Equitable Holdings, Inc.; *U.S. Public*, pg. 789

Company Index

ALLIANCEBERNSTEIN NATIONAL MUNICIPAL INCOME FUND, INC. CORPORATE AFFILIATIONS

ALLIANCEBERNSTEIN (SINGAPORE) LIMITED—See Equitable Holdings, Inc.; *U.S. Public*, pg. 789
ALLIANCEBERNSTEIN TAIWAN LIMITED—See Equitable Holdings, Inc.; *U.S. Public*, pg. 789
ALLIANCE BEVERAGE DISTRIBUTING COMPANY, LLC—See Breakthru Beverage Group, LLC; *U.S. Private*, pg. 643
ALLIANCE BIOTECH & ANALYTICAL LTD.—See HORIBA Ltd; *Int'l*, pg. 3474
ALLIANCE BOOTS HOLDINGS LIMITED—See Walgreens Boots Alliance, Inc.; *U.S. Public*, pg. 2321
ALLIANCE BOOTS SOURCING (HONG KONG) LIMITED—See Walgreens Boots Alliance, Inc.; *U.S. Public*, pg. 2321
ALLIANCE BROKERAGE CORP.; *U.S. Private*, pg. 181
ALLIANCE BUS GROUP, INC.—See Creative Bus Sales Inc.; *U.S. Private*, pg. 1088
ALLIANCE BUSINESS & COMMERCIAL INSURANCE SERVICES—See Inszone Insurance Services, LLC; *U.S. Private*, pg. 2096
ALLIANCE CASTINGS COMPANY, LLC—See The Greenbrier Companies, Inc.; *U.S. Public*, pg. 2085
ALLIANCE CHIMIE ALGERIE SPA—See BRENNTAG SE; *Int'l*, pg. 1146
ALLIANCE COACH INC.—See Lazydays Holdings, Inc.; *U.S. Public*, pg. 1294
ALLIANCE COMMERCIAL PEST CONTROL, INC.—See Thompson Street Capital Manager LLC; *U.S. Private*, pg. 4161
ALLIANCE COMMUNITY HOSPITAL; *U.S. Private*, pg. 181
ALLIANCE COMPRESSORS INC.—See Ingersoll Rand Inc.; *U.S. Public*, pg. 1120
ALLIANCE CONNECT, LLC—See Iowa Network Services Inc.; *U.S. Private*, pg. 2135
ALLIANCE CONSTRUCTION MATERIALS LTD.—See CK Hutchison Holdings Limited; *Int'l*, pg. 1636
ALLIANCE CONSTRUCTION MATERIALS LTD.—See Heidelberg Materials AG; *Int'l*, pg. 3311
ALLIANCE CONSTRUCTION SOLUTIONS LLC; *U.S. Private*, pg. 181
ALLIANCE CREATIVE GROUP, INC.; *U.S. Public*, pg. 79
ALLIANCE CREDIT UNION; *U.S. Private*, pg. 181
ALLIANCE DEFENDING FREEDOM, INC.; *U.S. Private*, pg. 181
ALLIANCE DEVELOPMENT GROUP; *U.S. Private*, pg. 182
ALLIANCE DEVELOPPEMENT CAPITAL SIIC SE; *Int'l*, pg. 338
ALLIANCE DIAGNOSTICOS, S.L.—See Life Healthcare Group Holdings Limited; *Int'l*, pg. 4493
ALLIANCE DISTRIBUTION SERVICES PTY LTD—See Vivendi SE; *Int'l*, pg. 8272
ALLIANCE ENERGY GROUP, LLC; *U.S. Private*, pg. 182
ALLIANCE ENERGY LLC—See Global Partners LP; *U.S. Public*, pg. 942
ALLIANCE ENERGY LTD. - REGINA OFFICE—See Alliance Energy Ltd.; *Int'l*, pg. 338
ALLIANCE ENERGY LTD.; *Int'l*, pg. 338
ALLIANCE ENERGY SERVICES, LLC; *U.S. Private*, pg. 182
ALLIANCE ENGINEERING INC.—See Alliance Engineering Inc.; *U.S. Private*, pg. 182
ALLIANCE ENGINEERING INC.; *U.S. Private*, pg. 182
ALLIANCE ENTERTAINMENT HOLDING CORPORATION; *U.S. Public*, pg. 79
ALLIANCE ENTERTAINMENT, LLC—See Alliance Entertainment Holding Corporation; *U.S. Public*, pg. 79
ALLIANCE ENTERTAINMENT SINGAPORE PTE. LTD—See PSC Corporation Ltd.; *Int'l*, pg. 6015
ALLIANCE ENTREPRENDRE SAS—See Groupe BPCE; *Int'l*, pg. 3092
ALLIANCE ENVIRONMENTAL GROUP, LLC; *U.S. Private*, pg. 182
ALLIANCE EXPRESS—See Delos Capital, LLC; *U.S. Private*, pg. 1198
ALLIANCE FAMILY OF COMPANIES, LLC—See Ancor Holdings, L.P.; *U.S. Private*, pg. 274
ALLIANCE FINANCE COMPANY PLC; *Int'l*, pg. 338
ALLIANCE FINANCIAL GROUP BERHAD; *Int'l*, pg. 338
ALLIANCE FINANCIAL GROUP, INC.; *U.S. Private*, pg. 182
ALLIANCE FINANCIAL SERVICES, INC.—See Lennar Corporation; *U.S. Public*, pg. 1305
ALLIANCE FOOD EQUIPMENT PROCESSING, LLC—See The Anderson Group, LLC; *U.S. Private*, pg. 3986
ALLIANCE FOODS COMPANY LLC—See International Holdings Company PJSC; *Int'l*, pg. 3750
ALLIANCE FOODS INC.; *U.S. Private*, pg. 182
ALLIANCE FOR AUDITED MEDIA; *U.S. Private*, pg. 182
ALLIANCE FOR BANGLADESH WORKER SAFETY; *U.S. Private*, pg. 182
ALLIANCE FOUNDATION OF FLORIDA, INC.; *U.S. Private*, pg. 182
ALLIANCE FRANCHISE BRANDS LLC; *U.S. Private*, pg. 182
ALLIANCE FUNDING GROUP, INC.; *U.S. Private*, pg. 182
ALLIANCE GLOBAL GROUP, INC.; *Int'l*, pg. 339
ALLIANCE GRAIN COMPANY INC.; *U.S. Private*, pg. 182
ALLIANCE GRAIN TERMINAL LTD.—See Paterson GlobalFoods Inc.; *Int'l*, pg. 5756
ALLIANCE GRAIN TRADERS (TIANJIN) CO. LTD.—See AGT Food and Ingredients Inc.; *Int'l*, pg. 221
ALLIANCE GRAPHICS PTE. LTD.—See Thai Beverage Public Company Limited; *Int'l*, pg. 7589
ALLIANCE GROUND INTERNATIONAL, LLC; *U.S. Private*, pg. 182
ALLIANCE GROUP LIMITED - DANNEVIRKE PLANT—See Alliance Group Limited; *Int'l*, pg. 339
ALLIANCE GROUP LIMITED - LEVIN PLANT—See Alliance Group Limited; *Int'l*, pg. 339
ALLIANCE GROUP LIMITED - LORNEVILLE PLANT—See Alliance Group Limited; *Int'l*, pg. 339
ALLIANCE GROUP LIMITED - MAKAREWA PLANT—See Alliance Group Limited; *Int'l*, pg. 339
ALLIANCE GROUP LIMITED - MATAURA PLANT—See Alliance Group Limited; *Int'l*, pg. 339
ALLIANCE GROUP LIMITED - NELSON PLANT—See Alliance Group Limited; *Int'l*, pg. 339
ALLIANCE GROUP LIMITED - PUKEURI PLANT—See Alliance Group Limited; *Int'l*, pg. 339
ALLIANCE GROUP LIMITED - SMITHFIELD PLANT—See Alliance Group Limited; *Int'l*, pg. 339
ALLIANCE GROUP LIMITED; *Int'l*, pg. 339
ALLIANCE GROUP (NZ) LTD—See Alliance Group Limited; *Int'l*, pg. 339
ALLIANCE GROUP SERVICES, INC.; *U.S. Private*, pg. 183
ALLIANCE GROWERS CORP.; *Int'l*, pg. 339
ALLIANCE HEALTHCARD, INC.—See Aon plc; *Int'l*, pg. 489
ALLIANCE HEALTHCARE DEUTSCHLAND AG—See Walgreens Boots Alliance, Inc.; *U.S. Public*, pg. 2322
ALLIANCE HEALTHCARE (DISTRIBUTION) LIMITED—See Walgreens Boots Alliance, Inc.; *U.S. Public*, pg. 2322
ALLIANCE HEALTHCARE ESPANA S.A.—See Walgreens Boots Alliance, Inc.; *U.S. Public*, pg. 2322
ALLIANCE HEALTHCARE FRANCE SA—See Walgreens Boots Alliance, Inc.; *U.S. Public*, pg. 2321
ALLIANCE HEALTHCARE GROUP FRANCE—See Walgreens Boots Alliance, Inc.; *U.S. Public*, pg. 2322
ALLIANCE HEALTHCARE GROUP FRANCE—See Walgreens Boots Alliance, Inc.; *U.S. Public*, pg. 2322
ALLIANCE HEALTHCARE GROUP LIMITED; *Int'l*, pg. 339
ALLIANCE HEALTHCARE ITALIA SPA—See Walgreens Boots Alliance, Inc.; *U.S. Public*, pg. 2322
ALLIANCE HEALTHCARE (IT SERVICES) LIMITED—See Walgreens Boots Alliance, Inc.; *U.S. Public*, pg. 2322
ALLIANCE HEALTHCARE LTD.—See Walgreens Boots Alliance, Inc.; *U.S. Public*, pg. 2321
ALLIANCE HEALTHCARE MANAGEMENT SERVICES LIMITED—See Walgreens Boots Alliance, Inc.; *U.S. Public*, pg. 2322
ALLIANCE HEALTHCARE NEDERLAND—See Walgreens Boots Alliance, Inc.; *U.S. Public*, pg. 2322
ALLIANCE HEALTHCARE NORGE A.S.—See Walgreens Boots Alliance, Inc.; *U.S. Public*, pg. 2322
ALLIANCE HEALTHCARE ROMANIA SRL—See Walgreens Boots Alliance, Inc.; *U.S. Public*, pg. 2322
ALLIANCE HEALTHCARE SERVICES, INC.—See Akumin, Inc.; *U.S. Public*, pg. 69
ALLIANCE HEALTHCARE SOLUTIONS, INC.—See Quatris Health LLC; *U.S. Private*, pg. 3324
ALLIANCE HEALTHCARE, S.R.O.—See Walgreens Boots Alliance, Inc.; *U.S. Public*, pg. 2322
ALLIANCE HEALTHCARE S.R.O.—See Walgreens Boots Alliance, Inc.; *U.S. Public*, pg. 2322
ALLIANCE HEALTH CENTER, INC.—See Universal Health Services, Inc.; *U.S. Public*, pg. 2255
ALLIANCE HEALTH, INC.; *U.S. Private*, pg. 183
ALLIANCE HOLDINGS GP, L.P.; *U.S. Private*, pg. 183
ALLIANCE HOLDINGS, INC.; *U.S. Private*, pg. 183
ALLIANCE HOME SERVICES INC; *U.S. Private*, pg. 183
ALLIANCE HOSPITALITY MANAGEMENT, LLC.; *U.S. Private*, pg. 183
THE ALLIANCE, INC.; *U.S. Private*, pg. 3984
ALLIANCE INDEMNITY COMPANY INC.—See Farmers Alliance Mutual Insurance Co., Inc.; *U.S. Private*, pg. 1476
ALLIANCE INSURANCE (PSC); *Int'l*, pg. 340
ALLIANCE INTEGRATED METALIKS LIMITED; *Int'l*, pg. 340
ALLIANCE INTEGRATED SYSTEMS, INC.—See Pentair plc; *Int'l*, pg. 5790
ALLIANCE INTERACTIVE INC.; *U.S. Private*, pg. 183
ALLIANCE INTERNATIONAL EDUCATION LEASING HOLDINGS LIMITED; *Int'l*, pg. 340
ALLIANCE INTERNATIONAL FORWARDERS, INC.; *U.S. Private*, pg. 183
ALLIANCE INVESTMENT BANK BHD—See Alliance Financial Group Berhad; *Int'l*, pg. 339
ALLIANCE LAUNDRY HOLDINGS LLC—See BDT Capital Partners, LLC; *U.S. Private*, pg. 502
ALLIANCE LAUNDRY SYSTEMS LLC—See BDT Capital Partners, LLC; *U.S. Private*, pg. 502
ALLIANCE MAGNESIUM INC.; *Int'l*, pg. 340
ALLIANCE MANAGEMENT, INC.; *U.S. Private*, pg. 183
ALLIANCE MANUFACTURERS REPRESENTATIVES INC.; *U.S. Private*, pg. 183
ALLIANCE MARINE RISK MANAGERS OF FLORIDA, INC.—See GTCR LLC; *U.S. Private*, pg. 1802
ALLIANCE MATERIAL HANDLING INC.; *U.S. Private*, pg. 183
ALLIANCE MEDIA GROUP; *U.S. Private*, pg. 183
ALLIANCE MEDIA HOLDINGS, INC.; *U.S. Public*, pg. 79
ALLIANCE MEDICAL BV—See Life Healthcare Group Holdings Limited; *Int'l*, pg. 4493
ALLIANCE MEDICAL DIAGNOSTIC IMAGING LTD—See Life Healthcare Group Holdings Limited; *Int'l*, pg. 4493
ALLIANCE MEDICAL GMBH—See Life Healthcare Group Holdings Limited; *Int'l*, pg. 4493
ALLIANCE MEDICAL GROUP LIMITED—See Life Healthcare Group Holdings Limited; *Int'l*, pg. 4493
ALLIANCE MEDICAL ITALIA S.R.L.—See Life Healthcare Group Holdings Limited; *Int'l*, pg. 4493
ALLIANCE MEDICAL PRODUCTS, INC.—See Siegfried Holding AG; *Int'l*, pg. 6884
ALLIANCE MEDINET PTE. LTD.—See Alliance Healthcare Group Limited; *Int'l*, pg. 339
ALLIANCE MINING CORP.; *Int'l*, pg. 340
ALLIANCE MOTORS AND DRIVES SDN BHD—See KVC Industrial Supplies Sdn. Bhd.; *Int'l*, pg. 4349
ALLIANCE NICKEL LIMITED; *Int'l*, pg. 340
ALLIANCE OFFICE SYSTEMS; *U.S. Private*, pg. 183
ALLIANCE OFFSHORE DRILLING PTE LIMITED—See CM Energy Tech Co., Ltd.; *Int'l*, pg. 1666
ALLIANCE OF PROFESSIONALS & CONSULTANTS, INC.; *U.S. Private*, pg. 183
ALLIANCE OIL COMPANY LTD.; *Int'l*, pg. 340
ALLIANCE ONCOLOGY, LLC—See Akumin, Inc.; *U.S. Public*, pg. 70
ALLIANCE ONE BRASIL EXPORTADORA DE TABACOS LTDA.—See Pyxus International, Inc.; *U.S. Public*, pg. 1740
ALLIANCE ONE BRASIL EXPORTADORA DE TABACOS LTDA.—See Pyxus International, Inc.; *U.S. Public*, pg. 1740
ALLIANCE ONE BRASIL EXPORTADORA DE TABACOS LTDA.—See Pyxus International, Inc.; *U.S. Public*, pg. 1740
ALLIANCE ONE BRASIL EXPORTADORA DE TABACOS LTDA.—See Pyxus International, Inc.; *U.S. Public*, pg. 1740
ALLIANCEONE INC.; *U.S. Private*, pg. 184
ALLIANCE ONE INTERNATIONAL A.G.—See Pyxus International, Inc.; *U.S. Public*, pg. 1740
ALLIANCE ONE INTERNATIONAL SERVICES LIMITED—See Pyxus International, Inc.; *U.S. Public*, pg. 1740
ALLIANCE ONE INTERNATIONAL SINGAPORE PTE LTD.—See Pyxus International, Inc.; *U.S. Public*, pg. 1740
ALLIANCE ONE INTERNATIONAL TABAK B.V.—See Pyxus International, Inc.; *U.S. Public*, pg. 1740
ALLIANCEONE LIMITED—See Teleperformance SE; *Int'l*, pg. 7539
ALLIANCE ONE MACEDONIA AD—See Pyxus International, Inc.; *U.S. Public*, pg. 1740
ALLIANCE ONE MYANMAR CO., LTD.—See Pyxus International, Inc.; *U.S. Public*, pg. 1740
ALLIANCEONE RECEIVABLES MANAGEMENT INC—See Teleperformance SE; *Int'l*, pg. 7539
ALLIANCE ONE ROTAG AG—See Pyxus International, Inc.; *U.S. Public*, pg. 1740
ALLIANCE ONE SERVICES (THAILAND) LIMITED—See Pyxus International, Inc.; *U.S. Public*, pg. 1740
ALLIANCE ONE SPECIALTY PRODUCTS LLC—See Pyxus International, Inc.; *U.S. Public*, pg. 1740
ALLIANCE ONE TABACO GUATEMALA S.A.—See Pyxus International, Inc.; *U.S. Public*, pg. 1740
ALLIANCE ONE TABACO MEXICO S.A. DE C.V.—See Pyxus International, Inc.; *U.S. Public*, pg. 1740
ALLIANCE ONE TOBACCO ARGENTINA S.A.—See Pyxus International, Inc.; *U.S. Public*, pg. 1740
ALLIANCE ONETOBACCO ARGENTINA S.A.—See Pyxus International, Inc.; *U.S. Public*, pg. 1740
ALLIANCE ONE TOBACCO BULGARIA EOOD—See Pyxus International, Inc.; *U.S. Public*, pg. 1740
ALLIANCE ONE TOBACCO CANADA, INC.—See Pyxus International, Inc.; *U.S. Public*, pg. 1740
ALLIANCE ONE TOBACCO GUATEMALA, S.A.—See Pyxus International, Inc.; *U.S. Public*, pg. 1740
ALLIANCE ONE TOBACCO (KENYA) LIMITED—See Pyxus International, Inc.; *U.S. Public*, pg. 1740
ALLIANCE ONE TOBACCO (MALAWI) LIMITED—See Pyxus International, Inc.; *U.S. Public*, pg. 1740
ALLIANCE ONE TOBACCO (MALAWI) LIMITED—See Pyxus International, Inc.; *U.S. Public*, pg. 1740
ALLIANCE ONE TOBACCO (MALAWI) LIMITED—See Pyxus International, Inc.; *U.S. Public*, pg. 1740
ALLIANCE ONE TOBACCO (MALAWI) LIMITED—See Pyxus International, Inc.; *U.S. Public*, pg. 1740
ALLIANCE ONE TOBACCO TANZANIA LTD.—See Pyxus International, Inc.; *U.S. Public*, pg. 1740

COMPANY NAME INDEX

ALLIANCE ONE TOBACCO (UGANDA) LIMITED—See Pyxus International, Inc.; *U.S. Public*, pg. 1740
ALLIANCE ONE TUTUN A.S.—See Pyxus International, Inc.; *U.S. Public*, pg. 1740
ALLIANCE ONE ZAMBIA LTD.—See Pyxus International, Inc.; *U.S. Public*, pg. 1740
ALLIANCE ONLINE LTD.—See Information Services Corporation; *Int'l*, pg. 3695
ALLIANCE PACKAGING-BEAVERTON DIVISION—See Alliance Packaging LLC; *U.S. Private*, pg. 184
ALLIANCE PACKAGING LLC; *U.S. Private*, pg. 184
ALLIANCE PACKAGING-SEATTLE CORRUGATED DIVISION—See Alliance Packaging LLC; *U.S. Private*, pg. 184
ALLIANCE PETROLEUM CORPORATION—See Van De Pol Enterprises, Inc.; *U.S. Private*, pg. 4339
ALLIANCE PHARMACEUTICALS GMBH—See Alliance Pharma PLC; *Int'l*, pg. 340
ALLIANCE PHARMACEUTICALS LIMITED—See Alliance Pharma PLC; *Int'l*, pg. 340
ALLIANCE PHARMACEUTICALS (THAILAND) CO., LTD.—See Alliance Pharma PLC; *Int'l*, pg. 340
ALLIANCE PHARMA PLC; *Int'l*, pg. 340
ALLIANCE PHARMA S.R.L.—See Alliance Pharma PLC; *Int'l*, pg. 340
ALLIANCE PHYSICAL THERAPY PARTNERS, LLC—See GPB Capital Holdings, LLC; *U.S. Private*, pg. 1748
ALLIANCE PIPELINE LIMITED PARTNERSHIP—See Enbridge Inc.; *Int'l*, pg. 2397
ALLIANCE PIPELINE L.P.—See Enbridge Inc.; *Int'l*, pg. 2397
ALLIANCE PIPELINE L.P.—See Pembina Pipeline Corporation; *Int'l*, pg. 5785
ALLIANCE PLASTICS, LLC; *U.S. Private*, pg. 184
ALLIANCE PRINTING & PUBLISHING, INC.—See Corporate Document Solutions, Inc.; *U.S. Private*, pg. 1054
ALLIANCE PRINT TECHNOLOGIES CO., LTD.—See Tien Wah Press Holdings Berhad; *Int'l*, pg. 7744
ALLIANCE PRODUCTS, LLC—See Sandstone Group, Inc.; *U.S. Private*, pg. 3545
ALLIANCE PROMOTIONS, LLC; *U.S. Private*, pg. 184
ALLIANCE PUBLISHING COMPANY INC., LLC—See Gannett Co., Inc.; *U.S. Public*, pg. 901
ALLIANCE PULSE PROCESSORS INC.—See AGT Food and Ingredients Inc.; *Int'l*, pg. 221
ALLIANCE REALTY ADVISORS; *U.S. Private*, pg. 184
ALLIANCE RECOVERY CORP.; *U.S. Public*, pg. 79
ALLIANCE RESOURCE PARTNERS, L.P.—See Alliance Holdings GP, L.P.; *U.S. Private*, pg. 183
ALLIANCE RESOURCES LIMITED; *Int'l*, pg. 340
ALLIANCE RUBBER COMPANY; *U.S. Private*, pg. 184
ALLIANCE (SA) PTY. LTD.—See Alliance Resources Limited; *Int'l*, pg. 341
ALLIANCE SEAFOODS INC.—See Yokorei Co.,Ltd.; *Int'l*, pg. 8595
ALLIANCE SECURITY INC.; *U.S. Private*, pg. 184
ALLIANCE SELECT FOODS INTERNATIONAL, INC.; *Int'l*, pg. 341
ALLIANCE SEMICONDUCTOR (INDIA) PRIVATE LIMITED—See Alimco Financial Corporation; *U.S. Private*, pg. 168
ALLIANCE SHIPPERS, INC.; *U.S. Private*, pg. 184
ALLIANCE SHIPPERS - TRANSPORTATION BROKER—See Alliance Shippers, Inc.; *U.S. Private*, pg. 184
ALLIANCE SOLUTIONS GROUP, INC.; *U.S. Private*, pg. 184
ALLIANCE SOLUTIONS GROUP; *U.S. Private*, pg. 184
ALLIANCE SOURCE TESTING LLC—See Align Capital Partners, LLC; *U.S. Private*, pg. 167
ALLIANCE SPACES PRIVATE LIMITED—See The Phoenix Mills Limited; *Int'l*, pg. 7673
ALLIANCE SPACESYSTEMS, LLC—See AE Industrial Partners, LP; *U.S. Private*, pg. 111
ALLIANCE SPORTS GROUP, L.P.; *U.S. Private*, pg. 184
ALLIANCES; *Int'l*, pg. 341
ALLIANCE STEEL, INC.—See Promus Holdings, LLC; *U.S. Private*, pg. 3284
ALLIANCE STORAGE TECHNOLOGIES, INC.; *U.S. Private*, pg. 184
ALLIANCE SUPPLY MANAGEMENT, LTD.—See Ship Supply of Florida, Inc.; *U.S. Private*, pg. 3637
ALLIANCE SURGICAL CENTER, LLC—See UnitedHealth Group Incorporated; *U.S. Public*, pg. 2238
ALLIANCE TECHNICAL GROUP, LLC—See Morgan Stanley; *U.S. Public*, pg. 1474
ALLIANCE TECHNOLOGIES; *U.S. Private*, pg. 184
ALLIANCE TECHNOLOGY GROUP, LLC; *U.S. Private*, pg. 184
ALLIANCE TECHNOLOGY SOLUTIONS, LLC.; *U.S. Private*, pg. 184
ALLIANCE TIRE COMPANY LTD.—See The Yokohama Rubber Co., Ltd.; *Int'l*, pg. 7702
ALLIANCE TIRE EUROPE B.V.—See The Yokohama Rubber Co., Ltd.; *Int'l*, pg. 7702
ALLIANCE TITLE & ESCROW CORPORATION—See Futura Corporation; *U.S. Private*, pg. 1626
ALLIANCE TRANSPORTATION, INC.—See GCC, S.A.B. de C.V.; *Int'l*, pg. 2894

ALLIANCE TRUCK AND EQUIPMENT, LLC; *U.S. Private*, pg. 184
ALLIANCE TRUST INVESTMENTS LIMITED—See Alliance Trust PLC; *Int'l*, pg. 341
ALLIANCE TRUST PLC; *Int'l*, pg. 341
ALLIANCE TRUST SAVINGS LIMITED—See abrdn PLC; *Int'l*, pg. 68
ALLIANCE TUNISIE S.A.R.L.—See BRENNTAG SE; *Int'l*, pg. 1146
ALLIANCE UNITED INSURANCE SERVICES, INC.—See Kemper Corporation; *U.S. Public*, pg. 1220
ALLIANCE WHOLESALE SUPPLY, INC.—See Hendricks Holding Company, Inc.; *U.S. Private*, pg. 1914
ALLIANCE WIRELESS TECHNOLOGIES, INC.—See Terex Corporation; *U.S. Public*, pg. 2019
ALLIANCE WORKFORCE SOLUTIONS LLC; *U.S. Private*, pg. 184
ALLIANDER AG—See Alliander N.V.; *Int'l*, pg. 341
ALLIANDER FINANCE B.V.—See Alliander N.V.; *Int'l*, pg. 341
ALLIANDER N.V.; *Int'l*, pg. 341
ALLIANT COMPANY LLC; *U.S. Private*, pg. 184
ALLIANT CREDIT UNION; *U.S. Private*, pg. 184
ALLIANT ENERGY CORPORATION; *U.S. Public*, pg. 79
ALLIANT GAS, LLC—See SHV Holdings N.V.; *Int'l*, pg. 6873
ALLIANT HEALTHCARE PRODUCTS; *U.S. Private*, pg. 185
ALLIANT HEALTH SOLUTIONS; *U.S. Private*, pg. 184
ALLIANT INSURANCE SERVICES HOUSTON LLC—See Stone Point Capital LLC; *U.S. Private*, pg. 3818
ALLIANT INSURANCE SERVICES, INC.—See Stone Point Capital LLC; *U.S. Private*, pg. 3818
ALLIANT INTEGRATORS, INC.—See Apollo Global Management, Inc.; *U.S. Public*, pg. 146
ALLIANT INTERNATIONAL UNIVERSITY-CAMPUS MEXICO, S.C.—See Bertelsmann SE & Co. KGaA; *Int'l*, pg. 990
ALLIANT INTERNATIONAL UNIVERSITY, INC.—See Bertelsmann SE & Co. KGaA; *Int'l*, pg. 990
ALLIANT/MESIROW INSURANCE SERVICES—See Stone Point Capital LLC; *U.S. Private*, pg. 3818
ALLIANT NATIONAL TITLE INSURANCE COMPANY; *U.S. Private*, pg. 185
ALLIANT SPECIALTY INSURANCE SERVICES, INC.—See Stone Point Capital LLC; *U.S. Private*, pg. 3818
ALLIANT STAFFING, LLC—See McLarty Capital Partners UK LLP; *U.S. Private*, pg. 2640
ALLIANZ ACTIO FRANCE—See Allianz SE; *Int'l*, pg. 343
ALLIANZ ACTIONS AEQUITAS—See Allianz SE; *Int'l*, pg. 343
ALLIANZ ACTIONS EURO VALUE—See Allianz SE; *Int'l*, pg. 343
ALLIANZ ACTIONS FRANCE MIDCAP—See Allianz SE; *Int'l*, pg. 343
ALLIANZ ACTIONS FRANCE—See Allianz SE; *Int'l*, pg. 343
ALLIANZ ACTIONS JAPON—See Allianz SE; *Int'l*, pg. 343
ALLIANZ AFRICA S.A.—See Allianz SE; *Int'l*, pg. 343
ALLIANZ ALAPKEZELO ZRT.—See Allianz SE; *Int'l*, pg. 343
ALLIANZ ALTERNATIVE ASSETS HOLDING GMBH—See Allianz SE; *Int'l*, pg. 343
ALLIANZ ARGENTINA COMPANIA DE SEGUROS S.A.—See Allianz SE; *Int'l*, pg. 343
ALLIANZ ASSET MANAGEMENT OF AMERICA L.P.—See Allianz SE; *Int'l*, pg. 343
ALLIANZ AUSTRALIA ADVANTAGE LTD.—See Allianz SE; *Int'l*, pg. 343
ALLIANZ AUSTRALIA INSURANCE LIMITED—See Allianz SE; *Int'l*, pg. 343
ALLIANZ AUSTRALIA LIFE INSURANCE LIMITED—See Allianz SE; *Int'l*, pg. 343
ALLIANZ AUSTRALIA LIMITED—See Allianz SE; *Int'l*, pg. 343
ALLIANZ AUSTRALIA SERVICES PTY LIMITED—See Allianz SE; *Int'l*, pg. 343
ALLIANZ AUSTRALIA WORKERS COMPENSATION (NSW) LIMITED—See Allianz SE; *Int'l*, pg. 343
ALLIANZ AUSTRALIA WORKERS COMPENSATION (SA) LIMITED—See Allianz SE; *Int'l*, pg. 344
ALLIANZ AUSTRALIA WORKERS COMPENSATION (VICTORIA) LIMITED—See Allianz SE; *Int'l*, pg. 344
ALLIANZ AUTOMOTIVE SERVICES GMBH—See Allianz SE; *Int'l*, pg. 344
ALLIANZ AUTOWELT GMBH—See Allianz SE; *Int'l*, pg. 344
ALLIANZ AVI 1 FONDS—See Allianz SE; *Int'l*, pg. 343
ALLIANZ AVIATION MANAGERS LLC—See Allianz SE; *Int'l*, pg. 344
ALLIANZ AVM B FONDS—See Allianz SE; *Int'l*, pg. 343
ALLIANZ AYUDHYA ASSURANCE PCL.—See Allianz Ayudhya Capital Public Company Limited; *Int'l*, pg. 341
ALLIANZ AYUDHYA ASSURANCE PCL—See Allianz SE; *Int'l*, pg. 344
ALLIANZ AYUDHYA CAPITAL PUBLIC COMPANY LIMITED; *Int'l*, pg. 341

ALLIANZ AYUDHYA GENERAL INSURANCE PUBLIC COMPANY LIMITED—See Allianz SE; *Int'l*, pg. 344
ALLIANZ AZL VERMOGENSVERWALTUNG GMBH—See Allianz SE; *Int'l*, pg. 343
ALLIANZ BANK FINANCIAL ADVISORS S.P.A.—See Allianz SE; *Int'l*, pg. 344
ALLIANZ BELGIUM S.A.—See Allianz SE; *Int'l*, pg. 343
ALLIANZ BENELUX S.A.—See Allianz SE; *Int'l*, pg. 344
ALLIANZ BERATUNGS- UND VERTRIEBS-AG—See Allianz SE; *Int'l*, pg. 344
ALLIANZ BIZNES SP. Z O.O.—See Allianz SE; *Int'l*, pg. 344
ALLIANZ BULGARIA HOLDING—See Allianz SE; *Int'l*, pg. 344
ALLIANZ BULGARIA PENSION COMPANY AD—See Allianz SE; *Int'l*, pg. 344
ALLIANZ BURKINA ASSURANCES VIE—See Allianz SE; *Int'l*, pg. 344
ALLIANZ BUSINESS SERVICES LIMITED—See Allianz SE; *Int'l*, pg. 348
ALLIANZ BUSINESS SERVICES S.R.O.—See Allianz SE; *Int'l*, pg. 345
ALLIANZ CAMEROUN ASSURANCES SA—See Allianz SE; *Int'l*, pg. 344
ALLIANZ CAMEROUN ASSURANCES VIE S.A.—See Allianz SE; *Int'l*, pg. 344
ALLIANZ CAPITAL PARTNERS GMBH—See Allianz SE; *Int'l*, pg. 344
ALLIANZ CAPITAL PARTNERS OF AMERICA LLC—See Allianz SE; *Int'l*, pg. 344
ALLIANZ CAPITAL PARTNERS VERWALTUNGS GMBH—See Allianz SE; *Int'l*, pg. 344
ALLIANZ CENTRAFRIQUE ASSURANCES—See Allianz SE; *Int'l*, pg. 344
ALLIANZ CHINA GENERAL INSURANCE COMPANY LTD.—See Allianz SE; *Int'l*, pg. 344
ALLIANZ CHINA LIFE INSURANCE CO., LTD.—See Allianz SE; *Int'l*, pg. 344
ALLIANZ CLIMATE SOLUTIONS GMBH—See Allianz SE; *Int'l*, pg. 344
ALLIANZ COMPAGNIA ITALIANA FINANZIAMENTI S.P.A.—See Allianz SE; *Int'l*, pg. 344
ALLIANZ COMPANIA DE SEGUROS Y REASEGUROS SA—See Allianz SE; *Int'l*, pg. 344
ALLIANZ CORNHILL INFORMATION SERVICES PRIVATE LTD.—See Allianz SE; *Int'l*, pg. 348
ALLIANZ COTE D'IVOIRE ASSURANCES—See Allianz SE; *Int'l*, pg. 344
ALLIANZ COTE D'IVOIRE ASSURANCES VIE SA—See Allianz SE; *Int'l*, pg. 344
ALLIANZ C.P. GENERAL INSURANCE CO., LTD.—See Allianz SE; *Int'l*, pg. 344
ALLIANZ C.P. GENERAL INSURANCE CO., LTD.—See Charoen Pokphand Group Co., Ltd.; *Int'l*, pg. 1453
ALLIANZ DEUTSCHLAND AG—See Allianz SE; *Int'l*, pg. 344
ALLIANZ DGD FONDS—See Allianz SE; *Int'l*, pg. 344
ALLIANZ DIRECT NEW EUROPE SP. Z O.O.—See Allianz SE; *Int'l*, pg. 344
ALLIANZ DIRECT S.P.A.—See Allianz SE; *Int'l*, pg. 344
ALLIANZ DIRECT S.R.O.—See Allianz SE; *Int'l*, pg. 344
ALLIANZ DIRECT VERSICHERUNGS-AG—See Allianz SE; *Int'l*, pg. 344
ALLIANZ DRESDNER BAUSPAR AG—See Allianz SE; *Int'l*, pg. 344
ALLIANZ DRESDNER PENSION CONSULT GMBH—See Allianz SE; *Int'l*, pg. 344
ALLIANZ ELEMENTAR LEBENSVERSICHERUNGS AG—See Allianz SE; *Int'l*, pg. 344
ALLIANZ ELEMENTAR VERSICHERUNGS AG—See Allianz SE; *Int'l*, pg. 344
ALLIANZ ELEMENTAR VERSICHERUNGS-AKTIENGESELLSCHAFT—See Allianz SE; *Int'l*, pg. 345
ALLIANZ EQUITY INVESTMENTS LTD.—See Allianz SE; *Int'l*, pg. 345
ALLIANZ EUROPE B.V.—See Allianz SE; *Int'l*, pg. 345
ALLIANZ FINANCE III B.V.—See Allianz SE; *Int'l*, pg. 345
ALLIANZ FINANCE PTY LTD.—See Allianz SE; *Int'l*, pg. 345
ALLIANZ FIRE AND MARINE INSURANCE JAPAN LTD.—See Allianz SE; *Int'l*, pg. 345
ALLIANZ FRANCE INFRASTRUCTURE 1—See Allianz SE; *Int'l*, pg. 345
ALLIANZ FRANCE—See Allianz SE; *Int'l*, pg. 345
ALLIANZ GENERAL INSURANCE COMPANY S.A.—See Allianz SE; *Int'l*, pg. 345
ALLIANZ GENERAL LAOS LTD.—See Allianz SE; *Int'l*, pg. 345
ALLIANZGI CAPITAL LLC—See Allianz SE; *Int'l*, pg. 346
ALLIANZGI DIVERSIFIED INCOME & CONVERTIBLE FUND; *U.S. Private*, pg. 185
ALLIANZ GLOBAL ASSISTANCE (AGA) INTERNATIONAL S.A.—See Allianz SE; *Int'l*, pg. 342
ALLIANZ GLOBAL ASSISTANCE - CANADA—See Allianz SE; *Int'l*, pg. 345
ALLIANZ GLOBAL ASSISTANCE INC.—See Allianz SE; *Int'l*, pg. 342

ALLIANZGI DIVERSIFIED INCOME & CONVERTIBLE FUND — CORPORATE AFFILIATIONS

ALLIANZ GLOBAL ASSISTANCE S.A.S.—See Allianz SE; *Int'l*, pg. 345
ALLIANZ GLOBAL ASSISTANCE—See Allianz SE; *Int'l*, pg. 342
ALLIANZ GLOBAL ASSISTANCE—See Allianz SE; *Int'l*, pg. 342
ALLIANZ GLOBAL ASSISTANCE USA—See Allianz SE; *Int'l*, pg. 345
ALLIANZ GLOBAL BENEFITS GMBH—See Allianz SE; *Int'l*, pg. 345
ALLIANZ GLOBAL CORPORATE & SPECIALTY AG—See Allianz SE; *Int'l*, pg. 345
ALLIANZ GLOBAL CORPORATE & SPECIALTY-AUSTRALIA—See Allianz SE; *Int'l*, pg. 345
ALLIANZ GLOBAL CORPORATE & SPECIALTY-AUSTRIA—See Allianz SE; *Int'l*, pg. 345
ALLIANZ GLOBAL CORPORATE & SPECIALTY-BELGIUM—See Allianz SE; *Int'l*, pg. 345
ALLIANZ GLOBAL CORPORATE & SPECIALTY-CANADA—See Allianz SE; *Int'l*, pg. 345
ALLIANZ GLOBAL CORPORATE & SPECIALTY (FRANCE) S.A.—See Allianz SE; *Int'l*, pg. 345
ALLIANZ GLOBAL CORPORATE & SPECIALTY-IRELAND—See Allianz SE; *Int'l*, pg. 345
ALLIANZ GLOBAL CORPORATE & SPECIALTY, NATIONAL INSURANCE COMPANY—See Allianz SE; *Int'l*, pg. 346
ALLIANZ GLOBAL CORPORATE & SPECIALTY-NETHERLANDS—See Allianz SE; *Int'l*, pg. 349
ALLIANZ GLOBAL CORPORATE & SPECIALTY-SINGAPORE—See Allianz SE; *Int'l*, pg. 345
ALLIANZ GLOBAL CORPORATE & SPECIALTY—See Allianz SE; *Int'l*, pg. 345
ALLIANZ GLOBAL CORPORATE & SPECIALTY—See Allianz SE; *Int'l*, pg. 345
ALLIANZ GLOBAL CORPORATE & SPECIALTY—See Allianz SE; *Int'l*, pg. 345
ALLIANZ GLOBAL CORPORATE & SPECIALTY—See Allianz SE; *Int'l*, pg. 345
ALLIANZ GLOBAL CORPORATE & SPECIALTY—See Allianz SE; *Int'l*, pg. 345
ALLIANZ GLOBAL CORPORATE & SPECIALTY—See Allianz SE; *Int'l*, pg. 345
ALLIANZ GLOBAL CORPORATE & SPECIALTY SOUTH AFRICA LTD.—See Allianz SE; *Int'l*, pg. 346
ALLIANZ GLOBAL CORPORATE & SPECIALTY-UK—See Allianz SE; *Int'l*, pg. 345
ALLIANZ GLOBAL INVESTORS AG—See Allianz SE; *Int'l*, pg. 346
ALLIANZ GLOBAL INVESTORS ASIA PACIFIC GMBH—See Allianz SE; *Int'l*, pg. 347
ALLIANZ GLOBAL INVESTORS ASIA PACIFIC LIMITED—See Allianz SE; *Int'l*, pg. 347
ALLIANZ GLOBAL INVESTORS ASSET MANAGEMENT (SHANGHAI) LIMITED—See Allianz SE; *Int'l*, pg. 347
ALLIANZ GLOBAL INVESTORS CAPITAL LLC—See Allianz SE; *Int'l*, pg. 347
ALLIANZ GLOBAL INVESTORS DISTRIBUTORS LLC—See Allianz SE; *Int'l*, pg. 347
ALLIANZ GLOBAL INVESTORS (FRANCE) S.A.—See Allianz SE; *Int'l*, pg. 346
ALLIANZ GLOBAL INVESTORS FUND MANAGEMENT LLC—See Allianz SE; *Int'l*, pg. 347
ALLIANZ GLOBAL INVESTORS GMBH—See Allianz SE; *Int'l*, pg. 346
ALLIANZ GLOBAL INVESTORS HONG KONG LIMITED—See Allianz SE; *Int'l*, pg. 346
ALLIANZ GLOBAL INVESTORS IRELAND LTD.—See Allianz SE; *Int'l*, pg. 347
ALLIANZ GLOBAL INVESTORS ITALIA S.P.A—See Allianz SE; *Int'l*, pg. 347
ALLIANZ GLOBAL INVESTORS JAPAN CO., LTD.—See Allianz SE; *Int'l*, pg. 347
ALLIANZ GLOBAL INVESTORS KAPITALANLAGEGESELLSCHAFT MBH—See Allianz SE; *Int'l*, pg. 346
ALLIANZ GLOBAL INVESTORS (LUXEMBOURG) S.A.—See Allianz SE; *Int'l*, pg. 346
ALLIANZ GLOBAL INVESTORS LUXEMBOURG S.A.; *Int'l*, pg. 341
ALLIANZ GLOBAL INVESTORS MANAGED ACCOUNTS LLC—See Allianz SE; *Int'l*, pg. 347
ALLIANZ GLOBAL INVESTORS NOMINEES (UK) LTD.—See Allianz SE; *Int'l*, pg. 347
ALLIANZ GLOBAL INVESTORS (SCHWEIZ) AG—See Allianz SE; *Int'l*, pg. 346
ALLIANZ GLOBAL INVESTORS SECURITIES INVESTMENT CONSULTING CO. LTD.—See Allianz SE; *Int'l*, pg. 346
ALLIANZ GLOBAL INVESTORS SINGAPORE LTD.—See Allianz SE; *Int'l*, pg. 346
ALLIANZ GLOBAL INVESTORS SOLUTIONS LLC—See Allianz SE; *Int'l*, pg. 347
ALLIANZ GLOBAL INVESTORS—See Allianz SE; *Int'l*, pg. 346
ALLIANZ GLOBAL INVESTORS—See Allianz SE; *Int'l*, pg. 346

ALLIANZ GLOBAL INVESTORS TAIWAN LTD.—See Allianz SE; *Int'l*, pg. 346
ALLIANZ GLOBAL INVESTORS (UK) LTD.—See Allianz SE; *Int'l*, pg. 346
ALLIANZ GLOBAL INVESTORS U.S. LLC—See Allianz SE; *Int'l*, pg. 347
ALLIANZ GLOBAL LIFE LTD.—See Allianz SE; *Int'l*, pg. 348
ALLIANZ GLOBAL RISKS US INSURANCE COMPANY—See Allianz SE; *Int'l*, pg. 345
ALLIANZ GROUP GREECE—See Allianz SE; *Int'l*, pg. 348
ALLIANZ HANDWERKER SERVICES GMBH—See Allianz SE; *Int'l*, pg. 350
ALLIANZ HAYAT VE EMEKLILIK AS—See Allianz SE; *Int'l*, pg. 348
ALLIANZ HAYAT VE EMEKLILIK A.S.—See Allianz SE; *Int'l*, pg. 345
ALLIANZ HELLAS INSURANCE COMPANY S.A.—See Allianz SE; *Int'l*, pg. 348
ALLIANZ HELLAS SINGLE MEMBER INSURANCE S.A.—See Allianz SE; *Int'l*, pg. 348
ALLIANZ HOLDING EINS GMBH—See Allianz SE; *Int'l*, pg. 348
ALLIANZ HOLDING FRANCE SAS—See Allianz SE; *Int'l*, pg. 348
ALLIANZ HOLDINGS PLC—See Allianz SE; *Int'l*, pg. 348
ALLIANZ HUNGARIA BIZTOSITO ZRT.—See Allianz SE; *Int'l*, pg. 348
ALLIANZ IARD S.A.—See Allianz SE; *Int'l*, pg. 348
ALLIANZ IMMOBILIEN GMBH—See Allianz SE; *Int'l*, pg. 348
ALLIANZ INSURANCE COMPANY-EGYPT S.A.E.—See Allianz SE; *Int'l*, pg. 348
ALLIANZ INSURANCE COMPANY LANKA LIMITED—See Allianz SE; *Int'l*, pg. 348
ALLIANZ INSURANCE COMPANY OF KENYA LIMITED—See Allianz SE; *Int'l*, pg. 348
ALLIANZ INSURANCE COMPANY OF SINGAPORE PTE LTD—See Allianz SE; *Int'l*, pg. 348
ALLIANZ INSURANCE LANKA LIMITED—See Allianz SE; *Int'l*, pg. 348
ALLIANZ INSURANCE LAOS CO. LTD.—See Allianz SE; *Int'l*, pg. 348
ALLIANZ INSURANCE LUXEMBOURG—See Allianz SE; *Int'l*, pg. 348
ALLIANZ INSURANCE MANAGEMENT ASIA PACIFIC PTE. LTD.—See Allianz SE; *Int'l*, pg. 344
ALLIANZ INSURANCE NEW ZEALAND—See Allianz SE; *Int'l*, pg. 348
ALLIANZ INSURANCE PLC—See Allianz SE; *Int'l*, pg. 348
ALLIANZ INVERSIONES S.A.—See Allianz SE; *Int'l*, pg. 348
ALLIANZ INVEST KAPITALANLAGEGESELLSCHAFT MBH—See Allianz SE; *Int'l*, pg. 348
ALLIANZ INVESTMENTBANK AG—See Allianz SE; *Int'l*, pg. 348
ALLIANZ INVESTMENT COMPANY LLC—See Allianz SE; *Int'l*, pg. 348
ALLIANZ INVESTMENT MANAGEMENT LLC—See Allianz SE; *Int'l*, pg. 348
ALLIANZ INVESTMENT MANAGEMENT SE—See Allianz SE; *Int'l*, pg. 348
ALLIANZ INVESTMENT PROPERTIES LTD.—See Allianz SE; *Int'l*, pg. 348
ALLIANZ ISLAND HF—See Islandsbanki hf.; *Int'l*, pg. 3820
ALLIANZ JINGDONG GENERAL INSURANCE COMPANY LTD.—See Allianz SE; *Int'l*, pg. 348
ALLIANZ KUNDE UND MARKT GMBH—See Allianz SE; *Int'l*, pg. 348
ALLIANZ LAD FONDS—See Allianz SE; *Int'l*, pg. 348
ALLIANZ LEBENCO FONDS—See Allianz SE; *Int'l*, pg. 348
ALLIANZ LEBENSVERSICHERUNGS-AG—See Allianz SE; *Int'l*, pg. 348
ALLIANZ LIETUVA GYVYBES DRAUDIMAS UAB—See Allianz SE; *Int'l*, pg. 348
ALLIANZ LIFE ASSURANCE COMPANY-EGYPT S.A.E.—See Allianz SE; *Int'l*, pg. 348
ALLIANZ LIFE (BERMUDA) LTD.—See Allianz SE; *Int'l*, pg. 348
ALLIANZ LIFE FINANCIAL SERVICES LLC—See Allianz SE; *Int'l*, pg. 347
ALLIANZ LIFE INSURANCE COMPANY OF GHANA LIMITED—See Allianz SE; *Int'l*, pg. 348
ALLIANZ LIFE INSURANCE COMPANY OF NEW YORK—See Allianz SE; *Int'l*, pg. 347
ALLIANZ LIFE INSURANCE COMPANY OF NORTH AMERICA—See Allianz SE; *Int'l*, pg. 347
ALLIANZ LIFE INSURANCE COMPANY S.A.—See Allianz SE; *Int'l*, pg. 348
ALLIANZ LIFE INSURANCE COMPANY—See Allianz SE; *Int'l*, pg. 348
ALLIANZ LIFE INSURANCE JAPAN LTD.—See Allianz SE; *Int'l*, pg. 348
ALLIANZ LIFE INSURANCE LANKA LTD.—See Allianz SE; *Int'l*, pg. 348
ALLIANZ LIFE INSURANCE MALAYSIA BERHAD—See Allianz SE; *Int'l*, pg. 348

ALLIANZ LIFE LUXEMBOURG S.A.—See Allianz SE; *Int'l*, pg. 348
ALLIANZ MADAGASCAR—See Allianz SE; *Int'l*, pg. 349
ALLIANZ MALAYSIA BERHAD—See Allianz SE; *Int'l*, pg. 349
ALLIANZ MALI ASSURANCES—See Allianz SE; *Int'l*, pg. 349
ALLIANZ MANAGED OPERATIONS & SERVICES SE—See Allianz SE; *Int'l*, pg. 349
ALLIANZ MAROC S.A.—See Allianz SE; *Int'l*, pg. 349
ALLIANZ MEXICO S.A. COMPANIA DE SEGUROS—See Allianz SE; *Int'l*, pg. 349
ALLIANZ MEXICO S.A.—See Allianz SE; *Int'l*, pg. 349
ALLIANZ NEDERLAND ASSET MANAGEMENT B.V.—See Allianz SE; *Int'l*, pg. 349
ALLIANZ NEDERLAND GROEP NV—See Allianz SE; *Int'l*, pg. 349
ALLIANZ NEDERLAND LEVENSVERZEKERING NV—See Allianz SE; *Int'l*, pg. 349
ALLIANZ NEDERLAND SCHADEVERZEKERING NV—See Allianz SE; *Int'l*, pg. 349
ALLIANZ NEDERLAND—See Allianz SE; *Int'l*, pg. 349
ALLIANZ NEW EUROPE HOLDING GMBH—See Allianz SE; *Int'l*, pg. 349
ALLIANZ NEW ZEALAND LTD.—See Allianz SE; *Int'l*, pg. 343
ALLIANZ NIGERIA INSURANCE PLC—See Allianz SE; *Int'l*, pg. 349
ALLIANZ NORTHERN IRELAND LTD—See Allianz SE; *Int'l*, pg. 349
ALLIANZ OF AMERICA, INC.—See Allianz SE; *Int'l*, pg. 351
ALLIANZ OF ASIA-PACIFIC AND AFRICA GMBH—See Allianz SE; *Int'l*, pg. 351
ALLIANZ OF NEW YORK—See Allianz SE; *Int'l*, pg. 347
ALLIANZ ONE - BUSINESS SOLUTIONS GMBH—See Allianz SE; *Int'l*, pg. 349
ALLIANZ PARTNERS DEUTSCHLAND GMBH—See Allianz SE; *Int'l*, pg. 349
ALLIANZ PARTNERS S.A.S.—See Allianz SE; *Int'l*, pg. 349
ALLIANZ PENSION CONSULT GMBH—See Allianz SE; *Int'l*, pg. 349
ALLIANZ PENSIONSFONDS AKTIENGESELLSCHAFT—See Allianz SE; *Int'l*, pg. 349
ALLIANZ PENSIONSKASSE AG—See Allianz SE; *Int'l*, pg. 349
ALLIANZ PENZIJNI FOND A.S.—See Allianz SE; *Int'l*, pg. 351
ALLIANZ PENZIJNI SPOLECNOST A.S.—See Allianz SE; *Int'l*, pg. 351
ALLIANZ PLC—See Allianz SE; *Int'l*, pg. 351
ALLIANZ PNB LIFE INSURANCE INC.—See Allianz SE; *Int'l*, pg. 349
ALLIANZ POJISTOVNA A/S—See Allianz SE; *Int'l*, pg. 349
ALLIANZ POLSKA SERVICES SP. Z O.O.—See Allianz SE; *Int'l*, pg. 349
ALLIANZ POPULAR S.L.—See Allianz SE; *Int'l*, pg. 349
ALLIANZ PORTUGAL—See Allianz SE; *Int'l*, pg. 349
ALLIANZ PRIVATE EQUITY PARTNERS GMBH—See Allianz SE; *Int'l*, pg. 344
ALLIANZ PRIVATE EQUITY PARTNERS VERWALTUNGS GMBH—See Allianz SE; *Int'l*, pg. 349
ALLIANZ PRIVATE KRANKENVERSICHERUNGS-AG—See Allianz SE; *Int'l*, pg. 349
ALLIANZ PRIVATE KRANKENVERSICHERUNGS-AKTIEN—See Allianz SE; *Int'l*, pg. 349
ALLIANZ PROPERTIES LIMITED—See Allianz SE; *Int'l*, pg. 349
ALLIANZ PROZESSFINANZ GMBH—See Allianz SE; *Int'l*, pg. 349
ALLIANZ REAL ESTATE ASIA PACIFIC—See Allianz SE; *Int'l*, pg. 349
ALLIANZ REAL ESTATE GERMANY GMBH—See Allianz SE; *Int'l*, pg. 349
ALLIANZ REAL ESTATE GMBH—See Allianz SE; *Int'l*, pg. 349
ALLIANZ RE DUBLIN LTD.—See Allianz SE; *Int'l*, pg. 351
ALLIANZ REINSURANCE AMERICA INC.—See Allianz SE; *Int'l*, pg. 349
ALLIANZ RENEWABLE ENERGY MANAGEMENT GMBH—See Allianz SE; *Int'l*, pg. 349
ALLIANZ RISK AUDIT—See Allianz SE; *Int'l*, pg. 348
ALLIANZ RISK CONSULTANTS B.V.—See Allianz SE; *Int'l*, pg. 349
ALLIANZ RISK CONSULTING GMBH—See Allianz SE; *Int'l*, pg. 349
ALLIANZ RISK TRANSFER AG—See Allianz SE; *Int'l*, pg. 349
ALLIANZ RISK TRANSFER AG—See Allianz SE; *Int'l*, pg. 345
ALLIANZ RISK TRANSFER (BERMUDA) LIMITED—See Allianz SE; *Int'l*, pg. 345
ALLIANZ RISK TRANSFER, INC.—See Allianz SE; *Int'l*, pg. 345
ALLIANZ RISK TRANSFER N.V.—See Allianz SE; *Int'l*, pg. 350

COMPANY NAME INDEX

ALLIANZ RISK TRANSFER (UK) LIMITED—See Allianz SE; *Int'l*, pg. 349
ALLIANZ ROSNO ASSET MANAGEMENT—See Allianz SE; *Int'l*, pg. 354
ALLIANZ ROSNO LIFE—See Allianz SE; *Int'l*, pg. 354
ALLIANZ SAUDE S.A.—See Allianz SE; *Int'l*, pg. 350
ALLIANZ SAUDI FRANSI COOPERATIVE INSURANCE COMPANY—See Allianz SE; *Int'l*, pg. 345
ALLIANZ SEGUROS DE VIDA S.A.—See Allianz SE; *Int'l*, pg. 350
ALLIANZ SEGUROS S.A.—See Allianz SE; *Int'l*, pg. 350
ALLIANZ SENEGAL ASSURANCES—See Allianz SE; *Int'l*, pg. 350
ALLIANZ SENEGAL ASSURANCES VIE—See Allianz SE; *Int'l*, pg. 350
ALLIANZ SENEGAL DOMMAGES—See Allianz SE; *Int'l*, pg. 350
ALLIANZ SENEGAL VIE—See Allianz SE; *Int'l*, pg. 350
ALLIANZ SERVICE CENTER GMBH—See Allianz SE; *Int'l*, pg. 350
ALLIANZ SERVICES PRIVATE LTD.—See Allianz SE; *Int'l*, pg. 350
ALLIANZ SE; *Int'l*, pg. 341
ALLIANZ SIGORTA A.S.—See Allianz SE; *Int'l*, pg. 345
ALLIANZ SLOVENSKA DOCHODKOVA SPRAVCOVSA SPOLOCNOST, A.S.—See Allianz SE; *Int'l*, pg. 350
ALLIANZ-SLOVENSKA DSS A.S.—See Allianz SE; *Int'l*, pg. 351
ALLIANZ SLOVENSKA POISTOVNA, A.S.—See Allianz SE; *Int'l*, pg. 350
ALLIANZ SNA SAL—See Allianz SE; *Int'l*, pg. 350
ALLIANZ SOA FONDS—See Allianz SE; *Int'l*, pg. 350
ALLIANZ—See Allianz SE; *Int'l*, pg. 343
ALLIANZ SOUTH AMERICA HOLDING B.V.—See Allianz SE; *Int'l*, pg. 350
ALLIANZ S.P.A.—See Allianz SE; *Int'l*, pg. 350
ALLIANZ SP. Z O.O.—See Allianz SE; *Int'l*, pg. 350
ALLIANZ SUBALPINA HOLDING S.P.A.—See Allianz SE; *Int'l*, pg. 350
ALLIANZ SUISSE IMMOBILIEN AG—See Allianz SE; *Int'l*, pg. 350
ALLIANZ SUISSE INSURANCE COMPANY—See Allianz SE; *Int'l*, pg. 350
ALLIANZ SUISSE VERSICHERUNGEN - ALLIANZ CU ISSE LEBEN—See Allianz SE; *Int'l*, pg. 350
ALLIANZ SUISSE VERSICHERUNGEN—See Allianz SE; *Int'l*, pg. 350
ALLIANZ SUISSE VERSICHERUNGS-GESELLSCHAFT AG—See Allianz SE; *Int'l*, pg. 350
ALLIANZ TAIWAN LIFE INSURANCE COMPANY LTD.—See Allianz SE; *Int'l*, pg. 350
ALLIANZ TAKAFUL B.S.C.(C)—See Allianz SE; *Int'l*, pg. 350
ALLIANZ TECHNOLOGY TRUST PLC; *Int'l*, pg. 356
ALLIANZ-TIRIAC ASIGURARI S.A.—See Allianz SE; *Int'l*, pg. 351
ALLIANZ-TIRIAC PENSII PRIVATE—See Allianz SE; *Int'l*, pg. 351
ALLIANZ TOGO ASSURANCES—See Allianz SE; *Int'l*, pg. 350
ALLIANZ (UK) LIMITED—See Allianz SE; *Int'l*, pg. 343
ALLIANZ UKRAINE SLC—See Allianz SE; *Int'l*, pg. 354
ALLIANZ UNDERWRITERS INSURANCE COMPANY, CORP.—See Allianz SE; *Int'l*, pg. 350
ALLIANZ US PRIVATE REIT LP—See Allianz SE; *Int'l*, pg. 350
ALLIANZ VERSICHERUNGS-AG (DUBAI BRANCH)—See Allianz SE; *Int'l*, pg. 350
ALLIANZ VERSICHERUNGS AG—See Allianz SE; *Int'l*, pg. 350
ALLIANZ VERSICHERUNGS AG—See Allianz SE; *Int'l*, pg. 350
ALLIANZ VERSICHERUNGS AG—See Allianz SE; *Int'l*, pg. 350
ALLIANZ VERSICHERUNGS AG—See Allianz SE; *Int'l*, pg. 350
ALLIANZ VIVA S.P.A.—See Allianz SE; *Int'l*, pg. 350
ALLIANZ VORSORGEKASSE AG—See Allianz SE; *Int'l*, pg. 350
ALLIANZ WORLDWIDE CARE LIMITED—See Allianz SE; *Int'l*, pg. 350
ALLIANZ YASAM VE EMEKLILIK A.S.—See Allianz SE; *Int'l*, pg. 351
ALLIANZ ZAGREB D.D.—See Allianz SE; *Int'l*, pg. 351
ALLIANZ ZENTRUM FUER TECHNIK GMBH—See Allianz SE; *Int'l*, pg. 352
ALLIB LEASING S.R.O.—See UniCredit S.p.A.; *Int'l*, pg. 8036
ALLIB NEKRETNINE D.O.O. ZA POSLOVANJE NEKRETNINAMA—See UniCredit S.p.A.; *Int'l*, pg. 8036
ALLIED 100, LLC—See Ridgemont Partners Management LLC; *U.S. Private*, pg. 3433
ALLIED ADVERTISING AGENCY, INC.; *U.S. Private*, pg. 185
ALLIED ADVERTISING PUBLIC RELATIONS OF CANADA, INC.—See AALP, Inc.; *U.S. Private*, pg. 32
ALLIED AEROFOAM PRODUCTS, LLC; *U.S. Private*, pg. 185

ALLIED AFFILIATED FUNDING, LP—See Axiom Bank, N.A.; *U.S. Private*, pg. 413
ALLIED AGRONOMY, LLC—See CHS INC.; *U.S. Public*, pg. 491
ALLIED AIR ENTERPRISES INC.—See Lennox International Inc.; *U.S. Public*, pg. 1307
ALLIED ALLOYS LP—See Stainless Steel Midwest LLC; *U.S. Private*, pg. 3776
ALLIED AMERICAN STEEL CORPORATION; *U.S. Private*, pg. 185
ALLIED ARABIA—See Allied International Ltd.; *Int'l*, pg. 357
ALLIED ARCHITECTS, INC.; *Int'l*, pg. 356
ALLIED ARTIST INTERNATIONAL, INC.; *U.S. Private*, pg. 185
ALLIED ASSOCIATES INTERNATIONAL, INC.—See Redhorse Corporation; *U.S. Private*, pg. 3378
ALLIED-BALTIC RUBBER, INC.—See Anhui Zhongding Holding (Group) Co., Ltd.; *Int'l*, pg. 470
ALLIED BANKING CORPORATION (HONG KONG) LIMITED—See Philippine National Bank; *Int'l*, pg. 5845
ALLIED BANK LIMITED—See Ibrahim Fibres Limited; *Int'l*, pg. 3576
ALLIED BEVERAGE GROUP L.L.C.; *U.S. Private*, pg. 185
ALLIED BIOTECH CORP.; *Int'l*, pg. 356
ALLIED BLENDERS AND DISTILLERS PVT. LTD.; *Int'l*, pg. 356
ALLIED BLENDING & INGREDIENTS, INC.—See Arsenal Capital Management LP; *U.S. Private*, pg. 337
ALLIED BUILDING CORP.; *U.S. Private*, pg. 185
ALLIED BUILDING MATERIALS INC.; *U.S. Private*, pg. 185
ALLIED BUILDING PRODUCTS CORP. - FERNDALE—See Beacon Roofing Supply, Inc.; *U.S. Public*, pg. 285
ALLIED BUILDING PRODUCTS CORP. - HICKORY HILLS - TRI-STATE WHOLESALE—See Beacon Roofing Supply, Inc.; *U.S. Public*, pg. 285
ALLIED BUILDING PRODUCTS CORPORATION—See Beacon Roofing Supply, Inc.; *U.S. Public*, pg. 285
ALLIED BUILDING PRODUCTS CORP. - ROCKVILLE—See Beacon Roofing Supply, Inc.; *U.S. Public*, pg. 285
ALLIED BUSINESS GROUP, INC.—See Mariner Wealth Advisors, LLC; *U.S. Private*, pg. 2575
ALLIED BUSINESS INTELLIGENCE, INC.; *U.S. Private*, pg. 185
ALLIED CAPITAL AND DEVELOPMENT OF SOUTH FLORIDA LLC; *U.S. Private*, pg. 185
ALLIED CEDAR INSURANCE GROUP LIMITED—See MS&AD Insurance Group Holdings, Inc.; *Int'l*, pg. 5066
ALLIED CHUCKER & ENGINEERING COMPANY; *U.S. Private*, pg. 185
ALLIED COMMUNICATIONS INC—See Bertelsmann SE & Co. KGaA; *Int'l*, pg. 993
ALLIED COMPUTERS INTERNATIONAL ASIA LTD.; *Int'l*, pg. 357
ALLIED CONCRETE COMPANY—See CRH plc; *Int'l*, pg. 1845
ALLIED CONCRETE PRODUCTS INC.; *U.S. Private*, pg. 185
ALLIED CONSTRUCTION CO. INC.; *U.S. Private*, pg. 185
ALLIED CONSTRUCTION PRODUCTS, LLC—See Sandvik AB; *Int'l*, pg. 6531
ALLIED CONSTRUCTION SERVICES INC.; *U.S. Private*, pg. 185
ALLIED CONVENTION SERVICE, INC.—See New State Capital Partners LLC; *U.S. Private*, pg. 2907
ALLIED COOPERATIVE INSURANCE GROUP; *Int'l*, pg. 357
ALLIED CORP.; *Int'l*, pg. 357
ALLIED CRITICAL METALS CORP.; *Int'l*, pg. 357
ALLIED DAIRY PRODUCTS INC.; *U.S. Private*, pg. 185
ALLIED DENTAL PRACTICES OF NEW JERSEY, LLC—See TriSpan LLP; *Int'l*, pg. 7927
ALLIED DIGITAL SERVICES LIMITED; *Int'l*, pg. 357
ALLIED DIGITAL SERVICES LLC—See Allied Digital Services Limited; *Int'l*, pg. 357
ALLIED DISCOUNT TIRE & BRAKE; *U.S. Private*, pg. 185
ALLIED DON VALLEY HOTEL INC.—See Allied Holdings Ltd.; *Int'l*, pg. 357
ALLIED ELECTRIC INC.; *U.S. Private*, pg. 185
ALLIED ELECTRIC MOTOR SERVICE; *U.S. Private*, pg. 186
ALLIED ELECTRONICS (CANADA) INC.—See RS Group plc; *Int'l*, pg. 6417
ALLIED ELECTRONICS INC.—See RS Group plc; *Int'l*, pg. 6417
ALLIED EMPLOYER GROUP; *U.S. Private*, pg. 186
ALLIED ENERGY CORPORATION—See CAMAC International Corporation; *U.S. Private*, pg. 725
ALLIED ENERGY CORP.; *U.S. Public*, pg. 80
ALLIED ENERGY, INC.; *U.S. Public*, pg. 80
ALLIED ENERGY INVESTMENT PTY. LTD.—See CAMAC International Corporation; *U.S. Private*, pg. 725
ALLIED ENERGY PLC—See CAMAC International Corporation; *U.S. Private*, pg. 725

ALLIED INTERNATIONAL LTD.

ALLIED ENTERPRISES INC.; *U.S. Private*, pg. 186
ALLIED ENVELOPE CO. INC.; *U.S. Private*, pg. 186
ALLIED ENVIRONMENTAL SOLUTIONS, INC.—See Allied Resource Corporation; *U.S. Private*, pg. 187
ALLIED EXHAUST SYSTEMS—See Allied Manufacturing Inc.; *U.S. Private*, pg. 186
ALLIED EXPERIENTIAL - LOS ANGELES—See AALP, Inc.; *U.S. Private*, pg. 32
ALLIED EXPERIENTIAL—See AALP, Inc.; *U.S. Private*, pg. 32
ALLIED FARMERS LIMITED; *Int'l*, pg. 357
ALLIED FASTENER & TOOL INC.; *U.S. Private*, pg. 186
ALLIED FEEDS INC.; *U.S. Private*, pg. 186
ALLIED FELT GROUP—See Central Shippee, Inc.; *U.S. Private*, pg. 824
ALLIED FINISHING INC.—See Decorative Castings Inc.; *U.S. Private*, pg. 1188
ALLIED FIRST BANCORP, INC.; *U.S. Private*, pg. 186
ALLIED FIRST BANK—See Allied First Bancorp, Inc.; *U.S. Private*, pg. 186
ALLIED FITTING LP; *U.S. Private*, pg. 186
ALLIED FOODS LIMITED—See DCC plc; *Int'l*, pg. 1989
ALLIED FRANCE—See Allied International Ltd.; *Int'l*, pg. 358
ALLIED GAMING & ENTERTAINMENT, INC.; *U.S. Public*, pg. 80
ALLIED GLASS CONTAINERS LTD.—See Verallia SA; *Int'l*, pg. 8164
ALLIED GOLD CORPORATION; *Int'l*, pg. 357
THE ALLIED GROUP INC.—See Atlantic Street Capital Management LLC; *U.S. Private*, pg. 374
ALLIED GROUP LIMITED; *Int'l*, pg. 357
ALLIED HANDLING EQUIPMENT CO—See Toyota Industries Corporation; *Int'l*, pg. 7869
ALLIED HEALTHCARE GROUP HOLDINGS LIMITED—See Charterhouse Capital Partners LLP; *Int'l*, pg. 1454
ALLIED HEALTHCARE GROUP HOLDINGS LIMITED—See CVC Capital Partners SICAV-FIS S.A.; *Int'l*, pg. 1882
ALLIED HEALTHCARE GROUP HOLDINGS LIMITED—See Permira Advisers LLP; *Int'l*, pg. 5803
ALLIED HEALTHCARE GROUP LIMITED—See Charterhouse Capital Partners LLP; *Int'l*, pg. 1455
ALLIED HEALTHCARE GROUP LIMITED—See CVC Capital Partners SICAV-FIS S.A.; *Int'l*, pg. 1882
ALLIED HEALTHCARE GROUP LIMITED—See Permira Advisers LLP; *Int'l*, pg. 5803
ALLIED HEALTHCARE HOLDINGS LIMITED—See Charterhouse Capital Partners LLP; *Int'l*, pg. 1454
ALLIED HEALTHCARE HOLDINGS LIMITED—See CVC Capital Partners SICAV-FIS S.A.; *Int'l*, pg. 1882
ALLIED HEALTHCARE HOLDINGS LIMITED—See Permira Advisers LLP; *Int'l*, pg. 5803
ALLIED HEALTHCARE INTERNATIONAL INC.—See Charterhouse Capital Partners LLP; *Int'l*, pg. 1454
ALLIED HEALTHCARE INTERNATIONAL INC.—See CVC Capital Partners SICAV-FIS S.A.; *Int'l*, pg. 1882
ALLIED HEALTHCARE INTERNATIONAL INC.—See Permira Advisers LLP; *Int'l*, pg. 5803
ALLIED HEALTHCARE—See Charterhouse Capital Partners LLP; *Int'l*, pg. 1454
ALLIED HEALTHCARE—See CVC Capital Partners SICAV-FIS S.A.; *Int'l*, pg. 1882
ALLIED HEALTHCARE—See Permira Advisers LLP; *Int'l*, pg. 5802
ALLIED HEALTH ELEMENTS COMPANY LIMITED—See Deson Development International Holdings Ltd; *Int'l*, pg. 2045
ALLIED HEALTH GROUP, LLC—See Cross Country Healthcare, Inc.; *U.S. Public*, pg. 595
ALLIED HEALTH PROFESSIONALS LIMITED—See Ares Management Corporation; *U.S. Public*, pg. 188
ALLIED HEALTH PROFESSIONALS LIMITED—See Old Oak Holdings Limited; *Int'l*, pg. 5552
ALLIED HERBALS LIMITED; *Int'l*, pg. 357
ALLIED HOLDINGS LTD.; *Int'l*, pg. 357
ALLIED HOME MEDICAL, INC.; *U.S. Private*, pg. 186
ALLIED HOME WARRANTY GP LLC—See NRG Energy, Inc.; *U.S. Public*, pg. 1549
ALLIED HOTEL PROPERTIES INC.—See Allied Holdings Ltd.; *Int'l*, pg. 357
ALLIED INDUSTRIES, INC.; *U.S. Private*, pg. 186
ALLIED INFORMATICS INC.; *U.S. Private*, pg. 186
ALLIED INSULATION SUPPLY CO., INC.; *U.S. Private*, pg. 186
ALLIED INSURANCE BROKERS LTD.—See GraceKennedy Limited; *Int'l*, pg. 3048
ALLIED INTEGRAL UNITED, INC.—See Clearday, Inc.; *U.S. Public*, pg. 512
ALLIED INTERNATIONAL CORP.; *U.S. Private*, pg. 186
ALLIED INTERNATIONAL EMERGENCY LLC—See Ambipar Participacoes e Empreendimentos SA; *Int'l*, pg. 414
ALLIED INTERNATIONAL HOLDINGS INC.—See AXA S.A.; *Int'l*, pg. 760
ALLIED INTERNATIONAL LTD.; *Int'l*, pg. 357
ALLIED IRISH BANKS (HOLDINGS & INVESTMENTS) LIMITED—See AIB Group plc; *Int'l*, pg. 228

ALLIED INTERNATIONAL LTD.

CORPORATE AFFILIATIONS

ALLIED IRISH FINANCE LIMITED—See AIB Group plc; *Int'l*, pg. 228
ALLIED LIVE—See AALP, Inc.; *U.S. Private*, pg. 32
ALLIED-LOCKE INDUSTRIES INCORPORATED; *U.S. Private*, pg. 191
ALLIED LUBE INC.; *U.S. Private*, pg. 186
ALLIED MACHINERY CORPORATION; *U.S. Private*, pg. 186
ALLIED MANUFACTURING INC.; *U.S. Private*, pg. 186
ALLIED MARBLE, INC.; *U.S. Private*, pg. 186
ALLIED MARINE & INDUSTRIAL INC.—See Upper Lakes Group Inc.; *Int'l*, pg. 8093
ALLIED MARINE LLC—See Shandong Heavy Industry Group Co., Ltd.; *Int'l*, pg. 6753
ALLIED MARKETING GROUP, INC.; *U.S. Private*, pg. 186
ALLIED MASTER CHEMISTS OF AUSTRALIA LIMITED—See Sigma Healthcare Ltd.; *Int'l*, pg. 6907
ALLIED MECHANICAL—See Tower Industries Inc.; *U.S. Private*, pg. 4194
ALLIED MEDIA—See Percept Holdings Pvt. Ltd.; *Int'l*, pg. 5796
ALLIED MEDICAL, LLC—See Flexicare (Group) Limited; *Int'l*, pg. 2705
ALLIED METAL COMPANY; *U.S. Private*, pg. 186
ALLIED METAL, LLC; *U.S. Private*, pg. 186
ALLIED METALLURG SOUTH AFRICA (AMETSA)—See Allied Mineral Products, Inc.; *U.S. Private*, pg. 186
ALLIED METALS CORP.; *U.S. Private*, pg. 186
ALLIED MINDS PLC; *U.S. Public*, pg. 80
ALLIED MINERAL PRODUCTS, ASIA—See Allied Mineral Products, Inc.; *U.S. Private*, pg. 187
ALLIED MINERAL PRODUCTS EUROPE BV—See Allied Mineral Products, Inc.; *U.S. Private*, pg. 187
ALLIED MINERAL PRODUCTS, INC.; *U.S. Private*, pg. 186
ALLIED MINERAL PRODUCTS, LATIN AMERICA—See Allied Mineral Products, Inc.; *U.S. Private*, pg. 187
ALLIED MINERAL PRODUCTS (TIANJIN) CO., LTD. (AMT)—See Allied Mineral Products, Inc.; *U.S. Private*, pg. 187
ALLIED MINERAL TECHNICAL SERVICES, INC.—See Allied Mineral Products, Inc.; *U.S. Private*, pg. 187
ALLIED MORTGAGE & FINANCIAL CORP.; *U.S. Private*, pg. 187
ALLIED MOTION CANADA INC.—See Allient Inc.; *U.S. Public*, pg. 80
ALLIED MOTION DORDRECHT B.V.—See Allient Inc.; *U.S. Public*, pg. 80
ALLIED MOTION PORTUGAL—See Allient Inc.; *U.S. Public*, pg. 80
ALLIED MOTION STOCKHOLM—See Allient Inc.; *U.S. Public*, pg. 80
ALLIED MOULDED ENCLOSURE PRODUCTS (INDIA) PVT LTD—See Allied Moulded Products Inc.; *U.S. Private*, pg. 187
ALLIED MOULDED PRODUCTS INC.; *U.S. Private*, pg. 187
ALLIED OIL & GAS SERVICES LLC—See Intervale Capital, LLC; *U.S. Private*, pg. 2127
ALLIED OIL & TIRE COMPANY, LLC—See AIP, LLC; *U.S. Private*, pg. 135
ALLIED OLD ENGLISH, INC.; *U.S. Private*, pg. 187
ALLIED ORTHOPEDIC APPLIANCES, INC.—See WCA Hospital; *U.S. Private*, pg. 4461
ALLIED PACIFIC—See Tower Industries Inc.; *U.S. Private*, pg. 4194
ALLIED PERSONNEL SERVICES, INC.; *U.S. Private*, pg. 187
ALLIED PHYSICIANS OF MICHIANA, LLC—See The South Bend Clinic, LLP; *U.S. Private*, pg. 4119
ALLIED PICKFORDS—See Madison Dearborn Partners, LLC; *U.S. Private*, pg. 2542
ALLIED PINNACLE PTY LTD—See Nisshin Seifun Group, Inc.; *Int'l*, pg. 5372
ALLIED PLASTICS HOLDINGS, LLC—See Alpha Industries, Inc.; *U.S. Private*, pg. 197
ALLIED PLASTIC SKYLIGHT; *Int'l*, pg. 358
ALLIED PLASTIC SUPPLY, INC.; *U.S. Private*, pg. 187
ALLIED POWER GROUP, LLC; *U.S. Private*, pg. 187
ALLIED POWER HOLDINGS, LLC—See Bernhard Capital Partners Management, LP; *U.S. Private*, pg. 536
ALLIEDPRA, INC.—See EagleTree Capital, LP; *U.S. Private*, pg. 1311
ALLIEDPRA MONACO—See Allied International Ltd.; *Int'l*, pg. 358
ALLIED PRECISION MANUFACTURING (M) SDN. BHD.—See Allied Technologies Ltd.; *Int'l*, pg. 358
ALLIED PRECISION TECHNOLOGIES (M) SDN. BHD.—See Allied Technologies Ltd.; *Int'l*, pg. 358
ALLIED PRECISION (THAILAND) CO., LTD.—See Allied Technologies Ltd.; *Int'l*, pg. 358
ALLIED PRINTING SERVICES, INC.; *U.S. Private*, pg. 187
ALLIED PROPANE SERVICE INC.; *U.S. Private*, pg. 187
ALLIED PROPERTIES (H.K.) LIMITED—See Allied Group Limited; *Int'l*, pg. 357
ALLIED PROPERTIES MANAGEMENT LIMITED PARTNERSHIP—See Allied Properties Real Estate Investment Trust; *Int'l*, pg. 358

ALLIED PROPERTIES REAL ESTATE INVESTMENT TRUST; *Int'l*, pg. 358
ALLIED PROTECTIVE SYSTEMS, INC.—See Summit Partners, L.P.; *U.S. Private*, pg. 3855
ALLIED READY MIX CONCRETE LIMITED—See Heidelberg Materials AG; *Int'l*, pg. 3308
ALLIED REALTY COMPANY; *U.S. Private*, pg. 187
ALLIED REFRACTORY PRODUCTS INDIA PRIVATE, LTD.—See Allied Mineral Products, Inc.; *U.S. Private*, pg. 187
ALLIED REFRIGERATION INC.; *U.S. Private*, pg. 187
ALLIED RELIABILITY INC.—See Shell plc; *Int'l*, pg. 6796
ALLIED RESOURCE CORPORATION; *U.S. Private*, pg. 187
ALLIED RESOURCES INC.; *U.S. Public*, pg. 80
ALLIED RICHARD BERTRAM MARINE GROUP INC.—See Shandong Heavy Industry Group Co., Ltd.; *Int'l*, pg. 6753
ALLIED RISK MANAGEMENT LIMITED—See Arthur J. Gallagher & Co.; *U.S. Public*, pg. 203
ALLIED RUBBER & RIGGING SUPPLY—See AEA Investors LP; *U.S. Private*, pg. 115
ALLIED SAFE & VAULT CO. INC.; *U.S. Private*, pg. 187
ALLIED SECURITY INNOVATIONS, INC.; *U.S. Public*, pg. 80
ALLIED SEED LLC; *U.S. Private*, pg. 187
ALLIEDSIGNAL AEROSPACE SERVICE CORPORATION—See Honeywell International Inc.; *U.S. Public*, pg. 1047
ALLIED SOFT LLC; *U.S. Private*, pg. 187
ALLIED SOLUTIONS LLC; *U.S. Private*, pg. 188
ALLIED SOLUTIONS LLC—See Allied Solutions LLC; *U.S. Private*, pg. 188
ALLIED SPAIN—See Allied International Ltd.; *Int'l*, pg. 358
ALLIED SPECIALTY INSURANCE INC.—See AXA S.A.; *Int'l*, pg. 760
ALLIED STEEL BUILDINGS, INC.; *U.S. Private*, pg. 188
ALLIED SUSTAINABILITY & ENVIRONMENTAL CONSULTANTS GROUP LIMITED; *Int'l*, pg. 358
ALLIED SYSTEMS COMPANY; *U.S. Private*, pg. 188
ALLIED SYSTEMS INC.; *U.S. Private*, pg. 188
ALLIED SYSTEMS—See Allied Systems Company; *U.S. Private*, pg. 188
ALLIED TECH BASE CO., LTD.—See Allied Architects, Inc.; *Int'l*, pg. 356
ALLIED TECH CAMP CO., LTD.—See Allied Architects, Inc.; *Int'l*, pg. 356
ALLIED TECHNOLOGIES HOLDINGS PTE. LTD.—See Allied Technologies Ltd.; *Int'l*, pg. 358
ALLIED TECHNOLOGIES LTD.; *Int'l*, pg. 358
ALLIED TECHNOLOGIES (SAIGON) CO., LTD.—See Allied Technologies Ltd.; *Int'l*, pg. 358
ALLIED TECHNOLOGY GROUP INC.—See The Carlyle Group Inc.; *U.S. Public*, pg. 2048
ALLIED TECHNOLOGY INC.—See Forum Energy Technologies, Inc.; *U.S. Public*, pg. 873
ALLIED TECH (S) PTE. LTD.—See Allied Technologies Ltd.; *Int'l*, pg. 358
ALLIED TELESIS CAPITAL CORP.—See ALLIED TELESIS HOLDINGS K.K.; *Int'l*, pg. 358
ALLIED TELESIS HOLDINGS K.K.; *Int'l*, pg. 358
ALLIED TELESIS (HONG KONG) LTD.—See ALLIED TELESIS HOLDINGS K.K.; *Int'l*, pg. 358
ALLIED TELESIS, INC.—See ALLIED TELESIS HOLDINGS K.K.; *Int'l*, pg. 358
ALLIED TELESIS INC.—See ALLIED TELESIS HOLDINGS K.K.; *Int'l*, pg. 358
ALLIED TELESIS INTERNATIONAL SERVICES LTD.—See ALLIED TELESIS HOLDINGS K.K.; *Int'l*, pg. 358
ALLIED TELESIS INTERNATIONAL S.L.U—See ALLIED TELESIS HOLDINGS K.K.; *Int'l*, pg. 358
ALLIED TELESIS LABS (PHILIPPINES) INC.—See ALLIED TELESIS HOLDINGS K.K.; *Int'l*, pg. 358
ALLIED TELESIS LABS S.R.L.—See ALLIED TELESIS HOLDINGS K.K.; *Int'l*, pg. 358
ALLIED TELESIS R&D CENTER K.K.—See ALLIED TELESIS HOLDINGS K.K.; *Int'l*, pg. 358
ALLIED TELESYN (CHINA) LTD.—See ALLIED TELESIS HOLDINGS K.K.; *Int'l*, pg. 358
ALLIED TELESYN INTERNATIONAL (ASIA) PTE. LTD.—See ALLIED TELESIS HOLDINGS K.K.; *Int'l*, pg. 358
ALLIED TELESYN INTERNATIONAL GMBH—See ALLIED TELESIS HOLDINGS K.K.; *Int'l*, pg. 358
ALLIED TELESYN INTERNATIONAL, INC.; *U.S. Private*, pg. 188
ALLIED TELESYN INTERNATIONAL LTD.—See ALLIED TELESIS HOLDINGS K.K.; *Int'l*, pg. 358
ALLIED TELESYN INTERNATIONAL S.A.—See ALLIED TELESIS HOLDINGS K.K.; *Int'l*, pg. 358
ALLIED TELESYN INTERNATIONAL S.R.L.—See ALLIED TELESIS HOLDINGS K.K.; *Int'l*, pg. 359
ALLIED TELESYN SOUTH ASIA PTE. LTD.—See ALLIED TELESIS HOLDINGS K.K.; *Int'l*, pg. 359
ALLIED TELESYN VERTRIEBSGESELLSCHAFT M.B.H.—See ALLIED TELESIS HOLDINGS K.K.; *Int'l*, pg. 359
ALLIED T-PRO INC.—See Fairfax Financial Holdings Limited; *Int'l*, pg. 2608

ALLIED TRANSMISSIONS (S.E.A.) PTE LTD—See Dana Incorporated; *U.S. Public*, pg. 621
ALLIED TUBE & CONDUIT CORPORATION—See Clayton, Dubilier & Rice, LLC; *U.S. Private*, pg. 919
ALLIED TUBE & CONDUIT—See Clayton, Dubilier & Rice, LLC; *U.S. Private*, pg. 919
ALLIED TURKISH BANK IBU LTD.—See Turkish Bank A.S.; *Int'l*, pg. 7975
ALLIED UK—See Allied International Ltd.; *Int'l*, pg. 358
ALLIED UNIKING CORPORATION; *U.S. Private*, pg. 188
ALLIED UNIVERSAL CORP.—See Allied Universal Holding Corporation; *U.S. Private*, pg. 188
ALLIED UNIVERSAL HOLDING CORPORATION; *U.S. Private*, pg. 188
ALLIED UNIVERSAL MANAGER LLC; *U.S. Private*, pg. 188
ALLIED UTILITY PRODUCTS, INC.—See WESCO International, Inc.; *U.S. Public*, pg. 2351
ALLIED VAN LINES, INC.—See Madison Dearborn Partners, LLC; *U.S. Private*, pg. 2542
ALLIED VAUGHN - CHICAGO—See Allied Vaughn Inc.; *U.S. Private*, pg. 191
ALLIED VAUGHN INC.; *U.S. Private*, pg. 191
ALLIED VAUGHN—See Allied Vaughn Inc.; *U.S. Private*, pg. 191
ALLIED VICTORY INVESTMENT LIMITED—See Wang On Group Ltd; *Int'l*, pg. 8341
ALLIED VISION TECHNOLOGIES (CANADA) INC.—See TKH Group N.V.; *Int'l*, pg. 7765
ALLIED VISION TECHNOLOGIES GMBH—See TKH Group N.V.; *Int'l*, pg. 7765
ALLIED VISION TECHNOLOGIES, INC.—See TKH Group N.V.; *Int'l*, pg. 7765
ALLIED VISION TECHNOLOGIES PTE. LTD.—See TKH Group N.V.; *Int'l*, pg. 7765
ALLIED VISION TECHNOLOGIES (SHANGHAI) CO., LTD.—See TKH Group N.V.; *Int'l*, pg. 7765
ALLIED WARRANTY LLC—See NRG Energy, inc.; *U.S. Public*, pg. 1549
ALLIED WASTE ENVIRONMENTAL MANAGEMENT GROUP, LLC—See Republic Services, Inc.; *U.S. Public*, pg. 1785
ALLIED WASTE, INC.—See Republic Services, Inc.; *U.S. Public*, pg. 1785
ALLIED WASTE INDUSTRIES, INC—See Republic Services, Inc.; *U.S. Public*, pg. 1785
ALLIED WASTE SERVICES OF CORVALLIS; *U.S. Private*, pg. 191
ALLIED WASTE SERVICES OF FORT WORTH, LLC—See Republic Services, Inc.; *U.S. Public*, pg. 1785
ALLIED WASTE SERVICES OF MASSACHUSETTS, LLC—See Republic Services, Inc.; *U.S. Public*, pg. 1785
ALLIED WASTE SERVICES OF PAGE, INC.—See Republic Services, Inc.; *U.S. Public*, pg. 1785
ALLIED WASTE SERVICES OF STILLWATER, INC.—See Republic Services, Inc.; *U.S. Public*, pg. 1785
ALLIED WASTE SYSTEMS OF ARIZONA, LLC—See Republic Services, Inc.; *U.S. Public*, pg. 1785
ALLIED WHOLESALE ELECTRICAL SUPPLY INCORPORATED; *U.S. Private*, pg. 191
ALLIED WIRE & CABLE INC. - MIDWESTERN DIVISION—See Allied Wire & Cable Inc.; *U.S. Private*, pg. 191
ALLIED WIRE & CABLE INC. - NEW ENGLAND DIVISION—See Allied Wire & Cable Inc.; *U.S. Private*, pg. 191
ALLIED WIRE & CABLE INC.; *U.S. Private*, pg. 191
ALLIED WIRE & CABLE INC.—See Allied Wire & Cable Inc.; *U.S. Private*, pg. 191
ALLIED WIRE & CABLE INC. - SOUTHEASTERN DIVISION—See Allied Wire & Cable Inc.; *U.S. Private*, pg. 191
ALLIED WIRE & CABLE INC. - WEST COAST DIVISION—See Allied Wire & Cable Inc.; *U.S. Private*, pg. 191
ALLIED WORK FORCE CHRISTCHURCH LIMITED—See AWF Madison Group Limited; *Int'l*, pg. 753
ALLIED WORK FORCE DUNEDIN LIMITED—See AWF Madison Group Limited; *Int'l*, pg. 753
ALLIED WORK FORCE HAMILTON LIMITED—See AWF Madison Group Limited; *Int'l*, pg. 753
ALLIED WORK FORCE NELSON LIMITED—See AWF Madison Group Limited; *Int'l*, pg. 753
ALLIED WORK FORCE PALMERSTON NORTH LIMITED—See AWF Madison Group Limited; *Int'l*, pg. 753
ALLIED WORK FORCE TAURANGA LIMITED—See AWF Madison Group Limited; *Int'l*, pg. 753
ALLIED WORK FORCE WELLINGTON LIMITED—See AWF Madison Group Limited; *Int'l*, pg. 753
ALLIED WORK FORCE WHANGAREI LIMITED—See AWF Madison Group Limited; *Int'l*, pg. 753
ALLIED WORLD ASSURANCE COMPANY (EUROPE) DESIGNATED ACTIVITY COMPANY—See Fairfax Financial Holdings Limited; *Int'l*, pg. 2605

COMPANY NAME INDEX

ALLIED WORLD ASSURANCE COMPANY HOLDINGS, LTD—See Fairfax Financial Holdings Limited; *Int'l*, pg. 2605
ALLIED WORLD ASSURANCE COMPANY, LTD—See Fairfax Financial Holdings Limited; *Int'l*, pg. 2606
ALLIED WORLD ASSURANCE COMPANY—See Fairfax Financial Holdings Limited; *Int'l*, pg. 2605
ALLIED WORLD ASSURANCE COMPANY (U.S.) INC.—See Fairfax Financial Holdings Limited; *Int'l*, pg. 2605
ALLIED WORLD ASSURANCE HOLDINGS (IRELAND) LTD—See Fairfax Financial Holdings Limited; *Int'l*, pg. 2606
ALLIED WORLD ASSURANCE HOLDINGS (U.S.) INC.—See Fairfax Financial Holdings Limited; *Int'l*, pg. 2606
ALLIED WORLD INSURANCE COMPANY—See Fairfax Financial Holdings Limited; *Int'l*, pg. 2606
ALLIED WORLD REINSURANCE COMPANY—See Fairfax Financial Holdings Limited; *Int'l*, pg. 2606
ALLIED WORLD SPECIALTY INSURANCE COMPANY—See Fairfax Financial Holdings Limited; *Int'l*, pg. 2606
ALLIED WORLD SURPLUS LINES INSURANCE COMPANY—See Fairfax Financial Holdings Limited; *Int'l*, pg. 2606
ALLIED WORLD SYNDICATE SERVICES (SINGAPORE) PTE. LTD.—See Fairfax Financial Holdings Limited; *Int'l*, pg. 2606
ALLIED ZURICH PLC—See Zurich Insurance Group Limited; *Int'l*, pg. 8697
ALLIENT INC.; *U.S. Public*, pg. 80
ALLIES INC.; *U.S. Private*, pg. 191
ALLIES INTERTRADE CO., LTD.—See Peerapat Technology Public Company Limited; *Int'l*, pg. 5779
ALLIES LIMITED; *U.S. Private*, pg. 191
ALLIES & ROSS MANAGEMENT AND DEVELOPMENT CORPORATION; *U.S. Private*, pg. 191
ALLIGATOR BIOSCIENCE AB; *Int'l*, pg. 359
ALLIGATOR BOOKS LIMITED—See IG Design Group Plc; *Int'l*, pg. 3600
ALLIGATOR COMPUTER SYSTEMS, INC.—See Health-Champion Partners LLC; *U.S. Private*, pg. 1895
ALLIGATOR DIESEL PERFORMANCE LLC; *U.S. Private*, pg. 192
ALLIGATOR ENERGY LIMITED; *Int'l*, pg. 359
ALLIGHTPRIMAX FZCO—See Seven Group Holdings Limited; *Int'l*, pg. 6732
ALLIGHT PTY LTD—See Seven Group Holdings Limited; *Int'l*, pg. 6733
ALLIKRISTE LLC; *U.S. Private*, pg. 192
ALLINA HEALTH SYSTEM, INC.; *U.S. Private*, pg. 192
ALLIN CORPORATION; *U.S. Public*, pg. 81
ALL INC.; *U.S. Private*, pg. 171
ALLIN DIGITAL IMAGING—See Allin Corporation; *U.S. Public*, pg. 81
ALL IN GAMES SA; *Int'l*, pg. 332
ALLIN INTERACTIVE CORPORATION—See Allin Corporation; *U.S. Public*, pg. 81
ALL IN MEDIA PTY. LTD.—See Adeia Inc.; *U.S. Private*, pg. 40
ALL IN ONE COMMUNICATION AG—See CTS Eventim AG & Co. KGAA; *Int'l*, pg. 1872
ALL IN ONE & MOORE BUILDING SYSTEMS, LLC—See Installed Building Products, Inc.; *U.S. Public*, pg. 1132
ALL-IN-ONE NETWORK SOLUTIONS, INC.; *U.S. Private*, pg. 173
ALL IN ONE VERMIETUNG GMBH—See BNP Paribas SA; *Int'l*, pg. 1079
ALLINOV INC.—See Astec Industries, Inc.; *U.S. Public*, pg. 216
ALL INSPIRE DEVELOPMENT PUBLIC COMPANY LIMITED; *Int'l*, pg. 332
ALL INVEST SECURITIES LTD.; *Int'l*, pg. 332
ALL IN WEST! CAPITAL CORPORATION; *Int'l*, pg. 332
ALL IPO PLC—See ADVFN PLC; *Int'l*, pg. 167
ALLIS COMMUNICATIONS CO., LTD.—See Allis Electric Co., Ltd.; *Int'l*, pg. 359
ALLIS ELECTRIC CO., LTD.; *Int'l*, pg. 359
ALLIS ELECTRIC (S) PTE. LTD.—See Allis Electric Co., Ltd.; *Int'l*, pg. 359
ALLISON AND PARTNERS K.K.—See Allison & Partners LLC; *U.S. Private*, pg. 192
ALLISON BAVARIAN—See AutoNation, Inc.; *U.S. Public*, pg. 232
ALLISON BAVARIAN—See AutoNation, Inc.; *U.S. Public*, pg. 232
ALLISON CHEVROLET INC.; *U.S. Private*, pg. 192
ALLISON & CHUMNEY, PC.; *U.S. Private*, pg. 192
ALLISON CORPORATION; *U.S. Private*, pg. 192
ALLISON DOOR SALES, INC.—See On-Point Group, LLC; *U.S. Private*, pg. 3019
ALLISON JAMES ESTATES & HOMES INC.; *U.S. Private*, pg. 192
ALLISON & PARTNERS LLC; *U.S. Private*, pg. 192
ALLISON & PARTNERS—See Allison & Partners LLC; *U.S. Private*, pg. 192
ALLISON & PARTNERS—See Allison & Partners LLC; *U.S. Private*, pg. 192
ALLISON & PARTNERS—See Allison & Partners LLC; *U.S. Private*, pg. 192
ALLISON & PARTNERS—See Allison & Partners LLC; *U.S. Private*, pg. 192
ALLISON & PARTNERS-WASHINGTON D.C.—See Allison & Partners LLC; *U.S. Private*, pg. 192
ALLISON REED GROUP, INC.; *U.S. Private*, pg. 192
ALLISON TRANSMISSION HOLDINGS, INC.; *U.S. Public*, pg. 81
ALLISON TRANSMISSION, INC.—See Allison Transmission Holdings, Inc.; *U.S. Public*, pg. 81
ALLISON TRANSMISSION JAPAN CO., LTD.—See Allison Transmission Holdings, Inc.; *U.S. Public*, pg. 81
ALLIS PARTICIPACOES S.A.; *Int'l*, pg. 359
ALLIS TOOL & MACHINE CORP.; *U.S. Private*, pg. 192
ALLITY PTY LTD—See Archer Capital Pty. Ltd.; *Int'l*, pg. 547
ALLIUM HEALTHCARE (SINGAPORE) PTE LTD—See G. K. Goh Holdings Limited; *Int'l*, pg. 2864
ALLIUM MEDICAL SOLUTIONS LTD.; *Int'l*, pg. 359
ALLIUM RENEWABLE ENERGY, LLC—See Lotus Infrastructure Partners LLC; *U.S. Private*, pg. 2497
ALLIXO TECHNOLOGIES, LLC; *U.S. Private*, pg. 192
ALL JOB POLAND SP. Z O.O.—See Cineworld Group plc; *Int'l*, pg. 1610
ALLKEM LIMITED; *Int'l*, pg. 359
ALL LEGAL STAFF INC.; *U.S. Private*, pg. 171
ALL-LIFT OF GEORGIA INC.; *U.S. Private*, pg. 173
ALL-LIFTS, INC.—See Altamont Capital Partners; *U.S. Private*, pg. 204
ALL-LIFT SYSTEMS, INC.—See Dunes Point Capital, LLC; *U.S. Private*, pg. 1288
ALL MAGNETICS INC.; *U.S. Private*, pg. 171
ALL MAKES OFFICE EQUIPMENT CO. INC.; *U.S. Private*, pg. 171
ALL MAKES OFFICE EQUIPMENT CO.—See All Makes Office Equipment Co. Inc.; *U.S. Private*, pg. 171
ALL MAKES OFFICE INTERIORS—See All Makes Office Equipment Co. Inc.; *U.S. Private*, pg. 171
ALLMAND BROS., INC.—See Briggs & Stratton Corporation; *U.S. Private*, pg. 650
ALL MARINE SPARES INTERNATIONAL, LLC; *U.S. Private*, pg. 171
ALLMA VOLKMANN ZWEIGNIEDERLASSUNG DER SAURER GERMANY GMDII & CO. KG Soo OC Oorlikon Corporation AG; *Int'l*, pg. 5514
ALLMED HEALTHCARE PROFESSIONALS PROPRIETARY LIMITED—See Workforce Holdings Ltd.; *Int'l*, pg. 8455
ALL MEDIA BALTICS—See Providence Equity Partners L.L.C.; *U.S. Private*, pg. 3291
ALL MEDIA CAPITAL, INC.—See Providence Capital Funding, Inc.; *U.S. Private*, pg. 3291
ALLMEDIA, INC.; *U.S. Private*, pg. 192
ALLMED MEDICAL PRODUCTS CO., LTD.; *Int'l*, pg. 359
ALL MED MEDICAL SUPPLY, LLC; *U.S. Private*, pg. 171
ALLMESS GMBH—See Itron, Inc.; *U.S. Public*, pg. 1175
ALLMETAL, INC.; *U.S. Private*, pg. 192
ALLMETAL RECYCLING, LLC; *U.S. Private*, pg. 192
ALLMETAL SCREW PRODUCTS CORP.; *U.S. Private*, pg. 192
ALL METAL SERVICES INDIA PRIVATE LIMITED—See Reliance Steel & Aluminum Co.; *U.S. Public*, pg. 1779
ALL METAL SERVICES LIMITED—See Reliance Steel & Aluminum Co.; *U.S. Public*, pg. 1779
ALL METAL SERVICES LTD.; *Int'l*, pg. 332
ALL METAL SERVICES LTD.—See Reliance Steel & Aluminum Co.; *U.S. Public*, pg. 1779
ALL METAL SERVICES LTD.—See Reliance Steel & Aluminum Co.; *U.S. Public*, pg. 1779
ALL METAL SERVICES (MALAYSIA) SDN. BHD.—See Reliance Steel & Aluminum Co.; *U.S. Public*, pg. 1779
ALL METALS PROCESSING & LOGISTICS, INC.—See Reliance Steel & Aluminum Co.; *U.S. Public*, pg. 1779
ALL METALS PROCESSING OF ORANGE COUNTY, LLC; *U.S. Private*, pg. 171
ALL METRO HEALTH CARE; *U.S. Private*, pg. 171
ALLM INC.—See Vector Inc.; *Int'l*, pg. 8144
ALL MOBILE VIDEO; *U.S. Private*, pg. 171
ALLMODES TRANSPORT INC.; *U.S. Private*, pg. 192
ALL MOTION TECHNOLOGY AB—See OEM International AB; *Int'l*, pg. 5528
ALL MOTORISTS INSURANCE AGENCY INC.—See Western General Insurance Co., Inc.; *U.S. Private*, pg. 4493
ALL NATION INSURANCE COMPANY; *U.S. Private*, pg. 171
ALLNATT LONDON PROPERTIES PLC—See SEGRO plc; *Int'l*, pg. 6683
ALL NEW YORK TITLE AGENCY, INC.—See Stewart Information Services Corporation; *U.S. Public*, pg. 1947
ALLNEX AUSTRIA GMBH—See Advent International Corporation; *U.S. Private*, pg. 98
ALLNEX BELGIUM SA/NV - DROGENBOS—See Advent International Corporation; *U.S. Private*, pg. 98
ALLNEX BELGIUM SA/NV - SCHOONAARDE—See Advent International Corporation; *U.S. Private*, pg. 98
ALLNEX BELGIUM SA/NV—See Advent International Corporation; *U.S. Private*, pg. 98
ALLNEX GERMANY GMBH - HAMBURG PLANT—See Advent International Corporation; *U.S. Private*, pg. 98
ALLNEX GERMANY GMBH—See Advent International Corporation; *U.S. Private*, pg. 98
ALLNEX HOLDING II GERMANY GMBH—See Advent International Corporation; *U.S. Private*, pg. 98
ALLNEX HOLDING S.A.R.L.—See Advent International Corporation; *U.S. Private*, pg. 98
ALLNEX NORGE KS—See Advent International Corporation; *U.S. Private*, pg. 98
ALLNEX RESINS AUSTRALIA PTY. LTD.—See Advent International Corporation; *U.S. Private*, pg. 98
ALLNEX USA, INC. - KALAMAZOO PLANT—See Advent International Corporation; *U.S. Private*, pg. 98
ALLNEX USA, INC.—See Advent International Corporation; *U.S. Private*, pg. 98
ALLNEX USA, INC. - STAMFORD R&D FACILITY—See Advent International Corporation; *U.S. Private*, pg. 98
ALLNEX USA, INC. - WALLINGFORD PLANT—See Advent International Corporation; *U.S. Private*, pg. 98
ALLNEX USA, INC. - WILLOW ISLAND PLANT—See Advent International Corporation; *U.S. Private*, pg. 98
ALL NIPPON AIRWAYS TRADING CO., LTD.—See ANA Holdings Inc.; *Int'l*, pg. 444
ALL NIPPON AIRWAYS WORLD TOURS CO., LTD.—See ANA Holdings Inc.; *Int'l*, pg. 444
ALL NOW LOGISTICS CO., LTD.—See C.P. All Public Company Limited; *Int'l*, pg. 1243
ALLNUTT FUNERAL SERVICE, INC.—See Service Corporation International; *U.S. Public*, pg. 1870
ALLOC AS—See Beaulieu International Group NV; *Int'l*, pg. 934
ALLOCATE SOFTWARE PLC—See Rothschild & Co SCA; *Int'l*, pg. 6403
ALLOCATE SOFTWARE PLC—See TA Associates, Inc.; *U.S. Private*, pg. 3917
ALLOCATE SOFTWARE PTY. LTD.—See Rothschild & Co SCA; *Int'l*, pg. 6403
ALLOCATE SOFTWARE PTY. LTD.—See TA Associates, Inc.; *U.S. Private*, pg. 3917
ALLOCATION NETWORK GMBH—See Thoma Bravo, L.P.; *U.S. Private*, pg. 4151
ALLOCATION SERVICES, INC.—See Brown & Brown, Inc.; *U.S. Public*, pg. 396
ALL OCEANS CLOSINGS LLC—See OneWater Marine Inc.; *U.S. Public*, pg. 1604
ALLO COMMUNICATIONS, LLC—See Nelnet, Inc.; *U.S. Public*, pg. 1504
ALLOGA AG—See CSL Limited; *Int'l*, pg. 1866
ALLOGA FRANCE—See Walgreens Boots Alliance, Inc.; *U.S. Public*, pg. 2322
ALLOGA (NEDERLAND) B.V.—See Walgreens Boots Alliance, Inc.; *U.S. Public*, pg. 2322
ALLOGA UK LIMITED—See Walgreens Boots Alliance, Inc.; *U.S. Public*, pg. 2322
ALLOGENE THERAPEUTICS, INC.; *U.S. Public*, pg. 81
ALLOGGIO GROUP LIMITED—See Next Capital Pty Limited; *Int'l*, pg. 5248
ALL OHIO READY MIX—See CRH plc; *Int'l*, pg. 1847
ALOMATIC PRODUCTS COMPANY—See Sun Capital Partners, Inc.; *U.S. Private*, pg. 3860
ALLONE HEALTH RESOURCES, INC.—See Highmark Health; *U.S. Private*, pg. 1940
ALL ORE MINERACAO PARTICIPACOES S.A.; *Int'l*, pg. 332
ALLOS GMBH—See PAI Partners S.A.S.; *Int'l*, pg. 5700
ALLOS HOF-MANUFAKTUR GMBH—See PAI Partners S.A.S.; *Int'l*, pg. 5699
ALLOSOURCE; *U.S. Private*, pg. 192
ALLOS SA; *Int'l*, pg. 359
ALLOS SCHWARZWALD GMBH—See PAI Partners S.A.S.; *Int'l*, pg. 5700
ALLO SUPPLIES—See Softimat SA; *Int'l*, pg. 7054
ALLOT COMMUNICATIONS (ASIA PACIFIC) PTE. LTD.—See Allot Ltd.; *Int'l*, pg. 360
ALLOT COMMUNICATIONS INC.—See Allot Ltd.; *Int'l*, pg. 360
ALLOT COMMUNICATIONS UK LIMITED—See Allot Ltd.; *Int'l*, pg. 360
ALLO TECHNOLOGY SDN. BHD.—See Tenaga Nasional Berhad; *Int'l*, pg. 7557
ALLOT LTD.; *Int'l*, pg. 359
ALLOVER MEDIA, INC.—See Audax Group, Limited Partnership; *U.S. Private*, pg. 386
ALLOVIR, INC.; *U.S. Public*, pg. 81
ALLOY BELLOWS & PRECISION WELDING—See Shelburne Corp.; *U.S. Private*, pg. 3630
ALLOY CARBIDE COMPANY; *U.S. Private*, pg. 193
ALLOY CAST PRODUCTS, INC.—See Altus Capital Partners, Inc.; *U.S. Private*, pg. 211
ALLOY COMPUTER PRODUCTS (AUSTRALIA) PTY. LTD.; *Int'l*, pg. 360
ALLOY COMPUTER PRODUCTS LLC—See Alloy Computer Products (Australia) Pty. Ltd.; *Int'l*, pg. 360
ALLOYCORP MINING INC.—See RCF Management LLC; *U.S. Private*, pg. 3362
ALLOY CUSTOM PRODUCTS, LLC—See Cryogenic Industrial Solutions, Inc.; *U.S. Private*, pg. 1115

ALLOY COMPUTER PRODUCTS (AUSTRALIA) PTY. LTD.　　　　　　　　　　　　　　　　　　　　**CORPORATE AFFILIATIONS**

ALLOYD BRANDS CONSUMER PACKAGING—See Sonoco Products Company; *U.S. Public*, pg. 1905
ALLOY DIE CASTING COMPANY—See Perella Weinberg Partners LP; *U.S. Public*, pg. 1674
ALLOY ENGINEERING COMPANY; *U.S. Private*, pg. 193
ALLOY HOLDINGS, LLC—See Trent Capital Partners, LLC; *U.S. Private*, pg. 4218
ALLOY MEDIA HOLDINGS, L.L.C.—See Warner Bros. Discovery, Inc.; *U.S. Public*, pg. 2327
ALLOY POLYMERS, INC.—See RTP Company; *U.S. Private*, pg. 3498
ALLOY POLYMERS TEXAS, LP—See RTP Company; *U.S. Private*, pg. 3498
ALLOY PRODUCTS CORP.; *U.S. Private*, pg. 193
ALLOY, SILVERSTEIN, SHAPIRO, ADAMS, MULFORD, CICALESE, WILSON & COMPANY; *U.S. Private*, pg. 193
ALLOY SOFTWARE, INC.; *U.S. Private*, pg. 193
ALLOY SPECIALTIES INC.—See J & E Precision Tool, LLC; *U.S. Private*, pg. 2152
ALLOY & STAINLESS FASTENERS, INC.; *U.S. Private*, pg. 193
ALLOY STEEL INTERNATIONAL, INC. - MOORESVILLE BRANCH—See Alloy Steel International, Inc.; *Int'l*, pg. 360
ALLOY STEEL INTERNATIONAL, INC.; *Int'l*, pg. 360
ALLOYS UNLIMITED PROCESSING—See Ampco-Pittsburgh Corporation; *U.S. Public*, pg. 126
ALLOY SURFACES COMPANY, INC.—See Chemring Group PLC; *Int'l*, pg. 1463
ALLOY TOOL STEEL, INC.—See Mitsubishi Corporation; *Int'l*, pg. 4940
ALLOY TOOL STEEL, INC.—See Sojitz Corporation; *Int'l*, pg. 7062
ALLOY WHEEL REPAIR SPECIALIST, INC.—See Soundcore Capital Partners, LLC; *U.S. Private*, pg. 3717
ALLOYWORKS, LLC—See Berkshire Hathaway Inc.; *U.S. Public*, pg. 313
ALL PACKAGING COMPANY—See Great Mill Rock LLC; *U.S. Private*, pg. 1766
ALLPACK INDUSTRIES LTD—See Aga Khan Development Network; *Int'l*, pg. 199
ALLPARTS MEDICAL, LLC—See Koninklijke Philips N.V.; *Int'l*, pg. 4269
ALLPAX PRODUCTS LLC—See Leonard Green & Partners, L.P.; *U.S. Private*, pg. 2427
ALLPER AG—See Exco Technologies Limited; *Int'l*, pg. 2580
ALL PHARMA (SHANGHAI) TRADING COMPANY LIMITED—See Aurobindo Pharma Ltd.; *Int'l*, pg. 712
ALLPHASE CLINICAL RESEARCH SERVICES INC.—See Calian Group Ltd.; *Int'l*, pg. 1263
ALL-PHASE ELECTRIC SUPPLY CO.—See Blackfriars Corp.; *U.S. Private*, pg. 574
ALL PHASE SECURITY, INC.—See Allied Universal Manager LLC; *U.S. Private*, pg. 191
ALLPIKE AUTOS PTY LTD—See Eagers Automotive Limited; *Int'l*, pg. 2263
ALLPIPES TECHNOLOGY SDN. BHD.—See Engtex Group Berhad; *Int'l*, pg. 2436
ALLPLAN CESKO S.R.O.—See Nemetschek SE; *Int'l*, pg. 5194
ALLPLAN DEUTSCHLAND GMBH—See Nemetschek SE; *Int'l*, pg. 5194
ALLPLAN FRANCE S.A.R.L.—See Nemetschek SE; *Int'l*, pg. 5194
ALLPLAN GMBH—See EVN AG; *Int'l*, pg. 2570
ALLPLAN INC.—See Nemetschek SE; *Int'l*, pg. 5194
ALLPLAN INFRASTRUCTURE GMBH—See Nemetschek SE; *Int'l*, pg. 5194
ALLPLAN ITALY SRL—See Nemetschek SE; *Int'l*, pg. 5194
ALLPLAN OSTERREICH GES.M.B.H.—See Nemetschek SE; *Int'l*, pg. 5194
ALLPLAN SCHWEIZ AG—See Nemetschek SE; *Int'l*, pg. 5194
ALLPLAN SLOVENSKO S.R.O.—See Nemetschek SE; *Int'l*, pg. 5194
ALLPLAN SYSTEMS ESPAHA S.A.—See Nemetschek SE; *Int'l*, pg. 5194
ALLPLAN UK LTD.—See Nemetschek SE; *Int'l*, pg. 5194
ALL POINTS COOPERATIVE; *U.S. Private*, pg. 171
ALL POINTS COOPERATIVE—See All Points Cooperative; *U.S. Private*, pg. 171
ALLPOINTS FOODSERVICE PARTS & SUPPLIES, INC.—See New Mountain Capital, LLC; *U.S. Private*, pg. 2901
ALL POINTS NORTH PLC; *Int'l*, pg. 332
ALL POWER MANUFACTURING CO.—See RBC Bearings Incorporated; *U.S. Public*, pg. 1766
ALL POWER PRODUCTS INC.—See Quanta Services, Inc.; *U.S. Public*, pg. 1750
ALLPRESS & MOORE RAILROAD SIGNAL CONTRACTORS INC.—See CDL Electric Company, Inc.; *U.S. Private*, pg. 802
ALL PRINTING RESOURCES INC.; *U.S. Public*, pg. 171
ALL-PRO FASTENERS INC.; *U.S. Private*, pg. 173
ALL PRO FREIGHT SYSTEMS INC.; *U.S. Private*, pg. 171

ALL PRO HORTICULTURE, INC.—See SiteOne Landscape Supply, Inc.; *U.S. Public*, pg. 1888
ALL-PRO IMAGING CORP.—See Air Techniques, Inc.; *U.S. Private*, pg. 140
ALLPRO PARKING, LLC—See Premium Parking Service, LLC; *U.S. Private*, pg. 3252
ALL PRO SALES, INC. - HOUSTON—See All Pro Sales, Inc.; *U.S. Private*, pg. 171
ALL PRO SALES, INC.; *U.S. Private*, pg. 171
ALL-PROTEC N.V.—See London Security PLC; *Int'l*, pg. 4546
ALL PURPOSE, INC.; *U.S. Private*, pg. 171
ALL QUALITY & SERVICES INC.; *U.S. Private*, pg. 171
ALLREAL FINANCE AG—See Allreal Holding AG; *Int'l*, pg. 360
ALLREAL GENERALUNTERNEHMUNG AG—See Allreal Holding AG; *Int'l*, pg. 360
ALLREAL HOLDING AG; *Int'l*, pg. 360
ALLREAL HOME AG—See Allreal Holding AG; *Int'l*, pg. 360
ALLREAL OFFICE AG—See Allreal Holding AG; *Int'l*, pg. 360
ALLREAL TONI AG—See Allreal Holding AG; *Int'l*, pg. 360
ALLREAL VULKAN AG—See Allreal Holding AG; *Int'l*, pg. 360
ALLREAL WEST AG—See Allreal Holding AG; *Int'l*, pg. 360
ALLRECIPES.COM, INC.—See Meredith Corporation; *U.S. Public*, pg. 1422
ALL RECYCLING, INC.—See Metro Metals Northwest Inc.; *U.S. Private*, pg. 2686
ALLRED'S INC.; *U.S. Private*, pg. 193
ALL RESPONSE MEDIA; *Int'l*, pg. 332
ALL RIGHT SOFTWARE INC.—See EPS Holdings, Inc.; *Int'l*, pg. 2465
ALL RING TECH CO., LTD.; *Int'l*, pg. 332
ALL RISKS, LTD.—See Ryan Specialty Holdings, Inc.; *U.S. Public*, pg. 1827
ALL ROADS COMPANY; *U.S. Private*, pg. 171
A.L.L. ROOFING MATERIALS OF SAN JOSE, LLC—See Leonard Green & Partners, L.P.; *U.S. Private*, pg. 2428
ALL ROUND FOODS BAKERY PRODUCTS INC.; *U.S. Private*, pg. 172
ALL R.V. SERVICE & REPAIR; *U.S. Private*, pg. 171
ALL SAFE INDUSTRIES, INC.; *U.S. Private*, pg. 172
ALLSAFE JAPAN LTD.—See Ashimori Industry Co., Ltd.; *Int'l*, pg. 607
ALLSAFE JAPAN LTD. - TOHOKU PLANT—See Ashimori Industry Co., Ltd.; *Int'l*, pg. 607
ALLSAFE JUNGFALK AUSTRALIA—See allsafe JUNGFALK GmbH & Co. KG; *Int'l*, pg. 360
ALLSAFE JUNGFALK BENELUX—See allsafe JUNGFALK GmbH & Co. KG; *Int'l*, pg. 360
ALLSAFE JUNGFALK GMBH & CO. KG; *Int'l*, pg. 360
ALL SAINTS COMMERCIAL PLC; *Int'l*, pg. 332
ALL SAINTS RETAIL LIMITED—See Lion Capital LLP; *Int'l*, pg. 4517
ALLSALE ELECTRIC INC.; *U.S. Private*, pg. 193
ALLSCRIPTS CANADA CORPORATION—See Veradigm Inc.; *U.S. Public*, pg. 2279
ALLSCRIPTS HEALTHCARE, LLC—See Veradigm Inc.; *U.S. Public*, pg. 2279
ALLSCRIPTS (INDIA) PRIVATE LIMITED—See Veradigm Inc.; *U.S. Public*, pg. 2279
ALLSCRIPTS INDIA—See Veradigm Inc.; *U.S. Public*, pg. 2280
ALLSCRIPTS SOFTWARE, LLC—See Veradigm Inc.; *U.S. Public*, pg. 2280
ALLSCRIPTS—See Veradigm Inc.; *U.S. Public*, pg. 2279
ALLSCRIPTS—See Veradigm Inc.; *U.S. Public*, pg. 2279
ALLSCRIPTS (UNITED KINGDOM) LIMITED—See Veradigm Inc.; *U.S. Public*, pg. 2279
ALL SEALS, INC.—See Diploma PLC; *Int'l*, pg. 2128
ALLSEAS MARINE SERVICES PTE LTD—See AMOS Group Limited; *Int'l*, pg. 430
ALL SEASONS HOTELS—See Accor S.A.; *Int'l*, pg. 91
ALL SEASONS RV & MARINE—See Camping World Holdings, Inc.; *U.S. Public*, pg. 427
ALL SEASONS TRAVEL AGENCY INC.; *U.S. Private*, pg. 172
ALLSECTECH MANILA INC.—See Quess Corp Limited; *Int'l*, pg. 6160
ALLSEC TECHNOLOGIES LIMITED—See Quess Corp Limited; *Int'l*, pg. 6160
ALLSECUR B.V.—See Allianz SE; *Int'l*, pg. 343
ALLSECUR DEUTSCHLAND AG—See Allianz SE; *Int'l*, pg. 343
ALL SENSORS ASIA PACIFIC K.K.—See Amphenol Corporation; *U.S. Public*, pg. 126
ALL SENSORS, CORP.; *U.S. Private*, pg. 172
ALL SENSORS GMBH—See Amphenol Corporation; *U.S. Public*, pg. 126
ALL SERV INDUSTRIAL LLC—See HCI Equity Management, L.P.; *U.S. Private*, pg. 1889
ALL SET MARINE LASHING AB—See Cargotec Corporation; *Int'l*, pg. 1326
ALLSHIPS LTD.; *Int'l*, pg. 360
ALLSHOES BENELUX B.V—See Bunzl plc; *Int'l*, pg. 1217

ALL SIZE CORRUGATED—See Buckeye Corrugated Inc.; *U.S. Private*, pg. 677
ALLSOP EUROPE LIMITED—See Allsop, Inc.; *U.S. Private*, pg. 193
ALLSOP, INC.; *U.S. Private*, pg. 193
ALL-SOUTH SUBCONTRACTORS INC.; *U.S. Private*, pg. 173
ALL SPANAWAY STORAGE LLC—See National Storage Affiliates Trust; *U.S. Public*, pg. 1498
ALL-SPEC INDUSTRIES, INC.—See Distribution Solutions Group, Inc.; *U.S. Public*, pg. 668
ALL SPORT COUTURE, LLC—See Lanco International Inc.; *U.S. Private*, pg. 2382
ALL-SPORTS LLC—See Peak Global Holdings, LLC; *U.S. Private*, pg. 3123
ALLSPRING GLOBAL DIVIDEND OPPORTUNITY FUND; *U.S. Public*, pg. 81
ALLSPRING INCOME OPPORTUNITIES FUND; *U.S. Public*, pg. 81
ALLSPRING UTILITIES & HIGH INCOME FUND; *U.S. Public*, pg. 81
ALLSTAFF AIRCONDITIONING (ACT) PTY LIMITED—See BSA Limited; *Int'l*, pg. 1201
ALLSTAFF AIRCONDITIONING (NSW) PTY LIMITED—See BSA Limited; *Int'l*, pg. 1201
ALLSTAFF AIRCONDITIONING (VIC) PTY LIMITED—See BSA Limited; *Int'l*, pg. 1201
ALL STAR AUTO LIGHTS, INC.—See Atlantic Street Capital Management LLC; *U.S. Private*, pg. 374
ALL STAR AUTOMOTIVE GROUP; *U.S. Private*, pg. 172
ALL STAR AUTOMOTIVE PRODUCTS; *U.S. Private*, pg. 172
ALL STAR BLEACHERS, INC.—See Summa Holdings, Inc.; *U.S. Private*, pg. 3852
ALLSTAR BUILDING MATERIALS LTD.; *U.S. Private*, pg. 193
ALL-STAR CHEVROLET GEO, INC.; *U.S. Private*, pg. 173
ALL STAR CONSULTING INC.; *U.S. Private*, pg. 172
ALL STAR DIRECTORIES, INC.; *U.S. Private*, pg. 172
ALL STAR DODGE CHRYSLER JEEP; *U.S. Private*, pg. 172
ALL STAR DODGE; *U.S. Private*, pg. 172
ALLSTAR ENERGY LIMITED—See 49 North Resources Inc.; *Int'l*, pg. 11
ALLSTAR FINANCIAL GROUP INC.; *U.S. Private*, pg. 193
ALL STAR FORD LLC; *U.S. Private*, pg. 172
ALL STAR GLASS CO. INC.; *U.S. Private*, pg. 172
ALLSTAR HEALTH BRANDS, INC.; *Int'l*, pg. 360
ALL STAR INCENTIVE MARKETING, INC.; *U.S. Private*, pg. 172
ALL STAR INTERNATIONAL TRUCKS INC.—See Yancey Bros. Co.; *U.S. Private*, pg. 4585
ALLSTAR MAGNETICS, INC.; *U.S. Private*, pg. 193
ALL STAR MARKETING INC.—See Morgan Distributing Company Inc.; *U.S. Private*, pg. 2783
ALL STAR NISSAN—See All Star Automotive Group; *U.S. Private*, pg. 172
ALLSTAR PRODUCTS GROUP LLC; *U.S. Private*, pg. 193
ALLSTAR REBAR LIMITED—See Penney Group; *Int'l*, pg. 5787
ALL STAR STRIPING LLC—See Investcorp Holdings B.S.C.; *Int'l*, pg. 3776
ALL STAR STRIPING LLC—See Trilantic Capital Management L.P.; *U.S. Private*, pg. 4231
ALL STAR TOYOTA—See All Star Automotive Group; *U.S. Private*, pg. 172
ALL STAR VACATION HOMES MANAGEMENT, INC.; *U.S. Private*, pg. 172
ALL-STATE BELTING COMPANY; *U.S. Private*, pg. 173
ALLSTATE BEVERAGE COMPANY LLC—See Gulf Distributing Holdings LLC; *U.S. Private*, pg. 1816
ALLSTATE CAN CORPORATION—See The Ohio Art Company, Inc.; *U.S. Private*, pg. 2118
ALL-STATE CAREER, INC.—See JLL Partners, LLC; *U.S. Private*, pg. 2212
ALL STATE COMMUNICATIONS, INC.—See Arvig Enterprises, Inc.; *U.S. Private*, pg. 344
ALLSTATE CONSTRUCTION INC.; *U.S. Private*, pg. 193
ALLSTATE CORPORATE SERVICES CORP.—See Apax Partners LLP; *Int'l*, pg. 503
THE ALLSTATE CORPORATION; *U.S. Public*, pg. 2032
ALL-STATE EXPRESS, INC.; *U.S. Private*, pg. 173
ALL STATE FASTENER CORPORATION; *U.S. Private*, pg. 172
ALLSTATE FLORAL & CRAFT, INC.; *U.S. Private*, pg. 193
ALL-STATE FORD TRUCK SALES—See Hesco Parts Corporation; *U.S. Private*, pg. 1927
ALLSTATE G.E.S. APPLIANCE, INC.; *U.S. Private*, pg. 193
ALL STATE HOMES, INC.; *U.S. Private*, pg. 172
ALLSTATE IMAGING INC.; *U.S. Private*, pg. 193
ALLSTATE INDIA PRIVATE LIMITED—See The Allstate Corporation; *U.S. Public*, pg. 2032
ALL-STATE INDUSTRIES INC.—See Blue Sage Capital, L.P.; *U.S. Private*, pg. 592
ALLSTATE INSURANCE COMPANY OF CANADA—See The Allstate Corporation; *U.S. Public*, pg. 2032

COMPANY NAME INDEX

ALLSTATE INSURANCE COMPANY—See The Allstate Corporation; *U.S. Public*, pg. 2032
ALL-STATE INTERNATIONAL, INC.; *U.S. Private*, pg. 173
ALLSTATE INVESTMENTS, LLC—See The Allstate Corporation; *U.S. Public*, pg. 2032
ALLSTATE LEASING, INC.—See Atlantic Automotive Corp.; *U.S. Private*, pg. 371
ALLSTATE LIFE INSURANCE COMPANY OF NEW YORK—See Vestar Capital Partners, LLC; *U.S. Private*, pg. 4373
ALLSTATE LIFE INSURANCE COMPANY—See The Allstate Corporation; *U.S. Public*, pg. 2032
ALLSTATE MORTGAGE CORP.; *U.S. Private*, pg. 193
ALLSTATE MOTOR CLUB, INC.—See The Allstate Corporation; *U.S. Public*, pg. 2032
ALLSTATE NEW JERSEY INSURANCE COMPANY—See The Allstate Corporation; *U.S. Public*, pg. 2032
ALLSTATE NON-INSURANCE HOLDINGS, INC.—See The Allstate Corporation; *U.S. Public*, pg. 2032
ALLSTATE NORTHBROOK INDEMNITY COMPANY—See The Allstate Corporation; *U.S. Public*, pg. 2033
ALLSTATE NORTHERN IRELAND LIMITED—See The Allstate Corporation; *U.S. Public*, pg. 2033
ALL STATE PACKAGING, INC.—See PMC Capital Partners, LLC; *U.S. Private*, pg. 3217
ALLSTATE POWER VAC, INC.—See Republic Services, Inc.; *U.S. Public*, pg. 1787
ALLSTATE RENT A FENCE, INC.—See American Fence Company, Inc.; *U.S. Private*, pg. 233
ALL STATES AG PARTS, LLC—See Kinderhook Industries, LLC; *U.S. Private*, pg. 2306
ALL STATES ASPHALT INC.; *U.S. Private*, pg. 172
ALLSTATE SOLUTIONS PRIVATE LIMITED—See The Allstate Corporation; *U.S. Public*, pg. 2033
ALLSTATE STEEL COMPANY INC.; *U.S. Private*, pg. 193
ALLSTATE SUGAR BOWL; *U.S. Private*, pg. 193
ALLSTATES WORLDCARGO, INC.; *U.S. Private*, pg. 193
ALL STATE TANK MANUFACTURING, LLC—See Cameron Holdings Corporation; *U.S. Public*, pg. 729
ALLSTATE TRAFFIC CONTROL, LLC—See Kohlberg & Company, LLC; *U.S. Private*, pg. 2337
ALL STEEL CONSULTANTS, INC.; *U.S. Private*, pg. 173
ALLSTEEL INC.—See HNI Corporation; *U.S. Public*, pg. 1042
ALLSTON-BRIGHTON TAB—See Gannett Co., Inc.; *U.S. Public*, pg. 901
ALLSTON SUPPLY CO., INC.—See Bain Capital, LP; *U.S. Private*, pg. 440
ALL STOR INDIAN TRAIL, LLC—See National Storage Affiliates Trust; *U.S. Public*, pg. 1498
ALL STOR MH—See National Storage Affiliates Trust; *U.S. Public*, pg. 1498
ALLSTREAM INC.—See DigitalBridge Group, Inc.; *U.S. Public*, pg. 665
ALLSTREAM INC.—See EQT AB; *Int'l*, pg. 2482
ALL STYLE APPAREL & ACTIVEWEAR; *U.S. Private*, pg. 173
ALLSUP ENTERPRISES INC.; *U.S. Private*, pg. 194
ALLSUP PETROLEUM INC.—See Allsup Enterprises Inc.; *U.S. Private*, pg. 194
ALLSUP'S CONVENIENCE STORES INC.—See BW Gas & Convenience Holdings, LLC; *U.S. Private*, pg. 700
ALL SYSTEMS GO, LLC; *U.S. Private*, pg. 173
ALL SYSTEMS INSTALLATION INC.; *U.S. Private*, pg. 173
ALLTAINER AB; *Int'l*, pg. 360
ALLTEC ANGEWANDTE LASERLICHT TECHNOLOGIE GMBH—See Danaher Corporation; *U.S. Public*, pg. 624
ALLTEC AUTOMATISIERUNGS- UND KOMMUNIKATIONSTECHNIK GMBH—See NORD Holding Unternehmensbeteiligungsgesellschaft mbH; *Int'l*, pg. 5416
ALLTEC GMBH—See Danaher Corporation; *U.S. Public*, pg. 632
ALLTECH APPLIED SCIENCE B.V.—See Standard Industries Holdings Inc.; *U.S. Private*, pg. 3779
ALL-TECH DECORATING COMPANY; *U.S. Private*, pg. 174
ALLTECH ENGINEERING CORP.; *U.S. Private*, pg. 194
ALLTECH FRANCE S.A.R.L.—See Standard Industries Holdings Inc.; *U.S. Private*, pg. 3779
ALLTECH GROM GMBH—See Standard Industries Holdings Inc.; *U.S. Private*, pg. 3779
ALLTECH, INC.; *U.S. Private*, pg. 194
ALLTECH ITALIA S.R.L.—See Standard Industries Holdings Inc.; *U.S. Private*, pg. 3779
ALL TECH MACHINERY & SUPPLY COMPANY—See Quaser Machine Tools, Inc.; *Int'l*, pg. 6156
ALLTECK LIMITED PARTNERSHIP—See Quanta Services, Inc.; *U.S. Public*, pg. 1750
ALLTECK LINE CONTRACTORS INC.—See Quanta Services, Inc.; *U.S. Public*, pg. 1750
ALLTEK MARINE ELECTRONICS CORP.—See Alltek Technology Corporation; *Int'l*, pg. 360
ALLTEK TECHNOLOGY CORPORATION; *Int'l*, pg. 360
ALLTEK TECHNOLOGY (SINGAPORE) PTE. LTD.—See Alltek Technology Corporation; *Int'l*, pg. 360
ALL TEMP, INC.—See AT Industries, Inc.; *U.S. Private*, pg. 363

ALL TEMPS PERSONNEL SERVICE; *U.S. Private*, pg. 173
ALLTERCO EUROPE GMBH—See Allterco JSCo; *Int'l*, pg. 360
ALLTERCO JSCO; *Int'l*, pg. 360
ALL TERIORS FLOOR COVERING, INC.; *U.S. Private*, pg. 173
ALLTERRA CENTRAL, INC.; *U.S. Private*, pg. 194
ALLTERRA DEUTSCHLAND GMBH—See Trimble, Inc.; *U.S. Public*, pg. 2190
ALLTERRA DEUTSCHLAND GMBH—See Trimble, Inc.; *U.S. Public*, pg. 2190
ALLTERRA IBERICA, S.L.U.—See Trimble, Inc.; *U.S. Public*, pg. 2190
ALL TERRAIN; *U.S. Private*, pg. 173
ALLTERRA OSTERREICH GMBH—See Trimble, Inc.; *U.S. Public*, pg. 2190
ALL-TEX ERECTION SYSTEMS INC.; *U.S. Private*, pg. 174
ALL-TEX INC.; *U.S. Private*, pg. 174
ALLTEX INDUSTRIES LTD.; *Int'l*, pg. 360
ALL-TEX PIPE & SUPPLY, INC.; *U.S. Private*, pg. 174
ALL-TEX ROOFING INC.; *U.S. Private*, pg. 174
ALL-TEX SUPPLY INC.—See The Sterling Group, L.P.; *U.S. Private*, pg. 4122
ALL THINGS MOBILE ANALYTIC, INC.; *U.S. Public*, pg. 78
ALL TILE INC.; *U.S. Private*, pg. 173
ALLTOOLS (PAKENHAM) PTY. LTD.—See Metcash Limited; *Int'l*, pg. 4852
ALLTOP ELECTRONICS (SUZHOU) LTD.—See Alltop Technology Co., Ltd.; *Int'l*, pg. 361
ALLTOP TECHNOLOGY CO., LTD.; *Int'l*, pg. 361
ALLTRADE TOOL LLC; *U.S. Private*, pg. 194
ALL TRAFFIC DATA SERVICES, LLC—See Rekor Systems, Inc.; *U.S. Public*, pg. 1778
ALL TRANS RISK SOLUTIONS, LLC—See Ambac Financial Group, Inc.; *U.S. Public*, pg. 92
ALL TREAT FARMS LIMITED—See Walker Industries Holdings Ltd.; *Int'l*, pg. 8333
ALL TRI-R INC.; *U.S. Private*, pg. 173
ALLTRISTA PLASTICS LLC—See One Rock Capital Partners, LLC; *U.S. Private*, pg. 3023
ALLTRONIOC HOLDINGS LIMITED; *Int'l*, pg. 361
ALLTRONICS MANUFACTURING (SHENZHEN) LIMITED—See Alltronics Holdings Limited; *Int'l*, pg. 361
ALLTRONICS TECH. MFTG. LIMITED—See Alltronics Holdings Limited; *Int'l*, pg. 361
ALLTRUST INSURANCE COMPANY OF CHINA LIMITED—See China Huaneng Group Co., Ltd.; *Int'l*, pg. 1509
ALLTRUST INSURANCE INC.; *U.S. Private*, pg. 194
ALLT SMORGAS—See Atria Plc; *Int'l*, pg. 694
ALLTUB BV—See OEP Capital Advisors, L.P.; *U.S. Private*, pg. 2997
ALLTUB CENTRAL EUROPE A.S.—See OEP Capital Advisors, L.P.; *U.S. Private*, pg. 2997
ALLTUB DEUTSCHLAND GMBH—See OEP Capital Advisors, L.P.; *U.S. Private*, pg. 2998
ALLTUB ITALIA SRL—See OEP Capital Advisors, L.P.; *U.S. Private*, pg. 2998
ALLTUB UK LIMITED—See OEP Capital Advisors, L.P.; *U.S. Private*, pg. 2998
ALLTUB USA, LLC—See OEP Capital Advisors, L.P.; *U.S. Private*, pg. 2998
ALLTURNA, LLC—See Search Discovery, Inc.; *U.S. Private*, pg. 3586
ALLU GROUP OY; *Int'l*, pg. 361
ALLUNITE—See Thornico A/S; *Int'l*, pg. 7719
ALLUP SILICA LIMITED; *Int'l*, pg. 361
ALLURA—See Grupo Empresarial Kaluz S.A. de C.V.; *Int'l*, pg. 3126
ALLURED PUBLISHING CORPORATION; *U.S. Private*, pg. 194
ALLURE GLOBAL SOLUTIONS, INC.—See Creative Realities, Inc.; *U.S. Public*, pg. 593
ALLURE HOME CREATIONS INC.; *U.S. Private*, pg. 194
ALLURESOFT, INC.; *U.S. Private*, pg. 194
ALLURION TECHNOLOGIES, INC.; *U.S. Public*, pg. 81
THE ALLUVIAN, LLC—See The Middleby Corporation; *U.S. Public*, pg. 2115
THE ALLUVIAN SPA, LLC—See The Middleby Corporation; *U.S. Public*, pg. 2115
ALLUVION STAFFING, INC.—See Olympus Partners; *U.S. Private*, pg. 3013
ALLUXA, INC.—See Enpro Inc.; *U.S. Public*, pg. 774
ALLVEST GMBH—See Allianz SE; *Int'l*, pg. 351
ALLVUE SYSTEMS HOLDINGS, INC.; *U.S. Private*, pg. 194
ALL WALL CONTRACTING, INC.; *U.S. Private*, pg. 173
ALL WATER SYSTEMS LIMITED—See The Bidvest Group Limited; *Int'l*, pg. 7622
ALL-WAYS ADVERTISING COMPANY; *U.S. Private*, pg. 174
ALL WEATHER INC.; *U.S. Private*, pg. 173
ALL WEATHER INSULATED PANELS—See Kingspan Group PLC; *Int'l*, pg. 4179
ALL WEATHER WINDOWS LTD.; *Int'l*, pg. 332

ALMACENES PITUSA INC.

ALL WEB LEADS, INC.—See Great Hill Partners, L.P.; *U.S. Private*, pg. 1763
ALLWEILER A/S—See KKR & Co. Inc.; *U.S. Public*, pg. 1242
ALLWEILER FINLAND OY AB—See KKR & Co. Inc.; *U.S. Public*, pg. 1242
ALLWEILER GMBH—See KKR & Co. Inc.; *U.S. Public*, pg. 1242
ALL WELD MACHINE & FABRICATION COMPANY; *U.S. Private*, pg. 173
ALLWELLNESS HOLDINGS GROUP LIMITED; *Int'l*, pg. 361
ALL WEST COACHLINES, INC.—See Variant Equity Advisors, LLC; *U.S. Public*, pg. 4346
ALL WEST COMMUNICATIONS INC.—See Novacap Management Inc.; *Int'l*, pg. 5453
ALL WEST/ SELECT SIRES, INC.—See Select Sires Inc.; *U.S. Private*, pg. 3601
ALLWINNER TECHNOLOGY CO., LTD.; *Int'l*, pg. 361
ALLWIN TELECOMMUNICATION CO., LTD.; *Int'l*, pg. 361
ALLWIRE INC.; *U.S. Private*, pg. 194
ALL WOMEN'S HEALTHCARE OF SAWGRASS, INC.—See KKR & Co. Inc.; *U.S. Public*, pg. 1244
ALL WOMEN'S HEALTHCARE OF WEST BROWARD, INC.—See KKR & Co. Inc.; *U.S. Public*, pg. 1244
ALL WOMEN'S HEALTHCARE SERVICES, INC.—See KKR & Co. Inc.; *U.S. Public*, pg. 1244
ALL WORLD MACHINERY SUPPLY, INC.—See Daikin Industries, Ltd.; *Int'l*, pg. 1932
ALL WORLD MACHINERY SUPPLY, INC.—See Daikin Industries, Ltd.; *Int'l*, pg. 1932
ALLWORLD PROJECT MANAGEMENT, LLC; *U.S. Private*, pg. 194
ALL WORLD TRAVEL INC.; *U.S. Private*, pg. 173
ALLWORTH FINANCIAL GROUP LP—See Lightyear Capital LLC; *U.S. Private*, pg. 2454
ALLWORTH FINANCIAL GROUP LP—See Ontario Teachers' Pension Plan; *Int'l*, pg. 5586
ALLWORTH FINANCIAL HOLDINGS, LLC—See Lightyear Capital LLC; *U.S. Private*, pg. 2454
ALLWORTH FINANCIAL HOLDINGS, LLC—See Ontario Teachers' Pension Plan; *Int'l*, pg. 5586
ALLWORTH FINANCIAL, LP—See Lightyear Capital LLC; *U.S. Private*, pg. 2454
ALLWORTH FINANCIAL, LP—See Ontario Teachers' Pension Plan; *Int'l*, pg. 5586
ALLWORX CORP.—See Windstream Holdings, Inc.; *U.S. Public*, pg. 2373
ALLWYN AG—See KKCG Group; *Int'l*, pg. 4198
ALLWYN ENTERTAINMENT AG—See KKCG Group; *Int'l*, pg. 4198
ALLWYN INTERNATIONAL A.S.—See KKCG Group; *Int'l*, pg. 4198
ALLWYN PRIORITIES, LLC—See NV5 Global, Inc.; *U.S. Public*, pg. 1557
ALLY AUTO ASSETS LLC; *U.S. Private*, pg. 194
ALLY BANK—See Ally Financial Inc.; *U.S. Public*, pg. 81
ALLY COMMERCIAL FINANCE LLC—See Ally Financial Inc.; *U.S. Public*, pg. 81
ALLY DATA TECHNOLOGY (BEIJING) CO., LTD.—See Zhewen Interactive Group Co Ltd; *Int'l*, pg. 8670
ALLY FINANCIAL INC.; *U.S. Public*, pg. 81
ALLY (HANGZHOU) INVESTMENT CO., LTD.—See Zhewen Interactive Group Co Ltd; *Int'l*, pg. 8670
ALLYIS, INC.; *U.S. Private*, pg. 194
ALLY LOGISTICS LLC; *U.S. Private*, pg. 194
ALLYSCA ASSISTANCE GMBH—See Munchener Ruckversicherungs AG; *Int'l*, pg. 5085
ALLY SERVICING, LLC—See Ally Financial Inc.; *U.S. Public*, pg. 81
ALLY WASTE SERVICES, LLC; *U.S. Private*, pg. 194
ALLY WHOLESALE ENTERPRISES LLC; *U.S. Private*, pg. 194
ALMA 360 CUSTOM MEDIA—See Alma Media Corporation; *Int'l*, pg. 361
ALMA AGENCY; *U.S. Private*, pg. 194
ALMAAK INTERNATIONAL GMBH—See HEXPOL AB; *Int'l*, pg. 3371
ALMAC CLINICAL SERVICES—See Almac Sciences Group Ltd.; *Int'l*, pg. 362
ALMAC CLINICAL TECHNOLOGIES—See Almac Sciences Group Ltd.; *Int'l*, pg. 362
ALMAC CO., LTD.; *Int'l*, pg. 362
ALMAC DIAGNOSTICS—See Almac Sciences Group Ltd.; *Int'l*, pg. 362
ALMACENADORA ACCEL, S. A.—See Accel, S.A.B. de C.V.; *Int'l*, pg. 79
ALMACENAJES, S.A.; *Int'l*, pg. 363
ALMACENES EXITO S.A.—See Calleja S.A. de C.V.; *Int'l*, pg. 1265
ALMACENES GENEVA S.A.—See Linde plc; *Int'l*, pg. 4508
ALMACENES METALURGICOS, S.A.U.; *Int'l*, pg. 363
ALMACENES PITUSA INC.; *U.S. Private*, pg. 195
ALMAC PHARMACEUTICAL SERVICES K.K.—See Almac Sciences Group Ltd.; *Int'l*, pg. 362
ALMAC PHARMACEUTICAL SERVICES PTE. LTD.—See Almac Sciences Group Ltd.; *Int'l*, pg. 362
ALMAC PHARMA SERVICES—See Almac Sciences Group Ltd.; *Int'l*, pg. 362

ALMAC SCIENCES GROUP LTD.

ALMAC SCIENCES GROUP LTD.; *Int'l*, pg. 362
ALMAC SCIENCES—See Almac Sciences Group Ltd.; *Int'l*, pg. 363
AL MADAR INVESTMENT CO K.S.C.P; *Int'l*, pg. 281
ALMADEN MINERALS LTD.; *Int'l*, pg. 363
ALMA DEVELOPMENT SP. Z O.O.—See Alma Market S.A.; *Int'l*, pg. 361
ALMADEX MINERALS LIMITED—See Abacus Mining & Exploration Corporation; *Int'l*, pg. 47
AL-MADINA FOR FINANCE & INVESTMENT COMPANY KSCC; *Int'l*, pg. 286
AL MADINA INSURANCE COMPANY SAOG; *Int'l*, pg. 281
AL MADINA LOGISTICS SERVICE S.A.O.C—See Global Financial Investments Holding SAOG; *Int'l*, pg. 2996
AL MADINA TAKAFUL CO. SAOG; *Int'l*, pg. 281
ALMA EXCHANGE BANK & TRUST—See South Banking Company; *U.S. Private*, pg. 3719
ALMA FOODS, LLC—See Hormel Foods Corporation; *U.S. Public*, pg. 1053
AL MAHA MODULAR INDUSTRIES LLC—See Alpha Dhabi Holding PJSC; *Int'l*, pg. 367
AL MAHA PETROLEUM PRODUCTS MARKETING COMPANY S.A.O.G.; *Int'l*, pg. 281
ALMA INTERMEDIA OY—See Alma Media Corporation; *Int'l*, pg. 361
ALMA JAPAN CORPORATION—See Seiren Co., Ltd.; *Int'l*, pg. 6691
AL MAJID INDUSTRIES L.L.C—See Juma Al Majid Group; *Int'l*, pg. 4025
AL MAJID PROPERTY CO LLC—See Juma Al Majid Group; *Int'l*, pg. 4025
AL MAJID TRAVEL AND TOURISM—See Juma Al Majid Group; *Int'l*, pg. 4025
ALMA LASERS, INC.—See Shanghai Fosun Pharmaceutical (Group) Co., Ltd.; *Int'l*, pg. 6767
ALMA LASERS LTD.—See Shanghai Fosun Pharmaceutical (Group) Co., Ltd.; *Int'l*, pg. 6767
AL-MAL INVESTMENT COMPANY KSCC; *Int'l*, pg. 286
AL-MAL SECURITIES & SERVICES LIMITED; *Int'l*, pg. 286
ALMA MANU OY—See Sanoma Oyj; *Int'l*, pg. 6553
ALMA MARITIME LIMITED; *Int'l*, pg. 361
ALMA MARKET S.A.; *Int'l*, pg. 361
ALMA MEDIA CORPORATION; *Int'l*, pg. 361
ALMA MEDIA INTERACTIVE OY—See Alma Media Corporation; *Int'l*, pg. 361
ALMA MEDIAPARTNERS OY—See Alma Media Corporation; *Int'l*, pg. 361
ALMA MEDIA VENTURES OY—See Alma Media Corporation; *Int'l*, pg. 361
ALMA METALS LIMITED; *Int'l*, pg. 361
AL-MAMOURA COMPANY FOR REAL ESTATE INVESTMENT; *Int'l*, pg. 286
AL MAMOURA REAL ESTATE INVESTMENTS CO.; *Int'l*, pg. 281
ALMANAC PUBLISHING CO.—See Geiger Brothers; *U.S. Private*, pg. 1656
ALMANAC REALTY INVESTORS, LLC—See Neuberger Berman Group LLC; *U.S. Private*, pg. 2890
AL MANAL PURIFICATION & BOTTLING OF MINERAL WATER LLC—See Agthia Group PJSC; *Int'l*, pg. 222
ALMANA NETWORKS SOLUTIONS; *Int'l*, pg. 363
AL-MANARA INSURANCE PLC CO.; *Int'l*, pg. 286
AL MANAR FINANCING & LEASING CO.; *Int'l*, pg. 281
ALMAND PLASTICS LTD.—See PannErgy Nyrt.; *Int'l*, pg. 5728
ALMAN ELECTRIC INC.; *U.S. Private*, pg. 195
ALMAN ELECTRIC; *U.S. Private*, pg. 195
ALMANIA INVESTMENTS (PROPRIETARY) LIMITED—See Hosken Consolidated Investments Limited; *Int'l*, pg. 3485
AL-MANSOUR AUTOMOTIVE COMPANY—See Mansour Group; *Int'l*, pg. 4676
AL MANSOUR COMPANY FOR PHARMACEUTICAL INDUSTRIES; *Int'l*, pg. 281
AL MANSOUR HOLDING COMPANY—See Mansour Group; *Int'l*, pg. 4676
AL-MANSOUR INVESTMENT BANK—See Qatar National Bank S.A.Q.; *Int'l*, pg. 6135
ALMAP BBDO—See Omnicom Group Inc.; *U.S. Public*, pg. 1573
ALMA PRODUCTS COMPANY—See Blue Point Capital Partners, LLC; *U.S. Private*, pg. 591
ALMA QUATTRO D.O.O.—See APG/SGA SA; *Int'l*, pg. 513
ALMARAI COMPANY LTD.; *Int'l*, pg. 363
ALMAR ASSOCIATES INC.; *U.S. Private*, pg. 195
ALMARISK NV—See KBC Group NV; *Int'l*, pg. 4106
AL MAROUF AND AL BARJAS COMBINED FOR GENERAL TRADING AND CONTRACTING COMPANY - ABDUL RAHMAN MOUSAA AL MAROUF AND PARTNER'S - W.L.L.—See Combined Group Contracting Company KSCC; *Int'l*, pg. 1709
ALMAR SALES CO. INC.; *U.S. Private*, pg. 195
AL-MASAKEN INTERNATIONAL FOR REAL ESTATE DEVELOPMENT CO. - K.S.C.; *Int'l*, pg. 286
AL MASANE AL KOBRA MINING COMPANY; *Int'l*, pg. 281

AL MASAOOD OIL INDUSTRY SUPPLIES & SERVICES CO.; *Int'l*, pg. 281
AL MASHRIQ FINANCIAL INVESTMENT CO. S.A.L.—See Arabia Insurance Co.; *Int'l*, pg. 533
AL-MASSALEH REAL ESTATE COMPANY K.S.C.C.; *Int'l*, pg. 286
ALMAST OJSC; *Int'l*, pg. 363
ALMA TALENT AB; *Int'l*, pg. 362
ALMA TALENT MEDIA AB—See Alma Talent AB; *Int'l*, pg. 362
ALMA TALENT OY—See Alma Media Corporation; *Int'l*, pg. 361
ALMATEC AG—See Knill Holding GmbH; *Int'l*, pg. 4208
ALMATEC GMBH—See Knill Holding GmbH; *Int'l*, pg. 4208
ALMA TELECOMMUNICATIONS KAZAKHSTAN JSC; *Int'l*, pg. 362
ALMATINSKIE ELEKTRICHESKIE SETI JSC; *Int'l*, pg. 363
ALMATIS B.V.—See Ordu Yardimlasma Kurumu Genel Mudurlugu; *Int'l*, pg. 5616
ALMATIS GMBH—See Ordu Yardimlasma Kurumu Genel Mudurlugu; *Int'l*, pg. 5616
ALMATIS INC.—See Ordu Yardimlasma Kurumu Genel Mudurlugu; *Int'l*, pg. 5616
ALMATIS LIMITED—See Morimura Bros., Inc.; *Int'l*, pg. 5046
ALMATIS LIMITED—See Ordu Yardimlasma Kurumu Genel Mudurlugu; *Int'l*, pg. 5616
ALMA TRACTOR & EQUIPMENT INC.; *U.S. Private*, pg. 195
ALMATYENERGOSBYT LLP—See Samruk-Energy JSC; *Int'l*, pg. 6508
ALMATY INTERNATIONAL AIRPORT JSC—See TAV Havalimanlari Holding A.S.; *Int'l*, pg. 7477
ALMATY POWER STATIONS JSC—See Samruk-Energy JSC; *Int'l*, pg. 6508
ALMATYTEMIR JSC; *Int'l*, pg. 363
ALMA UPPSALA AB—See Beijer Alma AB; *Int'l*, pg. 942
ALMAVIVA S.P.A.; *Int'l*, pg. 363
AL MAWARID MANPOWER CO.; *Int'l*, pg. 281
ALMAWAVE DO BRASIL LTDA.—See Almawave S.p.A.; *Int'l*, pg. 363
ALMAWAVE S.P.A.; *Int'l*, pg. 363
AL-MAZAYA HOLDING COMPANY K.S.C.P.; *Int'l*, pg. 287
ALMAZDORTRANS LLC—See PJSC Alrosa; *Int'l*, pg. 5878
ALM. BRAND A/S; *Int'l*, pg. 361
ALMCOE REFRIGERATION CO.—See Wind Point Advisors LLC; *U.S. Private*, pg. 4536
ALMCO, INC.—See Innovance, Inc.; *U.S. Private*, pg. 2081
ALMEC CO.,LTD.—See TIS Inc.; *Int'l*, pg. 7757
ALMEDA, A.S.—See Fresenius SE & Co. KGaA; *Int'l*, pg. 2777
ALMEDA GMBH—See Munchener Ruckversicherungs AG; *Int'l*, pg. 5092
ALMEDAHL-KINNA AB—See Almedahls Oy; *Int'l*, pg. 363
ALMEDAHLS OY; *Int'l*, pg. 363
ALMEDA MALL, INC.—See Buchanan Street Partners, Inc.; *U.S. Private*, pg. 676
ALMEDA VENTURES LP; *Int'l*, pg. 363
ALMEDA VERSICHERUNGS-AKTIENGESELLSCHAFT—See Munchener Ruckversicherungs AG; *Int'l*, pg. 5092
ALMEDIO, INC.; *Int'l*, pg. 363
AL MEERA CONSUMER GOODS COMPANY Q.S.C.; *Int'l*, pg. 281
AL MEEZAN INVESTMENT MANAGEMENT LIMITED—See Meezan Bank Limited; *Int'l*, pg. 4791
ALMEGA ENVIRONMENTAL & TECHNICAL SERVICES, INC.—See Align Capital Partners, LLC; *U.S. Private*, pg. 195
ALMEIDA & CARLSON INSURANCE AGENCY; *U.S. Private*, pg. 195
ALMENDRAL S.A.; *Int'l*, pg. 364
ALM EQUITY AB; *Int'l*, pg. 361
ALMER LTD.—See BERICAP GmbH & Co. KG; *Int'l*, pg. 980
ALMES—See Poulina Group Holding S.A.; *Int'l*, pg. 5942
ALMETAX MANUFACTURING CO., LTD.—See Sekisui House, Ltd.; *Int'l*, pg. 6697
AL-MET LIMITED—See Pressure Technologies Plc; *Int'l*, pg. 5965
ALMET NEDERLAND BV—See Henley Management Company; *U.S. Private*, pg. 1916
ALMET—See Henley Management Company; *U.S. Private*, pg. 1916
ALMEX INC.—See U-NEXT HOLDINGS Co.,Ltd; *Int'l*, pg. 7997
AL MINNERATH INC.; *U.S. Private*, pg. 147
ALMIRA DEVELOPMENT PTE LTD—See Hong Lai Huat Group Limited; *Int'l*, pg. 3467
ALMIRALL APS—See Almirall, S.A.; *Int'l*, pg. 364
ALMIRALL B.V.—See Almirall, S.A.; *Int'l*, pg. 364
ALMIRALL GMBH—See Almirall, S.A.; *Int'l*, pg. 364
ALMIRALL HERMAL GMBH—See Almirall, S.A.; *Int'l*, pg. 364
ALMIRALL LIMITED—See Almirall, S.A.; *Int'l*, pg. 364
ALMIRALL - PRODUTOS FARMACEUTICOS LDA.—See Almirall, S.A.; *Int'l*, pg. 364

CORPORATE AFFILIATIONS

ALMIRALL, S.A. DE C.V.—See Almirall, S.A.; *Int'l*, pg. 364
ALMIRALL, S.A.; *Int'l*, pg. 364
ALMIRALL, SAS—See Almirall, S.A.; *Int'l*, pg. 364
ALMIRALL, S.P.A.—See Almirall, S.A.; *Int'l*, pg. 364
ALMIRALL SP. Z O.O.—See Almirall, S.A.; *Int'l*, pg. 364
AL MIRFA POWER COMPANY—See Abu Dhabi Water & Electricity Authority; *Int'l*, pg. 73
ALMOAYYED CONTRACTING GROUP Y.K.—See Bahrain Duty Free Shop Complex BSC; *Int'l*, pg. 800
ALMO CORPORATION—See DCC plc; *Int'l*, pg. 1989
ALMO-ERZEUGNISSE E. BUSCH GMBH—See B. Braun Melsungen AG; *Int'l*, pg. 786
ALMOGIM HOLDINGS LTD.; *Int'l*, pg. 364
ALMOND PRODUCTS INC—See Quoin Inc.; *U.S. Private*, pg. 3329
ALMOND ROCA INTERNATIONAL—See Brown & Haley; *U.S. Private*, pg. 666
ALMONDZ CAPITAL MARKETS PVT. LTD.—See Almondz Global Securities Limited; *Int'l*, pg. 364
ALMONDZ COMMODITIES PVT. LTD.—See Almondz Global Securities Limited; *Int'l*, pg. 364
ALMONDZ GLOBAL SECURITIES LIMITED; *Int'l*, pg. 364
ALMONDZ INSURANCE BROKERS PVT. LTD.—See Almondz Global Securities Limited; *Int'l*, pg. 364
ALMONDZ REINSURANCE BROKERS PRIVATE LIMITED—See Almondz Global Securities Limited; *Int'l*, pg. 364
ALMON, INC.; *U.S. Private*, pg. 195
ALMONTY INDUSTRIES INC.; *Int'l*, pg. 364
ALMO PROFESSIONAL A/V—See DCC plc; *Int'l*, pg. 1989
THE ALMORE DYE HOUSE, INC.; *U.S. Private*, pg. 3984
ALMOST FAMILY, INC.—See UnitedHealth Group Incorporated; *U.S. Public*, pg. 2243
ALMOST FAMILY PC OF FT. LAUDERDALE, LLC—See UnitedHealth Group Incorporated; *U.S. Public*, pg. 2243
ALMOST FAMILY PC OF KENTUCKY, LLC—See UnitedHealth Group Incorporated; *U.S. Public*, pg. 2243
ALMOST FAMILY PC OF SW FLORIDA, LLC—See UnitedHealth Group Incorporated; *U.S. Public*, pg. 2243
ALMOST FAMILY PC OF WEST PALM, LLC—See UnitedHealth Group Incorporated; *U.S. Public*, pg. 2243
ALMOST HEAVEN SAUNAS LLC—See Harvia Oyj; *Int'l*, pg. 3281
ALMOST NEVER FILMS INC.; *U.S. Private*, pg. 195
AL-MOSUL FOR FUNFAIRS; *Int'l*, pg. 287
AL MOUWASAT MEDICAL SERVICES COMPANY; *Int'l*, pg. 281
AL MOWASAT HEALTHCARE COMPANY K.S.C.C.; *Int'l*, pg. 281
ALMRINS RORSERVICE AB—See YIT Corporation; *Int'l*, pg. 8586
ALMSTED ENTERPRISES INC.; *U.S. Private*, pg. 195
A.L.M.T. ASIA PACIFIC PTE. LTD.—See Sumitomo Electric Industries, Ltd.; *Int'l*, pg. 7277
A.L.M.T. CORP.—See Sumitomo Electric Industries, Ltd.; *Int'l*, pg. 7277
A.L.M.T. TECH INC. - ITAMI DIVISION—See Sumitomo Electric Industries, Ltd.; *Int'l*, pg. 7277
A.L.M.T. TECH INC. - SAKATA DIVISION NO.2 PLANT—See Sumitomo Electric Industries, Ltd.; *Int'l*, pg. 7277
A.L.M.T. TECH INC. - SAKATA DIVISION NO.3 PLANT—See Sumitomo Electric Industries, Ltd.; *Int'l*, pg. 7277
A.L.M.T. TECH INC. - SAKATA DIVISION (OHAMA PLANT)—See Sumitomo Electric Industries, Ltd.; *Int'l*, pg. 7277
A.L.M.T. TECH INC. - SAKATA DIVISION—See Sumitomo Electric Industries, Ltd.; *Int'l*, pg. 7277
A.L.M.T. TECH INC.—See Sumitomo Electric Industries, Ltd.; *Int'l*, pg. 7277
A.L.M.T. TECH INC. - TOYAMA DIVISION—See Sumitomo Electric Industries, Ltd.; *Int'l*, pg. 7277
A.L.M.T. (THAILAND) CO., LTD. - KORAT FACTORY—See Sumitomo Electric Industries, Ltd.; *Int'l*, pg. 7277
A.L.M.T. (THAILAND) CO., LTD.—See Sumitomo Electric Industries, Ltd.; *Int'l*, pg. 7277
AL MUDON INTERNATIONAL REAL ESTATE COMPANY - KPSC; *Int'l*, pg. 281
AL MUHAIDIB BUILDING MATERIALS COMPANY—See A.K. Al-Muhaidib & Sons Group of Companies; *Int'l*, pg. 24
AL MUHAIDIB CONTRACTING CO.—See A.K. Al-Muhaidib & Sons Group of Companies; *Int'l*, pg. 24
AL MUHAIDIB FOODS CO.—See A.K. Al-Muhaidib & Sons Group of Companies; *Int'l*, pg. 24
AL-MUHAIDIB HARDWARE—See A.K. Al-Muhaidib & Sons Group of Companies; *Int'l*, pg. 24
AL MUHAIDIB LAND TRANSPORT COMPANY—See A.K. Al-Muhaidib & Sons Group of Companies; *Int'l*, pg. 24
AL MUHAIDIB TECHNICAL SUPPLIES COMPANY—See A.K. Al-Muhaidib & Sons Group of Companies; *Int'l*, pg. 24
ALMUNEEF CO.; *Int'l*, pg. 364
AL-MUNTASER TRADING & CONTRACTING CO. W.L.L. - CONTRACTING DIVISION—See Al-Muntaser Trading & Contracting Co. W.L.L.; *Int'l*, pg. 287

COMPANY NAME INDEX

AL-MUNTASER TRADING & CONTRACTING CO. W.L.L.; *Int'l*, pg. 287
AL MUSAHA AL MUSHTARAKA CO.—See Fouad Alghanim & Sons Group of Companies; *Int'l*, pg. 2753
ALMUS FRANCE—See Walgreens Boots Alliance, Inc.; *U.S. Public*, pg. 2322
AL-MUTAWAA TRADING COMPANY LLC—See Suhail Bahwan Group (Holding) LLC; *Int'l*, pg. 7254
ALMY D.O.O.; *Int'l*, pg. 364
ALNA AB; *Int'l*, pg. 364
ALNAB ARMATUR AB—See Indutrade AB; *Int'l*, pg. 3677
AL-NABEEL FOR MARBLE & GRANITE COMPANY—See Jordan Marble Company; *Int'l*, pg. 3999
AL NABIL FOOD INDUSTRIES LLC—See Agthia Group PJSC; *Int'l*, pg. 222
ALNA INTELLIGENCE UAB—See Alna Ab; *Int'l*, pg. 364
ALNA SHARYO CO., LTD.—See Hankyu Hanshin Holdings Inc.; *Int'l*, pg. 3254
ALNA SOFTWARE UAB—See Alna Ab; *Int'l*, pg. 364
AL NASSER REAL ESTATE COMPANY S.A.R.L.—See Mohammed Abdulmohsin Al-Kharafi & Sons WLL; *Int'l*, pg. 5018
ALNA TRADING & EXPORTS LTD.; *Int'l*, pg. 364
AL-NAWADI HOLDING COMPANY - KPSC; *Int'l*, pg. 287
ALNA YUSOKI-YOHIN CO., LTD.—See Kawasaki Heavy Industries, Ltd.; *Int'l*, pg. 4095
ALNC, INC.; *U.S. Private*, pg. 195
AL NEYER, LLC; *U.S. Private*, pg. 147
AL-NISR AL-ARABI INSURANCE—See Arab Bank plc; *Int'l*, pg. 529
AL-NOOR SUGAR MILLS LIMITED; *Int'l*, pg. 287
ALNOVA TECHNOLOGIES CORPORATION S.L.—See Accenture plc; *Int'l*, pg. 86
ALNOX S.R.O; *Int'l*, pg. 365
ALNYLAM AUSTRIA GMBH—See Alnylam Pharmaceuticals, Inc.; *U.S. Public*, pg. 82
ALNYLAM BRASIL FARMACEUTICA LTDA.—See Alnylam Pharmaceuticals, Inc.; *U.S. Public*, pg. 82
ALNYLAM GERMANY GMBH—See Alnylam Pharmaceuticals, Inc.; *U.S. Public*, pg. 82
ALNYLAM PHARMACEUTICALS, INC.; *U.S. Public*, pg. 81
ALNYLAM PHARMACEUTICALS SPAIN SL—See Alnylam Pharmaceuticals, Inc.; *U.S. Public*, pg. 82
ALNYLAM UK LIMITED—See Alnylam Pharmaceuticals, Inc.; *U.S. Public*, pg. 82
ALOCS CORPORATION—See Akebono Brake Industry Co., Ltd.; *Int'l*, pg. 262
ALOE PHARMACEUTICAL CO., LTD.—See Kobayashi Pharmaceutical Co., Ltd.; *Int'l*, pg. 4216
ALOE PRIVATE EQUITY SAS; *Int'l*, pg. 365
ALOETTE COSMETICS, INC.; *U.S. Private*, pg. 195
ALOETTE COSMETICS OF CANADA—See Aloette Cosmetics, Inc.; *U.S. Private*, pg. 195
ALOFT CO., LTD.—See Daikoku Denki Co., Ltd.; *Int'l*, pg. 1937
ALOFT GROUP, INC.; *U.S. Private*, pg. 195
ALOG DATA CENTERS DO BRASIL S.A.—See Equinix, Inc.; *U.S. Public*, pg. 787
ALOGENT CORPORATION—See Battery Ventures, L.P.; *U.S. Private*, pg. 488
ALOHA AIR CARGO—See Saltchuk Resources Inc.; *U.S. Private*, pg. 3534
ALOHA AIR CONDITIONING, INC.—See Marathon HVAC Services, LLC; *U.S. Private*, pg. 2570
ALOHA AUTO GROUP, LTD.; *U.S. Private*, pg. 195
ALOHACARE; *U.S. Private*, pg. 195
ALOHA FREIGHT FORWARDERS, INC.; *U.S. Private*, pg. 195
ALOHA MEDICINALS, INC.—See American Botanicals, LLC; *U.S. Private*, pg. 225
ALOHA PETROLEUM, LTD.—See Sunoco LP; *U.S. Public*, pg. 1964
ALOHA RESTAURANTS, INC.; *U.S. Private*, pg. 195
ALOHA R.V., INC.—See Redwood Capital Investments, LLC; *U.S. Private*, pg. 3380
ALOI MATERIALS HANDLING INC; *U.S. Private*, pg. 195
ALOIS DALLMAYR AUTOMATEN-SERVICE GMBH HERXHEIM—See Alois Dallmayr KG; *Int'l*, pg. 365
ALOIS DALLMAYR GASTRO-SERVICE GMBH & CO KG—See Alois Dallmayr KG; *Int'l*, pg. 365
ALOIS DALLMAYR KAFFEE OHG—See Alois Dallmayr KG; *Int'l*, pg. 365
ALOIS DALLMAYR KG; *Int'l*, pg. 365
ALOIS FELSER GESELLSCHAFT M.B.H.—See PORR AG; *Int'l*, pg. 5922
ALOIS KASPER GMBH—See KONE Oyj; *Int'l*, pg. 4247
ALOJAS BIROJI SIA—See Eastnine AB; *Int'l*, pg. 2274
ALOK H&A LTD.—See Reliance - ADA Group Limited; *Int'l*, pg. 6261
ALOK INDUSTRIES LIMITED—See Reliance - ADA Group Limited; *Int'l*, pg. 6261
AL OLOUM BOOKSHOP LLC—See Tawoos LLC; *Int'l*, pg. 7477
AL OMANIYA FINANCIAL SERVICES (SAOG); *Int'l*, pg. 281
ALOMBARD SAS—See Schneider Electric SE; *Int'l*, pg. 6626
AL-OMRAN INDUSTRIAL TRADING CO.; *Int'l*, pg. 287

AL OMRAN REAL ESTATE DEVELOPMENT CO. K.S.C.—See Kuwait Real Estate Holding Company K.P.S.C.; *Int'l*, pg. 4348
ALON ASPHALT COMPANY—See Marathon Petroleum Corporation; *U.S. Public*, pg. 1363
ALON ASSETS, INC.—See Delek Group Ltd.; *Int'l*, pg. 2011
ALON BRANDS, INC.—See Delek Group Ltd.; *Int'l*, pg. 2011
ALON ISRAEL OIL COMPANY LTD.; *Int'l*, pg. 365
ALON NATURAL GAS EXPLORATION LTD.—See Alon Israel Oil Company Ltd.; *Int'l*, pg. 365
ALON REFINING KROTZ SPRINGS, INC.—See Delek Group Ltd.; *Int'l*, pg. 2011
ALON USA ENERGY, INC.—See Delek Group Ltd.; *Int'l*, pg. 2011
ALON USA PARTNERS, LP—See Delek Group Ltd.; *Int'l*, pg. 2011
ALONY HETZ GLOBAL LTD.—See Alony Hetz Properties and Investments Ltd.; *Int'l*, pg. 365
ALONY HETZ PROPERTIES AND INVESTMENTS LTD.; *Int'l*, pg. 365
ALOPEXX, INC.; *U.S. Private*, pg. 195
ALORICA INC.; *U.S. Private*, pg. 195
ALORO MINING CORP.; *Int'l*, pg. 365
ALOR SETAR HOLIDAY VILLA SDN. BHD.—See Advance Synergy Berhad; *Int'l*, pg. 156
AL-OSAIS CONTRACTING CO.—See Al-Osais International Holding Company; *Int'l*, pg. 287
AL-OSAIS HIRING CO.—See Al-Osais International Holding Company; *Int'l*, pg. 287
AL-OSAIS INDUSTRIAL & STRUCTURAL SUPPLY CO.—See Al-Osais International Holding Company; *Int'l*, pg. 287
AL-OSAIS INTERNATIONAL HOLDING COMPANY; *Int'l*, pg. 287
AL-OSAIS MCM CO. LTD.—See Al-Osais International Holding Company; *Int'l*, pg. 287
AL-OSAIS PETROLEUM SERVICES CO.—See Al-Osais International Holding Company; *Int'l*, pg. 287
AL-OSAIS REAL ESTATE CO.—See Al-Osais International Holding Company; *Int'l*, pg. 287
AL-OSAIS TRANSPORTATION & ROAD CONSTRUCTION CO.—See Al-Osais International Holding Company; *Int'l*, pg. 287
ALO SOLUTIONS, LLC; *U.S. Private*, pg. 195
ALOSRA SUPERMARKET W.L.L.—See BMMI B.S.C.; *Int'l*, pg. 1076
A LOT DECORATION SWEDEN AB—See Storskogen Group AB; *Int'l*, pg. 7227
AL-OTHAIM HOLDING COMPANY; *Int'l*, pg. 288
AL-OULA COMPANY; *Int'l*, pg. 288
AL OULA MIDDLE EAST LLC—See Al-Oula Company; *Int'l*, pg. 288
ALOYS F. DORNBRACHT GMBH & CO. KG; *Int'l*, pg. 365
ALOYS INC.; *Int'l*, pg. 365
ALOYSIUS, BUTLER & CLARK ASSOCIATES, INC.; *U.S. Private*, pg. 195
ALPABIO SAS—See Eurofins Scientific S.E.; *Int'l*, pg. 2535
ALPA CHIMIE ALIMENTAIRE SAS—See Eurofins Scientific S.E.; *Int'l*, pg. 2535
AL PACKER FORD - EAST—See Al Packer, Inc.; *U.S. Private*, pg. 147
AL PACKER, INC.; *U.S. Private*, pg. 147
ALPAC MARKETING SERVICES INC.; *U.S. Private*, pg. 196
ALPADIA S.A.—See Graham Holdings Company; *U.S. Public*, pg. 954
A.L.P.A. EQUIPMENT; *Int'l*, pg. 25
ALPAGEL GAP; *Int'l*, pg. 366
ALPAGRAPH TEAM GMBH—See Siris Capital Group, LLC; *U.S. Private*, pg. 3673
ALPA HYGIENE ALIMENTAIRE SAS—See Eurofins Scientific S.E.; *Int'l*, pg. 2535
ALPA LABORATORIES LTD; *Int'l*, pg. 365
ALPA LUMBER INC; *Int'l*, pg. 365
ALPA MICROBIOLOGIE ALIMENTAIRE SAS—See Eurofins Scientific S.E.; *Int'l*, pg. 2535
ALPAMSA S.A.—See Ledesma S.A.A.I.; *Int'l*, pg. 4439
ALPAR ARCHITECTURAL PRODUCTS, LLC—See Pawling Corporation; *U.S. Private*, pg. 3115
ALPARGATAS FRANCE S.A.R.L.—See Cambuhy Investimentos Ltda.; *Int'l*, pg. 1270
ALPARGATAS FRANCE S.A.R.L.—See Itausa - Investimentos Itau S.A.; *Int'l*, pg. 3830
ALPARGATAS ITALY S.R.L.—See Cambuhy Investimentos Ltda.; *Int'l*, pg. 1270
ALPARGATAS ITALY S.R.L.—See Itausa - Investimentos Itau S.A.; *Int'l*, pg. 3830
ALPARGATAS PORTUGAL LIMITED—See Cambuhy Investimentos Ltda.; *Int'l*, pg. 1270
ALPARGATAS PORTUGAL LIMITED—See Itausa - Investimentos Itau S.A.; *Int'l*, pg. 3830
ALPARGATAS S.A. - CAMPINA GRANDE PLANT—See Cambuhy Investimentos Ltda.; *Int'l*, pg. 1270
ALPARGATAS S.A. - CAMPINA GRANDE PLANT—See Itausa - Investimentos Itau S.A.; *Int'l*, pg. 3831

ALPARGATAS S.A. - DUPE PLANT—See Cambuhy Investimentos Ltda.; *Int'l*, pg. 1270
ALPARGATAS S.A. - DUPE PLANT—See Itausa - Investimentos Itau S.A.; *Int'l*, pg. 3831
ALPARGATAS SAIC—See Cambuhy Investimentos Ltda.; *Int'l*, pg. 1270
ALPARGATAS SAIC—See Itausa - Investimentos Itau S.A.; *Int'l*, pg. 3831
ALPARGATAS S.A. - JOAO PESSOA PLANT—See Cambuhy Investimentos Ltda.; *Int'l*, pg. 1270
ALPARGATAS S.A. - JOAO PESSOA PLANT—See Itausa - Investimentos Itau S.A.; *Int'l*, pg. 3831
ALPARGATAS S.A. - MOGI MIRIM PLANT—See Cambuhy Investimentos Ltda.; *Int'l*, pg. 1270
ALPARGATAS S.A. - MOGI MIRIM PLANT—See Itausa - Investimentos Itau S.A.; *Int'l*, pg. 3831
ALPARGATAS S.A. - SANTA RITA PLANT—See Cambuhy Investimentos Ltda.; *Int'l*, pg. 1270
ALPARGATAS S.A. - SANTA RITA PLANT—See Itausa - Investimentos Itau S.A.; *Int'l*, pg. 3831
ALPARGATAS S.A.—See Cambuhy Investimentos Ltda.; *Int'l*, pg. 1270
ALPARGATAS S.A.—See Itausa - Investimentos Itau S.A.; *Int'l*, pg. 3830
ALPARGATAS SPAIN S.L.U.—See Cambuhy Investimentos Ltda.; *Int'l*, pg. 1270
ALPARGATAS SPAIN S.L.U.—See Itausa - Investimentos Itau S.A.; *Int'l*, pg. 3831
ALPARGATAS UK LTD—See Cambuhy Investimentos Ltda.; *Int'l*, pg. 1270
ALPARGATAS UK LTD—See Itausa - Investimentos Itau S.A.; *Int'l*, pg. 3831
ALPARGATAS USA INC.—See Cambuhy Investimentos Ltda.; *Int'l*, pg. 1270
ALPARGATAS USA INC.—See Itausa - Investimentos Itau S.A.; *Int'l*, pg. 3831
ALPARK PETROLEUM, INC.; *U.S. Private*, pg. 196
ALP ASSOCIATES; *U.S. Private*, pg. 196
ALPAX COMERCIO DE PRODS.—See HORIBA Ltd; *Int'l*, pg. 3474
ALP CONSULTING LIMITED—See Bain Capital, LP; *U.S. Private*, pg. 433
ALPEK POLYESTER ARGENTINA S.A.—See ALFA, S.A.B. de C.V.; *Int'l*, pg. 313
ALPEK POLYESTER BRASIL S.A.—See ALFA, S.A.B. de C.V.; *Int'l*, pg. 313
ALPEK POLYESTER PERNAMBUCO S. A.—See ALFA, S.A.B. de C.V.; *Int'l*, pg. 313
ALPEK POLYESTER S.A. DE C.V.—See ALFA, S.A.B. de C.V.; *Int'l*, pg. 313
ALPEK POLYESTER UK LTD.—See ALFA, S.A.B. de C.V.; *Int'l*, pg. 313
ALPEK, S.A. DE C.V.—See ALFA, S.A.B. de C.V.; *Int'l*, pg. 313
ALPE METROLOGIA INDUSTRIAL, S.L.U.—See I Squared Capital Advisors (US) LLC; *U.S. Public*, pg. 2021
ALPE METROLOGIA INDUSTRIAL, S.L.U.—See TDR Capital LLP; *Int'l*, pg. 7491
THE ALPENA NEWS PUBLISHING CO. INC.—See The Nutting Company, Inc.; *U.S. Private*, pg. 4086
ALPENA POWER COMPANY; *U.S. Private*, pg. 196
ALPENA SUPERMARKET INC.; *U.S. Private*, pg. 196
ALPEN CO., LTD.; *Int'l*, pg. 366
ALPEN FOOD COMPANY SOUTH AFRICA (PTY) LTD.—See Post Holdings, Inc.; *U.S. Public*, pg. 1703
ALPENLANDISCHE GEMEINNUTZIGE WOHNBAU GMBH—See Vienna Insurance Group AG Wiener Versicherung Gruppe; *Int'l*, pg. 8193
ALPENPLAKAT AG—See APG/SGA SA; *Int'l*, pg. 513
ALPEN SRL—See Grimaldi Industri AB; *Int'l*, pg. 3086
ALPER CONSULTORIA E CORRETORA DE SEGUROS S.A.; *Int'l*, pg. 366
ALPERIA SPA; *Int'l*, pg. 366
ALPES ENTRETIEN DISTRIBUTION SAS—See Bunzl plc; *Int'l*, pg. 1217
ALPES INFORMATIQUE—See Vicat S.A.; *Int'l*, pg. 8185
ALPES PROVENCE AGNEAUX; *Int'l*, pg. 366
ALPETOUR - POTOVALNA AGENCIJA D.O.O.—See I Squared Capital Advisors (US) LLC; *U.S. Private*, pg. 2024
A.L.P. EUROPE LTD.—See A.A.G. STUCCHI s.r.l.; *Int'l*, pg. 22
ALP GROUP; *Int'l*, pg. 365
ALPHA 1 INDUCTION SERVICE CENTER—See Indel, Inc.; *U.S. Private*, pg. 2055
ALPHA 3 MANUFACTURING LIMITED—See Avnet, Inc.; *U.S. Public*, pg. 250
ALPHA ACTIVE INDUSTRIES SDN. BHD.—See Y.S.P. Southeast Asia Holding Berhad; *Int'l*, pg. 8543
ALPHA ADRIATIC D.D.; *Int'l*, pg. 366
ALPHA ADVISORS, INC.—See The Doctors Company; *U.S. Private*, pg. 4021
ALPHA AEOLIKI MOLAON LAKONIA S.A—See ELLAKTOR S.A.; *Int'l*, pg. 2364
ALPHA ALTERNATIVE ENERGY INC.—See EnerSys; *U.S. Public*, pg. 767
ALPHA AND OMEGA SEMICONDUCTOR INCORPORATED—See Alpha and Omega Semiconductor Limited; *Int'l*, pg. 366

ALPHA AND OMEGA SEMICONDUCTOR LIMITED

ALPHA AND OMEGA SEMICONDUCTOR LIMITED; *Int'l,* pg. 366
ALPHA AND OMEGA SEMICONDUCTOR (SHANGHAI) CO., LTD.—See Alpha and Omega Semiconductor Limited; *Int'l,* pg. 366
ALPHA AND OMEGA SEMICONDUCTOR (SHENZHEN) CO., LTD.—See Alpha and Omega Semiconductor Limited; *Int'l,* pg. 366
ALPHA AND OMEGA SEMICONDUCTOR (TAIWAN) LTD.—See Alpha and Omega Semiconductor Limited; *Int'l,* pg. 366
ALPHA ANIMATION & CULTURE CO., LTD. - CHENGHAI FACTORY—See Alpha Group Co., Ltd.; *Int'l,* pg. 368
ALPHA ASSEMBLY SOLUTIONS BELGIUM NV—See Element Solutions Inc.; *U.S. Public,* pg. 725
ALPHA ASSEMBLY SOLUTIONS BELGIUM NV—See Element Solutions Inc.; *U.S. Public,* pg. 726
ALPHA ASSEMBLY SOLUTIONS BRASIL SOLDAS LTDA—See Element Solutions Inc.; *U.S. Public,* pg. 726
ALPHA ASSEMBLY SOLUTIONS FRANCE SAS—See Element Solutions Inc.; *U.S. Public,* pg. 726
ALPHA ASSEMBLY SOLUTIONS KOREA LTD—See Element Solutions Inc.; *U.S. Public,* pg. 726
ALPHA ASSEMBLY SOLUTIONS KOREA LTD—See Element Solutions Inc.; *U.S. Public,* pg. 726
ALPHA ASSEMBLY SOLUTIONS NETHERLANDS B.V.—See Element Solutions Inc.; *U.S. Public,* pg. 726
ALPHA ASSEMBLY SOLUTIONS (SHENZEN) CO. LTD—See Element Solutions Inc.; *U.S. Public,* pg. 726
ALPHA ASSEMBLY SOLUTIONS SINGAPORE PTE LTD—See Element Solutions Inc.; *U.S. Public,* pg. 726
ALPHA ASSEMBLY SOLUTIONS (TAIWAN) LIMITED—See Element Solutions Inc.; *U.S. Public,* pg. 726
ALPHA ASSET MANAGEMENT A.E.D.A.K.—See Alpha Services and Holdings S.A.; *Int'l,* pg. 369
ALPHA ASSOCIATES, INC.; *U.S. Private,* pg. 196
ALPHA ASSOCIES CONSEIL SAS; *Int'l,* pg. 366
ALPHA ASTIKA AKINITA S.A.—See Alpha Services and Holdings S.A.; *Int'l,* pg. 369
ALPHA AUTOMATION INC.—See United Salt Corporation; *U.S. Private,* pg. 4297
ALPHA AUTOMOTIVE TECHNOLOGIES LLC—See IHI Corporation; *Int'l,* pg. 3604
ALPHA BAKING COMPANY, INC.; *U.S. Private,* pg. 196
ALPHA BANK ALBANIA SH.A.—See OTP Bank Plc; *Int'l,* pg. 5657
ALPHA BANK CYPRUS LIMITED—See Alpha Services and Holdings S.A.; *Int'l,* pg. 369
ALPHA BANK LONDON LTD—See Alpha Services and Holdings S.A.; *Int'l,* pg. 369
ALPHA BANK ROMANIA S.A.—See UniCredit S.p.A.; *Int'l,* pg. 8033
ALPHA BARNES REAL ESTATE SERVICES, LLC—See Asset Plus Companies LP; *U.S. Private,* pg. 354
ALPHA BETA GLOBAL TAPES & ADHESIVES CO., LTD.—See 3M Company; *U.S. Public,* pg. 7
ALPHABET AUSTRIA FUHRPARKMANAGEMENT GMBH—See Bayerische Motoren Werke Aktiengesellschaft; *Int'l,* pg. 910
ALPHABET BELGIUM LONG TERM RENTAL N.V.—See Bayerische Motoren Werke Aktiengesellschaft; *Int'l,* pg. 910
ALPHABET BELGIUM N.V./S.A.—See Bayerische Motoren Werke Aktiengesellschaft; *Int'l,* pg. 910
ALPHABET FRANCE FLEET MANAGEMENT S.N.C.—See Bayerische Motoren Werke Aktiengesellschaft; *Int'l,* pg. 910
ALPHABET FRANCE S.A.S.—See Bayerische Motoren Werke Aktiengesellschaft; *Int'l,* pg. 910
ALPHABET FUHRPARKMANAGEMENT GMBH—See Bayerische Motoren Werke Aktiengesellschaft; *Int'l,* pg. 910
ALPHABET FUHRPARKMANAGEMENT (SCHWEIZ) AG—See Bayerische Motoren Werke Aktiengesellschaft; *Int'l,* pg. 910
ALPHABET (GB) LTD.—See Bayerische Motoren Werke Aktiengesellschaft; *Int'l,* pg. 910
ALPHABET HOLDING COMPANY, INC.; *U.S. Private,* pg. 200
ALPHABET INC.; *U.S. Public,* pg. 82
ALPHABET ITALIA FLEET MANAGEMENT S.P.A.—See Bayerische Motoren Werke Aktiengesellschaft; *Int'l,* pg. 910
ALPHABET LUXEMBOURG S.A.—See Bayerische Motoren Werke Aktiengesellschaft; *Int'l,* pg. 910
ALPHABET NEDERLAND B.V.—See Bayerische Motoren Werke Aktiengesellschaft; *Int'l,* pg. 910
ALPHABET PLAYHOUSE AT EAST COAST PTE LTD—See NetDragon Websoft Holdings Limited; *Int'l,* pg. 5213
ALPHABET PLAYHOUSE CHILDCARE & LEARNING CENTRE PTE LTD—See NetDragon Websoft Holdings Limited; *Int'l,* pg. 5213
ALPHABET POLSKA FLEET MANAGEMENT SP. Z O.O.—See Bayerische Motoren Werke Aktiengesellschaft; *Int'l,* pg. 910
ALPHABET UK LTD.—See Bayerische Motoren Werke Aktiengesellschaft; *Int'l,* pg. 910

ALPHA BEVERAGES OY—See Altia Oyj; *Int'l,* pg. 392
ALPHA BILLION SDN. BHD.—See B.I.G. Industries Berhad; *Int'l,* pg. 790
ALPHA-BIO TEC LTD.—See Danaher Corporation; *U.S. Public,* pg. 628
ALPHA BIOTEC LTD.—See Danaher Corporation; *U.S. Public,* pg. 624
ALPHA BUILDING CENTER INC.; *U.S. Private,* pg. 196
ALPHA BULGARIA JSC; *Int'l,* pg. 367
ALPHACAN B.V.—See OpenGate Capital Management, LLC; *U.S. Private,* pg. 3030
ALPHACAN D.O.O.—See OpenGate Capital Management, LLC; *U.S. Private,* pg. 3031
ALPHACAN OMNIPLAST GMBH—See OpenGate Capital Management, LLC; *U.S. Private,* pg. 3031
ALPHACAN S.P.A.—See OpenGate Capital Management, LLC; *U.S. Private,* pg. 3031
ALPHA CAPITAL ACQUISITION COMPANY; *U.S. Public,* pg. 82
ALPHA CAPITAL PARTNERS, LTD.; *U.S. Private,* pg. 197
ALPHA CARD S.C.R.L./C.V.B.A.—See American Express Company; *U.S. Public,* pg. 100
ALPHA CARD SCRL—See American Express Company; *U.S. Public,* pg. 101
ALPHA CARD SERVICES INC.; *U.S. Private,* pg. 197
ALPHA CARD SYSTEMS, LLC—See Odyssey Investment Partners, LLC; *U.S. Private,* pg. 2994
ALPHACARE HOLDINGS, INC.—See Centene Corporation; *U.S. Public,* pg. 469
ALPHACARE OF NEW YORK, INC.—See Centene Corporation; *U.S. Public,* pg. 469
ALPHACAT MANAGERS LTD.—See American International Group, Inc.; *U.S. Public,* pg. 107
ALPHA CERAMICS GMBH—See Sacmi Imola S.C.A.R.L.; *Int'l,* pg. 6463
ALPHA CLOTHING LIMITED—See Pearl Global Industries Limited; *Int'l,* pg. 5774
ALPHA COAL RESOURCES COMPANY, LLC—See Alpha Natural Resources, Inc.; *U.S. Private,* pg. 199
ALPHA COAL SALES COMPANY, LLC—See Alpha Natural Resources, Inc.; *U.S. Private,* pg. 199
ALPHA COAL WEST, INC.—See Alpha Natural Resources, Inc.; *U.S. Private,* pg. 199
ALPHA COATINGS INC—See PPG Industries, Inc.; *U.S. Public,* pg. 1711
ALPHA COATING TECHNOLOGIES, LLC—See PPG Industries, Inc.; *U.S. Public,* pg. 1707
ALPHA COGNITION INC.; *Int'l,* pg. 367
ALPHA CO., LTD.; *Int'l,* pg. 367
ALPHACOM HOLDINGS, INC.; *Int'l,* pg. 370
ALPHA CONSULTANTS LIMITED—See Marsh & McLennan Companies, Inc.; *U.S. Public,* pg. 1374
ALPHA COPPER CORP.; *Int'l,* pg. 367
ALPHACORE CAPITAL LLC; *U.S. Private,* pg. 200
ALPHA CORPORATION - GUMMA PLANT—See ALPHA Corporation; *Int'l,* pg. 367
THE ALPHA CORPORATION OF TENNESSEE; *U.S. Private,* pg. 3984
ALPHA CORPORATION; *Int'l,* pg. 367
ALPHA CREDIT NEDERLAND B.V.—See ABN AMRO Group N.V.; *Int'l,* pg. 65
ALPHA CREDIT SA/NV—See BNP Paribas SA; *Int'l,* pg. 1084
ALPHA CUSTOM SERVICES LIMITED—See MOVe Logistics Group Limited; *Int'l,* pg. 5058
ALPHA DESIGN CO., LTD.—See MIMAKI ENGINEERING CO., LTD.; *Int'l,* pg. 4897
ALPHADETAIL, INC.—See IQVIA Holdings Inc.; *U.S. Public,* pg. 1169
ALPHA DEUREN INTERNATIONAL B.V.—See Sanwa Holdings Corporation; *Int'l,* pg. 6560
ALPHA DHABI HOLDING PJSC; *Int'l,* pg. 367
ALPHA DIVISIONS PUBLIC COMPANY LIMITED; *Int'l,* pg. 368
ALPHA DX GROUP LIMITED; *Int'l,* pg. 368
ALPHA DYNO NOBEL; *U.S. Private,* pg. 197
ALPHA ELECTRIC SUPPLY CORPORATION; *U.S. Private,* pg. 197
ALPHA ELECTRONICS CORP.—See Vishay Precision Group, Inc.; *U.S. Public,* pg. 2303
ALPHA-EN CORPORATION; *U.S. Public,* pg. 82
ALPHA ENERGIES RENOUVELABLES—See Rubis SCA; *Int'l,* pg. 6423
ALPHAEON CORPORATION; *U.S. Private,* pg. 200
ALPHA EXPLORATION ERITREA LIMITED—See Alpha Exploration Limited; *Int'l,* pg. 368
ALPHA EXPLORATION LIMITED; *Int'l,* pg. 368
ALPHA FINANCE A.E.P.E.Y.—See Alpha Services and Holdings S.A.; *Int'l,* pg. 369
ALPHA FINANCE ROMANIA S.A.—See Alpha Services and Holdings S.A.; *Int'l,* pg. 369
ALPHA FINANCIAL MARKETS CONSULTING INC.—See Bridgepoint Group Plc; *Int'l,* pg. 1153
ALPHA FINANCIAL MARKETS CONSULTING PLC—See Bridgepoint Group Plc; *Int'l,* pg. 1153
ALPHA FINANCIAL MARKETS CONSULTING S.A.S.—See Bridgepoint Group Plc; *Int'l,* pg. 1153
ALPHA FINANCIAL MARKETS CONSULTING SWITZERLAND S.A.—See Bridgepoint Group Plc; *Int'l,* pg. 1153

CORPORATE AFFILIATIONS

ALPHA FINANCIAL PRESS LIMITED—See Wonderful Sky Financial Group Holdings Limited; *Int'l,* pg. 8446
ALPHA FLIGHT A.S.—See The Emirates Group; *Int'l,* pg. 7639
ALPHA FLIGHT GROUP LIMITED—See The Emirates Group; *Int'l,* pg. 7639
ALPHA FLIGHT UK LIMITED—See The Emirates Group; *Int'l,* pg. 7639
ALPHA FLIGHT US, INC.—See The Emirates Group; *Int'l,* pg. 7638
ALPHA FLYING, INC.; *U.S. Private,* pg. 197
ALPHA FOODS INC.—See The Livekindly Company, Inc.; *U.S. Private,* pg. 4071
ALPHAFORM LTD—See Proto Labs, Inc.; *U.S. Public,* pg. 1729
ALPHAFORM—See Groupe Guillin SA; *Int'l,* pg. 3103
ALPHA FRANCE SAS—See Element Solutions Inc.; *U.S. Public,* pg. 726
ALPHA FX EUROPE LIMITED—See Alpha Group International plc; *Int'l,* pg. 368
ALPHA GARMENT INC.; *U.S. Private,* pg. 197
ALPHAGARY CORPORATION—See Grupo Empresarial Kaluz S.A. de C.V.; *Int'l,* pg. 3127
ALPHAGARY LIMITED—See Grupo Empresarial Kaluz S.A. de C.V.; *Int'l,* pg. 3127
ALPHAGEN INTELLIGENCE CORP.; *Int'l,* pg. 370
ALPHAGEO INDIA LTD; *Int'l,* pg. 370
ALPHAGILITY LLC; *U.S. Private,* pg. 200
ALPHA GRAPHIC INDIA LTD.; *Int'l,* pg. 368
ALPHAGRAPHICS, INC.—See MBE Worldwide S.p.A.; *Int'l,* pg. 4751
ALPHA GREEN ENERGY LIMITED; *U.S. Private,* pg. 197
ALPHA GRISSIN S.A.; *Int'l,* pg. 368
ALPHA GROUP CO., LTD.; *Int'l,* pg. 368
ALPHA GROUP INC.; *Int'l,* pg. 368
ALPHA GROUP INTERNATIONAL PLC; *Int'l,* pg. 368
ALPHA GROUP JERSEY LTD—See Alpha Services and Holdings S.A.; *Int'l,* pg. 369
THE ALPHA GROUP; *U.S. Private,* pg. 3984
THE ALPHA GROUP—See EnerSys; *U.S. Public,* pg. 767
ALPHA GROWTH MANAGEMENT INC.—See Alpha Growth PLC; *Int'l,* pg. 368
ALPHA GROWTH PLC; *Int'l,* pg. 368
ALPHA (GUANGZHOU) AUTOMOTIVEPARTS CO., LTD.—See ALPHA Corporation; *Int'l,* pg. 367
ALPHA HOLDINGS, INC.; *Int'l,* pg. 368
ALPHA HOLDING TWO B.V.—See HP Inc.; *U.S. Public,* pg. 1062
ALPHA HOSPITALS (NW) LIMITED—See Universal Health Services, Inc.; *U.S. Public,* pg. 2255
ALPHA HOUSING HARDWARE (THAILAND) CO., LTD.—See ALPHA Corporation; *Int'l,* pg. 367
ALPHA HPA LIMITED; *Int'l,* pg. 368
ALPHA HUNTER DRILLING, LLC—See Expand Energy Corporation; *U.S. Public,* pg. 808
ALPHA II, LLC - MONTGOMERY—See Alpha II, LLC; *U.S. Private,* pg. 197
ALPHA II, LLC; *U.S. Private,* pg. 197
ALPHA IMAGING, INC.—See Radon Medical Imaging Corp.; *U.S. Private,* pg. 3345
ALPHA IMAGING TECHNOLOGY CORPORATION—See MediaTek Inc.; *Int'l,* pg. 4773
ALPHA INDUSTRIES BHD.—See The Furukawa Electric Co., Ltd.; *Int'l,* pg. 7644
ALPHA INDUSTRIES INC.; *U.S. Private,* pg. 197
ALPHA INDUSTRIES, INC.; *U.S. Private,* pg. 197
ALPHA INDUSTRY QUERETARO, S.A. DE C.V.—See ALPHA Corporation; *Int'l,* pg. 367
ALPHA INDUSTRY (THAILAND) CO., LTD.—See ALPHA Corporation; *Int'l,* pg. 367
ALPHA-INNOTEC FRANCE EURL—See NIBE Industrier AB; *Int'l,* pg. 5259
ALPHA-INNOTEC GMBH—See NIBE Industrier AB; *Int'l,* pg. 5262
ALPHA-INNOTEC GMBH—See NIBE Industrier AB; *Int'l,* pg. 5262
ALPHA-INNOTEC NORGE AS—See NIBE Industrier AB; *Int'l,* pg. 5262
ALPHA-INNOTEC SUN GMBH—See NIBE Industrier AB; *Int'l,* pg. 5259
ALPHA INNOVATIONS MEXICO S DE R.L. DE C.V.—See EnerSys; *U.S. Public,* pg. 767
ALPHA INSULATION & WATER PROOFING COMPANY—See Installed Building Products, Inc.; *U.S. Public,* pg. 1132
ALPHA INSULATION & WATER PROOFING INC.—See Installed Building Products, Inc.; *U.S. Public,* pg. 1132
ALPHA INSURANCE LIMITED; *Int'l,* pg. 368
ALPHA INSURANCE LTD—See Alpha Services and Holdings S.A.; *Int'l,* pg. 369
ALPHA INSURANCE SA—See Enstar Group Limited; *Int'l,* pg. 2449
ALPHA INTERNATIONAL B.V.—See Droege Group AG; *Int'l,* pg. 2205
ALPHA INVESTMENT PARTNERS JAPAN KK—See Keppel Corporation Limited; *Int'l,* pg. 4130
ALPHA INVESTMENT PARTNERS LTD—See Keppel Corporation Limited; *Int'l,* pg. 4130
ALPHAKAT GMBH; *Int'l,* pg. 370

COMPANY NAME INDEX

ALPHAKINETIC LTD.—See Fidelity National Infor; *U.S. Public*, pg. 832
ALPHA LAB A.E.—See DIAGNOSTIC AND THERAPEUTIC CENTER OF ATHENS-HYGEIA S.A.; *Int'l*, pg. 2103
ALPHA LEASING A.E.—See Alpha Services and Holdings S.A.; *Int'l*, pg. 369
ALPHA LEASING ROMANIA IFN S.A.—See Alpha Services and Holdings S.A.; *Int'l*, pg. 369
ALPHA LENS COMPANY LTD.—See Carl-Zeiss-Stiftung; *Int'l*, pg. 1335
ALPHA LENS COMPANY LTD.—See EQT AB; *Int'l*, pg. 2472
ALPHALIFE A.A.E.Z.—See Alpha Services and Holdings S.A.; *Int'l*, pg. 369
ALPHA LINE SARL—See Savino Del Bene S.p.A.; *Int'l*, pg. 6600
ALPHALITE INCORPORATION—See Ka Shui International Holdings Limited; *Int'l*, pg. 4045
ALPHA LITHIUM CORPORATION—See Techint S.p.A.; *Int'l*, pg. 7504
ALPHALOGIC INDUSTRIES LIMITED; *Int'l*, pg. 370
ALPHALOGIC TECHSYS LTD.; *Int'l*, pg. 370
ALPHA MARKETING, INC.; *U.S. Private*, pg. 198
ALPHA MATERIAL HANDLING CO., INC.; *U.S. Private*, pg. 198
ALPHA MEDIA LLC; *U.S. Private*, pg. 198
ALPHA MEDICAL, S.R.O.—See Apax Partners LLP; *Int'l*, pg. 507
ALPHA MESS-STEUER-REGELTECHNIK GMBH—See Bilfinger SE; *Int'l*, pg. 1023
ALPHA METAL CO., LTD.—See Maruichi Steel Tube Ltd; *Int'l*, pg. 4713
ALPHA METALLURGICAL RESOURCES, INC.; *U.S. Public*, pg. 82
ALPHAMETAL MEXICO S.A. DE C.V.—See Maruichi Steel Tube Ltd; *Int'l*, pg. 4713
ALPHA METALS, INC.—See Element Solutions Inc; *U.S. Public*, pg. 726
ALPHA METALS (TAIWAN) INC—See Element Solutions Inc.; *U.S. Public*, pg. 726
ALPHAMETRIX, LLC; *U.S. Private*, pg. 200
ALPHA MICROELECTRONICS CORP.; *Int'l*, pg. 368
ALPHA MIDWEST HOLDING COMPANY—See Alpha Natural Resources, Inc.; *U.S. Private*, pg. 199
ALPHA MILLS CORP.; *U.S. Private*, pg. 198
ALPHAMIN RESOURCES CORP.; *Int'l*, pg. 370
ALPHAMIN S.A.—See BRENNTAG SE; *Int'l*, pg. 1146
ALPHA MONTICELLO, INC.—See Empire Resorts, Inc.; *U.S. Private*, pg. 1385
ALPHA MOS AMERICA INC—See Jolt Capital SAS; *Int'l*, pg. 3996
ALPHA MOS CHINA—See Jolt Capital SAS; *Int'l*, pg. 3996
ALPHA M.O.S. JAPAN K.K.—See Jolt Capital SAS; *Int'l*, pg. 3996
ALPHA MOS SA—See Jolt Capital SAS; *Int'l*, pg. 3996
ALPHANAM E&C JOINT STOCK COMPANY—See Alphanam Joint Stock Company; *Int'l*, pg. 370
ALPHANAM JOINT STOCK COMPANY; *Int'l*, pg. 370
ALPHA NATURAL RESOURCES, INC.; *U.S. Private*, pg. 198
ALPHA NATURAL RESOURCES, LLC—See Alpha Natural Resources, Inc.; *U.S. Private*, pg. 199
ALPHANCO VENTURE CORP.; *Int'l*, pg. 370
ALPHA NET CO., LTD.—See OTSUKA CORPORATION; *Int'l*, pg. 5658
ALPHA NETHERLANDS B.V.—See Element Solutions Inc.; *U.S. Public*, pg. 726
ALPHA NETWORK ALLIANCE VENTURES INC.; *U.S. Public*, pg. 82
ALPHA NETWORKS (CHANGSHU) CO., LTD.—See Alpha Networks Inc.; *Int'l*, pg. 369
ALPHA NETWORKS (CHENGDU) CO., LTD.—See Alpha Networks Inc.; *Int'l*, pg. 369
ALPHA NETWORKS (DONGGUAN) CO., LTD.—See Alpha Networks Inc.; *Int'l*, pg. 369
ALPHA NETWORKS INC.; *Int'l*, pg. 368
ALPHA NETWORKS INC.—See Alpha Networks Inc.; *Int'l*, pg. 369
ALPHA NETWORKS VIETNAM COMPANY LIMITED—See Alpha Networks Inc.; *Int'l*, pg. 369
ALPHANUMERIC SYSTEMS INC.; *U.S. Private*, pg. 200
ALPHA OFFICE SUPPLIES INC.; *U.S. Private*, pg. 199
ALPHA OMEGA INTEGRATION, LLC; *U.S. Private*, pg. 199
ALPHA OMEGA PUBLICATIONS—See Silver Lake Group, LLC; *U.S. Private*, pg. 3661
ALPHA & OMEGA SEMICONDUCTOR (HONG KONG) LIMITED—See Alpha and Omega Semiconductor Limited; *Int'l*, pg. 366
ALPHA & OMEGA SEMICONDUCTOR (SHENZHEN) LIMITED—See Alpha and Omega Semiconductor Limited; *Int'l*, pg. 366
ALPHA ONE LIMITED—See Digilife Technologies Limited; *Int'l*, pg. 2119
ALPHA PACIFIC PETROLEUM (S) PTE LTD—See AP Oil International Ltd.; *Int'l*, pg. 499
ALPHA PACKAGING INC.; *U.S. Private*, pg. 199

ALPHA PACKAGING LLC—See Irving Place Capital Management, L.P.; *U.S. Private*, pg. 2141
ALPHA PACKAGING LLC—See Irving Place Capital Management, L.P.; *U.S. Private*, pg. 2141
ALPHA PARK—See LAZ Parking Ltd, LLC; *U.S. Private*, pg. 2402
ALPHAPAY AG—See Otto GmbH & Co. KG; *Int'l*, pg. 5662
ALPHA PEAK LEISURE INC.; *Int'l*, pg. 369
ALPHAPET INC.—See Indorama Ventures Public Company Limited; *Int'l*, pg. 3658
ALPHAPHARM PTY LTD; *Int'l*, pg. 370
ALPHA-PLAN AG ROTHRIST—See Burkhalter Holding AG; *Int'l*, pg. 1224
ALPHA PLASTICS INC.; *U.S. Private*, pg. 199
ALPHAPOINTE ASSOCIATION FOR THE BLIND; *U.S. Private*, pg. 200
ALPHAPOLIS CO., LTD.; *Int'l*, pg. 370
ALPHA PRIME FOODS LIMITED—See Hang Sang (Siu Po) International Holding Company Limited; *Int'l*, pg. 3245
ALPHA PROCESS CONTROLS (INTERNATIONAL) LTD.—See ACCEDO Group Ltd.; *Int'l*, pg. 79
ALPHA PROPERTIES, INC.—See MetLife, Inc.; *U.S. Public*, pg. 1429
ALPHA PROPERTY & CASUALTY INSURANCE COMPANY—See Kemper Corporation; *U.S. Public*, pg. 1220
ALPHA PROTECH ENGINEERED PRODUCTS, INC.—See Alpha Pro Tech, Ltd.; *Int'l*, pg. 369
ALPHA PRO TECH, LTD.; *Int'l*, pg. 369
ALPHA PRO TECH-NOGALES—See Alpha Pro Tech, Ltd.; *Int'l*, pg. 369
ALPHAPURCHASE CO., LTD—See ASKUL Corporation; *Int'l*, pg. 625
ALPHA Q, INC.; *U.S. Private*, pg. 199
ALPHA RAE PERSONNEL INC.; *U.S. Private*, pg. 199
ALPHA RAIL TEAM GMBH & CO. KG—See Vossloh AG; *Int'l*, pg. 8309
ALPHA REAL ESTATE MANAGEMENT & INVESTMENTS S.A.—See Alpha Services and Holdings S.A.; *Int'l*, pg. 369
ALPHA REAL ESTATE SERVICES LLC—See Alpha Services and Holdings S.A.; *Int'l*, pg. 369
ALPHA REAL TRUST LIMITED; *Int'l*, pg. 369
ALPHA REPLY GMBH—See Reply S.p.A.; *Int'l*, pg. 6290
ALPHA RESINS, LLC—See Covia Holdings Corporation; *U.S. Private*, pg. 1072
ALPHA RESOURCE MANAGEMENT LTD—See Lagan Holdings Ltd.; *Int'l*, pg. 4393
ALPHA RESPIRATORY INC.—See Linde plc; *Int'l*, pg. 4505
ALPHARETTA TRANSFER STATION, LLC—See Waste Management, Inc.; *U.S. Public*, pg. 2330
ALPHA REVIEW CORPORATION—See Stone Point Capital LLC; *U.S. Private*, pg. 3823
ALPHA RHEINTAL BANK AG; *Int'l*, pg. 369
ALPHARMA DE ARGENTINA S.R.L.—See Zoetis, Inc.; *U.S. Public*, pg. 2409
ALPHARMA DO BRASIL LTDA.—See Zoetis, Inc.; *U.S. Public*, pg. 2409
ALPHARMA PHARMACEUTICALS LLC—See Pfizer Inc.; *U.S. Public*, pg. 1679
ALPHARM CO., LTD.—See Qol Holdings Co., Ltd.; *Int'l*, pg. 6147
ALPHA ROCAS SA—See The Emirates Group; *Int'l*, pg. 7639
ALPHA ROOFING INDUSTRIES, LLC; *U.S. Private*, pg. 199
ALPHA SANTANOL PTY. LTD.—See Mercer International Inc.; *Int'l*, pg. 4829
ALPHA SCHOOL BUS COMPANY INC—See Cook-Illinois Corp.; *U.S. Private*, pg. 1038
ALPHA SECURITY PRODUCTS—See CCL Industries Inc.; *Int'l*, pg. 1367
ALPHASENSE LIMITED—See AMETEK, Inc.; *U.S. Public*, pg. 119
ALPHASENSE USA, INC.—See AMETEK, Inc.; *U.S. Public*, pg. 120
ALPHASERVE TECHNOLOGIES, LLC.; *U.S. Private*, pg. 200
ALPHA SERVICER CO., LTD.—See SBI Shinsei Bank, Limited; *Int'l*, pg. 6606
ALPHA SERVICES AND HOLDINGS S.A.; *Int'l*, pg. 369
ALPHA SHIRT—See Bain Capital, LP; *U.S. Private*, pg. 437
ALPHASIMPLEX GROUP, LLC—See Virtus Investment Partners, Inc.; *U.S. Public*, pg. 2300
ALPHA SINTERED METALS, INC.—See O2 Investment Partners, LLC; *U.S. Private*, pg. 2982
ALPHASOFT SERVICES CORPORATION—See Agnite Education Limited; *Int'l*, pg. 212
ALPHA SOLUTIONS AG—See Bechtle AG; *Int'l*, pg. 937
ALPHA SOLUTIONS CO., LTD.—See Alpha Networks Inc.; *Int'l*, pg. 369
ALPHASON DESIGNS LIMITED—See Dorel Industries, Inc.; *U.S. Private*, pg. 2176
ALPHA SOURCE, INC.; *U.S. Private*, pg. 199
ALPHA SOUTHWEST, INC.—See Pike Street Capital, LP; *U.S. Private*, pg. 3180

ALPHAX FOOD SYSTEM CO., LTD.

ALPHA SPECIALTY PRODUCTS INC.; *U.S. Private*, pg. 199
ALPHASTAFF GROUP, INC.; *U.S. Private*, pg. 200
ALPHA STAMPING COMPANY—See The Alpha Group; *U.S. Private*, pg. 3984
ALPHA STAR ACQUISITION CORPORATION; *U.S. Public*, pg. 82
ALPHA STRATEGIC PLC—See Northill Capital LLP; *Int'l*, pg. 5445
ALPHA SYNOPSYS INC; *U.S. Private*, pg. 200
ALPHA SYSTEMS INC.; *Int'l*, pg. 369
ALPHA SYSTEMS INC.; *U.S. Private*, pg. 200
ALPHA TAU MEDICAL LTD.; *Int'l*, pg. 370
ALPHATECH ALI S.P.A.—See Ali Holding S.r.l; *Int'l*, pg. 320
ALPHA TECH ENERGY SOLUTIONS INDIA PRIVATE LIMITED—See EnerSys; *U.S. Public*, pg. 767
ALPHA TECHNICAL AND SERVICES INC.—See Alpha Networks Inc.; *Int'l*, pg. 369
ALPHA TECHNICAL SERVICES CORPORATION—See KKR & Co. Inc.; *U.S. Public*, pg. 1241
ALPHA TECHNICAL SERVICES INC.—See Alpha Networks Inc.; *Int'l*, pg. 369
ALPHATECHNO CO., LTD.—See Vision, Inc; *U.S. Public*, pg. 8253
ALPHA TECHNO CO., LTD.—See OTSUKA CORPORATION; *Int'l*, pg. 5658
ALPHA TECHNOLOGIES ASIA LTD.—See EnerSys; *U.S. Public*, pg. 767
ALPHA TECHNOLOGIES GMBH—See Roper Technologies, Inc.; *U.S. Public*, pg. 1810
ALPHA TECHNOLOGIES, INC.—See EnerSys; *U.S. Public*, pg. 767
ALPHA TECHNOLOGIES LTD.—See EnerSys; *U.S. Public*, pg. 767
ALPHA TECHNOLOGIES PTY. LTD.—See EnerSys; *U.S. Public*, pg. 767
ALPHA TECHNOLOGIES S.A.—See EnerSys; *U.S. Public*, pg. 767
ALPHA TECHNOLOGIES SERVICES, INC.—See EnerSys; *U.S. Public*, pg. 768
ALPHA TECHNOLOGIES SERVICES LLC—See Roper Technologies, Inc.; *U.S. Public*, pg. 1811
ALPHA TECHNOLOGY CORPORATION—See ALPHA Corporation; *Int'l*, pg. 367
ALPHA TECHNOLOGY GROUP LIMITED; *Int'l*, pg. 370
ALPHATEC HOLDINGS, INC.; *U.S. Public*, pg. 84
ALPHATEC SPINE, INC.—See Alphatec Holdings, Inc.; *U.S. Public*, pg. 84
ALPHA-TEC SYSTEMS, INC.—See StoneCalibre, LLC; *U.S. Private*, pg. 3827
ALPHA TEKNOVA, INC.; *U.S. Public*, pg. 82
ALPHA TELECOM INC.; *U.S. Private*, pg. 200
ALPHA TEL S.A.—See AT&T Inc.; *U.S. Public*, pg. 220
ALPHA TESTING, INC.—See Universal Engineering Sciences, LLC; *U.S. Private*, pg. 4304
ALPHA THAMES SUBSEA LTD.—See Saab AB; *Int'l*, pg. 6459
ALPHA THERAPEUTIC ITALIA, S.P.A.—See Grifols, S.A.; *Int'l*, pg. 3084
ALPHA TILES TRADING SDN. BHD.—See YB Ventures Berhad; *Int'l*, pg. 8573
ALPHATIME ACQUISITION CORP.; *U.S. Public*, pg. 84
ALPHA TRADING & SHIPPING AGENCIES LTD.—See The Al Fadl Group of Companies; *Int'l*, pg. 7612
ALPHA TRAINS—See Arcus Infrastructure Partners LLP; *Int'l*, pg. 552
ALPHA TRANSLATIONS CANADA INC.—See RWS Holdings plc; *Int'l*, pg. 6436
ALPHATRONICS B.V.—See TKH Group N.V.; *Int'l*, pg. 7763
ALPHATRON MARINE BEHEER B.V.—See Nisshinbo Holdings Inc.; *Int'l*, pg. 5372
ALPHA TRUST CORPORATION—See Roper Technologies, Inc.; *U.S. Public*, pg. 1810
ALPHA TRUST; *Int'l*, pg. 370
ALPHA UNIVERSAL MANAGEMENT PLC; *Int'l*, pg. 370
ALPHA URANIUM LTD.—See Strategic Minerals Corporation NL; *Int'l*, pg. 7236
ALPHA VENTURES A.E.—See Alpha Services and Holdings S.A.; *Int'l*, pg. 369
ALPHA VERTEILERTECHNIK GMBH—See Siemens Aktiengesellschaft; *Int'l*, pg. 6886
ALPHAVEST ACQUISITION CORP.; *U.S. Public*, pg. 85
ALPHA VIDEO & AUDIO, INC.; *U.S. Private*, pg. 200
ALPHAVILLE URBANISMO S.A.—See Blackstone Inc.; *U.S. Public*, pg. 360
ALPHAVILLE URBANISMO S.A.—See Patria Investimentos SA; *U.S. Public*, pg. 5757
ALPHA WASTEWATER, INC.; *Int'l*, pg. 370
ALPHAWAVE IP GROUP PLC; *Int'l*, pg. 370
ALPHAWEST SERVICES PTY LTD; *Int'l*, pg. 370
ALPHA WIRE COMPANY—See Belden, Inc.; *U.S. Public*, pg. 293
ALPHAX FOOD SYSTEM CO., LTD.; *Int'l*, pg. 370
ALPHEGA APOTHEKENPARTNER GMBH—See Walgreens Boots Alliance, Inc.; *U.S. Public*, pg. 2322
ALPHEGA—See Walgreens Boots Alliance, Inc.; *U.S. Public*, pg. 2322

115

ALPHEIDE-SENIORENZENTRUM GMBH—See Clariane SE; *Int'l*, pg. 1642
ALPHEUS COMMUNICATIONS LP—See Astra Capital Management LLC; *U.S. Private*, pg. 361
ALPHINAT INC.; *Int'l*, pg. 370
ALPHONSE CHARPIOT ET COMPAGNIE; *Int'l*, pg. 370
ALPHR TECHNOLOGY EUROPE SRL—See Indutrade AB; *Int'l*, pg. 3677
ALPHR TECHNOLOGY LTD.—See Indutrade AB; *Int'l*, pg. 3677
ALPI ADRIATICA SRL—See Albini & Pitigliani S.p.A.; *Int'l*, pg. 298
ALPI AIR & SEA A/S—See Albini & Pitigliani S.p.A.; *Int'l*, pg. 298
ALPI BELGIUM N.V.S.A.—See Albini & Pitigliani S.p.A.; *Int'l*, pg. 298
ALPIC BIOTECH LTD.—See Delta Plus Group; *Int'l*, pg. 2019
ALPICO HOLDINGS CO., LTD.; *Int'l*, pg. 371
ALPICO KOTSU CO., LTD.—See ALPICO Holdings Co., Ltd.; *Int'l*, pg. 371
ALPICO TAXI CO., LTD.—See ALPICO Holdings Co., Ltd.; *Int'l*, pg. 371
ALPIC S.A.—See Delta Plus Group; *Int'l*, pg. 2019
ALPI EESTI OU—See Albini & Pitigliani S.p.A.; *Int'l*, pg. 298
ALPI EXPRESS NORD SRL—See Albini & Pitigliani S.p.A.; *Int'l*, pg. 298
ALPI EXPRESS S.R.L.—See Albini & Pitigliani S.p.A.; *Int'l*, pg. 298
ALPI INTERNATIONAL, LTD; *U.S. Private*, pg. 200
ALPI KOREA LTD—See Albini & Pitigliani S.p.A.; *Int'l*, pg. 298
ALPI LAGHI S.R.L.—See Albini & Pitigliani S.p.A.; *Int'l*, pg. 298
ALPI LATVIA SIA—See Albini & Pitigliani S.p.A.; *Int'l*, pg. 298
ALPI LEVANTE SRL—See Albini & Pitigliani S.p.A.; *Int'l*, pg. 298
ALPI LISBOA LDA—See Albini & Pitigliani S.p.A.; *Int'l*, pg. 298
ALPI LIVORNO SRL—See Albini & Pitigliani S.p.A.; *Int'l*, pg. 298
ALPI LOGISTICS INC—See Albini & Pitigliani S.p.A.; *Int'l*, pg. 298
ALPI LUCCA SRL—See Albini & Pitigliani S.p.A.; *Int'l*, pg. 298
ALPINA BH, D.O.O.—See Alpina, d.d.; *Int'l*, pg. 371
ALPINA BROMY, D.O.O.—See Alpina, d.d.; *Int'l*, pg. 371
ALPINA CAPITAL PARTNERS LLP; *Int'l*, pg. 371
ALPINA CRO, D.O.O.—See Alpina, d.d.; *Int'l*, pg. 371
ALPINA, D.D.; *Int'l*, pg. 371
ALPINA FOODS, INC.—See Alpina Productos Alimenticios S.A.; *Int'l*, pg. 371
ALPINA PRODUCTOS ALIMENTICIOS S.A.; *Int'l*, pg. 371
ALPINA SIRO, S.R.L.—See Alpina, d.d.; *Int'l*, pg. 371
ALPINA SPORTS CORP.—See Alpina, d.d.; *Int'l*, pg. 371
ALPINA YUG, D.O.O.—See Alpina, d.d.; *Int'l*, pg. 371
ALP INDUSTRIES, INC.; *U.S. Private*, pg. 196
ALPINE 4 HOLDINGS, INC.; *U.S. Public*, pg. 85
ALPINE ACCESS CANADA, INC—See Creadev SAS; *Int'l*, pg. 1831
ALPINE ACQUISITION CORP.; *U.S. Public*, pg. 85
ALPINE AEROTECH LTD.; *Int'l*, pg. 371
ALPINE AGENCY INC.—See Blue Cross & Blue Shield of South Carolina; *U.S. Private*, pg. 587
ALPINE AIR EXPRESS, INC.—See AE Industrial Partners, LP; *U.S. Private*, pg. 111
ALPINE AMERICAN—See Hosokawa Micron Corporation; *Int'l*, pg. 3486
ALPINE APS—See ArchiMed SAS; *Int'l*, pg. 548
ALPINE ARMORING INC.; *U.S. Private*, pg. 200
ALPINE ASSOCIATES, L.P.; *U.S. Private*, pg. 200
ALPINE AUTO BROKERS INC.; *U.S. Public*, pg. 85
ALPINE AUTOMATION LIMITED—See Illinois Tool Works Inc.; *U.S. Public*, pg. 1101
ALPINE AVIATION INC—See AE Industrial Partners, LP; *U.S. Private*, pg. 111
ALPINE BANKS OF COLORADO; *U.S. Public*, pg. 85
ALPINE BANK—See Alpine Banks of Colorado; *U.S. Public*, pg. 85
ALPINE BAU CZ S. R. O.—See PORR AG; *Int'l*, pg. 5922
ALPINE BAU DEUTSCHLAND AG—See ALPINE Bau GmbH; *Int'l*, pg. 371
ALPINE BAU GMBH; *Int'l*, pg. 371
ALPINE BUICK, PONTIAC, GMC; *U.S. Private*, pg. 200
ALPINE COLONY ENTERPRISES INC.; *U.S. Private*, pg. 201
ALPINE COUNTRY CLUB; *U.S. Private*, pg. 201
ALPINE CUSTOMER SERVICE (USA), INC.—See Alps Alpine Co., Ltd.; *Int'l*, pg. 375
ALPINE DAIRY, LLC—See TINE SA; *Int'l*, pg. 7753
ALPINE DO BRASIL LTDA—See Alps Alpine Co., Ltd.; *Int'l*, pg. 375
ALPINE ELECTRONICS AUSTRALIA PTY. LIMITED—See Alps Alpine Co., Ltd.; *Int'l*, pg. 375
ALPINE ELECTRONICS (CHINA) COMPANY LIMITED—See Alps Alpine Co., Ltd.; *Int'l*, pg. 375

ALPINE ELECTRONICS DE ESPANA, S.A.—See Alps Alpine Co., Ltd.; *Int'l*, pg. 375
ALPINE ELECTRONICS (EUROPE) GMBH—See Alps Alpine Co., Ltd.; *Int'l*, pg. 375
ALPINE ELECTRONICS FRANCE S.A.R.L.—See Alps Alpine Co., Ltd.; *Int'l*, pg. 375
ALPINE ELECTRONICS GMBH—See Alps Alpine Co., Ltd.; *Int'l*, pg. 375
ALPINE ELECTRONICS, INC.—See Alps Alpine Co., Ltd.; *Int'l*, pg. 375
ALPINE ELECTRONICS MANUFACTURING OF EUROPE LTD.—See Alps Alpine Co., Ltd.; *Int'l*, pg. 375
ALPINE ELECTRONICS MARKETING INC.—See Alps Alpine Co., Ltd.; *Int'l*, pg. 375
ALPINE ELECTRONICS OF AMERICA, INC.—See Alps Alpine Co., Ltd.; *Int'l*, pg. 375
ALPINE ELECTRONICS OF CANADA, INC.—See Alps Alpine Co., Ltd.; *Int'l*, pg. 375
ALPINE ELECTRONICS OF MIDDLE EAST, FZCO—See Alps Alpine Co., Ltd.; *Int'l*, pg. 375
ALPINE ELECTRONICS OF SILICON VALLEY, INC.—See Alps Alpine Co., Ltd.; *Int'l*, pg. 375
ALPINE ELECTRONICS OF U.K. LIMITED—See Alps Alpine Co., Ltd.; *Int'l*, pg. 375
ALPINE-ENERGIE HOLDING AG—See ALPINE Bau GmbH; *Int'l*, pg. 371
ALPINE ENGINEERING SERVICES PTE LTD—See Sembcorp Industries Ltd.; *Int'l*, pg. 6703
THE ALPINE GROUP, INC.; *U.S. Private*, pg. 3984
ALPINE GROVE (NETHERLANDS) B.V.—See Alpine Grove Partners LLP; *U.S. Private*, pg. 201
ALPINE GROVE PARTNERS LLP; *U.S. Private*, pg. 201
ALPINE GROVE PARTNERS (US) LLC—See Alpine Grove Partners LLP; *U.S. Private*, pg. 201
ALPINE HOLDING COMPANY; *U.S. Private*, pg. 201
ALPINE HOLDING GMBH; *Int'l*, pg. 371
ALPINE HOUSING DEVELOPMENT CORPORATION LTD. - ALPINE ALLOYS DIVISION—See Alpine Housing Development Corporation Ltd.; *Int'l*, pg. 371
ALPINE HOUSING DEVELOPMENT CORPORATION LTD.; *Int'l*, pg. 371
ALPINE IMMUNE SCIENCES, INC.—See Vertex Pharmaceuticals Incorporated; *U.S. Public*, pg. 2287
ALPINE INCOME PROPERTY TRUST, INC.; *U.S. Public*, pg. 85
ALPINE, INC.—See Headspace Inc.; *U.S. Private*, pg. 1891
ALPINE INDUSTRIES, INC.—See Adama Technologies Corp.; *U.S. Private*, pg. 73
ALPINE INSULATION CO, INC.—See Installed Building Products, Inc.; *U.S. Public*, pg. 1132
ALPINE INSURANCE ASSOCIATES, INC.—See GTCR LLC; *U.S. Private*, pg. 1802
ALPINE INVESTORS; *U.S. Private*, pg. 201
ALPINE ITALIA S.P.A.—See Alps Alpine Co., Ltd.; *Int'l*, pg. 375
ALPINE LUMBER COMPANY INC.; *U.S. Private*, pg. 201
ALPINE MANUFACTURING, INC.—See Alps Alpine Co., Ltd.; *Int'l*, pg. 375
ALPINE MATERIALS LLC—See SiteOne Landscape Supply, Inc.; *U.S. Public*, pg. 1888
ALPINE MAYREDER CONSTRUCTION CO., LTD.—See ALPINE Bau GmbH; *Int'l*, pg. 371
ALPINE MEATS INC.; *U.S. Private*, pg. 201
ALPINE OCEAN SEISMIC SURVEY, INC.—See HAL Trust N.V.; *Int'l*, pg. 3226
ALPINE OF ASIA PACIFIC INDIA PVT., LTD.—See Alps Alpine Co., Ltd.; *Int'l*, pg. 375
ALPINE OIL CO., LTD.—See PTG Energy Public Company Limited; *Int'l*, pg. 6090
ALPINE PAYMENT SYSTEMS; *U.S. Private*, pg. 201
ALPINE PIPE MANUFACTURING SDN BHD—See Hiap Teck Venture Berhad; *Int'l*, pg. 3382
ALPINE POWER SYSTEMS INC.—See TFI Inc.; *U.S. Private*, pg. 3979
ALPINE PRECISION, INC.—See Alps Alpine Co., Ltd.; *Int'l*, pg. 375
ALPINE PRODUCTS INC.; *U.S. Private*, pg. 201
ALPINE PROPERTY MANAGEMENT LLC; *U.S. Private*, pg. 202
ALPINE RESEARCH OPTICS CORP.—See Altechna UAB; *Int'l*, pg. 389
ALPINE SALES INC.; *U.S. Private*, pg. 202
ALPINE SECURITY, LLC—See CISO Global, Inc.; *U.S. Public*, pg. 501
ALPINE SELECT AG; *Int'l*, pg. 371
ALPINES HARTSCHOTTERWERK GEORG KASSBOHRER & SOHN GMBH & CO. KG—See Strabag SE; *Int'l*, pg. 7229
ALPINE SUMMIT ENERGY PARTNERS, INC.; *U.S. Public*, pg. 85
ALPINE SYSTEMS CORPORATION—See Illinois Tool Works Inc.; *U.S. Public*, pg. 1101
ALPINE TECHNOLOGY MANUFACTURING, INC.—See Alps Alpine Co., Ltd.; *Int'l*, pg. 376
ALPINE TECHNOLOGY MANUFACTURING (THAILAND) CO., LTD.—See Alps Alpine Co., Ltd.; *Int'l*, pg. 375
ALPINE TERRACE—See Sava Senior Care LLC; *U.S. Private*, pg. 3555

ALPI NETHERLANDS B.V.—See Albini & Pitigliani S.p.A.; *Int'l*, pg. 298
ALPINE VALLEY BREAD COMPANY—See Flowers Foods, Inc.; *U.S. Public*, pg. 854
ALPINE WASTE & RECYCLING; *U.S. Private*, pg. 202
ALPIN HAUS SKI SHOP INC.; *U.S. Private*, pg. 200
ALPINION GUANGZHOU MEDICAL SYSTEMS CO., LTD.—See Iljin Display Co., Ltd.; *Int'l*, pg. 3614
ALPINION MEDICAL DEUTSCHLAND GMBH—See Iljin Display Co., Ltd.; *Int'l*, pg. 3614
ALPINION MEDICAL SYSTEMS CO., LTD.—See Iljin Display Co., Ltd.; *Int'l*, pg. 3614
ALPINION USA, INC.—See Iljin Display Co., Ltd.; *Int'l*, pg. 3614
ALPI NORD EST S.R.L.—See Albini & Pitigliani S.p.A.; *Int'l*, pg. 298
ALPINVEST PARTNERS B.V.—See The Carlyle Group Inc.; *U.S. Public*, pg. 2054
ALPINVEST PARTNERS INC.—See The Carlyle Group Inc.; *U.S. Public*, pg. 2054
ALPINVEST PARTNERS LIMITED—See The Carlyle Group Inc.; *U.S. Public*, pg. 2044
ALPI OLIMPIKA LTD—See Albini & Pitigliani S.p.A.; *Int'l*, pg. 298
ALPI PADANA S.R.L.—See Albini & Pitigliani S.p.A.; *Int'l*, pg. 298
AL-PI POLONIA SP. Z O.O.—See Albini & Pitigliani S.p.A.; *Int'l*, pg. 298
ALPI PORTUGAL LDA.—See Albini & Pitigliani S.p.A.; *Int'l*, pg. 298
ALPIQ AG—See Alpiq Holding AG; *Int'l*, pg. 372
ALPIQ ANLAGENTECHNIK GMBH—See Alpiq Holding AG; *Int'l*, pg. 372
ALPIQ CENTRAL EUROPE AG—See Alpiq Holding AG; *Int'l*, pg. 372
ALPIQ CSEPELI EROMU KFT—See Alpiq Holding AG; *Int'l*, pg. 372
ALPIQ CSEPELI SZOLGALTATO KFT.—See Alpiq Holding AG; *Int'l*, pg. 372
ALPIQ CSEPEL KFT.—See Alpiq Holding AG; *Int'l*, pg. 372
ALPIQ DEUTSCHLAND GMBH—See Alpiq Holding AG; *Int'l*, pg. 372
ALPIQ ECOPOWER LTD.—See Alpiq Holding AG; *Int'l*, pg. 372
ALPIQ ECOPOWER SCANDINAVIA AS—See Alpiq Holding AG; *Int'l*, pg. 373
ALPIQ ECOPOWER SWITZERLAND LTD.—See Alpiq Holding AG; *Int'l*, pg. 372
ALPIQ ECOSERVICES LTD.—See Bouygues S.A.; *Int'l*, pg. 1123
ALPIQ ENERGIA BULGARIA EOOD—See Alpiq Holding AG; *Int'l*, pg. 373
ALPIQ ENERGIA ESPANA S.A.U.—See Alpiq Holding AG; *Int'l*, pg. 372
ALPIQ ENERGIE DEUTSCHLAND GMBH—See Alpiq Holding AG; *Int'l*, pg. 373
ALPIQ ENERGIE FRANCE S.A.S.—See Alpiq Holding AG; *Int'l*, pg. 372
ALPIQ ENERGIJA BH D.O.O.—See Alpiq Holding AG; *Int'l*, pg. 372
ALPIQ ENERGIJA HRVATSKA D.O.O.—See Alpiq Holding AG; *Int'l*, pg. 372
ALPIQ ENERGIJA SKOPJE DOOEL—See Alpiq Holding AG; *Int'l*, pg. 373
ALPIQ ENERGY HELLAS S.A.—See Alpiq Holding AG; *Int'l*, pg. 373
ALPIQ ENERGY ITALY S.P.A.—See Alpiq Holding AG; *Int'l*, pg. 373
ALPIQ ENERGY SE—See Alpiq Holding AG; *Int'l*, pg. 373
ALPIQ ENERGY SE—See Alpiq Holding AG; *Int'l*, pg. 373
ALPIQ ENERGY UKRAINE LLC—See Alpiq Holding AG; *Int'l*, pg. 373
ALPIQ ENERTRANS AG—See Alpiq Holding AG; *Int'l*, pg. 372
ALPIQ FINANZBETEILIGUNGEN LTD.—See Alpiq Holding AG; *Int'l*, pg. 373
ALPIQ GENERATION (CZ) S.R.O.—See Sev.en Energy AG; *Int'l*, pg. 6730
ALPIQ GRID LTD.—See Alpiq Holding AG; *Int'l*, pg. 373
ALPIQ HOLDING AG; *Int'l*, pg. 371
ALPIQ HYDRO AARE AG—See Alpiq Holding AG; *Int'l*, pg. 373
ALPIQ INTEC EAST LTD.—See Bouygues S.A.; *Int'l*, pg. 1123
ALPIQ INTEC ROMANDIE SA—See Bouygues S.A.; *Int'l*, pg. 1123
ALPIQ ITALIA S.R.L.—See Alpiq Holding AG; *Int'l*, pg. 373
ALPIQ MANAGEMENT LTD.—See Alpiq Holding AG; *Int'l*, pg. 373
ALPIQ NARZOLE S.R.L.—See Alpiq Holding AG; *Int'l*, pg. 373
ALPIQ NORWAY AS—See Alpiq Holding AG; *Int'l*, pg. 373
ALPIQ PRODUCTION FRANCE MANAGEMENT S.A.S.—See Alpiq Holding AG; *Int'l*, pg. 372
ALPIQ RESEAU SA LAUSANNE—See Alpiq Holding AG; *Int'l*, pg. 373
ALPIQ ROMINDUSTRIES SRL—See Alpiq Holding AG; *Int'l*, pg. 373
ALPIQ SUISSE SA—See Alpiq Holding AG; *Int'l*, pg. 373

COMPANY NAME INDEX

ALPIQ SWISSTRADE LTD.—See Alpiq Holding AG; *Int'l*, pg. 373
ALPIQ TRADING LTD.—See Alpiq Holding AG; *Int'l*, pg. 373
ALPIQ VERCELLI S.R.L.—See Alpiq Holding AG; *Int'l*, pg. 373
ALPIQ ZLIN S.R.O.—See Alpiq Holding AG; *Int'l*, pg. 373
A.L.P.I. SARL—See London Security PLC; *Int'l*, pg. 4546
ALPI SERVIZIO MODA S.R.L.—See Albini & Pitigliani S.p.A.; *Int'l*, pg. 298
ALPI, S.P.A.—See Mondragon Corporation; *Int'l*, pg. 5029
ALPI SUISSE S.A.—See Albini & Pitigliani S.p.A.; *Int'l*, pg. 298
ALPI SUOMI OY—See Albini & Pitigliani S.p.A.; *Int'l*, pg. 298
ALPI TIRRENICA S.R.L.—See Albini & Pitigliani S.p.A.; *Int'l*, pg. 298
ALPITOUR S.P.A.; *Int'l*, pg. 373
ALPI UK LTD—See Albini & Pitigliani S.p.A.; *Int'l*, pg. 298
ALPI USA, INC.—See Albini & Pitigliani S.p.A.; *Int'l*, pg. 298
ALPI USA PACIFIC INC.—See Albini & Pitigliani S.p.A.; *Int'l*, pg. 298
ALPLA AVELLANEDA S.A.—See Alpla-Werke Alwin Lehner GmbH & Co. KG; *Int'l*, pg. 374
ALPLA BELGIUM N.V.—See Alpla-Werke Alwin Lehner GmbH & Co. KG; *Int'l*, pg. 374
ALPLA BH D.O.O. CITLUK—See Alpla-Werke Alwin Lehner GmbH & Co. KG; *Int'l*, pg. 374
ALPLA CARIBE INC.—See Alpla-Werke Alwin Lehner GmbH & Co. KG; *Int'l*, pg. 374
ALPLA COLOMBIA LTDA—See Alpla-Werke Alwin Lehner GmbH & Co. KG; *Int'l*, pg. 374
ALPLA DE VENEZUELA S.A.—See Alpla-Werke Alwin Lehner GmbH & Co. KG; *Int'l*, pg. 374
ALPLA D.O.O—See Alpla-Werke Alwin Lehner GmbH & Co. KG; *Int'l*, pg. 374
ALPLA FRANCE SAS—See Alpla-Werke Alwin Lehner GmbH & Co. KG; *Int'l*, pg. 374
ALPLA (GUANGZHOU) PLASTIC CO., LTD.—See Alpla-Werke Alwin Lehner GmbH & Co. KG; *Int'l*, pg. 373
ALPLA (HEFEI) PLASTIC CO., LTD—See Alpla-Werke Alwin Lehner GmbH & Co. KG; *Int'l*, pg. 374
ALPLA HONDURAS SA—See Alpla-Werke Alwin Lehner GmbH & Co. KG; *Int'l*, pg. 374
ALPLA IBERICA S.A.—See Alpla-Werke Alwin Lehner GmbH & Co. KG; *Int'l*, pg. 374
ALPLA INC.—See Alpla-Werke Alwin Lehner GmbH & Co. KG; *Int'l*, pg. 374
ALPLA INDIA PRIVATE LTD.—See Alpla-Werke Alwin Lehner GmbH & Co. KG; *Int'l*, pg. 374
ALPLA ITALIA S.R.L.—See Alpla-Werke Alwin Lehner GmbH & Co. KG; *Int'l*, pg. 374
ALPLA (JIANGSU) PLASTIC CO., LTD.—See Alpla-Werke Alwin Lehner GmbH & Co. KG; *Int'l*, pg. 374
ALPLA LLC—See Alpla-Werke Alwin Lehner GmbH & Co. KG; *Int'l*, pg. 374
ALPLA MEXICO S.A. DE C.V.—See Alpla-Werke Alwin Lehner GmbH & Co. KG; *Int'l*, pg. 374
ALPLA MUANYAG CSOMAGOLOIPARI KFT—See Alpla-Werke Alwin Lehner GmbH & Co. KG; *Int'l*, pg. 374
ALPLA NDM SP.Z.O.O—See Alpla-Werke Alwin Lehner GmbH & Co. KG; *Int'l*, pg. 374
ALPLA NEDERLAND B.V.—See Alpla-Werke Alwin Lehner GmbH & Co. KG; *Int'l*, pg. 374
ALPLA OPAKOWANIA Z TWORZYW SZTUCZNYCH SPOLKA Z.O.O.—See Alpla-Werke Alwin Lehner GmbH & Co. KG; *Int'l*, pg. 374
ALPLA PACKAGING LTD.—See Alpla-Werke Alwin Lehner GmbH & Co. KG; *Int'l*, pg. 374
ALPLA PACKAGING (VIETNAM) CO., LTD.—See Alpla-Werke Alwin Lehner GmbH & Co. KG; *Int'l*, pg. 374
ALPLA PLASTIK SANAYI VE TICARET LTD.—See Alpla-Werke Alwin Lehner GmbH & Co. KG; *Int'l*, pg. 374
ALPLA (SHANGHAI) PLASTIC CO., LTD—See Alpla-Werke Alwin Lehner GmbH & Co. KG; *Int'l*, pg. 374
ALPLA SPOL. S.R.O.—See Alpla-Werke Alwin Lehner GmbH & Co. KG; *Int'l*, pg. 374
ALPLA TASHKENT LRS—See Alpla-Werke Alwin Lehner GmbH & Co. KG; *Int'l*, pg. 374
ALPLA (TIANJIN) PLASTIC CO., LTD.—See Alpla-Werke Alwin Lehner GmbH & Co. KG; *Int'l*, pg. 374
ALPLA UK LIMITED—See Alpla-Werke Alwin Lehner GmbH & Co. KG; *Int'l*, pg. 374
ALPLA WAIDHOFEN GMBH—See Alpla-Werke Alwin Lehner GmbH & Co. KG; *Int'l*, pg. 374
ALPLA-WERKE ALWIN LEHNER GMBH & CO. KG; *Int'l*, pg. 373
ALPLA WERKE LEHNER GMBH & CO KG—See Alpla-Werke Alwin Lehner GmbH & Co. KG; *Int'l*, pg. 374
ALP LEASING CORPORATION—See ALP Industries, Inc.; *U.S. Private*, pg. 196
ALP LIGHTING & CEILING PRODUCTS, INC.; *U.S. Private*, pg. 196
ALP LIQUIDATING TRUST; *U.S. Private*, pg. 196
ALP MANAGEMENT CORP.—See ALP Industries, Inc.; *U.S. Private*, pg. 196
ALPOKAMI OU—See Nayax Ltd.; *Int'l*, pg. 5178

ALPOLIC CORP.—See Mitsubishi Chemical Group Corporation; *Int'l*, pg. 4930
ALPORIT AG—See swisspor Management AG; *Int'l*, pg. 7374
ALPOS ALU, D.O.O.—See ALPOS, d.d.; *Int'l*, pg. 374
ALPOS, D.D.; *Int'l*, pg. 374
ALPOS D.D.—See ALPOS, d.d.; *Int'l*, pg. 375
ALPOS D.O.O. ALEKSINAC—See ALPOS, d.d.; *Int'l*, pg. 375
ALPOS HANDELS GMBH—See ALPOS, d.d.; *Int'l*, pg. 374
ALPOS, INDUSTRIJA KOVINSKLH IZDELKOV ON OPREME, D.D.—See ALPOS, d.d.; *Int'l*, pg. 375
ALPOS MIZARSKA PROIZVODNJA, D.O.O.—See ALPOS, d.d.; *Int'l*, pg. 374
ALPOS OPREMA TRGOVIN D.O.O.—See ALPOS, d.d.; *Int'l*, pg. 374
ALPOS POHISTVO, D.O.O.—See ALPOS, d.d.; *Int'l*, pg. 374
ALPOS POSEBNE STORITVE, D.O.O.—See ALPOS, d.d.; *Int'l*, pg. 374
ALPOS PROIZVODNJA ORODIJ, D.O.O.—See ALPOS, d.d.; *Int'l*, pg. 374
ALPOS ROHR UND METALLHANDEL DEUTSCHLAND GMBH—See ALPOS, d.d.; *Int'l*, pg. 375
ALPOS SP. Z.O.O.—See ALPOS, d.d.; *Int'l*, pg. 375
ALP OVERSEAS PVT. LTD.—See ALP Group; *Int'l*, pg. 365
ALPOWA HEALTHCARE, INC.—See The Ensign Group, Inc.; *U.S. Public*, pg. 2070
ALPRESS OY—See Alma Media Corporation; *Int'l*, pg. 362
AL PRIME ENERGY CONSULTANT INC.; *U.S. Private*, pg. 147
ALPRINT ROVANIEMI—See Alma Media Corporation; *Int'l*, pg. 362
ALPRINT S.A.; *Int'l*, pg. 375
ALPRO A.D.; *Int'l*, pg. 375
A.L. PROCHOICE GROUP PUBLIC LTD.; *Int'l*, pg. 25
ALPRO COMM.VA—See Danone; *Int'l*, pg. 1967
ALPRO GMBH—See Danone; *Int'l*, pg. 1967
ALPRO HOLDINGS, BVBA—See Danone; *Int'l*, pg. 1967
ALPROP PTE LTD—See Singapore Land Group Limited; *Int'l*, pg. 6940
ALPRO SOJA NEDERLAND B.V.—See Danone; *Int'l*, pg. 1967
ALPRO (UK) LIMITED—See Danone; *Int'l*, pg. 1967
ALPS ACCOUNTING CENTRE—See Alps Alpine Co., Ltd.; *Int'l*, pg. 376
ALPS AGRI CAREER CORPORATION—See Altech Corporation; *Int'l*, pg. 389
ALPS ALPIN ASIA CO., LTD.—See Alps Alpine Co., Ltd.; *Int'l*, pg. 376
ALPS ALPINE CO., LTD.; *Int'l*, pg. 375
ALPS ALPINE NORTH AMERICA, INC.—See Alps Alpine Co., Ltd.; *Int'l*, pg. 376
ALPS ALPINE VIETNAM CO., LTD.—See Alps Alpine Co., Ltd.; *Int'l*, pg. 376
ALPS BUSINESS SERVICE CORPORATION—See Altech Corporation; *Int'l*, pg. 389
ALPS CAREER DESIGNING CORPORATION—See Altech Corporation; *Int'l*, pg. 389
ALPS CARE HEART CORPORATION—See Altech Corporation; *Int'l*, pg. 389
ALPS(CHINA)CO., LTD.—See Alps Alpine Co., Ltd.; *Int'l*, pg. 376
ALPS COMMUNICATION DEVICES TECHNOLOGY(SHANGHAI) CO., LTD.—See Alps Alpine Co., Ltd.; *Int'l*, pg. 375
ALPS CONSTRUCTION INC.; *U.S. Private*, pg. 202
ALPS CORPORATION; *U.S. Private*, pg. 202
ALPS DE MEXICO S. DE R.L. DE C.V.—See Alps Alpine Co., Ltd.; *Int'l*, pg. 376
ALPS ELECTRIC CO., LTD. - FURUKAWA PLANT—See Alps Alpine Co., Ltd.; *Int'l*, pg. 376
ALPS ELECTRIC CO., LTD. - KAKUDA PLANT—See Alps Alpine Co., Ltd.; *Int'l*, pg. 376
ALPS ELECTRIC CO., LTD. - NAGAOKA PLANT—See Alps Alpine Co., Ltd.; *Int'l*, pg. 376
ALPS ELECTRIC CO., LTD. - ONAHAMA PLANT—See Alps Alpine Co., Ltd.; *Int'l*, pg. 376
ALPS ELECTRIC CO., LTD. - TAIRA PLANT—See Alps Alpine Co., Ltd.; *Int'l*, pg. 376
ALPS ELECTRIC CO., LTD. - WAKUYA PLANT—See Alps Alpine Co., Ltd.; *Int'l*, pg. 376
ALPS ELECTRIC CZECH, S.R.O.—See Alps Alpine Co., Ltd.; *Int'l*, pg. 375
ALPS ELECTRIC EUROPA GMBH—See Alps Alpine Co., Ltd.; *Int'l*, pg. 376
ALPS ELECTRIC EUROPE GMBH - DORTMUND PLANT—See Alps Alpine Co., Ltd.; *Int'l*, pg. 376
ALPS ELECTRIC EUROPE GMBH—See Alps Alpine Co., Ltd.; *Int'l*, pg. 376
ALPS ELECTRIC EUROPE GMBH—See Alps Alpine Co., Ltd.; *Int'l*, pg. 376
ALPS ELECTRIC (INDIA) PRIVATE LIMITED—See Alps Alpine Co., Ltd.; *Int'l*, pg. 376
ALPS ELECTRIC (IRELAND) LIMITED—See Alps Alpine Co., Ltd.; *Int'l*, pg. 376
ALPS ELECTRIC KOREA CO., LTD.—See Alps Alpine Co., Ltd.; *Int'l*, pg. 376

ALROD ENTERPRISES INC.

ALPS ELECTRIC (MALAYSIA) SDN.BHD. - JENGKA PLANT—See Alps Alpine Co., Ltd.; *Int'l*, pg. 376
ALPS ELECTRIC (MALAYSIA) SDN. BHD.—See Alps Alpine Co., Ltd.; *Int'l*, pg. 376
ALPS ELECTRIC (NORTH AMERICA), INC.—See Alps Alpine Co., Ltd.; *Int'l*, pg. 376
ALPS ELECTRIC (SINGAPORE), PTE. LTD.—See Alps Alpine Co., Ltd.; *Int'l*, pg. 376
ALPS ELECTRIC (S) PTE. LTD.—See Alps Alpine Co., Ltd.; *Int'l*, pg. 376
ALPS ELECTRIC (THAILAND) CO., LTD.—See Alps Alpine Co., Ltd.; *Int'l*, pg. 375
ALPS ELECTRIC (USA), INC.—See Alps Alpine Co., Ltd.; *Int'l*, pg. 376
ALPS ELECTRONICS HONG KONG LIMITED—See Alps Alpine Co., Ltd.; *Int'l*, pg. 376
ALPS ELECTRONICS TAIWAN CO., LTD.—See Alps Alpine Co., Ltd.; *Int'l*, pg. 375
ALPSGIKEN MYANMAR CO., LTD.—See Altech Corporation; *Int'l*, pg. 389
ALPSGIKEN TAIWAN CO., LTD.—See Altech Corporation; *Int'l*, pg. 389
ALPS GREEN DEVICES CO., LTD.—See Alps Alpine Co., Ltd.; *Int'l*, pg. 375
ALPS HOLDINGS INC—See SS&C Technologies Holdings, Inc.; *U.S. Public*, pg. 1923
ALPS INDUSTRIES LIMITED; *Int'l*, pg. 377
ALPS LOGISTICS CO., LTD.; *Int'l*, pg. 377
ALPS LOGISTICS (GUANG DONG) CO., LTD.—See Alps Alpine Co., Ltd.; *Int'l*, pg. 376
ALPS PRECISION (MALAYSIA) SDN. BHD.—See Alps Alpine Co., Ltd.; *Int'l*, pg. 376
ALPS (SHANGHAI) INTERNATIONAL TRADING CO., LTD.—See Alps Alpine Co., Ltd.; *Int'l*, pg. 375
ALPS SOUTH LLC; *U.S. Private*, pg. 202
ALPS SPORTSWEAR MANUFACTURING CO., INC.; *U.S. Private*, pg. 202
ALPS TOOL CO., LTD.—See Citizen Watch Co., Ltd.; *Int'l*, pg. 1624
AL PUNTO ADVERTISING, INC.; *U.S. Private*, pg. 147
AL PURMORT INSURANCE INC.; *U.S. Private*, pg. 147
ALP USA, INC.—See ALP Group; *Int'l*, pg. 365
ALP'VERRE—See Compagnie de Saint-Gobain SA; *Int'l*, pg. 1722
ALPYBUS S.A.R.L.—See Mobico Group PLC; *Int'l*, pg. 5008
AL-QADIR TEXTILE MILLS LIMITED; *Int'l*, pg. 288
AL-QAIM TEXTILE MILLS LIMITED; *Int'l*, pg. 288
AL QUDS READYMIX; *Int'l*, pg. 282
AL QURAISHI ELECTRIC SERVICES OF SAUDI ARABIA—See Ali Zaid Al-Quraishi & Brothers Co.; *Int'l*, pg. 323
AL QURAISHI FURNITURE CORP.—See Ali Zaid Al-Quraishi & Brothers Co.; *Int'l*, pg. 323
AL QURAISHI LEISURE SERVICES—See Ali Zaid Al-Quraishi & Brothers Co.; *Int'l*, pg. 323
AL QURAISHI MARKETING CO. LTD.—See Ali Zaid Al-Quraishi & Brothers Co.; *Int'l*, pg. 323
AL QURAISHI SERVICES—See Ali Zaid Al-Quraishi & Brothers Co.; *Int'l*, pg. 323
ALRAI MEDIA GROUP COMPANY K.S.C.; *Int'l*, pg. 377
ALRAINE SHIPPING AGENCIES LTD.—See Financiere de L'Odet; *Int'l*, pg. 2665
AL RAJHI BANKING & INVESTMENT CORPORATION BHD—See Al Rajhi Bank; *Int'l*, pg. 282
AL RAJHI BANK - JORDAN LTD.—See Al Rajhi Bank; *Int'l*, pg. 282
AL RAJHI BANK - KUWAIT WLL—See Al Rajhi Bank; *Int'l*, pg. 282
AL RAJHI BANK - MALAYSIA SDN. BHD.—See Al Rajhi Bank; *Int'l*, pg. 282
AL RAJHI BANK; *Int'l*, pg. 282
AL RAJHI CAPITAL COMPANY—See Al Rajhi Bank; *Int'l*, pg. 282
AL RAJHI COMPANY FOR COOPERATIVE INSURANCE; *Int'l*, pg. 282
AL RAJHI DEVELOPMENT COMPANY LTD.—See Al Rajhi Bank; *Int'l*, pg. 282
AL-RAKAEZ PLC; *Int'l*, pg. 288
AL RAMZ CAPITAL LLC; *Int'l*, pg. 282
AL RAMZ CORPORATION INVESTMENT & DEVELOPMENT COMPANY PJSC—See Al Ramz Capital LLC; *Int'l*, pg. 282
ALRASHID-ABETONG CO. LTD.—See Heidelberg Materials AG; *Int'l*, pg. 3315
AL RASHID GROUP B.S.C. (C)—See Landmark Retail Holdings 1 Limited; *Int'l*, pg. 4407
AL RAWABI DAIRY COMPANY L.L.C.; *Int'l*, pg. 282
AL RAYAN BANK PLC—See Masraf Al Rayan (Q.S.C.); *Int'l*, pg. 4722
AL RAYAN HOLDING COMPANY K.S.C—See Kuwait Projects Company (Holding) K.S.C.P; *Int'l*, pg. 4346
AL RAYAN INVESTMENT L.L.C.—See Masraf Al Rayan (Q.S.C.); *Int'l*, pg. 4722
ALRESFORD SALADS LTD.—See Bakkavor Group plc; *Int'l*, pg. 805
ALROD ENTERPRISES INC.; *U.S. Private*, pg. 202
ALRO GMBH—See Gesco AG; *Int'l*, pg. 2945

117

ALROD ENTERPRISES INC.
CORPORATE AFFILIATIONS

ALRO METAL SERVICE CENTER, BOCA RATON—See Alro Steel Corporation; *U.S. Private*, pg. 202
ALRO METALS PLUS, CLEARWATER—See Alro Steel Corporation; *U.S. Private*, pg. 202
ALRO METALS PLUS, KALAMAZOO—See Alro Steel Corporation; *U.S. Private*, pg. 202
ALRO METALS SERVICE CENTER, ORLANDO—See Alro Steel Corporation; *U.S. Private*, pg. 202
ALROSA BELGIUM NV—See PJSC Alrosa; *Int'l*, pg. 5878
ALROSA CO. LTD.; *Int'l*, pg. 377
ALROSA HONG KONG LTD.—See PJSC Alrosa; *Int'l*, pg. 5878
ALROSA ISRAEL LTD.—See PJSC Alrosa; *Int'l*, pg. 5878
ALROSA S.A.—See Vimetco N.V.; *Int'l*, pg. 8207
ALROSA USA INC.—See PJSC Alrosa; *Int'l*, pg. 5878
ALRO SPECIALTY METALS, CHARLOTTE—See Alro Steel Corporation; *U.S. Private*, pg. 202
ALRO SPECIALTY METALS, MELROSE PARK—See Alro Steel Corporation; *U.S. Private*, pg. 202
ALRO SPECIALTY METALS, REDFORD—See Alro Steel Corporation; *U.S. Private*, pg. 202
ALROS PRODUCTS LIMITED; *Int'l*, pg. 377
ALRO STEEL CORPORATION - ALRO INDUSTRIAL SUPPLY DIVISION—See Alro Steel Corporation; *U.S. Private*, pg. 202
ALRO STEEL CORPORATION - ALRO PLASTICS DIVISION—See Alro Steel Corporation; *U.S. Private*, pg. 202
ALRO STEEL CORPORATION; *U.S. Private*, pg. 202
ALRO STEEL—See Alro Steel Corporation; *U.S. Private*, pg. 202
ALRQ STEEL—See Alro Steel Corporation; *U.S. Private*, pg. 202
ALROV PROPERTIES & LODGINGS LTD.; *Int'l*, pg. 377
AL-ROWAD NATIONAL PLASTIC CO.LTD—See National Industrialization Company; *Int'l*, pg. 5158
ALR TECHNOLOGIES INC.; *U.S. Public*, pg. 85
AL-RUBAIYAT COMPANY; *Int'l*, pg. 288
AL RUSHAID EASTMAN ARABIA LIMITED—See Compagnie de Saint-Gobain SA; *Int'l*, pg. 1730
AL SABAH TRADING & CONTRACTING INC.—See Ali Zaid Al-Quraishi & Brothers Co.; *Int'l*, pg. 323
ALSACHIM SAS—See Shimadzu Corporation; *Int'l*, pg. 6831
AL-SADEER HOTEL; *Int'l*, pg. 288
ALSAEED TRADING COMPANY LTD.—See Hayel Saeed Anam Group of Companies; *Int'l*, pg. 3290
AL-SAFAT INVESTMENT COMPANY K.S.C.C.; *Int'l*, pg. 288
AL SAFAT REAL ESTATE COMPANY K.P.S.C.; *Int'l*, pg. 282
AL SAFAT UNITED FOOD COMPANY K.S.C.—See Al-Safwa Group Holding Co. K.P.S.C.; *Int'l*, pg. 288
ALSAFE PREMIX CONCRETE PTY LTD—See Seven Group Holdings Limited; *Int'l*, pg. 6732
AL SAFI DANONE CO.—See Al Faisaliah Group; *Int'l*, pg. 277
AL SAFI DANONE CO.—See Danone; *Int'l*, pg. 1965
ALSAFIL SAS—See Nexans S.A.; *Int'l*, pg. 5240
AL-SAFWA GROUP HOLDING CO. K.P.S.C.; *Int'l*, pg. 288
ALSAGGAF TRADING CO.—See SMC Corporation; *Int'l*, pg. 7003
AL SAGR COOPERATIVE INSURANCE COMPANY—See Al-Sagr National Insurance Company; *Int'l*, pg. 288
AL-SAGR NATIONAL INSURANCE COMPANY; *Int'l*, pg. 288
ALSA GRUPO, S.L.U.—See Mobico Group PLC; *Int'l*, pg. 5008
AL SAHWA TRADING CO. LLC—See Al Hassan Engineering Company S.A.O.G.; *Int'l*, pg. 279
ALSAIF STORES FOR DEVELOPMENT & INVESTMENT COMPANY; *Int'l*, pg. 379
AL-SALAMA INSURANCE CO., LTD.; *Int'l*, pg. 288
AL-SALAMA AIRCRAFT COMPANY LTD—See National Industrialization Company; *Int'l*, pg. 5158
AL SALAM ASIA-PACIFIC PTE LTD.—See Al Salam Bank-Bahrain B.S.C.; *Int'l*, pg. 282
AL SALAM BANK-BAHRAIN B.S.C.; *Int'l*, pg. 282
AL SALAM BANK SEYCHELLES LIMITED—See Al Salam Bank-Bahrain B.S.C.; *Int'l*, pg. 282
AL SALAM BANK - SUDAN; *Int'l*, pg. 282
AL SALAM GROUP HOLDING COMPANY KSCC; *Int'l*, pg. 282
AL-SALAM REAL ESTATE INVESTMENT TRUST; *Int'l*, pg. 288
AL-SALBOOKH TRADING COMPANY K.S.C.; *Int'l*, pg. 288
AL-SANABEL INTERNATIONAL FOR ISLAMIC INVESTMENT (HOLDING) PLC; *Int'l*, pg. 288
AL SARH CO. FOR TRAVEL & TOURISM LTD.—See Seera Group Holding Co.; *Int'l*, pg. 6679
ALSATEL—See Eiffage S.A.; *Int'l*, pg. 2329
AL-SAWAM GENERAL CONTRACTING COMPANY LTD.—See Eng. Shabah Al-Shammery & Partners Co.; *Int'l*, pg. 2426
AL-SAWANI GROUP; *Int'l*, pg. 288
ALSAY INCORPORATED—See Venquest Capital Partners LLC; *U.S. Private*, pg. 4356
ALS BURKINA SARL—See ALS Limited; *Int'l*, pg. 377

ALS CANADA LTD—See ALS Limited; *Int'l*, pg. 378
ALS CHEMEX DE MEXICO S.A. DE C.V.—See ALS Limited; *Int'l*, pg. 378
ALS CHEMEX (GUANGZHOU) LTD.—See ALS Limited; *Int'l*, pg. 377
ALS CHEMEX SOUTH AFRICA (PROPRIETARY) LTD—See ALS Limited; *Int'l*, pg. 378
ALS CHITA LABORATORY LLC—See ALS Limited; *Int'l*, pg. 377
A.L. SCHUTZMAN COMPANY INC.; *U.S. Private*, pg. 27
ALS COAL - COLLIE—See ALS Limited; *Int'l*, pg. 378
ALSCO BERUFSKLEIDUNGS-SERVICE GMBH—See Alsco Inc.; *U.S. Private*, pg. 202
ALSCO INC.; *U.S. Private*, pg. 202
ALSCO ITALIA SRL—See Alsco Inc.; *U.S. Private*, pg. 202
AL'S CORNER OIL CO.; *U.S. Private*, pg. 148
ALSCO SERVITEX, INC.—See Alsco Inc.; *U.S. Private*, pg. 202
ALS CZECH REPUBLIC S.R.O.—See ALS Limited; *Int'l*, pg. 378
ALS DENMARK AS—See ALS Limited; *Int'l*, pg. 377
ALS DOMINICAN REPUBLIC SAS—See ALS Limited; *Int'l*, pg. 377
ALSEA, S.A.B. DE C.V.; *Int'l*, pg. 379
ALSEN MARKETING SP. Z O.O.—See AB S.A.; *Int'l*, pg. 41
ALSENTIS LLC—See Methode Electronics, Inc.; *U.S. Public*, pg. 1428
ALS ENVIRONMENTAL—See ALS Limited; *Int'l*, pg. 378
ALS ENVIRONMENTAL—See ALS Limited; *Int'l*, pg. 378
ALSERES PHARMACEUTICALS, INC.; *U.S. Public*, pg. 85
AL SERRA AUTO PLAZA; *U.S. Private*, pg. 147
AL SERRA CHEVROLET; *U.S. Private*, pg. 147
ALS FINLAND OY—See ALS Limited; *Int'l*, pg. 377
ALS FOOD & PHARMACEUTICAL POLSKA SP. Z O.O.—See ALS Limited; *Int'l*, pg. 377
ALSFORD PAGE & GEMS LIMITED—See PSC Insurance Group Limited; *Int'l*, pg. 6015
AL'S GARDEN CENTERS & GREENHOUSES, LLC.; *U.S. Private*, pg. 148
ALS GHANA LIMITED—See ALS Limited; *Int'l*, pg. 377
AL'S GOLDFISH LURE CO.—See Stuart Sports Specialties, Inc.; *U.S. Private*, pg. 3843
ALS GROUP USA, CORP—See ALS Limited; *Int'l*, pg. 378
AL SHAFAR DEVELOPMENT—See Al Shafar Group; *Int'l*, pg. 282
AL SHAFAR GROUP; *Int'l*, pg. 282
AL SHAHEER CORP.; *Int'l*, pg. 282
AL-SHAMEKHA FOR REAL ESTATE & FINANCIAL INVESTMENTS CO., LTD.; *Int'l*, pg. 288
ALSHAMEL INTERNATIONAL HOLDING COMPANY K.S.C.P; *Int'l*, pg. 379
AL SHAMS HOUSING & URBANIZATION; *Int'l*, pg. 282
AL SHANKLE CONSTRUCTION COMPANY; *U.S. Private*, pg. 147
AL SHARIF GROUP & KEC LTD. CO.—See KEC International Limited; *Int'l*, pg. 4113
AL SHARQ INVESTMENTS PROJECTS(HOLDING) P.L.C; *Int'l*, pg. 283
AL SHIPS GMBH—See Commerzbank AG; *Int'l*, pg. 1718
AL-SHOROUK HOSPITAL COMPANY S.A.E—See Cleopatra Hospitals; *Int'l*, pg. 1658
ALSIDE - BOTHELL PLANT—See Hellman & Friedman LLC; *U.S. Private*, pg. 1907
ALSIDE—See Hellman & Friedman LLC; *U.S. Private*, pg. 1907
ALSIM ALARKO SAN. TES. VE TIC. A.S.—See Alarko Holding A.S.; *Int'l*, pg. 291
ALSIM ALARKO S.R.L.—See Alarko Holding A.S.; *Int'l*, pg. 291
ALSINCO SA; *Int'l*, pg. 379
ALS INDUSTRIAL AUSTRALIA PTY. LTD.—See ALS Limited; *Int'l*, pg. 378
ALS INDUSTRIAL HOLDINGS PTY. LTD.—See ALS Limited; *Int'l*, pg. 378
ALS INSPECTION MOZAMBIQUE SERVICE, LDA.—See ALS Limited; *Int'l*, pg. 377
ALS INSPECTION NETHERLANDS BV—See ALS Limited; *Int'l*, pg. 377
ALS INSPECTION SOUTH KOREA LIMITED—See ALS Limited; *Int'l*, pg. 377
ALS INSPECTION UK LIMITED—See ALS Limited; *Int'l*, pg. 377
ALSIP HOTEL INVESTORS INC.; *U.S. Private*, pg. 202
ALS ITALIA S.R.L.—See ALS Limited; *Int'l*, pg. 377
ALS LABORATORIES (UK) LTD.—See ALS Limited; *Int'l*, pg. 377
ALS LABORATORY GROUP NORWAY AS—See ALS Limited; *Int'l*, pg. 377
ALS LABORATORY GROUP (THAILAND) CO. LTD—See ALS Limited; *Int'l*, pg. 378
ALS LEASING, INC.—See Brookdale Senior Living Inc.; *U.S. Public*, pg. 393
ALS LIMITED; *Int'l*, pg. 377
ALS METALLURGY - BURNIE—See ALS Limited; *Int'l*, pg. 378
ALS METALLURGY HOLDINGS PTY. LTD.—See ALS Limited; *Int'l*, pg. 378

ALSO A/S—See Droege Group AG; *Int'l*, pg. 2205
ALSO AS—See Droege Group AG; *Int'l*, pg. 2205
ALSO AUSTRIA GMBH—See Droege Group AG; *Int'l*, pg. 2205
ALSO CLOUD OY—See Droege Group AG; *Int'l*, pg. 2205
ALSO DEUTSCHLAND GMBH—See Droege Group AG; *Int'l*, pg. 2205
ALSO DIGITAL B.V—See Droege Group AG; *Int'l*, pg. 2205
ALSO EESTI OU—See Droege Group AG; *Int'l*, pg. 2205
ALSO ENERGY INC.; *U.S. Private*, pg. 202
ALSO FINLAND OY—See Droege Group AG; *Int'l*, pg. 2205
ALSO FRANCE S.A.S.—See Droege Group AG; *Int'l*, pg. 2205
ALSO HOLDING AG—See Droege Group AG; *Int'l*, pg. 2204
ALSO HUNGARY KFT.—See Droege Group AG; *Int'l*, pg. 2205
ALSOK ASAHI HARIMA CO., LTD.—See Sohgo Security Services Co., Ltd.; *Int'l*, pg. 7059
ALSOK CARE & SUPPORT CO., LTD.—See Sohgo Security Services Co., Ltd.; *Int'l*, pg. 7059
ALSOK INDIA PRIVATE LIMITED—See Sohgo Security Services Co., Ltd.; *Int'l*, pg. 7059
ALSOK MYANMAR SECURITY SERVICES CO., LTD.—See Sohgo Security Services Co., Ltd.; *Int'l*, pg. 7059
ALSOK THAI SECURITY SERVICES CO., LTD.—See Sohgo Security Services Co., Ltd.; *Int'l*, pg. 7059
ALSOK TRADING CO., LTD.—See Sohgo Security Services Co., Ltd.; *Int'l*, pg. 7059
ALSOK VIETNAM SECURITY SERVICES JOINT STOCK COMPANY—See Sohgo Security Services Co., Ltd.; *Int'l*, pg. 7059
ALSO MPS GMBH—See Droege Group AG; *Int'l*, pg. 2205
ALSO NEDERLAND B.V.—See Droege Group AG; *Int'l*, pg. 2205
ALSO NORDIC HOLDING OY—See Droege Group AG; *Int'l*, pg. 2205
ALSONS CONSOLIDATED RESOURCES, INC.—See Alcantara Group; *Int'l*, pg. 300
ALSONS DEVELOPMENT AND INVESTMENT CORPORATION—See Alcantara Group; *Int'l*, pg. 300
ALSON'S SHIPPING LTD.—See Albert Ballin KG; *Int'l*, pg. 294
ALSO POLSKA SP. Z O.O.—See Droege Group AG; *Int'l*, pg. 2205
AL SORAYAI GROUP; *Int'l*, pg. 283
ALSO SCHWEIZ AG—See Droege Group AG; *Int'l*, pg. 2205
ALSO SLOVAKIA S.R.O.—See Droege Group AG; *Int'l*, pg. 2205
ALSO SWEDEN AB—See Droege Group AG; *Int'l*, pg. 2205
ALSO TECHNOLOGY SRL—See Droege Group AG; *Int'l*, pg. 2205
ALS PATAGONIA S.A—See ALS Limited; *Int'l*, pg. 378
ALS PERU S.A.—See ALS Limited; *Int'l*, pg. 378
ALS POLAND SP. Z.O.O—See ALS Limited; *Int'l*, pg. 378
AL'S ROOFING SUPPLY, INC.—See Beacon Roofing Supply, Inc.; *U.S. Public*, pg. 285
ALS SCANDINAVIA AB—See ALS Limited; *Int'l*, pg. 377
ALS SERVICES PLC—See ALS Limited; *Int'l*, pg. 377
ALS SK, S.R.O.—See ALS Limited; *Int'l*, pg. 377
ALS TAIWAN CO. LTD—See ALS Limited; *Int'l*, pg. 378
ALSTA NASSAU BV—See ASSA ABLOY AB; *Int'l*, pg. 634
ALSTAR OILFIELD CONTRACTORS LTD.; *Int'l*, pg. 379
ALST CASINO HOLDCO, LLC—See Boyd Gaming Corporation; *U.S. Public*, pg. 379
ALS TECHNICHEM (HK) PTY LTD—See ALS Limited; *Int'l*, pg. 378
ALS TECHNICHEM (SINGAPORE) PTE LTD—See ALS Limited; *Int'l*, pg. 378
ALS TESTING SERVICES INDIA PRIVATE LIMITED—See ALS Limited; *Int'l*, pg. 377
ALS TESTING SERVICES NZ LIMITED—See ALS Limited; *Int'l*, pg. 377
ALS TESTING SERVICES (THAILAND) CO. LTD—See ALS Limited; *Int'l*, pg. 378
ALSTIN COMMUNICATIONS, INC.; *U.S. Private*, pg. 203
ALSTOM ALGERIE SOCIETE PAR ACTIONS—See Alstom S.A.; *Int'l*, pg. 379
ALSTOM ALGERIE S.P.A.—See Alstom S.A.; *Int'l*, pg. 380
ALSTOM ARGENTINA S.A.—See Alstom S.A.; *Int'l*, pg. 379
ALSTOM ASIA PACIFIC SDN. BHD.—See Alstom S.A.; *Int'l*, pg. 380
ALSTOM AUSTRALIA LTD—See Alstom S.A.; *Int'l*, pg. 380
ALSTOM AUSTRIA GMBH—See Alstom S.A.; *Int'l*, pg. 380
ALSTOM BALTICS SIA—See Alstom S.A.; *Int'l*, pg. 379
ALSTOM BELGIUM SA—See Alstom S.A.; *Int'l*, pg. 380
ALSTOM BRASIL LTDA.—See Alstom S.A.; *Int'l*, pg. 380
ALSTOM CARBON CAPTURE GMBH—See Alstom S.A.; *Int'l*, pg. 380
ALSTOM CHILE S.A—See Alstom S.A.; *Int'l*, pg. 380
ALSTOM (CHINA) INVESTMENT CO. LTD—See Alstom S.A.; *Int'l*, pg. 380

COMPANY NAME INDEX

ALSTOM CZECH REPUBLIC A.S.—See Alstom S.A.; *Int'l*, pg. 379
ALSTOM DANMARK A/S—See Alstom S.A.; *Int'l*, pg. 380
ALSTOM DEUTSCHLAND AG—See Alstom S.A.; *Int'l*, pg. 380
ALSTOM ESPANA IB—See Alstom S.A.; *Int'l*, pg. 380
ALSTOM FERROVIARIA PORTUGAL, S.A.—See Alstom S.A.; *Int'l*, pg. 379
ALSTOM FERROVIARIA S.P.A. - BOLOGNA—See Alstom S.A.; *Int'l*, pg. 381
ALSTOM FERROVIARIA S.P.A. - MODUGNO—See Alstom S.A.; *Int'l*, pg. 381
ALSTOM FERROVIARIA S.P.A.—See Alstom S.A.; *Int'l*, pg. 381
ALSTOM FINLAND OY—See Alstom S.A.; *Int'l*, pg. 380
ALSTOM FLERTEX S.A.S.—See Alstom S.A.; *Int'l*, pg. 379
ALSTOM GULF AREA—See Alstom S.A.; *Int'l*, pg. 380
ALSTOM HOLDINGS—See Alstom S.A.; *Int'l*, pg. 380
ALSTOM HONG KONG LTD.—See Alstom S.A.; *Int'l*, pg. 380
ALSTOM HUNGARY KFT.—See Alstom S.A.; *Int'l*, pg. 379
ALSTOM HYDRO—See Alstom S.A.; *Int'l*, pg. 380
ALSTOM INVESTMENT COMPANY LIMITED—See Alstom S.A.; *Int'l*, pg. 379
ALSTOM ISRAEL LTD.—See Alstom S.A.; *Int'l*, pg. 379
ALSTOM KAZAKHSTAN LLP—See Alstom S.A.; *Int'l*, pg. 379
ALSTOM KHADAMAT S.A.—See Alstom S.A.; *Int'l*, pg. 379
ALSTOM K.K.—See Alstom S.A.; *Int'l*, pg. 380
ALSTOM KONSTAL S.A.—See Alstom S.A.; *Int'l*, pg. 380
ALSTOM KOREA TRANSPORT LTD.—See Alstom S.A.; *Int'l*, pg. 379
ALSTOM LLC—See Alstom S.A.; *Int'l*, pg. 380
ALSTOM LOKOMOTIVEN SERVICE GMBH—See Alstom S.A.; *Int'l*, pg. 381
ALSTOM LTD.—See Alstom S.A.; *Int'l*, pg. 380
ALSTOM MEXICO SA DE CV—See Alstom S.A.; *Int'l*, pg. 381
ALSTOM NEDERLAND BV—See Alstom S.A.; *Int'l*, pg. 381
ALSTOM NETHERLANDS B.V.—See Alstom S.A.; *Int'l*, pg. 379
ALSTOM NEW ZEALAND LTD—See Alstom S.A.; *Int'l*, pg. 381
ALSTOM NORWAY AS—See Alstom S.A.; *Int'l*, pg. 381
ALSTOM N.V.—See Alstom S.A.; *Int'l*, pg. 381
ALSTOM PANAMA, S.A.—See Alstom S.A.; *Int'l*, pg. 379
ALSTOM POLSKA SPOLKA AKCYJNA—See Alstom S.A.; *Int'l*, pg. 379
ALSTOM POWER TURBOMACHINES SA—See General Electric Company; *U.S. Public*, pg. 917
ALSTOM PROJECTS INDIA LTD—See General Electric Company; *U.S. Public*, pg. 917
ALSTOM PROYECTOS DE TRANSPORTE, SRL—See Alstom S.A.; *Int'l*, pg. 379
ALSTOM RENEWABLE POWER CANADA INC.—See Alstom S.A.; *Int'l*, pg. 381
ALSTOM S.A.; *Int'l*, pg. 379
ALSTOM SCHIENENFAHRZEUGE AG—See Alstom S.A.; *Int'l*, pg. 379
ALSTOM S&E AFRICA (PTY) LTD—See Alstom S.A.; *Int'l*, pg. 381
ALSTOM SERVICES ITALIA S.P.A.—See Alstom S.A.; *Int'l*, pg. 379
ALSTOM SERVICES SDN. BHD.—See Alstom S.A.; *Int'l*, pg. 380
ALSTOM (SHARED SERVICES) PHILIPPINES, INC.—See Alstom S.A.; *Int'l*, pg. 380
ALSTOM SIGNALING INC.—See Alstom S.A.; *Int'l*, pg. 381
ALSTOM SIGNALING OPERATION, LLC—See Alstom S.A.; *Int'l*, pg. 381
ALSTOM SIGNALLING, LIMITED LIABILITY COMPANY—See Alstom S.A.; *Int'l*, pg. 379
ALSTOM SLOVAKIA, S.R.O.—See Alstom S.A.; *Int'l*, pg. 381
ALSTOM S.P.A.—See Alstom S.A.; *Int'l*, pg. 381
ALSTOM S.R.O.—See Alstom S.A.; *Int'l*, pg. 381
ALSTOM SWITZERLAND LTD—See Alstom S.A.; *Int'l*, pg. 381
ALSTOM TAIWAN LTD—See Alstom S.A.; *Int'l*, pg. 381
ALSTOM TRANSPORT AB—See Alstom S.A.; *Int'l*, pg. 381
ALSTOM TRANSPORTATION COLOMBIA S.A.S.—See Alstom S.A.; *Int'l*, pg. 380
ALSTOM TRANSPORTATION GERMANY GMBH—See Alstom S.A.; *Int'l*, pg. 380
ALSTOM TRANSPORTATION INC—See Alstom S.A.; *Int'l*, pg. 381
ALSTOM TRANSPORTATION INC—See Alstom S.A.; *Int'l*, pg. 381
ALSTOM TRANSPORT AUSTRALIA PTY LIMITED—See Alstom S.A.; *Int'l*, pg. 381
ALSTOM TRANSPORT AUSTRIA GMBH—See Alstom S.A.; *Int'l*, pg. 379
ALSTOM TRANSPORT AZERBAIJAN LLC—See Alstom S.A.; *Int'l*, pg. 380
ALSTOM TRANSPORT BELGIUM—See Alstom S.A.; *Int'l*, pg. 380

ALSTOM TRANSPORT B.V.—See Alstom S.A.; *Int'l*, pg. 381
ALSTOM TRANSPORT BV—See Alstom S.A.; *Int'l*, pg. 381
ALSTOM TRANSPORT CANADA INC.—See Alstom S.A.; *Int'l*, pg. 380
ALSTOM TRANSPORT DEUTSCHLAND GMBH—See Alstom S.A.; *Int'l*, pg. 380
ALSTOM TRANSPORTE SA DE CV—See Alstom S.A.; *Int'l*, pg. 381
ALSTOM TRANSPORTE SA—See Alstom S.A.; *Int'l*, pg. 380
ALSTOM TRANSPORT HUNGARY ZRT.—See Alstom S.A.; *Int'l*, pg. 380
ALSTOM TRANSPORT INDIA LIMITED—See Alstom S.A.; *Int'l*, pg. 380
ALSTOM TRANSPORT NEW ZEALAND LTD—See Alstom S.A.; *Int'l*, pg. 381
ALSTOM TRANSPORT NORWAY AS—See Alstom S.A.; *Int'l*, pg. 380
ALSTOM TRANSPORT REGIONAL TRAINS—See Alstom S.A.; *Int'l*, pg. 380
ALSTOM TRANSPORT SYSTEMS (MALAYSIA) SDN. BHD.—See Alstom S.A.; *Int'l*, pg. 380
ALSTOM TRANSPORT (THAILAND) CO., LTD.—See Alstom S.A.; *Int'l*, pg. 379
ALSTOM TRANSPORT VIETNAM LTD.—See Alstom S.A.; *Int'l*, pg. 380
ALSTOM UBUNYE (PTY) LTD.—See Alstom S.A.; *Int'l*, pg. 381
ALSTOM ULASIM ANONIM SIRKETI ANKARA SUBESI—See Alstom S.A.; *Int'l*, pg. 380
ALSTOM VANNKRAFT AS—See Alstom S.A.; *Int'l*, pg. 381
ALSTOM VIETNAM LTD.—See Alstom S.A.; *Int'l*, pg. 381
ALSTON & BIRD LLP; *U.S. Private*, pg. 203
ALSTON CAPITAL PARTNERS LLC; *U.S. Private*, pg. 203
ALSTONE TEXTILES (INDIA) LTD.; *Int'l*, pg. 383
ALSTONS BUILDING ENTERPRISES LIMITED—See ANSA McAL Limited; *Int'l*, pg. 477
ALSTONS LIMITED—See ANSA McAL Limited; *Int'l*, pg. 477
ALSTONS MARKETING COMPANY LIMITED—See ANSA McAL Limited; *Int'l*, pg. 477
ALSTONS SHIPPING LIMITED—See ANSA McAL Limited; *Int'l*, pg. 477
ALSTONS TRAVEL LIMITED—See ANSA McAL Limited; *Int'l*, pg. 477
ALSTRIA OFFICE REIT-AG; *Int'l*, pg. 383
ALSTYLE INTERNATIONAL SDN. BHD.—See Ossia International Limited; *Int'l*, pg. 5652
ALSUM FARMS & PRODUCT, INC.; *U.S. Private*, pg. 203
ALS USA, INC—See ALS Limited; *Int'l*, pg. 378
AL SUWADI POWER COMPANY SAOG; *Int'l*, pg. 283
ALSUWAIKET AGRICULTURE DIVISION—See AlSuwaiket Trading & Contracting Co.; *Int'l*, pg. 383
ALSUWAIKET EDUCATION DIVISION—See AlSuwaiket Trading & Contracting Co.; *Int'l*, pg. 383
ALSUWAIKET FURNITURE & HOME FURNISHING DIVISION—See AlSuwaiket Trading & Contracting Co.; *Int'l*, pg. 383
ALSUWAIKET TRADING & CONTRACTING CO. - CONSTRUCTION DIVISION—See AlSuwaiket Trading & Contracting Co.; *Int'l*, pg. 383
ALSUWAIKET TRADING & CONTRACTING CO.; *Int'l*, pg. 383
ALSUWAIKET TRADING & CONTRACTING CO. - TRADING DIVISION—See AlSuwaiket Trading & Contracting Co.; *Int'l*, pg. 383
ALSUWAIKET TRAVEL & TOURISM DIVISION—See AlSuwaiket Trading & Contracting Co.; *Int'l*, pg. 383
AL SWIDERSKI IMPLEMENT INC.; *U.S. Private*, pg. 147
AL.SYSTEMS GMBH—See Commerzbank AG; *Int'l*, pg. 1718
ALT5 SIGMA CORPORATION; *U.S. Public*, pg. 85
ALT 5 SIGMA INC.—See ALT5 Sigma Corporation; *U.S. Public*, pg. 85
ALTA AGRICORP—See Koepon Holdings B.V.; *Int'l*, pg. 4227
AL-TA'ALUF GENERAL TRANSPORTATION CO. LTD.—See Eng. Shabah Al-Shammery & Partners Co.; *Int'l*, pg. 2426
ALTA ASSOCIATES, INC.—See Diversified Search, LLC; *U.S. Private*, pg. 1243
ALTABA INC.; *U.S. Public*, pg. 86
ALTABANCORP—See Glacier Bancorp, Inc.; *U.S. Public*, pg. 938
ALTA BANKA A.D.; *Int'l*, pg. 383
ALTABANK—See Glacier Bancorp, Inc.; *U.S. Public*, pg. 938
ALTA BATES SUMMIT MEDICAL CENTER—See Sutter Health; *U.S. Private*, pg. 3887
ALTABOX S.A.—See Econocom Group SA; *Int'l*, pg. 2297
ALTA CAPITAL MANAGEMENT, LLC—See Guardian Capital Group Limited; *Int'l*, pg. 3169
ALTA COMMUNICATIONS, INC.; *U.S. Private*, pg. 203
ALTA COMPANY; *Int'l*, pg. 384
ALTA CRP AUBERGENVILLE SNC—See Altarea SCA; *Int'l*, pg. 385

ALTA-DENA CERTIFIED DAIRY, LLC—See Dean Foods Company; *U.S. Private*, pg. 1183
ALTA DEUTSCHLAND GMBH—See Koepon Holdings B.V.; *Int'l*, pg. 4227
ALTADIS DISTRIBUTION FRANCE S.A.S.—See Imperial Brands PLC; *Int'l*, pg. 3632
ALTADIS MIDDLE EAST FZCO.—See Imperial Brands PLC; *Int'l*, pg. 3632
ALTADIS S.A.—See Imperial Brands PLC; *Int'l*, pg. 3634
ALTADIS, S.A.U.—See Imperial Brands PLC; *Int'l*, pg. 3632
ALTADIS U.S.A. INC.—See Imperial Brands PLC; *Int'l*, pg. 3633
A.L.T. ADVERTISING & PROMOTION; *U.S. Private*, pg. 27
ALTADYN CORP.; *U.S. Private*, pg. 204
ALTADYN SA—See Altadyn Corp.; *U.S. Private*, pg. 204
ALTA EAST, INC.; *U.S. Private*, pg. 203
ALTA ENVIRONMENTAL CORPORATION; *U.S. Private*, pg. 203
ALTA EQUIPMENT GROUP INC.; *U.S. Public*, pg. 85
ALTA EQUIPMENT HOLDINGS, INC.—See Alta Equipment Group Inc.; *U.S. Public*, pg. 86
ALTA-FAB STRUCTURES LTD.; *Int'l*, pg. 384
ALTA FINANCIAL SERVICES, INC.—See Hanna Holdings, Inc.; *U.S. Private*, pg. 1854
ALTAFLEX—See OSI Systems, Inc.; *U.S. Public*, pg. 1621
ALTA FLIGHTS (CHARTERS) INC.; *Int'l*, pg. 384
ALTA FOREST PRODUCT, LLC—See ITOCHU Corporation; *Int'l*, pg. 3838
ALTAFRESH LLC; *U.S. Private*, pg. 204
ALTA FUELS, LLC—See World Kinect Corporation; *U.S. Public*, pg. 2380
ALTAGAS LTD.; *Int'l*, pg. 384
ALTAGAS OPERATING PARTNERSHIP—See AltaGas Ltd.; *Int'l*, pg. 384
ALTAGAS UTILITIES, INC.—See AltaGas Ltd.; *Int'l*, pg. 384
ALTAGAS UTILITY GROUP INC.—See AltaGas Ltd.; *Int'l*, pg. 384
ALTA GENETICS AUSTRALIA PTY. LTD.—See Koepon Holdings B.V.; *Int'l*, pg. 4227
ALTA GENETICS DO BRASIL LTDA.—See Koepon Holdings B.V.; *Int'l*, pg. 4227
ALTA GENETICS, INC.—See Koepon Holdings B.V.; *Int'l*, pg. 4227
ALTA GENETICS RUSSIA—See Koepon Holdings B.V.; *Int'l*, pg. 4227
ALTAGHENY INC.; *U.S. Private*, pg. 204
THE ALTA GROUP, LLC - ASSET MANAGEMENT PRACTICE—See The Alta Group, LLC; *U.S. Private*, pg. 3985
THE ALTA GROUP, LLC; *U.S. Private*, pg. 3984
ALTAI COMMUNICATIONS—See WPP plc; *Int'l*, pg. 8478
AL TAIF INVESTMENT COMPANY LLC—See Dubai Investments PJSC; *Int'l*, pg. 2219
AL TAIF TECHNICAL SERVICES PJSC—See Mubadala Investment Company PJSC; *Int'l*, pg. 5075
ALTAI-KOKS—See Novolipetski Metallurgicheski Komb OAO; *Int'l*, pg. 5466
ALTA INTERCONNECTION MANAGEMENT, LLC—See NRG Energy, Inc.; *U.S. Public*, pg. 1549
ALTAIR CHIMICA SPA—See Esseco Group SRL; *Int'l*, pg. 2509
ALTAIR CONTRACTING—See Irex Corporation; *U.S. Private*, pg. 2137
ALTAIR CORPORATION; *U.S. Public*, pg. 86
ALTAIR DISPOSAL SERVICES, LLC—See Clean Harbors, Inc.; *U.S. Public*, pg. 509
ALTAIR ENGINEERING AB—See Altair Engineering, Inc.; *U.S. Public*, pg. 86
ALTAIR ENGINEERING CANADA, LTD.—See Altair Engineering, Inc.; *U.S. Public*, pg. 86
ALTAIR ENGINEERING FRANCE, SARL—See Altair Engineering, Inc.; *U.S. Public*, pg. 86
ALTAIR ENGINEERING FRANCE S.A.S.—See Altair Engineering, Inc.; *U.S. Public*, pg. 86
ALTAIR ENGINEERING GMBH—See Altair Engineering, Inc.; *U.S. Public*, pg. 86
ALTAIR ENGINEERING, INC.; *U.S. Public*, pg. 86
ALTAIR ENGINEERING INDIA PVT. LTD.—See Altair Engineering, Inc.; *U.S. Public*, pg. 86
ALTAIR ENGINEERING ISRAEL LTD.—See Altair Engineering, Inc.; *U.S. Public*, pg. 86
ALTAIR ENGINEERING (PTY.) LTD.—See Altair Engineering, Inc.; *U.S. Public*, pg. 86
ALTAIR ENGINEERING SDN. BHD.—See Altair Engineering, Inc.; *U.S. Public*, pg. 86
ALTAIR ENGINEERING (SINGAPORE) PTE. LTD.—See Altair Engineering, Inc.; *U.S. Public*, pg. 86
ALTAI RESOURCES INC.; *Int'l*, pg. 384
ALTAIR EYEWEAR—See Vision Service Plan; *U.S. Private*, pg. 4391
ALTAIR GLOBAL RELOCATION; *U.S. Private*, pg. 204
ALTAIR INTERNATIONAL CORP.; *U.S. Public*, pg. 86
ALTAIRNANO, INC.—See Altair Nanotechnologies Inc.; *U.S. Private*, pg. 204
ALTAIR NANOTECHNOLOGIES INC.; *U.S. Private*, pg. 204

ALTAIR RESOURCES INC.

ALTAIR RESOURCES INC.; *Int'l*, pg. 384
ALTAIR SEMICONDUCTOR LTD.—See Sony Group Corporation; *Int'l*, pg. 7102
ALTAIR SOFTWARE AND SERVICES S.L.—See Altair Engineering, Inc.; *U.S. Public*, pg. 86
ALTAIR SOLAR, LLC—See EnBio Holdings Inc.; *Int'l*, pg. 2396
ALTAIR-STRICKLAND INCORPORATED; *U.S. Private*, pg. 204
ALTAIR US HOLDINGS, INC.—See Altair Nanotechnologies Inc.; *U.S. Private*, pg. 204
ALTAIR WATER & DRILLING SERVICES INC.—See Callidus Capital Corporation; *Int'l*, pg. 1265
ALTAI TECHNOLOGIES LIMITED—See Wongs International (Holdings) Ltd; *Int'l*, pg. 8447
ALTA IT SERVICES LLC—See System One Holdings, LLC; *U.S. Private*, pg. 3906
AL TAJAMOUAT FOR CATERING & HOUSING COMPANY, PLC.; *Int'l*, pg. 283
AL TAJAMOUAT FOR TOURISTIC PROJECTS CO. PLC; *Int'l*, pg. 283
AL TAJAMOUAT INVESTMENT COMPANY—See Specialized Investment Compounds Company, Plc.; *Int'l*, pg. 7129
ALTAK INC.; *U.S. Private*, pg. 204
ALTALEY MINING CORPORATION; *Int'l*, pg. 384
ALTA LIFT TRUCK SERVICES, INC.—See Alta Equipment Group Inc.; *U.S. Public*, pg. 86
ALTALINK INVESTMENTS, L.P.—See Berkshire Hathaway Inc.; *U.S. Public*, pg. 299
ALTALINK L.P.—See Berkshire Hathaway Inc.; *U.S. Public*, pg. 300
ALTA LOGISTICS, INC.—See Saltchuk Resources Inc.; *U.S. Private*, pg. 3534
ALTA LOMA PRODUCTIONS, INC.—See PLBY Group, Inc.; *U.S. Public*, pg. 1698
ALTAMA FOOTWEAR—See Brand Velocity Partners; *U.S. Private*, pg. 637
ALTAMAHA ELECTRIC MEMBERSHIP CORPORATION; *U.S. Private*, pg. 204
AL-TAMDEEN INVESTMENT COMPANY K.S.C.C.—See Tamdeen Real Estate Company K.S.C.C.; *Int'l*, pg. 7450
ALTAMED HEALTH SERVICES CORPORATION; *U.S. Private*, pg. 204
ALTA MESA HOLDINGS, L.P.—See Alta Mesa Resources, Inc.; *U.S. Private*, pg. 203
ALTA MESA RESOURCES, INC.; *U.S. Private*, pg. 203
ALTAMIN LIMITED; *Int'l*, pg. 384
ALTAMIRA GOLD CORP.; *Int'l*, pg. 385
ALTAMIRA INFORMATION SL—See Collecte Localisation Satellites; *Int'l*, pg. 1699
ALTAMIRA INSTRUMENTS, INC.—See SCIENTIFIC INDUSTRIES, INC.; *U.S. Public*, pg. 1849
ALTAMIRA TECHNOLOGIES CORPORATION; *U.S. Private*, pg. 204
ALTAMIRA THERAPEUTICS LTD.; *Int'l*, pg. 385
ALTAMIR S.C.A.; *Int'l*, pg. 385
ALTAMONT CAPITAL MANAGEMENT, LLC; *U.S. Private*, pg. 204
ALTAMONT CAPITAL PARTNERS; *U.S. Private*, pg. 204
THE ALTAMONTE SPRINGS FL ENDOSCOPY ASC, LLC—See KKR & Co. Inc.; *U.S. Public*, pg. 1247
ALTAMONT HOTEL ASSOCIATES LP—See Edison International; *U.S. Public*, pg. 719
ALTAMONT PHARMA ACQUISITION CORP.; *U.S. Private*, pg. 205
ALTANA AG—See SKion GmbH; *Int'l*, pg. 6986
ALTANA CHEMIE AG—See SKion GmbH; *Int'l*, pg. 6986
ALTA NEWSPAPER GROUP LIMITED PARTNERSHIP—See GVIC Communications Corp.; *Int'l*, pg. 3189
AL TANMYAH SERVICES L.L.C.—See Dubai Islamic Bank PSJ; *Int'l*, pg. 2219
ALTAN NEVADA MINERALS LIMITED; *Int'l*, pg. 385
ALTAN RIO MINERALS LIMITED; *Int'l*, pg. 385
ALTAPACIFIC BANCORP—See Banner Corporation; *U.S. Public*, pg. 275
ALTAPEX CORPORATION; *Int'l*, pg. 385
ALTA POLSKA SP. Z O.O.—See Koepon Holdings B.V.; *Int'l*, pg. 4227
ALTA PRODUCTIONS GROUP, INC.—See GMA Holdings, Inc.; *Int'l*, pg. 3012
ALTAREA COGEDIM CITALIS—See Altarea SCA; *Int'l*, pg. 385
ALTAREA ESPANA SL—See Altarea SCA; *Int'l*, pg. 385
ALTAREA FRANCE SAS—See Altarea SCA; *Int'l*, pg. 385
ALTAREA ITALIA S.R.L.—See Altarea SCA; *Int'l*, pg. 385
ALTAREA SCA; *Int'l*, pg. 385
ALTAREIT SCA—See Altarea SCA; *Int'l*, pg. 385
ALTA RESOURCES CORPORATION; *U.S. Private*, pg. 203
ALTA RESOURCES - PHILIPPINES—See Alta Resources Corporation; *U.S. Private*, pg. 203
ALTARIS CAPITAL PARTNERS, LLC; *U.S. Private*, pg. 205
ALTAROCK ENERGY INC.; *U.S. Private*, pg. 206
ALTA S.A.; *Int'l*, pg. 384

ALTASCIENCES CLINICAL LOS ANGELES, INC.—See Altasciences Company Inc.; *Int'l*, pg. 387
ALTASCIENCES COMPANY INC.; *Int'l*, pg. 387
AL TAS-HEELAT COMPANY—See Invest Bank; *Int'l*, pg. 3775
ALTA SKUPINA D.D.; *Int'l*, pg. 384
ALTAS PARTNERS LP; *Int'l*, pg. 386
ALTASTEEL, INC.—See Kyoei Steel Ltd.; *Int'l*, pg. 4362
ALTA TELECOM INTERNATIONAL LTD.—See TELUS CORPORATION; *Int'l*, pg. 7546
ALTATERRA KFT.—See VKR Holding A/S; *Int'l*, pg. 8281
ALTATERRA POLSKA SP. Z O.O.—See VKR Holding A/S; *Int'l*, pg. 8281
ALTA TRANSPORTATION, LLC—See World Kinect Corporation; *U.S. Public*, pg. 2380
AL TATWEER CONTRACTING L.L.C—See Belhasa Group of Companies; *Int'l*, pg. 963
ALTA UK LTD.—See Koepon Holdings B.V.; *Int'l*, pg. 4227
ALTAVIA ADVERTISING CO., LTD.—See Altavia S.A.; *Int'l*, pg. 387
ALTAVIA BELGIUM SA—See Altavia S.A.; *Int'l*, pg. 387
ALTAVIA CESKA SRO—See Altavia S.A.; *Int'l*, pg. 387
ALTA VIA CONSULTING, LLC—See Bluestone Investment Partners, LLC; *U.S. Private*, pg. 598
ALTAVIA DEUTSCHLAND GMBH—See Altavia S.A.; *Int'l*, pg. 387
ALTAVIA HELLAS AE—See Altavia S.A.; *Int'l*, pg. 387
ALTAVIA HTT LTD—See Altavia S.A.; *Int'l*, pg. 387
ALTAVIA HUNGARIA KFT—See Altavia S.A.; *Int'l*, pg. 387
ALTAVIA IBERICA CFA—See Altavia S.A.; *Int'l*, pg. 387
ALTAVIA ILETISIM AS—See Altavia S.A.; *Int'l*, pg. 387
ALTAVIA ITALIA SRL—See Altavia S.A.; *Int'l*, pg. 387
ALTAVIA LILLE SAS—See Altavia S.A.; *Int'l*, pg. 387
ALTAVIA OPTITRANS S.A.S.—See Altavia S.A.; *Int'l*, pg. 387
ALTAVIA POLSKA SP. Z.O.O.—See Altavia S.A.; *Int'l*, pg. 388
ALTAVIA ROMANIA COMMUNICATION SRL—See Altavia S.A.; *Int'l*, pg. 388
ALTAVIA RUS, OOO—See Altavia S.A.; *Int'l*, pg. 388
ALTAVIA S.A.; *Int'l*, pg. 387
ALTAVIA SWISS SA—See Altavia S.A.; *Int'l*, pg. 388
ALTAVIEW CONCRETE, LLC—See Summit Materials, Inc.; *U.S. Public*, pg. 1960
ALTA VISTA HEALTHCARE—See Apollo Global Management, Inc.; *U.S. Public*, pg. 156
ALTAVISTA MEMORIAL PARK LLC—See Axar Capital Management L.P.; *U.S. Private*, pg. 411
ALTA VISTA SOLUTIONS—See GI Manager L.P.; *U.S. Private*, pg. 1691
ALTA VISTA TECHNOLOGY LLC; *U.S. Private*, pg. 203
ALTAWEST GROUP; *Int'l*, pg. 388
AL TAWFIQ CO FOR PLASTIC & WOVEN SACKS INDUSTRIES LTD.—See Hayel Saeed Anam Group of Companies; *Int'l*, pg. 3290
AL TAWFIQ PLASTIC CO. FOR PLASTIC & WOVEN SACKS INDUSTRIES LTD.—See Zamil Group Holding Company; *Int'l*, pg. 8623
AL TAYER GROUP LLC; *Int'l*, pg. 283
AL TAYER STOCKS LLC—See Al Tayer Group LLC; *Int'l*, pg. 283
AL TAYER STOCKS LLC—See Stefanutti Stocks Holdings Limited; *Int'l*, pg. 7192
AL TAYYAR HOLIDAY TRAVEL GROUP—See Seera Group Holding Co.; *Int'l*, pg. 6679
AL-TAYYAR TRAVEL & TOURISM—See Seera Group Holding Co.; *Int'l*, pg. 6679
ALTC ACQUISITION CORP.; *U.S. Public*, pg. 87
ALT CO., LTD.; *Int'l*, pg. 383
ALTEA GREEN POWER S.P.A.; *Int'l*, pg. 388
ALTEAU S.A.—See Caisse des Depots et Consignations; *Int'l*, pg. 1257
ALTEC ENVIRONMENTAL CONSULTING, LLC—See Martin Resource Management Corporation; *U.S. Private*, pg. 2595
ALTECH ASIA PACIFIC VIETNAM CO., LTD.—See Altech Co., Ltd.; *Int'l*, pg. 388
ALTECH BATTERIES LIMITED; *Int'l*, pg. 388
ALTECH CO., LTD.; *Int'l*, pg. 388
ALTECH CORPORATION; *Int'l*, pg. 388
ALTECH ENGINEERING CO., LTD.—See Altech Co., Ltd.; *Int'l*, pg. 388
ALTECH IT INC.—See Altech Co., Ltd.; *Int'l*, pg. 388
ALTECHNA UAB; *Int'l*, pg. 389
ALTECH NEW MATERIAL CO., LTD.—See Altech Co., Ltd.; *Int'l*, pg. 388
ALTECH NEW MATERIALS (FUKUI) CO., LTD.—See Altech Co., Ltd.; *Int'l*, pg. 388
ALTECH NEW MATERIALS (SUZHOU) CO., LTD.—See Altech Co., Ltd.; *Int'l*, pg. 388
ALTECH HOLDINGS S.A.; *Int'l*, pg. 388
ALTECH SHANGHAI CO., LTD.—See Altech Co., Ltd.; *Int'l*, pg. 388
ALTECH SHINE CO., LTD.—See Altech Corporation; *Int'l*, pg. 389
ALTEC INDUSTRIES INC.; *U.S. Private*, pg. 206
ALTEC INDUSTRIES INC.—See Altec Industries Inc.; *U.S. Private*, pg. 206

CORPORATE AFFILIATIONS

ALTEC LANSING LLC—See Prophet Equity L.P.; *U.S. Private*, pg. 3286
ALTECNIC LTD.—See Caleffi S.p.A.; *Int'l*, pg. 1263
ALTECO MEDICAL AB; *Int'l*, pg. 389
ALTECO TECHNIK GMBH—See RPM International Inc.; *U.S. Public*, pg. 1819
ALTEC PRODUCTS INC.—See Beyond Limits, Inc.; *U.S. Private*, pg. 548
ALTEC UMWELTTECHNIK GMBH—See ALPINE Bau GmbH; *Int'l*, pg. 371
ALTEDIA SAS—See Adecco Group AG; *Int'l*, pg. 141
ALTE-GO KFT.—See MOL Magyar Olaj- es Gazipari Nyrt.; *Int'l*, pg. 5019
ALTEGRIS ADVISORS, LLC—See Aquiline Capital Partners LLC; *U.S. Private*, pg. 303
ALTEGRIS ADVISORS, LLC—See Genstar Capital, LLC; *U.S. Private*, pg. 1675
ALTEGRIS INVESTMENTS, INC.—See Aquiline Capital Partners LLC; *U.S. Private*, pg. 303
ALTEGRIS INVESTMENTS, INC.—See Genstar Capital, LLC; *U.S. Private*, pg. 1675
ALTEGRIS PORTFOLIO MANAGEMENT, INC.—See Aquiline Capital Partners LLC; *U.S. Private*, pg. 303
ALTEGRIS PORTFOLIO MANAGEMENT, INC.—See Genstar Capital, LLC; *U.S. Private*, pg. 1675
ALTEGRITY RISK INTERNATIONAL, INC.—See Corporate Risk Holdings LLC; *U.S. Private*, pg. 1056
ALTEHA ESV—See Sonic Healthcare Limited; *Int'l*, pg. 7096
ALTEK ALARKO ELEKTRIK SANT. TES. ISL. VE TIC. A.S.—See Alarko Holding A.S.; *Int'l*, pg. 291
ALTEK CORPORATION; *Int'l*, pg. 389
ALTEK ELECTRONICS INC.—See Cyient Limited; *Int'l*, pg. 1896
ALTEK LAB INC.—See Altek Corporation; *Int'l*, pg. 389
ALTE LEIPZIGER AUTOVERSICHERUNG—See Alte Leipziger Versicherung AG; *Int'l*, pg. 388
ALTE LEIPZIGER VERSICHERUNG AG; *Int'l*, pg. 388
ALTEN AUSTRIA SUD GMBH—See Alten S.A.; *Int'l*, pg. 389
ALTEN BELGIUM SPRL—See Alten S.A.; *Int'l*, pg. 389
ALTEN CALSOFT LABS, INC.—See Alten S.A.; *Int'l*, pg. 389
ALTEN CALSOFT LABS INDIA PRIVATE LTD.—See Alten S.A.; *Int'l*, pg. 389
ALTEN CANADA INC.—See Alten S.A.; *Int'l*, pg. 389
ALTEN CHINA LTD.—See Alten S.A.; *Int'l*, pg. 389
ALTEN DELIVERY CENTER IASI SRL—See Alten S.A.; *Int'l*, pg. 389
ALTENERGY ACQUISITION CORP.; *U.S. Public*, pg. 87
ALTEN GMBH—See Alten S.A.; *Int'l*, pg. 389
ALTEN ITALIA—See Alten S.A.; *Int'l*, pg. 390
ALTEN ITALIA SPA—See Alten S.A.; *Int'l*, pg. 389
ALTEN LTD—See Alten S.A.; *Int'l*, pg. 389
ALTEN LUXEMBOURG SARL—See Alten S.A.; *Int'l*, pg. 389
ALTEN NEDERLAND BV—See Alten S.A.; *Int'l*, pg. 389
ALTEN PCS—See Alten S.A.; *Int'l*, pg. 390
ALTEN-PFLEGEHEIM VEITSBRONN GMBH—See Clariane SE; *Int'l*, pg. 1642
ALTEN POLSKA SP. Z O.O.—See Alten S.A.; *Int'l*, pg. 389
ALTENRHEIN AVIATION LTD.—See Pilatus Aircraft Ltd.; *Int'l*, pg. 5866
ALTEN S.A.; *Int'l*, pg. 389
ALTEN SIR AND TELECOM—See Alten S.A.; *Int'l*, pg. 389
ALTEN SI-TECHNO ROMANIA SRL—See Alten S.A.; *Int'l*, pg. 389
ALTEN SPAIN SA—See Alten S.A.; *Int'l*, pg. 389
ALTEN SUD OUEST SAS—See Alten S.A.; *Int'l*, pg. 390
ALTEN SWEDEN AB—See Alten S.A.; *Int'l*, pg. 389
ALTEN SWITZERLAND SARL AG—See Alten S.A.; *Int'l*, pg. 389
ALTEN TECHNOLOGY GMBH—See Alten S.A.; *Int'l*, pg. 389
ALTEN-UND PFLEGEHEIM SIEGLAR GMBH—See Clariane SE; *Int'l*, pg. 1643
ALTEO ENERGIASZOLGALTATO NYRT—See MOL Magyar Olaj- es Gazipari Nyrt.; *Int'l*, pg. 5019
ALTEOGEN INC.; *Int'l*, pg. 391
ALTEO HOLDING SAS—See H.I.G. Capital, LLC; *U.S. Private*, pg. 1828
ALTEO LIMITED; *Int'l*, pg. 391
ALTEO-THERM KFT.—See MOL Magyar Olaj- es Gazipari Nyrt.; *Int'l*, pg. 5019
ALTE OY—See Alten S.A.; *Int'l*, pg. 390
ALTERA INFRASTRUCTURE L.P.—See Brookfield Corporation; *Int'l*, pg. 1175
ALTER ASSET MANAGEMENT, INC—See The Alter Group Ltd.; *U.S. Private*, pg. 3985
ALTERATION EARTH PLC; *Int'l*, pg. 391
ALTER BARGE LINE INC.; *U.S. Private*, pg. 206
ALTER+CARE—See The Alter Group Ltd.; *U.S. Private*, pg. 3985
ALTER COMPANIES; *U.S. Private*, pg. 206
ALTERCO S.A.; *Int'l*, pg. 391
ALTER DESIGN BUILDERS LLC—See The Alter Group Ltd.; *U.S. Private*, pg. 3985
ALTER DOMUS LUXEMBOURG SARL—See Permira Advisers LLP; *Int'l*, pg. 5803

COMPANY NAME INDEX

ALTER ECO; *U.S. Private*, pg. 206
ALTERE SECURITIZADORA S.A.; *Int'l*, pg. 391
THE ALTER GROUP LTD.; *U.S. Private*, pg. 3985
ALTERIAN DEUTSCHLAND GMBH—See RWS Holdings plc; *Int'l*, pg. 6437
ALTERIAN, INC.—See RWS Holdings plc; *Int'l*, pg. 6437
ALTERIAN LIMITED—See RWS Holdings plc; *Int'l*, pg. 6437
ALTERIAN (STAMFORD) INC.—See RWS Holdings plc; *Int'l*, pg. 6437
ALTERIAN TECHNOLOGIES INDIA PVT. LTD.—See RWS Holdings plc; *Int'l*, pg. 6437
ALTERI PARTNERS LLP; *Int'l*, pg. 391
ALTERIS INSURANCE SERVICES, INC.—See Brookfield Reinsurance Ltd.; *Int'l*, pg. 1193
ALTERITY INC.—See Symphony Technology Group, LLC; *U.S. Private*, pg. 3902
ALTERITY THERAPEUTICS INC.—See Alterity Therapeutics Limited; *Int'l*, pg. 391
ALTERITY THERAPEUTICS LIMITED; *Int'l*, pg. 391
ALTERMAN ENTERPRISES INC.—See Alterman, Inc.; *U.S. Private*, pg. 207
ALTERMAN, INC.; *U.S. Private*, pg. 207
ALTERNA CAPITAL PARTNERS LLC; *U.S. Private*, pg. 207
ALTERNA HOLDINGS CORP.—See Henkel AG & Co. KGaA; *Int'l*, pg. 3353
ALTERNATE HEALTH CORP.; *Int'l*, pg. 391
ALTERNATE SOLUTIONS HOMECARE; *U.S. Private*, pg. 207
ALTERNATE STAFFING INC.; *U.S. Private*, pg. 207
ALTERNATE TRANSIT ADVERTISING; *U.S. Private*, pg. 207
ALTERNATIFBANK A.S.—See The Commercial Bank (P.S.Q.C); *Int'l*, pg. 7635
ALTERNATIF FINANSAL KIRALAMA AS; *Int'l*, pg. 391
ALTERNATIF YATIRIM A.S.—See AG Anadolu Grubu Holding A.S.; *Int'l*, pg. 197
ALTERNATIVE APPAREL, INC.—See Hanesbrands Inc.; *U.S. Public*, pg. 982
ALTERNATIVE BILLING SOLUTIONS, INC.; *U.S. Private*, pg. 207
ALTERNATIVE CREDIT INVESTMENTS PLC; *Int'l*, pg. 391
ALTERNATIVE EARTH RESOURCES INC.; *Int'l*, pg. 391
ALTERNATIVE ENERGY STORE, LLC; *U.S. Private*, pg. 207
ALTERNATIVE FAMILY SERVICES; *U.S. Private*, pg. 207
ALTERNATIVE GLASS SUPPLIES PTY LIMITED—See MHG Glass Pty Ltd; *Int'l*, pg. 4872
ALTERNATIVE HOSE, INC.; *U.S. Private*, pg. 207
ALTERNATIVE INCOME REIT PLC; *Int'l*, pg. 391
ALTERNATIVE INVESTMENT CAPITAL LTD.—See Mitsubishi Corporation; *Int'l*, pg. 4937
ALTERNATIVE INVESTMENT CORPORATION; *U.S. Private*, pg. 207
ALTERNATIVE INVESTMENT MANAGEMENT LTD.—See Vontobel Holding AG; *Int'l*, pg. 8306
ALTERNATIVE INVESTMENT TRUST; *Int'l*, pg. 392
ALTERNATIVE LABORATORIES, LLC—See Alpine 4 Holdings, Inc.; *U.S. Public*, pg. 85
ALTERNATIVE LIVING SERVICES HOME CARE, INC.—See Brookdale Senior Living Inc.; *U.S. Public*, pg. 393
ALTERNATIVE MARKETING SOLUTIONS, INC.; *U.S. Private*, pg. 207
ALTERNATIVE REHABILITATION COMMUNITIES, INC.; *U.S. Private*, pg. 207
ALTERNATIVE RE LIMITED—See Arch Capital Group Ltd.; *Int'l*, pg. 546
ALTERNATIVE RESIDENCES TWO INC.; *U.S. Private*, pg. 207
ALTERNATIVE RISK MANAGEMENT LTD.; *U.S. Private*, pg. 207
ALTERNATIVE SCHOOLS NETWORK; *U.S. Private*, pg. 207
ALTERNATIVE SERVICES INC.; *U.S. Private*, pg. 207
ALTERNATIVES, INC.; *U.S. Private*, pg. 208
ALTERNATIVE SOLUTIONS, INC.; *U.S. Private*, pg. 207
ALTERNATIVE STAFFING INC.; *U.S. Private*, pg. 207
ALTERNATIVE STAINLESS COMPANY LIMITED—See Lohakit Metal Public Company Limited; *Int'l*, pg. 4543
ALTERNATIVE STRATEGIES GROUP, INC.—See Wells Fargo & Company; *U.S. Public*, pg. 2343
ALTERNATIVE TECHNOLOGY SOLUTIONS; *U.S. Private*, pg. 207
ALTERNATIVE UNDERWRITING SERVICES, LTD.—See Arch Capital Group Ltd.; *Int'l*, pg. 546
ALTERNATTIVA EMPRESA DE SERVICIOS TRANSITORIOS LIMITADA—See Empresaria Group Plc; *Int'l*, pg. 2388
ALTERN ENERGY LIMITED; *Int'l*, pg. 391
ALTERNERGY HOLDINGS CORPORATION; *Int'l*, pg. 392
ALTERNERGY LIMITED; *Int'l*, pg. 392
ALTERNET SYSTEMS, INC.; *U.S. Private*, pg. 208
ALTERNUS CLEAN ENERGY INC.; *U.S. Public*, pg. 87
ALTERNUS ENERGY GROUP PLC—See Alternus Clean Energy Inc.; *U.S. Public*, pg. 87
ALTERNUS ENERGY, INC.; *U.S. Public*, pg. 87

ALTERON REIT VARNA; *Int'l*, pg. 392
ALTERRA BANK—See First Business Financial Services, Inc.; *U.S. Public*, pg. 840
ALTERRA MOUNTAIN COMPANY—See KSL Capital Partners, LLC; *U.S. Private*, pg. 2354
ALTERRA POWER CORP.—See Innergex Renewable Energy Inc.; *Int'l*, pg. 3708
ALTER S.R.L.—See MKS Instruments, Inc.; *U.S. Public*, pg. 1452
ALTER TECHNOLOGY CHINA—See TUV NORD AG; *Int'l*, pg. 7979
ALTER TECHNOLOGY RUSSIA—See TUV NORD AG; *Int'l*, pg. 7979
ALTER TECHNOLOGY TUV NORD S.A.U.—See TUV NORD AG; *Int'l*, pg. 7979
ALTER TECHNOLOGY UK—See TUV NORD AG; *Int'l*, pg. 7979
ALTER TRADING CORPORATION; *U.S. Public*, pg. 206
ALTER TRUCKING AND TERMINAL CORP.—See Alter Companies; *U.S. Private*, pg. 206
ALTERWAY GROUP SARL—See Econocom Group SA; *Int'l*, pg. 2297
ALTERYX CZECH REPUBLIC S.R.O.—See Clearlake Capital Group, L.P.; *U.S. Private*, pg. 933
ALTERYX CZECH REPUBLIC S.R.O.—See Insight Venture Management, LLC; *U.S. Private*, pg. 2087
ALTERYX GMBH—See Clearlake Capital Group, L.P.; *U.S. Private*, pg. 933
ALTERYX GMBH—See Insight Venture Management, LLC; *U.S. Private*, pg. 2087
ALTERYX, INC.—See Clearlake Capital Group, L.P.; *U.S. Private*, pg. 933
ALTERYX, INC.—See Insight Venture Management, LLC; *U.S. Private*, pg. 2087
ALTES AMTSHAUS—See Wurth Verwaltungsgesellschaft mbH; *Int'l*, pg. 8506
ALTES LLC; *U.S. Private*, pg. 208
ALTEVA, INC.; *U.S. Private*, pg. 208
ALTEVA OF SYRACUSE, INC.—See Alteva, Inc.; *U.S. Private*, pg. 208
ALTEX CO., LTD.—See Toyota Industries Corporation; *Int'l*, pg. 7866
ALTEX ELECTRONICS, LTD.; *U.S. Private*, pg. 208
ALTEX INDUSTRIES, INC.; *U.S. Public*, pg. 87
ALTEX PACKAGING, INC.; *U.S. Private*, pg. 208
ALTEXSOFT, INC.; *U.S. Private*, pg. 208
ALTHEADX, INC.—See Castle Biosciences, Inc.; *U.S. Public*, pg. 447
ALTHEA GROUP HOLDINGS LIMITED; *Int'l*, pg. 392
ALTHEA PARK LIMITED—See Bridgepoint Group Plc; *Int'l*, pg. 1154
AL-THEMAR INTERNATIONAL HOLDING CO. (K.S.C.); *Int'l*, pg. 289
ALTHOFF INDUSTRIES INC.; *U.S. Private*, pg. 208
ALTIA CO., LTD.—See TPR Co., Ltd.; *Int'l*, pg. 7883
ALTIA CONSULTORES SA; *Int'l*, pg. 392
ALTIA EESTI AS—See Altia Oyj; *Int'l*, pg. 392
ALTIA NORWAY SERVICES AS—See Altia Oyj; *Int'l*, pg. 392
ALTIAN PHARMA—See Insud Pharma, S.L.; *Int'l*, pg. 3724
ALTIA OYJ; *Int'l*, pg. 392
ALTIA SWEDEN AB—See Altia Oyj; *Int'l*, pg. 392
ALTIA SWEDEN SERVICES AB—See Altia Oyj; *Int'l*, pg. 392
ALTIA SYSTEMS INC.—See GN Store Nord A/S; *Int'l*, pg. 3015
ALTICAST CORP.; *Int'l*, pg. 392
ALTICE EUROPE N.V.; *Int'l*, pg. 392
ALTICE FRANCE SA—See Tofane Global SAS; *Int'l*, pg. 7774
ALTICE LUXEMBOURG S.A.—See Altice Europe N.V.; *Int'l*, pg. 392
ALTICE USA, INC.; *U.S. Public*, pg. 87
ALTICOR CORPORATE ENTERPRISES—See Alticor Inc.; *U.S. Private*, pg. 208
ALTICOR INC.; *U.S. Private*, pg. 208
ALTIFORT FRANCE SAS; *Int'l*, pg. 393
ALTIGEN COMMUNICATIONS, INC.; *U.S. Public*, pg. 88
ALTIG INTERNATIONAL; *U.S. Private*, pg. 209
ALTI GLOBAL, INC.; *U.S. Public*, pg. 87
AL-TIJARI FINANCIAL BROKERAGE COMPANY K.S.C.—See Commercial Bank of Kuwait S.A.K.; *Int'l*, pg. 1715
ALTIMA DENTAL CANADA INC.—See Peloton Capital Management, Inc.; *Int'l*, pg. 5783
ALTIMA PARTNERS LLP; *Int'l*, pg. 393
ALTIMA RESOURCES LTD.; *Int'l*, pg. 393
ALTIMATE BELGIUM BVBA—See Arrow Electronics, Inc.; *U.S. Public*, pg. 195
ALTIMATE GROUP SAS—See Arrow Electronics, Inc.; *U.S. Public*, pg. 195
ALTIMATE MEDICAL, INC.—See Rockwood Equity Partners, LLC; *U.S. Private*, pg. 3468
ALTIMATE ND BELGIUM BVBA—See Arrow Electronics, Inc.; *U.S. Public*, pg. 195
ALTIMATE UK DISTRIBUTION LIMITED—See Arrow Electronics, Inc.; *U.S. Public*, pg. 195
ALTIMEDIA CORPORATION—See KT Corporation; *Int'l*, pg. 4314

ALTIME SPORT & LEISURE GMBH—See Cocreation Grass Co., Ltd.; *Int'l*, pg. 1687
ALTIMETER GROUP, LLC—See Prophet Brand Strategy, Inc.; *U.S. Private*, pg. 3285
ALTIMETER GROWTH CORP.; *U.S. Public*, pg. 88
ALTIMMUNE, INC; *U.S. Public*, pg. 88
ALTINA CAPITAL CORP.; *Int'l*, pg. 393
ALTINEX OIL DENMARK A/S—See BlueNord ASA; *Int'l*, pg. 1072
ALTINUM GVG MBH & CO. SONNENHOF—See Commerzbank AG; *Int'l*, pg. 1717
ALTINYAG KOMBINALARI AS; *Int'l*, pg. 393
ALTIN YUNUS TURISTIK TESISLER A.S.; *Int'l*, pg. 393
ALTIOR CONSULTING & TRAINING LIMITED—See Leeds Equity Partners, LLC; *U.S. Private*, pg. 2414
ALTIPLANO METALS INC.; *Int'l*, pg. 393
ALTIRA, INC.; *U.S. Private*, pg. 209
ALTIS AERO SYSTEMS LLC—See RTX Corporation; *U.S. Public*, pg. 1822
ALTISOURCE ASSET MANAGEMENT CORPORATION; *U.S. Public*, pg. 88
ALTISOURCE PORTFOLIO SOLUTIONS S.A.; *Int'l*, pg. 393
ALTISOURCE SOLUTIONS, INC.—See Altisource Portfolio Solutions S.A.; *Int'l*, pg. 393
ALTITUDE ACQUISITION CORP.; *U.S. Public*, pg. 88
ALTITUDE AEROSPACE INTERIORS LIMITED—See Air New Zealand Limited; *Int'l*, pg. 239
ALTITUDE DIGITAL, INC.; *U.S. Private*, pg. 209
ALTITUDE GROUP PLC; *Int'l*, pg. 393
ALTITUDE, INC.—See Accenture plc; *Int'l*, pg. 86
ALTITUDE INTERNATIONAL HOLDINGS, INC.; *U.S. Public*, pg. 88
ALTITUDE MARKETING; *U.S. Private*, pg. 209
ALTITUDE MARKETING—See Altitude Marketing; *U.S. Private*, pg. 209
ALTIUM B.V.—See Altium Limited; *Int'l*, pg. 393
ALTIUM EUROPE GMBH—See Altium Limited; *Int'l*, pg. 393
ALTIUM HEALTHCARE—See Loews Corporation; *U.S. Public*, pg. 1339
ALTIUM INFORMATION TECHNOLOGY (SHANGHAI) CO., LTD.—See Altium Limited; *Int'l*, pg. 393
ALTIUM JAPAN KK—See Altium Limited; *Int'l*, pg. 393
ALTIUM LIMITED; *Int'l*, pg. 393
ALTIUM NETHERLANDS BV—See Altium Limited; *Int'l*, pg. 393
ALTIUM PACKAGING CANADA—See Loews Corporation; *U.S. Public*, pg. 1339
ALTIUM PACKAGING LP—See Loews Corporation; *U.S. Public*, pg. 1339
ALTIUM UK LIMITED—See Altium Limited; *Int'l*, pg. 393
ALTIUS ENERGY CORPORATION—See Vitol Holding B.V.; *Int'l*, pg. 8260
ALTIUS MINERALS CORPORATION; *Int'l*, pg. 394
ALTIUSPAR, INC.—See Grupo Posadas S.A.B. de C.V.; *Int'l*, pg. 3134
ALTIUSPAR SOLUTIONS S.A. DE C.V.—See Grupo Posadas S.A.B. de C.V.; *Int'l*, pg. 3134
ALTIUS RESOURCES, INC.—See Altius Minerals Corporation; *Int'l*, pg. 394
ALTIVIA CORPORATION—See BRENNTAG SE; *Int'l*, pg. 1148
ALTIVIA OXIDE CHEMICALS, LLC—See BRENNTAG SE; *Int'l*, pg. 1148
ALTIVIA PETROCHEMICALS, LLC—See BRENNTAG SE; *Int'l*, pg. 1148
ALT+KELBER IMMOBILIENVERWALTUNG GMBH—See Vonovia SE; *Int'l*, pg. 8305
ALTLASTENSANIERUNG UND ABRAUMDEPONIE LANGES FELD GESELLSCHAFT M.B.H.—See PORR AG; *Int'l*, pg. 5922
ALTL INC.; *U.S. Private*, pg. 209
ALT LOGISTICS CO., LTD.—See Toyota Industries Corporation; *Int'l*, pg. 7865
ALTMAN-CHARTER COMPANY; *U.S. Private*, pg. 210
THE ALTMAN COMPANIES, INC.—See Hilton Grand Vacations Inc.; *U.S. Public*, pg. 1040
ALTMAN CONTRACTORS, INC.—See Hilton Grand Vacations Inc.; *U.S. Public*, pg. 1040
ALTMAN DEVELOPMENT CORPORATION—See Hilton Grand Vacations Inc.; *U.S. Public*, pg. 1040
THE ALTMAN GROUP; *U.S. Private*, pg. 3985
ALTMAN SPECIALTY PLANTS, INC.; *U.S. Private*, pg. 210
ALTMARKT-GALERIE DRESDEN GMBH & CO. KG—See Deutsche EuroShop AG; *Int'l*, pg. 2065
ALTMEYER HOME STORES INC.; *U.S. Private*, pg. 210
ALTO CONSTRUCTION CO., INC.; *U.S. Private*, pg. 210
ALTO DEVELOPMENT CORPORATION—See Zimmer Biomet Holdings, Inc.; *U.S. Public*, pg. 2405
ALTODIGITAL NETWORKS LIMITED—See Xerox Holdings Corporation; *U.S. Public*, pg. 2386
ALTO ENERGY LIMITED—See Grand Gulf Energy Limited; *Int'l*, pg. 3054
ALTO ENTERPRISES, INC.; *U.S. Private*, pg. 210
ALTOGETHER DIGITAL—See The Engine Group; *Int'l*, pg. 7640
ALTO INGREDIENTS, INC.; *U.S. Public*, pg. 88

ALTO INGREDIENTS, INC.

ALTOLA AG—See Vicat S.A.; *Int'l*, pg. 8185
ALTO MARKETING; *Int'l*, pg. 394
ALTO METALS LIMITED; *Int'l*, pg. 394
ALTONA RARE EARTHS PLC; *Int'l*, pg. 394
ALTONA RESOURCES, INC.; *U.S. Private*, pg. 210
ALTON BEAN TRUCKING INC.; *U.S. Private*, pg. 210
ALTON CASINO, LLC—See PENN Entertainment, Inc.; *U.S. Public*, pg. 1662
ALTON E. BLAKLEY COMPANY INC.; *U.S. Private*, pg. 210
ALTO NEUROSCIENCE, INC.; *U.S. Public*, pg. 88
ALTON GLASSHOUSES LIMITED—See Marshalls plc; *Int'l*, pg. 4702
ALTON INDUSTRY LTD.—See Suzhou Alton Electrical & Mechanical Industry Co., Ltd.; *Int'l*, pg. 7348
ALTON INTERNATIONAL (S) PTE LTD—See Federal International (2000) Ltd; *Int'l*, pg. 2630
ALTON JAPAN CO., LTD.—See Suzhou Alton Electrical & Mechanical Industry Co., Ltd.; *Int'l*, pg. 7348
ALTON SPORTS CO., LTD. - CHINA PLANT—See Alton Sports Co., Ltd.; *Int'l*, pg. 394
ALTON SPORTS CO., LTD.; *Int'l*, pg. 394
ALTON SPORTS CO., LTD. - YANGJU PLANT—See Alton Sports Co., Ltd.; *Int'l*, pg. 394
ALTON STEEL INC.; *U.S. Private*, pg. 210
THE (ALTON) TELEGRAPH—See Independence Capital Partners, LLC; *U.S. Private*, pg. 2057
ALTOONA CURVE BASEBALL CLUB—See Lozinak Professional Baseball LLC; *U.S. Private*, pg. 2507
ALTOONA WATER AUTHORITY; *U.S. Private*, pg. 210
ALTO PHARMACEUTICALS, INC.; *U.S. Private*, pg. 210
ALTO PLASTICS LTD.; *Int'l*, pg. 394
ALTO PRODUCTS CORP.; *U.S. Private*, pg. 210
ALTOR BIOSCIENCE, LLC—See NantWorks, LLC; *U.S. Private*, pg. 2833
ALTOR EQUITY PARTNERS AB; *Int'l*, pg. 394
ALTOR EQUITY PARTNERS A/S—See Altor Equity Partners AB; *Int'l*, pg. 394
ALTOR EQUITY PARTNERS OY—See Altor Equity Partners AB; *Int'l*, pg. 394
ALTORFER INC.; *U.S. Private*, pg. 210
ALTOR INDUSTRIE—See Altor; *Int'l*, pg. 394
ALTOR SOLUTIONS INC.—See Compass Diversified Holdings; *U.S. Public*, pg. 559
ALTOR; *Int'l*, pg. 394
ALTOS BIOLOGICS CO., LTD.—See Alteogen Inc.; *Int'l*, pg. 391
ALTO-SHAAM INC.; *U.S. Private*, pg. 210
ALTOS HORNOS DE MEXICO, S.A. DE C.V.—See Grupo Acerero del Norte S.A. de C.V.; *Int'l*, pg. 3118
ALTOS MANDOS DE NEGOCIOS, S.A. DE C.V.—See Desarrolladora Homex, S.A. de C.V.; *Int'l*, pg. 2044
ALTOSTRATUS SOLUTIONS, S.L.—See Telefonica, S.A.; *Int'l*, pg. 7535
ALTOUR INTERNATIONAL, INC.; *U.S. Private*, pg. 210
ALTOVIDA, INC.; *U.S. Private*, pg. 210
ALTOVISION INC.—See Experian plc; *Int'l*, pg. 2586
ALTOY SAVUNMA SANAYI VE HAVACILIK ANONIM SIRKETI—See AeroVironment, Inc.; *U.S. Public*, pg. 53
ALTPAPIER VERW WATTENSCHIED GMBH—See Stora Enso Oyj; *Int'l*, pg. 7223
ALTPLUS INC.; *Int'l*, pg. 397
ALTRAD ALUCON—See Altrad Investment Authority SAS; *Int'l*, pg. 397
ALTRAD AND B.V.B.A—See Altrad Investment Authority SAS; *Int'l*, pg. 397
ALTRAD ASIA LIMITED—See Altrad Investment Authority SAS; *Int'l*, pg. 397
ALTRAD BABCOCK LIMITED—See Altrad Investment Authority SAS; *Int'l*, pg. 397
ALTRAD BALLIAUW MULTISERVICES N.V.—See Altrad Investment Authority SAS; *Int'l*, pg. 397
ALTRAD BALLIAUW SP. Z O.O.—See Altrad Investment Authority SAS; *Int'l*, pg. 397
ALTRAD BAUMANN GMBH—See Altrad Investment Authority SAS; *Int'l*, pg. 397
ALTRAD BEAVER 84 LTD—See Altrad Investment Authority SAS; *Int'l*, pg. 397
ALTRAD BENELUX NV—See Altrad Investment Authority SAS; *Int'l*, pg. 397
ALTRAD BETONIERA SI ESAFODAJE ROMANIA S.R.L.—See Altrad Investment Authority SAS; *Int'l*, pg. 397
ALTRAD BRAGAGNOLO ITALIA SRL—See Altrad Investment Authority SAS; *Int'l*, pg. 397
ALTRAD CEDRIA—See Altrad Investment Authority SAS; *Int'l*, pg. 397
ALTRAD COLLECTIVITES SA—See Altrad Investment Authority SAS; *Int'l*, pg. 397
ALTRA D.D.; *Int'l*, pg. 397
ALTRAD FAMEA ECA S.A.S.—See Altrad Investment Authority SAS; *Int'l*, pg. 397
ALTRAD FORT BV—See Altrad Investment Authority SAS; *Int'l*, pg. 397
ALTRAD HAVICO N.V.—See Altrad Investment Authority SAS; *Int'l*, pg. 397
ALTRAD HOFMANINGER GMBH—See Altrad Investment Authority SAS; *Int'l*, pg. 397

ALTRAD HOLDING S.A.—See Altrad Investment Authority SAS; *Int'l*, pg. 397
ALTRAD INVESTMENT AUTHORITY SAS; *Int'l*, pg. 397
ALTRAD ITALIA SRL—See Altrad Investment Authority SAS; *Int'l*, pg. 397
ALTRAD - KONSKIE SPOLKA Z O.O.—See Altrad Investment Authority SAS; *Int'l*, pg. 397
ALTRAD LESCHA GMBH—See Altrad Investment Authority SAS; *Int'l*, pg. 397
ALTRAD LIMEX D.O.O.—See Altrad Investment Authority SAS; *Int'l*, pg. 397
ALTRAD LIV D.O.O.—See Altrad Investment Authority SAS; *Int'l*, pg. 397
ALTRAD MOSTOSTAL MONTAZ SP. Z O.O.—See Altrad Investment Authority SAS; *Int'l*, pg. 397
ALTRAD NSG LIMITED—See Altrad Investment Authority SAS; *Int'l*, pg. 397
ALTRAD PLETTAC ASSCO GMBH—See Altrad Investment Authority SAS; *Int'l*, pg. 397
ALTRAD PLETTAC IBERICA, S. L.—See Altrad Investment Authority SAS; *Int'l*, pg. 397
ALTRAD PLETTAC PRODUCTION GMBH—See Altrad Investment Authority SAS; *Int'l*, pg. 397
ALTRAD PLETTAC SARL—See Altrad Investment Authority SAS; *Int'l*, pg. 397
ALTRAD POLAND S.A.—See Altrad Investment Authority SAS; *Int'l*, pg. 397
ALTRAD-POMORZE SPOLKA Z O.O.—See Altrad Investment Authority SAS; *Int'l*, pg. 398
ALTRAD PROFIX BVBA—See Altrad Investment Authority SAS; *Int'l*, pg. 397
ALTRAD-PRYMAT SP. Z. O. O.—See Altrad Investment Authority SAS; *Int'l*, pg. 398
ALTRAD RICHARD FRAISSE SAS—See Altrad Investment Authority SAS; *Int'l*, pg. 397
ALTRAD RODISOLA S.A.—See Altrad Investment Authority SAS; *Int'l*, pg. 397
ALTRAD SAINT DENIS S.A.—See Altrad Investment Authority SAS; *Int'l*, pg. 397
ALTRAD SOFRAMAT ETEM S.A.—See Altrad Investment Authority SAS; *Int'l*, pg. 398
ALTRA ELECTRICALS LTD—See Schindler Holding AG; *Int'l*, pg. 6618
ALTRA INDUSTRIAL MOTION CORP.—See Regal Rexnord Corporation; *U.S. Public*, pg. 1772
ALTRA INDUSTRIAL MOTION, INC.—See Regal Rexnord Corporation; *U.S. Public*, pg. 1772
ALTRA INDUSTRIAL MOTION INDIA PRIVATE LTD.—See Regal Rexnord Corporation; *U.S. Public*, pg. 1772
ALTRA INDUSTRIAL MOTION RUSSIA OOO—See Regal Rexnord Corporation; *U.S. Public*, pg. 1772
ALTRA INDUSTRIAL MOTION SOUTH AFRICA (PTY.) LTD.—See Regal Rexnord Corporation; *U.S. Public*, pg. 1772
ALTRAN AG—See Capgemini SE; *Int'l*, pg. 1304
ALTRAN BELGIUM SA—See Capgemini SE; *Int'l*, pg. 1304
ALTRAN B.V.—See Capgemini SE; *Int'l*, pg. 1304
ALTRAN CANADA INC—See Capgemini SE; *Int'l*, pg. 1304
ALTRAN CIS FRANCE—See Capgemini SE; *Int'l*, pg. 1304
ALTRAN DEUTSCHLAND HOLDING GMBH—See Capgemini SE; *Int'l*, pg. 1304
ALTRAN INNOVACION S.L.U.—See Capgemini SE; *Int'l*, pg. 1304
ALTRAN INTERNATIONAL B.V.—See Capgemini SE; *Int'l*, pg. 1304
ALTRAN ITALIA S.P.A.—See Capgemini SE; *Int'l*, pg. 1304
ALTRAN LUXEMBOURG S.A.N.V.—See Capgemini SE; *Int'l*, pg. 1304
ALTRAN NORWAY AS—See Capgemini SE; *Int'l*, pg. 1304
ALTRAN OSTERREICH GMBH—See Capgemini SE; *Int'l*, pg. 1304
ALTRAN PORTUGAL S.A.—See Capgemini SE; *Int'l*, pg. 1305
ALTRAN PRAXIS LIMITED—See Capgemini SE; *Int'l*, pg. 1305
ALTRAN PRAXIS SAS—See Capgemini SE; *Int'l*, pg. 1305
ALTRAN S.A.N.V.—See Capgemini SE; *Int'l*, pg. 1305
ALTRAN SHANGAI LTD.—See Capgemini SE; *Int'l*, pg. 1305
ALTRAN SOLUTIONS CORP.—See Capgemini SE; *Int'l*, pg. 1305
ALTRAN SVERIGE AB—See Capgemini SE; *Int'l*, pg. 1305
ALTRAN (SWITZERLAND) S.A.—See Capgemini SE; *Int'l*, pg. 1305
ALTRAN TECHNOLOGIES INDIA LTD.—See Capgemini SE; *Int'l*, pg. 1305
ALTRAN TECHNOLOGIES SWEDEN AB—See Capgemini SE; *Int'l*, pg. 1305
ALTRAN TECHNOLOGIES UK LTD.—See Capgemini SE; *Int'l*, pg. 1305
ALTRAN UK LIMITED—See Capgemini SE; *Int'l*, pg. 1305
ALTRAN USA HOLDINGS INC.—See Capgemini SE; *Int'l*, pg. 1305
ALTRAN XYPE DEUTSCHLAND GMBH—See Capgemini SE; *Int'l*, pg. 1305
ALTRA S.P.A.—See CNH Industrial N.V.; *Int'l*, pg. 1675
ALTRAZEAL LIFE SCIENCES INC.; *U.S. Private*, pg. 210
ALTRIA CLIENT SERVICES INC.—See Altria Group, Inc.; *U.S. Public*, pg. 89

ALTRIA CONSUMER ENGAGEMENT SERVICES INC.—See Altria Group, Inc.; *U.S. Public*, pg. 89
ALTRIA GROUP, INC.; *U.S. Public*, pg. 88
ALTRI FLORESTAL, S.A.—See Altri, SGPS, S.A.; *Int'l*, pg. 398
ALTRI, PARTICIPACIONES Y TRADING, S.L.—See Altri, SGPS, S.A.; *Int'l*, pg. 398
ALTRI SALES, S.A.—See Altri, SGPS, S.A.; *Int'l*, pg. 398
ALTRI, SGPS, S.A.; *Int'l*, pg. 398
ALTROM AUTO GROUP LTD—See Genuine Parts Company; *U.S. Public*, pg. 932
ALTROM CANADA CORP.—See Genuine Parts Company; *U.S. Public*, pg. 932
ALTRON FINANCE (PTY) LIMITED—See Altron Limited.; *Int'l*, pg. 399
ALTRONICS MANUFACTURING, INC.—See Investissement Quebec; *Int'l*, pg. 3780
ALTRON LIMITED.; *Int'l*, pg. 398
ALTRU HEALTH SYSTEM; *U.S. Private*, pg. 210
ALTRUI BROTHERS TRUCK SALES, INC.; *U.S. Private*, pg. 210
ALTRUIS BENEFITS CONSULTING, INC.—See Reliance Global Group, Inc.; *U.S. Public*, pg. 1778
ALTRUISTA HEALTH, INC.—See Blackstone Inc.; *U.S. Public*, pg. 354
ALTRUIST CORP; *U.S. Private*, pg. 210
ALTRUIST TECHNOLOGIES PVT. LTD.; *Int'l*, pg. 399
ALTRUM—See Amsoil Inc.; *U.S. Private*, pg. 267
ALTRUST FINANCIAL SERVICES, INC.; *U.S. Public*, pg. 89
ALTRUST PRECISION TOOLING (DONGGUAN) CO., LTD.—See Combine Will International Holdings Limited; *Int'l*, pg. 1709
ALT STUDIOS—See Sigler Companies, Inc.; *U.S. Private*, pg. 3648
ALT TELECOM PCL; *Int'l*, pg. 383
ALTUGLAS INTERNATIONAL DENMARK A/S—See Arkema S.A.; *Int'l*, pg. 568
ALTUGLAS INTERNATIONAL S.A.S.—See Arkema S.A.; *Int'l*, pg. 568
ALTUGLAS INTERNATIONAL—See Arkema S.A.; *Int'l*, pg. 568
ALTUGLAS INTERNATIONAL—See Arkema S.A.; *Int'l*, pg. 568
ALTUGLAS INTERNATIONAL—See Arkema S.A.; *Int'l*, pg. 568
ALTUM PRECISION CO., LTD.—See Giovanni Agnelli B.V.; *Int'l*, pg. 2978
ALTUM PRECISION CO., LTD.—See PrimeMovers Equity (S) Pte. Ltd.; *Int'l*, pg. 5979
ALTUM PRECISION SDN. BHD.—See Giovanni Agnelli B.V.; *Int'l*, pg. 2978
ALTUM PRECISION SDN. BHD.—See PrimeMovers Equity (S) Pte. Ltd.; *Int'l*, pg. 5979
ALTURA COMMUNICATION SOLUTIONS, LLC—See Silver Oak Services Partners, LLC; *U.S. Private*, pg. 3661
ALTURA CREDIT UNION; *U.S. Private*, pg. 210
ALTURA HOMES DFW, LP.; *U.S. Private*, pg. 211
ALTURA MARKETS SOCIEDAD DE VALORES SA—See Societe Generale S.A.; *Int'l*, pg. 7038
ALTURAS MINERALS CORP.; *Int'l*, pg. 399
ALTUR INVESTISSEMENT S.C.A.; *Int'l*, pg. 399
ALTURNA DIRECT N.V.—See Amphenol Corporation; *U.S. Public*, pg. 126
ALTURNA INTEGRATION SERVICES N.V.—See Amphenol Corporation; *U.S. Public*, pg. 126
ALTURNA NETWORKS N.V.—See Amphenol Corporation; *U.S. Public*, pg. 126
ALTUR S.A.; *Int'l*, pg. 399
ALTUS BILISIM HIZMETLERI ANONIM SIRKETI—See Diebold Nixdorf, Inc.; *U.S. Public*, pg. 659
ALTUS CAPITAL PARTNERS, INC.; *U.S. Private*, pg. 211
ALTUSCIO NETWORKS—See Konica Minolta, Inc.; *Int'l*, pg. 4258
ALTUS FIRE & LIFE SAFETY—See Apax Partners LLP; *Int'l*, pg. 501
ALTUS GEOMATICS L.P.—See Altus Group Limited; *Int'l*, pg. 399
ALTUS GROUP LIMITED; *Int'l*, pg. 399
ALTUS GROUP U.S. INC.—See Altus Group Limited; *Int'l*, pg. 399
ALTUS HOLDINGS LIMITED; *Int'l*, pg. 399
ALTUS POWER, INC.; *U.S. Public*, pg. 89
ALTUS PROPERTY VENTURES, INC.; *Int'l*, pg. 399
ALTUS RENEWABLES LIMITED; *Int'l*, pg. 399
ALTUS RESOURCE CAPITAL LIMITED; *Int'l*, pg. 399
ALTUS S.A.; *Int'l*, pg. 399
ALTUS SISTEMAS DE AUTOMACAO S.A.; *Int'l*, pg. 399
ALTUS STRATEGIES PLC—See Elemental Altus Royalties Corp.; *Int'l*, pg. 2358
ALTUS TOWARZYSTWO FUNDUSZY INWESTYCYJNYCH S.A.; *Int'l*, pg. 399
AL-TUWAIRQI GROUP; *Int'l*, pg. 289
AL TUWAIRQI TRADING & CONTRACTING—See Al-Tuwairqi Group; *Int'l*, pg. 289
ALTVATER TERNOPIL LLC—See Veolia Environnement S.A.; *Int'l*, pg. 8153
ALTWOOD GARAGE DOORS LTD.; *Int'l*, pg. 399

COMPANY NAME INDEX

ALTYA, S.A. DE C.V.—See Promotora Ambiental S.A.B de C.V.; *Int'l*, pg. 5994
ALTYFOODS CO. LTD.—See AEON Co., Ltd.; *Int'l*, pg. 177
ALTYNEX COMPANY JSC; *Int'l*, pg. 399
ALTYNGOLD PLC; *Int'l*, pg. 399
ALTYNTAU KOKSHETAU JSC—See Glencore plc; *Int'l*, pg. 2991
ALUAR ALUMINIO ARGENTINO; *Int'l*, pg. 400
ALUBAR A/S—See ManpowerGroup Inc.; *U.S. Public*, pg. 1360
ALUCHEM INC.; *U.S. Private*, pg. 211
ALUCOAT CONVERSION, S.A.—See Aliberico, S.L.; *Int'l*, pg. 326
ALUCOBOND ASIA PACIFIC MANAGEMENT (SHANGHAI) LTD.—See Schweiter Technologies AG; *Int'l*, pg. 6645
ALUCOBOND COMPOSITES (JIANGSU) LTD.—See Schweiter Technologies AG; *Int'l*, pg. 6645
ALUCOBOND (FAR EAST) PTE. LTD.—See Schweiter Technologies AG; *Int'l*, pg. 6645
ALUCOIL S.A.—See Aliberico, S.L.; *Int'l*, pg. 326
ALUCON PUBLIC COMPANY LIMITED; *Int'l*, pg. 400
ALUCON S.R.O.—See Freudenberg SE; *Int'l*, pg. 2782
ALUE CO., LTD.; *Int'l*, pg. 400
ALUF HOLDINGS, INC.; *U.S. Public*, pg. 89
ALUFLEXPACK AG—See Global Equity Partners Beteiligungs-Management AG; *Int'l*, pg. 2996
ALUFLEX S.A.—See Quinenco S.A.; *Int'l*, pg. 6164
ALUFLEX SYSTEM AB—See Indutrade AB; *Int'l*, pg. 3677
ALUFLEX SYSTEM AS—See Indutrade AB; *Int'l*, pg. 3677
ALUFLUORIDE LIMITED; *Int'l*, pg. 400
ALUFOLD DIRECT LTD.—See Literacy Capital Plc; *Int'l*, pg. 4526
ALU-FORGE, INC.—See Berkshire Hathaway Inc.; *U.S. Public*, pg. 313
ALUFORM MARKETING PTE LTD.—See Compact Metal Industries Ltd.; *Int'l*, pg. 1721
ALUF PLASTICS; *U.S. Private*, pg. 211
ALUGLAS B.V.—See Indutrade AB; *Int'l*, pg. 3679
ALUJAIN CORPORATION—See Xenel Industries Ltd.; *Int'l*, pg. 8521
ALUKO CO., LTD; *Int'l*, pg. 400
ALUKON KG—See Hormann KG verkaufsgesellschaf, *Int'l*, pg. 3480
ALULA WATER PTY LTD; *Int'l*, pg. 400
ALUMACRAFT BOAT COMPANY—See Bain Capital, LP; *U.S. Private*, pg. 430
ALUMACRAFT BOAT COMPANY—See Bain Capital, LP; *U.S. Private*, pg. 431
ALUMA ENTERPRISES, INC.—See Brand Industrial Services, Inc.; *U.S. Private*, pg. 636
ALUMA-FORM INC.; *U.S. Private*, pg. 211
ALUMA-GLASS INDUSTRIES, INC.; *U.S. Private*, pg. 211
ALUMALSA S.A.—See Linamar Corporation; *Int'l*, pg. 4502
ALUMAROLL SPECIALTY CO. INC.; *U.S. Private*, pg. 211
ALUMASC EXTERIOR BUILDING PRODUCTS LIMITED—See The Alumasc Group plc; *Int'l*, pg. 7613
THE ALUMASC GROUP PLC; *Int'l*, pg. 7613
ALUMASC PRECISION COMPONENTS—See The Alumasc Group plc; *Int'l*, pg. 7613
ALUMASC PRECISION LIMITED—See The Alumasc Group plc; *Int'l*, pg. 7613
ALUMA SHIELD INDUSTRIES, INC.—See Metecno S.p.A.; *Int'l*, pg. 4853
ALUMA SYSTEMS—See Brand Industrial Services, Inc.; *U.S. Private*, pg. 636
ALUMA-WELD INC.; *U.S. Private*, pg. 211
ALUMCO S.A.—See Quinenco S.A.; *Int'l*, pg. 6164
ALUMETAL POLAND SP. Z O.O.—See Norsk Hydro ASA; *Int'l*, pg. 5433
ALUMETAL S.A.—See Norsk Hydro ASA; *Int'l*, pg. 5433
ALUMEX PLC—See Hayleys PLC; *Int'l*, pg. 3291
ALUMEXX N.V.; *Int'l*, pg. 400
ALUMICOR LIMITED—See Apogee Enterprises, Inc.; *U.S. Public*, pg. 145
ALUMI - COVER AWNING CO, INC.—See Style Crest, Inc.; *U.S. Private*, pg. 3846
ALUMIFUEL POWER CORPORATION; *U.S. Public*, pg. 89
ALUMIFUEL POWER INTERNATIONAL, INC.—See ALUMIFUEL POWER CORPORATION; *U.S. Public*, pg. 89
ALUMI-GUARD, INC.—See CRH plc; *Int'l*, pg. 1845
ALUMIL ALBANIA SHPK.—See Alumil Aluminium Industry S.A.; *Int'l*, pg. 400
ALUMIL ALUMINIUM INDUSTRY S.A.; *Int'l*, pg. 400
ALUMIL BULGARIA LTD.—See Alumil Aluminium Industry S.A.; *Int'l*, pg. 400
ALUMIL CY LTD.—See Alumil Aluminium Industry S.A.; *Int'l*, pg. 400
ALUMIL DEUTSCHLAND GMBH—See Alumil Aluminium Industry S.A.; *Int'l*, pg. 400
ALUMIL FRANCE S.A.S.—See Alumil Aluminium Industry S.A.; *Int'l*, pg. 400
ALUMIL GULF FZC—See Alumil Aluminium Industry S.A.; *Int'l*, pg. 400
ALUMIL HUNGARY K.T.F.—See Alumil Aluminium Industry S.A.; *Int'l*, pg. 400
ALUMIL ITALIA S.R.L.—See Alumil Aluminium Industry S.A.; *Int'l*, pg. 400
ALUMILITE, INC—See Arsenal Capital Management LP; *U.S. Private*, pg. 339
ALUMIL KOSOVA SHPK—See Alumil Aluminium Industry S.A.; *Int'l*, pg. 400
ALUMIL LLC—See Alumil Aluminium Industry S.A.; *Int'l*, pg. 400
ALUMIL MOLDAVIA—See Alumil Aluminium Industry S.A.; *Int'l*, pg. 400
ALUMIL OCEANIA PTY LTD—See Alumil Aluminium Industry S.A.; *Int'l*, pg. 400
ALUMIL POLSKA SP. Z O.O.—See Alumil Aluminium Industry S.A.; *Int'l*, pg. 400
ALUMIL ROM INDUSTRY S.A.—See Alumil Aluminium Industry S.A.; *Int'l*, pg. 400
ALUMIL S.A.—See Alumil Aluminium Industry S.A.; *Int'l*, pg. 400
ALUMIL SKOPJE D.O.O.—See Alumil Aluminium Industry S.A.; *Int'l*, pg. 400
ALUMIL SRB D.O.O.—See Alumil Aluminium Industry S.A.; *Int'l*, pg. 400
ALUMIL SYSTEMS UK LIMITED—See Alumil Aluminium Industry S.A.; *Int'l*, pg. 400
ALUMIL TECHNIC D.O.O.—See Alumil Aluminium Industry S.A.; *Int'l*, pg. 400
ALUMIL UKRAINE LTD.—See Alumil Aluminium Industry S.A.; *Int'l*, pg. 400
ALUMIL VARNA LTD.—See Alumil Aluminium Industry S.A.; *Int'l*, pg. 400
ALUMIL YU INDUSTRY A.D.—See Alumil Aluminium Industry S.A.; *Int'l*, pg. 400
ALUMINA A.D.; *Int'l*, pg. 400
ALUMINA ESPANOLA, S.A.—See Alcoa Corporation; *U.S. Public*, pg. 74
ALUMINA LIMITED—See Alcoa Corporation; *U.S. Public*, pg. 74
ALUMINA PARTNERS OF JAMAICA—See United Company RUSAL Plc; *Int'l*, pg. 8066
ALUMINERIE DE BECANCOUR INC.—See Alcoa Corporation; *U.S. Public*, pg. 74
ALUMINIJ D.D.; *Int'l*, pg. 401
ALUMINIUM AUSTRIA METALL QUEBEC INC.—See AMAG Austria Metall AG; *Int'l*, pg. 108
ALUMINIUM BAHRAIN B.S.C.; *Int'l*, pg. 401
ALUMINIUM & CHEMIE ROTTERDAM B.V.—See Rio Tinto plc; *Int'l*, pg. 6346
ALUMINIUM COMPANY OF MALAYSIA BERHAD; *Int'l*, pg. 401
ALUMINIUM DE GREECE S.A.—See Metlen Energy & Metals S.A.; *Int'l*, pg. 4854
ALUMINIUM DIE CASTING S.R.L.—See Regal Rexnord Corporation; *U.S. Public*, pg. 1772
ALUMINIUM DU MAROC SA; *Int'l*, pg. 401
ALUMINIUM EXTRUSION INDUSTRIES PLC; *Int'l*, pg. 401
ALUMINIUM FOIL CONVERTERS PROPRIETARY LIMITED—See The Bidvest Group Limited; *Int'l*, pg. 7621
ALUMINIUM GLASS INDUSTRIES (MAURITIUS) LIMITED—See AG Industries Limited; *Int'l*, pg. 198
ALUMINIUM KETY EMMI D.O.O.—See Grupa Kety S.A.; *Int'l*, pg. 3116
ALUMINIUM & LIGHT INDUSTRIES CO. LTD.—See GIBCA Limited; *Int'l*, pg. 2962
ALUMINIUM OF GREECE INDUSTRIAL & COMMERCIAL SOCIETE ANONYME—See Metlen Energy & Metals S.A.; *Int'l*, pg. 4854
ALUMINIUM OXID STADE GMBH—See Dadco Alumina & Chemicals Ltd.; *Int'l*, pg. 1904
THE ALUMINIUM POWDER COMPANY LIMITED—See AMG Critical Materials N.V.; *Int'l*, pg. 426
ALUMINIUM REGEAL AFFIMET—See Aurea, S.A.; *Int'l*, pg. 707
ALUMINIUM SERVICES UK LIMITED—See Reliance Steel & Aluminum Co.; *U.S. Public*, pg. 1779
ALUMINIUM TECHNOLOGIES SDN BHD—See Apply ASA; *Int'l*, pg. 521
ALUMINIUM VERKOOP ZUID B.V.—See CRH plc; *Int'l*, pg. 1842
ALUMINIUMWERK UNNA AG—See China Zhongwang Holdings Limited; *Int'l*, pg. 1567
ALUMINIUM WIRE & ROD CO., LTD.—See Nippon Light Metal Holdings Company, Ltd.; *Int'l*, pg. 5323
ALUMINUM AND STAINLESS, INC.—See Reliance Steel & Aluminum Co.; *U.S. Public*, pg. 1779
ALUMINUM COIL ANODIZING CORP.; *U.S. Private*, pg. 211
ALUMINUM COMPANY OF MALAYSIA BERHAD—See The Aditya Birla Group; *Int'l*, pg. 7611
ALUMINUM & COPPER RECYCLING CENTER CORPORATION—See Alconix Corporation; *Int'l*, pg. 302
ALUMINUM CORPORATION OF CHINA LIMITED; *Int'l*, pg. 401
ALUMINUM DELFZIJL B.V.—See Klesch & Company SA; *Int'l*, pg. 4201
ALUMINUM.IO, INC.; *U.S. Private*, pg. 211

ALVARADO CONSTRUCTION, INC.

ALUMINUM LINE PRODUCTS COMPANY; *U.S. Private*, pg. 211
ALUMINUM MAINTENANCE SYSTEMS OF TEXAS, INC.; *U.S. Private*, pg. 211
THE ALUMINUM POWDER COMPANY LIMITED—See AMG Critical Materials N.V.; *Int'l*, pg. 426
ALUMINUM PRECISION PRODUCTS INC.; *U.S. Private*, pg. 211
ALUMINUM PRODUCTS COMPANY LTD.; *Int'l*, pg. 401
ALUMINUM ROOFING SPECIALISTS INC.; *U.S. Private*, pg. 211
ALUMINUM SCRAP RECYCLE, L.L.C.—See Clayton, Dubilier & Rice, LLC; *U.S. Private*, pg. 921
ALUMINUM SCREEN MANUFACTURING CO.—See Kenner & Company, Inc.; *U.S. Private*, pg. 2285
ALUMINUM SCREEN MANUFACTURING CO.—See North Cove Partners; *U.S. Private*, pg. 2944
ALUMINUM SHAPES, LLC—See H.I.G. Capital, LLC; *U.S. Private*, pg. 1831
ALUMINUM WIRE ROD COMPANY LTD.—See Nippon Light Metal Holdings Company, Ltd.; *Int'l*, pg. 5323
ALUMNI AB—See DBAY Advisors Limited; *Int'l*, pg. 1987
ALUM S.A.; *Int'l*, pg. 400
ALUMTEK CORPORATION; *Int'l*, pg. 401
ALU-NASA ALUMINUM INDUSTRY LLC—See Salam International Investment Limited; *Int'l*, pg. 6491
ALUNG TECHNOLOGIES, INC.—See LivaNova PLC; *Int'l*, pg. 4529
ALUNORTE - ALUMINA DO NORTE DO BRASIL S.A.—See Norsk Hydro ASA; *Int'l*, pg. 5432
ALUPAR INVESTIMENTO S.A.; *Int'l*, pg. 401
ALUP CZ SPOL. S.R.O—See Atlas Copco AB; *Int'l*, pg. 677
ALUP GRASSAIR KOMPRESSOREN BV—See Atlas Copco AB; *Int'l*, pg. 677
ALUP KOMPRESSOREN B.V.—See Atlas Copco AB; *Int'l*, pg. 677
ALUP KOMPRESSOREN GMBH—See Atlas Copco AB; *Int'l*, pg. 677
ALUP KOMPRESSOREN POLSKA SP. Z.O.O.—See Atlas Copco AB; *Int'l*, pg. 677
ALUPLAST GMBH; *Int'l*, pg. 401
ALUPOL FILMS SP. Z O.O.—See Grupa Kety S.A.; *Int'l*, pg. 3116
ALUPOL PACKAGING KETY SP Z O.O.—See Grupa Kety S.A.; *Int'l*, pg. 3116
ALUPOL PACKAGING S.A.—See Grupa Kety S.A.; *Int'l*, pg. 3116
ALUPROF BELGIUM N.V.—See Grupa Kety S.A.; *Int'l*, pg. 3116
ALUPROF DEUTSCHLAND GMBH—See Grupa Kety S.A.; *Int'l*, pg. 3116
ALUPROF HUNGARY KFT.—See Grupa Kety S.A.; *Int'l*, pg. 3116
ALUPROF NETHERLANDS B.V.—See Grupa Kety S.A.; *Int'l*, pg. 3116
ALUPROF S.A.—See Grupa Kety S.A.; *Int'l*, pg. 3116
ALUPROF SYSTEM CZECH, S.R.O.—See Grupa Kety S.A.; *Int'l*, pg. 3117
ALUPROF SYSTEM - ROMANIA SRL—See Grupa Kety S.A.; *Int'l*, pg. 3116
ALUPROF UK LTD.—See Grupa Kety S.A.; *Int'l*, pg. 3116
ALURAME S.R.L—See Viohalco SA/NV; *Int'l*, pg. 8243
ALURECY, S.A.U.—See Cie Automotive S.A.; *Int'l*, pg. 1604
ALUSCAND AB—See Foga System International AB; *Int'l*, pg. 2720
ALUSH (THAILAND) CO., LTD.—See Asia Cassava Resources Holdings Limited; *Int'l*, pg. 611
AL-USOOL GENERAL TRADING COMPANY LTD.—See Eng. Shabah Al-Shammery & Partners Co.; *Int'l*, pg. 2426
ALUSSA ENERGY ACQUISITION CORP.; *Int'l*, pg. 401
ALUSYSTEM SRL—See Bog'Art S.R.L.; *Int'l*, pg. 1100
ALUTEC ANODISING & MACHINE TOOLS (PVT) LTD.—See Hayleys PLC; *Int'l*, pg. 3291
ALUTEC CO., LTD.; *Int'l*, pg. 401
ALUTEC LEICHTMETALLFELGEN GMBH—See UNIWHEELS Management (Switzerland) AG; *Int'l*, pg. 8083
ALUTEK—See LS Corp.; *Int'l*, pg. 4569
ALUTIIQ INTERNATIONAL SOLUTIONS, LLC; *U.S. Private*, pg. 211
ALUTIIQ, LLC—See Afognak Native Corporation; *U.S. Private*, pg. 123
ALUVO CORPORATION—See Morita Holdings Corporation; *Int'l*, pg. 5048
ALUWORKS LIMITED; *Int'l*, pg. 401
ALVA/AMCO PHARMACAL COMPANIES, INC.; *U.S. Private*, pg. 211
ALVA CONFECVOES, S.A.—See Toray Industries, Inc.; *Int'l*, pg. 7822
ALVADIS NV—See Vivendi SE; *Int'l*, pg. 8275
ALVAND ROUINKARAN CHEMICAL PRODUCTS COMPANY LTD.—See National Iranian Lead & Zinc Company; *Int'l*, pg. 5160
ALVAND TILE & CERAMIC COMPANY; *Int'l*, pg. 401
ALVAND TILE & CERAMIC INDUSTRIES CO.; *Int'l*, pg. 401
ALVARADO CONSTRUCTION, INC.; *U.S. Private*, pg. 211

ALVARADO HOSPITAL, LLC—See UC San Diego Health; *U.S. Private*, pg. 4273
ALVARADO HOSPITAL MEDICAL CENTER, INC.—See UC San Diego Health; *U.S. Private*, pg. 4273
ALVARADO MANUFACTURING CO. INC.—See dormakaba Holding AG; *Int'l*, pg. 2177
ALVARADO STAR—See Alden Global Capital LLC; *U.S. Private*, pg. 156
ALVARADO STREET BAKERY; *U.S. Private*, pg. 212
ALVAREZ HOMES, INC.; *U.S. Private*, pg. 214
ALVAREZ & MARSAL BUSINESS CONSULTING, LLC—See Alvarez & Marsal, Inc.; *U.S. Private*, pg. 213
ALVAREZ & MARSAL DISPUTE ANALYSIS & FORENSIC SERVICES, LLC—See Alvarez & Marsal, Inc.; *U.S. Private*, pg. 213
ALVAREZ & MARSAL HEALTHCARE INDUSTRY GROUP, LLC—See Alvarez & Marsal, Inc.; *U.S. Private*, pg. 213
ALVAREZ & MARSAL, INC.; *U.S. Private*, pg. 212
ALVAREZ & MARSAL NORTH AMERICA, LLC—See Alvarez & Marsal, Inc.; *U.S. Private*, pg. 212
ALVAREZ & MARSAL PUBLIC SECTOR SERVICES, LLC—See Alvarez & Marsal, Inc.; *U.S. Private*, pg. 213
ALVAREZ & MARSAL REAL ESTATE ADVISORY SERVICES, LLC—See Alvarez & Marsal, Inc.; *U.S. Private*, pg. 213
ALVAREZ & MARSAL TAXAND, LLC—See Alvarez & Marsal, Inc.; *U.S. Private*, pg. 213
ALVAREZ TECHNOLOGY GROUP, INC.; *U.S. Private*, pg. 214
ALVARIA, INC.—See Vector Capital Management, L.P.; *U.S. Private*, pg. 4350
ALVARION LTD.; *Int'l*, pg. 401
ALVARION SOUTH AFRICA (PTY) LTD—See SuperCom Ltd.; *Int'l*, pg. 7336
ALVARION TECHNOLOGIES—See SuperCom Ltd.; *Int'l*, pg. 7336
ALVARO P. ESCANDON, INC.; *U.S. Private*, pg. 214
ALVA STATE BANK & TRUST COMPANY—See Grace Investment Company, Inc.; *U.S. Private*, pg. 1749
ALVA SWEDEN AB—See Toray Industries, Inc.; *Int'l*, pg. 7822
ALVA TECHNIKA, UAB—See Cramo Plc; *Int'l*, pg. 1827
ALVA TUNISIA S.A.—See Toray Industries, Inc.; *Int'l*, pg. 7822
ALVEEN SA; *Int'l*, pg. 401
ALVEO LLC—See Stagwell, Inc.; *U.S. Public*, pg. 1925
ALVEST SAS—See Power Corporation of Canada; *Int'l*, pg. 5944
ALVEUS ROMANIA S.R.L.—See KJK Capital Oy; *Int'l*, pg. 4197
ALVEUS SP. Z O.O.—See KJK Capital Oy; *Int'l*, pg. 4198
ALVEUS VERTRIEBS GMBH—See KJK Capital Oy; *Int'l*, pg. 4198
ALVF, INC.—See EVI Industries, Inc.; *U.S. Public*, pg. 803
ALVG ANLAGENVERMIETUNG GMBH—See Landesbank Baden-Wuerttemberg; *Int'l*, pg. 4404
ALVIMAR GLOBAL INC.; *U.S. Private*, pg. 214
ALVIN EQUIPMENT COMPANY INC.; *U.S. Private*, pg. 214
ALV INFRASTRUCTURE DEVELOPMENT INVESTMENT JSC; *Int'l*, pg. 401
ALVIN H. BUTZ, INC.—See Butz Enterprises, Inc.; *U.S. Private*, pg. 698
ALVIN HOLLIS & CO. INC.; *U.S. Private*, pg. 214
ALVIN J. COLEMAN & SON INC.; *U.S. Private*, pg. 214
ALVIN MEDICAL CENTER LLC—See Adeptus Health Inc.; *U.S. Private*, pg. 78
ALVIS, INC.; *U.S. Private*, pg. 214
ALVIVA AB—See AB Volvo; *Int'l*, pg. 42
ALVIVA HOLDINGS LIMITED; *Int'l*, pg. 401
ALVOCOL N.V.—See Colruyt Group N.V.; *Int'l*, pg. 1705
ALVOGEN KOREA CO., LTD.—See Lotus Pharmaceutical Co., Ltd.; *Int'l*, pg. 4561
ALVOGEN KOREA HOLDINGS LTD.—See Lotus Pharmaceutical Co., Ltd.; *Int'l*, pg. 4561
ALVOG S.A.—See HORIBA Ltd; *Int'l*, pg. 3474
ALVO MINERALS LIMITED; *Int'l*, pg. 402
ALVOPETRO ENERGY LTD.; *Int'l*, pg. 402
ALVOPETRO S. A. EXTRACAO DE PETROLEO GAS NATURAL—See Alvopetro Energy Ltd.; *Int'l*, pg. 402
ALVORD-POLK INC.; *U.S. Private*, pg. 214
ALVTECHNOLOGIES PHILIPPINES INC.—See HORIBA Ltd; *Int'l*, pg. 3474
AL WAHA FOR SOFT DRINKS, JUICES, MINERAL WATER, PLASTICS, & PLASTIC CAPS PRODUCTION LLC—See Coca-Cola Icecek A.S.; *Int'l*, pg. 1686
AL WAHA MARITIME LLC—See Waha Capital PJSC; *Int'l*, pg. 8330
AL WARDHA FOOTWEAR & LEATHER PRODUCTS CO. LLC—See Omar Zawawi Establishment LLC; *Int'l*, pg. 5561
AL WASL MARINE LLC—See Tidewater Inc.; *U.S. Public*, pg. 2158
AL-WATANIAH TOWERS COMPANY; *Int'l*, pg. 289
AL-WATANIA INSURANCE COMPANY YSC; *Int'l*, pg. 289
AL WATHBA LUXURY COLLECTION DESERT RESORT & SPA - SOLE PROPRIETORSHIP LLC—See Alpha Dhabi Holding PJSC; *Int'l*, pg. 367

AL WATHBA NATIONAL INSURANCE COMPANY P.S.C.; *Int'l*, pg. 283
ALWAYS BAGELS, INC.; *U.S. Private*, pg. 214
ALWAYS FOR ME, LLC—See Waveland Investments, LLC; *U.S. Private*, pg. 4458
ALWAYS SUMMER LLC; *U.S. Private*, pg. 214
AL-WAZZAN HOLDING GROUP; *Int'l*, pg. 289
ALWERNIA FOSFORANY SP. Z.O.O.—See Kulczyk Investments S.A.; *Int'l*, pg. 4327
AL WIAAM FOR FINANCIAL INVESTMENT CO.; *Int'l*, pg. 283
AL WIDYAN COMPANY—See Saudi Real Estate Co.; *Int'l*, pg. 6594
A.L. WILSON CHEMICAL CO.; *U.S. Private*, pg. 27
A.L. WIZARD, INC.—See Thoma Bravo, L.P.; *U.S. Private*, pg. 4152
ALX ONCOLOGY HOLDINGS INC.; *U.S. Public*, pg. 89
ALX RESOURCES CORP.; *Int'l*, pg. 402
AL YAH SATELLITE COMMUNICATIONS COMPANY PJSC—See Bayanat AI PLC; *Int'l*, pg. 901
AL YAMAMAH STEEL INDUSTRIES COMPANY; *Int'l*, pg. 283
ALYAN PUMP CO.—See Bain Capital, LP; *U.S. Private*, pg. 432
ALYCE DESIGNS INC.; *U.S. Private*, pg. 214
ALY ENERGY SERVICES, INC.; *U.S. Public*, pg. 89
ALYESKA PIPELINE SERVICE COMPANY; *U.S. Private*, pg. 214
ALYESKA SEAFOODS, INC.—See Maruha Nichiro Corporation; *Int'l*, pg. 4711
AL YOUSEF GROUP; *Int'l*, pg. 283
ALYSIS LTD.—See Marfin Investment Group Holdings S.A.; *Int'l*, pg. 4691
AL YUSR INDUSTRIAL CONTRACTING COMPANY WLL; *Int'l*, pg. 283
ALYZIA—See Aeroports de Paris S.A.; *Int'l*, pg. 181
ALYZIA SURETE—See Aeroports de Paris S.A.; *Int'l*, pg. 181
AL-ZAMIN INVESTBANK; *Int'l*, pg. 289
AL-ZARQA EDUCATIONAL & INVESTMENT CO. P.L.C.; *Int'l*, pg. 289
AL ZAWRAA FINANCIAL INVESTMENT PLC; *Int'l*, pg. 283
AL ZAYANI INVESTMENTS WLL; *Int'l*, pg. 283
ALZCHEM GROUP AG; *Int'l*, pg. 402
ALZCHEM HOLDING GMBH—See BLUO SICAV-SIF; *Int'l*, pg. 1075
ALZCHEM LLC—See AlzChem Group AG; *Int'l*, pg. 402
ALZCHEM SHANGHAI CO., LTD.—See AlzChem Group AG; *Int'l*, pg. 402
ALZCHEM TROSTBERG GMBH—See BLUO SICAV-SIF; *Int'l*, pg. 1075
ALZCHEM UK LTD.—See AlzChem Group AG; *Int'l*, pg. 402
ALZECURE PHARMA AB; *Int'l*, pg. 402
ALZHEIMER'S ASSOCIATION; *U.S. Private*, pg. 214
ALZHEIMER'S RESOURCE CENTER OF CONNECTICUT, INC.; *U.S. Private*, pg. 214
ALZHEON, INC.; *U.S. Private*, pg. 214
ALZINOVA AB; *Int'l*, pg. 402
ALZWERKE GMBH—See Wacker Chemie AG; *Int'l*, pg. 8323
AMAAL COMMERCIAL BROKER LLC—See Belhasa Group of Companies; *Int'l*, pg. 963
AMAANAH REFUGEE SERVICES; *U.S. Private*, pg. 215
AMA - ASPHALTMISCHWERKE ANKLAM GMBH—See VINCI S.A.; *Int'l*, pg. 8211
AMAC CORPORATION—See Panasonic Holdings Corporation; *Int'l*, pg. 5720
A MACFRUGEL COMPANY INC.; *U.S. Private*, pg. 18
AMAC LOGISTICS, LLC—See ABRY Partners, LLC; *U.S. Private*, pg. 41
AMACOM HOLDING BV—See DCC plc; *Int'l*, pg. 1989
AMACON CONSTRUCTION LTD; *Int'l*, pg. 403
AMA CORPORATION PLC; *Int'l*, pg. 402
AMACPI INC.; *U.S. Private*, pg. 215
AMACS PROCESS TOWER INTERNALS—See Rockwood Equity Partners, LLC; *U.S. Private*, pg. 3468
AMADA AILINK SERVICE CO., LTD.—See Amada Holdings Co., Ltd.; *Int'l*, pg. 403
AMADA AMERICA, INC.—See Amada Holdings Co., Ltd.; *Int'l*, pg. 403
AMADA ASIA PTE. LTD.—See Amada Holdings Co., Ltd.; *Int'l*, pg. 403
AMADA AUSTRIA GMBH—See Amada Holdings Co., Ltd.; *Int'l*, pg. 403
AMADA BUTSURYU CO., LTD.—See Amada Holdings Co., Ltd.; *Int'l*, pg. 403
AMADA CANADA LTD.—See Amada Holdings Co., Ltd.; *Int'l*, pg. 404
AMADA CO., LTD, - ONO PLANT—See Amada Holdings Co., Ltd.; *Int'l*, pg. 403
AMADA CO., LTD.—See Amada Holdings Co., Ltd.; *Int'l*, pg. 403
AMADA CUTTING TECHNOLOGIES, INC.—See Amada Holdings Co., Ltd.; *Int'l*, pg. 404
AMADA DE MEXICO, S. DE R.L. DE C.V.—See Amada Holdings Co., Ltd.; *Int'l*, pg. 404

AMADA DO BRASIL LTDA.—See Amada Holdings Co., Ltd.; *Int'l*, pg. 404
AMADA DOCUMECH CO., LTD.—See Amada Holdings Co., Ltd.; *Int'l*, pg. 403
AMADA ENGINEERING CO., LTD.—See Amada Holdings Co., Ltd.; *Int'l*, pg. 403
AMADA ENGINEERING EUROPE S.P.A.—See Amada Holdings Co., Ltd.; *Int'l*, pg. 404
AMADA EUROPE S.A.—See Amada Holdings Co., Ltd.; *Int'l*, pg. 403
AMADA EUROPE SOFTWARE CENTER, S.A.S—See Amada Holdings Co., Ltd.; *Int'l*, pg. 403
AMADA FRANCHISE CENTER CO., LTD.—See Amada Holdings Co., Ltd.; *Int'l*, pg. 404
AMADA GMBH—See Amada Holdings Co., Ltd.; *Int'l*, pg. 404
AMADA HOLDINGS CO., LTD.; *Int'l*, pg. 403
AMADA HONG KONG CO., LTD.—See Amada Holdings Co., Ltd.; *Int'l*, pg. 404
AMADA (INDIA) PVT. LTD.—See Amada Holdings Co., Ltd.; *Int'l*, pg. 403
AMADA INTERNATIONAL INDUSTRY & TRADING (SHANGHAI) CO., LTD.—See Amada Holdings Co., Ltd.; *Int'l*, pg. 404
AMADA INTERNATIONAL TRADING (SHENZHEN) CO., LTD—See Amada Holdings Co., Ltd.; *Int'l*, pg. 404
AMADA ITALIA S.R.L.—See Amada Holdings Co., Ltd.; *Int'l*, pg. 404
AMADA KOREA CO., LTD.—See Amada Holdings Co., Ltd.; *Int'l*, pg. 404
AMADA LASER AMERICA INC.—See Amada Holdings Co., Ltd.; *Int'l*, pg. 404
AMADA LEASE CO., LTD.—See Tokyo Century Corporation; *Int'l*, pg. 7788
AMADA LIANYUNGANG MACHINERY CO., LTD.—See Amada Holdings Co., Ltd.; *Int'l*, pg. 404
AMADA LIANYUNGANG MACHINE TOOL CO., LTD—See Amada Holdings Co., Ltd.; *Int'l*, pg. 404
AMADA MACHINE TOOLS AMERICA, INC.—See Amada Holdings Co., Ltd.; *Int'l*, pg. 404
AMADA MACHINE TOOLS CO., LTD.—See Amada Holdings Co., Ltd.; *Int'l*, pg. 404
AMADA MACHINE TOOLS EUROPE GMBH FRANCE—See Amada Holdings Co., Ltd.; *Int'l*, pg. 404
AMADA MACHINE TOOLS EUROPE GMBH—See Amada Holdings Co., Ltd.; *Int'l*, pg. 404
AMADA MACHINE TOOLS (THAILAND) CO., LTD.—See Amada Holdings Co., Ltd.; *Int'l*, pg. 403
AMADA (MALAYSIA) SDN. BHD.—See Amada Holdings Co., Ltd.; *Int'l*, pg. 403
AMADA MAQUINARIA S.I.—See Amada Holdings Co., Ltd.; *Int'l*, pg. 404
AMADA NORTH AMERICA, INC.—See Amada Holdings Co., Ltd.; *Int'l*, pg. 404
AMADA OCEANIA PTY. LTD.—See Amada Holdings Co., Ltd.; *Int'l*, pg. 403
AMADA OUTILLAGE S.A.—See Amada Holdings Co., Ltd.; *Int'l*, pg. 404
AMADA PLANTECH CO., LTD.—See Amada Holdings Co., Ltd.; *Int'l*, pg. 404
AMADA S.A.—See Amada Holdings Co., Ltd.; *Int'l*, pg. 404
AMADAS GROUP INC. - ALBANY PLANT—See Amadas Group Inc.; *U.S. Private*, pg. 215
AMADAS GROUP INC.; *U.S. Private*, pg. 215
AMADA SHANGHAI MACHINE TECH CO., LTD.—See Amada Holdings Co., Ltd.; *Int'l*, pg. 404
AMADAS INDUSTRIES INC—See Amadas Group Inc.; *U.S. Private*, pg. 215
AMADA SINGAPORE (1989) PTE. LTD.—See Amada Holdings Co., Ltd.; *Int'l*, pg. 403
AMADA SOFT (INDIA) PVT. LTD.—See Amada Holdings Co., Ltd.; *Int'l*, pg. 403
AMADA SWEDEN AB—See Amada Holdings Co., Ltd.; *Int'l*, pg. 404
AMADA TAIWAN, INC.—See Amada Holdings Co., Ltd.; *Int'l*, pg. 404
AMADA (THAILAND) CO., LTD.—See Amada Holdings Co., Ltd.; *Int'l*, pg. 403
AMADA TOOL AMERICA, INC.—See Amada Holdings Co., Ltd.; *Int'l*, pg. 404
AMADA TOOL PRECISION CO., LTD.—See Amada Holdings Co., Ltd.; *Int'l*, pg. 404
AMADA TOYO CO., LTD.—See Amada Holdings Co., Ltd.; *Int'l*, pg. 404
AMADA TURKIYE MAKINA TEKNOLOJI SANAYI VE TICARET LTD.—See Amada Holdings Co., Ltd.; *Int'l*, pg. 404
AMADA UNITED KINGDOM LIMITED—See Amada Holdings Co., Ltd.; *Int'l*, pg. 404
AMADA VIETNAM CO., LTD.—See Amada Holdings Co., Ltd.; *Int'l*, pg. 403
AMADEO FARELL S.A.U.—See Kadant Inc.; *U.S. Public*, pg. 1212
AMADEUS AIRPORT IT GMBH—See Amadeus IT Group, S.A.; *Int'l*, pg. 405
AMADEUS ALBANIA SH.P.K.—See Amadeus IT Group, S.A.; *Int'l*, pg. 405
AMADEUS ARGENTINA S.A.—See Amadeus IT Group, S.A.; *Int'l*, pg. 405

COMPANY NAME INDEX

AMADEUS ASIA LIMITED—See Amadeus IT Group, S.A.; *Int'l*, pg. 405
AMADEUS AUSTRIA MARKETING GMBH—See Amadeus IT Group, S.A.; *Int'l*, pg. 405
AMADEUS (BEIJING) INFORMATION TECHNOLOGY CO., LTD.—See Amadeus IT Group, S.A.; *Int'l*, pg. 405
AMADEUS BENELUX N.V.—See Amadeus IT Group, S.A.; *Int'l*, pg. 405
AMADEUS BILGI TEKNOLOJISI HIZMETLERI A.S—See Amadeus IT Group, S.A.; *Int'l*, pg. 405
AMADEUS BOSNA D.O.O. ZA MARKETING SARAJEVO—See Amadeus IT Group, S.A.; *Int'l*, pg. 405
AMADEUS BRASIL LTDA.—See Amadeus IT Group, S.A.; *Int'l*, pg. 405
AMADEUS BULGARIA OOD—See Amadeus IT Group, S.A.; *Int'l*, pg. 405
AMADEUS CAPITAL PARTNERS LTD.; *Int'l*, pg. 404
AMADEUS CENTRAL AND WEST AFRICA S.A.—See Amadeus IT Group, S.A.; *Int'l*, pg. 405
AMADEUS CROATIA D.D.—See Croatia Airlines d.d.; *Int'l*, pg. 1851
AMADEUS CZECH REPUBLIC & SLOVAKIA S.R.O.—See Amadeus IT Group, S.A.; *Int'l*, pg. 405
AMADEUS DENMARK A/S—See Amadeus IT Group, S.A.; *Int'l*, pg. 405
AMADEUS EESTI AS—See Amadeus IT Group, S.A.; *Int'l*, pg. 405
AMADEUS EGYPT COMPUTERIZED RESERVATION SERVICES S.A.E.—See Amadeus IT Group, S.A.; *Int'l*, pg. 405
AMADEUS FINLAND OY—See Finnair Plc; *Int'l*, pg. 2675
AMADEUS FIRE AG; *Int'l*, pg. 405
AMADEUS FIRE INTERIM- UND PROJEKTMANAGEMENT GMBH—See Amadeus Fire AG; *Int'l*, pg. 405
AMADEUS FIRE SERVICES GMBH—See Amadeus Fire AG; *Int'l*, pg. 405
AMADEUS FRANCE S.A.—See Amadeus IT Group, S.A.; *Int'l*, pg. 405
AMADEUS FRANCE SNC—See Amadeus IT Group, S.A.; *Int'l*, pg. 405
AMADEUS GDS LLP—See Amadeus IT Group, S.A.; *Int'l*, pg. 405
AMADEUS GDS (MALAYSIA) SDN. BHD.—See Amadeus IT Group, S.A.; *Int'l*, pg. 405
AMADEUS GDS SINGAPORE PTE. LTD.—See Amadeus IT Group, S.A.; *Int'l*, pg. 406
AMADEUS GERMANY GMBH—See Amadeus IT Group, S.A.; *Int'l*, pg. 406
AMADEUSGLOBAL ECUADOR S.A.—See Amadeus IT Group, S.A.; *Int'l*, pg. 405
AMADEUS GLOBAL TRAVEL DISTRIBUTION LTD.—See Amadeus IT Group, S.A.; *Int'l*, pg. 405
AMADEUS GLOBAL TRAVEL ISRAEL LTD.—See Amadeus IT Group, S.A.; *Int'l*, pg. 406
AMADEUS GTD (MALTA) LIMITED—See Amadeus IT Group, S.A.; *Int'l*, pg. 406
AMADEUS GTD SOUTHERN AFRICA PTY. LTD.—See Amadeus IT Group, S.A.; *Int'l*, pg. 406
AMADEUS HELLAS ELECTRONIC TRAVEL INFORMATION SERVICES SINGLE MEMBER SOCIETE ANONYME—See Amadeus IT Group, S.A.; *Int'l*, pg. 405
AMADEUS HELLAS S.A.—See Amadeus IT Group, S.A.; *Int'l*, pg. 406
AMADEUS HONG KONG LIMITED—See Amadeus IT Group, S.A.; *Int'l*, pg. 406
AMADEUS HOSPITALITY AMERICAS, INC.—See Amadeus IT Group, S.A.; *Int'l*, pg. 405
AMADEUS HOSPITALITY ASIA PACIFIC PTE. LTD.—See Amadeus IT Group, S.A.; *Int'l*, pg. 405
AMADEUS HOSPITALITY NETHERLANDS B.V.—See Amadeus IT Group, S.A.; *Int'l*, pg. 405
AMADEUS HOSPITALITY UK LIMITED—See Amadeus IT Group, S.A.; *Int'l*, pg. 405
AMADEUS INFORMATION TECHNOLOGY LLC—See Amadeus IT Group, S.A.; *Int'l*, pg. 407
AMADEUS INTEGRATED SOLUTIONS PTY LTD—See Amadeus IT Group, S.A.; *Int'l*, pg. 407
AMADEUS ITALIA S.P.A.—See Amadeus IT Group, S.A.; *Int'l*, pg. 406
AMADEUS IT GROUP COLOMBIA S.A.S.—See Amadeus IT Group, S.A.; *Int'l*, pg. 405
AMADEUS IT GROUP S.A.—See Amadeus IT Group, S.A.; *Int'l*, pg. 405
AMADEUS IT GROUP, S.A.; *Int'l*, pg. 405
AMADEUS IT PACIFIC PTY. LTD.—See Amadeus IT Group, S.A.; *Int'l*, pg. 405
AMADEUS IT SERVICES UK LIMITED—See Amadeus IT Group, S.A.; *Int'l*, pg. 407
AMADEUS JAPAN K.K.—See Amadeus IT Group, S.A.; *Int'l*, pg. 407
AMADEUS KOREA, LTD.—See Amadeus IT Group, S.A.; *Int'l*, pg. 407
AMADEUS LEBANON S.A.R.L.—See Amadeus IT Group, S.A.; *Int'l*, pg. 407
AMADEUS LEISURE IT GMBH—See Amadeus IT Group, S.A.; *Int'l*, pg. 407

AMADEUS MACEDONIA DOOEL—See Amadeus IT Group, S.A.; *Int'l*, pg. 407
AMADEUS MAGYAROSZAG KFT—See Amadeus IT Group, S.A.; *Int'l*, pg. 406
AMADEUS MARKETING (GHANA) LTD.—See Amadeus IT Group, S.A.; *Int'l*, pg. 407
AMADEUS MARKETING IRELAND LTD.—See Amadeus IT Group, S.A.; *Int'l*, pg. 406
AMADEUS MARKETING NIGERIA LTD.—See Amadeus IT Group, S.A.; *Int'l*, pg. 407
AMADEUS MARKETING PHILS INC.—See Amadeus IT Group, S.A.; *Int'l*, pg. 406
AMADEUS MARKETING ROMANIA S.R.L.—See Amadeus IT Group, S.A.; *Int'l*, pg. 406
AMADEUS MARKETING (SCHWEIZ) A.G.—See Amadeus IT Group, S.A.; *Int'l*, pg. 406
AMADEUS MARKETING (UK) LTD.—See Amadeus IT Group, S.A.; *Int'l*, pg. 406
AMADEUS MAROC S.A.S.—See Amadeus IT Group, S.A.; *Int'l*, pg. 406
AMADEUS MEXICO, S.A. DE C.V.—See Amadeus IT Group, S.A.; *Int'l*, pg. 407
AMADEUS NORTH AMERICA, INC. - E-TRAVEL BUSINESS—See Amadeus IT Group, S.A.; *Int'l*, pg. 406
AMADEUS NORTH AMERICA, INC.—See Amadeus IT Group, S.A.; *Int'l*, pg. 406
AMADEUS NORWAY AS—See Amadeus IT Group, S.A.; *Int'l*, pg. 406
AMADEUS PARAGUAY S.R.L.—See Amadeus IT Group, S.A.; *Int'l*, pg. 406
AMADEUS PERU S.A.—See Amadeus IT Group, S.A.; *Int'l*, pg. 406
AMADEUS POLSKA SP. Z O.O.—See Amadeus IT Group, S.A.; *Int'l*, pg. 406
AMADEUS PURCHASE DEBT, S.A.—See Amadeus IT Group, S.A.; *Int'l*, pg. 406
AMADEUS REVENUE INTEGRITY INC.—See Amadeus IT Group, S.A.; *Int'l*, pg. 406
AMADEUS REZERVASYON DAGITIM SISTEMLERI A.S.—See Amadeus IT Group, S.A.; *Int'l*, pg. 406
AMADEUS S.A.S.—See Amadeus IT Group, S.A.; *Int'l*, pg. 407
AMADEUS SAUDI ARABIA LIMITED—See Amadeus IT Group, S.A.; *Int'l*, pg. 407
AMADEUS SCANDINAVIA AB.—See Amadeus IT Group, S.A.; *Int'l*, pg. 406
AMADEUS SERVICES LTD.—See Amadeus IT Group, S.A.; *Int'l*, pg. 406
AMADEUS SLOVENIJA, D.O.O.—See Amadeus IT Group, S.A.; *Int'l*, pg. 407
AMADEUS SOFIA LABS EOOD—See Amadeus IT Group, S.A.; *Int'l*, pg. 407
AMADEUS SOFTWARE LABS INDIA PRIVATE LIMITED—See Amadeus IT Group, S.A.; *Int'l*, pg. 407
AMADEUS SOFTWARE TECHNOLOGY (SHANGAI) CO., LTD.—See Amadeus IT Group, S.A.; *Int'l*, pg. 407
AMADEUS SOLUCIONES TECNOLOGICAS, S.A—See Amadeus IT Group, S.A.; *Int'l*, pg. 406
AMADEUS SWEDEN AB—See Amadeus IT Group, S.A.; *Int'l*, pg. 406
AMADEUS SYRIA LIMITED LIABILITY—See Amadeus IT Group, S.A.; *Int'l*, pg. 407
AMADEUS TAIWAN COMPANY LIMITED—See Amadeus IT Group, S.A.; *Int'l*, pg. 407
AMAD INVESTMENT & REAL ESTATE DEVELOPMENT PLC; *Int'l*, pg. 403
AMAECO S.R.L.—See Sesa S.p.A.; *Int'l*, pg. 6728
AMAERO INTERNATIONAL LIMITED; *Int'l*, pg. 407
AMAGASA CO., LTD.; *Int'l*, pg. 407
AMAG ASIA PACIFIC LTD.—See AMAG Austria Metall AG; *Int'l*, pg. 407
AMAG AUSTRIA METALL AG; *Int'l*, pg. 407
AMAG BENELUX B. V.—See AMAG Austria Metall AG; *Int'l*, pg. 407
AMAG CHINA LTD.—See AMAG Austria Metall AG; *Int'l*, pg. 407
AMAG COMPONENTS DEUTSCHLAND GMBH—See AMAG Austria Metall AG; *Int'l*, pg. 408
AMAG COMPONENTS KARLSRUHE GMBH—See AMAG Austria Metall AG; *Int'l*, pg. 408
AMAG DEUTSCHLAND GMBH—See AMAG Austria Metall AG; *Int'l*, pg. 407
AMAG FRANCE S.A.R.L.—See AMAG Austria Metall AG; *Int'l*, pg. 407
AMAGIC HOLOGRAPHICS, INC.—See K Laser Technology Inc.; *Int'l*, pg. 4037
AMAGIC HOLOGRAPHICS INDIA PVT. LTD.—See K Laser Technology Inc.; *Int'l*, pg. 4037
AMAG ITALIA S.R.L.—See AMAG Austria Metall AG; *Int'l*, pg. 408
AMAG METAL GMBH—See AMAG Austria Metall AG; *Int'l*, pg. 408
AMAG PHARMACEUTICALS, INC.; *U.S. Private*, pg. 215
AMAG ROLLING EASTERN EUROPE, S.R.O.—See AMAG Austria Metall AG; *Int'l*, pg. 408
AMAG ROLLING GMBH—See AMAG Austria Metall AG; *Int'l*, pg. 408

AMAG ROLLING IBERIA S.L.—See AMAG Austria Metall AG; *Int'l*, pg. 408
AMA GROUP LIMITED; *Int'l*, pg. 403
AMAG SERVICE GMBH—See AMAG Austria Metall AG; *Int'l*, pg. 408
AMAG TECHNOLOGY LTD.—See Allied Universal Manager LLC; *U.S. Private*, pg. 188
AMAG UK LTD.—See AMAG Austria Metall AG; *Int'l*, pg. 408
AMAG USA CORP.—See AMAG Austria Metall AG; *Int'l*, pg. 408
AMAIN.COM, INC.; *U.S. Private*, pg. 215
AMA INDUSTRIAL COMPANY; *Int'l*, pg. 403
AMAIZEINGLY GREEN PRODUCTS, L.P.; *Int'l*, pg. 408
AMAIZEINGLY GREEN VALUE PRODUCTS ULC—See Amaizeingly Green Products, L.P.; *Int'l*, pg. 408
AMAL ASSET MANAGEMENT LIMITED—See Balmain Corp.; *Int'l*, pg. 810
AMA LEO BURNETT—See Publicis Groupe S.A.; *Int'l*, pg. 6100
AMA LEO BURNETT—See Publicis Groupe S.A.; *Int'l*, pg. 6102
AMALFE BROS INC.; *U.S. Private*, pg. 215
AMALGAMATED BANK OF CHICAGO—See Amalgamated Investments Co.; *U.S. Private*, pg. 215
AMALGAMATED BANK—See Amalgamated Financial Corp.; *U.S. Public*, pg. 89
AMALGAMATED BEVERAGE INDUSTRIES—See Anheuser-Busch InBev SA/NV; *Int'l*, pg. 464
AMALGAMATED CONSTRUCTION (SCOTLAND) LTD.—See Renew Holdings plc; *Int'l*, pg. 6277
AMALGAMATED ELECTRICITY CO., LTD.; *Int'l*, pg. 408
AMALGAMATED ELECTRONIC CORPORATION LIMITED—See The Carlyle Group Inc.; *U.S. Public*, pg. 2045
AMALGAMATED FINANCIAL CORP.; *U.S. Public*, pg. 89
AMALGAMATED INSURANCE FUND; *U.S. Private*, pg. 215
AMALGAMATED INVESTMENTS CO.; *U.S. Private*, pg. 215
THE AMALGAMATED LIFE INSURANCE CO. INC.—See Amalgamated Insurance Fund; *U.S. Private*, pg. 215
AMALGAMATED METAL (AUSTRALIA) LTD—See Amalgamated Metal Corporation PLC; *Int'l*, pg. 408
AMALGAMATED METAL CORPORATION PLC; *Int'l*, pg. 408
AMALGAMATED METAL TRADING LTD—See Amalgamated Metal Corporation PLC; *Int'l*, pg. 408
AMALGAMATED REGIONAL TRADING (ART) HOLDINGS LTD.; *Int'l*, pg. 409
AMALGAMATED SECURITY SERVICES LIMITED; *Int'l*, pg. 409
AMALGAMATED SUGAR CO.—See Snake River Sugar Co.; *U.S. Private*, pg. 3699
AMALGAMATED SUGAR CO.—See Snake River Sugar Co.; *U.S. Private*, pg. 3699
AMALGAMATED SUGAR CO.—See Snake River Sugar Co.; *U.S. Private*, pg. 3699
AMALGAMATED TELECOM HOLDINGS KIRIBATI LIMITED—See Fiji National Provident Fund; *Int'l*, pg. 2661
AMALGAMATED TELECOM HOLDINGS LIMITED—See Fiji National Provident Fund; *Int'l*, pg. 2661
AMALGAME; *Int'l*, pg. 409
AMALGAMET CANADA—See Amalgamated Metal Corporation PLC; *Int'l*, pg. 409
AMALGAMET (SOUTH EAST ASIA) PTE LTD—See Amalgamated Metal Corporation PLC; *Int'l*, pg. 408
AMALGA N.V.—See Kendrion N.V.; *Int'l*, pg. 4126
AMALGA TRUST INC.—See Amalgamated Investments Co.; *U.S. Private*, pg. 215
AMALIE ARENA—See Tampa Bay Sports & Entertainment LLC; *U.S. Private*, pg. 3929
AMALIE OIL COMPANY; *U.S. Private*, pg. 215
AMAL LIMITED; *Int'l*, pg. 408
AMALLION ENTERPRISE (THAILAND) CORPORATION LTD.—See AE Multi Holdings Berhad; *Int'l*, pg. 170
AMAL NEW ZEALAND LIMITED—See Balmain Corp.; *Int'l*, pg. 809
AMALPAK LTD.—See Visy Industries Holdings Pty. Ltd.; *Int'l*, pg. 8255
AMAL SAMHA CO.; *Int'l*, pg. 408
AMA MARINE PUBLIC COMPANY LIMITED; *Int'l*, pg. 403
AMAMCO TOOL & SUPPLY CO., INC.—See OSG Corporation; *Int'l*, pg. 5648
AMANA AGRICULTURAL & INDUSTRIAL INVESTMENT CO.; *Int'l*, pg. 409
AMANACLIQ SHANGHAI LIMITED—See Amana Inc.; *Int'l*, pg. 409
AMANA COFFEE & TEA CO.—See Amana Society, Inc.; *U.S. Private*, pg. 216
AMANA COOPERATIVE INSURANCE COMPANY; *Int'l*, pg. 409
AMANA FARMS, INC.—See Amana Society, Inc.; *U.S. Private*, pg. 216
AMANAH HARTA TANAH PNB; *Int'l*, pg. 409
AMANAH LEASING PUBLIC COMPANY LIMITED; *Int'l*, pg. 409

AMANAH LEASING PUBLIC COMPANY LIMITED

CORPORATE AFFILIATIONS

AMANAH MUTUAL BERHAD—See Malayan Banking Berhad; *Int'l*, pg. 4659
AMANAHRAYA REAL ESTATE INVESTMENT TRUST; *Int'l*, pg. 409
AMANAH SAHAM NASIONAL BERHAD—See Permodalan Nasional Berhad; *Int'l*, pg. 5809
AMANA INC.; *Int'l*, pg. 409
AMANA-NORDSTROM MOTEL CO.—See Amana Society, Inc.; *U.S. Private*, pg. 216
AMANA SOCIETY, INC.; *U.S. Private*, pg. 216
AMANA SOCIETY SERVICE CO.—See Amana Society, Inc.; *U.S. Private*, pg. 216
AMANASU ENVIRONMENT CORPORATION; *U.S. Public*, pg. 90
AMANASU TECHNO HOLDINGS CORPORATION; *U.S. Public*, pg. 90
AMANA TAKAFUL (MALDIVES) PLC—See Amana Takaful PLC; *Int'l*, pg. 409
AMANA TAKAFUL PLC; *Int'l*, pg. 409
AMANAT HOLDINGS PJSC; *Int'l*, pg. 409
AMANAYA VENTURES LIMITED; *Int'l*, pg. 410
AMAN BUILDERS INC.; *Int'l*, pg. 409
AMANCO MEXICO—See Bharti Enterprises Limited; *Int'l*, pg. 1012
AMAN COTTON FIBROUS LIMITED; *Int'l*, pg. 409
AMANCRUISES COMPANY LIMITED—See DLF Limited; *Int'l*, pg. 2141
AMANDA STORESENTER AS—See BNP Paribas SA; *Int'l*, pg. 1079
AMANDO PENA INC.; *U.S. Private*, pg. 216
A.M. ANDREWS CO.; *U.S. Private*, pg. 27
AMANDUS D. MOYER LUMBER INCORPORATED; *U.S. Private*, pg. 216
AMANET MANAGEMENT & SYSTEMS LTD.; *Int'l*, pg. 410
AMAN FEED LTD.; *Int'l*, pg. 409
AMAN FREIGHT (MALAYSIA) SDN. BHD.—See DRB-HICOM Berhad; *Int'l*, pg. 2201
AMANGELDY GAS LLP; *Int'l*, pg. 410
AMANI FINANCIAL SERVICES SAOC—See Tawoos LLC; *Int'l*, pg. 7477
AMANI GOLD LIMITED; *Int'l*, pg. 410
AMANN GIRRBACH AG—See Capvis AG; *Int'l*, pg. 1318
AMANN GIRRBACH AMERICA INC.—See Capvis AG; *Int'l*, pg. 1318
AMANN GIRRBACH ASIA PTE. LTD.—See Capvis AG; *Int'l*, pg. 1318
AMANN GIRRBACH BRASIL LTDA.—See Capvis AG; *Int'l*, pg. 1318
AMANN GIRRBACH CHINA CO., LTD.—See Capvis AG; *Int'l*, pg. 1318
AMANN GIRRBACH GMBH—See Capvis AG; *Int'l*, pg. 1318
AMANO AGENCY CORP.—See Amano Corporation; *Int'l*, pg. 410
AMANO BUSINESS CREDIT—See Amano Corporation; *Int'l*, pg. 411
AMANO BUSINESS SOLUTIONS CORP.—See Amano Corporation; *Int'l*, pg. 410
AMANO CINCINNATI CANADA, INC.—See Amano Corporation; *Int'l*, pg. 410
AMANO CINCINNATI, INC.—See Amano Corporation; *Int'l*, pg. 410
AMANO CLEANTECH MALAYSIA SDN. BHD.—See Amano Corporation; *Int'l*, pg. 410
AMANO CORPORATION - HOSOE FACILITY—See Amano Corporation; *Int'l*, pg. 410
AMANO CORPORATION - MIYAKODA FACILITY—See Amano Corporation; *Int'l*, pg. 410
AMANO CORPORATION—See Amano Corporation; *Int'l*, pg. 410
AMANO CORPORATION; *Int'l*, pg. 410
AMANO CORPORATION—See Amano Corporation; *Int'l*, pg. 410
AMANO CORPORATION—See Amano Corporation; *Int'l*, pg. 410
AMANO CORPORATION - TSUKUI FACILITY—See Amano Corporation; *Int'l*, pg. 410
AMANO CORPORATION-YOKOHAMA FACILITY—See Amano Corporation; *Int'l*, pg. 410
AMANO ELECTRONICS EUROPE, N.V.—See Amano Corporation; *Int'l*, pg. 410
AMANO EUROPE HOLDINGS N.V.—See Amano Corporation; *Int'l*, pg. 410
AMANOHASHIDATE HOTEL CO., LTD.—See Hankyu Hanshin Holdings Inc.; *Int'l*, pg. 3255
AMANO INTERNATIONAL TRADING (SHANGHAI) CO., LTD.—See Amano Corporation; *Int'l*, pg. 410
AMANO KOREA CORPORATION—See Amano Corporation; *Int'l*, pg. 410
AMANO MAINTENANCE ENGINEERING CORP.—See Amano Corporation; *Int'l*, pg. 410
AMANO MALAYSIA SDN.BHD.—See Amano Corporation; *Int'l*, pg. 410
AMANO MANAGEMENT SERVICE CORP.—See Amano Corporation; *Int'l*, pg. 410
AMANO MCGANN CANADA INC.—See Amano Corporation; *Int'l*, pg. 411

AMANO MCGANN, INC.—See Amano Corporation; *Int'l*, pg. 411
AMANO MCGANN—See Amano Corporation; *Int'l*, pg. 411
AMANO MUSASHI ELECTRIC CORPORATION—See Amano Corporation; *Int'l*, pg. 411
AMANO PARKING SERVICE LTD.—See Amano Corporation; *Int'l*, pg. 411
AMANO SECURE JAPAN CORPORATION—See Amano Corporation; *Int'l*, pg. 411
AMANO SOFTWARE ENGINEERING (SHANGHAI) CO., LTD.—See Amano Corporation; *Int'l*, pg. 411
AMANO THAI INTERNATIONAL CO., LTD.—See Amano Corporation; *Int'l*, pg. 411
AMANO TIME & AIR SINGAPORE PTE. LTD.—See Amano Corporation; *Int'l*, pg. 411
AMANO TIME & ECOLOGY DE MEXICO S.A.DE C.V.—See Amano Corporation; *Int'l*, pg. 411
AMANO TIME & PARKING SPAIN, S.A.—See Amano Corporation; *Int'l*, pg. 411
AMANO UK LTD. - PARKING DIVISION—See Amano Corporation; *Int'l*, pg. 410
AMANO VIETNAM CO., LTD.—See Amano Corporation; *Int'l*, pg. 411
AMANOX SOLUTIONS AG—See Kontron AG; *Int'l*, pg. 4276
AMANRESORTS INTERNATIONAL PRIVATE LIMITED—See DLF Limited; *Int'l*, pg. 2141
AMANRESORTS LIMITED—See DLF Limited; *Int'l*, pg. 2141
AMANTA LAO CO., LTD.—See Amanta Resources Ltd.; *Int'l*, pg. 411
AMANTA RESOURCES LTD.; *Int'l*, pg. 411
A.MANZONI AND C. SPA—See Giovanni Agnelli B.V.; *Int'l*, pg. 2978
AMAPA FLORESTAL E CELULOSE S.A.—See Nippon Paper Industries Co., Ltd.; *Int'l*, pg. 5326
AMA PLASTICS; *U.S. Private*, pg. 215
AMA PLY LTD.—See Alam Group of Companies; *Int'l*, pg. 289
AMA PRECISION INC—See Pegatron Corporation; *Int'l*, pg. 5781
AMARA BRASIL, LTDA.—See Iberdrola, S.A.; *Int'l*, pg. 3570
AMARA HOLDINGS LTD.; *Int'l*, pg. 411
AMARA HOSPITALITY (THAILAND) CO., LTD.—See Amara Holdings Ltd.; *Int'l*, pg. 411
AMARA HOTEL PROPERTIES PTE LTD—See Amara Holdings Ltd.; *Int'l*, pg. 411
AMARA INTERNATIONAL HOTELS & RESORTS PTE LTD—See Amara Holdings Ltd.; *Int'l*, pg. 411
AMARAK CHEMICALS FZC—See Aries Agro Limited; *Int'l*, pg. 564
AMARANTUS BIOSCIENCE HOLDINGS, INC.; *U.S. Public*, pg. 90
AMARA RAJA ENERGY & MOBILITY LIMITED; *Int'l*, pg. 411
AMARA RAJA POWER SYSTEMS LIMITED—See Amara Raja Energy & Mobility Limited; *Int'l*, pg. 411
AM ARA REIT MANAGERS SDN BHD—See AMMB Holdings Berhad; *Int'l*, pg. 429
AMARAS AG—See Bechtle AG; *Int'l*, pg. 937
AMARA, S.A.—See ProA Capital de Inversiones SGEIC, S.A.; *Int'l*, pg. 5985
AMARA SENTOSA INVESTMENTS PTE LTD—See Amara Holdings Ltd.; *Int'l*, pg. 411
AMARATHAI RESTAURANT PTE LTD—See Amara Holdings Ltd.; *Int'l*, pg. 411
AMARAY—See Atlas Holdings, LLC; *U.S. Private*, pg. 378
AMAR CHITRA KATHA PRIVATE LIMITED—See Future Corporate Resources Limited; *Int'l*, pg. 2853
AMARC RESOURCES LTD.—See Hunter Dickinson Inc.; *Int'l*, pg. 3536
AMA RESEARCH LIMITED—See Informa plc; *Int'l*, pg. 3691
AMAR FINANCE & LEASING COMPANY (K.S.C.C.); *Int'l*, pg. 411
AMARI AUSTRIA GMBH—See Henley Management Company; *U.S. Private*, pg. 1916
AMARI HUNGARIA KFT.—See Henley Management Company; *U.S. Private*, pg. 1916
AMARILLO GEAR COMPANY INC.—See Berkshire Hathaway Inc.; *U.S. Public*, pg. 311
AMARILLO GLOBE-NEWS—See Gannett Co., Inc.; *U.S. Public*, pg. 901
AMARILLO GOLD CORPORATION—See Hochschild Mining plc; *Int'l*, pg. 3437
AMARILLO HARDWARE COMPANY; *U.S. Private*, pg. 216
AMARILLO MINERACAO DO BRASIL LIMITADA—See Hochschild Mining plc; *Int'l*, pg. 3438
AMARILLO NATIONAL BANCORP, INC.; *U.S. Private*, pg. 216
AMARILLO NATIONAL BANK—See Amarillo National Bancorp, Inc.; *U.S. Private*, pg. 216
AMARILLO WIND MACHINE COMPANY INC.—See Berkshire Hathaway Inc.; *U.S. Public*, pg. 311
AMARI METALS IBERICA SLU—See Henley Management Company; *U.S. Private*, pg. 1916

AMAR IMMUNODIAGNOSTICS PVT LTD—See Eurofins Scientific S.E.; *Int'l*, pg. 2535
AMARIN BOOK CENTER COMPANY LIMITED—See Amarin Printing & Publishing Public Company Limited; *Int'l*, pg. 412
AMARIN CORPORATION PLC; *Int'l*, pg. 412
AMARIN PHARMA, INC.—See AMARIN CORPORATION PLC; *Int'l*, pg. 412
AMARIN PRINTING & PUBLISHING PUBLIC COMPANY LIMITED; *Int'l*, pg. 412
AMARIN TELEVISION COMPANY LIMITED—See Amarin Printing & Publishing Public Company Limited; *Int'l*, pg. 412
AMARI PLASTICS PLC—See Blackfriars Corp.; *U.S. Private*, pg. 574
AMARITA BUXTEHUDE GMBH—See MK-Kliniken AG; *Int'l*, pg. 5001
AMARITA DATTELN GMBH—See MK-Kliniken AG; *Int'l*, pg. 5001
AMARITA HAMBURG MITTE PLUS GMBH—See MK-Kliniken AG; *Int'l*, pg. 5001
AMARITA OLDENBURG GMBH—See MK-Kliniken AG; *Int'l*, pg. 5001
AMARJOTHI SPINNING MILLS LTD - AMARJOTHI DYEING DIVISION—See Amarjothi Spinning Mills Ltd; *Int'l*, pg. 412
AMARJOTHI SPINNING MILLS LTD; *Int'l*, pg. 412
A-MARK PRECIOUS METALS, INC.; *U.S. Public*, pg. 10
THE AMARNA CO.—See H.I.G. Capital, LLC; *U.S. Private*, pg. 1832
AMARNATH SECURITIES LIMITED; *Int'l*, pg. 412
AMARO FOOD ENTERPRISES INC; *U.S. Private*, pg. 216
AMAR OIL CO. INC.; *U.S. Private*, pg. 216
AMARON BATTERIES (P) LTD.—See Amara Raja Energy & Mobility Limited; *Int'l*, pg. 411
AMAROQ MINERALS LIMITED; *Int'l*, pg. 412
AMARR COMPANY—See ASSA ABLOY AB; *Int'l*, pg. 634
A MARTINS & FERNANDES S.A—See Guerbet SA; *Int'l*, pg. 3172
A. MARTINS & FERNANDES—See Guerbet SA; *Int'l*, pg. 3172
AMART S.A.—See Ackermans & van Haaren NV; *Int'l*, pg. 104
AMARU, INC.; *Int'l*, pg. 412
AMAS-INVESTMENT AND PROJECT SERVICES LTD.—See Hinduja Group Ltd.; *Int'l*, pg. 3399
AMAS LIMITED—See Jones Lang LaSalle Incorporated; *U.S. Public*, pg. 1203
AMASSCOM CO., LTD.—See Sulzer Ltd.; *Int'l*, pg. 7257
AMASSE CAPITAL HOLDINGS LTD.; *Int'l*, pg. 412
A & M ASSOCIATES, INC—See U-Haul Holding Company; *U.S. Public*, pg. 2211
A.M. ASSOCIATES INSURANCE SERVICES LTD.—See R&Q Insurance Holdings Ltd.; *Int'l*, pg. 6168
AMASSURANCE BERHAD—See AMMB Holdings Berhad; *Int'l*, pg. 429
AMASTEN FASTIGHETS AB; *Int'l*, pg. 412
AMATA ASIA LIMITED—See Amata Corporation Public Company Limited; *Int'l*, pg. 412
AMATA B. GRIMM POWER 1 LIMITED—See Amata Corporation Public Company Limited; *Int'l*, pg. 412
AMATA B. GRIMM POWER 1 LIMITED—See EGAT Public Company Limited; *Int'l*, pg. 2322
AMATA B.GRIMM POWER 2 LTD.—See B. Grimm Group; *Int'l*, pg. 788
AMATA B.GRIMM POWER 3 LTD.—See B. Grimm Group; *Int'l*, pg. 788
AMATA B.GRIMM POWER HOLDING LTD.—See B. Grimm Group; *Int'l*, pg. 788
AMATA B.GRIMM POWER LTD.—See B. Grimm Group; *Int'l*, pg. 788
AMATA B. GRIMM POWER LTD.—See B. Grimm Group; *Int'l*, pg. 788
AMATA B.GRIMM POWER (RAYONG) 1 LTD.—See B. Grimm Group; *Int'l*, pg. 788
AMATA CITY CO. LTD.—See Amata Corporation Public Company Limited; *Int'l*, pg. 412
AMATA CITY HALONG JOINT STOCK COMPANY—See Amata Corporation Public Company Limited; *Int'l*, pg. 412
AMATA CITY RAYONG CO., LTD.—See Amata Corporation Public Company Limited; *Int'l*, pg. 412
AMATA CORPORATION PUBLIC COMPANY LIMITED; *Int'l*, pg. 412
AMATA FACILITY SERVICE CO. LTD.—See Amata Corporation Public Company Limited; *Int'l*, pg. 412
AMATA GLOBAL PTE. LTD.—See Amata Corporation Public Company Limited; *Int'l*, pg. 412
AMATA KWEG EDUCATION CO., LTD.—See Amata Corporation Public Company Limited; *Int'l*, pg. 412
AMATA NATURAL GAS DISTRIBUTION CO. LTD.—See Amata Corporation Public Company Limited; *Int'l*, pg. 412
AMATA NETWORK COMPANY LIMITED—See Advanced Info Service Plc; *Int'l*, pg. 159
AMATA SUMMIT GROWTH FREEHOLD & LEASEHOLD REAL ESTATE INVESTMENT TRUST; *Int'l*, pg. 413

COMPANY NAME INDEX — AMBIENTHESIS SPA

AMATA SUMMIT READY BUILT CO. LTD.—See Amata Corporation Public Company Limited; *Int'l*, pg. 413
AMATA (VIETNAM) JOINT STOCK COMPANY—See Amata Corporation Public Company Limited; *Int'l*, pg. 412
AMATA VN PCL—See Amata Corporation Public Company Limited; *Int'l*, pg. 413
AMATA WATER CO. LTD.—See Amata Corporation Public Company Limited; *Int'l*, pg. 413
AMATECH AG; *Int'l*, pg. 413
AMATECH CORPORATION—See Baxter International Inc.; *U.S. Public*, pg. 282
AMA TECHTEL COMMUNICATIONS; *U.S. Private*, pg. 215
AMATEI INCORPORATED; *Int'l*, pg. 413
AMATEK INDUSTRIES PTY LIMITED—See Fletcher Building Limited; *Int'l*, pg. 2699
AMATEUR ELECTRONIC SUPPLY LLC; *U.S. Private*, pg. 216
AMATHEON AGRI HOLDING N.V.; *Int'l*, pg. 413
AMATHUS CORPORATION LTD.—See Amathus Public Limited; *Int'l*, pg. 413
AMATHUS HOTELS LTD.—See Amathus Public Limited; *Int'l*, pg. 413
AMATHUS MARITIME LTD.—See Amathus Public Limited; *Int'l*, pg. 413
AMATHUS PUBLIC LIMITED; *Int'l*, pg. 413
AMATHUS TRAVEL LTD.—See Amathus Public Limited; *Int'l*, pg. 413
AMATHUS (UK) LTD.—See Amathus Public Limited; *Int'l*, pg. 413
AMATI AIM VCT PLC; *Int'l*, pg. 413
AMAT MUHIBAH SDN BHD—See Berjaya Corporation Berhad; *Int'l*, pg. 982
AMATO COLLISION CENTER, INC.; *U.S. Private*, pg. 216
AMATOM ELECTRONIC HARDWARE, INC.; *U.S. Private*, pg. 216
AMATO PHARMACEUTICAL PRODUCTS LTD.—See Takeda Pharmaceutical Company Limited; *Int'l*, pg. 7437
AMA TRANSPORTATION COMPANY, INC.—See Wadhams Enterprises Inc.; *U.S. Private*, pg. 4425
AMATSIAQUITAINE SAS—See Eurofins Scientific S.E.; *Int'l*, pg. 2535
AMATSUJI INDUSTRIAL CO., LTD.—See NSK Ltd.; *Int'l*, pg. 5478
AMATSUJI STEEL BALL MFG. CO., LTD. - SHIGA WORKS—See NSK Ltd.; *Int'l*, pg. 5478
AMATSUJI STEEL BALL MFG. CO., LTD.—See NSK Ltd.; *Int'l*, pg. 5478
AMAVITA APOTHEKEN GALENICARE AG—See CSL Limited; *Int'l*, pg. 1866
AMAVITA PHARMACY—See CSL Limited; *Int'l*, pg. 1866
AMAX GLOBAL SERVICES INC.; *U.S. Private*, pg. 216
AMAX INDUSTRIAL PRODUCTS; *U.S. Private*, pg. 216
AMA XPERTEYE GMBH—See AMA Corporation Plc; *Int'l*, pg. 403
AMA XPERTEYE INC.—See AMA Corporation Plc; *Int'l*, pg. 403
A- MAX TECHNOLOGY (CHINA) LTD.—See A-Max Technology Limited; *Int'l*, pg. 20
A-MAX TECHNOLOGY GMBH—See A-Max Technology Limited; *Int'l*, pg. 20
A-MAX TECHNOLOGY LIMITED; *Int'l*, pg. 20
A-MAX TECHNOLOGY MCO CO., LTD.—See A-Max Technology Limited; *Int'l*, pg. 20
AMAYA GLOBAL HOLDINGS CORP.; *U.S. Public*, pg. 90
AMAYA (INTERNATIONAL) LTD.—See Flutter Entertainment plc; *Int'l*, pg. 2715
AMAYSIM AUSTRALIA LIMITED—See WAM Capital Limited; *Int'l*, pg. 8337
AMAZE CO., LTD.; *Int'l*, pg. 413
AMAZE PLC—See Kin and Carta plc; *Int'l*, pg. 4164
AMAZE TECHNOLOGY LIMITED—See Kin and Carta plc; *Int'l*, pg. 4164
AMAZEUM; *U.S. Private*, pg. 216
AMAZIA, INC.; *Int'l*, pg. 413
AMAZING CHARTS LLC—See Constellation Software Inc.; *Int'l*, pg. 1773
AMAZING GRACE OUTREACH MINISTRIES & US FOOD RESCUE INC; *U.S. Private*, pg. 216
AMAZING LUXURY CARS; *U.S. Private*, pg. 216
AMAZING MICROELECTRONIC CORP.; *Int'l*, pg. 413
AMAZING SPECTACLES LTD.—See Prime Focus Limited; *Int'l*, pg. 5977
AMAZING SPEECH THERAPY PTE. LTD.—See OUE Limited; *Int'l*, pg. 5665
AMAZING SPEECH THERAPY SDN. BHD.—See OUE Limited; *Int'l*, pg. 5666
AMAZON ADVERTISING; *U.S. Private*, pg. 216
AMAZONAS FLORESTAL INC.; *U.S. Public*, pg. 91
AMAZONAS INDUSTRIAS ALIMENTICIAS S.A.—See Nichirei Corporation; *Int'l*, pg. 5269
AMAZON.COM.CA, INC.—See Amazon.com, Inc.; *U.S. Public*, pg. 90
AMAZON.COM.DEDC, LLC—See Amazon.com, Inc.; *U.S. Public*, pg. 90
AMAZON.COM, INC.; *U.S. Public*, pg. 90

AMAZON.CO.UK LTD.—See Amazon.com, Inc.; *U.S. Public*, pg. 90
AMAZON.DE GMBH—See Amazon.com, Inc.; *U.S. Public*, pg. 90
AMAZONE H. DREYER GMBH & CO. KG; *Int'l*, pg. 413
AMAZON ENERGY LIMITED—See Computacenter plc; *Int'l*, pg. 1758
AMAZON EU SARL—See Amazon.com, Inc.; *U.S. Public*, pg. 90
AMAZONIA MINERACAO LTDA; *Int'l*, pg. 413
AMAZON INSURANCE NV—See Baloise Holding AG; *Int'l*, pg. 811
AMAZON JAPAN K.K.—See Amazon.com, Inc.; *U.S. Public*, pg. 90
AMAZONLATERNA CO., LTD.—See Toei Co., Ltd.; *Int'l*, pg. 7773
AMAZON ROBOTICS LLC—See Amazon.com, Inc.; *U.S. Public*, pg. 90
AMAZON WEB SERVICES, INC.—See Amazon.com, Inc.; *U.S. Public*, pg. 90
AMAZOONE CERAMICS LIMITED—See Asian Granito India Limited; *Int'l*, pg. 617
AMAZULU INC.; *U.S. Private*, pg. 216
AMBAC ASSURANCE CORPORATION—See Ambac Financial Group, Inc.; *U.S. Public*, pg. 92
AMBAC ASSURANCE CORP—See Ambac Financial Group, Inc.; *U.S. Public*, pg. 92
AMBAC ASSURANCE UK LIMITED-MILAN BRANCH—See Ambac Financial Group, Inc.; *U.S. Public*, pg. 92
AMBAC ASSURANCE UK LIMITED—See Ambac Financial Group, Inc.; *U.S. Public*, pg. 92
AMBAC CAPITAL CORPORATION—See Ambac Financial Group, Inc.; *U.S. Public*, pg. 92
AMBAC FINANCIAL GROUP, INC.; *U.S. Public*, pg. 91
AMBACH ALI S.P.A.—See Ali Holding S.r.l.; *Int'l*, pg. 320
AMBAC INTERNATIONAL CORPORATION; *U.S. Private*, pg. 217
A&M BACON LIMITED—See Frenkel Topping Group plc; *Int'l*, pg. 2773
AMBA CO., PROIZVODNJA IN TRGOVINA D.O.O., LJUBLJANA—See CETIS, d.d.; *Int'l*, pg. 1424
AMBA ENTERPRISES LTD.; *Int'l*, pg. 413
AMB/AFCO CARGO, LLC—See Prologis, Inc.; *U.S. Public*, pg. 1727
AMBA HOLDINGS INC.—See Moody's Corporation; *U.S. Public*, pg. 1466
AMBAJI SYNTEX PRIVATE LIMITED—See Sumeet Industries Ltd; *Int'l*, pg. 7261
AMBALAL SARABHAI ENTERPRISES LTD.; *Int'l*, pg. 413
AMBANGAN PURI SDN. BHD—See Eastern & Oriental Berhad; *Int'l*, pg. 2271
AMBANG WIRA SDN. BHD.—See AWC Berhad; *Int'l*, pg. 752
AMBANI ORGOCHEM LIMITED; *Int'l*, pg. 413
AMBANK (M) BERHAD—See AMMB Holdings Berhad; *Int'l*, pg. 429
AMB APPARATE + MASCHINENBAU GMBH—See Meyer Burger Technology AG; *Int'l*, pg. 4869
AMBARELLA, INC.; *U.S. Public*, pg. 92
AMBARELLA SHANGHAI CO., LTD.—See Ambarella, Inc.; *U.S. Public*, pg. 92
AMBARELLA TAIWAN LTD.—See Ambarella, Inc.; *U.S. Public*, pg. 92
AMBAR ENERGIA LTDA—See J&F Investimentos S.A.; *Int'l*, pg. 3853
AMBA RESEARCH COSTA RICA SA—See Moody's Corporation; *U.S. Public*, pg. 1466
AMBA RESEARCH (INDIA) PRIVATE LIMITED—See Moody's Corporation; *U.S. Public*, pg. 1466
AMBA RESEARCH LANKA (PRIVATE) LIMITED—See Moody's Corporation; *U.S. Public*, pg. 1466
AMBA RESEARCH SINGAPORE PTE. LTD.—See Moody's Corporation; *U.S. Public*, pg. 1466
AMBA RESEARCH UK LIMITED—See Moody's Corporation; *U.S. Public*, pg. 1466
AMBA RESEARCH USA INC.—See Moody's Corporation; *U.S. Public*, pg. 1466
AMBA RIVER COKE LIMITED—See JSW Steel Ltd.; *Int'l*, pg. 4015
AMBAR PROTEIN INDUSTRIES LIMITED; *Int'l*, pg. 413
AMBASE CORPORATION; *U.S. Public*, pg. 92
AMBASSADAIR TRAVEL CLUB, INC.—See Grueninger Tours & Cruises Inc.; *U.S. Private*, pg. 1797
AMBASSADOR BOOK SERVICE, INC.; *U.S. Private*, pg. 217
AMBASSADOR ENTERPRISES, LLC; *U.S. Private*, pg. 217
AMBASSADOR FOOD SERVICES CORP.; *U.S. Private*, pg. 217
AMBASSADOR FOODS PTY LTD.—See Libstar Holdings Ltd.; *Int'l*, pg. 4487
THE AMBASSADOR HOTEL, LTD.; *Int'l*, pg. 7613
AMBASSADOR INC.; *U.S. Private*, pg. 217
AMBASSADOR INTRA HOLDINGS LTD.; *Int'l*, pg. 414
AMBASSADOR LIMOUSINE, INC.; *U.S. Private*, pg. 217
AMBASSADOR MACHINE TOOLS—See The 600 Group PLC; *Int'l*, pg. 7609
AMBASSADOR PROGRAMS, INC.; *U.S. Private*, pg. 217

AMBASSADOR SERVICES, INC.; *U.S. Private*, pg. 217
AMBASSADOR STEEL CORPORATION—See Nucor Corporation; *U.S. Public*, pg. 1553
AMBASSADOR SUPPLY, LLC—See Ambassador Enterprises, LLC; *U.S. Private*, pg. 217
AMBASSADOR THEATRE GROUP LIMITED; *Int'l*, pg. 414
AMBASSADOR TOURS S.A—See TUI AG; *Int'l*, pg. 7964
AMBASSADOR TRAVEL LTD.; *U.S. Private*, pg. 217
AMBASSADOR VAN LINES INC.; *U.S. Private*, pg. 217
AMBASSADOR WORLDWIDE MOVING, INC.—See Interstate Group Holdings, Inc.; *U.S. Private*, pg. 2125
AMBC INC.; *U.S. Private*, pg. 217
AMB DEVELOPMENT GROUP LLC; *U.S. Private*, pg. 217
AMBEA AB—See Triton Advisers Limited; *Int'l*, pg. 7929
AMBEE PHARMACEUTICALS LIMITED; *Int'l*, pg. 414
AMBEON HOLDINGS PLC; *Int'l*, pg. 414
AMBER CAPITAL, LP—See Amber Capital UK LLP; *Int'l*, pg. 414
AMBER CAPITAL UK LLP; *Int'l*, pg. 414
AMBERCARE CORPORATION—See Addus HomeCare Corporation; *U.S. Public*, pg. 40
THE AMBER CHEMICAL COMPANY LTD.—See Akoya Capital LLC; *U.S. Private*, pg. 146
THE AMBER CHEMICAL COMPANY LTD.—See Century Park Capital Partners, LLC; *U.S. Private*, pg. 833
AMBER DIAGNOSTICS CAMEROON SARL—See Amber Diagnostics, Inc.; *U.S. Private*, pg. 217
AMBER DIAGNOSTICS, INC.; *U.S. Private*, pg. 217
AMBER ENTERPRISES, INC.—See Hy-Vee, Inc.; *U.S. Private*, pg. 2016
AMBER ENTERPRISES INDIA LIMITED; *Int'l*, pg. 414
AMBERFIRE LIMITED—See London Security PLC; *Int'l*, pg. 4546
AMBER HILL FINANCIAL HOLDINGS LTD.; *Int'l*, pg. 414
AMBER HOMELOANS LIMITED—See The Skipton Building Society; *Int'l*, pg. 7686
AMBER PLASTICS PTY. LIMITED—See Berry Global Group, Inc; *U.S. Public*, pg. 320
AMBER RIDGE, LLC—See Hovnanian Enterprises, Inc.; *U.S. Public*, pg. 1056
AMBER ROAD CHINA, LTD.—See Insight Venture Management, LLC; *U.S. Private*, pg. 2087
AMBER ROAD, INC.—See Insight Venture Management, LLC; *U.S. Private*, pg. 2087
AMBER ROAD, INC.—See Insight Venture Management, LLC; *U.S. Private*, pg. 2087
AMBER ROAD LIMITED—See Insight Venture Management, LLC; *U.S. Private*, pg. 2087
AMBER ROAD SOFTWARE PRIVATE, LTD.—See Insight Venture Management, LLC; *U.S. Private*, pg. 2087
AMBERSAN MEDICAL TECHNOLOGY CO., LTD.—See Sigurd Microelectronics Corp.; *Int'l*, pg. 6913
AMBER SILICONES (TIANJIN) CO. LTD.—See Akoya Capital LLC; *U.S. Private*, pg. 146
AMBER SILICONES (TIANJIN) CO. LTD.—See Century Park Capital Partners, LLC; *U.S. Private*, pg. 834
AMBER TAVERNS LIMITED—See MxP Partners LLP; *Int'l*, pg. 5110
AMBERTECH LIMITED; *Int'l*, pg. 414
AMBER TECHNOLOGY (NZ) LIMITED—See Ambertech Limited; *Int'l*, pg. 414
AMBER TRAVEL, INC.—See Grueninger Tours & Cruises Inc.; *U.S. Private*, pg. 1797
AMBER WIRELESS GMBH—See Wurth Verwaltungsgesellschaft mbH; *Int'l*, pg. 8511
A.M. BEST COMPANY—See State Automobile Mutual Insurance Company; *U.S. Private*, pg. 3790
AMBETTER OF MAGNOLIA, INC.—See Centene Corporation; *U.S. Public*, pg. 468
AMBETTER OF NORTH CAROLINA, INC.—See Centene Corporation; *U.S. Public*, pg. 468
AMBETTER OF PEACH STATE INC.—See Centene Corporation; *U.S. Public*, pg. 468
AMBEV S.A.—See Anheuser-Busch InBev SA/NV; *Int'l*, pg. 465
AMB FINANCIAL CORP.; *U.S. Public*, pg. 91
AMBICA AGARBATHIES & AROMA INDUSTRIES LTD.; *Int'l*, pg. 414
AMBIC EQUIPMENT LIMITED—See Skellerup Holdings Limited; *Int'l*, pg. 6980
AMBICOM HOLDINGS, INC.; *U.S. Private*, pg. 217
AMBICOM, INC.—See AmbiCom Holdings, Inc.; *U.S. Private*, pg. 217
AMBIENCE PUBLICIS ADVERTISING PVT. LTD.—See Publicis Groupe S.A.; *Int'l*, pg. 6097
AMBIENTA SGR S.P.A; *Int'l*, pg. 414
AMBIENT CONSULTING, LLC; *U.S. Private*, pg. 217
AMBIENTE 2000 SRL—See Falck S.p.A.; *Int'l*, pg. 2610
AMBIENTE ENERGIA S.R.L—See Marzotto S.p.A.; *Int'l*, pg. 4718
AMBIENTE H2O INC.; *U.S. Private*, pg. 217
AMBIENT HEALTHCARE, INC.—See Harvest Partners L.P.; *U.S. Private*, pg. 1876
AMBIENTHESIS SPA; *Int'l*, pg. 414
AMBIENTIS RADIOPROTECAO LTDA—See Eckert & Ziegler Strahlen- und Medizintechnik AG; *Int'l*, pg. 2290
AMBIENT, LLC—See PAR Capital Management, Inc.; *U.S. Private*, pg. 3089

AMBIENTHESIS SPA

AMBIENT SERVICOS AMBIENTAIS DE RIBEIRAO PRETO, S.A.—See GS Holdings Corp.; *Int'l*, pg. 3142
AMBIENT TECHNOLOGIES, INC.; *U.S. Private*, pg. 217
AMBIENT TEMPERATURE CORP.—See Huron Capital Partners LLC; *U.S. Private*, pg. 2012
AMBIENT-TV SALES & SERVICES GMBH—See Stroer SE & Co. KGaA; *Int'l*, pg. 7241
AMBIENT WATER CORPORATION; *U.S. Private*, pg. 217
AMBIENT WEATHER CO.; *U.S. Private*, pg. 217
AMBIFACE & BUFFER SGPS LDA—See Waste Management, Inc.; *U.S. Public*, pg. 2332
AMBIKA COTTON MILLS LIMITED; *Int'l*, pg. 414
AMBIMED - GESTAO AMBIENTAL, LDA.—See Waste Management, Inc.; *U.S. Public*, pg. 2332
AMBIPAR EMERGENCY RESPONSE; *Int'l*, pg. 414
AMBIPAR PARTICIPACOES E EMPREENDIMENTOS SA; *Int'l*, pg. 414
AMBIPAR RESPONSE LIMITED—See Ambipar Participacoes e Empreendimentos SA; *Int'l*, pg. 414
AMBIR TECHNOLOGY, INC.; *U.S. Private*, pg. 218
AMBITECH ENGINEERING COPRORATION—See Zachry Holdings, Inc.; *U.S. Private*, pg. 4596
AMBIT ENERGY HOLDINGS, LLC—See Vistra Corp.; *U.S. Public*, pg. 2306
AMBIT GROUP LLC—See OceanSound Partners, LP; *U.S. Private*, pg. 2991
AMBITION DX HOLDINGS CO., LTD.; *Int'l*, pg. 415
AMBITION GROUP LIMITED - AMBITION TECHNOLOGY DIVISION—See Ambition Group Limited; *Int'l*, pg. 415
AMBITION GROUP LIMITED - FINANCE DIVISION—See Ambition Group Limited; *Int'l*, pg. 415
THE AMBITION GROUP LIMITED (HK)—See Ambition Group Limited; *Int'l*, pg. 415
AMBITION GROUP LIMITED; *Int'l*, pg. 415
THE AMBITION GROUP LIMITED (UK)—See Ambition Group Limited; *Int'l*, pg. 415
AMBITION GROUP SINGAPORE PTE LIMITED—See Ambition Group Limited; *Int'l*, pg. 415
AMBITION MICA LIMITED; *Int'l*, pg. 415
AMBITION RECRUIT PTY LIMITED—See Ambition Group Limited; *Int'l*, pg. 415
AMBITO DAS S.A.—See Corteva, Inc.; *U.S. Public*, pg. 581
AMBIUS B.V.—See Rentokil Initial plc; *Int'l*, pg. 6286
AMBIUS INC—See Rentokil Initial plc; *Int'l*, pg. 6286
AMBIUS, INC.—See Rentokil Initial plc; *Int'l*, pg. 6286
AMBIUS NV—See Rentokil Initial plc; *Int'l*, pg. 6286
AMBIUS SAS—See Rentokil Initial plc; *Int'l*, pg. 6286
AMBLER SAVINGS BANK; *U.S. Private*, pg. 218
AMBLING COMPANIES, INC.; *U.S. Private*, pg. 218
AMBO AGRITEC LIMITED; *Int'l*, pg. 415
AMBOILE SERVICES SAS—See Ecolab Inc.; *U.S. Public*, pg. 712
AMBONI PLANTATIONS LIMITED—See REA Vipingo Plantations Limited; *Int'l*, pg. 6230
AMBOW EDUCATION HOLDING LTD.; *Int'l*, pg. 415
AMBOY BANCORPORATION; *U.S. Private*, pg. 218
AMBOY BANK; *U.S. Private*, pg. 218
AMBRA BRANDS SP. Z O.O.—See Schloss Wachenheim AG; *Int'l*, pg. 6622
AMBRA PROPERTY S.R.L—See Unipol Gruppo S.p.A.; *Int'l*, pg. 8056
AMBRA S.A.; *Int'l*, pg. 415
AMBRA SP. Z O.O.—See Emperia Holding S.A; *Int'l*, pg. 2385
AMBRATEC GMBH—See Berner SE; *Int'l*, pg. 988
AMBRELL B.V.—See inTEST Corporation; *U.S. Public*, pg. 1159
AMBRELL CORPORATION—See inTEST Corporation; *U.S. Public*, pg. 1159
AMBRELL LIMITED—See inTEST Corporation; *U.S. Public*, pg. 1159
AMBRIAN METALS LIMITED—See Ambrian plc; *Int'l*, pg. 415
AMBRIAN PLC; *Int'l*, pg. 415
AMBRIDGE PARTNERS, LLC—See Fairfax Financial Holdings Limited; *Int'l*, pg. 2606
A.M. BRIGGS, INC.—See Sysco Corporation; *U.S. Public*, pg. 1973
AMBRILIA BIOPHARMA INC.; *Int'l*, pg. 415
THE AMBRIOLA COMPANY, INC.—See Gennaro Auricchio S.p.A.; *Int'l*, pg. 2924
AMBROISE BOUVIER TRANSPORTS; *Int'l*, pg. 415
AMBROISIE CAPITAL HOLDING S.A.S.; *Int'l*, pg. 415
AMBROMOBILIARE S.P.A.; *Int'l*, pg. 415
AMBRO SALES (PTY) LTD.—See Hudaco Industries Limited; *Int'l*, pg. 3521
AMBROSE CHINA LIMITED—See Dickson Concepts (International) Limited; *Int'l*, pg. 2112
AMBROSE EMPLOYER GROUP, LLC—See General Atlantic Service Company, L.P.; *U.S. Private*, pg. 1663
AMBROSIA SUBSTANCE ABUSE TREATMENT CENTER; *U.S. Private*, pg. 218
AMBROSI CUTLERY LTD.—See Birch Hill Equity Partners Management Inc.; *Int'l*, pg. 1046
AMBRX BIOPHARMA INC.—See Johnson & Johnson; *U.S. Public*, pg. 1194
AMBRX, INC.—See China Everbright Group Limited; *Int'l*, pg. 1501

AMBRX, INC.—See HOPU Investment Management Co., Ltd.; *Int'l*, pg. 3474
AMBRX, INC.—See Shanghai Fosun Pharmaceutical (Group) Co., Ltd.; *Int'l*, pg. 6767
AMBRX, INC.—See WuXi PharmaTech (Cayman) Inc.; *Int'l*, pg. 8515
AMBRY GENETICS CORP.—See Japan Investment Corporation; *Int'l*, pg. 3898
AMBRY GENETICS CORP.—See Konica Minolta, Inc.; *Int'l*, pg. 4257
AMBRY HILLS TECHNOLOGIES, LLC—See Air T, Inc.; *U.S. Public*, pg. 67
AMBU A/S; *Int'l*, pg. 416
AMBU AUSTRALIA PTY. LTD.—See Ambu A/S; *Int'l*, pg. 416
AMBU BV—See Ambu A/S; *Int'l*, pg. 416
AMBU (DEUTSCHLAND) GMBH—See Ambu A/S; *Int'l*, pg. 416
AMBU FRANCE S.A.R.L.—See Ambu A/S; *Int'l*, pg. 416
AMBU INC.—See Ambu A/S; *Int'l*, pg. 416
AMBU INDIA PRIVATE LIMITED—See Ambu A/S; *Int'l*, pg. 416
AMBUJA CEMENT RAJASTHAN LTD.—See Adani Enterprises Limited; *Int'l*, pg. 125
AMBUJA CEMENTS LTD—See Adani Enterprises Limited; *Int'l*, pg. 125
AMBU KK—See Ambu A/S; *Int'l*, pg. 416
AMBULANCE SERVICES OF DYERSBURG, INC.—See Community Health Systems, Inc.; *U.S. Public*, pg. 551
AMBULANCE SERVICES OF LEXINGTON, INC.—See Quorum Health Corporation; *U.S. Private*, pg. 3329
AMBULANCE SERVICES OF MCKENZIE, INC.—See Quorum Health Corporation; *U.S. Private*, pg. 3329
AMBULANCE SERVICES OF MCNAIRY, INC.—See Community Health Systems, Inc.; *U.S. Public*, pg. 551
AMBULANTA ZDRAVJE, ZDRAVSTVENE STORITVE, D.O.O.—See Assicurazioni Generali S.p.A.; *Int'l*, pg. 643
AMBULATORIEN BETRIEBSGESELLSCHAFT M.B.H.—See UNIQA Insurance Group AG; *Int'l*, pg. 8057
AMBULATORY ANESTHESIA ASSOCIATES INC.—See KKR & Co. Inc.; *U.S. Public*, pg. 1244
AMBULATORY CARE SOLUTIONS OF OHIO LLC—See Humana, Inc.; *U.S. Public*, pg. 1069
AMBULATORY ENDOSCOPY CLINIC OF DALLAS, LTD.—See HCA Healthcare, Inc.; *U.S. Public*, pg. 990
AMBULATORY SERVICES OF AMERICA, INC.—See U.S. Renal Care, Inc.; *U.S. Private*, pg. 4272
AMBULATORY SURGERY CENTER GROUP, LTD.—See HCA Healthcare, Inc.; *U.S. Public*, pg. 990
AMBULATORY SURGERY CENTER OF COOL SPRINGS, LLC—See Bain Capital, LP; *U.S. Private*, pg. 446
AMBULATORY SURGICAL ASSOCIATES, LLC—See Tenet Healthcare Corporation; *U.S. Public*, pg. 2009
AMBULATORY SURGICAL CENTER OF AIKEN, L.L.C.—See Universal Health Services, Inc.; *U.S. Public*, pg. 2255
AMBULATORY SURGICAL CENTER OF SOMERVILLE, LLC—See Tenet Healthcare Corporation; *U.S. Public*, pg. 2009
AMBU LLC—See Ambu A/S; *Int'l*, pg. 416
AMBU LTD.—See Ambu A/S; *Int'l*, pg. 416
AMBU LTD.—See Ambu A/S; *Int'l*, pg. 416
AMBU MEXICO OPERATIONS S. A. DE C. V.—See Ambu A/S; *Int'l*, pg. 416
AMBU NEW ZEALAND PTY. LTD.—See Ambu A/S; *Int'l*, pg. 416
AMBU NORDIC A/S—See Ambu A/S; *Int'l*, pg. 416
AMBUR INTERNATIONAL PTE. LTD.—See TT International Limited; *Int'l*, pg. 7960
AMBU SALES & SERVICES SDN. BHD.—See Ambu A/S; *Int'l*, pg. 416
AMBU S.R.L.—See Ambu A/S; *Int'l*, pg. 416
AMBU (XIAMEN) TRADING LTD.—See Ambu A/S; *Int'l*, pg. 416
AM BV—See Koninklijke BAM Groep N.V.; *Int'l*, pg. 4261
AMCAD BIOMED CORPORATION; *Int'l*, pg. 416
AMCAN BEVERAGES, INC.; *U.S. Private*, pg. 218
AM CAN—See Frozen Food Express Industries, Inc.; *U.S. Private*, pg. 1617
AM-CAN TRANSPORT SERVICE INC.; *U.S. Private*, pg. 215
A&M CAPITAL ADVISORS EUROPE, LLP—See Alvarez & Marsal, Inc.; *U.S. Private*, pg. 212
A&M CAPITAL ADVISORS, LLC—See Alvarez & Marsal, Inc.; *U.S. Private*, pg. 212
AMCAP MORTGAGE LLC—See Crosscountry Mortgage, LLC; *U.S. Private*, pg. 1106
A&M CASTING (THAILAND) CO., LTD.—See Akebono Brake Industry Co., Ltd.; *Int'l*, pg. 261
A.M. CASTLE & CO. (CANADA) INC.—See A. M. Castle & Co.; *U.S. Public*, pg. 11
A. M. CASTLE & CO. (CANADA) INC.—See A. M. Castle & Co.; *U.S. Public*, pg. 11
A. M. CASTLE & CO.; *U.S. Public*, pg. 10
A.M. CASTLE METAL MATERIALS (SHANGHAI) CO., LTD.—See A. M. Castle & Co.; *U.S. Public*, pg. 11

CORPORATE AFFILIATIONS

A.M. CASTLE METALS UK LIMITED—See A. M. Castle & Co.; *U.S. Public*, pg. 11
AMC BURGERS, INC.—See ICV Partners, LLC; *U.S. Private*, pg. 2034
AMCC FENETRES ET PORTES SAS—See Atrya SAS; *Int'l*, pg. 694
AMC CHILE S.A.—See Imdex Limited; *Int'l*, pg. 3623
AMCC JAPAN CO. LTD.—See MACOM Technology Solutions Holdings, Inc.; *U.S. Public*, pg. 1352
AMC ENTERTAINMENT HOLDINGS, INC.—See Dalian Wanda Group Corporation Ltd.; *Int'l*, pg. 1953
AMC ENTERTAINMENT INC.—See Dalian Wanda Group Corporation Ltd.; *Int'l*, pg. 1953
AMC FS, INC.—See CU Cooperative Systems, Inc.; *U.S. Private*, pg. 1119
AMC GROUP, INC.—See ICV Partners, LLC; *U.S. Private*, pg. 2034
AMCHI GENDYNAMY SCIENCE CORPORATION; *U.S. Private*, pg. 218
AMCICO POJISTOVNA A.S.—See MetLife, Inc.; *U.S. Public*, pg. 1429
AMCI INTERNATIONAL INC.—See KM Investment Corporation; *U.S. Private*, pg. 2321
AMCIL LIMITED; *Int'l*, pg. 416
AMC, INC.—See Blackstone Inc.; *U.S. Public*, pg. 350
AMCI—See Omnicom Group Inc.; *U.S. Public*, pg. 1573
AMCK AVIATION HOLDINGS IRELAND LIMITED—See Mitsubishi Corporation; *Int'l*, pg. 4937
AMC NETWORKS CENTRAL EUROPE KFT—See AMC Networks Inc.; *U.S. Public*, pg. 92
AMC NETWORKS INC.; *U.S. Public*, pg. 92
AMC NETWORKS INTERNATIONAL-CENTRAL EUROPE—See TVT Media; *Int'l*, pg. 7989
AMC NETWORKS LATIN AMERICA LLC—See TVT Media; *Int'l*, pg. 7989
AMC NORTH AMERICA LTD—See Imdex Limited; *Int'l*, pg. 3623
AMC/NORTH FULTON URGENT CARE #1, L.L.C.—See Tenet Healthcare Corporation; *U.S. Public*, pg. 2005
AMC/NORTH FULTON URGENT CARE #5, L.L.C.—See Tenet Healthcare Corporation; *U.S. Public*, pg. 2005
AMCO CORPORATION—See MITSUBA Corporation; *Int'l*, pg. 4928
AMCO ENGINEERING CO; *U.S. Private*, pg. 218
AMCO GIFFEN LTD.—See Renew Holdings plc; *Int'l*, pg. 6278
AMCO GROUP INC.; *U.S. Private*, pg. 218
AMCO GROUP LTD.—See Renew Holdings plc; *Int'l*, pg. 6278
A.M. COHRON & SON, INC.; *U.S. Private*, pg. 27
AMCO INDIA LTD.; *Int'l*, pg. 416
AMCOL AUSTRALIA PTY LTD—See Minerals Technologies, Inc.; *U.S. Public*, pg. 1448
A&M COLD STORAGE, LLC—See WillScot Mobile Mini Holdings Corp.; *U.S. Public*, pg. 2372
AMCOL INTERNATIONAL CORPORATION—See Minerals Technologies, Inc.; *U.S. Public*, pg. 1448
AMCOL MINERAL MADENCILIK SANAYI VE TICARET A.S.—See Minerals Technologies, Inc.; *U.S. Public*, pg. 1448
AMCOL MINERALS EUROPE LIMITED—See Minerals Technologies, Inc.; *U.S. Public*, pg. 1448
AMCO MANUFACTURING, INC.—See Yetter Manufacturing Co., Inc.; *U.S. Private*, pg. 4588
AMCOM INSURANCE SERVICES, INC.—See Stone Point Capital LLC; *U.S. Private*, pg. 3820
AM COMMUNICATIONS; *U.S. Private*, pg. 214
AMCON BLOCK & PRECAST INCORPORATED; *U.S. Private*, pg. 218
AMCON DISTRIBUTING COMPANY-CROSSVILLE—See AMCON Distributing Company; *U.S. Public*, pg. 92
AMCON DISTRIBUTING COMPANY, INC.—See AMCON Distributing Company; *U.S. Public*, pg. 92
AMCON DISTRIBUTING COMPANY; *U.S. Public*, pg. 92
AM CONSERVATION GROUP, INC.—See Kohlberg & Company, LLC; *U.S. Private*, pg. 2337
AM CONTRACTING LLC; *U.S. Private*, pg. 214
AMCO PLASTIC MATERIALS, INC.—See Ravago Holding S.A.; *Int'l*, pg. 6222
AMCOR FLEXIBLES ALZIRA S.L.U.—See Amcor plc; *Int'l*, pg. 417
AMCOR FLEXIBLES - ASHLAND INC—See Amcor plc; *Int'l*, pg. 417
AMCOR FLEXIBLES A/S—See Amcor plc; *Int'l*, pg. 416
AMCOR FLEXIBLES (AUSTRALIA) PTY LTD—See Amcor plc; *Int'l*, pg. 416
AMCOR FLEXIBLES BANGKOK PUBLIC COMPANY LIMITED—See Amcor plc; *Int'l*, pg. 417
AMCOR FLEXIBLES BARCELONA—See Amcor plc; *Int'l*, pg. 417
AMCOR FLEXIBLES BURGDORF GMBH—See Amcor plc; *Int'l*, pg. 417
AMCOR FLEXIBLES CRAMLINGTON LTD—See Amcor plc; *Int'l*, pg. 417
AMCOR FLEXIBLES DENMARK APS—See Amcor plc; *Int'l*, pg. 417
AMCOR FLEXIBLES EUROPA SUR S.L.—See Amcor plc; *Int'l*, pg. 417

COMPANY NAME INDEX

AMCOR FLEXIBLES EUROPE—See Amcor plc; *Int'l*, pg. 417
AMCOR FLEXIBLES GROUP PTY. LTD.—See Amcor plc; *Int'l*, pg. 416
AMCOR FLEXIBLES INC.—See Amcor plc; *Int'l*, pg. 417
AMCOR FLEXIBLES LUGO—See Amcor plc; *Int'l*, pg. 417
AMCOR FLEXIBLES (NEW ZEALAND) LTD.—See Amcor plc; *Int'l*, pg. 416
AMCOR FLEXIBLES PHETCHABURI CO., LTD.—See Amcor plc; *Int'l*, pg. 417
AMCOR FLEXIBLES PUERTO RICO INC.—See Amcor plc; *Int'l*, pg. 417
AMCOR FLEXIBLES RORSCHACH AG—See Amcor plc; *Int'l*, pg. 417
AMCOR FLEXIBLES SAINT MAUR—See Amcor plc; *Int'l*, pg. 417
AMCOR FLEXIBLES SARREBOURG S.A.S.—See Amcor plc; *Int'l*, pg. 417
AMCOR FLEXIBLES SINGAPORE PTE LTD—See Amcor plc; *Int'l*, pg. 417
AMCOR FLEXIBLES SINGEN GMBH—See Amcor plc; *Int'l*, pg. 417
AMCOR FLEXIBLES TRANSPAC B.V.B.A—See Amcor plc; *Int'l*, pg. 417
AMCOR FLEXIBLES UK LTD.—See Amcor plc; *Int'l*, pg. 417
AMCOR FLEXIBLES ZUTPHEN B.V.—See Amcor plc; *Int'l*, pg. 417
AMCOR INC.—See CRH plc; *Int'l*, pg. 1846
AMCOR INDUSTRIES, INC.—See Clearlake Capital Group, L.P.; *U.S. Private*, pg. 937
AMCOR PACKAGING UK LIMITED—See Amcor plc; *Int'l*, pg. 417
AMCORP GLOBAL LIMITED—See TEE International Limited; *Int'l*, pg. 7519
AMCORP GROUP BERHAD; *Int'l*, pg. 418
AMCOR PLC; *Int'l*, pg. 416
AMCORP PROPERTIES BERHAD—See Amcorp Group Berhad; *Int'l*, pg. 418
AMCOR PTY LTD—See Amcor plc; *Int'l*, pg. 416
AMCOR RIGID PLASTICS DE MEXICO S.A. DE C.V.—See Amcor plc; *Int'l*, pg. 417
AMCOR RIGID PLASTICS DE VENEZUELA S.A.—See Amcor plc; *Int'l*, pg. 417
AMCOR RIGID PLASTICS USA, INC.—See Amcor plc; *Int'l*, pg. 417
AMCOR RIGID PLASTICS USA, INC. - TUMWATER PLANT—See Amcor plc; *Int'l*, pg. 417
AMCOR TOBACCO PACKAGING BRABANT B.V.—See Amcor plc; *Int'l*, pg. 417
AMCOR TOBACCO PACKAGING NOVGOROD—See Amcor plc; *Int'l*, pg. 417
AMCOR TOBACCO PACKAGING POLSKA SPOLKA Z.O.O—See Amcor plc; *Int'l*, pg. 417
AMCOR TOBACCO PACKAGING SWITZERLAND GMBH—See Amcor plc; *Int'l*, pg. 417
AMCO-SAFT INDIA PVT LTD—See TotalEnergies SE; *Int'l*, pg. 7838
AMCO SP. Z O.O.—See International Flavors & Fragrances Inc.; *U.S. Public*, pg. 1151
AMCO SRL—See APG/SGA SA; *Int'l*, pg. 513
AMCO UNITED HOLDING LIMITED; *Int'l*, pg. 416
AMC PHYSICAL TRADING LTD—See Amalgamated Metal PLC; *Int'l*, pg. 408
AMCRAFT BUILDING PRODUCTS CO., INC.—See Hendricks Holding Company, Inc.; *U.S. Private*, pg. 1914
AMC RO STUDIOS S.R.L.—See Canada Pension Plan Investment Board; *Int'l*, pg. 1280
AMC RO STUDIOS S.R.L.—See EQT AB; *Int'l*, pg. 2482
AMC RO STUDIOS S.R.L.—See Temasek Holdings (Private) Limited; *Int'l*, pg. 7547
AMCS CORPORATION—See Advanced Manufacturing Control Systems Ltd.; *Int'l*, pg. 160
AMCS FRANCE SAS—See Advanced Manufacturing Control Systems Ltd.; *Int'l*, pg. 160
AMCS LTD—See Advanced Manufacturing Control Systems Ltd.; *Int'l*, pg. 160
AMCS SWEDEN AB—See Advanced Manufacturing Control Systems Ltd.; *Int'l*, pg. 160
AMC TECHNOLOGY, L.L.C.; *U.S. Private*, pg. 218
AMC TREASURY SERVICES LTD—See Amalgamated Metal Corporation PLC; *Int'l*, pg. 408
AMD ADVANCED MICRO DEVICES ISRAEL LTD.—See Advanced Micro Devices, Inc.; *U.S. Public*, pg. 48
AMD ADVANCED MICRO DEVICES (ROU) S.R.L.—See Advanced Micro Devices, Inc.; *U.S. Public*, pg. 48
AMD ADVANCED RESEARCH LLC—See Advanced Micro Devices, Inc.; *U.S. Public*, pg. 48
AMDAHL MOTORS; *U.S. Private*, pg. 218
AMDARIS BULGARIA EOOD—See Insight Enterprises, Inc.; *U.S. Public*, pg. 1129
AMDARIS GROUP LTD.—See Insight Enterprises, Inc.; *U.S. Public*, pg. 1129
AMDARIS ROMANIA S.R.L.—See Insight Enterprises, Inc.; *U.S. Public*, pg. 1129
AMDARIS S.R.L.—See Insight Enterprises, Inc.; *U.S. Public*, pg. 1129
AMDEX CORPORATION; *U.S. Private*, pg. 218

AMD FABRICATORS, INC.—See Astro Manufacturing & Design, Inc.; *U.S. Private*, pg. 362
AMD FAR EAST, LTD.—See Advanced Micro Devices, Inc.; *U.S. Public*, pg. 48
AMD INDIA PRIVATE LIMITED—See Advanced Micro Devices, Inc.; *U.S. Public*, pg. 48
AMD INDUSTRIES, INC.; *U.S. Private*, pg. 218
AMD INDUSTRIES LIMITED; *Int'l*, pg. 418
AMD INTERNATIONAL SALES & SERVICE, LTD.—See Advanced Micro Devices, Inc.; *U.S. Public*, pg. 48
AMD JAPAN LTD.—See Advanced Micro Devices, Inc.; *U.S. Public*, pg. 48
AMDOCS AUSTRALIA PROPRIETARY LIMITED—See Amdocs Limited; *Int'l*, pg. 419
AMDOCS BRAZIL LIMITADA—See Amdocs Limited; *Int'l*, pg. 419
AMDOCS B.V.—See Amdocs Limited; *Int'l*, pg. 419
AMDOCS CANADA, INC.—See Amdocs Limited; *Int'l*, pg. 419
AMDOCS CANADIAN MANAGED SERVICES, INC.—See Amdocs Limited; *Int'l*, pg. 419
AMDOCS CHAMPAIGN, INC.—See Amdocs Limited; *Int'l*, pg. 419
AMDOCS CHILE SPA—See Amdocs Limited; *Int'l*, pg. 419
AMDOCS (CR) S.R.O.—See Amdocs Limited; *Int'l*, pg. 419
AMDOCS DEVELOPMENT CENTRE INDIA PRIVATE LIMITED—See Amdocs Limited; *Int'l*, pg. 419
AMDOCS DEVELOPMENT LIMITED—See Amdocs Limited; *Int'l*, pg. 419
AMDOCS DIGITAL COMMERCE DIVISION—See Amdocs Limited; *Int'l*, pg. 419
AMDOCS (FINLAND) OY—See Amdocs Limited; *Int'l*, pg. 419
AMDOCS FRANCE—See Amdocs Limited; *Int'l*, pg. 419
AMDOCS HELLAS LTD.—See Amdocs Limited; *Int'l*, pg. 419
AMDOCS HOLDINGS ULC—See Amdocs Limited; *Int'l*, pg. 419
AMDOCS INC. - CALIFORNIA—See Amdocs Limited; *Int'l*, pg. 419
AMDOCS INC. - SAN JOSE—See Amdocs Limited; *Int'l*, pg. 419
AMDOCS INC. - SEATTLE—See Amdocs Limited; *Int'l*, pg. 419
AMDOCS INC.—See Amdocs Limited; *Int'l*, pg. 419
AMDOCS INTERNATIONAL GMBH—See Amdocs Limited; *Int'l*, pg. 419
AMDOCS INVESTMENTS SWITZERLAND LIMITED—See Amdocs Limited; *Int'l*, pg. 419
AMDOCS (ISRAEL) LIMITED—See Amdocs Limited; *Int'l*, pg. 419
AMDOCS (ITALY) SRL—See Amdocs Limited; *Int'l*, pg. 419
AMDOCS JAPAN—See Amdocs Limited; *Int'l*, pg. 419
AMDOCS LIMITED; *Int'l*, pg. 418
AMDOCS MANAGEMENT LIMITED—See Amdocs Limited; *Int'l*, pg. 419
AMDOCS MEXICO S. DE R.L. DE C.V.—See Amdocs Limited; *Int'l*, pg. 419
AMDOCS PHILIPPINES INC.—See Amdocs Limited; *Int'l*, pg. 419
AMDOCS (PORTUGAL) SOFTWARE, UNIPESSOAL LDA.—See Amdocs Limited; *Int'l*, pg. 419
AMDOCS QPASS INC.—See Amdocs Limited; *Int'l*, pg. 419
AMDOCS SINGAPORE PTE. LTD.—See Amdocs Limited; *Int'l*, pg. 419
AMDOCS SOFTWARE GMBH—See Amdocs Limited; *Int'l*, pg. 419
AMDOCS SOFTWARE SYSTEMS LTD.—See Amdocs Limited; *Int'l*, pg. 419
AMDOCS SYSTEMS EUROPE LIMITED—See Amdocs Limited; *Int'l*, pg. 419
AMDOCS SYSTEMS GROUP LIMITED—See Amdocs Limited; *Int'l*, pg. 419
AMDOCS SYSTEMS LIMITED—See Amdocs Limited; *Int'l*, pg. 419
AMDOCS TETHYS LIMITED—See Amdocs Limited; *Int'l*, pg. 420
AMDOCS (UK) LIMITED—See Amdocs Limited; *Int'l*, pg. 419
AMDOCS VIETNAM COMPANY LIMITED—See Amdocs Limited; *Int'l*, pg. 420
AMD RESEARCH & DEVELOPMENT CENTER INDIA PRIVATE LIMITED—See Advanced Micro Devices, Inc.; *U.S. Public*, pg. 48
AMD SOUTH AMERICA LTDA—See Advanced Micro Devices, Inc.; *U.S. Public*, pg. 48
AMD TECHNOLOGIES (CHINA) CO. LTD.—See Advanced Micro Devices, Inc.; *U.S. Public*, pg. 48
AMD TECHNOLOGY DEVELOPMENT (BEIJING) CO.—See Advanced Micro Devices, Inc.; *U.S. Public*, pg. 48
AMD TUV ARBEITS-MEDIZINISCHE DIENSTE GMBH—See TUV Rheinland Berlin-Brandenburg Pfalz e.V.; *Int'l*, pg. 7981
AMEC AZERBAIJAN—See John Wood Group PLC; *Int'l*, pg. 3982

AMEC CADE INGENIERIA Y DESARROLLO DE PROYECTOS LTDA.—See John Wood Group PLC; *Int'l*, pg. 3981
AMEC CADE SERVICIOS DE INGENIERIA LTDA.—See John Wood Group PLC; *Int'l*, pg. 3981
AMEC ENGINEERING & CONSULTING (SHANGHAI) CO., LTD—See John Wood Group PLC; *Int'l*, pg. 3981
AMEC ENVIRONMENT & INFRASTRUCTURE GMBH—See John Wood Group PLC; *Int'l*, pg. 3981
AMEC FOSTER WHEELER AES, INC.—See John Wood Group PLC; *Int'l*, pg. 3982
AMEC FOSTER WHEELER AMERICAS LIMITED—See John Wood Group PLC; *Int'l*, pg. 3982
AMEC FOSTER WHEELER AMERICAS LIMITED—See John Wood Group PLC; *Int'l*, pg. 3982
AMEC FOSTER WHEELER AUSTRALIA PTY. LTD.—See John Wood Group PLC; *Int'l*, pg. 3982
AMEC FOSTER WHEELER BIMAS BIRLESIK INSAAT VE MUHENDISLIK A.S.—See John Wood Group PLC; *Int'l*, pg. 3982
AMEC FOSTER WHEELER COLOMBIA SAS—See John Wood Group PLC; *Int'l*, pg. 3982
AMEC FOSTER WHEELER CONSTRUCTORS, INC.—See John Wood Group PLC; *Int'l*, pg. 3982
AMEC FOSTER WHEELER CONSULTING POLAND SP. Z O.O.—See John Wood Group PLC; *Int'l*, pg. 3982
AMEC FOSTER WHEELER E & I GMBH—See John Wood Group PLC; *Int'l*, pg. 3982
AMEC FOSTER WHEELER ENERGY LIMITED—See John Wood Group PLC; *Int'l*, pg. 3981
AMEC FOSTER WHEELER ENERGY & PARTNERS ENGINEERING COMPANY—See John Wood Group PLC; *Int'l*, pg. 3982
AMEC FOSTER WHEELER ENGINEERING AG—See John Wood Group PLC; *Int'l*, pg. 3982
AMEC FOSTER WHEELER ENVIRONMENT & INFRASTRUCTURE, INC.—See John Wood Group PLC; *Int'l*, pg. 3982
AMEC FOSTER WHEELER ENVIRONMENT & INFRASTRUCTURE—See John Wood Group PLC; *Int'l*, pg. 3982
AMEC FOSTER WHEELER FIRED HEATERS, LTD.—See John Wood Group PLC; *Int'l*, pg. 3982
AMEC FOSTER WHEELER FRANCE S.A.—See John Wood Group PLC; *Int'l*, pg. 3982
AMEC FOSTER WHEELER HOLDING (THAILAND) LIMITED—See John Wood Group PLC; *Int'l*, pg. 3982
AMEC FOSTER WHEELER IBERIA S.A.—See John Wood Group PLC; *Int'l*, pg. 3982
AMEC FOSTER WHEELER INC.—See John Wood Group PLC; *Int'l*, pg. 3982
AMEC FOSTER WHEELER INDIA PRIVATE LIMITED—See John Wood Group PLC; *Int'l*, pg. 3982
AMEC FOSTER WHEELER INTERNATIONAL INGENIERIA Y CONSTRUCCION LIMITADA—See John Wood Group PLC; *Int'l*, pg. 3982
AMEC FOSTER WHEELER ITALIANA, S.R.L.—See John Wood Group PLC; *Int'l*, pg. 3982
AMEC FOSTER WHEELER KAMTECH, INC.—See John Wood Group PLC; *Int'l*, pg. 3982
AMEC FOSTER WHEELER LIMITED—See John Wood Group PLC; *Int'l*, pg. 3981
AMEC FOSTER WHEELER NCL LIMITED—See John Wood Group PLC; *Int'l*, pg. 3981
AMEC FOSTER WHEELER NORTH AMERICA CORP.—See John Wood Group PLC; *Int'l*, pg. 3982
AMEC FOSTER WHEELER NUCLEAR UK LIMITED—See John Wood Group PLC; *Int'l*, pg. 3981
AMEC FOSTER WHEELER (PERU) S.A.—See John Wood Group PLC; *Int'l*, pg. 3981
AMEC FOSTER WHEELER PLC—See John Wood Group PLC; *Int'l*, pg. 3982
AMEC FOSTER WHEELER SERVICE (THAILAND) LIMITED—See John Wood Group PLC; *Int'l*, pg. 3982
AMEC FOSTER WHEELER USA CORPORATION—See John Wood Group PLC; *Int'l*, pg. 3982
AMEC FOSTER WHEELER VENEZUELA, C.A.—See John Wood Group PLC; *Int'l*, pg. 3982
AMEC GEOMATRIX CONSULTANTS, INC.—See John Wood Group PLC; *Int'l*, pg. 3982
AMEC GRD SA B.V—See John Wood Group PLC; *Int'l*, pg. 3981
AMEC INC.—See John Wood Group PLC; *Int'l*, pg. 3981
AMEC INC. - ST. JOHN'S—See John Wood Group PLC; *Int'l*, pg. 3982
AMEC INC. - VANCOUVER—See John Wood Group PLC; *Int'l*, pg. 3982
AMEC INTERNATIONAL INGENIERIA Y CONSTRUCCION LIMITADA—See John Wood Group PLC; *Int'l*, pg. 3981
AMEC INTERNATIONAL PTE LTD.—See Advanced Micro-Fabrication Equipment, Inc.; *Int'l*, pg. 161
AMEC JAPAN CO., INC.—See Advanced Micro-Fabrication Equipment, Inc.; *Int'l*, pg. 161
AMEC KML INC.—See Advanced Micro-Fabrication Equipment, Inc.; *Int'l*, pg. 161
AMEC KOREA LIMITED—See Advanced Micro-Fabrication Equipment, Inc.; *Int'l*, pg. 161
AMEC NANCHANG LTD.—See Advanced Micro-Fabrication Equipment, Inc.; *Int'l*, pg. 161

AMEC NEW ZEALAND LIMITED—See John Wood Group PLC; *Int'l*, pg. 3982
AMEC NORTH AMERICA, INC.—See Advanced Micro-Fabrication Equipment, Inc.; *Int'l*, pg. 161
AMEC NSS LIMITED—See John Wood Group PLC; *Int'l*, pg. 3981
AMECO CHILE S.A.—See Fluor Corporation; *U.S. Public*, pg. 857
AMEC OFFSHORE SERVICES LTD—See John Wood Group PLC; *Int'l*, pg. 3981
AMECO HOLDINGS, INC.—See OEP Capital Advisors, L.P.; *U.S. Private*, pg. 2998
AMECO MEXICO ADMINISTRACION Y SERVICIOS S DE RL/CV—See OEP Capital Advisors, L.P.; *U.S. Private*, pg. 2998
AME CONSTRUCTION SDN. BHD.—See AME Elite Consortium Berhad; *Int'l*, pg. 420
AMECO SERVICES, INC.—See OEP Capital Advisors, L.P.; *U.S. Private*, pg. 2998
AMECO SERVICES, INC.—See OEP Capital Advisors, L.P.; *U.S. Private*, pg. 2998
AMECO SERVICES, INC.—See OEP Capital Advisors, L.P.; *U.S. Private*, pg. 2998
AMECO SERVICES S DE RL DE CV—See OEP Capital Advisors, L.P.; *U.S. Private*, pg. 2998
AMECO SERVICES, S. DE R.L. DE C.V.—See OEP Capital Advisors, L.P.; *U.S. Private*, pg. 2998
AMECO SERVICES SRL—See OEP Capital Advisors, L.P.; *U.S. Private*, pg. 2998
AMECO SERVICES SRL—See OEP Capital Advisors, L.P.; *U.S. Private*, pg. 2998
AMECO SERVICES SRL—See OEP Capital Advisors, L.P.; *U.S. Private*, pg. 2998
AMECO SERVICES SRL—See OEP Capital Advisors, L.P.; *U.S. Private*, pg. 2998
AMECO SERVICES SRL—See OEP Capital Advisors, L.P.; *U.S. Private*, pg. 2998
AMECO SERVICES SRL—See OEP Capital Advisors, L.P.; *U.S. Private*, pg. 2998
AMEC PHILIPPINES—See John Wood Group PLC; *Int'l*, pg. 3981
AMEC PROCESS & ENERGY LTD.—See John Wood Group PLC; *Int'l*, pg. 3981
AMEC ROMANIA—See John Wood Group PLC; *Int'l*, pg. 3982
AMEC RUSSIA—See John Wood Group PLC; *Int'l*, pg. 3982
AMEC SERVICES LTD.—See John Wood Group PLC; *Int'l*, pg. 3981
AMEC SINGAPORE PTE LTD—See John Wood Group PLC; *Int'l*, pg. 3982
AMEC SOUTH AFRICA—See John Wood Group PLC; *Int'l*, pg. 3981
AMEC (SOUTH KOREA)—See John Wood Group PLC; *Int'l*, pg. 3981
AMEC TAIWAN LTD.—See Advanced Micro-Fabrication Equipment, Inc.; *Int'l*, pg. 161
AMEC TECHNOLOGIES LIMITED—See John Wood Group PLC; *Int'l*, pg. 3982
AMEC (UNITED ARAB EMIRATES)—See John Wood Group PLC; *Int'l*, pg. 3981
AMEC XIAMEN LTD.—See Advanced Micro-Fabrication Equipment, Inc.; *Int'l*, pg. 161
AMEC ZEKTIN PTY LIMITED—See John Wood Group PLC; *Int'l*, pg. 3981
AMEDEO AIR FOUR PLUS LIMITED; *Int'l*, pg. 420
AMEDEO RESOURCES PLC; *Int'l*, pg. 420
AMEDES BELGIUM N.V.—See DEKRA e.V.; *Int'l*, pg. 2007
AMEDES HOLDING GMBH—See BNP Paribas SA; *Int'l*, pg. 1093
AME DEVELOPMENT SDN. BHD.—See AME Elite Consortium Berhad; *Int'l*, pg. 420
AMEDIA AS; *Int'l*, pg. 420
AMEDISYS ARIZONA, L.L.C.—See Amedisys, Inc.; *U.S. Public*, pg. 93
AMEDISYS DELAWARE, L.L.C.—See Amedisys, Inc.; *U.S. Public*, pg. 93
AMEDISYS FLORIDA, L.L.C.—See Amedisys, Inc.; *U.S. Public*, pg. 93
AMEDISYS HOME HEALTH CARE - GASTONIA—See Amedisys, Inc.; *U.S. Public*, pg. 93
AMEDISYS HOME HEALTH CARE—See Amedisys, Inc.; *U.S. Public*, pg. 93
AMEDISYS HOME HEALTH CARE - WHEELING—See Amedisys, Inc.; *U.S. Public*, pg. 93
AMEDISYS HOME HEALTH, INC. OF ALABAMA—See Amedisys, Inc.; *U.S. Public*, pg. 93
AMEDISYS HOME HEALTH, INC. OF SOUTH CAROLINA—See Amedisys, Inc.; *U.S. Public*, pg. 93
AMEDISYS HOME HEALTH OF NEBRASKA, L.L.C.—See Amedisys, Inc.; *U.S. Public*, pg. 93
AMEDISYS, INC.; *U.S. Public*, pg. 93
AMEDISYS NEW HAMPSHIRE, L.L.C.—See Amedisys, Inc.; *U.S. Public*, pg. 93
AMEDISYS NEW JERSEY, L.L.C.—See Amedisys, Inc.; *U.S. Public*, pg. 93

AMEDISYS NORTH CAROLINA, L.L.C.—See Amedisys, Inc.; *U.S. Public*, pg. 93
AMEDISYS OKLAHOMA, L.L.C.—See Amedisys, Inc.; *U.S. Public*, pg. 93
AMEDISYS SPECIALIZED MEDICAL SERVICES, INC.—See Amedisys, Inc.; *U.S. Public*, pg. 93
AMEDISYS SP-IN, L.L.C.—See Amedisys, Inc.; *U.S. Public*, pg. 93
AMEDISYS SP-KY, L.L.C.—See Amedisys, Inc.; *U.S. Public*, pg. 93
AMEDISYS SP-OH, L.L.C.—See Amedisys, Inc.; *U.S. Public*, pg. 93
AMEDISYS TENNESSEE, L.L.C.—See Amedisys, Inc.; *U.S. Public*, pg. 93
AMED MANAGEMENT SERVICES LTD—See African Minerals Exploration & Development SICAR SCA; *Int'l*, pg. 192
AME ELITE CONSORTIUM BERHAD; *Int'l*, pg. 420
AME ENGINEERING INDUSTRIES SDN. BHD.—See AME Elite Consortium Berhad; *Int'l*, pg. 420
AMEEX TECHNOLOGIES CORPORATION—See EQT AB; *Int'l*, pg. 2483
AMEGA SALES INC.; *U.S. Private*, pg. 218
AMEGY BANK—See Zions Bancorporation, National Association; *U.S. Public*, pg. 2408
AME HOSPITALS PTY LIMITED—See Ramsay Health Care Limited; *Int'l*, pg. 6199
AME INCORPORATED; *U.S. Private*, pg. 218
AME INFO FZ LLC—See Apax Partners LLP; *Int'l*, pg. 507
AME INFO FZ LLC—See The Scott Trust Limited; *Int'l*, pg. 7681
AME INTERNATIONAL; *U.S. Private*, pg. 218
AMEI TECHNOLOGIES, INC.—See Orthofix Medical Inc.; *U.S. Public*, pg. 1619
AMEKAI METER (XIAMEN) CO.,LTD.—See AMETEK, Inc.; *U.S. Public*, pg. 120
AM ELEKTRISKA AB—See Bravida Holding AB; *Int'l*, pg. 1142
AMELIA BULLOCK REALTORS, INC.—See Kuper Realty Corp.; *U.S. Private*, pg. 2357
AMELIA ISLAND COMPANY; *U.S. Private*, pg. 218
AMELIA'S, LLC—See Grocery Outlet Holding Corp.; *U.S. Public*, pg. 970
AME LIFE LUX SA—See Enstar Group Limited; *Int'l*, pg. 2449
AMELKIS RESORTS S.A.—See Emaar Properties PJSC; *Int'l*, pg. 2372
AMELS—See Damen Shipyards Group; *Int'l*, pg. 1956
AME MARINE SERVICES SDN BHD—See Sapura Energy Berhad; *Int'l*, pg. 6574
AME MATERIAL ELECTRICO, S.A.U.—See Sonepar S.A.; *Int'l*, pg. 7090
A MENARINI INDUSTRIE FARMACEUTICHE RIUNITE SRL; *Int'l*, pg. 18
AMENDIA, INC.—See Kohlberg & Company, LLC; *U.S. Private*, pg. 2337
AMENDIS S.A.—See Veolia Environnement S.A.; *Int'l*, pg. 8153
AMENDOAS-HERDADE DA PALHETA I, LTD.; *Int'l*, pg. 420
AMENDOLAS FENCE CO.; *U.S. Private*, pg. 218
AMENDUNI NICOLA S.P.A.—See Acciaierie Valbruna S.p.A.; *Int'l*, pg. 89
AM ENGINEERING, INC.; *U.S. Private*, pg. 214
AMENITY HEALTH, INC.; *U.S. Private*, pg. 218
AMENITY SERVICE KANSAI CO., LTD.—See Nippon Telegraph & Telephone Corporation; *Int'l*, pg. 5354
AMEN PROPERTIES, INC.; *U.S. Public*, pg. 94
AMENTUM SERVICES, INC.; *U.S. Private*, pg. 218
AMERACRANE & HOIST, LLC—See Balance Point Capital Advisors, LLC; *U.S. Private*, pg. 457
AMERAMEX INTERNATIONAL, INC.; *U.S. Public*, pg. 94
AMERANT BANCORP INC.; *U.S. Public*, pg. 94
AMERANT BANK, N.A.—See Amerant Bancorp Inc.; *U.S. Public*, pg. 94
AMERANT MORTGAGE, LLC—See Amerant Bancorp Inc.; *U.S. Public*, pg. 94
AMERASIA BANK; *U.S. Private*, pg. 219
AMERBELLE TEXTILES, LLC; *U.S. Private*, pg. 219
AMERCABLE INCORPORATED; *U.S. Private*, pg. 219
AMERCAREROYAL, LLC—See HCI Equity Management, L.P.; *U.S. Private*, pg. 1889
AMERCHOL CORPORATION—See Dow Inc.; *U.S. Public*, pg. 686
AMERCO REAL ESTATE COMPANY OF TEXAS, INC.—See U-Haul Holding Company; *U.S. Public*, pg. 2211
AMERCO REAL ESTATE COMPANY—See U-Haul Holding Company; *U.S. Public*, pg. 2211
AMERC OY—See ANTA Sports Products Limited; *Int'l*, pg. 481
AMEREDEV II, LLC; *U.S. Private*, pg. 219
AMEREDIA INCORPORATED; *U.S. Private*, pg. 219
AMEREN CORPORATION; *U.S. Public*, pg. 94
AMEREN ENERGY FUELS & SERVICES CO.—See Ameren Corporation; *U.S. Public*, pg. 94
AMEREN ILLINOIS COMPANY—See Ameren Corporation; *U.S. Public*, pg. 94
AMERENIP—See Ameren Corporation; *U.S. Public*, pg. 94

AMEREN MICHIGAN GAS STORAGE, LLC—See Ameren Corporation; *U.S. Public*, pg. 94
AMEREN SERVICES INC.—See Ameren Corporation; *U.S. Public*, pg. 94
AMEREQUIP CORPORATION; *U.S. Private*, pg. 219
AMERESCO DMHS LLC—See Ameresco, Inc.; *U.S. Public*, pg. 95
AMERESCO FEDERAL SOLUTIONS, INC.—See Ameresco, Inc.; *U.S. Public*, pg. 95
AMERESCO GEORGIA LLC—See Ameresco, Inc.; *U.S. Public*, pg. 95
AMERESCO, INC.; *U.S. Public*, pg. 95
AMERESCO LIMITED—See Ameresco, Inc.; *U.S. Public*, pg. 95
AMERESCO SELECT, INC.—See Ameresco, Inc.; *U.S. Public*, pg. 95
AMERESCO SOLAR - SOLUTIONS INC.—See Ameresco, Inc.; *U.S. Public*, pg. 95
AMERESCOSOLUTIONS, INC.—See Ameresco, Inc.; *U.S. Public*, pg. 95
AMERESCO SOUTHWEST, INC.—See Ameresco, Inc.; *U.S. Public*, pg. 95
AMERESCO STAFFORD LLC—See Ameresco, Inc.; *U.S. Public*, pg. 95
AMEREX BROKERS LLC—See BGC Group, Inc.; *U.S. Public*, pg. 329
AMEREX CORPORATION; *U.S. Private*, pg. 219
AMEREX ENERGY SERVICES—See BGC Group, Inc.; *U.S. Public*, pg. 329
AMEREX FASHION GROUP—See Amerex Group, Inc.; *U.S. Private*, pg. 219
AMEREX GROUP, INC.; *U.S. Private*, pg. 219
AMEREX GROUP—See Amerex Group, Inc.; *U.S. Private*, pg. 219
AMEREX KID'S GROUP—See Amerex Group, Inc.; *U.S. Private*, pg. 219
AMEREX LADIES—See Amerex Group, Inc.; *U.S. Private*, pg. 219
AMERGENT HOSPITALITY GROUP, INC.; *U.S. Public*, pg. 95
AMERGENT, INC.—See Moore DM Group, LLC; *U.S. Private*, pg. 2780
AMERGERIS WEALTH MANAGEMENT AG—See Amergeris Wealth Management Group GmbH; *Int'l*, pg. 420
AMERGERIS WEALTH MANAGEMENT GROUP GMBH; *Int'l*, pg. 420
AMERGINT TECHNOLOGIES, INC.; *U.S. Private*, pg. 219
AMERGRAPH CORPORATION; *U.S. Private*, pg. 219
AMER GROUP HOLDING; *Int'l*, pg. 420
AMERGY MEXICANA, S.A. DE C.V.—See Iberdrola, S.A.; *Int'l*, pg. 3571
AMERHART LIMITED; *U.S. Private*, pg. 219
AMERIBANCSHARES, INC.; *U.S. Private*, pg. 220
AMERICA 1, LLC—See US 1 Industries, Inc.; *U.S. Private*, pg. 4317
AMERICA ACHIEVES; *U.S. Private*, pg. 220
AMERICA ACTION INC.—See Action Electronics Co., Ltd.; *Int'l*, pg. 119
AMERICA CHOICE RV—See Camping World Holdings, Inc.; *U.S. Public*, pg. 427
AMERICA CHUNG NAM LLC; *U.S. Private*, pg. 220
AMERICA CHUNG NAM TRANSPORTATION LLC—See America Chung Nam LLC; *U.S. Private*, pg. 220
AMERICA FUJIKURA LTD.—See Fujikura Ltd.; *Int'l*, pg. 2827
AMERICA GREAT HEALTH; *U.S. Public*, pg. 95
AMERICA II ELECTRONICS, INC.; *U.S. Public*, pg. 220
AMERICA II GROUP, LLC—See Wynnchurch Capital, L.P.; *U.S. Private*, pg. 4576
AMERICALL GROUP, INC.—See Teleperformance SE; *Int'l*, pg. 7541
AMERICA METAL EXPORT, INC.—See Yechiu Metal Recycling China Ltd.; *Int'l*, pg. 8575
AMERICA-MIDEAST EDUCATIONAL & TRAINING SERVICES, INC.; *U.S. Private*, pg. 221
AMERICA MIDWEST TRANSPORTATION, LLC.; *U.S. Private*, pg. 220
AMERICA MODERN GREEN DEVELOPMENT (HOUSTON), LLC—See Modern Land (China) Co., Ltd.; *Int'l*, pg. 5014
AMERICA MOVIL PERU, S.A.C.—See America Movil, S.A.B. de C.V.; *Int'l*, pg. 421
AMERICA MOVIL, S.A.B. DE C.V.; *Int'l*, pg. 421
AMERICAN ACADEMY OF DERMATOLOGY; *U.S. Private*, pg. 221
AMERICAN ACADEMY OF NEUROLOGY; *U.S. Private*, pg. 221
AMERICAN ACADEMY OF OTOLARYNGOLOGY-HEAD AND NECK SURGERY; *U.S. Private*, pg. 221
THE AMERICAN ACADEMY OF PEDIATRICS; *U.S. Private*, pg. 3985
AMERICAN ACADEMY OF PERIODONTOLOGY; *U.S. Private*, pg. 221
AMERICAN ACADEMY OF PHYSICAL MEDICINE & REHABILITATION; *U.S. Private*, pg. 221
AMERICAN ACADEMY OF SLEEP MEDICINE; *U.S. Private*, pg. 221

COMPANY NAME INDEX

AMERICAN ACCEPTANCE CORP.—See Unico American Corporation; *U.S. Public*, pg. 2225
AMERICAN ACCESS CASUALTY COMPANY—See Kemper Corporation; *U.S. Public*, pg. 1220
AMERICAN ACCESSORIES INC.—See Kinderhook Industries, LLC; *U.S. Private*, pg. 2306
AMERICAN ACCESSORIES INTERNATIONAL LLC; *U.S. Private*, pg. 221
AMERICAN ACCOUNTS & ADVISERS; *U.S. Private*, pg. 221
AMERICAN ACE INTERNATIONAL CO.; *U.S. Private*, pg. 221
AMERICAN ACHIEVEMENT CORPORATION—See Fenway Partners, LLC; *U.S. Private*, pg. 1495
AMERICANA COMPANIES, INC.; *U.S. Private*, pg. 258
AMERICANA COMPANIES INC.; *U.S. Private*, pg. 258
AMERICANA COMPANY INC.; *U.S. Private*, pg. 258
AMERICAN ACQUISITION OPPORTUNITY, INC.; *U.S. Public*, pg. 95
AMERICAN ACRYL LP—See Arkema S.A.; *Int'l*, pg. 569
AMERICAN ACRYL LP—See Nippon Shokubai Co., Ltd.; *Int'l*, pg. 5332
AMERICAN ACTION NETWORK; *U.S. Private*, pg. 221
AMERICAN ADDICTION CENTERS, INC.—See AAC Holdings, Inc.; *U.S. Private*, pg. 30
AMERICAN AGCO INC.; *U.S. Private*, pg. 221
AMERICAN AGCREDIT FLCA—See American AgCredit; *U.S. Private*, pg. 221
AMERICAN AGCREDIT PCA—See American AgCredit; *U.S. Private*, pg. 222
AMERICAN AGCREDIT; *U.S. Private*, pg. 221
AMERICAN AGENCIES CO. INC.; *U.S. Private*, pg. 222
AMERICAN AGENCY INC.; *U.S. Private*, pg. 222
AMERICAN AIRCRAFT PARTS MANUFACTURING CO.; *U.S. Private*, pg. 222
AMERICAN AIRES, INC.; *Int'l*, pg. 422
AMERICAN AIR FILTER INTERNATIONAL, INC.—See Daikin Industries, Ltd.; *Int'l*, pg. 1936
AMERICAN AIR FILTER MANUFACTURING SDN. BHD.—See Daikin Industries, Ltd.; *Int'l*, pg. 1932
AMERICAN AIR & HEAT, INC.—See Catterton Management Company, LLC; *U.S. Private*, pg. 793
AMERICAN AIRLINES CARGO—See American Airlines Group Inc.; *U.S. Public*, pg. 95
AMERICAN AIRLINES GROUP INC.; *U.S. Public*, pg. 95
AMERICAN AIRLINES, INC. - PUERTO RICO OFFICE—See American Airlines Group Inc.; *U.S. Public*, pg. 95
AMERICAN AIRLINES, INC.—See American Airlines Group Inc.; *U.S. Public*, pg. 95
AMERICAN AIR LIQUIDE HOLDINGS, INC.—See L'Air Liquide S.A.; *Int'l*, pg. 4370
AMERICAN AIRPORTS CORPORATION; *U.S. Private*, pg. 222
AMERICAN AIR SYSTEMS, INC.; *U.S. Private*, pg. 222
AMERICAN ALARM & COMMUNICATIONS, INC.; *U.S. Private*, pg. 222
AMERICANA LLC; *U.S. Private*, pg. 258
AMERICAN ALLOY STEEL INC.; *U.S. Private*, pg. 222
AMERICAN ALUMINUM EXTRUSION COMPANY, LLC; *U.S. Private*, pg. 222
AMERICAN AMBULANCE SERVICE, INC.—See Lundbeckfonden; *Int'l*, pg. 4580
AMERICAN-AMICABLE HOLDINGS, INC.—See iA Financial Corporation Inc.; *Int'l*, pg. 3567
AMERICAN-AMICABLE LIFE INSURANCE COMPANY OF TEXAS—See iA Financial Corporation Inc.; *Int'l*, pg. 3567
AMERICAN AMUSEMENTS LLC—See Trive Capital Inc.; *U.S. Private*, pg. 4240
AMERICAN ANALYTICAL CHEMISTRY LABORATORIES—See Intertek Group plc; *Int'l*, pg. 3762
AMERICAN ANESTHESIOLOGY OF NAPLES, INC.—See MEDNAX, Inc.; *U.S. Public*, pg. 1413
AMERICAN ANIMAL CONTROL, LLC—See Plunkett's Pest Control, Inc.; *U.S. Private*, pg. 3215
AMERICAN APPAREL AUSTRALIA PTY LTD—See American Apparel, Inc.; *U.S. Private*, pg. 222
AMERICAN APPAREL CANADA RETAIL INC.—See American Apparel, Inc.; *U.S. Private*, pg. 222
AMERICAN APPAREL (CARNABY) LIMITED—See American Apparel, Inc.; *U.S. Private*, pg. 222
AMERICAN APPAREL DEUTSCHLAND GMBH—See American Apparel, Inc.; *U.S. Private*, pg. 222
AMERICAN APPAREL DYEING & FINISHING, INC.—See American Apparel, Inc.; *U.S. Private*, pg. 222
AMERICAN APPAREL, INC.; *U.S. Private*, pg. 222
AMERICAN APPAREL, INC.; *U.S. Private*, pg. 222
AMERICAN APPAREL JAPAN YUGER KAISHA—See American Apparel, Inc.; *U.S. Private*, pg. 222
AMERICAN APPAREL (UK) LIMITED—See American Apparel, Inc.; *U.S. Private*, pg. 222
AMERICAN APPLIANCE PRODUCTS, INC.—See Trive Capital Inc.; *U.S. Private*, pg. 4240
AMERICAN ARBITRATION ASSOCIATION; *U.S. Private*, pg. 222
AMERICAN ARCHITECTURAL DESIGN SPECIALTIES, INC.; *U.S. Private*, pg. 222

AMERICANA RESTAURANTS INTERNATIONAL PLC; *Int'l*, pg. 423
AMERICAN ARMED FORCES MUTUAL AID ASSOCIATION; *U.S. Private*, pg. 222
AMERICAN ART CLAY CO., INC.; *U.S. Private*, pg. 222
AMERICAN ASPHALT PAVING CO.; *U.S. Private*, pg. 222
AMERICAN ASPHALT REPAIR & RESURFACING; *U.S. Private*, pg. 222
AMERICANAS S.A.; *Int'l*, pg. 423
AMERICAN ASSETS TRUST, INC.; *U.S. Public*, pg. 96
AMERICAN ASSETS TRUST, L.P.—See American Assets Trust, Inc.; *U.S. Public*, pg. 96
AMERICAN ASSOCIATION FOR CANCER RESEARCH; *U.S. Private*, pg. 222
AMERICAN ASSOCIATION FOR CLINICAL CHEMISTRY, INC.; *U.S. Private*, pg. 222
AMERICAN ASSOCIATION FOR LABORATORY ACCREDITATION; *U.S. Private*, pg. 223
AMERICAN ASSOCIATION FOR THE STUDY OF LIVER DISEASES; *U.S. Private*, pg. 223
AMERICAN ASSOCIATION OF AIRPORT EXECUTIVES; *U.S. Private*, pg. 223
AMERICAN ASSOCIATION OF NURSE ANESTHETISTS; *U.S. Private*, pg. 223
AMERICAN ASSOCIATION OF NURSE PRACTITIONERS; *U.S. Private*, pg. 223
AMERICAN ASSOCIATION OF ORAL AND MAXILLOFACIAL SURGEONS; *U.S. Private*, pg. 223
AMERICAN ASSOCIATION OF ORTHOPAEDIC SURGEONS; *U.S. Private*, pg. 223
AMERICAN ASSOCIATION OF STATE COLLEGES AND UNIVERSITIES; *U.S. Private*, pg. 223
AMERICAN ASSOCIATION OF STATE HIGHWAY & TRANSPORTATION OFFICIALS; *U.S. Private*, pg. 223
AMERICAN ATHLETIC INC.—See Berkshire Hathaway Inc.; *U.S. Public*, pg. 305
AMERICAN AUCTIONEERS LLC; *U.S. Private*, pg. 223
AMERICAN AUDIO COMPONENT INC.—See AAC Technologies Holdings Inc.; *Int'l*, pg. 31
AMERICAN AUDIO & VIDEO—See DCC plc; *Int'l*, pg. 1990
AMERICAN AUGERS, INC.—See The Toro Company; *U.S. Public*, pg. 2134
AMERICAN AUTO AUCTION GROUP, LLC—See Huron Capital Partners LLC; *U.S. Private*, pg. 2011
AMERICAN AUTOGARD LLC—See Zurn Elkay Water Solutions Corporation; *U.S. Public*, pg. 2412
AMERICAN AUTOMATED PAYROLL; *U.S. Private*, pg. 223
AMERICAN AUTO-MATRIX INC.—See ABB Ltd.; *Int'l*, pg. 56
THE AMERICAN AUTOMOBILE ASSOCIATION, INC.; *U.S. Private*, pg. 3985
AMERICAN AUTOMOBILE INSURANCE COMPANY, CORP.—See Allianz SE; *Int'l*, pg. 351
AMERICAN AVIATION SUPPLY LLC—See American Airlines Group Inc.; *U.S. Public*, pg. 96
AMERICAN AVIONIC TECHNOLOGIES CORPORATION—See RTX Corporation; *U.S. Public*, pg. 1822
AMERICAN AVK CO.—See AVK Holding A/S; *Int'l*, pg. 747
AMERICAN AXLE & MANUFACTURING DE MEXICO HOLDINGS S. DE R.L. DE C.V.—See American Axle & Manufacturing Holdings, Inc.; *U.S. Public*, pg. 96
AMERICAN AXLE & MANUFACTURING DE MEXICO S. DE R.L. DE C.V.—See American Axle & Manufacturing Holdings, Inc.; *U.S. Public*, pg. 96
AMERICAN AXLE & MANUFACTURING HOLDINGS, INC.; *U.S. Public*, pg. 96
AMERICAN AXLE & MANUFACTURING, INC.—See American Axle & Manufacturing Holdings, Inc.; *U.S. Public*, pg. 96
AMERICAN AZIDE CORPORATION—See H.I.G. Capital, LLC; *U.S. Private*, pg. 1829
AMERICAN BABY MAGAZINE—See Meredith Corporation; *U.S. Public*, pg. 1422
AMERICAN BACKGROUND SERVICES, INC.—See General Catalyst Partners; *U.S. Private*, pg. 1664
AMERICAN BACKGROUND SERVICES, INC.—See iSubscribed Inc.; *U.S. Private*, pg. 2147
AMERICAN BACKGROUND SERVICES, INC.—See WndrCo Holdings, LLC; *U.S. Private*, pg. 4552
AMERICAN BAILEY CORPORATION; *U.S. Private*, pg. 223
AMERICAN BALER COMPANY—See Avis Industrial Corporation; *U.S. Private*, pg. 407
AMERICAN BANCARD, LLC; *U.S. Private*, pg. 223
AMERICAN BANCOR, LTD.; *U.S. Private*, pg. 223
AMERICAN BANCORP, INC.; *U.S. Public*, pg. 97
AMERICAN BANCORP OF OKLAHOMA; *U.S. Private*, pg. 223
AMERICAN BANCORPORATION OF MINNESOTA, INC.; *U.S. Private*, pg. 223
THE AMERICAN BANKERS ASSOCIATION; *U.S. Private*, pg. 3985
AMERICAN BANKERS INSURANCE COMPANY OF FLORIDA—See Assurant, Inc.; *U.S. Public*, pg. 215
AMERICAN BANKERS LIFE ASSURANCE COMPANY OF FLORIDA—See Assurant, Inc.; *U.S. Public*, pg. 214

AMERICAN BOTANICALS, LLC

AMERICAN BANK HOLDING INC.; *U.S. Private*, pg. 223
AMERICAN BANK INCORPORATED; *U.S. Public*, pg. 97
AMERICAN BANKNOTE CORPORATION; *U.S. Private*, pg. 224
AMERICAN BANK—See American Bank Incorporated; *U.S. Public*, pg. 97
AMERICAN BANK—See Guaranty Development Company; *U.S. Private*, pg. 1809
AMERICAN BANK & TRUST COMPANY; *U.S. Private*, pg. 223
AMERICAN BANK & TRUST COMPANY—See American Bank Holding Inc.; *U.S. Private*, pg. 224
AMERICAN BANK & TRUST—See American Bancorp, Inc.; *U.S. Public*, pg. 97
AMERICAN BANK & TRUST—See Leackco Bank Holding Company, Inc.; *U.S. Private*, pg. 2405
AMERICAN BAPTIST HOMES OF THE MIDWEST; *U.S. Private*, pg. 224
THE AMERICAN BAR ASSOCIATION MEMBERS/NORTHERN TRUST COLLECTIVE TRUST; *U.S. Private*, pg. 3985
AMERICAN BARCODE AND RFID; *U.S. Private*, pg. 224
AMERICAN BASKETBALL ASSOCIATION, INC.; *U.S. Public*, pg. 97
AMERICAN BATH GROUP; *U.S. Private*, pg. 224
AMERICAN BATTERY CO. INC.; *U.S. Private*, pg. 224
AMERICAN BATTERY COMPANY—See East Penn Manufacturing Co., Inc.; *U.S. Private*, pg. 1317
AMERICAN BATTERY MATERIALS, INC.; *U.S. Public*, pg. 97
AMERICAN BATTERY METALS CORP.; *U.S. Public*, pg. 97
AMERICAN BATTERY TECHNOLOGY COMPANY; *U.S. Public*, pg. 97
AMERICAN BEACON ADVISORS—See Pharos Capital Group, LLC; *U.S. Private*, pg. 3166
AMERICAN BEACON ADVISORS—See TPG Capital, L.P.; *U.S. Public*, pg. 2175
AMERICAN BEAUTY CORP; *U.S. Private*, pg. 224
AMERICAN BENEFIT PLAN ADMINISTRATORS, INC.—See Water Street Healthcare Partners, LLC; *U.S. Private*, pg. 4452
AMERICAN BENEFITS GROUP—See Aon plc; *Int'l*, pg. 495
AMERICAN BEVERAGE ASSOCIATION; *U.S. Private*, pg. 224
AMERICAN BEVERAGE CORPORATION—See Brynwood Partners Management LLC; *U.S. Private*, pg. 674
AMERICAN BIAXIS INC.—See Sojitz Corporation; *Int'l*, pg. 7061
THE AMERICAN BICYCLE GROUP LLC; *U.S. Private*, pg. 3985
AMERICAN BICYCLE GROUP—See The American Bicycle Group LLC; *U.S. Private*, pg. 3985
AMERICAN BILTRITE FAR EAST, INC.—See American Biltrite Inc.; *U.S. Public*, pg. 97
AMERICAN BILTRITE INC.; *U.S. Public*, pg. 97
AMERICAN BILTRITE INTELLECTUAL PROPERTIES INC.—See American Biltrite Inc.; *U.S. Public*, pg. 97
AMERICAN BILTRITE LTD.—See American Biltrite Inc.; *U.S. Public*, pg. 97
AMERICAN BILTRITE—See American Biltrite Inc.; *U.S. Public*, pg. 97
AMERICAN BIOFUELS INC.; *Int'l*, pg. 422
AMERICAN BIO MEDICA CORPORATION; *U.S. Public*, pg. 98
AMERICAN BIOTECH LABS; *U.S. Private*, pg. 224
AMERICAN BIRD CONSERVANCY; *U.S. Private*, pg. 224
AMERICAN BISTRO SWEDEN AB—See Umoe Gruppen AS; *Int'l*, pg. 8026
AMERICAN BLANCHING COMPANY—See Post Holdings, Inc.; *U.S. Public*, pg. 1703
AMERICAN BLIMP CORP.—See Van Wagner Communications, LLC; *U.S. Private*, pg. 4341
AMERICAN BLOCKCHAINBIOCHAR CORPORATION; *U.S. Private*, pg. 224
AMERICAN BLUE RIBBON HOLDINGS, LLC—See Fidelity National Financial, Inc.; *U.S. Public*, pg. 830
AMERICAN BOARD COMPANIES, INC.—See The MATCO Group, Inc.; *U.S. Private*, pg. 4075
THE AMERICAN BOARD OF ANESTHESIOLOGY, INC.; *U.S. Private*, pg. 3986
AMERICAN BOARD OF MEDICAL SPECIALTIES; *U.S. Private*, pg. 224
THE AMERICAN BOARD OF PEDIATRICS; *U.S. Private*, pg. 3986
AMERICAN BOLT AND SCREW MANUFACTURING CORPORATION—See Nordic Capital AB; *Int'l*, pg. 5419
AMERICAN BORATE CORPORATION; *U.S. Private*, pg. 225
AMERICAN BOTANICALS, LLC; *U.S. Private*, pg. 225
AMERICAN BRIDGE COMPANY—See Continental Holdings Corp.; *Int'l*, pg. 1784
AMERICAN BRIDGE HOLDING COMPANY—See Continental Holdings Corp.; *Int'l*, pg. 1784
AMERICAN BRIDGE MANUFACTURING COMPANY—See Continental Holdings Corp.; *Int'l*, pg. 1784

AMERICAN BOTANICALS, LLC

AMERICAN BRIGHT SIGNS, INC.—See ACEP France; *Int'l*, pg. 98
AMERICAN BROADBAND HOLDING COMPANY—See Madison Dearborn Partners, LLC; *U.S. Private*, pg. 2540
AMERICAN BROADCASTING COMPANIES, INC.—See The Walt Disney Company; *U.S. Public*, pg. 2137
AMERICAN BRUSH COMPANY INC.—See A.H.I. Investment Inc.; *U.S. Private*, pg. 26
AMERICAN BUILDERS & CONTRACTORS SUPPLY CO., INC.—See Hendricks Holding Company, Inc.; *U.S. Private*, pg. 1914
AMERICAN BUILDERS SUPPLY, INC. - CLERMONT—See Kodiak Building Partners LLC; *U.S. Private*, pg. 2336
AMERICAN BUILDERS SUPPLY, INC.—See Kodiak Building Partners LLC; *U.S. Private*, pg. 2336
AMERICAN BUILDING COMPONENTS—See Clayton, Dubilier & Rice, LLC; *U.S. Private*, pg. 920
AMERICAN BUILDING & ROOFING—See Beacon Roofing Supply, Inc.; *U.S. Public*, pg. 285
AMERICAN BUILDINGS COMPANY—See Nucor Corporation; *U.S. Public*, pg. 1553
AMERICAN BUILDING SERVICES LLC—See Platinum Equity, LLC; *U.S. Private*, pg. 3208
AMERICAN BUILDING SUPPLY INC—See ONEX Corporation; *Int'l*, pg. 5579
AMERICAN BULK COMMODITIES INC.; *U.S. Private*, pg. 225
AMERICAN BUREAU OF SHIPPING; *U.S. Private*, pg. 225
AMERICAN BURN ASSOCIATION; *U.S. Private*, pg. 226
AMERICAN BUSINESS BANK; *U.S. Public*, pg. 98
AMERICAN BUSINESS LENDING, INC.—See Varde Partners, Inc.; *U.S. Private*, pg. 4346
AMERICAN BUSINESS MEDIA—See Software & Information Industry Association, Inc.; *U.S. Private*, pg. 3705
AMERICAN BUSINESS SOLUTIONS, INC.; *U.S. Private*, pg. 226
AMERICAN CABLE COMPANY INC.; *U.S. Private*, pg. 226
AMERICAN CABLING & COMMUNICATIONS INC.—See North American Video Corporation; *U.S. Private*, pg. 2941
AMERICAN CADASTRE, LLC—See Riverside Partners, LLC; *U.S. Private*, pg. 3445
AMERICAN CALIBRATION, INC.—See Concept Machine Tool Sales, LLC; *U.S. Private*, pg. 1008
AMERICAN CAMPUS COMMUNITIES, INC.—See Blackstone Inc.; *U.S. Public*, pg. 347
AMERICAN CAMPUS COMMUNITIES OPERATING PARTNERSHIP, LP—See Blackstone Inc.; *U.S. Public*, pg. 347
AMERICAN CAMPUS COMMUNITIES SERVICES, INC.—See Blackstone Inc.; *U.S. Public*, pg. 347
AMERICAN CANNABIS COMPANY, INC.; *U.S. Public*, pg. 98
AMERICAN CANNABIS INNOVATIONS CONGLOMERATED; *U.S. Private*, pg. 226
AMERICAN CAPITAL SENIOR FLOATING, LTD.; *U.S. Private*, pg. 226
AMERICAN CAPITAL TRUST I—See American Bank Incorporated; *U.S. Public*, pg. 97
AMERICAN CARGO EXPRESS, INC.—See LDI Ltd., LLC; *U.S. Private*, pg. 2404
AMERICAN CARPET ONE; *U.S. Private*, pg. 226
AMERICAN CARTAGE & DISTRIBUTION, LLC—See American Shipping Co. Inc.; *U.S. Private*, pg. 253
AMERICAN CASEIN COMPANY; *U.S. Private*, pg. 226
AMERICAN CASINO & ENTERTAINMENT PROPERTIES LLC—See Golden Entertainment, Inc.; *U.S. Public*, pg. 950
AMERICAN CASTING & MANUFACTURING CORPORATION; *U.S. Private*, pg. 226
AMERICAN CASTINGS—See American Cast Iron Pipe Company; *U.S. Private*, pg. 226
AMERICAN CAST IRON PIPE COMPANY; *U.S. Private*, pg. 226
AMERICAN CASUALTY COMPANY OF READING, PENNSYLVANIA—See Loews Corporation; *U.S. Public*, pg. 1339
AMERICAN CATCON, INC.—See Metalico Inc.; *U.S. Private*, pg. 2681
AMERICAN CENTRAL TRANSPORT, INC.—See The Kretsinger Group, Inc.; *U.S. Private*, pg. 4066
AMERICAN CENTURY BROKERAGE, INC.—See American Century Companies, Inc.; *U.S. Private*, pg. 226
AMERICAN CENTURY COMPANIES, INC.; *U.S. Private*, pg. 226
AMERICAN CENTURY INVESTMENTS—See American Century Companies, Inc.; *U.S. Private*, pg. 226
AMERICAN CHECKED, LLC—See Insight Venture Management, LLC; *U.S. Private*, pg. 2088
AMERICAN CHEMET CORPORATION; *U.S. Private*, pg. 227
AMERICAN CHEMET EXPORT CORPORATION—See American Chemet Corporation; *U.S. Private*, pg. 227
AMERICAN CHEMICALS, LLC—See Morgan Stanley; *U.S. Public*, pg. 1471

AMERICANCHURCH, INC.—See Our Sunday Visitor, Inc.; *U.S. Private*, pg. 3050
AMERICAN CHURCH MORTGAGE COMPANY; *U.S. Public*, pg. 98
AMERICAN CITY BUSINESS JOURNALS, INC.—See Advance Publications, Inc.; *U.S. Private*, pg. 84
AMERICAN CITY BUSINESS JOURNALS—See Advance Publications, Inc.; *U.S. Private*, pg. 84
AMERICAN CIVIL CONSTRUCTORS HOLDING INC.—See MasTec, Inc.; *U.S. Public*, pg. 1393
AMERICAN CIVIL CONSTRUCTORS WEST COAST LLC—See MasTec, Inc.; *U.S. Public*, pg. 1393
AMERICAN CLAIMS MANAGEMENT - ATLANTIC REGION, LLC—See Brown & Brown, Inc.; *U.S. Public*, pg. 396
AMERICAN CLAIMS MANAGEMENT, INC.—See Brown & Brown, Inc.; *U.S. Public*, pg. 397
AMERICAN CLASSIFIED SERVICES, INC.; *U.S. Private*, pg. 227
AMERICAN CLEANERS & LAUNDRY CO.; *U.S. Private*, pg. 227
AMERICAN CLEANING SYSTEMS, INC.—See Valcourt Building Services LLC; *U.S. Private*, pg. 4330
AMERICAN CLEAN RESOURCES GROUP, INC.; *U.S. Public*, pg. 98
AMERICAN COALITION FOR CLEAN COAL ELECTRICITY; *U.S. Private*, pg. 227
AMERICAN COASTAL INSURANCE COMPANY—See American Coastal Insurance Corporation; *U.S. Public*, pg. 98
AMERICAN COASTAL INSURANCE CORPORATION; *U.S. Public*, pg. 98
AMERICAN COATINGS; *U.S. Private*, pg. 227
AMERICAN COFFEE COMPANY, INC.; *U.S. Private*, pg. 227
AMERICAN COLD STORAGE; *U.S. Private*, pg. 227
AMERICAN COLLECTORS INSURANCE, INC.—See The Carlyle Group Inc.; *U.S. Public*, pg. 2050
AMERICAN COLLEGE OF CARDIOLOGY; *U.S. Private*, pg. 227
AMERICAN COLLEGE OF GASTROENTEROLOGY; *U.S. Private*, pg. 227
AMERICAN COLLEGE OF RHEUMATOLOGY, INC.; *U.S. Private*, pg. 227
AMERICAN COLLEGE OF SPORTS MEDICINE; *U.S. Private*, pg. 227
AMERICAN COLLEGIATE MARKETING; *U.S. Private*, pg. 227
AMERICAN COLLOID COMPANY—See Minerals Technologies, Inc.; *U.S. Public*, pg. 1448
AMERICAN COLONIAL INSURANCE COMPANY—See Conifer Holdings, Inc.; *U.S. Public*, pg. 567
AMERICAN COMMERCE INSURANCE COMPANY—See MAPFRE S.A.; *Int'l*, pg. 4684
AMERICAN COMMERCE SOLUTIONS, INC.; *U.S. Private*, pg. 227
AMERICAN COMMERCIAL LINES INC.—See Platinum Equity, LLC; *U.S. Private*, pg. 3201
AMERICAN COMMITTEE FOR THE WEIZMANN INSTITUTE OF SCIENCE, INC.; *U.S. Private*, pg. 227
AMERICAN COMMODITIES INC.; *U.S. Private*, pg. 227
AMERICAN COMMUNICATIONS GROUP, INC.; *U.S. Private*, pg. 227
AMERICAN COMMUNITY BANK OF INDIANA—See AMB Financial Corp.; *U.S. Public*, pg. 91
AMERICAN COMMUNITY PROPERTIES TRUST—See Federal Capital Partners; *U.S. Private*, pg. 1487
AMERICAN COMPACTION EQUIPMENT, INC.—See Toyota Industries Corporation; *Int'l*, pg. 7868
AMERICAN COMPENSATION INSURANCE COMPANY—See State Automobile Mutual Insurance Company; *U.S. Private*, pg. 3790
AMERICAN COMPLIANCE TECHNOLOGIES, INC.; *U.S. Private*, pg. 227
AMERICAN COMPRESSED GASES INC.; *U.S. Private*, pg. 227
AMERICAN COMPUTER DEVELOPMENT, INC.; *U.S. Private*, pg. 227
AMERICAN CONCEPT INSURANCE COMPANY—See Enstar Group Limited; *Int'l*, pg. 2448
AMERICAN CONCRETE PRODUCTS—See CRH plc; *Int'l*, pg. 1847
AMERICAN CONEC CORPORATION—See Amphenol Corporation; *U.S. Public*, pg. 126
AMERICAN CONSERVATORY THEATRE; *U.S. Private*, pg. 228
AMERICAN CONSOLIDATED INDUSTRIES; *U.S. Private*, pg. 228
AMERICAN CONSOLIDATED MEDIA LP; *U.S. Private*, pg. 228
AMERICAN CONSOLIDATED NATURAL RESOURCES, INC.; *U.S. Private*, pg. 228
AMERICAN CONSTRUCTION SOURCE, LLC—See Bain Capital, LP; *U.S. Private*, pg. 450
AMERICAN CONSTRUCTION SUPPLY, INC.—See Avalon Holdings Corporation; *U.S. Public*, pg. 239
AMERICAN CONSTRUCTION SUPPLY & RENTAL INC.; *U.S. Private*, pg. 228
AMERICAN CONSTRUCTORS LP; *U.S. Private*, pg. 228

CORPORATE AFFILIATIONS

AMERICAN CONSUMER CREDIT COUNSELING, INC.; *U.S. Private*, pg. 228
AMERICAN CONSUMER FINANCIAL NETWORK; *U.S. Private*, pg. 228
AMERICAN CONSUMER NEWS, LLC; *U.S. Private*, pg. 228
AMERICAN CONTINENTAL BANCORP; *U.S. Private*, pg. 228
AMERICAN CONTINENTAL BANK—See American Continental Bancorp; *U.S. Private*, pg. 228
AMERICAN CONTINENTAL INSURANCE COMPANY—See CVS Health Corporation; *U.S. Public*, pg. 615
AMERICAN CONTRACT BRIDGE LEAGUE, INC.; *U.S. Private*, pg. 228
AMERICAN CONTRACTING INC.; *U.S. Private*, pg. 228
AMERICAN CONTRACTING & SERVICES INC.—See Hughes Group, Inc.; *U.S. Private*, pg. 2003
AMERICAN CONTROLS INC.; *U.S. Private*, pg. 228
AMERICAN COOLER SERVICE, LLC—See JLL Partners, LLC; *U.S. Private*, pg. 2212
AMERICAN COPPER & BRASS, LLC—See Worth Investment Group, LLC; *U.S. Private*, pg. 4570
AMERICAN COPPER DEVELOPMENT CORPORATION; *Int'l*, pg. 422
AMERICAN CORNERSTONE INSURANCE LLC—See RightSure Insurance Group; *U.S. Private*, pg. 3436
AMERICAN CORRECTIONAL SOLUTIONS, INC.; *U.S. Private*, pg. 228
AMERICAN CORRUGATED PRODUCTS, INC.—See Welch Packaging Group, Inc.; *U.S. Private*, pg. 4473
AMERICAN COUNCIL FOR INTERNATIONAL STUDIES, INC. - ENCORE TOURS DIVISION—See American Institute for Foreign Study, Inc.; *U.S. Private*, pg. 237
AMERICAN COUNCIL FOR INTERNATIONAL STUDIES INC.—See American Institute for Foreign Study, Inc.; *U.S. Private*, pg. 237
AMERICAN COUNCIL OF LEARNED SOCIETIES; *U.S. Private*, pg. 229
AMERICAN COUNCIL ON THE TEACHING OF FOREIGN LANGUAGES; *U.S. Private*, pg. 229
AMERICAN COUNCILS FOR INTERNATIONAL EDUCATION; *U.S. Private*, pg. 229
AMERICAN COVERS, INC.—See Energizer Holdings, Inc.; *U.S. Public*, pg. 760
AMERICAN CRANE & EQUIPMENT CORPORATION - SERVICE, PARTS & STANDARD CRANE DIVISION—See American Crane & Equipment Corporation; *U.S. Private*, pg. 229
AMERICAN CRANE & EQUIPMENT CORPORATION; *U.S. Private*, pg. 229
AMERICAN CRANE & TRACTOR PARTS INCORPORATED—See GB Ricambi S.p.A.; *Int'l*, pg. 2893
AMERICAN CREDIT ALLIANCE INC.; *U.S. Private*, pg. 229
AMERICAN CREDIT CARD PROCESSING CORP.—See Priority Payment Systems, LLC; *U.S. Private*, pg. 3267
AMERICAN CREEK RESOURCES LTD.; *Int'l*, pg. 422
AMERICAN CREW, INC.—See MacAndrews & Forbes Incorporated; *U.S. Private*, pg. 2534
AMERICAN CRITICAL CARE SERVICES; *U.S. Private*, pg. 229
AMERICAN CRITICAL ELEMENTS INC.; *Int'l*, pg. 422
AMERICAN CRITTER COLLEGE, INC.; *U.S. Private*, pg. 229
AMERICAN CRYOSTEM CORPORATION; *U.S. Public*, pg. 98
AMERICAN CRYSTAL HOLDINGS, INC.; *U.S. Private*, pg. 229
AMERICAN CRYSTAL SUGAR COMPANY; *U.S. Public*, pg. 98
AMERICAN CURRENT CARE OF ARIZONA, P.A.—See Select Medical Holdings Corporation; *U.S. Public*, pg. 1857
AMERICAN CURRENT CARE OF ARKANSAS, P.A.—See Select Medical Holdings Corporation; *U.S. Public*, pg. 1857
AMERICAN CURRENT CARE OF MASSACHUSETTS, P.C.—See Select Medical Holdings Corporation; *U.S. Public*, pg. 1857
AMERICAN CURRENT CARE OF MICHIGAN, P.C.—See Select Medical Holdings Corporation; *U.S. Public*, pg. 1857
AMERICAN CURRENT CARE OF NEBRASKA, P.C.—See Select Medical Holdings Corporation; *U.S. Public*, pg. 1857
AMERICAN CURRENT CARE OF NEW JERSEY PA—See Select Medical Holdings Corporation; *U.S. Public*, pg. 1857
AMERICAN CURRENT CARE OF NORTH CAROLINA, P.C.—See Select Medical Holdings Corporation; *U.S. Public*, pg. 1857
AMERICAN CUSTOM YACHTS, INC.; *U.S. Private*, pg. 229
AMERICAN CUTTING EDGE, INC.—See CB Manufacturing & Sales Co., Inc.; *U.S. Private*, pg. 796
AMERICAN CYBERSYSTEMS, INC.; *U.S. Private*, pg. 229

COMPANY NAME INDEX

AMERICAN DAIRY QUEEN CORPORATION—See Berkshire Hathaway Inc.; *U.S. Public*, pg. 308
AMERICAN DAWN INC.; *U.S. Private*, pg. 230
AMERICAN DECORATIVE FABRICS, LLC; *U.S. Private*, pg. 230
AMERICAN DECORATIVE SURFACES, INC.—See Ares Management Corporation; *U.S. Public*, pg. 188
AMERICAN DEHYDRATED FOODS, INC.—See Symrise AG; *Int'l*, pg. 7380
AMERICAN DENTAL EDUCATION ASSOCIATION; *U.S. Private*, pg. 230
AMERICAN DENTAL PARTNERS, INC.—See JLL Partners, LLC; *U.S. Private*, pg. 2212
AMERICAN DE ROSA LAMPARTS, LLC—See Resilience Capital Partners, LLC; *U.S. Private*, pg. 3405
AMERICAN DESIGN LTD.; *U.S. Private*, pg. 230
AMERICAN DG ENERGY INC.—See Tecogen Inc.; *U.S. Public*, pg. 1989
AMERICAN DIGITAL TITLE INSURANCE COMPANY—See Munchener Ruckversicherungs AG; *Int'l*, pg. 5085
AMERICAN DINING CORPORATION; *U.S. Private*, pg. 230
AMERICAN DIRECT LLC—See Tidewater Direct LLC; *U.S. Private*, pg. 4168
AMERICAN DISPOSAL SERVICES OF WEST VIRGINIA, INC.—See Republic Services, Inc.; *U.S. Public*, pg. 1786
AMERICAN DISTILLING & MANUFACTURING CO.; *U.S. Private*, pg. 230
AMERICAN DIVERSIFIED HOLDINGS CORPORATION; *U.S. Public*, pg. 98
AMERICAN DORNIER MACHINERY CORPORATION—See Airbus SE; *Int'l*, pg. 242
AMERICAN DOUGLAS METALS INC.; *U.S. Private*, pg. 230
AMERICAN DRAPERY BLIND & CARPET, INC.; *U.S. Private*, pg. 230
AMERICAN DREAM HOME IMPROVEMENT, INC.; *U.S. Private*, pg. 230
AMERICAN DREW—See La-Z-Boy Incorporated; *U.S. Public*, pg. 1285
AMERICAN DRILL BUSHING CO.; *U.S. Private*, pg. 231
AMERICAN DRIVING RECORDS, INC.—See ABRY Partners, LLC; *U.S. Private*, pg. 43
AMERICAN DRYER CORPORATION—See Whirlpool Corporation; *U.S. Public*, pg. 2367
AMERICAN DRYER, LLC—See Zurn Elkay Water Solutions Corporation; *U.S. Public*, pg. 2412
AMERICAN DUCTILE IRON PIPE DIV.—See American Cast Iron Pipe Company; *U.S. Private*, pg. 226
AMERICAN EAGLE CO., INC.; *U.S. Private*, pg. 231
AMERICANEAGLE.COM, INC.; *U.S. Private*, pg. 258
AMERICAN EAGLE DISTRIBUTING CO.; *U.S. Private*, pg. 231
AMERICAN EAGLE EXPRESS INC.; *U.S. Private*, pg. 231
AMERICAN EAGLE LIFECARE CORPORATION; *U.S. Private*, pg. 231
AMERICAN EAGLE LOGISTICS, LLC—See Bennett International Group, Inc.; *U.S. Private*, pg. 527
AMERICAN EAGLE MORTGAGE CO., LLC; *U.S. Private*, pg. 231
AMERICAN EAGLE OUTFITTERS DUTCH OP CO B.V.—See American Eagle Outfitters, Inc.; *U.S. Public*, pg. 99
AMERICAN EAGLE OUTFITTERS, INC.; *U.S. Public*, pg. 98
AMERICAN EAGLE READY MIX UTAH, LLC—See Quanta Services, Inc.; *U.S. Public*, pg. 1750
AMERICAN EAGLE STEEL CORP.; *U.S. Private*, pg. 231
AMERICAN EAGLE SYSTEMS INC.; *U.S. Private*, pg. 231
AMERICAN EAGLE TANKERS AGENCIES INC.—See Petroliam Nasional Berhad; *Int'l*, pg. 5829
AMERICAN EAGLE WHEEL CORP.; *U.S. Private*, pg. 231
AMERICAN EAR HEARING AND AUDIOLOGY, LLC; *U.S. Private*, pg. 231
AMERICAN EDUCATIONAL PRODUCTS LLC—See Geneve Holdings Corp.; *U.S. Private*, pg. 1671
AMERICAN EDUCATIONAL RESEARCH ASSOCIATION; *U.S. Private*, pg. 231
AMERICAN EDUCATION CENTER, INC.; *U.S. Public*, pg. 99
AMERICAN EFFICIENT LLC; *U.S. Private*, pg. 231
AMERICAN & EFIRD (A&E EUROPE), SUKANCI D.O.O.—See The Kroger Co.; *U.S. Public*, pg. 2108
AMERICAN & EFIRD CANADA INCORPORATED—See The Kroger Co.; *U.S. Public*, pg. 2108
AMERICAN & EFIRD DE MEXICO, S.A. DE C.V—See The Kroger Co.; *U.S. Public*, pg. 2108
AMERICAN & EFIRD ENTERPRISES, INC.—See The Kroger Co.; *U.S. Public*, pg. 2108
AMERICAN & EFIRD (G.B.) LIMITED—See The Kroger Co.; *U.S. Public*, pg. 2108
AMERICAN & EFIRD, LLC—See Platinum Equity, LLC; *U.S. Public*, pg. 3201
AMERICAN & EFIRD (MALAYSIA) SDN. BHD.—See The Kroger Co.; *U.S. Public*, pg. 2108
AMERICAN & EFIRD MILLS (S) PTE. LTD.—See The Kroger Co.; *U.S. Public*, pg. 2108

AMERICAN EGG PRODUCTS, INC.—See Cal-Maine Foods, Inc.; *U.S. Public*, pg. 421
AMERICAN ELDERCARE, INC.—See Humana, Inc.; *U.S. Public*, pg. 1069
AMERICAN ELECTRICAL TESTING CO., INC.—See Asplundh Tree Expert Co.; *U.S. Private*, pg. 353
AMERICAN ELECTRIC CO. LLC; *U.S. Private*, pg. 231
AMERICAN ELECTRIC POWER COMPANY, INC.; *U.S. Public*, pg. 99
AMERICAN ELECTRIC POWER SERVICE CORPORATION—See American Electric Power Company, Inc.; *U.S. Public*, pg. 99
AMERICAN ELECTRIC SUPPLY INC.; *U.S. Private*, pg. 231
AMERICAN ELECTRONIC COMPONENTS, INC.; *U.S. Private*, pg. 231
AMERICAN ELECTRONIC COMPONENTS INC.; *U.S. Private*, pg. 231
AMERICAN ELECTRONIC RESOURCE; *U.S. Private*, pg. 231
AMERICAN ELECTRONICS, INC.—See Ducommun Incorporated; *U.S. Public*, pg. 689
AMERICAN ELEVATOR GROUP; *U.S. Private*, pg. 231
AMERICAN EMPIRE INSURANCE COMPANY—See American Financial Group, Inc.; *U.S. Public*, pg. 102
AMERICAN EMPIRE SURPLUS LINES INSURANCE COMPANY—See American Financial Group, Inc.; *U.S. Public*, pg. 102
AMERICAN EMPIRE UNDERWRITERS, INC.—See American Financial Group, Inc.; *U.S. Public*, pg. 102
AMERICAN ENDOWMENT FOUNDATION; *U.S. Private*, pg. 231
THE AMERICAN ENERGY GROUP, LTD.; *U.S. Public*, pg. 2034
AMERICAN ENERGY PARTNERS, INC.; *U.S. Public*, pg. 100
AMERICAN ENERGY PRODUCTION, INC.; *U.S. Private*, pg. 231
AMERICAN ENERGY TRANSPORT, LLC—See AET Holdings, LLC; *U.S. Private*, pg. 120
AMERICAN ENGINEERING ASSOCIATES - SOUTHEAST, P.A.; *U.S. Private*, pg. 232
AMERICAN ENTERPRISE GROUP, INC.—See American Enterprise Mutual Holding Company; *U.S. Private*, pg. 202
AMERICAN ENTERPRISE INSTITUTE FOR PUBLIC POLICY RESEARCH; *U.S. Private*, pg. 232
AMERICAN ENTERPRISE INVESTMENT SERVICES, INC.—See Ameriprise Financial, Inc.; *U.S. Public*, pg. 114
AMERICAN ENTERPRISE MUTUAL HOLDING COMPANY; *U.S. Private*, pg. 232
AMERICAN ENVIRONMENTAL CONSULTANTS, INC.—See TRC Companies, Inc.; *U.S. Private*, pg. 4215
AMERICAN ENVIRONMENTAL ENERGY, INC.; *U.S. Public*, pg. 100
AMERICAN ENVIRONMENTAL GROUP, INC.—See McLarens, Inc.; *U.S. Private*, pg. 2640
AMERICAN ENVIRONMENTAL GROUP LTD.—See Tetra Tech, Inc.; *U.S. Public*, pg. 2022
AMERICAN ENVIRONMENTAL SERVICES, INC.—See Enviri Corporation; *U.S. Public*, pg. 780
AMERICAN EQUIPMENT COMPANY, INC.—See OEP Capital Advisors, L.P.; *U.S. Private*, pg. 2998
AMERICAN EQUIPMENT, INC.—See Rotunda Capital Partners LLC; *U.S. Private*, pg. 3487
AMERICAN EQUIPMENT & TRAILER, INC.; *U.S. Private*, pg. 232
AMERICAN EQUITY INVESTMENT LIFE HOLDING COMPANY—See Brookfield Reinsurance Ltd.; *Int'l*, pg. 1193
AMERICAN EQUITY INVESTMENT LIFE INSURANCE COMPANY OF NEW YORK—See Brookfield Reinsurance Ltd.; *Int'l*, pg. 1193
AMERICAN EQUITY INVESTMENT LIFE INSURANCE COMPANY—See Brookfield Reinsurance Ltd.; *Int'l*, pg. 1193
AMERICAN EQUITY MORTGAGE INC.; *U.S. Private*, pg. 232
THE AMERICAN EQUITY UNDERWRITERS, INC.—See AmWINS Group, Inc.; *U.S. Private*, pg. 270
AMERICAN ESCROW COMPANY—See First American Financial Corporation; *U.S. Public*, pg. 835
AMERICAN ESOTERIC LABORATORIES, INC. - CENTRAL REGION LABORATORY—See Sonic Healthcare Limited; *Int'l*, pg. 7098
AMERICAN ESOTERIC LABORATORIES, INC. - EAST—See Sonic Healthcare Limited; *Int'l*, pg. 7098
AMERICAN ESOTERIC LABORATORIES, INC.—See Sonic Healthcare Limited; *Int'l*, pg. 7098
AMERICAN EUROPEAN GROUP, INC.; *U.S. Private*, pg. 232
AMERICAN EXCELSIOR COMPANY; *U.S. Private*, pg. 232
AMERICAN EXCHANGE GROUP; *U.S. Private*, pg. 232
AMERICAN EXHIBITIONS, INC.; *U.S. Private*, pg. 232
AMERICAN EXPRESS ARGENTINA S.A.—See American Express Company; *U.S. Public*, pg. 100

AMERICAN EXTERIORS, LLC

AMERICAN EXPRESS AUSTRIA BANK GMBH—See American Express Company; *U.S. Public*, pg. 100
AMERICAN EXPRESS BARCELO VIAJES SL—See American Express Company; *U.S. Public*, pg. 101
AMERICAN EXPRESS BRASIL ASSESSORIA EMPRESARIAL LTDA.—See American Express Company; *U.S. Public*, pg. 100
AMERICAN EXPRESS BUSINESS TRAVEL AB—See Global Business Travel Group, Inc.; *U.S. Public*, pg. 941
AMERICAN EXPRESS BUSINESS TRAVEL APS—See Global Business Travel Group, Inc.; *U.S. Public*, pg. 941
AMERICAN EXPRESS BUSINESS TRAVEL AS—See Global Business Travel Group, Inc.; *U.S. Public*, pg. 941
AMERICAN EXPRESS CARTE FRANCE SA—See American Express Company; *U.S. Public*, pg. 101
AMERICAN EXPRESS CENTURION BANK—See American Express Company; *U.S. Public*, pg. 101
AMERICAN EXPRESS CHANGE SAS—See American Express Company; *U.S. Public*, pg. 101
AMERICAN EXPRESS COMPANY AS—See American Express Company; *U.S. Public*, pg. 101
AMERICAN EXPRESS COMPANY (MEXICO) S.A. DE C.V.—See American Express Company; *U.S. Public*, pg. 101
AMERICAN EXPRESS COMPANY; *U.S. Public*, pg. 100
AMERICAN EXPRESS CORPORATE TRAVEL A/S—See American Express Company; *U.S. Public*, pg. 101
AMERICAN EXPRESS CORPORATE TRAVEL BVBA—See Global Business Travel Group, Inc.; *U.S. Public*, pg. 941
AMERICAN EXPRESS CREDIT CORPORATION—See American Express Company; *U.S. Public*, pg. 101
AMERICAN EXPRESS DENMARK A/S—See American Express Company; *U.S. Public*, pg. 101
AMERICAN EXPRESS EUROPE LIMITED—See American Express Company; *U.S. Public*, pg. 100
AMERICAN EXPRESS FRANCE SAS—See American Express Company; *U.S. Public*, pg. 101
AMERICAN EXPRESS GLOBAL COMMERCIAL CARD GROUP—See American Express Company; *U.S. Public*, pg. 100
AMERICAN EXPRESS GLOBAL INFORMATION SERVICES—See American Express Company; *U.S. Public*, pg. 100
AMERICAN EXPRESS HOLDING AB—See American Express Company; *U.S. Public*, pg. 101
AMERICAN EXPRESS HOLDINGS (FRANCE) SAS—See American Express Company; *U.S. Public*, pg. 100
AMERICAN EXPRESS HUNGARY KFT—See American Express Company; *U.S. Public*, pg. 101
AMERICAN EXPRESS INTERNATIONAL, INC.—See American Express Company; *U.S. Public*, pg. 101
AMERICAN EXPRESS INTERNATIONAL SA—See American Express Company; *U.S. Public*, pg. 101
AMERICAN EXPRESS INTERNATIONAL (TAIWAN), INC.—See American Express Company; *U.S. Public*, pg. 101
AMERICAN EXPRESS ITALIA S.R.L.—See American Express Company; *U.S. Public*, pg. 100
AMERICAN EXPRESS LOCAZIONI FINANZIARIE S.R.L.—See American Express Company; *U.S. Public*, pg. 101
AMERICAN EXPRESS (MALAYSIA) SDN. BHD.—See American Express Company; *U.S. Public*, pg. 100
AMERICAN EXPRESS NATIONAL BANK—See American Express Company; *U.S. Public*, pg. 101
AMERICAN EXPRESS NIPPON TRAVEL AGENCY, INC.—See American Express Company; *U.S. Public*, pg. 100
AMERICAN EXPRESS OVERSEAS CREDIT CORPORATION LIMITED—See American Express Company; *U.S. Public*, pg. 101
AMERICAN EXPRESS POLAND SP Z O O—See American Express Company; *U.S. Public*, pg. 101
AMERICAN EXPRESS REISEBURO GMBH—See American Express Company; *U.S. Public*, pg. 101
AMERICAN EXPRESS SERVICES EUROPE LIMITED—See American Express Company; *U.S. Public*, pg. 101
AMERICAN EXPRESS SERVICIOS PROFESIONALES, S. DE R.L. DE C.V.—See American Express Company; *U.S. Public*, pg. 101
AMERICAN EXPRESS SPOL. S.R.O.—See American Express Company; *U.S. Public*, pg. 101
AMERICAN EXPRESS (THAI) COMPANY LIMITED—See American Express Company; *U.S. Public*, pg. 101
AMERICAN EXPRESS TLS HK LIMITED—See American Express Company; *U.S. Public*, pg. 100
AMERICAN EXPRESS TRAVEL RELATED SERVICES COMPANY, INC.—See American Express Company; *U.S. Public*, pg. 101
AMERICAN EXPRESS VOYAGES SAS—See American Express Company; *U.S. Public*, pg. 101
AMERICAN EXTERIORS, LLC; *U.S. Private*, pg. 232
AMERICAN EXTRUDED PLASTICS, INC.—See Odyssey Investment Partners, LLC; *U.S. Private*, pg. 2995

AMERICAN FABRICATION CORPORATION

AMERICAN FABRICATION CORPORATION; *U.S. Private*, pg. 232
AMERICAN FABRICATORS, INC.; *U.S. Private*, pg. 232
AMERICAN FABRICATORS; *U.S. Private*, pg. 232
AMERICAN FACILITY SERVICES; *U.S. Private*, pg. 232
AMERICAN FAMILY ASSOCIATION, INC.; *U.S. Private*, pg. 232
AMERICAN FAMILY BROKERAGE, INC.—See American Family Mutual Insurance Company; *U.S. Private*, pg. 233
AMERICAN FAMILY CARE, INC.; *U.S. Private*, pg. 233
AMERICAN FAMILY FINANCIAL SERVICES, INC.—See American Family Mutual Insurance Company; *U.S. Private*, pg. 233
AMERICAN FAMILY HOME INSURANCE COMPANY—See Munchener Ruckversicherungs AG; *Int'l*, pg. 5090
AMERICAN FAMILY INSURANCE COMPANY—See American Family Mutual Insurance Company; *U.S. Private*, pg. 233
AMERICAN FAMILY LIFE ASSURANCE COMPANY OF COLUMBUS—See Aflac Incorporated; *U.S. Public*, pg. 57
AMERICAN FAMILY LIFE ASSURANCE COMPANY OF NEW YORK—See Aflac Incorporated; *U.S. Public*, pg. 57
AMERICAN FAMILY LIFE INSURANCE CO.—See American Family Mutual Insurance Company; *U.S. Private*, pg. 233
AMERICAN FAMILY MUTUAL INSURANCE COMPANY; *U.S. Private*, pg. 233
AMERICAN FARMLAND TRUST; *U.S. Private*, pg. 233
AMERICAN FARMS LLC; *U.S. Private*, pg. 233
AMERICAN FASTENERS INC.; *U.S. Private*, pg. 233
AMERICAN FAST FREIGHT, INC.—See The Jordan Company, L.P.; *U.S. Private*, pg. 4060
AMERICAN FEDERATION FOR AGING RESEARCH; *U.S. Private*, pg. 233
AMERICAN FEDERATION INSURANCE COMPANY—See Zurich Insurance Group Limited; *Int'l*, pg. 8698
AMERICAN FELT & FILTER COMPANY; *U.S. Private*, pg. 233
AMERICAN FENCE COMPANY, INC.; *U.S. Private*, pg. 233
AMERICAN FENCE COMPANY OF ARIZONA, INC.—See American Fence Company, Inc.; *U.S. Private*, pg. 233
AMERICAN FENCE & SECURITY COMPANY—See American Fence Company, Inc.; *U.S. Private*, pg. 233
AMERICAN FIBER & FINISHING INC.; *U.S. Private*, pg. 233
AMERICAN FIDELITY ASSURANCE COMPANY—See American Fidelity Corporation; *U.S. Private*, pg. 233
AMERICAN FIDELITY CORPORATION; *U.S. Private*, pg. 233
AMERICAN FIDELITY INTERNATIONAL HOLDINGS, INC.—See American Fidelity Corporation; *U.S. Private*, pg. 233
AMERICAN FIDELITY PROPERTY COMPANY—See American Fidelity Corporation; *U.S. Private*, pg. 234
AMERICAN FIDELITY SECURITIES, INC.—See American Fidelity Corporation; *U.S. Private*, pg. 233
AMERICAN FIELD PUBLISHING COMPANY, INC.—See United Kennel Club, Inc.; *U.S. Private*, pg. 4293
AMERICAN FILM INSTITUTE; *U.S. Private*, pg. 234
AMERICAN FILMS, INC.; *U.S. Public*, pg. 102
AMERICAN FINANCIAL & AUTOMOTIVE SERVICES, INC.—See Assurant, Inc.; *U.S. Public*, pg. 214
AMERICAN FINANCIAL ENTERPRISES, INC.—See American Financial Group, Inc.; *U.S. Public*, pg. 102
AMERICAN FINANCIAL GROUP, INC.; *U.S. Public*, pg. 102
AMERICAN FINANCIAL MARKETING INC.—See Allianz SE; *Int'l*, pg. 351
AMERICAN FINANCIAL RESOURCES, INC.—See Proprietary Capital LLC; *U.S. Private*, pg. 3286
AMERICAN FINANCIAL SOLUTIONS—See North Seattle Community College Foundation; *U.S. Private*, pg. 2946
AMERICAN FINANCIAL WARRANTY CORPORATION—See Assurant, Inc.; *U.S. Public*, pg. 214
AMERICAN FINDINGS CORPORATION; *U.S. Private*, pg. 234
AMERICAN FINE SINTER CO., LTD.—See Fine Sinter Co., Ltd.; *Int'l*, pg. 2673
AMERICAN FIRE & CASUALTY CO.—See Liberty Mutual Holding Company Inc.; *U.S. Private*, pg. 2446
AMERICAN FIREGLASS; *U.S. Private*, pg. 234
AMERICAN FIRE PROTECTION GROUP, INC.—See APi Group Corporation; *Int'l*, pg. 513
AMERICAN FIRE PROTECTION, INC.; *U.S. Private*, pg. 234
AMERICAN FIRE RESTORATION, LLC; *U.S. Private*, pg. 234
AMERICAN FIRE TECHNOLOGIES, INC.—See Littlejohn & Co., LLC; *U.S. Private*, pg. 2471
AMERICAN FIRST CREDIT UNION; *U.S. Private*, pg. 234
AMERICAN FIRST NATIONAL BANK NA; *U.S. Private*, pg. 234

AMERICAN FITNESS PROFESSIONALS & ASSOCIATES, LLC—See Moelis Asset Management LP; *U.S. Private*, pg. 2764
AMERICAN FITNESS WHOLESALERS LLC—See Gotham Cigars, LLC; *U.S. Private*, pg. 1745
AMERICAN FLANGE & MANUFACTURING CO., INC.—See Greif Inc.; *U.S. Public*, pg. 965
AMERICAN FLORIST SUPPLY INC.; *U.S. Private*, pg. 234
AMERICAN FLOW CONTROL—See American Cast Iron Pipe Company; *U.S. Private*, pg. 226
AMERICAN FOLIAGE MART—See Deli, Inc.; *U.S. Private*, pg. 1196
AMERICAN FOOD DISTRIBUTORS, LLC; *U.S. Private*, pg. 234
AMERICAN FOOD DISTRIBUTORS; *U.S. Private*, pg. 234
AMERICAN FOODSERVICE CORP.; *U.S. Private*, pg. 234
AMERICAN FOOD SERVICES INTERNATIONAL INC.—See Bellboy Corporation; *U.S. Private*, pg. 520
AMERICAN FOODS GROUP, LLC—See Rosens Diversified, Inc.; *U.S. Private*, pg. 3484
AMERICAN FOOD & VENDING CORP.; *U.S. Private*, pg. 234
AMERICAN FOREST PRODUCTS LLC; *U.S. Private*, pg. 234
AMERICAN FORK DIALYSIS, LLC—See DaVita Inc.; *U.S. Public*, pg. 636
AMERICAN FOUNDRY GROUP, INC.; *U.S. Private*, pg. 234
AMERICAN FOUNDRY—See American Foundry Group, Inc.; *U.S. Private*, pg. 234
AMERICAN FREIGHT, LLC—See B. Riley Financial, Inc.; *U.S. Public*, pg. 261
AMERICAN FREIGHT, LLC—See Irradiant Partners, LP; *U.S. Private*, pg. 2140
AMERICAN FROZEN FOODS, INC.; *U.S. Private*, pg. 234
AMERICAN FRUITS & FLAVORS LLC - JUICE DIVISION—See Monster Beverage Corporation; *U.S. Public*, pg. 1465
AMERICAN FRUITS & FLAVORS LLC—See Monster Beverage Corporation; *U.S. Public*, pg. 1465
AMERICAN FUEL AND PETROCHEMICAL MANUFACTURERS; *U.S. Private*, pg. 234
AMERICAN FUEL CELLS & COATED FABRICS CO—See Safran SA; *Int'l*, pg. 6477
AMERICAN FUJI SEAL, INC.—See Fuji Seal International, Inc.; *Int'l*, pg. 2816
AMERICAN FUJI SEAL, INC.—See Fuji Seal International, Inc.; *Int'l*, pg. 2816
AMERICAN FUJI TECHNICAL SERVICES, INC—See Fuji Seal International, Inc.; *Int'l*, pg. 2816
AMERICAN FUNDS DISTRIBUTORS, INC.—See The Capital Group Companies, Inc.; *U.S. Private*, pg. 4004
AMERICAN FUNERAL FINANCIAL, LLC—See Security National Financial Corporation; *U.S. Public*, pg. 1856
AMERICAN FURNITURE MANUFACTURING, INC.; *U.S. Private*, pg. 234
AMERICAN FURNITURE RENTAL; *U.S. Private*, pg. 234
AMERICAN FURNITURE WAREHOUSE; *U.S. Private*, pg. 235
AMERICAN FURUKAWA, INC.—See The Furukawa Electric Co., Ltd.; *Int'l*, pg. 7644
AMERICAN FUTURE SYSTEMS INC.; *U.S. Private*, pg. 235
AMERICAN GALVANIZING—See Valmont Industries, Inc.; *U.S. Public*, pg. 2273
AMERICAN GARDENWORKS; *U.S. Private*, pg. 235
AMERICAN GAS & CHEMICAL CO., LTD.; *U.S. Private*, pg. 235
AMERICAN GAS PRODUCTS, LLC—See Air Water Inc.; *Int'l*, pg. 239
AMERICAN GCI RESITOP, INC.—See Gun Ei Chemical Industry Co., Ltd.; *Int'l*, pg. 3183
AMERICAN GENE ENGINEER CORP.; *U.S. Private*, pg. 235
AMERICAN GENERAL ASSURANCE COMPANY—See American International Group, Inc.; *U.S. Public*, pg. 104
AMERICAN GENERAL FINANCE ADVISORS—See American International Group, Inc.; *U.S. Public*, pg. 106
AMERICAN GENERAL LIFE & ACCIDENT INSURANCE COMPANY—See American International Group, Inc.; *U.S. Public*, pg. 105
AMERICAN GENERAL LIFE & ACCIDENT INSURANCE COMPANY—See American International Group, Inc.; *U.S. Public*, pg. 105
AMERICAN GENERAL LIFE COMPANIES - SPRINGFIELD—See American International Group, Inc.; *U.S. Public*, pg. 105
AMERICAN GENERAL LIFE INSURANCE COMPANY—See American International Group, Inc.; *U.S. Public*, pg. 105
AMERICAN GENERAL SUPPLIES, INC.; *U.S. Private*, pg. 235
AMERICAN GENTOR CORPORATION—See Gentor, S.A. de C.V.; *Int'l*, pg. 2929
AMERICAN GIFT FUND; *U.S. Private*, pg. 235
AMERICAN GILSONITE CO.-BONANZA MINE—See Palladium Equity Partners, LLC; *U.S. Private*, pg. 3077
AMERICAN GILSONITE CO.—See Palladium Equity Partners, LLC; *U.S. Private*, pg. 3077

CORPORATE AFFILIATIONS

AMERICAN GIRL BRANDS, LLC—See Mattel, Inc.; *U.S. Public*, pg. 1398
AMERICAN GIRL LLC—See Mattel, Inc.; *U.S. Public*, pg. 1398
AMERICAN GIRL PLACE INC.—See Mattel, Inc.; *U.S. Public*, pg. 1398
AMERICAN GLASS RESEARCH—See Clayton, Dubilier & Rice, LLC; *U.S. Public*, pg. 924
AMERICAN GLOBAL HEALTH GROUP, LLC.; *U.S. Private*, pg. 235
AMERICAN GLOBAL LOGISTICS, LLC—See Moelis Asset Management LP; *U.S. Private*, pg. 2764
AMERICAN GOLF CORPORATION; *U.S. Private*, pg. 235
AMERICAN GOLF LTD.—See Sun Capital Partners, Inc.; *U.S. Private*, pg. 3861
AMERICAN GOLF OF ATLANTA—See Drive Shack Inc.; *U.S. Public*, pg. 688
AMERICAN GOVERNMENT SERVICES CORP.; *U.S. Private*, pg. 235
AMERICAN GOVERNOR CO.—See Emerson Electric Co.; *U.S. Public*, pg. 740
AMERICAN GRANBY, INC.; *U.S. Private*, pg. 235
AMERICAN GREEN, INC.; *U.S. Public*, pg. 103
AMERICAN GREETINGS CORP. - NORTH AMERICAN SOCIAL EXPRESSION PRODUCTS—See Clayton, Dubilier & Rice, LLC; *U.S. Public*, pg. 919
AMERICAN GREETINGS CORPORATION—See Clayton, Dubilier & Rice, LLC; *U.S. Public*, pg. 919
AMERICAN GREETINGS CORP. - RIPLEY FACILITY—See Clayton, Dubilier & Rice, LLC; *U.S. Private*, pg. 919
AMERICAN GRINDING AND MACHINE COMPANY; *U.S. Private*, pg. 235
AMERICAN GROUP, LLC.; *U.S. Private*, pg. 235
AMERICAN GUARANTEE AND LIABILITY INSURANCE COMPANY—See Zurich Insurance Group Limited; *Int'l*, pg. 8698
AMERICAN GUARANTEE INSURANCE COMPANY—See First Citizens BancShares, Inc.; *U.S. Public*, pg. 842
AMERICAN GUARANTY TITLE INSURANCE COMPANY—See Old Republic International Corporation; *U.S. Public*, pg. 1568
AMERICAN GYPSUM CO. LLC - DUKE PLANT—See Eagle Materials Inc.; *U.S. Public*, pg. 702
AMERICAN GYPSUM COMPANY LLC—See Eagle Materials Inc.; *U.S. Public*, pg. 702
AMERICAN HAKKO PRODUCTS, INC.; *U.S. Private*, pg. 235
AMERICAN HALLMARK INSURANCE COMPANY OF TEXAS—See Hallmark Financial Services, Inc.; *U.S. Public*, pg. 981
AMERICAN HALLMARK INSURANCE SERVICES, INC.—See Hallmark Financial Services, Inc.; *U.S. Public*, pg. 981
AMERICAN HANDLING SYSTEMS, INC.; *U.S. Private*, pg. 235
AMERICAN HARDWOOD INDUSTRIES, LLC—See Baillie Lumber Co., Inc.; *U.S. Private*, pg. 426
AMERICAN HARTFORD GOLD GROUP LLC; *U.S. Private*, pg. 235
AMERICAN HARVEST BAKING; *U.S. Private*, pg. 235
AMERICAN HAVAL MOTOR TECHNOLOGY, LLC—See Great Wall Motor Company Limited; *Int'l*, pg. 3065
AMERICAN HEALTHCARE INVESTORS LLC; *U.S. Private*, pg. 235
AMERICAN HEALTHCARE PRODUCTS, INC.; *U.S. Private*, pg. 236
AMERICAN HEALTHCARE REIT, INC.—See American Healthcare Investors LLC; *U.S. Private*, pg. 236
AMERICAN HEALTHCARE REIT, INC.—See Griffin Capital Corporation; *U.S. Private*, pg. 1787
AMERICAN HEALTHCARE SYSTEMS CORP., INC.; *U.S. Private*, pg. 236
AMERICAN HEALTH HOLDING INC.—See CVS Health Corporation; *U.S. Public*, pg. 615
AMERICAN HEALTH INFORMATION MANAGEMENT ASSOCIATION; *U.S. Private*, pg. 235
AMERICAN HEALTH LAWYERS ASSOCIATION INC.; *U.S. Private*, pg. 235
AMERICAN HEALTH NETWORK OF INDIANA, LLC—See UnitedHealth Group Incorporated; *U.S. Public*, pg. 2238
AMERICAN HEALTH NETWORK OF OHIO, LLC—See UnitedHealth Group Incorporated; *U.S. Public*, pg. 2238
AMERICAN HEALTH PACKAGING—See Cencora, Inc.; *U.S. Public*, pg. 466
AMERICAN HEALTHTECH, INC.—See PointClickCare Corp.; *Int'l*, pg. 5904
AMERICAN HEALTHWARE SYSTEMS—See Siemens Aktiengesellschaft; *Int'l*, pg. 6889
AMERICAN HEALTHWAYS SERVICES, INC.—See Stone Point Capital LLC; *U.S. Private*, pg. 3825
AMERICAN HEARING AID ASSOCIATES, INC.—See Demant A/S; *Int'l*, pg. 2023
AMERICAN HEARING SYSTEMS INC—See GN Store Nord A/S; *Int'l*, pg. 3016
AMERICAN HERITAGE AGENCY INC.—See Inszone Insurance Services, LLC; *U.S. Private*, pg. 2096

COMPANY NAME INDEX

AMERICAN HERITAGE BANK; *U.S. Private,* pg. 236
AMERICAN HERITAGE BILLIARDS, LLC—See Escalade, Incorporated; *U.S. Public,* pg. 793
AMERICAN HERITAGE LIFE INSURANCE COMPANY—See The Allstate Corporation; *U.S. Public,* pg. 2033
AMERICAN HERITAGE LIFE INVESTMENT CORPORATION—See The Allstate Corporation; *U.S. Public,* pg. 2033
AMERICAN HERITAGE NATIONAL BANK; *U.S. Private,* pg. 236
AMERICAN HERITAGE PUBLISHING COMPANY; *U.S. Private,* pg. 236
AMERICAN HIGHWAYS INSURANCE AGENCY, INC.—See American Financial Group, Inc.; *U.S. Public,* pg. 103
AMERICAN HOFMANN CORPORATION; *U.S. Private,* pg. 236
AMERICAN HOLDCO INC.; *U.S. Private,* pg. 236
AMERICAN HOLIDAYS (NI) LIMITED—See TUI AG; *Int'l,* pg. 7964
AMERICAN HOLT CORP.—See Arcline Investment Management LP; *U.S. Private,* pg. 313
AMERICAN HOME ASSURANCE CO., LTD.—See American International Group, Inc.; *U.S. Public,* pg. 104
AMERICAN HOME ASSURANCE COMPANY—See American International Group, Inc.; *U.S. Public,* pg. 106
AMERICAN HOME MEDICAL, INC.—See AdaptHealth Corp.; *U.S. Public,* pg. 38
AMERICAN HOME MORTGAGES; *U.S. Private,* pg. 236
AMERICAN HOME PARTNERS, INC.; *U.S. Private,* pg. 236
AMERICAN HOMEPATIENT, INC.—See Linde plc; *Int'l,* pg. 4505
AMERICAN HOMES 4 RENT, L.P.—See American Homes 4 Rent; *U.S. Public,* pg. 104
AMERICAN HOMES 4 RENT; *U.S. Public,* pg. 104
AMERICAN HOME SHIELD CORPORATION—See frontdoor, inc.; *U.S. Public,* pg. 887
AMERICAN HOMES, INC.; *U.S. Private,* pg. 236
AMERICAN HOMESTAR CORPORATION; *U.S. Private,* pg. 236
AMERICAN HOME TITLE & ESCROW COMPANY—See Sekisui House, Ltd.; *Int'l,* pg. 6697
AMERICAN HOMETOWN PUBLISHING, INC.—See West End Holdings LLC; *U.S. Private,* pg. 4485
AMERICAN HONDA FINANCE CORP.—See Honda Motor Co., Ltd.; *Int'l,* pg. 3459
AMERICAN HONDA MOTOR CO., INC.—See Honda Motor Co., Ltd.; *Int'l,* pg. 3459
AMERICAN HOSPICE LLC—See The Riverside Company; *U.S. Private,* pg. 4107
AMERICAN HOTEL INCOME PROPERTIES REIT LP; *Int'l,* pg. 422
AMERICAN HOTEL REGISTER COMPANY; *U.S. Private,* pg. 236
AMERICAN HOUSE; *U.S. Private,* pg. 236
AMERICAN HOUSING CORPORATION; *U.S. Private,* pg. 237
AMERICAN HUTS INC.; *U.S. Private,* pg. 237
AMERICAN HYDRAULICS—See The Greenbrier Companies, Inc.; *U.S. Public,* pg. 2086
AMERICAN HYDRO CORPORATION—See ITOCHU Corporation; *Int'l,* pg. 3838
AMERICAN IMAGING MANAGEMENT, INC.—See Elevance Health, Inc.; *U.S. Public,* pg. 728
AMERICAN IMMIGRATION LAWYERS ASSOCIATION; *U.S. Private,* pg. 237
AMERICAN IMPORTING COMPANY, INC.—See TreeHouse Foods, Inc.; *U.S. Public,* pg. 2187
AMERICAN INCOME HOLDING, INC.—See Globe Life Inc.; *U.S. Public,* pg. 946
AMERICAN INCOME LIFE INSURANCE COMPANY—See Globe Life Inc.; *U.S. Public,* pg. 946
AMERICAN INCORPORATORS LTD.; *U.S. Private,* pg. 237
AMERICAN INDEPENDENCE CORP.—See Geneve Holdings Corp.; *U.S. Private,* pg. 1670
AMERICAN INDEPENDENT MARKETING, INC.—See Integrity Marketing Group LLC; *U.S. Private,* pg. 2103
AMERICAN INDEPENDENT NETWORK INSURANCE COMPANY OF NEW YORK—See Penn Treaty American Corporation; *U.S. Private,* pg. 3135
AMERICAN INDIAN HEALTH & SERVICES CORP.—See KKR & Co. Inc.; *U.S. Public,* pg. 1239
AMERICAN INDUSTRIAL ACQUISITION CORPORATION; *U.S. Private,* pg. 237
AMERICAN INDUSTRIAL CORPORATION; *U.S. Private,* pg. 237
AMERICAN INDUSTRIAL HYGIENE ASSOCIATION; *U.S. Private,* pg. 237
AMERICAN INDUSTRIAL LEASING COMPANY INC.—See Elkin Co.; *U.S. Private,* pg. 1363
AMERICAN INDUSTRIAL MACHINE—See BP Energy Partners, LLC; *U.S. Private,* pg. 629
AMERICAN INDUSTRIAL MANUFACTURING SERVICES, INC.—See Denso Corporation; *Int'l,* pg. 2028

AMERICAN INDUSTRIAL PLASTIC, LLC—See Compagnie Generale des Etablissements Michelin SCA; *Int'l,* pg. 1744
AMERICAN INDUSTRIAL STEEL & SUPPLY, LLC—See Hendricks Holding Company, Inc.; *U.S. Private,* pg. 1915
AMERICAN INDUSTRIAL SYSTEMS, INC.—See Hon Hai Precision Industry Co., Ltd.; *Int'l,* pg. 3456
AMERICAN INDUSTRIES, INC—See Stone Canyon Industries, LLC; *U.S. Private,* pg. 3817
AMERICAN INKS & COATINGS CORPORATION—See Mosley Holdings Limited Partnership; *U.S. Private,* pg. 2793
AMERICAN INNOTEK, INC; *U.S. Private,* pg. 237
AMERICAN INNOVATIONS, LTD.—See HM International; *U.S. Private,* pg. 1954
AMERICAN INSTANTS, INC.; *U.S. Private,* pg. 237
AMERICAN INSTITUTE FOR CHARTERED PROPERTY CASUALTY UNDERWRITERS; *U.S. Private,* pg. 237
AMERICAN INSTITUTE FOR FOREIGN STUDY COLLEGE DIVISION—See American Institute for Foreign Study, Inc.; *U.S. Private,* pg. 237
AMERICAN INSTITUTE FOR FOREIGN STUDY (DEUTSCHLAND) GMBH—See American Institute for Foreign Study, Inc.; *U.S. Private,* pg. 237
AMERICAN INSTITUTE FOR FOREIGN STUDY, INC.; *U.S. Private,* pg. 237
AMERICAN INSTITUTE FOR FOREIGN STUDY—See American Institute for Foreign Study, Inc.; *U.S. Private,* pg. 237
AMERICAN INSTITUTE OF FINANCIAL INTELLIGENCE LLC—See American Education Center, Inc.; *U.S. Public,* pg. 99
AMERICAN INSTITUTE OF GASTRIC BANDING; *U.S. Private,* pg. 238
AMERICAN INSTITUTE OF PHYSICS INC.; *U.S. Private,* pg. 238
AMERICAN INSTITUTE OF STEEL CONSTRUCTION; *U.S. Private,* pg. 238
AMERICAN INSTITUTE OF TOXICOLOGY, INC.; *U.S. Private,* pg. 238
AMERICAN INSTITUTE OF TRUCKING, INC.—See Werner Enterprises, Inc.; *U.S. Public,* pg. 2349
AMERICAN INSTITUTIONAL FOODS—See A.I.G International, Inc.; *U.S. Private,* pg. 144
AMERICAN INSULATED GLASS, LLC—See Trulite Glass & Aluminum Solutions, LLC; *U.S. Private,* pg. 4249
AMERICAN INSULATED WIRE CORP.—See Leviton Manufacturing Company, Inc.; *U.S. Private,* pg. 2436
AMERICAN INSURANCE ACQUISITION INC.—See Atlas Financial Holdings, Inc.; *U.S. Public,* pg. 224
AMERICAN INSURANCE ADMINISTRATORS, INC.—See Genstar Capital, LLC; *U.S. Private,* pg. 1674
AMERICAN INSURANCE BROKERS, INC.—See Unico American Corporation; *U.S. Public,* pg. 2225
THE AMERICAN INSURANCE COMPANY, CORP.—See Allianz SE; *Int'l,* pg. 356
AMERICAN INSURANCE MANAGEMENT GROUP; *U.S. Private,* pg. 238
AMERICAN INSURANCE MARKETING SERVICES, INC.—See LTC Global, Inc.; *U.S. Private,* pg. 2509
AMERICAN INTEGRATION CONTRACTORS, LLC; *U.S. Private,* pg. 238
AMERICAN INTEGRATION TECHNOLOGIES LLC—See Ultra Clean Holdings, Inc.; *U.S. Public,* pg. 2223
AMERICAN INTEGRITY INSURANCE COMPANY OF FLORIDA, INC.; *U.S. Private,* pg. 238
AMERICAN INTERCONTINENTAL UNIVERSITY, INC.—See Perdoceo Education Corporation; *U.S. Public,* pg. 1673
AMERICAN INTERMODAL MANAGEMENT, LLC—See I Squared Capital Advisors (US) LLC; *U.S. Private,* pg. 2021
AMERICAN INTERNATIONAL CARGO SERVICES (CHINA) LIMITED—See American Shipping Co. Inc.; *U.S. Private,* pg. 253
AMERICAN INTERNATIONAL CARGO SERVICE—See American Shipping Co. Inc.; *U.S. Private,* pg. 253
AMERICAN INTERNATIONAL COMMUNICATIONS, INC.; *U.S. Private,* pg. 238
AMERICAN INTERNATIONAL COMMUNICATIONS JACKSONVILLE—See American International Communications, Inc.; *U.S. Private,* pg. 238
AMERICAN INTERNATIONAL CONTRACTORS INC.; *U.S. Private,* pg. 238
AMERICAN INTERNATIONAL DISTRIBUTION CORPORATION—See Investors Corporation of Vermont; *U.S. Private,* pg. 2132
AMERICAN INTERNATIONAL GROUP, INC.; *U.S. Public,* pg. 104
AMERICAN INTERNATIONAL GROUP UK LIMITED—See American International Group, Inc.; *U.S. Public,* pg. 106
AMERICAN INTERNATIONAL HEALTH ALLIANCE; *U.S. Private,* pg. 238
AMERICAN INTERNATIONAL HOLDINGS CORP.; *U.S. Public,* pg. 107
AMERICAN INTERNATIONAL INDUSTRIES COMPANY; *U.S. Private,* pg. 238

AMERICAN LEISURE HOLDINGS, INC.

AMERICAN INTERNATIONAL INDUSTRIES, INC.; *U.S. Public,* pg. 107
AMERICAN INTERNATIONAL INSURANCE COMPANY OF PUERTO RICO—See American International Group, Inc.; *U.S. Public,* pg. 106
AMERICAN INTERNATIONAL LIFE ASSURANCE COMPANY OF NEW YORK—See American International Group, Inc.; *U.S. Public,* pg. 105
AMERICAN INTERNATIONAL MANAGEMENT—See New York Fragrance Inc.; *U.S. Private,* pg. 2909
AMERICAN INTERNATIONAL MOVERS—See HI-Boy Group Inc.; *U.S. Private,* pg. 1931
AMERICAN INTERNATIONAL REALTY CORP.—See American International Group, Inc.; *U.S. Public,* pg. 106
AMERICAN INTERNATIONAL REINSURANCE COMPANY, LTD.—See American International Group, Inc.; *U.S. Public,* pg. 106
AMERICAN INTERNATIONAL RELOCATION SOLUTIONS LLC; *U.S. Private,* pg. 238
AMERICAN INTERNATIONAL SUPPLY INC.; *U.S. Private,* pg. 238
AMERICAN INTERNATIONAL TRAVEL LIMITED—See Flight Centre Travel Group Limited; *Int'l,* pg. 2705
AMERICAN INTERNATIONAL VENTURES, INC.; *U.S. Public,* pg. 108
AMERICAN INTERSTATE INSURANCE COMPANY INC.—See AMERISAFE, Inc.; *U.S. Public,* pg. 115
AMERICAN INVESTMENT LLC—See CenterOak Partners LLC; *U.S. Private,* pg. 816
AMERICAN IRON & STEEL COMPANY; *U.S. Private,* pg. 238
AMERICAN IRON WORKS; *U.S. Private,* pg. 238
AMERICAN ITALIAN PASTA COMPANY—See Conagra Brands, Inc.; *U.S. Public,* pg. 563
AMERICAN IT SOLUTIONS, INC. (AIT); *U.S. Private,* pg. 238
AMERICAN JEBCO CORPORATION; *U.S. Private,* pg. 238
AMERICAN JEREH INTERNATIONAL CORPORATION—See Yantai Jereh Oilfield Services Group Co., Ltd.; *Int'l,* pg. 8565
AMERICAN JEWELRY & LOAN; *U.S. Private,* pg. 239
AMERICAN JEWISH COMMITTEE; *U.S. Private,* pg. 239
AMERICAN JEWISH CONGRESS INC.; *U.S. Private,* pg. 239
AMERICAN JEWISH WORLD SERVICE, INC.; *U.S. Private,* pg. 239
AMERICAN JOURNAL EXPERTS, LLC; *U.S. Private,* pg. 239
AMERICAN JST CORP—See JST Transformateurs SA; *Int'l,* pg. 4014
THE AMERICAN JUNIOR GOLF ASSOCIATION; *U.S. Private,* pg. 3986
AMERICAN KENDA RUBBER IND. CO., LTD.—See Kenda Rubber Industrial Co., Ltd.; *Int'l,* pg. 4126
AMERICAN KITCHEN DELIGHTS; *U.S. Private,* pg. 239
AMERICAN KUHNE, INC.—See The Graham Group, Inc.; *U.S. Private,* pg. 4036
AMERICAN LABELMARK COMPANY INC.; *U.S. Private,* pg. 239
AMERICAN LABORATORIES INC.; *U.S. Private,* pg. 239
AMERICAN LABORATORIES; *U.S. Private,* pg. 239
AMERICAN LABORATORY PRODUCTS COMPANY, LTD.—See Ampersand Management LLC; *U.S. Private,* pg. 265
AMERICAN LAFRANCE LLC—See Patriarch Partners, LLC; *U.S. Private,* pg. 3109
AMERICAN LAMPRECHT TRANSPORT, INC.—See Lamprecht Transport AG; *Int'l,* pg. 4402
AMERICAN LAND DEVELOPMENT, LLC—See Peabody Energy Corporation; *U.S. Public,* pg. 1659
AMERICAN LANDFILL, INC.—See Waste Management, Inc.; *U.S. Public,* pg. 2330
AMERICAN LANDFILL MANAGEMENT, INC.—See Avalon Holdings Corporation; *U.S. Public,* pg. 239
AMERICAN LAND LEASE, INC.—See Green Courte Partners, LLC; *U.S. Private,* pg. 1772
AMERICAN LAND VENTURES, LLC; *U.S. Private,* pg. 239
AMERICAN LASER CENTERS; *U.S. Private,* pg. 239
AMERICAN LAUBSCHER CORPORATION; *U.S. Private,* pg. 239
AMERICAN LAWN MOWER COMPANY; *U.S. Private,* pg. 239
AMERICAN LAWYER MEDIA, INC.—See Apax Partners LLP; *Int'l,* pg. 504
AMERICAN LEAK DETECTION, INC.—See Water Intelligence plc; *U.S. Public,* pg. 2334
AMERICAN LEARNING CORPORATION; *U.S. Private,* pg. 239
AMERICAN LEATHER OPERATIONS, LLC—See Heartwood Partners, LLC; *U.S. Private,* pg. 1901
AMERICAN LEGAL SEARCH, LLC; *U.S. Private,* pg. 239
AMERICAN LEGEND COOPERATIVE; *U.S. Private,* pg. 239
THE AMERICAN LEGION MAGAZINE; *U.S. Private,* pg. 3986
AMERICAN LEISURE HOLDINGS, INC.; *U.S. Public,* pg. 108

AMERICAN LEISURE HOLDINGS, INC.

AMERICAN LIBERTY INSURANCE COMPANY—See Altaris Capital Partners, LLC; *U.S. Private*, pg. 206
AMERICAN LICORICE CO. INC.; *U.S. Private*, pg. 239
AMERICAN LIFAN INC.—See Lifan Technology (Group) Co., Ltd.; *Int'l*, pg. 4492
AMERICAN LIFE & ACCIDENT INSURANCE COMPANY—See Globe Life Inc.; *U.S. Public*, pg. 946
AMERICAN LIFE INSURANCE COMPANY—See MetLife, Inc.; *U.S. Public*, pg. 1429
AMERICAN LIFE & SECURITY CORP.—See Antarctica Capital, LLC; *U.S. Private*, pg. 287
AMERICAN LIFTING PRODUCTS INC.—See ALP Industries, Inc.; *U.S. Private*, pg. 196
AMERICAN LIFT TRUCK SERVICES LLC; *U.S. Private*, pg. 239
AMERICAN LIGHTING AND SIGNALIZATION, INC.—See Asplundh Tree Expert Co.; *U.S. Private*, pg. 353
AMERICAN LIGHTING, INC—See Tsinghua Tongfang Co., Ltd.; *Int'l*, pg. 7951
AMERICAN LIGHTING SUPPLY INC.—See ForceField Energy Inc.; *U.S. Private*, pg. 1563
AMERICAN LINEN SUPPLY CO.—See Alsco Inc.; *U.S. Private*, pg. 202
AMERICAN LIST COUNSEL, INC; *U.S. Private*, pg. 240
AMERICAN LITHIUM CORP.; *Int'l*, pg. 422
AMERICAN LITHIUM MINERALS, INC.; *U.S. Private*, pg. 240
AMERICAN LITHO INC.; *U.S. Private*, pg. 240
AMERICAN LOCKER COMPANY, INC.—See American Locker Group Incorporated; *U.S. Private*, pg. 240
AMERICAN LOCKER GROUP INCORPORATED; *U.S. Private*, pg. 240
AMERICAN LOCKER SECURITY SYSTEMS, INC.—See American Locker Group Incorporated; *U.S. Private*, pg. 240
AMERICAN LOUVER COMPANY; *U.S. Private*, pg. 240
AMERICAN LUBEFAST LLC—See MidOcean Partners, LLP; *U.S. Private*, pg. 2716
AMERICAN LUBRICANTS INC—See Battenfeld Management Inc.; *U.S. Private*, pg. 488
AMERICAN LUMBER COMPANY INCORPORATED; *U.S. Private*, pg. 240
AMERICAN LUMBER COMPANY LP; *U.S. Private*, pg. 240
AMERICAN MADE LINER SYSTEMS—See American Made, LLC; *U.S. Private*, pg. 240
AMERICAN MADE, LLC; *U.S. Private*, pg. 240
AMERICAN MANAGEMENT CORPORATION—See Novatae Risk Group, LLC; *U.S. Private*, pg. 2967
AMERICAN MANAGEMENT SERVICES LLC; *U.S. Private*, pg. 240
AMERICAN MANUFACTURERS MUTUAL INSURANCE COMPANY—See Lumbermens Mutual Group; *U.S. Private*, pg. 2514
AMERICAN MAPLAN CORPORATION—See Nimbus B.V.; *Int'l*, pg. 5296
AMERICAN MARAZZI TILE, INC.—See Mohawk Industries, Inc.; *U.S. Public*, pg. 1457
AMERICAN MARINE HOLDINGS, LLC; *U.S. Private*, pg. 240
AMERICAN MARITIME HOLDINGS, INC.; *U.S. Private*, pg. 240
AMERICAN MARKETING & MAILING SERVICES, INC.; *U.S. Private*, pg. 240
AMERICAN MARKING SYSTEMS, INC.; *U.S. Private*, pg. 241
AMERICAN-MARSH PUMPS; *U.S. Private*, pg. 258
AMERICAN MATERIALS COMPANY, LLC—See Summit Materials, Inc.; *U.S. Public*, pg. 1960
AMERICAN MEDIA, INC.—See Chatham Asset Management, LLC; *U.S. Public*, pg. 860
AMERICAN MEDIA INTERNATIONAL LTD.; *U.S. Private*, pg. 241
AMERICAN MEDICAL ADMINISTRATORS, INC.; *U.S. Private*, pg. 241
AMERICAN MEDICAL ALERT CORP.—See Tunstall Group Limited; *Int'l*, pg. 7973
AMERICAN MEDICAL GROUP LLC; *U.S. Private*, pg. 241
AMERICAN MEDICAL RESPONSE, INC.—See KKR & Co. Inc.; *U.S. Public*, pg. 1251
AMERICAN MEDICAL RESPONSE MID-ATLANTIC, INC.—See KKR & Co. Inc.; *U.S. Public*, pg. 1251
AMERICAN MEDICAL RESPONSE NORTHWEST, INC.—See KKR & Co. Inc.; *U.S. Public*, pg. 1251
AMERICAN MEDICAL RESPONSE OF COLORADO, INC.—See KKR & Co. Inc.; *U.S. Public*, pg. 1251
AMERICAN MEDICAL RESPONSE OF CONNECTICUT, INC.—See KKR & Co. Inc.; *U.S. Public*, pg. 1251
AMERICAN MEDICAL RESPONSE OF INLAND EMPIRE—See KKR & Co. Inc.; *U.S. Public*, pg. 1251
AMERICAN MEDICAL RESPONSE OF NEW YORK, LLC—See KKR & Co. Inc.; *U.S. Public*, pg. 1251
AMERICAN MEDICAL SECURITY LIFE INSURANCE COMPANY—See UnitedHealth Group Incorporated; *U.S. Public*, pg. 2251
AMERICAN MEDICAL SYSTEMS CANADA INC.—See Endo International plc; *Int'l*, pg. 2404
AMERICAN MEDICAL SYSTEMS DEUTSCHLAND GMBH—See Endo International plc; *Int'l*, pg. 2404

AMERICAN MEDICAL SYSTEMS EUROPE B.V.—See Endo International plc; *Int'l*, pg. 2404
AMERICAN MEDICAL SYSTEMS FRANCE S.A.S—See Endo International plc; *Int'l*, pg. 2404
AMERICAN MEDICAL SYSTEMS HOLDINGS, INC.—See Endo International plc; *Int'l*, pg. 2404
AMERICAN MEDICAL SYSTEMS IBERICA S.L.—See Endo International plc; *Int'l*, pg. 2404
AMERICAN MEDICAL SYSTEMS, INC.-SAN JOSE—See Endo International plc; *Int'l*, pg. 2404
AMERICAN MEDICAL SYSTEMS, INC.—See Endo International plc; *Int'l*, pg. 2404
AMERICAN MEDICAL SYSTEMS UK LIMITED—See Endo International plc; *Int'l*, pg. 2404
AMERICAN MEGATRENDS, INC.—See HGGC, LLC; *U.S. Private*, pg. 1928
AMERICAN MEGATRENDS INDIA PVT. LTD.—See HGGC, LLC; *U.S. Private*, pg. 1928
AMERICAN MEGATRENDS INFORMATION TECHNOLOGY (KUNSHAN) CO., LTD.—See HGGC, LLC; *U.S. Private*, pg. 1929
AMERICAN MEGATRENDS INTERNATIONAL GMBH—See HGGC, LLC; *U.S. Private*, pg. 1929
AMERICAN MEMORIAL LIFE INSURANCE COMPANY—See Assurant, Inc.; *U.S. Public*, pg. 214
AMERICAN MERCHANDISE LIQUIDATORS, INC.; *U.S. Private*, pg. 241
AMERICAN MERCHANTS CASUALTY CO.—See Motorists Mutual Insurance Co.; *U.S. Private*, pg. 2797
AMERICAN MERCURY INSURANCE COMPANY—See Mercury General Corporation; *U.S. Public*, pg. 1421
AMERICAN MERCURY LLOYDS INSURANCE COMPANY—See Mercury General Corporation; *U.S. Public*, pg. 1421
AMERICAN MERCURY MGA, INC.—See Mercury General Corporation; *U.S. Public*, pg. 1421
AMERICAN METALCAST TECHNOLOGIES—See Meridian International Group, Inc.; *U.S. Private*, pg. 2673
AMERICAN METAL MARKET—See Astorg Partners S.A.S.; *Int'l*, pg. 656
AMERICAN METAL MARKET—See Epiris Managers LLP; *Int'l*, pg. 2460
AMERICAN METAL MOULDING CORP.; *U.S. Private*, pg. 241
AMERICAN METAL & PLASTICS INC.; *U.S. Private*, pg. 241
AMERICAN METALS COAL INTRNATIONAL—See KM Investment Corporation; *U.S. Private*, pg. 2321
AMERICAN METALS COMPANY, INC.; *U.S. Private*, pg. 241
AMERICAN METALS CORPORATION—See Reliance Steel & Aluminum Co.; *U.S. Public*, pg. 1779
AMERICAN METAL SUPPLY CO, INC.—See MacArthur Co.; *U.S. Private*, pg. 2534
AMERICAN METAL TECHNOLOGIES, LLC; *U.S. Private*, pg. 241
AMERICAN METAL & TECHNOLOGY, INC.; *Int'l*, pg. 422
AMERICAN METAL TESTING INC.—See Aero Metals Inc.; *U.S. Private*, pg. 118
AMERICAN MICROWAVE CORPORATION—See Ironwave Technologies LLC; *U.S. Private*, pg. 2140
AMERICAN MIDSTREAM (MISSISSIPPI), LLC—See ArcLight Capital Holdings, LLC; *U.S. Private*, pg. 312
AMERICAN MIDWEST FLEET SOLUTIONS—See Genstar Capital, LLC; *U.S. Private*, pg. 1676
AMERICAN MILLS INCORPORATED; *U.S. Private*, pg. 241
AMERICAN MINING INSURANCE GROUP, LLC—See W.R. Berkley Corporation; *U.S. Public*, pg. 2316
AMERICAN MINI STORAGE-SAN ANTONIO, LLC—See National Storage Affiliates Trust; *U.S. Public*, pg. 1498
AMERICAN MINORITY BUSINESS FORMS, INC.; *U.S. Private*, pg. 241
AMERICAN MITSUBA CORP. - INDIANA PLANT—See MITSUBA Corporation; *Int'l*, pg. 4928
AMERICAN MITSUBA CORPORATION—See MITSUBA Corporation; *Int'l*, pg. 4928
AMERICAN MOBILE HEALTHCARE—See AMN Healthcare Services, Inc.; *U.S. Public*, pg. 125
AMERICAN MOBILE POWER INQ.—See Interpump Group S.p.A; *Int'l*, pg. 3756
AMERICAN MODERN HOME INSURANCE COMPANY—See Munchener Ruckversicherungs AG; *Int'l*, pg. 5090
AMERICAN MODERN INSURANCE GROUP, INC.—See Munchener Ruckversicherungs AG; *Int'l*, pg. 5090
AMERICAN MODERN LIFE INSURANCE COMPANY—See Munchener Ruckversicherungs AG; *Int'l*, pg. 5090
AMERICAN MODERN SURPLUS LINES INSURANCE COMPANY—See Munchener Ruckversicherungs AG; *Int'l*, pg. 5085
AMERICAN MOMENTUM BANK—See The Adam Corporation/Group; *U.S. Private*, pg. 3981
AMERICAN MONEY MANAGEMENT CORPORATION—See American Financial Group, Inc.; *U.S. Public*, pg. 102
AMERICAN MORTGAGE CONSULTANTS, INC.—See Stone Point Capital LLC; *U.S. Private*, pg. 3825

CORPORATE AFFILIATIONS

AMERICAN MORTGAGE SERVICE COMPANY—See Thrive Mortgage LLC; *U.S. Private*, pg. 4165
AMERICAN MORTGAGE SERVICES; *U.S. Private*, pg. 241
AMERICAN MOTEL MANAGEMENT; *U.S. Private*, pg. 241
AMERICAN MOTORISTS INSURANCE CO.—See Lumbermens Mutual Group; *U.S. Private*, pg. 2514
AMERICAN MOVIE CLASSICS COMPANY LLC—See AMC Networks Inc.; *U.S. Public*, pg. 92
AMERICAN MUNICIPAL POWER-OHIO, INC.; *U.S. Private*, pg. 241
AMERICAN MUSIC & SOUND LLC—See DCC plc; *Int'l*, pg. 1990
AMERICAN NANO SILICON TECHNOLOGIES, INC.; *Int'l*, pg. 422
AMERICAN NATIONAL BANK INC.—See American National Corporation; *U.S. Private*, pg. 241
AMERICAN NATIONAL BANK OF MINNESOTA—See American Bancorporation of Minnesota, Inc.; *U.S. Private*, pg. 223
AMERICAN NATIONAL BANKSHARES INC.—See Atlantic Union Bankshares Corporation; *U.S. Public*, pg. 223
AMERICAN NATIONAL BANK & TRUST—See AmeriBancShares, Inc.; *U.S. Private*, pg. 220
AMERICAN NATIONAL CORPORATION; *U.S. Private*, pg. 241
AMERICAN NATIONAL COUNTY MUTUAL INSURANCE COMPANY—See Brookfield Corporation; *Int'l*, pg. 1174
AMERICAN NATIONAL GROUP, INC.—See Brookfield Corporation; *Int'l*, pg. 1174
AMERICAN NATIONAL INSURANCE COMPANY OF NEW YORK—See Brookfield Corporation; *Int'l*, pg. 1174
AMERICAN NATIONAL INSURANCE COMPANY—See Brookfield Corporation; *Int'l*, pg. 1174
AMERICAN NATIONAL LIFE INSURANCE COMPANY OF NEW YORK—See Brookfield Corporation; *Int'l*, pg. 1174
AMERICAN NATIONAL LIFE INSURANCE COMPANY OF TEXAS—See Brookfield Corporation; *Int'l*, pg. 1174
AMERICAN NATIONAL PROPERTY & CASUALTY COMPANY—See Brookfield Corporation; *Int'l*, pg. 1174
AMERICAN NATIONAL REGISTERED INVESTMENT ADVISOR, INC.—See Brookfield Corporation; *Int'l*, pg. 1174
AMERICAN NATIONAL SKYLINE, INC.—See Valcourt Building Services LLC; *U.S. Private*, pg. 4330
AMERICAN NATIONAL TRADING CORP.—See Peregrine Financial Group, Inc.; *U.S. Private*, pg. 3147
AMERICAN NATIONAL TRUST & INVESTMENT MANAGEMENT CORP.—See Old National Bancorp; *U.S. Public*, pg. 1567
AMERICAN NATURAL ENERGY CORPORATION; *U.S. Private*, pg. 241
AMERICAN NATURAL GAS, LLC—See INNOVATE Corp.; *U.S. Public*, pg. 1125
AMERICAN NETWORK INSURANCE COMPANY—See Penn Treaty American Corporation; *U.S. Private*, pg. 3135
AMERICAN NEVADA COMPANY—See The Greenspun Corporation; *U.S. Private*, pg. 4039
AMERICAN NEWS COMPANY, LLC; *U.S. Private*, pg. 242
AMERICAN NEWSPAPER REPRESENTATIVES, INC.; *U.S. Private*, pg. 242
AMERICAN NICARAGUA FOUNDATION; *U.S. Private*, pg. 242
AMERICAN NIKE S.L.U.—See NIKE, Inc.; *U.S. Public*, pg. 1528
AMERICANN INC.; *U.S. Public*, pg. 113
AMERICAN NOBLE GAS, INC.; *U.S. Public*, pg. 108
AMERICAN NONWOVENS INC.—See Shinih Enterprise Co., Ltd.; *Int'l*, pg. 6845
AMERICAN NOVELTY INC; *U.S. Private*, pg. 242
AMERICAN NTN BEARING MFG. CORP.—See NTN Corporation; *Int'l*, pg. 5483
AMERICAN NURSING CARE INC.—See Catholic Health Initiatives; *U.S. Private*, pg. 789
AMERICAN NUTRITION, INC.—See J.H. Whitney & Co., LLC; *U.S. Private*, pg. 2166
AMERICAN OCCUPATIONAL THERAPY ASSOCIATION, INC.; *U.S. Private*, pg. 242
AMERICAN OFFICE EQUIPMENT CO. INC.; *U.S. Private*, pg. 242
AMERICAN & OHIO LOCOMOTIVE CRANE CO.—See ERS Industries Inc.; *U.S. Private*, pg. 1423
AMERICAN OIL RECOVERY, LLC—See Waste Management, Inc.; *U.S. Public*, pg. 2330
AMERICAN ONCOLOGY NETWORK, INC.; *U.S. Public*, pg. 108
AMERICAN ONCOLOGY NETWORK, LLC—See American Oncology Network, Inc.; *U.S. Public*, pg. 108
AMERICAN ONION INC.; *U.S. Private*, pg. 242
AMERICAN OPPORTUNITY FOR HOUSING, INC.; *U.S. Private*, pg. 242
AMERICAN OPTOMETRIC ASSOCIATION; *U.S. Private*, pg. 242
AMERICAN ORDINANCE LLC—See The Day & Zimmermann Group, Inc.; *U.S. Private*, pg. 4019

COMPANY NAME INDEX

AMERICAN ORIENTAL BIOENGINEERING, INC.; *Int'l*, pg. 422
AMERICAN OSMENT; *U.S. Private*, pg. 242
AMERICAN OSTEOPATHIC ASSOCIATION; *U.S. Private*, pg. 242
AMERICAN OUTCOMES MANAGEMENT, L.P.—See Ridgemont Partners Management LLC; *U.S. Private*, pg. 3433
AMERICAN OUTDOOR BRANDS, INC.; *U.S. Public*, pg. 108
AMERICAN OVERHEAD CONVEYOR—See Payson Casters, Inc.; *U.S. Private*, pg. 3117
AMERICAN OVERSEAS GROUP LIMITED; *Int'l*, pg. 422
AMERICAN OVERSEAS MARINE CORPORATION—See General Dynamics Corporation; *U.S. Public*, pg. 915
AMERICAN PACESETTERS ENTERPRISE LLC.; *U.S. Private*, pg. 242
AMERICAN PACIFIC CORPORATION—See H.I.G. Capital, LLC; *U.S. Private*, pg. 1828
AMERICAN PACIFIC GROUP, LLC; *U.S. Private*, pg. 242
AMERICAN PACIFIC INVESTCORP, LP; *U.S. Private*, pg. 242
AMERICAN PACIFIC MINING CORP.; *Int'l*, pg. 422
AMERICAN PACIFIC MORTGAGE; *U.S. Private*, pg. 242
AMERICAN PACKAGE EXPRESS—See Heritage Partners, Inc.; *U.S. Private*, pg. 1924
AMERICAN PACKAGING CORPORATION - EXTRUSION DIVISION—See American Packaging Corporation; *U.S. Private*, pg. 242
AMERICAN PACKAGING CORPORATION - FLEXOGRAPHIC DIVISION—See American Packaging Corporation; *U.S. Private*, pg. 242
AMERICAN PACKAGING CORPORATION - ROTO GRAUVRE DIVISION—See American Packaging Corporation; *U.S. Private*, pg. 242
AMERICAN PACKAGING CORPORATION—See American Packaging Corporation; *U.S. Private*, pg. 242
AMERICAN PACKAGING CORPORATION; *U.S. Private*, pg. 242
AMERICAN PAINTING AND RENOVATIONS, INC.; *U.S. Private*, pg. 242
AMERICAN PAINT PADDLE CO.—See Hyde Manufacturing Company; *U.S. Private*, pg. 2016
AMERICAN PANEL CORPORATION—See Mercury Systems, Inc.; *U.S. Public*, pg. 1422
AMERICAN PAPER CONVERTING LLC—See Ennis, Inc.; *U.S. Public*, pg. 768
AMERICAN PAPER OPTICS, LLC—See Westshore Capital Partners LLC; *U.S. Private*, pg. 4500
AMERICAN PAPER TOWEL CO. LLC; *U.S. Private*, pg. 243
AMERICAN PAPER & TWINE COMPANY; *U.S. Private*, pg. 243
AMERICAN PARA PROFESSIONAL SYSTEMS, INC.; *U.S. Private*, pg. 243
AMERICAN PARKING SYSTEM INC.; *U.S. Private*, pg. 243
AMERICAN PARK 'N SWAP—See Delaware North Companies, Inc.; *U.S. Private*, pg. 1194
AMERICAN PARKS COMPANY—See Court Square Capital Partners, L.P.; *U.S. Private*, pg. 1069
AMERICAN PARTNERS INC.; *U.S. Private*, pg. 243
AMERICAN PASTEURIZATION COMPANY; *U.S. Private*, pg. 243
AMERICAN PATRIOT BRANDS, INC.; *U.S. Private*, pg. 243
AMERICAN PATRIOT OIL & GAS LIMITED; *Int'l*, pg. 422
AMERICAN PAVING CO. INC.—See Lyles Diversified Inc.; *U.S. Private*, pg. 2520
AMERICAN PAWN & JEWELRY, INC.; *U.S. Private*, pg. 243
AMERICAN PAYDAY LOANS INC.; *U.S. Private*, pg. 243
AMERICAN PELLET MILL SERVICES, INC.—See Buhler AG; *Int'l*, pg. 1212
AMERICAN PENSION SERVICES, INC.; *U.S. Private*, pg. 243
AMERICAN PERFORMANCE INDUSTRIES; *U.S. Private*, pg. 243
AMERICAN PEST CONTROL-MNTGMRY—See EQT AB; *Int'l*, pg. 2467
AMERICAN PEST MANAGEMENT, INC.—See EQT AB; *Int'l*, pg. 2467
AMERICAN PETRO-HUNTER INC.; *U.S. Private*, pg. 243
AMERICAN PETROLEUM EQUIPMENT & CONSTRUCTION COMPANY, INC.; *U.S. Private*, pg. 243
AMERICAN PETROLEUM TANKERS II LLC—See Kinder Morgan, Inc.; *U.S. Public*, pg. 1232
AMERICAN PETROLEUM TANKERS LLC—See Kinder Morgan, Inc.; *U.S. Public*, pg. 1232
AMERICAN PETROLEUM TANKERS PARTNERS LP; *U.S. Private*, pg. 243
AMERICAN PHILOSOPHICAL SOCIETY; *U.S. Private*, pg. 243
AMERICAN PHOENIX INC.; *U.S. Private*, pg. 243
AMERICAN PHOTOCOPY EQUIPMENT COMPANY OF PITTSBURGH, LLC—See Xerox Holdings Corporation; *U.S. Public*, pg. 2387
AMERICAN PHOTONICS CO.; *U.S. Private*, pg. 243
AMERICAN PHYSICAL SOCIETY; *U.S. Private*, pg. 243

AMERICAN PHYSICIAN PARTNERS, LLC; *U.S. Private*, pg. 243
AMERICAN PHYSICIANS ASSURANCE CORPORATION—See The Doctors Company; *U.S. Private*, pg. 4021
AMERICAN PILEDRIVING EQUIPMENT, INC.; *U.S. Private*, pg. 243
AMERICAN PIPE & CONSTRUCTION INTERNATIONAL—See NOV, Inc.; *U.S. Public*, pg. 1543
AMERICAN PIPE & PLASTICS, INC.—See Clayton, Dubilier & Rice, LLC; *U.S. Private*, pg. 811
AMERICAN PIPING PRODUCTS INC.—See Center Rock Capital Partners, LP; *U.S. Private*, pg. 811
AMERICAN PIZZA PARTNERS LP; *U.S. Private*, pg. 243
AMERICAN PLANNING ASSOCIATION; *U.S. Private*, pg. 243
AMERICAN PLANT FOOD CORP.; *U.S. Private*, pg. 243
AMERICAN PLASTIC MOLDING CORP.; *U.S. Private*, pg. 244
AMERICAN PLASTIC PIPE AND SUPPLY, L.L.C.—See The Shaw Group Inc.; *U.S. Private*, pg. 4117
AMERICAN PLASTICS, LLC—See Highview Capital, LLC; *U.S. Private*, pg. 1942
AMERICAN PLASTICS, LLC—See Victory Park Capital Advisors, LLC; *U.S. Private*, pg. 4379
AMERICAN PLASTIC TECHNOLOGIES, INC.—See Rao Design International, Inc.; *U.S. Private*, pg. 3355
AMERICAN PLASTIC TOYS INC.; *U.S. Private*, pg. 244
AMERICAN PLAST S.A.—See Amcor plc; *Int'l*, pg. 418
AMERICAN PLATINUM PROPERTY & CASUALTY INSURANCE COMPANY—See Universal Insurance Holdings, Inc.; *U.S. Public*, pg. 2261
AMERICAN PNEUMATIC TOOLS—See Atlas Copco AB; *Int'l*, pg. 681
AMERICAN POLICE BEAT—See Regent, L.P.; *U.S. Private*, pg. 3388
AMERICAN POLY-FOAM CO. LTD—See Future Foam, Inc.; *U.S. Private*, pg. 1626
AMERICAN POOL ENTERPRISES INC.—See FirstService Corporation; *Int'l*, pg. 2690
AMERICAN POOL MANAGEMENT CORP.; *U.S. Private*, pg. 244
AMERICAN POOLPLAYERS ASSOCIATION INC.; *U.S. Private*, pg. 244
AMERICAN POP CORN COMPANY; *U.S. Private*, pg. 244
AMERICAN POTASH CORP.; *Int'l*, pg. 422
AMERICAN POWER CONVERSION CORP (A.P.C.) BV—See Schneider Electric SE; *Int'l*, pg. 6626
AMERICAN POWER GROUP CORPORATION; *U.S. Public*, pg. 108
AMERICAN POWER SYSTEMS, LLC; *U.S. Private*, pg. 244
AMERICAN PRECAST REFRACTORIES DIVISION—See Allied Mineral Products, Inc.; *U.S. Private*, pg. 187
AMERICAN PRECISION INDUSTRIES INC.—See Fortive Corporation; *U.S. Public*, pg. 870
AMERICAN PRECLINICAL SERVICES LLC—See ArchiMed SAS; *Int'l*, pg. 549
AMERICAN PREMIUM WATER CORPORATION; *U.S. Public*, pg. 108
AMERICAN PRESS LLC; *U.S. Private*, pg. 244
AMERICAN PRINTING COMPANY INC.; *U.S. Private*, pg. 244
AMERICAN PROCESS, INC.—See GranInvestimentos SA; *Int'l*, pg. 3059
AMERICAN PRODUCT DISTRIBUTORS, INC.; *U.S. Private*, pg. 244
AMERICAN PRODUCTS, L.L.C.; *U.S. Private*, pg. 244
AMERICAN PROMOTIONAL EVENTS, INC.—See Anderson Companies, Inc.; *U.S. Private*, pg. 276
AMERICAN PROMOTIONAL EVENTS, INC.—See Anderson Companies, Inc.; *U.S. Private*, pg. 276
AMERICAN PROPERTY GROUP OF SARASOTA INC.; *U.S. Private*, pg. 244
AMERICAN PROPERTY MANAGEMENT CORPORATION; *U.S. Private*, pg. 244
AMERICAN PROSTHETIC COMPONENTS, LLC—See The Jordan Company, L.P.; *U.S. Private*, pg. 4060
AMERICAN PROTEIN CORPORATION INC.—See Lauridsen Group Inc.; *U.S. Private*, pg. 2399
AMERICAN PROTEINS INC.; *U.S. Private*, pg. 244
AMERICAN PRUDENTIAL CAPITAL, INC.—See Stellar Bancorp, Inc.; *U.S. Public*, pg. 1944
AMERICAN PSYCHIATRIC ASSOCIATION; *U.S. Private*, pg. 244
AMERICAN PSYCHOLOGICAL ASSOCIATION; *U.S. Private*, pg. 244
AMERICAN PUBLIC EDUCATION, INC.; *U.S. Public*, pg. 108
AMERICAN PUBLIC MEDIA GROUP; *U.S. Private*, pg. 244
AMERICAN PUBLIC MEDIA—See American Public Media Group; *U.S. Private*, pg. 244
AMERICAN PUBLIC TELEVISION; *U.S. Private*, pg. 245
AMERICAN PUBLIC UNIVERSITY SYSTEM, INC.—See American Public Education, Inc.; *U.S. Public*, pg. 108
AMERICAN PUBLIC WORKS ASSOCIATION; *U.S. Private*, pg. 245

AMERICAN PUBLISHERS LLC—See M2 Media Group, LLC; *U.S. Private*, pg. 2530
AMERICAN PULVERIZER COMPANY; *U.S. Private*, pg. 245
AMERICAN QUALITY FOODS; *U.S. Private*, pg. 245
AMERICAN QUILTER'S SOCIETY—See Schroeder Publishing Company; *U.S. Private*, pg. 3569
AMERICAN RADIO CORP.—See VOXX International Corporation; *U.S. Public*, pg. 2310
AMERICAN RADIOLOGY SERVICES, LLC—See RadNet, Inc.; *U.S. Public*, pg. 1760
AMERICAN RADIOLOGY SERVICES OF DELAWARE, INC.—See RadNet, Inc.; *U.S. Public*, pg. 1760
AMERICAN RADIONIC CO. INC.—See Vladmir, Ltd.; *U.S. Private*, pg. 4407
AMERICAN RAILCAR INDUSTRIES, INC—See ITE Management L.P.; *U.S. Private*, pg. 2149
AMERICAN RAILCAR LEASING, LLC—See ITE Management L.P.; *U.S. Private*, pg. 2149
AMERICAN RANGE CORPORATION—See Hatco Corporation; *U.S. Private*, pg. 1879
AMERICAN RARE EARTHS & MATERIALS, CORP.; *Int'l*, pg. 423
AMERICAN READING COMPANY; *U.S. Private*, pg. 245
AMERICAN READY MIX INC.; *U.S. Private*, pg. 245
AMERICAN REALTY ADVISORS; *U.S. Private*, pg. 245
AMERICAN REALTY CAPITAL DAILY NET ASSET VALUE TRUST, INC.—See AR Global Investments, LLC; *U.S. Private*, pg. 306
AMERICAN REALTY CAPITAL GLOBAL TRUST II, INC.—See AR Global Investments, LLC; *U.S. Private*, pg. 306
AMERICAN REALTY CAPITAL NEW YORK CITY REIT II, INC.—See AR Global Investments, LLC; *U.S. Private*, pg. 306
AMERICAN REALTY CAPITAL - RETAIL CENTERS OF AMERICA II, INC.—See AR Global Investments, LLC; *U.S. Private*, pg. 306
AMERICAN REALTY INVESTORS, INC.; *U.S. Public*, pg. 108
AMERICAN REALTY TRUST, INC.—See American Realty Investors, Inc.; *U.S. Public*, pg. 108
AMERICAN REBEL HOLDINGS, INC.; *U.S. Public*, pg. 109
AMERICAN RECOVERY SERVICE INC.; *U.S. Private*, pg. 245
AMERICAN RED BALL TRANSIT CO. INC.—See Interstate Group Holdings, Inc.; *U.S. Private*, pg. 2125
AMERICAN RED CROSS; *U.S. Private*, pg. 245
AMERICAN REFINING GROUP INC.; *U.S. Private*, pg. 245
AMERICAN REFRACTORIES CO.—See RGP Holding, Inc.; *U.S. Private*, pg. 3420
AMERICAN REFRIGERATION COMPANY, LLC—See Southfield Capital Advisors, LLC; *U.S. Private*, pg. 3736
AMERICAN REFRIGERATION LLC—See EMC Company; *U.S. Private*, pg. 1379
AMERICAN REFRIGERATION SUPPLIES, INC.—See Kitchell Corporation; *U.S. Private*, pg. 2316
AMERICAN REGENT, INC.—See Daiichi Sankyo Co., Ltd.; *Int'l*, pg. 1930
AMERICAN REGISTRY FOR DIAGNOSTIC MEDICAL SONOGRAPHY, INC.; *U.S. Private*, pg. 245
AMERICAN REGISTRY FOR INTERNET NUMBERS, LTD.; *U.S. Private*, pg. 245
THE AMERICAN REGISTRY OF PATHOLOGY, INC.; *U.S. Private*, pg. 3986
AMERICAN RELIABLE INSURANCE COMPANY—See Paine Schwartz Partners, LLC; *U.S. Private*, pg. 3075
AMERICAN RELIANCE INC.; *U.S. Private*, pg. 245
AMERICAN RENAISSANCE CAPITAL, INC.; *U.S. Private*, pg. 245
AMERICAN RENAL ASSOCIATES HOLDINGS, INC.—See Nautic Partners, LLC; *U.S. Private*, pg. 2868
AMERICAN RENAL TEXAS, L.P.—See Nautic Partners, LLC; *U.S. Private*, pg. 2869
AMERICAN RENOLIT CORPORATION—See RENOLIT SE; *Int'l*, pg. 6284
AMERICAN RENTAL MANAGEMENT COMPANY—See Federal Capital Partners; *U.S. Private*, pg. 1487
AMERICAN REPERTORY THEATER; *U.S. Private*, pg. 246
AMERICAN REPORTING COMPANY, LLC; *U.S. Private*, pg. 246
AMERICAN REPROGRAPHICS COMPANY, LLC—See ARC DOCUMENT SOLUTIONS, INC.; *U.S. Public*, pg. 179
AMERICAN REPUBLIC INSURANCE COMPANY—See American Enterprise Mutual Holding Company; *U.S. Private*, pg. 232
AMERICAN REPUBLIC INVESTMENT CO.—See AMREP Corporation; *U.S. Public*, pg. 133
AMERICAN RESIDENTIAL MORTGAGE LP; *U.S. Private*, pg. 246
AMERICAN RESIDENTIAL SERVICES LLC—See Del-Air Heating, Air Conditioning & Refrigeration Corp.; *U.S. Private*, pg. 1193
AMERICAN RESOURCES CORPORATION; *U.S. Public*, pg. 109

AMERICAN RESTAURANT GROUP, INC.

AMERICAN RESTAURANT GROUP, INC.; *U.S. Private*, pg. 246
AMERICAN RESTAURANT HOLDINGS, INC.; *U.S. Private*, pg. 246
AMERICAN RESTAURANTS, LLC—See American Restaurant Holdings, Inc.; *U.S. Private*, pg. 246
AMERICAN RESURGENS MANAGEMENT CORPORATION; *U.S. Private*, pg. 246
AMERICAN RETAIL ALLIANCE CORP.—See Leone Asset Management, Inc.; *U.S. Public*, pg. 1308
AMERICAN RETIREMENT CORPORATION—See Brookdale Senior Living Inc.; *U.S. Public*, pg. 393
AMERICAN RHEINMETALL MUNITION INC.—See Rheinmetall AG; *Int'l*, pg. 6324
AMERICAN RICE, INC.-FREEPORT—See Ebro Foods S.A.; *Int'l*, pg. 2287
AMERICAN RICE, INC.—See Ebro Foods S.A.; *Int'l*, pg. 2287
AMERICAN RIGGING & SUPPLY—See The Carpenter Group; *U.S. Private*, pg. 4005
AMERICAN RIVER BANKSHARES—See Bank of Marin Bancorp; *U.S. Public*, pg. 273
AMERICAN RIVER-PACKAGEONE INC.; *U.S. Private*, pg. 246
AMERICAN RIVER TRANSPORTATION COMPANY—See Archer-Daniels-Midland Company; *U.S. Public*, pg. 183
AMERICAN RIVER VENTURES, LLC; *U.S. Private*, pg. 246
AMERICAN RIVIERA BANK; *U.S. Public*, pg. 109
THE AMERICAN ROAD INSURANCE COMPANY—See Ford Motor Company; *U.S. Public*, pg. 867
AMERICAN ROAD LINE, INC.; *U.S. Private*, pg. 246
AMERICAN ROAD SERVICES COMPANY LLC—See Ford Motor Company; *U.S. Public*, pg. 864
AMERICAN ROADSIDE BURGERS SMITHTOWN, INC.—See Sonnet BioTherapeutics Holdings, Inc; *U.S. Public*, pg. 1903
AMERICAN ROADS, LLC—See DIF Management Holding B.V.; *Int'l*, pg. 2117
AMERICAN ROBOTICS, INC.—See Ondas Holdings, Inc.; *U.S. Public*, pg. 1602
AMERICAN ROCK SALT COMPANY LLC; *U.S. Private*, pg. 246
AMERICAN ROCKWOOL, INC.—See Owens Corning; *U.S. Public*, pg. 1626
AMERICAN ROLAND FOOD CORP.—See Vestar Capital Partners, LLC; *U.S. Private*, pg. 4371
AMERICAN ROLLER BEARING CO., INC.; *U.S. Private*, pg. 246
AMERICAN ROLLER BEARING COMPANY; *U.S. Private*, pg. 246
AMERICAN ROLLER COMPANY; *U.S. Private*, pg. 246
AMERICAN ROLL FORMED PRODUCTS CORP.; *U.S. Private*, pg. 246
AMERICAN ROOFING & METAL CO. INC.; *U.S. Private*, pg. 246
AMERICAN SAFETY INSURANCE COMPANY—See Atlantic American Corporation; *U.S. Public*, pg. 222
AMERICAN SAFETY TECHNOLOGIES—See Illinois Tool Works Inc.; *U.S. Public*, pg. 1101
AMERICAN SALE, INC.; *U.S. Private*, pg. 246
AMERICAN SALES COMPANY, INC.—See The Shurtleff & Andrews Corp.; *U.S. Private*, pg. 4117
AMERICAN SALES COMPANY, LLC—See Koninklijke Ahold Delhaize N.V.; *Int'l*, pg. 4260
AMERICAN SANDS ENERGY CORP.; *U.S. Private*, pg. 246
AMERICAN SANITATION, INC.—See Republic Services, Inc.; *U.S. Public*, pg. 1786
AMERICAN SAVINGS BANK, F.S.B.—See Hawaiian Electric Industries, Inc.; *U.S. Public*, pg. 989
AMERICAN SCAFFOLD—See J.F. Lehman & Company, Inc.; *U.S. Private*, pg. 2162
AMERICAN SCALE CO. LLC—See Rotunda Capital Partners LLC; *U.S. Private*, pg. 3487
AMERICAN SCHOOL OF CORRESPONDENCE; *U.S. Private*, pg. 246
AMERICAN SCIENCE AND ENGINEERING, INC.—See OSI Systems, Inc.; *U.S. Public*, pg. 1621
AMERICAN SEAFOOD PARTNERS LP—See American Pizza Partners LP; *U.S. Private*, pg. 243
AMERICAN SEAFOODS COMPANY—See American Seafoods, LP; *U.S. Private*, pg. 246
AMERICAN SEAFOODS GROUP LLC—See American Seafoods, LP; *U.S. Private*, pg. 246
AMERICAN SEAFOODS, LP; *U.S. Private*, pg. 246
AMERICAN SEALANTS, INC.—See Arsenal Capital Management LP; *U.S. Private*, pg. 339
AMERICAN SEAL & PACKAGING, INC.—See Align Capital Partners, LLC; *U.S. Private*, pg. 167
AMERICAN SEATING COMPANY; *U.S. Private*, pg. 247
AMERICAN SEAWAY FOODS, INC.—See Giant Eagle, Inc.; *U.S. Private*, pg. 1694
AMERICAN SECURITIES LLC; *U.S. Private*, pg. 247
AMERICAN SECURITY LIFE INSURANCE COMPANY LIMITED—See American International Group, Inc.; *U.S. Public*, pg. 106

AMERICAN SECURITY LIFE INSURANCE COMPANY—See American International Group, Inc.; *U.S. Public*, pg. 106
AMERICAN SECURITY, L.L.C.; *U.S. Private*, pg. 253
AMERICAN SECURITY PROGRAMS INC.—See Allied Universal Manager LLC; *U.S. Private*, pg. 191
AMERICAN SEEDS, LLC—See Bayer Aktiengesellschaft; *Int'l*, pg. 908
AMERICAN SENIOR BENEFITS, LLC—See Integrity Marketing Group LLC; *U.S. Private*, pg. 2103
AMERICAN SENIORS ASSOCIATION HOLDING GROUP, INC.; *U.S. Public*, pg. 109
AMERICAN SENIOR SERVICES, INC.; *U.S. Private*, pg. 253
AMERICAN SENIORS FOUNDATION INC; *U.S. Private*, pg. 253
AMERICAN SENSOR TECHNOLOGIES, INC.—See TE Connectivity Ltd.; *Int'l*, pg. 7494
AMERICAN SERVICE CENTER ASSOCIATES LLC; *U.S. Private*, pg. 253
AMERICAN SERVICE COMPANY—See The Riverside Company; *U.S. Private*, pg. 4107
AMERICAN SERVICE INSURANCE COMPANY—See Atlas Financial Holdings, Inc.; *U.S. Public*, pg. 224
AMERICAN SERVICES, INC.—See Allied Universal Manager LLC; *U.S. Private*, pg. 188
AMERICANS FOR JOB SECURITY; *U.S. Private*, pg. 259
AMERICANS FOR PROSPERITY; *U.S. Private*, pg. 259
AMERICAN SHALE OIL, LLC—See Genie Energy Ltd.; *U.S. Public*, pg. 930
AMERICAN SHARED HOSPITAL SERVICES; *U.S. Public*, pg. 109
AMERICAN SHARED RADIOSURGERY SERVICES—See American Shared Hospital Services; *U.S. Public*, pg. 109
AMERICAN SHARE INSURANCE; *U.S. Private*, pg. 253
AMERICAN SHIPPING CO., INC.; *U.S. Private*, pg. 253
AMERICAN SHIPYARD CO., LLC—See Sun Communities, Inc.; *U.S. Public*, pg. 1963
AMERICAN SHIZUKI CORPORATION—See Shizuki Electric Company, Inc.; *Int'l*, pg. 6855
AMERICAN SHOE S.A.—See Air Products & Chemicals, Inc.; *U.S. Public*, pg. 66
AMERICAN SHOPPING CARTS INC—See Americana Companies, Inc.; *U.S. Private*, pg. 258
AMERICAN SHOWA, INC.—See Hitachi Astemo, Ltd.; *Int'l*, pg. 3409
AMERICAN SILVER MINING CO.; *U.S. Public*, pg. 109
AMERICAN SINTERED TECHNOLOGIES, INC.—See Fansteel, Inc.; *U.S. Private*, pg. 1472
AMERICAN SKANDIA MARKETING, INCORPORATED—See Prudential Financial, Inc.; *U.S. Public*, pg. 1732
AMERICAN SKIN FOOD GROUP LLC—See WH Group Limited; *Int'l*, pg. 8395
AMERICAN SLATE COMPANY—See Hendricks Holding Company, Inc.; *U.S. Private*, pg. 1914
AMERICAN SLIDE-CHART CO.; *U.S. Private*, pg. 253
AMERICAN SMALL BUSINESS ALLIANCE, INC.; *U.S. Private*, pg. 253
AMERICAN SMOOTH WAVE VENTURES, INC.; *U.S. Private*, pg. 253
AMERICAN SNUFF COMPANY, LLC—See British American Tobacco plc; *Int'l*, pg. 1168
AMERICAN SOCCER COMPANY, INC—See Brand Velocity Partners; *U.S. Private*, pg. 637
AMERICAN SOCCER CORPORATION; *U.S. Private*, pg. 253
AMERICAN SOCIETY FOR BIOCHEMISTRY AND MOLECULAR BIOLOGY; *U.S. Private*, pg. 253
AMERICAN SOCIETY FOR CLINICAL PATHOLOGY; *U.S. Private*, pg. 253
AMERICAN SOCIETY FOR GASTROINTESTINAL ENDOSCOPY; *U.S. Private*, pg. 253
AMERICAN SOCIETY FOR MICROBIOLOGY; *U.S. Private*, pg. 253
AMERICAN SOCIETY FOR RADIATION ONCOLOGY; *U.S. Private*, pg. 254
AMERICAN SOCIETY FOR TESTING & MATERIALS; *U.S. Private*, pg. 254
AMERICAN SOCIETY FOR THE PREVENTION OF CRUELTY TO ANIMALS; *U.S. Private*, pg. 254
AMERICAN SOCIETY FOR YAD VASHEM; *U.S. Private*, pg. 254
AMERICAN SOCIETY OF ANESTHESIOLOGISTS; *U.S. Private*, pg. 254
AMERICAN SOCIETY OF APPRAISERS; *U.S. Private*, pg. 254
AMERICAN SOCIETY OF CATARACT AND REFRACTIVE SURGERY; *U.S. Private*, pg. 254
AMERICAN SOCIETY OF MECHANICAL ENGINEERS; *U.S. Private*, pg. 254
AMERICAN SOCIETY OF NEPHROLOGY; *U.S. Private*, pg. 254
AMERICAN SOCIETY OF PENSION PROFESSIONALS & ACTUARIES, INC.; *U.S. Private*, pg. 254

CORPORATE AFFILIATIONS

AMERICAN SOCIETY OF RADIOLOGIC TECHNOLOGISTS; *U.S. Private*, pg. 254
AMERICAN SOCIETY OF SAFETY ENGINEERS; *U.S. Private*, pg. 254
AMERICAN SOFTWARE CAPITAL INC.—See ASC Global Inc.; *U.S. Private*, pg. 345
AMERICAN SOFTWARE, INC.; *U.S. Public*, pg. 109
AMERICAN SOIL TECHNOLOGIES, INC.; *U.S. Private*, pg. 254
AMERICAN SOLAR & ALTERNATIVE POWER LLC—See Kingspan Group PLC; *Int'l*, pg. 4176
AMERICAN SOLAR ELECTRIC, INC.; *U.S. Private*, pg. 254
AMERICAN SOLUTIONS FOR BUSINESS; *U.S. Private*, pg. 254
AMERICAN SOUTHERN HOMES, LLC; *U.S. Private*, pg. 254
AMERICAN SOUTHERN INSURANCE COMPANY—See Atlantic American Corporation; *U.S. Public*, pg. 222
AMERICAN SOUTHWEST INSURANCE MANAGERS, INC.—See AmWINS Group, Inc.; *U.S. Private*, pg. 269
AMERICAN SOYBEAN ASSOCIATION; *U.S. Private*, pg. 255
AMERICAN SPECIALTIES INC.; *U.S. Private*, pg. 255
AMERICAN SPECIALTY GLASS, INC.—See Littlejohn & Co., LLC; *U.S. Private*, pg. 2471
AMERICAN SPECIALTY HEALTH, INC.; *U.S. Private*, pg. 255
AMERICAN SPECIALTY INSURANCE & RISK SERVICES, INC.—See Brown & Brown, Inc.; *U.S. Public*, pg. 396
AMERICAN SPEECH-LANGUAGE-HEARING ASSOCIATION; *U.S. Private*, pg. 255
AMERICAN SPICE COMPANY INC.; *U.S. Private*, pg. 255
AMERICAN SPIRALWELD PIPE COMPANY, LLC—See American Cast Iron Pipe Company; *U.S. Private*, pg. 226
AMERICAN SPIRIT GRAPHICS CORPORATION; *U.S. Private*, pg. 255
AMERICAN SPORTING GOODS CORPORATION—See Caleres, Inc.; *U.S. Public*, pg. 422
AMERICAN SPRING WIRE CORP.; *U.S. Private*, pg. 255
AMERICAN STAINLESS TUBING, INC.—See Ascent Industries Co.; *U.S. Public*, pg. 210
AMERICAN STAIR CORPORATION; *U.S. Private*, pg. 255
AMERICAN STANDARD B&K MEXICO, S. DE R.L. DE C.V.—See Sun Capital Partners, Inc.; *U.S. Private*, pg. 3858
AMERICAN STANDARD B&K (THAILAND) PUBLIC COMPANY LTD.—See LIXIL Group Corporation; *Int'l*, pg. 4534
AMERICAN STANDARD CANADA, INC.—See Sun Capital Partners, Inc.; *U.S. Private*, pg. 3858
AMERICAN STANDARD INSURANCE COMPANY OF WISCONSIN—See American Family Mutual Insurance Company; *U.S. Private*, pg. 233
AMERICAN STANDARD JIANGMEN FITTINGS CO. LTD.—See LIXIL Group Corporation; *Int'l*, pg. 4533
AMERICAN STANDARD KOREA INC.—See LIXIL Group Corporation; *Int'l*, pg. 4534
AMERICAN STANDARD PHILIPPINES LIMITED, CO.—See LIXIL Group Corporation; *Int'l*, pg. 4533
AMERICAN STANDARD TESTING BUREAU; *U.S. Private*, pg. 255
AMERICAN STARLINGER-SAHM, INC.—See Starlinger & Co. GmbH; *Int'l*, pg. 7178
AMERICAN STATE BANCSHARES, INC.; *U.S. Private*, pg. 255
AMERICAN STATE BANK HOLDING COMPANY, INC.; *U.S. Private*, pg. 255
AMERICAN STATE BANK—See Steele Holdings, Inc.; *U.S. Private*, pg. 3796
AMERICAN STATE BANK & TRUST COMPANY OF WILLISTON—See American State Bank Holding Company, Inc.; *U.S. Private*, pg. 255
AMERICAN STATE BANK & TRUST COMPANY—See American State Bancshares, Inc.; *U.S. Private*, pg. 255
AMERICAN STATE EQUIPMENT CO. INC.; *U.S. Private*, pg. 255
AMERICAN STATES UTILITY SERVICES, INC.—See American States Water Company; *U.S. Public*, pg. 110
AMERICAN STATES WATER COMPANY; *U.S. Public*, pg. 109
AMERICAN STATIONERY CO., INC.; *U.S. Private*, pg. 255
AMERICAN STEAMSHIP COMPANY—See AIP, LLC; *U.S. Private*, pg. 135
AMERICAN STEEL & ALUMINUM CORPORATION—See Nova Steel Inc.; *Int'l*, pg. 5452
AMERICAN STEEL FOUNDRIES—See AMSTED Industries Incorporated; *U.S. Private*, pg. 267
AMERICAN STEEL INC.; *U.S. Private*, pg. 255
AMERICAN STEEL PIPE DIV.—See American Cast Iron Pipe Company; *U.S. Private*, pg. 226
AMERICAN STEEL & SUPPLY INC.; *U.S. Private*, pg. 255
AMERICAN STOCK TRANSFER & TRUST COMPANY, LLC—See Pacific Equity Partners Pty. Limited; *Int'l*, pg. 5688
AMERICAN STRATEGIC INSURANCE CORP.; *U.S. Private*, pg. 256

COMPANY NAME INDEX

AMERICAN STRATEGIC INVESTMENT CO.—See AR Global Investments, LLC; *U.S. Private*, pg. 306
AMERICAN STRUCTUREPOINT INC.; *U.S. Private*, pg. 256
AMERICAN STUDENT ASSISTANCE; *U.S. Private*, pg. 256
AMERICAN SUBSTANCE ABUSE PROFESSIONALS, INC.; *U.S. Private*, pg. 256
AMERICAN SUESSEN CORPORATION—See Rieter Holding Ltd.; *Int'l*, pg. 6339
AMERICAN SUGAR REFINING, INC.—See Florida Crystals Corporation; *U.S. Private*, pg. 1548
AMERICAN SUMMIT INSURANCE COMPANY—See Re-Align Capital Strategies; *U.S. Private*, pg. 3368
AMERICAN SUNNY FOODS, INC.—See Western Milling, LLC; *U.S. Private*, pg. 4494
AMERICAN SUNREX CORPORATION; *U.S. Private*, pg. 256
AMERICAN SUNROOF CORPORATION; *U.S. Private*, pg. 256
AMERICAN SUPERCONDUCTOR CORPORATION; *U.S. Public*, pg. 110
AMERICAN SUPERIOR FEEDS INC.; *U.S. Private*, pg. 256
AMERICAN SUPPORT LLC; *U.S. Private*, pg. 256
AMERICAN SURGICAL HOLDINGS, INC.—See Great Point Partners, LLC; *U.S. Private*, pg. 1767
AMERICAN SUZUKI MOTOR CORPORATION—See Suzuki Motor Corporation; *Int'l*, pg. 7354
AMERICAN SWISS PRODUCTS CO, INC.; *U.S. Private*, pg. 256
AMERICAN SYNERGY CORPORATION; *U.S. Private*, pg. 256
AMERICAN SYNTHETIC RUBBER COMPANY—See Compagnie Generale des Etablissements Michelin SCA; *Int'l*, pg. 1743
AMERICAN SYSTEMS CORPORATION; *U.S. Private*, pg. 256
AMERICAN TACK & HARDWARE CO. INC.—See Amertac Holdings Inc.; *U.S. Private*, pg. 261
AMERICAN TANK & FABRICATING COMPANY; *U.S. Private*, pg. 256
AMERICAN TANK & VESSEL INC.; *U.S. Private*, pg. 256
AMERICAN TEC CO. LTD—See North Asia Strategic Holdings Limited; *Int'l*, pg. 5440
AMERICAN TEC ELECTRONIC INDIA PVT LTD.—See Fuji Corporation; *Int'l*, pg. 2809
AMERICAN TECHNICAL CERAMICS (CHINA) LTD.—See KYOCERA Corporation; *Int'l*, pg. 4359
AMERICAN TECHNICAL CERAMICS CORP.—See KYOCERA Corporation; *Int'l*, pg. 4359
AMERICAN TECHNICAL CERAMICS (FLORIDA), INC.—See KYOCERA Corporation; *Int'l*, pg. 4359
AMERICAN TECHNICAL CERAMICS - HYDERABAD—See KYOCERA Corporation; *Int'l*, pg. 4359
AMERICAN TECHNICAL MOLDING, INC.—See Integer Holdings Corporation; *U.S. Public*, pg. 1135
AMERICAN TECHNICAL PUBLISHERS, INC.; *U.S. Private*, pg. 256
AMERICAN TECHNOLOGIES, INC.; *U.S. Private*, pg. 256
AMERICAN TECHNOLOGY SERVICES INC; *U.S. Private*, pg. 256
AMERICAN TEL-A-SYSTEMS INC.; *U.S. Private*, pg. 256
AMERICAN TELECARE, INC.; *U.S. Private*, pg. 257
AMERICAN TELECOMMUNICATIONS INC.; *U.S. Private*, pg. 257
AMERICAN TELEMEDICINE, INC.—See MEDNAX, Inc.; *U.S. Public*, pg. 1414
AMERICAN TELETIMER CORP.; *U.S. Private*, pg. 257
AMERICAN TERATEC, INC.—See Makke LLC; *U.S. Private*, pg. 2556
AMERICAN TERMINALS DISTRIBUTION CORP—See H&M International Transportation Inc.; *U.S. Private*, pg. 1823
AMERICAN TEXTILE HOLDINGS, LLC—See Monomoy Capital Partners LLC; *U.S. Private*, pg. 2772
AMERICAN TEXTILE INDUSTRIES, LLC—See Monomoy Capital Partners LLC; *U.S. Private*, pg. 2772
AMERICAN TEXTILE MAINTENANCE COMPANY; *U.S. Private*, pg. 257
AMERICAN THEATRE SUPPLY INC.—See Eastern Federal Corp.; *U.S. Private*, pg. 1319
AMERICAN THERMOPLASTIC COMPANY; *U.S. Private*, pg. 257
AMERICAN TIRE DISTRIBUTORS HOLDINGS, INC.—See TPG Capital, L.P.; *U.S. Public*, pg. 2166
AMERICAN TIRE DISTRIBUTORS, INC.—See TPG Capital, L.P.; *U.S. Public*, pg. 2166
AMERICAN TITLE COMPANY OF HOUSTON—See Anywhere Real Estate Inc.; *U.S. Public*, pg. 142
AMERICAN TITLE INC.—See Assurant, Inc.; *U.S. Public*, pg. 214
AMERICAN TOOL COMPANIES HOLDING B.V.—See Newell Brands Inc.; *U.S. Public*, pg. 1513
AMERICAN TOOLING CENTER, INC.; *U.S. Private*, pg. 257
AMERICAN TORCH TIP CO. INC.; *U.S. Private*, pg. 257

AMERICAN TOWER CORPORATION; *U.S. Public*, pg. 110
AMERICAN TOWER INTERNATIONAL, INC.—See American Tower Corporation; *U.S. Public*, pg. 110
AMERICAN TOWER INVESTMENTS LLC—See American Tower Corporation; *U.S. Public*, pg. 110
AMERICAN TRADING INTERNATIONAL; *U.S. Private*, pg. 257
AMERICAN TRADING & PRODUCTION CORPORATION; *U.S. Private*, pg. 257
AMERICAN TRAFFIC SOLUTIONS, INC.—See Platinum Equity, LLC; *U.S. Private*, pg. 3201
AMERICAN TRAILER RENTAL GROUP—See Wind Point Advisors LLC; *U.S. Private*, pg. 4533
AMERICAN TRAILER WORKS, INC.—See Bain Capital, LP; *U.S. Private*, pg. 436
AMERICAN TRANSIT INSURANCE COMPANY—See United Security Life and Health Insurance Company; *U.S. Private*, pg. 4297
AMERICAN TRANSIT MIX CEMEX—See CEMEX, S.A.B. de C.V.; *Int'l*, pg. 1399
AMERICAN TRANSMISSION COMPANY LLC—See ATC Management Inc.; *U.S. Private*, pg. 365
AMERICAN TRIM - CULLMAN—See American Trim LLC; *U.S. Private*, pg. 257
AMERICAN TRIM LLC; *U.S. Private*, pg. 257
AMERICAN TRUCK & BUS INC.; *U.S. Private*, pg. 257
AMERICAN TRUCKING ASSOCIATION; *U.S. Private*, pg. 257
AMERICAN TRUST SENIOR CARE LLC; *U.S. Private*, pg. 257
AMERICAN TRUST—See Mid Atlantic Capital Group, Inc.; *U.S. Private*, pg. 2705
AMERICAN TRUTZSCHLER INC—See Trutzschler GmbH & Co. KG; *Int'l*, pg. 7945
AMERICAN T-SHIRT CO—See Watumull Brothers Ltd. Inc.; *U.S. Private*, pg. 4456
AMERICAN TUBE CORP.; *U.S. Private*, pg. 257
AMERICAN TUBING INC.—See National Tube Holding Company Inc.; *U.S. Private*, pg. 2864
AMERICAN TURNED PRODUCTS, INC.; *U.S. Private*, pg. 257
AMERICAN TV & APPLIANCE OF MADISON, INC.; *U.S. Private*, pg. 257
AMERICAN UNDERWATER PRODUCTS; *U.S. Private*, pg. 257
AMERICAN UNIC CORP.—See Spelna, Inc.; *U.S. Private*, pg. 3754
AMERICAN UNIFORM CO.—See Alsco Inc.; *U.S. Private*, pg. 202
AMERICAN UNITED MUTUAL INSURANCE HOLDING COMPANY; *U.S. Private*, pg. 257
AMERICAN UNIVERSAL-HOCKESSIN, LLC—See Nautic Partners, LLC; *U.S. Private*, pg. 2869
AMERICAN URBAN RADIO NETWORKS - CHICAGO SALES—See Sheridan Broadcasting Corporation; *U.S. Private*, pg. 3633
AMERICAN URBAN RADIO NETWORKS - NEW YORK SALES—See Sheridan Broadcasting Corporation; *U.S. Private*, pg. 3633
AMERICAN URBAN RADIO NETWORKS—See Sheridan Broadcasting Corporation; *U.S. Private*, pg. 3633
AMERICAN UTILITY MANAGEMENT, INC.—See Thoma Bravo, L.P.; *U.S. Private*, pg. 4152
AMERICAN VALVE & HYDRANT CO.—See American Cast Iron Pipe Company; *U.S. Private*, pg. 226
AMERICAN VAN EQUIPMENT INC.; *U.S. Private*, pg. 258
AMERICAN VANGUARD CORPORATION; *U.S. Public*, pg. 111
AMERICAN VANPAC CARRIERS, INC.—See Atlas World Group, Inc.; *U.S. Private*, pg. 380
AMERICAN VENDING MACHINES, INC.—See Vendors Exchange International, Inc.; *U.S. Private*, pg. 4356
AMERICAN VENDING SALES, INC.; *U.S. Private*, pg. 258
AMERICAN VETERINARY PHARMACEUTICALS—See CSR Company Inc.; *U.S. Private*, pg. 1117
AMERICAN VIDEO TELECONFERENCING CORP.; *U.S. Public*, pg. 112
AMERICAN VIETNAMESE BIOTECH INCORPORATION; *Int'l*, pg. 423
AMERICAN VIRTUAL CLOUD TECHNOLOGIES, INC.; *U.S. Public*, pg. 112
AMERICAN VISION WINDOWS, INC.; *U.S. Private*, pg. 258
AMERICAN WAGERING, INC.—See William Hill Plc; *Int'l*, pg. 8413
AMERICAN WAL-BOARD LLC—See American Securities LLC; *U.S. Private*, pg. 248
AMERICAN WASTE INDUSTRIES; *U.S. Private*, pg. 258
AMERICAN WASTE, LLC—See BC Partners LLP; *Int'l*, pg. 924
AMERICAN WASTE MANAGEMENT SERVICES, INC.—See Avalon Holdings Corporation; *U.S. Public*, pg. 239
AMERICAN WATER ACCIONA AGUA LLC—See American Water Works Company, Inc.; *U.S. Public*, pg. 112
AMERICAN WATER CAPITAL CORPORATION—See American Water Works Company, Inc.; *U.S. Public*, pg. 112

AMERICAN WATER HEATER COMPANY—See A. O. Smith Corporation; *U.S. Public*, pg. 11
AMERICAN WATER TREATMENT, INC.—See Nolan Capital, Inc.; *U.S. Private*, pg. 2934
AMERICAN WATER WORKS COMPANY, INC.; *U.S. Public*, pg. 112
AMERICAN WAY MOTORS, INC.—See AutoNation, Inc.; *U.S. Public*, pg. 232
AMERICAN WEB INC.; *U.S. Private*, pg. 258
AMERICAN WELDING & GAS, INC.—See Advance Auto Parts, Inc.; *U.S. Public*, pg. 44
AMERICAN WELDING & TANK CO.—See Wind Point Advisors LLC; *U.S. Private*, pg. 4536
AMERICAN WELL CORPORATION; *U.S. Public*, pg. 112
AMERICAN WESTBROOK INSURANCE SERVICES, LLC—See GTCR LLC; *U.S. Private*, pg. 1802
AMERICAN WEST HOMES INC.; *U.S. Private*, pg. 258
AMERICAN WEST INSURANCE COMPANY—See Nodak Insurance Company; *U.S. Private*, pg. 2933
AMERICAN WEST METALS LIMITED; *Int'l*, pg. 423
AMERICAN WEST WORLDWIDE EXPRESS INC.; *U.S. Private*, pg. 258
AMERICAN WHOLESALE BOOK COMPANY INC.—See Books-A-Million, Inc.; *U.S. Private*, pg. 616
AMERICAN WHOLESALERS INC.; *U.S. Private*, pg. 258
AMERICAN WINDOW FILM INC—See Solar Art Window Film, Inc.; *U.S. Private*, pg. 3707
AMERICAN WINDOW & GLASS INC.; *U.S. Private*, pg. 258
AMERICAN WIRE & CABLE COMPANY; *U.S. Private*, pg. 258
AMERICAN WOOD FIBERS, INC.; *U.S. Private*, pg. 258
AMERICAN WOODMARK CORPORATION; *U.S. Public*, pg. 112
AMERICAN WOOD MOULDING, LLC; *U.S. Private*, pg. 258
AMERICAN WORDATA, INC.; *U.S. Private*, pg. 258
AMERICANWORK, INC.—See ATAR Capital, LLC; *U.S. Private*, pg. 364
AMERICAN WRECKING INC.; *U.S. Private*, pg. 258
AMERICAN XANTHAN CORPORATION; *U.S. Private*, pg. 258
AMERICAN YEAST SALES INC—See Lallemand, Inc.; *Int'l*, pg. 4399
AMERICAN YOUTH SOCCER ORGANIZATION; *U.S. Private*, pg. 258
AMERICAN ZETTLER INCORPORATED—See Zettler Components, Inc.; *U.S. Private*, pg. 4603
AMERICAN ZINC RECYCLING CORP.—See Befesa S.A.; *Int'l*, pg. 939
AMERICAN ZURICH INSURANCE COMPANY—See Zurich Insurance Group Limited; *Int'l*, pg. 8698
AMERICAP INSURANCE GROUP, LLC—See Galiot Insurance Services, Inc.; *U.S. Private*, pg. 1637
AMERICA PRECISION INDUSTRY - SURFACE MOUNT DIVISION—See Danaher Corporation; *U.S. Public*, pg. 626
AMERICARX.COM; *U.S. Private*, pg. 259
AMERICA'S 1ST CHOICE OF SOUTH CAROLINA, INC.—See Elevance Health, Inc.; *U.S. Public*, pg. 728
AMERICA'S AUTO AUCTION INC.—See Trinity Hunt Management, L.P.; *U.S. Private*, pg. 4234
AMERICA'S BEST CONTACTS & EYEGLASSES—See KKR & Co. Inc.; *U.S. Public*, pg. 1261
AMERICA'S BEVERAGE CO.—See The Kroger Co.; *U.S. Public*, pg. 2107
AMERICA'S BODY COMPANY; *U.S. Private*, pg. 220
AMERICAS CALL CENTER, LLC—See Porch Group, Inc.; *U.S. Public*, pg. 1702
AMERICA'S CAPITAL PARTNERS, LLC; *U.S. Private*, pg. 220
AMERICA'S CAR MART, INC.—See America's Car-Mart, Inc.; *U.S. Public*, pg. 95
AMERICA'S CAR-MART, INC.; *U.S. Public*, pg. 95
AMERICA'S CATCH, INC.; *U.S. Private*, pg. 220
AMERICA'S CHARITIES; *U.S. Private*, pg. 221
AMERICAS CHOICE INC—See Pearson plc; *Int'l*, pg. 5777
AMERICA'S CHRISTIAN CREDIT UNION; *U.S. Private*, pg. 221
AMERICA'S FINANCIAL CHOICE, LLC—See Finbond Group Limited; *Int'l*, pg. 2670
AMERICA'S FLOOD SERVICES, INC.—See The Seibels Bruce Group, Inc.; *U.S. Private*, pg. 4116
AMERICAS FOOD TECHNOLOGIES, INC.—See The Jordan Company, L.P.; *U.S. Private*, pg. 4062
AMERICAS GOLD AND SILVER CORPORATION; *Int'l*, pg. 423
AMERICA'S HEALTH CARE AT HOME, INC.—See AdaptHealth Corp.; *U.S. Public*, pg. 39
AMERICA'S HEALTH CARE PLAN/RX AGENCY, INC.—See Aon plc; *Int'l*, pg. 489
AMERICA'S HOME PLACE INC.; *U.S. Private*, pg. 221
AMERICA'S INCREDIBLE PIZZA COMPANY; *U.S. Private*, pg. 221
AMERICAS INSURANCE CO—See IMF Bentham Limited; *Int'l*, pg. 3624
AMERICA'S JOB EXCHANGE LLC—See Ontario Teachers' Pension Plan; *Int'l*, pg. 5586

AMERICA'S MORTGAGE PROFESSIONALS — CORPORATE AFFILIATIONS

AMERICA'S MORTGAGE PROFESSIONALS; *U.S. Private*, pg. 221
AMERICAS OFFICE SOURCE, INC.—See The ODP Corporation; *U.S. Public*, pg. 2117
AMERICAS POTASH PERU S.A.—See Coloured Ties Capital Inc.; *Int'l*, pg. 1704
AMERICA'S POWERSPORTS INC.; *U.S. Private*, pg. 221
AMERICAS PRODUCTS & DISTRIBUTION, INC.—See CRH plc; *Int'l*, pg. 1842
AMERICA'S SCHOOLHOUSE COUNCIL, LLC—See Tetra Tech, Inc.; *U.S. Public*, pg. 2022
AMERICA'S SERVICE LINE, LLC—See Rosens Diversified, Inc.; *U.S. Private*, pg. 3484
AMERICA'S SUPER PAWN, INC.; *U.S. Private*, pg. 221
AMERICAS TECHNOLOGY ACQUISITION CORP.; *U.S. Public*, pg. 113
AMERICAS TEST KITCHEN LIMITED PARTNERSHIP—See Marquee Brands LLC; *U.S. Private*, pg. 2586
AMERICA'S WINDOW, LLC—See West Shore Window & Door, Inc.; *U.S. Private*, pg. 4487
AMERICA TAMPAS S/A—See Evora S.A.; *Int'l*, pg. 2573
AMERICATEL CORPORATION—See Blue Casa Communications, Inc.; *U.S. Private*, pg. 586
AMERICATEL CORPORATION—See Garrison Investment Group LP; *U.S. Private*, pg. 1646
AMERICATEL SISTEMAS DE COMUNICACION C.A.—See The Cisneros Group of Companies; *Int'l*, pg. 7632
AMERICA, THE BEAUTIFUL DREAMER, INC.; *U.S. Private*, pg. 221
AMERICATOWNE HOLDINGS, INC.; *U.S. Private*, pg. 259
AMERICA VOTES; *U.S. Private*, pg. 220
AMERICA WORKS OF NEW YORK INC.; *U.S. Private*, pg. 220
AMERICA YOUCARE PHARMA, INC.—See Youcare Pharmaceutical Group Co., Ltd.; *Int'l*, pg. 8601
AMERIC DISC, INC.—See Transcontinental Inc.; *Int'l*, pg. 7897
AMERICH CORPORATION; *U.S. Private*, pg. 259
AMERICHEM INC.; *U.S. Private*, pg. 259
AMERICHIP, INC.; *U.S. Private*, pg. 259
AMERICHOICE CORPORATION—See UnitedHealth Group Incorporated; *U.S. Public*, pg. 2238
AMERICLEAN TILE & GROUT, LLC—See Midwest Remediation Inc.; *U.S. Private*, pg. 2723
AMERIC MACHINERY CORPORATION—See Mitsubishi Corporation; *Int'l*, pg. 4942
AMERI-CO CARRIERS, INC.—See Minerals Technologies, Inc.; *U.S. Public*, pg. 1448
AMERICO CHEMICAL PRODUCTS, INC.—See Harbour Group Industries, Inc.; *U.S. Private*, pg. 1860
AMERICO FINANCIAL LIFE & ANNUITY INSURANCE COMPANY—See Financial Holding Corp.; *U.S. Private*, pg. 1507
AMERICOLD BARCELONA PALAU S.A.—See Americold Realty Trust, Inc.; *U.S. Public*, pg. 113
AMERICOLD CASCADE COLD INC.—See Americold Realty Trust, Inc.; *U.S. Public*, pg. 113
AMERICOLD FORWARDING AGENCY B.V.—See Americold Realty Trust, Inc.; *U.S. Public*, pg. 113
AMERICOLD LEIXOES UNIPESSOAL LDA—See Americold Realty Trust, Inc.; *U.S. Public*, pg. 113
AMERICOLD LOGISTICS, LLC—See Americold Realty Trust, Inc.; *U.S. Public*, pg. 113
AMERICOLD MAASVLAKTE B.V.—See Americold Realty Trust, Inc.; *U.S. Public*, pg. 113
AMERICOLD REALTY LLC—See Americold Realty Trust, Inc.; *U.S. Public*, pg. 113
AMERICOLD REALTY TRUST, INC.; *U.S. Public*, pg. 113
AMERICOLD SINES UNIPESSOAL LDA—See Americold Realty Trust, Inc.; *U.S. Public*, pg. 113
AMERICOLD URK B.V.—See Americold Realty Trust, Inc.; *U.S. Public*, pg. 113
AMERICOLD VALENCIA S.L.U.—See Americold Realty Trust, Inc.; *U.S. Public*, pg. 113
AMERICO LIFE, INC.—See Financial Holding Corp.; *U.S. Private*, pg. 1507
AMERICOLLECT, INC.; *U.S. Private*, pg. 259
AMERICO LOGISTICS, INC.—See Minerals Technologies, Inc.; *U.S. Public*, pg. 1448
AMERICO MANUFACTURING CO., INC.—See Branford Castle, Inc.; *U.S. Private*, pg. 639
AMERICOM GOVERNMENT SERVICES, INC.—See SES S.A.; *Int'l*, pg. 6727
AMERICOMMERCE, L.P.—See Cart.Com, Inc.; *U.S. Private*, pg. 775
AMERICOM TECHNOLOGY, INC.—See Crestone Services Group LLC; *U.S. Private*, pg. 1097
AMERICON EQUIPMENT SERVICES, INC.—See Babcock & Wilcox Enterprises, Inc.; *U.S. Public*, pg. 262
AMERICON, LLC—See Babcock & Wilcox Enterprises, Inc.; *U.S. Public*, pg. 262
AMERICRAFT CARTON GROUP, INC.—See Americraft Carton, Inc.; *U.S. Private*, pg. 259
AMERICRAFT CARTON, INC. - LOWELL PLANT—See Americraft Carton, Inc.; *U.S. Private*, pg. 259
AMERICRAFT CARTON, INC. - MEMPHIS PLANT—See Americraft Carton, Inc.; *U.S. Private*, pg. 259

AMERICRAFT CARTON, INC. - NORWALK PLANT—See Americraft Carton, Inc.; *U.S. Private*, pg. 259
AMERICRAFT CARTON, INC.; *U.S. Private*, pg. 259
AMERICRAFT CARTON INC.—See Americraft Carton, Inc.; *U.S. Private*, pg. 259
AMERICRAFT CARTON, INC.—See Americraft Carton, Inc.; *U.S. Private*, pg. 259
AMERICRAFT CARTON, INC.—See Americraft Carton, Inc.; *U.S. Private*, pg. 259
AMERICRAFT CARTON, INC.—See Americraft Carton, Inc.; *U.S. Private*, pg. 259
AMERICRAFT CARTON, INC.—See Americraft Carton, Inc.; *U.S. Private*, pg. 259
AMERICRAFT CARTON, INC. - ST. PAUL PLANT—See Americraft Carton, Inc.; *U.S. Private*, pg. 259
AMERICRAFT CARTON, INC. - STURGIS PLANT—See Americraft Carton, Inc.; *U.S. Private*, pg. 259
AMERICRAFT CARTON, INC. - WINSTON-SALEM PLANT—See Americraft Carton, Inc.; *U.S. Private*, pg. 259
AMERICRAFT MARINE GROUP LLC—See Libra Group Limited; *Int'l*, pg. 4486
AMERICREDIT FINANCIAL SERVICES, INC.—See General Motors Company; *U.S. Public*, pg. 925
AMERICREW INC.; *U.S. Public*, pg. 113
AMERICROWN SERVICE CORPORATION—See National Association for Stock Car Auto Racing, Inc.; *U.S. Private*, pg. 2845
AMERIDIAL, INC.; *U.S. Private*, pg. 259
AMERIDIAN SPECIALTY SERVICES INC.; *U.S. Private*, pg. 259
AMERIDRIVES COUPLINGS—See Regal Rexnord Corporation; *U.S. Public*, pg. 1772
AMERIDRIVES INTERNATIONAL, LLC—See Regal Rexnord Corporation; *U.S. Public*, pg. 1772
AMERI FINANCIAL GROUP, INC.; *U.S. Private*, pg. 220
AMERIFIRST FINANCIAL CORPORATION—See Union Home Mortgage Corp.; *U.S. Private*, pg. 4284
AMERIFIRST HOME MORTGAGE; *U.S. Private*, pg. 259
AMERI-FORCE CRAFT SERVICES, INC.—See Ameri-Force, Inc.; *U.S. Private*, pg. 220
AMERI-FORCE, INC.; *U.S. Private*, pg. 220
AMERI-FORCE INDUSTRIAL SERVICES, INC.—See Ameri-Force, Inc.; *U.S. Private*, pg. 220
AMERI-FORCE LABOR SERVICES, INC.—See Ameri-Force, Inc.; *U.S. Private*, pg. 220
AMERI-FORCE PROFESSIONAL SERVICES, INC.—See Ameri-Force, Inc.; *U.S. Private*, pg. 220
AMERIFRESH, INC.—See US Foods Holding Corp.; *U.S. Public*, pg. 2266
AMERIGAS EAGLE PROPANE, INC.—See UGI Corporation; *U.S. Public*, pg. 2221
AMERIGAS FINANCE CORP.—See UGI Corporation; *U.S. Public*, pg. 2221
AMERIGAS, INC.—See UGI Corporation; *U.S. Public*, pg. 2221
AMERIGAS PARTNERS, L.P.—See UGI Corporation; *U.S. Public*, pg. 2221
AMERIGAS POLSKA SP. Z.O.O.—See UGI Corporation; *U.S. Public*, pg. 2221
AMERIGAS PROPANE, INC.—See UGI Corporation; *U.S. Public*, pg. 2221
AMERIGAS PROPANE, L.P.—See UGI Corporation; *U.S. Public*, pg. 2221
AMERIGLOBE FIBC SOLUTIONS; *U.S. Private*, pg. 259
AMERIGO RESOURCES LTD.; *Int'l*, pg. 423
AMERIGO RESTAURANT CORPORATION; *U.S. Private*, pg. 259
AMERIGROUP COMMUNITY CARE OF NEW MEXICO, INC.—See Elevance Health, Inc.; *U.S. Public*, pg. 728
AMERIGROUP CORPORATION—See Elevance Health, Inc.; *U.S. Public*, pg. 728
AMERIGROUP DISTRICT OF COLUMBIA, INC.—See Elevance Health, Inc.; *U.S. Public*, pg. 728
AMERIGROUP IOWA, INC.—See Elevance Health, Inc.; *U.S. Public*, pg. 728
AMERIGROUP LOUISIANA, INC.—See Elevance Health, Inc.; *U.S. Public*, pg. 728
AMERIGROUP MARYLAND, INC.—See Elevance Health, Inc.; *U.S. Public*, pg. 728
AMERIGROUP NEW JERSEY, INC.—See Elevance Health, Inc.; *U.S. Public*, pg. 728
AMERIGROUP NEW YORK, LLC—See Elevance Health, Inc.; *U.S. Public*, pg. 728
AMERIGROUP TENNESSEE, INC.—See Elevance Health, Inc.; *U.S. Public*, pg. 728
AMERIGROUP TEXAS, INC.—See Elevance Health, Inc.; *U.S. Public*, pg. 728
AMERIGROUP WASHINGTON, INC.—See Elevance Health, Inc.; *U.S. Public*, pg. 728
AMERIGROW RECYCLING - DELRAY, LIMITED PARTNERSHIP; *U.S. Private*, pg. 259
AMERIGUARD SECURITY SERVICES, INC.; *U.S. Public*, pg. 113
AMERIHEALTH NEW JERSEY; *U.S. Private*, pg. 259
AMERIHOST FRANCHISE SYSTEMS, INC.—See Travel & Leisure Co.; *U.S. Public*, pg. 2185
AMERIJET INTERNATIONAL INC.—See ZS Fund L.P.; *U.S. Private*, pg. 4609
AMERIKAN LLC—See Myers Industries, Inc.; *U.S. Public*, pg. 1488

AMERI-KART CORP.—See Myers Industries, Inc.; *U.S. Public*, pg. 1488
AMERIKAS, INC.; *U.S. Private*, pg. 260
AMERI-KLEEN; *U.S. Private*, pg. 220
AMERIKOHL MINING INC.; *U.S. Private*, pg. 260
AMERILAB TECHNOLOGIES, INC.—See DCC plc; *Int'l*, pg. 1990
AMERILIFE GROUP, LLC—See Thomas H. Lee Partners, L.P.; *U.S. Private*, pg. 4156
AMERI LIFE & HEALTH SERVICES; *U.S. Private*, pg. 220
AMERILUX INTERNATIONAL, LLC.; *U.S. Private*, pg. 260
AMERIMARK DIRECT, LLC—See JH Partners LLC; *U.S. Private*, pg. 2207
AMERIMARK DIRECT, LLC—See Prudential Financial, Inc.; *U.S. Public*, pg. 1732
AMERIMARK GROUP AG; *Int'l*, pg. 423
AMERIMAX HOME PRODUCTS—See Omnimax Holdings, Inc.; *U.S. Private*, pg. 3017
AMERIMED, INC.—See Catholic Health Initiatives; *U.S. Private*, pg. 789
AMERI METRO, INC.; *U.S. Private*, pg. 220
AMERINAC HOLDING CORP.; *U.S. Private*, pg. 260
AMERINDIA TECHNOLOGIES, INC.; *U.S. Private*, pg. 260
AMERINIC, INC.—See Universal Corporation; *U.S. Public*, pg. 2254
AMERINST INSURANCE GROUP, LTD.; *Int'l*, pg. 423
AMER INTERNATIONAL GROUP CO., LTD.; *Int'l*, pg. 420
AMERI-PAC, INC.—See Wilbur-Ellis Company; *U.S. Private*, pg. 4517
AMERI & PARTNERS INC.—See Enveric Biosciences, Inc.; *U.S. Public*, pg. 780
AMERIPATH CONSOLIDATED LABS, INC.—See Quest Diagnostics, Inc.; *U.S. Public*, pg. 1755
AMERIPATH CONSULTING PATHOLOGY SERVICES, P.A.—See Quest Diagnostics, Inc.; *U.S. Public*, pg. 1755
AMERIPATH, INC.—See Quest Diagnostics, Inc.; *U.S. Public*, pg. 1755
AMERIPATH INDIANAPOLIS, P.C.—See Quest Diagnostics, Inc.; *U.S. Public*, pg. 1755
AMERIPATH PITTSBURGH, P.C.—See Quest Diagnostics, Inc.; *U.S. Public*, pg. 1755
AMERIPEC, INC.—See Uni-President Enterprises Corporation; *Int'l*, pg. 8029
AMERIPIPE SUPPLY, INC.; *U.S. Private*, pg. 260
AMERIPLAN CORPORATION; *U.S. Private*, pg. 260
AMERIPRIDE LINEN & UNIFORM SERVICES, INC.—See Aramark; *U.S. Public*, pg. 177
AMERIPRIDE SERVICES INC.—See Aramark; *U.S. Public*, pg. 177
AMERIPRINT CORPORATION—See Ennis, Inc.; *U.S. Public*, pg. 768
AMERIPRISE ADVISOR SERVICES, INC.—See Ameriprise Financial, Inc.; *U.S. Public*, pg. 114
AMERIPRISE AUTO & HOME INSURANCE AGENCY INC.—See American Family Mutual Insurance Company; *U.S. Private*, pg. 233
AMERIPRISE CERTIFICATE COMPANY—See Ameriprise Financial, Inc.; *U.S. Public*, pg. 114
AMERIPRISE FINANCIAL, INC.; *U.S. Public*, pg. 113
AMERIPRISE FINANCIAL SERVICES, INC.—See Ameriprise Financial, Inc.; *U.S. Public*, pg. 114
AMERIPRISE TRUST COMPANY—See Ameriprise Financial, Inc.; *U.S. Public*, pg. 114
AMERIPRO HEALTH LLC; *U.S. Private*, pg. 260
AMERIQUAL GROUP, LLC—See Harlan Bakeries LLC; *U.S. Private*, pg. 1865
AMERIQUEST BUSINESS SERVICES; *U.S. Private*, pg. 260
AMERIQUEST CAPITAL CORPORATION; *U.S. Private*, pg. 260
AMERI-QUIPT OF NORTH CAROLINA, INC.—See AdaptHealth Corp.; *U.S. Public*, pg. 38
AMERISAFE INC.—See Dunes Point Capital, LLC; *U.S. Private*, pg. 1289
AMERISAFE, INC.; *U.S. Public*, pg. 115
AMERISAFE RISK SERVICES, INC.—See AMERISAFE, Inc.; *U.S. Public*, pg. 115
AMERIS BANCORP; *U.S. Public*, pg. 114
AMERIS BANK—See Ameris Bancorp; *U.S. Public*, pg. 114
AMERISCAPE USA, INC.; *U.S. Private*, pg. 260
AMERISE BIOSCIENCES LTD; *Int'l*, pg. 423
AMERISERVE FOOD MANAGEMENT SERVICES—See Charterhouse Capital Partners LLP; *Int'l*, pg. 1455
AMERISERV FINANCIAL BANK—See Ameriserv Financial, Inc.; *U.S. Public*, pg. 115
AMERISERV FINANCIAL, INC.; *U.S. Public*, pg. 115
AMERISERV TRUST & FINANCIAL SERVICES CO.—See Ameriserv Financial, Inc.; *U.S. Public*, pg. 115
AMERISOURCEBERGEN CONSULTING SERVICES, INC.—See Cencora, Inc.; *U.S. Public*, pg. 466
AMERISOURCEBERGEN DRUG CORPORATION—See Cencora, Inc.; *U.S. Public*, pg. 466
AMERISOURCEBERGEN SERVICES CORPORATION—See Cencora, Inc.; *U.S. Public*, pg. 466
AMERISOURCEBERGEN—See Cencora, Inc.; *U.S. Public*, pg. 466

COMPANY NAME INDEX

AMERISOURCEBERGEN—See Cencora, Inc.; *U.S. Public*, pg. 466
AMERISOURCEBERGEN—See Cencora, Inc.; *U.S. Public*, pg. 466
AMERISOURCEBERGEN—See Cencora, Inc.; *U.S. Public*, pg. 466
AMERISOURCEBERGEN—See Cencora, Inc.; *U.S. Public*, pg. 466
AMERISOURCEBERGEN—See Cencora, Inc.; *U.S. Public*, pg. 466
AMERISOURCEBERGEN—See Cencora, Inc.; *U.S. Public*, pg. 466
AMERISOURCEBERGEN—See Cencora, Inc.; *U.S. Public*, pg. 466
AMERISOURCEBERGEN—See Cencora, Inc.; *U.S. Public*, pg. 466
AMERISOURCEBERGEN—See Cencora, Inc.; *U.S. Public*, pg. 466
AMERISOURCEBERGEN—See Cencora, Inc.; *U.S. Public*, pg. 466
AMERISOURCEBERGEN—See Cencora, Inc.; *U.S. Public*, pg. 466
AMERISOURCEBERGEN SPECIALTY GROUP—See Cencora, Inc.; *U.S. Public*, pg. 466
AMERISOURCE HEALTH SERVICES CORPORATION—See Cencora, Inc.; *U.S. Public*, pg. 466
AMERISPEC LLC—See Roark Capital Group Inc.; *U.S. Private*, pg. 3456
AMERISTAR AGENCY, INC.—See Marsh & McLennan Companies, Inc.; *U.S. Public*, pg. 1380
AMERISTAR CASINO BLACK HAWK, LLC—See PENN Entertainment, Inc.; *U.S. Public*, pg. 1662
AMERISTAR CASINO COUNCIL BLUFFS, LLC—See PENN Entertainment, Inc.; *U.S. Public*, pg. 1662
AMERISTAR CASINO EAST CHICAGO, LLC—See PENN Entertainment, Inc.; *U.S. Public*, pg. 1662
AMERISTAR CASINO KANSAS CITY, LLC—See Boyd Gaming Corporation; *U.S. Public*, pg. 377
AMERISTAR CASINO ST. CHARLES, LLC—See Boyd Gaming Corporation; *U.S. Public*, pg. 377
AMERISTAR CASINO VICKSBURG, LLC—See PENN Entertainment, Inc.; *U.S. Public*, pg. 1662
AMERISTAR JET CHARTER INC.; *U.S. Private*, pg. 260
AMERISTAR MEATS, INC.—See US Foods Holding Corp.; *U.S. Public*, pg. 2266
AMERISTAR NETWORK, INC.; *U.S. Public*, pg. 115
AMERISTAR PERIMETER SECURITY USA, INC.—See ASSA ABLOY AB; *Int'l*, pg. 638
AMERISURE INSURANCE COMPANY INC—See Amerisure Mutual Insurance Company; *U.S. Private*, pg. 260
AMERISURE MUTUAL INSURANCE COMPANY; *U.S. Private*, pg. 260
AMERISUR RESOURCES PLC—See GeoPark Limited; *Int'l*, pg. 2934
AMERITA, INC.—See KKR & Co. Inc.; *U.S. Public*, pg. 1262
AMERITAPE, INC.—See Sur-Seal LLC; *U.S. Private*, pg. 3883
AMERITAS INVESTMENT CORP.—See Ameritas Mutual Holding Company; *U.S. Private*, pg. 261
AMERITAS INVESTMENT PARTNERS, INC.—See Ameritas Mutual Holding Company; *U.S. Private*, pg. 261
AMERITAS LIFE INSURANCE CORP.—See Ameritas Mutual Holding Company; *U.S. Private*, pg. 261
AMERITAS MUTUAL HOLDING COMPANY; *U.S. Private*, pg. 260
AMERITEC CORPORATION; *U.S. Private*, pg. 261
AMERI-TECH KIDNEY CENTER- ARLINGTON, LLC—See Nautic Partners, LLC; *U.S. Private*, pg. 2869
AMERI-TECH KIDNEY CENTER- BEDFORD, LLC—See Nautic Partners, LLC; *U.S. Private*, pg. 2869
AMERITEK VENTURES; *U.S. Public*, pg. 115
AMERITEL CORPORATION; *U.S. Private*, pg. 261
AMERITEL INNS INCORPORATED; *U.S. Private*, pg. 261
AMERITEMPS INC.; *U.S. Private*, pg. 261
AMERITEX FABRIC SYSTEMS—See LCI Industries; *U.S. Public*, pg. 1295
AMERIT FLEET SOLUTIONS, INC.—See Brightstar Capital Partners, L.P.; *U.S. Private*, pg. 652
AMERITRANS BUS, INC.—See ABC Bus Companies, Inc.; *U.S. Private*, pg. 35
AMERITRANS CAPITAL CORPORATION; *U.S. Public*, pg. 115
AMERITRUST CORPORATION; *U.S. Public*, pg. 115
AMERITRUST MORTGAGE CORPORATION; *U.S. Private*, pg. 261
AMERITYRE CORPORATION; *U.S. Public*, pg. 115
AMERIWEST LITHIUM INC.; *Int'l*, pg. 423
AMERIWOOD INDUSTRIES, INC.—See Dorel Industries, Inc.; *Int'l*, pg. 2176
AMERIWORKS FINANCIAL SERVICES, INC.; *U.S. Public*, pg. 115
AMERIX CORPORATION—See Ascend One Corporation; *U.S. Private*, pg. 346
AMERLING COMPANY; *U.S. Private*, pg. 261

AMERLUX, LLC—See Delta Electronics, Inc.; *Int'l*, pg. 2017
AMERMAN INSURANCE SERVICES, LLC—See Galiot Insurance Services, Inc.; *U.S. Private*, pg. 1638
AME ROBOTICS CORPORATION—See Sapura Energy Berhad; *Int'l*, pg. 6574
AMEROCK CORPORATION—See Nova Capital Management Limited; *Int'l*, pg. 5450
AMERON BRASIL INDUSTRIA E COMERCIO DE TUBOS LTDA—See NOV, Inc.; *U.S. Public*, pg. 1543
AMERON HAWAII—See NOV, Inc.; *U.S. Public*, pg. 1543
AMERON HOLDINGS II PTE LTD—See NOV, Inc.; *U.S. Public*, pg. 1543
AMERON INTERNATIONAL CORPORATION—See NOV, Inc.; *U.S. Public*, pg. 1543
AMERON INTERNATIONAL WATER TRANSMISSION GROUP—See NOV, Inc.; *U.S. Public*, pg. 1544
AMERON POLE PRODUCTS LLC—See Arcosa, Inc.; *U.S. Public*, pg. 186
AMERON PROTECTIVE LININGS CO—See NOV, Inc.; *U.S. Public*, pg. 1544
AMEROPA AG; *Int'l*, pg. 423
AMEROPA ASIA PTE LTD—See Ameropa AG; *Int'l*, pg. 423
AMEROPA AUSTRALIA PTY LTD—See Ameropa AG; *Int'l*, pg. 423
AMEROPA (BEIJING) TRADING CO. LTD.—See Ameropa AG; *Int'l*, pg. 423
AMEROPA CHILE - SAS—See Ameropa AG; *Int'l*, pg. 423
AMEROPA COMMODITIES (PTY) LTD.—See Ameropa AG; *Int'l*, pg. 423
AMEROPA CONOSUR SRL.—See Ameropa AG; *Int'l*, pg. 423
AMEROPA DO BRASIL COMERCIAL AGRICOLA LTDA.—See Ameropa AG; *Int'l*, pg. 423
AMEROPA DUNGEMITTEL GMBH—See Ameropa AG; *Int'l*, pg. 423
AMEROPA EGYPT—See Ameropa AG; *Int'l*, pg. 424
AMEROPA FRANCE S.A.R.L—See Ameropa AG; *Int'l*, pg. 424
AMEROPA GESELLSCHAFT M.B.H.—See Ameropa AG; *Int'l*, pg. 424
AMEROPA GRAINS SA; *Int'l*, pg. 424
AMEROPA IBERIA S.L.—See Ameropa AG; *Int'l*, pg. 424
AMEROPA INDIA PVT LTD—See Ameropa AG; *Int'l*, pg. 424
AMEROPA ITALIA SRL—See Ameropa AG; *Int'l*, pg. 424
AMEROPA LJUBLJANA D.O.O.—See Ameropa AG; *Int'l*, pg. 424
AMEROPA MIDDLE EAST - DMCC—See Ameropa AG; *Int'l*, pg. 424
AMEROPA NORTH AMERICA, INC.—See Ameropa AG; *Int'l*, pg. 424
AMEROPA POLSKA SP Z O.O.—See Ameropa AG; *Int'l*, pg. 424
AMEROPA-REISEN GMBH—See Deutsche Bahn AG; *Int'l*, pg. 2049
AMEROPA ROMANIA SERVICES S.R.L.—See Ameropa AG; *Int'l*, pg. 424
AMEROPA TURKEY—See Ameropa AG; *Int'l*, pg. 424
AMEROPA UK LTD.—See Ameropa AG; *Int'l*, pg. 424
AMEROPA VIETNAM—See Ameropa AG; *Int'l*, pg. 424
AMEROPA ZITNI TERMINAL D.O.O.—See Ameropa AG; *Int'l*, pg. 424
AMEROP PRODUCTS; *U.S. Private*, pg. 261
AMERPLAST AB—See Chiltern Capital LLP; *Int'l*, pg. 1479
AMERPLAST LTD.—See Chiltern Capital LLP; *Int'l*, pg. 1479
AMERPLAST SP. Z O.O.—See Chiltern Capital LLP; *Int'l*, pg. 1479
AMERRA CAPITAL MANAGEMENT LLC; *Int'l*, pg. 424
AMERSOL, INC.—See Solar Art Window Film, Inc.; *U.S. Private*, pg. 3707
AMER SPORT OY—See ANTA Sports Products Limited; *Int'l*, pg. 479
AMER SPORTS ASIA SERVICES LIMITED—See ANTA Sports Products Limited; *Int'l*, pg. 479
AMER SPORTS AUSTRALIA PTY. LTD.—See ANTA Sports Products Limited; *Int'l*, pg. 481
AMER SPORTS AUSTRIA GMBH—See ANTA Sports Products Limited; *Int'l*, pg. 479
AMER SPORTS CANADA, INC.—See ANTA Sports Products Limited; *Int'l*, pg. 479
AMER SPORTS CHINA—See ANTA Sports Products Limited; *Int'l*, pg. 479
AMER SPORTS COMPANY—See ANTA Sports Products Limited; *Int'l*, pg. 480
AMER SPORTS CORPORATION—See ANTA Sports Products Limited; *Int'l*, pg. 479
AMERSPORTS CZECH REPUBLIC—See ANTA Sports Products Limited; *Int'l*, pg. 481
AMER SPORTS CZECH REPUBLIC S.R.O.—See ANTA Sports Products Limited; *Int'l*, pg. 480
AMER SPORTS DENMARK APS—See ANTA Sports Products Limited; *Int'l*, pg. 480
AMER SPORTS DEUTSCHLAND GMBH—See ANTA Sports Products Limited; *Int'l*, pg. 480
AMERSPORTS DEUTSCHLAND GMBH—See ANTA Sports Products Limited; *Int'l*, pg. 481

AMER SPORTS ESTONIA—See ANTA Sports Products Limited; *Int'l*, pg. 480
AMER SPORTS EUROPEAN CENTER AG—See ANTA Sports Products Limited; *Int'l*, pg. 480
AMER SPORTS EUROPE GMBH—See ANTA Sports Products Limited; *Int'l*, pg. 480
AMER SPORTS EUROPE SERVICES GMBH—See ANTA Sports Products Limited; *Int'l*, pg. 480
AMER SPORTS FINANCE OY—See ANTA Sports Products Limited; *Int'l*, pg. 480
AMER SPORTS FRANCE—See ANTA Sports Products Limited; *Int'l*, pg. 480
AMER SPORTS HOLDING GMBH—See ANTA Sports Products Limited; *Int'l*, pg. 480
AMER SPORTS HOLDING S.A.S.—See ANTA Sports Products Limited; *Int'l*, pg. 480
AMER SPORTS ITALIA S.P.A.—See ANTA Sports Products Limited; *Int'l*, pg. 480
AMER SPORTS JAPAN, INC.—See ANTA Sports Products Limited; *Int'l*, pg. 481
AMER SPORTS KOREA LTD.—See ANTA Sports Products Limited; *Int'l*, pg. 481
AMER SPORTS LATIN AMERICA—See ANTA Sports Products Limited; *Int'l*, pg. 480
AMER SPORTS MALAYSIA SDN BHD—See ANTA Sports Products Limited; *Int'l*, pg. 481
AMER SPORTS NETHERLANDS—See ANTA Sports Products Limited; *Int'l*, pg. 480
AMER SPORTS NORGE A/S—See ANTA Sports Products Limited; *Int'l*, pg. 480
AMER SPORTS POLAND SP. Z.O.O.—See ANTA Sports Products Limited; *Int'l*, pg. 480
AMERSPORT SP. Z O.O. SP. K.—See Penta Investments Limited; *Int'l*, pg. 5788
AMER SPORTS RUSSIA—See ANTA Sports Products Limited; *Int'l*, pg. 480
AMER SPORTS SA—See ANTA Sports Products Limited; *Int'l*, pg. 480
AMER SPORTS SHANGHAI TRADING LTD.—See ANTA Sports Products Limited; *Int'l*, pg. 480
AMER SPORTS SLOVAKIA—See ANTA Sports Products Limited; *Int'l*, pg. 480
AMER SPORTS SOURCING LTD.—See ANTA Sports Products Limited; *Int'l*, pg. 480
AMER SPORTS SPAIN S.A.—See ANTA Sports Products Limited; *Int'l*, pg. 481
AMER SPORTS SUOMI OY—See ANTA Sports Products Limited; *Int'l*, pg. 481
AMER SPORTS SVERIGE AB—See ANTA Sports Products Limited; *Int'l*, pg. 480
AMER SPORTS TAIWAN—See ANTA Sports Products Limited; *Int'l*, pg. 481
AMER SPORTS UK & IRELAND LTD—See ANTA Sports Products Limited; *Int'l*, pg. 480
AMER SPORTS UK LIMITED—See ANTA Sports Products Limited; *Int'l*, pg. 481
AMER SPORTS UK LOGISTICS CENTER—See ANTA Sports Products Limited; *Int'l*, pg. 480
AMER SPORTS UK LTD. - LOGISTICS CENTER—See ANTA Sports Products Limited; *Int'l*, pg. 481
AMER SPORTS WINTER & OUTDOOR COMPANY—See ANTA Sports Products Limited; *Int'l*, pg. 480
AMERTAC HOLDINGS INC.; *U.S. Private*, pg. 261
AMERTEK COMPUTER (SHENZHEN) CO. LTD.—See FIC Global, Inc.; *Int'l*, pg. 2653
AMERTEK LIMITED—See VIA Technologies, Inc.; *Int'l*, pg. 8182
AMER TOBACCO LTD.—See ANTA Sports Products Limited; *Int'l*, pg. 480
AMERTRON TECHNOLOGY (KUNSHAN) CO. LTD.—See Inari Amertron Berhad; *Int'l*, pg. 3645
AMER TUNISIA SARL—See Brookfield Corporation; *Int'l*, pg. 1178
AMER TUNISIA SARL—See Elliott Management Corporation; *U.S. Private*, pg. 1370
AMERY CAPITAL LIMITED; *Int'l*, pg. 424
AMERY REGIONAL MEDICAL CENTER; *U.S. Private*, pg. 261
AMESBURY NEWS—See Gannett Co., Inc.; *U.S. Public*, pg. 901
AMESBURY TRUTH—See Quanex Building Products Corp.; *U.S. Public*, pg. 1749
THE AMES COMPANIES, INC.—See Griffon Corporation; *U.S. Public*, pg. 969
THE AMES COMPANIES UK LTD.—See Griffon Corporation; *U.S. Public*, pg. 969
AMES CONSTRUCTION, INC.; *U.S. Private*, pg. 261
AMES CORPORATION—See Grafoid, Inc.; *Int'l*, pg. 3050
A.M.E. SERVICES, INC.; *U.S. Private*, pg. 27
AMES GOLDSMITH CORP.; *U.S. Private*, pg. 261
AMES GOLDSMITH UK LTD—See Ames Goldsmith Corp.; *U.S. Private*, pg. 261
AMES GROUP LIMITED—See Rollins, Inc.; *U.S. Public*, pg. 1808
AMES INTERNATIONAL INC.—See Puyallup Tribe of Indians; *U.S. Private*, pg. 3308
AMESITE INC.; *U.S. Public*, pg. 116
AMES NATIONAL CORPORATION; *U.S. Public*, pg. 115
A MESSAGE CENTER INC.; *U.S. Private*, pg. 18

A MESSAGE CENTER INC.

CORPORATE AFFILIATIONS

AMES SAND & GRAVEL, INC.—See MDU Resources Group, Inc.; *U.S. Public*, pg. 1409
AMES SCULLIN O'HAIRE; *U.S. Private*, pg. 262
AMES TAPING TOOLS CO. OF CANADA LIMITED—See Aurora Capital Group, LLC; *U.S. Private*, pg. 394
AMES TAPING TOOL SYSTEMS CO.—See Sun Capital Partners, Inc.; *U.S. Private*, pg. 3858
AMES TEXTILE CORPORATION; *U.S. Private*, pg. 262
AMES TRUE TEMPER - BERNIE—See Griffon Corporation; *U.S. Public*, pg. 969
A.M.E.'S UNIFORMS, INC.; *U.S. Private*, pg. 27
AMES WALKER INTERNATIONAL INC.; *U.S. Private*, pg. 262
AMES WATSON HOLDING LLC; *U.S. Private*, pg. 262
AMESYS CANADA INC.—See Atos SE; *Int'l*, pg. 691
AMESYS S.A.—See Atos SE; *Int'l*, pg. 691
A METAVERSE COMPANY; *Int'l*, pg. 18
A. METAXIOTIS S.A.; *Int'l*, pg. 21
AMETEK ADVANCED INDUSTRIES, INC.—See AMETEK, Inc.; *U.S. Public*, pg. 117
AMETEK AEGIS, INC.—See AMETEK, Inc.; *U.S. Public*, pg. 116
AMETEK AEROSPACE & DEFENSE DIVISION—See AMETEK, Inc.; *U.S. Public*, pg. 116
AMETEK AIRCRAFT PARTS & ACCESSORIES, INC.—See AMETEK, Inc.; *U.S. Public*, pg. 117
AMETEK AIRTECHNOLOGY GROUP LTD.—See AMETEK, Inc.; *U.S. Public*, pg. 116
AMETEK AMERON, LLC—See AMETEK, Inc.; *U.S. Public*, pg. 117
AMETEK AUTOMATION & PROCESS TECHNOLOGIES—See AMETEK, Inc.; *U.S. Public*, pg. 117
AMETEK CANADA, LLC—See AMETEK, Inc.; *U.S. Public*, pg. 116
AMETEK CERAMICS, INC.—See AMETEK, Inc.; *U.S. Public*, pg. 116
AMETEK CHATILLON FORCE MEASUREMENT PRODUCTS—See AMETEK, Inc.; *U.S. Public*, pg. 117
AMETEK CHEMICAL PRODUCTS—See AMETEK, Inc.; *U.S. Public*, pg. 117
AMETEK CTS EUROPE GMBH—See AMETEK, Inc.; *U.S. Public*, pg. 119
AMETEK CTS GERMANY GMBH—See AMETEK, Inc.; *U.S. Public*, pg. 120
AMETEK DENMARK—See AMETEK, Inc.; *U.S. Public*, pg. 116
AMETEK DREXELBROOK—See AMETEK, Inc.; *U.S. Public*, pg. 117
AMETEK ELECTROMECHANICAL GROUP—See AMETEK, Inc.; *U.S. Public*, pg. 116
AMETEK ELECTRONIC INSTRUMENTS GROUP—See AMETEK, Inc.; *U.S. Public*, pg. 116
AMETEK FLOORCARE SPECIALTY MOTORS DIVISION—See AMETEK, Inc.; *U.S. Public*, pg. 116
AMETEK GERMANY GMBH—See AMETEK, Inc.; *U.S. Public*, pg. 120
AMETEK GMBH—See AMETEK, Inc.; *U.S. Public*, pg. 119
AMETEK HDR POWER SYSTEMS, INC.—See AMETEK, Inc.; *U.S. Public*, pg. 119
AMETEK HSA, INC.—See AMETEK, Inc.; *U.S. Public*, pg. 117
AMETEK HUGHES-TREITLER—See AMETEK, Inc.; *U.S. Public*, pg. 116
AMETEK, INC.; *U.S. Public*, pg. 116
AMETEK INSTRUMENTOS, S.L.—See AMETEK, Inc.; *U.S. Public*, pg. 120
AMETEK ITALIA—See AMETEK, Inc.; *U.S. Public*, pg. 119
AMETEK LAMB ELECTRIC DIVISION—See AMETEK, Inc.; *U.S. Public*, pg. 116
AMETEK LAMB MOTORES DE MEXICO, S. DE R.L. DE C.V.—See AMETEK, Inc.; *U.S. Public*, pg. 119
AMETEK LAND, INC.—See AMETEK, Inc.; *U.S. Public*, pg. 118
AMETEK MATERIAL ANALYSIS HOLDINGS GMBH—See AMETEK, Inc.; *U.S. Public*, pg. 119
AMETEK MEASUREMENT & CALIBRATION TECHNOLOGIES—See AMETEK, Inc.; *U.S. Public*, pg. 117
AMETEK MIDDLE EAST FZE—See AMETEK, Inc.; *U.S. Public*, pg. 119
AMETEK MOTORS (SHANGHAI) CO., LTD.—See AMETEK, Inc.; *U.S. Public*, pg. 119
AMETEK MRO FLORIDA, INC.—See AMETEK, Inc.; *U.S. Public*, pg. 117
AMETEK NORDIC AB—See AMETEK, Inc.; *U.S. Public*, pg. 119
AMETEK PANALARM PRODUCTS—See AMETEK, Inc.; *U.S. Public*, pg. 117
AMETEK POWER INSTRUMENTS—See AMETEK, Inc.; *U.S. Public*, pg. 117
AMETEK PRECISION MOTION CONTROL - ROTRON/NAUTILAIR BLOWERS—See AMETEK, Inc.; *U.S. Public*, pg. 117
AMETEK PROCESS & ANALYTICAL INSTRUMENTS DIVISION—See AMETEK, Inc.; *U.S. Public*, pg. 117
AMETEK PROGRAMMABLE POWER, INC.—See AMETEK, Inc.; *U.S. Public*, pg. 118

AMETEK ROTRON - EL CAJON—See AMETEK, Inc.; *U.S. Public*, pg. 117
AMETEK ROTRON—See AMETEK, Inc.; *U.S. Public*, pg. 117
AMETEK SCP, INC.—See AMETEK, Inc.; *U.S. Public*, pg. 119
AMETEK SOLARTRON ISA—See AMETEK, Inc.; *U.S. Public*, pg. 117
AMETEK SOLID STATE CONTROLS—See AMETEK, Inc.; *U.S. Public*, pg. 118
AMETEK SPECIALTY METAL PRODUCTS DIVISION—See AMETEK, Inc.; *U.S. Public*, pg. 116
AMETEK S.R.L.—See AMETEK, Inc.; *U.S. Public*, pg. 119
AMETEK THERMAL SYSTEMS, INC—See AMETEK, Inc.; *U.S. Public*, pg. 119
AMETEK U.S. GAUGE—See AMETEK, Inc.; *U.S. Public*, pg. 118
AMETEK VEHICULAR INSTRUMENTATION SYSTEMS—See AMETEK, Inc.; *U.S. Public*, pg. 118
AMETHYST GROUP LIMITED—See Cathay Investments Limited; *Int'l*, pg. 1360
AMETHYSTUM STORAGE TECHNOLOGY CO., LTD.; *Int'l*, pg. 424
AMETROS FINANCIAL CORPORATION—See Webster Financial Corporation; *U.S. Public*, pg. 2341
AMEUBLEMENTS TANGUAY INC.—See BMTC Group, Inc.; *Int'l*, pg. 1078
AMEX AGENZIA ASSICURATIVA S.R.L.—See American Express Company; *U.S. Public*, pg. 101
AMEX AL OMANIA LLC—See American Express Company; *U.S. Public*, pg. 101
AMEX ASESORES DE SEGUROS, S.A. (SOCIEDAD UNIPERSONAL)—See American Express Company; *U.S. Public*, pg. 101
AMEX ASESORES DE SEGUROS, S.A.—See American Express Company; *U.S. Public*, pg. 101
AMEX BANK OF CANADA—See American Express Company; *U.S. Public*, pg. 101
AMEX CANADA INC.—See American Express Company; *U.S. Public*, pg. 101
AMEX CARD SERVICES COMPANY—See American Express Company; *U.S. Public*, pg. 101
AMEXCOM ELECTRONICS, INC.—See Compal Electronics, Inc.; *Int'l*, pg. 1746
AMEXDRUG CORPORATION; *U.S. Public*, pg. 122
AMEX EGYPT COMPANY LIMITED LIABILITY COMPANY—See American Express Company; *U.S. Public*, pg. 102
AMEX EXPLORATION INC.; *Int'l*, pg. 424
AMEX (MIDDLE EAST) QFC LLC—See American Express Company; *U.S. Public*, pg. 100
AMEY INFRASTRUCTURE SERVICES LTD.—See Ferrovial S.A.; *Int'l*, pg. 2644
AMEY RAIL LTD.—See Ferrovial S.A.; *Int'l*, pg. 2644
AMEY ROADSTONE INTERNATIONAL LIMITED—See Heidelberg Materials AG; *Int'l*, pg. 3308
AMEY TPT LIMITED—See Ferrovial S.A.; *Int'l*, pg. 2644
AMEY UK PLC—See Ferrovial S.A.; *Int'l*, pg. 2644
AMFAC HAWAII LLC—See Walton Street Capital, LLC; *U.S. Private*, pg. 4435
AMFAR; *U.S. Private*, pg. 262
AMF AUTOMATION TECHNOLOGIES, LLC—See Markel Group Inc.; *U.S. Public*, pg. 1367
AMF BAKERY SYSTEMS—See Markel Group Inc.; *U.S. Public*, pg. 1368
AMF BAKE-TECH—See Markel Group Inc.; *U.S. Public*, pg. 1368
AMF BOWLING CENTERS, INC.—See Bowlero Corp; *U.S. Public*, pg. 376
AMF BOWLING WORLDWIDE, INC.—See Bowlero Corp; *U.S. Public*, pg. 376
AMF-BRUNS GMBH & CO. KG; *Int'l*, pg. 424
A & M FEBCON LIMITED; *Int'l*, pg. 17
AMFED COMPANIES, LLC; *U.S. Private*, pg. 262
AMF ELECTRICAL CONTRACTORS, INC.; *U.S. Private*, pg. 262
AMF GROUP JSC; *Int'l*, pg. 424
AMFI CORP.; *Int'l*, pg. 424
AMFIL TECHNOLOGIES INC.; *Int'l*, pg. 424
AMFINE CHEMICAL CORPORATION—See Mitsubishi Corporation; *Int'l*, pg. 4937
AMFIN FINANCIAL CORP.; *U.S. Public*, pg. 122
AMFIRST REAL ESTATE INVESTMENT TRUST; *Int'l*, pg. 424
A M FORD SALES LTD; *Int'l*, pg. 18
AMFORGE INDUSTRIES LTD.; *Int'l*, pg. 424
AMF SUPPORT SURFACES INC.; *U.S. Private*, pg. 262
AMFUNDS MANAGEMENT BERHAD—See AMMB Holdings Berhad; *Int'l*, pg. 429
AMFUTURES SDN BHD—See AMMB Holdings Berhad; *Int'l*, pg. 429
AMG ADVANCED METALLURGICAL GROUP INVESTMENT BV—See AMG Critical Materials N.V.; *Int'l*, pg. 425
AMG ADVANCED METALLURGICAL GROUP N.V.—See AMG Critical Materials N.V.; *Int'l*, pg. 425
AMG ALLIANCE LLC—See AMG Resources Corp.; *U.S. Private*, pg. 262

AMG ALPOCO UK LIMITED—See AMG Critical Materials N.V.; *Int'l*, pg. 425
AMG ALUMINUM CHINA LIMITED—See AMG Critical Materials N.V.; *Int'l*, pg. 425
AMG ALUMINUM MEXICO, S.A. DE CV—See AMG Critical Materials N.V.; *Int'l*, pg. 426
AMG ALUMINUM NORTH AMERICA, LLC - HENDERSON PLANT—See AMG Critical Materials N.V.; *Int'l*, pg. 425
AMG ALUMINUM NORTH AMERICA, LLC—See AMG Critical Materials N.V.; *Int'l*, pg. 425
AMG ALUMINUM NORTH AMERICA, LLC - WENATCHEE PLANT—See AMG Critical Materials N.V.; *Int'l*, pg. 425
AMG ALUMINUM UK LIMITED—See AMG Critical Materials N.V.; *Int'l*, pg. 425
AMG ANALYTICAL SERVICES LIMITED—See AMG Critical Materials N.V.; *Int'l*, pg. 425
AMGAS BLU S.R.L.—See Ascopiave S.p.A.; *Int'l*, pg. 603
AMG & ASSOCIATES, INC.; *U.S. Private*, pg. 262
AMGAZIT F.K. LTD.—See Stanley Black & Decker, Inc.; *U.S. Public*, pg. 1933
AMG BIOENERGY RESOURCES HOLDINGS LTD.; *Int'l*, pg. 425
AMG BRAZILIAN HOLDING BV—See AMG Critical Materials N.V.; *Int'l*, pg. 425
AMG BRAZIL S.A.—See AMG Critical Materials N.V.; *Int'l*, pg. 425
AMG CANADA CORP.—See Affiliated Managers Group, Inc.; *U.S. Public*, pg. 53
AMG COATING TECHNOLOGIES GMBH—See AMG Critical Materials N.V.; *Int'l*, pg. 425
AMG CRITICAL MATERIALS N.V.; *Int'l*, pg. 425
AMGEN AB—See Amgen Inc.; *U.S. Public*, pg. 122
AMGEN AUSTRALIA PTY LTD.—See Amgen Inc.; *U.S. Public*, pg. 122
AMGEN AUSTRALIA PTY LTD.—See Amgen Inc.; *U.S. Public*, pg. 122
AMGEN BELGIUM S.A. N.V.—See Amgen Inc.; *U.S. Public*, pg. 122
AMGEN-BIO-FARMACEUTICA, LDA.—See Amgen Inc.; *U.S. Public*, pg. 123
AMGEN B.V.—See Amgen Inc.; *U.S. Public*, pg. 122
AMGEN CANADA INC.—See Amgen Inc.; *U.S. Public*, pg. 122
AMGEN COLORADO, INC.—See Amgen Inc.; *U.S. Public*, pg. 122
AMGEN DEVELOPMENT CORPORATION—See Amgen Inc.; *U.S. Public*, pg. 122
AM GENERAL AFTERMARKET FULFILLMENT AND TRAINING CENTER—See MacAndrews & Forbes Incorporated; *U.S. Private*, pg. 2531
AM GENERAL AFTERMARKET FULFILLMENT AND TRAINING CENTER—See The Renco Group Inc.; *U.S. Private*, pg. 4104
AM GENERAL CONTRACTORS SPA—See Westinghouse Air Brake Technologies Corporation; *U.S. Public*, pg. 2356
AM GENERAL LLC—See MacAndrews & Forbes Incorporated; *U.S. Private*, pg. 2531
AM GENERAL LLC—See The Renco Group Inc.; *U.S. Private*, pg. 4104
AM GENERAL TECHNOLOGY AND ENGINEERING CENTER—See MacAndrews & Forbes Incorporated; *U.S. Private*, pg. 2531
AM GENERAL TECHNOLOGY AND ENGINEERING CENTER—See The Renco Group Inc.; *U.S. Private*, pg. 4104
AMGEN EUROPE B.V.—See Amgen Inc.; *U.S. Public*, pg. 122
AMGEN (EUROPE) GMBH—See Amgen Inc.; *U.S. Public*, pg. 122
AMGEN FREMONT INC.—See Amgen Inc.; *U.S. Public*, pg. 123
AMGEN GLOBAL FINANCE B.V.—See Amgen Inc.; *U.S. Public*, pg. 123
AMGEN GMBH—See Amgen Inc.; *U.S. Public*, pg. 122
AMGEN GMBH—See Amgen Inc.; *U.S. Public*, pg. 123
AMGEN HOLDING, INC.—See Amgen Inc.; *U.S. Public*, pg. 123
AMGEN INC. - GOVERNMENT AFFAIRS OFFICE—See Amgen Inc.; *U.S. Public*, pg. 123
AMGEN INC. - SAN FRANCISCO—See Amgen Inc.; *U.S. Public*, pg. 123
AMGEN INC.; *U.S. Public*, pg. 122
AMGEN LIMITED—See Amgen Inc.; *U.S. Public*, pg. 123
AMGEN MANUFACTURING, LIMITED—See Amgen Inc.; *U.S. Public*, pg. 123
AMGEN RESEARCH (MUNICH) GMBH—See Amgen Inc.; *U.S. Public*, pg. 123
AMGEN ROCKVILLE, INC.—See Amgen Inc.; *U.S. Public*, pg. 123
AMGEN S.A.—See Amgen Inc.; *U.S. Public*, pg. 123
AMGEN S.A.—See Amgen Inc.; *U.S. Public*, pg. 123
AMGEN S.A.S.—See Amgen Inc.; *U.S. Public*, pg. 123
AMGEN SINGAPORE MANUFACTURING PTE. LTD.—See Amgen Inc.; *U.S. Public*, pg. 123
AMGEN S.P.A.—See Amgen Inc.; *U.S. Public*, pg. 123
AMGENTECH INC.—See Telco Cuba, Inc.; *U.S. Public*, pg. 1992
AMGEN USA INC.—See Amgen Inc.; *U.S. Public*, pg. 123

COMPANY NAME INDEX

AMG EURO HOLDINGS CV—See AMG Critical Materials N.V.; *Int'l*, pg. 425
AMG FUNDS LLC—See Affiliated Managers Group, Inc.; *U.S. Public*, pg. 53
AMG HOLDINGS CO., LTD.; *Int'l*, pg. 426
AMG IDEALCAST SOLAR CORPORATION—See AMG Critical Materials N.V.; *Int'l*, pg. 425
AMG INSURANCE BERHAD—See AMMB Holdings Berhad; *Int'l*, pg. 429
AMG LITHIUM GMBH—See AMG Critical Materials N.V.; *Int'l*, pg. 425
AMG-LIVINGSTON, LLC—See Apollo Global Management, Inc.; *U.S. Public*, pg. 154
AMGLO KEMLITE LABORATORIES INC.; *U.S. Private*, pg. 262
AMG MEDIA NETWORKS LIMITED—See Adani Enterprises Limited; *Int'l*, pg. 124
AMG MINERACAO S.A.—See AMG Critical Materials N.V.; *Int'l*, pg. 425
AMG NATIONAL TRUST BANK; *U.S. Private*, pg. 262
AMGOORIE INDIA LIMITED—See Camellia Plc; *Int'l*, pg. 1271
AMG PACKAGING & PAPER COMPANY LTD.; *Int'l*, pg. 426
AMGP GEORGIA MANAGED CARE COMPANY, INC.—See Elevance Health, Inc.; *U.S. Public*, pg. 728
THE AMGRAPH GROUP; *U.S. Private*, pg. 3986
AMGRAPH PACKAGING INC.; *U.S. Private*, pg. 262
AMG RESOURCES CORP. - BALTIMORE FACILITY—See AMG Resources Corp.; *U.S. Private*, pg. 262
AMG RESOURCES CORP. - GARY FACILITY—See AMG Resources Corp.; *U.S. Private*, pg. 262
AMG RESOURCES CORP. - LLANELLI FACILITY—See AMG Resources Corp.; *U.S. Private*, pg. 262
AMG RESOURCES CORP. - MILWAUKEE FACILITY—See AMG Resources Corp.; *U.S. Private*, pg. 262
AMG RESOURCES CORP. - NEWARK FACILITY—See AMG Resources Corp.; *U.S. Private*, pg. 262
AMG RESOURCES CORP.; *U.S. Private*, pg. 262
AMG RESOURCES CORP. - ST. JOSEPH FACILITY—See AMG Resources Corp.; *U.S. Private*, pg. 262
AMG RESOURCES CORP. - ST. PAUL FACILITY—See AMG Resources Corp.; *U.S. Private*, pg. 262
AMG RESOURCES PACIFIC CORP—See AMG Resources Corp.; *U.S. Private*, pg. 262
AM GROUP HOLDINGS LIMITED; *Int'l*, pg. 402
AMG-SOUTHERN TENNESSEE, LLC—See Apollo Global Management, Inc.; *U.S. Public*, pg. 154
AMG SUPERALLOYS UK LIMITED—See AMG Critical Materials N.V.; *Int'l*, pg. 426
AMG-THAI UNION FEEDMILL (PRIVATE) LIMITED—See Thai Union Group Public Company Limited; *Int'l*, pg. 7596
AMG VANADIUM, INC.—See AMG Critical Materials N.V.; *Int'l*, pg. 425
AM&G WATERPROOFING, LLC; *U.S. Private*, pg. 215
AMHEARST GLEN, INC.; *U.S. Private*, pg. 262
AMHERST ALARM, INC.—See Pye-Barker Fire & Safety, LLC; *U.S. Private*, pg. 3309
AMHERST MADISON, INC.—See Port Amherst, Ltd.; *U.S. Private*, pg. 3229
AMHERST SECURITIES GROUP LP; *U.S. Private*, pg. 263
AMHERST SYSTEMS, INC.—See Northrop Grumman Corporation; *U.S. Public*, pg. 1540
AMHIL EUROPA SP. Z O.O.—See Wentworth Technologies Co. Ltd.; *Int'l*, pg. 8377
AM HOLDINGS LLC—See American International Group, Inc.; *U.S. Public*, pg. 106
AMH PORTFOLIO ONE, LLC—See American Homes 4 Rent; *U.S. Public*, pg. 104
AMHULT 2 AB; *Int'l*, pg. 426
AMIAD FILTRATION SYSTEMS INDIA PVT LTD—See Amiad Water Systems Ltd.; *Int'l*, pg. 427
AMIAD USA INC.—See Amiad Water Systems Ltd.; *Int'l*, pg. 427
AMIAD WATER SYSTEMS EUROPE SAS—See Amiad Water Systems Ltd.; *Int'l*, pg. 427
AMIAD WATER SYSTEMS LTD.; *Int'l*, pg. 427
AMIAD WATER SYSTEMS SAS—See Amiad Water Systems Ltd.; *Int'l*, pg. 427
AMIA ENERGY GMBH; *Int'l*, pg. 426
AMIANTIT FIBERGLASS INDUSTRIAL, LTD.—See Owens Corning; *U.S. Public*, pg. 1626
AMIAT S.P.A.—See Iren S.p.A.; *Int'l*, pg. 3808
AMI BEARINGS, INC.; *U.S. Private*, pg. 263
AMICA APPAREL CORP—See Maran Inc.; *U.S. Private*, pg. 2569
AMICA INTERNATIONAL GMBH—See Amica S.A.; *Int'l*, pg. 427
AMICA LLOYD'S OF TEXAS—See Amica Mutual Insurance Co.; *U.S. Private*, pg. 263
AMICALOLA ELECTRIC MEMBERSHIP CORPORATION; *U.S. Private*, pg. 263
AMICA MATURE LIFESTYLES INC.—See Ontario Teachers' Pension Plan; *Int'l*, pg. 5587
AMICA MUTUAL INSURANCE CO.; *U.S. Private*, pg. 263
AMICA S.A.; *Int'l*, pg. 427
AMICCOM ELECTRONICS CORP.; *Int'l*, pg. 427

AMICK CONSTRUCTION, INC.; *U.S. Private*, pg. 263
AMICK PROCESSING INC.; *U.S. Private*, pg. 263
AMICO CANADA, INC.—See Gibraltar Industries, Inc.; *U.S. Public*, pg. 935
AMICO FONTANA—See Gibraltar Industries, Inc.; *U.S. Public*, pg. 935
AMICOGEN, INC. - 2ND MANUFACTURING FACILITY—See Amicogen, Inc.; *Int'l*, pg. 427
AMICOGEN, INC.; *Int'l*, pg. 427
AMICO HOUSTON—See Gibraltar Industries, Inc.; *U.S. Public*, pg. 935
AMICO LAKELAND—See Gibraltar Industries, Inc.; *U.S. Public*, pg. 935
AMI CO., LTD.—See Astena Holdings Co., Ltd.; *Int'l*, pg. 653
AMI COMMUNICATIONS SLOVAKIA—See Daniel J. Edelman, Inc.; *U.S. Private*, pg. 1154
AMI COMMUNICATIONS—See Daniel J. Edelman, Inc.; *U.S. Private*, pg. 1154
AMICO OREM—See Gibraltar Industries, Inc.; *U.S. Public*, pg. 935
AMICORP GROUP AG; *Int'l*, pg. 427
AMICORP NETHERLANDS B.V.—See Amicorp Group AG; *Int'l*, pg. 427
AMICORP SWITZERLAND AG—See Amicorp Group AG; *Int'l*, pg. 427
AMICO—See Gibraltar Industries, Inc.; *U.S. Public*, pg. 935
AMICO—See EssilorLuxottica SA; *Int'l*, pg. 2512
AMICUS INSURANCE SOLUTIONS LIMITED—See Brown & Brown, Inc.; *U.S. Public*, pg. 396
AMICUS LEGAL LTD.—See Munchener Ruckversicherungs AG; *Int'l*, pg. 5085
AMICUS SEARCH GROUP LLC; *U.S. Private*, pg. 263
AMICUS THERAPEUTICS B.V.—See Amicus Therapeutics, Inc.; *U.S. Public*, pg. 124
AMICUS THERAPEUTICS CANADA INC.—See Amicus Therapeutics, Inc.; *U.S. Public*, pg. 124
AMICUS THERAPEUTICS GMBH—See Amicus Therapeutics, Inc.; *U.S. Public*, pg. 124
AMICUS THERAPEUTICS, INC.; *U.S. Public*, pg. 124
AMICUS THERAPEUTICS K.K.—See Amicus Therapeutics, Inc.; *U.S. Public*, pg. 124
AMICUS THERAPEUTICS OAC—See Amicus Therapeutics, Inc.; *U.S. Public*, pg. 124
AMICUS THERAPEUTICS S.L.—See Amicus Therapeutics, Inc.; *U.S. Public*, pg. 124
AMICUS THERAPEUTICS S.L.U.—See Amicus Therapeutics, Inc.; *U.S. Public*, pg. 124
AMICUS THERAPEUTICS S.R.L.—See Amicus Therapeutics, Inc.; *U.S. Public*, pg. 124
AMICUS THERAPEUTICS UK OPERATIONS LIMITED—See Amicus Therapeutics, Inc.; *U.S. Public*, pg. 124
AMIDA CARE INC.; *U.S. Private*, pg. 263
AMIDA HOLDING CO., LTD.—See RAKSUL, Inc.; *Int'l*, pg. 6194
AMIDATA S.A.—See RS Group plc; *Int'l*, pg. 6417
AMIDATA S.A.—See RS Group plc; *Int'l*, pg. 6417
AMI EDUCATION SOLUTIONS LTD—See Constellation Software Inc.; *Int'l*, pg. 1773
AMIENS INJECTION S.A.—See Plastiques du Val de Loire S.A.; *Int'l*, pg. 5892
AMI ENTERTAINMENT NETWORK, INC.—See Konica Minolta, Inc.; *Int'l*, pg. 4258
AMI EXCHANGERS LTD.—See DMI UK Ltd.; *Int'l*, pg. 2145
AMIFA CO., LTD.; *Int'l*, pg. 427
AMIGO CHEVROLET; *U.S. Private*, pg. 263
AMIGO HOLDINGS PLC; *Int'l*, pg. 427
AMIGO LOANS INTERNATIONAL LIMITED; *Int'l*, pg. 427
AMIGO LOANS IRELAND LIMITED—See Amigo Loans International Limited; *Int'l*, pg. 427
AMIGO LOANS LIMITED—See Amigo Holdings PLC; *Int'l*, pg. 427
AMIGO MOBILITY INTERNATIONAL, INC.; *U.S. Private*, pg. 263
AMIGOS LIBRARY SERVICES; *U.S. Private*, pg. 263
AMIGO TRUCK & EQUIPMENT, LLC.; *U.S. Private*, pg. 263
AMI (HOLDINGS), LLC—See Apollo Global Management, Inc.; *U.S. Public*, pg. 146
AMI INDUSTRIES, INC.; *U.S. Private*, pg. 263
AMI INVESTMENTS, LLC—See McWane, Inc.; *U.S. Private*, pg. 2645
AMIKAM & PARAS DIAMOND CORPORATION; *U.S. Private*, pg. 263
AMIKIDS, INC.; *U.S. Private*, pg. 263
AMIL ASSISTENCIA MEDICA INTERNACIONAL S.A.—See UnitedHealth Group Incorporated; *U.S. Public*, pg. 2239
AMILOT CAPITAL INC.; *Int'l*, pg. 427
AMIL PARTICIPACOES SA; *Int'l*, pg. 427
AMI MANCHESTER, LLC; *U.S. Private*, pg. 263
AMI MECHANICAL, INC.—See Colorado Mechanical Services, LLC; *U.S. Private*, pg. 974
AMI METALS EUROPE SPRL—See Reliance Steel & Aluminum Co.; *U.S. Public*, pg. 1779

AMI METALS FRANCE SAS—See Reliance Steel & Aluminum Co.; *U.S. Public*, pg. 1779
AMI METALS, INC.—See Reliance Steel & Aluminum Co.; *U.S. Public*, pg. 1779
AMI METALS UK LIMITED—See Reliance Steel & Aluminum Co.; *U.S. Public*, pg. 1779
AMIMON, LTD.; *Int'l*, pg. 427
AMINCO CHOLINE CHLORIDE (SHANGHAI) CO., LTD.—See Eastman Chemical Company; *U.S. Public*, pg. 706
AMINCO INTERNATIONAL (USA) INC.; *U.S. Private*, pg. 263
AMINCOR, INC.; *U.S. Public*, pg. 124
AMIND SOLUTIONS, LLC—See Trinity Hunt Management, L.P.; *U.S. Private*, pg. 4234
AMINES & PLASTICIZERS LIMITED; *Int'l*, pg. 427
AMINES & PLASTICIZERS LIMITED - UNIT-II—See AMINES & PLASTICIZERS LIMITED; *Int'l*, pg. 428
AMINES & PLASTICIZERS LIMITED - UNIT-I—See AMINES & PLASTICIZERS LIMITED; *Int'l*, pg. 428
AMINEX PETROLEUM SERVICES LIMITED—See Aminex PLC; *Int'l*, pg. 428
AMINEX PLC; *Int'l*, pg. 428
AMINO CHEMICALS LIMITED—See ABA Chemicals Corporation; *Int'l*, pg. 47
AMINO COMMUNICATIONS AB—See Aferian plc; *Int'l*, pg. 185
AMINO COMMUNICATIONS LIMITED—See Aferian plc; *Int'l*, pg. 185
AMINOLOGICS CO., LTD.; *Int'l*, pg. 428
AMIN PHARMACEUTICAL COMPANY; *Int'l*, pg. 427
AMIN'S PATHOLOGY LABORATORY PRIVATE LIMITED—See Metropolis Healthcare Ltd.; *Int'l*, pg. 4863
AMIN TANNERY LIMITED; *Int'l*, pg. 427
AMINTERNATIONAL (L) LTD—See AMMB Holdings Berhad; *Int'l*, pg. 429
AMIN TYRE LTD.—See Bridgestone Corporation; *Int'l*, pg. 1155
AMINVESTMENT BANK GROUP—See AMMB Holdings Berhad; *Int'l*, pg. 429
AMINVESTMENT SERVICES BERHAD—See AMMB Holdings Berhad; *Int'l*, pg. 429
AMION, INC.—See Doximity, Inc.; *U.S. Public*, pg. 686
AMI OPERATING, INC.—See Brynwood Partners Management LLC; *U.S. Private*, pg. 674
AMI ORGANICS LIMITED; *Int'l*, pg. 426
AMIRA NATURE FOODS LTD.; *Int'l*, pg. 428
AMIR MARKETING & INVESTMENTS IN AGRICULTURE LTD.; *Int'l*, pg. 428
AMIR SEMEL PACKAGING & CHEMICALS LTD.—See BERICAP GmbH & Co. KG; *Int'l*, pg. 980
AMI SAUDI ARABIA LTD.—See Xenel Industries Ltd.; *Int'l*, pg. 8521
AMISCO INDUSTRIES LTD.—See Gestion Martin Poitras Inc; *Int'l*, pg. 2946
AMI SEMICONDUCTOR CANADA COMPANY—See ON Semiconductor Corporation; *U.S. Public*, pg. 1600
AMISLAMIC BANK BERHAD—See AMMB Holdings Berhad; *Int'l*, pg. 429
AMISTCO SEPARATION PRODUCTS, INC.—See Rockwood Equity Partners, LLC; *U.S. Private*, pg. 3468
AMISUB (SFH), INC.—See Tenet Healthcare Corporation; *U.S. Public*, pg. 2007
AMITA HOLDINGS CO., LTD.; *Int'l*, pg. 428
AMITAL SPINNING CORP.; *U.S. Private*, pg. 263
AMI (TANZANIA) LTD.—See Financiere de L'Odet; *Int'l*, pg. 2665
AMITA TECHNOLOGIES INC.—See Energy Absolute Public Company Limited; *Int'l*, pg. 2422
AMITA TECHNOLOGY (THAILAND) CO., LTD.—See Energy Absolute Public Company Limited; *Int'l*, pg. 2422
AMIT CHILDREN, INC.; *U.S. Private*, pg. 263
AMITE BIOENERGY LLC—See Drax Group plc; *Int'l*, pg. 2200
AMITECH GERMANY GMBH—See Saudi Arabian Amiantit Company; *Int'l*, pg. 6588
AMITE CITY FORD INC.; *U.S. Private*, pg. 263
AMITEC OY; *Int'l*, pg. 428
AMIT GMBH—See Kontron AG; *Int'l*, pg. 4276
AMIT INTERNATIONAL LIMITED; *Int'l*, pg. 428
AMITRONIC OY—See Addtech AB; *Int'l*, pg. 131
AMIT SECURITIES LIMITED; *Int'l*, pg. 428
AMIT SPINNING INDUSTRIES LIMITED—See CLC Industries Limited; *Int'l*, pg. 1653
AMIT SRL—See Vivaticket; *Int'l*, pg. 8265
AMITY INSURANCE AGENCY, INC.—See Brown & Brown, Inc.; *U.S. Public*, pg. 399
AMITY TECHNOLOGY LLC; *U.S. Private*, pg. 263
AMIVAC S.A.S—See HomeToGo SE; *Int'l*, pg. 3455
AMIVOICE THAI CO., LTD.—See Advanced Media, Inc.; *Int'l*, pg. 160
AMIYA CORPORATION; *Int'l*, pg. 428
AMIYAKI TEI CO., LTD.; *Int'l*, pg. 428
AMJ CAMPBELL, INC.; *Int'l*, pg. 428
AMJ GLOBAL TECHNOLOGY; *U.S. Public*, pg. 124
AMJ LAND HOLDINGS LIMITED; *Int'l*, pg. 428
A & M JUMBO BAGS LTD.; *Int'l*, pg. 17
AMK INSURANCE AGENCY, INC.; *U.S. Private*, pg. 263

AMK INSURANCE AGENCY, INC.

AMKOR ADVANCED TECHNOLOGY TAIWAN, INC.—See Amkor Technology, Inc.; *U.S. Public*, pg. 124
AMKOR ASSEMBLY & TEST (SHANGHAI) CO., LTD.—See Amkor Technology, Inc.; *U.S. Public*, pg. 124
AMKOR TECHNOLOGY EUROSERVICES, S.A.R.L.—See Amkor Technology, Inc.; *U.S. Public*, pg. 124
AMKOR TECHNOLOGY GERMANY GMBH—See Amkor Technology, Inc.; *U.S. Public*, pg. 124
AMKOR TECHNOLOGY, INC.; *U.S. Public*, pg. 124
AMKOR TECHNOLOGY JAPAN, K.K.—See Amkor Technology, Inc.; *U.S. Public*, pg. 124
AMKOR TECHNOLOGY KOREA, INC.—See Amkor Technology, Inc.; *U.S. Public*, pg. 124
AMKOR TECHNOLOGY MALAYSIA SDN. BHD.—See Amkor Technology, Inc.; *U.S. Public*, pg. 124
AMKOR TECHNOLOGY PHILIPPINES, INC.—See Amkor Technology, Inc.; *U.S. Public*, pg. 124
AMKOR TECHNOLOGY SINGAPORE HOLDING PTE. LTD.—See Amkor Technology, Inc.; *U.S. Public*, pg. 124
AMKOR TECHNOLOGY TAIWAN LTD.—See Amkor Technology, Inc.; *U.S. Public*, pg. 124
AMKO SERVICE COMPANY—See FIBA Technologies Inc.; *U.S. Private*, pg. 1501
AML3D LIMITED; *Int'l*, pg. 429
AMLAB SERVICES PTE. LTD.—See Blackstone Inc.; *U.S. Public*, pg. 354
AMLAK FINANCE PJSC—See Emaar Properties PJSC; *Int'l*, pg. 2372
AMLAN INTERNATIONAL—See Oil-Dri Corporation of America; *U.S. Public*, pg. 1565
AMLEX HOLDINGS BHD; *Int'l*, pg. 429
AML FOODS LTD.; *Int'l*, pg. 428
AMLI RESIDENTIAL PROPERTIES TRUST—See Morgan Stanley; *U.S. Public*, pg. 1475
AMLOGIC SHANGHAI CO., LTD.; *Int'l*, pg. 429
A.M. LOGISTICS, INC.; *U.S. Private*, pg. 27
AMLOID CORPORATION; *U.S. Private*, pg. 264
AML RIGHTSOURCE LLC; *U.S. Private*, pg. 263
AML SYSTEMS SAS—See Johnson Electric Holdings Limited; *Int'l*, pg. 3990
AMLY CHEMICALS CO., LTD.—See Matex International Limited; *Int'l*, pg. 4727
AMMAN ASIA ELECTRIC POWER COMPANY—See Korea Electric Power Corporation; *Int'l*, pg. 4283
AMMAN CHAMBER OF COMMERCE LIMITED—See Jordan Loan Guarantee Corporation; *Int'l*, pg. 3998
AMMAN CHAMBER OF INDUSTRY LTD.—See Jordan Loan Guarantee Corporation; *Int'l*, pg. 3998
AMMANN + SCHMID AG—See VINCI S.A.; *Int'l*, pg. 8212
AMMANN SWITZERLAND LTD; *Int'l*, pg. 429
AMMAN STOCK EXCHANGE; *Int'l*, pg. 429
AMMARS INC.; *U.S. Private*, pg. 264
AMMB HOLDINGS BERHAD; *Int'l*, pg. 429
AMMCON CORP.—See Arcline Investment Management LP; *U.S. Private*, pg. 313
AMMD, LLC; *U.S. Private*, pg. 264
AMMED CANCER CENTER (CENTRAL) LIMITED—See HKR International Limited; *Int'l*, pg. 3429
AMMEGA—See Advent International Corporation; *U.S. Private*, pg. 98
AMMERAAL BELTECH HOLDING BV—See Advent International Corporation; *U.S. Private*, pg. 98
AMMERAAL BELTECH INC.—See Advent International Corporation; *U.S. Private*, pg. 98
AMMERAAL BELTECH SA—See Advent International Corporation; *U.S. Private*, pg. 98
AMMERCHANT BANK BERHAD—See AMMB Holdings Berhad; *Int'l*, pg. 429
AMMERTECH B.V.—See Indutrade AB; *Int'l*, pg. 3679
AMMETLIFE INSURANCE BERHAD—See MetLife, Inc.; *U.S. Public*, pg. 1429
AMMETLIFE TAKAFUL BERHAD—See MetLife, Inc.; *U.S. Public*, pg. 1429
AMMEX PLASTICS, LLC—See Echo Engineering & Production Supplies, Inc.; *U.S. Private*, pg. 1327
AMMO BROTHERS; *U.S. Private*, pg. 264
AMMO, INC.; *U.S. Public*, pg. 124
AMMON & RIZOS COMPANY INC.; *U.S. Private*, pg. 264
A & M MOTORS INC.; *U.S. Private*, pg. 18
AMMO VAREJO LTDA—See Coteminas Companhia de Tecidos Norte de Minas; *Int'l*, pg. 1817
AMM SPA—See Link Mobility Group Holding ASA; *Int'l*, pg. 4513
AMMUNITION LLC; *U.S. Private*, pg. 264
AMN ALLIED SERVICES, LLC—See AMN Healthcare Services, Inc.; *U.S. Public*, pg. 125
AMNAV MARITIME SERVICES—See Saltchuk Resources Inc.; *U.S. Private*, pg. 3534
AMNEAL PHARMACEUTICALS COMPANY GMBH—See Amneal Pharmaceuticals, Inc.; *U.S. Public*, pg. 125
AMNEAL PHARMACEUTICALS, INC.; *U.S. Public*, pg. 125
AMNEAL PHARMACEUTICALS LLC—See Amneal Pharmaceuticals, Inc.; *U.S. Public*, pg. 125
AMNEAL PHARMACEUTICALS OF NEW YORK LLC—See Amneal Pharmaceuticals, Inc.; *U.S. Public*, pg. 125

AMNET BROADBAND PTY. LTD.—See Aware Super Pty Ltd; *Int'l*, pg. 752
AMNET BROADBAND PTY. LTD.—See Macquarie Group Limited; *Int'l*, pg. 4629
AMNET DATA SOLUTIONS INC.; *U.S. Private*, pg. 264
AMNET NEW YORK, INC.; *U.S. Private*, pg. 264
AM NETWORKS; *U.S. Private*, pg. 214
AM NEW YORK—See Altice USA, Inc.; *U.S. Public*, pg. 87
AM NGV (S) PTE. LTD.—See Asian Micro Holdings Ltd.; *Int'l*, pg. 618
AM NGV (T) CO., LTD.—See Asian Micro Holdings Ltd.; *Int'l*, pg. 618
AMN HEALTHCARE ALLIED, INC.—See AMN Healthcare Services, Inc.; *U.S. Public*, pg. 125
AMN HEALTHCARE, INC.—See AMN Healthcare Services, Inc.; *U.S. Public*, pg. 125
AMN HEALTHCARE SERVICES, INC.; *U.S. Public*, pg. 124
AMNIMO INC.—See Yokogawa Electric Corporation; *Int'l*, pg. 8592
AMNIR RECYCLING INDUSTRIES LTD.—See Veridis Environment Ltd; *Int'l*, pg. 8168
AMNIS THERAPEUTICS LTD.; *Int'l*, pg. 429
AMNITEC B.V.—See Smiths Group plc; *Int'l*, pg. 7012
AMNITEC LIMITED—See Smiths Group plc; *Int'l*, pg. 7012
AMN NOMINEES PTY. LTD.—See Kairos Minerals Limited; *Int'l*, pg. 4052
AMNODE AB; *Int'l*, pg. 429
AM NOMINEES (TEMPATAN) SDN BHD—See AMMB Holdings Berhad; *Int'l*, pg. 429
AM/NS CALVERT—See ArcelorMittal S.A.; *Int'l*, pg. 543
AM/NS CALVERT—See Nippon Steel Corporation; *Int'l*, pg. 5334
AMN SERVICES, LLC—See AMN Healthcare Services, Inc.; *U.S. Public*, pg. 125
AMN STAFFING SERVICES, LLC—See AMN Healthcare Services, Inc.; *U.S. Public*, pg. 125
AMOAD, INC.—See CyberAgent, Inc.; *Int'l*, pg. 1892
AMOBEE EMEA LIMITED—See Temasek Holdings (Private) Limited; *Int'l*, pg. 7552
AMOBEE, INC.—See Nexxen International Ltd.; *Int'l*, pg. 5251
AMOBEE LTD—See Temasek Holdings (Private) Limited; *Int'l*, pg. 7552
AMOCO ARGENTINA OIL CO.—See BP plc; *Int'l*, pg. 1126
AMO COMMUNICATIONS—See Percept Holdings Pvt. Ltd.; *Int'l*, pg. 5796
AMOCO TRINIDAD GAS B.V.—See BP plc; *Int'l*, pg. 1126
AMODAIMI OIL COMPANY, LTD.—See China Petrochemical Corporation; *Int'l*, pg. 1539
AMODIAG ENVIRONNEMENT—See Hiolle Industries S.A.; *Int'l*, pg. 3401
AMOEBA BIOCIDE SAS; *Int'l*, pg. 429
AMOEBA CULTURE CO., LTD.—See CJ Corporation; *Int'l*, pg. 1631
AMOEBA TECHNOLOGIES INC.—See Keysight Technologies, Inc.; *U.S. Public*, pg. 1226
AMOENA GMBH & CO. KG—See Coloplast A/S; *Int'l*, pg. 1702
AMOGREENTECH CO., LTD.; *Int'l*, pg. 429
AMOL DICALITE LTD.—See Lalbhai Group; *Int'l*, pg. 4398
AMOL DICALITE LTD.—See RGP Holding, Inc.; *U.S. Private*, pg. 3420
AMON CARTER MUSEUM OF AMERICAN ART; *U.S. Private*, pg. 264
A MONTEVERDI INC.; *U.S. Private*, pg. 18
AMORA CERAMICS PRIVATE LIMITED—See Somany Ceramics Limited; *Int'l*, pg. 7083
A. MORANTE Y CIA SA—See Lectra SA; *Int'l*, pg. 4437
AMORE CONSTRUCTION CO.; *U.S. Private*, pg. 264
AMOREG; *Int'l*, pg. 429
AMOREPACIFIC AUSTRALIA PTY. LTD.—See Amorepacific Corp.; *Int'l*, pg. 430
AMOREPACIFIC CANADA INC.—See Amorepacific Corp.; *Int'l*, pg. 430
AMOREPACIFIC CORP.; *Int'l*, pg. 429
AMOREPACIFIC EUROPE S.A.S—See Amorepacific Corp.; *Int'l*, pg. 430
AMOREPACIFIC GLOBAL OPERATIONS LIMITED—See Amorepacific Corp.; *Int'l*, pg. 430
AMOREPACIFIC GROUP; *Int'l*, pg. 430
AMOREPACIFIC HONG KONG CO., LIMITED—See Amorepacific Corp.; *Int'l*, pg. 430
AMOREPACIFIC JAPAN CO., LTD.—See Amorepacific Corp.; *Int'l*, pg. 430
AMOREPACIFIC (SHANGHAI) R&I CENTER CO., LTD.—See Amorepacific Corp.; *Int'l*, pg. 430
AMOREPACIFIC SINGAPORE PTE CO LTD.—See Amorepacific Corp.; *Int'l*, pg. 430
AMOREPACIFIC TAIWAN CO., LTD.—See Amorepacific Corp.; *Int'l*, pg. 430
AMOREPACIFIC VIETNAM LTD.—See Amorepacific Corp.; *Int'l*, pg. 430
AMORIM AUSTRALASIA PTY. LTD.—See CORTICEIRA AMORIM, S.G.P.S., S.A.; *Int'l*, pg. 1807
AMORIM BENELUX B.V.—See CORTICEIRA AMORIM, S.G.P.S., S.A.; *Int'l*, pg. 1807
AMORIM CORK AMERICA, INC.—See CORTICEIRA AMORIM, S.G.P.S., S.A.; *Int'l*, pg. 1807

CORPORATE AFFILIATIONS

AMORIM CORK BEIJING LTD.—See CORTICEIRA AMORIM, S.G.P.S., S.A.; *Int'l*, pg. 1807
AMORIM CORK BULGARIA EOOD—See CORTICEIRA AMORIM, S.G.P.S., S.A.; *Int'l*, pg. 1807
AMORIM CORK COMPOSITES INC.—See CORTICEIRA AMORIM, S.G.P.S., S.A.; *Int'l*, pg. 1807
AMORIM CORK COMPOSITES, S. A.—See CORTICEIRA AMORIM, S.G.P.S., S.A.; *Int'l*, pg. 1807
AMORIM CORK DEUTSCHLAND GMBH & CO KG—See CORTICEIRA AMORIM, S.G.P.S., S.A.; *Int'l*, pg. 1807
AMORIM CORK FLOORING, S.A.—See CORTICEIRA AMORIM, S.G.P.S., S.A.; *Int'l*, pg. 1807
AMORIM CORK HUNGARY ZRT—See CORTICEIRA AMORIM, S.G.P.S., S.A.; *Int'l*, pg. 1807
AMORIM CORK INSULATION, S.A.—See CORTICEIRA AMORIM, S.G.P.S., S.A.; *Int'l*, pg. 1807
AMORIM CORK ITALIA, SPA—See CORTICEIRA AMORIM, S.G.P.S., S.A.; *Int'l*, pg. 1807
AMORIM CORK SOUTH AFRICA (PTY) LTD.—See CORTICEIRA AMORIM, S.G.P.S., S.A.; *Int'l*, pg. 1807
AMORIM CORK VENTURES, LDA.—See CORTICEIRA AMORIM, S.G.P.S., S.A.; *Int'l*, pg. 1807
AMORIM DEUTSCHLAND, GMBH—See CORTICEIRA AMORIM, S.G.P.S., S.A.; *Int'l*, pg. 1807
AMORIM FLOORING AUSTRIA GMBH—See CORTICEIRA AMORIM, S.G.P.S., S.A.; *Int'l*, pg. 1807
AMORIM FLOORING NORTH AMERICA INC.—See CORTICEIRA AMORIM, S.G.P.S., S.A.; *Int'l*, pg. 1807
AMORIM FLOORING SWEDEN AB—See CORTICEIRA AMORIM, S.G.P.S., S.A.; *Int'l*, pg. 1807
AMORIM FLOORING (SWITZERLAND) AG—See CORTICEIRA AMORIM, S.G.P.S., S.A.; *Int'l*, pg. 1807
AMORIM FLORESTAL ESPANA, SL—See CORTICEIRA AMORIM, S.G.P.S., S.A.; *Int'l*, pg. 1807
AMORIM FLORESTAL MEDITERRANEO, SL—See CORTICEIRA AMORIM, S.G.P.S., S.A.; *Int'l*, pg. 1807
AMORIM FLORESTAL, S.A.—See CORTICEIRA AMORIM, S.G.P.S., S.A.; *Int'l*, pg. 1807
AMORIM & IRMAOS, SGPS, S.A.—See CORTICEIRA AMORIM, S.G.P.S., S.A.; *Int'l*, pg. 1807
AMORIM ISOLAMENTOS, S.A.—See CORTICEIRA AMORIM, S.G.P.S., S.A.; *Int'l*, pg. 1807
AMORIM JAPAN CORPORATION—See CORTICEIRA AMORIM, S.G.P.S., S.A.; *Int'l*, pg. 1807
AMORIM REVESTIMENTOS, S.A.—See CORTICEIRA AMORIM, S.G.P.S., S.A.; *Int'l*, pg. 1807
AMORIM SPORTS, LDA.—See CORTICEIRA AMORIM, S.G.P.S., S.A.; *Int'l*, pg. 1807
AMORIM TOP SERIES, S.A.—See CORTICEIRA AMORIM, S.G.P.S., S.A.; *Int'l*, pg. 1807
AMORIM TUNISIE, S.A.R.L.—See CORTICEIRA AMORIM, S.G.P.S., S.A.; *Int'l*, pg. 1807
AMORIM (UK) LTD.—See CORTICEIRA AMORIM, S.G.P.S., S.A.; *Int'l*, pg. 1807
A.M. ORTEGA CONSTRUCTION INC.; *U.S. Private*, pg. 27
A + MORTGAGE SERVICES, INC.; *U.S. Private*, pg. 18
A. MORTON THOMAS & ASSOCIATES INC.; *U.S. Private*, pg. 23
AMORY HMA, LLC—See Curae Health, Inc.; *U.S. Private*, pg. 1124
AMOS & ANDREWS INC.—See Andrews Group; *U.S. Private*, pg. 280
AMOS AUSTRIA GMBH—See Allianz SE; *Int'l*, pg. 342
AMOS AZERBAIJAN LLC—See AMOS Group Limited; *Int'l*, pg. 430
AMOS CO., LTD.—See Amorepacific Corp.; *Int'l*, pg. 430
AMOS & CONNORS, INC.; *U.S. Private*, pg. 264
AMOS CRAFT PUBLISHING—See Amos Press, Inc.; *U.S. Private*, pg. 264
AMOSEALTEX CORK CO., LTD.—See CORTICEIRA AMORIM, S.G.P.S., S.A.; *Int'l*, pg. 1807
AMOSENSE CO., LTD.; *Int'l*, pg. 430
AMOS EUROPE (UK) LIMITED—See AMOS Group Limited; *Int'l*, pg. 430
AMOS GROUP LIMITED; *Int'l*, pg. 430
AMO (SHANGHAI) MEDICAL DEVICES TRADING CO., LTD.—See Johnson & Johnson; *U.S. Public*, pg. 1193
AMOS-HILL ASSOCIATES, INC.; *U.S. Private*, pg. 264
AMOS INTERNATIONAL (HK) LIMITED—See AMOS Group Limited; *Int'l*, pg. 430
AMOS INTERNATIONAL (SHANGHAI) CO., LTD.—See AMOS Group Limited; *Int'l*, pg. 430
AMOS INTERNATIONAL (S) PTE LTD—See AMOS Group Limited; *Int'l*, pg. 430
AMOS KAZAKHSTAN LLP—See AMOS Group Limited; *Int'l*, pg. 430
AMOSKEAG BEVERAGES INC.; *U.S. Private*, pg. 264
AMOS KOREA CO LTD—See AMOS Group Limited; *Int'l*, pg. 430
AMOS LUZON DEVELOPMENT AND ENERGY GROUP LTD.; *Int'l*, pg. 430
AMOS MALAYSIA SDN BHD—See AMOS Group Limited; *Int'l*, pg. 430
AMOS MIDDLE EAST FZE—See AMOS Group Limited; *Int'l*, pg. 430
AMOS MIDDLE EAST HOLDINGS FZE—See AMOS Group Limited; *Int'l*, pg. 430
AMOS PRESS, INC.; *U.S. Private*, pg. 264

COMPANY NAME INDEX

AMOSSCO LIMITED—See Aminex PLC; *Int'l*, pg. 428
AMOS SUPPLY KOREA CO., LTD.—See AMOS Group Limited; *Int'l*, pg. 430
AMOS SUPPLY PTE LTD—See AMOS Group Limited; *Int'l*, pg. 430
AMOS VIETNAM PTE LTD—See AMOS Group Limited; *Int'l*, pg. 430
AMOT CONTROLS CORPORATION—See Roper Technologies, Inc.; *U.S. Public*, pg. 1810
AMOT CONTROLS GMBH—See Roper Technologies, Inc.; *U.S. Public*, pg. 1810
AMOTECH CO., LTD. - ANTENNA DIVISION—See Amotech Co Ltd; *Int'l*, pg. 431
AMOTECH CO., LTD. - MOTOR DIVISION—See Amotech Co Ltd; *Int'l*, pg. 431
AMOTECH CO., LTD. - SHANDONG FACTORY—See Amotech Co Ltd; *Int'l*, pg. 431
AMOTECH CO LTD; *Int'l*, pg. 430
AMOTECH CO., LTD. - VARISTOR DIVISION—See Amotech Co Ltd; *Int'l*, pg. 431
AMOTECH KOREA INC.—See Amotech Co Ltd; *Int'l*, pg. 430
AMOTEC, INC.; *U.S. Private*, pg. 264
AMOTEK S.R.L.—See OPTIMA Packaging Group GmbH; *Int'l*, pg. 5603
AMOTIV LIMITED; *Int'l*, pg. 431
AMO TOYS A/S—See Thunderful Group AB; *Int'l*, pg. 7722
AMOUN INTERNATIONAL FOR INVESTMENT P.L.C; *Int'l*, pg. 431
AMOUN PHARMACEUTICAL COMPANY S.A.E.; *Int'l*, pg. 431
AMOVA GMBH—See SMS Holding GmbH; *Int'l*, pg. 7015
AMOY DIAGNOSTICS CO., LTD.; *Int'l*, pg. 431
AMOY FOOD LTD.—See CITIC Group Corporation; *Int'l*, pg. 1619
AMPA 2P SAS—See Dorel Industries, Inc.; *Int'l*, pg. 2176
AMPAC ENTERPRISES INC.; *U.S. Private*, pg. 264
AMPACET CORPORATION; *U.S. Private*, pg. 264
AMPACET EUROPE, S.A.—See Ampacet Corporation; *U.S. Private*, pg. 264
AMPACET SHANGHAI (TRADING) CO., LTD.—See Ampacet Corporation; *U.S. Private*, pg. 264
AMPACET SOUTH AMERICA S.R.L.—See Ampacet Corporation; *U.S. Private*, pg. 264
AMPACET SPECIALTY PRODUCTS PRIVATE LTD.—See Ampacet Corporation; *U.S. Private*, pg. 264
AMPACET (THAILAND) COMPANY, LTD.—See Ampacet Corporation; *U.S. Private*, pg. 264
AMPAC EUROPE LIMITED—See Halma plc; *Int'l*, pg. 3230
AMPAC FINE CHEMICALS LLC—See SK Inc.; *Int'l*, pg. 6971
AMPAC FINE CHEMICALS TEXAS, LLC—See SK Inc.; *Int'l*, pg. 6971
AMPAC FLEXIBLES AG—See The Pritzker Group - Chicago, LLC; *U.S. Private*, pg. 4099
AMPAC FLEXIBLES GMBH—See The Pritzker Group - Chicago, LLC; *U.S. Private*, pg. 4099
AMPAC HOLDINGS, LLC—See The Pritzker Group - Chicago, LLC; *U.S. Private*, pg. 4099
AMPACK GMBH—See Robert Bosch GmbH; *Int'l*, pg. 6358
AMPAC NZ LIMITED—See Halma plc; *Int'l*, pg. 3230
AMPAC PTY LIMITED—See Halma plc; *Int'l*, pg. 3230
AMPAC SCIENTIFIC INC.; *U.S. Private*, pg. 264
AM-PAC TIRE DISTRIBUTORS, INC.—See TPG Capital, L.P.; *U.S. Public*, pg. 2166
AMPA DEVELOPPEMENT SAS—See Dorel Industries, Inc.; *Int'l*, pg. 2176
AMP (AGENCE ET MESSAGERIE DE PRESSE)—See Vivendi SE; *Int'l*, pg. 8271
AMP AGENCY; *U.S. Private*, pg. 264
AMP AMERMEX, S.A. DE C.V.—See TE Connectivity Ltd.; *Int'l*, pg. 7494
AMPAM PARKS MECHANICAL, INC.—See Gemspring Capital Management, LLC; *U.S. Private*, pg. 1658
AMPANG PUTERI SPECIALIST HOSPITAL SDN BHD—See KPJ Healthcare Berhad; *Int'l*, pg. 4296
AMPAS MAJU SDN BHD—See IJM Corporation Berhad; *Int'l*, pg. 3608
AM-PAT INCORPORATED; *U.S. Private*, pg. 265
AMP AUSTRALIAN FINANCIAL SERVICES HOLDINGS LIMITED—See AMP Limited; *Int'l*, pg. 431
AMP BANK LIMITED—See AMP Limited; *Int'l*, pg. 431
AMP CAPITAL HOLDINGS LIMITED—See AMP Limited; *Int'l*, pg. 431
AMP CAPITAL INVESTMENTS LIMITED—See AMP Limited; *Int'l*, pg. 431
AMP CAPITAL INVESTORS INTERNATIONAL HOLDINGS LIMITED—See AMP Limited; *Int'l*, pg. 431
AMP CAPITAL INVESTORS LIMITED—See AMP Limited; *Int'l*, pg. 431
AMP CAPITAL INVESTORS (LUXEMBOURG) S.A R.L.—See AMP Limited; *Int'l*, pg. 431
AMP CAPITAL INVESTORS (NEW ZEALAND) LIMITED—See AMP Limited; *Int'l*, pg. 432
AMP CAPITAL INVESTORS PROPERTY JAPAN KK—See AMP Limited; *Int'l*, pg. 432
AMP CAPITAL INVESTORS (US) LIMITED—See AMP Limited; *Int'l*, pg. 431

AMP CAPITAL OFFICE AND INDUSTRIAL PTY LIMITED—See AMP Limited; *Int'l*, pg. 432
AMPCO MARKETING, L.L.C.—See Chevron Corporation; *U.S. Public*, pg. 487
AMPCO MARKETING, L.L.C.—See ConocoPhillips; *U.S. Public*, pg. 568
AMPCO METAL DEUTSCHLAND GMBH—See Ampco Metal SA; *Int'l*, pg. 433
AMPCO METAL (FOSHAN) CO. LTD.—See Ampco Metal SA; *Int'l*, pg. 433
AMPCO METAL, INC.—See Ampco Metal SA; *Int'l*, pg. 433
AMPCO METAL, INC. - WELDING PRODUCTS DIVISION—See Ampco Metal SA; *Int'l*, pg. 433
AMPCO METAL INDIA PVT LTD—See Ampco Metal SA; *Int'l*, pg. 433
AMPCO METAL KOREA CO., LTD.—See Ampco Metal SA; *Int'l*, pg. 433
AMPCO METAL LTD.—See Ampco Metal SA; *Int'l*, pg. 433
AMPCO METAL PORTUGAL LTDA.—See Ampco Metal SA; *Int'l*, pg. 433
AMPCO METAL SA - AREOSPACE DIVISION—See Ampco Metal SA; *Int'l*, pg. 433
AMPCO METAL SA; *Int'l*, pg. 433
AMPCO METAL SAS—See Ampco Metal SA; *Int'l*, pg. 433
AMPCO METAL SRL—See Ampco Metal SA; *Int'l*, pg. 433
AMPCO METAL S.R.O.—See Ampco Metal SA; *Int'l*, pg. 433
AMPCONTROL PTY. LTD.—See Washington H. Soul Pattinson & Company Limited; *Int'l*, pg. 8351
AMPCONTROL UK LTD.—See Washington H. Soul Pattinson & Company Limited; *Int'l*, pg. 8351
AMPCO-PITTSBURGH CORPORATION; *U.S. Public*, pg. 126
AMPCO PRODUCTS INC.; *U.S. Private*, pg. 265
AMPCO SERVICES, LLC—See Chevron Corporation; *U.S. Public*, pg. 487
AMPCO SERVICES, LLC—See ConocoPhillips; *U.S. Public*, pg. 569
AMPCO SYSTEM PARKING—See ABM Industries, Inc.; *U.S. Public*, pg. 26
AMPCO SYSTEM PARKING—See ABM Industries, Inc.; *U.S. Public*, pg. 26
AMPCO SYSTEM PARKING—See ABM Industries, Inc.; *U.S. Public*, pg. 26
AMPCO SYSTEM PARKING—See ABM Industries, Inc.; *U.S. Public*, pg. 26
AMPCO SYSTEM PARKING—See ABM Industries, Inc.; *U.S. Public*, pg. 26
AMPCO SYSTEM PARKING—See ABM Industries, Inc.; *U.S. Public*, pg. 26
AMPCUS INC.; *U.S. Private*, pg. 265
AMP CUSTODIAN SERVICES (NZ) LIMITED—See AMP Limited; *Int'l*, pg. 432
AMPD VENTURES, INC.; *Int'l*, pg. 433
AMPED WIRELESS LIMITED; *U.S. Private*, pg. 265
AMPEGON AG—See Parter Capital Group GmbH; *Int'l*, pg. 5748
AMPEGON ANTENNA SYSTEMS GMBH—See Parter Capital Group GmbH; *Int'l*, pg. 5748
AMPEGON SCIENCE & TECHNOLOGY (BEIJING) CO., LTD.—See Parter Capital Group GmbH; *Int'l*, pg. 5748
AMP ELECTRIC INC.—See Morse Electric Incorporated; *U.S. Private*, pg. 2790
AMPERAGE, LLC; *U.S. Private*, pg. 265
AMPERAGE MARKETING—See AMPERAGE, LLC; *U.S. Private*, pg. 265
AMPERE COMPUTING LLC; *U.S. Private*, pg. 265
AMPERE LIMITED; *Int'l*, pg. 433
AMPER KLINIKEN AG—See Fresenius SE & Co. KGaA; *Int'l*, pg. 2778
AMPERO GMBH—See BayWa AG; *Int'l*, pg. 915
AMPER PROGRAMAS DE ELECTRONICA Y COMUNICACIONES S.A—See Thales S.A.; *Int'l*, pg. 7603
AMPERSAND CONSTRUCTION, LLC; *U.S. Private*, pg. 265
AMPERSAND INC.—See ULVAC, Inc.; *Int'l*, pg. 8020
AMPERSAND MANAGEMENT LLC; *U.S. Private*, pg. 265
AMPER, S.A.; *Int'l*, pg. 433
AMPEX CORPORATION - COLORADO SPRINGS SERVICE FACILITY—See Ampex Corporation; *U.S. Private*, pg. 266
AMPEX CORPORATION; *U.S. Private*, pg. 266
AMPEX DATA INTERNATIONAL CORPORATION—See Ampex Corporation; *U.S. Private*, pg. 266
AMPEX DATA SYSTEMS CORPORATION—See Ampex Corporation; *U.S. Private*, pg. 266
AMPEX GREAT BRITAIN LTD.—See Ampex Corporation; *U.S. Private*, pg. 266
AMPEX JAPAN LTD.—See Ampex Corporation; *U.S. Private*, pg. 266
AMP FINANCE SERVICES LIMITED—See AMP Limited; *Int'l*, pg. 432
AMP FINANCIAL PLANNING PTY LIMITED—See AMP Limited; *Int'l*, pg. 432
AMP GBS LIMITED—See AMP Limited; *Int'l*, pg. 432
AMP GERMAN CANNABIS GROUP INC.; *Int'l*, pg. 431
AMP GROUP FINANCE SERVICES LIMITED—See AMP Limited; *Int'l*, pg. 432

AMPHENOL CORPORATION

AMP GROUP HOLDINGS LIMITED—See AMP Limited; *Int'l*, pg. 432
AMP GROUP SERVICES LIMITED—See AMP Limited; *Int'l*, pg. 432
AMPHASTAR PHARMACEUTICALS, INC.; *U.S. Public*, pg. 126
AMPHENOL ADVANCED SENSORS PUERTO RICO, LLC—See Amphenol Corporation; *U.S. Public*, pg. 126
AMPHENOL ADVANCED SENSORS—See Amphenol Corporation; *U.S. Public*, pg. 126
AMPHENOL AEROSPACE & INDUSTRIAL OPERATIONS—See Amphenol Corporation; *U.S. Public*, pg. 126
AMPHENOL AIR LB GMBH—See Amphenol Corporation; *U.S. Public*, pg. 128
AMPHENOL AIR LB NORTH AMERICA, INC.—See Amphenol Corporation; *U.S. Public*, pg. 128
AMPHENOL ALDEN PRODUCTS COMPANY—See Amphenol Corporation; *U.S. Public*, pg. 128
AMPHENOL ALDEN PRODUCTS MEXICO, S.A. DE C.V.—See Amphenol Corporation; *U.S. Public*, pg. 128
AMPHENOL ANTENNA SOLUTIONS, INC.—See Amphenol Corporation; *U.S. Public*, pg. 128
AMPHENOL ASSEMBLETECH (XIAMEN) CO., LTD.—See Amphenol Corporation; *U.S. Public*, pg. 128
AMPHENOL AUSTRALIA PTY. LTD.—See Amphenol Corporation; *U.S. Public*, pg. 128
AMPHENOL BAR-TEC, LTD—See Amphenol Corporation; *U.S. Public*, pg. 127
AMPHENOL BENELUX B.V.—See Amphenol Corporation; *U.S. Public*, pg. 127
AMPHENOL BORISCH TECHNOLOGIES, INC—See Amphenol Corporation; *U.S. Public*, pg. 126
AMPHENOL CABLES ON DEMAND CORP.—See Amphenol Corporation; *U.S. Public*, pg. 127
AMPHENOL CANADA CORP.—See Amphenol Corporation; *U.S. Public*, pg. 127
AMPHENOL (CHANGZHOU) ADVANCED CONNECTOR CO. LTD.—See Amphenol Corporation; *U.S. Public*, pg. 126
AMPHENOL CNT (XIAN) TECHNOLOGY CO., LTD.—See Amphenol Corporation; *U.S. Public*, pg. 127
AMPHENOL COMMERCIAL AND INDUSTRIAL UK, LIMITED—See Amphenol Corporation; *U.S. Public*, pg. 127
AMPHENOL COMMERCIAL INTERCONNECT KOREA CO. LTD.—See Amphenol Corporation; *U.S. Public*, pg. 127
AMPHENOL COMMERCIAL PRODUCTS (CHENGDU) CO. LTD.—See Amphenol Corporation; *U.S. Public*, pg. 127
AMPHENOL CONNEXUS AB—See Amphenol Corporation; *U.S. Public*, pg. 128
AMPHENOL CONNEXUS AEOU—See Amphenol Corporation; *U.S. Public*, pg. 128
AMPHENOL CONNEXUS OU—See Amphenol Corporation; *U.S. Public*, pg. 127
AMPHENOL CORPORATION; *U.S. Public*, pg. 126
AMPHENOL CUSTOM CABLE, INC.—See Amphenol Corporation; *U.S. Public*, pg. 127
AMPHENOL DAESHIN ELECTRONIC & PRECISION CO., LTD.—See Amphenol Corporation; *U.S. Public*, pg. 127
AMPHENOL DC ELECTRONICS—See Amphenol Corporation; *U.S. Public*, pg. 127
AMPHENOL DO BRASIL LTDA.—See Amphenol Corporation; *U.S. Public*, pg. 129
AMPHENOL EAST ASIA ELECTRONIC TECHNOLOGY (SHENZHEN) CO. LTD.—See Amphenol Corporation; *U.S. Public*, pg. 127
AMPHENOL EAST ASIA ELECT. TECH. SHENZHEN CO., LTD.—See Amphenol Corporation; *U.S. Public*, pg. 127
AMPHENOL EEC, INC.—See Amphenol Corporation; *U.S. Public*, pg. 127
AMPHENOL FCI ASIA PTE. LTD.—See Amphenol Corporation; *U.S. Public*, pg. 127
AMPHENOL FCI BESANCON SA—See Amphenol Corporation; *U.S. Public*, pg. 127
AMPHENOL FCI CONNECTORS SINGAPORE PTE. LTD.—See Amphenol Corporation; *U.S. Public*, pg. 127
AMPHENOL FCI CONNECTORS SINGAPORE PTE LTD - THAILAND REPRESENTATIVE OFFICE—See Amphenol Corporation; *U.S. Public*, pg. 127
AMPHENOL FIBER OPTIC TECHNOLOGY (SHENZHEN) CO., LTD.—See Amphenol Corporation; *U.S. Public*, pg. 127
AMPHENOL FIBER TECHNOLOGY (SHENZHEN) CO., LTD.—See Amphenol Corporation; *U.S. Public*, pg. 127
AMPHENOL FILEC, S.A.S.—See Amphenol Corporation; *U.S. Public*, pg. 127
AMPHENOL FINLAND OY—See Amphenol Corporation; *U.S. Public*, pg. 127
AMPHENOL GESELLSCHAFT M.B.H.—See Amphenol Corporation; *U.S. Public*, pg. 127
AMPHENOL GLOBAL INTERCONNECT SYSTEMS—See Amphenol Corporation; *U.S. Public*, pg. 127
AMPHENOL GRIFFITH ENTERPRISES, LLC—See Amphenol Corporation; *U.S. Public*, pg. 128

AMPHENOL CORPORATION
CORPORATE AFFILIATIONS

AMPHENOL INTERCONNECT INDIA PRIVATE LIMITED—See Amphenol Corporation; *U.S. Public*, pg. 128
AMPHENOL INTERCONNECT PRODUCTS CORPORATION—See Amphenol Corporation; *U.S. Public*, pg. 128
AMPHENOL INTERCON SYSTEMS, INC.—See Amphenol Corporation; *U.S. Public*, pg. 128
AMPHENOL INTERNATIONAL MILITARY AEROSPACE & INDUSTRIAL OPERATIONS—See Amphenol Corporation; *U.S. Public*, pg. 128
AMPHENOL INVOTEC LIMITED—See Amphenol Corporation; *U.S. Public*, pg. 128
AMPHENOL JAPAN, LTD.—See Amphenol Corporation; *U.S. Public*, pg. 128
AMPHENOL KAI JACK (SHENAHEN) CO. LTD.—See Amphenol Corporation; *U.S. Public*, pg. 128
AMPHENOL LIMITED—See Amphenol Corporation; *U.S. Public*, pg. 128
AMPHENOL LTW TECHNOLOGY CO., LTD—See Amphenol Corporation; *U.S. Public*, pg. 128
AMPHENOL MALAYSIA SDN BHD—See Amphenol Corporation; *U.S. Public*, pg. 128
AMPHENOL MCP KOREA LIMITED—See Amphenol Corporation; *U.S. Public*, pg. 128
AMPHENOL MOBILE CONNECTOR SOLUTIONS (CHANGZHOU) CO., LTD.—See Amphenol Corporation; *U.S. Public*, pg. 128
AMPHENOL MOBILE CONSUMER PRODUCTS GROUP—See Amphenol Corporation; *U.S. Public*, pg. 128
AMPHENOL NELSON DUNN TECHNOLOGIES, INC.—See Amphenol Corporation; *U.S. Public*, pg. 128
AMPHENOL NETWORK SOLUTIONS, INC.—See Amphenol Corporation; *U.S. Public*, pg. 128
AMPHENOL OMNICONNECT INDAI PRIVATE LIMITED—See Amphenol Corporation; *U.S. Public*, pg. 128
AMPHENOL OPTIMIZE MEXICO S.A. DE C.V.—See Amphenol Corporation; *U.S. Public*, pg. 128
AMPHENOL PCD INC.—See Amphenol Corporation; *U.S. Public*, pg. 128
AMPHENOL PCD (SHENZHEN) CO., LTD.—See Amphenol Corporation; *U.S. Public*, pg. 128
AMPHENOL PHITEK LIMITED—See Amphenol Corporation; *U.S. Public*, pg. 128
AMPHENOL PRECISION OPTICS GMBH—See Zech Group SE; *Int'l*, pg. 8628
AMPHENOL PRINTED CIRCUITS, INC.—See Amphenol Corporation; *U.S. Public*, pg. 128
AMPHENOL PROCOM, INC.—See Amphenol Corporation; *U.S. Public*, pg. 128
AMPHENOL PROVENS SAS—See Amphenol Corporation; *U.S. Public*, pg. 128
AMPHENOL RF ASIA LIMITED—See Amphenol Corporation; *U.S. Public*, pg. 128
AMPHENOL RF—See Amphenol Corporation; *U.S. Public*, pg. 128
AMPHENOL SENSING KOREA COMPANY LIMITED—See Amphenol Corporation; *U.S. Public*, pg. 128
AMPHENOL SHOUH MIN INDUSTRY (SHENZHEN) COMPANY—See Amphenol Corporation; *U.S. Public*, pg. 128
AMPHENOL STEWARD ENTERPRISES, INC.—See Amphenol Corporation; *U.S. Public*, pg. 126
AMPHENOL TAIWAN CORP.—See Amphenol Corporation; *U.S. Public*, pg. 128
AMPHENOL TCS DE MEXICO S.A. DE C.V.—See Amphenol Corporation; *U.S. Public*, pg. 129
AMPHENOL TCS IRELAND LTD.—See Amphenol Corporation; *U.S. Public*, pg. 129
AMPHENOL TCS (MALAYSIA) SDN BHD—See Amphenol Corporation; *U.S. Public*, pg. 129
AMPHENOL TCS SDN BHD—See Amphenol Corporation; *U.S. Public*, pg. 129
AMPHENOL TCS—See Amphenol Corporation; *U.S. Public*, pg. 129
AMPHENOL TECHNICAL PRODUCTS INTERNATIONAL—See Amphenol Corporation; *U.S. Public*, pg. 127
AMPHENOL TECHNOLOGY MACEDONIA—See Amphenol Corporation; *U.S. Public*, pg. 129
AMPHENOL TECHNOLOGY (SHENZHEN) CO. LTD.—See Amphenol Corporation; *U.S. Public*, pg. 127
AMPHENOL TECVOX LLC—See Amphenol Corporation; *U.S. Public*, pg. 129
AMPHENOL TEL-AD LIMITED—See Amphenol Corporation; *U.S. Public*, pg. 129
AMPHENOL-TFC (CHANGZHOU) COMMUNICATIONS EQUIPMENT CO., LTD.—See Amphenol Corporation; *U.S. Public*, pg. 132
AMPHENOL TFC DO BRASIL LTDA—See Amphenol Corporation; *U.S. Public*, pg. 132
AMPHENOL THERMOMETRICS, INC.—See Amphenol Corporation; *U.S. Public*, pg. 129
AMPHENOL THERMOMETRICS (UK) LIMITED—See Amphenol Corporation; *U.S. Public*, pg. 129
AMPHENOL THERMOMETRICS (UK) LIMITED—See Amphenol Corporation; *U.S. Public*, pg. 129
AMPHENOL TIANJIN CO. LTD.—See Amphenol Corporation; *U.S. Public*, pg. 129
AMPHENOL T&M ANTENNAS, INC.—See Amphenol Corporation; *U.S. Public*, pg. 128
AMPHENOL TRACKWISE DESIGNS LIMITED—See Amphenol Corporation; *U.S. Public*, pg. 129
AMPHENOL-TUCHEL ELECTRONICS GMBH—See Amphenol Corporation; *U.S. Public*, pg. 129
AMPHENOL TUCHEL INDUSTRIAL GMBH—See Amphenol Corporation; *U.S. Public*, pg. 129
AMPHENOL TURKEY BAGLANTI COZUMLERI LIMITED SIRKETI—See Amphenol Corporation; *U.S. Public*, pg. 129
AMPHENOL (XIAMEN) HIGH SPEED CABLE CO., LTD.—See Amphenol Corporation; *U.S. Public*, pg. 126
AMPHIL; *U.S. Private*, pg. 266
AMPHION INNOVATIONS PLC; *Int'l*, pg. 433
AMPHION INNOVATIONS US, INC.—See Amphion Innovations plc; *Int'l*, pg. 433
AMPHION MEDICAL SOLUTIONS, LLC—See iMedX, Inc.; *U.S. Private*, pg. 2046
AMPHITECH; *Int'l*, pg. 433
AMPHIVENA THERAPEUTICS INC.—See Affimed N.V.; *Int'l*, pg. 186
AMP HOLDINGS LIMITED—See AMP Limited; *Int'l*, pg. 432
AMPHORA, INC.; *U.S. Private*, pg. 266
AMPHOS GMBH—See TRUMPF SE + Co. KG; *Int'l*, pg. 7942
AMP HUNGARY TRADING CO. LTD.—See TE Connectivity Ltd.; *Int'l*, pg. 7494
AM PIERCE & ASSOCIATES, INC.; *U.S. Private*, pg. 214
AMP INSURANCE INVESTMENT HOLDINGS PTY LIMITED—See AMP Limited; *Int'l*, pg. 432
AMP INVESTMENT SERVICES PTY LIMITED—See AMP Limited; *Int'l*, pg. 432
AMPIO PHARMACEUTICALS, INC.; *U.S. Public*, pg. 132
AMPIRE AUTO PARTS (SHANGHAI) CO. LTD.—See New Hoong Fatt Holdings Berhad; *Int'l*, pg. 5224
AMPIRE CO., LTD.; *Int'l*, pg. 433
AMPIRICAL SOLUTIONS LLC; *U.S. Private*, pg. 266
AMPLA ENERGIA E SERVICOS, S.A.—See Enel S.p.A.; *Int'l*, pg. 2412
AMPLE ELECTRONIC TECHNOLOGY CO., LTD.; *Int'l*, pg. 433
AMPLE INDUSTRIES, INC.—See Ares Management Corporation; *U.S. Public*, pg. 190
AMPLE ORGANICS INC.—See Wilcompute Systems Group, Inc.; *Int'l*, pg. 8409
AMPLE TECHNOLOGY CO. LTD.—See A.A.G. STUCCHI s.r.l.; *Int'l*, pg. 22
AMPLE WEALTH ENTERPRISE LTD.—See Eson Precision Ind. Co., Ltd.; *Int'l*, pg. 2504
AMPLEX AB; *Int'l*, pg. 433
AMPLEX INC.; *U.S. Private*, pg. 266
AMPLEXOR, INC.—See Rheinische-Bergische Verlagsgesellschaft mbH; *Int'l*, pg. 6321
AMPLEXOR INTERNATIONAL S.A.—See Rheinische-Bergische Verlagsgesellschaft mbH; *Int'l*, pg. 6321
AMPLEXOR SINGAPORE PTE. LTD.—See Rheinische-Bergische Verlagsgesellschaft mbH; *Int'l*, pg. 6321
AMPLIA THERAPEUTICS LIMITED; *Int'l*, pg. 435
AMPLIDAN A/S—See L3Harris Technologies, Inc.; *U.S. Public*, pg. 1280
AMPLIDATA N.V.—See Western Digital Corporation; *U.S. Public*, pg. 2355
AMP LIFE LTD.—See Resolution Life Group Holdings LP; *Int'l*, pg. 6297
AMPLIFIED DIGITAL, LLC—See Lee Enterprises, Incorporated; *U.S. Public*, pg. 1298
AMPLIFIER RESEARCH CORP.—See AMETEK, Inc.; *U.S. Public*, pg. 120
AMPLIFIER TECHNOLOGIES, INC.; *U.S. Private*, pg. 266
AMPLIFON AG—See Amplifon S.p.A.; *Int'l*, pg. 435
AMPLIFON BEHEER BV—See Amplifon S.p.A.; *Int'l*, pg. 435
AMPLIFON COTE D'AZUR SAS—See Amplifon S.p.A.; *Int'l*, pg. 435
AMPLIFON DEUTSCHLAND GMBH—See Amplifon S.p.A.; *Int'l*, pg. 435
AMPLIFON FRANCE SA—See Amplifon S.p.A.; *Int'l*, pg. 435
AMPLIFON GROUPE FRANCE SA—See Amplifon S.p.A.; *Int'l*, pg. 435
AMPLIFON IBERICA SA—See Amplifon S.p.A.; *Int'l*, pg. 435
AMPLIFON INDIA PVT LTD.—See Amplifon S.p.A.; *Int'l*, pg. 435
AMPLIFON ITALIA S.P.A.—See Amplifon S.p.A.; *Int'l*, pg. 435
AMPLIFON MAGYARORSZAG LTD.—See Amplifon S.p.A.; *Int'l*, pg. 435
AMPLIFON MIDDLE EAST SA—See Amplifon S.p.A.; *Int'l*, pg. 435
AMPLIFON SIETECH LTD.—See Amplifon S.p.A.; *Int'l*, pg. 435
AMPLIFON S.P.A.; *Int'l*, pg. 435
AMPLIFON SUD OUEST SAS—See Amplifon S.p.A.; *Int'l*, pg. 435
AMPLIFON USA—See Amplifon S.p.A.; *Int'l*, pg. 435
AMPLIFY EDUCATION, INC.—See News Corporation; *U.S. Public*, pg. 1518
AMPLIFY ENERGY CORP.; *U.S. Public*, pg. 133
AMPLIFY ENERGY HOLDINGS LLC—See Amplify Energy Corp.; *U.S. Public*, pg. 133
AMPLIFY SNACK BRANDS, INC.—See The Hershey Co.; *U.S. Public*, pg. 2088
AMP LIMITED—See TE Connectivity Ltd.; *Int'l*, pg. 7494
AMP LIMITED; *Int'l*, pg. 431
AMPLINXT PRIVATE LIMITED—See SoftTech Engineers Limited; *Int'l*, pg. 7056
AMPLIO DIGITAL, LLC; *U.S. Private*, pg. 266
AMPLIO INGREDIENTS SDN. BHD.—See Sunzen Biotech Berhad; *Int'l*, pg. 7333
AMPLION ASSET MANAGEMENT OY—See Catella AB; *Int'l*, pg. 1359
AMPLI SA; *Int'l*, pg. 435
AMPLITECH GROUP, INC.; *U.S. Public*, pg. 133
AMPLITUDE AUSTRALIA PTY LTD.—See PAI Partners S.A.S.; *Int'l*, pg. 5699
AMPLITUDE AUTOMOBILES; *Int'l*, pg. 436
AMPLITUDE GMBH—See PAI Partners S.A.S.; *Int'l*, pg. 5699
AMPLITUDE, INC.; *U.S. Public*, pg. 133
AMPLITUDE LASER INC.—See Amplitude Technologies SA; *Int'l*, pg. 436
AMPLITUDE LATIN AMERICA S.A.—See PAI Partners S.A.S.; *Int'l*, pg. 5699
AMPLITUDE SAS—See PAI Partners S.A.S.; *Int'l*, pg. 5699
AMPLITUDE SURGICAL SAS—See PAI Partners S.A.S.; *Int'l*, pg. 5699
AMPLITUDE SYSTEMES, S.A.—See Amplitude Technologies SA; *Int'l*, pg. 436
AMPLITUDE TECHNOLOGIES SA; *Int'l*, pg. 436
AMPLIVOX LTD.—See Demant A/S; *Int'l*, pg. 2023
AMPLOGIX TECHNOLOGY SDN. BHD.—See Cabnet Holding Berhad; *Int'l*, pg. 1246
AMPLO S.A.; *Int'l*, pg. 436
AMPLUS ASSET DEVELOPMENT INC.—See AK Holdings, Inc.; *Int'l*, pg. 259
AMPLYFI LTD; *Int'l*, pg. 436
AMPLYX PHARMACEUTICALS INC.—See Pfizer Inc.; *U.S. Public*, pg. 1679
AM/PM ADVERTISING INC.; *U.S. Private*, pg. 215
AMPM, INC. DETROIT—See AMPM, Inc.; *U.S. Private*, pg. 266
AMPM, INC.; *U.S. Private*, pg. 266
AM/PM PROPERTY MANAGEMENT, INC.—See Trive Capital Inc.; *U.S. Private*, pg. 4240
A M P M—See BP plc; *Int'l*, pg. 1126
AM PM SYSTEMS; *Int'l*, pg. 402
AM PM USA SERVICE, LLC—See AM PM Systems; *Int'l*, pg. 402
A.M. PNEUMATIK D.O.O.—See SMC Corporation; *Int'l*, pg. 7003
AMPN USA LLC—See Minerva Bunkering; *Int'l*, pg. 4907
AMPOL BENDIGO PTY LTD—See Ampol Limited; *Int'l*, pg. 436
AMPOL FOOD PROCESSING LTD.; *Int'l*, pg. 436
AMPOL LIMITED; *Int'l*, pg. 436
AMPOL METRO FUELS PTY LTD—See Ampol Limited; *Int'l*, pg. 436
AMPORTS ATLANTIC TERMINAL—See AGF Management Limited; *Int'l*, pg. 206
AMPORTS ATLANTIC TERMINAL—See Instar Group Inc.; *Int'l*, pg. 3723
AMPORTS, INC.—See AGF Management Limited; *Int'l*, pg. 206
AMPORTS, INC.—See Instar Group Inc.; *Int'l*, pg. 3723
AMPORTS MEXICO ALTAMIRA TERMINAL—See AGF Management Limited; *Int'l*, pg. 207
AMPORTS MEXICO ALTAMIRA TERMINAL—See Instar Group Inc.; *Int'l*, pg. 3723
AMPPARIT OY—See Otava Ltd.; *Int'l*, pg. 5656
AMP PRODUCTS PACIFIC LIMITED—See TE Connectivity Ltd.; *Int'l*, pg. 7494
AMPRIO GMBH—See Rheinmetall AG; *Int'l*, pg. 6321
AMPRION GMBH; *Int'l*, pg. 437
AMPRITE ELECTRIC COMPANY INC.; *U.S. Private*, pg. 266
AMPRIUS TECHNOLOGIES, INC.; *U.S. Public*, pg. 133
AMPRO ADLINK TECHNOLOGY, INC.—See ADLINK Technology, Inc.; *Int'l*, pg. 151
A.M. PRODUCTIONS—See Financiere de L'Odet; *Int'l*, pg. 2666
AMPRO INC.; *U.S. Private*, pg. 266
AMPRO INDUSTRIES INC.; *U.S. Private*, pg. 266
AMPRO LABORATORIES, INC.—See American Proteins Inc.; *U.S. Private*, pg. 244
AMPROPERTY TRUST MANAGEMENT BERHAD—See AMMB Holdings Berhad; *Int'l*, pg. 429
AMPRO PRODUCTS INC.—See American Proteins Inc.; *U.S. Private*, pg. 244
AMP SECURITY; *U.S. Private*, pg. 264
AMP SERVICES HOLDINGS LIMITED—See AMP Limited; *Int'l*, pg. 432

COMPANY NAME INDEX

AMP SERVICES LIMITED—See AMP Limited; *Int'l*, pg. 432
AMP SERVICES (NZ) LIMITED—See AMP Limited; *Int'l*, pg. 432
AMP SERVICES (NZ) LIMITED—See AMP Limited; *Int'l*, pg. 432
AMP SUPERANNUATION LIMITED—See AMP Limited; *Int'l*, pg. 432
AMP SUPERANNUATION (NZ) LIMITED—See AMP Limited; *Int'l*, pg. 432
AMPTECH, INC.—See New Water Capital, L.P.; *U.S. Private*, pg. 2908
AMPTEK, INC.—See AMETEK, Inc.; *U.S. Public*, pg. 120
AMPTHILL METAL COMPANY LTD.—See Madison Dearborn Partners, LLC; *U.S. Private*, pg. 2541
AMPVOLTS LIMITED; *Int'l*, pg. 437
AMP WARRINGAH MALL PTY LTD—See AMP Limited; *Int'l*, pg. 432
AMPYR GLOBAL ENERGY HOLDINGS PTE. LTD.; *Int'l*, pg. 437
AMQ SOLUTIONS—See Steelcase Inc.; *U.S. Public*, pg. 1944
AMQUIP CRANE—See Apollo Global Management, Inc.; *U.S. Public*, pg. 153
AMRA LTD—See Reach PLC; *Int'l*, pg. 6231
A.M. RAMP & CO. GMBH—See Sakata INX Corporation; *Int'l*, pg. 6487
AMRAPALI CAPITAL AND FINANCE SERVICES LIMITED; *Int'l*, pg. 437
AMRAPALI FINCAP LIMITED; *Int'l*, pg. 437
AMRAPALI GROUP; *Int'l*, pg. 437
AMRAPALI INDUSTRIES LIMITED; *Int'l*, pg. 437
AMRAWORLD AGRICO LTD.; *Int'l*, pg. 437
AMREIT MANAGERS SDN BHD—See AMMB Holdings Berhad; *Int'l*, pg. 429
AMRELI STEELS LTD.; *Int'l*, pg. 437
AMRENT INC.—See CBC Companies Inc.; *U.S. Private*, pg. 796
AMREP CORPORATION; *U.S. Public*, pg. 133
AMREP, INC.—See New Mountain Capital, LLC; *U.S. Private*, pg. 2904
AMREP SOUTHWEST, INC.—See AMREP Corporation; *U.S. Public*, pg. 133
AM RESOURCES CORP.; *Int'l*, pg. 402
AMREST COFFEE DEUTSCHLAND SP. Z O.O. & CO. KG—See AmRest Holdings SE; *Int'l*, pg. 437
AMREST COFFEE SP. Z. O. O.—See Starbucks Corporation; *U.S. Public*, pg. 1939
AMREST COFFEE S.R.O.—See Starbucks Corporation; *U.S. Public*, pg. 1939
AMREST HOLDINGS SE; *Int'l*, pg. 437
AMREST KFT—See AmRest Holdings SE; *Int'l*, pg. 437
AMREST, LLC—See AmRest Holdings SE; *Int'l*, pg. 437
AMRESTORE INC.—See Triton Advisers Limited; *Int'l*, pg. 7933
AMREST PIZZA GMBH—See AmRest Holdings SE; *Int'l*, pg. 437
AMREST SP. Z O.O.—See AmRest Holdings SE; *Int'l*, pg. 437
AMREST S.R.O.—See AmRest Holdings SE; *Int'l*, pg. 437
AMRE SUPPLY CANADA INC.—See Ferguson plc; *Int'l*, pg. 2637
AMREYAH CEMENT COMPANY S.A.E.—See Camargo Correa S.A.; *Int'l*, pg. 1267
AMREYAH CIMPOR CEMENT COMPANY S.A.E.—See Camargo Correa S.A.; *Int'l*, pg. 1267
AMRI INC.—See KSB SE & Co. KGaA; *Int'l*, pg. 4310
AMR INTERACTIVE GROUP PTY LIMITED—See WPP plc; *Int'l*, pg. 8462
AMRISC, LP—See Clayton, Dubilier & Rice, LLC; *U.S. Private*, pg. 927
AMRISC, LP—See Mubadala Investment Company PJSC; *Int'l*, pg. 5076
AMRISC, LP—See Stone Point Capital LLC; *U.S. Private*, pg. 3826
AMRIT CORP. LIMITED; *Int'l*, pg. 438
AMRIT CORP LTD; *Int'l*, pg. 438
AMROCK, LLC—See Rocket Companies, Inc.; *U.S. Public*, pg. 1804
AMROCK TITLE INSURANCE COMPANY—See Rocket Companies, Inc.; *U.S. Public*, pg. 1804
AMROD CORP; *U.S. Private*, pg. 266
AMRO FABRICATING CORPORATION; *U.S. Private*, pg. 266
AMRON INTERNATIONAL INC.; *U.S. Private*, pg. 266
AMRON—See National Presto Industries, Inc; *U.S. Public*, pg. 1497
AMROSE OIL COMPANY; *U.S. Private*, pg. 266
AMRS (AUST) PTY LTD—See Service Stream Limited; *Int'l*, pg. 6725
AMRU AND HANWHA INTERNATIONAL CO., LTD.—See Hanwha Group; *Int'l*, pg. 3265
AMRUMBANK-WEST GMBH—See E.ON SE; *Int'l*, pg. 2252
AMRUTANJAN HEALTH CARE LIMITED; *Int'l*, pg. 438
AMRYT PHARMA PLC—See Chiesi Farmaceutici SpA; *Int'l*, pg. 1477
A.M.S. 2000—See BATM Advanced Communications Ltd.; *Int'l*, pg. 890

AMSAC RIVERS ESCROW, INC.—See Stewart Information Services Corporation; *U.S. Public*, pg. 1947
AMS ADVANCED MEDICAL SERVICES GMBH—See AMS Advanced Medical Services GmbH; *Int'l*, pg. 438
AMS ADVANCED MEDICAL SERVICES GMBH; *Int'l*, pg. 438
AMS ADVANCED MEDICAL SERVICES LTD.—See AMS Advanced Medical Services GmbH; *Int'l*, pg. 438
AMSAFE AVIATION (CHONGQING), LTD.—See TransDigm Group Incorporated; *U.S. Public*, pg. 2181
AMSAFE BRIDPORT LIMITED—See TransDigm Group Incorporated; *U.S. Public*, pg. 2182
AMSAFE BRIDPORT NITTAMBUWA—See TransDigm Group Incorporated; *U.S. Public*, pg. 2182
AMSAFE COMMERCIAL PRODUCTS—See TransDigm Group Incorporated; *U.S. Public*, pg. 2182
AMSAFE-C SAFE, INC.—See TransDigm Group Incorporated; *U.S. Public*, pg. 2182
AMSAFE DEFENSE—See TransDigm Group Incorporated; *U.S. Public*, pg. 2182
AMSAFE GLOBAL SERVICES (PRIVATE) LIMITED—See TransDigm Group Incorporated; *U.S. Public*, pg. 2182
AMSAFE, INC.—See TransDigm Group Incorporated; *U.S. Public*, pg. 2181
AMSAFE KUNSHAN—See TransDigm Group Incorporated; *U.S. Public*, pg. 2182
AMS AG; *Int'l*, pg. 438
AMS - AMERICAN MEDICAL SYSTEMS DO BRASIL PRODUTOS UROLOGICOS E GINECOLOGICOS LTDA.—See Endo International plc; *Int'l*, pg. 2404
AMS AMEROPA MARKETING & SALES AG—See Ameropa AG; *Int'l*, pg. 423
AMSA SPA—See A2A S.p.A.; *Int'l*, pg. 29
AM'S BRAIN INC.—See TOKAI Holdings Corporation; *Int'l*, pg. 7779
AMSCAN INC.—See Thomas H. Lee Partners, L.P.; *U.S. Private*, pg. 4156
AMSC ASA; *Int'l*, pg. 441
AMSC AUSTRIA GMBH—See American Superconductor Corporation; *U.S. Public*, pg. 110
AMSC CO., LTD.; *Int'l*, pg. 441
AMSC INDIA PRIVATE LIMITED—See American Superconductor Corporation; *U.S. Public*, pg. 110
AMSCO CAST PRODUCTS (CANADA) INC.—See Black Cat Blades Ltd.; *Int'l*, pg. 1050
AMSCOMATIC, INC.—See M&R Holdings Inc.; *U.S. Private*, pg. 2525
AMS CORPORATION; *U.S. Private*, pg. 266
AMS CORPORATION—See Japan Meat Co., Ltd.; *Int'l*, pg. 3899
AMSCO SCHOOL PUBLICATIONS, INC.; *U.S. Private*, pg. 267
AMSCO STEEL COMPANY; *U.S. Private*, pg. 267
AMSCOT CORPORATION—See Amscot Holdings Inc.; *U.S. Private*, pg. 267
AMSCOT HOLDINGS INC.; *U.S. Private*, pg. 267
AMSCO WEAR PRODUCTS INC.; *U.S. Private*, pg. 267
AMSC WINDTEC GMBH—See American Superconductor Corporation; *U.S. Public*, pg. 110
AMSDELL COMPANIES; *U.S. Private*, pg. 267
AMSEC LLC—See Huntington Ingalls Industries, Inc.; *U.S. Public*, pg. 1072
AMSEC NOMINEES (ASING) SDN BHD—See AMMB Holdings Berhad; *Int'l*, pg. 429
AMSEC NOMINEES (TEMPATAN) SDN BHD—See AMMB Holdings Berhad; *Int'l*, pg. 429
AMSECO EXPLORATION LTD.; *Int'l*, pg. 441
AMS ELECTRONICS LTD.—See PCB Technologies Ltd.; *Int'l*, pg. 5766
AM SERVICES, INC.—See A-Mark Precious Metals, Inc.; *U.S. Public*, pg. 10
AMS FULFILLMENT , INC.; *U.S. Private*, pg. 266
AMS GMBH; *Int'l*, pg. 440
AMS IMAGING, LLC—See Konica Minolta, Inc.; *Int'l*, pg. 4258
AMS, INC.—See The Why How Do Company, Inc; *Int'l*, pg. 7701
AMS INTERNATIONAL AG—See ams AG; *Int'l*, pg. 440
AMSI PROPERTY MANAGEMENT - HOUSTON OFFICE—See Koch Industries, Inc.; *U.S. Private*, pg. 2330
AMSI PROPERTY MANAGEMENT—See Koch Industries, Inc.; *U.S. Private*, pg. 2330
AMSITO OILWELL SERVICES (MALAYSIA) SDN. BHD.—See Reservoir Link Energy Berhad; *Int'l*, pg. 6296
AMSIVE DIGITAL INC.—See H.I.G. Capital, LLC; *U.S. Private*, pg. 1829
AMSIVE LLC—See H.I.G. Capital, LLC; *U.S. Private*, pg. 1829
AMSKY TECHNOLOGY CO., LTD.; *Int'l*, pg. 441
AM SLEEP INC.; *U.S. Private*, pg. 214
AMS MARINE PTE. LTD.—See Destini Berhad; *Int'l*, pg. 2046
AMS MECHANICAL SYSTEMS, INC.; *U.S. Private*, pg. 266
AMS MEDICAL SYSTEMS IRELAND LIMITED—See Endo International plc; *Int'l*, pg. 2404
AMSOIL INC.; *U.S. Private*, pg. 267

AMT DATASOUTH CORPORATION

AMSONS APPARELS LTD; *Int'l*, pg. 441
AMSONS GROUP; *Int'l*, pg. 441
AMS OSIGURANJE A.D.; *Int'l*, pg. 440
AMSPHERE LIMITED; *Int'l*, pg. 441
AMS PICTURES; *U.S. Private*, pg. 267
AMS PLASTICS, INC.—See BlackBern Partners LLC; *U.S. Private*, pg. 573
AMS PLASTICS, INC.—See Lee Equity Partners LLC; *U.S. Private*, pg. 2412
AMS POLYMERS LTD.; *Int'l*, pg. 440
AMS PRESS INC.; *U.S. Private*, pg. 267
AMS PUBLIC TRANSPORT HOLDINGS LIMITED; *Int'l*, pg. 441
AMS SEMICONDUCTORS INDIA PVT LTD—See ams AG; *Int'l*, pg. 440
AMS SPECTRAL UV—See Forsyth Capital Investors LLC; *U.S. Private*, pg. 1573
AMS STAFF LEASING; *U.S. Private*, pg. 267
AM STABILIZERS CORP.—See Adeka Corporation; *Int'l*, pg. 142
AMSTAN LOGISTICS INC.—See Sun Capital Partners, Inc.; *U.S. Private*, pg. 3858
AMSTAT CORP.—See The Hearst Corporation; *U.S. Private*, pg. 4044
AMSTED CANADA INC.—See AMSTED Industries Incorporated; *U.S. Private*, pg. 267
AMSTED INDUSTRIES INCORPORATED; *U.S. Private*, pg. 267
AMSTED RAIL COMPANY, INC. - ASF KEYSTONE—See AMSTED Industries Incorporated; *U.S. Private*, pg. 267
AMSTED RAIL COMPANY, INC.—See AMSTED Industries Incorporated; *U.S. Private*, pg. 267
AMSTED RPS—See AMSTED Industries Incorporated; *U.S. Private*, pg. 267
AMSTEEL MILLS MARKETING SDN BHD—See Lion Industries Corporation Berhad; *Int'l*, pg. 4519
AMSTEEL MILLS SDN BHD—See Lion Group Management Services Sdn Bhd; *Int'l*, pg. 4518
AMSTEK METAL; *U.S. Private*, pg. 268
AMSTERDAM DUNGEON B.V.—See Merlin Entertainments plc; *Int'l*, pg. 4837
AMSTERDAM HOUSE CONTINUING CARE RETIREMENT COMMUNITY, INC.; *U.S. Private*, pg. 268
AMSTERDAM PRINTING & LITHO—See Taylor Corporation; *U.S. Private*, pg. 3938
AMSTERDAM SCHIPHOL PIJPLEIDING C.V.—See Air France-KLM S.A.; *Int'l*, pg. 236
AMSTERDAM SOFTWARE B.V.—See World Kinect Corporation; *U.S. Public*, pg. 2380
AMSTERDAM TRADE BANK N.V.—See ABH Holdings S.A.; *Int'l*, pg. 60
AMSTER KIRTZ CO.; *U.S. Private*, pg. 268
AMSTORE CORPORATION; *U.S. Private*, pg. 268
AMSTRONG INDUSTRY CORPORATION—See Hota Industrial Mfg. Co., Ltd.; *Int'l*, pg. 3487
AMSUM & ASH, INC.—See Tab India Granites Pvt. Ltd.; *Int'l*, pg. 7401
A&M SUPPLY CORP.; *U.S. Private*, pg. 20
AMSURG BURBANK, INC.—See KKR & Co. Inc.; *U.S. Public*, pg. 1244
AMSURG CINCINNATI ANESTHESIA, LLC—See KKR & Co. Inc.; *U.S. Public*, pg. 1244
AMSURG CITRUS ANESTHESIA, LLC—See KKR & Co. Inc.; *U.S. Public*, pg. 1244
AMSURG CORP. - CENTRAL REGIONAL OFFICE—See KKR & Co. Inc.; *U.S. Public*, pg. 1244
AMSURG CORP.—See KKR & Co. Inc.; *U.S. Public*, pg. 1244
AMSURG EL PASO, INC.—See KKR & Co. Inc.; *U.S. Public*, pg. 1244
AMSURG FRESNO CA, INC.—See KKR & Co. Inc.; *U.S. Public*, pg. 1244
AMSURG GREENSBORO ANESTHESIA, LLC—See KKR & Co. Inc.; *U.S. Public*, pg. 1244
AMSURG HERMITAGE ANESTHESIA, LLC—See KKR & Co. Inc.; *U.S. Public*, pg. 1244
AMSURG KENTUCKY OPHTHALMOLOGY, LLC—See KKR & Co. Inc.; *U.S. Public*, pg. 1244
AMSURG LOUISVILLE GI, LLC—See KKR & Co. Inc.; *U.S. Public*, pg. 1244
AMSURG NORTHERN KENTUCKY GI, LLC—See KKR & Co. Inc.; *U.S. Public*, pg. 1244
AMSURG ROCKLEDGE FL ANESTHESIA, LLC—See KKR & Co. Inc.; *U.S. Public*, pg. 1244
AMSURG ST. GEORGE ANESTHESIA, LLC—See KKR & Co. Inc.; *U.S. Public*, pg. 1246
AMSURG TAMPA BAY ANESTHESIA, LLC—See KKR & Co. Inc.; *U.S. Public*, pg. 1244
AMSURG TOLEDO ANESTHESIA, LLC—See KKR & Co. Inc.; *U.S. Public*, pg. 1244
AMT - ADVANCED MOULD TECHNOLOGY INDIA PRIVATE LTD.—See Intek Group S.p.A.; *Int'l*, pg. 3732
AMT ASSURANCES SARL—See CVC Capital Partners SICAV-FIS S.A.; *Int'l*, pg. 1882
AMT CO., LTD.—See Mitsui-Soko Holdings Co., Ltd.; *Int'l*, pg. 4993
AMT DATASOUTH CORPORATION—See AMT Datasouth Corporation; *U.S. Private*, pg. 268
AMT DATASOUTH CORPORATION; *U.S. Private*, pg. 268

AMTD DIGITAL INC.—See AMTD Group Company Limited; *Int'l*, pg. 441
AMTD GROUP COMPANY LIMITED; *Int'l*, pg. 441
AMTD IDEA GROUP—See AMTD Group Company Limited; *Int'l*, pg. 441
AMTDIRECT, LLC—See GI Manager L.P.; *U.S. Private*, pg. 1693
AMTEC CORPORATION—See National Presto Industries, Inc; *U.S. Public*, pg. 1497
AMTEC CORPORATION; *U.S. Private*, pg. 268
AMTECH DRIVES, INC.—See Amtech Electronics India Limited; *Int'l*, pg. 441
AMTECH ELECTRONICS INDIA LIMITED; *Int'l*, pg. 441
AMTECH GMBH—See Wentworth Technologies Co. Ltd.; *Int'l*, pg. 8377
AMTECH GROUP LIMITED—See Trimble, Inc.; *U.S. Public*, pg. 2190
AMTECH LIGHTING SERVICES—See WESCO International, Inc.; *U.S. Public*, pg. 2352
AM TECHNICAL SOLUTIONS, INC.; *U.S. Private*, pg. 215
AMTECH POWER LIMITED—See Amtech Electronics India Limited; *Int'l*, pg. 441
AMTECH SYSTEMS, INC.; *U.S. Public*, pg. 133
AMTECH WORLD CORPORATION—See Roper Technologies, Inc.; *U.S. Public*, pg. 1810
AMTECK, LLC—See Comfort Systems USA, Inc.; *U.S. Public*, pg. 543
AMTECK OF KENTUCKY, LLC—See Comfort Systems USA, Inc.; *U.S. Public*, pg. 543
AMTEC MOULDED PRODUCTS INC.—See Ucal Ltd.; *Int'l*, pg. 8010
AMTEK AUTO LIMITED; *Int'l*, pg. 441
AMTEK DEUTSCHLAND GMBH—See Amtek Auto Limited; *Int'l*, pg. 441
AMTEK GERMANY HOLDING GMBH & CO. KG—See Amtek Auto Limited; *Int'l*, pg. 441
AMTEK HOLDINGS BERHAD; *Int'l*, pg. 441
AMTEK INVESTMENTS U.K. LIMITED—See Amtek Auto Limited; *Int'l*, pg. 441
AMTEK MARKETING SERVICES PTE. LTD.—See Pensonic Holdings Berhad; *Int'l*, pg. 5787
AMTEK PRECISION ENGINEERING (SHANGHAI) CO., LTD.—See Blackstone Inc.; *U.S. Public*, pg. 354
AMTEK TRANSPORTATION SYSTEMS LIMITED—See Amtek Auto Limited; *Int'l*, pg. 441
AMTEL CELLULAR SDN. BHD.—See Amtel Holdings Berhad; *Int'l*, pg. 442
AMTEL HOLDINGS BERHAD; *Int'l*, pg. 442
AMTEL, INC.—See StoneCalibre, LLC; *U.S. Private*, pg. 3828
AMTEL RESOURCES SDN. BHD.—See Amtel Holdings Berhad; *Int'l*, pg. 442
AMTEL SECURITY SYSTEMS, INC.; *U.S. Private*, pg. 268
AMTEX BANCSHARES INC.; *U.S. Private*, pg. 268
AMTEX INC.—See Hayashi Telempu Co., Ltd.; *Int'l*, pg. 3289
AMTEX LIMITED; *Int'l*, pg. 442
AMTEX SYSTEMS INC.; *U.S. Private*, pg. 268
AMT FUTURES LIMITED—See Amalgamated Metal Corporation PLC; *Int'l*, pg. 408
AMTICO INTERNATIONAL LTD.—See Mannington Mills, Inc.; *U.S. Private*, pg. 2565
AMTICO USA, LLC—See Mannington Mills, Inc.; *U.S. Private*, pg. 2565
AMT, INC.—See 3D Systems Corporation; *U.S. Public*, pg. 4
AMT NORTH AMERICA INC—See Magontec Limited; *Int'l*, pg. 4642
A.M. TODD BOTANICAL THERAPEUTICS—See A.M. Todd Company; *U.S. Private*, pg. 27
A.M. TODD COMPANY; *U.S. Private*, pg. 27
A.M. TODD - INGREDIENTS & FLAVORS—See A.M. Todd Company; *U.S. Private*, pg. 27
AMTOON INCORPORATION—See China Merchants Group Limited; *Int'l*, pg. 1521
AMTOPP CORPORATION—See Inteplast Group, Ltd.; *U.S. Private*, pg. 2106
AMTOTE AUSTRALASIA PTY LTD—See The Stronach Group Inc.; *Int'l*, pg. 7689
AMTOTE INTERNATIONAL, INC.—See The Stronach Group Inc.; *Int'l*, pg. 7689
AMT PUMP COMPANY—See The Gorman-Rupp Company; *U.S. Public*, pg. 2085
AMTRAC OF OHIO, INC.; *U.S. Private*, pg. 268
AMTRADA HOLDING B.V.; *Int'l*, pg. 442
AM TRANS EXPEDITE, INC.—See Hudson Hill Capital LLC; *U.S. Private*, pg. 2002
AM TRANSPORT SERVICES, INC.; *U.S. Private*, pg. 215
AMTRAN TECHNOLOGY; *Int'l*, pg. 442
AMTRAN VIETNAM TECHNOLOGY COMPANY LIMITED—See AmTRAN Technology; *Int'l*, pg. 442
AMTREX, INC.; *U.S. Private*, pg. 268
AMTRION GMBH—See Gesco AG; *Int'l*, pg. 2945
AMTROL-ALFA METALOMECANICA, S.A.—See Worthington Industries, Inc.; *U.S. Public*, pg. 2382
AMTROL HOLDINGS INC.—See Worthington Industries, Inc.; *U.S. Public*, pg. 2382
AMTROL INC.—See Worthington Industries, Inc.; *U.S. Public*, pg. 2382

AMTRUST AGRICULTURE INSURANCE SERVICES, LLC—See Stone Point Capital LLC; *U.S. Private*, pg. 3820
AMTRUST AT LLOYD'S LIMITED—See Stone Point Capital LLC; *U.S. Private*, pg. 3820
AMTRUST CENTRAL BUREAU OF SERVICES LTD.—See Stone Point Capital LLC; *U.S. Private*, pg. 3820
AMTRUST CLAIMS MANAGEMENT SRL—See Stone Point Capital LLC; *U.S. Private*, pg. 3820
AMTRUST CORPORATE MEMBER LIMITED—See Stone Point Capital LLC; *U.S. Private*, pg. 3820
AMTRUST EUROPE LEGAL, LTD.—See Stone Point Capital LLC; *U.S. Private*, pg. 3820
AMTRUST EUROPE LTD.—See Stone Point Capital LLC; *U.S. Private*, pg. 3820
AMTRUST FINANCIAL SERVICES, INC.—See Stone Point Capital LLC; *U.S. Private*, pg. 3819
AMTRUST GESTION BOLIVIA S.R.L.—See Stone Point Capital LLC; *U.S. Private*, pg. 3820
AMTRUST GESTION PARAGUAY S.A.—See Stone Point Capital LLC; *U.S. Private*, pg. 3820
AMTRUST GESTION PERU S.A.C.—See Stone Point Capital LLC; *U.S. Private*, pg. 3820
AMTRUST INSURANCE LUXEMBOURG S.A.—See Stone Point Capital LLC; *U.S. Private*, pg. 3820
AMTRUST INSURANCE SERVICES NORWAY AS—See Stone Point Capital LLC; *U.S. Private*, pg. 3820
AMTRUST INSURANCE SPAIN, S. L.—See Liberty Mutual Holding Company Inc.; *U.S. Private*, pg. 2445
AMTRUST INTERNATIONAL INSURANCE LTD.—See Stone Point Capital LLC; *U.S. Private*, pg. 3820
AMTRUST INTERNATIONAL UNDERWRITERS LIMITED—See Stone Point Capital LLC; *U.S. Private*, pg. 3820
AMTRUST NORDIC AB—See Stone Point Capital LLC; *U.S. Private*, pg. 3820
AMTRUST NORTH AMERICA, INC.—See Stone Point Capital LLC; *U.S. Private*, pg. 3820
AMTRUST NORTH AMERICA OF FLORIDA, INC.—See Stone Point Capital LLC; *U.S. Private*, pg. 3820
AMTRUST NORTH AMERICA—See Stone Point Capital LLC; *U.S. Private*, pg. 3820
AMTRUST RE ARIES S.A.—See Stone Point Capital LLC; *U.S. Private*, pg. 3820
AMTRUST UNDERWRITERS, INC.—See Stone Point Capital LLC; *U.S. Private*, pg. 3820
AMTRUST UNDERWRITING LIMITED—See Stone Point Capital LLC; *U.S. Private*, pg. 3820
AMT-SYBEX LTD.—See Capita plc; *Int'l*, pg. 1308
AMULET CAPITAL PARTNERS, L.P.; *U.S. Private*, pg. 268
AMUNDSEN DAVIS LLC; *U.S. Private*, pg. 269
AMUNEAL MANUFACTURING CORPORATION; *U.S. Private*, pg. 269
AMURCON CORPORATION OF VIRGINIA—See Amurcon Corporation; *U.S. Private*, pg. 269
AMURCON CORPORATION; *U.S. Private*, pg. 269
AMUR MINERALS CORPORATION; *Int'l*, pg. 442
AMUSE EDUTAINMENT INC.—See Amuse Inc.; *Int'l*, pg. 442
AMUSE GROUP HOLDING LTD.; *Int'l*, pg. 442
AMUSE INC.; *Int'l*, pg. 442
AMUSEMENT SALES & SERVICE INC.—See United Gaming, LLC; *U.S. Private*, pg. 4293
AMUSEMENTS OF AMERICA INC.; *U.S. Private*, pg. 269
AMUSE SOFT ENTERTAINMENT, INC.—See Amuse Inc.; *Int'l*, pg. 442
AMUZA; *U.S. Private*, pg. 269
AMVAC CHEMICAL CORPORATION—See American Vanguard Corporation; *U.S. Public*, pg. 111
AMVAC CHEMICAL CORPORATION—See American Vanguard Corporation; *U.S. Public*, pg. 111
AMVAC CHEMICAL UK LTD.—See American Vanguard Corporation; *U.S. Public*, pg. 111
AMVAC MEXICO S. DE R.L. DE C.V.—See American Vanguard Corporation; *U.S. Public*, pg. 111
AMVAC NETHERLANDS BV—See American Vanguard Corporation; *U.S. Public*, pg. 111
AMV CAPITAL CORPORATION; *U.S. Private*, pg. 442
AMVENTURE INSURANCE AGENCY, INC.—See Stone Point Capital LLC; *U.S. Private*, pg. 3820
AMVERTON BERHAD; *Int'l*, pg. 443
AMVI APLICA. MECANICAS VALVULAS INDUSTRIALES, S.A.—See KSB SE & Co. KGaA; *Int'l*, pg. 4310
AMVIG HOLDINGS LIMITED; *Int'l*, pg. 442
AMVIS HOLDINGS, INC.; *Int'l*, pg. 443
AMWAAL TRADE & ENGINEERING CO., LTD.—See BERICAP GmbH & Co. KG; *Int'l*, pg. 980
AMWAJ CATERING SERVICES LIMITED—See Qatar Petroleum; *Int'l*, pg. 6135
AMWAL INTERNATIONAL INVESTMENT COMPANY KSCC—See SHUAA Capital psc; *Int'l*, pg. 6868
AMWAL INVEST PLC; *Int'l*, pg. 443
AMWARE LOGISTICS SERVICES, INC.—See Rotunda Capital Partners LLC; *U.S. Private*, pg. 3487
AMWAT MOVING WAREHOUSING & STORAGE; *U.S. Private*, pg. 269
AMWAY ARGENTINA, INC.—See Alticor Inc.; *U.S. Private*, pg. 208

AMWAY BELGIUM CO—See Alticor Inc.; *U.S. Private*, pg. 208
AMWAY CANADA CORPORATION—See Alticor Inc.; *U.S. Private*, pg. 208
AMWAY CORPORATION—See Alticor Inc.; *U.S. Private*, pg. 208
AMWAY CZECH REPUBLIC—See Alticor Inc.; *U.S. Private*, pg. 208
AMWAY DE ESPANA, S.A.—See Alticor Inc.; *U.S. Private*, pg. 209
AMWAY DE GUATEMALA, S.A.—See Alticor Inc.; *U.S. Private*, pg. 209
AMWAY DENMARK APS—See Alticor Inc.; *U.S. Private*, pg. 209
AMWAY DE PANAMA S.A.—See Alticor Inc.; *U.S. Private*, pg. 209
AMWAY DE PORTUGAL, INC.—See Alticor Inc.; *U.S. Private*, pg. 209
AMWAY DOMINICAN REPUBLIC, LLC—See Alticor Inc.; *U.S. Private*, pg. 209
AMWAY (EUROPE) LTD.—See Alticor Inc.; *U.S. Private*, pg. 208
AMWAY FRANCE—See Alticor Inc.; *U.S. Private*, pg. 209
AMWAY GMBH—See Alticor Inc.; *U.S. Private*, pg. 209
AMWAY GRAND PLAZA HOTEL—See Alticor Inc.; *U.S. Private*, pg. 209
AMWAY HELLAS—See Alticor Inc.; *U.S. Private*, pg. 209
AMWAY HONG KONG LTD.—See Alticor Inc.; *U.S. Private*, pg. 209
AMWAY HUNGARIA MARKETING KFT.—See Alticor Inc.; *U.S. Private*, pg. 208
AMWAY INDONESIA—See Alticor Inc.; *U.S. Private*, pg. 209
AMWAY ITALIA S.R.L.—See Alticor Inc.; *U.S. Private*, pg. 209
AMWAY (JAPAN) LIMITED—See Alticor Inc.; *U.S. Private*, pg. 208
AMWAY KOREA, LTD.—See Alticor Inc.; *U.S. Private*, pg. 209
AMWAY (MALAYSIA) SDN. BHD.—See Alticor Inc.; *U.S. Private*, pg. 208
AMWAY NEDERLAND LTD.—See Alticor Inc.; *U.S. Private*, pg. 209
AMWAY OF AUSTRALIA—See Alticor Inc.; *U.S. Private*, pg. 209
AMWAY OF NEW ZEALAND—See Alticor Inc.; *U.S. Private*, pg. 209
AMWAY PHILIPPINES—See Alticor Inc.; *U.S. Private*, pg. 209
AMWAY POLAND—See Alticor Inc.; *U.S. Private*, pg. 209
AMWAY ROMANIA MARKETING S.R.L.—See Alticor Inc.; *U.S. Private*, pg. 209
AMWAY (SCHWEIZ) AG—See Alticor Inc.; *U.S. Private*, pg. 208
AMWAY SLOVENIA L.L.C.—See Alticor Inc.; *U.S. Private*, pg. 209
AMWAY SLOVENSKO, S.R.O.—See Alticor Inc.; *U.S. Private*, pg. 209
AMWAY SOUTH AFRICA—See Alticor Inc.; *U.S. Private*, pg. 209
AMWAY TAIWAN, LTD.—See Alticor Inc.; *U.S. Private*, pg. 209
AMWAY (THAILAND) LIMITED—See Alticor Inc.; *U.S. Private*, pg. 208
AMWAY TURKEY LTD.—See Alticor Inc.; *U.S. Private*, pg. 209
AMWAY (U.K.) LIMITED—See Alticor Inc.; *U.S. Private*, pg. 208
AMWAY URUGUAY—See Alticor Inc.; *U.S. Private*, pg. 209
AMW CAPITAL LEASING & FINANCE PLC; *Int'l*, pg. 443
AMWELD BUILDING PRODUCTS INC.; *U.S. Private*, pg. 269
AMWELL INC.—See The Walt Disney Company; *U.S. Public*, pg. 2140
A&M WHOLESALE HARDWARE SUPPLY COMPANY; *U.S. Private*, pg. 20
AMWINS GROUP, INC. - REDONDO BEACH—See AmWINS Group, Inc.; *U.S. Private*, pg. 269
AMWINS GROUP, INC.; *U.S. Private*, pg. 269
AM WIRELESS URUGUAY, S.A.—See America Movil, S.A.B. de C.V.; *Int'l*, pg. 421
AMX INTERNATIONAL, INC.; *U.S. Private*, pg. 270
AMX LLC—See Samsung Group; *Int'l*, pg. 6512
AMX PARAGUAY, S.A.—See America Movil, S.A.B. de C.V.; *Int'l*, pg. 421
AMX USA HOLDING, S.A. DE C.V.—See America Movil, S.A.B. de C.V.; *Int'l*, pg. 421
AMYCEL, INC.—See Monterey Mushrooms, Inc.; *U.S. Private*, pg. 2776
AMYLON S.A.—See Boromir Prod SA Buzau; *Int'l*, pg. 1114
AMYLUM BULGARIA EAD—See Archer-Daniels-Midland Company; *U.S. Public*, pg. 183
AMYLUM NISASTA SANAYI TICARET ANONIM SIRKETI—See Archer-Daniels-Midland Company; *U.S. Public*, pg. 183

COMPANY NAME INDEX

AMYLUM NISASTA SANAYI VE TICARET ANONIM SIRKETI—See Archer-Daniels-Midland Company; *U.S. Public*, pg. 183
AMY LYNN, INC.; *U.S. Private*, pg. 270
AMYLYX PHARMACEUTICALS, INC.; *U.S. Public*, pg. 134
AMYNTA AGENCY, INC.—See Fairfax Financial Holdings Limited; *Int'l*, pg. 2606
AMYNTA SURETY SOLUTIONS—See Fairfax Financial Holdings Limited; *Int'l*, pg. 2606
AMYRIS BRASIL LTDA.—See Koninklijke DSM N.V.; *Int'l*, pg. 4262
AMYRIS, INC.; *U.S. Public*, pg. 134
AMY'S KITCHEN, INC.; *U.S. Private*, pg. 270
AMYX, INC.; *U.S. Private*, pg. 270
AMZAK CAPITAL MANAGEMENT, LLC; *U.S. Private*, pg. 270
AMZA LIMITED—See Element Solutions Inc.; *U.S. Public*, pg. 725
AMZ FINANCIAL INSURANCE SERVICES, LLC; *U.S. Private*, pg. 270
AMZUR TECHNOLOGIES, INC.; *U.S. Private*, pg. 270
AMZUR TECHNOLOGIES (I) PRIVATE LIMITED—See Amzur Technologies, Inc.; *U.S. Private*, pg. 271
AN2 THERAPEUTICS, INC.; *U.S. Public*, pg. 134
ANA AERO SUPPLY SYSTEMS CO., LTD.—See ANA Holdings Inc.; *Int'l*, pg. 443
ANA AIRCRAFT MAINTENANCE CO., LTD—See ANA Holdings Inc.; *Int'l*, pg. 444
ANA AIR SERVICE FUKUSHIMA CO., LTD.—See ANA Holdings Inc.; *Int'l*, pg. 444
ANA AIR SERVICE MATSUYAMA CO., LTD.—See ANA Holdings Inc.; *Int'l*, pg. 444
ANA AIR SERVICE SAGA CO., LTD.—See ANA Holdings Inc.; *Int'l*, pg. 444
ANAAM INTERNATIONAL HOLDING COMPANY GROUP; *Int'l*, pg. 444
ANA BASE MAINTENANCE TECHNICS CO., LTD.—See ANA Holdings Inc.; *Int'l*, pg. 444
ANABATIC TECHNOLOGIES PHILIPPINES INC.—See PT Anabatic Technologies Tbk; *Int'l*, pg. 6021
ANABELLE BITS PTY LTD.; *Int'l*, pg. 444
ANABIOS CORPORATION; *U.S. Private*, pg. 271
ANABOLIC LABORATORIES INC.; *U.S. Private*, pg. 271
ANABOND LIMITED; *Int'l*, pg. 444
ANABUKI KOSAN INC.; *Int'l*, pg. 444
ANA BUSINESS CREATE CO., LTD—See ANA Holdings Inc.; *Int'l*, pg. 444
ANA BUSINESS JET INC.—See ANA Holdings Inc.; *Int'l*, pg. 444
ANACACHO WIND FARM, LLC—See E.ON SE; *Int'l*, pg. 2251
ANACACIA CAPITAL PTY LTD; *Int'l*, pg. 445
ANACAP FINANCIAL PARTNERS LLP; *Int'l*, pg. 445
ANA CARGO INC.—See ANA Holdings Inc.; *Int'l*, pg. 444
ANA CATERING SERVICE CO., LTD.—See ANA Holdings Inc.; *Int'l*, pg. 444
ANACHEM LIMITED—See Mettler-Toledo International, Inc.; *U.S. Public*, pg. 1432
ANACLE SYSTEMS LIMITED; *Int'l*, pg. 445
ANACLE SYSTEMS SDN BHD—See Anacle Systems Limited; *Int'l*, pg. 445
ANACO & GREEVE INTERNATIONAL B.V.—See Dole plc; *Int'l*, pg. 2158
ANACOMP, INC.; *U.S. Public*, pg. 134
ANACOMP (NEDERLAND) B.V.—See Anacomp, Inc.; *U.S. Public*, pg. 134
ANA COMPONENT TECHNICS CO., LTD.—See ANA Holdings Inc.; *Int'l*, pg. 444
ANACONDA SPORTS, INC.; *U.S. Private*, pg. 271
ANADARKO ALGERIA COMPANY, LLC—See Occidental Petroleum Corporation; *U.S. Public*, pg. 1561
ANADARKO GATHERING COMPANY LLC—See Western Midstream Partners, LP; *U.S. Public*, pg. 2356
ANADARKO INDUSTRIES, LLC; *U.S. Private*, pg. 271
ANADARKO OIL & GAS COMPANY—See Occidental Petroleum Corporation; *U.S. Public*, pg. 1561
ANADARKO PETROLEUM CORPORATION—See Occidental Petroleum Corporation; *U.S. Public*, pg. 1561
ANADARKO UINTAH MIDSTREAM, LLC—See Occidental Petroleum Corporation; *U.S. Public*, pg. 1561
ANADARKO US OFFSHORE CORPORATION—See Occidental Petroleum Corporation; *U.S. Public*, pg. 1561
ANADARKO WATTENBERG COMPANY, LLC—See Western Midstream Partners, LP; *U.S. Public*, pg. 2356
ANADIS CO., LTD.—See TSI Holdings Co., Ltd.; *Int'l*, pg. 7950
ANADOLU ANONIM TURK SIGORTA SIRKETI; *Int'l*, pg. 445
ANADOLU ARACLAR TICARET A.S.—See AG Anadolu Grubu Holding A.S.; *Int'l*, pg. 197
ANADOLU BILISIM HIZMETLERI A.S.—See AG Anadolu Grubu Holding A.S.; *Int'l*, pg. 197
ANADOLU CAM ESKISEHIR SANAYI A.S.—See Turkiye Sise ve Cam Fabrikalari A.S.; *Int'l*, pg. 7977
ANADOLU CAM YENISEHIR SANAYI A.S.—See Turkiye Sise ve Cam Fabrikalari A.S.; *Int'l*, pg. 7977
ANADOLU EFES BIRACILIK VE MALT SANAYII A.S.; *Int'l*, pg. 445

ANADOLU ELEKTRIK A.S.—See Statkraft AS; *Int'l*, pg. 7185
ANADOLU ENDUSTRI HOLDING A.S.—See AG Anadolu Grubu Holding A.S.; *Int'l*, pg. 197
ANADOLU ENDUSTRI HOLDING UND CO. KG—See AG Anadolu Grubu Holding A.S.; *Int'l*, pg. 197
ANADOLU ETAP PENKON GIDA VE TARIM URUNLERI SAN VE TIC. A.S.—See Anadolu Efes Biracilik ve Malt Sanayii A.S.; *Int'l*, pg. 445
ANADOLU FLYGT POMPA PAZARLAMA VE TICARET AS—See Xylem Inc.; *U.S. Public*, pg. 2396
ANADOLU GIRISIM SERMAYESI YATIRIM ORTAKLIGI A.S.; *Int'l*, pg. 445
ANADOLU HAYAT EMEKLILIK A.S.—See Turkiye Is Bankasi A.S.; *Int'l*, pg. 7976
ANADOLU ISUZU OTOMOTIV SANAYI VE TICARET A.S.—See Isuzu Motors Limited; *Int'l*, pg. 3825
ANADOLU JAPAN TURIZM A.S.—See Fiba Holding A.S.; *Int'l*, pg. 2651
ANADOLU MOTOR URETIM VE PAZARLAMA A.S.—See AG Anadolu Grubu Holding A.S.; *Int'l*, pg. 197
ANADOLU RESTORAN ISLETMELERI LIMITED SIRKETI—See AG Anadolu Grubu Holding A.S.; *Int'l*, pg. 197
ANADOLU VARLIK YONETIM A.S.—See AG Anadolu Grubu Holding A.S.; *Int'l*, pg. 197
ANA ENGINE TECHNICS CO., LTD.—See ANA Holdings Inc.; *Int'l*, pg. 444
ANAEROBICOS SRL—See Illinois Tool Works Inc.; *U.S. Public*, pg. 1101
ANAFI PLUS—See Assystem S.A.; *Int'l*, pg. 650
ANA FOODS CO., LTD.—See ANA Holdings Inc.; *Int'l*, pg. 444
ANAGENICS LIMITED; *Int'l*, pg. 446
ANAGEST SA—See Texaf SA; *Int'l*, pg. 7582
ANAGRAM INTERNATIONAL, INC.—See Thomas H. Lee Partners, L.P.; *U.S. Private*, pg. 4156
ANAHEIM AMATEUR HOCKEY ASSOCIATION; *U.S. Private*, pg. 271
ANAHEIM BAND INSTRUMENTS, INC.—See Bain Capital, LP; *U.S. Private*, pg. 440
ANAHEIM DUCKS HOCKEY CLUB, LLC; *U.S. Private*, pg. 271
ANAHEIM EXTRUSION CO. INC.—See UMC Acquisition Corp.; *U.S. Private*, pg. 4278
ANAHEIM HILLS MEDICAL IMAGING, L.L.C.—See UCI Health; *U.S. Private*, pg. 4274
ANAHEIM MANUFACTURING COMPANY—See Western Industries, Inc.; *U.S. Private*, pg. 4494
ANAHEIM REGIONAL MEDICAL CENTER—See AHMC & AHMC Healthcare Inc.; *U.S. Private*, pg. 130
ANAHEIM TRANSPORTATION NETWORK; *U.S. Private*, pg. 271
ANA HOLDINGS INC.; *Int'l*, pg. 443
ANAHOL S.A.—See Illinois Tool Works Inc.; *U.S. Public*, pg. 1101
ANA HOTEL UBE LTD.—See UBE Corporation; *Int'l*, pg. 8000
ANAHUAC SOUTH CAROLINA ELASTIC S.A. DE C.V.—See Rhode Island Textile Company, Inc.; *U.S. Private*, pg. 3422
ANA INFORMATION SYSTEMS PLANNING CO., LTD.—See ANA Holdings Inc.; *Int'l*, pg. 444
ANAJET INC.—See Ricoh Company, Ltd.; *Int'l*, pg. 6335
ANALABS RESOURCES BERHAD; *Int'l*, pg. 446
ANALCLINIC SA—See Eurofins Scientific S.E.; *Int'l*, pg. 2535
ANA LINE MAINTENANCE TECHNICS CO., LTD.—See ANA Holdings Inc.; *Int'l*, pg. 444
ANALIZY ONLINE S.A; *Int'l*, pg. 446
ANALOG DEVICES AB—See Analog Devices, Inc.; *U.S. Public*, pg. 134
ANALOG DEVICES AS—See Analog Devices, Inc.; *U.S. Public*, pg. 134
ANALOG DEVICES AUSTRALIA PTY. LTD.—See Analog Devices, Inc.; *U.S. Public*, pg. 134
ANALOG DEVICES (CHINA) CO. LTD.—See Analog Devices, Inc.; *U.S. Public*, pg. 134
ANALOG DEVICES GMBH—See Analog Devices, Inc.; *U.S. Public*, pg. 134
ANALOG DEVICES GMBH—See Analog Devices, Inc.; *U.S. Public*, pg. 134
ANALOG DEVICES GMBH-TECHNISCHES BURO WEST—See Analog Devices, Inc.; *U.S. Public*, pg. 134
ANALOG DEVICES, INC. - GREENSBORO—See Analog Devices, Inc.; *U.S. Public*, pg. 135
ANALOG DEVICES, INC. - SAN JOSE—See Analog Devices, Inc.; *U.S. Public*, pg. 135
ANALOG DEVICES, INC.; *U.S. Public*, pg. 134
ANALOG DEVICES, INC. - WILMINGTON—See Analog Devices, Inc.; *U.S. Public*, pg. 135
ANALOG DEVICES INDIA PVT. LTD.—See Analog Devices, Inc.; *U.S. Public*, pg. 134
ANALOG DEVICES INTERNATIONAL FINANCIAL SERVICES LIMITED—See Analog Devices, Inc.; *U.S. Public*, pg. 134
ANALOG DEVICES INTERNATIONAL U.C.—See Analog Devices, Inc.; *U.S. Public*, pg. 134

ANALYTICA LIMITED

ANALOG DEVICES IRELAND LTD.—See Analog Devices, Inc.; *U.S. Public*, pg. 134
ANALOG DEVICES, (ISRAEL) LTD.—See Analog Devices, Inc.; *U.S. Public*, pg. 135
ANALOG DEVICES K.K.—See Analog Devices, Inc.; *U.S. Public*, pg. 135
ANALOG DEVICES KOREA, LTD.—See Analog Devices, Inc.; *U.S. Public*, pg. 135
ANALOG DEVICES LTD.—See Analog Devices, Inc.; *U.S. Public*, pg. 135
ANALOG DEVICES NEDERLAND B.V.—See Analog Devices, Inc.; *U.S. Public*, pg. 135
ANALOG DEVICES S.A.S—See Analog Devices, Inc.; *U.S. Public*, pg. 135
ANALOG DEVICES (SHANGHAI) CO. LTD.—See Analog Devices, Inc.; *U.S. Public*, pg. 134
ANALOG DEVICES S.L.—See Analog Devices, Inc.; *U.S. Public*, pg. 135
ANALOG DEVICES SRL—See Analog Devices, Inc.; *U.S. Public*, pg. 135
ANALOG DEVICES TAIWAN, LTD.—See Analog Devices, Inc.; *U.S. Public*, pg. 135
ANALOGIC CANADA CORPORATION—See Altaris Capital Partners, LLC; *U.S. Private*, pg. 205
ANALOGIC CORPORATION—See Altaris Capital Partners, LLC; *U.S. Private*, pg. 205
ANALOGIC ITALIA S.R.L—See Altaris Capital Partners, LLC; *U.S. Private*, pg. 205
ANALOGIC MEDICAL EQUIPMENT (SHANGHAI) CO. LTD.—See Altaris Capital Partners, LLC; *U.S. Private*, pg. 205
ANALOG INTEGRATIONS CORP.; *Int'l*, pg. 446
ANA LOGISTIC SERVICE CO., LTD—See ANA Holdings Inc.; *Int'l*, pg. 444
ANALOG MODULES, INC.—See HEICO Corporation; *U.S. Public*, pg. 1020
ANALOG TECH KK—See Analog Devices, Inc.; *U.S. Public*, pg. 135
ANALOGUE HOLDINGS LIMITED; *Int'l*, pg. 446
ANALOZBE D.O.O—See OTP Bank Plc; *Int'l*, pg. 5657
ANALYSER SERVICES TRINIDAD LTD.—See Addtech AB; *Int'l*, pg. 131
ANALYSIS, DESIGN & DIAGNOSTICS, INC.—See SEACORP, LLC; *U.S. Private*, pg. 3584
ANALYSIS GROUP, INC.; *U.S. Private*, pg. 271
ANALYSIS LAB S.A.—See PHM Group Holding Oyj; *Int'l*, pg. 5848
ANALYSIS & MEASUREMENT SERVICES CORPORATION; *U.S. Private*, pg. 271
ANALYSIS-ONE—See Financial Index Australia Pty Ltd.; *Int'l*, pg. 2665
ANALYSIS S.A.—See Sartorius AG; *Int'l*, pg. 6578
ANALYST IMS INVESTMENT MANAGEMENT SERVICES LTD.; *Int'l*, pg. 446
ANALYSTS INTERNATIONAL CORPORATION—See American CyberSystems, Inc.; *U.S. Private*, pg. 229
ANALYSTS INTERNATIONAL-LAWSON PRACTICE—See American CyberSystems, Inc.; *U.S. Private*, pg. 229
ANALYSTS INTERNATIONAL-MANAGED SERVICES GROUP—See American CyberSystems, Inc.; *U.S. Private*, pg. 229
ANALYSYS MASON AS—See Datatec Limited; *Int'l*, pg. 1980
ANALYSYS MASON FZ LLC—See Datatec Limited; *Int'l*, pg. 1980
ANALYSYS MASON GROUP LIMITED—See Datatec Limited; *Int'l*, pg. 1980
ANALYSYS MASON INDIA PVT. LIMITED—See Datatec Limited; *Int'l*, pg. 1980
ANALYSYS MASON LIMITED—See Bridgepoint Group Plc; *Int'l*, pg. 1154
ANALYSYS MASON LIMITED—See Datatec Limited; *Int'l*, pg. 1980
ANALYSYS MASON LIMITED—See Datatec Limited; *Int'l*, pg. 1980
ANALYSYS MASON LIMITED—See Bridgepoint Group Plc; *Int'l*, pg. 1154
ANALYSYS MASON PTE LIMITED—See Datatec Limited; *Int'l*, pg. 1980
ANALYSYS MASON SAS—See Datatec Limited; *Int'l*, pg. 1980
ANALYSYS MASON SPAIN S.L.—See Datatec Limited; *Int'l*, pg. 1980
ANALYSYS MASON S.R.L.—See Datatec Limited; *Int'l*, pg. 1980
ANALYSYS MASON VENTURES FUND NORDIC 1 AS—See Datatec Limited; *Int'l*, pg. 1980
ANALYT DE CENTROAMERICA SA—See HORIBA Ltd; *Int'l*, pg. 3474
ANALYTICA BIO-ENERGY CORP.; *Int'l*, pg. 446
ANALYTICA INC.—See The Aleut Corporation; *U.S. Private*, pg. 3984
ANALYTICAL DEVELOPMENT COMPANY LIMITED—See Halma plc; *Int'l*, pg. 3230
ANALYTICAL ENVIRONMENTAL SERVICES—See Montrose Environmental Group, Inc.; *U.S. Public*, pg. 1466
ANALYTICAL GRAPHICS INC.—See ANSYS, Inc.; *U.S. Public*, pg. 138
ANALYTICA LIMITED; *Int'l*, pg. 446

ANALYTICA LIMITED

ANALYTICAL INDUSTRIES INC.—See Battery Ventures, L.P.; *U.S. Private*, pg. 489
ANALYTICAL INSTRUMENTS SA—See HORIBA Ltd; *Int'l*, pg. 3474
ANALYTICAL MAINTENANCE SERVICES, INC.—See CBRE Group, Inc.; *U.S. Public*, pg. 460
ANALYTICAL RESEARCH LABORATORIES LIMITED—See Ravensdown Limited; *Int'l*, pg. 6223
ANALYTICAL SERVICES, INC.—See Arctic Slope Regional Corporation; *U.S. Private*, pg. 316
ANALYTICAL SERVICES & MATERIALS, INC.; *U.S. Private*, pg. 271
ANALYTICAL SPECTRAL DEVICES, INC.—See Spectris Plc; *Int'l*, pg. 7131
ANALYTICAL SURVEYS, INC.—See RAMTeCH Software Solutions Pvt. Ltd.; *Int'l*, pg. 6200
ANALYTICAL TECHNOLOGY & CONTROL LIMITED; *Int'l*, pg. 446
ANALYTICAL TECHNOLOGY, INC.—See Badger Meter, Inc.; *U.S. Public*, pg. 263
ANALYTICAL WIZARDS, INC.—See Definitive Healthcare Corp.; *U.S. Public*, pg. 648
ANALYTIC INVESTORS, LLC—See Wells Fargo & Company; *U.S. Public*, pg. 2343
ANALYTICO BV—See Eurofins Scientific S.E.; *Int'l*, pg. 2535
ANALYTICO MILIEU NV—See Eurofins Scientific S.E.; *Int'l*, pg. 2535
ANALYTICON DISCOVERY GMBH—See BRAIN Biotech AG; *Int'l*, pg. 1137
ANALYTICON DISCOVERY LLC—See BRAIN Biotech AG; *Int'l*, pg. 1137
ANALYTICS8, LLC; *U.S. Private*, pg. 271
ANALYTIC SERVICES, INC.; *U.S. Private*, pg. 271
ANALYTICS NETWORK SRL—See Sesa S.p.A.; *Int'l*, pg. 6728
ANALYTICS PARTNERS, LLC—See HealthAxis Group, LLC; *U.S. Private*, pg. 1895
ANALYTIC STRESS RELIEVING, INC.—See The Cap-Street Group LLC; *U.S. Private*, pg. 4004
ANALYTIK JENA AG—See Endress+Hauser (International) Holding AG; *Int'l*, pg. 2405
ANALYTIK JENA JAPAN CO., LTD.—See Endress+Hauser (International) Holding AG; *Int'l*, pg. 2405
ANALYTIK JENA SHANGHAI INSTRUMENTS CO., LTD.—See Endress+Hauser (International) Holding AG; *Int'l*, pg. 2405
ANALYTIK JENA US, INC.—See Endress+Hauser (International) Holding AG; *Int'l*, pg. 2405
ANALYTIXINSIGHT INC.; *Int'l*, pg. 446
ANALYTIX ON DEMAND, INC.; *U.S. Private*, pg. 271
ANAM ELECTRONICS CO., LTD - CONSUMER A/V DIVISION—See Anam Electronics Co., Ltd.; *Int'l*, pg. 446
ANAM ELECTRONICS CO., LTD.; *Int'l*, pg. 446
ANAMET CANADA, INC.—See Anamet Inc.; *U.S. Private*, pg. 271
ANAMET EUROPE B.V.—See Anamet Inc.; *U.S. Private*, pg. 271
ANAMET INC.; *U.S. Private*, pg. 271
ANAMET SA—See Viohalco SA/NV; *Int'l*, pg. 8243
ANAM INC.; *U.S. Private*, pg. 271
ANAMIZU ELECTRONICS INDUSTRIES, LTD.—See Murata Manufacturing Co., Ltd.; *Int'l*, pg. 5096
ANAMIZU MURATA MANUFACTURING CO., LTD.—See Murata Manufacturing Co., Ltd.; *Int'l*, pg. 5096
ANA MOTOR SERVICE CO., LTD.—See ANA Holdings Inc.; *Int'l*, pg. 444
ANANDA DEVELOPMENT PUBLIC COMPANY LIMITED; *Int'l*, pg. 447
ANANDA FOOD PTY. LTD.—See Elixinol Wellness Limited; *Int'l*, pg. 2363
ANAND I-POWER LIMITED—See Apollo Global Management, Inc.; *U.S. Public*, pg. 160
ANAND PROJECTS LIMITED; *Int'l*, pg. 446
ANAND RATHI WEALTH LIMITED; *Int'l*, pg. 446
ANAND RAYONS LTD.; *Int'l*, pg. 446
ANANGEL-AMERICAN SHIPHOLDINGS LIMITED; *Int'l*, pg. 447
ANAN HIGH TRUST CO., LTD.—See Takuma Co., Ltd.; *Int'l*, pg. 7442
ANANIA & ASSOCIATES INVESTMENT COMPANY LLC; *U.S. Private*, pg. 272
ANAN INTERNATIONAL LIMITED; *Int'l*, pg. 446
ANANTI INC.; *Int'l*, pg. 447
ANANT RAJ LIMITED; *Int'l*, pg. 447
ANAPAC—See Enerpac Tool Group Corp.; *U.S. Public*, pg. 765
ANAPASS, INC.; *Int'l*, pg. 447
ANAP INC.; *Int'l*, pg. 447
ANAPLAN, INC.; *U.S. Public*, pg. 136
ANAPTYSBIO, INC.; *U.S. Public*, pg. 136
ANAQUA, INC.—See Insight Venture Management, LLC; *U.S. Private*, pg. 2087
ANARAFE SL; *Int'l*, pg. 447
ANAREN CERAMICS, INC.—See TTM Technologies, Inc.; *U.S. Public*, pg. 2203
ANAREN COMMUNICATIONS SUZHOU CO., LTD.—See TTM Technologies, Inc.; *U.S. Public*, pg. 2203

ANAREN, INC.—See TTM Technologies, Inc.; *U.S. Public*, pg. 2203
ANAREN MICROWAVE (EUROPE), INC.—See TTM Technologies, Inc.; *U.S. Public*, pg. 2203
ANAREN MICROWAVE, INC.—See TTM Technologies, Inc.; *U.S. Public*, pg. 2203
ANA SALES CO., LTD.—See ANA Holdings Inc.; *Int'l*, pg. 444
ANASIA - EGYPT (S.A.E.)—See Endress+Hauser (International) Holding AG; *Int'l*, pg. 2405
ANAS INTERNATIONAL ENTERPRISE S.P.A.—See Ferrovie dello Stato Italiane S.p.A.; *Int'l*, pg. 2645
ANA SKY BUILDING SERVICE CO., LTD.—See ANA Holdings Inc.; *Int'l*, pg. 444
ANASPEC INC.—See Kaneka Corporation; *Int'l*, pg. 4066
ANASTASIA CONFECTIONS, INC.—See Hilton Grand Vacations Inc.; *U.S. Public*, pg. 1039
ANASTASI CONSTRUCTION COMPANY, L.L.C.; *U.S. Private*, pg. 272
ANASTASI DEVELOPMENT COMPANY, LLC.; *U.S. Private*, pg. 272
ANASTORIA SDN. BHD.—See South Malaysia Industries Berhad; *Int'l*, pg. 7116
ANASYS INSTRUMENTS CORP.—See Bruker Corporation; *U.S. Public*, pg. 404
ANATARA LIFESCIENCES LTD.; *Int'l*, pg. 447
ANATEC AG—See STMicroelectronics N.V.; *Int'l*, pg. 7217
ANATECH CORP.—See Muncherner Ruckversicherungs AG; *Int'l*, pg. 5090
ANATECH, LTD.—See Cancer Diagnostics, Inc.; *U.S. Private*, pg. 733
ANA TELEMART CO., LTD.—See ANA Holdings Inc.; *Int'l*, pg. 444
ANATOMY IT, LLC; *U.S. Private*, pg. 272
ANATOMY SUPPLY PARTNERS; *U.S. Private*, pg. 272
ANATRACE PRODUCTS, LLC—See StoneCalibre, LLC; *U.S. Private*, pg. 3827
ANA TRADING DUTY FREE CO., LTD.—See ANA Holdings Inc.; *Int'l*, pg. 444
A. NATTERMANN & CIE. GMBH—See Sanofi; *Int'l*, pg. 6547
ANAVEO SAS—See Bridgepoint Group Plc; *Int'l*, pg. 1154
ANAVEX LIFE SCIENCES CORP.; *U.S. Public*, pg. 136
ANA WING FELLOWS VIE OJI CO., LTD.—See ANA Holdings Inc.; *Int'l*, pg. 444
ANA WINGS—See ANA Holdings Inc.; *Int'l*, pg. 444
ANAWON TRUST—See Bristol County Savings Bank; *U.S. Private*, pg. 656
ANAX METALS LIMITED; *Int'l*, pg. 447
ANAZAOHEALTH INC.—See Fagron NV; *Int'l*, pg. 2602
ANBANG INSURANCE GROUP CO., LTD.; *Int'l*, pg. 447
ANBANG LIFE INSURANCE INC.—See Anbang Insurance Group Co., Ltd.; *Int'l*, pg. 447
ANBAO CORP.—See SECOM Co., Ltd.; *Int'l*, pg. 6670
ANBAO INSURANCE PTE LTD—See Orica Limited; *Int'l*, pg. 5619
ANB BANK—See The Sturm Financial Group, Inc.; *U.S. Private*, pg. 4124
ANBC, INC.; *Int'l*, pg. 447
ANB INVEST—See Arab National Bank; *Int'l*, pg. 531
A.N.B. LABORATORIES CO., LTD.—See Bangkok Dusit Medical Services Public Company Limited; *Int'l*, pg. 833
A.N.B. LABORATORY CO., LTD.—See Bangkok Dusit Medical Services Public Company Limited; *Int'l*, pg. 833
ANBO INC—See ANDRITZ AG; *Int'l*, pg. 455
AN CADILLAC OF WPB, LLC—See AutoNation, Inc.; *U.S. Public*, pg. 231
ANCA DO BRASIL—See ANCA Pty Ltd; *Int'l*, pg. 448
ANCA GMBH—See ANCA Pty Ltd; *Int'l*, pg. 447
ANCA JAPAN—See ANCA Pty Ltd; *Int'l*, pg. 447
ANCALA PARTNERS LLP; *Int'l*, pg. 447
ANCA MACHINE TOOL (SHANGHAI) CO. LTD—See ANCA Pty Ltd; *Int'l*, pg. 447
ANCA MACHINE TOOLS PRIVATE LTD—See ANCA Pty Ltd; *Int'l*, pg. 448
ANCA MOTION PTY. LTD.—See ANCA Pty Ltd; *Int'l*, pg. 448
ANCA MOTION TAIWAN CO., LTD—See ANCA Pty Ltd; *Int'l*, pg. 448
ANCAP MANAGEMENT INC.; *U.S. Private*, pg. 272
ANCA PTY LTD; *Int'l*, pg. 447
ANCA (THAILAND) LTD—See ANCA Pty Ltd; *Int'l*, pg. 447
ANCA (UK) LTD—See ANCA Pty Ltd; *Int'l*, pg. 447
ANCA (USA) INC—See ANCA Pty Ltd; *Int'l*, pg. 447
ANC CAPITAL VENTURES, INC.; *Int'l*, pg. 447
ANCELIN SAS—See VINCI S.A.; *Int'l*, pg. 8212
AN CENTRAL REGION MANAGEMENT, LLC—See AutoNation, Inc.; *U.S. Public*, pg. 231
ANCERO, LLC; *U.S. Private*, pg. 272
ANCESTRY.COM EUROPE S.A R.L.—See Blackstone Inc.; *U.S. Public*, pg. 348
ANCESTRY.COM LLC—See Blackstone Inc.; *U.S. Public*, pg. 347
AN/CF ACQUISITION CORP.—See AutoNation, Inc.; *U.S. Public*, pg. 232
ANCHENG PROPERTY & CASUALTY INSURANCE CO., LTD.; *Int'l*, pg. 448
AN CHEVROLET - ARROWHEAD, INC.—See AutoNation, Inc.; *U.S. Public*, pg. 231

CORPORATE AFFILIATIONS

ANCHIN, BLOCK & ANCHIN LLP; *U.S. Private*, pg. 272
ANCHIN CAPITAL ADVISORS LLC—See Anchin, Block & Anchin LLP; *U.S. Private*, pg. 272
ANCHORAGE CAPITAL GROUP, L.L.C.; *U.S. Private*, pg. 273
ANCHORAGE CAPITAL PARTNERS PTY. LIMITED; *Int'l*, pg. 448
ANCHORAGE MEDIA GROUP—See Shivers Trading & Operating Company; *U.S. Private*, pg. 3638
ANCHOR AGENCY, INC.—See Pioneer Savings Bank; *U.S. Private*, pg. 3188
ANCHORAGE SAND & GRAVEL COMPANY, INC.—See MDU Resources Group, Inc.; *U.S. Public*, pg. 1409
ANCHORAGE SURGICENTER, LLC—See HCA Healthcare, Inc.; *U.S. Public*, pg. 990
ANCHORAGE SUZUKI ARCTIC CAT; *U.S. Private*, pg. 274
ANCHOR BANK; *U.S. Private*, pg. 272
ANCHOR BAY ENTERTAINMENT, LLC—See Lions Gate Entertainment Corp.; *Int'l*, pg. 4521
ANCHOR BLOCK COMPANY—See CRH plc; *Int'l*, pg. 1845
ANCHOR BRAKE SHOE COMPANY LLC—See Knorr-Bremse AG; *Int'l*, pg. 4209
ANCHOR BREWERS & DISTILLERS, LLC—See The Griffin Group, LLC; *U.S. Private*, pg. 4039
ANCHOR CAPITAL ADVISORS LLC; *U.S. Private*, pg. 272
ANCHOR CAPITAL PROPRIETARY LIMITED—See Anchor Group Limited; *Int'l*, pg. 448
ANCHOR CHEMICALS (PTY) LTD—See Hobart Enterprises Ltd; *Int'l*, pg. 3436
THE ANCHOR CIGAR & CANDY COMPANY INC.—See Tri County Wholesale Distributors Inc.; *U.S. Private*, pg. 4220
ANCHOR CNGO CORP.; *U.S. Private*, pg. 272
ANCHOR COMMERCIAL REALTY CORP.; *U.S. Private*, pg. 272
ANCHOR COMPUTER INC.; *U.S. Private*, pg. 272
ANCHOR COMPUTER INC.—See Anchor Computer Inc.; *U.S. Private*, pg. 272
ANCHOR CONCRETE PRODUCTS INC.—See CRH plc; *Int'l*, pg. 1845
ANCHOR CONSTRUCTION CORPORATION; *U.S. Private*, pg. 273
ANCHOR CONSTRUCTION INDUSTRIAL PRODUCTS LTD; *Int'l*, pg. 448
ANCHOR COUPLING, INC.—See Caterpillar, Inc.; *U.S. Public*, pg. 449
THE ANCHOR DANLY COMPANY—See Connell Limited Partnership; *U.S. Private*, pg. 1017
ANCHOR DIE TECHNOLOGIES—See Anchor Manufacturing Group, Inc.; *U.S. Private*, pg. 273
ANCHOR DRILLING FLUIDS USA, LLC—See Palladium Equity Partners, LLC; *U.S. Private*, pg. 3078
ANCHOR FABRICATION LTD.; *U.S. Private*, pg. 273
ANCHOR FIRE PROTECTION CO.—See The Carlyle Group Inc.; *U.S. Public*, pg. 2053
ANCHORFREE, INC.; *U.S. Private*, pg. 274
ANCHOR GASOLINE CORPORATION; *U.S. Private*, pg. 273
ANCHOR GENERAL INSURANCE AGENCY, INC.; *U.S. Private*, pg. 273
ANCHOR GLASS CONTAINER CORPORATION—See BA Glass B.V.; *Int'l*, pg. 791
ANCHOR GLASS CONTAINER CORPORATION—See CVC Capital Partners SICAV-FIS S.A.; *Int'l*, pg. 1884
ANCHOR GROUP LIMITED; *Int'l*, pg. 448
ANCHOR GRUP S.A.—See Fiba Holding A.S.; *Int'l*, pg. 2651
ANCHOR HOCKING, CANADA, INC.—See EveryWare Global, Inc.; *U.S. Private*, pg. 1441
ANCHOR HOCKING, LLC—See EveryWare Global, Inc.; *U.S. Private*, pg. 1441
ANCHOR INDUSTRIES, INC. - LEISURE POOLS FACTORY—See Anchor Industries, Inc.; *U.S. Private*, pg. 273
ANCHOR INDUSTRIES, INC.; *U.S. Private*, pg. 273
ANCHOR INNOVATION, INC.; *U.S. Private*, pg. 273
ANCHOR INSULATION CO., INC.—See Installed Building Products, Inc.; *U.S. Public*, pg. 1132
ANCHOR INSURANCE GROUP, INC.—See Vitol Holding B.V.; *Int'l*, pg. 8260
ANCHOR INSURANCE S.A.—See Vitol Holding B.V.; *Int'l*, pg. 8261
ANCHOR INTERNATIONAL BV—See IG Design Group Plc; *Int'l*, pg. 3600
ANCHOR KING LTD.—See Clean Harbors, Inc.; *U.S. Public*, pg. 510
ANCHOR LAMINA AMERICA, INC.—See MISUMI Group Inc.; *Int'l*, pg. 4921
ANCHOR LAND HOLDINGS, INC.; *Int'l*, pg. 448
ANCHOR LAS AB; *Int'l*, pg. 448
ANCHOR MANUFACTURING GROUP, INC.; *U.S. Private*, pg. 273
ANCHOR METAL PROCESSING—See Anchor Manufacturing Group, Inc.; *U.S. Private*, pg. 273
ANCHOR PAINT CO. OF DENVER INC.—See Anchor Paint Manufacturing Co. Inc.; *U.S. Private*, pg. 273

COMPANY NAME INDEX

ANCHOR PAINT CO. OF OKLAHOMA CITY INC.—See Anchor Paint Manufacturing Co. Inc.; *U.S. Private*, pg. 273
ANCHOR PAINT MANUFACTURING CO. INC.; *U.S. Private*, pg. 273
ANCHOR PAPER COMPANY; *U.S. Private*, pg. 273
ANCHOR PHARMACY & MEDICAL SUPPLIES; *U.S. Private*, pg. 273
ANCHOR POST PRODUCTS OF TEXAS, INC.; *U.S. Private*, pg. 273
ANCHOR PRINTING COMPANY—See Harvest Partners L.P.; *U.S. Private*, pg. 1876
ANCHOR QEA, LLC; *U.S. Private*, pg. 273
ANCHOR RESOURCES LIMITED; *Int'l*, pg. 448
ANCHOR RETAIL INVESTMENTS N.V.—See Fiba Holding A.S.; *Int'l*, pg. 2651
ANCHOR RISK SERVICES GMBH—See Kuehne + Nagel International AG; *Int'l*, pg. 4324
ANCHOR RUBBER PRODUCTS, LLC—See Align Capital Partners, LLC; *U.S. Private*, pg. 167
ANCHOR SECURITIES PRIVATE CLIENTS PROPRIETARY LIMITED—See Anchor Group Limited; *Int'l*, pg. 448
ANCHOR SEMICONDUCTOR, INC.—See KLA Corporation; *U.S. Public*, pg. 1267
ANCHOR (SHANGHAI) SEMICONDUCTOR INC.—See KLA Corporation; *U.S. Public*, pg. 1267
ANCHOR SOFTWARE LLC—See Anchor Computer Inc.; *U.S. Private*, pg. 272
ANCHOR STAFFING, INC.—See Lyneer Staffing Solutions, LLC; *U.S. Private*, pg. 2521
ANCHOR STONE COMPANY; *U.S. Private*, pg. 273
ANCHORSTONE HOLDINGS LTD.; *Int'l*, pg. 448
ANCHOR SUBARU; *U.S. Private*, pg. 273
ANCHOR SYSTEMS PTY LTD—See Deluxe Corporation; *U.S. Public*, pg. 652
ANCHOR TAMPA, INC.; *U.S. Private*, pg. 273
ANCHOR WALL SYSTEMS—See CRH plc; *Int'l*, pg. 1845
ANCHOR WORLDWIDE, LLC; *U.S. Private*, pg. 273
ANCHOR YEAST (PTY) LTD.—See Lallemand, Inc.; *Int'l*, pg. 4399
ANCHUN INTERNATIONAL HOLDINGS LTD.; *Int'l*, pg. 449
ANCILLA SYSTEMS INCORPORATED; *U.S. Private*, pg. 274
ANCIRA ENTERPRISES INC.; *U.S. Private*, pg. 274
ANCO ANIMAL NUTRITION COMPETENCE GMBH—See Archer-Daniels-Midland Company; *U.S. Public*, pg. 183
ANCOFER STAHLHANDEL GMBH—See AG der Dillinger Huttenwerke; *Int'l*, pg. 197
ANCOFERWALDRAM STEELPLATES B.V.—See AG der Dillinger Huttenwerke; *Int'l*, pg. 197
ANCO INSURANCE MANAGERS INC.; *U.S. Private*, pg. 274
ANCO INSURANCE SERVICES—See Anco Insurance Managers Inc.; *U.S. Private*, pg. 274
AN COLLISION CENTER FTL SOUTH, INC.—See AutoNation, Inc.; *U.S. Public*, pg. 231
AN COLLISION CENTER OF ADDISON, INC.—See AutoNation, Inc.; *U.S. Public*, pg. 231
AN COLLISION CENTER OF LAS VEGAS, INC.—See AutoNation, Inc.; *U.S. Public*, pg. 231
AN COLLISION CENTER OF NORTH HOUSTON, INC.—See AutoNation, Inc.; *U.S. Public*, pg. 231
AN COLLISION CENTER OF SARASOTA, INC.—See AutoNation, Inc.; *U.S. Public*, pg. 231
AN COLLISION CENTER OF TEMPE, INC.—See AutoNation, Inc.; *U.S. Public*, pg. 231
ANCOM BIOSCIENCE SDN. BHD.—See Ancom Nylex Berhad; *Int'l*, pg. 449
ANCOM-CHEMQUEST TERMINALS SDN. BHD.—See Ancom Logistics Berhad; *Int'l*, pg. 449
ANCOM COMPONENTS SDN. BHD.—See Ancom Nylex Berhad; *Int'l*, pg. 449
ANCOM CROP CARE SDN. BHD.—See Ancom Nylex Berhad; *Int'l*, pg. 449
ANCOM LOGISTICS BERHAD; *Int'l*, pg. 449
ANCOM NYLEX BERHAD; *Int'l*, pg. 449
ANCOM NYLEX TERMINALS SDN. BHD.—See Ancom Logistics Berhad; *Int'l*, pg. 449
ANCONA ENTERPRISES INC.; *U.S. Private*, pg. 274
ANCONA GRAIN INC.; *U.S. Private*, pg. 274
ANCON BUILDING PRODUCTS PTY LTD—See CRH plc; *Int'l*, pg. 1842
ANCON CONSTRUCTION COMPANY; *U.S. Private*, pg. 274
ANCON KOT LOGISTICS—See Ancon Marine, LLC; *U.S. Private*, pg. 274
ANCON LIMITED—See CRH plc; *Int'l*, pg. 1843
ANCON MARINE, LLC; *U.S. Private*, pg. 274
ANCO PRODUCTS, INC.—See APi Group Corporation; *Int'l*, pg. 513
ANCORA CHUMBADORES LTDA.; *Int'l*, pg. 449
ANCORA COFFEE & TEA; *U.S. Private*, pg. 275
ANCOR HOLDINGS, L.P.; *U.S. Private*, pg. 274
ANCOR INFORMATION MANAGEMENT LLC—See GI Manager L.P.; *U.S. Private*, pg. 1692
AN CORPUS CHRISTI CHEVROLET, LP—See AutoNation, Inc.; *U.S. Public*, pg. 231

AN CORPUS CHRISTI MOTORS, INC.—See AutoNation, Inc.; *U.S. Public*, pg. 231
AN CORPUS CHRISTI T. IMPORTS, LP—See AutoNation, Inc.; *U.S. Public*, pg. 231
ANCO SP. Z O.O.—See E.ON SE; *Int'l*, pg. 2251
ANCOTECH AG—See INDUS Holding AG; *Int'l*, pg. 3662
ANCOTECH GMBH—See INDUS Holding AG; *Int'l*, pg. 3662
AN COUNTY LINE FORD, INC.—See AutoNation, Inc.; *U.S. Public*, pg. 231
ANCRA ABT AB—See The Heico Companies, L.L.C.; *U.S. Private*, pg. 4050
ANCRA AUSTRALIA PTY. LTD.—See The Heico Companies, L.L.C.; *U.S. Private*, pg. 4050
ANCRA ESPANA S.L.—See The Heico Companies, L.L.C.; *U.S. Private*, pg. 4050
ANCRA ESPANA—See The Heico Companies, L.L.C.; *U.S. Private*, pg. 4050
ANCRA INTERNATIONAL LLC - CARGO DIVISION—See The Heico Companies, L.L.C.; *U.S. Private*, pg. 4050
ANCRA INTERNATIONAL LLC—See The Heico Companies, L.L.C.; *U.S. Private*, pg. 4050
ANCRA INTERNATIONAL LLC—See The Heico Companies, L.L.C.; *U.S. Private*, pg. 4050
ANCRA INTERNATIONAL LLC—See The Heico Companies, L.L.C.; *U.S. Private*, pg. 4050
ANCRA INTERNATIONAL LLC—See The Heico Companies, L.L.C.; *U.S. Private*, pg. 4050
ANCRA INTERNATIONAL SARL—See The Heico Companies, L.L.C.; *U.S. Private*, pg. 4050
ANCRA JAPAN LTD.—See allsafe JUNGFALK GmbH & Co. KG; *Int'l*, pg. 360
ANCRA NEW ZEALAND LIMITED—See The Heico Companies, L.L.C.; *U.S. Private*, pg. 4050
ANCRA SYSTEMS BV—See The Heico Companies, L.L.C.; *U.S. Private*, pg. 4050
ANC RESEARCH & DEVELOPMENT LLC - CONSTRUCTION DIVISION—See Cook Inlet Region, Inc.; *U.S. Private*, pg. 1038
ANC RESEARCH & DEVELOPMENT LLC—See Cook Inlet Region, Inc.; *U.S. Private*, pg. 1038
ANCRONA AB—See FMCG Business Partner AB; *Int'l*, pg. 2717
ANC SPORTS ENTERPRISES, LLC—See Atairos Group, Inc.; *U.S. Private*, pg. 363
AN CUONG WOOD-WORKING JOINT STOCK COMPANY—See Sumitomo Forestry Co., Ltd.; *Int'l*, pg. 7285
ANC WORLDCHOICE HOLIDAYS LTD.—See Amathus Public Limited; *Int'l*, pg. 413
ANDACOR S.A.; *Int'l*, pg. 449
ANDA, INC.—See Teva Pharmaceutical Industries, Ltd.; *Int'l*, pg. 7580
ANDA INSURANCE AGENCIES PTE. LTD.—See Marsh & McLennan Companies, Inc.; *U.S. Public*, pg. 1374
ANDALAY SOLAR, INC.; *U.S. Private*, pg. 275
ANDALE FARMERS COOPERATIVE CO.; *U.S. Private*, pg. 275
ANDALE INC.; *U.S. Private*, pg. 275
ANDALUSIA DISTRIBUTING COMPANY INC.; *U.S. Private*, pg. 275
ANDALUSIA T.V. INC.—See Koninklijke Philips N.V.; *Int'l*, pg. 4269
ANDALUSI BEVERAGES S.L.; *Int'l*, pg. 275
ANDALUZA DE GASES S.A.—See Mitsubishi Chemical Group Corporation; *Int'l*, pg. 4937
AND ANADOLU GAYRIMENKUL YATIRIMLARI A.S.—See Ag Anadolu Grubu Holding Anonim Sirketi; *Int'l*, pg. 197
ANDA PHARMACEUTICALS, INC.—See Teva Pharmaceutical Industries, Ltd.; *Int'l*, pg. 7580
ANDARA TOOLS AND PLANT HIRE LTD—See Bryen & Langley Ltd.; *Int'l*, pg. 1201
ANDA SEMICONDUCTOR TECHNOLOGY (SUZHOU) CO., LTD.—See Everlight Chemical Industrial Co.; *Int'l*, pg. 2567
ANDATEE CHINA MARINE FUEL SERVICES CORPORATION; *Int'l*, pg. 449
ANDAVO TRAVEL; *U.S. Private*, pg. 275
ANDAZ AMSTERDAM PRINSENGRACHT—See Hyatt Hotels Corporation; *U.S. Public*, pg. 1076
ANDAZ LIVERPOOL STREET—See Hyatt Hotels Corporation; *U.S. Public*, pg. 1076
ANDCO CONSULTING, LLC; *U.S. Private*, pg. 275
AND COMPANY CO., LTD.—See TAKE AND GIVE. NEEDS Co. Ltd.; *Int'l*, pg. 7436
ANDEAN PRECIOUS METALS CORP.; *Int'l*, pg. 449
ANDEAN SILVER LIMITED; *Int'l*, pg. 449
ANDEAVOR LLC—See Marathon Petroleum Corporation; *U.S. Public*, pg. 1363
ANDEAVOR LOGISTICS LP—See Marathon Petroleum Corporation; *U.S. Public*, pg. 1364
ANDELCARE, INC.; *U.S. Private*, pg. 275
ANDEL'S BERLIN HOTELBETRIEBS GMBH—See U City Public Company Limited; *Int'l*, pg. 7996
ANDEN CO., LTD.—See Denso Corporation; *Int'l*, pg. 2028
ANDEN (THAILAND) CO., LTD.—See Denso Corporation; *Int'l*, pg. 2028
ANDERA PARTNERS SCA; *Int'l*, pg. 449
ANDERCO, INC—See Metrie Canada Limited; *Int'l*, pg. 4856
ANDERCO INVESTMENT PTE LTD; *Int'l*, pg. 450

A.N. DERINGER, INC.; *U.S. Private*, pg. 27
ANDERMATT ALPINE DESTINATION COMPANY AG—See Orascom Development Holding AG; *Int'l*, pg. 5613
ANDEROL B.V.—See LANXESS AG; *Int'l*, pg. 4415
ANDERSCH AG—See FTI Consulting, Inc.; *U.S. Public*, pg. 890
ANDERSELITE LTD. - LONDON—See AndersElite Ltd.; *Int'l*, pg. 450
ANDERSELITE LTD.; *Int'l*, pg. 450
ANDERSEN & ASSOCIATES INC.; *U.S. Private*, pg. 275
ANDERSEN & CHRISTENSEN AALBORG APS—See Matas A/S; *Int'l*, pg. 4726
ANDERSEN COMMERCIAL PLUMBING, INC.—See Sun Capital Partners, Inc.; *U.S. Public*, pg. 3858
ANDERSEN CORPORATION; *U.S. Private*, pg. 275
ANDERSEN DAIRY INC.; *U.S. Private*, pg. 275
ANDERSEN & MARTINI HOLDING A/S; *Int'l*, pg. 450
ANDERSEN OG AKSNES RORLEGGERBEDRIFT AS—See Instalco AB; *Int'l*, pg. 3721
ANDERSEN WINDOWS, INC.—See Andersen Corporation; *U.S. Private*, pg. 275
ANDERS + KERN (U.K.) LIMITED—See Aukett Swanke Group Plc; *Int'l*, pg. 704
ANDERSON AMERICA CORP.—See Anderson Industrial Corporation; *Int'l*, pg. 450
ANDERSON ANDERSON & BROWN LLP; *Int'l*, pg. 450
ANDERSON ASHCROFT LIMITED—See Brown & Brown, Inc.; *U.S. Public*, pg. 396
ANDERSON AUTOMOTIVE GROUP INC.; *U.S. Private*, pg. 276
ANDERSON AUTOMOTIVE GROUP; *U.S. Private*, pg. 276
ANDERSON AUTO PARTS CO. INC.; *U.S. Private*, pg. 276
ANDERSON BAUMAN TOURTELLOT VOS & CO.—See B. Riley Financial, Inc.; *U.S. Public*, pg. 260
ANDERSON BONELESS BEEF, INC.—See FoodMaven Corporation; *U.S. Private*, pg. 1562
ANDERSON BROTHERS CONSTRUCTION CO. BRAINERD, INC.; *U.S. Private*, pg. 276
ANDERSON CARGO SERVICES, LLC—See Argosy Capital Group, LLC; *U.S. Private*, pg. 321
ANDERSON CARGO SERVICES, LLC—See Headhaul Capital Partners LLC; *U.S. Private*, pg. 1891
ANDERSON CHEMICAL COMPANY INC.—See NCH Corporation; *U.S. Private*, pg. 2876
ANDERSON CHRYSLER JEEP INC.; *U.S. Private*, pg. 276
ANDERSON COLUMBIA CO. INC.; *U.S. Private*, pg. 276
ANDERSON COMPANIES, INC.; *U.S. Private*, pg. 276
ANDERSON CONCRETE CORP.; *U.S. Private*, pg. 276
ANDERSON CONSTRUCTION COMPANY OF FORT GAINES; *U.S. Private*, pg. 276
ANDERSON CONSTRUCTION LTD—See Anderson Group Limited; *Int'l*, pg. 450
ANDERSON-COOK INC. - CLINTON TWP. PLANT—See Anderson-Cook Inc.; *U.S. Private*, pg. 278
ANDERSON-COOK INC. - FRASER PLANT—See Anderson-Cook Inc.; *U.S. Private*, pg. 278
ANDERSON-COOK INC. - SHANGHAI PLANT—See Anderson-Cook Inc.; *U.S. Private*, pg. 278
ANDERSON-COOK INC.; *U.S. Private*, pg. 278
ANDERSON-COOK INC. - STRATFORD PLANT—See Anderson-Cook Inc.; *U.S. Private*, pg. 278
ANDERSON COUNTY LANDFILL, INC.—See Waste Connections, Inc.; *Int'l*, pg. 8353
ANDERSON CUSTOM PROCESSING, INC. - BELLEVILLE PLANT—See Anderson Custom Processing, Inc.; *U.S. Private*, pg. 276
ANDERSON CUSTOM PROCESSING, INC.; *U.S. Private*, pg. 276
ANDERSON & DAHLEN INC.—See Gray Inc.; *U.S. Private*, pg. 1759
ANDERSON DAIRY, INC.; *U.S. Private*, pg. 276
ANDERSON DDB HEALTH & LIFESTYLE—See Omnicom Group Inc.; *U.S. Public*, pg. 1579
ANDERSON DDB HEALTH & LIFESTYLE—See Omnicom Group Inc.; *U.S. Public*, pg. 1579
ANDERSON DDB SANTE.VIE.ESPRIT.—See Omnicom Group Inc.; *U.S. Public*, pg. 1579
ANDERSON DESIGN & BUILD—See Anderson Group Limited; *Int'l*, pg. 450
ANDERSON DEVELOPMENT COMPANY—See Mitsui Chemicals, Inc.; *Int'l*, pg. 4982
ANDERSON DRILLING INC.—See Keller Group plc; *Int'l*, pg. 4119
ANDERSON ELECTRICAL PRODUCTS—See Hubbell Incorporated; *U.S. Public*, pg. 1066
ANDERSON ELECTRIC, INC.; *U.S. Private*, pg. 276
ANDERSON ENTERPRISES & EQUIPMENT, LLC—See Tym Corporation; *U.S. Private*, pg. 7994
ANDERSON EQUIPMENT CO., INC.; *U.S. Private*, pg. 276
ANDERSON ERICKSON DAIRY COMPANY; *U.S. Private*, pg. 276
ANDERSON EUROPE GMBH—See Anderson Industrial Corporation; *Int'l*, pg. 450
ANDERSON FORD MAZDA LLC; *U.S. Private*, pg. 276

ANDERSON FOREST PRODUCTS INC.

CORPORATE AFFILIATIONS

ANDERSON FOREST PRODUCTS INC.; *U.S. Private*, pg. 277
ANDERSON & FRYER EXPORTS INC.—See Twin Rivers Group Inc.; *U.S. Private*, pg. 4265
ANDERSON GAS & PROPANE INC.; *U.S. Private*, pg. 277
ANDERSON-GILYARD; *U.S. Private*, pg. 278
ANDERSON GROUP LIMITED; *Int'l*, pg. 450
THE ANDERSON GROUP, LLC; *U.S. Private*, pg. 3986
THE ANDERSON GROUP; *U.S. Private*, pg. 3986
ANDERSON HARDWOOD FLOORS; *U.S. Private*, pg. 277
ANDERSON HAY & GRAIN CO. INC.; *U.S. Private*, pg. 277
ANDERSON HILL INSURANCE LIMITED—See PepsiCo, Inc.; *U.S. Public*, pg. 1668
ANDERSON & HOWARD ELECTRIC INC.; *U.S. Private*, pg. 275
ANDERSON & HOWARD ELECTRIC, INC.; *U.S. Private*, pg. 275
ANDERSON INDEPENDENT MAIL, LLC—See Gannett Co., Inc.; *U.S. Public*, pg. 898
ANDERSON INDUSTRIAL CORPORATION - HOULUNG FACTORY—See Anderson Industrial Corporation; *Int'l*, pg. 450
ANDERSON INDUSTRIAL CORPORATION; *Int'l*, pg. 450
ANDERSON INDUSTRIAL HONG KONG LIMITED—See Anderson Industrial Corporation; *Int'l*, pg. 450
ANDERSON INDUSTRIES LLC; *U.S. Private*, pg. 277
ANDERSON INSTRUMENT CO., INC.—See Fortive Corporation; *U.S. Public*, pg. 870
ANDERSON INSURANCE & INVESTMENT AGENCY—See Associated Banc-Corp; *U.S. Public*, pg. 214
ANDERSON INTERNATIONAL CORP.; *U.S. Private*, pg. 277
ANDERSON LA, INC.—See Chatham Asset Management, LLC; *U.S. Private*, pg. 862
ANDERSON LANDFILL, INC.—See Waste Management, Inc.; *U.S. Public*, pg. 2330
ANDERSON LANDFILL, INC.—See Waste Management, Inc.; *U.S. Public*, pg. 2330
ANDERSON MACHINERY COMPANY; *U.S. Private*, pg. 277
ANDERSON MACHINERY (SINGAPORE) PTE. LTD.—See Anderson Industrial Corporation; *Int'l*, pg. 450
ANDERSON MANUFACTURING CO., INC—See Big Shoulders Capital LLC; *U.S. Private*, pg. 554
ANDERSON MANUFACTURING INC.—See Keller Group plc; *Int'l*, pg. 4119
ANDERSON MARKETING GROUP; *U.S. Private*, pg. 277
ANDERSON-MCQUEEN COMPANY; *U.S. Private*, pg. 278
ANDERSON MERCHANDISERS, L.P.—See Anderson Companies, Inc.; *U.S. Private*, pg. 276
ANDERSON METALS, LLC—See Gemspring Capital Management, LLC; *U.S. Private*, pg. 1659
ANDERSON & MIDDLETON COMPANY; *U.S. Private*, pg. 275
ANDERSON MOTORS; *U.S. Private*, pg. 277
ANDERSON OIL COMPANY INCORPORATED; *U.S. Private*, pg. 277
ANDERSON PARTNERS; *U.S. Private*, pg. 277
ANDERSONPENNA PARTNERS, INC.—See Littlejohn & Co., LLC; *U.S. Private*, pg. 2469
ANDERSON PERFORMANCE IMPROVEMENT COMPANY, INC.—See Business Impact Group LLC; *U.S. Private*, pg. 694
ANDERSON PERU MINING AND EXPLORATION S.A.C.—See Silver North Resources Ltd.; *Int'l*, pg. 6924
ANDERSON POWER PRODUCTS, LTD.—See IDEAL Industries Inc; *U.S. Private*, pg. 2036
ANDERSON POWER PRODUCTS—See IDEAL Industries Inc; *U.S. Private*, pg. 2036
ANDERSON PRESS INC; *U.S. Private*, pg. 277
ANDERSON PRODUCTS, INC.—See Weiler Corporation; *U.S. Private*, pg. 4471
ANDERSON REGENERATE—See Anderson Group Limited; *Int'l*, pg. 450
ANDERSON REGIONAL HEALTH SYSTEM; *U.S. Private*, pg. 277
ANDERSON REGIONAL MEDICAL CENTER—See Anderson Regional Health System; *U.S. Private*, pg. 277
THE ANDERSONS CANADA LIMITED—See The Andersons Incorporated; *U.S. Public*, pg. 2034
THE ANDERSONS CLYMERS ETHANOL LLC—See The Andersons Incorporated; *U.S. Public*, pg. 2034
THE ANDERSONS DENISON ETHANOL LLC—See The Andersons Incorporated; *U.S. Public*, pg. 2035
ANDERSON SEAL, INC.—See Trelleborg AB; *Int'l*, pg. 7913
ANDERSON SERVICES; *U.S. Private*, pg. 277
ANDERSON'S FORMAL WEAR INC.—See Frana & Associates Inc.; *U.S. Private*, pg. 1586
THE ANDERSONS, INC. - AUBURN GRAIN—See The Andersons Incorporated; *U.S. Public*, pg. 2035
THE ANDERSONS INCORPORATED; *U.S. Public*, pg. 2034

THE ANDERSONS LAWN FERTILIZER DIVISION, INC.—See The Andersons Incorporated; *U.S. Public*, pg. 2035
THE ANDERSONS MARATHON ETHANOL LLC—See The Andersons Incorporated; *U.S. Public*, pg. 2035
ANDERSON SPRATT GROUP; *Int'l*, pg. 450
THE ANDERSONS, SOUTHERN REGION—See The Andersons Incorporated; *U.S. Public*, pg. 2034
ANDERSON STEEL SUPPLY, INC.; *U.S. Private*, pg. 277
ANDERSONS (WHOLESALE) LIMITED—See Kitwave Group Plc; *Int'l*, pg. 4195
ANDERSON TAIWAN (CENTRAL)—See Anderson Industrial Corporation; *Int'l*, pg. 450
ANDERSON TECHNOLOGIES INC.; *U.S. Private*, pg. 277
ANDERSON TRUCKING SERVICE INC.; *U.S. Private*, pg. 277
ANDERSON-TULLY CO.; *U.S. Private*, pg. 278
ANDERSON & VREELAND INC.—See Anderson & Vreeland, Inc.; *U.S. Private*, pg. 276
ANDERSON & VREELAND, INC.; *U.S. Private*, pg. 276
ANDERSON WATER SYSTEMS LIMITED—See Veolia Environnement S.A.; *Int'l*, pg. 8155
ANDERSON WEBER TOYOTA-LINCOLN-MERCURY; *U.S. Private*, pg. 277
ANDERSON ZAKS LIMITED—See Global Payments Inc.; *U.S. Public*, pg. 943
ANDERSON ZURMUEHLEN & CO., PC; *U.S. Private*, pg. 277
ANDERSSON & PARTNERS; *Int'l*, pg. 450
ANDERTON CONCRETE PRODUCTS LTD.—See Ibstock plc; *Int'l*, pg. 3577
ANDES 7, INC.; *U.S. Private*, pg. 278
ANDES CANDIES LP—See Tootsie Roll Industries, Inc.; *U.S. Public*, pg. 2163
ANDES CHEMICAL CORPORATION—See IMCD N.V.; *Int'l*, pg. 3621
ANDES CORPORACION MINERA S.A.—See McEwen Mining Inc.; *Int'l*, pg. 4758
ANDES GOLD CORP.; *U.S. Public*, pg. 136
ANDES MANUFACTURING LLC—See Tootsie Roll Industries, Inc.; *U.S. Public*, pg. 2163
ANDES SOLAR SPA—See The AES Corporation; *U.S. Public*, pg. 2031
ANDES TECHNOLOGY CORPORATION; *Int'l*, pg. 450
ANDES TECHNOLOGY USA CORPORATION—See Andes Technology Corporation; *Int'l*, pg. 450
ANDEX INDUSTRIES INC.; *U.S. Private*, pg. 278
AND FACTORY, INC.; *Int'l*, pg. 449
ANDFJORD SALMON AS; *Int'l*, pg. 450
ANDGAR CORPORATION; *U.S. Private*, pg. 278
AND GLOBAL PTE. LTD.—See Marubeni Corporation; *Int'l*, pg. 4705
ANDHRA BANK—See Union Bank of India; *Int'l*, pg. 8051
ANDHRA CEMENTS LIMITED—See Jaiprakash Associates Limited; *Int'l*, pg. 3873
ANDHRA PAPER LIMITED—See West Coast Paper Mills Ltd.; *Int'l*, pg. 8383
THE ANDHRA PETROCHEMICALS LIMITED; *Int'l*, pg. 7613
ANDHRA PRADESH TANNERIES LTD.; *Int'l*, pg. 451
THE ANDHRA SUGARS LIMITED; *Int'l*, pg. 7613
ANDIAMO CORPORATION; *U.S. Public*, pg. 136
ANDI ASISTENCIA, S.A.—See MAPFRE S.A.; *Int'l*, pg. 4684
ANDINA BOTTLING INVESTMENTS SA—See Embotelladora Andina S.A.; *Int'l*, pg. 2375
ANDINO CEMENTS USA, LLC; *U.S. Private*, pg. 278
ANDIS ADVERTISING; *U.S. Private*, pg. 278
ANDISCH, INC.; *U.S. Private*, pg. 278
ANDIS COMPANY; *U.S. Private*, pg. 278
ANDLAND OVERSEAS S.A.—See Abbott Laboratories; *U.S. Public*, pg. 19
ANDLAUER HEALTHCARE GROUP, INC.; *Int'l*, pg. 451
ANDLINGER & COMPANY CVBA—See Andlinger & Company, Inc.; *U.S. Private*, pg. 278
ANDLINGER & COMPANY GMBH—See Andlinger & Company, Inc.; *U.S. Private*, pg. 278
ANDLINGER & COMPANY, INC.; *U.S. Private*, pg. 278
A N D MUSIC CORP.—See Young Chang Akki Co. Ltd.; *Int'l*, pg. 8602
ANDO HOLDINGS LTD.; *Int'l*, pg. 451
ANDON HEALTH CO., LTD.; *Int'l*, pg. 451
ANDOR CO., LTD.—See TCS Holdings Co., Ltd.; *Int'l*, pg. 7485
ANDOR SYSTEM SUPPORT CO., LTD.—See Sobal Corporation; *Int'l*, pg. 7030
ANDOR TECHNOLOGY CHINA—See Oxford Instruments Plc; *Int'l*, pg. 5674
ANDOR TECHNOLOGY JAPAN—See Oxford Instruments Plc; *Int'l*, pg. 5674
ANDOR TECHNOLOGY LTD.—See Oxford Instruments Plc; *Int'l*, pg. 5674
ANDOR TECHNOLOGY (USA)—See Oxford Instruments Plc; *Int'l*, pg. 5674
ANDORVER PLACE APTS. L.L.C.—See Veris Residential, Inc.; *U.S. Public*, pg. 2281
ANDOVER BANCORP, INC.; *U.S. Private*, pg. 278
ANDOVER BANK—See Andover Bancorp, Inc.; *U.S. Public*, pg. 136

ANDOVER CAPITAL CORPORATION; *Int'l*, pg. 451
ANDOVER COMMUNICATIONS, INC.; *U.S. Private*, pg. 279
THE ANDOVER COMPANIES; *U.S. Private*, pg. 3986
ANDOVER HEALTHCARE, INC.—See Milliken & Company; *U.S. Private*, pg. 2737
ANDOVER HOUSE LLC—See UDR, Inc.; *U.S. Public*, pg. 2218
ANDOVER NATIONAL CORPORATION; *U.S. Private*, pg. 279
ANDPAK, INC.—See ADDEV Material SAS; *Int'l*, pg. 128
ANDRADA MINING LIMITED; *Int'l*, pg. 451
ANDRADE & CANELLAS ENERGIA S.A.; *Int'l*, pg. 451
ANDRADE GUTIERREZ CONCESSOES S.A.; *Int'l*, pg. 451
ANDRADE GUTIERREZ PARTICIPACOES S.A.—See Andrade Gutierrez Concessoes S.A.; *Int'l*, pg. 451
ANDRA PRADESH EXPRESSWAY LIMITED—See Infrastructure Leasing & Financial Services Limited; *Int'l*, pg. 3697
ANDREA ELECTRONICS CORPORATION; *U.S. Public*, pg. 136
ANDREA INTERNATIONAL—See American International Industries Company; *U.S. Private*, pg. 238
ANDREAS BONIFER, SPEDITION- UND VERKEHRSUN-TERNEHMENS VERWALTUNGS-GMBH—See Metropolitan European Transport Limited; *Int'l*, pg. 4864
ANDREAS FURNITURE COMPANY INC.; *U.S. Private*, pg. 279
ANDREAS SIMONSEN GMBH FROZEN FISH DIVISION—See Andreas Simonsen GmbH; *Int'l*, pg. 451
ANDREAS SIMONSEN GMBH; *Int'l*, pg. 451
ANDREAS STIHL AG & CO.; *Int'l*, pg. 451
ANDRE-BOUDIN BAKERIES INC.; *U.S. Private*, pg. 279
ANDREESSEN HOROWITZ; *U.S. Private*, pg. 279
ANDREINI & COMPANY—See PCF Insurance Services of The West, LLC; *U.S. Private*, pg. 3120
ANDRELL INC.; *U.S. Private*, pg. 279
ANDREOLI/MS&L—See Publicis Groupe S.A.; *Int'l*, pg. 6102
ANDRE PROST, INC.; *U.S. Private*, pg. 279
ANDRE-ROMBERG INSURANCE AGENCY, INC.—See Stone Point Capital LLC; *U.S. Private*, pg. 3818
ANDRES CONSTRUCTION SERVICES INC.; *U.S. Private*, pg. 279
ANDRESEN TOWERS A/S—See IAI Holding A/S; *Int'l*, pg. 3568
ANDRESS ENGINEERING ASSOCIATES INC.; *U.S. Private*, pg. 279
ANDRE TECHNOLOGIES & STATRON SA—See Statron AG; *Int'l*, pg. 7185
ANDRETTI PETROLEUM, LLC; *U.S. Private*, pg. 279
ANDRETTI WINERY; *U.S. Private*, pg. 279
ANDRE VOSS ERDBAU UND TRANSPORT GMBH; *Int'l*, pg. 451
ANDREW BETHELL ASSOCIATES LIMITED—See Pico (Thailand) Public Company Limited; *Int'l*, pg. 5860
ANDREW CHRISTIAN, INC.; *U.S. Private*, pg. 279
ANDREW CONSTRUCTION CO II, INC.; *U.S. Private*, pg. 279
ANDREW HARPER, LLC—See Travel Leaders Group, LLC; *U.S. Private*, pg. 4213
ANDREW HENDRIKS & SONS GREENHOUSES; *Int'l*, pg. 451
ANDREW INDUSTRIAL TEXTILE MANUFACTURING COMPANY (WUXI) LIMITED—See Lydall, Inc.; *U.S. Public*, pg. 1349
ANDREW INSURANCE ASSOCIATES, INC.—See Arthur J. Gallagher & Co.; *U.S. Public*, pg. 202
ANDREW JONES TRAVEL PTY LTD.—See Corporate Travel Management Limited; *Int'l*, pg. 1805
ANDREW LAUREN CO. INC.; *U.S. Private*, pg. 279
ANDREW MACALLISTER SA; *Int'l*, pg. 451
ANDREW MUIRHEAD & SON LIMITED—See Scottish Leather Group Ltd.; *Int'l*, pg. 6653
ANDREW PELLER LIMITED; *Int'l*, pg. 451
ANDREW P.M. PETRIDES & SONS LTD.—See Max Weishaupt GmbH; *Int'l*, pg. 4735
ANDREW R. MANCINI ASSOCIATES, INC.; *U.S. Private*, pg. 279
ANDREW SATCOM AFTICA (PTY.) LTD.—See CommScope Holding Company, Inc.; *U.S. Public*, pg. 548
ANDREWS & CO, LLC; *U.S. Private*, pg. 280
ANDREWS CONNECTICUT—See Chatham Asset Management, LLC; *U.S. Private*, pg. 866
ANDREWS DIALYSIS, LLC—See DaVita Inc.; *U.S. Public*, pg. 636
ANDREWS DISTRIBUTING COMPANY, LLC; *U.S. Private*, pg. 280
ANDREWS DISTRIBUTING COMPANY OF NORTH TEXAS, LLC—See Andrews Distributing Company, LLC; *U.S. Private*, pg. 280
THE ANDREWS ENGINEERING COMPANY INCORPORATED—See Davis & Floyd, Inc.; *U.S. Private*, pg. 1172
ANDREWS GROUP; *U.S. Private*, pg. 280
ANDREW SHERET LIMITED; *Int'l*, pg. 452

ANDREWS INTERNATIONAL GOVERNMENT SERVICES, INC.—See Audax Group, Limited Partnership; *U.S. Private*, pg. 386
ANDREWS INTERNATIONAL—See Audax Group, Limited Partnership; *U.S. Private*, pg. 386
ANDREWS INTERNATIONAL—See Audax Group, Limited Partnership; *U.S. Private*, pg. 386
ANDREWS LIGHTING & HARDWARE GALLERY—See Ferguson plc; *Int'l*, pg. 2637
ANDREWS LOGISTICS, INC.; *U.S. Private*, pg. 280
ANDREWS MCMEEL UNIVERSAL; *U.S. Private*, pg. 280
THE ANDREWS MOVING & STORAGE COMPANY INC.; *U.S. Private*, pg. 3986
ANDREWS OIL BUYERS, INC.—See NGL Energy Partners LP; *U.S. Public*, pg. 1527
ANDREWS OIL COMPANY; *U.S. Private*, pg. 280
ANDREW SPORTS CLUB INC.; *U.S. Private*, pg. 279
ANDREWS PUBLICATIONS—See Thomson Reuters Corporation; *Int'l*, pg. 7715
ANDREWS REALTY LTD; *Int'l*, pg. 452
ANDREWS SYKES BVBA—See ANDREWS SYKES GROUP PLC; *Int'l*, pg. 452
ANDREWS SYKES B.V.—See ANDREWS SYKES GROUP PLC; *Int'l*, pg. 452
ANDREWS SYKES GROUP PLC; *Int'l*, pg. 452
ANDREWS SYKES LUXEMBOURG SARL—See ANDREWS SYKES GROUP PLC; *Int'l*, pg. 452
ANDREWS TRANSPORTATION, INC.—See Andrews Logistics, Inc.; *U.S. Private*, pg. 280
ANDREW & SUZANNE CO. INC.—See G-III Apparel Group, Ltd.; *U.S. Public*, pg. 893
ANDREW TELECOMMUNICATIONS DE REYNOSA S DE RL DE CV—See CommScope Holding Company, Inc.; *U.S. Public*, pg. 548
ANDREW TELECOMMUNICATIONS INDIA PVT. LTD. (ATGV)—See CommScope Holding Company, Inc.; *U.S. Public*, pg. 548
ANDREW TOYOTA; *U.S. Private*, pg. 280
ANDREW W. BYRD & CO., LLC; *U.S. Private*, pg. 280
ANDREW YULE & COMPANY LTD.; *Int'l*, pg. 452
ANDRIE, INC.—See Auxo Investment Partners, LLC; *U.S. Private*, pg. 402
ANDRITZ AB—See ANDRITZ AG; *Int'l*, pg. 452
ANDRITZ AG - RUSSIA REPRESENTATIVE OFFICE—See ANDRITZ AG; *Int'l*, pg. 452
ANDRITZ AG—See ANDRITZ AG; *Int'l*, pg. 455
ANDRITZ AG—See ANDRITZ AG; *Int'l*, pg. 455
ANDRITZ AG; *Int'l*, pg. 452
ANDRITZ AG - TAIWAN REPRESENTATIVE OFFICE—See ANDRITZ AG; *Int'l*, pg. 452
ANDRITZ ASSELIN-THIBEAU—See ANDRITZ AG; *Int'l*, pg. 454
ANDRITZ AUTOMATION LTD.—See ANDRITZ AG; *Int'l*, pg. 454
ANDRITZ BIAX S.A.S.—See ANDRITZ AG; *Int'l*, pg. 454
ANDRITZ BOISFER IGGESUND S.A.S.—See ANDRITZ AG; *Int'l*, pg. 454
ANDRITZ BRASIL LTDA.—See ANDRITZ AG; *Int'l*, pg. 452
ANDRITZ B.V.—See ANDRITZ AG; *Int'l*, pg. 455
ANDRITZ CHILE LTDA.—See ANDRITZ AG; *Int'l*, pg. 452
ANDRITZ CHILE LTDA.—See ANDRITZ AG; *Int'l*, pg. 452
ANDRITZ (CHINA) LTD.—See ANDRITZ AG; *Int'l*, pg. 452
ANDRITZ CONSTRUCOES E MONTAGENS LTDA.—See ANDRITZ AG; *Int'l*, pg. 455
ANDRITZ DELKOR (PTY) LTD.—See ANDRITZ AG; *Int'l*, pg. 454
ANDRITZ DIATEC S.R.L.—See ANDRITZ AG; *Int'l*, pg. 452
ANDRITZ DIES & ROLLS B.V.—See ANDRITZ AG; *Int'l*, pg. 452
ANDRITZ ENERGY & ENVIRONMENT GMBH—See ANDRITZ AG; *Int'l*, pg. 452
ANDRITZ ENVIRONMENTAL ENGINEERING (SHANGHAI) CO., LTD.—See ANDRITZ AG; *Int'l*, pg. 455
ANDRITZ EUROSLOT FRANCE SAS—See ANDRITZ AG; *Int'l*, pg. 455
ANDRITZ FABRICS AND ROLLS LIMITED—See ANDRITZ AG; *Int'l*, pg. 453
ANDRITZ FABRICS AND ROLLS OY—See ANDRITZ AG; *Int'l*, pg. 453
ANDRITZ FABRICS & ROLLS AG—See ANDRITZ AG; *Int'l*, pg. 455
ANDRITZ FABRICS & ROLLS INC.—See ANDRITZ AG; *Int'l*, pg. 455
ANDRITZ FABRICS & ROLLS S.A. DE C.V.—See ANDRITZ AG; *Int'l*, pg. 455
ANDRITZ FBB GMBH—See ANDRITZ AG; *Int'l*, pg. 455
ANDRITZ FEED & BIOFUEL A/S—See ANDRITZ AG; *Int'l*, pg. 452
ANDRITZ FEED & BIOFUEL A/S - VENEZUELA REPRESENTATIVE OFFICE—See ANDRITZ AG; *Int'l*, pg. 452
ANDRITZ FEED & BIOFUEL A/S - VIETNAM REPRESENTATIVE OFFICE—See ANDRITZ AG; *Int'l*, pg. 453
ANDRITZ FEED & BIOFUEL BRASIL LTDA.—See ANDRITZ AG; *Int'l*, pg. 452
ANDRITZ FEED & BIOFUEL B.V.—See ANDRITZ AG; *Int'l*, pg. 453
ANDRITZ FEED & BIOFUEL CANADA INC.—See ANDRITZ AG; *Int'l*, pg. 453

ANDRITZ FEED & BIOFUEL LTD.—See ANDRITZ AG; *Int'l*, pg. 453
ANDRITZ FEED & BIOFUEL MEXICO—See ANDRITZ AG; *Int'l*, pg. 452
ANDRITZ FEED & BIOFUEL—See ANDRITZ AG; *Int'l*, pg. 452
ANDRITZ FIBER DRYING LTD.—See ANDRITZ AG; *Int'l*, pg. 454
ANDRITZ FIEDLER GMBH—See ANDRITZ AG; *Int'l*, pg. 453
ANDRITZ FLIESSBETT SYSTEME GMBH—See ANDRITZ AG; *Int'l*, pg. 453
ANDRITZ FRAUTECH S.R.L.—See ANDRITZ AG; *Int'l*, pg. 453
ANDRITZ FZCO—See ANDRITZ AG; *Int'l*, pg. 455
ANDRITZ GOUDA B.V.—See ANDRITZ AG; *Int'l*, pg. 455
ANDRITZ HYDRO AB—See ANDRITZ AG; *Int'l*, pg. 453
ANDRITZ HYDRO AG ABMB BULACH—See ANDRITZ AG; *Int'l*, pg. 453
ANDRITZ HYDRO AG—See ANDRITZ AG; *Int'l*, pg. 453
ANDRITZ HYDRO AG—See ANDRITZ AG; *Int'l*, pg. 453
ANDRITZ HYDRO AS—See ANDRITZ AG; *Int'l*, pg. 453
ANDRITZ HYDRO BRASIL LTDA.—See ANDRITZ AG; *Int'l*, pg. 453
ANDRITZ HYDRO CANADA INC.—See ANDRITZ AG; *Int'l*, pg. 455
ANDRITZ HYDRO C.A.—See ANDRITZ AG; *Int'l*, pg. 453
ANDRITZ HYDRO CORP.—See ANDRITZ AG; *Int'l*, pg. 453
ANDRITZ HYDRO DRC SARL—See ANDRITZ AG; *Int'l*, pg. 455
ANDRITZ HYDRO GMBH—See ANDRITZ AG; *Int'l*, pg. 453
ANDRITZ HYDRO GMBH—See ANDRITZ AG; *Int'l*, pg. 453
ANDRITZ HYDRO GMBH - UKRAINE REPRESENTATIVE OFFICE—See ANDRITZ AG; *Int'l*, pg. 453
ANDRITZ HYDRO GMBH - VIETNAM REPRESENTATIVE OFFICE—See ANDRITZ AG; *Int'l*, pg. 453
ANDRITZ HYDRO HAMMERFEST (UK) LIMITED—See ANDRITZ AG; *Int'l*, pg. 455
ANDRITZ HYDRO, INC.—See ANDRITZ AG; *Int'l*, pg. 453
ANDRITZ HYDRO LTDA.—See ANDRITZ AG; *Int'l*, pg. 453
ANDRITZ HYDRO LTDA.—See ANDRITZ AG; *Int'l*, pg. 455
ANDRITZ HYDRO LTD. STI.—See ANDRITZ AG; *Int'l*, pg. 453
ANDRITZ HYDRO LTEE/LTD.—See ANDRITZ AG; *Int'l*, pg. 453
ANDRITZ HYDRO NEPAL PVT. LTD.—See ANDRITZ AG; *Int'l*, pg. 453
ANDRITZ HYDRO OY—See ANDRITZ AG; *Int'l*, pg. 455
ANDRITZ HYDRO PRIVATE LIMITED—See ANDRITZ AG; *Int'l*, pg. 453
ANDRITZ HYDRO (PTY.) LTD.—See ANDRITZ AG; *Int'l*, pg. 455
ANDRITZ HYDRO S.A. DE C.V.—See ANDRITZ AG; *Int'l*, pg. 453
ANDRITZ HYDRO SA—See ANDRITZ AG; *Int'l*, pg. 453
ANDRITZ HYDRO S.A.—See ANDRITZ AG; *Int'l*, pg. 453
ANDRITZ HYDRO S.A.S.—See ANDRITZ AG; *Int'l*, pg. 453
ANDRITZ HYDRO S.L.—See ANDRITZ AG; *Int'l*, pg. 453
ANDRITZ HYDRO S.R.L. UNIPERSONALE—See ANDRITZ AG; *Int'l*, pg. 453
ANDRITZ HYDRO S.R.O.—See ANDRITZ AG; *Int'l*, pg. 453
ANDRITZ HYDRO (SU), LDA.—See ANDRITZ AG; *Int'l*, pg. 455
ANDRITZ HYDRO, UNIPESSOAL LDA.—See ANDRITZ AG; *Int'l*, pg. 455
ANDRITZ IGGESUND TOOLS AB—See ANDRITZ AG; *Int'l*, pg. 452
ANDRITZ IGGESUND TOOLS CANADA INC.—See ANDRITZ AG; *Int'l*, pg. 454
ANDRITZ INC. - GLEN FALLS—See ANDRITZ AG; *Int'l*, pg. 453
ANDRITZ INC. - KUSTERS DIVISION—See ANDRITZ AG; *Int'l*, pg. 453
ANDRITZ INC. - PELL CITY—See ANDRITZ AG; *Int'l*, pg. 453
ANDRITZ INC.—See ANDRITZ AG; *Int'l*, pg. 453
ANDRITZ INDIA PRIVATE LIMITED—See ANDRITZ AG; *Int'l*, pg. 454
ANDRITZ INGENIERIA S.A.—See ANDRITZ AG; *Int'l*, pg. 454
ANDRITZ JOCHMAN S.R.O.—See ANDRITZ AG; *Int'l*, pg. 454
ANDRITZ KAISER GMBH—See ANDRITZ AG; *Int'l*, pg. 454
ANDRITZ KFT.—See ANDRITZ AG; *Int'l*, pg. 454
ANDRITZ K.K.—See ANDRITZ AG; *Int'l*, pg. 454
ANDRITZ KMPT GMBH—See ANDRITZ AG; *Int'l*, pg. 454
ANDRITZ KMPT INC.—See ANDRITZ AG; *Int'l*, pg. 453
ANDRITZ KUFFERATH GMBH—See ANDRITZ AG; *Int'l*, pg. 454
ANDRITZ KUFFERATH S.R.O.—See ANDRITZ AG; *Int'l*, pg. 454
ANDRITZ KUSTERS GMBH—See ANDRITZ AG; *Int'l*, pg. 454

ANDRITZ LTD./LTEE—See ANDRITZ AG; *Int'l*, pg. 454
ANDRITZ LTD.—See ANDRITZ AG; *Int'l*, pg. 454
ANDRITZ MAERZ GMBH—See ANDRITZ AG; *Int'l*, pg. 454
ANDRITZ METALS FRANCE S.A.S.—See ANDRITZ AG; *Int'l*, pg. 454
ANDRITZ METALS GERMANY GMBH—See ANDRITZ AG; *Int'l*, pg. 454
ANDRITZ METALS NETHERLANDS B.V.—See ANDRITZ AG; *Int'l*, pg. 454
ANDRITZ METALS USA INC—See ANDRITZ AG; *Int'l*, pg. 454
ANDRITZ MEWA GMBH—See ANDRITZ AG; *Int'l*, pg. 455
ANDRITZ MEWA KFT.—See ANDRITZ AG; *Int'l*, pg. 455
ANDRITZ NOVIMPIANTI S.R.L.—See ANDRITZ AG; *Int'l*, pg. 454
ANDRITZ (NZ) LTD.—See ANDRITZ AG; *Int'l*, pg. 456
ANDRITZ O&M PRIVATE LIMITED—See ANDRITZ AG; *Int'l*, pg. 454
ANDRITZ OY—See ANDRITZ AG; *Int'l*, pg. 454
ANDRITZ PAPERCHINE—See ANDRITZ AG; *Int'l*, pg. 454
ANDRITZ PAPER MACHINERY LTD.—See ANDRITZ AG; *Int'l*, pg. 454
ANDRITZ PERFOJET S.A.S.—See ANDRITZ AG; *Int'l*, pg. 454
ANDRITZ POWER SDN. BHD.—See ANDRITZ AG; *Int'l*, pg. 454
ANDRITZ PTY. LTD.—See ANDRITZ AG; *Int'l*, pg. 454
ANDRITZ PULP & PAPER—See ANDRITZ AG; *Int'l*, pg. 454
ANDRITZ PUMPS GERMANY GMBH—See ANDRITZ AG; *Int'l*, pg. 454
ANDRITZ RITZ GMBH—See ANDRITZ AG; *Int'l*, pg. 454
ANDRITZ RITZ IMMOBILIEN GMBH—See ANDRITZ AG; *Int'l*, pg. 454
ANDRITZ RITZ PTE. LTD.—See ANDRITZ AG; *Int'l*, pg. 455
ANDRITZ SAS—See ANDRITZ AG; *Int'l*, pg. 454
ANDRITZ SAVONLINNA WORKS OY—See ANDRITZ AG; *Int'l*, pg. 454
ANDRITZ SDN. BHD.—See ANDRITZ AG; *Int'l*, pg. 455
ANDRITZ SELAS S.A.S.—See ANDRITZ AG; *Int'l*, pg. 454
ANDRITZ SEPARATION GMBH—See ANDRITZ AG; *Int'l*, pg. 454
ANDRITZ SEPARATION INC.—See ANDRITZ AG; *Int'l*, pg. 453
ANDRITZ SEPARATION (INDIA) PRIVATE LTD.—See ANDRITZ AG; *Int'l*, pg. 454
ANDRITZ SEPARATION INDUSTRIA E COMERCIO DE EQUIPAMENTOS DE FILTRACAO LTDA.—See ANDRITZ AG; *Int'l*, pg. 452
ANDRITZ SEPARATION ITALY S.R.L.—See ANDRITZ AG; *Int'l*, pg. 454
ANDRITZ SEPARATION LTDA.—See ANDRITZ AG; *Int'l*, pg. 452
ANDRITZ SEPARATION & PUMP TECHNOLOGIES INDIA PRIVATE LIMITED—See ANDRITZ AG; *Int'l*, pg. 455
ANDRITZ SEPARATION—See ANDRITZ AG; *Int'l*, pg. 454
ANDRITZ (SHANGHAI) EQUIPMENT & ENGINEERING CO., LTD.—See ANDRITZ AG; *Int'l*, pg. 455
ANDRITZ SINGAPORE PTE. LTD.—See ANDRITZ AG; *Int'l*, pg. 454
ANDRITZ SINGAPORE PTE. LTD.—See ANDRITZ AG; *Int'l*, pg. 455
ANDRITZ SLOVAKIA S.R.O.—See ANDRITZ AG; *Int'l*, pg. 455
ANDRITZ SOUTEC AG—See ANDRITZ AG; *Int'l*, pg. 455
ANDRITZ S.R.L.—See ANDRITZ AG; *Int'l*, pg. 454
ANDRITZ SUNDWIG GMBH—See ANDRITZ AG; *Int'l*, pg. 455
ANDRITZ TECHNOLOGIES AB—See ANDRITZ AG; *Int'l*, pg. 455
ANDRITZ TECHNOLOGIES H.K. LTD.—See ANDRITZ AG; *Int'l*, pg. 455
ANDRITZ TECHNOLOGIES PVT. LTD.—See ANDRITZ AG; *Int'l*, pg. 452
ANDRITZ (THAILAND) LTD.—See ANDRITZ AG; *Int'l*, pg. 452
ANDRITZ THERMTEC B.V.—See ANDRITZ AG; *Int'l*, pg. 455
ANDRITZ URUGUAY S.A.—See ANDRITZ AG; *Int'l*, pg. 455
ANDRITZ VIETNAM COMPANY LIMITED—See ANDRITZ AG; *Int'l*, pg. 455
ANDRITZ - WOLFENSBERGER SPECIAL ALLOY FOUNDRY CO., LTD.—See ANDRITZ AG; *Int'l*, pg. 455
ANDROMEDA METALS LIMITED; *Int'l*, pg. 457
ANDROMEDA NOMINEES PTY. LTD.—See Singapore Post Limited; *Int'l*, pg. 6941
ANDROMEDA SYSTEMS INC.; *U.S. Private*, pg. 280
ANDRON GMBH—See Korber AG; *Int'l*, pg. 4281
ANDRONICO'S COMMUNITY MARKETS—See Renovo Capital, LLC; *U.S. Private*, pg. 3399
ANDROSCOGGIN HOME HEALTH SERVICES, INC.; *U.S. Private*, pg. 280
ANDROSCOGGIN SAVINGS BANK; *U.S. Private*, pg. 280
ANDROSCOGGIN VALLEY HOSPITAL; *U.S. Private*, pg. 280

ANDROSCOGGIN VALLEY HOSPITAL — CORPORATE AFFILIATIONS

Company Index

ANDROS INCORPORATED—See Advanced Energy Industries, Inc.; *U.S. Public*, pg. 47
ANDULELA INVESTMENT HOLDINGS LIMITED; *Int'l*, pg. 457
AN DUONG THAO DIEN REAL ESTATE TRADING INVESTMENT JOINT STOCK COMPANY; *Int'l*, pg. 443
ANDURIL INDUSTRIES, INC.; *U.S. Private*, pg. 280
ANDWIN CORPORATION; *U.S. Private*, pg. 281
ANDY BUSINESS CONGLOMERATE, USA; *U.S. Private*, pg. 281
ANDY GUMP INC.; *U.S. Private*, pg. 281
ANDY M. CAMACHO INC.; *U.S. Private*, pg. 281
ANDY MOHR BUICK GMC; *U.S. Private*, pg. 281
ANDY MOHR FORD; *U.S. Private*, pg. 281
ANDY MOHR NISSAN, INC.; *U.S. Private*, pg. 281
ANDY MOHR TRUCK CENTER; *U.S. Private*, pg. 281
ANDY'S ASSURANCE AGENCY; *U.S. Private*, pg. 281
ANDYS CAR AND TRUCK CENTER, INC.—See Glockner Chevrolet Co. Inc.; *U.S. Private*, pg. 1720
ANDY SHAW FORD; *U.S. Private*, pg. 281
ANDY'S RESTAURANTS, INC.; *U.S. Private*, pg. 281
ANEBULO PHARMACEUTICALS, INC.; *U.S. Public*, pg. 136
ANE (CAYMAN) INC.; *Int'l*, pg. 457
ANEKA JARINGAN HOLDINGS BERHAD; *Int'l*, pg. 457
ANEK LINES SA—See Attica Group; *Int'l*, pg. 696
ANEL DOGA ENTEGRE GERI DONUSUM ENDUSTRI A.S—See Anel Electrical Project Contracting Trade Inc.; *Int'l*, pg. 457
ANEL ELECTRICAL PROJECT CONTRACTING TRADE INC.; *Int'l*, pg. 457
ANEL ELEKTRIK PROJE TAAHHUT TIC. A.S—See Anel Electrical Project Contracting Trade Inc.; *Int'l*, pg. 457
ANEL ELEKTRIK PROJE TAAHHUT VE TICARET A.S—See Anel Electrical Project Contracting Trade Inc.; *Int'l*, pg. 457
ANEL ELEKTRIK PROJE TAAHHUT VE TICARET A.S—See Anel Electrical Project Contracting Trade Inc.; *Int'l*, pg. 457
ANEL ELEKTRIK PROJE TAAHHUT VE TICARET A.S—See Anel Electrical Project Contracting Trade Inc.; *Int'l*, pg. 457
ANELEMIRATES GENERAL CONTRACTING LLC—See Anel Electrical Project Contracting Trade Inc.; *Int'l*, pg. 458
ANEL ENGINEERING & CONTRACTING LIMITED—See Anel Electrical Project Contracting Trade Inc.; *Int'l*, pg. 458
ANELMARIN GEMI ELK. ELKT. SIS. TIC. VE SAN. A.S.—See Anel Electrical Project Contracting Trade Inc.; *Int'l*, pg. 458
ANELSIS MUHENDISLIK SAN. VE TIC. LTD. STI.—See Anel Electrical Project Contracting Trade Inc.; *Int'l*, pg. 458
ANEMOI INTERNATIONAL LTD; *Int'l*, pg. 458
ANEMOI LLC; *U.S. Private*, pg. 458
ANEMOS ATALANTIS SA—See ELLAKTOR S.A.; *Int'l*, pg. 2364
ANEMOSTAT PRODUCTS—See Mestek, Inc.; *U.S. Public*, pg. 1426
ANEMOS THRAKIS SA—See ELLAKTOR S.A.; *Int'l*, pg. 2364
ANERI FINCAP LIMITED; *Int'l*, pg. 458
ANESCO LIMITED—See Ara Partners Group; *U.S. Private*, pg. 306
ANESTHESIA ASSOCIATES OF PINELLAS COUNTY DIVISION, LLC—See KKR & Co. Inc.; *U.S. Public*, pg. 1244
ANESTHESIA BUSINESS CONSULTANTS; *U.S. Private*, pg. 281
ANESTHESIA SPECIAL OPERATIONS, LLC—See Blackstone Inc.; *U.S. Public*, pg. 359
ANESTHESIOLOGISTS OF GREATER ORLANDO, INC.—See KKR & Co. Inc.; *U.S. Public*, pg. 1244
ANESTHESIOLOGY ASSOCIATES OF TALLAHASSEE, INC.—See KKR & Co. Inc.; *U.S. Public*, pg. 1244
ANESTHESIOLOGY PROFESSIONAL SERVICES, INC.—See Bain Capital, LP; *U.S. Private*, pg. 445
ANEST IWATA AIR ENGINEERING INC.—See ANEST IWATA Corporation; *Int'l*, pg. 458
ANEST IWATA AUSTRALIA PTY LTD—See ANEST IWATA Corporation; *Int'l*, pg. 458
ANEST IWATA CORPORATION; *Int'l*, pg. 458
ANEST IWATA DEUTSCHLAND GMBH—See ANEST IWATA Corporation; *Int'l*, pg. 458
ANEST IWATA EUROPE GMBH—See ANEST IWATA Corporation; *Int'l*, pg. 458
ANEST IWATA EUROPE S.R.L—See ANEST IWATA Corporation; *Int'l*, pg. 458
ANEST IWATA FRANCE S.A.—See ANEST IWATA Corporation; *Int'l*, pg. 458
ANEST IWATA IBERICA S.L.—See ANEST IWATA Corporation; *Int'l*, pg. 458
ANEST IWATA ITALIA S.R.L.—See ANEST IWATA Corporation; *Int'l*, pg. 458
ANEST IWATA KOREA CORPORATION—See ANEST IWATA Corporation; *Int'l*, pg. 458
ANEST IWATA-MEDEA INC—See ANEST IWATA Corporation; *Int'l*, pg. 458

ANEST IWATA MOTHERSON COATING EQUIPMENT PRIVATE LTD.—See ANEST IWATA Corporation; *Int'l*, pg. 458
ANEST IWATA MOTHERSON LIMITED—See ANEST IWATA Corporation; *Int'l*, pg. 458
ANEST IWATA RUS LLC—See ANEST IWATA Corporation; *Int'l*, pg. 458
ANEST IWATA SCANDINAVIA AKTIERBOLAG—See ANEST IWATA Corporation; *Int'l*, pg. 458
ANEST IWATA SEGI CORPORATION—See ANEST IWATA Corporation; *Int'l*, pg. 458
ANEST IWATA SHANGHAI COATING MACHINERY CO., LTD.—See ANEST IWATA Corporation; *Int'l*, pg. 458
ANEST IWATA (SHANGHAI) CORPORATION—See ANEST IWATA Corporation; *Int'l*, pg. 458
ANEST IWATA SOUTH AFRICA PTY. LTD.—See ANEST IWATA Corporation; *Int'l*, pg. 458
ANEST IWATA SOUTHEAST ASIA CO., LTD.—See ANEST IWATA Corporation; *Int'l*, pg. 458
ANEST IWATA SPARMAX CO., LTD.—See ANEST IWATA Corporation; *Int'l*, pg. 458
ANEST IWATA TAIWAN CORPORATION—See ANEST IWATA Corporation; *Int'l*, pg. 458
ANEST IWATA (U.K.) LTD.—See ANEST IWATA Corporation; *Int'l*, pg. 458
ANEST IWATA USA INC.—See ANEST IWATA Corporation; *Int'l*, pg. 458
ANEST IWATA VIETNAM CO., LTD.—See ANEST IWATA Corporation; *Int'l*, pg. 458
ANETA BELYSNING AB—See Byggma ASA; *Int'l*, pg. 1235
ANETA LIGHTING AS—See Byggma ASA; *Int'l*, pg. 1235
ANETSBERGER, INC.—See The Middleby Corporation; *U.S. Public*, pg. 2113
ANEVIA SA—See ATEME S.A.; *Int'l*, pg. 668
ANEWA ENGINEERING PRIVATE LIMITED—See Alpha Dhabi Holding PJSC; *Int'l*, pg. 367
A NEW LEAF; *U.S. Private*, pg. 18
ANEW MARKETING GROUP; *U.S. Private*, pg. 281
ANEW MARKETING GROUP—See ANEW Marketing Group; *U.S. Private*, pg. 281
ANEXINET CORP.—See Guggenheim Partners, LLC; *U.S. Private*, pg. 1811
ANEXIO, INC.; *U.S. Private*, pg. 281
ANEXO GROUP PLC; *Int'l*, pg. 459
ANF DATA SPOL. S R.O.—See Siemens Aktiengesellschaft; *Int'l*, pg. 6886
ANFIELD ENERGY INC.; *Int'l*, pg. 459
ANFIMA NV—See Ackermans & van Haaren NV; *Int'l*, pg. 104
ANF IMMOBILIER—See Caisse des Depots et Consignations; *Int'l*, pg. 1258
AN FORT MYERS IMPORTS, LLC—See AutoNation, Inc.; *U.S. Public*, pg. 231
AN FREMONT LUXURY IMPORTS, INC.—See AutoNation, Inc.; *U.S. Public*, pg. 231
ANF SPECIALTIES INC.—See Texas Farm Products Company; *U.S. Private*, pg. 3975
ANFU.CE LINK LIMITED; *Int'l*, pg. 459
ANGANG GROUP HONG KONG CO. LTD.—See Anshan Iron & Steel Group Corporation; *Int'l*, pg. 479
ANGANG STEEL COMPANY LTD.—See Anshan Iron & Steel Group Corporation; *Int'l*, pg. 479
ANGARAI INTERNATIONAL, INC.; *U.S. Private*, pg. 281
ANGARI PTY LTD—See Origin Energy Ltd.; *Int'l*, pg. 5629
ANGAS SECURITIES LIMITED; *Int'l*, pg. 459
ANGELALIGN TECHNOLOGY INC.; *Int'l*, pg. 459
ANGEL ASSOCIATES (TAIWAN) INC—See YungShin Global Holding Corporation; *Int'l*, pg. 8614
ANGEL BROTHERS ENTERPRISES INC.; *U.S. Private*, pg. 281
ANGELCARE HOLDING INC.; *Int'l*, pg. 459
ANGELCARE MONITORS INC.—See Angelcare Holding Inc.; *Int'l*, pg. 459
ANGEL CITY PRESS—See Los Angeles Public Library Docents; *U.S. Private*, pg. 2497
ANGEL.COM INCORPORATED—See Permira Advisers LLP; *Int'l*, pg. 5804
ANGELES EQUITY PARTNERS, LLC; *U.S. Private*, pg. 281
ANGELES HOME HEALTH CARE, INC.—See The Ensign Group, Inc.; *U.S. Public*, pg. 2070
ANGELES WELDING & MFG., INC.; *U.S. Private*, pg. 282
ANGEL FIBERS LIMITED; *Int'l*, pg. 459
ANGEL FINCAP PRIVATE LIMITED—See Angel One Limited; *Int'l*, pg. 459
ANGEL GOLD CORP.; *Int'l*, pg. 459
ANGEL GROUP LTD.; *Int'l*, pg. 459
ANGEL HOLDINGS GODO KAISHA; *Int'l*, pg. 459
ANGEL HUMAN RESOUCES LTD; *Int'l*, pg. 459
ANGELICA CORPORATION—See KKR & Co. Inc.; *U.S. Public*, pg. 1239
ANGELICA RIVERFRONT REDEVELOPMENT INC.—See Lange-Stegmann Co., Inc.; *U.S. Private*, pg. 2389
ANGELICA TEXTILE SERVICES, INC.—See KKR & Co. Inc.; *U.S. Public*, pg. 1239
ANGELIC BAKEHOUSE, INC.—See Benford Capital Partners, LLC; *U.S. Private*, pg. 526
ANGELI-MENOMINEE INC.; *U.S. Private*, pg. 282
ANGELINI ACRAF S.P.A.; *Int'l*, pg. 460

ANGELINI FARMACEUTICA LDA.—See Angelini ACRAF S.p.A.; *Int'l*, pg. 460
ANGELINI FARMACEUTICA S.A.—See Angelini ACRAF S.p.A.; *Int'l*, pg. 460
ANGELINI ILAC SAN. VE TIC. A.S.—See Angelini ACRAF S.p.A.; *Int'l*, pg. 460
ANGELINI PHARMA BULGARIA EOOD—See Angelini ACRAF S.p.A.; *Int'l*, pg. 460
ANGELINI PHARMA CESKA REPUBLIKA S.R.O.—See Angelini ACRAF S.p.A.; *Int'l*, pg. 460
ANGELINI PHARMACEUTICALS (PVT) LTD—See Angelini ACRAF S.p.A.; *Int'l*, pg. 460
ANGELINI PHARMACEUTICALS ROMANIA S.R.L.—See Angelini ACRAF S.p.A.; *Int'l*, pg. 460
ANGELINI PHARMA HELLAS S.A.—See Angelini ACRAF S.p.A.; *Int'l*, pg. 460
ANGELINI PHARMA INC.—See Angelini ACRAF S.p.A.; *Int'l*, pg. 460
ANGELINI PHARMA MAGYARORSZAG KFT.—See Angelini ACRAF S.p.A.; *Int'l*, pg. 460
ANGELINI PHARMA OSTERREICH GMBH—See Angelini ACRAF S.p.A.; *Int'l*, pg. 460
ANGELINI PHARMA POLSKA SP.Z.O.O.—See Angelini ACRAF S.p.A.; *Int'l*, pg. 460
ANGELINI PHARMA RUS LLC—See Angelini ACRAF S.p.A.; *Int'l*, pg. 460
ANGELINI PHARMA SLOVENSKA REPUBLIKA S. R. O.—See Angelini ACRAF S.p.A.; *Int'l*, pg. 460
ANGEL ISLAND CAPITAL, L.P.—See Golden Gate Capital Management II, LLC; *U.S. Private*, pg. 1730
ANGEL ISLAND CAPITAL MANAGEMENT, LLC—See Golden Gate Capital Management II, LLC; *U.S. Private*, pg. 1731
ANGELL-DEMMEL EUROPE GMBH—See Demmel AG; *Int'l*, pg. 2025
ANGELL-DEMMEL NORTH AMERICA CORPORATION—See American Trim LLC; *U.S. Private*, pg. 257
ANGELL-DEMMEL NORTH AMERICA—See American Trim LLC; *U.S. Private*, pg. 257
ANGELLE CONCRETE GROUP, LLC; *U.S. Private*, pg. 282
ANGEL METAL CO., LTD.—See ASSA ABLOY AB; *Int'l*, pg. 638
ANGEL OAK MORTGAGE REIT, INC.; *U.S. Public*, pg. 136
ANGELO, GORDON & CO., L.P.—See TPG Capital, L.P.; *U.S. Public*, pg. 2166
THE ANGELO IAFRATE COMPANIES; *U.S. Private*, pg. 3986
ANGELO IAFRATE CONSTRUCTION COMPANY—See The Angelo Iafrate Companies; *U.S. Private*, pg. 3986
ANGELO MORATTI S.A.P.A.; *Int'l*, pg. 460
ANGEL ONE LIMITED; *Int'l*, pg. 459
ANGELO'S FRESH FOOD MARKET, LLC—See Angelo's Fresh Market, Inc.; *U.S. Private*, pg. 282
ANGELO'S FRESH MARKET, INC.; *U.S. Private*, pg. 282
ANGELO'S SUPPLIES, INC.—See SiteOne Landscape Supply, Inc.; *U.S. Public*, pg. 1889
ANGELOU ECONOMIC ADVISORS INC.; *U.S. Private*, pg. 282
ANGELOU ECONOMIC ADVISORS INC.—See Angelou Economic Advisors Inc.; *U.S. Private*, pg. 282
ANGEL PARK CO., LTD.—See J. Front Retailing Co., Ltd.; *Int'l*, pg. 3855
ANGEL PARK GOLF, LLC; *U.S. Private*, pg. 281
ANGELPOINTS, LLC—See Blackbaud, Inc.; *U.S. Public*, pg. 341
ANGEL POND HOLDINGS CORPORATION; *U.S. Public*, pg. 136
ANGEL PRODUCTIONS SASU—See Vivendi SE; *Int'l*, pg. 8275
ANGEL RISK MANAGEMENT LIMITED—See AXA S.A.; *Int'l*, pg. 760
ANGELS BASEBALL, L.P.; *U.S. Private*, pg. 282
ANGEL'S ESTATE SA—See Purcari Wineries Public Company Limited; *Int'l*, pg. 6121
ANGELS INSTRUMENTATION, INC.—See Transcat, Inc.; *U.S. Public*, pg. 2179
ANGELS MODEL MANAGEMENT SARL—See Elite World S.A.; *Int'l*, pg. 2362
ANGEL STAFFING, INC.; *U.S. Private*, pg. 281
ANGEL'S TOUCH HOME CARE, INC.—See Formation Capital, LLC; *U.S. Private*, pg. 1571
ANGEL TELECOM CORP.; *Int'l*, pg. 459
ANGEL TRAINS LIMITED—See AMP Limited; *Int'l*, pg. 432
ANGEL TRAINS LIMITED—See Public Sector Pension Investment Board; *Int'l*, pg. 6095
ANGELUS BLOCK CO. INC.; *U.S. Private*, pg. 282
ANGELUS FURNITURE OUTLET INC.; *U.S. Private*, pg. 283
ANGELVISION TECHNOLOGIES, INC.; *U.S. Private*, pg. 283
ANGEL WAREHOUSE INC.; *U.S. Private*, pg. 281
ANGEL WATCH HOME CARE, L.L.C.—See Amedisys, Inc.; *U.S. Public*, pg. 93
ANGEL YEAST COMPANY LIMITED; *Int'l*, pg. 459
ANGER MACHINING GMBH—See Tong-Tai Machine Tool Co., Ltd.; *Int'l*, pg. 7806

ANGER MACHINING INC.—See Tong-Tai Machine Tool Co., Ltd.; *Int'l*, pg. 7806
ANGERMAYER, BRUMM & LANGE UNTERNEHMENSGRUPPE GMBH; *Int'l*, pg. 460
ANGES, INC.; *Int'l*, pg. 460
ANGIANG FISHERIES IMPORT & EXPORT JOINT STOCK COMPANY; *Int'l*, pg. 460
AN GIANG IMPORT-EXPORT COMPANY; *Int'l*, pg. 443
ANGI ENERGY SYSTEMS, INC.—See Vontier Corporation; *U.S. Public*, pg. 2308
ANGIE'S LIST, INC.—See IAC Inc.; *U.S. Public*, pg. 1081
ANGI INC.—See IAC Inc.; *U.S. Public*, pg. 1081
ANG INDUSTRIES LIMITED; *Int'l*, pg. 459
ANGIODYNAMICS CANADA INC.—See AngioDynamics, Inc.; *U.S. Public*, pg. 137
ANGIODYNAMICS, INC.; *U.S. Public*, pg. 136
ANGIODYNAMICS NETHERLANDS B. V.—See AngioDynamics, Inc.; *U.S. Public*, pg. 137
ANGIODYNAMICS UK LIMITED—See AngioDynamics, Inc.; *U.S. Public*, pg. 137
ANGIOGENEX, INC.; *U.S. Public*, pg. 137
ANGIOGRAFIA E HEMODINAMICA MADRE THEODORA LTDA.—See UnitedHealth Group Incorporated; *U.S. Public*, pg. 2239
ANGIOLAB, INC.; *Int'l*, pg. 460
ANGIOLOGIKUM GMBH—See Asklepios Kliniken GmbH & Co. KGaA; *Int'l*, pg. 622
ANGKARA SETIA DEVELOPMENT SDN. BHD.—See Advance Information Marketing Berhad; *Int'l*, pg. 156
ANGKASA AMSTEEL PTE LTD—See Daehan Steel Co., Ltd.; *Int'l*, pg. 1907
ANGKASA AMSTEEL PTE LTD—See LTC Corporation Limited; *Int'l*, pg. 4571
ANGKASA JASA SDN. BHD.—See Press Metal Aluminium Holdings Bhd; *Int'l*, pg. 5965
ANGKA-TAN MOTOR SDN BHD—See Warisan TC Holdings Berhad; *Int'l*, pg. 8345
ANGKOR DAIRY PRODUCTS CO., LTD.—See Vietnam Dairy Products Joint Stock Company; *Int'l*, pg. 8198
ANGKOR RESOURCES CORP.; *Int'l*, pg. 460
ANGLATROLL AB—See Egmont Fonden; *Int'l*, pg. 2325
ANGLE PLC; *Int'l*, pg. 460
ANGLER GAMING PLC; *Int'l*, pg. 461
THE ANGLER'S BOUTIQUE RESORT—See Coral Hospitality, LLC; *U.S. Private*, pg. 1046
ANGLERS MARINE; *U.S. Private*, pg. 283
ANGLESEY MINING PLC; *Int'l*, pg. 461
ANGLE TECHNOLOGY LIMITED—See ANGLE plc; *Int'l*, pg. 461
ANGLE TECHNOLOGY LLC—See ANGLE plc; *Int'l*, pg. 460
ANGLE TECHNOLOGY VENTURES LIMITED—See ANGLE plc; *Int'l*, pg. 461
ANGLIA COMPONENTS PLC—See STMicroelectronics N.V.; *Int'l*, pg. 7217
ANGLIA CROWN LIMITED—See Romy Foods Corporation Ltd.; *Int'l*, pg. 6395
ANGLIA HARVESTERS LTD.—See Claas KGaA mbH; *Int'l*, pg. 1641
ANGLIAN WATER GROUP LIMITED—See Canada Pension Plan Investment Board; *Int'l*, pg. 1278
ANGLIAN WATER GROUP LIMITED—See Commonwealth Bank of Australia; *Int'l*, pg. 1720
ANGLIAN WATER GROUP LIMITED—See Industry Super Holdings Pty. Ltd.; *Int'l*, pg. 3675
ANGLIAN WATER SERVICES LIMITED—See Canada Pension Plan Investment Board; *Int'l*, pg. 1278
ANGLIAN WATER SERVICES LIMITED—See Commonwealth Bank of Australia; *Int'l*, pg. 1720
ANGLIAN WATER SERVICES LIMITED—See Industry Super Holdings Pty. Ltd.; *Int'l*, pg. 3676
ANGLIA TELECOM CENTRES LIMITED—See Daisy Group Limited; *Int'l*, pg. 1942
ANG LIFESCIENCES INDIA LIMITED; *Int'l*, pg. 459
ANGLING DIRECT PLC; *Int'l*, pg. 461
ANGLIN REICHMANN SNELLGROVE & ARMSTRONG, P.C.; *U.S. Private*, pg. 283
ANGLISS CHINA LIMITED—See The Bidvest Group Limited; *Int'l*, pg. 7621
ANGLISS GUANGZHOU FOOD SERVICE COMPANY LIMITED—See The Bidvest Group Limited; *Int'l*, pg. 7621
ANGLISS HONG KONG FOOD SERVICE LIMITED—See The Bidvest Group Limited; *Int'l*, pg. 7621
ANGLISS MACAU FOOD SERVICE LIMITED—See The Bidvest Group Limited; *Int'l*, pg. 7621
ANGLISS SHANGHAI FOOD SERVICE LIMITED—See The Bidvest Group Limited; *Int'l*, pg. 7621
ANGLISS SINGAPORE PTE LIMITED—See The Bidvest Group Limited; *Int'l*, pg. 7621
ANGLO AFRICAN OIL & GAS PLC; *Int'l*, pg. 461
ANGLO AMERICAN AUSTRALIA LIMITED—See Anglo American PLC; *Int'l*, pg. 461
ANGLO AMERICAN BRASIL LIMITADA—See Anglo American PLC; *Int'l*, pg. 461
ANGLO AMERICAN CHILE—See Anglo American PLC; *Int'l*, pg. 461
ANGLO AMERICAN METALLURGICAL COAL HOLDINGS LIMITED—See Anglo American PLC; *Int'l*, pg. 461

ANGLO AMERICAN MINERIO DE FERRO BRASIL S.A.—See Anglo American PLC; *Int'l*, pg. 461
ANGLO AMERICAN NIQUEL BRASIL LTDA.—See Anglo American PLC; *Int'l*, pg. 461
ANGLO AMERICAN PERU S.A.—See Anglo American PLC; *Int'l*, pg. 461
ANGLO AMERICAN PLATINUM LIMITED—See Anglo American PLC; *Int'l*, pg. 461
ANGLO AMERICAN PLC; *Int'l*, pg. 461
ANGLO AMERICAN PROJECTS (UK) LTD.—See Anglo American PLC; *Int'l*, pg. 461
ANGLO AMERICAN RESOURCES TRADING (CHINA) CO. LTD.—See Anglo American PLC; *Int'l*, pg. 461
ANGLO AMERICAN SOUTH AFRICA LIMITED—See Anglo American PLC; *Int'l*, pg. 461
ANGLO AMERICAN SUR SA—See Anglo American PLC; *Int'l*, pg. 461
ANGLO AMERICAN WOODSMITH LIMITED—See Anglo American PLC; *Int'l*, pg. 461
ANGLO ARDMORE SHIP MANAGEMENT LIMITED—See Ardmore Shipping Corporation; *U.S. Public*, pg. 556
ANGLO ASIA ALLOYS VIETNAM CO., LTD.—See Daiki Aluminium Industry Co., Ltd.; *Int'l*, pg. 1931
ANGLO ASIAN MINING PLC; *Int'l*, pg. 462
AN GLOBAL I.T. S.A.P.I. DE C.V.; *U.S. Private*, pg. 271
ANGLOBAL LTD.—See TSI Holdings Co., Ltd.; *Int'l*, pg. 7950
ANGLO BASE METALS (IRELAND) LTD.—See Anglo American PLC; *Int'l*, pg. 461
ANGLO-BOMARC MINES LTD.; *Int'l*, pg. 463
ANGLO COAL (GERMAN CREEK) PTY LTD—See Anglo American PLC; *Int'l*, pg. 461
ANGLO-DANISH FIBRE INDUSTRIES LTD—See Freudenberg SE; *Int'l*, pg. 2789
ANGLO DUTCH WATER CARBONS LTD.—See Cabot Corporation; *U.S. Public*, pg. 416
ANGLO-EASTERN PLANTATIONS (M) SDN. BHD.—See Anglo Eastern Plantations PLC; *Int'l*, pg. 463
ANGLO EASTERN PLANTATIONS PLC; *Int'l*, pg. 462
ANGLO-EASTERN UNIVAN GROUP; *Int'l*, pg. 463
ANGLO EUROPEAN AVIATION AG; *Int'l*, pg. 463
ANGLO-EUROPEAN (U.K.) LTD—See Anglo European Aviation AG; *Int'l*, pg. 463
ANGLO FERROUS BRAZIL S.A.—See Anglo American PLC; *Int'l*, pg. 461
ANGLO FERROUS MINAS RIO MINEHACAU SA—See Anglo American PLC; *Int'l*, pg. 461
ANGLOGOLD ASHANTI NORTH AMERICA INC.—See AngloGold Ashanti plc; *Int'l*, pg. 463
ANGLOGOLD ASHANTI PLC; *Int'l*, pg. 463
ANGLO HIBERNIAN BLOODSTOCK INSURANCE SERVICES LIMITED—See Brown & Brown, Inc.; *U.S. Public*, pg. 396
ANGLOLAB S.A.—See The British United Provident Association Limited; *Int'l*, pg. 7629
ANGLO-MAURITIUS STOCKBROKERS LIMITED—See SWAN General Ltd.; *Int'l*, pg. 7360
ANGLO OPERATIONS (PTY) LTD.—See Anglo American PLC; *Int'l*, pg. 461
ANGLO PHILIPPINE HOLDINGS CORPORATION; *Int'l*, pg. 463
ANGLO PLATINUM MARKETING LIMITED—See Anglo American PLC; *Int'l*, pg. 461
ANGLORAND SECURITIES LIMITED—See Ningbo Construction Co., Ltd.; *Int'l*, pg. 5301
ANGLO SCOTTISH ASSET FINANCE LIMITED; *Int'l*, pg. 463
ANGLO-SIBERIAN OIL COMPANY (CYPRUS) LIMITED—See OJSC Rosneftegaz; *Int'l*, pg. 5541
ANGLO-THAI CO. LTD.—See Hup Soon Global Corporation Limited; *Int'l*, pg. 3538
ANGOFLEX LIMITADA—See TechnipFMC plc; *Int'l*, pg. 7507
ANGOLA JAPAN OIL CO., LTD.—See Mitsubishi Corporation; *Int'l*, pg. 4937
ANGOLA WIRE PRODUCTS INC.; *U.S. Private*, pg. 283
ANGOORAN MINERS COMPANY LIMITED—See National Iranian Lead & Zinc Company; *Int'l*, pg. 5160
ANGO PRODUCTION—See Vivendi SE; *Int'l*, pg. 8275
ANGOSTURA HOLDINGS LIMITED; *Int'l*, pg. 463
ANGOSTURA LIMITED—See Angostura Holdings Limited; *Int'l*, pg. 463
ANGO WORLD HOLDINGS, INC.; *U.S. Public*, pg. 137
AN GRIANAN GRAIN COMPANY LIMITED—See Donegal Investment Group Plc; *Int'l*, pg. 2163
ANGROPREDUZECE D.D.; *Int'l*, pg. 463
ANGROPROMET PREHRANA A.D.; *Int'l*, pg. 463
ANGROPROMET TIKVESANKA AD; *Int'l*, pg. 463
ANGSANA MESTIKA SDN. BHD.—See WCE Holdings Berhad; pg. 8361
ANGST+PFISTER SENSORS & POWER AG—See P-Duke Technology Co., Ltd.; *Int'l*, pg. 5681
ANGSTROHM PRECISION, INC.—See Vishay Intertechnology, Inc.; *U.S. Public*, pg. 2302
ANGSTROM GRAPHICS INC. - ANGSTROM GRAPHICS CREATIVE DIVISION—See Mittera Group, Inc.; *U.S. Private*, pg. 2751
ANGSTROM GRAPHICS INC.-MIDWEST—See Mittera Group, Inc.; *U.S. Private*, pg. 2751

ANGSTROM GRAPHICS INC.—See Mittera Group, Inc.; *U.S. Private*, pg. 2751
ANGSTROM TECHNOLOGIES INC.; *U.S. Public*, pg. 137
ANGSTROM TECHNOLOGY LTD.—See ASGARD Partners & Co., LLC; *U.S. Private*, pg. 349
ANGSTROM USA, LLC.; *U.S. Public*, pg. 283
ANG TONG SENG BROTHERS ENTERPRISES PTE. LTD.—See Ocean Sky International Limited; *Int'l*, pg. 5516
ANG TONG SENG CONSTRUCTION PTE. LTD.—See Ocean Sky International Limited; *Int'l*, pg. 5516
ANGUS CHEMICAL COMPANY—See Golden Gate Capital Management II, LLC; *U.S. Private*, pg. 1730
ANGUS CHEMIE GMBH—See Golden Gate Capital Management II, LLC; *U.S. Private*, pg. 1730
ANGUS COUNTY PRESS LTD—See JPIMedia Holdings Limited; *Int'l*, pg. 4006
ANGUS ENERGY PLC; *Int'l*, pg. 463
ANGUS FIRE (S.A.) LIMITED—See Carrier Global Corporation; *U.S. Public*, pg. 440
ANGUS GOLD, INC.; *Int'l*, pg. 463
ANGUS MONTGOMERY LTD.; *Int'l*, pg. 463
ANGUS RESOURCES INC.; *Int'l*, pg. 463
ANGY (CHINA) MEDICAL LIMITED; *Int'l*, pg. 464
ANGY (GUANGZHOU) MEDICAL TECHNOLOGY CO., LTD.—See Angy (China) Medical Limited; *Int'l*, pg. 464
ANHANGUERA EDUCACIONAL PARTICIPACOES S.A.—See Cogna Educacao S.A.; *Int'l*, pg. 1695
ANHEUSER-BUSCH AMERICAS HOLDINGS LLC—See Anheuser-Busch InBev SA/NV; *Int'l*, pg. 465
ANHEUSER-BUSCH EMPLOYEES BENEFIT TRUST; *U.S. Private*, pg. 283
ANHEUSER-BUSCH COMPANIES, LLC—See Anheuser-Busch InBev SA/NV; *Int'l*, pg. 465
ANHEUSER-BUSCH COS., INC.—See Anheuser-Busch InBev SA/NV; *Int'l*, pg. 465
ANHEUSER-BUSCH INBEV GERMANY HOLDING GMBH—See Anheuser-Busch InBev SA/NV; *Int'l*, pg. 465
ANHEUSER BUSCH INBEV ITALIA SPA—See Anheuser-Busch InBev SA/NV; *Int'l*, pg. 465
ANHEUSER-BUSCH INBEV SA/NV; *Int'l*, pg. 464
ANHEUSER-BUSCH, INC.—See Anheuser-Busch InBev SA/NV; *Int'l*, pg. 465
ANHEUSER-BUSCH INTERNATIONAL, INC.—See Anheuser-Busch InBev SA/NV; *Int'l*, pg. 465
ANHEUSER-BUSCH PACKAGING GROUP, INC.—See Anheuser-Busch InBev SA/NV; *Int'l*, pg. 465
ANHEUSER-BUSCH RECYCLING CORPORATION—See Anheuser-Busch InBev SA/NV; *Int'l*, pg. 465
ANHEUSER-BUSCH SALES OF HAWAII—See Anheuser-Busch InBev SA/NV; *Int'l*, pg. 465
ANHEUSER-BUSCH SALES OF LIMA—See Anheuser-Busch InBev SA/NV; *Int'l*, pg. 465
ANHEUSER-BUSCH SALES POMONA—See Anheuser-Busch InBev SA/NV; *Int'l*, pg. 465
ANH HUY CONSTRUCTION CO., LTD—See Hoa Binh Construction Group JSC; *Int'l*, pg. 3435
AN H. IMPORTS OF ATLANTA, LLC—See AutoNation, Inc.; *U.S. Public*, pg. 231
AN-HO METAL INDUSTRIAL CO., LTD.—See Sanwa Holdings Corporation; *Int'l*, pg. 6560
ANH REFRACTORIES EUROPE LIMITED—See Platinum Equity, LLC; *U.S. Private*, pg. 3203
ANHUI ANFU BATTERY TECHNOLOGY CO., LTD.; *Int'l*, pg. 466
ANHUI ANKAI AUTOMOBILE CO., LTD.—See Anhui Jianghuai Automobile Group Corp., Ltd.; *Int'l*, pg. 468
ANHUI ANLI MATERIAL TECHNOLOGY CO., LTD.; *Int'l*, pg. 466
ANHUI ANNADA TITANIUM INDUSTRY CO., LTD.; *Int'l*, pg. 466
ANHUI BAILU ELECTRONIC TECHNOLOGY CO., LTD.—See Anhui Wanyi Science & Technology Co., Ltd.; *Int'l*, pg. 470
ANHUI BAOYE CONSTRUCTION ENGINEERING GROUP CO., LTD.—See Baoye Group Company Limited; *Int'l*, pg. 857
ANHUI BRC & MA STEEL WELDMESH CO. LTD.—See China Baowu Steel Group Corp., Ltd.; *Int'l*, pg. 1486
ANHUI CABLE CO., LTD.—See Far East Smarter Energy Co., Ltd.; *Int'l*, pg. 2617
ANHUI CHANGFENG CONCH CEMENT CO., LTD.—See Anhui Conch Cement Company Limited; *Int'l*, pg. 466
ANHUI CHANGFENG YANGZI AUTOMOBILE MANUFACTURING CO., LTD.—See Changfeng (Group) Co., Ltd.; *Int'l*, pg. 1443
ANHUI CHAOYUE ENVIRONMENTAL TECHNOLOGY CO., LTD.; *Int'l*, pg. 466
ANHUI CLEAN ENVIRONMENT BIOTECHNOLOGY CO., LTD.—See Tritech Group Limited; *Int'l*, pg. 7928
ANHUI COFCO BIOCHEMICAL & GALACTIC LACTIC ACID CO., LTD.—See Cofco Biotechnology Co., Ltd.; *Int'l*, pg. 1691
ANHUI COFCO BIOCHEMICAL & GALACTIC LACTIC ACID CO., LTD.—See Finasucre S.A.; *Int'l*, pg. 2670
ANHUI CONCH CEMENT COMPANY LIMITED; *Int'l*, pg. 466

ANHUI CONCH CEMENT COMPANY LIMITED — CORPORATE AFFILIATIONS

ANHUI CONCH KAWASAKI ENERGY CONSERVATION EQUIPMENT MANUFACTURING CO., LTD.—See Kawasaki Heavy Industries, Ltd.; *Int'l*, pg. 4095

ANHUI CONCH KAWASAKI ENGINEERING CO., LTD.—See Kawasaki Heavy Industries, Ltd.; *Int'l*, pg. 4095

ANHUI CONCH KAWASAKI EQUIPMENT MANUFACTURING CO., LTD.—See Kawasaki Heavy Industries, Ltd.; *Int'l*, pg. 4095

ANHUI CONSTRUCTION ENGINEERING GROUP CORPORATION LIMITED; *Int'l*, pg. 467

ANHUI COREACH TECHNOLOGY CO., LTD.; *Int'l*, pg. 467

ANHUI DELI HOUSEHOLD GLASS CO., LTD.; *Int'l*, pg. 467

ANHUI DONGHUA ENVIRONMENT & MUNICIPAL ENGINEERING CO., LTD.—See East China Engineering Science & Technology Co., Ltd.; *Int'l*, pg. 2269

ANHUI EARTH-PANDA ADVANCED MAGNETIC MATERIAL CO., LTD.—See Earth-Panda Advance Magnetic Material Co., Ltd.; *Int'l*, pg. 2268

ANHUI EDSCHA AUTOMOTIVE PARTS, CO. LTD.—See Corporacion Gestamp SL; *Int'l*, pg. 1804

ANHUI ELECTRIC POWER COMPANY—See State Grid Corporation of China; *Int'l*, pg. 7182

ANHUI EXPRESSWAY COMPANY LIMITED; *Int'l*, pg. 467

ANHUI FENGYUAN PHARMACEUTICAL CO., LTD.; *Int'l*, pg. 467

ANHUI FUHUANG STEEL STRUCTURE CO., LTD.; *Int'l*, pg. 467

ANHUI FURUN MEAT PROCESSING CO., LTD—See China Yurun Food Group Limited; *Int'l*, pg. 1566

ANHUI GENUINE PAPER PACKING CO., LTD.; *Int'l*, pg. 467

ANHUI GOLDEN SEED WINERY CO., LTD.; *Int'l*, pg. 467

ANHUI GOURGEN TRAFFIC CONSTRUCTION CO., LTD.; *Int'l*, pg. 467

ANHUI GREAT WALL MILITARY INDUSTRY CO., LTD.; *Int'l*, pg. 467

ANHUI GUANGXIN AGROCHEMICAL CO., LTD.; *Int'l*, pg. 467

ANHUI GUJING DISTILLERY CO., LTD.—See Anhui Gujing Group Co., Ltd.; *Int'l*, pg. 467

ANHUI GUJING GROUP CO., LTD.; *Int'l*, pg. 467

ANHUI GUOFENG NEW MATERIALS CO., LTD.; *Int'l*, pg. 467

ANHUI HANYANG PRECISE MACHINERY CO., LTD.—See Shanghai Hanbell Precise Machinery Co., Ltd.; *Int'l*, pg. 6769

ANHUI HEFEI XIANGDA CAMEL FEED CO., LTD—See Tangrenshen Group Co., Ltd.; *Int'l*, pg. 7458

ANHUI HELI CO., LTD.; *Int'l*, pg. 467

ANHUI HENGYUAN COAL INDUSTRY & ELECTRICITY POWER CO., LTD.; *Int'l*, pg. 468

ANHUI HIGHLY PRECISION CASTING CO., LTD.—See Shanghai Highly (Group) Co., Ltd.; *Int'l*, pg. 6770

ANHUI HONGLU STEEL CONSTRUCTION (GROUP) CO., LTD.; *Int'l*, pg. 468

ANHUI HONGYU WUZHOU MEDICAL MANUFACTURER CO., LTD.; *Int'l*, pg. 468

ANHUI HUAERTAI CHEMICAL CO., LTD.; *Int'l*, pg. 468

ANHUI HUAHENG BIOTECHNOLOGY CO., LTD.; *Int'l*, pg. 468

ANHUI HUALI PACKAGING CO., LTD.—See Overseas Chinese Town (Asia) Holdings Limited; *Int'l*, pg. 5672

ANHUI HUAMAO IMPORT & EXPORT CO., LTD.—See Anhui Huamao Textile Company Limited; *Int'l*, pg. 468

ANHUI HUAMAO TEXTILE COMPANY LIMITED; *Int'l*, pg. 468

ANHUI HUANGSHAN CAPSULE CO., LTD.; *Int'l*, pg. 468

ANHUI HUAQI ENVIRONMENTAL PROTECTION & TECHNOLOGY CO., LTD.; *Int'l*, pg. 468

ANHUI HUAYE AROMAS HEFEI CO., LTD.—See Anhui Hyea Aromas Co., Ltd.; *Int'l*, pg. 468

ANHUI HUILONG AGRICULTURAL MEANS OF PRODUCTION CO., LTD.; *Int'l*, pg. 468

ANHUI HYEA AROMAS CO., LTD.; *Int'l*, pg. 468

ANHUI JIANCHENG INTERNATIONAL ECONOMIC & TECHNICAL COOPERATION CO., LTD—See JC International Group Ltd; *Int'l*, pg. 3919

ANHUI JIANGHUAI AUTOMOBILE GROUP CORP., LTD.; *Int'l*, pg. 468

ANHUI JIANGNAN CHEMICAL INDUSTRY CO., LTD.; *Int'l*, pg. 468

ANHUI JIANHUAI PIPELINE ENGINEERING CO., LTD.—See Beijing Hanjian Heshan Pipeline Co.,LTD.; *Int'l*, pg. 951

ANHUI JINCHEN NONWOVEN CO., LTD.; *Int'l*, pg. 468

ANHUI JINHE INDUSTRIAL CO., LTD.; *Int'l*, pg. 468

ANHUI JINXUAN TECHNOLOGICAL CO., LTD.—See Anhui Jinhe Industrial Co., Ltd.; *Int'l*, pg. 468

ANHUI JIUHUA MOUNTAIN TOURISM DEVELOPMENT CO., LTD; *Int'l*, pg. 468

ANHUI JUAN KUANG ELECTRIC CO., LTD.; *Int'l*, pg. 469

ANHUI KEDA INDUSTRIAL CO., LTD.—See Keda Industrial Group Co., Ltd.; *Int'l*, pg. 4114

ANHUI KEDA SMART ENERGY TECHNOLOGY CO., LTD.—See Keda Industrial Group Co., Ltd.; *Int'l*, pg. 4114

ANHUI KORRUN CO., LTD.; *Int'l*, pg. 469

ANHUI KOUZI DISTILLERY CO., LTD.; *Int'l*, pg. 469

ANHUI KUBOTA SANLIAN PUMP CO., LTD.—See Kubota Corporation; *Int'l*, pg. 4320

ANHUI LANDUN PHOTOELECTRON CO., LTD.; *Int'l*, pg. 469

ANHUI LEOCH POWER SUPPLY CORP.—See Leoch International Technology Limited; *Int'l*, pg. 4457

ANHUI LIUGONG CRANE CO., LTD.—See Guangxi Liugong Machinery Co., Ltd.; *Int'l*, pg. 3163

ANHUI LIUGUO CHEMICAL CO., LTD.; *Int'l*, pg. 469

ANHUI LONGQUAN PIPELINE ENGINEERING CO., LTD.—See Shandong Longquan Pipeline Engineering Co., Ltd.; *Int'l*, pg. 6756

ANHUI MEIZHI COMPRESSOR CO., LTD.—See Midea Group Co., Ltd.; *Int'l*, pg. 4884

ANHUI MENOVO PHARMACEUTICAL CO., LTD.—See Ningbo Menovo Pharmaceutical Co., Ltd.; *Int'l*, pg. 5304

ANHUI PROVINCE NATURAL GAS DEVELOPMENT CO., LTD.—See Henderson Land Development Co. Ltd.; *Int'l*, pg. 3344

ANHUI PROVINCIAL ARCHITECTURAL DESIGN & RESEARCH INSTITUTE CO., LTD.; *Int'l*, pg. 469

ANHUI QIAOFENG PACKAGE PRINTING CO., LTD.—See Tesson Holdings Limited; *Int'l*, pg. 7575

ANHUI QUANCHAI ENGINE CO., LTD.; *Int'l*, pg. 469

ANHUI RONGEN ENVIRONMENTAL PROTECTION TECHNOLOGY CO., LTD.—See Tennant Company; *U.S. Public*, pg. 2016

ANHUI SAN'AN OPTOELECTRONICS CO., LTD.—See San'an Optoelectronics Co., Ltd.; *Int'l*, pg. 6522

ANHUI SAN'AN TECHNOLOGY CO., LTD.—See San'an Optoelectronics Co., Ltd.; *Int'l*, pg. 6522

ANHUI SHENGYUN ENVIRONMENT PROTECTION GROUP CO., LTD.; *Int'l*, pg. 469

ANHUI SHENJIAN NEW MATERIALS CO., LTD.; *Int'l*, pg. 469

ANHUI SHINY ELECTRONIC TECHNOLOGY COMPANY LIMITED; *Int'l*, pg. 469

ANHUI SIERTE FERTILIZER INDUSTRY CO., LTD.; *Int'l*, pg. 469

ANHUI SINONET & XINLONG SCIENCE & TECHNOLOGY CO., LTD.; *Int'l*, pg. 469

ANHUI SMITH NEW MATERIAL TECHNOLOGY CO., LTD.—See Shanghai Smith Adhesive New Material Co., Ltd.; *Int'l*, pg. 6779

ANHUI SUN-CREATE ELECTRONICS CO., LTD.; *Int'l*, pg. 469

ANHUI SUNHERE PHARMACEUTICAL EXCIPIENTS CO., LTD.; *Int'l*, pg. 469

ANHUI TATFOOK TECHNOLOGY CO., LTD; *Int'l*, pg. 469

ANHUI TEC TOWER CO., LTD.—See Telidyne Inc.; *U.S. Public*, pg. 1998

ANHUI TIANDA OIL PIPE COMPANY LIMITED—See Vallourec SA; *Int'l*, pg. 8118

ANHUI TONGFENG ELECTRONICS CO., LTD.; *Int'l*, pg. 469

ANHUI TONGGUAN COPPER FOIL GROUP CO., LTD.; *Int'l*, pg. 470

ANHUI TONGYUAN ENVIRONMENT ENERGY SAVING CO., LTD.; *Int'l*, pg. 470

ANHUI TRANSPORT CONSULTING & DESIGN INSTITUTE CO., LTD.; *Int'l*, pg. 470

ANHUI TRUCHUM ADVANCED MATERIALS AND TECHNOLOGY CO., LTD.; *Int'l*, pg. 470

ANHUI TUOSHAN HEAVY INDUSTRIES CO., LTD.; *Int'l*, pg. 470

ANHUI WANTONG POSTS & TELECOMMUNICATION COMPANY LIMITED—See ZTE Corporation; *Int'l*, pg. 8691

ANHUI WANTONG TECHNOLOGY CO., LTD.; *Int'l*, pg. 470

ANHUI WANWEI UPDATED HI-TECH MATERIAL INDUSTRY COMPANY LIMITED; *Int'l*, pg. 470

ANHUI WANYI SCIENCE & TECHNOLOGY CO., LTD.; *Int'l*, pg. 470

AN HUI WENERGY CO., LTD.; *Int'l*, pg. 443

ANHUI XINBO ALUMINUM CO., LTD.; *Int'l*, pg. 470

ANHUI XINHUA MEDIA CO., LTD.; *Int'l*, pg. 470

ANHUI XINLI FINANCE CO., LTD.; *Int'l*, pg. 470

ANHUI YINGJIA DISTILLERY CO., LTD.; *Int'l*, pg. 470

ANHUI YINGLIU ELECTROMECHANICAL CO., LTD.; *Int'l*, pg. 470

ANHUI YONGDA BAOYI AUTOMOBILE SALES AND SERVICES CO., LTD.—See China Yongda Automobiles Services Holdings Limited; *Int'l*, pg. 1564

ANHUI YONGMAO TAI ALUMINUM CO. LTD.—See Shanghai Yongmaotai Automotive Technology Co., Ltd.; *Int'l*, pg. 6782

ANHUI YONGMAOTAI AUTO PARTS CO. LTD.—See Shanghai Yongmaotai Automotive Technology Co., Ltd.; *Int'l*, pg. 6782

ANHUI YUANCHEN ENVIRONMENTAL PROTECTION SCIENCE & TECHNOLOGY CO., LTD.; *Int'l*, pg. 470

ANHUI ZHONGDING HOLDING (GROUP) CO., LTD.; *Int'l*, pg. 470

ANHUI ZHONGDING SEALING PARTS CO., LTD.—See Anhui Zhongding Holding (Group) Co., Ltd.; *Int'l*, pg. 470

ANHUI ZHONGHUAN ENVIRONMENTAL PROTECTION TECHNOLOGY CO., LTD.; *Int'l*, pg. 471

ANHUI ZHONGYUAN NEW MATERIALS CO., LTD.; *Int'l*, pg. 471

ANH VIET MECHANICAL & ALUMINUM GLASS CORPORATION—See Hoa Binh Construction Group JSC; *Int'l*, pg. 3435

ANHYDRO A/S—See Lone Star Funds; *U.S. Private*, pg. 2486

ANHYDRO S.A.S—See Lone Star Funds; *U.S. Private*, pg. 2485

ANICH INDUSTRIES, INC.—See DoALL Company; *U.S. Private*, pg. 1250

ANICOM HOLDINGS, INC.; *Int'l*, pg. 471

ANICOM INSURANCE, INC.—See Anicom Holdings, Inc.; *Int'l*, pg. 471

ANICOM PAFE, INC.—See Anicom Holdings, Inc.; *Int'l*, pg. 471

ANICOM SPECIALTY MEDICAL INSTITUTE, INC.—See Anicom Holdings, Inc.; *Int'l*, pg. 471

ANIDAPORT - INVESTIMENTOS IMOBILIARIOS, UNIPESSOAL, LTDA—See Banco Bilbao Vizcaya Argentaria, S.A.; *Int'l*, pg. 817

A. NIEDERMUHLBICHLER BAUGESELLSCHAFT M.B.H.—See PORR AG; *Int'l*, pg. 5922

ANIELLO INSURANCE AGENCY, INC.—See GTCR LLC; *U.S. Private*, pg. 1802

ANI INTEGRATED SERVICES LIMITED; *Int'l*, pg. 471

ANI JOINT STOCK COMPANY; *Int'l*, pg. 471

ANIKA THERAPEUTICS, INC.; *U.S. Public*, pg. 137

ANIK FERRO-ALLOYS PVT. LTD—See Anik Industries Ltd.; *Int'l*, pg. 471

ANIK INDUSTRIES LTD.; *Int'l*, pg. 471

ANI LEASING IFN S.A.—See UniCredit S.p.A.; *Int'l*, pg. 8036

ANILLO INDUSTRIES, INC.—See KKR & Co. Inc.; *U.S. Public*, pg. 1262

ANIL SPECIAL STEEL INDUSTRIES LTD.; *Int'l*, pg. 471

ANIMA ALTERNATIVE SGR S.P.A.—See ANIMA Holding S.p.A.; *Int'l*, pg. 471

ANIMA ALTERNATIVE S.P.A.—See ANIMA Holding S.p.A.; *Int'l*, pg. 471

ANIMA HOLDING SA; *Int'l*, pg. 471

ANIMA HOLDING S.P.A.; *Int'l*, pg. 471

ANIMAID PET HOSPITAL; *U.S. Private*, pg. 283

ANIMALCARE GROUP PLC; *Int'l*, pg. 471

ANIMALCARE LIMITED—See Animalcare Group plc; *Int'l*, pg. 471

ANIMALCO A.S.—See Agrofert Holding, a.s.; *Int'l*, pg. 218

ANIMAL DERMATOLOGY & ALLERGY—See Percheron Investment Management LP; *U.S. Private*, pg. 3146

ANIMAL DERMATOLOGY CLINIC—See Percheron Investment Management LP; *U.S. Private*, pg. 3146

ANIMAL DERMATOLOGY GROUP, INC.—See Percheron Investment Management LP; *U.S. Private*, pg. 3146

ANIMAL DERMATOLOGY REFERRAL CLINIC—See Percheron Investment Management LP; *U.S. Private*, pg. 3146

ANIMAL EMERGENCY CENTRE CENTRAL COAST PTY LTD.—See TPG Capital, L.P.; *U.S. Public*, pg. 2176

ANIMAL EMERGENCY CENTRE (FRANKSTON) PTY LTD.—See TPG Capital, L.P.; *U.S. Public*, pg. 2176

ANIMAL EMERGENCY CENTRE HALLAM PTY LTD.—See TPG Capital, L.P.; *U.S. Public*, pg. 2176

ANIMAL EMERGENCY CENTRE PTY LTD.—See TPG Capital, L.P.; *U.S. Public*, pg. 2176

ANIMAL EMERGENCY CENTRE WOOLLOONGABBA PTY LTD.—See TPG Capital, L.P.; *U.S. Public*, pg. 2176

ANIMALFEEDS INTERNATIONAL CORPORATION; *U.S. Private*, pg. 283

ANIMAL FEED SUPPLEMENT INC.—See Carr's Group PLC; *Int'l*, pg. 1343

ANIMAL GENERAL MEDICAL CENTER CORPORATION—See Olympic Group Corporation; *Int'l*, pg. 5555

ANIMAL HAVEN INC.; *U.S. Private*, pg. 283

ANIMAL HEALTH CENTRE LIMITED—See CVS Group Plc; *Int'l*, pg. 1890

ANIMAL HEALTH INTERNATIONAL, INC.—See Patterson Companies, Inc.; *U.S. Public*, pg. 1654

ANIMAL HUMANE SOCIETY; *U.S. Private*, pg. 283

ANIMAL PHARM CARE USA, INC.—See Swedencare AB; *Int'l*, pg. 7365

ANIMAL PLANET EUROPE P/S—See Warner Bros. Discovery, Inc.; *U.S. Public*, pg. 2326

ANIMAL PLANET, LLC—See Warner Bros. Discovery, Inc.; *U.S. Public*, pg. 2326

ANIMAL REPRODUCTION SYSTEMS—See Dupree, Inc.; *U.S. Private*, pg. 1291

ANIMAL RESCUE LEAGUE OF BOSTON; *U.S. Private*, pg. 283

ANIMALSCAN MRI-NC SCHOOL OF VETERINARY MEDICINE—See AnimalScan; *U.S. Private*, pg. 283

ANIMALSCAN MRI—See AnimalScan; *U.S. Private*, pg. 283

ANIMALSCAN MRI—See AnimalScan; *U.S. Private*, pg. 283
ANIMALSCAN MRI—See AnimalScan; *U.S. Private*, pg. 283
ANIMALSCAN; *U.S. Private*, pg. 283
ANIMAL SUPPLY COMPANY LLC—See Summit Partners, L.P.; *U.S. Private*, pg. 3855
ANIMAL SUPPLY CO. WEST—See Summit Partners, L.P.; *U.S. Private*, pg. 3855
ANIMANA B.V.—See IDEXX Laboratories, Inc.; *U.S. Public*, pg. 1092
ANIMA NV—See Ackermans & van Haaren NV; *Int'l*, pg. 104
ANIMART INC.; *U.S. Private*, pg. 283
ANIMAS DIALYSIS, LLC—See DaVita Inc.; *U.S. Public*, pg. 636
ANIMA SGR S.P.A.—See ANIMA Holding S.p.A.; *Int'l*, pg. 471
ANIMAS LLC—See Johnson & Johnson; *U.S. Public*, pg. 1194
ANIMAS SURGICAL HOSPITAL, LLC—See Bain Capital, LP; *U.S. Private*, pg. 446
ANIMAS VALLEY MALL, LLC—See Brookfield Corporation; *Int'l*, pg. 1185
ANIMATED DESIGNS LLC; *U.S. Private*, pg. 283
ANIMATE FOTOFIXE E MAQUINAS AUTOMATICAS LDA—See ME Group International plc; *Int'l*, pg. 4762
ANIMATICS CORP.—See Moog Inc.; *U.S. Public*, pg. 1470
ANIMATICS GMBH—See Moog Inc.; *U.S. Public*, pg. 1469
ANIMATION COLLECTIVE; *U.S. Private*, pg. 283
ANIMAX DESIGNS INC.—See Cityneon Holdings Limited; *Int'l*, pg. 1629
ANIMAX LTD.—See Carr's Group PLC; *Int'l*, pg. 1343
ANIMED DIRECT LIMITED—See CVS Group Plc; *Int'l*, pg. 1890
ANIMEDICA GMBH—See AGRAVIS Raiffeisen AG; *Int'l*, pg. 216
ANIMEDICA INTERNATIONAL GMBH—See AGRAVIS Raiffeisen AG; *Int'l*, pg. 216
ANIMEDICA LATINO AMERICA S.A. DE C.V.—See AGRAVIS Raiffeisen AG; *Int'l*, pg. 215
ANIMEIGO INC.; *U.S. Private*, pg. 283
ANIMEX FISH SP. Z O.O.—See WH Group Limited; *Int'l*, pg. 8395
ANIMEX FOODS SP. Z.O.O. S.K.A.—See WH Group Limited; *Int'l*, pg. 8395
ANIMEX GRUPA DROBIARSKA SP Z.O.O.—See WH Group Limited; *Int'l*, pg. 8395
ANIMEX GRUPA PASZOWA S.A.—See WH Group Limited; *Int'l*, pg. 8395
ANIMEX-PASZE SP. Z O.O.—See WH Group Limited; *Int'l*, pg. 8395
ANIMEX SF SP. Z.O.O PASZE S.K.A.—See WH Group Limited; *Int'l*, pg. 8395
ANIMEX SP. Z O.O.—See WH Group Limited; *Int'l*, pg. 8395
ANIMIX, LLC—See Benford Capital Partners, LLC; *U.S. Private*, pg. 525
ANIMOCA BRANDS CORPORATION LIMITED; *Int'l*, pg. 471
ANIMOTO, INC.—See Redbrick Technologies Inc.; *Int'l*, pg. 6245
AN IMPORTS OF FT. LAUDERDALE, INC.—See AutoNation, Inc.; *U.S. Public*, pg. 231
AN IMPORTS OF SPOKANE, INC.—See AutoNation, Inc.; *U.S. Public*, pg. 231
AN IMPORTS OF STEVENS CREEK, INC.—See AutoNation, Inc.; *U.S. Public*, pg. 231
AN IMPORTS ON WESTON ROAD, INC.—See AutoNation, Inc.; *U.S. Public*, pg. 231
ANIMUS SOLUTIONS INC.; *U.S. Private*, pg. 283
ANINO INTERNATIONAL PLC; *Int'l*, pg. 471
AN INTERNET GROUP; *U.S. Private*, pg. 271
ANION QUIMICA INDUSTRIAL S.A.—See Element Solutions Inc.; *U.S. Public*, pg. 725
ANIPARK CO., LTD.—See CJ Corporation; *Int'l*, pg. 1631
ANIPET ANIMAL SUPPLIES INC.; *Int'l*, pg. 472
ANI PHARMACEUTICALS, INC.; *U.S. Public*, pg. 137
ANIPLUS INT'L; *Int'l*, pg. 472
ANISA INTERNATIONAL, INC.; *U.S. Private*, pg. 283
ANISERCO S.A.; *Int'l*, pg. 472
ANIS OPAKOWANIA SP. Z.O.O—See Groupe Guillin SA; *Int'l*, pg. 3103
ANITA'S MEXICAN FOODS CORP.—See La Reina Company; *U.S. Private*, pg. 2369
ANITOX CORP—See The Riverside Company; *U.S. Private*, pg. 4107
ANITOX (M) SDN. BHD.—See SCC Holdings Berhad; *Int'l*, pg. 6614
ANITTEL GROUP LIMITED—See 5G Networks Limited; *Int'l*, pg. 13
ANITTEL PTY. LTD.—See 5G Networks Limited; *Int'l*, pg. 13
ANIXA BIOSCIENCES, INC.; *U.S. Public*, pg. 137
ANIXTER AUSTRALIA PTY. LTD.—See WESCO International, Inc.; *U.S. Public*, pg. 2350
ANIXTER AUSTRIA GMBH—See WESCO International, Inc.; *U.S. Public*, pg. 2350
ANIXTER BELGIUM B.V.B.A.—See WESCO International, Inc.; *U.S. Public*, pg. 2350
ANIXTER BULGARIA EOOD—See WESCO International, Inc.; *U.S. Public*, pg. 2350
ANIXTER CANADA, INC.—See WESCO International, Inc.; *U.S. Public*, pg. 2350
ANIXTER (CIS) LLC—See WESCO International, Inc.; *U.S. Public*, pg. 2350
ANIXTER DANMARK A.S.—See WESCO International, Inc.; *U.S. Public*, pg. 2350
ANIXTER DEUTSCHLAND GMBH—See WESCO International, Inc.; *U.S. Public*, pg. 2350
ANIXTER EGYPT LLC—See WESCO International, Inc.; *U.S. Public*, pg. 2350
ANIXTER ESPANA S.L.—See WESCO International, Inc.; *U.S. Public*, pg. 2350
ANIXTER EUROFIN B.V.—See WESCO International, Inc.; *U.S. Public*, pg. 2350
ANIXTER ILETISIM SISTEMLERI PAZARLAMA VE TICARET A.S.—See WESCO International, Inc.; *U.S. Public*, pg. 2350
ANIXTER, INC.-CONNECTICUT—See WESCO International, Inc.; *U.S. Public*, pg. 2350
ANIXTER INC—See WESCO International, Inc.; *U.S. Public*, pg. 2350
ANIXTER INC. - WAUKESHA—See WESCO International, Inc.; *U.S. Public*, pg. 2350
ANIXTER INDIA PRIVATE LIMITED—See WESCO International, Inc.; *U.S. Public*, pg. 2350
ANIXTER INTERNATIONAL INC.—See WESCO International, Inc.; *U.S. Public*, pg. 2350
ANIXTER ITALIA S.R.L.—See WESCO International, Inc.; *U.S. Public*, pg. 2350
ANIXTER JORVEX S.A.C.—See WESCO International, Inc.; *U.S. Public*, pg. 2350
ANIXTER LIMITED—See WESCO International, Inc.; *U.S. Public*, pg. 2350
ANIXTER LOGISTICA DO BRASIL LTDA—See WESCO International, Inc.; *U.S. Public*, pg. 2350
ANIXTER NEW ZEALAND LIMITED—See WESCO International, Inc.; *U.S. Public*, pg. 2350
ANIXTER NORGE A.N.S.—See WESCO International, Inc.; *U.S. Public*, pg. 2350
ANIXTER POLAND SP.Z.O.O.—See WESCO International, Inc.; *U.S. Public*, pg. 2350
ANIXTER PORTUGAL S.A.—See WESCO International, Inc.; *U.S. Public*, pg. 2350
ANIXTER POWER SOLUTIONS CANADA INC.—See WESCO International, Inc.; *U.S. Public*, pg. 2350
ANIXTER PUERTO RICO, INC.—See WESCO International, Inc.; *U.S. Public*, pg. 2350
ANIXTER SAUDI ARABIA LIMITED—See WESCO International, Inc.; *U.S. Public*, pg. 2350
ANIXTER SINGAPORE PTE. LTD.—See WESCO International, Inc.; *U.S. Public*, pg. 2350
ANIXTER SVERIGE AB—See WESCO International, Inc.; *U.S. Public*, pg. 2350
ANIXTER SWITZERLAND SARL—See WESCO International, Inc.; *U.S. Public*, pg. 2350
ANIXTER THAILAND INC.—See WESCO International, Inc.; *U.S. Public*, pg. 2350
ANIXTER (U.K.) LIMITED—See WESCO International, Inc.; *U.S. Public*, pg. 2350
ANJAC SAS; *Int'l*, pg. 472
ANJANEY ALLOYS LTD.—See Bhagwati Syndicate Pvt. Ltd.; *Int'l*, pg. 1010
ANJANEYAP GLOBAL INC.; *U.S. Private*, pg. 284
ANJANI ETECH SOLUTIONS, INC.; *U.S. Private*, pg. 284
ANJANI FINANCE LIMITED; *Int'l*, pg. 472
ANJANI FOODS LIMITED; *Int'l*, pg. 472
ANJANI PORTLAND CEMENT LTD. - NALGONDA WORKS—See Anjani Portland Cement Ltd.; *Int'l*, pg. 472
ANJANI PORTLAND CEMENT LTD.; *Int'l*, pg. 472
ANJANI SYNTHETICS LTD. - AHMEDABAD PLANT—See Anjani Synthetics Ltd.; *Int'l*, pg. 472
ANJANI SYNTHETICS LTD.; *Int'l*, pg. 472
ANJIE USA INC.—See Suzhou Anjie Technology Co., Ltd.; *Int'l*, pg. 7349
ANJIE WIRELESS TECHNOLOGY (SUZHOU) CO., LTD.—See Suzhou Anjie Technology Co., Ltd.; *Int'l*, pg. 7349
ANJI FOODSTUFF CO., LTD.; *Int'l*, pg. 472
ANJI FUJIKURA RUBBER CO., LTD.—See Fujikura Composites Inc.; *Int'l*, pg. 2826
ANJI MICROELECTRONICS TECHNOLOGY SHANGHAI CO., LTD.; *Int'l*, pg. 472
ANJI-NYK LOGISTICS (THAILAND) CO., LTD.—See Nippon Yusen Kabushiki Kaisha; *Int'l*, pg. 5357
ANJI TECHNOLOGY CO., LTD.; *Int'l*, pg. 472
ANJO ISUZU CORPORATION—See Mitsubishi Corporation; *Int'l*, pg. 4937
ANJOST CORP.; *U.S. Private*, pg. 284
ANJU SOFTWARE, INC.—See ABRY Partners, LLC; *U.S. Private*, pg. 40
ANKA BEHAVIORAL HEALTH, INC.; *U.S. Private*, pg. 284
ANKA INDIA LIMITED; *Int'l*, pg. 472
ANKAMA SAS; *Int'l*, pg. 472
ANKAM INC.; *U.S. Public*, pg. 137
ANKARSRUM ASSISTENT AB—See Duroc AB; *Int'l*, pg. 2229
ANKARSRUM DIE CASTING AB—See AB Monsteras Metall; *Int'l*, pg. 41
ANKARSRUM INDUSTRIES AB—See Duroc AB; *Int'l*, pg. 2229
ANKARSRUM MOTORS AB—See Duroc AB; *Int'l*, pg. 2229
ANKARSRUM UNIVERSAL MOTORS AB—See Duroc AB; *Int'l*, pg. 2229
ANKATEKS TURIZM INSAAT TEKSTIL TEMIZLEME SANAYI VE TICARET LTD.—See Servizi Italia SpA; *Int'l*, pg. 6726
ANKENY PHYSICAL & SPORTS THERAPY, LIMITED PARTNERSHIP—See U.S. Physical Therapy, Inc.; *U.S. Public*, pg. 2213
ANKER AB—See Per Aarsleff Holding A/S; *Int'l*, pg. 5795
ANKER AMSTERDAM SPIRITS B.V.—See B&S Group S.A.; *Int'l*, pg. 784
ANKER INDUSTRIES—See Speyside Equity LLC; *U.S. Private*, pg. 3756
ANKER INNOVATIONS TECHNOLOGY CO., LTD.; *Int'l*, pg. 472
ANKER INTERNATIONAL PLC—See IG Design Group Plc; *Int'l*, pg. 3600
ANKER-TEPPICHBODEN GEBRUDER SCHOELLER GMBH & CO. KG - AVIATION DIVISION—See ANKER-Teppichboden Gebruder Schoeller GmbH & Co. KG; *Int'l*, pg. 472
ANKER-TEPPICHBODEN GEBRUDER SCHOELLER GMBH & CO. KG; *Int'l*, pg. 472
AN KHANH NEW CITY DEVELOPMENT JOINT VENTURE COMPANY LIMITED—See Vietnam Construction Stock Corporation; *Int'l*, pg. 8197
ANKHU KHOLA HYDROPOWER COMPANY LTD; *Int'l*, pg. 472
ANKIT FASTENERS PVT LTD.—See LISI S.A.; *Int'l*, pg. 4523
ANKIT METAL & POWER LTD.; *Int'l*, pg. 472
ANKMAR, LLC—See E.E. Newcomer Enterprises Inc.; *U.S. Private*, pg. 1305
ANKOR ENERGY, LLC.; *U.S. Private*, pg. 284
ANKOR E&P HOLDINGS CORP.—See Korea National Oil Corporation; *Int'l*, pg. 4286
ANKURA CONSULTING GROUP, LLC; *U.S. Private*, pg. 284
ANKUR DISTRIBUTORS PVT. LTD.—See Sangani Hospitals Limited; *Int'l*, pg. 6537
ANKUSH FINSTOCK LIMITED; *Int'l*, pg. 473
ANL (CHINA) LIMITED—See CMA CGM S.A.; *Int'l*, pg. 1666
ANL CONTAINER LINE PTY LIMITED—See CMA CGM S.A.; *Int'l*, pg. 1666
ANLEV (UK) HOLDINGS LIMITED—See Analogue Holdings Limited; *Int'l*, pg. 446
ANLI FINANCIAL COMMUNICATIONS LIMITED—See China Success Finance Group Holdings Limited; *Int'l*, pg. 1556
ANLI INTERNATIONAL CO., LTD.; *Int'l*, pg. 473
ANLIMA TEXTILE LIMITED—See Anlima Yarn Dyeing Limited; *Int'l*, pg. 473
ANLIMA YARN DYEING LIMITED; *Int'l*, pg. 473
ANLIN INDUSTRIES; *U.S. Private*, pg. 284
ANL SINGAPORE—See CMA CGM S.A.; *Int'l*, pg. 1666
ANLU JIAXU NATURAL GAS COMPANY LIMITED—See Renaissance United Limited; *Int'l*, pg. 6273
AN LUXURY IMPORTS GP, LLC—See AutoNation, Inc.; *U.S. Public*, pg. 231
AN LUXURY IMPORTS, LTD.—See AutoNation, Inc.; *U.S. Public*, pg. 231
AN LUXURY IMPORTS OF COCONUT CREEK, INC.—See AutoNation, Inc.; *U.S. Public*, pg. 231
AN LUXURY IMPORTS OF MARIETTA, LLC—See AutoNation, Inc.; *U.S. Public*, pg. 231
AN LUXURY IMPORTS OF PALM BEACH, INC.—See AutoNation, Inc.; *U.S. Public*, pg. 231
AN LUXURY IMPORTS OF PEMBROKE PINES, INC.—See AutoNation, Inc.; *U.S. Public*, pg. 231
AN LUXURY IMPORTS OF PHOENIX, INC.—See AutoNation, Inc.; *U.S. Public*, pg. 231
AN LUXURY IMPORTS OF SANFORD, INC.—See AutoNation, Inc.; *U.S. Public*, pg. 231
AN LUXURY IMPORTS OF SARASOTA, INC.—See AutoNation, Inc.; *U.S. Public*, pg. 231
AN LUXURY IMPORTS OF SPOKANE, INC.—See AutoNation, Inc.; *U.S. Public*, pg. 231
AN LUXURY IMPORTS OF TUCSON, INC.—See AutoNation, Inc.; *U.S. Public*, pg. 231
ANMAR CONSTRUCTION AFRICA (PTY) LTD—See Anmar Mechanical and Electrical Contractors Ltd.; *Int'l*, pg. 473
ANMAR MECHANICAL AND ELECTRICAL CONTRACTORS LTD.; *Int'l*, pg. 473
ANMAR METROLOGY, INC.—See Transcat, Inc.; *U.S. Public*, pg. 2179
ANMECO N.V.—See Ackermans & van Haaren NV; *Int'l*, pg. 104

ANMAR MECHANICAL AND ELECTRICAL CONTRACTORS LTD. CORPORATE AFFILIATIONS

ANMED ENCOMPASS HEALTH REHABILITATION HOSPITAL, LLC—See Encompass Health Corporation; *U.S. Public*, pg. 754
ANMED HEALTH MEDICAL CENTER—See AnMed Health; *U.S. Private*, pg. 284
ANMED HEALTH; *U.S. Private*, pg. 284
AN/MNI ACQUISITION CORP.—See AutoNation, Inc.; *U.S. Public*, pg. 232
AN/MNI ACQUISITION CORP.—See AutoNation, Inc.; *U.S. Public*, pg. 232
ANMOL INDIA LIMITED; *Int'l*, pg. 473
AN MOTORS OF BROOKSVILLE, INC.—See AutoNation, Inc.; *U.S. Public*, pg. 231
AN MOTORS OF DALLAS, INC.—See AutoNation, Inc.; *U.S. Public*, pg. 231
AN MOTORS OF MEMPHIS, INC.—See AutoNation, Inc.; *U.S. Public*, pg. 231
AN MOTORS OF PEMBROKE, LLC—See AutoNation, Inc.; *U.S. Public*, pg. 231
AN MOTORS OF SCOTTSDALE, LLC—See AutoNation, Inc.; *U.S. Public*, pg. 231
AN MOTORS ON FEDERAL HIGHWAY, LLC—See AutoNation, Inc.; *U.S. Public*, pg. 231
AN MOTORS ON SOUTH PADRE, LP—See AutoNation, Inc.; *U.S. Public*, pg. 231
ANNABELLE AG—See TX Group AG; *Int'l*, pg. 7991
ANNABELLE CANDY COMPANY, INC.; *U.S. Private*, pg. 284
ANNABIDIOL CORP.; *U.S. Public*, pg. 137
ANNA CLINIC CORP.—See Quorum Health Corporation; *U.S. Private*, pg. 3329
ANNADEL CAPITAL INC.—See Defined Financial Planning, LLC; *U.S. Private*, pg. 1191
ANNAGEN, LLC; *U.S. Private*, pg. 284
ANNA HOSPITAL CORPORATION—See Quorum Health Corporation; *U.S. Private*, pg. 3329
ANNAIK LIMITED; *Int'l*, pg. 473
ANN AIK PTE LTD—See AnnAik Limited; *Int'l*, pg. 473
ANNA INFRASTRUCTURES LIMITED; *Int'l*, pg. 473
ANNA INTERNATIONAL LIMITED—See BWT Aktiengesellschaft; *Int'l*, pg. 1232
ANNALY CAPITAL MANAGEMENT, INC.; *U.S. Public*, pg. 137
ANNALY COMMERCIAL REAL ESTATE GROUP, INC.—See Annaly Capital Management, Inc.; *U.S. Public*, pg. 137
ANNA MARIA VACATIONS; *U.S. Private*, pg. 284
ANNAMS SYSTEMS, CORP.—See CGI Inc.; *Int'l*, pg. 1432
ANNAN & BIRD LITHOGRAPHERS, INC.—See Chatham Asset Management, LLC; *U.S. Private*, pg. 862
ANNAPOLIS INFLATABLES—See Fawcett Marine Supplies LLC; *U.S. Private*, pg. 1484
ANNAPOLIS JUNCTION NFM LLC—See Boston Properties, Inc.; *U.S. Public*, pg. 372
ANNAPOLIS MICRO SYSTEMS, INC.; *U.S. Private*, pg. 284
ANNAPOLIS OUTBACK, INC.—See Bloomin' Brands, Inc.; *U.S. Public*, pg. 362
ANNAPURNA BHASKARI GROUP; *Int'l*, pg. 473
ANNAPURNA ELECTRONICS & SERVICES PVT. LTD.—See Annapurna Bhaskari Group; *Int'l*, pg. 473
ANNAPURNA KENMORE TUBE PRODUCTS PVT. LTD.—See Annapurna Bhaskari Group; *Int'l*, pg. 473
ANNAPURNA KENMORE TUBE PRODUCTS PVT. LTD.—See Parker Hannifin Corporation; *U.S. Public*, pg. 1640
ANN ARBOR ANNUITY EXCHANGE INC.—See Allianz SE; *Int'l*, pg. 351
ANN ARBOR CEILING & PARTITION CO.—See National Construction Enterprises Inc.; *U.S. Private*, pg. 2851
ANN ARBOR FIRE PROTECTION INC.; *U.S. Private*, pg. 284
ANNAR DIAGNOSTICA IMPORT SAS—See HORIBA Ltd; *Int'l*, pg. 3474
ANNAX GMBH—See Westinghouse Air Brake Technologies Corporation; *U.S. Public*, pg. 2357
ANNAX POLSKA SP. Z O.O.—See Westinghouse Air Brake Technologies Corporation; *U.S. Public*, pg. 2357
ANNAX SCHEIZ AG—See Westinghouse Air Brake Technologies Corporation; *U.S. Public*, pg. 2357
ANNAX (SUZHOU) RAIL SYSTEMS CO., LTD.—See Westinghouse Air Brake Technologies Corporation; *U.S. Public*, pg. 2357
ANN BEE (M) SDN. BHD.—See Muhibbah Engineering (M) Bhd.; *Int'l*, pg. 5078
ANNE ARUNDEL BROADBAND, LLC—See WideOpenWest, Inc.; *U.S. Public*, pg. 2369
ANNE ARUNDEL DERMATOLOGY MANAGEMENT LLC—See Ridgemont Partners Management LLC; *U.S. Private*, pg. 3433
ANNE ARUNDEL DERMATOLOGY P.A.—See NMS Capital Services, LLC; *U.S. Private*, pg. 2931
ANNEBERGS LIMTRAE A/S—See Kingspan Group PLC; *Int'l*, pg. 4178
ANNEC GREEN REFRACTORIES CORPORATION; *Int'l*, pg. 473
ANNEHEM BYGG OCH PROJEKT AB—See Peab AB; *Int'l*, pg. 5771

ANNE KLEIN COMMUNICATIONS GROUP, LLC; *U.S. Private*, pg. 284
ANNELIESE KOSTER GMBH & CO. KG—See INDUS Holding AG; *Int'l*, pg. 3662
ANNEMARIE BORLIND SA—See Boerlind Gesellschaft fuer Erzeugnisse mbH; *Int'l*, pg. 1100
ANNEX CAPITAL MANAGEMENT LLC; *U.S. Private*, pg. 285
ANNEX CONSULTING GROUP INC.—See Cornell Capital LLC; *U.S. Private*, pg. 1051
ANNEX CONSULTING GROUP INC.—See TorQuest Partners Inc.; *Int'l*, pg. 7830
ANNEX MANUFACTURING, INC.; *U.S. Private*, pg. 285
ANNEXON, INC.; *U.S. Public*, pg. 138
ANNEX PUBLISHING & PRINTING INC.; *Int'l*, pg. 474
ANNEX-TECHNIK GMBH—See LKQ Corporation; *U.S. Public*, pg. 1333
ANN HARVEY DIVISION—See Sun Capital Partners, Inc.; *U.S. Private*, pg. 3861
ANN & HOPE INC.; *U.S. Private*, pg. 284
ANNICA HOLDINGS LIMITED; *Int'l*, pg. 474
ANNICK GOUTAL S.A.S.—See Amorepacific Corp.; *Int'l*, pg. 430
ANNIDIS CORPORATION; *Int'l*, pg. 474
ANNIE'S ENTERPRISES, INC.—See General Mills, Inc.; *U.S. Public*, pg. 921
ANNIE'S HOMEGROWN, INC.—See General Mills, Inc.; *U.S. Public*, pg. 921
ANNIE'S, INC.—See General Mills, Inc.; *U.S. Public*, pg. 921
ANNIE'S PUBLISHING, LLC—See Dynamic Resource Group, Inc.; *U.S. Private*, pg. 1298
ANNIL CO., LTD.; *Int'l*, pg. 474
ANNIN & COMPANY; *U.S. Private*, pg. 285
ANN INC.—See Sycamore Partners Management, LP; *U.S. Private*, pg. 3895
ANNING DECCO FINE CHEMICAL CO.,LIMITED.—See UPL Limited; *Int'l*, pg. 8089
ANNING JOHNSON COMPANY—See Anson Industries, Inc.; *U.S. Private*, pg. 286
ANNING JOHNSON COMPANY—See Anson Industries, Inc.; *U.S. Private*, pg. 286
ANNING JOHNSON CO.—See Anson Industries, Inc.; *U.S. Private*, pg. 286
ANNING JOHNSON SAN FRANCISCO—See Anson Industries, Inc.; *U.S. Private*, pg. 286
ANNINMUIZAS IPASUMS SIA—See Africa Israel Investments Ltd.; *Int'l*, pg. 190
ANNISTON HMA, LLC—See The Health Care Authority of the City of Anniston; *U.S. Private*, pg. 4043
ANNIVERSAIRE INC.—See AOKI Holdings Inc.; *Int'l*, pg. 488
ANNIVERSARY TRAVEL CO., LTD.—See TAKE AND GIVE. NEEDS Co. Ltd.; *Int'l*, pg. 7436
ANN JOO GREEN ENERGY SDN. BHD.—See Ann Joo Resources Berhad; *Int'l*, pg. 473
ANN JOO INTEGRATED STEEL SDN. BHD.—See Ann Joo Resources Berhad; *Int'l*, pg. 473
ANN JOO MANAGEMENT SERVICES SDN. BHD.—See Ann Joo Resources Berhad; *Int'l*, pg. 473
ANN JOO METAL SDN. BHD.—See Ann Joo Resources Berhad; *Int'l*, pg. 473
ANN JOO METAL (SINGAPORE) PTE. LTD.—See Ann Joo Resources Berhad; *Int'l*, pg. 473
ANN JOO RESOURCES BERHAD; *Int'l*, pg. 473
ANNKISSAM LLC—See Homecare Software Solutions LLC; *U.S. Private*, pg. 1973
ANNONA ENERGY INC.; *Int'l*, pg. 474
ANNOOR TEXTILE MILLS LIMITED; *Int'l*, pg. 474
AN NORTH PHOENIX COLLISION, INC.—See AutoNation, Inc.; *U.S. Public*, pg. 231
ANNOVA LNG, LLC—See Constellation Energy Corporation; *U.S. Public*, pg. 571
ANNOVATION BIOPHARMA, INC.—See Novartis AG; *Int'l*, pg. 5460
ANNOVIS BIO, INC.; *U.S. Public*, pg. 138
ANN & ROBERT H. LURIE CHILDREN'S HOSPITAL OF CHICAGO; *U.S. Private*, pg. 284
ANN SACKS TILE & STONE, INC.—See Kohler Company; *U.S. Private*, pg. 2339
ANN STORCK CENTER, INC.; *U.S. Private*, pg. 284
ANNTAYLOR, INC.—See Sycamore Partners Management, LP; *U.S. Private*, pg. 3895
ANNTAYLOR RETAIL, INC.—See Sycamore Partners Management, LP; *U.S. Private*, pg. 3895
ANNUAL REVIEWS; *U.S. Private*, pg. 285
ANNUITY INVESTORS LIFE INSURANCE COMPANY—See Massachusetts Mutual Life Insurance Company; *U.S. Private*, pg. 2605
ANNUITY & LIFE REASSURANCE, LTD.—See Annuity & Life Re (Holdings), Ltd.; *Int'l*, pg. 474
ANNUITY & LIFE RE (HOLDINGS), LTD.; *Int'l*, pg. 474
THE ANNUITY STORE FINANCIAL & INSURANCE SERVICES LLC—See Allianz SE; *Int'l*, pg. 356
ANNUM BERHAD; *Int'l*, pg. 474
ANOCOIL CORPORATION; *U.S. Private*, pg. 285
ANOD BANK; *Int'l*, pg. 474
ANODYNE MEDICAL DEVICE, INC.—See Baxter International Inc.; *U.S. Public*, pg. 282

ANOKA HENNEPIN SCHOOL DISTRICT CREDIT UNION, INC.; *U.S. Private*, pg. 285
ANOMALY B.V—See Stagwell, Inc.; *U.S. Public*, pg. 1925
ANOMALY INC.—See Stagwell, Inc.; *U.S. Public*, pg. 1925
ANOMALY LONDON LLP—See Stagwell, Inc.; *U.S. Public*, pg. 1926
ANOMALY PARTNERS LLC—See Stagwell, Inc.; *U.S. Public*, pg. 1926
ANOMATIC CORPORATION—See Thyssen'sche Handelsgesellschaft m.b.H.; *Int'l*, pg. 7723
ANOMET INC.—See A.A.G. STUCCHI s.r.l.; *Int'l*, pg. 22
ANONYMOUS INTELLIGENCE COMPANY INC; *Int'l*, pg. 474
ANOPLATE CORPORATION; *U.S. Private*, pg. 285
ANORD MARDIX (IRELAND) LTD.—See Flex Ltd.; *Int'l*, pg. 2702
ANORD MARDIX (UK) LIMITED—See Flex Ltd.; *Int'l*, pg. 2702
ANOTA FAHRZEUG SERVICE- UND VERTRIEBSGESELLSCHAFT MBH—See Mercedes-Benz Group AG; *Int'l*, pg. 4820
ANOTECH DO BRASIL LTDA—See Alten S.A.; *Int'l*, pg. 390
ANOTECH ENERGY DOHA LLC—See Alten S.A.; *Int'l*, pg. 390
ANOTECH ENERGY NIGERIA LIMITED—See Alten S.A.; *Int'l*, pg. 390
ANOTECH ENERGY SA—See Alten S.A.; *Int'l*, pg. 389
ANOTECH ENERGY SINGAPORE PTE. LTD.—See Alten S.A.; *Int'l*, pg. 390
ANOTECH ENERGY USA INC.—See Alten S.A.; *Int'l*, pg. 390
ANOTEROS, INC.; *U.S. Private*, pg. 285
ANOTHER BROKEN EGG OF AMERICA LLC—See The Beekman Group, LLC; *U.S. Private*, pg. 3992
ANOTHER CHANCE PROPERTIES PTE LTD—See Second Chance Properties Ltd.; *Int'l*, pg. 6672
ANOTO GROUP AB; *Int'l*, pg. 474
ANOTO INC.—See Anoto Group AB; *Int'l*, pg. 474
ANOTO K.K.—See Anoto Group AB; *Int'l*, pg. 474
ANOTSUGIKEN CO., LTD.—See Meidensha Corporation; *Int'l*, pg. 4797
ANOVA HEALTHCARE SERVICES, INC.; *U.S. Private*, pg. 285
ANOVA MICROSYSTEMS INC.; *U.S. Private*, pg. 285
A NOVO COMLINK ESPANA SL—See Hainan Traffic Administration Holding Co., Ltd.; *Int'l*, pg. 3213
ANOVO NORDIC AB—See Francisco Partners Management, LP; *U.S. Private*, pg. 1588
A NOVO POLSKA SP.Z.O.O.—See Hainan Traffic Administration Holding Co., Ltd.; *Int'l*, pg. 3213
ANOVO S.A.—See Hainan Traffic Administration Holding Co., Ltd.; *Int'l*, pg. 3213
ANOXKALDNES AB—See Veolia Environnement S.A.; *Int'l*, pg. 8161
ANPARIO INC.—See Anpario plc; *Int'l*, pg. 474
ANPARIO MALAYSIA SDN. BHD.—See Anpario plc; *Int'l*, pg. 475
ANPARIO PLC; *Int'l*, pg. 474
ANPARIO PTY. LTD.—See Anpario plc; *Int'l*, pg. 475
ANPARIO SAUDE E NUTRICAO ANIMAL LTDA.—See Anpario plc; *Int'l*, pg. 475
ANPARIO (SHANGHAI) BIOTECH CO., LTD.—See Anpario plc; *Int'l*, pg. 474
ANPARIO (THAILAND) LTD.—See Anpario plc; *Int'l*, pg. 474
ANP BLACKSTONE ENERGY COMPANY, LLC—See ENGIE SA; *Int'l*, pg. 2433
AN/PF ACQUISITION CORP.—See AutoNation, Inc.; *U.S. Public*, pg. 232
ANPHA-AG JOINT STOCK COMPANY—See Konoike Transport Co., Ltd.; *Int'l*, pg. 4274
AN PHA PETROLEUM GROUP JOINT STOCK COMPANY; *Int'l*, pg. 443
AN PHAT BIOPLASTICS; *Int'l*, pg. 443
AN PHAT PLASTIC & GREEN ENVIRONMENT JOINT STOCK COMPANY - FACTORY NO 2—See An Phat Bioplastics; *Int'l*, pg. 443
ANP HOLDING B.V.; *Int'l*, pg. 474
AN PHU IRRADIATION J.S.C.; *Int'l*, pg. 443
ANPLE LABORATORY TECHNOLOGIES (SHANGHAI) INC.—See Focused Photonics (Hangzhou), Inc.; *Int'l*, pg. 2720
AN POST BILLPOST PROCESSING SERVICES LIMITED—See An Post LLC; *Int'l*, pg. 443
AN POST DIRECT LIMITED—See An Post LLC; *Int'l*, pg. 443
AN POST LLC; *Int'l*, pg. 443
AN POST NATIONAL LOTTERY CO.—See An Post LLC; *Int'l*, pg. 443
AN-PRO COMPANY—See The Procter & Gamble Company; *U.S. Public*, pg. 2120
ANPULO FOOD DEVELOPMENT, INC.; *Int'l*, pg. 475
ANPULO FOOD, INC.; *Int'l*, pg. 475
ANP USA INC.—See Advanced Nano Products Co., Ltd.; *Int'l*, pg. 161
ANQING ART TP PISTONS CO., LTD.—See TPR Co., Ltd.; *Int'l*, pg. 7883

ANQING ATGE ENGINEERING CO., LTD.—See TPR Co., Ltd.; *Int'l*, pg. 7883
ANQING HUAPENG CHANGJIANG GLASS CO., LTD.—See Shangdong Huapeng Glass Co., Ltd.; *Int'l*, pg. 6760
ANQING TIANZHUSHAN AIRPORT CO., LTD.—See Hainan Traffic Administration Holding Co., Ltd.; *Int'l*, pg. 3212
ANQING TP POWDER METALLURGY CO., LTD.—See TPR Co., Ltd.; *Int'l*, pg. 7883
ANQING TPR ENGINEERING PLASTIC CO., LTD.—See TPR Co., Ltd.; *Int'l*, pg. 7883
ANQORE B.V.—See CVC Capital Partners SICAV-FIS S.A.; *Int'l*, pg. 1886
ANQUIRO VENTURES LTD.; *Int'l*, pg. 475
ANRAKUTEI CO., LTD.; *Int'l*, pg. 475
ANR BBDO—See Omnicom Group Inc.; *U.S. Public*, pg. 1573
ANR BBDO—See Omnicom Group Inc.; *U.S. Public*, pg. 1573
ANREDER & COMPANY—See Anreder & Co.; *U.S. Private*, pg. 285
ANREDER & CO.; *U.S. Private*, pg. 285
ANRIKA GROUP SCANDINAVIA AB; *Int'l*, pg. 475
ANRIKA QUALITY SERVICES AB—See Anrika Group Scandinavia AB; *Int'l*, pg. 475
ANRITSU AB—See Anritsu Corporation; *Int'l*, pg. 475
ANRITSU AB—See Anritsu Corporation; *Int'l*, pg. 475
ANRITSU A/S—See Anritsu Corporation; *Int'l*, pg. 475
ANRITSU (CHINA) CO., LTD.—See Anritsu Corporation; *Int'l*, pg. 475
ANRITSU CO. LTD.—See Anritsu Corporation; *Int'l*, pg. 475
ANRITSU COMPANY, INC.—See Anritsu Corporation; *Int'l*, pg. 475
ANRITSU COMPANY LIMITED—See Anritsu Corporation; *Int'l*, pg. 475
ANRITSU COMPANY, S.A. DE C.V—See Anritsu Corporation; *Int'l*, pg. 475
ANRITSU COMPANY—See Anritsu Corporation; *Int'l*, pg. 475
ANRITSU CORPORATION; *Int'l*, pg. 475
ANRITSU CUSTOMER SUPPORT CO., LTD.—See Anritsu Corporation; *Int'l*, pg. 475
ANRITSU DEVICES CO., LTD.—See Anritsu Corporation; *Int'l*, pg. 475
ANRITSU ELECTRONICA, LTDA.—See Anritsu Corporation; *Int'l*, pg. 475
ANRITSU ELECTRONICS LTD—See Anritsu Corporation; *Int'l*, pg. 475
ANRITSU EMEA GMBH—See Anritsu Corporation; *Int'l*, pg. 475
ANRITSU EMEA LTD—See Anritsu Corporation; *Int'l*, pg. 475
ANRITSU GMBH—See Anritsu Corporation; *Int'l*, pg. 475
ANRITSU INDIA PRIVATE LIMITED—See Anritsu Corporation; *Int'l*, pg. 475
ANRITSU INDUSTRIAL SOLUTIONS (SHANGHAI) CO., LTD.—See Anritsu Corporation; *Int'l*, pg. 475
ANRITSU INFIVIS B.V.—See Anritsu Corporation; *Int'l*, pg. 475
ANRITSU INFIVIS CO., LTD.—See Anritsu Corporation; *Int'l*, pg. 475
ANRITSU INFIVIS INC.—See Anritsu Corporation; *Int'l*, pg. 475
ANRITSU INFIVIS LTD.—See Anritsu Corporation; *Int'l*, pg. 475
ANRITSU INFIVIS (THAILAND) CO., LTD.—See Anritsu Corporation; *Int'l*, pg. 475
ANRITSU KOUSAN CO., LTD.—See Anritsu Corporation; *Int'l*, pg. 475
ANRITSU LIMITED—See Anritsu Corporation; *Int'l*, pg. 475
ANRITSU PHILIPPINES, INC.—See Anritsu Corporation; *Int'l*, pg. 475
ANRITSU PTE. LTD—See Anritsu Corporation; *Int'l*, pg. 476
ANRITSU PTY. LTD—See Anritsu Corporation; *Int'l*, pg. 476
ANRITSU REAL ESTATE CO., LTD.—See Anritsu Corporation; *Int'l*, pg. 476
ANRITSU S.A—See Anritsu Corporation; *Int'l*, pg. 476
ANRITSU SOLUTIONS SK, S.R.O.—See Anritsu Corporation; *Int'l*, pg. 476
ANRITSU SOLUTIONS S.R.L—See Anritsu Corporation; *Int'l*, pg. 476
ANRITSU S.R.L—See Anritsu Corporation; *Int'l*, pg. 476
ANRO INC.; *U.S. Private*, pg. 285
ANR PIPELINE COMPANY—See TC Energy Corporation; *Int'l*, pg. 7482
ANR STORAGE COMPANY—See TC Energy Corporation; *Int'l*, pg. 7482
ANSA AUTOMOTIVE LIMITED—See ANSA McAl Limited; *Int'l*, pg. 477
ANSA COATINGS JAMAICA LIMITED—See ANSA McAl Limited; *Int'l*, pg. 477
ANSA COATINGS LIMITED—See ANSA McAl Limited; *Int'l*, pg. 476
ANS ADVANCED NETWORK SERVICES, LLC—See Charge Enterprises, Inc.; *U.S. Public*, pg. 479

ANSA FINANCIAL HOLDINGS (BARBADOS) LIMITED—See ANSA McAl Limited; *Int'l*, pg. 476
ANSAFONE CONTACT CENTERS; *U.S. Private*, pg. 285
ANSAH ASIA SDN. BHD.—See Keller Group plc; *Int'l*, pg. 4119
ANSA HOTEL KL SDN BHD—See Berjaya Corporation Berhad; *Int'l*, pg. 982
ANSAL BUILDWELL LTD; *Int'l*, pg. 477
ANSAL CLUBS PVT. LIMITED—See Ahsal Housing Ltd; *Int'l*, pg. 478
ANSALDOBREDA INC.—See Leonardo S.p.A.; *Int'l*, pg. 4458
ANSALDOCALDAI BOILERS INDIA PRIVATE LIMITED—See Gammon India Limited; *Int'l*, pg. 2879
ANSALDO ENERGIA S.P.A.—See Cassa Depositi e Prestiti S.p.A.; *Int'l*, pg. 1354
ANSALDO ENERGIA SWITZERLAND AG—See Cassa Depositi e Prestiti S.p.A.; *Int'l*, pg. 1354
ANSALDO ENERGY INC.—See Hanwha Group; *Int'l*, pg. 3265
ANSALDO NUCLEARE SPA—See Cassa Depositi e Prestiti S.p.A.; *Int'l*, pg. 1354
ANSALDO RUSSIA LLC—See Cassa Depositi e Prestiti S.p.A.; *Int'l*, pg. 1354
ANSALDO SISTEMI INDUSTRIALI SA—See Nidec Corporation; *Int'l*, pg. 5274
ANSALDO STS FRANCE SAS—See Hitachi, Ltd.; *Int'l*, pg. 3417
ANSALDO STS IRELAND—See Hitachi, Ltd.; *Int'l*, pg. 3417
ANSALDO STS SWEDEN AB—See Hitachi, Ltd.; *Int'l*, pg. 3417
ANSALDO THOMASSEN GULF LLC—See Cassa Depositi e Prestiti S.p.A.; *Int'l*, pg. 1354
ANSAL HOUSING LTD; *Int'l*, pg. 477
ANSAL IT CITY & PARKS LTD.—See Ansal Properties & Infrastructure Limited; *Int'l*, pg. 478
ANSAL PROPERTIES & INFRASTRUCTURE LIMITED; *Int'l*, pg. 478
ANSA MCAL (BARBADOS) LIMITED—See ANSA McAl Limited; *Int'l*, pg. 476
ANSA MCAL CHEMICALS LTD.—See ANSA McAl Limited; *Int'l*, pg. 476
ANSA MCAL ENTERPRISES LIMITED—See ANSA McAl Limited; *Int'l*, pg. 476
ANSA MCAL LIMITED; *Int'l*, pg. 476
ANSA MCAL TRADING INC.—See ANSA McAl Limited; *Int'l*, pg. 476
ANSA MCAL TRADING LIMITED—See ANSA McAl Limited; *Int'l*, pg. 476
ANSA MCAL (U.S.) INC.—See ANSA McAl Limited; *Int'l*, pg. 476
ANSA MERCHANT BANK LIMITED—See ANSA McAl Limited; *Int'l*, pg. 476
ANSAM METALS LLC—See Audax Group, Limited Partnership; *U.S. Private*, pg. 390
ANSA MOTORS GUYANA INC.—See ANSA McAl Limited; *Int'l*, pg. 477
ANSA MOTORS LIMITED—See ANSA McAl Limited; *Int'l*, pg. 476
AN SAN JOSE LUXURY IMPORTS, INC.—See AutoNation, Inc.; *U.S. Public*, pg. 231
ANSA POLYMER—See ANSA McAl Limited; *Int'l*, pg. 477
ANSARADA GROUP LIMITED; *Int'l*, pg. 478
ANSARADA HONG KONG LIMITED—See Ansarada Group Limited; *Int'l*, pg. 478
ANSARADA PTE. LIMITED—See Ansarada Group Limited; *Int'l*, pg. 478
ANSARADA UK LIMITED—See Ansarada Group Limited; *Int'l*, pg. 478
ANSA RE LIMITED—See ANSA McAl Limited; *Int'l*, pg. 476
ANSAR FINANCIAL AND DEVELOPMENT CORPORATION; *Int'l*, pg. 478
ANSARI & AUJAN COMPANY L.L.C.—See Aujan Industries Co., L.L.C.; *Int'l*, pg. 704
ANSARI SUGAR MILLS LIMITED; *Int'l*, pg. 478
ANSA SECURITIES LIMITED—See ANSA McAl Limited; *Int'l*, pg. 476
ANSA TECHNOLOGIES LIMITED—See ANSA McAl Limited; *Int'l*, pg. 477
ANSAY & ASSOCIATES INC.; *U.S. Private*, pg. 285
ANSAY & ASSOCIATES, LLC.; *U.S. Private*, pg. 285
ANSCA HOMES; *U.S. Private*, pg. 285
ANSCHLUSS PTE LTD—See Sakae Holdings Ltd.; *Int'l*, pg. 6486
ANSCHUETZ SINGAPORE PTE. LTD.—See DMB Dr. Dieter Murmann Beteiligungsgesellschaft mbH; *Int'l*, pg. 2142
THE ANSCHUTZ CORPORATION; *U.S. Private*, pg. 3986
ANSCHUTZ ENTERTAINMENT GROUP—See The Anschutz Corporation; *U.S. Private*, pg. 3986
ANSCHUTZ FILM GROUP, LLC—See The Anschutz Corporation; *U.S. Private*, pg. 3986
ANSCHUTZ GMBH—See DMB Dr. Dieter Murmann Beteiligungsgesellschaft mbH; *Int'l*, pg. 2142
ANSCO & ASSOCIATES, LLC—See Dycom Industries, Inc.; *U.S. Public*, pg. 698

ANS DISTRIBUTING LLC—See MidOcean Partners, LLP; *U.S. Private*, pg. 2716
ANSEARCH.COM.AU PTY LTD—See Adslot Ltd.; *Int'l*, pg. 154
ANSELL CANADA INC.—See Ansell Limited; *Int'l*, pg. 478
ANSELL COMMERCIAL MEXICO S.A. DE C.V.—See Ansell Limited; *Int'l*, pg. 478
ANSELL ELECTRICAL PRODUCTS LIMITED—See ENDO Lighting Corporation; *Int'l*, pg. 2404
ANSELL HEALTHCARE EUROPE N.V.—See Ansell Limited; *Int'l*, pg. 478
ANSELL HEALTHCARE JAPAN CO. LTD.—See Ansell Limited; *Int'l*, pg. 478
ANSELL HEALTHCARE LLC—See Ansell Limited; *Int'l*, pg. 478
ANSELL (HONG KONG) LIMITED—See Ansell Limited; *Int'l*, pg. 478
ANSELL INTERNATIONAL—See Ansell Limited; *Int'l*, pg. 478
ANSELL LIMITED; *Int'l*, pg. 478
ANSELL NORWAY AS—See Ansell Limited; *Int'l*, pg. 478
ANSELL PROTECTIVE SOLUTIONS AB—See Ansell Limited; *Int'l*, pg. 478
ANSELL (SALES & DISTRIBUTION) LIMITED—See ENDO Lighting Corporation; *Int'l*, pg. 2404
ANSELL SANDEL MEDICAL SOLUTIONS LLC—See Ansell Limited; *Int'l*, pg. 478
ANSELMO LEON DISTRIBUCION, S.L.—See Iberdrola, S.A.; *Int'l*, pg. 3570
ANSELMO L. MORVILLO, S.A.—See Quad/Graphics, Inc.; *U.S. Public*, pg. 1744
ANSEM BV—See Cyient Limited; *Int'l*, pg. 1895
ANSEM NV—See Cyient Limited; *Int'l*, pg. 1895
ANSEN CORPORATION; *U.S. Private*, pg. 285
ANSER ADVISORY LLC—See Accenture plc; *Int'l*, pg. 86
ANS GROUP LIMITED—See Inflexion Private Equity Partners LLP; *Int'l*, pg. 3688
ANSHAN HIFICHEM CO., LTD.; *Int'l*, pg. 479
ANSHAN HYMSON SCIENCE & TECHNOLOGY CO., LTD.—See Hymson Laser Technology Group Co Ltd; *Int'l*, pg. 3549
ANSHAN IRON & STEEL GROUP CORPORATION; *Int'l*, pg. 479
ANSHAN LISHAN DISTRICT AOXIN Q & M STOMATOLOGY POLYCLINIC CO., LTD.—See Aoxin Q & M Dental Group Limited; *Int'l*, pg. 498
ANSHAN SENYUAN ROAD & BRIDGE CO., LTD.; *Int'l*, pg. 479
ANSHAN TIANXING PARKSON SHOPPING CENTRE CO LTD—See Parkson Holdings Berhad; *Int'l*, pg. 5744
AN-SHIN FOOD SERVICES CO., LTD.; *Int'l*, pg. 443
ANSHIN GUARANTOR SERVICE CO., LTD.; *Int'l*, pg. 479
ANSHIN STEEL INDUSTRIES SDN. BHD.—See Ann Joo Resources Berhad; *Int'l*, pg. 473
ANSHIN STEEL PROCESSOR SDN. BHD.—See Ann Joo Resources Berhad; *Int'l*, pg. 473
ANSHUNI COMMERCIALS LIMITED; *Int'l*, pg. 479
ANS INDUSTRIES LIMITED; *Int'l*, pg. 476
ANSIRA PARTNERS, INC.; *U.S. Private*, pg. 285
ANSI SYSTEMS SDN. BHD.—See Zen Tech International Berhad; *Int'l*, pg. 8632
ANSLEY ATLANTA REAL ESTATE,LLC; *U.S. Private*, pg. 286
ANSLEY GOLF CLUB; *U.S. Private*, pg. 286
ANSOFT CORPORATION—See ANSYS, Inc.; *U.S. Public*, pg. 138
ANSON ADVISORS INC; *Int'l*, pg. 479
ANSONIA COPPER & BRASS INC.; *U.S. Private*, pg. 286
ANSONIA CREDIT DATA, INC.—See Equifax Inc.; *U.S. Public*, pg. 786
ANSON INDUSTRIES, INC.; *U.S. Private*, pg. 286
ANSON OIL INDUSTRIES BERHAD—See MHC Plantations Bhd; *Int'l*, pg. 4872
ANSON PARTNERS LLC; *U.S. Private*, pg. 286
ANSON RESOURCES LIMITED; *Int'l*, pg. 479
ANSON-STONER INC.; *U.S. Private*, pg. 286
ANSORGE LOGISTICA S.R.L—See Spedition Ansorge GmbH & Co.KG; *Int'l*, pg. 7132
THE ANSPACH EFFORT, LLC—See Johnson & Johnson; *U.S. Public*, pg. 1200
ANSTAFF BANK—See First National Bancorp, Inc.; *U.S. Private*, pg. 1521
ANSTALT FUR STROMUNGSMASCHINEN GMBH—See ANDRITZ AG; *Int'l*, pg. 455
ANST, CHINA RESOURCES MICRO-ASSEMBLY TECHNOLOGY CO., LTD.—See China Resources (Holdings) Co., Ltd.; *Int'l*, pg. 1548
AN SUBARU MOTORS, INC.—See AutoNation, Inc.; *U.S. Public*, pg. 231
AN SUBARU MOTORS, INC.—See AutoNation, Inc.; *U.S. Public*, pg. 232
ANSUL BV—See London Security PLC; *Int'l*, pg. 4546
ANSUL MEXICO, S.A. DE C.V.—See Johnson Controls International plc; *Int'l*, pg. 3989
ANSUL S.A.—See London Security PLC; *Int'l*, pg. 4546
ANSUL SOLUTIONS B.V.—See London Security PLC; *Int'l*, pg. 4546
ANSUNG GLASS CO., LTD.—See KC Green Holdings Co., Ltd.; *Int'l*, pg. 4108

ANSON-STONER INC.

ANSVAR INSURANCE LIMITED—See Ecclesiastical Insurance Office plc; *Int'l*, pg. 2288
ANSWEAR.COM SA; *Int'l*, pg. 479
ANSWER-1 COMMUNICATIONS; *U.S. Private*, pg. 286
ANSWER AND CONSULTING CO., LTD—See Core Corporation; *Int'l*, pg. 1797
ANSWER DRIVES S.R.L.—See Nidec Corporation; *Int'l*, pg. 5274
ANSWER FINANCIAL, INC.—See The Allstate Corporation; *U.S. Public*, pg. 2033
ANSWERFIRST COMMUNICATIONS, INC.; *U.S. Private*, pg. 286
THE ANSWER GROUP INC.—See Teleperformance SE; *Int'l*, pg. 7541
ANSWERNET EDUCATION SERVICES, INC.; *U.S. Private*, pg. 286
ANSWERNET, INC.; *U.S. Private*, pg. 286
ANSWERPHONE; *U.S. Private*, pg. 286
ANSWER PRODUCTS, INC.—See LDI Ltd., LLC; *U.S. Private*, pg. 2404
ANSWERS CORPORATION—See Apax Partners LLP; *Int'l*, pg. 501
ANSWER TECHNOLOGY CO., LTD.; *Int'l*, pg. 479
ANSYS BELGIUM SA—See ANSYS, Inc.; *U.S. Public*, pg. 138
ANSYS CANADA LTD.—See ANSYS, Inc.; *U.S. Public*, pg. 138
ANSYS CHINA—See ANSYS, Inc.; *U.S. Public*, pg. 138
ANSYS FLUENT INDIA PVT. LTD.—See ANSYS, Inc.; *U.S. Public*, pg. 138
ANSYS FLUENT SHANGHAI ENGINEERING SOFTWARE TRADING COMPANY LTD.—See ANSYS, Inc.; *U.S. Public*, pg. 138
ANSYS FRANCE SAS—See ANSYS, Inc.; *U.S. Public*, pg. 138
ANSYS GERMANY GMBH—See ANSYS, Inc.; *U.S. Public*, pg. 138
ANSYS GOVERNMENT INITIATIVES, INC. AGI—See ANSYS, Inc.; *U.S. Public*, pg. 138
ANSYS HONG KONG LTD.—See ANSYS, Inc.; *U.S. Public*, pg. 138
ANSYS HORSHAM—See ANSYS, Inc.; *U.S. Public*, pg. 138
ANSYS IBERIA S.L.—See ANSYS, Inc.; *U.S. Public*, pg. 138
ANSYS ICEM CFD INC.—See ANSYS, Inc.; *U.S. Public*, pg. 138
ANSYS, INC.; *U.S. Public*, pg. 138
ANSYS, INC.—See ANSYS, Inc.; *U.S. Public*, pg. 138
ANSYS ITALIA, S.R.L.—See ANSYS, Inc.; *U.S. Public*, pg. 138
ANSYS JAPAN K.K.—See ANSYS, Inc.; *U.S. Public*, pg. 138
ANSYS KOREA LLC—See ANSYS, Inc.; *U.S. Public*, pg. 138
ANSYS OOO—See ANSYS, Inc.; *U.S. Public*, pg. 138
ANSYS SOFTWARE PVT. LTD.—See ANSYS, Inc.; *U.S. Public*, pg. 138
ANSYS SWEDEN AB—See ANSYS, Inc.; *U.S. Public*, pg. 138
ANSYS SWITZERLAND GMBH—See ANSYS, Inc.; *U.S. Public*, pg. 138
ANSYS TECHNOLOGY (SHANGHAI) CO., LTD.—See ANSYS, Inc.; *U.S. Public*, pg. 138
ANSYS UK, LTD.—See ANSYS, Inc.; *U.S. Public*, pg. 138
ANTAEAN SOLUTIONS, LLC; *U.S. Private*, pg. 286
ANTAEUS FASHIONS INC.—See Eclat Textile Co., Ltd.; *Int'l*, pg. 2291
ANTAH SCHINDLER SDN. BHD.—See Schindler Holding AG; *Int'l*, pg. 6620
ANTAI-HEYUAN NUCLEAR ENERGY TECHNOLOGY & MATERIALS CO., LTD.—See Advanced Technology & Materials Co., Ltd.; *Int'l*, pg. 162
ANTALIS GROUPE SAS—See Sequana SA; *Int'l*, pg. 6719
ANTALIS OY—See Metsaliitto Osuuskunta; *Int'l*, pg. 4864
ANTALIS SA—See KPP Group Holdings Co., Ltd.; *Int'l*, pg. 4297
ANTALIS VENTURES CORP.; *Int'l*, pg. 481
ANTALYA FREE TRADE ZONE OPERATING CO., INC.—See Tekfen Holding A.S.; *Int'l*, pg. 7526
ANTA NETHERLANDS B.V.—See ANTA Sports Products Limited; *Int'l*, pg. 479
ANTARA ASSISTED CARE SERVICES LIMITED—See Max India Limited; *Int'l*, pg. 4734
ANTARA HOLIDAY VILLAS SDN. BHD.—See Advance Synergy Berhad; *Int'l*, pg. 156
ANTARA MEGAH SDN. BHD.—See Bertam Alliance Berhad; *Int'l*, pg. 989
ANTARA SENIOR LIVING LIMITED—See Max Financial Services Limited; *Int'l*, pg. 4734
ANTARA STEEL MILLS SDN BHD—See Lion Industries Corporation Berhad; *Int'l*, pg. 4519
ANTARCHILE S.A.; *Int'l*, pg. 481
ANTAR CRANES SERVICES PTE. LTD.—See JP Nelson Equipment Pte Ltd; *Int'l*, pg. 4005
ANTARCTICA CAPITAL, LLC; *U.S. Private*, pg. 286
ANTARES CAPITAL CORPORATION; *U.S. Private*, pg. 287

ANTARES CAPITAL LP—See Canada Pension Plan Investment Board; *Int'l*, pg. 1278
ANTARES-DESENVOLVIMENTO DE SOFTWARE, LDA.—See FARO Technologies, Inc.; *U.S. Public*, pg. 823
ANTARES GLOBAL MANAGEMENT LIMITED—See Qatar Insurance Company S.A.Q.; *Int'l*, pg. 6134
ANTARES GROUP, INC.; *U.S. Public*, pg. 287
ANTARES GROUP, INC.; *U.S. Private*, pg. 287
ANTARES HOMES, LTD.—See Landsea Homes Corp.; *U.S. Public*, pg. 1292
ANTARES, INC.; *U.S. Private*, pg. 287
ANTARES MANAGING AGENCY LIMITED—See Qatar Insurance Company S.A.Q.; *Int'l*, pg. 6134
ANTARES NAVIERA S.A.—See Ultramar Ltda.; *Int'l*, pg. 8018
ANTARES PHARMA AG—See Halozyme Therapeutics, Inc.; *U.S. Public*, pg. 981
ANTARES PHARMA, INC.—See Halozyme Therapeutics, Inc.; *U.S. Public*, pg. 981
ANTARES RESTAURANT GROUP LIMITED—See Blackstone Inc.; *U.S. Public*, pg. 360
ANTARES TECHNOLOGY SOLUTIONS, INC.—See Guggenheim Partners, LLC; *U.S. Private*, pg. 1812
ANTARES UNDERWRITING ASIA PTE. LIMITED—See Qatar Insurance Company S.A.Q.; *Int'l*, pg. 6134
ANTARES VISION ASIA PACIFIC LIMITED—See Antares Vision SpA; *Int'l*, pg. 482
ANTARES VISION DO BRASIL—See Antares Vision SpA; *Int'l*, pg. 482
ANTARES VISION FRANCE SAS—See Antares Vision SpA; *Int'l*, pg. 482
ANTARES VISION INDIA PRIVATE LIMITED—See Antares Vision SpA; *Int'l*, pg. 482
ANTARES VISION NORTH AMERICA LLC—See Antares Vision SpA; *Int'l*, pg. 482
ANTARES VISION RUS OOO—See Antares Vision SpA; *Int'l*, pg. 482
ANTARES VISION SPA; *Int'l*, pg. 482
ANTARGAZ BELGIUM N.V.—See UGI Corporation; *U.S. Public*, pg. 2222
ANTARGAZ LUXEMBOURG S.A.—See UGI Corporation; *U.S. Public*, pg. 2222
ANTARGAZ NEDERLAND B.V.—See UGI Corporation; *U.S. Public*, pg. 2222
ANTARGAZ S.A.—See UGI Corporation; *U.S. Public*, pg. 2222
ANTARIKSH INDUSTRIES LIMITED; *Int'l*, pg. 482
ANTARRA COMMUNICATIONS; *U.S. Private*, pg. 287
ANTARRA COMMUNICATIONS—See Antarra Communications; *U.S. Private*, pg. 287
ANT ASIA CO., LTD.—See ANT Neuro B.V.; *Int'l*, pg. 479
ANTA SPORTS PRODUCTS LIMITED; *Int'l*, pg. 479
ANTAYA TECHNOLOGIES CORPORATION—See Aptiv PLC; *Int'l*, pg. 524
ANTAYA TECHNOLOGIES CORPORATION (ZHUHAI) LTD.—See Aptiv PLC; *Int'l*, pg. 524
ANT CAPITAL PARTNERS CO., LTD.—See The Norinchukin Bank; *Int'l*, pg. 7671
ANTEA BELGIUM N.V.—See Centric Holding B.V.; *Int'l*, pg. 1412
ANTE APS—See Karnov Group AB; *Int'l*, pg. 4084
ANTEA S.A.S.—See Centric Holding B.V.; *Int'l*, pg. 1412
ANTEA USA, INC.—See Centric Holding B.V.; *Int'l*, pg. 1412
ANTEC BIOTECH CO., LTD.—See YungShin Global Holding Corporation; *Int'l*, pg. 8614
ANTECH DIAGNOSTICS CANADA LTD.—See Mars, Incorporated; *U.S. Private*, pg. 2590
ANTEC INCORPORATED; *U.S. Private*, pg. 287
ANTEC INTERNATIONAL LTD.—See LANXESS AG; *Int'l*, pg. 4414
ANTECO SA; *Int'l*, pg. 482
ANTEC SERVICEPOOL GMBH—See Morgan Stanley; *U.S. Public*, pg. 1473
ANTEKS HOME FURNISHINGS INC.; *U.S. Private*, pg. 287
ANTELEC LTD.—See Kinden Corporation; *Int'l*, pg. 4165
ANTELEC S.A.S.—See Nokia Corporation; *Int'l*, pg. 5404
ANTELOPE COAL LLC—See Cloud Peak Energy Inc.; *U.S. Public*, pg. 946
ANTELOPE ENTERPRISE HOLDINGS LTD.; *Int'l*, pg. 482
ANTELOPE MEMORIAL HOSPITAL; *U.S. Private*, pg. 287
ANTELOPE OIL TOOL & MANUFACTURING COMPANY—See Intervale Capital, LLC; *U.S. Private*, pg. 2127
ANTELOPE VALLEY CHEVROLET, INC.—See General Motors Company; *U.S. Public*, pg. 923
ANTELOPE VALLEY EAST KERN WATER AGENCY; *U.S. Private*, pg. 287
ANTELOPE VALLEY FORD; *U.S. Private*, pg. 287
ANTELOPE VALLEY NEWSPAPER INC.; *U.S. Private*, pg. 287
ANTELOPE VALLEY RECYCLING AND DISPOSAL FACILITY, INC.—See Waste Management, Inc.; *U.S. Public*, pg. 2330
ANTELOPE VALLEY SCHOOL TRANSPORTATION AGENCY; *U.S. Private*, pg. 287

CORPORATE AFFILIATIONS

ANTELOPE VALLEY SURGERY CENTER, L.P.—See UnitedHealth Group Incorporated; *U.S. Public*, pg. 2239
ANTENA 3 DE RADIO DE MELILLA, S.A.—See Promotora de Informaciones S.A.; *Int'l*, pg. 5995
ANTENA 3 EVENTOS S.L.U.—See Atresmedia Corporacion de Medios de Comunicacion, S.A.; *Int'l*, pg. 693
ANTENA 3 FILMS S.L.U.—See Atresmedia Corporacion de Medios de Comunicacion, S.A.; *Int'l*, pg. 693
ANTENEX, INC—See DuPont de Nemours, Inc.; *U.S. Public*, pg. 693
ANTENGENE CORPORATION LIMITED; *Int'l*, pg. 482
ANTENNACRAFT CO.—See RS Legacy Corporation; *U.S. Private*, pg. 3496
ANTENNA DEVELOPMENT CORPORATION—See Blue Canyon Technologies LLC; *U.S. Private*, pg. 586
ANTENNA DEXTERRA ASIA PACIFIC PTY LTD.—See Pegasystems Inc.; *U.S. Public*, pg. 1660
ANTENNA GROUP, INC.—See Beckerman Group; *U.S. Private*, pg. 511
ANTENNA GROUP; *Int'l*, pg. 482
ANTENNA HOUSE, INC.—See Antenna House, Inc.; *Int'l*, pg. 482
ANTENNA HOUSE, INC.; *Int'l*, pg. 482
ANTENNA INTERNATIONAL—See The Wicks Group of Companies, LLC; *U.S. Private*, pg. 4135
ANTENNA MAST INCORPORATED—See The Will-Burt Co., Inc.; *U.S. Private*, pg. 4136
ANTENNA PLUS, LLC—See Airgain, Inc.; *U.S. Public*, pg. 68
ANTENNA PRODUCTS CORPORATION—See Phazar Corp.; *U.S. Private*, pg. 3166
ANTENNA RESEARCH ASSOCIATES, INCORPORATED; *U.S. Private*, pg. 287
ANTENNAS DIRECT; *U.S. Private*, pg. 287
ANTENNAS SOFTWARE, LLC—See Pegasystems Inc.; *U.S. Public*, pg. 1660
ANTENNA & TECHNOLOGY CORP.—See Ace Technologies Corp.; *Int'l*, pg. 95
ANTENNA.TV S.A.—See Antenna Group; *Int'l*, pg. 482
ANTENN CONSULTING AB—See Randstad N.V.; *Int'l*, pg. 6202
ANTENNE NIEDERSACHSEN GMBH & CO. KG—See Bertelsmann SE & Co. KGaA; *Int'l*, pg. 993
ANTENNENTECHNIK ABB BAD BLANKENBURG GMBH—See Huizhou Desay SV Automotive Co., Ltd.; *Int'l*, pg. 3527
ANTEOTECH LTD; *Int'l*, pg. 482
ANTEPRIMA SRL—See Credito Emiliano S.p.A.; *Int'l*, pg. 1836
ANTERIA CO., LTD.—See Soft99 Corporation; *Int'l*, pg. 7051
ANTERIO INC.—See Nippon Telegraph & Telephone Corporation; *Int'l*, pg. 5350
ANTERIS TECHNOLOGIES LTD.; *Int'l*, pg. 482
ANTERIST + SCHNEIDER ZEEBRUGGE B.V.—See Deutsche Bahn AG; *Int'l*, pg. 2049
ANTERIX INC.; *U.S. Public*, pg. 139
ANTEROGEN CO., LTD—See Bukwang Pharmaceutical Co., Ltd.; *Int'l*, pg. 1213
ANTERO MIDSTREAM CORPORATION; *U.S. Public*, pg. 139
ANTERO MIDSTREAM LLC—See Antero Resources Corporation; *U.S. Public*, pg. 140
ANTERO MIDSTREAM PARTNERS LP—See Antero Midstream Corporation; *U.S. Public*, pg. 140
ANTERO RESOURCES CORPORATION; *U.S. Public*, pg. 140
ANTEROS LAGERHANTERING AB—See Bjorn Borg AB; *Int'l*, pg. 1054
ANTEVENIO SA; *Int'l*, pg. 482
AN TEXTILE MILLS LIMITED; *Int'l*, pg. 443
ANTEX WESTERN LTD.; *Int'l*, pg. 482
ANTHEM BEHAVIORAL HEALTH—See Elevance Health, Inc.; *U.S. Public*, pg. 728
ANTHEM BENEFIT ADMINISTRATORS INC.—See Elevance Health, Inc.; *U.S. Public*, pg. 728
ANTHEM BLUE CROSS & BLUE SHIELD OF MISSOURI—See Elevance Health, Inc.; *U.S. Public*, pg. 729
ANTHEM BLUE CROSS LIFE AND HEALTH INSURANCE COMPANY—See Elevance Health, Inc.; *U.S. Public*, pg. 729
THE ANTHEM COMPANIES, INC.—See Elevance Health, Inc.; *U.S. Public*, pg. 730
ANTHEM CREDENTIALING SERVICES, INC.—See Elevance Health, Inc.; *U.S. Public*, pg. 729
ANTHEM DENTAL—See Elevance Health, Inc.; *U.S. Public*, pg. 729
ANTHEM! DESIGN PTY. LTD.—See Matthews International Corporation; *U.S. Public*, pg. 1400
ANTHEM GOLF & COUNTRY CLUB—See Apollo Global Management, Inc.; *U.S. Public*, pg. 149
ANTHEM HEALTH PLANS, INC.—See Elevance Health, Inc.; *U.S. Public*, pg. 729
ANTHEM HEALTH PLANS OF KENTUCKY—See Elevance Health, Inc.; *U.S. Public*, pg. 729
ANTHEM HEALTH PLANS OF MAINE, INC—See Elevance Health, Inc.; *U.S. Public*, pg. 729

COMPANY NAME INDEX

ANTHEM HEALTH PLANS OF NEW HAMPSHIRE—See Elevance Health, Inc.; *U.S. Public*, pg. 729
ANTHEM HEALTH PLANS OF VIRGINIA—See Elevance Health, Inc.; *U.S. Public*, pg. 729
ANTHEM HOLDING CORP.—See Elevance Health, Inc.; *U.S. Public*, pg. 729
ANTHEM INSURANCE COMPANIES, INC.—See Elevance Health, Inc.; *U.S. Public*, pg. 729
ANTHEMIS EXPONENTIAL VENTURES LLP—See Momentum Group Limited; *Int'l*, pg. 5023
ANTHEM LIFE INSURANCE COMPANY—See Meiji Yasuda Life Insurance Company; *Int'l*, pg. 4802
ANTHEM MARKETING, LLC—See Quad/Graphics, Inc.; *U.S. Public*, pg. 1744
ANTHEMONA LTD.—See PPF Group N.V.; *Int'l*, pg. 5950
ANTHEM PROPERTIES GROUP, LTD.—See Anthem Works Ltd.; *Int'l*, pg. 483
ANTHEM SECURITIES, INC—See Atlas Energy Group, LLC; *U.S. Public*, pg. 223
ANTHEM VISION—See Elevance Health, Inc.; *U.S. Public*, pg. 729
ANTHEM WORKS LTD.; *Int'l*, pg. 483
ANTHEM WORLDWIDE - CINCINNATI—See Matthews International Corporation; *U.S. Public*, pg. 1401
ANTHEM WORLDWIDE - NEW YORK—See Matthews International Corporation; *U.S. Public*, pg. 1401
ANTHEM WORLDWIDE—See Matthews International Corporation; *U.S. Public*, pg. 1401
ANTHEM WORLDWIDE - TORONTO—See Matthews International Corporation; *U.S. Public*, pg. 1401
ANTHERA PHARMACEUTICALS, INC.; *U.S. Public*, pg. 140
ANTHILL BV—See bpost NV/SA; *Int'l*, pg. 1133
ANTHOGYR S.A.—See Straumann Holding AG; *Int'l*, pg. 7237
ANTHOGYR SAS—See Straumann Holding AG; *Int'l*, pg. 7237
ANTHOLOGY INC.—See Leeds Equity Partners, LLC; *U.S. Private*, pg. 2414
ANTHOLOGY INC.—See Veritas Capital Fund Management, LLC; *U.S. Private*, pg. 4360
ANTHON EIENDOM AS—See Fastighets AB Balder; *Int'l*, pg. 2622
AN THONG MINING INVESTMENT JSC—See Hoa Phat Group Joint Stock Company; *Int'l*, pg. 3435
ANTHONY BEST DYNAMICS LIMITED—See AB Dynamics plc; *Int'l*, pg. 39
ANTHONY CHEVROLET CADILLAC; *U.S. Private*, pg. 287
ANTHONY EQUITY HOLDINGS, INC.—See Dover Corporation; *U.S. Public*, pg. 678
ANTHONY FARMERS COOP ELEVATOR CO.; *U.S. Private*, pg. 287
ANTHONY FOREST PRODUCTS CO., INC. - ARKANSAS LAMINATING PLANT—See Canfor Corporation; *Int'l*, pg. 1290
ANTHONY FOREST PRODUCTS CO., INC. - ARKANSAS SAWMILL—See Canfor Corporation; *Int'l*, pg. 1290
ANTHONY FOREST PRODUCTS CO., INC. - GEORGIA LAMINATING PLANT—See Canfor Corporation; *Int'l*, pg. 1290
ANTHONY FOREST PRODUCTS CO., INC. - TEXAS CHIP MILL—See Canfor Corporation; *Int'l*, pg. 1290
ANTHONY FOREST PRODUCTS COMPANY, LLC—See Canfor Corporation; *Int'l*, pg. 1290
ANTHONY HARDWOOD COMPOSITES INC—See Anthony Timberlands, Inc.; *U.S. Private*, pg. 288
ANTHONY HODGES CONSULTING LIMITED—See Arthur J. Gallagher & Co.; *U.S. Public*, pg. 202
ANTHONY, INC.; *U.S. Private*, pg. 288
ANTHONY INSURANCE INCORPORATED—See Intact Financial Corporation; *Int'l*, pg. 3726
ANTHONY INTERNATIONAL, INC.—See Avista Capital Partners, L.P.; *U.S. Private*, pg. 408
ANTHONY MEXICO HOLDINGS S. DE R.L. DE C.V.—See Dover Corporation; *U.S. Public*, pg. 678
ANTHONY PARASSON INC.; *U.S. Private*, pg. 287
ANTHONY PONTIAC GMC BUICK, INC.; *U.S. Private*, pg. 288
ANTHONY REFRESH GROUP, LLC—See Dover Corporation; *U.S. Public*, pg. 678
THE ANTHONY ROBBINS COMPANY—See Robbins Research International; *U.S. Private*, pg. 3457
ANTHONY ROOFING LTD.—See Altas Partners LP; *Int'l*, pg. 386
ANTHONY-ROSS COMPANY—See Clyde Blowers Capital IM LLP; *Int'l*, pg. 1665
ANTHONY'S COAL FIRED PIZZA OF AVENTURA, LLC—See BurgerFi International, Inc.; *U.S. Public*, pg. 412
ANTHONY'S COAL FIRED PIZZA OF BOCA RATON, LLC—See BurgerFi International, Inc.; *U.S. Public*, pg. 412
ANTHONY'S COAL FIRED PIZZA OF EDISON, LLC—See BurgerFi International, Inc.; *U.S. Public*, pg. 412
ANTHONY'S COAL FIRED PIZZA OF LITTLETON, LLC—See BurgerFi International, Inc.; *U.S. Public*, pg. 412
ANTHONY'S COAL FIRED PIZZA OF MONROEVILLE, LLC—See BurgerFi International, Inc.; *U.S. Public*, pg. 412
ANTHONY'S COAL FIRED PIZZA OF PLANTATION, LLC—See BurgerFi International, Inc.; *U.S. Public*, pg. 412
ANTHONY'S COAL FIRED PIZZA OF READING, LLC—See BurgerFi International, Inc.; *U.S. Public*, pg. 412
ANTHONY'S COAL FIRED PIZZA OF SOUTH TAMPA, LLC—See BurgerFi International, Inc.; *U.S. Public*, pg. 412
ANTHONY'S COAL FIRED PIZZA OF STONY BROOK, LLC—See BurgerFi International, Inc.; *U.S. Public*, pg. 412
ANTHONY'S COAL FIRED PIZZA OF TREXLERTOWN LLC—See BurgerFi International, Inc.; *U.S. Public*, pg. 412
ANTHONY'S COAL FIRED PIZZA OF WYNNEWOOD, LLC—See BurgerFi International, Inc.; *U.S. Public*, pg. 412
ANTHONY'S COAL FIRED PIZZA; *U.S. Private*, pg. 288
ANTHONY'S FISH GROTTO; *U.S. Private*, pg. 288
ANTHONY'S INC.; *U.S. Private*, pg. 288
ANTHONY SPECIALTY GLASS LLC—See Dover Corporation; *U.S. Public*, pg. 678
ANTHONY & SYLVAN POOLS CORPORATION; *U.S. Private*, pg. 287
ANTHONY & SYLVAN POOLS CORPORATION—See Anthony & Sylvan Pools Corporation; *U.S. Private*, pg. 287
ANTHONY TECHNICAL GLASS (SHANGHAI) CO. LTD—See Dover Corporation; *U.S. Public*, pg. 678
ANTHONY-THOMAS CANDY COMPANY; *U.S. Private*, pg. 288
ANTHONY TIMBERLANDS, INC.; *U.S. Private*, pg. 288
ANTHONY UNDERWOOD AUTOMOTIVE, INC.; *U.S. Private*, pg. 288
ANTHONY VEDER GROUP N.V.—See HAL Trust N.V.; *Int'l*, pg. 3223
ANTHONY VINEYARDS; *U.S. Private*, pg. 288
ANTHONY WILDING RETIREMENT VILLAGE LIMITED—See Ryman Healthcare Ltd.; *Int'l*, pg. 6439
ANTHRACITE INDUSTRIES, INC.—See Great Mill Rock LLC; *U.S. Private*, pg. 1765
ANTHRACITE POWER AND LIGHT—See Reading Anthracite Company; *U.S. Private*, pg. 3366
ANTHROPOLOGIE, INC.—See Urban Outfitters, Inc.; *U.S. Public*, pg. 2265
ANTHROPOS CAPITAL CORP.; *U.S. Public*, pg. 140
ANTHURIUM AND ORCHIDS LIMITED—See ENL Limited; *Int'l*, pg. 2441
ANTI-AGING HOUSE HOLDING LIMITED; *Int'l*, pg. 483
ANTIAGING QUANTUM LIVING INC.; *U.S. Public*, pg. 140
ANTIBE THERAPEUTICS INC.; *Int'l*, pg. 483
ANTIBIOTICE S.A.; *Int'l*, pg. 483
ANTIBODIES INCORPORATED—See Janel Corporation; *U.S. Public*, pg. 1187
ANTICA DITTA MARCHISIO S.P.A.; *Int'l*, pg. 483
ANTICIMEX AB—See EQT AB; *Int'l*, pg. 2467
ANTICIMEX A/S—See EQT AB; *Int'l*, pg. 2467
ANTICIMEX AS—See EQT AB; *Int'l*, pg. 2468
ANTICIMEX BENELUX B.V.—See EQT AB; *Int'l*, pg. 2468
ANTICIMEX FORSAKRINGAR AB—See EQT AB; *Int'l*, pg. 2468
ANTICIMEX GMBH & CO. KG—See EQT AB; *Int'l*, pg. 2468
ANTICIMEX INTERNATIONAL AB—See EQT AB; *Int'l*, pg. 2467
ANTICIPA REAL ESTATE, SLU—See Blackstone Inc.; *U.S. Public*, pg. 360
ANTICLINE DISPOSAL, LLC—See NGL Energy Partners LP; *U.S. Public*, pg. 1527
ANTIEN INDUSTRIES JOINT STOCK COMPANY; *Int'l*, pg. 483
ANTIETAM CABLE TELEVISION, INC.—See Schurz Communications, Inc.; *U.S. Private*, pg. 3571
ANTI-FRICTION ENTERPRISES 1985—See Magni Group Inc.; *U.S. Private*, pg. 2547
ANTIGO DAILY JOURNAL—See Adams Publishing Group, LLC; *U.S. Private*, pg. 74
ANTI-HYDRO INTERNATIONAL, INC.; *U.S. Private*, pg. 288
ANTILIA GROUP, CORP.; *Int'l*, pg. 483
ANTIL INC.—See Vector Inc.; *Int'l*, pg. 8144
ANTILLEAN MARINE SHIPPING CORP.; *U.S. Private*, pg. 288
ANTILLES CLEANING SERVICE INC.; *U.S. Private*, pg. 288
ANTILLES GOLD LIMITED; *Int'l*, pg. 483
ANTIMITE ASSOCIATES INC.—See Terminix Service, Inc.; *U.S. Private*, pg. 3969
AN T. IMPORTS OF ATLANTA, LLC—See AutoNation, Inc.; *U.S. Public*, pg. 232
ANTINEA S.R.L.—See Giorgio Armani S.p.A.; *Int'l*, pg. 2978
ANT-INFORMATIK AG—See NEXUS AG; *Int'l*, pg. 5250
ANT-INFORMATIK GMBH—See NEXUS AG; *Int'l*, pg. 5250
ANTING SENDIRIAN BERHAD—See Mega First Corporation Berhad; *Int'l*, pg. 4792
ANTIN INFRASTRUCTURE PARTNERS SAS; *Int'l*, pg. 483
ANTIOCH CHRYSLER JEEP DODGE; *U.S. Private*, pg. 288
ANTIOCH TIRE INC.; *U.S. Private*, pg. 288
ANTIOQUIA GOLD INC.; *Int'l*, pg. 483
ANTIPA MINERALS LTD.; *Int'l*, pg. 483
ANTIPHON AB; *Int'l*, pg. 483
ANTIPODES GLOBAL INVESTMENT COMPANY LIMITED; *Int'l*, pg. 483
ANTIPODES VOYAGES SA; *Int'l*, pg. 483
ANTIQUARY CARE HOME ARBROATH—See Balhousie Holdings Limited; *Int'l*, pg. 808
ANTIQUELAND USA INC.; *U.S. Private*, pg. 288
ANTIQUITAS VERWALTUNGSGESELLSCHAFT MBH—See DMG MORI Co., Ltd.; *Int'l*, pg. 2144
ANTISEPTICA CHEM.-PHARM PRODUKTE GMBH; *Int'l*, pg. 483
ANTLER GOLD, INC.; *Int'l*, pg. 483
ANTLER HILL MINING LTD.; *Int'l*, pg. 484
ANTLER HOMES PLC—See Literacy Capital Plc; *Int'l*, pg. 4526
ANTLER LTD—See Centurion Group Ltd; *Int'l*, pg. 1417
ANTN CO., LTD.; *Int'l*, pg. 484
ANT NEURO B.V.; *Int'l*, pg. 479
ANT NORTH AMERICA, INC.—See ANT Neuro B.V.; *Int'l*, pg. 479
ANTOFAGASTA MINERALS S.A.—See Antofagasta plc; *Int'l*, pg. 484
ANTOFAGASTA PLC; *Int'l*, pg. 484
ANTOINE MOUEIX SAS—See AdVini S.A.; *Int'l*, pg. 168
ANTOK NYOMDAIPARI KFT—See CirclePrinters Holding BV; *Int'l*, pg. 1618
ANTOLINI LUIGI & C. S.P.A.; *Int'l*, pg. 484
ANTON/BAUER INCORPORATED; *U.S. Private*, pg. 288
ANTON/BAUER INC.—See Videndum plc; *Int'l*, pg. 8190
ANTON BORER IMMOBILIEN AG; *Int'l*, pg. 484
ANTON CASTRO LAW, LLC; *U.S. Private*, pg. 288
ANTON COLLINS MITCHELL, LLP—See BDO USA, LLP; *U.S. Public*, pg. 501
ANTON DEBATIN GMBH; *Int'l*, pg. 484
ANTONETTI CAPITAL MANAGEMENT, LLC; *U.S. Private*, pg. 288
ANTONG HOLDINGS CO., LTD.; *Int'l*, pg. 485
ANTON HUBNER GMBH & CO. KG—See Dermapharm Holding SE; *Int'l*, pg. 2043
ANTONIO PUIG, S.A.—See Puig Brands S.A.; *Int'l*, pg. 6115
ANTONIO'S MANUFACTURING INC.; *U.S. Private*, pg. 288
ANTONIO SOFO & SON IMPORTING CO. INC.; *U.S. Private*, pg. 288
ANTON OILFIELD SERVICES GROUP LIMITED; *Int'l*, pg. 484
ANTONOV AUTOMOTIVE TECHNOLOGIES B.V.—See Antonov plc; *Int'l*, pg. 485
ANTONOV AUTOMOTIVE TECHNOLOGIES LTD—See Antonov plc; *Int'l*, pg. 485
ANTONOV PLC; *Int'l*, pg. 485
ANTON PAAR AUSTRALIA PTY LTD—See Anton Paar GmbH; *Int'l*, pg. 484
ANTON PAAR AUSTRIA GMBH—See Anton Paar GmbH; *Int'l*, pg. 484
ANTON PAAR BENELUX BVBA—See Anton Paar GmbH; *Int'l*, pg. 484
ANTON PAAR BRASIL LTDA.—See Anton Paar GmbH; *Int'l*, pg. 484
ANTON PAAR CANADA INC.—See Anton Paar GmbH; *Int'l*, pg. 484
ANTON PAAR COLOMBIA S.A.S.—See Anton Paar GmbH; *Int'l*, pg. 484
ANTON PAAR CROATIA D.O.O.—See Anton Paar GmbH; *Int'l*, pg. 484
ANTON PAAR CZECH REPUBLIC S.R.O.—See Anton Paar GmbH; *Int'l*, pg. 484
ANTON PAAR FRANCE S.A.S.—See Anton Paar GmbH; *Int'l*, pg. 484
ANTON PAAR GERMANY GMBH—See Anton Paar GmbH; *Int'l*, pg. 484
ANTON PAAR GMBH; *Int'l*, pg. 484
ANTON PAAR HUNGARY KFT—See Anton Paar GmbH; *Int'l*, pg. 484
ANTON PAAR INDIA PVT. LTD.—See Anton Paar GmbH; *Int'l*, pg. 484
ANTON PAAR IRELAND LTD.—See Anton Paar GmbH; *Int'l*, pg. 484
ANTON PAAR ITALIA S.R.L.—See Anton Paar GmbH; *Int'l*, pg. 484
ANTON PAAR JAPAN K.K.—See Anton Paar GmbH; *Int'l*, pg. 484
ANTON PAAR KOREA LTD.—See Anton Paar GmbH; *Int'l*, pg. 484
ANTON PAAR LTD.—See Anton Paar GmbH; *Int'l*, pg. 484
ANTON PAAR MALAYSIA SDN BHD—See Anton Paar GmbH; *Int'l*, pg. 484

ANTON PAAR GMBH

CORPORATE AFFILIATIONS

ANTON PAAR NEW ZEALAND LIMITED—See Anton Paar GmbH; *Int'l*, pg. 485
ANTON PAAR NORDIC AB—See Anton Paar GmbH; *Int'l*, pg. 485
ANTON PAAR OLCUM ALETLERI TICARET LTD. STI.—See Anton Paar GmbH; *Int'l*, pg. 485
ANTON PAAR OPTOTEC GMBH—See Anton Paar GmbH; *Int'l*, pg. 485
ANTON PAAR POLAND, SP.Z.O.O.—See Anton Paar GmbH; *Int'l*, pg. 485
ANTON PAAR PROVETEC GMBH—See Anton Paar GmbH; *Int'l*, pg. 485
ANTON PAAR QUANTATEC INC.—See Anton Paar GmbH; *Int'l*, pg. 485
ANTON PAAR SHANGHAI TRADING CO., LTD.—See Anton Paar GmbH; *Int'l*, pg. 485
ANTON PAAR SHAPETEC BA D.O.O.—See Anton Paar GmbH; *Int'l*, pg. 485
ANTON PAAR SINGAPORE PTE LTD.—See Anton Paar GmbH; *Int'l*, pg. 485
ANTON PAAR SLOVAKIA S.R.O.—See Anton Paar GmbH; *Int'l*, pg. 485
ANTON PAAR SOUTHERN AFRICA (PTY) LTD—See Anton Paar GmbH; *Int'l*, pg. 485
ANTON PAAR SPAIN S.L.U.—See Anton Paar GmbH; *Int'l*, pg. 485
ANTON PAAR SWITZERLAND AG—See Anton Paar GmbH; *Int'l*, pg. 485
ANTON PAAR TAIWAN CO. LTD.—See Anton Paar GmbH; *Int'l*, pg. 485
ANTON PAAR (THAILAND) LTD.—See Anton Paar GmbH; *Int'l*, pg. 484
ANTON PAAR TRITEC SA—See Anton Paar GmbH; *Int'l*, pg. 485
ANTON PAAR USA, INC.—See Anton Paar GmbH; *Int'l*, pg. 485
ANTONY LARA ENVIRO SOLUTIONS PRIVATE LIMITED—See Antony Waste Handling Cell Limited; *Int'l*, pg. 485
ANTONY WASTE HANDLING CELL LIMITED; *Int'l*, pg. 485
ANT PRECISION INDUSTRY CO., LTD.; *Int'l*, pg. 479
ANTREPRIZA DE REPARATII SI LUCRARI A R L CLUJ S.A.—See STRABAG SE; *Int'l*, pg. 7229
ANTRIEBSTECHNIK KATT HESSEN GMBH—See WEG S.A.; *Int'l*, pg. 8367
ANTRIM CONSTRUCTION COMPANY LTD; *Int'l*, pg. 485
ANTRIM ENERGY INC.; *Int'l*, pg. 485
ANTRONIX INC.; *U.S. Private*, pg. 288
ANTROPE SNC—See Eiffage S.A.; *Int'l*, pg. 2330
ANT SINAI VE TIC.URUNLERI PAZ. A.S—See Ag Anadolu Grubu Holding Anonim Sirketi; *Int'l*, pg. 197
ANTS SOFTWARE INC.; *U.S. Private*, pg. 288
ANTTILA OY—See 4K Invest International; *Int'l*, pg. 12
ANTUIT, INC.; *U.S. Private*, pg. 289
ANTUR TURIZM A.S.—See Dogus Holding AS; *Int'l*, pg. 2154
ANTWERP BULK TERMINAL NV—See SEA-invest Group; *Int'l*, pg. 6661
ANTWERP DIAMOND BANK—See KBC Group NV; *Int'l*, pg. 4105
ANTWERP DIAMOND DISTRIBUTORS INC.; *U.S. Private*, pg. 289
ANTWERPEN MOTOR CARS LTD.; *U.S. Private*, pg. 289
ANTWERPES AG—See DocCheck AG; *Int'l*, pg. 2153
ANTWERPSE BOUWWERKEN NV—See Eiffage S.A.; *Int'l*, pg. 2329
ANTWERPSE DIAMANTBANK N.V.—See KBC Group NV; *Int'l*, pg. 4105
ANTWERP SPACE N.V.—See OHB SE; *Int'l*, pg. 5532
ANTWERPS SPORTPALEIS N.V.—See Live Nation Entertainment, Inc.; *U.S. Public*, pg. 1328
ANTWERP TERMINAL & PROCESSING COMPANY N.V.—See Industry Super Holdings Pty. Ltd.; *Int'l*, pg. 3676
ANTWERP TERMINAL & PROCESSING COMPANY N.V.—See Vitol Holding B.V.; *Int'l*, pg. 8261
ANTWERP TOWAGE NV—See Fairplay Schleppdampfschiffs-Reederei Richard Borchard GmbH; *Int'l*, pg. 2609
ANTWORKS PTE. LTD.; *Int'l*, pg. 485
ANTYCIP IBERICA SL—See HENSOLDT AG; *Int'l*, pg. 3355
ANTYCIP TECHNOLOGIES S.A.S.—See HENSOLDT AG; *Int'l*, pg. 3355
ANTZ CO., LTD.; *Int'l*, pg. 485
ANUBHAV INFRASTRUCTURE LIMITED; *Int'l*, pg. 485
ANUGRAH MADISON ADVERTISING PVT. LTD.—See Madison Communications; *Int'l*, pg. 4634
ANUH PHARMA LTD.; *Int'l*, pg. 485
ANUKARAN COMMERCIAL ENTERPRISES LIMITED; *Int'l*, pg. 485
ANULEX TECHNOLOGIES, INC.; *U.S. Private*, pg. 289
ANUPAM FINSERV LTD.; *Int'l*, pg. 485
ANUPAM RASAYAN INDIA LIMITED; *Int'l*, pg. 486
ANUP ENGINEERING LIMITED—See Lalbhai Group; *Int'l*, pg. 4398
ANUP MALLEABLES LIMITED; *Int'l*, pg. 485
ANU RESOURCES, INC.; *U.S. Private*, pg. 289

ANUROOP PACKAGING LIMITED; *Int'l*, pg. 486
ANUTRA CORP; *U.S. Private*, pg. 289
ANUVU—See PAR Capital Management, Inc.; *U.S. Private*, pg. 3089
ANVA ARION SWEDEN AB—See AnVa Tubes & Components AB; *Int'l*, pg. 486
ANVA GMBH—See AnVa Tubes & Components AB; *Int'l*, pg. 486
ANVA KSG AB—See AnVa Tubes & Components AB; *Int'l*, pg. 486
ANVA ROSTFRITT & SMIDE AB—See AnVa Tubes & Components AB; *Int'l*, pg. 486
ANVAR PARAWOOD CO., LTD.—See Sri Trang Agro-Industry Public Company Limited; *Int'l*, pg. 7150
ANVA TITECH SYSTEM AB—See AnVa Tubes & Components AB; *Int'l*, pg. 486
ANVATO, INC.—See Alphabet Inc.; *U.S. Public*, pg. 83
ANVA TUBES & COMPONENTS AB; *Int'l*, pg. 486
ANVIA HOLDINGS CORPORATION; *U.S. Public*, pg. 140
ANVICOM-COMMAND FEDERAL, INC.—See Bridge Growth Partners, LLC; *U.S. Private*, pg. 649
ANVICOM-COMMAND FEDERAL, INC.—See Frontenac Company LLC; *U.S. Private*, pg. 1614
ANVIFISH JOINT-STOCK COMPANY; *Int'l*, pg. 486
ANVIL ATTACHMENTS, LLC; *U.S. Private*, pg. 289
ANVIL ATTACHMENTS, LLC—See Woodvine Group, LLC; *U.S. Private*, pg. 4561
ANVIL CASES, INC.—See Caltron Case Company; *U.S. Private*, pg. 724
ANVIL FENCE & SUPPLY CO. INC.—See The Fort Miller Group Inc.; *U.S. Private*, pg. 4029
ANVIL HOLDINGS, INC.—See Gildan Activewear Inc.; *Int'l*, pg. 2973
ANVIL INTERNATIONAL, LLC—See Tailwind Capital Group, LLC; *U.S. Private*, pg. 3923
ANVIL KNITWEAR, INC.—See Gildan Activewear Inc.; *Int'l*, pg. 2973
ANVIL MEDIA, INC.—See Deksia LLC; *U.S. Private*, pg. 1192
ANVIS AUTOMOTIVE SPAIN S.A.U.—See Sumitomo Riko Company Limited; *Int'l*, pg. 7297
ANVIS AVT S.R.O.—See Sumitomo Riko Company Limited; *Int'l*, pg. 7297
ANVIS AVT S.R.O.—See Sumitomo Riko Company Limited; *Int'l*, pg. 7297
ANVIS DEUTSCHLAND GMBH—See Sumitomo Riko Company Limited; *Int'l*, pg. 7297
ANVIS FRANCE DECIZE S.A.S.—See Sumitomo Riko Company Limited; *Int'l*, pg. 7297
ANVIS FRANCE EPINAL S.A.S.—See Sumitomo Riko Company Limited; *Int'l*, pg. 7297
ANVIS GROUP GMBH—See Sumitomo Riko Company Limited; *Int'l*, pg. 7297
ANVISGROUP MEXICO S.A.P.I. DE C.V.—See Sumitomo Riko Company Limited; *Int'l*, pg. 7297
ANVIS INDUSTRY S.A.S.—See Sumitomo Riko Company Limited; *Int'l*, pg. 7297
ANVIS ROM SRL—See Sumitomo Riko Company Limited; *Int'l*, pg. 7297
ANVIS RUS—See Sumitomo Riko Company Limited; *Int'l*, pg. 7297
ANVIS SD FRANCE S.A.S.—See Sumitomo Riko Company Limited; *Int'l*, pg. 7297
ANVIS (WUXI) RUBBER ANTI-VIBRATION CO., LTD.—See Sumitomo Riko Company Limited; *Int'l*, pg. 7297
ANVL, INC.—See Vista Equity Partners, LLC; *U.S. Private*, pg. 4395
ANV SECURITY GROUP, INC.; *Int'l*, pg. 486
ANV SERVICES US INC.—See ACNOVER, S.L.; *Int'l*, pg. 107
ANV SYNDICATE MANAGEMENT LIMITED—See ACNOVER, S.L.; *Int'l*, pg. 107
ANWAY ENTERPRISES LIMITED—See Kaisun Holdings Limited; *Int'l*, pg. 4053
A.N. WEBBER INC.; *U.S. Private*, pg. 27
ANWELL PRECISION TECHNOLOGY (HK) LIMITED—See Anwell Technologies Ltd.; *Int'l*, pg. 486
ANWELL SOLAR TECHNOLOGIES LIMITED—See Anwell Technologies Ltd.; *Int'l*, pg. 486
ANWELL TECHNOLOGIES LTD.; *Int'l*, pg. 486
ANWIL SA—See Orlen S.A.; *Int'l*, pg. 5640
ANWORTH MORTGAGE ASSET CORPORATION—See Waterfall Asset Management LLC; *U.S. Private*, pg. 4453
ANX E-BUSINESS CORP.; *U.S. Private*, pg. 289
ANXIAN YUAN CHINA HOLDINGS LIMITED; *Int'l*, pg. 486
ANXIAN YUAN (HK) LIMITED—See Anxian Yuan China Holdings Limited; *Int'l*, pg. 486
ANXIN-CHINA HOLDINGS LIMITED; *Int'l*, pg. 486
ANXIN TRUST CO., LTD.; *Int'l*, pg. 486
ANYA HINDMARCH JAPAN CORPORATION—See ASHS Ltd.; *Int'l*, pg. 609
ANYANG IRON & STEEL GROUP CO., LTD.; *Int'l*, pg. 486
ANYANG IRON & STEEL INC.—See Anyang Iron & Steel Group Co., Ltd.; *Int'l*, pg. 487
ANYANG XIANGYU MEDICAL EQUIPMENT CO., LTD.—See Xiangyu Medical Co., Ltd.; *Int'l*, pg. 8527

ANYBET GMBH—See mybet Holding SE; *Int'l*, pg. 5111
ANY BREAKERS, INC.; *U.S. Private*, pg. 289
ANYCOLOR INC.; *Int'l*, pg. 487
ANY-G B.V.—See World Kinect Corporation; *U.S. Public*, pg. 2380
ANYGEN CO LTD; *Int'l*, pg. 487
ANYHELP BRASIL ASSESSORIA E SERVICOS EM SISTEMAS DE INFORMACAO LTDA.—See ManpowerGroup Inc.; *U.S. Public*, pg. 1357
ANYHELP INTERNATIONAL, S.L.U.—See ManpowerGroup Inc.; *U.S. Public*, pg. 1357
ANYMEDI CO., LTD.; *Int'l*, pg. 487
ANYMIND GROUP, INC.; *Int'l*, pg. 487
ANY MOUNTAIN LTD.; *U.S. Private*, pg. 289
ANYONG BIOTECHNOLOGY CO., LTD.—See TOPCO Scientific Co., Ltd.; *Int'l*, pg. 7814
ANYONG FRESHMART, INC.—See TOPCO Scientific Co., Ltd.; *Int'l*, pg. 7814
ANYPAY SDN. BHD.—See Revenue Group Bhd; *Int'l*, pg. 6313
ANY SECURITY PRINTING COMPANY PLC; *Int'l*, pg. 486
ANYTECH INC.—See JFE Holdings, Inc.; *Int'l*, pg. 3935
ANYTEK TECHNOLOGY CORPORATION LTD—See Amphenol Corporation; *U.S. Public*, pg. 129
ANYTHING CO., LTD.—See Rentracks Co., Ltd.; *Int'l*, pg. 6289
ANYTHINGWEATHER COMMUNICATIONS, INC.; *U.S. Private*, pg. 289
ANYTIME FITNESS LLC—See Self Esteem Brands LLC; *U.S. Private*, pg. 3602
ANYUAN COAL INDUSTRY GROUP CO., LTD.; *Int'l*, pg. 487
ANYWAY SOLUTION SAS—See VINCI S.A.; *Int'l*, pg. 8212
ANYWHERE REAL ESTATE GROUP LLC—See Anywhere Real Estate Inc.; *U.S. Public*, pg. 140
ANYWHERE REAL ESTATE INC.; *U.S. Public*, pg. 140
ANYWIRE CORPORATION; *Int'l*, pg. 487
ANZA AB—See Orkla ASA; *Int'l*, pg. 5638
ANZAG ROSTOCK GMBH & CO. KG—See Walgreens Boots Alliance, Inc.; *U.S. Public*, pg. 2321
ANZA HEALTHCARE, INC.—See The Ensign Group, Inc.; *U.S. Public*, pg. 2070
ANZA INC.—See Holien Inc.; *U.S. Private*, pg. 1963
ANZ ASIA LIMITED—See Australia & New Zealand Banking Group Limited; *Int'l*, pg. 719
ANZ ASIA PACIFIC DIVISION—See Australia & New Zealand Banking Group Limited; *Int'l*, pg. 719
ANZ AUSTRALIAN CAPITAL TERRITORY—See Australia & New Zealand Banking Group Limited; *Int'l*, pg. 722
ANZ BANK (EUROPE) LIMITED—See Australia & New Zealand Banking Group Limited; *Int'l*, pg. 720
ANZ BANK (KIRIBATI) LIMITED—See Australia & New Zealand Banking Group Limited; *Int'l*, pg. 720
ANZ BANK (SAMOA) LIMITED—See Australia & New Zealand Banking Group Limited; *Int'l*, pg. 719
ANZ BANK SOLOMON ISLANDS—See Australia & New Zealand Banking Group Limited; *Int'l*, pg. 719
ANZ BANK (THAI) PUBLIC COMPANY LIMITED—See Australia & New Zealand Banking Group Limited; *Int'l*, pg. 720
ANZ BANK (VANUATU) LIMITED—See Australia & New Zealand Banking Group Limited; *Int'l*, pg. 719
ANZCHEM PTY LIMITED—See The Garfield Weston Foundation; *Int'l*, pg. 7648
ANZCO FOODS AUSTRALIA PTY LTD—See Itoham Yonekyu Holdings Inc.; *Int'l*, pg. 3842
ANZCO FOODS (EUROPE) LTD—See Itoham Yonekyu Holdings Inc.; *Int'l*, pg. 3842
ANZCO FOODS JAPAN LTD.—See Itoham Yonekyu Holdings Inc.; *Int'l*, pg. 3842
ANZCO FOODS LTD. CANTERBURY FACILITY—See Itoham Yonekyu Holdings Inc.; *Int'l*, pg. 3842
ANZCO FOODS LTD. ELTHAM FACILITY—See Itoham Yonekyu Holdings Inc.; *Int'l*, pg. 3842
ANZCO FOODS LTD. GREEN ISLAND FACILITY—See Itoham Yonekyu Holdings Inc.; *Int'l*, pg. 3842
ANZCO FOODS LTD. KOKIRI FACILITY—See Itoham Yonekyu Holdings Inc.; *Int'l*, pg. 3842
ANZCO FOODS LTD. MANAWATU FACILITY—See Itoham Yonekyu Holdings Inc.; *Int'l*, pg. 3842
ANZCO FOODS LTD. MARLBOROUGH FACILITY—See Itoham Yonekyu Holdings Inc.; *Int'l*, pg. 3842
ANZCO FOODS LTD. RAKAIA FACILITY—See Itoham Yonekyu Holdings Inc.; *Int'l*, pg. 3842
ANZCO FOODS LTD. RANGITIKEI FACILITY—See Itoham Yonekyu Holdings Inc.; *Int'l*, pg. 3842
ANZCO FOODS LTD.—See Itoham Yonekyu Holdings Inc.; *Int'l*, pg. 3842
ANZCO FOODS LTD. WAITARA FACILITY—See Itoham Yonekyu Holdings Inc.; *Int'l*, pg. 3842
ANZCO FOODS NORTH AMERICA INC.—See Itoham Yonekyu Holdings Inc.; *Int'l*, pg. 3842
ANZCO FOODS TAIWAN LIMITED—See Itoham Yonekyu Holdings Inc.; *Int'l*, pg. 3842
ANZCO FOODS (UK) LTD—See Itoham Yonekyu Holdings Inc.; *Int'l*, pg. 3842
ANZ COOK ISLANDS—See Australia & New Zealand Banking Group Limited; *Int'l*, pg. 719

COMPANY NAME INDEX

ANZ (DELAWARE) INC.—See Australia & New Zealand Banking Group Limited; *Int'l*, pg. 719
ANZEA TEXTILES, INC.—See C F Stinson, Inc.; *U.S. Private*, pg. 701
ANZEN DENGU (HUI ZHOU) CO., LTD.—See Tamura Corporation; *Int'l*, pg. 7452
ANZEN YUSO CO., LTD.—See Senko Group Holdings Co., Ltd.; *Int'l*, pg. 6709
ANZ FIJI—See Australia & New Zealand Banking Group Limited; *Int'l*, pg. 719
ANZ GERMANY—See Australia & New Zealand Banking Group Limited; *Int'l*, pg. 720
ANZ GUAM INC.—See Australia & New Zealand Banking Group Limited; *Int'l*, pg. 720
ANZHENG FASHION GROUP CO., LTD.; *Int'l*, pg. 487
ANZ INSTITUTIONAL DIVISION—See Australia & New Zealand Banking Group Limited; *Int'l*, pg. 720
ANZ INTERNATIONAL (HONG KONG) LTD.—See Australia & New Zealand Banking Group Limited; *Int'l*, pg. 719
ANZ INTERNATIONAL PTE. LTD.—See Australia & New Zealand Banking Group Limited; *Int'l*, pg. 719
ANZ INVESTMENT SERVICES (NEW ZEALAND) LIMITED—See Australia & New Zealand Banking Group Limited; *Int'l*, pg. 720
ANZIO WHEELS POLAND SP. Z.O.O.—See UNIWHEELS Management (Switzerland) AG; *Int'l*, pg. 8083
ANZ JAPAN—See Australia & New Zealand Banking Group Limited; *Int'l*, pg. 719
ANZ KOREA—See Australia & New Zealand Banking Group Limited; *Int'l*, pg. 719
ANZ LENDERS MORTGAGE INSURANCE PTY. LIMITED—See Australia & New Zealand Banking Group Limited; *Int'l*, pg. 720
ANZ MALAYSIA—See Australia & New Zealand Banking Group Limited; *Int'l*, pg. 719
ANZ NATIONAL BANK LTD.—See Australia & New Zealand Banking Group Limited; *Int'l*, pg. 720
ANZ NATIONAL BANK LTD.—See Australia & New Zealand Banking Group Limited; *Int'l*, pg. 720
ANZ NEW ZEALAND INVESTMENTS LIMITED—See Australia & New Zealand Banking Group Limited; *Int'l*, pg. 720
ANZ NEW ZEALAND SECURITIES LIMITED—See Australia & New Zealand Banking Group Limited; *Int'l*, pg. 720
ANZ NORTHERN TERRITORY—See Australia & New Zealand Banking Group Limited; *Int'l*, pg. 720
ANZPAC SERVICES (AUSTRALIA) PTY LIMITED—See Tien Wah Press Holdings Berhad; *Int'l*, pg. 7744
ANZ PHILIPPINES—See Australia & New Zealand Banking Group Limited; *Int'l*, pg. 719
ANZ PRIVATE BANK—See Australia & New Zealand Banking Group Limited; *Int'l*, pg. 720
ANZ SECURITIES INC.—See Australia & New Zealand Banking Group Limited; *Int'l*, pg. 719
ANZ SECURITIES LIMITED—See Australia & New Zealand Banking Group Limited; *Int'l*, pg. 720
ANZ SHANGHAI—See Australia & New Zealand Banking Group Limited; *Int'l*, pg. 719
ANZ SINGAPORE LIMITED—See Australia & New Zealand Banking Group Limited; *Int'l*, pg. 719
ANZ TAIWAN—See Australia & New Zealand Banking Group Limited; *Int'l*, pg. 719
ANZ THAILAND—See Australia & New Zealand Banking Group Limited; *Int'l*, pg. 719
ANZ TONGA—See Australia & New Zealand Banking Group Limited; *Int'l*, pg. 720
ANZ UK—See Australia & New Zealand Banking Group Limited; *Int'l*, pg. 720
ANZU PARTNERS, LLC; *U.S. Private*, pg. 289
AO 12 AIRCRAFT REPAIR PLANT—See Russian Technologies State Corporation; *Int'l*, pg. 6431
AO 150 AIRCRAFT REPAIR PLANT—See Russian Technologies State Corporation; *Int'l*, pg. 6431
AO 356 AIRCRAFT REPAIR PLANT—See Russian Technologies State Corporation; *Int'l*, pg. 6431
AO 419 AIRCRAFT REPAIR PLANT—See Russian Technologies State Corporation; *Int'l*, pg. 6431
AO 810 AIRCRAFT REPAIR PLANT—See Russian Technologies State Corporation; *Int'l*, pg. 6431
AO AD PLASTIK TOGLIATTI—See AD Plastik d.d.; *Int'l*, pg. 122
AO AK BARS LEASING—See OJSC AK BARS Bank; *Int'l*, pg. 5539
AO ALFA LAVAL POTOK—See Alfa Laval AB; *Int'l*, pg. 308
AOBA PHARMACY CO., LTD.—See Polaris Capital Group Co., Ltd.; *Int'l*, pg. 5907
AO CAPITAL PARTNERS, LLC—See Azalea Health Innovations, Inc.; *U.S. Private*, pg. 415
AOC B.V. UK LTD.—See Saudi Arabian Oil Company; *Int'l*, pg. 6589
A.O.C. CANADA, INC.—See The Alpha Corporation of Tennessee; *U.S. Private*, pg. 3984
AOC DO BRASIL MONITORES LTDA.—See TPV Technology Co., Ltd.; *Int'l*, pg. 7885
AOC EGYPT PETROLEUM COMPANY, LTD—See Fuji Oil Company; *Int'l*, pg. 2815

A.O.C. FOODMARTS INC.—See R.K. Allen Oil Co., Inc.; *U.S. Private*, pg. 3338
AOC INDIA PVT. LTD.—See The Alpha Corporation of Tennessee; *U.S. Private*, pg. 3984
AOC INTERNATIONAL (EUROPE) GMBH—See TPV Technology Co., Ltd.; *Int'l*, pg. 7885
AOC KEY SOLUTIONS, INC.; *U.S. Private*, pg. 289
AOC, LLC - AOC CALIFORNIA PLANT—See The Alpha Corporation of Tennessee; *U.S. Private*, pg. 3984
AOC, LLC - AOC FLORIDA PLANT—See The Alpha Corporation of Tennessee; *U.S. Private*, pg. 3984
AOC, LLC - AOC INDIANA PLANT—See The Alpha Corporation of Tennessee; *U.S. Private*, pg. 3984
AOC, LLC - AOC MEXICO PLANT—See The Alpha Corporation of Tennessee; *U.S. Private*, pg. 3984
AOC, LLC - AOC ONTARIO PLANT—See The Alpha Corporation of Tennessee; *U.S. Private*, pg. 3984
AOC, LLC - AOC TENNESSEE PLANT—See The Alpha Corporation of Tennessee; *U.S. Private*, pg. 3984
AOC, LLC—See The Alpha Corporation of Tennessee; *U.S. Private*, pg. 3984
AOC NEDERLAND B.V.—See CVC Capital Partners SICAV-FIS S.A.; *Int'l*, pg. 1886
A.O. CONSTRUCTION COMPANY, INC.; *U.S. Private*, pg. 27
AOC SOLUTIONS, INC.; *U.S. Private*, pg. 289
AOC TECHNO CO., LTD.—See Asahi Yukizai Corporation; *Int'l*, pg. 598
AOC TRANSPORT, INC.—See Getty Realty Corp.; *U.S. Public*, pg. 935
AOC (UK) LTD.—See The Alpha Corporation of Tennessee; *U.S. Private*, pg. 3984
AO DEUTSCHLAND LIMITED—See AO World PLC; *Int'l*, pg. 487
AOE FREIGHT (HK) LTD.—See Beijing Sports & Entertainment Industry Group Limited; *Int'l*, pg. 957
AOE FREIGHT (SHENZHEN) LTD.—See Beijing Sports & Entertainment Industry Group Limited; *Int'l*, pg. 957
AOE FREIGHT (SHENZHEN) LTD.—See Beijing Sports & Entertainment Industry Group Limited; *Int'l*, pg. 957
AOE FREIGHT (SHENZHEN) LTD.—See Beijing Sports & Entertainment Industry Group Limited; *Int'l*, pg. 957
AOE FREIGHT (SHENZHEN) LTD.—See Beijing Sports & Entertainment Industry Group Limited; *Int'l*, pg. 957
AOE FREIGHT (SHENZHEN) LTD.—See Beijing Sports & Entertainment Industry Group Limited; *Int'l*, pg. 957
AOE FREIGHT (SHENZHEN) LTD.—See Beijing Sports & Entertainment Industry Group Limited; *Int'l*, pg. 957
AOF IMAGING TECHNOLOGY, JAPAN LTD.—See Asia Optical Co., Inc.; *Int'l*, pg. 613
AOF IMAGING TECHNOLOGY LIMITED—See Asia Optical Co., Inc.; *Int'l*, pg. 613
AOFRIO LIMITED; *Int'l*, pg. 487
AOFR PTY. LTD.—See Aegis Lightwave, Inc.; *U.S. Private*, pg. 116
AOG CORPORATION—See Summit Utilities Inc.; *U.S. Private*, pg. 3857
AOGIN BUSINESS SERVICE CO., LTD.—See The Aomori Bank, Ltd.; *Int'l*, pg. 7613
AOGIN CREDIT CARD CO., LTD.—See The Aomori Bank, Ltd.; *Int'l*, pg. 7613
AOGIN LEASE CO., LTD.—See The Aomori Bank, Ltd.; *Int'l*, pg. 7613
A.O. HARDEE & SON, INC.; *U.S. Private*, pg. 27
AOHATA CORPORATION, JAM FACTORY—See Aohata Corporation; *Int'l*, pg. 487
AOHATA CORPORATION; *Int'l*, pg. 487
AO HELICOPTER SERVICE COMPANY—See Russian Technologies State Corporation; *Int'l*, pg. 6431
AOI ELECTRONICS CO., LTD.; *Int'l*, pg. 487
AOI INDUSTRIES CO., LTD.—See Kurita Water Industries Ltd.; *Int'l*, pg. 4340
AOI MACHINE INDUSTRY CO., LTD.—See Toyota Motor Corporation; *Int'l*, pg. 7870
AOI MEDICAL, INC.; *U.S. Private*, pg. 289
AO, INC.—See Kodiak Building Partners LLC; *U.S. Private*, pg. 2336
AOI PHARMACEUTICALS, INC.—See Akebia Therapeutics, Inc.; *U.S. Public*, pg. 69
AOI PRO. INC.—See AOI TYO Holdings Inc.; *Int'l*, pg. 488
AOI SURGICENTER, LLC—See HCA Healthcare, Inc.; *U.S. Public*, pg. 990
AO ITAB SHOP CONCEPT RUSSIA—See ITAB Shop Concept AB; *Int'l*, pg. 3827
AOITEC CO., LTD.—See Koito Manufacturing Co., Ltd.; *Int'l*, pg. 4230
AOI TYO HOLDINGS INC.; *Int'l*, pg. 488
AO KARELSKY OKATYSH—See PAO Severstal; *Int'l*, pg. 5731
AOKI HOLDINGS INC.; *Int'l*, pg. 488
AOKI INC.—See AOKI Holdings Inc.; *Int'l*, pg. 488
AOKI MARINE CO., LTD.—See Takamatsu Construction Group Co., Ltd.; *Int'l*, pg. 7429
AOKI SUPER CO., LTD.; *Int'l*, pg. 488
AO KUMERTAU AVIATION PRODUCTION ENTERPRISE—See Russian Technologies State Corporation; *Int'l*, pg. 6431
AOL DEUTSCHLAND MEDIEN GMBH—See Apollo Global Management, Inc.; *U.S. Public*, pg. 167

AO MACHINERY SERVICE GMBH—See Seika Corporation; *Int'l*, pg. 6685
AO MAPEI—See Mapei SpA; *Int'l*, pg. 4681
AO MIL MOSCOW HELICOPTER PLANT—See Russian Technologies State Corporation; *Int'l*, pg. 6431
AO MIZUHO BANK (MOSCOW)—See Mizuho Financial Group, Inc.; *Int'l*, pg. 4997
AOMORI ATOM CO., LTD.—See Takamiya Co., Ltd.; *Int'l*, pg. 7430
THE AOMORI BANK, LTD.; *Int'l*, pg. 7613
AOMORI DAIYA CO., LTD.—See Mitsubishi Heavy Industries, Ltd.; *Int'l*, pg. 4953
AOMORI DDK LTD.—See Fujikura Ltd.; *Int'l*, pg. 2827
AOMORI FUJIKURA KANAYA LTD.—See Fujikura Ltd.; *Int'l*, pg. 2827
AOMORI HINO MOTOR LTD.—See Toyota Motor Corporation; *Int'l*, pg. 7870
AOMORI OLYMPUS CO., LTD.—See Olympus Corporation; *Int'l*, pg. 5556
AOMORI RIVER TECHNO CO., LTD.—See River Eletec Corporation; *Int'l*, pg. 6352
AO MUFG BANK (EURASIA)—See Mitsubishi UFJ Financial Group, Inc.; *Int'l*, pg. 4969
AON ADJUDICATION SERVICES LTD—See Aon plc; *Int'l*, pg. 489
AON ADVISORS, INC.—See Aon plc; *Int'l*, pg. 489
AON AFFINITY CHILE LTDA.—See Aon plc; *Int'l*, pg. 489
AON AFFINITY SP ZOO—See Aon plc; *Int'l*, pg. 489
AON/ALBERT G. RUBEN INSURANCE SERVICES, INC.—See Aon plc; *Int'l*, pg. 494
AON ASIA PACIFIC LIMITED—See Aon plc; *Int'l*, pg. 489
AON AUSTRIA VERSICHERUNGSMAKLER GMBH—See Aon plc; *Int'l*, pg. 489
AON BAHRAIN W.L.L.—See Aon plc; *Int'l*, pg. 489
AON BELGIUM NV—See Aon plc; *Int'l*, pg. 489
AON BENFIELD BRATISLAVA S.R.O.—See Aon plc; *Int'l*, pg. 489
AON BENFIELD CANADA—See Aon plc; *Int'l*, pg. 489
AON BENFIELD (CHILE) CORREDORES DE REASEGUROS LTDA.—See Aon plc; *Int'l*, pg. 489
AON BENFIELD CHINA LIMITED—See Aon plc; *Int'l*, pg. 489
AON BENFIELD COLOMBIA LTDA. CORREDORES DE REASEGUROS—See Aon plc; *Int'l*, pg. 489
AON BENFIELD FAC INC.—See Aon plc; *Int'l*, pg. 489
AON BENFIELD GREECE SA—See Aon plc; *Int'l*, pg. 489
AON BENFIELD IBERIA, CORREDURIA DE REASEGUROS SA—See Aon plc; *Int'l*, pg. 489
AON BENFIELD INC.—See Aon plc; *Int'l*, pg. 489
AON BENFIELD INC.—See Aon plc; *Int'l*, pg. 489
AON BENFIELD ISRAEL LIMITED—See Aon plc; *Int'l*, pg. 489
AON BENFIELD ITALIA SPA—See Aon plc; *Int'l*, pg. 489
AON BENFIELD LIMITED—See Aon plc; *Int'l*, pg. 489
AON BENFIELD MALAYSIA LIMITED—See Aon plc; *Int'l*, pg. 489
AON BENFIELD NETHERLANDS CV—See Aon plc; *Int'l*, pg. 489
AON BENFIELD (NEW ZEALAND) LIMITED—See Aon plc; *Int'l*, pg. 489
AON BENFIELD PERU CORREDORES REASEGUROS SA—See Aon plc; *Int'l*, pg. 489
AON BENFIELD PTE. LTD.—See Aon plc; *Int'l*, pg. 490
AON BENFIELD PTY. LTD.—See Aon plc; *Int'l*, pg. 490
AON BENFIELD RUCKVERSICHERUNGSMAKLER GES.MBH—See Aon plc; *Int'l*, pg. 490
AON BENFIELD S.A. DE C.V.—See Aon plc; *Int'l*, pg. 490
AON BENFIELD SECURITIES, INC.—See Aon plc; *Int'l*, pg. 490
AON BENFIELD (SOUTH AFRICA) PTY LTD—See Aon plc; *Int'l*, pg. 490
AON (BERMUDA) LTD.—See Aon plc; *Int'l*, pg. 489
AON BETEILIGUNGSMANAGEMENT DEUTSCHLAND GMBH & CO. KG—See Aon plc; *Int'l*, pg. 490
AON BOLIVIA SA CORREDORES DE SEGUROS—See Aon plc; *Int'l*, pg. 490
AON BULGARIA EOOD—See Aon plc; *Int'l*, pg. 490
AON BUSINESS CONSULTING LTD.—See Aon plc; *Int'l*, pg. 490
AON CANADA INC.—See Aon plc; *Int'l*, pg. 490
AON CAPTIVE SERVICES GROUP—See Aon plc; *Int'l*, pg. 490
AON CASH MANAGEMENT B.V.—See Aon plc; *Int'l*, pg. 490
AON CENTRAL AND EASTERN EUROPE AS—See Aon plc; *Int'l*, pg. 490
AON CENTRE FOR INNOVATION AND ANALYTICS LTD—See Aon plc; *Int'l*, pg. 490
AON-COFCO INSURANCE BROKERAGE CO., LTD.—See COFCO Limited; *Int'l*, pg. 1691
AON-COFCO INSURANCE BROKERS CO., LTD.—See Aon plc; *Int'l*, pg. 494
AON CONSULTING ARGENTINA SA—See Aon plc; *Int'l*, pg. 490
AON CONSULTING (BENEFITS) LIMITED—See Aon plc; *Int'l*, pg. 490
AON CONSULTING - CHICAGO—See Aon plc; *Int'l*, pg. 490
AON CONSULTING, INC.—See Aon plc; *Int'l*, pg. 490

THE AOMORI BANK, LTD.
CORPORATE AFFILIATIONS

AON CONSULTING & INSURANCE SERVICES—See Aon plc; *Int'l*, pg. 490
AON CONSULTING LESOTHO (PTY) LTD.—See Aon plc; *Int'l*, pg. 490
AON CONSULTING NEW ZEALAND LTD.—See Aon plc; *Int'l*, pg. 490
AON CONSULTING (PNG) LTD.—See Aon plc; *Int'l*, pg. 490
AON CONSULTING - SAN FRANCISCO—See Aon plc; *Int'l*, pg. 490
AON CONSULTING—See Aon plc; *Int'l*, pg. 490
AON CONSULTING—See Aon plc; *Int'l*, pg. 490
AON CONSULTING—See Aon plc; *Int'l*, pg. 490
AON CONSULTING SOUTH AFRICA (PTY) LTD.—See Aon plc; *Int'l*, pg. 490
AON CONSULTING (THAILAND) LTD.—See Aon plc; *Int'l*, pg. 490
AON CORPORATION AUSTRALIA—See Aon plc; *Int'l*, pg. 490
AON CORPORATION—See Aon plc; *Int'l*, pg. 488
AON CORP.—See Aon plc; *Int'l*, pg. 491
AON CORP.—See Aon plc; *Int'l*, pg. 491
AON CREDIT INTERNATIONAL SCHWEIZ AG—See Aon plc; *Int'l*, pg. 491
AON CR SRL—See Aon plc; *Int'l*, pg. 490
AON DENMARK A/S—See Aon plc; *Int'l*, pg. 491
AON DEUTSCHLAND BETEILIGUNGS GMBH—See Aon plc; *Int'l*, pg. 491
AON (DIFC) GULF LLC—See Aon plc; *Int'l*, pg. 489
AON DIRECT GROUP ESPANA SL—See Aon plc; *Int'l*, pg. 491
AON DIRECT GROUP INC—See Aon plc; *Int'l*, pg. 491
A ONE ALFORM CO., LTD.; *Int'l*, pg. 18
AONE PLUS CO., LTD.—See Iida Group Holdings Co., Ltd.; *Int'l*, pg. 3607
A-ONE SEIMITSU INC.; *Int'l*, pg. 20
AO NEVA-METALL—See PAO Severstal; *Int'l*, pg. 5731
AON FINLAND OY—See Aon plc; *Int'l*, pg. 491
AON FRANCE FINANCE SA—See Aon plc; *Int'l*, pg. 491
AON GIL Y CARVAJAL CORREDURIA DE SEGUROS SA—See Aon plc; *Int'l*, pg. 491
AON GLOBAL LIMITED—See Aon plc; *Int'l*, pg. 495
AON GLOBAL RISK CONSULTING AB—See Aon plc; *Int'l*, pg. 491
AON GLOBAL RISK CONSULTING LUXEMBOURG SARL—See Aon plc; *Int'l*, pg. 491
AON GLOBAL RISK CONSULTING—See Aon plc; *Int'l*, pg. 490
AON GLOBAL SERVICES, INC.—See Aon plc; *Int'l*, pg. 491
AON GREECE S.A.—See Aon plc; *Int'l*, pg. 491
AON GROUP HOLDINGS INTERNATIONAL 1 B.V.—See Aon plc; *Int'l*, pg. 491
AON GROUP, INC.—See Aon plc; *Int'l*, pg. 491
AON GROUP JAPAN LTD.—See Aon plc; *Int'l*, pg. 490
AON HEALTHCARE—See Aon plc; *Int'l*, pg. 491
AON HEALTHCARE—See Aon plc; *Int'l*, pg. 491
AON HEWITT BELGIUM—See Alight, Inc.; *U.S. Public*, pg. 76
AON HEWITT CONSULTING KOREA INC.—See Aon plc; *Int'l*, pg. 491
AON HEWITT (CYPRUS) LIMITED—See Alight, Inc.; *U.S. Public*, pg. 76
AON HEWITT ESPANA S.A.U.—See Alight, Inc.; *U.S. Public*, pg. 76
AON HEWITT FINANCIAL ADVICE LTD.—See Aon plc; *Int'l*, pg. 491
AON HEWITT GMBH—See Alight, Inc.; *U.S. Public*, pg. 76
AON HEWITT GMBH—See Alight, Inc.; *U.S. Public*, pg. 76
AON HEWITT GMBH—See Alight, Inc.; *U.S. Public*, pg. 76
AON HEWITT HR ONE CORPORATION—See Alight, Inc.; *U.S. Public*, pg. 76
AON HEWITT KOREA—See Alight, Inc.; *U.S. Public*, pg. 76
AON HEWITT LIMITED—See Alight, Inc.; *U.S. Public*, pg. 76
AON HEWITT MALAYSIA SDN. BHD—See Alight, Inc.; *U.S. Public*, pg. 76
AON HEWITT - MONTREAL—See Aon plc; *Int'l*, pg. 490
AON HEWITT (PNG) LTD.—See Alight, Inc.; *U.S. Public*, pg. 76
AON HEWITT RISK & CONSULTING SRL—See Alight, Inc.; *U.S. Public*, pg. 76
AON HEWITT S.A.—See Alight, Inc.; *U.S. Public*, pg. 76
AON HEWITT SAUDI ARABIA LLC—See Aon plc; *Int'l*, pg. 491
AON HEWITT SINGAPORE PTE. LTD.—See Alight, Inc.; *U.S. Public*, pg. 76
AON HEWITT SP. Z O.O.—See Alight, Inc.; *U.S. Public*, pg. 76
AON HEWITT (SWITZERLAND) S.A.—See Alight, Inc.; *U.S. Public*, pg. 76
AON HEWITT (THAILAND) LTD.—See Alight, Inc.; *U.S. Public*, pg. 76
AON HEWITT - TORONTO—See Alight, Inc.; *U.S. Public*, pg. 76
AON HEWITT WEALTH MANAGEMENT PTE. LTD.—See Alight, Inc.; *U.S. Public*, pg. 76

AON HOLDING DEUTSCHLAND GMBH—See Aon plc; *Int'l*, pg. 491
AON HOLDINGS CORRETORES DE SEGUROS LTDA—See Aon plc; *Int'l*, pg. 491
AON HOLDINGS HONG KONG LIMITED—See Aon plc; *Int'l*, pg. 491
AON HOLDINGS LIMITED—See Aon plc; *Int'l*, pg. 491
AON HOLDINGS NORWAY AS—See Aon plc; *Int'l*, pg. 491
AON HONG KONG LIMITED—See Alight, Inc.; *U.S. Public*, pg. 76
AON HUNTINGTON T BLOCK INSURANCE AGENCY—See Aon plc; *Int'l*, pg. 493
AON INC.; *Int'l*, pg. 488
AON INSURANCE BROKERS (MALAYSIA) SDN BHD—See Aon plc; *Int'l*, pg. 491
AON INSURANCE BROKERS (PVT) LTD.—See Aon plc; *Int'l*, pg. 491
AON INSURANCE MANAGERS (BARBADOS) LTD.—See Aon plc; *Int'l*, pg. 491
AON INSURANCE MANAGERS (DUBLIN) LTD.—See Aon plc; *Int'l*, pg. 492
AON INSURANCE MANAGERS GIBRALTAR LTD.—See Aon plc; *Int'l*, pg. 492
AON INSURANCE MANAGERS (GUERNSEY) LTD.—See Aon plc; *Int'l*, pg. 494
AON INSURANCE MANAGERS (ISLE OF MAN) LTD.—See Aon plc; *Int'l*, pg. 492
AON INSURANCE MANAGERS (LIECHTENSTEIN) AG—See Aon plc; *Int'l*, pg. 492
AON INSURANCE MANAGERS (LUXEMBOURG) SA—See Aon plc; *Int'l*, pg. 492
AON INSURANCE MANAGERS (MALTA) LTD.—See Aon plc; *Int'l*, pg. 492
AON INSURANCE MANAGERS (SHANNON) LIMITED—See Aon plc; *Int'l*, pg. 492
AON INSURANCE MANAGERS (SINGAPORE) PTE LTD—See Aon plc; *Int'l*, pg. 492
AON INSURANCE MANAGERS (SWITZERLAND) AG—See Aon plc; *Int'l*, pg. 492
AON INSURANCE SERVICES—See Aon plc; *Int'l*, pg. 490
AON INTERNATIONAL HOLDINGS, INC.—See Aon plc; *Int'l*, pg. 492
AON INVESTMENTS USA INC.—See Aon plc; *Int'l*, pg. 492
AON ITALIA SPA—See Aon plc; *Int'l*, pg. 492
AON JAUCH & HUBENER EMPLOYEE BENEFIT CONSULTING GES.MBH—See Aon plc; *Int'l*, pg. 491
AON JAUCH & HUEBENER GMBH—See Aon plc; *Int'l*, pg. 491
AON JAUCH & HUEBENER GMBH—See Aon plc; *Int'l*, pg. 491
AON KENYA INSURANCE BROKERS LTD—See Aon plc; *Int'l*, pg. 492
AON KOREA INC.—See Aon plc; *Int'l*, pg. 492
AON LATVIA SIA—See Aon plc; *Int'l*, pg. 492
AON LESOTHO (PTY) LTD.—See Aon plc; *Int'l*, pg. 492
AON LIMPOPO (PTY) LTD—See Aon plc; *Int'l*, pg. 492
A-ONLINE CAPITAL LTD.; *Int'l*, pg. 20
AON LUXEMBOURG SA—See Aon plc; *Int'l*, pg. 492
AON MACDONAGH BOLAND GROUP LTD—See Aon plc; *Int'l*, pg. 492
AON MAJAN LLC—See Aon plc; *Int'l*, pg. 492
AON MANAGEMENT CONSULTING/RATH & STRONG INC.—See Aon plc; *Int'l*, pg. 491
AON MANAGEMENT SOLUTIONS SAU—See Aon plc; *Int'l*, pg. 492
AON MIDDLE EAST CO LLC—See Aon plc; *Int'l*, pg. 492
AON MONIA OY—See Aon plc; *Int'l*, pg. 492
AON NAMIBIA (PTY) LTD.—See Aon plc; *Int'l*, pg. 492
AON NATIONAL FLOOD SERVICES, INC.—See Aon plc; *Int'l*, pg. 492
AON NETHERLANDS OPERATIONS BV—See Aon plc; *Int'l*, pg. 492
AON NEW ZEALAND—See Aon plc; *Int'l*, pg. 492
AO NNK-AMURNEFTEPRODUCT—See Alliance Oil Company Ltd.; *Int'l*, pg. 340
AO NNK-PRIMORNEFTEPRODUCT—See Alliance Oil Company Ltd.; *Int'l*, pg. 340
AON NORWAY AS—See Aon plc; *Int'l*, pg. 492
AON OF ARIZONA INC.—See Aon plc; *Int'l*, pg. 494
AO NORTH AMERICA; *U.S. Private*, pg. 289
AO NOVOSIBIRSK AIRCRAFT REPAIR PLANT—See Russian Technologies State Corporation; *Int'l*, pg. 6431
AON PARIZEAU INC.—See Aon plc; *Int'l*, pg. 492
AON PENSIONS INSURANCE BROKERS GMBH—See Aon plc; *Int'l*, pg. 492
AON PHILIPPINES, INC.—See Aon plc; *Int'l*, pg. 492
AON PLC; *Int'l*, pg. 488
AON PMI INTERNATIONAL LIMITED—See Aon plc; *Int'l*, pg. 492
AON POLAND SP. Z.O.O.—See Alight, Inc.; *U.S. Public*, pg. 76
AON POLSKA SERVICES SP. Z.O.O.—See Aon plc; *Int'l*, pg. 492
AON POLSKA SP. ZOO—See Aon plc; *Int'l*, pg. 492
AON PREMIUM FINANCE, LLC—See Aon plc; *Int'l*, pg. 492
AON PRIVATE CONSULTING A/S—See Aon plc; *Int'l*, pg. 492

AON QATAR LLC—See Aon plc; *Int'l*, pg. 492
AON REED STENHOUSE, INC.—See Aon plc; *Int'l*, pg. 491
AON REINSURANCE SOLUTIONS ASIA PTE. LTD.—See Aon plc; *Int'l*, pg. 490
AON REINSURANCE SOLUTIONS MENA LIMITED—See Aon plc; *Int'l*, pg. 490
AON RE MIDDLE EAST WLL—See Aon plc; *Int'l*, pg. 492
AON RE SWITZERLAND—See Aon plc; *Int'l*, pg. 492
AON RISK INSURANCE SERVICES WEST, INC.—See Aon plc; *Int'l*, pg. 493
AON RISKMINDER A/S—See Aon plc; *Int'l*, pg. 494
AON RISK SERVICE OF TEXAS INC.—See Aon plc; *Int'l*, pg. 493
AON RISK SERVICES AUSTRALIA LTD.—See Aon plc; *Int'l*, pg. 493
AON RISK SERVICES (CHILE) SA—See Aon plc; *Int'l*, pg. 493
AON RISK SERVICES COMPANIES, INC.—See Aon plc; *Int'l*, pg. 492
AON RISK SERVICES INC. FLORIDA—See Aon plc; *Int'l*, pg. 493
AON RISK SERVICES INC. (LA)—See Aon plc; *Int'l*, pg. 493
AON RISK SERVICES, INC. OF CENTRAL CALIFORNIA—See Aon plc; *Int'l*, pg. 493
AON RISK SERVICES INC. OF COLORADO—See Aon plc; *Int'l*, pg. 493
AON RISK SERVICES INC. OF INDIANA—See Aon plc; *Int'l*, pg. 493
AON RISK SERVICES, INC. OF MASSACHUSETTS—See Aon plc; *Int'l*, pg. 493
AON RISK SERVICES INC. OF NJ—See Aon plc; *Int'l*, pg. 493
AON RISK SERVICES INC.—See Aon plc; *Int'l*, pg. 492
AON RISK SERVICES INC.—See Aon plc; *Int'l*, pg. 493
AON RISK SERVICES INC.—See Aon plc; *Int'l*, pg. 493
AON RISK SERVICES INC.—See Aon plc; *Int'l*, pg. 493
AON RISK SERVICES INC.—See Aon plc; *Int'l*, pg. 493
AON RISK SERVICES INC.—See Aon plc; *Int'l*, pg. 493
AON RISK SERVICES INC.—See Aon plc; *Int'l*, pg. 493
AON RISK SERVICES INC.—See Aon plc; *Int'l*, pg. 493
AON RISK SERVICES INC.—See Aon plc; *Int'l*, pg. 493
AON RISK SERVICES INC.—See Aon plc; *Int'l*, pg. 493
AON RISK SERVICES INC.—See Aon plc; *Int'l*, pg. 493
AON RISK SERVICES INC.—See Aon plc; *Int'l*, pg. 493
AON RISK SERVICES, JAPAN, LTD.—See Aon plc; *Int'l*, pg. 493
AON RISK SERVICES (NI) LIMITED—See Aon plc; *Int'l*, pg. 492
AON RISK SERVICES OF OREGON—See Aon plc; *Int'l*, pg. 493
AON RISK SERVICES OF PUERTO RICO INC—See Aon plc; *Int'l*, pg. 493
AON RISK SERVICES OF TEXAS—See Aon plc; *Int'l*, pg. 493
AON RISK SERVICES—See Aon plc; *Int'l*, pg. 493
AON RISK SERVICES SOUTHWEST, INC.—See Aon plc; *Int'l*, pg. 493
AON RISK SERVICES TAIWAN LTD.—See Aon plc; *Int'l*, pg. 493
AON RISK SERVICES (THAILAND) LTD.—See Aon plc; *Int'l*, pg. 493
AON RISK SOLUTIONS (CAYMAN) LTD.—See Aon plc; *Int'l*, pg. 493
AON ROMANIA BROKER DE ASIGURARE - RE ASIGURARE SRL—See Aon plc; *Int'l*, pg. 494
AON RUS INSURANCE BROKERS LLC—See Aon plc; *Int'l*, pg. 494
AON (SCHWEIZ) AG—See Aon plc; *Int'l*, pg. 491
AON SECURITIES INC.—See Aon plc; *Int'l*, pg. 494
AON SINGAPORE (BROKING CENTRE) PTE. LTD.—See Aon plc; *Int'l*, pg. 494
AON SINGAPORE PTE LTD—See Aon plc; *Int'l*, pg. 493
AON SLOVAKIA—See Aon plc; *Int'l*, pg. 491
AON SOLUTIONS IRELAND LIMITED—See Alight, Inc.; *U.S. Public*, pg. 76
AON SOLUTIONS JAPAN LTD—See Alight, Inc.; *U.S. Public*, pg. 76
AON SOLUTIONS MIDDLE EAST LIMITED—See Alight, Inc.; *U.S. Public*, pg. 76
AON SOLUTIONS SWEDEN AB—See Alight, Inc.; *U.S. Public*, pg. 76
AON SPECIALIST SERVICES PRIVATE LIMITED—See Aon plc; *Int'l*, pg. 494
AON SPECIALTY RE, INC.—See Aon plc; *Int'l*, pg. 494
AON SWEDEN AB—See Aon plc; *Int'l*, pg. 494
AON TAIWAN LTD.—See Aon plc; *Int'l*, pg. 494
AON TANZANIA LTD.—See Aon plc; *Int'l*, pg. 494
AON TARIZEAU INC.—See Aon plc; *Int'l*, pg. 490
AON (THAILAND) LTD.—See Aon plc; *Int'l*, pg. 489
AON TUNISIA SO.CAR.GEST S.A.—See Aon plc; *Int'l*, pg. 494
AON TUNISIE S.A.—See Aon plc; *Int'l*, pg. 494
AON UK LIMITED—See Aon plc; *Int'l*, pg. 494
AON US HOLDINGS, INC.—See Aon plc; *Int'l*, pg. 494

COMPANY NAME INDEX

AON VERSICHERUNGSAGENTUR DEUTSCHLAND GMBH—See Aon plc; *Int'l*, pg. 494
AON VERSICHERUNGSMAKLER DEUTSCHLAND GMBH—See Aon plc; *Int'l*, pg. 494
AON VIETNAM LIMITED—See Aon plc; *Int'l*, pg. 494
AON ZAMBIA LTD—See Aon plc; *Int'l*, pg. 494
AON ZAMBIA PENSION FUND ADMINISTRATORS LIMITED—See Aon plc; *Int'l*, pg. 494
AON ZIMBABWE (PVT) LTD.—See Masawara PLC; *Int'l*, pg. 4719
AO OLCON—See PAO Severstal; *Int'l*, pg. 5731
AO OPK OBORONPROM—See Russian Technologies State Corporation; *Int'l*, pg. 6430
AOOVAC LIMITED—See ATI Inc.; *U.S. Public*, pg. 222
AOPEN INC.—See Acer Incorporated; *Int'l*, pg. 98
AOPEN INTERNATIONAL (SHANGHAI) CO., LTD—See Wistron Corporation; *Int'l*, pg. 8438
AO PRECISION MANUFACTURING LLC—See Juno Investments LLC; *U.S. Private*, pg. 2244
AO "LINDE URALTECHGAZ"—See Linde plc; *Int'l*, pg. 4505
AO RANBAXY—See Sun Pharmaceutical Industries Ltd.; *Int'l*, pg. 7307
AORA VENDING SP. Z O.O.—See IVS Group S.A.; *Int'l*, pg. 3848
AO RECYCLING LIMITED—See AO World PLC; *Int'l*, pg. 487
AO REDUCTOR-PM—See Russian Technologies State Corporation; *Int'l*, pg. 6431
A.O. REED & CO.—See Blackstone Inc.; *U.S. Public*, pg. 355
AORERE RESOURCES LIMITED; *Int'l*, pg. 498
AOS ADS; *U.S. Private*, pg. 289
AO SEVERSTAL STEEL SOLUTIONS—See PAO Severstal; *Int'l*, pg. 5731
AOSHIKANG TECHNOLOGY CO., LTD.; *Int'l*, pg. 498
AOS INC.—See SES S.A.; *Int'l*, pg. 6727
AOSKGL, INC.—See Christy Sports LLC; *U.S. Private*, pg. 892
A. O. SMITH (CHINA) ENVIRONMENTAL PRODUCTS CO., LTD.—See A. O. Smith Corporation; *U.S. Public*, pg. 11
A. O. SMITH CORPORATION; *U.S. Public*, pg. 11
A.O. SMITH ELECTRICAL PRODUCTS GMBH—See Regal Rexnord Corporation; *U.S. Public*, pg. 1772
A. O. SMITH ENTERPRISES LTD.—See A. O. Smith Corporation; *U.S. Public*, pg. 11
A. O. SMITH INDIA WATER PRODUCTS PRIVATE LIMITED—See A. O. Smith Corporation; *U.S. Public*, pg. 11
A.O. SMITH - PROTECTIVE COATINGS DIVISION—See A. O. Smith Corporation; *U.S. Public*, pg. 11
A.O. SMITH VIETNAM COMPANY LIMITED—See A. O. Smith Corporation; *U.S. Public*, pg. 11
A. O. SMITH WATER FZE—See A. O. Smith Corporation; *U.S. Public*, pg. 11
A. O. SMITH WATER PRODUCTS CO. - CHARLOTTE PLANT—See A. O. Smith Corporation; *U.S. Public*, pg. 11
A.O. SMITH WATER PRODUCTS COMPANY B.V.—See A. O. Smith Corporation; *U.S. Public*, pg. 11
A. O. SMITH WATER PRODUCTS—See A. O. Smith Corporation; *U.S. Public*, pg. 11
AOSP INVESTMENTS, LLC—See Pyxus International, Inc.; *U.S. Public*, pg. 1740
AOSS MEDICAL SUPPLY, INC.; *U.S. Private*, pg. 289
AOSTE FILIALE (SUISSE) SARL—See ALFA, S.A.B. de C.V.; *Int'l*, pg. 313
AO STUPINO MACHINE PRODUCTION PLANT—See Russian Technologies State Corporation; *Int'l*, pg. 6431
AO SVERIGE AB—See Brodrene A & O Johansen A/S; *Int'l*, pg. 1173
AO TARKETT—See Tarkett S.A.; *Int'l*, pg. 7462
AOT BUSINESS CONSULTING (SHANGHAI) INC.—See Helloworld Travel Limited; *Int'l*, pg. 3337
AOTCO METAL FINISHING LLC; *U.S. Private*, pg. 289
AOT DEUTSCHLAND GMBH—See Transcor Astra Group S.A.; *Int'l*, pg. 7897
AOTEA PATHOLOGY LIMITED—See BGH Capital Pty Ltd; *Int'l*, pg. 1007
AOTEA PATHOLOGY LIMITED—See Ontario Teachers' Pension Plan; *Int'l*, pg. 5585
AOTECAR NEW ENERGY TECHNOLOGY CO., LTD.; *Int'l*, pg. 498
AOTEK S. COOP.—See Mondragon Corporation; *Int'l*, pg. 5028
AO TELIA CARRIER RUSSIA—See Telia Company AB; *Int'l*, pg. 7543
AOT ENERGY POLAND SP. Z O.O.—See Transcor Astra Group S.A.; *Int'l*, pg. 7897
THE AOT GROUP PTY. LTD.—See Helloworld Travel Limited; *Int'l*, pg. 3337
AOTO ELECTRONICS (US) LLC—See Shenzhen AOTO Electronics Co., Ltd.; *Int'l*, pg. 6804
AOT TRADING AG—See Transcor Astra Group S.A.; *Int'l*, pg. 7897
AO ULAN-UDE AVIATION PLANT—See Russian Technologies State Corporation; *Int'l*, pg. 6431
AO VORKUTAUGOL—See PAO Severstal; *Int'l*, pg. 5731

AOVO TOURISTIK AG; *Int'l*, pg. 498
A. O. WATER PRODUCTS COMPANY—See A. O. Smith Corporation; *U.S. Public*, pg. 11
AOWEI HOLDING LIMITED; *Int'l*, pg. 498
AO WORLD PLC; *Int'l*, pg. 487
AO WURTH-RUS—See Wurth Verwaltungsgesellschaft mbH; *Int'l*, pg. 8503
AOXING PHARMACEUTICAL COMPANY, INC.; *U.S. Private*, pg. 289
AOXIN Q & M DENTAL GROUP LIMITED; *Int'l*, pg. 498
AOX PTY LTD—See Australian Agricultural Projects Ltd; *Int'l*, pg. 721
AOYAMA CAPITAL CO., LTD.—See AOYAMA TRADING Co. Ltd.; *Int'l*, pg. 498
AOYAMA GARDEN CO., LTD.—See Takasho Co.,Ltd.; *Int'l*, pg. 7436
AOYAMA KIKO CO., LTD.—See Hazama Ando Corporation; *Int'l*, pg. 3294
AOYAMA-KOGEN WIND FARM CO., LTD.—See Chubu Electric Power Co., Inc.; *Int'l*, pg. 1593
AOYAMA SEISAKUSHO CO., LTD.—See OSG Corporation; *Int'l*, pg. 5648
AOYAMA TRADING CO. LTD.; *Int'l*, pg. 498
AOYAMA ZAISAN NETWORKS CO., LTD.; *Int'l*, pg. 499
AOYUAN BEAUTY VALLEY TECHNOLOGY CO., LTD.; *Int'l*, pg. 499
AOYUAN HEALTHY LIFE GROUP COMPANY LIMITED; *Int'l*, pg. 499
AOYUAN MEIGU TECHNOLOGY CO., LTD.; *Int'l*, pg. 499
AOZORA BANK, LTD.—See Cerberus Capital Management, L.P.; *U.S. Private*, pg. 836
AOZORA INVESTMENT CO., LTD.—See Cerberus Capital Management, L.P.; *U.S. Private*, pg. 836
AOZORA LOAN SERVICES CO., LTD.—See Cerberus Capital Management, L.P.; *U.S. Private*, pg. 836
AOZORA SECURITIES CO., LTD.—See Cerberus Capital Management, L.P.; *U.S. Private*, pg. 836
AOZORA TRUST BANK, LTD.—See Cerberus Capital Management, L.P.; *U.S. Private*, pg. 837
APAACO, INC.—See Astrana Health Inc.; *U.S. Public*, pg. 217
APA-AUSTRIA PRESSE AGENTUR EG; *Int'l*, pg. 500
APAC-ARKANSAS - ARKHOLA DIVISION—See CRH plc; *Int'l*, pg. 1846
APAC-ARKANSAS - MCCLINTON ANCHOR DIVISION—See CRH plc; *Int'l*, pg. 1846
APAC-ATLANTIC - ASHEVILLE DIVISION—See CRH plc; *Int'l*, pg. 1846
APAC-ATLANTIC - HARRISON DIVISION—See CRH plc; *Int'l*, pg. 1846
APACE MUSIC LIMITED—See Content Ventures Limited; *Int'l*, pg. 1779
APACER ELECTRONIC (SHANGHAI) CO., LTD.—See Apacer Technology Inc.; *Int'l*, pg. 500
APACER MEMORY AMERICA, INC.—See Apacer Technology Inc.; *Int'l*, pg. 500
APACER TECHNOLOGIES PVT LTD.—See Apacer Technology Inc.; *Int'l*, pg. 500
APACER TECHNOLOGY CORP.—See Apacer Technology Inc.; *Int'l*, pg. 500
APACER TECHNOLOGY INC.; *Int'l*, pg. 500
APACHE ARGENTINA CORP.—See YPF S.A.; *Int'l*, pg. 8605
APACHE CASINO HOTEL—See Fort Sill Apache Tribe of Oklahoma; *U.S. Private*, pg. 1575
APACHE COMMUNICATION INC.—See WPG Holdings Limited; *Int'l*, pg. 8461
APACHE CONSTRUCTION COMPANY, INC.; *U.S. Private*, pg. 290
APACHE CORPORATION—See APA Corporation; *U.S. Public*, pg. 143
APACHE CRUDE OIL MARKETING, INC.—See APA Corporation; *U.S. Public*, pg. 143
APACHE DELAWARE INVESTMENT LLC—See APA Corporation; *U.S. Public*, pg. 143
APACHE DESIGN, INC.—See ANSYS, Inc.; *U.S. Public*, pg. 139
APACHE DESIGN SOLUTIONS INC.—See ANSYS, Inc.; *U.S. Public*, pg. 139
APACHE DESIGN SOLUTIONS, INC.—See ANSYS, Inc.; *U.S. Public*, pg. 139
APACHE DESIGN SOLUTIONS K.K.—See ANSYS, Inc.; *U.S. Public*, pg. 139
APACHE DESIGN SOLUTIONS YUHAN HOESA—See ANSYS, Inc.; *U.S. Public*, pg. 139
APACHE EGYPT COMPANIES—See APA Corporation; *U.S. Public*, pg. 143
APACHE ENTERPRISES, INC.—See Sowell & Co., Inc.; *U.S. Private*, pg. 3743
APACHE FINANCE CANADA CORPORATION—See APA Corporation; *U.S. Public*, pg. 143
APACHE GROUP OF MINNESOTA, INC.—See Bain Capital, LP; *U.S. Private*, pg. 440
APACHE INC.—See Genuine Parts Company; *U.S. Public*, pg. 933
APACHE INDUSTRIES, INC.—See Sinca Industries, Inc.; *U.S. Private*, pg. 3669
APACHE INTERNATIONAL, INC.—See APA Corporation; *U.S. Public*, pg. 143

APARTMENT LIFE

APACHE JUNCTION INDEPENDENT—See Independent Newspapers, Inc.; *U.S. Private*, pg. 2060
APACHE JUNCTION LANDFILL CORPORATION—See Republic Services, Inc.; *U.S. Public*, pg. 1786
APACHE KOREA CORP.—See WPG Holdings Limited; *Int'l*, pg. 8461
APACHE LOUISIANA MINERALS LLC—See APA Corporation; *U.S. Public*, pg. 143
APACHE MILLS INC.; *U.S. Private*, pg. 290
APACHE MOTORCYCLES INC.; *U.S. Private*, pg. 290
APACHE NITROGEN PRODUCTS, INC.; *U.S. Private*, pg. 290
APACHE NORTH SEA INVESTMENT—See APA Corporation; *U.S. Public*, pg. 143
APACHE NORTH SEA LIMITED—See APA Corporation; *U.S. Public*, pg. 143
APACHE OFFSHORE INVESTMENT PARTNERSHIP—See APA Corporation; *U.S. Public*, pg. 143
APACHE POWER SOLUTIONS ISRAEL LTD.—See ANSYS, Inc.; *U.S. Public*, pg. 139
APACHE RAILWAY COMPANY—See PT Sinar Mas Group; *Int'l*, pg. 6073
APACHE STAINLESS EQUIPMENT CORP.; *U.S. Private*, pg. 290
APACHE STONE LLC—See Trilantic Capital Management L.P.; *U.S. Private*, pg. 4231
APACHE SUPPLY, INC.—See Ram Tool & Supply Co. Inc.; *U.S. Private*, pg. 3351
APACHE SURINAME 58 HOLDINGS CORPORATION LDC—See APA Corporation; *U.S. Public*, pg. 143
APACHETA CORPORATION—See ResMed Inc.; *U.S. Public*, pg. 1790
APAC-KANSAS - KANSAS CITY DIVISION—See CRH plc; *Int'l*, pg. 1846
APAC-KANSAS - SHEARS DIVISION—See CRH plc; *Int'l*, pg. 1846
APAC MID-SOUTH, INC.—See CRH plc; *Int'l*, pg. 1846
APAC-MISSISSIPPI, INC.—See CRH plc; *Int'l*, pg. 1846
APAC-OKLAHOMA, INC.—See CRH plc; *Int'l*, pg. 1846
APAC OPTO ELECTRONICS, INC.; *Int'l*, pg. 500
APA CORPORATION; *U.S. Public*, pg. 143
AP ACQUISITION CORP.; *Int'l*, pg. 499
APAC REALTY LIMITED—See Morgan Stanley; *U.S. Public*, pg. 1471
APAC RESOURCES ASIA LIMITED—See APAC Resources Limited; *Int'l*, pg. 500
APAC RESOURCES LIMITED; *Int'l*, pg. 500
APAC RUBBER, INC.; *U.S. Private*, pg. 290
APAC-SOUTHEAST - SOUTHERN FLORIDA DIVISION—See CRH plc; *Int'l*, pg. 1846
APACS; *Int'l*, pg. 500
APACT CO., LTD.; *Int'l*, pg. 500
APAC-TENNESSEE, INC.—See CRH plc; *Int'l*, pg. 1846
APAC-TEXAS - TROTTI & THOMSON DIVISION—See CRH plc; *Int'l*, pg. 1846
APA ENGINEERING PRIVATE LTD.—See TAKE Solutions Limited; *Int'l*, pg. 7436
APA GASNET AUSTRALIA (OPERATIONS) PTY. LTD.—See APA Group; *Int'l*, pg. 500
APA GASNET AUSTRALIA PTY LIMITED—See APA Group; *Int'l*, pg. 500
APA GROUP; *Int'l*, pg. 499
A&P AG STRUCTURES INC.; *U.S. Private*, pg. 20
APA HOLDINGS CO., LTD.; *Int'l*, pg. 500
APAK BEAM LTD—See Axway Software SA; *Int'l*, pg. 772
APAK GROUP LTD.—See Axway Software SA; *Int'l*, pg. 772
APALUX AG—See Allreal Holding AG; *Int'l*, pg. 360
APAMAN CO., LTD.; *Int'l*, pg. 500
APAMAN ENERGY CO., LTD.—See Apaman Co., Ltd.; *Int'l*, pg. 500
APAMA (UK) LIMITED—See Progress Software Corporation; *U.S. Public*, pg. 1725
A PANAYIDES CONTRACTING PUBLIC LTD; *Int'l*, pg. 18
AP ANLAGE & PRIVATBANK AG—See Ripplewood Holdings LLC; *U.S. Private*, pg. 3439
APA NOVA BUCURESTI SRL—See Veolia Environnement S.A.; *Int'l*, pg. 8153
APAPA BULK TERMINAL LIMITED—See Flour Mills of Nigeria Plc.; *Int'l*, pg. 2709
APAQ TECHNOLOGY CO., LTD.; *Int'l*, pg. 500
APAQ TECHNOLOGY CO., LTD. - WUXI FACTORY—See Apaq Technology Co., Ltd.; *Int'l*, pg. 501
AP ARBEITPARTNER GMBH & CO. KG—See DEKRA e.V.; *Int'l*, pg. 2007
APARCAMIENTOS TRIANA SA—See Indigo Group S.A.S.; *Int'l*, pg. 3655
APAR INDUSTRIES LTD.; *Int'l*, pg. 501
APARTAMENTUL SA; *Int'l*, pg. 501
APARTMENT EXPRESS CORPORATE HOUSING INC.; *U.S. Private*, pg. 290
APARTMENT INCOME REIT LLC—See Blackstone Inc.; *U.S. Public*, pg. 349
APARTMENT INCOME REIT, L.P.—See Blackstone Inc.; *U.S. Public*, pg. 349
APARTMENT INVESTMENT AND MANAGEMENT COMPANY; *U.S. Public*, pg. 143
APARTMENT LIFE; *U.S. Private*, pg. 290

APARTMENT LIST

APARTMENT LIST; *U.S. Private*, pg. 290
APARTMENT REALTY ADVISORS OF ARIZONA, LLLP—See BGC Group, Inc.; *U.S. Public*, pg. 327
APARTMENT REALTY ADVISORS OF FLORIDA, INC.—See BGC Group, Inc.; *U.S. Public*, pg. 328
APARTMENTS, LLC—See CoStar Group, Inc.; *U.S. Public*, pg. 585
APARTMENTS OF MANDALAY BAY, LLC—See RAIT Financial Trust; *U.S. Private*, pg. 3348
APARTOTEL, S.A.—See Melia Hotels International, S.A.; *Int'l*, pg. 4809
A PASS EDUCATIONAL GROUP LLC; *U.S. Private*, pg. 18
APATECH LIMITED—See Baxter International Inc.; *U.S. Public*, pg. 280
APATIT, OJSC—See PJSC PhosAgro; *Int'l*, pg. 5883
AP ATLANTIC DISTRIBUTION, INC.; *U.S. Private*, pg. 290
APATOR CONTROL SP. Z O.O.—See Apator S.A.; *Int'l*, pg. 501
APATOR ELKOMTECH S.A.—See Apator S.A.; *Int'l*, pg. 501
APATOR GMBH—See Apator S.A.; *Int'l*, pg. 501
APATOR KFAP SP. Z O.O.—See Apator S.A.; *Int'l*, pg. 501
APATOR METRIX S.A—See Apator S.A.; *Int'l*, pg. 501
APATOR MINING SP. Z O.O.—See Apator S.A.; *Int'l*, pg. 501
APATOR POWOGAZ S.A.—See Apator S.A.; *Int'l*, pg. 501
APATOR RECTOR SP. Z O.O.—See Apator S.A.; *Int'l*, pg. 501
APATOR S.A.; *Int'l*, pg. 501
APATOR TELEMETRIA SP. Z O.O.—See Apator S.A.; *Int'l*, pg. 501
A & P AUTO PARTS, INC.—See Stellex Capital Management LP; *U.S. Private*, pg. 3800
APAVE SA; *Int'l*, pg. 501
APAWAMIS CLUB; *U.S. Private*, pg. 290
APAX GLOBAL ALPHA LTD.; *Int'l*, pg. 501
APAX INVESTMENT (SHANGHAI) COMPANY LTD—See Apax Partners LLP; *Int'l*, pg. 501
APAX PARTNERS BETEILIGUNGSBERATUNG GMBH—See Apax Partners LLP; *Int'l*, pg. 501
APAX PARTNERS BRAZIL CONSULTORIA LTDA.—See Apax Partners LLP; *Int'l*, pg. 501
APAX PARTNERS ESPANA, S.L.—See Apax Partners LLP; *Int'l*, pg. 501
APAX PARTNERS HONG KONG LTD—See Apax Partners LLP; *Int'l*, pg. 501
APAX PARTNERS INDIA ADVISERS PRIVATE LIMITED—See Apax Partners LLP; *Int'l*, pg. 501
APAX PARTNERS (ISRAEL) LTD—See Apax Partners LLP; *Int'l*, pg. 501
APAX PARTNERS LLP; *Int'l*, pg. 501
APAX PARTNERS, L.P.—See Apax Partners LLP; *Int'l*, pg. 502
APAX PARTNERS SAS—See Apax Partners LLP; *Int'l*, pg. 501
APAX PARTNERS (UK) LTD—See Apax Partners LLP; *Int'l*, pg. 501
APB APPARATEBAU SCHWEISSTECHNIK GMBH—See Christof Holding AG; *Int'l*, pg. 1587
APB APRANGA—See MG Baltic UAB; *Int'l*, pg. 4871
APB RESOURCES BERHAD; *Int'l*, pg. 507
AP CAPITAL INVESTMENT, LP; *U.S. Private*, pg. 290
APC AUSTRALIA PTY. LIMITED—See Schneider Electric SE; *Int'l*, pg. 6625
APC AUTOMOTIVE TECHNOLOGIES, LLC—See Audax Group, Limited Partnership; *U.S. Private*, pg. 386
APC AUTOMOTIVE TECHNOLOGIES, LLC—See Harvest Partners L.P.; *U.S. Private*, pg. 1876
APCB INC.; *Int'l*, pg. 508
APC BRANDS, INC.—See Court Square Capital Partners, L.P.; *U.S. Private*, pg. 1069
APC BRASIL LTDA—See Schneider Electric SE; *Int'l*, pg. 6625
APC ELINSTALLATOREN AB—See Instalco AB; *Int'l*, pg. 3721
APC GROUP, INC.; *Int'l*, pg. 507
APC HOLDINGS BV—See Schneider Electric SE; *Int'l*, pg. 6625
APCI, INC.; *U.S. Private*, pg. 290
APC INDIA PRIVATE LTD—See Schneider Electric SE; *Int'l*, pg. 6625
APC INTERNATIONAL CORPORATION BV—See Schneider Electric SE; *Int'l*, pg. 6625
APC INTERNATIONAL HOLDINGS BV—See Schneider Electric SE; *Int'l*, pg. 6625
AP CITY LIMITED—See Hang Lung Group Limited; *Int'l*, pg. 3244
APC JAPAN, INC.—See Schneider Electric SE; *Int'l*, pg. 6625
APC LOGISTICS AB—See Nippon Express Holdings, Inc.; *Int'l*, pg. 5314
APC LOGISTICS AB—See Nippon Express Holdings, Inc.; *Int'l*, pg. 5314
APC LOGISTICS AB—See Nippon Express Holdings, Inc.; *Int'l*, pg. 5314
APC LOGISTICS A/S—See Nippon Express Holdings, Inc.; *Int'l*, pg. 5314

APC-MGE—See Schneider Electric SE; *Int'l*, pg. 6633
APC-MGE—See Schneider Electric SE; *Int'l*, pg. 6633
APC-MGE—See Schneider Electric SE; *Int'l*, pg. 6633
APC-MGE—See Schneider Electric SE; *Int'l*, pg. 6633
APC-MGE—See Schneider Electric SE; *Int'l*, pg. 6633
APC-MGE—See Schneider Electric SE; *Int'l*, pg. 6633
APC NUTRITION, INC.—See Lauridsen Group Inc.; *U.S. Private*, pg. 2399
APC NUTRITION, LTD.—See Lauridsen Group Inc.; *U.S. Private*, pg. 2899
APCOA BELGIUM N.V.—See Centerbridge Partners, L.P.; *U.S. Private*, pg. 811
APCOA PARKING AG—See Centerbridge Partners, L.P.; *U.S. Private*, pg. 811
APCOA PARKING AUSTRIA GMBH—See Centerbridge Partners, L.P.; *U.S. Private*, pg. 811
APCOA PARKING DEUTSCHLAND GMBH—See Centerbridge Partners, L.P.; *U.S. Private*, pg. 811
APCOA PARKING ESPANA S.A.—See Centerbridge Partners, L.P.; *U.S. Private*, pg. 811
APCOA PARKING IRELAND LTD.—See Centerbridge Partners, L.P.; *U.S. Private*, pg. 812
APCOA PARKING ITALIA S.P.A.—See Centerbridge Partners, L.P.; *U.S. Private*, pg. 812
APCOA PARKING NEDERLAND B.V.—See Centerbridge Partners, L.P.; *U.S. Private*, pg. 812
APCOA PARKING POLSKA SP.Z O.O.—See Centerbridge Partners, L.P.; *U.S. Private*, pg. 812
APCOA PARKING SWITZERLAND AG—See Centerbridge Partners, L.P.; *U.S. Private*, pg. 812
APCOA PARKING TURKEY—See Centerbridge Partners, L.P.; *U.S. Private*, pg. 812
APCOA PARKING (UK) LTD—See Centerbridge Partners, L.P.; *U.S. Private*, pg. 811
A&P COAT, APRON & LINEN SUPPLY; *U.S. Private*, pg. 20
APCO COATINGS LTD.—See Asian Paints Limited; *Int'l*, pg. 618
APCO COATINGS—See Asian Paints Limited; *Int'l*, pg. 618
APCO EMPLOYEES CREDIT UNION; *U.S. Private*, pg. 290
APCO GRAPHICS INC.; *U.S. Private*, pg. 290
APCO HOLDINGS, LLC—See Ontario Teachers' Pension Plan; *Int'l*, pg. 5587
APCO, INC.—See Winsupply, Inc.; *U.S. Private*, pg. 4544
APCO INDUSTRIES CO. LIMITED; *Int'l*, pg. 508
APCOM INC. - COOKEVILLE PLANT—See A. O. Smith Corporation; *U.S. Public*, pg. 11
APCOM INC.—See A. O. Smith Corporation; *U.S. Public*, pg. 11
AP COMPANY USA, INC.—See AP Holdings Co., Ltd; *Int'l*, pg. 499
AP CONSTRUCTION INC.; *U.S. Private*, pg. 290
A&P CONSULTING TRANSPORTATION ENGINEERS CORP.—See H.I.G. Capital, LLC; *U.S. Private*, pg. 1827
APCO SERVICE STATIONS PTY. LTD.; *Int'l*, pg. 508
APCO SYSTEMS LIMITED—See Harvest Technology PLC; *Int'l*, pg. 3281
APCOTEX INDUSTRIES LIMITED; *Int'l*, pg. 508
APCO WORLDWIDE - PARIS—See APCO Worldwide; *U.S. Private*, pg. 291
APCO WORLDWIDE; *U.S. Private*, pg. 290
APCO WORLDWIDE—See APCO Worldwide; *U.S. Private*, pg. 291
APCO WORLDWIDE—See APCO Worldwide; *U.S. Private*, pg. 291
APCO WORLDWIDE—See APCO Worldwide; *U.S. Private*, pg. 290
APCO WORLDWIDE—See APCO Worldwide; *U.S. Private*, pg. 291
APCO WORLDWIDE—See APCO Worldwide; *U.S. Private*, pg. 291
APCO WORLDWIDE—See APCO Worldwide; *U.S. Private*, pg. 291
APCO WORLDWIDE—See APCO Worldwide; *U.S. Private*, pg. 291
APCO WORLDWIDE—See APCO Worldwide; *U.S. Private*, pg. 291
APCO WORLDWIDE—See APCO Worldwide; *U.S. Private*, pg. 291
APCO WORLDWIDE—See APCO Worldwide; *U.S. Private*, pg. 291
APCO WORLDWIDE—See APCO Worldwide; *U.S. Private*, pg. 291
APCO WORLDWIDE—See APCO Worldwide; *U.S. Private*, pg. 291

CORPORATE AFFILIATIONS

APCO WORLDWIDE—See APCO Worldwide; *U.S. Private*, pg. 291
APCO WORLDWIDE—See APCO Worldwide; *U.S. Private*, pg. 291
APC PAPER CO. INC.—See The Pritzker Group - Chicago, LLC; *U.S. Private*, pg. 4099
APC POLSKA SP. Z O.O.—See Lauridsen Group Inc.; *U.S. Private*, pg. 2399
APC POSTAL LOGISTICS, LLC; *U.S. Private*, pg. 290
APC POWER AND COOLING, UK LTD—See Schneider Electric SE; *Int'l*, pg. 6625
APC SWEDEN AB—See Schneider Electric SE; *Int'l*, pg. 6633
APC TECHNOLOGY GROUP PLC; *Int'l*, pg. 507
APCT, INC.—See IGP Industries, LLC; *U.S. Private*, pg. 2039
APC UK LTD—See Schneider Electric SE; *Int'l*, pg. 6625
APC WIRELESS; *U.S. Private*, pg. 290
APDC, INC.—See I Squared Capital Advisors (US) LLC; *U.S. Private*, pg. 2025
APD COMMUNICATIONS LTD—See NEC Corporation; *Int'l*, pg. 5186
APDM, INC.—See Astorg Partners S.A.S.; *Int'l*, pg. 657
APDM, INC.—See Nordic Capital AB; *Int'l*, pg. 5421
APDM, INC.—See Novo Nordisk Fonden; *Int'l*, pg. 5465
APE ANGEWANDTE PHYSIK & ELEKTRONIK GMBH; *Int'l*, pg. 508
APEC (ASIA) LIMITED—See Freudenberg SE; *Int'l*, pg. 2782
APEC LIMITED—See Blackstone Inc.; *U.S. Public*, pg. 359
APE COMMERCIAL PROPERTY A.E.—See Alpha Services and Holdings S.A.; *Int'l*, pg. 369
APEEJAY SURRENDRA GROUP LTD.; *Int'l*, pg. 508
APEF MANAGEMENT COMPANY 5 LIMITED—See Alpha Associes Conseil SAS; *Int'l*, pg. 366
APEGELEC INDUSTRIES—See Hiolle Industries S.A.; *Int'l*, pg. 3401
APEIRON CAPITAL INVESTMENT CORP.; *U.S. Public*, pg. 144
APEIRON SYSTEMS, INC.—See KonaTel, Inc.; *U.S. Public*, pg. 1271
APELDOORN FLEXIBLE PACKAGING B.V.—See Jindal Poly Films Ltd.; *Int'l*, pg. 3967
APELEM SAS—See Diagnostic Medical Systems S.A.; *Int'l*, pg. 2103
APEL INTERNATIONAL, LLC—See Align Capital Partners, LLC; *U.S. Private*, pg. 167
APELLA CAPITAL LLC; *U.S. Private*, pg. 291
APELLIS PHARMACEUTICALS, INC.; *U.S. Public*, pg. 144
APELOA PHARMACEUTICAL CO., LTD.; *Int'l*, pg. 508
APELON INC.; *U.S. Private*, pg. 291
APEM AB—See IDEC Corporation; *Int'l*, pg. 3589
APEM BENELUX NV/SA—See IDEC Corporation; *Int'l*, pg. 3589
APEM COMPONENTS LTD.—See IDEC Corporation; *Int'l*, pg. 3589
APEM GMBH—See IDEC Corporation; *Int'l*, pg. 3589
APEM, INC.—See IDEC Corporation; *Int'l*, pg. 3589
AP EMISSIONS TECHNOLOGIES, LLC; *U.S. Private*, pg. 290
APEM ITALIA S.R.L.—See IDEC Corporation; *Int'l*, pg. 3589
APEM S.A.—See IDEC Corporation; *Int'l*, pg. 3589
APE PTACEK ENGINEERING GMBH; *Int'l*, pg. 508
APE PUMPS (PTY) LIMITED—See WPIL Limited; *Int'l*, pg. 8462
AP EQUIPMENT RENTALS (SINGAPORE) PTE. LTD.—See AP Rentals Holdings Ltd.; *Int'l*, pg. 499
APERAM ALLOYS IMPHY—See Aperam SA; *Int'l*, pg. 508
APERAM ALLOYS RESCAL SAS—See Aperam SA; *Int'l*, pg. 508
APERAM BIOENERGIA LTDA—See Aperam SA; *Int'l*, pg. 508
APERAM ISTANBUL PASLANMAZ CELIK SANAYI VE TICARET A.S.—See Aperam SA; *Int'l*, pg. 508
APERAM SA - MONTEVIDEO UNIT—See Aperam SA; *Int'l*, pg. 508
APERAM SA - RIBEIRAO PIRES UNIT—See Aperam SA; *Int'l*, pg. 508
APERAM SA; *Int'l*, pg. 508
APERAM SA - SUMARE UNIT—See Aperam SA; *Int'l*, pg. 508
APERAM STAINLESS BELGIUM N.V.—See Aperam SA; *Int'l*, pg. 508
APERAM STAINLESS EUROPE S.A.—See Aperam SA; *Int'l*, pg. 508
APERAM STAINLESS PRECISION EUROPE—See Aperam SA; *Int'l*, pg. 508
APERAM STAINLESS SERVICES & SOLUTIONS ARGENTINA S.A—See Aperam SA; *Int'l*, pg. 508
APERAM STAINLESS SERVICES & SOLUTIONS BRAZIL—See Aperam SA; *Int'l*, pg. 508
APERAM STAINLESS SERVICES & SOLUTIONS FRANCE S.A.—See Aperam SA; *Int'l*, pg. 508
APERAM STAINLESS SERVICES & SOLUTIONS GERMANY GMBH—See Aperam SA; *Int'l*, pg. 508
APERAM STAINLESS SERVICES & SOLUTIONS IBERICA SL—See Aperam SA; *Int'l*, pg. 508

COMPANY NAME INDEX

APERAM STAINLESS SERVICES & SOLUTIONS INTERNATIONAL S.A.—See Aperam SA; *Int'l*, pg. 508
APERAM STAINLESS SERVICES & SOLUTIONS ITALY SRL—See Aperam SA; *Int'l*, pg. 508
APERAM STAINLESS SERVICES & SOLUTIONS LUXEMBOURG SA—See Aperam SA; *Int'l*, pg. 508
APERAM STAINLESS SERVICES & SOLUTIONS POLAND SP. Z O.O—See Aperam SA; *Int'l*, pg. 508
APERAM STAINLESS SERVICES & SOLUTIONS TUBES BRAZIL—See Aperam SA; *Int'l*, pg. 508
APERAM STAINLESS SERVICES & SOLUTIONS TUBES CZECH REPUBLIC—See Aperam SA; *Int'l*, pg. 508
APERAM STAINLESS SERVICES & SOLUTIONS TUBES EUROPE SAS—See Mutares SE & Co. KGaA; *Int'l*, pg. 5104
APERAM STAINLESS SERVICES & SOLUTIONS UK LTD—See Aperam SA; *Int'l*, pg. 508
APERAM STAINLESS SERVICES & SOLUTIONS USA, LLC—See Aperam SA; *Int'l*, pg. 508
APERE ENTERPRISE STORAGE SOLUTIONS INDIA PVT. LTD.—See Elliott Management Corporation; *U.S. Private*, pg. 1366
APERE ENTERPRISE STORAGE SOLUTIONS INDIA PVT. LTD.—See Vista Equity Partners, LLC; *U.S. Private*, pg. 4395
A. PERIN ROOFING & SIDING, INC.; *U.S. Private*, pg. 23
APERIO GROUP LLC—See BlackRock, Inc.; *U.S. Public*, pg. 344
APERION MANAGEMENT GROUP LLC; *U.S. Private*, pg. 291
APERION MANAGEMENT; *U.S. Private*, pg. 291
APERIO TECHNOLOGIES, INC.—See Danaher Corporation; *U.S. Public*, pg. 628
APERLEASING SRL—See Econocom Group SA; *Int'l*, pg. 2297
APERTURE ACQUISITION CORP.; *U.S. Public*, pg. 144
APERTURE DEBT SOLUTIONS LLP; *Int'l*, pg. 508
APERTURE TECHNOLOGIES INC.—See Vertiv Holdings Co; *U.S. Public*, pg. 2288
APET INC.; *U.S. Private*, pg. 291
APETIT KALA OY—See Apetit Plc; *Int'l*, pg. 509
APETIT KASVIOLJY OY—See Apetit Plc; *Int'l*, pg. 509
APETIT PAKASTE OY—See Apetit Plc; *Int'l*, pg. 509
APETIT PLC; *Int'l*, pg. 509
APETIT SUOMI OY—See Apetit Plc; *Int'l*, pg. 509
APEVA SE—See Aixtron SE; *Int'l*, pg. 255
APEX 2, INC.; *U.S. Private*, pg. 291
APEX ACCOUNTING AND TAX, INC.; *U.S. Private*, pg. 291
APEX ACE HOLDING LIMITED; *Int'l*, pg. 509
APEXA CORP.—See MIB Group Inc.; *U.S. Private*, pg. 2697
APEX ADVANCED TECHNOLOGY LLC—See Cadsys (India) Ltd.; *Int'l*, pg. 1248
APEX ANALYTIX, LLC—See KKR & Co. Inc.; *U.S. Public*, pg. 1239
APEX ASIA PACIFIC PRIVATE LIMITED—See Apex International Co., Ltd.; *Int'l*, pg. 511
APEX BANK—See Clayton HC, Inc.; *U.S. Private*, pg. 918
APEX BBDO PUBLICIDAD—See Omnicom Group Inc.; *U.S. Public*, pg. 1573
APEX BIOTECHNOLOGY CORP.; *Int'l*, pg. 509
APEX BIOTECHNOLOGY SUZHOU CORPORATION—See Apex Biotechnology Corp.; *Int'l*, pg. 509
APEX BULK COMMODITIES INC.; *U.S. Private*, pg. 291
APEX CAPITAL & FINANCE LIMITED; *Int'l*, pg. 509
APEXCCTV; *U.S. Private*, pg. 293
APEX CIRCUIT (THAILAND) CO., LTD.—See Apex International Co., Ltd.; *Int'l*, pg. 511
APEX CLAIMS SERVICES OF NEW ENGLAND—See Aquiline Capital Partners LLC; *U.S. Private*, pg. 305
APEX CLEARING CORPORATION—See Apex Fintech Solutions LLC; *U.S. Private*, pg. 292
APEX COMMERCIAL KITCHEN CO—See Osceola Capital Management, LLC; *U.S. Private*, pg. 3046
APEX COMPANIES, LLC; *U.S. Private*, pg. 292
APEX COMPOSITES INC.—See Apex Engineering Inc.; *U.S. Private*, pg. 292
APEX CONTRACTING & RESTORATION, INC.; *U.S. Private*, pg. 292
APEX CORPORATE SERVICES (NETHERLANDS) B.V.—See Apex Fund Services Holdings Ltd.; *Int'l*, pg. 509
APEX COVANTAGE; *U.S. Private*, pg. 292
APEX CREDIT MANAGEMENT LIMITED—See Encore Capital Group, Inc.; *U.S. Public*, pg. 759
APEX CREDIT SOLUTIONS INC.—See Chailease Holding Company Limited; *Int'l*, pg. 1436
APEX DENTAL PARTNERS, LP; *U.S. Private*, pg. 292
APEX DEVELOPMENT PUBLIC COMPANY LIMITED; *Int'l*, pg. 509
APEX DISTRIBUTION INC—See Russel Metals Inc.; *Int'l*, pg. 6430
APEX DYNAMICS SWEDEN AB—See OEM International AB; *Int'l*, pg. 5528
APEX ELECTRIC—See Motor City Electric Co., Inc.; *U.S. Private*, pg. 2796

APEX ELECTRONICS (SHEN ZHEN) CO., LTD.—See Apex International Co., Ltd.; *Int'l*, pg. 511
APEX ELEVATOR CORP.—See KONE Oyj; *Int'l*, pg. 4249
APEX ENGINEERING INC.; *U.S. Private*, pg. 292
APEX ENGINEERS (INDIA) PRIVATE LIMITED—See Cadsys (India) Ltd.; *Int'l*, pg. 1248
APEX ENTERPRISES LIMITED—See Apex Footwear Limited; *Int'l*, pg. 509
APEX EQUITY CAPITAL SDN. BHD.—See Apex Equity Holdings Berhad; *Int'l*, pg. 509
APEX EQUITY HOLDINGS BERHAD; *Int'l*, pg. 509
APEX EUROPE B.V.—See Apex International Co., Ltd.; *Int'l*, pg. 511
APEX EXPERT SOLUTIONS LLC—See SAP SE; *Int'l*, pg. 6566
APEX FACILITY RESOURCES, INC.; *U.S. Private*, pg. 292
APEX FAMILY MEDICINE LLC—See Skylight Health Group Inc.; *Int'l*, pg. 6994
APEX FINANCIAL SERVICES, INC.—See Apex Fund Services Holdings Ltd.; *Int'l*, pg. 510
APEX FINTECH SOLUTIONS LLC; *U.S. Private*, pg. 292
APEX FLEET INC.—See Deutsche Bank Aktiengesellschaft; *Int'l*, pg. 2055
APEX FOODS LIMITED—See Apex Holding Limited; *Int'l*, pg. 511
APEX FOOTWEAR LIMITED; *Int'l*, pg. 509
APEX FREIGHT SERVICES, INC.—See ABRY Partners, LLC; *U.S. Private*, pg. 41
APEX FROZEN FOODS LIMITED; *Int'l*, pg. 509
APEX FUND & CORPORATE SERVICES (GUERNSEY) LIMITED—See Apex Fund Services Holdings Ltd.; *Int'l*, pg. 510
APEX FUND & CORPORATE SERVICES (JERSEY) LIMITED—See Apex Fund Services Holdings Ltd.; *Int'l*, pg. 510
APEX FUND & CORPORATE SERVICES (UK) LIMITED—See Apex Fund Services Holdings Ltd.; *Int'l*, pg. 510
APEX FUND SERVICES (ABU DHABI) LTD.—See Apex Fund Services Holdings Ltd.; *Int'l*, pg. 510
APEX FUND SERVICES BAHRAIN WLL—See Apex Fund Services Holdings Ltd.; *Int'l*, pg. 510
APEX FUND SERVICES (BULGARIA) EOOD—See Apex Fund Services Holdings Ltd.; *Int'l*, pg. 510
APEX FUND SERVICES (CANADA) LTD.—See Apex Fund Services Holdings Ltd.; *Int'l*, pg. 510
APEX FUND SERVICES (CHARLOTTE) LLC—See Apex Fund Services Holdings Ltd.; *Int'l*, pg. 510
APEX FUND SERVICES (CHICAGO) LLC—See Apex Fund Services Holdings Ltd.; *Int'l*, pg. 510
APEX FUND SERVICES (HK) LIMITED—See Apex Fund Services Holdings Ltd.; *Int'l*, pg. 510
APEX FUND SERVICES HOLDINGS LTD.; *Int'l*, pg. 509
APEX FUND SERVICES (IOM) LTD.—See Apex Fund Services Holdings Ltd.; *Int'l*, pg. 510
APEX FUND SERVICES (IRELAND) LTD.—See Apex Fund Services Holdings Ltd.; *Int'l*, pg. 510
APEX FUND SERVICES LIMITED—See Apex Fund Services Holdings Ltd.; *Int'l*, pg. 510
APEX FUND SERVICES LLP—See Apex Fund Services Holdings Ltd.; *Int'l*, pg. 510
APEX FUND SERVICES LTD.—See Apex Fund Services Holdings Ltd.; *Int'l*, pg. 510
APEX FUND SERVICES (MALTA) LTD.—See Apex Fund Services Holdings Ltd.; *Int'l*, pg. 510
APEX FUND SERVICES (MAURITIUS) LTD.—See Apex Fund Services Holdings Ltd.; *Int'l*, pg. 510
APEX FUND SERVICES (SINGAPORE) PTE. LTD.—See Apex Fund Services Holdings Ltd.; *Int'l*, pg. 510
APEX FUND SERVICES (SYDNEY) PTY LIMITED—See Apex Fund Services Holdings Ltd.; *Int'l*, pg. 510
APEX FUND SERVICES (UK) LTD.—See Apex Fund Services Holdings Ltd.; *Int'l*, pg. 510
APEX FUND SERVICES (URUGUAY) S.A.—See Apex Fund Services Holdings Ltd.; *Int'l*, pg. 510
APEX FUND SERVICES US INC—See Apex Fund Services Holdings Ltd.; *Int'l*, pg. 510
APEX GLOBAL BRANDS INC.; *U.S. Private*, pg. 292
APEX GROUP LTD.—See Apex Fund Services Holdings Ltd.; *Int'l*, pg. 510
APEX HCG ONCOLOGY HOSPITALS LLP—See Healthcare Global Enterprises Limited; *Int'l*, pg. 3304
APEX HEALTHCARE BERHAD; *Int'l*, pg. 510
APEX HOLDING LIMITED; *Int'l*, pg. 511
APEX HOME LOANS, INC.; *U.S. Private*, pg. 292
APEX HOMES INC.; *U.S. Private*, pg. 292
APEX HOSPICE LLC—See Encompass Health Corporation; *U.S. Public*, pg. 754
APEXICAL, INC.; *U.S. Private*, pg. 293
APEXIGEN, INC.—See Pyxis Oncology, Inc.; *U.S. Public*, pg. 1740
APEX-I INTERNATIONAL CO., LTD.—See Gallant Precision Machining Co., Ltd.; *Int'l*, pg. 2873
APEX INCORPORATED; *U.S. Private*, pg. 292
APEX INFINITE SOLUTIONS LLC; *U.S. Private*, pg. 292
APEX INFORMATION TECHNOLOGIES; *U.S. Private*, pg. 292
APEX INSTRUMENTS, INC.; *U.S. Private*, pg. 292

APEX RESOURCES, INC.

APEX INSURANCE AGENCY, INC.—See Brown & Brown, Inc.; *U.S. Public*, pg. 396
APEX INTEC CO., LTD.; *Int'l*, pg. 511
APEX INTEGRATED SECURITY SOLUTIONS, LLC—See GTCR LLC; *U.S. Private*, pg. 1801
APEX INTERNATIONAL CO., LTD.; *Int'l*, pg. 511
APEX INTERNATIONAL FINANCIAL ENGINEERING RESEARCH & TECHNOLOGY CO., LIMITED; *Int'l*, pg. 511
APEX INVESTMENT CONSULTING (SHANGHAI) CO., LTD.—See Apex Fund Services Holdings Ltd.; *Int'l*, pg. 510
APEX INVESTMENT SERVICES BERHAD; *Int'l*, pg. 511
APEX ITALY S.R.L.—See Apex International Co., Ltd.; *Int'l*, pg. 511
APEX KINGWIN INTERNATIONAL CO., LTD.—See Apex International Financial Engineering Research & Technology Co., Limited; *Int'l*, pg. 511
APEX KYOKUYO CO., LTD.—See Kyokuyo Co. Ltd.; *Int'l*, pg. 4363
APEX LEARNING, INC.—See The Vistria Group, LP; *U.S. Private*, pg. 4131
APEX LIMITED PARTNERSHIP; *Int'l*, pg. 511
APEX LINGERIE LIMITED—See Apex Holding Limited; *Int'l*, pg. 511
APEX MACHINE CO.; *U.S. Private*, pg. 292
APEX MACHINE TOOL COMPANY, INC.—See Hanwha Group; *Int'l*, pg. 3264
APEX MARITIME CO. INC.—See Kerry Logistics Network Limited; *Int'l*, pg. 4140
APEX MEDICAL COMMUNICATIONS, INC.; *U.S. Private*, pg. 293
APEX MEDICALCORP INDIA PVT. LTD.—See Wellell Inc.; *Int'l*, pg. 8374
APEX MEDICAL CORPORATION - NORWELL EXECUTIVE OFFICE—See Tenex Capital Management, L.P.; *U.S. Private*, pg. 3966
APEX MEDICAL CORPORATION—See Tenex Capital Management, L.P.; *U.S. Private*, pg. 3966
APEX MEDICAL FRANCE SASU—See Wellell Inc.; *Int'l*, pg. 8374
APEX MEDICAL (KUNSHAN) CO., LTD.—See Wellell Inc.; *Int'l*, pg. 8374
APEX MEDICAL (KUNSHAN) CORP.—See Wellell Inc.; *Int'l*, pg. 8374
APEX MEDICAL LIMITED—See Wellell Inc.; *Int'l*, pg. 8374
APEX MEDICAL S.L.—See Wellell Inc.; *Int'l*, pg. 8374
APEX MEDICAL THAILAND CO., LTD.—See Wellell Inc.; *Int'l*, pg. 8374
APEX MEDICAL USA CORP.—See Wellell Inc.; *Int'l*, pg. 8374
APEX MICROTECHNOLOGY, CORP.—See HEICO Corporation; *U.S. Public*, pg. 1020
APEX MILLS CORPORATION; *U.S. Private*, pg. 293
APEX MINING CO., INC.; *Int'l*, pg. 512
APEX (NANTONG) TEXTILE CO., LTD.—See De Licacy Industrial Co., Ltd.; *Int'l*, pg. 1996
APEX OFFICE PRODUCTS, INC.; *U.S. Private*, pg. 293
APEX OIL COMPANY, INC.; *U.S. Private*, pg. 293
APEX OPTICAL COMPANY INC—See EssilorLuxottica SA; *Int'l*, pg. 2513
APEX OUTSOURCING, INC.; *U.S. Private*, pg. 293
APEX PARKS GROUP, LLC—See Edgewater Services, LLC; *U.S. Private*, pg. 1335
APEX PARTNERS PROPRIETARY LIMITED; *Int'l*, pg. 512
APEX PARTNERS PTY LTD; *Int'l*, pg. 512
APEX PHARMACY CORPORATE SDN. BHD.—See Apex Healthcare Berhad; *Int'l*, pg. 511
APEX PHARMACY MARKETING SDN. BHD.—See Apex Healthcare Berhad; *Int'l*, pg. 511
APEX PHARMA LIMITED—See Apex Footwear Limited; *Int'l*, pg. 509
APEX PHARMA MARKETING PTE. LTD.—See Apex Healthcare Berhad; *Int'l*, pg. 511
APEX PLASTICS INC.—See Container Services LLC; *U.S. Private*, pg. 1027
APEX-POWER GREEN TECHNOLOGY CO., LTD.—See Apex International Financial Engineering Research & Technology Co., Limited; *Int'l*, pg. 511
APEX PRECISION POWER—See Cirrus Logic, Inc.; *U.S. Public*, pg. 496
APEX PRECISION TECHNOLOGY INC.; *U.S. Private*, pg. 293
APEX PRINT LTD.—See Ringier Trade Media Ltd.; *Int'l*, pg. 6344
APEX PRINT TECHNOLOGIES, LLC—See GTCR LLC; *U.S. Private*, pg. 1806
APEX PRODUCTS COMPANY—See Keystone Laboratories, Inc.; *U.S. Private*, pg. 2300
APEX REALTY VENTURES LLP—See Prestige Estates Projects Ltd.; *Int'l*, pg. 5966
APEX REFORESTATION LTD; *Int'l*, pg. 512
APEX RENT A CAR LTD.—See Avis Budget Group, Inc.; *U.S. Public*, pg. 248
APEX RESOURCES INC.; *Int'l*, pg. 512
APEX RESOURCES, INC.; *U.S. Private*, pg. 293
APEX RESOURCE TECHNOLOGIES, INC.—See DuPont de Nemours, Inc.; *U.S. Public*, pg. 694

APEX RESTAURANT MANAGEMENT, INC.

APEX RESTAURANT MANAGEMENT, INC.; *U.S. Private*, pg. 293
APEX RETAIL SDN BHD—See Apex Healthcare Berhad; *Int'l*, pg. 511
APEX SCIENCE & ENGINEERING CORP.; *Int'l*, pg. 512
APEX SERVICE PARTNERS LLC; *U.S. Private*, pg. 293
APEX SIGNAL CORPORATION—See North Atlantic Industries Inc.; *U.S. Private*, pg. 2942
APEX SOFTWARE TECHNOLOGIES, LLC—See HgCapital Trust plc; *Int'l*, pg. 3376
APEX SPINNING & KNITTING MILLS LIMITED—See Apex Holding Limited; *Int'l*, pg. 511
APEXSQL, LLC—See Francisco Partners Management, LP; *U.S. Private*, pg. 1591
APEX SUPPLY COMPANY; *U.S. Private*, pg. 293
APEX SYSTEMS, INC.—See ASGN Incorporated; *U.S. Public*, pg. 210
APEX TANNERY LIMITED; *Int'l*, pg. 512
APEX TECHNOLOGY GROUP, INC.; *U.S. Private*, pg. 293
APEXTERIORS INC.; *U.S. Private*, pg. 293
APEX TEXTILE PRINTING MILLS LIMITED—See Apex Holding Limited; *Int'l*, pg. 511
APEX TOOL GROUP GERMANY GMBH—See Bain Capital, LP; *U.S. Private*, pg. 430
APEX TOOL GROUP GMBH & CO. OHG—See Bain Capital, LP; *U.S. Private*, pg. 430
APEX TOOL GROUP, LLC - DAYTON POWER TOOLS PLANT—See Bain Capital, LP; *U.S. Private*, pg. 430
APEX TOOL GROUP, LLC - POWER TOOL DIVISION—See Bain Capital, LP; *U.S. Private*, pg. 430
APEX TOOL GROUP, LLC—See Bain Capital, LP; *U.S. Private*, pg. 430
APEX TOOL GROUP, LLC—See Bain Capital, LP; *U.S. Private*, pg. 430
APEX TOOL GROUP PTY. LTD.—See Bain Capital, LP; *U.S. Private*, pg. 430
APEX TOOLS & ORTHOPEDICS CO.—See Berkshire Hathaway Inc.; *U.S. Public*, pg. 308
APEX TOOL S.R.L.—See Bain Capital, LP; *U.S. Private*, pg. 430
APEX TOWER LIMITED—See CLS Holdings plc; *Int'l*, pg. 1663
APEX TOWING COMPANY—See Apex Oil Company, Inc.; *U.S. Private*, pg. 293
APEX VALVES LIMITED—See Watts Water Technologies, Inc.; *U.S. Public*, pg. 2337
APEX YARN DYEING LIMITED—See Apex Holding Limited; *Int'l*, pg. 511
A.P. FORD PTY LTD—See Eagers Automotive Limited; *Int'l*, pg. 2263
AP FORMULATORS—See Highlander Partners, LP; *U.S. Private*, pg. 1939
APFT BERHAD; *Int'l*, pg. 512
APG, ALLGEMEINE PLAKATGESELLSCHAFT APG—See APG/SGA SA; *Int'l*, pg. 513
APG ASSET MANAGEMENT NV; *Int'l*, pg. 512
APG CANADA—See CRH plc; *Int'l*, pg. 1845
APG & CO., PTY. LTD.; *Int'l*, pg. 512
APG ELECTRIC INC.; *U.S. Private*, pg. 293
APG EUROPE B.V.—See Indutrade AB; *Int'l*, pg. 3677
APG-EUROPE GMBH—See APG International Inc.; *U.S. Private*, pg. 293
APG EUROPE LTD.—See APG International Inc.; *U.S. Private*, pg. 293
APG FAR EAST LTD.—See APG International Inc.; *U.S. Private*, pg. 293
APG GEO-SYSTEMS SDN BHD—See Yanlord Land Group Limited; *Int'l*, pg. 8562
APG INTERNATIONAL INC.; *U.S. Private*, pg. 293
APG L.P. - KNOXVILLE—See The CapStreet Group LLC; *U.S. Private*, pg. 4004
APG L.P.—See The CapStreet Group LLC; *U.S. Private*, pg. 4004
APG MIDDLE EAST FZC—See APG International Inc.; *U.S. Private*, pg. 293
APG POLYTECH, LLC; *U.S. Private*, pg. 293
AP GREEN DE MEXICO, S.A. DE C.V.—See Platinum Equity, LLC; *U.S. Private*, pg. 3203
A.P. GREEN REFRACTORIES, INC.—See Platinum Equity, LLC; *U.S. Private*, pg. 3203
APG SECURITIES JOINT STOCK COMPANY; *Int'l*, pg. 512
APG SECURITY LLC—See Allied Universal Manager LLC; *U.S. Private*, pg. 190
APG/SGA SA; *Int'l*, pg. 513
APG-SGA TRAFFIC SA—See APG/SGA SA; *Int'l*, pg. 513
APG SYSTEMS (EM) SDN BHD—See Yanlord Land Group Limited; *Int'l*, pg. 8562
APHEX BIOCLEANSE SYSTEMS, INC; *U.S. Public*, pg. 144
APHEX SYSTEMS LTD.—See RODE Microphones; *Int'l*, pg. 6382
APH INC.; *U.S. Private*, pg. 293
AP HOLDINGS CO., LTD; *Int'l*, pg. 499
APHRIA INC.—See Tilray Brands, Inc.; *Int'l*, pg. 7748
APHRODITE CO., LTD.—See Senko Group Holdings Co., Ltd.; *Int'l*, pg. 6709
A.P. HUBBARD WHOLESALE LUMBER; *U.S. Private*, pg. 27

APIAM ANIMAL HEALTH LIMITED; *Int'l*, pg. 515
A.P.I. APPLICAZIONI PLASTICHE INDUSTRIALI S.P.A.—See RPM International Inc.; *U.S. Public*, pg. 1818
APIARY CAPITAL LLP; *Int'l*, pg. 515
APIARY MEDICAL, INC.; *U.S. Private*, pg. 294
API BETRIEBS GEMEINNUTZIGE GMBH—See Fresenius SE & Co. KGaA; *Int'l*, pg. 2777
APICA CO., LTD.—See Oji Holdings Corporation; *Int'l*, pg. 5536
APICAL INDUSTRIES—See Bristow Group, Inc.; *U.S. Public*, pg. 387
API (CANBERRA) PTY LIMITED—See Wesfarmers Limited; *Int'l*, pg. 8380
APICARE PAIN SPECIALIST PTE. LTD.—See Livingstone Health Holdings Limited; *Int'l*, pg. 4532
APIC ASSIST CORPORATION—See Yamaha Corporation; *Int'l*, pg. 8550
APICINQ NV—See KBC Group NV; *Int'l*, pg. 4105
API CIUDAD DE MEXICO—See Grupo TMM, S.A.B.; *Int'l*, pg. 3137
API CONSTRUCTION COMPANY—See APi Group Corporation; *Int'l*, pg. 513
API CONTROL SYSTEMS SOLUTIONS INC; *U.S. Private*, pg. 294
APICORE US LLC—See Viatris Inc.; *U.S. Public*, pg. 2293
API CORPORATION - FUKUROI PLANT—See UBE Corporation; *Int'l*, pg. 8000
API CORPORATION - IWAKI PLANT—See UBE Corporation; *Int'l*, pg. 8000
API CORPORATION—See UBE Corporation; *Int'l*, pg. 8000
API CORPORATION - YOSHITOMI PLANT—See UBE Corporation; *Int'l*, pg. 8000
APICORP PETROLEUM SHIPPING FUND LIMITED—See Arab Petroleum Investments Corporation; *Int'l*, pg. 531
APICS CO., LTD.—See Futaba Industrial Co., Ltd.; *Int'l*, pg. 2851
APIC YAMADA CORPORATION - APIC YAMADA AMERICA PLANT—See Yamaha Corporation; *Int'l*, pg. 8550
APIC YAMADA CORPORATION—See Yamaha Corporation; *Int'l*, pg. 8550
APIC YAMADA CORPORATION - YOSHINO PLANT—See Yamaha Corporation; *Int'l*, pg. 8550
APIC YAMADA DISTRIBUTORS INC.—See Yamaha Corporation; *Int'l*, pg. 8550
APIC YAMADA SINGAPORE PTE. LTD - FACTORY—See Yamaha Corporation; *Int'l*, pg. 8550
APIC YAMADA SINGAPORE PTE. LTD.—See Yamaha Corporation; *Int'l*, pg. 8550
APIC YAMADA TECHNOLOGY (SHANGHAI) CO., LTD.—See Yamaha Corporation; *Int'l*, pg. 8550
APIC YAMADA (THAILAND) COMPANY LIMITED—See Yamaha Corporation; *Int'l*, pg. 8550
API DELEVAN, INC.—See Danaher Corporation; *U.S. Public*, pg. 623
API FABRICACION, S.A.—See ACS, Actividades de Construccion y Servicios, S.A.; *Int'l*, pg. 110
APIFIX LTD.—See OrthoPediatrics Corp.; *U.S. Public*, pg. 1619
API FOILMAKERS LIMITED—See Aldus Pty. Ltd.; *Int'l*, pg. 305
API FOILS HOLDINGS LIMITED—See Aldus Pty. Ltd.; *Int'l*, pg. 305
API FOILS (NEW ZEALAND) LIMITED—See Aldus Pty. Ltd.; *Int'l*, pg. 305
API FOILS PTY LIMITED—See Aldus Pty. Ltd.; *Int'l*, pg. 305
API FOILS SAS—See Aldus Pty. Ltd.; *Int'l*, pg. 305
API FOX PLAZA LLC—See Equity Residential; *U.S. Public*, pg. 791
APIGATE SDN BHD—See Axiata Group Berhad; *Int'l*, pg. 768
APIGEE CORPORATION—See Alphabet Inc.; *U.S. Public*, pg. 712
API GROUP CORPORATION; *Int'l*, pg. 513
API GROUP, INC.—See APi Group Corporation; *Int'l*, pg. 513
API GROUP PLC—See Steel Partners Holdings L.P.; *U.S. Public*, pg. 1942
API HEALTHCARE CORPORATION - SAN DIEGO—See Clearlake Capital Group, L.P.; *U.S. Private*, pg. 937
API HEALTHCARE CORPORATION - SAN DIEGO—See SkyKnight Capital LLC; *U.S. Private*, pg. 3685
API HEALTHCARE CORPORATION—See Clearlake Capital Group, L.P.; *U.S. Private*, pg. 937
API HEALTHCARE CORPORATION—See SkyKnight Capital LLC; *U.S. Private*, pg. 3685
API HEALTHCARE HOLDINGS (NZ) LIMITED—See Wesfarmers Limited; *Int'l*, pg. 8380
API HEAT TRANSFER, INC.—See Guggenheim Partners, LLC; *U.S. Private*, pg. 1811
API HEAT TRANSFER, INC.—See Littlejohn & Co., LLC; *U.S. Private*, pg. 2469
A-PIHVI KAUHAJOKI OY—See Atria Plc; *Int'l*, pg. 693
API, INC.; *U.S. Private*, pg. 294
API INDUSTRIES INC.; *U.S. Private*, pg. 294

CORPORATE AFFILIATIONS

API / INMET, INC.—See AEA Investors LP; *U.S. Private*, pg. 113
API INTERNATIONAL INC.; *U.S. Private*, pg. 294
API LAMINATES LIMITED—See Steel Partners Holdings L.P.; *U.S. Public*, pg. 1942
AP IMAGES—See The Associated Press; *U.S. Private*, pg. 3989
API MICROELECTRONICS LIMITED—See AEA Investors LP; *U.S. Private*, pg. 113
API MOVILIDAD, S.A.—See ACS, Actividades de Construccion y Servicios, S.A.; *Int'l*, pg. 110
API NATIONAL SERVICE GROUP—See APi Group Corporation; *Int'l*, pg. 513
APINES, INC.—See Denso Corporation; *Int'l*, pg. 2028
AP INSTITUTIONAL ADVISORS LLC.—See Actua Corporation; *U.S. Private*, pg. 71
APIO (AFRICA) LTD; *Int'l*, pg. 515
API POWER COMPANY LIMITED; *Int'l*, pg. 514
API RESEARCH LABORATORIES—See UBE Corporation; *Int'l*, pg. 8000
APISCENT LABS, LLC; *U.S. Private*, pg. 294
APIS INDIA LIMITED; *Int'l*, pg. 515
APISMELLIS HOMECARE LLC—See The Ensign Group, Inc.; *U.S. Public*, pg. 2070
APIS PARTNERS, LLP; *Int'l*, pg. 515
API SUPPLY, INC.—See APi Group Corporation; *Int'l*, pg. 513
API SYSTEMS GROUP, INC.—See APi Group Corporation; *Int'l*, pg. 513
API SYSTEMS INTEGRATORS—See APi Group Corporation; *Int'l*, pg. 513
API TECHNOLOGIES CORP.—See AEA Investors LP; *U.S. Private*, pg. 113
API TECHNOLOGIES SAS—See Exel Industries SA; *Int'l*, pg. 2582
API (USA) HOLDINGS LIMITED—See Steel Partners Holdings L.P.; *U.S. Public*, pg. 1942
API USA, INC.—See RPM International Inc.; *U.S. Public*, pg. 1818
APIVIO SYSTEMS INC.—See NuriFlex Co., Ltd.; *Int'l*, pg. 5490
API / WEINSCHEL, INC.—See AEA Investors LP; *U.S. Private*, pg. 113
APIX INTERNATIONAL CO., LTD.—See Denkyo Group Holdings Co.,Ltd.; *Int'l*, pg. 2028
APIXIO INC.—See New Mountain Capital, LLC; *U.S. Private*, pg. 2900
APJ ASSET PROTECTION JERSEY LIMITED—See Apollo Global Management, Inc.; *U.S. Public*, pg. 147
A.P. JOHN & SONS PTY LTD—See Tonnellerie Francois Freres; *Int'l*, pg. 7810
AP JOY LIMITED—See Hang Lung Group Limited; *Int'l*, pg. 3244
APKV US PRIVATE REIT GP LLC—See Allianz SE; *Int'l*, pg. 342
APKV US PRIVATE REIT LP—See Allianz SE; *Int'l*, pg. 343
APLAB LIMITED-MUMBAI—See Aplab Limited; *Int'l*, pg. 515
APLAB LIMITED; *Int'l*, pg. 515
A PLACE FOR MOM, INC.—See General Atlantic Service Company, L.P.; *U.S. Private*, pg. 1662
A PLACE FOR MOM, INC.—See Silver Lake Group, LLC; *U.S. Private*, pg. 3655
A PLACE TO CALL HOME, INC.—See KKR & Co. Inc.; *U.S. Public*, pg. 1262
APL (AMERICA) LLC—See CMA CGM S.A.; *Int'l*, pg. 1668
APL APOLLO TUBES LTD.; *Int'l*, pg. 515
APLAS LTD.—See China Tianying Inc.; *Int'l*, pg. 1559
APLAYA CREATIONS LIMITED; *Int'l*, pg. 515
APL BANGLADESH PVT. LTD.—See CMA CGM S.A.; *Int'l*, pg. 1668
APL CHEMI NATURA LTD.—See Aurobindo Pharma Ltd.; *Int'l*, pg. 712
APL CO. PTE. LTD. - EUROPE OFFICE—See CMA CGM S.A.; *Int'l*, pg. 1668
APL CO. PTE. LTD. - MIDDLE EAST OFFICE—See CMA CGM S.A.; *Int'l*, pg. 1668
APL CO. PTE. LTD.—See CMA CGM S.A.; *Int'l*, pg. 1668
APL DO BRASIL LTDA—See NOV, Inc.; *U.S. Public*, pg. 1543
APL ENGINEERED MATERIALS, INC.—See Saratoga Partners,L.P.; *U.S. Private*, pg. 3549
APLEONA AHR CARECATERING GMBH—See EQT AB; *Int'l*, pg. 2468
APLEONA AHR CARECLEAN GMBH—See EQT AB; *Int'l*, pg. 2468
APLEONA AHR HEALTHCARE & SERVICES GMBH—See EQT AB; *Int'l*, pg. 2468
APLEONA GMBH—See EQT AB; *Int'l*, pg. 2468
APLEONA HSG AG—See EQT AB; *Int'l*, pg. 2468
APLEONA HSG A/S—See EQT AB; *Int'l*, pg. 2468
APLEONA HSG CULINARESS GMBH—See EQT AB; *Int'l*, pg. 2468
APLEONA HSG EOOD—See EQT AB; *Int'l*, pg. 2468
APLEONA HSG EVENT SERVICES GMBH—See EQT AB; *Int'l*, pg. 2468
APLEONA HSG GMBH—See EQT AB; *Int'l*, pg. 2468
APLEONA HSG GMBH—See EQT AB; *Int'l*, pg. 2468

COMPANY NAME INDEX

APLEONA HSG KFT.—See EQT AB; *Int'l*, pg. 2468
APLEONA HSG LIMITED—See EQT AB; *Int'l*, pg. 2468
APLEONA HSG LIMITED—See EQT AB; *Int'l*, pg. 2468
APLEONA HSG NORD GMBH—See EQT AB; *Int'l*, pg. 2468
APLEONA HSG NORDOST GMBH—See EQT AB; *Int'l*, pg. 2468
APLEONA HSG O.O.O.—See EQT AB; *Int'l*, pg. 2468
APLEONA HSG OST GMBH—See EQT AB; *Int'l*, pg. 2468
APLEONA HSG RHEIN-MAIN GMBH—See EQT AB; *Int'l*, pg. 2468
APLEONA HSG S.A.R.L.—See EQT AB; *Int'l*, pg. 2469
APLEONA HSG S.A.—See EQT AB; *Int'l*, pg. 2468
APLEONA HSG SECURITY & SERVICES GMBH—See EQT AB; *Int'l*, pg. 2468
APLEONA HSG S.P.A.—See EQT AB; *Int'l*, pg. 2468
APLEONA HSG SP. Z O.O.—See EQT AB; *Int'l*, pg. 2468
APLEONA HSG SRL—See EQT AB; *Int'l*, pg. 2468
APLEONA HSG S.R.O.—See EQT AB; *Int'l*, pg. 2469
APLEONA HSG S.R.O.—See EQT AB; *Int'l*, pg. 2469
APLEONA HSG SUDOST GMBH—See EQT AB; *Int'l*, pg. 2468
APLEONA HSG TOV—See EQT AB; *Int'l*, pg. 2468
APLEONA HSG WURTTEMBERG GMBH—See EQT AB; *Int'l*, pg. 2469
APLEONA PPP LIMITED—See EQT AB; *Int'l*, pg. 2468
APLEONA REAL ESTATE GMBH—See Bilfinger SE; *Int'l*, pg. 1024
APLEONA R&M AUSBAU BERLIN GMBH—See Bilfinger SE; *Int'l*, pg. 1024
APLEONA R&M AUSBAU FRANKFURT GMBH—See Bilfinger SE; *Int'l*, pg. 1024
APLEONA R&M AUSBAU GMBH—See Bilfinger SE; *Int'l*, pg. 1024
APLEONA R&M AUSBAU MANNHEIM GMBH—See Bilfinger SE; *Int'l*, pg. 1024
APLEONA R&M AUSBAU MUNCHEN GMBH—See Bilfinger SE; *Int'l*, pg. 1024
APLEONA R&M AUSBAU STUTTGART GMBH—See Bilfinger SE; *Int'l*, pg. 1024
APLEX TECHNOLOGY, INC.; *Int'l*, pg. 515
APLF LIMITED—See Informa plc; *Int'l*, pg. 3691
APLICACIONES TECNICAS DE LA ENERGIA, S.L.—See Elecnor, S.A.; *Int'l*, pg. 2347
APLICACIONES Y TRATAMIENTOS DE SISTEMAS S.A.; *Int'l*, pg. 515
APLICARE INC.—See The Clorox Company; *U.S. Public*, pg. 2062
APLICA SOLUCIONES TECNOLOGICAS CHILE LIMITADA—See Banco Bilbao Vizcaya Argentaria, S.A.; *Int'l*, pg. 817
APLISENS S.A.; *Int'l*, pg. 515
APLITT S.A.; *Int'l*, pg. 515
APLIX CORPORATION; *Int'l*, pg. 516
APLIX KOREA CORPORATION—See Aplix Corporation; *Int'l*, pg. 516
APLJ CAPITAL MANAGEMENT LLC; *U.S. Private*, pg. 294
APL LOGISTICS CAMBODIA PVT. LTD.—See Kintetsu Group Holdings Co.,Ltd.; *Int'l*, pg. 4183
APL LOGISTICS CHINA, LTD.—See Kintetsu Group Holdings Co.,Ltd.; *Int'l*, pg. 4183
APL LOGISTICS HONDURAS S. DE R.L.—See Kintetsu Group Holdings Co.,Ltd.; *Int'l*, pg. 4183
APL LOGISTICS (HONG KONG) LTD.—See Kintetsu Group Holdings Co.,Ltd.; *Int'l*, pg. 4183
APL LOGISTICS, INC.—See Kintetsu Group Holdings Co.,Ltd.; *Int'l*, pg. 4183
APL LOGISTICS, LTD.—See Kintetsu Group Holdings Co.,Ltd.; *Int'l*, pg. 4183
APL LOGISTICS LTD.—See Kintetsu Group Holdings Co.,Ltd.; *Int'l*, pg. 4183
APL LOGISTICS SVCS. THAILAND LTD.—See Kintetsu Group Holdings Co.,Ltd.; *Int'l*, pg. 4183
APL LOGISTICS UK—See Kintetsu Group Holdings Co.,Ltd.; *Int'l*, pg. 4183
APL LOGISTICS WMS DE MEXICO, S.A. DE C.V.—See Kintetsu Group Holdings Co.,Ltd.; *Int'l*, pg. 4183
APL MANAGEMENT PTE LTD—See NOV, Inc.; *U.S. Public*, pg. 1543
APL MARITIME, LTD.—See CMA CGM S.A.; *Int'l*, pg. 1668
APL-NOL (M) SDN. BHD.—See CMA CGM S.A.; *Int'l*, pg. 1668
APL NORWAY AS—See NOV, Inc.; *U.S. Public*, pg. 1543
APL RESEARCH CENTRE LIMITED—See Aurobindo Pharma Ltd.; *Int'l*, pg. 712
APL SWIFT SERVICES (MALTA) LTD.—See Aurobindo Pharma Ltd.; *Int'l*, pg. 712
APL THAI LIMITED—See Aurobindo Pharma Ltd.; *Int'l*, pg. 712
A PLUS 2 COMPUTER LIMITED—See Mobicon Group Limited; *Int'l*, pg. 5009
A PLUS ASSET ADVISOR CO., LTD.; *Int'l*, pg. 18
APLUS FINANCIAL CO., LTD.—See SBI Shinsei Bank, *Int'l*, pg. 6606
A.PLUS GROUP HOLDINGS LIMITED; *Int'l*, pg. 28
A PLUS HEALTH CARE, INC.—See Addus HomeCare Corporation; *U.S. Public*, pg. 40
A PLUS INTERNATIONAL INC.; *U.S. Private*, pg. 19

APLUS PRODUCTS LLC—See Diversified Electronics Inc.; *U.S. Private*, pg. 1242
A PLUS S.R.L.—See Sesa S.p.A.; *Int'l*, pg. 6728
A PLUS TREE, LLC; *U.S. Private*, pg. 19
APL VIETNAM LIMITED—See CMA CGM S.A.; *Int'l*, pg. 1668
APM ALUMINIUM CASTINGS SDN. BHD.—See APM Automotive Holdings Berhad; *Int'l*, pg. 516
AP MARINE, LLC—See Genesis Energy, L.P.; *U.S. Public*, pg. 930
A&P MARKETS—See Williams, Inc.; *U.S. Private*, pg. 4527
APM AUTO COMPONENTS (THAILAND) LTD.—See APM Automotive Holdings Berhad; *Int'l*, pg. 516
APM AUTO COMPONENTS (USA) INC.—See APM Automotive Holdings Berhad; *Int'l*, pg. 516
APM AUTO COMPONENTS (VIETNAM) CO. LTD.—See APM Automotive Holdings Berhad; *Int'l*, pg. 516
APM AUTO ELECTRICS SDN. BHD.—See APM Automotive Holdings Berhad; *Int'l*, pg. 516
A.P.M. AUTOMATION SOLUTIONS LTD.—See Emerson Electric Co.; *U.S. Public*, pg. 745
APM AUTOMOTIVE HOLDINGS BERHAD; *Int'l*, pg. 516
APM AUTOMOTIVE S.R.O.—See LKQ Corporation; *U.S. Public*, pg. 1333
APM AUTO PARTS MARKETING (MALAYSIA) SDN. BHD.—See APM Automotive Holdings Berhad; *Int'l*, pg. 516
APM AUTO PARTS MARKETING SDN. BHD.—See APM Automotive Holdings Berhad; *Int'l*, pg. 516
APM AUTO SAFETY SYSTEMS SDN. BHD.—See APM Automotive Holdings Berhad; *Int'l*, pg. 516
APM CLIMATE CONTROL SDN. BHD.—See APM Automotive Holdings Berhad; *Int'l*, pg. 516
APM-COACHAIR SDN. BHD.—See APM Automotive Holdings Berhad; *Int'l*, pg. 516
APM COIL SPRINGS SDN. BHD.—See APM Automotive Holdings Berhad; *Int'l*, pg. 516
APM COMMUNICATION INC.—See Unimicron Technology Corporation; *Int'l*, pg. 8050
APM DELTA SEATING SYSTEMS SDN. BHD.—See APM Automotive Holdings Berhad; *Int'l*, pg. 516
AP MEDIA PTE. LTD.—See Oceanus Group Limited; *Int'l*, pg. 5518
AP MEMORY TECHNOLOGY CORPORATION; *Int'l*, pg. 499
APM ENGINEERING & RESEARCH SDN. BHD.—See APM Automotive Holdings Berhad; *Int'l*, pg. 516
APM GROUP LTD.; *Int'l*, pg. 516
APM HUMAN SERVICES INTERNATIONAL LIMITED—See Madison Dearborn Partners, LLC; *U.S. Private*, pg. 2540
APM, INC.; *U.S. Private*, pg. 294
APM INDUSTRIES LIMITED; *Int'l*, pg. 516
APM INTERNATIONAL SAS—See Wilmington plc; *Int'l*, pg. 8421
APM MEDIA SARL—See Wilmington plc; *Int'l*, pg. 8421
A.P. MOLLER HOLDING A/S; *Int'l*, pg. 25
A.P. MOLLER-MAERSK A/S; *Int'l*, pg. 25
A.P. MOLLER SINGAPORE PTE. LTD.—See A.P. Moller-Maersk A/S; *Int'l*, pg. 25
A.P. MOTORS (NO.2) PTY LTD—See Eagers Automotive Limited; *Int'l*, pg. 2263
A.P. MOTORS (NO.3) PTY LTD—See Eagers Automotive Limited; *Int'l*, pg. 2263
APM PLASTICS SDN. BHD.—See APM Automotive Holdings Berhad; *Int'l*, pg. 516
APM PRINT D.O.O.—See Axel Springer SE; *Int'l*, pg. 765
APM PROPERTY MANAGEMENT PTE. LTD.—See ESR Group Limited; *Int'l*, pg. 2507
APM SEATINGS SDN. BHD.—See APM Automotive Holdings Berhad; *Int'l*, pg. 516
APM SHOCK ABSORBERS SDN. BHD.—See APM Automotive Holdings Berhad; *Int'l*, pg. 516
APM SPRINGS SDN. BHD.—See APM Automotive Holdings Berhad; *Int'l*, pg. 516
APM SPRINGS (VIETNAM) CO. LTD.—See APM Automotive Holdings Berhad; *Int'l*, pg. 516
APM TACHI-S SEATING SYSTEMS SDN. BHD.—See APM Automotive Holdings Berhad; *Int'l*, pg. 516
APM TERMINAL PACIFIC LTD.—See A.P. Moller-Maersk A/S; *Int'l*, pg. 25
APM TERMINALS - AARHUS A/S—See A.P. Moller-Maersk A/S; *Int'l*, pg. 25
APM TERMINALS ALGECIRAS S.A.—See A.P. Moller-Maersk A/S; *Int'l*, pg. 25
APM TERMINALS APAPA LTD.—See A.P. Moller-Maersk A/S; *Int'l*, pg. 25
APM TERMINALS BAHRAIN B.S.C.—See A.P. Moller-Maersk A/S; *Int'l*, pg. 25
APM TERMINALS B.V.—See A.P. Moller-Maersk A/S; *Int'l*, pg. 25
APM TERMINALS CALLAO S.A.—See A.P. Moller-Maersk A/S; *Int'l*, pg. 25
APM TERMINALS - CARGO SERVICE A/S—See A.P. Moller-Maersk A/S; *Int'l*, pg. 25
APM TERMINALS ELIZABETH, LLC—See A.P. Moller-Maersk A/S; *Int'l*, pg. 25

APOLLO ACQUISITION CORPORATION

APM TERMINALS GOTHENBURG AB—See A.P. Moller-Maersk A/S; *Int'l*, pg. 25
APM TERMINALS INDIA PVT. LTD.—See A.P. Moller-Maersk A/S; *Int'l*, pg. 25
APM TERMINALS INTERNATIONAL B.V.—See A.P. Moller-Maersk A/S; *Int'l*, pg. 25
APM TERMINALS LAZARO CARDENAS S.A. DE C.V.—See A.P. Moller-Maersk A/S; *Int'l*, pg. 25
APM TERMINALS LIBERIA LTD—See A.P. Moller-Maersk A/S; *Int'l*, pg. 25
APM TERMINALS MAASVLAKTE II B.V.—See A.P. Moller-Maersk A/S; *Int'l*, pg. 25
APM TERMINALS MANAGEMENT B.V.—See A.P. Moller-Maersk A/S; *Int'l*, pg. 25
APM TERMINALS MOBILE, LLC—See A.P. Moller-Maersk A/S; *Int'l*, pg. 25
APM TERMINALS MOIN S.A.—See A.P. Moller-Maersk A/S; *Int'l*, pg. 25
APM TERMINALS NORTH AMERICA B.V.—See A.P. Moller-Maersk A/S; *Int'l*, pg. 25
APM TERMINALS NORTH AMERICA, INC.—See A.P. Moller-Maersk A/S; *Int'l*, pg. 25
APM TERMINALS PACIFIC LLC—See A.P. Moller-Maersk A/S; *Int'l*, pg. 25
APM TERMINALS ROTTERDAM B.V.—See A.P. Moller-Maersk A/S; *Int'l*, pg. 25
APM TERMINALS—See A.P. Moller-Maersk A/S; *Int'l*, pg. 25
APM TERMINALS TANGIER SA—See A.P. Moller-Maersk A/S; *Int'l*, pg. 25
APM TERMINALS VALENCIA S.A.—See A.P. Moller-Maersk A/S; *Int'l*, pg. 25
APM-TS B.V.—See APM Automotive Holdings Berhad; *Int'l*, pg. 516
APNA MICROFINANCE BANK LIMITED; *Int'l*, pg. 516
APN DIGITAL PTY. LTD.—See ARN Media Limited; *Int'l*, pg. 576
APN EDUCATIONAL MEDIA (NZ) LIMITED—See ARN Media Limited; *Int'l*, pg. 576
APN EDUCATIONAL MEDIA—See ARN Media Limited; *Int'l*, pg. 576
APN EUROPEAN RETAIL PROPERTY GROUP; *Int'l*, pg. 516
APN MEDIA (NZ) LIMITED—See ARN Media Limited; *Int'l*, pg. 576
APN NEW ZEALAND LIMITED—See ARN Media Limited; *Int'l*, pg. 576
APN ONLINE (AUSTRALIA) PTY LIMITED—See ARN Media Limited; *Int'l*, pg. 576
APN OUTDOOR PTY. LTD.—See JCDecaux S.A.; *Int'l*, pg. 3920
APN PROPERTY GROUP LIMITED—See DEXUS; *Int'l*, pg. 2093
APN SPECIALIST PUBLICATIONS NZ LIMITED—See ARN Media Limited; *Int'l*, pg. 576
APN SUPERANNUATION PTY LTD—See ARN Media Limited; *Int'l*, pg. 576
APO ASSET MANAGEMENT GMBH—See Deutsche Apotheker- und Arztebank eG; *Int'l*, pg. 2049
APOCELL, INC.—See Precision Medicine Group, Inc.; *U.S. Private*, pg. 3245
APO CEMENT CORPORATION—See CEMEX, S.A.B. de C.V.; *Int'l*, pg. 1398
APODACA INVERSIONES INMOBILIARIAS SOCIMI, S.A.; *Int'l*, pg. 517
APODACA WALL SYSTEMS, INC.; *U.S. Private*, pg. 294
APODANNORDIC PHARMAPACKAGING A/S—See Fagron NV; *Int'l*, pg. 2603
APOFINANZ GMBH—See Deutsche Apotheker- und Arztebank eG; *Int'l*, pg. 2049
APOGEE CORPORATION (JERSEY) LIMITED—See HP Inc.; *U.S. Public*, pg. 1062
APOGEE ENTERPRISES, INC.; *U.S. Public*, pg. 145
APOGEE JETS; *U.S. Private*, pg. 294
APOGEE MINERALS LTD.; *Int'l*, pg. 517
APOGEE OPTOCOM CO., LTD.; *Int'l*, pg. 517
APOGEE RESULTS; *U.S. Private*, pg. 294
APOGEE SOUND INTERNATIONAL, LLC—See Bogen Communications International Inc.; *U.S. Public*, pg. 367
APOGEE THERAPEUTICS, INC.; *U.S. Public*, pg. 145
APO HOLDINGS INC.; *U.S. Private*, pg. 294
A. P. O'HORO COMPANY; *U.S. Private*, pg. 23
AP OIL INTERNATIONAL LTD.; *Int'l*, pg. 499
AP OIL PTE LTD—See AP Oil International Ltd.; *Int'l*, pg. 499
AP OIL SINGAPORE (CHONGQING) LTD.—See AP Oil International Ltd.; *Int'l*, pg. 499
AP OIL SINGAPORE (SHANGHAI) LIMITED—See AP Oil International Ltd.; *Int'l*, pg. 499
APO IMMOBILIEN-KAG—See Deutsche Apotheker- und Arztebank eG; *Int'l*, pg. 2049
APOKJEDEN A/S—See PHOENIX Pharmahandel GmbH & Co. KG; *Int'l*, pg. 5854
APOLLO 8 MAINTENANCE SERVICES LTD.; *Int'l*, pg. 517
APOLLO ACQUISITION CORPORATION; *U.S. Private*, pg. 294

APOLLO ACQUISITION CORPORATION

CORPORATE AFFILIATIONS

APOLLO AEROSPACE COMPONENTS INDIA PRIVATE LIMITED—See Park-Ohio Holdings Corp.; *U.S. Public*, pg. 1638
APOLLO AEROSPACE COMPONENTS LIMITED—See Park-Ohio Holdings Corp.; *U.S. Public*, pg. 1638
APOLLO AEROSPACE COMPONENTS SP.Z.O.O.—See Park-Ohio Holdings Corp.; *U.S. Public*, pg. 1638
APOLLO AF LOAN TRUST—See Aflac Incorporated; *U.S. Public*, pg. 57
APOLLO AMERICA INC.—See Halma plc; *Int'l*, pg. 3231
APOLLO ASSET MANAGEMENT, INC.—See Apollo Global Management, Inc.; *U.S. Public*, pg. 145
APOLLO BANCORP, INC.; *U.S. Public*, pg. 145
APOLLO BANCSHARES, INC.—See Seacoast Banking Corporation of Florida; *U.S. Public*, pg. 1851
APOLLO BANK—See Seacoast Banking Corporation of Florida; *U.S. Public*, pg. 1851
APOLLO (BEIJING) FIRE PRODUCTS CO. LTD.—See Halma plc; *Int'l*, pg. 3230
APOLLO BELL INTERNATIONAL PLC; *Int'l*, pg. 517
APOLLO CARE CONNECT, INC.—See Astrana Health Inc.; *U.S. Public*, pg. 217
APOLLO CASUALTY INSURANCE CO.; *U.S. Private*, pg. 294
APOLLO CHEMICAL CORP.; *U.S. Private*, pg. 294
APOLLO CHEMICALS LIMITED—See H.B. Fuller Company; *U.S. Public*, pg. 977
APOLLO COLORS INC.; *U.S. Private*, pg. 294
APOLLO COMMERCIAL REAL ESTATE FINANCE, INC.—See Apollo Global Management, Inc.; *U.S. Public*, pg. 146
APOLLO CONSOLIDATED LIMITED; *Int'l*, pg. 517
APOLLO CONSULTING SERVICES CORPORATION—See Indotronix International Corporation; *U.S. Private*, pg. 2064
APOLLO COSMETIC SURGICAL CENTRE PVT LIMITED—See Apollo Hospitals Enterprise Limited; *Int'l*, pg. 517
APOLLO CVHF LIMITED—See Apollo Hospitals Enterprise Limited; *Int'l*, pg. 517
APOLLO DEBT SOLUTIONS BDC; *U.S. Private*, pg. 294
APOLLO DEVELOPMENT ASSOCIATES LP—See Edison International; *U.S. Public*, pg. 719
APOLLO DISPLAY TECHNOLOGIES CORP.; *U.S. Private*, pg. 294
APOLLO EARTHMOVERS LTD.—See Gujarat Apollo Industries Limited; *Int'l*, pg. 3176
APOLLO EDUCATION GROUP, INC.—See Apollo Global Management, Inc.; *U.S. Public*, pg. 146
APOLLO EDUCATION GROUP, INC.—See The Vistria Group, LP; *U.S. Private*, pg. 4131
APOLLO ENDOSURGERY COSTA RICA S.R.L.—See Boston Scientific Corporation; *U.S. Public*, pg. 373
APOLLO ENDOSURGERY, INC.—See Boston Scientific Corporation; *U.S. Public*, pg. 373
APOLLO ENDOSURGERY UK LTD.—See Boston Scientific Corporation; *U.S. Public*, pg. 373
APOLLO ENDOSURGERY US, INC.—See Boston Scientific Corporation; *U.S. Public*, pg. 373
APOLLO ENTERPRISE SOLUTIONS, INC.—See Apollo Enterprise Solutions, Ltd.; *U.S. Private*, pg. 294
APOLLO ENTERPRISE SOLUTIONS, LTD.; *U.S. Private*, pg. 294
APOLLO FINVEST (INDIA) LIMITED; *Int'l*, pg. 517
APOLLO FIRE DETECTORS LIMITED—See Halma plc; *Int'l*, pg. 3230
APOLLO FOOD HOLDINGS BERHAD; *Int'l*, pg. 517
APOLLO FOREST PRODUCTS LTD; *Int'l*, pg. 517
APOLLO FUTURE MOBILITY GROUP LIMITED; *Int'l*, pg. 517
APOLLO GESELLSCHAFT FUR MELDETECHNOLOGIE MBH—See Halma plc; *Int'l*, pg. 3230
APOLLO GIKEN CO., LTD.—See Meitec Corporation; *Int'l*, pg. 4804
APOLLO GLENEAGLES PET-CT LIMITED—See Apollo Hospitals Enterprise Limited; *Int'l*, pg. 517
APOLLO GLENEAGLES PET-CT LIMITED—See Khazanah Nasional Berhad; *Int'l*, pg. 4152
APOLLO GLOBAL CAPITAL, INC.; *Int'l*, pg. 517
APOLLO GLOBAL MANAGEMENT, INC.; *U.S. Public*, pg. 145
APOLLO GLOBAL REAL ESTATE MANAGEMENT, L.P—See Apollo Global Management, Inc.; *U.S. Public*, pg. 146
APOLLO GMBH—See Halma plc; *Int'l*, pg. 3230
APOLLO GOESSNITZ GMBH—See HMS Hydraulic Machines & Systems Group plc; *Int'l*, pg. 3432
APOLLO HAIR SYSTEMS INC; *U.S. Private*, pg. 294
APOLLO HEALTH AND LIFESTYLE LIMITED—See Apollo Hospitals Enterprise Limited; *Int'l*, pg. 517
APOLLO HEALTH STREET, INC.—See Sutherland Global Services, Inc.; *U.S. Private*, pg. 3886
APOLLO HEALTH STREET LTD—See Sutherland Global Services, Inc.; *U.S. Private*, pg. 3886
APOLLO HOLDING B.V.—See Newell Brands Inc.; *U.S. Public*, pg. 1513
APOLLO HOSPITALS ENTERPRISE LIMITED; *Int'l*, pg. 517
APOLLO, INC.; *U.S. Private*, pg. 295

APOLLO INDUSTRIES INC.; *U.S. Private*, pg. 294
APOLLO INTERACTIVE, INC. - DALLAS—See Apollo Interactive, Inc.; *U.S. Private*, pg. 295
APOLLO INTERACTIVE, INC.; *U.S. Private*, pg. 294
APOLLO INTERNATIONAL FORWARDERS, INC.; *U.S. Private*, pg. 295
APOLLO INTERNATIONAL MANAGEMENT, L.P.—See Apollo Global Management, Inc.; *U.S. Public*, pg. 146
APOLLO INVESTMENT MANAGEMENT, L.P.—See Apollo Global Management, Inc.; *U.S. Public*, pg. 146
APOLLO JETS LLC; *U.S. Private*, pg. 295
APOLLO KORAMANGALA CRADLE LIMITED—See Apollo Hospitals Enterprise Limited; *Int'l*, pg. 517
APOLLO LAVASA HEALTH CORPORATION LIMITED—See Apollo Hospitals Enterprise Limited; *Int'l*, pg. 517
APOLLO MACHINE & WELDING LTD.; *Int'l*, pg. 518
APOLLO MANAGEMENT INTERNATIONAL LLP—See Apollo Global Management, Inc.; *U.S. Public*, pg. 146
APOLLO MASCHINENBAU GMBH—See Gujarat Apollo Industries Limited; *Int'l*, pg. 3176
APOLLOMD, INC.; *U.S. Private*, pg. 295
APOLLOMED ACCOUNTABLE CARE ORGANIZATION, INC.—See Astrana Health Inc.; *U.S. Public*, pg. 217
APOLLO MEDICAL HOLDINGS INC.—See Alfresa Holdings Corporation; *Int'l*, pg. 317
APOLLO MEDICAL MANAGEMENT, INC.—See Astrana Health Inc.; *U.S. Public*, pg. 217
APOLLO MED INNOVATIONS LLC; *U.S. Private*, pg. 295
APOLLO METALS, LTD.—See Tata Sons Limited; *Int'l*, pg. 7473
APOLLO MICRO SYSTEMS LIMITED; *Int'l*, pg. 518
APOLLOMICS (AUSTRALIA) PTY, LTD.—See Apollomics Inc.; *U.S. Public*, pg. 168
APOLLOMICS INC.; *U.S. Public*, pg. 168
APOLLO MINERALS LIMITED; *Int'l*, pg. 518
APOLLO MOTORHOME HOLIDAYS PTY. LTD.—See Tourism Holdings Limited; *Int'l*, pg. 7848
APOLLO NELLORE HOSPITAL LIMITED—See Apollo Hospitals Enterprise Limited; *Int'l*, pg. 517
APOLLON HOCHSCHULE DER GESUNDHEITSWIRTSCHAFT GMBH—See Ernst Klett AG; *Int'l*, pg. 2495
APOLLO OIL LLC; *U.S. Private*, pg. 295
APOLLO PARTNERS LLC; *U.S. Private*, pg. 295
APOLLO PIPES LIMITED; *Int'l*, pg. 518
APOLLO PLASTICS CORP.—See Specialty Manufacturers, Inc.; *U.S. Private*, pg. 3750
APOLLO RAJSHREE HOSPITALS PRIVATE LIMITED—See Apollo Hospitals Enterprise Limited; *Int'l*, pg. 517
APOLLO REALTY INCOME SOLUTIONS, INC.; *U.S. Private*, pg. 295
APOLLORETAILING CO., LTD.—See Idemitsu Kosan Co., Ltd.; *Int'l*, pg. 3590
APOLLO ROOFING SOLUTIONS LIMITED—See H.B. Fuller Company; *U.S. Public*, pg. 977
APOLLO RV SERVICE & REPAIR CENTRE PTY. LTD.—See Tourism Holdings Limited; *Int'l*, pg. 7848
APOLLO SCIENTIFIC LIMITED—See Central Glass Co., Ltd.; *Int'l*, pg. 1406
APOLLO SENIOR FLOATING RATE FUND INC.—See Apollo Global Management, Inc.; *U.S. Public*, pg. 146
APOLLO SHEET METAL INC.; *U.S. Private*, pg. 295
APOLLO SIGN & MILLWORK LTD.; *Int'l*, pg. 518
APOLLO SILVER CORP.; *Int'l*, pg. 518
APOLLO SINDOORI HOTELS LIMITED; *Int'l*, pg. 518
APOLLO SOLAR ENERGY, INC.; *Int'l*, pg. 518
APOLLO (SOUTH AFRICA) HOLDINGS (PTY)—See Apollo Tyres Ltd.; *Int'l*, pg. 518
APOLLO S.R.L.—See Terra Firma Capital Partners Ltd.; *Int'l*, pg. 7566
APOLLO ST DEBT ADVISORS LLC—See Apollo Global Management, Inc.; *U.S. Public*, pg. 146
APOLLO SUGAR CLINICS LIMITED—See Apollo Hospitals Enterprise Limited; *Int'l*, pg. 517
APOLLO SUNGUARD SYSTEMS, INC.; *U.S. Private*, pg. 295
APOLLO TACTICAL INCOME FUND INC.—See Apollo Global Management, Inc.; *U.S. Public*, pg. 147
APOLLOTEX. CO. LTD—See Okamoto Industries, Inc.; *Int'l*, pg. 5544
APOLLO (THAILAND) CO., LTD.—See Idemitsu Kosan Co., Ltd.; *Int'l*, pg. 3590
APOLLO TIRES (US) INC.—See Apollo Tyres Ltd.; *Int'l*, pg. 518
APOLLO TOURISM & LEISURE LTD.—See Tourism Holdings Limited; *Int'l*, pg. 7848
APOLLO TRICOAT TUBES LIMITED—See Apl Apollo Tubes Ltd.; *Int'l*, pg. 515
APOLLO TRUST COMPANY—See Apollo Bancorp, Inc.; *U.S. Public*, pg. 145
APOLLO TYRES AG—See Apollo Tyres Ltd.; *Int'l*, pg. 518
APOLLO TYRES (AUSTRIA) GESELLSCHAFT M.B.H.—See Apollo Tyres Ltd.; *Int'l*, pg. 518
APOLLO TYRES (BELUX) S.A.—See Apollo Tyres Ltd.; *Int'l*, pg. 518
APOLLO TYRES B.V.—See Apollo Tyres Ltd.; *Int'l*, pg. 518

APOLLO TYRES (GERMANY) GMBH—See Apollo Tyres Ltd.; *Int'l*, pg. 518
APOLLO TYRES GLOBAL R & D B.V.—See Apollo Tyres Ltd.; *Int'l*, pg. 518
APOLLO TYRES HOLDINGS (SINGAPORE) PTE. LTD.—See Apollo Tyres Ltd.; *Int'l*, pg. 518
APOLLO TYRES (HUNGARY) KFT.—See Apollo Tyres Ltd.; *Int'l*, pg. 518
APOLLO TYRES (HUNGARY) SALES KFT.—See Apollo Tyres Ltd.; *Int'l*, pg. 518
APOLLO TYRES IBERICA S.A.U.—See Apollo Tyres Ltd.; *Int'l*, pg. 518
APOLLO TYRES LTD.; *Int'l*, pg. 518
APOLLO TYRES (MALAYSIA) SDN BHD—See Apollo Tyres Ltd.; *Int'l*, pg. 518
APOLLO TYRES (MIDDLE EAST) FZE.—See Apollo Tyres Ltd.; *Int'l*, pg. 518
APOLLO TYRES (R&D) GMBH—See Apollo Tyres Ltd.; *Int'l*, pg. 518
APOLLO TYRES (THAILAND) LIMITED—See Apollo Tyres Ltd.; *Int'l*, pg. 518
APOLLO TYRES (UK) HOLDINGS LTD.—See Apollo Tyres Ltd.; *Int'l*, pg. 518
APOLLO TYRES (UK) PVT. LTD.—See Apollo Tyres Ltd.; *Int'l*, pg. 518
APOLLO TYRES (UK) SALES LTD.—See Apollo Tyres Ltd.; *Int'l*, pg. 518
APOLLO VREDESTEIN B.V.—See Apollo Tyres Ltd.; *Int'l*, pg. 518
APOLLO VREDESTEIN KFT.—See Apollo Tyres Ltd.; *Int'l*, pg. 519
APOLLO VREDESTEIN OPONY POLSKA SP. Z.O.O.—See Apollo Tyres Ltd.; *Int'l*, pg. 519
APOLLO VREDESTEIN SCHWEIZ AG—See Apollo Tyres Ltd.; *Int'l*, pg. 518
APOLLO VREDESTEIN TIRES INC.—See Apollo Tyres Ltd.; *Int'l*, pg. 519
APOLLO VREDESTEIN (UK) LTD.—See Apollo Tyres Ltd.; *Int'l*, pg. 518
APOLLO WOOD RECOVERY INC.; *U.S. Private*, pg. 295
APOLO TOOL & DIE MANUFACTURING INC.—See TEOCO Corporation; *U.S. Private*, pg. 3969
APOLO TUBULARS S.A.—See United States Steel Corporation; *U.S. Public*, pg. 2236
A. POMERANTZ & COMPANY; *U.S. Private*, pg. 23
APONSA AB—See Solteq Oyj; *Int'l*, pg. 7076
APONTIS PHARMA AG—See Advent International Corporation; *U.S. Private*, pg. 108
APONTIS PHARMA DEUTSCHLAND GMBH & CO. KG—See Advent International Corporation; *U.S. Private*, pg. 108
A. POORTMAN (LONDON) LTD.—See AGT Food and Ingredients Inc.; *Int'l*, pg. 221
APOORVA LEASING FINANCE & INVESTMENT COMPANY LTD.; *Int'l*, pg. 519
APOPLEX MEDICAL TECHNOLOGIES GMBH—See Geratherm Medical AG; *Int'l*, pg. 2942
APO PLUS STATION CO., LTD.—See Qol Holdings Co., Ltd.; *Int'l*, pg. 6147
APO PLUS STATION (THAILAND) CO., LTD.—See Qol Holdings Co., Ltd.; *Int'l*, pg. 6147
APO PUMPS & COMPRESSORS, LLC—See DXP Enterprises, Inc.; *U.S. Public*, pg. 697
APORTER SP. Z. O.O.—See WDX S.A.; *Int'l*, pg. 8362
A-PORT S.A.—See Flughafen Zurich AG; *Int'l*, pg. 2713
APOS A.D.; *Int'l*, pg. 519
APOSENSE LTD.; *Int'l*, pg. 519
APOS GMBH—See Nynomic AG; *Int'l*, pg. 5501
APOSITION—See Dentsu Group Inc.; *Int'l*, pg. 2035
APOSPHARE GMBH—See IQVIA Holdings Inc.; *U.S. Public*, pg. 1168
APOTEFROTIRAS SA—See ELLAKTOR S.A.; *Int'l*, pg. 2364
APOTEK HJARTAT AB—See ICA Gruppen AB; *Int'l*, pg. 3577
APOTEKSTJANST SWEDEN AB—See Bonver AB; *Int'l*, pg. 1109
APOTEX CORP.—See SK Capital Partners, LP; *U.S. Private*, pg. 3678
APOTEX EUROPE B.V.—See Aurobindo Pharma Ltd.; *Int'l*, pg. 712
APOTEX ILAC SAN.TIC.LTD.STI.—See SK Capital Partners, LP; *U.S. Private*, pg. 3678
APOTEX INC.—See SK Capital Partners, LP; *U.S. Private*, pg. 3678
APOTEX NETHERLANDS BV—See SK Capital Partners, LP; *U.S. Private*, pg. 3678
APOTEX NICARAGUA, S.A.—See SK Capital Partners, LP; *U.S. Private*, pg. 3679
APOTEX NZ LTD—See SK Capital Partners, LP; *U.S. Private*, pg. 3678
APOTEX PANAMA, S.A.—See SK Capital Partners, LP; *U.S. Private*, pg. 3679
APOTEX PHARMACEUTICAL HOLDINGS INC—See SK Capital Partners, LP; *U.S. Private*, pg. 3678
APOTEX POLSKA SP. Z.O.O.—See Aurobindo Pharma Ltd.; *Int'l*, pg. 712
APOTEX PTY LTD.—See SK Capital Partners, LP; *U.S. Private*, pg. 3679

COMPANY NAME INDEX

APOTEX RESEARCH PRIVATE LIMITED.—See SK Capital Partners, LP; *U.S. Private*, pg. 3679
APOTHECARY HOLDCO, LLC—See Wells Fargo & Company; *U.S. Public*, pg. 2344
APOTHECARY PRODUCTS, LLC—See Wells Fargo & Company; *U.S. Public*, pg. 2344
APOTHECON B.V.—See Viatris Inc.; *U.S. Public*, pg. 2293
APOTHECON, INC.—See Bristol-Myers Squibb Company; *U.S. Public*, pg. 384
APOTHEEK HAGI B.V.—See Walgreens Boots Alliance, Inc.; *U.S. Public*, pg. 2322
A-POWER ENERGY GENERATION SYSTEMS, LTD.; *Int'l*, pg. 20
APOWER HOLDINGS LIMITED—See Mobicon Group Limited; *Int'l*, pg. 5009
A POWER LIMITED—See Mobicon Group Limited; *Int'l*, pg. 5009
APOYOS Y ESTRUCTURAS METALICAS S.A.—See Siemens Energy AG; *Int'l*, pg. 6902
AP PACKAGING (HANOI) CO.,LTD.—See Rengo Co., Ltd.; *Int'l*, pg. 6279
APPALACHIA COAL SALES COMPANY, INC.—See Alpha Natural Resources, Inc.; *U.S. Private*, pg. 198
APPALACHIA MIDSTREAM SERVICES, L.L.C.—See The Williams Companies, Inc.; *U.S. Public*, pg. 2143
APPALACHIAN CAST PRODUCTS, INC.; *U.S. Private*, pg. 295
APPALACHIAN CONSUMER RATE RELIEF FUNDING LLC—See American Electric Power Company, Inc.; *U.S. Public*, pg. 99
APPALACHIAN EMERGENCY PHYSICIANS; *U.S. Private*, pg. 295
APPALACHIAN LOG STRUCTURES; *U.S. Private*, pg. 295
APPALACHIAN MOUNTAIN BREWERY, INC.—See Anheuser-Busch InBev SA/NV; *Int'l*, pg. 465
APPALACHIAN POWER COMPANY—See American Electric Power Company, Inc.; *U.S. Public*, pg. 99
APPALACHIAN REGIONAL HEALTHCARE, INC.; *U.S. Private*, pg. 295
APPALACHIAN TIRE PRODUCTS INC.; *U.S. Private*, pg. 295
APPALACHIAN UNDERWRITERS, INC. - OAK RIDGE—See Appalachian Underwriters, Inc.; *U.S. Private*, pg. 295
APPALACHIAN UNDERWRITERS, INC.; *U.S. Private*, pg. 295
APP ANNIE LTD.; *Int'l*, pg. 519
THE A.P. PAPER MILLS LTD - CP UNIT—See West Coast Paper Mills Ltd.; *Int'l*, pg. 8383
APPARATEBAU GAUTING GESELLSCHAFT MIT BESCHRANKTER HAFTUNG—See Diehl Stiftung & Co. KG; *Int'l*, pg. 2114
APPARATUS, INC.—See EQT AB; *Int'l*, pg. 2471
APPAREL BUSINESS SYSTEMS, LLC—See TA Associates, Inc.; *U.S. Private*, pg. 3914
THE APPAREL GROUP, LTD.; *U.S. Private*, pg. 3987
APPAREL GROUP PTY. LTD.; *Int'l*, pg. 519
APPAREL MAGAZINE—See RFE Investment Partners; *U.S. Private*, pg. 3419
APPAREL RESOURCES INC.; *U.S. Private*, pg. 295
APPARELWAY, INC.; *U.S. Private*, pg. 295
APPAREO SYSTEMS, LLC; *U.S. Private*, pg. 295
APPASIA BERHAD; *Int'l*, pg. 519
APPASIA STREAM SDN. BHD.—See AppAsia Berhad; *Int'l*, pg. 519
APPBANK INC.; *Int'l*, pg. 519
APPCAST, INC.—See Axel Springer SE; *Int'l*, pg. 766
APPCELERATOR INC.—See Axway Software SA; *Int'l*, pg. 772
APPCENTRAL, INC.—See BlueRun Ventures; *U.S. Private*, pg. 597
APP CORPORATION PTY LIMITED—See Bureau Veritas S.A.; *Int'l*, pg. 1221
APPDIRECT INC.; *U.S. Private*, pg. 296
APP-DNA, INC.—See Elliott Management Corporation; *U.S. Private*, pg. 1366
APP-DNA, INC.—See Vista Equity Partners, LLC; *U.S. Private*, pg. 4395
APPDYNAMICS INTERNATIONAL LTD.—See Cisco Systems, Inc.; *U.S. Public*, pg. 497
APPDYNAMICS, LLC—See Cisco Systems, Inc.; *U.S. Public*, pg. 497
APPDYNAMICS TECHNOLOGIES INDIA PRIVATE LIMITED—See Cisco Systems, Inc.; *U.S. Public*, pg. 497
APPEAL-DEMOCRAT—See Horizon Publications Inc.; *U.S. Private*, pg. 1982
APPEG SA—See Fagron NV; *Int'l*, pg. 2602
APP-ELEARN PTY. LTD.—See MPS Limited; *Int'l*, pg. 5063
APP ENGINEERING SDN BHD—See APP Systems Services Pte. Ltd.; *Int'l*, pg. 519
APPENINN NYRT.; *Int'l*, pg. 519
APPEN JAPAN PTY LTD—See Appen Limited; *Int'l*, pg. 519
APPEN LIMITED; *Int'l*, pg. 519
AP PENSION LIVSFORSIKRINGSAKTIESELSKAB—See Foreningen AP Pension f.m.b.a.; *Int'l*, pg. 2731

APPENTURE D.O.O—See Adveritas Limited; *Int'l*, pg. 167
APPERIAN, INC.—See TPG Capital, L.P.; *U.S. Public*, pg. 2173
APPERSON PRINT RESOURCES, INC. - APPERSON EDUCATION PRODUCTS DIVISION—See Apperson Print Resources, Inc.; *U.S. Private*, pg. 296
APPERSON PRINT RESOURCES, INC.; *U.S. Private*, pg. 296
APPETITO PROVISION CO., INC.—See Premio Foods, Inc.; *U.S. Private*, pg. 3251
APPEX SAS—See VINCI S.A.; *Int'l*, pg. 8212
APPFIRST, INC.—See ScienceLogic LLC; *U.S. Private*, pg. 3573
APPFOG, INC.—See Lumen Technologies, Inc.; *U.S. Public*, pg. 1345
APPFOLIO, INC.; *U.S. Public*, pg. 168
APPGATE, INC.; *U.S. Public*, pg. 168
APPHARVEST, INC.; *U.S. Public*, pg. 168
APPH AVIATION SERVICES LTD.—See Heroux-Devtek Inc.; *Int'l*, pg. 3364
APPH (BOLTON) LTD.—See Heroux-Devtek Inc.; *Int'l*, pg. 3364
APPH LTD.—See Heroux-Devtek Inc.; *Int'l*, pg. 3364
APPH NOTTINGHAM LTD.—See Heroux-Devtek Inc.; *Int'l*, pg. 3364
APP HUNG YEN COMPANY LIMITED—See Agriculture Printing & Packaging Joint Stock Company; *Int'l*, pg. 217
APPH WICHITA, INC.—See Heroux-Devtek Inc.; *Int'l*, pg. 3364
APPIA COMMUNICATIONS, INC.—See CallTower Inc.; *U.S. Private*, pg. 723
APPIA ENERGY S.R.L.—See Marcegaglia S.p.A.; *Int'l*, pg. 4688
APPIA GRANDS TRAVAUX SNC—See Eiffage S.A.; *Int'l*, pg. 2330
APPIA LIANTS EMULSION RHONE ALPES—See Eiffage S.A.; *Int'l*, pg. 2330
APPIAN CAPITAL ADVISORY LLP; *Int'l*, pg. 520
APPIAN CORPORATION; *U.S. Public*, pg. 168
APPIAN EUROPE LTD.—See Appian Corporation; *U.S. Public*, pg. 169
APPIAN FRANCE SARL—See Appian Corporation; *U.S. Public*, pg. 169
APPIAN NETHERLANDS BV—See Appian Corporation; *U.S. Public*, pg. 169
APPIAN SINGAPORE PTE. LTD.—See Appian Corporation; *U.S. Public*, pg. 169
APPIAN SOFTWARE GERMANY GMBH—See Appian Corporation; *U.S. Public*, pg. 169
APPIAN SOFTWARE INTERNATIONAL GMBH—See Appian Corporation; *U.S. Public*, pg. 169
APPIAN SOFTWARE SWITZERLAND LLC—See Appian Corporation; *U.S. Public*, pg. 169
APPIAN SPAIN, S.L.—See Appian Corporation; *U.S. Public*, pg. 169
APPIA RARE EARTHS & URANIUM CORP.; *Int'l*, pg. 520
APPIER GROUP, INC.; *Int'l*, pg. 520
APPIER PTE LTD.—See Appier Group, Inc.; *Int'l*, pg. 520
APPIFY INFOTECH LLP—See Mankind Pharma Ltd.; *Int'l*, pg. 4673
APPI GEOTHERMAL ENERGY CORPORATION—See Mitsubishi Gas Chemical Company, Inc.; *Int'l*, pg. 4948
APPILI THERAPEUTICS, INC.; *Int'l*, pg. 520
APP INCLINE CORPORATION; *U.S. Private*, pg. 295
APP INTERNATIONAL MARKETING. LTD.—See Pabrik Kertas Tjiwi Kimia Tbk; *Int'l*, pg. 5684
APP INTERNATIONAL MARKETING PTE. LTD.—See Pabrik Kertas Tjiwi Kimia Tbk; *Int'l*, pg. 5684
APP INTERNATIONAL MARKETING (THAILAND) CO., LTD.—See Pabrik Kertas Tjiwi Kimia Tbk; *Int'l*, pg. 5684
APPIRIO INC.—See Wipro Limited; *Int'l*, pg. 8432
APPIRITS, INC.; *Int'l*, pg. 520
APP ITALY S.R.L.—See Pabrik Kertas Tjiwi Kimia Tbk; *Int'l*, pg. 5684
APP JAPAN LTD.—See Pabrik Kertas Tjiwi Kimia Tbk; *Int'l*, pg. 5684
APPLANIX CORPORATION—See Trimble, Inc.; *U.S. Public*, pg. 2190
APPLANIX LLC—See Trimble, Inc.; *U.S. Public*, pg. 2190
A.P. PLASMAN, INC.—See Insight Equity Holdings LLC; *U.S. Private*, pg. 2086
APPLAUSE APP QUALITY, INC.—See Vista Equity Partners, LLC; *U.S. Private*, pg. 4395
APPLE AB—See Apple Inc.; *U.S. Public*, pg. 169
APPLE AMERICAN GROUP LLC; *U.S. Private*, pg. 296
APPLE ASIA LIMITED—See Apple Inc.; *U.S. Public*, pg. 169
APPLE AUTO AUCTION (THAILAND) COMPANY LIMITED—See MBK Public Company Limited; *Int'l*, pg. 4754
APPLE AUTO GLASS, LTD.—See s.a. D'Ieteren n.v.; *Int'l*, pg. 6447
APPLE BANK FOR SAVINGS; *U.S. Private*, pg. 296
APPLEBEE'S FRANCHISOR LLC—See Dine Brands Global, Inc.; *U.S. Public*, pg. 666
APPLEBEE'S INTERNATIONAL, INC.—See Dine Brands Global, Inc.; *U.S. Public*, pg. 666

APPLEBEE'S RESTAURANTS NORTH, LLC—See Dine Brands Global, Inc.; *U.S. Public*, pg. 666
APPLEBEE'S RESTAURANTS TEXAS, LLC—See Dine Brands Global, Inc.; *U.S. Public*, pg. 666
APPLEBEE'S RESTAURANTS VERMONT, INC.—See Dine Brands Global, Inc.; *U.S. Public*, pg. 667
APPLEBEE'S SERVICES, INC.—See Dine Brands Global, Inc.; *U.S. Public*, pg. 667
APPLE BELL JOHNSON & CO. PA—See Gilliam Bell Moser LLP; *U.S. Private*, pg. 1700
APPLE BENELUX B.V. - BELGIUM OFFICE—See Apple Inc.; *U.S. Public*, pg. 169
APPLE BENELUX B.V.—See Apple Inc.; *U.S. Public*, pg. 169
APPLE BUS COMPANY; *U.S. Private*, pg. 296
APPLEBY LEARNING AND CHILD CARE CENTRE INC.—See Ontario Teachers' Pension Plan; *Int'l*, pg. 5587
APPLEBY & STERLING, INC.; *U.S. Private*, pg. 297
APPLEBY & WYMAN INSURANCE AGENCY, INC.—See Cross Financial Corporation; *U.S. Private*, pg. 1104
APPLE CANADA INC.—See Apple Inc.; *U.S. Public*, pg. 169
APPLECARE MEDICAL MANAGEMENT, LLC—See UnitedHealth Group Incorporated; *U.S. Public*, pg. 2239
APPLE CARR VILLAGE MOBILE HOME PARK, LLC—See Sun Communities, Inc.; *U.S. Public*, pg. 1961
APPLECHEM INC.—See Societe la Biochimie Appliquee SAS; *Int'l*, pg. 7043
APPLE CHEVROLET INCORPORATED; *U.S. Private*, pg. 296
APPLE COMPUTER MEXICO S.A. DE C.V.—See Apple Inc.; *U.S. Public*, pg. 169
APPLE CORE ENTERPRISES INC.; *U.S. Private*, pg. 296
APPLE CREEK BANC CORP.; *U.S. Private*, pg. 296
THE APPLE CREEK BANKING COMPANY—See Apple Creek Banc Corp.; *U.S. Private*, pg. 296
APPLEDORE MEDICAL GROUP, INC.—See HCA Healthcare, Inc.; *U.S. Public*, pg. 990
APPLEDORE MEDICAL GROUP, INC.—See HCA Healthcare, Inc.; *U.S. Public*, pg. 990
APPLEDORE SHIPBUILDERS (2004) LIMITED—See Babcock International Group PLC; *Int'l*, pg. 792
APPLE & EVE LLC—See Lassonde Industries, Inc.; *Int'l*, pg. 4421
APPLE EXPRESS COURIER INC.—See bpost NV/SA; *Int'l*, pg. 1133
APPLE EXPRESS COURIER LTD.—See bpost NV/SA; *Int'l*, pg. 1133
APPLE FABRICATION COMPANY—See Triton Consolidated, Inc.; *U.S. Private*, pg. 4239
APPLE FARM SERVICE INC.; *U.S. Private*, pg. 296
APPLE FILM CO., LTD.—See Inabata & Co. Ltd.; *Int'l*, pg. 3643
APPLE FILM DA NANG CO., LTD.—See Inabata & Co. Ltd.; *Int'l*, pg. 3643
APPLE FLAVOR & FRAGRANCE GROUP CO., LTD.; *Int'l*, pg. 520
APPLE FLAVOR & FRAGRANCE USA CORP.—See Apple Flavor & Fragrance Group Co., Ltd.; *Int'l*, pg. 520
APPLE FORD INC.; *U.S. Private*, pg. 296
APPLE FORD; *U.S. Private*, pg. 296
APPLE FRANCE SARL—See Apple Inc.; *U.S. Public*, pg. 169
APPLEGATE, INC.; *U.S. Private*, pg. 297
APPLEGATE LIVESTOCK EQUIPMENT, INC.—See Ag Growth International Inc.; *Int'l*, pg. 198
APPLEGATE MEDIA GROUP; *U.S. Private*, pg. 297
APPLEGATE RECOVERY, LLC—See Webster Equity Partners, LLC; *U.S. Private*, pg. 4466
APPLE GES.MBH—See Apple Inc.; *U.S. Public*, pg. 169
APPLE GMBH—See Apple Inc.; *U.S. Public*, pg. 169
APPLE GRAPHICS, INC.—See Chatham Asset Management, LLC; *U.S. Private*, pg. 862
APPLE GREEN HOLDING, INC.; *Int'l*, pg. 520
APPLEGREEN PLC; *Int'l*, pg. 520
APPLE GROWTH PARTNERS; *U.S. Private*, pg. 296
APPLE HEALTH CARE INC.; *U.S. Private*, pg. 296
APPLE HOMECARE MEDICAL SUPPLY, LLC—See InTandem Capital Partners, LLC; *U.S. Private*, pg. 2097
APPLE HOME HEALTH CARE LTD—See Addus HomeCare Corporation; *U.S. Public*, pg. 40
APPLE HOSPITALITY REIT, INC.—See Apple Suites Realty Group, Inc.; *U.S. Private*, pg. 297
APPLE INC.; *U.S. Public*, pg. 169
APPLE INDIA PRIVATE LIMITED—See Apple Inc.; *U.S. Public*, pg. 169
APPLE INTERNATIONAL CO., LTD.; *Int'l*, pg. 520
APPLEJAM INC.; *U.S. Private*, pg. 297
APPLEJAM OF GA INC.—See Applejam Inc.; *U.S. Private*, pg. 297
APPLEJAM OF TX INC.—See Applejam Inc.; *U.S. Private*, pg. 297
APPLE JAPAN, INC.—See Apple Inc.; *U.S. Public*, pg. 169
APPLE LEISURE GROUP; *U.S. Private*, pg. 296
APPLE METRO INC.; *U.S. Private*, pg. 297
APPLE ONE SERVICE ARIZONA INC.; *U.S. Private*, pg. 297
APPLEONE SERVICES LTD; *Int'l*, pg. 521

APPLE OPERATIONS EUROPE—See Apple Inc.; *U.S. Public*, pg. 169
APPLE OPERATIONS INTERNATIONAL—See Apple Inc.; *U.S. Public*, pg. 169
APPLEPIE CAPITAL, INC.; *U.S. Private*, pg. 297
APPLE PRESS LTD—See The Quarto Group, Inc.; *Int'l*, pg. 7677
APPLE PTY. LIMITED—See Apple Inc.; *U.S. Public*, pg. 169
APPLE ROCK; *U.S. Private*, pg. 297
APPLE RUBBER PRODUCTS INC.; *U.S. Private*, pg. 297
APPLE RUSH CO, INC.; *U.S. Public*, pg. 169
APPLE SALES INTERNATIONAL—See Apple Inc.; *U.S. Public*, pg. 169
APPLE SAUCE, INC.; *U.S. Private*, pg. 297
APPLESEED'S, INC.—See Bluestem Brands, Inc.; *U.S. Private*, pg. 598
APPLE SEEDS; *U.S. Private*, pg. 297
APPLE SUITES REALTY GROUP, INC.; *U.S. Private*, pg. 297
APPLETISER SA (PTY) LTD.—See The Coca-Cola Company; *U.S. Public*, pg. 2063
APPLETON CORPORATION—See The O'Connell Companies, Incorporated; *U.S. Private*, pg. 4087
APPLETON ELECTRIC, S.A. DE C.V.—See Emerson Electric Co.; *U.S. Public*, pg. 740
APPLETON GROUP CANADA, LTD.—See Emerson Electric Co.; *U.S. Public*, pg. 740
APPLETON GROUP - CHERRYVILLE—See Emerson Electric Co.; *U.S. Public*, pg. 740
APPLETON GROUP - FULLERTON—See Emerson Electric Co.; *U.S. Public*, pg. 740
APPLETON GROUP - MEMPHIS—See Emerson Electric Co.; *U.S. Public*, pg. 740
APPLETON GROUP - SOUTH MILWAUKEE—See Emerson Electric Co.; *U.S. Public*, pg. 740
APPLETON GROUP - STEPHENVILLE—See Emerson Electric Co.; *U.S. Public*, pg. 740
APPLETON GRP LLC—See Emerson Electric Co.; *U.S. Public*, pg. 740
APPLETON LEARNING CORPORATION; *U.S. Private*, pg. 297
APPLETON SECURITY CORP.—See The O'Connell Companies, Incorporated; *U.S. Private*, pg. 4087
APPLETON SUPPLY CO., INC.—See Gibraltar Industries, Inc.; *U.S. Public*, pg. 935
APPLETREE ANSWERING SERVICES, INC.; *U.S. Private*, pg. 297
APPLE TREE HONDA; *U.S. Private*, pg. 297
APPLETREE MARKETS; *U.S. Private*, pg. 297
APPLE TREE PRODUCTIONS APS—See ITV plc; *Int'l*, pg. 3844
APPLE TUCK & ASSOCIATES, INC.—See Sunland Builders; *U.S. Private*, pg. 3868
APPLE VACATIONS, LLC—See Apple Leisure Group; *U.S. Private*, pg. 296
APPLE VALLEY INSULATION, A BDI COMPANY, INC.—See Installed Building Products, Inc.; *U.S. Public*, pg. 1132
APPLEWAY CHEVROLET, INC.—See AutoNation, Inc.; *U.S. Public*, pg. 232
APPLEWHITE DENTAL LLC—See NMS Capital Services, LLC; *U.S. Private*, pg. 2931
APPLIANCE FACTORY OUTLET & MATTRESSES, INC.; *U.S. Private*, pg. 297
APPLIANCE PARTS DEPOT INC.; *U.S. Private*, pg. 297
APPLIANCES COMPONENTS COMPANIES SPAIN, S.A.—See Guangzhou Wanbao Group Co., Ltd.; *Int'l*, pg. 3168
APPLIANCESMART HOLDINGS LLC—See Live Ventures Incorporated; *U.S. Public*, pg. 1332
APPLIANCESMART, INC.—See Live Ventures Incorporated; *U.S. Public*, pg. 1332
APPLIANCESMART—See Live Ventures Incorporated; *U.S. Public*, pg. 1332
APPLIANCESMART—See Live Ventures Incorporated; *U.S. Public*, pg. 1332
APPLIANCE WAREHOUSE OF AMERICA, INC.—See Pamplona Capital Management LLP; *Int'l*, pg. 5711
APPLIANCE WAREHOUSE OF EXETER; *U.S. Private*, pg. 298
APPLICABLE LIMITED—See Nippon Telegraph & Telephone Corporation; *Int'l*, pg. 5340
APPLICA CANADA CORPORATION—See Spectrum Brands Holdings, Inc.; *U.S. Public*, pg. 1916
APPLICA CONSUMER PRODUCTS, INC.—See Spectrum Brands Holdings, Inc.; *U.S. Public*, pg. 1916
APPLICAD PUBLIC COMPANY LIMITED; *Int'l*, pg. 521
APPLICA SERVICIOS DE MEXICO, S. DE R.L. DE C.V.—See Spectrum Brands Holdings, Inc.; *U.S. Public*, pg. 1916
APPLICATION CONSULTING GROUP; *U.S. Private*, pg. 298
APPLICATION CONSULTING TRAINING SOLUTIONS INC.; *U.S. Private*, pg. 298
APPLICATION DEVELOPMENT CONSULTANTS, LLC; *U.S. Private*, pg. 298
APPLICATION DEVELOPMENT RESOURCES, INC.; *U.S. Private*, pg. 298

APPLICATION SPECIALTIES, INC.—See DXP Enterprises, Inc.; *U.S. Public*, pg. 697
APPLICATIONS SOFTWARE TECHNOLOGY LLC; *U.S. Private*, pg. 298
APPLICATOR SALES & SERVICE; *U.S. Private*, pg. 298
APPLICHEM GMBH—See Illinois Tool Works Inc.; *U.S. Public*, pg. 1101
APPLICHEM, INC.—See Illinois Tool Works Inc.; *U.S. Public*, pg. 1101
APPLICON CONSULTING SWEDEN HOLDING AB—See Origo hf.; *Int'l*, pg. 5630
APPLICON EHF.—See Origo hf.; *Int'l*, pg. 5630
APPLICON HOLDING EHF—See Origo hf.; *Int'l*, pg. 5630
APPLICON SOLUTIONS LTD—See Origo hf.; *Int'l*, pg. 5630
APPLIDE CORPORATION; *Int'l*, pg. 521
APPLIED AEROSPACE STRUCTURES, CORP.—See Greenbriar Equity Group, L.P.; *U.S. Private*, pg. 1775
APPLIED ANALYTIX INC.—See QueBIT Consulting, LLC; *U.S. Private*, pg. 3325
APPLIED AVIONICS, INC.; *U.S. Private*, pg. 298
APPLIED BIOCHEMIST INC.—See SePRO Corporation; *U.S. Private*, pg. 3611
APPLIED BIOCODE CORP.; *U.S. Public*, pg. 169
APPLIED BIOSCIENCES CORP.; *U.S. Public*, pg. 170
APPLIED BIOSYSTEMS DE MEXICO S. DE R.L. DE C.V.—See Thermo Fisher Scientific Inc.; *U.S. Public*, pg. 2148
APPLIED BIOSYSTEMS INTERNATIONAL, INC. RUSSIA REP OFFICE—See Thermo Fisher Scientific Inc.; *U.S. Public*, pg. 2145
APPLIED BIOSYSTEMS, LLC—See Thermo Fisher Scientific Inc.; *U.S. Public*, pg. 2148
APPLIED BIOSYSTEMS TRADING (SHANGHAI) COMPANY LTD.—See Thermo Fisher Scientific Inc.; *U.S. Public*, pg. 2145
APPLIED BUSINESS SYSTEMS SDN. BHD.—See Omesti Berhad; *Int'l*, pg. 5562
APPLIED CANADA, ULC—See Applied Industrial Technologies, Inc.; *U.S. Public*, pg. 170
APPLIED CARD HOLDINGS INC.; *U.S. Private*, pg. 298
APPLIED CARD SYSTEMS INC.; *U.S. Private*, pg. 298
APPLIED CARE & DEVELOPMENT LIMITED—See Sheikh Holdings Group (Investments) Limited; *Int'l*, pg. 6793
APPLIED CLINICAL INTELLIGENCE, LLC—See Leonard Green & Partners, L.P.; *U.S. Private*, pg. 2429
APPLIED CO., LTD.; *Int'l*, pg. 521
APPLIED COMMUNICATIONS IRELAND LIMITED—See ACI Worldwide, Inc.; *U.S. Public*, pg. 34
APPLIED COMPOSITES AB—See GKN plc; *Int'l*, pg. 2986
APPLIED COMPOSITES ENGINEERING, INC.—See AE Industrial Partners, LP; *U.S. Private*, pg. 111
APPLIED COMPRESSION SYSTEMS LTD.—See Xebec Adsorption Inc.; *Int'l*, pg. 8520
APPLIED COMPUTER RESEARCH, INC.—See Wired Real Estate Group Inc.; *U.S. Private*, pg. 4546
APPLIED COMPUTER SOLUTIONS—See Pivot Technology Solutions, Inc.; *U.S. Public*, pg. 1695
APPLIED CONSTRUCTION & ENGINEERING (M) SDN BHD—See Yanlord Land Group Limited; *Int'l*, pg. 8562
APPLIED CONTROL ENGINEERING, INC.; *U.S. Private*, pg. 298
APPLIED CONTROL TECHNOLOGY, LLC.—See ACS, Actividades de Construccion y Servicios, S.A.; *Int'l*, pg. 111
APPLIED COOLING TECHNOLOGY LLC—See DMI UK Ltd.; *Int'l*, pg. 2145
APPLIED CRYO TECHNOLOGIES, INC.—See Plug Power Inc.; *U.S. Public*, pg. 1699
APPLIED DB PUBLIC COMPANY LIMITED; *Int'l*, pg. 521
APPLIED DEFENSE SOLUTIONS, INC.—See L3Harris Technologies, Inc.; *U.S. Public*, pg. 1280
APPLIED DEVELOPMENT HOLDINGS LIMITED; *Int'l*, pg. 521
APPLIED DIGITAL CORPORATION; *U.S. Public*, pg. 170
APPLIED DNA SCIENCES, INC.; *U.S. Public*, pg. 170
APPLIED DRILLING TECHNOLOGY INC.—See Transocean Ltd.; *Int'l*, pg. 7903
APPLIED DRILLING TECHNOLOGY INTERNATIONAL—See Transocean Ltd.; *Int'l*, pg. 7903
APPLIED DYNAMICS INTERNATIONAL, LTD.—See Applied Dynamics International; *U.S. Private*, pg. 298
APPLIED DYNAMICS INTERNATIONAL; *U.S. Private*, pg. 298
APPLIED ECOLOGICAL SERVICES, INC.—See KKR & Co. Inc.; *U.S. Public*, pg. 1263
APPLIED ENERGETICS, INC.; *U.S. Public*, pg. 170
APPLIED ENERGY GROUP, INC.—See Ameresco, Inc.; *U.S. Public*, pg. 95
APPLIED ENERGY LLC—See I Squared Capital Advisors (US) LLC; *U.S. Private*, pg. 2025
APPLIED ENERGY SOLUTIONS; *U.S. Private*, pg. 298
APPLIED ENGINEERING PTE. LTD.; *Int'l*, pg. 521
APPLIED FELTS, INC.—See Vortex Company, LLC; *U.S. Private*, pg. 4413
APPLIED FIBER MANUFACTURING, LLC; *U.S. Private*, pg. 298
APPLIED FLUID POWER INC.; *U.S. Private*, pg. 298

APPLIED FOOD TECHNOLOGIES, INC.; *U.S. Private*, pg. 298
APPLIED FUSION INC.—See Francisco Partners Management, LP; *U.S. Private*, pg. 1590
APPLIED GENETIC TECHNOLOGIES CORPORATION—See Syncona Ltd.; *Int'l*, pg. 7382
APPLIED GEOGRAPHICS, INC.—See The Sanborn Map Company, Inc.; *U.S. Private*, pg. 4114
APPLIED GEOMECHANICS INC—See CARBO Ceramics Inc.; *U.S. Private*, pg. 748
APPLIED GLOBAL TECHNOLOGIES; *U.S. Private*, pg. 298
APPLIED GRAPHENE MATERIALS PLC; *Int'l*, pg. 521
APPLIED HANDLING INC.; *U.S. Private*, pg. 298
APPLIED HEALTH CARE, LTD.—See Option Care Health, Inc.; *U.S. Public*, pg. 1609
APPLIED IMAGE GROUP INC.; *U.S. Private*, pg. 298
APPLIED IMAGING INTERNATIONAL LTD.—See Danaher Corporation; *U.S. Public*, pg. 624
APPLIED INDUSTRIAL CONTROLS, INC.—See Frontenac Company LLC; *U.S. Private*, pg. 1614
APPLIED INDUSTRIAL TECHNOLOGIES - CA LLC—See Applied Industrial Technologies, Inc.; *U.S. Public*, pg. 170
APPLIED INDUSTRIAL TECHNOLOGIES - DBB, INC.—See Applied Industrial Technologies, Inc.; *U.S. Public*, pg. 170
APPLIED INDUSTRIAL TECHNOLOGIES, INC. - LONDON—See Applied Industrial Technologies, Inc.; *U.S. Public*, pg. 170
APPLIED INDUSTRIAL TECHNOLOGIES, INC.; *U.S. Public*, pg. 170
APPLIED INDUSTRIAL TECHNOLOGIES - INDIANA LLC—See Applied Industrial Technologies, Inc.; *U.S. Public*, pg. 170
APPLIED INDUSTRIAL TECHNOLOGIES, LP—See Applied Industrial Technologies, Inc.; *U.S. Public*, pg. 170
APPLIED INDUSTRIAL TECHNOLOGIES, LTD.—See Applied Industrial Technologies, Inc.; *U.S. Public*, pg. 170
APPLIED INDUSTRIAL TECHNOLOGIES - MBC, INC.—See Applied Industrial Technologies, Inc.; *U.S. Public*, pg. 170
APPLIED INDUSTRIAL TECHNOLOGIES - PA LLC—See Applied Industrial Technologies, Inc.; *U.S. Public*, pg. 170
APPLIED INDUSTRIAL TECHNOLOGIES PTY LTD.—See Applied Industrial Technologies, Inc.; *U.S. Public*, pg. 170
APPLIED INDUSTRIAL TECHNOLOGIES - TX LP—See Applied Industrial Technologies, Inc.; *U.S. Public*, pg. 170
APPLIED INFORMATION GROUP INC.—See Aquiline Capital Partners LLC; *U.S. Private*, pg. 304
APPLIED INFORMATION SCIENCES, INC.; *U.S. Private*, pg. 298
APPLIED INSIGHT, LLC—See CACI International Inc.; *U.S. Public*, pg. 417
APPLIED INSTRUMENT TECHNOLOGIES, INC.—See Schneider Electric SE; *Int'l*, pg. 6627
APPLIED INTERNATIONAL INFORMATICS GMBH—See Atos SE; *Int'l*, pg. 690
APPLIED INTUITION, INC.; *U.S. Private*, pg. 299
APPLIED INVESTMENT (ASIA) LIMITED—See Applied Development Holdings Limited; *Int'l*, pg. 521
APPLIED KILOVOLTS LIMITED—See L3Harris Technologies, Inc.; *U.S. Public*, pg. 1280
APPLIED LANGUAGE SOLUTIONS—See Capita plc; *Int'l*, pg. 1308
APPLIED LASER SALISBURY—See RCR Tomlinson Ltd.; *Int'l*, pg. 6228
APPLIED LASER TULLAMARINE—See RCR Tomlinson Ltd.; *Int'l*, pg. 6228
APPLIED LASER WETHERILL PARK—See RCR Tomlinson Ltd.; *Int'l*, pg. 6228
APPLIED MACHINE & MOTION CONTROL, INC.—See Genuine Parts Company; *U.S. Public*, pg. 933
APPLIED MAINTENANCE SUPPLIES & SOLUTIONS, LLC—See Applied Industrial Technologies, Inc.; *U.S. Public*, pg. 170
APPLIED MAINTENANCE SUPPLIES & SOLUTIONS—See Applied Industrial Technologies, Inc.; *U.S. Public*, pg. 170
APPLIED MATERIALS CANADA, INC.—See Applied Materials, Inc.; *U.S. Public*, pg. 172
APPLIED MATERIALS (CHINA) HOLDINGS, LTD.—See Applied Materials, Inc.; *U.S. Public*, pg. 172
APPLIED MATERIALS (CHINA), INC.—See Applied Materials, Inc.; *U.S. Public*, pg. 172
APPLIED MATERIALS CORP.—See Applied Materials, Inc.; *U.S. Public*, pg. 172
APPLIED MATERIALS DEUTSCHLAND HOLDING GMBH—See Applied Materials, Inc.; *U.S. Public*, pg. 172
APPLIED MATERIALS EUROPE BV—See Applied Materials, Inc.; *U.S. Public*, pg. 172
APPLIED MATERIALS FRANCE SARL—See Applied Materials, Inc.; *U.S. Public*, pg. 172
APPLIED MATERIALS GMBH & CO., KG—See Applied Materials, Inc.; *U.S. Public*, pg. 172

APPLIED MATERIALS GMBH—See Applied Materials, Inc.; *U.S. Public*, pg. 172
APPLIED MATERIALS, INC.; *U.S. Public*, pg. 172
APPLIED MATERIALS, INC.—See Applied Materials, Inc.; *U.S. Public*, pg. 172
APPLIED MATERIALS INDIA PRIVATE LIMITED—See Applied Materials, Inc.; *U.S. Public*, pg. 172
APPLIED MATERIALS IRELAND LTD.—See Applied Materials, Inc.; *U.S. Public*, pg. 172
APPLIED MATERIALS ISRAEL, LTD.—See Applied Materials, Inc.; *U.S. Public*, pg. 172
APPLIED MATERIALS ITALIA S.R.L.—See Applied Materials, Inc.; *U.S. Public*, pg. 172
APPLIED MATERIALS JAPAN, INC.—See Applied Materials, Inc.; *U.S. Public*, pg. 172
APPLIED MATERIALS KOREA, LTD.—See Applied Materials, Inc.; *U.S. Public*, pg. 172
APPLIED MATERIALS SINGAPORE TECHNOLOGY PTE. LTD.—See Applied Materials, Inc.; *U.S. Public*, pg. 172
APPLIED MATERIALS SOUTH EAST ASIA PTE. LTD.—See Applied Materials, Inc.; *U.S. Public*, pg. 172
APPLIED MATERIALS SPV2, INC.—See Applied Materials, Inc.; *U.S. Public*, pg. 172
APPLIED MATERIALS TAIWAN, LTD.—See Applied Materials, Inc.; *U.S. Public*, pg. 172
APPLIED MATERIALS UK LIMITED—See Applied Materials, Inc.; *U.S. Public*, pg. 172
APPLIED MATERIALS WEB COATING GMBH—See Applied Materials, Inc.; *U.S. Public*, pg. 172
APPLIED MATERIALS (XIAN), LTD.—See Applied Materials, Inc.; *U.S. Public*, pg. 172
APPLIED MATHS INC.—See KBC Group NV; *Int'l*, pg. 4104
APPLIED MATHS NV—See Institut Merieux; *Int'l*, pg. 3724
APPLIED MECHANICAL SYSTEMS, INC.; *U.S. Private*, pg. 299
APPLIED MEDICAL CORPORATION; *U.S. Private*, pg. 299
APPLIED MEXICO HOLDINGS, S.A. DE C.V.—See Applied Industrial Technologies, Inc.; *U.S. Public*, pg. 170
APPLIED MEXICO, S.A. DE C.V.—See Applied Industrial Technologies, Inc.; *U.S. Public*, pg. 170
APPLIED MICRO CIRCUITS CORPORATION CANADA—See MACOM Technology Solutions Holdings, Inc.; *U.S. Public*, pg. 1352
APPLIED MICRO CIRCUITS CORPORATION—See MACOM Technology Solutions Holdings, Inc.; *U.S. Public*, pg. 1352
APPLIED MINERALS, INC.; *U.S. Public*, pg. 173
APPLIED MOLECULAR TRANSPORT INC.—See Cyclo Therapeutics, Inc.; *U.S. Public*, pg. 617
APPLIED MOTION PRODUCTS INC.—See Shanghai Moons' Electric Co., Ltd.; *Int'l*, pg. 6775
APPLIED NANOTECH, INC.; *U.S. Private*, pg. 299
APPLIED NATURAL GAS FUELS, INC.; *U.S. Private*, pg. 299
APPLIED OPTICAL SYSTEMS, INC.—See Optical Cable Corporation; *U.S. Public*, pg. 1609
APPLIED OPTOELECTRONICS, INC.; *U.S. Public*, pg. 173
APPLIED PATHWAYS LLC—See Elevance Health, Inc.; *U.S. Public*, pg. 728
APPLIED PETROLEUM TECHNOLOGY A.S.—See Weatherford International plc; *U.S. Public*, pg. 2339
APPLIED PETROLEUM TECHNOLOGY (UK) LIMITED—See Weatherford International plc; *U.S. Public*, pg. 2339
APPLIED PHYSICAL SCIENCES CORP.—See General Dynamics Corporation; *U.S. Public*, pg. 913
APPLIED PHYSICS TECHNOLOGIES, INC.—See Hitachi, Ltd.; *Int'l*, pg. 3412
APPLIED POWER PRODUCTS INC.; *U.S. Private*, pg. 299
APPLIED PREDICTIVE TECHNOLOGIES, INC.—See Mastercard Incorporated; *U.S. Public*, pg. 1394
APPLIED PROCESS, INC.—See High Street Capital Management, Inc.; *U.S. Private*, pg. 1937
APPLIED PRODUCTS, INC.—See Goldner Hawn Johnson & Morrison Inc.; *U.S. Private*, pg. 1735
APPLIED RAPID TECHNOLOGIES CORP.—See Obsidian Solutions Group LLC; *U.S. Private*, pg. 2988
APPLIED RESEARCH ASSOCIATES EMERALD COAST DIVISION—See Applied Research Associates, Inc.; *U.S. Private*, pg. 299
APPLIED RESEARCH ASSOCIATES, INC.; *U.S. Private*, pg. 299
APPLIED RESEARCH ASSOCIATES MID-ATLANTIC DIVISION—See Applied Research Associates, Inc.; *U.S. Private*, pg. 299
APPLIED RESEARCH ASSOCIATES MIDWEST DIVISION—See Applied Research Associates, Inc.; *U.S. Private*, pg. 299
APPLIED RESEARCH ASSOCIATES NORTH FLORIDA DIVISION—See Applied Research Associates, Inc.; *U.S. Private*, pg. 299
APPLIED RESEARCH ASSOCIATES ROCKY MOUNTAIN DIVISION—See Applied Research Associates, Inc.; *U.S. Private*, pg. 299

APPLIED RESEARCH ASSOCIATES SHOCK PHYSICS DIVISION—See Applied Research Associates, Inc.; *U.S. Private*, pg. 299
APPLIED RESEARCH ASSOCIATES SOUTHEAST DIVISION—See Applied Research Associates, Inc.; *U.S. Private*, pg. 299
APPLIED RESEARCH ASSOCIATES SOUTHWEST DIVISION—See Applied Research Associates, Inc.; *U.S. Private*, pg. 299
APPLIED RIGAKU TECHNOLOGIES, INC.—See Rigaku Corporation; *Int'l*, pg. 6339
APPLIED SATELLITE TECHNOLOGY AUSTRALIA PTY LTD—See HAL Trust N.V.; *Int'l*, pg. 3226
APPLIED SATELLITE TECHNOLOGY LTD—See HAL Trust N.V.; *Int'l*, pg. 3226
APPLIED SATELLITE TECHNOLOGY SYSTEMS LTD—See HAL Trust N.V.; *Int'l*, pg. 3226
APPLIED SATELLITE TECHNOLOGY SYSTEMS US LLC—See HAL Trust N.V.; *Int'l*, pg. 3226
APPLIED SCIENCE ASSOCIATES, INC.—See RPS Group plc; *Int'l*, pg. 6415
APPLIED SCIENCES DIVISION—See Caddock Electronics, Inc.; *U.S. Private*, pg. 712
APPLIED SCIENTIFIC INSTRUMENTATION, INC.; *U.S. Private*, pg. 299
APPLIED SIGNAL TECHNOLOGY, INC.—See RTX Corporation; *U.S. Public*, pg. 1825
APPLIED SIGNAL TECHNOLOGY—See RTX Corporation; *U.S. Public*, pg. 1825
APPLIED SIGNAL TECHNOLOGY—See RTX Corporation; *U.S. Public*, pg. 1825
APPLIED SOFTWARE TECHNOLOGY, INC.; *U.S. Private*, pg. 299
APPLIED STEMCELL, INC.—See QHP Capital, L.P.; *U.S. Private*, pg. 3313
APPLIED SUPER CONETICS, INC.—See Japan Industrial Partners, Inc.; *Int'l*, pg. 3892
APPLIED SYSTEMS INC.—See Hellman & Friedman LLC; *U.S. Private*, pg. 1907
APPLIED SYSTEMS INC.—See JMI Services, Inc.; *U.S. Private*, pg. 2215
APPLIED TECHNICAL SERVICES CORPORATION—See Goldberg Lindsay & Co., LLC; *U.S. Private*, pg. 1729
APPLIED TECHNICAL SERVICES, INC.—See Odyssey Investment Partners, LLC; *U.S. Private*, pg. 2994
APPLIED TECHNOLOGIES ASSOCIATES; *U.S. Private*, pg. 299
APPLIED TECHNOLOGIES INC.—See French Gerleman Electric Co., Inc.; *U.S. Private*, pg. 1608
APPLIED TECHNOLOGIES INTERNET SAS; *Int'l*, pg. 521
APPLIED TECHNOLOGY CO., LTD.; *Int'l*, pg. 521
APPLIED TECHNOLOGY SERVICES, INC.; *U.S. Private*, pg. 299
APPLIED TECH SOLUTIONS INC—See PLATTE RIVER NETWORKS INC.; *U.S. Private*, pg. 3211
APPLIED THERAPEUTICS, INC.; *U.S. Public*, pg. 173
APPLIED THERMAL SYSTEMS—See Gryphon Investors, LLC; *U.S. Private*, pg. 1799
APPLIED TOYS LIMITED—See Applied Development Holdings Limited; *Int'l*, pg. 521
APPLIED TRAINING SYSTEMS INC—See Ontario Teachers' Pension Plan; *Int'l*, pg. 5586
APPLIED TRUST ENGINEERING, INC.—See GI Manager L.P.; *U.S. Private*, pg. 1693
APPLIED UNDERWRITERS CAPTIVE RISK ASSURANCE COMPANY, INC.—See Quadrant Management, Inc.; *U.S. Private*, pg. 3316
APPLIED UNDERWRITERS, INC.—See Quadrant Management, Inc.; *U.S. Private*, pg. 3316
APPLIED UTILITY SYSTEMS, INC.—See Johnson Matthey PLC; *Int'l*, pg. 3991
APPLIED UV, INC.; *U.S. Public*, pg. 173
APPLIED VALUE LLC; *U.S. Private*, pg. 300
APPLIED VENTURES, LLC—See Applied Materials, Inc.; *U.S. Public*, pg. 172
APPLIED VISIONS, INC.; *U.S. Private*, pg. 300
APPLIED VISUAL SCIENCES, INC.; *U.S. Public*, pg. 173
APPLIED VOICE & SPEECH TECHNOLOGIES, INC.—See StoneCalibre, LLC; *U.S. Private*, pg. 3827
APPLIED WASTEWATER SYSTEMS—See Pentair plc; *Int'l*, pg. 5790
APPLIED WEATHER TECHNOLOGY, INC.—See Alfa Laval AB; *Int'l*, pg. 312
APPLIFE DIGITAL SOLUTIONS, INC.; *U.S. Public*, pg. 173
APPLIKE GROUP GMBH—See Bertelsmann SE & Co. KGaA; *Int'l*, pg. 990
APPLIKON BIOTECHNOLOGY B.V.—See Getinge AB; *Int'l*, pg. 2947
APPLING HEALTHCARE SYSTEM; *U.S. Private*, pg. 300
APPLING INSURANCE AGENCY—See Inszone Insurance Services, LLC; *U.S. Private*, pg. 2096
APPLIQATE, INC.; *U.S. Public*, pg. 173
APPLITEK NV/SA; *Int'l*, pg. 521
APPLOVIN CORP.; *U.S. Public*, pg. 173
APPLUS ARGENTINA, S.A.—See I Squared Capital Advisors (US) LLC; *U.S. Private*, pg. 2021
APPLUS ARGENTINA, S.A.—See TDR Capital LLP; *Int'l*, pg. 7491

APPLUS CAR TESTING SERVICE, LTD.—See I Squared Capital Advisors (US) LLC; *U.S. Private*, pg. 2021
APPLUS CAR TESTING SERVICE, LTD.—See TDR Capital LLP; *Int'l*, pg. 7491
APPLUS CHILE, S.A.—See I Squared Capital Advisors (US) LLC; *U.S. Private*, pg. 2021
APPLUS CHILE, S.A.—See TDR Capital LLP; *Int'l*, pg. 7491
APPLUS COSTA RICA, S.A.—See I Squared Capital Advisors (US) LLC; *U.S. Private*, pg. 2021
APPLUS COSTA RICA, S.A.—See TDR Capital LLP; *Int'l*, pg. 7491
APPLUS CZECH REPUBLIC, S.R.O.—See I Squared Capital Advisors (US) LLC; *U.S. Private*, pg. 2021
APPLUS CZECH REPUBLIC, S.R.O.—See TDR Capital LLP; *Int'l*, pg. 7491
APPLUS DANMARK, A/S—See I Squared Capital Advisors (US) LLC; *U.S. Private*, pg. 2021
APPLUS DANMARK, A/S—See TDR Capital LLP; *Int'l*, pg. 7491
APPLUS FOMENTO DE CONTROL, S.A.—See I Squared Capital Advisors (US) LLC; *U.S. Private*, pg. 2021
APPLUS FOMENTO DE CONTROL, S.A.—See TDR Capital LLP; *Int'l*, pg. 7491
APPLUS II MEIO AMBIENTE PORTUGAL, LDA.—See I Squared Capital Advisors (US) LLC; *U.S. Private*, pg. 2021
APPLUS II MEIO AMBIENTE PORTUGAL, LDA.—See TDR Capital LLP; *Int'l*, pg. 7491
APPLUS INDIA PRIVATE LIMITED—See I Squared Capital Advisors (US) LLC; *U.S. Private*, pg. 2021
APPLUS INDIA PRIVATE LIMITED—See TDR Capital LLP; *Int'l*, pg. 7491
APPLUS INGENIERIA Y CONSULTORIA, SAS—See I Squared Capital Advisors (US) LLC; *U.S. Private*, pg. 2021
APPLUS INGENIERIA Y CONSULTORIA, SAS—See TDR Capital LLP; *Int'l*, pg. 7491
APPLUS ITALY, S.R.L.—See I Squared Capital Advisors (US) LLC; *U.S. Private*, pg. 2021
APPLUS ITALY, S.R.L.—See TDR Capital LLP; *Int'l*, pg. 7491
APPLUS ITEUVE GALICIA, S.L.U.—See I Squared Capital Advisors (US) LLC; *U.S. Private*, pg. 2021
APPLUS ITEUVE GALICIA, S.L.U.—See TDR Capital LLP; *Int'l*, pg. 7491
APPLUS JAPAN KK.—See I Squared Capital Advisors (US) LLC; *U.S. Private*, pg. 2022
APPLUS JAPAN KK.—See TDR Capital LLP; *Int'l*, pg. 7491
APPLUS K2 AMERICA, LLC—See I Squared Capital Advisors (US) LLC; *U.S. Private*, pg. 2022
APPLUS K2 AMERICA, LLC—See TDR Capital LLP; *Int'l*, pg. 7491
APPLUS KAZAKHSTAN LLC—See I Squared Capital Advisors (US) LLC; *U.S. Private*, pg. 2022
APPLUS KAZAKHSTAN LLC—See TDR Capital LLP; *Int'l*, pg. 7491
APPLUS LABORATORIES, AS—See I Squared Capital Advisors (US) LLC; *U.S. Private*, pg. 2022
APPLUS LABORATORIES, AS—See TDR Capital LLP; *Int'l*, pg. 7491
APPLUS MEXICO, S.A. DE C.V.—See I Squared Capital Advisors (US) LLC; *U.S. Private*, pg. 2022
APPLUS MEXICO, S.A. DE C.V.—See TDR Capital LLP; *Int'l*, pg. 7491
APPLUS MONGOLIA, LLC—See I Squared Capital Advisors (US) LLC; *U.S. Private*, pg. 2022
APPLUS MONGOLIA, LLC—See TDR Capital LLP; *Int'l*, pg. 7491
APPLUS NORCONTROL GUATEMALA, S.A.—See I Squared Capital Advisors (US) LLC; *U.S. Private*, pg. 2022
APPLUS NORCONTROL GUATEMALA, S.A.—See TDR Capital LLP; *Int'l*, pg. 7491
APPLUS NORCONTROL PERU, S.A.C.—See I Squared Capital Advisors (US) LLC; *U.S. Private*, pg. 2022
APPLUS NORCONTROL PERU, S.A.C.—See TDR Capital LLP; *Int'l*, pg. 7491
APPLUS NORCONTROL REPUBLICA DOMINICANA, S.R.L.—See I Squared Capital Advisors (US) LLC; *U.S. Private*, pg. 2022
APPLUS NORCONTROL REPUBLICA DOMINICANA, S.R.L.—See TDR Capital LLP; *Int'l*, pg. 7491
APPLUS NORCONTROL, S.L.—See I Squared Capital Advisors (US) LLC; *U.S. Private*, pg. 2022
APPLUS NORCONTROL, S.L.—See TDR Capital LLP; *Int'l*, pg. 7491
APPLUS PANAMA, S.A.—See I Squared Capital Advisors (US) LLC; *U.S. Private*, pg. 2022
APPLUS PANAMA, S.A.—See TDR Capital LLP; *Int'l*, pg. 7491
APPLUS PNG LIMITED—See I Squared Capital Advisors (US) LLC; *U.S. Private*, pg. 2022
APPLUS PNG LIMITED—See TDR Capital LLP; *Int'l*, pg. 7491
APPLUS PORTUGAL, LDA.—See I Squared Capital Advisors (US) LLC; *U.S. Private*, pg. 2022

APPLUS PORTUGAL, LDA.—See TDR Capital LLP; *Int'l*, pg. 7491
APPLUS PTY, LTD.—See I Squared Capital Advisors (US) LLC; *U.S. Private*, pg. 2022
APPLUS PTY, LTD.—See TDR Capital LLP; *Int'l*, pg. 7491
APPLUS QUALITEC SERVICOS DE ENGENHARIA, LTDA.—See I Squared Capital Advisors (US) LLC; *U.S. Private*, pg. 2022
APPLUS QUALITEC SERVICOS DE ENGENHARIA, LTDA.—See TDR Capital LLP; *Int'l*, pg. 7491
APPLUS RTD DEUTSCHLAND INSPEKTIONSGESELL-SCHAFT, GMBH—See I Squared Capital Advisors (US) LLC; *U.S. Private*, pg. 2022
APPLUS RTD DEUTSCHLAND INSPEKTIONSGESELL-SCHAFT, GMBH—See TDR Capital LLP; *Int'l*, pg. 7491
APPLUS RTD PTE, LTD.—See I Squared Capital Advisors (US) LLC; *U.S. Private*, pg. 2022
APPLUS RTD PTE, LTD.—See TDR Capital LLP; *Int'l*, pg. 7491
APPLUS RTD—See I Squared Capital Advisors (US) LLC; *U.S. Private*, pg. 2022
APPLUS RTD—See TDR Capital LLP; *Int'l*, pg. 7491
APPLUS RTD USA, INC.—See I Squared Capital Advisors (US) LLC; *U.S. Private*, pg. 2022
APPLUS RTD USA, INC.—See TDR Capital LLP; *Int'l*, pg. 7491
APPLUS SERVICES, S.A.—See I Squared Capital Advisors (US) LLC; *U.S. Private*, pg. 2021
APPLUS SERVICES, S.A.—See TDR Capital LLP; *Int'l*, pg. 7490
APPLUS (SHANGAI) QUALITY INSPECTION CO, LTD.—See I Squared Capital Advisors (US) LLC; *U.S. Private*, pg. 2021
APPLUS (SHANGAI) QUALITY INSPECTION CO, LTD.—See TDR Capital LLP; *Int'l*, pg. 7491
APPLUS SINGAPORE PTE LTD—See I Squared Capital Advisors (US) LLC; *U.S. Private*, pg. 2022
APPLUS SINGAPORE PTE LTD—See TDR Capital LLP; *Int'l*, pg. 7491
APPLUS STEEL TEST (PTY.) LTD.—See I Squared Capital Advisors (US) LLC; *U.S. Private*, pg. 2022
APPLUS STEEL TEST (PTY.) LTD.—See TDR Capital LLP; *Int'l*, pg. 7491
APPLUS+ TECHNOLOGIES, INC.—See Searchlight Capital Partners, L.P.; *U.S. Private*, pg. 3590
APPLUS TURKEY GOZETIM HIZMETLERI LIMITED SIRKETI—See I Squared Capital Advisors (US) LLC; *U.S. Private*, pg. 2022
APPLUS TURKEY GOZETIM HIZMETLERI LIMITED SIRKETI—See TDR Capital LLP; *Int'l*, pg. 7491
APPLUS UK LTD—See I Squared Capital Advisors (US) LLC; *U.S. Private*, pg. 2022
APPLUS UK LTD—See TDR Capital LLP; *Int'l*, pg. 7491
APPLUS URUGUAY, S.A.—See I Squared Capital Advisors (US) LLC; *U.S. Private*, pg. 2022
APPLUS URUGUAY, S.A.—See TDR Capital LLP; *Int'l*, pg. 7491
APPLUS VELOSI SA (PTY) LTD.—See I Squared Capital Advisors (US) LLC; *U.S. Private*, pg. 2022
APPLUS VELOSI SA (PTY) LTD.—See TDR Capital LLP; *Int'l*, pg. 7491
APPLUS+ VELOSI—See I Squared Capital Advisors (US) LLC; *U.S. Private*, pg. 2023
APPLUS+ VELOSI—See TDR Capital LLP; *Int'l*, pg. 7493
APPLY ADVANCED MOBILE TECHNOLOGIES LTD.; *Int'l*, pg. 521
APPLY-A-LINE, LLC—See The Sterling Group, L.P.; *U.S. Private*, pg. 4121
APPLY ASA; *Int'l*, pg. 521
APPLY CAPNOR POLAND SP. Z O.O.—See Apply ASA; *Int'l*, pg. 521
APPLY CAPNOR US, INC.—See Apply ASA; *Int'l*, pg. 521
APPLY EMTUNGA AB—See Apply ASA; *Int'l*, pg. 521
APPLY LEIRVIK AS—See Apply ASA; *Int'l*, pg. 521
APPLY LEIRVIK INTERNATIONAL PTE LTD—See Apply ASA; *Int'l*, pg. 522
APPLY LQ PARTNER AS—See Apply ASA; *Int'l*, pg. 521
APPLY POLAND SP. Z O.O.—See Apply ASA; *Int'l*, pg. 522
APPLY RIG & MODULES AS—See Apply ASA; *Int'l*, pg. 522
APPLY SORCO AS—See Apply ASA; *Int'l*, pg. 522
APPMIRAL B.V.B.A.—See CM.com N.V.; *Int'l*, pg. 1666
APPOGEE, LLC; *U.S. Private*, pg. 300
APPOINTECH, INC.—See ADTRAN Holdings, Inc.; *U.S. Public*, pg. 44
THE APPOINTMENT GROUP LIMITED—See ECI Partners LLP; *Int'l*, pg. 2289
THE APPOINTMENT GROUP (UK) LIMITED—See ECI Partners LLP; *Int'l*, pg. 2289
APPOLLO ISPAT COMPLEX LIMITED; *Int'l*, pg. 522
APPOMATTOX IMAGING, LLC—See HCA Healthcare, Inc.; *U.S. Public*, pg. 990
APPOSITE CAPITAL LLP; *Int'l*, pg. 522
APPOTRONICS CORP., LTD.; *Int'l*, pg. 522
APP PAPER CO., LTD.—See Pabrik Kertas Tjiwi Kimia Tbk; *Int'l*, pg. 5684
APP PHARMACEUTICALS, INC.—See Fresenius SE & Co. KGaA; *Int'l*, pg. 2777

APP (PHILIPPINES), INC.—See Pabrik Kertas Tjiwi Kimia Tbk; *Int'l*, pg. 5684
APPRAISAL PROPERTY MANAGEMENT SDN BHD—See Jones Lang LaSalle Incorporated; *U.S. Public*, pg. 1201
APPRECIA TECHNOLOGY, INC.—See Tazmo Co., Ltd.; *Int'l*, pg. 7479
APPRECIATE GROUP PLC—See PayPoint plc; *Int'l*, pg. 5763
APPRECIATE HOLDINGS, INC.; *U.S. Public*, pg. 173
APPREDEEM, INC.—See Perk.com, Inc.; *Int'l*, pg. 5801
APPRENTICE & JOURNEYMEN TRAINING TRUST FUND OF THE SOUTHERN CALIFORNIA PLUMBING & PIPING INDUSTRY; *U.S. Private*, pg. 300
APPRIO INC.; *U.S. Private*, pg. 300
APPRISE MEDIA, LLC; *U.S. Private*, pg. 300
APPRISE SOFTWARE, INC.—See TA Associates, Inc.; *U.S. Private*, pg. 3914
APPRISS HOLDINGS, INC.; *U.S. Private*, pg. 300
APPRISS, INC.—See Appriss Holdings, Inc.; *U.S. Private*, pg. 300
APPRISS RETAIL—See Appriss Holdings, Inc.; *U.S. Private*, pg. 300
APPRIVER AG—See Open Text Corporation; *Int'l*, pg. 5598
APPRIVER CANADA ULC—See Open Text Corporation; *Int'l*, pg. 5598
APPRIVER, LLC—See Open Text Corporation; *Int'l*, pg. 5598
APPRIVER UK LTD.—See Open Text Corporation; *Int'l*, pg. 5598
APPROACH EXCELLENCE TRADING LTD.—See Apex International Co., Ltd.; *Int'l*, pg. 511
APPROACH OIL & GAS INC.—See Approach Resources Inc.; *U.S. Public*, pg. 300
APPROACH OPERATING, LLC—See Approach Resources Inc.; *U.S. Private*, pg. 300
APPROACH RESOURCES INC.; *U.S. Private*, pg. 300
APPROACH SIGNS LIMITED—See Fletcher Building Limited; *Int'l*, pg. 2699
APPROACH (UK) LIMITED—See General Motors Company; *U.S. Public*, pg. 927
APPRO DEVELOPMENT, INC.; *U.S. Private*, pg. 300
AP PROFESSIONALS OF WNY LLC; *U.S. Private*, pg. 290
APPROFRAIS S.A.—See Allianz SE; *Int'l*, pg. 351
APPRO INTERNATIONAL, INC.—See Hewlett Packard Enterprise Company; *U.S. Public*, pg. 1030
AP PROPERTIES LIMITED—See Hang Lung Group Limited; *Int'l*, pg. 3244
APPROVED MORTGAGE BROKERS LIMITED—See RTO Limited; *Int'l*, pg. 6420
APPROVISIONNEMENT ELECTRIQUE—See Sonepar S.A.; *Int'l*, pg. 7090
APPROXY INC.—See Numecent Holdings Ltd.; *U.S. Private*, pg. 2973
APPS ASSOCIATES GMBH—See Quad-C Management, Inc.; *U.S. Private*, pg. 3315
APPS ASSOCIATES LLC—See Quad-C Management, Inc.; *U.S. Private*, pg. 3315
APPS ASSOCIATES PVT. LTD.—See Quad-C Management, Inc.; *U.S. Private*, pg. 3315
APPS CARTAGE INC.—See Mullen Group Ltd.; *Int'l*, pg. 5079
APPSCATTER GROUP PLC; *Int'l*, pg. 522
APPSCIENCE, INC.—See Sabio Holdings Inc.; *Int'l*, pg. 6462
APPSENSE LTD.; *Int'l*, pg. 522
APPSFLYER INC.; *U.S. Private*, pg. 300
APPSILAN ASIA PTE. LTD.—See MIRAIT ONE Corporation; *Int'l*, pg. 4917
APPSOFT TECHNOLOGIES, INC.; *U.S. Public*, pg. 173
APP START-UP AB—See Instalco AB; *Int'l*, pg. 3721
APPS TRANSPORT GROUP INC.—See Mullen Group Ltd.; *Int'l*, pg. 5079
APPSWARM, INC.; *U.S. Public*, pg. 174
APP SYSTEMS SERVICES (INDIA) PVT LTD—See APP Systems Services Pte. Ltd.; *Int'l*, pg. 519
APP SYSTEMS SERVICES PTE. LTD.; *Int'l*, pg. 519
APP SYSTEMS SERVICES PTE. LTD.—See APP Systems Services Pte. Ltd.; *Int'l*, pg. 519
APP SYSTEMS SERVICES (THAILAND) CO. LTD.—See APP Systems Services Pte. Ltd.; *Int'l*, pg. 519
APPTECH INC.; *U.S. Private*, pg. 300
APPTECH PAYMENTS CORP.; *U.S. Public*, pg. 174
APP-TEK INTERNATIONAL PTY LTD—See Thermo Fisher Scientific Inc.; *U.S. Public*, pg. 2145
APPTENTIVE, INC.—See KKR & Co. Inc.; *U.S. Public*, pg. 1239
APPTIO EUROPE LIMITED—See International Business Machines Corporation; *U.S. Public*, pg. 1145
APPTIO FRANCE SAS—See International Business Machines Corporation; *U.S. Public*, pg. 1145
APPTIO, INC.—See International Business Machines Corporation; *U.S. Public*, pg. 1145
APPTIO ITALY S.R.L.—See International Business Machines Corporation; *U.S. Public*, pg. 1145
APPTIO PTY LTD.—See International Business Machines Corporation; *U.S. Public*, pg. 1145

APPTIS, INC.—See New Mountain Capital, LLC; *U.S. Private*, pg. 2900
APPTNESS MEDIA GROUP, LLC—See Zeta Global Holdings Corp.; *U.S. Public*, pg. 2403
APPULSE CORPORATION; *Int'l*, pg. 522
APPVION OPERATIONS, INC.—See Franklin Resources, Inc.; *U.S. Public*, pg. 880
APPWORX LLC; *U.S. Private*, pg. 300
APPYEA, INC.; *U.S. Public*, pg. 174
APQ GLOBAL LIMITED; *Int'l*, pg. 522
APRAAVA ENERGY PRIVATE LIMITED—See CLP Holdings Limited; *Int'l*, pg. 1663
AP RACING LTD.—See Brembo S.p.A.; *Int'l*, pg. 1144
APRANGA UAB—See MG Baltic UAB; *Int'l*, pg. 4871
APRA PORTER NOVELLI—See Omnicom Group Inc.; *U.S. Public*, pg. 1590
APR CONSULTING INC.; *U.S. Public*, pg. 300
APREA THERAPEUTICS, INC.; *U.S. Public*, pg. 174
APRENDERE SKOLOR AB; *Int'l*, pg. 522
APR ENERGY, LLC—See ACON Investments, LLC; *U.S. Private*, pg. 62
APR ENERGY, LLC—See Fairfax Financial Holdings Limited; *Int'l*, pg. 2605
APR ENERGY PLC—See ACON Investments, LLC; *U.S. Private*, pg. 62
APR ENERGY PLC—See Fairfax Financial Holdings Limited; *Int'l*, pg. 2605
AP RENEWABLES LTD.—See Ardova Plc.; *Int'l*, pg. 557
AP RENTALS HOLDINGS LTD.; *Int'l*, pg. 499
APRESA - PLP SPAIN, S. A.—See Preformed Line Products Company; *U.S. Public*, pg. 1714
A P RESINAS, S.A. DE C.V.—See PPG Industries, Inc.; *U.S. Public*, pg. 1707
APRESTO CO., LTD.—See Kyoritsu Electric Corporation; *Int'l*, pg. 4364
AP RETI GAS NORD EST S.R.L.—See Ascopiave S.p.A.; *Int'l*, pg. 603
AP RETI GAS ROVIGO S.R.L.—See Ascopiave S.p.A.; *Int'l*, pg. 603
AP RETI GAS S.P.A.—See Ascopiave S.p.A.; *Int'l*, pg. 603
APRIA HEALTHCARE GROUP INC.—See Blackstone Inc.; *U.S. Public*, pg. 348
APRICA CHILDCARE INSTITUTE-APRICA IKUJI KENKY-USH KABUSHIKI KAISHA—See Newell Brands Inc.; *U.S. Public*, pg. 1513
APRICA CHILDREN'S PRODUCTS KK—See Newell Brands Inc.; *U.S. Public*, pg. 1513
APRICA HEALTHCARE PRIVATE LIMITED—See Eris Life-sciences Limited; *Int'l*, pg. 2493
APRICA KOREA CO., LTD.—See Newell Brands Inc.; *U.S. Public*, pg. 1513
APRICA (SHANGHAI) TRADING CO., LTD.—See Newell Brands Inc.; *U.S. Public*, pg. 1513
APRICA SPA—See A2A S.p.A.; *Int'l*, pg. 29
APRICOT OFFICE SUPPLIES & FURNITURE, INC.; *U.S. Private*, pg. 301
APRIL CORNELL HOLDINGS; *U.S. Private*, pg. 301
APRIL CORPORATE BROKING SARL—See CVC Capital Partners SICAV-FIS S.A.; *Int'l*, pg. 1882
APRIL COVER SARL—See CVC Capital Partners SICAV-FIS S.A.; *Int'l*, pg. 1882
APRIL DEUTSCHLAND AG—See CVC Capital Partners SICAV-FIS S.A.; *Int'l*, pg. 1882
APRIL ENTREPRISE LYON—See CVC Capital Partners SICAV-FIS S.A.; *Int'l*, pg. 1882
APRIL GERMANY AG—See CVC Capital Partners SICAV-FIS S.A.; *Int'l*, pg. 1882
APRIL GROUP SA—See CVC Capital Partners SICAV-FIS S.A.; *Int'l*, pg. 1882
APRIL IARD SARL—See CVC Capital Partners SICAV-FIS S.A.; *Int'l*, pg. 1882
APRILIA SPA—See Immsi S.p.a.; *Int'l*, pg. 3628
APRIL IBERIA SARL—See CVC Capital Partners SICAV-FIS S.A.; *Int'l*, pg. 1882
APRIL MARINE—See CVC Capital Partners SICAV-FIS S.A.; *Int'l*, pg. 1882
APRIL MARKETING SOLUTIONS SARL—See CVC Capital Partners SICAV-FIS S.A.; *Int'l*, pg. 1882
APRIL MON ASSURANCE LYON—See CVC Capital Partners SICAV-FIS S.A.; *Int'l*, pg. 1882
APRIL PATRIMOINE SARL—See CVC Capital Partners SICAV-FIS S.A.; *Int'l*, pg. 1882
APRIL SIX GMBH—See The Mission Group Public Limited Company; *Int'l*, pg. 7667
APRIL SIX INC.—See The Mission Group Public Limited Company; *Int'l*, pg. 7667
APRIL-SIX LTD—See The Mission Group Public Limited Company; *Int'l*, pg. 7667
APRIL SIX (MOBILITY) LTD.—See The Mission Group Public Limited Company; *Int'l*, pg. 7667
APRIL SIX PROOF LTD.—See The Mission Group Public Limited Company; *Int'l*, pg. 7667
APRIL SIX PTE. LTD.—See The Mission Group Public Limited Company; *Int'l*, pg. 7667
APRIMA MEDICAL SOFTWARE, INC.—See CompuGroup Medical SE & Co. KGaA; *Int'l*, pg. 1757
APRINNOVA, LLC—See Amyris, Inc.; *U.S. Public*, pg. 134
APRIO BENEFIT ADVISORS, LLC—See Aprio, LLP; *U.S. Private*, pg. 301

COMPANY NAME INDEX

APRIO, LLP; *U.S. Private*, pg. 301
APRIORI CAPITAL PARTNERS L.P.; *U.S. Private*, pg. 301
APRIORI TECHNOLOGIES, INC.; *U.S. Private*, pg. 302
APRIO WEALTH MANAGEMENT, LLC—See Aprio, LLP; *U.S. Private*, pg. 301
APRISMA MANAGEMENT TECHNOLOGIES—See The Gores Group, LLC; *U.S. Private*, pg. 4034
APRIVIA SA—See PBG S.A.; *Int'l*, pg. 5765
A-PRO CO., LTD.; *Int'l*, pg. 20
APROGEN BIOLOGICS, INC.; *Int'l*, pg. 522
APROGEN HEALTHCARE & GAMES INC.; *Int'l*, pg. 522
APROGEN KIC INC.; *Int'l*, pg. 522
APROLIS, SAS—See Monnoyeur SAS; *Int'l*, pg. 5034
A PROMOTORA, SOCIEDADE DE CAPITAL DE RISCO, S.A.R.L.—See Caixa Geral de Depositos S.A.; *Int'l*, pg. 1260
APROS CO., LTD.—See Astena Holdings Co., Ltd.; *Int'l*, pg. 653
APR SUPPLY CO.; *U.S. Private*, pg. 300
APRYSE SOFTWARE INC.—See Thoma Bravo, L.P.; *U.S. Private*, pg. 4146
APS ALKON A.S.—See VINCI S.A.; *Int'l*, pg. 8230
APS ALTPAPIER SERVICE SCHWEIZ AG—See CPH Chemie + Papier Holding AG; *Int'l*, pg. 1824
APSALYS SARL—See Micropole SA; *Int'l*, pg. 4880
APSA—See L'Air Liquide S.A.; *Int'l*, pg. 4375
APS - ASSISTENCIA PERSONALIZADA A SAUDE LTDA.—See UnitedHealth Group Incorporated; *U.S. Public*, pg. 2238
APS BUILDING SERVICES, INC.; *U.S. Private*, pg. 302
APS B.V.—See LKQ Corporation; *U.S. Public*, pg. 1333
APS CHINA CORPORATION—See APS Holdings Corporation; *Int'l*, pg. 523
APSCO APPLIANCE & TV CENTERS, INC.; *U.S. Private*, pg. 302
APS CO., LTD.—See Eastern Polymer Group Public Company Limited; *Int'l*, pg. 2273
APSE CAPITAL LTD.; *Int'l*, pg. 523
APS ELECTRONIC AG—See Kiepe Electric GmbH; *Int'l*, pg. 4158
APS ENERGIA CAUCASUS LTD.—See APS Energia SA; *Int'l*, pg. 522
APS ENERGIA CZECH S.R.O.—See APS Energia SA; *Int'l*, pg. 522
APS ENERGIA SA; *Int'l*, pg. 522
APS ENERGIA TURK ELEKTRIK SANAYI VE TICARET LTD.—See APS Energia SA; *Int'l*, pg. 522
APS ENTERPRISES HOLDING COMPANY, INC.—See Cencora, Inc.; *U.S. Public*, pg. 466
A.P. SERVICES, LLC—See Curtiss-Wright Corporation; *U.S. Public*, pg. 612
APS FRANCE S.A.R.L.—See Brother Industries, Ltd.; *Int'l*, pg. 1197
APS HEALTHCARE, INC.—See Centene Corporation; *U.S. Public*, pg. 471
APS HOLDINGS CORPORATION; *Int'l*, pg. 523
APS IRELAND, INC.—See Hancom, Inc.; *Int'l*, pg. 3242
APS KOREA, INC.—See Hancom, Inc.; *Int'l*, pg. 3242
APS MATERIALS, INC.—See Hancom, Inc.; *Int'l*, pg. 3242
APSN LIFESCIENCE SDN. BHD.—See Rhone Ma Holdings Berhad; *Int'l*, pg. 6327
APSONIC SDN. BHD.—See Engtex Group Berhad; *Int'l*, pg. 2436
APS POWER SOLUTIONS LLC—See Emek Elektrik Endustrisi A.S.; *Int'l*, pg. 2377
APS RESOURCES—See ASSA ABLOY AB; *Int'l*, pg. 633
APS SINERGIA S.P.A.—See ACEGAS-APS SpA; *Int'l*, pg. 95
APSS S.R.L.—See L3Harris Technologies, Inc.; *U.S. Public*, pg. 1280
APS TECHNOLOGY GROUP, INC.—See ABB Ltd.; *Int'l*, pg. 52
APS TECHNOLOGY, INC.; *U.S. Private*, pg. 302
AP SUCCESS LIMITED—See Hang Lung Group Limited; *Int'l*, pg. 3244
APS VERWALTUNGS-GMBH—See Sealed Air Corporation; *U.S. Public*, pg. 1852
APS VIETANM CO. LTD.—See APS Holdings Corporation; *Int'l*, pg. 523
APSYS RISK ENGINEERING UK LIMITED—See Airbus SE; *Int'l*, pg. 246
APSYS—See Airbus SE; *Int'l*, pg. 246
APSYS UK—See Airbus SE; *Int'l*, pg. 246
APTABIO THERAPEUTICS INC.; *Int'l*, pg. 523
APT ADVANCED POLYMER TUBING GMBH—See Masterflex SE; *Int'l*, pg. 4725
APTAMER GROUP PLC; *Int'l*, pg. 523
APTAMER SCIENCES INC.; *Int'l*, pg. 523
APTARA—See iEnergizer Limited; *Int'l*, pg. 3597
APTAR BALLINASLOE LIMITED—See AptarGroup, Inc.; *U.S. Public*, pg. 174
APTAR CALI SAS—See AptarGroup, Inc.; *U.S. Public*, pg. 174
APTAR CKYNE S.R.O.—See AptarGroup, Inc.; *U.S. Public*, pg. 174
APTAR CSP TECHNOLOGIES, INC.—See AptarGroup, Inc.; *U.S. Public*, pg. 174
APTAR FRANCE S.A.S.—See AptarGroup, Inc.; *U.S. Public*, pg. 174

APTAR FREYUNG GMBH—See AptarGroup, Inc.; *U.S. Public*, pg. 174
APTARGROUP, INC.- CONGERS—See AptarGroup, Inc.; *U.S. Public*, pg. 175
APTARGROUP, INC.; *U.S. Public*, pg. 174
APTARIS LLC; *U.S. Private*, pg. 302
APTAR ITALIA S.P.A.—See AptarGroup, Inc.; *U.S. Public*, pg. 174
APTAR LEEDS—See AptarGroup, Inc.; *U.S. Public*, pg. 175
APTAR MEZZOVICO S.A.—See AptarGroup, Inc.; *U.S. Public*, pg. 174
APTAR MEZZOVICO S.A.—See AptarGroup, Inc.; *U.S. Public*, pg. 175
APTAR RADOLFZELL GMBH—See AptarGroup, Inc.; *U.S. Public*, pg. 174
APTAR (THAILAND) LTD.—See AptarGroup, Inc.; *U.S. Public*, pg. 174
APTAR TORELLO, S.A.—See AptarGroup, Inc.; *U.S. Public*, pg. 174
APTAR VILLINGEN GMBH—See AptarGroup, Inc.; *U.S. Public*, pg. 174
APT CONTROLS LIMITED—See SWARCO AG; *Int'l*, pg. 7360
APTEAN - GOMEMBERS AMS—See TA Associates, Inc.; *U.S. Private*, pg. 3914
APTEAN, INC.—See TA Associates, Inc.; *U.S. Private*, pg. 3914
APTEAN - MADE2MANAGE ERP—See TA Associates, Inc.; *U.S. Private*, pg. 3914
APTEAN - TRADEBEAM SCM—See TA Associates, Inc.; *U.S. Private*, pg. 3914
APTECH GROUP, INC.; *U.S. Private*, pg. 302
APTECH LIMITED; *Int'l*, pg. 523
APTEC HOLDING EGYPT LLC—See Hainan Traffic Administration Holding Co., Ltd.; *Int'l*, pg. 3213
APTEC HOLDINGS LIMITED—See Hainan Traffic Administration Holding Co., Ltd.; *Int'l*, pg. 3213
AP-TELA OY—See Lone Star Funds; *U.S. Private*, pg. 2487
APTERYX IMAGING INC.—See Level Equity Management, LLC; *U.S. Private*, pg. 2434
APTEVO THERAPEUTICS INC.; *U.S. Public*, pg. 175
APT FACILITY MANAGEMENT PTY. LTD.—See APA Group; *Int'l*, pg. 500
APT GOLDFIELDS PTY. LTD.—See APA Group; *Int'l*, pg. 500
AP (THAILAND) PUBLIC COMPANY LIMITED; *Int'l*, pg. 499
APTICOM S.R.L.—See Hexatronic Group AB; *Int'l*, pg. 3370
APTIFY—See Insight Venture Management, LLC; *U.S. Private*, pg. 2088
APTILO NETWORKS AB—See Norvestor Equity AS; *Int'l*, pg. 5447
APTILO NETWORKS, INC.—See Norvestor Equity AS; *Int'l*, pg. 5447
APTIMA, INC.; *U.S. Private*, pg. 302
APTIM GOVERNMENT SOLUTIONS, LLC—See McDermott International, Inc.; *U.S. Public*, pg. 1405
APTINA INDIA PRIVATE LIMITED—See ON Semiconductor Corporation; *U.S. Public*, pg. 1600
APTINA (UK) LIMITED—See ON Semiconductor Corporation; *U.S. Public*, pg. 1600
APT, INC.; *U.S. Private*, pg. 302
APTINYX, INC.; *U.S. Public*, pg. 175
APTITO, LLC—See Mullen Automotive, Inc.; *U.S. Public*, pg. 1486
APTITUDE SOFTWARE (CANADA) LIMITED—See Aptitude Software Group Plc; *Int'l*, pg. 523
APTITUDE SOFTWARE GROUP PLC; *Int'l*, pg. 523
APTIV INTERNATIONAL BV—See ICON plc; *Int'l*, pg. 3584
APTIV INTERNATIONAL LTD.—See ICON plc; *Int'l*, pg. 3584
APTIV INTERNATIONAL LTD.—See ICON plc; *Int'l*, pg. 3584
APTIV INTERNATIONAL SARL—See ICON plc; *Int'l*, pg. 3584
APTIV INTERNATIONAL SP. Z O.O.—See ICON plc; *Int'l*, pg. 3584
APTIV PLC; *Int'l*, pg. 524
APTIV SAFETY & MOBILITY SERVICES SINGAPORE PTE. LTD—See Aptiv PLC; *Int'l*, pg. 524
APTIV SOLUTIONS, INC. - MARYLAND—See ICON plc; *Int'l*, pg. 3584
APTIV SOLUTIONS, INC.—See ICON plc; *Int'l*, pg. 3584
APT MEDICAL, INC.; *Int'l*, pg. 523
APT MOTO VOX GROUP, INC.; *U.S. Public*, pg. 174
APT O&M SERVICES PTY LTD—See APA Group; *Int'l*, pg. 500
APTORUM GROUP LIMITED; *Int'l*, pg. 526
APTOSE BIOSCIENCES INC.; *Int'l*, pg. 526
APTO SOLUTIONS, INC.; *U.S. Private*, pg. 302
APT PACKAGING LTD.; *Int'l*, pg. 523
APT PARMELIA PTY. LTD.—See APA Group; *Int'l*, pg. 500
APT PHARMA LIMITED—See Jacobson Pharma Corporation Limited; *Int'l*, pg. 3865

APYX MEDICAL CORPORATION

APT PIPELINES (QLD) PTY LIMITED—See APA Group; *Int'l*, pg. 500
A-P-T RESEARCH, INC.; *U.S. Private*, pg. 22
APT RESOURCES & SERVICES SRL; *Int'l*, pg. 523
APT SATELLITE HOLDINGS LIMITED—See APT Satellite International Company Limited; *Int'l*, pg. 523
APT SATELLITE INTERNATIONAL COMPANY LIMITED; *Int'l*, pg. 523
APTS B.V.—See VDL Groep B.V.; *Int'l*, pg. 8140
APT SYSTEMS, INC.; *U.S. Public*, pg. 174
APTUIT, LLC—See Evotec SE; *Int'l*, pg. 2573
APTUIT (OXFORD) LIMITED—See Evotec SE; *Int'l*, pg. 2573
APTUIT (VERONA) SRL—See Evotec SE; *Int'l*, pg. 2573
APTUS COURT REPORTING, LLC; *U.S. Private*, pg. 302
APTUS FINANCE INDIA PRIVATE LIMITED—See Aptus Value Housing Finance India Limited; *Int'l*, pg. 526
APTUS HEALTH, INC.—See KKR & Co. Inc.; *U.S. Public*, pg. 1253
APTUS HEALTH INTERNATIONAL FRANCE—See Merck & Co., Inc.; *U.S. Public*, pg. 1415
APTUS VALUE HOUSING FINANCE INDIA LIMITED; *Int'l*, pg. 526
APUESTAS INTERNACIONALES, S.A. DE C.V.—See Grupo Televisa, S.A.B.; *Int'l*, pg. 3136
AP UNIVERSAL LIMITED—See Hang Lung Group Limited; *Int'l*, pg. 3244
APURES CO LTD.; *Int'l*, pg. 526
APURVA IND PVT. LTD.—See Sika AG; *Int'l*, pg. 6914
APV BENELUX NV—See Lone Star Funds; *U.S. Private*, pg. 2485
AP VERITAS—See Management Recruiters International, Inc.; *U.S. Private*, pg. 2560
APV LTD.—See Lone Star Funds; *U.S. Private*, pg. 2485
A.P. WAGNER INC.; *U.S. Private*, pg. 27
AP WIN LIMITED—See Hang Lung Group Limited; *Int'l*, pg. 3244
AP WINNER (CHANGZHOU) CHEMICAL TECHNOLOGY CO., LTD.—See Wurth Verwaltungsgesellschaft mbH; *Int'l*, pg. 8503
AP WINNER INDUSTRIA E COMERCIO DE PRODUTOS QUIMI-COS LTD. A.—See Wurth Verwaltungsgesellschaft mbH; *Int'l*, pg. 8503
APW INTERNATIONAL (USA), INC.—See Auto Parts Warehouse Inc.; *U.S. Private*, pg. 397
AP WIP INVESTMENTS HOLDINGS, LP—See EQT AB; *Int'l*, pg. 2479
AP WIP INVESTMENTS HOLDINGS, LP—See Public Sector Pension Investment Board; *Int'l*, pg. 6096
AP WIRELESS AUSTRALIA PTY LTD—See EQT AB; *Int'l*, pg. 2479
AP WIRELESS AUSTRALIA PTY LTD—See Public Sector Pension Investment Board; *Int'l*, pg. 6096
AP WIRELESS BELGIUM, BVBA—See EQT AB; *Int'l*, pg. 2479
AP WIRELESS BELGIUM, BVBA—See Public Sector Pension Investment Board; *Int'l*, pg. 6096
AP WIRELESS CANADA, ULC—See EQT AB; *Int'l*, pg. 2479
AP WIRELESS CANADA, ULC—See Public Sector Pension Investment Board; *Int'l*, pg. 6096
APWIRELESS INFRASTRUCTURE PARTNERS, LLC—See EQT AB; *Int'l*, pg. 2479
APWIRELESS INFRASTRUCTURE PARTNERS, LLC—See Public Sector Pension Investment Board; *Int'l*, pg. 6096
AP WIRELESS IRELAND INVESTMENTS LTD.—See EQT AB; *Int'l*, pg. 2479
AP WIRELESS IRELAND INVESTMENTS LTD.—See Public Sector Pension Investment Board; *Int'l*, pg. 6096
AP WIRELESS (UK) LIMITED—See EQT AB; *Int'l*, pg. 2479
AP WIRELESS (UK) LIMITED—See Public Sector Pension Investment Board; *Int'l*, pg. 6096
A.P. WOODSON CO.—See Star Group, L.P.; *U.S. Public*, pg. 1937
AP WORLD LIMITED—See Hang Lung Group Limited; *Int'l*, pg. 3244
APW PRESIDENT SYSTEMS LTD.—See Schneider Electric SE; *Int'l*, pg. 6625
APWPT II INVESTIMENTOS, S.A.—See EQT AB; *Int'l*, pg. 2479
APWPT II INVESTIMENTOS, S.A.—See Public Sector Pension Investment Board; *Int'l*, pg. 6096
APW WYOTT FOOD SERVICE EQUIPMENT, INC.—See Standex International; *U.S. Public*, pg. 1931
APW WYOTT FOOD SERVICE EQUIPMENT, INC.—See Standex International; *U.S. Public*, pg. 1931
APX GROUP HOLDINGS, INC.—See NRG Energy, Inc.; *U.S. Public*, pg. 1551
APX TECHNOLOGIE SP. Z O.O.—See Nicolas Correa S.A.; *Int'l*, pg. 5272
APYRON TECHNOLOGIES, INC.—See Streamline Capital, Inc.; *U.S. Private*, pg. 3838
APYX MEDICAL CORPORATION; *U.S. Public*, pg. 175
APZ AUTO-PFLEGE-ZENTRUM GMBH—See TUV SUD AG; *Int'l*, pg. 7984
AQ1 SYSTEMS PTY. LTD.—See Aktieselskabet Schouw & Co.; *Int'l*, pg. 265

175

AQ1 SYSTEMS S.A.—See Aktieselskabet Schouw & Co.; Int'l, pg. 265
AQABA NATIONAL REAL ESTATE PROJECTS COMPANY—See National Real Estate Company K.S.C.; Int'l, pg. 5162
AQABA PROCESSING COMPANY LTD—See Ricegrowers Limited; Int'l, pg. 6329
AQABA TECHNOLOGIES; U.S. Private, pg. 302
AQALAT COMPANY LIMITED—See Saudi Telecom Company; Int'l, pg. 6594
AQ ANTON KFT—See AQ Group AB; Int'l, pg. 526
AQAR REAL ESTATE INVESTMENTS COMPANY - K.S.C.; Int'l, pg. 527
AQC CORPORATION—See Yamashin-Filter Corp.; Int'l, pg. 8553
AQ COMPONENTS MJALLOM AB—See AQ Group AB; Int'l, pg. 526
AQ COMPONENTS SUZHOU CO., LTD.—See AQ Group AB; Int'l, pg. 526
AQ COMPONENTS VASTERAS AB—See AQ Group AB; Int'l, pg. 526
AQ ELECTRIC AD—See AQ Group AB; Int'l, pg. 526
AQ ELECTRIC & ENCLOSURES SUZHOU CO., LTD.—See AQ Group AB; Int'l, pg. 526
AQ ELECTRIC SUZHOU CO., LTD.—See AQ Group AB; Int'l, pg. 526
AQ ENCLOSURE SOLLEFTEA AB—See AQ Group AB; Int'l, pg. 526
AQERO VERTRIEBS GMBH—See Development Bank of Japan, Inc.; Int'l, pg. 2087
AQERO VERTRIEBS GMBH—See LIXIL Group Corporation; Int'l, pg. 4533
AQ GROUP AB; Int'l, pg. 526
AQ INDUCTIVES HUNGARY KFT—See AQ Group AB; Int'l, pg. 526
AQIWO; U.S. Private, pg. 302
AQ LASERTOOL OU—See AQ Group AB; Int'l, pg. 526
AQL DECORATING CO., INC.—See O. Berk Company L.L.C.; U.S. Private, pg. 2981
AQL EMC LIMITED—See Eurofins Scientific S.E.; Int'l, pg. 2535
AQL SRL—See El.En. S.p.A.; Int'l, pg. 2341
AQ MAGNETICA ITALY S.R.L.—See AQ Group AB; Int'l, pg. 526
AQ MAGNIT AD—See AQ Group AB; Int'l, pg. 526
AQM VIETNAM LIMITED—See Eurofins Scientific S.E.; Int'l, pg. 2535
AQ PARKOPRINT AB—See AQ Group AB; Int'l, pg. 526
AQ PLASTRONIC AD—See AQ Group AB; Int'l, pg. 526
AQR CAPITAL MANAGEMENT, LLC; U.S. Private, pg. 302
AQRS THE BUILDING COMPANY SDN. BHD.—See Gabungan AQRS Berhad; Int'l, pg. 2868
AQSEPTENCE GROUP GMBH—See Brookfield Corporation; Int'l, pg. 1181
AQSEPTENCE GROUP - HANAU—See Brookfield Corporation; Int'l, pg. 1181
AQSEPTENCE GROUP SRL.—See Brookfield Corporation; Int'l, pg. 1182
AQS MANAGEMENT SYSTEMS, INC.—See DEKRA e.V.; Int'l, pg. 2007
AQ SPECIAL SHEET METAL AB—See AQ Group AB; Int'l, pg. 526
AQ TRAFO AB—See AQ Group AB; Int'l, pg. 526
AQ TRAFOTEK AS—See AQ Group AB; Int'l, pg. 526
AQ TRAFOTEK OY—See AQ Group AB; Int'l, pg. 526
AQ TRANSFORMER SOLUTIONS INC.—See AQ Group AB; Int'l, pg. 527
AQUA-AEROBIC SYSTEMS, INC.—See METAWATER Co., Ltd.; Int'l, pg. 4851
AQUA AIR PRODUCTS INC.; U.S. Private, pg. 302
AQUA ART CO., LTD.—See Fuyo General Lease Co., Ltd.; Int'l, pg. 2859
AQUA-ASTON HOSPITALITY, LLC—See Marriott Vacations Worldwide Corporation; U.S. Public, pg. 1373
AQUABEST SEAFOOD, LLC; U.S. Private, pg. 303
AQUABIO LTD.—See Freudenberg SE; Int'l, pg. 2782
AQUA BIO TECHNOLOGY ASA; Int'l, pg. 527
AQUA BLASTING CORP.—See Battle Investment Group LLC; U.S. Private, pg. 489
AQUABOND TECHNOLOGIES, INC.—See Universal Photonics, Inc.; U.S. Private, pg. 4306
AQUABOTIX TECHNOLOGY CORPORATION—See UUV Aquabotix Ltd; Int'l, pg. 8102
AQUABOUNTY TECHNOLOGIES, INC.; U.S. Public, pg. 175
AQUA CAPITAL; Int'l, pg. 527
AQUACARE—See Sembcorp Industries Ltd.; Int'l, pg. 6704
AQUA-CHEM, INC.—See Crimson Investment; U.S. Private, pg. 1100
AQUA CLARA TOHOKU CORPORATION—See Yurtec Corporation; Int'l, pg. 8617
AQUA CORPORATION PUBLIC COMPANY LIMITED; Int'l, pg. 527
AQUA CURE LIMITED (UK)—See Castik Capital S.a.r.l.; Int'l, pg. 1356
AQUA CURE (SCOTLAND) LIMITED—See Castik Capital S.a.r.l.; Int'l, pg. 1356

AQUA DATA INC.—See AtkinsRealis Group Inc.; Int'l, pg. 671
AQUA DERMATOLOGY MANAGEMENT, LLC—See Raj Patel, MD LLC; U.S. Private, pg. 3349
AQUADIAGNOSTICS WATER RESEARCH & TECHNOLOGY CENTER LIMITED—See Shapoorji Pallonji & Co. Ltd.; Int'l, pg. 6788
AQUA DIRECT LTD.—See Arjun Infrastructure Partners Limited; Int'l, pg. 568
AQUADRILL LLC—See SeaDrill Limited; Int'l, pg. 6662
AQUADUS VVS AB—See Instalco AB; Int'l, pg. 3721
AQUAESSENCE PTY LTD—See Beston Global Food Company Limited; Int'l, pg. 1000
AQUA EYE LTD—See H2O Creative; Int'l, pg. 3200
AQUAFAX LIMITED—See LKQ Corporation; U.S. Public, pg. 1333
AQUAFIDES SCHWEIZ AG—See Katadyn Holding AG; Int'l, pg. 4088
AQUAFIL S.P.A.—See Aquafin Holding S.p.A.; Int'l, pg. 527
AQUAFIL U.S.A., INC.—See Aquafin Holding S.p.A.; Int'l, pg. 527
AQUA FINANCE, INC.—See Blackstone Inc.; U.S. Public, pg. 348
AQUAFINE CORPORATION—See Danaher Corporation; U.S. Public, pg. 624
AQUAFINE GMBH—See Danaher Corporation; U.S. Public, pg. 624
AQUAFIN HOLDING S.P.A.; Int'l, pg. 527
AQUA-FLO SDN. BHD.—See Kumpulan Darul Ehsan Berhad; Int'l, pg. 4331
AQUAFLOW LTD—See Veolia Environnement S.A.; Int'l, pg. 8161
AQUAFUNDALIA - AGUA DO FUNDAO, S.A.—See Fomento de Construcciones y Contratas, S.A.; Int'l, pg. 2722
AQUA-GAS MANUFACTURING LTD.—See AVK Holding A/S; Int'l, pg. 747
AQUAGESTION CAPACITACION S.A.—See Abbott Laboratories; U.S. Public, pg. 19
AQUAGESTION S.A.—See Abbott Laboratories; U.S. Public, pg. 19
AQUAGIB LIMITED—See CK Hutchison Holdings Limited; Int'l, pg. 1637
AQUAGOLD INTERNATIONAL, INC.; Int'l, pg. 527
AQUA-GON INC.; U.S. Private, pg. 303
AQUA GUARDIAN GROUP LIMITED; Int'l, pg. 527
AQUAHEAT NEW ZEALAND LIMITED—See Eastern Bay Energy Trust; Int'l, pg. 2271
AQUA HOSPITALITY LLC—See Marriott Vacations Worldwide Corporation; U.S. Public, pg. 1373
AQUA ILLINOIS, INC.—See Essential Utilities Inc.; U.S. Public, pg. 795
AQUA ILLINOIS—See Essential Utilities Inc.; U.S. Public, pg. 795
AQUA ILLINOIS - VERMILION COUNTY DIVISION—See Essential Utilities Inc.; U.S. Public, pg. 795
AQUA INDIANA, INC.—See Essential Utilities Inc.; U.S. Public, pg. 795
AQUAINTEC CORPORATION—See Air Water Inc.; Int'l, pg. 240
AQUALIA CZECH, S.L.—See Fomento de Construcciones y Contratas, S.A.; Int'l, pg. 2722
AQUALIA GESTION INTEGRAL DEL AGUA S.A.—See Fomento de Construcciones y Contratas, S.A.; Int'l, pg. 2722
AQUALIA INFRAESTRUCTURAS D.O.O.—See Fomento de Construcciones y Contratas, S.A.; Int'l, pg. 2722
AQUALIA INFRAESTRUCTURAS D.O.O.—See Fomento de Construcciones y Contratas, S.A.; Int'l, pg. 2722
AQUALIA INFRAESTRUCTURAS MONTENEGRO (AIM) D.O.O.—See Fomento de Construcciones y Contratas, S.A.; Int'l, pg. 2722
AQUALIA MEXICO, S.A. DE C.V.—See Fomento de Construcciones y Contratas, S.A.; Int'l, pg. 2722
AQUALINE LTD.; Int'l, pg. 527
AQUALISA PRODUCTS LIMITED; Int'l, pg. 527
AQUALISBRAEMAR TECHNICAL SERVICES (ADJUSTING) LIMITED—See ABL Group ASA; Int'l, pg. 62
AQUALISBRAEMAR TECHNICAL SERVICES LTD.—See ABL Group ASA; Int'l, pg. 62
AQUA LOGISTICS LIMITED; Int'l, pg. 527
AQUALON FRANCE B.V.—See Ashland Inc.; U.S. Public, pg. 212
AQUA LUANA OPERATOR LLC—See Marriott Vacations Worldwide Corporation; U.S. Public, pg. 1373
AQUA LUNG AMERICA, INC.—See Montagu Private Equity LLP; Int'l, pg. 5036
AQUA LUNG CANADA—See L'Air Liquide S.A.; Int'l, pg. 4374
AQUALUNG ESPANA—See L'Air Liquide S.A.; Int'l, pg. 4375
AQUA LUNG FRANCE—See L'Air Liquide S.A.; Int'l, pg. 4374
AQUA LUNG JAPAN, LTD—See L'Air Liquide S.A.; Int'l, pg. 4374
AQUALUNG TAUCHSPORTARTIKEL GMBH—See L'Air Liquide S.A.; Int'l, pg. 4375

AQUALUX PRODUCTS HOLDINGS LTD.—See Fetim B.V.; Int'l, pg. 2648
AQUALUX PRODUCTS LTD.—See Fetim B.V.; Int'l, pg. 2648
AQUAMAIOR - AGUAS DE CAMPO MAIOR, S.A.—See Fomento de Construcciones y Contratas, S.A.; Int'l, pg. 2722
AQUAMAR, INC.—See Huron Capital Partners LLC; U.S. Private, pg. 2012
AQUAMARINE SHIPPING CO., LTD.—See Albert Ballin KG; Int'l, pg. 294
AQUAMARINE SUBSEA AS—See HitecVision AS; Int'l, pg. 3426
AQUAMARINE SUBSEA HOUSTON, INC.—See HitecVision AS; Int'l, pg. 3426
AQUAMARINE SUBSEA STAVANGER AS—See HitecVision AS; Int'l, pg. 3426
AQUA METALS, INC.; U.S. Public, pg. 175
AQUAMETRO AG—See INTEGRA Holding AG; Int'l, pg. 3729
AQUAMETRO BELGIUM SPRL.—See INTEGRA Holding AG; Int'l, pg. 3729
AQUAMETRO (CHINA) PTE LTD.—See INTEGRA Holding AG; Int'l, pg. 3729
AQUAMETRO KOREA LTD.—See INTEGRA Holding AG; Int'l, pg. 3729
AQUAMETRO MARINE GMBH—See INTEGRA Holding AG; Int'l, pg. 3729
AQUAMETRO ME JLT—See INTEGRA Holding AG; Int'l, pg. 3729
AQUAMETRO MESSTECHNIK GMBH—See INTEGRA Holding AG; Int'l, pg. 3729
AQUAMETRO SA—See INTEGRA Holding AG; Int'l, pg. 3729
AQUAMETRO (S.E.A.) PTE LTD.—See INTEGRA Holding AG; Int'l, pg. 3729
AQUAMINE, LLC—See Victaulic Company; U.S. Private, pg. 4377
AQUA MIZER INC.; U.S. Private, pg. 302
AQUA NEW JERSEY, INC.—See Essential Utilities Inc.; U.S. Public, pg. 795
AQUA NEW JERSEY—See Essential Utilities Inc.; U.S. Public, pg. 795
AQUA NEW YORK, INC.—See American Water Works Company, Inc.; U.S. Public, pg. 112
AQUANEX, SERVICIO DOMICILIARIO DEL AGUA DE EXTREMADURA SA; Int'l, pg. 527
AQUANTIA B.V.—See Marvell Technology Group Ltd.; Int'l, pg. 4717
AQUANTIA CORP.—See Marvell Technology Group Ltd.; Int'l, pg. 4716
AQUANTIA SEMICONDUCTOR INDIA PVT. LTD.—See Marvell Technology Group Ltd.; Int'l, pg. 4717
AQUA OHIO, INC.—See Essential Utilities Inc.; U.S. Public, pg. 795
AQUA OHIO, INC.—See Essential Utilities Inc.; U.S. Public, pg. 795
AQUA OHIO - LAKE SHORE DIVISION—See Essential Utilities Inc.; U.S. Public, pg. 795
AQUA OHIO - MARION DIVISION—See Essential Utilities Inc.; U.S. Public, pg. 795
AQUA ONLINE; Int'l, pg. 527
AQUA PENNSYLVANIA, INC.—See Essential Utilities Inc.; U.S. Public, pg. 795
AQUA PENNSYLVANIA - ROARING CREEK DIVISION—See Essential Utilities Inc.; U.S. Public, pg. 795
AQUA PENNSYLVANIA - SHENANGO VALLEY DIVISION—See Essential Utilities Inc.; U.S. Public, pg. 795
AQUA PHARMACEUTICAL HOLDINGS INC.—See Almirall, S.A.; Int'l, pg. 364
AQUA PLUS WASSER- UND RECYCLINGSYSTEME GMBH—See Element Solutions Inc.; U.S. Public, pg. 725
AQUA POOL & SPA, INC.; U.S. Private, pg. 303
AQUAPORIN ASIA PTE. LTD.—See Aquaporin A/S; Int'l, pg. 528
AQUAPORIN A/S; Int'l, pg. 527
AQUAPORIN US INC.—See Aquaporin A/S; Int'l, pg. 528
AQUA POWER SYSTEMS INC.; Int'l, pg. 527
AQUA PRODUCT CORPORATION—See Nippon Filcon Co., Ltd.; Int'l, pg. 5317
AQUA PROTECH LABORATORIES, INC.—See Leonard Green & Partners, L.P.; U.S. Private, pg. 2426
AQUA-PURE VENTURES INC.; Int'l, pg. 527
AQUA-REHAB, INC.—See Caisse de Depot et Placement du Quebec; Int'l, pg. 1255
AQUARIAN, LLC—See Shepard Exposition Services Inc.; U.S. Private, pg. 3632
AQUARION WATER COMPANY OF CONNECTICUT—See Macquarie Group Limited; Int'l, pg. 4627
AQUARION WATER COMPANY OF MASSACHUSETTS, INC.—See Eversource Energy; U.S. Public, pg. 801
AQUARION WATER COMPANY OF MASSACHUSETTS & NEW HAMPSHIRE—See Macquarie Group Limited; Int'l, pg. 4627
AQUARION WATER COMPANY OF NEW HAMPSHIRE, INC.—See Eversource Energy; U.S. Public, pg. 801

COMPANY NAME INDEX

AQUARION WATER COMPANY—See Eversource Energy; *U.S. Public*, pg. 801
AQUARION WATER COMPANY—See Macquarie Group Limited; *Int'l*, pg. 4626
AQUARIUM GEANT DE SAINT MALO SAS—See Compagnie des Alpes S.A.; *Int'l*, pg. 1737
AQUARIUM SOFTWARE LIMITED—See Trupanion, Inc.; *U.S. Public*, pg. 2201
AQUARIUS AI, INC.; *Int'l*, pg. 528
AQUARIUS IRRIGATION SUPPLY INC.; *U.S. Private*, pg. 303
AQUARIUS LTD. INC.; *U.S. Private*, pg. 303
AQUARIUS SURGICAL TECHNOLOGIES INC.; *Int'l*, pg. 528
AQUARON ACQUISITION CORP.; *U.S. Public*, pg. 175
AQUASANA, INC.—See A. O. Smith Corporation; *U.S. Public*, pg. 11
AQUA SECURITIES, L.P.—See BGC Group, Inc.; *U.S. Public*, pg. 328
AQUA-SERV ENGINEERS INC.—See Harpure Enterprises Inc.; *U.S. Private*, pg. 1868
AQUA SERVICE AICHI CO.—See METAWATER Co., Ltd.; *Int'l*, pg. 4851
AQUA SERVICES, INC.—See Fort Point Capital, LLC; *U.S. Private*, pg. 1574
AQUASHIELD, INC.—See Komline-Sanderson Corporation; *U.S. Private*, pg. 2342
AQUA SIGNAL GMBH; *Int'l*, pg. 527
AQUASIGN—See Ecolab Inc.; *U.S. Public*, pg. 712
AQUASIUM TECHNOLOGY LIMITED; *Int'l*, pg. 528
AQUASOL MORELIA S.A. DE C.V.—See Empresas Publicas de Medellin ESP; *Int'l*, pg. 2391
AQUASOURCE SAS—See Veolia Environnement S.A.; *Int'l*, pg. 8155
AQUA SUN PROPERTIES; *U.S. Private*, pg. 303
AQUATAS PTY LTD—See Tassal Group Limited; *Int'l*, pg. 7466
AQUATECH ENVIRONMENTAL, INC.—See MPW Industrial Services Group, Inc.; *U.S. Private*, pg. 2804
AQUATECH INTERNATIONAL CORP.; *U.S. Private*, pg. 303
AQUATEC INC.; *U.S. Private*, pg. 303
AQUATEC OPERATIONS GMBH—See Invacare Corporation; *U.S. Private*, pg. 2130
AQUATERRA CONSULTING PTY LIMITED—See RPS Group plc; *Int'l*, pg. 6415
AQUATERRA CORPORATION—See Primo Water Corporation; *U.S. Public*, pg. 1718
AQUATERRA ENVIRONMENTAL SOLUTIONS, INC.—See SCS Engineers; *U.S. Private*, pg. 3580
AQUATERRA, LLC—See Terracon Consultants, Inc.; *U.S. Private*, pg. 3970
AQUA-TERRA LOGISTICS PTE. LTD.—See KS Energy Limited; *Int'l*, pg. 4309
AQUA-TERRA OILFIELD EQUIPMENT & SERVICES PTE. LTD.—See KS Energy Limited; *Int'l*, pg. 4309
AQUA-TERRA SUPPLY CO. LTD.—See KS Energy Limited; *Int'l*, pg. 4309
AQUA TEXAS, INC.—See Essential Utilities Inc.; *U.S. Public*, pg. 795
AQUATHERM INTERNATIONAL; *U.S. Private*, pg. 303
AQUATIC AMUSEMENT ASSOCIATES LTD.—See Aquatic Development Group, Inc.; *U.S. Private*, pg. 303
AQUATICA—See United Parks & Resorts Inc.; *U.S. Public*, pg. 2234
AQUATIC BUILDERS LTD.—See Aquatic Development Group, Inc.; *U.S. Private*, pg. 303
AQUATIC CONSTRUCTION LTD.—See Aquatic Development Group, Inc.; *U.S. Private*, pg. 303
AQUATIC CO.—See The Sterling Group, L.P.; *U.S. Private*, pg. 4121
AQUATIC DEVELOPMENT GROUP, INC.; *U.S. Private*, pg. 303
AQUATIC ENGINEERING & CONSTRUCTION LIMITED—See H2 Equity Partners B.V.; *Int'l*, pg. 3199
AQUATIC VEGETATION CONTROL INC.; *U.S. Private*, pg. 303
AQUATIS A.S.—See Safichem Group AG; *Int'l*, pg. 6471
AQUATIS SPOL S.R.O.—See AFRY AB; *Int'l*, pg. 194
AQUATREAT CHEMICAL PRODUCTS LIMITED—See Marlowe Plc; *Int'l*, pg. 4698
AQUATROL CORPORATION—See JM Process Systems Inc.; *U.S. Private*, pg. 2214
AQUATROL—See Momar, Inc.; *U.S. Private*, pg. 2767
AQUATRO - PROJECTOS E ENGENHARIA, S.A.—See Jose de Mello, SGPS, S.A.; *Int'l*, pg. 4001
AQUATUS A.D.; *Int'l*, pg. 528
AQUAVENTURE HOLDINGS LIMITED—See BDT Capital Partners, LLC; *U.S. Private*, pg. 502
AQUAWORLD PRODUCTS—See Chem-Tainer Industries, Inc.; *U.S. Private*, pg. 871
AQUA YIELD OPERATIONS, LLC; *U.S. Private*, pg. 303
AQUAZANIA AFRICA PROPRIETARY LIMITED—See The Bidvest Group Limited; *Int'l*, pg. 7621
AQUEDUCT CAPITAL S.A R.L.—See Deutsche Bank Aktiengesellschaft; *Int'l*, pg. 2055
AQUENTA CONSULTING PTY LTD—See Jacobs Engineering Group, Inc.; *U.S. Public*, pg. 1183

AQUENT GMBH & CO. KG—See Aquent Inc.; *U.S. Private*, pg. 303
AQUENT INC.; *U.S. Private*, pg. 303
AQUEOUS MANAGEMENT LIMITED—See Willis Towers Watson Public Limited Company; *Int'l*, pg. 8414
AQUESTA BANK—See United Community Banks, Inc.; *U.S. Public*, pg. 2230
AQUESTA FINANCIAL HOLDINGS, INC.—See United Community Banks, Inc.; *U.S. Public*, pg. 2230
AQUESTIVE THERAPEUTICS, INC.—See Kuraray Co., Ltd.; *Int'l*, pg. 4336
AQUILA ACQUISITION CORPORATION; *Int'l*, pg. 528
AQUILA GMBH—See VPK Packaging Group NV; *Int'l*, pg. 8312
AQUILA GROUP HOLDINGS LIMITED—See Siris Capital Group, LLC; *U.S. Private*, pg. 3673
AQUILA RESOURCES INC.—See Gold Resource Corporation; *U.S. Public*, pg. 949
AQUILA RESOURCES PTY LIMITED—See China Baowu Steel Group Corp., Ltd.; *Int'l*, pg. 1485
AQUILA SA; *Int'l*, pg. 528
AQUILA SERVICES GROUP PLC; *Int'l*, pg. 528
AQUILA SOFTWARE—See Constellation Software Inc.; *Int'l*, pg. 1775
AQUILA SP. Z O.O.—See VPK Packaging Group NV; *Int'l*, pg. 8312
AQUILA TECHNOLOGY CORP.—See RPG Group; *Int'l*, pg. 6415
AQUILA TREASURY & FINANCE SOLUTIONS LIMITED—See Aquila Services Group PLC; *Int'l*, pg. 528
AQUILES CHILE SPA.—See Bridgepoint Group Plc; *Int'l*, pg. 1154
AQUILEX ARABIA, LTD.—See Ali Abdullah Al Tamimi Company; *Int'l*, pg. 319
AQUILEX SPECIALTY REPAIR & OVERHAUL INC.—See AZZ, Inc.; *U.S. Public*, pg. 259
AQUILEX WELDING SERVICES, B.V.—See AZZ, Inc.; *U.S. Public*, pg. 259
AQUILEX WELDING SERVICES POLAND SP. Z O.O.—See AZZ, Inc.; *U.S. Public*, pg. 259
AQUILEX WSI NUCLEAR SERVICES—See AZZ, Inc.; *U.S. Public*, pg. 259
AQUILINE CAPITAL PARTNERS LLC; *U.S. Private*, pg. 303
AQUILINI INVESTMENT GROUP; *Int'l*, pg. 528
AQUILLA INSURANCE BROKERS LIMITED—See Brown & Brown, Inc.; *U.S. Public*, pg. 396
AQUIMISA S.L.—See ALS Limited; *Int'l*, pg. 377
AQUION ENERGY LLC—See bluesky.energy Gmbh; *Int'l*, pg. 1074
AQUION PARTNERS L.P.; *U.S. Private*, pg. 305
AQUIRIAN LIMITED; *Int'l*, pg. 528
AQUIRIAN TECHNOLOGY PTY LTD—See Aquirian Limited; *Int'l*, pg. 528
AQUIRIS SA—See Veolia Environnement S.A.; *Int'l*, pg. 8153
AQUIS ENTERTAINMENT LIMITED; *Int'l*, pg. 528
AQUIS EXCHANGE PLC; *Int'l*, pg. 528
AQUIS STOCK EXCHANGE LIMITED—See CME Group, Inc.; *U.S. Public*, pg. 516
AQUITAINE RHONE GAZ—See UGI Corporation; *U.S. Public*, pg. 2222
AQUITY SOLUTIONS, LLC—See Rare Enterprises Ltd.; *Int'l*, pg. 6211
A QUOTE INSURANCE SERVICES LIMITED—See Highway Insurance Holdings Plc; *Int'l*, pg. 3389
AQUTIA CO., LTD.—See AEON Co., Ltd.; *Int'l*, pg. 177
AQ WIRING SYSTEMS CANADA INC.—See AQ Group AB; *Int'l*, pg. 527
AQ WIRING SYSTEMS NY, INC.—See AQ Group AB; *Int'l*, pg. 527
AQ WIRING SYSTEMS S.A. DE C.V.—See AQ Group AB; *Int'l*, pg. 527
AQ WIRING SYSTEMS SP.Z.O.O.—See AQ Group AB; *Int'l*, pg. 527
AQ WIRING SYSTEMS UAB—See AQ Group AB; *Int'l*, pg. 527
ARA-ADELPHI LLC—See Nautic Partners, LLC; *U.S. Private*, pg. 2869
ARA ASSET MANAGEMENT LIMITED—See ESR Group Limited; *Int'l*, pg. 2507
ARA ASSET MANAGEMENT (PROSPERITY) LIMITED—See ESR Group Limited; *Int'l*, pg. 2507
ARA-AUGUSTA CLINIC LLC—See Nautic Partners, LLC; *U.S. Private*, pg. 2869
ARA-AVENTURA LLC—See Nautic Partners, LLC; *U.S. Private*, pg. 2869
ARAB AFRICAN INTERNATIONAL BANK; *Int'l*, pg. 529
ARAB AFRICAN INVESTMENT MANAGEMENT—See Arab African International Bank; *Int'l*, pg. 529
ARAB ALUMINIUM INDUSTRY CO. LTD.; *Int'l*, pg. 529
ARAB AMERICAN INTERNATIONAL EXPRESS COMPANY—See Aramex PJSC; *Int'l*, pg. 535
THE ARAB ASSURERS INSURANCE CO. PSC; *Int'l*, pg. 7613
ARAB BANK AUSTRALIA LTD—See Arab Bank plc; *Int'l*, pg. 529

ARABIAN CEMENT COMPANY

ARAB BANKING CORPORATION ALGERIA SPA—See Arab Banking Corporation B.S.C.; *Int'l*, pg. 529
ARAB BANKING CORPORATION B.S.C.; *Int'l*, pg. 529
ARAB BANKING CORPORATION - EGYPT S.A.E.—See Arab Banking Corporation B.S.C.; *Int'l*, pg. 529
ARAB BANKING CORPORATION (JORDAN)—See Arab Banking Corporation B.S.C.; *Int'l*, pg. 529
ARAB BANKING CORPORATION TUNISIA, S.A.—See Arab Banking Corporation B.S.C.; *Int'l*, pg. 529
ARAB BANK PLC; *Int'l*, pg. 529
ARAB BANK (SWITZERLAND) LTD.—See Arab Bank plc; *Int'l*, pg. 529
ARAB BANK-SYRIA—See Arab Bank plc; *Int'l*, pg. 529
ARAB CABLES COMPANY—See El Sewedy Electric Company; *Int'l*, pg. 2341
ARAB CENTER FOR PHARMACEUTICAL & CHEMICAL INDUSTRIES CO.; *Int'l*, pg. 529
ARAB COMPANY FOR LAND RECLAMATION S.A.E.; *Int'l*, pg. 530
ARAB COMPANY FOR PAINT PRODUCTS; *Int'l*, pg. 530
ARAB COTTON GINNING COMPANY; *Int'l*, pg. 530
THE ARAB DAIRY PRODUCTS CO.; *Int'l*, pg. 7613
ARAB DEVELOPMENT INVESTMENT COMPANY; *Int'l*, pg. 530
ARAB DRIP IRRIGATION TECHNOLOGY COMPANY LTD.—See Adritec Group International, E.C.; *Int'l*, pg. 153
ARAB DRIP IRRIGATION TECHNOLOGY COMPANY LTD.—See Sleiman Agricultural Establishment; *Int'l*, pg. 6996
THE ARAB-EASTERN INSURANCE COMPANY LIMITED E.C.—See Tokio Marine Holdings, Inc.; *Int'l*, pg. 7783
ARAB EAST INVESTMENT COMPANY; *Int'l*, pg. 530
ARAB ELECTRICAL INDUSTRIES; *Int'l*, pg. 530
ARABELLA ADVISORS, LLC; *U.S. Private*, pg. 306
ARABELLA EXPLORATION, INC.; *U.S. Private*, pg. 307
ARABELLA HOSPITALITY GMBH & CO. KG—See Schorghuber Stiftung & Co. Holding KG; *Int'l*, pg. 6638
ARABESQUE GRC—See Kassem Darwish Fakhro & Sons; *Int'l*, pg. 4088
ARAB FERTILIZERS AND CHEMICALS INDUSTRIES LTD.—See Arab Potash Company PLC; *Int'l*, pg. 531
ARAB FINANCE HOUSE (AFH) S.A.L.—See Qatar Islamic Bank (S.A.Q.); *Int'l*, pg. 6134
THE ARAB FINANCIAL INVESTMENT CO.; *Int'l*, pg. 7613
ARAB FINANCIAL SERVICES B.S.C.; *Int'l*, pg. 530
ARAB FINANCIAL SERVICES COMPANY B.S.C.—See Arab Banking Corporation B.S.C.; *Int'l*, pg. 529
ARAB HEAVY INDUSTRIES P.J.S.C; *Int'l*, pg. 530
THE ARAB HOTELS COMPANY; *Int'l*, pg. 7613
ARABIA FELIX INDUSTRIAL LTD.—See Hayel Saeed Anam Group of Companies; *Int'l*, pg. 3290
ARABI AGRICULTURE CO.—See Arabi Holding Group Company K.S.C.C.; *Int'l*, pg. 532
ARABIA INSURANCE COMPANY S.A.L.—See Arabia Insurance Company; *Int'l*, pg. 533
ARABIA INSURANCE COMPANY; *Int'l*, pg. 533
ARABIA INSURANCE COMPANY - SYRIA S.A.—See Arabia Insurance Co.; *Int'l*, pg. 533
ARABIA INSURANCE COOPERATIVE COMPANY; *Int'l*, pg. 533
ARABIA INSURANCE CO.; *Int'l*, pg. 533
ARABIAN AGRICULTURAL SERVICES CO.; *Int'l*, pg. 533
ARABIAN ALKALI COMPANY—See NAMA Chemicals Company; *Int'l*, pg. 5134
ARABIAN AMINES COMPANY—See Huntsman Corporation; *U.S. Public*, pg. 1073
ARABIAN AUTOMOBILES CO.—See Nissan Motor Co., Ltd.; *Int'l*, pg. 5367
ARABIAN AXLES AND FOUNDRIES AND SPARE PARTS COMPANY LTD.—See National Industrialization Company; *Int'l*, pg. 5158
ARABIAN BULK TRADE LTD.—See Xenel Industries Ltd.; *Int'l*, pg. 8521
ARABIAN BULK TRADE PTE. LTD.—See Xenel Industries Ltd.; *Int'l*, pg. 8521
ARABIAN BUSINESS MACHINES COMPANY—See The Olayan Group; *Int'l*, pg. 7672
ARABIAN CAN INDUSTRY LLC—See Al Ghurair Group; *Int'l*, pg. 277
ARABIAN CBI LTD.—See McDermott International, Inc.; *U.S. Public*, pg. 1405
ARABIAN CEMENT COMPANY LTD.; *Int'l*, pg. 533
ARABIAN CEMENT COMPANY; *Int'l*, pg. 533
ARABIAN CEMENT CO.—See Arabian Cement Company Ltd.; *Int'l*, pg. 533
ARABIAN CHEMICAL CARRIERS LTD. CO.—See Albert Ballin KG; *Int'l*, pg. 296
ARABIAN CHEMICAL COMPANY (LATEX) LTD.—See Dow Inc.; *U.S. Public*, pg. 683
ARABIAN CHEMICAL COMPANY (LATEX) LTD.—See E.A. Juffali & Brothers Company; *Int'l*, pg. 2250
ARABIAN CHEMICAL COMPANY (POLYSTYRENE) LIMITED—See Dow Inc.; *U.S. Public*, pg. 683
ARABIAN CHEMICAL COMPANY (POLYSTYRENE) LIMITED—See E.A. Juffali & Brothers Company; *Int'l*, pg. 2251

ARABIAN CEMENT COMPANY / CORPORATE AFFILIATIONS

Company Index

ARABIAN DARB GENERAL TRADING & CONTRACTING COMPANY—See Endress+Hauser (International) Holding AG; *Int'l*, pg. 2405
ARABIAN ELEVATOR & ESCALATOR CO. LTD.—See KONE Oyj; *Int'l*, pg. 4247
ARABIAN FIBERGLASS INSULATION CO.—See Owens Corning; *U.S. Public*, pg. 1626
ARABIAN FOOD & DAIRY FACTORIES—See HAK Al-gahtani Group of Companies; *Int'l*, pg. 3219
ARABIAN FOOD INDUSTRIES COMPANY; *Int'l*, pg. 533
ARABIAN GULF INVESTMENTS (FAR EAST) LIMITED—See HSBC Holdings plc; *Int'l*, pg. 3503
ARABIAN INTERNATIONAL HEALTHCARE HOLDING COMPANY; *Int'l*, pg. 533
ARABIAN INTERNET AND COMMUNICATIONS SERVICES COMPANY—See Saudi Telecom Company; *Int'l*, pg. 6594
ARABIAN JAPANESE MEMBRANE COMPANY, LLC—See Toyobo Co., Ltd.; *Int'l*, pg. 7860
ARABIAN METERING COMPANY—See Itron, Inc.; *U.S. Public*, pg. 1175
ARABIAN NEON W.L.L.—See Dadabhai Group; *Int'l*, pg. 1904
ARABIAN OIL COMPANY, LTD.—See Fuji Oil Company, Ltd.; *Int'l*, pg. 2815
ARABIAN OUD COMPANY; *Int'l*, pg. 533
ARABIAN PACKAGING CO. LLC—See Al Ghurair Group; *Int'l*, pg. 277
ARABIAN PAPER PRODUCTS COMPANY—See Huhtamaki Oyj; *Int'l*, pg. 3524
ARABIAN PAPER PRODUCTS COMPANY—See The Olayan Group; *Int'l*, pg. 7672
ARABIAN PETROCHEMICAL CO.—See Saudi Basic Industries Corporation; *Int'l*, pg. 6590
ARABIAN PETROLEUM LIMITED; *Int'l*, pg. 533
ARABIAN PIPELINE & SERVICES CO. LTD.—See Al-Osais International Holding Company; *Int'l*, pg. 287
ARABIAN PIPES COMPANY; *Int'l*, pg. 533
ARABIAN PLASTIC INDUSTRIAL CO. LTD.; *Int'l*, pg. 533
ARABIAN PLASTIC MANUFACTURING COMPANY—See Georg Fischer AG; *Int'l*, pg. 2935
ARABIAN PROFILE COMPANY LIMITED—See GIBCA Limited; *Int'l*, pg. 2962
ARABIAN SHIELD COOPERATIVE INSURANCE COMPANY; *Int'l*, pg. 533
ARABIAN SOIL CONTRACTORS LTD.—See Trevi Finanziaria Industriale SpA.; *Int'l*, pg. 7916
ARABIAN STEEL PIPES MFG CO. LTD; *Int'l*, pg. 533
ARABIAN STORES COMPANY LTD.; *Int'l*, pg. 534
ARABIA S.A.L. HOLDING COMPANY—See Arabia Insurance Co.; *Int'l*, pg. 533
ARABIC COMPUTER SYSTEMS LTD.—See National Technology Group; *Int'l*, pg. 5164
ARABI COMPANY W.L.L.—See Arabi Holding Group Company K.S.C.C.; *Int'l*, pg. 532
ARABI ENERTECH COMPANY K.S.C.—See Arabi Holding Group Company K.S.C.C.; *Int'l*, pg. 532
ARABI ENGINEERING CO.—See Arabi Holding Group Company K.S.C.C.; *Int'l*, pg. 532
ARABI GULF SERVICES & INDUSTRIAL SUPPLIES CO.—See Arabi Holding Group Company K.S.C.C.; *Int'l*, pg. 532
ARABI HOLDING GROUP COMPANY K.S.C.C.; *Int'l*, pg. 532
ARABI INDUSTRIAL SERVICES & SUPPLIES CO.—See Arabi Holding Group Company K.S.C.C.; *Int'l*, pg. 532
ARABI MEDICAL & SCIENTIFIC EQUIPMENT CO. W.L.L.—See Arabi Holding Group Company K.S.C.C.; *Int'l*, pg. 532
ARAB INFORMATION MANAGEMENT SERVICES; *Int'l*, pg. 530
ARAB INSURANCE GROUP B.S.C.; *Int'l*, pg. 530
ARAB INTERNATIONAL CO. FOR EDUCATION & INVESTMENT PLC; *Int'l*, pg. 530
ARAB INTERNATIONAL FOOD FACTORIES & INVESTMENT COMPANY; *Int'l*, pg. 530
ARAB INTERNATIONAL HOTELS PLC.; *Int'l*, pg. 530
ARAB INTERNATIONAL OPTRONICS—See Thales S.A.; *Int'l*, pg. 7605
ARAB INVESTMENT BANK S.A.L.—See Arab Bank plc; *Int'l*, pg. 529
ARAB INVESTORS UNION CO. FOR REAL ESTATES DEVELOPING P.L.C; *Int'l*, pg. 530
ARAB ISLAMIC BANK; *Int'l*, pg. 530
ARAB JORDANIAN INSURANCE GROUP; *Int'l*, pg. 530
ARAB JORDAN INVESTMENT BANK (QATAR) L.L.C.—See Arab Jordan Investment Bank; *Int'l*, pg. 530
ARAB JORDAN INVESTMENT BANK; *Int'l*, pg. 530
ARAB LEASING COMPANY PSC—See Arab Palestinian Investment Company; *Int'l*, pg. 531
ARABLE CAPITAL PARTNERS LLC; *U.S. Private*, pg. 307
ARAB LIFE & ACCIDENT INSURANCE COMPANY P.S.C.; *Int'l*, pg. 531
ARAB MEDICAL & SCIENTIFIC ALLIANCE CO.—See HORIBA Ltd; *Int'l*, pg. 3474
ARAB MISR INSURANCE GROUP—See Fairfax Financial Holdings Limited; *Int'l*, pg. 2607

ARAB MOLTAQA INVESTMENTS COMPANY; *Int'l*, pg. 531
ARAB NATIONAL BANK; *Int'l*, pg. 531
ARAB NATIONAL LEASING COMPANY LTD—See Arab Bank plc; *Int'l*, pg. 529
ARA-BOCA RATON DIALYSIS LLC—See Nautic Partners, LLC; *U.S. Private*, pg. 2869
ARAB ORIENT INSURANCE CO. LTD.—See Fairfax Financial Holdings Limited; *Int'l*, pg. 2607
ARAB PALESTINIAN INVESTMENT COMPANY; *Int'l*, pg. 531
ARAB PALESTINIAN SHOPPING CENTERS—See Arab Palestinian Investment Company; *Int'l*, pg. 531
THE ARAB PESTICIDES & VETERINARY DRUGS MFG. CO. - IRBID FACTORY—See The Arab Pesticides & Veterinary Drugs Mfg. Co.; *Int'l*, pg. 7614
THE ARAB PESTICIDES & VETERINARY DRUGS MFG. CO.; *Int'l*, pg. 7613
ARAB PETROLEUM INVESTMENTS CORPORATION; *Int'l*, pg. 531
ARAB PHARMACEUTICAL MANUFACTURING CO.—See Hikma Pharmaceuticals PLC; *Int'l*, pg. 3390
ARAB PHOENIX HOLDINGS; *Int'l*, pg. 531
ARAB POLVARA COMPANY FOR SPINNING & WEAVING COMPANY; *Int'l*, pg. 531
ARAB POTASH COMPANY LTD - POTASH PLANT—See Arab Potash Company PLC; *Int'l*, pg. 531
ARAB POTASH COMPANY PLC; *Int'l*, pg. 531
ARAB REAL ESTATE COMPANY K.S.C.C; *Int'l*, pg. 531
ARAB REAL ESTATE DEVELOPMENT COMPANY PSC; *Int'l*, pg. 531
ARAB SATELLITE COMMUNICATIONS ORGANIZATION; *Int'l*, pg. 531
ARAB SEA INFORMATION SYSTEM CO; *Int'l*, pg. 531
ARAB SHIPBUILDING & REPAIR YARD CO.; *Int'l*, pg. 531
ARAB SHIP MANAGEMENT LTD.—See Jordan Nation Shipping Lines P.L.C; *Int'l*, pg. 3999
ARAB SUDANESE BANK LIMITED—See Arab Bank plc; *Int'l*, pg. 529
ARAB SUPPLY & TRADING CO. - FOOD SUPPLY DIVISION—See Arab Supply & Trading Co.; *Int'l*, pg. 532
ARAB SUPPLY & TRADING CO.; *Int'l*, pg. 532
ARABTEC ENGINEERING SERVICES L.L.C.—See Arabtec Holding PJSC; *Int'l*, pg. 534
ARABTEC HOLDING PJSC; *Int'l*, pg. 534
ARAB TOWER CONTRACTING COMPANY LTD.—See Enjaz for Development & Multi Projects Company P.L.C.; *Int'l*, pg. 2439
ARAB TUNISIAN BANK—See Arab Bank plc; *Int'l*, pg. 529
ARAB UNION INTERNATIONAL INSURANCE CO. LTD.; *Int'l*, pg. 532
ARAB WEAVERS UNION COMPANY P.L.C.; *Int'l*, pg. 532
A. RACKE GMBH; *Int'l*, pg. 21
ARACLON BIOTECH, S.L.—See Grifols, S.A.; *Int'l*, pg. 3084
ARACO CO., LTD.—See Toyota Boshoku Corporation; *Int'l*, pg. 7863
ARACOMA COAL COMPANY, INC.—See Alpha Natural Resources, Inc.; *U.S. Private*, pg. 198
ARACOMA DRUG CO. INC.; *U.S. Private*, pg. 307
ARA-DAYTONA BEACH DIALYSIS LLC—See Nautic Partners, LLC; *U.S. Private*, pg. 2869
ARADHANA FOODS AND JUICES PRIVATE LIMITED—See PepsiCo, Inc.; *U.S. Public*, pg. 1668
ARA DIALYSIS UNIT AT OHIO VALLEY HOSPITAL, LLC—See Nautic Partners, LLC; *U.S. Private*, pg. 2869
ARADIANT CORP.; *U.S. Private*, pg. 307
ARADIGM CORPORATION; *U.S. Public*, pg. 175
ARAD INVESTMENT & INDUSTRIAL DEVELOPMENT LTD.; *Int'l*, pg. 534
ARA DIRECT COMMUNICATIONS—See Omnicom Group Inc.; *U.S. Public*, pg. 1596
ARAD LTD.; *Int'l*, pg. 534
ARAD-OPHIR LTD.; *Int'l*, pg. 534
ARAFA HOLDING; *Int'l*, pg. 534
ARAFURA RARE EARTHS LIMITED; *Int'l*, pg. 534
ARAG ARGENTINA S.A.U.—See Nordson Corporation; *U.S. Public*, pg. 1532
ARAG AUSTRALIA PTY LTD.—See Nordson Corporation; *U.S. Public*, pg. 1532
ARAG DO BRASIL S.A.—See Nordson Corporation; *U.S. Public*, pg. 1532
ARAGEN BIOSCIENCE, INC.—See GVK Power and Infrastructure Limited; *Int'l*, pg. 3190
ARAGEN BIOTECHNOLOGY LTD.—See The Jordanian Pharmaceutical Manufacturing Co., P.L.C.; *Int'l*, pg. 7660
ARAG INSURANCE COMPANY INC.; *U.S. Private*, pg. 307
ARAGON ENTERTAINMENT CENTER, INC.—See Live Nation Entertainment, Inc.; *U.S. Public*, pg. 1328
ARAGON-ERH, SAS—See Econocom Group SA; *Int'l*, pg. 2297
ARAGONESA DE POSTVENTA S.L.U.—See Brookfield Corporation; *Int'l*, pg. 1188
THE ARAGON GROUP—See Boyd Gaming Corporation; *U.S. Public*, pg. 378

ARAGON LLC.; *U.S. Private*, pg. 307
ARAGONNE WIND LLC—See Infigen Energy Limited; *Int'l*, pg. 3685
ARAGON PHARMACEUTICALS, INC.—See Johnson & Johnson; *U.S. Public*, pg. 1194
ARA GROEP B.V.—See Omnicom Group Inc.; *U.S. Public*, pg. 1596
ARA GROUP LIMITED; *Int'l*, pg. 528
ARAG S.A. R.L.—See Nordson Corporation; *U.S. Public*, pg. 1532
ARAG SERVICES LLC—See Arag Insurance Company Inc.; *U.S. Private*, pg. 307
ARAG SE; *Int'l*, pg. 534
ARAH EDAR (M) SDN. BHD.—See Dancomech Holdings Berhad; *Int'l*, pg. 1959
ARAI & CO., LTD.; *Int'l*, pg. 534
ARAI INDUSTRIAL CO., LTD.—See Nippon Steel Corporation; *Int'l*, pg. 5337
ARAIKE MACHINERY CO.,LTD.—See Nippon Coke & Engineering Co., Ltd.; *Int'l*, pg. 5313
ARAIKE MATERIALS CO.,LTD.—See Nippon Coke & Engineering Co., Ltd.; *Int'l*, pg. 5313
ARA INTERACTIVE—See Omnicom Group Inc.; *U.S. Public*, pg. 1596
A RAIZE-INSTITUICAO DE PAGAMENTOS S.A.; *Int'l*, pg. 18
ARA-JOHNSTON DIALYSIS LLC—See Nautic Partners, LLC; *U.S. Private*, pg. 2869
ARAKAWA CHEMICAL (CHINA) INC.—See Arakawa Chemical Industries, Ltd.; *Int'l*, pg. 534
ARAKAWA CHEMICAL INDUSTRIES, LTD - FUJI PLANT—See Arakawa Chemical Industries, Ltd.; *Int'l*, pg. 534
ARAKAWA CHEMICAL INDUSTRIES, LTD - KUSHIRO PLANT—See Arakawa Chemical Industries, Ltd.; *Int'l*, pg. 534
ARAKAWA CHEMICAL INDUSTRIES, LTD. - MIZUSHIMA PLANT—See Arakawa Chemical Industries, Ltd.; *Int'l*, pg. 534
ARAKAWA CHEMICAL INDUSTRIES, LTD. - ONAHAMA PLANT—See Arakawa Chemical Industries, Ltd.; *Int'l*, pg. 534
ARAKAWA CHEMICAL INDUSTRIES, LTD - OSAKA PLANT—See Arakawa Chemical Industries, Ltd.; *Int'l*, pg. 534
ARAKAWA CHEMICAL INDUSTRIES, LTD.; *Int'l*, pg. 534
ARAKAWA CHEMICAL INDUSTRIES, LTD. - TOKUSHIMA PLANT—See Arakawa Chemical Industries, Ltd.; *Int'l*, pg. 534
ARAKAWA CHEMICAL INDUSTRIES, LTD - TSURUSAKI PLANT—See Arakawa Chemical Industries, Ltd.; *Int'l*, pg. 534
ARAKAWA CHEMICAL (TAIPEI), LTD.—See Arakawa Chemical Industries, Ltd.; *Int'l*, pg. 534
ARAKAWA CHEMICAL (USA) INC.—See Arakawa Chemical Industries, Ltd.; *Int'l*, pg. 534
ARAKAWA EUROPE GMBH—See Arakawa Chemical Industries, Ltd.; *Int'l*, pg. 534
ARAKELIAN ENTERPRISES, INC.; *U.S. Private*, pg. 307
ARAKOR CO. LTD.—See Aramark; *U.S. Public*, pg. 177
ARA KOREA LIMITED—See ESR Group Limited; *Int'l*, pg. 2508
ARALIA SYSTEMS, INC.—See Aralia Systems Ltd.; *Int'l*, pg. 535
ARALIA SYSTEMS LTD.; *Int'l*, pg. 535
ARA LOGOS LOGISTICS TRUST; *Int'l*, pg. 528
ARA - LUDLOW DIALYSIS, LLC—See Nautic Partners, LLC; *U.S. Private*, pg. 2868
ARAMARK AMERICAN FOOD SERVICES, LLC—See Aramark; *U.S. Public*, pg. 176
ARAMARK/CAMPBELL CATERING—See Aramark; *U.S. Public*, pg. 177
ARAMARK CANADA LTD.—See Aramark; *U.S. Public*, pg. 176
ARAMARK CANADA LTD.—See Aramark; *U.S. Public*, pg. 176
ARAMARK CATERING LIMITED—See Aramark; *U.S. Public*, pg. 176
ARAMARK CHINA HOLDINGS LIMITED—See Aramark; *U.S. Public*, pg. 177
ARAMARK CHINA—See Aramark; *U.S. Public*, pg. 176
ARAMARK CHUGACH ALASKA SERVICES, LLC—See Aramark; *U.S. Public*, pg. 177
ARAMARK COLOMBIA SAS—See Aramark; *U.S. Public*, pg. 177
ARAMARK CO. LTD.—See Aramark; *U.S. Public*, pg. 177
ARAMARK CORPORATION—See Aramark; *U.S. Public*, pg. 175
ARAMARK DENMARK APS—See Aramark; *U.S. Public*, pg. 177
ARAMARK EDUCATIONAL GROUP, LLC—See Aramark; *U.S. Public*, pg. 176
ARAMARK ENTERTAINMENT, LLC—See Aramark; *U.S. Public*, pg. 176
ARAMARK ENTERTAINMENT SERVICES (CANADA), INC.—See Aramark; *U.S. Public*, pg. 176
ARAMARK FACILITIES MANAGEMENT, LLC—See Aramark; *U.S. Public*, pg. 176

COMPANY NAME INDEX

ARAMARK FACILITY SERVICES, LLC—See Aramark; *U.S. Public*, pg. 176
ARAMARK FACILITY SERVICES—See Aramark; *U.S. Public*, pg. 176
ARAMARK FHC BUSINESS SERVICES, LLC—See Aramark; *U.S. Public*, pg. 176
ARAMARK FHC, LLC—See Aramark; *U.S. Public*, pg. 176
ARAMARK FOOD AND SUPPORT SERVICES GROUP, INC.—See Aramark; *U.S. Public*, pg. 176
ARAMARK GMBH—See Aramark; *U.S. Public*, pg. 176
ARAMARK HARRISON LODGING—See Aramark; *U.S. Public*, pg. 176
ARAMARK HEALTHCARE SUPPORT SERVICES, LLC—See Aramark; *U.S. Public*, pg. 176
ARAMARK HEALTHCARE TECHNOLOGIES, LLC—See Ascension Health Alliance; *U.S. Private*, pg. 346
ARAMARK HOLDINGS GMBH & CO. KG—See Aramark; *U.S. Public*, pg. 176
ARAMARK INDIA PRIVATE LIMITED—See Aramark; *U.S. Public*, pg. 177
ARAMARK INTERMEDIATE HOLDCO CORPORATION—See Aramark; *U.S. Public*, pg. 175
ARAMARK IRELAND HOLDINGS LIMITED—See Aramark; *U.S. Public*, pg. 177
ARAMARK LIMITED—See Aramark; *U.S. Public*, pg. 176
ARAMARK MANAGEMENT GMBH—See Aramark; *U.S. Public*, pg. 177
ARAMARK MANNING SERVICES LIMITED—See Aramark; *U.S. Public*, pg. 176
ARAMARK MEXICO S.A. DE C.V.—See Aramark; *U.S. Public*, pg. 176
ARAMARK NEDERLAND—See Aramark; *U.S. Public*, pg. 176
ARAMARK PERU, S.A.C.—See Aramark; *U.S. Public*, pg. 177
ARAMARK PROPERTY SERVICES LIMITED—See Aramark; *U.S. Public*, pg. 177
ARAMARK QUEBEC, INC.—See Aramark; *U.S. Public*, pg. 176
ARAMARK REFRESHMENT SERVICES, INC.—See Aramark; *U.S. Public*, pg. 176
ARAMARK REFRESHMENT SERVICES, LLC—See Aramark; *U.S. Public*, pg. 176
ARAMARK REFRESHMENT SERVICES OF TAMPA, LLC—See Aramark; *U.S. Public*, pg. 176
ARAMARK REMOTE WORKPLACE SERVICES LTD.—See Aramark; *U.S. Public*, pg. 177
ARAMARK RESTAURATIONS GMBH—See Aramark; *U.S. Public*, pg. 176
ARAMARK SARL—See Aramark; *U.S. Public*, pg. 177
ARAMARK S.A.—See Aramark; *U.S. Public*, pg. 176
ARAMARK SERVICE INDUSTRIES (CHINA) CO., LTD.—See Aramark; *U.S. Public*, pg. 177
ARAMARK SERVICES OF PUERTO RICO, INC.—See Aramark; *U.S. Public*, pg. 176
ARAMARK SERVICIOS DE CATERING, S.L.—See Aramark; *U.S. Public*, pg. 177
ARAMARK SERVICIOS INTEGRALES, S.A.—See Aramark; *U.S. Public*, pg. 177
ARAMARK SERVICIOS SRL—See Aramark; *U.S. Public*, pg. 177
ARAMARK; *U.S. Public*, pg. 175
ARAMARK SPORTS & ENTERTAINMENT SERVICES, LLC—See Aramark; *U.S. Public*, pg. 176
ARAMARK, S.R.O.—See Aramark; *U.S. Public*, pg. 177
ARAMARK UNIFORM & CAREER APPAREL GROUP, INC.—See Vestis Corp; *U.S. Public*, pg. 2290
ARAMARK UNIFORM & CAREER APPAREL, LLC—See Vestis Corp; *U.S. Public*, pg. 2290
ARAMARK UNIFORM & CAREER—See Vestis Corp; *U.S. Public*, pg. 2290
ARAMARK UNIFORM SERVICES (BALTIMORE) LLC—See Vestis Corp; *U.S. Public*, pg. 2290
ARAMARK UNIFORM SERVICES (CANADA) LTD.—See Aramark; *U.S. Public*, pg. 177
ARAMARK UNIFORM SERVICES JAPAN CORPORATION—See Aramark; *U.S. Public*, pg. 177
ARAMARK UNIFORM SERVICES JAPAN CORPORATION—See Mitsui & Co., Ltd.; *Int'l*, pg. 4973
ARAMARK UNIFORM SERVICES (ROCHESTER) LLC—See Vestis Corp; *U.S. Public*, pg. 2290
ARAMARK UNIFORM SERVICES (SANTA ANA) LLC—See Vestis Corp; *U.S. Public*, pg. 2290
ARAMARK UNIFORM SERVICES (SYRACUSE) LLC—See Vestis Corp; *U.S. Public*, pg. 2290
ARAMARK UNIFORM SERVICES (TEXAS) LLC—See Vestis Corp; *U.S. Public*, pg. 2290
ARAMARK WORKPLACE SOLUTIONS (UK) LTD.—See Aramark; *U.S. Public*, pg. 177
ARAMARK WORKPLACE SOLUTIONS YONETIM HIZMETLERI LIMITED SIRKETI—See Aramark; *U.S. Public*, pg. 177
ARAMBHAN GROUP; *Int'l*, pg. 535
ARAMBHAN HOSPITALITY SERVICES LIMITED—See Arambhan Group; *Int'l*, pg. 535
ARAMCO ASIA INDIA PRIVATE LIMITED—See Saudi Arabian Oil Company; *Int'l*, pg. 6589
ARAMCO ASIA JAPAN K.K.—See Saudi Arabian Oil Company; *Int'l*, pg. 6589

ARAMCO ASIA SINGAPORE PTE. LTD.—See Saudi Arabian Oil Company; *Int'l*, pg. 6589
ARAMCO ASSOCIATED COMPANY—See Saudi Arabian Oil Company; *Int'l*, pg. 6589
ARAMCO FAR EAST (BEIJING) BUSINESS SERVICES COMPANY—See Saudi Arabian Oil Company; *Int'l*, pg. 6589
ARAMCO FINANCIAL SERVICES COMPANY—See Saudi Arabian Oil Company; *Int'l*, pg. 6590
ARAMCO OVERSEAS COMPANY BV—See Saudi Arabian Oil Company; *Int'l*, pg. 6589
ARAMCO OVERSEAS COMPANY—See Saudi Arabian Oil Company; *Int'l*, pg. 6589
ARAMCO OVERSEAS COMPANY UK, LIMITED—See Saudi Arabian Oil Company; *Int'l*, pg. 6589
ARAMCO OVERSEAS MALAYSIA SDN. BHD.—See Saudi Arabian Oil Company; *Int'l*, pg. 6589
ARAMCO SERVICES COMPANY—See Saudi Arabian Oil Company; *Int'l*, pg. 6589
ARAMCO TRADING COMPANY—See Saudi Arabian Oil Company; *Int'l*, pg. 6590
ARAMCO TRADING FUJAIRAH FZE—See Saudi Arabian Oil Company; *Int'l*, pg. 6590
ARAMCO TRADING LIMITED—See Saudi Arabian Oil Company; *Int'l*, pg. 6590
ARAMCO TRADING SINGAPORE PTE. LTD.—See Saudi Arabian Oil Company; *Int'l*, pg. 6590
ARAMEA ASSET MANAGEMENT AG—See Niiio Finance Group AG; *Int'l*, pg. 5288
ARAMENDIA PLUMBING, HEATING & AIR, LTD.—See Brookfield Infrastructure Partners L.P.; *Int'l*, pg. 1190
ARAMEX AMMAN—See Aramex PJSC; *Int'l*, pg. 535
ARAMEX EMIRATES LLC—See Aramex PJSC; *Int'l*, pg. 535
ARAMEX HONG KONG LIMITED—See Aramex PJSC; *Int'l*, pg. 535
ARAMEX INDIA PRIVATE LIMITED—See Aramex PJSC; *Int'l*, pg. 535
ARAMEX INTERNATIONAL EGYPT FOR AIR & LOCAL SERVICES (S.A.E)—See Aramex PJSC; *Int'l*, pg. 535
ARAMEX INTERNATIONAL EGYPT—See Aramex PJSC; *Int'l*, pg. 535
ARAMEX INTERNATIONAL HAVA KARGO VE KERYE ANONIM SIRKETI—See Aramex PJSC; *Int'l*, pg. 535
ARAMEX INTERNATIONAL LIMITED—See Aramex PJSC; *Int'l*, pg. 535
ARAMEX INTERNATIONAL LOGISTICS PRIVATE LTD.—See Aramex PJSC; *Int'l*, pg. 535
ARAMEX IRELAND—See Aramex PJSC; *Int'l*, pg. 535
ARAMEX JORDAN LTD.—See Aramex PJSC; *Int'l*, pg. 535
ARAMEX KUWAIT KSE—See Aramex PJSC; *Int'l*, pg. 535
ARAMEX NEDERLAND BV—See Aramex PJSC; *Int'l*, pg. 535
ARAMEX PJSC; *Int'l*, pg. 535
ARAMEX SAUDI LIMITED COMPANY—See Aramex PJSC; *Int'l*, pg. 535
ARAMEX SOUTH AFRICA PTY LTD—See Aramex PJSC; *Int'l*, pg. 535
ARAMEX (UK) LIMITED—See Aramex PJSC; *Int'l*, pg. 535
ARAM GROUP P.J.S.C; *Int'l*, pg. 535
ARAMIJAYA SDN. BHD.—See PLS Plantations Berhad; *Int'l*, pg. 5898
ARAM INCORPORATED; *U.S. Private*, pg. 307
ARAMIS GROUP SAS; *Int'l*, pg. 535
ARAMIT CEMENT LTD.; *Int'l*, pg. 535
ARAMIT GROUP; *Int'l*, pg. 535
ARAMIT LIMITED—See Aramit Group; *Int'l*, pg. 535
ARAMIT THAI ALUMINIUM LIMITED—See Aramit Group; *Int'l*, pg. 535
ARAMO SHIPPING (SINGAPORE) PTE LTD—See Fuji Oil Company, Ltd.; *Int'l*, pg. 2815
ARAMSCO, INC.—See American Securities LLC; *U.S. Private*, pg. 247
ARA M/V—See Omnicom Group Inc.; *U.S. Public*, pg. 1596
ARA-NAPLES DIALYSIS CENTER LLC—See Nautic Partners, LLC; *U.S. Private*, pg. 2869
ARA-NAPLES SOUTH DIALYSIS CENTER LLC—See Nautic Partners, LLC; *U.S. Private*, pg. 2869
ARA NATIONAL LAND SERVICES, LLC—See BGC Group, Inc.; *U.S. Public*, pg. 328
ARAN BIOMEDICAL TEORANTA LTD.—See Integer Holdings Corporation; *U.S. Public*, pg. 1134
ARANDELL CORPORATION—See Saothair Capital Partners LLC; *U.S. Private*, pg. 3548
ARANEO LIMITED—See Vital Limited; *Int'l*, pg. 8258
ARANETA PROPERTIES, INC.; *Int'l*, pg. 536
ARANJIN RESOURCES LIMITED; *Int'l*, pg. 536
A-RANK BERHAD; *Int'l*, pg. 20
ARAN RESEARCH & DEVELOPMENT (1982) LTD.; *Int'l*, pg. 535
ARAN WORLD S.R.L.—See Masco Corporation; *U.S. Public*, pg. 1391
ARA-ORANGE PARK LLC—See Nautic Partners, LLC; *U.S. Private*, pg. 2869
ARAPAHOE BASIN SKI AREA—See KSL Capital Partners, LLC; *U.S. Private*, pg. 2354

ARAPAHOE GASTROENTEROLOGY ANASTHESIA ASSOCIATES LLC—See WELL Health Technologies Corp.; *Int'l*, pg. 8372
ARAPAHOE HOUSE; *U.S. Private*, pg. 307
ARAPAHOE MOTORS, INC.; *U.S. Private*, pg. 307
ARAPAHOE SURGICENTER, LLC—See HCA Healthcare, Inc.; *U.S. Public*, pg. 990
ARA PARTNERS GROUP, LLC—See Affiliated Managers Group, Inc.; *U.S. Public*, pg. 53
ARA PARTNERS GROUP; *U.S. Private*, pg. 306
ARAPRINT B.V.—See Cimpress plc; *Int'l*, pg. 1609
ARA-PROVIDENCE DIALYSIS LLC—See Nautic Partners, LLC; *U.S. Private*, pg. 2869
A. RAPTIS & SONS PTY. LTD.; *Int'l*, pg. 21
ARARA, INC.; *Int'l*, pg. 536
ARARATBANK OJSC; *Int'l*, pg. 536
ARARAT HOME OF LOS ANGELES, INC.; *U.S. Private*, pg. 307
ARA REAL ESTATE INVESTORS XVIII PTE. LTD—See ESR Group Limited; *Int'l*, pg. 2508
ARA-RHODE ISLAND DIALYSIS II LLC—See Nautic Partners, LLC; *U.S. Private*, pg. 2869
ARASCO CHEMICAL CO.—See Arabian Agricultural Services Co.; *Int'l*, pg. 533
ARASCO COLD STORE CO.—See Arabian Agricultural Services Co.; *Int'l*, pg. 533
ARASCO FEED MILL CO.—See Arabian Agricultural Services Co.; *Int'l*, pg. 533
ARAS CORP; *U.S. Private*, pg. 307
ARASCO TRANSPORT, HANDLING AND SHIPPING CO.—See Arabian Agricultural Services Co.; *Int'l*, pg. 533
ARA-SOUTH LABURNUM DIALYSIS LLC—See Nautic Partners, LLC; *U.S. Private*, pg. 2869
ARAS SECURITY AB—See Lagercrantz Group AB; *Int'l*, pg. 4393
ARAS SECURITY A/S—See Lagercrantz Group AB; *Int'l*, pg. 4393
ARAT AB—See Storskogen Group AB; *Int'l*, pg. 7227
ARATA CORPORATION; *Int'l*, pg. 536
ARATANA THERAPEUTICS, INC.—See Elanco Animal Health Incorporated; *U.S. Public*, pg. 722
ARATANA THERAPEUTICS NV—See Elanco Animal Health Incorporated; *U.S. Public*, pg. 722
ARATA (THAILAND) CO., LTD.—See Arata Corporation; *Int'l*, pg. 536
ARATA VIETNAM COMPANY LIMITED—See Arata Corporation; *Int'l*, pg. 536
ARA-TITUSVILLE DIALYSIS LLC—See Nautic Partners, LLC; *U.S. Private*, pg. 2869
ARA-TIVERTON DIALYSIS LLC—See Nautic Partners, LLC; *U.S. Private*, pg. 2869
ARATRON AB—See Addtech AB; *Int'l*, pg. 131
ARATRON A/S—See THK CO., LTD.; *Int'l*, pg. 7711
ARATRON HYDRAULIKK AS—See Addtech AB; *Int'l*, pg. 132
ARATRON KURT WIIG AS—See Addtech AB; *Int'l*, pg. 132
ARA TRUST MANAGEMENT (SUNTEC) LIMITED—See ESR Group Limited; *Int'l*, pg. 2508
ARAUCO DO BRASIL SA—See AntarChile S.A.; *Int'l*, pg. 481
ARA US HOSPITALITY TRUST; *Int'l*, pg. 529
ARAVALI SECURITIES & FINANCE LIMITED; *Int'l*, pg. 536
ARAVANIS INSOLVENCY PTY LTD—See FSA Group Limited; *Int'l*, pg. 2798
ARAVIVE, INC.; *U.S. Public*, pg. 178
ARAWAK CEMENT COMPANY LIMITED—See CEMEX, S.A.B. de C.V.; *Int'l*, pg. 1400
ARAWAK ENERGY CORPORATION—See Vitol Holding B.V.; *Int'l*, pg. 8260
ARAWAK ENERGY INTERNATIONAL LTD.—See Vitol Holding B.V.; *Int'l*, pg. 8260
ARAWAK PAVING CO. INC.; *U.S. Private*, pg. 308
ARAWATA ASSETS LIMITED—See Australia & New Zealand Banking Group Limited; *Int'l*, pg. 720
ARA-WEST JACKSONVILLE LLC—See Nautic Partners, LLC; *U.S. Private*, pg. 2869
ARAYA INDUSTRIAL CO., LTD.; *Int'l*, pg. 536
A RAYMOND AUTOMOTIVE FASTENERS (ZHENJIANG) CO., LTD.—See A. Raymond & Cie SCS; *Int'l*, pg. 21
A RAYMOND BAGLANTI ELEMANLARI LTD. STI—See A. Raymond & Cie SCS; *Int'l*, pg. 21
A. RAYMOND BRASIL LTDA—See A. Raymond & Cie SCS; *Int'l*, pg. 22
A. RAYMOND & CIE SCS; *Int'l*, pg. 21
A RAYMOND FASTENERS INDIA PRIVATE LIMITED—See A. Raymond & Cie SCS; *Int'l*, pg. 22
A. RAYMOND GMBH & CO. KG—See A. Raymond & Cie SCS; *Int'l*, pg. 22
ARAYMOND INDUSTRIAL—See A. Raymond & Cie SCS; *Int'l*, pg. 22
A RAYMOND ITALIANA S.R.L—See A. Raymond & Cie SCS; *Int'l*, pg. 22
A. RAYMOND JABLONEC S.R.O.—See A. Raymond & Cie SCS; *Int'l*, pg. 22
A RAYMOND JAPAN CO., LTD.—See A. Raymond & Cie SCS; *Int'l*, pg. 21

A. RAYMOND & CIE SCS

A. RAYMOND KOREA CO. LTD.—See A. Raymond & Cie SCS; *Int'l*, pg. 22
A. RAYMOND LTD.—See A. Raymond & Cie SCS; *Int'l*, pg. 22
A RAYMOND - PACIFIC SIGHT LTD—See A. Raymond & Cie SCS; *Int'l*, pg. 21
A. RAYMOND RUS LLC—See A. Raymond & Cie SCS; *Int'l*, pg. 22
A. RAYMOND SINGAPORE PTE. LTD.—See A. Raymond & Cie SCS; *Int'l*, pg. 22
A.RAYMOND SLOVAKIA, S.R.O.—See A. Raymond & Cie SCS; *Int'l*, pg. 22
A RAYMOND TECNIACERO SAU—See A. Raymond & Cie SCS; *Int'l*, pg. 21
A. RAYMOND TINNERMAN AUTOMOTIVE INC.—See A. Raymond & Cie SCS; *Int'l*, pg. 22
A. RAYMOND TINNERMAN AUTOMOTIVE MEXICO S. DE R.L. DE C.V.—See A. Raymond & Cie SCS; *Int'l*, pg. 22
ARAYMOND TINNERMAN INDUSTRIAL INC.—See A. Raymond & Cie SCS; *Int'l*, pg. 22
A.RAYMOND TINNERMAN MANUFACTURING HAMILTON, INC.—See A. Raymond & Cie SCS; *Int'l*, pg. 22
A RAYMOND TINNERMAN MANUFACTURING, INC.—See A. Raymond & Cie SCS; *Int'l*, pg. 22
ARA-YUBA CITY DIALYSIS LLC—See Nautic Partners, LLC; *U.S. Private*, pg. 2869
ARAZU INCORPORATED; *Int'l*, pg. 536
ARB BERHAD; *Int'l*, pg. 536
ARB CORPORATION LIMITED; *Int'l*, pg. 536
AR-BE DOORS INC.; *U.S. Private*, pg. 306
ARBEE ASSOCIATES INC.; *U.S. Private*, pg. 308
ARBEITSGEMEINSCHAFT ZELLENKUHLERANLAGE KKW ISAR GEA ENERGIETECHNIK GMBH-ALPINE BAU DEUTSCHLAND AG—See GEA Group Aktiengesellschaft; *Int'l*, pg. 2897
ARBEIT-TIMES CO., LTD.; *Int'l*, pg. 537
ARBEJDERNES LANDSBANK A/S; *Int'l*, pg. 537
ARBEJDSMARKEDETS TILLAEGSPENSION; *Int'l*, pg. 537
ARBEL GROUP—See AGT Food and Ingredients Inc.; *Int'l*, pg. 221
ARBELLA INCORPORATED—See Arbella Insurance Group; *U.S. Private*, pg. 308
ARBELLA INDEMNITY INSURANCE CO.—See Arbella Insurance Group; *U.S. Private*, pg. 308
ARBELLA INSURANCE GROUP—See Arbella Insurance Group; *U.S. Private*, pg. 308
ARBELLA INSURANCE GROUP; *U.S. Private*, pg. 308
ARBELLA MUTUAL INSURANCE CO.—See Arbella Insurance Group; *U.S. Private*, pg. 308
ARBELLA PROTECTION INSURANCE COMPANY INC.—See Arbella Insurance Group; *U.S. Private*, pg. 308
ARBELLA SERVICE COMPANY INC.—See Arbella Insurance Group; *U.S. Private*, pg. 308
ARBEN GROUP LLC.; *U.S. Private*, pg. 308
ARBEN GROUP; *U.S. Private*, pg. 308
ARB HOLDINGS LIMITED; *Int'l*, pg. 536
ARBICO EAST LLC; *U.S. Private*, pg. 308
ARBICO PLC.; *Int'l*, pg. 537
ARBILL INDUSTRIES INC.; *U.S. Private*, pg. 308
ARB, INC.—See Primoris Services Corporation; *U.S. Public*, pg. 1718
ARB IOT GROUP LIMITED; *Int'l*, pg. 537
ARBITECH; *U.S. Private*, pg. 308
ARBITRATION FORUMS, INC.; *U.S. Private*, pg. 308
ARBIZ CO., LTD.—See USS Co., Ltd.; *Int'l*, pg. 8099
ARB MIDSTREAM, LLC; *U.S. Private*, pg. 308
ARBOC SPECIALTY VEHICLES, LLC—See NFI Group Inc.; *Int'l*, pg. 5252
ARBOGA-DARENTH LTD—See Nederman Holding AB; *Int'l*, pg. 5188
ARBOL INC.; *U.S. Private*, pg. 308
ARBONA AB; *Int'l*, pg. 537
ARBON EQUIPMENT CORPORATION—See Rite-Hite Holding Corporation; *U.S. Private*, pg. 3441
ARBON EQUIPMENT PTY LIMITED—See Rite-Hite Holding Corporation; *U.S. Private*, pg. 3442
ARBONIA AG; *Int'l*, pg. 537
ARBONIA FRANCE S.A.R.L.—See Arbonia AG; *Int'l*, pg. 537
ARBONIA MANAGEMENT AG—See Arbonia AG; *Int'l*, pg. 537
ARBONIA RIESA GMBH—See Arbonia AG; *Int'l*, pg. 538
ARBONIA SERVICES AG—See Arbonia AG; *Int'l*, pg. 538
ARBONIA SOLUTIONS AG—See Arbonia AG; *Int'l*, pg. 538
ARBONIS—See VINCI S.A.; *Int'l*, pg. 8211
ARBONNE INTERNATIONAL, LLC—See Groupe Rocher Operations SAS; *Int'l*, pg. 3110
ARBORA & AUSONIA, S.L.—See The Procter & Gamble Company; *U.S. Public*, pg. 2120
ARBOR ART TREE CARE INC.—See Apax Partners LLP; *Int'l*, pg. 506
ARBOR BANCORP, INC.; *U.S. Private*, pg. 308
ARBOR BIOSCIENCES (BIODISCOVERY LLC)—See Daicel Corporation; *Int'l*, pg. 1918
ARBORCHEM PRODUCTS—See Asplundh Tree Expert Co.; *U.S. Private*, pg. 353

ARBOR CONSULTING RESOURCES INC.; *U.S. Private*, pg. 308
ARBOR CONTRACT CARPET INC.; *U.S. Private*, pg. 308
ARBOR-CROWLEY, LLC—See AZZ, Inc.; *U.S. Public*, pg. 259
ARBORETUM MALL, LLC—See Washington Prime Group Inc.; *U.S. Private*, pg. 4448
ARBORGEN HOLDINGS LIMITED; *Int'l*, pg. 538
ARBORGEN INC.—See ArborGen Holdings Limited; *Int'l*, pg. 538
ARBORGUARD, INC.—See The Davey Tree Expert Company; *U.S. Private*, pg. 4018
ARBOR HOMES, LLC—See Berkshire Hathaway Inc.; *U.S. Public*, pg. 304
ARBOR INVESTMENT GROUP; *U.S. Private*, pg. 308
ARBORINVEST, S.A.U.—See The Procter & Gamble Company; *U.S. Public*, pg. 2120
ARBOR ITALIA S.R.L.—See Arbor Technology Corp.; *Int'l*, pg. 538
ARBORITE; *Int'l*, pg. 538
ARBOR MATERIAL HANDLING INC.; *U.S. Private*, pg. 308
ARBOR MEMORIAL SERVICES INC.—See Fairfax Financial Holdings Limited; *Int'l*, pg. 2606
ARBOR MEMORIAL SERVICES INC.—See JC Clark Ltd.; *Int'l*, pg. 3919
ARBOR METALS CORP.; *Int'l*, pg. 538
ARBORMETRICS SOLUTIONS, INC.—See Asplundh Tree Expert Co.; *U.S. Private*, pg. 353
ARBOR NETWORKS UK LTD—See Danaher Corporation; *U.S. Public*, pg. 624
ARBOR-NOMICS TURF, INC.—See Senske Lawn & Tree Care, Inc.; *U.S. Private*, pg. 3608
ARBOR PHARMACEUTICALS LLC—See NovaQuest Capital Management, LLC; *U.S. Private*, pg. 2967
ARBOR PRIVATE INVESTMENT COMPANY, LLC; *U.S. Private*, pg. 309
ARBOR REALTY FUNDING, LLC—See Arbor Realty Trust, Inc.; *U.S. Public*, pg. 178
ARBOR REALTY SR, INC.—See Arbor Realty Trust, Inc.; *U.S. Public*, pg. 178
ARBOR REALTY TRUST, INC.; *U.S. Public*, pg. 178
ARBOR TECHNOLOGY CORP.; *Int'l*, pg. 538
ARBORTECH—See Berkshire Hathaway Inc.; *U.S. Public*, pg. 299
ARBOR TRAILS, LLC—See Hovnanian Enterprises, Inc.; *U.S. Public*, pg. 1056
ARBOR TREE SERVICE INC.—See The Davey Tree Expert Company; *U.S. Private*, pg. 4018
ARBOR WALK MALL, LLC—See Washington Prime Group Inc.; *U.S. Private*, pg. 4448
ARBORWELL, INC.—See Apax Partners LLP; *Int'l*, pg. 506
ARBOS CO., LTD.—See Nippon Fine Chemical Co., Ltd.; *Int'l*, pg. 5318
ARBOUR CLO LIMITED—See Brookfield Corporation; *Int'l*, pg. 1181
ARBOUR ELDER SERVICES, INC.—See Universal Health Services, Inc.; *U.S. Public*, pg. 2255
ARBOUR FOUNDATION, INC.—See Universal Health Services, Inc.; *U.S. Public*, pg. 2255
THE ARBOUR HOSPITAL—See Universal Health Services, Inc.; *U.S. Public*, pg. 2260
ARBOUR-HRI HOSPITAL—See Universal Health Services, Inc.; *U.S. Public*, pg. 2260
ARBOUR NATIONAL; *U.S. Private*, pg. 309
ARB STRUCTURES—See Primoris Services Corporation; *U.S. Public*, pg. 1718
A&R BULK-PAK, INC.—See Nova Infrastructure Management, LLC; *U.S. Private*, pg. 2965
ARBURG AG—See Arburg GmbH & Co.; *Int'l*, pg. 539
ARBURG A/S—See Arburg GmbH & Co.; *Int'l*, pg. 539
ARBURG BV—See Arburg GmbH & Co.; *Int'l*, pg. 539
ARBURG GESMBH—See Arburg GmbH & Co.; *Int'l*, pg. 539
ARBURG GMBH & CO.; *Int'l*, pg. 539
ARBURG (HK) LTD.—See Arburg GmbH & Co.; *Int'l*, pg. 539
ARBURG HUNGARIA KFT.—See Arburg GmbH & Co.; *Int'l*, pg. 539
ARBURG, INC.—See Arburg GmbH & Co.; *Int'l*, pg. 539
ARBURG LTDA.—See Arburg GmbH & Co.; *Int'l*, pg. 539
ARBURG N.V.—See Arburg GmbH & Co.; *Int'l*, pg. 539
ARBURG POLSKA SP. Z O.O.—See Arburg GmbH & Co.; *Int'l*, pg. 539
ARBURG, S.A. DE C.V.—See Arburg GmbH & Co.; *Int'l*, pg. 539
ARBURG SDN BHD—See Arburg GmbH & Co.; *Int'l*, pg. 539
ARBURG SPOL. S R. O.—See Arburg GmbH & Co.; *Int'l*, pg. 539
ARBURG (THAILAND) CO., LTD.—See Arburg GmbH & Co.; *Int'l*, pg. 539
ARBUTHNOT BANKING GROUP PLC; *Int'l*, pg. 539
ARBUTHNOT LATHAM & CO. LIMITED—See Arbuthnot Banking Group plc; *Int'l*, pg. 539
ARBUTUS BIOPHARMA CORPORATION; *U.S. Public*, pg. 178
ARBUTUS PARK RETIREMENT COMMUNITY; *U.S. Private*, pg. 309

CORPORATE AFFILIATIONS

ARBY'S CANADA, INC.—See Roark Capital Group Inc.; *U.S. Private*, pg. 3455
ARBY'S RESTAURANT GROUP, INC.—See Roark Capital Group Inc.; *U.S. Private*, pg. 3455
ARC3 ARCHITECTURE, INC.; *U.S. Private*, pg. 309
ARCA ASSICURAZIONI S.P.A.—See Unipol Gruppo S.p.A.; *Int'l*, pg. 8056
ARC ABATEMENT, INC.; *U.S. Private*, pg. 309
ARCA BIOPHARMA, INC.; *U.S. Public*, pg. 179
ARCA BIRU SDN BHD—See Khazanah Nasional Berhad; *Int'l*, pg. 4152
ARCA CALIFORNIA—See ALT5 Sigma Corporation; *U.S. Public*, pg. 85
ARCA CANADA INC.—See ALT5 Sigma Corporation; *U.S. Public*, pg. 85
ARCA CAPITAL BOHEMIA, A.S.—See Arca Capital Slovakia, A.S.; *Int'l*, pg. 539
ARCA CAPITAL FINANCE GROUP, A.S.—See Arca Capital Slovakia, A.S.; *Int'l*, pg. 540
ARCA CAPITAL SLOVAKIA, A.S.; *Int'l*, pg. 539
ARCA CONTINENTAL, S.A.B. DE C.V.; *Int'l*, pg. 540
ARCADE CHINA ACQUISITION CORP.; *U.S. Private*, pg. 309
ARCADIA AEROSPACE INDUSTRIES LLC—See X-Ray Industries Inc.; *U.S. Private*, pg. 4579
ARCADIA BIOSCIENCES, INC.; *U.S. Public*, pg. 179
THE ARCADIA CA ENDOSCOPY ASC, L.P.—See KKR & Co. Inc.; *U.S. Public*, pg. 1247
ARCADIA CHEVROLET BUICK PONTIAC INC.; *U.S. Private*, pg. 309
ARCADIA DEVELOPMENT PTE. LTD.—See Allgreen Properties Ltd.; *Int'l*, pg. 338
ARCADIA GROUP LIMITED; *Int'l*, pg. 540
ARCADIA INC.—See DMC Global Inc.; *U.S. Public*, pg. 671
ARCADIA JEWELLERY LIMITED—See Affluent Partners Holdings Limited; *Int'l*, pg. 188
ARCADIA LIVE GMBH—See CTS Eventim AG & Co. KGAA; *Int'l*, pg. 1872
ARCADIA MINERALS LIMITED; *Int'l*, pg. 540
ARCADIAN HEALTHCARE; *U.S. Private*, pg. 310
ARCADIAN WOOL BROKERS LIMITED—See Nutrien Ltd.; *Int'l*, pg. 5492
ARCADIA OPTRONIX INC.—See Advanced Fiber Resources (Zhuhai) Ltd; *Int'l*, pg. 159
ARCADIA PUBLISHING, INC.; *U.S. Private*, pg. 309
ARCADIA SOLUTIONS, LLC—See Ferrer Freeman & Company, LLC; *U.S. Private*, pg. 1498
ARCADIE SA—See Safestay Plc; *Int'l*, pg. 6470
ARCADIS ASIA—See ARCADIS N.V.; *Int'l*, pg. 540
ARCADIS AUSTRALIA PACIFIC HOLDINGS PTY. LTD.—See ARCADIS N.V.; *Int'l*, pg. 541
ARCADIS BELGIUM HOLDING NV—See ARCADIS N.V.; *Int'l*, pg. 540
ARCADIS BELGIUM N.V.—See ARCADIS N.V.; *Int'l*, pg. 540
ARCADIS BOUW BV—See ARCADIS N.V.; *Int'l*, pg. 541
ARCADIS CHILE SA—See ARCADIS N.V.; *Int'l*, pg. 540
ARCADIS CZ A.S.—See ARCADIS N.V.; *Int'l*, pg. 540
ARCADIS DEUTSCHLAND GMBH—See ARCADIS N.V.; *Int'l*, pg. 540
ARCADIS ESG—See ARCADIS N.V.; *Int'l*, pg. 540
ARCADIS EUROMETUDES S.A.—See ARCADIS N.V.; *Int'l*, pg. 540
ARCADIS FRANCE S.A.S.—See ARCADIS N.V.; *Int'l*, pg. 541
ARCADIS G&M, INC.—See ARCADIS N.V.; *Int'l*, pg. 541
ARCADIS HOLDING FRANCE S.A.S.—See ARCADIS N.V.; *Int'l*, pg. 540
ARCADIS INFRA B.V.—See ARCADIS N.V.; *Int'l*, pg. 541
ARCADIS ITALIA SRL—See ARCADIS N.V.; *Int'l*, pg. 540
ARCADIS LLP—See ARCADIS N.V.; *Int'l*, pg. 541
ARCADIS LOGOS LTDA.—See ARCADIS N.V.; *Int'l*, pg. 540
ARCADIS, LTD.—See ARCADIS N.V.; *Int'l*, pg. 541
ARCADIS - MIDDLE EAST—See ARCADIS N.V.; *Int'l*, pg. 541
ARCADIS NEDERLAND BV—See ARCADIS N.V.; *Int'l*, pg. 541
ARCADIS N.V.; *Int'l*, pg. 540
ARCADIS PERU—See ARCADIS N.V.; *Int'l*, pg. 540
ARCADIS - PHILIPPINES—See ARCADIS N.V.; *Int'l*, pg. 541
ARCADIS RUIWITELIJKE OHTWILLEUNG BV—See ARCADIS N.V.; *Int'l*, pg. 541
ARCADIS SPATIAL INFORMATION—See ARCADIS N.V.; *Int'l*, pg. 541
ARCADIS SP. Z.O.O.—See ARCADIS N.V.; *Int'l*, pg. 541
ARCADIS - SYDNEY—See ARCADIS N.V.; *Int'l*, pg. 540
ARCADIS (UK) LIMITED—See ARCADIS N.V.; *Int'l*, pg. 541
ARCADIS U.S., INC. - AUSTIN—See ARCADIS N.V.; *Int'l*, pg. 541
ARCADIS U.S., INC.—See ARCADIS N.V.; *Int'l*, pg. 541
ARCADIS U.S., INC. - TAMPA—See ARCADIS N.V.; *Int'l*, pg. 541
ARCADYAN TECHNOLOGY CORPORATION—See Compal Electronics, Inc.; *Int'l*, pg. 1746
ARCA IMPRESA GESTIONI SGR S.P.A.; *Int'l*, pg. 540

COMPANY NAME INDEX

ARCA INVESTMENTS, A.S.; *Int'l*, pg. 540
ARCALIS—See Allianz SE; *Int'l*, pg. 342
ARCAM AB—See General Electric Company; *U.S. Public*, pg. 919
ARCAMAX PUBLISHING, INC.; *U.S. Private*, pg. 310
ARCA MINNESOTA—See ALT5 Sigma Corporation; *U.S. Public*, pg. 85
ARC AMSTERDAM—See Publicis Groupe S.A.; *Int'l*, pg. 6097
ARCANA POOL SYSTEMS GMBH—See BWT Aktiengesellschaft; *Int'l*, pg. 1233
ARCANE LTD.—See JFLA Holdings Inc.; *Int'l*, pg. 3939
ARCANE S.A.R.L.—See JFLA Holdings Inc.; *Int'l*, pg. 3939
ARCAPITA BANK B.S.C. (C)—See Arcapita Group Holdings Limited; *Int'l*, pg. 542
ARCAPITA GROUP HOLDINGS LIMITED; *Int'l*, pg. 542
ARCAPITA, INC.—See Arcapita Group Holdings Limited; *Int'l*, pg. 542
ARCAPITA INVESTMENT ADVISORS UK LIMITED—See Arcapita Group Holdings Limited; *Int'l*, pg. 542
ARCAPITA INVESTMENT MANAGEMENT B.S.C.(C)—See Arcapita Group Holdings Limited; *Int'l*, pg. 543
ARCAPITA INVESTMENT MANAGEMENT SINGAPORE PTE. LTD.—See Arcapita Group Holdings Limited; *Int'l*, pg. 542
AR CAPITAL, LLC—See AR Global Investments, LLC; *U.S. Private*, pg. 306
ARCA REGLER GMBH; *Int'l*, pg. 540
ARCAROMA AB—See OptiCept Technologies AB; *Int'l*, pg. 5602
A&R CARTON AB—See CVC Capital Partners SICAV-FIS S.A.; *Int'l*, pg. 1881
A&R CARTON A/S—See CVC Capital Partners SICAV-FIS S.A.; *Int'l*, pg. 1881
A&R CARTON CDF SA—See CVC Capital Partners SICAV-FIS S.A.; *Int'l*, pg. 1881
A&R CARTON LUND AB—See CVC Capital Partners SICAV-FIS S.A.; *Int'l*, pg. 1881
A&R CARTON NORTH AMERICA INC.—See CVC Capital Partners SICAV-FIS S.A.; *Int'l*, pg. 1881
A&R CARTON OY—See CVC Capital Partners SICAV-FIS S.A.; *Int'l*, pg. 1881
A&R CARTON—See CVC Capital Partners SICAV-FIS S.A.; *Int'l*, pg. 1881
A&R CARTON ST PETERSBURG ZAO—See CVC Capital Partners SICAV-FIS S.A.; *Int'l*, pg. 1881
ARC ASPICIO LLC; *U.S. Private*, pg. 309
ARCA.TECH SYSTEMS, L.L.C.—See BC Partners LLP; *Int'l*, pg. 924
ARC AUTOMOTIVE, INC.—See Yinyi Co., Ltd.; *Int'l*, pg. 8585
ARCA VALVULAS S.A. DE C.V.—See ARCA Regler GmbH; *Int'l*, pg. 540
ARCA VITA S.P.A.—See Unipol Gruppo S.p.A.; *Int'l*, pg. 8056
ARC BAY PINES INC—See Brookdale Senior Living Inc.; *U.S. Public*, pg. 393
ARCBEST CORPORATION; *U.S. Public*, pg. 179
ARCBEST INTERNATIONAL, INC.—See ArcBest Corporation; *U.S. Public*, pg. 180
ARCBEST LOGISTICS, INC.—See ArcBest Corporation; *U.S. Public*, pg. 180
ARCBEST TECHNOLOGIES, INC.—See ArcBest Corporation; *U.S. Public*, pg. 180
ARC BOYNTON BEACH LLC—See Brookdale Senior Living Inc.; *U.S. Public*, pg. 393
ARC BRADENTON HC, INC.—See Brookdale Senior Living Inc.; *U.S. Public*, pg. 393
ARC BRANDYWINE, LP—See Brookdale Senior Living Inc.; *U.S. Public*, pg. 393
ARC COCONUT CREEK LLC—See Brookdale Senior Living Inc.; *U.S. Public*, pg. 393
ARC-COM FABRICS INCORPORATED; *U.S. Private*, pg. 309
ARC CONSULTING LLC—See CBIZ, Inc.; *U.S. Public*, pg. 456
ARC CONTRACTING, INC.; *U.S. Private*, pg. 309
ARC COUNTRYSIDE LLC—See Brookdale Senior Living Inc.; *U.S. Public*, pg. 393
ARC DOCUMENT SOLUTIONS, INC. - ATLANTA—See ARC DOCUMENT SOLUTIONS, INC.; *U.S. Public*, pg. 179
ARC DOCUMENT SOLUTIONS, INC.—See ARC DOCUMENT SOLUTIONS, INC.; *U.S. Public*, pg. 179
ARC DOCUMENT SOLUTIONS, INC.—See ARC DOCUMENT SOLUTIONS, INC.; *U.S. Public*, pg. 179
ARC DOCUMENT SOLUTIONS, INC.—See ARC DOCUMENT SOLUTIONS, INC.; *U.S. Public*, pg. 179
ARC DOCUMENT SOLUTIONS, INC.—See ARC DOCUMENT SOLUTIONS, INC.; *U.S. Public*, pg. 179
ARC DOCUMENT SOLUTIONS, INC.—See ARC DOCUMENT SOLUTIONS, INC.; *U.S. Public*, pg. 179
ARC DOCUMENT SOLUTIONS, INC.; *U.S. Public*, pg. 178
ARC DOCUMENT SOLUTIONS, LLC—See ARC DOCUMENT SOLUTIONS, INC.; *U.S. Public*, pg. 179
ARC DOCUMENT SOLUTIONS - TEXAS—See ARC DOCUMENT SOLUTIONS, INC.; *U.S. Public*, pg. 178

ARC E-COMMERCE AB—See BHG Group AB; *Int'l*, pg. 1014
ARCEE INDUSTRIES LIMITED; *Int'l*, pg. 543
ARCELIK A.S.—See Koc Holding A.S.; *Int'l*, pg. 4222
ARCELIK HITACHI HOME APPLIANCES SALES HONG KONG LIMITED—See Koc Holding A.S.; *Int'l*, pg. 4222
ARCELIK HITACHI HOME APPLIANCES SALES MALAYSIA SDN. BHD.—See Koc Holding A.S.; *Int'l*, pg. 4222
ARCELIK HITACHI HOME APPLIANCES SALES MIDDLE EAST FZE—See Koc Holding A.S.; *Int'l*, pg. 4222
ARCELIK HITACHI HOME APPLIANCES SALES (SINGAPORE) PTE. LTD.—See Koc Holding A.S.; *Int'l*, pg. 4222
ARCELIK HITACHI HOME APPLIANCES SALES VIETNAM CO., LTD.—See Koc Holding A.S.; *Int'l*, pg. 4222
ARCELIK HITACHI HOME APPLIANCES (THAILAND) LTD.—See Koc Holding A.S.; *Int'l*, pg. 4222
ARCELIK MOTOR PLANTS—See Koc Holding A.S.; *Int'l*, pg. 4222
ARCELLX, INC.; *U.S. Public*, pg. 180
ARCELOR INTERNATIONAL EXPORT S.A.—See ArcelorMittal S.A.; *Int'l*, pg. 543
ARCELORMITTAL AMBALAJ CELIGI SANAYI VE TICARET A.S.—See ArcelorMittal S.A.; *Int'l*, pg. 543
ARCELORMITTAL ANCENIS—See ArcelorMittal S.A.; *Int'l*, pg. 543
ARCELORMITTAL ANNABA SPA—See ArcelorMittal S.A.; *Int'l*, pg. 543
ARCELORMITTAL - ARCELORMITTAL AVELLINO MILL—See ArcelorMittal S.A.; *Int'l*, pg. 543
ARCELORMITTAL - ARCELORMITTAL CANOSSA MILL—See ArcelorMittal S.A.; *Int'l*, pg. 543
ARCELORMITTAL - ARCELORMITTAL DESVRES MILL—See ArcelorMittal S.A.; *Int'l*, pg. 543
ARCELORMITTAL - ARCELORMITTAL DUNKERQUE MILL—See ArcelorMittal S.A.; *Int'l*, pg. 543
ARCELORMITTAL - ARCELORMITTAL ETXEBARRI MILL—See ArcelorMittal S.A.; *Int'l*, pg. 543
ARCELORMITTAL - ARCELORMITTAL MARDYCK MILL—See ArcelorMittal S.A.; *Int'l*, pg. 543
ARCELORMITTAL - ARCELORMITTAL MONTATAIRE MILL—See ArcelorMittal S.A.; *Int'l*, pg. 543
ARCELORMITTAL - ARCELORMITTAL MOUZON MILL—See ArcelorMittal S.A.; *Int'l*, pg. 543
ARCELORMITTAL ASTURIAS S.A.—See ArcelorMittal S.A.; *Int'l*, pg. 545
ARCELORMITTAL ATLANTIQUE ET LORRAINE S.A.S.—See ArcelorMittal S.A.; *Int'l*, pg. 543
ARCELORMITTAL BELVAL & DIFFERDANGE S.A.—See ArcelorMittal S.A.; *Int'l*, pg. 543
ARCELORMITTAL BERYSLAV—See ArcelorMittal S.A.; *Int'l*, pg. 543
ARCELORMITTAL BISSEN S.A.—See ArcelorMittal S.A.; *Int'l*, pg. 543
ARCELORMITTAL BRAMPTON—See ArcelorMittal S.A.; *Int'l*, pg. 544
ARCELORMITTAL BRASIL S.A.—See ArcelorMittal S.A.; *Int'l*, pg. 543
ARCELORMITTAL BREMEN GMBH—See ArcelorMittal S.A.; *Int'l*, pg. 543
ARCELORMITTAL CARIACICA—See ArcelorMittal S.A.; *Int'l*, pg. 544
ARCELORMITTAL CELAYA S.A. DE C.V.—See ArcelorMittal S.A.; *Int'l*, pg. 544
ARCELORMITTAL COATESVILLE—See Cleveland-Cliffs, Inc.; *U.S. Public*, pg. 514
ARCELORMITTAL COMMERCIAL RPS DEUTSCHLAND GMBH—See ArcelorMittal S.A.; *Int'l*, pg. 544
ARCELORMITTAL - COTEAU DU LAC—See ArcelorMittal S.A.; *Int'l*, pg. 543
ARCELORMITTAL DISTRIBUTION S.A.S.—See ArcelorMittal S.A.; *Int'l*, pg. 544
ARCELORMITTAL DISTRIBUTION SOLUTIONS—See ArcelorMittal S.A.; *Int'l*, pg. 544
ARCELORMITTAL DOFASCO INC.—See ArcelorMittal S.A.; *Int'l*, pg. 544
ARCELORMITTAL DUDELANGE S.A.—See GFG Alliance Limited; *Int'l*, pg. 2956
ARCELORMITTAL DUISBURG GMBH—See ArcelorMittal S.A.; *Int'l*, pg. 544
ARCELORMITTAL EAST CHICAGO—See Cleveland-Cliffs, Inc.; *U.S. Public*, pg. 514
ARCELORMITTAL EISENHUTTENSTADT GMBH—See ArcelorMittal S.A.; *Int'l*, pg. 544
ARCELORMITTAL ESCAZU SA—See ArcelorMittal S.A.; *Int'l*, pg. 544
ARCELORMITTAL ESPANA S.A.—See ArcelorMittal S.A.; *Int'l*, pg. 544
ARCELORMITTAL FLAT CARBON EUROPE S.A.—See ArcelorMittal S.A.; *Int'l*, pg. 544
ARCELORMITTAL FRANCE S.A.—See ArcelorMittal S.A.; *Int'l*, pg. 544
ARCELORMITTAL GALATI S.A.—See GFG Alliance Limited; *Int'l*, pg. 2956
ARCELORMITTAL GANDRANGE S.A—See ArcelorMittal S.A.; *Int'l*, pg. 544
ARCELORMITTAL GEEL—See ArcelorMittal S.A.; *Int'l*, pg. 544

ARCELORMITTAL GENK N.V.—See ArcelorMittal S.A.; *Int'l*, pg. 543
ARCELORMITTAL GENK STAINLESS SERVICE BELGIUM N.V.—See ArcelorMittal S.A.; *Int'l*, pg. 544
ARCELORMITTAL GENT N.V.—See ArcelorMittal S.A.; *Int'l*, pg. 544
ARCELORMITTAL GENT—See ArcelorMittal S.A.; *Int'l*, pg. 544
ARCELORMITTAL GIPUZKOA S.L.—See ArcelorMittal S.A.; *Int'l*, pg. 544
ARCELORMITTAL GUAPILES—See ArcelorMittal S.A.; *Int'l*, pg. 545
ARCELORMITTAL HAMBURG GMBH—See ArcelorMittal S.A.; *Int'l*, pg. 544
ARCELORMITTAL HAMILTON INC.—See ArcelorMittal S.A.; *Int'l*, pg. 543
ARCELORMITTAL HAUTMONT—See ArcelorMittal S.A.; *Int'l*, pg. 544
ARCELORMITTAL HUNEDOARA S.A.—See ArcelorMittal S.A.; *Int'l*, pg. 544
ARCELORMITTAL INFRASTRUCTURE G.P—See ArcelorMittal S.A.; *Int'l*, pg. 544
ARCELORMITTAL INTERNATIONAL ANTWERP SA—See ArcelorMittal S.A.; *Int'l*, pg. 543
ARCELORMITTAL INTERNATIONAL LUXEMBOURG S.A.—See ArcelorMittal S.A.; *Int'l*, pg. 544
ARCELORMITTAL ITAUNA—See ArcelorMittal S.A.; *Int'l*, pg. 544
ARCELORMITTAL JUBAIL—See ArcelorMittal S.A.; *Int'l*, pg. 544
ARCELORMITTAL JUIZ DE FORA.—See ArcelorMittal S.A.; *Int'l*, pg. 544
ARCELORMITTAL-KISWIRE LLC—See ArcelorMittal S.A.; *Int'l*, pg. 545
ARCELORMITTAL KRYVIY RIH—See ArcelorMittal S.A.; *Int'l*, pg. 544
ARCELORMITTAL LAPLACE—See Cleveland-Cliffs, Inc.; *U.S. Public*, pg. 514
ARCELORMITTAL LAZARO CARDENAS S.A. DE C.V.—See ArcelorMittal S.A.; *Int'l*, pg. 544
ARCELORMITTAL LESAKA S.A.—See ArcelorMittal S.A.; *Int'l*, pg. 543
ARCELORMITTAL LIEGE SA—See GFG Alliance Limited; *Int'l*, pg. 2956
ARCELORMITTAL LOGISTICS BELGIUM—See ArcelorMittal S.A.; *Int'l*, pg. 544
ARCELORMITTAL LONDON—See ArcelorMittal S.A.; *Int'l*, pg. 544
ARCELORMITTAL LONG PRODUCTS CANADA G.P.—See ArcelorMittal S.A.; *Int'l*, pg. 544
ARCELORMITTAL MADRID S.L.—See ArcelorMittal S.A.; *Int'l*, pg. 544
ARCELORMITTAL MEDITERRANEE S.A.S.—See ArcelorMittal S.A.; *Int'l*, pg. 544
ARCELORMITTAL MEXICO S.A. DE C.V.—See ArcelorMittal S.A.; *Int'l*, pg. 545
ARCELORMITTAL MINES CANADA INC.—See ArcelorMittal S.A.; *Int'l*, pg. 544
ARCELORMITTAL MONLEVADE S.A.—See ArcelorMittal S.A.; *Int'l*, pg. 545
ARCELORMITTAL MONTERREY—See ArcelorMittal S.A.; *Int'l*, pg. 545
ARCELORMITTAL MONTREAL INC.—See ArcelorMittal S.A.; *Int'l*, pg. 545
ARCELORMITTAL OSTRAVA A.S.—See GFG Alliance Limited; *Int'l*, pg. 2956
ARCELORMITTAL PIOMBINO S.P.A.—See GFG Alliance Limited; *Int'l*, pg. 2956
ARCELORMITTAL POINT LISAS LTD—See ArcelorMittal S.A.; *Int'l*, pg. 545
ARCELORMITTAL POLAND S.A.—See ArcelorMittal S.A.; *Int'l*, pg. 545
ARCELORMITTAL PROJECTS BELGIUM NV—See ArcelorMittal S.A.; *Int'l*, pg. 545
ARCELORMITTAL PROJECTS NETHERLANDS BV—See ArcelorMittal S.A.; *Int'l*, pg. 545
ARCELORMITTAL RODANGE & SCHIFFLANGE S.A.—See ArcelorMittal S.A.; *Int'l*, pg. 545
ARCELORMITTAL RONGCHENG—See ArcelorMittal S.A.; *Int'l*, pg. 545
ARCELORMITTAL RUHRORT GMBH—See ArcelorMittal S.A.; *Int'l*, pg. 545
ARCELORMITTAL SAGUNTO SL—See ArcelorMittal S.A.; *Int'l*, pg. 543
ARCELORMITTAL S.A.; *Int'l*, pg. 543
ARCELORMITTAL SESTAO S.L.U—See ArcelorMittal S.A.; *Int'l*, pg. 543
ARCELORMITTAL SHIPPING LTD.—See ArcelorMittal S.A.; *Int'l*, pg. 545
ARCELORMITTAL SKOPJE (CRM) AD—See GFG Alliance Limited; *Int'l*, pg. 2956
ARCELORMITTAL SOUTH AFRICA LTD. - NEWCASTLE WORKS—See ArcelorMittal S.A.; *Int'l*, pg. 545
ARCELORMITTAL SOUTH AFRICA LTD. - PRETORIA WORKS—See ArcelorMittal S.A.; *Int'l*, pg. 545
ARCELORMITTAL SOUTH AFRICA LTD. - SALDANHA WORKS—See ArcelorMittal S.A.; *Int'l*, pg. 545
ARCELORMITTAL SOUTH AFRICA LTD.—See ArcelorMittal S.A.; *Int'l*, pg. 545

ARCELORMITTAL S.A.

ARCELORMITTAL SOUTH AFRICA LTD. - VANDERBIJL-PARK WORKS—See ArcelorMittal S.A.; *Int'l*, pg. 545
ARCELORMITTAL SOUTH AFRICA LTD. - VEREENIGING WORKS—See ArcelorMittal S.A.; *Int'l*, pg. 545
ARCELORMITTAL SSC UK LTD—See ArcelorMittal S.A.; *Int'l*, pg. 545
ARCELORMITTAL ST. CHELY D'APCHER MILL—See ArcelorMittal S.A.; *Int'l*, pg. 545
ARCELORMITTAL STEEL NORTH AMERICA—See ArcelorMittal S.A.; *Int'l*, pg. 545
ARCELORMITTAL STEELTON LLC—See Cleveland-Cliffs, Inc.; *U.S. Public*, pg. 514
ARCELORMITTAL STEEL USA INC.—See Cleveland-Cliffs, Inc.; *U.S. Public*, pg. 514
ARCELORMITTAL TAILORED BLANKS—See Cleveland-Cliffs, Inc.; *U.S. Public*, pg. 514
ARCELORMITTAL TALLINN OU—See ArcelorMittal S.A.; *Int'l*, pg. 545
ARCELORMITTAL TEMIRTAU—See National Managing Holding Baiterek JSC; *Int'l*, pg. 5161
ARCELORMITTAL TUBARAO—See ArcelorMittal S.A.; *Int'l*, pg. 543
ARCELORMITTAL TUBULAR PRODUCTS IASI SA—See ArcelorMittal S.A.; *Int'l*, pg. 545
ARCELORMITTAL TUBULAR PRODUCTS KARVINA A.S.—See ArcelorMittal S.A.; *Int'l*, pg. 545
ARCELORMITTAL TUBULAR PRODUCTS ROMAN S.A.—See ArcelorMittal S.A.; *Int'l*, pg. 545
ARCELORMITTAL VINTON, INC—See Cleveland-Cliffs, Inc.; *U.S. Public*, pg. 514
ARCELORMITTAL WARSZAWA SP. Z.O.O.—See ArcelorMittal S.A.; *Int'l*, pg. 545
ARCELORMITTAL WOODSTOCK—See ArcelorMittal S.A.; *Int'l*, pg. 544
ARCELOR RPS—See ArcelorMittal S.A.; *Int'l*, pg. 543
ARCENEAUX FORD INC.; *U.S. Private*, pg. 310
ARC ENTERTAINMENT LLC; *U.S. Private*, pg. 309
ARCES S.A.—See P&V Assurances SCRL; *Int'l*, pg. 5681
ARCET EQUIPMENT COMPANY; *U.S. Private*, pg. 310
ARC EUROBANAN, S.L.—See Dole plc; *Int'l*, pg. 2158
ARC EXCESS & SURPLUS LLC; *U.S. Private*, pg. 309
ARC EXCESS & SURPLUS OF MIDSOUTH, LLC—See ARC Excess & Surplus LLC; *U.S. Private*, pg. 309
ARC EXCESS & SURPLUS OF NEW ENGLAND, LLC—See ARC Excess & Surplus LLC; *U.S. Private*, pg. 309
ARC FABRICATORS, LLC—See MDU Resources Group, Inc.; *U.S. Public*, pg. 1409
ARC FINANCE LIMITED; *Int'l*, pg. 539
ARC FINANCIAL CORP.; *Int'l*, pg. 539
ARC FREEDOM SQUARE LLC—See Brookdale Senior Living Inc.; *U.S. Public*, pg. 393
ARC FUNDS LIMITED; *Int'l*, pg. 539
ARC GALLERIA WOODS INC—See Brookdale Senior Living Inc.; *U.S. Public*, pg. 393
ARC GREENWOOD VILLAGE INC—See Brookdale Senior Living Inc.; *U.S. Public*, pg. 393
ARC GROUP, INC.; *U.S. Public*, pg. 179
ARC GROUP WORLDWIDE, INC.; *U.S. Public*, pg. 179
ARCHAEA ENERGY INC.—See BP plc; *Int'l*, pg. 1126
ARCHANA SOFTWARE LIMITED; *Int'l*, pg. 547
ARCHARDS IRRIGATION PTY. LTD.—See Nutrien Ltd.; *Int'l*, pg. 5492
ARCH AUTO PARTS CORP.—See Blue Point Capital Partners, LLC; *U.S. Private*, pg. 590
ARCH BIOPARTNERS INC.; *Int'l*, pg. 546
ARCHBOLD CONTAINER CORPORATION—See Green Bay Packaging Inc.; *U.S. Private*, pg. 1771
ARCHBROOK CAPITAL MANAGEMENT LLC; *U.S. Private*, pg. 310
ARCH CAPITAL GROUP LTD.; *Int'l*, pg. 546
ARCH CAPITAL GROUP (U.S.) INC—See Arch Capital Group Ltd.; *Int'l*, pg. 546
ARCH CAPITAL PARTNERS AG—See Liechtensteinische Landesbank AG; *Int'l*, pg. 4491
ARCH CAPITAL SERVICES INC.—See Arch Capital Group Ltd.; *Int'l*, pg. 546
ARCH CHEMICALS B.V.—See Lonza Group AG; *Int'l*, pg. 4552
ARCH CHEMICALS (CHINA) CO., LTD.—See Lonza Group AG; *Int'l*, pg. 4552
ARCH CHEMICALS FAR EAST LTD.—See Lonza Group AG; *Int'l*, pg. 4552
ARCH CHEMICALS GMBH—See Lonza Group AG; *Int'l*, pg. 4552
ARCH CHEMICALS, INC. - KUALA LUMPUR—See Lonza Group AG; *Int'l*, pg. 4553
ARCH CHEMICALS, INC. - MISSISSAUGA—See Lonza Group AG; *Int'l*, pg. 4553
ARCH CHEMICALS, INC. - NEW ZEALAND—See Lonza Group AG; *Int'l*, pg. 4553
ARCH CHEMICALS, INC.—See Lonza Group AG; *Int'l*, pg. 4552
ARCH CHEMICALS, INC. - SYDNEY—See Lonza Group AG; *Int'l*, pg. 4553
ARCH CHEMICALS IRELAND B.V.—See Lonza Group AG; *Int'l*, pg. 4552
ARCH CHEMICALS JAPAN, INC.—See Lonza Group AG; *Int'l*, pg. 4552

ARCH CHEMICALS LTD.—See Lonza Group AG; *Int'l*, pg. 4552
ARCH CHEMICALS (PTY) LTD.—See Lonza Group AG; *Int'l*, pg. 4552
ARCH CHEMICALS SAS—See Lonza Group AG; *Int'l*, pg. 4553
ARCH CHEMICALS SINGAPORE PTE, LTD.—See Lonza Group AG; *Int'l*, pg. 4553
ARCH COAL, INC.—See Arch Resources, Inc.; *U.S. Public*, pg. 180
ARCH COAL TERMINAL, INC.—See Arch Resources, Inc.; *U.S. Public*, pg. 180
ARCH CUTTING TOOLS CORP.—See The Jordan Company, L.P.; *U.S. Private*, pg. 4060
ARCH CUTTING TOOLS - FLUSHING, LLC—See The Jordan Company, L.P.; *U.S. Private*, pg. 4060
ARC HEALTH HOLDINGS, LLC—See Thurston Group, LLC; *U.S. Private*, pg. 4166
ARCHEAN CHEMICAL INDUSTRIES LIMITED; *Int'l*, pg. 547
ARCHEAN STAR RESOURCES INC.; *Int'l*, pg. 547
ARCHE DE VIE SA—See Clariane SE; *Int'l*, pg. 1642
ARCHELON LLC; *U.S. Private*, pg. 310
ARCHEMICS LTD—See Harel Mallac & Co. Ltd.; *Int'l*, pg. 3274
ARCHEM QUIMICA LTDA—See Illinois Tool Works Inc.; *U.S. Public*, pg. 1101
ARCHENFIELD INSURANCE MANAGEMENT LIMITED—See Brown & Brown, Inc.; *U.S. Public*, pg. 396
ARCHEO, INC.—See Marchex, Inc.; *U.S. Public*, pg. 1364
ARCH EQUITY PARTNERS, LLC; *U.S. Private*, pg. 310
ARCHER A. ASSOCIATES, INC.—See GTCR LLC; *U.S. Private*, pg. 1802
ARCHER AVIATION INC.; *U.S. Public*, pg. 180
ARCHER AVIATION OPERATING CORP.—See Archer Aviation Inc.; *U.S. Public*, pg. 180
ARCHER CAPITAL PTY. LTD.; *Int'l*, pg. 547
ARCHER COMMUNICATIONS, INC.; *U.S. Private*, pg. 310
ARCHER DANIELS MIDLAND ASIA PACIFIC, LIMITED—See Archer-Daniels-Midland Company; *U.S. Public*, pg. 183
ARCHER DANIELS MIDLAND CO. (ADM)—See Archer-Daniels-Midland Company; *U.S. Public*, pg. 184
ARCHER-DANIELS-MIDLAND COMPANY - CORN PROCESSING—See Archer-Daniels-Midland Company; *U.S. Public*, pg. 184
ARCHER-DANIELS-MIDLAND COMPANY; *U.S. Public*, pg. 180
ARCHER DANIELS MIDLAND COMPNAY - CLINTON—See Archer-Daniels-Midland Company; *U.S. Public*, pg. 184
ARCHER DANIELS MIDLAND CO.—See Archer-Daniels-Midland Company; *U.S. Public*, pg. 183
ARCHER DANIELS MIDLAND CO.—See Archer-Daniels-Midland Company; *U.S. Public*, pg. 183
ARCHER DANIELS MIDLAND CO.—See Archer-Daniels-Midland Company; *U.S. Public*, pg. 183
ARCHER DANIELS MIDLAND CO.—See Archer-Daniels-Midland Company; *U.S. Public*, pg. 184
ARCHER DANIELS MIDLAND CO.—See Archer-Daniels-Midland Company; *U.S. Public*, pg. 183
ARCHER DANIELS MIDLAND CO.—See Archer-Daniels-Midland Company; *U.S. Public*, pg. 183
ARCHER DANIELS MIDLAND CO.—See Archer-Daniels-Midland Company; *U.S. Public*, pg. 183
ARCHER DANIELS MIDLAND CO.—See Archer-Daniels-Midland Company; *U.S. Public*, pg. 183
ARCHER DANIELS MIDLAND CO.—See Archer-Daniels-Midland Company; *U.S. Public*, pg. 183
ARCHER DANIELS MIDLAND CO.—See Archer-Daniels-Midland Company; *U.S. Public*, pg. 183
ARCHER DANIELS MIDLAND CO.—See Archer-Daniels-Midland Company; *U.S. Public*, pg. 183
ARCHER DANIELS MIDLAND CO.—See Archer-Daniels-Midland Company; *U.S. Public*, pg. 183
ARCHER DANIELS MIDLAND CO.—See Archer-Daniels-Midland Company; *U.S. Public*, pg. 183
ARCHER DANIELS MIDLAND CO.—See Archer-Daniels-Midland Company; *U.S. Public*, pg. 183
ARCHER DANIELS MIDLAND CO.—See Archer-Daniels-Midland Company; *U.S. Public*, pg. 183
ARCHER DANIELS MIDLAND CO.—See Archer-Daniels-Midland Company; *U.S. Public*, pg. 183
ARCHER DANIELS MIDLAND CO.—See Archer-Daniels-Midland Company; *U.S. Public*, pg. 183

CORPORATE AFFILIATIONS

ARCHER DANIELS MIDLAND CO.—See Archer-Daniels-Midland Company; *U.S. Public*, pg. 183
ARCHER DANIELS MIDLAND CO.—See Archer-Daniels-Midland Company; *U.S. Public*, pg. 184
ARCHER DANIELS MIDLAND CO.—See Archer-Daniels-Midland Company; *U.S. Public*, pg. 184
ARCHER DANIELS MIDLAND CO.—See Archer-Daniels-Midland Company; *U.S. Public*, pg. 183
ARCHER DANIELS MIDLAND CO.—See Archer-Daniels-Midland Company; *U.S. Public*, pg. 183
ARCHER DANIELS MIDLAND CO.—See Archer-Daniels-Midland Company; *U.S. Public*, pg. 183
ARCHER DANIELS MIDLAND CO.—See Archer-Daniels-Midland Company; *U.S. Public*, pg. 183
ARCHER DANIELS MIDLAND CO.—See Archer-Daniels-Midland Company; *U.S. Public*, pg. 183
ARCHER DANIELS MIDLAND CO.-WEST PLANT—See Archer-Daniels-Midland Company; *U.S. Public*, pg. 184
ARCHER DANIELS MIDLAND EUROPE BV—See Archer-Daniels-Midland Company; *U.S. Public*, pg. 184
ARCHER DANIELS MIDLAND KOREA LLC—See Archer-Daniels-Midland Company; *U.S. Public*, pg. 184
ARCHER-DANIELS-MIDLAND PHILIPPINES, INC.—See Archer-Daniels-Midland Company; *U.S. Public*, pg. 184
ARCHER DANIELS MIDLAND SINGAPORE, PTE. LTD.—See Archer-Daniels-Midland Company; *U.S. Public*, pg. 184
ARCHER EXPLORATION CORP.; *Int'l*, pg. 547
ARCHER EXTERIORS; *U.S. Private*, pg. 310
ARCHER FINANCIAL SERVICES, INC. (AFS)—See Archer-Daniels-Midland Company; *U.S. Public*, pg. 182
ARCHER & GREINER P.C.; *U.S. Private*, pg. 310
THE ARCHER GROUP; *U.S. Private*, pg. 3987
ARCHERHALL, LLC; *U.S. Private*, pg. 311
ARCHER LIMITED; *Int'l*, pg. 547
ARCHER MALMO; *U.S. Private*, pg. 310
ARCHER MATERIALS LIMITED; *Int'l*, pg. 548
ARCHERMIND TECHNOLOGY (NANJING) CO., LTD.; *Int'l*, pg. 548
ARCHER OIL TOOLS AS—See Archer Limited; *Int'l*, pg. 547
ARCHERPOINT, L.L.C.—See Cherry Bekaert LLP; *U.S. Private*, pg. 874
ARCHER PRESSURE PUMPING LLC—See Archer Limited; *Int'l*, pg. 547
ARCHER RV; *U.S. Private*, pg. 310
ARCHER SCREW PRODUCTS INC.; *U.S. Private*, pg. 310
ARCHER (UK) LIMITED—See Archer Limited; *Int'l*, pg. 547
ARCHER WEALTH MANAGEMENT LLC—See HighTower Holding LLC; *U.S. Public*, pg. 1941
ARCHER WELL COMPANY (AUSTRALIA) PTY LTD.—See Archer Limited; *Int'l*, pg. 547
ARCHER WESTERN CONTRACTORS—See The Walsh Group; *U.S. Private*, pg. 4133
ARCHETYPE AGENCY AB—See Next 15 Group plc; *Int'l*, pg. 5245
ARCHETYPE AGENCY BEIJING LIMITED—See Next 15 Group plc; *Int'l*, pg. 5245
ARCHETYPE AGENCY GMBH—See Next 15 Group plc; *Int'l*, pg. 5245
ARCHETYPE AGENCY LIMITED—See Next 15 Group plc; *Int'l*, pg. 5245
ARCHETYPE AGENCY LIMITED—See Next 15 Group plc; *Int'l*, pg. 5245
ARCHETYPE AGENCY PRIVATE LIMITED—See Next 15 Group plc; *Int'l*, pg. 5245
ARCHETYPE AGENCY PTE LIMITED—See Next 15 Group plc; *Int'l*, pg. 5245
ARCHETYPE AGENCY PTY LIMITED—See Next 15 Group plc; *Int'l*, pg. 5246
ARCHETYPE AGENCY SARL—See Next 15 Group plc; *Int'l*, pg. 5246
ARCHETYPE AGENCY SDN. BHD.—See Next 15 Group plc; *Int'l*, pg. 5246
ARCHETYPE AGENCY S.L.—See Next 15 Group plc; *Int'l*, pg. 5246
ARCHETYPE AGENCY SRL—See Next 15 Group plc; *Int'l*, pg. 5246
ARCH EXCESS & SURPLUS INSURANCE COMPANY—See Arch Capital Group Ltd.; *Int'l*, pg. 546
ARCH FINANCIAL HOLDINGS AUSTRALIA PTY LTD—See Arch Capital Group Ltd.; *Int'l*, pg. 546
ARCHGATE TMS SOLUTIONS LLC; *U.S. Private*, pg. 311
ARCH GLOBAL PRECISION LLC—See The Jordan Company, L.P.; *U.S. Private*, pg. 4060
ARCHIAL NORR LIMITED—See The Ingenium Group Inc.; *Int'l*, pg. 7655
ARCHIBALD INGALL STRETTON; *Int'l*, pg. 548
ARCHIBUS, INC.—See Eptura, Inc.; *U.S. Private*, pg. 1414
ARCHICOM SA—See Echo Investment S.A.; *Int'l*, pg. 2289
ARCHIDPLY DECOR LIMITED; *Int'l*, pg. 548
ARCHIDPLY INDUSTRIES LTD; *Int'l*, pg. 548
ARCHIE COMIC PUBLICATIONS INC.; *U.S. Private*, pg. 311
ARCHIES LIMITED; *Int'l*, pg. 548
ARCHIMEDES GLOBAL, INC.; *U.S. Private*, pg. 311
ARCHIMED SAS; *Int'l*, pg. 548
ARCHIMICA S.P.A.—See PI Industries Ltd.; *Int'l*, pg. 5859

COMPANY NAME INDEX

ARCH INDEMNITY INSURANCE COMPANY—See Arch Capital Group Ltd.; *Int'l*, pg. 546
ARCH INSURANCE CANADA LTD.—See Arch Capital Group Ltd.; *Int'l*, pg. 546
ARCH INSURANCE COMPANY (EUROPE) LTD.—See Arch Capital Group Ltd.; *Int'l*, pg. 546
ARCH INSURANCE COMPANY—See Arch Capital Group Ltd.; *Int'l*, pg. 546
ARCH INSURANCE (EU) DESIGNATED ACTIVITY COMPANY—See Arch Capital Group Ltd.; *Int'l*, pg. 546
ARCH INSURANCE GROUP, INC.—See Arch Capital Group Ltd.; *Int'l*, pg. 546
ARCH INSURANCE (UK) LIMITED—See Arch Capital Group Ltd.; *Int'l*, pg. 546
ARCH INTERNATIONAL TRADING (SHANGHAI) CO., LTD.—See Lonza Group AG; *Int'l*, pg. 4552
ARCH INVESTMENT MANAGEMENT LTD.—See Arch Capital Group Ltd.; *Int'l*, pg. 546
ARCHIPELAGO LEARNING, INC.—See The Vistria Group, LP; *U.S. Private*, pg. 4131
ARCHI-RO KFT.—See Deutsche Steinzeug Cremer & Breuer AG; *Int'l*, pg. 2083
ARCHISH GALLERY CO., LTD.—See VT Holdings Co., Ltd.; *Int'l*, pg. 8315
ARCHITEC HOUSEWARES; *U.S. Private*, pg. 311
ARCHITECTED BUSINESS SOLUTIONS SRL—See Logo Yazilim Sanayi ve Ticaret A.S.; *Int'l*, pg. 4543
ARCHITECTS ORANGE LLP; *U.S. Private*, pg. 311
ARCHITECTS STUDIO JAPAN INC.; *Int'l*, pg. 549
ARCHITECTURAL AREA LIGHTING/MOLDCAST CO.—See Hubbell Incorporated; *U.S. Public*, pg. 1066
ARCHITECTURAL ART MFG. INC.—See Pittcon Industries; *U.S. Private*, pg. 3191
ARCHITECTURAL BUILDING SUPPLY CO.—See Platinum Equity, LLC; *U.S. Private*, pg. 3208
ARCHITECTURAL COMPONENTS GROUP, INC.—Armstrong World Industries, Inc.; *U.S. Public*, pg. 194
ARCHITECTURAL COMPUTER SERVICES, INC.—See Alpine Investors; *U.S. Private*, pg. 201
ARCHITECTURAL DIGEST—See Advance Publications, Inc.; *U.S. Private*, pg. 85
ARCHITECTURAL DOORS INC.; *U.S. Private*, pg. 311
ARCHITECTURAL DOORS & WINDOWS; *U.S. Private*, pg. 311
ARCHITECTURAL FLOORING RESOURCE, INC.; *U.S. Private*, pg. 311
ARCHITECTURAL GLASS & ALUMINUM CO. INC.; *U.S. Private*, pg. 311
ARCHITECTURAL GLASS & GLAZING—See Aluma-Glass Industries, Inc.; *U.S. Public*, pg. 211
ARCHITECTURAL GRANITE & MARBLE, LLC—See Architectural Surfaces Group, LLC; *U.S. Private*, pg. 311
ARCHITECTURAL PANEL PRODUCTS, INC.; *U.S. Private*, pg. 311
ARCHITECTURAL PLASTICS LIMITED—See Allied Plastic Skylight; *Int'l*, pg. 358
ARCHITECTURAL RECORD—See BNP Media, Inc.; *U.S. Private*, pg. 602
ARCHITECTURAL STONE—See Haines & Kibblehouse Inc.; *U.S. Private*, pg. 1840
ARCHITECTURAL SURFACES GROUP, LLC; *U.S. Private*, pg. 311
ARCHITECTURAL SYSTEMS INC.; *U.S. Private*, pg. 311
ARCHITECTURAL TESTING, INC.—See Intertek Group plc; *Int'l*, pg. 3762
ARCHITECTURAL WINDOWS & DOORS—See Peter Pan Bus Lines, Inc.; *U.S. Private*, pg. 3159
ARCHITECTURAL WOODS INC.; *U.S. Private*, pg. 311
ARCHITECTURE DESIGN COLLABORATIVE, INC.; *U.S. Private*, pg. 311
ARCHITECTUREPLUS INTERNATIONAL, INC.; *U.S. Private*, pg. 311
ARCHITEX INTERNATIONAL; *U.S. Private*, pg. 311
ARCHIT ORGANOSYS LTD.; *Int'l*, pg. 549
ARCHITRAVE DESIGN & PLANNING SERVICES PTE. LTD.—See Banyan Tree Holdings Ltd.; *Int'l*, pg. 855
ARCHIVAGES ET SERVICES—See Iron Mountain Incorporated; *U.S. Public*, pg. 1172
ARCHIV BUNEK S.R.O.—See Esperite N.V.; *Int'l*, pg. 2506
ARCHIVE 2000 LTD.—See Taavura Holdings, Ltd.; *Int'l*, pg. 7401
ARCHIVES CORP.—See Berkshire Partners LLC; *U.S. Private*, pg. 534
ARCHIVEX S.A.—See Iron Mountain Incorporated; *U.S. Public*, pg. 1172
ARCHIVIT S.R.L.—See Villar International Ltd.; *Int'l*, pg. 8206
ARCH LMI PTY LTD—See Arch Capital Group Ltd.; *Int'l*, pg. 546
ARCH LOGISTICS, LLC—See Bunzl plc; *Int'l*, pg. 1217
ARCHLYNK, LLC; *U.S. Private*, pg. 311
ARCH MEDICAL SOLUTIONS CORP—See The Jordan Company, L.P.; *U.S. Private*, pg. 4060
ARCH MI ASIA LIMITED—See Arch Capital Group Ltd.; *Int'l*, pg. 546
ARCH MORTGAGE ASSURANCE COMPANY—See Arch Capital Group Ltd.; *Int'l*, pg. 546
ARCH MORTGAGE INSURANCE COMPANY—See Arch Capital Group Ltd.; *Int'l*, pg. 546

ARCH MORTGAGE INSURANCE LIMITED—See Arch Capital Group Ltd.; *Int'l*, pg. 546
ARCH OF WYOMING, LLC—See Arch Resources, Inc.; *U.S. Public*, pg. 180
ARCH OHIO, INC.—See Trulite Glass & Aluminum Solutions, LLC; *U.S. Private*, pg. 4249
ARCHON CORPORATION; *U.S. Public*, pg. 185
ARCHON GROUP EUROPE GMBH—See The Goldman Sachs Group, Inc.; *U.S. Public*, pg. 2076
ARCHON GROUP, L.P.—See The Goldman Sachs Group, Inc.; *U.S. Public*, pg. 2076
ARCHONIC, LLC—See Marchex, Inc.; *U.S. Public*, pg. 1364
ARCHON INFORMATION SYSTEMS, L.L.C.; *U.S. Private*, pg. 312
ARCHONIX SYSTEMS, LLC—See ABRY Partners, LLC; *U.S. Private*, pg. 41
ARCHON MINERALS LIMITED; *Int'l*, pg. 549
ARCHON TECHNOLOGIES LTD; *Int'l*, pg. 549
ARCHOSAUR GAMES INC.; *Int'l*, pg. 549
ARCHOS GMBH—See Archos S.A.; *Int'l*, pg. 549
ARCHOS INC.—See Archos S.A.; *Int'l*, pg. 549
ARCHOS S.A.; *Int'l*, pg. 549
ARCHOS UK LTD.—See Archos S.A.; *Int'l*, pg. 549
ARCH PERSONAL CARE PRODUCTS, L.P.—See Lonza Group AG; *Int'l*, pg. 4553
ARCH PHARMALABS LIMITED; *Int'l*, pg. 547
ARCH PHYSICAL THERAPY AND SPORTS MEDICINE, LIMITED PARTNERSHIP—See U.S. Physical Therapy, Inc.; *U.S. Public*, pg. 2213
ARCH PRECISION COMPONENTS CORP.—See Madison Dearborn Partners, LLC; *U.S. Private*, pg. 2540
ARCH PROMO GROUP LLC; *U.S. Private*, pg. 310
ARCH PROTECTION CHEMICALS PVT. LTD.—See Lonza Group AG; *Int'l*, pg. 4553
ARCH QUIMICA ARGENTINA S.R.L.—See Lonza Group AG; *Int'l*, pg. 4553
ARCH QUIMICA BRASIL LTDA.—See Lonza Group AG; *Int'l*, pg. 4553
ARCH QUIMICA COLOMBIA S.A.—See Lonza Group AG; *Int'l*, pg. 4553
ARCH QUIMICA, S.A. DE C.V.—See Lonza Group AG; *Int'l*, pg. 4553
ARCH QUIMICA URUGUAY S.A.—See Lonza Group AG; *Int'l*, pg. 4553
ARCH RE ACCIDENT & HEALTH APS—See Arch Capital Group Ltd.; *Int'l*, pg. 546
ARCH RE FACULTATIVE UNDERWRITERS INC.—See Arch Capital Group Ltd.; *Int'l*, pg. 546
ARCH REINSURANCE COMPANY INC.—See Arch Capital Group Ltd.; *Int'l*, pg. 546
ARCH REINSURANCE EUROPE UNDERWRITING LIMITED—See Arch Capital Group Ltd.; *Int'l*, pg. 546
ARCH REINSURANCE LTD.—See Arch Capital Group Ltd.; *Int'l*, pg. 546
ARCH RESOURCES, INC.; *U.S. Public*, pg. 180
ARCHRIVAL, INC.; *U.S. Private*, pg. 312
ARCHROCK, INC.; *U.S. Public*, pg. 185
ARCHROCK PARTNERS, L.P.—See Archrock, Inc.; *U.S. Public*, pg. 186
ARCHROMA MANAGEMENT GMBH—See SK Capital Partners, LP; *U.S. Private*, pg. 3679
ARCHROMA PAKISTAN LTD.—See SK Capital Partners, LP; *U.S. Private*, pg. 3679
ARCHROMA U.S., INC.—See SK Capital Partners, LP; *U.S. Private*, pg. 3679
ARCHSAT INVESTMENTS (GAUTENG)(PTY) LTD—See Ellies Holdings Limited; *Int'l*, pg. 2366
ARCHSAT INVESTMENTS (NATAL) (PTY) LTD—See Ellies Holdings Limited; *Int'l*, pg. 2366
ARCH SOLUTIONS AGENCY LLC—See Reinsurance Group of America, Inc.; *U.S. Public*, pg. 1777
ARCH SPECIALTY INSURANCE AGENCY INC.—See Arch Capital Group Ltd.; *Int'l*, pg. 546
ARCH SPECIALTY INSURANCE COMPANY—See Arch Capital Group Ltd.; *Int'l*, pg. 546
ARCHSTONE BOCA RATON REIT LP—See AvalonBay Communities, Inc.; *U.S. Public*, pg. 240
ARCHSTONE B.V.—See Equity Residential; *U.S. Public*, pg. 791
ARCHSTONE CRONIN'S LANDING LLC—See Equity Residential; *U.S. Public*, pg. 791
ARCHSTONE FINANCIAL SERVICES LLC—See AvalonBay Communities, Inc.; *U.S. Public*, pg. 240
ARCHSTONE REDWOOD SHORES LLC—See Equity Residential; *U.S. Public*, pg. 791
ARCH THERAPEUTICS, INC.; *U.S. Public*, pg. 180
ARCH TIMBER PROTECTION AB—See Lonza Group AG; *Int'l*, pg. 4553
ARCH TIMBER PROTECTION BV—See Lonza Group AG; *Int'l*, pg. 4553
ARCHTIS EU GMBH—See archTIS Limited; *Int'l*, pg. 549
ARCHTIS LIMITED; *Int'l*, pg. 549
ARCHTIS UK LIMITED—See archTIS Limited; *Int'l*, pg. 549
ARCHTIS US, INC.—See archTIS Limited; *Int'l*, pg. 549
ARCH UK BIOCIDES LTD.—See Lonza Group AG; *Int'l*, pg. 4553

ARCO-IRIS GOLD CORPORATION

ARCH UNDERWRITERS INC.—See Arch Capital Group Ltd.; *Int'l*, pg. 546
ARCH UNDERWRITING AGENCY (AUSTRALIA) PTY. LTD.—See Arch Capital Group Ltd.; *Int'l*, pg. 546
ARCH UNDERWRITING AT LLOYD'S (AUSTRALIA) PTY LTD—See Arch Capital Group Ltd.; *Int'l*, pg. 547
ARCH U.S. MI HOLDINGS INC.—See Arch Capital Group Ltd.; *Int'l*, pg. 546
ARCH VENTURE PARTNERS; *U.S. Private*, pg. 310
ARCH WATER PRODUCTS FRANCE S.A.S—See Lonza Group AG; *Int'l*, pg. 4553
ARCH WATER PRODUCTS—See Lonza Group AG; *Int'l*, pg. 4553
ARCH WATER PRODUCTS SOUTH AFRICA PTY. LIMITED—See Lonza Group AG; *Int'l*, pg. 4552
ARCHWAY FINANCE & OPERATIONS, INC.—See SEI Investments Company; *U.S. Public*, pg. 1856
ARCHWAY MARKETING SERVICES, INC.—See Investcorp Holdings B.S.C.; *Int'l*, pg. 3776
THE ARCHWAY PROGRAMS, INC.; *U.S. Private*, pg. 3987
ARCHWAY SALES, LLC—See One Rock Capital Partners, LLC; *U.S. Private*, pg. 3022
ARCH WOOD PROTECTION (FIJI) LTD—See Lonza Group AG; *Int'l*, pg. 4553
ARCH WOOD PROTECTION, INC. - CONLEY PLANT—See Lonza Group AG; *Int'l*, pg. 4553
ARCH WOOD PROTECTION, INC.—See Lonza Group AG; *Int'l*, pg. 4553
ARCH WOOD PROTECTION (M) SDN. BHD.—See Lonza Group AG; *Int'l*, pg. 4553
ARCH WOOD PROTECTION (NZ) LIMITED—See Lonza Group AG; *Int'l*, pg. 4553
ARCH WOOD PROTECTION (SA) (PROPERIETARY) LIMITED—See Lonza Group AG; *Int'l*, pg. 4552
ARCIMOTO, INC.; *U.S. Public*, pg. 186
ARC INTERNATIONAL NORTH AMERICA INC.—See Jacques Georges Durand Industries, S.A.; *Int'l*, pg. 3866
ARC INTERNATIONAL SA—See Jacques Georges Durand Industries, S.A.; *Int'l*, pg. 3866
ARCIS EQUITY PARTNERS LLC; *U.S. Private*, pg. 312
ARC ITALIA—See Publicis Groupe S.A.; *Int'l*, pg. 6100
ARCKARINGA ENERGY PTY LTD—See Altona Rare Earths PLC; *Int'l*, pg. 394
ARCLAND RESOURCES, INC.; *Int'l*, pg. 549
ARCLANDS CORP; *Int'l*, pg. 549
ARCLAND SERVICE HOLDINGS CO., LTD.—See Arclands Corp; *Int'l*, pg. 549
ARC LEGAL ASSISTANCE LIMITED—See Stone Point Capital LLC; *U.S. Private*, pg. 3820
ARCLIGHT CAPITAL HOLDINGS, LLC; *U.S. Private*, pg. 312
ARCLIGHT CAPITAL PARTNERS, LLC—See ArcLight Capital Holdings, LLC; *U.S. Private*, pg. 312
ARCLIGHT CINEMA COMPANY; *U.S. Private*, pg. 312
ARCLINE INVESTMENT MANAGEMENT LP; *U.S. Private*, pg. 312
ARCLIN INC.—See Lone Star Funds; *U.S. Private*, pg. 2484
ARCLIN USA, LLC—See Lone Star Funds; *U.S. Private*, pg. 2484
ARC LOGISTICS LLC—See Warburg Pincus LLC; *U.S. Private*, pg. 4440
ARC MACHINES GMBH—See Enovis Corporation; *U.S. Public*, pg. 770
ARC MACHINES INC.—See Enovis Corporation; *U.S. Public*, pg. 771
THE ARC MERCER, INC.; *U.S. Private*, pg. 3987
ARC MIDATLANTIC—See ARC Excess & Surplus LLC; *U.S. Private*, pg. 309
ARC MIDCO L.L.C.—See ARC DOCUMENT SOLUTIONS, INC.; *U.S. Public*, pg. 179
ARC MIDDLE EAST—See Publicis Groupe S.A.; *Int'l*, pg. 6100
ARC MINERALS LTD; *Int'l*, pg. 539
A.R.C. NETWORKS, INC.—See Windstream Holdings, Inc.; *U.S. Public*, pg. 2373
ARCOA GHANA LTD.—See HORIBA Ltd; *Int'l*, pg. 3474
ARCO AM PM—See BP plc; *Int'l*, pg. 1126
ARCOA RISK RETENTION GROUP, INC.—See U-Haul Holding Company; *U.S. Public*, pg. 2211
ARCOBASSO FOODS, INC.—See Golding Farms Foods, Inc.; *U.S. Private*, pg. 1735
ARCO CONSTRUCTION COMPANY INC.; *U.S. Private*, pg. 315
ARCO DEVELOPMENT SIA—See Arco Vara AS; *Int'l*, pg. 550
ARCO ELECTRIC, INC.; *U.S. Private*, pg. 315
ARC OF GEORGIA, LLC—See Bain Capital, LP; *U.S. Private*, pg. 445
ARC OF GREATER NEW ORLEANS; *U.S. Private*, pg. 309
ARC OF THE UNITED STATES; *U.S. Private*, pg. 309
ARCO INCORPORATED; *U.S. Private*, pg. 315
ARCO INDUSTRIAL SALES INC.; *U.S. Private*, pg. 315
ARCO-IRIS GOLD CORPORATION; *Int'l*, pg. 550
ARCO LAB PRIVATE LIMITED—See Strides Pharma Science Limited; *Int'l*, pg. 7240

183

ARCOLAB SA—See Strides Pharma Science Limited; *Int'l*, pg. 7240
ARCOMA AB; *Int'l*, pg. 550
ARCOMA NORTH AMERICA INC.—See Stille AB; *Int'l*, pg. 7215
ARCOMET ASIA PTE LTD—See Arcomet & Co.; *Int'l*, pg. 550
ARCOMET & CO.; *Int'l*, pg. 550
ARCOMET DEUTSCHLAND GMBH & CO. KG—See Arcomet & Co.; *Int'l*, pg. 550
ARCOMET (HONG KONG) LTD—See Arcomet & Co.; *Int'l*, pg. 550
ARCOMET ITALIA SPA—See Arcomet & Co.; *Int'l*, pg. 550
ARCOMET TORENKRANEN NEDERLAND BV—See Arcomet & Co.; *Int'l*, pg. 550
ARCO MOTOR INDUSTRY COMPANY LIMITED—See Motus Holdings Limited; *Int'l*, pg. 5056
ARCOM PUBLISHING INC.; *U.S. Private*, pg. 315
ARCO/MURRAY NATIONAL CONSTRUCTION COMPANY, INC.; *U.S. Private*, pg. 315
ARCONA AB—See Veidekke ASA; *Int'l*, pg. 8148
ARCONA INTERNATIONAL (PTY) LTD.—See A.A.G. STUCCHI s.r.l.; *Int'l*, pg. 22
ARCON CONSTRUCTION & MANAGEMENT SERVICES, INC.; *U.S. Private*, pg. 315
ARCON ELECTRIC, LLC—See ARCON Construction & Management Services, Inc.; *U.S. Private*, pg. 315
ARCONIC ARCHITECTURAL PRODUCTS SAS—See Howmet Aerospace Inc.; *U.S. Public*, pg. 1062
ARCONIC (CHINA) INVESTMENT COMPANY LTD.—See Howmet Aerospace Inc.; *U.S. Public*, pg. 1062
ARCONIC DOMESTIC LLC—See Howmet Aerospace Inc.; *U.S. Public*, pg. 1061
ARCONIC FASTENERS SAS - US OPERATIONS—See Howmet Aerospace Inc.; *U.S. Public*, pg. 1061
ARCONIC FASTENING SYSTEMS & RINGS-AUSTRALIA PTY. LTD.—See Howmet Aerospace Inc.; *U.S. Public*, pg. 1061
ARCONIC FASTENING SYSTEMS & RINGS - CARSON—See Howmet Aerospace Inc.; *U.S. Public*, pg. 1061
ARCONIC FASTENING SYSTEMS & RINGS - KINGSTON—See Howmet Aerospace Inc.; *U.S. Public*, pg. 1061
ARCONIC FASTENING SYSTEMS & RINGS - TUCSON—See Howmet Aerospace Inc.; *U.S. Public*, pg. 1061
ARCONIC FASTENING SYSTEMS & RINGS - WACO—See Howmet Aerospace Inc.; *U.S. Public*, pg. 1061
ARCONIC GLOBAL FASTENERS LIMITED - LEICESTER—See Howmet Aerospace Inc.; *U.S. Public*, pg. 1062
ARCONIC GLOBAL FASTENERS LIMITED - REDDITCH—See Howmet Aerospace Inc.; *U.S. Public*, pg. 1062
ARCONIC GLOBAL FASTENERS LIMITED - TELFORD—See Howmet Aerospace Inc.; *U.S. Public*, pg. 1062
ARCONIC GLOBAL FASTENERS & RINGS, INC.—See Howmet Aerospace Inc.; *U.S. Public*, pg. 1061
ARCONIC GMBH—See Howmet Aerospace Inc.; *U.S. Public*, pg. 1062
ARCONIC INTERNATIONAL (ASIA) LIMITED—See Howmet Aerospace Inc.; *U.S. Public*, pg. 1062
ARCONIC INTERNATIONAL HOLDING COMPANY LLC—See Howmet Aerospace Inc.; *U.S. Public*, pg. 1062
ARCONIC INVERSIONES ESPANA S.L.—See Howmet Aerospace Inc.; *U.S. Public*, pg. 1062
ARCON SOLAR A/S—See VKR Holding A/S; *Int'l*, pg. 8281
ARCONTECH GROUP PLC; *Int'l*, pg. 550
ARCONTECH LTD.—See Arcontech Group PLC; *Int'l*, pg. 550
ARCOPAR S.A.—See Arcor Sociedad Anonima, Industrial y Comercial; *Int'l*, pg. 550
ARCOPLAST INC.—See Germfree Laboratories Inc.; *U.S. Private*, pg. 1687
ARCO PLATFORM LIMITED—See Dragoneer Investment Group, LLC; *U.S. Private*, pg. 1271
ARCO PLATFORM LIMITED—See General Atlantic Service Company, L.P.; *U.S. Private*, pg. 1662
ARCO (QLD) PTY LTD—See Bunka Shutter Co., Ltd.; *Int'l*, pg. 1216
ARCOR AG & CO. KG—See Vodafone Group Plc; *Int'l*, pg. 8285
ARCOR A.G.—See Arcor Sociedad Anonima, Industrial y Comercial; *Int'l*, pg. 550
ARCOR CANADA INC.—See Arcor Sociedad Anonima, Industrial y Comercial; *Int'l*, pg. 550
ARCOR DE PERU S.A.—See Arcor Sociedad Anonima, Industrial y Comercial; *Int'l*, pg. 550
ARCOR DO BRASIL LIMITADA—See Arcor Sociedad Anonima, Industrial y Comercial; *Int'l*, pg. 550
ARCOR ECUADOR—See Arcor Sociedad Anonima, Industrial y Comercial; *Int'l*, pg. 550
ARCOR ONLINE GMBH—See Vodafone Group Plc; *Int'l*, pg. 8285

ARCOR SOCIEDAD ANONIMA, INDUSTRIAL Y COMERCIAL; *Int'l*, pg. 550
ARCOR TRADING (SHANGHAI) CO. LTD.—See Arcor Sociedad Anonima, Industrial y Comercial; *Int'l*, pg. 550
ARCOR U.S.A. INC.—See Arcor Sociedad Anonima, Industrial y Comercial; *Int'l*, pg. 550
ARCOSA AGGREGATES GULF COAST, LLC—See Arcosa, Inc.; *U.S. Public*, pg. 186
ARCOSA AGGREGATES OHIO RIVER VALLEY, LLC—See Arcosa, Inc.; *U.S. Public*, pg. 186
ARCOSA AGGREGATES TEXAS, LLC—See Arcosa, Inc.; *U.S. Public*, pg. 186
ARCOSA AGGREGATES WEST, LLC—See Arcosa, Inc.; *U.S. Public*, pg. 186
ARCOSA, INC.; *U.S. Public*, pg. 186
ARCOSA WIND TOWERS, INC.—See Arcosa, Inc.; *U.S. Public*, pg. 186
ARCOS COMMUNICATIONS; *U.S. Private*, pg. 315
ARCOS DORADOS ARUBA N.V.—See Arcos Dorados Holdings Inc.; *Int'l*, pg. 550
ARCOS DORADOS COLOMBIA S.A.S—See Arcos Dorados Holdings Inc.; *Int'l*, pg. 550
ARCOS DORADOS COSTA RICA ADCR, S.A.—See Arcos Dorados Holdings Inc.; *Int'l*, pg. 550
ARCOS DORADOS HOLDINGS INC.; *Int'l*, pg. 550
ARCOS DORADOS PUERTO RICO, LLC—See Arcos Dorados Holdings Inc.; *Int'l*, pg. 550
ARCOS DOURADOS COMERCIO DE ALIMENTOS LTDA.—See Arcos Dorados Holdings Inc.; *Int'l*, pg. 550
ARCOS HONG KONG LTD.—See ALROSA Co. Ltd.; *Int'l*, pg. 377
ARCOS INDUSTRIES LLC; *U.S. Private*, pg. 315
ARCOS LIMITED—See ALROSA Co. Ltd.; *Int'l*, pg. 377
ARCOS LLC—See The Riverside Company; *U.S. Private*, pg. 4107
ARCOS MENDOCINOS S.A.—See Arcos Dorados Holdings Inc.; *Int'l*, pg. 550
ARCO—See BP plc; *Int'l*, pg. 1126
ARCOS SERCAL INMOBILIARIA, S. DE R.L. DE C.V.—See Arcos Dorados Holdings Inc.; *Int'l*, pg. 550
ARCOT DEUTSCHLAND GMBH—See Broadcom Inc.; *U.S. Public*, pg. 388
ARCOTECH LTD.; *Int'l*, pg. 551
ARCO TOWERS REIT; *Int'l*, pg. 549
ARCOT R&D SOFTWARE PRIVATE LTD.—See Broadcom Inc.; *U.S. Public*, pg. 388
ARCOT SYSTEMS INC.—See Broadcom Inc.; *U.S. Public*, pg. 388
ARCOUR SA—See VINCI S.A.; *Int'l*, pg. 8212
ARC OUTDOORS; *U.S. Private*, pg. 309
ARCO VARA AS; *Int'l*, pg. 549
ARC OVERLAND PARK LLC—See Welltower Inc.; *U.S. Public*, pg. 2347
ARC PA-QRS TRUST—See Realty Income Corporation; *U.S. Public*, pg. 1768
ARC PARKLANE INC—See Brookdale Senior Living, Inc.; *U.S. Public*, pg. 393
ARC PHILADELPHIA—See ARC DOCUMENT SOLUTIONS, INC.; *U.S. Public*, pg. 179
ARC PHYSICAL THERAPY PLUS, LIMITED PARTNERSHIP—See U.S. Physical Therapy, Inc.; *U.S. Public*, pg. 2213
ARCPLUS GROUP PLC—See Shanghai Guosheng (Group) Co., Ltd.; *Int'l*, pg. 6768
ARCPOINT GROUP LLC—See ARCpoint Inc.; *U.S. Public*, pg. 186
ARCPOINT INC.; *U.S. Public*, pg. 186
ARC PRODUCTS, INC.—See Lincoln Electric Holdings, Inc.; *U.S. Public*, pg. 1317
ARCQUS GMBH—See ManpowerGroup Inc.; *U.S. Public*, pg. 1357
ARC RESOURCES LTD.; *Int'l*, pg. 539
ARC RICHMOND HEIGHTS LLC—See Brookdale Senior Living, Inc.; *U.S. Public*, pg. 393
ARC RICHMOND PLACE INC—See Brookdale Senior Living Inc.; *U.S. Public*, pg. 393
ARCROYAL UNLIMITED—See Owens & Minor, Inc.; *U.S. Public*, pg. 1625
ARC SANTA CATALINA INC—See Brookdale Senior Living Inc.; *U.S. Public*, pg. 393
ARCS COMPANY LIMITED; *Int'l*, pg. 551
ARCSERVE (USA) LLC—See Marlin Equity Partners, LLC; *U.S. Private*, pg. 2583
ARCSIGHT HONG KONG LIMITED—See Micro Focus International plc; *Int'l*, pg. 4876
ARCSIGHT, LLC—See Micro Focus International plc; *Int'l*, pg. 4876
ARCS INVESTMENTS, LLC; *U.S. Private*, pg. 315
ARC SLIMLINE LIMITED—See Heidelberg Materials AG; *Int'l*, pg. 3308
ARCSOFT CORP., LTD.; *Int'l*, pg. 551
ARCSOFT, INC.; *U.S. Private*, pg. 315
ARC SOLUTIONS (INTERNATIONAL) LIMITED—See Enghouse Systems Limited; *Int'l*, pg. 2427
ARCSOURCE GROUP, INC.; *U.S. Private*, pg. 315
ARC SOUTH, LLC—See ARC Excess & Surplus LLC; *U.S. Private*, pg. 309
ARC SPECIALTY BROKERAGE, LLC—See ARC Excess & Surplus LLC; *U.S. Private*, pg. 309

ARC SUN CITY WEST, LLC—See Welltower Inc.; *U.S. Public*, pg. 2347
ARC TECHNOLOGIES, INC.—See Hexcel Corporation; *U.S. Public*, pg. 1032
ARCTECH SOLAR (CHANGZHOU) CO., LTD.—See Arctech Solar Holding Co., Ltd.; *Int'l*, pg. 551
ARCTECH SOLAR HOLDING CO., LTD.; *Int'l*, pg. 551
ARCTECH SOLAR, INC.—See Arctech Solar Holding Co., Ltd.; *Int'l*, pg. 551
ARCTECH SOLAR INDIA PVT. LTD.—See Arctech Solar Holding Co., Ltd.; *Int'l*, pg. 551
ARCTECH SOLAR (JAPAN) CO., LTD.—See Arctech Solar Holding Co., Ltd.; *Int'l*, pg. 551
ARCTECH SOLAR (SHANGHAI) COMPANY—See Arctech Solar Holding Co., Ltd.; *Int'l*, pg. 551
ARCTEK INDUSTRIAL CO., LTD.—See Taiwan Fu Hsing Industrial Co., Ltd.; *Int'l*, pg. 7420
ARCTEK SECURITY TECHNOLOGIES (SHANGHAI) CO., LTD.—See Taiwan Fu Hsing Industrial Co., Ltd.; *Int'l*, pg. 7420
ARC TERMINALS HOLDINGS LLC—See Warburg Pincus LLC; *U.S. Private*, pg. 4440
ARC TERMINALS JOLIET HOLDINGS LLC—See Warburg Pincus LLC; *U.S. Private*, pg. 4440
ARCTERN CONSULTING PRIVATE LIMITED—See American CyberSystems, Inc.; *U.S. Private*, pg. 229
ARCTERN, INC.—See American CyberSystems, Inc.; *U.S. Private*, pg. 229
ARC'TERYX EQUIPMENT, INC.—See ANTA Sports Products Limited; *Int'l*, pg. 480
ARCTIC BIOSCIENCE AS; *Int'l*, pg. 551
ARCTIC BLUE BEVERAGES AB; *Int'l*, pg. 551
ARCTIC CANADIAN DIAMOND COMPANY LTD.—See Burgundy Diamond Mines Limited; *Int'l*, pg. 1224
ARCTIC CAT ESPANA S.L.—See Textron Inc.; *U.S. Public*, pg. 2028
ARCTIC CAT GMBH—See Textron Inc.; *U.S. Public*, pg. 2028
ARCTIC CAT INC.—See Textron Inc.; *U.S. Public*, pg. 2028
ARCTIC CAT UK LTD—See Textron Inc.; *U.S. Public*, pg. 2028
ARCTIC CIRCLE ENTERPRISES INC.; *U.S. Private*, pg. 315
ARCTIC CIRCLE RESTAURANTS, INC.—See Artic Circle, Inc; *U.S. Public*, pg. 342
ARCTIC CONTAINER OPERATION A/S—See Royal Arctic Line A/S; *Int'l*, pg. 6409
ARCTIC CO-OPERATIVES LIMITED; *Int'l*, pg. 551
ARCTIC ENGINEERING CO., INC.—See Partners Group Holding AG; *Int'l*, pg. 5750
ARCTIC EXPRESS INC.; *U.S. Private*, pg. 315
ARCTIC EXPRESS INSULATION LLC—See Installed Building Products, Inc.; *U.S. Public*, pg. 1132
ARCTIC FALLS SPRING WATER, INC.; *U.S. Private*, pg. 315
ARCTIC FINANCIAL LTD.—See VersaBank; *Int'l*, pg. 8173
ARCTIC FISH HOLDING AS; *Int'l*, pg. 551
ARCTIC FOX LITHIUM CORP.; *Int'l*, pg. 551
ARCTIC FOX, LLC—See Harbour Group Industries, Inc.; *U.S. Private*, pg. 1860
ARCTIC GLACIER HOLDINGS INC.—See H.I.G. Capital, LLC; *U.S. Private*, pg. 1829
ARCTIC GLACIER INC.—See H.I.G. Capital, LLC; *U.S. Private*, pg. 1829
ARCTIC GLACIER PENNSYLVANIA, INC.—See H.I.G. Capital, LLC; *U.S. Private*, pg. 1829
ARCTIC GLACIER U.S.A., INC.—See H.I.G. Capital, LLC; *U.S. Private*, pg. 1829
ARCTIC LEASING LLC—See AIP, LLC; *U.S. Private*, pg. 136
ARCTIC MINERALS AB; *Int'l*, pg. 551
ARCTIC OFFICE MACHINE INC.; *U.S. Private*, pg. 315
ARCTIC OFFSHORE FARMING AS—See Salmar ASA; *Int'l*, pg. 6494
ARCTIC OIL AND GAS SERVICES LTD—See Inuvialuit Regional Corporation; *Int'l*, pg. 3772
THE ARCTICOM GROUP, LLC; *U.S. Private*, pg. 3987
ARCTIC PAPER BALTIC STATES SIA—See Arctic Paper S.A.; *Int'l*, pg. 551
ARCTIC PAPER BENELUX S.A.—See Arctic Paper S.A.; *Int'l*, pg. 551
ARCTIC PAPER DANMARK A/S—See Arctic Paper S.A.; *Int'l*, pg. 551
ARCTIC PAPER DEUTSCHLAND GMBH—See Arctic Paper S.A.; *Int'l*, pg. 551
ARCTIC PAPER ESPANA SL—See Arctic Paper S.A.; *Int'l*, pg. 551
ARCTIC PAPER FRANCE SAS—See Arctic Paper S.A.; *Int'l*, pg. 551
ARCTIC PAPER GRYCKSBO AB—See Arctic Paper S.A.; *Int'l*, pg. 551
ARCTIC PAPER ITALIA SRL—See Arctic Paper S.A.; *Int'l*, pg. 551
ARCTIC PAPER KOSTRZYN S.A.—See Arctic Paper S.A.; *Int'l*, pg. 551
ARCTIC PAPER MOCHENWANGEN GMBH—See Arctic Paper S.A.; *Int'l*, pg. 551

COMPANY NAME INDEX

ARCTIC PAPER MUNKEDALS AB—See Arctic Paper S.A.; *Int'l*, pg. 551
ARCTIC PAPER NORGE AS—See Arctic Paper S.A.; *Int'l*, pg. 551
ARCTIC PAPER PAPIERHANDELS GMBH—See Arctic Paper S.A.; *Int'l*, pg. 551
ARCTIC PAPER POLSKA SP. Z O.O.—See Arctic Paper S.A.; *Int'l*, pg. 552
ARCTIC PAPER S.A.; *Int'l*, pg. 551
ARCTIC PAPER SCHWEIZ AG—See Arctic Paper S.A.; *Int'l*, pg. 552
ARCTIC PAPER SVERIGE AB—See Arctic Paper S.A.; *Int'l*, pg. 552
ARCTIC PAPER UK LIMITED—See Arctic Paper S.A.; *Int'l*, pg. 552
ARCTIC PIPE ENGINEERING, INC.—See Arctic Slope Regional Corporation; *U.S. Private*, pg. 316
ARCTIC PIPE INSPECTION, INC.—See Arctic Slope Regional Corporation; *U.S. Private*, pg. 316
ARCTIC SLOPE REGIONAL CORPORATION; *U.S. Private*, pg. 315
ARCTIC SNOW & ICE CONTROL INC.; *U.S. Private*, pg. 316
ARCTIC SPIRIT PROMOTIONS—See Nunasi Corporation; *Int'l*, pg. 5489
ARCTIC STAR EXPLORATION CORP.; *Int'l*, pg. 552
ARCTIC STRUCTURES LLC; *U.S. Private*, pg. 316
ARCTICZYMES TECHNOLOGIES ASA; *Int'l*, pg. 552
ARC TITUCAZ001, LLC—See Realty Income Corporation; *U.S. Public*, pg. 1768
ARCTOS NORTHSTAR ACQUISITION CORP.; *U.S. Public*, pg. 186
ARCTOUCH LLC—See WPP plc; *Int'l*, pg. 8469
ARC TRAINING INTERNATIONAL LIMITED—See MITIE Group Plc; *Int'l*, pg. 4926
ARCTURUS REALTY CORPORATION—See AtkinsRealis Group Inc.; *Int'l*, pg. 671
ARCTURUS THERAPEUTICS HOLDINGS INC.; *U.S. Public*, pg. 186
ARCTURUS THERAPEUTICS LTD.—See Arcturus Therapeutics Holdings Inc.; *U.S. Public*, pg. 187
ARCTURUS UAV, INC.—See AeroVironment, Inc.; *U.S. Public*, pg. 53
ARCULUS GMBH—See Jungheinrich AG; *Int'l*, pg. 4027
ARCULUS HOLDINGS, L.L.C.—See CompoSecure, Inc.; *U.S. Public*, pg. 561
ARCURE; *Int'l*, pg. 552
ARCUS ASA; *Int'l*, pg. 552
ARCUS AS—See Arcus ASA; *Int'l*, pg. 552
ARCUS BIOSCIENCES, INC.; *U.S. Public*, pg. 187
ARCUS DEVELOPMENT GROUP INC.; *Int'l*, pg. 552
ARCUS FINLAND OY—See Arcus ASA; *Int'l*, pg. 552
ARCUS-GRUPPEN AS—See Arcus ASA; *Int'l*, pg. 552
ARCUS INFRASTRUCTURE PARTNERS LLP; *Int'l*, pg. 552
ARCUS INSTALLATION N.V.—See Deufol SE; *Int'l*, pg. 2048
ARCUS S.A.; *Int'l*, pg. 553
ARCUS SWEDEN AB—See Arcus ASA; *Int'l*, pg. 552
ARCUS SYSTEMY INFORMATYCZNE SP. Z O.O.—See Arcus S.A.; *Int'l*, pg. 553
ARCUS WINE BRANDS AS—See Arcus ASA; *Int'l*, pg. 552
ARCUTIS BIOTHERAPEUTICS, INC.; *U.S. Public*, pg. 187
ARCVIA MINERVA SA; *Int'l*, pg. 553
ARCVISION TECHNOLOGY CORP.—See Ac&C International Co., Ltd.; *Int'l*, pg. 74
ARCWASTE COLLECTION S.R.L.—See Koc Holding A.S.; *Int'l*, pg. 4222
ARCWEST EXPLORATION INC.; *Int'l*, pg. 553
ARCW INSURANCE, INC.; *U.S. Private*, pg. 316
ARC WIRELESS, INC.—See ARC Group Worldwide, Inc.; *U.S. Public*, pg. 179
ARC WIRELESS, LLC—See ARC Group Worldwide, Inc.; *U.S. Public*, pg. 179
ARC WORCESTER CENTER L.P.—See Tenet Healthcare Corporation; *U.S. Public*, pg. 2009
ARC WORLDWIDE, ASIA PACIFIC—See Publicis Groupe S.A.; *Int'l*, pg. 6100
ARC WORLDWIDE, EUROPE, MIDDLE EAST & AFRICA—See Publicis Groupe S.A.; *Int'l*, pg. 6100
ARC WORLDWIDE, NORTH AMERICA—See Publicis Groupe S.A.; *Int'l*, pg. 6100
ARC WORLDWIDE—See Publicis Groupe S.A.; *Int'l*, pg. 6100
ARC WORLDWIDE—See Publicis Groupe S.A.; *Int'l*, pg. 6100
ARC WORLDWIDE—See Publicis Groupe S.A.; *Int'l*, pg. 6100
ARC WORLDWIDE—See Publicis Groupe S.A.; *Int'l*, pg. 6100
ARC WORLDWIDE—See Publicis Groupe S.A.; *Int'l*, pg. 6100
ARC WORLDWIDE—See Publicis Groupe S.A.; *Int'l*, pg. 6100
ARC WORLDWIDE—See Publicis Groupe S.A.; *Int'l*, pg. 6100
ARC WORLDWIDE—See Publicis Groupe S.A.; *Int'l*, pg. 6100
ARC WORLDWIDE—See Publicis Groupe S.A.; *Int'l*, pg. 6100
ARC WORLDWIDE—See Publicis Groupe S.A.; *Int'l*, pg. 6100
ARC WORLDWIDE—See Publicis Groupe S.A.; *Int'l*, pg. 6100
ARC WORLDWIDE—See Publicis Groupe S.A.; *Int'l*, pg. 6100
ARC WORLDWIDE—See Publicis Groupe S.A.; *Int'l*, pg. 6100
ARC WORLDWIDE—See Publicis Groupe S.A.; *Int'l*, pg. 6100
ARC WORLDWIDE—See Publicis Groupe S.A.; *Int'l*, pg. 6100
ARDAGH GLASS HOLMEGAARD A/S—See Ardagh Group S.A.; *Int'l*, pg. 553
ARDAGH GLASS INC. - BRIDGETON—See Ardagh Group S.A.; *Int'l*, pg. 553
ARDAGH GLASS INC. - DUNKIRK—See Ardagh Group S.A.; *Int'l*, pg. 553
ARDAGH GLASS INC. - MADERA—See Ardagh Group S.A.; *Int'l*, pg. 553
ARDAGH GLASS INC.—See Ardagh Group S.A.; *Int'l*, pg. 553
ARDAGH GLASS ITALY S.R.L.—See Ardagh Group S.A.; *Int'l*, pg. 553
ARDAGH GLASS LIMITED—See Ardagh Group S.A.; *Int'l*, pg. 553
ARDAGH GLASS LIMMARED AB—See Ardagh Group S.A.; *Int'l*, pg. 553
ARDAGH GLASS SALES LIMITED—See Ardagh Group S.A.; *Int'l*, pg. 553
ARDAGH GROUP S.A.; *Int'l*, pg. 553
ARDAGH METAL BEVERAGE EUROPE GMBH—See Ardagh Group S.A.; *Int'l*, pg. 553
ARDAGH METAL PACKAGING NETHERLANDS B.V.—See Ardagh Group S.A.; *Int'l*, pg. 553
ARDAGH METAL PACKAGING S.A.; *Int'l*, pg. 553
ARDAGH METAL PACKAGING UK LIMITED—See Ardagh Group S.A.; *Int'l*, pg. 553
ARDAGH METAL PACKAGING UK LTD. - SUTTON-IN-ASHFIELD PLANT—See Ardagh Group S.A.; *Int'l*, pg. 553
ARDAGH METAL PACKAGING USA, INC.—See Ardagh Group S.A.; *Int'l*, pg. 553
ARDAGH PACKAGING GROUP LIMITED—See Ardagh Group S.A.; *Int'l*, pg. 553
ARDAKAN INDUSTRIAL CERAMICS CO.; *Int'l*, pg. 553
ARDAMAN & ASSOCIATES, INC.—See Tetra Tech, Inc.; *U.S. Public*, pg. 2022
ARDANTA N.V.—See ASR Nederland N.V.; *Int'l*, pg. 632
ARDATEM—See Gerard Perrier Industrie S.A.; *Int'l*, pg. 2942
ARD CONTRACTING, INC.; *U.S. Private*, pg. 317
ARDCO/TRAVERSE LIFT—See The Heico Companies, L.L.C.; *U.S. Private*, pg. 4050
ARD DISTRIBUTORS INC.; *U.S. Private*, pg. 317
ARDEA RESOURCES LIMITED; *Int'l*, pg. 554
ARDE-BARINCO, INC.—See L3Harris Technologies, Inc.; *U.S. Public*, pg. 1279
ARDE, INC.—See L3Harris Technologies, Inc.; *U.S. Public*, pg. 1279
THE ARDELL GROUP; *U.S. Private*, pg. 3987
ARDELL INTERNATIONAL, INC.—See American International Industries Company; *U.S. Private*, pg. 238
ARDEL STEEL; *Int'l*, pg. 554
ARDELYX, INC.; *U.S. Public*, pg. 187
ARDEN COMPANIES; *U.S. Private*, pg. 317
ARDEN ENGINEERING CONSTRUCTORS LLC; *U.S. Private*, pg. 317
ARDEN ENGINEERING, INC.—See Arlington Capital Partners LLC; *U.S. Private*, pg. 327
ARDEN GROUP, INC.—See TPG Capital, L.P.; *U.S. Public*, pg. 2168
ARDEN LANDFILL, INC.—See Waste Management, Inc.; *U.S. Public*, pg. 2330
ARDEN MAIDSTONE LIMITED—See Lithia Motors, Inc.; *U.S. Public*, pg. 1821
ARDEN PARK VENTURES, LLC—See Beazer Homes USA, Inc.; *U.S. Public*, pg. 287
ARDEN PARTNERS PLC—See Zeus Group Limited; *Int'l*, pg. 8640
ARDEN SOFTWARE LTD.; *Int'l*, pg. 554
AR DENTAL SUPPLIES SDN. BHD.—See Q&M Dental Group (Singapore) Limited; *Int'l*, pg. 6129
ARDENT CONCEPTS, INC.—See Amphenol Corporation; *U.S. Public*, pg. 129
ARDENTEC CORPORATION; *Int'l*, pg. 554
ARDENT ENVIRONMENTAL GROUP, INC.—See Brookfield Corporation; *Int'l*, pg. 1182
ARDENTE SUPPLY CO. INC.; *U.S. Private*, pg. 317
ARDENT LEISURE MANAGEMENT LIMITED—See Coast Entertainment Holdings Limited; *Int'l*, pg. 1681
ARDENT MANAGEMENT CONSULTING, INC; *U.S. Private*, pg. 317
ARDENT MILLS, LLC—See Cargill, Inc.; *U.S. Private*, pg. 754
ARDENT MILLS, LLC—See CHS INC.; *U.S. Public*, pg. 491
ARDENT MILLS, LLC—See Conagra Brands, Inc.; *U.S. Public*, pg. 563
ARDENT MILLS—See Cargill, Inc.; *U.S. Private*, pg. 754
ARDENT MILLS—See CHS INC.; *U.S. Public*, pg. 491
ARDENT MILLS—See Conagra Brands, Inc.; *U.S. Public*, pg. 563
ARDEN TRUST COMPANY—See Warburg Pincus LLC; *U.S. Private*, pg. 4439
ARDENT SERVICES, LLC - KENNER—See EMCOR Group, Inc.; *U.S. Public*, pg. 736
ARDENT SERVICES, LLC—See EMCOR Group, Inc.; *U.S. Public*, pg. 736
ARDENT SUPPORT TECHNOLOGIES, LLC—See Charlesbank Capital Partners, LLC; *U.S. Private*, pg. 856
ARDENT SUPPORT TECHNOLOGIES, LLC—See GTCR LLC; *U.S. Private*, pg. 1806
ARDEN TUNBRIDGE WELLS LIMITED—See Lithia Motors, Inc.; *U.S. Public*, pg. 1321
ARDEO EDUCATION SOLUTIONS, LLC; *U.S. Private*, pg. 317
ARDEPRO CO. LTD.; *Int'l*, pg. 554
ARDEVOL—See LDC SA; *Int'l*, pg. 4430
ARD FINANCE S.A.; *Int'l*, pg. 553
ARD GRUP BILISIM TEKNOLOJILERI A.S.; *Int'l*, pg. 553
ARDIAN GERMANY GMBH—See Ardian SAS; *Int'l*, pg. 554
ARDIAN INVESTMENT SINGAPORE PTE. LTD.—See Ardian SAS; *Int'l*, pg. 554
ARDIAN INVESTMENT SWITZERLAND AG—See Ardian SAS; *Int'l*, pg. 554
ARDIAN INVESTMENT UK LIMITED—See Ardian SAS; *Int'l*, pg. 554
ARDIAN ITALY S.R.L.—See Ardian SAS; *Int'l*, pg. 554
ARDIAN SAS; *Int'l*, pg. 554
ARDIAN US LLC—See Ardian SAS; *Int'l*, pg. 554
ARDICOM DIGITAL COMMUNICATIONS INC.—See Arctic Co-Operatives Limited; *Int'l*, pg. 551
ARDIDEN LIMITED; *Int'l*, pg. 556
ARDI INVESTMENTS & TRADING COMPANY LIMITED; *Int'l*, pg. 554
ARDILES IMPORT S.A.C.—See Einhell Germany AG; *Int'l*, pg. 2332
ARD INC.; *U.S. Private*, pg. 317
ARDISEIS FZCO—See CGG; *Int'l*, pg. 1431
ARDMONA FOODS LIMITED—See Perma Funds Management; *Int'l*, pg. 5802
ARDMONA FOODS LIMITED—See Perma Funds Management; *Int'l*, pg. 5802
ARDMONA FOODS LIMITED—See The Eights Group Pty Ltd.; *Int'l*, pg. 7638
ARDMONA FOODS LIMITED—See The Eights Group Pty Ltd.; *Int'l*, pg. 7638
ARDMORE CONSTRUCTION LIMITED; *Int'l*, pg. 556
ARDMORE NISSAN; *U.S. Private*, pg. 317
ARDMORE SHIPPING (ASIA) PTE LIMITED—See Ardmore Shipping Corporation; *Int'l*, pg. 556
ARDMORE SHIPPING CORPORATION; *Int'l*, pg. 556
ARDMORE SHIPPING SERVICES (IRELAND) LIMITED—See Ardmore Shipping Corporation; *Int'l*, pg. 556
ARDO A/B—See Ardo N.V.; *Int'l*, pg. 556
ARDO A/S—See Ardo N.V.; *Int'l*, pg. 556
ARDO AUSTRIA FROST GMBH—See Ardo N.V.; *Int'l*, pg. 557
ARDO B.V.—See Ardo N.V.; *Int'l*, pg. 557
ARDOFOODS IRELAND LTD.—See Ardo N.V.; *Int'l*, pg. 557
ARDO GMBH—See Ardo N.V.; *Int'l*, pg. 557
ARDOISIERES D'ANGERS—See Groupe Bruxelles Lambert SA; *Int'l*, pg. 3099
ARDO ITALIA SRL—See Ardo N.V.; *Int'l*, pg. 557
ARDO MOCHOV S.R.O.—See Ardo N.V.; *Int'l*, pg. 556
THE ARDONAGH GROUP LIMITED; *Int'l*, pg. 7614
ARDO N.V.; *Int'l*, pg. 556
ARDO SA—See Ardo N.V.; *Int'l*, pg. 557
ARDO SHANGAI MARKETING CO. LTD—See Ardo N.V.; *Int'l*, pg. 557
ARDO SP.Z.O.O.—See Ardo N.V.; *Int'l*, pg. 557
ARDO UK LTD.—See Ardo N.V.; *Int'l*, pg. 557
ARDOUR WORLD LIMITED; *Int'l*, pg. 557
ARDOVA PLC; *Int'l*, pg. 557
ARDOVRIES ESPANA S.A.—See Ardo N.V.; *Int'l*, pg. 557
ARDSHINBANK CJSC; *Int'l*, pg. 557
ARDSLEY PARTNERS; *U.S. Private*, pg. 317
ARDUMAN KLIMA SANAYI SERVISI AS—See Johnson Controls International plc; *Int'l*, pg. 3985
ARDURRA GROUP, LLC—See Littlejohn & Co., LLC; *U.S. Private*, pg. 2469
AREA 21 SOFTWARE GMBH—See ELMOS Semiconductor AG; *Int'l*, pg. 2368

ARDSLEY PARTNERS

AREA 3 EQUIPAMIENTO Y DISENO INTERIORISMO, S.L.U.—See Elecnor, S.A.; *Int'l*, pg. 2347
AREA AGENCY ON AGING FOR SOUTHWEST FLORIDA INC.; *U.S. Private*, pg. 317
AREA AGENCY ON AGING OF CENTRAL FLORIDA; *U.S. Private*, pg. 317
AREA AGENCY ON AGING OF PALM BEACH/TREASURE COAST, INC.; *U.S. Private*, pg. 317
AREA AGENCY ON AGING OF WESTERN ARKANSAS, INC.; *U.S. Private*, pg. 317
AREA AGENCY ON AGING, PSA2; *U.S. Private*, pg. 317
AREA AGENCY ON AGING REGION 9, INC.; *U.S. Private*, pg. 317
A.R.E. ACCESSORIES, LLC; *U.S. Private*, pg. 27
AREA COOPERATIVE EDUCATIONAL SERVICES; *U.S. Private*, pg. 317
AREA DE SERVICIO COIROS SL—See Infrastructure Leasing & Financial Services Limited; *Int'l*, pg. 3697
AREA ENERGY AND ELECTRIC INC.; *U.S. Private*, pg. 317
AREA ENERGY & ELECTRIC, INC.; *U.S. Private*, pg. 317
AREA ERECTORS INC.; *U.S. Private*, pg. 317
AREA FIVE AGENCY ON AGING & COMMUNITY SERVICES, INC.; *U.S. Private*, pg. 317
AREAGOLFE - GESTAO, CONSTRUCAO E MANUTENCAO DE CAMPOS DE GOLFE, S.A.—See Mota-Engil SGPS, S.A.; *Int'l*, pg. 5052
AREALINK CO. LTD.; *Int'l*, pg. 557
AREALIS LIEGENSCHAFTSMANAGEMENT GMBH—See Vienna Insurance Group AG Wiener Versicherung Gruppe; *Int'l*, pg. 8193
AREA QUEST INC.; *Int'l*, pg. 557
AREA SOCIETE DES AUTOROUTES RHONES-ALPES SA—See Eiffage S.A.; *Int'l*, pg. 2331
AREA SOCIETE DES AUTOROUTES RHONES-ALPES SA—See Macquarie Group Limited; *Int'l*, pg. 4626
AREAS, SAU—See PAI Partners S.A.S.; *Int'l*, pg. 5699
AREA TRAVEL AGENCY LTD.—See Finnair Plc; *Int'l*, pg. 2675
AREA WHOLESALE TIRE COMPANY, LLC; *U.S. Private*, pg. 318
AREAWIDE COUNCIL ON AGING OF BROWARD COUNTY, INC.; *U.S. Private*, pg. 318
AREAWIDE MEDIA INC.—See Rust Communications; *U.S. Private*, pg. 3507
AREA ZERO CONSULTING DE ARQUITECTURA E INTERIORISMO, S.L.—See Jones Lang LaSalle Incorporated; *U.S. Public*, pg. 1201
ARECONT VISION LLC—See IDIS Co., Ltd.; *Int'l*, pg. 3595
ARECOR THERAPEUTICS PLC; *Int'l*, pg. 557
AREEJ VEGETABLE OILS & DERIVATIVES SAOG—See Omar Zawawi Establishment LLC; *Int'l*, pg. 5561
AREEYA PROPERTY PUBLIC COMPANY LIMITED; *Int'l*, pg. 557
AREF INVESTMENT GROUP K.S.C.C.—See Kuwait Finance House K.S.C.; *Int'l*, pg. 4344
AREF THALASSA SOCIMI, S.A.U.; *Int'l*, pg. 557
AREHNA ENGINEERING, INC.; *U.S. Private*, pg. 318
ARE HOLDINGS, INC.; *Int'l*, pg. 557
AREIAS SYSTEMS, INC.; *U.S. Private*, pg. 318
AREIT, INC.; *Int'l*, pg. 558
A-RELIABLE AUTO PARTS & WRECKERS, INC.—See LKQ Corporation; *U.S. Public*, pg. 1333
ARELIS SAS; *Int'l*, pg. 558
ARELLANO CONSTRUCTION COMPANY—See Grupo Villar Mir, S.A.U.; *Int'l*, pg. 3139
AREMAI PETROLEUM (PRIVATE) LIMITED,—See Pakistan State Oil Limited; *Int'l*, pg. 5704
AREM PACIFIC CORP.; *Int'l*, pg. 558
ARENA AGROINDUSTRIE ALIMENTARI SPA—See Arena Holding S.p.A.; *Int'l*, pg. 558
ARENA AUTO AUCTION—See Cox Enterprises, Inc.; *U.S. Private*, pg. 1076
ARENA BERLIN BETRIEBS GMBH—See CTS Eventim AG & Co. KGAA; *Int'l*, pg. 1872
ARENA BILGISAYAR SANAYI VE TICARET A.S.; *Int'l*, pg. 558
ARENA BRANDS INC.—See Kainos Capital, LLC; *U.S. Private*, pg. 2254
ARENA BROKER S.R.L.—See Banco BPM S.p.A.; *Int'l*, pg. 818
ARENA COMMUNICATIONS; *U.S. Private*, pg. 318
ARENA EVENTS GROUP PLC—See International Holdings Company PJSC; *Int'l*, pg. 3750
ARENA FAKTORING A.S.; *Int'l*, pg. 558
ARENA FORTIFY ACQUISITION CORP.; *U.S. Public*, pg. 187
THE ARENA GROUP HOLDINGS, INC; *U.S. Public*, pg. 2035
ARENA GROUP LIMITED—See Xerox Holdings Corporation; *U.S. Public*, pg. 2386
ARENA HOLDING S.P.A. - CREMERIA DEL LATTAITO PLANT—See Arena Holding S.p.A.; *Int'l*, pg. 558
ARENA HOLDING S.P.A. - GARBINI PLANT—See Arena Holding S.p.A.; *Int'l*, pg. 558
ARENA HOLDING S.P.A. - LA FARAONA PLANT—See Arena Holding S.p.A.; *Int'l*, pg. 558
ARENA HOLDING S.P.A. - MARE PRONTO PLANT—See Arena Holding S.p.A.; *Int'l*, pg. 558
ARENA HOLDING S.P.A. - MARSILI PLANT—See Arena Holding S.p.A.; *Int'l*, pg. 558
ARENA HOLDING S.P.A. - NATURICCHI PLANT—See Arena Holding S.p.A.; *Int'l*, pg. 558
ARENA HOLDING S.P.A.; *Int'l*, pg. 558
ARENA HOLDING S.P.A. - TU IN CUCINA PLANT—See Arena Holding S.p.A.; *Int'l*, pg. 558
ARENA HOSPITALITY GROUP D.D.; *Int'l*, pg. 558
ARENA INVESTMENT MANAGEMENT LIMITED; *Int'l*, pg. 558
ARENA INVESTORS, LP; *U.S. Private*, pg. 318
ARENA LEISURE CATERING LIMITED—See Reuben Brothers SA; *Int'l*, pg. 6311
ARENA LEISURE RACING LIMITED—See Reuben Brothers SA; *Int'l*, pg. 6311
ARENA MANAGEMENT GMBH—See CTS Eventim AG & Co. KGAA; *Int'l*, pg. 1872
ARENA MEDIA LIMITED—See Vivendi SE; *Int'l*, pg. 8269
ARENA MINERALS INC.—See Lithium Americas Corp.; *Int'l*, pg. 4526
ARENANET, INC.—See NCsoft Corporation; *Int'l*, pg. 5181
ARENA ONE GMBH—See E.ON SE; *Int'l*, pg. 2251
ARENA OPERATIONS, LLC—See Atlanta Hawks, L.P.; *U.S. Private*, pg. 370
ARENA PHARMACEUTICALS, INC.—See Pfizer Inc.; *U.S. Public*, pg. 1679
ARENA.PL SA; *Int'l*, pg. 558
ARENA RACING CORPORATION LIMITED—See Reuben Brothers SA; *Int'l*, pg. 6311
ARENA REIT—See Arena Investment Management Limited; *Int'l*, pg. 558
ARENARIA S.R.L.—See Societa Esercizi Commerciali Industriali; *Int'l*, pg. 7034
ARENA SA—See Enstar Group Limited; *Int'l*, pg. 2448
ARENA SOLUTIONS, INC.—See PTC Inc.; *U.S. Public*, pg. 1734
ARENA STAGE; *U.S. Private*, pg. 318
ARENDAL LUFTHAVN GULLKNAPP AS—See Arendals Fossekompani ASA; *Int'l*, pg. 558
ARENDALS FOSSEKOMPANI ASA; *Int'l*, pg. 558
ARENDS-AWE INC.; *U.S. Private*, pg. 318
ARENDS BROS. INC.; *U.S. Private*, pg. 318
ARENDS, INC.; *U.S. Private*, pg. 318
ARENSON OFFICE FURNISHINGS INC.; *U.S. Private*, pg. 318
ARENTFOX SCHIFF LLP; *U.S. Private*, pg. 318
ARENT, INC.; *Int'l*, pg. 559
ARE OY—See Onvest Oy; *Int'l*, pg. 5592
ARE - QRS CORP.—See Alexandria Real Estate Equities, Inc.; *U.S. Public*, pg. 75
ARES ACQUISITION CORPORATION; *U.S. Public*, pg. 187
ARES ADMINISTRATIVE SERVICES (DIFC) LIMITED—See Ares Management Corporation; *U.S. Public*, pg. 187
ARES ASIA LIMITED; *Int'l*, pg. 559
ARES ASIA MANAGEMENT (HK), LIMITED—See Ares Management Corporation; *U.S. Public*, pg. 187
ARES CAPITAL CORPORATION—See Ares Management Corporation; *U.S. Public*, pg. 187
ARES CAPITAL EUROPE LIMITED—See Ares Management Corporation; *U.S. Public*, pg. 188
ARES CAPITAL MANAGEMENT LLC—See Ares Management Corporation; *U.S. Public*, pg. 187
ARES CIMENTO INSAAT SAN. VE TIC. A.S.—See Bursa Cimento Fabrikasi A.S.; *Int'l*, pg. 1226
ARES COMMERCIAL REAL ESTATE CORPORATION—See Ares Management Corporation; *U.S. Public*, pg. 188
ARES DYNAMIC CREDIT ALLOCATION FUND, INC.—See Ares Management Corporation; *U.S. Public*, pg. 188
ARES EIF MANAGEMENT, LLC—See Ares Management Corporation; *U.S. Public*, pg. 188
ARESGAS EAD—See Hera S.p.A.; *Int'l*, pg. 3356
ARES GENETICS GMBH—See OpGen, Inc.; *U.S. Public*, pg. 1607
ARES GREEN TECHNOLOGY CORPORATION—See Frontken Corporation Berhad; *Int'l*, pg. 2796
ARES GROUP, INC.; *U.S. Private*, pg. 318
ARES INDUSTRIAL FURNACE (TIANJIN) CO., LTD.—See SMS Holding GmbH; *Int'l*, pg. 7015
ARES INSURANCE SOLUTIONS LLC—See Ares Management Corporation; *U.S. Public*, pg. 187
ARES INTERNATIONAL CORPORATION; *Int'l*, pg. 559
ARESI S.P.A.—See Robert Bosch GmbH; *Int'l*, pg. 6358
ARES MANAGEMENT CORPORATION; *U.S. Public*, pg. 187
ARES MANAGEMENT LIMITED—See Ares Management Corporation; *U.S. Public*, pg. 188
ARES MANAGEMENT LLC-CAPITAL MARKETS GROUP—See Ares Management Corporation; *U.S. Public*, pg. 188
ARES MANAGEMENT LLC-PRIVATE DEBT GROUP—See Ares Management Corporation; *U.S. Public*, pg. 188
ARES MANAGEMENT LLC-PRIVATE EQUITY GROUP—See Ares Management Corporation; *U.S. Public*, pg. 188
ARES MANAGEMENT LLC-REAL ESTATE GROUP—See Ares Management Corporation; *U.S. Public*, pg. 188
ARES MANAGEMENT LLC—See Ares Management Corporation; *U.S. Public*, pg. 187
ARES MANAGEMENT UK LIMITED—See Ares Management Corporation; *U.S. Public*, pg. 188
ARES & MERCURY CO., LTD.—See Zappallas, Inc.; *Int'l*, pg. 8625
ARES REAL ESTATE INCOME TRUST INC.—See Black Creek Group, LLC; *U.S. Private*, pg. 570
ARES SPORTSWEAR, LTD.; *U.S. Private*, pg. 318
ARES SPORTSWEAR—See Dyenomite, LLC; *U.S. Private*, pg. 1296
ARES STRATEGIC MINING INC.; *Int'l*, pg. 559
ARETE ACQUISITIONS, LLC; *U.S. Private*, pg. 318
ARETE ASSOCIATES; *U.S. Private*, pg. 318
ARETEC GROUP, INC.—See RCAP Holdings, LLC; *U.S. Private*, pg. 3361
ARE - TECH SQUARE, LLC—See Alexandria Real Estate Equities, Inc.; *U.S. Public*, pg. 75
ARETE INDUSTRIES, INC.; *U.S. Public*, pg. 191
ARETE M PTE. LTD.—See 8Telecom International Holdings Co. Ltd.; *Int'l*, pg. 16
ARETI SPA—See ACEA S.p.A.; *Int'l*, pg. 95
ARETTO WELLNESS INC.; *Int'l*, pg. 559
ARETT SALES CORPORATION; *U.S. Private*, pg. 318
ARETUM HOLDINGS, LLC—See Renovus Capital Partners; *U.S. Private*, pg. 3399
AREVALO'S TORTILLIARIA INC.; *U.S. Private*, pg. 318
AREVA NC AUSTRALIA PTY LTD—See Orano SA; *Int'l*, pg. 5611
AREVA RENEWABLES GMBH—See Orano SA; *Int'l*, pg. 5611
AREV LIFE SCIENCES GLOBAL CORP.; *Int'l*, pg. 559
AREWAY LLC; *U.S. Private*, pg. 319
AREX INDUSTRIES LIMITED; *Int'l*, pg. 559
AR-EX LTD.; *U.S. Private*, pg. 306
AREX—See Societe Anonyme d'Explosifs et de Produits Chimiques; *Int'l*, pg. 7035
AREY COMPANY; *U.S. Private*, pg. 319
AREZZO INDUSTRIA E COMERCIO S.A.; *Int'l*, pg. 560
ARFA ENTERPRISES INC.; *U.S. Private*, pg. 319
ARFIN INDIA LIMITED; *Int'l*, pg. 560
ARFMAN HEKWERK B.V.—See CRH plc; *Int'l*, pg. 1842
A&R FOODS INC.; *U.S. Private*, pg. 20
ARGA CONTROLS, INC.—See Electro Switch Corporation; *U.S. Private*, pg. 1353
ARGAMAN INDUSTRIES LTD.; *Int'l*, pg. 560
ARGAND PARTNERS, LP; *U.S. Private*, pg. 319
ARGAN, INC.; *U.S. Public*, pg. 191
ARGANO, LLC—See Trinity Hunt Management, L.P.; *U.S. Private*, pg. 4234
ARGAN SA; *Int'l*, pg. 560
ARGE AUTOBAHNWERBUNG GMBH—See JCDecaux S.A.; *Int'l*, pg. 3920
ARGENCOBRA, S.A.—See ACS, Actividades de Construccion y Servicios, S.A.; *Int'l*, pg. 110
ARGEN CORPORATION; *U.S. Private*, pg. 319
ARGENCOS SA—See Godrej & Boyce Mfg. Co. Ltd.; *Int'l*, pg. 3020
ARGENE INC.—See Institut Merieux; *Int'l*, pg. 3724
ARGENE SA—See Institut Merieux; *Int'l*, pg. 3724
ARGENE SRL—See Institut Merieux; *Int'l*, pg. 3724
ARGENIA, LLC—See Truist Financial Corporation; *U.S. Public*, pg. 4234
ARGENICA THERAPEUTICS LIMITED; *Int'l*, pg. 560
ARGENT ADVISORS, INC.—See Argent Financial Group, Inc.; *U.S. Private*, pg. 320
ARGENTA ENERGIA S.A.—See Azabache Energy Inc.; *Int'l*, pg. 776
ARGENTAL S.A.R.L.—See Danish Crown AmbA; *Int'l*, pg. 1964
ARGENTA OIL AND GAS T&T LIMITED—See Azabache Energy Inc.; *Int'l*, pg. 776
ARGENT ASSOCIATES INC.; *U.S. Private*, pg. 319
ARGENTA UNDERWRITING ASIA PTE. LTD.—See Talanx AG; *Int'l*, pg. 7443
ARGENT CAPITAL MANAGEMENT, LLC; *U.S. Private*, pg. 319
ARGENTEA SRL—See GPI S.p.A.; *Int'l*, pg. 3046
ARGENTEX GROUP PLC; *Int'l*, pg. 561
ARGENT FIDUCIARY CONSULTING SERVICES, LLC—See Argent Financial Group, Inc.; *U.S. Private*, pg. 320
ARGENT FINANCIAL GROUP, INC.; *U.S. Private*, pg. 319
ARGENT GROUP EUROPE LIMITED; *Int'l*, pg. 560
ARGENTIL CAPITAL PARTNERS LIMITED; *Int'l*, pg. 561
ARGENTINA CLEARING S.A.—See Banco Macro S.A.; *Int'l*, pg. 823
ARGENTINA LITHIUM & ENERGY CORP.; *Int'l*, pg. 561
ARGENTINA PORTER NOVELLI—See Omnicom Group Inc.; *U.S. Public*, pg. 1590
ARGENT INDUSTRIAL LIMITED; *Int'l*, pg. 560
ARGENTINE BETTERMENT CORPORATION; *U.S. Private*, pg. 320
ARGENT INTERNATIONAL; *U.S. Private*, pg. 320

COMPANY NAME INDEX

ARGENT MINERALS LIMITED; *Int'l*, pg. 561
ARGENT OPTICAL MANUFACTORY LIMITED—See Arts Optical International Holdings Ltd; *Int'l*, pg. 585
ARGENT PROPERTY SERVICES, LLC—See Argent Financial Group, Inc.; *U.S. Private*, pg. 320
ARGENTS EXPRESS GROUP LTD; *U.S. Private*, pg. 320
ARGENT STEEL GROUP (PTY) LTD—See ARGENT INDUSTRIAL LIMITED; *Int'l*, pg. 560
ARGENT TRUST COMPANY, N.A.—See Argent Financial Group, Inc.; *U.S. Private*, pg. 320
ARGENT TRUST COMPANY OF TENNESSEE—See Argent Financial Group, Inc.; *U.S. Private*, pg. 320
ARGENTUM 47, INC.; *Int'l*, pg. 561
THE ARGENTUM GROUP; *U.S. Private*, pg. 3987
ARGENTUM SILVER CORP.; *Int'l*, pg. 561
ARGENT VENTURES, LLC; *U.S. Private*, pg. 320
ARGENX JAPAN KK—See ARGENX SE; *Int'l*, pg. 561
ARGENX SE; *Int'l*, pg. 561
ARGEO AS; *Int'l*, pg. 561
ARGES GMBH—See Novanta Inc.; *U.S. Public*, pg. 1548
ARGETON GMBH—See Wienerberger AG; *Int'l*, pg. 8407
ARGEX TITANIUM INC.; *Int'l*, pg. 561
ARG FINANCIAL STAFFING; *U.S. Private*, pg. 319
ARGHA KARYA PRIMA INDUSTRY TBK; *Int'l*, pg. 561
ARGIBETAO SA—See SODIM, SGPS, SA; *Int'l*, pg. 7049
ARGIBETAO - SOCIEDADE DE NOVOS PRODUTOS DE ARGILA E BETAO, S.A.—See SODIM, SGPS, SA; *Int'l*, pg. 7049
ARGI FINANCIAL GROUP; *U.S. Private*, pg. 320
ARGILETUM MERCHANT S.P.A.; *Int'l*, pg. 561
ARGIL, INC.—See Gentex Corporation; *U.S. Public*, pg. 931
ARG, INC.; *U.S. Private*, pg. 319
ARGIS-GALAC SEA; *Int'l*, pg. 561
ARGIS LIMITED—See Steadfast Group Limited; *Int'l*, pg. 7187
ARGIX DIRECT INC.; *U.S. Private*, pg. 320
AR GLOBAL INVESTMENTS, LLC; *U.S. Private*, pg. 306
ARG MBH & CO. KG; *Int'l*, pg. 560
ARGO AB—See Copperstone Resources AB; *Int'l*, pg. 1794
ARGO AG—See Coop-Gruppe Genossenschaft; *Int'l*, pg. 1789
ARGO BLOCKCHAIN PLC; *Int'l*, pg. 561
ARGO BUSINESS SERVICES INC.—See Argo Graphics Inc.; *Int'l*, pg. 562
ARGO CAPITAL MANAGEMENT (CYPRUS) LIMITED—See Argo Group Limited; *Int'l*, pg. 562
ARGO CAPITAL MANAGEMENT LIMITED—See Argo Group Limited; *Int'l*, pg. 562
ARGO DATA RESOURCE CORPORATION; *U.S. Private*, pg. 320
ARGO DIRECT, LTD.—See Brookfield Reinsurance Ltd.; *Int'l*, pg. 1193
ARGO EXPLORATION LIMITED; *Int'l*, pg. 561
ARGO FINANZIARIA S.P.A.; *Int'l*, pg. 561
ARGOGLOBAL ASSICURAZIONI S.P.A.—See Brookfield Reinsurance Ltd.; *Int'l*, pg. 1194
ARGO GLOBAL LISTED INFRASTRUCTURE LIMITED; *Int'l*, pg. 562
ARGOGLOBAL SE—See Brookfield Reinsurance Ltd.; *Int'l*, pg. 1194
ARGOGLOBAL UNDERWRITING ASIA PACIFIC PTE LTD.—See Brookfield Reinsurance Ltd.; *Int'l*, pg. 1194
ARGOGLOBAL UNDERWRITING (DUBAI) LIMITED—See Brookfield Reinsurance Ltd.; *Int'l*, pg. 1194
ARGO GOLD INC.; *Int'l*, pg. 562
ARGO GRAPHICS INC.; *Int'l*, pg. 562
ARGO GROUP INTERNATIONAL HOLDINGS, LTD. - ALTERIS PUBLIC RISK SOLUTIONS DIVISION—See Brookfield Reinsurance Ltd.; *Int'l*, pg. 1193
ARGO GROUP INTERNATIONAL HOLDINGS, LTD.—See Brookfield Reinsurance Ltd.; *Int'l*, pg. 1193
ARGO GROUP LIMITED; *Int'l*, pg. 562
ARGO GROUP US, INC.—See Brookfield Reinsurance Ltd.; *Int'l*, pg. 1193
ARGO INFRASTRUCTURE PARTNERS LLC; *U.S. Private*, pg. 320
ARGO INTERNATIONAL CORPORATION—See Argo Turboserve Corporation; *U.S. Private*, pg. 320
ARGO INVESTMENTS LIMITED; *Int'l*, pg. 562
ARGO KONZERTE GMBH—See CTS Eventim AG & Co. KGAA; *Int'l*, pg. 1872
ARGOLINA D O O—See OTP Bank Plc; *Int'l*, pg. 5657
ARGO LIVING SOILS CORP.; *Int'l*, pg. 562
ARGO LTD—See Lotte Co., Ltd.; *Int'l*, pg. 4560
ARGO MANAGEMENT GROUP, LLC—See Kingsway Financial Services Inc.; *U.S. Public*, pg. 1234
ARGO MANAGEMENT HOLDINGS, LTD.—See Brookfield Reinsurance Ltd.; *Int'l*, pg. 1193
ARGO MANAGING AGENCY LIMITED—See Brookfield Reinsurance Ltd.; *Int'l*, pg. 1193
ARGONAUTA ENERGY SERVICES LLC—See Reiten & Co AS; *Int'l*, pg. 6259
ARGONAUT CLAIMS MANAGEMENT, LLC—See Brookfield Reinsurance Ltd.; *Int'l*, pg. 1194
ARGONAUT CLAIMS SERVICES, LTD.—See Brookfield Reinsurance Ltd.; *Int'l*, pg. 1194

ARGONAUT CONSTRUCTORS, INC.; *U.S. Private*, pg. 321
ARGONAUT EXPLORATION INC.; *Int'l*, pg. 563
ARGONAUT GOLD INC.; *U.S. Public*, pg. 191
ARGONAUT INSURANCE COMPANY—See Brookfield Reinsurance Ltd.; *Int'l*, pg. 1194
ARGONAUT LIMITED RISK INSURANCE COMPANY—See Brookfield Reinsurance Ltd.; *Int'l*, pg. 1194
ARGONAUT MANAGEMENT SERVICES, INC.—See Brookfield Reinsurance Ltd.; *Int'l*, pg. 1194
ARGONAUT-MIDWEST INSURANCE COMPANY—See Brookfield Reinsurance Ltd.; *Int'l*, pg. 1194
ARGONAUT PRIVATE EQUITY, LLC; *U.S. Private*, pg. 321
ARGONAUT RESOURCES LAOS CO LIMITED—See Orpheus Uranium Limited; *Int'l*, pg. 5643
ARGONAUT-SOUTHWEST INSURANCE COMPANY—See Brookfield Reinsurance Ltd.; *Int'l*, pg. 1194
ARGON DENIMS LIMITED; *Int'l*, pg. 562
ARGON MEDICAL DEVICES, INC. - GAINESVILLE PLANT—See Shandong Weigao Group Medical Polymer Company Limited; *Int'l*, pg. 6759
ARGON MEDICAL DEVICES, INC.—See Shandong Weigao Group Medical Polymer Company Limited; *Int'l*, pg. 6758
ARGONNE CAPITAL GROUP, LLC; *U.S. Private*, pg. 321
ARGON ST, INC.—See The Boeing Company; *U.S. Public*, pg. 2039
ARGON TECHNOLOGIES, INC.—See Centre Partners Management LLC; *U.S. Private*, pg. 828
ARGON VERLAG GMBH—See Verlagsgruppe Georg von Holtzbrinck GmbH; *Int'l*, pg. 8169
ARGO PANTES TBK; *Int'l*, pg. 562
ARGO PRODUCTS CO.; *U.S. Private*, pg. 320
ARGO PRO—See Brookfield Reinsurance Ltd.; *Int'l*, pg. 1193
ARGO REAL ESTATE OPPORTUNITIES FUND—See Argo Group Limited; *Int'l*, pg. 562
ARGO RE DIFC, LTD.—See Brookfield Reinsurance Ltd.; *Int'l*, pg. 1193
ARGO RE, LTD.—See Brookfield Reinsurance Ltd.; *Int'l*, pg. 1194
ARGOS BUSINESS SOLUTIONS LIMITED—See J Sainsbury plc; *Int'l*, pg. 3852
ARGOS CARPETS & FLOORING; *Int'l*, pg. 563
ARGO SEGURAS BRASIL, SA—See GP Investments, Ltd.; *Int'l*, pg. 3045
ARGOS GESTION, S.L.U.—See RPM International Inc.; *U.S. Public*, pg. 1816
ARGOS GUATEMALA S.A.—See Grupo Argos S.A.; *Int'l*, pg. 3120
ARGOS LTD.—See J Sainsbury plc; *Int'l*, pg. 3852
ARGO SOLUTIONS, SA—See Brookfield Reinsurance Ltd.; *Int'l*, pg. 1194
ARGO—See Ontario Drive & Gear Limited; *Int'l*, pg. 5583
ARGOS USA CORPORATION - GAINESVILLE BLOCK/READY-MIX—See Grupo Argos S.A.; *Int'l*, pg. 3120
ARGOS USA CORPORATION - LINEBAUGH READY-MIX—See Grupo Argos S.A.; *Int'l*, pg. 3120
ARGOS USA CORPORATION - PALMETTO READY-MIX—See Grupo Argos S.A.; *Int'l*, pg. 3120
ARGOS USA LLC—See Grupo Argos S.A.; *Int'l*, pg. 3120
ARGOS WITYU FRANCE SAS—See Argos Wityu S.A.; *Int'l*, pg. 563
ARGOS WITYU ITALIA S.P.A.—See Argos Wityu S.A.; *Int'l*, pg. 563
ARGOS WITYU S.A.; *Int'l*, pg. 563
ARGOSY CAPITAL GROUP, LLC; *U.S. Private*, pg. 321
ARGOSY CONSOLE, INC.; *U.S. Private*, pg. 321
ARGOSY EDUCATION GROUP, INC.—See Dream Center Foundation, a California Nonprofit Corp.; *U.S. Private*, pg. 1272
ARGOSY HEALTHCARE PARTNERS—See Argosy Capital Group, LLC; *U.S. Private*, pg. 321
ARGOSY INTERNATIONAL INC.; *U.S. Private*, pg. 322
ARGOSY MINERALS LIMITED; *Int'l*, pg. 563
ARGOSY PROPERTY LIMITED; *Int'l*, pg. 563
ARGOSY REAL ESTATE MANAGEMENT, LLC—See Argosy Capital Group, LLC; *U.S. Private*, pg. 321
ARGOSY RESEARCH, INC.; *Int'l*, pg. 563
ARGOSY TRADING CO. LTD—See N.K. Shacolas (Holdings) Ltd.; *Int'l*, pg. 5116
ARGOSY UNIVERSITY/ATLANTA—See Dream Center Foundation, a California Nonprofit Corp.; *U.S. Private*, pg. 1273
ARGOSY UNIVERSITY/CHICAGO—See Dream Center Foundation, a California Nonprofit Corp.; *U.S. Private*, pg. 1273
ARGOSY UNIVERSITY/DALLAS—See Dream Center Foundation, a California Nonprofit Corp.; *U.S. Private*, pg. 1273
ARGOSY UNIVERSITY FAMILY CENTER, INC.—See Dream Center Foundation, a California Nonprofit Corp.; *U.S. Private*, pg. 1272
ARGOSY UNIVERSITY/HONOLULU—See Dream Center Foundation, a California Nonprofit Corp.; *U.S. Private*, pg. 1273

ARGOSY UNIVERSITY OF FLORIDA, INC.—See Dream Center Foundation, a California Nonprofit Corp.; *U.S. Private*, pg. 1272
ARGOSY UNIVERSITY/ORANGE COUNTY—See Dream Center Foundation, a California Nonprofit Corp.; *U.S. Private*, pg. 1273
ARGOSY UNIVERSITY/PHOENIX—See Dream Center Foundation, a California Nonprofit Corp.; *U.S. Private*, pg. 1273
ARGOSY UNIVERSITY/SARASOTA—See Dream Center Foundation, a California Nonprofit Corp.; *U.S. Private*, pg. 1273
ARGOSY UNIVERSITY/SCHAUMBURG—See Dream Center Foundation, a California Nonprofit Corp.; *U.S. Private*, pg. 1273
ARGOSY UNIVERSITY/SEATTLE—See Dream Center Foundation, a California Nonprofit Corp.; *U.S. Private*, pg. 1273
ARGOSY UNIVERSITY—See Dream Center Foundation, a California Nonprofit Corp.; *U.S. Private*, pg. 1272
ARGOSY UNIVERSITY/TAMPA—See Dream Center Foundation, a California Nonprofit Corp.; *U.S. Private*, pg. 1273
ARGOSY UNIVERSITY/TWIN CITIES—See Dream Center Foundation, a California Nonprofit Corp.; *U.S. Private*, pg. 1273
ARGOSY UNIVERSITY/WASHINGTON DC—See Dream Center Foundation, a California Nonprofit Corp.; *U.S. Private*, pg. 1273
ARGOTEC DEUTSCHLAND GMBH—See Mativ Holdings, Inc.; *U.S. Public*, pg. 1396
ARGO TECHNOLOGY, INC. - USA—See TerraVest Industries, Inc.; *Int'l*, pg. 7568
ARGOTEK, INC.—See Parsons Corporation; *U.S. Public*, pg. 1650
ARGOT PARTNERS, LLC—See Avesi Partners, LLC; *U.S. Private*, pg. 405
ARGO TRANSDATA CORPORATION—See The Eastern Company; *U.S. Public*, pg. 2069
ARGO TURBOSERVE CORPORATION; *U.S. Private*, pg. 320
ARGO UNDERWRITING AGENCY, LTD.—See Brookfield Reinsurance Ltd.; *Int'l*, pg. 1194
ARGOX INFORMATION CO., LTD.—See SATO Holdings Corporation; *Int'l*, pg. 6585
ARGPEX S.A.—See Golan Plastic Products Ltd.; *Int'l*, pg. 3023
ARG TRUCKING CORP—See Wadhams Enterprises Inc.; *U.S. Private*, pg. 4424
ARGUINDEGUI OIL COMPANY; *U.S. Private*, pg. 322
ARGUS CAMERA COMPANY, LLC—See Impero Electronics, Inc.; *U.S. Private*, pg. 2050
ARGUS CAPITAL CORP.; *U.S. Public*, pg. 191
ARGUS CARRIERS LTD.—See Mullen Group Ltd.; *Int'l*, pg. 5079
ARGUS CONTRACTING, INC—See Irex Corporation; *U.S. Private*, pg. 2137
ARGUS-COURIER—See Gannett Co., Inc.; *U.S. Public*, pg. 905
ARGUS DENTAL PLAN, INC.; *U.S. Private*, pg. 322
ARGUS ENERGY LLC.; *U.S. Private*, pg. 322
ARGUS GMBH & CO. K.G.—See Flowserve Corporation; *U.S. Public*, pg. 855
ARGUS GROUP HOLDINGS LIMITED; *Int'l*, pg. 563
ARGUS HEALTH SYSTEMS, INC.—See SS&C Technologies Holdings, Inc.; *U.S. Public*, pg. 1923
ARGUS IMAGING B.V.—See Koninklijke Philips N.V.; *Int'l*, pg. 4270
ARGUS INFORMATION & ADVISORY SERVICES, LLC—See Verisk Analytics, Inc.; *U.S. Public*, pg. 2282
ARGUS INVESTORS' COUNSEL, INC.—See The Argus Research Group, Inc.; *U.S. Private*, pg. 3988
ARGUS KREDITT AS—See TowerBrook Capital Partners, L.P.; *U.S. Private*, pg. 4194
ARGUS LEADER—See Gannett Co., Inc.; *U.S. Public*, pg. 897
ARGUS LIMITED; *U.S. Private*, pg. 322
ARGUS MEDIA, INC. - NEW YORK—See General Atlantic Service Company, L.P.; *U.S. Private*, pg. 1662
ARGUS MEDIA, INC. - NEW YORK—See HgCapital Trust plc; *Int'l*, pg. 3376
ARGUS MEDIA, INC.—See General Atlantic Service Company, L.P.; *U.S. Private*, pg. 1662
ARGUS MEDIA, INC.—See HgCapital Trust plc; *Int'l*, pg. 3376
ARGUS MEDIA, INC. - WASHINGTON, D.C.—See General Atlantic Service Company, L.P.; *U.S. Private*, pg. 1662
ARGUS MEDIA, INC. - WASHINGTON, D.C.—See HgCapital Trust plc; *Int'l*, pg. 3376
ARGUS MEDIA LIMITED—See General Atlantic Service Company, L.P.; *U.S. Private*, pg. 1662
ARGUS MEDIA LIMITED—See HgCapital Trust plc; *Int'l*, pg. 3376
ARGUS MEDIA LTD. - JAPAN—See General Atlantic Service Company, L.P.; *U.S. Private*, pg. 1662
ARGUS MEDIA LTD. - JAPAN—See HgCapital Trust plc; *Int'l*, pg. 3376

ARGUS LIMITED

ARGUS MEDIA LTD. - RUSSIA—See General Atlantic Service Company, L.P.; *U.S. Private*, pg. 1662
ARGUS MEDIA LTD. - RUSSIA—See HgCapital Trust plc; *Int'l*, pg. 3376
ARGUS PACIFIC, INC.—See Terracon Consultants, Inc.; *U.S. Private*, pg. 3970
ARGUS RESEARCH COMPANY—See The Argus Research Group, Inc.; *U.S. Private*, pg. 3988
THE ARGUS RESEARCH GROUP, INC.; *U.S. Private*, pg. 3988
ARGUS, S.A.; *Int'l*, pg. 563
ARGUS, S.A.—See Nippon Sheet Glass Co. Ltd.; *Int'l*, pg. 5330
ARGUS SECURITY S.R.L.—See Halma plc; *Int'l*, pg. 3230
ARGUS (SHANGHAI) TEXTILE AUXILIARY CO., LTD.—See Argus (Shanghai) Textile Chemicals Co., Ltd.; *Int'l*, pg. 563
ARGUS (SHANGHAI) TEXTILE CHEMICALS CO., LTD.; *Int'l*, pg. 563
ARGUS SOFTWARE, INC.—See Altus Group Limited; *Int'l*, pg. 399
THE ARGUS—See Alden Global Capital LLC; *U.S. Private*, pg. 155
ARGUS; *U.S. Private*, pg. 322
ARGUS TECHNICAL SERVICES INC.; *U.S. Private*, pg. 322
ARGUS TECHNOLOGIES, INC.—See EnerSys; *U.S. Public*, pg. 768
ARGUS VICKERS AMERICAN EQUITY RESEARCH LTD.—See The Argus Research Group, Inc.; *U.S. Private*, pg. 3988
ARGUS WORLDWIDE CORP.; *U.S. Public*, pg. 191
ARGYLE COMMUNICATIONS—See Publicis Groupe S.A.; *Int'l*, pg. 6106
ARGYLE DIALYSIS, LLC—See DaVita Inc.; *U.S. Public*, pg. 636
ARGYLE DIAMONDS AUSTRALIA—See Rio Tinto plc; *Int'l*, pg. 6346
ARGYLE DIAMONDS LIMITED—See Rio Tinto plc; *Int'l*, pg. 6346
ARGYLE EXECUTIVE FORUM, LLC; *U.S. Private*, pg. 322
ARGYLE PINK DIAMONDS—See Rio Tinto plc; *Int'l*, pg. 6347
ARGYLE STREET MANAGEMENT LIMITED; *Int'l*, pg. 563
ARGYLL INSURANCE SERVICES LIMITED—See Marsh & McLennan Companies, Inc.; *U.S. Public*, pg. 1374
ARGYLL PARTNERS LTD.; *Int'l*, pg. 563
ARGYLL SCOTT HONG KONG LTD.—See Hydrogen Group Plc; *Int'l*, pg. 3547
ARGYLL SCOTT INTERNATIONAL (SINGAPORE) LTD.—See Hydrogen Group Plc; *Int'l*, pg. 3547
ARGYLL SCOTT MALAYSIA SDN BHD—See Hydrogen Group Plc; *Int'l*, pg. 3547
ARGYLL SCOTT RECRUITMENT (THAILAND) LTD.—See Hydrogen Group Plc; *Int'l*, pg. 3547
ARGYNNIS GROUP AB—See Pomona-Gruppen AB; *Int'l*, pg. 5918
ARGY, WILTSE & ROBINSON, P.C.; *U.S. Private*, pg. 322
ARHC ATLARFL01 TRS, LLC—See Ventas, Inc.; *U.S. Public*, pg. 2278
ARHC BTFMYFL01 TRS, LLC—See Ventas, Inc.; *U.S. Public*, pg. 2278
ARHC BTNAPFL01 TRS, LLC—See Ventas, Inc.; *U.S. Public*, pg. 2278
ARH III INSURANCE CO., INC.—See NJ Transit Corporation; *U.S. Private*, pg. 2930
ARHITEKTURA THOLOS PROJEKTIRANJE D.O.O.—See INSTITUT IGH d.d.; *Int'l*, pg. 3723
ARHT MEDIA INC.; *Int'l*, pg. 563
ARIA BAY RETIREMENT VILLAGE LIMITED—See Arvida Group Limited; *Int'l*, pg. 587
ARIA CREMATION SERVICES, LLC—See The John P. Brooks Family Corporation; *U.S. Private*, pg. 4059
ARIAD CUSTOM PUBLISHING LIMITED—See High Road Capital Partners, LLC; *U.S. Private*, pg. 1936
ARIADNE AUSTRALIA LIMITED; *Int'l*, pg. 563
ARIA ENERGY LLC—See BP plc; *Int'l*, pg. 1126
ARIAFINA CO. LTD.—See Elica S.p.A.; *Int'l*, pg. 2361
ARIA GARDENS LIMITED—See Arvida Group Limited; *Int'l*, pg. 587
ARIA HOTELS AND CONSULTANCY SERVICES PVT. LTD.—See Asian Hotels (West) Limited; *Int'l*, pg. 618
ARIAKE FARM CO., LTD.—See ARIAKE JAPAN Co., Ltd.; *Int'l*, pg. 563
ARIAKE JAPAN CO LTD - KYUSHU PLANT—See ARIAKE JAPAN Co., Ltd.; *Int'l*, pg. 563
ARIAKE JAPAN CO., LTD.; *Int'l*, pg. 563
ARIAKE U.S.A., INC.—See Kerry Group plc; *Int'l*, pg. 4138
ARIANA RESOURCES PLC; *Int'l*, pg. 564
ARIANESPACE—See Airbus SE; *Int'l*, pg. 245
ARIANESPACE, INC.—See Safran SA; *Int'l*, pg. 6472
ARIANESPACE SAS—See Airbus SE; *Int'l*, pg. 245
ARIANESPACE SAS—See Safran SA; *Int'l*, pg. 6472
ARIANESPACE SINGAPORE PTE. LTD.—See Airbus SE; *Int'l*, pg. 245
ARIANESPACE SINGAPORE PTE. LTD.—See Safran SA; *Int'l*, pg. 6472
ARIANNE PHOSPHATE INC.; *Int'l*, pg. 564

ARIAN RESOURCES CORP.; *Int'l*, pg. 564
ARIAN SILVER MEXICO S.A. DE C.V.MEXICO—See Alien Metals Ltd.; *Int'l*, pg. 327
ARIA PARK RETIREMENT VILLAGE LIMITED—See Arvida Group Limited; *Int'l*, pg. 587
ARIA PROPERTY GROUP (PTY) LIMITED—See Trematon Capital Investments Ltd.; *Int'l*, pg. 7915
ARIA RESORT & CASINO, LLC—See MGM Resorts International; *U.S. Public*, pg. 1435
ARIAS INTEL CORP.; *U.S. Private*, pg. 322
ARIA SOLUTIONS INC.—See TTEC Holdings, Inc.; *U.S. Public*, pg. 2203
ARIAT INTERNATIONAL, INC.; *U.S. Private*, pg. 322
ARIBA BELGIUM—See SAP SE; *Int'l*, pg. 6567
ARIBA CZECH S.R.O.—See SAP SE; *Int'l*, pg. 6566
ARIBA DEUTSCHLAND GMBH—See SAP SE; *Int'l*, pg. 6567
ARIBA FRANCE SARL—See SAP SE; *Int'l*, pg. 6567
ARIBA IBERIA, S.L.—See SAP SE; *Int'l*, pg. 6567
ARIBA IBERIA, S.L.—See SAP SE; *Int'l*, pg. 6567
ARIBA, INC.—See SAP SE; *Int'l*, pg. 6567
ARIBA, INC.—See SAP SE; *Int'l*, pg. 6567
ARIBA, INC.—See SAP SE; *Int'l*, pg. 6567
ARIBA SLOVAK REPUBLIC, S.R.O.—See SAP SE; *Int'l*, pg. 6566
ARIBA SWEDEN AB—See SAP SE; *Int'l*, pg. 6567
ARIBA SWITZERLAND GMBH SARL LLC—See SAP SE; *Int'l*, pg. 6567
ARIBA TECHNOLOGIES INDIA PRIVATE LIMITED—See SAP SE; *Int'l*, pg. 6566
ARIBA TECHNOLOGIES NETHERLANDS B.V.—See SAP SE; *Int'l*, pg. 6567
ARIBA TECHNOLOGIES PVT LTD—See SAP SE; *Int'l*, pg. 6567
ARI. BATTERJEE & BROS COMPANY—See HORIBA Ltd; *Int'l*, pg. 3475
ARIBA U.K. LIMITED—See SAP SE; *Int'l*, pg. 6567
ARIBEX, INC.—See Danaher Corporation; *U.S. Public*, pg. 628
ARI CASUALTY COMPANY—See Stone Point Capital LLC; *U.S. Private*, pg. 3820
ARICH ENTERPRISE CO., LTD.; *Int'l*, pg. 564
ARIDOS ESPECIALES SPA—See VINCI S.A.; *Int'l*, pg. 8212
ARIDOS SANZ S.L.U.—See Heidelberg Materials AG; pg. 3308
ARIDOS VELILLA, S.A.—See Heidelberg Materials AG; *Int'l*, pg. 3308
ARIDTEC PTE LTD.—See Eneco Refresh Limited; *Int'l*, pg. 2411
ARIE DARMA ENTERPRISES (S) PTE. LTD.—See Max Weishaupt GmbH; *Int'l*, pg. 4735
ARIEL CAPITAL MANAGEMENT LLC; *U.S. Private*, pg. 322
ARIEL CLINICAL SERVICES; *U.S. Private*, pg. 322
ARIEL CORPORATION; *U.S. Private*, pg. 322
THE ARIEL GROUP LLC; *U.S. Private*, pg. 3988
ARIEL RE BDA LIMITED—See Brookfield Reinsurance Ltd.; *Int'l*, pg. 1194
ARIENS COMPANY INC.; *U.S. Private*, pg. 322
ARIENS SPECIALTY BRANDS, LLC—See The Riverside Company; *U.S. Private*, pg. 4108
ARIES 94 S.R.O.—See Linde plc; *Int'l*, pg. 4504
ARIES AGRO LIMITED; *Int'l*, pg. 564
ARIES AUTOMOTIVE ACCESSORIES, INC.—See LCI Industries; *U.S. Public*, pg. 1295
ARIES BUILDING SYSTEMS, LLC - PNW MAJOR PROJECTS—See Reliant Asset Management LLC; *U.S. Private*, pg. 3395
ARIES BUILDING SYSTEMS, LLC—See Reliant Asset Management LLC; *U.S. Private*, pg. 3395
ARIES CANADA LTD.—See Aries Industries Inc.; *U.S. Private*, pg. 322
ARIES CO. LTD.—See Nisshinbo Holdings Inc.; *Int'l*, pg. 5372
ARIES ELECTRONICS INC.; *U.S. Private*, pg. 322
ARIES GLOBAL LOGISTICS, INC.; *U.S. Private*, pg. 322
ARIES INDUSTRIES INC.; *U.S. Private*, pg. 322
ARIES MARINE CORPORATION; *U.S. Private*, pg. 323
ARIES MOTOR SP. Z O.O.—See Kanematsu Corporation; *Int'l*, pg. 4068
ARIES OPTICAL LTD.—See EssilorLuxottica SA; *Int'l*, pg. 2512
ARIES POWER EQUIPMENT LTD.—See Kanematsu Corporation; *Int'l*, pg. 4068
ARIES PREPARED BEEF CO.; *U.S. Private*, pg. 323
ARIES SYSTEMS CORPORATION—See RELX plc; *Int'l*, pg. 6264
ARI EUROPE B.V.—See True Wind Capital Management, L.P.; *U.S. Private*, pg. 4248
ARIF HABIB CONSULTANCY (PVT.) LIMITED—See Aisha Steel Mills Limited; *Int'l*, pg. 251
ARIF HABIB CORPORATION LIMITED; *Int'l*, pg. 564
ARIF HABIB DMCC—See Arif Habib Corporation Limited; *Int'l*, pg. 564
ARI FINANCIAL SERVICES, INC.—See Holman Automotive Group, Inc.; *U.S. Private*, pg. 1967
ARI FLEET SERVICES OF CANADA, INC.—See ITE Management L.P.; *U.S. Private*, pg. 2149

CORPORATE AFFILIATIONS

ARIGATOU SERVICES CO., LTD.; *Int'l*, pg. 564
ARIG CAPITAL LIMITED—See Arab Insurance Group B.S.C.; *Int'l*, pg. 530
ARIHANT CAPITAL (IFSC) LIMITED—See Arihant Capital Markets Ltd.; *Int'l*, pg. 564
ARIHANT CAPITAL MARKETS LTD.; *Int'l*, pg. 564
ARIHANT FOUNDATIONS & HOUSING LIMITED; *Int'l*, pg. 564
ARIHANT INSTITUTE LIMITED; *Int'l*, pg. 564
ARIHANT MULTI COMMERCIAL LIMITED; *Int'l*, pg. 564
ARIHANT'S SECURITIES LIMITED; *Int'l*, pg. 565
ARIHANT SUPERSTRUCTURES LIMITED; *Int'l*, pg. 564
ARIHANT TOURNESOL LTD.; *Int'l*, pg. 565
ARIHANT VATIKA REALTY PRIVATE LIMITED—See Arihant Superstructures Limited; *Int'l*, pg. 565
ARI-INDUSTRIAL PRODUCTS GROUP—See ITE Management L.P.; *U.S. Private*, pg. 2149
ARI INTERNATIONAL CORPORATION—See Parker Corporation; *Int'l*, pg. 5743
ARIIX, LLC—See NewAge, Inc.; *U.S. Public*, pg. 1513
ARI JACKSON MANUFACTURING—See ITE Management L.P.; *U.S. Private*, pg. 2149
ARILI PLASTIK SANAYII AS—See Solvay S.A.; *Int'l*, pg. 7077
ARI LONGTRAIN, INC.—See ITE Management L.P.; *U.S. Private*, pg. 2149
ARIMA COMMUNICATIONS CORPORATION—See Arima Photovoltaic & Optical Corp.; *Int'l*, pg. 565
ARIMA DISPLAY CORPORATION—See Arima Photovoltaic & Optical Corp.; *Int'l*, pg. 565
ARIMA, INC.—See Lions Gate Entertainment Corp.; *Int'l*, pg. 4520
ARIMA INSURANCE SOFTWARE W.L.L.—See Arab Insurance Group B.S.C.; *Int'l*, pg. 530
ARIMA OPTOELECTRONICS CORPORATION—See Arima Photovoltaic & Optical Corp.; *Int'l*, pg. 565
ARIMA PHOTOVOLTAIC & OPTICAL CORP.; *Int'l*, pg. 565
ARIMA REAL ESTATE SOCIMI SA; *Int'l*, pg. 565
ARIMA VIEW HOTEL CO., LTD.—See Hankyu Hanshin Holdings Inc.; *Int'l*, pg. 3255
ARIMELIA ITG SOCIMI, S.A.; *Int'l*, pg. 565
ARIMON TECHNOLOGIES INC.; *U.S. Private*, pg. 323
ARI NETWORK SERVICES, INC.—See True Wind Capital Management, L.P.; *U.S. Private*, pg. 4248
ARING EQUIPMENT COMPANY INC.; *U.S. Private*, pg. 323
ARINSIRI LAND PUBLIC COMPANY LIMITED; *Int'l*, pg. 565
ARIOLA EURODISC INC.—See Universal Music Group N.V.; *Int'l*, pg. 8081
ARION BANK HF.; *Int'l*, pg. 565
ARION BANKI HF; *Int'l*, pg. 565
ARION GROUP CORP.; *U.S. Public*, pg. 192
ARION TECHNOLOGY INC.; *Int'l*, pg. 565
ARIOSA DIAGNOSTICS, INC.—See Roche Holding AG; *Int'l*, pg. 6374
ARIPAEV, AS—See Bonnier AB; *Int'l*, pg. 1108
ARIP PUBLIC COMPANY LIMITED; *Int'l*, pg. 565
ARI PRODUCTS INC.; *U.S. Private*, pg. 322
ARISAWA FIBER GLASS CO., LTD.—See Arisawa Manufacturing Co., Ltd.; *Int'l*, pg. 565
ARISAWA JUSHI KOGYO CO., LTD.—See Arisawa Manufacturing Co., Ltd.; *Int'l*, pg. 565
ARISAWA KENPAN CO., LTD.—See Arisawa Manufacturing Co., Ltd.; *Int'l*, pg. 565
ARISAWA MANUFACTURING CO., LTD. - 3D MATERIAL DIVISION—See Arisawa Manufacturing Co., Ltd.; *Int'l*, pg. 565
ARISAWA MANUFACTURING CO., LTD. - CIRCUIT MATERIAL DIVISION—See Arisawa Manufacturing Co., Ltd.; *Int'l*, pg. 565
ARISAWA MANUFACTURING CO., LTD. - ELECTRICAL INSULATING & COMPOSITE MATERIAL DIVISION—See Arisawa Manufacturing Co., Ltd.; *Int'l*, pg. 565
ARISAWA MANUFACTURING CO., LTD. - ELECTRONIC MATERIAL DIVISION—See Arisawa Manufacturing Co., Ltd.; *Int'l*, pg. 565
ARISAWA MANUFACTURING CO., LTD. - NAKADAHARA FACTORY—See Arisawa Manufacturing Co., Ltd.; *Int'l*, pg. 565
ARISAWA MANUFACTURING CO., LTD. - NAKADAHARA-NISHI FACTORY—See Arisawa Manufacturing Co., Ltd.; *Int'l*, pg. 566
ARISAWA MANUFACTURING CO., LTD.; *Int'l*, pg. 565
ARISAWA SOGYO CO., LTD.—See Arisawa Manufacturing Co., Ltd.; *Int'l*, pg. 566
ARISE AB; *Int'l*, pg. 566
ARISE BOILER INSPECTION AND INSURANCE COMPANY RISK RETENTION GROUP—See TUV SUD AG; *Int'l*, pg. 7984
ARISE HEALTH PLAN—See Wisconsin Physicians Service Insurance Corporation; *U.S. Private*, pg. 4549
ARISE, INC.—See TUV SUD AG; *Int'l*, pg. 7984
ARISE INNOVATION, INC.—See Japan Pulp and Paper Company Limited; *U.S. Private*, pg. 3903
ARISE SERVICE & PROJEKTERING AB—See Arise AB; *Int'l*, pg. 566

COMPANY NAME INDEX — ARIZON COMPANIES

ARISE VIRTUAL SOLUTIONS, INC.—See Warburg Pincus LLC; *U.S. Private*, pg. 4440
ARISE WIND FARM 3 AB—See Arise AB; *Int'l*, pg. 566
ARISE WIND FARM 4 AB—See Arise AB; *Int'l*, pg. 566
ARIS GLOBAL LLC—See Nordic Capital AB; *Int'l*, pg. 5419
ARIS HORTICULTURAL SERVICES—See Aris Horticulture, Inc.; *U.S. Private*, pg. 323
ARIS HORTICULTURE, INC.; *U.S. Private*, pg. 323
ARIS INTERNATIONAL LIMITED—See BRCCA Services Private Limited; *Int'l*, pg. 1143
ARISIT PTY LIMITED—See Harvey Norman Holdings Ltd; *Int'l*, pg. 3281
ARIS MAURITIUS LIMITED—See Endress+Hauser (International) Holding AG; *Int'l*, pg. 2405
ARISON HOLDINGS (1998) LTD.; *Int'l*, pg. 566
ARISON INVESTMENTS LTD.—See Arison Holdings (1998) Ltd.; *Int'l*, pg. 566
ARIS SOLUTIONS INC.; *U.S. Private*, pg. 323
ARISTA AIR CONDITIONING CORPORATION; *U.S. Private*, pg. 323
ARISTA CAPITAL LTD.—See Arista Financial Corp.; *U.S. Private*, pg. 323
ARISTA FINANCIAL CORP.; *U.S. Private*, pg. 323
ARISTA INVESTORS CORP.; *U.S. Private*, pg. 323
ARISTA LABORATORIES EUROPE LTD.—See MPAC Group PLC; *Int'l*, pg. 5060
ARISTA LABORATORIES INC.—See MPAC Group PLC; *Int'l*, pg. 5060
ARISTA MOLECULAR, INC.—See Danaher Corporation; *U.S. Public*, pg. 625
ARISTA NETWORKS AUSTRALIA PTY LTD—See Arista Networks, Inc.; *U.S. Public*, pg. 192
ARISTA NETWORKS EURL—See Arista Networks, Inc.; *U.S. Public*, pg. 192
ARISTA NETWORKS GMBH—See Arista Networks, Inc.; *U.S. Public*, pg. 192
ARISTA NETWORKS, INC.; *U.S. Public*, pg. 192
ARISTA NETWORKS INDIA PRIVATE LIMITED—See Arista Networks, Inc.; *U.S. Public*, pg. 192
ARISTA NETWORKS SINGAPORE PRIVATE LTD.—See Arista Networks, Inc.; *U.S. Public*, pg. 192
ARISTA POWER, INC.; *U.S. Public*, pg. 192
ARISTA WINES—See Lassonde Industries, Inc.; *Int'l*, pg. 4421
ARISTECH ACRYLICS LLC - AVONITE SURFACES—See SK Capital Partners, LP; *U.S. Private*, pg. 3679
ARISTECH ACRYLICS LLC—See SK Capital Partners, LP; *U.S. Private*, pg. 3679
ARIS TELERADIOLOGY, LLC—See Great Point Partners, LLC; *U.S. Private*, pg. 1767
ARISTEYA LLC—See AFI Development PLC; *Int'l*, pg. 189
ARIS TITLE INSURANCE CORPORATION—See Brookfield Reinsurance Ltd.; *Int'l*, pg. 1193
ARISTOCRAT ARGENTINA S.A.—See Aristocrat Leisure Limited; *Int'l*, pg. 566
ARISTOCRAT BEREA SKILLED NURSING AND REHABILITATION CENTER—See Communicare, Inc.; *U.S. Private*, pg. 988
ARISTOCRAT GROUP CORP.; *U.S. Public*, pg. 192
ARISTOCRAT INTERNATIONAL PTY LTD—See Aristocrat Leisure Limited; *Int'l*, pg. 566
ARISTOCRAT LEISURE CYPRUS LIMITED—See Aristocrat Leisure Limited; *Int'l*, pg. 566
ARISTOCRAT LEISURE LIMITED; *Int'l*, pg. 566
ARISTOCRAT (MACAU) PTY LIMITED—See Aristocrat Leisure Limited; *Int'l*, pg. 566
ARISTOCRAT PROPERTIES PTY LTD—See Aristocrat Leisure Limited; *Int'l*, pg. 566
ARISTOCRAT SERVICE MEXICO, S.A. DE C.V.—See Aristocrat Leisure Limited; *Int'l*, pg. 566
ARISTOCRAT TECHNICAL SERVICES PTY LTD—See Aristocrat Leisure Limited; *Int'l*, pg. 566
ARISTOCRAT TECHNOLOGIES AUSTRALIA PTY. LTD.—See Aristocrat Leisure Limited; *Int'l*, pg. 566
ARISTOCRAT TECHNOLOGIES EUROPE (HOLDINGS) LIMITED—See Aristocrat Leisure Limited; *Int'l*, pg. 566
ARISTOCRAT TECHNOLOGIES EUROPE LIMITED—See Aristocrat Leisure Limited; *Int'l*, pg. 566
ARISTOCRAT TECHNOLOGIES, INC.—See Aristocrat Leisure Limited; *Int'l*, pg. 566
ARISTOCRAT TECHNOLOGIES INDIA PRIVATE LTD—See Aristocrat Leisure Limited; *Int'l*, pg. 566
ARISTOCRAT TECHNOLOGIES MACAU LIMITED—See Aristocrat Leisure Limited; *Int'l*, pg. 566
ARISTOCRAT TECHNOLOGIES NZ LIMITED—See Aristocrat Leisure Limited; *Int'l*, pg. 566
ARISTOCRAT TECHNOLOGIES SPAIN S.L—See Aristocrat Leisure Limited; *Int'l*, pg. 566
ARISTOCRAT TECHNOLOGY GAMING SYSTEMS PTY LIMITED—See Aristocrat Leisure Limited; *Int'l*, pg. 566
ARISTOCRAT VOLKSWAGEN INC.; *U.S. Private*, pg. 323
ARISTON DEUTSCHLAND GMBH—See Ariston Holding N.V.; *Int'l*, pg. 567
ARISTON HOLDING N.V.; *Int'l*, pg. 567
ARISTON THERMO CZ S.R.O.—See Ariston Holding N.V.; *Int'l*, pg. 567
ARISTON THERMO MAROC S.A.—See Ariston Holding N.V.; *Int'l*, pg. 567

ARISTON THERMO ROMANIA S.R.L.—See Ariston Holding N.V.; *Int'l*, pg. 567
ARISTON THERMO S.P.A.; *Int'l*, pg. 567
ARISTON THERMO UK LTD.—See Ariston Holding N.V.; *Int'l*, pg. 567
ARISTON THERMO USA LLC—See Ariston Holding N.V.; *Int'l*, pg. 567
ARISTON THERMO VIETNAM LTD.—See Ariston Holding N.V.; *Int'l*, pg. 567
THE ARISTOS GROUP; *U.S. Private*, pg. 3988
ARISTOTLE CAPITAL MANAGEMENT, LLC; *U.S. Private*, pg. 323
THE ARISTOTLE CORPORATION—See Geneve Holdings Corp.; *U.S. Private*, pg. 1671
ARISTOTLE PACIFIC CAPITAL, LLC—See Aristotle Capital Management, LLC; *U.S. Private*, pg. 323
ARIS TRADING LTD.—See Endress+Hauser (International) Holding AG; *Int'l*, pg. 2405
ARISTRO CAPITAL MARKETS LIMITED—See U. Y. Fincorp Limited; *Int'l*, pg. 7998
ARIS WATER SOLUTIONS, INC.; *U.S. Public*, pg. 192
ARISZ ACQUISITION CORP.; *U.S. Public*, pg. 192
ARITA ENGINEERING SDN. BHD.—See UNIMECH Group Berhad; *Int'l*, pg. 8048
ARITA FLANGES INDUSTRIES SDN. BHD.—See UNIMECH Group Berhad; *Int'l*, pg. 8049
ARITA VALVE MFG. (M) SDN. BHD.—See UNIMECH Group Berhad; *Int'l*, pg. 8049
ARITCO DE GMBH—See Investment AB Latour; *Int'l*, pg. 3782
ARITCO HOMELIFT LTD.—See Investment AB Latour; *Int'l*, pg. 3782
ARITCO LIFT AB—See Investment AB Latour; *Int'l*, pg. 3782
ARITHMETICA CONSULTING GMBH—See Vienna Insurance Group AG Wiener Versicherung Gruppe; *Int'l*, pg. 8196
ARITHMETIC INC.—See Aeria Inc.; *Int'l*, pg. 179
ARITHNEA GMBH—See adesso SE; *Int'l*, pg. 144
ARITZIA, INC.; *Int'l*, pg. 567
ARITZIA LP—See Aritzia, Inc.; *Int'l*, pg. 567
ARIUS SA—See BNP Paribas SA; *Int'l*, pg. 1079
ARIUS TECHNOLOGY INC.; *Int'l*, pg. 567
ARIUS TECHNOLOGY INC. - VAUGHAN—See Arius Technology Inc.; *Int'l*, pg. 567
ARI UTARA SDN. BHD.—See Ajiya Berhad; *Int'l*, pg. 258
ARIVA MORTGAGE SERVICES, LLC—See Hilltop Holdings Inc.; *U.S. Public*, pg. 1038
ARIWA ABWASSERREINIGUNG IM WALDVIERTEL GMBH—See PORR AG; *Int'l*, pg. 5922
ARIXA MANAGEMENT, LLC; *U.S. Private*, pg. 323
ARIX BIOSCIENCE PLC; *Int'l*, pg. 567
ARIZANT DEUTSCHLAND GMBH—See 3M Company; *U.S. Public*, pg. 8
ARIZANT FRANCE SAS—See 3M Company; *U.S. Public*, pg. 8
ARIZANT HOLDINGS INC.—See 3M Company; *U.S. Public*, pg. 8
ARIZANT, INC.—See 3M Company; *U.S. Public*, pg. 8
ARIZANT INTERNATIONAL CORPORATION—See 3M Company; *U.S. Public*, pg. 8
ARIZANT OSTERREICH GMBH—See 3M Company; *U.S. Public*, pg. 8
ARIZANT UK LIMITED—See 3M Company; *U.S. Public*, pg. 8
ARIZONA-AMERICAN WATER COMPANY—See EPCOR Utilities, Inc.; *Int'l*, pg. 2459
ARIZONA AUTO AUCTION—See Cox Enterprises, Inc.; *U.S. Private*, pg. 1076
ARIZONA BANK & TRUST—See Heartland Financial USA, Inc.; *U.S. Public*, pg. 1018
ARIZONA BEHAVIORAL HEALTH CORPORATION; *U.S. Private*, pg. 323
ARIZONA BIKE WEEK CHARITIES; *U.S. Private*, pg. 323
ARIZONA BIODYNE—See Centene Corporation; *U.S. Public*, pg. 469
ARIZONA BLINDS; *U.S. Private*, pg. 323
ARIZONA BRAKE & CLUTCH SUPPLY—See Platinum Equity, LLC; *U.S. Private*, pg. 3209
ARIZONA & CALIFORNIA RAILROAD COMPANY—See Brookfield Infrastructure Partners L.P.; *Int'l*, pg. 1190
ARIZONA & CALIFORNIA RAILROAD COMPANY—See GIC Pte. Ltd.; *Int'l*, pg. 2965
ARIZONA CAPACITORS, INC.—See Electro Technik Industries; *U.S. Private*, pg. 1354
ARIZONA CARDINALS FOOTBALL CLUB, INC.; *U.S. Private*, pg. 323
ARIZONA CARE NETWORK - NEXT, LLC.—See Tenet Healthcare Corporation; *U.S. Public*, pg. 2001
ARIZONA CENTRAL CREDIT UNION; *U.S. Private*, pg. 324
ARIZONA COMMERCIAL TRUCK SALES, LLC.; *U.S. Private*, pg. 324
THE ARIZONA DAILY STAR—See Gannett Co., Inc.; *U.S. Public*, pg. 899
THE ARIZONA DAILY STAR—See Lee Enterprises, Incorporated; *U.S. Public*, pg. 1300
ARIZONA DAILY SUN—See Lee Enterprises, Incorporated; *U.S. Public*, pg. 1298

ARIZONA DIAMONDBACKS; *U.S. Private*, pg. 324
ARIZONA EASTERN RAILWAY COMPANY—See Brookfield Infrastructure Partners L.P.; *Int'l*, pg. 1190
ARIZONA EASTERN RAILWAY COMPANY—See GIC Pte. Ltd.; *Int'l*, pg. 2965
ARIZONA ELECTRIC POWER COOPERATIVE INC.; *U.S. Private*, pg. 324
ARIZONA FUEL DISTRIBUTORS LLC; *U.S. Private*, pg. 324
ARIZONA GALVANIZING INC.—See AZZ, Inc.; *U.S. Public*, pg. 259
ARIZONA GRAINS INC.; *U.S. Private*, pg. 324
ARIZONA GRAIN VALLEY SEED—See Arizona Grains Inc.; *U.S. Private*, pg. 324
ARIZONA HEALTH PARTNERS, LLC—See Tenet Healthcare Corporation; *U.S. Public*, pg. 2014
ARIZONA HEART HOSPITAL, LLC—See Tenet Healthcare Corporation; *U.S. Public*, pg. 2014
ARIZONA HOUSING, INC.; *U.S. Private*, pg. 324
ARIZONA HUMANE SOCIETY; *U.S. Private*, pg. 324
ARIZONA INDUSTRIAL & MUNICIPAL SERVICES LLC—See Mack Operations LLC; *U.S. Private*, pg. 2536
ARIZONA INSTRUMENT LLC; *U.S. Private*, pg. 324
ARIZONA LABOR FORCE INC.; *U.S. Private*, pg. 324
ARIZONA LEATHER COMPANY INC.; *U.S. Private*, pg. 324
ARIZONA MACHINERY CO.; *U.S. Private*, pg. 324
ARIZONA MILLS—See Simon Property Group, Inc.; *U.S. Public*, pg. 1882
ARIZONA MIST INC.—See Platinum Equity, LLC; *U.S. Private*, pg. 3207
ARIZONA MUTUAL TRADING CO., INC.—See Takara Holdings, Inc.; *Int'l*, pg. 7433
ARIZONA NEWS SERVICE, LLC—See The Dolan Company; *U.S. Private*, pg. 4022
ARIZONA OFFICE TECHNOLOGIES—See Xerox Holdings Corporation; *U.S. Public*, pg. 2389
ARIZONA PARTSMASTER INC.; *U.S. Private*, pg. 324
ARIZONA PAVEMENT PROFILING—See Nesbitt Investment Company; *U.S. Private*, pg. 2886
ARIZONA PEPPER PRODUCTS CO., INC.; *U.S. Private*, pg. 324
ARIZONA PIPE LINE COMPANY INC.; *U.S. Private*, pg. 324
ARIZONA POLYMER FLOORING—See Audax Group, Limited Partnership; *U.S. Private*, pg. 388
ARIZONA PROFESSIONAL BASEBALL LTD PARTNERSHIP—See Pinnacle West Capital Corporation; *U.S. Public*, pg. 1692
ARIZONA PUBLIC SERVICE COMPANY—See Pinnacle West Capital Corporation; *U.S. Public*, pg. 1692
THE ARIZONA REPUBLIC—See Gannett Co., Inc.; *U.S. Public*, pg. 899
ARIZONA RV CENTERS, LLC—See Camping World Holdings, Inc.; *U.S. Public*, pg. 427
ARIZONA'S BEST EQUIPMENT INC.—See Tym Corporation; *Int'l*, pg. 7994
ARIZONA'S CHILDREN ASSOCIATION; *U.S. Private*, pg. 325
ARIZONA SILVER EXPLORATION INC.; *Int'l*, pg. 567
ARIZONA SONORAN COPPER COMPANY INC.; *Int'l*, pg. 567
ARIZONA SPINE AND JOINT HOSPITAL LLC—See Bain Capital, LP; *U.S. Private*, pg. 445
ARIZONA STAIRS, INC.—See McDonough Corporation; *U.S. Private*, pg. 2632
ARIZONA STATE CREDIT UNION; *U.S. Private*, pg. 324
ARIZONA STATE TRAILERS SALES, INC.; *U.S. Private*, pg. 324
ARIZONA STATE UNIVERSITY; *U.S. Private*, pg. 325
ARIZONA STONE & ARCHITECTURAL, LLC.; *U.S. Private*, pg. 325
ARIZONA TILE-ANAHEIM—See Arizona Tile Supply, Inc.; *U.S. Private*, pg. 325
ARIZONA TILE SUPPLY, INC.; *U.S. Private*, pg. 325
ARIZONA TRENCH COMPANY, LLC—See Quanta Services, Inc.; *U.S. Public*, pg. 1750
ARIZONA UROLOGY SPECIALISTS, P.L.L.C.—See Audax Group, Limited Partnership; *U.S. Private*, pg. 387
ARIZONA WATER COMPANY—See Fontana Water Company; *U.S. Private*, pg. 1560
ARIZONA WHOLESALE SUPPLY COMPANY; *U.S. Private*, pg. 325
ARIZON COMPANIES; *U.S. Private*, pg. 323
ARIZON RFID TECHNOLOGY CO., LTD.—See YFY, Inc.; *Int'l*, pg. 8579
ARJAE SHEET METAL COMPANY, INC.—See Ares Management Corporation; *U.S. Public*, pg. 189
ARJO AB—See Getinge AB; *Int'l*, pg. 2947
ARJO AUSTRIA GMBH—See Getinge AB; *Int'l*, pg. 2947
ARJO EQUIPEMENTS HOSPITALIERS S.A.—See Getinge AB; *Int'l*, pg. 2947
ARJO FAR EAST LTD.—See Getinge AB; *Int'l*, pg. 2947
ARJO HOSPITAL EQUIPMENT AB—See Getinge AB; *Int'l*, pg. 2947
ARJO HOSPITAL EQUIPMENT PTY LTD.—See Getinge AB; *Int'l*, pg. 2948

ARIZON COMPANIES

ARJO HOSPITAL EQUIPMENT S.R.O.—See Getinge AB; *Int'l*, pg. 2948
ARJOHUNTLEIGH AB—See Getinge AB; *Int'l*, pg. 2948
ARJOHUNTLEIGH AG—See Getinge AB; *Int'l*, pg. 2948
ARJOHUNTLEIGH A/S—See Getinge AB; *Int'l*, pg. 2948
ARJOHUNTLEIGH CANADA INC.—See Getinge AB; *Int'l*, pg. 2948
ARJOHUNTLEIGH GMBH—See Getinge AB; *Int'l*, pg. 2948
ARJOHUNTLEIGH HEALTHCARE INDIA PVT. LTD.—See Getinge AB; *Int'l*, pg. 2948
ARJOHUNTLEIGH HEALTHCARE POLSKA SP. Z O.O.—See Getinge AB; *Int'l*, pg. 2948
ARJOHUNTLEIGH (HONG KONG) LTD—See Getinge AB; *Int'l*, pg. 2948
ARJOHUNTLEIGH HOSPITAL EQUIPMENT AB—See Getinge AB; *Int'l*, pg. 2948
ARJOHUNTLEIGH IBERICA S.L.—See Getinge AB; *Int'l*, pg. 2948
ARJOHUNTLEIGH INC—See Getinge AB; *Int'l*, pg. 2948
ARJOHUNTLEIGH INTERNATIONAL AB—See Getinge AB; *Int'l*, pg. 2949
ARJOHUNTLEIGH INTERNATIONAL LTD—See Getinge AB; *Int'l*, pg. 2948
ARJOHUNTLEIGH LTD—See Getinge AB; *Int'l*, pg. 2948
ARJOHUNTLEIGH MAGOG INC.—See Getinge AB; *Int'l*, pg. 2948
ARJOHUNTLEIGH MIDDLE EAST—See Getinge AB; *Int'l*, pg. 2948
ARJOHUNTLEIGH NEDERLAND B.V.—See Getinge AB; *Int'l*, pg. 2948
ARJOHUNTLEIGH NORWAY A/S—See Getinge AB; *Int'l*, pg. 2948
ARJOHUNTLEIGH NV/SA—See Getinge AB; *Int'l*, pg. 2948
ARJOHUNTLEIGH POLSKA SP. Z.O.O.—See Getinge AB; *Int'l*, pg. 2948
ARJOHUNTLEIGH PTY LTD.—See Getinge AB; *Int'l*, pg. 2948
ARJOHUNTLEIGH SAS—See Getinge AB; *Int'l*, pg. 2948
ARJOHUNTLEIGH (SHANGHAI) MEDICAL TRADING CO. LTD—See Getinge AB; *Int'l*, pg. 2948
ARJOHUNTLEIGH SINGAPORE PTE LTD—See Getinge AB; *Int'l*, pg. 2948
ARJOHUNTLEIGH SOUTH AFRICA (PTY) LTD—See Getinge AB; *Int'l*, pg. 2948
ARJOHUNTLEIGH SPA—See Getinge AB; *Int'l*, pg. 2948
ARJOHUNTLEIGH S.R.O.—See Getinge AB; *Int'l*, pg. 2948
ARJOHUNTLEIGH UK AND IRELAND—See Getinge AB; *Int'l*, pg. 2948
ARJOHUNTLEIGH UK—See Getinge AB; *Int'l*, pg. 2948
ARJOHUNTLEIGH - UK—See Getinge AB; *Int'l*, pg. 2948
ARJO ITALIA S.P.A.—See Getinge AB; *Int'l*, pg. 2948
ARJO LTD MED. AB—See Getinge AB; *Int'l*, pg. 2948
ARJO LTD—See Getinge AB; *Int'l*, pg. 2948
ARJO SPAIN S.A.—See Getinge AB; *Int'l*, pg. 2948
ARJOWIGGINS FINE PAPERS LIMITED—See WEPA Hygieneprodukte GmbH & Co. KG; *Int'l*, pg. 8378
ARJOWIGGINS GRAPHIC BENELUX—See WEPA Hygieneprodukte GmbH & Co. KG; *Int'l*, pg. 8378
ARJOWIGGINS SAS—See WEPA Hygieneprodukte GmbH & Co. KG; *Int'l*, pg. 8378
ARJOWIGGINS SECURITY SAS; *Int'l*, pg. 567
ARJUN INFRASTRUCTURE PARTNERS LIMITED; *Int'l*, pg. 567
ARK AC BURGER BAR LLC—See Ark Restaurants Corp.; *U.S. Public*, pg. 192
ARKADIA CAPITAL CORP.; *Int'l*, pg. 568
ARKADIN, INC.—See Nippon Telegraph & Telephone Corporation; *Int'l*, pg. 5344
ARKADIN SAS—See Nippon Telegraph & Telephone Corporation; *Int'l*, pg. 5344
ARKADIUM, INC.; *U.S. Private*, pg. 325
ARKADY WROCLAWSKIE S.A.—See Develia S.A.; *Int'l*, pg. 2087
ARKA FINCAP LIMITED—See Kirloskar Oil Engines Limited; *Int'l*, pg. 4191
ARKAL AUTOMOTIVE LTD. - AUBURN PLANT—See RAVAL ACS Ltd.; *Int'l*, pg. 6222
ARKAL AUTOMOTIVE LTD. - AUENGRUND PLANT—See RAVAL ACS Ltd.; *Int'l*, pg. 6222
ARKAL AUTOMOTIVE LTD. - DONGGUAN PLANT—See RAVAL ACS Ltd.; *Int'l*, pg. 6222
ARKAL AUTOMOTIVE LTD. - LEON PLANT—See RAVAL ACS Ltd.; *Int'l*, pg. 6222
ARKAL AUTOMOTIVE LTD. - LONDON PLANT—See RAVAL ACS Ltd.; *Int'l*, pg. 6222
ARKAL AUTOMOTIVE LTD. - ORKOIEN PLANT—See RAVAL ACS Ltd.; *Int'l*, pg. 6222
ARKAL AUTOMOTIVE LTD.—See RAVAL ACS Ltd.; *Int'l*, pg. 6222
ARK AMSTERDAM—See Publicis Groupe S.A.; *Int'l*, pg. 6100
ARKAN AL-KUWAIT REAL ESTATE COMPANY KSCC; *Int'l*, pg. 568
ARKAN HOLDING COMPANY K.S.C.—See Bayan Investment Holding Company K.S.C.C.; *Int'l*, pg. 901

ARKANOVA ENERGY CORPORATION; *U.S. Public*, pg. 193
ARKANSAS BLUE CROSS AND BLUE SHIELD—See USAble Corporation; *U.S. Private*, pg. 4322
ARKANSAS CASUALTY INVESTMENT—See Arkansas Farm Bureau Federation; *U.S. Private*, pg. 325
ARKANSAS CHILDREN'S HOSPITAL; *U.S. Private*, pg. 325
THE ARKANSAS CITY TRAVELER—See Winfield Publishing Co.; *U.S. Private*, pg. 4540
ARKANSAS DEMOCRAT-GAZETTE, INC.—See Wehco Media, Inc.; *U.S. Private*, pg. 4469
ARKANSAS ELDER OUTREACH OF LITTLE ROCK, INC.; *U.S. Private*, pg. 325
ARKANSAS ELECTRICAL OUTLET INC.; *U.S. Private*, pg. 325
ARKANSAS ELECTRIC COOPERATIVES, INC.; *U.S. Private*, pg. 325
ARKANSAS EXTENDED CARE, LLC—See UnitedHealth Group Incorporated; *U.S. Public*, pg. 2244
ARKANSAS FARM BUREAU FEDERATION; *U.S. Private*, pg. 325
ARKANSAS FARM BUREAU INVESTMENT—See Arkansas Farm Bureau Federation; *U.S. Private*, pg. 325
ARKANSAS FEDERAL CREDIT UNION; *U.S. Private*, pg. 326
ARKANSAS FOUNDATION FOR MEDICAL CARE, INC.; *U.S. Private*, pg. 326
ARKANSAS GALVANIZING INC.—See AZZ, Inc.; *U.S. Public*, pg. 259
ARKANSAS GLASS CONTAINER CORP.; *U.S. Private*, pg. 326
ARKANSAS HEALTH & WELLNESS HEALTH PLAN, INC.—See Centene Corporation; *U.S. Public*, pg. 468
ARKANSAS HEARST ARGYLE TELEVISION, INC.—See The Hearst Corporation; *U.S. Private*, pg. 4048
ARKANSAS HOMECARE OF FULTON, LLC—See UnitedHealth Group Incorporated; *U.S. Public*, pg. 2244
ARKANSAS HOME HOSPICE, LLC—See UnitedHealth Group Incorporated; *U.S. Public*, pg. 2244
ARKANSAS HOSPICE, INC.; *U.S. Private*, pg. 326
ARKANSAS INFORMATION CONSORTIUM, LLC—See Tyler Technologies, Inc.; *U.S. Public*, pg. 2208
ARKANSAS KENWORTH INC.—See Murphy-Hoffman Company; *U.S. Private*, pg. 2816
THE ARKANSAS LIGHTHOUSE FOR THE BLIND—See Winston-Salem Industries for The Blind, Inc.; *U.S. Private*, pg. 4544
ARKANSAS LIME COMPANY—See United States Lime & Minerals, Inc.; *U.S. Public*, pg. 2236
ARKANSAS LOUISIANA & MISSISSIPPI RAILROAD CO.—See Brookfield Infrastructure Partners L.P.; *Int'l*, pg. 1190
ARKANSAS LOUISIANA & MISSISSIPPI RAILROAD CO.—See GIC Pte. Ltd.; *Int'l*, pg. 2965
ARKANSAS METHODIST MEDICAL CENTER; *U.S. Private*, pg. 326
ARKANSAS MIDLAND RAILROAD—See Brookfield Infrastructure Partners L.P.; *Int'l*, pg. 1190
ARKANSAS MIDLAND RAILROAD—See GIC Pte. Ltd.; *Int'l*, pg. 2965
ARKANSAS MILL SUPPLY COMPANY; *U.S. Private*, pg. 326
ARKANSAS & MISSOURI RAILROAD CO.; *U.S. Private*, pg. 325
ARKANSAS PACKAGING PRODUCTS, INC.; *U.S. Private*, pg. 326
ARKANSAS PHYSICAL THERAPY SERVICES OF CONWAY, LLC—See UnitedHealth Group Incorporated; *U.S. Public*, pg. 2244
ARKANSAS RECLAMATION COMPANY, LLC—See Waste Connections, Inc.; *Int'l*, pg. 8354
ARKANSAS REGIONAL ORGAN RECOVERY AGENCY; *U.S. Private*, pg. 326
ARKANSAS RICE DEPOT, INC.; *U.S. Private*, pg. 326
ARKANSAS TELEVISION COMPANY—See TEGNA Inc.; *U.S. Public*, pg. 1990
ARKANSAS TOTAL CARE, INC.—See Centene Corporation; *U.S. Public*, pg. 468
ARKANSAS TRAILER MANUFACTURING CO., INC.; *U.S. Private*, pg. 326
ARKANSAS VALLEY ELECTRIC COOPERATIVE CORPORATION; *U.S. Private*, pg. 326
ARKANSAS VALLEY STATE BANK; *U.S. Private*, pg. 326
ARKANSAS WHOLESALE LUMBER, LLC—See Bain Capital, LP; *U.S. Private*, pg. 451
ARKAS ALGERIE S.P.A.—See Albert Ballin KG; *Int'l*, pg. 294
ARKAS SHIPPING & TRANSPORT S.A.—See Albert Ballin KG; *Int'l*, pg. 294
ARK ATLANTIC CITY CORP.—See Ark Restaurants Corp.; *U.S. Public*, pg. 192
ARK ATLANTIC CITY RESTAURANT CORP.—See Ark Restaurants Corp.; *U.S. Public*, pg. 192
A&R KATZ MANAGEMENT INC.; *U.S. Private*, pg. 20
ARKAY PACKAGING CORPORATION; *U.S. Private*, pg. 326
ARK BRYANT PARK CORP.—See Ark Restaurants Corp.; *U.S. Public*, pg. 192

CORPORATE AFFILIATIONS

ARK BRYANT PARK SOUTHWEST LLC—See Ark Restaurants Corp.; *U.S. Public*, pg. 192
ARK CONFERENCES LIMITED—See Wilmington plc; *Int'l*, pg. 8421
ARK CONNECTICUT BRANCHES CORP.—See Ark Restaurants Corp.; *U.S. Public*, pg. 192
A.R.K. CONTRACTING SERVICES LLC.; *U.S. Private*, pg. 27
ARKCORE, INC.; *U.S. Private*, pg. 568
ARK D.C. KIOSK, INC.—See Ark Restaurants Corp.; *U.S. Public*, pg. 192
ARKEL CONSTRUCTORS, INC.; *U.S. Private*, pg. 326
ARKEL INTERNATIONAL INC.; *U.S. Private*, pg. 326
ARKEMA B.V.—See Arkema S.A.; *Int'l*, pg. 568
ARKEMA CANADA INC.—See Arkema S.A.; *Int'l*, pg. 569
ARKEMA CANADA INC.—See Arkema S.A.; *Int'l*, pg. 569
ARKEMA CHANGSHU CHEMICALS CO. LTD—See Arkema S.A.; *Int'l*, pg. 568
ARKEMA (CHANGSHU) FLUOROCHEMICAL CO. LTD—See Arkema S.A.; *Int'l*, pg. 568
ARKEMA (CHANGSHU) POLYAMIDES CO., LTD.—See Arkema S.A.; *Int'l*, pg. 568
ARKEMA CHEMICALS INDIA PRIVATE LTD.—See Arkema S.A.; *Int'l*, pg. 568
ARKEMA CHEMICALS SAUDI ARABIA—See Arkema S.A.; *Int'l*, pg. 568
ARKEMA CHINA INVESTMENT CO. LTD—See Arkema S.A.; *Int'l*, pg. 568
ARKEMA COATEX BRASIL INDUSTRIA E COMERCIO LTDA.—See Arkema S.A.; *Int'l*, pg. 569
ARKEMA COATING RESINS - ALSIP—See Arkema S.A.; *Int'l*, pg. 569
ARKEMA COATING RESINS LTD.—See Arkema S.A.; *Int'l*, pg. 569
ARKEMA COATING RESINS MALAYSIA SDN. BHD.—See Arkema S.A.; *Int'l*, pg. 569
ARKEMA COATING RESINS—See Arkema S.A.; *Int'l*, pg. 569
ARKEMA COATING RESINS - TORRANCE PLANT—See Arkema S.A.; *Int'l*, pg. 569
ARKEMA COATINGS RESINS, S.A.U.—See Arkema S.A.; *Int'l*, pg. 569
ARKEMA CO. LTD—See Arkema S.A.; *Int'l*, pg. 569
ARKEMA COMPANY LTD.—See Arkema S.A.; *Int'l*, pg. 569
ARKEMA DEUTSCHLAND GMBH—See Arkema S.A.; *Int'l*, pg. 569
ARKEMA EUROPE SA—See Arkema S.A.; *Int'l*, pg. 569
ARKEMA GMBH—See Arkema S.A.; *Int'l*, pg. 569
ARKEMA HYDROGEN PEROXIDE CO., LTD.—See Arkema S.A.; *Int'l*, pg. 569
ARKEMA INC.—See Arkema S.A.; *Int'l*, pg. 569
ARKEMA INICIADORES SA DE CV—See Arkema S.A.; *Int'l*, pg. 569
ARKEMA KIMYA SANAYI VE TICARET AS—See Arkema S.A.; *Int'l*, pg. 569
ARKEMA K.K.—See Arkema S.A.; *Int'l*, pg. 569
ARKEMA KOREA HOLDING CO., LTD.—See Arkema S.A.; *Int'l*, pg. 569
ARKEMA LTD—See Arkema S.A.; *Int'l*, pg. 569
ARKEMA MEXICO S.A DE C.V—See Arkema S.A.; *Int'l*, pg. 569
ARKEMA NORTH EUROPE B.V.—See Arkema S.A.; *Int'l*, pg. 569
ARKEMA PTE LTD—See Arkema S.A.; *Int'l*, pg. 569
ARKEMA PTY. LTD.—See Arkema S.A.; *Int'l*, pg. 569
ARKEMA QUIMICA LTDA—See Arkema S.A.; *Int'l*, pg. 569
ARKEMA QUIMICA S.A—See Arkema S.A.; *Int'l*, pg. 569
ARKEMA RESEARCH CENTER—See Arkema S.A.; *Int'l*, pg. 569
ARKEMA ROTTERDAM BV—See Arkema S.A.; *Int'l*, pg. 568
ARKEMA S.A.; *Int'l*, pg. 568
ARKEMA SHANGHAI DISTRIBUTION CO. LTD—See Arkema S.A.; *Int'l*, pg. 569
ARKEMA SP Z.O.O.—See Arkema S.A.; *Int'l*, pg. 570
ARKEMA SRL—See Arkema S.A.; *Int'l*, pg. 570
ARKEMA (SUZHOU) POLYAMIDES CO., LTD.—See Arkema S.A.; *Int'l*, pg. 569
ARKEMA VLISSINGEN B.V.—See Arkema S.A.; *Int'l*, pg. 568
ARKEMA YOSHITOMI, LTD.—See Mitsubishi Chemical Group Corporation; *Int'l*, pg. 4935
ARKEN POP INTERNATIONAL LIMITED—See Writtle Holdings Limited; *Int'l*, pg. 8495
ARKEO INC.—See Groupe Crit, S.A.; *Int'l*, pg. 3101
ARKESSA LIMITED—See Montagu Private Equity LLP; *Int'l*, pg. 5036
ARK GROUP AUSTRALIA PTY LIMITED—See Wilmington plc; *Int'l*, pg. 8422
ARK GROUP LIMITED—See Wilmington plc; *Int'l*, pg. 8422
ARKIL HOLDING A/S; *Int'l*, pg. 571
ARK INSAAT AS—See Koc Holding A.S.; *Int'l*, pg. 4222
ARKION LIFE SCIENCES L.L.C.; *U.S. Private*, pg. 326
ARK ISLAND BEACH RESORT LLC—See Ark Restaurants Corp.; *U.S. Public*, pg. 192
ARKIVA AB—See Addnode Group AB; *Int'l*, pg. 130

COMPANY NAME INDEX

ARKIVE INFORMATION MANAGEMENT LLC—See SPP Management Services, LLC; *U.S. Private*, pg. 3762
ARK JUPITER RI, LLC—See Ark Restaurants Corp.; *U.S. Public*, pg. 192
ARKKITEHTITOIMISTO BRUNOW & MAUNULA OY—See Sweco AB; *Int'l*, pg. 7363
ARK LAS VEGAS RESTAURANT CORP.—See Ark Restaurants Corp.; *U.S. Public*, pg. 192
ARKLE PRINT LTD; *Int'l*, pg. 571
ARKLE RESOURCES PLC; *Int'l*, pg. 571
ARK-LES CONNECTORS—See Milestone Partners Ltd.; *U.S. Private*, pg. 2729
ARK LIFE ASSURANCE COMPANY DAC—See Phoenix Group Holdings PLC; *Int'l*, pg. 5851
ARK MEADOWLANDS LLC—See Ark Restaurants Corp.; *U.S. Public*, pg. 192
ARK MINES LTD; *Int'l*, pg. 568
ARKNETMEDIA INC.; *U.S. Private*, pg. 326
ARKO HOLDINGS LTD.—See Haymaker Acquisition Corp.; *U.S. Private*, pg. 1885
ARK OPERATING CORP.—See Ark Restaurants Corp.; *U.S. Public*, pg. 192
ARKOSE ENERGY CORP.; *U.S. Public*, pg. 193
ARKOS FIELD SERVICES, LP—See Burckhardt Compression Holding AG; *Int'l*, pg. 1220
ARKOS GROUP LLC—See Burckhardt Compression Holding AG; *Int'l*, pg. 1220
ARKO TECHNOLOGY A.S.—See VINCI S.A.; *Int'l*, pg. 8212
ARK OYSTER HOUSE GULF SHORES I, LLC—See Ark Restaurants Corp.; *U.S. Public*, pg. 192
ARKPHIRE GROUP LTD.—See BC Partners LLP; *Int'l*, pg. 925
ARK POTOMAC CORPORATION—See Ark Restaurants Corp.; *U.S. Public*, pg. 192
ARKRAY CO. LTD., INC.—See ARKRAY, Inc.; *Int'l*, pg. 571
ARKRAY EUROPE, B.V.—See ARKRAY, Inc.; *Int'l*, pg. 571
ARKRAY FACTORY, INC. - KUSATSU FACTORY—See ARKRAY, Inc.; *Int'l*, pg. 571
ARKRAY FACTORY, INC.—See ARKRAY, Inc.; *Int'l*, pg. 571
ARKRAY FACTORY LTD.—See ARKRAY, Inc.; *Int'l*, pg. 571
ARKRAY FACTORY PINGHU, INC.—See ARKRAY, Inc.; *Int'l*, pg. 571
ARKRAY FACTORY SHANGHAI, INC.—See ARKRAY, Inc.; *Int'l*, pg. 571
ARKRAY GLOBAL BUSINESS, INC.—See ARKRAY, Inc.; *Int'l*, pg. 571
ARKRAY HEALTHCARE PVT. LTD.—See ARKRAY, Inc.; *Int'l*, pg. 571
ARKRAY, INC.; *Int'l*, pg. 571
ARKRAY INDUSTRY, INC.—See ARKRAY, Inc.; *Int'l*, pg. 571
ARKRAY LTD.—See ARKRAY, Inc.; *Int'l*, pg. 571
ARKRAY MARKETING SHANGHAI, INC.—See ARKRAY, Inc.; *Int'l*, pg. 572
ARKRAY & PARTNERS PTE. LTD.—See ARKRAY, Inc.; *Int'l*, pg. 571
ARKRAY TECH XI'AN, INC.—See ARKRAY, Inc.; *Int'l*, pg. 572
ARKRAY USA, INC.—See ARKRAY, Inc.; *Int'l*, pg. 572
ARK RESOURCES HOLDINGS SDN BHD; *Int'l*, pg. 568
ARK RESTAURANTS CORP.; *U.S. Public*, pg. 192
ARK ROYAL INSURANCE COMPANY; *U.S. Private*, pg. 325
ARK SOUTHWEST D.C. CORP.—See Ark Restaurants Corp.; *U.S. Public*, pg. 192
ARK SYSTEMS CO., LTD.—See CAC Holdings Corporation; *Int'l*, pg. 1247
ARK TECHNOLOGIES INC.; *U.S. Private*, pg. 325
ARKTON SP. Z O.O.—See Berling S.A.; *Int'l*, pg. 986
ARKU COIL SYSTEMS INC—See ARKU Maschinenbau GmbH; *Int'l*, pg. 572
ARKU LEVELING SYSTEMS (KUNSHAN) CO., LTD.—See ARKU Maschinenbau GmbH; *Int'l*, pg. 572
ARKU MASCHINENBAU GMBH; *Int'l*, pg. 572
ARK UNION STATION, INC.—See Ark Restaurants Corp.; *U.S. Public*, pg. 192
ARKWIN INDUSTRIES, INC.—See TransDigm Group Incorporated; *U.S. Public*, pg. 2182
ARKWRIGHT ADVANCED COATING, INC.—See ANDRITZ AG; *Int'l*, pg. 455
ARLAB S.A.—See Biotronik GmbH & Co.; *Int'l*, pg. 1044
ARLA DP HOLDING A/S—See Arla Foods amba; *Int'l*, pg. 572
ARLA FOODS AB—See Arla Foods amba; *Int'l*, pg. 572
ARLA FOODS AMBA; *Int'l*, pg. 572
ARLA FOODS ARTIS LTD—See Arla Foods amba; *Int'l*, pg. 572
ARLA FOODS AS—See Arla Foods amba; *Int'l*, pg. 572
ARLA FOODS BANGLADESH LTD.—See Arla Foods amba; *Int'l*, pg. 572
ARLA FOODS B.V.—See Arla Foods amba; *Int'l*, pg. 572
ARLA FOODS DEUTSCHLAND GMBH—See Arla Foods amba; *Int'l*, pg. 572
ARLA FOODS FINANCIAL SERVICES CENTRE SP. Z O.O.—See Arla Foods amba; *Int'l*, pg. 572

ARLA FOODS GMBH—See Arla Foods amba; *Int'l*, pg. 572
ARLA FOODS HELLAS S.A.—See Arla Foods amba; *Int'l*, pg. 572
ARLA FOODS INC.—See Arla Foods amba; *Int'l*, pg. 572
ARLA FOODS INC.—See Arla Foods amba; *Int'l*, pg. 572
ARLA FOODS INGREDIENTS AMBA—See Arla Foods amba; *Int'l*, pg. 572
ARLA FOODS INGREDIENTS GMBH—See Arla Foods amba; *Int'l*, pg. 572
ARLA FOODS INGREDIENTS, INC.—See Arla Foods amba; *Int'l*, pg. 572
ARLA FOODS INGREDIENTS K.K.—See Arla Foods amba; *Int'l*, pg. 572
ARLA FOODS INGREDIENTS KOREA CO., LTD.—See Arla Foods amba; *Int'l*, pg. 572
ARLA FOODS INGREDIENTS S.A. DE C.V.—See Arla Foods amba; *Int'l*, pg. 572
ARLA FOODS INGREDIENTS S.A.—See Arla Foods amba; *Int'l*, pg. 572
ARLA FOODS KASEREINEN GMBH—See Arla Foods amba; *Int'l*, pg. 572
ARLA FOODS LIMITED—See Arla Foods amba; *Int'l*, pg. 573
ARLA FOODS LTDA—See Arla Foods amba; *Int'l*, pg. 573
ARLA FOODS PRODUCTION LLC—See Arla Foods amba; *Int'l*, pg. 572
ARLA FOODS S.A.R.L.—See Arla Foods amba; *Int'l*, pg. 573
ARLA FOODS S.A.—See Arla Foods amba; *Int'l*, pg. 573
ARLA FOODS SA—See Arla Foods amba; *Int'l*, pg. 573
ARLA FOODS—See Arla Foods amba; *Int'l*, pg. 573
ARLA FOODS SP. Z O.O.—See Arla Foods amba; *Int'l*, pg. 573
ARLA FOODS S.R.L.—See Arla Foods amba; *Int'l*, pg. 573
ARLA FOODS TRADING A/S—See Arla Foods amba; *Int'l*, pg. 573
ARLA FOODS UK PLC-OSWESTRY PACKING FACILITY—See Arla Foods amba; *Int'l*, pg. 573
ARLA FOODS UK PLC—See Arla Foods amba; *Int'l*, pg. 573
ARLA FOODS (WESTBURY) LTD—See Arla Foods amba; *Int'l*, pg. 573
ARLA INGMAN OY AB—See Arla Foods amba; *Int'l*, pg. 572
ARLANDASTAD GROUP AB; *Int'l*, pg. 573
ARLAND TOOL & MANUFACTURING INC.; *U.S. Private*, pg. 326
ARLANIS REPLY LTD.—See Reply S.p.A.; *Int'l*, pg. 6290
ARLAN'S MARKET INC.; *U.S. Private*, pg. 326
ARLAN WAGONS LLP; *U.S. Private*, pg. 326
ARLANXEO BELGIUM N.V.—See Saudi Arabian Oil Company; *Int'l*, pg. 6589
ARLANXEO CANADA INC.—See Saudi Arabian Oil Company; *Int'l*, pg. 6589
ARLANXEO ELASTOMERES FRANCE S.A.S.—See Saudi Arabian Oil Company; *Int'l*, pg. 6589
ARLANXEO EMULSION RUBBER FRANCE S.A.S—See Saudi Arabian Oil Company; *Int'l*, pg. 6589
ARLANXEO HOLDING B.V.—See Saudi Arabian Oil Company; *Int'l*, pg. 6589
ARLANXEO NETHERLANDS B.V.—See Saudi Arabian Oil Company; *Int'l*, pg. 6589
ARLANXEO USA LLC—See Saudi Arabian Oil Company; *Int'l*, pg. 6589
ARLA PLAST AB; *Int'l*, pg. 573
ARLEE HOME FASHIONS INC.; *U.S. Private*, pg. 326
ARLEIGH INTERNATIONAL LIMITED—See LKQ Corporation; *U.S. Public*, pg. 1333
THE ARLEN GROUP, INC.—See Stone Point Capital LLC; *U.S. Private*, pg. 3819
ARLEY WHOLESALE INC.; *U.S. Private*, pg. 326
ARLIGHT AYDINLATMA A.S.—See Fagerhult Group AB; *Int'l*, pg. 2601
THE ARLINGTON ADVOCATE—See Gannett Co., Inc.; *U.S. Public*, pg. 903
ARLINGTON ASSET INVESTMENT CORP.—See Ellington Management Group, L.L.C.; *U.S. Public*, pg. 1364
ARLINGTON CAPITAL PARTNERS LLC; *U.S. Private*, pg. 326
ARLINGTON COAL & LUMBER CO. INC.; *U.S. Private*, pg. 328
ARLINGTON COMPUTER PRODUCTS; *U.S. Private*, pg. 329
ARLINGTON CONTACT LENS SERVICE, INC.; *U.S. Private*, pg. 329
ARLINGTON DIALYSIS CENTER, LLC—See Nautic Partners, LLC; *U.S. Private*, pg. 2869
THE ARLINGTON EYE CENTER, INC.—See Centre Partners Management LLC; *U.S. Private*, pg. 828
ARLINGTON INDUSTRIES INC.; *U.S. Private*, pg. 329
ARLINGTON INVESTMENT COMPANY—See Credit Acceptance Corporation; *U.S. Public*, pg. 593
ARLINGTON MACHINE & TOOL CO.—See Rift Valley Equity Partners, LLC; *U.S. Private*, pg. 3435
ARLINGTON METALS CORPORATION; *U.S. Private*, pg. 329

ARMADA MERCANTILE LTD.

ARLINGTON ORTHOPEDIC AND SPINE HOSPITAL, LLC—See Tenet Healthcare Corporation; *U.S. Public*, pg. 2009
ARLINGTON PARK—See Churchill Downs, Inc.; *U.S. Public*, pg. 493
ARLINGTON PATHOLOGY ASSOCIATION 5.01(A) CORPORATION—See Quest Diagnostics, Inc.; *U.S. Public*, pg. 1755
ARLINGTON PLATING COMPANY—See Enameled Steel; *U.S. Private*, pg. 1389
ARLINGTON PLATING COMPANY—See Midwestern Rust Proof Co.; *U.S. Private*, pg. 2724
ARLINGTON RACK & PACKAGING CO.; *U.S. Private*, pg. 329
THE ARLINGTON RESORT HOTEL & SPA; *U.S. Private*, pg. 3988
ARLINGTON RESOURCES, INC.; *U.S. Private*, pg. 329
ARLINGTON SALVAGE & WRECKER CO.; *U.S. Private*, pg. 329
ARLINGTON TOMORROW FOUNDATION; *U.S. Private*, pg. 329
ARLITECH ELECTRONIC CORP.; *Int'l*, pg. 573
ARL NETWORK—See US 1 Industries, Inc.; *U.S. Private*, pg. 4316
A.R. LOCKHART DEVELOPMENT CO.; *U.S. Private*, pg. 27
ARLON EMD LLC—See CriticalPoint Capital, LLC; *U.S. Private*, pg. 1102
ARLON GRAPHICS, LLC—See FLEXcon Corporation; *U.S. Private*, pg. 1543
ARLON GROUP LLC—See Continental Grain Company; *U.S. Private*, pg. 1029
ARLO TECHNOLOGIES, INC.; *U.S. Public*, pg. 193
ARLO TECHNOLOGIES INTERNATIONAL LTD.—See Arlo Technologies, Inc.; *U.S. Public*, pg. 193
ARL TRANSPORT, LLC—See US 1 Industries, Inc.; *U.S. Private*, pg. 4316
ARLUN FLOOR COVERINGS INC.; *U.S. Private*, pg. 329
ARLUN, INC.—See The Sterling Group, L.P.; *U.S. Private*, pg. 4121
ARMACELL ASIA LTD.—See PAI Partners S.A.S.; *Int'l*, pg. 5699
ARMACELL AUSTRALIA PTY. LTD.—See PAI Partners S.A.S.; *Int'l*, pg. 5699
ARMACELL BRASIL, LTDA.—See PAI Partners S.A.S.; *Int'l*, pg. 5699
ARMACELL FRANCE SA—See PAI Partners S.A.S.; *Int'l*, pg. 5699
ARMACELL GMBH—See Blackstone Inc.; *U.S. Public*, pg. 360
ARMACELL GMBH—See Kirkbi A/S; *Int'l*, pg. 4189
ARMACELL (GUANGZHOU) LIMITED—See PAI Partners S.A.S.; *Int'l*, pg. 5699
ARMACELL IBERIA, S.L.—See PAI Partners S.A.S.; *Int'l*, pg. 5699
ARMACELL INDIA PRIVATE LTD.—See PAI Partners S.A.S.; *Int'l*, pg. 5699
ARMACELL INTERNATIONAL HOLDING GMBH—See PAI Partners S.A.S.; *Int'l*, pg. 5699
ARMACELL INTERNATIONAL S.A.—See PAI Partners S.A.S.; *Int'l*, pg. 5699
ARMACELL ITALIA S.R.L.—See PAI Partners S.A.S.; *Int'l*, pg. 5699
ARMACELL KOREA LLC—See PAI Partners S.A.S.; *Int'l*, pg. 5699
ARMACELL LLC - DALLAS PLANT—See PAI Partners S.A.S.; *Int'l*, pg. 5700
ARMACELL LLC—See PAI Partners S.A.S.; *Int'l*, pg. 5699
ARMACELL POLAND SP. Z O.O.—See PAI Partners S.A.S.; *Int'l*, pg. 5700
ARMACELL (THAILAND) LIMITED—See PAI Partners S.A.S.; *Int'l*, pg. 5699
ARMACELL UK LTD.—See PAI Partners S.A.S.; *Int'l*, pg. 5700
ARMACELL - ZAMIL MIDDLE EAST CO.—See PAI Partners S.A.S.; *Int'l*, pg. 5699
ARMACERO INDUSTRIAL Y COMERCIAL LTDA—See CAP S.A.; *Int'l*, pg. 1300
ARMACUP MARITIME SERVICES LTD.—See Wallenius Wilhelmsen ASA; *Int'l*, pg. 8334
ARMADA DATA CORPORATION; *Int'l*, pg. 573
ARMADA ENTERPRISES, LP; *U.S. Private*, pg. 329
THE ARMADA GROUP, INC.—See Stone Point Capital LLC; *U.S. Private*, pg. 3823
ARMADA GROUP, LTD.; *U.S. Private*, pg. 329
ARMADA HOFFLER PROPERTIES, INC.; *U.S. Public*, pg. 193
ARMADA HOLDINGS PTY LTD—See BlackWall Limited; *Int'l*, pg. 1062
ARMADA INVESTMENT HOLDING LTD—See CIMB Group Holdings Berhad; *Int'l*, pg. 1607
ARMADALE CAPITAL LTD.; *U.S. Private*, pg. 329
ARMADALE CAPITALL PLC; *Int'l*, pg. 574
ARMADALE COMMERCIAL LTD.—See Avis Budget Group, Inc.; *U.S. Public*, pg. 248
ARMADA MARINE CONTRACTORS CASPIAN PTE. LTD.—See Bumi Armada Berhad; *Int'l*, pg. 1215
ARMADA MATERIALS, LLC; *U.S. Private*, pg. 329
ARMADA MERCANTILE LTD.; *U.S. Public*, pg. 193

ARMADA METALS LIMITED — CORPORATE AFFILIATIONS

ARMADA METALS LIMITED; *Int'l*, pg. 573
ARMADA NANO TECHNOLOGIES GROUP INC.; *U.S. Private*, pg. 329
ARMADAN A/S—See Beijer Ref AB; *Int'l*, pg. 944
ARMADA NUTRITION LLC—See Nagase & Co., Ltd.; *Int'l*, pg. 5126
ARMADA PARENT, INC.—See Stellex Capital Management LP; *U.S. Private*, pg. 3800
ARMADA SUPPLY CHAIN SOLUTIONS, LLC—See Armada Group, Ltd.; *U.S. Private*, pg. 329
ARMADA TIMES—See Alden Global Capital LLC; *U.S. Private*, pg. 159
ARMADA TOOLWORKS LIMITED; *Int'l*, pg. 574
ARMADA WATER ASSETS, INC.; *U.S. Private*, pg. 329
ARMADILLO CONSTRUCTION COMPANY, LTD.; *U.S. Private*, pg. 329
ARMADILLO ENTERPRISES, INC.; *U.S. Private*, pg. 329
ARMADILLO EVEN EMPREENDIMENTOS IMOBILIARIOS LTDA.—See Even Construtora e Incorporadora S.A.; *Int'l*, pg. 2561
ARMADILLO RESOURCES LTD.; *Int'l*, pg. 574
ARMAEC ENERGY GROUP PLC; *Int'l*, pg. 574
ARMA GLOBAL CORP.; *U.S. Private*, pg. 329
ARMA GROUP HOLDINGS PTY. LTD.—See Credit Clear Limited; *Int'l*, pg. 1835
ARMAKA AG—See Tulikivi Corporation; *Int'l*, pg. 7969
ARMALY SPONGE COMPANY, INC.; *U.S. Private*, pg. 330
ARMAND COLIN SAS—See Vivendi SE; *Int'l*, pg. 8272
ARMANDO TESTA BRUSSELS NV—See Armando Testa S.p.A.; *Int'l*, pg. 574
ARMANDO TESTA GMBH—See Armando Testa S.p.A.; *Int'l*, pg. 574
ARMANDO TESTA LTD.—See Armando Testa S.p.A.; *Int'l*, pg. 574
ARMANDO TESTA SL—See Armando Testa S.p.A.; *Int'l*, pg. 574
ARMANDO TESTA—See Armando Testa S.p.A.; *Int'l*, pg. 574
ARMANDO TESTA S.P.A.; *Int'l*, pg. 574
ARMANDO TESTA S.P.A.—See Armando Testa S.p.A.; *Int'l*, pg. 574
ARMANDO TESTA S.P.A.—See Armando Testa S.p.A.; *Int'l*, pg. 574
ARMAND PRODUCTS COMPANY—See Church & Dwight Co., Inc.; *U.S. Public*, pg. 493
ARMAND PRODUCTS COMPANY—See Occidental Petroleum Corporation; *U.S. Public*, pg. 1561
ARMAN FINANCIAL SERVICES LTD.; *Int'l*, pg. 574
ARMAN HOLDINGS LIMITED; *Int'l*, pg. 574
ARMANINO FOODS OF DISTINCTION, INC.; *U.S. Public*, pg. 193
ARMANINO LLP; *U.S. Private*, pg. 330
ARMANINO LLP; *U.S. Private*, pg. 330
ARMA SERVICES, INC.; *U.S. Private*, pg. 193
ARMATA PHARMACEUTICALS, INC.; *U.S. Public*, pg. 193
ARMAT GMBH & CO. KG—See TUV SUD AG; *Int'l*, pg. 7984
ARMATIS SA—See Activa Capital S.A.S.; *Int'l*, pg. 119
ARMATRON INTERNATIONAL, INC.; *U.S. Private*, pg. 330
ARMATURA CO., LTD.—See Zkteco Co., Ltd.; *Int'l*, pg. 8687
ARMATURE AD; *Int'l*, pg. 574
ARMATURE DNS 2000 INC.; *Int'l*, pg. 574
ARMATUREN AICHHORN GMBH—See Indutrade AB; *Int'l*, pg. 3677
ARMATURENWERK ALTENBURG GMBH—See BITZER SE; *Int'l*, pg. 1051
ARMATURES BOIS-FRANCS INC.; *Int'l*, pg. 574
ARMATURTEKNIK I OSBY AB—See Metso Oyj; *Int'l*, pg. 4866
ARMBUSINESSBANK CJSC; *Int'l*, pg. 574
ARM CEMENT LIMITED; *Int'l*, pg. 573
ARM CLAIMS INCORPORATED—See TorQuest Partners Inc.; *Int'l*, pg. 7830
ARMC, L.P.—See Community Health Systems, Inc.; *U.S. Public*, pg. 550
ARMCO CAPITAL INC.; *Int'l*, pg. 574
THE ARMCO GROUP INC.; *U.S. Private*, pg. 3988
ARMCO METALS HOLDINGS, INC.; *U.S. Private*, pg. 330
ARMCO METALS (SHANGHAI) HOLDINGS, LTD.—See Armco Metals Holdings, Inc.; *U.S. Private*, pg. 330
ARMCOR AIR SOLUTIONS PTY. LTD.—See Beijer Ref AB; *Int'l*, pg. 943
ARMECONOMBANK OJSC; *Int'l*, pg. 574
ARMED FORCES BANK, N.A.—See Dickinson Financial Corporation; *U.S. Private*, pg. 1227
ARMED FORCES COMMUNICATIONS, INC. - CRANBURY—See Armed Forces Communications, Inc.; *U.S. Private*, pg. 330
ARMED FORCES COMMUNICATIONS, INC.; *U.S. Private*, pg. 330
ARMED FORCES FINANCIAL NETWORK, LLC—See Fidelity National Infor; *U.S. Public*, pg. 832
ARMED FORCES INSURANCE EXCHANGE; *U.S. Private*, pg. 330

ARMED FORCES SERVICES CORPORATION—See Centene Corporation; *U.S. Public*, pg. 469
ARMEDIA LLC; *U.S. Private*, pg. 330
AR MEDIA; *U.S. Private*, pg. 306
A.R. MEDICOM INC. (ASIA) LTD.—See A.R. Medicom Inc.; *Int'l*, pg. 28
A.R. MEDICOM INC. HEALTHCARE (SHANGHAI) LTD.—See A.R. Medicom Inc.; *Int'l*, pg. 28
A.R. MEDICOM INC. (JAPAN) LTD.—See A.R. Medicom Inc.; *Int'l*, pg. 28
A.R. MEDICOM INC.; *Int'l*, pg. 28
A.R. MEDICOM INC. (TAIWAN) LTD.—See A.R. Medicom Inc.; *Int'l*, pg. 28
ARMELLINI AIR EXPRESS, INC.—See Armellini Industries, Inc.; *U.S. Private*, pg. 330
ARMELLINI EXPRESS LINES INC.—See Armellini Industries, Inc.; *U.S. Private*, pg. 330
ARMELLINI INDUSTRIES, INC.; *U.S. Private*, pg. 330
ARMEN CADILLAC; *U.S. Private*, pg. 330
ARMENIA AMBULATORY SURGERY CENTER, LLC—See Bain Capital, LP; *U.S. Private*, pg. 445
ARMENIAN CARD CJSC—See Central Bank of Armenia; *Int'l*, pg. 1404
ARMENIA SECURITIES EXCHANGE—See Nasdaq, Inc.; *U.S. Public*, pg. 1491
ARMENI CONSULTING SERVICES, LLC—See KCI Holdings Inc.; *U.S. Private*, pg. 2269
ARMET ALARM & ELECTRONICS INC.; *U.S. Private*, pg. 330
AR METALLIZING GMBH—See Nissha Co., Ltd.; *Int'l*, pg. 5371
AR METALLIZING LTD.—See H.I.G. Capital, LLC; *U.S. Private*, pg. 1828
ARMETALLIZING N.V.—See H.I.G. Capital, LLC; *U.S. Private*, pg. 1828
AR METALLIZING PRODUTOS METALIZADOS LTDA.—See Nissha Co., Ltd.; *Int'l*, pg. 5371
AR METALLIZING SRL—See H.I.G. Capital, LLC; *U.S. Private*, pg. 1828
ARMETAL METAL INDUSTRIES COMPANY LTD.—See Al-Hejailan Group; *Int'l*, pg. 286
ARMEYSKI HOLDING AD; *Int'l*, pg. 574
ARMFIELD, HARRISON & THOMAS, INC.—See The Baldwin Insurance Group, Inc.; *U.S. Public*, pg. 2035
ARM FRANCE SAS—See SoftBank Group Corp.; *Int'l*, pg. 7051
ARM FRANCE—See SoftBank Group Corp.; *Int'l*, pg. 7051
ARMGOLD/HARMONY FREEGOLD JOINT VENTURE COMPANY (PROPRIETARY) LIMITED—See Harmony Gold Mining Company Limited; *Int'l*, pg. 3278
ARM & HAMMER CONSUMER PRODUCTS—See Church & Dwight Co., Inc.; *U.S. Public*, pg. 493
ARM HOLDINGS LIMITED—See SoftBank Group Corp.; *Int'l*, pg. 7051
ARMIDALE HOSPITAL PTY LIMITED—See Ramsay Health Care Limited; *Int'l*, pg. 6199
ARMILAR BUSINESS SERVICES S.L.—See Byggfakta Group Nordic HoldCo AB; *Int'l*, pg. 1234
ARMINAK & ASSOCIATES, INC.—See TriMas Corporation; *U.S. Public*, pg. 2189
ARMINTOOL MANUFACTURING & ARMIN MOLD CORPORATION; *U.S. Private*, pg. 330
ARMISTEAD MECHANICAL INC.; *U.S. Private*, pg. 330
ARMISTEAD NH II, INC.—See Nova Leap Health Corp.; *Int'l*, pg. 5451
ARMISTEAD SENIOR CARE—See Nova Leap Health Corp.; *Int'l*, pg. 5451
ARMITAGE PET CARE LIMITED—See Spectrum Brands Holdings, Inc.; *U.S. Public*, pg. 1915
ARMITRON WATCH DIVISION—See E. Gluck Corp.; *U.S. Private*, pg. 1304
ARM KK—See SoftBank Group Corp.; *Int'l*, pg. 7051
ARM KOREA LIMITED—See SoftBank Group Corp.; *Int'l*, pg. 7051
ARM LTD. - MAIDENHEAD—See SoftBank Group Corp.; *Int'l*, pg. 7051
ARM LTD. - SHEFFIELD—See SoftBank Group Corp.; *Int'l*, pg. 7051
ARM LTD.—See SoftBank Group Corp.; *Int'l*, pg. 7051
ARM, LTD.—See SoftBank Group Corp.; *Int'l*, pg. 7051
ARM, LTD. - TEXAS—See SoftBank Group Corp.; *Int'l*, pg. 7051
ARM NATIONAL FOOD INC.; *U.S. Private*, pg. 329
ARMO BIOSCIENCES, INC.—See Eli Lilly & Company; *U.S. Public*, pg. 731
ARMO CO., LTD.—See Kajima Corporation; *Int'l*, pg. 4053
ARMOIRES FABRITEC LTEE.-COOKSHIRE—See Armoires Fabritec Ltee.; *Int'l*, pg. 574
ARMOIRES FABRITEC LTEE.; *Int'l*, pg. 574
ARMON INC.; *U.S. Private*, pg. 330
THE ARMOR ALL/STP PRODUCTS COMPANY—See Energizer Holdings, Inc.; *U.S. Public*, pg. 760
ARMORBLOX LLC—See Cisco Systems, Inc.; *U.S. Public*, pg. 497
ARMORCAST PRODUCTS COMPANY; *U.S. Private*, pg. 331
ARMORCAST ROTATIONAL MOLDING—See Armorcast Products Company; *U.S. Private*, pg. 331

ARMOR CONNECTIC SAS—See Eiffage S.A.; *Int'l*, pg. 2329
ARMOR DESIGNS, INC.; *U.S. Private*, pg. 331
ARMORED AUTOGROUP AUSTRALIA PTY LTD—See Energizer Holdings, Inc.; *U.S. Public*, pg. 760
ARMORED AUTOGROUP CANADA ULC—See Energizer Holdings, Inc.; *U.S. Public*, pg. 760
ARMORED AUTOGROUP INC.—See Energizer Holdings, Inc.; *U.S. Public*, pg. 760
ARMORED AUTOGROUP PARENT, INC.—See Spectrum Brands Holdings, Inc.; *U.S. Public*, pg. 1915
ARMORED AUTO (UK) LP—See Energizer Holdings, Inc.; *U.S. Public*, pg. 760
ARMORED TEXTILES, INC.—See Kuriyama Holdings Corporation; *Int'l*, pg. 4341
ARMORFLEX INTERNATIONAL LIMITED—See Valmont Industries, Inc.; *U.S. Public*, pg. 2273
THE ARMOR GROUP, INC.; *U.S. Private*, pg. 3988
ARMOR INOX S.A.—See The Middleby Corporation; *U.S. Public*, pg. 2113
ARMOR INOX UK LTD.—See The Middleby Corporation; *U.S. Public*, pg. 2114
ARMORIZE TECHNOLOGIES, INC.—See Thoma Bravo, L.P.; *U.S. Private*, pg. 4151
ARMORLINK SH CORP.—See IEI Integration Corp.; *Int'l*, pg. 3597
ARMOR MINERALS INC.; *Int'l*, pg. 574
ARMOR SAFE TECHNOLOGIES—See Phelps Tointon Inc.; *U.S. Private*, pg. 3167
ARMORTEX, INC.—See TETCO, Inc.; *U.S. Private*, pg. 3973
ARMORWORKS ENTERPRISES, LLC—See Littlejohn & Co., LLC; *U.S. Private*, pg. 2470
THE ARMORY SHOW INC.—See Vornado Realty Trust; *U.S. Public*, pg. 2310
ARMOUR AUTOMOTIVE GROUP LIMITED—See AAMP of Florida, Inc.; *U.S. Private*, pg. 32
ARMOUR AUTOMOTIVE LIMITED—See AAMP of Florida, Inc.; *U.S. Private*, pg. 32
ARMOUR COURIER SERVICES INC.—See Armour Transportation Systems; *Int'l*, pg. 575
ARMOUR-ECKRICH MEATS, LLC—See WH Group Limited; *Int'l*, pg. 8395
ARMOUR ENERGY LIMITED; *Int'l*, pg. 575
ARMOUR HOME ELECTRONICS LIMITED—See Q Acoustics Limited; *Int'l*, pg. 6129
ARMOUR HONG KONG LIMITED—See Q Acoustics Limited; *Int'l*, pg. 6129
ARMOUR LOGISTICS SERVICES INC.—See Armour Transportation Systems; *Int'l*, pg. 575
ARMOUR NORDIC AB—See AAMP of Florida, Inc.; *U.S. Private*, pg. 32
ARMOUR NORDIC AS—See AAMP of Florida, Inc.; *U.S. Private*, pg. 32
ARMOUR PLASTICS LIMITED - ENGINEERING DIVISION—See Armour Plastics Limited; *Int'l*, pg. 575
ARMOUR PLASTICS LIMITED - RENAISSANCE BATHS DIVISION—See Armour Plastics Limited; *Int'l*, pg. 575
ARMOUR PLASTICS LIMITED; *Int'l*, pg. 575
ARMOUR RESIDENTIAL REIT, INC.; *U.S. Public*, pg. 193
ARMOUR TRANSPORTATION SYSTEMS; *Int'l*, pg. 575
ARMOUR TRANSPORT INC—See Armour Transportation Systems; *Int'l*, pg. 575
ARM RESEARCH LABS, LLC—See Open Text Corporation; *Int'l*, pg. 5598
ARMS ACRES INC.—See Liberty Management Group, Inc.; *U.S. Private*, pg. 2444
A.R.M. SOLUTIONS, INC.; *U.S. Private*, pg. 28
ARMSTRONG CYCLE PARTS (SDN). BERHAD—See Oriental Holdings Berhad; *Int'l*, pg. 5624
ARMSTRONG AEROSPACE, INC.—See Astronics Corporation; *U.S. Public*, pg. 217
ARMSTRONG AIR & HEATING INC.; *U.S. Private*, pg. 331
ARMSTRONG AUTO PARTS SDN. BERHAD—See Oriental Holdings Berhad; *Int'l*, pg. 5624
ARMSTRONG BUICK VOLKSWAGEN; *U.S. Private*, pg. 331
ARMSTRONG BUILDING PRODUCTS B.V.—See Armstrong World Industries, Inc.; *U.S. Public*, pg. 194
ARMSTRONG CHINA HOLDINGS, LIMITED—See Armstrong World Industries, Inc.; *U.S. Public*, pg. 194
ARMSTRONG COMPONENT PARTS (VIETNAM) CO., LTD.—See Oriental Holdings Berhad; *Int'l*, pg. 5624
ARMSTRONG CONSULTANTS, INC.—See H.W. Lochner, Inc.; *U.S. Private*, pg. 1836
ARMSTRONG CORK FINANCE LLC—See Armstrong World Industries, Inc.; *U.S. Public*, pg. 194
ARMSTRONG COUNTY MEMORIAL HOSPITAL; *U.S. Private*, pg. 331
ARMSTRONG CRANE & RIGGING INC.—See Barnhart Crane & Rigging Co.; *U.S. Private*, pg. 478
ARMSTRONG CRAVEN LIMITED; *Int'l*, pg. 575
ARMSTRONG CYCLE PARTS (SDN.) BERHAD - ALOR GAJAH FACTORY—See Oriental Holdings Berhad; *Int'l*, pg. 5624
ARMSTRONG DEVELOPMENT PROPERTIES, INC.—See Armstrong Holdings, Inc.; *U.S. Private*, pg. 331

ARMSTRONG DLW AG—See Armstrong World Industries, Inc.; *U.S. Public*, pg. 194
ARMSTRONG ENERGY GLOBAL LIMITED; *Int'l*, pg. 575
ARMSTRONG FLOORING HONG KONG LIMITED—See Armstrong Flooring, Inc.; *U.S. Public*, pg. 193
ARMSTRONG FLOORING, INC.; *U.S. Public*, pg. 193
ARMSTRONG FLOORING PTY. LTD.—See Armstrong Flooring, Inc.; *U.S. Public*, pg. 193
ARMSTRONG FLUID HANDLING—See Armstrong International, Inc.; *U.S. Private*, pg. 331
ARMSTRONG FORENSIC ENGINEERS, INC.; *U.S. Private*, pg. 331
ARMSTRONG GARDEN CENTERS, INC.; *U.S. Private*, pg. 331
ARMSTRONG GLOBAL HOLDINGS, INC.—See Armstrong International, Inc.; *U.S. Private*, pg. 331
ARMSTRONG HEAT TRANSFER GROUP—See Armstrong International, Inc.; *U.S. Private*, pg. 331
ARMSTRONG HOLDEN BROOKE PULLEN LIMITED—See S.A. Armstrong Limited; *Int'l*, pg. 6447
ARMSTRONG HOLDINGS, INC.; *U.S. Private*, pg. 331
ARMSTRONG HYDRAULICS SOUTH AFRICA (PTY.) LTD.—See Apollo Global Management, Inc.; *U.S. Public*, pg. 160
ARMSTRONG INDUSTRIAL CORPORATION LTD.; *Int'l*, pg. 575
ARMSTRONG INDUSTRIES SDN. BHD.—See Oriental Holdings Berhad; *Int'l*, pg. 5624
ARMSTRONG INTEGRATED SYSTEMS LIMITED—See S.A. Armstrong Limited; *Int'l*, pg. 6447
ARMSTRONG INTERNATIONAL, INC.; *U.S. Private*, pg. 331
ARMSTRONG INTERNATIONAL ITALIANA S.R.L—See Armstrong International, Inc.; *U.S. Private*, pg. 331
ARMSTRONG INTERNATIONAL MEXICO S DE RL DE CV—See Armstrong International, Inc.; *U.S. Private*, pg. 331
ARMSTRONG INTERNATIONAL PRIVATE LIMITED—See Armstrong International, Inc.; *U.S. Private*, pg. 331
ARMSTRONG INTERNATIONAL, S.A.—See Armstrong International, Inc.; *U.S. Private*, pg. 331
ARMSTRONG INTERNATIONAL SA—See Armstrong International, Inc.; *U.S. Private*, pg. 331
ARMSTRONG LABORATORIOS DE MEXICO S.A. DE C.V.—See Bago Group; *Int'l*, pg. 799
ARMSTRONG MCCALL HOLDINGS, INC.—See Sally Beauty Holdings, Inc.; *U.S. Public*, pg. 1838
ARMSTRONG MCCALL, L.P.—See Sally Beauty Holdings, Inc.; *U.S. Public*, pg. 1838
ARMSTRONG MECHANICAL COMPONENTS COMPANY LIMITED—See Armstrong Industrial Corporation Ltd.; *Int'l*, pg. 575
ARMSTRONG METALLDECKEN GMBH—See Aurelius Equity Opportunities SE & Co. KGaA; *Int'l*, pg. 707
ARMSTRONG METALLDECKEN HOLDINGS AG—See Armstrong World Industries, Inc.; *U.S. Public*, pg. 194
ARMSTRONG MOLD CORP.; *U.S. Private*, pg. 332
ARMSTRONG MOVING & STORAGE INC.; *U.S. Private*, pg. 332
ARMSTRONG ODENWALD CHANGCHUN (AOC) TECHNOLOGY CO LTD—See Armstrong Industrial Corporation Ltd.; *Int'l*, pg. 575
ARMSTRONG ODENWALD TECHNOLOGY (TIANJIN) CO LTD—See Armstrong Industrial Corporation Ltd.; *Int'l*, pg. 575
ARMSTRONG ODENWALD TECHNOLOGY (WUHAN) CO LTD—See Armstrong Industrial Corporation Ltd.; *Int'l*, pg. 575
ARMSTRONG PHARMACEUTICALS, INC.—See Amphastar Pharmaceuticals, Inc.; *U.S. Public*, pg. 126
ARMSTRONG PRODUCE LTD.—See Sysco Corporation; *U.S. Public*, pg. 1974
ARMSTRONG PUMPS INC.—See S.A. Armstrong Limited; *Int'l*, pg. 6447
ARMSTRONG REALTY SDN. BHD.—See Oriental Holdings Berhad; *Int'l*, pg. 5624
ARMSTRONG/ROBITAILLE/RIEGLE BUSINESS & INSURANCE SOLUTIONS—See Genstar Capital, LLC; *U.S. Private*, pg. 1674
ARMSTRONG RUBBER & CHEMICAL PRODUCTS COMPANY LIMITED—See Armstrong Industrial Corporation Ltd.; *Int'l*, pg. 575
ARMSTRONG RUBBER MANUFACTURING PTE LTD—See Armstrong Industrial Corporation Ltd.; *Int'l*, pg. 575
ARMSTRONG RUBBER TECHNOLOGY (THAILAND) COMPANY LIMITED—See Armstrong Industrial Corporation Ltd.; *Int'l*, pg. 575
ARMSTRONG SECURITIES, INC.—See BDO Unibank, Inc.; *Int'l*, pg. 930
ARMSTRONG SERVICE FRANCE S.A.—See Armstrong International, Inc.; *U.S. Private*, pg. 331
ARMSTRONG SERVICE, INC.—See Armstrong International, Inc.; *U.S. Private*, pg. 332
ARMSTRONG STEEL; *U.S. Private*, pg. 332
ARMSTRONG TEASDALE LLP; *U.S. Private*, pg. 332
ARMSTRONG TECHNOLOGY INC.; *U.S. Private*, pg. 332
ARMSTRONG TECHNOLOGY (SUZHOU) CO LTD—See Armstrong Industrial Corporation Ltd.; *Int'l*, pg. 575

ARMSTRONG TECHNOLOGY (WUXI) CO LTD—See Armstrong Industrial Corporation Ltd.; *Int'l*, pg. 575
ARMSTRONG TELEPHONE COMPANY—See Armstrong Holdings, Inc.; *U.S. Private*, pg. 331
ARMSTRONG TRADING & SUPPLIES SDN. BHD.—See Oriental Holdings Berhad; *Int'l*, pg. 5624
ARMSTRONG UTILITIES, INC.—See Armstrong Holdings, Inc.; *U.S. Private*, pg. 331
ARMSTRONG WOOD PRODUCTS, INC.—See AIP, LLC; *U.S. Private*, pg. 134
ARMSTRONG WORLD INDUSTRIES (AUSTRALIA) PTY. LTD.—See Armstrong World Industries, Inc.; *U.S. Public*, pg. 194
ARMSTRONG WORLD INDUSTRIES CANADA LTD.—See Armstrong World Industries, Inc.; *U.S. Public*, pg. 194
ARMSTRONG WORLD INDUSTRIES (H.K.) LIMITED—See Armstrong World Industries, Inc.; *U.S. Public*, pg. 194
ARMSTRONG WORLD INDUSTRIES, INC.; *U.S. Public*, pg. 193
ARMSTRONG WORLD INDUSTRIES LTD.—See Aurelius Equity Opportunities SE & Co. KGaA; *Int'l*, pg. 707
ARMSTRONG-YOSHITAKE, INC.—See Armstrong International, Inc.; *U.S. Private*, pg. 332
ARMSTRONG-YOSHITAKE, INC.—See Yoshitake Inc.; *Int'l*, pg. 8601
ARMSTRONG Y&R—See WPP plc; *Int'l*, pg. 8491
ARMTEC COUNTERMEASURES CO. - DEFENSE TECHNOLOGIES-ARO—See TransDigm Group Incorporated; *U.S. Public*, pg. 2180
ARMTEC COUNTERMEASURES CO.—See TransDigm Group Incorporated; *U.S. Public*, pg. 2180
ARMTEC COUTERMEASURES CO.—See TransDigm Group Incorporated; *U.S. Public*, pg. 2180
ARMTECH, INC.; *U.S. Private*, pg. 332
ARMTEC LP—See Brookfield Corporation; *Int'l*, pg. 1175
ARMY EMERGENCY RELIEF; *U.S. Private*, pg. 332
ARMY FLEET SUPPORT LLC—See L3Harris Technologies, Inc.; *U.S. Public*, pg. 1280
ARMY & NAVY DEPARTMENT STORES LIMITED; *Int'l*, pg. 575
ARMY TIMES PUBLISHING COMPANY—See Regent, L.P.; *U.S. Private*, pg. 3388
ARMY WELFARE TRUST LLC; *U.S. Private*, pg. 575
ARNARLAX EHF—See Salmar ASA; *Int'l*, pg. 6494
ARNAVA SAS—See Scientific Brain Training SA; *Int'l*, pg. 6648
ARNAV CORPORATION LIMITED; *Int'l*, pg. 576
ARNAV INDUSTRIES, INC.; *U.S. Private*, pg. 332
ARNAWAT LIMITED—See Sansiri pcl; *Int'l*, pg. 6556
ARNE B. CORNELIUSSEN AS—See Orkla ASA; *Int'l*, pg. 5638
ARNECKE SIEBOLD RECHTSANWALTE PARTNER-SCHAFTSGESELLSCHAFT; *Int'l*, pg. 576
ARNELL—See Omnicom Group Inc.; *U.S. Public*, pg. 1573
ARNELL-WEST INC.; *U.S. Private*, pg. 332
ARNE OLAV LUND A/S—See Peab AB; *Int'l*, pg. 5771
ARNESES Y CONEXIONES, S. A. DE C.V—See Onamba Co., Ltd.; *Int'l*, pg. 5573
ARNEST ONE CORPORATION—See Iida Group Holdings Co., Ltd.; *Int'l*, pg. 3607
ARNES WELDING LTD.; *Int'l*, pg. 576
ARNETT & BURGESS ENERGY SERVICES LP—See Quanta Services, Inc.; *U.S. Public*, pg. 1750
ARNETT & BURGESS OIL FIELD CONSTRUCTION LIMITED—See Quanta Services, Inc.; *U.S. Public*, pg. 1750
ARNETT & BURGESS PIPELINERS LTD.—See Quanta Services, Inc.; *U.S. Public*, pg. 1750
ARNETT & BURGESS PIPELINERS (ROCKIES) LLC—See Quanta Services, Inc.; *U.S. Public*, pg. 1750
ARNETTE POLYMERS, LLC—See RPM International Inc.; *U.S. Public*, pg. 1818
ARNEXX S.A.—See Echeverria Izquierdo S.A.; *Int'l*, pg. 2289
ARNGAR, INC.—See Sonic Automotive, Inc.; *U.S. Public*, pg. 1902
ARNHOLD & COMPANY, LIMITED—See Summit Ascent Holdings Limited; *Int'l*, pg. 7301
ARNHOLD DESIGN CENTRES LIMITED—See Summit Ascent Holdings Limited; *Int'l*, pg. 7301
ARNHOLD INVESTMENTS LIMITED—See Summit Ascent Holdings Limited; *Int'l*, pg. 7301
ARNHOLD (MACAU) LIMITED—See Summit Ascent Holdings Limited; *Int'l*, pg. 7301
ARNHOLD MARBLE LIMITED—See Summit Ascent Holdings Limited; *Int'l*, pg. 7301
ARNHOLD SOURCING LIMITED—See Summit Ascent Holdings Limited; *Int'l*, pg. 7302
ARNICA DENTAL CARE LIMITED—See The British United Provident Association Limited; *Int'l*, pg. 7629
ARNIE BAUER, INC.; *U.S. Private*, pg. 332
ARNIES RESTAURANT; *U.S. Private*, pg. 332
ARNIS INC.; *U.S. Private*, pg. 332
ARN MEDIA LIMITED; *Int'l*, pg. 576
ARNO FRIEDRICHS HARTMETALL GMBH & CO. KG—See KKR & Co. Inc.; *U.S. Public*, pg. 1253
ARNOLD AG—See The Poul Due Jensen Foundation; *Int'l*, pg. 7674

ARNOLD AUTOMOTIVE AND OIL CO.; *U.S. Private*, pg. 333
ARNOLD-BAKER CHEVROLET; *U.S. Private*, pg. 333
ARNOLD BERNHARD & CO.; *U.S. Private*, pg. 333
ARNOLD BROS. TRANSPORT LTD; *Int'l*, pg. 576
ARNOLD CHATZ CARS CONSTANTIA KLOOF PROPRIETARY LIMITED—See Super Group Limited; *Int'l*, pg. 7334
ARNOLD CLARK AUTOMOBILES LIMITED; *Int'l*, pg. 576
ARNOLD CLARK FINANCE LIMITED—See Arnold Clark Automobiles Limited; *Int'l*, pg. 576
ARNOLD CLARK INSURANCE SERVICES LIMITED—See Arnold Clark Automobiles Limited; *Int'l*, pg. 576
THE ARNOLD ENGINEERING CO.—See Compass Diversified Holdings; *U.S. Public*, pg. 560
ARNOLD FASTENERS (SHENYANG) CO., LTD.—See Wurth Verwaltungsgesellschaft mbH; *Int'l*, pg. 8504
ARNOLD FASTENING SYSTEMS, INC.—See Wurth Verwaltungsgesellschaft mbH; *Int'l*, pg. 8511
ARNOLD HOLDINGS LIMITED; *Int'l*, pg. 576
ARNOLD J THOMAS & SON INC—See Thomas & Sons Distributors; *U.S. Private*, pg. 4154
ARNOLD KLP LTD.—See Vivendi SE; *Int'l*, pg. 8267
ARNOLD LUMBER COMPANY; *U.S. Private*, pg. 333
ARNOLD MACHINERY CO - CONSTRUCTION & MINING DIVISION—See Arnold Machinery Company; *U.S. Private*, pg. 333
ARNOLD MACHINERY COMPANY - MATERIAL HANDLING DIVISION—See Arnold Machinery Company; *U.S. Private*, pg. 333
ARNOLD MACHINERY COMPANY; *U.S. Private*, pg. 333
ARNOLD MAGNETIC TECHNOLOGIES AG—See Compass Diversified Holdings; *U.S. Public*, pg. 559
ARNOLD MAGNETIC TECHNOLOGIES CORPORATION—See Compass Diversified Holdings; *U.S. Public*, pg. 560
ARNOLD MAGNETIC TECHNOLOGIES LTD.—See Compass Diversified Holdings; *U.S. Public*, pg. 560
ARNOLD MOTOR SUPPLY, LLP; *U.S. Private*, pg. 333
ARNOLDNYC—See Vivendi SE; *Int'l*, pg. 8267
ARNOLD OIL CO. INC.; *U.S. Private*, pg. 333
ARNOLDO MONDADORI EDITORE S.P.A.—See Fininvest S.p.A.; *Int'l*, pg. 2675
ARNOLD & O'SHERIDAN, INC.; *U.S. Private*, pg. 332
ARNOLD PALMER'S BAY HILL CLUB & LODGE; *U.S. Private*, pg. 333
ARNOLD & PORTER KAYE SCHOLER LLP; *U.S. Private*, pg. 332
ARNOLD SHAPIRO PRODUCTIONS, INC.; *U.S. Private*, pg. 333
ARNOLD & SHINJO GMBH & CO. KG—See Wurth Verwaltungsgesellschaft mbH; *Int'l*, pg. 8504
ARNOLD'S OF WILLMAR INCORPORATED; *U.S. Private*, pg. 333
ARNOLD STEEL COMPANY, INC.; *U.S. Private*, pg. 333
ARNOLD TECHNIQUE FRANCE—See Wurth Verwaltungsgesellschaft mbH; *Int'l*, pg. 8504
ARNOLD UMFORMTECHNIK GMBH & CO. KG—See Wurth Verwaltungsgesellschaft mbH; *Int'l*, pg. 8504
ARNOLD-WILBERT CORP.; *U.S. Private*, pg. 333
ARNOLD WORLDWIDE—See Vivendi SE; *Int'l*, pg. 8267
ARNOLD WRAGG LTD.—See ALA SpA; *Int'l*, pg. 289
ARNOMIJ B.V.—See Aliaxis S.A./N.V.; *Int'l*, pg. 323
ARNON CORPORATION; *Int'l*, pg. 577
ARNONE LOWTH WILSON & LEIBOWITZ INC.—See Aon plc; *Int'l*, pg. 495
ARNO THERAPEUTICS, INC.; *U.S. Public*, pg. 194
ARNOTT, INC.—See MidOcean Partners, LLP; *U.S. Private*, pg. 2716
ARNOTT'S BISCUITS LTD.—See Campbell Soup Company; *U.S. Public*, pg. 426
ARNOTTS (FRUIT) LIMITED—See Sysco Corporation; *U.S. Public*, pg. 1973
ARNOTTS LTD.; *Int'l*, pg. 577
ARNOTT'S NEW ZEALAND LIMITED—See Campbell Soup Company; *U.S. Public*, pg. 426
ARNPRIOR AEROSPACE INC.—See Consolidated Industries, Inc.; *U.S. Private*, pg. 1021
ARNS, INC.—See Ares Management Corporation; *U.S. Public*, pg. 191
ARNS, INC.—See Pretium Partners, LLC; *U.S. Private*, pg. 3257
ARNTZEN CORPORATION; *U.S. Private*, pg. 333
AROA BIOSURGERY LIMITED; *Int'l*, pg. 577
AROBS TRANSILVANIA SOFTWARE S.A.; *Int'l*, pg. 577
AROCA DEL PINAR SOCIMI, S.A.; *Int'l*, pg. 577
AROCELL AB; *Int'l*, pg. 577
AROGAS INC.; *U.S. Private*, pg. 334
ARO GMBH—See Ingersoll Rand Inc.; *U.S. Public*, pg. 1120
AROGO CAPITAL ACQUISITION CORP.; *U.S. Public*, pg. 194
AROG PHARMACEUTICALS, INC.; *U.S. Private*, pg. 333
ARO GRANITE INDUSTRIES LTD.; *Int'l*, pg. 577
ARO GRANITE INDUSTRIES LTD. - UNIT II—See Aro Granite Industries Ltd.; *Int'l*, pg. 577
ARO GRANITE INDUSTRIES LTD. - UNIT I—See Aro Granite Industries Ltd.; *Int'l*, pg. 577
AROHERBS SPAIN S.L.—See Dole plc; *Int'l*, pg. 2157

AROK INC.

CORPORATE AFFILIATIONS

AROK INC.; *U.S. Private*, pg. 334
ARO LIQUIDATION, INC.; *U.S. Private*, pg. 333
AROMA AD; *Int'l*, pg. 577
AROMA CELTE SA; *Int'l*, pg. 577
AROMA COFFEE (SHANGHAI) CO., LTD.—See Marubeni Corporation; *Int'l*, pg. 4705
AROMA COSMETICS AD; *Int'l*, pg. 577
AROMA ENTERPRISES (INDIA) LIMITED; *Int'l*, pg. 577
AROMA S.A.—See International Flavors & Fragrances Inc.; *U.S. Public*, pg. 1151
AROMASCAPE DEVELOPMENT CENTRE GMBH—See Huabao International Holdings Limited; *Int'l*, pg. 3510
AROMATECH HOLDING COMPANY—See Jordan Industries, Inc.; *U.S. Private*, pg. 2235
AROMATHERAPY ASSOCIATES, INC—See Walgreens Boots Alliance, Inc.; *U.S. Public*, pg. 2322
AROMATHERAPY ASSOCIATES LTD.—See B&B Investment Partners LLP; *U.S. Private*, pg. 783
AROMATIC FUSION; *U.S. Private*, pg. 334
AROMATIQUE INC.; *U.S. Private*, pg. 334
AROMCO LTD.—See International Flavors & Fragrances Inc.; *U.S. Public*, pg. 1151
AROMOR FLAVORS & FRAGRANCES INC.—See International Flavors & Fragrances Inc.; *U.S. Public*, pg. 1151
ARONA CORPORATION; *U.S. Private*, pg. 334
ARON EVER GRIP LTD.—See Toagosei Co. Ltd.; *Int'l*, pg. 7769
ARONKASEI CO., LTD.—See Toagosei Co. Ltd.; *Int'l*, pg. 7769
ARON PACKAGING CO., LTD.—See Toagosei Co. Ltd.; *Int'l*, pg. 7769
ARONSON ASSOCIATES INC.; *U.S. Private*, pg. 334
ARONSON-CAMPBELL INDUSTRIAL SUPPLY INC.; *U.S. Private*, pg. 334
ARONSON LLC; *U.S. Private*, pg. 334
AROOT CO., LTD.; *Int'l*, pg. 577
AROPAC S.R.L—See Thornico A/S; *Int'l*, pg. 7719
ARO PALACE S.A.; *Int'l*, pg. 577
AROPE INSURANCE SAL—See BLOM Bank, S.A.L.; *Int'l*, pg. 1064
ARORA ENGINEERS, INC.; *U.S. Private*, pg. 334
ARORA HOTELS LIMITED; *Int'l*, pg. 577
ARORA-MATTHEY LIMITED; *Int'l*, pg. 577
ARORA-MATTHEY LIMITED VISAKHAPATNAM UNIT—See Arora-Matthey Limited; *Int'l*, pg. 577
ARO RECRUITMENT (SINGAPORE) PTE. LTD.—See Bain Capital, LP; *U.S. Private*, pg. 433
AROS DEL PACIFICO S.A.C.—See Titan International, Inc.; *U.S. Public*, pg. 2160
AROS DEL PACIFICO S.A.—See Titan International, Inc.; *U.S. Public*, pg. 2160
AROSELLOS, S.A. DE C.V.—See Parker Hannifin Corporation; *U.S. Public*, pg. 1640
A ROSENTHAL (CAPE) (PTY) LTD.—See Agra Limited; *Int'l*, pg. 213
A ROSENTHAL (PTY) LTD.—See Agra Limited; *Int'l*, pg. 213
AROS MINERAL AB—See Barclays PLC; *Int'l*, pg. 859
ARO-SYSTEMS INC.; *U.S. Private*, pg. 333
AROTECH CORPORATION—See Greenbriar Equity Group, L.P.; *U.S. Private*, pg. 1775
AROT POLSKA SP.Z.O.O.—See Bharti Enterprises Limited; *Int'l*, pg. 1012
AROTZ FOODS, S.A.—See Ebro Foods S.A.; *Int'l*, pg. 2286
THE AROUNDCAMPUS GROUP; *U.S. Private*, pg. 3988
AROUND NOON FOODS LIMITED; *Int'l*, pg. 577
AROUND THE CLOCK A/C SERVICE, LLC; *U.S. Private*, pg. 334
AROUND THE CLOCK FREIGHTLINER GROUP LLC—See Penske Automotive Group, Inc.; *U.S. Public*, pg. 1664
AROUNDTOWN SA; *Int'l*, pg. 577
AROVELLA THERAPEUTICS LIMITED; *Int'l*, pg. 578
AROWANA INC.; *Int'l*, pg. 578
AROWAY ENERGY INC.; *Int'l*, pg. 578
ARO WELDING TECHNOLOGIES AB—See Langley Holdings Plc; *Int'l*, pg. 4409
ARO WELDING TECHNOLOGIES GMBH—See Langley Holdings Plc; *Int'l*, pg. 4409
ARO WELDING TECHNOLOGIES INC—See Langley Holdings Plc; *Int'l*, pg. 4409
ARO WELDING TECHNOLOGIES S.A. DE C.V.—See Langley Holdings Plc; *Int'l*, pg. 4409
ARO WELDING TECHNOLOGIES SA-NV—See Langley Holdings Plc; *Int'l*, pg. 4409
ARO WELDING TECHNOLOGIES SAS—See Langley Holdings Plc; *Int'l*, pg. 4409
ARO WELDING TECHNOLOGIES S.A.U—See Langley Holdings Plc; *Int'l*, pg. 4409
ARO WELDING TECHNOLOGIES S.R.O.—See Langley Holdings Plc; *Int'l*, pg. 4409
ARO WELDING TECHNOLOGIES (WUHAN) CO., LTD.—See Langley Holdings Plc; *Int'l*, pg. 4409
A&R PACKAGING & DISTRIBUTION SERVICES, INC.—See A&R Transport, Inc.; *U.S. Private*, pg. 20
A&R PACKAGING & DISTRIBUTION SERVICES, INC.—See A&R Transport, Inc.; *U.S. Private*, pg. 20

AR PACKAGING GROUP AB—See CVC Capital Partners SICAV-FIS S.A.; *Int'l*, pg. 1881
A&R PACKING CO.; *U.S. Private*, pg. 20
ARPAC LLC—See Warburg Pincus LLC; *U.S. Private*, pg. 4437
ARPADIS GROUP; *Int'l*, pg. 578
ARPA INDUSTRIALE S.P.A.—See Averbuch Formica Center Ltd.; *Int'l*, pg. 739
ARPAK INTERNATIONAL INVESTMENTS LTD.; *Int'l*, pg. 578
ARPA-SEVAN OJSC; *Int'l*, pg. 578
ARPE AG—See BKW AG; *Int'l*, pg. 1054
ARPEGE SAS—See Fosun International Limited; *Int'l*, pg. 2751
ARP EUROPE AG—See Bechtle AG; *Int'l*, pg. 937
ARP GMBH—See Bechtle AG; *Int'l*, pg. 937
ARPICO ATARAXIA ASSET MANAGEMENT (PVT) LTD.—See Richard Pieris & Co. Ltd.; *Int'l*, pg. 6330
ARPICO FINANCE COMPANY PLC—See Associated Motor Finance Company PLC; *Int'l*, pg. 649
ARPICO FLEXIFOAM (PVT) LTD.—See Richard Pieris & Co, Ltd.; *Int'l*, pg. 6330
ARPICO INSURANCE PLC; *Int'l*, pg. 578
ARPICO INTERIORS (PVT) LTD—See Richard Pieris & Co. Ltd.; *Int'l*, pg. 6330
ARPIDAG INTERNATIONAL (PVT) LTD.—See Richard Pieris & Co. Ltd.; *Int'l*, pg. 6330
ARPITECH (PVT) LTD.—See Richard Pieris & Co. Ltd.; *Int'l*, pg. 6330
ARPLAMA N.V.; *Int'l*, pg. 578
A & R PLUMBING, INC.; *U.S. Private*, pg. 18
ARP NEDERLAND B.V.—See Bechtle AG; *Int'l*, pg. 937
ARP NV—See Bechtle AG; *Int'l*, pg. 937
ARP SAS—See Bechtle AG; *Int'l*, pg. 937
ARP SCHWEIZ AG—See Bechtle AG; *Int'l*, pg. 937
ARQIT QUANTUM INC.; *Int'l*, pg. 578
ARQIVA LIMITED—See Canada Pension Plan Investment Board; *Int'l*, pg. 1278
ARQIVA LIMITED—See Canada Pension Plan Investment Board; *Int'l*, pg. 1278
ARQUATI S.P.A.; *Int'l*, pg. 578
ARQUEONAUTAS WORLDWIDE - ARQUEOLOGIA SUBAQUATICA S.A.; *Int'l*, pg. 578
ARQUEST INC.; *U.S. Private*, pg. 334
ARQUIMED S.A.—See HORIBA Ltd; *Int'l*, pg. 3475
ARQULE, INC.—See Merck & Co., Inc.; *U.S. Public*, pg. 1419
ARRABELLE AT VAIL SQUARE, LLC—See Vail Resorts, Inc.; *U.S. Public*, pg. 2271
ARRAID, LLC.—See Reactive Group; *Int'l*, pg. 6232
ARRAIL G ROUP LIMITED; *Int'l*, pg. 578
ARRAN CHEMICAL COMPANY—See Almac Sciences Group Ltd.; *Int'l*, pg. 363
ARRAN ISLE LTD.—See ASSA ABLOY AB; *Int'l*, pg. 638
ARRANTA BIO HOLDINGS LLC—See Recipharm AB; *Int'l*, pg. 6235
THE ARRAS GROUP—See The Adcom Group, Inc.; *U.S. Private*, pg. 3981
ARRAS GROUP S.P.A; *Int'l*, pg. 578
ARRAS KEATHLEY ADVERTISING—See The Adcom Group, Inc.; *U.S. Private*, pg. 3981
ARRASMITH, JUDD, RAPP, CHOVAN, INC.—See Schmidt Associates, Inc.; *U.S. Private*, pg. 3565
ARRAY ASIA LTD.—See Array Marketing Group Inc.; *Int'l*, pg. 578
ARRAYA SOLUTIONS, INC.; *U.S. Private*, pg. 334
ARRAY BIOPHARMA INC.—See Pfizer Inc.; *U.S. Public*, pg. 1679
ARRAYCOMM, INC.—See Ygomi LLC; *U.S. Private*, pg. 4589
ARRAY ELECTRONICS (CHINA) LIMITED—See Willas-Array Electronics (Holdings) Ltd.; *Int'l*, pg. 8412
ARRAYENT, INC.—See Prodea Systems, Inc.; *U.S. Private*, pg. 3272
ARRAY INFORMATION TECHNOLOGY, INC.; *U.S. Private*, pg. 334
ARRAYIT CORP.; *U.S. Public*, pg. 194
ARRAYIT DIAGNOSTICS, INC.—See Arrayit Corp.; *U.S. Public*, pg. 194
ARRAY LIGHTING—See Revolution Lighting Technologies, Inc.; *U.S. Public*, pg. 1793
ARRAY MARKETING GROUP INC. - ARRAY BRADFORD FIXTURE DIVISION—See Array Marketing Group Inc.; *Int'l*, pg. 578
ARRAY MARKETING GROUP INC.; *Int'l*, pg. 578
ARRAY NETWORKS, INC.; *U.S. Private*, pg. 334
ARRAY NEW YORK—See Array Marketing Group Inc.; *Int'l*, pg. 578
ARRAY PRODUCTS COMPANY, LLC; *U.S. Private*, pg. 334
ARRAY PUBLICATIONS BV—See Roularta Media Group NV; *Int'l*, pg. 6407
ARRAY TECHNOLOGIES, INC.; *U.S. Public*, pg. 194
AR-RAZI SAUDI METHANOL CO.—See Saudi Basic Industries Corporation; *Int'l*, pg. 6590
ARR CRAIB TRANSPORT LTD.—See Gregory Distribution (Holdings) Limited; *Int'l*, pg. 3078
ARRC TECHNOLOGY; *U.S. Private*, pg. 334

ARREDONDO, ZEPEDA & BRUNZ, LLC—See Littlejohn & Co., LLC; *U.S. Private*, pg. 2469
ARRENDADORA JOHN DEERE S.A. DE C.V.—See Deere & Company; *U.S. Public*, pg. 646
ARRENDADORA KCSM, S. DE R.L. DE C.V.—See Canadian Pacific Kansas City Limited; *Int'l*, pg. 1285
ARRENDADORA VALMEX—See Grupo BAL; *Int'l*, pg. 3121
ARRESTAGE INTERNATIONAL, INC.; *U.S. Private*, pg. 334
ARREVA LLC; *U.S. Private*, pg. 334
ARRHYTHMIA NETWORK TECHNOLOGY SL; *Int'l*, pg. 578
ARRIBATEC GROUP ASA; *Int'l*, pg. 578
ARRIBATEC HOSPITALITY AS—See Arribatec Group ASA; *Int'l*, pg. 579
ARRIBATEC SOLUTIONS ASA; *Int'l*, pg. 579
ARRICANO REAL ESTATE PLC; *Int'l*, pg. 579
ARRINGTON LUMBER & PALLET COMPANY, INC.; *U.S. Private*, pg. 335
ARR INVESTMENTS, LLC; *U.S. Private*, pg. 334
ARRIS BELGIUM BVBA—See CommScope Holding Company, Inc.; *U.S. Public*, pg. 547
ARRIS - BOCA RATON—See CommScope Holding Company, Inc.; *U.S. Public*, pg. 548
ARRIS BROADBAND SOLUTIONS, LTD.—See CommScope Holding Company, Inc.; *U.S. Public*, pg. 548
ARRIS COMMUNICATIONS IRELAND LIMITED—See CommScope Holding Company, Inc.; *U.S. Public*, pg. 548
ARRISCRAFT INTERNATIONAL LP—See Wienerberger AG; *Int'l*, pg. 8404
ARRIS DE MEXICO S.A. DE C.V.—See CommScope Holding Company, Inc.; *U.S. Public*, pg. 548
ARRIS ENTERPRISES, INC.—See CommScope Holding Company, Inc.; *U.S. Public*, pg. 548
ARRIS ENTERPRISES LLC—See CommScope Holding Company, Inc.; *U.S. Public*, pg. 547
ARRIS FRANCE S.A.S.—See CommScope Holding Company, Inc.; *U.S. Public*, pg. 548
ARRIS GLOBAL LTD.—See CommScope Holding Company, Inc.; *U.S. Public*, pg. 548
ARRIS GROUP B.V.—See CommScope Holding Company, Inc.; *U.S. Public*, pg. 548
ARRIS GROUP DE MEXICO S.A. DE C.V.—See CommScope Holding Company, Inc.; *U.S. Public*, pg. 548
ARRIS GROUP EUROPE HOLDING B.V.—See CommScope Holding Company, Inc.; *U.S. Public*, pg. 548
ARRIS GROUP, INC. - GLOBAL STRATEGIES—See CommScope Holding Company, Inc.; *U.S. Public*, pg. 547
ARRIS GROUP, INC. - OPERATIONS—See CommScope Holding Company, Inc.; *U.S. Public*, pg. 547
ARRIS GROUP INDIA PRIVATE LIMITED—See CommScope Holding Company, Inc.; *U.S. Public*, pg. 548
ARRIS GROUP JAPAN K.K.—See CommScope Holding Company, Inc.; *U.S. Public*, pg. 548
ARRIS GROUP KOREA, INC.—See CommScope Holding Company, Inc.; *U.S. Public*, pg. 548
ARRIS GROUP RUSSIA LLC—See CommScope Holding Company, Inc.; *U.S. Public*, pg. 548
ARRIS - HONG KONG—See CommScope Holding Company, Inc.; *U.S. Public*, pg. 548
ARRIS INTERNATIONAL IBERIA S.L.—See CommScope Holding Company, Inc.; *U.S. Public*, pg. 548
ARRIS INTERNATIONAL PLC—See CommScope Holding Company, Inc.; *U.S. Public*, pg. 547
ARRIS SINGAPORE PTE. LTD.—See CommScope Holding Company, Inc.; *U.S. Public*, pg. 548
ARRIS SOLUTIONS, INC. - CHICAGO—See CommScope Holding Company, Inc.; *U.S. Public*, pg. 548
ARRIS SOLUTIONS, INC. - HORSHAM—See CommScope Holding Company, Inc.; *U.S. Public*, pg. 548
ARRIS SOLUTIONS, INC.—See CommScope Holding Company, Inc.; *U.S. Public*, pg. 548
ARRIS SOLUTIONS SPAIN S.L.—See CommScope Holding Company, Inc.; *U.S. Public*, pg. 548
ARRIS SOLUTIONS U.K., LTD.—See CommScope Holding Company, Inc.; *U.S. Public*, pg. 548
ARRIS SWEDEN A.B.—See CommScope Holding Company, Inc.; *U.S. Public*, pg. 548
ARRIS TAIWAN, LTD.—See CommScope Holding Company, Inc.; *U.S. Public*, pg. 548
ARRIS TECHNOLOGY, INC.—See CommScope Holding Company, Inc.; *U.S. Public*, pg. 548
ARRIS TECHNOLOGY (SHENZHEN) CO., LTD.—See CommScope Holding Company, Inc.; *U.S. Public*, pg. 548
ARRIS TELECOMUNICACIONES CHILE LTDA—See CommScope Holding Company, Inc.; *U.S. Public*, pg. 548
ARRIS TELECOMUNICACOES DO BRASIL LTDA—See CommScope Holding Company, Inc.; *U.S. Public*, pg. 548
ARRIVA BUS & COACH LTD.—See I Squared Capital Advisors (US) LLC; *U.S. Private*, pg. 2024
ARRIVA CITY S.R.O.—See Deutsche Bahn AG; *Int'l*, pg. 2049

ARRIVA CROYDON&NORTH SURREY LIMITED—See I Squared Capital Advisors (US) LLC; *U.S. Private*, pg. 2024
ARRIVA DANMARK A/S—See Mutares SE & Co. KGaA; *Int'l*, pg. 5104
ARRIVA EAST HERTS & ESSEX LTD—See I Squared Capital Advisors (US) LLC; *U.S. Private*, pg. 2024
ARRIVA GALICIA S.L.—See Deutsche Bahn AG; *Int'l*, pg. 2049
ARRIVA HOLDING CESKA REPUBLIKA S.R.O—See I Squared Capital Advisors (US) LLC; *U.S. Private*, pg. 2024
ARRIVA HUNGARY ZRT.—See I Squared Capital Advisors (US) LLC; *U.S. Private*, pg. 2024
ARRIVA INSURANCE—See I Squared Capital Advisors (US) LLC; *U.S. Private*, pg. 2024
ARRIVA INSURANCE COMPANY (GIBRALTAR) LIMITED—See I Squared Capital Advisors (US) LLC; *U.S. Private*, pg. 2024
ARRIVA ITALIA S.R.L.—See I Squared Capital Advisors (US) LLC; *U.S. Private*, pg. 2024
ARRIVA LIORBUS, A. S.—See Deutsche Bahn AG; *Int'l*, pg. 2049
ARRIVA LITAS D.O.O.—See Mutares SE & Co. KGaA; *Int'l*, pg. 5104
ARRIVA LONDON LTD—See I Squared Capital Advisors (US) LLC; *U.S. Private*, pg. 2024
ARRIVA MADRID MOVILIDAD S.L.—See Deutsche Bahn AG; *Int'l*, pg. 2049
ARRIVA MEDICAL PHILIPPINES, INC.—See Abbott Laboratories; *U.S. Public*, pg. 19
ARRIVA MICHALOVCE, A.S.—See I Squared Capital Advisors (US) LLC; *U.S. Private*, pg. 2024
ARRIVA MIDDLE EAST FZE—See I Squared Capital Advisors (US) LLC; *U.S. Private*, pg. 2024
ARRIVA MIDLANDS LIMITED—See I Squared Capital Advisors (US) LLC; *U.S. Private*, pg. 2024
ARRIVA MIDLANDS NORTH LIMITED—See I Squared Capital Advisors (US) LLC; *U.S. Private*, pg. 2024
ARRIVA NEDERLAND B.V.—See I Squared Capital Advisors (US) LLC; *U.S. Private*, pg. 2024
ARRIVA NITRA A.S—See I Squared Capital Advisors (US) LLC; *U.S. Private*, pg. 2024
ARRIVA NOROESTE SL—See I Squared Capital Advisors (US) LLC; *U.S. Private*, pg. 2024
ARRIVA NORTH EAST LIMITED—See I Squared Capital Advisors (US) LLC; *U.S. Private*, pg. 2025
ARRIVA NORTH EAST - NEWCASTLE UPON TYNE—See I Squared Capital Advisors (US) LLC; *U.S. Private*, pg. 2025
ARRIVA NORTH WEST & WALES—See I Squared Capital Advisors (US) LLC; *U.S. Private*, pg. 2025
ARRIVA NOVE ZAMKY, A.S.—See I Squared Capital Advisors (US) LLC; *U.S. Private*, pg. 2025
ARRIVA OSTGOTAPENDELN AB—See I Squared Capital Advisors (US) LLC; *U.S. Private*, pg. 2025
ARRIVA PLC—See I Squared Capital Advisors (US) LLC; *U.S. Private*, pg. 2024
ARRIVA PORTUGAL - TRANSPORTES LDA—See I Squared Capital Advisors (US) LLC; *U.S. Private*, pg. 2024
ARRIVA PRAHA S.R.O.—See I Squared Capital Advisors (US) LLC; *U.S. Private*, pg. 2025
ARRIVA RAIL LONDON LIMITED—See Deutsche Bahn AG; *Int'l*, pg. 2049
ARRIVA RP SP. Z O.O.—See I Squared Capital Advisors (US) LLC; *U.S. Private*, pg. 2025
ARRIVA SERVICE S.R.O.—See I Squared Capital Advisors (US) LLC; *U.S. Private*, pg. 2025
ARRIVA SLOVAKIA A.S.—See Deutsche Bahn AG; *Int'l*, pg. 2049
ARRIVA SOUTHERN COUNTIES—See I Squared Capital Advisors (US) LLC; *U.S. Private*, pg. 2025
ARRIVA STAJERSKA, DRUZBA ZA PREVOZ POTNIKOV, D.D.—See I Squared Capital Advisors (US) LLC; *U.S. Private*, pg. 2025
ARRIVA STREDNI CECHY S.R.O.—See Deutsche Bahn AG; *Int'l*, pg. 2049
ARRIVA SVERIGE AB—See VR-Group Plc; *Int'l*, pg. 8313
ARRIVA TAG AB—See I Squared Capital Advisors (US) LLC; *U.S. Private*, pg. 2025
ARRIVA TEPLICE S.R.O—See I Squared Capital Advisors (US) LLC; *U.S. Private*, pg. 2025
ARRIVA THE SHIRES—See I Squared Capital Advisors (US) LLC; *U.S. Private*, pg. 2025
ARRIVA TOG A/S—See I Squared Capital Advisors (US) LLC; *U.S. Private*, pg. 2025
ARRIVA TOURING BV—See I Squared Capital Advisors (US) LLC; *U.S. Private*, pg. 2025
ARRIVA TRAINS WALES/TRENAU ARRIVA CYMRU LIMITED—See I Squared Capital Advisors (US) LLC; *U.S. Private*, pg. 2025
ARRIVA TRANSPORT SOLUTIONS LIMITED—See I Squared Capital Advisors (US) LLC; *U.S. Private*, pg. 2025
ARRIVA TRNAVA, A. S.—See Deutsche Bahn AG; *Int'l*, pg. 2049
ARRIVA VYCHODNI CECHY A.S.—See I Squared Capital Advisors (US) LLC; *U.S. Private*, pg. 2025
ARRIVA YORKSHIRE LTD.—See I Squared Capital Advisors (US) LLC; *U.S. Private*, pg. 2025
ARRIVA YORKSHIRE NORTH LTD—See I Squared Capital Advisors (US) LLC; *U.S. Private*, pg. 2025
ARRIVA YORKSHIRE WEST LTD—See I Squared Capital Advisors (US) LLC; *U.S. Private*, pg. 2025
ARRIVENT BIOPHARMA, INC.; *U.S. Public*, pg. 194
ARRIVER US, INC.—See QUALCOMM Incorporated; *U.S. Public*, pg. 1747
ARRIVE—See LDC SA; *Int'l*, pg. 4430
ARRIVE WEALTH MANAGEMENT LIMITED—See AMP Limited; *Int'l*, pg. 432
ARRIVIA—See 3i Group plc; *Int'l*, pg. 8
ARRIYADH DEVELOPMENT COMPANY; *Int'l*, pg. 579
ARRK CORPORATION—See Mitsui Chemicals, Inc.; *Int'l*, pg. 4981
ARRMA-DURANGO LTD.—See Hobbico, Inc.; *U.S. Private*, pg. 1958
ARRMAZ CHEMICALS (YUNNAN) CO., LTD.—See Arkema S.A.; *Int'l*, pg. 570
ARR-MAZ DO BRASIL LTDA.—See Arkema S.A.; *Int'l*, pg. 570
ARRMAZ GULF CHEMICAL COMPANY LTD.—See Arkema S.A.; *Int'l*, pg. 570
ARRMAZ MOROCCO SARLAU—See Arkema S.A.; *Int'l*, pg. 570
ARRMAZ PRODUCTS, LP—See Golden Gate Capital Management II, LLC; *U.S. Private*, pg. 1731
AR ROBOTICS AND AUTOMATION PTE. LTD.—See ISDN Holdings Limited; *Int'l*, pg. 3813
ARROHEALTH—See New Mountain Capital, LLC; *U.S. Private*, pg. 2901
ARRONDA IMMOBILIENVERWALTUNGS GMBH—See UniCredit S.p.A.; *Int'l*, pg. 8033
ARROWAC FISHERIES INC.; *U.S. Public*, pg. 336
ARROW ACQUISITION LLC—See Affiliated Managers Group, Inc.; *U.S. Public*, pg. 53
ARROW ALTECH DISTRIBUTION (PTY) LTD.—See Arrow Electronics, Inc.; *U.S. Public*, pg. 195
ARROW ALTECH HOLDINGS (PTY) LTD.—See Arrow Electronics, Inc.; *U.S. Public*, pg. 195
ARROW ARGENTINA S.A.—See Arrow Electronics, Inc.; *U.S. Public*, pg. 195
ARROW ASIA PAC LTD.—See Arrow Electronics, Inc.; *U.S. Public*, pg. 195
ARROW BRASIL S.A.—See Arrow Electronics, Inc.; *U.S. Public*, pg. 195
ARROW BUILDING CENTER - POST FRAME DIVISION—See Consolidated Lumber Co.; *U.S. Private*, pg. 1021
ARROW BUILDING CENTERS—See Consolidated Lumber Co.; *U.S. Private*, pg. 1021
ARROW BUSINESS CONSULTING CORPORATION—See Chiyoda Corporation; *Int'l*, pg. 1574
ARROW CAPITAL CORP.; *Int'l*, pg. 579
ARROW CAPITAL MANAGEMENT, INC.; *Int'l*, pg. 579
ARROW CARS INTERNATIONAL, INC.; *Int'l*, pg. 579
ARROW CENTRAL EUROPE GMBH—See Arrow Electronics, Inc.; *U.S. Public*, pg. 195
ARROW CENTRAL EUROPE HOLDING MUNICH GMBH—See Arrow Electronics, Inc.; *U.S. Public*, pg. 195
ARROW (CHINA) ELECTRONICS TRADING CO. LTD.—See Arrow Electronics, Inc.; *U.S. Public*, pg. 195
ARROW COACH LINES, INC.—See Village Charters, Inc.; *U.S. Private*, pg. 4383
ARROW COATED PRODUCTS (UK) LIMITED—See Arrow Greentech Limited; *Int'l*, pg. 579
ARROW-COMMUNICATION LABS INC.—See Northern CATV Sales Inc.; *U.S. Private*, pg. 2952
ARROW COMPANIES, LLC; *U.S. Private*, pg. 335
ARROW COMPONENTS (M) SDN BHD—See Arrow Electronics, Inc.; *U.S. Public*, pg. 195
ARROW COMPONENTS (NZ)—See Arrow Electronics, Inc.; *U.S. Public*, pg. 195
ARROW COMPONENTS—See Arrow Electronics, Inc.; *U.S. Public*, pg. 195
ARROW COMPONENTS SWEDEN AB—See Arrow Electronics, Inc.; *U.S. Public*, pg. 195
ARROW CONCRETE COMPANY; *U.S. Private*, pg. 335
ARROW CONSTRUCTION PRODUCTS LIMITED; *Int'l*, pg. 579
ARROWCREST GROUP PTY. LTD.; *Int'l*, pg. 579
ARROW DENMARK, APS—See Arrow Electronics, Inc.; *U.S. Public*, pg. 195
ARROW DISPOSAL SERVICE, LLC—See Waste Management, Inc.; *U.S. Public*, pg. 2330
ARROW EC INCOME ADVANTAGE ALTERNATIVE FUND; *Int'l*, pg. 579
ARROW ECS AG—See Arrow Electronics, Inc.; *U.S. Public*, pg. 195
ARROW ECS AG—See Arrow Electronics, Inc.; *U.S. Public*, pg. 195
ARROW ECS ANZ LIMITED—See Arrow Electronics, Inc.; *U.S. Public*, pg. 195
ARROW ECS ANZ PTY LTD—See Arrow Electronics, Inc.; *U.S. Public*, pg. 195
ARROW ECS ASIA PTE. LTD—See Arrow Electronics, Inc.; *U.S. Public*, pg. 195
ARROW ECS A.S.—See Arrow Electronics, Inc.; *U.S. Public*, pg. 196
ARROW ECS AUSTRALIA PTY. LIMITED—See Arrow Electronics, Inc.; *U.S. Public*, pg. 195
ARROW ECS BALTIC OU—See Arrow Electronics, Inc.; *U.S. Public*, pg. 196
ARROW ECS BELGIUM—See Arrow Electronics, Inc.; *U.S. Public*, pg. 196
ARROW ECS BRASIL DISTRIBUIDORA LTDA.—See Arrow Electronics, Inc.; *U.S. Public*, pg. 196
ARROW ECS B.V.—See Arrow Electronics, Inc.; *U.S. Public*, pg. 196
ARROW ECS B.V.—See Arrow Electronics, Inc.; *U.S. Public*, pg. 196
ARROW ECS CANADA LTD.—See Arrow Electronics, Inc.; *U.S. Public*, pg. 198
ARROW ECS DENMARK A/S—See Arrow Electronics, Inc.; *U.S. Public*, pg. 196
ARROW ECS D.O.O.—See Arrow Electronics, Inc.; *U.S. Public*, pg. 196
ARROW ECS FINLAND OY—See Arrow Electronics, Inc.; *U.S. Public*, pg. 196
ARROW ECS FZCO—See Arrow Electronics, Inc.; *U.S. Public*, pg. 196
ARROW ECS GMBH—See Arrow Electronics, Inc.; *U.S. Public*, pg. 196
ARROW ECS INTERNET SECURITY AG - BRUTTISELLEN—See Arrow Electronics, Inc.; *U.S. Public*, pg. 196
ARROW ECS INTERNET SECURITY AG—See Arrow Electronics, Inc.; *U.S. Public*, pg. 196
ARROW ECS INTERNET SECURITY, S.L.—See Arrow Electronics, Inc.; *U.S. Public*, pg. 196
ARROW ECS (IRELAND) LIMITED—See Arrow Electronics, Inc.; *U.S. Public*, pg. 195
ARROW ECS KFT.—See Arrow Electronics, Inc.; *U.S. Public*, pg. 196
ARROW ECS LTD.—See Arrow Electronics, Inc.; *U.S. Public*, pg. 196
ARROW ECS LTD.—See Arrow Electronics, Inc.; *U.S. Public*, pg. 196
ARROW ECS NETWORK & SECURITY SAS—See Arrow Electronics, Inc.; *U.S. Public*, pg. 196
ARROW ECS (NI) LIMITED—See Arrow Electronics, Inc.; *U.S. Public*, pg. 195
ARROW ECS NORDIC A/S—See Arrow Electronics, Inc.; *U.S. Public*, pg. 196
ARROW ECS NORWAY AS—See Arrow Electronics, Inc.; *U.S. Public*, pg. 196
ARROWECS PORTUGAL SOCIEDADE UNIPESSOAL LDA.—See Arrow Electronics, Inc.; *U.S. Public*, pg. 195
ARROW ECS PTY LTD.—See Arrow Electronics, Inc.; *U.S. Public*, pg. 196
ARROW ECS SA NV—See Arrow Electronics, Inc.; *U.S. Public*, pg. 196
ARROW ECS SARL—See Arrow Electronics, Inc.; *U.S. Public*, pg. 196
ARROW ECS, SAS—See Arrow Electronics, Inc.; *U.S. Public*, pg. 195
ARROW ECS SERVICES SP.Z.O.O.—See Arrow Electronics, Inc.; *U.S. Public*, pg. 196
ARROW ECS SPA—See Arrow Electronics, Inc.; *U.S. Public*, pg. 196
ARROW ECS SP.Z.O.O.—See Arrow Electronics, Inc.; *U.S. Public*, pg. 196
ARROW ECS S.R.O.—See Arrow Electronics, Inc.; *U.S. Public*, pg. 196
ARROW ECS SWEDEN AB—See Arrow Electronics, Inc.; *U.S. Public*, pg. 196
ARROWEDGE LTD.; *Int'l*, pg. 580
ARROW ELECTRIC CO. INC.; *U.S. Private*, pg. 335
ARROW ELECTRONICE S.R.L.—See Arrow Electronics, Inc.; *U.S. Public*, pg. 196
ARROW ELECTRONICS ANZ HOLDINGS PTY LTD.—See Arrow Electronics, Inc.; *U.S. Public*, pg. 196
ARROW ELECTRONICS ASIA (S) PTE LTD.—See Arrow Electronics, Inc.; *U.S. Public*, pg. 196
ARROW ELECTRONICS ASIA (S) PTE LTD.—See Arrow Electronics, Inc.; *U.S. Public*, pg. 196
ARROW ELECTRONICS AUSTRALIA PTY LTD.—See Arrow Electronics, Inc.; *U.S. Public*, pg. 196
ARROW ELECTRONICS AUSTRALIA PTY LTD.—See Arrow Electronics, Inc.; *U.S. Public*, pg. 196
ARROW ELECTRONICS CANADA LTD.—See Arrow Electronics, Inc.; *U.S. Public*, pg. 196
ARROW ELECTRONICS CHINA LTD.—See Arrow Electronics, Inc.; *U.S. Public*, pg. 196
ARROW ELECTRONICS COMPONENTS—See Arrow Electronics, Inc.; *U.S. Public*, pg. 197
ARROW ELECTRONICS COMPONENTS—See Arrow Electronics, Inc.; *U.S. Public*, pg. 196
ARROW ELECTRONICS COMPONENTS—See Arrow Electronics, Inc.; *U.S. Public*, pg. 196
ARROW ELECTRONICS COMPONENTS—See Arrow Electronics, Inc.; *U.S. Public*, pg. 197
ARROW ELECTRONICS COMPONENTS—See Arrow Electronics, Inc.; *U.S. Public*, pg. 197
ARROW ELECTRONICS COMPONENTS—See Arrow Electronics, Inc.; *U.S. Public*, pg. 197

ARROW ELECTRIC CO. INC.

CORPORATE AFFILIATIONS

ARROW ELECTRONICS COMPONENTS—See Arrow Electronics, Inc.; *U.S. Public*, pg. 197
ARROW ELECTRONICS COMPONENTS—See Arrow Electronics, Inc.; *U.S. Public*, pg. 197
ARROW ELECTRONICS COMPONENTS—See Arrow Electronics, Inc.; *U.S. Public*, pg. 197
ARROW ELECTRONICS COMPONENTS—See Arrow Electronics, Inc.; *U.S. Public*, pg. 197
ARROW ELECTRONICS COMPONENTS—See Arrow Electronics, Inc.; *U.S. Public*, pg. 197
ARROW ELECTRONICS COMPONENTS—See Arrow Electronics, Inc.; *U.S. Public*, pg. 197
ARROW ELECTRONICS COMPONENTS—See Arrow Electronics, Inc.; *U.S. Public*, pg. 197
ARROW ELECTRONICS COMPONENTS—See Arrow Electronics, Inc.; *U.S. Public*, pg. 197
ARROW ELECTRONICS COMPONENTS—See Arrow Electronics, Inc.; *U.S. Public*, pg. 197
ARROW ELECTRONICS COMPONENTS—See Arrow Electronics, Inc.; *U.S. Public*, pg. 197
ARROW ELECTRONICS COMPONENTS—See Arrow Electronics, Inc.; *U.S. Public*, pg. 197
ARROW ELECTRONICS COMPONENTS—See Arrow Electronics, Inc.; *U.S. Public*, pg. 197
ARROW ELECTRONICS COMPONENTS—See Arrow Electronics, Inc.; *U.S. Public*, pg. 197
ARROW ELECTRONICS COMPONENTS—See Arrow Electronics, Inc.; *U.S. Public*, pg. 197
ARROW ELECTRONICS COMPONENTS—See Arrow Electronics, Inc.; *U.S. Public*, pg. 197
ARROW ELECTRONICS COMPONENTS—See Arrow Electronics, Inc.; *U.S. Public*, pg. 197
ARROW ELECTRONICS COMPONENTS—See Arrow Electronics, Inc.; *U.S. Public*, pg. 197
ARROW ELECTRONICS COMPONENTS—See Arrow Electronics, Inc.; *U.S. Public*, pg. 197
ARROW ELECTRONICS COMPONENTS—See Arrow Electronics, Inc.; *U.S. Public*, pg. 197
ARROW ELECTRONICS COMPONENTS—See Arrow Electronics, Inc.; *U.S. Public*, pg. 197
ARROW ELECTRONICS COMPONENTS—See Arrow Electronics, Inc.; *U.S. Public*, pg. 197
ARROW ELECTRONICS COMPONENTS—See Arrow Electronics, Inc.; *U.S. Public*, pg. 197
ARROW ELECTRONICS CZECH REPUBLIC S.R.O.—See Arrow Electronics, Inc.; *U.S. Public*, pg. 197
ARROW ELECTRONICS D.O.O.—See Arrow Electronics, Inc.; *U.S. Public*, pg. 197
ARROW ELECTRONICS EMEASA S.R.L.—See Arrow Electronics, Inc.; *U.S. Public*, pg. 197
ARROW ELECTRONICS ESTONIA OU—See Arrow Electronics, Inc.; *U.S. Public*, pg. 197
ARROW ELECTRONICS GK—See Arrow Electronics, Inc.; *U.S. Public*, pg. 197
ARROW ELECTRONICS HELLAS S.A.—See Arrow Electronics, Inc.; *U.S. Public*, pg. 197
ARROW ELECTRONICS HOLDINGS PTY LTD.—See Arrow Electronics, Inc.; *U.S. Public*, pg. 197
ARROW ELECTRONICS, INC.; *U.S. Public*, pg. 194
ARROW ELECTRONICS, INC.—See Arrow Electronics, Inc.; *U.S. Public*, pg. 198
ARROW ELECTRONICS INDIA LTD.—See Arrow Electronics, Inc.; *U.S. Public*, pg. 197
ARROW ELECTRONICS INDIA PRIVATE LTD.—See Arrow Electronics, Inc.; *U.S. Public*, pg. 195
ARROW ELECTRONICS INTERNATIONAL, INC.—See Arrow Electronics, Inc.; *U.S. Public*, pg. 197
ARROW ELECTRONICS ITALIA S.R.L.—See Arrow Electronics, Inc.; *U.S. Public*, pg. 197
ARROW ELECTRONICS JAPAN K.K.—See Arrow Electronics, Inc.; *U.S. Public*, pg. 197
ARROW ELECTRONICS KOREA LTD.—See Arrow Electronics, Inc.; *U.S. Public*, pg. 195
ARROW ELECTRONICS, LTD.—See Arrow Electronics, Inc.; *U.S. Public*, pg. 198
ARROW ELECTRONICS MEXICO, S. DE R.L. DE C.V.—See Arrow Electronics, Inc.; *U.S. Public*, pg. 197
ARROW ELECTRONICS NORWEGIAN HOLDINGS AS—See Arrow Electronics, Inc.; *U.S. Public*, pg. 197
ARROW ELECTRONICS POLAND SP.Z.O.O.—See Arrow Electronics, Inc.; *U.S. Public*, pg. 195
ARROW ELECTRONICS (SHANGHAI) CO. LTD.—See Arrow Electronics, Inc.; *U.S. Public*, pg. 196
ARROW ELECTRONICS (SHENZHEN) CO. LTD.—See Arrow Electronics, Inc.; *U.S. Public*, pg. 196
ARROW ELECTRONICS SLOVAKIA S.R.O.—See Arrow Electronics, Inc.; *U.S. Public*, pg. 198
ARROW ELECTRONICS—See Arrow Electronics, Inc.; *U.S. Public*, pg. 196
ARROW ELECTRONICS (S) PTE LTD.—See Arrow Electronics, Inc.; *U.S. Public*, pg. 195
ARROW ELECTRONICS (SWEDEN) KB—See Arrow Electronics, Inc.; *U.S. Public*, pg. 196
ARROW ELECTRONICS TAIWAN LTD.—See Arrow Electronics, Inc.; *U.S. Public*, pg. 195

ARROW ELECTRONICS (THAILAND) LIMITED—See Arrow Electronics, Inc.; *U.S. Public*, pg. 196
ARROW ELECTRONICS (THAILAND) LIMITED—See Arrow Electronics, Inc.; *U.S. Public*, pg. 196
ARROW ELECTRONICS (UK) LTD.—See Arrow Electronics, Inc.; *U.S. Public*, pg. 196
ARROW ELECTRONICS UKRAINE, LLC—See Arrow Electronics, Inc.; *U.S. Public*, pg. 198
ARROW ELECTRONICS UKRAINE, LLC—See Arrow Electronics, Inc.; *U.S. Public*, pg. 198
ARROW ELEKTRONIK TICARET, A.S.—See Arrow Electronics, Inc.; *U.S. Public*, pg. 198
ARROW ENERGY PTY. LTD.—See China National Petroleum Corporation; *Int'l*, pg. 1533
ARROW ENERGY PTY. LTD.—See Shell plc; *Int'l*, pg. 6796
ARROW ENGINE COMPANY—See TriMas Corporation; *U.S. Public*, pg. 2189
ARROW ENTERPRISE COMPUTING SOLUTIONS, INC.—See Arrow Electronics, Inc.; *U.S. Public*, pg. 198
ARROW ENTERPRISE COMPUTING SOLUTIONS LTD. - NOTTINGHAM OFFICE—See Arrow Electronics, Inc.; *U.S. Public*, pg. 198
ARROW ENTERPRISE COMPUTING SOLUTIONS LTD.—See Arrow Electronics, Inc.; *U.S. Public*, pg. 198
ARROW ENTERPRISE COMPUTING SOLUTIONS LTD.—See Arrow Electronics, Inc.; *U.S. Public*, pg. 198
ARROW ENTERPRISE COMPUTING SOLUTIONS S3—See Arrow Electronics, Inc.; *U.S. Public*, pg. 198
ARROW ENTERPRISE COMPUTING SOLUTIONS S3—See Arrow Electronics, Inc.; *U.S. Public*, pg. 198
ARROW ENTERPRISE COMPUTING SOLUTIONS, S.A.—See Arrow Electronics, Inc.; *U.S. Public*, pg. 198
ARROW EXPLORATION CORP.; *Int'l*, pg. 579
ARROW EXTERMINATORS INC.; *U.S. Private*, pg. 335
ARROW FASTENER CO., LLC—See Masco Corporation; *U.S. Public*, pg. 1389
ARROW FASTENER (U.K.) LIMITED—See Masco Corporation; *U.S. Public*, pg. 1391
ARROW FINANCIAL CORPORATION; *U.S. Public*, pg. 200
ARROW FINANCIAL SERVICES LLC—See SLM Corporation; *U.S. Public*, pg. 1894
ARROW FINLAND OY—See Arrow Electronics, Inc.; *U.S. Public*, pg. 198
ARROW FLUID POWER—See Arrow Pneumatics Inc.; *U.S. Private*, pg. 335
ARROW FORD INC.; *U.S. Private*, pg. 335
ARROW FREIGHT CORPORATION—See Benguet Corporation; *Int'l*, pg. 974
ARROW GAMES CORPORATION—See Arrow International, Inc.; *U.S. Private*, pg. 335
ARROW GEAR COMPANY; *U.S. Private*, pg. 335
ARROW GLASS & MIRROR, INC.; *U.S. Private*, pg. 335
ARROW GLOBAL GROUP PLC; *Int'l*, pg. 579
ARROW GLOBAL LIMITED—See Arrow Global Group PLC; *Int'l*, pg. 579
ARROW GREENTECH LIMITED; *Int'l*, pg. 579
ARROW GROUP INDUSTRIES, INC.—See Leonard Green & Partners, L.P.; *U.S. Private*, pg. 2424
ARROWHEAD ADVERTISING; *U.S. Private*, pg. 336
ARROWHEAD BEHAVIORAL HEALTH, LLC—See Universal Health Services, Inc.; *U.S. Public*, pg. 2256
ARROWHEAD CONTAINERS INC.—See Southern Missouri Container Packaging Group; *U.S. Private*, pg. 3733
ARROWHEAD CONVEYOR CORPORATION, INC.; *U.S. Private*, pg. 336
ARROWHEAD CREDIT UNION; *U.S. Private*, pg. 336
ARROWHEAD ELECTRICAL PRODUCTS, INC.—See The Riverside Company; *U.S. Private*, pg. 4107
ARROWHEAD ENDOSCOPY AND PAIN MANAGEMENT CENTER, LLC—See Tenet Healthcare Corporation; *U.S. Public*, pg. 2009
ARROWHEAD EQUIPMENT INC.; *U.S. Private*, pg. 336
ARROWHEAD GENERAL INSURANCE AGENCY HOLDING CORP.—See Brown & Brown, Inc.; *U.S. Public*, pg. 396
ARROWHEAD GENERAL INSURANCE AGENCY, INC.—See Brown & Brown, Inc.; *U.S. Public*, pg. 396
ARROWHEAD INSURANCE RISK MANAGERS, LLC—See Brown & Brown, Inc.; *U.S. Public*, pg. 396
ARROWHEAD INTERNATIONAL CORPORATION—See Chiyoda Corporation; *Int'l*, pg. 1574
ARROWHEAD MADISON, INC.—See Arrowhead Pharmaceuticals, Inc.; *U.S. Public*, pg. 201
ARROWHEAD MEDICAL, LLC—See Evome Medical Technologies Inc.; *U.S. Public*, pg. 805
ARROWHEAD MILLS, INC.—See Brynwood Partners Management LLC; *U.S. Private*, pg. 674
ARROWHEAD MOUNTAIN SPRING WATER COMPANY—See Metropoulos & Co.; *U.S. Private*, pg. 2690
ARROWHEAD MOUNTAIN SPRING WATER COMPANY—See Metropoulos & Co.; *U.S. Private*, pg. 2690
ARROWHEAD MOUNTAIN SPRING WATER COMPANY—See Metropoulos & Co.; *U.S. Private*, pg. 2690

ARROWHEAD MOUNTAIN SPRING WATER COMPANY—See One Rock Capital Partners, LLC; *U.S. Private*, pg. 3021
ARROWHEAD MOUNTAIN SPRING WATER COMPANY—See One Rock Capital Partners, LLC; *U.S. Private*, pg. 3021
ARROWHEAD MOUNTAIN SPRING WATER COMPANY—See One Rock Capital Partners, LLC; *U.S. Private*, pg. 3021
ARROWHEAD MOUNTAIN SPRING WATER COMPANY—See Metropoulos & Co.; *U.S. Private*, pg. 2690
ARROWHEAD MOUNTAIN SPRING WATER COMPANY—See One Rock Capital Partners, LLC; *U.S. Private*, pg. 3021
ARROWHEAD PHARMACEUTICALS, INC.; *U.S. Public*, pg. 200
ARROWHEAD PIPE & SUPPLY CO—See Mack Energy Corporation; *U.S. Private*, pg. 2536
ARROWHEAD PLASTIC ENGINEERING, INC.; *U.S. Private*, pg. 336
ARROWHEAD PROMOTION & FULFILLMENT COMPANY, INC.; *U.S. Private*, pg. 336
ARROWHEAD RANCH INDEPENDENT—See Independent Newspapers, Inc.; *U.S. Private*, pg. 2060
ARROWHEAD RESOURCES (U.S.A.) LTD.—See Bucking Horse Energy Inc.; *Int'l*, pg. 1210
ARROWHEAD STEEL FABRICATORS—See Chief Industries, Inc.; *U.S. Private*, pg. 881
ARROWHEAD TOWNE CENTER LLC—See The Macerich Company; *U.S. Public*, pg. 2109
ARROWHEAD WATER—See Metropoulos & Co.; *U.S. Private*, pg. 2690
ARROWHEAD WATER—See Metropoulos & Co.; *U.S. Private*, pg. 2690
ARROWHEAD WATER—See One Rock Capital Partners, LLC; *U.S. Private*, pg. 3021
ARROWHEAD WATER—See One Rock Capital Partners, LLC; *U.S. Private*, pg. 3021
ARROWHEAD WEST, INC.; *U.S. Private*, pg. 336
ARROWHEAD WHOLESALE INSURANCE SERVICES, LLC—See Brown & Brown, Inc.; *U.S. Public*, pg. 397
ARROW HOLDINGS S.A.R.L.—See TDR Capital LLP; *Int'l*, pg. 7493
ARROW HOME GROUP CO., LTD.; *Int'l*, pg. 579
ARROW IBERIA ELECTRONICA, S.L.U.—See Arrow Electronics, Inc.; *U.S. Public*, pg. 198
ARROW INFORMATION CO., LTD.—See Yumeshin Holdings Co., Ltd.; *Int'l*, pg. 8613
ARROW-INTECHRA LLC—See Arrow Electronics, Inc.; *U.S. Public*, pg. 198
ARROW INTERACTIVE LTD—See Reach PLC; *Int'l*, pg. 6231
ARROW INTERNATIONAL, INC.; *U.S. Private*, pg. 335
ARROW INTERVENTIONAL, INC.—See Teleflex Incorporated; *U.S. Public*, pg. 1995
ARROW LUMBER & HARDWARE LLC; *U.S. Private*, pg. 335
ARROW MAPS—See Langenscheidt Kommanditgesellschaft; *Int'l*, pg. 4409
ARROWMARK FINANCIAL CORP.; *U.S. Public*, pg. 201
ARROW MEDICAL LIMITED—See Vicplas International Ltd; *Int'l*, pg. 8187
ARROW MIDSTREAM HOLDINGS, LLC—See Crestwood Equity Partners LP; *U.S. Public*, pg. 594
ARROW MINERALS LTD; *Int'l*, pg. 579
ARROW NORDIC COMPONENTS AB—See Arrow Electronics, Inc.; *U.S. Public*, pg. 198
ARROW NORWAY A/S—See Arrow Electronics, Inc.; *U.S. Public*, pg. 198
ARROWOOD INDEMNITY COMPANY—See Arrowpoint Capital Corp.; *U.S. Private*, pg. 336
ARROWOOD-SOUTHERN COMPANY—See Norfolk Southern Corporation; *U.S. Public*, pg. 1535
ARROWOOD SURPLUS LINES INSURANCE COMPANY—See MS&AD Insurance Group Holdings, Inc.; *Int'l*, pg. 5066
ARROWOOD VINEYARDS & WINERY—See Jackson Family Wines, Inc.; *U.S. Private*, pg. 2176
ARROWPAC INCORPORATED; *U.S. Private*, pg. 336
ARROW PARTNERSHIP, LLC; *U.S. Private*, pg. 335
ARROW PHYSICAL THERAPY, LIMITED PARTNERSHIP—See U.S. Physical Therapy, Inc.; *U.S. Public*, pg. 2213
ARROW PNEUMATICS INC.; *U.S. Private*, pg. 335
ARROWPOINT ADVISORY LLP—See Rothschild & Co SCA; *Int'l*, pg. 6402
ARROWPOINT ASSET MANAGEMENT LLC; *U.S. Private*, pg. 336
ARROWPOINT CAPITAL CORP.; *U.S. Private*, pg. 336
ARROWPOINT CORPORATION; *U.S. Private*, pg. 336
ARROWPOINTE CORP.—See The Ascent Group LLC; *U.S. Private*, pg. 3988
ARROW/RAPAC, LTD.—See Arrow Electronics, Inc.; *U.S. Public*, pg. 198
ARROW RESOURCES DEVELOPMENT, INC.; *U.S. Private*, pg. 335
ARROW ROAD CONSTRUCTION COMPANY; *U.S. Private*, pg. 335

ARROW SAFETY DEVICE COMPANY; *U.S. Private*, pg. 336
ARROW S.A.—See Omnicom Group Inc.; *U.S. Public*, pg. 1573
ARROW SECURITY, INC.; *U.S. Private*, pg. 336
ARROW SHIPPING AGENCY CO.,LTD.—See Regional Container Lines Public Company Limited; *Int'l*, pg. 6254
ARROW SHIRT CO.—See PVH Corp.; *U.S. Public*, pg. 1739
ARROW SINTERED PRODUCTS—See Arrow Pneumatics Inc.; *U.S. Private*, pg. 335
ARROW S-TECH NORWAY AS—See Arrow Electronics, Inc.; *U.S. Public*, pg. 198
ARROW STRATEGIES, LLC; *U.S. Private*, pg. 336
ARROWSTREAM, INC.—See Buyers Edge Platform LLC; *U.S. Private*, pg. 699
ARROW SYNDICATE PUBLIC COMPANY LIMITED; *Int'l*, pg. 579
ARROW TANK & ENGINEERING CO.; *U.S. Private*, pg. 336
ARROW TECH HIGH PURITY DIVISION—See Arrow Tank & Engineering Co.; *U.S. Private*, pg. 336
ARROW TECHNOLOGIES, LLC; *U.S. Private*, pg. 336
ARROW TEXTILES LTD.—See Delta Manufacturing Ltd; *Int'l*, pg. 2019
ARROW THOMPSON METALS, INC.—See The Thompson Companies; *U.S. Private*, pg. 4126
ARROW TRUCK SALES INCORPORATED; *U.S. Private*, pg. 336
ARROW TRU-LINE, INC.—See MiddleGround Management, LP; *U.S. Private*, pg. 2711
ARROW TRUST SYSTEMS CO., LTD.—See Open Up Group Inc; *Int'l*, pg. 5598
ARROW UEC JAPAN, KK—See Arrow Electronics, Inc.; *U.S. Public*, pg. 198
ARROW UNIFORM-TAYLOR LLC—See UniFirst Corporation; *U.S. Public*, pg. 2226
ARROW VALUE RECOVERY BELGIUM BVBA—See Arrow Electronics, Inc.; *U.S. Public*, pg. 198
ARROW VALUE RECOVERY CZECH REPUBLIC SRO—See Arrow Electronics, Inc.; *U.S. Public*, pg. 198
ARROW VALUE RECOVERY DENMARK APS—See Arrow Electronics, Inc.; *U.S. Public*, pg. 198
ARROW VALUE RECOVERY EMEA BV—See Arrow Electronics, Inc.; *U.S. Public*, pg. 198
ARROW VALUE RECOVERY FRANCE SAS—See Arrow Electronics, Inc.; *U.S. Public*, pg. 198
ARROW VALUE RECOVERY GERMANY GMBH—See Arrow Electronics, Inc.; *U.S. Public*, pg. 198
ARROW VALUE RECOVERY NETHERLANDS BV—See Arrow Electronics, Inc.; *U.S. Public*, pg. 198
ARROW VALUE RECOVERY NORWAY AS—See Arrow Electronics, Inc.; *U.S. Public*, pg. 198
ARROW VALUE RECOVERY UK LTD—See Arrow Electronics, Inc.; *U.S. Public*, pg. 198
ARROWWOOD CABINETRY, INC.; *U.S. Private*, pg. 336
ARROYO & COMPANY; *U.S. Private*, pg. 336
ARROYO PROCESS EQUIPMENT INC.; *U.S. Private*, pg. 337
ARROZEIRAS MUNDIARROZ, S.A.—See Ebro Foods S.A.; *Int'l*, pg. 2286
ARR PLANNER CO., LTD.; *Int'l*, pg. 578
ARRYX, INC.—See Haemonetics Corporation; *U.S. Public*, pg. 979
ARS ADVERTISING, LLC.; *U.S. Private*, pg. 337
ARS ADVERTISING—See ARS Advertising, LLC.; *U.S. Private*, pg. 337
ARS ADVERTISING—See ARS Advertising, LLC.; *U.S. Private*, pg. 337
ARSALON TECHNOLOGIES, LLC; *U.S. Private*, pg. 337
AR SANDRI INC.; *U.S. Private*, pg. 306
ARSAN TEKSTIL TICARET VE SANAYI AS; *Int'l*, pg. 580
A.R. SAVAGE & SON, LLC; *U.S. Private*, pg. 27
ARS CHEMICAL (THAILAND) CO., LTD.—See Otsuka Holdings Co., Ltd.; *Int'l*, pg. 5659
A.R. SCHMEIDLER & CO., INC.—See Pine Street Alternative Asset Management LP; *U.S. Private*, pg. 3183
AR'S CO., LTD.—See CHINO Corporation; *Int'l*, pg. 1570
ARS DREAM PNG LTD.—See IBJ Inc.; *Int'l*, pg. 3576
ARS DREAM TRAVEL & TOURS CORP.—See IBJ Inc.; *Int'l*, pg. 3576
ARSEDITION GMBH—See Bonnier AB; *Int'l*, pg. 1108
ARSENAL CAPITAL MANAGEMENT LP; *U.S. Private*, pg. 337
ARSENAL GROUP, LLC; *U.S. Private*, pg. 339
ARSENAL SECURITY GROUP, INC.; *U.S. Private*, pg. 339
ARSENAL STRENGTH LLC; *U.S. Private*, pg. 339
ARSEUS BV—See Fagron NV; *Int'l*, pg. 2603
ARSEUS DENTAL NEDERLAND B.V.—See Fagron NV; *Int'l*, pg. 2603
ARSEUS HOSPITAL NV—See Arseus Medical NV; *Int'l*, pg. 580
ARSEUS MEDICAL NV; *Int'l*, pg. 580
ARSEUS TEC NV—See Fagron NV; *Int'l*, pg. 2603
ARSHIYA LIMITED; *Int'l*, pg. 580
ARSIN CORP.—See SemanticSpace Technologies; *U.S. Private*, pg. 3603

ARS INTERNATIONAL LLC—See The Aleut Corporation; *U.S. Private*, pg. 3984
ARS INTERNATIONAL PRIVATE LIMITED—See Accuracy Shipping Limited; *Int'l*, pg. 94
ARSO RADIO CORPORATION; *U.S. Private*, pg. 339
ARS PHARMACEUTICALS, INC.; *U.S. Public*, pg. 201
ARS PROBATA GMBH—See Eurofins Scientific S.E.; *Int'l*, pg. 2535
ARS PUBLICIDAD—See Omnicom Group Inc.; *U.S. Public*, pg. 1579
ARSS INFRASTRUCTURE PROJECTS LIMITED; *Int'l*, pg. 580
ARSTAKLINIKEN AB—See Vimian Group AB; *Int'l*, pg. 8208
ARS THANEA S.A.—See Syzygy AG; *Int'l*, pg. 7394
ARSTIDERNE ARKITEKTER AS—See Sweco AB; *Int'l*, pg. 7363
AR SULTAN LTD—See Schindler Holding AG; *Int'l*, pg. 6618
ARS-UNIKAI GMBH—See Hamburger Hafen und Logistik AG; *Int'l*, pg. 3236
ARS WEALTH ADVISORS, LLC; *U.S. Private*, pg. 337
ARSYS INTERNET S.L.—See United Internet AG; *Int'l*, pg. 8069
ARTA CAPITAL SGEIC SA; *Int'l*, pg. 580
ART ADVANCED RESEARCH TECHNOLOGIES INC.; *Int'l*, pg. 580
ARTAFLEX INC.; *Int'l*, pg. 581
ARTAG HOLDINGS, INC.—See Quarles Petroleum Incorporated; *U.S. Private*, pg. 3324
ARTAL GROUP S.A.; *Int'l*, pg. 581
ARTAL LUXEMBOURG S.A.—See Artal Group S.A.; *Int'l*, pg. 581
ARTANES MINING GROUP AD; *Int'l*, pg. 581
ARTA TECHFIN CORPORATION LIMITED; *Int'l*, pg. 580
ARTCOBELL CORPORATION—See CounterPoint Capital Partners, LLC; *U.S. Private*, pg. 1066
ARTCO-BELL CORPORATION—See CounterPoint Capital Partners, LLC; *U.S. Private*, pg. 1066
ARTCO GROUP INTERNATIONAL, INC.; *U.S. Private*, pg. 340
ART.COM INC.—See Trends International LLC; *U.S. Private*, pg. 4218
ART COMMUNICATION SYSTEM, INC—See TBS Holdings, Inc.; *Int'l*, pg. 7481
ART CORPORATION LIMITED - KADOMA PAPER MILLS DIVISION—See Amalgamated Regional Trading (ART) Holdings Ltd.; *Int'l*, pg. 409
ARTCO (US), INC.—See Taylor Corporation; *U.S. Private*, pg. 3938
THE ARTCRAFT COMPANY; *U.S. Private*, pg. 3988
ARTCRAFT PROMOTIONAL CONCEPTS; *U.S. Private*, pg. 340
ART CRAFT TECHNOLOGY PTE LTD—See Min Aik Technology Co., Ltd.; *Int'l*, pg. 4898
ARTCURIAL HOLDING SA—See Groupe Industriel Marcel Dassault S.A.; *Int'l*, pg. 3104
ART DESIGN & COMMUNICATION JOINT STOCK COMPANY; *Int'l*, pg. 580
A.R.T. DIGITAL HOLDINGS CORP.; *U.S. Public*, pg. 12
ARTEA SA; *Int'l*, pg. 581
ARTEC AQUA AS—See Endur ASA; *Int'l*, pg. 2409
ARTEC CONSTRUCTION LTD.; *Int'l*, pg. 581
ARTEC GLOBAL MEDIA, INC.; *U.S. Public*, pg. 201
ARTEC GMBH—See Rheinmetall AG; *Int'l*, pg. 6321
ARTECH CHINA LIMITED—See Artech Information Systems LLC; *U.S. Private*, pg. 340
ARTECH CHINA LIMITED—See Artech Information Systems LLC; *U.S. Private*, pg. 340
ARTECH CHINA-SHANGHAI—See Artech Information Systems LLC; *U.S. Private*, pg. 340
ARTECH DIGITAL ENTERTAINMENTS, INC.—See BCE Inc.; *Int'l*, pg. 927
ARTECH INFORMATION SYSTEMS LLC; *U.S. Private*, pg. 340
ARTECH INFOSYSTEMS PRIVATE LIMITED—See Artech Information Systems LLC; *U.S. Private*, pg. 340
ARTECH INFOSYSTEMS PRIVATE LIMITED—See Artech Information Systems LLC; *U.S. Private*, pg. 340
ARTECH POWER & TRADING LTD.; *Int'l*, pg. 581
ARTECH ULTRASONIC SYSTEMS AG—See Crest Group Inc.; *U.S. Private*, pg. 1095
ARTEC PULVERISATION SAS—See Bucher Industries AG; *Int'l*, pg. 1206
ARTEC TECHNOLOGIES AG; *Int'l*, pg. 581
ARTE DE MEXICO INCORPORATED; *U.S. Private*, pg. 340
ARTEFACT INFRASTRUCTURE LTD.—See Artefact Projects Ltd.; *Int'l*, pg. 581
ARTEFACT PROJECTS LTD.; *Int'l*, pg. 581
ARTEFACT S.A.—See Ardian SAS; *Int'l*, pg. 554
ARTEFACT; *U.S. Private*, pg. 340
ARTE GRAFICO EDITORIAL ARGENTINO S.A.—See Grupo Clarin S.A.; *Int'l*, pg. 3124
ARTEGRAFT INC—See LeMaitre Vascular, Inc.; *U.S. Public*, pg. 1304
ARTEGY LTD.—See BNP Paribas SA; *Int'l*, pg. 1079
ARTEGY SAS—See BNP Paribas SA; *Int'l*, pg. 1079
ARTEK OY AB—See Vitra AG; *Int'l*, pg. 8261

ARTELCOM GRAND SUD SAS—See Artelcom S.A.; *Int'l*, pg. 581
ARTELCOM S.A.; *Int'l*, pg. 581
THE ARTEL GROUP PTY LIMITED—See Navis Capital Partners Limited; *Int'l*, pg. 5176
ARTELIA HOLDING SA; *Int'l*, pg. 581
ARTEL, INC.; *U.S. Private*, pg. 340
ARTELO BIOSCIENCES, INC.; *U.S. Public*, pg. 201
ARTEL—See Atrel VideoSystems; *U.S. Private*, pg. 382
ARTEMA MEDICAL AB—See Getinge AB; *Int'l*, pg. 2951
ARTEMIS ACQUISITION CORP.; *U.S. Public*, pg. 201
ARTEMIS ALPHA TRUST PLC; *Int'l*, pg. 581
ARTEMIS CAPITAL PARTNERS MANAGEMENT CO., LLC; *U.S. Private*, pg. 340
ARTEMIS CONSULTING, INC.—See Renovus Capital Partners; *U.S. Private*, pg. 3399
ARTEMIS ELECTRICALS & PROJECTS LTD.; *Int'l*, pg. 581
ARTEMIS ELECTRONICS LLC; *U.S. Private*, pg. 341
ARTEMIS FINLAND OY—See ESW Capital, LLC; *U.S. Private*, pg. 1430
ARTEMIS GLOBAL LIFE SCIENCES LIMITED; *Int'l*, pg. 581
ARTEMIS GOLD, INC.; *Int'l*, pg. 581
ARTEMIS HOLDING AG; *Int'l*, pg. 582
ARTEMIS IMMOBILIEN AG—See Artemis Holding AG; *Int'l*, pg. 582
ARTEMIS INFORMATION MANAGEMENT S.A.—See INFORMER GROUP S.A.; *Int'l*, pg. 3695
ARTEMIS INTELLIGENT POWER LTD.—See Mitsubishi Heavy Industries, Ltd.; *Int'l*, pg. 4953
ARTEMIS INTERNATIONAL FRANCE—See ESW Capital, LLC; *U.S. Private*, pg. 1430
ARTEMIS INTERNATIONAL GMBH—See ESW Capital, LLC; *U.S. Private*, pg. 1430
ARTEMIS INTERNATIONAL SOLUTIONS CORPORATION—See ESW Capital, LLC; *U.S. Private*, pg. 1430
ARTEMIS INTERNATIONAL SRL—See ESW Capital, LLC; *U.S. Private*, pg. 1430
ARTEMIS INVESTMENT MANAGEMENT LIMITED; *Int'l*, pg. 582
ARTEMIS INVESTMENT MANAGEMENT LLP—See Affiliated Managers Group, Inc.; *U.S. Public*, pg. 53
ARTEMIS MEDICARE SERVICES LIMITED; *Int'l*, pg. 582
ARTEMIS OPTICAL LIMITED—See Gooch & Housego PLC; *Int'l*, pg. 3038
ARTEMIS REAL ESTATE SRL—See Artemis Holding AG; *Int'l*, pg. 582
ARTEMIS RESOURCES LTD; *Int'l*, pg. 583
ARTEMIS S.A.—See Financiere Pinault SCA; *Int'l*, pg. 2668
ARTEMIS STRATEGIC INVESTMENT CORPORATION; *U.S. Public*, pg. 201
ARTEMIS THERAPEUTICS, INC.; *U.S. Public*, pg. 201
ARTEMIS TRANSMISSORA DE ENERGIA, LTDA.—See ACS, Actividades de Construcción y Servicios, S.A.; *Int'l*, pg. 110
ARTEMIS VCT PLC; *Int'l*, pg. 583
ARTENIUS ITALIA S.P.A.—See La Seda de Barcelona, S.A.; *Int'l*, pg. 4389
ARTENIUS TURKPET, A.S.—See La Seda de Barcelona, S.A.; *Int'l*, pg. 4389
ARTE RADIOTELEVISIVO ARGENTINO S.A.—See Grupo Clarin S.A.; *Int'l*, pg. 3124
ARTERA SERVICES, LLC—See Clayton, Dubilier & Rice, LLC; *U.S. Private*, pg. 919
ARTERIA NETWORKS CORP.; *Int'l*, pg. 583
ARTERIAN, INC.—See The Aldridge Company; *U.S. Private*, pg. 3983
ARTERIA S.A.; *Int'l*, pg. 583
ARTERIS, INC.; *U.S. Public*, pg. 201
ARTERIS S.A.—See Brookfield Corporation; *Int'l*, pg. 1175
ARTERIS S.A.—See Arteris, Inc.; *U.S. Public*, pg. 201
ARTERRA BIOSCIENCE SRL; *Int'l*, pg. 583
ARTERRA WINES CANADA, INC.—See Ontario Teachers' Pension Plan; *Int'l*, pg. 5587
ARTERYEX INC.—See Eisai Co., Ltd.; *Int'l*, pg. 2334
THE ARTERY GROUP, LLC; *U.S. Private*, pg. 3988
ARTERY TECHNOLOGY COMPANY—See Faraday Technology Corporation; *Int'l*, pg. 2617
ARTERY TECHNOLOGY CORPORATION, LTD.—See Faraday Technology Corporation; *Int'l*, pg. 2618
ARTE SALON HOLDINGS, INC.; *Int'l*, pg. 581
ARTESANIAS BAJA, S. A. DE C.V.—See Hubbell Incorporated; *U.S. Public*, pg. 1066
ARTES ASSEKURANZSERVICE GMBH—See Munchener Ruckversicherungs AG; *Int'l*, pg. 5085
ARTES CORPORATION—See Kajima Corporation; *Int'l*, pg. 4053
ARTES GRAFICAS RIOPLATENSE S.A.—See Grupo Clarin S.A.; *Int'l*, pg. 3124
ARTESIA DIALYSIS, LLC—See DaVita Inc.; *U.S. Public*, pg. 636
ARTESIAN DEVELOPMENT CORPORATION—See Artesian Resources Corporation; *U.S. Public*, pg. 201
ARTESIAN RESOURCES CORPORATION; *U.S. Public*, pg. 201

ARTESIAN RESOURCES CORPORATION / CORPORATE AFFILIATIONS

ARTESIAN WASTEWATER MANAGEMENT, INC.—See Artesian Resources Corporation; *U.S. Public*, pg. 201
ARTESIAN WATER COMPANY, INC.—See Artesian Resources Corporation; *U.S. Public*, pg. 202
ARTESIAN WATER MARYLAND, INC.—See Artesian Resources Corporation; *U.S. Public*, pg. 202
ARTESIAN WATER PENNSYLVANIA, INC.—See Artesian Resources Corporation; *U.S. Public*, pg. 202
ARTE STRAITS HOLDINGS PTE. LTD.—See ARTE Salon Holdings, Inc.; *Int'l*, pg. 581
ARTES VALVE & SERVICE GMBH—See ARCA Regler GmbH; *Int'l*, pg. 540
ARTESYN BIOSOLUTIONS ESTONIA OU—See Repligen Corporation; *U.S. Public*, pg. 1784
ARTESYN BIOSOLUTIONS IRELAND LIMITED—See Repligen Corporation; *U.S. Public*, pg. 1784
ARTESYN BIOSOLUTIONS USA, LLC—See Repligen Corporation; *U.S. Public*, pg. 1784
ARTESYN EMBEDDED COMPUTING, INC.—See Penguin Solutions, Inc.; *U.S. Public*, pg. 1661
ARTESYN EMBEDDED POWER—See Advanced Energy Industries, Inc.; *U.S. Public*, pg. 47
ARTESYN EMBEDDED TECHNOLOGIES, INC.—See Platinum Equity, LLC; *U.S. Private*, pg. 3201
ARTESYN HOLDING GMBH—See Advanced Energy Industries, Inc.; *U.S. Public*, pg. 47
ARTESYS SA—See Capgemini SE; *Int'l*, pg. 1303
ARTEX RISK SOLUTIONS (GIBRALTAR) LIMITED—See Arthur J. Gallagher & Co.; *U.S. Public*, pg. 202
ARTEX RISK SOLUTIONS, INC.—See Arthur J. Gallagher & Co.; *U.S. Public*, pg. 202
ARTEX RISK SOLUTIONS, INC.—See Arthur J. Gallagher & Co.; *U.S. Public*, pg. 203
ARTEX RISK SOLUTIONS (MALTA) LIMITED—See Arthur J. Gallagher & Co.; *U.S. Public*, pg. 202
ARTEX RISK SOLUTIONS (SINGAPORE) PTE. LTD.—See Arthur J. Gallagher & Co.; *U.S. Public*, pg. 202
ARTEX S.A.—See Weatherford International plc; *U.S. Public*, pg. 2339
ARTEX SECURITIES CORPORATION—See SONG DA 9 JOINT STOCK COMPANY; *Int'l*, pg. 7095
ARTEX TRADING COMPANY LTD.—See Hayel Saeed Anam Group of Companies; *Int'l*, pg. 3290
ART FORCE JAPAN CO., LTD.; *Int'l*, pg. 580
ART FORCE LLC—See General Finance & Development, Inc.; *U.S. Public*, pg. 921
ARTFORUM INTERNATIONAL MAGAZINE, INC.—See Penske Media Corporation; *U.S. Private*, pg. 3139
ART & FRAME DIRECT INC.; *U.S. Private*, pg. 339
ART GAMBLIN MOTORS; *U.S. Private*, pg. 339
ARTGEN BIOTECH PJSC; *Int'l*, pg. 583
ARTGO HOLDINGS LIMITED; *Int'l*, pg. 583
ARTGREEN CO., LTD.; *Int'l*, pg. 583
ART GROUP HOLDINGS LIMITED; *Int'l*, pg. 580
ART GUILD INC.; *U.S. Private*, pg. 339
ARTHALAND CORPORATION; *Int'l*, pg. 583
ART HAUSER INSURANCE, INC.; *U.S. Private*, pg. 339
ART HILL INC.; *U.S. Private*, pg. 339
A.R. THOMSON GROUP; *Int'l*, pg. 28
ARTHREX BVBA—See Arthrex, Inc.; *U.S. Private*, pg. 341
ARTHREX CALIFORNIA INC.—See Arthrex, Inc.; *U.S. Private*, pg. 341
ARTHREX DANMARK A/S—See Arthrex, Inc.; *U.S. Private*, pg. 341
ARTHREX DO BRAZIL—See Arthrex, Inc.; *U.S. Private*, pg. 341
ARTHREX ESPANA & PORTUGAL—See Arthrex, Inc.; *U.S. Private*, pg. 341
ARTHREX GESMBH—See Arthrex, Inc.; *U.S. Private*, pg. 341
ARTHREX, INC.; *U.S. Private*, pg. 341
ARTHREX KOREA—See Arthrex, Inc.; *U.S. Private*, pg. 341
ARTHREX LTD.—See Arthrex, Inc.; *U.S. Private*, pg. 341
ARTHREX MEDIZINISCHE INSTRUMENTE GMBH—See Arthrex, Inc.; *U.S. Private*, pg. 341
ARTHREX MEXICO, S.A. DE C.V.—See Arthrex, Inc.; *U.S. Private*, pg. 341
ARTHREX NEDERLAND B.V.—See Arthrex, Inc.; *U.S. Private*, pg. 341
ARTHREX S.A.S.—See Arthrex, Inc.; *U.S. Private*, pg. 341
ARTHREX SVERIGE AB—See Arthrex, Inc.; *U.S. Private*, pg. 341
ARTHREX SWISS AG—See Arthrex, Inc.; *U.S. Private*, pg. 341
ARTHRITIS FOUNDATION, INC.; *U.S. Private*, pg. 341
ARTHRITIS SPECIALISTS OF NASHVILLE, INC.—See HCA Healthcare, Inc.; *U.S. Public*, pg. 990
ARTHROCARE CORPORATION—See Smith & Nephew plc; *Int'l*, pg. 7008
ARTHROCARE MEDICAL CORPORATION—See Smith & Nephew plc; *Int'l*, pg. 7009
ARTHROCARE SINGAPORE PTE. LTD.—See Smith & Nephew plc; *Int'l*, pg. 7009
ARTHROGEN B.V.—See MeiraGTx Holdings plc; *U.S. Public*, pg. 1414
ARTHROSCOPY ASSOCIATION OF NORTH AMERICA; *U.S. Private*, pg. 341

ARTHROSURFACE INCORPORATED—See Anika Therapeutics, Inc.; *U.S. Public*, pg. 137
ARTHUR BRETT & SONS LIMITED—See McLaren Construction Group; *Int'l*, pg. 4759
ARTHUR BROWN & BRO., INC.; *U.S. Private*, pg. 341
ARTHUR COMPANIES INC.; *U.S. Private*, pg. 341
ARTHUR D. LITTLE AB—See Arthur D. Little SAS; *Int'l*, pg. 583
ARTHUR D. LITTLE AB—See Arthur D. Little SAS; *Int'l*, pg. 583
ARTHUR D. LITTLE ASIA PACIFIC LTD.—See Arthur D. Little SAS; *Int'l*, pg. 583
ARTHUR D. LITTLE ASIA PTD. LTD.—See Arthur D. Little SAS; *Int'l*, pg. 583
ARTHUR D. LITTLE AUSTRIA GMBH—See Arthur D. Little SAS; *Int'l*, pg. 583
ARTHUR D. LITTLE BENELUX N.V.—See Arthur D. Little SAS; *Int'l*, pg. 583
ARTHUR D. LITTLE BENELUX S.A.—See Arthur D. Little SAS; *Int'l*, pg. 583
ARTHUR D. LITTLE CHINA LIMITED—See Arthur D. Little SAS; *Int'l*, pg. 583
ARTHUR D. LITTLE GMBH—See Arthur D. Little SAS; *Int'l*, pg. 583
ARTHUR D. LITTLE GMBH—See Arthur D. Little SAS; *Int'l*, pg. 583
ARTHUR D. LITTLE HONG KONG—See Arthur D. Little SAS; *Int'l*, pg. 583
ARTHUR D. LITTLE, INC.—See Arthur D. Little SAS; *Int'l*, pg. 584
ARTHUR D. LITTLE JAPAN, INC.—See Arthur D. Little SAS; *Int'l*, pg. 583
ARTHUR D. LITTLE KOREA—See Arthur D. Little SAS; *Int'l*, pg. 583
ARTHUR D. LITTLE LIMITED—See Arthur D. Little SAS; *Int'l*, pg. 583
ARTHUR D. LITTLE MIDDLE EAST FZ LLC—See Arthur D. Little SAS; *Int'l*, pg. 583
ARTHUR D. LITTLE (M) SDN BHD—See Arthur D. Little SAS; *Int'l*, pg. 583
ARTHUR D. LITTLE SAS; *Int'l*, pg. 583
ARTHUR D. LITTLE SAUDI ARABIA—See Arthur D. Little SAS; *Int'l*, pg. 583
ARTHUR D. LITTLE (SCHWEIZ) AG—See Arthur D. Little SAS; *Int'l*, pg. 583
ARTHUR D. LITTLE S.L.—See Arthur D. Little SAS; *Int'l*, pg. 584
ARTHUR D. LITTLE—See Arthur D. Little SAS; *Int'l*, pg. 583
ARTHUR D. LITTLE—See Arthur D. Little SAS; *Int'l*, pg. 584
ARTHUR D. LITTLE S.P.A.—See Arthur D. Little SAS; *Int'l*, pg. 584
ARTHUR F. BELL, JR. & ASSOCIATES, LLC—See Cohen & Company; *U.S. Private*, pg. 962
ARTHUR G. LOMBARD & SONS INC.; *U.S. Private*, pg. 341
ARTHUR HEYMANN GMBH & CO. KG—See Thai Union Group Public Company Limited; *Int'l*, pg. 7597
ARTHUR J. GALLAGHER (AUS) PTY. LTD.—See Arthur J. Gallagher & Co.; *U.S. Public*, pg. 203
ARTHUR J. GALLAGHER AUSTRALASIA HOLDINGS PTY. LTD.—See Arthur J. Gallagher & Co.; *U.S. Public*, pg. 203
ARTHUR J. GALLAGHER BROKERAGE & RISK MANAGEMENT SERVICES, LLC—See Arthur J. Gallagher & Co.; *U.S. Public*, pg. 203
ARTHUR J. GALLAGHER & CO. (AUS) LTD—See Arthur J. Gallagher & Co.; *U.S. Public*, pg. 203
ARTHUR J. GALLAGHER & CO. (BERMUDA) LIMITED—See Arthur J. Gallagher & Co.; *U.S. Public*, pg. 202
ARTHUR J. GALLAGHER & CO. (ILLINOIS)—See Arthur J. Gallagher & Co.; *U.S. Public*, pg. 202
ARTHUR J. GALLAGHER & CO. INSURANCE BROKERS OF CALIFORNIA, INC.—See Arthur J. Gallagher & Co.; *U.S. Public*, pg. 202
ARTHUR J. GALLAGHER & CO. NEWPORT BEACH—See Arthur J. Gallagher & Co.; *U.S. Public*, pg. 202
ARTHUR J. GALLAGHER & CO. ROCKVILLE—See Arthur J. Gallagher & Co.; *U.S. Public*, pg. 205
ARTHUR J. GALLAGHER & CO.; *U.S. Public*, pg. 202
ARTHUR J. GALLAGHER HOUSING LIMITED—See Arthur J. Gallagher & Co.; *U.S. Public*, pg. 202
ARTHUR J. GALLAGHER INTERMEDIARIES (BERMUDA) LIMITED—See Arthur J. Gallagher & Co.; *U.S. Public*, pg. 202
ARTHUR J. GALLAGHER MANAGEMENT (BERMUDA) LIMITED—See Arthur J. Gallagher & Co.; *U.S. Public*, pg. 202
ARTHUR J. GALLAGHER MIDDLE EAST BSC—See Arthur J. Gallagher & Co.; *U.S. Public*, pg. 202
ARTHUR J. GALLAGHER REINSURANCE AUSTRALASIA PTY. LTD.—See Arthur J. Gallagher & Co.; *U.S. Public*, pg. 203
ARTHUR J. GALLAGHER RISK MANAGEMENT SERVICES (HAWAII), INC.—See Arthur J. Gallagher & Co.; *U.S. Public*, pg. 203

ARTHUR J. GALLAGHER RISK MANAGEMENT SERVICES, INC.—See Arthur J. Gallagher & Co.; *U.S. Public*, pg. 203
ARTHUR J. GALLAGHER SWEDEN AB—See Arthur J. Gallagher & Co.; *U.S. Public*, pg. 203
ARTHUR J. GALLAGHER (UK) LIMITED—See Arthur J. Gallagher & Co.; *U.S. Public*, pg. 202
ARTHUR J. GLATFELTER AGENCY INC.—See American International Group, Inc.; *U.S. Public*, pg. 106
ARTHUR J. HURLEY COMPANY, INC.; *U.S. Private*, pg. 341
ARTHUR J. ROGERS & CO; *U.S. Private*, pg. 342
ARTHUR LAUER, INC.; *U.S. Private*, pg. 342
ARTHUR L DAVIS PUBLISHING AGENCY, INC.—See Ziff Davis, Inc.; *U.S. Public*, pg. 2404
ARTHUR MURRAY ENTERPRISES, INC.—See Arthur Murray International, Inc.; *U.S. Private*, pg. 342
ARTHUR MURRAY INTERNATIONAL, INC.; *U.S. Private*, pg. 342
ARTHUR & PAT LAING ENTERTAINMENT PTY LTD—See LOV Group Invest SAS; *Int'l*, pg. 4563
ARTHUR RUTENBERG HOMES INC.; *U.S. Private*, pg. 342
ARTHUR SANDERSON & SONS LTD.—See Sanderson Design Group PLC; *Int'l*, pg. 6525
ARTHUR SANDERSON & SONS SARL—See Sanderson Design Group PLC; *Int'l*, pg. 6525
ARTHUR SCHUMAN INC. (ASI); *U.S. Private*, pg. 342
ARTHUR'S ENTERPRISES, INC.; *U.S. Private*, pg. 342
ARTHUR'S GARDEN DELI INC.; *U.S. Private*, pg. 342
ARTHUR SHUSTER INC.; *U.S. Private*, pg. 342
ARTHUR STATE BANK; *U.S. Private*, pg. 342
ARTICAD LTD—See COFRA Holding AG; *Int'l*, pg. 1693
ARTIC CIRCLE, INC.; *U.S. Private*, pg. 342
ARTICLE ONE PARTNERS, LLC—See RWS Holdings plc; *Int'l*, pg. 6436
ARTIC TEMP, INC.—See Imperial Brown Inc.; *U.S. Private*, pg. 2049
ARTICULATE COMMUNICATIONS INC.; *U.S. Private*, pg. 342
ARTICULATE COMMUNICATIONS INC.—See Articulate Communications Inc.; *U.S. Private*, pg. 342
ARTICUS LTD. MARKETING COMMUNICATIONS; *U.S. Private*, pg. 342
ARTIFAX; *U.S. Private*, pg. 342
ARTIFEX MUNDI S.A.; *Int'l*, pg. 584
ARTIFEX SOFTWARE INC.—See Epapyrus, Inc.; *Int'l*, pg. 2458
ARTIFEX TECHNOLOGY CONSULTING, INC.; *U.S. Private*, pg. 342
ARTIFICIAL ELECTRONICS INTELLIGENT MATERIAL LIMITED; *Int'l*, pg. 584
ARTIFICIAL INTELLIGENCE TECHNOLOGY SOLUTIONS INC.; *U.S. Public*, pg. 208
ARTIFICIAL LABS LTD.—See Capita plc; *Int'l*, pg. 1308
ARTIFICIAL LIFE ASIA LIMITED—See Artificial Life, Inc.; *Int'l*, pg. 584
ARTIFICIAL LIFE, INC.; *Int'l*, pg. 584
ARTIFICIAL LIFE SOURCE HOLDING PLC—See Artificial Life, Inc.; *Int'l*, pg. 584
ARTIFICIAL MIND & MOVEMENT; *Int'l*, pg. 584
ARTIFICIAL SOLUTIONS BV—See Teneo AI AB; *Int'l*, pg. 7559
ARTIFICIAL SOLUTIONS GERMANY GMBH—See Teneo AI AB; *Int'l*, pg. 7559
ARTIFICIAL SOLUTIONS HOLDING ASH AB—See Teneo AI AB; *Int'l*, pg. 7559
ARTIFICIAL SOLUTIONS IBERIA, S. L.—See Teneo AI AB; *Int'l*, pg. 7559
ARTIFICIAL SOLUTIONS INC—See Teneo AI AB; *Int'l*, pg. 7559
ARTIFICIAL TURF SUPPLY LLC—See Blackford Capital LLC; *U.S. Private*, pg. 574
ARTIGIANCASSA SPA—See BNP Paribas SA; *Int'l*, pg. 1079
ARTILA ELECTRONICS CO., LTD.—See Ningbo Techmation Co., Ltd.; *Int'l*, pg. 5306
ARTILIUM N.V.—See Pareteum Corporation; *U.S. Public*, pg. 1637
ARTILIUM PLC—See Pareteum Corporation; *U.S. Public*, pg. 1637
ARTILLERY MARKETING COMMUNICATIONS LLC; *U.S. Private*, pg. 343
ARTIMAS FASHIONS PRIVATE LIMITED—See Lux Industries Limited; *Int'l*, pg. 4587
ARTIM BILISIM COZUM VE DAGITIM A.S.—See Indeks Bilgisayar Sistemleri Muhendislik Sanayi ve Ticaret A.S.; *Int'l*, pg. 3649
THE ARTIME GROUP; *U.S. Private*, pg. 3988
ARTINI HOLDINGS LIMITED; *Int'l*, pg. 584
ARTINOVA AB; *Int'l*, pg. 584
ARTINOVA POLAND SP. Z O.O.—See Artinova AB; *Int'l*, pg. 584
ARTIN PAPIERVERTRIEBS GMBH—See Artinova AB; *Int'l*, pg. 584
THE ART INSTITUTE OF ATLANTA, LLC—See Dream Center Foundation, a California Nonprofit Corp.; *U.S. Private*, pg. 1274

COMPANY NAME INDEX

THE ART INSTITUTE OF AUSTIN, INC.—See Dream Center Foundation, a California Nonprofit Corp.; *U.S. Private*, pg. 1274
THE ART INSTITUTE OF CALIFORNIA - HOLLYWOOD, INC.—See Dream Center Foundation, a California Nonprofit Corp.; *U.S. Private*, pg. 1274
THE ART INSTITUTE OF CALIFORNIA - INLAND EMPIRE, INC.—See Dream Center Foundation, a California Nonprofit Corp.; *U.S. Private*, pg. 1274
THE ART INSTITUTE OF CALIFORNIA - LOS ANGELES, INC.—See Dream Center Foundation, a California Nonprofit Corp.; *U.S. Private*, pg. 1274
THE ART INSTITUTE OF CALIFORNIA - ORANGE COUNTY, INC.—See Dream Center Foundation, a California Nonprofit Corp.; *U.S. Private*, pg. 1274
THE ART INSTITUTE OF CALIFORNIA - SACRAMENTO, INC.—See Dream Center Foundation, a California Nonprofit Corp.; *U.S. Private*, pg. 1274
THE ART INSTITUTE OF CALIFORNIA - SUNNYVALE, INC.—See Dream Center Foundation, a California Nonprofit Corp.; *U.S. Private*, pg. 1274
THE ART INSTITUTE OF CHARLESTON, INC.—See Dream Center Foundation, a California Nonprofit Corp.; *U.S. Private*, pg. 1274
THE ART INSTITUTE OF CHARLOTTE, LLC—See Dream Center Foundation, a California Nonprofit Corp.; *U.S. Private*, pg. 1274
THE ART INSTITUTE OF COLORADO, INC.—See Dream Center Foundation, a California Nonprofit Corp.; *U.S. Private*, pg. 1274
THE ART INSTITUTE OF DALLAS, INC.—See Dream Center Foundation, a California Nonprofit Corp.; *U.S. Private*, pg. 1274
THE ART INSTITUTE OF FORT LAUDERDALE, INC.—See Dream Center Foundation, a California Nonprofit Corp.; *U.S. Private*, pg. 1274
THE ART INSTITUTE OF FORT WORTH, INC.—See Dream Center Foundation, a California Nonprofit Corp.; *U.S. Private*, pg. 1274
THE ART INSTITUTE OF HOUSTON, INC.—See Dream Center Foundation, a California Nonprofit Corp.; *U.S. Private*, pg. 1274
THE ART INSTITUTE OF INDIANAPOLIS, LLC—See Dream Center Foundation, a California Nonprofit Corp.; *U.S. Private*, pg. 1274
THE ART INSTITUTE OF JACKSONVILLE, INC.—See Dream Center Foundation, a California Nonprofit Corp.; *U.S. Private*, pg. 1274
THE ART INSTITUTE OF LAS VEGAS, INC.—See Dream Center Foundation, a California Nonprofit Corp.; *U.S. Private*, pg. 1275
THE ART INSTITUTE OF MICHIGAN, INC.—See Dream Center Foundation, a California Nonprofit Corp.; *U.S. Private*, pg. 1275
THE ART INSTITUTE OF NEW YORK CITY, INC.—See Dream Center Foundation, a California Nonprofit Corp.; *U.S. Private*, pg. 1274
THE ART INSTITUTE OF OHIO - CINCINNATI, INC.—See Dream Center Foundation, a California Nonprofit Corp.; *U.S. Private*, pg. 1275
THE ART INSTITUTE OF PHILADELPHIA LLC—See Dream Center Foundation, a California Nonprofit Corp.; *U.S. Private*, pg. 1274
THE ART INSTITUTE OF PITTSBURGH LLC—See Dream Center Foundation, a California Nonprofit Corp.; *U.S. Private*, pg. 1274
THE ART INSTITUTE OF PORTLAND, INC.—See Dream Center Foundation, a California Nonprofit Corp.; *U.S. Private*, pg. 1274
THE ART INSTITUTE OF RALEIGH-DURHAM, INC.—See Dream Center Foundation, a California Nonprofit Corp.; *U.S. Private*, pg. 1274
THE ART INSTITUTE OF SALT LAKE CITY, INC.—See Dream Center Foundation, a California Nonprofit Corp.; *U.S. Private*, pg. 1275
THE ART INSTITUTE OF SAN ANTONIO, INC.—See Dream Center Foundation, a California Nonprofit Corp.; *U.S. Private*, pg. 1275
THE ART INSTITUTE OF SEATTLE, INC.—See Dream Center Foundation, a California Nonprofit Corp.; *U.S. Private*, pg. 1275
THE ART INSTITUTE OF ST. LOUIS, INC.—See Dream Center Foundation, a California Nonprofit Corp.; *U.S. Private*, pg. 1274
THE ART INSTITUTE OF TAMPA, INC.—See Dream Center Foundation, a California Nonprofit Corp.; *U.S. Private*, pg. 1275
THE ART INSTITUTE OF TENNESSEE - NASHVILLE, INC.—See Dream Center Foundation, a California Nonprofit Corp.; *U.S. Private*, pg. 1275
THE ART INSTITUTE OF TUCSON, INC.—See Dream Center Foundation, a California Nonprofit Corp.; *U.S. Private*, pg. 1275
THE ART INSTITUTE OF VIRGINIA BEACH LLC—See Dream Center Foundation, a California Nonprofit Corp.; *U.S. Private*, pg. 1274
THE ART INSTITUTE OF WASHINGTON - DULLES LLC—See Dream Center Foundation, a California Nonprofit Corp.; *U.S. Private*, pg. 1275
THE ART INSTITUTE OF WASHINGTON, INC.—See Dream Center Foundation, a California Nonprofit Corp.; *U.S. Private*, pg. 1275
THE ART INSTITUTE OF WISCONSIN LLC—See Dream Center Foundation, a California Nonprofit Corp.; *U.S. Private*, pg. 1275
THE ART INSTITUTE OF YORK-PENNSYLVANIA LLC—See Dream Center Foundation, a California Nonprofit Corp.; *U.S. Private*, pg. 1275
THE ART INSTITUTE ONLINE—See Dream Center Foundation, a California Nonprofit Corp.; *U.S. Private*, pg. 1274
THE ART INSTITUTES INTERNATIONAL - KANSAS CITY, INC.—See Dream Center Foundation, a California Nonprofit Corp.; *U.S. Private*, pg. 1275
THE ART INSTITUTES INTERNATIONAL LLC—See Dream Center Foundation, a California Nonprofit Corp.; *U.S. Private*, pg. 1274
THE ART INSTITUTES INTERNATIONAL MINNESOTA, INC.—See Dream Center Foundation, a California Nonprofit Corp.; *U.S. Private*, pg. 1275
ART-INVEST REAL ESTATE MANAGEMENT GMBH & CO. KG; *Int'l*, pg. 580
ARTIO GLOBAL INVESTORS INC.—See abrdn PLC; *Int'l*, pg. 68
ART IRON, INC.; *U.S. Private*, pg. 340
ARTISAN ACQUISITION CORP.; *Int'l*, pg. 584
ARTISANAL BRANDS, INC.; *U.S. Private*, pg. 343
THE ARTISANAL SPIRITS COMPANY PLC; *Int'l*, pg. 7614
ARTISAN BREAD CO., LLC—See Tyson Foods, Inc.; *U.S. Public*, pg. 2209
ARTISAN CONFECTIONS COMPANY—See The Hershey Co.; *U.S. Public*, pg. 2088
ARTISAN CONSUMER GOODS, INC.; *U.S. Public*, pg. 208
ARTISAN CONTAINER SERVICE LLC—See NLM Inc.; *U.S. Private*, pg. 2931
ARTISAN DESIGN GROUP, LLC—See The Sterling Group, L.P.; *U.S. Private*, pg. 4121
ARTISAN DESIGN GROUP; *U.S. Private*, pg. 343
ARTISAN DISPLAY & PACKAGING—See President Container Group, Inc.; *U.S. Private*, pg. 3254
ARTISAN ENERGY CORPORATION; *Int'l*, pg. 584
ARTISAN INFRASTRUCTURE INC.; *U.S. Private*, pg. 343
ARTISAN PARTNERS ASSET MANAGEMENT INC.; *U.S. Public*, pg. 208
ARTISAN PARTNERS HOLDINGS LP—See Artisan Partners Asset Management Inc.; *U.S. Public*, pg. 208
ARTISAN PARTNERS LIMITED PARTNERSHIP—See Artisan Partners Asset Management Inc.; *U.S. Public*, pg. 208
ARTISAN PARTNERS UK LLP—See Artisan Partners Asset Management Inc.; *U.S. Public*, pg. 208
ARTISANS' BANK; *U.S. Private*, pg. 343
ARTISANS INC.; *U.S. Private*, pg. 343
ARTISAN SPECIALTY FOODS, INC.—See Innovative Food Holdings, Inc.; *U.S. Public*, pg. 1126
ARTISAN (UK) DEVELOPMENTS LIMITED—See Artisan (UK) plc; *Int'l*, pg. 584
ARTISAN (UK) PLC; *Int'l*, pg. 584
ARTISAN (UK) PROJECTS LIMITED—See Artisan (UK) plc; *Int'l*, pg. 584
ARTISAN (UK) PROPERTIES LIMITED—See Artisan (UK) plc; *Int'l*, pg. 584
ARTISENT, LLC—See Gentex Corporation; *U.S. Private*, pg. 1679
ARTIS TD CO.—See TCS TurControlSysteme AG; *Int'l*, pg. 7485
ARTIS-NAPLES; *U.S. Private*, pg. 343
ARTISON INVESTMENTS, LTD.; *U.S. Private*, pg. 343
ARTIS REAL ESTATE INVESTMENT TRUST; *Int'l*, pg. 584
ARTISSIMO DESIGNS INC.—See Artissimo Holdings, Inc.; *U.S. Private*, pg. 343
ARTISSIMO HOLDINGS, INC.; *U.S. Private*, pg. 343
ARTISSIMO U.S., LLC—See Artissimo Holdings, Inc.; *U.S. Private*, pg. 343
ARTISTA CHOCOLATES SA—See Compagnie du Bois Sauvage SA; *Int'l*, pg. 1740
ARTIST & BUSINESS TRANSPORT GROUP B.V.—See Live Nation Entertainment, Inc.; *U.S. Public*, pg. 1328
ARTISTDIRECT, INC.—See Relativity Media, LLC; *U.S. Private*, pg. 3393
ARTISTE HOLDING LIMITED—See EZCORP, Inc.; *U.S. Public*, pg. 817
ARTISTIC CARTON COMPANY - AUBURN DIVISION—See Graphic Packaging Holding Company; *U.S. Public*, pg. 958
ARTISTIC CARTON COMPANY—See Graphic Packaging Holding Company; *U.S. Public*, pg. 958
ARTISTIC COUNTERS, INC.; *U.S. Private*, pg. 343
ARTISTIC DENIM MILLS LIMITED; *Int'l*, pg. 584
ARTISTIC FRAME CO., INC.; *U.S. Private*, pg. 343
ARTISTIC FRAMING INC.; *U.S. Private*, pg. 343
ARTISTIC PAVERS MANUFACTURING, INC.; *U.S. Private*, pg. 343
ARTISTIC STUDIOS, LTD—See Irving Place Capital Management, L.P.; *U.S. Private*, pg. 2141
ARTISTIC TILE INC.; *U.S. Private*, pg. 343
ARTISTMSS INTERNATIONAL GROUP, INC.; *U.S. Public*, pg. 208
ARTISTREE LANDSCAPE MAINTENANCE & DESIGN; *U.S. Private*, pg. 343
ARTISTS' FRAME SERVICE, INC.; *U.S. Private*, pg. 343
ARTITALIA GROUP INC.; *Int'l*, pg. 585
ARTIVA BIOTHERAPEUTICS, INC.; *U.S. Private*, pg. 343
ARTIVION, INC.; *U.S. Public*, pg. 208
ARTIVISION TECHNOLOGIES PTE. LTD.; *Int'l*, pg. 585
ARTI YATIRIM HOLDING A.S.; *Int'l*, pg. 585
ARTIZA NETWORKS, INC. - RANCHO PALOS VERDES BRANCH—See Artiza Networks, Inc.; *Int'l*, pg. 585
ARTIZA NETWORKS, INC.; *Int'l*, pg. 585
ARTIZA (SHANGHAI) SOFTWARE DEVELOPMENT CO., LTD.—See Artiza Networks, Inc.; *Int'l*, pg. 585
ART LEWIN & CO.; *U.S. Private*, pg. 340
ART LINE INC.; *U.S. Private*, pg. 340
ARTLINK TECHNOLOGY CO. LTD.—See Arrow Electronics, Inc.; *U.S. Public*, pg. 198
ART & LOGIC, INC.; *U.S. Private*, pg. 339
ARTMAR INC.; *U.S. Private*, pg. 343
ART MARINE LLC—See Abraaj Capital Limited; *Int'l*, pg. 67
ARTMARKET.COM; *Int'l*, pg. 585
ART MARKETING SYNDICATE SA—See Agora S.A.; *Int'l*, pg. 212
ART MORAN PONTIAC-GMC TRUCK-MITSUBISHI INC.; *U.S. Private*, pg. 340
ARTNATURE INC.; *Int'l*, pg. 585
ARTNATURE MALAYSIA SDN. BHD.—See Artnature Inc.; *Int'l*, pg. 585
ARTNATURE (SHANGHAI) INC.—See Artnature Inc.; *Int'l*, pg. 585
ARTNATURE SINGAPORE PTE. LTD.—See Artnature Inc.; *Int'l*, pg. 585
ARTNER CO., LTD.; *Int'l*, pg. 585
ARTNET AG; *Int'l*, pg. 585
ARTNET UK LTD.—See artnet AG; *Int'l*, pg. 585
ARTNET WORLDWIDE CORPORATION—See artnet AG; *Int'l*, pg. 585
ARTNEX INC.—See Aucnet Inc.; *Int'l*, pg. 700
ART NIRMAN LTD.; *Int'l*, pg. 580
ART NOUVEAU PALACE HOTEL-PRAGUE—See Warimpex Finanz- und Beteiligungs AG; *Int'l*, pg. 8345
ART OF BUSINESS, INC.; *U.S. Private*, pg. 340
THE ART OF SHAVING - FL, LLC—See The Procter & Gamble Company; *U.S. Public*, pg. 2124
ART OTEL BERLIN CITY CENTER WEST GMBH—See PPHE Hotel Group Limited; *Int'l*, pg. 5951
ART OTEL BUDAPEST SZALLODAUZEMELTETO KFT—See PPHE Hotel Group Limited; *Int'l*, pg. 5951
ARTPRESTO CO., LTD.—See BANDAI NAMCO Holdings Inc.; *Int'l*, pg. 828
ARTQUEST INTERNATIONAL ALLIANCES, INC.; *Int'l*, pg. 585
ARTRA GROUP CORPORATION; *Int'l*, pg. 585
A&R TRANSPORT, INC.; *U.S. Private*, pg. 20
ART RESOURCE, INC.; *U.S. Private*, pg. 340
ART ROBBINS INSTRUMENTS, LLC—See Argosy Capital Group, LLC; *U.S. Private*, pg. 321
ARTRONIQ BERHAD; *Int'l*, pg. 585
ARTRONIQ INNOVATION SDN BHD—See ARTRONIQ BERHAD; *Int'l*, pg. 585
ARTRONIX SDN. BHD.—See ARTRONIQ BERHAD; *Int'l*, pg. 585
ARTRYA LIMITED; *Int'l*, pg. 585
ARTSAKHHEK OJSC; *Int'l*, pg. 586
ARTS ALLIANCE VENTURES; *Int'l*, pg. 585
ARTSANA ARGENTINA S.A.—See BI-Invest Advisors S.A.; *Int'l*, pg. 1016
ARTSANA BELGIUM SA—See BI-Invest Advisors S.A.; *Int'l*, pg. 1016
ARTSANA FRANCE S.A.S.—See BI-Invest Advisors S.A.; *Int'l*, pg. 1016
ARTSANA GERMANY GMBH—See BI-Invest Advisors S.A.; *Int'l*, pg. 1016
ARTSANA PORTUGAL, S.A.—See BI-Invest Advisors S.A.; *Int'l*, pg. 1016
ARTSANA SPAIN S.A.U.—See BI-Invest Advisors S.A.; *Int'l*, pg. 1016
ARTSANA S.P.A.—See BI-Invest Advisors S.A.; *Int'l*, pg. 1016
ARTSANA SUISSE S.A.—See BI-Invest Advisors S.A.; *Int'l*, pg. 1016
ARTSANA TURKEY BEBEK VE SAGLIK URUNLERI A.S.—See BI-Invest Advisors S.A.; *Int'l*, pg. 1016
ARTSANA USA, INC.—See BI-Invest Advisors S.A.; *Int'l*, pg. 1016
ARTS & COMMUNICATIONS COUNSELORS—See Ruder Finn Group, Inc.; *U.S. Private*, pg. 3501
ARTS GROUP CO., LTD.; *Int'l*, pg. 585
ART SHIPPING INTERNATIONAL SAS—See Clasquin S.A.; *Int'l*, pg. 1652
THE ART SHOPPE LTD.; *Int'l*, pg. 7614
ARTSON ENGINEERING LTD; *Int'l*, pg. 586
ARTSONIA, LLC; *U.S. Private*, pg. 344
ARTS OPTICAL COMPANY LIMITED—See Arts Optical International Holdings Ltd; *Int'l*, pg. 585

ARTS OPTICAL INTERNATIONAL HOLDINGS LTD

ARTS OPTICAL INTERNATIONAL HOLDINGS LTD; *Int'l*, pg. 585
ARTSPACE PROJECTS INC; *U.S. Private*, pg. 344
ARTSQUEST; *U.S. Private*, pg. 344
ARTS STUDIO LIMITED—See Arts Optical International Holdings Ltd.; *Int'l*, pg. 585
ART STONE THEATRICAL CORP.; *U.S. Private*, pg. 340
A.R.T. STUDIO CLAY COMPANY, INC.—See T.J. Haggerty, Inc.; *U.S. Private*, pg. 3912
ART SUPPLY ENTERPRISES INC.; *U.S. Private*, pg. 340
ART'S-WAY MANUFACTURING CO., INC.; *U.S. Public*, pg. 201
ARTS-WAY MANUFACTURING INTERNATIONAL LTD—See Art's-Way Manufacturing Co., Inc.; *U.S. Public*, pg. 201
ART'S WAY SCIENTIFIC, INC.—See Art's-Way Manufacturing Co., Inc.; *U.S. Public*, pg. 201
ART'S WAY VESSELS, INC.—See Art's-Way Manufacturing Co., Inc.; *U.S. Public*, pg. 201
ART TECHNOLOGIES, INC.—See The C. M. Paula Company; *U.S. Private*, pg. 4003
ARTUR EXPRESS, INC.; *U.S. Private*, pg. 344
ARTUR HEYMANN GMBH—See Thai Union Group Public Company Limited; *Int'l*, pg. 7596
ARTUS CORPORATION; *U.S. Private*, pg. 344
ARTUS MINERALQUELLEN GMBH & CO. KG—See Solvay S.A.; *Int'l*, pg. 7080
ARTUSO PASTRY FOODS, CORP; *U.S. Private*, pg. 344
ARTUS SAS—See Parker Hannifin Corporation; *U.S. Public*, pg. 1643
ARTVIEW CO. LTD—See N.K. Shacolas (Holdings) Ltd.; *Int'l*, pg. 5116
ART VIVANT CO., LTD.; *Int'l*, pg. 580
ARTWALK TILE, INC.; *U.S. Private*, pg. 344
ARTWELL ENTERPRISES LIMITED—See Asia Cassava Resources Holdings Limited; *Int'l*, pg. 611
ART WILSON COMPANY—See Arcosa, Inc.; *U.S. Public*, pg. 186
ARUBA NETWORKS, INC.—See HP Inc.; *U.S. Public*, pg. 1062
ARUBA NETWORKS INDIA PVT. LTD.—See HP Inc.; *U.S. Public*, pg. 1062
ARUHI CORPORATION—See SBI Holdings, Inc.; *Int'l*, pg. 6604
ARUJ INDUSTRIES LTD.; *Int'l*, pg. 586
ARUMA RESOURCES LIMITED; *Int'l*, pg. 586
ARUNA HOTELS LTD.; *Int'l*, pg. 586
ARUNDEL AG; *Int'l*, pg. 586
ARUNDEL COMMUNITY DEVELOPMENT SERVICES, INC.; *U.S. Private*, pg. 344
ARUNDEL FORD; *U.S. Private*, pg. 344
ARUNDEL GROUP LIMITED—See Arundel AG; *Int'l*, pg. 586
ARUNDEL MACHINE TOOL CO.—See The Jordan Company, L.P.; *U.S. Private*, pg. 4060
ARUNDEL (MAURITIUS) LIMITED—See Arundel AG; *Int'l*, pg. 586
ARUNDEL MILLS—See Simon Property Group, Inc.; *U.S. Public*, pg. 1882
ARUNIS ABODE LTD.; *Int'l*, pg. 586
ARUNJYOTI BIO VENTURES LIMITED; *Int'l*, pg. 586
ARUN KABELI POWER LIMITED—See Ridi Power Company Limited; *Int'l*, pg. 6338
ARUNODAYA HOSPITALS PRIVATE LIMITED—See Krishna Institute of Medical Sciences Limited; *Int'l*, pg. 4302
ARUN TECHNOLOGY LTD.—See Focused Photonics (Hangzhou), Inc.; *Int'l*, pg. 2720
ARUN VALLEY HYDROPOWER DEVELOPMENT CO. LTD.; *Int'l*, pg. 586
ARUP ADVISORY INC.—See Arup Group Ltd.; *Int'l*, pg. 586
ARUP AMERICAS, INC.—See Arup Group Ltd.; *Int'l*, pg. 586
ARUP ASSOCIATES LIMITED—See Arup Group Ltd.; *Int'l*, pg. 586
ARUP BOTSWANA LIMITED—See Arup Group Ltd.; *Int'l*, pg. 586
ARUP BRASIL CONSULTORIA LTDA—See Arup Group Ltd.; *Int'l*, pg. 586
ARUP B.V.—See Arup Group Ltd.; *Int'l*, pg. 586
ARUP CANADA INC.—See Arup Group Ltd.; *Int'l*, pg. 586
ARUP CHINA LIMITED—See Arup Group Ltd.; *Int'l*, pg. 586
ARUP COLOMBIA S.A.S.—See Arup Group Ltd.; *Int'l*, pg. 586
ARUP DEUTSCHLAND GMBH—See Arup Group Ltd.; *Int'l*, pg. 586
ARUP D.O.O.—See Arup Group Ltd.; *Int'l*, pg. 587
ARUP GOVERNMENT PROJECTS INC.—See Arup Group Ltd.; *Int'l*, pg. 586
ARUP GROUP LTD.; *Int'l*, pg. 586
ARUP IRELAND LIMITED—See Arup Group Ltd.; *Int'l*, pg. 586
ARUP ITALIA S.R.L.—See Arup Group Ltd.; *Int'l*, pg. 586
ARUP LABORATORIES; *U.S. Private*, pg. 344
ARUP LATIN AMERICA S.A.U.—See Arup Group Ltd.; *Int'l*, pg. 586

ARUP MUHENDISLIK VE MUSAVIRLIK LIMITED SIRKETI—See Arup Group Ltd.; *Int'l*, pg. 586
ARUP NEW ZEALAND LIMITED—See Arup Group Ltd.; *Int'l*, pg. 586
ARUP PARTNER PTY LIMITED—See Arup Group Ltd.; *Int'l*, pg. 587
ARUP (PTY) LIMITED—See Arup Group Ltd.; *Int'l*, pg. 586
ARUP PTY LIMITED—See Arup Group Ltd.; *Int'l*, pg. 587
ARUP - S.I.G.M.A. LTD—See Arup Group Ltd.; *Int'l*, pg. 586
ARUP SINGAPORE PRIVATE LIMITED—See Arup Group Ltd.; *Int'l*, pg. 587
ARUP TEXAS INC.—See Arup Group Ltd.; *Int'l*, pg. 587
ARUP VIETNAM LIMITED—See Arup Group Ltd.; *Int'l*, pg. 587
ARUZE USA, INC.—See Universal Entertainment Corporation; *Int'l*, pg. 8078
ARVADA CARE & REHABILITATION CENTER—See The Ensign Group, Inc.; *U.S. Public*, pg. 2070
ARVADA EXCAVATING CO.; *U.S. Private*, pg. 344
ARVADA HOUSE PRESERVATION LIMITED PARTNERSHIP—See Apartment Investment and Management Company; *U.S. Public*, pg. 144
ARVADA MERIDIAN, LLC—See Brookdale Senior Living Inc.; *U.S. Public*, pg. 393
ARVADA RENT-ALLS; *U.S. Private*, pg. 344
ARVAL AB—See BNP Paribas SA; *Int'l*, pg. 1080
ARVAL AS—See BNP Paribas SA; *Int'l*, pg. 1080
ARVAL AUSTRIA GMBH—See BNP Paribas SA; *Int'l*, pg. 1080
ARVAL BELGIUM—See BNP Paribas SA; *Int'l*, pg. 1080
ARVAL BENELUX BV—See BNP Paribas SA; *Int'l*, pg. 1080
ARVAL BRASIL LTDA—See BNP Paribas SA; *Int'l*, pg. 1080
ARVAL B.V.—See BNP Paribas SA; *Int'l*, pg. 1080
ARVAL CZ S.R.O.—See BNP Paribas SA; *Int'l*, pg. 1080
ARVAL DEUTSCHLAND GMBH—See BNP Paribas SA; *Int'l*, pg. 1080
ARVAL ECL SAS—See BNP Paribas SA; *Int'l*, pg. 1080
ARVAL FRANCE—See BNP Paribas SA; *Int'l*, pg. 1080
ARVAL INDIA PRIVATE LTD.—See BNP Paribas SA; *Int'l*, pg. 1080
ARVAL LUXEMBOURG—See BNP Paribas SA; *Int'l*, pg. 1080
ARVAL MAGYARORSZAG KFT.—See BNP Paribas SA; *Int'l*, pg. 1080
ARVAL MAROC—See BNP Paribas SA; *Int'l*, pg. 1080
ARVAL OOO—See BNP Paribas SA; *Int'l*, pg. 1080
ARVAL OY—See BNP Paribas SA; *Int'l*, pg. 1080
ARVAL PHH SERVICE LEASE CZ S.R.O.—See BNP Paribas SA; *Int'l*, pg. 1080
ARVAL PORTUGAL—See BNP Paribas SA; *Int'l*, pg. 1080
ARVAL SCHWEIZ AG—See BNP Paribas SA; *Int'l*, pg. 1080
ARVAL SERVICE GMBH—See BNP Paribas SA; *Int'l*, pg. 1080
ARVAL SERVICE LEASE ALUGER OPERATIONAL AUTOMOVEIS SA—See BNP Paribas SA; *Int'l*, pg. 1080
ARVAL SERVICE LEASE ITALIA S.P.A.—See BNP Paribas SA; *Int'l*, pg. 1080
ARVAL SERVICE LEASE POLSKA SP. Z O.O.—See BNP Paribas SA; *Int'l*, pg. 1080
ARVAL SERVICE LEASE ROMANIA SRL—See BNP Paribas SA; *Int'l*, pg. 1080
ARVAL SERVICE LEASE SA—See BNP Paribas SA; *Int'l*, pg. 1080
ARVAL SERVICE LEASE, S.A.—See BNP Paribas SA; *Int'l*, pg. 1080
ARVAL SLOVAKIA, S.R.O.—See BNP Paribas SA; *Int'l*, pg. 1080
ARVAL TRADING SAS—See BNP Paribas SA; *Int'l*, pg. 1080
ARVAL UK LTD.—See BNP Paribas SA; *Int'l*, pg. 1080
ARVANA INC.; *U.S. Public*, pg. 208
ARVANDAN OIL & GAS COMPANY—See National Iranian Oil Company; *Int'l*, pg. 5160
ARVAND PETROCHEMICAL COMPANY—See Persian Gulf Petrochemical Industry Commercial Company; *Int'l*, pg. 5815
ARVAN INC.—See Churchill Equity, Inc.; *U.S. Private*, pg. 894
ARVATO AG—See Bertelsmann SE & Co. KGaA; *Int'l*, pg. 996
ARVATO CRM NORDHORN GMBH—See Bertelsmann SE & Co. KGaA; *Int'l*, pg. 996
ARVATO CROSSMARKETING GMBH—See Bertelsmann SE & Co. KGaA; *Int'l*, pg. 996
ARVATO DE MEXICO, S.A. DE C.V.—See Bertelsmann SE & Co. KGaA; *Int'l*, pg. 990
ARVATO DIGITAL SERVICES LIMITED—See Bertelsmann SE & Co. KGaA; *Int'l*, pg. 990
ARVATO DIGITAL—See Bertelsmann SE & Co. KGaA; *Int'l*, pg. 990
ARVATO DIRECT SERVICES BRANDENBURG GMBH—See Bertelsmann SE & Co. KGaA; *Int'l*, pg. 997
ARVATO DIRECT SERVICES COTTBUS GMBH—See Bertelsmann SE & Co. KGaA; *Int'l*, pg. 997

CORPORATE AFFILIATIONS

ARVATO DIRECT SERVICES DORTMUND GMBH—See Bertelsmann SE & Co. KGaA; *Int'l*, pg. 997
ARVATO DIRECT SERVICES EIWEILER GMBH—See Bertelsmann SE & Co. KGaA; *Int'l*, pg. 997
ARVATO DIRECT SERVICES FRANKFURT GMBH—See Bertelsmann SE & Co. KGaA; *Int'l*, pg. 997
ARVATO DIRECT SERVICES MUNSTER GMBH—See Bertelsmann SE & Co. KGaA; *Int'l*, pg. 997
ARVATO DIRECT SERVICES NECKARSULM GMBH—See Bertelsmann SE & Co. KGaA; *Int'l*, pg. 997
ARVATO DIRECT SERVICES NEUBRANDENBURG GMBH—See Bertelsmann SE & Co. KGaA; *Int'l*, pg. 997
ARVATO DIRECT SERVICES POTSDAM GMBH—See Bertelsmann SE & Co. KGaA; *Int'l*, pg. 997
ARVATO DIRECT SERVICES SCHWERIN GMBH—See Bertelsmann SE & Co. KGaA; *Int'l*, pg. 997
ARVATO DIRECT SERVICES STRALSUND GMBH—See Bertelsmann SE & Co. KGaA; *Int'l*, pg. 997
ARVATO DIRECT SERVICES WILHELMSHAVEN GMBH—See Bertelsmann SE & Co. KGaA; *Int'l*, pg. 997
ARVATO FINANCE AS—See Bertelsmann SE & Co. KGaA; *Int'l*, pg. 996
ARVATO FINANCIAL SOLUTIONS LIMITED—See Bertelsmann SE & Co. KGaA; *Int'l*, pg. 996
ARVATO INFOSCORE GMBH—See Bertelsmann SE & Co. KGaA; *Int'l*, pg. 997
ARVATO MEDIA GMBH—See Bertelsmann SE & Co. KGaA; *Int'l*, pg. 997
ARVATO P.S. GMBH—See Bertelsmann SE & Co. KGaA; *Int'l*, pg. 997
ARVATO SCM IRELAND LIMITED—See Bertelsmann SE & Co. KGaA; *Int'l*, pg. 996
ARVATO SERVICES CHEMNITZ GMBH—See Bertelsmann SE & Co. KGaA; *Int'l*, pg. 997
ARVATO SERVICES DRESDEN GMBH—See Bertelsmann SE & Co. KGaA; *Int'l*, pg. 997
ARVATO SERVICES DUISBURG GMBH—See Bertelsmann SE & Co. KGaA; *Int'l*, pg. 997
ARVATO SERVICES ESSEN GMBH—See Bertelsmann SE & Co. KGaA; *Int'l*, pg. 997
ARVATO SERVICES K.S.—See Bertelsmann SE & Co. KGaA; *Int'l*, pg. 990
ARVATO SERVICES TECHNICAL INFORMATION GMBH—See Bertelsmann SE & Co. KGaA; *Int'l*, pg. 997
ARVATO SE—See Bertelsmann SE & Co. KGaA; *Int'l*, pg. 990
ARVATO SUPPLY CHAIN SOLUTIONS SE—See Bertelsmann SE & Co. KGaA; *Int'l*, pg. 990
ARVATO SYSTEMS PERDATA GMBH—See Bertelsmann SE & Co. KGaA; *Int'l*, pg. 997
ARVATO SYSTEMS S4M GMBH—See Bertelsmann SE & Co. KGaA; *Int'l*, pg. 997
ARVATO TELCO SERVICES ERFURT GMBH—See Bertelsmann SE & Co. KGaA; *Int'l*, pg. 997
ARVCO CONTAINER CORPORATION; *U.S. Private*, pg. 344
ARVEE LABORATORIES (INDIA) LIMITED; *Int'l*, pg. 587
ARVE INTERIM SAS—See Randstad N.V.; *Int'l*, pg. 6201
ARVEL INDUSTRIES SARL—See Bucher Industries AG; *Int'l*, pg. 1206
ARVESTA BV; *Int'l*, pg. 587
ARVEST ASSET MANAGEMENT—See Arvest Bank Group, Inc.; *U.S. Private*, pg. 344
ARVEST BANK GROUP, INC.; *U.S. Private*, pg. 344
ARVEST BANK OPERATIONS, INC.—See Arvest Bank Group, Inc.; *U.S. Private*, pg. 344
ARVEST BANK—See Arvest Bank Group, Inc.; *U.S. Private*, pg. 344
ARVEST MORTGAGE COMPANY—See Arvest Bank Group, Inc.; *U.S. Private*, pg. 344
ARVIDA GROUP LIMITED; *Int'l*, pg. 587
ARVID NILSSON LOGISTICS & TRADE (SHANGHAI) CO., LTD.—See Wurth Verwaltungsgesellschaft mbH; *Int'l*, pg. 8504
ARVID NILSSON SVERIGE AB—See Wurth Verwaltungsgesellschaft mbH; *Int'l*, pg. 8504
ARVIG COMMUNICATIONS SYSTEMS—See Arvig Enterprises, Inc.; *U.S. Private*, pg. 344
ARVIG ENTERPRISES, INC.; *U.S. Private*, pg. 344
ARVINAS, INC.; *U.S. Public*, pg. 208
ARVIND ACCEL LIMITED—See Lalbhai Group; *Int'l*, pg. 4398
ARVIND & COMPANY SHIPPING AGENCIES LIMITED; *Int'l*, pg. 587
ARVIND ENVISOL LIMITED—See Arvind Fashions Ltd.; *Int'l*, pg. 587
ARVIND FASHIONS LTD.; *Int'l*, pg. 587
ARVIND INFRACON LLP—See Lalbhai Group; *Int'l*, pg. 4398
ARVIND INTERNATIONAL LTD.; *Int'l*, pg. 587
ARVIND LIFESTYLE BRANDS LIMITED—See Lalbhai Group; *Int'l*, pg. 4398
ARVIND LIMITED - DENIM DIVISION—See Lalbhai Group; *Int'l*, pg. 4398

ARVIND LIMITED - KHAKHI DIVISION—See Lalbhai Group; *Int'l*, pg. 4398
ARVIND LIMITED - KNITS DIVISION—See Lalbhai Group; *Int'l*, pg. 4398
ARVIND LIMITED - SHIRTING DIVISION—See Lalbhai Group; *Int'l*, pg. 4398
ARVIND LIMITED—See Lalbhai Group; *Int'l*, pg. 4398
ARVIND MAFATLAL GROUP; *Int'l*, pg. 587
ARVIND REMEDIES LTD; *Int'l*, pg. 588
ARVIND RETAIL LIMITED—See Lalbhai Group; *Int'l*, pg. 4398
ARVIND SMARTSPACES LIMITED—See Lalbhai Group; *Int'l*, pg. 4399
ARVIND WORLDWIDE INC.—See Lalbhai Group; *Int'l*, pg. 4399
ARVIN-EDISON WATER STORAGE DISTRICT; *U.S. Private*, pg. 345
ARVIN EUROPEAN HOLDINGS (UK) LIMITED—See Cummins Inc.; *U.S. Public*, pg. 608
ARVIN INTERNATIONAL HOLLAND B.V.—See Cummins Inc.; *U.S. Public*, pg. 608
ARVINMERITOR B.V.—See Cummins Inc.; *U.S. Public*, pg. 608
ARVINMERITOR CV AFTERMARKET GMBH—See Cummins Inc.; *U.S. Public*, pg. 608
ARVINMERITOR CVS (SHANGHAI) CO., LTD.—See Cummins Inc.; *U.S. Public*, pg. 608
ARVINMERITOR HEAVY VEHICLE SYSTEMS ESPANIA S.A.—See Cummins Inc.; *U.S. Public*, pg. 608
ARVINMERITOR LIGHT VEHICLE AFTERMARKET GROUP—See Cummins Inc.; *U.S. Public*, pg. 608
ARVINMERITOR LIGHT VEHICLE SYSTEMS-FRANCE—See Cummins Inc.; *U.S. Public*, pg. 608
ARVINMERITOR SWEDEN AB—See Cummins Inc.; *U.S. Public*, pg. 608
ARVIN MOTION CONTROL LIMITED—See Cummins Inc.; *U.S. Public*, pg. 608
ARVIN SANGO, INC.—See Sango Co., Ltd.; *Int'l*, pg. 6537
ARVIN SANGO, INC.—See Sango Co., Ltd.; *Int'l*, pg. 6537
ARVIXE, LLC; *U.S. Private*, pg. 345
ARVO COMMUNICATIONS, INC.; *U.S. Private*, pg. 345
ARVOG; *Int'l*, pg. 588
ARVOS GMBH - DUSSELDORF—See Triton Advisers Limited; *Int'l*, pg. 7928
ARVOS GMBH—See Triton Advisers Limited; *Int'l*, pg. 7928
ARVOS HOLDING GMBH—See Triton Advisers Limited; *Int'l*, pg. 7928
ARWA MINERAL WATER COMPANY LTD.—See Hayel Saeed Anam Group of Companies; *Int'l*, pg. 3290
ARWAY CORPORATION; *Int'l*, pg. 588
AR WILFLEY & SONS INC.; *U.S. Private*, pg. 306
ARWOOD MACHINE CORPORATION—See VulcanForms Inc.; *U.S. Private*, pg. 4416
ARXAN TECHNOLOGIES, INC.—See TPG Capital, L.P.; *U.S. Public*, pg. 2173
ARX AUTOMATIZACION DE FARMACIAS, S.L.U.—See Becton, Dickinson & Company; *U.S. Public*, pg. 288
ARX BVBA—See Becton, Dickinson & Company; *U.S. Public*, pg. 288
ARXCEO CORPORATION—See Japan Communications, Inc.; *Int'l*, pg. 3887
ARX EQUITY PARTNERS S.R.O.; *Int'l*, pg. 588
ARX GOLD CORPORATION; *Int'l*, pg. 588
ARX HOLDING CORP.—See The Progressive Corporation; *U.S. Public*, pg. 2124
ARX INC.—See DocuSign, Inc.; *U.S. Public*, pg. 672
ARX INSURANCE COMPANY—See Fairfax Financial Holdings Limited; *Int'l*, pg. 2605
ARX LIMITED—See Becton, Dickinson & Company; *U.S. Public*, pg. 288
ARX, LLC—See Adhesive Research, Inc.; *U.S. Private*, pg. 79
ARX SA—See Becton, Dickinson & Company; *U.S. Public*, pg. 288
ARX SAS—See Becton, Dickinson & Company; *U.S. Public*, pg. 288
ARYA ELECTRONICS IRAN CO.; *Int'l*, pg. 588
ARYA INSTRUMENT CO.—See Endress+Hauser (International) Holding AG; *Int'l*, pg. 2405
ARYAKA NETWORKS INC.; *U.S. Private*, pg. 345
ARYAKA NETWORKS INDIA PVT. LTD.—See Aryaka Networks Inc.; *U.S. Private*, pg. 345
ARYAMAN CAPITAL MARKETS LTD—See ARYAMAN FINANCIAL SERVICES LTD; *Int'l*, pg. 588
ARYAMAN FINANCIAL SERVICES LTD; *Int'l*, pg. 588
ARYAN INFRASTRUCTURE INVESTMENTS PVT. LTD.—See IRB Infrastructure Developers Ltd.; *Int'l*, pg. 3805
ARYAN SHARES & STOCK BROKERS LTD.; *Int'l*, pg. 588
ARYAN TOLL ROAD PVT. LTD.—See IRB Infrastructure Developers Ltd.; *Int'l*, pg. 3805
ARYA OFFSHORE SERVICES PVT. LTD.—See Sembcorp Industries Ltd.; *Int'l*, pg. 6703
ARYA OMNITALK WIRELESS SOLUTIONS PRIVATE LIMITED—See Arvind Fashions Ltd.; *Int'l*, pg. 587
ARYA RESOURCES LTD.; *Int'l*, pg. 588
ARYA SCIENCES ACQUISITION CORP.; *U.S. Private*, pg. 345
ARYAVAN ENTERPRISE LIMITED; *Int'l*, pg. 588
ARYLUX HUNGARY ELEKTROMECHANIKUS ALKATRESZGYARTO KFT—See Illinois Tool Works Inc.; *U.S. Public*, pg. 1101
ARYSTA AGROQUIMICOS Y FERTILZANTES URUGUAY SA—See UPL Limited; *Int'l*, pg. 8088
ARYSTA HEALTH AND NUTRITION SCIENCES CORPORATION—See UPL Limited; *Int'l*, pg. 8088
ARYSTA LIFESCIENCE ARGENTINA SA—See UPL Limited; *Int'l*, pg. 8088
ARYSTA LIFESCIENCE BENELUX SRL—See UPL Limited; *Int'l*, pg. 8088
ARYSTA LIFESCIENCE CENTROAMERICA SA—See UPL Limited; *Int'l*, pg. 8088
ARYSTA LIFESCIENCE CHILE SA—See UPL Limited; *Int'l*, pg. 8088
ARYSTA LIFESCIENCE COLOMBIA SA—See UPL Limited; *Int'l*, pg. 8088
ARYSTA LIFESCIENCE CORPORATION—See UPL Limited; *Int'l*, pg. 8088
ARYSTA LIFESCIENCE ESPANA SA—See UPL Limited; *Int'l*, pg. 8088
ARYSTA LIFESCIENCE EUROPE SARL—See UPL Limited; *Int'l*, pg. 8088
ARYSTA LIFESCIENCE FINECHEMICAL EUROPE GMBH—See UPL Limited; *Int'l*, pg. 8088
ARYSTA LIFESCIENCE FRANCE SAS—See UPL Limited; *Int'l*, pg. 8088
ARYSTA LIFESCIENCE HOLDINGS FRANCE SAS—See UPL Limited; *Int'l*, pg. 8088
ARYSTA LIFESCIENCE IBERIA SLU—See UPL Limited; *Int'l*, pg. 8088
ARYSTA LIFESCIENCE INC.—See UPL Limited; *Int'l*, pg. 8088
ARYSTA LIFESCIENCE INDIA LIMITED—See UPL Limited; *Int'l*, pg. 8088
ARYSTA LIFESCIENCE ITALIA S.R.L—See UPL Limited; *Int'l*, pg. 8088
ARYSTA LIFESCIENCE KENYA LTD—See UPL Limited; *Int'l*, pg. 8088
ARYSTA LIFESCIENCE MAGYARORSZAG KFT—See UPL Limited; *Int'l*, pg. 8088
ARYSTA LIFESCIENCE PAKISTAN (PVT) LTD—See UPL Limited; *Int'l*, pg. 8088
ARYSTA LIFESCIENCE POLSKA SP ZOO—See UPL Limited; *Int'l*, pg. 8088
ARYSTA LIFESCIENCE RUS LLC—See UPL Limited; *Int'l*, pg. 8088
ARYSTA LIFESCIENCE (SHANGHAI) CO LTD—See UPL Limited; *Int'l*, pg. 8088
ARYSTA LIFESCIENCE SLOVAKIA SRO—See UPL Limited; *Int'l*, pg. 8088
ARYSTA LIFESCIENCE SOUTH AFRICA (PTY) LTD—See UPL Limited; *Int'l*, pg. 8088
ARYSTA LIFESCIENCE UK LTD—See UPL Limited; *Int'l*, pg. 8088
ARYSTA LIFESCIENCE UKRAINE LLC—See UPL Limited; *Int'l*, pg. 8088
ARYSTA LIFESCIENCE VIETNAM CO LTD—See UPL Limited; *Int'l*, pg. 8088
ARYSTA LIFESCIENCE VOSTOK LLC—See UPL Limited; *Int'l*, pg. 8088
ARYT INDUSTRIES LTD.; *Int'l*, pg. 588
ARYZTA AG; *Int'l*, pg. 588
ARYZTA BAKERIES DEUTSCHLAND GMBH—See ARYZTA AG; *Int'l*, pg. 588
ARYZTA FOOD SOLUTIONS GMBH—See ARYZTA AG; *Int'l*, pg. 588
ARYZTA FOOD SOLUTIONS JAPAN CO., LTD.—See ARYZTA AG; *Int'l*, pg. 589
ARYZTA FOOD SOLUTIONS SCHWEIZ AG—See ARYZTA AG; *Int'l*, pg. 588
ARYZTA HOLDINGS ASIA PACIFIC BV—See ARYZTA AG; *Int'l*, pg. 588
ARYZTA LTD.—See ARYZTA AG; *Int'l*, pg. 588
ARYZTA POLSKA SP.Z O.O.—See ARYZTA AG; *Int'l*, pg. 588
ARZAN FINANCIAL GROUP FOR FINANCING & INVESTMENT K.S.P.C.; *Int'l*, pg. 589
ARZAN SECURITIES BROKERAGE CO. SAE—See Arzan Financial Group for Financing & Investment K.S.P.C.; *Int'l*, pg. 589
ARZAN WEALTH (DIFC) CO. LIMITED—See Arzan Financial Group for Financing & Investment K.S.P.C.; *Int'l*, pg. 589
AR ZINC S.A.—See Glencore plc; *Int'l*, pg. 2990
ARZNEIMITTEL PROSTRAKAN GMBH—See Kirin Holdings Company, Limited; *Int'l*, pg. 4189
ARZNEIWERK AG VIDA; *Int'l*, pg. 589
ARZON LIMITED; *Int'l*, pg. 589
ARZTPARTNER ALMEDA AG—See Munchener Ruckversicherungs AG; *Int'l*, pg. 5085
ARZUM ELEKTRIKLI EV ALETLERI SANAYI VE TICARET A.S.; *Int'l*, pg. 589
AS24 BELGIE N.V.—See TotalEnergies SE; *Int'l*, pg. 7835
AS24 ESPANOLA S.A.—See TotalEnergies SE; *Int'l*, pg. 7835
AS24 FUEL CARDS LIMITED—See TotalEnergies SE; *Int'l*, pg. 7835
AS24 POLSKA SP Z O.O.—See TotalEnergies SE; *Int'l*, pg. 7835
AS24—See TotalEnergies SE; *Int'l*, pg. 7835
.A.S.A. ABFALL SERVICE AG—See Fomento de Construcciones y Contratas, S.A.; *Int'l*, pg. 2722
.A.S.A. ABFALL SERVICE HALBENRAIN GMBH—See Fomento de Construcciones y Contratas, S.A.; *Int'l*, pg. 2722
.A.S.A. ABFALL SERVICE NEUNKIRCHEN GMBH—See Fomento de Construcciones y Contratas, S.A.; *Int'l*, pg. 2722
A.S.A. ABFALL SERVICE WIENER NEUSTADT GMBH—See Fomento de Construcciones y Contratas, S.A.; *Int'l*, pg. 2722
ASA ALEASING D.O.O.—See ASA Holding d.o.o.; *Int'l*, pg. 591
ASA APPLE INC.; *U.S. Private*, pg. 345
.A.S.A. AREAL SPOL. S.R.O—See Fomento de Construcciones y Contratas, S.A.; *Int'l*, pg. 2722
ASA AUTOMOTIVE SYSTEMS, LLC—See Constellation Software Inc.; *Int'l*, pg. 1773
ASA BANKA D.D. SARAJEVO; *Int'l*, pg. 591
ASA BANKA D.D.; *Int'l*, pg. 591
ASABIKIWAKADORI CO., LTD.—See Kobe Bussan Co., Ltd.; *Int'l*, pg. 4217
ASA CONS ROMANIA S.R.L.—See Bain Capital, LP; *U.S. Private*, pg. 438
ASADA SHOJI CO., LTD.—See Kumiai Chemical Industry Co., Ltd.; *Int'l*, pg. 4330
ASADA U CO., LTD.—See Chori Co., Ltd.; *Int'l*, pg. 1583
ASA ELECTRONICS LLC—See VOXX International Corporation; *U.S. Public*, pg. 2310
ASAEL FARR & SONS COMPANY; *U.S. Private*, pg. 345
ASA EPITOIPARI KFT.—See Bain Capital, LP; *U.S. Private*, pg. 438
A'SAFFA FOODS S.A.O.G; *Int'l*, pg. 19
ASAFFA LOGISTICS LLC—See A'Saffa Foods S.A.O.G; *Int'l*, pg. 19
ASAG AIR SYSTEM AG—See BKW AG; *Int'l*, pg. 1054
ASAGAMI CORPORATION; *Int'l*, pg. 592
ASA GOLD & PRECIOUS METALS LTD.; *U.S. Public*, pg. 209
ASAHI AGENCY CO., LTD.—See Kitano Construction Corp.; *Int'l*, pg. 4195
ASAHI AIRPORT SERVICE CO., LTD.—See The Asahi Shimbun Company; *Int'l*, pg. 7614
ASAHI AIR SUPPLY, INC.—See Mikuni Corporation; *Int'l*, pg. 4893
ASAHI/AMERICA, INC.—See Asahi Yukizai Corporation; *Int'l*, pg. 598
ASAHI ARCHITECTS OFFICE CO., LTD.—See Adeka Corporation; *Int'l*, pg. 142
ASAHI AREA ADVERTISING INC.—See Hakuhodo DY Holdings Incorporated; *Int'l*, pg. 3220
ASAHI AREA ADVERTISING WAKAYAMA INC.—See Hakuhodo DY Holdings Incorporated; *Int'l*, pg. 3220
ASAHI AREA AVERTISING NARA INC.—See Hakuhodo DY Holdings Incorporated; *Int'l*, pg. 3220
ASAHI ASIA PACIFIC PTE. LTD.—See Asahi Yukizai Corporation; *Int'l*, pg. 598
ASAHI AV EUROPE GMBH—See Asahi Yukizai Corporation; *Int'l*, pg. 598
ASAHI AV TRADING CO ,LTD—See Asahi Yukizai Corporation; *Int'l*, pg. 598
ASAHI AV VALVE (SHANGHAI) CO., LTD.—See Asahi Yukizai Corporation; *Int'l*, pg. 598
ASAHI BANK BUSINESS SERVICE CO., LTD.—See Resona Holdings, Inc.; *Int'l*, pg. 6298
ASAHI BANK CAREER SERVICE CO., LTD.—See Resona Holdings, Inc.; *Int'l*, pg. 6298
ASAHI BANK FINANCE SERVICE CO., LTD.—See Resona Holdings, Inc.; *Int'l*, pg. 6298
ASAHI BANK PROPERTY CO., LTD.—See Resona Holdings, Inc.; *Int'l*, pg. 6298
ASAHI BEER (CHINA) INVESTMENT CO., LTD.—See Asahi Group Holdings Ltd.; *Int'l*, pg. 593
ASAHI BEER COMMUNICATION CO., LTD.—See Pasona Group Inc.; *Int'l*, pg. 5753
ASAHI BEER TAIWAN CO., LTD.—See Asahi Group Holdings Ltd.; *Int'l*, pg. 593
ASAHI BEER U.S.A., INC.—See Asahi Group Holdings Ltd.; *Int'l*, pg. 593
ASAHI BEVERAGES (NZ) LTD.—See Asahi Group Holdings Ltd.; *Int'l*, pg. 593
ASAHI BEVERAGES PTY LTD—See Asahi Group Holdings Ltd.; *Int'l*, pg. 593
ASAHI BIOCYCLE CO. LTD.—See Asahi Group Holdings Ltd.; *Int'l*, pg. 593
ASAHI BREWERIES, LTD.—See Asahi Group Holdings Ltd.; *Int'l*, pg. 593
ASAHI BROADCASTING GROUP HOLDINGS CORPORATION; *Int'l*, pg. 592
ASAHI BROILER CO.—See Meiji Holdings Co., Ltd.; *Int'l*, pg. 4800
ASAHI BUILDING CO., LTD.—See The Asahi Shimbun Company; *Int'l*, pg. 7614

ASAHI BROADCASTING GROUP HOLDINGS CORPORATION

ASAHI CALPIS BEVERAGES CO., LTD.—See Asahi Group Holdings Ltd.; *Int'l*, pg. 593
ASAHI CALPIS WELLNESS CO., LTD.—See Asahi Group Holdings Ltd.; *Int'l*, pg. 593
ASAHI CARBON CO., LTD.—See Bridgestone Corporation; *Int'l*, pg. 1155
ASAHI CHEMICAL CO., LTD.—See Sumitomo Chemical Company, Limited; *Int'l*, pg. 7264
ASAHI CHEMICAL (H.K.) LTD.—See Asahi Kasei Corporation; *Int'l*, pg. 594
ASAHI CHEMICAL MANUFACTURING CO., LTD.—See OAT Agrio Co., Ltd.; *Int'l*, pg. 5507
ASAHI CO., LTD.; *Int'l*, pg. 592
ASAHI CONCRETE WORKS CO., LTD.; *Int'l*, pg. 592
ASAHI CREATE CO., LTD.—See Seino Holdings Co., Ltd.; *Int'l*, pg. 6690
ASAHI CULTURE CENTER K.K.—See The Asahi Shimbun Company; *Int'l*, pg. 7614
ASAHI DANBORU CO., LTD.—See Rengo Co., Ltd.; *Int'l*, pg. 6279
ASAHI-DENPA CO., LTD.—See Neturen Co., Ltd.; *Int'l*, pg. 5216
ASAHI DENSHI CO., LTD.—See Hokuriku Electric Industry Co., Ltd.; *Int'l*, pg. 3444
ASAHI DIAMOND AMERICA, INC.—See Asahi Diamond Industrial Co. Ltd.; *Int'l*, pg. 592
ASAHI DIAMOND DE MEXICO, S.A. DE C.V.—See Asahi Diamond Industrial Co. Ltd.; *Int'l*, pg. 592
ASAHI DIAMOND INDUSTRIAL AUSTRALIA PTY., LTD.—See Asahi Diamond Industrial Co. Ltd.; *Int'l*, pg. 592
ASAHI DIAMOND INDUSTRIAL CO. LTD. - CHIBA NO.2 FACTORY—See Asahi Diamond Industrial Co. Ltd.; *Int'l*, pg. 592
ASAHI DIAMOND INDUSTRIAL CO. LTD. - CHIBA TSURUMAI FACTORY—See Asahi Diamond Industrial Co. Ltd.; *Int'l*, pg. 592
ASAHI DIAMOND INDUSTRIAL CO. LTD. - MIE FACTORY—See Asahi Diamond Industrial Co. Ltd.; *Int'l*, pg. 592
ASAHI DIAMOND INDUSTRIAL CO. LTD.; *Int'l*, pg. 592
ASAHI DIAMOND INDUSTRIAL CO. LTD. - TAMAGAWA FACTORY—See Asahi Diamond Industrial Co. Ltd.; *Int'l*, pg. 592
ASAHI DIAMOND INDUSTRIAL EUROPE SAS—See Asahi Diamond Industrial Co. Ltd.; *Int'l*, pg. 592
ASAHI DIAMOND INDUSTRIAL GERMANY GMBH—See Asahi Diamond Industrial Co. Ltd.; *Int'l*, pg. 592
ASAHI DIAMOND INDUSTRIAL MALAYSIA SDN. BHD.—See Asahi Diamond Industrial Co. Ltd.; *Int'l*, pg. 592
ASAHI DIAMOND INDUSTRIAL SCANDINAVIA AB—See Asahi Diamond Industrial Co. Ltd.; *Int'l*, pg. 592
ASAHI DIAMOND (THAILAND) CO., LTD.—See Asahi Diamond Industrial Co. Ltd.; *Int'l*, pg. 592
ASAHI EITO CO., LTD.; *Int'l*, pg. 593
ASAHI ELECTRIC WORKS CO., LTD.—See The Furukawa Electric Co., Ltd.; *Int'l*, pg. 7644
ASAHI ELECTRONICS CO., LTD.—See Nippon Signal Co., Ltd.; *Int'l*, pg. 5333
ASAHI ENGINEERING (MALAYSIA) SDN. BHD.—See Asahi Kogyosha Co., Ltd.; *Int'l*, pg. 598
ASAHI ENTERPRISE CO., LTD.—See Seino Holdings Co., Ltd.; *Int'l*, pg. 6690
ASAHI FACILITIES INC.—See Takenaka Corporation; *Int'l*, pg. 7441
ASAHI FINANCE (AUSTRALIA) LTD.—See Resona Holdings, Inc.; *Int'l*, pg. 6298
ASAHI FOOD & HEALTHCARE CO., LTD.—See Asahi Group Holdings Ltd.; *Int'l*, pg. 593
ASAHI FORGE OF AMERICA CORP.—See NTN Corporation; *Int'l*, pg. 5483
ASAHI FR R&D CO., LTD.—See Parker Corporation; *Int'l*, pg. 5743
ASAHI GAKUSEI SHIMBUN PUBLISHING COMPANY K.K.—See The Asahi Shimbun Company; *Int'l*, pg. 7614
ASAHI GLASS CO., LTD. - AICHI PLANT (TAKETOYO)—See AGC Inc.; *Int'l*, pg. 203
ASAHI GLASS CO., LTD. - AICHI PLANT (TOYOTA)—See AGC Inc.; *Int'l*, pg. 203
ASAHI GLASS CO., LTD. - CHIBA PLANT—See AGC Inc.; *Int'l*, pg. 203
ASAHI GLASS CO., LTD. - KANSAI PLANT—See AGC Inc.; *Int'l*, pg. 203
ASAHI GLASS CO., LTD. - KASHIMA PLANT—See AGC Inc.; *Int'l*, pg. 203
ASAHI GLASS CO., LTD. - KEIHIN PLANT—See AGC Inc.; *Int'l*, pg. 203
ASAHI GLASS CO., LTD. - KITAKYUSHU PLANT—See AGC Inc.; *Int'l*, pg. 203
ASAHI GLASS CO., LTD. - SAGAMI PLANT—See AGC Inc.; *Int'l*, pg. 203
ASAHI GLASS CO., LTD. - TAKASAGO PLANT—See AGC Inc.; *Int'l*, pg. 203
ASAHI GLASS FINE TECHNO KOREA CO., LTD.—See Asahi Kasei Corporation; *Int'l*, pg. 594
ASAHI GROUP FOODS, LTD.—See Asahi Group Holdings Ltd.; *Int'l*, pg. 593

ASAHI GROUP HOLDINGS LTD.; *Int'l*, pg. 593
ASAHI G&S SDN. BHD.—See ARE Holdings, Inc.; *Int'l*, pg. 557
ASAHI INDIA GLASS, LTD. - AIS (AUTO) HARYANA WORKS.—See AGC Inc.; *Int'l*, pg. 204
ASAHI INDIA GLASS, LTD. - AIS (FLOAT) WORKS—See AGC Inc.; *Int'l*, pg. 204
ASAHI INDIA GLASS LTD.—See AGC Inc.; *Int'l*, pg. 203
ASAHI INDUSTRIES CO., LTD. - CHIBA PLANT—See Godo Steel, Ltd.; *Int'l*, pg. 3020
ASAHI INDUSTRIES CO., LTD. - KANSAI PLANT—See Godo Steel, Ltd.; *Int'l*, pg. 3020
ASAHI INDUSTRIES CO., LTD. - SAITAMA PLANT—See Godo Steel, Ltd.; *Int'l*, pg. 3020
ASAHI INDUSTRIES CO., LTD.—See Godo Steel, Ltd.; *Int'l*, pg. 3020
ASAHI INDUSTRIES LIMITED; *Int'l*, pg. 594
ASAHI INDUSTRY CO., LTD.—See Hisaka Works, Ltd.; *Int'l*, pg. 3406
ASAHI INFRASTRUCTURE & PROJECTS LIMITED; *Int'l*, pg. 594
ASAHI INTECC CO., LTD.; *Int'l*, pg. 594
ASAHI INTECC EUROPE B.V.—See Asahi Intecc Co., Ltd.; *Int'l*, pg. 594
ASAHI INTECC GMA CO., LTD.—See Asahi Intecc Co., Ltd.; *Int'l*, pg. 594
ASAHI INTECC HANOI CO., LTD.—See Asahi Intecc Co., Ltd.; *Int'l*, pg. 594
ASAHI INTECC J-SALES, INC.—See Asahi Intecc Co., Ltd.; *Int'l*, pg. 594
ASAHI INTECC LATIN PROMACAO DE VENDAS LTDA—See Asahi Intecc Co., Ltd.; *Int'l*, pg. 594
ASAHI INTECC LATIN PROMOCAO DE VENDAS E COMERCIO DE PRODUTOS CIRURGICOS LTDA.—See Asahi Intecc Co., Ltd.; *Int'l*, pg. 594
ASAHI INTECC SCIENTIFIC (BEIJING) CO., LTD.—See Asahi Intecc Co., Ltd.; *Int'l*, pg. 594
ASAHI INTECC THAILAND CO., LTD.—See Asahi Intecc Co., Ltd.; *Int'l*, pg. 594
ASAHI INTECC USA, INC.—See Asahi Intecc Co., Ltd.; *Int'l*, pg. 594
ASAHI INTELLIGENCE SERVICE CO.,LTD.; *Int'l*, pg. 594
ASAHI INTERNATIONAL, LTD.—See Asahi Group Holdings Ltd.; *Int'l*, pg. 593
ASAHI JINZAI SERVICE CO., LTD.—See Asahi Printing Co., Ltd.; *Int'l*, pg. 598
ASAHI KAGAKU KOGYO CO., LTD.—See Sumitomo Mitsui Trust Holdings, Inc.; *Int'l*, pg. 7296
ASAHI KAKO CO., LTD.—See Daiwabo Holdings Co., Ltd.; *Int'l*, pg. 1949
ASAHI KASEI ADVANCE CORP.—See Asahi Kasei Corporation; *Int'l*, pg. 595
ASAHI KASEI ADVANCE (SHANGHAI) CO., LTD.—See Asahi Kasei Corporation; *Int'l*, pg. 594
ASAHI KASEI ADVANCE THAILAND CO., LTD.—See Asahi Kasei Corporation; *Int'l*, pg. 595
ASAHI KASEI AMERICA, INC.—See Asahi Kasei Corporation; *Int'l*, pg. 595
ASAHI KASEI AMIDAS CO., LTD.—See Asahi Kasei Corporation; *Int'l*, pg. 595
ASAHI KASEI-BEIJING—See Asahi Kasei Corporation; *Int'l*, pg. 596
ASAHI KASEI BIOPROCESS EUROPE SA/NV—See Asahi Kasei Corporation; *Int'l*, pg. 595
ASAHI KASEI BIOPROCESS, INC.—See Asahi Kasei Corporation; *Int'l*, pg. 595
ASAHI KASEI BUSINESS MANAGEMENT (SHANGHAI) CO., LTD.—See Asahi Kasei Corporation; *Int'l*, pg. 595
ASAHI KASEI CHEMICALS CORPORATION—See Asahi Kasei Corporation; *Int'l*, pg. 595
ASAHI KASEI CHEMICALS KOREA CO., LTD.—See Asahi Kasei Corporation; *Int'l*, pg. 595
ASAHI KASEI (CHINA) CO., LTD.—See Asahi Kasei Corporation; *Int'l*, pg. 594
ASAHI KASEI CONSTRUCTION MATERIALS—See Asahi Kasei Corporation; *Int'l*, pg. 595
ASAHI KASEI CORPORATION; *Int'l*, pg. 594
ASAHI KASEI E-MATERIALS CORP.—See Asahi Kasei Corporation; *Int'l*, pg. 595
ASAHI KASEI EMD CORPORATION—See Asahi Kasei Corporation; *Int'l*, pg. 595
ASAHI KASEI EPOXY CO., LTD.—See Asahi Kasei Corporation; *Int'l*, pg. 595
ASAHI KASEI EUROPE GMBH—See Asahi Kasei Corporation; *Int'l*, pg. 595
ASAHI KASEI FIBERS (H.K.) LTD.—See Asahi Kasei Corporation; *Int'l*, pg. 595
ASAHI KASEI FIBERS ITALY SRL—See Asahi Kasei Corporation; *Int'l*, pg. 595
ASAHI KASEI FINECHEM CO., LTD.—See Asahi Kasei Corporation; *Int'l*, pg. 595
ASAHI KASEI GEOTECHNOLOGIES CO., LTD.—See Asahi Kasei Corporation; *Int'l*, pg. 595
ASAHI KASEI HOME PRODUCTS CORP.—See Asahi Kasei Corporation; *Int'l*, pg. 595
ASAHI KASEI HOMES CORP.—See Asahi Kasei Corporation; *Int'l*, pg. 595
ASAHI KASEI INDIA PVT. LTD.—See Asahi Kasei Corporation; *Int'l*, pg. 595

CORPORATE AFFILIATIONS

ASAHI KASEI MEDICAL CO., LTD.—See Asahi Kasei Corporation; *Int'l*, pg. 595
ASAHI KASEI MEDICAL EUROPE GMBH—See Asahi Kasei Corporation; *Int'l*, pg. 595
ASAHI KASEI MEDICAL EUROPE GMBH—See Asahi Kasei Corporation; *Int'l*, pg. 595
ASAHI KASEI MEDICAL (HANGZHOU) CO., LTD.—See Asahi Kasei Corporation; *Int'l*, pg. 595
ASAHI KASEI MEDICAL TRADING (KOREA) CO., LTD.—See Asahi Kasei Corporation; *Int'l*, pg. 595
ASAHI KASEI MICRODEVICES CORP.—See Asahi Kasei Corporation; *Int'l*, pg. 595
ASAHI KASEI MICRODEVICES EUROPE GMBH—See Asahi Kasei Corporation; *Int'l*, pg. 595
ASAHI KASEI MICRODEVICES EUROPE SAS—See Asahi Kasei Corporation; *Int'l*, pg. 595
ASAHI KASEI MICRODEVICES KOREA CORP.—See Asahi Kasei Corporation; *Int'l*, pg. 595
ASAHI KASEI MICRODEVICES (SHANGHAI) CO., LTD.—See Asahi Kasei Corporation; *Int'l*, pg. 595
ASAHI KASEI MICRODEVICES TAIWAN CORP.—See Asahi Kasei Corporation; *Int'l*, pg. 595
ASAHI KASEI MICROSYSTEMS CO., LTD.—See Asahi Kasei Corporation; *Int'l*, pg. 596
ASAHI KASEI MICROZA (HANGZHOU) CO., LTD.—See Asahi Kasei Corporation; *Int'l*, pg. 596
ASAHI KASEI MORTGAGE CORPORATION—See Asahi Kasei Corporation; *Int'l*, pg. 596
ASAHI KASEI PHARMA (BEIJING) CO., LTD.—See Asahi Kasei Corporation; *Int'l*, pg. 596
ASAHI KASEI PHARMA—See Asahi Kasei Corporation; *Int'l*, pg. 596
ASAHIKASEI PLASTICS (AMERICA) INC.—See Asahi Kasei Corporation; *Int'l*, pg. 596
ASAHI KASEI PLASTICS (GUANGZHOU) CO., LTD.—See Asahi Kasei Corporation; *Int'l*, pg. 596
ASAHI KASEI PLASTICS (HONG KONG) CO., LTD.—See Asahi Kasei Corporation; *Int'l*, pg. 596
ASAHI KASEI PLASTICS LTD.—See Asahi Kasei Corporation; *Int'l*, pg. 595
ASAHI KASEI PLASTICS NORTH AMERICA, INC.—See Asahi Kasei Corporation; *Int'l*, pg. 595
ASAHIKASEI PLASTICS (SHANGHAI) CO., LTD.—See Asahi Kasei Corporation; *Int'l*, pg. 596
ASAHI KASEI PLASTICS SINGAPORE PTE. LTD.—See Asahi Kasei Corporation; *Int'l*, pg. 596
ASAHIKASEI PLASTICS (THAILAND) CO., LTD.—See Asahi Kasei Corporation; *Int'l*, pg. 596
ASAHI KASEI PLASTICS VIETNAM CO., LTD.—See Asahi Kasei Corporation; *Int'l*, pg. 596
ASAHI KASEI REFORM CO., LTD.—See Asahi Kasei Corporation; *Int'l*, pg. 596
ASAHI KASEI-SHANGHAI—See Asahi Kasei Corporation; *Int'l*, pg. 596
ASAHI KASEI SPANDEX AMERICA, INC.—See Asahi Kasei Corporation; *Int'l*, pg. 596
ASAHI KASEI SPANDEX EUROPE GMBH—See Asahi Kasei Corporation; *Int'l*, pg. 596
ASAHI KASEI SYNTHETIC RUBBER SINGAPORE PTE. LTD.—See Asahi Kasei Corporation; *Int'l*, pg. 596
ASAHI KASEI TECHNOPLUS CO., LTD.—See Asahi Kasei Corporation; *Int'l*, pg. 596
ASAHI KASEI TECHNOSYSTEM CORP.—See Asahi Kasei Corporation; *Int'l*, pg. 596
ASAHI KASEI TRADING CO., LTD.—See Asahi Kasei Corporation; *Int'l*, pg. 596
ASAHI KASEI ZOLL MEDICAL CORP.—See Asahi Kasei Corporation; *Int'l*, pg. 596
ASAHI KISEN KAISHA, LTD.—See Kawasaki Kisen Kaisha, Ltd.; *Int'l*, pg. 4098
ASAHI KOGYOSHA CO., LTD. - EQUIPMENT DIVISION—See Asahi Kogyosha Co., Ltd.; *Int'l*, pg. 598
ASAHI KOGYOSHA CO., LTD.; *Int'l*, pg. 598
ASAHI KOHATSU CORPORATION—See K. Wah International Holdings Limited; *Int'l*, pg. 4043
ASAHIKOUSEKI CO., LTD.—See Daiei Kankyo Co., Ltd.; *Int'l*, pg. 1924
ASAHI L&C CORP.—See Hurxley Corporation; *Int'l*, pg. 3538
ASAHI MANUFACTURING CO., LTD.—See Denso Corporation; *Int'l*, pg. 2028
ASAHIMATSU FOODS CO., LTD.; *Int'l*, pg. 599
ASAHI METALS (HONG KONG) LTD.—See Singapore Asahi Chemical & Solder Industries Pte. Ltd.; *Int'l*, pg. 6939
ASAHI METALS (SHENZHEN) LTD.—See Singapore Asahi Chemical & Solder Industries Pte. Ltd.; *Int'l*, pg. 6939
ASAHI MODI MATERIALS PVT., LTD.—See Asahi Yukizai Corporation; *Int'l*, pg. 598
ASAHI MOTOR CO., LTD.—See Tobu Railway Co., Ltd.; *Int'l*, pg. 7771
ASAHI MOTOR CORPORATION—See Tobu Railway Co., Ltd.; *Int'l*, pg. 7771
ASAHI MUTUAL LIFE INSURANCE COMPANY—See Tokio Marine Holdings, Inc.; *Int'l*, pg. 7782
ASAHI NET, INC.; *Int'l*, pg. 598
ASAHI NEW TRANSPORT DEVELOPMENT CO., LTD.—See SBS Holdings Inc.; *Int'l*, pg. 6607

COMPANY NAME INDEX

ASAHI ORGANIC CHEMICALS INDUSTRY CO., LTD. - AICHI PLANT—See Asahi Yukizai Corporation; *Int'l*, pg. 598
ASAHI ORGANIC CHEMICALS INDUSTRY CO., LTD. - HIROSIMA PLANT—See Asahi Yukizai Corporation; *Int'l*, pg. 598
ASAHI ORGANIC CHEMICALS (NANTONG) CO., LTD.—See Asahi Yukizai Corporation; *Int'l*, pg. 598
ASAHI ORGANIC CHEMICALS TRADING (SHANGHAI) CO., LTD.—See Asahi Yukizai Corporation; *Int'l*, pg. 598
ASAHI ORIKOMI INC.—See The Asahi Shimbun Company; *Int'l*, pg. 7614
ASAHI ORIKOMI OSAKA INC.—See The Asahi Shimbun Company; *Int'l*, pg. 7614
ASAHIOZU CORPORATION; *Int'l*, pg. 599
ASAHI PD GLASS KOREA CO., LTD.—See AGC Inc.; *Int'l*, pg. 204
ASAHIPEN CORPORATION; *Int'l*, pg. 599
ASAHI PHOTOPRODUCTS EUROPE N.V./S.A.—See Asahi Kasei Corporation; *Int'l*, pg. 595
ASAHI PHOTOPRODUCTS (UK) LTD.—See Asahi Kasei Corporation; *Int'l*, pg. 596
ASAHI PRETEC CORPORATION—See ARE Holdings, Inc.; *Int'l*, pg. 557
ASAHI PRETEC KOREA CO., LTD.—See ARE Holdings, Inc.; *Int'l*, pg. 557
ASAHI PRINTING BUSINESS SUPPORT CO., LTD.—See Asahi Printing Co., Ltd.; *Int'l*, pg. 598
ASAHI PRINTING CO., LTD.; *Int'l*, pg. 598
ASAHI PROCESSING CO., LTD.—See Daiwabo Holdings Co., Ltd.; *Int'l*, pg. 1949
ASAHI REFINING CANADA LTD.—See ARE Holdings, Inc.; *Int'l*, pg. 557
ASAHI REFINING FLORIDA, LLC—See ARE Holdings, Inc.; *Int'l*, pg. 557
ASAHI REFINING USA INC.—See ARE Holdings, Inc.; *Int'l*, pg. 557
ASAHI RESEARCH CENTER CO., LTD.—See Asahi Kasei Corporation; *Int'l*, pg. 596
ASAHI RUBBER INC. - FUKUSHIMA FACTORY—See Parker Corporation; *Int'l*, pg. 5743
ASAHI RUBBER INC. - SHIRAKAWA FACTORY—See Parker Corporation; *Int'l*, pg. 5743
ASAHI RUBBER INC.—See Parker Corporation; *Int'l*, pg. 5743
ASAHI SANGYO CO.—See Ryobi Limited; *Int'l*, pg. 6440
ASAHI-SCHWEBEL (TAIWAN) CO., LTD.—See Asahi Kasei Corporation; *Int'l*, pg. 596
ASAHI SECURITY CO., LTD.—See Toyota Industries Corporation; *Int'l*, pg. 7866
ASAHI SEIKI CO., LTD.—See NSK Ltd.; *Int'l*, pg. 5478
ASAHI-SEIKI MANUFACTURING CO., LTD MACHINERY DIVISION—See Asahi-Seiki Manufacturing Co., Ltd.; *Int'l*, pg. 599
ASAHI-SEIKI MANUFACTURING CO., LTD. PRECISION ENGINEERING DIVISION—See Asahi-Seiki Manufacturing Co., Ltd.; *Int'l*, pg. 599
ASAHI-SEIKI MANUFACTURING CO., LTD.; *Int'l*, pg. 599
ASAHI SEIREN CO., LTD.; *Int'l*, pg. 598
ASAHI SEISAKUSHO CO., LTD.—See Ferrotec Holdings Corporation; *Int'l*, pg. 2643
ASAHI SHIKO CO., LTD.—See Rengo Co., Ltd.; *Int'l*, pg. 6279
ASAHI SHIMBUN AMERICA, INC.—See The Asahi Shimbun Company; *Int'l*, pg. 7614
ASAHI SHIMBUN AMERICA, INC.—See The Asahi Shimbun Company; *Int'l*, pg. 7614
THE ASAHI SHIMBUN COMPANY; *Int'l*, pg. 7614
ASAHI SHIMBUN INTERNATIONAL LTD.—See The Asahi Shimbun Company; *Int'l*, pg. 7614
ASAHI SKB CO., LTD.—See Asahi Kasei Corporation; *Int'l*, pg. 596
ASAHI SOFT DRINKS CO., LTD.—See Asahi Group Holdings Ltd.; *Int'l*, pg. 593
ASAHI SOLDER TECHNOLOGY (BEIJING) CO. LTD.—See Singapore Asahi Chemical & Solder Industries Pte. Ltd.; *Int'l*, pg. 6939
ASAHI SOLDER TECHNOLOGY (THAILAND) CO. LTD—See Singapore Asahi Chemical & Solder Industries Pte. Ltd.; *Int'l*, pg. 6939
ASAHI SOLDER TECHNOLOGY (WUXI) CO. LTD.—See Singapore Asahi Chemical & Solder Industries Pte. Ltd.; *Int'l*, pg. 6939
ASAHI SONGWON COLORS LTD.; *Int'l*, pg. 598
ASAHI SUISAN CO., LTD.—See Kuze Co., Ltd.; *Int'l*, pg. 4348
ASAHI SUNAC MACHINERY SERVICE (THAILAND) CO., LTD.—See Seika Corporation; *Int'l*, pg. 6685
ASAHI SURGICAL ROBOTICS CO., LTD.—See Asahi Intecc Co., Ltd.; *Int'l*, pg. 594
ASAHI SYNCHROTECH CO., LTD.—See Chubu Electric Power Co., Inc.; *Int'l*, pg. 1593
ASAHI TANKER CO., LTD.—See Mitsui O.S.K. Lines, Ltd.; *Int'l*, pg. 4988
ASAHI TATEMONO KANRI K.K.—See The Asahi Shimbun Company; *Int'l*, pg. 7614
ASAHI TEC ALUMINIUM (THAILAND) COMPANY LIMITED—See Topy Industries, Ltd.; *Int'l*, pg. 7821
ASAHI TEC CORP., LTD.—See Topy Industries, Ltd.; *Int'l*, pg. 7821
ASAHI TENNANTS COLOR PRIVATE LIMITED—See Asahi Songwon Colors Ltd.; *Int'l*, pg. 598
ASAHI TOSTEM EXTERIOR BUILDING MATERIALS CO., LTD.—See LIXIL Group Corporation; *Int'l*, pg. 4533
ASAHI UK LTD.—See Asahi Group Holdings Ltd.; *Int'l*, pg. 593
ASAHI UNYU KAISHA, LTD.—See Nippon Yusen Kabushiki Kaisha; *Int'l*, pg. 5357
ASAHI WELLNESS FOODS CO., LTD.—See Gourmet Kineya Co., Ltd.; *Int'l*, pg. 3044
ASAHI YUKI HANBAI NISHI-NIHON K.K.—See Asahi Yukizai Corporation; *Int'l*, pg. 598
ASAHI YUKIZAI CORPORATION; *Int'l*, pg. 598
ASAHI YUKIZAI MEXICO S.A. DE C.V.—See Asahi Yukizai Corporation; *Int'l*, pg. 598
A.S.A. HODMEZOVASARHELY KOZTLSZTASAGL KFT—See Fomento de Construcciones y Contratas, S.A.; *Int'l*, pg. 2722
ASA HOLDING D.O.O.; *Int'l*, pg. 591
ASA INTERNATIONAL GROUP PLC; *Int'l*, pg. 591
ASA INTERNATIONAL INDIA MICROFINANCE LIMITED—See ASA International Group plc; *Int'l*, pg. 591
ASA INTERNATIONAL LTD.; *U.S. Private*, pg. 345
ASAIS S.A.S.—See Itron, Inc.; *U.S. Public*, pg. 1175
ASA ITALIA SARL—See ASA San Marino S.p.A.; *Int'l*, pg. 592
ASA JOINT STOCK COMPANY; *Int'l*, pg. 592
ASAKA INDUSTRIAL CO., LTD.; *Int'l*, pg. 599
ASAKA KOUUN CO., LTD.—See Asaka Riken Co., Ltd.; *Int'l*, pg. 599
ASAKA MISONO UTILITY SERVICES CORPORATION—See Hitachi, Ltd.; *Int'l*, pg. 3412
ASAKA RIKEN CO., LTD. - FUKUYAMA PLANT—See Asaka Riken Co., Ltd.; *Int'l*, pg. 599
ASAKA RIKEN CO., LTD. - IWAKI PLANT—See Asaka Riken Co., Ltd.; *Int'l*, pg. 599
ASAKA RIKEN CO., LTD.; *Int'l*, pg. 599
ASAKAWA LENS WORKS CO., LTD.—See CHINO Corporation; *Int'l*, pg. 1570
ASAKUMA CO., LTD.; *Int'l*, pg. 599
ASAKUSA HAM CO., LTD.—See Itoham Yonekyu Holdings Inc.; *Int'l*, pg. 3842
A/S ALDARIS—See Carlsberg A/S; *Int'l*, pg. 1339
AS A. LE COQ—See Olvi Oyj; *Int'l*, pg. 5554
ASALEO CARE LIMITED—See Essity Aktiebolag; *Int'l*, pg. 2516
ASALEO CARE LIMITED—See Essity Aktiebolag; *Int'l*, pg. 2516
AS ALL MEDIA EESTI—See Providence Equity Partners L.L.C.; *U.S. Private*, pg. 3291
ASAMA COLDWATER MFG.—See Honda Motor Co., Ltd.; *Int'l*, pg. 3460
ASAMAGIKEN CO., LTD. - MISATO PLANT—See Sumitomo Corporation; *Int'l*, pg. 7268
ASAMA GIKEN CO., LTD.—See Sumitomo Corporation; *Int'l*, pg. 7268
ASA MARKETING; *U.S. Private*, pg. 345
ASAMA; *U.S. Private*, pg. 345
ASAM BETRIEBS-GMBH—See Stroer SE & Co. KGaA; *Int'l*, pg. 7241
AS AMBULANCES SERVICES SA—See AEVIS VICTORIA SA; *Int'l*, pg. 183
ASAMER BAUSTOFFE AG; *Int'l*, pg. 599
AS AMERICA, INC.—See Sun Capital Partners, Inc.; *U.S. Private*, pg. 3858
ASA MICROFINANCE (TANZANIA) LTD.—See ASA International Group plc; *Int'l*, pg. 591
ASA MICROFINANCE (UGANDA) LIMITED—See ASA International Group plc; *Int'l*, pg. 592
ASAM RESOURCES SA (PROPRIETARY) LIMITED—See Firestone Diamonds plc; *Int'l*, pg. 2679
ASA MULTIPLATE SDN BHD—See Advanced Systems Automation Limited; *Int'l*, pg. 162
ASANA BIOSCIENCES, LLC—See Erasca, Inc.; *U.S. Public*, pg. 792
ASANA, INC.; *U.S. Public*, pg. 209
ASANE BYGGMESTERFORRETNING AS—See AF Gruppen ASA; *Int'l*, pg. 184
ASANGHA REALTY COMPANY LIMITED—See Raimon Land Public Company Limited; *Int'l*, pg. 6189
AS ANNE SOOJUS—See Fortum Oyj; *Int'l*, pg. 2740
ASANO CONCRETE CO., LTD.—See Taiheiyo Cement Corporation; *Int'l*, pg. 7411
ASANO LABORATORIES CO., LTD.—See Daiichi Jitsugyo Co. Ltd.; *Int'l*, pg. 1927
ASANO TAISEIKISO ENGINEERING CO., LTD.—See Oriental Consultants Holdings Company Limited; *Int'l*, pg. 5623
ASAN SUNGWOO HITECH CO., LTD.—See Sungwoo Hitech Co., Ltd.; *Int'l*, pg. 7315
ASAN TECHNO VALLEY CO., LTD.—See Hanwha Group; *Int'l*, pg. 3264
ASANTE GOLD CORPORATION; *Int'l*, pg. 599
ASANTE INCORPORATED; *Int'l*, pg. 599
ASANTE TECHNOLOGIES, INC.; *U.S. Private*, pg. 345

ASANUMA CONSTRUCTION LTD.—See Asanuma Corporation; *Int'l*, pg. 599
ASANUMA CORPORATION - PRECAST CONCRETE PLANT—See Asanuma Corporation; *Int'l*, pg. 599
ASANUMA CORPORATION; *Int'l*, pg. 599
ASAOKA SPICE K.K.—See House Foods Group Inc.; *Int'l*, pg. 3490
ASA PAKISTAN LIMITED—See ASA International Group plc; *Int'l*, pg. 592
ASAP EXPEDITING & LOGISTICS, LLC—See Littlejohn & Co., LLC; *U.S. Private*, pg. 2470
ASAP, INC.—See Grossman Marketing Group; *U.S. Private*, pg. 1792
ASAP INDUSTRIAL SUPPLY, INC.—See Winsupply, Inc.; *U.S. Private*, pg. 4544
A.S.A.P. INDUSTRIES MANUFACTURING, LLC—See Boyne Capital Management, LLC; *U.S. Private*, pg. 628
ASAP PRINTING CORP—See 4OVER, Inc.; *U.S. Private*, pg. 15
ASAP SDN. BHD.—See Aldrich Resources Bhd; *Int'l*, pg. 305
ASAP SOLUTIONS GROUP, LLC; *U.S. Private*, pg. 345
ASA PSS D.O.O—See ASA Holding d.o.o.; *Int'l*, pg. 591
A.S.A.P. SUPPLIES LIMITED—See LKQ Corporation; *U.S. Public*, pg. 1333
ASAP TOWING & STORAGE COMPANY; *U.S. Private*, pg. 345
A S ARBURY & SONS, INC.—See Hellman & Friedman LLC; *U.S. Private*, pg. 1908
AS ARCHIVU SERVISS—See Iron Mountain Incorporated; *U.S. Public*, pg. 1172
ASARCO INCORPORATED—See Grupo Mexico, S.A.B. de C.V.; *Int'l*, pg. 3132
ASA RESOURCE GROUP PLC; *Int'l*, pg. 592
ASARFI HOSPITAL LIMITED; *Int'l*, pg. 599
ASARINA PHARMA AB; *Int'l*, pg. 599
ASA SAFETY SUPPLY—See Trivest Partners, LP; *U.S. Private*, pg. 4240
ASA SAN MARINO S.P.A.; *Int'l*, pg. 592
ASA SAVINGS & LOANS LIMITED—See ASA International Group plc; *Int'l*, pg. 592
ASAS CAPITAL LTD; *Int'l*, pg. 599
ASAS DUNIA BERHAD; *Int'l*, pg. 599
ASAS MUTIARA SDN. BHD.—See Asas Dunia Berhad; *Int'l*, pg. 599
ASA SPA—See Hera S.p.A.; *Int'l*, pg. 3356
ASAS REAL ESTATE COMPANY—See Sharjah Islamic Bank PJSC; *Int'l*, pg. 6790
ASA SRL—See El.En. S.p.A.; *Int'l*, pg. 2341
ASA STEEL (M) SDN. BHD.—See Leon Fuat Berhad; *Int'l*, pg. 4457
ASATSU CENTURY (SHANGHAI) ADVERTISING CO.,LTD.—See Bain Capital, LP; *U.S. Private*, pg. 428
ASATSU-DK MALAYSIA SDN. BHD.—See Bain Capital, LP; *U.S. Private*, pg. 428
ASATSU-DK SINGAPORE PTE. LTD.—See Bain Capital, LP; *U.S. Private*, pg. 428
ASATSU-DK VIETNAM INC.—See Bain Capital, LP; *U.S. Private*, pg. 428
ASATSU (THAILAND) CO., LTD.—See Bain Capital, LP; *U.S. Private*, pg. 428
AS AUDIO-SERVICE GESELLSCHAFT MIT BESCHRANKTER HAFTUNG—See Siemens Aktiengesellschaft; *Int'l*, pg. 6886
AS AUFZUGE AG—See Schindler Holding AG; *Int'l*, pg. 6618
ASAVIE TECHNOLOGIES LIMITED—See Akamai Technologies, Inc.; *U.S. Public*, pg. 69
ASAVIE UK LIMITED—See Akamai Technologies, Inc.; *U.S. Public*, pg. 69
ASAX CO., LTD.; *Int'l*, pg. 599
AS BALTIKA—See KJK Capital Oy; *Int'l*, pg. 4197
ASB BANK LIMITED—See Commonwealth Bank of Australia; *Int'l*, pg. 1719
ASB-BEBIDAS E ALIMENTOS LTDA—See Nestle S.A.; *Int'l*, pg. 5202
ASB CAPITAL MANAGEMENT, LLC; *U.S. Private*, pg. 345
ASB CONSULT LLC—See Belarusbank; *Int'l*, pg. 963
ASB GROUP INVESTMENTS LIMITED—See Commonwealth Bank of Australia; *Int'l*, pg. 1719
ASB HAWAII, INC.—See Hawaiian Electric Industries, Inc.; *U.S. Public*, pg. 989
ASBI JOINT STOCK COMPANY; *Int'l*, pg. 600
ASB INTERNATIONAL PVT. LTD.—See NISSEI ASB MACHINE CO., LTD.; *Int'l*, pg. 5370
ASBIS BALTICS SIA—See ASBISc Enterprises Plc; *Int'l*, pg. 600
ASBIS-BALTIK AS—See ASBISc Enterprises Plc; *Int'l*, pg. 600
ASBIS BULGARIA LIMITED—See ASBISc Enterprises Plc; *Int'l*, pg. 600
ASBIS CA LLC—See ASBISc Enterprises Plc; *Int'l*, pg. 600
ASBISC-CR D.O.O.—See ASBISc Enterprises Plc; *Int'l*, pg. 600
ASBISC ENTERPRISES PLC; *Int'l*, pg. 600
ASBIS CR D.O.O.—See ASBISc Enterprises Plc; *Int'l*, pg. 600

ASBIS CZ, SPOL. S R.O.—See ASBISc Enterprises Plc; *Int'l*, pg. 600
ASBIS D.O.O.—See ASBISc Enterprises Plc; *Int'l*, pg. 600
ASBIS D.O.O.—See ASBISc Enterprises Plc; *Int'l*, pg. 600
ASBIS EUROPE BV—See ASBISc Enterprises Plc; *Int'l*, pg. 600
ASBIS HELLAS SINGLE MEMBER S.A.—See ASBISc Enterprises Plc; *Int'l*, pg. 600
ASBIS HUNGARY COMMERCIAL LTD—See ASBISc Enterprises Plc; *Int'l*, pg. 600
ASBIS IT SOLUTIONS HUNGARY KFT.—See ASBISc Enterprises Plc; *Int'l*, pg. 600
ASBIS KAZAKHSTAN LLP—See ASBISc Enterprises Plc; *Int'l*, pg. 600
ASBIS KYPROS LTD—See ASBISc Enterprises Plc; *Int'l*, pg. 600
ASBIS LTD.—See ASBISc Enterprises Plc; *Int'l*, pg. 600
ASBIS LV SIA—See ASBISc Enterprises Plc; *Int'l*, pg. 600
ASBIS ME FZE—See ASBISc Enterprises Plc; *Int'l*, pg. 600
ASBIS MIDDLE EAST FZE—See ASBISc Enterprises Plc; *Int'l*, pg. 600
ASBIS PL SP.Z O.O.—See ASBISc Enterprises Plc; *Int'l*, pg. 600
ASBIS POLAND SP. Z O.O.—See ASBISc Enterprises Plc; *Int'l*, pg. 600
ASBIS ROMANIA S.R.L.—See ASBISc Enterprises Plc; *Int'l*, pg. 600
ASBIS SK SP.L SR.O—See ASBISc Enterprises Plc; *Int'l*, pg. 600
ASBIS SLOVENIA D.O.O.—See ASBISc Enterprises Plc; *Int'l*, pg. 600
ASBIS TR BILGISAYAR LIMITED SIRKETI—See ASBISc Enterprises Plc; *Int'l*, pg. 600
ASBIS UKRAINE LTD.—See ASBISc Enterprises Plc; *Int'l*, pg. 600
ASBIS VILNIUS UAB—See ASBISc Enterprises Plc; *Int'l*, pg. 600
ASB LEASING LLC—See Belarusbank; *Int'l*, pg. 963
A&S BMW MOTORCYCLES; *U.S. Private*, pg. 21
AS BOMINFLOT ESTONIA—See Marquard & Bahls AG; *Int'l*, pg. 4699
ASB PTE (THAILAND) CO., LTD.—See NISSEI ASB MACHINE CO., LTD.; *Int'l*, pg. 5370
AS BRAKE SYSTEMS, INC.—See AISIN Corporation; *Int'l*, pg. 252
A.S. BRYDEN & SONS (BARBADOS) LTD.—See ANSA McAL Limited; *Int'l*, pg. 476
A/S BRYGGERIET VESTFYEN—See Olvi Oyj; *Int'l*, pg. 5554
ASB SANATORIY SOLNECHNY UE—See Belarusbank; *Int'l*, pg. 963
ASB SECURITIES LIMITED—See Commonwealth Bank of Australia; *Int'l*, pg. 1719
A&S BUILDING SYSTEMS, INC.—See Clayton, Dubilier & Rice, LLC; *U.S. Private*, pg. 920
ASBURY ATLANTA AU L.L.C.—See Asbury Automotive Group, Inc.; *U.S. Public*, pg. 209
ASBURY ATLANTA HON LLC—See Asbury Automotive Group, Inc.; *U.S. Public*, pg. 209
ASBURY ATLANTA LEX LLC—See Asbury Automotive Group, Inc.; *U.S. Public*, pg. 209
ASBURY ATLANTA NIS LLC—See Asbury Automotive Group, Inc.; *U.S. Public*, pg. 210
ASBURY ATLANTA TOY 2 L.L.C.—See Asbury Automotive Group, Inc.; *U.S. Public*, pg. 209
ASBURY ATLANTA TOY LLC—See Asbury Automotive Group, Inc.; *U.S. Public*, pg. 210
ASBURY AUTOMOTIVE GROUP, INC.; *U.S. Public*, pg. 209
ASBURY AUTOMOTIVE JACKSONVILLE, L.P.—See Asbury Automotive Group, Inc.; *U.S. Public*, pg. 209
ASBURY CARBONS, INC. - GRAPHITOS MEXICANOS DE ASBURY DIVISION—See Great Mill Rock LLC; *U.S. Private*, pg. 1765
ASBURY CARBONS INC.—See Great Mill Rock LLC; *U.S. Private*, pg. 1765
ASBURY CARBONS, INC.—See Great Mill Rock LLC; *U.S. Private*, pg. 1765
ASBURY CARBONS, INC. - SOUTHWESTERN GRAPHITE DIVISION—See Great Mill Rock LLC; *U.S. Private*, pg. 1765
ASBURY COMMUNITIES, INC.; *U.S. Private*, pg. 345
ASBURY EQUIPMENT—See Great Mill Rock LLC; *U.S. Private*, pg. 1765
ASBURY FT. WORTH FORD, L.L.C.—See Asbury Automotive Group, Inc.; *U.S. Public*, pg. 209
ASBURY GRAPHITE INC. OF CALIFORNIA—See Great Mill Rock LLC; *U.S. Private*, pg. 1765
ASBURY GRAPHITE MILLS, INC. - ASBURY PLANT—See Great Mill Rock LLC; *U.S. Private*, pg. 1766
ASBURY GRAPHITE MILLS, INC. - KITTANNING PLANT—See Great Mill Rock LLC; *U.S. Private*, pg. 1766
ASBURY GRAPHITE MILLS, INC.—See Great Mill Rock LLC; *U.S. Private*, pg. 1766
ASBURY GRAPHITE—See Great Mill Rock LLC; *U.S. Private*, pg. 1765

ASBURY JAX FORD, LLC—See Asbury Automotive Group, Inc.; *U.S. Public*, pg. 209
ASBURY LOUISIANA, INC.—See Great Mill Rock LLC; *U.S. Private*, pg. 1766
ASBURY PARK PRESS—See Gannett Co., Inc.; *U.S. Public*, pg. 897
ASBURY PARTNERS, LLC—See Safehold Inc.; *U.S. Public*, pg. 1834
ASBURY WILKINSON, INC. - BURLINGTON PLANT—See Great Mill Rock LLC; *U.S. Private*, pg. 1766
ASBURY WILKINSON, INC.—See Great Mill Rock LLC; *U.S. Private*, pg. 1766
AS BYGGFORM—See Byggma ASA; *Int'l*, pg. 1235
ASCADE MIDDLE EAST FZ-LLC—See CSG Systems International, Inc.; *U.S. Public*, pg. 601
ASCALON CAPITAL MANAGERS LIMITED—See Generation Development Group; *Int'l*, pg. 2920
AS CAMBREX TALLINN—See Permira Advisers LLP; *Int'l*, pg. 5803
ASC AMERICAS L.P.—See ASC telecom AG; *Int'l*, pg. 600
AS CAPITAL, INC.; *U.S. Private*, pg. 345
AS. CA. S.P.A.—See Cremonini S.p.A.; *Int'l*, pg. 1838
ASCC, INC.; *U.S. Private*, pg. 346
ASC COMMUNICATIONS, LLC; *U.S. Private*, pg. 345
ASC CONSTRUCTION EQUIPMENT USA, INC.—See AB Volvo; *Int'l*, pg. 43
ASCELIA PHARMA AB; *Int'l*, pg. 601
ASCELIA PHARMA INC.—See Ascelia Pharma AB; *Int'l*, pg. 601
ASCENA GLOBAL SOURCING HONG KONG LIMITED—See Mahwah Bergen Retail Group, Inc.; *U.S. Private*, pg. 2550
ASCENCIA INVESTMENT MANAGEMENT LIMITED—See Frenkel Topping Group plc; *Int'l*, pg. 2773
ASCENCIA LIMITED; *Int'l*, pg. 601
ASCENCIO S.A.; *Int'l*, pg. 601
ASCENDANT COMPLIANCE MANAGEMENT; *U.S. Private*, pg. 346
ASCENDANT RESOURCES INC.; *Int'l*, pg. 601
ASCENDAS HOSPITALITY TRUST; *Int'l*, pg. 601
ASCEND CLINICAL LLC—See Eurofins Scientific S.E.; *Int'l*, pg. 2535
ASCEND DVPT HWD, LLC—See Macquarie Group Limited; *Int'l*, pg. 4627
ASCENDENT CAPITAL PARTNERS (ASIA) LIMITED; *Int'l*, pg. 601
ASCEND FUNDRAISING SOLUTIONS—See Orange Capital Ventures GP, LLC; *U.S. Private*, pg. 3036
ASCEND GENE AND CELL THERAPIES GMBH; *Int'l*, pg. 601
ASCEND GMBH—See Alkem Laboratories Ltd.; *Int'l*, pg. 330
ASCENDIA INC.—See Future Corporation; *Int'l*, pg. 2853
ASCENDIA S.A.; *Int'l*, pg. 601
ASCEND INTEGRATED MEDIA, LLC; *U.S. Private*, pg. 346
ASCENDIO CO., LTD.; *Int'l*, pg. 601
ASCENDIS ANIMAL HEALTH (PTY) LTD—See Ascendis Health Limited; *Int'l*, pg. 601
ASCENDIS HEALTH DIRECT (PTY) LTD—See Ascendis Health Limited; *Int'l*, pg. 601
ASCENDIS HEALTH LIMITED; *Int'l*, pg. 601
ASCENDIS PHARMA A/S; *Int'l*, pg. 602
ASCENDIS PHARMA ENDOCRINOLOGY, INC.—See Ascendis Pharma A/S; *Int'l*, pg. 602
ASCENDIS PHARMA GMBH—See Ascendis Pharma A/S; *Int'l*, pg. 602
ASCENDIS PHARMA, INC.—See Ascendis Pharma A/S; *Int'l*, pg. 602
ASCEND LABORATORIES LLC—See Alkem Laboratories Ltd.; *Int'l*, pg. 330
ASCEND LABORATORIES SDN. BHD.—See Alkem Laboratories Ltd.; *Int'l*, pg. 330
ASCEND LABORATORIES SPA—See Alkem Laboratories Ltd.; *Int'l*, pg. 330
ASCEND LEARNING, LLC—See Blackstone Inc.; *U.S. Public*, pg. 348
ASCEND LEARNING, LLC—See Canada Pension Plan Investment Board; *Int'l*, pg. 1278
ASCEND MANAGEMENT INNOVATIONS LLC; *U.S. Private*, pg. 346
ASCENDO ACADEMY PTE. LTD.—See Ascendo International Holdings Pte. Ltd.; *Int'l*, pg. 602
ASCENDO INTERNATIONAL HOLDINGS PTE. LTD.; *Int'l*, pg. 602
ASCEND ONE CORPORATION; *U.S. Private*, pg. 346
ASCENDO RESOURCES, LLC; *U.S. Private*, pg. 346
ASCEND PERFORMANCE MATERIALS LLC—See SK Capital Partners, LP; *U.S. Private*, pg. 3679
ASCEND PLASTIC SURGERY PARTNERS; *U.S. Private*, pg. 346
ASCEND SOLUTIONS SDN BHD—See Genting Berhad; *Int'l*, pg. 2928
ASCENDTECH, INC.; *U.S. Private*, pg. 346
ASCEND TECHNOLOGIES, LLC—See TAC Partners, Inc.; *U.S. Private*, pg. 3920
ASCEND TECHNOLOGIES, LLC; *U.S. Private*, pg. 346
ASCENDUM SOLUTIONS LLC—See Vora Ventures LLC; *U.S. Private*, pg. 4412

ASCEND VENTURE GROUP, LLC; *U.S. Private*, pg. 346
ASCEND WELLNESS HOLDINGS, INC.; *U.S. Public*, pg. 210
ASC ENGINEERED SOLUTIONS, LLC—See Tailwind Capital Group, LLC; *U.S. Private*, pg. 3923
ASCENSEURS DRIEUX-COMBALUZIER S.A.S.—See ThyssenKrupp AG; *Int'l*, pg. 7723
ASCENSEURS SOULIER S.N.C.—See KONE Oyj; *Int'l*, pg. 4247
ASCENSEURS TECHNOLOGIE SERRURERIE (S.A)—See KONE Oyj; *Int'l*, pg. 4247
ASCENSIA DIABETES CARE CANADA INC.—See PHC Holdings Corporation; *Int'l*, pg. 5843
ASCENSIA DIABETES CARE HOLDINGS AG—See PHC Holdings Corporation; *Int'l*, pg. 5843
ASCENSIA DIABETES CARE UK LIMITED—See PHC Holdings Corporation; *Int'l*, pg. 5843
ASCENSIA DIABETES CARE US INC.—See PHC Holdings Corporation; *Int'l*, pg. 5843
ASCENSION BENEFITS & INSURANCE SOLUTIONS—See Aquiline Capital Partners LLC; *U.S. Private*, pg. 305
ASCENSION BORGESS LEE HOSPITAL—See Ascension Health Alliance; *U.S. Private*, pg. 346
ASCENSION CAPITAL GROUP, INC.—See Encore Capital Group, Inc.; *U.S. Public*, pg. 759
ASCENSION COLLEGIATE SOLUTIONS—See Aquiline Capital Partners LLC; *U.S. Private*, pg. 305
ASCENSION HEALTH ALLIANCE; *U.S. Private*, pg. 346
ASCENSION ORTHOPEDICS, INC.—See Integra LifeSciences Holdings Corporation; *U.S. Public*, pg. 1135
ASCENSION ORTHOPEDICS, LTD.—See Integra LifeSciences Holdings Corporation; *U.S. Public*, pg. 1135
ASCENSION PROPERTIES LIMITED—See Rebosis Property Fund Ltd.; *Int'l*, pg. 6235
ASCENSION SAINT THOMAS LEBANON SURGERY CENTER, LLC—See Tenet Healthcare Corporation; *U.S. Public*, pg. 2001
ASCENSION ST JOHN FOUNDATION; *U.S. Private*, pg. 348
ASCENSION TECHNOLOGY CORPORATION—See Roper Technologies, Inc.; *U.S. Public*, pg. 1810
ASCENSION WASTEWATER TREATMENT—See Bernhard Capital Partners Management, LP; *U.S. Private*, pg. 536
ASCENSION WATER CO.—See Baton Rouge Water Works Company; *U.S. Private*, pg. 487
ASCENSORES ANDINO SAS—See Schindler Holding AG; *Int'l*, pg. 6618
ASCENSORES BIDASOA S.L.—See KONE Oyj; *Int'l*, pg. 4247
ASCENSORES MURALLA, S.A.—See KONE Oyj; *Int'l*, pg. 4247
ASCENSORES R CASADO, S.A.—See KONE Oyj; *Int'l*, pg. 4247
ASCENSORES SCHINDLER (CHILE) S.A.—See Schindler Holding AG; *Int'l*, pg. 6618
ASCENSORES SCHINDLER DE COLOMBIA S.A.—See Schindler Holding AG; *Int'l*, pg. 6618
ASCENSORES SCHINDLER DEL PERU S.A.—See Schindler Holding AG; *Int'l*, pg. 6618
ASCENSORES SCHINDLER S.A.—See Schindler Holding AG; *Int'l*, pg. 6618
ASCENSORES SCHINDLER S.A.—See Schindler Holding AG; *Int'l*, pg. 6618
ASCENS SERVICES SAS—See Financiere de L'Odet; *Int'l*, pg. 2665
ASCENSUS, LLC—See Aquiline Capital Partners LLC; *U.S. Private*, pg. 303
ASCENSUS, LLC—See Genstar Capital, LLC; *U.S. Private*, pg. 1675
ASCENSUS SPECIALTIES LLC—See Wind Point Advisors LLC; *U.S. Private*, pg. 4533
ASCENT AEROSPACE—See AIP, LLC; *U.S. Private*, pg. 133
ASCENTAGE PHARMA GROUP INC.—See Ascentage Pharma Group International; *Int'l*, pg. 602
ASCENTAGE PHARMA GROUP INTERNATIONAL; *Int'l*, pg. 602
ASCENT AVIATION GROUP, INC.—See World Kinect Corporation; *U.S. Public*, pg. 2380
ASCENT AVIATION SERVICES CORP.—See Marana Aerospace Solutions, Inc.; *U.S. Private*, pg. 2569
ASCENT BANCORP; *U.S. Private*, pg. 348
ASCENT BRIDGE LIMITED; *Int'l*, pg. 602
ASCENT BUILDING LLC—See Pennar Industries Limited; *Int'l*, pg. 5786
ASCENT CAPITAL GROUP, INC.; *U.S. Private*, pg. 348
ASCENT CLOUD LLC—See The Ascent Group LLC; *U.S. Private*, pg. 3988
ASCENT DEVELOPMENT CO., LTD; *Int'l*, pg. 602
ASCENTECH, K.K.; *Int'l*, pg. 602
ASCENTEK, INC.—See Synagex, Inc; *U.S. Private*, pg. 3902
ASCENTEK INTERNATIONAL COMPANY LIMITED—See Fuji Corporation; *Int'l*, pg. 2809
ASCENTEX INDUSTRY CORP.—See Fuji Corporation; *Int'l*, pg. 2809

COMPANY NAME INDEX

ASCENT GLOBAL LOGISTICS, LLC—See Elliott Management Corporation; *U.S. Private*, pg. 1365
THE ASCENT GROUP LLC; *U.S. Private*, pg. 3988
ASCENTIAL PLC—See Informa plc; *Int'l*, pg. 3691
ASCENT INDUSTRIES CO.; *U.S. Public*, pg. 210
ASCENT INNOVATIONS LLC; *U.S. Private*, pg. 348
ASCENT INVESTMENT PARTNERS, LLC—See Mariner Wealth Advisors, LLC; *U.S. Private*, pg. 2575
ASCENTIS CORPORATION—See Hellman & Friedman LLC; *U.S. Private*, pg. 1910
ASCENTIUM CAPITAL LLC—See Regions Financial Corporation; *U.S. Public*, pg. 1776
ASCENTIUM CORPORATION; *U.S. Private*, pg. 348
ASCENTIUM-MWR—See Ascentium Corporation; *U.S. Private*, pg. 348
ASCENT KEYBOARDLABS TECH PVT. LTD.—See Reliable Data Services Ltd.; *Int'l*, pg. 6261
ASCENT MEDIA GROUP, LLC—See Ascent Capital Group, Inc.; *U.S. Private*, pg. 348
ASCENT PREP INTERNATIONAL EDUCATION LIMITED—See Bexcellent Group Holdings Limited; *Int'l*, pg. 1005
ASCENT RESOURCES PLC; *Int'l*, pg. 602
ASCENTRON, INC.—See Crestview Partners, L.P.; *U.S. Private*, pg. 1098
THE ASCENT SERVICES GROUP; *U.S. Private*, pg. 3989
ASCENT SOLAR TECHNOLOGIES, INC.; *U.S. Public*, pg. 210
ASCENTY DATA CENTERS E TELECOMUNICOES S.A—See Digital Realty Trust, Inc.; *U.S. Public*, pg. 663
A/S CERBO NORGE—See Nolato AB; *Int'l*, pg. 5407
ASCER PTE. LTD.—See Ascendo International Holdings Pte. Ltd.; *Int'l*, pg. 602
ASCERTIA LTD.—See Tinexta S.p.A.; *Int'l*, pg. 7753
ASCERTIA SOFTWARE TRADING LLC—See Tinexta S.p.A.; *Int'l*, pg. 7753
A/S CESU ALUS—See Olvi Oyj; *Int'l*, pg. 5554
ASC GLOBAL INC.; *U.S. Private*, pg. 345
ASCHAUER ZIMMEREI GMBH—See PORR AG; *Int'l*, pg. 5922
ASCHE CHIESI GMBH—See Chiesi Farmaceutici SpA; *Int'l*, pg. 1477
ASCH/GROSSBARDT, INC., *U.S. Private*, pg. 040
AS CHILE ENERGY GROUP SA—See Edenred S.A.; *Int'l*, pg. 2307
ASCHINGER ELECTRIC CO.; *U.S. Private*, pg. 348
A. SCHONBEK & CO.; *U.S. Private*, pg. 23
A/S CHRISTIAN BERNER—See Christian Berner Tech Trade AB; *Int'l*, pg. 1586
A. SCHULMAN BELGIUM—See LyondellBasell Industries N.V.; *Int'l*, pg. 4606
A. SCHULMAN CASTELLON, S.L.—See LyondellBasell Industries N.V.; *Int'l*, pg. 4606
A. SCHULMAN CUSTOM COMPOUNDING NE, INC.—See LyondellBasell Industries N.V.; *Int'l*, pg. 4606
A. SCHULMAN DE MEXICO, S.A. DE C.V.—See LyondellBasell Industries N.V.; *Int'l*, pg. 4607
A. SCHULMAN EUROPE VERWALTUNGS GMBH—See LyondellBasell Industries N.V.; *Int'l*, pg. 4606
A. SCHULMAN GAINSBOROUGH LTD—See LyondellBasell Industries N.V.; *Int'l*, pg. 4608
A. SCHULMAN GMBH—See LyondellBasell Industries N.V.; *Int'l*, pg. 4606
A. SCHULMAN HUNGARY KFT.—See LyondellBasell Industries N.V.; *Int'l*, pg. 4606
A. SCHULMAN, INC. - EAST CHICAGO—See LyondellBasell Industries N.V.; *Int'l*, pg. 4607
A. SCHULMAN, INC. - FILLED & REINFORCED PLASTICS—See LyondellBasell Industries N.V.; *Int'l*, pg. 4607
A. SCHULMAN INC. LIMITED—See LyondellBasell Industries N.V.; *Int'l*, pg. 4606
A. SCHULMAN, INC. - LIQUID COATINGS & DISPERSIONS—See LyondellBasell Industries N.V.; *Int'l*, pg. 4607
A. SCHULMAN, INC. - PLASTIC COLORANTS—See LyondellBasell Industries N.V.; *Int'l*, pg. 4607
A. SCHULMAN, INC.—See LyondellBasell Industries N.V.; *Int'l*, pg. 4606
A. SCHULMAN, INC. - SPECIALTY PLASTICS, CARPENTERSVILLE PLANT—See LyondellBasell Industries N.V.; *Int'l*, pg. 4607
A. SCHULMAN INTERNATIONAL SERVICES BVBA—See LyondellBasell Industries N.V.; *Int'l*, pg. 4606
A. SCHULMAN L'ARBRESLE SAS—See LyondellBasell Industries N.V.; *Int'l*, pg. 4606
A. SCHULMAN NORDIC AB—See LyondellBasell Industries N.V.; *Int'l*, pg. 4606
A. SCHULMAN PLASTICOS DO BRASIL LTDA.—See LyondellBasell Industries N.V.; *Int'l*, pg. 4606
A. SCHULMAN PLASTICS, BV—See LyondellBasell Industries N.V.; *Int'l*, pg. 4606
A. SCHULMAN PLASTICS S.L.—See LyondellBasell Industries N.V.; *Int'l*, pg. 4606
A. SCHULMAN PLASTICS SPA—See LyondellBasell Industries N.V.; *Int'l*, pg. 4606

A. SCHULMAN PLASTICS S.R.O.—See LyondellBasell Industries N.V.; *Int'l*, pg. 4606
A. SCHULMAN PLASTIK SANAYI VE TIC A.S.—See LyondellBasell Industries N.V.; *Int'l*, pg. 4606
A. SCHULMAN POZNAN SP ZOO—See LyondellBasell Industries N.V.; *Int'l*, pg. 4606
A. SCHULMAN SAINT GERMAIN LAVAL S.A.S.—See LyondellBasell Industries N.V.; *Int'l*, pg. 4606
A. SCHULMAN, S.A.S.—See LyondellBasell Industries N.V.; *Int'l*, pg. 4607
A. SCHULMAN THERMOPLASTIC COMPOUNDS LIMITED—See LyondellBasell Industries N.V.; *Int'l*, pg. 4607
A. SCHULMAN THERMOPLASTIC COMPOUNDS SDN. BHD.—See LyondellBasell Industries N.V.; *Int'l*, pg. 4607
ASCIANO LIMITED—See BlackRock, Inc.; *U.S. Public*, pg. 345
ASCIANO LIMITED—See Canada Pension Plan Investment Board; *Int'l*, pg. 1279
ASCIANO LIMITED—See China Investment Corporation; *Int'l*, pg. 1513
ASCIANO LIMITED—See Qube Holdings Limited; *Int'l*, pg. 6157
ASCI DIRECT, S.A.—See Vivendi SE; *Int'l*, pg. 8269
THE ASCII GROUP, INC.; *U.S. Private*, pg. 3989
ASC INDUSTRIES INC.—See Crowne Group LLC; *U.S. Private*, pg. 1112
ASCIO GMBH—See HgCapital Trust plc; *Int'l*, pg. 3377
ASCIO TECHNOLOGIES INC.—See Tucows, Inc.; *Int'l*, pg. 7963
AS CITADELE BANKA EESTI FILIAAL—See Ripplewood Holdings LLC; *U.S. Private*, pg. 3439
AS CITADELE BANKA—See Ripplewood Holdings LLC; *U.S. Private*, pg. 3439
ASC JAPAN INC.—See ASC telecom AG; *Int'l*, pg. 600
ASCLEPION LASER TECHNOLOGIES GMBH—See El.En. S.p.A.; *Int'l*, pg. 2341
ASCLEPIUS CONSULTING & TECHNOLOGIES PVT LTD.—See Virinchi Ltd.; *Int'l*, pg. 8248
ASCLETIS PHARMA, INC.; *Int'l*, pg. 602
ASC MACARTHUR SQUARE PTY LTD.—See Wesfarmers Limited; *Int'l*, pg. 8380
A&C MACHINE TOOLS INC.; *U.S. Private*, pg. 345
ASC NETWORK, LLC—See UnitedHealth Group Incorporated; *U.S. Public*, pg. 2238
ASCO AEROSPACE CANADA LTD.—See ASCO Industries NV/SA; *Int'l*, pg. 602
ASCO AEROSPACE DO BRASIL—See ASCO Industries NV/SA; *Int'l*, pg. 602
ASCO AEROSPACE USA, LLC—See ASCO Industries NV/SA; *Int'l*, pg. 602
AS COCA-COLA HBC EESTI—See Coca-Cola HBC AG; *Int'l*, pg. 1685
ASCO CO., LTD.—See Sala Corporation; *Int'l*, pg. 6490
ASCO CONSTRUCTION LTD.; *Int'l*, pg. 602
ASCO CORP.—See Sala Corporation; *Int'l*, pg. 6490
ASCO DEUTSCHLAND GMBH—See ASCO Industries NV/SA; *Int'l*, pg. 602
ASCO EG S.P.A.—See Ascopiave S.p.A.; *Int'l*, pg. 603
ASCO EQUIPMENT SAN ANTONIO—See Associated Supply Company Inc.; *U.S. Private*, pg. 357
ASCO EXTINGUISHERS COMPANY LIMITED—See London Security PLC; *Int'l*, pg. 4547
ASCO FREIGHT MANAGEMENT LTD.—See Endless LLP; *Int'l*, pg. 2403
ASCO FREIGHT MANAGEMENT—See Endless LLP; *Int'l*, pg. 2403
ASCO GROUP LIMITED—See Endless LLP; *Int'l*, pg. 2403
ASCO INDUSTRIES NV/SA; *Int'l*, pg. 602
ASCO INDUSTRIES SAS—See Swiss Steel Holding AG; *Int'l*, pg. 7372
ASCO JOUCOMATIC PTY. LTD.—See Emerson Electric Co.; *U.S. Public*, pg. 741
ASCOLTA, LLC—See Management Science & Innovation LLC; *U.S. Private*, pg. 2561
ASCOMATICA S.A. DE C.V.—See Emerson Electric Co.; *U.S. Public*, pg. 741
ASCOMATION PTY. LTD.—See Emerson Electric Co.; *U.S. Public*, pg. 741
ASCOM (BELGIUM) NV—See Ascom Holding AG; *Int'l*, pg. 603
ASCOM B.V.—See Ascom Holding AG; *Int'l*, pg. 603
ASCOM CARBONATE & CHEMICAL MANUFACTURING COMPANY—See ASEC Company for Mining; *Int'l*, pg. 605
ASCOM COLOMBIA S.A.—See Ascom Holding AG; *Int'l*, pg. 603
ASCOM DANMARK A/S—See Ascom Holding AG; *Int'l*, pg. 603
ASCOM DANMARK A/S—See Ascom Holding AG; *Int'l*, pg. 603
ASCOM DEUTSCHLAND GMBH—See Ascom Holding AG; *Int'l*, pg. 603
ASCOM (FINLAND) OY—See Ascom Holding AG; *Int'l*, pg. 602
ASCOM (FRANCE) SA—See Ascom Holding AG; *Int'l*, pg. 602

ASCOM-HG, LLC—See Huizenga Manufacturing Group, Inc.; *U.S. Private*, pg. 2004
ASCOM HOLDING AG; *Int'l*, pg. 602
ASCOM HPF SA—See Ascom Holding AG; *Int'l*, pg. 603
ASCOM IMMOBILIEN AG—See Ascom Holding AG; *Int'l*, pg. 602
ASCOM INDIA PVT LTD—See Ascom Holding AG; *Int'l*, pg. 603
ASCOM INTEGRATED WIRELESS PTY LTD—See Ascom Holding AG; *Int'l*, pg. 603
ASCOM LEASING & INVESTMENTS LTD.; *Int'l*, pg. 603
ASCOM (MALAYSIA) SDN BHD—See Ascom Holding AG; *Int'l*, pg. 602
ASCOM (NEDERLAND) BV—See Ascom Holding AG; *Int'l*, pg. 603
ASCOM NETWORK TESTING AB—See Ascom Holding AG; *Int'l*, pg. 603
ASCOM NETWORK TESTING AG—See Ascom Holding AG; *Int'l*, pg. 602
ASCOM NORWAY—See Ascom Holding AG; *Int'l*, pg. 603
AS COMPANY S.A.; *Int'l*, pg. 589
ASCOM POLAND SP. Z.O.O.—See Ascom Holding AG; *Int'l*, pg. 603
ASCOM PRECIOUS METALS MINING SAE—See ASEC Company for Mining; *Int'l*, pg. 605
ASCOM (SCHWEIZ) AG—See Ascom Holding AG; *Int'l*, pg. 602
ASCOM SECURITY SOLUTIONS AG—See Ascom Holding AG; *Int'l*, pg. 603
ASCOM SOLUTIONS (SINGAPORE) PTE LTD—See Ascom Holding AG; *Int'l*, pg. 603
ASCOM (SWEDEN) AB—See Ascom Holding AG; *Int'l*, pg. 603
ASCOM SYSTEC AG—See Ascom Holding AG; *Int'l*, pg. 603
ASCOM TATECO AB—See Ascom Holding AG; *Int'l*, pg. 603
ASCOM UK GROUP LTD.—See Ascom Holding AG; *Int'l*, pg. 603
ASCOM (UK) LTD.—See Ascom Holding AG; *Int'l*, pg. 603
ASCOM UMS S.R.L.—See Ascom Holding AG; *Int'l*, pg. 603
ASCOM (US) INC.—See Ascom Holding AG; *Int'l*, pg. 603
ASCON CO., LTD.—See AOYAMA TRADING Co. Ltd.; *Int'l*, pg. 498
ASCON HOSTING FACILITIES B.V.—See CompuGroup Medical SE & Co. KGaA; *Int'l*, pg. 1755
ASCON SOFTWARE B.V.—See CompuGroup Medical SE & Co. KGaA; *Int'l*, pg. 1755
ASCO/NUMATICS GMBH—See Emerson Electric Co.; *U.S. Public*, pg. 740
ASCO NUMATICS (INDIA) PRIVATE LIMITED—See Emerson Electric Co.; *U.S. Public*, pg. 740
ASCO NUMATICS, S.A.—See Emerson Electric Co.; *U.S. Public*, pg. 740
ASCO NUMATICS SIRAI SRL—See Emerson Electric Co.; *U.S. Public*, pg. 740
ASCOPIAVE ENERGIE S.P.A.—See Ascopiave S.p.A.; *Int'l*, pg. 603
ASCOPIAVE S.P.A.; *Int'l*, pg. 603
ASCO POWER TECHNOLOGIES LIMITED—See Emerson Electric Co.; *U.S. Public*, pg. 740
ASCO POWER TECHNOLOGIES LOAD BANK—See Schneider Electric SE; *Int'l*, pg. 6633
ASCO POWER TECHNOLOGIES, L.P. - ANAHEIM—See Schneider Electric SE; *Int'l*, pg. 6633
ASCO POWER TECHNOLOGIES, L.P. - HOUSTON—See Schneider Electric SE; *Int'l*, pg. 6633
ASCO POWER TECHNOLOGIES, L.P.—See Schneider Electric SE; *Int'l*, pg. 6633
ASCO POWER TECHNOLOGIES, L.P. - WOODBRIDGE—See Schneider Electric SE; *Int'l*, pg. 6633
ASCOR CHIMICI S.R.L.—See Vetoquinol S.A.; *Int'l*, pg. 8180
ASCO RENEWABLES S.P.A.—See Ascopiave S.p.A.; *Int'l*, pg. 603
ASCORIUM NORTH AMERICA, INC.—See Recticel S.A.; *Int'l*, pg. 6241
ASCORP, INC.; *U.S. Private*, pg. 348
ASCO SAS—See Emerson Electric Co.; *U.S. Public*, pg. 740
ASCO SINTERING CO.; *U.S. Private*, pg. 348
ASCOT ASSET CONSULTING CORP.—See Ascot Corp.; *Int'l*, pg. 604
ASCOT CORP.; *Int'l*, pg. 603
ASCOTECH S.A. DE C.V.—See Emerson Electric Co.; *U.S. Public*, pg. 741
ASCOT ENTERPRISES, INC.; *U.S. Private*, pg. 348
ASCOT RESOURCES LTD.; *Int'l*, pg. 604
THE ASCOTT CAPITAL PTE LTD—See CapitaLand Investment Limited; *Int'l*, pg. 1314
THE ASCOTT (EUROPE) PTE LTD—See CapitaLand Investment Limited; *Int'l*, pg. 1314
ASCOTT INTERNATIONAL MANAGEMENT (2001) PTE LTD—See CapitaLand Investment Limited; *Int'l*, pg. 1314
THE ASCOTT LIMITED—See CapitaLand Investment Limited; *Int'l*, pg. 1314

ASCOTT PROPERTY MANAGEMENT (BEIJING) CO., LTD—See CapitaLand Investment Limited; *Int'l*, pg. 1314
ASCOTT RESIDENCE TRUST MANAGEMENT LIMITED—See CapitaLand Investment Limited; *Int'l*, pg. 1314
ASCOTT SALES INTEGRATION PTY. LTD.—See IQVIA Holdings Inc.; *U.S. Public*, pg. 1168
ASCOVAL INDUSTRIA E COMMERCIO LTDA.—See Emerson Electric Co.; *U.S. Public*, pg. 741
ASCOVAL S.A.S.—See Vallourec SA; *Int'l*, pg. 8117
ASCO VALVE, INC.—See Emerson Electric Co.; *U.S. Public*, pg. 750
ASCO VALVE MANUFACTURING, LLC—See Schneider Electric SE; *Int'l*, pg. 6633
ASC PROFILES INC.—See BlueScope Steel Limited; *Int'l*, pg. 1073
ASC PTY. LTD.; *Int'l*, pg. 600
AS CRAMO ESTONIA—See Cramo Plc; *Int'l*, pg. 1827
A.S. CREATION (FRANCE) SAS—See A.S. Creation Tapeten AG; *Int'l*, pg. 28
A.S. CREATION (NL) B.V.—See A.S. Creation Tapeten AG; *Int'l*, pg. 28
A.S. CREATION TAPETEN AG; *Int'l*, pg. 28
A.S. CREATION TEXTIL GMBH—See A.S. Creation Tapeten AG; *Int'l*, pg. 28
AS CREATION (UK) LIMITED—See A.S. Creation Tapeten AG; *Int'l*, pg. 28
ASC SCHWEIZ AG—See ASC telecom AG; *Int'l*, pg. 600
ASC SIGNAL DIVISION, INC.—See Kratos Defense & Security Solutions, Inc.; *U.S. Public*, pg. 1275
ASC SIGNAL DIVISION - MANUFACTURING—See Kratos Defense & Security Solutions, Inc.; *U.S. Public*, pg. 1275
ASC TECHNOLOGIES AG—See ASC telecom AG; *Int'l*, pg. 600
ASC TECHNOLOGIES GMBH—See ASC telecom AG; *Int'l*, pg. 601
ASC TECHNOLOGIES S.A.S.—See ASC telecom AG; *Int'l*, pg. 601
ASC TELECOM AG; *Int'l*, pg. 600
ASC TELECOM SINGAPORE PTE. LTD.—See ASC telecom AG; *Int'l*, pg. 601
ASC UK TECHNOLOGIES LTD—See ASC telecom AG; *Int'l*, pg. 601
ASCUTNEY METAL PRODUCTS—See Spirol International Corporation; *U.S. Private*, pg. 3758
ASC WARRINGAH MALL PTY LTD.—See Wesfarmers Limited; *Int'l*, pg. 8380
ASC WFO SOLUTIONS DO BRASIL LTDA.—See ASC telecom AG; *Int'l*, pg. 601
ASDA'A BCW—See WPP plc; *Int'l*, pg. 8467
ASDAG BAUGESELLSCHAFT M.B.H.—See PORR AG; *Int'l*, pg. 5922
ASDA GROUP LIMITED—See TDR Capital LLP; *Int'l*, pg. 7490
A/S DANSK SHELL—See Shell plc; *Int'l*, pg. 6796
AS DBT—See Public Joint Stock Company Acron; *Int'l*, pg. 6094
ASDCO—See APi Group Corporation; *Int'l*, pg. 514
A.S. DESIGN LIMITED—See JAKKS Pacific, Inc.; *U.S. Public*, pg. 1186
ASDEX CORPORATION—See Aichi Steel Corporation; *Int'l*, pg. 230
ASD HEALTHCARE—See Cencora, Inc.; *U.S. Public*, pg. 466
ASD INTERPIPE LTD.—See Klockner & Co. SE; *Int'l*, pg. 4202
ASDION BERHAD.; *Int'l*, pg. 604
AS DITTON PIEVADKEZU RUPNICA; *Int'l*, pg. 589
ASD LIMITED—See Klockner & Co. SE; *Int'l*, pg. 4202
ASD METAL SERVICES LTD.—See Klockner & Co. SE; *Int'l*, pg. 4202
AS DOMZALE MOTO CENTER D.O.O.—See Honda Motor Co., Ltd.; *Int'l*, pg. 3459
ASD SPECIALTY HEALTHCARE, INC.—See Cencora, Inc.; *U.S. Public*, pg. 466
ASD WESTOK LIMITED—See Klockner & Co. SE; *Int'l*, pg. 4202
ASEA BROWN BOVERI INC.—See ABB Ltd.; *Int'l*, pg. 55
ASEA BROWN BOVERI LTDA.—See ABB Ltd.; *Int'l*, pg. 55
ASEA BROWN BOVERI LTD.—See ABB Ltd.; *Int'l*, pg. 55
ASEA BROWN BOVERI LTD—See ABB Ltd.; *Int'l*, pg. 55
ASEA BROWN BOVERI (PTY) LTD—See ABB Ltd.; *Int'l*, pg. 55
ASEA BROWN BOVERI S.A. DE C.V.—See ABB Ltd.; *Int'l*, pg. 53
ASEA BROWN BOVERI S.A.E.—See ABB Ltd.; *Int'l*, pg. 55
ASEA BROWN BOVERI, S.A.—See ABB Ltd.; *Int'l*, pg. 55
ASEA BROWN BOVERI, S.A.—See ABB Ltd.; *Int'l*, pg. 55
ASEA BROWN BOVERI, S.A.—See ABB Ltd.; *Int'l*, pg. 55
ASEA BROWN BOVERI S.A.—See ABB Ltd.; *Int'l*, pg. 54
ASEA BROWN BOVERI S.A.—See ABB Ltd.; *Int'l*, pg. 55
ASEA BROWN BOVERI S.A.—See ABB Ltd.; *Int'l*, pg. 55
ASEAN ADVISORY PTE. LTD.—See Zico Holdings Inc.; *Int'l*, pg. 8681

ASEANA HOLDINGS, INC.—See DM Wenceslao & Associates, Inc.; *Int'l*, pg. 2142
ASEANA PROPERTIES LTD.; *Int'l*, pg. 605
ASE ASSEMBLY & TEST (SHANGHAI) LIMITED—See ASE Technology Holding Co., Ltd.; *Int'l*, pg. 604
ASEC CEMENT CO.—See Citadel Capital S.A.E.; *Int'l*, pg. 1619
ASEC COMPANY FOR MINING; *Int'l*, pg. 605
ASE (CHUNG LI), INC.—See ASE Technology Holding Co., Ltd.; *Int'l*, pg. 604
ASECO INTEGRATED SYSTEMS LTD.; *Int'l*, pg. 605
ASEC S.A.—See Vector Software Sp. z o. o.; *Int'l*, pg. 8145
A+ SECURE PACKAGING, LLC—See Cardinal Health, Inc.; *U.S. Public*, pg. 433
AS ECZA DEPOSU TICARET A.S.—See Selcuk Ecza Deposu Ticaret ve Sanayi AS; *Int'l*, pg. 6699
ASEED HOLDINGS CO., LTD.; *Int'l*, pg. 605
ASE ELECTRONICS (M) SDN. BHD.—See ASE Technology Holding Co., Ltd.; *Int'l*, pg. 604
ASEEM GLOBAL LTD.; *Int'l*, pg. 605
AS EESTI GAAS—See AS Infortar; *Int'l*, pg. 590
AS EESTI KREDIIDIPANK LATVIJAS—See PJSC VTB Bank; *Int'l*, pg. 5886
ASEFA PUBLIC COMPANY LIMITED; *Int'l*, pg. 605
ASEGONIA CO., LTD.—See Tsunagu Group Holdings Inc.; *Int'l*, pg. 7957
ASEGUA THERAPEUTICS, LLC—See Gilead Sciences, Inc.; *U.S. Public*, pg. 936
ASEGURADORA GENERAL S.A.; *Int'l*, pg. 605
ASEGURADORA PORVENIR GNP—See Grupo BAL; *Int'l*, pg. 3121
ASEGURADORA VALENCIANA SA DE SEGUROS Y REASEGUROS—See MAPFRE S.A.; *Int'l*, pg. 4683
ASE JAPAN CO., LTD.—See ASE Technology Holding Co., Ltd.; *Int'l*, pg. 604
ASE KAOHSIUNG—See ASE Technology Holding Co., Ltd.; *Int'l*, pg. 604
ASE KOREA INC.—See ASE Technology Holding Co., Ltd.; *Int'l*, pg. 604
AS EKSPRESS GRUPP; *Int'l*, pg. 589
ASE (KUNSHAN) INC.—See ASE Technology Holding Co., Ltd.; *Int'l*, pg. 604
ASEKURACJA CASH HANDLING SP. Z.O.O.—See Impel S.A.; *Int'l*, pg. 3631
ASEL ART SUPPLY INC.; *U.S. Private*, pg. 348
ASEL ASCENSORES S.L.—See ThyssenKrupp AG; *Int'l*, pg. 7723
A SELF-ADMINISTERED REAL ESTATE INVESTMENT TRUST INC.; *Int'l*, pg. 18
A/S ELIF—See Schindler Holding AG; *Int'l*, pg. 6618
AS ELION ESINDUS—See Telia Company AB; *Int'l*, pg. 7543
ASELSAN ELEKTRONIK SANAYI VE TICARET AS; *Int'l*, pg. 605
ASEM, S.R.L.—See Rockwell Automation, Inc.; *U.S. Public*, pg. 1805
ASENCE PHARMA PVT. LTD.—See Ambalal Sarabhai Enterprises Ltd.; *Int'l*, pg. 413
ASENDIA MANAGEMENT SAS—See Die Schweizerische Post AG; *Int'l*, pg. 2112
ASENDIA MANAGEMENT SAS—See La Poste S.A.; *Int'l*, pg. 4388
ASENDIA USA—See Die Schweizerische Post AG; *Int'l*, pg. 2112
ASENDIA USA—See La Poste S.A.; *Int'l*, pg. 4388
AS ENERGOFIRMA JAUDA; *Int'l*, pg. 590
ASENOVA KREPOST AD; *Int'l*, pg. 606
ASENSUS SURGICAL, INC.—See Karl Storz GmbH & Co.; *Int'l*, pg. 4083
ASENSUS SURGICAL ITALIA, S.R.L.—See Karl Storz GmbH & Co.; *Int'l*, pg. 4083
ASENTA MANAGEMENT CONSULTANTS—See Stanwick Management Consultants; *Int'l*, pg. 7172
ASENTEC CO., LTD.—See SJG Sejong Co., Ltd.; *Int'l*, pg. 6969
ASENTINEL, LLC—See Marlin Equity Partners, LLC; *U.S. Private*, pg. 2583
ASEPCO CORP.—See Spirax-Sarco Engineering plc; *Int'l*, pg. 7139
ASEP MEDICAL HOLDINGS INC.; *Int'l*, pg. 606
ASEPTIC SOLUTIONS USA VENTURES, LLC—See Glanbia Co-Operative Society Limited; *Int'l*, pg. 2987
ASEPTIC SYSTEMS CO., LTD.—See Dai Nippon Printing Co., Ltd.; *Int'l*, pg. 1914
ASEPT INTERNATIONAL AB—See Lagercrantz Group AB; *Int'l*, pg. 4393
ASERA INC.; *U.S. Private*, pg. 348
AS ERAKUTE—See Veolia Environnement S.A.; *Int'l*, pg. 8156
ASE RENT, S.A. DE C.V.—See MAPFRE S.A.; *Int'l*, pg. 4684
A SERVIDONE INC; *U.S. Private*, pg. 19
AS ESAB—See Enovis Corporation; *U.S. Public*, pg. 770
ASE SINGAPORE PTE. LTD.—See ASE Technology Holding Co., Ltd.; *Int'l*, pg. 604
ASESORES Y GESTORES FINANCIEROS SA—See Banque Cantonale Vaudoise; *Int'l*, pg. 853
ASESORES/Y&R S.A.—See WPP plc; *Int'l*, pg. 8491

ASESORIA DEPORTIVA ESPECIALIZADA, S.A. DE C.V.—See ANTA Sports Products Limited; *Int'l*, pg. 480
ASESORIA MEXICANA EMPRESARIAL, S. DE R.L DE C.V.—See Samvardhana Motherson International Limited; *Int'l*, pg. 6517
ASESORIAS E INVERSIONES AMERICAN EXPRESS CHILE LIMITADA—See American Express Company; *U.S. Public*, pg. 102
ASESORIAS Y REPRESENTACIONES ANALITICAS S.R.L.—See HORIBA Ltd; *Int'l*, pg. 3475
ASESORIA TECNICA Y GESTION ADMINISTRATIVA, S.A. DE C.V.—See Empresas ICA S.A.B. de C.V.; *Int'l*, pg. 2390
ASESORIA Y CONTROL EN PROTECCION RADIOLOGICA, S.L.—See TUV NORD AG; *Int'l*, pg. 7979
AS ESPAK—See Einhell Germany AG; *Int'l*, pg. 2332
ASE S.P.A.; *Int'l*, pg. 604
AS ESTONIAN CELL—See Heinzel Holding GmbH; *Int'l*, pg. 3325
AS ETAL GROUP—See Amplex AB; *Int'l*, pg. 434
ASE TECHNOLOGY HOLDING CO., LTD.; *Int'l*, pg. 604
ASE TECHNOLOGY INC.; *U.S. Private*, pg. 348
ASETEK A/S; *Int'l*, pg. 606
ASETEK DANMARK A/S—See Asetek A/S; *Int'l*, pg. 606
ASE TEST, INC.—See ASE Technology Holding Co., Ltd.; *Int'l*, pg. 604
ASE TEST, LIMITED—See ASE Technology Holding Co., Ltd.; *Int'l*, pg. 604
ASETRONICS AG; *Int'l*, pg. 606
ASFALTBELAGGNINGAR I BODEN AB—See Peab AB; *Int'l*, pg. 5771
ASFALTOS ESPANOLES, S.A.—See Mubadala Investment Company PJSC; *Int'l*, pg. 5074
ASFALTOS Y CONSTRUCCIONES ELSAN, S.A.—See Grupo Villar Mir, S.A.U.; *Int'l*, pg. 3138
ASFALT REMIX AS—See YIT Corporation; *Int'l*, pg. 8586
ASFALTTI-SYSTEM OY—See Peab AB; *Int'l*, pg. 5771
ASFD, INC.—See eBay Inc.; *U.S. Public*, pg. 709
AS FEB—See Ahlsell AB; *Int'l*, pg. 223
ASFG, INC.; *U.S. Private*, pg. 348
ASF GROUP LIMITED; *Int'l*, pg. 606
ASF HOLLAND B.V.—See Dole plc; *Int'l*, pg. 2157
ASF (HONG KONG) LTD.—See ASF Group Limited; *Int'l*, pg. 606
AS FINANCIERING—See Sparebanken Ost; *Int'l*, pg. 7125
AS FISKENETT—See Egersund Group AS; *Int'l*, pg. 2323
ASFLOW CO LTD.; *Int'l*, pg. 606
AS FORTUM POWER & HEAT—See Fortum Oyj; *Int'l*, pg. 2741
AS FORTUM TARTU—See Fortum Oyj; *Int'l*, pg. 2740
AS FORUM CINEMAS—See Ratos AB; *Int'l*, pg. 6218
AS FUJITSU ESTONIA—See Fujitsu Limited; *Int'l*, pg. 2835
AS G4S EESTI—See Allied Universal Manager LLC; *U.S. Private*, pg. 188
ASG AIRPORT SERVICE GESELLSCHAFT MBH—See Fraport AG; *Int'l*, pg. 2763
ASG AMBULANZ LEIPZIG GMBH—See Lundbeckfonden; *Int'l*, pg. 4580
ASGARD CORPORATION—See Aeria Inc.; *Int'l*, pg. 179
ASGARD FINANCIAL SERVICES LTD—See Arnotts Ltd.; *Int'l*, pg. 577
ASGARD INVESTMENT HOTELS SOCIMI SA; *Int'l*, pg. 606
ASGARD PARTNERS & CO., LLC; *U.S. Private*, pg. 348
ASGARD WEALTH SOLUTIONS LTD. MELBOURNE—See Westpac Banking Corporation; *Int'l*, pg. 8391
ASGARD WEALTH SOLUTIONS LTD.—See Westpac Banking Corporation; *Int'l*, pg. 8391
ASGCO MANUFACTURING, INC.; *U.S. Private*, pg. 349
A/S GELSTED BYGNINGSINDUSTRI—See VKR Holding A/S; *Int'l*, pg. 8281
ASGENT, INC.; *Int'l*, pg. 606
ASG GROUP LIMITED—See Nomura Research Institute, Ltd.; *Int'l*, pg. 5412
ASG JERGENS INC.—See Jergens Inc.; *U.S. Private*, pg. 2201
AS GLAMOX HE—See Triton Advisers Limited; *Int'l*, pg. 7931
ASG LTD—See Anderson Spratt Group; *Int'l*, pg. 450
ASG MARKETING SDN. BHD.—See Ajiya Berhad; *Int'l*, pg. 258
ASGM AUSTRIAN STRATEGIC GAS STORAGE MANAGEMENT GMBH—See Verbund AG; *Int'l*, pg. 8165
ASGN INCORPORATED; *U.S. Public*, pg. 210
AS GREINER PACKAGING—See Greiner Holding AG; *Int'l*, pg. 3078
A & S GROUP (HOLDINGS) LIMITED; *Int'l*, pg. 17
ASG SOFTWARE SOLUTIONS—See Allen Systems Group, Inc.; *U.S. Private*, pg. 180
ASG SOFTWARE SOLUTIONS—See Allen Systems Group, Inc.; *U.S. Private*, pg. 180
A/S GUNNEBO NORDIC—See Gunnebo AB; *Int'l*, pg. 3184
AS GUSTAF—See AS Merko Ehitus; *Int'l*, pg. 590
ASHAKACEM PLC—See Holcim Ltd.; *Int'l*, pg. 3448
ASHANTI GOLD CORP.—See Desert Gold Ventures Inc.; *Int'l*, pg. 2044

ASHANTI SANKOFA INC.; *Int'l*, pg. 606
A/S HANZAS MAIZNICAS—See Lantmännen ek for; *Int'l*, pg. 4414
ASHA PHILLIP SECURITIES LTD—See Phillip Capital Pte. Ltd.; *Int'l*, pg. 5846
ASHAPURA INTERNATIONAL LIMITED—See Ashapura Minechem Limited; *Int'l*, pg. 606
ASHAPURA MIDGULF NV—See Ashapura Minechem Limited; *Int'l*, pg. 606
ASHAPURA MINECHEM LIMITED; *Int'l*, pg. 606
ASHAPURA PERFOCLAY LIMITED—See Ashapura Minechem Limited; *Int'l*, pg. 606
ASHAPURI GOLD ORNAMENT LTD.; *Int'l*, pg. 606
ASHARI AGENCIES LTD.; *Int'l*, pg. 606
AS HARJU ELEKTER TELETEHNIKA—See Harju Elekter AS; *Int'l*, pg. 3277
A' SHARQIYA INVESTMENT HOLDING CO. SAOG; *Int'l*, pg. 19
ASHAWAY LINE & TWINE MFG. CO.; *U.S. Private*, pg. 349
ASHBRIDGE OIL CO. INC.; *U.S. Private*, pg. 349
ASH BROKERAGE CORP.; *U.S. Private*, pg. 349
ASHBURN CONSULTING LLC—See IMB Partners; *U.S. Private*, pg. 2046
ASHBURN OFFSHORE OIL & GAS EQUIPMENT & ENGINEERING (TIANJIN) CO. LTD.—See Wah Seong Corporation Berhad; *Int'l*, pg. 8329
ASHBURTON; *Int'l*, pg. 606
ASHBY LUMBER CO.; *U.S. Private*, pg. 349
ASHBY STREET OUTDOOR LLC—See Lamar Advertising Company; *U.S. Public*, pg. 1290
ASHCO EXTERIORS INC.; *U.S. Private*, pg. 349
ASH CO., LTD.—See ARTE Salon Holdings, Inc.; *Int'l*, pg. 581
ASHCOR TECHNOLOGIES LTD.—See ATCO Ltd.; *Int'l*, pg. 666
ASH CREEK ENTERPRISES, INC.; *U.S. Private*, pg. 349
ASHCROFT HOUSE LIMITED—See Sheikh Holdings Group (Investments) Limited; *Int'l*, pg. 6793
ASHCROFT INSTRUMENTS GMBH—See Nagano Keiki Co., Ltd.; *Int'l*, pg. 5125
ASHCROFT INSTRUMENTS MEXICO, S.A. DE C.V.C—See Nagano Keiki Co., Ltd.; *Int'l*, pg. 5125
ASHCROFT INSTRUMENTS SINGAPORE PTE LTD—See Nagano Keiki Co., Ltd.; *Int'l*, pg. 5125
ASHCROFT INSTRUMENTS (SUZHOU) CO., LTD.—See Nagano Keiki Co., Ltd.; *Int'l*, pg. 5125
ASHCROFT-NAGANO KEIKI HOLDINGS, INC.—See Nagano Keiki Co., Ltd.; *Int'l*, pg. 5125
ASHEBORO ELASTICS CORPORATION; *U.S. Private*, pg. 349
ASHEBORO PAPER & PACKAGING, INC.; *U.S. Private*, pg. 349
A. SHEFTEL AND SONS, INC.; *U.S. Private*, pg. 23
ASHER AGENCY, INC. - LEXINGTON—See Asher Agency, Inc.; *U.S. Private*, pg. 349
ASHER AGENCY, INC.; *U.S. Private*, pg. 349
ASHER MEDIA, INC.; *U.S. Private*, pg. 349
ASHER'S CHOCOLATES, INC.; *U.S. Private*, pg. 349
ASHEVILLE CHEVROLET INC.; *U.S. Private*, pg. 349
ASHEVILLE CITIZEN-TIMES—See Gannett Co., Inc.; *U.S. Public*, pg. 897
ASHEVILLE MALL CMBS, LLC—See CBL & Associates Properties, Inc.; *U.S. Public*, pg. 457
ASHFAQ TEXTILE MILLS LIMITED; *Int'l*, pg. 606
ASHFIELD CAPITAL PARTNERS, LLC; *U.S. Private*, pg. 349
ASHFIELD HEALTHCARE GMBH—See Clayton, Dubilier & Rice, LLC; *U.S. Private*, pg. 927
ASHFIELD HEALTHCARE IRELAND LIMITED—See Clayton, Dubilier & Rice, LLC; *U.S. Private*, pg. 927
ASHFORD ADVISORS, INC.—See Ashford Inc.; *U.S. Public*, pg. 211
ASHFORD ANCHORAGE LP—See Ashford Hospitality Trust, Inc.; *U.S. Public*, pg. 211
ASHFORD HOSPITALITY ADVISORS LLC—See Ashford Inc.; *U.S. Public*, pg. 211
ASHFORD HOSPITALITY TRUST, INC.; *U.S. Public*, pg. 211
ASHFORD INC.; *U.S. Public*, pg. 211
ASHFORD PITTSBURGH WATERFRONT LP—See Ashford Hospitality Trust, Inc.; *U.S. Public*, pg. 211
ASHFORD PROPERTIES, LLC—See TransDigm Group Incorporated; *U.S. Public*, pg. 2180
ASHFORD TRS FIVE LLC—See Ashford Hospitality Trust, Inc.; *U.S. Public*, pg. 211
ASHFORD TRS FLAGSTAFF LLC—See Ashford Hospitality Trust, Inc.; *U.S. Public*, pg. 211
ASHFORD TRS FORT TOWER I LLC—See Ashford Hospitality Trust, Inc.; *U.S. Public*, pg. 211
ASHFORD TRS LE PAVILLON LLC—See Ashford Hospitality Trust, Inc.; *U.S. Public*, pg. 211
ASHFORD TRS MINNEAPOLIS AIRPORT LLC—See Ashford Hospitality Trust, Inc.; *U.S. Public*, pg. 211
ASHFORD TRS PIER HOUSE LLC—See Braemar Hotels & Resorts, Inc.; *U.S. Public*, pg. 379
ASHFORD TRS PITTSBURGH SOUTHPOINTE LLC—See Ashford Hospitality Trust, Inc.; *U.S. Public*, pg. 211

ASHFORD TRS POOL A LLC—See Ashford Hospitality Trust, Inc.; *U.S. Public*, pg. 211
ASHFORD TRS POOL C1 LLC—See Ashford Hospitality Trust, Inc.; *U.S. Public*, pg. 211
ASHFORD TRS SIX LLC—See Ashford Hospitality Trust, Inc.; *U.S. Public*, pg. 211
ASHFORD TRS WICHITA LLC—See Ashford Hospitality Trust, Inc.; *U.S. Public*, pg. 211
ASHFORD UNIVERSITY LLC—See University of Arizona; *U.S. Private*, pg. 4308
THE ASH GROUP, INC.; *U.S. Private*, pg. 3989
ASH GROVE AGGREGATES, INC.—See CRH plc; *Int'l*, pg. 1842
ASH GROVE AGGREGATES—See CRH plc; *Int'l*, pg. 1842
ASH GROVE CEMENT COMPANY, CEMENT PLT—See CRH plc; *Int'l*, pg. 1842
ASH GROVE CEMENT COMPANY—See CRH plc; *Int'l*, pg. 1842
ASH GROVE CEMENT PLANT—See CRH plc; *Int'l*, pg. 1842
ASH GROVE MATERIALS CORP.—See CRH plc; *Int'l*, pg. 1842
ASH GROVE TEXAS—See CRH plc; *Int'l*, pg. 1843
ASHH, INC.; *U.S. Private*, pg. 349
ASHIANA AGRO INDUSTRIES LIMITED; *Int'l*, pg. 607
ASHIANA HOUSING LTD; *Int'l*, pg. 607
ASHIANA ISPAT LTD.; *Int'l*, pg. 607
ASHIHARA DRIVING SCHOOL COMPANY—See Nitta Corporation; *Int'l*, pg. 5382
ASHIKA CAPITAL LIMITED; *Int'l*, pg. 607
THE ASHIKAGA BANK, LTD.—See Mebuki Financial Group, Inc.; *Int'l*, pg. 4763
ASHIMA LTD.; *Int'l*, pg. 607
ASHIMORI ENGINEERING CO., LTD.—See Ashimori Industry Co., Ltd.; *Int'l*, pg. 607
ASHIMORI INDIA PRIVATE LIMITED—See Ashimori Industry Co., Ltd.; *Int'l*, pg. 607
ASHIMORI INDUSTRIA DE MEXICO, S.A. DE C.V—See Ashimori Industry Co., Ltd.; *Int'l*, pg. 607
ASHIMORI INDUSTRY CO., LTD. - FUKUI PLANT—See Ashimori Industry Co., Ltd.; *Int'l*, pg. 607
ASHIMORI INDUSTRY CO., LTD. - HAMAMATSU PLANT—See Ashimori Industry Co., Ltd.; *Int'l*, pg. 607
ASHIMORI INDUSTRY CO., LTD - SASAYAMA PLANT—See Ashimori Industry Co., Ltd.; *Int'l*, pg. 607
ASHIMORI INDUSTRY CO., LTD.; *Int'l*, pg. 607
ASHIMORI INDUSTRY YAMAGUCHI CO., LTD.—See Ashimori Industry Co., Ltd.; *Int'l*, pg. 607
ASHIMORI KOREA CO., LTD.—See Ashimori Industry Co., Ltd.; *Int'l*, pg. 607
ASHIMORI TECHNOLOGY (WUXI) CO., LTD.—See Ashimori Industry Co., Ltd.; *Int'l*, pg. 607
ASHIMORI TEXTILE MANUFACTURING CO., LTD.—See Ashimori Industry Co., Ltd.; *Int'l*, pg. 607
ASHIMORI (THAILAND) CO., LTD.—See Ashimori Industry Co., Ltd.; *Int'l*, pg. 607
ASHINCKIY METZAVOD PAO; *Int'l*, pg. 607
ASHIRVAD PIPES PVT. LTD—See Aliaxis S.A./N.V.; *Int'l*, pg. 323
ASHIRWAD CAPITAL LIMITED; *Int'l*, pg. 607
ASHIRWAD STEELS & INDUSTRIES LIMITED; *Int'l*, pg. 607
ASHISH POLYPLAST LTD.; *Int'l*, pg. 607
ASHIYA JOSUI CO., LTD.—See Daiei Kankyo Co., Ltd.; *Int'l*, pg. 1924
AS HKSCAN ESTONIA—See HKFoods Plc; *Int'l*, pg. 3429
ASH & LACY BUILDING SYSTEMS LTD; *Int'l*, pg. 606
ASHLAND CANADA CORP.—See Ashland Inc.; *U.S. Public*, pg. 211
ASHLAND CHEMICAL HISPANIA, S.L.—See Ashland Inc.; *U.S. Public*, pg. 211
ASHLAND (CHINA) HOLDINGS CO., LTD.—See Ashland Inc.; *U.S. Public*, pg. 211
ASHLAND CZ S.R.O.—See Ashland Inc.; *U.S. Public*, pg. 211
ASHLAND DAILY TIDINGS—See Rosebud Media, LLC; *U.S. Private*, pg. 3482
ASHLAND DANMARK APS—See Ashland Inc.; *U.S. Public*, pg. 211
ASHLAND FINLAND OY—See Ashland Inc.; *U.S. Public*, pg. 211
ASHLAND FOUNDRY & MACHINE WORKS, LLC—See Speyside Equity LLC; *U.S. Private*, pg. 3756
ASHLAND FRANCE SAS—See Ashland Inc.; *U.S. Public*, pg. 211
ASHLAND HARDWARE SYSTEMS—See Quanex Building Products Corp.; *U.S. Public*, pg. 1749
ASHLAND HOME NET—See Jefferson Public Radio; *U.S. Private*, pg. 2198
ASHLAND INC.; *U.S. Public*, pg. 211
ASHLAND INDUSTRIES AUSTRIA GMBH—See Ashland Inc.; *U.S. Public*, pg. 212
ASHLAND INDUSTRIES BELGIUM BVBA—See Ashland Inc.; *U.S. Public*, pg. 212
ASHLAND INDUSTRIES DEUTSCHLAND GMBH—See Ashland Inc.; *U.S. Public*, pg. 212
ASHLAND INDUSTRIES EUROPE GMBH—See Ashland Inc.; *U.S. Public*, pg. 211

ASHLAND INDUSTRIES FINLAND OY—See Ashland Inc.; *U.S. Public*, pg. 212
ASHLAND INDUSTRIES FRANCE SAS—See Ashland Inc.; *U.S. Public*, pg. 212
ASHLAND INDUSTRIES ITALIA S.R.L.—See Ashland Inc.; *U.S. Public*, pg. 212
ASHLAND INDUSTRIES NEDERLAND B.V.—See Ashland Inc.; *U.S. Public*, pg. 212
ASHLAND INDUSTRIES SWEDEN AB—See Ashland Inc.; *U.S. Public*, pg. 212
ASHLAND INDUSTRIES UK LIMITED—See Ashland Inc.; *U.S. Public*, pg. 212
ASHLAND INTERNATIONAL HOLDINGS, INC.—See Ashland Inc.; *U.S. Public*, pg. 211
ASHLAND MANAGEMENT AGENCY, LLC—See Fifth Third Bancorp; *U.S. Public*, pg. 833
ASHLAND OFFICE SUPPLY, INC.; *U.S. Private*, pg. 349
ASHLAND PERFORMANCE MATERIALS - OAK CREEK—See Ashland Inc.; *U.S. Public*, pg. 211
ASHLAND PERFORMANCE MATERIALS—See Ashland Inc.; *U.S. Public*, pg. 211
ASHLAND PHYSICAL THERAPY, LIMITED PARTNERSHIP—See U.S. Physical Therapy, Inc.; *U.S. Public*, pg. 2213
ASHLAND PUBLISHING CO., LLC—See Gannett Co., Inc.; *U.S. Public*, pg. 901
ASHLAND RHINE HOLDINGS B.V.—See Ashland Inc.; *U.S. Public*, pg. 212
ASHLAND RHONE HOLDINGS B.V.—See Ashland Inc.; *U.S. Public*, pg. 212
ASHLAND SERVICES B.V.—See Ashland Inc.; *U.S. Public*, pg. 211
ASHLAND SPECIALTIES BELGIUM BVBA—See Ashland Inc.; *U.S. Public*, pg. 212
ASHLAND SPECIALTIES HISPANIA S.L.—See Ashland Inc.; *U.S. Public*, pg. 212
ASHLAND SPECIALTIES SOUTH AFRICA PROPRIETARY LIMITED—See Ashland Inc.; *U.S. Public*, pg. 212
ASHLAND SPECIALTIES SVERIGE AB—See Ashland Inc.; *U.S. Public*, pg. 212
ASHLAND SPECIALTIES UK LIMITED—See Ashland Inc.; *U.S. Public*, pg. 212
ASHLAND SPECIALTY INGREDIENTS—See Ashland Inc.; *U.S. Public*, pg. 212
ASHLAND SPECIALTY INGREDIENTS—See Ashland Inc.; *U.S. Public*, pg. 212
ASHLAND SWITZERLAND HOLDINGS GMBH—See Ashland Inc.; *U.S. Public*, pg. 212
ASHLAND TAB—See Gannett Co., Inc.; *U.S. Public*, pg. 901
ASHLAND TECHNOLOGIES, INC.; *U.S. Private*, pg. 349
ASHLEY AVERY'S COLLECTIBLES—See Franchise Concepts, Inc.; *U.S. Private*, pg. 1587
ASHLEY CAPITAL LLC; *U.S. Private*, pg. 349
ASHLEY DISTRIBUTION SERVICES, LTD.—See Ashley Furniture Industries, Inc.; *U.S. Private*, pg. 350
ASHLEY ELLIS LLC—See GEE Group Inc.; *U.S. Public*, pg. 909
ASHLEY FURNITURE INDUSTRIES, INC.; *U.S. Private*, pg. 350
ASHLEY F. WARD, INC.; *U.S. Private*, pg. 350
ASHLEY GINNING SERVICES PTY LTD—See Louis Dreyfus Company B.V.; *Int'l*, pg. 4562
ASHLEY HOMESTORES, LTD.—See Ashley Furniture Industries, Inc.; *U.S. Private*, pg. 350
ASHLEY HOUSE PLC; *Int'l*, pg. 607
ASHLEY IMPORTS, LLC; *U.S. Private*, pg. 350
ASHLEY-MARTIN MANUFACTURING LLC—See Designs for Health, Inc.; *U.S. Private*, pg. 1215
ASHLEY SERVICES GROUP LIMITED; *Int'l*, pg. 607
ASHLEY STEWART, INC.—See The Invus Group, LLC; *U.S. Private*, pg. 4057
ASHLEY VALLEY MEDICAL CENTER, LLC—See Apollo Global Management, Inc.; *U.S. Public*, pg. 154
ASHLY AUDIO INC—See DCC plc; *Int'l*, pg. 1990
ASHMORE BROS., INC.; *U.S. Private*, pg. 350
ASHMORE EMERGING MARKETS INCOME FUND; *Int'l*, pg. 607
ASHMORE GLOBAL OPPORTUNITIES LTD.; *Int'l*, pg. 607
ASHMORE GROUP PLC; *Int'l*, pg. 607
ASHMORE INVESTMENT MANAGEMENT INDIA LLP—See Ashmore Group plc; *Int'l*, pg. 608
ASHMORE INVESTMENT MANAGEMENT LIMITED—See Ashmore Group plc; *Int'l*, pg. 608
ASHNISHA INDUSTRIES LTD.; *Int'l*, pg. 608
ASHNOOR TEXTILE MILLS LIMITED; *Int'l*, pg. 608
ASHOKA BUILDCON LTD.; *Int'l*, pg. 608
ASHOKA CONCESSIONS LIMITED—See Ashoka Buildcon Ltd.; *Int'l*, pg. 608
ASHOKA INDIA EQUITY INVESTMENT TRUST PLC; *Int'l*, pg. 608
ASHOK ALCO CHEM LIMITED; *Int'l*, pg. 608
ASHOKA METCAST LIMITED; *Int'l*, pg. 608
ASHOKA REFINERIES LIMITED; *Int'l*, pg. 608
ASHOKA; *U.S. Private*, pg. 350
ASHOKA TECHNOLOGIES PRIVATE LIMITED—See Ashoka Buildcon Ltd.; *Int'l*, pg. 608

ASHOK LELAND FINANCE LTD.—See Hinduja Group Ltd.; *Int'l*, pg. 3398
ASHOK LEYLAND LTD.—See Hinduja Group Ltd.; *Int'l*, pg. 3398
ASHOK LEYLAND (NIGERIA) LIMITED—See Hinduja Group Ltd.; *Int'l*, pg. 3398
ASHOK PIRAMAL GROUP; *Int'l*, pg. 608
AS HOLMEN METS—See Holmen AB; *Int'l*, pg. 3452
ASHOT ASHKELON INDUSTRIES LTD.—See First Israel Mezzanine Investors Ltd.; *Int'l*, pg. 2685
ASH PLASTIC PRODUCTS LIMITED—See Hill & Smith PLC; *Int'l*, pg. 3391
ASHRAM ONLINE.COM LIMITED; *Int'l*, pg. 608
ASHRING HOUSE LIMITED—See Sheikh Holdings Group (Investments) Limited; *Int'l*, pg. 6793
ASH-SHARQIYAH DEVELOPMENT COMPANY; *Int'l*, pg. 606
ASH SHIPPING, INC., *U.S. Private*, pg. 349
ASHS LTD.; *Int'l*, pg. 609
ASH STEVENS INC.—See Piramal Enterprises Ltd.; *Int'l*, pg. 5874
ASH STEVENS, INC.—See Piramal Enterprises Ltd.; *Int'l*, pg. 5874
ASHTEAD FINANCING LIMITED—See Ashtead Group Plc; *Int'l*, pg. 609
ASHTEAD GROUP PLC; *Int'l*, pg. 609
ASHTEAD PLANT HIRE CO. LTD.—See Ashtead Group Plc; *Int'l*, pg. 609
ASHTEAD TECHNOLOGY HOLDINGS PLC; *Int'l*, pg. 609
ASHTEAD TECHNOLOGY LTD.—See Ashtead Technology Holdings Plc; *Int'l*, pg. 609
ASHTON ATLANTA RESIDENTIAL LLC; *U.S. Private*, pg. 350
ASHTON BANCSHARES, INC.; *U.S. Private*, pg. 350
ASHTON COAL OPERATIONS PTY LIMITED—See Yankuang Group Co., Limited; *Int'l*, pg. 8562
ASHTON COMPANY, INC., *U.S. Private*, pg. 350
THE ASHTON COMPANY; *U.S. Private*, pg. 3989
ASHTON-DRAKE GALLERIES, LTD.—See The Bradford Group; *U.S. Private*, pg. 3999
ASHTON GARDENS HOUSTON; *U.S. Private*, pg. 350
ASHTON STATE BANK AGENCY, INC.—See Ashton Bancshares, Inc.; *U.S. Private*, pg. 350
ASHTON STATE BANK—See Ashton Bancshares, Inc.; *U.S. Private*, pg. 350
ASHTON WOODS HOMES; *U.S. Private*, pg. 350
ASHTROM GROUP LTD.; *Int'l*, pg. 609
ASHTRUR PROPERTIES LTD.; *Int'l*, pg. 609
ASHUR INTERNATIONAL BANK FOR INVESTMENT; *Int'l*, pg. 609
ASH VENTURE LLC—See SER Capital Partners LLC; *U.S. Private*, pg. 3612
ASHWA TECHNOLOGIES CO. LTD.—See Henkel AG & Co. KGaA; *Int'l*, pg. 3348
ASHWICK (VIC) NO 102 PTY. LTD.—See Elders Limited; *Int'l*, pg. 2346
ASHWOOD PARK RETIREMENT VILLAGE LIMITED—See Arvida Group Limited; *Int'l*, pg. 587
ASHWOOD UK LIMITED—See Eurofins Scientific S.E.; *Int'l*, pg. 2535
ASHWORTH BELTS B.V.—See Ashworth Bros., Inc.; *U.S. Private*, pg. 350
ASHWORTH BROS., INC.; *U.S. Private*, pg. 350
ASHWORTH COLLEGE—See IAC Inc.; *U.S. Public*, pg. 1083
ASHWORTH EUROPE, LTD—See Ashworth Bros., Inc.; *U.S. Private*, pg. 350
ASHWORTH FACTORY SERVICE CORPORATION—See Ashworth Bros., Inc.; *U.S. Private*, pg. 350
ASHWORTH JAPAN K.K.—See Ashworth Bros., Inc.; *U.S. Private*, pg. 350
ASHWORTH—See Compagnie de Saint-Gobain SA; *Int'l*, pg. 1722
ASIA ACCESS TELECOM, INC.; *U.S. Private*, pg. 351
ASIA AGRICULTURAL MACHINERY CO., LTD. - FIRST FACTORY—See Asia Agricultural Machinery Co., Ltd.; *Int'l*, pg. 609
ASIA AGRICULTURAL MACHINERY CO., LTD.; *Int'l*, pg. 609
ASIA AIRPORT HOTEL CO., LTD.—See Asia Hotel Public Company Limited; *Int'l*, pg. 613
ASIA AIR SURVEY CO., LTD.; *Int'l*, pg. 609
ASIA AIR SURVEY MYANMAR CO., LTD—See Asia Air Survey Co., Ltd.; *Int'l*, pg. 609
ASIA ALLIED INFRASTRUCTURE HOLDINGS LIMITED; *Int'l*, pg. 609
ASIA ALUMINIUM HOLDINGS LIMITED; *Int'l*, pg. 610
ASIA AMALGAMATED HOLDINGS CORPORATION; *Int'l*, pg. 610
ASIA AMERICA CORPORATION—See Argosy Capital Group, LLC; *U.S. Private*, pg. 321
ASIA AQUACULTURE (M) SDN. BHD.—See Charoen Pokphand Foods Public Company Limited; *Int'l*, pg. 1451
ASIA ASSET ADVISORY CO., LTD.—See Land & Houses Public Company Limited; *Int'l*, pg. 4403
ASIA ASSET FINANCE PLC—See Asia Capital PLC; *Int'l*, pg. 610

ASIA ASSET PROPERTY GROUP LTD—See Hopefluent Group Holdings Ltd; *Int'l*, pg. 3473
ASIA ASSET PROPERTY SERVICES (SHANGHAI) CO., LTD.—See Hopefluent Group Holdings Ltd; *Int'l*, pg. 3473
ASIA AVIATION PUBLIC COMPANY LIMITED; *Int'l*, pg. 610
ASIABASEMETALS INC.; *Int'l*, pg. 616
ASIA-BENI STEEL INDUSTRIES (PTE) LTD—See Asia Enterprises Holding Limited; *Int'l*, pg. 612
ASIABEST GROUP INTERNATIONAL INC.—See Universal Entertainment Corporation; *Int'l*, pg. 8078
ASIA BIOMASS PUBLIC COMPANY LIMITED; *Int'l*, pg. 610
ASIA BOOKS COMPANY LTD—See Thames & Hudson Ltd; *Int'l*, pg. 7607
ASIA BRANDS BERHAD; *Int'l*, pg. 610
ASIA BROADBAND, INC.; *U.S. Public*, pg. 213
THE ASIA BUSINESS DAILY CO., LTD.; *Int'l*, pg. 7614
ASIA CABLE ENGINEERING CO., PTE. LTD.—See Sojitz Corporation; *Int'l*, pg. 7061
ASIA CABLE ENGINEERING CO., PTE. LTD.—See The Furukawa Electric Co., Ltd.; *Int'l*, pg. 7644
ASIA CAN MANUFACTURING CO., LTD.—See Carabao Group Public Company Limited; *Int'l*, pg. 1319
ASIA CAPITAL GROUP PUBLIC COMPANY LIMITED; *Int'l*, pg. 610
ASIA CAPITAL LTD.; *Int'l*, pg. 610
ASIA CAPITAL PLC; *Int'l*, pg. 610
ASIA CAPITAL PUBLIC COMPANY LIMITED; *Int'l*, pg. 610
ASIA CARBON INDUSTRIES, INC.; *Int'l*, pg. 610
ASIA CASSAVA RESOURCES HOLDINGS LIMITED; *Int'l*, pg. 610
ASIACELL COMMUNICATIONS PJSC—See Ooredoo Q.S.C.; *Int'l*, pg. 5594
ASIA CEMEDINE CO., LTD.—See Kaneka Corporation; *Int'l*, pg. 4066
ASIA CEMENT (CHINA) HOLDINGS CORPORATION—See Asia Cement Corporation; *Int'l*, pg. 611
ASIA CEMENT CO., LTD.—See Asia Holdings Co., Ltd.; *Int'l*, pg. 612
ASIA CEMENT CORPORATION - HSINCHU PLANT—See Asia Cement Corporation; *Int'l*, pg. 611
ASIA CEMENT CORPORATION - HUALIEN PLANT—See Asia Cement Corporation; *Int'l*, pg. 611
ASIA CEMENT CORPORATION; *Int'l*, pg. 611
ASIA CEMENT (SINGAPORE) PTE. LTD.—See Asia Cement Corporation; *Int'l*, pg. 611
ASIA CENTER KFT.—See STRABAG SE; *Int'l*, pg. 7229
ASIA CHEMICAL CORPORATION INC.; *U.S. Private*, pg. 351
ASIA COAL LIMITED; *Int'l*, pg. 611
ASIA COMMERCIAL BANK; *Int'l*, pg. 611
ASIA COMMERCIAL HOLDINGS LIMITED; *Int'l*, pg. 611
ASIACOM PHILIPPINES, INC.—See Deutsche Telekom AG; *Int'l*, pg. 2083
ASIA CONSOLIDATED DMC PTE. LTD.—See Yatra Online, Inc.; *Int'l*, pg. 8571
ASIA CONTINENT INVESTMENT HOLDINGS PTE. LTD.—See Asia Cement Corporation; *Int'l*, pg. 611
ASIA CREATIVE TOURS CO., LTD.—See Japan Airlines Co., Ltd.; *Int'l*, pg. 3884
ASIACREDIT BANK JSC; *Int'l*, pg. 616
ASIA CUANON TECHNOLOGY (SHANGHAI) CO., LTD.; *Int'l*, pg. 611
ASIA DEVELOPMENT CAPITAL CO., LTD.; *Int'l*, pg. 611
ASIA DIGITAL ENGINEERING SDN. BHD.—See Capital A Bhd; *Int'l*, pg. 1309
ASIA DRAGON INTERNATIONAL LIMITED—See Alco Holdings Limited; *Int'l*, pg. 301
ASIA ELECTRONICS HK TECHNOLOGIES LIMITED—See Computime Group Limited; *Int'l*, pg. 1760
ASIA ENERGY LOGISTICS GROUP LIMITED; *Int'l*, pg. 611
ASIA ENTERPRISES HOLDING LIMITED; *Int'l*, pg. 612
ASIA ENVIRONMENTAL PARTNERS, L.P.—See Olympus Capital Holdings Asia; *U.S. Private*, pg. 3012
ASIA EQUITY EXCHANGE GROUP INC.; *Int'l*, pg. 612
ASIAEURO INTERNATIONAL BEVERAGE (HONG KONG) LIMITED—See Thai Beverage Public Company Limited; *Int'l*, pg. 7589
ASIA EURO OIL PLC; *Int'l*, pg. 612
ASIA-EXPRESS LOGISTICS HOLDINGS LIMITED; *Int'l*, pg. 616
ASIA FASHION HOLDINGS LIMITED; *Int'l*, pg. 612
ASIA FIBER PUBLIC COMPANY LIMITED; *Int'l*, pg. 612
ASIA FILE CORPORATION BHD.; *Int'l*, pg. 612
ASIA FINANCIAL HOLDINGS LIMITED—See Mitsubishi UFJ Financial Group, Inc.; *Int'l*, pg. 4969
ASIAFIN HOLDINGS CORP.; *Int'l*, pg. 616
ASIAFLEX PRODUCTS SDN BHD—See TechnipFMC plc; *Int'l*, pg. 7507
THE ASIA FOUNDATION; *U.S. Private*, pg. 3989
ASIA GAME SHOW HOLDINGS LTD.—See Pico Far East Holdings Limited; *Int'l*, pg. 5860

ASIA GENERAL HOLDING CO.,LTD.—See Topcon Corporation; *Int'l*, pg. 7814
ASIA GIKEN CO., LTD.—See Carlit Co., Ltd.; *Int'l*, pg. 1338
ASIA GLOBAL CROSSING LTD.; *Int'l*, pg. 612
ASIA GLOBAL HEALTH LTD.—See Bumrungrad Hospital Public Company Limited; *Int'l*, pg. 1215
ASIA GLOBAL RESEARCH CO., LTD.—See Bumrungrad Hospital Public Company Limited; *Int'l*, pg. 1215
ASIA GREEN AGRICULTURE CORPORATION; *Int'l*, pg. 612
ASIA GREEN BIOTECHNOLOGY CORP.; *Int'l*, pg. 612
ASIA GREEN ENERGY PUBLIC COMPANY LIMITED; *Int'l*, pg. 612
ASIA GROCERY DISTRIBUTION LIMITED; *Int'l*, pg. 612
ASIA GROUND SERVICE CO., LTD.—See Triple i Logistics Public Company Limited; *Int'l*, pg. 7926
ASIA HOLDINGS CO., LTD. - DAEJEON PLANT—See Asia Holdings Co., Ltd.; *Int'l*, pg. 612
ASIA HOLDINGS CO., LTD. - HONGSEONG PLANT—See Asia Holdings Co., Ltd.; *Int'l*, pg. 612
ASIA HOLDINGS CO., LTD. - JECHEON PLANT—See Asia Holdings Co., Ltd.; *Int'l*, pg. 612
ASIA HOLDINGS CO., LTD. - JUNGBU PLANT—See Asia Holdings Co., Ltd.; *Int'l*, pg. 612
ASIA HOLDINGS CO., LTD. - SEOUL REMICON PLANT—See Asia Holdings Co., Ltd.; *Int'l*, pg. 612
ASIA HOLDINGS CO., LTD.; *Int'l*, pg. 612
ASIA HOLDINGS CO., LTD. - SUWON PLANT—See Asia Holdings Co., Ltd.; *Int'l*, pg. 612
ASIA HOLDINGS CO., LTD. - YONGIN PLANT—See Asia Holdings Co., Ltd.; *Int'l*, pg. 612
ASIA HOTEL PUBLIC COMPANY LIMITED; *Int'l*, pg. 613
ASIAHUB TRADING SDN. BHD.—See Fajarbaru Builder Group Bhd.; *Int'l*, pg. 2610
ASIA ICOM INC.—See ICOM INCORPORATED; *Int'l*, pg. 3582
ASIA INDUSTRY CO., LTD.—See Tosoh Corporation; *Int'l*, pg. 7832
ASIA INDUSTRY DEVELOPMENT CO., LTD.—See Asia Holdings Co., Ltd.; *Int'l*, pg. 613
ASIA INFIASTRUCTURE MANAGEMENT (THAILAND) CO., LTD.—See Thoresen Thai Agencies Public Company Limited; *Int'l*, pg. 7718
ASIA INFLIGHT LTD.—See Ringier Trade Media Ltd.; *Int'l*, pg. 6344
ASIAINFO, INC.—See CITIC Group Corporation; *Int'l*, pg. 1619
ASIAINFO INTERNATIONAL PTE. LTD.—See CITIC Group Corporation; *Int'l*, pg. 1619
ASIA INSURANCE COMPANY LIMITED—See Mitsubishi UFJ Financial Group, Inc.; *Int'l*, pg. 4969
ASIA INSURANCE CO.; *Int'l*, pg. 613
ASIA INSURANCE LIMITED; *Int'l*, pg. 613
ASIA INTERACTIVE MEDIA INC.; *Int'l*, pg. 613
ASIA INTERNET HOLDING CO., LTD.—See Internet Initiative Japan Inc.; *Int'l*, pg. 3753
ASIA INVEST BANK CJSC—See National Bank for Foreign Economic Activity of the Republic of Uzbekistan; *Int'l*, pg. 5151
ASIA INVESTMENT AND SUPERMARKET TRADING DO. LTD.—See Jardine Matheson Holdings Limited; *Int'l*, pg. 3909
ASIA JET PARTNERS MALAYSIA SDN BHD—See Berjaya Corporation Berhad; *Int'l*, pg. 982
ASIA JET SDN. BHD.—See Berjaya Corporation Berhad; *Int'l*, pg. 982
ASIA KELMET CO., LTD.—See Daido Metal Corporation; *Int'l*, pg. 1921
ASIA LIFELINE MEDICAL SERVICES PTE. LTD.—See Pacific Healthcare Holdings Ltd.; *Int'l*, pg. 5689
ASIALINK TECHNOLOGY DEVELOPMENT LIMITED—See FSBM Holdings Berhad; *Int'l*, pg. 2798
ASIA LOGISTICS (CHINA) LIMITED; *Int'l*, pg. 613
ASIA MEDIA CO., LTD.; *Int'l*, pg. 613
ASIA MEDIA GROUP BERHAD; *Int'l*, pg. 613
ASIA MEDICAL & AGRICULTURAL LABORATORY & RESEARCH CENTER COMPANY LIMITED—See Ladprao General Hospital Public Company Limited; *Int'l*, pg. 4392
ASIAMEDIC ASTIQUE THE AESTHETIC CLINIC PTE LTD—See AsiaMedic Ltd.; *Int'l*, pg. 616
ASIAMEDIC EYE CENTRE PTE. LTD.—See AsiaMedic Ltd.; *Int'l*, pg. 616
ASIAMEDIC LTD.; *Int'l*, pg. 616
ASIAMEDIC PET/CT CENTRE PTE LTD—See AsiaMedic Ltd.; *Int'l*, pg. 616
ASIA METAL PUBLIC COMPANY LIMITED; *Int'l*, pg. 613
ASIAMET EDUCATION GROUP BERHAD—See Creador Sdn. Bhd.; *Int'l*, pg. 1831
ASIAMET EDUCATION GROUP BERHAD—See SMRT Holdings Berhad; *Int'l*, pg. 7014
ASIAMET RESOURCES LIMITED; *Int'l*, pg. 617
ASIA MEWAH RESOURCES SDN. BHD.—See Haisan Resources Berhad; *Int'l*, pg. 3217
ASIA MIDDLE EAST TOURS (L.L.C.)—See Asiatravel.com Holdings Limited; *Int'l*, pg. 620
ASIA MILES LIMITED—See Cathay Pacific Airways Limited; *Int'l*, pg. 1360

COMPANY NAME INDEX

ASIA MINERAL JOINT STOCK COMPANY; *Int'l*, pg. 613
ASIA MODIFIED STARCH CO., LTD.—See Mitsubishi Corporation; *Int'l*, pg. 4937
ASIAMOST SDN. BHD.—See AME Elite Consortium Berhad; *Int'l*, pg. 420
ASIANA ABACUS INC.—See Kumho Asiana Group; *Int'l*, pg. 4330
ASIANA AIRLINES, INC.—See Korean Air Lines Co., Ltd.; *Int'l*, pg. 4288
ASIANA AIRLINES—See Korean Air Lines Co., Ltd.; *Int'l*, pg. 4288
ASIANA AIRPORT INC.—See Kumho Asiana Group; *Int'l*, pg. 4330
ASIANA CUISINE ENTERPRISES, INC.; *U.S. Private*, pg. 351
ASIANA DEVELOPMENT CO LTD—See Kumho Asiana Group; *Int'l*, pg. 4330
ASIAN AGE HOLDINGS LTD.—See Deccan Chronicle Holdings Ltd.; *Int'l*, pg. 1999
ASIANA IDT, INC.—See Korean Air Lines Co., Ltd.; *Int'l*, pg. 4288
ASIAN ALLIANCE INSURANCE PLC - ICT DIVISION—See Softlogic Holdings PLC; *Int'l*, pg. 7056
ASIAN ALLIANCE INTERNATIONAL CO., LTD.—See Asian Sea Corporation Public Company Limited; *Int'l*, pg. 619
ASIAN AMERICAN COAL INC.—See Banpu Public Company Limited; *Int'l*, pg. 851
ASIAN AMERICAN DRUG ABUSE PROGRAM; *U.S. Private*, pg. 351
ASIAN AMERICAN HOME CARE, INC.—See Humana, Inc.; *U.S. Public*, pg. 1069
ASIAN AMERICAN MEDICAL GROUP LIMITED; *Int'l*, pg. 617
ASIAN AUTOPARTS CO., LTD.—See Honda Motor Co., Ltd.; *Int'l*, pg. 3460
ASIAN AVIATION CENTRE OF EXCELLENCE SDN BHD.—See AirAsia X Berhad; *Int'l*, pg. 241
ASIAN AVIATION TRAINING CENTRE LTD.—See L3Harris Technologies, Inc.; *U.S. Public*, pg. 1280
ASIAN BAMBOO AG; *Int'l*, pg. 617
ASIAN BEARING LTD.; *Int'l*, pg. 617
ASIANBEAUTYWHOLESALE (HONG KONG) LIMITED—See YesAsia Holdings Ltd.; *Int'l*, pg. 8578
ASIAN BUSINESS SOFTWARE SOLUTIONS SDN. BHD.—See Bain Capital, LP; *U.S. Private*, pg. 441
ASIAN CAPITAL RESOURCES (HOLDINGS) LIMITED; *Int'l*, pg. 617
ASIAN CITRUS (H.K.) COMPANY LIMITED—See Asian Citrus Holdings Limited; *Int'l*, pg. 617
ASIAN CITRUS HOLDINGS LIMITED; *Int'l*, pg. 617
ASIAN CONSUMER CARE PRIVATE LIMITED—See Dabur India Ltd.; *Int'l*, pg. 1903
ASIAN COUNSELING & REFERRAL SERVICE; *U.S. Private*, pg. 351
ASIAN DEVELOPMENT BANK; *Int'l*, pg. 617
ASIAN ELECTRONIC TECHNOLOGY PTE. LTD.—See Seiko Group Corporation; *Int'l*, pg. 6688
ASIAN ENERGY SERVICES LTD.—See OilMax Energy Pvt. Ltd.; *Int'l*, pg. 5536
ASIA NEO TECH INDUSTRIAL CO., LTD.; *Int'l*, pg. 613
ASIANET STAR COMMUNICATIONS PRIVATE LIMITED—See The Walt Disney Company; *U.S. Public*, pg. 2137
ASIA NETWORK INTERNATIONAL CO., LTD.—See Triple i Logistics Public Company Limited; *Int'l*, pg. 7926
ASIAN EUROPEAN FOOTWEAR; *Int'l*, pg. 617
ASIAN EYE INSTITUTE INC.—See Lopez, Inc.; *Int'l*, pg. 4556
ASIAN FINANCE LTD.—See Nation Lanka Finance PLC; *Int'l*, pg. 5149
ASIAN FLORA LIMITED; *Int'l*, pg. 617
ASIAN GRANITO INDIA LIMITED - GUJARAT UNIT—See Asian Granito India Limited; *Int'l*, pg. 617
ASIAN GRANITO INDIA LIMITED; *Int'l*, pg. 617
ASIAN GROUP SCS EUROPE GMBH—See Asian Sea Corporation Public Company Limited; *Int'l*, pg. 619
ASIAN GROUP SERVICES CO., LTD.—See Asian Sea Corporation Public Company Limited; *Int'l*, pg. 619
ASIAN GROWTH PROPERTIES LIMITED; *Int'l*, pg. 617
ASIAN HALL ALGERIE SARL—See Toyota Tsusho Corporation; *Int'l*, pg. 7875
ASIAN HEALTHCARE SPECIALISTS LIMITED—See Doctor Anywhere Pte Ltd.; *Int'l*, pg. 2153
ASIAN HEALTH SERVICES; *U.S. Private*, pg. 351
ASIAN HONDA MOTOR CO., LTD.—See Honda Motor Co., Ltd.; *Int'l*, pg. 3460
ASIAN HOTELS (EAST) LIMITED; *Int'l*, pg. 617
ASIAN HOTELS (NORTH) LIMITED; *Int'l*, pg. 617
ASIAN HOTELS & PROPERTIES PLC; *Int'l*, pg. 617
ASIAN HOTELS (WEST) LIMITED; *Int'l*, pg. 617
ASIAN INDUSTRY AND INFORMATION SERVICES PVT LTD.—See The Braj Binani Group; *Int'l*, pg. 7627
ASIAN INFORMATION TECHNOLOGY INC.—See WPG Holdings Limited; *Int'l*, pg. 8460
ASIAN INSULATORS PUBLIC COMPANY LIMITED; *Int'l*, pg. 618
ASIAN LIFE CO., LTD.—See Asian Phytoceuticals Public Company Limited; *Int'l*, pg. 619

ASIANLIFE FINANCIAL ASSURANCE CORPORATION—See Malayan Banking Berhad; *Int'l*, pg. 4660
ASIANLIFE & GENERAL ASSURANCE CORPORATION—See Malayan Banking Berhad; *Int'l*, pg. 4660
ASIAN LIFE INSURANCE COMPANY; *Int'l*, pg. 618
ASIAN LIFT PTE LTD—See HAL Trust N.V.; *Int'l*, pg. 3227
ASIAN LIFT PTE LTD—See Sembcorp Industries Ltd.; *Int'l*, pg. 6703
ASIAN LINK CO., LTD.—See LAC Co., Ltd.; *Int'l*, pg. 4391
ASIANLOGIC LIMITED; *Int'l*, pg. 619
ASIAN MARINE SERVICES PUBLIC COMPANY LIMITED; *Int'l*, pg. 618
ASIAN MARUYAMA (THAILAND) CO., LTD.—See Maruyama Mfg. Co., Inc.; *Int'l*, pg. 4715
ASIAN MICRO CO. LTD.—See Asian Micro Holdings Ltd.; *Int'l*, pg. 618
ASIAN MICRO HOLDINGS LTD.; *Int'l*, pg. 618
ASIAN MICRO TECHNOLOGY CO. LTD.—See Asian Micro Holdings Ltd.; *Int'l*, pg. 618
ASIAN MICRO (THAILAND) CO., LTD.—See Asian Micro Holdings Ltd.; *Int'l*, pg. 618
ASIAN PAC HOLDINGS BERHAD; *Int'l*, pg. 618
ASIAN - PACIFIC BANK PJSC—See Central Bank of the Russian Federation; *Int'l*, pg. 1405
ASIAN-PACIFIC CAN CO LTD—See Thai Union Group Public Company Limited; *Int'l*, pg. 7596
ASIAN PACIFIC HEALTH CARE VENTURE, INC.; *U.S. Private*, pg. 351
ASIAN PACIFIC TIMBER MARKETING PTY LTD—See Asian Pacific Timber Marketing Pty Ltd; *Int'l*, pg. 618
ASIAN PACIFIC TIMBER MARKETING PTY LTD; *Int'l*, pg. 618
ASIAN PAINTS (BANGLADESH) LIMITED—See Asian Paints Limited; *Int'l*, pg. 618
ASIAN PAINTS INDUSTRIAL COATINGS LTD.—See Asian Paints Limited; *Int'l*, pg. 618
ASIAN PAINTS INTERNATIONAL PRIVATE LIMITED—See Asian Paints Limited; *Int'l*, pg. 618
ASIAN PAINTS (LANKA) LIMITED—See Asian Paints Limited; *Int'l*, pg. 618
ASIAN PAINTS LIMITED; *Int'l*, pg. 618
ASIAN PAINTS (NEPAL) PVT. LIMITED—See Asian Paints Limited; *Int'l*, pg. 618
ASIAN PAINTS (S.I.) LIMITED—See Asian Paints Limited; *Int'l*, pg. 618
ASIAN PAINTS (VANUATU) LIMITED—See Asian Paints Limited; *Int'l*, pg. 618
ASIAN PAY TELEVISION TRUST; *Int'l*, pg. 619
ASIAN PETROPRODUCTS & EXPORTS LIMITED; *Int'l*, pg. 619
ASIAN PETS CARE CORPORATION CO., LTD.—See Asian Sea Corporation Public Company Limited; *Int'l*, pg. 619
ASIAN PHYTOCEUTICALS PUBLIC COMPANY LIMITED; *Int'l*, pg. 619
ASIAN PLASTIC MACHINERY CO. LTD.—See Chen Hsong Holdings Ltd.; *Int'l*, pg. 1464
ASIAN PORCELAIN SDN. BHD.—See CSH Alliance Berhad; *Int'l*, pg. 1865
ASIAN POTTERY HOME & GARDEN SDN. BHD.—See CSH Alliance Berhad; *Int'l*, pg. 1865
ASIAN POTTERY (PENANG) SDN. BHD.—See CSH Alliance Berhad; *Int'l*, pg. 1865
ASIAN SEA CORPORATION PUBLIC COMPANY LIMITED; *Int'l*, pg. 619
ASIAN SEALAND ENGINEERING PTE LTD—See Lanco Construction & Engineering Pte Ltd; *Int'l*, pg. 4402
ASIAN SEALAND OFFSHORE & MARINE PTE. LTD.—See Beng Kuang Marine Limited; *Int'l*, pg. 973
ASIAN STANLEY INTERNATIONAL CO., LTD.—See Stanley Electric Co., Ltd.; *Int'l*, pg. 7170
ASIAN STAR ANCHOR CHAIN CO., LTD. JIANGSU; *Int'l*, pg. 619
ASIAN STAR COMPANY LIMITED (USA)—See Asian Star Company Ltd; *Int'l*, pg. 619
ASIAN STAR COMPANY LTD; *Int'l*, pg. 619
ASIAN STAR CO.; *Int'l*, pg. 619
ASIAN STAR JEWELS PRIVATE LIMITED—See Asian Star Company Ltd; *Int'l*, pg. 619
ASIAN STEEL COMPANY LTD.—See Sumitomo Corporation; *Int'l*, pg. 7268
ASIAN STEEL PRODUCT CO., LTD—See Italian-Thai Development pcl; *Int'l*, pg. 3829
ASIAN SURFACE TECHNOLOGIES PTE. LTD.—See The Carlyle Group Inc.; *U.S. Public*, pg. 2054
ASIAN TANAKA BANGKOK CO., LTD.—See Tanaka Seimitsu Kogyo Co., Ltd.; *Int'l*, pg. 7456
ASIAN TEA & EXPORTS LIMITED; *Int'l*, pg. 619
ASIAN TELEVISION NETWORK INC.—See Asian Television Network International Ltd.; *Int'l*, pg. 619
ASIAN TELEVISION NETWORK INTERNATIONAL LTD.; *Int'l*, pg. 619
ASIAN TERMINALS, INC.; *Int'l*, pg. 619
ASIAN TIGERS K.C.DAT (CHINA) LTD.—See Yamatane Corporation; *Int'l*, pg. 8553
ASIAN TIGERS TRANSPO INTERNATIONAL LTD.—See Yamatane Corporation; *Int'l*, pg. 8553

ASIAN TIGERS TRANSPO INTERNATIONAL (VIETNAM) LTD.—See Yamatane Corporation; *Int'l*, pg. 8553
ASIAN TRAILS LTD.—See Fairfax Financial Holdings Limited; *Int'l*, pg. 2608
ASIAN TRAILS TOUR LTD.—See Fairfax Financial Holdings Limited; *Int'l*, pg. 2608
ASIAN TRANSMISSION CORP.—See Mitsubishi Motors Corporation; *Int'l*, pg. 4966
ASIAN WEEK FOUNDATION—See AsianWeek; *U.S. Private*, pg. 351
ASIANWEEK; *U.S. Private*, pg. 351
ASIAN WORLD OF MARTIAL ARTS, INC.; *U.S. Private*, pg. 351
ASIA OFFSHORE DRILLING LIMITED—See SeaDrill Limited; *Int'l*, pg. 6662
ASIAONE ONLINE PTE. LTD.—See mm2 Asia Ltd.; *Int'l*, pg. 5004
ASIA OPTICAL CO., INC.; *Int'l*, pg. 613
ASIA OPTICAL INTERNATIONAL LTD.—See Asia Optical Co., Inc.; *Int'l*, pg. 613
ASIA ORIENT COMPANY LIMITED—See Asia Orient Holdings Limited; *Int'l*, pg. 613
ASIA ORIENT HOLDINGS LIMITED; *Int'l*, pg. 613
ASIA-PAC FINANCIAL INVESTMENT COMPANY LIMITED; *Int'l*, pg. 616
ASIA PACIFIC BEVERAGE PTE. LTD.—See LT Group, Inc.; *Int'l*, pg. 4571
THE ASIA-PACIFIC CENTRE FOR RESEARCH, INC.; *Int'l*, pg. 7614
ASIA PACIFIC DATA CENTRE—See NEXTDC Limited; *Int'l*, pg. 5248
ASIA PACIFIC DIVISION PTE LTD.—See Hankook & Company Co., Ltd.; *Int'l*, pg. 3253
ASIA PACIFIC ELITE CORP.—See Tong-Tai Machine Tool Co., Ltd.; *Int'l*, pg. 7806
ASIA PACIFIC FREIGHT SYSTEM SDN. BHD.—See DRB-HICOM Berhad; *Int'l*, pg. 2201
THE ASIA PACIFIC FUND, INC.; *U.S. Private*, pg. 3989
ASIA PACIFIC GENERAL INSURANCE CO. LIMITED; *Int'l*, pg. 613
ASIA PACIFIC GLASS CO., LTD.—See Carabao Group Public Company Limited; *Int'l*, pg. 1319
ASIA PACIFIC HOLDINGS LIMITED—See InterContinental Hotels Group PLC; *Int'l*, pg. 3736
ASIA-PACIFIC INFORMATION SERVICES SDN. BHD.—See Deutsche Post AG; *Int'l*, pg. 2071
ASIA - PACIFIC INVESTMENT JOINT STOCK COMPANY; *Int'l*, pg. 609
ASIA-PACIFIC LIGHT ALLOY (NANTONG) TECHNOLOGY CO., LTD.—See Jiangsu Asia-Pacific Light Alloy Technology Co., Ltd.; *Int'l*, pg. 3943
ASIA PACIFIC MARINE CORPORATION—See Nippon Yusen Kabushiki Kaisha; *Int'l*, pg. 5357
ASIA PACIFIC MICROSYSTEMS, INC.—See Unimicron Technology Corporation; *Int'l*, pg. 8050
ASIA PACIFIC RESOURCES INTERNATIONAL HOLDINGS LTD.; *Int'l*, pg. 613
ASIA PACIFIC SATELLITE LNC.; *Int'l*, pg. 614
ASIA-PACIFIC SECURITIES JOINT STOCK COMPANY; *Int'l*, pg. 616
ASIA PACIFIC SOLUTIONS PTE. LTD.—See VINCI S.A.; *Int'l*, pg. 8217
ASIA-PACIFIC SPECIAL NUTRIENTS SDN. BHD.—See Rhone Ma Holdings Berhad; *Int'l*, pg. 6327
ASIA-PACIFIC STRATEGIC INVESTMENTS LIMITED; *Int'l*, pg. 616
ASIA PACIFIC TELECOM CO., LTD.; *Int'l*, pg. 614
ASIA PACIFIC TRADING & INVESTMENT CO LIMITED—See KBC Group NV; *Int'l*, pg. 4104
ASIA PACIFIC WIRE & CABLE CORPORATION LIMITED; *Int'l*, pg. 614
ASIA PACKAGING MANUFACTURING CO., LTD.—See Carabao Group Public Company Limited; *Int'l*, pg. 1319
ASIA PACK LIMITED; *Int'l*, pg. 614
ASIAPAC RECYCLING PTE LTD—See Livingstone Health Holdings Limited; *Int'l*, pg. 4532
ASIAPAC TECHNOLOGY PTE. LTD.—See Keppel Corporation Limited; *Int'l*, pg. 4130
ASIA PAPER MANUFACTURING CO., LTD.; *Int'l*, pg. 614
ASIA PARAGON INTERNATIONAL LIMITED—See Delong Holdings Limited; *Int'l*, pg. 2015
ASIA PARKING INVESTMENT PTE. LTD.—See Nissei Build Kogyo Co., Ltd.; *Int'l*, pg. 5370
ASIA PATTAYA HOTEL CO., LTD—See Asia Hotel Public Company Limited; *Int'l*, pg. 613
ASIAPHARMA HOLDINGS LTD.; *Int'l*, pg. 620
ASIAPHOS LIMITED; *Int'l*, pg. 620
ASIA PILE HOLDINGS CORPORATION; *Int'l*, pg. 614
ASIA PIONEER ENTERTAINMENT HOLDINGS LIMITED; *Int'l*, pg. 614
ASIA PIONEER ENTERTAINMENT LIMITED—See Asia Pioneer Entertainment Holdings Limited; *Int'l*, pg. 614
ASIA PLASTIC RECYCLING HOLDING LIMITED; *Int'l*, pg. 614
ASIA PLUS ADVISORY COMPANY LIMITED—See Asia Plus Group Holdings Public Company Limited; *Int'l*, pg. 614
ASIA PLUS GROUP HOLDINGS PUBLIC COMPANY LIMITED; *Int'l*, pg. 614

ASIA PLUS SECURITIES COMPANY LIMITED—See Asia Plus Group Holdings Public Company Limited; *Int'l*, pg. 614
ASIA POLY HOLDINGS BERHAD; *Int'l*, pg. 614
ASIA POLY INDUSTRIAL SDN. BHD.—See Asia Poly Holdings Berhad; *Int'l*, pg. 615
ASIA POLYMER CORPORATION - LIN YUAN PLANT—See Asia Polymer Corporation; *Int'l*, pg. 615
ASIA POLYMER CORPORATION; *Int'l*, pg. 615
ASIA-POTASH INTERNATIONAL INVESTMENT (GUANGZHOU) CO., LTD.; *Int'l*, pg. 616
ASIA POWER CORPORATION LIMITED; *Int'l*, pg. 615
ASIA POWER PROJECTS PRIVATE LTD.—See Cassa Depositi e Prestiti S.p.A.; *Int'l*, pg. 1354
ASIA PRECISION PUBLIC COMPANY LIMITED; *Int'l*, pg. 615
ASIA PROCESS INDUSTRIES PTE. LTD.—See Hiap Seng Engineering Limited; *Int'l*, pg. 3382
ASIA PROJECTS ENGINEERING PTE LTD.—See Kyudenko Corporation; *Int'l*, pg. 4366
ASIA PROPERTIES, INC.; *U.S. Public*, pg. 213
ASIA PULP & PAPER AUSTRIA GMBH—See Pabrik Kertas Tjiwi Kimia Tbk; *Int'l*, pg. 5684
ASIA PULP & PAPER (CANADA) LTD.—See Pabrik Kertas Tjiwi Kimia Tbk; *Int'l*, pg. 5684
ASIA PULP & PAPER—See PT Sinar Mas Group; *Int'l*, pg. 6072
ASIARAY MEDIA GROUP LIMITED; *Int'l*, pg. 620
ASIA RECYCLE TECHNOLOGY COMPANY LIMITED—See Seven Utilities and Power Public Co., Ltd.; *Int'l*, pg. 6734
ASIA RECYCLING RESOURCES PTE. LTD.—See K.L. Resources Pte. Ltd.; *Int'l*, pg. 4044
ASIA REFRACTORIES CO., LTD.—See Nippon Crucible Co., Ltd.; *Int'l*, pg. 5313
ASIA RESOURCES HOLDINGS LIMITED; *Int'l*, pg. 615
ASIA SATELLITE TELECOMMUNICATIONS CO., LTD.—See CITIC Group Corporation; *Int'l*, pg. 1619
ASIA SATELLITE TELECOMMUNICATIONS CO., LTD.—See The Carlyle Group Inc.; *U.S. Public*, pg. 2045
ASIA SATELLITE TELECOMMUNICATIONS HOLDINGS LIMITED—See CITIC Group Corporation; *Int'l*, pg. 1619
ASIA SATELLITE TELECOMMUNICATIONS HOLDINGS LIMITED—See The Carlyle Group Inc.; *U.S. Public*, pg. 2045
ASIASEC PROPERTIES LIMITED—See Tian An China Investments Company Limited; *Int'l*, pg. 7737
ASIA SEED CO., LTD.; *Int'l*, pg. 615
ASIA SERMKIJ LEASING PUBLIC COMPANY LIMITED; *Int'l*, pg. 615
ASIA SILICONES MONOMER LTD.—See Shin-Etsu Chemical Co. Ltd.; *Int'l*, pg. 6838
ASIA SIYAKA COMMODITIES PLC; *Int'l*, pg. 615
ASIASOFT ONLINE PTE. LTD.—See Asphere Innovations Public Company Limited; *Int'l*, pg. 630
ASIA SPORTS VENTURES PTE LTD—See Bertelsmann SE & Co, KGaA; *Int'l*, pg. 993
ASIA STABILIZERS CO., LTD.—See Miwon Commercial Co., Ltd.; *Int'l*, pg. 4995
ASIA STANDARD HOTEL GROUP LIMITED—See Asia Standard International Group Limited; *Int'l*, pg. 615
ASIA STANDARD INTERNATIONAL GROUP LIMITED; *Int'l*, pg. 615
ASIA STRATEGIC HOLDINGS LIMITED; *Int'l*, pg. 615
ASIA TECH IMAGE, INC.; *Int'l*, pg. 615
ASIA TECHNICAL SUPPORT LABORATORY PTE. LTD.—See Zeon Corporation; *Int'l*, pg. 8635
ASIA TELE-NET & TECHNOLOGY CORPORATION LIMITED; *Int'l*, pg. 615
ASIATIC CARPETS LTD; *Int'l*, pg. 620
ASIATIC GROUP (HOLDINGS) LIMITED; *Int'l*, pg. 620
ASIATIC MARKETING COMMUNICATIONS, LTD.—See WPP plc; *Int'l*, pg. 8479
ASIA TIMBER PRODUCTS GROUP—See CVC Capital Partners SICAV-FIS S.A.; *Int'l*, pg. 1885
ASIA TIME CORPORATION; *Int'l*, pg. 616
ASIATIQUE RIVERFRONT CO., LTD.—See Asset World Corp Public Company Limited; *Int'l*, pg. 643
ASIA TODAY LIMITED—See Essel Corporate Resources Pvt. Ltd.; *Int'l*, pg. 2510
ASIATRAK (TIANJIN) LTD.—See Caterpillar, Inc.; *U.S. Public*, pg. 449
ASIATRAVEL.COM HOLDINGS LIMITED; *Int'l*, pg. 620
ASIA TRAVEL NETWORK LTD.—See Asiatravel.com Holdings Limited; *Int'l*, pg. 620
ASIA TRAVEL NETWORK LTD—See Asiatravel.com Holdings Limited; *Int'l*, pg. 620
ASIATRAVEL ONLINE SDN BHD—See Asiatravel.com Holdings Limited; *Int'l*, pg. 620
ASIA TRUST CO., LTD.—See Shinhan Financial Group Co., Ltd.; *Int'l*, pg. 6843
ASIA TV LIMITED—See Essel Corporate Resources Pvt. Ltd.; *Int'l*, pg. 2509
ASIA UNION ELECTRONIC CHEMICAL CORP.—See MiTAC International Corp.; *Int'l*, pg. 4923
ASIA UNITED BANK CORPORATION; *Int'l*, pg. 616
ASI AUTOMATIKK AS—See Addtech AB; *Int'l*, pg. 131

ASIA VETS HOLDINGS LTD.; *Int'l*, pg. 616
ASI AVIATION, INC.; *U.S. Private*, pg. 350
ASIA VITAL COMPONENTS CO., LTD. - AVC TAIPEI FACTORY—See Asia Vital Components Co., Ltd.; *Int'l*, pg. 616
ASIA VITAL COMPONENTS CO., LTD.; *Int'l*, pg. 616
ASIA WEB DIRECT CO., LTD.—See Expedia Group, Inc.; *U.S. Public*, pg. 809
ASIA WEB DIRECT (HK) LIMITED—See Expedia Group, Inc.; *U.S. Public*, pg. 809
ASIA WHEEL CO., LTD.—See Zhejiang Jingu Co., Ltd.; *Int'l*, pg. 8657
ASIA YAMAICHI ELECTRONICS INC.—See YAMAICHI ELECTRONICS Co Ltd; *Int'l*, pg. 8552
ASIA YAMAICHI ELECTRONICS INC. - UMSONG PLANT—See YAMAICHI ELECTRONICS Co Ltd; *Int'l*, pg. 8552
ASIA YOSHINOYA INTERNATIONAL SDN. BHD.—See Yoshinoya Holdings Co., Ltd.; *Int'l*, pg. 8600
ASI BUILDING PRODUCTS; *U.S. Private*, pg. 350
ASI BUSINESS SOLUTIONS INC.; *U.S. Private*, pg. 350
ASI BUSINESS SOLUTIONS, LLC—See Xerox Holdings Corporation; *U.S. Public*, pg. 2387
ASIC ENGINEERING SDN BHD—See Beng Kuang Marine Limited; *Int'l*, pg. 973
ASICENTRUM SPOL. S.R.O—See The Swatch Group Ltd.; *Int'l*, pg. 7691
ASICO LLC—See Audax Group, Limited Partnership; *U.S. Private*, pg. 388
ASI CONSTRUCTORS INC.—See Patel Engineering Ltd.; *Int'l*, pg. 5755
ASI CORPORATION; *U.S. Private*, pg. 350
ASICS AMERICA CORPORATION—See ASICS Corporation; *Int'l*, pg. 620
ASICS APPAREL INDUSTRY CORP.—See ASICS Corporation; *Int'l*, pg. 620
ASICS ASIA PTE. LTD.—See ASICS Corporation; *Int'l*, pg. 620
ASICS AUSTRIA GMBH—See ASICS Corporation; *Int'l*, pg. 620
ASICS CANADA CORPORATION—See ASICS Corporation; *Int'l*, pg. 620
ASICS CHINA TRADING CO., LTD.—See ASICS Corporation; *Int'l*, pg. 620
ASICS CORPORATION; *Int'l*, pg. 620
ASICS DENMARK A/S—See ASICS Corporation; *Int'l*, pg. 620
ASICS DEUTSCHLAND GMBH—See ASICS Corporation; *Int'l*, pg. 620
ASICS EUROPE B.V.—See ASICS Corporation; *Int'l*, pg. 620
ASICS FRANCE S.A.S.—See ASICS Corporation; *Int'l*, pg. 620
ASICS HONG KONG LIMITED—See ASICS Corporation; *Int'l*, pg. 620
ASICS IBERIA S.L.—See ASICS Corporation; *Int'l*, pg. 621
ASICS INDIA PRIVATE LIMITED—See ASICS Corporation; *Int'l*, pg. 621
ASICS ITALIA S.R.L.—See ASICS Corporation; *Int'l*, pg. 621
ASICS KOREA CORPORATION—See ASICS Corporation; *Int'l*, pg. 621
ASICS MALAYSIA SDN. BHD.—See ASICS Corporation; *Int'l*, pg. 621
ASICS MIDDLE EAST TRADING LLC—See ASICS Corporation; *Int'l*, pg. 621
ASICS NORGE AS—See ASICS Corporation; *Int'l*, pg. 621
ASICS OCEANIA PTY. LTD.—See ASICS Corporation; *Int'l*, pg. 621
ASICS POLSKA SP.ZO.O.—See ASICS Corporation; *Int'l*, pg. 621
ASICS SOURCING (VIETNAM) CO., LTD.—See ASICS Corporation; *Int'l*, pg. 621
ASICS SOUTH AFRICA PTY. LTD.—See ASICS Corporation; *Int'l*, pg. 621
ASICS SPORTS COMPLEX CORP.—See ASICS Corporation; *Int'l*, pg. 621
ASICS SPORTS MEXICO, S.A. DE C.V.—See ASICS Corporation; *Int'l*, pg. 621
ASICS SVERIGE AB—See ASICS Corporation; *Int'l*, pg. 621
ASICS TAIWAN CORPORATION—See ASICS Corporation; *Int'l*, pg. 621
ASICS THAILAND CO., LTD.—See ASICS Corporation; *Int'l*, pg. 621
ASICS TRADING CO., LTD.—See ASICS Corporation; *Int'l*, pg. 621
ASICS TRYUS SERVICE CORP.—See ASICS Corporation; *Int'l*, pg. 621
ASICS UK LIMITED—See ASICS Corporation; *Int'l*, pg. 621
ASIENS APPLIANCE, INC.—See 1847 Holdings LLC; *U.S. Public*, pg. 2
ASIENTOS DE CASTILLA LEON, S.A.—See Stellantis N.V.; *Int'l*, pg. 7201
ASIENTOS DE GALICIA, S.L.—See Stellantis N.V.; *Int'l*, pg. 7201
ASIENTOS DEL NORTE, S.A.—See Stellantis N.V.; *Int'l*, pg. 7201

ASIFINA S.A.—See Willis Towers Watson Public Limited Company; *Int'l*, pg. 8415
AS IF KINNISVARAHALDUS—See Sampo plc; *Int'l*, pg. 6507
ASI GLOBAL, LLC—See UnitedHealth Group Incorporated; *U.S. Public*, pg. 2241
ASIGNET USA, INC.; *U.S. Private*, pg. 351
ASIGURAREA ROMANEASCA - ASIROM VIENNA INSURANCE GROUP S.A.—See Vienna Insurance Group AG Wiener Versicherung Gruppe; *Int'l*, pg. 8193
A.S.I. HASTINGS, INC.—See Odyssey Investment Partners, LLC; *U.S. Private*, pg. 2995
ASI INDUSTRIAL SYSTEMS BEIJING CO. LTD.—See Nidec Corporation; *Int'l*, pg. 5274
ASI INDUSTRIES LIMITED; *Int'l*, pg. 609
ASI INNOVATION SAS; *Int'l*, pg. 609
ASI INVESTMENTS HOLDING CO.—See LyondellBasell Industries N.V.; *Int'l*, pg. 4607
ASIL CELIK SANAYI VE TICARET A.S.; *Int'l*, pg. 621
ASIMCO INTERNATIONAL CASTING (SHANXI) CO., LTD.—See Zhengzhou Coal Mining Machinery Group Co., Ltd.; *Int'l*, pg. 8670
ASIMCO INTERNATIONAL INC.—See Bain Capital, LP; *U.S. Private*, pg. 428
ASIMCO MEILIAN BRAKING SYSTEM (LANGFANG) CO., LTD.—See Bain Capital, LP; *U.S. Private*, pg. 428
ASIMCO SHUANGHUAN PISTON RING (YIZHENG) CO., LTD.—See Zhengzhou Coal Mining Machinery Group Co., Ltd.; *Int'l*, pg. 8670
ASIMCO TECHNOLOGIES LIMITED—See Bain Capital, LP; *U.S. Private*, pg. 428
ASIMCO TIANWEI FUEL INJECTION EQUIPMENT STOCK CO., LTD.—See Bain Capital, LP; *U.S. Private*, pg. 428
ASIMEX ANTERIST + SCHNEIDER IMPORT - EXPORT SAS—See Deutsche Bahn AG; *Int'l*, pg. 2049
ASIMILAR GROUP PLC; *Int'l*, pg. 621
ASIMOV'S SCIENCE FICTION MAGAZINE—See Penny Publications, LLC; *U.S. Private*, pg. 3137
ASIM TEXTILE MILLS LTD.—See National Group of Companies LLC; *Int'l*, pg. 5158
A&S, INC.; *U.S. Private*, pg. 21
A/S INDUSTEK—See Indutrade AB; *Int'l*, pg. 3677
AS INFORTAR; *Int'l*, pg. 590
AS INPRO GMBH—See Deutsche Lufthansa AG; *Int'l*, pg. 2066
AS INSIGNIA—See Bilia AB; *Int'l*, pg. 1029
AS INTERNATIONAL GROUP—See Neurones S.A.; *Int'l*, pg. 5219
ASI PROPERTIES, INC.—See American Software, Inc.; *U.S. Public*, pg. 109
AS-IP TECH, INC.; *U.S. Public*, pg. 209
ASIRI CENTRAL HOSPITALS PLC—See Softlogic Holdings PLC; *Int'l*, pg. 7055
ASIRI DIAGNOSTICS SERVICES (PVT) LTD.—See Softlogic Holdings PLC; *Int'l*, pg. 7055
ASIRI HOSPITAL HOLDINGS PLC—See Softlogic Holdings PLC; *Int'l*, pg. 7055
ASIRI HOSPITALS MATARA (PVT) LTD—See Softlogic Holdings PLC; *Int'l*, pg. 7055
ASIRI SURGICAL HOSPITAL PLC—See Softlogic Holdings PLC; *Int'l*, pg. 7055
ASIRO INC.; *Int'l*, pg. 621
AS IRON MOUNTAIN LATVIA AS—See Iron Mountain Incorporated; *U.S. Public*, pg. 1172
ASIRVAD MICRO FINANCE LIMITED—See Manappuram Finance Limited; *Int'l*, pg. 4667
ASI SERVICES, INC.—See The Progressive Corporation; *U.S. Public*, pg. 2124
THE ASI SOLUTIONS; *Int'l*, pg. 7614
ASISTENCIA OFFSHORE, S.A.—See ACS, Actividades de Construccion y Servicios, S.A.; *Int'l*, pg. 110
ASI SYSTEM INTEGRATION, INC.; *U.S. Private*, pg. 350
ASIT C.MEHTA FINANCIAL SERVICES LTD.; *Int'l*, pg. 621
ASITE SOLUTIONS LTD.; *Int'l*, pg. 621
ASITE SOLUTIONS PRIVATE LIMITED—See Asite Solutions Ltd.; *Int'l*, pg. 621
ASIX ELECTRONICS CO. LTD.; *Int'l*, pg. 621
ASJADE TECHNOLOGY INC.—See ASRock, Inc.; *Int'l*, pg. 632
A/S JARVAKANDI KLAAS—See O-I Glass, Inc.; *U.S. Public*, pg. 1560
ASJ COMMERCE INC.—See ASJ Inc.; *Int'l*, pg. 621
ASJ COMPONENTS (M) SDN. BHD.—See Yageo Corporation; *Int'l*, pg. 8545
ASJ HOLDINGS LIMITED—See Ralec Electronic Corporation; *Int'l*, pg. 6196
ASJ INC.; *Int'l*, pg. 621
ASJ PTE. LTD.—See Ralec Electronic Corporation; *Int'l*, pg. 6196
ASKA ANIMAL HEALTH CO., LTD.—See ASKA Pharmaceutical Co., Ltd.; *Int'l*, pg. 621
AS KANAL 2—See UP Invest OU; *Int'l*, pg. 8086
ASKANIA MEDIA FILMPRODUKTION GMBH—See Bavaria Film GmbH; *Int'l*, pg. 899
ASKA PHARMACEUTICAL CO., LTD.; *Int'l*, pg. 621
ASK APPLICATIONS, INC.—See IAC Inc.; *U.S. Public*, pg. 1082

ASKARI AVIATION SERVICES PVT LTD.—See Army Welfare Trust LLC; *Int'l*, pg. 575
ASKARI BANK LTD.—See Fauji Foundation; *Int'l*, pg. 2623
ASKARI DEVELOPMENT HOLDINGS PVT LTD—See Army Welfare Trust LLC; *Int'l*, pg. 575
ASKARI ENTERPRISES PVT LTD—See Army Welfare Trust LLC; *Int'l*, pg. 575
ASKARI GENERAL INSURANCE COMPANY LIMITED; *Int'l*, pg. 621
ASKARI GUARDS (PVT) LIMITED—See Army Welfare Trust LLC; *Int'l*, pg. 575
ASKARI INVESTMENT MANAGEMENT LIMITED—See Fauji Foundation; *Int'l*, pg. 2623
ASKARII RESOURCES, LLC—See Petrolia Energy Corporation; *U.S. Public*, pg. 1678
ASKARI LIFE ASSURANCE COMPANY LIMITED—See Army Welfare Trust LLC; *Int'l*, pg. 575
ASKARI METALS LIMITED; *Int'l*, pg. 621
ASKARI REAL ESTATE LTD.—See Army Welfare Trust LLC; *Int'l*, pg. 576
ASKA TECHNOLOGIES (KS) INC.—See Jess-Link Products Co., Ltd.; *Int'l*, pg. 3932
ASK CHEMICALS BENELUX B.V.—See Rhone Group, LLC; *U.S. Private*, pg. 3423
ASK CHEMICALS GMBH—See Rhone Group, LLC; *U.S. Private*, pg. 3423
ASK CHEMICALS GMBH - WERK WULFRATH—See Rhone Group, LLC; *U.S. Private*, pg. 3423
ASK CHEMICALS LP—See Rhone Group, LLC; *U.S. Private*, pg. 3423
A/S KELVIN HUGHES—See HENSOLDT AG; *Int'l*, pg. 3355
AS KEMIVESI—See Kemira Oyj; *Int'l*, pg. 4123
ASKER MUNAI EXPLORATION JSC; *Int'l*, pg. 621
A-SKETCH INC.—See Amuse Inc.; *Int'l*, pg. 442
ASKEY COMPUTER CORP.—See ASUSTeK Computer Inc.; *Int'l*, pg. 663
ASKEY DO BRASIL TECNOLOGIA LTDA.—See ASUSTeK Computer Inc.; *Int'l*, pg. 663
ASKEY INTERNATIONAL CORP.—See ASUSTeK Computer Inc.; *Int'l*, pg. 663
ASKEY TECHNOLOGY (JIANGSU) LTD.—See ASUSTeK Computer Inc.; *Int'l*, pg. 663
ASK FOODS INC.; *U.S. Private*, pg. 351
AS KIDS TOYS S.R.L.—See AS COMPANY S.A.; *Int'l*, pg. 589
ASK INDUSTRIES S.P.A.—See JVCKENWOOD Corporation; *Int'l*, pg. 4032
AS KINNISVARAPORTAAL—See Alma Media Corporation; *Int'l*, pg. 361
ASK JEEVES UK PARTNERSHIP—See IAC Inc.; *U.S. Public*, pg. 1082
ASKLEP CHINA INC.—See Nippon Telegraph & Telephone Corporation; *Int'l*, pg. 5350
ASKLEP INC.—See Nippon Telegraph & Telephone Corporation; *Int'l*, pg. 5350
ASKLEP INC.—See Nippon Telegraph & Telephone Corporation; *Int'l*, pg. 5350
ASKLEPIOS - ASB KRANKENHAUS RADEBERG GMBH—See Asklepios Kliniken GmbH & Co. KGaA; *Int'l*, pg. 622
ASKLEPIOS FACHKLINIKEN BRANDENBURG GMBH—See Asklepios Kliniken GmbH & Co. KGaA; *Int'l*, pg. 622
ASKLEPIOS FACHKLINIKUM STADTRODA GMBH—See Asklepios Kliniken GmbH & Co. KGaA; *Int'l*, pg. 622
ASKLEPIOS GESUNDHEITSZENTRUM BAD TOLZ GMBH—See Asklepios Kliniken GmbH & Co. KGaA; *Int'l*, pg. 622
ASKLEPIOS HARZKLINIKEN GMBH—See Asklepios Kliniken GmbH & Co. KGaA; *Int'l*, pg. 622
ASKLEPIOS KLINIK ALSBACH GMBH—See Asklepios Kliniken GmbH & Co. KGaA; *Int'l*, pg. 622
ASKLEPIOS KLINIK ALTONA—See Asklepios Kliniken GmbH & Co. KGaA; *Int'l*, pg. 622
ASKLEPIOS KLINIK AM KURPARK BAD SCHWARTAU—See Asklepios Kliniken GmbH & Co. KGaA; *Int'l*, pg. 622
ASKLEPIOS KLINIK BAD GRIESBACH GMBH & CIE OHG—See Asklepios Kliniken GmbH & Co. KGaA; *Int'l*, pg. 622
ASKLEPIOS KLINIK BAD SALZUNGEN GMBH—See Asklepios Kliniken GmbH & Co. KGaA; *Int'l*, pg. 622
ASKLEPIOS KLINIK BAD WILDUNGEN GMBH—See Asklepios Kliniken GmbH & Co. KGaA; *Int'l*, pg. 622
ASKLEPIOS KLINIK BARMBEK GMBH—See Asklepios Kliniken GmbH & Co. KGaA; *Int'l*, pg. 622
ASKLEPIOS KLINIK DR. WALB HOMBERG/OHM—See Asklepios Kliniken GmbH & Co. KGaA; *Int'l*, pg. 622
ASKLEPIOS KLINIKEN GMBH & CO. KGAA; *Int'l*, pg. 622
ASKLEPIOS KLINIKEN LANGEN-SELIGENSTADT GMBH—See Asklepios Kliniken GmbH & Co. KGaA; *Int'l*, pg. 622
ASKLEPIOS KLINIKEN VERWALTUNGS - GESELLSCHAFT MBH - LABOR & COLLECTIVE BARGAINING LAW DIVISION—See Asklepios Kliniken GmbH & Co. KGaA; *Int'l*, pg. 622

ASKLEPIOS KLINIKEN VERWALTUNGS - GESELLSCHAFT MBH - MEDICINE & SCIENCE DIVISION—See Asklepios Kliniken GmbH & Co. KGaA; *Int'l*, pg. 622
ASKLEPIOS KLINIKEN WEISSENFELS - HOHENMOLSEN GMBH—See Asklepios Kliniken GmbH & Co. KGaA; *Int'l*, pg. 622
ASKLEPIOS KLINIK GAUTING GMBH—See Asklepios Kliniken GmbH & Co. KGaA; *Int'l*, pg. 622
ASKLEPIOS KLINIK LENGGRIES GMBH—See Asklepios Kliniken GmbH & Co. KGaA; *Int'l*, pg. 622
ASKLEPIOS KLINIK LICH GMBH—See Asklepios Kliniken GmbH & Co. KGaA; *Int'l*, pg. 622
ASKLEPIOS KLINIK LINDAU GMBH—See Asklepios Kliniken GmbH & Co. KGaA; *Int'l*, pg. 622
ASKLEPIOS KLINIK LINDENLOHE GMBH—See Asklepios Kliniken GmbH & Co. KGaA; *Int'l*, pg. 622
ASKLEPIOS KLINIK NORD GMBH—See Asklepios Kliniken GmbH & Co. KGaA; *Int'l*, pg. 622
ASKLEPIOS KLINIK PASEWALK GMBH—See Asklepios Kliniken GmbH & Co. KGaA; *Int'l*, pg. 622
ASKLEPIOS KLINIK SANKT AUGUSTIN GMBH—See Asklepios Kliniken GmbH & Co. KGaA; *Int'l*, pg. 622
ASKLEPIOS KLINIK SCHAUFLING GMBH—See Asklepios Kliniken GmbH & Co. KGaA; *Int'l*, pg. 622
ASKLEPIOS KLINIK SOBERNHEIM GMBH—See Asklepios Kliniken GmbH & Co. KGaA; *Int'l*, pg. 622
ASKLEPIOS KLINIK ST. GEORG—See Asklepios Kliniken GmbH & Co. KGaA; *Int'l*, pg. 622
ASKLEPIOS KLINIKUM BAD ABBACH GMBH—See Asklepios Kliniken GmbH & Co. KGaA; *Int'l*, pg. 622
ASKLEPIOS KLINIKUM HARBURG—See Asklepios Kliniken GmbH & Co. KGaA; *Int'l*, pg. 622
ASKLEPIOS KLINIKUM UCKERMARK GMBH—See Asklepios Kliniken GmbH & Co. KGaA; *Int'l*, pg. 622
ASKLEPIOS KLINIK WANDSBEK—See Asklepios Kliniken GmbH & Co. KGaA; *Int'l*, pg. 622
ASKLEPIOS KLINIK WIESBADEN GMBH—See Asklepios Kliniken GmbH & Co. KGaA; *Int'l*, pg. 622
ASKLEPIOS MEDI TOP PFLEGEDIENST & SERVICE GMBH—See Asklepios Kliniken GmbH & Co. KGaA; *Int'l*, pg. 623
ASKLEPIOS MVZ BAYERN GMBH—See Asklepios Kliniken GmbH & Co. KGaA; *Int'l*, pg. 622
ASKLEPIOS MVZ BRANDENBURG GMBH—See Asklepios Kliniken GmbH & Co. KGaA; *Int'l*, pg. 622
ASKLEPIOS MVZ HESSEN GMBH—See Asklepios Kliniken GmbH & Co. KGaA; *Int'l*, pg. 622
ASKLEPIOS MVZ MITTELDEUTSCHLAND GMBH—See Asklepios Kliniken GmbH & Co. KGaA; *Int'l*, pg. 622
ASKLEPIOS MVZ NIEDERSACHSEN GMBH—See Asklepios Kliniken GmbH & Co. KGaA; *Int'l*, pg. 622
ASKLEPIOS MVZ NORD SCHLESWIG HOLSTEIN GMBH—See Asklepios Kliniken GmbH & Co. KGaA; *Int'l*, pg. 622
ASKLEPIOS MVZ SACHSEN-ANHALT GMBH—See Asklepios Kliniken GmbH & Co. KGaA; *Int'l*, pg. 622
ASKLEPIOS NORDSEEKLINIK WESTERLAND GMBH—See Asklepios Kliniken GmbH & Co. KGaA; *Int'l*, pg. 622
ASKLEPIOS POLAND SP. Z O.O.—See Asklepios Kliniken GmbH & Co. KGaA; *Int'l*, pg. 622
ASKLEPIOS PSYCHIATRIE NIEDERSACHSEN GMBH—See Asklepios Kliniken GmbH & Co. KGaA; *Int'l*, pg. 622
ASKLEPIOS REHAKLINIK BAD OLDESLOE GMBH—See Asklepios Kliniken GmbH & Co. KGaA; *Int'l*, pg. 622
ASKLEPIOS SCHWALM-EDER-KLINIKEN GMBH—See Asklepios Kliniken GmbH & Co. KGaA; *Int'l*, pg. 622
ASKLEPIOS STADTKLINIK BAD TOLZ GMBH—See Asklepios Kliniken GmbH & Co. KGaA; *Int'l*, pg. 623
ASKLEPIOS SUDPFALZKLINIKEN GMBH—See Asklepios Kliniken GmbH & Co. KGaA; *Int'l*, pg. 623
ASKLEPIOS THERAPIE GMBH—See Asklepios Kliniken GmbH & Co. KGaA; *Int'l*, pg. 623
ASKLEPIOS WESERBERGLAND-KLINIK GMBH—See Asklepios Kliniken GmbH & Co. KGaA; *Int'l*, pg. 623
ASKLEPIOS WESTKLINIKUM HAMBURG GMBH—See Asklepios Kliniken GmbH & Co. KGaA; *Int'l*, pg. 623
ASKME CORPORATION—See Abalance Corporation Ltd.; *Int'l*, pg. 48
ASKNET GMBH—See Signpost NV; *Int'l*, pg. 6912
ASKNET K.K.—See Signpost NV; *Int'l*, pg. 6912
ASKO HOLDING A.S.; *Int'l*, pg. 624
ASKO, INC.—See ANDRITZ AG; *Int'l*, pg. 455
ASK OKINAWA CORPORATION—See A&A Material Corporation; *Int'l*, pg. 18
ASKOLL EVA SPA; *Int'l*, pg. 625
ASKOMA AG—See NIBE Industrier AB; *Int'l*, pg. 5259
ASKOMA SDN. BHD.—See NIBE Industrier AB; *Int'l*, pg. 5259
AS KONE—See KONE Oyj; *Int'l*, pg. 4247
ASKO NORGE AS—See NorgesGruppen ASA; *Int'l*, pg. 5427
ASKO-STRAKHOVANIE PJSC; *Int'l*, pg. 625
ASKOYVAERINGEN AS—See Schibsted ASA; *Int'l*, pg. 6617
ASK PRODUCTS, INC.—See Equistone Partners Europe Limited; *Int'l*, pg. 2487

AS KROONPRESS—See UP Invest OU; *Int'l*, pg. 8086
ASK SANSHIN ENGINEERING CORPORATION—See A&A Material Corporation; *Int'l*, pg. 18
ASK STAFFING, INC.; *U.S. Private*, pg. 351
ASK TECHNICA CORPORATION—See A&A Material Corporation; *Int'l*, pg. 18
ASK TECHNOLOGY GROUP LIMITED—See PC Partner Group Limited; *Int'l*, pg. 5766
ASKUL CORPORATION; *Int'l*, pg. 625
ASKUL LOGIST CORPORATION—See ASKUL Corporation; *Int'l*, pg. 625
ASKUL (SHANGHAI) TRADING CO., LTD.—See ASKUL Corporation; *Int'l*, pg. 625
ASL ACQUISITION, INC.—See NetXposure, Inc.; *U.S. Private*, pg. 2890
ASL AIRLINES (IRELAND) LIMITED—See STAR Capital Partners Limited; *Int'l*, pg. 7173
ASL ANALYTIK SERVICE LABOR GMBH & CO.—See Korber AG; *Int'l*, pg. 4280
ASLAN CEMENT A.S.; *Int'l*, pg. 625
ASLAN CONSTRUCTION INC.; *U.S. Private*, pg. 351
ASLAN PHARMACEUTICALS LIMITED; *Int'l*, pg. 625
ASLAN PHARMACEUTICALS (SHANGHAI) CO. LTD.—See ASLAN Pharmaceuticals Limited; *Int'l*, pg. 625
ASLAN PHARMACEUTICALS TAIWAN LTD.—See ASLAN Pharmaceuticals Limited; *Int'l*, pg. 625
AS LATVIJAS BALZAMS; *Int'l*, pg. 590
AS LATVIJAS CENTRALAIS DEPOZITARIJS—See Nasdaq, Inc.; *U.S. Public*, pg. 1491
A.S. LATVIJAS LIFTS SCHINDLER—See Schindler Holding AG; *Int'l*, pg. 6618
AS LATVIJAS METALS—See PAO Severstal; *Int'l*, pg. 5731
AS LATVO—See Rigas Elektromasinbuves Rupnica AS; *Int'l*, pg. 6340
ASL AUTOMATED (THAILAND) LTD.—See Beijing Teamsun Technology Co., Ltd.; *Int'l*, pg. 958
ASL AVIATION HOLDINGS DAC—See STAR Capital Partners Limited; *Int'l*, pg. 7173
ASL DISTRIBUTION SERVICES LIMITED—See Consolidated Fastfrate Inc.; *Int'l*, pg. 1770
ASLE CORPORATION SINGAPORE PTE. LTD.—See Onamba Co., Ltd.; *Int'l*, pg. 5573
ASLE ELECTRONICS (CAMBODIA) CO., LTD.—See Onamba Co., Ltd.; *Int'l*, pg. 5573
ASLE ELECTRONICS CO., LTD—See Onamba Co., Ltd.; *Int'l*, pg. 5573
ASL HOLDINGS LIMITED—See Halma plc; *Int'l*, pg. 3230
ASL INDUSTRIES LIMITED; *Int'l*, pg. 625
ASL INTERPRETER REFERRAL SERVICE, INC.; *U.S. Private*, pg. 351
ASL MARINE HOLDINGS LTD; *Int'l*, pg. 625
ASL MARKETING, LLC—See Vivendi SE; *Int'l*, pg. 8267
ASMAK QURIYAT INTERNATIONAL LLC—See International Holdings Company PJSC; *Int'l*, pg. 3750
ASMAK SEAFOOD PROCESSING CO. LLC—See International Holdings Company PJSC; *Int'l*, pg. 3750
ASMALLWORLD AG; *Int'l*, pg. 627
ASM AMERICA INC.—See ASM INTERNATIONAL N.V.; *Int'l*, pg. 626
A.S. MANAGEMENT CORPORATION; *U.S. Private*, pg. 28
ASMARQ CO., LTD.; *Int'l*, pg. 627
ASMAR; *Int'l*, pg. 627
A-SMART COMMERCE PTE LTD—See A-Smart Holdings Ltd.; *Int'l*, pg. 20
A-SMART HOLDINGS LTD.; *Int'l*, pg. 20
A-SMART LIFE PTE LTD—See A-Smart Holdings Ltd.; *Int'l*, pg. 20
A-SMART MEDIA PTE LTD—See A-Smart Holdings Ltd.; *Int'l*, pg. 20
A-SMART PROPERTY HOLDINGS PTE LTD—See A-Smart Holdings Ltd.; *Int'l*, pg. 20
A-SMART TECHNOLOGIES PTE LTD—See A-Smart Holdings Ltd.; *Int'l*, pg. 20
ASMARU CORPORATION—See ASKUL Corporation; *Int'l*, pg. 625
ASM ASSEMBLY AUTOMATION LTD.—See ASM INTERNATIONAL N.V.; *Int'l*, pg. 626
ASM ASSEMBLY EQUIPMENT BANGKOK LIMITED—See ASM INTERNATIONAL N.V.; *Int'l*, pg. 626
ASM ASSEMBLY EQUIPMENT (M) SDN. BHD.—See ASM INTERNATIONAL N.V.; *Int'l*, pg. 626
ASM ASSEMBLY SYSTEMS LLC—See ASM INTERNATIONAL N.V.; *Int'l*, pg. 626
ASM ASSEMBLY TECHNOLOGY CO. LIMITED—See ASM INTERNATIONAL N.V.; *Int'l*, pg. 626
ASM BELGIUM N.V.—See ASM INTERNATIONAL N.V.; *Int'l*, pg. 626
ASM CHINA LTD—See ASM INTERNATIONAL N.V.; *Int'l*, pg. 626
ASM DIGITAL TECHNOLOGIES INC.—See ASM Technologies Limited; *Int'l*, pg. 627
ASM DIGITAL TECHNOLOGIES PTE LTD.—See ASM Technologies Limited; *Int'l*, pg. 627
ASMEA S.R.L.—See A2A S.p.A.; *Int'l*, pg. 29
ASMECO (THAILAND) LTD.; *Int'l*, pg. 627
ASMEDIA TECHNOLOGY INC.; *Int'l*, pg. 627

ASMEDIA TECHNOLOGY INC.

CORPORATE AFFILIATIONS

ASM ENERGIA E AMBIENTE S.R.L.—See A2A S.p.A.; *Int'l*, pg. 29
ASM ENERGY SRL—See A2A S.p.A.; *Int'l*, pg. 29
ASMENT DE TEMARA S.A.—See Camargo Correa S.A.; *Int'l*, pg. 1267
AS MERKO EHITUS EESTI—See AS Merko Ehitus; *Int'l*, pg. 590
AS MERKO EHITUS; *Int'l*, pg. 590
AS MERKO INFRA—See AS Merko Ehitus; *Int'l*, pg. 590
AS MERKO TARTU—See AS Merko Ehitus; *Int'l*, pg. 590
A&S METALS - MODESTO—See SGS Enterprises Inc.; *U.S. Private*, pg. 3622
ASM EUROPE B.V.—See ASM INTERNATIONAL N.V.; *Int'l*, pg. 626
ASM FAR EAST MARKETING LTD.—See ASM INTERNATIONAL N.V.; *Int'l*, pg. 626
ASM FRANCE S.A.R.L.—See ASM INTERNATIONAL N.V.; *Int'l*, pg. 626
ASM FRONT-END MANUFACTURING SINGAPORE PTE LTD—See ASM INTERNATIONAL N.V.; *Int'l*, pg. 626
ASM FRONT-END SALES AND SERVICES TAIWAN CO. LTD—See ASM INTERNATIONAL N.V.; *Int'l*, pg. 626
ASM GENITECH KOREA LTD.—See ASM INTERNATIONAL N.V.; *Int'l*, pg. 626
ASM GERMANY SALES B.V.—See ASM INTERNATIONAL N.V.; *Int'l*, pg. 626
ASM GROUP S.A.; *Int'l*, pg. 625
ASMIK ACE, INC.—See Sumitomo Corporation; *Int'l*, pg. 7269
ASM INDUSTRIES INC.—See SERFILCO, Ltd.; *U.S. Private*, pg. 3613
ASM INTERNATIONAL N.V.; *Int'l*, pg. 626
ASM IP HOLDING B.V.—See ASM INTERNATIONAL N.V.; *Int'l*, pg. 626
ASMIQ AG—See Die Schweizerische Post AG; *Int'l*, pg. 2112
ASMITA GARDENS SRL—See Alpha Services and Holdings S.A.; *Int'l*, pg. 369
A. SMITH BOWMAN DISTILLERY—See Sazerac Company, Inc.; *U.S. Private*, pg. 3559
ASM JAPAN K.K. - NAGAOKA FACTORY—See ASM INTERNATIONAL N.V.; *Int'l*, pg. 626
ASM JAPAN K.K.—See ASM INTERNATIONAL N.V.; *Int'l*, pg. 626
ASMJ S.R.O.—See Fomento de Construcciones y Contratas, S.A.; *Int'l*, pg. 2722
ASM LASER SEPARATION INTERNATIONAL (ALSI) B.V.—See ASM INTERNATIONAL N.V.; *Int'l*, pg. 626
ASML AUSTIN.—See ASML Holding N.V.; *Int'l*, pg. 627
ASML BELGIUM BVBA—See ASML Holding N.V.; *Int'l*, pg. 627
ASML CAPITAL US, INC.—See ASML Holding N.V.; *Int'l*, pg. 627
ASML EQUIPMENT MALAYSIA SDN. BHD.—See ASML Holding N.V.; *Int'l*, pg. 627
ASML FRANCE S.A.R.L.—See ASML Holding N.V.; *Int'l*, pg. 627
ASML GERMANY GMBH—See ASML Holding N.V.; *Int'l*, pg. 627
ASML HOLDING N.V.; *Int'l*, pg. 627
ASML HONG KONG LTD.—See ASML Holding N.V.; *Int'l*, pg. 627
ASML IRELAND LTD.—See ASML Holding N.V.; *Int'l*, pg. 627
ASML JAPAN CO. LTD.—See ASML Holding N.V.; *Int'l*, pg. 627
ASML KOREA CO., LTD.—See ASML Holding N.V.; *Int'l*, pg. 627
ASML NETHERLANDS B.V.—See ASML Holding N.V.; *Int'l*, pg. 627
ASM LOGISTICS (S) PTE LIMITED—See Santova Ltd.; *Int'l*, pg. 6559
ASML PARTICIPATION US INC.—See ASML Holding N.V.; *Int'l*, pg. 627
ASML (SHANGHAI) INTERNATIONAL TRADING CO., LTD—See ASML Holding N.V.; *Int'l*, pg. 627
ASML SINGAPORE PTE. LTD.—See ASML Holding N.V.; *Int'l*, pg. 627
ASML TAIWAN LTD.—See ASML Holding N.V.; *Int'l*, pg. 627
ASML (TIANJIN) CO. LTD.—See ASML Holding N.V.; *Int'l*, pg. 627
ASML US, INC.—See ASML Holding N.V.; *Int'l*, pg. 627
ASML VENTURES 1 INC.—See ASML Holding N.V.; *Int'l*, pg. 627
ASM MANAGEMENT CO., LTD.—See Thai Beverage Public Company Limited; *Int'l*, pg. 7589
ASM MESSEPROFIS AG; *Int'l*, pg. 626
ASM MODULAR SYSTEMS INC.—See Kingspan Group PLC; *Int'l*, pg. 4176
ASM NUTOOL, INC.—See ASM INTERNATIONAL N.V.; *Int'l*, pg. 626
AS MOBILE WHOLESALE—See Telia Company AB; *Int'l*, pg. 7543
ASMO CATERING MALAYSIA SDN. BHD.—See Asmo Corporation; *Int'l*, pg. 628
ASMO CO., LTD—See Denso Corporation; *Int'l*, pg. 2028
ASMO CORPORATION; *Int'l*, pg. 628

ASMO CZECH S.R.O.—See Denso Corporation; *Int'l*, pg. 2028
ASMO DETROIT, INC—See Denso Corporation; *Int'l*, pg. 2028
ASMO GREENVILLE OF NORTH CAROLINA, INC.—See Denso Corporation; *Int'l*, pg. 2028
ASMO NORTH CAROLINA, INC.—See Denso Corporation; *Int'l*, pg. 2028
ASM PACIFIC ASSEMBLY PRODUCTS, INC.—See ASM INTERNATIONAL N.V.; *Int'l*, pg. 626
ASM PACIFIC HOLDING B.V.—See ASM INTERNATIONAL N.V.; *Int'l*, pg. 626
ASM PACIFIC TECHNOLOGY LTD.—See ASM INTERNATIONAL N.V.; *Int'l*, pg. 626
ASMPT GMBH & CO. KG; *Int'l*, pg. 628
ASM RESEARCH LLC—See Accenture plc; *Int'l*, pg. 85
ASM SALES FORCE AGENCY SP. Z O.O.—See ASM Group S.A.; *Int'l*, pg. 625
ASM SEMICONDUCTOR MATERIALS (SHENZHEN) CO. LTD.—See ASM INTERNATIONAL N.V.; *Int'l*, pg. 626
ASM SERVICES AND SUPPORT IRELAND LTD.—See ASM INTERNATIONAL N.V.; *Int'l*, pg. 626
ASM SERVICES AND SUPPORT ISRAEL LTD—See ASM INTERNATIONAL N.V.; *Int'l*, pg. 626
ASM TECHNOLOGIES LIMITED; *Int'l*, pg. 626
ASM TECHNOLOGY (HUIZHOU) CO. LIMITED—See ASM INTERNATIONAL N.V.; *Int'l*, pg. 626
ASM TECHNOLOGY (M) SDN. BHD.—See ASM INTERNATIONAL N.V.; *Int'l*, pg. 626
ASM TECHNOLOGY SINGAPORE PTE LTD—See ASM INTERNATIONAL N.V.; *Int'l*, pg. 626
ASM UNITED KINGDOM SALES B.V—See ASM INTERNATIONAL N.V.; *Int'l*, pg. 626
ASMUSSEN GMBH—See Compagnie des Levures Lesaffre SA; *Int'l*, pg. 1738
ASM VERCELLI S.P.A.—See Iren S.p.A.; *Int'l*, pg. 3808
ASM WAFER PROCESS EQUIPMENT SINGAPORE PTE LTD—See ASM INTERNATIONAL N.V.; *Int'l*, pg. 626
ASN AG—See Swiss Life Holding; *Int'l*, pg. 7368
ASNAS CO., LTD.—See H2O Retailing Corp.; *Int'l*, pg. 3200
ASN BROKER PCL; *Int'l*, pg. 628
A/S NESTLE NORGE—See Nestle S.A.; *Int'l*, pg. 5202
ASNM NEW MEDIA AG—See Unister Holding GmbH; *Int'l*, pg. 8062
AS NOREMCO CONSTRUCTION—See Veidekke ASA; *Int'l*, pg. 8148
AS NORMA—See Autoliv, Inc.; *Int'l*, pg. 728
A/S NORSKE SHELL—See Shell plc; *Int'l*, pg. 6796
ASN TANFORAN CROSSING II LLC—See AvalonBay Communities, Inc.; *U.S. Public*, pg. 240
ASN TECHNOLOGIES, INC.—See Equity Residential; *U.S. Public*, pg. 791
THE ASNY CORPORATION; *U.S. Private*, pg. 3989
ASOCIACION DE COOPERATIVAS ARGENTINAS C.L.; *Int'l*, pg. 628
ASOCIACION PUERTORRIQUENOS EN MARCHA FOR EVERYONE; *U.S. Private*, pg. 351
ASO CO., LTD.; *Int'l*, pg. 628
A&S OF CASTROVILLE INC—See SGS Enterprises Inc.; *U.S. Private*, pg. 3622
ASO FOAM CRETE CO., LTD.; *Int'l*, pg. 628
AS OLAINFARM; *Int'l*, pg. 590
ASOLID TECHNOLOGY CO., LTD.; *Int'l*, pg. 628
ASOLO GOLF CLUB S.R.L—See Edizione S.r.l.; *Int'l*, pg. 2312
ASOLO NORTH AMERICA INC.—See Asolo S.p.A.; *Int'l*, pg. 628
ASOLO S.P.A.; *Int'l*, pg. 628
ASOLVA, INC.—See Constellation Software Inc.; *Int'l*, pg. 1773
AS ONE CORPORATION; *Int'l*, pg. 591
AS ONE SHANGHAI CORPORATION—See AS ONE Corporation; *Int'l*, pg. 591
A-SONIC AEROSPACE LIMITED; *Int'l*, pg. 20
A-SONIC AVIATION SOLUTIONS PTE LTD—See A-Sonic Aerospace Limited; *Int'l*, pg. 20
A-SONIC EXPRESS LOGISTICS (INDIA) PRIVATE LIMITED—See A-Sonic Aerospace Limited; *Int'l*, pg. 20
A-SONIC LOGISTICS (AUSTRALIA) PTY LTD—See A-Sonic Aerospace Limited; *Int'l*, pg. 20
A-SONIC LOGISTICS (H.K.) LIMITED—See A-Sonic Aerospace Limited; *Int'l*, pg. 21
A-SONIC LOGISTICS (KOREA) CO., LTD.—See A-Sonic Aerospace Limited; *Int'l*, pg. 21
A-SONIC LOGISTICS (NETHERLANDS) B.V.—See A-Sonic Aerospace Limited; *Int'l*, pg. 21
A-SONIC LOGISTICS PTE. LTD.—See A-Sonic Aerospace Limited; *Int'l*, pg. 20
A-SONIC LOGISTICS (UK) LTD.—See A-Sonic Aerospace Limited; *Int'l*, pg. 21
A-SONIC LOGISTICS (USA), INC.—See A-Sonic Aerospace Limited; *Int'l*, pg. 21
A-SONIC LOGISTICS (VIETNAM) COMPANY LIMITED—See A-Sonic Aerospace Limited; *Int'l*, pg. 21
AS ONLINE SDN. BHD.—See Asphere Innovations Public Company Limited; *Int'l*, pg. 629
A. SORIANO AIR CORPORATION—See A. Soriano Corporation; *Int'l*, pg. 22

A. SORIANO CORPORATION; *Int'l*, pg. 22
AS ORIOLA—See Oriola Corporation; *Int'l*, pg. 5631
ASO SAVINGS & LOANS PLC.; *Int'l*, pg. 628
ASOS PLC; *Int'l*, pg. 628
A/S OSTBIRK BYGNINGSINDUSTRI—See VKR Holding A/S; *Int'l*, pg. 8281
ASOTA GMBH—See Duroc AB; *Int'l*, pg. 2230
A SOUTHERN SEASON INC.; *U.S. Private*, pg. 19
AS OUTOKUMPU STAINLESS TUBULAR PRODUCTS—See Outokumpu Oyj; *Int'l*, pg. 5668
ASPA BELGIUM N.V.—See HAL Trust N.V.; *Int'l*, pg. 3223
ASPA BENELUX B.V.—See HAL Trust N.V.; *Int'l*, pg. 3223
ASPAC INC.—See Canon Inc.; *Int'l*, pg. 1292
ASPAC LUBRICANTS (MALAYSIA) SDN. BHD.—See BP plc; *Int'l*, pg. 1126
ASPACOIL LTD; *Int'l*, pg. 628
ASP AG—See TKH Group N.V.; *Int'l*, pg. 7763
ASPARITY DECISION SOLUTIONS, INC.—See Automatic Data Processing, Inc.; *U.S. Public*, pg. 230
AS PAROC—See Owens Corning; *U.S. Public*, pg. 1626
A/S PARTS LIMITED—See Ingersoll Rand Inc.; *U.S. Public*, pg. 1120
ASPASIEL S.R.L.—See ThyssenKrupp AG; *Int'l*, pg. 7723
A&S PAVING, INC.; *U.S. Private*, pg. 21
ASP CO.,LTD.—See Septeni Holdings Co., Ltd.; *Int'l*, pg. 6718
ASP. COMMUNICATIONS CO., LTD.—See PRONEXUS INC.; *Int'l*, pg. 5996
ASPECT8 LIMITED—See Schroders plc; *Int'l*, pg. 6639
ASPECT CONSULTING, INC.; *U.S. Private*, pg. 351
ASPECT EDUCATION LIMITED—See Graham Holdings Company; *U.S. Public*, pg. 955
ASPECT HOLDINGS, LLC; *U.S. Private*, pg. 351
ASPECT IMAGING LTD.—See Level Biotechnology, Inc.; *Int'l*, pg. 4470
ASPECT INTERNATIONALE SPRACHSCHULE GMBH—See Graham Holdings Company; *U.S. Public*, pg. 955
ASPECT MANAGEMENT, LLC—See Integrity Marketing Group LLC; *U.S. Private*, pg. 2103
ASPECT RATIO INC.; *U.S. Private*, pg. 351
ASPECT SOFTWARE ASIA PACIFIC PTE LTD.—See Vector Capital Management, L.P.; *U.S. Private*, pg. 4350
ASPECT SOFTWARE GROUP HOLDINGS LTD.; *U.S. Private*, pg. 351
ASPECT SOFTWARE, INC.—See Vector Capital Management, L.P.; *U.S. Private*, pg. 4350
ASPECT SOFTWARE—See Vector Capital Management, L.P.; *U.S. Private*, pg. 4350
ASPEED TECHNOLOGY INC.; *Int'l*, pg. 628
ASPEED TECHNOLOGY (U.S.A.) INC.—See ASPEED Technology Inc.; *Int'l*, pg. 628
ASPEKT TELEFILM-PRODUKTION GMBH—See SPIEGEL-Verlag Rudolf Augstein GmbH & Co.; *Int'l*, pg. 7135
ASPEM S.P.A.—See A2A S.p.A.; *Int'l*, pg. 29
ASPEN AERIALS, INC.—See The Sterling Group, L.P.; *U.S. Private*, pg. 4123
ASPEN AEROGELS, INC.; *U.S. Public*, pg. 213
ASPEN AIR CONDITIONING, INC.—See Del-Air Heating, Air Conditioning & Refrigeration Corp.; *U.S. Private*, pg. 1193
ASPEN APARTMENTS—See American Management Services LLC; *U.S. Private*, pg. 240
ASPEN API INC.—See Aspen Pharmacare Holdings Limited; *Int'l*, pg. 629
ASPEN ASIA COMPANY LIMITED—See Aspen Pharmacare Holdings Limited; *Int'l*, pg. 629
THE ASPEN BRANDS; *U.S. Private*, pg. 3989
ASPEN CAPITAL ADVISORS INC.—See Apollo Global Management, Inc.; *U.S. Public*, pg. 147
ASPEN COLOMBIANA S.A.S.—See Aspen Pharmacare Holdings Limited; *Int'l*, pg. 629
ASPENCORE, LLC—See Arrow Electronics, Inc.; *U.S. Public*, pg. 198
ASPENCORE MEDIA GMBH—See Arrow Electronics, Inc.; *U.S. Public*, pg. 198
ASPEN COURT, LLC—See TPG Capital, L.P.; *U.S. Public*, pg. 2168
ASPEN DENTAL MANAGEMENT, INC.—See Ares Management Corporation; *U.S. Public*, pg. 188
ASPEN DISTRIBUTION SERVICES, INC.; *U.S. Private*, pg. 351
ASPEN EDUCATION GROUP, INC.—See Acadia Healthcare Company, Inc.; *U.S. Public*, pg. 28
ASPEN ELECTRONICS LIMITED—See APC Technology Group plc; *Int'l*, pg. 508
ASPEN EQUIPMENT COMPANY INC.—See The Manitowoc Company, Inc.; *U.S. Public*, pg. 2111
ASPEN EQUITY INVESTMENTS PTY. LIMITED—See Aspen Group Limited; *Int'l*, pg. 628
ASPEN EXTERIORS, INC.; *U.S. Private*, pg. 351
ASPEN FOODS—See Koch Foods, Inc.; *U.S. Private*, pg. 2326
ASPEN FRANCE SAS—See Aspen Pharmacare Holdings Limited; *Int'l*, pg. 629
ASPEN FUNDS MANAGEMENT LTD.—See Aspen Group Limited; *Int'l*, pg. 629

COMPANY NAME INDEX

ASPEN GERMANY GMBH—See Aspen Pharmacare Holdings Limited; *Int'l*, pg. 629
ASPEN GLEN CLUB—See Apollo Global Management, Inc.; *U.S. Public*, pg. 149
ASPEN GLOBAL INCORPORATED—See Aspen Pharmacare Holdings Limited; *Int'l*, pg. 629
ASPEN (GROUP) HOLDINGS LIMITED; *Int'l*, pg. 628
THE ASPEN GROUP, INC.; *U.S. Private*, pg. 3989
ASPEN GROUP, INC.; *U.S. Public*, pg. 213
ASPEN GROUP LIMITED; *Int'l*, pg. 628
ASPEN GROUP LTD.; *Int'l*, pg. 629
ASPEN GROUP RESOURCES CORP.; *Int'l*, pg. 629
ASPEN GROVE LANDSCAPE COMPANIES, LLC; *U.S. Private*, pg. 352
ASPEN HEALTHCARE FZ LLC—See Aspen Pharmacare Holdings Limited; *Int'l*, pg. 629
ASPEN HEALTHCARE LIMITED—See NMC Health PLC; *Int'l*, pg. 5392
ASPEN HEALTHCARE MALTA LTD.—See Aspen Pharmacare Holdings Limited; *Int'l*, pg. 629
ASPEN HEALTHCARE SERVICES; *U.S. Private*, pg. 352
ASPEN HEALTHCARE TAIWAN LIMITED—See Aspen Pharmacare Holdings Limited; *Int'l*, pg. 629
ASPEN INSURANCE HOLDINGS LIMITED—See Apollo Global Management, Inc.; *U.S. Public*, pg. 147
ASPEN INSURANCE UK LIMITED—See Apollo Global Management, Inc.; *U.S. Public*, pg. 147
ASPEN INSURANCE U.S. SERVICES INC—See Apollo Global Management, Inc.; *U.S. Public*, pg. 147
ASPEN INTERNATIONAL HOLDINGS, INC.; *U.S. Public*, pg. 213
ASPEN LABORATORIES, INC.—See CONMED Corporation; *U.S. Public*, pg. 567
ASPENLEAF ENERGY LIMITED; *Int'l*, pg. 629
ASPEN LEAF YOGURT, LLC—See Rocky Mountain Chocolate Factory, Inc.; *U.S. Public*, pg. 1807
ASPEN MARKETING SERVICES, INC. - ATLANTA—See Publicis Groupe S.A.; *Int'l*, pg. 6098
ASPEN MARKETING SERVICES, INC. - AUBURN HILLS—See Publicis Groupe S.A.; *Int'l*, pg. 6098
ASPEN MARKETING SERVICES, INC. - COSTA MESA—See Publicis Groupe S.A.; *Int'l*, pg. 6098
ASPEN MARKETING SERVICES, INC. - IRVING—See Publicis Groupe S.A.; *Int'l*, pg. 6098
ASPEN MARKETING SERVICES, INC. - NEW YORK—See Publicis Groupe S.A.; *Int'l*, pg. 6098
ASPEN MARKETING SERVICES, INC. - PARSIPPANY—See Publicis Groupe S.A.; *Int'l*, pg. 6098
ASPEN MARKETING SERVICES, INC. - SAINT PETERSBURG—See Publicis Groupe S.A.; *Int'l*, pg. 6098
ASPEN MARKETING SERVICES, INC. - SAN DIEGO—See Publicis Groupe S.A.; *Int'l*, pg. 6098
ASPEN MARKETING SERVICES, INC. - SCOTTSDALE—See Publicis Groupe S.A.; *Int'l*, pg. 6098
ASPEN MARKETING SERVICES, LLC—See Publicis Groupe S.A.; *Int'l*, pg. 6098
ASPEN MARKETING SERVICES—See Publicis Groupe S.A.; *Int'l*, pg. 6098
ASPEN MARKETING SERVICES—See Publicis Groupe S.A.; *Int'l*, pg. 6098
ASPEN MARKETING SERVICES—See Publicis Groupe S.A.; *Int'l*, pg. 6098
ASPENMARK ROOFING SOLUTIONS LLC—See Restoration Builders Inc.; *U.S. Private*, pg. 3410
ASPEN MEDICAL EUROPE LIMITED—See Baxter International Inc.; *U.S. Public*, pg. 283
ASPEN MEDICAL EUROPE LIMITED (UK)—See Baxter International Inc.; *U.S. Public*, pg. 283
ASPEN MEDICAL PRODUCTS MALAYSIA SDN. BHD.—See Aspen Pharmacare Holdings Limited; *Int'l*, pg. 629
ASPEN MORTGAGE CORP.; *U.S. Private*, pg. 352
ASPEN NOTRE DAME DE BONDEVILLE SAS—See Aspen Pharmacare Holdings Limited; *Int'l*, pg. 629
ASPEN NUTRITIONALS (PTY) LTD—See Groupe Lactalis SA; *Int'l*, pg. 3105
ASPEN OF DC; *U.S. Private*, pg. 352
ASPEN PHARMACARE AUSTRALIA PTY. LTD.—See Aspen Pharmacare Holdings Limited; *Int'l*, pg. 629
ASPEN PHARMACARE CANADA INC.—See Aspen Pharmacare Holdings Limited; *Int'l*, pg. 629
ASPEN PHARMACARE ESPANA S.L.—See Aspen Pharmacare Holdings Limited; *Int'l*, pg. 629
ASPEN PHARMACARE HOLDINGS LIMITED; *Int'l*, pg. 629
ASPEN PHARMACARE NIGERIA LIMITED—See Aspen Pharmacare Holdings Limited; *Int'l*, pg. 629
ASPEN PHARMACARE UK LIMITED—See Aspen Pharmacare Holdings Limited; *Int'l*, pg. 629
ASPEN PHARMA - INDUSTRIA FARMACEUTICA LTDA—See Aspen Pharmacare Holdings Limited; *Int'l*, pg. 629
ASPEN PHARMA IRELAND LIMITED—See Aspen Pharmacare Holdings Limited; *Int'l*, pg. 629
ASPEN PHARMA (PTY) LIMITED—See Aspen Pharmacare Holdings Limited; *Int'l*, pg. 629

ASPEN PHARMA TRADING LIMITED—See Aspen Pharmacare Holdings Limited; *Int'l*, pg. 629
ASPEN PHILIPPINES INCORPORATED—See Aspen Pharmacare Holdings Limited; *Int'l*, pg. 629
ASPEN PLACE, INC.—See Webster Financial Corporation; *U.S. Public*, pg. 2341
ASPENPOINTE; *U.S. Private*, pg. 352
ASPEN PROPERTY MANAGEMENT LTD.—See CML Global Capital Ltd.; *Int'l*, pg. 1671
ASPEN PROPERTY TRUST—See Aspen Group Limited; *Int'l*, pg. 629
ASPEN PUBLISHERS, INC.—See Wolters Kluwer n.v.; *Int'l*, pg. 8445
ASPEN REFRIGERANTS, INC.—See Hudson Technologies, Inc.; *U.S. Public*, pg. 1068
ASPEN REFRIGERANTS, INC.—See Hudson Technologies, Inc.; *U.S. Public*, pg. 1068
ASPEN RISK MANAGEMENT GROUP—See Tristar Insurance Group, Inc.; *U.S. Private*, pg. 4238
ASPEN RISK MANAGEMENT LIMITED—See Apollo Global Management, Inc.; *U.S. Public*, pg. 147
ASPENS CO., LTD.—See Namutech Co., Ltd.; *Int'l*, pg. 5137
ASPEN SINGAPORE PTE. LTD.—See Apollo Global Management, Inc.; *U.S. Public*, pg. 147
ASPEN SKIING COMPANY, LLC—See Henry Crown & Company; *U.S. Private*, pg. 1917
ASPEN SPECIALTY INSURANCE COMPANY—See Apollo Global Management, Inc.; *U.S. Public*, pg. 147
ASPEN SPECIALTY INSURANCE SOLUTIONS, LLC—See Apollo Global Management, Inc.; *U.S. Public*, pg. 147
ASPEN SQUARE MANAGEMENT, INC.; *U.S. Private*, pg. 352
ASPEN SURGICAL PRODUCTS, INC.—See Audax Group, Limited Partnership; *U.S. Private*, pg. 386
ASPEN SURGICAL PUERTO RICO CORP.—See Audax Group, Limited Partnership; *U.S. Private*, pg. 386
ASPENTECH ARGENTINA S.R.L.—See Emerson Electric Co.; *U.S. Public*, pg. 741
ASPENTECH (BEIJING) CO., LTD.—See Emerson Electric Co.; *U.S. Public*, pg. 741
ASPENTECH CANADA LTD.—See Emerson Electric Co.; *U.S. Public*, pg. 741
ASPENTECH CORPORATION—See Emerson Electric Co.; *U.S. Public*, pg. 741
ASPENTECH DE MEXICO S. DE R.L. DE C.V.—See Emerson Electric Co.; *U.S. Public*, pg. 741
ASPENTECH EUROPE B.V.—See Emerson Electric Co.; *U.S. Public*, pg. 741
ASPENTECH EUROPE SA/NV—See Emerson Electric Co.; *U.S. Public*, pg. 741
ASPENTECH, INC.—See Emerson Electric Co.; *U.S. Public*, pg. 741
ASPENTECH INDIA PVT. LTD.—See Emerson Electric Co.; *U.S. Public*, pg. 741
ASPENTECH JAPAN CO., LTD.—See Emerson Electric Co.; *U.S. Public*, pg. 741
ASPENTECH LTD.—See Emerson Electric Co.; *U.S. Public*, pg. 741
ASPEN TECHNOLOGY AUSTRALIA PTY LTD.—See Emerson Electric Co.; *U.S. Public*, pg. 741
ASPEN TECHNOLOGY, INC.—See Emerson Electric Co.; *U.S. Public*, pg. 741
ASPEN TECHNOLOGY LLC—See Emerson Electric Co.; *U.S. Public*, pg. 741
ASPEN TECHNOLOGY S.A.S.—See Emerson Electric Co.; *U.S. Public*, pg. 741
ASPEN TECHNOLOGY S.L.—See Emerson Electric Co.; *U.S. Public*, pg. 741
ASPEN TECHNOLOGY S.R.L.—See Emerson Electric Co.; *U.S. Public*, pg. 741
ASPEN TECHNOLOGY WLL—See Emerson Electric Co.; *U.S. Public*, pg. 741
ASPENTECH NORWAY AS—See Emerson Electric Co.; *U.S. Public*, pg. 742
ASPENTECH PTE. LTD.—See Emerson Electric Co.; *U.S. Public*, pg. 741
ASPENTECH (SHANGHAI) CO., LTD.—See Emerson Electric Co.; *U.S. Public*, pg. 741
ASPENTECH SOFTWARE BRAZIL LTDA.—See Emerson Electric Co.; *U.S. Public*, pg. 741
ASPENTECH SOLUTIONS SDN. BHD.—See Emerson Electric Co.; *U.S. Public*, pg. 741
ASPENTECH S.R.L.—See Emerson Electric Co.; *U.S. Public*, pg. 741
ASPENTECH (THAILAND) LTD.—See Emerson Electric Co.; *U.S. Public*, pg. 741
ASPEN TECH (THAILAND) LTD.—See Emerson Electric Co.; *U.S. Public*, pg. 741
ASPENTECH VENEZUELA, C.A.—See Emerson Electric Co.; *U.S. Public*, pg. 741
ASPEN TRANSPORTATION, LLC; *U.S. Private*, pg. 352
ASPEN UNIVERSITY INC.—See Aspen Group, Inc.; *U.S. Public*, pg. 213
ASPEN VALLEY LANDSCAPE SUPPLY, INC.—See SiteOne Landscape Supply, Inc.; *U.S. Public*, pg. 1889
ASPEN VETERINARY RESOURCES, LTD—See Patterson Companies, Inc.; *U.S. Public*, pg. 1653

ASPEN VISION CITY SDN. BHD.—See Aspen (Group) Holdings Limited; *Int'l*, pg. 628
ASPEN WALK (EIGHT ASH GREEN) MANAGEMENT COMPANY LIMITED—See Bellway plc; *Int'l*, pg. 967
ASPENWARE, INC.; *U.S. Private*, pg. 352
ASPEN WASTE SYSTEM OF MISSOURI—See Aspen Waste Systems Inc.; *U.S. Private*, pg. 352
ASPEN WASTE SYSTEMS INC.; *U.S. Private*, pg. 352
ASPENWOOD SQUARE APARTMENTS, LP—See Synovus Financial Corp.; *U.S. Public*, pg. 1971
ASPENWOOD SQUARE APARTMENTS, LP—See Synovus Financial Corp.; *U.S. Public*, pg. 1971
ASPEN YOUTH, INC.—See Acadia Healthcare Company, Inc.; *U.S. Public*, pg. 28
ASPERA GMBH—See USU Software AG; *Int'l*, pg. 8099
ASPERA, INC.—See International Business Machines Corporation; *U.S. Public*, pg. 1148
ASPERA INSURANCE SERVICES, INC.—See Kinsale Capital Group, Inc.; *U.S. Public*, pg. 1235
ASPER BV—See ABO-Group NV/SA; *Int'l*, pg. 66
ASPERITY EMPLOYEE BENEFITS INC.—See Inflexion Private Equity Partners LLP; *Int'l*, pg. 3688
ASPERITY EMPLOYEE BENEFITS LTD.—See Inflexion Private Equity Partners LLP; *Int'l*, pg. 3688
ASPERITY EMPLOYEE BENEFITS LTD.—See Inflexion Private Equity Partners LLP; *Int'l*, pg. 3688
ASPERITY EMPLOYEE BENEFITS PTY. LTD.—See Inflexion Private Equity Partners LLP; *Int'l*, pg. 3688
ASPERMONT LIMITED; *Int'l*, pg. 629
ASPERMONT MEDIA—See Aspermont Limited; *Int'l*, pg. 629
ASPEX CORPORATION—See Thermo Fisher Scientific Inc.; *U.S. Public*, pg. 2146
ASP FIBERMARK HOLDINGS LLC.; *U.S. Private*, pg. 351
ASPF II - VERWALTUNGS - GMBH & CO. KG—See Prudential Financial, Inc.; *U.S. Public*, pg. 1731
ASPHALT & BETON GMBH—See STRABAG SE; *Int'l*, pg. 7229
ASPHALT COMMERCE EOOD LTD.—See Trace Group Hold PLC; *Int'l*, pg. 7886
ASPHALT COMMERCE LTD.—See Trace Group Hold PLC; *Int'l*, pg. 7886
ASPHALT CONTRACTORS INC.; *U.S. Private*, pg. 352
ASPHALT GESELLSCHAFT RIEGLER GMBH—See STRABAG SE; *Int'l*, pg. 7229
ASPHALT MATERIALS INC.—See Heritage Group; *U.S. Private*, pg. 1923
ASPHALTMISCHWERK GREINSFURTH GMBH & CO OG—See PORR AG; *Int'l*, pg. 5922
ASPHALTMISCHWERK LEOPOLDAU - TEERAG- ASDAG + MAYREDER-BAU GMBH & CO. KG—See PORR AG; *Int'l*, pg. 5922
ASPHALT PAVING COMPANY OF AUSTIN, LLC—See Summit Materials, Inc.; *U.S. Public*, pg. 1960
ASPHALT PAVING & SUPPLY INC.—See McCormick Incorporated; *U.S. Private*, pg. 2630
ASPHALT SPECIALTIES CO. INC.; *U.S. Private*, pg. 352
ASPHALT SURFACING COMPANY—See Henry Carlson Company; *U.S. Private*, pg. 1917
ASPHALT-UNTERNEHMUNG CARL GUNTHER GESELLSCHAFT M.B.H.—See PORR AG; *Int'l*, pg. 5922
ASPHALTUNTERNEHMUNG RAIMUND GUCKLER BAU-UNTERNEHMUNG GESELLSCHAFT M.B.H.—See PORR AG; *Int'l*, pg. 5922
ASPHERE INNOVATIONS PUBLIC COMPANY LIMITED; *Int'l*, pg. 629
ASP-HOLMBLAD A/S—See Gies Holding GmbH; *Int'l*, pg. 2969
ASPHOLMEN FASTIGHETER AB—See Castellum AB; *Int'l*, pg. 1356
ASPIAIR GMBH—See ATON GmbH; *Int'l*, pg. 688
ASPIAL CORPORATION LIMITED; *Int'l*, pg. 630
ASPIAL-LEE HWA JEWELLERY PTE. LTD.—See Aspial Corporation Limited; *Int'l*, pg. 630
ASPIAL LIFESTYLE LIMITED; *Int'l*, pg. 630
ASPIAL LIFESTYLE LIMITED—See Aspial Corporation Limited; *Int'l*, pg. 630
ASPINWALL & CO. LTD., - COFFEE DIVISION—See Aspinwall & Co. Ltd.,; *Int'l*, pg. 630
ASPINWALL & CO. LTD., - LOGISTICS DIVISION—See Aspinwall & Co. Ltd.,; *Int'l*, pg. 630
ASPINWALL & CO. LTD., - NATURAL FIBRE DIVISION—See Aspinwall & Co. Ltd.,; *Int'l*, pg. 630
ASPINWALL & CO. LTD., - SANDY SPRINGS BRANCH—See Aspinwall & Co. Ltd.,; *Int'l*, pg. 630
ASPINWALL & CO. LTD.,; *Int'l*, pg. 630
ASPINWALL COOPERATIVE CO.; *U.S. Private*, pg. 352
ASPIRA LABS, INC.—See Aspira Women's Health Inc.; *U.S. Public*, pg. 213
ASPIRANET; *U.S. Private*, pg. 352
ASPIRANT GROUP, INC.; *Int'l*, pg. 630
ASPIRA PATHLAB & DIAGNOSTICS LIMITED; *Int'l*, pg. 630
ASPIRATIONS CARE LTD.—See Elysian Capital LLP; *Int'l*, pg. 2372
ASPIRA WOMEN'S HEALTH INC.; *U.S. Public*, pg. 213
ASPIRE CHICAGO; *U.S. Private*, pg. 352
ASPIRE CONSULTING GROUP LLC; *U.S. Private*, pg. 352

ASPIRE CONSULTING GROUP LLC

ASPIRE DEFENCE CAPITAL WORKS JV—See KBR, Inc.; *U.S. Public*, pg. 1215
ASPIRE ENERGY OF OHIO, LLC—See Chesapeake Utilities Corporation; *U.S. Public*, pg. 485
ASPIRE FINANCIAL SERVICES, LLC—See PCS Retirement, LLC; *U.S. Private*, pg. 3121
ASPIRE GLOBAL INC.; *Int'l*, pg. 631
THE ASPIRE GROUP, INC.—See Playfly Sports Properties, LLC; *U.S. Private*, pg. 3212
ASPIRE HEALTH, INC.—See Elevance Health, Inc.; *U.S. Public*, pg. 729
ASPIRE HEALTH PARTNERS - FERNPARK FACILITY—See Aspire Health Partners, Inc.; *U.S. Private*, pg. 352
ASPIRE HEALTH PARTNERS, INC.; *U.S. Private*, pg. 352
ASPIRE HEALTH PARTNERS - PRINCETON PLAZA—See Aspire Health Partners, Inc.; *U.S. Private*, pg. 352
ASPIREHR; *U.S. Private*, pg. 352
ASPIRE MINERALS PTY LTD.—See Apollo Consolidated Limited; *Int'l*, pg. 517
ASPIRE MINING LIMITED; *Int'l*, pg. 631
ASPIRENT CONSULTING LLC—See Nippon Telegraph & Telephone Corporation; *Int'l*, pg. 5348
ASPIRE OF ILLINOIS; *U.S. Private*, pg. 352
ASPIRE OF WESTERN NEW YORK, INC.; *U.S. Private*, pg. 352
ASPIRE REAL ESTATE INVESTORS, INC.; *U.S. Private*, pg. 352
ASPIRE SCOTLAND LIMITED.—See Acadia Healthcare Company, Inc.; *U.S. Public*, pg. 28
ASPIRE SOFTWARE—See Valsef Group; *Int'l*, pg. 8122
ASPIRE TECHNOLOGY SOLUTIONS LTD.—See Lloyds Banking Group plc; *Int'l*, pg. 4537
ASPIRIANT HOLDINGS, LLC; *U.S. Private*, pg. 352
ASPIRION HEALTH RESOURCES, LLC—See Linden LLC; *U.S. Private*, pg. 2460
ASPIRITY HOLDINGS, LLC; *U.S. Private*, pg. 353
ASPIRO AB—See Block, Inc.; *U.S. Public*, pg. 362
ASPIS INSURANCE BROKERAGE SA—See Eurobank Ergasias Services and Holdings S.A.; *Int'l*, pg. 2533
ASPIS INTERNATIONAL AEDAK—See Eurobank Ergasias Services and Holdings S.A.; *Int'l*, pg. 2533
ASPIS LEASING S.A.—See Eurobank Ergasias Services and Holdings S.A.; *Int'l*, pg. 2533
ASPIT AS—See Nordhealth AS; *Int'l*, pg. 5419
ASPLEX SP. Z.O.O.—See Acer Incorporated; *Int'l*, pg. 99
ASPLUND CO., LTD.—See World Co., Ltd.; *Int'l*, pg. 8456
ASPLUNDH BRUSH CONTROL CO.—See Asplundh Tree Expert Co.; *U.S. Private*, pg. 353
ASPLUNDH CANADA ULC—See Asplundh Tree Expert Co.; *U.S. Private*, pg. 353
ASPLUNDH ENVIRONMENTAL SERVICES, INC.—See Asplundh Tree Expert Co.; *U.S. Private*, pg. 353
ASPLUNDH FAMILY PUBLIC FOUNDATION INC.; *U.S. Private*, pg. 353
ASPLUNDH TREE EXPERT (AUSTRALIA) PTY LTD—See Asplundh Tree Expert Co.; *U.S. Private*, pg. 353
ASPLUNDH TREE EXPERT CO.; *U.S. Private*, pg. 353
ASPLUNDH TREE EXPERT (NZ) LTD—See Asplundh Tree Expert Co.; *U.S. Private*, pg. 353
ASPLUNDH TREE SERVICE ULC—See Asplundh Tree Expert Co.; *U.S. Private*, pg. 353
ASPOCOMP AB—See Aspocomp Group Oyj; *Int'l*, pg. 632
ASPOCOMP GROUP OYJ; *Int'l*, pg. 632
ASPOCOMP OY—See Aspocomp Group Oyj; *Int'l*, pg. 632
ASPOCOMP (THAILAND) CO., LTD.—See Aspocomp Group Oyj; *Int'l*, pg. 632
ASPOKEM INTERNATIONAL B.V.—See Aspo Oyj; *Int'l*, pg. 631
ASP ONE.FR SAS—See Tessi S.A.; *Int'l*, pg. 7574
ASPONE LTD.—See Ekwienox Limited; *Int'l*, pg. 2340
ASPO OYJ; *Int'l*, pg. 631
AS POSTIMEES GRUPP—See UP Invest OU; *Int'l*, pg. 8086
AS POSTIMEES—See UP Invest OU; *Int'l*, pg. 8086
ASP PLASTICS PTY LIMITED—See Cleanaway Waste Management Limited; *Int'l*, pg. 1654
A/S PREBEN Z JENSEN—See Beijer Alma AB; *Int'l*, pg. 942
AS PREMIA FFL—See PRFoods AS; *Int'l*, pg. 5968
AS PREMIUM BRANDS NORWAY—See Pernod Ricard S.A.; *Int'l*, pg. 5810
ASPRESEG SAS—See Delta Plus Group; *Int'l*, pg. 2019
ASPREVA INTERNATIONAL LIMITED—See CSL Limited; *Int'l*, pg. 1866
ASPREY; *Int'l*, pg. 632
AS PRICEWATERHOUSECOOPERS; *Int'l*, pg. 591
AS PRINTALL—See AS Ekspress Grupp; *Int'l*, pg. 589
ASPROFOS ENGINEERING S.A.—See HELLENiQ ENERGY Holdings S.A.; *Int'l*, pg. 3334
ASP SERVEUR SAS—See Econocom Group SA; *Int'l*, pg. 2297
A-SPV D.O.O.—See Raiffeisen Bank International AG; *Int'l*, pg. 6182
ASP WESTWARD, L.P.—See American Securities LLC; *U.S. Private*, pg. 247
ASPYRA-EAST COAST OFFICE—See ASPYRA, INC.; *U.S. Public*, pg. 214

ASPYRA, INC.; *U.S. Public*, pg. 213
ASPYRA TECHNOLOGIES LTD.—See ASPYRA, INC.; *U.S. Public*, pg. 213
ASPYR MEDIA, INC.—See Embracer Group AB; *Int'l*, pg. 2375
A SQUARED ENTERTAINMENT LLC—See Kartoon Studios, Inc.; *U.S. Public*, pg. 1214
A SQUARED PRODUCTIONS GROUP, INC.—See Duncan Channon; *U.S. Private*, pg. 1287
A SQUARED PRODUCTIONS GROUP, INC.; *U.S. Private*, pg. 19
ASRA MINERALS LIMITED; *Int'l*, pg. 632
ASRC CIVIL CONSTRUCTION, LLC—See Arctic Slope Regional Corporation; *U.S. Private*, pg. 316
ASRC CONSTRUCTION HOLDING COMPANY, LLC—See Arctic Slope Regional Corporation; *U.S. Private*, pg. 316
ASRC ENERGY SERVICES POWER & COMMUNICATIONS, LLC—See Arctic Slope Regional Corporation; *U.S. Private*, pg. 316
ASRC ENERGY SERVICES—See Arctic Slope Regional Corporation; *U.S. Private*, pg. 316
ASRC FEDERAL HOLDING COMPANY—See Arctic Slope Regional Corporation; *U.S. Private*, pg. 316
ASRC INDUSTRIAL SERVICES LLC—See Arctic Slope Regional Corporation; *U.S. Private*, pg. 316
ASRC MANAGEMENT SERVICES, INC.—See Arctic Slope Regional Corporation; *U.S. Private*, pg. 316
ASRCO LOGISTICS LTD.—See Beijing Sports & Entertainment Industry Group Limited; *Int'l*, pg. 957
ASRC SERVICE CENTER, INC.—See Arctic Slope Regional Corporation; *U.S. Private*, pg. 316
ASRC SKW ESKIMOS, INC.—See Arctic Slope Regional Corporation; *U.S. Private*, pg. 316
A.S.R. ELECTRICAL CONTRACTING; *U.S. Private*, pg. 28
AS REOLA GAAS—See Neste Oyj; *Int'l*, pg. 5201
ASR EUROPE LOGISTICS LTD.—See Beijing Sports & Entertainment Industry Group Limited; *Int'l*, pg. 957
AS REVERTA; *Int'l*, pg. 591
AS RIGAS AUTOELEKTROAPARATU RUPNICA; *Int'l*, pg. 591
ASR INTERNATIONAL CORPORATION; *U.S. Private*, pg. 353
ASR LOGISTICS LTD.—See Beijing Sports & Entertainment Industry Group Limited; *Int'l*, pg. 957
ASR NEDERLAND N.V.; *Int'l*, pg. 632
ASROCK AMERICA, INC.—See ASRock Inc.; *Int'l*, pg. 632
ASROCK EUROPE B.V.—See ASRock Inc.; *Int'l*, pg. 632
ASROCK INC.; *Int'l*, pg. 632
A/S ROCKWOOL—See ROCKWOOL A/S; *Int'l*, pg. 6379
A.S. ROMA S.P.A.—See The Friedkin Group, Inc.; *U.S. Private*, pg. 4031
ASRR CAPITAL LTD.; *Int'l*, pg. 632
ASR REAL ESTATE B.V.—See ASR Nederland N.V.; *Int'l*, pg. 632
ASR RECYCLING KASHIMA CO., LTD.—See Konoike Transport Co., Ltd.; *Int'l*, pg. 4274
A/S RUKO—See ASSA ABLOY AB; *Int'l*, pg. 632
A & S RV CENTER, INC.—See Redwood Capital Investments, LLC; *U.S. Private*, pg. 3380
ASR VERMOGENSBEHEER N.V.—See ASR Nederland N.V.; *Int'l*, pg. 632
ASR VERZEKERINGEN N.V.—See ASR Nederland N.V.; *Int'l*, pg. 632
ASRY MARKETING SERVICES LTD.—See Arab Shipbuilding & Repair Yard Co.; *Int'l*, pg. 532
ASSA ABLOY AB; *Int'l*, pg. 632
ASSA ABLOY ASIA HOLDING AB—See ASSA ABLOY AB; *Int'l*, pg. 633
ASSA ABLOY ASIA PACIFIC LTD—See ASSA ABLOY AB; *Int'l*, pg. 633
ASSA ABLOY AUSTRALIA PACIFIC PTY LTD—See ASSA ABLOY AB; *Int'l*, pg. 633
ASSA ABLOY AUSTRALIA PTY LTD—See ASSA ABLOY AB; *Int'l*, pg. 633
ASSA ABLOY AUSTRIA GMBH—See ASSA ABLOY AB; *Int'l*, pg. 633
ASSA ABLOY BALTIC AS—See ASSA ABLOY AB; *Int'l*, pg. 633
ASSA ABLOY CHILE LTDA—See ASSA ABLOY AB; *Int'l*, pg. 633
ASSA ABLOY COLOMBIA S.A.S.—See ASSA ABLOY AB; *Int'l*, pg. 633
ASSA ABLOY DANMARK A/S—See ASSA ABLOY AB; *Int'l*, pg. 633
ASSA ABLOY DEUTSCHLAND GMBH—See ASSA ABLOY AB; *Int'l*, pg. 633
ASSA ABLOY DOOR SECURITY SOLUTIONS—See ASSA ABLOY AB; *Int'l*, pg. 636
ASSA ABLOY EAST AFRICA LTD.—See ASSA ABLOY AB; *Int'l*, pg. 633
ASSA ABLOY ENTRANCE SYSTEMS AB—See ASSA ABLOY AB; *Int'l*, pg. 633
ASSA ABLOY ENTRANCE SYSTEMS AUSTRALIA PTY LTD—See ASSA ABLOY AB; *Int'l*, pg. 634
ASSA ABLOY ENTRANCE SYSTEMS AUSTRIA GMBH—See ASSA ABLOY AB; *Int'l*, pg. 635

CORPORATE AFFILIATIONS

ASSA ABLOY ENTRANCE SYSTEMS DENMARK A/S—See ASSA ABLOY AB; *Int'l*, pg. 633
ASSA ABLOY ENTRANCE SYSTEMS FINLAND OY—See ASSA ABLOY AB; *Int'l*, pg. 633
ASSA ABLOY ENTRANCE SYSTEMS FRANCE SAS—See ASSA ABLOY AB; *Int'l*, pg. 633
ASSA ABLOY ENTRANCE SYSTEMS GMBH—See ASSA ABLOY AB; *Int'l*, pg. 633
ASSA ABLOY ENTRANCE SYSTEMS IDDS AB—See ASSA ABLOY AB; *Int'l*, pg. 635
ASSA ABLOY ENTRANCE SYSTEMS ITALY S.P.A.—See ASSA ABLOY AB; *Int'l*, pg. 633
ASSA ABLOY ENTRANCE SYSTEMS ITALY SRL—See ASSA ABLOY AB; *Int'l*, pg. 633
ASSA ABLOY ENTRANCE SYSTEMS KFT.—See ASSA ABLOY AB; *Int'l*, pg. 633
ASSA ABLOY ENTRANCE SYSTEMS NORWAY AS—See ASSA ABLOY AB; *Int'l*, pg. 633
ASSA ABLOY ENTRANCE SYSTEMS NV—See ASSA ABLOY AB; *Int'l*, pg. 633
ASSA ABLOY ENTRANCE SYSTEMS (PORTO)—See ASSA ABLOY AB; *Int'l*, pg. 634
ASSA ABLOY ENTRANCE SYSTEMS, SPOL. S R.O.—See ASSA ABLOY AB; *Int'l*, pg. 633
ASSA ABLOY ENTRANCE SYSTEMS (SUZHOU) CO., LTD.—See ASSA ABLOY AB; *Int'l*, pg. 633
ASSA ABLOY ENTRANCE SYSTEMS SWEDEN AB—See ASSA ABLOY AB; *Int'l*, pg. 633
ASSA ABLOY ENTRANCE SYSTEMS UK & IRELAND—See ASSA ABLOY AB; *Int'l*, pg. 634
ASSA ABLOY ES PRODUCTION S.R.O—See ASSA ABLOY AB; *Int'l*, pg. 633
ASSA ABLOY FORSAKRINGS AB—See ASSA ABLOY AB; *Int'l*, pg. 635
ASSA ABLOY GECIS SISTEMLERI A.S.—See ASSA ABLOY AB; *Int'l*, pg. 635
ASSA ABLOY GLOBAL SOLUTIONS AB—See ASSA ABLOY AB; *Int'l*, pg. 635
ASSA ABLOY GUOQIANG (SHANDONG) HARDWARE TECHNOLOGY CO., LTD—See ASSA ABLOY AB; *Int'l*, pg. 635
ASSA ABLOY HOLDING ITALIA S.P.A.—See ASSA ABLOY AB; *Int'l*, pg. 635
ASSA ABLOY HOLDINGS (SA) LTD—See ASSA ABLOY AB; *Int'l*, pg. 635
ASSA ABLOY HONG KONG LIMITED—See ASSA ABLOY AB; *Int'l*, pg. 635
ASSA ABLOY HOSPITALITY (CANADA) LTD.—See ASSA ABLOY AB; *Int'l*, pg. 635
ASSA ABLOY HOSPITALITY GMBH—See ASSA ABLOY AB; *Int'l*, pg. 635
ASSA ABLOY HOSPITALITY IBERICA, S.L.—See ASSA ABLOY AB; *Int'l*, pg. 635
ASSA ABLOY HOSPITALITY LTD—See ASSA ABLOY AB; *Int'l*, pg. 635
ASSA ABLOY HOSPITALITY LTD—See ASSA ABLOY AB; *Int'l*, pg. 635
ASSA ABLOY HOSPITALITY LTD—See ASSA ABLOY AB; *Int'l*, pg. 635
ASSA ABLOY HOSPITALITY PTE LTD—See ASSA ABLOY AB; *Int'l*, pg. 635
ASSA ABLOY HOSPITALITY SAS—See ASSA ABLOY AB; *Int'l*, pg. 635
ASSA ABLOY HOSPITALITY SHANGHAI LTD—See ASSA ABLOY AB; *Int'l*, pg. 635
ASSA ABLOY HUNGARY KERESKEDELMI KFT.—See ASSA ABLOY AB; *Int'l*, pg. 635
ASSA ABLOY IDENTIFICATION TECHNOLOGY GROUP AB—See ASSA ABLOY AB; *Int'l*, pg. 635
ASSA ABLOY, INC.—See ASSA ABLOY AB; *Int'l*, pg. 636
ASSA ABLOY INDIA PRIVATE LTD.—See ASSA ABLOY AB; *Int'l*, pg. 635
ASSA ABLOY INDUSTRIETORE GMBH—See ASSA ABLOY AB; *Int'l*, pg. 635
ASSA ABLOY IP AB—See ASSA ABLOY AB; *Int'l*, pg. 635
ASSA ABLOY ITALIA S.P.A.—See ASSA ABLOY AB; *Int'l*, pg. 635
ASSA ABLOY JAPAN CO LTD—See ASSA ABLOY AB; *Int'l*, pg. 636
ASSA ABLOY KOREA CO., LTD.—See ASSA ABLOY AB; *Int'l*, pg. 636
ASSA ABLOY KREDIT AB—See ASSA ABLOY AB; *Int'l*, pg. 636
ASSA ABLOY LIMITED—See ASSA ABLOY AB; *Int'l*, pg. 636
ASSA ABLOY MALAYSIA SDN BHD—See ASSA ABLOY AB; *Int'l*, pg. 636
ASSA ABLOY MERCOR DOORS SP. Z O.O.—See ASSA ABLOY AB; *Int'l*, pg. 633
ASSA ABLOY MEXICO, S.A DE CV.—See ASSA ABLOY AB; *Int'l*, pg. 636
ASSA ABLOY MOBILE SERVICES AB—See ASSA ABLOY AB; *Int'l*, pg. 636
ASSA ABLOY NEDERLAND B.V.—See ASSA ABLOY AB; *Int'l*, pg. 636
ASSA ABLOY NEW ZEALAND LIMITED—See ASSA ABLOY AB; *Int'l*, pg. 636
ASSA ABLOY NV—See ASSA ABLOY AB; *Int'l*, pg. 636

COMPANY NAME INDEX

ASSA ABLOY OCCIDENTE, SA DE CV—See ASSA ABLOY AB; *Int'l*, pg. 636
ASSA ABLOY POLAND SP. Z O.O.—See ASSA ABLOY AB; *Int'l*, pg. 636
ASSA ABLOY PORTUGAL, LDA.—See ASSA ABLOY AB; *Int'l*, pg. 636
ASSA ABLOY PORTUGAL, UNIPESSOAL, LDA—See ASSA ABLOY AB; *Int'l*, pg. 636
ASSA ABLOY SALES & MARKETING GROUP, INC.—See ASSA ABLOY AB; *Int'l*, pg. 637
ASSA ABLOY (SA) (PTY) LTD—See ASSA ABLOY AB; *Int'l*, pg. 632
ASSA ABLOY SICHERHEITSTECHNIK GMBH - BERLIN PLANT—See ASSA ABLOY AB; *Int'l*, pg. 636
ASSA ABLOY SICHERHEITSTECHNIK GMBH—See ASSA ABLOY AB; *Int'l*, pg. 636
ASSA ABLOY SINGAPORE PTE LTD—See ASSA ABLOY AB; *Int'l*, pg. 636
ASSA ABLOY SOUTH ASIA PTE LTD—See ASSA ABLOY AB; *Int'l*, pg. 636
ASSA ABLOY SVENSK FASTIGHETS AB—See ASSA ABLOY AB; *Int'l*, pg. 636
ASSA ABLOY (SWITZERLAND) LTD.—See ASSA ABLOY AB; *Int'l*, pg. 636
ASSA ABLOY THAILAND LTD—See ASSA ABLOY AB; *Int'l*, pg. 636
ASSA ABLOY (ZHONGSHAN) SECURITY TECHNOLOGY COMPANY LIMITED—See ASSA ABLOY AB; *Int'l*, pg. 633
ASSAB CELIK VE ISIL ISLEM A.S.—See voestalpine AG; *Int'l*, pg. 8287
ASSABET VALLEY BANCORP; *U.S. Private*, pg. 353
ASSAB JAPAN KK—See voestalpine AG; *Int'l*, pg. 8287
ASSAB STEELS (CHINA) LTD.—See voestalpine AG; *Int'l*, pg. 8287
ASSAB STEELS (HK) LTD.—See voestalpine AG; *Int'l*, pg. 8287
ASSAB STEELS (KOREA) CO., LTD.—See voestalpine AG; *Int'l*, pg. 8287
ASSAB STEELS (MALAYSIA) SDN BHD—See voestalpine AG; *Int'l*, pg. 8287
ASSAB STEELS SINGAPORE (PTE) LTD.—See voestalpine AG; *Int'l*, pg. 8287
ASSAB STEELS (TAIWAN) LTD.—See voestalpine AG; *Int'l*, pg. 8287
ASSAB STEELS (THAILAND) LTD.—See voestalpine AG; *Int'l*, pg. 8287
ASSAB STEELS VIETNAM COMPANY LIMITED—See voestalpine AG; *Int'l*, pg. 8287
ASSAB TOOLING (BEIJING) CO., LTD.—See voestalpine AG; *Int'l*, pg. 8287
ASSAB TOOLING (DONG GUAN) CO., LTD.—See voestalpine AG; *Int'l*, pg. 8287
ASSAB TOOLING (QING DAO) CO., LTD.—See voestalpine AG; *Int'l*, pg. 8287
ASSAB TOOLING TECHNOLOGY (CHONGQING) CO., LTD.—See voestalpine AG; *Int'l*, pg. 8287
ASSAB TOOLING TECHNOLOGY (NINGBO) CO., LTD.—See voestalpine AG; *Int'l*, pg. 8287
ASSAB TOOLING TECHNOLOGY (SHANGHAI) CO., LTD.—See voestalpine AG; *Int'l*, pg. 8287
ASSAB TOOLING (XIAMEN) CO., LTD.—See voestalpine AG; *Int'l*, pg. 8287
ASSA COMPANIA DE SEGUROS, S.A.—See Grupo ASSA, S.A.; *Int'l*, pg. 3121
A/S SAF TEHNIKA; *Int'l*, pg. 28
ASSA, INC—See ASSA ABLOY AB; *Int'l*, pg. 637
ASSA INDUSTRIE AB—See ASSA ABLOY AB; *Int'l*, pg. 639
ASSAM CARBON PRODUCTS LTD.—See Morgan Advanced Materials plc; *Int'l*, pg. 5041
ASSAM COMPANY INDIA LIMITED—See BRS Ventures Investment Ltd; *Int'l*, pg. 1199
ASSAM ENTRADE LIMITED; *Int'l*, pg. 641
ASSAM PETRO-CHEMICALS LTD.; *Int'l*, pg. 641
AS SANGAR; *Int'l*, pg. 591
ASSANTE WEALTH MANAGEMENT (CANADA) LTD.—See CI Financial Corporation; *Int'l*, pg. 1600
ASSA OEM AB—See ASSA ABLOY AB; *Int'l*, pg. 637
ASSAS FOR CONCRETE PRODUCTS CO. LTD.; *Int'l*, pg. 641
A/S SCANCEM CHEMICALS—See Heidelberg Materials AG; *Int'l*, pg. 3315
ASSCENT INFOSERVE PVT. LTD.—See Accentia Technologies Limited; *Int'l*, pg. 82
AS SCHENKER—See Deutsche Bahn AG; *Int'l*, pg. 2052
ASSCOM INSURANCE BROKERS SRL—See Aon plc; *Int'l*, pg. 494
ASSECO AUSTRIA GMBH—See Asseco Poland S.A.; *Int'l*, pg. 641
ASSECO BUSINESS SOLUTIONS S.A.—See Asseco Poland S.A.; *Int'l*, pg. 641
ASSECO CENTRAL EUROPE, A.S.—See Asseco Poland S.A.; *Int'l*, pg. 641
ASSECO DENMARK A/S—See Asseco Poland S.A.; *Int'l*, pg. 641
ASSECO GERMANY AG—See Asseco Poland S.A.; *Int'l*, pg. 641
ASSECO POLAND S.A.; *Int'l*, pg. 641

ASSECO SEE D.O.O.E.L.—See Asseco Poland S.A.; *Int'l*, pg. 641
ASSECO SEE D.O.O.—See Asseco Poland S.A.; *Int'l*, pg. 641
ASSECO SEE D.O.O.—See Asseco Poland S.A.; *Int'l*, pg. 641
ASSECO SEE D.O.O.—See Asseco Poland S.A.; *Int'l*, pg. 641
ASSECO SEE D.O.O.—See Asseco Poland S.A.; *Int'l*, pg. 641
ASSECO SEE D.O.O.—See Asseco Poland S.A.; *Int'l*, pg. 641
ASSECO SEE D.O.O.—See Asseco Poland S.A.; *Int'l*, pg. 641
ASSECO SEE SH.P.K.—See Asseco Poland S.A.; *Int'l*, pg. 641
ASSECO SEE SH.P.K.—See Asseco Poland S.A.; *Int'l*, pg. 641
ASSECO SEE TEKNOLOJI A.S.—See Asseco Poland S.A.; *Int'l*, pg. 641
ASSECO SOUTH EASTERN EUROPE S.A.—See Asseco Poland S.A.; *Int'l*, pg. 641
ASSECO SPAIN SA—See Asseco Poland S.A.; *Int'l*, pg. 641
AS SELECTA S.R.O.—See Allianz SE; *Int'l*, pg. 343
ASSELIN-THIBEAU SITE D'ELBEUF—See NSC Groupe SA; *Int'l*, pg. 5476
ASSELIN-THIBEAU SITE DE TOURCOING—See NSC Groupe SA; *Int'l*, pg. 5476
ASSEMBLA INC.—See HGGC, LLC; *U.S. Private*, pg. 1929
ASSEMBLIES ON TIME, INC.—See Crestview Partners, L.P.; *U.S. Private*, pg. 1098
ASSEMBLIN AB; *Int'l*, pg. 642
ASSEMBLIN VENTILATION AB—See Triton Advisers Limited; *Int'l*, pg. 7933
ASSEMBLY BIOSCIENCES, INC.; *U.S. Public*, pg. 214
ASSEMBLY FASTENERS INC.; *U.S. Private*, pg. 353
ASSEMBLY & MANUFACTURING SYSTEMS, INC.; *U.S. Private*, pg. 353
ASSEMBLY ORGANIZING OY—See Telia Company AB; *Int'l*, pg. 7543
ASSEMBLY PHARMACEUTICALS, INC.—See Assembly Biosciences, Inc.; *U.S. Public*, pg. 214
ASSEMBLY ROW CONDOMINIUM, INC.—See Federal Realty Investment Trust; *U.S. Public*, pg. 825
ASSEMBLY SERVICES SDN BHD—See Sime Darby Berhad; *Int'l*, pg. 6930
ASSEMBLY—See Stagwell, Inc.; *U.S. Public*, pg. 1926
ASSEMBLY & TEST - EUROPE GMBH—See ATS Corporation; *Int'l*, pg. 695
ASSEM-PAK, INC.—See OEP Capital Advisors, L.P.; *U.S. Private*, pg. 2999
ASSEMS INC.; *Int'l*, pg. 642
ASSEMTI SA—See The Swatch Group Ltd.; *Int'l*, pg. 7691
ASS END OF ARM TOOLING, INC.—See INDUS Holding AG; *Int'l*, pg. 3662
ASSENT CONSULTING—See Cross Country Healthcare, Inc.; *U.S. Public*, pg. 595
AS SERTIFITSEERIMISKESKUS—See Telia Company AB; *Int'l*, pg. 7543
ASSERTIO HOLDINGS, INC.; *U.S. Public*, pg. 214
A&S SERVICES GROUP, LLC—See McCain Foods Limited; *Int'l*, pg. 4756
AS SERVICIOS DE PUBLICIDAD S.A.—See Vivendi SE; *Int'l*, pg. 8269
THE ASSESSMENT COMPANY LTD—See Pearson plc; *Int'l*, pg. 5778
ASSESSMENT TECHNOLOGIES INSTITUTE, LLC—See Blackstone Inc.; *U.S. Public*, pg. 348
ASSESSMENT TECHNOLOGIES INSTITUTE, LLC—See Canada Pension Plan Investment Board; *Int'l*, pg. 1279
ASSESSMENT TECHNOLOGY, INC.—See Silver Lake Group, LLC; *U.S. Private*, pg. 3661
ASSET ACCEPTANCE CAPITAL CORP.—See Encore Capital Group, Inc.; *U.S. Public*, pg. 759
ASSET ACCEPTANCE, LLC—See Encore Capital Group, Inc.; *U.S. Public*, pg. 759
THE ASSET ADVISORY GROUP, INC.—See Genstar Capital, LLC; *U.S. Private*, pg. 1677
THE ASSET ADVISORY GROUP, INC.—See Keystone Group, L.P.; *U.S. Private*, pg. 2298
ASSET ALLIANCE ADVISORS INC—See Asset Alliance Corporation; *U.S. Private*, pg. 354
ASSET ALLIANCE CORPORATION; *U.S. Private*, pg. 353
ASSET ALLIANCE HOLDING GROUP—See Asset Alliance Corporation; *U.S. Private*, pg. 354
ASSETANDO REAL ESTATE GMBH—See Ernst Russ AG; *Int'l*, pg. 2495
ASSET APPRAISAL SERVICES, INC.—See RB Global, Inc.; *Int'l*, pg. 6226
ASSETCO FREIGHT BROKERS INC.; *U.S. Private*, pg. 354
ASSETCO PLC; *Int'l*, pg. 643
ASSETCORE LTD.—See Aquila Services Group PLC; *Int'l*, pg. 528
ASSETCO TECHNICAL RESCUE—See AssetCo plc; *Int'l*, pg. 643
ASSETCO UAE—See AssetCo plc; *Int'l*, pg. 643
ASSET DATA SOLUTIONS, LLC—See Emerson Electric Co.; *U.S. Public*, pg. 748

ASSET WORLD CORP PUBLIC COMPANY LIMITED

ASSET DEVELOPMENT GROUP, INC.—See West Partners LLC; *U.S. Private*, pg. 4486
ASSET ENTITIES INC.; *U.S. Public*, pg. 214
ASSET EXCHANGE, INC.—See Fidelity National Infor; *U.S. Public*, pg. 832
ASSET FINANCE DIVISION—See National Bank of Malawi; *Int'l*, pg. 5154
ASSET FIVE GROUP PUBLIC COMPANY LIMITED; *Int'l*, pg. 642
ASSETGATE GMBH—See Intrum AB; *Int'l*, pg. 3770
ASSET INGATLAN MANAGEMENT KFT.—See Metro AG; *Int'l*, pg. 4859
ASSET INTELLIGENCE, LLC—See PowerFleet, Inc.; *U.S. Public*, pg. 1706
ASSET INTERNATIONAL AUSTRALIA PTY LTD—See Genstar Capital, LLC; *U.S. Private*, pg. 1675
ASSET INTERNATIONAL HONG KONG LTD.—See Genstar Capital, LLC; *U.S. Private*, pg. 1675
ASSET INTERNATIONAL INC.—See Genstar Capital, LLC; *U.S. Private*, pg. 1675
ASSET INTERNATIONAL LTD—See Hill & Smith PLC; *Int'l*, pg. 3391
ASSET INTERTECH, INC.; *U.S. Private*, pg. 354
ASSET KINETICS PTY. LTD.—See Engenco Limited; *Int'l*, pg. 2426
ASSET MANAGEMENT COMPANY, LLC; *U.S. Private*, pg. 354
THE ASSET MANAGEMENT CORPORATION LIMITED—See PCF Group plc; *Int'l*, pg. 5768
ASSET MANAGEMENT ONE CO., LTD.—See Dai-ichi Life Holdings, Inc.; *Int'l*, pg. 1917
ASSET MANAGEMENT ONE CO., LTD.—See Mizuho Financial Group, Inc.; *Int'l*, pg. 4997
ASSET MANAGEMENT ONE HONG KONG LIMITED—See Dai-ichi Life Holdings, Inc.; *Int'l*, pg. 1917
ASSET MANAGEMENT ONE HONG KONG LIMITED—See Mizuho Financial Group, Inc.; *Int'l*, pg. 4997
ASSET MANAGEMENT ONE INTERNATIONAL LTD.—See Mizuho Financial Group, Inc.; *Int'l*, pg. 4997
ASSET MANAGEMENT ONE SINGAPORE PTE. LTD.—See Dai-ichi Life Holdings, Inc.; *Int'l*, pg. 1917
ASSET MANAGEMENT ONE SINGAPORE PTE. LTD.—See Mizuho Financial Group, Inc.; *Int'l*, pg. 4997
ASSET MANAGEMENT SERVICE S.R.L.—See I.M.A. Industria Macchine Automatiche S.p.A.; *Int'l*, pg. 3566
ASSET MANAGEMENT SLOVENSKEJ SPORITELNE SPRAV SPOL A S.—See Erste Group Bank AG; *Int'l*, pg. 2498
ASSET MARKETING SYSTEMS INSURANCE SERVICES, LLC; *U.S. Private*, pg. 354
ASSETMARK FINANCIAL HOLDINGS, INC.—See GTCR LLC; *U.S. Private*, pg. 1802
ASSETMARK, INC.—See Huatai Securities Co., Ltd.; *Int'l*, pg. 3514
ASSETNATION, INC.—See RB Global, Inc.; *Int'l*, pg. 6226
ASSETOWL LIMITED; *Int'l*, pg. 643
ASSET PLUS COMPANIES LP; *U.S. Private*, pg. 354
ASSET PLUS FUND MANAGEMENT COMPANY LIMITED—See Asia Plus Group Holdings Public Company Limited; *Int'l*, pg. 614
ASSET PLUS LIMITED; *Int'l*, pg. 642
ASSET PRESERVATION, INC.—See Stewart Information Services Corporation; *U.S. Public*, pg. 1947
ASSET PROPERTY MANAGEMENT LTD.—See Pan Pacific International Holdings Corporation; *Int'l*, pg. 5715
ASSET PROTECTION ASSOCIATES, INC.—See Allied Universal Manager LLC; *U.S. Private*, pg. 190
ASSET PROTECTION, INC.—See Hellman & Friedman LLC; *U.S. Private*, pg. 1908
ASSET PROTECTION & SECURITY SERVICES, L. P.; *U.S. Private*, pg. 354
ASSET REALTY GROUP; *U.S. Private*, pg. 354
ASSET REALTY—See Asset Realty Group; *U.S. Private*, pg. 354
ASSET REALTY—See Asset Realty Group; *U.S. Private*, pg. 354
ASSET RESOLUTION LIMITED; *Int'l*, pg. 642
ASSET SOURCE INTERNATIONAL, INC.—See STA International Inc.; *U.S. Private*, pg. 3774
ASSET STAFFING INCORPORATED; *U.S. Private*, pg. 354
ASSET STRATEGY RETIREMENT CONSULTANTS, LLC; *U.S. Private*, pg. 354
ASSETT, INC.; *U.S. Private*, pg. 354
ASSETTRACKR PRIVATE LTD.—See ZF Friedrichshafen AG; *Int'l*, pg. 8641
ASSET VANTAGE INC.—See Asset Vantage Systems Pvt. Ltd.; *Int'l*, pg. 642
ASSET VANTAGE SYSTEMS PVT. LTD.; *Int'l*, pg. 642
ASSET WAVE CORPORATION, INC.—See ORIX Corporation; *Int'l*, pg. 5634
ASSETWISE PUBLIC COMPANY LIMITED; *Int'l*, pg. 643
ASSETWORKS, INC.—See Constellation Software Inc.; *Int'l*, pg. 1775
ASSET WORLD CORP PUBLIC COMPANY LIMITED; *Int'l*, pg. 642
AS SEVERSTALLAT—See PAO Severstal; *Int'l*, pg. 5731

ASSET WORLD CORP PUBLIC COMPANY LIMITED

ASSICURAZIONI GENERALI—See Assicurazioni Generali S.p.A.; *Int'l*, pg. 643
ASSICURAZIONI GENERALI S.P.A. - GENERALI GLOBAL LONDON UNIT—See Assicurazioni Generali S.p.A.; *Int'l*, pg. 643
ASSICURAZIONI GENERALI S.P.A.; *Int'l*, pg. 643
ASSIETTA PRIVATE EQUITY SGR S.P.A.; *Int'l*, pg. 648
ASSIGNED COUNSEL INCORPORATED.; *U.S. Private*, pg. 354
ASSIGNED RISK SOLUTIONS LTD.—See The Allstate Corporation; *U.S. Public*, pg. 2033
ASSIGNMENT AMERICA, LLC—See Cross Country Healthcare, Inc.; *U.S. Public*, pg. 595
ASSIGN NAVI, INC.—See LTS, Inc.; *Int'l*, pg. 4571
ASSIMA A/S—See Fonds de Solidarite des Travailleurs du Quebec; *Int'l*, pg. 2725
ASSIMA CANADA, INC.—See Fonds de Solidarite des Travailleurs du Quebec; *Int'l*, pg. 2725
ASSIMA FRANCE SAS—See Fonds de Solidarite des Travailleurs du Quebec; *Int'l*, pg. 2725
ASSIMA, INC.—See Fonds de Solidarite des Travailleurs du Quebec; *Int'l*, pg. 2725
ASSIMA PLC—See Fonds de Solidarite des Travailleurs du Quebec; *Int'l*, pg. 2725
ASSIMA SOFTWARE ESPAFIA, S.L.—See Fonds de Solidarite des Travailleurs du Quebec; *Int'l*, pg. 2725
ASSIMA SWITZERLAND SA—See Fonds de Solidarite des Travailleurs du Quebec; *Int'l*, pg. 2725
ASSIMOCO VITA S.P.A.—See DZ BANK AG Deutsche Zentral-Genossenschaftsbank; *Int'l*, pg. 2243
ASSIOPAY S.R.L.—See TXT e-Solutions S.p.A.; *Int'l*, pg. 7993
ASSISTANCE COURTAGE D'ASSURANCE ET DE REASSURANCE S.A.—See Allianz SE; *Int'l*, pg. 351
ASSISTANS PA GOTLAND AB—See Humana AB; *Int'l*, pg. 3529
ASSIST DIGITAL S.P.A.—See Ardian SAS; *Int'l*, pg. 555
ASSISTEC CO. LTD.—See FUJIFILM Holdings Corporation; *Int'l*, pg. 2821
ASSISTECH CIA. LTDA.—See SMC Corporation; *Int'l*, pg. 7003
ASSISTED 4 LIVING, INC.; *U.S. Public*, pg. 214
ASSISTED LIVING CONCEPTS, LLC—See TPG Capital, L.P.; *U.S. Public*, pg. 2168
ASSISTED LIVING PROPERTIES INC.—See Brookdale Senior Living Inc.; *U.S. Public*, pg. 393
ASSIST GMBH—See Advent International Corporation; *U.S. Private*, pg. 104
ASSIST INFORMATICA S.R.L.—See Sesa S.p.A.; *Int'l*, pg. 6728
ASSISTIVE TECHNOLOGY GROUP, INC.—See Audax Group, Limited Partnership; *U.S. Private*, pg. 386
AS SISUSTAJA—See Carrier Global Corporation; *U.S. Public*, pg. 441
ASSITECA AGRICOLTURA S.R.L.—See Assiteca SpA; *Int'l*, pg. 648
ASSITECA BSA S.R.L.—See Assiteca SpA; *Int'l*, pg. 648
ASSITECA CONSULTING S.R.L.—See Assiteca SpA; *Int'l*, pg. 648
ASSITECA SPA; *Int'l*, pg. 648
ASSIUT CEMENT COMPANY—See CEMEX, S.A.B. de C.V.; *Int'l*, pg. 1398
ASSIUT ISLAMIC TRADING; *Int'l*, pg. 648
ASSMANN BERATEN + PLANEN GMBH; *Int'l*, pg. 648
ASS MASCHINENBAU GMBH—See INDUS Holding AG; *Int'l*, pg. 3662
ASSOCIATED ACCEPTANCE, INC.—See Rush Enterprises, Inc.; *U.S. Public*, pg. 1826
ASSOCIATED ADVERTISING AGENCY, INC.; *U.S. Private*, pg. 354
ASSOCIATED AGENCY GROUP, LLC—See Aon plc; *Int'l*, pg. 495
ASSOCIATED AIRCRAFT COMPANY LLC; *U.S. Private*, pg. 354
ASSOCIATED AIRCRAFT MANUFACTURING & SALES, INC.; *U.S. Private*, pg. 354
ASSOCIATED ALCOHOLS & BREWERIES LTD.; *Int'l*, pg. 648
ASSOCIATED ALUMINUM PRODUCTS CO., LLC; *U.S. Private*, pg. 354
ASSOCIATED AMERICAN INDUSTRIES, INC.—See Standex International; *U.S. Public*, pg. 1930
ASSOCIATED ASPHALT INC.—See Ergon, Inc.; *U.S. Private*, pg. 1418
ASSOCIATED ASSET MANAGEMENT CORPORATION B.V.—See Munchener Ruckversicherungs AG; *Int'l*, pg. 5085
ASSOCIATED AUTO PARTS; *U.S. Private*, pg. 354
ASSOCIATED BANC-CORP; *U.S. Public*, pg. 214
ASSOCIATED BANK, NA—See Associated Banc-Corp; *U.S. Public*, pg. 214
ASSOCIATED BATTERY MANUFACTURERS (CEYLON) LIMITED—See EXIDE INDUSTRIES LIMITED; *Int'l*, pg. 2585
ASSOCIATED BILLING SERVICES, INC.—See Northwell Health, Inc.; *U.S. Private*, pg. 2958
ASSOCIATED BILLING SERVICES, INC.—See Pamplona Capital Management LLP; *Int'l*, pg. 5711

ASSOCIATED BRANDS INC.—See TreeHouse Foods, Inc.; *U.S. Public*, pg. 2187
ASSOCIATED BRANDS INDUSTRIES LIMITED - BISCUIT DIVISION—See Associated Brands Industries Limited; *Int'l*, pg. 648
ASSOCIATED BRANDS INDUSTRIES LIMITED; *Int'l*, pg. 648
ASSOCIATED BRIGHAM CONTRACTORS; *U.S. Private*, pg. 354
ASSOCIATED BRITISH ENGINEERING PLC; *Int'l*, pg. 648
ASSOCIATED BRITISH FOODS PLC—See The Garfield Weston Foundation; *Int'l*, pg. 7647
ASSOCIATED BRITISH PORTS HOLDINGS LTD.—See GIC Pte. Ltd.; *Int'l*, pg. 2964
ASSOCIATED BRITISH PORTS HOLDINGS LTD.—See M&G Group Limited; *Int'l*, pg. 4612
ASSOCIATED BRITISH PORTS HOLDINGS LTD.—See Ontario Municipal Employees Retirement System; *Int'l*, pg. 5583
ASSOCIATED BRITISH PORTS HOLDINGS LTD.—See The Goldman Sachs Group, Inc.; *U.S. Public*, pg. 2076
ASSOCIATED BROKERS LTD—See The Mauritius Union Assurance Company Limited; *Int'l*, pg. 7666
ASSOCIATED BUILDING COMPANY—See Tata Sons Limited; *Int'l*, pg. 7468
ASSOCIATED BUYERS, LLC—See Rainforest Distribution Corp; *U.S. Private*, pg. 3348
ASSOCIATED CABLES PVT. LTD.—See Prysmian S.p.A.; *Int'l*, pg. 6010
ASSOCIATED CAPITAL GROUP, INC.; *U.S. Public*, pg. 214
ASSOCIATED CERAMICS LIMITED; *Int'l*, pg. 648
ASSOCIATED CITRUS PACKERS, INC.—See Limoneira Company; *U.S. Public*, pg. 1316
ASSOCIATED CLAIMS ENTERPRISES INC.—See Cameron General Corporation; *U.S. Private*, pg. 728
ASSOCIATED CLINICAL LABORATORIES—See Quest Diagnostics, Inc.; *U.S. Public*, pg. 1755
ASSOCIATED COMMUNITY BANCORP, INC.; *U.S. Private*, pg. 355
ASSOCIATED CONSTRUCTION PUBLICATIONS LLC; *U.S. Private*, pg. 355
ASSOCIATED CONSULTING INTERNATIONAL, INC.; *U.S. Private*, pg. 355
ASSOCIATED COST ENGINEERS INC.; *U.S. Private*, pg. 355
ASSOCIATED COUNSEL FOR THE ACCUSED; *U.S. Private*, pg. 355
ASSOCIATED CRAFTS, INC.; *U.S. Private*, pg. 355
ASSOCIATED CREDITORS EXCHANGE, INC.; *U.S. Private*, pg. 355
ASSOCIATED CREDIT UNION OF TEXAS; *U.S. Private*, pg. 355
ASSOCIATED DATA SERVICES, INC.—See Asure Software, Inc.; *U.S. Public*, pg. 218
ASSOCIATED DRYWALL SUPPLIERS, INC.—See American Securities LLC; *U.S. Private*, pg. 248
ASSOCIATED ELECTRIC COOPERATIVE INC.; *U.S. Private*, pg. 355
ASSOCIATED ELECTRONIC INC.—See Thunder Tiger Corp.; *Int'l*, pg. 7722
ASSOCIATED ENGINEERS, LTD.; *Int'l*, pg. 648
ASSOCIATED ENGINEERS ZHUHAI S.E.Z. LTD.—See Associated Engineers, Ltd.; *Int'l*, pg. 648
ASSOCIATED ENVIRONMENTAL SYSTEMS; *U.S. Private*, pg. 355
ASSOCIATED EQUIPMENT COMPANY OF DELAWARE; *U.S. Private*, pg. 355
ASSOCIATED EQUIPMENT SALES CO.; *U.S. Private*, pg. 355
ASSOCIATED ESTATES REALTY CORPORATION—See Brookfield Corporation; *Int'l*, pg. 1175
ASSOCIATED EYE SURGICAL CENTER, LLC—See KKR & Co. Inc.; *U.S. Public*, pg. 1249
ASSOCIATED FABRICS CORPORATION; *U.S. Private*, pg. 355
ASSOCIATED FINANCIAL CORP.; *U.S. Private*, pg. 355
ASSOCIATED FINANCIAL GROUP, LLC—See Caisse de Depot et Placement du Quebec; *Int'l*, pg. 1256
ASSOCIATED FINANCIAL GROUP, LLC—See KKR & Co. Inc.; *U.S. Public*, pg. 1264
ASSOCIATED FINANCIAL GROUP, LLC - WAUKESHA OFFICE—See Caisse de Depot et Placement du Quebec; *Int'l*, pg. 1256
ASSOCIATED FINANCIAL GROUP, LLC - WAUKESHA OFFICE—See KKR & Co. Inc.; *U.S. Public*, pg. 1265
ASSOCIATED FIRE PROTECTION; *U.S. Private*, pg. 355
ASSOCIATED FOOD STORES, INC.; *U.S. Private*, pg. 355
ASSOCIATED FOOD STORES, INC.; *U.S. Private*, pg. 355
ASSOCIATED FUEL PUMP SYSTEMS CORP.—See Denso Corporation; *Int'l*, pg. 2031
ASSOCIATED FUEL PUMP SYSTEMS CORP.—See Robert Bosch GmbH; *Int'l*, pg. 6366
ASSOCIATED FUIG LLC; *U.S. Public*, pg. 355
THE ASSOCIATED GENERAL CONTRACTORS OF AMERICA; *U.S. Private*, pg. 3989

CORPORATE AFFILIATIONS

ASSOCIATED GLASS, INC.; *U.S. Private*, pg. 355
ASSOCIATED GLOBAL SYSTEMS, INC.—See Nippon Express Holdings, Inc.; *Int'l*, pg. 5317
ASSOCIATED GROCERS, INC.; *U.S. Private*, pg. 356
ASSOCIATED GROCERS OF FLORIDA, INC.—See United Natural Foods, Inc.; *U.S. Public*, pg. 2231
ASSOCIATED GROCERS OF NEW ENGLAND, INC.; *U.S. Private*, pg. 355
ASSOCIATED GROCERS OF THE SOUTH, INC.; *U.S. Private*, pg. 356
ASSOCIATED HANGAR INC.; *U.S. Private*, pg. 356
ASSOCIATED HEALTH SERVICES INC; *U.S. Private*, pg. 356
ASSOCIATED HOME CARE, LLC—See Amedisys, Inc.; *U.S. Public*, pg. 93
ASSOCIATED HYGIENIC PRODUCTS LLC—See PT Sinar Mas Group; *Int'l*, pg. 6072
ASSOCIATED INDEMNITY CORP.—See Allianz SE; *Int'l*, pg. 347
ASSOCIATED INDUSTRIES CHINA, INC.; *Int'l*, pg. 649
ASSOCIATED INDUSTRIES INSURANCE COMPANY, INC.—See Stone Point Capital LLC; *U.S. Private*, pg. 3820
ASSOCIATED INDUSTRIES OF MASSACHUSETTS MUTUAL INSURANCE COMPANY; *U.S. Private*, pg. 356
ASSOCIATED INDUSTRIES; *U.S. Private*, pg. 356
ASSOCIATED INSURANCE AGENTS, INC.—See CBIZ, Inc.; *U.S. Public*, pg. 456
ASSOCIATED INTERNATIONAL HOTELS LTD.; *Int'l*, pg. 649
ASSOCIATED INVESTMENT SERVICES, INC.—See Associated Banc-Corp; *U.S. Public*, pg. 214
ASSOCIATED KAOLIN INDUSTRIES SDN. BHD.—See Doka Wawasan TKH Holdings Berhad; *Int'l*, pg. 2156
ASSOCIATED LEASE CORP.—See Associated Grocers of New England, Inc.; *U.S. Private*, pg. 356
ASSOCIATED LIGHTING REPRESENTATIVES, INC.; *U.S. Private*, pg. 356
ASSOCIATED MATERIAL HANDLING INDUSTRIES INC.—See Toyota Industries Corporation; *Int'l*, pg. 7869
ASSOCIATED MATERIALS GROUP, INC.—See Hellman & Friedman LLC; *U.S. Private*, pg. 1907
ASSOCIATED MATERIALS, LLC—See Hellman & Friedman LLC; *U.S. Private*, pg. 1907
ASSOCIATED MEAT PACKERS (PRIVATE) LIMITED—See Innscor Africa Ltd.; *Int'l*, pg. 3713
ASSOCIATED MICROBREWERIES LTD.; *U.S. Private*, pg. 356
ASSOCIATED MILK PRODUCERS, INC.; *U.S. Private*, pg. 356
ASSOCIATED MOTOR FINANCE COMPANY PLC; *Int'l*, pg. 649
ASSOCIATED MOTOR HOLDINGS (PTY) LIMITED—See Dubai World Corporation; *Int'l*, pg. 2221
ASSOCIATED MUSIC PUBLISHERS—See Music Sales Corporation; *U.S. Private*, pg. 2817
ASSOCIATED NEWSPAPERS LTD.—See Daily Mail & General Trust plc; *Int'l*, pg. 1937
ASSOCIATED OF LOS ANGELES; *U.S. Private*, pg. 356
ASSOCIATED OILS PTY LTD—See Cleanaway Waste Management Limited; *Int'l*, pg. 1655
ASSOCIATED OUTDOOR CLUBS, INC.; *U.S. Private*, pg. 356
ASSOCIATED PACKAGING INC.; *U.S. Private*, pg. 356
ASSOCIATED PAINTERS, INC.—See Vance Street Capital LLC; *U.S. Private*, pg. 4342
ASSOCIATED PAPER INC.; *U.S. Private*, pg. 356
ASSOCIATED PARTNERS, LP; *U.S. Private*, pg. 356
ASSOCIATED PENSION CONSULTANTS, INC.—See Lightyear Capital LLC; *U.S. Private*, pg. 2454
ASSOCIATED PETROLEUM CARRIERS; *U.S. Private*, pg. 356
ASSOCIATED PETROLEUM PRODUCTS INC.; *U.S. Private*, pg. 356
ASSOCIATED PHARMACIES INC.; *U.S. Private*, pg. 356
ASSOCIATED PIPE LINE CONTRACTORS, INC.; *U.S. Private*, pg. 356
ASSOCIATED POWER, INC.; *U.S. Private*, pg. 357
THE ASSOCIATED PRESS AB—See The Associated Press; *U.S. Private*, pg. 3989
THE ASSOCIATED PRESS A/S—See The Associated Press; *U.S. Private*, pg. 3989
THE ASSOCIATED PRESS (BELGIUM) S.A.—See The Associated Press; *U.S. Private*, pg. 3989
THE ASSOCIATED PRESS DE VENEZUELA, S.A.—See The Associated Press; *U.S. Private*, pg. 3989
THE ASSOCIATED PRESS, INC.—See The Associated Press; *U.S. Private*, pg. 3989
THE ASSOCIATED PRESS, LTD.—See The Associated Press; *U.S. Private*, pg. 3989
THE ASSOCIATED PRESS; *U.S. Private*, pg. 3989
THE ASSOCIATED PRESS—See The Associated Press; *U.S. Private*, pg. 3989
ASSOCIATED PRESS TELEVISION NEWS—See The Associated Press; *U.S. Private*, pg. 3989
ASSOCIATED PRODUCE DEALERS & BROKERS OF L.A - INSURANCE TRUST; *U.S. Private*, pg. 357
ASSOCIATED PRODUCTION SERVICE; *U.S. Private*, pg. 357

ASSOCIATED PUBLISHING COMPANY—See The Hearst Corporation; *U.S. Private*, pg. 4047
ASSOCIATED RACK CORPORATION; *U.S. Private*, pg. 357
ASSOCIATED READY MIX CONCRETE; *U.S. Private*, pg. 357
ASSOCIATED RECOVERY SYSTEMS; *U.S. Private*, pg. 357
ASSOCIATED RECREATION COUNCIL; *U.S. Private*, pg. 357
ASSOCIATED RESEARCH INC.—See Ikonix Group, Inc.; *U.S. Private*, pg. 2041
ASSOCIATED RESOURCES, INC.—See Avisto Capital Partners, LLC; *U.S. Private*, pg. 409
ASSOCIATED RETAILERS LIMITED; *Int'l*, pg. 649
ASSOCIATED RISK CONSULTANTS LIMITED—See Epiris Managers LLP; *Int'l*, pg. 2461
ASSOCIATED SALES & BAG COMPANY INCORPORATED; *U.S. Private*, pg. 357
ASSOCIATED SERVICES LIMITED; *Int'l*, pg. 649
ASSOCIATED SERVICE SPECIALIST; *U.S. Private*, pg. 357
ASSOCIATED; *U.S. Private*, pg. 354
ASSOCIATED SPECIALTY CONTRACTING, INC.; *U.S. Private*, pg. 357
ASSOCIATED SPRING-ASIA PTE. LTD.—See OEP Capital Advisors, L.P.; *U.S. Private*, pg. 2998
ASSOCIATED SPRING CORPORATION—See OEP Capital Advisors, L.P.; *U.S. Private*, pg. 2998
ASSOCIATED SPRING MEXICO, S.A.—See OEP Capital Advisors, L.P.; *U.S. Private*, pg. 2998
ASSOCIATED SPRING RAYMOND GMBH—See Barnes Group Inc.; *U.S. Public*, pg. 276
ASSOCIATED SPRING RAYMOND (SHANGHAI) CO., LTD.—See OEP Capital Advisors, L.P.; *U.S. Private*, pg. 2998
ASSOCIATED SPRING RAYMOND—See OEP Capital Advisors, L.P.; *U.S. Private*, pg. 2998
ASSOCIATED SPRING—See OEP Capital Advisors, L.P.; *U.S. Private*, pg. 2998
ASSOCIATED SPRING—See OEP Capital Advisors, L.P.; *U.S. Private*, pg. 2998
ASSOCIATED SPRING (U.K.) LTD.—See OEP Capital Advisors, L.P.; *U.S. Private*, pg. 2998
ASSOCIATED STEEL GROUP, LLC—See Promus Holdings, LLC; *U.S. Private*, pg. 3283
ASSOCIATED STEEL WORKERS, LTD.; *U.S. Private*, pg. 357
ASSOCIATED SUBSTATION ENGINEERING INC.—See Aubrey Silvey Enterprises Inc.; *U.S. Private*, pg. 385
ASSOCIATED SUPPLY COMPANY INC.; *U.S. Private*, pg. 357
ASSOCIATED SUPPLY COMPANY INC; *U.S. Private*, pg. 357
ASSOCIATED TECHNICAL SERVICES LTD.—See Power Assets Holdings Limited; *Int'l*, pg. 5943
ASSOCIATED TELEPHONE DESIGN INC.; *U.S. Private*, pg. 357
ASSOCIATED TERMINALS LLC; *U.S. Private*, pg. 357
ASSOCIATED TEXTILE RENTAL SERVICES—See Vestis Corp; *U.S. Public*, pg. 2290
ASSOCIATED THIRD PARTY ADMINISTRATORS; *U.S. Private*, pg. 357
ASSOCIATED TIME & PARKING CONTROLS, INC.; *U.S. Private*, pg. 357
ASSOCIATED TOOLMAKERS LTD.—See The Eastern Company; *U.S. Public*, pg. 2069
ASSOCIATED TRANSFER & STORAGE INC.; *U.S. Private*, pg. 357
ASSOCIATED TRUST COMPANY, NA—See Associated Banc-Corp; *U.S. Public*, pg. 214
ASSOCIATED TUBE INDUSTRIES—See Samuel, Son & Co., Limited; *Int'l*, pg. 6515
ASSOCIATED TUBE USA, INC.—See Samuel, Son & Co., Limited; *Int'l*, pg. 6515
ASSOCIATED TYRE SPECIALISTS LIMITED—See Compagnie Generale des Etablissements Michelin SCA; *Int'l*, pg. 1744
ASSOCIATED VALVE—See Canerector Inc.; *Int'l*, pg. 1290
ASSOCIATED WELDING SUPPLY INC.; *U.S. Private*, pg. 357
ASSOCIATED WHOLESALE ELECTRIC CO.—See Associated of Los Angeles; *U.S. Private*, pg. 356
ASSOCIATED WHOLESALE GROCERS, INC.; *U.S. Private*, pg. 357
ASSOCIATE GLOBAL PARTNERS LIMITED; *Int'l*, pg. 648
ASSOCIATE PARTNERS LABORATORIES SDN BHD—See Nexgram Holdings Berhad; *Int'l*, pg. 5244
ASSOCIATES FOR INTERNATIONAL RESEARCH, INC.—See Relo Group, Inc.; *Int'l*, pg. 6265
ASSOCIATES IN ADVERTISING LIMITED—See Gemspring Capital Management, LLC; *U.S. Private*, pg. 1659
ASSOCIATES IN MEDICAL PHYSICS, LLC; *U.S. Private*, pg. 358
ASSOCIATES INSURANCE AGENCY, INC.; *U.S. Private*, pg. 358
ASSOCIATES OF CAPE COD, INC.—See Seikagaku Corporation; *Int'l*, pg. 6686

ASSOCIATION CASUALTY INSURANCE COMPANY—See Columbia Insurance Group, Inc.; *U.S. Private*, pg. 977
ASSOCIATION DES CENTRES DISTRIBUTEURS E. LECLERC; *Int'l*, pg. 649
ASSOCIATION FOR ADVANCED LIFE UNDERWRITING; *U.S. Private*, pg. 358
ASSOCIATION FOR COMPUTING MACHINERY; *U.S. Private*, pg. 358
ASSOCIATION FOR MOLECULAR PATHOLOGY; *U.S. Private*, pg. 358
ASSOCIATION FOR TALENT DEVELOPMENT; *U.S. Private*, pg. 358
ASSOCIATION FOR THE DEVELOPMENTALLY DISABLED; *U.S. Private*, pg. 358
ASSOCIATION HEADQUARTERS, LLC—See Corridor Capital, LLC; *U.S. Private*, pg. 1058
ASSOCIATION MEMBER BENEFITS ADVISORS, LLC; *U.S. Private*, pg. 358
ASSOCIATION OF AMERICAN RAILROADS; *U.S. Private*, pg. 358
ASSOCIATION OF BANKS IN JORDAN LTD.—See Jordan Loan Guarantee Corporation; *Int'l*, pg. 3998
ASSOCIATION OF CERTIFIED ANTI-MONEY LAUNDERING SPECIALISTS LLC—See Wendel S.A.; *Int'l*, pg. 8376
ASSOCIATION OF CHRISTIAN SCHOOLS INTERNATIONAL; *U.S. Private*, pg. 358
ASSOCIATION OF GOVERNING BOARDS OF UNIVERSITIES AND COLLEGES; *U.S. Private*, pg. 358
ASSOCIATION OF NATIONAL ADVERTISERS, INC.; *U.S. Private*, pg. 358
ASSOCIATION OF PERIOPERATIVE REGISTERED NURSES; *U.S. Private*, pg. 358
THE ASSOCIATION OF PLASTIC RECYCLERS; *U.S. Private*, pg. 3989
ASSOCIATION OF PRIVATE SECTOR COLLEGES AND UNIVERSITIES; *U.S. Private*, pg. 358
ASSOCIATION OF PUBLIC HEALTH LABORATORIES; *U.S. Private*, pg. 358
ASSOCIATION OF SCHOOLS AND PROGRAMS OF PUBLIC HEALTH; *U.S. Private*, pg. 359
ASSOCIATION OF SOCIAL WORK BOARDS; *U.S. Private*, pg. 359
ASSOCIATION OF TEXAS PROFESSIONAL EDUCATORS; *U.S. Private*, pg. 359
ASSOCIATION OF THE UNITED STATES ARMY; *U.S. Private*, pg. 359
ASSOCIATION OF WOMEN'S HEALTH, OBSTETRIC & NEONATAL NURSES; *U.S. Private*, pg. 359
ASSOCIATIONS, INC.; *U.S. Private*, pg. 359
ASSOCIAZIONE CALCIO MILAN S.P.A.—See RedBird Capital Partners L.P.; *U.S. Private*, pg. 3377
ASSOCIAZIONE DEI FONOGRAFICI ITALIANI; *Int'l*, pg. 649
ASSORE LIMITED; *Int'l*, pg. 649
AS SPACECOM—See Globaltrans Investment PLC; *Int'l*, pg. 3004
ASS/ SPIELKARTENFABRIK ALTENBURG GMBH—See Cartamundi N.V.; *Int'l*, pg. 1347
AS STAR FM—See Providence Equity Partners L.L.C.; *U.S. Private*, pg. 3291
AS STOCKMANN—See Stockmann plc; *Int'l*, pg. 7220
AS STORA ENSO LATVIJA—See Stora Enso Oyj; *Int'l*, pg. 7222
AS STUBER, ZNL DER SERGIO LO STANCO ELEKTRO AG—See Burkhalter Holding AG; *Int'l*, pg. 1224
ASSUMPTION COOPERATIVE GRAIN COMPANY; *U.S. Private*, pg. 359
ASSUMPTION MUTUAL LIFE INSURANCE COMPANY; *Int'l*, pg. 649
THE ASSUMPTION VILLAGE—See Catholic Healthcare Partners; *U.S. Private*, pg. 792
AS SUNNINGDALE TECH (LATVIA)—See Sunningdale Tech Ltd; *Int'l*, pg. 7317
ASSURA INVESTMENTS LIMITED—See Assura plc; *Int'l*, pg. 649
ASSURAMED, INC.—See Cardinal Health, Inc.; *U.S. Public*, pg. 433
ASSURANCEAMERICA CORPORATION; *U.S. Private*, pg. 359
ASSURANCE COMPANY OF AMERICA—See Zurich Insurance Group Limited; *Int'l*, pg. 8698
ASSURANCE FORENSIC ACCOUNTING CPAS, LLC; *U.S. Private*, pg. 359
ASSURANCE IQ, LLC—See Prudential Financial, Inc.; *U.S. Public*, pg. 1731
ASSURANCES BIAT—See Banque Internationale Arabe de Tunisie; *Int'l*, pg. 854
ASSURANCES CONTINENTALES - CONTINENTALE VERZEKERINGEN N.V.—See The Hartford Financial Services Group, Inc.; *U.S. Public*, pg. 2088
ASSURANCES GENERALES DU LAOS—See Allianz SE; *Int'l*, pg. 343
ASSURANCES MEDICALES SA—See Allianz SE; *Int'l*, pg. 351
ASSURANCE SERVICES CORPORATION—See Marsh & McLennan Companies, Inc.; *U.S. Public*, pg. 1374
ASSURANCE SOFTWARE, INC.—See Resurgens Technology Partners, LLC; *U.S. Private*, pg. 3410

ASSURANCE TECHNOLOGY CORPORATION; *U.S. Private*, pg. 359
ASSURANCE VIE ET PREVOYANCE (AVIP) S.A.—See Allianz SE; *Int'l*, pg. 351
ASSURANT ARGENTINA COMPANIA DE SEGUROS SOCIEDAD ANONIMA—See Assurant, Inc.; *U.S. Public*, pg. 214
ASSURANT CONSULTING COMPANY, LIMITED.—See Assurant, Inc.; *U.S. Public*, pg. 215
ASSURANT DEUTSCHLAND GMBH—See Assurant, Inc.; *U.S. Public*, pg. 215
ASSURANT FRANCE—See Assurant, Inc.; *U.S. Public*, pg. 215
ASSURANT, INC.; *U.S. Public*, pg. 214
ASSURANT INTERMEDIARY LTD.—See Assurant, Inc.; *U.S. Public*, pg. 215
ASSURANT LIFE OF CANADA—See Assurant, Inc.; *U.S. Public*, pg. 215
ASSURANT SERVICES CANADA, INC.—See Assurant, Inc.; *U.S. Public*, pg. 215
ASSURANT SERVICES IRELAND, LTD.—See Assurant, Inc.; *U.S. Public*, pg. 215
ASSURANT SOLUTIONS - PRENEED DIVISION—See Assurant, Inc.; *U.S. Public*, pg. 215
ASSURANT SOLUTIONS—See Assurant, Inc.; *U.S. Public*, pg. 215
ASSURANT SOLUTIONS SPAIN, S.A.—See Assurant, Inc.; *U.S. Public*, pg. 215
ASSURANT SPECIALTY PROPERTY—See Assurant, Inc.; *U.S. Public*, pg. 215
ASSURA PHARMACY LIMITED—See Assura plc; *Int'l*, pg. 649
ASSURA PLC; *Int'l*, pg. 649
ASSURA PROPERTIES LIMITED—See Assura plc; *Int'l*, pg. 649
ASSURA PROPERTIES UK LIMITED—See Assura plc; *Int'l*, pg. 649
ASSURA PROPERTY MANAGEMENT LIMITED—See Assura plc; *Int'l*, pg. 649
ASSURE AMERICA CORP.; *U.S. Private*, pg. 359
ASSURECARE, LLC—See Vora Ventures LLC; *U.S. Private*, pg. 4412
ASSURED AGGREGATES COMPANY; *U.S. Private*, pg. 359
ASSURED ASSISTANCE INC.—See Royal Bank of Canada; *Int'l*, pg. 6410
ASSURED COVER PTY LTD—See PSC Insurance Group Limited; *Int'l*, pg. 6015
ASSURED FLOW SOLUTIONS LLC—See Sentinel Capital Partners, L.L.C.; *U.S. Private*, pg. 3609
THE ASSURED GROUP; *U.S. Private*, pg. 3989
ASSURED GUARANTY CORP.—See Assured Guaranty Ltd.; *Int'l*, pg. 649
ASSURED GUARANTY CORP.—See Assured Guaranty Ltd.; *Int'l*, pg. 650
ASSURED GUARANTY (EUROPE) PLC—See Assured Guaranty Ltd.; *Int'l*, pg. 649
ASSURED GUARANTY (EUROPE) SA.—See Assured Guaranty Ltd.; *Int'l*, pg. 649
ASSURED GUARANTY (LONDON) PLC—See Assured Guaranty Ltd.; *Int'l*, pg. 649
ASSURED GUARANTY LTD.; *Int'l*, pg. 649
ASSURED GUARANTY MORTGAGE INSURANCE COMPANY—See Assured Guaranty Ltd.; *Int'l*, pg. 650
ASSURED GUARANTY MUNICIPAL HOLDINGS INC.—See Assured Guaranty Ltd.; *Int'l*, pg. 650
ASSURED GUARANTY RE LTD.—See Assured Guaranty Ltd.; *Int'l*, pg. 649
ASSURED GUARANTY RE OVERSEAS LTD—See Assured Guaranty Ltd.; *Int'l*, pg. 649
ASSURED GUARANTY US HOLDINGS INC—See Assured Guaranty Ltd.; *Int'l*, pg. 649
ASSURED HEALTH CARE, INC.—See Regional Health Properties, Inc.; *U.S. Public*, pg. 1775
ASSURED HEALTHCARE PARTNERS LLC—See Assured Guaranty Ltd.; *Int'l*, pg. 650
ASSURED INFORMATION SECURITY, INC.; *U.S. Private*, pg. 359
ASSURED INVESTMENT MANAGEMENT LLC—See Sound Point Capital Management, LP; *U.S. Private*, pg. 3717
ASSURED INVESTMENT MANAGEMENT (LONDON) LLP—See Assured Guaranty Ltd.; *Int'l*, pg. 650
ASSURED NEACE LUKENS INSURANCE AGENCY, INC.—See GTCR LLC; *U.S. Private*, pg. 1802
ASSUREDPARTNERS, INC.—See GTCR LLC; *U.S. Private*, pg. 1802
ASSURED QUALITY TECHNOLOGY, LTD.—See Atlas Fibre Company; *U.S. Private*, pg. 376
ASSURED QUALITY TESTING SERVICES, LLC—See LKQ Corporation; *U.S. Public*, pg. 1333
ASSURED TELEMATICS INC.—See Pegasus TransTech, LLC; *U.S. Private*, pg. 3130
ASSURED TRANSPORTATION SERVICES; *U.S. Private*, pg. 359
ASSURE HOLDINGS CORP.; *U.S. Public*, pg. 216
ASSURE HOLDINGS, LLC; *U.S. Private*, pg. 359
ASSURE HOME HEALTHCARE—See Bain Capital, LP; *U.S. Private*, pg. 439

ASSURESIGN LLC—See TPG Capital, L.P.; *U.S. Public*, pg. 2175
ASSURESOUTH, INC.—See GTCR LLC; *U.S. Private*, pg. 1802
ASSUREVAULT LLC—See The HF Group LLC; *U.S. Private*, pg. 4052
ASSUREWEB LIMITED—See Aviva plc; *Int'l*, pg. 745
ASSUREX HEALTH, INC.—See Myriad Genetics, Inc.; *U.S. Public*, pg. 1489
ASSURIA BELEGGINGSMAATSCHAPPIJ N.V.—See Assuria N.V.; *Int'l*, pg. 650
ASSURIA LEVENSVERZEKERING N.V.—See Assuria N.V.; *Int'l*, pg. 650
ASSURIA LIFE (GY) INC.—See Assuria N.V.; *Int'l*, pg. 650
ASSURIA MEDISCHE VERZEKERING N.V.—See Assuria N.V.; *Int'l*, pg. 650
ASSURIA N.V.; *Int'l*, pg. 650
ASSURIA SCHADEVERZEKERING N.V.—See Assuria N.V.; *Int'l*, pg. 650
ASSURITY LIFE INSURANCE COMPANY—See Assurity Security Group Inc.; *U.S. Private*, pg. 359
ASSURITY SECURITY GROUP INC.; *U.S. Private*, pg. 359
AS SYNERGIE—See Neurones S.A.; *Int'l*, pg. 5219
ASSYRIAN NATIONAL COUNCIL OF ILLINOIS; *U.S. Private*, pg. 359
ASSYRIAN UNIVERSAL ALLIANCE FOUNDATION, INC.; *U.S. Private*, pg. 360
ASSYSTEMBRIME PORTUGAL—See Assystem S.A.; *Int'l*, pg. 651
ASSYSTEM DEUTSCHLAND HOLDING GMBH—See Assystem S.A.; *Int'l*, pg. 650
ASSYSTEM DEVELOPPEMENT—See Assystem S.A.; *Int'l*, pg. 650
ASSYSTEM ENGINEERING & CONSULTING (SHANGHAI) CO , LTD—See Assystem S.A.; *Int'l*, pg. 650
ASSYSTEM ENVIRONNEMENT—See Assystem S.A.; *Int'l*, pg. 650
ASSYSTEM ENVY A.S.—See Assystem S.A.; *Int'l*, pg. 650
ASSYSTEM FACILITIES—See Assystem S.A.; *Int'l*, pg. 650
ASSYSTEM FRANCE—See Assystem S.A.; *Int'l*, pg. 650
ASSYSTEM GMBH—See Assystem S.A.; *Int'l*, pg. 650
ASSYSTEM GROUP UK LTD—See Assystem S.A.; *Int'l*, pg. 651
ASSYSTEM IBERIA—See Assystem S.A.; *Int'l*, pg. 651
ASSYSTEM INDIA PVT LTD—See Assystem S.A.; *Int'l*, pg. 651
ASSYSTEM INNOVATION—See Assystem S.A.; *Int'l*, pg. 651
ASSYSTEM (IOM) LTD—See Assystem S.A.; *Int'l*, pg. 650
ASSYSTEM ITALIA SRL—See Assystem S.A.; *Int'l*, pg. 651
ASSYSTEM PORTUGAL—See Assystem S.A.; *Int'l*, pg. 651
ASSYSTEM ROMANIA SRL—See Assystem S.A.; *Int'l*, pg. 651
ASSYSTEM S.A.; *Int'l*, pg. 650
ASSYSTEM SERVICES DEUTSCHLAND GMBH—See Assystem S.A.; *Int'l*, pg. 650
ASSYSTEM TECHNOLOGIES & SERVICES SA—See Assystem S.A.; *Int'l*, pg. 651
ASTA AG—See Arbonia AG; *Int'l*, pg. 538
ASTA CO LTD; *Int'l*, pg. 651
ASTA CONDUCTORS CO., LTD.—See Global Equity Partners Beteiligungs-Management AG; *Int'l*, pg. 2996
ASTA DEVELOPMENT GMBH—See Eleco Plc; *Int'l*, pg. 2348
ASTA DEVELOPMENT PLC—See Eleco Plc; *Int'l*, pg. 2348
ASTADIA CONSULTING - INDIA—See The Gores Group, LLC; *U.S. Private*, pg. 4034
ASTADIA CONSULTING UK LIMITED—See The Gores Group, LLC; *U.S. Private*, pg. 4034
ASTADIA, INC.-ATLANTA—See The Gores Group, LLC; *U.S. Private*, pg. 4034
ASTADIA INC.—See The Gores Group, LLC; *U.S. Private*, pg. 4034
ASTA ELEKTRODRAHT GMBH & CO KG—See Global Equity Partners Beteiligungs-Management AG; *Int'l*, pg. 2996
ASTA FUNDING, INC.; *U.S. Private*, pg. 360
ASTA HOLDINGS GMBH—See Global Equity Partners Beteiligungs-Management AG; *Int'l*, pg. 2996
ASTA INDIA PRIVATE LIMITED—See Global Equity Partners Beteiligungs-Management AG; *Int'l*, pg. 2996
ASTAIRE GROUP PLC; *Int'l*, pg. 651
ASTAKA HOLDINGS LIMITED; *Int'l*, pg. 651
ASTAKOS TERMINAL S.A.—See AEGEK Group; *Int'l*, pg. 173
ASTALDI ARABIA LTD.—See Salini Costruttori S.p.A.; *Int'l*, pg. 6492
ASTALDI CONSTRUCTION CORPORATION—See Salini Costruttori S.p.A.; *Int'l*, pg. 6492
ASTALDI S.P.A.—See Salini Costruttori S.p.A.; *Int'l*, pg. 6492
ASTALLAS PHARMA SP—See Astellas Pharma Inc.; *Int'l*, pg. 652
AS TALLINK BALTIC—See AS Infortar; *Int'l*, pg. 590

AS TALLINK DUTY FREE—See AS Infortar; *Int'l*, pg. 590
AS TALLINK GRUPP—See AS Infortar; *Int'l*, pg. 590
AS TALLINNA TEED—See AS Merko Ehitus; *Int'l*, pg. 590
AS TALLINNA VESI; *Int'l*, pg. 591
ASTANA FINANCE, JSC; *Int'l*, pg. 651
ASTANAGAS KMG JSC; *Int'l*, pg. 651
ASTANA INTERNATIONAL EXCHANGE LIMITED; *Int'l*, pg. 651
ASTANA INVESTMENT HOUSE JSC—See Central-Asian Power Energy Company JSC; *Int'l*, pg. 1410
ASTANA SOLAR LLP—See Canadian Solar Inc.; *Int'l*, pg. 1286
ASTANA SOLAR LLP—See ECM Technologies SAS; *Int'l*, pg. 2292
ASTANA SOLAR LLP—See Kasen International Holdings Limited; *Int'l*, pg. 4087
ASTANA SOLAR LLP—See Yadran-Oil Group; *Int'l*, pg. 8544
ASTARA, INC.; *U.S. Private*, pg. 360
ASTAREAL AB—See Fuji Chemical Industries Co., Ltd; *Int'l*, pg. 2809
ASTAREAL (AUSTRALIA) PTY LTD—See Fuji Chemical Industries Co., Ltd; *Int'l*, pg. 2809
ASTAREAL CO., LTD. - NAGOYA—See Fuji Chemical Industries Co., Ltd; *Int'l*, pg. 2809
ASTAREAL CO., LTD. - OSAKA—See Fuji Chemical Industries Co., Ltd; *Int'l*, pg. 2809
ASTAREAL CO., LTD.—See Fuji Chemical Industries Co., Ltd; *Int'l*, pg. 2809
ASTAREAL CO., LTD. - TOYAMA—See Fuji Chemical Industries Co., Ltd; *Int'l*, pg. 2809
ASTAREAL HOLDINGS CO., LTD.—See Fuji Chemical Industries Co., Ltd; *Int'l*, pg. 2808
ASTAREAL, INC.—See Fuji Chemical Industries Co., Ltd; *Int'l*, pg. 2809
ASTAREAL, INC. - WASHINGTON—See Fuji Chemical Industries Co., Ltd; *Int'l*, pg. 2809
ASTAREAL (INDIA) PRIVATE LIMITED—See Fuji Chemical Industries Co., Ltd; *Int'l*, pg. 2809
ASTAREAL PTE. LTD.—See Fuji Chemical Industries Co., Ltd; *Int'l*, pg. 2809
A STAR ELECTRIC COMPANY; *U.S. Private*, pg. 19
ASTAR HEATING & AIR, LLC—See Morgan Stanley; *U.S. Public*, pg. 1474
ASTARO GMBH & CO. KG—See Apax Partners LLP; *Int'l*, pg. 506
ASTAR PIMA ROADSCOTTSDALE LLC—See Safehold Inc.; *U.S. Public*, pg. 1834
ASTAR STEEL SDN. BHD.—See YKGI Holdings Berhad; *Int'l*, pg. 8587
ASTARTA HOLDING N.V.; *Int'l*, pg. 651
ASTARTI DEVELOPMENT PLC—See Libra Holidays Group Public Ltd.; *Int'l*, pg. 4486
AS TARTU JOUJAAM—See Fortum Oyj; *Int'l*, pg. 2740
AS TARTU KESKKATLAMAJA—See Fortum Oyj; *Int'l*, pg. 2740
ASTATINE CAPITAL PARTNERS LLC—See Astatine Investment Partners LLC; *U.S. Private*, pg. 360
ASTATINE INVESTMENT PARTNERS LLC; *U.S. Private*, pg. 360
ASTAVITA, INC.—See Fuji Chemical Industries Co., Ltd; *Int'l*, pg. 2809
A.S.T. BAUGESELLSCHAFT M.B.H.—See Swietelsky Baugesellschaft m.b.H.; *Int'l*, pg. 7367
AST BEARINGS LLC—See Genuine Parts Company; *U.S. Public*, pg. 933
AST CO., LTD.—See Pyeong Hwa Automotive Co., Ltd; *Int'l*, pg. 6127
AST DISTRIBUTION ASIA PTE LTD—See HAL Trust N.V.; *Int'l*, pg. 3226
AST DOCUMENT SOLUTIONS—See Pacific Equity Partners Pty. Limited; *Int'l*, pg. 5689
ASTEA FRANCE—See EQT AB; *Int'l*, pg. 2477
ASTEA INTERNATIONAL AUSTRALIAN PTY LTD.—See EQT AB; *Int'l*, pg. 2477
ASTEA INTERNATIONAL, INC.—See EQT AB; *Int'l*, pg. 2477
ASTEA INTERNATIONAL INC.—See EQT AB; *Int'l*, pg. 2477
ASTEA INTERNATIONAL JAPAN, INC.—See EQT AB; *Int'l*, pg. 2477
ASTEA ISRAEL LTD.—See EQT AB; *Int'l*, pg. 2477
ASTEA SERVICE & DISTRIBUTION SYSTEMS, BV.—See EQT AB; *Int'l*, pg. 2477
ASTEA (UK) LTD.—See EQT AB; *Int'l*, pg. 2477
ASTEC AUSTRALIA PTY LTD—See Astec Industries, Inc.; *U.S. Public*, pg. 216
ASTEC CO., LTD.—See Medipal Holdings Corporation; *Int'l*, pg. 4779
ASTEC CUSTOM POWER (SINGAPORE) PTE LTD—See Advanced Energy Industries, Inc.; *U.S. Public*, pg. 47
ASTEC EUROPE LIMITED—See Advanced Energy Industries, Inc.; *U.S. Public*, pg. 47
AS TECHNOLOGIE—See Neurones S.A.; *Int'l*, pg. 5219
ASTEC, INC.—See Astec Industries, Inc.; *U.S. Public*, pg. 216
ASTEC INDUSTRIES AFRICA MIDDLE EAST (PTY) LTD.—See Astec Industries, Inc.; *U.S. Public*, pg. 216
ASTEC INDUSTRIES, INC.; *U.S. Public*, pg. 216

ASTEC LIFESCIENCES LTD; *Int'l*, pg. 651
ASTEC MOBILE MACHINERY GMBH—See Astec Industries, Inc.; *U.S. Public*, pg. 216
ASTEC MOBILE SCREENS, INC.—See Astec Industries, Inc.; *U.S. Public*, pg. 216
ASTECO PROPERTY MANAGEMENT LLC—See ALDAR Properties PJSC; *Int'l*, pg. 304
ASTEC POWER PHILIPPINES, INC.—See Advanced Energy Industries, Inc.; *U.S. Public*, pg. 47
ASTEEL AJIYA SDN. BHD.—See YKGI Holdings Berhad; *Int'l*, pg. 8587
ASTEELFLASH BEDFORD LIMITED—See ASE Technology Holding Co., Ltd.; *Int'l*, pg. 604
ASTEELFLASH BONN GMBH—See ASE Technology Holding Co., Ltd.; *Int'l*, pg. 604
ASTEELFLASH DESIGN SOLUTIONS HAMBURG GMBH—See ASE Technology Holding Co., Ltd.; *Int'l*, pg. 604
ASTEELFLASH DEVELOPPEMENT—See ASE Technology Holding Co., Ltd.; *Int'l*, pg. 604
ASTEELFLASH EBERBACH GMBH—See ASE Technology Holding Co., Ltd.; *Int'l*, pg. 604
ASTEELFLASH EST—See ASE Technology Holding Co., Ltd.; *Int'l*, pg. 604
ASTEELFLASH FREMONT—See ASE Technology Holding Co., Ltd.; *Int'l*, pg. 604
ASTEELFLASH GERMANY GMBH—See ASE Technology Holding Co., Ltd.; *Int'l*, pg. 605
ASTEELFLASH GROUP—See ASE Technology Holding Co., Ltd.; *Int'l*, pg. 604
ASTEELFLASH HERSFELD GMBH—See ASE Technology Holding Co., Ltd.; *Int'l*, pg. 605
ASTEELFLASH HERSFELD GMBH—See ASE Technology Holding Co., Ltd.; *Int'l*, pg. 605
ASTEELFLASH MEXICO S.A. DE C.V.—See ASE Technology Holding Co., Ltd.; *Int'l*, pg. 605
ASTEELFLASH NORMANDIE—See ASE Technology Holding Co., Ltd.; *Int'l*, pg. 605
ASTEELFLASH PLZEN S.R.O.—See ASE Technology Holding Co., Ltd.; *Int'l*, pg. 605
ASTEELFLASH SCHWANDORF GMBH—See ASE Technology Holding Co., Ltd.; *Int'l*, pg. 605
ASTEELFLASH SUZHOU—See ASE Technology Holding Co., Ltd.; *Int'l*, pg. 605
ASTEELFLASH TIJUANA—See ASE Technology Holding Co., Ltd.; *Int'l*, pg. 605
ASTEELFLASH TUNISIE S.A.—See ASE Technology Holding Co., Ltd.; *Int'l*, pg. 605
ASTEELFLASH USA CORP.—See ASE Technology Holding Co., Ltd.; *Int'l*, pg. 605
ASTEEL RESOURCES SDN. BHD.—See YKGI Holdings Berhad; *Int'l*, pg. 8587
ASTEEL (SABAH) SDN. BHD.—See YKGI Holdings Berhad; *Int'l*, pg. 8587
ASTEEL SDN BHD.—See YKGI Holdings Berhad; *Int'l*, pg. 8587
ASTEEL SYNERGY SDN. BHD.—See YKGI Holdings Berhad; *Int'l*, pg. 8587
ASTEK GROUP PLC; *Int'l*, pg. 651
ASTEK INNOVATIONS LTD.—See The Jordan Company, L.P.; *U.S. Private*, pg. 4063
ASTEK WALLCOVERING, INC.; *U.S. Private*, pg. 360
ASTEL JSC; *Int'l*, pg. 651
ASTELLAS ANALYTICAL SCIENCE LABORATORIES, INC.—See Astellas Pharma Inc.; *Int'l*, pg. 651
ASTELLAS BUSINESS SERVICE CO., LTD.—See Astellas Pharma Inc.; *Int'l*, pg. 651
ASTELLAS B.V.—See Astellas Pharma Inc.; *Int'l*, pg. 652
ASTELLAS FARMA COLOMBIA SAS—See Astellas Pharma Inc.; *Int'l*, pg. 651
ASTELLAS FARMA LIMITADA—See Astellas Pharma Inc.; *Int'l*, pg. 651
ASTELLAS IRELAND—See Astellas Pharma Inc.; *Int'l*, pg. 652
ASTELLAS LEARNING INSTITUTE CO., LTD.—See Astellas Pharma Inc.; *Int'l*, pg. 651
ASTELLAS LTD.—See Astellas Pharma Inc.; *Int'l*, pg. 652
ASTELLAS PHARMA AB—See Astellas Pharma Inc.; *Int'l*, pg. 652
ASTELLAS PHARMA AE—See Astellas Pharma Inc.; *Int'l*, pg. 652
ASTELLAS PHARMA A.G.—See Astellas Pharma Inc.; *Int'l*, pg. 652
ASTELLAS PHARMA A/S—See Astellas Pharma Inc.; *Int'l*, pg. 652
ASTELLAS PHARMA AUSTRALIA PTY LTD—See Astellas Pharma Inc.; *Int'l*, pg. 652
ASTELLAS PHARMA B.V.—See Astellas Pharma Inc.; *Int'l*, pg. 652
ASTELLAS PHARMA B.V.—See Astellas Pharma Inc.; *Int'l*, pg. 652
ASTELLAS PHARMA CANADA, INC.—See Astellas Pharma Inc.; *Int'l*, pg. 652
ASTELLAS PHARMA CO., LIMITED—See Astellas Pharma Inc.; *Int'l*, pg. 653
ASTELLAS PHARMA DMCC—See Astellas Pharma Inc.; *Int'l*, pg. 652

ASTELLAS PHARMA D.O.O.—See CEZ, a.s.; *Int'l*, pg. 1426
ASTELLAS PHARMA EUROPE B.V.—See Astellas Pharma Inc.; *Int'l*, pg. 652
ASTELLAS PHARMA EUROPE LTD.—See Astellas Pharma Inc.; *Int'l*, pg. 652
ASTELLAS PHARMA EUROPE—See Astellas Pharma Inc.; *Int'l*, pg. 652
ASTELLAS PHARMA GES.MBH—See Astellas Pharma Inc.; *Int'l*, pg. 652
ASTELLAS PHARMA GMBH—See Astellas Pharma Inc.; *Int'l*, pg. 652
ASTELLAS PHARMA GMBH—See Astellas Pharma Inc.; *Int'l*, pg. 652
ASTELLAS PHARMA HONG KONG CO., LTD.—See Astellas Pharma Inc.; *Int'l*, pg. 652
ASTELLAS PHARMA ILAC TICARET VE SANAYI A.S.—See Astellas Pharma Inc.; *Int'l*, pg. 652
ASTELLAS PHARMA INC.; *Int'l*, pg. 651
ASTELLAS PHARMA INDIA PRIVATE LIMITED—See Astellas Pharma Inc.; *Int'l*, pg. 652
ASTELLAS PHARMA INTERNATIONAL B.V.—See Astellas Pharma Inc.; *Int'l*, pg. 652
ASTELLAS PHARMA KFT.—See Astellas Pharma Inc.; *Int'l*, pg. 652
ASTELLAS PHARMA KOREA, INC.—See Astellas Pharma Inc.; *Int'l*, pg. 652
ASTELLAS PHARMA LTDA—See Astellas Pharma Inc.; *Int'l*, pg. 652
ASTELLAS PHARMA LTD.—See Astellas Pharma Inc.; *Int'l*, pg. 652
ASTELLAS PHARMA MALAYSIA SDN. BHD.—See Astellas Pharma Inc.; *Int'l*, pg. 652
ASTELLAS PHARMA PHILIPPINES INC.—See Astellas Pharma Inc.; *Int'l*, pg. 652
ASTELLAS PHARMA (PTY) LIMITED—See Astellas Pharma Inc.; *Int'l*, pg. 652
ASTELLAS PHARMA SARL—See Astellas Pharma Inc.; *Int'l*, pg. 652
ASTELLAS PHARMA, S.A.—See Astellas Pharma Inc.; *Int'l*, pg. 652
ASTELLAS PHARMA S.A.S—See Astellas Pharma Inc.; *Int'l*, pg. 652
ASTELLAS PHARMA SINGAPORE PTE. LTD.—See Astellas Pharma Inc.; *Int'l*, pg. 652
ASTELLAS PHARMA S.P.A—See Astellas Pharma Inc.; *Int'l*, pg. 652
ASTELLAS PHARMA SP.Z.O.O.—See Astellas Pharma Inc.; *Int'l*, pg. 652
ASTELLAS PHARMA S.R.O—See Astellas Pharma Inc.; *Int'l*, pg. 652
ASTELLAS PHARMA TAIWAN, INC.—See Astellas Pharma Inc.; *Int'l*, pg. 652
ASTELLAS PHARMA TECH CO., LTD.—See Astellas Pharma Inc.; *Int'l*, pg. 652
ASTELLAS PHARMA (THAILAND) CO., LTD.—See Astellas Pharma Inc.; *Int'l*, pg. 652
ASTELLAS PHARMA US, INC.—See Astellas Pharma Inc.; *Int'l*, pg. 653
ASTELLAS RESEARCH INSTITUTE OF AMERICA LLC—See Astellas Pharma Inc.; *Int'l*, pg. 653
ASTELLAS RESEARCH TECHNOLOGIES CO., LTD.—See Astellas Pharma Inc.; *Int'l*, pg. 653
ASTELLAS TOKAI CO., LTD.—See Astellas Pharma Inc.; *Int'l*, pg. 653
ASTELLAS US HOLDING, INC.—See Astellas Pharma Inc.; *Int'l*, pg. 653
ASTELLAS US LLC—See Astellas Pharma Inc.; *Int'l*, pg. 653
ASTELLAS US TECHNOLOGIES, INC.—See Astellas Pharma Inc.; *Int'l*, pg. 653
ASTELLAS VENTURE MANAGEMENT LLC—See Astellas Pharma Inc.; *Int'l*, pg. 653
ASTENA HOLDINGS CO., LTD.; *Int'l*, pg. 653
AST-ENG CORP.—See MIRAIT ONE Corporation; *Int'l*, pg. 4917
ASTENJOHNSON, INC. - KANATA R&D FACILITY—See AstenJohnson, Inc.; *U.S. Private*, pg. 360
ASTENJOHNSON, INC.; *U.S. Private*, pg. 360
AST EQUITY PLAN SOLUTIONS, INC.—See Pacific Equity Partners Pty. Limited; *Int'l*, pg. 5688
ASTERAND INC.—See Stemgent, Inc.; *U.S. Private*, pg. 3801
ASTER DM HEALTHCARE LTD.; *Int'l*, pg. 653
ASTER GROUP, INC.—See Nippon Telegraph & Telephone Corporation; *Int'l*, pg. 5347
ASTERIA CORPORATION; *Int'l*, pg. 654
ASTERIAS BIOTHERAPEUTICS, INC.—See Lineage Cell Therapeutics, Inc.; *U.S. Public*, pg. 1320
ASTERIAS S.A.—See Hellenic Fishfarming S.A.; *Int'l*, pg. 3333
ASTERI HOLDINGS; *U.S. Private*, pg. 360
ASTERIKS INC.—See DTS Corporation; *Int'l*, pg. 2217
ASTER INFORMATIQUE—See Poulina Group Holding S.A.; *Int'l*, pg. 5942
ASTERION BELGIUM, NV—See Exela Technologies, Inc.; *U.S. Public*, pg. 806
ASTERION DENMARK A/S—See Exela Technologies, Inc.; *U.S. Public*, pg. 806

ASTERION DM FINLAND A.B.—See Exela Technologies, Inc.; *U.S. Public*, pg. 806
ASTERION FRANCE S.A.S.—See Exela Technologies, Inc.; *U.S. Public*, pg. 806
ASTERION INDUSTRIAL PARTNERS SGEIC SA; *Int'l*, pg. 654
ASTERION INTERNATIONAL GMBH—See Exela Technologies, Inc.; *U.S. Public*, pg. 806
ASTERM SAS—See IMI plc; *Int'l*, pg. 3624
ASTERON ADVISORY SERVICES LIMITED—See Dai-ichi Life Holdings, Inc.; *Int'l*, pg. 1918
ASTERON LIFE LIMITED—See Suncorp Group Limited; *Int'l*, pg. 7311
ASTERON LIMITED—See Dai-ichi Life Holdings, Inc.; *Int'l*, pg. 1918
ASTERON PORTFOLIO SERVICES LIMITED—See Dai-ichi Life Holdings, Inc.; *Int'l*, pg. 1918
ASTER PHARMACIES GROUP LLC—See Aster DM Healthcare Ltd.; *Int'l*, pg. 654
ASTERSPRING INTERNATIONAL SDN. BHD.—See Esthetics International Group Berhad; *Int'l*, pg. 2518
ASTEX GMBH—See MKS Instruments, Inc.; *U.S. Public*, pg. 1452
ASTEX PHARMACEUTICALS, INC.—See Otsuka Holdings Co., Ltd.; *Int'l*, pg. 5660
AST FARMA B.V.—See EQT AB; *Int'l*, pg. 2474
AST FUND SOLUTIONS, LLC—See Pacific Equity Partners Pty. Limited; *Int'l*, pg. 5688
AST GROUPE SA; *Int'l*, pg. 651
ASTHMATX, INC.—See Boston Scientific Corporation; *U.S. Public*, pg. 373
ASTI CORPORATION - FUKUROI FACTORY—See ASTI Corporation; *Int'l*, pg. 654
ASTI CORPORATION - HAMAMATSU FACTORY—See ASTI Corporation; *Int'l*, pg. 654
ASTI CORPORATION - IWATA FACTORY—See ASTI Corporation; *Int'l*, pg. 654
ASTI CORPORATION - KAKEGAWA FACTORY—See ASTI Corporation; *Int'l*, pg. 654
ASTI CORPORATION - MIYAKODA FACTORY—See ASTI Corporation; *Int'l*, pg. 654
ASTI CORPORATION; *Int'l*, pg. 654
ASTIDVALE PTE LTD—See SC Global Developments Limited; *Int'l*, pg. 6609
ASTI ELECTRONICS CORPORATION—See ASTI Corporation; *Int'l*, pg. 654
ASTI ELECTRONICS INDIA PRIVATE LIMITED—See ASTI Corporation; *Int'l*, pg. 654
ASTI HOLDINGS LIMITED; *Int'l*, pg. 654
ASTIKA HOLDINGS, INC.; *Int'l*, pg. 655
AS TIKKURILA—See PPG Industries, Inc.; *U.S. Public*, pg. 1710
ASTILLAS EXPORTACIONES LIMITADA—See Mitsubishi Corporation; *Int'l*, pg. 4938
ASTINO BERHAD; *Int'l*, pg. 655
ASTINO (MALAYSIA) COLOUR STEEL SHEET SDN. BHD.—See Astino Berhad; *Int'l*, pg. 655
ASTINO SOUTHERN SDN. BHD.—See Astino Berhad; *Int'l*, pg. 655
ASTI RESEARCH & DEVELOPMENT VIETNAM CORPORATION—See ASTI Corporation; *Int'l*, pg. 654
ASTIR IT SOLUTIONS, INC.; *U.S. Private*, pg. 360
ASTIR PALACE VOULIAGMENIS S.A.—See National Bank of Greece S.A.; *Int'l*, pg. 5153
ASTI TRANSPORTATION SYSTEMS INC.—See New Enterprise Stone & Lime Co., Inc.; *U.S. Private*, pg. 2895
ASTI (USA), INC.—See ASTI Holdings Limited; *Int'l*, pg. 655
ASTIVITA LIMITED—See TAMAWOOD LIMITED; *Int'l*, pg. 7449
ASTIVITA LIMITED; *Int'l*, pg. 655
ASTLEFORD INTERNATIONAL TRUCKS, INC.; *U.S. Private*, pg. 360
AST MARINE SCIENCES LTD—See HAL Trust N.V.; *Int'l*, pg. 3226
ASTMAX ENERGY, INC.—See ASTMAX Trading, Inc.; *Int'l*, pg. 655
ASTMAX INVESTMENTS MANAGEMENT, INC.—See ASTMAX Trading, Inc.; *Int'l*, pg. 655
ASTMAX TRADING, INC.; *Int'l*, pg. 655
ASTM S.P.A.—See Argo Finanziaria S.p.A.; *Int'l*, pg. 561
ASTOCO INC.—See Envipro Holdings Inc.; *Int'l*, pg. 2454
ASTOM CORPORATION—See Tokuyama Corporation; *Int'l*, pg. 7786
ASTOMOS ENERGY CORPORATION—See Idemitsu Kosan Co., Ltd.; *Int'l*, pg. 3590
ASTON AIR CONTROL PTE LTD—See Anderco Investment Pte Ltd; *Int'l*, pg. 450
ASTON BAY HOLDINGS LTD.; *Int'l*, pg. 655
ASTON CHEMICALS LTD.—See Sunjin Beauty Science Co., Ltd.; *Int'l*, pg. 7316
ASTONE HOLDINGS PTY LTD—See SUTL Enterprise Limited; *Int'l*, pg. 7347
ASTON HOTELS & RESORTS; *U.S. Private*, pg. 360
ASTONISH; *U.S. Private*, pg. 360
ASTON MARTIN JAPAN GK—See Aston Martin Lagonda Global Holdings Plc; *Int'l*, pg. 655
ASTON MARTIN LAGONDA GLOBAL HOLDINGS PLC; *Int'l*, pg. 655

ASTON MARTIN LAGONDA LIMITED—See Efad Real Estate Company; *Int'l*, pg. 2318
ASTON MARTIN LAGONDA OF NORTH AMERICA, INC.—See Efad Real Estate Company; *Int'l*, pg. 2318
ASTON MARTIN LAGONDA—See Efad Real Estate Company; *Int'l*, pg. 2318
ASTON MINERALS LIMITED; *Int'l*, pg. 655
ASTON PHOTONIC TECHNOLOGIES LIMITED—See Moog Inc.; *U.S. Public*, pg. 1469
ASTON VILLA FOOTBALL CLUB LIMITED—See Aston Villa Limited; *Int'l*, pg. 655
ASTON VILLA LIMITED; *Int'l*, pg. 655
AS TOOTSI TURVAS—See Vapo Oy; *Int'l*, pg. 8131
ASTOR & BLACK CUSTOM CLOTHIERS, LTD.; *U.S. Private*, pg. 360
ASTOR CHOCOLATE CORP.; *U.S. Private*, pg. 360
THE ASTOR CROWNE PLAZA NEW ORLEANS; *U.S. Private*, pg. 3989
ASTORE VALVES & FITTINGS S.R.L.—See Aliaxis S.A./N.V.; *Int'l*, pg. 323
ASTORG FORD LINCOLN-MERCURY OF PARKERSBURG, INC.; *U.S. Private*, pg. 361
ASTORG MOTOR CO.; *U.S. Private*, pg. 361
ASTORG PARTNERS S.A.S.; *Int'l*, pg. 655
ASTORG PARTNERS UK—See Astorg Partners S.A.S.; *Int'l*, pg. 655
ASTORIA A.D.; *Int'l*, pg. 657
ASTORIA D.O.O.—See Adris Grupa d.d.; *Int'l*, pg. 153
ASTORIA ENERGY LLC—See APG Asset Management NV; *Int'l*, pg. 512
ASTORIA ENERGY LLC—See IDB Development Corporation Ltd.; *Int'l*, pg. 3588
ASTORIA ENERGY LLC—See Munchener Ruckversicherungs AG; *Int'l*, pg. 5085
ASTOR PARK WOHNANLAGE LANGEN GMBH—See MK-Kliniken AG; *Int'l*, pg. 5001
ASTOR & SANDERS CORPORATION; *U.S. Private*, pg. 360
ASTORY CO LTD.; *Int'l*, pg. 657
ASTOS DIZAINAS MCCANN ERICKSON VILNIUS—See The Interpublic Group of Companies, Inc.; *U.S. Public*, pg. 2097
ASTOUND BROADBAND, LLC—See Stonepeak Partners L.P.; *U.S. Private*, pg. 3829
ASTOUND COMMERCE CORP.; *U.S. Private*, pg. 361
AST PERSONAL WEALTH SOLUTIONS, LLC—See Pacific Equity Partners Pty. Limited; *Int'l*, pg. 5689
ASTRA AGRICULTURAL CO. LTD.—See Arab Supply & Trading Co.; *Int'l*, pg. 532
ASTRA BENELUX B.V.—See SES S.A.; *Int'l*, pg. 6727
ASTRA CAPITAL MANAGEMENT LLC; *U.S. Private*, pg. 361
ASTRA CENTRE FOR WOMEN & FERTILITY PTE. LTD.—See Singapore Medical Group Limited; *Int'l*, pg. 6940
ASTRACHEM MOROCCO CO.—See ASTRA INDUSTRIAL GROUP COMPANY; *Int'l*, pg. 657
ASTRACHEM SAUDI ARABIA CO.—See ASTRA INDUSTRIAL GROUP COMPANY; *Int'l*, pg. 657
ASTRACHEM TURKEY—See ASTRA INDUSTRIAL GROUP COMPANY; *Int'l*, pg. 657
ASTRACHEM UKRAINE LTD.—See ASTRA INDUSTRIAL GROUP COMPANY; *Int'l*, pg. 657
ASTRA DEUTSCHLAND GMBH—See SES S.A.; *Int'l*, pg. 6727
ASTRA ENERGY INC.; *U.S. Public*, pg. 216
ASTRA EXPLORATION INC.; *Int'l*, pg. 657
ASTRAFLEX (PTY) LTD—See Berry Global Group, Inc; *U.S. Public*, pg. 323
ASTRA FOOD PROCESSING CO.—See Arab Supply & Trading Co.; *Int'l*, pg. 532
ASTRA FOODS, INC.; *U.S. Private*, pg. 361
ASTRA FRANCE S.A.—See SES S.A.; *Int'l*, pg. 6727
ASTRA GAMES LTD.—See Novomatic AG; *Int'l*, pg. 5466
ASTRA (GB) LIMITED—See SES S.A.; *Int'l*, pg. 6727
ASTRAGON ENTERTAINMENT GMBH—See Team17 Group plc; *Int'l*, pg. 7500
ASTRA GRAIN TRADE DIVISION—See Arab Supply & Trading Co.; *Int'l*, pg. 532
ASTRAIA SOFTWARE GMBH—See NEXUS AG; *Int'l*, pg. 5250
ASTRA INC.; *U.S. Private*, pg. 361
ASTRA INDUSTRIAL COMPLEX CO. FOR FERTILIZERS & AGROCHEMICALS—See ASTRA INDUSTRIAL GROUP COMPANY; *Int'l*, pg. 657
ASTRA INDUSTRIAL COMPLEX CO. FOR FERTILIZERS AND PESTICIDES LTD.—See ASTRA INDUSTRIAL GROUP COMPANY; *Int'l*, pg. 657
ASTRA INDUSTRIAL COMPLEX CO. LTD.—See ASTRA INDUSTRIAL GROUP COMPANY; *Int'l*, pg. 657
ASTRA INDUSTRIAL COMPLEX FOR FERTILIZERS & AGROCHEMICALS CO. LTD.—See Arab Supply & Trading Co.; *Int'l*, pg. 532
ASTRA INDUSTRIAL GROUP COMPANY; *Int'l*, pg. 657
ASTRA INDUSTRIES LTD.—See Kansai Paint Co., Ltd.; *Int'l*, pg. 4071
ASTRAKHAN POWER SALE COMPANY PAO; *Int'l*, pg. 658

ASTRA-KLK PTE. LTD.—See Kuala Lumpur Kepong Berhad; *Int'l*, pg. 4318
ASTRAL ASIA BERHAD; *Int'l*, pg. 658
ASTRAL - BAZENOVE PRISLUSENSTVI, S.R.O.—See Fluidra SA; *Int'l*, pg. 2713
ASTRAL BRANDS, INC.; *U.S. Private*, pg. 361
ASTRAL EXPORT, S.A—See Fluidra SA; *Int'l*, pg. 2713
ASTRAL EXTRACTS, LTD.; *U.S. Private*, pg. 361
ASTRAL FOODS LIMITED; *Int'l*, pg. 658
ASTRAL IMAGES CORPORATION—See Astrotech Corporation; *U.S. Public*, pg. 218
ASTRAL INDIA PRIVATE LTD—See Fluidra SA; *Int'l*, pg. 2713
ASTRALIS A/S; *Int'l*, pg. 658
ASTRALIS NEXUS APS—See Astralis A/S; *Int'l*, pg. 658
ASTRAL ITALIA SPA—See Fluidra SA; *Int'l*, pg. 2713
ASTRAL LIMITED; *Int'l*, pg. 658
ASTRALLOY STEEL PRODUCTS INC.—See SSAB AB; *Int'l*, pg. 7155
ASTRAL MARAZUL—See Fluidra SA; *Int'l*, pg. 2713
ASTRAL NIGERIA LTD—See Fluidra SA; *Int'l*, pg. 2713
ASTRAL OPERATIONS LIMITED - EARLYBIRD FARM DIVISION—See Astral Foods Limited; *Int'l*, pg. 658
ASTRAL OPERATIONS LIMITED—See Astral Foods Limited; *Int'l*, pg. 658
ASTRAL OUT-OF-HOME—See BCE Inc.; *Int'l*, pg. 927
ASTRAL PISCINE S.A.S—See Fluidra SA; *Int'l*, pg. 2713
ASTRAL POOL AUSTRALIA PTY LIMITED—See Fluidra SA; *Int'l*, pg. 2713
ASTRALPOOL CHILE LTD—See Fluidra SA; *Int'l*, pg. 2713
ASTRALPOOL CHINA—See Fluidra SA; *Int'l*, pg. 2713
ASTRALPOOL CYPRUS LTD—See Fluidra SA; *Int'l*, pg. 2714
ASTRAL POOL HELLAS SA—See Fluidra SA; *Int'l*, pg. 2713
ASTRAL POOL S.A.—See Fluidra SA; *Int'l*, pg. 2713
ASTRAL POOL SWIMMING POOL EQUIPMENT (SHANGHAI) LTD., CO—See Fluidra SA; *Int'l*, pg. 2713
ASTRALPOOL SWITZERLAND S.A.—See Fluidra SA; *Int'l*, pg. 2714
ASTRALPOOL THAILAND CO., LTD—See Fluidra SA; *Int'l*, pg. 2714
ASTRAL RESOURCES NL; *Int'l*, pg. 658
ASTRAL SCANDINAVIA A/S—See Fluidra SA; *Int'l*, pg. 2713
ASTRAL SNG—See Fluidra SA; *Int'l*, pg. 2713
ASTRAL SWEDEN AB—See Fluidra SA; *Int'l*, pg. 2713
ASTRAL UK LTD—See Fluidra SA; *Int'l*, pg. 2714
ASTRA MANUFACTURING, INC.—See ShoreView Industries, LLC; *U.S. Private*, pg. 3642
ASTRA MARKETING GMBH—See SES S.A.; *Int'l*, pg. 6727
ASTRA MARKETING LTD.—See SES S.A.; *Int'l*, pg. 6727
ASTRAMATIC S.A.U.—See Fluidra SA; *Int'l*, pg. 2714
ASTRA MICROWAVE PRODUCTS LIMITED; *Int'l*, pg. 658
ASTRA MICROWAVE PRODUCTS LIMITED - UNIT-II—See Astra Microwave Products Limited; *Int'l*, pg. 658
ASTRA MICROWAVE PRODUCTS LIMITED - UNIT-I—See Astra Microwave Products Limited; *Int'l*, pg. 658
ASTRA MINING COMPANY LIMITED—See Saudi Lime Industries Company; *Int'l*, pg. 6594
ASTRANA HEALTH INC.; *U.S. Public*, pg. 216
ASTRA NOVA CO.—See ASTRA INDUSTRIAL GROUP COMPANY; *Int'l*, pg. 657
ASTRA OIL COMPANY PTE LTD—See Transcor Astra Group S.A.; *Int'l*, pg. 7897
ASTRAPAK GAUTENG (PTY) LTD—See Berry Global Group, Inc; *U.S. Public*, pg. 323
ASTRAPAK KWAZULU-NATAL (PTY) LTD—See Berry Global Group, Inc; *U.S. Public*, pg. 323
ASTRAPAK LIMITED - CINQPLAST PLASTOP DENVER DIVISION—See Berry Global Group, Inc; *U.S. Public*, pg. 323
ASTRAPAK LIMITED - CITY PACKAGING DIVISION—See Berry Global Group, Inc; *U.S. Public*, pg. 323
ASTRAPAK LIMITED - PACKAGING CONSULTANTS DIVISION—See Berry Global Group, Inc; *U.S. Public*, pg. 323
ASTRAPAK LIMITED - PENINSULA PACKAGING DIVISION—See Berry Global Group, Inc; *U.S. Public*, pg. 323
ASTRAPAK LIMITED - PLASTFORM DIVISION—See Berry Global Group, Inc; *U.S. Public*, pg. 323
ASTRAPAK LIMITED - PLASTOP BRONKHORSTSPRUIT DIVISION—See Berry Global Group, Inc; *U.S. Public*, pg. 323
ASTRAPAK LIMITED - TRISTAR PLASTICS DIVISION—See Berry Global Group, Inc; *U.S. Public*, pg. 323
ASTRAPAK LIMITED - ULTRAPAK DIVISION—See Berry Global Group, Inc; *U.S. Public*, pg. 323
ASTRAPAK MANUFACTURING HOLDINGS (PTY) LTD—See Berry Global Group, Inc; *U.S. Public*, pg. 323
ASTRAPE CONSULTING LLC—See TA Associates, Inc.; *U.S. Public*, pg. 3917
ASTRA PLATFORM SERVICES GMBH—See SES S.A.; *Int'l*, pg. 6727

ASTRA POLSKA—See SES S.A.; *Int'l*, pg. 6727
ASTRA POLYMER COMPOUNDING CO. LTD.—See ASTRA INDUSTRIAL GROUP COMPANY; *Int'l*, pg. 657
ASTRA SPACE, INC.; *U.S. Private*, pg. 361
ASTRA SUPERMARKET AND COMMERCIAL DIVISION—See Arab Supply & Trading Co.; *Int'l*, pg. 532
ASTRA TRANSCOR FRANCE SAS—See Transcor Astra Group S.A.; *Int'l*, pg. 7897
ASTRA VEICOLI INDUSTRIALI S.P.A.—See CNH Industrial N.V.; *Int'l*, pg. 1675
ASTRAZENECA AB, O.Z.—See AstraZeneca PLC; *Int'l*, pg. 659
ASTRAZENECA AB—See AstraZeneca PLC; *Int'l*, pg. 659
ASTRAZENECA AG—See AstraZeneca PLC; *Int'l*, pg. 659
ASTRAZENECA ARGENTINA S.A.—See AstraZeneca PLC; *Int'l*, pg. 660
ASTRAZENECA A/S—See AstraZeneca PLC; *Int'l*, pg. 659
ASTRAZENECA AS—See AstraZeneca PLC; *Int'l*, pg. 659
ASTRAZENECA BELGIUM—See AstraZeneca PLC; *Int'l*, pg. 659
ASTRAZENECA BULGARIA—See AstraZeneca PLC; *Int'l*, pg. 659
ASTRAZENECA B.V.—See AstraZeneca PLC; *Int'l*, pg. 659
ASTRAZENECA CANADA INC.—See AstraZeneca PLC; *Int'l*, pg. 660
ASTRAZENECA CHILE S.A.—See AstraZeneca PLC; *Int'l*, pg. 660
ASTRAZENECA CLINICAL RESEARCH REGION CEE (HU)—See AstraZeneca PLC; *Int'l*, pg. 660
ASTRAZENECA COLOMBIA S.A.—See AstraZeneca PLC; *Int'l*, pg. 660
ASTRAZENECA CORPORATE IS—See AstraZeneca PLC; *Int'l*, pg. 659
ASTRAZENECA CZECH REPUBLIC—See AstraZeneca PLC; *Int'l*, pg. 659
ASTRAZENECA DO BRASIL LTDA.—See AstraZeneca PLC; *Int'l*, pg. 660
ASTRAZENECA DOMINICAN REPUBLIC—See AstraZeneca PLC; *Int'l*, pg. 659
ASTRAZENECA D.O.O.—See AstraZeneca PLC; *Int'l*, pg. 661
ASTRAZENECA EGYPT LLC—See AstraZeneca PLC; *Int'l*, pg. 661
ASTRAZENECA FARMACEUTICA SPAIN S.A.—See AstraZeneca PLC; *Int'l*, pg. 660
ASTRAZENECA FRANCE—See AstraZeneca PLC; *Int'l*, pg. 660
ASTRAZENECA FZ-LLC—See AstraZeneca PLC; *Int'l*, pg. 660
ASTRAZENECA GMBH—See AstraZeneca PLC; *Int'l*, pg. 660
ASTRAZENECA GULF FZ LLC—See AstraZeneca PLC; *Int'l*, pg. 660
ASTRAZENECA HOLDING GMBH—See AstraZeneca PLC; *Int'l*, pg. 660
ASTRAZENECA HONG KONG LTD.—See AstraZeneca PLC; *Int'l*, pg. 660
ASTRAZENECA ICELAND—See AstraZeneca PLC; *Int'l*, pg. 660
ASTRAZENECA ILAC SANAYI VE TICARET LIMITED—See AstraZeneca PLC; *Int'l*, pg. 661
ASTRAZENECA INDIA PVT LIMITED—See AstraZeneca PLC; *Int'l*, pg. 660
ASTRAZENECA (ISRAEL) LTD.—See AstraZeneca PLC; *Int'l*, pg. 659
ASTRAZENECA KFT.—See AstraZeneca PLC; *Int'l*, pg. 660
ASTRAZENECA KK—See AstraZeneca PLC; *Int'l*, pg. 660
ASTRAZENECA KK—See AstraZeneca PLC; *Int'l*, pg. 660
ASTRAZENECA KONTOR EESTIS—See AstraZeneca PLC; *Int'l*, pg. 661
ASTRAZENECA KOREA (SOUTH)—See AstraZeneca PLC; *Int'l*, pg. 660
ASTRAZENECA LATVIA—See AstraZeneca PLC; *Int'l*, pg. 660
ASTRAZENECA LIETUVA UAB—See AstraZeneca PLC; *Int'l*, pg. 660
ASTRAZENECA LIMITED—See AstraZeneca PLC; *Int'l*, pg. 660
ASTRAZENECA LLAC SANAYI VE TIC. LTD. STI.—See AstraZeneca PLC; *Int'l*, pg. 661
ASTRAZENECA LP—See AstraZeneca PLC; *Int'l*, pg. 660
ASTRAZENECA LP—See AstraZeneca PLC; *Int'l*, pg. 660
ASTRAZENECA LUXEMBOURG S.A.R.L.—See AstraZeneca PLC; *Int'l*, pg. 660
ASTRAZENECA NIJMEGEN B.V.—See AstraZeneca PLC; *Int'l*, pg. 661
ASTRAZENECA OSTERREICH GMBH—See AstraZeneca PLC; *Int'l*, pg. 660
ASTRAZENECA OY—See AstraZeneca PLC; *Int'l*, pg. 660
ASTRAZENECA PERU S.A.—See AstraZeneca PLC; *Int'l*, pg. 660
ASTRAZENECA PHARMACEUTICAL CO. LTD.—See AstraZeneca PLC; *Int'l*, pg. 660
ASTRAZENECA PHARMACEUTICALS (IRELAND) LTD.—See AstraZeneca PLC; *Int'l*, pg. 660
ASTRAZENECA PHARMACEUTICALS LP—See AstraZeneca PLC; *Int'l*, pg. 660

ASTRAZENECA PHARMACEUTICALS PAKISTAN (PRIVATE) LIMITED—See AstraZeneca PLC; *Int'l*, pg. 661
ASTRAZENECA PHARMACEUTICALS (PHILS.) INC.—See AstraZeneca PLC; *Int'l*, pg. 660
ASTRAZENECA PHARMACEUTICALS (PTY) LTD—See AstraZeneca PLC; *Int'l*, pg. 660
ASTRAZENECA PHARMA INDIA LIMITED—See AstraZeneca PLC; *Int'l*, pg. 660
ASTRAZENECA PHARMA POLAND SP. Z.O.O.—See AstraZeneca PLC; *Int'l*, pg. 660
ASTRAZENECA (PHILIPPINES) INC.—See AstraZeneca PLC; *Int'l*, pg. 659
ASTRAZENECA PLC; *Int'l*, pg. 659
ASTRAZENECA PRODUTOS FARMACEUTICOS, LDA.—See AstraZeneca PLC; *Int'l*, pg. 661
ASTRAZENECA - PRODUTOS FARMACEUTICOS, LDA.—See AstraZeneca PLC; *Int'l*, pg. 661
ASTRAZENECA PTY. LTD.—See AstraZeneca PLC; *Int'l*, pg. 661
ASTRAZENECA R&D MOLNDAL—See AstraZeneca PLC; *Int'l*, pg. 659
ASTRAZENECA R&D SODERTALJE—See AstraZeneca PLC; *Int'l*, pg. 659
ASTRAZENECA ROMANIA—See AstraZeneca PLC; *Int'l*, pg. 661
ASTRAZENECA RUSSIA—See AstraZeneca PLC; *Int'l*, pg. 661
ASTRAZENECA S.A. DE C.V.—See AstraZeneca PLC; *Int'l*, pg. 660
ASTRAZENECA S.A.—See AstraZeneca PLC; *Int'l*, pg. 661
ASTRAZENECA SDN BHD.—See AstraZeneca PLC; *Int'l*, pg. 661
ASTRAZENECA (SINGAPORE) PTE. LTD.—See AstraZeneca PLC; *Int'l*, pg. 659
ASTRAZENECA SOUTH AFRICA—See AstraZeneca PLC; *Int'l*, pg. 661
ASTRAZENECA S.P.A.—See AstraZeneca PLC; *Int'l*, pg. 661
ASTRAZENECA TAIWAN LIMITED—See AstraZeneca PLC; *Int'l*, pg. 661
ASTRAZENECA (THAILAND) LTD.—See AstraZeneca PLC; *Int'l*, pg. 659
ASTRAZENECA TREASURY LIMITED—See AstraZeneca PLC; *Int'l*, pg. 661
ASTRAZENECA UK LTD.—See AstraZeneca PLC; *Int'l*, pg. 661
ASTRAZENECA UK MANUFACTURING—See AstraZeneca PLC; *Int'l*, pg. 661
ASTRAZENECA UKRAINE LLC—See AstraZeneca PLC; *Int'l*, pg. 661
ASTRAZENECA URUGUAY SA—See AstraZeneca PLC; *Int'l*, pg. 661
ASTRAZENECA VENEZUELA S.A.—See AstraZeneca PLC; *Int'l*, pg. 661
ASTRAZENECA VIETNAM COMPANY LIMITED—See AstraZeneca PLC; *Int'l*, pg. 661
ASTREA ACQUISITION CORP.; *U.S. Public*, pg. 217
ASTRE CORPORATION; *U.S. Private*, pg. 361
ASTREE ASSURANCES—See Allianz SE; *Int'l*, pg. 343
ASTRENSKA INSURANCE LIMITED—See The Collinson Group Limited; *Int'l*, pg. 7634
ASTREX ELECTRONICS INC.—See Berkshire Hathaway Inc.; *U.S. Public*, pg. 316
ASTREYA PARTNERS, INC.; *U.S. Private*, pg. 361
ASTRIA HEALTH; *U.S. Private*, pg. 361
ASTRIA REGIONAL MEDICAL CENTER—See Astria Health; *U.S. Private*, pg. 361
ASTRIA SEMICONDUCTOR HOLDINGS, INC—See FormFactor, Inc.; *U.S. Public*, pg. 868
ASTRIA SUNNYSIDE HOSPITAL—See Astria Health; *U.S. Private*, pg. 361
ASTRIA THERAPEUTICS, INC.; *U.S. Public*, pg. 217
ASTRIA TOPPENISH HOSPITAL—See Astria Health; *U.S. Private*, pg. 361
ASTRID TM A.S.—See Gr. Sarantis S.A.; *Int'l*, pg. 3047
AS TRIGON CAPITAL GROUP; *Int'l*, pg. 591
ASTRIMEX B.V.—See Blackstone Inc.; *U.S. Public*, pg. 356
ASTRIMEX UTRECHT—See Blackstone Inc.; *U.S. Public*, pg. 356
ASTRIUM GMBH—See Airbus SE; *Int'l*, pg. 245
ASTRIUM HOLDING S.A.S.—See Airbus SE; *Int'l*, pg. 245
ASTRIUM NORTH AMERICA, INC.—See Airbus SE; *Int'l*, pg. 245
ASTRIUM SPACE TRANSPORTATION GMBH—See Airbus SE; *Int'l*, pg. 245
ASTRIUM SPACE TRANSPORTATION—See Airbus SE; *Int'l*, pg. 245
ASTRIUM (UK) LIMITED—See Airbus SE; *Int'l*, pg. 245
ASTRIX TECHNOLOGY GROUP, INC.; *U.S. Private*, pg. 361
ASTRO AEROSPACE LTD.; *U.S. Public*, pg. 217
ASTRO ALL ASIA NETWORKS PLC; *Int'l*, pg. 661
ASTRO APPAREL, INC.; *U.S. Private*, pg. 362
ASTRO BUILDINGS INC.—See Roberts Trading Corporation; *U.S. Private*, pg. 3460
ASTRO CARPET MILLS LLC—See Live Ventures Incorporated; *U.S. Public*, pg. 1332

COMPANY NAME INDEX

ASTROCAST SA; *Int'l*, pg. 662
ASTRO-CENTURY EDUCATION & TECHNOLOGY CO., LTD.; *Int'l*, pg. 662
ASTROCHEF, INC.; *U.S. Private*, pg. 362
ASTRO COMMUNICATIONS SERVICES, INC.; *U.S. Private*, pg. 362
ASTRO CORP.—See Mitsubishi Chemical Group Corporation; *Int'l*, pg. 4930
ASTRO DIGITAL PUBLICATIONS SDN BHD—See Astro Malaysia Holdings Bhd; *Int'l*, pg. 662
ASTRODYNE CORPORATION—See Tinicum Enterprises, Inc.; *U.S. Private*, pg. 4173
ASTRO GAMING, INC.—See Logitech International S.A.; *U.S. Public*, pg. 1341
ASTRO GS SHOP SDN. BHD.—See Astro Malaysia Holdings Bhd; *Int'l*, pg. 662
ASTRO INC.; *U.S. Private*, pg. 362
ASTROL ELECTRONIC AG—See Sun.King Technology Group Limited; *Int'l*, pg. 7309
ASTRO LINCOLN, MERCURY, INC.; *U.S. Private*, pg. 362
ASTRO MACHINE CORP.—See AstroNova, Inc.; *U.S. Public*, pg. 218
ASTRO MALAYSIA HOLDINGS BHD; *Int'l*, pg. 662
ASTRO MANUFACTURING & DESIGN, INC.; *U.S. Private*, pg. 362
ASTRO-MED GMBH—See AstroNova, Inc.; *U.S. Public*, pg. 218
ASTRONAUTICS C.A. LTD.—See Astronautics Corporation of America; *U.S. Private*, pg. 362
ASTRONAUTICS CORPORATION OF AMERICA - PLANT 4—See Astronautics Corporation of America; *U.S. Private*, pg. 362
ASTRONAUTICS CORPORATION OF AMERICA; *U.S. Private*, pg. 362
ASTRONAUTICS U.K.—See Astronautics Corporation of America; *U.S. Private*, pg. 362
ASTRON BUILDINGS LLC—See Lindab International AB; *Int'l*, pg. 4503
ASTRON BUILDINGS S.A.—See Lindab International AB; *Int'l*, pg. 4503
ASTRON BUILDINGS SP. Z O.O.—See Lindab International AB; *Int'l*, pg. 4503
ASTRON BUILDINGS S.R.O.—See Lindab International AB; *Int'l*, pg. 4503
ASTRON CONNECT, INC.; *Int'l*, pg. 662
ASTRON CORPORATION LIMITED; *Int'l*, pg. 662
ASTRON ENERGY—See Glencore plc; *Int'l*, pg. 2990
ASTRONERGY GMBH—See Chint Group Corporation; *Int'l*, pg. 1571
ASTRONERGY SOLAR COMPANY CO., LTD.—See Chint Group Corporation; *Int'l*, pg. 1571
ASTRONERGY SOLAR, INC.—See Chint Group Corporation; *Int'l*, pg. 1571
ASTRONERGY SOLAR KOREA CO., LTD.—See Chint Group Corporation; *Int'l*, pg. 1571
ASTRONERGY SOLAR THAILAND CO., LTD.—See Chint Group Corporation; *Int'l*, pg. 1571
ASTRONERGY—See Chint Group Corporation; *Int'l*, pg. 1571
ASTRONICS ADVANCED ELECTRONIC SYSTEMS CORP.—See Astronics Corporation; *U.S. Public*, pg. 217
ASTRONICS AEROSAT CORPORATION—See Astronics Corporation; *U.S. Public*, pg. 217
ASTRONICS CONNECTIVITY SYSTEMS & CERTIFICATION CORP.—See Astronics Corporation; *U.S. Public*, pg. 217
ASTRONICS CORPORATION; *U.S. Public*, pg. 217
ASTRONICS CUSTOM CONTROLS CONCEPTS INC.—See Astronics Corporation; *U.S. Public*, pg. 217
ASTRONICS TEST SYSTEMS INC.—See Astronics Corporation; *U.S. Public*, pg. 217
ASTRON KESTRELL, LTD.—See Minor International PCL; *Int'l*, pg. 4911
ASTRONOVA GMBH—See AstroNova, Inc.; *U.S. Public*, pg. 218
ASTRONOVA, INC.; *U.S. Public*, pg. 217
ASTRONOVA (SHANGHAI) TRADING CO., LTD—See AstroNova, Inc.; *U.S. Public*, pg. 218
ASTRONOVA (SINGAPORE) PTE LTD.—See AstroNova, Inc.; *U.S. Public*, pg. 218
ASTRON PAPER & BOARD MILL LIMITED; *Int'l*, pg. 662
ASTRON RESEARCH LIMITED—See Intas Pharmaceuticals Ltd.; *Int'l*, pg. 3728
ASTRO PAK CORPORATION; *U.S. Private*, pg. 362
ASTROPLAST KUNSTSTOFFTECHNIK GMBH & CO. KG—See Gesco AG; *Int'l*, pg. 2945
ASTRO PRODUCTIONS SDN. BHD.—See Astro Malaysia Holdings Bhd; *Int'l*, pg. 662
ASTRO RADIO SDN. BHD.—See Astro Malaysia Holdings Bhd; *Int'l*, pg. 662
ASTRO RESOURCES N.L.; *Int'l*, pg. 662
ASTROSEAL PRODUCTS MFG CORPORATION—See HEICO Corporation; *U.S. Public*, pg. 1019
ASTRO SHAW SDN. BHD.—See Astro Malaysia Holdings Bhd; *Int'l*, pg. 662
ASTRO SPAR, INC.—See Arlington Capital Partners LLC; *U.S. Private*, pg. 327
ASTRO STROBEL KOMMUNIKATIONSSYSTEME GMBH; *Int'l*, pg. 662
ASTRO STUDIOS, INC.—See The Carlyle Group Inc.; *U.S. Public*, pg. 2051
ASTROSYSTEMS AUTOMATION—See North Atlantic Industries Inc.; *U.S. Private*, pg. 2942
ASTROTECH CORPORATION; *U.S. Public*, pg. 218
ASTRO TECHNOLOGIES LTD.—See Fuji Corporation; *Int'l*, pg. 2809
ASTROTECH SPACE OPERATIONS, INC. - VANDENBERG AIR FORCE BASE—See Lockheed Martin Corporation; *U.S. Public*, pg. 1338
ASTROTECH SPACE OPERATIONS, LLC—See Lockheed Martin Corporation; *U.S. Public*, pg. 1338
ASTRO-TEC MANUFACTURING, INC.; *U.S. Private*, pg. 362
ASTRO-TEK INDUSTRIES INC.—See White Wolf Capital LLC; *U.S. Private*, pg. 4510
ASTROTEK IRELAND LIMITED—See Rexel, S.A.; *Int'l*, pg. 6316
ASTRUM CAPITAL MANAGEMENT LIMITED—See Astrum Financial Holdings Limited; *Int'l*, pg. 662
ASTRUM FINANCIAL HOLDINGS LIMITED; *Int'l*, pg. 662
ASTRUP DRUGS, INC.; *U.S. Private*, pg. 362
ASTRY LOAN SERVICES CORPORATION—See AIFUL Corporation; *Int'l*, pg. 232
AST SERVICE GMBH—See L'Air Liquide S.A.; *Int'l*, pg. 4370
AST SPACEMOBILE, INC.; *U.S. Public*, pg. 216
AST TELECOM, LLC—See Fiji National Provident Fund; *Int'l*, pg. 2661
A. STUCKI COMPANY—See Stone Canyon Industries, LLC; *U.S. Private*, pg. 3817
ASTURIANA DE LAMINADOS SA; *Int'l*, pg. 663
ASTURIANA DE ZINC S.A.—See Glencore plc; *Int'l*, pg. 2990
ASTUTE, INC.; *U.S. Private*, pg. 362
ASTUTE MEDICAL INC.—See Institut Merieux; *Int'l*, pg. 3724
AS TV PLAY BALTICS—See Providence Equity Partners L.L.C.; *U.S. Private*, pg. 3291
AS'TY INC.—See Yondashi Holdings Inc.; *Int'l*, pg. 8596
ASTYRA CORPORATION; *U.S. Private*, pg. 362
ASTYX GMBH—See General Motors Company; *U.S. Public*, pg. 923
ASUBIO PHAMACEUTICALS, INC.—See Daiichi Sankyo Co., Ltd.; *Int'l*, pg. 1930
ASUBIO PHARMA CO., LTD.—See Daiichi Sankyo Co., Ltd.; *Int'l*, pg. 1929
ASU GROUP; *U.S. Public*, pg. 362
ASUKA ASSET MANAGEMENT CO., LTD.—See Aizawa Securities Group Co., Ltd.; *Int'l*, pg. 255
ASUKA FOODS CO., LTD.—See Showa Holdings Co., Ltd.; *Int'l*, pg. 6861
ASUKANET COMPANY LIMITED; *Int'l*, pg. 663
ASUKASOKEN CO., LTD.—See JFE Holdings, Inc.; *Int'l*, pg. 3935
ASULAB S.A.—See The Swatch Group Ltd.; *Int'l*, pg. 7691
ASUMIRAI CO., LTD.—See J-Lease Co., Ltd.; *Int'l*, pg. 3854
ASUNA CO., LTD.—See Arisawa Manufacturing Co., Ltd.; *Int'l*, pg. 566
ASUNARO AOKI CONSTRUCTION CO., LTD.—See Takamatsu Construction Group Co., Ltd.; *Int'l*, pg. 7429
A/S UNION—See Norske Skog ASA; *Int'l*, pg. 5437
ASUNTOSALKKU OY; *Int'l*, pg. 663
ASURAGEN, INC.—See Bio-Techne Corporation; *U.S. Public*, pg. 334
ASURANSI AXA INDONESIA—See AXA S.A.; *Int'l*, pg. 759
ASURANSI DAYIN MITRA TBK; *Int'l*, pg. 663
ASURANSI MULTI ARTHA GUNA TBK; *Int'l*, pg. 663
ASURE PAYROLL TAX MANAGEMENT LLC—See Asure Software, Inc.; *U.S. Public*, pg. 218
ASURE, INC.; *U.S. Private*, pg. 218
ASURE SOFTWARE UK LTD.—See KKR & Co. Inc.; *U.S. Public*, pg. 1239
ASURION LLC; *U.S. Private*, pg. 362
ASURIS NORTHWEST HEALTH—See Cambia Health Solutions, Inc.; *U.S. Private*, pg. 726
ASUS COMPUTER CZECH REPUBLIC S. R. O.—See ASUSTeK Computer Inc.; *Int'l*, pg. 663
ASUS COMPUTER GMBH—See ASUSTeK Computer Inc.; *Int'l*, pg. 663
ASUS COMPUTER INTERNATIONAL, INC.—See ASUSTeK Computer Inc.; *Int'l*, pg. 663
ASUS CZECH SERVICE S. R. O.—See ASUSTeK Computer Inc.; *Int'l*, pg. 663
ASUS EUROPE B.V.—See ASUSTeK Computer Inc.; *Int'l*, pg. 663
ASUS FRANCE SARL—See ASUSTeK Computer Inc.; *Int'l*, pg. 663
ASUS HOLLAND B.V.—See ASUSTeK Computer Inc.; *Int'l*, pg. 663
ASUS KOREA CO., LTD.—See ASUSTeK Computer Inc.; *Int'l*, pg. 663
ASUS MEXICO, S. A. DE C. V.—See ASUSTeK Computer Inc.; *Int'l*, pg. 663
ASUS NORDIC AB—See ASUSTeK Computer Inc.; *Int'l*, pg. 663
ASUS POLSKA SP. Z O. O.—See ASUSTeK Computer Inc.; *Int'l*, pg. 663
ASUSPOWER INVESTMENT CO., LTD.—See Pegatron Corporation; *Int'l*, pg. 5781
ASUS SERVICE AUSTRALIA PTY LIMITED—See ASUSTeK Computer Inc.; *Int'l*, pg. 663
ASUS TECHNOLOGY (HONG KONG) LIMITED—See ASUSTeK Computer Inc.; *Int'l*, pg. 663
ASUS TECHNOLOGY LICENSING INC.—See ASUSTeK Computer Inc.; *Int'l*, pg. 663
ASUS TECHNOLOGY PTE. LIMITED—See ASUSTeK Computer Inc.; *Int'l*, pg. 663
ASUS TECHNOLOGY (VIETNAM) CO., LTD.—See ASUSTeK Computer Inc.; *Int'l*, pg. 663
ASUSTEK COMPUTER INC.; *Int'l*, pg. 663
ASUSTEK COMPUTER MALAYSIA SDN. BHD.—See ASUSTeK Computer Inc.; *Int'l*, pg. 663
ASUSTEK COMPUTER (S) PTE. LTD.—See ASUSTeK Computer Inc.; *Int'l*, pg. 663
ASUSTEK COMPUTERS (PTY) LIMITED—See ASUSTeK Computer Inc.; *Int'l*, pg. 664
ASUSTEK ITALY S. R. L.—See ASUSTeK Computer Inc.; *Int'l*, pg. 664
ASUSTEK (UK) LIMITED—See ASUSTeK Computer Inc.; *Int'l*, pg. 663
ASUTORO PUBLISHING CO., LTD.—See TOPPAN Holdings Inc.; *Int'l*, pg. 7816
ASUTOSH ENTERPRISES LIMITED; *Int'l*, pg. 664
A. SUTTER AG—See CRS Holding AG; *Int'l*, pg. 1859
ASUWA ELECTRONICS INDUSTRIES, LTD.—See Murata Manufacturing Co., Ltd.; *Int'l*, pg. 5096
ASUWA MURATA MANUFACTURING CO., LTD.—See Murata Manufacturing Co., Ltd.; *Int'l*, pg. 5097
AS VEOLIA KESKKONNATEENUSED—See Veolia Environnement S.A.; *Int'l*, pg. 8159
ASV HOLDINGS, INC.—See Yanmar Co., Ltd.; *Int'l*, pg. 8563
AS VIRU OLU—See Harboes Bryggeri A/S; *Int'l*, pg. 3271
AS VORU JUUST—See Valio Ltd.; *Int'l*, pg. 8116
ASWAAQ—See Investment Corporation of Dubai; *Int'l*, pg. 3785
ASWAN VILLAGE ASSOCIATES, LLC—See Bank of America Corporation; *U.S. Public*, pg. 270
ASWARE CO., LTD.—See SOLXYZ Co., Ltd.; *Int'l*, pg. 7083
ASW-ASPHALT- UND SCHOTTERWERK NEUSTIFT GMBH AND CO. KG—See PORR AG; *Int'l*, pg. 5922
A.S. WATSON RETAIL (HK) LTD—See CK Hutchison Holdings Limited; *Int'l*, pg. 1636
ASW HOLDING CORPORATION; *U.S. Private*, pg. 363
ASW LOGISTICS INC.; *U.S. Private*, pg. 363
A/S WODSCHOW & CO.—See The Middleby Corporation; *U.S. Public*, pg. 2113
A.S.W. SERVICES INC.; *U.S. Private*, pg. 28
ASW STEEL INC.—See Acciaierie Valbruna S.p.A.; *Int'l*, pg. 89
ASX CLEARING CORPORATION LIMITED—See ASX Limited; *Int'l*, pg. 664
ASX LIMITED; *Int'l*, pg. 664
ASX OPERATIONS PTY. LIMITED—See ASX Limited; *Int'l*, pg. 664
ASX SETTLEMENT CORPORATION LIMITED—See ASX Limited; *Int'l*, pg. 664
ASYAD HOLDING GROUP; *Int'l*, pg. 664
ASYA INFOSOFT LTD.; *Int'l*, pg. 664
AS YIT EHITUS—See YIT Corporation; *Int'l*, pg. 8586
ASYLUM RECORDS LLC—See Access Industries, Inc.; *U.S. Private*, pg. 52
ASYLUM RESEARCH CORP.—See Oxford Instruments Plc; *Int'l*, pg. 5674
THE ASYLUM; *U.S. Private*, pg. 3989
ASYMCHEM LABORATORIES TIAN JIN CO LTD; *Int'l*, pg. 664
ASYMMETRIK, LTD.—See Arlington Capital Partners LLC; *U.S. Private*, pg. 327
ASYSTEL ITALIA SPA—See Econocom Group SA; *Int'l*, pg. 2297
ATA - A.T APPARELS, INC.; *U.S. Private*, pg. 363
AT ABATEMENT SERVICES, INC.—See AT Industries, Inc.; *U.S. Private*, pg. 363
ATAB AUTOMATIONSTEKNIK AB—See Investment AB Latour; *Int'l*, pg. 3780
A TABLE MATSUYA CO., LTD.—See ALPICO Holdings Co., Ltd.; *Int'l*, pg. 371
ATA BYGG-OCH MARKPRODUKTER AB; *Int'l*, pg. 665
ATACADAO S.A.—See Carrefour SA; *Int'l*, pg. 1343
ATACAMA RESOURCES INTERNATIONAL, INC.; *U.S. Public*, pg. 220
ATA CASTING TECHNOLOGY CO., LTD.—See Daido Metal Corporation; *Int'l*, pg. 1921
ATA CASTING TECHNOLOGY JAPAN CO., LTD.—See Daido Metal Corporation; *Int'l*, pg. 1921
A.T.A. CO., LTD.—See Takashimaya Company, Limited; *Int'l*, pg. 7435
ATA CREATIVITY GLOBAL; *Int'l*, pg. 665
ATAC RESOURCES LTD.—See Hecla Mining Company; *U.S. Public*, pg. 1018
ATAC SAS—See Auchan Holding S.A.; *Int'l*, pg. 699
AT ADRIA D.O.O.—See Avtotehna, d.d.; *Int'l*, pg. 751

ATA CREATIVITY GLOBAL

ATAD STEEL STRUCTURE CORP.—See Kanematsu Corporation; *Int'l*, pg. 4068
ATA ELEKTRIK ENERJISI TOPTAN SATIS A.S.—See Verusa Holding A.S.; *Int'l*, pg. 8175
ATAER HOLDING A.S.—See OYAK Cement Group; *Int'l*, pg. 5677
ATAF GESTIONI S.R.L.—See Ferrovie dello Stato Italiane S.p.A.; *Int'l*, pg. 2645
ATAG ASSET MANAGEMENT AG—See Basellandschaftliche Kantonalbank; *Int'l*, pg. 871
ATAG ASSET MANAGEMENT (LUXEMBOURG) S.A.—See Basellandschaftliche Kantonalbank; *Int'l*, pg. 871
ATA GAYRIMENKUL YATIRIM ORTAKLIGI AS; *Int'l*, pg. 665
ATAG BELGIE NV—See Hisense Co., Ltd.; *Int'l*, pg. 3407
ATAG HEATING B.V.—See Ariston Holding N.V.; *Int'l*, pg. 567
ATAG HEIZUNGSTECHNIK GMBH—See Ariston Holding N.V.; *Int'l*, pg. 567
ATAG PRIVATE CLIENT SERVICES AG—See Basellandschaftliche Kantonalbank; *Int'l*, pg. 871
ATAG VERWARMING BELGIE B.V.B.A.—See Ariston Holding N.V.; *Int'l*, pg. 567
ATA HILL & SMITH AB—See Hill & Smith PLC; *Int'l*, pg. 3391
ATA HILL & SMITH AS—See Hill & Smith PLC; *Int'l*, pg. 3391
ATAHUAMPA PIC S.A.—See Genus Plc; *Int'l*, pg. 2931
ATAI FUJI ELECTRIC CO., LTD.—See Fuji Electric Co., Ltd.; *Int'l*, pg. 2810
ATAI LIFE SCIENCES AG; *Int'l*, pg. 665
ATAI LIFE SCIENCES N.V.; *Int'l*, pg. 665
ATAI LIFE SCIENCES US INC.—See ATAI Life Sciences N.V.; *Int'l*, pg. 665
ATA IMS BERHAD; *Int'l*, pg. 665
ATAIN INSURANCE COMPANIES—See H.W. Kaufman Financial Group, Inc.; *U.S. Private*, pg. 1836
ATAIROS GROUP, INC.; *U.S. Private*, pg. 363
ATA IT LTD.—See National Bank of Canada; *Int'l*, pg. 5152
ATAKA ASANO CO., LTD.—See Hitachi Zosen Corporation; *Int'l*, pg. 3410
ATAK OOO—See Auchan Holding S.A.; *Int'l*, pg. 699
ATAKULE GAYRIMENKUL YATIRIM ORTAKLIGI AS; *Int'l*, pg. 665
ATALANTA CORPORATION—See Gellert Global Group; *U.S. Private*, pg. 1656
ATALANTA FURNITURE SRL—See Gellert Global Group; *U.S. Private*, pg. 1656
ATALANTA NOVA SRL—See Gellert Global Group; *U.S. Private*, pg. 1656
ATALANTA SOSNOFF CAPITAL, LLC; *U.S. Private*, pg. 364
ATALASOFT, INC.—See Clearlake Capital Group, L.P.; *U.S. Private*, pg. 935
ATALASOFT, INC.—See TA Associates, Inc.; *U.S. Private*, pg. 3916
ATALAYA CAPITAL MANAGEMENT LP—See Blue Owl Capital Inc.; *U.S. Public*, pg. 364
ATALAYA FINANCING LIMITED—See Atalaya Mining plc; *Int'l*, pg. 665
ATALAYA MINING PLC; *Int'l*, pg. 665
ATAL BUILDWELL PVT. LTD.—See Setubandhan Infrastructure Limited; *Int'l*, pg. 6730
ATALIAN GLOBAL SERVICES; *Int'l*, pg. 665
ATALIAN SERVEST FOOD CO. LIMITED—See La Financiere Atalian SAS; *Int'l*, pg. 4387
ATALLAH GROUP, INC.; *Int'l*, pg. 666
ATAL REALTECH LIMITED; *Int'l*, pg. 665
ATAL S.A.; *Int'l*, pg. 665
ATAL SPOL S.R.O.—See Actia Group SA; *Int'l*, pg. 118
ATALY, INC.; *U.S. Private*, pg. 364
ATAMEKEN-AGRO JSC; *Int'l*, pg. 666
ATAMIAN VOLKSWAGEN & HONDA, INC.; *U.S. Private*, pg. 364
ATAMI DAIICHI TRAFFIC CO., LTD.—See Daiichi Koutsu Sangyo Co., Ltd.; *Int'l*, pg. 1928
ATAM VALVES LIMITED; *Int'l*, pg. 666
ATANA LIMITED—See Marlowe Plc; *Int'l*, pg. 4698
ATARA BIOTHERAPEUTICS, INC.; *U.S. Public*, pg. 220
ATARA BIOTHERAPEUTICS SWITZERLAND GMBH—See Atara Biotherapeutics, Inc.; *U.S. Public*, pg. 220
ATAR CAPITAL, LLC; *U.S. Private*, pg. 364
ATA RECRUITMENT LIMITED—See RTC Group Plc; *Int'l*, pg. 6420
ATARI, INC.—See Atari, SA; *Int'l*, pg. 666
ATARI, SA; *Int'l*, pg. 666
ATAR URGUU JSC; *Int'l*, pg. 666
ATASAY KUYUMCULUK; *Int'l*, pg. 666
ATASCOSA NATIONAL BANK; *U.S. Private*, pg. 365
ATASEHIR RESTORAN ISLETMELERI GIDA TURIZM TICARET A.S.—See Dogus Holding AS; *Int'l*, pg. 2154
ATASUN OPTIK A.S.—See HAL Trust N.V.; *Int'l*, pg. 3223
ATA TESTING AUTHORITY (BEIJING) LIMITED—See ATA Creativity Global; *Int'l*, pg. 665
AT AUTOMOBILES; *Int'l*, pg. 664
ATB ANTRIEBSTECHNIK GMBH—See Wolong Holding Group Co., Ltd.; *Int'l*, pg. 8443

ATB AUFZUGTECHNIK BERLIN GMBH—See KONE Oyj; *Int'l*, pg. 4247
ATB AUSTRIA ANTRIEBSTECHNIK AG—See Wolong Holding Group Co., Ltd.; *Int'l*, pg. 8443
ATB AUTOMATION NV—See Indutrade AB; *Int'l*, pg. 3677
ATB CAPITAL MARKETS INC.—See Alberta Treasury Branches; *Int'l*, pg. 298
ATB FOD BOR D.O.O.—See Wolong Holding Group Co., Ltd.; *Int'l*, pg. 8443
ATB LAURENCE SCOTT LTD.—See Wolong Holding Group Co., Ltd.; *Int'l*, pg. 8443
ATB MORLEY LTD.—See Wolong Holding Group Co., Ltd.; *Int'l*, pg. 8443
ATB MOTORENTECHNIK GMBH—See Wolong Holding Group Co., Ltd.; *Int'l*, pg. 8443
ATB MOTORENWERKE GMBH—See Wolong Holding Group Co., Ltd.; *Int'l*, pg. 8443
ATB MOTORS B.V.—See Wolong Holding Group Co., Ltd.; *Int'l*, pg. 8443
ATB MOTORS (WUHAN) CO., LTD.—See Wolong Electric Group Co., Ltd.; *Int'l*, pg. 8443
ATB SECURITIES INC.—See Alberta Treasury Branches; *Int'l*, pg. 298
ATB SEVER D.O.O.—See Wolong Holding Group Co., Ltd.; *Int'l*, pg. 8443
AT B.V.—See Excellent Retail Brands B.V.; *Int'l*, pg. 2578
ATC ADHESIVE TAPE CONVERTING AB—See OEM International AB; *Int'l*, pg. 5528
ATC AFRICAN TRAVEL CONCEPT PROPRIETARY LIMITED—See TUI AG; *Int'l*, pg. 7963
ATC ALLOYS LTD.; *Int'l*, pg. 666
AT CAPITAL PTE LIMITED; *Int'l*, pg. 664
ATC EUROPE—See KYOCERA Corporation; *Int'l*, pg. 4359
ATC EUROPE - UNITED KINGDOM—See KYOCERA Corporation; *Int'l*, pg. 4359
ATC FIBRA DE COLOMBIA, S.A.S.—See American Tower Corporation; *U.S. Public*, pg. 110
ATC FRANCE HOLDING S.A.S.—See American Tower Corporation; *U.S. Public*, pg. 110
ATC GERMANY HOLDINGS GMBH—See American Tower Corporation; *U.S. Public*, pg. 110
ATC GERMANY OPERATING 1 GMBH—See American Tower Corporation; *U.S. Public*, pg. 110
ATC GERMANY SERVICES GMBH—See American Tower Corporation; *U.S. Public*, pg. 110
ATC GROUP, INC.; *U.S. Private*, pg. 365
ATC GROUP SERVICES (CT) INC.—See GI Manager L.P.; *U.S. Private*, pg. 1691
ATC GROUP SERVICES LLC—See Bernhard Capital Partners Management, LP; *U.S. Private*, pg. 536
ATCHAFALAYA MEASUREMENT, INC.—See Sentinel Capital Partners, L.L.C.; *U.S. Private*, pg. 3609
ATC HEALTHCARE, INC.; *U.S. Private*, pg. 365
ATC HEALTHCARE SERVICES, INC.—See ATC Healthcare, Inc.; *U.S. Private*, pg. 365
A & T CHEVROLET, INCORPORATED; *U.S. Private*, pg. 18
ATC HOLDINGS CO., LTD.—See Topy Industries, Ltd.; *Int'l*, pg. 7821
ATC (ITALIA) S.R.L.—See Airtac International Group; *Int'l*, pg. 248
A.T. CLAYTON & COMPANY, INC.; *U.S. Private*, pg. 28
ATC LEASING COMPANY—See TFI International Inc.; *Int'l*, pg. 7586
ATC LIGHTING & PLASTICS INC.—See ATC Group, Inc.; *U.S. Private*, pg. 365
ATC MANAGEMENT INC.; *U.S. Private*, pg. 365
ATC MARKETING (UGANDA) LIMITED—See American Tower Corporation; *U.S. Public*, pg. 110
ATC NYMOLD CORPORATION—See ATC Group, Inc.; *U.S. Private*, pg. 365
ATCOAT GMBH; *Int'l*, pg. 667
ATCOAT HAMBURG GMBH—See ATCOAT GmbH; *Int'l*, pg. 667
ATCO AUSTRALIA PTY. LTD.—See ATCO Ltd.; *Int'l*, pg. 666
ATCO BLUE FLAME KITCHEN—See ATCO Ltd.; *Int'l*, pg. 666
ATCO ELECTRIC LTD.—See ATCO Ltd.; *Int'l*, pg. 667
ATCO ENERGY LTD.—See ATCO Ltd.; *Int'l*, pg. 666
ATCO ENERGYSENSE—See ATCO Ltd.; *Int'l*, pg. 666
ATCO ENERGY SOLUTIONS LTD—See ATCO Ltd.; *Int'l*, pg. 666
ATCO FRONTEC EUROPA KFT-SUCURSAL EM PORTUGAL—See ATCO Ltd.; *Int'l*, pg. 666
ATCO FRONTEC EUROPE LTD.—See ATCO Ltd.; *Int'l*, pg. 666
ATCO GAS AUSTRALIA PTY. LTD.—See ATCO Ltd.; *Int'l*, pg. 666
ATCO GAS & PIPELINES LTD.—See ATCO Ltd.; *Int'l*, pg. 667
ATCO GAS—See ATCO Ltd.; *Int'l*, pg. 667
ATCO INCORPORATED; *U.S. Private*, pg. 365
ATCO INTERNATIONAL CORPORATION; *U.S. Private*, pg. 365
ATCO I-TEK AUSTRALIA—See ATCO Ltd.; *Int'l*, pg. 666
ATCO LTD.; *Int'l*, pg. 666

CORPORATE AFFILIATIONS

ATCO MIDSTREAM NWT LTD.—See ATCO Ltd.; *Int'l*, pg. 666
ATCOM, INC.; *U.S. Private*, pg. 365
ATCO MINING INC.; *Int'l*, pg. 667
ATCOM INTERNET & MULTIMEDIA LTD.—See Dionic Industrial & Trading S.A; *Int'l*, pg. 2127
ATCOMM PUBLISHING CORP.; *U.S. Private*, pg. 365
AT COMPUS S.R.O.—See AB S.A.; *Int'l*, pg. 41
AT COMPUTERS HOLDING A.S.—See AB S.A.; *Int'l*, pg. 41
ATCOM SA—See Dionic Industrial & Trading S.A; *Int'l*, pg. 2128
ATCOM TECHNOLOGIES LTD.; *Int'l*, pg. 667
AT CONFERENCE, INC.; *U.S. Private*, pg. 363
A-T CONTROLS, INC—See MiddleGround Management, LP; *U.S. Private*, pg. 2712
ATCO PIPELINES—See ATCO Ltd.; *Int'l*, pg. 667
ATCO POWER AUSTRALIA PTY LTD—See ATCO Ltd.; *Int'l*, pg. 666
ATCO POWER LTD.—See ATCO Ltd.; *Int'l*, pg. 666
ATCO PRODUCTS, INC.—See Blue Point Capital Partners, LLC; *U.S. Private*, pg. 591
ATCORE SYSTEMS, LLC—See Faye Business Systems Group Inc.; *U.S. Private*, pg. 1484
ATCORE TECHNOLOGY LTD.—See Inflexion Private Equity Partners LLP; *Int'l*, pg. 3688
ATCOR MEDICAL INC.—See CardieX Limited; *Int'l*, pg. 1321
ATCOR MEDICAL PTY LIMITED—See CardieX Limited; *Int'l*, pg. 1321
A&T CORPORATION—See Tokuyama Corporation; *Int'l*, pg. 7786
ATCO RUBBER PRODUCTS INC.—See Mueller Industries, Inc.; *U.S. Public*, pg. 1484
ATCO STRUCTURES & LOGISTICS LTD.—See ATCO Ltd.; *Int'l*, pg. 666
ATCO STRUCTURES & LOGISTICS PTY LTD.—See ATCO Ltd.; *Int'l*, pg. 666
ATCO STRUCTURES & LOGISTICS UK LTD.—See ATCO Ltd.; *Int'l*, pg. 666
ATCO STRUCTURES & LOGISTICS (USA) INC. - ALASKA—See ATCO Ltd.; *Int'l*, pg. 666
ATCO STRUCTURES & LOGISTICS (USA) INC.—See ATCO Ltd.; *Int'l*, pg. 666
ATCO WATER, LTD.—See ATCO Ltd.; *Int'l*, pg. 666
ATCO PARAGUAY S.R.L.—See American Tower Corporation; *U.S. Public*, pg. 110
ATC PVT. LTD.—See Bridgestone Corporation; *Int'l*, pg. 1155
ATC REALTY ONE, LLC—See Wells Fargo & Company; *U.S. Public*, pg. 2343
ATC REALTY SIXTEEN, INC.—See Wells Fargo & Company; *U.S. Public*, pg. 2343
A.T. CROSS COMPANY—See Transom Capital Group, LLC; *U.S. Private*, pg. 4209
A.T. CROSS (FRANCE) S.A.—See Transom Capital Group, LLC; *U.S. Private*, pg. 4209
A.T. CROSS LIMITED—See Transom Capital Group, LLC; *U.S. Private*, pg. 4209
A.T. CROSS LIMITED—See Transom Capital Group, LLC; *U.S. Private*, pg. 4209
ATC SEQUOIA LLC—See American Tower Corporation; *U.S. Public*, pg. 110
ATC SOUTH AFRICA SERVICES PTY LTD—See American Tower Corporation; *U.S. Public*, pg. 110
ATC TELECOM INFRASTRUCTURE PRIVATE LIMITED—See Brookfield Corporation; *Int'l*, pg. 1174
ATC TIRES AP PRIVATE LTD.—See The Yokohama Rubber Co., Ltd.; *Int'l*, pg. 7702
ATC TIRES PVT. LTD.—See The Yokohama Rubber Co., Ltd.; *Int'l*, pg. 7702
ATC TOWER (GHANA) LIMITED—See American Tower Corporation; *U.S. Public*, pg. 110
ATC VENTURE GROUP INC.; *U.S. Private*, pg. 365
ATD-AMERICAN CO. INC.; *U.S. Private*, pg. 365
ATD CORPORATION—See TPG Capital, L.P.; *U.S. Public*, pg. 2166
ATD JSC—See Societe Anonyme d'Explosifs et de Produits Chimiques; *Int'l*, pg. 7035
ATD PORTER NOVELLI—See Omnicom Group Inc.; *U.S. Public*, pg. 1590
ATEA ASA; *Int'l*, pg. 667
ATEA AS—See Atea ASA; *Int'l*, pg. 667
ATEA A/S—See Atea ASA; *Int'l*, pg. 667
ATEA BALTIC UAB—See Atea ASA; *Int'l*, pg. 667
ATEA FINLAND OY—See Atea ASA; *Int'l*, pg. 667
ATEA GLOBAL SERVICES SIA.—See Atea ASA; *Int'l*, pg. 667
ATEA LOGISTICS AB—See Atea ASA; *Int'l*, pg. 667
ATEAM CONNECT INC.—See Ateam Inc.; *Int'l*, pg. 667
ATEAM INC.; *Int'l*, pg. 667
THE A TEAM, LLC; *U.S. Private*, pg. 3980
THE A TEAM PROMOTIONAL—See The A Team, LLC; *U.S. Private*, pg. 3980
ATEA PHARMACEUTICALS, INC.; *U.S. Public*, pg. 220
ATEA SIA.—See Atea ASA; *Int'l*, pg. 667
ATEA SVERIGE AB—See Atea ASA; *Int'l*, pg. 667
ATEA UAB—See Atea ASA; *Int'l*, pg. 667

COMPANY NAME INDEX

ATEB CANADA LTD.—See Omnicell, Inc.; *U.S. Public*, pg. 1572
ATEB, INC.—See Omnicell, Inc.; *U.S. Public*, pg. 1572
ATEC BUSINESS INFORMATION GMBH—See Management Capital Holding AG; *Int'l*, pg. 4666
ATEC CO., LTD.—See Iwatani Corporation; *Int'l*, pg. 3850
A-TEC CO., LTD.—See Oriental Consultants Holdings Company Limited; *Int'l*, pg. 5623
A-TECH CORP.; *U.S. Private*, pg. 22
A'TECH ENTERPRISES INT'L LTD.—See V-TAC Technology Co., Ltd.; *Int'l*, pg. 8105
ATECH OEM, INC.; *Int'l*, pg. 667
ATECH PERIPHERALS, INC.—See Aten International Co., Ltd.; *Int'l*, pg. 668
A-TECH SOLUTION CO., LTD. - CHEONAN FACTORY—See A-TECH Solution Co., Ltd.; *Int'l*, pg. 21
A-TECH SOLUTION CO., LTD. - GWANG-JU FACTORY—See A-TECH Solution Co., Ltd.; *Int'l*, pg. 21
A-TECH SOLUTION CO., LTD.; *Int'l*, pg. 21
A-TECH; *U.S. Private*, pg. 22
ATEC, INC.; *U.S. Private*, pg. 365
A-TEC INDUSTRIES AG; *Int'l*, pg. 21
ATEC MOBILITY CO., LTD—See Iwatani Corporation; *Int'l*, pg. 3849
ATECO TOBLER AG—See Indutrade AB; *Int'l*, pg. 3677
ATECS AG—See Zech Group SE; *Int'l*, pg. 8628
ATEC SYSTEMS, INC.—See Cadiz Inc.; *U.S. Public*, pg. 419
ATEC SYSTEMS, LTD.—See Armada Group, Ltd.; *U.S. Private*, pg. 329
ATECT CORPORATION; *Int'l*, pg. 667
ATECT KOREA CORPORATION—See Atect Corporation; *Int'l*, pg. 668
ATEECO, INC.; *U.S. Private*, pg. 365
ATE-ELECTRONICS S.R.L.—See NIBE Industrier AB; *Int'l*, pg. 5259
ATE ENERGY INTERNATIONAL CO., LTD.; *Int'l*, pg. 667
ATEGI S.COOP—See Mondragon Corporation; *Int'l*, pg. 5031
ATEGO GROUP LTD.—See PTC Inc.; *U.S. Public*, pg. 1734
ATEGO SAS—See PTC Inc.; *U.S. Public*, pg. 1734
ATEK ACCESS TECHNOLOGIES, LLC—See ATEK Companies, Inc.; *U.S. Private*, pg. 365
ATEK COMPANIES, INC.; *U.S. Private*, pg. 365
ATEK METAL TECHNOLOGIES, LLC—See ATEK Companies, Inc.; *U.S. Private*, pg. 365
ATEL 14, LLC—See ATEL Capital Group; *U.S. Private*, pg. 366
ATEL 15, LLC—See ATEL Capital Group; *U.S. Private*, pg. 366
ATEL CAPITAL GROUP; *U.S. Private*, pg. 366
ATE LEASING S.A.—See Piraeus Financial Holdings S.A.; *Int'l*, pg. 5873
ATEL EQUIPMENT CORPORATION—See ATEL Capital Group; *U.S. Private*, pg. 366
ATEL FINANCIAL SERVICES—See ATEL Capital Group; *U.S. Private*, pg. 366
ATEL GROWTH CAPITAL FUND 8, LLC—See ATEL Capital Group; *U.S. Private*, pg. 366
ATEL HELLAS S.A.—See Alpiq Holding AG; *Int'l*, pg. 373
ATELIER DE PRODUCTION ET DE CREATION; *Int'l*, pg. 668
ATELIER D'OEUVRES DE FORGE—See Ateliers Perrault Freres; *Int'l*, pg. 668
ATELIER DU GRANIER S.A.R.L—See Vicat S.A.; *Int'l*, pg. 8185
ATELIER GARDEUR GMBH; *Int'l*, pg. 668
ATELIER P.V. HYDRAULIQUE 2004 INC—See Applied Industrial Technologies, Inc.; *U.S. Public*, pg. 170
ATELIERS BUSCH S.A.—See Dr. Ing. K. Busch GmbH; *Int'l*, pg. 2192
ATELIERS D ORVAL SA—See Ermewa Interservices Sarl; *Int'l*, pg. 2494
ATELIER SERVICES—See BNP Paribas SA; *Int'l*, pg. 1080
ATELIERS FERIGNAC SA—See Ateliers Perrault Freres; *Int'l*, pg. 668
ATELIERS HUBERT GERKEN S.A.—See Westinghouse Air Brake Technologies Corporation; *U.S. Public*, pg. 2357
ATELIERS NORMAND SA—See Media 6 SA; *Int'l*, pg. 4770
ATELIERS PERRAULT FRERES; *Int'l*, pg. 668
ATELIERS TOFER SAS—See Figeac-Aero SA; *Int'l*, pg. 2660
ATEL INVESTOR SERVICES—See ATEL Capital Group; *U.S. Private*, pg. 366
ATELJE A.D.; *Int'l*, pg. 668
ATELJE LYKTAN AB—See Fagerhult Group AB; *Int'l*, pg. 2601
ATELJE MARGARETHA AB—See Litorina Capital Management AB; *Int'l*, pg. 4527
ATEL LEASING CORPORATION—See ATEL Capital Group; *U.S. Private*, pg. 366
ATEL SECURITIES CORPORATION—See ATEL Capital Group; *U.S. Private*, pg. 366

ATEL VENTURES, INC.—See ATEL Capital Group; *U.S. Private*, pg. 366
ATEMAX NORD-EST S.A.S.—See Tessenderlo Group NV; *Int'l*, pg. 7573
ATEME S.A.; *Int'l*, pg. 668
ATEMPO DEUTSCHLAND GMBH—See Atempo S.A.; *Int'l*, pg. 668
ATEMPO, INC.—See Atempo S.A.; *Int'l*, pg. 668
ATEM POLSKA SP. Z O.O.—See VINCI S.A.; *Int'l*, pg. 8212
ATEMPO S.A.; *Int'l*, pg. 668
ATEMZENTRUM BAD LIPPSPRINGE GMBH—See PAUL HARTMANN AG; *Int'l*, pg. 5760
ATEN ADVANCE CO.,LTD—See Aten International Co., Ltd.; *Int'l*, pg. 668
ATEN SHANGHAI CO., LTD.—See Rentracks Co., Ltd.; *Int'l*, pg. 6289
ATEN CANADA TECHNOLOGIES INC.—See Aten International Co., Ltd.; *Int'l*, pg. 668
ATEN CHINA CO., LTD.—See Aten International Co., Ltd.; *Int'l*, pg. 668
ATENDE MEDICA SP. Z O.O.—See Atende S.A.; *Int'l*, pg. 668
ATENDE S.A.; *Int'l*, pg. 668
ATENDE SOFTWARE SP. Z O.O.—See Atende S.A.; *Int'l*, pg. 668
ATENEA COMUNICACION Y MECENAZGO, S.A.—See Lone Star Funds; *U.S. Private*, pg. 2485
AT ENGINEERING SOLUTION SDN. BHD.—See AT Systematization Berhad; *Int'l*, pg. 664
ATEN INFOTECH N.V.—See Aten International Co., Ltd.; *Int'l*, pg. 668
ATEN INTERNATIONAL CO., LTD.; *Int'l*, pg. 668
ATEN JAPAN CO., LTD—See Aten International Co., Ltd.; *Int'l*, pg. 668
ATEN NEW JERSEY INC—See Aten International Co., Ltd.; *Int'l*, pg. 668
ATENOR S.A.; *Int'l*, pg. 668
ATEN TECHNOLOGY INC.—See Aten International Co., Ltd.; *Int'l*, pg. 668
ATENTO COLOMBIA, S.A.—See Telefonica, S.A.; *Int'l*, pg. 7535
ATENTO INVERSIONES Y TELESERVICIOS, S.A.U.—See Bain Capital, LP; *U.S. Private*, pg. 430
ATENTO S.A.—See Bain Capital, LP; *U.S. Private*, pg. 430
ATENTO TELESERVICIOS ESPANA, S.A.U.—See Bain Capital, LP; *U.S. Private*, pg. 430
ATEN U.K. LIMITED—See Aten International Co., Ltd.; *Int'l*, pg. 668
ATEP - AMKOR TECHNOLOGY PORTUGAL, S.A.—See Amkor Technology, Inc.; *U.S. Public*, pg. 124
ATERIAN, INC.; *U.S. Public*, pg. 220
ATERIAN INVESTMENT MANAGEMENT, L.P.; *U.S. Private*, pg. 366
ATERIAN PLC; *Int'l*, pg. 668
ATESCO INDUSTRIAL CARTERING JOINT STOCK COMPANY; *Int'l*, pg. 668
ATET D.O.O.—See Petrol, Slovenska energetska druzba, d.d.; *Int'l*, pg. 5827
ATETSU LIME CO., LTD.—See Nittetsu Mining Co., Ltd.; *Int'l*, pg. 5383
ATEVIA AG; *Int'l*, pg. 669
ATEX GROUP LTD.—See Kistefos AS; *Int'l*, pg. 4192
ATEXIA SAS—See VINCI S.A.; *Int'l*, pg. 8212
ATEXIS FRANCE SAS—See Alten S.A.; *Int'l*, pg. 390
ATEXIS GMBH—See Alten S.A.; *Int'l*, pg. 390
ATEXIS SPAIN SL—See Alten S.A.; *Int'l*, pg. 390
ATEXIS SRL—See Alten S.A.; *Int'l*, pg. 390
ATEX MEDIA INC.—See Vista Equity Partners, LLC; *U.S. Private*, pg. 4398
AT EXPRESS PTE. LTD.—See Asiatravel.com Holdings Limited; *Int'l*, pg. 620
ATEX RESOURCES, INC.; *Int'l*, pg. 669
AT&F ADVANCED METALS LLC—See American Tank & Fabricating Company; *U.S. Private*, pg. 256
ATF AEROSPACE LLC—See ATF, Inc.; *U.S. Private*, pg. 367
ATFBANK JSC—See UniCredit S.p.A.; *Int'l*, pg. 8039
ATF CAPITAL B.V.—See UniCredit S.p.A.; *Int'l*, pg. 8039
A.T. FERRELL COMPANY, INC. - CLIPPER SEPARATION DIVISION—See A.T. Ferrell Company, Inc.; *U.S. Private*, pg. 28
A.T. FERRELL COMPANY, INC.; *U.S. Private*, pg. 28
ATFIELDS MANUFACTURING TECHNOLOGY CORPORATION—See Nuvoton Technology Corporation; *Int'l*, pg. 5495
AT FILMS INC.—See Berry Global Group, Inc; *U.S. Public*, pg. 320
ATF, INC.; *U.S. Private*, pg. 367
AT&F INDIA FABRICATION PVT. LTD.—See American Tank & Fabricating Company; *U.S. Private*, pg. 256
ATFIN GMBH—See Camellia Plc; *Int'l*, pg. 1271
AT&F MARINE—See American Tank & Fabricating Company; *U.S. Private*, pg. 256
ATF MINING ELECTRICS PTY LTD—See Washington H. Soul Pattinson & Company Limited; *Int'l*, pg. 8351
ATF SERVICES PTY. LTD.—See CHAMP Private Equity Pty. Ltd.; *Int'l*, pg. 1439
ATG ACCESS LTD.—See Hill & Smith PLC; *Int'l*, pg. 3391

ATHENS ADMINISTRATORS

AT GLOBAL MARKETS (UK) LIMITED; *Int'l*, pg. 664
ATG-LUTHER & MAELZER ASIA LTD.—See Cohu, Inc.; *U.S. Public*, pg. 530
ATG MEDIA LTD—See Mobeus Equity Partners LLP; *Int'l*, pg. 5008
ATG TITLE; *U.S. Private*, pg. 367
ATG TRANSPORTATION LLC—See Palladium Equity Partners, LLC; *U.S. Private*, pg. 3078
ATG TRUST COMPANY—See Midland States Bancorp, Inc.; *U.S. Public*, pg. 1445
ATG UV TECHNOLOGY LIMITED—See Xylem Inc.; *U.S. Public*, pg. 2393
ATHABASCA MINERALS INC.; *Int'l*, pg. 669
ATHABASCA OIL CORP.; *Int'l*, pg. 669
ATHA ENERGY CORP.; *Int'l*, pg. 669
ATH APLICACIONES TECNICAS HIDRAULICAS S.L.—See Fluidra SA; *Int'l*, pg. 2713
ATHARV ENTERPRISES LIMITED; *Int'l*, pg. 669
ATHAS HEALTH, LLC—See Nobilis Health Corp.; *U.S. Private*, pg. 2932
ATH AUFZUGSTECHNIK HEILBRONN GMBH & CO. KG—See KONE Oyj; *Int'l*, pg. 4247
A&T HAUSGERATE AG—See AB Electrolux; *Int'l*, pg. 40
ATH CALL CENTRE LIMITED—See Fiji National Provident Fund; *Int'l*, pg. 2661
A & T HEALTH CARE LLC.; *U.S. Private*, pg. 18
ATHEEB GROUP; *Int'l*, pg. 669
ATHEEB INTERGRAPH SAUDI COMPANY - RIYADH—See Hexagon AB; *Int'l*, pg. 3368
ATHEEB (UK) LTD.—See Atheeb Group; *Int'l*, pg. 669
ATHELNEY TRUST PLC; *Int'l*, pg. 669
ATHENA BITCOIN GLOBAL; *U.S. Public*, pg. 221
ATHENA CAPITAL ADVISORS LLC—See Franklin Resources, Inc.; *U.S. Public*, pg. 880
ATHENA CONSEIL LUX S.A.; *Int'l*, pg. 669
ATHENA CONSTRUCTIONS LIMITED; *Int'l*, pg. 669
ATHENA CONSUMER ACQUISITION CORP.; *U.S. Public*, pg. 221
ATHENA DIAGNOSTICS, INC.—See Quest Diagnostics, Inc.; *U.S. Public*, pg. 1755
ATHENA DYNAMICS PTE. LTD.—See BH Global Corporation Limited; *Int'l*, pg. 1009
ATHENA EMIRATES LLC—See ATHENA S.A.; *Int'l*, pg. 670
ATHENA FUJAIRAH LLC—See ATHENA S.A.; *Int'l*, pg. 670
ATHENA GLOBAL TECHNOLOGIES LTD.; *Int'l*, pg. 669
ATHENA GOLD CORPORATION; *U.S. Public*, pg. 221
ATHENA HEALTH CARE SYSTEMS; *U.S. Private*, pg. 367
ATHENAHEALTH, INC.—See Bain Capital, LP; *U.S. Private*, pg. 452
ATHENAHEALTH, INC.—See Hellman & Friedman LLC; *U.S. Private*, pg. 1911
ATHENA INVESTMENTS A/S; *Int'l*, pg. 669
ATHENA MANUFACTURING, LP; *U.S. Private*, pg. 367
ATHENA MINES LIMITED—See Argo Exploration Limited; *Int'l*, pg. 561
ATHENA PROPERTIES LIMITED—See Centum Investment Company Limited; *Int'l*, pg. 1416
ATHENA RESOURCES LIMITED; *Int'l*, pg. 669
ATHENA S.A.; *Int'l*, pg. 670
ATHENE ANNUITY & LIFE ASSURANCE COMPANY OF NEW YORK—See Apollo Global Management, Inc.; *U.S. Public*, pg. 147
ATHENE ANNUITY & LIFE ASSURANCE COMPANY—See Apollo Global Management, Inc.; *U.S. Public*, pg. 147
ATHENE ASSET MANAGEMENT, L.P.—See Apollo Global Management, Inc.; *U.S. Public*, pg. 147
ATHENEE PALACE HILTON BUCHAREST HOTEL; *Int'l*, pg. 670
ATHENE HOLDING LTD.—See Apollo Global Management, Inc.; *U.S. Public*, pg. 147
ATHENE LEBENSVERSICHERUNG AG—See Apollo Global Management, Inc.; *U.S. Public*, pg. 147
ATHENE LIFE RE LTD.—See Apollo Global Management, Inc.; *U.S. Public*, pg. 147
ATHENE USA CORPORATION—See Apollo Global Management, Inc.; *U.S. Public*, pg. 147
ATHENEX, INC.; *U.S. Public*, pg. 221
ATHENEX PHARMACEUTICAL DIVISION, LLC—See Athenex, Inc.; *U.S. Public*, pg. 221
ATHENEX PHARMA SOLUTIONS, LLC—See Athenex, Inc.; *U.S. Public*, pg. 221
ATHENIAN BREWERY S.A.—See L'Arche Green N.V.; *Int'l*, pg. 4376
ATHENIAN VENTURE PARTNERS LP; *U.S. Private*, pg. 367
ATHENIUM ANALYTICS LLC; *U.S. Private*, pg. 367
ATHENIUM, LLC—See Athenium Analytics LLC; *U.S. Private*, pg. 367
ATHENS ADMINISTRATORS; *U.S. Private*, pg. 367
ATHENS BANNER-HERALD—See Gannett Co., Inc.; *U.S. Public*, pg. 901
ATHENS BEHAVIORAL HEALTH CLINIC—See Hopewell Health Centers Inc.; *U.S. Private*, pg. 1979
ATHENS CHEVROLET, INC.—See General Motors Company; *U.S. Public*, pg. 923

223

ATHENS EXCHANGE S.A.—See Hellenic Exchanges-Athens Stock Exchange S.A.; *Int'l*, pg. 3333
ATHENS FOODS, INC.; *U.S. Private*, pg. 367
ATHENS INTERNATIONAL AIRPORT S.A.; *Int'l*, pg. 670
ATHENS-LIMESTONE HOMECARE, LLC—See United-Health Group Incorporated; *U.S. Public*, pg. 2244
ATHENS MARINA S.A.—See Avax S.A.; *Int'l*, pg. 737
ATHENS MEDICAL CENTERS SA; *Int'l*, pg. 670
THE ATHENS MESSENGER—See American Consolidated Media LP; *U.S. Private*, pg. 228
ATHENS PAPER CO. - DISTRIBUTION—See Athens Paper Company, Inc.; *U.S. Private*, pg. 368
ATHENS PAPER COMPANY, INC.; *U.S. Private*, pg. 367
ATHENS PAPER CO.—See Athens Paper Company, Inc.; *U.S. Private*, pg. 367
ATHENS PAPER CO.—See Athens Paper Company, Inc.; *U.S. Private*, pg. 367
ATHENS PARK HOMES, LLC—See Champion Homes, Inc.; *U.S. Public*, pg. 477
ATHENS SEED COMPANY; *U.S. Private*, pg. 368
ATHENS SURGERY CENTER, LLC—See Apollo Global Management, Inc.; *U.S. Public*, pg. 154
ATHENS SURGERY CENTER PARTNER, LLC—See Apollo Global Management, Inc.; *U.S. Public*, pg. 154
ATHENS UTILITY BOARD; *U.S. Private*, pg. 368
ATHENS WATER SUPPLY & SEWERAGE S.A.; *Int'l*, pg. 670
ATHERONOVA INC.; *U.S. Private*, pg. 368
ATHEROTECH, INC.—See Behrman Brothers Management Corp.; *U.S. Private*, pg. 515
ATHERSYS, INC.—See Healios K.K.; *Int'l*, pg. 3302
ATHERTON BAPTIST HOMES; *U.S. Private*, pg. 368
ATHEZZA; *Int'l*, pg. 670
ATHIO DIALYSIS, LLC—See DaVita Inc.; *U.S. Public*, pg. 636
ATHIRA PHARMA, INC.; *U.S. Public*, pg. 221
ATHLEISURE INC.; *U.S. Private*, pg. 368
ATHLETA (ITM) INC.—See The Gap, Inc.; *U.S. Public*, pg. 2074
ATHLETA—See The Gap, Inc.; *U.S. Public*, pg. 2074
ATHLETES FIRST, LLC—See General Catalyst Partners; *U.S. Private*, pg. 1664
ATHLETES FIRST, LLC—See Mastry Management LLC; *U.S. Private*, pg. 2608
THE ATHLETE'S FOOT AUSTRALIA PTY LIMITED—See Accent Group Limited; *Int'l*, pg. 81
ATHLETE'S FOOT BRANDS, LLC—See INTERSPORT International Corporation; *Int'l*, pg. 3761
ATHLETES' PERFORMANCE, INC.; *U.S. Private*, pg. 368
ATHLETICA INC.; *U.S. Private*, pg. 368
ATHLETICA SPORT SYSTEMS INC.—See Fulcrum Capital Partners Inc.; *Int'l*, pg. 2841
ATHLETIC CLUB AJACCIEN ACA FOOTBALL; *Int'l*, pg. 670
ATHLETIC CLUB AT ONE CLEVELAND—See Walton Street Capital, LLC; *U.S. Private*, pg. 4435
ATHLETICO LTD.; *U.S. Private*, pg. 368
ATHLETICS INVESTMENT GROUP, LLC; *U.S. Private*, pg. 368
ATHLETICS UNLIMITED, INC.—See Bain Capital, LP; *U.S. Private*, pg. 451
ATHLETIC TRAINING EQUIPMENT COMPANY, INC.—See ANTA Sports Products Limited; *Int'l*, pg. 481
ATHLETX SPORTS GROUP, LLC; *U.S. Private*, pg. 368
ATHLON ACQUISITION CORP.; *U.S. Public*, pg. 221
ATHLON BELGIUM N.V.—See Mercedes-Benz Group AG; *Int'l*, pg. 4821
ATHLON CAR LEASE INTERNATIONAL B.V.—See Mercedes-Benz Group AG; *Int'l*, pg. 4821
ATHLON CAR LEASE POLSKA SP. Z O.O.—See Mercedes-Benz Group AG; *Int'l*, pg. 4821
ATHLONE EXTRUSIONS LTD.—See Schweiter Technologies AG; *Int'l*, pg. 6645
ATHLONE EXTRUSIONS (UK) LTD.—See Schweiter Technologies AG; *Int'l*, pg. 6645
ATHLON FRANCE S.A.—See Mercedes-Benz Group AG; *Int'l*, pg. 4821
ATHLON GERMANY GMBH & CO. KG—See Mercedes-Benz Group AG; *Int'l*, pg. 4821
ATHLON HOLDING N.V.—See Cooperatieve Centrale Raiffeisen-Boerenleenbank B.A.; *Int'l*, pg. 1791
ATHLON HOLDINGS, INC.; *U.S. Private*, pg. 368
ATHLON ITALY SRL A SOCIO UNICO—See Mercedes-Benz Group AG; *Int'l*, pg. 4821
ATHLON LUXEMBOURG S.A.—See Mercedes-Benz Group AG; *Int'l*, pg. 4821
ATHLON PORTUGAL, LDA.—See Mercedes-Benz Group AG; *Int'l*, pg. 4821
ATHLON SPAIN, S.A.—See Mercedes-Benz Group AG; *Int'l*, pg. 4821
ATHLON SPORTS COMMUNICATIONS, INC.—See Athlon Holdings, Inc.; *U.S. Private*, pg. 368
ATHLON SWEDEN—See Mercedes-Benz Group AG; *Int'l*, pg. 4821
ATHOC, INC.—See BlackBerry Limited; *Int'l*, pg. 1060
ATHOL SAVINGS BANK INC.; *U.S. Private*, pg. 368
AT HOME GROUP INC.—See Hellman & Friedman LLC; *U.S. Private*, pg. 1907

AT HOME PROPERTIES LLC—See Hellman & Friedman LLC; *U.S. Private*, pg. 1907
ATHON SA; *Int'l*, pg. 670
ATHORA HOLDING LTD.—See Apollo Global Management, Inc.; *U.S. Public*, pg. 147
ATHOS AERONAUTIQUE—See Assystem S.A.; *Int'l*, pg. 651
ATHOS IMMOBILIEN AG; *Int'l*, pg. 670
ATHOS SERVICE GMBH; *Int'l*, pg. 670
ATH POWER CONSULTING CORPORATION; *U.S. Private*, pg. 367
ATHRIS HOLDING AG; *Int'l*, pg. 670
ATHWAL EYE ASSOCIATES PC—See Chicago Pacific Founders; *U.S. Private*, pg. 878
ATIAC—See Groupe Crit, S.A.; *Int'l*, pg. 3101
ATIA GROUP LTD.; *U.S. Private*, pg. 369
ATI AIRTEST TECHNOLOGIES INC.; *Int'l*, pg. 670
ATI CASTING SERVICE—See ATI Inc.; *U.S. Public*, pg. 221
ATICO INTERNATIONAL USA, INC.; *U.S. Private*, pg. 369
ATICO MINING CORPORATION COLOMBIA SAS—See Atico Mining Corporation; *Int'l*, pg. 670
ATICO MINING CORPORATION; *Int'l*, pg. 670
ATI ENTERPRISES, INC.—See BC Partners LLP; *Int'l*, pg. 922
ATIEVA, INC.—See Lucid Group, Inc.; *U.S. Public*, pg. 1345
ATIF HOLDINGS LIMITED; *Int'l*, pg. 670
ATI FLOWFORM PRODUCTS, LLC—See ATI Inc.; *U.S. Public*, pg. 221
ATI FORGED PRODUCTS—See ATI Inc.; *U.S. Public*, pg. 221
ATI GARRYSON LTD.—See ATI Inc.; *U.S. Public*, pg. 221
ATI GARRYSON—See ATI Inc.; *U.S. Public*, pg. 221
ATI INC.; *U.S. Public*, pg. 221
ATI, INC.—See CNH Industrial N.V.; *Int'l*, pg. 1674
ATI INDUSTRIAL AUTOMATION, INC.—See Novanta Inc.; *U.S. Public*, pg. 1548
ATI JET, INC.; *U.S. Private*, pg. 368
ATIKA GMBH & CO. KG—See Altrad Investment Authority SAS; *Int'l*, pg. 397
ATI LADISH DIECAST TOOLING—See ATI Inc.; *U.S. Public*, pg. 221
ATIL-COBRA, S.A.—See ACS, Actividades de Construccion y Servicios, S.A.; *Int'l*, pg. 110
ATILIM FAKTORING A.S.; *Int'l*, pg. 670
ATILZE DIGITAL SDN. BHD.—See G3 Global Berhad; *Int'l*, pg. 2866
ATIMONAN ONE ENERGY, INC.—See Manila Electric Company; *Int'l*, pg. 4671
ATIMO PERSONEELSTECHNIEK B.V.—See dormakaba Holding AG; *Int'l*, pg. 2177
AT INDIA AUTO PARTS PVT. LTD.—See AISIN Corporation; *Int'l*, pg. 253
AT INDUSTRIAL SHEET METAL, INC.—See AT Industries, Inc.; *U.S. Private*, pg. 363
AT INDUSTRIES, INC.; *U.S. Private*, pg. 363
ATI NETWORKS INC; *U.S. Public*, pg. 222
AT INFORMATION PRODUCTS; *U.S. Private*, pg. 363
AT INTERNET BRAZIL—See Applied Technologies Internet SAS; *Int'l*, pg. 521
AT INTERNET GMBH—See Applied Technologies Internet SAS; *Int'l*, pg. 521
AT INTERNET INC.—See Applied Technologies Internet SAS; *Int'l*, pg. 521
AT INTERNET LTD—See Applied Technologies Internet SAS; *Int'l*, pg. 521
AT INTERNET PTE. LTD—See Applied Technologies Internet SAS; *Int'l*, pg. 521
AT INTERNET SL—See Applied Technologies Internet SAS; *Int'l*, pg. 521
ATINUM E&P, INC.—See Atinum Investment Co., Ltd; *Int'l*, pg. 670
ATINUM INVESTMENT CO., LTD; *Int'l*, pg. 670
AT INVESTMENT ADVISERS, INC.—See Canadian Imperial Bank of Commerce; *Int'l*, pg. 1283
ATI OPERATING HOLDINGS, LLC—See ATI Inc.; *U.S. Public*, pg. 221
ATI PHARMED PHARMACEUTICAL COMPANY—See Alborz Investment Company; *Int'l*, pg. 299
ATI PHYSICAL THERAPY, INC.—See SoftBank Group Corp.; *Int'l*, pg. 7052
ATI PHYSICAL THERAPY, INC.—See Advent International Corporation; *U.S. Private*, pg. 96
ATIS CORPORATION—See Nihon Enterprise Co., Ltd.; *Int'l*, pg. 5284
ATIS GROUP INC.—See Fonciere Volta SA; *Int'l*, pg. 2725
ATIS GROUP INC.—See Fonds de Solidarite des Travailleurs du Quebec; *Int'l*, pg. 2725
ATISHAY LIMITED; *Int'l*, pg. 670
ATIS IBERICA DERICHEBOURG ATIS AERONAUTIQUE SL—See Derichebourg S.A.; *Int'l*, pg. 2041
ATI SPECIALTY ALLOYS AND COMPONENTS—See ATI Inc.; *U.S. Public*, pg. 221
ATI SPECIALTY MATERIALS—See ATI Inc.; *U.S. Public*, pg. 221
ATI STELLRAM S.A—See ATI Inc.; *U.S. Public*, pg. 221
ATI TECHNOLOGIES (L) INC.—See Advanced Micro Devices, Inc.; *U.S. Public*, pg. 48

ATI TECHNOLOGIES ULC—See Advanced Micro Devices, Inc.; *U.S. Public*, pg. 48
ATITECH S.P.A.—See Meridie S.p.A.; *Int'l*, pg. 4836
ATI TELECOM INTERNATIONAL COMPANY; *Int'l*, pg. 670
ATI TITANIUM, LLC—See ATI Inc.; *U.S. Public*, pg. 221
ATIVA S.P.A.—See Argo Finanziaria S.p.A.; *Int'l*, pg. 561
ATI WAREHOUSE INC.; *U.S. Private*, pg. 369
ATI WINDOWS; *U.S. Private*, pg. 369
ATI ZKM FORGING SP. Z O.O.—See ATI Inc.; *U.S. Public*, pg. 221
AT JAPAN CO., LTD—See AEON Co., Ltd.; *Int'l*, pg. 177
ATK AEROSPACE GROUP—See Northrop Grumman Corporation; *U.S. Public*, pg. 1540
ATK AEROSPACE SYSTEMS—See Northrop Grumman Corporation; *U.S. Public*, pg. 1540
ATK AEROSPACE SYSTEMS—See Northrop Grumman Corporation; *U.S. Public*, pg. 1540
ATKA KUNSTSTOFFVERARBEITUNG GMBH; *Int'l*, pg. 670
ATKA US, LLC—See Salesforce, Inc.; *U.S. Public*, pg. 1836
A.T. KEARNEY, INC.; *U.S. Private*, pg. 28
ATK ENERGY EU LIMITED—See AtkinsRealis Group Inc.; *Int'l*, pg. 673
ATKINS AUSTRALASIA PTY LTD.—See AtkinsRealis Group Inc.; *Int'l*, pg. 673
ATKINS CHINA LIMITED—See AtkinsRealis Group Inc.; *Int'l*, pg. 673
ATKINS DANMARK A/S—See AtkinsRealis Group Inc.; *Int'l*, pg. 673
ATKINS ENERGY GOVERNMENT GROUP, INC.—See AtkinsRealis Group Inc.; *Int'l*, pg. 673
ATKINS INC.; *U.S. Private*, pg. 369
ATKINS KROLL INC.—See Inchcape plc; *Int'l*, pg. 3647
ATKINS KROLL (SAIPAN) INC.—See Inchcape plc; *Int'l*, pg. 3647
ATKINS NORTH AMERICA INC.—See AtkinsRealis Group Inc.; *Int'l*, pg. 673
ATKINS NORTH AMERICA—See AtkinsRealis Group Inc.; *Int'l*, pg. 673
ATKINS NORTH AMERICA—See AtkinsRealis Group Inc.; *Int'l*, pg. 673
ATKINS NUCLEAR SOLUTIONS US, INC.—See AtkinsRealis Group Inc.; *Int'l*, pg. 673
ATKINS NUTRITIONALS, INC.—See The Simply Good Foods Company; *U.S. Public*, pg. 2130
ATKINSON-BAKER, INC; *U.S. Private*, pg. 369
ATKINSON CANDY COMPANY; *U.S. Private*, pg. 369
ATKINSON CONSTRUCTION—See Clark Enterprises, Inc.; *U.S. Private*, pg. 912
ATKINSON-CRAWFORD SALES CO.; *U.S. Private*, pg. 369
ATKINSON GRAIN & FERTILIZER INC.; *U.S. Private*, pg. 369
ATKINSON INVESTMENT CORPORATION—See Dilmar Oil Company Inc.; *U.S. Private*, pg. 1232
ATKINSON MATERIALS—See Haines & Kibblehouse Inc.; *U.S. Private*, pg. 1840
ATKINSON'S MARKET INC.; *U.S. Private*, pg. 369
ATKINSON TRUCK SALES INC.; *U.S. Private*, pg. 369
ATKINSON UNDERGROUND GROUP—See Clark Enterprises, Inc.; *U.S. Private*, pg. 913
ATKINSREALIS GROUP INC.; *Int'l*, pg. 670
ATK LAUNCH SYSTEMS INC—See Northrop Grumman Corporation; *U.S. Public*, pg. 1540
ATK MISSLE SYSTEMS—See Northrop Grumman Corporation; *U.S. Public*, pg. 1540
ATKORE INC.—See Clayton, Dubilier & Rice, LLC; *U.S. Private*, pg. 919
ATKORE INTERNATIONAL HOLDINGS INC.—See Clayton, Dubilier & Rice, LLC; *U.S. Private*, pg. 919
ATKORE INTERNATIONAL, INC.—See Clayton, Dubilier & Rice, LLC; *U.S. Private*, pg. 919
ATK SPACE SYSTEMS INC.—See Northrop Grumman Corporation; *U.S. Public*, pg. 1540
ATLANCE FRANCE SAS—See Econocom Group SA; *Int'l*, pg. 2297
ATLANCE SA/NV—See Econocom Group SA; *Int'l*, pg. 2297
ATLANCE SAS—See Econocom Group SA; *Int'l*, pg. 2297
ATLAND VOISIN SAS—See Fonciere Atland SA; *Int'l*, pg. 2724
ATLAN DYESS INC.—See Ishii Hyoki Co., Ltd.; *Int'l*, pg. 3817
ATLAN HOLDINGS BERHAD; *Int'l*, pg. 673
ATLAN MEDIA INC.; *Int'l*, pg. 674
ATLAN PLASTICS INC.; *U.S. Private*, pg. 370
ATLANTA ASSOCIATION FOR CONVALESCENT AGED PERSONS INC.; *U.S. Private*, pg. 370
ATLANTA ASSURANCES; *Int'l*, pg. 674
ATLANTA ATTACHMENT COMPANY, INC.; *U.S. Private*, pg. 370
ATLANTA AUTO AUCTION, INC.—See Cox Enterprises, Inc.; *U.S. Private*, pg. 1076
ATLANTA BEVERAGE CO.; *U.S. Private*, pg. 370
ATLANTA BONDED WAREHOUSE CORPORATION; *U.S. Private*, pg. 370

COMPANY NAME INDEX

ATLANTA BOTANICAL GARDEN, INC.; *U.S. Private,* pg. 370
ATLANTA BRAVES HOLDINGS, INC.; *U.S. Public,* pg. 222
ATLANTA BRAVES, INC.—See Atlanta Braves Holdings, Inc.; *U.S. Private,* pg. 222
THE ATLANTA BREAD COMPANY; *U.S. Private,* pg. 3990
ATLANTA BUSINESS CHRONICLE—See Advance Publications, Inc.; *U.S. Private,* pg. 84
ATLANTA CAFE HOLDINGS CORP.; *U.S. Private,* pg. 370
ATLANTA CAPITAL MANAGEMENT COMPANY, LLC—See Morgan Stanley; *U.S. Public,* pg. 1471
ATLANTA COMMERCIAL GLAZING INC.—See Installed Building Products, Inc.; *U.S. Public,* pg. 1132
ATLANTA COMMERCIAL TIRE INC.; *U.S. Private,* pg. 370
ATLANTA DATACOM INC.; *U.S. Private,* pg. 370
ATLANTA DEVCON LIMITED; *Int'l,* pg. 674
ATLANTA ELECTRICAL DISTRIBUTORS, LLC—See WESCO International, Inc.; *U.S. Public,* pg. 2351
ATLANTA ENERGY PRIVATE LIMITED—See Atlanta Limited; *Int'l,* pg. 674
ATLANTA EQUIPMENT COMPANY INC—See Road Machinery & Supplies Company; *U.S. Private,* pg. 3453
ATLANTA FALCONS FOOTBALL CLUB, LLC; *U.S. Private,* pg. 370
ATLANTA FINANCIAL ASSOCIATES INC.—See Genstar Capital, LLC; *U.S. Private,* pg. 1677
ATLANTA FINANCIAL ASSOCIATES INC.—See Keystone Group, L.P.; *U.S. Private,* pg. 2298
ATLANTA FIXTURE & SALES COMPANY INC.—See Sysco Corporation; *U.S. Public,* pg. 1973
ATLANTA FORKLIFTS, INC.; *U.S. Private,* pg. 370
ATLANTA FREIGHTLINER TRUCK SALES & SERVICE—See Mercedes-Benz Group AG; *Int'l,* pg. 4823
ATLANTA GAS LIGHT COMPANY—See The Southern Company; *U.S. Public,* pg. 2131
ATLANTA GOLD INC.; *Int'l,* pg. 674
ATLANTA GOLD INC.—See Atlanta Gold Inc.; *Int'l,* pg. 674
ATLANTA HARDWOOD CORPORATION - AHC CRYSTAL SPRING DIVISION—See Atlanta Hardwood Corporation; *U.S. Private,* pg. 370
ATLANTA HARDWOOD CORPORATION - AHC NORTH GEORGIA DIVISION—See Atlanta Hardwood Corporation; *U.S. Private,* pg. 370
ATLANTA HARDWOOD CORPORATION; *U.S. Private,* pg. 370
ATLANTA HAWKS, L.P.; *U.S. Private,* pg. 370
ATLANTA HISTORY CENTER; *U.S. Private,* pg. 370
ATLANTA INTERNATIONAL INSURANCE COMPANY—See Aon plc; *Int'l,* pg. 488
THE ATLANTA JOURNAL-CONSTITUTION—See Apollo Global Management, Inc.; *U.S. Public,* pg. 163
ATLANTA LEGAL AID SOCIETY, INC.; *U.S. Private,* pg. 370
ATLANTA LIFE FINANCIAL GROUP; *U.S. Private,* pg. 371
ATLANTA LIFE INSURANCE COMPANY—See Atlanta Life Financial Group; *U.S. Private,* pg. 371
ATLANTA LIMITED; *Int'l,* pg. 674
ATLANTA MOTOR SPEEDWAY, INC.—See Sonic Financial Corporation; *U.S. Private,* pg. 3713
ATLANTA NATIONAL LEAGUE BASEBALL CLUB, LLC—See Atlanta Braves Holdings, Inc.; *U.S. Public,* pg. 222
ATLANTA OFFICE TECHNOLOGIES, INC.; *U.S. Private,* pg. 371
ATLANTA ORIENTAL FOOD WHOLESALE CO.; *U.S. Private,* pg. 371
ATLANTA OUTLET SHOPPES, LLC—See CBL & Associates Properties, Inc.; *U.S. Public,* pg. 457
ATLANTA OUTPATIENT SURGERY CENTER—See HCA Healthcare, Inc.; *U.S. Public,* pg. 990
THE ATLANTA PALM—See Palm Restaurant Group; *U.S. Private,* pg. 3080
ATLANTA PEDIATRIC THERAPY, INC.; *U.S. Private,* pg. 371
ATLANTA PLUMBERS & STEAMFITTERS; *U.S. Private,* pg. 371
ATLANTA POLAND S.A.; *Int'l,* pg. 674
ATLANTA POSTAL CREDIT UNION; *U.S. Private,* pg. 371
ATLANTA POWERTRAIN & HYDRAULICS, INC.—See Force America Inc.; *U.S. Private,* pg. 1563
ATLANTA RADIO, LLC—See Cumulus Media Inc.; *U.S. Public,* pg. 609
ATLANTA REFRIGERATION SERVICE COMPANY, INC.; *U.S. Private,* pg. 371
ATLANTA ROOFING SUPPLY INC—See Leonard Green & Partners, L.P.; *U.S. Private,* pg. 2428
ATLANTA STEEL ERECTORS, INC.—See Williams Enterprises of Georgia, Inc.; *U.S. Private,* pg. 4525
ATLANTA SURGERY CENTER, LTD.—See HCA Healthcare, Inc.; *U.S. Public,* pg. 991
ATLANTA SYMPHONY ORCHESTRA; *U.S. Private,* pg. 371
ATLANTA VILLA SDN. BHD.—See WCT Holdings Berhad; *Int'l,* pg. 8361

ATLANTA WEST CARPETS, LLC—See The Sterling Group, L.P.; *U.S. Private,* pg. 4121
ATLANTA WHIRLPOOL—See AGCO Inc.; *U.S. Private,* pg. 126
ATLANTE SRL—See VINCI S.A.; *Int'l,* pg. 8212
ATLANTIC 10 CONFERENCE; *U.S. Private,* pg. 371
ATLANTICA COMPANHIA DE SEGUROS S.A.—See Banco Bradesco S.A.; *Int'l,* pg. 819
ATLANTICA DE HANDLING—See Binter Canarias, S.A.; *Int'l,* pg. 1034
THE ATLANTIC ADVERTISING SALES—See National Journal Group; *U.S. Private,* pg. 2858
ATLANTICA HELLAS S.A.—See TUI AG; *Int'l,* pg. 7964
ATLANTICA HOTELS & RESORTS LTD; *Int'l,* pg. 676
ATLANTICA, INC.; *U.S. Public,* pg. 223
ATLANTIC AIRWAYS; *Int'l,* pg. 674
ATLANTIC ALLIANCE PARTNERSHIP CORP.; *U.S. Public,* pg. 222
ATLANTIC ALUMINUM, LLC—See H.I.G. Capital, LLC; *U.S. Private,* pg. 1829
ATLANTIC AMERICAN CORPORATION; *U.S. Public,* pg. 222
ATLANTIC AMERICAN FIRE EQUIPMENT COMPANY INC.; *U.S. Private,* pg. 371
ATLANTIC AMERICAN PARTNERS, LLC; *U.S. Private,* pg. 371
ATLANTIC AND GENERAL INVESTMENT TRUST LIMITED—See RIT Capital Partners plc; *Int'l,* pg. 6351
ATLANTIC AND WESTERN RAILWAY LP—See Brookfield Infrastructure Partners L.P.; *Int'l,* pg. 1190
ATLANTIC AND WESTERN RAILWAY LP—See GIC Pte. Ltd.; *Int'l,* pg. 2965
ATLANTIC AQUA FARMS, LTD.—See Ontario Teachers' Pension Plan; *Int'l,* pg. 5587
ATLANTICARE BEHAVIORAL HEALTH, INC.—See Geisinger Health System; *U.S. Private,* pg. 1656
ATLANTICARE HEALTH SYSTEM, INC.—See Geisinger Health System; *U.S. Private,* pg. 1656
ATLANTICARE OCCUPATIONAL HEALTH—See Geisinger Health System; *U.S. Private,* pg. 1656
ATLANTICARE REGIONAL MEDICAL CENTER, INC.—See Geisinger Health System; *U.S. Private,* pg. 1656
ATLANTIC ARGETA D.O.O.—See ATLANTIC GRUPA d.d.; *Int'l,* pg. 674
ATLANTIC ASSOCIATES, INC.—See Poch Personnel, Inc.; *U.S. Private,* pg. 3219
ATLANTICA SUSTAINABLE INFRASTRUCTURE PLC; *Int'l,* pg. 676
ATLANTIC AUTOMALL; *U.S. Private,* pg. 371
ATLANTIC AUTOMOBILES SAS—See General Motors Company; *U.S. Public,* pg. 927
ATLANTIC AUTOMOTIVE CORP.; *U.S. Private,* pg. 371
ATLANTIC AVENUE ACQUISITION CORP; *U.S. Public,* pg. 222
ATLANTIC AVIATION FBO, INC.—See Macquarie Group Limited; *Int'l,* pg. 4627
ATLANTIC AVIATION FLIGHT SUPPORT, INC.—See Macquarie Group Limited; *Int'l,* pg. 4627
ATLANTIC AVIATION-KANSAS CITY LLC—See Macquarie Group Limited; *Int'l,* pg. 4627
ATLANTIC AVIATION LLC-PHF—See Macquarie Group Limited; *Int'l,* pg. 4627
ATLANTIC AVIATION OF SANTA MONICA, L.P.—See Macquarie Group Limited; *Int'l,* pg. 4627
ATLANTIC AVIATION OKLAHOMA CITY INC.—See Macquarie Group Limited; *Int'l,* pg. 4627
ATLANTIC AVIATION OREGON FBO, INC.—See Macquarie Group Limited; *Int'l,* pg. 4627
ATLANTIC AVIATION-ORLANDO EXECUTIVE LLC—See Macquarie Group Limited; *Int'l,* pg. 4627
ATLANTIC AVIATION-ORLANDO LLC—See Macquarie Group Limited; *Int'l,* pg. 4627
ATLANTIC AVIATION PHILADELPHIA, INC.—See Macquarie Group Limited; *Int'l,* pg. 4627
ATLANTIC AVIATION-ST. AUGUSTINE LLC—See Macquarie Group Limited; *Int'l,* pg. 4627
ATLANTIC AVIATION-STEAMBOAT-HAYDEN LLC—See Macquarie Group Limited; *Int'l,* pg. 4627
ATLANTIC AVIATION STEWART LLC—See Macquarie Group Limited; *Int'l,* pg. 4627
ATLANTIC AVIATION-STUART LLC—See Macquarie Group Limited; *Int'l,* pg. 4627
ATLANTIC AVIATION-WEST PALM BEACH LLC—See Macquarie Group Limited; *Int'l,* pg. 4627
ATLANTIC BAY MORTGAGE GROUP LLC; *U.S. Private,* pg. 371
ATLANTIC BOOKS—See Grove/Atlantic, Inc.; *U.S. Private,* pg. 1794
ATLANTIC BOTTLING COMPANY; *U.S. Private,* pg. 371
ATLANTIC BRIDGE VENTURES; *Int'l,* pg. 674
ATLANTIC BROADBAND GROUP LLC—See Gestion Audem, Inc.; *Int'l,* pg. 2946
ATLANTIC BUSINESS SYSTEMS—See Perpetual Capital, LLC; *U.S. Private,* pg. 2946
ATLANTIC BUSINESS TECHNOLOGIES, INC.; *U.S. Private,* pg. 372
ATLANTIC CAPITAL BANCSHARES, INC.—See SouthState Corporation; *U.S. Public,* pg. 1912

ATLANTIC CAPITAL BANK, N.A.—See SouthState Corporation; *U.S. Public,* pg. 1912
ATLANTIC CAPITAL GROUP, INC.; *U.S. Private,* pg. 372
ATLANTIC CASTING & ENGINEERING CORPORATION; *U.S. Private,* pg. 372
ATLANTIC CEDEVITA D.O.O.—See ATLANTIC GRUPA d.d.; *Int'l,* pg. 674
ATLANTIC CENTRAL ENTERPRISES, INC.; *U.S. Private,* pg. 372
ATLANTIC CHINA WELDING CONSUMABLES, INC.; *Int'l,* pg. 674
ATLANTIC CITY ELECTRIC COMPANY—See Exelon Corporation; *U.S. Public,* pg. 807
ATLANTIC CITY MUNICIPAL UTILITIES AUTHORITY; *U.S. Private,* pg. 372
THE ATLANTIC CITY PALM—See Palm Restaurant Group; *U.S. Private,* pg. 3080
ATLANTIC CLIMATISATION ET VENTILATION S.A.S.—See Atlantic Societe Francaise Develop Thermique S.A.; *Int'l,* pg. 675
ATLANTIC COASTAL ACQUISITION CORP.; *U.S. Private,* pg. 372
ATLANTIC COASTAL ELECTRONICS; *U.S. Private,* pg. 372
ATLANTIC COASTAL SUPPLY, INC—See Winsupply, Inc.; *U.S. Private,* pg. 4545
ATLANTIC COAST CONFERENCE; *U.S. Private,* pg. 372
ATLANTIC COAST FIBERS, INC.—See Casella Waste Systems, Inc.; *U.S. Public,* pg. 445
ATLANTIC COAST FOODS, INC.; *U.S. Private,* pg. 372
ATLANTIC COAST MEDIA GROUP; *U.S. Private,* pg. 372
ATLANTIC COAST SURGICAL SUITES, LLC—See Tenet Healthcare Corporation; *U.S. Public,* pg. 2001
ATLANTIC COMMODITIES VIETNAM LTD—See Ecom Agroindustrial Corporation Ltd.; *Int'l,* pg. 2296
ATLANTIC COMMUNICATIONS-HOUSTON OFFICE—See International Exhibitions, Inc.; *U.S. Private,* pg. 2116
ATLANTIC COMMUNITY BANKERS BANK; *U.S. Private,* pg. 372
ATLANTIC CONCRETE PRODUCTS, INC. - COCKEYSVILLE PLANT—See Atlantic Concrete Products, Inc.; *U.S. Private,* pg. 372
ATLANTIC CONCRETE PRODUCTS, INC.; *U.S. Private,* pg. 372
ATLANTIC CONTAINER SERVICE INC.; *U.S. Private,* pg. 372
ATLANTIC CONTRACTING & SPECIALTIES LLC—See Irex Corporation; *U.S. Private,* pg. 2137
ATLANTIC COPPER, S.A.—See Freeport-McMoRan Inc.; *U.S. Public,* pg. 884
ATLANTIC COPPER, S.L.U.—See Freeport-McMoRan Inc.; *U.S. Public,* pg. 884
ATLANTIC CORPORATE INTERIORS, INC.; *U.S. Private,* pg. 372
ATLANTIC CORPORATION - CHARLESTON FACILITY—See Atlantic Corporation; *U.S. Private,* pg. 372
ATLANTIC CORPORATION - CHARLOTTE FACILITY—See Atlantic Corporation; *U.S. Private,* pg. 372
ATLANTIC CORPORATION - GREENSBORO FACILITY—See Atlantic Corporation; *U.S. Private,* pg. 372
ATLANTIC CORPORATION; *U.S. Private,* pg. 372
ATLANTIC COUNTY UTILITIES AUTHORITY; *U.S. Private,* pg. 372
ATLANTIC CREDIT & FINANCE, INC.—See Encore Capital Group, Inc.; *U.S. Public,* pg. 759
ATLANTIC DATA SERVICES, INC.; *U.S. Private,* pg. 373
ATLANTIC DETROIT DIESEL-ALLISON, LLC; *U.S. Private,* pg. 373
ATLANTIC DETROIT DIESEL-ALLISON - POWER SYSTEMS—See Atlantic Detroit Diesel-Allison, LLC; *U.S. Private,* pg. 373
ATLANTIC DETROIT DIESEL-ALLISON—See Mercedes-Benz Group AG; *Int'l,* pg. 4823
ATLANTIC DETROIT DIESEL-ALLISON—See Atlantic Detroit Diesel-Allison, LLC; *U.S. Private,* pg. 373
ATLANTIC DIALYSIS, LLC—See DaVita Inc.; *U.S. Public,* pg. 636
ATLANTIC DROGA KOLINSKA D.O.O.—See ATLANTIC GRUPA d.d.; *Int'l,* pg. 674
ATLANTIC DUCT CLEANING, INC.—See The Operand Group II LLC; *U.S. Public,* pg. 4088
ATLANTIC-DURANT TECHNOLOGY INC.—See Atlantic Tool & Die Company Inc.; *U.S. Private,* pg. 375
ATLANTIC DYNAMICS SDN. BHD.—See Daiman Development Berhad; *Int'l,* pg. 1938
ATLANTIC ELECTRIC, LLC—See Comfort Systems USA, Inc.; *U.S. Public,* pg. 543
ATLANTIC EMPLOYERS INSURANCE COMPANY—See Chubb Limited; *Int'l,* pg. 1590
ATLANTIC ENERGIAS RENOVAVEIS S/A—See General Atlantic Service Company, L.P.; *U.S. Private,* pg. 1661
ATLANTIC ENERGY CONCEPTS, INC.—See Schaedler/Yesco Distribution, Inc.; *U.S. Private,* pg. 3563
ATLANTIC ENGINEERING LABORATORIES INC.—See GI Manager L.P.; *U.S. Private,* pg. 1691

ATLANTIC DETROIT DIESEL-ALLISON, LLC

CORPORATE AFFILIATIONS

ATLANTIC FASTENERS CO., INC.—See Applied Industrial Technologies, Inc.; *U.S. Public*, pg. 170

ATLANTIC FASTENERS, INC.—See Wurth Verwaltungsgesellschaft mbH; *Int'l*, pg. 8511

ATLANTIC FIELD PLUME DE VEAU INC.; *U.S. Private*, pg. 373

ATLANTIC FILTER CORP.—See A. O. Smith Corporation; *U.S. Public*, pg. 11

ATLANTIC FISH & DISTRIBUTING CO.; *U.S. Private*, pg. 373

ATLANTIC FISHING ENTERPRISES (PTY) LTD—See African Equity Empowerment Investmts Limited; *Int'l*, pg. 191

ATLANTIC FLOATS DENMARK A/S—See SP Group A/S; *Int'l*, pg. 7122

ATLANTIC FORFAITIERUNGS AG—See Dr. August Oetker KG; *Int'l*, pg. 2190

ATLANTIC FRANCO BELGE—See Atlantic Societe Francaise Develop Thermique S.A.; *Int'l*, pg. 675

ATLANTIC FS S.A.S.—See Grupo Nutresa S.A.; *Int'l*, pg. 3133

ATLANTIC GASKET CORP.; *U.S. Private*, pg. 373

ATLANTIC GOLD CORPORATION—See St Barbara Limited; *Int'l*, pg. 7157

ATLANTIC GOLD EXPLORATION PTY. LTD.—See St Barbara Limited; *Int'l*, pg. 7157

ATLANTIC GREAT DANE INC.; *U.S. Private*, pg. 373

ATLANTIC GROUP; *U.S. Private*, pg. 373

ATLANTIC GROUP; *Int'l*, pg. 674

ATLANTIC GRUPA D.D.; *Int'l*, pg. 674

ATLANTIC GUILLOT—See Atlantic Societe Francaise Develop Thermique S.A.; *Int'l*, pg. 675

ATLANTIC HEALTH PARTNERS, LLC—See Roper Technologies, Inc.; *U.S. Public*, pg. 1810

ATLANTIC HEALTH SYSTEM INC.; *U.S. Private*, pg. 373

ATLANTIC HOSIERY, INC.; *U.S. Private*, pg. 373

ATLANTIC HOTEL EXPLOITATIE, B.V.—See Minor International PCL; *Int'l*, pg. 4911

ATLANTIC HOUSING FOUNDATION, INC.; *U.S. Private*, pg. 373

ATLANTIC HOUSING PARTNERS, LLLP; *U.S. Private*, pg. 373

ATLANTIC INSURANCE COMPANY PUBLIC LTD; *Int'l*, pg. 675

ATLANTIC INTERNATIONAL CORP.; *U.S. Public*, pg. 222

ATLANTIC INTERNATIONAL DISTRIBUTORS, INC.—See The Riverside Company; *U.S. Private*, pg. 4108

ATLANTIC INVESTMENT COMPANY—See Norfolk Southern Corporation; *U.S. Public*, pg. 1535

ATLANTIC INVESTMENT COMPANY; *U.S. Private*, pg. 373

ATLANTIC IRRIGATION OF CANADA INC.—See SiteOne Landscape Supply, Inc.; *U.S. Public*, pg. 1888

ATLANTIC LEAF PROPERTIES LIMITED; *Int'l*, pg. 675

ATLANTIC LIFT TRUCK INC.; *U.S. Private*, pg. 373

ATLANTIC LIMOUSINE INC.; *U.S. Private*, pg. 373

ATLANTIC LITHIUM LIMITED; *Int'l*, pg. 675

ATLANTIC LUGGAGE COMPANY LTD—See LVMH Moet Hennessy Louis Vuitton SE; *Int'l*, pg. 4592

ATLANTIC LUMPUS AS; *Int'l*, pg. 675

ATLANTICLUX LEBENSVERSICHERUNG S.A.—See FWU AG; *Int'l*, pg. 2859

ATLANTIC MARINE ELECTRONICS, INC—See Viking Yacht Company; *U.S. Private*, pg. 4382

ATLANTIC MARINE SERVICE EGYPT S.A.E.—See KS Energy Limited; *Int'l*, pg. 4310

ATLANTIC MARINE SERVICES BV—See KS Energy Limited; *Int'l*, pg. 4310

ATLANTIC MARINE SERVICES (CYPRUS) GROUP LIMITED—See KS Energy Limited; *Int'l*, pg. 4310

ATLANTIC MARITIME GROUP FZE—See Atlantic Navigation Holdings (Singapore) Limited; *Int'l*, pg. 675

ATLANTIC MARITIME SERVICES LLC—See Valaris Limited; *Int'l*, pg. 8110

ATLANTIC MBH & CO. KG—See Rickmers Holding AG; *Int'l*, pg. 6333

ATLANTIC MEDIA SERVICES; *U.S. Private*, pg. 373

ATLANTIC MEDICAL, INC.—See AdaptHealth Corp.; *U.S. Public*, pg. 38

ATLANTIC MEMORIAL HEALTHCARE ASSOCIATES, INC.—See The Ensign Group, Inc.; *U.S. Public*, pg. 2070

ATLANTIC MERCHANT CAPITAL INVESTORS, LLC; *U.S. Private*, pg. 373

ATLANTIC METHANOL ASSOCIATES LLC—See Chevron Corporation; *U.S. Public*, pg. 487

ATLANTIC METHANOL ASSOCIATES LLC—See ConocoPhillips; *U.S. Public*, pg. 569

ATLANTIC METRO COMMUNICATIONS, INC.—See Stonecourt Capital LP; *U.S. Private*, pg. 3828

THE ATLANTIC MONTHLY GROUP, INC.—See National Journal Group; *U.S. Private*, pg. 2858

ATLANTIC MULTIPOWER GERMANY GMBH & CO.—See Reckitt Benckiser Group plc; *Int'l*, pg. 6237

ATLANTIC MULTIPOWER GMBH & CO. OHG—See ATLANTIC GRUPA d.d.; *Int'l*, pg. 674

ATLANTIC MULTIPOWER SRL—See ATLANTIC GRUPA d.d.; *Int'l*, pg. 674

ATLANTIC MULTIPOWER UK LTD—See ATLANTIC GRUPA d.d.; *Int'l*, pg. 674

ATLANTIC MUTUAL COMPANIES; *U.S. Private*, pg. 373

ATLANTIC MUTUAL INSURANCE COMPANY—See Atlantic Mutual Companies; *U.S. Private*, pg. 373

ATLANTIC NAVIGATION HOLDINGS (SINGAPORE) LIMITED; *Int'l*, pg. 675

ATLANTIC.NET, INC.; *U.S. Private*, pg. 375

ATLANTIC OILFIELD SERVICES EUROPE B.V.—See KS Energy Limited; *Int'l*, pg. 4310

ATLANTIC OILFIELD SERVICES LTD.—See KS Energy Limited; *Int'l*, pg. 4310

ATLANTIC ONSHORE SERVICES BV—See KS Energy Limited; *Int'l*, pg. 4310

ATLANTIC PACKAGING AS—See Atlantic Group; *Int'l*, pg. 674

ATLANTIC PACKAGING PRODUCTS LTD.; *Int'l*, pg. 675

ATLANTIC PARTNERS CORP.; *U.S. Private*, pg. 373

ATLANTIC PASTE & GLUE CO. INC.; *U.S. Private*, pg. 374

ATLANTIC PETROLEUM UK LIMITED—See P/F Atlantic Petroleum; *Int'l*, pg. 5683

ATLANTIC PLASTICS LTD.—See Triton Advisers Limited; *Int'l*, pg. 7934

ATLANTIC PLUMBING SUPPLY CORP.; *U.S. Private*, pg. 374

ATLANTIC POULTRY INC. - EGG DIVISION—See Atlantic Poultry Inc.; *Int'l*, pg. 675

ATLANTIC POULTRY INC. - FEED MILL—See Atlantic Poultry Inc.; *Int'l*, pg. 675

ATLANTIC POULTRY INC. - HATCHERY DIVISION—See Atlantic Poultry Inc.; *Int'l*, pg. 675

ATLANTIC POULTRY INC.; *Int'l*, pg. 675

ATLANTIC POWER CORPORATION—See I Squared Capital Advisors (US) LLC; *U.S. Private*, pg. 2025

ATLANTIC POWER LIMITED PARTNERSHIP—See I Squared Capital Advisors (US) LLC; *U.S. Private*, pg. 2025

ATLANTIC PRECISION, INC.—See Berkshire Hathaway Inc.; *U.S. Public*, pg. 313

ATLANTIC PROJECTS COMPANY, INC.—See Argan, Inc.; *U.S. Public*, pg. 191

ATLANTIC PROJECTS COMPANY LIMITED—See Argan, Inc.; *U.S. Public*, pg. 191

ATLANTIC PROMOTIONS INC.; *Int'l*, pg. 675

ATLANTIC PRO-NUTRIENTS, INC.; *U.S. Private*, pg. 374

ATLANTIC QUEST CATERING COMPANY—See LM Restaurants, Inc.; *U.S. Private*, pg. 2476

ATLANTIC REAL ESTATE CO., LTD.—See Land & Houses Public Company Limited; *Int'l*, pg. 4403

ATLANTIC REALTY PROFESSIONALS, INC.—See Wilkinson & Associates Real Estate; *U.S. Private*, pg. 4521

ATLANTIC RECORDS GROUP—See Access Industries, Inc.; *U.S. Private*, pg. 52

ATLANTIC REEFER TERMINALS INC.—See F.W. Bryce, Inc.; *U.S. Private*, pg. 1457

ATLANTIC RELOCATION SYSTEMS; *U.S. Private*, pg. 374

ATLANTIC RENEWABLE ENERGY CORPORATION—See Iberdrola, S.A.; *Int'l*, pg. 3570

ATLANTIC RISK SPECIALISTS, INC.—See AmWINS Group, Inc.; *U.S. Private*, pg. 269

ATLANTIC SAPPHIRE ASA; *U.S. Public*, pg. 222

ATLANTIC SEAFOOD AS—See Atlantic Group; *Int'l*, pg. 674

ATLANTIC SECURITIES LTD.—See Atlantic Insurance Company Public Ltd; *Int'l*, pg. 675

ATLANTIC SECURITY INSURANCE COMPANY INC.—See Strickland Insurance Group Inc.; *U.S. Private*, pg. 3839

ATLANTIC SELF STORAGE; *U.S. Private*, pg. 374

ATLANTIC SERVICE CO. LTD.—See Steel Partners Holdings L.P.; *U.S. Public*, pg. 1943

ATLANTIC SERVICE CO. (U.K.) LTD.—See Steel Partners Holdings L.P.; *U.S. Public*, pg. 1943

ATLANTIC SERVICES GROUP, INC.—See Propark, Inc.; *U.S. Private*, pg. 3284

ATLANTIC SERVICES; *U.S. Private*, pg. 374

ATLANTIC SERVICE & SUPPLY LLC—See Watsco, Inc.; *U.S. Public*, pg. 2336

ATLANTIC SFDT—See Atlantic Societe Francaise Develop Thermique S.A.; *Int'l*, pg. 675

ATLANTIC SHIPPERS INC.—See Animalfeeds International Corporation; *U.S. Private*, pg. 283

ATLANTIC SHIPPERS OF TEXAS, INC.—See Animalfeeds International Corporation; *U.S. Private*, pg. 283

ATLANTIC SHORES HOSPITAL, LLC—See Universal Health Services, Inc.; *U.S. Public*, pg. 2256

ATLANTIC SMO HOLDINGS LLC—See Macquarie Group Limited; *Int'l*, pg. 4627

ATLANTIC SOCIETE FRANCAISE DEVELOP THERMIQUE S.A.; *Int'l*, pg. 675

ATLANTIC SOUTHERN PAVING & SEALCOATING, CO.—See Harbor Beach Capital, LLC; *U.S. Private*, pg. 1858

ATLANTIC SPECIALTY LINES, INC.—See Ryan Specialty Holdings, Inc.; *U.S. Public*, pg. 1828

ATLANTIC SPECIALTY WIRE INC.—See AEB International Inc.; *U.S. Private*, pg. 116

ATLANTIC SPRING—See American Securities LLC; *U.S. Private*, pg. 249

ATLANTIC S.R.L.—See ATLANTIC GRUPA d.d.; *Int'l*, pg. 675

ATLANTIC STARK D.O.O.—See ATLANTIC GRUPA d.d.; *Int'l*, pg. 674

ATLANTIC STATES CAST IRON PIPE COMPANY—See McWane, Inc.; *U.S. Private*, pg. 2645

ATLANTIC STATES INSURANCE COMPANY—See Donegal Group Inc.; *U.S. Public*, pg. 676

ATLANTIC STATES INSURANCE COMPANY—See Donegal Group Inc.; *U.S. Public*, pg. 676

ATLANTIC STATES INSURANCE COMPANY—See Donegal Group Inc.; *U.S. Public*, pg. 676

ATLANTIC STATES INSURANCE COMPANY—See Donegal Group Inc.; *U.S. Public*, pg. 676

ATLANTIC STEWARDSHIP BANK—See Columbia Financial, Inc.; *U.S. Public*, pg. 534

ATLANTIC STREET CAPITAL MANAGEMENT LLC; *U.S. Private*, pg. 374

ATLANTIC SUPER MARKET S.A.; *Int'l*, pg. 675

ATLANTIC TACTICAL, INC.—See Kanders & Company, Inc.; *U.S. Private*, pg. 2259

ATLANTIC TESTING LABORATORIES, LTD.; *U.S. Private*, pg. 374

ATLANTIC THEATER COMPANY; *U.S. Private*, pg. 374

ATLANTIC TOOL & DIE COMPANY INC.; *U.S. Private*, pg. 374

ATLANTIC TOYOTA; *U.S. Private*, pg. 375

ATLANTIC TRACK & TURNOUT CO.; *U.S. Private*, pg. 375

ATLANTIC TRACTOR—See McCombie Group, LLC; *U.S. Private*, pg. 2629

ATLANTIC TRADE D.O.O., LJUBLJANA—See ATLANTIC GRUPA d.d.; *Int'l*, pg. 675

ATLANTIC TRADING & MARKETING, INC.—See TotalEnergies SE; *Int'l*, pg. 7839

ATLANTIC TRAITEUR INNOVATION—See LDC SA; *Int'l*, pg. 4430

ATLANTIC TREE NURSERY, INC.—See The Robert Baker Companies; *U.S. Private*, pg. 675

ATLANTIC TRUST GROUP, LLC - BALTIMORE—See Canadian Imperial Bank of Commerce; *Int'l*, pg. 1283

ATLANTIC TRUST GROUP, LLC - BOSTON—See Canadian Imperial Bank of Commerce; *Int'l*, pg. 1283

ATLANTIC TRUST GROUP, LLC—See Canadian Imperial Bank of Commerce; *Int'l*, pg. 1283

ATLANTIC UNION BANKSHARES CORPORATION; *U.S. Public*, pg. 222

ATLANTIC UNION BANK—See Atlantic Union Bankshares Corporation; *U.S. Public*, pg. 223

ATLANTIC (USA), INC., USA—See Ecom Agroindustrial Corporation Ltd.; *Int'l*, pg. 2296

ATLANTICUS HOLDINGS CORPORATION; *U.S. Public*, pg. 223

ATLANTIC UTILITY TRAILER SALES, INC.; *U.S. Private*, pg. 375

ATLANTIC VENEER CORPORATION; *U.S. Private*, pg. 375

ATLANTIC VENTILATION—See Atlantic Societe Francaise Develop Thermique S.A.; *Int'l*, pg. 675

ATLANTIC VIDEO INC.—See Family Federation for World Peace & Unification; *U.S. Private*, pg. 1469

ATLANTIC WASTE DISPOSAL, INC.—See Waste Management, Inc.; *U.S. Public*, pg. 2330

ATLANTIC WATER GARDENS—See Argand Partners, LP; *U.S. Private*, pg. 319

ATLANTIC WHARF JV LLC—See Boston Properties, Inc.; *U.S. Public*, pg. 373

ATLANTIC WHOLESALERS LTD.—See George Weston Limited; *Int'l*, pg. 2938

ATLANTIC WIND & SOLAR, INC.; *Int'l*, pg. 675

ATLANTIC ZEISER (ASIA) SDN. BHD.—See Atlantic Zeiser GmbH & Co.; *Int'l*, pg. 676

ATLANTIC ZEISER GMBH & CO.; *Int'l*, pg. 676

ATLANTIC ZEISER, INC.—See Atlantic Zeiser GmbH & Co.; *Int'l*, pg. 676

ATLANTIC ZEISER LTD—See Atlantic Zeiser GmbH & Co.; *Int'l*, pg. 676

ATLANTIC ZEISER S.A.—See Atlantic Zeiser GmbH & Co.; *Int'l*, pg. 676

ATLANTIC ZEISER S.A.S.—See Atlantic Zeiser GmbH & Co.; *Int'l*, pg. 676

ATLANTIC ZEISER SRL—See Atlantic Zeiser GmbH & Co.; *Int'l*, pg. 676

ATLANTIQUE DRAGAGE SARL—See HAL Trust N.V.; *Int'l*, pg. 3224

ATLANTIQUE MENUISERIES FERMETURES (A.M.F.)—See Compagnie de Saint-Gobain SA; *Int'l*, pg. 1722

ATLANTIQUE PRODUCTIONS SA—See Vivendi SE; *Int'l*, pg. 8275

ATLANTIS ADVENTURES, LLC—See Atlantis Submarines International Inc.; *Int'l*, pg. 676

ATLANTIS CO., LTD.—See Gree Inc.; *Int'l*, pg. 3069

ATLANTIS FIRE PROTECTION—See Capital Alignment Partners, Inc.; *U.S. Private*, pg. 738

ATLANTIS FIRE PROTECTION—See Lynch Holdings, LLC; *U.S. Private*, pg. 2520

COMPANY NAME INDEX

ATLANTIS FOUNDRIES (PTY.) LTD.—See Mercedes-Benz Group AG; *Int'l*, pg. 4820
ATLANTIS GLORY INC.; *U.S. Public*, pg. 223
ATLANTIS INTERNATIONAL SERVICE COMPANY LTD.—See Uttam Galva Steels Limited; *Int'l*, pg. 8101
ATLANTIS INTERNET GROUP CORP.; *U.S. Public*, pg. 223
ATLANTIS OUTPATIENT CENTER—See HCA Healthcare, Inc.; *U.S. Public*, pg. 991
ATLANTIS OUTPATIENT CENTER—See HCA Healthcare, Inc.; *U.S. Public*, pg. 991
ATLANTIS S.A.; *Int'l*, pg. 676
ATLANTIS SUBMARINES HAWAII, INC.—See Atlantis Submarines International Inc.; *Int'l*, pg. 676
ATLANTIS SUBMARINES INTERNATIONAL INC.; *Int'l*, pg. 676
ATLANTIS SYSTEMS CORP.—See BPLI Holdings Inc.; *Int'l*, pg. 1132
ATLANTIS SYSTEMS INTERNATIONAL INC.—See BPLI Holdings Inc.; *Int'l*, pg. 1133
ATLANTIS TRAVEL & TOURS—See ECI Partners LLP; *Int'l*, pg. 2289
ATLANTIS (UK) LTD.—See PGS ASA; *Int'l*, pg. 5838
ATLANTIS YATIRIM HOLDING A.S.; *Int'l*, pg. 676
ATLANTIX GLOBAL SYSTEMS, LLC—See H.I.G. Capital, LLC; *U.S. Private*, pg. 1829
ATLANTIX PARTNERS LLC; *U.S. Private*, pg. 375
ATLANTO AG—See Helvetia Holding AG; *Int'l*, pg. 3339
ATLANTSKA PLOVIDBA D.D.—See Tankerska plovidba d.d; *Int'l*, pg. 7459
AT LAOS CO., LTD.—See Fairfax Financial Holdings Limited; *Int'l*, pg. 2608
ATLAPAC CORP.—See H.I.G. Capital, LLC; *U.S. Private*, pg. 1834
ATLAPAC TRADING COMPANY, INC.; *U.S. Private*, pg. 375
ATLAS ADMINISTRATORS INC.—See USA Managed Care Organization; *U.S. Private*, pg. 4321
ATLAS ADVERTISING, LLC; *U.S. Private*, pg. 375
ATLAS AIR, INC.—See Apollo Global Management, Inc.; *U.S. Public*, pg. 148
ATLAS AIR, INC.—See J.F. Lehman & Company, Inc.; *U.S. Private*, pg. 2162
ATLAS AIR WORLDWIDE HOLDINGS, INC.—See Apollo Global Management, Inc.; *U.S. Public*, pg. 148
ATLAS AIR WORLDWIDE HOLDINGS, INC.—See J.F. Lehman & Company, Inc.; *U.S. Private*, pg. 2162
ATLAS ALARM CORPORATION; *U.S. Private*, pg. 375
ATLAS AMERICAN CORPORATION; *U.S. Private*, pg. 375
ATLAS ANTIBODIES AB—See Investor AB; *Int'l*, pg. 3785
ATLAS ASIA PACIFIC INCORPORATED; *U.S. Private*, pg. 375
ATLAS ASPHALT INC.; *U.S. Private*, pg. 375
ATLAS ASSET MANAGEMENT LIMITED—See Atlas Group of Companies; *Int'l*, pg. 685
ATLAS AUTOS (PRIVATE) LIMITED - KARACHI PLANT—See Atlas Group of Companies; *Int'l*, pg. 685
ATLAS AUTOS (PRIVATE) LIMITED - SHEIKHUPURA PLANT—See Atlas Group of Companies; *Int'l*, pg. 685
ATLAS AUTOS (PRIVATE) LIMITED—See Atlas Group of Companies; *Int'l*, pg. 685
ATLAS AXILLIA CO. (PVT) LTD.—See Hemas Holdings PLC; *Int'l*, pg. 3340
ATLAS BANGLADESH LIMITED; *Int'l*, pg. 676
ATLAS BATTERY LTD.—See Atlas Group of Companies; *Int'l*, pg. 685
ATLAS BATTERY LTD.—See GS Yuasa Corporation; *Int'l*, pg. 3143
ATLAS BOBCAT, INC.—See Atlas Lift Truck Rentals & Sales, Inc.; *U.S. Private*, pg. 379
ATLAS BOLT & SCREW COMPANY—See Berkshire Hathaway Inc.; *U.S. Public*, pg. 310
ATLAS BOX & CRATING CO. INC.; *U.S. Private*, pg. 375
ATLAS BRONZE; *U.S. Private*, pg. 375
ATLAS BUTLER HEATING & COOLING; *U.S. Private*, pg. 375
ATLASBX CO., LTD.—See Hankook Tire & Technology Co., Ltd.; *Int'l*, pg. 3253
ATLAS CAPITAL ENERGY LLC—See Scatec ASA; *Int'l*, pg. 6613
ATLAS CAPITAL GROUP, LLC; *U.S. Private*, pg. 375
ATLAS CLEAN AIR LTD.; *Int'l*, pg. 676
ATLAS COMFORT SYSTEMS USA, INC.—See Comfort Systems USA, Inc.; *U.S. Public*, pg. 543
ATLAS COMMUNICATIONS, INC.—See North 6th Agency, Inc.; *U.S. Private*, pg. 2939
THE ATLAS COMPANIES, INC.—See Betco Corporation; *U.S. Private*, pg. 545
ATLAS COMPANIES, LLC; *U.S. Private*, pg. 375
ATLAS CONSOLIDATED INDUSTRIES (PTY) LIMITED—See AECI Limited; *Int'l*, pg. 171
ATLAS CONSOLIDATED MINING & DEVELOPMENT CORPORATION; *Int'l*, pg. 676
ATLAS CONSTRUCTION SUPPLY INC.; *U.S. Private*, pg. 375
ATLAS CONSULTING—See Atlas Development Corporation; *U.S. Private*, pg. 376

ATLAS CONTAINER CORPORATION; *U.S. Private*, pg. 375
ATLAS CONTAINER LLC—See Atlas Container Corporation; *U.S. Private*, pg. 375
ATLAS CONVERTING EQUIPMENT (INDIA) PVT. LTD.—See Atlas Converting Equipment Limited; *Int'l*, pg. 676
ATLAS CONVERTING EQUIPMENT LIMITED; *Int'l*, pg. 676
ATLAS CONVERTING NORTH AMERICA, INC.—See Atlas Converting Equipment Limited; *Int'l*, pg. 676
ATLAS COPCO AB; *Int'l*, pg. 676
ATLAS COPCO AIRPOWER N.V.—See Atlas Copco AB; *Int'l*, pg. 678
ATLAS COPCO AIRTEC—See Atlas Copco AB; *Int'l*, pg. 678
ATLAS COPCO ANGOLA LDA—See Atlas Copco AB; *Int'l*, pg. 677
ATLAS COPCO ANLEGG- OG GRUVETEKNIKK A/S—See Atlas Copco AB; *Int'l*, pg. 677
ATLAS COPCO APPLICATION CENTER EUROPE GMBH—See Atlas Copco AB; *Int'l*, pg. 679
ATLAS COPCO APPLICATIONS INDUSTRIELLES S.A.S.—See Atlas Copco AB; *Int'l*, pg. 678
ATLAS COPCO ARGENTINA S.A.C.I.—See Atlas Copco AB; *Int'l*, pg. 677
ATLAS COPCO ASAP N.V.—See Atlas Copco AB; *Int'l*, pg. 678
ATLAS COPCO ASSEMBLY SYSTEMS LLC—See Atlas Copco AB; *Int'l*, pg. 681
ATLAS COPCO ASSISTANCE TECHNIQUE—See Atlas Copco AB; *Int'l*, pg. 678
ATLAS COPCO A/S—See Atlas Copco AB; *Int'l*, pg. 677
ATLAS COPCO AUSTRALIA PTY LTD—See Atlas Copco AB; *Int'l*, pg. 677
ATLAS COPCO BALTIC SIA—See Atlas Copco AB; *Int'l*, pg. 677
ATLAS COPCO BANGLADESH LTD.—See Atlas Copco AB; *Int'l*, pg. 677
ATLAS COPCO BEHEER B.V.—See Atlas Copco AB; *Int'l*, pg. 679
ATLAS COPCO BELGIUM N.V.—See Atlas Copco AB; *Int'l*, pg. 678
ATLAS COPCO BH D.O.O.—See Atlas Copco AB; *Int'l*, pg. 677
ATLAS COPCO BLM S.R.L.—See Atlas Copco AB; *Int'l*, pg. 677
ATLAS COPCO BOLIVIANA SA—See Atlas Copco AB; *Int'l*, pg. 678
ATLAS COPCO (BOTSWANA) (PTY) LTD—See Atlas Copco AB; *Int'l*, pg. 677
ATLAS COPCO BRASIL LTDA—See Atlas Copco AB; *Int'l*, pg. 678
ATLAS COPCO BULGARIA EOOD—See Atlas Copco AB; *Int'l*, pg. 678
ATLAS COPCO CANADA INC.—See Atlas Copco AB; *Int'l*, pg. 681
ATLAS COPCO CENTRAL ASIA LLP—See Atlas Copco AB; *Int'l*, pg. 678
ATLAS COPCO CHILENA S.A.C.—See Atlas Copco AB; *Int'l*, pg. 678
ATLAS COPCO CHINA/HONG KONG LTD—See Atlas Copco AB; *Int'l*, pg. 678
ATLAS COPCO (CHINA) INVESTMENT CO., LTD.—See Atlas Copco AB; *Int'l*, pg. 678
ATLAS COPCO CMT SWEDEN AB—See Atlas Copco AB; *Int'l*, pg. 678
ATLAS COPCO CMT USA INC.—See Atlas Copco AB; *Int'l*, pg. 680
ATLAS COPCO COLOMBIA LTDA—See Atlas Copco AB; *Int'l*, pg. 678
ATLAS COPCO COMPRESSEURS S.A.S—See Atlas Copco AB; *Int'l*, pg. 678
ATLAS COPCO COMPRESSOR AB—See Atlas Copco AB; *Int'l*, pg. 678
ATLAS COPCO COMPRESSOR CANADA—See Atlas Copco AB; *Int'l*, pg. 681
ATLAS COPCO COMPRESSORS LLC—See Atlas Copco AB; *Int'l*, pg. 680
ATLAS COPCO COMPTEC LLC—See Atlas Copco AB; *Int'l*, pg. 680
ATLAS COPCO CONSTRUCTION TOOLS AB—See Atlas Copco AB; *Int'l*, pg. 677
ATLAS COPCO CONSTRUCTION TOOLS GMBH—See Atlas Copco AB; *Int'l*, pg. 678
ATLAS COPCO CONSTRUCTION TOOLS SARL—See Atlas Copco AB; *Int'l*, pg. 678
ATLAS COPCO CRAELIUS—See Atlas Copco AB; *Int'l*, pg. 678
ATLAS COPCO CREPELLE S.A.S.—See Atlas Copco AB; *Int'l*, pg. 678
ATLAS COPCO CUSTOMER FINANCE AB—See Atlas Copco AB; *Int'l*, pg. 678
ATLAS COPCO CUSTOMER FINANCE AUSTRALIA PTY LTD—See Atlas Copco AB; *Int'l*, pg. 678
ATLAS COPCO CUSTOMER FINANCE CHILE LTDA—See Atlas Copco AB; *Int'l*, pg. 678
ATLAS COPCO (CYPRUS) LTD—See Atlas Copco AB; *Int'l*, pg. 677

ATLAS COPCO D.O.O.—See Atlas Copco AB; *Int'l*, pg. 681
ATLAS COPCO DRC SPRL—See Atlas Copco AB; *Int'l*, pg. 678
ATLAS COPCO DRILLING SOLUTIONS LLC—See Atlas Copco AB; *Int'l*, pg. 681
ATLAS COPCO DRILLING SOLUTIONS—See Atlas Copco AB; *Int'l*, pg. 681
ATLAS COPCO DYNAPAC AB—See FAYAT SAS; *Int'l*, pg. 2624
ATLAS COPCO EASTERN AFRICA LTD—See Atlas Copco AB; *Int'l*, pg. 678
ATLAS COPCO ENERGAS GMBH—See Atlas Copco AB; *Int'l*, pg. 679
ATLAS COPCO EQUIPMENT EGYPT S.A.E.—See Atlas Copco AB; *Int'l*, pg. 678
ATLAS COPCO FINANCE DAC—See Atlas Copco AB; *Int'l*, pg. 678
ATLAS COPCO FORAGE ET CONSTRUCTION S.A.S.—See Atlas Copco AB; *Int'l*, pg. 678
ATLAS COPCO FRANCE HOLDING S.A.—See Atlas Copco AB; *Int'l*, pg. 678
ATLAS COPCO FRANCE SAS—See Atlas Copco AB; *Int'l*, pg. 678
ATLAS COPCO GES.M.B.H.—See Atlas Copco AB; *Int'l*, pg. 679
ATLAS COPCO GHANA LTD—See Atlas Copco AB; *Int'l*, pg. 679
ATLAS COPCO HELLAS AE—See Atlas Copco AB; *Int'l*, pg. 679
ATLAS COPCO HOLDING GMBH—See Atlas Copco AB; *Int'l*, pg. 679
ATLAS COPCO HOLDINGS SOUTH AFRICA (PTY) LTD—See Atlas Copco AB; *Int'l*, pg. 679
ATLAS COPCO HURRICANE LLC—See Atlas Copco AB; *Int'l*, pg. 680
ATLAS COPCO IAS GMBH—See Atlas Copco AB; *Int'l*, pg. 679
ATLAS COPCO (INDIA) LTD.—See Atlas Copco AB; *Int'l*, pg. 677
ATLAS COPCO INDUSTRIAL AIR—See Atlas Copco AB; *Int'l*, pg. 678
ATLAS COPCO INDUSTRIAL TECHNIQUE AB—See Atlas Copco AB; *Int'l*, pg. 679
ATLAS COPCO INDUSTRIAL TECHNIQUE S.R.L.—See Atlas Copco AB; *Int'l*, pg. 680
ATLAS COPCO INDUSTRIAL ZAMBIA LIMITED—See Atlas Copco AB; *Int'l*, pg. 679
ATLAS COPCO IRAN AB—See Atlas Copco AB; *Int'l*, pg. 679
ATLAS COPCO IRAQ LLC—See Atlas Copco AB; *Int'l*, pg. 679
ATLAS COPCO (IRELAND) LTD—See Atlas Copco AB; *Int'l*, pg. 677
ATLAS COPCO ITALIA S.P.A.—See Atlas Copco AB; *Int'l*, pg. 679
ATLAS COPCO KFT—See Atlas Copco AB; *Int'l*, pg. 679
ATLAS COPCO KK—See Atlas Copco AB; *Int'l*, pg. 679
ATLAS COPCO KOMPRESSOREN UND DRUCK-LUFTTECHNIK GMBH—See Atlas Copco AB; *Int'l*, pg. 679
ATLAS COPCO KOMPRESSORTEKNIK A/S—See Atlas Copco AB; *Int'l*, pg. 679
ATLAS COPCO KOMPRESSORTEKNIKK AS—See Atlas Copco AB; *Int'l*, pg. 679
ATLAS COPCO KOREA CO., LTD.—See Atlas Copco AB; *Int'l*, pg. 679
ATLAS COPCO LATVIJA SIA—See Atlas Copco AB; *Int'l*, pg. 679
ATLAS COPCO LEVANT S.A.L—See Atlas Copco AB; *Int'l*, pg. 679
ATLAS COPCO LIETUVA UAB—See Atlas Copco AB; *Int'l*, pg. 679
ATLAS COPCO LIFTON EOOD—See Atlas Copco AB; *Int'l*, pg. 679
ATLAS COPCO LLC—See Atlas Copco AB; *Int'l*, pg. 679
ATLAS COPCO LTD—See Atlas Copco AB; *Int'l*, pg. 681
ATLAS COPCO MAFI-TRENCH COMPANY LLC—See Atlas Copco AB; *Int'l*, pg. 680
ATLAS COPCO MAKINALARI IMALAT AS—See Atlas Copco AB; *Int'l*, pg. 679
ATLAS COPCO (MALAYSIA) SDN. BHD.—See Atlas Copco AB; *Int'l*, pg. 677
ATLAS COPCO MAROC SA—See Atlas Copco AB; *Int'l*, pg. 679
ATLAS COPCO MCT GMBH—See Atlas Copco AB; *Int'l*, pg. 679
ATLAS COPCO MEXICANA S.A. DE C.V.—See Atlas Copco AB; *Int'l*, pg. 679
ATLAS COPCO NAMIBIA (PTY) LTD—See Atlas Copco AB; *Int'l*, pg. 679
ATLAS COPCO NEDERLAND B.V.—See Atlas Copco AB; *Int'l*, pg. 679
ATLAS COPCO NIGERIA LTD.—See Atlas Copco AB; *Int'l*, pg. 680
ATLAS COPCO (NI) LTD—See Atlas Copco AB; *Int'l*, pg. 681
ATLAS COPCO NORTH AMERICA LLC—See Atlas Copco AB; *Int'l*, pg. 680

ATLAS COPCO AB

ATLAS COPCO (N.Z.) LTD—See Atlas Copco AB; *Int'l*, pg. 677
ATLAS COPCO OIL-FREE AIR—See Atlas Copco AB; *Int'l*, pg. 678
ATLAS COPCO PAKISTAN (PVT) LTD—See Atlas Copco AB; *Int'l*, pg. 680
ATLAS COPCO PERUANA SA—See Atlas Copco AB; *Int'l*, pg. 680
ATLAS COPCO PERU S.A.C.—See Atlas Copco AB; *Int'l*, pg. 680
ATLAS COPCO (PHILIPPINES) INC.—See Atlas Copco AB; *Int'l*, pg. 677
ATLAS COPCO POLSKA SP. Z.O.O.—See Atlas Copco AB; *Int'l*, pg. 680
ATLAS COPCO PORTABLE AIR—See Atlas Copco AB; *Int'l*, pg. 678
ATLAS COPCO POWERCRUSHER GMBH—See Atlas Copco AB; *Int'l*, pg. 679
ATLAS COPCO POWER TECHNIQUE GMBH—See Atlas Copco AB; *Int'l*, pg. 680
ATLAS COPCO REINSURANCE SA—See Atlas Copco AB; *Int'l*, pg. 680
ATLAS COPCO RENTAL B.V.—See Atlas Copco AB; *Int'l*, pg. 679
ATLAS COPCO RENTAL EUROPE N.V.—See Atlas Copco AB; *Int'l*, pg. 678
ATLAS COPCO RENTAL LLC—See Atlas Copco AB; *Int'l*, pg. 680
ATLAS COPCO ROCK DRILLS AB—See Atlas Copco AB; *Int'l*, pg. 680
ATLAS COPCO ROMANIA S.R.L.—See Atlas Copco AB; *Int'l*, pg. 680
ATLAS COPCO S.A.E.—See Atlas Copco AB; *Int'l*, pg. 680
ATLAS COPCO (SCHWEIZ) AG—See Atlas Copco AB; *Int'l*, pg. 677
ATLAS COPCO SECOROC AB—See Atlas Copco AB; *Int'l*, pg. 680
ATLAS COPCO SECOROC LLC—See Atlas Copco AB; *Int'l*, pg. 680
ATLAS COPCO SERVICES MIDDLE EAST OMC—See Atlas Copco AB; *Int'l*, pg. 680
ATLAS COPCO SERVICES MIDDLE EAST SPC—See Atlas Copco AB; *Int'l*, pg. 680
ATLAS COPCO (SHANGHAI) EQUIPMENT RENTAL CO LTD—See Atlas Copco AB; *Int'l*, pg. 677
ATLAS COPCO (SHANGHAI) PROCESS EQUIPMENT CO LTD—See Atlas Copco AB; *Int'l*, pg. 677
ATLAS COPCO (SHANGHAI) TRADING CO., LTD.—See Atlas Copco AB; *Int'l*, pg. 677
ATLAS COPCO (SHENYANG) CONSTRUCTION AND MINING EQUIPMENT LTD—See Atlas Copco AB; *Int'l*, pg. 677
ATLAS COPCO SOUTH AFRICA (PTY) LTD—See Atlas Copco AB; *Int'l*, pg. 679
ATLAS COPCO (SOUTH EAST ASIA) PTE LTD—See Atlas Copco AB; *Int'l*, pg. 677
ATLAS COPCO SPECIALTY RENTAL LLC—See Atlas Copco AB; *Int'l*, pg. 680
ATLAS COPCO SRBIJA DOO—See Atlas Copco AB; *Int'l*, pg. 681
ATLAS COPCO S.R.O.—See Atlas Copco AB; *Int'l*, pg. 680
ATLAS COPCO S.R.O.—See Atlas Copco AB; *Int'l*, pg. 681
ATLAS COPCO S.R.O.—See Atlas Copco AB; *Int'l*, pg. 681
ATLAS COPCO TAIWAN LTD—See Atlas Copco AB; *Int'l*, pg. 681
ATLAS COPCO TANZANIA LTD—See Atlas Copco AB; *Int'l*, pg. 681
ATLAS COPCO (THAILAND) LTD—See Atlas Copco AB; *Int'l*, pg. 677
ATLAS COPCO TOOLS AB—See Atlas Copco AB; *Int'l*, pg. 681
ATLAS COPCO TOOLS & ASSEMBLY SYSTEMS LLC—See Atlas Copco AB; *Int'l*, pg. 681
ATLAS COPCO TOOLS A/S—See Atlas Copco AB; *Int'l*, pg. 677
ATLAS COPCO TOOLS CENTRAL EUROPE GMBH—See Atlas Copco AB; *Int'l*, pg. 679
ATLAS COPCO TOOLS GMBH—See Atlas Copco AB; *Int'l*, pg. 679
ATLAS COPCO UK HOLDINGS LTD—See Atlas Copco AB; *Int'l*, pg. 681
ATLAS COPCO VENEZUELA SA—See Atlas Copco AB; *Int'l*, pg. 681
ATLAS COPCO VIETNAM COMPANY LTD—See Atlas Copco AB; *Int'l*, pg. 681
ATLAS COPCO (ZAMBIA) LTD—See Atlas Copco AB; *Int'l*, pg. 677
ATLAS CORPORATION S.R.L. - APLA DIVISION—See Atlas Corporation S.R.L.; *Int'l*, pg. 685
ATLAS CORPORATION S.R.L.; *Int'l*, pg. 684
ATLAS CSF SDN BHD—See CSF Group plc; *Int'l*, pg. 1864
ATLAS CYCLES (HARYANA) LTD.; *Int'l*, pg. 685
ATLAS DEVELOPMENT CORPORATION; *U.S. Private*, pg. 375

ATLAS DID (PRIVATE) LTD.—See Daido Kogyo Co., Ltd.; *Int'l*, pg. 1920
ATLAS DIE, LLC - ATLANTA PLANT—See Auxo Investment Partners, LLC; *U.S. Private*, pg. 402
ATLAS DIE, LLC - CHEM-MILLING DIVISION—See Auxo Investment Partners, LLC; *U.S. Private*, pg. 402
ATLAS DIE, LLC - CHICAGO PLANT—See Auxo Investment Partners, LLC; *U.S. Private*, pg. 402
ATLAS DIE, LLC - GREENSBORO PLANT—See Auxo Investment Partners, LLC; *U.S. Private*, pg. 402
ATLAS DIE, LLC—See Auxo Investment Partners, LLC; *U.S. Private*, pg. 402
ATLAS ELECTRICA, S.A.—See Controladora Mabe S.A. de C.V.; *Int'l*, pg. 1785
ATLAS ELEKTRONIK FINLAND OY—See Airbus SE; *Int'l*, pg. 242
ATLAS ELEKTRONIK FINLAND OY—See ThyssenKrupp AG; *Int'l*, pg. 7723
ATLAS ELEKTRONIK GMBH—See Airbus SE; *Int'l*, pg. 241
ATLAS ELEKTRONIK GMBH—See ThyssenKrupp AG; *Int'l*, pg. 7723
ATLAS ELEKTRONIK INDIA PRIVATE LIMITED—See ThyssenKrupp AG; *Int'l*, pg. 7723
ATLAS ELEKTRONIK UK LTD.—See Airbus SE; *Int'l*, pg. 242
ATLAS ELEKTRONIK UK LTD.—See ThyssenKrupp AG; *Int'l*, pg. 7723
ATLAS ELEVATORS GENERAL TRADING & CONTRACTING COMPANY; *Int'l*, pg. 685
ATLAS ENERGY GROUP, LLC; *U.S. Public*, pg. 223
ATLAS ENERGY SOLUTIONS INC.; *U.S. Public*, pg. 223
ATLAS ENGINEERED PRODUCTS LTD.; *Int'l*, pg. 685
ATLAS ENGINEERING LIMITED—See Atlas Group of Companies; *Int'l*, pg. 685
ATLAS EPS—See Atlas Roofing Corp.; *U.S. Private*, pg. 380
ATLAS ESTATES COOPERATIEF U.A.—See Atlas Estates Limited; *Int'l*, pg. 685
ATLAS ESTATES LIMITED; *Int'l*, pg. 685
ATLAS EXCAVATING INC.; *U.S. Private*, pg. 376
ATLAS FARMACEUTICA S.A.—See Abbott Laboratories; *U.S. Public*, pg. 19
ATLAS FERTILIZER CORPORATION—See Sojitz Corporation; *Int'l*, pg. 7061
ATLAS FIBRE COMPANY; *U.S. Private*, pg. 376
ATLAS FINANCIAL HOLDINGS, INC.; *U.S. Public*, pg. 224
ATLAS FOOD SYSTEMS & SERVICES, INC.; *U.S. Private*, pg. 376
ATLAS FOR LAND RECLAMATION & AGRICULTURAL PROCESSING; *Int'l*, pg. 685
ATLAS FUND SERVICES (USA) LLC—See Zedra Trust Co. Ltd; *Int'l*, pg. 8629
ATLAS FUTURES FUND, LIMITED PARTNERSHIP; *U.S. Private*, pg. 376
ATLAS GENERAL HOLDINGS, LLC—See Arthur J. Gallagher & Co.; *U.S. Public*, pg. 203
ATLAS GENTECH (NZ) LIMITED—See WESCO International, Inc.; *U.S. Public*, pg. 2350
ATLAS GLOBAL FZE—See Atlas Group of Companies; *Int'l*, pg. 685
ATLAS GROUP OF COMPANIES; *Int'l*, pg. 685
THE ATLAS GROUP; *U.S. Private*, pg. 3990
ATLAS GROWTH ACQUISITION LTD.; *Int'l*, pg. 685
ATLAS GROWTH PARTNERS, L.P.; *U.S. Private*, pg. 376
ATLAS HEALTH CARE LINEN SERVICES CO.; *U.S. Private*, pg. 376
ATLAS HEALTHCARE SOFTWARE INDIA PRIVATE LIMITED—See Roper Technologies, Inc.; *U.S. Public*, pg. 1810
ATLAS HEAVY ENGINEERING PTY LTD—See Caterpillar, Inc.; *U.S. Public*, pg. 449
ATLAS HITEC (PVT). LIMITED—See Atlas Group of Companies; *Int'l*, pg. 685
ATLAS HOLDINGS, LLC; *U.S. Private*, pg. 376
ATLAS HOMEWARES, INC.—See The Jordan Company, L.P.; *U.S. Private*, pg. 4062
ATLAS HONDA LIMITED—See Atlas Group of Companies; *Int'l*, pg. 685
ATLAS HONDA LIMITED—See Honda Motor Co., Ltd.; *Int'l*, pg. 3460
ATLAS HOTELS, INC.; *U.S. Private*, pg. 378
ATLAS INDUSTRIAL CONTRACTORS, LLC; *U.S. Private*, pg. 378
ATLAS INDUSTRIES INC.; *U.S. Private*, pg. 379
ATLAS INFORMATION TECHNOLOGY, S.A.—See Nippon Telegraph & Telephone Corporation; *Int'l*, pg. 5344
THE ATLAS INSURANCE AGENCY, INC.—See Munchener Ruckversicherungs AG; *Int'l*, pg. 5092
ATLAS INSURANCE LIMITED; *Int'l*, pg. 685
ATLAS INTERMEDIATE HOLDINGS LLC—See GI Manager L.P.; *U.S. Private*, pg. 1691
ATLAS INTERNATIONAL LIFT TRUCKS—See Atlas Lift Truck Rentals & Sales, Inc.; *U.S. Private*, pg. 379
ATLASINVEST; *Int'l*, pg. 686
ATLAS IRON LIMITED; *Int'l*, pg. 686
ATLAS JEWELLERY INDIA LIMITED; *Int'l*, pg. 686

CORPORATE AFFILIATIONS

ATLAS LIFT TRUCK RENTALS & SALES, INC.; *U.S. Private*, pg. 379
ATLAS LIGHTING PRODUCTS, INC.—See LSI Industries Inc.; *U.S. Public*, pg. 1344
ATLAS LITHIUM CORPORATION; *Int'l*, pg. 686
ATLAS LOGISTICS INC.—See Atlas World Group, Inc.; *U.S. Private*, pg. 380
ATLAS LOGISTICS PVT. LTD.—See SBS Holdings Inc.; *Int'l*, pg. 6607
ATLAS MACHINE AND SUPPLY INC.; *U.S. Private*, pg. 379
ATLAS MACHINING & WELDING, INC.; *U.S. Private*, pg. 379
ATLAS MARA LIMITED; *Int'l*, pg. 686
ATLAS MARIDAN APS—See Airbus SE; *Int'l*, pg. 242
ATLAS MARIDAN APS—See ThyssenKrupp AG; *Int'l*, pg. 7723
ATLAS MASCHINEN GMBH—See Terex Corporation; *U.S. Public*, pg. 2019
ATLAS MATERIAL TESTING TECHNOLOGY GMBH—See AMETEK, Inc.; *U.S. Public*, pg. 117
ATLAS MATERIAL TESTING TECHNOLOGY LLC—See AMETEK, Inc.; *U.S. Public*, pg. 117
ATLAS MEDICAL—See Atlas Development Corporation; *U.S. Private*, pg. 376
ATLAS MENKUL KIYMETLER YATIRIM ORTAKLIGI A.S.; *Int'l*, pg. 686
ATLAS MERCHANT CAPITAL LLC; *U.S. Private*, pg. 379
ATLAS MERCHANT CAPITAL UK LLP—See Atlas Merchant Capital LLC; *U.S. Private*, pg. 379
ATLAS METAL INDUSTRIES INC.—See Mercury Aircraft Inc.; *U.S. Private*, pg. 2670
ATLAS METAL & IRON CORPORATION; *U.S. Private*, pg. 379
ATLAS METAL PRODUCTS COMPANY; *U.S. Private*, pg. 379
ATLAS MINERALS & CHEMICALS, INC.; *U.S. Private*, pg. 379
ATLAS MORTGAGE & INSURANCE CO., INC.; *U.S. Private*, pg. 379
ATLAS NAVAL SYSTEMS MALAYSIA SDN BHD—See Airbus SE; *Int'l*, pg. 242
ATLAS NAVAL SYSTEMS MALAYSIA SDN BHD—See ThyssenKrupp AG; *Int'l*, pg. 7723
ATLAS NORTH AMERICA, LLC—See Airbus SE; *Int'l*, pg. 242
ATLAS NORTH AMERICA, LLC—See ThyssenKrupp AG; *Int'l*, pg. 7723
ATLAS OIL COMPANY—See Simon Holdings LLC; *U.S. Private*, pg. 3666
ATLAS OPERATIONS, INC.; *U.S. Private*, pg. 379
ATLAS PACIFIC ENGINEERING COMPANY, INC.; *U.S. Private*, pg. 379
ATLAS PAPER MILLS, LLC—See PT Sinar Mas Group; *Int'l*, pg. 6073
ATLAS PEARLS LTD.; *Int'l*, pg. 686
ATLAS PEN & PENCIL CORP.; *U.S. Private*, pg. 379
ATLAS PETROLEUM EXPLORATION WORLDWIDE, LTD.—See Corcel plc; *Int'l*, pg. 1795
ATLAS PHARMA INC.—See SUNSHINE BIOPHARMA, INC.; *Int'l*, pg. 7322
ATLAS PIPELINE MID-CONTINENT WESTTEX, LLC—See Targa Resources Corp.; *U.S. Public*, pg. 1982
ATLAS PODIATRY PTE. LTD.—See Livingstone Health Holdings Limited; *Int'l*, pg. 4532
ATLAS POWER LIMITED—See Atlas Group of Companies; *Int'l*, pg. 685
ATLAS PROFESSIONALS B.V.—See HAL Trust N.V.; *Int'l*, pg. 3223
ATLAS PROFESSIONAL SERVICES, INC.; *U.S. Private*, pg. 379
ATLAS PUBLIC HEALTH—See Atlas Development Corporation; *U.S. Private*, pg. 376
ATLAS PUMPING SERVICE—See Audax Group, Limited Partnership; *U.S. Private*, pg. 388
ATLAS RAILROAD CONSTRUCTION CO., INC.—See Brookfield Infrastructure Partners L.P.; *Int'l*, pg. 1190
ATLAS RAILROAD CONSTRUCTION CO., INC.—See GIC Pte. Ltd.; *Int'l*, pg. 2965
ATLAS REAL ESTATE PARTNERS; *U.S. Private*, pg. 379
ATLAS REFINERY, INC.; *U.S. Private*, pg. 379
ATLAS REPLY S.R.L.—See Reply S.p.A.; *Int'l*, pg. 6290
ATLAS RESOURCE PARTNERS GP, LLC—See Atlas Energy Group, LLC; *U.S. Public*, pg. 223
ATLAS RESOURCES INTERNATIONAL, INC.; *U.S. Public*, pg. 224
ATLAS RFID SOLUTIONS, INC.; *U.S. Private*, pg. 379
ATLAS RHYTHM SDN. BHD.—See AbleGroup Berhad; *Int'l*, pg. 63
ATLAS ROOFING CORP.—See Atlas Roofing Corp.; *U.S. Private*, pg. 380
ATLAS ROOFING CORP.—See Atlas Roofing Corp.; *U.S. Private*, pg. 380
ATLAS ROOFING CORP.—See Atlas Roofing Corp.; *U.S. Private*, pg. 380
ATLAS ROOFING CORP.; *U.S. Private*, pg. 380
ATLAS SALT INC.—See Vulcan Minerals Inc.; *Int'l*, pg. 8318

ATLAS, S.A.—See Mubadala Investment Company PJSC; *Int'l*, pg. 5074
ATLASS HARDWARE CORPORATION—See Frontenac Company LLC; *U.S. Private*, pg. 1613
ATLASSIAN B.V.—See Atlassian Corporation; *Int'l*, pg. 686
ATLASSIAN CORPORATION; *Int'l*, pg. 686
ATLASSIAN, INC.—See Atlassian Corporation; *Int'l*, pg. 686
ATLASSIAN K.K.—See Atlassian Corporation; *Int'l*, pg. 686
ATLASSIAN PHILIPPINES, INC.—See Atlassian Corporation; *Int'l*, pg. 686
ATLASSIAN PTY. LTD.—See Atlassian Corporation; *Int'l*, pg. 686
ATLAS—See Meta Platforms, Inc.; *U.S. Public*, pg. 1426
ATLAS—See Meta Platforms, Inc.; *U.S. Public*, pg. 1427
ATLAS SOUND—See MiTek Corporation; *U.S. Private*, pg. 2751
ATLAS-SSI, INC.—See XPV Water Partners; *Int'l*, pg. 8538
ATLAS STAFFING INC.; *U.S. Private*, pg. 380
ATLAS STEEL PRODUCTS CO. INC.; *U.S. Private*, pg. 380
ATLAS SUPPLY, INC.—See Beacon Roofing Supply, Inc.; *U.S. Public*, pg. 285
ATLAS TAG & LABEL—See Ennis, Inc.; *U.S. Public*, pg. 768
ATLAS TECHNICAL CONSULTANTS, INC.—See GI Manager L.P.; *U.S. Private*, pg. 1691
ATLAS TECHNOLOGIES CORPORATION; *Int'l*, pg. 686
ATLAS TERMINAL CO. INC—See Atlas World Group, Inc.; *U.S. Private*, pg. 380
ATLAST FULFILLMENT; *U.S. Private*, pg. 381
ATLAS THERAPEUTICS AB—See Alligator Bioscience AB; *Int'l*, pg. 359
AT LAST NATURALS, INC.; *U.S. Private*, pg. 363
ATLAS TOOL INC.; *U.S. Private*, pg. 380
ATLAS TOYOTA MATERIAL HANDLING INC—See Atlas Lift Truck Rentals & Sales, Inc.; *U.S. Private*, pg. 379
ATLAS TRADE DISTRIBUTION SRL—See ANY Security Printing Company PLC; *Int'l*, pg. 486
ATLAS TRANSFER & STORAGE CO.; *U.S. Private*, pg. 380
ATLAS TRANSPORT, INC.—See Republic Services, Inc.; *U.S. Public*, pg. 1786
ATLAS TRAVEL INTERNATIONAL; *U.S. Private*, pg. 380
ATLAS TRILLO HEATING & AIR CONDITIONING, INC.—See Del-Air Heating, Air Conditioning & Refrigeration Corp.; *U.S. Private*, pg. 1193
ATLAS TUBE INC. - CHICAGO—See Zekelman Industries Inc.; *U.S. Private*, pg. 4600
ATLAS TUBE INC. - PLYMOUTH—See Zekelman Industries Inc.; *U.S. Private*, pg. 4600
ATLAS TUBE INC.—See Zekelman Industries Inc.; *U.S. Private*, pg. 4600
ATLAS TUBULAR LP; *U.S. Private*, pg. 380
ATLAS-TUCK CONCRETE, INC.—See Vulcan Materials Company; *U.S. Public*, pg. 2313
ATLAS VAN LINES (CANADA) LTD.—See Atlas World Group, Inc.; *U.S. Private*, pg. 380
ATLAS VAN LINES, INC.—See Atlas World Group, Inc.; *U.S. Private*, pg. 380
ATLAS VAN LINES INTL.—See Atlas World Group, Inc.; *U.S. Private*, pg. 380
ATLAS WATER SYSTEMS, INC.; *U.S. Private*, pg. 380
ATLAS WEATHERING DSET LABORATORIES—See AMETEK, Inc.; *U.S. Public*, pg. 117
ATLAS WIRE CORPORATION; *U.S. Private*, pg. 380
ATLAS WORLD-CLASS TRAVEL—See Atlas World Group, Inc.; *U.S. Private*, pg. 380
ATLAS WORLD GROUP, INC.; *U.S. Private*, pg. 380
ATLAS WORLDWIDE GENERAL TRADING LLC—See Atlas Group of Companies; *Int'l*, pg. 685
ATLATEC HOLDINGS, S.A. DE C.V.—See Mitsui & Co., Ltd.; *Int'l*, pg. 4973
ATLATSA RESOURCES CORPORATION; *Int'l*, pg. 686
ATLE AB—See 3i Group plc; *Int'l*, pg. 8
ATLED CO., LTD.—See Softcreate Holdings Corp.; *Int'l*, pg. 7054
ATLIFIC INC.—See Ocean Properties, Ltd.; *U.S. Private*, pg. 2989
ATLINKS GROUP LIMITED; *Int'l*, pg. 687
ATL LEASING; *Int'l*, pg. 673
AT-LOAN CO., LTD.—See Sumitomo Mitsui Financial Group, Inc.; *Int'l*, pg. 7293
ATL PARTNERS, LLC; *U.S. Private*, pg. 369
ATL PUEBLA—See Grupo TMM, S.A.B.; *Int'l*, pg. 3137
AT&L RAILROAD—See Wheeler Brothers Grain Co.; *U.S. Private*, pg. 4505
ATL TECHNOLOGY, INC.; *U.S. Private*, pg. 369
ATL TELECOM LIMITED; *Int'l*, pg. 673
ATLUS CO. LTD.—See Sega Sammy Holdings, Inc.; *Int'l*, pg. 6680
AT&M AMORPHOUS TECHNOLOGY CO., LTD.—See Advanced Technology & Materials Co., Ltd.; *Int'l*, pg. 162
ATMA PARTICIPACOES S.A.; *Int'l*, pg. 687
A.T. MASSEY COAL COMPANY, INC.—See Alpha Natural Resources, Inc.; *U.S. Private*, pg. 198
AT&M BIOMATERIALS CO., LTD.—See Advanced Technology & Materials Co., Ltd.; *Int'l*, pg. 162
ATM B.V.—See Renewi plc; *Int'l*, pg. 6278

ATM COMPUTERSYSTEME GMBH—See Krauss-Maffei Wegmann GmbH & Co. KG; *Int'l*, pg. 4300
ATM CONSTRUCT S.A.; *Int'l*, pg. 687
ATM CORPORATION OF AMERICA; *U.S. Private*, pg. 381
ATMD ELECTRONICS (SHANGHAI) LIMITED—See Tomen Devices Corporation; *Int'l*, pg. 7800
ATMD ELECTRONICS (SHENZHEN) LIMITED—See Tomen Devices Corporation; *Int'l*, pg. 7800
ATMD ELECTRONICS (SINGAPORE) LIMITED—See Tomen Devices Corporation; *Int'l*, pg. 7800
ATMD (HONG KONG) LIMITED—See Tomen Devices Corporation; *Int'l*, pg. 7800
AT MEDIA-HUNGARY KFT—See TVT Media; *Int'l*, pg. 7989
AT MEDIA SP. Z O O—See Liberty Global plc; *Int'l*, pg. 4484
AT MEDICS HOLDINGS LLP—See Centene Corporation; *U.S. Public*, pg. 467
AT MEDICS LTD.—See Centene Corporation; *U.S. Public*, pg. 467
ATM ELECTRONIC CORPORATION (HK) LIMITED—See Arrow Electronics, Inc.; *U.S. Public*, pg. 195
ATM ELECTRONIC CORP.—See Arrow Electronics, Inc.; *U.S. Public*, pg. 195
ATM ELECTRONICS TECHNOLOGY (SHENZHEN) CO. LTD.—See Arrow Electronics, Inc.; *U.S. Public*, pg. 195
ATM ENTSORGUNG DEUTSCHLAND GMBH—See Renewi plc; *Int'l*, pg. 6278
AT&M ENVIRONMENTAL ENGINEERING TECHNOLOGY CO., LTD.—See Advanced Technology & Materials Co., Ltd.; *Int'l*, pg. 162
ATMEQUIPMENT.COM—See Grant Victor; *U.S. Private*, pg. 1757
ATM EXECUTION LLC—See The Toronto-Dominion Bank; *Int'l*, pg. 7695
ATM GRUPA S.A.; *Int'l*, pg. 687
ATMI DYNACORE LLC; *U.S. Private*, pg. 381
ATMI INTERNATIONAL TRADING CO. LTD.—See Entegris, Inc.; *U.S. Public*, pg. 776
ATM INWESTYCJE SP. Z.O.O.—See ATM Grupa S.A.; *Int'l*, pg. 687
ATMI PRECAST INC.; *U.S. Private*, pg. 381
ATMIRA ESPACIO DE CONSULTORIA S.L.; *Int'l*, pg. 687
ATMI TAIWAN CO. LTD.—See Entegris, Inc.; *U.S. Public*, pg. 776
ATM NATIONAL, LLC—See NCR Voyix Corporation.; *U.S. Public*, pg. 1501
ATM NETWORK, INC.—See NCR Voyix Corporation.; *U.S. Public*, pg. 1501
ATMOKY GMBH; *Int'l*, pg. 687
ATMOR INDUSTRIES LTD.—See Ariston Holding N.V.; *Int'l*, pg. 567
ATMOS CO., LTD.—See Copro Holdings Co., Ltd.; *Int'l*, pg. 1794
ATMOS ENERGY CORPORATION; *U.S. Public*, pg. 224
ATMOS ENERGY HOLDINGS, INC.—See Atmos Energy Corporation; *U.S. Public*, pg. 224
ATMOS ENERGY SERVICES, LLC—See Atmos Energy Corporation; *U.S. Public*, pg. 224
ATMOSERA, INC.; *U.S. Private*, pg. 381
ATMOS GATHERING COMPANY, LLC—See Atmos Energy Corporation; *U.S. Public*, pg. 224
ATMOSPHERE COMMERCIAL INTERIORS, LLC—See HNI Corporation; *U.S. Public*, pg. 1043
ATMOSPHERE HEAT TREATING INC.—See AFC-Holcroft LLC; *U.S. Private*, pg. 121
ATMOSPHERIC & ENVIRONMENTAL RESEARCH - AIR QUALITY—See Verisk Analytics, Inc.; *U.S. Public*, pg. 2283
ATMOSPHERIC & ENVIRONMENTAL RESEARCH, INC.—See Verisk Analytics, Inc.; *U.S. Public*, pg. 2282
ATMOS PIPELINE AND STORAGE, LLC—See Atmos Energy Corporation; *U.S. Public*, pg. 224
ATMOS POWER SYSTEMS, INC.—See Atmos Energy Corporation; *U.S. Public*, pg. 224
ATM PARTS COMPANY LTD.—See discoverIE Group plc; *Int'l*, pg. 2132
ATM RECYCLING, INC.; *U.S. Private*, pg. 381
ATM ROZRYWKA SP. Z.O.O.—See ATM Grupa S.A.; *Int'l*, pg. 687
ATM S.A.—See MCI Capital Alternatywna Spolka Inwestycyjna S.A.; *Int'l*, pg. 4758
AT&M STAR ELECTRONIC COMPONENT CO., LTD.—See Advanced Technology & Materials Co., Ltd.; *Int'l*, pg. 162
ATM STUDIO SP. Z.O.O.—See ATM Grupa S.A.; *Int'l*, pg. 687
ATM SYSTEM SP. Z.O.O.—See ATM Grupa S.A.; *Int'l*, pg. 687
ATM-TURAUTOMATIK GMBH—See dormakaba Holding AG; *Int'l*, pg. 2177
ATMUS FILTRATION TECHNOLOGIES INC.; *U.S. Public*, pg. 224
AT&M VENTURE CAPITAL INVESTMENT (SHENZHEN) CO., LTD.—See Advanced Technology & Materials Co., Ltd.; *Int'l*, pg. 162
ATNA RESOURCES LTD.; *U.S. Private*, pg. 381
AT-NET SERVICES-GREENVILLE, INC.—See At-Net Services, Inc.; *U.S. Private*, pg. 363

AT-NET SERVICES, INC.; *U.S. Private*, pg. 363
ATN HOLDINGS, INC.; *Int'l*, pg. 687
ATN INTERNATIONAL, INC.; *U.S. Public*, pg. 224
ATN INTERNATIONAL LIMITED; *Int'l*, pg. 687
ATO ABFALLWIRTSCHAFT TORGAU-OSCHATZ GMBH—See Alba SE; *Int'l*, pg. 293
ATO-ASIA TURNOUTS LIMITED—See Vossloh AG; *Int'l*, pg. 8308
ATOBATC SHIPPING AB—See Aspo Oyj; *Int'l*, pg. 631
ATOBATC SHIPPING CYPRUS LTD.—See Aspo Oyj; *Int'l*, pg. 631
ATODIA AB—See Platinum Equity, LLC; *U.S. Private*, pg. 3201
ATOJ, INC.—See Softcreate Holdings Corp.; *Int'l*, pg. 7054
ATOK-BIG WEDGE CO., INC.; *Int'l*, pg. 687
ATOL CO., LTD.—See Medipal Holdings Corporation; *Int'l*, pg. 4779
ATOLL SAS—See Randstad N.V.; *Int'l*, pg. 6201
ATOM42 LIMITED—See Samsung Group; *Int'l*, pg. 6511
ATOMATIC MECHANICAL SERVICES, INC.; *U.S. Private*, pg. 381
ATOM CORPORATION; *Int'l*, pg. 687
ATOME ENERGY PLC; *Int'l*, pg. 687
ATOM EMPREENDIMENTOS E PARTICIPACOES S.A.; *Int'l*, pg. 687
ATOMENERGOREMONT PLC; *Int'l*, pg. 687
ATOM ENTERTAINMENT INC.—See National Amusements, Inc.; *U.S. Private*, pg. 2841
ATOMERA INCORPORATED; *U.S. Public*, pg. 225
ATOMHAWK DESIGN LIMITED—See Sumo Group plc; *Int'l*, pg. 7302
ATOMIC AUSTRIA GMBH—See ANTA Sports Products Limited; *Int'l*, pg. 480
ATOMIC CREDIT UNION, INC.; *U.S. Private*, pg. 381
ATOMIC DATA, LLC.; *U.S. Private*, pg. 381
ATOMIC DIRECT, LLC; *U.S. Private*, pg. 381
ATOMIC ENERGY OF CANADA LIMITED; *Int'l*, pg. 687
ATOMIC MINERALS CORPORATION; *Int'l*, pg. 687
ATOMIC OBJECT LLC; *U.S. Private*, pg. 381
ATOMI CORP.—See Dugan Production Corp.; *U.S. Private*, pg. 1285
ATOMIC PLAYPEN; *U.S. Private*, pg. 381
ATOMIC SKI USA INC.—See ANTA Sports Products Limited; *Int'l*, pg. 480
ATOMIC SPORTS CANADA—See ANTA Sports Products Limited; *Int'l*, pg. 480
ATOMIC TATTOOS, LLC; *U.S. Private*, pg. 381
ATOM INSTRUMENT LLC—See Advanced Holdings Ltd.; *Int'l*, pg. 159
ATOMIX CO., LTD.; *Int'l*, pg. 688
ATOM LIVIN TECH CO., LTD.; *Int'l*, pg. 687
ATOMMIX INDUSTRIA E COMERCIO LTDA.—See Komatsu Ltd.; *Int'l*, pg. 4234
ATOMO DIAGNOSTICS LIMITED; *Int'l*, pg. 688
ATOMOS; *Int'l*, pg. 688
ATOM POWER, INC.—See SK Inc.; *Int'l*, pg. 6971
ATOM PRODUCTIONS, INC.—See Lions Gate Entertainment Corp.; *Int'l*, pg. 4520
ATOMSYSTEM CO., LTD.; *Int'l*, pg. 688
ATOM TECHNOLOGIES LTD.—See Nippon Telegraph & Telephone Corporation; *Int'l*, pg. 5346
ATOMWIDE LIMITED—See Macquarie Group Limited; *Int'l*, pg. 4630
ATON GMBH; *Int'l*, pg. 688
ATON GREEN STORAGE S.P.A.; *Int'l*, pg. 689
ATON LLC; *Int'l*, pg. 689
ATON PHARMA, INC.—See Bausch Health Companies Inc.; *U.S. Private*, pg. 898
ATON PROJECTS V.O.F.—See E.ON SE; *Int'l*, pg. 2251
ATON RESOURCES INC.; *Int'l*, pg. 689
ATON SYSTEMES S.A.—See Actia Group SA; *Int'l*, pg. 118
A TOOL SHED INC.; *U.S. Private*, pg. 19
ATOPTECH, INC.—See Avatar Integrated Systems, Inc.; *U.S. Private*, pg. 404
ATORKA GROUP HF; *Int'l*, pg. 690
ATOS AG—See Atos SE; *Int'l*, pg. 690
ATOS ARGENTINA SA—See Atos SE; *Int'l*, pg. 690
ATOS (AUSTRALIA) PTY. LTD.—See Atos SE; *Int'l*, pg. 690
ATOS BELGIUM SA—See Atos SE; *Int'l*, pg. 690
ATOS BILISIM DANISMANLIK VE MUSTERI HIZMETLERI SANAYI VE TICARET A/S—See Atos SE; *Int'l*, pg. 690
ATOS CONSLUTING CANAROIAS, SA—See Atos SE; *Int'l*, pg. 690
ATOS CONSULTING FRANCE—See Atos SE; *Int'l*, pg. 690
ATOS CONSUMER PRODUCTS PTE LTD—See Fitgenes Australia Pty Ltd.; *Int'l*, pg. 2695
ATOS CONVERGENCE CREATORS GMBH—See Atos SE; *Int'l*, pg. 690
ATOS CONVERGENCE CREATORS SRL—See Atos SE; *Int'l*, pg. 690
ATOS COVICS BUSINESS SOLUTIONS CO., LTD.—See Atos SE; *Int'l*, pg. 690
ATOS FRANCE S.A.S.—See Atos SE; *Int'l*, pg. 690
ATOS GLOBAL DELIVERY CENTER MEXICO, S. DE R.L. DE C.V.—See Atos SE; *Int'l*, pg. 690

ATOS GLOBAL DELIVERY CENTER PHILIPPINES, INC.—See Atos SE; *Int'l*, pg. 690
ATOS INDIA PRIVATE LIMITED—See Atos SE; *Int'l*, pg. 690
ATOS INFORMATION TECHNOLOGY (CHINA) CO., LTD.—See Atos SE; *Int'l*, pg. 690
ATOS INFORMATION TECHNOLOGY GMBH—See Atos SE; *Int'l*, pg. 690
ATOS INFORMATION TECHNOLOGY HK LTD.—See Atos SE; *Int'l*, pg. 691
ATOS INFORMATION TECHNOLOGY INC.—See Atos SE; *Int'l*, pg. 691
ATOS INFORMATION TECHNOLOGY (NANJING) CO., LTD.—See Atos SE; *Int'l*, pg. 690
ATOS INFORMATION TECHNOLOGY SAE—See Atos SE; *Int'l*, pg. 691
ATOS INFORMATION TECHNOLOGY (SINGAPORE) PTE. LTD.—See Atos SE; *Int'l*, pg. 690
ATOS INTERNATIONAL GERMANY GMBH—See Atos SE; *Int'l*, pg. 691
ATOS IT-DIENSTLEISTUNG UND BERATUNG GMBH—See Atos SE; *Int'l*, pg. 690
ATOS IT SERVICES PRIVATE LTD—See Atos SE; *Int'l*, pg. 690
ATOS IT SERVICES SARL—See Atos SE; *Int'l*, pg. 690
ATOS IT SERVICES UK LIMITED—See Atos SE; *Int'l*, pg. 690
ATOS IT SERVICIOS DO BRAZIL LTDA—See Atos SE; *Int'l*, pg. 690
ATOS ITS NEARSHORE CENTER MAROC S.A.R.L.—See Atos SE; *Int'l*, pg. 690
ATOS IT SOLUTIONS AND SERVICES D.O.O.—See Atos SE; *Int'l*, pg. 690
ATOS IT SOLUTIONS AND SERVICES GMBH—See Atos SE; *Int'l*, pg. 690
ATOS IT SOLUTIONS AND SERVICES GMBH—See Atos SE; *Int'l*, pg. 690
ATOS IT SOLUTIONS AND SERVICES, INC.—See Atos SE; *Int'l*, pg. 690
ATOS IT SOLUTIONS & SERVICES A/S—See Atos SE; *Int'l*, pg. 690
ATOS IT SOLUTIONS & SERVICES LLC—See Atos SE; *Int'l*, pg. 690
ATOS IT SOLUTIONS & SERVICES LTD.—See Atos SE; *Int'l*, pg. 690
ATOS IT SOLUTIONS & SERVICES OY—See Atos SE; *Int'l*, pg. 690
ATOS IT SOLUTIONS & SERVICES S.A.S.—See Atos SE; *Int'l*, pg. 690
ATOS IT SOLUTIONS & SERVICES S.R.O.—See Atos SE; *Int'l*, pg. 690
ATOS KK—See Atos SE; *Int'l*, pg. 691
ATOS LUXEMBOURG PSF S.A.—See Atos SE; *Int'l*, pg. 691
ATOS LUXEMBOURG SF S.A.—See Atos SE; *Int'l*, pg. 691
ATOS MAGYARORSZAG KFT.—See Atos SE; *Int'l*, pg. 691
ATOS MEDICAL AB—See PAI Partners S.A.S.; *Int'l*, pg. 5700
ATOS MEDICAL APS—See Coloplast A/S; *Int'l*, pg. 1703
ATOS MEDICAL AUSTRIA GMBH—See Coloplast A/S; *Int'l*, pg. 1703
ATOS MEDICAL BRASIL LTDA.—See Coloplast A/S; *Int'l*, pg. 1703
ATOS MEDICAL B.V.B.A.—See Coloplast A/S; *Int'l*, pg. 1703
ATOS MEDICAL B.V.—See Coloplast A/S; *Int'l*, pg. 1703
ATOS MEDICAL CANADA INC.—See Coloplast A/S; *Int'l*, pg. 1703
ATOS MEDICAL GMBH—See Coloplast A/S; *Int'l*, pg. 1703
ATOS MEDICAL INC.—See Coloplast A/S; *Int'l*, pg. 1703
ATOS MEDICAL JAPAN INC.—See Coloplast A/S; *Int'l*, pg. 1703
ATOS MEDICAL LTD.—See Coloplast A/S; *Int'l*, pg. 1703
ATOS MEDICAL POLAND SP. Z O.O.—See Coloplast A/S; *Int'l*, pg. 1703
ATOS MEDICAL PTY. LTD.—See Coloplast A/S; *Int'l*, pg. 1703
ATOS MEDICAL S.A.S.—See Coloplast A/S; *Int'l*, pg. 1703
ATOS MEDICAL S.L.—See Coloplast A/S; *Int'l*, pg. 1703
ATOS MEDICAL S.R.L.—See Coloplast A/S; *Int'l*, pg. 1703
ATOS MEDICAL UK LTD.—See Coloplast A/S; *Int'l*, pg. 1703
ATOS NEDERLAND B.V.—See Atos SE; *Int'l*, pg. 691
ATOS ORIGIN BRASIL LTDA—See Atos SE; *Int'l*, pg. 691
ATOS ORIGIN CONSULTING CANARIAS, SA—See Atos SE; *Int'l*, pg. 691
ATOS ORIGIN FORMATION S.A—See Atos SE; *Int'l*, pg. 691
ATOS ORIGIN FZ LLC—See Atos SE; *Int'l*, pg. 691
ATOS ORIGIN INDONESIA PT—See Atos SE; *Int'l*, pg. 691
ATOS ORIGIN INFORMATION TECHNOLOGY (CHINA) CO. LTD—See Atos SE; *Int'l*, pg. 691
ATOS ORIGIN INTEGRATION SAS—See Atos SE; *Int'l*, pg. 691
ATOS ORIGIN MANAGEMENT FRANCE SAS—See Atos SE; *Int'l*, pg. 691

ATOS ORIGIN SERVICOS DE TECNOLOGIA DA INFORMACAO DO BRASIL LTDA—See Atos SE; *Int'l*, pg. 691
ATOS POLAND GLOBAL SERVICE SP ZOO—See Atos SE; *Int'l*, pg. 691
ATOS POLSKA SA—See Atos SE; *Int'l*, pg. 691
ATOS PROPERTY MANAGEMENT GMBH—See CORESTATE Capital Holding SA; *Int'l*, pg. 1799
ATOS PTY. LTD.—See Atos SE; *Int'l*, pg. 691
ATOS QATAR LLC—See Atos SE; *Int'l*, pg. 691
ATOSSA THERAPEUTICS, INC.; *U.S. Public*, pg. 225
ATOS SAUDI COMPANY—See Atos SE; *Int'l*, pg. 691
ATOSS CSD SOFTWARE GMBH—See ATOSS Software AG; *Int'l*, pg. 692
ATOS SERVICES (MALAYSIA) SDN BHD—See Atos SE; *Int'l*, pg. 691
ATOS SE; *Int'l*, pg. 690
ATOS SINGAPORE—See Atos SE; *Int'l*, pg. 691
ATOS SOLUCOES E SERIVCOS PARA TECNOLOGIAS DE INFORMACAO, UNIPESSOAL, LTDA.—See Atos SE; *Int'l*, pg. 691
ATOS SOLUCOES E SERVICOS PARA TECNOLOGIAS DE INFORMACAO, UNIPESSOAL, LTDA.—See Atos SE; *Int'l*, pg. 691
ATOS SPAIN SA—See Atos SE; *Int'l*, pg. 691
ATOSS SOFTWARE AG—See ATOSS Software AG; *Int'l*, pg. 693
ATOSS SOFTWARE AG; *Int'l*, pg. 692
ATOSS SOFTWARE GESELLSCHAFT M.B.H.—See ATOSS Software AG; *Int'l*, pg. 693
ATOSS SOFTWARE S.R.L.—See ATOSS Software AG; *Int'l*, pg. 693
ATOS TAIWAN LTD—See Atos SE; *Int'l*, pg. 691
ATOS UK IT LIMITED—See Atos SE; *Int'l*, pg. 691
ATOS WELLNESS PTE LTD—See Fitgenes Australia Pty Ltd.; *Int'l*, pg. 2695
ATOTECH ARGENTINA S.A.—See TotalEnergies SE; *Int'l*, pg. 7836
ATOTECH ASIA PACIFIC LTD—See TotalEnergies SE; *Int'l*, pg. 7836
ATOTECH CANADA LTD.—See TotalEnergies SE; *Int'l*, pg. 7836
ATOTECH CZ, A.S.—See TotalEnergies SE; *Int'l*, pg. 7836
ATOTECH DE MEXICO S.A. DE C.V.—See TotalEnergies SE; *Int'l*, pg. 7837
ATOTECH DEUTSCHLAND GMBH—See TotalEnergies SE; *Int'l*, pg. 7836
ATOTECH DEUTSCHLAND GMBH—See TotalEnergies SE; *Int'l*, pg. 7836
ATOTECH DEUTSCHLAND GMBH—See TotalEnergies SE; *Int'l*, pg. 7836
ATOTECH DO BRASIL GALVANOTECNICA LTDA.—See TotalEnergies SE; *Int'l*, pg. 7837
ATOTECH ESPANA S.A—See TotalEnergies SE; *Int'l*, pg. 7836
ATOTECH FRANCE SA—See TotalEnergies SE; *Int'l*, pg. 7836
ATOTECH ISTANBUL KIMYA SANAYI TIC. LTD. STI.—See TotalEnergies SE; *Int'l*, pg. 7836
ATOTECH ITALIA S.R.L.—See TotalEnergies SE; *Int'l*, pg. 7836
ATOTECH JAPAN K.K.—See TotalEnergies SE; *Int'l*, pg. 7836
ATOTECH KOREA LTD.—See TotalEnergies SE; *Int'l*, pg. 7836
ATOTECH (MALAYSIA) SDN BHD—See TotalEnergies SE; *Int'l*, pg. 7836
ATOTECH NEDERLAND B.V.—See TotalEnergies SE; pg. 7836
ATOTECH OSTERREICH GMBH—See TotalEnergies SE; *Int'l*, pg. 7836
ATOTECH OSTERREICH GMBH—See TotalEnergies SE; *Int'l*, pg. 7836
ATOTECH POLAND SP.Z O.O.—See TotalEnergies SE; *Int'l*, pg. 7836
ATOTECH S.E.A (PHILS) PTE LTD—See TotalEnergies SE; *Int'l*, pg. 7836
ATOTECH S.E.A PTE LTD—See TotalEnergies SE; *Int'l*, pg. 7836
ATOTECH SKANDINAVIEN AB—See TotalEnergies SE; *Int'l*, pg. 7836
ATOTECH SLOVENIJA, PROIZVODNJA KEMICNIH IZDELKOV, D.D.—See TotalEnergies SE; *Int'l*, pg. 7836
ATOTECH SPAIN SA—See TotalEnergies SE; *Int'l*, pg. 7836
ATOTECH SRL ITALIA LAINATE—See TotalEnergies SE; *Int'l*, pg. 7836
ATOTECH TAIWAN LTD. - GUANYIN PLANT—See TotalEnergies SE; *Int'l*, pg. 7836
ATOTECH TAIWAN LTD.—See TotalEnergies SE; *Int'l*, pg. 7836
ATOTECH (THAILAND) CO., LTD.—See TotalEnergies SE; *Int'l*, pg. 7836
ATOTECH UK LTD.—See TotalEnergies SE; *Int'l*, pg. 7836
ATOTECH USA INC.—See TotalEnergies SE; *Int'l*, pg. 7836
ATOTECH VIETNAM CO., LTD.—See TotalEnergies SE; *Int'l*, pg. 7837
ATOUR LIFESTYLE HOLDINGS LIMITED; *Int'l*, pg. 693

A TOUTE VITESSE SA; *Int'l*, pg. 18
A TO ZMEDIA; *U.S. Private*, pg. 19
A TO Z SERVICE CO., LTD.—See AEON Co., Ltd.; *Int'l*, pg. 178
A TO Z TIRE & BATTERY INC.; *U.S. Private*, pg. 19
ATP AUTOMOTIVE TESTING PAPENBURG GMBH—See Adecco Group AG; *Int'l*, pg. 140
ATPE-AMIB S.A.—See KONE Oyj; *Int'l*, pg. 4247
ATP EJENDOMME A/S—See Arbejdsmarkedets Tillaegspension; *Int'l*, pg. 537
ATP ELECTRONICS, INC.—See Actiontec Electronics, Inc.; *U.S. Private*, pg. 68
ATP EUROPE BVBA—See ATP Tour, Inc.; *U.S. Private*, pg. 381
AT PHIL., INC.—See Asiatravel.com Holdings Limited; *Int'l*, pg. 620
ATPI LIMITED; *Int'l*, pg. 693
ATP INTERNATIONAL GROUP—See ATP Tour, Inc.; *U.S. Private*, pg. 381
ATP LONDON—See ATP Tour, Inc.; *U.S. Private*, pg. 381
ATP PRIVATE EQUITY ADVISORS APS—See Arbejdsmarkedets Tillaegspension; *Int'l*, pg. 537
AT PRECISION TOOLING SDN. BHD.—See AT Systematization Berhad; *Int'l*, pg. 664
ATP TOUR, INC.; *U.S. Private*, pg. 381
ATRACCO AUTO AB—See LKQ Corporation; *U.S. Public*, pg. 1333
A TRACKS PTE LTD—See ISDN Holdings Limited; *Int'l*, pg. 3813
ATRACK TECHNOLOGY, INC.; *Int'l*, pg. 693
ATRACK TECHNOLOGY (TOKYO) INC.—See ATrack Technology, Inc.; *Int'l*, pg. 693
ATRACSYS SARL—See Smith & Nephew plc; *Int'l*, pg. 7007
ATRADA TRADING NETWORK AG—See Deutsche Telekom AG; *Int'l*, pg. 2083
ATRADIUS COLLECTIONS B.V.—See Grupo Catalana Occidente, S.A.; *Int'l*, pg. 3124
ATRADIUS COLLECTIONS, INC.—See Grupo Catalana Occidente, S.A.; *Int'l*, pg. 3124
ATRADIUS CREDIT INSURANCE NV—See Grupo Catalana Occidente, S.A.; *Int'l*, pg. 3124
ATRADIUS N.V.—See Grupo Catalana Occidente, S.A.; *Int'l*, pg. 3124
ATRADIUS—See Grupo Catalana Occidente, S.A.; *Int'l*, pg. 3124
ATRADIUS—See Grupo Catalana Occidente, S.A.; *Int'l*, pg. 3124
ATRADIUS TRADE CREDIT INSURANCE, INC.—See Grupo Catalana Occidente, S.A.; *Int'l*, pg. 3124
ATRAE, INC.; *Int'l*, pg. 693
ATR ASSET MANAGEMENT, INC.—See Malayan Banking Berhad; *Int'l*, pg. 4660
ATRATO ONSITE ENERGY PLC; *Int'l*, pg. 693
ATRAVEO GMBH—See HomeToGo SE; *Int'l*, pg. 3456
ATRAX MARKETING; *U.S. Private*, pg. 382
ATRECA, INC.; *U.S. Public*, pg. 225
A.TREDS LTD.—See Axis Bank Limited; *Int'l*, pg. 769
ATREL VIDEOSYSTEMS; *U.S. Private*, pg. 382
ATREM S.A.; *Int'l*, pg. 693
ATREND USA; *U.S. Private*, pg. 382
ATRENEW INC.; *Int'l*, pg. 693
ATRENTA INC.—See Synopsys, Inc.; *U.S. Public*, pg. 1970
ATR EQUIPMENT SOLUTIONS LTD.—See National Bank of Greece S.A.; *Int'l*, pg. 5153
ATRES ADVERTISING S.L.U.—See Atresmedia Corporacion de Medios de Comunicacion, S.A.; *Int'l*, pg. 693
AT RESERVATION PTE LTD—See Asiatravel.com Holdings Limited; *Int'l*, pg. 620
ATRESMEDIA CORPORACION DE MEDIOS DE COMUNICACION, S.A.; *Int'l*, pg. 693
ATREX INC.; *U.S. Private*, pg. 382
ATREYU CAPITAL MARKETS LTD.; *Int'l*, pg. 693
ATR GROUP LTD.—See National Bank of Greece S.A.; *Int'l*, pg. 5153
ATR HOLDINGS LTD—See Centurion Group Ltd; *Int'l*, pg. 1417
ATRIA CONCEPT AB—See Atria Plc; *Int'l*, pg. 693
ATRIA CONCEPT SP Z.O.O—See Atria Plc; *Int'l*, pg. 693
ATRIA CONSULTING, LLC; *U.S. Private*, pg. 382
ATRIA CONVERGENCE TECHNOLOGIES PRIVATE LIMITED—See India Value Fund Advisors Pvt Ltd.; *Int'l*, pg. 3652
ATRIA DANMARK A/S—See Atria Plc; *Int'l*, pg. 693
ATRIA EESTI AS—See Atria Plc; *Int'l*, pg. 693
ATRIA FINLAND OY—See Atria Plc; *Int'l*, pg. 693
ATRIA FOODSERVICE AB—See Atria Plc; *Int'l*, pg. 693
ATRIA GUILDERLAND—See Atria Senior Living, Inc.; *U.S. Private*, pg. 382
ATRIA HUNTINGTON—See Atria Senior Living, Inc.; *U.S. Private*, pg. 382
ATRIA MANAGEMENT CANADA, ULC—See Ventas, Inc.; *U.S. Public*, pg. 2278
ATRIA NORTHPARK PARK, LLC—See Ventas, Inc.; *U.S. Public*, pg. 2278
ATRIA PALM DESERT—See Atria Senior Living, Inc.; *U.S. Private*, pg. 382
ATRIA PAN DENTAL GROUP PTE. LTD.—See Pacific Healthcare Holdings Ltd.; *Int'l*, pg. 5689

COMPANY NAME INDEX

ATRIA PLC; *Int'l*, pg. 693
ATRIA RETAIL AB—See Atria Plc; *Int'l*, pg. 694
ATRIA SCANDINAVIA AB—See Atria Plc; *Int'l*, pg. 693
ATRIA SENIOR LIVING, INC.; *U.S. Private*, pg. 382
ATRIA VISTA DEL RIO, LLC—See Ventas, Inc.; *U.S. Public*, pg. 2278
ATRIA WEALTH SOLUTIONS, LLC—See Lee Equity Partners LLC; *U.S. Private*, pg. 2412
ATRICURE EUROPE, B.V.—See AtriCure, Inc.; *U.S. Public*, pg. 225
ATRICURE HONG KONG LIMITED,—See AtriCure, Inc.; *U.S. Public*, pg. 225
ATRICURE, INC.; *U.S. Public*, pg. 225
ATRIK D.O.O.—See Avtotehna, d.d.; *Int'l*, pg. 751
ATRILOGY SOLUTIONS GROUP, INC.—See DIVERSANT, LLC; *U.S. Private*, pg. 1240
ATR INDUSTRIE-ELEKTRONIK GMBH—See G. Siempelkamp GmbH & Co. KG; *Int'l*, pg. 2864
ATR INFRASTRUCTURE PVT. LTD.—See IRB Infrastructure Developers Ltd.; *Int'l*, pg. 3805
ATR INTERNATIONAL AG—See Stahlgruber Otto Gruber GmbH & Co. KG; *Int'l*, pg. 7164
ATR INTERNATIONAL, INC.; *U.S. Private*, pg. 381
ATRION CORPORATION—See Nordson Corporation; *U.S. Public*, pg. 1532
ATRION LEASING COMPANY LLC—See Nordson Corporation; *U.S. Public*, pg. 1532
ATRION MEDICAL PRODUCTS, INC.—See Nordson Corporation; *U.S. Public*, pg. 1532
ATRITECH, INC.—See Boston Scientific Corporation; *U.S. Public*, pg. 373
ATRIUM 21 SP. Z O.O.—See City Service SE; *Int'l*, pg. 1627
ATRIUM AT WESTON PLACE, LLC—See Ventas, Inc.; *U.S. Public*, pg. 2278
ATRIUM AUSTRALIA-PACIFIC RIM PTY. LTD—See Getinge AB; *Int'l*, pg. 2949
ATRIUM BIRE, SIGI, S.A., *Int'l*, pg. 694
ATRIUM CENTERS, LLC; *U.S. Private*, pg. 382
ATRIUM COMPANIES, INC.—See Kenner & Company, Inc.; *U.S. Private*, pg. 2285
ATRIUM COMPANIES, INC.—See North Cove Partners; *U.S. Private*, pg. 2944
ATRIUM CORPORATION—See Kenner & Company, Inc.; *U.S. Private*, pg. 2285
ATRIUM CORPORATION—See North Cove Partners; *U.S. Private*, pg. 2944
ATRIUM DEVELOPMENT INC.; *U.S. Private*, pg. 382
ATRIUM DOOR & WINDOW CO.—See Kenner & Company, Inc.; *U.S. Private*, pg. 2285
ATRIUM DOOR & WINDOW CO.—See North Cove Partners; *U.S. Private*, pg. 2944
ATRIUM EUROPE BV—See Getinge AB; *Int'l*, pg. 2949
ATRIUM HOTEL, L.L.C—See Hyatt Hotels Corporation; *U.S. Public*, pg. 1076
ATRIUM INNOVATIONS INC.—See Nestle S.A.; *Int'l*, pg. 5206
ATRIUM LJUNGBERG AB; *Int'l*, pg. 694
ATRIUM MALL LLC—See Winthrop Realty Liquidating Trust; *U.S. Public*, pg. 2374
ATRIUM MEDICAL CORPORATION—See Getinge AB; *Int'l*, pg. 2951
ATRIUM MEDICAL INDIA PVT LTD—See Getinge AB; *Int'l*, pg. 2949
ATRIUM MORTGAGE INVESTMENT CORPORATION; *Int'l*, pg. 694
ATRIUM REAL ESTATE INVESTMENT TRUST; *Int'l*, pg. 694
ATRIUM RISK MANAGEMENT SERVICES (WASHINGTON) LTD.—See Enstar Group Limited; *Int'l*, pg. 2448
ATRIUM SOFTWARE LTD—See Trimble, Inc.; *U.S. Public*, pg. 2190
ATRIUM STAFFING SERVICES LTD.; *U.S. Private*, pg. 382
ATRIUM UNDERWRITERS LTD.—See Enstar Group Limited; *Int'l*, pg. 2448
ATRIUM UNDERWRITING GROUP LTD.—See Enstar Group Limited; *Int'l*, pg. 2448
ATRIUM WINDOWS & DOORS, INC.—See Kenner & Company, Inc.; *U.S. Private*, pg. 2285
ATRIUM WINDOWS & DOORS, INC.—See North Cove Partners; *U.S. Private*, pg. 2944
ATRIUS HEALTH, INC.; *U.S. Private*, pg. 382
ATR KIMENG LAND, INC.—See Malayan Banking Berhad; *Int'l*, pg. 4660
ATR-LEARNING TECHNOLOGY CORPORATION—See Uchida Yoko Co., Ltd.; *Int'l*, pg. 8012
ATR LIGHTING ENTERPRISES, INC.; *U.S. Private*, pg. 381
ATRM HOLDINGS, INC.—See Star Equity Holdings, Inc.; *U.S. Public*, pg. 1937
ATRONIX INC.; *U.S. Private*, pg. 382
ATRO PROVITA GMBH—See Gelita AG; *Int'l*, pg. 2913
ATR-TREK CO., LTD.—See AI Co., Ltd.; *Int'l*, pg. 226
ATRUM COAL LIMITED; *Int'l*, pg. 694
ATR WIRE & CABLE CO. INC.—See ITOCHU Corporation; *Int'l*, pg. 3838
ATRYA SAS; *Int'l*, pg. 694
ATRYS HEALTH SA; *Int'l*, pg. 694

ATS ACOUSTICS; *U.S. Private*, pg. 382
ATS ADVANCED MANUFACTURING DIVISION—See ATS Corporation; *Int'l*, pg. 694
AT&S AMERICAS LLC—See AT&S Austria Technologie & Systemtechnik Aktiengesellschaft; *Int'l*, pg. 665
ATS ARITIM TEKNOLOJILERI SANAYI TIC AS—See Veolia Environnement S.A.; *Int'l*, pg. 8161
AT&S ASIA PACIFIC LIMITED—See AT&S Austria Technologie & Systemtechnik Aktiengesellschaft; *Int'l*, pg. 665
ATS ASPHALTTECHNIK GMBH—See FAYAT SAS; *Int'l*, pg. 2624
ATS ASSEMBLY & TEST, INC. - DAYTON—See ATS Corporation; *Int'l*, pg. 695
ATS ASSEMBLY & TEST, INC.—See ATS Corporation; *Int'l*, pg. 695
ATS-ATPE S.A.S.—See KONE Oyj; *Int'l*, pg. 4247
AT&S AUSTRIA TECHNOLOGIE & SYSTEMTECHNIK AKTIENGESELLSCHAFT; *Int'l*, pg. 664
ATS AUTOMATION ASIA PTE LTD—See ATS Corporation; *Int'l*, pg. 695
ATS AUTOMATION ASIA (TIANJIN) CO., LTD.—See ATS Corporation; *Int'l*, pg. 695
ATS AUTOMATION INC.; *U.S. Private*, pg. 382
ATS AUTOMATION MALAYSIA SDN. BHD.—See ATS Corporation; *Int'l*, pg. 695
ATS AUTOMATION—See ATS Corporation; *Int'l*, pg. 695
ATS AUTOMATION TOOLING SYSTEMS GMBH—See ATS Corporation; *Int'l*, pg. 695
ATS AUTOMATION TOOLING SYSTEMS GMBH - WINNENDEN—See ATS Corporation; *Int'l*, pg. 695
ATS-AVANTE TECHNOLOGY & SERVICE LTD.—See Sungwoo Techron Co., Ltd.; *Int'l*, pg. 7316
ATS CAROLINA INC.—See ATS Corporation; *Int'l*, pg. 695
AT&S CHINA CO. LTD.—See AT&S Austria Technologie & Systemtechnik Aktiengesellschaft; *Int'l*, pg. 665
ATSCO FOOTWEAR GROUP; *U.S. Private*, pg. 382
ATS CO., LTD.—See Daifuku Co., Ltd.; *Int'l*, pg. 1924
ATS CORPORATION; *Int'l*, pg. 694
AT&S DEUTSCHLAND GMBH—See AT&S Austria Technologie & Systemtechnik Aktiengesellschaft; *Int'l*, pg. 665
ATS ELECTRIC, INC.; *U.S. Private*, pg. 382
ATS ELGI LIMITED—See ELGI Equipments Limited; *Int'l*, pg. 2359
AT SEMICON CO., LTD.; *Int'l*, pg. 664
ATS ENGINEERING LTD.; *Int'l*, pg. 696
ATS EUROMASTER LIMITED—See Compagnie Generale des Etablissements Michelin SCA; *Int'l*, pg. 1741
ATS GROUP, LLC; *U.S. Private*, pg. 382
ATS-HELLMANN WORLDWIDE LOGISTICS LTD.—See Hellmann Worldwide Logistics GmbH & Co. KG; *Int'l*, pg. 3335
ATSIGN, INC.; *U.S. Private*, pg. 382
AT&S INDIA PRIVATE LIMITED—See AT&S Austria Technologie & Systemtechnik Aktiengesellschaft; *Int'l*, pg. 665
ATS INDUSTRIAL SUPPLY, S. DE R.L. DE C.V.—See MSC Industrial Direct Co., Inc.; *U.S. Public*, pg. 1483
AT SINGAPORE (GLOBAL) PTE. LTD.—See Agilent Technologies, Inc.; *U.S. Public*, pg. 60
ATS JAPAN CORP.—See RTX Corporation; *U.S. Public*, pg. 1822
ATS JAPAN KABUSHIKI KAISHA—See RTX Corporation; *U.S. Public*, pg. 1822
AT&S KLAGENFURT LEITERPLATTEN GMBH—See AT&S Austria Technologie & Systemtechnik Aktiengesellschaft; *Int'l*, pg. 665
ATS KOREA—See RTX Corporation; *U.S. Public*, pg. 1822
ATS KRAFTSERVICE AB—See Peab AB; *Int'l*, pg. 5771
ATS LABORATORIES INC.—See Abbott Laboratories; *U.S. Public*, pg. 18
ATS LEICHTMETALLRADER GMBH—See UNIWHEELS Management (Switzerland) AG; *Int'l*, pg. 8083
ATSL HOLDINGS B.V.—See Gammon India Limited; *Int'l*, pg. 2879
ATS LOGISTICS, INC.—See Nova Infrastructure Management, LLC; *U.S. Private*, pg. 2965
ATS MACHINE TOOL DIVISION—See ATS Corporation; *Int'l*, pg. 695
AT+S N.V.—See Deufol SE; *Int'l*, pg. 2048
AT&S OF DELAWARE, INC.—See Acadia Healthcare Company, Inc.; *U.S. Public*, pg. 27
ATS OHIO INC.—See ATS Corporation; *Int'l*, pg. 695
ATS PACIFIC FIJI LIMITED—See Helloworld Travel Limited; *Int'l*, pg. 3337
ATS PACIFIC (NZ) LTD—See Helloworld Travel Limited; *Int'l*, pg. 3337
ATS PRECISION METAL COMPONENTS—See ATS Corporation; *Int'l*, pg. 695
ATS PRECISION PLASTIC COMPONENTS—See ATS Corporation; *Int'l*, pg. 695
ATS PROCESSING SERVICES, L.L.C.—See Verra Mobility Corporation; *U.S. Public*, pg. 2286
ATS PRODUCTS INC.; *U.S. Private*, pg. 382
ATS RETAIL SOLUTIONS—See TFI International Inc.; *Int'l*, pg. 7585
ATS SERVICE AB—See Peab AB; *Int'l*, pg. 5771

AT & S SKANDINAVIA AB—See AT&S Austria Technologie & Systemtechnik Aktiengesellschaft; *Int'l*, pg. 665
ATS SORTIMAT USA LLC—See ATS Corporation; *Int'l*, pg. 695
ATS SPECIALIZED, INC.—See Anderson Trucking Service Inc.; *U.S. Private*, pg. 277
A.T.S. SRL—See Vitrolife AB; *Int'l*, pg. 8262
ATS STAHLSCHMIDT & MAIWORM GMBH—See UNIWHEELS Management (Switzerland) AG; *Int'l*, pg. 8083
ATS STAHLSCHMIDT & MAIWORM SP. Z O.O.—See UNIWHEELS Management (Switzerland) AG; *Int'l*, pg. 8083
ATS SYSTEMS OREGON INC.—See ATS Corporation; *Int'l*, pg. 695
AT&S (TAIWAN) CO., LTD.—See AT&S Austria Technologie & Systemtechnik Aktiengesellschaft; *Int'l*, pg. 665
ATS-TANNER BANDING SYSTEMS AG; *Int'l*, pg. 696
ATS TEST INC.—See ATS Corporation; *Int'l*, pg. 695
ATS TRAINING, LLC; *U.S. Private*, pg. 382
ATSUGI CO., LTD.; *Int'l*, pg. 696
ATSUGI ISEHARA CABLE NETWORK CORPORATION—See TOKAI Holdings Corporation; *Int'l*, pg. 7779
ATSUGI SENKO TRANSPORT CO., LTD.—See Senko Group Holdings Co., Ltd.; *Int'l*, pg. 6709
ATSUGISENSO CO., LTD.—See The Sumitomo Warehouse Co. Ltd.; *Int'l*, pg. 7689
AT SURGICAL COMPANY, INC.; *U.S. Private*, pg. 363
ATSUTA SHIKI CO., LTD.—See Tomoku Co., Ltd.; *Int'l*, pg. 7801
ATS WICKEL-UND MONTAGETECHNIK AG—See ATS Corporation; *Int'l*, pg. 695
AT SYSTEMATIZATION BERHAD; *Int'l*, pg. 664
A&T SYSTEMS INC.; *U.S. Private*, pg. 21
A&T SYSTEMS—See A&T Systems Inc.; *U.S. Private*, pg. 21
ATTABOX INDUSTRIAL ENCLOSURES—See Robroy Industries, Inc.; *U.S. Private*, pg. 3463
ATTACHE; *U.S. Private*, pg. 382
ATTACK MARKETING, LLC; *U.S. Private*, pg. 383
ATTACQ LIMITED; *Int'l*, pg. 696
ATTADALE HOSPITAL PROPERTY PTY LIMITED—See Ramsay Health Care Limited; *Int'l*, pg. 6199
AT&T ADVANCED SOLUTIONS, INC.—See AT&T Inc.; *U.S. Public*, pg. 219
AT-TAHUR LTD.; *Int'l*, pg. 665
ATTAINED PTY. LTD.—See Adisyn Ltd; *Int'l*, pg. 149
ATTAIN FINANCE CANADA, INC.—See CURO Group Holdings Corp.; *U.S. Public*, pg. 611
ATTAINIA, INC.—See TA Associates, Inc.; *U.S. Private*, pg. 3918
ATTAIN, LLC; *U.S. Private*, pg. 383
ATTAKROC INC.—See Mincon Group PLC; *Int'l*, pg. 4900
AT&T ALASCOM—See Arlington Capital Partners LLC; *U.S. Private*, pg. 328
ATTANA AB; *Int'l*, pg. 696
ATTARCO INC.; *U.S. Private*, pg. 383
ATTARD & CO. FOODSTUFFS LTD.—See Attard & Co. Ltd.; *Int'l*, pg. 696
ATTARD & CO. INDUSTRIAL LTD.—See Attard & Co. Ltd.; *Int'l*, pg. 696
ATTARD & CO. LTD.; *Int'l*, pg. 696
AT&T ARKANSAS—See AT&T Inc.; *U.S. Public*, pg. 219
ATTAS ALARKO TURISTIK TESISLER A.S.—See Alarko Holding A.S.; *Int'l*, pg. 291
ATTC MANUFACTURING, INC.—See AISIN Corporation; *Int'l*, pg. 253
AT&T COMMUNICATIONS CORP.—See AT&T Inc.; *U.S. Public*, pg. 219
AT&T COMUNICACIONES DIGITALES, S. DE R.L. DE C.V.—See AT&T Inc.; *U.S. Public*, pg. 219
ATT CONSULTANTS COMPANY LIMITED—See Team Consulting Engi; *Int'l*, pg. 7500
ATTEA & ATTEA, P.C.; *U.S. Private*, pg. 383
ATTEBURY GRAIN, LLC; *U.S. Private*, pg. 383
AT TECHMAC CO., LTD.—See Anritsu Corporation; *Int'l*, pg. 475
ATTEL INGENIERIE-SATCO—See TXCOM S.A.; *Int'l*, pg. 7993
ATTEMA B.V.—See ABN AMRO Group N.V.; *Int'l*, pg. 65
ATTENDEE INTERACTIVE, LLC—See Insight Venture Management, LLC; *U.S. Private*, pg. 2088
ATTENDO AB; *Int'l*, pg. 696
ATTENDS AB—See PT Sinar Mas Group; *Int'l*, pg. 6072
ATTENDS AS—See PT Sinar Mas Group; *Int'l*, pg. 6072
ATTENDS BVBA—See PT Sinar Mas Group; *Int'l*, pg. 6072
ATTENDS EUROPE GMBH—See PT Sinar Mas Group; *Int'l*, pg. 6072
ATTENDS GMBH—See PT Sinar Mas Group; *Int'l*, pg. 6072
ATTENDS GMBH—See PT Sinar Mas Group; *Int'l*, pg. 6072
ATTENDS HEALTHCARE AB—See PT Sinar Mas Group; *Int'l*, pg. 6072
ATTENDS HEALTHCARE GROUP LTD.—See PT Sinar Mas Group; *Int'l*, pg. 6072
ATTENDS HEALTHCARE LTD.—See PT Sinar Mas Group; *Int'l*, pg. 6073

231

ATTENDS HEALTHCARE PRODUCTS, INC.—See PT Sinar Mas Group; *Int'l*, pg. 6073
ATTENDS HEALTHCARE PRODUCTS, INC.—See PT Sinar Mas Group; *Int'l*, pg. 6073
ATTENDS LTD—See PT Sinar Mas Group; *Int'l*, pg. 6073
ATTENDS OY—See PT Sinar Mas Group; *Int'l*, pg. 6073
ATTENSITY CORPORATION—See Attensity Group, Inc.; *U.S. Private*, pg. 383
ATTENSITY GROUP, INC.; *U.S. Private*, pg. 383
AT&T ENTERPRISE CANADA CO.—See AT&T Inc.; *U.S. Public*, pg. 219
ATTENTI LTD.—See Apax Partners LLP; *Int'l*, pg. 502
ATTENTI US, INC.—See Apax Partners LLP; *Int'l*, pg. 502
ATTERBERY TRUCK SALES, INC.; *U.S. Private*, pg. 383
ATTERO TECH, LLC—See QSC, LLC; *U.S. Private*, pg. 3314
ATTESTOR LIMITED; *Int'l*, pg. 696
ATTEWELL LIMITED—See Inflexion Private Equity Partners LLP; *Int'l*, pg. 3688
AT&T EXTERNAL AFFAIRS—See Frontier Communications Parent, Inc.; *U.S. Public*, pg. 887
AT&T GOVERNMENT SOLUTIONS, INC.—See Arlington Capital Partners LLC; *U.S. Private*, pg. 328
AT&T GOVERNMENT SOLUTIONS—See AT&T Inc.; *U.S. Public*, pg. 219
AT THE TABLE PUBLIC RELATIONS; *U.S. Private*, pg. 363
ATT HOLDING COMPANY—See Griffon Corporation; *U.S. Public*, pg. 969
ATTICABANK PROPERTIES S.A—See ATTICA BANK S.A.; *Int'l*, pg. 696
ATTICA BANK S.A.; *Int'l*, pg. 696
ATTICA CONSULTING S.A—See ATTICA BANK S.A.; *Int'l*, pg. 696
ATTICA DEPARTMENT STORES S.A.—See Folli Follie S.A.; *Int'l*, pg. 2721
ATTICA GROUP; *Int'l*, pg. 696
ATTICA HOLDINGS (UK) LIMITED—See Integrated Asset Management plc; *Int'l*, pg. 3730
ATTICA HYDRAULIC EXCHANGE, INC.—See Clearlake Capital Group, L.P.; *U.S. Private*, pg. 933
ATTICA PUBLICATIONS S.A.; *Int'l*, pg. 696
ATTICA VENTURES S.A.—See ATTICA BANK S.A.; *Int'l*, pg. 696
ATTICA WEALTH MANAGEMENT S.A.—See ATTICA BANK S.A.; *Int'l*, pg. 696
ATTIC LIGHT ENTERTAINMENT, INC.; *U.S. Private*, pg. 383
ATTIJARIWAFA BANK EGYPT S.A.E—See Banco Santander, S.A.; *Int'l*, pg. 825
ATTIJARIWAFA BANK—See Banco Santander, S.A.; *Int'l*, pg. 825
ATTI-KAT SA; *Int'l*, pg. 696
ATTIKI ODOS S.A—See ELLAKTOR S.A.; *Int'l*, pg. 2364
ATTIKI SA—See Viohalco SA/NV; *Int'l*, pg. 8243
ATTILAN GROUP LIMITED; *Int'l*, pg. 696
AT&T INC.; *U.S. Public*, pg. 218
ATTIS INDUSTRIES INC.; *U.S. Private*, pg. 383
ATTIS OIL AND GAS LIMITED—See Helium One Global Ltd.; *Int'l*, pg. 3331
ATTITASH MOUNTAIN RESORT—See Vail Resorts, Inc.; *U.S. Public*, pg. 2271
ATTITUDE DRINK COMPANY, INC.—See Attitude Drinks Incorporated; *U.S. Private*, pg. 383
ATTITUDE DRINKS INCORPORATED; *U.S. Private*, pg. 383
ATTITUDES IN DRESSING INC.; *U.S. Private*, pg. 383
ATTIVO GROUP; *Int'l*, pg. 696
AT&T KANSAS—See AT&T Inc.; *U.S. Public*, pg. 219
ATTL ADVANCED MATERIALS CO., LTD.—See Advanced Technology & Materials Co., Ltd.; *Int'l*, pg. 162
AT&T MESSAGING—See AT&T Inc.; *U.S. Public*, pg. 219
AT&T MISSOURI—See AT&T Inc.; *U.S. Public*, pg. 219
AT&T MOBILITY LLC—See AT&T Inc.; *U.S. Public*, pg. 219
AT&T MOBILITY LLC—See AT&T Inc.; *U.S. Public*, pg. 219
AT&T MOBILITY LLC—See AT&T Inc.; *U.S. Public*, pg. 219
AT&T MOBILITY LLC—See AT&T Inc.; *U.S. Public*, pg. 219
AT&T MOBILITY LLC—See AT&T Inc.; *U.S. Public*, pg. 219
AT&T MOBILITY LLC—See AT&T Inc.; *U.S. Public*, pg. 219
AT&T MOBILITY LLC—See AT&T Inc.; *U.S. Public*, pg. 219
ATTOCK CEMENT PAKISTAN LIMITED; *Int'l*, pg. 697
ATTOCK PETROLEUM LIMITED—See Attock Refinery Ltd; *Int'l*, pg. 697
ATTOCK REFINERY LTD; *Int'l*, pg. 697
AT&T OF PUERTO RICO, INC.—See AT&T Inc.; *U.S. Public*, pg. 219
AT&T OHIO—See AT&T Inc.; *U.S. Public*, pg. 219
AT&T OKLAHOMA—See AT&T Inc.; *U.S. Public*, pg. 219
AT TOKYO CORPORATION—See SECOM Co., Ltd.; *Int'l*, pg. 6670
AT&T OPERATIONS, INC.—See AT&T Inc.; *U.S. Public*, pg. 219

ATTORNEYS' TITLE FUND SERVICES, LLC—See Attorneys' Title Insurance Fund; *U.S. Private*, pg. 383
ATTORNEYS' TITLE GUARANTY FUND, INC.; *U.S. Private*, pg. 383
ATTORNEYS' TITLE GUARANTY FUND, INC.—See Guaranteed Rate, Inc.; *U.S. Private*, pg. 1809
ATTORNEYS' TITLE GUARANTY FUND—See Guaranteed Rate, Inc.; *U.S. Private*, pg. 1809
ATTORNEYS' TITLE INSURANCE FUND; *U.S. Private*, pg. 383
ATTO TECHNOLOGY, INC.; *U.S. Private*, pg. 383
ATTRACTIVE VENTURE (JB) SDN. BHD.—See D'nonce Technology Bhd.; *Int'l*, pg. 1899
ATTRACTIVE VENTURE (KL) SDN. BHD.—See D'nonce Technology Bhd.; *Int'l*, pg. 1899
ATTRACTIVE VENTURE SDN. BHD.—See D'nonce Technology Bhd.; *Int'l*, pg. 1899
A-T TRADE INC.; *U.S. Private*, pg. 22
ATTRAQT GROUP PLC—See CrownPeak Technology, Inc.; *U.S. Private*, pg. 1112
ATTRAX S.A.—See DZ BANK AG Deutsche Zentral-Genossenschaftsbank; *Int'l*, pg. 2245
ATTRELL AUTO HOLDINGS LIMITED; *Int'l*, pg. 697
ATTREZZOAUTO.COM S.R.L.—See s.a. D'Ieteren n.v.; *Int'l*, pg. 6447
ATTRONICA COMPUTERS INC.; *U.S. Private*, pg. 383
AT&T SERVICES INC—See AT&T Inc.; *U.S. Public*, pg. 219
AT&T—See Frontier Communications Parent, Inc.; *U.S. Public*, pg. 887
AT&T—See AT&T Inc.; *U.S. Public*, pg. 218
AT&T—See AT&T Inc.; *U.S. Public*, pg. 219
AT&T—See AT&T Inc.; *U.S. Public*, pg. 218
AT&T—See AT&T Inc.; *U.S. Public*, pg. 218
AT&T—See AT&T Inc.; *U.S. Public*, pg. 218
AT&T—See AT&T Inc.; *U.S. Public*, pg. 219
AT&T—See AT&T Inc.; *U.S. Public*, pg. 219
AT&T—See AT&T Inc.; *U.S. Public*, pg. 219
AT&T—See AT&T Inc.; *U.S. Public*, pg. 219
AT&T—See AT&T Inc.; *U.S. Public*, pg. 219
AT&T—See AT&T Inc.; *U.S. Public*, pg. 218
AT&T—See AT&T Inc.; *U.S. Public*, pg. 219
AT&T—See AT&T Inc.; *U.S. Public*, pg. 218
AT&T—See AT&T Inc.; *U.S. Public*, pg. 218
AT&T SOUTHEAST—See AT&T Inc.; *U.S. Public*, pg. 218
AT&T SOUTHEAST—See AT&T Inc.; *U.S. Public*, pg. 219
AT&T TECHNICAL SERVICES COMPANY—See Arlington Capital Partners LLC; *U.S. Private*, pg. 328
AT&T TELEHOLDINGS, INC—See AT&T Inc.; *U.S. Public*, pg. 219
AT&T TEXAS—See AT&T Inc.; *U.S. Public*, pg. 219
ATTUNE FOODS, INC.; *U.S. Private*, pg. 383
ATTUNE HEARING PTY. LTD.—See Amplifon S.p.A.; *Int'l*, pg. 435
ATTUNITY (HONG KONG) LTD.—See Thoma Bravo, L.P.; *U.S. Private*, pg. 4152
ATTUNITY INC.—See Thoma Bravo, L.P.; *U.S. Private*, pg. 4152
ATTUNITY ISRAEL (1992) LTD—See Thoma Bravo, L.P.; *U.S. Private*, pg. 4152
ATTUNITY LTD.—See Thoma Bravo, L.P.; *U.S. Private*, pg. 4152
ATTUNITY (UK) LIMITED—See Thoma Bravo, L.P.; *U.S. Private*, pg. 4152
ATTUNIX CORPORATION; *U.S. Private*, pg. 383
ATTURRA HOLDINGS PTY LTD—See Atturra Ltd.; *Int'l*, pg. 697
ATTURRA LTD.; *Int'l*, pg. 697
AT&T WEST—See AT&T Inc.; *U.S. Public*, pg. 219
ATTWOOD CORPORATION—See Brunswick Corporation; *U.S. Public*, pg. 407
A.T.U AUTO-TEILE-UNGER GMBH & CO. KG—See Mobivia Groupe SA; *Int'l*, pg. 5012
ATUL AUTO LTD.; *Int'l*, pg. 697
ATUL GREEN AUTOMOTIVE PRIVATE LIMITED—See Atul Auto Ltd.; *Int'l*, pg. 697
ATUL LTD.—See Lalbhai Group; *Int'l*, pg. 4399
ATUL SUGAR SCREENS PRIVATE LIMITED—See IDEX Corp; *U.S. Public*, pg. 1089
ATUM LIFE PRIVATE LIMITED—See Visaka Industries Limited; *Int'l*, pg. 8249
ATUTOR I.C. SP. Z.O.O—See PROCHEM S.A.; *Int'l*, pg. 5986
ATVEXA AB; *Int'l*, pg. 697
ATVIQ BIOTECH LTD.—See Orgenesis Inc.; *U.S. Public*, pg. 1617
ATV PRIVAT TV GMBH & CO KG—See ProSiebenSat.1 Media SE; *Int'l*, pg. 6000
ATV PRODUCTIONS LTD.—See Best Medical International, Inc.; *U.S. Private*, pg. 543
ATV PROJECTS INDIA LIMITED; *Int'l*, pg. 697
A.T. WALL COMPANY; *U.S. Private*, pg. 28
ATWATER REAL ESTATE; *U.S. Private*, pg. 384
ATWATER TIRE SERVICES INC.—See Delray Tire & Retreading Inc.; *U.S. Private*, pg. 1199
ATW COMPANIES INC.; *U.S. Private*, pg. 384
ATWEC TECHNOLOGIES, INC.; *U.S. Public*, pg. 225
ATWELL AZ, LLC—See Atwell, LLC; *U.S. Private*, pg. 384
ATWELL, LLC; *U.S. Private*, pg. 384
ATWELL MEDIA SERVICES, INC.; *U.S. Private*, pg. 384

A.T. WILLIAMS OIL COMPANY; *U.S. Private*, pg. 28
ATWOOD AUSTRALIAN WATERS DRILLING PTY. LTD.—See Valaris Limited; *Int'l*, pg. 8110
ATWOOD CHEVROLET INC.; *U.S. Private*, pg. 384
ATWOOD DEEP SEAS, LTD.—See Valaris Limited; *Int'l*, pg. 8110
ATWOOD DISTRIBUTING, INC.; *U.S. Private*, pg. 384
ATWOOD DRILLING, INC.—See Valaris Limited; *Int'l*, pg. 8110
ATWOOD ENTERPRISES INC.; *U.S. Private*, pg. 384
ATWOOD FENCE COMPANY INC.; *U.S. Private*, pg. 384
ATWOOD HUNTER CO.—See Valaris Limited; *Int'l*, pg. 8110
ATWOOD OCEANICS AUSTRALIA PTY. LTD.—See Valaris Limited; *Int'l*, pg. 8110
ATWOOD OCEANICS, INC.—See Valaris Limited; *Int'l*, pg. 8110
ATWOOD OCEANICS MANAGEMENT, LP—See Valaris Limited; *Int'l*, pg. 8110
ATWORKGROUP LLC; *U.S. Private*, pg. 384
ATW TECH INC.; *Int'l*, pg. 697
ATX COMMUNICATIONS, INC.—See Windstream Holdings, Inc.; *U.S. Public*, pg. 2373
ATX INC.—See Kadokawa Corporation; *Int'l*, pg. 4047
ATX NETWORKS CORP.—See H.I.G. Capital, LLC; *U.S. Private*, pg. 1828
ATX S.A.—See Emerson Electric Co.; *U.S. Public*, pg. 740
ATYAB BAKERY LLC—See Oman Flour Mills Co SAOG; *Int'l*, pg. 5559
ATYAB FOODTECH LLC—See Oman Flour Mills Co SAOG; *Int'l*, pg. 5559
ATYAB INVESTMENTS LLC—See Oman Flour Mills Co SAOG; *Int'l*, pg. 5559
ATYATI TECHNOLOGIES PRIVATE LIMITED—See Genpact Limited; *Int'l*, pg. 2926
AT YOUR SERVICE LIMOUSINES, INC.—See Unique Limousine, Inc.; *U.S. Private*, pg. 4286
ATYPON SYSTEMS JORDAN—See John Wiley & Sons, Inc.; *U.S. Public*, pg. 1192
ATYPON SYSTEMS, LLC—See John Wiley & Sons, Inc.; *U.S. Public*, pg. 1192
ATYPON SYSTEMS UK—See John Wiley & Sons, Inc.; *U.S. Public*, pg. 1192
ATYR PHARMA, INC.; *U.S. Public*, pg. 225
ATZENHOFFER CHEVROLET COMPANY; *U.S. Private*, pg. 384
AU10TIX B.V.—See ICTS International, N.V.; *Int'l*, pg. 3587
AUA BETEILIGUNGEN GESELLSCHAFT M.B.H.—See Deutsche Lufthansa AG; *Int'l*, pg. 2066
AUA PRIVATE EQUITY PARTNERS LLC; *U.S. Private*, pg. 384
AUBADE HANDELS GMBH—See Calida Holding AG; *Int'l*, pg. 1264
AUBADE ITALIA S.R.L.—See Calida Holding AG; *Int'l*, pg. 1264
AUBADE PARIS SAS—See Calida Holding AG; *Int'l*, pg. 1264
AUBADE PARIS (UK) LTD.—See Calida Holding AG; *Int'l*, pg. 1264
AUBASS CO., LTD.—See Denso Corporation; *Int'l*, pg. 2028
AUBAY ITALIA S.P.A.—See Aubay SA; *Int'l*, pg. 698
AUBAY LUXEMBOURG S.A.—See Aubay SA; *Int'l*, pg. 698
AUBAY PORTUGAL—See Aubay SA; *Int'l*, pg. 698
AUBAY SA; *Int'l*, pg. 698
AUBAY SPAIN S.L.—See Aubay SA; *Int'l*, pg. 698
AUBAY UK LIMITED—See Aubay SA; *Int'l*, pg. 698
AUBERGEDUSOLEIL; *U.S. Private*, pg. 384
AUBERLE; *U.S. Private*, pg. 384
AUBERT & DUVAL SAS - FIRMINY PLANT—See Eramet SA; *Int'l*, pg. 2489
AUBERT & DUVAL SAS - GENNEVILLIERS PLANT—See Eramet SA; *Int'l*, pg. 2489
AUBERT & DUVAL SAS - IMPHY PLANT—See Eramet SA; *Int'l*, pg. 2489
AUBERT & DUVAL SAS - ISSOIRE INTERFORGE PLANT—See Eramet SA; *Int'l*, pg. 2489
AUBERT & DUVAL SAS - LES ANCIZES PLANT—See Eramet SA; *Int'l*, pg. 2489
AUBERT & DUVAL SAS - PAMIERS PLANT—See Eramet SA; *Int'l*, pg. 2489
AUBERT & DUVAL—See Eramet SA; *Int'l*, pg. 2489
AUBES PRODUCTIONS—See Vivendi SE; *Int'l*, pg. 8275
AUBEX CORPORATION; *Int'l*, pg. 698
AUB GROUP LIMITED; *Int'l*, pg. 697
AUB GROUP NZ LIMITED—See AUB Group Limited; *Int'l*, pg. 698
AUBO PRODUCTION A/S—See TCM Group A/S; *Int'l*, pg. 7484
AUBREY GROUP, INC.—See Elbit Systems Limited; *Int'l*, pg. 2344
AUBREY ORGANICS INC.; *U.S. Private*, pg. 385
AUBREY SILVEY ENTERPRISES INC.; *U.S. Private*, pg. 385
AUBRY LOGISTIQUE; *Int'l*, pg. 698
AUBUCHON HOMES, INC.; *U.S. Private*, pg. 385
AUBURN BANCORP, INC.; *U.S. Public*, pg. 225

COMPANY NAME INDEX

AUBURNBANK—See Auburn National Bancorporation, Inc.; *U.S. Public*, pg. 225
AUBURN COMMUNITY HOSPITAL; *U.S. Private*, pg. 385
AUBURN CORPORATION; *U.S. Private*, pg. 385
AUBURN DAIRY PRODUCTS, INC.—See Instantwhip Foods, Inc.; *U.S. Private*, pg. 2092
AUBURN ENTERPRISES LLC—See Aptiv PLC; *Int'l*, pg. 524
AUBURN FILTERSENSE LLC—See Nederman Holding AB; *Int'l*, pg. 5188
AUBURN GEAR, INC.—See North River Capital LLC; *U.S. Private*, pg. 2946
AUBURN HOSIERY MILLS, INC.—See GMM Capital LLC; *U.S. Private*, pg. 1722
AUBURN INVESTMENTS INC.—See Drury Inn Inc.; *U.S. Private*, pg. 1280
AUBURN JOURNAL INC.—See Brehm Communications Inc.; *U.S. Private*, pg. 644
AUBURN LEATHER CO.—See ISA Industrial Ltd.; *Int'l*, pg. 3812
AUBURN MANOR APARTMENTS LP—See Edison International; *U.S. Public*, pg. 719
THE AUBURN MANUFACTURING COMPANY; *U.S. Private*, pg. 3990
AUBURN MANUFACTURING INC.; *U.S. Private*, pg. 385
AUBURN MOTOR SALES; *U.S. Private*, pg. 385
AUBURN NATIONAL BANCORPORATION, INC.; *U.S. Public*, pg. 225
AUBURN REGIONAL MEDICAL CENTER—See Universal Health Services, Inc.; *U.S. Public*, pg. 2260
AUBURN ROAD FAMILY MEDICAL CENTRE PTY LIMITED—See Sonic Healthcare Limited; *Int'l*, pg. 7096
AUBURN SAVINGS BANK—See Auburn Bancorp, Inc.; *U.S. Public*, pg. 225
AUBURN SUPPLY CO. INC.; *U.S. Private*, pg. 385
AUBURN TRADER—See Brehm Communications Inc.; *U.S. Private*, pg. 644
AUCFAN CO., LTD.; *Int'l*, pg. 698
AUC FINANCIAL PARTNERS INC—See Aucnet Inc.; *Int'l*, pg. 700
AUCHAN (CHINA) INVESTMENT CO., LTD.—See Alibaba Group Holding Limited; *Int'l*, pg. 326
AUCHAN COORDINATION SERVICES S.A.—See Auchan Holding S.A.; *Int'l*, pg. 699
AUCHAN E-COMMERCE FRANCE S.A.S.—See Auchan Holding S.A.; *Int'l*, pg. 699
AUCHAN E-COMMERCE POLSKA SP. Z O.O.—See Auchan Holding S.A.; *Int'l*, pg. 699
AUCHAN HOLDING S.A.; *Int'l*, pg. 699
AUCHAN HUNGARY—See Auchan Holding S.A.; *Int'l*, pg. 699
AUCHAN POLSKA—See Auchan Holding S.A.; *Int'l*, pg. 699
AUCHAN ROMANIA S.A.—See Auchan Holding S.A.; *Int'l*, pg. 699
AUCHAN SHANGHAI HYPERMARKET—See Auchan Holding S.A.; *Int'l*, pg. 699
AUCHAN—See Auchan Holding S.A.; *Int'l*, pg. 699
AUCHAN—See Auchan Holding S.A.; *Int'l*, pg. 699
AUCHAN—See Auchan Holding S.A.; *Int'l*, pg. 699
AUCHAN SPA; *Int'l*, pg. 699
AUCHAN UKRAINE—See Auchan Holding S.A.; *Int'l*, pg. 699
AUCHTERARDER CARE HOME—See Balhousie Holdings Limited; *Int'l*, pg. 808
AUCKLAND AUTO COLLECTION LIMITED—See Eagers Automotive Limited; *Int'l*, pg. 2263
AUCKLAND DENTAL GROUP—See BGH Capital Pty Ltd; *Int'l*, pg. 1008
AUCKLAND DENTAL GROUP—See Ontario Teachers' Pension Plan; *Int'l*, pg. 5585
AUCKLAND FISH MARKET LIMITED—See Sanford Limited; *Int'l*, pg. 6536
AUCKLAND HEARING LTD.—See Amplifon S.p.A.; *Int'l*, pg. 435
AUCKLAND INTERNATIONAL AIRPORT LIMITED; *Int'l*, pg. 699
AUCKLAND REAL ESTATE TRUST; *Int'l*, pg. 699
AUCLERT SAS; *Int'l*, pg. 699
AUCMA CO., LTD.; *Int'l*, pg. 699
AUCNET ADVANCE INC.—See Aucnet Inc.; *Int'l*, pg. 700
AUCNET CONSUMER PRODUCTS USA, LLC—See Aucnet Inc.; *Int'l*, pg. 700
AUCNET DIGITAL PRODUCTS INC.—See Aucnet Inc.; *Int'l*, pg. 700
AUCNET HK LIMITED—See Aucnet Inc.; *Int'l*, pg. 699
AUCNET IBS INC.—See Aucnet Inc.; *Int'l*, pg. 700
AUCNET INC.; *Int'l*, pg. 699
AUCNET MEDICAL INC.—See Aucnet Inc.; *Int'l*, pg. 700
AUCNET SALES AND SUPPORT INC.—See Aucnet Inc.; *Int'l*, pg. 700
AUCONET GMBH—See SPARTA AG; *Int'l*, pg. 7127
AUC SERVICE INC.—See Aucnet Inc.; *Int'l*, pg. 700
AUCTANE LLC—See Thoma Bravo, L.P.; *U.S. Private*, pg. 4153
AUCTION BROADCASTING CO. LLC; *U.S. Private*, pg. 385
AUCTION FRONTIER, LLC—See OPENLANE, Inc.; *U.S. Public*, pg. 1607

AUCTION SYSTEMS AUCTIONEERS & APPRAISERS, INC.; *U.S. Private*, pg. 385
AUCTION TECHNOLOGY GROUP PLC; *Int'l*, pg. 700
AUCTION WORLD USA, LLC; *U.S. Private*, pg. 385
AUCTIVA CORPORATION—See Alibaba Group Holding Limited; *Int'l*, pg. 326
AUCTUS CAPITAL PARTNERS AG; *Int'l*, pg. 700
AUCTUS INVESTMENT GROUP LIMITED; *Int'l*, pg. 700
AUCTUS MINERALS PTY. LTD.—See Denham Capital Management LP; *U.S. Private*, pg. 1205
AUDACIA SA; *Int'l*, pg. 700
AUDACIOUS INQUIRY, LLC; *U.S. Private*, pg. 385
AUDACY, INC.; *U.S. Public*, pg. 226
AUDALIA RESOURCES LIMITED; *Int'l*, pg. 700
AUDANT INVESTMENTS PTY. LTD.; *Int'l*, pg. 700
AUDATEX AUSTRALIA PTY LTD.—See Vista Equity Partners, LLC; *U.S. Private*, pg. 4399
AUDATEX CANADA, ULC—See Vista Equity Partners, LLC; *U.S. Private*, pg. 4400
AUDATEX DATEN INTERNATIONALE DATENENTWICKLUNGSGESELLSCHAFT MBH—See Vista Equity Partners, LLC; *U.S. Private*, pg. 4399
AUDATEX ESPANA S.A.—See Vista Equity Partners, LLC; *U.S. Private*, pg. 4399
AUDATEX INFORMATION SYSTEM (CHINA) CO., LTD.—See Vista Equity Partners, LLC; *U.S. Private*, pg. 4399
AUDATEX LTN S. DE R.L. DE C.V.—See Vista Equity Partners, LLC; *U.S. Private*, pg. 4400
AUDATEX NETWORK SERVICES NETHERLANDS B.V.—See Vista Equity Partners, LLC; *U.S. Private*, pg. 4400
AUDATEX NORTH AMERICA, INC.—See Vista Equity Partners, LLC; *U.S. Private*, pg. 4400
AUDATEX OSTERREICH GES.MBH—See Vista Equity Partners, LLC; *U.S. Private*, pg. 4400
AUDATEX POLSKA SP. Z.O.O.—See Vista Equity Partners, LLC; *U.S. Private*, pg. 4400
AUDATEX PORTUGAL PERITAGENS INFORMATIZADAS DERIVADAS DE ACIDENTES, S.A.—See Vista Equity Partners, LLC; *U.S. Private*, pg. 4400
AUDATEX SERVICES SRL—See Vista Equity Partners, LLC; *U.S. Private*, pg. 4400
AUDATEX SINGAPORE PTE LTD—See Vista Equity Partners, LLC; *U.S. Private*, pg. 4400
AUDATEX SLOVAKIA S.R.O.—See Vista Equity Partners, LLC; *U.S. Private*, pg. 4400
AUDATEX SWITZERLAND GMBH—See Vista Equity Partners, LLC; *U.S. Private*, pg. 4400
AUDATEX SYSTEMS BILGI TEKNOLOJILERI HIZMETLERI LIMTED SIRKETI—See Vista Equity Partners, LLC; *U.S. Private*, pg. 4400
AUDATEX SYSTEMS S.R.O.—See Vista Equity Partners, LLC; *U.S. Private*, pg. 4400
AUDATEX (UK) LIMITED—See Vista Equity Partners, LLC; *U.S. Private*, pg. 4399
AUDAX CREDIT BDC INC.; *U.S. Private*, pg. 385
AUDAX ENERGY GMBH—See ADX Energy Limited; *Int'l*, pg. 169
AUDAX ENERGY SRL—See ADX Energy Limited; *Int'l*, pg. 169
AUDAX GROUP, LIMITED PARTNERSHIP; *U.S. Private*, pg. 385
AUDAX-KECK GMBH; *Int'l*, pg. 700
AUDAX LTD.—See AUDAX-Keck GmbH; *Int'l*, pg. 700
AUDAX MANAGEMENT COMPANY, LLC—See Audax Group, Limited Partnership; *U.S. Private*, pg. 385
AUDAX MEZZANINE—See Audax Group, Limited Partnership; *U.S. Private*, pg. 390
AUDAX RENOVABLES, S.A.; *Int'l*, pg. 700
AUDCO INDIA LTD.—See Larsen & Toubro Limited; *Int'l*, pg. 4418
AUDDIA INC.; *U.S. Public*, pg. 227
AUDEARA LIMITED; *Int'l*, pg. 700
AUDECA, S.L.U.—See Elecnor, S.A.; *Int'l*, pg. 2347
AUDELI, S.A.—See ACS, Actividades de Construccion y Servicios, S.A.; *Int'l*, pg. 110
AUDEMARS PIGUET & CIE; *Int'l*, pg. 700
AUDEMARS PIGUET DEUTSCHLAND—See Audemars Piguet & Cie; *Int'l*, pg. 701
AUDEMARS PIGUET FRANCE—See Audemars Piguet & Cie; *Int'l*, pg. 701
AUDEMARS PIGUET ITALIA S.P.A.—See Audemars Piguet & Cie; *Int'l*, pg. 701
AUDEMARS PIGUET (NORTH AMERICA)—See Audemars Piguet & Cie; *Int'l*, pg. 700
AUDEMARS PIGUET (SUISSE) S.A.—See Audemars Piguet & Cie; *Int'l*, pg. 701
AUDEN TECHNO CORP.; *Int'l*, pg. 701
AUDENTES THERAPEUTICS, INC.—See Astellas Pharma Inc.; *Int'l*, pg. 653
AUDERA; *Int'l*, pg. 701
AUDETTE CADILLAC, INC.; *U.S. Private*, pg. 390
AUDEX FUJAIRAH LL FZE—See PEC Ltd.; *Int'l*, pg. 5778
AUDI AG—See Porsche Automobil Holding SE; *Int'l*, pg. 5926
AUDIA INTERNATIONAL, INC.; *U.S. Private*, pg. 390

AUDI AKADEMIE GESELLSCHAFT FUR PERSONAL UND ORGANISATIONS ENTWICKLUNG MBH—See Porsche Automobil Holding SE; *Int'l*, pg. 5926
AUDIBLE GMBH—See Amazon.com, Inc.; *U.S. Public*, pg. 90
AUDIBLE, INC.—See Amazon.com, Inc.; *U.S. Public*, pg. 90
AUDIBLE LIMITED—See Amazon.com, Inc.; *U.S. Public*, pg. 90
AUDI BRAZIL DISTRIBUIDORA DE VEICULOS LTD.—See Porsche Automobil Holding SE; *Int'l*, pg. 5926
AUDI CAPITAL (KSA) CJSC—See Bank Audi sal; *Int'l*, pg. 837
AUDI CAPITAL (SYRIA) LLC—See Bank Audi sal; *Int'l*, pg. 837
AUDI CORAL SPRINGS—See Lithia Motors, Inc.; *U.S. Public*, pg. 1321
AUDIENCE LABS SA; *Int'l*, pg. 701
AUDIENCE PARTNERS, LLC—See Altice USA, Inc.; *U.S. Public*, pg. 87
AUDIENCE PRODUCTIONS, INC.; *U.S. Private*, pg. 391
AUDIENCESCIENCE INC.; *U.S. Private*, pg. 391
AUDIENCE SYSTEMS LIMITED—See Kotobuki Corporation; *Int'l*, pg. 4292
AUDIENCEVIEW TICKETING CORPORATION; *Int'l*, pg. 701
AUDI FARMINGTON HILLS—See Lithia Motors, Inc.; *U.S. Public*, pg. 1321
AUDIGY GROUP LLC—See GN Store Nord A/S; *Int'l*, pg. 3016
AUDI HUNGARIA MOTOR KFT.—See Porsche Automobil Holding SE; *Int'l*, pg. 5926
AUDI JAPAN K.K.—See Porsche Automobil Holding SE; *Int'l*, pg. 5926
AUDIKA AB—See Demant A/S; *Int'l*, pg. 2023
AUDIKA AG—See Demant A/S; *Int'l*, pg. 2023
AUDIKA APS—See Demant A/S; *Int'l*, pg. 2023
AUDIKA GROUPE SA—See Demant A/S; *Int'l*, pg. 2023
AUDIMATION SERVICES, INC.—See CaseWare International, Inc.; *Int'l*, pg. 1352
AUDINATE GROUP LIMITED; *Int'l*, pg. 701
AUDINATE, INC.—See Audinate Group Limited; *Int'l*, pg. 701
AUDINATE LIMITED—See Audinate Group Limited; *Int'l*, pg. 701
AUDINATE LIMITED—See Audinate Group Limited; *Int'l*, pg. 701
AUDINATE PTY LIMITED—See Audinate Group Limited; *Int'l*, pg. 701
AUDIOBOOM GROUP PLC; *Int'l*, pg. 701
AUDIOBOOM LIMITED—See Audioboom Group plc; *Int'l*, pg. 701
AUDIOCODES ARGENTINA S.A.—See AudioCodes Ltd.; *Int'l*, pg. 701
AUDIOCODES, BEIJING—See AudioCodes Ltd.; *Int'l*, pg. 702
AUDIOCODES BRASIL EQUIPAMENTOS DE VOZ SOBRE IP LTDA.—See AudioCodes Ltd.; *Int'l*, pg. 701
AUDIOCODES CALIFORNIA—See AudioCodes Ltd.; *Int'l*, pg. 701
AUDIOCODES EUROPE LIMITED—See AudioCodes Ltd.; *Int'l*, pg. 701
AUDIOCODES GMBH—See AudioCodes Ltd.; *Int'l*, pg. 701
AUDIOCODES, INC.—See AudioCodes Ltd.; *Int'l*, pg. 702
AUDIOCODES INDIA PVT. LTD.—See AudioCodes Ltd.; *Int'l*, pg. 702
AUDIOCODES KOREA LTD.—See AudioCodes Ltd.; *Int'l*, pg. 702
AUDIOCODES LTD.; *Int'l*, pg. 701
AUDIOCODES LTD.—See AudioCodes Ltd.; *Int'l*, pg. 702
AUDIOCODES MEXICO—See AudioCodes Ltd.; *Int'l*, pg. 702
AUDIOCODES SINGAPORE—See AudioCodes Ltd.; *Int'l*, pg. 702
AUDIOCODES USA—See AudioCodes Ltd.; *Int'l*, pg. 702
AUDIODEV FAR EAST LTD.—See Nok9 AB; *Int'l*, pg. 5403
AUDIODEV USA—See Nok9 AB; *Int'l*, pg. 5403
AUDIO-DIGEST FOUNDATION; *U.S. Private*, pg. 391
AUDIO.DIGITAL NRW GMBH—See Deutsche Post AG; *Int'l*, pg. 2083
AUDIOEYE, INC.; *U.S. Public*, pg. 227
AUDI OF AMERICA, INC.—See Porsche Automobil Holding SE; *Int'l*, pg. 5926
AUDI OF BERNARDSVILLE; *U.S. Private*, pg. 390
AUDIO FIDELITY COMMUNICATIONS CORP.; *U.S. Private*, pg. 391
AUDIO GROUP GREECE B.V.; *Int'l*, pg. 701
AUDIO HEALTH HEARING CARE(SHATIN) LIMITED—See Town Health International Medical Group Limited; *Int'l*, pg. 7851
THE AUDIO HOUSE, INC.—See National Amusements, Inc.; *U.S. Private*, pg. 2844
AUDIO INTERVISUAL DESIGN, INC.—See Advanced Systems Group, LLC; *U.S. Private*, pg. 92
AUDIOLIB SA—See Vivendi SE; *Int'l*, pg. 8271
AUDIOLOGY SERVICES COMPANY LLC—See Demant A/S; *Int'l*, pg. 2023

AUDIO GROUP GREECE B.V.

AUDIOMICRO, INC.—See Zealot Networks, Inc.; *U.S. Private*, pg. 4598
AUDIONAMIX SA—See Eurovestech Plc; *Int'l*, pg. 2558
AUDIO NETWORK LIMITED—See Lions Gate Entertainment Corp.; *Int'l*, pg. 4520
AUDIONOMKLINIKEN SVERIGE AB—See Synsam AB; *Int'l*, pg. 7386
AUDIONOVA DENMARK—See HAL Trust N.V.; *Int'l*, pg. 3223
AUDIONOVA FRANCE—See HAL Trust N.V.; *Int'l*, pg. 3223
AUDIONOVA INTERNATIONAL B.V.—See Sonova Holding AG; *Int'l*, pg. 7100
THE AUDIO PARTNERS, INC.—See Blackstone Audio, Inc.; *U.S. Private*, pg. 576
AUDIO PIXELS HOLDINGS LIMITED; *Int'l*, pg. 701
AUDIOPOLE JSC—See Transition Evergreen; *Int'l*, pg. 7900
AUDIO PRECISION, INC.—See Battery Ventures, L.P.; *U.S. Private*, pg. 488
AUDIO PRO HEILBRONN ELEKTROAKUSTIK GMBH—See Transition Evergreen; *Int'l*, pg. 7900
AUDIO RESEARCH CORPORATION—See Fine Sounds S.p.A.; *Int'l*, pg. 2673
AUDIO SAT SP. Z.O.O.—See Siemens Aktiengesellschaft; *Int'l*, pg. 6886
AUDIOSEARS CORPORATION; *U.S. Private*, pg. 391
AUDIO SELECCION S.L.—See Demant A/S; *Int'l*, pg. 2023
AUDIOSONIC—See KKR & Co. Inc.; *U.S. Public*, pg. 1261
AUDIOTECH HEALTHCARE CORPORATION; *Int'l*, pg. 702
AUDIO-TECHNICA CENTRAL EUROPE LTD—See Audio-Technica Corporation; *Int'l*, pg. 701
AUDIO-TECHNICA CORPORATION; *Int'l*, pg. 701
AUDIO-TECHNICA (GREATER CHINA) LIMITED—See Audio-Technica Corporation; *Int'l*, pg. 701
AUDIO-TECHNICA LIMITED (UK)—See Audio-Technica Corporation; *Int'l*, pg. 701
AUDIO-TECHNICA NIEDERLASSUNG DEUTSCHLAND—See Audio-Technica Corporation; *Int'l*, pg. 701
AUDIO-TECHNICA SAS—See Audio-Technica Corporation; *Int'l*, pg. 701
AUDIO-TECHNICA (S.E.A.) PTE. LTD.—See Audio-Technica Corporation; *Int'l*, pg. 701
AUDIO-TECHNICA TAIWAN CO., LTD.—See Audio-Technica Corporation; *Int'l*, pg. 701
AUDIO-TECHNICA U.S., INC.—See Audio-Technica Corporation; *Int'l*, pg. 701
AUDIOTEL CORPORATION—See Jack Henry & Associates, Inc.; *U.S. Public*, pg. 1182
AUDIOTEL INTERNATIONAL LTD—See Security Research Group plc; *Int'l*, pg. 6677
AUDIO TOURS AND TRAVEL HONG KONG LIMITED—See TUI AG; *Int'l*, pg. 7964
AUDIOVALLEY; *Int'l*, pg. 702
AUDIO-VIDEO G+M LTD.—See Swisscom AG; *Int'l*, pg. 7373
AUDIO VIDEO SYSTEMS, INC. (AVS); *U.S. Private*, pg. 391
AUDIO VISUAL MANAGEMENT SOLUTIONS, INC.; *U.S. Private*, pg. 391
AUDIO VISUAL MATERIAL LIMITED—See Northamber plc; *Int'l*, pg. 5441
AUDIO VISUAL SERVICES CORPORATION—See Blackstone Inc.; *U.S. Public*, pg. 348
AUDIO VISUAL SERVICES GROUP, LLC—See Blackstone Inc.; *U.S. Public*, pg. 348
AUDIOVOX ATLANTA CORP.—See VOXX International Corporation; *U.S. Public*, pg. 2310
AUDIOVOX AUDIO VISUAL DIVISION—See VOXX International Corporation; *U.S. Public*, pg. 2310
AUDIOVOX ELECTRONICS CORPORATION—See VOXX International Corporation; *U.S. Public*, pg. 2310
AUDIOVOX MEXICO, S DE RR DE CV—See VOXX International Corporation; *U.S. Public*, pg. 2310
AUDIOVOX SOUTHEAST—See VOXX International Corporation; *U.S. Public*, pg. 2311
AUDIOWISE TECHNOLOGY INC.—See PixArt Imaging, Inc.; *Int'l*, pg. 5876
AUDIOXTRA PTY. LTD.—See Autobacs Seven Co., Ltd.; *Int'l*, pg. 725
AUDI PEMBROKE PINES; *U.S. Private*, pg. 390
AUDI SARADAR INVESTMENT BANK SAL—See Bank Audi sal; *Int'l*, pg. 837
AUDI SARADAR PRIVATE BANK SAL—See Bank Audi sal; *Int'l*, pg. 837
AUDI SYNKO GMBH—See Porsche Automobil Holding SE; *Int'l*, pg. 5926
AUDITECH BV—See Amplifon S.p.A.; *Int'l*, pg. 435
AUDITOIRE—See Omnicom Group Inc.; *U.S. Public*, pg. 1596
AUDITORY LEARNING FOUNDATION; *U.S. Private*, pg. 391
AUDIT SERVICES, INC.—See Aquiline Capital Partners LLC; *U.S. Private*, pg. 305
AUDITUDE, INC.—See Adobe Inc.; *U.S. Public*, pg. 42
AUDITWERX—See Carr, Riggs & Ingram, LLC; *U.S. Private*, pg. 771

AUDITZ, LLC—See TransUnion; *U.S. Public*, pg. 2184
AUDIUS AG; *Int'l*, pg. 702
AUDIUS SE—See audius AG; *Int'l*, pg. 702
AUDIX CORPORATION; *Int'l*, pg. 702
AUDIX HI-TECH INVESTMENT CO., LTD.—See Audix Corporation; *Int'l*, pg. 702
AUDIX TECHNOLOGY (WUJIANG) CO., LTD.—See Audix Corporation; *Int'l*, pg. 702
AUDIX TECHNOLOGY (XIAMEN) CO., LTD.—See Audix Corporation; *Int'l*, pg. 702
AUDI ZENTRUM AACHEN JACOBS AUTO GMBH—See Penske Automotive Group, Inc.; *U.S. Public*, pg. 1664
AUDI ZENTRUM HANNOVER GMBH—See Porsche Automobil Holding SE; *Int'l*, pg. 5926
AUDLEY CAPITAL ADVISORS LLP; *Int'l*, pg. 702
AUDLEY TRAVEL US, INC.; *U.S. Private*, pg. 391
AUDMET OY—See Demant A/S; *Int'l*, pg. 2023
AUDUBON ENGINEERING; *U.S. Private*, pg. 391
AUDUBON MAGAZINE—See National Audubon Society, Inc.; *U.S. Private*, pg. 2847
AUDUBON MACHINERY CORP.; *U.S. Private*, pg. 391
AUDUBON MANUFACTURING CORPORATION—See Oshkosh Corporation; *U.S. Public*, pg. 1620
AUDUBON MATERIALS LLC—See Eagle Materials Inc.; *U.S. Public*, pg. 702
AUDUBON METALS LLC—See Koch Enterprises, Inc.; *U.S. Private*, pg. 2326
AUDUBON NATURE INSTITUTE; *U.S. Private*, pg. 391
AUDUBON PHYSICAL THERAPY, LIMITED PARTNERSHIP—See U.S. Physical Therapy, Inc.; *U.S. Public*, pg. 2214
AUDUBON READYMIX LLC—See Eagle Materials Inc.; *U.S. Public*, pg. 702
AUDUBON URBAN INVESTMENTS, LLC—See Bank of America Corporation; *U.S. Public*, pg. 270
AUER - DIE BAUSOFTWARE GMBH—See Nemetschek SE; *Int'l*, pg. 5193
AUER FORMENBAU GMBH—See L. Possehl & Co. mbH; *Int'l*, pg. 4381
AUERHAMMER METALLWERK GMBH—See Wickeder Westfalenstahl GmbH; *Int'l*, pg. 8401
AUER LIGHTING GMBH—See Saratoga Partners L.P.; *U.S. Private*, pg. 3549
AUER STEEL & HEATING SUPPLY CO. INC.; *U.S. Private*, pg. 391
AUER STEEL & HEATING SUPPLY COMPANY, TWIN CITIES, INC.—See Auer Steel & Heating Supply Co. Inc.; *U.S. Private*, pg. 391
AUER VERLAG GMBH—See Ernst Klett AG; *Int'l*, pg. 2495
AUFBAU UND HANDELSGESELLSCHAFT MBH—See DZ BANK AG Deutsche Zentral-Genossenschaftsbank; *Int'l*, pg. 2243
AUFEMININ S.A.—See Television Francaise 1 S.A.; *Int'l*, pg. 7542
AUFFENBERG IMPORTS INC.; *U.S. Private*, pg. 391
AUFFENBERG OF CARBONDALE—See Chris Auffenberg Ford Inc.; *U.S. Private*, pg. 889
AU FINANCIAL HOLDINGS CORPORATION—See KDDI Corporation; *Int'l*, pg. 4111
AUFWIND SCHMACK ELSO BIOGAZ SZOLGALTATO KFT.—See BayWa AG; *Int'l*, pg. 915
AUGA GROUP, AB; *Int'l*, pg. 702
AUGA GRUDUVA, UAB—See AUGA group, AB; *Int'l*, pg. 702
AUGA JURBARKAI, ZUB—See AUGA group, AB; *Int'l*, pg. 702
AUGA LANKESA, ZUB—See AUGA group, AB; *Int'l*, pg. 702
AUGA MANTVILISKIS, ZUB—See AUGA group, AB; *Int'l*, pg. 702
AUGA NAUSODE, ZUB—See AUGA group, AB; *Int'l*, pg. 702
AUGA SKEMIAI, ZUB—See AUGA group, AB; *Int'l*, pg. 702
AUGA SMILGIAI, ZUB—See AUGA group, AB; *Int'l*, pg. 702
AUGA SPINDULYS, ZUB—See AUGA group, AB; *Int'l*, pg. 703
AUGA ZELSVELE, ZUB—See AUGA group, AB; *Int'l*, pg. 703
AUGEAN NORTH LIMITED—See Ancala Partners LLP; *Int'l*, pg. 448
AUGEAN NORTH LIMITED—See Fiera Capital Corporation; *Int'l*, pg. 2659
AUGEAN NORTH SEA SERVICES LIMITED—See Ancala Partners LLP; *Int'l*, pg. 448
AUGEAN NORTH SEA SERVICES LIMITED—See Fiera Capital Corporation; *Int'l*, pg. 2659
AUGEAN PLC—See Ancala Partners LLP; *Int'l*, pg. 448
AUGEAN PLC—See Fiera Capital Corporation; *Int'l*, pg. 2659
AUGEAN SOUTH LIMITED—See Ancala Partners LLP; *Int'l*, pg. 448
AUGEAN SOUTH LIMITED—See Fiera Capital Corporation; *Int'l*, pg. 2659
AUGEAN TREATMENT LIMITED—See Ancala Partners LLP; *Int'l*, pg. 448
AUGEAN TREATMENT LIMITED—See Fiera Capital Corporation; *Int'l*, pg. 2659

CORPORATE AFFILIATIONS

AUGEO AFFINITY MARKETING, INC.; *U.S. Private*, pg. 391
AUGERE CONSTRUCTION; *U.S. Private*, pg. 392
AUGER SERVICES, INC.—See Primoris Services Corporation; *U.S. Public*, pg. 1718
AUGER SITE INVESTIGATIONS LTD.—See Sdiptech AB; *Int'l*, pg. 6658
AUGES SALES & SERVICE; *U.S. Private*, pg. 392
AUGE TECHNOLOGY CORPORATION; *Int'l*, pg. 703
AUGHINISH ALUMINA LIMITED—See United Company RUSAL Plc; *Int'l*, pg. 8066
AUG. LAUKHUFF GMBH & CO. KG; *Int'l*, pg. 702
AUGMEDIX, INC.—See HCA Healthcare, Inc.; *U.S. Public*, pg. 994
AUGMENTITY SYSTEMS; *U.S. Private*, pg. 392
AUGMENTUM FINTECH PLC; *Int'l*, pg. 703
AUG. PRIEN IMMOBILIEN PE VERWALTUNG BRAHMSQUARTIER GMBH—See Allianz SE; *Int'l*, pg. 343
AUG. RATH JUN. GMBH—See Rath AG; *Int'l*, pg. 6214
AUGROS COSMETIC PACKAGING; *Int'l*, pg. 703
AUGSBURG FORTRESS CANADA—See Augsburg Fortress; *U.S. Private*, pg. 392
AUGSBURG FORTRESS; *U.S. Private*, pg. 392
AUGUR CAPITAL AG; *Int'l*, pg. 703
AUGURE SA; *Int'l*, pg. 703
AUGUSTA APARTMENTS NEVADA, LLC—See RAIT Financial Trust; *U.S. Private*, pg. 3348
AUGUST A. BUSCH & COMPANY OF MASSACHUSETTS, INC.—See Anheuser-Busch InBev SA/NV; *Int'l*, pg. 465
THE AUGUSTA CHRONICLE—See Gannett Co., Inc.; *U.S. Public*, pg. 904
AUGUSTA COATING & MANUFACTURING, LLC; *U.S. Private*, pg. 392
AUGUSTA COCA-COLA BOTTLING COMPANY—See Coca-Cola Bottling Co. United, Inc.; *U.S. Private*, pg. 958
AUGUSTA COOPERATIVE FARM BUREAU, INC.; *U.S. Private*, pg. 392
AUGUSTA CYBERKNIFE, LLC—See HCA Healthcare, Inc.; *U.S. Public*, pg. 991
AUGUSTA DODGE INC.; *U.S. Private*, pg. 392
AUGUSTA GOLD CORP.; *Int'l*, pg. 703
AUGUSTA HEALTH SYSTEM, LLC—See Quorum Health Corporation; *U.S. Private*, pg. 3329
AUGUSTA IRON & STEEL WORKS; *U.S. Private*, pg. 392
AUGUSTA MEMORIAL PARK PERPETUAL CARE COMPANY—See Axar Capital Management L.P.; *U.S. Private*, pg. 411
AUGUSTA PHYSICIAN SERVICES, LLC—See Quorum Health Corporation; *U.S. Private*, pg. 3329
AUGUSTA POINTE, LLC—See Century Communities, Inc.; *U.S. Public*, pg. 475
AUGUSTA PRIMARY CARE SERVICES, LLC—See HCA Healthcare, Inc.; *U.S. Public*, pg. 991
AUGUSTA READY MIX INC.; *U.S. Private*, pg. 392
AUGUSTA REGIONAL CLINIC; *U.S. Private*, pg. 392
AUGUSTA RESOURCE CENTER ON AGING, INC.—See Life Care Companies, LLC; *U.S. Private*, pg. 2448
AUGUSTA SPORTSWEAR, INC.—See Platinum Equity, LLC; *U.S. Private*, pg. 3207
AUGUSTA SURGICAL CENTER—See HCA Healthcare, Inc.; *U.S. Public*, pg. 991
AUGUSTA SYMPHONY INC.; *U.S. Private*, pg. 392
AUGUSTA SYSTEMS, INC.—See Hexagon AB; *Int'l*, pg. 3368
AUGUST BROTJE GMBH—See BDR Thermea Group B.V.; *Int'l*, pg. 930
AUGUST CAPITAL; *U.S. Private*, pg. 392
AUGUST EQUITY LLP; *Int'l*, pg. 703
AUGUSTE THOUARD EXPERTISE, SAS—See BNP Paribas SA; *Int'l*, pg. 1080
AUGUSTE VICTORIA GMBH—See RAG-Stiftung; *Int'l*, pg. 6179
AUGUST FALLER GMBH & CO. KG; *Int'l*, pg. 703
AUGUST FRANCE HOLDING COMPANY S.A.S.—See Sensata Technologies Holding plc; *U.S. Public*, pg. 1865
AUGUST HALL, LLC—See Live Nation Entertainment, Inc.; *U.S. Public*, pg. 1328
AUGUST HILDEBRANDT GMBH; *Int'l*, pg. 703
AUGUST HOME PUBLISHING COMPANY; *U.S. Private*, pg. 392
AUGUSTINE VENTURES INC.—See Red Pine Exploration Inc.; *Int'l*, pg. 6244
AUGUST & JEAN HILPERT GMBH & CO. KG—See STRABAG SE; *Int'l*, pg. 7229
AUGUST, LANG & HUSAK, INC.; *U.S. Private*, pg. 392
AUGUSTOWIANKA SP. Z.O.O.—See Marie Brizard Wine & Spirits S.A.; *Int'l*, pg. 4693
AUGUST PACKAGING INC.; *U.S. Private*, pg. 392
AUGUST RUEGGEBERG GMBH & CO. KG PFERDWERKZEUGE; *Int'l*, pg. 703
AUGUST SILK INC.—See High Fashion International Limited; *Int'l*, pg. 3385
AUGUSTUS MARTIN LTD.; *Int'l*, pg. 704
AUGUST WINTER & SONS INC.; *U.S. Private*, pg. 392
AUGWIND ENERGY TECH STORAGE LTD.; *Int'l*, pg. 704

COMPANY NAME INDEX

AUI CONTRACTORS, LLC.; *U.S. Private*, pg. 392
AUI, INC.; *U.S. Private*, pg. 392
AUJAN INDUSTRIES CO., L.L.C.; *Int'l*, pg. 704
AUJARD SAS—See Brookfield Corporation; *Int'l*, pg. 1188
AUKAMM KLINIK FUR OPERATIVE RHEUMATOLOGIE UND ORTHOPADIE GMBH—See Fresenius SE & Co. KGaA; *Int'l*, pg. 2778
AUK CORP.—See Kodenshi Corporation; *Int'l*, pg. 4225
AUKETT FITZROY ROBINSON LIMITED—See Aukett Swanke Group Plc; *Int'l*, pg. 704
AUKETT FITZROY ROBINSON SP. Z.O.O.—See Aukett Swanke Group Plc; *Int'l*, pg. 704
AUKETT SRO—See Aukett Swanke Group Plc; *Int'l*, pg. 704
AUKETT SWANKE GROUP PLC; *Int'l*, pg. 704
AUKING MINING LIMITED; *Int'l*, pg. 704
AUKLAND MEDICINE DISTRIBUTORS (PROPRIETARY) LIMITED—See Remgro Limited; *Int'l*, pg. 6270
AU LAC SOFTWARE DEVELOPMENT COMPANY LIMITED—See ALTA Company; *Int'l*, pg. 384
AU LAC TECHNOLOGY APPLICATIONS PLASTICS COMPANY LIMITED—See ALTA Company; *Int'l*, pg. 384
AULAND CO., LTD.—See Sumitomo Electric Industries, Ltd.; *Int'l*, pg. 7278
AULBACH ENTGRATUNGSTECHNIK GMBH; *Int'l*, pg. 704
AUL BROTHERS TOOL & DIE INC.—See Mursix Corporation; *U.S. Private*, pg. 2816
A U L CORP.—See Dai-ichi Life Holdings, Inc.; *Int'l*, pg. 1917
AULDHOUSE COMPUTER TRAINING LIMITED—See AWN Holdings Limited; *Int'l*, pg. 753
AULD PHILLIPS LTD.; *Int'l*, pg. 704
AUL REINSURANCE MANAGEMENT SERVICES, LLC—See American United Mutual Insurance Holding Company; *U.S. Private*, pg. 258
AULSON CO. INC.; *U.S. Private*, pg. 393
AULT ALLIANCE, INC.; *U.S. Public*, pg. 227
AULT DISRUPTIVE TECHNOLOGIES CORPORATION; *U.S. Public*, pg. 227
AUMA ACTUATORS (CHINA) CO., LTD.—See AUMA Riester GmbH & Co. KG; *Int'l*, pg. 704
AUMA ACTUATORS LTD.—See AUMA Riester GmbH & Co. KG; *Int'l*, pg. 704
AUMA ACTUATORS MIDDLE EAST WLL—See AUMA Riester GmbH & Co. KG; *Int'l*, pg. 705
AUMA ACTUATORS (SINGAPORE) PTE LTD.—See AUMA Riester GmbH & Co. KG; *Int'l*, pg. 704
AUMA ACTUATORS (S) PTE. LTD.—See AUMA Riester GmbH & Co. KG; *Int'l*, pg. 704
AUMA-ARMATURENANTRIEBE GES.M.B.H.—See AUMA Riester GmbH & Co. KG; *Int'l*, pg. 705
AUMA AUTOMACAO DO BRASIL LTDA.—See AUMA Riester GmbH & Co. KG; *Int'l*, pg. 705
AUMA BENELUX B.V.B.A.—See AUMA Riester GmbH & Co. KG; *Int'l*, pg. 704
AUMA BENELUX B.V.—See AUMA Riester GmbH & Co. KG; *Int'l*, pg. 704
AUMA ENDUSTRI KONTROL SISTEMLERI LIMITED SIRKETI—See AUMA Riester GmbH & Co. KG; *Int'l*, pg. 704
AUMA FINLAND OY—See AUMA Riester GmbH & Co. KG; *Int'l*, pg. 704
AUMA FRANCE S.A.R.L.—See AUMA Riester GmbH & Co. KG; *Int'l*, pg. 704
AUMA INDIA PRIVATE LIMITED—See AUMA Riester GmbH & Co. KG; *Int'l*, pg. 704
AUMA ITALIANA S.R.L.—See AUMA Riester GmbH & Co. KG; *Int'l*, pg. 704
AUMA JAPAN CO., LTD.—See AUMA Riester GmbH & Co. KG; *Int'l*, pg. 704
AUMAKE LIMITED; *Int'l*, pg. 705
AUMA-LUSA REPRESENTATIVE OFFICE, LDA.—See AUMA Riester GmbH & Co. KG; *Int'l*, pg. 705
AUMA MEXICO S. DE R.L. DE C.V.—See AUMA Riester GmbH & Co. KG; *Int'l*, pg. 704
AUMANN AG—See MBB SE; *Int'l*, pg. 4751
AUMANN BEELEN GMBH—See MBB SE; *Int'l*, pg. 4751
AUMAN'S, INC.—See Service Corporation International; *U.S. Public*, pg. 1871
AUMA POLSKA SP. Z O.O.—See AUMA Riester GmbH & Co. KG; *Int'l*, pg. 704
AUMA RIESTER GMBH & CO. KG; *Int'l*, pg. 704
AUMA (SCHWEIZ) AG—See AUMA Riester GmbH & Co. KG; *Int'l*, pg. 704
AUMA SERVOPOHONY SPOL. S.R.O.—See AUMA Riester GmbH & Co. KG; *Int'l*, pg. 704
AUMA SOUTH AFRICA (PTY) LTD.—See AUMA Riester GmbH & Co. KG; *Int'l*, pg. 705
AUMA TECHNOLOGY AUTOMATIONS LTD—See AUMA Riester GmbH & Co. KG; *Int'l*, pg. 704
AUMEGA METALS LTD.; *Int'l*, pg. 705
AU MIN AFRICA PTY LTD; *Int'l*, pg. 697
AU MINERA CORP; *Int'l*, pg. 697
AUMO, INC.—See Gree Inc.; *Int'l*, pg. 3069
AUNALYTICS, INC., *U.S. Private*, pg. 393
AUNA OPERADORES DE TELECOMUNICACIONES, S.A.—See Orange S.A.; *Int'l*, pg. 5610
AUNA S.A.A.; *Int'l*, pg. 705
AUNA TELECOMUNICACIONES S.A.—See Orange S.A.; *Int'l*, pg. 5610
AU NATUREL INC.—See HGGC, LLC; *U.S. Private*, pg. 1930
AUN CONSULTING, INC.; *Int'l*, pg. 705
AUNDE ACHTER & EBELS GMBH; *Int'l*, pg. 705
AUNDE BRAZIL S.A.—See AUNDE Achter & Ebels GmbH; *Int'l*, pg. 705
AUNDE CORPORATION—See AUNDE Achter & Ebels GmbH; *Int'l*, pg. 705
AUNDE FRANCE SA—See AUNDE Achter & Ebels GmbH; *Int'l*, pg. 705
AUNDE KFT—See AUNDE Achter & Ebels GmbH; *Int'l*, pg. 705
AUNDE KULMBACH GMBH—See AUNDE Achter & Ebels GmbH; *Int'l*, pg. 705
AUNDE MEXICO S.A. DE C.V.—See AUNDE Achter & Ebels GmbH; *Int'l*, pg. 705
AUNDE POLAND SP. Z O.O.—See AUNDE Achter & Ebels GmbH; *Int'l*, pg. 705
AUNDE S.A.—See AUNDE Achter & Ebels GmbH; *Int'l*, pg. 705
AUN GLOBAL MARKETING PTE. LTD.—See AUN Consulting, Inc.; *Int'l*, pg. 705
AUN HONG KONG MARKETING CO., LTD.—See AUN Consulting, Inc.; *Int'l*, pg. 705
AUN THAI LABORATORIES CO., LTD.—See AUN Consulting, Inc.; *Int'l*, pg. 705
AUNTIE ANNE'S INC.—See Roark Capital Group Inc.; *U.S. Private*, pg. 3454
AUNT KITTY'S FOODS, INC—See Hanover Foods Corporation; *U.S. Public*, pg. 984
AUNT SARAH'S LLC; *U.S. Private*, pg. 393
AUO CORPORATION; *Int'l*, pg. 706
AUO GREEN ENERGY AMERICA CORP.—See AUO Corporation; *Int'l*, pg. 706
AUO GREEN ENERGY EUROPE B.V.—See AUO Corporation; *Int'l*, pg. 706
AU OPTRONICS CORPORATION AMERICA—See AUO Corporation; *Int'l*, pg. 706
AU OPTRONICS CORPORATION JAPAN—See AUO Corporation; *Int'l*, pg. 706
AU OPTRONICS EUROPE B.V.—See AUO Corporation; *Int'l*, pg. 706
AU OPTRONICS KOREA LTD.—See AUO Corporation; *Int'l*, pg. 706
AU OPTRONICS MANUFACTURING (SHANGHAI) CORP.—See AUO Corporation; *Int'l*, pg. 706
AU OPTRONICS (SHANGHAI) CO., LTD.—See AUO Corporation; *Int'l*, pg. 706
AU OPTRONICS (SLOVAKIA) S.R.O.—See AUO Corporation; *Int'l*, pg. 706
AU PAIR IN AMERICA—See American Institute for Foreign Study, Inc.; *U.S. Private*, pg. 237
AUPLATA SAS; *Int'l*, pg. 706
AUPU HOME STYLE CORPORATION LTD.; *Int'l*, pg. 706
AUQ GOLD MINING INC.; *Int'l*, pg. 706
AURA BIOSCIENCES, INC.; *U.S. Public*, pg. 227
AURA CE CO., LTD.—See RAITO KOGYO Co., Ltd.; *Int'l*, pg. 6191
AURA ENERGY LIMITED; *Int'l*, pg. 706
AURA ENGINEERING SOLUTION CO., LTD.—See Segula Technologies SA; *Int'l*, pg. 6683
AURA FINANCIAL CORPORATION; *U.S. Private*, pg. 393
AURAFIN LLC—See Berkshire Hathaway Inc.; *U.S. Public*, pg. 316
AURAFIN OROAMERICA—See Berkshire Hathaway Inc.; *U.S. Public*, pg. 316
AURA HARDWOOD LUMBER INC.—See Hardwoods Distribution Inc.; *Int'l*, pg. 3273
AURA INVESTMENTS LTD.; *Int'l*, pg. 706
AURA LIGHT AB—See FSN Capital Partners AS; *Int'l*, pg. 2798
AURA LIGHT APS—See FSN Capital Partners AS; *Int'l*, pg. 2799
AURA LIGHT A/S—See FSN Capital Partners AS; *Int'l*, pg. 2798
AURA LIGHT FRANCE SARL—See FSN Capital Partners AS; *Int'l*, pg. 2799
AURA LIGHT GMBH—See FSN Capital Partners AS; *Int'l*, pg. 2799
AURA LIGHT GREECE—See FSN Capital Partners AS; *Int'l*, pg. 2799
AURA LIGHT INTERNATIONAL AB—See FSN Capital Partners AS; *Int'l*, pg. 2798
AURA LIGHT ITALY S.R.L.—See FSN Capital Partners AS; *Int'l*, pg. 2799
AURA LIGHT OY—See FSN Capital Partners AS; *Int'l*, pg. 2799
AURALIGHT POLSKA SP. Z O.O.—See FSN Capital Partners AS; *Int'l*, pg. 2799
AURA LIGHT PORTUGAL UNIPESSOAL, LDA—See FSN Capital Partners AS; *Int'l*, pg. 2799
AURA LIGHT SPAIN, S.L.U.—See FSN Capital Partners AS; *Int'l*, pg. 2799
AURA LIGHT TRADING (SHANGHAI) CO., LTD—See FSN Capital Partners AS; *Int'l*, pg. 2799
AURA LIGHT USA INC—See FSN Capital Partners AS; *Int'l*, pg. 2799
AURA LONG LIFE LAMPS LTD.—See FSN Capital Partners AS; *Int'l*, pg. 2799
AURA MINERALS INC.—See Northwestern Enterprises Ltd.; *Int'l*, pg. 5447
AURA MINERALS (ONTARIO) INC.—See Northwestern Enterprises Ltd.; *Int'l*, pg. 5447
AURAMO OY—See Hyster-Yale Materials Handling, Inc.; *U.S. Public*, pg. 1079
AURANGABAD DISTILLERY LIMITED; *Int'l*, pg. 706
AURANIA RESOURCES LTD.; *Int'l*, pg. 707
AURA OSIGURANJE A.D.; *Int'l*, pg. 706
AURA RENEWABLE ACQUISITIONS PLC; *Int'l*, pg. 706
AURASOURCE, INC.; *U.S. Public*, pg. 227
AURAS TECHNOLOGY CO., LTD.; *Int'l*, pg. 707
AURA SYSTEMS, INC.; *U.S. Public*, pg. 227
AURATOR ASSET MANAGEMENT LTD.—See Evli Pankki Oyj; *Int'l*, pg. 2570
AURCANA SILVER CORPORATION; *Int'l*, pg. 707
AURDEL SWEDEN AB—See DistIT AB; *Int'l*, pg. 2136
AUREA ENERGY SOLUTIONS, INC.—See ESW Capital, LLC; *U.S. Private*, pg. 1429
AUREA, S.A.; *Int'l*, pg. 707
AUREA SOFTWARE GMBH—See ESW Capital, LLC; *U.S. Private*, pg. 1429
AUREA SOFTWARE, INC.—See ESW Capital, LLC; *U.S. Private*, pg. 1429
AUREC PTY. LTD.—See Randstad N.V.; *Int'l*, pg. 6201
AU-REKA GOLD CORPORATION—See Equinox Gold Corp.; *Int'l*, pg. 2485
AUREL BGC—See BGC Group, Inc.; *U.S. Public*, pg. 328
AURELIA METALS LTD; *Int'l*, pg. 707
AURELIAN ECUADOR S.A.—See Kinross Gold Corporation; *Int'l*, pg. 4182
AURELIAN OIL & GAS LIMITED—See San Leon Energy plc; *Int'l*, pg. 6521
AURELIAN OIL & GAS POLAND SP. Z O.O.—See San Leon Energy plc; *Int'l*, pg. 6521
AURELIO RESOURCE CORPORATION; *U.S. Private*, pg. 393
AURELIUS ACTIVE MANAGEMENT HOLDING GMBH—See Aurelius Equity Opportunities SE & Co. KGaA; *Int'l*, pg. 707
AURELIUS ALPHA LIMITED—See Aurelius Equity Opportunities SE & Co. KGaA; *Int'l*, pg. 707
AURELIUS BETEILIGUNGSBERATUNGS AG—See Aurelius Equity Opportunities SE & Co. KGaA; *Int'l*, pg. 707
AURELIUS COMMERCIAL BETEILIGUNGS GMBH—See Aurelius Equity Opportunities SE & Co. KGaA; *Int'l*, pg. 707
AURELIUS EQUITY OPPORTUNITIES SE & CO. KGAA; *Int'l*, pg. 707
AURELIUS FINANCE COMPANY LTD.—See Aurelius Equity Opportunities SE & Co. KGaA; *Int'l*, pg. 707
AURELIUS MINERALS LIMITED; *Int'l*, pg. 710
AURELIUS NEDERLAND B.V.—See Aurelius Equity Opportunities SE & Co. KGaA; *Int'l*, pg. 707
AURELIUS NORDICS AB—See Aurelius Equity Opportunities SE & Co. KGaA; *Int'l*, pg. 707
AURELIUS TRANSAKTIONSBERATUNGS AG—See Aurelius Equity Opportunities SE & Co. KGaA; *Int'l*, pg. 707
AUREOLE BUSINESS COMPONENTS & DEVICES INC.—See Mitani Sangyo Co., Ltd.; *Int'l*, pg. 4924
AUREOLE CONSTRUCTION SOFTWARE DEVELOPMENT INC.—See Mitani Sangyo Co., Ltd.; *Int'l*, pg. 4924
AUREOLE EXPERT INTEGRATORS INC.—See Mitani Sangyo Co., Ltd.; *Int'l*, pg. 4924
AUREOLE FINE CHEMICAL PRODUCTS INC.—See Mitani Sangyo Co., Ltd.; *Int'l*, pg. 4924
AUREOLE INFORMATION TECHNOLOGY INC.—See Mitani Sangyo Co., Ltd.; *Int'l*, pg. 4924
AUREOLE MITANI CHEMICAL & ENVIRONMENT INC.—See Mitani Sangyo Co., Ltd.; *Int'l*, pg. 4924
AUREOLE UNIT-DEVICES MANUFACTURING SERVICE INC.—See Mitani Sangyo Co., Ltd.; *Int'l*, pg. 4924
AUREON BIOSCIENCES, INC; *U.S. Private*, pg. 393
AURES GMBH—See Aures Technologies; *Int'l*, pg. 710
AURES TECHNOLOGIES GMBH—See Aures Technologies; *Int'l*, pg. 710
AURES TECHNOLOGIES INC.—See Aures Technologies; *Int'l*, pg. 710
AURES TECHNOLOGIES LTD.—See Aures Technologies; *Int'l*, pg. 710
AURES TECHNOLOGIES PTY. LTD.—See Aures Technologies; *Int'l*, pg. 710
AURES TECHNOLOGIES; *Int'l*, pg. 710
AURES USA INC—See Aures Technologies; *Int'l*, pg. 710
AUREX B.V.—See Aurobindo Pharma Ltd.; *Int'l*, pg. 712
AUREX ENERGY CORP.; *Int'l*, pg. 710
AURIANT MINING AB; *Int'l*, pg. 710
AURIA WIRELESS PTY LIMITED—See Etherstack PLC; *Int'l*, pg. 2263
AURIC ASSET MANAGEMENT PTE LTD—See Lippo Limited; *Int'l*, pg. 4522
AURIC CHUN YIP SDN BHD—See Lippo Limited; *Int'l*, pg. 4522
AURIC MINING LIMITED; *Int'l*, pg. 710
AURIC PACIFIC FOOD INDUSTRIES PTE LTD—See Lippo Limited; *Int'l*, pg. 4522

AURIC MINING LIMITED

CORPORATE AFFILIATIONS

AURIC PACIFIC FOOD PROCESSING SDN BHD—See Lippo Limited; *Int'l*, pg. 4522
AURIC PACIFIC GROUP LIMITED—See Lippo Limited; *Int'l*, pg. 4521
AURIC PACIFIC MARKETING PTE LTD—See Diethelm Keller Holding Limited; *Int'l*, pg. 2116
AURIC PACIFIC (M) SDN BHD—See Diethelm Keller Holding Limited; *Int'l*, pg. 2116
AURIC POOL, S.A.—See Fluidra SA; *Int'l*, pg. 2714
AURIC RESOURCES INTERNATIONAL, INC.; *U.S. Private*, pg. 393
AURIEMMA CONSULTING GROUP, INC., *U.S. Private*, pg. 393
AURIGA INDUSTRIES A/S; *Int'l*, pg. 710
AURIGA INTERNATIONAL S.A.—See Laboratorios del Dr. Esteve, S.A.; *Int'l*, pg. 4390
AURIGA POLYMERS INC.—See Indorama Ventures Public Company Limited; *Int'l*, pg. 3658
AURIGENE DISCOVERY TECHNOLOGIES LIMITED—See Dr. Reddy's Laboratories Limited; *Int'l*, pg. 2195
AURIGENE DISCOVERY TECHNOLOGIES (MALAYSIA) SDN BHD—See Dr. Reddy's Laboratories Limited; *Int'l*, pg. 2195
AURIGEN SA—See Sonic Healthcare Limited; *Int'l*, pg. 7096
AURIGO SOFTWARE TECHNOLOGIES INC.; *U.S. Private*, pg. 393
AURI, INC.; *U.S. Public*, pg. 227
AURINIA PHARMACEUTICALS INC.; *Int'l*, pg. 711
AURIN INVESTMENT GROUP GMBH; *Int'l*, pg. 711
AURINKO OU—See Finnair Plc; *Int'l*, pg. 2675
AURION CORPORATION PTY LIMITED—See Recruit Holdings Co., Ltd.; *Int'l*, pg. 6240
AURIONPRO SCM PTE LTD.—See Aurionpro Solutions Limited; *Int'l*, pg. 711
AURIONPRO SOLUTIONS (HK) LTD.—See Aurionpro Solutions Limited; *Int'l*, pg. 711
AURIONPRO SOLUTIONS LIMITED; *Int'l*, pg. 711
AURIONPRO SOLUTIONS PTY LTD.—See Aurionpro Solutions Limited; *Int'l*, pg. 711
AURIONPRO SOLUTIONS, SPC—See Aurionpro Solutions Limited; *Int'l*, pg. 711
AURIONPRO TRANSIT PTE. LTD.—See Aurionpro Solutions Limited; *Int'l*, pg. 711
AURION RESOURCES AB—See Aurion Resources Ltd.; *Int'l*, pg. 711
AURION RESOURCES LTD.; *Int'l*, pg. 711
AURIS AG; *Int'l*, pg. 711
AURISCO PHARMACEUTICAL CO., LTD.; *Int'l*, pg. 711
AURIS HEALTH, INC.—See Johnson & Johnson; *U.S. Public*, pg. 1194
AURIS HEALTH, INC.—See Johnson & Johnson; *U.S. Public*, pg. 1194
AURIS MEDICAL LTD.—See Altamira Therapeutics Ltd.; *Int'l*, pg. 385
AURIS MINERALS LIMITED; *Int'l*, pg. 711
AURIZON HOLDINGS LIMITED; *Int'l*, pg. 711
AURIZON OPERATIONS LIMITED—See Aurizon Holdings Limited; *Int'l*, pg. 711
AURIZON PORT SERVICES NSW PTY. LTD.—See Aurizon Holdings Limited; *Int'l*, pg. 711
AURIZON PORT SERVICES PTY LTD—See Aurizon Holdings Limited; *Int'l*, pg. 711
AUROBINDO (DATONG) BIO-PHARMA CO. LTD.—See Aurobindo Pharma Ltd.; *Int'l*, pg. 712
AUROBINDO (H.K.) LIMITED—See Aurobindo Pharma Ltd.; *Int'l*, pg. 712
AUROBINDO ILAC SANAYI VE TICARET LTD—See Aurobindo Pharma Ltd.; *Int'l*, pg. 712
AUROBINDO PHARMA B.V.—See Aurobindo Pharma Ltd.; *Int'l*, pg. 712
AUROBINDO PHARMA COLOMBIA SAS—See Aurobindo Pharma Ltd.; *Int'l*, pg. 712
AUROBINDO PHARMA FRANCE SARL—See Aurobindo Pharma Ltd.; *Int'l*, pg. 712
AUROBINDO PHARMA GMBH—See Aurobindo Pharma Ltd.; *Int'l*, pg. 712
AUROBINDO PHARMA INDUSTRIA FARMACEUTICA LTDA—See Aurobindo Pharma Ltd.; *Int'l*, pg. 712
AUROBINDO PHARMA (ITALIA) S.R.L—See Aurobindo Pharma Ltd.; *Int'l*, pg. 712
AUROBINDO PHARMA JAPAN K.K—See Aurobindo Pharma Ltd.; *Int'l*, pg. 712
AUROBINDO PHARMA LTD.; *Int'l*, pg. 712
AUROBINDO PHARMA (MALTA) LIMITED—See Aurobindo Pharma Ltd.; *Int'l*, pg. 712
AUROBINDO PHARMA (PORTUGAL) UNIPESSOAL LDA—See Aurobindo Pharma Ltd.; *Int'l*, pg. 712
AUROBINDO PHARMA PRODUCTOS FARMACEUTICOS LTDA—See Aurobindo Pharma Ltd.; *Int'l*, pg. 712
AUROBINDO PHARMA PRODUTOS FARMACEUTICOS LTDA.—See Aurobindo Pharma Ltd.; *Int'l*, pg. 712
AUROBINDO PHARMA (PTY) LIMITED—See Aurobindo Pharma Ltd.; *Int'l*, pg. 712
AUROBINDO PHARMA ROMANIA SRL—See Aurobindo Pharma Ltd.; *Int'l*, pg. 712
AUROBINDO PHARMA USA INC.—See Aurobindo Pharma Ltd.; *Int'l*, pg. 712

AUROBINDO SWITZERLAND AG—See Aurobindo Pharma Ltd.; *Int'l*, pg. 712
AUROBINDO TONGLING (DATONG) PHARMACEUTICAL CO. LTD.—See Aurobindo Pharma Ltd.; *Int'l*, pg. 712
AURO HEALTH LLC—See Aurobindo Pharma Ltd.; *Int'l*, pg. 712
AURO HOLDINGS BERHAD; *Int'l*, pg. 711
AURO IMPEX & CHEMICALS LIMITED; *Int'l*, pg. 711
AURO LABORATORIES LIMITED; *Int'l*, pg. 711
AUROLIFE PHARMA LLC—See Aurobindo Pharma Ltd.; *Int'l*, pg. 712
AUROMA COKE LIMITED; *Int'l*, pg. 713
AUROMA TECHNOLOGIES CO. DBA ACCESS LASER COMPANY—See TRUMPF SE + Co. KG; *Int'l*, pg. 7942
AUROMEDICS PHARMA LLC—See Aurobindo Pharma Ltd.; *Int'l*, pg. 712
AUROPHARMA INC.—See Aurobindo Pharma Ltd.; *Int'l*, pg. 712
AURORA ABSOLUTE RETURN FUND; *Int'l*, pg. 713
AURORA BEARING CO—See The Timken Company; *U.S. Public*, pg. 2132
AURORA BLACKTOP INC.; *U.S. Private*, pg. 393
AURORA CANNABIS INC.; *Int'l*, pg. 713
AURORA CAPITAL GROUP, LLC; *U.S. Private*, pg. 393
AURORA CAPITAL HOLDINGS LLC—See Saudi Arabian Oil Company; *Int'l*, pg. 6590
AURORA CASKET COMPANY, LLC—See Matthews International Corporation; *U.S. Public*, pg. 1399
AURORA CIVIL ENGINEERING INC.; *U.S. Private*, pg. 394
AURORA COMMUNITY SERVICES; *U.S. Private*, pg. 394
AURORA COOPERATIVE; *U.S. Private*, pg. 394
AURORA CORP. OF AMERICA—See Aurora Corporation; *Int'l*, pg. 713
AURORA CORPORATION; *Int'l*, pg. 713
AURORA DESIGN PUBLIC COMPANY LIMITED; *Int'l*, pg. 713
AURORA DEUTSCHLAND GMBH—See Aurora Cannabis Inc.; *Int'l*, pg. 713
AURORA DIAGNOSTICS HOLDINGS, LLC; *U.S. Private*, pg. 394
AURORA DIAGNOSTICS, LLC—See Sonic Healthcare Limited; *Int'l*, pg. 7096
AURORA EIENDOM AS; *Int'l*, pg. 713
AURORA ENERGY LTD.—See Paladin Energy Ltd.; *Int'l*, pg. 5705
AURORA FINANCIAL GROUP INC.—See Cherry Hill Mortgage Investment Corporation; *U.S. Public*, pg. 485
AURORA FLIGHT SCIENCES CORPORATION—See The Boeing Company; *U.S. Public*, pg. 2039
THE AURORA FUNDS INC.; *U.S. Private*, pg. 3990
AURORA FUNDS MANAGEMENT LIMITED; *Int'l*, pg. 713
AURORA GAS LLC—See Aurora Power Resources Inc.; *U.S. Private*, pg. 395
AURORA GESUNDHEIT GMBH—See Shop Apotheke Europe N.V.; *Int'l*, pg. 6859
AURORA GLOBAL INCOME TRUST; *Int'l*, pg. 713
AURORA GROUP DANMARK A/S—See DistIT AB; *Int'l*, pg. 2136
AURORA GROUP FINLAND OY—See DistIT AB; *Int'l*, pg. 2136
AURORA GROUP NORGE AS—See DistIT AB; *Int'l*, pg. 2136
AURORA GROUP SVERIGE AB—See DistIT AB; *Int'l*, pg. 2136
AURORA HEALTH CARE, INC.—See Advocate Health Care Network; *U.S. Private*, pg. 111
AURORA INNOVATION, INC.; *U.S. Public*, pg. 227
AURORA INNOVATIONS, LLC—See Hydrofarm Holdings Group, Inc.; *U.S. Public*, pg. 1079
AURORA INVESTMENT TRUST PLC; *Int'l*, pg. 713
AURORA ISI ARACLARI SAN. VE TIC. LTD. STI—See INDUS Holding AG; *Int'l*, pg. 3662
AURORA JAPAN CORP.—See Aurora Corporation; *Int'l*, pg. 713
AURORA JET CENTER—See The Sterling Group, L.P.; *U.S. Private*, pg. 4122
AURORA KENDRICK JAMES LIMITED—See Daisy Group Limited; *Int'l*, pg. 1943
AURORA KONRAD G. SCHULZ GMBH & CO. KG—See INDUS Holding AG; *Int'l*, pg. 3662
AURORA KUNSTSTOFFE GMBH—See MOL Magyar Olajes Gazipari Nyrt.; *Int'l*, pg. 5019
AURORA LABS LIMITED; *Int'l*, pg. 714
AURORALIGHT, INC.—See Kuzco Lighting, Inc.; *Int'l*, pg. 4348
AURORA LOAN SERVICES LLC—See Lehman Brothers Holdings Inc. Plan Trust; *U.S. Private*, pg. 2419
AURORA METALS DIVISION LLC—See Hiler Industries; *U.S. Private*, pg. 1944
AURORA MOBILE LIMITED; *Int'l*, pg. 714
AURORA MUHLEN GMBH—See Raiffeisen-Holding Niederosterreich-Wien reg. Gen.m.b.H.; *Int'l*, pg. 6185
AURORA NATIONAL LIFE ASSURANCE COMPANY—See Financiere Pinault SCA; *Int'l*, pg. 2668
AURORA NORTH AMERICA LLC—See INDUS Holding AG; *Int'l*, pg. 3662

AURORA OFFICE AUTOMATION CORPORATION—See Aurora Corporation; *Int'l*, pg. 713
AURORA OFFICE AUTOMATION SALES, CO., LTD.—See Aurora Corporation; *Int'l*, pg. 713
AURORA OFFICE FURNITURE CO., LTD.—See Aurora Corporation; *Int'l*, pg. 713
AURORA OPTOELECTRONICS CO., LTD.; *Int'l*, pg. 714
AURORA ORGANIC DAIRY CORPORATION—See Charlesbank Capital Partners, LLC; *U.S. Private*, pg. 854
AURORA PACKING CO., INC.; *U.S. Private*, pg. 395
AURORA PEAT PRODUCTS ULC—See Hydrofarm Holdings Group, Inc.; *U.S. Public*, pg. 1079
AURORA PLASTICS, LLC—See Nautic Partners, LLC; *U.S. Private*, pg. 2868
AURORA POLSKA SP. Z O.O.—See Raiffeisen-Holding Niederosterreich-Wien reg. Gen.m.b.H.; *Int'l*, pg. 6185
AURORA POWER RESOURCES INC.; *U.S. Private*, pg. 395
AURORA PROPERTY BUY-WRITE INCOME TRUST—See Aurora Funds Management Limited; *Int'l*, pg. 713
AURORA PUMP—See Pentair plc; *Int'l*, pg. 5791
AURORA RESEARCH INSTITUTE, LLC—See Sonic Healthcare Limited; *Int'l*, pg. 7096
AURORA RESURGENCE MANAGEMENT PARTNERS LLC—See Aurora Capital Group, LLC; *U.S. Private*, pg. 393
AURORA ROYALTIES INC.; *Int'l*, pg. 714
AURORA S.A.; *Int'l*, pg. 714
AURORA SINGAPORE CORP.—See Aurora Corporation; *Int'l*, pg. 713
AURORA SOLAR TECHNOLOGIES INC.; *Int'l*, pg. 714
AURORA SPECIALTY TEXTILES GROUP, INC.—See Meridian Industries, Inc.; *U.S. Private*, pg. 2673
AURORA SPINE CORPORATION; *U.S. Public*, pg. 228
AURORA SYSTEMS CONSULTING, INC.—See Plurilock Security, Inc.; *Int'l*, pg. 5898
AURORA SYSTEMS CORPORATION—See Aurora Corporation; *Int'l*, pg. 713
AURORA TANKERS USA INC.—See IMC Pan Asia Alliance Pte. Ltd.; *Int'l*, pg. 3621
AURORA TECHNOLOGIES INC.; *U.S. Private*, pg. 395
AURORA TECHNOLOGY B.V.—See GomSpace Group AB; *Int'l*, pg. 3037
AURORA TELECOM CORPORATION—See Aurora Corporation; *Int'l*, pg. 713
AURORA WELL SERVICE, LLC—See Aurora Power Resources Inc.; *U.S. Private*, pg. 395
AURORA WORLD CORPORATION; *Int'l*, pg. 714
AURORIUM HOLDINGS LLC—See The Pritzker Group - Chicago, LLC; *U.S. Private*, pg. 4098
AUROS TECHNOLOGY CO., LTD.; *Int'l*, pg. 714
AURO SUNDRAM PLY & DOOR PVT. LTD.—See Century Plyboards (I) Ltd.; *Int'l*, pg. 1419
AUROTECH CORPORATION—See Disco Corporation; *Int'l*, pg. 2131
AUROTEK CORPORATION; *Int'l*, pg. 714
AUROTEK CORPORATION - TAOYUAN FACTORY—See Aurotek Corporation; *Int'l*, pg. 714
AUROTEK (JAPAN) INC.—See Aurotek Corporation; *Int'l*, pg. 714
AUROVALLIS SARL—See Aurania Resources Ltd.; *Int'l*, pg. 707
AUROVIDA FARMACEUTICA S.A. DE C.V.—See Aurobindo Pharma Ltd.; *Int'l*, pg. 712
AUROVITAS PHARMA POLSKA SP. Z O.O.—See Aurobindo Pharma Ltd.; *Int'l*, pg. 712
AUROVITAS SPAIN SA.—See Aurobindo Pharma Ltd.; *Int'l*, pg. 713
AUROVITAS SPOL S.R.O—See Aurobindo Pharma Ltd.; *Int'l*, pg. 713
AUROVITAS UNIPESSOAL LDA.—See Aurobindo Pharma Ltd.; *Int'l*, pg. 712
AURRENAK S. COOP.—See Mondragon Corporation; *Int'l*, pg. 5028
AURRENAK SERVICE S.A. DE C.V.—See Mondragon Corporation; *Int'l*, pg. 5028
AURRIGO INTERNATIONAL PLC; *Int'l*, pg. 714
AURRIGO PTE. LTD.—See Aurrigo International Plc; *Int'l*, pg. 714
AURSKOG SPAREBANK; *Int'l*, pg. 714
AURUBIS AG; *Int'l*, pg. 714
AURUBIS BERANGO S.L.U.—See Aurubis AG; *Int'l*, pg. 714
AURUBIS BUFFALO, INC.—See Aurubis AG; *Int'l*, pg. 714
AURUBIS BULGARIA AD—See Aurubis AG; *Int'l*, pg. 715
AURUBIS ENGINEERING EAD—See Aurubis AG; *Int'l*, pg. 714
AURUBIS FINLAND OY—See Aurubis AG; *Int'l*, pg. 714
AURUBIS ITALIA SRL—See Aurubis AG; *Int'l*, pg. 715
AURUBIS METAL PRODUCTS (SHANGHAI) CO., LTD—See Aurubis AG; *Int'l*, pg. 714
AURUBIS MIDDLE EAST FZE—See Aurubis AG; *Int'l*, pg. 714
AURUBIS MORTARA S.P.A.—See Aurubis AG; *Int'l*, pg. 715
AURUBIS NETHERLANDS B.V.—See Aurubis AG; *Int'l*, pg. 714
AURUBIS NV/SA - OLEN—See Aurubis AG; *Int'l*, pg. 715

COMPANY NAME INDEX

AURUBIS NV/SA—See Aurubis AG; *Int'l*, pg. 715
AURUBIS RUS LLC—See Aurubis AG; *Int'l*, pg. 715
AURUBIS SLOVAKIA S.R.O.—See Aurubis AG; *Int'l*, pg. 714
AURUBIS STOLBERG GMBH & CO. KG—See Aurubis AG; *Int'l*, pg. 714
AURUBIS STOLBERG VERWALTUNGS GMBH—See Aurubis AG; *Int'l*, pg. 714
AURUBIS SWEDEN AB—See Aurubis AG; *Int'l*, pg. 714
AURUBIS SWEDEN—See Aurubis AG; *Int'l*, pg. 715
AURUBIS UK LIMITED—See Aurubis AG; *Int'l*, pg. 715
AURUM ANALYTICA PRIVATE LIMITED—See Aurum PropTech Ltd.; *Int'l*, pg. 715
AURUM GROUP LIMITED—See Apollo Global Management, Inc.; *U.S. Public*, pg. 167
AURUMIN LIMITED; *Int'l*, pg. 715
AURUM MEDICAL CO, LTD.—See Ship Healthcare Holdings, Inc.; *Int'l*, pg. 6851
AURUM PACIFIC (CHINA) GROUP LIMITED; *Int'l*, pg. 715
AURUM PRESS LIMITED—See The Quarto Group, Inc.; *Int'l*, pg. 7677
AURUM PROPTECH LTD.; *Int'l*, pg. 715
AURUM RESOURCES LIMITED; *Int'l*, pg. 715
AURUM SOFTWARES AND SOLUTIONS PRIVATE LIMITED—See Aurum PropTech Ltd.; *Int'l*, pg. 715
AURVANDIL ACQUISITION CORP.; *U.S. Public*, pg. 228
AURWEST RESOURCES CORPORATION; *Int'l*, pg. 715
AURYN MINING CORPORATION; *U.S. Public*, pg. 228
AUSA LIFE INSURANCE CO.—See Aegon N.V.; *Int'l*, pg. 174
AUS ASIA MINERALS LIMITED; *Int'l*, pg. 715
AUSBILDUNG.DE GMBH—See Bertelsmann SE & Co. KGaA; *Int'l*, pg. 990
AUSBIL INVESTMENT MANAGEMENT—See Dexia SA; *Int'l*, pg. 2092
AUSCANN GROUP HOLDINGS PTY LTD; *Int'l*, pg. 715
AUSCOL PTY LTD—See GrainCorp Limited; *Int'l*, pg. 3052
AUSCO PRODUCTS, INC.; *U.S. Private*, pg. 228
AUSCOTT LIMITED—See Australian Food & Fibre Ltd.; *Int'l*, pg. 721
AUSCRETE CORPORATION; *U.S. Public*, pg. 228
AUSDRILL (GHANA) PTY. LTD.—See Perenti Global Limited; *Int'l*, pg. 5797
AUSDRILL MINING SERVICES PTY. LTD.—See Perenti Global Limited; *Int'l*, pg. 5797
AUSDRILL NORTHWEST PTY. LTD.—See Perenti Global Limited; *Int'l*, pg. 5797
AUSECO, S.A.—See Lone Star Funds; *U.S. Private*, pg. 2485
AUSENCO LIMITED—See RCF Management LLC; *U.S. Private*, pg. 3362
AUSENCO PSI LLC—See RCF Management LLC; *U.S. Private*, pg. 3362
AUSENCO SERVICES PTY. LTD.—See RCF Management LLC; *U.S. Private*, pg. 3362
AUSGOLD LIMITED; *Int'l*, pg. 715
AUSGROUP CORPORATION CO., LTD.—See AusGroup Limited; *Int'l*, pg. 716
AUSGROUP LIMITED; *Int'l*, pg. 715
AUSHANG.ONLINE GMBH—See FORTEC Elektronik AG; *Int'l*, pg. 2738
AUS HOLDCO PTY. LIMITED—See Brunswick Corporation; *U.S. Public*, pg. 407
AUSHON BIOSYSTEMS, INC.—See Quanterix Corporation; *U.S. Public*, pg. 1753
AUSILIA S.R.L.—See Sesa S.p.A.; *Int'l*, pg. 6728
AUSIMONT INDUSTRIES, INC.—See Solvay S.A.; *Int'l*, pg. 7079
AUSINO PTY LTD.—See China Machinery Engineering Corporation; *Int'l*, pg. 1515
AUSIRON DEVELOPMENT CORPORATION PTY. LTD.—See Metso Oyj; *Int'l*, pg. 4865
AUSLEY ASSOCIATES INC.—See MAG DS Corp.; *U.S. Private*, pg. 2545
AU SMALL FINANCE BANK LIMITED; *Int'l*, pg. 697
AUSMA MOTORENREVISIE B.V.—See DEUTZ AG; *Int'l*, pg. 2085
AUSMANI LIMITED; *Int'l*, pg. 716
AUSMEDIC AUSTRALIA PTY LIMITED—See Madison Dearborn Partners, LLC; *U.S. Private*, pg. 2542
AUSMON RESOURCES LIMITED; *Int'l*, pg. 716
AUSNET SERVICES LTD.—See Brookfield Corporation; *Int'l*, pg. 1175
AUSNUTRIA DAIRY CORPORATION LTD—See Inner Mongolia Yili Industrial Group Co., Ltd.; *Int'l*, pg. 3708
AUSOM ENTERPRISE LIMITED; *Int'l*, pg. 716
AUSON AB; *Int'l*, pg. 716
AUSPCHIP TECHNOLOGIES CO., LTD.—See T&S Communications Co.,Ltd.; *Int'l*, pg. 7395
AUSPLASTICS PTY LTD—See CTI Logistics Limited; *Int'l*, pg. 1871
AUSQUEST LIMITED; *Int'l*, pg. 716
AUSRA EQUIPMENT & SUPPLY COMPANY INC.—See Tym Corporation; *Int'l*, pg. 7994
AUSREP PTY LTD—See Navis Capital Partners Limited; *Int'l*, pg. 5176
AUSSEE OATS MILLING (PRIVATE) LIMITED—See Future Corporate Resources Limited; *Int'l*, pg. 2853

AUSSIE BROADBAND LTD.; *Int'l*, pg. 716
AUSSIEFIT; *U.S. Private*, pg. 395
AUSSIE FOODS, LLC—See Downs Food Group; *U.S. Private*, pg. 1269
AUSSIE PET MOBILE, INC.; *U.S. Private*, pg. 395
AUSTAGENCIES PTY. LTD.—See AUB Group Limited; *Int'l*, pg. 698
AUSTAL CAIRNS PTY. LTD.—See Austal Limited; *Int'l*, pg. 716
AUSTAL LIMITED; *Int'l*, pg. 716
AUSTAL MUSCAT LLC—See Austal Limited; *Int'l*, pg. 716
AUSTAL USA LLC—See Austal Limited; *Int'l*, pg. 716
AUSTAL VIET NAM CO., LTD.—See Austal Limited; *Int'l*, pg. 716
AUSTAR COAL MINE PTY LIMITED—See Yankuang Group Co., Limited; *Int'l*, pg. 8562
AUSTAR GOLD LIMITED; *Int'l*, pg. 716
AUSTAR HEARING SCIENCE & TECHNOLOGY (XIAMEN) CO., LTD.—See Merry Electronics Co., Ltd.; *Int'l*, pg. 4838
AUSTAR LIFESCIENCES LIMITED; *Int'l*, pg. 716
AUSTASIA GROUP LTD.; *Int'l*, pg. 716
AUSTBORE PTY. LTD.—See Austin Engineering Ltd.; *Int'l*, pg. 718
AUSTBRECK PTY LIMITED—See Westinghouse Air Brake Technologies Corporation; *U.S. Public*, pg. 2358
AUSTBRECK PTY, LTD.—See Westinghouse Air Brake Technologies Corporation; *U.S. Public*, pg. 2357
AUSTBROKERS CANBERRA PTY. LTD.—See AUB Group Limited; *Int'l*, pg. 698
AUSTBROKERS CE MCDONALD PTY. LTD.—See AUB Group Limited; *Int'l*, pg. 698
AUSTBROKERS CENTRAL COAST PTY. LTD.—See AUB Group Limited; *Int'l*, pg. 698
AUSTBROKERS CORPORATE PTY. LTD.—See AUB Group Limited; *Int'l*, pg. 698
AUSTBROKERS LIFE PTY LTD—See AUB Group Limited; *Int'l*, pg. 698
AUSTBROKERS PREMIER PTY. LTD.—See AUB Group Limited; *Int'l*, pg. 698
AUSTBROKERS PROFESSIONAL SERVICES PTY. LTD.—See AUB Group Limited; *Int'l*, pg. 698
AUSTBROKERS PTY. LTD.—See AUB Group Limited; *Int'l*, pg. 698
AUSTBROKERS RWA PTY. LTD.—See AUB Group Limited; *Int'l*, pg. 698
AUSTBROKERS SYDNEY PTY. LTD.—See AUB Group Limited; *Int'l*, pg. 698
AUSTBROKERS TERRACE INSURANCE BROKERS PTY. LTD.—See AUB Group Limited; *Int'l*, pg. 698
AUSTBROKERS TERRACE INSURANCE PTY LTD.—See AUB Group Limited; *Int'l*, pg. 698
AUSTBROKERS TRADE CREDIT PTY. LTD.—See AUB Group Limited; *Int'l*, pg. 698
AUSTCHINA HOLDINGS LTD; *Int'l*, pg. 716
AUSTCO COMMUNICATIONS SYSTEMS PTY. LTD.—See Azure Healthcare Limited; *Int'l*, pg. 782
AUSTCOLD REFRIGERATION PTY LTD—See Enovis Corporation; *U.S. Public*, pg. 770
AUSTCO MARKETING & SERVICE (ASIA) PTE. LTD.—See Azure Healthcare Limited; *Int'l*, pg. 782
AUSTCO MARKETING & SERVICE (CANADA) LTD.—See Azure Healthcare Limited; *Int'l*, pg. 782
AUSTCO MARKETING & SERVICE (UK) LTD.—See Azure Healthcare Limited; *Int'l*, pg. 782
AUSTCO MARKETING & SERVICE (USA) LTD.—See Azure Healthcare Limited; *Int'l*, pg. 782
AUSTDAC PTY. LIMITED—See Hubbell Incorporated; *U.S. Public*, pg. 1066
AUSTECH INSTRUMENTS PTY LTD—See Washington H. Soul Pattinson & Company Limited; *Int'l*, pg. 8351
AUSTELL NATURAL GAS SYSTEM; *U.S. Private*, pg. 395
AUSTEM CO., LTD. - SEJONG PLANT 1—See Austem Co., Ltd.; *Int'l*, pg. 717
AUSTEM CO., LTD. - SEJONG PLANT 2—See Austem Co., Ltd.; *Int'l*, pg. 717
AUSTEM CO., LTD.; *Int'l*, pg. 716
AUSTEMPER INC.—See AFC-Holcroft LLC; *U.S. Private*, pg. 121
AUSTENITIC CREATIONS PRIVATE LIMITED—See Jindal Holdings Limited; *Int'l*, pg. 3966
AUSTEN MARITIME SERVICES PTE LTD—See STENA AB; *Int'l*, pg. 7206
AUSTEN RIGGS CENTER; *U.S. Private*, pg. 395
AUSTEREO GROUP LIMITED—See Southern Cross Media Group Limited; *Int'l*, pg. 391
AUSTERLITZ ACQUISITION CORP I; *U.S. Private*, pg. 395
AUSTEVOLL FISKEINDUSTRI AS—See Austevoll Seafood ASA; *Int'l*, pg. 717
AUSTEVOLL SEAFOOD ASA; *Int'l*, pg. 717
AUSTEX DIES PTY LIMITED—See Capral Limited; *Int'l*, pg. 1315
AUSTEX OIL LIMITED; *Int'l*, pg. 718
AUS-TEX PRINTING & MAILING; *U.S. Private*, pg. 395
AUST & HACHMANN E.K.; *Int'l*, pg. 716
AUSTIN BANK CORP., INC.; *U.S. Private*, pg. 395
AUSTIN BANK, TEXAS N.A.—See Austin Bank Corp., Inc.; *U.S. Private*, pg. 395

AUSTIN BENN LTD.—See HFBG Holding B.V.; *Int'l*, pg. 3374
AUSTIN BRIDGE & ROAD, INC.—See Austin Industries, Inc.; *U.S. Private*, pg. 395
AUSTIN BROCKENBROUGH & ASSOCIATES, LLP—See Godspeed Capital Management LP; *U.S. Private*, pg. 1725
AUSTIN CANADA INC.—See Austin Engineering Ltd.; *Int'l*, pg. 718
AUSTIN CAPITAL BANK; *U.S. Private*, pg. 395
AUSTIN CENTER FOR OUTPATIENT SURGERY, L.P.—See UnitedHealth Group Incorporated; *U.S. Public*, pg. 2239
AUSTIN CHEMICAL COMPANY INC.; *U.S. Private*, pg. 395
AUSTIN COCA-COLA BOTTLING COMPANY—See The Coca-Cola Company; *U.S. Public*, pg. 2064
AUSTIN COMMERCIAL, INC.—See Austin Industries, Inc.; *U.S. Private*, pg. 395
AUSTIN COMPANY; *U.S. Private*, pg. 395
THE AUSTIN COMPANY—See Kajima Corporation; *Int'l*, pg. 4055
AUSTIN CONSOLIDATED HOLDINGS, INC.—See Equifax Inc.; *U.S. Public*, pg. 785
AUSTIN CONSULTING GROUP, INC.—See Arthur J. Gallagher & Co.; *U.S. Public*, pg. 203
AUSTINCSI, LLC—See Cognizant Technology Solutions Corporation; *U.S. Public*, pg. 523
AUSTIN DATA, INC.—See D.R. Horton, Inc.; *U.S. Public*, pg. 619
THE AUSTIN DIAGNOSTIC CLINIC, PLLC—See HCA Healthcare, Inc.; *U.S. Public*, pg. 1011
AUSTIN DISTRIBUTING & MANUFACTURING CORP.; *U.S. Private*, pg. 395
AUSTIN ENDOSCOPY CENTER I, LP—See KKR & Co. Inc.; *U.S. Public*, pg. 1244
AUSTIN ENERGY (ASIA) PTE. LTD.—See Nordic Group Limited; *Int'l*, pg. 5422
AUSTIN ENERGY OFFSHORE PTE. LTD.—See Nordic Group Limited; *Int'l*, pg. 5422
AUSTIN ENERGY; *U.S. Private*, pg. 395
AUSTIN ENGINEERING CO., INC.; *U.S. Private*, pg. 395
AUSTIN ENGINEERING CO. LTD.; *U.S. Private*, pg. 395
AUSTIN ENGINEERING LTD.; *Int'l*, pg. 718
AUSTIN ETT AFRICA LIMITED—See Austin Engineering Ltd.; *Int'l*, pg. 718
AUSTIN FOAM PLASTICS INC.—See IQZAN Holding Berhad; *Int'l*, pg. 3804
AUSTIN FRASER GMBH—See Austin Fraser Limited; *Int'l*, pg. 718
AUSTIN FRASER INC—See Austin Fraser Limited; *Int'l*, pg. 718
AUSTIN FRASER LIMITED; *Int'l*, pg. 718
AUSTIN GEOMODELING, INC.; *U.S. Private*, pg. 395
AUSTIN GOLD CORP.; *Int'l*, pg. 718
AUSTIN HARDWARE & SUPPLY INC.; *U.S. Private*, pg. 395
AUSTIN HEART, PLLC—See HCA Healthcare, Inc.; *U.S. Public*, pg. 991
AUSTIN INDUSTRIAL, INC.—See Austin Industries, Inc.; *U.S. Private*, pg. 396
AUSTIN INDUSTRIES, INC.; *U.S. Private*, pg. 395
AUSTIN LAWRENCE GROUP; *U.S. Private*, pg. 396
AUSTIN LAZ & COMPANY PLC; *Int'l*, pg. 718
AUSTIN MANUFACTURING SERVICES LP; *U.S. Private*, pg. 396
AUSTIN MATERIALS, LLC—See Summit Materials, Inc.; *U.S. Public*, pg. 1960
AUSTIN-MCGREGOR INTERNATIONAL; *U.S. Private*, pg. 396
AUSTIN MUTUAL INSURANCE GROUP; *U.S. Private*, pg. 396
AUSTIN POWDER COMPANY—See Davis Mining & Manufacturing Inc.; *U.S. Private*, pg. 1174
AUSTIN PRESTRESS CO—See Abrams International LLP; *U.S. Private*, pg. 40
AUSTIN PRODUCTIONS INC.; *U.S. Private*, pg. 396
AUSTIN PUMP & SUPPLY COMPANY INC; *U.S. Private*, pg. 396
AUSTIN QUALITY FOODS, INC.—See Kellanova; *U.S. Public*, pg. 1217
AUSTINREALESTATE.COM; *U.S. Private*, pg. 396
AUSTIN REED LIMITED—See Alteri Partners LLP; *Int'l*, pg. 391
AUSTIN RESOURCES LTD.; *Int'l*, pg. 718
AUSTIN RIBBON & COMPUTER SUPPLIES, INC.—See Pivot Technology Solutions, Inc.; *U.S. Public*, pg. 1695
AUSTIN SCIENTIFIC COMPANY—See Oxford Instruments Plc; *Int'l*, pg. 5674
AUSTIN-SMITH:LORD ABU DHABI—See Austin-Smith:Lord LLP; *Int'l*, pg. 718
AUSTIN-SMITH:LORD LLP; *Int'l*, pg. 718
AUSTIN-SMITH:LORD LLP—See Austin-Smith:Lord LLP; *Int'l*, pg. 718
AUSTIN-SMITH:LORD LLP—See Austin-Smith:Lord LLP; *Int'l*, pg. 718
AUSTIN-SMITH:LORD LLP—See Austin-Smith:Lord LLP; *Int'l*, pg. 718

AUSTIN-SMITH:LORD LLP—See Austin-Smith:Lord LLP; Int'l, pg. 718
AUSTIN TELE-SERVICES PARTNERS, L.P.—See Genesis Networks Enterprises, LLC; U.S. Private, pg. 1669
AUSTIN TRAFFIC SIGNAL CONSTRUCTION CO., LP; U.S. Private, pg. 396
AUSTIN TRI-HAWK AUTOMOTIVE, INC.—See G-TEKT Corporation; Int'l, pg. 2863
AUSTIN UROGYNECOLOGY, PLLC—See HCA Healthcare, Inc.; U.S. Public, pg. 991
AUSTIN VENTURES, LP; U.S. Private, pg. 396
AUSTIN WHITE LIME COMPANY; U.S. Private, pg. 396
AUSTIN & WILLIAMS; U.S. Private, pg. 395
AUSTNAM JOINT STOCK CORPORATION—See Vietnam Industrial Investments Limited; Int'l, pg. 8200
AUSTOFIX GROUP LIMITED; Int'l, pg. 718
AUSTOFIX SURGICAL PTY LTD—See Austofix Group Limited; Int'l, pg. 718
AUSTON CAPITAL CORP.; Int'l, pg. 719
AUSTPAC RESOURCES NL - NEWCASTLE DEMONSTRATION PLANT—See Austpac Resources N.L.; Int'l, pg. 719
AUSTPAC RESOURCES N.L.; Int'l, pg. 719
AUSTRAK PTY. LTD.—See Vossloh AG; Int'l, pg. 8308
AUSTRALAND HK COMPANY LIMITED—See Frasers Property Limited; Int'l, pg. 2766
AUSTRALAND WHOLESALE HOLDINGS LIMITED—See Frasers Property Limited; Int'l, pg. 2766
AUSTRAL ASIA LINE - AUSTRALIA—See Schoeller Holdings Ltd.; Int'l, pg. 6637
AUSTRAL ASIA LINE BV—See Schoeller Holdings Ltd.; Int'l, pg. 6637
THE AUSTRALASIAN ADVERTISING COMPANY PTY LIMITED—See JCDecaux S.A.; Int'l, pg. 3920
AUSTRALASIAN LUBRICANTS MANUFACTURING COMPANY PTY LTD—See Ampol Limited; Int'l, pg. 436
AUSTRALASIAN METALS LIMITED; Int'l, pg. 719
THE AUSTRAL BRICK COMPANY PTY. LIMITED—See Brickworks Limited; Int'l, pg. 1152
AUSTRAL BRICKS (NSW) PTY LTD—See Brickworks Limited; Int'l, pg. 1151
AUSTRAL BRICKS (QLD) PTY LTD—See Brickworks Limited; Int'l, pg. 1151
AUSTRAL BRICKS (SA) PTY LTD—See Brickworks Limited; Int'l, pg. 1151
AUSTRAL BRICKS (TASMANIA) PTY LTD.—See Brickworks Limited; Int'l, pg. 1152
AUSTRAL BRICKS (VIC) PTY LTD—See Brickworks Limited; Int'l, pg. 1152
AUSTRAL BRICKS (WA) PTY LTD—See Brickworks Limited; Int'l, pg. 1152
AUSTRAL CONSTRUCTION PTY. LTD.—See Keller Group plc; Int'l, pg. 4119
AUSTRAL FISHERIES PTY. LTD.—See Maruha Nichiro Corporation; Int'l, pg. 4711
AUSTRAL GOLD LIMITED; Int'l, pg. 719
AUSTRAL GROUP S.A.A.—See Austevoll Seafood ASA; Int'l, pg. 717
AUSTRALIA BALDOR PTY LTD—See ABB Ltd.; Int'l, pg. 51
AUSTRALIA CHINA HOLDINGS LIMITED; Int'l, pg. 720
AUSTRALIA CHINA INVESTMENTS CORPORATION PTY LTD—See Sandfire Resources Limited; Int'l, pg. 6525
AUSTRALIA FINANCE GROUP LTD; Int'l, pg. 720
AUSTRALIA & INTERNATIONAL HOLDINGS LIMITED; Int'l, pg. 719
AUSTRALIA MINJAR GOLD PTY LTD.—See Jinan High Tech Development Co., Ltd.; Int'l, pg. 3965
AUSTRALIAN ADMINISTRATION SERVICES PTY LTD.—See Pacific Equity Partners Pty. Limited; Int'l, pg. 5689
AUSTRALIAN ADVENTURE TOURISM GROUP LIMITED—See Income Asset Management Group Limited; Int'l, pg. 3648
AUSTRALIAN AEROSPACE COMPOSITES PTY LTD.—See Airbus SE; Int'l, pg. 243
AUSTRALIAN AEROSPACE LIMITED—See Airbus SE; Int'l, pg. 243
AUSTRALIAN AGRICULTURAL COMPANY LIMITED; Int'l, pg. 720
AUSTRALIAN AGRICULTURAL PROJECTS LTD; Int'l, pg. 720
AUSTRALIAN AIRCONDITIONING DISTRIBUTORS PTY. LTD.—See Beijer Ref AB; Int'l, pg. 943
AUSTRALIAN AIR EXPRESS PTY. LTD.—See Australian Postal Corporation; Int'l, pg. 722
AUSTRALIAN AIR EXPRESS PTY. LTD.—See Qantas Airways Limited; Int'l, pg. 6132
AUSTRALIAN AIRLINE PILOT ACADEMY PTY LIMITED—See REGIONAL EXPRESS HOLDINGS LIMITED; Int'l, pg. 6254
AUSTRALIAN AMALGAMATED TERMINALS PTY. LTD.—See Qube Holdings Limited; Int'l, pg. 6157
AUSTRALIAN ARROW PTY. LTD.—See Yazaki Corporation; Int'l, pg. 8572
AUSTRALIAN ASSET AGGREGATION PTY LTD—See BNK Banking Corporation Limited; Int'l, pg. 1079
AUSTRALIAN ASSOCIATED MOTOR INSURERS LIMITED; Int'l, pg. 721

AUSTRALIAN ASSOCIATED PRESS PTY LTD; Int'l, pg. 721
AUSTRALIAN AUTOMOTIVE ELECTRICAL WHOLESALE PTY LTD—See Bapcor Limited; Int'l, pg. 857
AUSTRALIAN AUTOMOTIVE GROUP PROPRIETARY LIMITED—See Motus Holdings Limited; Int'l, pg. 5056
AUSTRALIAN AVIONICS PTY. LTD.—See General Dynamics Corporation; U.S. Public, pg. 913
AUSTRALIAN BIOTECHNOLOGIES PTY. LTD.—See EBOS Group Limited; Int'l, pg. 2285
AUSTRALIAN BOND EXCHANGE HOLDINGS LIMITED; Int'l, pg. 721
AUSTRALIAN BOND EXCHANGE PTY LTD.—See Australian Bond Exchange Holdings Limited; Int'l, pg. 721
AUSTRALIAN BRAKE CONTROLS—See ZF Friedrichshafen AG; Int'l, pg. 8641
AUSTRALIAN CAPITAL HOME LOANS PTY LTD—See BNK Banking Corporation Limited; Int'l, pg. 1079
AUSTRALIAN CAREERS NETWORK LIMITED; Int'l, pg. 721
AUSTRALIAN CENTRAL CREDIT UNION LTD; Int'l, pg. 721
AUSTRALIAN CLASSING SERVICES PTY LTD.—See Louis Dreyfus Company B.V.; Int'l, pg. 4562
AUSTRALIAN CLINICAL LABS LIMITED—See Crescent Capital Partners Ltd.; Int'l, pg. 1839
AUSTRALIAN COAL HOLDINGS PTY LIMITED—See Rio Tinto plc; Int'l, pg. 6347
AUSTRALIAN COLLEGE OF APPLIED PSYCHOLOGY PTY. LTD.—See Navitas Limited; Int'l, pg. 5176
AUSTRALIAN COMMERCIAL PROPERTY MANAGEMENT LIMITED—See Australia & New Zealand Banking Group Limited; Int'l, pg. 720
AUSTRALIAN CONSOLIDATED INSURANCE LIMITED—See Insured Group Limited; Int'l, pg. 3726
AUSTRALIAN CONSTRUCTION PRODUCTS PTY LIMITED—See Fletcher Building Limited; Int'l, pg. 2699
AUSTRALIAN CONSULATE GENERAL—See Australian Trade and Investment Commission; Int'l, pg. 722
AUSTRALIAN COTTON GINNING COMPANY PTY LTD.—See Louis Dreyfus Company B.V.; Int'l, pg. 4562
AUSTRALIAN DAIRY NUTRITIONALS GROUP; Int'l, pg. 721
AUSTRALIAN ENERGY MARKET OPERATOR LIMITED; Int'l, pg. 721
AUSTRALIAN ETHICAL INVESTMENT LIMITED; Int'l, pg. 721
AUSTRALIAN ETHICAL SUPERANNUATION PTY LIMITED—See Australian Ethical Investment Limited; Int'l, pg. 721
AUSTRALIA & NEW ZEALAND BANKING GROUP LIMITED; Int'l, pg. 719
AUSTRALIA & NEW ZEALAND BANKING GROUP (PNG) LIMITED—See Kina Securities Limited; Int'l, pg. 4164
AUSTRALIAN EXECUTOR TRUSTEES (NSW) LIMITED—See Insignia Financial Ltd.; Int'l, pg. 3719
AUSTRALIAN EXECUTOR TRUSTEES (SA) LIMITED—See Insignia Financial Ltd.; Int'l, pg. 3719
AUSTRALIAN FACTORING COMPANY PTY. LTD.—See Butn Limited; Int'l, pg. 1229
AUSTRALIAN FIBRE GLASS PTY LIMITED—See Fletcher Building Limited; Int'l, pg. 2699
AUSTRALIAN FILM INSTITUTE; Int'l, pg. 721
AUSTRALIAN FINANCIAL REVIEW—See Nine Entertainment Co. Holdings Limited; Int'l, pg. 5298
AUSTRALIAN FISHING ENTERPRISES PTY LTD—See Sarin Group Pty Ltd; Int'l, pg. 6577
AUSTRALIAN FOOD & FIBRE LTD.; Int'l, pg. 721
AUSTRALIAN FOOTWEAR PTY LTD—See Fusion Retail Brands, Pty. Ltd.; Int'l, pg. 2849
AUSTRALIAN FOUNDATION INVESTMENT COMPANY LIMITED; Int'l, pg. 721
AUSTRALIAN FULFILMENT SERVICES PTY LTD—See CTI Logistics Limited; Int'l, pg. 1871
THE AUSTRALIAN GAS LIGHT COMPANY—See AGL Energy Limited; Int'l, pg. 211
AUSTRALIAN GAS NETWORKS LIMITED; Int'l, pg. 721
AUSTRALIAN GLASS GROUP HOLDING PTY. LTD.—See Metro Performance Glass Limited; Int'l, pg. 4861
AUSTRALIAN GOLD & COPPER LIMITED; Int'l, pg. 721
AUSTRALIAN GOLDFIELDS LIMITED; Int'l, pg. 721
AUSTRALIAN GOLD REAGENTS PTY LTD—See Wesfarmers Limited; Int'l, pg. 8380
AUSTRALIAN GRAND PRIX CORPORATION PTY. LTD.; Int'l, pg. 721
AUSTRALIAN GRAPHICS PTY LTD—See Wesfarmers Limited; Int'l, pg. 8380
AUSTRALIAN HEALTHCARE ACADEMY PTY LTD—See PeopleIn Limited; Int'l, pg. 5794
AUSTRALIAN HOSPITAL CARE (COMO) PTY. LTD.—See Brookfield Corporation; Int'l, pg. 1176
AUSTRALIAN HOSPITAL CARE (DORSET) PTY. LTD.—See Brookfield Corporation; Int'l, pg. 1176
AUSTRALIAN HOSPITAL CARE (KNOX) PTY. LTD.—See Brookfield Corporation; Int'l, pg. 1176
AUSTRALIAN HOSPITAL CARE (LATROBE) PTY LIMITED—See Ramsay Health Care Limited; Int'l, pg. 6199

AUSTRALIAN HOSPITAL CARE (MASADA) PTY LIMITED—See Ramsay Health Care Limited; Int'l, pg. 6199
AUSTRALIAN HOSPITAL CARE (MSH) PTY LIMITED—See Ramsay Health Care Limited; Int'l, pg. 6199
AUSTRALIAN HOSPITAL CARE (PINDARA) PTY LIMITED—See Ramsay Health Care Limited; Int'l, pg. 6199
AUSTRALIAN HOSPITAL CARE (THE AVENUE) PTY LIMITED—See Ramsay Health Care Limited; Int'l, pg. 6199
AUSTRALIAN INDUSTRIAL ABRASIVES PTY. LTD.—See Robert Bosch GmbH; Int'l, pg. 6358
AUSTRALIAN INVESTMENT COMPANY SERVICES LIMITED—See Australian Foundation Investment Company Limited; Int'l, pg. 721
AUSTRALIAN LABORATORY GROUP (ZAMBIA) LIMITED—See ALS Limited; Int'l, pg. 377
AUSTRALIAN LABORATORY SERVICES (ALS) (CAMBODIA) CO., LTD.—See ALS Limited; Int'l, pg. 377
AUSTRALIAN LABORATORY SERVICES PTY. LTD.—See ALS Limited; Int'l, pg. 378
AUSTRALIAN LABORATORY SERVICES SURINAME N.V.—See ALS Limited; Int'l, pg. 378
AUSTRALIAN LEARNING GROUP PTY. LIMITED—See UCW Limited; Int'l, pg. 8013
AUSTRALIAN LEISURE & ENTERTAINMENT PROPERTY MANAGEMENT LIMITED—See Charter Hall Limited; Int'l, pg. 1454
AUSTRALIAN LEISURE & ENTERTAINMENT PROPERTY MANAGEMENT LIMITED—See Host-Plus Pty. Limited; Int'l, pg. 3486
AUSTRALIAN LEISURE & ENTERTAINMENT PROPERTY TRUST—See Charter Hall Limited; Int'l, pg. 1454
AUSTRALIAN LEISURE & ENTERTAINMENT PROPERTY TRUST—See Host-Plus Pty. Limited; Int'l, pg. 3486
AUSTRALIAN LIFT COMPONENTS PTY. LTD.—See Dewhurst Group plc; Int'l, pg. 2091
AUSTRALIAN LIQUOR MARKETERS PTY LIMITED—See Metcash Limited; Int'l, pg. 4852
AUSTRALIAN LIQUOR MARKETERS (QLD) PTY. LTD.—See Metcash Limited; Int'l, pg. 4852
AUSTRALIAN LIQUOR MARKETERS (WA) PTY. LTD.—See Metcash Limited; Int'l, pg. 4852
AUSTRALIAN LOCAL SEARCH PTY. LTD.—See Thryv Holdings, Inc.; U.S. Public, pg. 2157
AUSTRALIAN LONGLINE PTY. LTD.—See Nissui Corporation; Int'l, pg. 5377
AUSTRALIAN LUNG HEALTH INITIATIVE PTY LTD.—See 4DMedical Limited; Int'l, pg. 11
AUSTRALIAN MAGNESIUM CORPORATION LIMITED—See Magontec Limited; Int'l, pg. 4642
AUSTRALIAN MEAT INDUSTRY SUPERANNUATION TRUST PTY LTD.; Int'l, pg. 721
AUSTRALIAN MINES LIMITED; Int'l, pg. 721
AUSTRALIAN MUD COMPANY PTY LTD.—See Imdex Limited; Int'l, pg. 3623
AUSTRALIAN NATURAL MILK ASSOCIATION PTY LTD—See Jatcorp Limited; Int'l, pg. 3913
AUSTRALIAN NEWS CHANNEL PTY. LTD.—See News Corporation; U.S. Public, pg. 1519
AUSTRALIAN OIL & GAS CORP.; Int'l, pg. 722
AUSTRALIAN OILSEEDS HOLDINGS LIMITED; Int'l, pg. 722
AUSTRALIAN OILSEEDS INVESTMENTS PTY LTD.—See Australian Oilseeds Holdings Limited; Int'l, pg. 722
AUSTRALIAN ONLINE TRAVEL PTY. LTD.—See Helloworld Travel Limited; Int'l, pg. 3337
AUSTRALIAN OPCO PTY. LTD.—See Flight Centre Travel Group Limited; Int'l, pg. 2706
AUSTRALIAN ORTHOPAEDIC FIXATIONS PTY LTD—See Austofix Group Limited; Int'l, pg. 718
AUSTRALIAN PACIFIC COAL LTD.; Int'l, pg. 722
AUSTRALIAN PHARMACEUTICAL INDUSTRIES LIMITED—See Wesfarmers Limited; Int'l, pg. 8380
AUSTRALIAN PLASTIC PROFILES PTY. LTD.—See Legrand S.A.; Int'l, pg. 4444
AUSTRALIAN POLLUTION ENGINEERING PTY LTD—See Cleanaway Waste Management Limited; Int'l, pg. 1654
AUSTRALIAN PORTABLE BUILDINGS PTY LIMITED—See Black Diamond Group Limited; Int'l, pg. 1059
AUSTRALIAN POSTAL CORPORATION; Int'l, pg. 722
AUSTRALIAN POTASH LIMITED; Int'l, pg. 722
AUSTRALIAN PROPERTY MONITORS PTY LIMITED—See Nine Entertainment Co. Holdings Limited; Int'l, pg. 5298
AUSTRALIAN PROVINCIAL NEWSPAPERS INTERNATIONAL PTY LIMITED—See ARN Media Limited; Int'l, pg. 576
AUSTRALIAN PROVINCIAL NEWSPAPERS LTD—See ARN Media Limited; Int'l, pg. 576
AUSTRALIAN RADIO NETWORK PTY. LIMITED—See ARN Media Limited; Int'l, pg. 576
AUSTRALIAN RARE EARTHS LIMITED; Int'l, pg. 722
THE AUSTRALIAN REINFORCING COMPANY; Int'l, pg. 7614

COMPANY NAME INDEX

AUSTRALIAN REIT INCOME FUND—See Harvest Portfolios Group Inc.; *Int'l*, pg. 3281
AUSTRALIAN RENEWABLE FUELS ADELAIDE PTY LTD—See Thorney Technologies Ltd; *Int'l*, pg. 7719
AUSTRALIAN RESOURCE RECOVERY PTY LTD—See Cleanaway Waste Management Limited; *Int'l*, pg. 1655
AUSTRALIAN RETIREMENT HOMES LIMITED—See Brookfield Corporation; *Int'l*, pg. 1185
AUSTRALIAN RUGBY UNION; *Int'l*, pg. 722
AUSTRALIAN SANDSTONE INDUSTRIES PTY. LTD.—See ChongHerr Investments Ltd.; *Int'l*, pg. 1578
AUSTRALIAN SECURITIES EXCHANGE LIMITED—See ASX Limited; *Int'l*, pg. 664
AUSTRALIAN SECURITY GROUP PTY LTD.—See China Security Co., Ltd.; *Int'l*, pg. 1550
AUSTRALIAN SILICA QUARTZ GROUP LTD.—See Sandon Capital Investments Limited; *Int'l*, pg. 6526
AUSTRALIAN SPORTS TOURS PTY LTD—See TUI AG; *Int'l*, pg. 7964
AUSTRALIAN STRATEGIC MATERIALS LIMITED; *Int'l*, pg. 722
AUSTRALIANSUPER PTY LTD; *Int'l*, pg. 723
AUSTRALIAN TERMINAL SERVICES PTY LTD—See Cleanaway Waste Management Limited; *Int'l*, pg. 1654
AUSTRALIAN TIMKEN PROPRIETARY LTD.—See The Timken Company; *U.S. Public*, pg. 2132
AUSTRALIAN TOURS MANAGEMENT PTY LTD.—See Fairfax Financial Holdings Limited; *Int'l*, pg. 2608
AUSTRALIAN TRADE AND INVESTMENT COMMISSION; *Int'l*, pg. 722
THE AUSTRALIAN TRAFFIC NETWORK PTY. LIMITED—See GTCR LLC; *U.S. Private*, pg. 1805
AUSTRALIAN TUBE MILLS PTY. LIMITED—See GFG Alliance Limited; *Int'l*, pg. 2956
AUSTRALIAN TURF CLUB (ATC); *Int'l*, pg. 722
AUSTRALIAN UNITED GROCERS PTY LTD—See Australian United Retailers Limited; *Int'l*, pg. 722
AUSTRALIAN UNITED INVESTMENT COMPANY LTD; *Int'l*, pg. 722
AUSTRALIAN UNITED RETAILERS LIMITED; *Int'l*, pg. 722
AUSTRALIAN UNITY BOWRAL DEVELOPMENT PTY LTD—See Australian Unity Limited; *Int'l*, pg. 722
AUSTRALIAN UNITY CARE SERVICES PTY LTD—See Australian Unity Limited; *Int'l*, pg. 722
AUSTRALIAN UNITY FUNDS MANAGEMENT LIMITED—See Australian Unity Limited; *Int'l*, pg. 723
AUSTRALIAN UNITY GROUP SERVICES PROPRIETARY LIMITED—See Australian Unity Limited; *Int'l*, pg. 723
AUSTRALIAN UNITY HEALTH CARE LIMITED—See Australian Unity Limited; *Int'l*, pg. 723
AUSTRALIAN UNITY HEALTH LIMITED—See Australian Unity Limited; *Int'l*, pg. 723
AUSTRALIAN UNITY INVESTMENT BONDS LIMITED—See Australian Unity Limited; *Int'l*, pg. 723
AUSTRALIAN UNITY LIMITED; *Int'l*, pg. 722
AUSTRALIAN UNITY NOMINEES PTY LTD—See Australian Unity Limited; *Int'l*, pg. 723
AUSTRALIAN UNITY PROPERTY LIMITED—See Australian Unity Limited; *Int'l*, pg. 723
AUSTRALIAN UNITY RETIREMENT LIVING SERVICES LIMITED—See Australian Unity Limited; *Int'l*, pg. 723
AUSTRALIAN URANIUM LTD—See Australian Vanadium Limited; *Int'l*, pg. 723
AUSTRALIAN VALVE GROUP PTY LTD—See Watts Water Technologies, Inc.; *U.S. Public*, pg. 2337
AUSTRALIAN VANADIUM LIMITED; *Int'l*, pg. 723
AUSTRALIAN VINTAGE LTD.; *Int'l*, pg. 723
AUSTRALIAN VINTAGE (UK) LTD.—See Australian Vintage Ltd.; *Int'l*, pg. 723
AUSTRALIAN VINYLS CORPORATION PTY LTD—See Wesfarmers Limited; *Int'l*, pg. 8381
AUSTRALIAN WEALTH MANAGEMENT LIMITED—See Insignia Financial Ltd.; *Int'l*, pg. 3719
AUSTRALIAN WINDOW FURNISHINGS (NSW) PTY. LTD.—See 3G Capital Partners L.P.; *U.S. Private*, pg. 12
AUSTRALIAN WOOL INDUSTRIES LTD.—See Alrov Properties & Lodgings Ltd.; *Int'l*, pg. 377
AUSTRALIAN WOOL INNOVATION LIMITED (AWI); *Int'l*, pg. 723
AUSTRALIAN WOOL TESTING AUTHORITY LTD. - AWTA PRODUCT TESTING DIVISION—See Australian Wool Testing Authority Ltd.; *Int'l*, pg. 723
AUSTRALIAN WOOL TESTING AUTHORITY LTD. - AWTA RAW WOOL DIVISION—See Australian Wool Testing Authority Ltd.; *Int'l*, pg. 723
AUSTRALIAN WOOL TESTING AUTHORITY LTD.; *Int'l*, pg. 723
AUSTRALIA PACIFIC ELECTRIC CABLES PTY., LTD.—See Asia Pacific Wire & Cable Corporation Limited; *Int'l*, pg. 614
AUSTRALIA SANDSTONE MERCHANTS PTY. LTD.; *Int'l*, pg. 720
AUSTRALIA SKYDIVE PTY. LTD.—See Experience Co Limited; *Int'l*, pg. 2588
AUSTRALIA UNITED MINING LIMITED; *Int'l*, pg. 720
AUSTRALIA ZOO PTY LTD; *Int'l*, pg. 720
AUSTRALIE SASU; *Int'l*, pg. 723

AUSTRALIS CAPITAL, INC.; *U.S. Public*, pg. 228
AUSTRALIS OIL & GAS LIMITED; *Int'l*, pg. 723
AUSTRALIS SEAFOODS S.A.—See Joyvio Food Co., Ltd.; *Int'l*, pg. 4005
AUSTRALIS TMS INC.—See Australis Oil & Gas Limited; *Int'l*, pg. 723
AUSTRAL MASONRY (NSW) PTY LTD—See Brickworks Limited; *Int'l*, pg. 1152
AUSTRAL MASONRY (QLD) PTY LTD—See Brickworks Limited; *Int'l*, pg. 1152
AUSTRAL MASONRY (VIC) PTY LTD—See Brickworks Limited; *Int'l*, pg. 1152
AUSTRAL PRECAST PTY LTD—See Brickworks Limited; *Int'l*, pg. 1152
AUSTRAL PRECAST (QLD) PTY LTD—See Brickworks Limited; *Int'l*, pg. 1152
AUSTRAL PTY LTD—See Eagers Automotive Limited; *Int'l*, pg. 2263
AUSTRAL RESOURCES AUSTRALIA LTD.; *Int'l*, pg. 719
AUSTRAL WRIGHT METALS—See Fletcher Building Limited; *Int'l*, pg. 2699
AUSTRIA CARD GMBH—See INFORM P. LYKOS S.A.; *Int'l*, pg. 3691
AUSTRIACARD HOLDINGS AG; *Int'l*, pg. 723
AUSTRIA CARD POLSKA SP.Z.O.O.—See INFORM P. LYKOS S.A.; *Int'l*, pg. 3691
AUSTRIA CARD TURKEY KART OPERASYONLARI AS—See Austriacard Holdings AG; *Int'l*, pg. 724
AUSTRIA EMAIL AG—See Treibacher Industrie AG; *Int'l*, pg. 7910
AUSTRIA HOTELS BETRIEBS CZ S.R.O.—See UNIQA Insurance Group AG; *Int'l*, pg. 8057
AUSTRIA HOTELS INTERNATIONAL BETRIEBS-GMBH; *Int'l*, pg. 723
AUSTRIA HOTELS LIEGENSCHAFTSBESITZ AG—See UNIQA Insurance Group AG; *Int'l*, pg. 8057
AUSTRIA HOTELS LIEGENSCHAFTSBESITZ CZ S.R.O.—See UNIQA Insurance Group AG; *Int'l*, pg. 8057
AUSTRIA JUICE GERMANY GMBH—See AGRANA Beteiligungs-AG; *Int'l*, pg. 214
AUSTRIA JUICE GMBH—See AGRANA Beteiligungs-AG; *Int'l*, pg. 214
AUSTRIA JUICE GMBH—See BayWa AG; *Int'l*, pg. 919
AUSTRIA JUICE ROMANIA S.R.L.—See AGRANA Beteiligungs-AG; *Int'l*, pg. 214
AUSTRIA JUICE UKRAINE TOV—See AGRANA Beteiligungs-AG; *Int'l*, pg. 214
AUSTRIA LEASING GMBH—See UniCredit S.p.A.; *Int'l*, pg. 8033
AUSTRIALS PTY LTD—See Healius Limited; *Int'l*, pg. 3302
AUSTRIAMICROSYSTEMS FRANCE S.A.R.L.—See ams AG; *Int'l*, pg. 440
AUSTRIAMICROSYSTEMS GERMANY GMBH—See ams AG; *Int'l*, pg. 440
AUSTRIAMICROSYSTEMS ITALY S.R.L.—See ams AG; *Int'l*, pg. 440
AUSTRIAMICROSYSTEMS JAPAN CO. LTD—See ams AG; *Int'l*, pg. 440
AUSTRIAMICROSYSTEMS (PHILIPPINES) INC.—See ams AG; *Int'l*, pg. 440
AUSTRIAMICROSYSTEMS SPAIN S.L.—See ams AG; *Int'l*, pg. 440
AUSTRIAMICROSYSTEMS USA INC—See ams AG; *Int'l*, pg. 440
AUSTRIAN AIRLINES AG—See Deutsche Lufthansa AG; *Int'l*, pg. 2066
AUSTRIAN AIRLINES TECHNIK-BRATISLAVA, S.R.O.—See Deutsche Lufthansa AG; *Int'l*, pg. 2066
AUSTRIAN GAMING INDUSTRIES GMBH—See Novomatic AG; *Int'l*, pg. 5466
AUSTRIAN MYHOLIDAY—See Deutsche Lufthansa AG; *Int'l*, pg. 2066
AUSTRIAN POST INTERNATIONAL DEUTSCHLAND GMBH—See Osterreichische Post AG; *Int'l*, pg. 5653
AUSTRIAN RECYCLING S.R.O.—See Heinzel Holding GmbH; *Int'l*, pg. 3325
AUSTRIA PUMA DASSLER GMBH—See Puma SE; *Int'l*, pg. 6117
AUSTRIA TABAK GMBH—See Japan Tobacco Inc.; *Int'l*, pg. 3906
AUSTRO ENGINEERING CAPE (PTY) LIMITED—See enX Group Limited; *Int'l*, pg. 2456
AUSTRO ENGINE GMBH—See Diamond Aircraft Industries Gmbh; *Int'l*, pg. 2105
AUSTROPLANT ARZNEIMITTEL GMBH—See Dr. Willmar Schwabe GmbH & Co. KG; *Int'l*, pg. 2195
AUSTRO (PTY) LIMITED—See enX Group Limited; *Int'l*, pg. 2456
AUSTRO WOOD (PTY) LIMITED—See enX Group Limited; *Int'l*, pg. 2456
AUSTRO WOODWORKING MACHINES & TOOLS—See enX Group Limited; *Int'l*, pg. 2456
AUSTUBE PTY LIMITED—See Bain Capital, LP; *U.S. Private*, pg. 439
AUSTUBE PTY LIMITED—See Investec Limited; *Int'l*, pg. 3777

AUSUPREME INTERNATIONAL HOLDINGS LIMITED; *Int'l*, pg. 724
AUSWEST SEEDS PTY LIMITED—See Agria Corporation; *Int'l*, pg. 216
AUSWEST TIMBERS HOLDINGS PTY LTD—See Brickworks Limited; *Int'l*, pg. 1152
AUSWEST TIMBERS PTY LTD.—See Brickworks Limited; *Int'l*, pg. 1152
AUSWIDE BANK LTD.; *Int'l*, pg. 724
AUSY BELGIUM—See Randstad N.V.; *Int'l*, pg. 6201
AUSY CONSULTING GMBH—See Randstad N.V.; *Int'l*, pg. 6201
AUSY LUXEMBOURG PSF SA—See Randstad N.V.; *Int'l*, pg. 6201
AUSYPT LDA.—See Randstad N.V.; *Int'l*, pg. 6201
AUSY SA—See Randstad N.V.; *Int'l*, pg. 6201
AUSY SERVICIOS DE INGENIERIA S.L.—See Randstad N.V.; *Int'l*, pg. 6201
AUSY SWEDEN—See Randstad N.V.; *Int'l*, pg. 6201
AUSY SWITZERLAND AG—See Randstad N.V.; *Int'l*, pg. 6201
AUSY TECHNOLOGIES GERMANY AG—See Randstad N.V.; *Int'l*, pg. 6201
AUSY TECHNOLOGIES ROMANIA SRL—See Randstad N.V.; *Int'l*, pg. 6201
AUT 6 PTY LTD—See Eagers Automotive Limited; *Int'l*, pg. 2263
AUTANIA AG—See Dr. Helmut Rothenberger Holding GmbH; *Int'l*, pg. 2191
AUTCO DISTRIBUTING INC.; *U.S. Private*, pg. 396
AUTCTION LLC—See OJSC Sberbank of Russia; *Int'l*, pg. 5541
AUTEC AUTOMATENBETRIEBSGMBH—See Novomatic AG; *Int'l*, pg. 5466
AUTECH CORPORATION - GYEONGJU FACTORY—See Autech Corporation; *Int'l*, pg. 724
AUTECH CORPORATION; *Int'l*, pg. 724
AUTECH CORPORATION - YESAN FACTORY—See Autech Corporation; *Int'l*, pg. 724
AUTECH JAPAN, INC.—See Nissan Motor Co., Ltd.; *Int'l*, pg. 5367
AUTECO MINERALS LTD.; *Int'l*, pg. 724
AUTEFA SOLUTIONS GERMANY GMBH—See OC Oerlikon Corporation AG; *Int'l*, pg. 5512
AUTELAN TECHNOLOGY INTERNATIONAL LIMITED—See Beijing AUTELAN Technology Co. Ltd.; *Int'l*, pg. 945
AUTEL INTELLIGENT TECHNOLOGY CORP., LTD.; *Int'l*, pg. 724
AUTEL S.R.L.—See Trevisan Cometal SpA; *Int'l*, pg. 7917
AUTENSYS GMBH—See EnBW Energie Baden-Wurttemberg AG; *Int'l*, pg. 2398
AUTESTS SIA—See TUV Rheinland Berlin-Brandenburg Pfalz e.V.; *Int'l*, pg. 7981
AUTEURS ASSOCIES SAS—See Mediawan SA; *Int'l*, pg. 4774
AUTEX INC.; *U.S. Private*, pg. 396
AUTHEN-TECH COMMUNICATIONS CANADA INC.; *Int'l*, pg. 724
AUTHENTEC K.K.—See Apple Inc.; *U.S. Public*, pg. 169
AUTHENTEC (SHANGHAI) CO., LTD—See Apple Inc.; *U.S. Public*, pg. 169
AUTHENTIC AUTOGRAPHS UNLIMITED, INC.; *U.S. Private*, pg. 396
AUTHENTIC BRANDS GROUP LLC—See Leonard Green & Partners, L.P.; *U.S. Private*, pg. 2424
AUTHENTIC CUSTOM HOMES, LLC; *U.S. Private*, pg. 396
AUTHENTIC ENTERTAINMENT, INC.—See LOV Group Invest SAS; *Int'l*, pg. 4564
AUTHENTIC ENTERTAINMENT—See mcm Entertainment Group Limited; *Int'l*, pg. 4760
AUTHENTIC EQUITY ACQUISITION CORP.; *U.S. Public*, pg. 228
AUTHENTIC HEALTHCARE SERVICES PVT. LTD.—See Reliable Data Services Ltd.; *Int'l*, pg. 6261
AUTHENTIC HEROES, INC.—See AUTHENTIC HOLDINGS, INC.; *U.S. Public*, pg. 228
AUTHENTIC HOLDINGS, INC.; *U.S. Public*, pg. 228
AUTHENTICOM, INC.; *U.S. Private*, pg. 396
AUTHENTIC RESTAURANT BRANDS—See Garnett Station Partners, LP; *U.S. Private*, pg. 1645
AUTHENTIC SPECIALTY FOODS, INC.—See Grupo Kuo, S.A.B. de C.V.; *Int'l*, pg. 3131
AUTHENTIDATE, INC.—See Aeon Global Health Corp.; *U.S. Private*, pg. 117
AUTHENTIFY, INC.—See Wells Fargo & Company; *U.S. Public*, pg. 2343
AUTHID.AI,; *U.S. Public*, pg. 228
AUTHORISED INVESTMENT FUND LTD.; *Int'l*, pg. 724
AUTHORITY BRANDS, LLC—See Apax Partners LLP; *Int'l*, pg. 502
AUTHORITY BRANDS US HOME SERVICES, INC.—See Apax Partners LLP; *Int'l*, pg. 502
AUTHORIZE.NET HOLDINGS, INC.—See Visa, Inc.; *U.S. Public*, pg. 2301
AUTHOR SOLUTIONS, LLC—See Najafi Companies, LLC; *U.S. Private*, pg. 2831

AUTHUM INVESTMENT INFRASTRUCTURE LTD.

CORPORATE AFFILIATIONS

AUTHUM INVESTMENT INFRASTRUCTURE LTD.; *Int'l*, pg. 724
AUTINS AB—See Autins Group plc; *Int'l*, pg. 724
AUTINS GMBH—See Autins Group plc; *Int'l*, pg. 724
AUTINS GROUP PLC; *Int'l*, pg. 724
AUTINS LIMITED—See Autins Group plc; *Int'l*, pg. 724
AUTINS TECHNICAL CENTRE LIMITED—See Autins Group plc; *Int'l*, pg. 724
THE AUTISM PROGRAM OF VIRGINIA, INC.; *U.S. Private*, pg. 3990
AUTISM SERVICES, INC.; *U.S. Private*, pg. 396
AUTISM SOCIETY OF NORTH CAROLINA, INC.; *U.S. Private*, pg. 396
AUTO1.COM GMBH—See AUTO1 Group SE; *Int'l*, pg. 725
AUTO1 CZECHIA S.R.O.—See AUTO1 Group SE; *Int'l*, pg. 725
AUTO1 GROUP SE; *Int'l*, pg. 725
AUTO ACCESSORIES GARAGE INC.; *U.S. Private*, pg. 396
AUTOAGENT DATA SOLUTIONS, LLC—See Stella Point Capital, LP; *U.S. Private*, pg. 3799
AUTO AIRCON (INDIA) LIMITED—See Tata Sons Limited; *Int'l*, pg. 7473
AUTOALLIANCE INTERNATIONAL INC.—See Ford Motor Company; *U.S. Public*, pg. 864
AUTOALLIANCE INTERNATIONAL INC.—See Mazda Motor Corporation; *Int'l*, pg. 4748
AUTOANYTHING, INC.—See Kingswood Capital Management LLC; *U.S. Private*, pg. 2312
AUTOBACS CAR SERVICE MALAYSIA SDN. BHD.—See Autobacs Seven Co., Ltd.; *Int'l*, pg. 725
AUTOBACS FINANCIAL SERVICE CO., LTD.—See Autobacs Seven Co., Ltd.; *Int'l*, pg. 725
AUTOBACS FRANCE SAS—See Autobacs Seven Co., Ltd.; *Int'l*, pg. 725
AUTOBACS MANAGEMENT SERVICE CO., LTD.—See Autobacs Seven Co., Ltd.; *Int'l*, pg. 726
AUTOBACS NAGASAKI CO., LTD.—See Autobacs Seven Co., Ltd.; *Int'l*, pg. 726
AUTOBACS SEVEN CO., LTD.; *Int'l*, pg. 725
AUTOBACS VENTURE SINGAPORE PTE. LTD.—See Autobacs Seven Co., Ltd.; *Int'l*, pg. 726
AUTOBAHN MOTORCAR GROUP; *U.S. Private*, pg. 398
AUTOBAHNPLUS SERVICES GMBH—See BERGER Holding GmbH; *Int'l*, pg. 979
AUTOBAHN TANK & RAST GMBH—See Abu Dhabi Investment Authority; *Int'l*, pg. 71
AUTOBAHN TANK & RAST GMBH—See Allianz SE; *Int'l*, pg. 351
AUTOBAHN TANK & RAST GMBH—See Munchener Ruckversicherungs AG; *Int'l*, pg. 5085
AUTOBAHN TANK & RAST GMBH—See Ontario Municipal Employees Retirement System; *Int'l*, pg. 5584
AUTO-BAKE PTY LTD—See The Middleby Corporation; *U.S. Public*, pg. 2113
AUTOBANK AG; *Int'l*, pg. 726
AUTOBAR GROUP LTD.—See CVC Capital Partners SICAV-FIS S.A.; *Int'l*, pg. 1882
AUTO-BAR S.R.L.—See IVS Group S.A.; *Int'l*, pg. 3848
AUTOBASE, INC.—See Irish Times; *U.S. Private*, pg. 2138
AUTOBAX (PTY.) LTD.—See Invicta Holdings Limited; *Int'l*, pg. 3788
AUTOBENEX, SPOL S.R.O—See Stahlgruber Otto Gruber GmbH & Co. KG; *Int'l*, pg. 7164
AUTO-BERNER KOUVOLA—See Berner Oy; *Int'l*, pg. 988
AUTO-BERNER—See Berner Oy; *Int'l*, pg. 988
AUTOBIO DIAGNOSTICS CO., LTD; *Int'l*, pg. 726
AUTOBIZ SA—See Stellantis N.V.; *Int'l*, pg. 7201
AUTOBODY SUPPLY COMPANY, INC.—See LKQ Corporation; *U.S. Public*, pg. 1336
AUTO BODY TOOLMART; *U.S. Private*, pg. 396
AUTO BUSINESS PTE. LTD.—See Tan Chong International Limited; *Int'l*, pg. 7452
AUTOBUTLER APS—See Stellantis N.V.; *Int'l*, pg. 7201
AUTO BUTLER INC.; *U.S. Private*, pg. 397
AUTOBYTEL DEALER SERVICES, INC.—See One Planet Group LLC; *U.S. Private*, pg. 3020
AUTOBYTEL FLORIDA, INC.—See One Planet Group LLC; *U.S. Private*, pg. 3020
AUTOCAM (CHINA) AUTOMOTIVE COMPONENTS CO., LTD—See NN, Inc.; *U.S. Public*, pg. 1530
AUTOCAM CORPORATION BOUVERAT INDUSTRIES—See NN, Inc.; *U.S. Public*, pg. 1530
AUTOCAM CORPORATION, INC.—See NN, Inc.; *U.S. Public*, pg. 1530
AUTOCAM CORPORATION—See NN, Inc.; *U.S. Public*, pg. 1530
AUTOCAM CORPORATION—See NN, Inc.; *U.S. Public*, pg. 1530
AUTOCAM DE BRASIL USINAGEM LTDA—See NN, Inc.; *U.S. Public*, pg. 1530
AUTOCAM INTERNATIONAL, LTD—See NN, Inc.; *U.S. Public*, pg. 1530
AUTOCAMIONALE DELLA CISA S.P.A.—See Argo Finanziaria S.p.A.; *Int'l*, pg. 562
AUTOCAM POLAND SP. Z.O.O.—See NN, Inc.; *U.S. Public*, pg. 1530
AUTOCANADA INC.; *Int'l*, pg. 726
AUTOCAPITAL CANADA INC.; *Int'l*, pg. 726

AUTOCARES MALLORCA, S.L.—See Deutsche Bahn AG; *Int'l*, pg. 2049
AUTO CAR, INC.—See AutoNation, Inc.; *U.S. Public*, pg. 232
AUTOCAST AND FORGE PTY LTD—See KPS Capital Partners, LP; *U.S. Private*, pg. 2346
AUTOCENTAR BH D.O.O.—See Zavarovalnica Triglav, d.d.; *Int'l*, pg. 8626
AUTOCENTER KOCH GMBH—See Koch Gruppe Automobile AG; *Int'l*, pg. 4224
AUTO CENTER SA; *Int'l*, pg. 724
AUTOCESTA ZAGREB-MACELJ D.O.O.—See STRABAG SE; *Int'l*, pg. 7229
AUTO CHASSIS INTERNATIONAL (ACI) LE MANS—See Renault S.A.; *Int'l*, pg. 6273
AUTOCHIM SA—See VINCI S.A.; *Int'l*, pg. 8212
AUTO CIRCUITOS DE OBREGON, S.A. DE C.V.—See Yazaki Corporation; *Int'l*, pg. 8572
AUTOCLAIMS DIRECT, INC.; *U.S. Private*, pg. 398
AUTO CLEARING CHRYSLER DODGE JEEP RAM; *Int'l*, pg. 724
AUTOCLENZ SERVICES LIMITED—See Mi-Pay Group plc; *Int'l*, pg. 4873
AUTOCLERK, INC.—See Best Western International, Inc.; *U.S. Private*, pg. 544
AUTOCLIK BY ACG COMPANY LIMITED—See Autocorp Holding Public Company Limited; *Int'l*, pg. 726
THE AUTO CLUB GROUP; *U.S. Private*, pg. 3990
AUTO CLUB INSURANCE ASSOCIATION—See The American Automobile Association, Inc.; *U.S. Private*, pg. 3985
AUTO CLUB SPEEDWAY—See National Association for Stock Car Auto Racing, Inc.; *U.S. Private*, pg. 2845
AUTO CLUB TRUST, FSB - OMAHA (132ND ST.) BRANCH—See The Auto Club Group; *U.S. Private*, pg. 3990
AUTO CLUB TRUST, FSB—See The Auto Club Group; *U.S. Private*, pg. 3990
AUTOCOM ASSOCIATES; *U.S. Private*, pg. 398
AUTOCOM COMPONENTES AUTOMOTIVOS DO BRASIL LTDA.—See Cie Automotive S.A.; *Int'l*, pg. 1604
AUTOCOM DIAGNOSTIC PARTNER AB—See Wurth Verwaltungsgesellschaft mbH; *Int'l*, pg. 8504
AUTO COMPANY VIII, INC.—See AutoNation, Inc.; *U.S. Public*, pg. 232
AUTO COMPANY VII, INC.—See AutoNation, Inc.; *U.S. Public*, pg. 232
AUTO COMPANY VI, INC.—See AutoNation, Inc.; *U.S. Public*, pg. 232
AUTO COMPANY XIII, INC.—See AutoNation, Inc.; *U.S. Public*, pg. 232
AUTO COMPANY XII, INC.—See AutoNation, Inc.; *U.S. Public*, pg. 232
AUTO COMPANY XI, INC.—See AutoNation, Inc.; *U.S. Public*, pg. 232
AUTO COMPANY XIV, INC.—See AutoNation, Inc.; *U.S. Public*, pg. 232
AUTO COMPANY XIX, INC.—See AutoNation, Inc.; *U.S. Public*, pg. 232
AUTO COMPANY XVII, INC.—See AutoNation, Inc.; *U.S. Public*, pg. 232
AUTO COMPANY XXIII, INC.—See AutoNation, Inc.; *U.S. Public*, pg. 232
AUTO COMPANY XXII, INC.—See AutoNation, Inc.; *U.S. Public*, pg. 232
AUTO COMPANY XXI, INC.—See AutoNation, Inc.; *U.S. Public*, pg. 232
AUTO COMPANY XXVII, INC.—See AutoNation, Inc.; *U.S. Public*, pg. 232
AUTO COMPANY XXV, INC.—See AutoNation, Inc.; *U.S. Public*, pg. 232
AUTO CONECTORES DE CHIHUAHUA ELCOM S. DE R.L. DE C.V.—See Yazaki Corporation; *Int'l*, pg. 8572
AUTOC ONE K.K.—See SBI Holdings, Inc.; *Int'l*, pg. 6604
AUTOCONT A.S.—See AutoCont Control Systems, s.r.o.; *Int'l*, pg. 726
AUTOCONT CONTROL SYSTEMS, S.R.O.; *Int'l*, pg. 726
AUTOCONT ONLINE A/S—See AutoCont Control Systems, s.r.o.; *Int'l*, pg. 726
AUTOCORA OBCHODNI SPOL S.R.O—See Stahlgruber Otto Gruber GmbH & Co. KG; *Int'l*, pg. 7164
AUTOCORP HOLDING PUBLIC COMPANY LIMITED; *Int'l*, pg. 726
AUTOCOUNT DOTCOM BERHAD; *Int'l*, pg. 726
AUTO CRAFT TOOL & DIE CO.—See Arsenal Capital Management LP; *U.S. Private*, pg. 338
AUTO CRANE COMPANY—See Gridiron Capital, LLC; *U.S. Private*, pg. 1786
AUTOCRAT, LLC; *U.S. Private*, pg. 398
AUTO CREDIT EXPRESS, INC.—See KKR & Co. Inc.; *U.S. Public*, pg. 1253
AUTO CREDIT INVESTMENTS OF GEORGIA INC.—See Scott-McRae Automotive Group Inc.; *U.S. Private*, pg. 3578
AUTO CREDIT OF FLORIDA INC.—See Scott-McRae Automotive Group Inc.; *U.S. Private*, pg. 3578
AUTO CREDIT OF GEORGIA INC.—See Scott-McRae Automotive Group Inc.; *U.S. Private*, pg. 3578

AUTOCRIB EMEA GMBH—See Snap-on Incorporated; *U.S. Public*, pg. 1897
AUTOCRIB, INC.—See Snap-on Incorporated; *U.S. Public*, pg. 1897
AUTOCRUISE S.A.S.—See ZF Friedrichshafen AG; *Int'l*, pg. 8645
AUTO CUSTOM CARPETS INC.; *U.S. Private*, pg. 397
AUTO DATA, INC.; *U.S. Private*, pg. 397
AUTODATA SOLUTIONS, INC.—See Thoma Bravo, L.P.; *U.S. Private*, pg. 4146
AUTO DEALERS EXCHANGE OF CONCORD, LLC—See OPENLANE, Inc.; *U.S. Public*, pg. 1607
AUTO DEALERS EXCHANGE OF MEMPHIS, LLC—See OPENLANE, Inc.; *U.S. Public*, pg. 1607
AUTO DEALERSHIP III, LLC—See AutoNation, Inc.; *U.S. Public*, pg. 232
AUTO DEALERSHIP IV, LLC—See AutoNation, Inc.; *U.S. Public*, pg. 232
AUTO DEALERSHIP VI, LLC—See AutoNation, Inc.; *U.S. Public*, pg. 232
AUTO DEALERSHIP V, LLC—See AutoNation, Inc.; *U.S. Public*, pg. 232
AUTODEMO LLC; *U.S. Private*, pg. 398
AUTODESCUENTO, S.L.—See Banco Santander, S.A.; *Int'l*, pg. 825
AUTODESK AB—See Autodesk, Inc.; *U.S. Public*, pg. 228
AUTODESK APS—See Autodesk, Inc.; *U.S. Public*, pg. 228
AUTODESK ASIA PTE. LTD.—See Autodesk, Inc.; *U.S. Public*, pg. 229
AUTODESK ASIA PTE. LTD.—See Autodesk, Inc.; *U.S. Public*, pg. 228
AUTODESK BENELUX B.V.—See Autodesk, Inc.; *U.S. Public*, pg. 228
AUTODESK B.V.—See Autodesk, Inc.; *U.S. Public*, pg. 229
AUTODESK CANADA CO.—See Autodesk, Inc.; *U.S. Public*, pg. 229
AUTODESK CANADA CO.—See Autodesk, Inc.; *U.S. Public*, pg. 229
AUTODESK (CHINA) SOFTWARE RESEARCH AND DEVELOPMENT CO., LTD.—See Autodesk, Inc.; *U.S. Public*, pg. 228
AUTODESK DE MEXICO S.A. DE C.V.—See Autodesk, Inc.; *U.S. Public*, pg. 229
AUTODESK DEVELOPMENT SARL—See Autodesk, Inc.; *U.S. Public*, pg. 228
AUTODESK DO BRASIL LTDA—See Autodesk, Inc.; *U.S. Public*, pg. 228
AUTODESK (EMEA) SARL—See Autodesk, Inc.; *U.S. Public*, pg. 228
AUTODESK GESMBH—See Autodesk, Inc.; *U.S. Public*, pg. 228
AUTODESK GMBH—See Autodesk, Inc.; *U.S. Public*, pg. 228
AUTODESK, INC.; *U.S. Public*, pg. 228
AUTODESK, INC. - UK—See Autodesk, Inc.; *U.S. Public*, pg. 229
AUTODESK INDIA PRIVATE LIMITED—See Autodesk, Inc.; *U.S. Public*, pg. 228
AUTODESK LIMITED—See Autodesk, Inc.; *U.S. Public*, pg. 228
AUTODESK LTD. JAPAN—See Autodesk, Inc.; *U.S. Public*, pg. 229
AUTODESK SA—See Autodesk, Inc.; *U.S. Public*, pg. 229
AUTODESK SOFTWARE (CHINA) CO., LTD.—See Autodesk, Inc.; *U.S. Public*, pg. 228
AUTODESK SOFTWARE, UNIPESSOAL, LDA.—See Autodesk, Inc.; *U.S. Public*, pg. 229
AUTODESK S.R.L.—See Autodesk, Inc.; *U.S. Public*, pg. 229
AUTODIE LLC—See Stellantis N.V.; *Int'l*, pg. 7199
AUTODIS ITALIA S.R.L.—See s.a. D'Ieteren n.v.; *Int'l*, pg. 6447
AUTODISTRIBUTION BENELUX B.V.—See LKQ Corporation; *U.S. Public*, pg. 1333
AUTODOME SDN. BHD.—See YTL Corporation Berhad; *Int'l*, pg. 8606
AUTODRIVE1; *U.S. Private*, pg. 398
AUTO DRIVEAWAY FRANCHISE SYSTEMS, LLC—See Evanston Partners, LLC; *U.S. Private*, pg. 1435
THE AUTODROME PLC; *Int'l*, pg. 7614
AUTODROM SOSNOVA U CESKE LIPY A.S—See Vienna Insurance Group AG Wiener Versicherung Gruppe; *Int'l*, pg. 8193
AUTO ELECTRA NAALDWIJK B.V.—See LKQ Corporation; *U.S. Public*, pg. 1333
AUTOELECTRIC OF AMERICA INC—See Nexans S.A.; *Int'l*, pg. 5242
AUTOENGINUITY LLC—See Searchlight Capital Partners, L.P.; *U.S. Private*, pg. 3590
AUTO EQUIPMENT INC.; *U.S. Private*, pg. 397
AUTO ESCAPE GROUP—See Expedia Group, Inc.; *U.S. Public*, pg. 809
AUTO ESCAPE SA—See Expedia Group, Inc.; *U.S. Public*, pg. 809
AUTO ESCAPE UK—See Expedia Group, Inc.; *U.S. Public*, pg. 809

240

AUTOESTRADAS DE GALICIA, S.A.—See Sacyr, S.A.; *Int'l*, pg. 6465
AUTOEUROPA AUTOMOVELS LDA.—See Porsche Automobil Holding SE; *Int'l*, pg. 5926
AUTO EUROPE, LLC; *U.S. Private*, pg. 397
AUTOEVER SYSTEMS EUROPE GMBH—See Hyundai Motor Company; *Int'l*, pg. 3558
AUTO EXECUTIVES; *U.S. Private*, pg. 397
AUTO EXPEDITING INC.; *U.S. Private*, pg. 397
AUTO EXPRESS FRONTERA NORTE, S. A. DE C. V.—See Grupo Traxion, S. A. B. de C. V.; *Int'l*, pg. 3138
AUTOFEED CORPORATION; *Int'l*, pg. 726
AUTOFIL WORLDWIDE LIMITED—See Indorama Ventures Public Company Limited; *Int'l*, pg. 3658
AUTOFORJAS, LTDA.—See Cie Automotive S.A.; *Int'l*, pg. 1604
AUTOFORM TOOL & MANUFACTURING, LLC—See Park-Ohio Holdings Corp.; *U.S. Public*, pg. 1639
AUTO FORNEBU AS—See General Motors Company; *U.S. Public*, pg. 926
AUTOFORUM KOCH GMBH—See Koch Gruppe Automobile AG; *Int'l*, pg. 4224
AUTOGARD ASIA PACIFIC PTY LTD—See Zurn Elkay Water Solutions Corporation; *U.S. Public*, pg. 2412
AUTOGARD HOLDINGS LIMITED—See Zurn Elkay Water Solutions Corporation; *U.S. Public*, pg. 2412
AUTOGATOR, INC.; *U.S. Private*, pg. 398
AUTO & GENERAL INSURANCE COMPANY LIMITED—See BGL Group Limited; *Int'l*, pg. 1008
AUTOGENOMICS, INC.—See Prescient Medicine Holdings LLC; *Int'l*, pg. 3253
AUTOGERMA S.P.A—See Porsche Automobil Holding SE; *Int'l*, pg. 5926
AUTO GLASS NOW LLC—See Driven Brands Holdings Inc.; *U.S. Public*, pg. 688
AUTO GLASS SERVICE LLC.; *U.S. Private*, pg. 397
AUTO GLASS SPECIALISTS, INC.—See s.a. D'Ieteren n.v.; *Int'l*, pg. 6447
AUTO GLOBAL PARTS INDUSTRIES SDN. BHD.—See New Hoong Fatt Holdings Berhad; *Int'l*, pg. 5224
AUTOGRANA A.D.; *Int'l*, pg. 726
AUTOGRILL CATERING UK LIMITED—See Avolta AG; *Int'l*, pg. 749
AUTOGRILL IBERIA S.L.U—See Avolta AG; *Int'l*, pg. 749
AUTOGRILL SCHWEIZ A.G.—See Edizione S.r.l.; *Int'l*, pg. 2311
AUTOGRILL S.P.A.—See Avolta AG; *Int'l*, pg. 749
AUTOGRILL VFS F&B CO. LTD—See Edizione S.r.l.; *Int'l*, pg. 2311
AUTOHAUS24 GMBH—See Banco Santander, S.A.; *Int'l*, pg. 825
AUTOHAUS ARIZONA, INC.; *U.S. Private*, pg. 398
AUTOHAUS AUGSBURG GMBH—See Penske Automotive Group, Inc.; *U.S. Public*, pg. 1664
AUTOHAUS BILIA GMBH & CO. KG—See Bilia AB; *Int'l*, pg. 1029
AUTOHAUS BMW; *U.S. Private*, pg. 398
AUTOHAUS CAR RENTAL SDN. BHD.—See Permaju Industries Berhad; *Int'l*, pg. 5802
AUTOHAUS G.V.O. GMBH—See General Motors Company; *U.S. Public*, pg. 926
AUTOHAUS HANSA NORD GMBH—See Ernst Dello GmbH & Co. KG; *Int'l*, pg. 2494
AUTOHAUS HEINRICH SENDEN GMBH; *Int'l*, pg. 726
AUTOHAUS HOLDINGS, INC.—See AutoNation, Inc.; *U.S. Public*, pg. 233
AUTOHAUS KOCH GMBH—See Koch Gruppe Automobile AG; *Int'l*, pg. 4224
AUTOHAUS KRETTER GMBH; *Int'l*, pg. 726
AUTOHAUS LANCASTER, INC.; *U.S. Private*, pg. 398
AUTOHAUS NIX GMBH—See Penske Automotive Group, Inc.; *U.S. Public*, pg. 1664
AUTOHAUS ON EDENS INC.; *U.S. Private*, pg. 398
AUTOHAUS WIDMANN + WINTERHOLLER GMBH - FARCHANT—See Autohaus Widmann + Winterholler GmbH; *Int'l*, pg. 727
AUTOHAUS WIDMANN + WINTERHOLLER GMBH; *Int'l*, pg. 727
AUTOHELLAS S.A.; *Int'l*, pg. 727
AUTOHERO BELGIUM B.V.—See AUTO1 Group SE; *Int'l*, pg. 725
AUTOHERO GMBH—See AUTO1 Group SE; *Int'l*, pg. 725
AUTOHERO ITALIA S.R.L.—See AUTO1 Group SE; *Int'l*, pg. 725
AUTOHERO NL B.V.—See AUTO1 Group SE; *Int'l*, pg. 725
AUTOHERO OSTERREICH GMBH—See AUTO1 Group SE; *Int'l*, pg. 725
AUTOHERO PLUS SPAIN S.L.—See AUTO1 Group SE; *Int'l*, pg. 725
AUTOHERO POLAND SP. Z O.O.—See AUTO1 Group SE; *Int'l*, pg. 725
AUTOHOME INC.—See Ping An Insurance (Group) Company of China, Ltd.; *Int'l*, pg. 5869
AUTO HRVATSKA D.D.; *Int'l*, pg. 724
AUTO IMPEX JOINT STOCK COMPANY; *Int'l*, pg. 724
AUTOINFO, INC.—See Comvest Group Holdings LLC; *U.S. Private*, pg. 1007

AUTO INJURY SOLUTIONS, INC.—See Advent International Corporation; *U.S. Private*, pg. 98
AUTO INSURANCE SPECIALISTS, LLC—See Mercury General Corporation; *U.S. Public*, pg. 1421
AUTO INSURANCE SPECIALISTS—See Mercury General Corporation; *U.S. Public*, pg. 1421
AUTO INVESTMENT INC.—See ITOCHU Corporation; *Int'l*, pg. 3838
AUTO ITALIA EAD—See Eurohold Bulgaria AD; *Int'l*, pg. 2553
AUTO ITALIA HOLDINGS LIMITED; *Int'l*, pg. 724
AUTO ITALIA LIMITED—See Auto Italia Holdings Limited; *Int'l*, pg. 724
AUTO KELLY A.S.—See LKQ Corporation; *U.S. Public*, pg. 1333
AUTO KELLY SLOVAKIA S.R.O.—See LKQ Corporation; *U.S. Public*, pg. 1333
AUTOKINITON GLOBAL GROUP, LP—See KPS Capital Partners, LP; *U.S. Private*, pg. 2346
AUTOKOMERC A.D.; *Int'l*, pg. 727
AUTOKORAN A.D.; *Int'l*, pg. 727
AUTOKRAFT GMBH—See Deutsche Bahn AG; *Int'l*, pg. 2049
AUTOKRAZ HOLDING CO.; *Int'l*, pg. 727
AUTO KUCA 21. MAJ A.D.; *Int'l*, pg. 725
AUTO KUCA LESKOVAC AD; *Int'l*, pg. 725
AUTOKUCA RAKETA AD; *Int'l*, pg. 727
AUTO KUCA VOZDOVAC A.D.; *Int'l*, pg. 725
AUTO KUCA ZEMUN A.D.; *Int'l*, pg. 725
AUTOKUHLER GMBH & CO. KG; *Int'l*, pg. 727
AUTO-LACKIER-CENTER GMBH—See Porsche Automobil Holding SE; *Int'l*, pg. 5933
AUTOLAND, INC.—See Mission Federal Credit Union; *U.S. Private*, pg. 2747
AUTOLIGHTS, LLC—See Atlantic Street Capital Management LLC; *U.S. Private*, pg. 374
AUTOLINE DESIGN SOFTWARE LIMITED—See Autoline Industries Limited; *Int'l*, pg. 727
AUTOLINE INDUSTRIES LIMITED - BHOSARI UNIT III—See Autoline Industries Limited; *Int'l*, pg. 728
AUTOLINE INDUSTRIES LIMITED - BHOSARI UNIT II—See Autoline Industries Limited; *Int'l*, pg. 727
AUTOLINE INDUSTRIES LIMITED - BHOSARI UNIT I—See Autoline Industries Limited; *Int'l*, pg. 727
AUTOLINE INDUSTRIES LIMITED - CHAKAN UNIT III—See Autoline Industries Limited; *Int'l*, pg. 728
AUTOLINE INDUSTRIES LIMITED - CHAKAN UNIT I—See Autoline Industries Limited; *Int'l*, pg. 728
AUTOLINE INDUSTRIES LIMITED; *Int'l*, pg. 727
AUTOLITE (INDIA) LIMITED; *Int'l*, pg. 728
AUTOLITE MANUFACTURING LIMITED—See Autolite (India) Limited; pg. 728
AUTOLIV AB—See Autoliv, Inc.; *Int'l*, pg. 728
AUTOLIV - AIRBAG INFLATOR FACILITY—See Autoliv, Inc.; *Int'l*, pg. 729
AUTOLIV ARGENTINA S.A.—See Autoliv, Inc.; *Int'l*, pg. 728
AUTOLIV ASIA PACIFIC—See Autoliv, Inc.; *Int'l*, pg. 728
AUTOLIV ASP B.V.—See Autoliv, Inc.; *Int'l*, pg. 728
AUTOLIV ASP, INC.—See Autoliv, Inc.; *Int'l*, pg. 729
AUTOLIV AUSTRALIA PTY. LTD.—See Autoliv, Inc.; *Int'l*, pg. 728
AUTOLIV BEIJING SAFETY SYSTEMS—See Autoliv, Inc.; *Int'l*, pg. 728
AUTOLIV BKI S.A.—See Autoliv, Inc.; *Int'l*, pg. 728
AUTOLIV BV & CO. KG—See Autoliv, Inc.; *Int'l*, pg. 728
AUTOLIV B.V. & CO. KG, WERK NORD—See Autoliv, Inc.; *Int'l*, pg. 728
AUTOLIV CANADA, INC.—See Autoliv, Inc.; *Int'l*, pg. 728
AUTOLIV CANKOR OTOMOTIV EMNIYET SISTEMLERI SANAYI VE TICARET A.S.—See Autoliv, Inc.; *Int'l*, pg. 728
AUTOLIV CANKOR—See Autoliv, Inc.; *Int'l*, pg. 728
AUTOLIV (CHANGCHUN) MAWHUNG VEHICLE SAFETY SYSTEMS CO., LTD.—See Autoliv, Inc.; *Int'l*, pg. 728
AUTOLIV (CHINA) ELECTRONICS CO., LTD.—See Autoliv, Inc.; *Int'l*, pg. 728
AUTOLIV (CHINA) STEERING WHEEL CO., LTD.—See Autoliv, Inc.; *Int'l*, pg. 728
AUTOLIV CORPORATION—See Autoliv, Inc.; *Int'l*, pg. 728
AUTOLIV DE MEXICO S.A. DE C.V.—See Autoliv, Inc.; *Int'l*, pg. 730
AUTOLIV DEVELOPMENT AB—See Autoliv, Inc.; *Int'l*, pg. 728
AUTOLIV DO BRASIL LTDA—See Autoliv, Inc.; *Int'l*, pg. 730
AUTOLIV DO BRASIL—See Autoliv, Inc.; *Int'l*, pg. 730
AUTOLIV ELECTRONICS AB—See Autoliv, Inc.; *Int'l*, pg. 728
AUTOLIV ELECTRONICS AB—See Autoliv, Inc.; *Int'l*, pg. 728
AUTOLIV ELECTRONICS AMERICA—See Autoliv, Inc.; *Int'l*, pg. 729
AUTOLIV ELECTRONICS CANADA, INC.—See Autoliv, Inc.; *Int'l*, pg. 729
AUTOLIV ELECTRONICS, PONTOISE—See Autoliv, Inc.; *Int'l*, pg. 728

AUTOLIV ELECTRONICS SAS, ROUEN—See Autoliv, Inc.; *Int'l*, pg. 728
AUTOLIV FRANCE, GOURNAY—See Autoliv, Inc.; *Int'l*, pg. 728
AUTOLIV FRANCE—See Autoliv, Inc.; *Int'l*, pg. 728
AUTOLIV GMBH, BRAUNSCHWEIG—See Autoliv, Inc.; *Int'l*, pg. 728
AUTOLIV GMBH, WERK SUD—See Autoliv, Inc.; *Int'l*, pg. 728
AUTOLIV HIROTAKO SAFETY SDN. BHD.—See Autoliv, Inc.; *Int'l*, pg. 729
AUTOLIV HIROTAKO SAFETY SDN. BHD.—See MBM Resources Berhad; *Int'l*, pg. 4754
AUTOLIV HIROTAKO SDN. BHD.—See Autoliv, Inc.; *Int'l*, pg. 728
AUTOLIV HIROTAKO SDN. BHD.—See MBM Resources Berhad; *Int'l*, pg. 4754
AUTOLIV HIROTAKO SRS SDN. BHD.—See Autoliv, Inc.; *Int'l*, pg. 729
AUTOLIV HIROTAKO SRS SDN. BHD.—See MBM Resources Berhad; *Int'l*, pg. 4754
AUTOLIV HOLDING AB—See Autoliv, Inc.; *Int'l*, pg. 729
AUTOLIV, INC.; *Int'l*, pg. 728
AUTOLIV INFLATORS—See Autoliv, Inc.; *Int'l*, pg. 729
AUTOLIV INITIATORS—See Autoliv, Inc.; *Int'l*, pg. 729
AUTOLIV ISODELTA SAS—See Autoliv, Inc.; *Int'l*, pg. 729
AUTOLIV ISODELTA—See Autoliv, Inc.; *Int'l*, pg. 729
AUTOLIV ITALIA SPA—See Autoliv, Inc.; *Int'l*, pg. 729
AUTOLIV IZUMI PHILIPPINES, INC.—See Autoliv, Inc.; *Int'l*, pg. 729
AUTOLIV JAPAN LTD. - ATSUGI FACILITY—See Autoliv, Inc.; *Int'l*, pg. 729
AUTOLIV JAPAN LTD. - FUJISAWA FACILITY—See Autoliv, Inc.; *Int'l*, pg. 729
AUTOLIV JAPAN LTD.—See Autoliv, Inc.; *Int'l*, pg. 729
AUTOLIV KFT.—See Autoliv, Inc.; *Int'l*, pg. 729
AUTOLIV KK—See Autoliv, Inc.; *Int'l*, pg. 729
AUTOLIV KLE S.A.—See Autoliv, Inc.; *Int'l*, pg. 729
AUTOLIV KLE S.A.U.—See Autoliv, Inc.; *Int'l*, pg. 729
AUTOLIV MANDO CORPORATION—See Autoliv, Inc.; *Int'l*, pg. 729
AUTOLIV MEKAN AB—See Autoliv, Inc.; *Int'l*, pg. 728
AUTOLIV NORTH AMERICA AIRBAG INFLATOR FACILITY—See Autoliv, Inc.; *Int'l*, pg. 729
AUTOLIV NORTH AMERICA AIRBAG MODULE FACILITY—See Autoliv, Inc.; *Int'l*, pg. 729
AUTOLIV NORTH AMERICA, AMERICAN TECHNICAL CENTER—See Autoliv, Inc.; *Int'l*, pg. 729
AUTOLIV NORTH AMERICA SEAT BELT FACILITY—See Autoliv, Inc.; *Int'l*, pg. 729
AUTOLIV NORTH AMERICA SERVICE PARTS FACILITY—See Autoliv, Inc.; *Int'l*, pg. 729
AUTOLIV NORTH AMERICA—See Autoliv, Inc.; *Int'l*, pg. 729
AUTOLIV NORTH AMERICA STEERING WHEEL FACILITY—See Autoliv, Inc.; *Int'l*, pg. 729
AUTOLIV POLAND RESTRAINT SYSTEMS—See Autoliv, Inc.; *Int'l*, pg. 729
AUTOLIV POLAND SP.Z.O.O.—See Autoliv, Inc.; *Int'l*, pg. 729
AUTOLIV QB, INC.—See Autoliv, Inc.; *Int'l*, pg. 729
AUTOLIV ROMANIA S.A.—See Autoliv, Inc.; *Int'l*, pg. 729
AUTOLIV SAFETY TECHNOLOGY—See Autoliv, Inc.; *Int'l*, pg. 729
AUTOLIV (SHANGHAI) MANAGEMENT CO., LTD.—See Autoliv, Inc.; *Int'l*, pg. 728
AUTOLIV (SHANGHAI) VEHICLE SAFETY SYSTEMS CO., LTD.—See Autoliv, Inc.; *Int'l*, pg. 728
AUTOLIV SICHERHEITSTECHNIK GMBH, WERK OST—See Autoliv, Inc.; *Int'l*, pg. 729
AUTOLIV SOUTHERN AFRICA (PTY) LTD.—See Autoliv, Inc.; *Int'l*, pg. 729
AUTOLIV SPRING DYNAMICS—See Autoliv, Inc.; *Int'l*, pg. 730
AUTOLIV STEERING WHEELS MEXICO S. DE R.L. DE C.V.—See Autoliv, Inc.; *Int'l*, pg. 730
AUTOLIV STEERING WHEELS S.R.L. DE C.V.—See Autoliv, Inc.; *Int'l*, pg. 730
AUTOLIV TEXTILES—See Autoliv, Inc.; *Int'l*, pg. 730
AUTOLIV THAILAND LIMITED—See Autoliv, Inc.; *Int'l*, pg. 730
AUTOLOGIC DIAGNOSTICS, INC.—See Searchlight Capital Partners, L.P.; *U.S. Private*, pg. 3590
AUTOLOGIC DIAGNOSTICS LTD.—See Searchlight Capital Partners, L.P.; *U.S. Private*, pg. 3590
AUTOLOGIC DIAGNOSTICS PTY. LTD.—See Searchlight Capital Partners, L.P.; *U.S. Private*, pg. 3590
AUTOLOGIC HOLDINGS LIMITED—See DBAY Advisors Limited; *Int'l*, pg. 1986
AUTOLOGISTIC POLAND SP. Z O. O.—See Deutsche Bahn AG; *Int'l*, pg. 2050
AUTOLUM PROCESSING CO.—See Ferragon Corporation; *U.S. Private*, pg. 1498
AUTOLUS THERAPEUTICS PLC; *Int'l*, pg. 730
AUTOLUTION INDUSTRIAL PTE LTD—See Tan Chong International Limited; *Int'l*, pg. 7452
AUTOMAG GMBH—See Bayerische Motoren Werke Aktiengesellschaft; *Int'l*, pg. 910
AUTOMAKEDONIJA A.D.; *Int'l*, pg. 730

AUTO MALL 46, INC.

AUTO MALL 46, INC.; *U.S. Private*, pg. 397
AUTO MANAGEMENT INC.; *U.S. Private*, pg. 397
AUTOMARKET/LOTUS OF ORANGE COUNTY; *U.S. Private*, pg. 398
AUTOMATA S.A.—See Krones AG; *Int'l*, pg. 4305
AUTOMATED BENEFIT SERVICES—See US Health Holdings Ltd.; *U.S. Private*, pg. 4319
AUTOMATED BENEFITS INC.—See Insight Venture Management, LLC; *U.S. Private*, pg. 2089
AUTOMATED BENEFITS INC.—See Stone Point Capital LLC; *U.S. Private*, pg. 3823
AUTOMATED BUILDING COMPANY—See TCS TurControlSysteme AG; *Int'l*, pg. 7485
AUTOMATED BUILDING COMPONENTS, INC.; *U.S. Private*, pg. 399
AUTOMATED BUILDING COMPONENTS, INC.—See Bain Capital, LP; *U.S. Private*, pg. 450
AUTOMATED BUSINESS PRODUCTS, INC.—See Ricoh Company, Ltd.; *Int'l*, pg. 6336
AUTOMATED COLLECTION SERVICES, INC. (ACSI); *U.S. Private*, pg. 399
AUTOMATED ENVIRONMENTS LLC—See Munters Group AB; *Int'l*, pg. 5094
AUTOMATED EQUIPMENT COMPANY INC.—See Diamond Parking Services LLC; *U.S. Private*, pg. 1223
AUTOMATED FINANCIAL SYSTEMS INC.; *U.S. Private*, pg. 399
AUTOMATED GATE SERVICES, INC.—See Aurora Capital Group, LLC; *U.S. Private*, pg. 394
AUTOMATED GRAPHIC SYSTEMS, INC.—See Chatham Asset Management, LLC; *U.S. Private*, pg. 862
AUTOMATED HEALTHCARE SOLUTIONS, LLC; *U.S. Private*, pg. 399
AUTOMATED IMAGING SYSTEMS, INC.—See R.J. Young Co., Inc.; *U.S. Private*, pg. 3337
AUTOMATED INDUSTRIAL MACHINERY, INC.; *U.S. Private*, pg. 399
AUTOMATED LOGIC AUSTRALIA PTY. LIMITED—See Carrier Global Corporation; *U.S. Public*, pg. 440
AUTOMATED LOGIC CORPORATION—See Carrier Global Corporation; *U.S. Public*, pg. 440
AUTOMATED MEASUREMENT & CONTROL CORPORATION—See Makke LLC; *U.S. Private*, pg. 2556
AUTOMATED MEDICAL SYSTEMS INC.—See DAS Health Ventures, Inc.; *U.S. Private*, pg. 1161
AUTOMATED METAL TECHNOLOGIES, INC.—See Naimor, Inc.; *U.S. Private*, pg. 2831
AUTOMATED OUTLET, INC.; *U.S. Private*, pg. 399
AUTOMATED PACKAGING SYSTEMS COMERCIALE IMPORTACAO DO BRASIL LTDA.—See Sealed Air Corporation; *U.S. Public*, pg. 1852
AUTOMATED PACKAGING SYSTEMS EUROPE—See Sealed Air Corporation; *U.S. Public*, pg. 1852
AUTOMATED PACKAGING SYSTEMS GMBH & CO. KG—See Sealed Air Corporation; *U.S. Public*, pg. 1852
AUTOMATED PACKAGING SYSTEMS INC.—See Sealed Air Corporation; *U.S. Public*, pg. 1852
AUTOMATED PACKAGING SYSTEMS LIMITED—See Sealed Air Corporation; *U.S. Public*, pg. 1852
AUTOMATED PAYMENT HIGHWAY, INC—See Lovell Minnick Partners LLC; *U.S. Private*, pg. 2501
AUTOMATED PETROLEUM & ENERGY COMPANY, INC.; *U.S. Private*, pg. 399
AUTOMATED POWER EXCHANGE INC.; *U.S. Private*, pg. 399
AUTOMATEDQA CORP.; *U.S. Private*, pg. 399
AUTOMATED RESOURCE MANAGEMENT ASSOCIATES, INC.; *U.S. Private*, pg. 399
AUTOMATED SYSTEMS COMPANY K.S.C—See Kuwait Airways Corporation; *Int'l*, pg. 4343
AUTOMATED SYSTEMS DESIGN, INC.—See RAF Industries, Inc.; *U.S. Private*, pg. 3345
AUTOMATED SYSTEMS GROUP LTD—See Mobeus Equity Partners LLP; *Int'l*, pg. 5008
AUTOMATED SYSTEMS HOLDINGS LIMITED—See Beijing Teamsun Technology Co., Ltd.; *Int'l*, pg. 958
AUTOMATED SYSTEMS INC.; *U.S. Private*, pg. 399
THE AUTOMATED TECHNOLOGY GROUP LIMITED—See John Wood Group PLC; *Int'l*, pg. 3984
THE AUTOMATED TECHNOLOGY GROUP (SLOVAKIA) S.R.O.—See John Wood Group PLC; *Int'l*, pg. 3984
AUTOMATED TECHNOLOGY MACHINES INCORPORATED; *U.S. Private*, pg. 399
AUTOMATED TOUCHSTONE MACHINES LIMITED; *Int'l*, pg. 730
AUTOMATED WASTE SERVICES LLC—See BC Partners LLP; *Int'l*, pg. 924
AUTO/MATE, INC.—See Vista Equity Partners, LLC; *U.S. Private*, pg. 398
AUTOMATIC APARTMENT LAUNDRIES, INC.; *U.S. Private*, pg. 399
AUTOMATIC BAR CONTROLS, INC.—See The Middleby Corporation; *U.S. Public*, pg. 2113
AUTOMATIC CONTROL SYSTEMS INC.—See Financiere de L'Odet; *Int'l*, pg. 2665
AUTOMATIC DATA PROCESSING, INC.; *U.S. Public*, pg. 229

AUTOMATIC DATA PROCESSING INSURANCE AGENCY, INC.—See Automatic Data Processing, Inc.; *U.S. Public*, pg. 230
AUTOMATIC DATA PROCESSING LIMITED—See Automatic Data Processing, Inc.; *U.S. Public*, pg. 230
AUTOMATIC DATA PROCESSING LIMITED—See Automatic Data Processing, Inc.; *U.S. Public*, pg. 230
AUTOMATIC ELECTRIC EUROPE B.V.; *Int'l*, pg. 730
AUTOMATIC ENTRANCES OF WISCONSIN, INC.—See Alpine Investors; *U.S. Private*, pg. 201
AUTOMATIC EQUIPMENT CORPORATION; *U.S. Private*, pg. 399
AUTOMATIC EQUIPMENT MANUFACTURING CO.; *U.S. Private*, pg. 399
AUTOMATIC FEED COMPANY—See Nidec Corporation; *Int'l*, pg. 5274
AUTOMATIC FIRE SPRINKLERS, INC.—See Pye-Barker Fire & Safety, LLC; *U.S. Private*, pg. 3309
AUTOMATIC MACHINE PRODUCTS COMPANY; *U.S. Private*, pg. 399
AUTOMATIC PROCESSING INCORPORATED—See AZZ, Inc.; *U.S. Public*, pg. 259
AUTOMATIC PRODUCTS INTERNATIONAL LTD.—See Crane NXT, Co.; *U.S. Public*, pg. 591
AUTOMATIC PRODUCTS (UK) LTD.—See Crane NXT, Co.; *U.S. Public*, pg. 591
AUTOMATIC RETAILING (NORTHERN) LIMITED—See Kitwave Group Plc; *Int'l*, pg. 4196
AUTOMATIC ROLLS OF BALTIMORE, INC.—See H&S Bakery Inc.; *U.S. Private*, pg. 1823
AUTOMATIC ROLLS OF NEW ENGLAND, INC.—See H&S Bakery Inc.; *U.S. Private*, pg. 1823
AUTOMATIC ROLLS OF NEW JERSEY, INC.—See H&S Bakery Inc.; *U.S. Private*, pg. 1823
AUTOMATIC ROLLS OF NORTH CAROLINA, LLC—See H&S Bakery Inc.; *U.S. Private*, pg. 1823
AUTOMATIC SCREW MACHINE PRODUCTS COMPANY, INC.—See Dubai Holding LLC; *Int'l*, pg. 2218
AUTOMATIC SPRING COILING—See American Securities LLC; *U.S. Private*, pg. 249
AUTOMATIC SPRING PRODUCTS CORP.; *U.S. Private*, pg. 399
AUTOMATIC SYSTEMS (BELGIUM) SA—See Financiere de L'Odet; *Int'l*, pg. 2665
AUTOMATIC SYSTEMS EQUIPMENT UK LTD.—See Financiere de L'Odet; *Int'l*, pg. 2665
AUTOMATIC SYSTEMS ESPANOLA SA—See Financiere de L'Odet; *Int'l*, pg. 2665
AUTOMATIC TERRAZZO TILES FACTORY LLC—See Badr Investment Group LLC; *Int'l*, pg. 796
AUTOMATIC TIMING & CONTROLS—See Desco Corporation; *U.S. Private*, pg. 1211
AUTOMATIKA SP. Z O.O.—See Zaklady Chemiczne POLICE S.A.; *Int'l*, pg. 8621
AUTOMATIK DO BRAZIL MAQUINAS PARA INDUSTRIA DO PLASTICO LTDA.—See Dover Corporation; *U.S. Public*, pg. 681
AUTOMATIKOS IRANGA UAB—See Harju Elekter AS; *Int'l*, pg. 3277
AUTOMATIK PLASTICS MACHINERY GMBH—See Dover Corporation; *U.S. Public*, pg. 681
AUTOMATIK PLASTICS MACHINERY SDN. BHD.—See Dover Corporation; *U.S. Public*, pg. 681
AUTOMATIK PLASTICS MACHINERY (TAIWAN) LTD.—See Dover Corporation; *U.S. Public*, pg. 681
AUTOMATION COMPONENTS, INC.—See Arcline Investment Management LP; *U.S. Private*, pg. 313
AUTOMATION & CONTROL CONCEPTS, INC.—See Hamilton Robinson LLC; *U.S. Private*, pg. 1848
AUTOMATION & CONTROLS ENGINEERING LTD.; *Int'l*, pg. 730
AUTOMATIONDIRECT, INC.—See Koyo Electronics Industries Co., Ltd.; *Int'l*, pg. 4295
AUTOMATION ENGINEERING CO., INC.; *U.S. Private*, pg. 399
AUTOMATION ENGINEERING CORPORATION; *U.S. Private*, pg. 399
AUTOMATION GROUP INC.; *U.S. Private*, pg. 399
AUTOMATION GROUP LIMITED—See Teaminvest Private Group Limited; *Int'l*, pg. 7501
AUTOMATION, INC.—See Applied Industrial Technologies, Inc.; *U.S. Public*, pg. 171
AUTOMATION INVESTMENT EUROPE B.V.—See OMRON Corporation; *Int'l*, pg. 5564
AUTOMATION & MODULAR COMPONENTS, INC.; *U.S. Private*, pg. 399
AUTOMATION PERSONNEL SERVICES, INC.; *U.S. Private*, pg. 399
AUTOMATION SOLUTIONS LTD.—See Endress+Hauser (International) Holding AG; *Int'l*, pg. 2405
AUTOMATION SPECIALISTS, INC.; *U.S. Private*, pg. 399
AUTOMATION TECHNIQUE SA; *Int'l*, pg. 730
AUTOMATION TECHNIQUES PTY. LTD.—See Graco, Inc.; *U.S. Public*, pg. 953
AUTOMATION TECHNOLOGIES, INC.; *U.S. Private*, pg. 400
AUTOMATION TOOL COMPANY; *U.S. Private*, pg. 400
AUTOMATION TOOLING SYSTEMS ENTERPRISES, INC.—See ATS Corporation; *Int'l*, pg. 695

CORPORATE AFFILIATIONS

AUTOMATION-X CORPORATION; *U.S. Private*, pg. 400
AUTOMATISMES BATIMENT SA—See ASSA ABLOY AB; *Int'l*, pg. 638
AUTOMATISMES BFT FRANCE S.A.S.—See Somfy SA; *Int'l*, pg. 7084
AUTOMATISMO CROUZET DE MEXICO, S.A. DE C.V.—See Schneider Electric SE; *Int'l*, pg. 6626
AUTOMATISMOS PUJOL SL—See Somfy SA; *Int'l*, pg. 7084
AUTOMAT PICTURES, INC.; *U.S. Private*, pg. 398
AUTOMATTIC INC.; *U.S. Private*, pg. 400
AUTOMAX CHRYSLER DODGE JEEP RAM; *U.S. Private*, pg. 400
AUTOMAX CO., LTD.—See Kyokuto Boeki Kaisha, Ltd.; *Int'l*, pg. 4362
AUTOMAXI INTERNATIONAL—See Accent Equity Partners AB; *Int'l*, pg. 81
AUTOMECANICA SA—See Rheinmetall AG; *Int'l*, pg. 6323
AUTOMED TECHNOLOGIES (CANADA), INC.—See Cencora, Inc.; *U.S. Public*, pg. 467
AUTOMED TECHNOLOGIES, INC.—See Cencora, Inc.; *U.S. Public*, pg. 467
AUTOMESTER DANMARK APS—See Hella GmbH & Co. KGaA; *Int'l*, pg. 3331
AUTOMETAL S.A.—See Cie Automotive S.A.; *Int'l*, pg. 1604
AUTOMETAL SBC INJECAO E PINTURA DE PLASTICOS LTDA.—See Cie Automotive S.A.; *Int'l*, pg. 1604
AUTO METER PRODUCTS, INC.—See Promus Holdings, LLC; *U.S. Private*, pg. 3284
AUTOMIC SOFTWARE GMBH—See Broadcom Inc.; *U.S. Public*, pg. 388
AUTOMIC SOFTWARE, INC.—See Broadcom Inc.; *U.S. Public*, pg. 388
AUTO MISSION LTD.—See AutoNation, Inc.; *U.S. Public*, pg. 232
AUTO MISSION LTD.—See AutoNation, Inc.; *U.S. Public*, pg. 232
THE AUTOMOBILE ASSOCIATION LIMITED—See Charterhouse Capital Partners LLP; *Int'l*, pg. 1455
THE AUTOMOBILE ASSOCIATION LIMITED—See CVC Capital Partners SICAV-FIS S.A.; *Int'l*, pg. 1882
THE AUTOMOBILE ASSOCIATION LIMITED—See Permira Advisers LLP; *Int'l*, pg. 5803
AUTOMOBILE CONTROLE TECHNIQUE S.A.R.L.—See DEKRA e.V.; *Int'l*, pg. 2007
AUTOMOBILE CORPORATION OF GOA LTD; *Int'l*, pg. 730
AUTOMOBILE INSPECTION SYSTEM INC.—See Aucnet Inc.; *Int'l*, pg. 700
AUTOMOBILE INSURANCE PLANS SERVICE OFFICE; *U.S. Private*, pg. 400
AUTOMOBILE MAGAZINE—See TEN: The Enthusiast Network, Inc.; *U.S. Private*, pg. 3964
AUTOMOBILE & PCB INC.; *Int'l*, pg. 730
AUTOMOBILE PROTECTION CORPORATION—See Ontario Teachers' Pension Plan; *Int'l*, pg. 5587
AUTOMOBILE PROVENCE INNOVATION; *Int'l*, pg. 730
AUTOMOBILES CHATENET; *Int'l*, pg. 730
AUTOMOBILES CITROEN SA—See Stellantis N.V.; *Int'l*, pg. 7201
AUTOMOBILES MAUGER FORD; *Int'l*, pg. 730
AUTOMOBILES OF STATESVILLE, INC.; *U.S. Private*, pg. 400
AUTOMOBILES ORTHEZIENNES; *Int'l*, pg. 730
AUTOMOBILES PEUGEOT SA—See Stellantis N.V.; *Int'l*, pg. 7201
AUTOMOBILI LAMBORGHINI HOLDING S.P.A.—See Porsche Automobil Holding SE; *Int'l*, pg. 5926
AUTOMOBILI LAMBORGHINI S.P.A.—See Porsche Automobil Holding SE; *Int'l*, pg. 5926
AUTOMOBILMANUFAKTUR DRESDEN GMBH—See Porsche Automobil Holding SE; *Int'l*, pg. 5926
AUTOMOBILWOCHE—See Crain Communications, Inc.; *U.S. Private*, pg. 1083
THE AUTOMOBLOX COMPANY—See Audax Group, Limited Partnership; *U.S. Private*, pg. 390
AUTOMODULAR ASSEMBLIES, INC.—See HLS Therapeutics, Inc.; *Int'l*, pg. 3431
AUTOMOTIVA USIMINAS S.A.—See Techint S.p.A.; *Int'l*, pg. 7505
AUTOMOTIVE ACADEMY B.V.—See LKQ Corporation; *U.S. Public*, pg. 1333
AUTOMOTIVE AFTER MARKET INC.; *U.S. Private*, pg. 400
AUTOMOTIVE ASSURANCE GROUP, LLC—See Stone Point Capital LLC; *U.S. Private*, pg. 3820
AUTOMOTIVE AXLES LIMITED—See Cummins Inc.; *U.S. Public*, pg. 608
AUTOMOTIVE AXLES LIMITED—See Kalyani Group; *Int'l*, pg. 4058
AUTOMOTIVE CAPITAL SERVICES, INC.—See Onity Group Inc.; *U.S. Public*, pg. 1604
AUTOMOTIVE CLEANING CHEMICALS LTD.—See Berner SE; *Int'l*, pg. 988
AUTOMOTIVE CLIMATE CONTROL, INC.; *U.S. Private*, pg. 400
AUTOMOTIVE COLOR & SUPPLY, LLC—See WILsquare Capital LLC; *U.S. Private*, pg. 4532

COMPANY NAME INDEX

AUTOMOTIVE COMPONENT CARRIER LLC—See Penske Corporation; *U.S. Private*, pg. 3138
AUTOMOTIVE COMPONENTS EUROPE S.A.—See Grupo Industrial Saltillo S.A. de C.V.; *Int'l*, pg. 3130
AUTOMOTIVE COMPONENTS LIMITED—See Massy Holdings Ltd.; *Int'l*, pg. 4723
AUTOMOTIVE CONCEPTS OF NORTH AMERICA; *U.S. Private*, pg. 400
AUTOMOTIVE CORPORATION (MALAYSIA) SDN BHD—See DRB-HICOM Berhad; *Int'l*, pg. 2201
AUTOMOTIVE DATA SERVICES LIMITED—See LKQ Corporation; *U.S. Public*, pg. 1333
AUTOMOTIVE DATA SERVICES PTY. LTD.—See carsales.com Limited; *Int'l*, pg. 1346
AUTOMOTIVE DEVELOPMENT GROUP, LLC—See Ontario Teachers' Pension Plan; *Int'l*, pg. 5587
AUTOMOTIVE DISTRIBUTORS CO., INC.; *U.S. Private*, pg. 400
AUTOMOTIVE ELECTRONIC CONTROLS—See Methode Electronics, Inc.; *U.S. Public*, pg. 1428
AUTOMOTIVE EXPORT SUPPLIES LTD.—See KJAER GROUP A/S; *Int'l*, pg. 4197
AUTOMOTIVE FASTENERS INC.; *U.S. Private*, pg. 400
AUTOMOTIVE FINANCE CORPORATION—See OPENLANE, Inc.; *U.S. Public*, pg. 1607
AUTOMOTIVE FINANCIAL SERVICES PTY LTD—See Solvar Limited; *Int'l*, pg. 7077
AUTOMOTIVE FINCO CORP.; *Int'l*, pg. 730
AUTOMOTIVE HARD PARTS INC.; *U.S. Private*, pg. 400
AUTOMOTIVE HOLDINGS GROUP LIMITED—See Eagers Automotive Limited; *Int'l*, pg. 2263
AUTOMOTIVE IMPORTING MANUFACTURING, INC.; *U.S. Private*, pg. 400
AUTOMOTIVE INDUSTRIES SENDIRIAN BERHAD—See Sime Darby Berhad; *Int'l*, pg. 6930
AUTOMOTIVE INTERNET MEDIA, INC.; *U.S. Private*, pg. 400
AUTOMOTIVE LEASE GUIDE (ALG), INC.—See TrueCar, Inc.; *U.S. Public*, pg. 2199
AUTOMOTIVE LIGHTING BROTTERODE GMBH—See Stellantis N.V.; *Int'l*, pg. 7196
AUTOMOTIVE LIGHTING ITALIA S.P.A.—See Stellantis N.V.; *Int'l*, pg. 7196
AUTOMOTIVE LIGHTING JAPAN K.K.—See Stellantis N.V.; *Int'l*, pg. 7196
AUTOMOTIVE LIGHTING POLSKA SP. Z O.O.—See Stellantis N.V.; *Int'l*, pg. 7196
AUTOMOTIVE LIGHTING REAR LAMPS FRANCE S.A.S.—See Stellantis N.V.; *Int'l*, pg. 7196
AUTOMOTIVE LIGHTING REUTLINGEN GMBH—See Stellantis N.V.; *Int'l*, pg. 7196
AUTOMOTIVE LIGHTING S.R.O.—See Stellantis N.V.; *Int'l*, pg. 7196
AUTOMOTIVE MANAGEMENT GROUP, INC.; *U.S. Private*, pg. 400
AUTOMOTIVE MANAGEMENT SERVICES, INC.; *U.S. Private*, pg. 400
AUTOMOTIVE MANUFACTURING & SUPPLY CO.; *U.S. Private*, pg. 400
AUTOMOTIVE MEDIA, LLC—See Penske Automotive Group, Inc.; *U.S. Public*, pg. 1664
AUTOMOTIVE MOLD TECHNOLOGY CO., LTD.—See Nagase & Co., Ltd.; *Int'l*, pg. 5126
AUTOMOTIVE NEWS—See Crain Communications, Inc.; *U.S. Private*, pg. 1083
AUTOMOTIVE PARTS DISTRIBUTION INTERNATIONAL, LLC.—See Enterex International Limited; *Int'l*, pg. 2451
AUTOMOTIVE PARTS EXPRESS INC.; *U.S. Private*, pg. 400
AUTOMOTIVE PARTS HEADQUARTERS, INC.; *U.S. Private*, pg. 400
AUTOMOTIVE PETROLEUM AND ALLIED INDUSTRIES EMPLOYEES WELFARE FUND; *U.S. Private*, pg. 400
AUTOMOTIVE PRODUCT CONSULTANTS, INC.; *U.S. Private*, pg. 400
AUTOMOTIVE PROPERTIES REAL ESTATE INVESTMENT TRUST; *Int'l*, pg. 731
AUTOMOTIVE RACING PRODUCTS; *U.S. Private*, pg. 400
AUTOMOTIVE RECOVERY SERVICES, INC.—See RB Global, Inc.; *Int'l*, pg. 6226
AUTOMOTIVE REFINISH TECHNOLOGIES LLC—See BASF SE; *Int'l*, pg. 875
AUTOMOTIVE RENTALS, INC.—See Holman Automotive Group, Inc.; *U.S. Private*, pg. 1967
AUTOMOTIVE SANDOUVILLE—See Stellantis N.V.; *Int'l*, pg. 7201
AUTOMOTIVE SERVICE INC.; *U.S. Private*, pg. 401
AUTOMOTIVE SERVICE NETWORK, INC.; *U.S. Private*, pg. 401
AUTOMOTIVE SOLUTIONS GROUP LIMITED—See AMA Group Limited; *Int'l*, pg. 403
AUTOMOTIVE STAMPINGS & ASSEMBLIES LIMITED—See Tata AutoComp Systems Limited; *Int'l*, pg. 7466
AUTOMOTIVE SUPPLY ASSOCIATES, INC.; *U.S. Private*, pg. 401
AUTOMOTIVE TESTING AND DEVELOPMENT SERVICES, INC.; *U.S. Private*, pg. 401

AUTOMOTIVE TRAINING GMBH—See Mercedes-Benz Group AG; *Int'l*, pg. 4820
AUTOMOTIVE TRAINING INSTITUTE, LLC—See Driven Brands Holdings Inc.; *U.S. Public*, pg. 688
AUTOMOTIVE TRIM DEVELOPMENTS; *Int'l*, pg. 731
AUTOMOTIVE WAREHOUSE, INC.—See Advance Auto Parts, Inc.; *U.S. Public*, pg. 45
AUTOMOTORES FRANCO-CHILENA S.A.—See Stellantis N.V.; *Int'l*, pg. 7201
AUTO MOTORS OF ENGLEWOOD, LLC—See AutoNation, Inc.; *U.S. Public*, pg. 232
AUTOMOULD (PTY) LIMITED—See Morgan Advanced Materials plc; *Int'l*, pg. 5041
AUTOMOVEIS CITROEN S.A.—See Stellantis N.V.; *Int'l*, pg. 7201
AUTOMOVILES CITROEN ESPANA S.A.—See Stellantis N.V.; *Int'l*, pg. 7203
AUTOMOVILISMO Y TURISMO SA; *Int'l*, pg. 731
AUTO NATIE WOMMELGEM N.V.—See s.a. D'Ieteren n.v.; *Int'l*, pg. 6447
AUTONATION CHEVROLET CADILLAC CORPUS CHRISTI—See AutoNation, Inc.; *U.S. Public*, pg. 232
AUTONATION CHEVROLET FORT LAUDERDALE—See AutoNation, Inc.; *U.S. Public*, pg. 233
AUTONATION CHEVROLET SPOKANE VALLEY—See AutoNation, Inc.; *U.S. Public*, pg. 233
AUTONATIONDIRECT.COM, INC.—See AutoNation, Inc.; *U.S. Public*, pg. 233
AUTONATION DODGE OF PEMBROKE PINES, INC.—See AutoNation, Inc.; *U.S. Public*, pg. 232
AUTONATION FLEET SERVICES, LLC—See AutoNation, Inc.; *U.S. Public*, pg. 232
AUTONATION FORD AMHERST—See AutoNation, Inc.; *U.S. Public*, pg. 232
AUTONATION FORD BURLESON—See AutoNation, Inc.; *U.S. Public*, pg. 232
AUTONATION FORD EAST—See AutoNation, Inc.; *U.S. Public*, pg. 233
AUTONATION FORD FRISCO—See AutoNation, Inc.; *U.S. Public*, pg. 232
AUTONATION FORD MEMPHIS—See AutoNation, Inc.; *U.S. Public*, pg. 232
AUTONATION FORD PANAMA CITY—See AutoNation, Inc.; *U.S. Public*, pg. 232
AUTONATION FORD SOUTH FORT WORTH—See AutoNation, Inc.; *U.S. Public*, pg. 232
AUTONATION FORD TUSTIN—See AutoNation, Inc.; *U.S. Public*, pg. 232
AUTONATION FORD WOLFCASE—See AutoNation, Inc.; *U.S. Public*, pg. 233
AUTONATION FORT WORTH MOTORS, LTD.—See AutoNation, Inc.; *U.S. Public*, pg. 233
AUTONATION IMPORTS OF KATY, L.P.—See AutoNation, Inc.; *U.S. Public*, pg. 233
AUTONATION IMPORTS OF LITHIA SPRINGS, INC.—See AutoNation, Inc.; *U.S. Public*, pg. 233
AUTONATION IMPORTS OF LONGWOOD, INC.—See AutoNation, Inc.; *U.S. Public*, pg. 233
AUTONATION IMPORTS OF PALM BEACH, INC.—See AutoNation, Inc.; *U.S. Public*, pg. 233
AUTONATION IMPORTS OF WINTER PARK, INC.—See AutoNation, Inc.; *U.S. Public*, pg. 233
AUTONATION IMPORTS OF WINTER PARK, INC.—See AutoNation, Inc.; *U.S. Public*, pg. 233
AUTONATION, INC.; *U.S. Public*, pg. 230
AUTONATION NISSAN LEWISVILLE—See AutoNation, Inc.; *U.S. Public*, pg. 233
AUTONATION NISSAN ORANGE PARK—See AutoNation, Inc.; *U.S. Public*, pg. 233
AUTONATION TOYOTA CERRITOS—See AutoNation, Inc.; *U.S. Public*, pg. 233
AUTONATION TOYOTA CORPUS CHRISTI—See AutoNation, Inc.; *U.S. Public*, pg. 233
AUTONATION USA OF PERRINE, INC.—See HGreg.com; *U.S. Private*, pg. 1931
AUTONATION V. IMPORTS OF DELRAY BEACH, LLC—See AutoNation, Inc.; *U.S. Public*, pg. 233
AUTONAVI HOLDINGS LIMITED—See Alibaba Group Holding Limited; *Int'l*, pg. 326
AUTONAVI SOFTWARE CO., LTD.—See Alibaba Group Holding Limited; *Int'l*, pg. 326
AUTO NEJMA MAROC SA; *Int'l*, pg. 725
AUTO NETWORKS INTERNATIONAL CORPORATION; *Int'l*, pg. 725
AUTONETWORKS TECHNOLOGIES, LTD.—See Sumitomo Electric Industries, Ltd.; *Int'l*, pg. 7277
AUTONEUM BELGIUM N.V.—See Autoneum Holding Ltd.; *Int'l*, pg. 731
AUTONEUM CANADA LTD.—See Autoneum Holding Ltd.; *Int'l*, pg. 731
AUTONEUM (CHONGQING) SOUND-PROOF PARTS CO. LTD.—See Autoneum Holding Ltd.; *Int'l*, pg. 731
AUTONEUM CZ S.R.O.—See Autoneum Holding Ltd.; *Int'l*, pg. 731
AUTONEUM ERKURT OTOMOTIV AS—See Autoneum Holding Ltd.; *Int'l*, pg. 731
AUTONEUM FELTEX (PTY) LIMITED—See Autoneum Holding Ltd.; *Int'l*, pg. 731

AUTO PARTS COMPANY

AUTONEUM FELTEX (PTY) LTD.—See Steinhoff International Holdings N.V.; *Int'l*, pg. 7194
AUTONEUM FRANCE S.A.S.U.—See Autoneum Holding Ltd.; *Int'l*, pg. 731
AUTONEUM GERMANY GMBH—See Autoneum Holding Ltd.; *Int'l*, pg. 731
AUTONEUM GREAT BRITAIN LTD. - HECKMONDWIKE—See Autoneum Holding Ltd.; *Int'l*, pg. 731
AUTONEUM GREAT BRITAIN LTD.—See Autoneum Holding Ltd.; *Int'l*, pg. 731
AUTONEUM HOLDING LTD.; *Int'l*, pg. 731
AUTONEUM INDIA PVT. LTD.—See Autoneum Holding Ltd.; *Int'l*, pg. 731
AUTONEUM KOREA LTD.—See Autoneum Holding Ltd.; *Int'l*, pg. 731
AUTONEUM MANAGEMENT AG—See Autoneum Holding Ltd.; *Int'l*, pg. 731
AUTONEUM MEXICO OPERATIONS, S.A. DE C.V.—See Autoneum Holding Ltd.; *Int'l*, pg. 731
AUTONEUM MEXICO, S. DE R.L. DE C.V.—See Autoneum Holding Ltd.; *Int'l*, pg. 731
AUTONEUM NETHERLANDS B.V.—See Autoneum Holding Ltd.; *Int'l*, pg. 731
AUTONEUM NITTOKU (GUANGZHOU) SOUND-PROOF CO. LTD.—See Autoneum Holding Ltd.; *Int'l*, pg. 731
AUTONEUM NITTOKU SOUND PROOF PRODUCTS INDIA PVT. LTD.—See Autoneum Holding Ltd.; *Int'l*, pg. 731
AUTONEUM NORTH AMERICA, INC. - AIKEN—See Autoneum Holding Ltd.; *Int'l*, pg. 731
AUTONEUM NORTH AMERICA, INC. - BLOOMSBURG—See Autoneum Holding Ltd.; *Int'l*, pg. 731
AUTONEUM NORTH AMERICA, INC.—See Autoneum Holding Ltd.; *Int'l*, pg. 731
AUTONEUM POLAND SP. Z.O.O.—See Autoneum Holding Ltd.; *Int'l*, pg. 731
AUTONEUM PORTUGAL LDA.—See Autoneum Holding Ltd.; *Int'l*, pg. 731
AUTONEUM RUS LLC—See Autoneum Holding Ltd.; *Int'l*, pg. 731
AUTONEUM (SHANGHAI) MANAGEMENT CO. LTD.—See Autoneum Holding Ltd.; *Int'l*, pg. 731
AUTONEUM SPAIN NORTHWEST S.L.U.—See Autoneum Holding Ltd.; *Int'l*, pg. 731
AUTONEUM SPAIN S.A.U.—See Autoneum Holding Ltd.; *Int'l*, pg. 731
AUTONEUM SWITZERLAND AG—See Autoneum Holding Ltd.; *Int'l*, pg. 731
AUTONEUM TECHNOLOGIES AG—See Autoneum Holding Ltd.; *Int'l*, pg. 731
AUTONEXUS PTY. LTD.—See Inchcape plc; *Int'l*, pg. 3647
AUTONOMIX MEDICAL, INC.; *U.S. Public*, pg. 238
AUTONOMOUS ELECTRIC MOBILITY PVT. LTD.—See Digilife Technologies Limited; *Int'l*, pg. 2119
AUTONOMOUS SURFACE VEHICLES LIMITED—See L3Harris Technologies, Inc.; *U.S. Public*, pg. 1280
AUTONOMOUSTUFF LLC—See Hexagon AB; *Int'l*, pg. 3367
AUTO ONE AUSTRALIA PTY. LTD.; *Int'l*, pg. 725
AUTOONLINE B.V.—See Vista Equity Partners, LLC; *U.S. Private*, pg. 4399
AUTOONLINE ITALIA S.R.L.—See Vista Equity Partners, LLC; *U.S. Private*, pg. 4399
AUTOONLINE MAGYAROSZAG KFT.—See Vista Equity Partners, LLC; *U.S. Private*, pg. 4399
AUTOONLINE OTOMOTIV BILGI ISLEM ANONIM SIRKETI—See Vista Equity Partners, LLC; *U.S. Private*, pg. 4399
AUTOONLINE SISTEME INFORMATICE SRL—See Vista Equity Partners, LLC; *U.S. Private*, pg. 4399
AUTO-OWNERS INSURANCE COMPANY—See Auto-Owners Insurance Group; *U.S. Private*, pg. 397
AUTO-OWNERS INSURANCE GROUP; *U.S. Private*, pg. 397
AUTO-OWNERS LIFE INSURANCE CO.—See Auto-Owners Insurance Group; *U.S. Private*, pg. 397
AUTO PAINT—See Auto-Wares, LLC; *U.S. Private*, pg. 398
AUTOPAL INC—See Autolite (India) Limited; *Int'l*, pg. 728
AUTO PARK POZNAN SP. Z O.O.—See Eiffage S.A.; *Int'l*, pg. 2329
AUTOPARK, S.A.—See Industry Super Holdings Pty. Ltd.; *Int'l*, pg. 3676
AUTOPARTES DE PRECISION DE SANTANA, S.A. DE C.V.—See Equistone Partners Europe Limited; *Int'l*, pg. 2487
AUTOPARTES WALKER, S. DE R.L. DE C.V.—See Apollo Global Management, Inc.; *U.S. Public*, pg. 163
AUTOPART INTERNATIONAL INC.—See Advance Auto Parts, Inc.; *U.S. Public*, pg. 44
AUTO PARTNER SA; *Int'l*, pg. 725
AUTO PARTS 4LESS GROUP, INC.; *U.S. Public*, pg. 228
AUTO PARTS ALLIANCE (CHINA) LTD.—See G-TEKT Corporation; *Int'l*, pg. 2863
AUTOPARTS ARMETAL S.A.—See Fras-le S.A.; *Int'l*, pg. 2765
AUTO PARTS COMPANY; *U.S. Private*, pg. 397

AUTO PARTS COMPANY

AUTO PARTS KOMEHYO KK—See Komehyo Holdings Co., Ltd.; *Int'l*, pg. 4241
AUTO PARTS MANUFACTURERS CO. SDN. BHD.—See APM Automotive Holdings Berhad; *Int'l*, pg. 516
AUTO PARTS MANUFACTURING MISSISSIPPI INC.—See Toyota Motor Corporation; *Int'l*, pg. 7872
AUTO PARTS OF JUPITER, INC.—See Genuine Parts Company; *U.S. Public*, pg. 932
AUTOPARTS PROSEC NV—See LKQ Corporation; *U.S. Public*, pg. 1333
AUTO PARTS WAREHOUSE INC.; *U.S. Private*, pg. 397
AUTO PERFORMANCE, INC.—See Auto-Wares, LLC; *U.S. Private*, pg. 398
AUTOPIA, LTD.—See Topy Industries, Ltd.; *Int'l*, pg. 7821
AUTO PINS INDIA LTD.; *Int'l*, pg. 725
AUTOPISTA CONCESIONARIA ASTUR-LEONESA, S.A.—See Sacyr, S.A.; *Int'l*, pg. 6465
AUTOPISTA DEL SOL, CONCESIONARIA ESPANOLA, S.A.—See Meridiam Infrastructure Partners SAS; *Int'l*, pg. 4835
AUTOPISTA DE NAVARRA, S.A.—See Sacyr, S.A.; *Int'l*, pg. 6465
AUTOPISTA FERNAO DIAS, S.A.—See Industry Super Holdings Pty. Ltd.; *Int'l*, pg. 3676
AUTOPISTA FLUMINENSE, S.A.—See Industry Super Holdings Pty. Ltd.; *Int'l*, pg. 3676
AUTOPISTAS DE BIZKAIA, S.A.—See Sacyr, S.A.; *Int'l*, pg. 6465
AUTOPISTAS DEL ATLANTICO, C.E.S.A.—See Sacyr, S.A.; *Int'l*, pg. 6465
AUTOPISTAS DEL CAFE S.A.—See Grupo Argos S.A.; *Int'l*, pg. 3120
AUTOPISTAS DE LEON, S.A.C.E.—See ACS, Actividades de Construccion y Servicios, S.A.; *Int'l*, pg. 112
AUTOPISTAS DEL NORDESTE S.A.—See Grupo Argos S.A.; *Int'l*, pg. 3120
AUTOPISTA URBANA NORTE, S.A. DE C.V.—See Industry Super Holdings Pty. Ltd.; *Int'l*, pg. 3675
THE AUTOPLANET GROUP INC.; *Int'l*, pg. 7614
AUTOPLEX AUTOMOTIVE LP; *U.S. Private*, pg. 401
AUTOPLEX BMW—See Autoplex Automotive LP; *U.S. Private*, pg. 401
AUTO POINT, INC.—See Vista Equity Partners, LLC; *U.S. Private*, pg. 4400
AUTO PORTFOLIO SERVICES, LLC—See OPENLANE, Inc.; *U.S. Public*, pg. 1607
AUTOPORT LIMITED—See Canadian National Railway Company; *Int'l*, pg. 1284
AUTO POSTO IMPERIO LTDA.—See Companhia Brasileira de Distribuicao; *Int'l*, pg. 1746
AUTOPREVOZ AD BANJA LUKA; *Int'l*, pg. 731
AUTOPREVOZ GORNJI MILANOVAC A.D.; *Int'l*, pg. 732
AUTOPREVOZ JANJUSEVIC A.D.; *Int'l*, pg. 732
AUTOPREVOZTURIST A.D.; *Int'l*, pg. 732
AUTOPROMETNO PODUZECE D.D.—See Deutsche Bahn AG; *Int'l*, pg. 2049
AUTOQUIP CORPORATION—See Miner Enterprises, Inc.; *U.S. Private*, pg. 2741
AUTOQUOTES LLC—See TA Associates, Inc.; *U.S. Private*, pg. 3914
AUTORAD, INC.—See Alfa Laval AB; *Int'l*, pg. 309
AUTORAMA INC.; *U.S. Private*, pg. 401
AUTO RECAMBIOS VILBER, S.L.—See s.a. D'Ieteren n.v.; *Int'l*, pg. 6447
AUTO RECYCLE AKITA CO., LTD.—See Dowa Holdings Co., Ltd.; *Int'l*, pg. 2182
AUTO RECYCLERS LLC; *U.S. Private*, pg. 397
AUTO REFINISH DISTRIBUTORS HOLDING CORP.; *U.S. Private*, pg. 397
AUTO REFINISH DISTRIBUTORS—See Auto Refinish Distributors Holding Corp.; *U.S. Private*, pg. 397
AUTO RELAIS SAGLIO; *Int'l*, pg. 725
AUTORE OIL & PROPANE COMPANY; *U.S. Private*, pg. 401
AUTO RESEARCH AND DEVELOPMENT SDN. BHD.—See Tan Chong Motor Holdings Berhad; *Int'l*, pg. 7453
AUTORESIDUOS S.L.U.—See Copart, Inc.; *U.S. Public*, pg. 574
AUTOREVO, LTD; *U.S. Private*, pg. 401
AUTORIDERS INTERNATIONAL LTD.; *Int'l*, pg. 732
AUTOROBOT-STREFA SP Z.O.O.—See EFORT Intelligent Equipment Co., Ltd.; *Int'l*, pg. 2321
AUTOROLL UK LTD.—See Indutrade AB; *Int'l*, pg. 3677
AUTOROUTES DU SUD DE LA FRANCE—See VINCI S.A.; *Int'l*, pg. 8230
AUTOROUTES PARIS-RHIN-RHONE—See Eiffage S.A.; *Int'l*, pg. 2331
AUTOROUTES PARIS-RHIN-RHONE—See Macquarie Group Limited; *Int'l*, pg. 4626
AUTOROUTES TRAFIC SAS—See VINCI S.A.; *Int'l*, pg. 8212
AUTO SAFETY HOUSE—See OEP Capital Advisors, L.P.; *U.S. Private*, pg. 3000
AUTOSAINT LIMITED—See White Mountains Insurance Group, Ltd.; *U.S. Public*, pg. 2368
AUTOSALES, INC.; *U.S. Private*, pg. 401

AUTOSCOPE TECHNOLOGIES CORPORATION; *U.S. Public*, pg. 238
AUTOSCOUT24 BELGIUM S.A.—See Scout24 SE; *Int'l*, pg. 6653
AUTOSCOUT24 FRANCE SAS—See Scout24 SE; *Int'l*, pg. 6653
AUTOSCOUT24 GMBH—See Hellman & Friedman LLC; *U.S. Private*, pg. 1907
AUTOSCOUT24 ITALIA S.R.L.—See Scout24 SE; *Int'l*, pg. 6653
AUTOSCOUT24 NEDERLAND B.V.—See Scout24 SE; *Int'l*, pg. 6653
AUTOSCRIPT LIMITED—See Videndum plc; *Int'l*, pg. 8190
AUTOSEIS, INC.—See Global Geophysical Services, Inc.; *U.S. Private*, pg. 1714
AUTO SENATEUR INC; *Int'l*, pg. 725
AUTOSERVER CO., LTD.; *Int'l*, pg. 732
AUTOS ETC INC.; *U.S. Private*, pg. 401
AUTO'S ETC. LTD.; *U.S. Private*, pg. 397
AUTOSHOP SOLUTIONS INC.; *U.S. Private*, pg. 401
AUTO SHRED RECYCLING, LLC—See European Metal Recycling Limited; *Int'l*, pg. 2557
AUTOSISTEMAS DE TORREON S.A. DE C.V.—See Sumitomo Electric Industries, Ltd.; *Int'l*, pg. 7277
AUTO SOUND COMPANY INCORPORATED; *U.S. Private*, pg. 397
AUTOSOURCE MOTORS LLC; *U.S. Private*, pg. 401
AUTO SPACE S.R.L.—See Societatea de Asigurari-Reasigurari Moldcargo S.A.; *Int'l*, pg. 7034
AUTO-SPAN OY—See Kesko Corporation; *Int'l*, pg. 4143
AUTOSPLICE INC.; *U.S. Private*, pg. 401
AUTOSPORTS GROUP LIMITED; *Int'l*, pg. 732
AUTOSPORT USA, INC.—See RumbleON, Inc.; *U.S. Public*, pg. 1826
AUTOSPORT WILLY SA—See LKQ Corporation; *U.S. Public*, pg. 1334
AUTOS RODRIGUEZ EOCAR, S.L.—See Mobico Group PLC.; *Int'l*, pg. 5008
AUTOSTADT GMBH—See Porsche Automobil Holding SE; *Int'l*, pg. 5926
AUTOSTAR SOLUTIONS, INC.—See Vista Equity Partners, LLC; *U.S. Private*, pg. 4400
AUTOSTOP LEUVEN NV—See LKQ Corporation; *U.S. Public*, pg. 1334
AUTOSTORE HOLDINGS LTD.; *Int'l*, pg. 732
AUTOSTRADA ASTI-CUNEO S.P.A.—See Argo Finanziaria S.p.A.; *Int'l*, pg. 562
AUTOSTRADA DEL BRENNERO S.P.A.—See Edizione S.r.l.; *Int'l*, pg. 2311
AUTOSTRADA EKSPLOATACJA SA—See Groupe Egis S.A.; *Int'l*, pg. 3102
AUTOSTRADA LIGURE TOSCANA S.P.A.—See Argo Finanziaria S.p.A.; *Int'l*, pg. 562
AUTOSTRADE CONCESSIONI E COSTRUZIONI S.P.A.—See Edizione S.r.l.; *Int'l*, pg. 2311
AUTOSTRADE PER L'ITALIA S.P.A.—See Edizione S.r.l.; *Int'l*, pg. 2312
AUTOSTRADE TEC SPA—See Edizione S.r.l.; *Int'l*, pg. 2312
AUTO STYLING TRUCKMAN GROUP LIMITED—See ARB Corporation Limited; *Int'l*, pg. 536
AUTO SUPPLIERS LIMITED—See Freudenberg SE; *Int'l*, pg. 2782
AUTO SUPPLY COMPANY INC.; *U.S. Private*, pg. 397
AUTOSURE PTY. LTD.—See The Bidvest Group Limited; *Int'l*, pg. 7621
AUTOS VEGA INC.; *U.S. Private*, pg. 401
AUTOTAC, INC.—See Oakland Standard Co., LLC; *U.S. Private*, pg. 2985
AUTO TAG OF AMERICA LLC—See Verra Mobility Corporation; *U.S. Public*, pg. 2286
AUTOTAL BIZTOSITASI SZOLGALTATO KFT.—See Assicurazioni Generali S.p.A.; *Int'l*, pg. 646
AUTOTASK CORPORATION—See Vista Equity Partners, LLC; *U.S. Private*, pg. 4395
AUTOTASK (UK) LIMITED—See Vista Equity Partners, LLC; *U.S. Private*, pg. 4395
AUTOTECH ENGINEERING DEUTSCHLAND, GMBH—See Acek Desarrollo y Gestion Industrial SL; *Int'l*, pg. 96
AUTOTECH ENGINEERING; *U.S. Private*, pg. 401
AUTOTECHNICA FLEET SERVICES S.R.L.—See AUTOHELLAS S.A.; *Int'l*, pg. 727
AUTOTECHNICA LTD.—See AUTOHELLAS S.A.; *Int'l*, pg. 727
AUTOTECHNICA MONTENEGRO DOO—See AUTOHELLAS S.A.; *Int'l*, pg. 727
AUTOTECHNICA SERBIA DOO—See AUTOHELLAS S.A.; *Int'l*, pg. 727
AUTOTECHNIK TUNING PTY. LTD.—See WEDS CO., LTD.; *Int'l*, pg. 8367
AUTOTECH TECH LIMITED PARTNERSHIP—See AVG Advanced Technologies LP; *U.S. Private*, pg. 406
AUTOTEC LLC; *U.S. Public*, pg. 401
AUTOTEHNA A.D; *Int'l*, pg. 732
AUTOTEHNA A.D.; *Int'l*, pg. 732
AUTOTEILE SUPERMARKT GMBH—See LKQ Corporation; *U.S. Public*, pg. 1334
AUTO TEMP, INC.; *U.S. Private*, pg. 397

CORPORATE AFFILIATIONS

AUTOTEST-TOUR S.R.O.—See DEKRA e.V.; *Int'l*, pg. 2007
AUTO TODO MEXICANA S.A. DE C.V.—See Genuine Parts Company; *U.S. Public*, pg. 932
AUTOTRADER.COM INC.—See Cox Enterprises, Inc.; *U.S. Private*, pg. 1076
AUTOTRADER GROUP, INC.—See Cox Enterprises, Inc.; *U.S. Private*, pg. 1076
AUTO TRADER GROUP PLC—See Apax Partners LLP; *Int'l*, pg. 502
AUTO TRADING LEASING IFN S.A.—See Banco BPM S.p.A.; *Int'l*, pg. 818
AUTOTRANS D.D.—See Deutsche Bahn AG; *Int'l*, pg. 2049
AUTOTRANSPORT A.D.; *Int'l*, pg. 732
AUTOTRANSPORT A.D.; *Int'l*, pg. 732
AUTOTRANSPORT A.D.; *Int'l*, pg. 732
AUTOTRANSPORTES MIGUEL MEZA SANCHEZ, S. A. P. I. DE C. V.—See Grupo Traxion, S. A. B. de C. V.; *Int'l*, pg. 3138
AUTO TREND PRODUCTS—See Punch Press Products, Inc.; *U.S. Private*, pg. 3304
AUTO-TROL TECHNOLOGY AUSTRALIA—See Auto-trol Technology Corporation; *U.S. Private*, pg. 398
AUTO-TROL TECHNOLOGY CANADA LTD.—See Auto-trol Technology Corporation; *U.S. Private*, pg. 398
AUTO-TROL TECHNOLOGY CORPORATION; *U.S. Private*, pg. 398
AUTO-TROL TECHNOLOGY GMBH—See Auto-trol Technology Corporation; *U.S. Private*, pg. 398
AUTOTRONIC CONTROLS CORPORATION—See Z Capital Group, LLC; *U.S. Public*, pg. 4595
AUTO TRUCK GROUP, LLC—See Holman Automotive Group, Inc.; *U.S. Private*, pg. 1967
AUTO TRUCK TRANSPORT CORPORATION—See TFI International Inc.; *Int'l*, pg. 7586
AUTO TRUCK TRANSPORT USA, LLC—See TFI International Inc.; *Int'l*, pg. 7586
AUTOTYPE HOLDINGS (USA), INC.—See Element Solutions Inc.; *U.S. Public*, pg. 725
AUTOVALLEY, SAS—See BNP Paribas SA; *Int'l*, pg. 1080
AUTOVANTI BRIANZA S.R.L.—See Penske Automotive Group, Inc.; *U.S. Public*, pg. 1664
AUTOVANTI MONZA S.R.L.—See Penske Automotive Group, Inc.; *U.S. Public*, pg. 1664
AUTOVATIVE TECHNOLOGIES, INC.; *U.S. Private*, pg. 401
AUTOV CORPORATION BERHAD—See Globaltec Formation Berhad; *Int'l*, pg. 3004
AUTOV CORPORATION SDN. BHD.—See Globaltec Formation Berhad; *Int'l*, pg. 3004
AUTO-VEHICLE PARTS LLC—See GHK Capital Partners LP; *U.S. Private*, pg. 1690
AUTOVEICOLI ERZELLI S.P.A.; *Int'l*, pg. 732
AUTOVENTIL A.D.; *Int'l*, pg. 732
AUTOVENTURE CORPORATION SDN. BHD.—See Globaltec Formation Berhad; *Int'l*, pg. 3004
AUTOVENTURE MANDO SDN. BHD.—See Globaltec Formation Berhad; *Int'l*, pg. 3004
AUTOVIA DE ARAGON TRAMO 1, S.A.—See Industry Super Holdings Pty. Ltd.; *Int'l*, pg. 3676
AUTOVIA DE LA MANCHA, S.A—See ACS, Actividades de Construccion y Servicios, S.A.; *Int'l*, pg. 110
AUTOVIA DEL CAMP DEL TURIA, S.A.—See ACS, Actividades de Construccion y Servicios, S.A.; *Int'l*, pg. 110
AUTOVIA DEL ERESMA CONC. DE LA JUNTA DE CASTILLA Y LEON, S.A.—See Sacyr, S.A.; *Int'l*, pg. 6465
AUTOVIA DEL PIRINEO, S.A.—See ACS, Actividades de Construccion y Servicios, S.A.; *Int'l*, pg. 110
AUTOVIA MEDINACELI-CALATAYUD SOC.CONCES.ESTADO, S.A.—See ACS, Actividades de Construccion y Servicios, S.A.; *Int'l*, pg. 110
AUTOVIA MITLA-TEHUANTEPEC, S.A. DE C.V.—See Empresas ICA S.A.B. de C.V.; *Int'l*, pg. 2390
AUTOVIA PARADORES Y SERVICIOS, S.A. DE C.V.—See Empresas ICA S.A.B. de C.V.; *Int'l*, pg. 2390
AUTOVIAS, S.A.—See Industry Super Holdings Pty. Ltd.; *Int'l*, pg. 3676
AUTOVIN CANADA INC.—See OPENLANE, Inc.; *U.S. Public*, pg. 1607
AUTOVIN, INC.—See OPENLANE, Inc.; *U.S. Public*, pg. 1607
AUTOVISION (SCOTLAND) LIMITED—See General Motors Company; *U.S. Public*, pg. 927
AUTOWALLIS PUBLIC LIMITED COMPANY; *Int'l*, pg. 732
AUTO WAREHOUSING COMPANY; *U.S. Private*, pg. 397
AUTO-WARES, LLC; *U.S. Private*, pg. 398
AUTO-WARES OE—See Auto-Wares, LLC; *U.S. Private*, pg. 398
AUTO-WARES TOOLS, INC.—See Auto-Wares, LLC; *U.S. Private*, pg. 398
AUTOWAVE CO., LTD.; *Int'l*, pg. 732
AUTOWAY CO., LTD.—See PROTO CORPORATION; *Int'l*, pg. 6006
AUTOWEB.COM, INC.—See One Planet Group LLC; *U.S. Private*, pg. 3020
AUTOWEB, INC.—See One Planet Group LLC; *U.S. Private*, pg. 3020

COMPANY NAME INDEX

AUTOWEB, INC.—See One Planet Group LLC; *U.S. Private*, pg. 3020
AUTOWEEK—See Crain Communications, Inc.; *U.S. Private*, pg. 1083
AUTO WESSEL B.V.—See LKQ Corporation; *U.S. Public*, pg. 1333
AUTO WEST GROUP; *Int'l*, pg. 725
AUTOWORKS MARKHAM, LP—See Lithia Motors, Inc.; *U.S. Public*, pg. 1321
AUTOWORLD.COM.MY SDN. BHD.—See JcbNEXT Berhad; *Int'l*, pg. 3920
AUTOWORLD KIA; *U.S. Private*, pg. 401
AUTO X CO., LTD.—See SCB X Public Company Limited; *Int'l*, pg. 6614
AUTOXY S.P.A.—See Motork Plc; *Int'l*, pg. 5054
AUTOZENTRUM KOCH GMBH—See Koch Gruppe Automobile AG; *Int'l*, pg. 4224
AUTOZENTRUM WEST KOLN GMBH—See General Motors Company; *U.S. Public*, pg. 926
AUTOZONE.COM, INC.—See AutoZone, Inc.; *U.S. Public*, pg. 239
AUTOZONE DEVELOPMENT LLC—See AutoZone, Inc.; *U.S. Public*, pg. 239
AUTOZONE, INC.; *U.S. Public*, pg. 239
AUTOZONE NORTHEAST, INC.—See AutoZone, Inc.; *U.S. Public*, pg. 239
AUTOZONE PARTS, INC.—See AutoZone, Inc.; *U.S. Public*, pg. 239
AUTOZONE RETAIL AND DISTRIBUTION (PTY) LTD—See TRG Management LP; *U.S. Private*, pg. 4219
AUTOZONE STORES, INC.—See AutoZone, Inc.; *U.S. Public*, pg. 239
AUTOZONE TEXAS, L.P.—See AutoZone, Inc.; *U.S. Public*, pg. 239
AUTRANS CORPORATION - INGERSOLL PLANT—See Sojitz Corporation; *Int'l*, pg. 7061
AUTRANS DE VENEZUELA, S.A.—See Sojitz Corporation; *Int'l*, pg. 7061
AUTRANS INDIA PRIVATE LIMITED—See Sojitz Corporation; *Int'l*, pg. 7061
AUTRANS (THAILAND) CO., LTD.—See Sojitz Corporation; *Int'l*, pg. 7061
AUTRIAL S.L.—See WEG S.A.; *Int'l*, pg. 8367
AUTRONICA FIRE AND SECURITY AS—See Carrier Global Corporation; *U.S. Public*, pg. 440
AUTRONIC PLASTICS INC.; *U.S. Private*, pg. 401
AUTRONICS CORPORATION—See Curtiss-Wright Corporation; *U.S. Public*, pg. 611
AUTRONIC STEUER- UND REGELTECHNIK GMBH—See FORTEC Elektronik AG; *Int'l*, pg. 2738
AUTRY GREER & SONS, INC.; *U.S. Private*, pg. 402
AUTUMN BUILDERS LIMITED; *Int'l*, pg. 732
AUTUMN CORPORATION—See Saber Healthcare Group LLC; *U.S. Private*, pg. 3520
AUTUMNPAPER MALAYSIA SDN BHD—See Kering S.A.; *Int'l*, pg. 4133
AUTUMN SENIOR LIVING, LLC; *U.S. Private*, pg. 402
AUVERGNE AERONAUTIQUE SAS—See Figeac-Aero SA; *Int'l*, pg. 2660
AUVERGNE CREATIONS—See Groupe Limagrain Holding SA; *Int'l*, pg. 3107
AUVERGNE ISOLATION—See Compagnie de Saint-Gobain SA; *Int'l*, pg. 1722
AUVERGNE PRODUCTIQUE INGENIERIE SAS—See VINCI S.A.; *Int'l*, pg. 8212
AU VIET SECURITIES CORPORATION; *Int'l*, pg. 697
AUVIL FRUIT COMPANY, INC.; *U.S. Private*, pg. 402
AUVI ONE—See Videlio SA; *Int'l*, pg. 8190
AUVITRONICS LIMITED - MANUFACTURING UNIT-1—See House of Habib; *Int'l*, pg. 3491
AUVITRONICS LIMITED - MANUFACTURING UNIT-2—See House of Habib; *Int'l*, pg. 3491
AUVITRONICS LIMITED—See House of Habib; *Int'l*, pg. 3491
AUWA-CHEMIE GMBH & CO. KG—See WashTec AG; *Int'l*, pg. 8351
AUWELD INTERNATIONAL PTE LTD—See Mitsubishi Chemical Group Corporation; *Int'l*, pg. 4936
AUWELD SDN BHD—See Mitsubishi Chemical Group Corporation; *Int'l*, pg. 4936
AUXEL FTG SHANGHAI CO., LTD.—See Amphenol Corporation; *U.S. Public*, pg. 126
AUXICOGENT HOLDINGS PRIVATE LIMITED—See John Keells Holdings PLC; *Int'l*, pg. 3978
AUXICOGENT INTERNATIONAL (PVT) LTD—See John Keells Holdings PLC; *Int'l*, pg. 3978
AUXICO RESOURCES CANADA, INC.; *Int'l*, pg. 732
AUXIDEICO GESTION, S.A.—See ECE Projektmanagement GmbH & Co KG; *Int'l*, pg. 2288
AUXILIA GRAPHICA S.R.L.—See Sycamore Partners Management, LP; *U.S. Private*, pg. 3896
AUXILIAR LOGISTICA AEROPUERTUARIA, S.A.—See International Consolidated Airlines Group S.A.; *Int'l*, pg. 3745
AUXILLIUM ENERGY, INC.; *U.S. Private*, pg. 402
AUXIMIO AG—See IGP Advantag AG; *Int'l*, pg. 3603
AUX INTERNATIONAL HOLDINGS LIMITED; *Int'l*, pg. 732

AUXITEC BATIMENT SAS—See Artelia Holding SA; *Int'l*, pg. 581
AUXITROL S.A.—See TransDigm Group Incorporated; *U.S. Public*, pg. 2180
AUXLY CANNABIS GROUP INC.; *Int'l*, pg. 733
AUX MINERACAO DE OURO—See EBX Group Ltd.; *Int'l*, pg. 2287
AUXO INVESTMENT PARTNERS, LLC; *U.S. Private*, pg. 402
AUXORA (SHENZHEN) INC.—See Suzhou TFC Optical Communication Co., Ltd.; *Int'l*, pg. 7352
AUX RESOURCES CORPORATION—See Scottie Resources Corp.; *Int'l*, pg. 6652
AUX SABLE CANADA L.P.—See Enbridge Inc.; *Int'l*, pg. 2397
AUX SABLE CANADA L.P.—See Pembina Pipeline Corporation; *Int'l*, pg. 5785
AUX SABLE CANADA LTD.—See Enbridge Inc.; *Int'l*, pg. 2397
AUX SABLE LIQUID PRODUCTS INC.—See The Williams Companies, Inc.; *U.S. Public*, pg. 2142
AUX SABLE LIQUID PRODUCTS LP; *U.S. Private*, pg. 402
AUX SABLE MIDSTREAM LLC—See The Williams Companies, Inc.; *U.S. Public*, pg. 2143
AUZO LAGUN S.COOP.—See Mondragon Corporation; *Int'l*, pg. 5028
AVA ADVERTISING; *U.S. Private*, pg. 402
AVA AFRICA S.A.R.L.—See Newpark Resources, Inc.; *U.S. Public*, pg. 1517
AVAAK, INC—See NETGEAR, Inc.; *U.S. Public*, pg. 1508
AVAAP INC.; *U.S. Private*, pg. 403
AVA BENELUX B.V.—See Enterex International Limited; *Int'l*, pg. 2450
AVA CEE SP. Z O.O.—See Enterex International Limited; *Int'l*, pg. 2451
AVAC, LTD.; *Int'l*, pg. 733
AVACO CO., LTD - DAEGU 1ST FACTORY—See AVACO CO., Ltd; *Int'l*, pg. 733
AVACO CO., LTD; *Int'l*, pg. 733
AVACON WASSER GMBH—See E.ON SE; *Int'l*, pg. 2251
AVA COOLING UK LIMITED—See Enterex International Limited; *Int'l*, pg. 2451
AVACTA ANIMAL HEALTH LIMITED—See Avacta Group plc; *Int'l*, pg. 733
AVACTA GROUP PLC; *Int'l*, pg. 733
AVACTA LIFE SCIENCES LIMITED—See Avacta Group plc; *Int'l*, pg. 733
AVADA GROUP LIMITED; *Int'l*, pg. 733
AVA DANMARK A/S—See Enterex International Limited; *Int'l*, pg. 2450
AVADEL PHARMACEUTICALS PLC; *Int'l*, pg. 734
AVADH SNACKS PRIVATE LIMITED—See Prataap Snacks Limited; *Int'l*, pg. 5955
AVADH SUGAR & ENERGY LIMITED; *Int'l*, pg. 734
AVADIAN CREDIT UNION; *U.S. Private*, pg. 403
AVADIM HEALTH, INC.—See British Columbia Investment Management Corp.; *Int'l*, pg. 1169
AVAD LLC—See Kingswood Capital Management LLC; *U.S. Private*, pg. 2312
AVA EASTERN EUROPE D.F.& S., S.R.L.—See Newpark Resources, Inc.; *U.S. Public*, pg. 1517
AVA GALLERY & ART CENTER; *U.S. Private*, pg. 402
AVAGO TECHNOLOGIES U.S. INC.—See Broadcom Inc.; *U.S. Public*, pg. 388
AVAGO TECHNOLOGIES WIRELESS (U.S.A.) MANUFACTURING INC.—See Broadcom Inc.; *U.S. Public*, pg. 388
AVAILABLE FINANCE LIMITED; *Int'l*, pg. 734
AVAILITY, LLC—See GuideWell Mutual Holding Corporation; *U.S. Private*, pg. 1813
AVAILITY, LLC—See Humana, Inc.; *U.S. Public*, pg. 1069
AVAILITY, L.L.C.—See Humana, Inc.; *U.S. Public*, pg. 1069
AVAILO AB—See EQT AB; *Int'l*, pg. 2475
AVAILO NETWORKS AB—See EQT AB; *Int'l*, pg. 2475
AVAILPRO SAS—See Accor S.A.; *Int'l*, pg. 91
AVAIL RESOURCE MANAGEMENT, INC.—See Atlas World Group, Inc.; *U.S. Private*, pg. 380
AVAIL-TVN; *U.S. Private*, pg. 403
AVA ITALIA S.R.L.—See Enterex International Limited; *Int'l*, pg. 2451
AVA KUHLERCENTER AUSTRIA GMBH—See Enterex International Limited; *Int'l*, pg. 2451
AVALA A.D.; *Int'l*, pg. 734
AVALANCHE HEALTHCARE, INC.—See The Ensign Group, Inc.; *U.S. Public*, pg. 2070
AVALANCHE INTERNATIONAL CORP.; *U.S. Public*, pg. 239
AVALANCHE SEARCH MARKETING INC.; *Int'l*, pg. 734
AVALAND BERHAD; *Int'l*, pg. 734
AVALAN WIRELESS SYSTEMS, INC.—See Dover Corporation; *U.S. Public*, pg. 678
AVALARA, INC.—See Vista Equity Partners, LLC; *U.S. Private*, pg. 4395
AVALARA TECHNOLOGIES PVT. LTD.—See Vista Equity Partners, LLC; *U.S. Private*, pg. 4395
AVALDATA CORPORATION; *Int'l*, pg. 734

AVALON HOLDINGS CORPORATION

AVALERE HEALTH, LLC—See Lloyds Banking Group plc; *U.S. Public*, pg. 4537
AVALEX TECHNOLOGIES CORPORATION; *U.S. Private*, pg. 403
AVALIGN CASES & TRAYS—See Arlington Capital Partners LLC; *U.S. Private*, pg. 327
AVALIGN TECHNOLOGIES, INC.—See Arlington Capital Partners LLC; *U.S. Private*, pg. 327
AVALON ACQUISITION INC.—See GWG Holdings, Inc.; *U.S. Public*, pg. 975
AVALON ACTON, INC.—See AvalonBay Communities, Inc.; *U.S. Public*, pg. 240
AVALON ADVANCED MATERIALS INC.; *Int'l*, pg. 734
AVALON ANAHEIM STADIUM, L.P.—See AvalonBay Communities, Inc.; *U.S. Public*, pg. 240
AVALON ARUNDEL CROSSING, LLC—See AvalonBay Communities, Inc.; *U.S. Public*, pg. 240
AVALON AT BALLSTON, LLC—See AvalonBay Communities, Inc.; *U.S. Public*, pg. 240
AVALON AT DIAMOND HEIGHTS, L.P.—See AvalonBay Communities, Inc.; *U.S. Public*, pg. 240
AVALON AT INVERNESS, LLC—See Century Communities, Inc.; *U.S. Public*, pg. 475
AVALON AT PROVIDENCE PARK, LLC—See AvalonBay Communities, Inc.; *U.S. Public*, pg. 240
AVALON AVIATION ACADEMY PRIVATE LIMITED—See Aptech Limited; *Int'l*, pg. 523
AVALONBAY ASSEMBLY ROW, INC.—See AvalonBay Communities, Inc.; *U.S. Public*, pg. 240
AVALONBAY COMMUNITIES, INC.; *U.S. Public*, pg. 239
AVALONBAY GROSVENOR, INC.—See AvalonBay Communities, Inc.; *U.S. Public*, pg. 240
AVALONBAY SHREWSBURY, INC.—See AvalonBay Communities, Inc.; *U.S. Public*, pg. 240
AVALONBAY TRAVILLE, LLC—See AvalonBay Communities, Inc.; *U.S. Public*, pg. 240
AVALON BONTERRA, LLC—See AvalonBay Communities, Inc.; *U.S. Public*, pg. 240
AVALON CAMPBELL SOLAR, LLC—See AvalonBay Communities, Inc.; *U.S. Public*, pg. 240
AVALON CERRITOS, L.P.—See AvalonBay Communities, Inc.; *U.S. Public*, pg. 240
AVALON COLUMBIA PIKE, LLC—See AvalonBay Communities, Inc.; *U.S. Public*, pg. 240
AVALON CONSULTING, LLC; *U.S. Private*, pg. 403
AVALON COPY CENTERS OF AMERICA, INC.—See Surge Private Equity LLC; *U.S. Private*, pg. 3884
AVALON CORPUS CHRISTI TRANSITIONAL CENTER, LLC—See Corecivic, Inc.; *U.S. Public*, pg. 577
AVALON CORRECTIONAL SERVICES, INC.—See Corecivic, Inc.; *U.S. Public*, pg. 577
AVALON COUNTRY CLUB AT SHARON, INC.—See Avalon Holdings Corporation; *U.S. Public*, pg. 239
AVALON DEL REY APARTMENTS, LLC—See AvalonBay Communities, Inc.; *U.S. Public*, pg. 240
AVALON DOCUMENTS SERVICES; *U.S. Private*, pg. 403
AVALON ENCINO, L.P.—See AvalonBay Communities, Inc.; *U.S. Public*, pg. 240
AVALON EUROPE S.L.—See Lonsdale Capital Partners LLP; *Int'l*, pg. 4552
AVALON EXHIBITS, INC.; *U.S. Private*, pg. 403
AVALON FASHION VALLEY, L.P.—See AvalonBay Communities, Inc.; *U.S. Public*, pg. 240
AVALON FORD SALES LTD.; *Int'l*, pg. 734
AVALON GLASS & MIRROR COMPANY; *U.S. Private*, pg. 403
AVALON GLOBAL GROUP, INC.; *U.S. Private*, pg. 403
AVALON GLOBOCARE CORP.; *U.S. Public*, pg. 239
AVALON GOLF AND COUNTRY CLUB, INC.—See Avalon Holdings Corporation; *U.S. Public*, pg. 239
AVALON HEALTH SERVICES, LLC; *U.S. Private*, pg. 403
AVALON HOBOKEN, LLC—See AvalonBay Communities, Inc.; *U.S. Public*, pg. 240
AVALON HOLDINGS CORPORATION; *U.S. Public*, pg. 239
AVALON HOSPICE IOWA, LLC—See Humana, Inc.; *U.S. Public*, pg. 1069
AVALON HOSPICE MINNESOTA, LLC—See Humana, Inc.; *U.S. Public*, pg. 1069
AVALON HOSPICE MISSOURI, LLC—See Humana, Inc.; *U.S. Public*, pg. 1069
AVALON HOSPICE OHIO, LLC—See Humana, Inc.; *U.S. Public*, pg. 1069
AVALON IRVINE, L.P.—See AvalonBay Communities, Inc.; *U.S. Public*, pg. 240
AVALON LABORATORIES LLC—See Nordson Corporation; *U.S. Public*, pg. 1532
AVALON LAKES GOLF, INC.—See Avalon Holdings Corporation; *U.S. Public*, pg. 239
AVALON (MANSFIELD) MANAGEMENT COMPANY LIMITED—See Persimmon plc; *Int'l*, pg. 5815
AVALON MINERALS ADAK AB—See Sunstone Metals Ltd; *Int'l*, pg. 7324
AVALON MINERALS VISCARIA AB—See Copperstone Resources AB; *Int'l*, pg. 1794
AVALON MORTUARY SERVICE CORP.—See The John P. Brooks Family Corporation; *U.S. Private*, pg. 4059
AVALON NATURAL PRODUCTS, INC.—See The Hain Celestial Group, Inc.; *U.S. Public*, pg. 2086

AVALON HOLDINGS CORPORATION

AVALON NEW CANAAN, LLC—See AvalonBay Communities, Inc.; *U.S. Public*, pg. 240
AVALON NEWPORT, L.P.—See AvalonBay Communities, Inc.; *U.S. Public*, pg. 240
AVALON NORTH BERGEN, LLC—See AvalonBay Communities, Inc.; *U.S. Public*, pg. 240
AVALON OAKS, INC.—See AvalonBay Communities, Inc.; *U.S. Public*, pg. 240
AVALON OCEAN AVENUE, L.P.—See AvalonBay Communities, Inc.; *U.S. Public*, pg. 240
AVALON PARK CREST, LLC—See AvalonBay Communities, Inc.; *U.S. Public*, pg. 240
AVALON PARK GROUP MANAGEMENT, INC.; *U.S. Private*, pg. 403
AVALON PARK—See Avalon Park Group Management, Inc.; *U.S. Private*, pg. 403
AVALON PETROLEUM COMPANY; *U.S. Private*, pg. 403
AVALON PORTICO AT SILVER SPRING METRO, LLC—See AvalonBay Communities, Inc.; *U.S. Public*, pg. 240
AVALON PRECISION CASTING COMPANY, LLC—See Argand Partners, LP; *U.S. Private*, pg. 319
AVALON PRECISION METALSMITHS—See Argand Partners, LP; *U.S. Private*, pg. 319
AVALON RESORTS, INC.—See Avalon Holdings Corporation; *U.S. Public*, pg. 239
AVALON RISK MANAGEMENT, INC.; *U.S. Private*, pg. 403
AVALON RIVERVIEW NORTH, LLC—See AvalonBay Communities, Inc.; *U.S. Public*, pg. 240
AVALON SHARON, INC.—See AvalonBay Communities, Inc.; *U.S. Public*, pg. 240
AVALON SOLUTIONS INC.—See Devoteam SA; *Int'l*, pg. 2089
AVALON SOMERS, LLC—See AvalonBay Communities, Inc.; *U.S. Public*, pg. 240
AVALON SOMERVILLE STATION URBAN RENEWAL, LLC—See AvalonBay Communities, Inc.; *U.S. Public*, pg. 240
AVALON STAFFING, LLC—See Corecivic, Inc.; *U.S. Public*, pg. 577
AVALON TECHNOLOGIES LIMITED; *Int'l*, pg. 734
AVALON TINTON FALLS, LLC—See AvalonBay Communities, Inc.; *U.S. Public*, pg. 240
AVALON TOWERS BELLEVUE, LLC—See AvalonBay Communities, Inc.; *U.S. Public*, pg. 240
AVALON TRANSITIONAL CENTER DALLAS, LLC—See Corecivic, Inc.; *U.S. Public*, pg. 577
AVALON TRAVEL, INC.—See Avalon Holdings Corporation; *U.S. Public*, pg. 239
AVALON TRUSTEE COMPANY LIMITED—See Lonsdale Capital Partners LLP; *Int'l*, pg. 4552
AVALON TULSA, LLC—See Corecivic, Inc.; *U.S. Public*, pg. 577
AVALON UNION CITY, L.P.—See AvalonBay Communities, Inc.; *U.S. Public*, pg. 240
AVALON WEST LONG BRANCH, LLC—See AvalonBay Communities, Inc.; *U.S. Public*, pg. 240
AVALON WOODLAND HILLS, L.P.—See AvalonBay Communities, Inc.; *U.S. Public*, pg. 240
AVALOQ ASIA PACIFIC PTE. LTD.—See NEC Corporation; *Int'l*, pg. 5183
AVALOQ AUSTRALIA PTY. LTD.—See NEC Corporation; *Int'l*, pg. 5183
AVALOQ EVOLUTION AG—See NEC Corporation; *Int'l*, pg. 5183
AVALOQ FRANCE SAS—See NEC Corporation; *Int'l*, pg. 5183
AVALOQ GROUP AG—See NEC Corporation; *Int'l*, pg. 5183
AVALOQ HONG KONG LIMITED—See NEC Corporation; *Int'l*, pg. 5183
AVALOQ LICENCE AG—See NEC Corporation; *Int'l*, pg. 5183
AVALOQ LUXEMBOURG SARL—See NEC Corporation; *Int'l*, pg. 5183
AVALOQ SOURCING (DEUTSCHLAND) AG—See NEC Corporation; *Int'l*, pg. 5183
AVALOQ UK LTD.—See NEC Corporation; *Int'l*, pg. 5183
AVALO THERAPEUTICS, INC.; *U.S. Public*, pg. 239
AVALOTIS CORPORATION; *U.S. Private*, pg. 403
AVALT, LLC; *U.S. Private*, pg. 403
AVA MORADIA SAS—See Enterex International Limited; *Int'l*, pg. 2451
AVANA BAKERIES LTD.—See Boparan Holdings Limited; *Int'l*, pg. 1111
AVANADE ASIA PTE LTD.—See Accenture plc; *Int'l*, pg. 85
AVANADE AUSTRALIA PTY LTD.—See Accenture plc; *Int'l*, pg. 85
AVANADE BELGIUM SPRL—See Accenture plc; *Int'l*, pg. 85
AVANADE CANADA INC.—See Accenture plc; *Int'l*, pg. 85
AVANADE DENMARK APS—See Accenture plc; *Int'l*, pg. 85
AVANADE DEUTSCHLAND GMBH—See Accenture plc; *Int'l*, pg. 85
AVANADE DO BRASIL LTDA—See Accenture plc; *Int'l*, pg. 85
AVANADE FINLAND OY—See Accenture plc; *Int'l*, pg. 85

AVANADE FRANCE—See Accenture plc; *Int'l*, pg. 85
AVANADE GUANGZHOU—See Accenture plc; *Int'l*, pg. 85
AVANADE INC.—See Accenture plc; *Int'l*, pg. 85
AVANADE IRELAND LIMITED—See Accenture plc; *Int'l*, pg. 86
AVANADE ITALY SRL—See Accenture plc; *Int'l*, pg. 85
AVANADE JAPAN KK—See Accenture plc; *Int'l*, pg. 85
AVANADE MALAYSIA SDN BHD—See Accenture plc; *Int'l*, pg. 85
AVANADE NETHERLANDS BV—See Accenture plc; *Int'l*, pg. 85
AVANADE NORWAY AS—See Accenture plc; *Int'l*, pg. 85
AVANADE OSTERREICH GMBH—See Accenture plc; *Int'l*, pg. 86
AVANADE POLAND SP. Z O.O.—See Accenture plc; *Int'l*, pg. 86
AVANADE SCHWEIZ GMBH—See Accenture plc; *Int'l*, pg. 85
AVANADE SOUTH AFRICA—See Accenture plc; *Int'l*, pg. 85
AVANADE SPAIN SL—See Accenture plc; *Int'l*, pg. 85
AVANADE SWEDEN AB—See Accenture plc; *Int'l*, pg. 85
AVANADE UK LTD.—See Accenture plc; *Int'l*, pg. 85
AVAN AS—See ManpowerGroup Inc.; *U.S. Public*, pg. 1357
AVANCE CORPORATION—See Olympic Group Corporation; *Int'l*, pg. 5555
AVANCE GAS AS—See Avance Gas Holding Ltd.; *Int'l*, pg. 734
AVANCE GAS HOLDING LTD.; *Int'l*, pg. 734
AVANCE INVESTMENT MANAGEMENT, LLC; *U.S. Private*, pg. 403
AVANCEON LP—See Endress+Hauser (International) Holding AG; *Int'l*, pg. 2405
AVANCEON LTD.; *U.S. Private*, pg. 403
AVANCE TECHNOLOGIES LTD.; *Int'l*, pg. 734
AVANEA ENERGY ACQUISITION CORP.; *U.S. Public*, pg. 241
AVANGARD CAPITAL GROUP, INC.; *U.S. Private*, pg. 404
AVANGARDCO INVESTMENTS PUBLIC LIMITED; *Int'l*, pg. 734
AVANGATE B.V.—See Francisco Partners Management, LP; *U.S. Private*, pg. 1588
AVANGATE INC.—See Francisco Partners Management, LP; *U.S. Private*, pg. 1588
AVANGRID, INC.—See Iberdrola, S.A.; *Int'l*, pg. 3570
AVANGRID RENEWABLES, LLC—See Iberdrola, S.A.; *Int'l*, pg. 3570
AVANI RESOURCES PTE LTD.; *Int'l*, pg. 734
AVANIR PHARMACEUTICALS, INC.—See Otsuka Holdings Co., Ltd.; *Int'l*, pg. 5660
AVANKIA LLC; *U.S. Private*, pg. 404
AVANOS MEDICAL AUSTRALIA PTY LTD.—See Avanos Medical, Inc.; *U.S. Public*, pg. 241
AVANOS MEDICAL DEUTSCHLAND GMBH—See Avanos Medical, Inc.; *U.S. Public*, pg. 241
AVANOS MEDICAL, INC.; *U.S. Public*, pg. 241
AVANOS MEDICAL SINGAPORE PTE. LTD.—See Avanos Medical, Inc.; *U.S. Public*, pg. 241
AVANPRO, S.A.—See HORIBA Ltd.; *Int'l*, pg. 3475
AVANQUEST CHINA—See Claranova SA; *Int'l*, pg. 1642
AVANQUEST DEUTSCHLAND GMBH—See Claranova SA; *Int'l*, pg. 1642
AVANQUEST FRANCE—See Claranova SA; *Int'l*, pg. 1642
AVANQUEST IBERICA S.L.—See Claranova SA; *Int'l*, pg. 1642
AVANQUEST ITALIA SRL—See Claranova SA; *Int'l*, pg. 1642
AVANQUEST PUBLISHING USA—See Claranova SA; *Int'l*, pg. 1642
AVANQUEST SOFTWARE USA—See Claranova SA; *Int'l*, pg. 1642
AVANQUEST UK LTD—See Claranova SA; *Int'l*, pg. 1642
AVANSSUR S.A.—See AXA S.A.; *Int'l*, pg. 759
AVANSTRATE INC.—See Vedanta Resources Ltd; *Int'l*, pg. 8146
AVANSTRATE KOREA INC.—See Hoya Corporation; *Int'l*, pg. 3495
AVANSTRATE TAIWAN INC.—See Hoya Corporation; *Int'l*, pg. 3495
AVANT AEROSPACE, LLC—See The Sterling Group, L.P.; *U.S. Private*, pg. 4123
AVANTAGE REPLY (BELGIUM) SPRL—See Reply S.p.A.; *Int'l*, pg. 6290
AVANTAGE REPLY GMBH—See Reply S.p.A.; *Int'l*, pg. 6290
AVANTAGE REPLY LIMITED—See Reply S.p.A.; *Int'l*, pg. 6291
AVANTAGE REPLY (LUXEMBOURG) SARL—See Reply S.p.A.; *Int'l*, pg. 6290
AVANTAGE REPLY (NETHERLANDS) BV—See Reply S.p.A.; *Int'l*, pg. 6290
AVANTA SERVICED OFFICE GROUP PLC—See Old Oak Holdings Limited; *Int'l*, pg. 5552
AVANTAS, LLC—See AMN Healthcare Services, Inc.; *U.S. Public*, pg. 125
AVANT ASSOCIATES, INC.—See Kajima Corporation; *Int'l*, pg. 4053

CORPORATE AFFILIATIONS

AVANTAX, INC.—See Genstar Capital, LLC; *U.S. Private*, pg. 1676
AVANTAX PLANNING PARTNERS, INC.—See Genstar Capital, LLC; *U.S. Private*, pg. 1676
AVANTAX WEALTH MANAGEMENT, INC.—See Genstar Capital, LLC; *U.S. Private*, pg. 1676
AVANTAZH GROUP; *Int'l*, pg. 735
AVANT BRANDS INC.; *Int'l*, pg. 734
AVANT COMMUNICATIONS, INC.; *U.S. Private*, pg. 404
AVANT CORPORATION; *Int'l*, pg. 735
AVANT CREDIT CORP.; *U.S. Private*, pg. 404
AVANT DIAGNOSTICS, INC.—See Theralink Technologies, Inc.; *U.S. Public*, pg. 2144
AVANTE CAPITAL PARTNERS; *U.S. Private*, pg. 404
AVANTEC AUSTRIA GMBH—See AVANTEC Zerspantechnik GmbH; *Int'l*, pg. 735
AVANTEC HEALTHCARE LTD.—See Omnicell, Inc.; *U.S. Public*, pg. 1572
AVANTECH, INC.; *U.S. Private*, pg. 404
AVANTEC ITALY S.R.L.—See AVANTEC Zerspantechnik GmbH; *Int'l*, pg. 735
AVANTE CORP; *Int'l*, pg. 735
AVANTEC SARL—See Thermo Fisher Scientific Inc.; *U.S. Public*, pg. 2148
AVANTEC USA, LLC—See AVANTEC Zerspantechnik GmbH; *Int'l*, pg. 735
AVANTEC VASCULAR CORP.—See Nipro Corporation; *Int'l*, pg. 5361
AVANTEC ZERSPANTECHNIK GMBH; *Int'l*, pg. 735
AVANTEL LTD.; *Int'l*, pg. 735
AVANTE MEZZANINE PARTNERS, INC.; *U.S. Private*, pg. 404
AVANTEOS INVESTMENTS LIMITED—See Commonwealth Bank of Australia; *Int'l*, pg. 1719
AVANTE PROPERTY ASSET MANAGEMENT SERVICES—See Ocean & Oil Holdings Limited; *Int'l*, pg. 5515
AVANTES B.V.—See Nynomic AG; *Int'l*, pg. 5501
AVANTES CHINA LTD.—See Nynomic AG; *Int'l*, pg. 5501
AVANTE SECURITY INC.—See Avante Corp; *Int'l*, pg. 735
AVANTES INC.—See Nynomic AG; *Int'l*, pg. 5501
AVANTE SYSTEMS, INC.; *Int'l*, pg. 735
AVANT-GARDE ADVISORS LLC; *U.S. Private*, pg. 404
AVANTHA BUSINESS SOLUTIONS LIMITED—See Avantha Group; *Int'l*, pg. 735
AVANTHA BUSINESS SOLUTIONS USA, INC.—See Avantha Group; *Int'l*, pg. 735
AVANTHA GROUP; *Int'l*, pg. 735
AVANTHA POWER & INFRASTRUCTURE LIMITED—See Avantha Group; *Int'l*, pg. 735
AVANT HEALTHCARE PROFESSIONALS, LLC—See Jackson Healthcare, LLC; *U.S. Private*, pg. 2177
AVANTIA CO., LTD.; *Int'l*, pg. 736
AVANTI ACQUISITION CORP.; *Int'l*, pg. 736
AVANTI BROADBAND LIMITED—See Avanti Communications Group plc; *Int'l*, pg. 736
AVANTI CAPITAL PLC; *Int'l*, pg. 736
AVANTI CIGAR CORPORATION; *U.S. Private*, pg. 404
AVANTI COMMUNICATIONS GROUP PLC; *Int'l*, pg. 736
AVANTI COMMUNICATIONS LIMITED—See Avanti Communications Group plc; *Int'l*, pg. 736
AVANTI FEEDS LTD. - PRAWN FEED/FISH FEED FACTORIES—See Avanti Feeds Ltd.; *Int'l*, pg. 736
AVANTI FEEDS LTD.; *Int'l*, pg. 736
AVANTI GMBH—See OMV Aktiengesellschaft; *Int'l*, pg. 5568
AVANTI GOLD CORPORATION; *Int'l*, pg. 736
AVANTI HEALTH SYSTEMS; *U.S. Private*, pg. 404
AVANTI HELIUM CORP.; *Int'l*, pg. 736
AVANTI LINENS, INC.; *U.S. Private*, pg. 404
AVANT IMAGING & INFORMATION MANAGEMENT, INC.; *Int'l*, pg. 735
AVANTI POLAR LIPIDS, INC.—See Croda International plc; *Int'l*, pg. 1851
AVANTI PRODUCTS, LLC—See The Legacy Companies; *U.S. Private*, pg. 4069
AVANTIQ AG—See Wolters Kluwer n.v.; *Int'l*, pg. 8445
AVANTIQ OCEANIA PTY LTD—See Wolters Kluwer n.v.; *Int'l*, pg. 8445
AVANTI SPACE LIMITED—See Avanti Communications Group plc; *Int'l*, pg. 736
AVANTI STAFF CORPORATION—See Persol Holdings Co., Ltd.; *Int'l*, pg. 5818
AVANTI THAI AQUA FEEDS PRIVATE LIMITED—See Avanti Feeds Ltd.; *Int'l*, pg. 736
AVANTIUM HOLDING BV; *Int'l*, pg. 736
AVANT MARKETING GROUP; *U.S. Private*, pg. 404
AVANT NORTH AMERICA—See ACI Group; *U.S. Private*, pg. 59
AVANTOR FLUID HANDLING, LLC—See Avantor, Inc.; *U.S. Public*, pg. 241
AVANTOR, INC.; *U.S. Public*, pg. 241
AVANTOR PERFORMANCE MATERIALS INDIA LIMITED—See Avantor, Inc.; *U.S. Public*, pg. 241
AVANTOR PERFORMANCE MATERIALS KOREA LIMITED—See Avantor, Inc.; *U.S. Public*, pg. 241
AVANTOR PERFORMANCE MATERIALS, LLC—See Avantor, Inc.; *U.S. Public*, pg. 241

COMPANY NAME INDEX

AVANTOR PERFORMANCE MATERIALS POLAND S.A.—See Kulczyk Investments S.A.; *Int'l*, pg. 4327
AVANTOR PERFORMANCE MATERIALS S.A. DE C.V.—See Avantor, Inc.; *U.S. Public*, pg. 241
AVANTOR PERFORMANCE MATERIALS SDN BHD—See Avantor, Inc.; *U.S. Public*, pg. 241
AVANTOR PERFORMANCE MATERIALS TAIWAN CO., LTD.—See Avantor, Inc.; *U.S. Public*, pg. 241
AVANTOR VWR (SHANGHAI) CO., LTD.—See Avantor, Inc.; *U.S. Public*, pg. 242
AVANT PUBLICATIONS LLC; *U.S. Private*, pg. 404
AVANT SERVICES CORPORATION; *U.S. Private*, pg. 404
AVANT TECHNOLOGIES OF PR, INC.; *U.S. Private*, pg. 404
AVANTUS AEROSPACE LIMITED—See Inflexion Private Equity Partners LLP; *Int'l*, pg. 3688
AVANZA BANK HOLDING AB; *Int'l*, pg. 736
AVA PACIFIC BEACH SOLAR, LLC—See AvalonBay Communities, Inc.; *U.S. Public*, pg. 240
AVA PASADENA SOLAR, LLC—See AvalonBay Communities, Inc.; *U.S. Public*, pg. 240
AVARA AIKEN PHARMACEUTICAL SERVICES, INC.—See American Industrial Acquisition Corporation; *U.S. Private*, pg. 237
AVARA PHARMACEUTICAL SERVICES, INC.—See American Industrial Acquisition Corporation; *U.S. Private*, pg. 237
AVARA PHARMACEUTICAL TECHNOLOGIES, INC.—See American Industrial Acquisition Corporation; *U.S. Private*, pg. 237
AVARDA AB—See TF Bank AB; *Int'l*, pg. 7585
AVARDA OY—See TF Bank AB; *Int'l*, pg. 7585
AVARGA LIMITED; *Int'l*, pg. 736
AVA RISK GROUP LIMITED; *Int'l*, pg. 733
AVARN SECURITY GROUP HOLDING AS; *Int'l*, pg. 737
AVARN SECURITY OY—See Avarn Security Group Holding AS; *Int'l*, pg. 737
AVARONE METALS INC.; *Int'l*, pg. 737
AVA-RUHA CORP.; *U.S. Private*, pg. 402
AVARUS AG—See CRONIMET Holding GmbH; *Int'l*, pg. 1854
AVARY HOLDING INVESTMENT (SHENZHEN) CO., LTD.—See Zhen Ding Technology Holding Limited; *Int'l*, pg. 8669
AVARY HOLDINGS (SHENZHEN) CO., LTD.—See Zhen Ding Technology Holding Limited; *Int'l*, pg. 8669
AVARY JAPAN CO., LTD.—See Zhen Ding Technology Holding Limited; *Int'l*, pg. 8669
AVARY LOGISTICS SERVICES (SHENZHEN) CO., LTD.—See Zhen Ding Technology Holding Limited; *Int'l*, pg. 8669
AVARY SINGAPORE PRIVATE LIMITED—See Zhen Ding Technology Holding Limited; *Int'l*, pg. 8669
AVARY TECHNOLOGY (INDIA) PRIVATE LIMITED—See Zhen Ding Technology Holding Limited; *Int'l*, pg. 8669
AVASANT LLC; *U.S. Private*, pg. 404
AVASARA FINANCE LIMITED; *Int'l*, pg. 737
AVASCENT GROUP—See Marsh & McLennan Companies, Inc.; *U.S. Public*, pg. 1386
AVAS ENGINEERING LLC—See Endress+Hauser (International) Holding AG; *Int'l*, pg. 2405
AVA, S.P.A.—See Newpark Resources, Inc.; *U.S. Public*, pg. 1517
AVAST SOFTWARE B.V.—See Gen Digital Inc.; *U.S. Public*, pg. 910
AVAST SOFTWARE, INC.—See Gen Digital Inc.; *U.S. Public*, pg. 910
AVAST SOFTWARE S.R.O.—See Gen Digital Inc.; *U.S. Public*, pg. 910
AVATAR INTEGRATED SYSTEMS, INC.; *U.S. Private*, pg. 404
AVATAR STUDIOS; *U.S. Private*, pg. 404
AVATAR SYSTEMS, INC.; *U.S. Public*, pg. 242
AVATEC CO., LTD.; *Int'l*, pg. 737
AVATECH OF FLORIDA INC.—See Rand Worldwide, Inc.; *U.S. Public*, pg. 1762
AVATECH OF NEBRASKA INC.—See Rand Worldwide, Inc.; *U.S. Public*, pg. 1762
AVATEL TECHNOLOGIES, INC.; *U.S. Private*, pg. 404
AVATION PLC; *Int'l*, pg. 737
AVATRIA INC.; *U.S. Private*, pg. 404
AVAX S.A.; *Int'l*, pg. 737
AVAYA AUSTRALIA PTY LTD—See Silver Lake Group, LLC; *U.S. Private*, pg. 3655
AVAYA AUSTRALIA PTY LTD—See TPG Capital, L.P.; *U.S. Public*, pg. 2168
AVAYA BELGIUM SPRL—See Silver Lake Group, LLC; *U.S. Private*, pg. 3655
AVAYA BELGIUM SPRL—See TPG Capital, L.P.; *U.S. Public*, pg. 2169
AVAYA CANADA CORP.—See Silver Lake Group, LLC; *U.S. Private*, pg. 3655
AVAYA CANADA CORP.—See TPG Capital, L.P.; *U.S. Public*, pg. 2169
AVAYA CHINA - BEIJING OFFICE—See Silver Lake Group, LLC; *U.S. Private*, pg. 3655
AVAYA CHINA - BEIJING OFFICE—See TPG Capital, L.P.; *U.S. Public*, pg. 2168

AVAYA CHINA - GUANGZHOU OFFICE—See Silver Lake Group, LLC; *U.S. Private*, pg. 3655
AVAYA CHINA - GUANGZHOU OFFICE—See TPG Capital, L.P.; *U.S. Public*, pg. 2168
AVAYA CHINA - SHANGHAI OFFICE—See Silver Lake Group, LLC; *U.S. Private*, pg. 3655
AVAYA CHINA - SHANGHAI OFFICE—See TPG Capital, L.P.; *U.S. Public*, pg. 2168
AVAYA CZECH REPUBLIC—See Silver Lake Group, LLC; *U.S. Private*, pg. 3655
AVAYA CZECH REPUBLIC—See TPG Capital, L.P.; *U.S. Public*, pg. 2169
AVAYA DEUTSCHLAND GMBH—See Silver Lake Group, LLC; *U.S. Private*, pg. 3656
AVAYA DEUTSCHLAND GMBH—See TPG Capital, L.P.; *U.S. Public*, pg. 2169
AVAYA FRANCE S.A.—See Silver Lake Group, LLC; *U.S. Private*, pg. 3656
AVAYA FRANCE S.A.—See TPG Capital, L.P.; *U.S. Public*, pg. 2169
AVAYA GMBH & CO. KG—See Silver Lake Group, LLC; *U.S. Private*, pg. 3656
AVAYA GMBH & CO. KG—See TPG Capital, L.P.; *U.S. Public*, pg. 2169
AVAYA GOVERNMENT SOLUTIONS INC.—See Silver Lake Group, LLC; *U.S. Private*, pg. 3656
AVAYA GOVERNMENT SOLUTIONS INC.—See TPG Capital, L.P.; *U.S. Public*, pg. 2169
AVAYA HOLDINGS CORP.—See Silver Lake Group, LLC; *U.S. Private*, pg. 3655
AVAYA HOLDINGS CORP.—See TPG Capital, L.P.; *U.S. Public*, pg. 2168
AVAYA HONG KONG CO. LTD.—See Silver Lake Group, LLC; *U.S. Private*, pg. 3655
AVAYA HONG KONG CO. LTD.—See TPG Capital, L.P.; *U.S. Public*, pg. 2168
AVAYA INC.—See Silver Lake Group, LLC; *U.S. Private*, pg. 3655
AVAYA INC.—See TPG Capital, L.P.; *U.S. Public*, pg. 2168
AVAYA ISRAEL—See Silver Lake Group, LLC; *U.S. Private*, pg. 3656
AVAYA ISRAEL—See TPG Capital, L.P.; *U.S. Public*, pg. 2169
AVAYA JAPAN—See Silver Lake Group, LLC; *U.S. Private*, pg. 3655
AVAYA JAPAN—See TPG Capital, L.P.; *U.S. Public*, pg. 2168
AVAYA KOREA—See Silver Lake Group, LLC; *U.S. Private*, pg. 3655
AVAYA KOREA—See TPG Capital, L.P.; *U.S. Public*, pg. 2168
AVAYA, LLC—See Silver Lake Group, LLC; *U.S. Private*, pg. 3656
AVAYA, LLC—See TPG Capital, L.P.; *U.S. Public*, pg. 2169
AVAYA MALAYSIA—See Silver Lake Group, LLC; *U.S. Private*, pg. 3655
AVAYA MALAYSIA—See TPG Capital, L.P.; *U.S. Public*, pg. 2168
AVAYA NEDERLAND B.V.—See Silver Lake Group, LLC; *U.S. Private*, pg. 3656
AVAYA NEDERLAND B.V.—See TPG Capital, L.P.; *U.S. Public*, pg. 2169
AVAYA PHILIPPINES—See Silver Lake Group, LLC; *U.S. Private*, pg. 3655
AVAYA PHILIPPINES—See TPG Capital, L.P.; *U.S. Public*, pg. 2168
AVAYA SINGAPORE—See Silver Lake Group, LLC; *U.S. Private*, pg. 3655
AVAYA SINGAPORE—See TPG Capital, L.P.; *U.S. Public*, pg. 2168
AVAYA THAILAND—See Silver Lake Group, LLC; *U.S. Private*, pg. 3655
AVAYA THAILAND—See TPG Capital, L.P.; *U.S. Public*, pg. 2168
AVAYA UK - SCOTLAND OFFICE—See Silver Lake Group, LLC; *U.S. Private*, pg. 3656
AVAYA UK - SCOTLAND OFFICE—See TPG Capital, L.P.; *U.S. Public*, pg. 2169
AVAYA UK—See Silver Lake Group, LLC; *U.S. Private*, pg. 3656
AVAYA UK—See TPG Capital, L.P.; *U.S. Public*, pg. 2169
AVBA HI TECH SERVICES LTD.; *Int'l*, pg. 737
AVB, INC.—See Flowers Foods, Inc.; *U.S. Public*, pg. 854
AV BRECONRIDGE LIMITED—See Sanmina Corporation; *U.S. Public*, pg. 1840
AV BUILDER CORP.; *U.S. Private*, pg. 402
AV CAPITAL HOLDINGS MANAGEMENT, LLC; *U.S. Private*, pg. 402
AVC CHEMICAL CORPORATION—See Ishihara Sangyo Kaisha, Ltd.; *Int'l*, pg. 3817
AVC CHEMICAL CORPORATION—See Resins, Inc.; *Int'l*, pg. 6297
AVC CORP.; *U.S. Private*, pg. 404
AV CELL INC.—See The Aditya Birla Group; *Int'l*, pg. 7610
AVCENTER INC.; *U.S. Private*, pg. 404
AVCHEM, INC.—See Platinum Equity, LLC; *U.S. Private*, pg. 3210
AVC IMMEDIA LIMITED; *Int'l*, pg. 737

AVCO CORPORATION—See Textron Inc.; *U.S. Public*, pg. 2028
AVCO DISPOSAL INC.—See Burrtec Waste Industries, Inc.; *U.S. Private*, pg. 692
AV CONCEPT HOLDINGS LTD; *Int'l*, pg. 733
AV CONCEPT LIMITED—See AV Concept Holdings Ltd; *Int'l*, pg. 733
AV CONCEPT SINGAPORE PTE LTD.—See AV Concept Holdings Ltd; *Int'l*, pg. 733
AVCON INDUSTRIES, INC.—See Butler National Corporation; *U.S. Public*, pg. 413
AVCON INFORMATION TECHNOLOGY CO., LTD.; *Int'l*, pg. 737
AVCO ROOFING INC.—See Restoration Builders Inc.; *U.S. Private*, pg. 3409
AVCORP INDUSTRIES, INC.—See Searchlight Capital Partners, L.P.; *U.S. Private*, pg. 3588
AVC TECHNOLOGY (INTERNATIONAL) LIMITED—See AV Concept Holdings Ltd; *Int'l*, pg. 733
AVD CONSULTANCY N.V.—See Lundbeckfonden; *Int'l*, pg. 4580
AVDEL FRANCE SAS—See Stanley Black & Decker, Inc.; *U.S. Public*, pg. 1931
AVDEL ITALIA S.R.L.—See Stanley Black & Decker, Inc.; *U.S. Public*, pg. 1931
AVDEL SPAIN SA—See Stanley Black & Decker, Inc.; *U.S. Public*, pg. 1931
AVDEL UK LTD.—See Stanley Black & Decker, Inc.; *U.S. Public*, pg. 1934
AVDEL USA LLC—See Stanley Black & Decker, Inc.; *U.S. Public*, pg. 1934
AVEANNA HEALTHCARE HOLDINGS INC.; *U.S. Public*, pg. 242
AVEANNA HEALTHCARE, LLC; *U.S. Private*, pg. 405
AVECHO BIOTECHNOLOGY LTD.; *Int'l*, pg. 737
AVECIA LTD. - CINCINNATI FACILITY—See Avecia Ltd.; *Int'l*, pg. 737
AVECIA LTD. - MILFORD FACILITY—See Avecia Ltd.; *Int'l*, pg. 737
AVECIA LTD.; *Int'l*, pg. 737
AVECIA NV/SA—See Avecia Ltd.; *Int'l*, pg. 737
AVECIA SPAIN S.L.—See Avecia Ltd.; *Int'l*, pg. 737
AVECPALM MARKETING RESOURCES SDN. BHD.—See CB Industrial Product Holding Berhad; *Int'l*, pg. 1364
AVECTO LIMITED—See Francisco Partners Management, LP; *U.S. Private*, pg. 1589
AVEDA CORPORATION—See The Estee Lauder Companies Inc.; *U.S. Public*, pg. 2073
AVEDA SERVICES INC.—See The Estee Lauder Companies Inc.; *U.S. Public*, pg. 2073
AVEDA TRANSPORTATION AND ENERGY SERVICES INC.—See Daseke, Inc.; *U.S. Private*, pg. 1161
AVEDIS FOUNDATION; *U.S. Private*, pg. 405
AVEDIS ZILDJIAN COMPANY INC.; *U.S. Private*, pg. 405
AVEDORE DYREKLINIK APS—See Vimian Group AB; *Int'l*, pg. 8208
AVEDRO, INC.—See Glaukos Corporation; *U.S. Public*, pg. 939
AVEGA GROUP AB—See TietoEVRY Oyj; *Int'l*, pg. 7745
AVE GESELLSCHAFT FUR HORFUNKBETEILIGUNGEN MBH—See Bertelsmann SE & Co. KGaA; *Int'l*, pg. 993
A/V/E GMBH—See RWE AG; *Int'l*, pg. 6433
AVELANA—See Chargeurs SA; *Int'l*, pg. 1449
AVELEAD CONSULTING, LLC—See Streamline Health Solutions, Inc.; *U.S. Public*, pg. 1954
AVELLA OF DEER VALLEY, INC.; *U.S. Private*, pg. 405
AVELLA OF PHOENIX III, INC.—See UnitedHealth Group Incorporated; *U.S. Public*, pg. 2239
AVELLA OF SACRAMENTO, INC.—See UnitedHealth Group Incorporated; *U.S. Public*, pg. 2239
AVELLA OF SCOTTSDALE, INC.—See Avella of Deer Valley, Inc.; *U.S. Private*, pg. 405
AVEMCO INSURANCE COMPANY—See Tokio Marine Holdings, Inc.; *Int'l*, pg. 7783
AVEMIO AG; *Int'l*, pg. 737
AVEMIS SAS—See Vesuvius plc; *Int'l*, pg. 8178
AVEM PARTNERS, LLC; *U.S. Private*, pg. 405
AVENAL PARK LLC—See BlackRock, Inc.; *U.S. Public*, pg. 345
THE AVENAL PROGRESS—See Lee Enterprises, Incorporated; *U.S. Public*, pg. 1300
AVENAMITE S.A.—See L'Oreal S.A.; *Int'l*, pg. 4378
AVENANCE ITALIA S.P.A—See Charterhouse Capital Partners LLP; *Int'l*, pg. 1455
AVENA NORDIC GRAIN OY—See Apetit Plc; *Int'l*, pg. 509
AVENDRA, LLC—See Aramark; *U.S. Public*, pg. 177
A VENDRE A LOUER SAS—See Schibsted ASA; *Int'l*, pg. 6616
AVENGA; *Int'l*, pg. 738
AVENG E+PC ENGINEERING & PROJECTS COMPANY LIMITED—See Aveng Limited; *Int'l*, pg. 738
AVENG LIMITED; *Int'l*, pg. 738
AVENG WATER PTY LTD; *Int'l*, pg. 738
AVENICA—See University Ventures Funds Management LLC; *U.S. Public*, pg. 4310
AVENIDA NAPERVILLE PARTNERS LLC—See Safehold Inc.; *U.S. Public*, pg. 1834
AVENIDA PARTNERS LLC—See Ashmore Group plc; *Int'l*, pg. 608

AVENIRA LIMITED

AVENIRA LIMITED; *Int'l*, pg. 738
AVENIR CONSEIL FORMATION SA—See Alten S.A; *Int'l*, pg. 390
AVENIR ELECTRIQUE DE LIMOGES; *Int'l*, pg. 738
AVENIR ENERGIE SA; *Int'l*, pg. 738
AVENIR FINANCE CORPORATE—See Advenis; *Int'l*, pg. 166
AVENIR FINANCE GESTION—See Advenis; *Int'l*, pg. 166
AVENIR FINANCE INVESTMENT MANAGERS (AFIM)—See Advenis; *Int'l*, pg. 166
AVENIR FINANCE PARTENAIRES—See Advenis; *Int'l*, pg. 167
AVENIR FINANCE SECURITIES—See Advenis; *Int'l*, pg. 167
AVENIR GLOBAL, INC—See RES PUBLICA Consulting Group Inc.; *Int'l*, pg. 6295
AVENIR PRAHA & JCDECAUX NEONLIGHT—See JCDecaux S.A.; *Int'l*, pg. 3920
AVENIR—See JCDecaux S.A.; *Int'l*, pg. 3920
AVENIR TELECOM FRANCE—See Avenir Telecom S.A.; *Int'l*, pg. 738
AVENIR TELECOM ROMANIA—See Avenir Telecom S.A.; *Int'l*, pg. 738
AVENIR TELECOM S.A.; *Int'l*, pg. 738
AVENIR TELECOM SPAIN—See Avenir Telecom S.A.; *Int'l*, pg. 738
AVENIR WELLNESS SOLUTIONS, INC.; *U.S. Public*, pg. 242
AVENIR WELLNESS SOLUTIONS OF CALIFORNIA, LLC—See Avenir Wellness Solutions, Inc.; *U.S. Public*, pg. 242
AVENIS SA—See Alpiq Holding AG; *Int'l*, pg. 373
AVENSIA AB; *Int'l*, pg. 738
AVENSYS UK LTD.—See Fresenius SE & Co. KGaA; *Int'l*, pg. 2777
AVENTAS MANUFACTURING GROUP LIMITED; *Int'l*, pg. 738
AVENT HOLDINGS LIMITED—See Koninklijke Philips N.V.; *Int'l*, pg. 4267
AVENTIC PARTNERS AG—See UBS Group AG; *Int'l*, pg. 8007
AVENTICS AB—See Emerson Electric Co.; *U.S. Public*, pg. 742
AVENTICS AG—See Emerson Electric Co.; *U.S. Public*, pg. 742
AVENTICS AS—See Emerson Electric Co.; *U.S. Public*, pg. 742
AVENTICS B.V.—See Emerson Electric Co.; *U.S. Public*, pg. 742
AVENTICS GMBH—See Emerson Electric Co.; *U.S. Public*, pg. 742
AVENTICS GMBH—See Emerson Electric Co.; *U.S. Public*, pg. 742
AVENTICS HUNGARY KFT.—See Emerson Electric Co.; *U.S. Public*, pg. 742
AVENTICS INDIA PRIVATE LIMITED—See Emerson Electric Co.; *U.S. Public*, pg. 742
AVENTICS MEXICO, S. DE R.L. DE C.V.—See Emerson Electric Co.; *U.S. Public*, pg. 742
AVENTICS OY—See Emerson Electric Co.; *U.S. Public*, pg. 742
AVENTICS PNEUMATICS EQUIPMENT (CHANGZHOU) CO., LTD.—See Emerson Electric Co.; *U.S. Public*, pg. 742
AVENTICS PNEUMATICS TRADING (SHANGHAI) CO., LTD.—See Emerson Electric Co.; *U.S. Public*, pg. 742
AVENTICS S.A.S.—See Emerson Electric Co.; *U.S. Public*, pg. 742
AVENTICS, SPOL. S.R.O.—See Emerson Electric Co.; *U.S. Public*, pg. 742
AVENTICS SP. Z O.O.—See Emerson Electric Co.; *U.S. Public*, pg. 742
AVENTICS S.R.L.—See Emerson Electric Co.; *U.S. Public*, pg. 742
AVENTIS HOLDINGS INC.—See Sanofi; *Int'l*, pg. 6550
AVENTIS PHARMA, LDA.—See Sanofi; *Int'l*, pg. 6550
AVENTIS PHARMA LIMITED—See Sanofi; *Int'l*, pg. 6550
AVENTIS PHARMA (MANUFACTURING) PTE. LTD—See Sanofi; *Int'l*, pg. 6551
AVENTIS PHARMA SA—See Sanofi; *Int'l*, pg. 6550
AVENTIS PHARMA—See Sanofi; *Int'l*, pg. 6550
AVENTIS SYSTEMS; *U.S. Private*, pg. 405
AVENT LIMITED—See Koninklijke Philips N.V.; *Int'l*, pg. 4267
AVENTRI, INC.—See HGGC, LLC; *U.S. Private*, pg. 1929
AVENTURA ENERGY, INC.—See Vermilion Energy Inc.; *Int'l*, pg. 8172
AVENTURA GROUP AB; *Int'l*, pg. 739
AVENTURA HEALTHCARE SPECIALISTS LLC—See HCA Healthcare, Inc.; *U.S. Public*, pg. 991
AVENTURA HOSPITAL & MEDICAL CENTER—See HCA Healthcare, Inc.; *U.S. Public*, pg. 991
AVENTURE AVIATION; *U.S. Private*, pg. 405
AVENT USI—See Avnet, Inc.; *U.S. Public*, pg. 249
AVENUE100 MEDIA SOLUTIONS INC.; *U.S. Private*, pg. 405
AVENUE 365 LENDER SERVICES, LLC—See Rithm Capital Corp.; *U.S. Public*, pg. 1799
THE AVENUE AT WHITE MARSH BUSINESS TRUST—See Federal Realty Investment Trust; *U.S. Public*, pg. 826
AVENUE CAPITAL GROUP, LLC; *U.S. Private*, pg. 405
AVENUE CAPITAL MANAGEMENT II, L.P.—See Avenue Capital Group, LLC; *U.S. Private*, pg. 405
AVENUE CAPITAL MORTGAGE REIT INC.—See Avenue Capital Group, LLC; *U.S. Private*, pg. 405
AVENUE CARS OF GLOUCESTER LIMITED; *Int'l*, pg. 739
AVENUE CODE LLC—See Universo Online S.A.; *Int'l*, pg. 8083
AVENUE INDUSTRIAL SUPPLY CO. LTD.—See Franz Haniel & Cie. GmbH; *Int'l*, pg. 2763
AVENUE M INTERNATIONAL SCA—See LVMH Moet Hennessy Louis Vuitton SE; *Int'l*, pg. 4590
AVENUE MORTGAGE CORPORATION—See CIB Marine Bancshares, Inc.; *U.S. Public*, pg. 494
AVENUE MOULD SOLUTIONS LTD.—See Nolato AB; *Int'l*, pg. 5407
AVENUE MOVING AND STORAGE LIMITED; *Int'l*, pg. 739
AVENUE NISSAN SALES LTD.; *Int'l*, pg. 739
AVENUES HEALTHCARE, INC.—See The Ensign Group, Inc.; *U.S. Public*, pg. 2070
AVENUE STORES, LLC—See Independence Capital Partners, LLC; *U.S. Private*, pg. 2057
AVENUE SUPERMARTS LIMITED; *Int'l*, pg. 739
AVENUES WORLD FZ-LLC—See Infibeam Avenues Limited; *Int'l*, pg. 3684
AVENUE THERAPEUTICS, INC.; *U.S. Public*, pg. 242
AVENU INSIGHTS & ANALYTICS LLC—See Arlington Capital Partners LLC; *U.S. Private*, pg. 327
AVENZA HOLDINGS INC.; *Int'l*, pg. 739
AVENZA SYSTEMS INC.—See Avenza Holdings Inc.; *Int'l*, pg. 739
AVEO GROUP LIMITED—See Brookfield Corporation; *Int'l*, pg. 1185
AVEO HEALTHCARE LIMITED—See Brookfield Corporation; *Int'l*, pg. 1186
THE AVEON GROUP L.P.; *U.S. Private*, pg. 3990
AVEO PHARMACEUTICALS, INC.—See LG Chem Ltd.; *Int'l*, pg. 4473
AVE-PLAZA LLC—See UNIQA Insurance Group AG; *Int'l*, pg. 8057
AVEPOINT, INC.; *U.S. Public*, pg. 243
AVERA HEALTH; *U.S. Private*, pg. 405
AVER ASIA (S) PTE. LTD.—See Sumitomo Corporation; *Int'l*, pg. 7268
AVERA TYLER HOSPITAL—See Avera Health; *U.S. Private*, pg. 405
AVERBUCH FORMICA CENTER LTD.; *Int'l*, pg. 739
AVERE SYSTEMS, INC.—See Microsoft Corporation; *U.S. Public*, pg. 1439
AVER INFORMATION INC.—See AVer Information Inc.; *Int'l*, pg. 739
AVER INFORMATION, INC.—See AVer Information Inc.; *Int'l*, pg. 739
AVER INFORMATION INC.; *Int'l*, pg. 739
AVERITT EXPRESS INC.; *U.S. Private*, pg. 405
AVERMEDIA TECHNOLOGIES INC.; *Int'l*, pg. 739
AVERNA TECHNOLOGIES INC.; *Int'l*, pg. 739
AVERNA TEST SYSTEMS INC.—See Averna Technologies Inc.; *Int'l*, pg. 739
AVERON PARK LIMITED; *Int'l*, pg. 739
AVEROX INC.; *Int'l*, pg. 739
AVEROX (PVT.) LTD.—See AVEROX INC.; *Int'l*, pg. 739
AVERTEST, LLC; *U.S. Private*, pg. 405
AVERTEX UTILITY SOLUTIONS INC.; *Int'l*, pg. 739
AVERTIUM, LLC—See Sunstone Partners Management LLC; *U.S. Private*, pg. 3873
AVERTIUM TENNESSEE, INC.—See Sunstone Partners Management LLC; *U.S. Private*, pg. 3873
AVERY BERKEL FRANCE SAS—See Illinois Tool Works Inc.; *U.S. Public*, pg. 1101
AVERY BREWING COMPANY—See Mahou, S.A.; *Int'l*, pg. 4649
AVERY DENNISON BELGIE BVBA—See Avery Dennison Corporation; *U.S. Public*, pg. 243
AVERY DENNISON BELGIUM MANAGEMENT SERVICES SPRL—See Avery Dennison Corporation; *U.S. Public*, pg. 243
AVERY DENNISON CENTRAL EUROPE GMBH—See Avery Dennison Corporation; *U.S. Public*, pg. 243
AVERY DENNISON CHILE S.A.—See Avery Dennison Corporation; *U.S. Public*, pg. 243
AVERY DENNISON COLOMBIA S. A.—See Avery Dennison Corporation; *U.S. Public*, pg. 243
AVERY DENNISON CORPORATION; *U.S. Public*, pg. 243
AVERY DENNISON CORP. - RETAIL BRANDING & INFORMATION SOLUTIONS—See Avery Dennison Corporation; *U.S. Public*, pg. 243
AVERY DENNISON DO BRASIL LTDA.—See Avery Dennison Corporation; *U.S. Public*, pg. 244
AVERY DENNISON FASSON CANADA, INC.—See Avery Dennison Corporation; *U.S. Public*, pg. 244
AVERY DENNISON (FUZHOU) CONVERTED PRODUCTS LIMITED—See Avery Dennison Corporation; *U.S. Public*, pg. 243

CORPORATE AFFILIATIONS

AVERY DENNISON GROUP SINGAPORE (PTE) LIMITED—See Avery Dennison Corporation; *U.S. Public*, pg. 244
AVANTOR PERFORMANCE MATERIAL S [sic]
AVERY DENNISON GULF FZCO—See Avery Dennison Corporation; *U.S. Public*, pg. 244
AVERY DENNISON HOLDING LIMITED—See Avery Dennison Corporation; *U.S. Public*, pg. 243
AVERY DENNISON HONG KONG HOLDING I B.V.—See Avery Dennison Corporation; *U.S. Public*, pg. 243
AVERY DENNISON (HONG KONG) LTD.—See Avery Dennison Corporation; *U.S. Public*, pg. 243
AVERY DENNISON - INDUSTRIAL & AUTOMOTIVE PRODUCTS DIVISION—See Avery Dennison Corporation; *U.S. Public*, pg. 243
AVERY DENNISON IRELAND LTD.—See Avery Dennison Corporation; *U.S. Public*, pg. 244
AVERY DENNISON ITALIA S.P.A.—See Avery Dennison Corporation; *U.S. Public*, pg. 244
AVERY DENNISON JAPAN MATERIALS COMPANY LTD.—See Avery Dennison Corporation; *U.S. Public*, pg. 243
AVERY DENNISON (KENYA) PRIVATE LIMITED—See Avery Dennison Corporation; *U.S. Public*, pg. 243
AVERY DENNISON MANAGEMENT GMBH—See Avery Dennison Corporation; *U.S. Public*, pg. 244
AVERY DENNISON MATERIALS GMBH—See Avery Dennison Corporation; *U.S. Public*, pg. 244
AVERY DENNISON MATERIALS PTY LTD—See Avery Dennison Corporation; *U.S. Public*, pg. 244
AVERY DENNISON (NEDERLAND) B.V.—See Avery Dennison Corporation; *U.S. Public*, pg. 243
AVERY DENNISON NTP A.S.—See Avery Dennison Corporation; *U.S. Public*, pg. 244
AVERY DENNISON OVERSEAS CORPORATION—See Avery Dennison Corporation; *U.S. Public*, pg. 243
AVERY DENNISON - PERFORMANCE FILMS DIVISION, SCHERERVILLE—See Avery Dennison Corporation; *U.S. Public*, pg. 243
AVERY DENNISON PERFORMANCE POLYMERS—See Avery Dennison Corporation; *U.S. Public*, pg. 244
AVERY DENNISON PRAHA SPOL. S.R.O.—See Avery Dennison Corporation; *U.S. Public*, pg. 244
AVERY DENNISON PRINTER SYSTEMS DIVISION—See Avery Dennison Corporation; *U.S. Public*, pg. 243
AVERY DENNISON RBIS PTY LTD—See Avery Dennison Corporation; *U.S. Public*, pg. 243
AVERY DENNISON - REFLECTIVE FILMS DIVISION, NILES—See Avery Dennison Corporation; *U.S. Public*, pg. 243
AVERY DENNISON RETAIL BRANDING & INFORMATION SOLUTIONS - FAIR LAWN—See Avery Dennison Corporation; *U.S. Public*, pg. 243
AVERY DENNISON RETAIL BRANDING & INFORMATION SOLUTIONS - GREENSBORO—See Avery Dennison Corporation; *U.S. Public*, pg. 243
AVERY DENNISON RETAIL BRANDING & INFORMATION SOLUTIONS - LENOIR—See Avery Dennison Corporation; *U.S. Public*, pg. 243
AVERY DENNISON RETAIL BRANDING & INFORMATION SOLUTIONS - SAYRE—See Avery Dennison Corporation; *U.S. Public*, pg. 244
AVERY DENNISON RETAIL INFORMATION SERVICES DE MEXICO, S.A. DE C.V.—See Avery Dennison Corporation; *U.S. Public*, pg. 244
AVERY DENNISON RETAIL INFORMATION SERVICES LLC—See Avery Dennison Corporation; *U.S. Public*, pg. 243
AVERY DENNISON RIS DOMINICAN REPUBLIC—See Avery Dennison Corporation; *U.S. Public*, pg. 243
AVERY DENNISON R.I.S. FRANCE S. A. S.—See Avery Dennison Corporation; *U.S. Public*, pg. 243
AVERY DENNISON R.I.S. ITALIA S.R.L.—See Avery Dennison Corporation; *U.S. Public*, pg. 243
AVERY DENNISON RIS KOREA LTD.—See Avery Dennison Corporation; *U.S. Public*, pg. 243
AVERY DENNISON R.I.S. POLSKA SP.ZO.O—See Avery Dennison Corporation; *U.S. Public*, pg. 243
AVERY DENNISON RIS TAIWAN LTD.—See Avery Dennison Corporation; *U.S. Public*, pg. 243
AVERY DENNISON RIS VIETNAM CO. LTD.—See Avery Dennison Corporation; *U.S. Public*, pg. 244
AVERY DENNISON, S.A. DE C.V.—See Avery Dennison Corporation; *U.S. Public*, pg. 244
AVERY DENNISON SCANDINAVIA AB—See Avery Dennison Corporation; *U.S. Public*, pg. 243
AVERY DENNISON SINGAPORE (PTE) LTD.—See Avery Dennison Corporation; *U.S. Public*, pg. 244
AVERY DENNISON - SPECIALTY TAPE U.S.—See Avery Dennison Corporation; *U.S. Public*, pg. 243
AVERY DENNISON S.R.L.—See Avery Dennison Corporation; *U.S. Public*, pg. 243
AVERY DENNISON (SUZHOU) CO. LIMITED—See Avery Dennison Corporation; *U.S. Public*, pg. 243
AVERY DENNISON SYSTEMES D'ETIQUETAGE FRANCE S.A.S.—See Avery Dennison Corporation; *U.S. Public*, pg. 243
AVERY DENNISON (THAILAND) LTD.—See Avery Dennison Corporation; *U.S. Public*, pg. 243

COMPANY NAME INDEX

AVERY DENNISON U.K. LTD.—See Avery Dennison Corporation; *U.S. Public*, pg. 244
AVERY ETICHETTE ITALIA S.P.A.—See Avery Dennison Corporation; *U.S. Public*, pg. 244
AVERY GRAPHICS AND REFLECTIVE PRODUCTS DIVISION—See Avery Dennison Corporation; *U.S. Public*, pg. 244
AVERY HEALTHCARE GROUP LIMITED—See Welltower Inc.; *U.S. Public*, pg. 2347
AVERY HOLDINGS, INC.—See Billing Services Group, LLC; *U.S. Private*, pg. 559
AVERY INDIA LIMITED—See Illinois Tool Works Inc.; *U.S. Public*, pg. 1101
AVERY JOURNAL-TIMES—See Adams Publishing Group, LLC; *U.S. Private*, pg. 75
AVERY MALAYSIA SDN BHD—See Illinois Tool Works Inc.; *U.S. Public*, pg. 1101
AVERY MANOR NURSING, L.L.C.—See Apollo Global Management, Inc.; *U.S. Public*, pg. 156
A VERY NORMAL COMPANY PTE. LTD.—See Omnibridge Holdings Limited; *Int'l*, pg. 5564
AVERY OFFICE PRODUCTS PTY. LTD.—See CCL Industries Inc.; *Int'l*, pg. 1367
AVERY OFFICE PRODUCTS PUERTO RICO L.L.C.—See CCL Industries Inc.; *Int'l*, pg. 1367
AVERY PRODUCTS CORPORATION—See CCL Industries Inc.; *Int'l*, pg. 1367
AVERYS SA—See Blackstone Inc.; *U.S. Public*, pg. 348
AVERY TICO S.R.L.—See CCL Industries Inc.; *Int'l*, pg. 1367
AVERY WEIGH-TRONIX HOLDINGS LIMITED—See Illinois Tool Works Inc.; *U.S. Public*, pg. 1101
AVERY WEIGH-TRONIX, INC.—See Illinois Tool Works Inc.; *U.S. Public*, pg. 1101
AVERY WEIGH-TRONIX INTERNATIONAL LIMITED—See Illinois Tool Works Inc.; *U.S. Public*, pg. 1101
AVERY WEIGH-TRONIX, LLC—See Illinois Tool Works Inc.; *U.S. Public*, pg. 1101
AVERY WEIGH-TRONIX (SUZHOU) WEIGHING TECHNOLOGY CO. LTD.—See Illinois Tool Works Inc.; *U.S. Public*, pg. 1101
AVERY WEIGH-TRONIX UK LIMITED—See Illinois Tool Works Inc.; *U.S. Public*, pg. 1101
AVERY WOODS REPORTING SERVICE—See Stevens Koenig Reporting; *U.S. Private*, pg. 3909
AVERY ZWECKFORM GMBH—See Avery Dennison Corporation; *U.S. Public*, pg. 244
AVE S.A.; *Int'l*, pg. 737
AVESCO MARKETING CORPORATION; *Int'l*, pg. 739
AVESI PARTNERS, LLC; *U.S. Private*, pg. 405
AVESIS, INC.—See The Guardian Life Insurance Company of America; *U.S. Private*, pg. 4040
AVES ONE AG; *Int'l*, pg. 739
AVESORO HOLDINGS LIMITED; *Int'l*, pg. 739
AVESORO JERSEY LIMITED—See Avesoro Holdings Limited; *Int'l*, pg. 740
AVESORO RESOURCES INC.—See Avesoro Holdings Limited; *Int'l*, pg. 740
AVESTA COMPUTER SERVICES LTD.; *U.S. Private*, pg. 405
AVESTA HOMES LLC; *U.S. Private*, pg. 406
AVESTA HOUSING DEVELOPMENT CORP.; *U.S. Private*, pg. 406
AVESTA KLIPPCENTER AB—See Outokumpu Oyj; *Int'l*, pg. 5667
AVESTA WELDING AB—See voestalpine AG; *Int'l*, pg. 8291
AVESTA WELDING LLC—See voestalpine AG; *Int'l*, pg. 8291
AVEST CO., LTD—See Dynavest Pte. Ltd.; *Int'l*, pg. 2242
AVESTHAGEN, INC.—See Avesthagen Limited; *Int'l*, pg. 740
AVESTHAGEN LIMITED; *Int'l*, pg. 740
AVESTHAGEN PTE. LTD.—See Avesthagen Limited; *Int'l*, pg. 740
AVESTHAGEN PVT. LTD.—See Avesthagen Limited; *Int'l*, pg. 740
AVESZT BT.—See PHOENIX Pharmahandel GmbH & Co. KG; *Int'l*, pg. 5854
AVETAS VERSICHERUNGS-AKTIENGESELLSCHAFT—See Baloise Holding AG; *Int'l*, pg. 811
AVETHAGEN M-E FZ-LLC—See Avesthagen Limited; *Int'l*, pg. 740
AVETTA, LLC—See Welsh, Carson, Anderson & Stowe; *U.S. Private*, pg. 4479
AVEVA AB—See Schneider Electric SE; *Int'l*, pg. 6623
AVEVA ASIA PACIFIC SDN BHD—See Schneider Electric SE; *Int'l*, pg. 6623
AVEVA ASIA PACIFIC - SHANGHAI—See Schneider Electric SE; *Int'l*, pg. 6623
AVEVA AS—See Schneider Electric SE; *Int'l*, pg. 6623
AVEVA DENMARK A/S—See Schneider Electric SE; *Int'l*, pg. 6623
AVEVA DO BRASIL INFORMATICA LTDA—See Schneider Electric SE; *Int'l*, pg. 6623
AVEVA DRUG DELIVERY SYSTEMS, INC—See DifGen Pharmaceuticals Pvt. Ltd.; *Int'l*, pg. 2118
AVEVA GMBH—See Schneider Electric SE; *Int'l*, pg. 6623

AVEVA GROUP PLC—See Schneider Electric SE; *Int'l*, pg. 6623
AVEVA INFORMATION TECHNOLOGY INDIA PRIVATE LIMITED—See Schneider Electric SE; *Int'l*, pg. 6623
AVEVA PTY LIMITED—See Schneider Electric SE; *Int'l*, pg. 6623
AVEVA SA—See Schneider Electric SE; *Int'l*, pg. 6623
AVEVA SOFTWARE SINGAPORE PTE. LTD.—See Schneider Electric SE; *Int'l*, pg. 6623
AVEVA SOLUTIONS LIMITED—See Schneider Electric SE; *Int'l*, pg. 6623
AVEX ASIA PTE. LTD.—See Avex Inc.; *Int'l*, pg. 740
AVEX CLASSICS INTERNATIONAL INC.—See Avex Inc.; *Int'l*, pg. 740
AVEX ENTERTAINMENT INC.—See Avex Inc.; *Int'l*, pg. 740
AVEX & HIROTSU BIO EMPOWER LLC—See Avex Inc.; *Int'l*, pg. 740
AVEX HONG KONG LTD.—See Avex Inc.; *Int'l*, pg. 740
AVEX INC.; *Int'l*, pg. 740
AVEX MANAGEMENT INC.—See Avex Inc.; *Int'l*, pg. 740
AVEX MARKETING INC.—See Avex Inc.; *Int'l*, pg. 740
AVEX PHARMACEUTICALS PTE. LTD.—See Apex Healthcare Berhad; *Int'l*, pg. 511
AVFAST (INDIA) PVT. LTD.—See Stanley Black & Decker, Inc.; *U.S. Public*, pg. 1932
AVF GULF JLT—See AVK Holding A/S; *Int'l*, pg. 746
AVFUEL CORPORATION; *U.S. Private*, pg. 406
AVFX, LLC—See Harbor Beach Capital, LLC; *U.S. Private*, pg. 1858
AVG ABFALL-VERWERTUNGS-GESELLSCHAFT MBH—See Katoen Natie N.V.; *Int'l*, pg. 4090
AVG ADVANCED TECHNOLOGIES LP; *U.S. Private*, pg. 406
AVG LOGISTICS LTD.; *Int'l*, pg. 740
AVG-LTI LP—See AVG Advanced Technologies LP; *U.S. Private*, pg. 406
AVGOL INDUSTRIES 1953 LTD.—See Indorama Ventures Public Company Limited; *Int'l*, pg. 3658
AVG TECHNOLOGIES B.V.—See Gen Digital Inc.; *U.S. Public*, pg. 910
AVG TECHNOLOGIES CZ S.R.O.—See Gen Digital Inc.; *U.S. Public*, pg. 910
AVGUSTA TRADE LTD.—See Trace Group Hold PLC; *Int'l*, pg. 7886
AVH CAROLINAS, LLC—See Brookfield Corporation; *Int'l*, pg. 1183
AVH DAIRY TRADE B.V.—See Emmi AG; *Int'l*, pg. 2384
AVH NORTH FLORIDA, LLC—See Brookfield Corporation; *Int'l*, pg. 1183
AV HOMES, INC.—See Brookfield Corporation; *Int'l*, pg. 1183
AV HOMES OF ARIZONA, LLC—See Brookfield Corporation; *Int'l*, pg. 1183
AVIAAM LEASING AB; *Int'l*, pg. 741
AVIA ASHOK LEYLAND MOTORS S.R.O—See Hinduja Group Ltd.; *Int'l*, pg. 3398
AVIA ASHOK LEYLAND RUS—See Hinduja Group Ltd.; *Int'l*, pg. 3398
AVIA CAPITAL SERVICES LLC—See Russian Technologies State Corporation; *Int'l*, pg. 6431
AVIACION INTERCONTINENTAL, A.I.E.—See Banco Santander, S.A.; *Int'l*, pg. 825
AVIACION REGIONAL CANTABRA, A.I.E.—See Banco Santander, S.A.; *Int'l*, pg. 825
AVIACODE INCORPORATED—See ChrysCapital Management Co.; *Int'l*, pg. 1588
AVIACOMP SAS—See Sogeclair; *Int'l*, pg. 7058
AVIAGEN INCORPORATED—See EW GROUP GmbH; *Int'l*, pg. 2575
AVIAGEN INC.—See EW GROUP GmbH; *Int'l*, pg. 2575
AVIAGEN LIMITED—See EW GROUP GmbH; *Int'l*, pg. 2575
AVIALL AUSTRALIA PTY. LTD.—See The Boeing Company; *U.S. Public*, pg. 2039
AVIALLIANCE CAPITAL VERWALTUNGS GMBH & CO. KG—See Public Sector Pension Investment Board; *Int'l*, pg. 6095
AVIALLIANCE GMBH—See Public Sector Pension Investment Board; *Int'l*, pg. 6095
AVIALL NEW ZEALAND—See The Boeing Company; *U.S. Public*, pg. 2039
AVIALL PTE LTD—See The Boeing Company; *U.S. Public*, pg. 2039
AVIANCA GROUP INTERNATIONAL LIMITED—See Synergy Group; *Int'l*, pg. 7384
A'VIANDS, LLC—See Charterhouse Capital Partners LLP; *Int'l*, pg. 1455
AVIAN ENGINEERING, LLC; *U.S. Private*, pg. 406
AVIAN ENTERPRISES, LLC; *U.S. Private*, pg. 406
AVIAN MOBILE LTD.—See Nationwide Fleet Installations Ltd.; *Int'l*, pg. 5165
AVIAOK INTERNATIONAL LLC; *Int'l*, pg. 741
AVIAQ AB—See AVTECH Sweden AB; *Int'l*, pg. 751
AVIAREPS AG; *Int'l*, pg. 741
AVIAREPS MARKETING GARDEN LTD.; *Int'l*, pg. 741
AVIAREPS MARKETING GARDEN LTD.—See AVIAREPS Marketing Garden Ltd.; *Int'l*, pg. 741

AVIAREPS MARKETING GARDEN—See AVIAREPS Marketing Garden Ltd.; *Int'l*, pg. 741
AVIA SOLUTIONS GROUP AB; *Int'l*, pg. 741
AVIAT COMMUNICATIONS TECHNOLOGY (SHENZHEN) COMPANY LTD.—See Aviat Networks, Inc.; *U.S. Public*, pg. 245
AVIATECH CORPORATION; *U.S. Private*, pg. 406
AVIATION BLADE SERVICES, INC.—See First Equity Group, Inc.; *U.S. Private*, pg. 1517
AVIATION CAPITAL GROUP LLC—See Tokyo Century Corporation; *Int'l*, pg. 7788
AVIATION CHARTER INC.; *U.S. Private*, pg. 406
AVIATION COMMUNICATION & SURVEILLANCE SYSTEMS, LLC—See L3Harris Technologies, Inc.; *U.S. Public*, pg. 1281
AVIATION COMMUNICATION & SURVEILLANCE SYSTEMS, LLC—See Thales S.A.; *Int'l*, pg. 7602
AVIATION CONSTRUCTORS, INC.—See Cleveland Group, Inc.; *U.S. Private*, pg. 941
AVIATION CONTRACT SERVICES, INC.—See Macquarie Group Limited; *Int'l*, pg. 4627
AVIATION EQUIPMENT LEASING (AUSTRALIA) PTY LTD—See Goldbell Corporation; *Int'l*, pg. 3027
AVIATION EQUIPMENT LEASING PTE LTD—See Goldbell Corporation; *Int'l*, pg. 3027
AVIATION FACILITIES COMPANY, INC.; *U.S. Private*, pg. 406
AVIATION FUEL INTERNATIONAL, INC.—See FUELSTREAM, INC.; *U.S. Public*, pg. 891
AVIATION GROUND EQUIPMENT CORP.—See Nexus Capital Management LP; *U.S. Private*, pg. 2922
AVIATION GROUND SERVICE COMPANY LTD.—See Cam Ranh International Airport Services JSC; *Int'l*, pg. 1266
AVIATION INDUSTRY CORPORATION OF CHINA; *Int'l*, pg. 741
AVIATION INSTITUTE OF MAINTENANCE - INDIANAPOLIS—See Centura College; *U.S. Private*, pg. 830
AVIATION INSTITUTE OF MAINTENANCE—See Centura College; *U.S. Private*, pg. 830
AVIATION INVENTORY RESOURCES, INC.; *U.S. Private*, pg. 406
AVIATION LABORATORIES, INC.; *U.S. Private*, pg. 406
AVIATION LEASE AND FINANCE COMPANY K.S.C.C.—See Kuwait Finance House K.S.C.; *Int'l*, pg. 4344
AVIATION LINKS LTD.; *Int'l*, pg. 742
AVIATION LOGISTICS CORP.—See The Boeing Company; *U.S. Public*, pg. 2041
AVIATION MANUFACTURING GROUP, LLC—See Loar Group, Inc.; *U.S. Private*, pg. 2477
AVIATION MINING SOLUTIONS, INC.; *U.S. Private*, pg. 406
AVIATION PARTNERSHIP (PHILIPPINES) CORPORATION—See JG Summit Holdings, Inc.; *Int'l*, pg. 3939
AVIATION PARTNERS, INC.—See Washington Corporations; *U.S. Private*, pg. 4446
AVIATION, POWER & MARINE, INC.—See Pfingsten Partners, LLC; *U.S. Private*, pg. 3164
AVIATIONPOWER TECHNICAL SERVICES GMBH—See ManpowerGroup Inc.; *U.S. Public*, pg. 1357
AVIATIONPOWER UK LTD.—See ManpowerGroup Inc.; *U.S. Public*, pg. 1357
AVIATION QUALITY SERVICES GMBH—See Deutsche Lufthansa AG; *Int'l*, pg. 2068
AVIATION SERVICE SERVIS LETAL, DOO, LJUBLJANA—See Textron Inc.; *U.S. Public*, pg. 2028
AVIATION SOLUTIONS, LLC—See Marsh & McLennan Companies, Inc.; *U.S. Public*, pg. 1380
AVIATION SPARES & SERVICES INTERNATIONAL CO.; *U.S. Private*, pg. 406
AVIATIONSTAFFMANAGEMENT GMBH—See ManpowerGroup Inc.; *U.S. Public*, pg. 1357
AVIATIONSTAFF MANAGEMENT—See ManpowerGroup Inc.; *U.S. Public*, pg. 1357
AVIATION TECHNICAL SERVICES INC.—See JLL Partners, LLC; *U.S. Private*, pg. 2212
AVIATION TECHNOLOGIES, INC.—See TransDigm Group Incorporated; *U.S. Public*, pg. 2182
AVIAT NETWORKS (AUSTRALIA) PTY. LTD.—See Aviat Networks, Inc.; *U.S. Public*, pg. 245
AVIAT NETWORKS BRASIL SERVICOS EM COMMUNICACOES LTDA.—See Aviat Networks, Inc.; *U.S. Public*, pg. 245
AVIAT NETWORKS CANADA ULC—See Aviat Networks, Inc.; *U.S. Public*, pg. 245
AVIAT NETWORKS COMMUNICATION SOLUTIONS LIMITED—See Aviat Networks, Inc.; *U.S. Public*, pg. 245
AVIAT NETWORKS COTE D'IVOIRE—See Aviat Networks, Inc.; *U.S. Public*, pg. 245
AVIAT NETWORKS DE MEXICO, S.A. DE C.V.—See Aviat Networks, Inc.; *U.S. Public*, pg. 245
AVIAT NETWORKS GHANA LIMITED—See Aviat Networks, Inc.; *U.S. Public*, pg. 245
AVIAT NETWORKS, INC.; *U.S. Public*, pg. 245

AVIAT NETWORKS, INC.

AVIAT NETWORKS (INDIA) PRIVATE LIMITED—See Aviat Networks, Inc.; *U.S. Public*, pg. 245
AVIAT NETWORKS MALAYSIA SDN. BHD.—See Aviat Networks, Inc.; *U.S. Public*, pg. 245
AVIAT NETWORKS (NZ) LIMITED—See Aviat Networks, Inc.; *U.S. Public*, pg. 245
AVIAT NETWORKS PHILIPPINES, INC.—See Aviat Networks, Inc.; *U.S. Public*, pg. 245
AVIAT NETWORKS POLSKA SP. Z.O.O.—See Aviat Networks, Inc.; *U.S. Public*, pg. 245
AVIAT NETWORKS SAUDI ARABIA—See Aviat Networks, Inc.; *U.S. Public*, pg. 245
AVIAT NET WORKS SAUDI TELECOM & INFORMATION TECHNOLOGY CO.—See Aviat Networks, Inc.; *U.S. Public*, pg. 245
AVIAT NETWORKS (S) PTE. LTD.—See Aviat Networks, Inc.; *U.S. Public*, pg. 245
AVIAT NETWORKS (THAILAND) LTD.—See Aviat Networks, Inc.; *U.S. Public*, pg. 245
AVIAT NETWORKS (UK) LIMITED—See Aviat Networks, Inc.; *U.S. Public*, pg. 245
AVIATOR AIRPORT ALLIANCE EUROPE AB—See Avia Solutions Group AB; *Int'l*, pg. 741
AVIATOR DENMARK A/S—See Avia Solutions Group AB; *Int'l*, pg. 741
AVIATOR LLC—See Flutter Entertainment plc; *Int'l*, pg. 2715
AVIAT STORITVENO PODJETJE, D.O.O.—See Aviat Networks, Inc.; *U.S. Public*, pg. 246
AVIAT U.S., INC. - SAN ANTONIO—See Aviat Networks, Inc.; *U.S. Public*, pg. 246
AVIAT U.S., INC.—See Aviat Networks, Inc.; *U.S. Public*, pg. 245
AVIBANK MFG., INC.—See Berkshire Hathaway Inc.; *U.S. Public*, pg. 314
AVIBANK SERVICES, LLC—See Berkshire Hathaway Inc.; *U.S. Public*, pg. 313
AVI BIOPHARMA INTERNATIONAL LIMITED—See Sarepta Therapeutics, Inc.; *U.S. Public*, pg. 1841
AVIC AIRBORNE SYSTEMS CO., LTD.; *Int'l*, pg. 742
AVICANNA, INC.; *Int'l*, pg. 743
AVIC AVIATION HIGH-TECHNOLOGY CO., LTD.—See Aviation Industry Corporation of China; *Int'l*, pg. 741
AVIC ELECTROMECHANICAL SYSTEMS CO., LTD.—See Aviation Industry Corporation of China; *Int'l*, pg. 741
AVICENNA TECHNOLOGY, INC.—See AMETEK, Inc.; *U.S. Public*, pg. 120
AVIC FORSTAR SCIENCE & TECHNOLOGY CO., LTD.—See Aviation Industry Corporation of China; *Int'l*, pg. 741
AVIC (HAINAN) SPECIAL GLASS MATERIAL CO., LTD.—See Hainan Development Holdings Nanhai Co., Ltd.; *Int'l*, pg. 3211
AVIC HEAVY MACHINERY CO., LTD.—See Aviation Industry Corporation of China; *Int'l*, pg. 741
AVIC HELICOPTER CO., LTD.—See Aviation Industry Corporation of China; *Int'l*, pg. 741
AVICHINA INDUSTRY & TECHNOLOGY CO., LTD.—See Aviation Industry Corporation of China; *Int'l*, pg. 741
AVIC INDUSTRY-FINANCE HOLDINGS CO., LTD.—See Aviation Industry Corporation of China; *Int'l*, pg. 741
AVIC INTERNATIONAL BEIJING COMPANY LIMITED—See AVIC International Holdings Limited; *Int'l*, pg. 742
AVIC INTERNATIONAL HOLDINGS LIMITED; *Int'l*, pg. 742
AVIC INTERNATIONAL MARITIME HOLDINGS LIMITED—See China Merchants Group Limited; *Int'l*, pg. 1520
AVIC INTERNATIONAL OFFSHORE (XIAMEN) CO., LTD.—See China Merchants Group Limited; *Int'l*, pg. 1520
AVIC INTERNATIONAL SHIP DEVELOPMENT (CHINA) CO., LTD.—See China Merchants Group Limited; *Int'l*, pg. 1520
AVIC JONHON OPTRONIC TECHNOLOGY CO., LTD.—See Aviation Industry Corporation of China; *Int'l*, pg. 741
AVIC JOY HOLDINGS (HK) LIMITED; *Int'l*, pg. 742
AVICOLA BRASOV S.A.; *Int'l*, pg. 743
AVICOLA CREVEDIA—See Agroli Group; *Int'l*, pg. 220
AVICOLA MOLISANA SRL—See Arena Holding S.p.A.; *Int'l*, pg. 558
AVICOLA S.A.—See SIF Muntenia S.A.; *Int'l*, pg. 6905
AVICOLA SLOBOZIA SA; *Int'l*, pg. 743
AVICOM MARKETING COMMUNICATIONS; *U.S. Private*, pg. 406
AVICOM MARKETING COMMUNICATIONS—See Avicom Marketing Communications; *U.S. Private*, pg. 406
AVICOR CONSTRUCTION; *Int'l*, pg. 743
AVIC SANXIN SOLAR GLASS CO., LTD.—See Hainan Development Holdings Nanhai Co., Ltd.; *Int'l*, pg. 3211
AVIC WEIHAI SHIPYARD CO., LTD.—See AVIC International Holdings Limited; *Int'l*, pg. 742
AVIC XIAN AIRCRAFT INDUSTRY GROUP COMPANY LTD.—See Aviation Industry Corporation of China; *Int'l*, pg. 741
AVIDBANK HOLDINGS, INC.; *U.S. Public*, pg. 246

AVIDBANK—See Avidbank Holdings, Inc.; *U.S. Public*, pg. 246
AVID BIOSERVICES, INC.; *U.S. Public*, pg. 246
AVID CENTER; *U.S. Private*, pg. 406
AVID COMMUNICATIONS LLC—See Nelnet, Inc.; *U.S. Public*, pg. 1504
AVID DATING LIFE INC.—See Avid Life Media Inc.; *Int'l*, pg. 743
AVID DEVELOPMENT GMBH—See Symphony Technology Group, LLC; *U.S. Private*, pg. 3901
AVIDE DEVELOPMENTS INC.—See Co-op Atlantic; *Int'l*, pg. 1679
AVID GENERAL PARTNER B.V.—See Symphony Technology Group, LLC; *U.S. Private*, pg. 3901
AVIDIA BANK—See Assabet Valley Bancorp; *U.S. Private*, pg. 353
AVIDIAN GOLD CORP.; *Int'l*, pg. 743
AVIDIAN TECHNOLOGIES, INC.; *U.S. Private*, pg. 407
AVIDIAN WEALTH SOLUTIONS, LLC; *U.S. Private*, pg. 407
AVIDITY BIOSCIENCES, INC.; *U.S. Public*, pg. 246
AVID LIFE MEDIA INC.; *Int'l*, pg. 743
AVIDLY OY—See Adelis Equity Partners AB; *Int'l*, pg. 142
AVID MEDICAL, INC.—See Owens & Minor, Inc.; *U.S. Public*, pg. 1625
AVID NORTH ASIA LIMITED—See Symphony Technology Group, LLC; *U.S. Private*, pg. 3901
AVID PALLET SERVICES, LLC—See Hendricks Holding Company, Inc.; *U.S. Private*, pg. 1915
AVID PROPERTY GROUP; *Int'l*, pg. 743
AVID RADIOPHARMACEUTICALS, INC.—See Eli Lilly & Company; *U.S. Public*, pg. 731
AVIDSEN—See HF Company; *Int'l*, pg. 3374
AVID SYSTEMS, INC.—See Symphony Technology Group, LLC; *U.S. Private*, pg. 3901
AVID TECHNICAL RESOURCES, INC.; *U.S. Private*, pg. 407
AVID TECHNOLOGIES, INC.—See Avnet, Inc.; *U.S. Public*, pg. 254
AVID TECHNOLOGIES, INC.—See Avnet, Inc.; *U.S. Public*, pg. 249
AVID TECHNOLOGY CANADA CORP.—See Symphony Technology Group, LLC; *U.S. Private*, pg. 3901
AVID TECHNOLOGY EUROPE LTD—See Symphony Technology Group, LLC; *U.S. Private*, pg. 3901
AVID TECHNOLOGY GMBH—See Symphony Technology Group, LLC; *U.S. Private*, pg. 3901
AVID TECHNOLOGY HOLDING GMBH—See Symphony Technology Group, LLC; *U.S. Private*, pg. 3901
AVID TECHNOLOGY, INC. - MADISON—See Symphony Technology Group, LLC; *U.S. Private*, pg. 3901
AVID TECHNOLOGY, INC. (S.E. ASIA) PTE. LTD.—See Symphony Technology Group, LLC; *U.S. Private*, pg. 3901
AVID TECHNOLOGY, INC.—See Symphony Technology Group, LLC; *U.S. Private*, pg. 3901
AVID TECHNOLOGY INTERNATIONAL B.V.—See Symphony Technology Group, LLC; *U.S. Private*, pg. 3901
AVID TECHNOLOGY K.K.—See Symphony Technology Group, LLC; *U.S. Private*, pg. 3901
AVID TECHNOLOGY SALES LIMITED—See Symphony Technology Group, LLC; *U.S. Private*, pg. 3901
AVID TECHNOLOGY S.A.R.L—See Symphony Technology Group, LLC; *U.S. Private*, pg. 3901
AVID TECHNOLOGY (S.E. ASIA) PTE LTD—See Symphony Technology Group, LLC; *U.S. Private*, pg. 3901
AVID TECHNOLOGY S.L.—See Symphony Technology Group, LLC; *U.S. Private*, pg. 3901
AVIDXCHANGE HOLDINGS, INC.; *U.S. Public*, pg. 246
AVIDXCHANGE, INC.—See AvidXchange Holdings, Inc.; *U.S. Public*, pg. 246
AVIEL ELECTRONICS—See RF Industries, Ltd.; *U.S. Public*, pg. 1796
AVIENT ARGENTINA S.A.—See Avient Corporation; *U.S. Public*, pg. 246
AVIENT CANADA ULC—See Avient Corporation; *U.S. Public*, pg. 246
AVIENT CHILE S.P.A.—See Avient Corporation; *U.S. Public*, pg. 246
AVIENT COLORANTS BELGIUM SA—See Avient Corporation; *U.S. Public*, pg. 246
AVIENT COLORANTS ITALY S.R.L.—See Avient Corporation; *U.S. Public*, pg. 246
AVIENT COLORANTS MALAYSIA SDN. BHD.—See Avient Corporation; *U.S. Public*, pg. 246
AVIENT COLORANTS SINGAPORE PTE. LTD.—See Avient Corporation; *U.S. Public*, pg. 247
AVIENT COLORANTS SWITZERLAND AG—See Avient Corporation; *U.S. Public*, pg. 247
AVIENT COLORANTS (THAILAND) LTD.—See Avient Corporation; *U.S. Public*, pg. 246
AVIENT CORPORATION; *U.S. Public*, pg. 246
AVIENT FINLAND OY—See Avient Corporation; *U.S. Public*, pg. 247
AVIENT JAPAN K.K.—See Avient Corporation; *U.S. Public*, pg. 247
AVIENT LUXEMBOURG S.A R.L—See Avient Corporation; *U.S. Public*, pg. 247

AVIENT NEW ZEALAND LIMITED—See Avient Corporation; *U.S. Public*, pg. 247
AVIENT SAUDI INDUSTRIES CO., LTD.—See Avient Corporation; *U.S. Public*, pg. 247
AVIENT SINGAPORE PTE. LTD.—See Avient Corporation; *U.S. Public*, pg. 247
AVIENT (THAILAND) CO., LTD.—See Avient Corporation; *U.S. Public*, pg. 246
AVIENT TH. BERGMANN GMBH—See Avient Corporation; *U.S. Public*, pg. 247
AVIFIL SAS—See Parker Hannifin Corporation; *U.S. Public*, pg. 1640
AVI FINANCIAL SERVICES (PTY) LIMITED—See AVI Limited; *Int'l*, pg. 740
AVI FOODSYSTEMS INC.; *U.S. Private*, pg. 406
AVIGILON CORPORATION—See Motorola Solutions, Inc.; *U.S. Public*, pg. 1477
AVI GLOBAL TRUST PLC; *Int'l*, pg. 740
AVIGNON CAPITAL LIMITED; *Int'l*, pg. 743
THE AVI GROUP; *U.S. Private*, pg. 3990
AVI INTEGRATORS INC.—See Gemspring Capital Management, LLC; *U.S. Private*, pg. 1658
AVI JAPAN OPPORTUNITY TRUST PLC; *Int'l*, pg. 740
AVIKO B.V.—See Royal Cosun U.A.; *Int'l*, pg. 6411
AVILA CONSTRUCTION COMPANY INC; *U.S. Private*, pg. 407
AVILA'S GARDEN ART; *U.S. Private*, pg. 407
AVILA THERAPEUTICS, INC.—See Bristol-Myers Squibb Company; *U.S. Public*, pg. 386
AVILAVES GREDOS—See LDC SA; *Int'l*, pg. 4430
AVILEN, INC.; *Int'l*, pg. 743
AVI LIMITED; *Int'l*, pg. 740
AVI LION HOLDINGS LLC—See Access Value Investors LLC; *U.S. Private*, pg. 53
AVI LION HOLDINGS LLC—See Lion Equity Partners, LLC; *U.S. Private*, pg. 2463
AVILLION BERHAD; *Int'l*, pg. 743
AVILO MARKETING GESELLSCHAFT M. B. H.—See Metro AG; *Int'l*, pg. 4856
AVIMAC PTE. LTD.—See Frencken Group Limited; *Int'l*, pg. 2772
AVIMA (PTY) LTD—See Ascendis Health Limited; *Int'l*, pg. 601
AVINCO LTD.; *Int'l*, pg. 743
AVINEON, INC.; *U.S. Private*, pg. 407
AVINEON INDIA PRIVATE LIMITED—See Avineon, Inc.; *U.S. Private*, pg. 407
AVI NETWORKS B.V.—See Dell Technologies Inc.; *U.S. Public*, pg. 649
AVI NETWORKS GERMANY GMBH—See Dell Technologies Inc.; *U.S. Public*, pg. 649
AVI NETWORKS INDIA PRIVATE LIMITED—See Dell Technologies Inc.; *U.S. Public*, pg. 649
AVINGER, INC.; *U.S. Public*, pg. 248
AVINGTRANS PLC; *Int'l*, pg. 743
AVINODE AKTIEBOLAG—See World Kinect Corporation; *U.S. Public*, pg. 2380
AVINODE GROUP AB—See The Hearst Corporation; *U.S. Private*, pg. 4044
AVINODE, INC.—See World Kinect Corporation; *U.S. Public*, pg. 2380
AVIN OIL S.A.—See Motor Oil (Hellas) Corinth Refineries S. A.; *Int'l*, pg. 5053
AVINOR AS; *Int'l*, pg. 744
AVINOR FLYSIKRING AS—See Avinor AS; *Int'l*, pg. 744
AVINO SILVER & GOLD MINES LTD.; *Int'l*, pg. 744
AVINS INDUSTRIAL PRODUCTS CORPORATION; *U.S. Private*, pg. 407
AVINS USA, INC.—See Baoshida International Holding Group Co., Ltd.; *Int'l*, pg. 856
AVINTIV INC.—See Berry Global Group, Inc; *U.S. Public*, pg. 320
AVINTIV SPECIALTY MATERIALS INC.—See Berry Global Group, Inc; *U.S. Public*, pg. 320
AVINTOS AG—See Indutrade AB; *Int'l*, pg. 3677
AVIOANE CRAIOVA S.A.; *Int'l*, pg. 744
AVIO CREDIT, INC.—See CURO Group Holdings Corp.; *U.S. Public*, pg. 611
AVIO-DIEPEN B.V.—See Kirkhill Aircraft Parts Co.; *U.S. Private*, pg. 2314
AVIO-DIEPEN INC.—See Kirkhill Aircraft Parts Co.; *U.S. Private*, pg. 2314
AVIO EXCELENTE, S.A. DE C.V.—See KYOCERA Corporation; *Int'l*, pg. 4359
AVIO GLOBAL, INC.; *U.S. Private*, pg. 407
AVIO, INC.—See General Electric Company; *U.S. Public*, pg. 916
AVION DRONE (MALAYSIA) SDN. BHD.—See OCK Group Berhad; *Int'l*, pg. 5520
AVIONIC DESIGN GMBH—See Deutsche Lufthansa AG; *Int'l*, pg. 2066
AVIONIC INSTRUMENTS INC.—See TransDigm Group Incorporated; *U.S. Public*, pg. 2182
AVION LOGISTICS LIMITED—See General Dynamics Corporation; *U.S. Public*, pg. 913
AVIONOS, LLC—See AEA Investors LP; *U.S. Private*, pg. 114
AVIONS DE TRANSPORT REGIONAL—See Airbus SE; *Int'l*, pg. 246

COMPANY NAME INDEX

AVIONS DE TRANSPORT REGIONAL—See Leonardo S.p.A.; *Int'l*, pg. 4458
AVION SOLUTIONS, INC.; *U.S. Private*, pg. 407
AVIONTE; *U.S. Private*, pg. 407
AVIONYX, S.A.—See Joby Aviation, Inc.; *U.S. Public*, pg. 1190
AVIOPORT SPA—See Schiphol Group NV; *Int'l*, pg. 6621
AVIOQ INC.—See Shandong Oriental Ocean Sci-Tech Co., Ltd.; *Int'l*, pg. 6757
AVIOR INTEGRATED PRODUCTS—See Searchlight Capital Partners, L.P.; *U.S. Private*, pg. 3588
AVIOS GROUP LTD.—See International Consolidated Airlines Group S.A.; *Int'l*, pg. 3745
AVIO S.P.A.; *Int'l*, pg. 744
AVIOSUPPORT, INC.—See Avio Global, Inc.; *U.S. Private*, pg. 407
AVIOSYS TECHNOLOGIES CO., LTD.—See Korea Aerospace Industries Ltd.; *Int'l*, pg. 4281
AVI PARTNERS, LLC; *U.S. Private*, pg. 406
AVI POLYMERS LIMITED; *Int'l*, pg. 740
AVI PRODUCTS INDIA LIMITED; *Int'l*, pg. 741
AVIQUIPO DE PORTUGAL, LTDA—See Aerotech World Trade Corp.; *U.S. Private*, pg. 120
AVIRA RESOURCES LTD.; *Int'l*, pg. 744
AVIRE ELEVATOR TECHNOLOGY INDIA PTE. LTD.—See Halma plc; *Int'l*, pg. 3230
AVIRE ELEVATOR TECHNOLOGY SHANGHAI LTD.—See Halma plc; *Int'l*, pg. 3230
AVIRE GLOBAL PTE. LTD.—See Halma plc; *Int'l*, pg. 3230
AVIRE LIMITED—See Halma plc; *Int'l*, pg. 3230
AVIRE S.R.O.—See Halma plc; *Int'l*, pg. 3230
AVISA DIAGNOSTICS INC.; *Int'l*, pg. 744
AVIS AUTOVERMIETUNG AG—See Avis Budget Group, Inc.; *U.S. Public*, pg. 248
AVIS AUTOVERMIETUNG GESELLSCHAFT M.B.H—See Avis Budget Group, Inc.; *U.S. Public*, pg. 248
AVIS AUTOVERMIETUNG GMBH & CO KG—See Avis Budget Group, Inc.; *U.S. Public*, pg. 248
AVIS BELGIUM SA—See Avis Budget Group, Inc.; *U.S. Public*, pg. 248
AVIS BUDGET AUTO SERVICE GMBH—See Avis Budget Group, Inc.; *U.S. Public*, pg. 248
AVIS BUDGET AUTOVERHUUR BV—See Avis Budget Group, Inc.; *U.S. Public*, pg. 248
AVIS BUDGET AUTOVERMIETUNG AG—See Avis Budget Group, Inc.; *U.S. Public*, pg. 248
AVIS BUDGET DENMARK AS—See Avis Budget Group, Inc.; *U.S. Public*, pg. 248
AVIS BUDGET EMEA LTD—See Avis Budget Group, Inc.; *U.S. Public*, pg. 248
AVIS BUDGET EUROPE INTERNATIONAL REINSURANCE LIMITED—See Avis Budget Group, Inc.; *U.S. Public*, pg. 248
AVIS BUDGET GROUP, INC.; *U.S. Public*, pg. 248
AVIS BUDGET SERVICES LIMITED—See Avis Budget Group, Inc.; *U.S. Public*, pg. 248
AVIS BUDGET TECHNOLOGY INNOVATIONS PRIVATE LIMITED—See Avis Budget Group, Inc.; *U.S. Public*, pg. 248
AVIS CAR SALES, LLC—See Avis Budget Group, Inc.; *U.S. Public*, pg. 248
AVIS CAR SALES UTD, LLC—See Avis Budget Group, Inc.; *U.S. Public*, pg. 248
AVISCO INC.; *U.S. Private*, pg. 408
AVISENA, INC.; *U.S. Private*, pg. 408
AVISEN BV—See 1Spatial Plc; *Int'l*, pg. 3
AVISEN UK LIMITED—See 1Spatial Plc; *Int'l*, pg. 3
AVIS EUROPE PLC—See Avis Budget Group, Inc.; *U.S. Public*, pg. 248
AVIS FINANCE COMPANY PLC—See Avis Budget Group, Inc.; *U.S. Public*, pg. 248
AVIS FINANCIAL CORP.; *Int'l*, pg. 744
AVIS FORD INC.; *U.S. Private*, pg. 407
AVIS INDUSTRIAL CORPORATION; *U.S. Private*, pg. 407
AVISION BRASIL LTDA.—See Avision Inc.; *Int'l*, pg. 744
AVISION EUROPE GMBH—See Avision Inc.; *Int'l*, pg. 744
AVISION INC.; *Int'l*, pg. 744
AVISION LABS., INC.—See Avision Inc.; *Int'l*, pg. 744
AVISION SALES GROUP—See Osceola Capital Management, LLC; *U.S. Private*, pg. 3046
AVISION (SUZHOU) CO., LTD.—See Avision Inc.; *Int'l*, pg. 744
AVIS LOCATION DE VOITURES S.A R.L—See Avis Budget Group, Inc.; *U.S. Public*, pg. 248
AVISONIC TECHNOLOGY CORP.—See ELAN Microelectronic Corp.; *Int'l*, pg. 2342
AVISON YOUNG (CANADA) INC.; *Int'l*, pg. 744
AVISON YOUNG (USA) INC. - LOS ANGELES, NORTH—See Avison Young (Canada) Inc.; *Int'l*, pg. 744
AVISON YOUNG (USA) INC. - NEW JERSEY—See Avison Young (Canada) Inc.; *Int'l*, pg. 744
AVISON YOUNG (USA) INC. - RALEIGH-DURHAM—See Avison Young (Canada) Inc.; *Int'l*, pg. 744
AVISON YOUNG (USA) INC.—See Avison Young (Canada) Inc.; *Int'l*, pg. 744
AVISON YOUNG (USA) INC. - SOUTH FLORIDA-FORT LAUDERDALE—See Avison Young (Canada) Inc.; *Int'l*, pg. 745

AVISON YOUNG (USA) INC. - TAMPA—See Avison Young (Canada) Inc.; *Int'l*, pg. 745
AVI SPA SDN BHD—See Avillion Berhad; *Int'l*, pg. 743
AVI-SPL, INC. - CHICAGO—See Marlin Equity Partners, LLC; *U.S. Private*, pg. 2583
AVI-SPL, INC. - DALLAS—See Marlin Equity Partners, LLC; *U.S. Private*, pg. 2583
AVI-SPL, INC. - FORT LAUDERDALE—See Marlin Equity Partners, LLC; *U.S. Private*, pg. 2583
AVI-SPL, INC. - JACKSONVILLE—See Marlin Equity Partners, LLC; *U.S. Private*, pg. 2583
AVI-SPL, INC. - ORLANDO—See Marlin Equity Partners, LLC; *U.S. Private*, pg. 2583
AVI-SPL, INC.—See Marlin Equity Partners, LLC; *U.S. Private*, pg. 2583
AVI-SPL, INC. - TALLAHASSEE—See Marlin Equity Partners, LLC; *U.S. Private*, pg. 2583
AVI-SPL, INC. - WASHINGTON, D.C.—See Marlin Equity Partners, LLC; *U.S. Private*, pg. 2583
AVIS RENT A CAR LIMITED—See Avis Budget Group, Inc.; *U.S. Public*, pg. 248
AVIS RENT A CAR SYSTEM, LLC—See Avis Budget Group, Inc.; *U.S. Public*, pg. 248
AVISRETUR AS—See Schibsted ASA; *Int'l*, pg. 6618
AVI S.R.L.—See Interpump Group S.p.A.; *Int'l*, pg. 3756
AVIS SOUTHERN AFRICA LTD.—See Barloworld Ltd.; *Int'l*, pg. 866
AVISTA CAPITAL HOLDINGS, L.P.—See Avista Capital Partners, L.P.; *U.S. Private*, pg. 408
AVISTA CAPITAL, INC.—See Avista Corporation; *U.S. Public*, pg. 249
AVISTA CAPITAL PARTNERS, L.P.; *U.S. Private*, pg. 408
AVISTA CORPORATION; *U.S. Public*, pg. 249
AVISTA INCORPORATED—See AE Industrial Partners, LP; *U.S. Private*, pg. 111
AVISTA OIL AG; *Int'l*, pg. 745
AVISTA OIL DANMARK A/S—See Avista Oil AG; *Int'l*, pg. 745
AVISTA TECHNOLOGIES, INC.—See Kurita Water Industries Ltd.; *Int'l*, pg. 4340
AVISTA TECHNOLOGIES (UK) LTD.—See Kurita Water Industries Ltd.; *Int'l*, pg. 4340
AVISTA UTILITIES—See Avista Corporation; *U.S. Public*, pg. 249
AVISTO CAPITAL PARTNERS, LLC; *U.S. Private*, pg. 409
AVI SYSTEMS COMPANY—See AVI Systems, Inc.; *U.S. Private*, pg. 406
AVI SYSTEMS, INC.; *U.S. Private*, pg. 406
AVITA DRUGS LLC—See Tailwind Capital Group, LLC; *U.S. Private*, pg. 3924
AVITA HEALTH SYSTEM; *U.S. Private*, pg. 409
AVITA MEDICAL AMERICAS LLC—See Avita Medical, Inc.; *U.S. Public*, pg. 249
AVITA MEDICAL EUROPE LTD.—See Avita Medical, Inc.; *U.S. Public*, pg. 249
AVITA MEDICAL, INC.; *U.S. Public*, pg. 249
AVITAS INC.; *U.S. Private*, pg. 409
AVITEA GMBH—See Hella GmbH & Co. KGaA; *Int'l*, pg. 3333
AVITEA INDUSTRIESERVICE GMBH—See Hella GmbH & Co. KGaA; *Int'l*, pg. 3333
AVI-TECH ELECTRONICS PTE. LTD.—See Avi-Tech Holdings Limited; *Int'l*, pg. 741
AVITECH GMBH—See Indra Sistemas, S.A.; *Int'l*, pg. 3659
AVI-TECH HOLDINGS LIMITED; *Int'l*, pg. 741
AVI-TECH, INC.—See Avi-Tech Holdings Limited; *Int'l*, pg. 741
AVITECH S.R.O.—See Indra Sistemas, S.A.; *Int'l*, pg. 3659
AVITIDE, INC.; *U.S. Private*, pg. 409
AVIT LTD.; *Int'l*, pg. 745
AVITOOLS (SUZHOU) CO., LTD.—See Nordic Group Limited; *Int'l*, pg. 5422
AVITRON PRIVATE LIMITED—See SAM Engineering & Equipment (M) Berhad; *Int'l*, pg. 6500
AVITRU, LLC—See Roper Technologies, Inc.; *U.S. Public*, pg. 1810
AVITUM S.R.L—See B. Braun Melsungen AG; *Int'l*, pg. 786
AVITUS ORTHOPAEDICS, INC.—See Zimmer Biomet Holdings, Inc.; *U.S. Public*, pg. 2405
AVIVA ANNUITY UK LIMITED—See Aviva plc; *Int'l*, pg. 745
AVIVA ASSURANCES SA—See Aema Groupe; *Int'l*, pg. 175
AVIVA CANADA INC.—See Aviva plc; *Int'l*, pg. 745
AVIVA CENTRAL SERVICES UK LIMITED—See Aviva plc; *Int'l*, pg. 745
AVIVA-COFCO LIFE INSURANCE CO., LTD.—See COFCO Limited; *Int'l*, pg. 1691
AVIVA EQUITY RELEASE UK LIMITED—See Aviva plc; *Int'l*, pg. 745
AVIVA FRANCE—See Aema Groupe; *Int'l*, pg. 175
AVIVA GROUP HOLDINGS LIMITED—See Aviva plc; *Int'l*, pg. 745
AVIVA GROUP IRELAND PLC—See Aviva plc; *Int'l*, pg. 745
AVIVA HEALTH UK LIMITED—See Aviva plc; *Int'l*, pg. 745
AVIVA INDUSTRIES LIMITED; *Int'l*, pg. 745
AVIVA INSURANCE COMPANY OF CANADA—See Aviva plc; *Int'l*, pg. 745

AVIVA INSURANCE EUROPE SE—See Aviva plc; *Int'l*, pg. 745
AVIVA INSURANCE IRELAND DESIGNATED ACTIVITY COMPANY—See Aviva plc; *Int'l*, pg. 745
AVIVA INSURANCE LIMITED—See Aviva plc; *Int'l*, pg. 745
AVIVA INSURANCE UK LIMITED—See Aviva plc; *Int'l*, pg. 745
AVIVA INVESTORS AUSTRALIA LIMITED—See National Australia Bank Limited; *Int'l*, pg. 5151
AVIVA INVESTORS CANADA INC.—See Aviva plc; *Int'l*, pg. 745
AVIVA INVESTORS FRANCE SA—See Aviva plc; *Int'l*, pg. 745
AVIVA INVESTORS GLOBAL SERVICES LIMITED—See Aviva plc; *Int'l*, pg. 745
AVIVA INVESTORS HOLDINGS LIMITED—See Aviva plc; *Int'l*, pg. 745
AVIVA INVESTORS NORTH AMERICA, INC.—See Aviva plc; *Int'l*, pg. 745
AVIVA INVESTORS REAL ESTATE FRANCE S.A.—See Aviva plc; *Int'l*, pg. 746
AVIVA INVESTORS SCHWEIZ GMBH—See Aviva plc; *Int'l*, pg. 746
AVIVA INVESTORS UK FUND SERVICES LIMITED—See Aviva plc; *Int'l*, pg. 745
AVIVA ITALIA HOLDING S.P.A—See Aviva plc; *Int'l*, pg. 746
AVIVA ITALIA S.P.A—See Allianz SE; *Int'l*, pg. 350
AVIVA LIFE & PENSIONS IRELAND LTD.—See Aviva plc; *Int'l*, pg. 745
AVIVA LIFE & PENSIONS UK LIMITED—See Aviva plc; *Int'l*, pg. 746
AVIVA LIMITED—See Aviva plc; *Int'l*, pg. 746
AVIVA PLC; *Int'l*, pg. 745
AVIVA POWSZECHNE TOWARZYSTWO EMERYTALNE AVIVA BZ WBK S.A.—See Aviva plc; *Int'l*, pg. 746
AVIVA RISK MANAGEMENT SOLUTIONS UK LIMITED—See Aviva plc; *Int'l*, pg. 746
AVIVA SYSTEM BIOLOGY CORPORATION—See Level Biotechnology, Inc.; *Int'l*, pg. 4470
AVIVA TOWARZYSTWO UBEZPIECZEN NA ZYCIE SA—See Aviva plc; *Int'l*, pg. 746
AVIVA TOWARZYSTWO UBEZPIECZEN OGOLNYCH SA—See Aviva plc; *Int'l*, pg. 746
AVIVA VIE S.A.—See Aema Groupe; *Int'l*, pg. 175
AVIV CENTERS FOR LIVING; *U.S. Private*, pg. 409
AVIX, INC.; *Int'l*, pg. 746
AVIX TECHNOLOGIES, INC.; *U.S. Public*, pg. 249
AVIZIA INC.—See American Well Corporation; *U.S. Public*, pg. 112
AVJENNINGS LIMITED—See SC Global Developments Limited; *Int'l*, pg. 6609
AVJET ASIA CO., LTD.—See Avjet Corporation; *U.S. Private*, pg. 409
AVJET CORPORATION; *U.S. Private*, pg. 409
AVKARE, INC.—See Amneal Pharmaceuticals, Inc.; *U.S. Public*, pg. 125
AVK ARMADAN SP. Z O.O.—See AVK Holding A/S; *Int'l*, pg. 746
AVK AUSTRALIA PTY LTD—See AVK Holding A/S; *Int'l*, pg. 746
AVK BELGIUM NV—See AVK Holding A/S; *Int'l*, pg. 746
AVK FINLAND OY—See AVK Holding A/S; *Int'l*, pg. 746
AVK FLOW CONTROL A/S—See AVK Holding A/S; *Int'l*, pg. 746
AVK FRANCE S.A.S.—See AVK Holding A/S; *Int'l*, pg. 746
AVK GUMMI A/S—See AVK Holding A/S; *Int'l*, pg. 746
AVK HAUT MARNAISE S.A.S.—See AVK Holding A/S; *Int'l*, pg. 747
AVK HOLDING A/S; *Int'l*, pg. 746
AVK INDUSTRIAL PTY LTD—See AVK Holding A/S; *Int'l*, pg. 747
AVK INDUSTRIAL VALVE SINGAPORE PTE. LTD.—See AVK Holding A/S; *Int'l*, pg. 747
AVK ITALIA S.R.L.—See AVK Holding A/S; *Int'l*, pg. 747
AVK MITTELMANN ARMATUREN GMBH—See AVK Holding A/S; *Int'l*, pg. 747
AVK NEDERLAND B.V.—See AVK Holding A/S; *Int'l*, pg. 747
AVK NORGE AS—See AVK Holding A/S; *Int'l*, pg. 747
AVK PHILIPPINES INC.—See AVK Holding A/S; *Int'l*, pg. 747
AVK PLAST A/S—See AVK Holding A/S; *Int'l*, pg. 747
AVK PLASTICS B.V.—See AVK Holding A/S; *Int'l*, pg. 747
AVK SEALING TECHNOLOGY (KUNSHAN) CO. LTD.—See AVK Holding A/S; *Int'l*, pg. 747
AVK SVERIGE AB—See AVK Holding A/S; *Int'l*, pg. 747
AVK SYDDAL LTD.—See AVK Holding A/S; *Int'l*, pg. 747
AVK SYNTEC (ANHUI) CO. LTD.—See AVK Holding A/S; *Int'l*, pg. 747
AVK TOOLING A/S—See AVK Holding A/S; *Int'l*, pg. 747
AVK UK LIMITED—See AVK Holding A/S; *Int'l*, pg. 747
AVK VALVES (ANHUI) CO., LTD.—See AVK Holding A/S; *Int'l*, pg. 747
AVK VALVES (BEIJING) CO LTD—See AVK Holding A/S; *Int'l*, pg. 747
AVK VALVES COMPANY HONG KONG LTD.—See AVK Holding A/S; *Int'l*, pg. 747

AVK HOLDING A/S

AVK VALVES INDIA PVT. LTD.—See AVK Holding A/S; *Int'l*, pg. 747
AVK VALVES KOREA CO., LTD.—See AVK Holding A/S; *Int'l*, pg. 747
AVK VALVES MANUFACTURING MALAYSIA SDN. BHD.—See AVK Holding A/S; *Int'l*, pg. 747
AVK VALVES (SHANGHAI) CO. LTD.—See AVK Holding A/S; *Int'l*, pg. 747
AVK VALVES SOUTHERN AFRICA PTY. LTD.—See AVK Holding A/S; *Int'l*, pg. 747
AVK VALVULAS DO BRASIL LTDA.—See AVK Holding A/S; *Int'l*, pg. 747
AVK VALVULAS S.A.—See AVK Holding A/S; *Int'l*, pg. 747
AVK VIETNAM CO., LTD.—See AVK Holding A/S; *Int'l*, pg. 747
AVK VOD-KA A.S.—See AVK Holding A/S; *Int'l*, pg. 747
AVLA PERU COMPANIA DE SEGUROS SA; *Int'l*, pg. 748
AVL AST D.O.O.—See AVL List GmbH; *Int'l*, pg. 748
AVL AUTOKUT ENGINEERING LTD.—See AVL List GmbH; *Int'l*, pg. 748
AVL CECHY SPOL. S R.O.—See AVL List GmbH; *Int'l*, pg. 748
AVL DEUTSCHLAND GMBH—See AVL List GmbH; *Int'l*, pg. 748
AVL FRANCE S.A.—See AVL List GmbH; *Int'l*, pg. 748
AVL IBERICA S.A.—See AVL List GmbH; *Int'l*, pg. 748
AVL ITALY S.R.L.—See AVL List GmbH; *Int'l*, pg. 748
AVL LIST GMBH; *Int'l*, pg. 748
AVL LIST NORDISKA AB—See AVL List GmbH; *Int'l*, pg. 748
AVL MICHIGAN HOLDING CORPORATION—See AVL List GmbH; *Int'l*, pg. 748
AVL NORTH AMERICA INC.—See AVL List GmbH; *Int'l*, pg. 748
AVL POWERTRAIN ENGINEERING, INC.—See AVL List GmbH; *Int'l*, pg. 748
AVL UNITED KINGDOM LIMITED—See AVL List GmbH; *Int'l*, pg. 748
AVM ASSOCIATES LLC; *U.S. Private*, pg. 409
A V MATTERS—See Harbor Beach Capital, LLC; *U.S. Private*, pg. 1858
AVMAX AVIONICS—See Avmax Group Inc.; *Int'l*, pg. 748
AVMAX ENGINEERING—See Avmax Group Inc.; *Int'l*, pg. 748
AVMAX GROUP INC.; *Int'l*, pg. 748
AVMAX MONTANA, INC.—See Avmax Group Inc.; *Int'l*, pg. 748
AVMAX SPARES EAST AFRICA LIMITED—See Avmax Group Inc.; *Int'l*, pg. 748
AVMED HEALTH PLANS—See SantaFe Healthcare, Inc.; *U.S. Private*, pg. 3547
AVM IMPACT LTD.—See Kinly Holding B.V.; *Int'l*, pg. 4181
AVM, INC.—See Cummins Inc.; *U.S. Public*, pg. 608
AVMOR LTEE; *Int'l*, pg. 748
AVN ABFALLVERWERTUNG NIEDEROSTERREICH GMBH—See EVN AG; *Int'l*, pg. 2570
AV NACKAWIC INC—See The Aditya Birla Group; *Int'l*, pg. 7612
AVN CORPORATION; *U.S. Private*, pg. 409
AVNERA CORPORATION—See Skyworks Solutions, Inc.; *U.S. Public*, pg. 1893
AVNET ABACUS HERLEV—See TD Synnex Corp; *U.S. Public*, pg. 1985
AVNET ABACUS MADRID—See TD Synnex Corp; *U.S. Public*, pg. 1985
AVNET ASIA PTE LTD—See Ingredion Incorporated; *U.S. Public*, pg. 1123
AVNET ASIC ISRAEL LTD—See Avnet, Inc.; *U.S. Public*, pg. 250
AVNET B.V.—See Avnet, Inc.; *U.S. Public*, pg. 250
AVNET CHILE S.A.—See Avnet, Inc.; *U.S. Public*, pg. 250
AVNET COMPONENTS BRASIL PARTICIPACOES LTDA.—See Avnet, Inc.; *U.S. Public*, pg. 250
AVNET COMPONENTS ISRAEL LIMITED—See Avnet, Inc.; *U.S. Public*, pg. 250
AVNET COMPONENTS LTD.—See Avnet, Inc.; *U.S. Public*, pg. 250
AVNET COMPUTER SERVICE (HONG KONG) LIMITED—See Avnet, Inc.; *U.S. Public*, pg. 250
AVNET COMPUTER SERVICE (MACAU) LIMITED—See Avnet, Inc.; *U.S. Public*, pg. 250
AVNET DE MEXICO, S.A. DE C.V.—See Avnet, Inc.; *U.S. Public*, pg. 252
AVNET DE PUERTO RICO, INC.—See Avnet, Inc.; *U.S. Public*, pg. 252
AVNET DO BRASIL LTDA—See Avnet, Inc.; *U.S. Public*, pg. 252
AVNET D.O.O. BEOGRAD—See Avnet, Inc.; *U.S. Public*, pg. 252
AVNET D. O. O.—See Avnet, Inc.; *U.S. Public*, pg. 252
AVNET ELECTRONICS MARKETING (AUSTRALIA) PTY LTD—See Ingredion Incorporated; *U.S. Public*, pg. 1123
AVNET ELECTRONICS MARKETING—See Avnet, Inc.; *U.S. Public*, pg. 250
AVNET ELECTRONICS MARKETING—See Avnet, Inc.; *U.S. Public*, pg. 250
AVNET ELECTRONICS MARKETING—See Avnet, Inc.; *U.S. Public*, pg. 250
AVNET ELECTRONICS MARKETING—See Avnet, Inc.; *U.S. Public*, pg. 250
AVNET ELECTRONICS MARKETING—See Avnet, Inc.; *U.S. Public*, pg. 250
AVNET ELECTRONICS MARKETING—See Avnet, Inc.; *U.S. Public*, pg. 250
AVNET ELECTRONICS MARKETING—See Avnet, Inc.; *U.S. Public*, pg. 250
AVNET ELECTRONICS MARKETING—See Avnet, Inc.; *U.S. Public*, pg. 250
AVNET ELECTRONICS MARKETING—See Avnet, Inc.; *U.S. Public*, pg. 250
AVNET ELECTRONICS TECHNOLOGY (SHENZHEN) LIMITED—See Avnet, Inc.; *U.S. Public*, pg. 251
AVNET ELECTRONICS TURKEY ITHALAT IHRACAT SANAYI VE TICARET LIMITED SIRKETI—See Avnet, Inc.; *U.S. Public*, pg. 251
AVNET EMBEDDED (FREIBURG) GMBH—See Avnet, Inc.; *U.S. Public*, pg. 251
AVNET EMBEDDED GMBH—See Avnet, Inc.; *U.S. Public*, pg. 251
AVNET EMBEDDED INDUSTRIA E COMERCIO LTDA—See Avnet, Inc.; *U.S. Public*, pg. 251
AVNET EMG AG—See Avnet, Inc.; *U.S. Public*, pg. 250
AVNET EMG ELEKTRONISCHE BAUELEMENTE GMBH—See Avnet, Inc.; *U.S. Public*, pg. 250
AVNET EMG ELEKTRONISCHE BAUELMENTE GMBH—See Avnet, Inc.; *U.S. Public*, pg. 250
AVNET EMG FRANCE S.A.—See Avnet, Inc.; *U.S. Public*, pg. 250
AVNET EMG FRANCE—See Avnet, Inc.; *U.S. Public*, pg. 250
AVNET EMG GMBH—See Avnet, Inc.; *U.S. Public*, pg. 250
AVNET EMG ITALY S.R.L.—See Avnet, Inc.; *U.S. Public*, pg. 250
AVNET EMG LTD.—See Avnet, Inc.; *U.S. Public*, pg. 250
AVNET EM SP. Z O O.—See Avnet, Inc.; *U.S. Public*, pg. 250
AVNET EM SP. Z O O.—See Avnet, Inc.; *U.S. Public*, pg. 250
AVNET ENTERPRISE SOLUTIONS—See Avnet, Inc.; *U.S. Public*, pg. 251
AVNET EUROPE BV—See Avnet, Inc.; *U.S. Public*, pg. 251
AVNET EUROPE EXECUTIVE BVBA—See Avnet, Inc.; *U.S. Public*, pg. 251
AVNET FINANCE B.V.—See Avnet, Inc.; *U.S. Public*, pg. 251
AVNET (HOLDINGS) LTD—See Avnet, Inc.; *U.S. Public*, pg. 250
AVNET HOLDINGS UK LIMITED—See Avnet, Inc.; *U.S. Public*, pg. 251
AVNET HONG KONG LIMITED—See Avnet, Inc.; *U.S. Public*, pg. 251
AVNET IBERIA S.A.—See Avnet, Inc.; *U.S. Public*, pg. 251
AVNET, INC.; *U.S. Public*, pg. 249
AVNET INTEGRATED RESOURCES REPARO DE ELETRONICOS LTDA.—See Avnet, Inc.; *U.S. Public*, pg. 251
AVNET INTERNATIONAL (CANADA) LTD.—See Avnet, Inc.; *U.S. Public*, pg. 251
AVNET JAPAN (ASIA) LIMITED—See Avnet, Inc.; *U.S. Public*, pg. 251
AVNET JAPAN (HK) LIMITED—See Avnet, Inc.; *U.S. Public*, pg. 251
AVNET JAPAN (MALAYSIA) SDN. BHD.—See Avnet, Inc.; *U.S. Public*, pg. 251
AVNET JAPAN (SINGAPORE) PTE LTD.—See Avnet, Inc.; *U.S. Public*, pg. 251
AVNET KABUSHIKI KAISHA—See Avnet, Inc.; *U.S. Public*, pg. 251
AVNET KOPP (PTY) LIMITED—See Avnet, Inc.; *U.S. Public*, pg. 251
AVNET KOREA, INC.—See Ingredion Incorporated; *U.S. Public*, pg. 1123
AVNET LOGISTICS B.V.B.A.—See Avnet, Inc.; *U.S. Public*, pg. 251
AVNET LOGISTICS DO BRASIL LTDA.—See Avnet, Inc.; *U.S. Public*, pg. 251
AVNET LOGISTICS GMBH—See Avnet, Inc.; *U.S. Public*, pg. 251
AVNET LOGISTICS PMC STUTENSEE GMBH—See Avnet, Inc.; *U.S. Public*, pg. 251
AVNET LOGISTICS—See Avnet, Inc.; *U.S. Public*, pg. 251
AVNET LOGISTICS STUTENSEE GMBH—See Avnet, Inc.; *U.S. Public*, pg. 251
AVNET MALAYSIA SDN BHD—See Avnet, Inc.; *U.S. Public*, pg. 251
AVNET MAX LIMITED—See STMicroelectronics N.V.; *Int'l*, pg. 7217
AVNET NORTEC AB—See Avnet, Inc.; *U.S. Public*, pg. 252
AVNET NORTEC A/S—See Avnet, Inc.; *U.S. Public*, pg. 252
AVNET NORTEC AS—See Avnet, Inc.; *U.S. Public*, pg. 252
AVNET NORTEC OY—See Avnet, Inc.; *U.S. Public*, pg. 252
AVNET (NZ)—See Avnet, Inc.; *U.S. Public*, pg. 250
AVNET PARTNER SOLUTIONS, S. DE R.L. DE C.V.—See Avnet, Inc.; *U.S. Public*, pg. 252

CORPORATE AFFILIATIONS

AVNET (SHANGHAI) LIMITED—See Ingredion Incorporated; *U.S. Public*, pg. 1123
AVNET SILICA—See Avnet, Inc.; *U.S. Public*, pg. 250
AVNET SILICA—See Avnet, Inc.; *U.S. Public*, pg. 250
AVNET SILICA—See Avnet, Inc.; *U.S. Public*, pg. 250
AVNET SILICA—See Avnet, Inc.; *U.S. Public*, pg. 250
AVNET SILICA—See Avnet, Inc.; *U.S. Public*, pg. 251
AVNET SOLUTIONS PTE. LTD.—See Avnet, Inc.; *U.S. Public*, pg. 252
AVNET SP. Z.O.O.—See Avnet, Inc.; *U.S. Public*, pg. 252
AVNET S.R.L.—See Avnet, Inc.; *U.S. Public*, pg. 252
AVNET S.R.O.—See Avnet, Inc.; *U.S. Public*, pg. 252
AVNET TECHNOLOGY ELECTRONICS MARKETING (TAIWAN) CO., LTD.—See Avnet, Inc.; *U.S. Public*, pg. 252
AVNET TECHNOLOGY SOLUTIONS (CHINA) LTD—See TD Synnex Corp; *U.S. Public*, pg. 1985
AVNET TECHNOLOGY SOLUTIONS—See TD Synnex Corp; *U.S. Public*, pg. 1985
AVNET TECHNOLOGY SOLUTIONS (TIANJIN) LTD—See TD Synnex Corp; *U.S. Public*, pg. 1985
AVNET TECHNOLOGY (THAILAND) LTD.—See TD Synnex Corp; *U.S. Public*, pg. 1985
AVNET TIME—See Avnet, Inc.; *U.S. Public*, pg. 251
AVNET UNIDUX (HK) LIMITED—See Avnet, Inc.; *U.S. Public*, pg. 252
AVNET UNIDUX (MALAYSIA) SDN. BHD.—See Avnet, Inc.; *U.S. Public*, pg. 252
AVNET UNIDUX (THAILAND) COMPANY LIMITED—See Avnet, Inc.; *U.S. Public*, pg. 252
AVOCADO RESEARCH CHEMICALS LIMITED—See Thermo Fisher Scientific Inc.; *U.S. Public*, pg. 2145
THE AVOCA GROUP, INC.—See Leonard Green & Partners, L.P.; *U.S. Private*, pg. 2430
AVOCA HANDWEAVERS DESIGNS LIMITED—See Aramark; *U.S. Public*, pg. 178
AVOCA HANDWEAVERS LIMITED—See Aramark; *U.S. Public*, pg. 177
AVOCA HANDWEAVERS SHOPS LIMITED—See Aramark; *U.S. Public*, pg. 177
AVOCA, INC.—See Ashland Inc.; *U.S. Public*, pg. 213
AVOCENT BELGIUM LIMITED BVBA/SPRL—See Vertiv Holdings Co; *U.S. Public*, pg. 2288
AVOCENT CORPORATION—See Vertiv Holdings Co; *U.S. Public*, pg. 2288
AVOCENT DO BRASIL INFORMATICA S.A.—See Vertiv Holdings Co; *U.S. Public*, pg. 2288
AVOCENT FREMONT CORP.—See Vertiv Holdings Co; *U.S. Public*, pg. 2288
AVOCENT HUNTSVILLE, LLC—See Vertiv Holdings Co; *U.S. Public*, pg. 2288
AVOCENT INTERNATIONAL LIMITED—See Vertiv Holdings Co; *U.S. Public*, pg. 2288
AVOCENT JAPAN KK—See Emerson Electric Co.; *U.S. Public*, pg. 742
AVOCENT REDMOND CORP.—See Vertiv Holdings Co; *U.S. Public*, pg. 2288
AVOCENT SWEDEN AB—See Vertiv Holdings Co; *U.S. Public*, pg. 2288
AVOCET GOLD LIMITED—See Avocet Mining PLC; *Int'l*, pg. 749
AVOCET HARDWARE LTD.; *Int'l*, pg. 748
AVOCET MINING PLC; *Int'l*, pg. 749
A.V.O.D. KURUTULMUS GIDA VE TARIM URUNLERI SAN. TIC. A.S.; *Int'l*, pg. 28
AVOFUN EUROPE S.L.—See Dole plc; *Int'l*, pg. 2157
AVOKA TECHNOLOGIES PTY LIMITED—See Temenos AG; *Int'l*, pg. 7554
AVOLON HOLDINGS LIMITED—See Hainan Traffic Administration Holding Co., Ltd.; *Int'l*, pg. 3213
A.V. OLSSON TRADING CO. INC.; *U.S. Private*, pg. 28
AVOLTA AG; *Int'l*, pg. 749
AVOMARK INSURANCE CO.—See Liberty Mutual Holding Company Inc.; *U.S. Private*, pg. 2446
AVO MULTI-AMP CORPORATION—See Megger Group Limited; *Int'l*, pg. 4794
AVO MULTI-AMP CORP. - VALLEY FORGE—See Megger Group Limited; *Int'l*, pg. 4794
AVON BEAUTY PRODUCTS INDIA PVT. LTD.—See Natura & Co Holding S.A.; *Int'l*, pg. 5166
AVON BEAUTY PRODUCTS, SARL—See Natura & Co Holding S.A.; *Int'l*, pg. 5166
AVON CITY MOTORCYCLES LTD.—See The Colonial Motor Company Limited; *Int'l*, pg. 7634
AVON CITY MOTORS LTD—See The Colonial Motor Company Limited; *Int'l*, pg. 7634
AVON COLOMBIA LTDA.—See Natura & Co Holding S.A.; *Int'l*, pg. 5166
AVON CORPORATION LTD.; *Int'l*, pg. 749
AVON COSMETICAS, LTD.—See Natura & Co Holding S.A.; *Int'l*, pg. 5166
AVON COSMETICOS, LTDA.—See Natura & Co Holding S.A.; *Int'l*, pg. 5166
AVON COSMETICS BULGARIA EOOD—See Natura & Co Holding S.A.; *Int'l*, pg. 5166
AVON COSMETICS DE VENEZUELA, C.A.—See Natura & Co Holding S.A.; *Int'l*, pg. 5166
AVON COSMETICS EGYPT, S.A.E—See Natura & Co Holding S.A.; *Int'l*, pg. 5166

COMPANY NAME INDEX

AVON COSMETICS FINLAND OY—See Natura & Co Holding S.A.; *Int'l*, pg. 5166
AVON COSMETICS GMBH—See Natura & Co Holding S.A.; *Int'l*, pg. 5166
AVON COSMETICS (GREECE) SOLE PARTNER LTD.—See Natura & Co Holding S.A.; *Int'l*, pg. 5166
AVON COSMETICS HUNGARY KOZMETIKAI CIKK KERESKEDELMI KFT.—See Natura & Co Holding S.A.; *Int'l*, pg. 5166
AVON COSMETICS, INC.—See Natura & Co Holding S.A.; *Int'l*, pg. 5166
AVON COSMETICS LIMITED—See Natura & Co Holding S.A.; *Int'l*, pg. 5166
AVON COSMETICS LTD.—See Natura & Co Holding S.A.; *Int'l*, pg. 5166
AVON COSMETICS (MALAYSIA) SDN. BHD.—See Natura & Co Holding S.A.; *Int'l*, pg. 5166
AVON COSMETICS (MOLDOVA) S.R.L.—See Natura & Co Holding S.A.; *Int'l*, pg. 5166
AVON COSMETICS POLSKA SP ZOO—See Natura & Co Holding S.A.; *Int'l*, pg. 5166
AVON COSMETICS (ROMANIA) S.R.L.—See Natura & Co Holding S.A.; *Int'l*, pg. 5166
AVON COSMETICS, S.A. DE C.V.—See Natura & Co Holding S.A.; *Int'l*, pg. 5167
AVON COSMETICS, S.A.—See Natura & Co Holding S.A.; *Int'l*, pg. 5167
AVON COSMETICS SIA—See Natura & Co Holding S.A.; *Int'l*, pg. 5166
AVON COSMETICS, S.P.A.—See Natura & Co Holding S.A.; *Int'l*, pg. 5167
AVON COSMETICS S.R.L. A SOCIO UNICO—See Natura & Co Holding S.A.; *Int'l*, pg. 5166
AVON COSMETICS SRO—See Natura & Co Holding S.A.; *Int'l*, pg. 5166
AVON COSMETICS (TAIWAN) LTD.—See Natura & Co Holding S.A.; *Int'l*, pg. 5166
AVON COSMETICS (THAILAND) LTD.—See Natura & Co Holding S.A.; *Int'l*, pg. 5166
AVON COSMETICS (UKRAINE)—See Natura & Co Holding S.A.; *Int'l*, pg. 5166
AVON COSMETICS (VIETNAM) LIMITED—See Natura & Co Holding S.A.; *Int'l*, pg. 5166
AVONDALE ADVISORS, LLC—See Avondale Partners, LLC; *U.S. Private*, pg. 410
AVONDALE CONSULTING; *U.S. Private*, pg. 410
AVONDALE FOOD STORES LIMITED; *Int'l*, pg. 750
AVONDALE PARTNERS, LLC; *U.S. Private*, pg. 410
AVONDALE SECURITIES S.A.—See Bank of Ireland Group plc; *Int'l*, pg. 844
AVONDALE STRATEGIC PARTNERS; *U.S. Private*, pg. 410
THE AVON-DIXON AGENCY, LLC—See Genstar Capital, LLC; *U.S. Private*, pg. 1675
AVON EESTI OU—See Natura & Co Holding S.A.; *Int'l*, pg. 5167
AVON EMEA FINANCE SERVICE CENTRE SPOLKA Z O.O.—See Natura & Co Holding S.A.; *Int'l*, pg. 5167
AVON ENGINEERED FABRICATIONS, INC—See Avon Protection plc; *Int'l*, pg. 750
AVON FOUNDATION—See Natura & Co Holding S.A.; *Int'l*, pg. 5167
AVON HI-LIFE INC.—See Avon Protection plc; *Int'l*, pg. 750
AVON INDUSTRIAL LTDA.—See Natura & Co Holding S.A.; *Int'l*, pg. 5167
AVON INFLATABLES LTD.—See The Carlyle Group Inc.; *U.S. Public*, pg. 2057
AVON KOZMETIKA DOO—See Natura & Co Holding S.A.; *Int'l*, pg. 5167
AVON KOZMETIK URUNLERI SANAYI VE TICARET ANONIM SIRKETI—See Natura & Co Holding S.A.; *Int'l*, pg. 5167
AVON LAKE ENVIRONMENTAL REDEVELOPMENT GROUP, LLC—See SER Capital Partners LLC; *U.S. Private*, pg. 3612
AVON LIPPIATT HOBBS (CONTRACTING) LIMITED; *Int'l*, pg. 749
AVON MACHINING LLC—See Auxo Investment Partners, LLC; *U.S. Private*, pg. 402
AVON MERCANTILE LIMITED; *Int'l*, pg. 749
AVON MILK-RITE USA INC.—See Avon Protection plc; *Int'l*, pg. 750
AVONMORE CAPITAL & MANAGEMENT SERVICES LTD.; *Int'l*, pg. 750
AVON OPERATIONS POLSKA SP. Z O.O.—See Natura & Co Holding S.A.; *Int'l*, pg. 5167
AVON PLASTICS, INC.; *U.S. Private*, pg. 410
AVON POLYMER PRODUCTS LIMITED—See Avon Protection plc; *Int'l*, pg. 750
AVON PRODUCTS (CHINA) CO., LTD.—See Natura & Co Holding S.A.; *Int'l*, pg. 5167
AVON PRODUCTS (FEBO) LTD.—See Natura & Co Holding S.A.; *Int'l*, pg. 5167
AVON PRODUCTS, INC.—See Natura & Co Holding S.A.; *Int'l*, pg. 5166
AVON PRODUCTS MANUFACTURING, INC.—See Natura & Co Holding S.A.; *Int'l*, pg. 5167

AVON PRODUCTS PTY. LTD.—See Natura & Co Holding S.A.; *Int'l*, pg. 5167
AVON PROTECTION PLC; *Int'l*, pg. 749
AVON PROTECTION SYSTEMS, INC.—See Avon Protection plc; *Int'l*, pg. 750
AVON RUBBER OVERSEAS LIMITED—See Avon Protection plc; *Int'l*, pg. 750
AVON RUBBER PENSION TRUST LIMITED—See Avon Protection plc; *Int'l*, pg. 750
AVON RUBBER & PLASTICS INC.—See Avon Protection plc; *Int'l*, pg. 750
AVON SAS—See Natura & Co Holding S.A.; *Int'l*, pg. 5167
AVONSIDE GROUP SERVICES LIMITED; *Int'l*, pg. 750
AVON SOLUTIONS & LOGISTICS PRIVATE LIMITED—See Updater Services Limited; *Int'l*, pg. 8087
AVON WESCO—See WESCO International, Inc.; *U.S. Public*, pg. 2351
AVO PHOTONICS, INC.—See Halma plc; *Int'l*, pg. 3230
AVO SA—See Mersen S.A.; *Int'l*, pg. 4838
AVOW HOSPICE, INC.; *U.S. Private*, pg. 410
AVOX SYSTEMS INC.—See Safran SA; *Int'l*, pg. 6477
AVOX SYSTEMS, INC. - VAN NUYS—See Safran SA; *Int'l*, pg. 6477
AVOYELLES HOSPITAL—See Progressive Acute Care LLC; *U.S. Private*, pg. 3278
AVP ENGINEERING (M) SDN. BHD.—See CB Industrial Product Holding Berhad; *Int'l*, pg. 1364
AVP, INC.; *U.S. Public*, pg. 254
AVPLAN TRIP SUPPORT—See Avfuel Corporation; *U.S. Private*, pg. 406
AV PLASTICS SDN. BHD.—See D'nonce Technology Bhd.; *Int'l*, pg. 1899
AVP MANAGEMENT SERVICES, INC.—See Austin Ventures, LP; *U.S. Private*, pg. 396
AV POUND & CO LTD—See Hobart Enterprises Ltd; *Int'l*, pg. 3436
AV PROMOTIONS HOLDINGS LIMITED; *Int'l*, pg. 733
AVR-AFVALVERWERKING B.V.—See CK Hutchison Holdings Limited; *Int'l*, pg. 1636
AVRA SURGICAL ROBOTICS, INC.; *U.S. Private*, pg. 410
AVRASYA GAYRIMENKUL YATIRIM ORTAKLIGI A.S.; *Int'l*, pg. 750
AVRASYA PETROL VE TURISTIK TESISLER YATIRIMLARI AS; *Int'l*, pg. 750
AVREAFOSTER INC.—See Omnicom Group Inc.; *U.S. Public*, pg. 753
AVRETT FREE GINSBERG—See The Interpublic Group of Companies, Inc.; *U.S. Public*, pg. 2097
AVRICORE HEALTH INC.; *Int'l*, pg. 750
AVRIL SCA; *Int'l*, pg. 750
AVRIO VENTURES LTD.; *Int'l*, pg. 750
AVRO INDIA LIMITED; *Int'l*, pg. 750
AVROT INDUSTRIES LTD.; *Int'l*, pg. 750
AVROY SHLAIN COSMETICS (PTY.) LTD.—See Tupperware Brands Corporation; *U.S. Public*, pg. 2204
AVR REALTY COMPANY, LLC; *U.S. Private*, pg. 410
AVRUPA MINERALS LTD.; *Int'l*, pg. 750
AVRUPA YATIRIM HOLDING AS; *Int'l*, pg. 750
AVS CARGO MANAGEMENT SERVICES PRIVATE LIMITED—See Expolanka Holdings PLC; *Int'l*, pg. 2589
AVS CO., LTD.—See Olympus Corporation; *Int'l*, pg. 5556
A.V. SIMULATION SAS—See Sogeclair; *Int'l*, pg. 7058
AVSL INDUSTRIES LTD.; *Int'l*, pg. 750
AV SOLAR RANCH 1, LLC—See Constellation Energy Corporation; *U.S. Public*, pg. 571
AVS-PHOENIX MECANO GMBH—See Phoenix Mecano AG; *Int'l*, pg. 5851
AVS SYSTEMS INC.—See Information Services Corporation; *Int'l*, pg. 3695
AVSURANCE CORPORATION—See Avfuel Corporation; *U.S. Private*, pg. 406
AVT BEIJING CO., LTD.—See VINCI S.A.; *Int'l*, pg. 8211
AV TECH CORPORATION - CCTV PRODUCT DIVISION—See Av Tech Corporation; *Int'l*, pg. 733
AV TECH CORPORATION - SANCHONG FACTORY—See Av Tech Corporation; *Int'l*, pg. 733
AV TECH CORPORATION; *Int'l*, pg. 733
AVTECH CORPORATION—See TransDigm Group Incorporated; *U.S. Public*, pg. 2182
AVTECH FRANCE SARL—See AVTECH Sweden AB; *Int'l*, pg. 751
AVTECH MIDDLE EAST LLC—See AVTECH Sweden AB; *Int'l*, pg. 751
AVTEC HOMES; *U.S. Private*, pg. 410
AVTECH SWEDEN AB; *Int'l*, pg. 751
AVTECHTYEE, INC.—See TransDigm Group Incorporated; *U.S. Public*, pg. 2182
AVTEC INC.; *U.S. Private*, pg. 410
AVTEC SYSTEMS, INC.—See Kratos Defense & Security Solutions, Inc.; *U.S. Public*, pg. 1276
AVTENTA.SI, D.O.O.—See Telekom Slovenije, d.d.; *Int'l*, pg. 7538
AVTERA D.O.O.—See Avtotehna, d.d.; *Int'l*, pg. 751
AV TERRACE BAY INC.—See The Aditya Birla Group; *Int'l*, pg. 7612
AVT EUROPE NV—See VINCI S.A.; *Int'l*, pg. 8211
AVTEX SOLUTIONS, LLC—See TTEC Holdings, Inc.; *U.S. Public*, pg. 2203

AV THERAPEUTICS, INC.; *U.S. Private*, pg. 402
AV THOMAS PRODUCE; *U.S. Private*, pg. 402
AVTIL ENTERPRISE LIMITED; *Int'l*, pg. 751
AVT INDUSTRITEKNIK AB—See Addtech AB; *Int'l*, pg. 131
AVT INTERNATIONAL LIMITED—See Apex Ace Holding Limited; *Int'l*, pg. 509
AVT MCCORMICK INGREDIENTS PVT LTD.—See McCormick & Company, Incorporated; *U.S. Public*, pg. 1403
AVT NATURAL PRODUCTS LTD.; *Int'l*, pg. 751
AVTO AKTIV SLO D.O.O.—See AutoWallis Public Limited Company; *Int'l*, pg. 732
AVTODOM OAO; *Int'l*, pg. 751
AVTOTEHNA, D.D.; *Int'l*, pg. 751
AVTOTEHNA OPREMA D.O.O.—See Avtotehna, d.d.; *Int'l*, pg. 751
AVTOTEHNA VIS D.O.O.—See Avtotehna, d.d.; *Int'l*, pg. 751
AVTO UNION AD—See Eurohold Bulgaria AD; *Int'l*, pg. 2552
AVTPUMP APS—See AESSEAL Plc; *Int'l*, pg. 183
AVT RELIABILITY LTD.—See AESSEAL Plc; *Int'l*, pg. 182
AVTRON AEROSPACE, INC.—See Odyssey Investment Partners, LLC; *U.S. Private*, pg. 2994
AVTRON INDUSTRIAL AUTOMATION, INC.—See Nidec Corporation; *Int'l*, pg. 5275
AVT SIMULATION INC.; *U.S. Private*, pg. 410
AVT TEA SERVICES NORTH AMERICA LLC—See AVT Natural Products Ltd.; *Int'l*, pg. 751
AVT-URAL LLC—See Evraz plc; *Int'l*, pg. 2573
AVURE TECHNOLOGIES INC.—See John Bean Technologies Corporation; *U.S. Public*, pg. 1191
AVVAA WORLD HEALTH CARE PRODUCTS INC.; *Int'l*, pg. 751
AVVASHYA CCI LOGISTICS PRIVATE LIMITED—See Allcargo Logistics Limited; *Int'l*, pg. 333
AVVENTA WORLDWIDE, LLC—See Accenture plc; *Int'l*, pg. 86
AVVIO REPLY LTD.—See Reply S.p.A.; *Int'l*, pg. 6290
AVVIO REPLY S.R.L.—See Reply S.p.A.; *Int'l*, pg. 6290
AVVO, INC.—See KKR & Co. Inc.; *U.S. Public*, pg. 1253
AVX CZECH REPUBLIC S.R.O.—See KYOCERA Corporation; *Int'l*, pg. 4358
AVX DESIGN & INTEGRATION, INC.—See Focus Universal Inc.; *U.S. Public*, pg. 862
AVX ELECTRONIC COMPONENTS & INTERCONNECT SOLUTIONS CORPORATION—See KYOCERA Corporation; *Int'l*, pg. 4355
AVX ELECTRONICS (TIANJIN) CO. LTD.—See KYOCERA Corporation; *Int'l*, pg. 4358
AVX FILTERS CORPORATION—See KYOCERA Corporation; *Int'l*, pg. 4358
AVX ISRAEL LTD.—See KYOCERA Corporation; *Int'l*, pg. 4358
AVX/KYOCERA ASIA LTD.—See KYOCERA Corporation; *Int'l*, pg. 4359
AVX/KYOCERA (SHANGHAI) INTERNATIONAL TRADING CO., LTD.—See KYOCERA Corporation; *Int'l*, pg. 4359
AVX/KYOCERA YUHAN HOESA—See KYOCERA Corporation; *Int'l*, pg. 4359
AVX LTD.—See KYOCERA Corporation; *Int'l*, pg. 4358
AVX TANTALUM CORPORATION—See KYOCERA Corporation; *Int'l*, pg. 4358
AVY CO., LTD.—See AVY Precision Technology, Inc.; *Int'l*, pg. 751
AVY PRECISION METAL COMPONENTS (SUZHOU) CO., LTD—See AVY Precision Technology, Inc.; *Int'l*, pg. 751
AVY PRECISION TECHNOLOGY, INC.; *Int'l*, pg. 751
AWA AMERICAS LLC—See BITZER SE; *Int'l*, pg. 1051
THE AWA BANK, LTD.; *Int'l*, pg. 7614
AWAD BROTHERS INC.; *U.S. Private*, pg. 410
AWAFI FOODSTUFF LND. CO. L.L.C.—See Juma Al Majid Group; *Int'l*, pg. 4025
AWAJI STEEL PIPE CO., LTD.—See Nippon Steel Corporation; *Int'l*, pg. 5337
AWAKE SECURITY LLC—See Arista Networks, Inc.; *U.S. Public*, pg. 192
AWAKN LIFE SCIENCES CORP.; *Int'l*, pg. 751
AWAL DAIRY COMPANY W.L.L.—See Trafco Group B.S.C.; *Int'l*, pg. 7889
AWALE RESOURCES LTD.; *Int'l*, pg. 751
AWANBIRU TECHNOLOGY BERHAD; *Int'l*, pg. 751
AWA PAPER (SHANGHAI) CO., LTD.—See Awa Paper & Technological Company Inc.; *Int'l*, pg. 751
AWA PAPER & TECHNOLOGICAL COMPANY INC.; *Int'l*, pg. 751
AWARDIT AB; *Int'l*, pg. 752
AWARD METALS INC.; *U.S. Private*, pg. 410
AWARDS.COM LLC—See TWS Partnership LLC; *U.S. Private*, pg. 4267
AWARD SOLUTIONS, INC.—See Accenture plc; *Int'l*, pg. 86
AWARE, INC.; *U.S. Public*, pg. 254
AWAREMD, INC.—See WELL Health Technologies Corp.; *Int'l*, pg. 8372
AWARENESS CANADA—See Awareness, Inc.; *U.S. Private*, pg. 410
AWARENESS, INC.; *U.S. Private*, pg. 410

AWARENESS, INC.

AWARENESS TECHNOLOGIES, INC.—See TZP Group LLC; *U.S. Private*, pg. 4269
AWARENESS TECHNOLOGY INC.; *U.S. Private*, pg. 410
AWAREPOINT CORP.; *U.S. Private*, pg. 410
AWARE SECURITY CORPORATION—See Aware, Inc.; *U.S. Public*, pg. 254
AWARE SUPER PTY LTD; *Int'l*, pg. 752
AWAS - MIAMI—See Terra Firma Capital Partners Ltd.; *Int'l*, pg. 7566
AWAS—See Terra Firma Capital Partners Ltd.; *Int'l*, pg. 7566
A. WATTS, INC.; *U.S. Private*, pg. 24
AWAX S.P.A.; *Int'l*, pg. 752
A.W. AYRES AGENCY, INC.—See The Ayres Group, LLC; *U.S. Private*, pg. 3990
AWAY RESORTS LTD.—See COFRA Holding AG; *Int'l*, pg. 1693
AWAYSIS CAPITAL, INC.; *U.S. Public*, pg. 254
A&W BEARINGS & SUPPLY CO.; *U.S. Private*, pg. 21
AWB GRAINFLOW PTY. LTD.—See Cargill, Inc.; *U.S. Private*, pg. 755
AWBREY GLEN GOLF CLUB, INC.—See Brooks Resources Corporation; *U.S. Private*, pg. 664
AWBREY HOUSE, LLC—See TPG Capital, L.P.; *U.S. Public*, pg. 2168
AWC BERHAD; *Int'l*, pg. 752
AWC FRAC VALVES INC.; *U.S. Private*, pg. 410
A.W. CHESTERTON CO. LTD.—See A.W. Chesterton Company; *U.S. Private*, pg. 28
A.W. CHESTERTON COMPANY; *U.S. Private*, pg. 28
AWC HOLDING COMPANY—See Clayton, Dubilier & Rice, LLC; *U.S. Private*, pg. 921
AWC INC.; *U.S. Private*, pg. 410
AWD DEUTSCHLAND GMBH—See Swiss Life Holding; *Int'l*, pg. 7369
AWD D.O.O.—See Swiss Life Holding; *Int'l*, pg. 7370
AWD HUNGARY—See Swiss Life Holding; *Int'l*, pg. 7369
AW DIRECT, INC.—See The Riverside Company; *U.S. Private*, pg. 4108
AWD ROMANIA—See Swiss Life Holding; *Int'l*, pg. 7369
AWD SP. Z O.O.—See Swiss Life Holding; *Int'l*, pg. 7370
AWD S.R.O.—See Swiss Life Holding; *Int'l*, pg. 7370
AWD SWITZERLAND—See Swiss Life Holding; *Int'l*, pg. 7369
AWD - VERSICHERUNGSMAKLER UND -BERATUNGS GMBH—See Swiss Life Holding; *Int'l*, pg. 7368
AWE ACQUISITION, INC.—See Blackstreet Capital Management, LLC; *U.S. Private*, pg. 577
AWEA MECHANTRONIC CO., LTD.; *Int'l*, pg. 753
AWEA MECHANTRONIC CO., LTD. - TAIWAN TAICHUNG FACTORY—See Awea Mechantronic Co., Ltd.; *Int'l*, pg. 753
AWEA MECHANTRONIC (SUZHOU) LTD.—See Awea Mechantronic Co., Ltd.; *Int'l*, pg. 753
AWEBA WERKZEUGBAU GMBH—See ANDRITZ AG; *Int'l*, pg. 455
AWEBER COMMUNICATIONS, INC.; *U.S. Private*, pg. 411
AWECOMM TECHNOLOGIES, LLC—See Audax Group, Limited Partnership; *U.S. Private*, pg. 387
AWEK MICRODATA GMBH—See Fujitsu Limited; *Int'l*, pg. 2837
AWEL Y MOR OFFSHORE WIND FARM LIMITED—See RWE AG; *Int'l*, pg. 6433
AWE PLC; *Int'l*, pg. 752
AWESOME AGENT CO., LTD.—See ZIGExN Co., Ltd.; *Int'l*, pg. 8682
AWESOME TRANSPORTATION, INC.—See Western Beef, Inc.; *U.S. Private*, pg. 4491
AWESTRUCK MARKETING GROUP; *U.S. Private*, pg. 411
AWETA -AUTOLINE, INC.—See FPS Food Processing Systems B.V.; *Int'l*, pg. 2757
AWETA FRANCE S.A.S.—See FPS Food Processing Systems B.V.; *Int'l*, pg. 2757
AWETA G&P—See FPS Food Processing Systems B.V.; *Int'l*, pg. 2757
AWETA HOLDING B.V.—See FPS Food Processing Systems B.V.; *Int'l*, pg. 2757
AWETA SISTEMI S.P.A.—See FPS Food Processing Systems B.V.; *Int'l*, pg. 2757
AW EUROPE S.A.—See AISIN Corporation; *Int'l*, pg. 252
A.W. FABER-CASTELL ARGENTINA S.A.—See Faber-Castell AG; *Int'l*, pg. 2598
A.W. FABER-CASTELL (AUST.) PTY. LTD.—See Faber-Castell AG; *Int'l*, pg. 2598
A.W. FABER-CASTELL AUSTRIA GMBH—See Faber-Castell AG; *Int'l*, pg. 2599
A.W. FABER-CASTELL COLOMBIA LTDA.—See Faber-Castell AG; *Int'l*, pg. 2599
A.W. FABER-CASTELL DE MEXICO SA DE CV—See Faber-Castell AG; *Int'l*, pg. 2599
A.W. FABER-CASTELL GES.M.B.H.—See Faber-Castell AG; *Int'l*, pg. 2599
A.W. FABER-CASTELL GUANGZHOU STATIONERY CO., LTD.—See Faber-Castell AG; *Int'l*, pg. 2599
A.W. FABER-CASTELL (H.K.) LTD.—See Faber-Castell AG; *Int'l*, pg. 2598
A.W. FABER-CASTELL (INDIA) LTD.—See Faber-Castell AG; *Int'l*, pg. 2598

A.W. FABER-CASTELL ITALIA S.R.L.—See Faber-Castell AG; *Int'l*, pg. 2599
A.W. FABER-CASTELL (M) SDN. BHD.—See Faber-Castell AG; *Int'l*, pg. 2598
A.W. FABER-CASTELL NORDIC APS—See Faber-Castell AG; *Int'l*, pg. 2599
A.W. FABER-CASTELL (NZ) LTD.—See Faber-Castell AG; *Int'l*, pg. 2598
A.W. FABER-CASTELL PERUANA S.A.—See Faber-Castell AG; *Int'l*, pg. 2599
A.W. FABER-CASTELL S.A.R.L.—See Faber-Castell AG; *Int'l*, pg. 2599
A.W. FABER-CASTELL S.A.—See Faber-Castell AG; *Int'l*, pg. 2599
A.W. FABER-CASTELL SCHWEIZ AG—See Faber-Castell AG; *Int'l*, pg. 2599
A.W. FABER-CASTELL SPOL. S RO.—See Faber-Castell AG; *Int'l*, pg. 2599
A.W. FABER-CASTELL (S) PTE. LTD.—See Faber-Castell AG; *Int'l*, pg. 2598
A.W. FABER-CASTELL USA INC—See Faber-Castell AG; *Int'l*, pg. 2599
A.W. FABER-CASTELL VERTRIEB GMBH—See Faber-Castell AG; *Int'l*, pg. 2599
AWF MADISON GROUP LIMITED; *Int'l*, pg. 753
A&W FOOD SERVICES OF CANADA INC.—See TorQuest Partners Inc.; *Int'l*, pg. 7830
A.W. FRASER LTD.; *Int'l*, pg. 28
AWG FITTINGS GMBH—See IDEX Corp; *U.S. Public*, pg. 1089
AW GOLDEN INC.; *U.S. Private*, pg. 410
AWG PROPERTY LIMITED—See Canada Pension Plan Investment Board; *Int'l*, pg. 1278
AWG PROPERTY LIMITED—See Commonwealth Bank of Australia; *Int'l*, pg. 1720
AWG PROPERTY LIMITED—See Industry Super Holdings Pty. Ltd.; *Int'l*, pg. 3675
A W HAINSWORTH & SONS LTD.; *Int'l*, pg. 18
A.W. HASTINGS & CO. INC.; *U.S. Private*, pg. 28
A.W. HERNDON OIL CO. INC.; *U.S. Private*, pg. 28
AWH PARTNERS, LLC—See Winston Harton Holdings, LLC; *U.S. Private*, pg. 4544
AWIB PTY. LTD.—See PSC Insurance Group Limited; *Int'l*, pg. 6015
AWI, INC.—See VIP Wireless, Inc.; *U.S. Private*, pg. 4387
A. WILBERT'S SONS ISLAND, LLC—See A. Wilbert's Sons, LLC; *U.S. Private*, pg. 24
A. WILBERT'S SONS, LLC; *U.S. Private*, pg. 24
AWILCO DRILLING PLC; *Int'l*, pg. 753
AWILCO LNG 1 AS—See Awilco LNG ASA; *Int'l*, pg. 753
AWILCO LNG 2 AS—See Awilco LNG ASA; *Int'l*, pg. 753
AWILCO LNG 3 AS—See Awilco LNG ASA; *Int'l*, pg. 753
AWILCO LNG 4 AS—See Awilco LNG ASA; *Int'l*, pg. 753
AWILCO LNG 5 AS—See Awilco LNG ASA; *Int'l*, pg. 753
AWILCO LNG 6 AS—See Awilco LNG ASA; *Int'l*, pg. 753
AWILCO LNG 7 AS—See Awilco LNG ASA; *Int'l*, pg. 753
AWILCO LNG ASA; *Int'l*, pg. 753
AWI LICENSING COMPANY—See Armstrong World Industries, Inc.; *U.S. Public*, pg. 194
AWI MANUFACTURING, INC.—See William Hill Plc; *Int'l*, pg. 8413
A. WIMPFHEIMER & BROS., INC.; *U.S. Private*, pg. 24
AWIN AB—See Axel Springer SE; *Int'l*, pg. 765
AWIN AG—See Axel Springer SE; *Int'l*, pg. 765
AWIN B.V.—See Axel Springer SE; *Int'l*, pg. 765
AW INDUSTRIES, INC.; *U.S. Private*, pg. 410
AWIN INC.—See Axel Springer SE; *Int'l*, pg. 765
A-WIN INSURANCE LTD.—See Rogers Insurance Ltd.; *Int'l*, pg. 6383
AWIN LEASING COMPANY, INC.—See Republic Services, Inc.; *U.S. Public*, pg. 1785
AWIN LTD.—See Axel Springer SE; *Int'l*, pg. 766
AWIN SAS—See Axel Springer SE; *Int'l*, pg. 765
AWIN SP. Z.O.O.—See Axel Springer SE; *Int'l*, pg. 765
AWIN SRL—See Axel Springer SE; *Int'l*, pg. 765
AWIN VEICULACAO DE PUBLICIDADE NA INTERNET LTDA—See Axel Springer SE; *Int'l*, pg. 766
AW-I S CO., LTD.—See AISIN Corporation; *Int'l*, pg. 252
AWISCO NY CORPORATION; *U.S. Private*, pg. 411
AWISTA GESELLSCHAFT FUR ABFALLWIRTSCHAFT UND STADTREINIGUNG MBH—See EnBW Energie Baden-Wurttemberg AG; *Int'l*, pg. 2397
AWISTA LOGISTIK GMBH—See EnBW Energie Baden-Wurttemberg AG; *Int'l*, pg. 2398
AWK GROUP AG—See DPE Deutsche Private Equity GmbH; *Int'l*, pg. 2187
A&W (MALAYSIA) SDN BHD—See Malayan United Industries Berhad; *Int'l*, pg. 4661
A.W. MILLER—See A.W. Miller Technical Sales Inc.; *U.S. Private*, pg. 28
A.W. MILLER TECHNICAL SALES, INC.—See A.W. Miller Technical Sales Inc.; *U.S. Private*, pg. 28
A.W. MILLER TECHNICAL SALES INC.; *U.S. Private*, pg. 28
AWM MOLD SERVICE US INC.—See Adval Tech Holding AG; *Int'l*, pg. 155
AWM MOLD TECH INTERNATIONAL TRADING (SHANGHAI) CO. LTD.—See Adval Tech Holding AG; *Int'l*, pg. 155

CORPORATE AFFILIATIONS

AWM PLASTPACK LTD.—See Adval Tech Holding AG; *Int'l*, pg. 155
AWMS HOLDINGS, LLC—See Avalon Holdings Corporation; *U.S. Public*, pg. 239
AWM S.P.A.—See Viohalco SA/NV; *Int'l*, pg. 8243
AW NAZCA SAATCHI & SAATCHI—See Publicis Groupe S.A.; *Int'l*, pg. 6107
AWNCLEAN U. S. A., INC.—See Valcourt Building Services LLC; *U.S. Private*, pg. 4330
AWN HOLDINGS LIMITED; *Int'l*, pg. 753
AW NORTH CAROLINA, INC.—See AISIN Corporation; *Int'l*, pg. 252
A WOMAN'S PLACE, LLC—See Community Health Systems, Inc.; *U.S. Public*, pg. 550
A WORK OF ART INC.; *U.S. Private*, pg. 19
A WORLD OF TILE LLC; *U.S. Private*, pg. 19
AWP ASSISTANCE UK LTD.—See Allianz SE; *Int'l*, pg. 343
AWP AUSTRALIA PTY. LTD.—See Allianz SE; *Int'l*, pg. 343
A.W. PERRY INC.; *U.S. Private*, pg. 29
AWP FRANCE SAS—See Allianz SE; *Int'l*, pg. 343
AWP GMBH—See E.ON SE; *Int'l*, pg. 2251
AWP, INC.—See Kohlberg & Company, LLC; *U.S. Private*, pg. 2337
AWP INDUSTRIES INC.; *U.S. Private*, pg. 411
AWP LLC; *U.S. Private*, pg. 411
AWP P&C S.A.—See Allianz SE; *Int'l*, pg. 343
AW PROPERTY CO.; *U.S. Private*, pg. 410
AWQUIS JAPAN CO., LTD.—See AISIN Corporation; *Int'l*, pg. 253
AWR-APLAC CORPORATION—See Cadence Design Systems, Inc.; *U.S. Public*, pg. 418
AWR-APLAC OY—See National Instruments Corporation; *U.S. Private*, pg. 2856
AWR CORPORATION—See Cadence Design Systems, Inc.; *U.S. Public*, pg. 418
A&W RESTAURANTS, INC.; *U.S. Private*, pg. 21
A&W REVENUE ROYALTIES INCOME FUND—See TorQuest Partners Inc.; *Int'l*, pg. 7830
AWR JAPAN KK—See National Instruments Corporation; *U.S. Private*, pg. 2856
AW ROSTAMANI LOGISTICS LLC—See Mitsui-Soko Holdings Co., Ltd.; *Int'l*, pg. 4992
AWR SPORTS LLC—See Peak Global Holdings, LLC; *U.S. Private*, pg. 3123
AWS ACHSLAGERWERK STASSFURT GMBH; *Int'l*, pg. 753
AWS (BEIJING), LTD.—See Ubicom Holdings, Inc.; *Int'l*, pg. 8003
AWS ENTSORGUNG GMBH—See BayWa AG; *Int'l*, pg. 915
AWS. GMBH—See Gelsenwasser AG; *Int'l*, pg. 2913
AWS (KUNSHAN), LTD.—See Ubicom Holdings, Inc.; *Int'l*, pg. 8003
AWS:PWU PERSONALMARKETING GMBH—See WPP plc; *Int'l*, pg. 8481
AWT INTERNATIONAL (ASIA) SDN. BHD.—See NauticAWT Limited; *Int'l*, pg. 5172
AWT INTERNATIONAL TRADE AG—See UniCredit S.p.A.; *Int'l*, pg. 8038
A&W TRADE MARKS LIMITED PARTNERSHIP—See TorQuest Partners Inc.; *Int'l*, pg. 7830
AW TRANSMISSION ENGINEERING U.S.A., INC.—See AISIN Corporation; *Int'l*, pg. 252
A. W. TROUTMAN CO.; *U.S. Private*, pg. 23
AWU ABFALLWIRTSCHAFTS-UNION OBERHAVEL GMBH—See Alba SE; *Int'l*, pg. 293
AWU LOGISTIK OPR GMBH—See Alba SE; *Int'l*, pg. 293
AW UNDERWRITERS INC.—See Fairfax Financial Holdings Limited; *Int'l*, pg. 2606
AWU OSTPRIGNITZ-RUPPIN GMBH—See Alba SE; *Int'l*, pg. 293
AWWAL MODARABA MANAGEMENT LIMITED; *Int'l*, pg. 753
A&W WATER SERVICE, INC.—See Superior Energy Services, Inc.; *U.S. Private*, pg. 3877
AWX PTY LTD—See PeopleIn Limited; *Int'l*, pg. 5794
A. W. ZENGELER CLEANERS, INC.; *U.S. Private*, pg. 24
AXA ADVISORS, LLC—See Equitable Holdings, Inc.; *U.S. Public*, pg. 788
AXA ADVISORS, LLC—See Equitable Holdings, Inc.; *U.S. Public*, pg. 788
AXA-ARAG PROTECTION JURIDIQUE SA—See AXA S.A.; *Int'l*, pg. 759
AXA-ARAG RECHTSSCHUTZ AG—See AXA S.A.; *Int'l*, pg. 759
AXA ART FRANCE—See AXA S.A.; *Int'l*, pg. 754
AXA ART INSURANCE CORPORATION - CANADA—See AXA S.A.; *Int'l*, pg. 754
AXA ART INSURANCE CORPORATION—See AXA S.A.; *Int'l*, pg. 754
AXA ART LUXEMBOURG—See AXA S.A.; *Int'l*, pg. 754
AXA ART - NEDERLAND—See AXA S.A.; *Int'l*, pg. 754
AXA ART—See AXA S.A.; *Int'l*, pg. 754
AXA ART—See AXA S.A.; *Int'l*, pg. 754
AXA ART VERSICHERUNG AG—See AXA S.A.; *Int'l*, pg. 754

COMPANY NAME INDEX

AXA ART VERSICHERUNG AG—See AXA S.A.; *Int'l*, pg. 757
AXA ASIA PACIFIC HOLDINGS LIMITED—See AMP Limited; *Int'l*, pg. 432
AXA ASSICURAZIONI—See AXA S.A.; *Int'l*, pg. 754
AXA ASSISTANCE (BEIJING) CO., LTD.—See AXA S.A.; *Int'l*, pg. 754
AXA ASSISTANCE CANADA INC.—See AXA S.A.; *Int'l*, pg. 754
AXA ASSISTANCE CHILE S.A—See AXA S.A.; *Int'l*, pg. 754
AXA ASSISTANCE DEUTSCHLAND GMBH—See AXA S.A.; *Int'l*, pg. 754
AXA ASSISTANCE FRANCE—See AXA S.A.; *Int'l*, pg. 754
AXA ASSISTANCE JAPAN CO., LTD.—See AXA S.A.; *Int'l*, pg. 754
AXA ASSISTANCE MEXICO SA DE CV—See AXA S.A.; *Int'l*, pg. 754
AXA ASSISTANCE OCEAN INDIEN LTD—See AXA S.A.; *Int'l*, pg. 754
AXA ASSISTANCE PANAMA SA.—See AXA S.A.; *Int'l*, pg. 754
AXA ASSISTANCE S.A.—See AXA S.A.; *Int'l*, pg. 754
AXA ASSISTANCE—See AXA S.A.; *Int'l*, pg. 754
AXA ASSISTANCE (UK) LTD—See AXA S.A.; *Int'l*, pg. 754
AXA ASSISTANCE USA, INC.—See AXA S.A.; *Int'l*, pg. 754
AXA ASSURANCE MAROC—See AXA S.A.; *Int'l*, pg. 755
AXA ASSURANCES GABON—See AXA S.A.; *Int'l*, pg. 755
AXA ASSURANCES LUXEMBOURG S.A.—See AXA S.A.; *Int'l*, pg. 755
AXA ASSURANCES SENEGAL—See AXA S.A.; *Int'l*, pg. 755
AXA ASSURANCES—See AXA S.A.; *Int'l*, pg. 755
AXA ASSURANCES VIE LUXEMBOURG—See AXA S.A.; *Int'l*, pg. 755
AXA AURORA IBERICA S.A. DE SEGUROS Y REASEGUROS—See AXA S.A.; *Int'l*, pg. 757
AXA AURORA VIDA SA DE SEGUROS Y REASEGUROS—See AXA S.A.; *Int'l*, pg. 757
AXA AUSTRALIA—See AMP Limited; *Int'l*, pg. 432
AXA BANK AG.—See AXA S.A.; *Int'l*, pg. 757
AXA BANK BELGIUM SABELGIUM SA—See AXA S.A.; *Int'l*, pg. 756
AXA BANK EUROPE CZECH REPUBLIC—See AXA S.A.; *Int'l*, pg. 755
AXA BANK EUROPE SLOVAKIA—See AXA S.A.; *Int'l*, pg. 755
AXA BANQUE—See AXA S.A.; *Int'l*, pg. 756
AXA BELGIUM S.A.—See AXA S.A.; *Int'l*, pg. 756
AXA BUSINESS SERVICES PRIVATE LIMITED—See AXA S.A.; *Int'l*, pg. 755
AXA CESKA REPUBLIKA S.R.O.—See AXA S.A.; *Int'l*, pg. 755
AXA CESSIONS—See AXA S.A.; *Int'l*, pg. 755
AXA CHINA REGION INSURANCE COMPANY (BERMUDA) LIMITED—See AXA S.A.; *Int'l*, pg. 755
AXA CHINA REGION INSURANCE COMPANY LIMITED—See AXA S.A.; *Int'l*, pg. 755
AXA CHINA REGION LTD.—See AXA S.A.; *Int'l*, pg. 755
AXA COLONIA INSURANCE LIMITED—See AXA S.A.; *Int'l*, pg. 755
AXA CONSEIL—See AXA S.A.; *Int'l*, pg. 755
AXA COOPERATIVE INSURANCE COMPANY; *Int'l*, pg. 754
AXA CORPORATE SOLUTIONS ASSURANCE S.A—See AXA S.A.; *Int'l*, pg. 755
AXA CORPORATE SOLUTIONS AUSTRALIA—See AXA S.A.; *Int'l*, pg. 755
AXA CORPORATE SOLUTIONS DUBAI—See AXA S.A.; *Int'l*, pg. 755
AXA CORPORATE SOLUTIONS GERMANY—See AXA S.A.; *Int'l*, pg. 755
AXA CORPORATE SOLUTIONS HONG KONG—See AXA S.A.; *Int'l*, pg. 755
AXA CORPORATE SOLUTIONS INSURANCE—See Equitable Holdings, Inc.; *U.S. Public*, pg. 788
AXA CORPORATE SOLUTIONS LIFE REINSURANCE COMPANY—See Equitable Holdings, Inc.; *U.S. Public*, pg. 788
AXA CORPORATE SOLUTIONS—See AXA S.A.; *Int'l*, pg. 755
AXA CORPORATE SOLUTIONS—See Equitable Holdings, Inc.; *U.S. Public*, pg. 788
AXA CORPORATE SOLUTIONS—See AXA S.A.; *Int'l*, pg. 755
AXA CORPORATE SOLUTIONS SWITZERLAND—See AXA S.A.; *Int'l*, pg. 755
AXA CORPORATE SOLUTIONS UK—See AXA S.A.; *Int'l*, pg. 755
AXA CORP. SOLUTIONS INSURANCE COMPANY—See Equitable Holdings, Inc.; *U.S. Public*, pg. 788
AXA COTE D'IVOIRE—See AXA S.A.; *Int'l*, pg. 755
AXACTOR ESPANA PLATFORM SA—See Axactor SE; *Int'l*, pg. 761
AXACTOR FINLAND OY—See Axactor SE; *Int'l*, pg. 761

AXACTOR GERMANY HOLDING GMBH—See Axactor SE; *Int'l*, pg. 761
AXACTOR ITALY SPA—See Axactor SE; *Int'l*, pg. 761
AXACTOR NORWAY AS—See Axactor SE; *Int'l*, pg. 761
AXACTOR SE; *Int'l*, pg. 761
AXACTOR SWEDEN AB—See Axactor SE; *Int'l*, pg. 761
AXA CUSTOMER SERVICES LTD—See AXA S.A.; *Int'l*, pg. 755
AXA CZECH REPUBLIC INSURANCE—See AXA S.A.; *Int'l*, pg. 755
AXA CZECH REPUBLIC PENSION FUNDS—See AXA S.A.; *Int'l*, pg. 755
AXA D.D.S., A.S.—See AXA S.A.; *Int'l*, pg. 759
AXA DIRECT KOREA—See AXA S.A.; *Int'l*, pg. 756
AXA DIRECT—See AXA S.A.; *Int'l*, pg. 756
AXA DISTRIBUTORS, LLC.—See Equitable Holdings, Inc.; *U.S. Public*, pg. 788
AXA EPARGNE ENTREPRISE—See AXA S.A.; *Int'l*, pg. 756
AXA EQUITABLE LIFE ASSURANCE COMPANY—See Equitable Holdings, Inc.; *U.S. Public*, pg. 788
AXA FINE ART CHINA—See AXA S.A.; *Int'l*, pg. 754
AXA FINE ART HONG KONG—See AXA S.A.; *Int'l*, pg. 754
AXA FINE ART SINGAPORE—See AXA S.A.; *Int'l*, pg. 754
AXA FRAMLINGTON—See AXA S.A.; *Int'l*, pg. 756
AXA FRAMLINGTON—See AXA S.A.; *Int'l*, pg. 756
AXA FRANCE ASSURANCE SAS—See AXA S.A.; *Int'l*, pg. 756
AXA FRANCE IARD—See AXA S.A.; *Int'l*, pg. 756
AXA FRANCE VIE S.A—See AXA S.A.; *Int'l*, pg. 756
AXA GENERAL INSURANCE CO., LTD.—See AXA S.A.; *Int'l*, pg. 756
AXA GENERAL INSURANCE HONG KONG—See AXA S.A.; *Int'l*, pg. 756
AXA GENERAL INSURANCE - LTD.—See AXA S.A.; *Int'l*, pg. 759
AXA GLOBAL RE SA—See AXA S.A.; *Int'l*, pg. 756
AXA GLOBAL STRUCTURED PRODUCTS INC.—See Equitable Holdings, Inc.; *U.S. Public*, pg. 788
AXA GROUP OPERATIONS SWITZERLAND AG—See AXA S.A.; *Int'l*, pg. 756
AXA HOLDING MAROC S.A.—See AXA S.A.; *Int'l*, pg. 756
AXA HOLDINGS BELGIUM—See AXA S.A.; *Int'l*, pg. 756
AXA INSURANCE A.E.—See AXA S.A.; *Int'l*, pg. 757
AXA INSURANCE GULF—See AXA S.A.; *Int'l*, pg. 756
AXA INSURANCE GULF—See AXA S.A.; *Int'l*, pg. 756
AXA INSURANCE LIMITED—See AXA S.A.; *Int'l*, pg. 756
AXA INSURANCE PCL—See AXA S.A.; *Int'l*, pg. 756
AXA INSURANCE PLC—See AXA S.A.; *Int'l*, pg. 758
AXA INSURANCE PTE. LTD.—See HSBC Holdings plc; *Int'l*, pg. 3506
AXA INSURANCE S.A.—See Assicurazioni Generali S.p.A.; *Int'l*, pg. 643
AXA INSURANCE (SAUDI ARABIA) B.S.C.—See AXA S.A.; *Int'l*, pg. 756
AXA INSURANCE SINGAPORE PTE LTD—See AXA S.A.; *Int'l*, pg. 756
AXA INSURANCE—See Equitable Holdings, Inc.; *U.S. Public*, pg. 788
AXA INSURANCE—See AXA S.A.; *Int'l*, pg. 756
AXA INSURANCE UK PLC—See AXA S.A.; *Int'l*, pg. 758
AXA INTERLIFE S.P.A.—See AXA S.A.; *Int'l*, pg. 757
AXA INVESTICNI SPOLECNOST A.S.—See AXA S.A.; *Int'l*, pg. 759
AXA INVESTICNI SPOLECNOST A.S.—See AXA S.A.; *Int'l*, pg. 759
AXA INVESTMENT MANAGERS ASIA LIMITED—See AXA S.A.; *Int'l*, pg. 756
AXA INVESTMENT MANAGERS ASIA (SINGAPORE) LTD.—See AXA S.A.; *Int'l*, pg. 756
AXA INVESTMENT MANAGERS BENELUX SA/NV - NETHERLANDS—See AXA S.A.; *Int'l*, pg. 756
AXA INVESTMENT MANAGERS BENELUX SA/NV—See AXA S.A.; *Int'l*, pg. 756
AXA INVESTMENT MANAGERS DEUTSCHLAND GMBH—See AXA S.A.; *Int'l*, pg. 756
AXA INVESTMENT MANAGERS GS LIMITED—See AXA S.A.; *Int'l*, pg. 756
AXA INVESTMENT MANAGERS GS LTD., SUCURSAL EN ESPANA—See AXA S.A.; *Int'l*, pg. 756
AXA INVESTMENT MANAGERS, INC.—See AXA S.A.; *Int'l*, pg. 756
AXA INVESTMENT MANAGERS ITALIA S.P.A.—See AXA S.A.; *Int'l*, pg. 756
AXA INVESTMENT MANAGERS JAPAN LTD.—See AXA S.A.; *Int'l*, pg. 756
AXA INVESTMENT MANAGERS LLC—See AXA S.A.; *Int'l*, pg. 756
AXA INVESTMENT MANAGERS PARIS S.A.—See AXA S.A.; *Int'l*, pg. 756
AXA INVESTMENT MANAGERS S.A.—See AXA S.A.; *Int'l*, pg. 756
AXA INVESTMENT MANAGERS SCHWEIZ AG—See AXA S.A.; *Int'l*, pg. 756
AXA INVESTMENT MANAGERS UK LIMITED—See AXA S.A.; *Int'l*, pg. 756
AXA IRELAND LIMITED—See AXA S.A.; *Int'l*, pg. 757
AXA ITALIA S.P.A.—See AXA S.A.; *Int'l*, pg. 757

AXAR CAPITAL MANAGEMENT L.P.

AXA JAPAN HOLDING CO.—See AXA S.A.; *Int'l*, pg. 757
AXA KONZERN AG—See AXA S.A.; *Int'l*, pg. 757
AXA KRANKENVERSICHERUNG AG—See AXA S.A.; *Int'l*, pg. 757
AXA LIABILITIES MANAGERS BELGIUM—See AXA S.A.; *Int'l*, pg. 757
AXA LIABILITIES MANAGERS INC.—See Equitable Holdings, Inc.; *U.S. Public*, pg. 788
AXA LIABILITIES MANAGERS SAS—See AXA S.A.; *Int'l*, pg. 757
AXA LIABILITIES MANAGERS UK LIMITED—See AXA S.A.; *Int'l*, pg. 757
AXA LIFE EUROPE LIMITED—See AXA S.A.; *Int'l*, pg. 757
AXA LIFE INSURANCE COMPANY LIMITED—See AXA S.A.; *Int'l*, pg. 757
AXA LIFE LTD.—See AXA S.A.; *Int'l*, pg. 757
AXALTA COATING SYSTEMS AUSTRALIA PTY LTD—See Axalta Coating Systems Ltd.; *U.S. Public*, pg. 255
AXALTA COATING SYSTEMS BELGIUM BVBA—See Axalta Coating Systems Ltd.; *U.S. Public*, pg. 254
AXALTA COATING SYSTEMS CANADA COMPANY—See Axalta Coating Systems Ltd.; *U.S. Public*, pg. 255
AXALTA COATING SYSTEMS FRANCE SAS—See Axalta Coating Systems Ltd.; *U.S. Public*, pg. 255
AXALTA COATING SYSTEMS, LLC—See Axalta Coating Systems Ltd.; *U.S. Public*, pg. 255
AXALTA COATING SYSTEMS LTD.; *U.S. Public*, pg. 254
AXALTA COATING SYSTEMS MEXICO, S. DE R.L. DE C.V.—See Axalta Coating Systems Ltd.; *U.S. Public*, pg. 255
AXALTA COATING SYSTEMS UK LIMITED—See Axalta Coating Systems Ltd.; *U.S. Public*, pg. 255
AXALTA POWDER COATING SYSTEMS USA, INC.—See Axalta Coating Systems Ltd.; *U.S. Public*, pg. 255
AXALTO PARTICIPATIONS S.A.S.—See Thales S.A.; *Int'l*, pg. 7599
AXA LUXEMBOURG SA—See AXA S.A.; *Int'l*, pg. 757
AXA MANSARD HEALTH LIMITED—See AXA S.A.; *Int'l*, pg. 757
AXA MANSARD INSURANCE PLC—See AXA S.A.; *Int'l*, pg. 757
AXA MANSARD INVESTMENTS LIMITED—See AXA S.A.; *Int'l*, pg. 757
AXA MBASK IC OJSC—See AXA S.A.; *Int'l*, pg. 757
AXA MEDITERRANEAN HOLDING, S.A.—See AXA S.A.; *Int'l*, pg. 757
AXA MERKENS FONDS GMBH—See AXA S.A.; *Int'l*, pg. 757
AXA MIDDLE EAST—See AXA S.A.; *Int'l*, pg. 757
AXA MULTI MANAGER—See Equitable Holdings, Inc.; *U.S. Public*, pg. 788
AXANCE SA—See Devoteam SA; *Int'l*, pg. 2089
AXA NETWORK, LLC—See Equitable Holdings, Inc.; *U.S. Public*, pg. 788
AXA PENSION SOLUTIONS AG—See AXA S.A.; *Int'l*, pg. 757
AXA PENZIJNI SPOLECNOST A.S.—See UBS Group AG; *Int'l*, pg. 8005
AXA PHILIPPINES—See AXA S.A.; *Int'l*, pg. 757
AXA POJISOVNA A.S.—See AXA S.A.; *Int'l*, pg. 759
AXA POLAND PENSION FUNDS—See AXA S.A.; *Int'l*, pg. 758
AXA POLSKA S.A.—See AXA S.A.; *Int'l*, pg. 758
AXA PORTUGAL COMPANHIA DE SEGUROS DE VIDA SA—See AXA S.A.; *Int'l*, pg. 758
AXA PORTUGAL - COMPANHIA DE SEGUROS S.A.—See AXA S.A.; *Int'l*, pg. 758
AXA POWER APS—See Illinois Tool Works Inc.; *U.S. Public*, pg. 1103
AXA POWSZECHNE TOWARZYSTWO EMERYTALNE S.A.—See AXA S.A.; *Int'l*, pg. 758
AXA PPP HEALTHCARE GROUP PLC—See AXA S.A.; *Int'l*, pg. 758
AXA PROTECTION JURIDIQUE—See AXA S.A.; *Int'l*, pg. 758
AXAR ACQUISITION CORP.—See Axar Capital Management L.P.; *U.S. Private*, pg. 411
AXARA; *Int'l*, pg. 761
AXAR CAPITAL MANAGEMENT L.P.; *U.S. Private*, pg. 411
AXA REAL ESTATE INVESTMENT MANAGERS - HUNGARY—See AXA S.A.; *Int'l*, pg. 757
AXA REAL ESTATE INVESTMENT MANAGERS ITALIA S.R.L.—See AXA S.A.; *Int'l*, pg. 757
AXA REAL ESTATE INVESTMENT MANAGERS JAPAN KK—See AXA S.A.; *Int'l*, pg. 757
AXA REAL ESTATE INVESTMENT MANAGERS NEDERLAND B.V.—See AXA S.A.; *Int'l*, pg. 757
AXA REAL ESTATE INVESTMENT MANAGERS S.A.—See AXA S.A.; *Int'l*, pg. 757
AXA REAL ESTATE INVESTMENT MANAGERS - SPAIN—See AXA S.A.; *Int'l*, pg. 757
AXA REAL ESTATE INVESTMENT MANAGERS - SWITZERLAND—See AXA S.A.; *Int'l*, pg. 757
AXA REAL ESTATE INVESTMENT MANAGERS - UK—See AXA S.A.; *Int'l*, pg. 757
AXA ROSENBERG CANADA CO.—See AXA S.A.; *Int'l*, pg. 758

AXA ROSENBERG INVESTMENT MANAGEMENT ASIA PACIFIC LTD.—See AXA S.A.; *Int'l*, pg. 758
AXA ROSENBERG INVESTMENT MANAGEMENT LIMITED—See AXA S.A.; *Int'l*, pg. 758
AXA ROSENBERG INVESTMENT MANAGEMENT LLC—See Equitable Holdings, Inc.; *U.S. Public*, pg. 788
AXA S.A.; *Int'l*, pg. 754
AXAS CORPORATION—See AXAS Holdings Co., Ltd.; *Int'l*, pg. 761
AXA SEGUROS GENERALES SA DE SEGUROS Y REASEGUROS—See AXA S.A.; *Int'l*, pg. 757
AXA SEGUROS MEXICO—See AXA S.A.; *Int'l*, pg. 758
AXA SEGUROS SA DE CV—See AXA S.A.; *Int'l*, pg. 758
AXA SEGUROS URUGUAY SA—See AXA S.A.; *Int'l*, pg. 758
AXA SERVICES SAS—See AXA S.A.; *Int'l*, pg. 758
AXAS HOLDINGS CO., LTD.; *Int'l*, pg. 761
AXA SIGORTA A.S.—See AXA S.A.; *Int'l*, pg. 758
AXA SPACE, INC.—See Equitable Holdings, Inc.; *U.S. Public*, pg. 788
AXA SPDB INVESTMENT MANAGERS CO., LTD—See AXA S.A.; *Int'l*, pg. 758
AXA SR—See AXA S.A.; *Int'l*, pg. 758
AXA STENMAN DEUTSCHLAND GMBH—See Allegion Public Limited Company; *Int'l*, pg. 335
AXA STENMAN FRANCE S.A.S.—See Allegion Public Limited Company; *Int'l*, pg. 335
AXA STENMAN INDUSTRIES B.V.—See Allegion Public Limited Company; *Int'l*, pg. 335
AXA STENMAN NEDERLAND B.V.—See Allegion Public Limited Company; *Int'l*, pg. 335
AXA STENMAN POLAND SP.Z.O.O.—See Allegion Public Limited Company; *Int'l*, pg. 335
AXA SUN LIFE PLC—See AXA S.A.; *Int'l*, pg. 758
AXA TECHNOLOGY SERVICES AMERICA INC—See Equitable Holdings, Inc.; *U.S. Public*, pg. 788
AXA TECHNOLOGY SERVICES AUSTRALIA—See AXA S.A.; *Int'l*, pg. 758
AXA TECHNOLOGY SERVICES GERMANY GMBH—See AXA S.A.; *Int'l*, pg. 758
AXA TECHNOLOGY SERVICES JAPAN K.K—See AXA S.A.; *Int'l*, pg. 758
AXA TECHNOLOGY SERVICES PORTUGAL—See AXA S.A.; *Int'l*, pg. 758
AXA TECHNOLOGY SERVICES SAS.—See AXA S.A.; *Int'l*, pg. 758
AXA TECHNOLOGY SERVICES SOUTH EAST ASIA—See AXA S.A.; *Int'l*, pg. 758
AXA TECHNOLOGY SERVICES UK PLC—See AXA S.A.; *Int'l*, pg. 758
AXA TIANPING PROPERTY & CASUALTY INSURANCE COMPANY LTD, (AXATP)—See AXA S.A.; *Int'l*, pg. 758
AXA TOWARZYSTWO FUNDUSZY INWESTYCYJNYCH S.A.—See Equitable Holdings, Inc.; *U.S. Public*, pg. 789
AXA TOWARZYSTWO UBEZPIECZEN S.A.—See AXA S.A.; *Int'l*, pg. 758
AXA TURKEY HOLDING A.S.—See AXA S.A.; *Int'l*, pg. 758
AXA UBEZPIECZENIA TOWARZYSTWO UBEZPIECZEN I REASEKURACJI S.A.—See AXA S.A.; *Int'l*, pg. 758
AXA UK PLC—See AXA S.A.; *Int'l*, pg. 758
AXA UKRAINE—See AXA S.A.; *Int'l*, pg. 758
AXA VERSICHERUNG AG—See AXA S.A.; *Int'l*, pg. 758
AXA VERSICHERUNGEN AG—See AXA S.A.; *Int'l*, pg. 758
AXA VIE GABON—See AXA S.A.; *Int'l*, pg. 758
AXA WEALTH LTD—See AXA S.A.; *Int'l*, pg. 759
AXA WEALTH MANAGEMENT (HK) LIMITED—See AXA S.A.; *Int'l*, pg. 755
AXA WEALTH MANAGEMENT SINGAPORE PTE LTD—See AXA S.A.; *Int'l*, pg. 759
AXA WINTERTHUR PENSIONES—See AXA S.A.; *Int'l*, pg. 758
AXA XL GROUP LTD.—See AXA S.A.; *Int'l*, pg. 759
AXA ZIVOTNI POJISTOVNA, A.S.—See AXA S.A.; *Int'l*, pg. 759
AXA ZIVOTNI POJISTOVNA A.S.—See AXA S.A.; *Int'l*, pg. 759
AXA ZYCIE TOWARZYSTWO UBEZPIECZEN S.A.—See AXA S.A.; *Int'l*, pg. 759
AXBERG HEATING—See Black Diamond Plumbing & Mechanical, Inc.; *U.S. Private*, pg. 571
AXCAP VENTURES INC.; *Int'l*, pg. 761
AXCELIS TECHNOLOGIES GMBH—See Axcelis Technologies, Inc.; *U.S. Public*, pg. 255
AXCELIS TECHNOLOGIES, INC.; *U.S. Public*, pg. 255
AXCELIS TECHNOLOGIES LTD.—See Axcelis Technologies, Inc.; *U.S. Public*, pg. 255
AXCELIS TECHNOLOGIES LTD.—See Axcelis Technologies, Inc.; *U.S. Public*, pg. 255
AXCELIS TECHNOLOGIES PTE. LTD.—See Axcelis Technologies, Inc.; *U.S. Public*, pg. 255
AXCELIS TECHNOLOGIES, S.A.R.L.—See Axcelis Technologies, Inc.; *U.S. Public*, pg. 255
AXCELIS TECHNOLOGIES, S.R.L.—See Axcelis Technologies, Inc.; *U.S. Public*, pg. 255
AXCELLA HEALTH INC.; *U.S. Public*, pg. 255

AXCELL TECHNOLOGIES, INC.—See Switchfast Technologies LLC; *U.S. Private*, pg. 3894
AXCEL MANAGEMENT A/S; *Int'l*, pg. 761
AXCEN PHOTONICS CORPORATION; *Int'l*, pg. 762
AXCERA, LLC—See GigaHertz LLC; *U.S. Private*, pg. 1697
AXCESS INTERNATIONAL, INC.; *U.S. Private*, pg. 412
AXCHEM SOLUTIONS INC.; *U.S. Private*, pg. 412
AXCIS INFORMATION NETWORK INC.—See Equibase Company LLC; *U.S. Private*, pg. 1415
AXCO INSURANCE INFORMATION SERVICES LIMITED—See Wilmington plc; *Int'l*, pg. 8422
AX CONSTRUCTION LIMITED—See AX Investments PLC; *Int'l*, pg. 754
AXEDA SYSTEMS INC.; *U.S. Private*, pg. 412
AXE DISTRIBUTION SOLUTIONS TRINIDAD, LTD.—See WESCO International, Inc.; *U.S. Public*, pg. 2350
AXELACARE HOLDINGS, INC.—See Harvest Partners L.P.; *U.S. Private*, pg. 1876
AXELAIR S.A.—See Thermador Groupe; *Int'l*, pg. 7707
AXEL AMERICAS LLC; *U.S. Private*, pg. 412
AXELERATE; *U.S. Private*, pg. 412
AXELERO SPA; *Int'l*, pg. 767
AXELGAARD MANUFACTURING CO., LTD.; *U.S. Private*, pg. 412
AXEL JOHNSON AB—See Axel Johnson Gruppen AB; *Int'l*, pg. 762
AXEL JOHNSON GRUPPEN AB; *Int'l*, pg. 762
AXEL JOHNSON INC.—See Axel Johnson Gruppen AB; *Int'l*, pg. 765
AXEL JOHNSON INTERNATIONAL AB—See Axel Johnson Gruppen AB; *Int'l*, pg. 762
AXEL JOHNSON INTERNATIONAL AS—See Axel Johnson Gruppen AB; *Int'l*, pg. 764
AXEL JOHNSON LAB SYSTEMS A/S—See Axel Johnson Gruppen AB; *Int'l*, pg. 764
AXELL CORPORATION; *Int'l*, pg. 767
AXEL LINDGREN AB; *Int'l*, pg. 765
AXELLUS AB—See Orkla ASA; *Int'l*, pg. 5637
AXELLUS AS—See Orkla ASA; *Int'l*, pg. 5637
AXELLUS SP. Z.O.O.—See Orkla ASA; *Int'l*, pg. 5637
AXELLUS S.R.O—See Orkla ASA; *Int'l*, pg. 5637
AXEL MARK INC.; *Int'l*, pg. 765
AXELON SERVICES CORPORATION; *U.S. Private*, pg. 412
AXEL PLASTICS RESEARCH LABORATORIES, INC.; *U.S. Private*, pg. 412
AXEL POLYMERS LIMITED; *Int'l*, pg. 765
AXELROD FOODS, INC.—See Catamount Dairy Holdings L.P.; *U.S. Private*, pg. 787
AXEL SEMRAU GMBH & CO. KG—See Abbott Laboratories; *U.S. Public*, pg. 20
AXEL SPRINGER BUDAPEST GMBH—See Axel Springer SE; *Int'l*, pg. 766
AXEL SPRINGER CORPORATE SOLUTIONS GMBH & CO. KG—See Axel Springer SE; *Int'l*, pg. 766
AXEL SPRINGER DIGITAL VENTURES GMBH—See Axel Springer SE; *Int'l*, pg. 766
AXEL SPRINGER ESPANA S.A.—See Axel Springer SE; *Int'l*, pg. 766
AXEL SPRINGER HY GMBH—See Axel Springer SE; *Int'l*, pg. 766
AXEL SPRINGER IDEAS ENGINEERING GMBH—See Axel Springer SE; *Int'l*, pg. 766
AXEL SPRINGER MEDIAHOUSE BERLIN GMBH—See Axel Springer SE; *Int'l*, pg. 766
AXEL SPRINGER NORWAY AS—See Axel Springer SE; *Int'l*, pg. 766
AXEL SPRINGER POLSKA SP.Z.O.O.—See Axel Springer SE; *Int'l*, pg. 766
AXEL SPRINGER SE; *Int'l*, pg. 765
AXEL SPRINGER SYNDICATION GMBH—See Axel Springer SE; *Int'l*, pg. 766
AXENERGY LTD.—See Meier Capital AG; *Int'l*, pg. 4799
AXENICS, INC.; *U.S. Private*, pg. 412
AXEN SARL—See Alten S.A.; *Int'l*, pg. 389
AXENTA AG—See Swiss Life Holding; *Int'l*, pg. 7370
AXENT/AEGON N.V.—See Aegon N.V.; *Int'l*, pg. 174
AXENT NABESTAANDENZORG N.V.—See Egeria Capital Management B.V.; *Int'l*, pg. 2323
AXEPT BUSINESS SOFTWARE LTD.—See Swisscom AG; *Int'l*, pg. 7373
AXEREAL UNION DE COOPERATIVES AGRICOLES; *Int'l*, pg. 767
AXERIA IARD S.A.—See Arch Capital Group Ltd.; *Int'l*, pg. 547
AXERIA PREVOYANCE SARL—See CVC Capital Partners SICAV-FIS S.A.; *Int'l*, pg. 1882
AXESA SERVICIOS DE INFORMACION, S. EN C,—See Caribe Media, Inc.; *U.S. Private*, pg. 761
AXES CO., LTD.—See Scroll Corporation; *Int'l*, pg. 6656
AXESS CORPORATION; *U.S. Private*, pg. 412
AXESS INTERNATIONAL NETWORK, INC.—See Japan Airlines Co., Ltd.; *Int'l*, pg. 3881
AXESS LIMITED—See ENL Limited; *Int'l*, pg. 2441
AXESSTEL, INC.; *U.S. Private*, pg. 412
AXESSTEL KOREA, INC.—See Axesstel, Inc.; *U.S. Private*, pg. 412

AXESS ULTRASOUND, LLC—See Ascension Health Alliance; *Int'l*, pg. 346
AXETURE CORP; *U.S. Private*, pg. 412
AXFAST AB—See Axel Johnson Gruppen AB; *Int'l*, pg. 762
AXFLOW AB—See Axel Johnson Gruppen AB; *Int'l*, pg. 762
AXFLOW A/S—See Axel Johnson Gruppen AB; *Int'l*, pg. 762
AXFLOW AS—See Axel Johnson Gruppen AB; *Int'l*, pg. 763
AXFLOW B.V.—See Axel Johnson Gruppen AB; *Int'l*, pg. 763
AXFLOW DC B.V.—See Axel Johnson Gruppen AB; *Int'l*, pg. 762
AXFLOW GESMBH—See Axel Johnson Gruppen AB; *Int'l*, pg. 762
AXFLOW GMBH—See Axel Johnson Gruppen AB; *Int'l*, pg. 763
AXFLOW HOLDING AB—See Axel Johnson Gruppen AB; *Int'l*, pg. 762
AXFLOW KFT—See Axel Johnson Gruppen AB; *Int'l*, pg. 762
AXFLOW LDA.—See Axel Johnson Gruppen AB; *Int'l*, pg. 763
AXFLOW LIMITED—See Axel Johnson Gruppen AB; *Int'l*, pg. 762
AXFLOW LTD.—See Axel Johnson Gruppen AB; *Int'l*, pg. 763
AXFLOW LTD.—See Axel Johnson Gruppen AB; *Int'l*, pg. 763
AXFLOW N.V. / S.A.—See Axel Johnson Gruppen AB; *Int'l*, pg. 763
AXFLOW OY—See Axel Johnson Gruppen AB; *Int'l*, pg. 763
AXFLOW SA—See Axel Johnson Gruppen AB; *Int'l*, pg. 763
AXFLOW SAS—See Axel Johnson Gruppen AB; *Int'l*, pg. 763
AXFLOW SPA—See Axel Johnson Gruppen AB; *Int'l*, pg. 763
AXFLOW SP. Z O.O.—See Axel Johnson Gruppen AB; *Int'l*, pg. 763
AXFLOW SRL—See Axel Johnson Gruppen AB; *Int'l*, pg. 762
AXFLOW S.R.O., O.Z.P.Z.O.—See Axel Johnson Gruppen AB; *Int'l*, pg. 763
AXFLOW S.R.O.—See Axel Johnson Gruppen AB; *Int'l*, pg. 763
AXFLOW SYSTEMS B.V.—See Axel Johnson Gruppen AB; *Int'l*, pg. 763
AXFOOD AB—See Axel Johnson Gruppen AB; *Int'l*, pg. 764
AXFOOD IT AB—See Axel Johnson Gruppen AB; *Int'l*, pg. 764
AXFOOD NARLIVS AB—See Axel Johnson Gruppen AB; *Int'l*, pg. 764
AXFOOD SVERIGE AB—See Axel Johnson Gruppen AB; *Int'l*, pg. 764
AXF RESOURCES PTY LTD.; *Int'l*, pg. 767
AXIA CONSULTING, LLC; *U.S. Private*, pg. 412
AXIA INCORPORATED—See Aurora Capital Group, LLC; *U.S. Private*, pg. 394
AXIALL CORPORATION—See Westlake Corporation; *U.S. Public*, pg. 2360
AXIALOG S.A.—See ITS Group SA; *Int'l*, pg. 3844
AXIAL R/C, INC.—See Hobbico, Inc.; *U.S. Private*, pg. 1958
AXIAL RETAILING INC.; *Int'l*, pg. 768
AXIANE MEUNERIE—See Axereal Union de Cooperatives Agricoles; *Int'l*, pg. 767
AXIA NETMEDIA CORPORATION—See BCE Inc.; *Int'l*, pg. 926
AXIANS AB—See VINCI S.A.; *Int'l*, pg. 8212
AXIANS AB—See Electricite de France S.A.; *Int'l*, pg. 2351
AXIANS AUDIOVISUAL BELGIUM NV—See VINCI S.A.; *Int'l*, pg. 8211
AXIANS BELGIUM—See VINCI S.A.; *Int'l*, pg. 8239
AXIANS BUSINESS SOLUTIONS BV—See VINCI S.A.; *Int'l*, pg. 8212
AXIANS EWASTE GMBH—See VINCI S.A.; *Int'l*, pg. 8212
AXIANS GNS AG—See VINCI S.A.; *Int'l*, pg. 8212
AXIANS ICT AB—See VINCI S.A.; *Int'l*, pg. 8212
AXIANS ICT AUSTRIA GMBH—See VINCI S.A.; *Int'l*, pg. 8212
AXIANS ICT BV—See VINCI S.A.; *Int'l*, pg. 8212
AXIANS IKVS AG—See VINCI S.A.; *Int'l*, pg. 8212
AXIANS IKVS GMBH—See VINCI S.A.; *Int'l*, pg. 8212
AXIANS INDUSTRIAL APPLICATIONS & SERVICES GMBH—See VINCI S.A.; *Int'l*, pg. 8212
AXIANS INFOMA (SCHWEIZ) A.G.—See Electricite de France S.A.; *Int'l*, pg. 2351
AXIANS INFORMA GMBH—See Electricite de France S.A.; *Int'l*, pg. 2351
AXIANS IOT NORDIC AB—See VINCI S.A.; *Int'l*, pg. 8212
AXIANS IT SECURITY GMBH—See VINCI S.A.; *Int'l*, pg. 8212
AXIANS IT&T AG—See VINCI S.A.; *Int'l*, pg. 8212
AXIANS LYNX GMBH—See VINCI S.A.; *Int'l*, pg. 8212
AXIANS MICATEL AG—See VINCI S.A.; *Int'l*, pg. 8212

COMPANY NAME INDEX

AXIANS NEO SOLUTIONS & TECHNOLOGY GMBH—See VINCI S.A.; *Int'l*, pg. 8212
AXIANS NETLINK B.V.—See VINCI S.A.; *Int'l*, pg. 8236
AXIANS NETWORK SERVICES—See VINCI S.A.; *Int'l*, pg. 8236
AXIANS NETWORKS LIMITED—See VINCI S.A.; *Int'l*, pg. 8212
AXIANS NETWORKS POLAND SP. Z O.O—See VINCI S.A.; *Int'l*, pg. 8212
AXIANS NETWORKS & SOLUTIONS GMBH—See VINCI S.A.; *Int'l*, pg. 8212
AXIANS (NK NETWORKS & SERVICES GMBH)—See VINCI S.A.; *Int'l*, pg. 8238
AXIANS PERFORMANCE SOLUTIONS BV—See VINCI S.A.; *Int'l*, pg. 8212
AXIANS REDTOO INC.—See VINCI S.A.; *Int'l*, pg. 8212
AXIANS REDTOO S.R.O—See VINCI S.A.; *Int'l*, pg. 8212
AXIANS SAIV S.P.A.—See VINCI S.A.; *Int'l*, pg. 8212
AXIANS SA—See VINCI S.A.; *Int'l*, pg. 8236
AXIANS SIRECOM SRL—See VINCI S.A.; *Int'l*, pg. 8212
AXIANS SIRECOM US INC.—See VINCI S.A.; *Int'l*, pg. 8212
AXIANS—See VINCI S.A.; *Int'l*, pg. 8238
AXIANS TECNINFO ANGOLA S.A.—See VINCI S.A.; *Int'l*, pg. 8212
AXIANS TELEMATICS BV—See VINCI S.A.; *Int'l*, pg. 8212
AXIA POWER HOLDINGS, B.V.—See Marubeni Corporation; *Int'l*, pg. 4707
AXIA PUBLIC RELATIONS; *U.S. Private*, pg. 412
AXIARE PATRIMONIO SOCIMI S.A.—See Inmobiliaria Colonial SOCIMI SA; *Int'l*, pg. 3706
AXIA STRATEGIES, INC.—See Aquiline Capital Partners LLC; *U.S. Private*, pg. 304
AXIATA BUSINESS SERVICES SDN BHD—See Axiata Group Berhad; *Int'l*, pg. 768
AXIATA DIGITAL ADVERTISING SDN BHD—See Axiata Group Berhad; *Int'l*, pg. 768
AXIATA DIGITAL CAPITAL SDN BHD—See Axiata Group Berhad; *Int'l*, pg. 768
AXIATA DIGITAL ECODE SDN BHD—See Axiata Group Berhad; *Int'l*, pg. 768
AXIATA DIGITAL LABS (PRIVATE) LIMITED—See Axiata Group Berhad; *Int'l*, pg. 768
AXIATA DIGITAL LABS SDN. BHD.—See Axiata Group Berhad; *Int'l*, pg. 768
AXIATA DIGITAL SERVICES SDN BHD—See Axiata Group Berhad; *Int'l*, pg. 768
AXIATA GROUP BERHAD; *Int'l*, pg. 768
AXICA KONGRESS- UND TAGUNGSZENTRUM PARISER PLATZ 3 GMBH—See DZ BANK AG Deutsche Zentral-Genossenschaftsbank; *Int'l*, pg. 2243
AXICHEM AB; *Int'l*, pg. 768
AXICOM COHN & WOLFE—See WPP plc; *Int'l*, pg. 8469
AXICOM PTY LIMITED—See AustralianSuper Pty Ltd; *Int'l*, pg. 723
AXICOM—See WPP plc; *Int'l*, pg. 8469
AXICOM—See WPP plc; *Int'l*, pg. 8469
AXICOM—See WPP plc; *Int'l*, pg. 8469
AXICOM—See WPP plc; *Int'l*, pg. 8469
AXICOM SRL—See WPP plc; *Int'l*, pg. 8469
AXICORP GMBH—See Dermapharm Holding SE; *Int'l*, pg. 2043
AXI EDUCATION SOLUTIONS, LLC—See Rotunda Capital Partners LLC; *U.S. Private*, pg. 3488
AXIELL GROUP AB; *Int'l*, pg. 768
AXIM BIOTECHNOLOGIES, INC.; *U.S. Public*, pg. 255
AXIM GEOSPATIAL, LLC—See NV5 Global, Inc.; *U.S. Public*, pg. 1557
AXIMUM—See Bouygues S.A.; *Int'l*, pg. 1122
AX INC.—See Axell Corporation; *Int'l*, pg. 767
AXINDUSTRIES AB—See Axel Johnson Gruppen AB; *Int'l*, pg. 763
AXINGTON INC.; *Int'l*, pg. 768
AX INVESTMENTS PLC; *Int'l*, pg. 754
AXIO GROUP MANAGEMENT LTD.—See Epiris Managers LLP; *Int'l*, pg. 2461
AXIOHM S.A.S.—See TXCOM S.A.; *Int'l*, pg. 7993
AXIOHM USA LLC—See TXCOM S.A.; *Int'l*, pg. 7993
AXIOLOGIC SOLUTIONS, LLC; *U.S. Private*, pg. 412
AXIOMA ARGENTINA S.A.U—See Deutsche Borse AG; *Int'l*, pg. 2063
AXIOMA (CH) GMBH—See Deutsche Borse AG; *Int'l*, pg. 2063
AXIOMA GERMANY GMBH—See Deutsche Borse AG; *Int'l*, pg. 2063
AXIOMA, INC.—See Deutsche Borse AG; *Int'l*, pg. 2064
AXIOMA INSURANCE (CYPRUS) LTD—See Allianz SE; *Int'l*, pg. 343
AXIOMA JAPAN G.K—See Deutsche Borse AG; *Int'l*, pg. 2063
AXIOMA S.A.S.U—See Deutsche Borse AG; *Int'l*, pg. 2063
AXIOM AUTOMOTIVE TECHNOLOGIES, INC.—See Blue Point Capital Partners, LLC; *U.S. Private*, pg. 590
AXIOM AUTOMOTIVE TECHNOLOGIES, INC; *U.S. Private*, pg. 413
AXIOM BANK, N.A.; *U.S. Private*, pg. 413
AXIOM CAPITAL ADVISORS, INC.; *Int'l*, pg. 768
AXIOM CONSULTING PARTNERS, LLC; *U.S. Private*, pg. 413
AXIOM CORDAGES LIMITED—See Responsive Industries Ltd; *Int'l*, pg. 6302
AXIOM CORPORATION; *U.S. Private*, pg. 413
AXIOM CORP.; *Int'l*, pg. 769
AXIOM EPM—See Vizient, Inc.; *U.S. Private*, pg. 4407
AXIOMETRICS LLC—See Thoma Bravo, L.P.; *U.S. Private*, pg. 4152
THE AXIOM GROUP, INC.—See Apax Partners LLP; *Int'l*, pg. 503
AXIOM, INC.; *U.S. Private*, pg. 413
AXIOM LABEL, LLC—See Ares Management Corporation; *U.S. Public*, pg. 190
AXIOM LEGAL, INC.-SAN FRANCISCO—See Axiom Automotive Technologies, Inc; *U.S. Private*, pg. 413
AXIOM LEGAL LONDON—See Axiom Automotive Technologies, Inc; *U.S. Private*, pg. 413
AXIOM MANUFACTURING SERVICES LIMITED—See Elate Holdings Limited; *Int'l*, pg. 2343
AXIOM MATERIALS, INC.—See Haci Omer Sabanci Holding A.S.; *Int'l*, pg. 3204
AXIOM (MAURITIUS) EQUITY FUND LTD.—See United Investments Ltd.; *Int'l*, pg. 8069
AXIOM MINING LIMITED; *Int'l*, pg. 769
AXIOM OIL AND GAS CORP.; *U.S. Private*, pg. 413
AXIOM PROPERTIES LIMITED; *Int'l*, pg. 769
AXIOM RAIL COMPONENTS LIMITED—See Deutsche Bahn AG; *Int'l*, pg. 2050
AXIOM RAIL LIMITED—See Deutsche Bahn AG; *Int'l*, pg. 2050
AXIOM RAIL (STOKE) LIMITED—See Deutsche Bahn AG; *Int'l*, pg. 2050
AXIOM RE, INC.—See Aquiline Capital Partners LLC; *U.S. Private*, pg. 304
AXIOM SALES FORCE DEVELOPMENT LLC; *U.S. Private*, pg. 413
AXIOMSL HOLDINGS BV—See Nasdaq, Inc.; *U.S. Public*, pg. 1491
AXIOM; *U.S. Private*, pg. 413
AXIOM TECHNOLOGY INC—See Axiomtek Co., Ltd; *Int'l*, pg. 769
AXIOMTEK CO., LTD; *Int'l*, pg. 769
AXIOMTEK DEUTSCHLAND GMBH—See Axiomtek Co., Ltd; *Int'l*, pg. 769
AXIOMTEK ITALIA S.R.L—See Axiomtek Co., Ltd; *Int'l*, pg. 769
AXIOMTEK (M) SDN. BHD.—See Axiomtek Co., Ltd; *Int'l*, pg. 769
AXIOMTEK TECHNOLOGY (SHEN ZHENG) CO., LTD.—See Axiomtek Co., Ltd; *Int'l*, pg. 769
AXIOMTEK TEKDEUTSCHLAND GMBH—See Axiomtek Co., Ltd; *Int'l*, pg. 769
AXIOMTEK (THAILAND) CO., LTD.—See Axiomtek Co., Ltd; *Int'l*, pg. 769
AXIOM TEST EQUIPMENT, INC.—See Transcat, Inc.; *U.S. Public*, pg. 2179
AXIOM VETERINARY LABORATORIES LIMITED—See CVS Group Plc; *Int'l*, pg. 1890
AXIOM WORLDWIDE INC.; *U.S. Private*, pg. 413
AXION ENERGY—See BP plc; *Int'l*, pg. 1131
AXION ENERGY—See Bridas Corporation; *Int'l*, pg. 1152
AXIO-NET GMBH—See Trimble, Inc.; *U.S. Public*, pg. 2190
AXION GLOBAL DIGITS TECHNOLOGY (HONG KONG) LIMITED—See Edvance International Holdings Limited; *Int'l*, pg. 2316
AXION HEALTH INC.—See Thoma Bravo, L.P.; *U.S. Private*, pg. 4146
AXION POWER INTERNATIONAL, INC.; *U.S. Public*, pg. 255
AXION VENTURES INC.; *Int'l*, pg. 769
AXIO RESEARCH, LLC—See New Mountain Capital, LLC; *U.S. Private*, pg. 2900
AXIOS INC.; *U.S. Private*, pg. 413
AXIOS SUSTAINABLE GROWTH ACQUISITION CORPORATION; *U.S. Public*, pg. 255
AXIOS SYSTEMS PLC.—See EQT AB; *Int'l*, pg. 2477
AXIOS VALUATION SOLUTIONS, LLC—See Assurant, Inc.; *U.S. Public*, pg. 215
AXIS41, INC.—See Dentsu Group Inc.; *Int'l*, pg. 2036
AXIS AB—See Canon Inc.; *Int'l*, pg. 1293
AXIS ASSET MANAGEMENT COMPANY LTD.—See Axis Bank Limited; *Int'l*, pg. 769
AXIS AUTO FINANCE INC.; *Int'l*, pg. 769
AXIS BANK LIMITED - CORPORATE OFFICE—See Axis Bank Limited; *Int'l*, pg. 769
AXIS BANK LIMITED; *Int'l*, pg. 769
AXIS BANK UK LTD.—See Axis Bank Limited; *Int'l*, pg. 769
AXISBIOTIX LIMITED—See Skinbiotherapeutics plc; *Int'l*, pg. 6986
AXIS BUSINESS SOLUTIONS, INC.; *U.S. Private*, pg. 413
AXISCADES GMBH—See Axiscades Technologies Ltd.; *Int'l*, pg. 770
AXISCADES INC.—See Axiscades Technologies Ltd.; *Int'l*, pg. 770
AXISCADES TECHNOLOGIES LTD.; *Int'l*, pg. 770
AXISCADES TECHNOLOGY CANADA INC.—See Axiscades Technologies Ltd.; *Int'l*, pg. 770

AXISS ADVERTISING

AXISCADES UK LIMITED—See Axiscades Technologies Ltd.; *Int'l*, pg. 770
AXIS CAPITAL HOLDINGS LIMITED - AXIS GLOBAL ACCIDENT & HEALTH DIVISION—See AXIS Capital Holdings Limited; *Int'l*, pg. 769
AXIS CAPITAL HOLDINGS LIMITED; *Int'l*, pg. 769
AXIS CAPITAL USA LLC—See Axis Bank Limited; *Int'l*, pg. 769
AXIS COMMUNICATIONS AB—See Canon Inc.; *Int'l*, pg. 1293
AXIS COMMUNICATIONS BV—See Canon Inc.; *Int'l*, pg. 1293
AXIS COMMUNICATIONS GMBH—See Canon Inc.; *Int'l*, pg. 1293
AXIS COMMUNICATIONS KK—See Canon Inc.; *Int'l*, pg. 1293
AXIS COMMUNICATIONS KOREA CO. LTD.—See Canon Inc.; *Int'l*, pg. 1293
AXIS COMMUNICATIONS OOO—See Canon Inc.; *Int'l*, pg. 1293
AXIS COMMUNICATIONS PTY LTD—See Canon Inc.; *Int'l*, pg. 1293
AXIS COMMUNICATIONS (SA) (PTY) LTD—See Canon Inc.; *Int'l*, pg. 1293
AXIS COMMUNICATIONS—See Canon Inc.; *Int'l*, pg. 1293
AXIS COMMUNICATIONS; *U.S. Private*, pg. 413
AXIS COMMUNICATIONS (S) PTE LTD—See Canon Inc.; *Int'l*, pg. 1293
AXIS COMMUNICATIONS TAIWAN CO., LTD.—See Canon Inc.; *Int'l*, pg. 1293
AXIS COMMUNICATIONS (UK) LTD—See Canon Inc.; *Int'l*, pg. 1293
AXIS CONSULTING 2000 LTD—See 4iG Nyrt.; *Int'l*, pg. 12
AXIS CONSULTING CORPORATION; *Int'l*, pg. 770
AXIS CREATE INC.—See Open Up Group Inc; *Int'l*, pg. 5598
AXIS DEVICE TECHNOLOGY CO., LTD.—See Sanshin Electronics Co., Ltd.; *Int'l*, pg. 6556
AXIS ELECTRONICS LIMITED—See Cicor Technologies Ltd.; *Int'l*, pg. 1603
AXIS ENERGY SERVICES HOLDINGS INC.—See Precision Drilling Corporation; *Int'l*, pg. 5957
AXIS EXPLORATION, LLC—See Civitas Resources, Inc.; *U.S. Public*, pg. 507
AXIS FINANCE LTD.—See Axis Bank Limited; *Int'l*, pg. 769
AXIS GEOSPATIAL LLC—See Peak Rock Capital LLC; *U.S. Private*, pg. 3124
AXIS GLOBAL SYSTEMS LLC; *U.S. Private*, pg. 413
AXIS GROUP, INC.—See Jack Cooper Transport Co., Inc.; *U.S. Private*, pg. 2173
AXIS GROUP, LLC; *U.S. Private*, pg. 413
AXIS GROUP SERVICES, INC.—See AXIS Capital Holdings Limited; *Int'l*, pg. 769
AXIS INFORMATION SYSTEMS; *Int'l*, pg. 770
AXIS INSURANCE COMPANY—See AXIS Capital Holdings Limited; *Int'l*, pg. 769
AXISMATERIA LTD.—See Sumitomo Electric Industries, Ltd.; *Int'l*, pg. 7277
AXIS MEDIA; *U.S. Private*, pg. 413
AXIS MUNDI SA—See Nippon Telegraph & Telephone Corporation; *Int'l*, pg. 5349
AXIS MUTUAL FUND TRUSTEE LTD.—See Axis Bank Limited; *Int'l*, pg. 769
AXIS PRIVATE EQUITY LIMITED—See Axis Bank Limited; *Int'l*, pg. 769
AXIS REAL ESTATE INVESTMENT TRUST; *Int'l*, pg. 770
AXIS REINSURANCE COMPANY—See AXIS Capital Holdings Limited; *Int'l*, pg. 769
AXIS RE LIMITED—See AXIS Capital Holdings Limited; *Int'l*, pg. 769
AXIS RE SE—See AXIS Capital Holdings Limited; *Int'l*, pg. 769
AXIS RISK CONSULTING SERVICES PVT. LTD.—See Genpact Limited; *Int'l*, pg. 2926
AXISS ADVERTISING; *U.S. Private*, pg. 414
AXIS SECURITIES LTD.—See Axis Bank Limited; *Int'l*, pg. 769
AXIS-SHIELD AS—See Abbott Laboratories; *U.S. Public*, pg. 19
AXIS-SHIELD DIAGNOSTICS LIMITED—See Abbott Laboratories; *U.S. Public*, pg. 19
AXIS-SHIELD LIMITED—See Abbott Laboratories; *U.S. Public*, pg. 19
AXISSOFT CORPORATION—See Sojitz Corporation; *Int'l*, pg. 7062
AXIS SPECIALTY EUROPE LIMITED—See AXIS Capital Holdings Limited; *Int'l*, pg. 770
AXIS SPECIALTY FINANCE LLC—See AXIS Capital Holdings Limited; *Int'l*, pg. 770
AXIS SPECIALTY INSURANCE CO.—See AXIS Capital Holdings Limited; *Int'l*, pg. 770
AXIS SPECIALTY LIMITED—See AXIS Capital Holdings Limited; *Int'l*, pg. 770
AXIS SPECIALTY UK HOLDINGS LIMITED—See AXIS Capital Holdings Limited; *Int'l*, pg. 770
AXIS SURPLUS INSURANCE COMPANY—See AXIS Capital Holdings Limited; *Int'l*, pg. 770

AXIS TECHNOLOGIES GROUP, INC.

AXIS TECHNOLOGIES GROUP, INC.; *U.S. Public*, pg. 255
AXIS TECHNOLOGY, LLC—See Clearlake Capital Group, L.P.; *U.S. Private*, pg. 936
AXIS TECHNOLOGY, LLC—See Francisco Partners Management, LP; *U.S. Private*, pg. 1591
AXIS-TEC PTE. LTD.—See Ellipsiz Ltd.; *Int'l*, pg. 2366
AXIS TEKNOLOGIES; *U.S. Private*, pg. 414
AXIS TRUSTEE SERVICES LIMITED—See Raymond Limited; *Int'l*, pg. 6224
AXIS UNDERWRITING SERVICES PTY LTD—See Steadfast Group Limited; *Int'l*, pg. 7187
AXITA COTTON LTD.; *Int'l*, pg. 770
AXITEA S.P.A—See Stirling Square Capital Partners LLP; *Int'l*, pg. 7216
AXIUM HEALTHCARE PHARMACY, INC.—See The Kroger Co.; *U.S. Public*, pg. 2107
AXIUM INFRASTRUCTURE INC.; *U.S. Private*, pg. 414
AXIUM INSPECTIONS, LLC—See RFE Investment Partners; *U.S. Private*, pg. 3419
AXIUM PHARMACEUTICALS, INC.; *U.S. Private*, pg. 414
AXIUM PHARMACY HOLDINGS, INC.—See The Kroger Co.; *U.S. Public*, pg. 2107
AXIUM XTS CORPORATION; *U.S. Private*, pg. 414
AXIUS WATER—See KKR & Co. Inc.; *U.S. Public*, pg. 1239
AXIUS WATER—See XPV Water Partners; *Int'l*, pg. 8538
AXIVION GMBH—See Qt Group Plc; *Int'l*, pg. 6148
AXIZ BOTSWANA PROPRIETARY LIMITED—See Alviva Holdings Limited; *Int'l*, pg. 401
AXJO KABEL AG—See Nexans S.A.; *Int'l*, pg. 5241
AXLBIT, INC.—See Equinix, Inc.; *U.S. Public*, pg. 787
AXLE GROUP HOLDINGS LIMITED—See Halfords Group plc; *Int'l*, pg. 3229
AXLES INDIA LIMITED—See Sundaram Brake Linings Limited; *Int'l*, pg. 7312
AXLETECH DO BRASIL SISTEMAS AUTOMOTIVOS LTDA.—See Cummins Inc.; *U.S. Public*, pg. 608
AXLETECH INTERNATIONAL HOLDINGS, INC.—See Cummins Inc.; *U.S. Public*, pg. 608
AXLETECH INTERNATIONAL, LLC—See Cummins Inc.; *U.S. Public*, pg. 608
AXLETECH INTERNATIONAL SAS—See Cummins Inc.; *U.S. Public*, pg. 608
AXL MUSICAL INSTRUMENTS CO., LTD., CORP.; *U.S. Private*, pg. 414
AXLOAD AB—See Axel Johnson Gruppen AB; *Int'l*, pg. 763
AXLY PRODUCTION MACHINING INC.—See Gemini Group, Inc.; *U.S. Private*, pg. 1657
AXMIN, INC.; *Int'l*, pg. 770
AXM PHARMA, INC.; *U.S. Private*, pg. 414
AXN LATIN AMERICA INC.—See Sony Group Corporation; *Int'l*, pg. 7107
AXOGEN CORPORATION—See AxoGen, Inc.; *U.S. Public*, pg. 255
AXOGEN, INC.; *U.S. Public*, pg. 255
AXOLABS GMBH—See Roche Holding AG; *Int'l*, pg. 6373
AXO LIGHT S.R.L.—See Dexelance S.p.A.; *Int'l*, pg. 2092
AXOLOT SOLUTIONS HOLDING AB; *Int'l*, pg. 770
AXOM TECHNOLOGIES, LLC—See Sagewind Capital LLC; *U.S. Private*, pg. 3527
AXON ACTIVE AG; *Int'l*, pg. 770
AXON COMMUNICATIONS INC.—See Mountaingate Capital Management, L.P.; *U.S. Private*, pg. 2801
AXONE BV—See LGM; *Int'l*, pg. 4477
AXONE GMBH—See LGM; *Int'l*, pg. 4477
AXON ENTERPRISE, INC.; *U.S. Public*, pg. 255
AXON GROUP LIMITED—See HCL Technologies Ltd.; *Int'l*, pg. 3298
AXON HOLDINGS S.A.; *Int'l*, pg. 770
AXONICS, INC.; *U.S. Public*, pg. 256
AX-ON INC—See Nippon Television Holdings Inc.; *Int'l*, pg. 5356
AXON LAB AG—See HORIBA Ltd; *Int'l*, pg. 3475
AXON LAB AG—See HORIBA Ltd; *Int'l*, pg. 3475
AXON LAB B.V.—See HORIBA Ltd; *Int'l*, pg. 3475
AXON LAB D.O.O.—See HORIBA Ltd; *Int'l*, pg. 3475
AXON LAB NV—See HORIBA Ltd; *Int'l*, pg. 3475
AXON LAB SPOL. S R.O.—See HORIBA Ltd; *Int'l*, pg. 3475
AXON LLC—See Leonard Green & Partners, L.P.; *U.S. Private*, pg. 2427
AXON NEUROSCIENCE SE—See ISTROKAPITAL SE; *Int'l*, pg. 3824
AXONOM, INC.—See TA Associates, Inc.; *U.S. Private*, pg. 3914
AXON PARTNERS GROUP SA; *Int'l*, pg. 771
AXONPRIME INFRASTRUCTURE ACQUISITION CORP.; *U.S. Public*, pg. 256
AXON PUBLIC SAFETY UK LIMITED—See Axon Enterprise, Inc.; *U.S. Public*, pg. 256
AXON SECURITIES S.A.—See AXON Holdings S.A.; *Int'l*, pg. 770
AXON SOLUTIONS LIMITED—See HCL Technologies Ltd.; *Int'l*, pg. 3298
AXON SOLUTIONS SDN BHD—See HCL Technologies Ltd.; *Int'l*, pg. 3298
AXON VENTURES LIMITED; *Int'l*, pg. 771

AXOS BANK—See Axos Financial, Inc.; *U.S. Public*, pg. 256
AXOS CLEARING LLC—See Axos Financial, Inc.; *U.S. Public*, pg. 256
AXOS DIGITAL ASSETS LLC—See Axos Financial, Inc.; *U.S. Public*, pg. 256
AXOS FINANCIAL, INC.; *U.S. Public*, pg. 256
AXP ENERGY LIMITED; *Int'l*, pg. 771
AXPO ALBANIA SH.A.—See Axpo Holding AG; *Int'l*, pg. 771
AXPO AUSTRIA GMBH—See Axpo Holding AG; *Int'l*, pg. 771
AXPO BENELUX S.A.—See Axpo Holding AG; *Int'l*, pg. 771
AXPO BH DOO—See Axpo Holding AG; *Int'l*, pg. 771
AXPO BULGARIA EAD—See Axpo Holding AG; *Int'l*, pg. 771
AXPO DEUTSCHLAND GMBH—See Axpo Holding AG; *Int'l*, pg. 771
AXPO D.O.O. BEOGRAD—See Axpo Holding AG; *Int'l*, pg. 771
AXPO DOOEL MK—See Axpo Holding AG; *Int'l*, pg. 771
AXPO D.O.O.—See Axpo Holding AG; *Int'l*, pg. 771
AXPO ENERGY ROMANIA S.A.—See Axpo Holding AG; *Int'l*, pg. 771
AXPO FINLAND OY—See Axpo Holding AG; *Int'l*, pg. 771
AXPO FRANCE S.A.S.—See Axpo Holding AG; *Int'l*, pg. 771
AXPO GAS SERVICE ITALIA SPA—See Axpo Holding AG; *Int'l*, pg. 771
AXPO HOLDING AG; *Int'l*, pg. 771
AXPO HOLZ + ENERGIE AG—See Axpo Holding AG; *Int'l*, pg. 771
AXPO IBERIA S.L.—See Axpo Holding AG; *Int'l*, pg. 771
AXPO INFORMATIK AG—See Axpo Holding AG; *Int'l*, pg. 771
AXPO INTERNATIONAL S.A.—See Axpo Holding AG; *Int'l*, pg. 771
AXPO ITALIA S.P.A.—See Axpo Holding AG; *Int'l*, pg. 771
AXPO KOMPOGAS AG—See Axpo Holding AG; *Int'l*, pg. 771
AXPO NORDIC AS—See Axpo Holding AG; *Int'l*, pg. 771
AXPO POLSKA SP.Z.O.O.—See Axpo Holding AG; *Int'l*, pg. 771
AXPO SINGAPORE PTE. LTD.—See Axpo Holding AG; *Int'l*, pg. 771
AXPO SLOVENSKO, S.R.O.—See Axpo Holding AG; *Int'l*, pg. 771
AXPO SOLUTIONS AG—See Axpo Holding AG; *Int'l*, pg. 771
AXPO SVERIGE AB—See Axpo Holding AG; *Int'l*, pg. 771
AXPO TEGRA AG—See Axpo Holding AG; *Int'l*, pg. 771
AXPO TRADING AG - HEAD OFFICE & TRADING CENTER—See Axpo Holding AG; *Int'l*, pg. 771
AXPO TRGOVINA D.O.O.—See Axpo Holding AG; *Int'l*, pg. 771
AXPO TURKEY ENERJI A.S.—See Axpo Holding AG; *Int'l*, pg. 771
AXPO UK LTD.—See Axpo Holding AG; *Int'l*, pg. 771
AXPO UKRAINE LLC—See Axpo Holding AG; *Int'l*, pg. 771
AXPO U.S. LLC—See Axpo Holding AG; *Int'l*, pg. 771
AXPRO FRANCE S.A.—See Axel Johnson Gruppen AB; *Int'l*, pg. 762
AXRO HOLDING AB—See Sweco AB; *Int'l*, pg. 7363
AXSCEND LTD.—See SAF-Holland S.A.; *Int'l*, pg. 6467
AXSESSTODAY LIMITED—See Cerberus Capital Management, L.P.; *U.S. Private*, pg. 837
AXSOME THERAPEUTICS, INC.; *U.S. Public*, pg. 256
AXSON CENTRAL EUROPE S.R.O.—See Sika AG; *Int'l*, pg. 6918
AXSON INDIA PVT. LTD.—See Sika AG; *Int'l*, pg. 6916
AXSON ITALIA S.R.L.—See Sika AG; *Int'l*, pg. 6916
AXSON JAPAN K.K.—See Sika AG; *Int'l*, pg. 6917
AXSON MEXICO, S.A. DE C.V.—See Sika AG; *Int'l*, pg. 6917
AXSON TECHNOLOGIES SHANGHAI CO., LTD.—See Sika AG; *Int'l*, pg. 6915
AXSON TECHNOLOGIES SPAIN S.L.—See Sika AG; *Int'l*, pg. 6918
AXSON TECHNOLOGIES US, INC.—See Sika AG; *Int'l*, pg. 6916
AXSON UK LTD.—See Sika AG; *Int'l*, pg. 6917
AXS PTE LTD—See DBS Group Holdings Ltd.; *Int'l*, pg. 1988
AXSTORES AB—See Axel Johnson Gruppen AB; *Int'l*, pg. 764
AXSUN TECHNOLOGIES, INC.—See AEA Investors LP; *U.S. Private*, pg. 113
AXTEL INDUSTRIES LIMITED; *Int'l*, pg. 772
AXTELL-TAYLOR GM, LLC; *U.S. Private*, pg. 414
AXTERIA GROUP BERHAD; *Int'l*, pg. 772
AXT, INC.; *U.S. Public*, pg. 256
AXTONE GMBH—See ITT Inc.; *U.S. Public*, pg. 1177
AXTONE HSW SP. Z.O.O.—See ITT Inc.; *U.S. Public*, pg. 1177
AXTONE S.A.—See ITT Inc.; *U.S. Public*, pg. 1177
AXTONE S.R.O.—See ITT Inc.; *U.S. Public*, pg. 1177
AXUS FINLAND OY—See Societe Generale S.A.; *Int'l*, pg. 7038

CORPORATE AFFILIATIONS

AXUS ITALIANA SRL—See Societe Generale S.A.; *Int'l*, pg. 7038
AXUS NEDERLAND BV—See Societe Generale S.A.; *Int'l*, pg. 7038
AXUS SA/NV—See Societe Generale S.A.; *Int'l*, pg. 7038
AXWAY ASIA PACIFIC PTE LTD—See Axway Software SA; *Int'l*, pg. 772
AXWAY BELGIUM SA—See Axway Software SA; *Int'l*, pg. 772
AXWAY BULGARIA—See Axway Software SA; *Int'l*, pg. 772
AXWAY BV—See Axway Software SA; *Int'l*, pg. 772
AXWAY GMBH—See Axway Software SA; *Int'l*, pg. 772
AXWAY INC.—See Axway Software SA; *Int'l*, pg. 772
AXWAY IRELAND LIMITED—See Axway Software SA; *Int'l*, pg. 772
AXWAY LIMITED—See Axway Software SA; *Int'l*, pg. 772
AXWAY LTD.—See Axway Software SA; *Int'l*, pg. 772
AXWAY NORDIC AB—See Axway Software SA; *Int'l*, pg. 772
AXWAY PTE. LTD.—See Axway Software SA; *Int'l*, pg. 772
AXWAY PTY LTD—See Axway Software SA; *Int'l*, pg. 772
AXWAY ROMANIA SRL—See Axway Software SA; *Int'l*, pg. 772
AXWAY SOFTWARE CHINA—See Axway Software SA; *Int'l*, pg. 772
AXWAY SOFTWARE DO BRASIL LTDA.—See Axway Software SA; *Int'l*, pg. 772
AXWAY SOFTWARE GMBH—See Axway Software SA; *Int'l*, pg. 772
AXWAY SOFTWARE IBERIA—See Axway Software SA; *Int'l*, pg. 772
AXWAY SOFTWARE MALAYSIA SDN BHD—See Axway Software SA; *Int'l*, pg. 772
AXWAY SOFTWARE SA; *Int'l*, pg. 772
AXWAY—See Axway Software SA; *Int'l*, pg. 772
AXWAY SRL—See Axway Software SA; *Int'l*, pg. 772
AXWAY UK LTD—See Axway Software SA; *Int'l*, pg. 772
AXXCELERA BROADBAND WIRELESS INC.—See Moseley Associates, Inc.; *U.S. Private*, pg. 2793
AXXE REISEGASTRONOMIE GMBH—See Abu Dhabi Investment Authority; *Int'l*, pg. 71
AXXE REISEGASTRONOMIE GMBH—See Allianz SE; *Int'l*, pg. 351
AXXE REISEGASTRONOMIE GMBH—See Munchener Ruckversicherungs AG; *Int'l*, pg. 5085
AXXE REISEGASTRONOMIE GMBH—See Ontario Municipal Employees Retirement System; *Int'l*, pg. 5584
AXXESS CAPITAL; *Int'l*, pg. 772
AXXESS TECHNOLOGY SOLUTIONS, INC; *U.S. Private*, pg. 414
AXXIOME AG; *Int'l*, pg. 772
AXXIOME AMERICAS, INC.—See Axxiome AG; *Int'l*, pg. 772
AXXIOME ASIA PACIFIC PTE. LTD.—See Axxiome AG; *Int'l*, pg. 772
AXXIOME BENELUX BV—See Axxiome AG; *Int'l*, pg. 772
AXXIOME BRASIL LTDA.—See Axxiome AG; *Int'l*, pg. 773
AXXIOME CANADA LTD.—See Axxiome AG; *Int'l*, pg. 773
AXXIOME CIS LLC.—See Axxiome AG; *Int'l*, pg. 773
AXXIOME COLOMBIA S.A.S.—See Axxiome AG; *Int'l*, pg. 773
AXXIOME DEUTSCHLAND GMBH—See Axxiome AG; *Int'l*, pg. 773
AXXIOME POLSKA SP. Z O.O—See Axxiome AG; *Int'l*, pg. 773
AXXIOME S.A.—See Axxiome AG; *Int'l*, pg. 773
AXXIOME UK LTD.—See Axxiome AG; *Int'l*, pg. 773
AXXIOME URUGUAY S.A.—See Axxiome AG; *Int'l*, pg. 773
AXXIOME USA LLC—See Axxiome AG; *Int'l*, pg. 773
AXXIOM SOLUCOES TECNOLOGICAS S.A.—See Light S.A.; *Int'l*, pg. 4496
AXXION ASSET MANAGEMENT SAC; *Int'l*, pg. 773
AXXIS CONSULTING (S) PTE. LTD.—See BIPROGY Inc.; *Int'l*, pg. 1045
AXXIS DRILLING INC.—See Ensign Energy Services Inc.; *Int'l*, pg. 2447
THE AXXON GROUP SERVICOS DE CONSULTORIA E ASSESSORIA LTDA—See Groupe BPCE; *Int'l*, pg. 3096
AXXON WERTPAPIERHANDELSBANK AG; *Int'l*, pg. 773
AXXSYS DANMARK APS—See Bridgepoint Group Plc; *Int'l*, pg. 1153
AXXZIA, INC.; *Int'l*, pg. 773
AXYGEN BIOSCIENCE, INC.—See Corning Incorporated; *U.S. Public*, pg. 578
AXYGEN, INC.—See Corning Incorporated; *U.S. Public*, pg. 578
AXYNTIS SAS—See Argos Wityu S.A.; *Int'l*, pg. 563
AXYON CONSULTING, LLC; *U.S. Private*, pg. 414
AXYS GROUP LTD.—See United Investments Ltd.; *Int'l*, pg. 8070
AXYS INDUSTRIAL SOLUTIONS, INC.; *U.S. Private*, pg. 414
AXYS INVESTMENT PARTNERS LTD.—See United Investments Ltd.; *Int'l*, pg. 8070
AXYS; *U.S. Private*, pg. 414

COMPANY NAME INDEX

AXYS STOCKBROKING LTD.—See United Investments Ltd.; *Int'l*, pg. 8070
AXYZ AUTOMATION GROUP INC.; *Int'l*, pg. 773
AXYZ AUTOMATION INC.—See AXYZ Automation Group Inc.; *Int'l*, pg. 773
AXYZ CO., LTD.; *Int'l*, pg. 773
AXYZ OHIO VALLEY REGION, INC.—See AXYZ Automation Group Inc.; *Int'l*, pg. 773
AYABE ENGINEERING PLASTICS CO., LTD.—See Gunze Limited; *Int'l*, pg. 3185
AYABE TOYO RUBBER CO.,LTD—See Toyo Tire Corporation; *Int'l*, pg. 7859
AYA CONSTRUCTION CO., LTD.—See Senko Group Holdings Co., Ltd.; *Int'l*, pg. 6709
AYA GOLD & SILVER INC.; *Int'l*, pg. 773
AYA GOLD & SILVER MAROC S.A.—See Aya Gold & Silver Inc.; *Int'l*, pg. 773
AYA KITCHENS & BATHS, LTD.; *Int'l*, pg. 773
AYALA AUTOMOTIVE HOLDINGS CORPORATION—See Ayala Corporation; *Int'l*, pg. 773
AYALA AVIATION CORPORATION—See Ayala Corporation; *Int'l*, pg. 773
AYALA CORPORATION; *Int'l*, pg. 773
AYALA FOUNDATION, INC.—See Ayala Corporation; *Int'l*, pg. 774
AYALA HOTELS, INC.—See Ayala Corporation; *Int'l*, pg. 774
AYALA INTERNATIONAL PTE. LTD.—See Ayala Corporation; *Int'l*, pg. 774
AYALA LAND, INC.—See Ayala Corporation; *Int'l*, pg. 774
AYALALAND LOGISTICS HOLDINGS CORP.; *Int'l*, pg. 774
AYALA PHARMACEUTICALS, INC.; *U.S. Public*, pg. 256
AYALON INSURANCE COMPANY LTD.; *Int'l*, pg. 774
AYAMAS FOOD CORPORATION SDN. BHD.—See Johor Corporation; *Int'l*, pg. 3994
AYAMAS SHOPPE SDN BHD—See Johor Corporation; *Int'l*, pg. 3994
AYANDA GMBH—See Sirio Pharma Co., Ltd.; *Int'l*, pg. 6961
A YARD & A HALF LANDSCAPING LLC; *U.S. Private*, pg. 19
AYARS & AYARS INCORPORATED; *U.S. Private*, pg. 414
AYAS ENERJI URETIM VETICARET A.S.—See OYAK Cement Group; *Int'l*, pg. 5677
AYASE SEIMITSU CO., LTD—See NHK Spring Co., Ltd.; *Int'l*, pg. 5257
AYATTI INNOVATIVE PRIVATE LIMITED—See Paras Defence & Space Technologies Ltd.; *Int'l*, pg. 5739
AYCASH GMBH—See Fiserv, Inc.; *U.S. Public*, pg. 851
AYCOCK, LLC—See Enerfab, Inc.; *U.S. Private*, pg. 1392
THE AYCO COMPANY, L.P.—See The Goldman Sachs Group, Inc.; *U.S. Public*, pg. 2082
AYCO FARMS INC.; *U.S. Private*, pg. 414
AYCO GRUPO INMOBILIARIO, S.A.; *Int'l*, pg. 774
AYDEM YENILENEBILIR ENERJI A.S.; *Int'l*, pg. 774
AYDIN DISPLAYS, INC.—See Elbit Systems Limited; *Int'l*, pg. 2344
AYEN ELECTRIC TRADING INC.—See Ayen Enerji AS; *Int'l*, pg. 774
AYEN ELEKTRIK TICARET A.S.—See Ayen Enerji AS; *Int'l*, pg. 774
AYEN ENERGIJA D.O.O—See Ayen Enerji AS; *Int'l*, pg. 774
AYEN ENERGY TRADING D.O.O—See Ayen Enerji AS; *Int'l*, pg. 775
AYEN ENERGY TRADING SHA—See Ayen Enerji AS; *Int'l*, pg. 775
AYEN ENERJI AS; *Int'l*, pg. 774
AYEPEE LAMITUBES LIMITED; *Int'l*, pg. 775
AYER HITAM LAND SDN. BHD.—See Gromutual Berhad; *Int'l*, pg. 3087
AYER HOLDINGS BERHAD; *Int'l*, pg. 775
AYER SALES INC.; *U.S. Private*, pg. 414
AYERS BASEMENT SYSTEMS, LLC.; *U.S. Private*, pg. 414
AYERS CHEVROLET & OLDSMOBILE, INC.; *U.S. Private*, pg. 414
AYERS EXPLORATION INC.; *Int'l*, pg. 775
AYERS GROUP INC.—See Silver Oak Services Partners, LLC; *U.S. Private*, pg. 3661
AYERS MUSIC CO.—See Wan Shyh Shing Co., Ltd.; *Int'l*, pg. 8340
AYERS OIL CO. INC.; *U.S. Private*, pg. 414
AYERST-WYETH PHARMACEUTICALS LLC—See Pfizer Inc.; *U.S. Public*, pg. 1679
AYES CELIK HASIR VE CIT SANAYI A.S.; *Int'l*, pg. 775
AYFIE GROUP AS; *Int'l*, pg. 775
AYGAZ A.S.—See Koc Holding A.S.; *Int'l*, pg. 4222
AYGAZ DOGAL GAZ TOPTAN SATIS A.S.—See Koc Holding A.S.; *Int'l*, pg. 4222
AYIMA LIMITED—See New Equity Venture Int. AB; *Int'l*, pg. 5223
AYKLEY WOODS (DURHAM) MANAGEMENT COMPANY LIMITED—See Persimmon plc; *Int'l*, pg. 5815
AYLA OASIS DEVELOPMENT COMPANY—See Arab Supply & Trading Co.; *Int'l*, pg. 532
AYLESWORTH FLEMING LIMITED—See You & Mr Jones Inc.; *U.S. Private*, pg. 4591

AY MANUFACTURING LTD.—See Honda Motor Co., Ltd.; *Int'l*, pg. 3464
A.Y. MCDONALD MANUFACTURING CO.; *U.S. Private*, pg. 29
A.Y.M. INC.—See A.Y. McDonald Manufacturing Co.; *U.S. Private*, pg. 29
AYM SYNTEX LIMITED—See Welspun Group; *Int'l*, pg. 8375
AYNGARAN INTERNATIONAL LTD.; *Int'l*, pg. 775
AYNGARAN INTERNATIONAL MEDIA PVT. LTD.—See Ayngaran International Ltd.; *Int'l*, pg. 775
AYNOR FOODS INC.—See W. Lee Flowers & Company Inc.; *U.S. Private*, pg. 4418
AYON CYBERSECURITY, INC.—See Video Display Corporation; *U.S. Public*, pg. 2296
AYONDO LTD.; *Int'l*, pg. 775
AYON VISUAL SOLUTIONS—See Video Display Corporation; *U.S. Public*, pg. 2296
AYO TECHNOLOGY SOLUTIONS LTD.; *Int'l*, pg. 775
AYOUBCO GENERAL CONTRACTING; *Int'l*, pg. 775
AYR ENVIRONMENTAL SERVICES LIMITED—See CK Hutchison Holdings Limited; *Int'l*, pg. 1637
AYR ENVIRONMENTAL SERVICES OPERATIONS LIMITED—See CK Hutchison Holdings Limited; *Int'l*, pg. 1637
AYRES ASSOCIATES INC.; *U.S. Private*, pg. 414
THE AYRES COMPANY—See Ayres-Delta Implement, Inc.; *U.S. Private*, pg. 415
AYRES-DELTA IMPLEMENT, INC.; *U.S. Private*, pg. 414
AYRES-DELTA IMPLEMENT OF BELZONI, INC.—See Ayres-Delta Implement, Inc.; *U.S. Private*, pg. 414
THE AYRES GROUP, LLC; *U.S. Private*, pg. 3990
AYRES KAHLER + SACCO; *U.S. Private*, pg. 414
AYRES-RICE INSURANCE AGENCY, INC.—See The Ayres Group, LLC; *U.S. Private*, pg. 3990
AYR MOTOR EXPRESS INC.; *Int'l*, pg. 775
AYRO, INC.; *U.S. Public*, pg. 256
AYRTON DRUGS MANUFACTURING COMPANY LIMITED; *Int'l*, pg. 775
AYR WELLNESS INC.; *Int'l*, pg. 775
AYS (FZ) SDN. BHD.—See AYS Ventures Berhad; *Int'l*, pg. 775
AYSLING LLC—See Valsef Group; *Int'l*, pg. 8123
AYS METAL PRODUCTS & ENGINEERING SDN. BHD.—See AYS Ventures Berhad; *Int'l*, pg. 775
AYSON GEOTEKNIK VE DENIZ INSAAT A.S.—See Dogus Holding AS; *Int'l*, pg. 2154
AYS PLACEMENTS & WORKSHOP S.R.O—See Randstad N.V.; *Int'l*, pg. 6201
AYS VENTURES BERHAD; *Int'l*, pg. 775
AYS WIRE PRODUCTS SDN. BHD.—See AYS Ventures Berhad; *Int'l*, pg. 776
AYTAC GIDA YATIRIM SANAYI VE TICARET A.S.—See Yildiz Holding AS; *Int'l*, pg. 8583
AYTEMIZ AKARYAKIT DAGITIM A.S.—See PJSC Tatneft; *Int'l*, pg. 5885
AYTU BIOPHARMA, INC.; *U.S. Public*, pg. 256
AYUDA MANAGEMENT CORPORATION; *U.S. Private*, pg. 415
AYUDHYA CAPITAL AUTO LEASE PLC—See Mitsubishi UFJ Financial Group, Inc.; *Int'l*, pg. 4969
AYUDHYA CAPITAL SERVICES COMPANY LIMITED—See Mitsubishi UFJ Financial Group, Inc.; *Int'l*, pg. 4969
AYUDHYA DEVELOPMENT LEASING CO., LTD.—See Mitsubishi UFJ Financial Group, Inc.; *Int'l*, pg. 4969
AYUJOY HERBALS LTD.; *U.S. Public*, pg. 257
AYURA LABORATORIES INC.—See AIN Holdings Inc.; *Int'l*, pg. 234
AYURVEDAGRAM HERITAGE WELLNESS CENTRE PVT. LTD.—See Kerala Ayurveda Ltd.; *Int'l*, pg. 4132
AYU TECHNOLOGY SOLUTIONS LLC; *U.S. Private*, pg. 415
AYUTTHAYA GLASS INDUSTRY CO., LTD.—See BG Container Glass Public Company Limited; *Int'l*, pg. 1006
AYVALIK MARINA VE YAT ISLETMECILIGI SAN. VE TIC. A.S.—See Koc Holding A.S.; *Int'l*, pg. 4222
AYYAN INVESTMENT CO.; *Int'l*, pg. 776
AYZENBERG GROUP, INC.; *U.S. Private*, pg. 415
AZABACHE ENERGY INC.; *Int'l*, pg. 776
AZADEGAN PETROLEUM DEVELOPMENT, LTD.—See INPEX CORPORATION; *Int'l*, pg. 3716
AZAD ENGINEERING LIMITED; *Int'l*, pg. 776
AZAD INTERNATIONAL INC.; *U.S. Private*, pg. 415
AZALEA CAPITAL, LLC; *U.S. Private*, pg. 415
AZALEA COLOR COMPANY; *U.S. Private*, pg. 415
AZALEA GARDENS OF MOBILE—See Management Seven, LLC; *U.S. Private*, pg. 2561
AZALEA HEALTH INNOVATIONS, INC.; *U.S. Private*, pg. 415
AZAM EKUITI SDN BHD—See IJM Corporation Berhad; *Int'l*, pg. 3608
AZ ANZEIGER AG—See BT Holding AG; *Int'l*, pg. 1204
AZARAB INDUSTRIES; *Int'l*, pg. 776
AZARA HEALTHCARE LLC; *U.S. Private*, pg. 415
AZARBAIJAN INVESTMENT DEVELOPMENT COMPANY; *Int'l*, pg. 776
AZARGA METALS CORP.; *Int'l*, pg. 776
AZARGA URANIUM CORP.; *Int'l*, pg. 776

AZ-ARGES VERMOGENSVERWALTUNGSGESELLSCHAFT MBH—See Allianz SE; *Int'l*, pg. 343
AZ-ARGOS 50 VERMOGENSVERWALTUNGSGESELLSCHAFT MBH & CO. KG—See Allianz SE; *Int'l*, pg. 343
AZ-ARGOS 51 VERMOGENSVERWALTUNGSGESELLSCHAFT MBH & CO. KG—See Allianz SE; *Int'l*, pg. 343
AZ-ARGOS 56 VERMOGENSVERWALTUNGSGESELLSCHAFT MBH—See Allianz SE; *Int'l*, pg. 343
AZAR INCORPORATED; *U.S. Private*, pg. 415
AZAR INTERNATIONAL CORP.; *Int'l*, pg. 776
AZARIT COMPANY; *Int'l*, pg. 776
AZAR REFRACTORIES CO.; *Int'l*, pg. 776
AZART-SAT SP ZOO—See Liberty Global plc; *Int'l*, pg. 4484
AZAVEA INCORPORATED; *U.S. Private*, pg. 415
AZAZIE, INC.; *U.S. Private*, pg. 415
AZBAR LTD—See Tipperary Co-operative Creamery Ltd.; *Int'l*, pg. 7756
AZBIL BRAZIL LIMITED—See Azbil Corporation; *Int'l*, pg. 777
AZBIL CONTROL INSTRUMENTS (DALIAN) CO., LTD.—See Azbil Corporation; *Int'l*, pg. 777
AZBIL CONTROL INSTRUMENT TRADING (DALIAN) CO., LTD.—See Azbil Corporation; *Int'l*, pg. 777
AZBIL CONTROL SOLUTIONS (SHANGHAI) CO., LTD.—See Azbil Corporation; *Int'l*, pg. 777
AZBIL CORPORATION; *Int'l*, pg. 776
AZBIL EUROPE NV—See Azbil Corporation; *Int'l*, pg. 777
AZBIL EUROPE NV—See Azbil Corporation; *Int'l*, pg. 777
AZBIL HONG KONG LIMITED—See Azbil Corporation; *Int'l*, pg. 777
AZBIL INDIA PRIVATE LIMITED—See Azbil Corporation; *Int'l*, pg. 777
AZBIL INFORMATION TECHNOLOGY CENTER (DALIAN) CO., LTD.—See Azbil Corporation; *Int'l*, pg. 777
AZBIL KIMMON CO., LTD.—See Azbil Corporation; *Int'l*, pg. 777
AZBIL KIMMON TECHNOLOGY CORPORATION—See Azbil Corporation; *Int'l*, pg. 777
AZBIL KOREA CO., LTD.—See Azbil Corporation; *Int'l*, pg. 777
AZBIL KYOTO CO., LTD.—See Azbil Corporation; *Int'l*, pg. 777
AZBIL MALAYSIA SDN. BHD.—See Azbil Corporation; *Int'l*, pg. 777
AZBIL MEXICO, S. DE R.L.DE C.V.—See Azbil Corporation; *Int'l*, pg. 777
AZBIL NORTH AMERICA, INC.—See Azbil Corporation; *Int'l*, pg. 777
AZBIL NORTH AMERICA RESEARCH & DEVELOPMENT, INC.—See Azbil Corporation; *Int'l*, pg. 777
AZBIL PHILIPPINES CORPORATION—See Azbil Corporation; *Int'l*, pg. 777
AZBIL PRODUCTION (THAILAND) CO., LTD.—See Azbil Corporation; *Int'l*, pg. 777
AZBIL ROYALCONTROLS CO., LTD.—See Azbil Corporation; *Int'l*, pg. 777
AZBIL SAUDI LIMITED—See Azbil Corporation; *Int'l*, pg. 777
AZBIL SINGAPORE PTE. LTD.—See Azbil Corporation; *Int'l*, pg. 777
AZBIL TAISHIN CO., LTD.—See Azbil Corporation; *Int'l*, pg. 777
AZBIL TAIWAN CO., LTD.—See Azbil Corporation; *Int'l*, pg. 777
AZBIL TELSTAR, S.L.U.—See Azbil Corporation; *Int'l*, pg. 777
AZBIL (THAILAND) CO., LTD.—See Azbil Corporation; *Int'l*, pg. 776
AZBIL TRADING CO., LTD.—See Azbil Corporation; *Int'l*, pg. 777
AZBIL VIETNAM CO., LTD.—See Azbil Corporation; *Int'l*, pg. 777
AZBIL YAMATAKE FRIENDLY CO., LTD.—See Azbil Corporation; *Int'l*, pg. 777
AZBTC CO.—See State Oil Fund of the Republic of Azerbaijan; *Int'l*, pg. 7184
A-Z BUS SALES, INC.; *U.S. Private*, pg. 22
AZCO INC.—See Burns & McDonnell, Inc.; *U.S. Private*, pg. 690
AZ-COM DATA SECURITY CO., LTD.—See AZ-COM MARUWA Holdings Inc.; *Int'l*, pg. 776
AZCO MICA INC.—See Santa Fe Gold Corp.; *U.S. Public*, pg. 1841
AZ-COM MARUWA HOLDINGS INC.; *Int'l*, pg. 776
AZCON CORP.—See Blue Tee Corporation; *U.S. Private*, pg. 594
A/Z CORPORATION—See Cianbro Corporation; *U.S. Private*, pg. 896
AZCO STEEL COMPANY—See Berkshire Hathaway Inc.; *U.S. Public*, pg. 309
AZDAMAN SDN. BHD.—See Oilcorp Berhad; *Int'l*, pg. 5535
AZ DIRECT AG—See Bertelsmann SE & Co. KGaA; *Int'l*, pg. 989
AZ DIRECT GMBH—See Bertelsmann SE & Co. KGaA; *Int'l*, pg. 993

AZ-COM MARUWA HOLDINGS INC.

Company Index

AZ DIRECT OSTERREICH GMBH—See Bertelsmann SE & Co. KGaA; *Int'l*, pg. 989
AZ DISPLAYS, INC.—See Zettler Components, Inc.; *U.S. Private*, pg. 4603
AZEAL INC.—See Amuse Inc.; *Int'l*, pg. 442
AZEARTH CORPORATION; *Int'l*, pg. 778
AZEGO COMPONENTS AG—See HPI AG; *Int'l*, pg. 3500
THE AZEK COMPANY INC.; *U.S. Public*, pg. 2035
THE AZEK GROUP LLC—See The AZEK Company Inc.; *U.S. Public*, pg. 2035
AZELIS AMERICAS—See EQT AB; *Int'l*, pg. 2469
AZELIS A/S—See EQT AB; *Int'l*, pg. 2469
AZELIS AUSTRALIA PTY. LIMITED—See EQT AB; *Int'l*, pg. 2469
AZELIS BULGARIA EAD—See EQT AB; *Int'l*, pg. 2469
AZELIS CANADA, INC.—See EQT AB; *Int'l*, pg. 2469
AZELIS CZECH REPUBLIC, S.R.O.—See EQT AB; *Int'l*, pg. 2469
AZELIS DEUTSCHLAND GMBH—See EQT AB; *Int'l*, pg. 2469
AZELIS DEUTSCHLAND KOSMETIK GMBH—See EQT AB; *Int'l*, pg. 2469
AZELIS ESPANA, S.A.—See EQT AB; *Int'l*, pg. 2469
AZELIS FOOD & HEALTH—See EQT AB; *Int'l*, pg. 2469
AZELIS FRANCE SAS—See EQT AB; *Int'l*, pg. 2469
AZELIS GROUP NV—See EQT AB; *Int'l*, pg. 2469
AZELIS INDIA PRIVATE LIMITED—See EQT AB; *Int'l*, pg. 2469
AZELIS RUSSIA—See EQT AB; *Int'l*, pg. 2469
AZELIS S.A.—See EQT AB; *Int'l*, pg. 2469
AZELIS SERBIA—See EQT AB; *Int'l*, pg. 2469
AZELIS UK LIFE SCIENCES LTD—See EQT AB; *Int'l*, pg. 2469
A-ZENITH HOME FURNISHINGS CO., LTD.; *Int'l*, pg. 21
AZEN MANUFACTURING PTE. LTD.—See Twin City Fan Companies, Ltd.; *U.S. Private*, pg. 4265
AZENN SA; *Int'l*, pg. 778
AZENTA BEIJING TECHNOLOGIES LIMITED—See Azenta, Inc.; *U.S. Public*, pg. 257
AZENTA GERMANY GMBH—See Azenta, Inc.; *U.S. Public*, pg. 257
AZENTA (GUANGZHOU) LIFE SCIENCE CO., LTD.—See Azenta, Inc.; *U.S. Public*, pg. 257
AZENTA, INC.; *U.S. Public*, pg. 257
AZENTA LIFE SCIENCES CANADA, INC.—See Azenta, Inc.; *U.S. Public*, pg. 257
AZENTA SINGAPORE PTE. LTD.—See Azenta, Inc.; *U.S. Public*, pg. 257
AZENTA (TIANJIN) BIOTECHNOLOGY CO., LTD.—See Azenta, Inc.; *U.S. Public*, pg. 257
AZENTIO SOFTWARE PTE. LTD.—See Apax Partners LLP; *Int'l*, pg. 502
AZERBAIJAN (BTC) LTD—See State Oil Co. of Azerbaijan Republic; *Int'l*, pg. 7184
AZERBAIJAN COCA-COLA BOTTLERS LIMITED LIABILITY COMPANY—See Coca-Cola Icecek A.S.; *Int'l*, pg. 1686
AZERBAIJAN INTERNATIONAL MINING COMPANY LIMITED—See Anglo Asian Mining plc; *Int'l*, pg. 462
AZERBAIJAN (SCP) LTD—See State Oil Co. of Azerbaijan Republic; *Int'l*, pg. 7184
AZERBAIJAN SUGAR PRODUCTION ASSOCIATION—See International Sun Group FZCO; *Int'l*, pg. 3752
A. ZEREGA'S SONS, INC.; *U.S. Private*, pg. 24
AZERICARD LTD.—See International Bank of Azerbaijan; *Int'l*, pg. 3743
AZERION GROUP N.V.; *Int'l*, pg. 778
AZERION PORTUGAL LDA.—See Azerion Group N.V.; *Int'l*, pg. 778
AZERKOSMOS OJSC; *Int'l*, pg. 778
AZERSUN HOLDING - KHIRDALAN CARDBOARD FACTORY—See International Sun Group FZCO; *Int'l*, pg. 3753
AZERSUN HOLDING—See International Sun Group FZCO; *Int'l*, pg. 3752
AZES PTY LTD—See Azeus Systems Holdings Ltd.; *Int'l*, pg. 778
AZEUS SYSTEMS (DALIAN) CO., LTD.—See Azeus Systems Holdings Ltd.; *Int'l*, pg. 778
AZEUS SYSTEMS HOLDINGS LTD.; *Int'l*, pg. 778
AZEUS SYSTEMS LIMITED—See Azeus Systems Holdings Ltd.; *Int'l*, pg. 778
AZEUS UK LIMITED—See Azeus Systems Holdings Ltd.; *Int'l*, pg. 778
AZEVEDO & TRAVASSOS S.A.; *Int'l*, pg. 778
AZ FACHVERLAGE AG—See BT Holding AG; *Int'l*, pg. 1204
AZF AUTOMOTIVE GROUP INC.; *U.S. Private*, pg. 415
AZFIN SEMICONDUCTORS PTE LTD—See Aztech Group Ltd.; *Int'l*, pg. 781
AZFIT CO., LTD.—See Ozu Corporation; *Int'l*, pg. 5679
AZ FRANCE S.A.S.—See Orsero S.p.A.; *Int'l*, pg. 5644
AZGARD NINE LIMITED; *Int'l*, pg. 778
A&Z HAYWARD, INC.—See Allison Reed Group, Inc.; *U.S. Private*, pg. 192
AZIA AVTO JSC; *Int'l*, pg. 778
AZIEL CORP.; *U.S. Private*, pg. 415

AZIENDA BRESCIANA PETROLI NOCIVELLI S.P.A.; *Int'l*, pg. 778
AZIENDA ELETTRICA TICINESE; *Int'l*, pg. 778
AZIENDA INFORMATICA ITALIANA S.R.L.—See CY4Gate S.p.A.; *Int'l*, pg. 1891
AZIENDA SERVIZI VALTROMPIA S.P.A.—See A2A S.p.A.; *Int'l*, pg. 29
AZILLIAN HEALTHCARE PRIVATE LIMITED—See Medico Intercontinental Limited; *Int'l*, pg. 4776
AZIMA DLI, LLC—See Fortive Corporation; *U.S. Public*, pg. 870
AZIMUT BENETTI SERVICES USA, INC.—See Azimut-Benetti S.p.A.; *Int'l*, pg. 780
AZIMUT-BENETTI S.P.A.; *Int'l*, pg. 780
AZIMUT CONSULENZA SIM SPA—See Azimut Holding SpA; *Int'l*, pg. 779
AZIMUT (DIFC) LIMITED—See Azimut Holding SpA; *Int'l*, pg. 779
AZIMUT EGYPT ASSET MANAGEMENT S.A.E.—See Azimut Holding SpA; *Int'l*, pg. 779
AZIMUT EXPLORATION INC.; *Int'l*, pg. 779
AZIMUT FINANCIAL INSURANCE S.P.A.—See Azimut Holding SpA; *Int'l*, pg. 779
AZIMUTH FULL SCREEN PUBLICATIONS INC.; *U.S. Private*, pg. 415
AZIMUT HOLDING SPA; *Int'l*, pg. 779
AZIMUTH SYSTEMS, INC.—See Anritsu Corporation; *Int'l*, pg. 476
AZIMUT INVESTMENTS SA AGF—See Azimut Holding SpA; *Int'l*, pg. 779
AZIMUT INVESTMENTS S.A.—See Azimut Holding SpA; *Int'l*, pg. 779
AZIMUT INVESTMENTS SA—See Azimut Holding SpA; *Int'l*, pg. 779
AZIMUT LIFE DAC—See Azimut Holding SpA; *Int'l*, pg. 779
AZIMUT (ME) LIMITED—See Azimut Holding SpA; *Int'l*, pg. 779
AZIMUT PORTFOY YONETIMI A.S.—See Azimut Holding SpA; *Int'l*, pg. 779
AZINCOURT ENERGY CORP.; *Int'l*, pg. 780
AZINCOURT ENERGY CORP.; *Int'l*, pg. 780
AZ INVESTMENT MANAGEMENT—See Azimut Holding SpA; *Int'l*, pg. 779
AZION CORP.; *Int'l*, pg. 780
AZITRA INC.; *U.S. Public*, pg. 258
AZIZ FATIMAH MEDICAL AND DENTAL COLLEGE—See Sitara Chemical Industries Ltd.; *Int'l*, pg. 6964
AZIZ PIPES CORP.; *Int'l*, pg. 780
AZ JUPITER 4 B.V.—See Allianz SE; *Int'l*, pg. 343
AZ JUPITER 8 B.V.—See Allianz SE; *Int'l*, pg. 343
AZ JUPITER 9 B.V.—See Allianz SE; *Int'l*, pg. 343
AZ KLIMA A.S.—See CEZ, a.s.; *Int'l*, pg. 1426
AZ KLIMA SK, S.R.O.—See CEZ, a.s.; *Int'l*, pg. 1426
AZKOYEN COMERCIAL DEUTSCHLAND GMBH—See AZKOYEN S.A.; *Int'l*, pg. 780
AZKOYEN INDUSTRIAL, S.A.—See AZKOYEN S.A.; *Int'l*, pg. 780
AZKOYEN MEDIOS DE PAGO, S.A.—See AZKOYEN S.A.; *Int'l*, pg. 780
AZKOYEN S.A.; *Int'l*, pg. 780
AZLAN GROUP PLC—See TD Synnex Corp; *U.S. Public*, pg. 1986
AZLAN LOGISTICS LIMITED—See TD Synnex Corp; *U.S. Public*, pg. 1985
AZLAN SCANDINAVIA AB—See TD Synnex Corp; *U.S. Public*, pg. 1985
AZLE ANTIQUE MALL; *U.S. Private*, pg. 415
AZLEWAY, INC.; *U.S. Private*, pg. 415
AZ LIFE LTD—See Azimut Holding SpA; *Int'l*, pg. 779
AZ MASTER (M) SDN. BHD.—See KVC Industrial Supplies Sdn. Bhd.; *Int'l*, pg. 4349
AZMAYESH INDUSTRIAL FACTORIES COMPANY; *Int'l*, pg. 780
AZ MEDIEN AG—See BT Holding AG; *Int'l*, pg. 1204
AZN CAPITAL CORP.; *Int'l*, pg. 780
AZO CONTROLS GMBH—See AZO GmbH & Co. KG; *Int'l*, pg. 780
AZO EURL—See AZO GmbH & Co. KG; *Int'l*, pg. 780
AZOFF MSG ENTERTAINMENT LLC—See Azoff Music Management; *U.S. Private*, pg. 415
AZOFF MSG ENTERTAINMENT LLC—See Madison Square Garden Sports Corp.; *U.S. Public*, pg. 1354
AZOFF MUSIC MANAGEMENT; *U.S. Private*, pg. 415
AZO GMBH & CO. KG; *Int'l*, pg. 780
AZO, INC.—See AZO GmbH & Co. KG; *Int'l*, pg. 780
AZO INGREDIENTS AUTOMATION SYSTEM (TIANJIN) CO., LTD.—See AZO GmbH & Co. KG; *Int'l*, pg. 780
AZO LIQUIDS GMBH—See AZO GmbH & Co. KG; *Int'l*, pg. 780
AZO LTD.—See AZO GmbH & Co. KG; *Int'l*, pg. 780
AZOLVER DANMARK APS—See Francotyp-Postalia Holding AG; *Int'l*, pg. 2760
AZOLVER ITALY S.R.L.—See Francotyp-Postalia Holding AG; *Int'l*, pg. 2760
AZOLVER NORGE AS—See Francotyp-Postalia Holding AG; *Int'l*, pg. 2760

CORPORATE AFFILIATIONS

AZOLVER SUOMI OY—See Francotyp-Postalia Holding AG; *Int'l*, pg. 2760
AZOLVER SVENSKA AS—See Francotyp-Postalia Holding AG; *Int'l*, pg. 2761
AZOLVER SWITZERLAND AG—See Francotyp-Postalia Holding AG; *Int'l*, pg. 2761
AZOMURES S.A.—See Ameropa AG; *Int'l*, pg. 424
AZONIX CORPORATION—See Crane NXT, Co.; *U.S. Public*, pg. 589
AZON USA INC.; *U.S. Private*, pg. 415
AZO N.V.—See AZO GmbH & Co. KG; *Int'l*, pg. 780
AZOOM CO., LTD.; *Int'l*, pg. 780
A. ZORBAS & SONS PUBLIC LTD.; *Int'l*, pg. 22
AZOREAN-AQUATIC TECHNOLOGIES SA; *Int'l*, pg. 781
AZORIM INVESTMENT DEVELOPMENT & CONSTRUCTION CO., LTD.; *Int'l*, pg. 781
AZO UK LTD.—See AZO GmbH & Co. KG; *Int'l*, pg. 780
AZPECT PHOTONICS AB; *Int'l*, pg. 781
AZPLANNING CO., LTD.; *Int'l*, pg. 781
AZ.PL SP. Z O.O.—See United Internet AG; *Int'l*, pg. 8069
AZRIELI GROUP LTD.; *Int'l*, pg. 781
AZ-SGD PRIVATE EQUITY FONDS GMBH—See Allianz SE; *Int'l*, pg. 343
AZ SWISS S.A.—See Azimut Holding SpA; *Int'l*, pg. 779
AZTALAN ENGINEERING, INC.; *U.S. Private*, pg. 415
AZTAR INDIANA GAMING COMPANY, LLC—See Caesars Entertainment, Inc.; *U.S. Public*, pg. 420
AZTAR RIVERBOAT HOLDING COMPANY, LLC—See Caesars Entertainment, Inc.; *U.S. Public*, pg. 420
AZTECA AMERICA, INC.—See Grupo Salinas, S.A. de C.V.; *Int'l*, pg. 3135
AZTECA FOODS, INCORPORATED; *U.S. Private*, pg. 416
AZTECA MILLING LP—See Gruma, S.A.B. de C.V.; *Int'l*, pg. 3114
THE AZTECA-OMEGA GROUP; *U.S. Private*, pg. 3990
AZTECA RESTAURANT ENTERPRISES; *U.S. Private*, pg. 416
AZTECA SYSTEMS, LLC—See Trimble, Inc.; *U.S. Public*, pg. 2190
AZTEC COMMUNICATIONS LTD.; *U.S. Private*, pg. 415
AZTEC COMPONENTS, INC.; *U.S. Private*, pg. 415
AZTEC CROWLEY—See AZZ, Inc.; *U.S. Public*, pg. 259
AZTEC ENTERPRISES, INC.; *U.S. Private*, pg. 416
AZTEC EVENTS & TENTS, INC.—See Milestone Capital, Inc.; *U.S. Private*, pg. 2728
AZTEC FACILITY SERVICES INCORPORATED; *U.S. Private*, pg. 416
AZTECH CONTROLS CORPORATION; *U.S. Private*, pg. 416
AZTEC HEALTHCARE, INC.—See The Ensign Group, Inc.; *U.S. Public*, pg. 2070
AZTEC ELECTRIC INC.; *U.S. Private*, pg. 416
AZTECH GROUP LTD.; *Int'l*, pg. 781
AZTECH LABS INC.—See Aztech Group Ltd.; *Int'l*, pg. 781
AZ-TECHNOLOGY SDN BHD—See Aztech Group Ltd.; *Int'l*, pg. 781
AZTECH PROFESSIONAL SERVICES, INC.—See EGS, Inc.; *U.S. Private*, pg. 1346
AZTECH TECHNOLOGIES, INC.—See LaBella Associates, D.P.C.; *U.S. Private*, pg. 2370
AZTECHWB CO., LTD.; *Int'l*, pg. 781
AZTEC, INC.—See Activar, Inc.; *U.S. Private*, pg. 68
AZTEC INDUSTRIES, INC.—See AZZ, Inc.; *U.S. Public*, pg. 259
AZTEC MANUFACTURING PARTNERSHIP, LTD.—See AZZ, Inc.; *U.S. Public*, pg. 259
AZTEC MANUFACTURING - WASKOM PARTNERSHIP, LTD.—See AZZ, Inc.; *U.S. Public*, pg. 259
AZTEC MATERIAL SERVICE CORP.; *U.S. Private*, pg. 416
AZTEC MINERALS CORP.; *Int'l*, pg. 781
AZTEC NETWORKS, INC.; *U.S. Private*, pg. 416
AZTEC SHOPS LTD. INC.; *U.S. Private*, pg. 416
AZTEC SOLAR, INC.—See Sigora Solar, LLC; *U.S. Private*, pg. 3651
AZTEC TUBULAR PRODUCTS—See AZZ, Inc.; *U.S. Public*, pg. 258
AZTEC WELL SERVICING CO. INC.; *U.S. Private*, pg. 416
AZTEK TECHNOLOGIES (1984) LTD.—See Sky Israel Private Equity Fund; *Int'l*, pg. 6992
A-Z TERMINAL CORPORATION—See ITOCHU Corporation; *Int'l*, pg. 3840
A-Z TERMINAL CORPORATION—See Marubeni Corporation; *Int'l*, pg. 4709
AZTEX INTERNATIONAL; *U.S. Private*, pg. 416
AZTX CATTLE CO., LTD.; *U.S. Private*, pg. 416
AZU AUTOTEILE UND ZUBEHOR VERTRIEBS GMBH—See Porsche Automobil Holding SE; *Int'l*, pg. 5926
AZUL AZUL SA; *Int'l*, pg. 781
AZU LIFE CARE CO., LTD.—See Leopalace21 Corporation; *Int'l*, pg. 4465
AZULIS CAPITAL; *Int'l*, pg. 781
AZUL PARTNERS, INC.; *U.S. Private*, pg. 416
AZUL S.A.; *Int'l*, pg. 781
AZUL SYSTEMS, INC.; *U.S. Private*, pg. 416
AZUL SYSTEMS UNITED KINGDOM LIMITED—See Azul Systems, Inc.; *U.S. Private*, pg. 416

AZUMA BUSSAN LTD.—See BASF SE; *Int'l*, pg. 871
AZUMA CIS, LLC—See Azuma Shipping Co., Ltd.; *Int'l*, pg. 781
AZUMA HOUSE CO., LTD.; *Int'l*, pg. 781
AZUMAH RESOURCES LIMITED; *Int'l*, pg. 782
AZUMA KIRIN INDUSTRIA E COMERCIO DE BEBIDAS E ALIMENTOS LTDA.—See Kirin Holdings Company, Limited; *Int'l*, pg. 4186
AZUMA KIRIN INDUSTRIA E COMERCIO DE BEBIDAS E ALIMENTOS LTDA.—See Kirin Holdings Company, Limited; *Int'l*, pg. 4186
AZUMA LOGITEC CO., LTD.—See Azuma Shipping Co., Ltd.; *Int'l*, pg. 781
AZUMA MACHINERY CO., LTD.—See Mitsui E&S Holdings Co., Ltd.; *Int'l*, pg. 4984
AZUMA SHIPPING CO., LTD. - CHUBU BUSINESS DIVISION—See Azuma Shipping Co., Ltd.; *Int'l*, pg. 781
AZUMA SHIPPING CO., LTD. - KANTO BUSINESS DIVISION—See Azuma Shipping Co., Ltd.; *Int'l*, pg. 781
AZUMA SHIPPING CO., LTD. - KANTO BUSINESS DIVISION—See Azuma Shipping Co., Ltd.; *Int'l*, pg. 781
AZUMA SHIPPING CO., LTD. - KEIHIN BUSINESS DIVISION—See Azuma Shipping Co., Ltd.; *Int'l*, pg. 781
AZUMA SHIPPING CO., LTD. - KEIHIN BUSINESS DIVISION—See Azuma Shipping Co., Ltd.; *Int'l*, pg. 781
AZUMA SHIPPING CO., LTD. - KYUSHU BUSINESS DIVISION—See Azuma Shipping Co., Ltd.; *Int'l*, pg. 781
AZUMA SHIPPING CO., LTD. - MARITIME TRANSPORTATION DIVISION—See Azuma Shipping Co., Ltd.; *Int'l*, pg. 782
AZUMA SHIPPING CO., LTD.; *Int'l*, pg. 781
AZUMA SHIPPING MONGOLIA LLC—See Azuma Shipping Co., Ltd.; *Int'l*, pg. 782
AZUMA SHIPPING (QINGDAO) CO., LTD.—See Azuma Shipping Co., Ltd.; *Int'l*, pg. 781
AZUMA TRANSPORT SERVICES (THAILAND) CO., LTD.—See Azuma Shipping Co., Ltd.; *Int'l*, pg. 782
AZUMI MURATA MANUFACTURING CO., LTD.—See Murata Manufacturing Co., Ltd.; *Int'l*, pg. 5097
AZURE ACRES TREATMENT CENTER, LLC—See Acadia Healthcare Company, Inc.; *U.S. Public*, pg. 28
AZURE CAPITAL PARTNERS, LP; *U.S. Private*, pg. 416
AZURE HEALTHCARE LIMITED; *Int'l*, pg. 782
AZURE HOLDING GROUP CORP.; *U.S. Private*, pg. 416
AZURE MIDSTREAM ENERGY LLC—See Clearfork Midstream LLC; *U.S. Private*, pg. 933
AZURE MINERALS LIMITED—See Hancock Prospecting Pty. Ltd.; *Int'l*, pg. 3242
AZURE MINERALS LIMITED—See Sociedad Quimica y Minera de Chile S.A.; *Int'l*, pg. 7032
AZURE POWER GLOBAL LIMITED; *Int'l*, pg. 782
AZURE STANDARD; *U.S. Private*, pg. 416
AZURE SUMMIT TECHNOLOGY, INC.—See CACI International Inc.; *U.S. Public*, pg. 417
AZURE WATER LLC—See Isodiol International, Inc.; *Int'l*, pg. 3820
AZUREWAVE TECHNOLOGIES, INC.; *Int'l*, pg. 782
AZUR INDUSTRIES; *Int'l*, pg. 782
AZURI TECHNOLOGIES LTD.—See Marubeni Corporation; *Int'l*, pg. 4705
AZURITY PHARMACEUTICALS, INC.—See NovaQuest Capital Management, LLC; *U.S. Private*, pg. 2967
THE AZUR SELECTION S.A.; *Int'l*, pg. 7614
AZUR SPACE SOLAR POWER GMBH—See 5N Plus Inc.; *Int'l*, pg. 13
AZUSA HIGHLANDER—See Alden Global Capital LLC; *U.S. Private*, pg. 158
AZ VERS US PRIVATE REIT GP LLC—See Allianz SE; *Int'l*, pg. 343
AZ VERS US PRIVATE REIT LP—See Allianz SE; *Int'l*, pg. 343
AZX INC.—See MK SEIKO CO., LTD.; *Int'l*, pg. 5001
AZZALIN SRL; *Int'l*, pg. 782
AZZAM JORDAN; *U.S. Private*, pg. 416
AZZARO SAS—See L'Oreal S.A.; *Int'l*, pg. 4378
AZZ CALVERT—See AZZ, Inc.; *U.S. Public*, pg. 258
AZZ CANADA LIMITED—See AZZ, Inc.; *U.S. Public*, pg. 258
AZZ CENTRAL ELECTRIC—See AZZ, Inc.; *U.S. Public*, pg. 258
AZZ CGIT—See AZZ, Inc.; *U.S. Public*, pg. 258
AZZEDINE ALAIA S.A.S.; *Int'l*, pg. 783
AZZ ELECTRICAL/INDUSTRIAL PRODUCTS—See AZZ, Inc.; *U.S. Public*, pg. 258
AZZ ENCLOSURE SYSTEMS - CHATTANOOGA LLC—See AZZ, Inc.; *U.S. Public*, pg. 258
AZZ ENCLOSURE SYSTEMS LLC—See AZZ, Inc.; *U.S. Public*, pg. 258
AZZ GALVANIZING – CHATTANOOGA LLC—See AZZ, Inc.; *U.S. Public*, pg. 259
AZZ GALVANIZING - BIG SPRING, LLC—See AZZ, Inc.; *U.S. Public*, pg. 258

AZZ GALVANIZING - BRISTOL LLC—See AZZ, Inc.; *U.S. Public*, pg. 258
AZZ GALVANIZING - CHATTANOOGA LLC—See AZZ, Inc.; *U.S. Public*, pg. 258
AZZ GALVANIZING - KENNEDALE, LLC—See AZZ, Inc.; *U.S. Public*, pg. 258
AZZ GALVANIZING - KOSCIUSKO, LLC—See AZZ, Inc.; *U.S. Public*, pg. 258
AZZ GALVANIZING - MORGAN CITY, LLC—See AZZ, Inc.; *U.S. Public*, pg. 259
AZZ GALVANIZING - NASHVILLE—See AZZ, Inc.; *U.S. Public*, pg. 259
AZZ GALVANIZING - NEBRASKA, LLC—See AZZ, Inc.; *U.S. Public*, pg. 259
AZZ GALVANIZING - SAN ANTONIO, LLC—See AZZ, Inc.; *U.S. Public*, pg. 259
AZZ GALVANIZING SERVICES—See AZZ, Inc.; *U.S. Public*, pg. 259
AZZ GALVANIZING - VIRGINIA LLC—See AZZ, Inc.; *U.S. Public*, pg. 259
AZZ HOLDINGS, INC.—See AZZ, Inc.; *U.S. Public*, pg. 259
AZZ, INC.; *U.S. Public*, pg. 258
AZZ R-A-L—See AZZ, Inc.; *U.S. Public*, pg. 258
AZZ SMS LLC—See CenterGate Capital, LP; *U.S. Private*, pg. 816
AZZ SURFACE TECHNOLOGIES – ROWLETT LLC—See AZZ, Inc.; *U.S. Public*, pg. 259
AZZ SURFACE TECHNOLOGIES - GAINESVILLE LLC—See AZZ, Inc.; *U.S. Public*, pg. 259
AZZ SURFACE TECHNOLOGIES - GARLAND SOUTH LLC—See AZZ, Inc.; *U.S. Public*, pg. 259
AZZ SURFACE TECHNOLOGIES - TAMPA LLC—See AZZ, Inc.; *U.S. Public*, pg. 259
AZZ SURFACE TECHNOLOGIES - TERRELL LLC—See AZZ, Inc.; *U.S. Public*, pg. 259
AZZ TEXAS WELDED WIRE, LLC—See AZZ, Inc.; *U.S. Public*, pg. 259
AZZ TRADING (SHANGHAI) CO., LTD—See AZZ, Inc.; *U.S. Public*, pg. 259
AZZUR GROUP, LLC; *U.S. Private*, pg. 416
AZZURRO SOLUTIONS CORP.; *Int'l*, pg. 783
AZZ WSI B.V.—See AZZ, Inc.; *U.S. Public*, pg. 259
AZZ WSI CANADA, ULC—See AZZ, Inc.; *U.S. Public*, pg. 259
AZZ WSI DO BRASIL LTDA.—See AZZ, Inc.; *U.S. Public*, pg. 259
AZZ WSI HOLDING B.V.—See AZZ, Inc.; *U.S. Public*, pg. 259
AZZ WSI, INC.—See AZZ, Inc.; *U.S. Public*, pg. 259

B

B12 CAPITAL PARTNERS LLC; *U.S. Private*, pg. 421
B1BANK—See Business First Bancshares, Inc.; *U.S. Public*, pg. 413
B27, LLC—See DXP Enterprises, Inc.; *U.S. Public*, pg. 697
B2A, LLC; *U.S. Private*, pg. 421
B2B BANK—See Laurentian Bank of Canada; *Int'l*, pg. 4425
B2B CFO PARTNERS, LLC; *U.S. Private*, pg. 421
B2B CHIPS, LTD.—See SINOHUB, INC.; *Int'l*, pg. 6952
B2B COMPUTER PRODUCTS, LLC; *U.S. Private*, pg. 421
B2B INDUSTRIAL PACKAGING, LLC—See GenNx360 Capital Partners, L.P.; *U.S. Private*, pg. 1672
B2B INDUSTRIES LLC.; *U.S. Private*, pg. 421
B2B MEDIA—See Vomela Specialty Company; *U.S. Private*, pg. 4412
B2 BREDBAND AB—See Telenor ASA; *Int'l*, pg. 7538
B2B SALUD S.L.U.—See Centene Corporation; *U.S. Public*, pg. 468
B2B SOFTECH INC.—See B2B Software Technologies Limited; *Int'l*, pg. 790
B2B SOFTWARE TECHNOLOGIES KASSEL GMBH—See B2B Software Technologies Limited; *Int'l*, pg. 790
B2B SOFTWARE TECHNOLOGIES LIMITED; *Int'l*, pg. 790
B2B STAFFING SERVICES, INC.; *U.S. Private*, pg. 421
B2B TECHNOLOGIES, LLC—See Source Capital, LLC; *U.S. Private*, pg. 3718
B 2 BUSINESS SYSTEMS LIMITED—See Xerox Holdings Corporation; *U.S. Public*, pg. 2386
B2C2 LTD.—See SBI Holdings, Inc.; *Int'l*, pg. 6604
B2E CORPORATION—See Central Garden & Pet Company; *U.S. Public*, pg. 473
B2EN CO., LTD.; *Int'l*, pg. 790
B2GOLD CORP.; *Int'l*, pg. 790
B2HOLDING AS; *Int'l*, pg. 790
B2I AUTOMOTIVE—See Alten S.A.; *Int'l*, pg. 390
B2 INTERACTIVE; *U.S. Private*, pg. 421
B2 KAPTIAL D.O.O—See B2Holding AS; *Int'l*, pg. 790
B2X CARE SOLUTIONS GMBH—See Barkawi Holding GmbH; *Int'l*, pg. 865
B3 CONSULTING GROUP AB; *Int'l*, pg. 791
B3 S.A.; *Int'l*, pg. 791
B3 SOLUTIONS, LLC; *U.S. Private*, pg. 421
B3SYSTEM S.A.; *Int'l*, pg. 791
B4HEALTH, LLC—See AMN Healthcare Services, Inc.; *U.S. Public*, pg. 125

B4S SOLUTIONS PVT LTD.; *Int'l*, pg. 791
B4UTRADE.COM, CORP.; *U.S. Private*, pg. 421
B-52 CAPITAL PUBLIC COMPANY LIMITED; *Int'l*, pg. 784
B7 INTERACTIVE, LLC—See Scaleworks, Inc.; *U.S. Private*, pg. 3561
B90 HOLDINGS PLC; *Int'l*, pg. 791
BAADER BANK AG; *Int'l*, pg. 791
BAADER & HEINS CAPITAL MANAGEMENT AG—See Baader Bank AG; *Int'l*, pg. 791
BAADER HEINS & SEITZ CAPITAL MANAGEMENT AG—See Baader Bank AG; *Int'l*, pg. 791
BAADER HELVEA AG—See Baader Bank AG; *Int'l*, pg. 791
BAADER HELVEA INC.—See Baader Bank AG; *Int'l*, pg. 791
BAADER HELVEA LTD.—See Baader Bank AG; *Int'l*, pg. 791
BAADER HERMES/Y&R—See WPP plc; *Int'l*, pg. 8491
BAAN ROCK GARDEN PUBLIC COMPANY LIMITED; *Int'l*, pg. 792
BAANX GROUP LTD.; *Int'l*, pg. 792
BAAN YING PTE. LTD.—See Raimon Land Public Company Limited; *Int'l*, pg. 6189
BAARSMA SOUTH AFRICA PTY. LTD.—See Union InVivo - Union de Cooperatives Agricoles; *Int'l*, pg. 8053
BAARSMA WINE GROUP HOLDING B.V.—See Union InVivo - Union de Cooperatives Agricoles; *Int'l*, pg. 8053
BAARSMA WINES BV—See Union InVivo - Union de Cooperatives Agricoles; *Int'l*, pg. 8053
BAAZEEM TRADING COMPANY; *Int'l*, pg. 792
BABA ARTS LTD.; *Int'l*, pg. 792
BABA FARID SUGAR MILLS LIMITED—See Fecto Group of Companies; *Int'l*, pg. 2629
BABALON PTY LTD—See Sapura Energy Berhad; *Int'l*, pg. 6574
BABAWEST LTD.—See Samarkand Group Plc; *Int'l*, pg. 6501
BABBEL—See Lesson Nine GmbH; *Int'l*, pg. 4469
BABBITT FORD LINCOLN-MERCURY LLC; *U.S. Private*, pg. 421
BABBOE B.V.—See Accell Group N.V.; *Int'l*, pg. 80
BABCN LLC—See Accenture plc; *Int'l*, pg. 86
BABCOCK AFRICA (PTY) LTD—See Babcock International Group PLC; *Int'l*, pg. 792
BABCOCK AFRICA SERVICES (PTY) LIMITED—See Babcock International Group PLC; *Int'l*, pg. 792
BABCOCK AIRPORTS—See Babcock International Group PLC; *Int'l*, pg. 792
BABCOCK BORSIG POWER USLUGE D.O.O.—See Bilfinger SE; *Int'l*, pg. 1024
BABCOCK BORSIG SERVICE ARABIA LTD.—See Bilfinger SE; *Int'l*, pg. 1024
BABCOCK BORSIG SERVICE GMBH—See Bilfinger SE; *Int'l*, pg. 1027
BABCOCK BORSIG STEINMULLER CZ S.R.O.—See Bilfinger SE; *Int'l*, pg. 1027
BABCOCK BORSIG STEINMULLER GMBH—See Bilfinger SE; *Int'l*, pg. 1024
BABCOCK CANADA INC.—See Babcock International Group PLC; *Int'l*, pg. 792
BABCOCK CENTER, INC.; *U.S. Private*, pg. 421
BABCOCK DEFENCE & SECURITY SERVICES—See Babcock International Group PLC; *Int'l*, pg. 792
BABCOCK DESIGN & TECHNOLOGY LIMITED—See Babcock International Group PLC; *Int'l*, pg. 792
BABCOCK EAGLETON INC.—See Babcock International Group PLC; *Int'l*, pg. 792
BABCOCK EDUCATION & SKILLS LIMITED—See Babcock International Group PLC; *Int'l*, pg. 792
BABCOCK ENGINEERING SERVICES LTD.—See Babcock International Group PLC; *Int'l*, pg. 792
BABCOCK-HITACHI DONGFANG BOILER CO., LTD.—See Hitachi, Ltd.; *Int'l*, pg. 3423
BABCOCK-HITACHI DONGFANG BOILER CO., LTD.—See Mitsubishi Heavy Industries, Ltd.; *Int'l*, pg. 4960
BABCOCK-HITACHI (PHILIPPINES) INC.—See Hitachi, Ltd.; *Int'l*, pg. 3423
BABCOCK-HITACHI (PHILIPPINES) INC.—See Mitsubishi Heavy Industries, Ltd.; *Int'l*, pg. 4960
BABCOCK INTEGRATED TECHNOLOGY LIMITED—See Babcock International Group PLC; *Int'l*, pg. 792
BABCOCK INTERNATIONAL FRANCE AVIATION SAS—See Babcock International Group PLC; *Int'l*, pg. 792
BABCOCK INTERNATIONAL GROUP PLC; *Int'l*, pg. 792
BABCOCK INTERNATIONAL GROUP—See Babcock International Group PLC; *Int'l*, pg. 792
BABCOCK INTERNATIONAL HOLDINGS BV—See Babcock International Group PLC; *Int'l*, pg. 792
BABCOCK INTERNATIONAL ITALY S.P.A.—See Babcock International Group PLC; *Int'l*, pg. 792
BABCOCK INTERNATIONAL LIMITED—See Babcock International Group PLC; *Int'l*, pg. 792
BABCOCK INTERNATIONAL SPAIN S.L.U.—See Babcock International Group PLC; *Int'l*, pg. 792

BABCOCK INTERNATIONAL GROUP PLC

BABCOCK INTERNATIONAL SUPPORT SERVICES LIMITED—See Babcock International Group PLC; *Int'l*, pg. 792
BABCOCK & JENKINS, INC.; *U.S. Private*, pg. 421
BABCOCK KRAFTWERKSERVICE GMBH—See Bilfinger SE; *Int'l*, pg. 1024
BABCOCK LAND LIMITED—See Babcock International Group PLC; *Int'l*, pg. 792
BABCOCK LUMBER COMPANY - FINEWOOD DIVISION—See Babcock Lumber Company; *U.S. Private*, pg. 422
BABCOCK LUMBER COMPANY; *U.S. Private*, pg. 422
BABCOCK MARINE (CLYDE) LIMITED—See Babcock International Group PLC; *Int'l*, pg. 792
BABCOCK MARINE—See Babcock International Group PLC; *Int'l*, pg. 792
BABCOCK NTUTHUKO ENGINEERING (PTY) LIMITED—See Babcock International Group PLC; *Int'l*, pg. 792
BABCOCK (NZ) LTD—See Babcock International Group PLC; *Int'l*, pg. 792
BABCOCK POWER ENVIRONMENTAL INC.—See Babcock Power, Inc.; *U.S. Private*, pg. 422
BABCOCK POWER, INC.; *U.S. Private*, pg. 422
BABCOCK POWER RENEWABLES LLC—See Babcock Power, Inc.; *U.S. Private*, pg. 422
BABCOCK POWER SERVICES INC.—See Babcock Power, Inc.; *U.S. Private*, pg. 422
BABCOCK POWER UK LTD.—See Babcock Power, Inc.; *U.S. Private*, pg. 422
BABCOCK PTY LTD—See Babcock International Group PLC; *Int'l*, pg. 792
BABCOCK RAIL—See Babcock International Group PLC; *Int'l*, pg. 792
BABCOCK SERVICES, INC.—See CNIM Constructions Industrielles de la Mediterranee SA; *Int'l*, pg. 1676
BABCOCK WANSON AG—See CNIM Constructions Industrielles de la Mediterranee SA; *Int'l*, pg. 1676
BABCOCK WANSON CALDEIRAS LDA—See CNIM Constructions Industrielles de la Mediterranee SA; *Int'l*, pg. 1677
BABCOCK WANSON ESPANA SA—See CNIM Constructions Industrielles de la Mediterranee SA; *Int'l*, pg. 1677
BABCOCK WANSON HOLDING SA—See CNIM Constructions Industrielles de la Mediterranee SA; *Int'l*, pg. 1676
BABCOCK WANSON ITALIANA—See CNIM Constructions Industrielles de la Mediterranee SA; *Int'l*, pg. 1677
BABCOCK WANSON MAROC—See CNIM Constructions Industrielles de la Mediterranee SA; *Int'l*, pg. 1677
BABCOCK WANSON SA - MANUFACTURING FACILITY—See Fonds de Consolidation et de Developpement des Entreprises; *Int'l*, pg. 2725
BABCOCK WANSON SA—See Fonds de Consolidation et de Developpement des Entreprises; *Int'l*, pg. 2725
BABCOCK WANSON UK LTD.—See CNIM Constructions Industrielles de la Mediterranee SA; *Int'l*, pg. 1677
BABCOCK WEST SUSSEX CAREERS LIMITED—See Babcock International Group PLC; *Int'l*, pg. 792
BABCOCK & WILCOX BEIJING CO., LTD.—See Babcock & Wilcox Enterprises, Inc.; *U.S. Public*, pg. 262
BABCOCK & WILCOX DE MONTERREY, S.A. DE C.V.—See Babcock & Wilcox Enterprises, Inc.; *U.S. Public*, pg. 263
BABCOCK & WILCOX ENTERPRISES, INC.; *U.S. Public*, pg. 262
BABCOCK & WILCOX INVESTMENT COMPANY—See BWX Technologies, Inc.; *U.S. Public*, pg. 413
BABCOCK & WILCOX LOIBL GMBH—See Deutsche Invest Capital Partners GmbH; *Int'l*, pg. 2066
BABCOCK & WILCOX MEGTEC, LLC—See Durr AG; *Int'l*, pg. 2231
BABCOCK & WILCOX ME HOLDINGS LIMITED—See Babcock & Wilcox Enterprises, Inc.; *U.S. Public*, pg. 262
BABCOCK & WILCOX POWER GENERATION GROUP, INC.—See Babcock & Wilcox Enterprises, Inc.; *U.S. Public*, pg. 262
BABCOCK & WILCOX SPIG, INC.—See Babcock & Wilcox Enterprises, Inc.; *U.S. Public*, pg. 262
BABCOCK & WILCOX VOLUND AB—See AUCTUS Capital Partners AG; *Int'l*, pg. 700
BABCOCK & WILCOX VOLUND A/S—See Babcock & Wilcox Enterprises, Inc.; *U.S. Public*, pg. 262
BABCOCK & WILCOX VOLUND LIMITED—See Babcock & Wilcox Enterprises, Inc.; *U.S. Public*, pg. 262
BABCO CONSTRUCTION INC.; *U.S. Private*, pg. 421
BABCOX PUBLICATIONS INC.; *U.S. Private*, pg. 422
BABEL MEDIA INDIA PRIVATE LIMITED—See Canada Pension Plan Investment Board; *Int'l*, pg. 1280
BABEL MEDIA INDIA PRIVATE LIMITED—See EQT AB; *Int'l*, pg. 2482
BABEL MEDIA INDIA PRIVATE LIMITED—See Temasek Holdings (Private) Limited; *Int'l*, pg. 7547
BABEL MEDIA LIMITED—See Canada Pension Plan Investment Board; *Int'l*, pg. 1280
BABEL MEDIA LIMITED—See EQT AB; *Int'l*, pg. 2482
BABEL MEDIA LIMITED—See Temasek Holdings (Private) Limited; *Int'l*, pg. 7547
BABELON INVESTMENTS CO. P.L.C.; *Int'l*, pg. 793

BABER INVESTMENT GROUP, INC.; *U.S. Private*, pg. 422
BABERS INC.; *U.S. Private*, pg. 422
BABIES TRENDYLAND LIMITED—See Mansion International Holdings Limited; *Int'l*, pg. 4676
BAB IKON GMBH SCHLIESSTECHNIK—See ASSA ABLOY AB; *Int'l*, pg. 639
BAB, INC.; *U.S. Public*, pg. 262
BABIS VOVOS INTERNATIONAL CONSTRUCTION S.A.; *Int'l*, pg. 793
BA BLACKTOP LTD.—See VINCI S.A.; *Int'l*, pg. 8218
BABLER DIALYSIS, LLC—See DaVita Inc.; *U.S. Public*, pg. 636
BABOR COSMETICS AMERICA CORP.—See Dr. BABOR GmbH & Co. KG; *Int'l*, pg. 2190
BABRI COTTON MILLS LIMITED—See Bibojee Services Private Limited; *Int'l*, pg. 1018
BABSCO SUPPLY, INC.; *U.S. Private*, pg. 422
BABS PAYLINK AB—See British Columbia Investment Management Corp.; *Int'l*, pg. 1170
BABS PAYLINK AB—See Francisco Partners Management, LP; *U.S. Private*, pg. 1592
BAB SYSTEMS, INC.—See BAB, Inc.; *U.S. Public*, pg. 262
BABY BUNTING GROUP LIMITED; *Int'l*, pg. 793
BABY CALENDAR, INC.; *Int'l*, pg. 793
BABYCARE LTD.—See Gull Holdings, Ltd.; *U.S. Private*, pg. 1817
BABYCENTER, LLC—See Ziff Davis, Inc.; *U.S. Public*, pg. 2404
BABY COW PRODUCTIONS LIMITED—See British Broadcasting Corporation; *Int'l*, pg. 1169
BABY DM SCANDINAVIA AB—See Ratos AB; *Int'l*, pg. 6215
BABYEARTH; *U.S. Private*, pg. 422
THE BABY EINSTEIN COMPANY, LLC—See The Walt Disney Company; *U.S. Public*, pg. 2139
THE BABY FOLD; *U.S. Private*, pg. 3990
BABYHAVEN.COM INC.; *U.S. Private*, pg. 422
THE BABY JOGGER COMPANY—See Newell Brands Inc.; *U.S. Public*, pg. 1515
BABYLISS SA—See American Securities LLC; *U.S. Private*, pg. 247
BABYLON BANK S.A.; *Int'l*, pg. 793
BABYLON HOLDINGS LIMITED; *U.S. Public*, pg. 263
BABYLON HOTEL; *Int'l*, pg. 793
BABYLON LTD.; *Int'l*, pg. 793
BABYLON PUMP & POWER LIMITED; *Int'l*, pg. 793
BABYLON SOFTWARE LTD.—See Babylon Ltd.; *Int'l*, pg. 793
BABY-MARKT.DE GMBH—See Tengelmann Warenhandelsgesellschaft KG; *Int'l*, pg. 7559
BABYSAM AMBA—See AAC Capital Partners Holding B.V.; *Int'l*, pg. 30
BABYSAM AMBA—See Polaris Management A/S; *Int'l*, pg. 5908
THE BABY SHOP LLC—See Landmark Retail Holdings 1 Limited; *Int'l*, pg. 4407
BABYSTEPS LIMITED—See Cornerstone Financial Holdings Limited; *Int'l*, pg. 1801
BABY TOGS, INC.; *U.S. Private*, pg. 422
BABYTREE GROUP; *Int'l*, pg. 793
BABY TREND, INC.—See Alpha Group Co., Ltd.; *Int'l*, pg. 368
BABY TULA POLAND—See Compass Diversified Holdings; *U.S. Public*, pg. 559
BA-CA ANDANTE LEASING GMBH—See UniCredit S.p.A.; *Int'l*, pg. 8036
BACA CENA IMMOBILIEN LEASING GMBH—See UniCredit S.p.A.; *Int'l*, pg. 8037
BACA CHEOPS LEASING GMBH—See UniCredit S.p.A.; *Int'l*, pg. 8034
BACA HYDRA LEASING GESELLSCHAFT M.B.H.—See UniCredit S.p.A.; *Int'l*, pg. 8036
BA-CA INFRASTRUCTURE FINANCE ADVISORY GMBH—See UniCredit S.p.A.; *Int'l*, pg. 8034
BACA KOMMUNALLEASING GMBH—See UniCredit S.p.A.; *Int'l*, pg. 8036
BACAL ALPHA DOO ZA POSLOVANJE NEKRETNINAMA—See UniCredit S.p.A.; *Int'l*, pg. 8036
BA/CA-LEASING BETEILIGUNGEN GMBH—See UniCredit S.p.A.; *Int'l*, pg. 8034
BACA LEASING CARMEN GMBH—See UniCredit S.p.A.; *Int'l*, pg. 8037
BA/CA-LEASING FINANZIERUNG GMBH—See UniCredit S.p.A.; *Int'l*, pg. 8036
BA-CA LEASING MAR IMMOBILIEN LEASING GMBH—See UniCredit S.p.A.; *Int'l*, pg. 8036
BA-CA LEASING VERSICHERUNGSSERVICE GMBH—See UniCredit S.p.A.; *Int'l*, pg. 8036
BACANORA LITHIUM LTD.; *Int'l*, pg. 793
BA-CA PRESTO LEASING GMBH—See UniCredit S.p.A.; *Int'l*, pg. 8036
BACARDI AB—See Bacardi Limited; *Int'l*, pg. 793
BACARDI BOTTLING CORPORATION—See Bacardi Limited; *Int'l*, pg. 794
BACARDI CANADA, INC.—See Bacardi Limited; *Int'l*, pg. 793
BACARDI CAPITAL LIMITED—See Bacardi Limited; *Int'l*, pg. 793

BACARDI CENTROAMERICA, S.A.—See Bacardi Limited; *Int'l*, pg. 794
BACARDI CHINA LIMITED—See Bacardi Limited; *Int'l*, pg. 793
BACARDI & COMPANY LIMITED—See Bacardi Limited; *Int'l*, pg. 793
BACARDI CORPORATION—See Bacardi Limited; *Int'l*, pg. 793
BACARDI ESPANA S.A.—See Bacardi Limited; *Int'l*, pg. 794
BACARDI FRANCE S.A.S.—See Bacardi Limited; *Int'l*, pg. 794
BACARDI GLOBAL BRANDS INC.—See Bacardi Limited; *Int'l*, pg. 794
BACARDI GLOBAL BRANDS LIMITED—See Bacardi Limited; *Int'l*, pg. 794
BACARDI GMBH—See Bacardi Limited; *Int'l*, pg. 794
BACARDI INTERNATIONAL LIMITED—See Bacardi Limited; *Int'l*, pg. 794
BACARDI LIMITED; *Int'l*, pg. 793
BACARDI-MARTINI ASIA-PACIFIC LIMITED—See Bacardi Limited; *Int'l*, pg. 794
BACARDI-MARTINI BELGIUM NV—See Bacardi Limited; *Int'l*, pg. 794
BACARDI-MARTINI BV—See Bacardi Limited; *Int'l*, pg. 794
BACARDI-MARTINI CHILE S.A.—See Bacardi Limited; *Int'l*, pg. 794
BACARDI-MARTINI DANMARK A/S—See Bacardi Limited; *Int'l*, pg. 794
BACARDI-MARTINI FINLAND—See Bacardi Limited; *Int'l*, pg. 794
BACARDI-MARTINI FRANCE—See Bacardi Limited; *Int'l*, pg. 794
BACARDI-MARTINI GMBH—See Bacardi Limited; *Int'l*, pg. 794
BACARDI-MARTINI HUNGARY KFT.—See Bacardi Limited; *Int'l*, pg. 794
BACARDI-MARTINI INDIA LIMITED—See Bacardi Limited; *Int'l*, pg. 794
BACARDI-MARTINI PACIFIC PTY. LTD.—See Bacardi Limited; *Int'l*, pg. 794
BACARDI MARTINI PATRON INTERNATIONAL GMBH—See Bacardi Limited; *Int'l*, pg. 794
BACARDI-MARTINI POLSKA SP Z O.O.—See Bacardi Limited; *Int'l*, pg. 794
BACARDI-MARTINI RUSSIA—See Bacardi Limited; *Int'l*, pg. 794
BACARDI-MARTINI (SUISSE) S.A.R.L.—See Bacardi Limited; *Int'l*, pg. 794
BACARDI-MARTINI UK LIMITED—See Bacardi Limited; *Int'l*, pg. 794
BACARDI-MARTINI URUGUAY S.A.—See Bacardi Limited; *Int'l*, pg. 794
BACARDI NEDERLAND N.V.—See Bacardi Limited; *Int'l*, pg. 794
BACARDI NORGE AS—See Bacardi Limited; *Int'l*, pg. 794
BACARDI RUS LLC—See Bacardi Limited; *Int'l*, pg. 794
BACARDI SHANGHAI LIMITED—See Bacardi Limited; *Int'l*, pg. 794
BACARDI USA, INC.—See Bacardi Limited; *Int'l*, pg. 794
BACARDI VENEZUELA C.A.—See Bacardi Limited; *Int'l*, pg. 794
BACARDI Y COMPANIA, S.A. DE C.V.—See Bacardi Limited; *Int'l*, pg. 794
BA CA SECUND LEASING GMBH—See UniCredit S.p.A.; *Int'l*, pg. 8036
BA-CA WIEN MITTE HOLDING GMBH—See UniCredit S.p.A.; *Int'l*, pg. 8039
BAC BV—See Thermo Fisher Scientific Inc.; *U.S. Public*, pg. 2145
BACCARAT, INC.—See Fortune Fountain (Beijing) Holding Group Co., Ltd.; *Int'l*, pg. 2743
BACCARAT SA—See Fortune Fountain (Beijing) Holding Group Co., Ltd.; *Int'l*, pg. 2743
BACCHUS IMPORTERS, LTD.—See Breakthru Beverage Group, LLC; *U.S. Private*, pg. 643
BACCO CONSTRUCTION CO.; *U.S. Private*, pg. 422
BAC COOLING SYSTEMS (SUZHOU) CO., LTD.—See AMSTED Industries Incorporated; *U.S. Private*, pg. 267
BAC DALIAN CO., LTD.—See AMSTED Industries Incorporated; *U.S. Private*, pg. 267
BACE COMERCIO INTERNACIONAL LTDA.—See PAUL HARTMANN AG; *Int'l*, pg. 5760
BAC FLORIDA BANK—See Banco Bradesco S.A.; *Int'l*, pg. 819
BAC FLORIDA INVESTMENTS—See Banco Bradesco S.A.; *Int'l*, pg. 819
BAC GIANG EXPLOITABLE MINERAL JOINT STOCK COMPANY; *Int'l*, pg. 793
BAC GOURMET HOUSE CO., LTD.—See Bangkok Airways Public Company Limited; *Int'l*, pg. 832
BACHARACH INC.—See FFL Partners, LLC; *U.S. Private*, pg. 1500
BACH COMPOSITE INDUSTRY A/S—See Jupiter Bach A/S; *Int'l*, pg. 4029
BACHEM AG—See Bachem Holding AG; *Int'l*, pg. 794
BACHEM AMERICAS, INC.—See Bachem Holding AG; *Int'l*, pg. 795

COMPANY NAME INDEX

BACHEM DISTRIBUTION SERVICES GMBH—See Bachem Holding AG; *Int'l*, pg. 795
BACHEM HOLDING AG; *Int'l*, pg. 794
BACHEM JAPAN K.K.—See Bachem Holding AG; *Int'l*, pg. 795
BACHEM SA—See Bachem Holding AG; *Int'l*, pg. 795
BACHEM (UK) LTD.—See Bachem Holding AG; *Int'l*, pg. 794
BACHER AG—See INDUS Holding AG; *Int'l*, pg. 3662
BACHLE LOGISTICS GMBH—See Die Schweizerische Post AG; *Int'l*, pg. 2112
BACHMAN AUTO GROUP; *U.S. Private*, pg. 422
BACHMAN-BERNARD AUTO MALLS; *U.S. Private*, pg. 423
BACHMANN ASIA LIMITED—See Kader Holdings Company Limited; *Int'l*, pg. 4046
BACHMANN (CHINA) LIMITED—See Kader Holdings Company Limited; *Int'l*, pg. 4046
BACHMANN EUROPE PLC—See Kader Holdings Company Limited; *Int'l*, pg. 4046
BACHMANN INDUSTRIES, INC.—See Kader Holdings Company Limited; *Int'l*, pg. 4046
BACHMAN SERVICES INC.—See Innospec Inc.; *U.S. Public*, pg. 1125
BACHMAN'S, INC.; *U.S. Private*, pg. 423
BACHOCO AGUASCALIENTES—See Industrias Bachoco S.A.B. de C.V.; *Int'l*, pg. 3673
BACHOCO CELAYA—See Industrias Bachoco S.A.B. de C.V.; *Int'l*, pg. 3673
BACHOCO CHINAMECA—See Industrias Bachoco S.A.B. de C.V.; *Int'l*, pg. 3673
BACHOCO CUAUTLA—See Industrias Bachoco S.A.B. de C.V.; *Int'l*, pg. 3673
BACHOCO CULIACAN—See Industrias Bachoco S.A.B. de C.V.; *Int'l*, pg. 3673
BACHOCO GOMEZ PALACIO—See Industrias Bachoco S.A.B. de C.V.; *Int'l*, pg. 3673
BACHOCO HERMOSILLO—See Industrias Bachoco S.A.B. de C.V.; *Int'l*, pg. 3673
BACHOCO LAGOS DE MORENO—See Industrias Bachoco S.A.B. de C.V.; *Int'l*, pg. 3673
BACHOCO MERIDA—See Industrias Bachoco S.A.B. de C.V.; *Int'l*, pg. 3673
BACHOCO MEXICO—See Industrias Bachoco S.A.D. de C.V.; *Int'l*, pg. 3673
BACHOCO MONTERREY—See Industrias Bachoco S.A.B. de C.V.; *Int'l*, pg. 3673
BACHOCO PUEBLA—See Industrias Bachoco S.A.B. de C.V.; *Int'l*, pg. 3673
BACHOCO, S.A. DE C.V.—See Industrias Bachoco S.A.B. de C.V.; *Int'l*, pg. 3673
BACHOCO SALTILLO—See Industrias Bachoco S.A.B. de C.V.; *Int'l*, pg. 3673
BACHOCO TECAMACHALCO—See Industrias Bachoco S.A.B. de C.V.; *Int'l*, pg. 3673
BACHOCO VERCRUZ—See Industrias Bachoco S.A.B. de C.V.; *Int'l*, pg. 3673
BACHOFEN-AG—See THK CO., LTD.; *Int'l*, pg. 7711
BAC HOLDING INTERNATIONAL CORP.; *Int'l*, pg. 793
BACH PLUMBING & HEATING COMPANY OF CLAYTON, INC.—See Heidelberg Materials AG; *Int'l*, pg. 3313
BACHRACH CLOTHING, INC.—See Sun Capital Partners, Inc.; *U.S. Private*, pg. 3858
BACHRODT MOTORS INC.; *U.S. Private*, pg. 423
BACH TO ROCK MUSIC SCHOOL, INC.; *U.S. Private*, pg. 422
BACHY BELGIQUE—See VINCI S.A.; *Int'l*, pg. 8231
BACHY FUNDACIONES SA—See VINCI S.A.; *Int'l*, pg. 8231
BACHY SOLETANCHE AUSTRALIA PTY. LTD.—See VINCI S.A.; *Int'l*, pg. 8213
BACHY SOLETANCHE GROUP LTD—See VINCI S.A.; *Int'l*, pg. 8231
BACHY SOLETANCHE LIMITED—See VINCI S.A.; *Int'l*, pg. 8234
BACHY SOLETANCHE SINGAPORE PTE LTD—See VINCI S.A.; *Int'l*, pg. 8231
BACHY SOLETANCHE VIETNAM CO., LTD.—See VINCI S.A.; *Int'l*, pg. 8231
BACIL PHARMA LIMITED; *Int'l*, pg. 795
BAC INSURANCE CORP—See Banco Bradesco S.A.; *Int'l*, pg. 819
BAC IP BV—See Thermo Fisher Scientific Inc.; *U.S. Public*, pg. 2145
BAC JAPAN CO., LTD.—See AMSTED Industries Incorporated; *U.S. Private*, pg. 267
BACKA A.D.; *Int'l*, pg. 795
BAC KAN MINERAL JOINT STOCK CORPORATION; *Int'l*, pg. 793
BACKA PALANKA A.D.; *Int'l*, pg. 795
BACKBLAZE, INC.; *U.S. Public*, pg. 263
BACK BONE ELECTRONICS CO., LTD.—See Korea Electric Terminal Co., Ltd.; *Int'l*, pg. 4284
BACKBONE ENTERTAINMENT—See Foundation 9 Entertainment, Inc.; *U.S. Private*, pg. 1579
BACKBONE MEDIA, INC.; *U.S. Private*, pg. 423
BACKBRIDGE (MALMESBURY) MANAGEMENT COMPANY LIMITED—See Persimmon plc; *Int'l*, pg. 5815

BACKCOUNTRY.COM, INC.—See TSG Consumer Partners LLC; *U.S. Private*, pg. 4252
BACKDRAFT BREWING COMPANY; *U.S. Private*, pg. 423
BACKE DIGITAL BRAND MARKETING; *U.S. Private*, pg. 423
BACKER AB—See NIBE Industrier AB; *Int'l*, pg. 5259
BACKER ALPE S. DE R.L. DE C.V.—See NIBE Industrier AB; *Int'l*, pg. 5259
BACKER BHV AB - CALESCO DIVISION—See NIBE Industrier AB; *Int'l*, pg. 5259
BACKER BHV AB—See NIBE Industrier AB; *Int'l*, pg. 5259
BACKER BHV-CALESCO DIV.—See NIBE Industrier AB; *Int'l*, pg. 5259
BACKER BHV/CALESCO FRANCE SARL—See NIBE Industrier AB; *Int'l*, pg. 5259
BACKER CELLNERGY ENGINEERING PTE. LTD.—See NIBE Industrier AB; *Int'l*, pg. 5259
BACKER EHP AB—See NIBE Industrier AB; *Int'l*, pg. 5261
BACKER EHP INC—See NIBE Industrier AB; *Int'l*, pg. 5259
BACKER ELC AG—See NIBE Industrier AB; *Int'l*, pg. 5259
BACKER ELEKTRO CZ A.S.—See NIBE Industrier AB; *Int'l*, pg. 5259
BACKER ELTOP S.R.O.—See NIBE Industrier AB; *Int'l*, pg. 5259
BACKER FACSA S.L.—See NIBE Industrier AB; *Int'l*, pg. 5259
BACKER FER S.R.L.—See NIBE Industrier AB; *Int'l*, pg. 5259
BACKER GRAND HEATER CO., LTD.—See NIBE Industrier AB; *Int'l*, pg. 5259
BACKERHAUS VEIT LTD.—See Swander Pace Capital, LLC; *U.S. Private*, pg. 3889
BACKER HEATING TECHNOLOGIES CO., LTD.—See NIBE Industrier AB; *Int'l*, pg. 5259
BACKER HEATING TECHNOLOGIES FRANCE SARL—See NIBE Industrier AB; *Int'l*, pg. 5259
BACKER HEATING TECHNOLOGIES, INC.—See NIBE Industrier AB; *Int'l*, pg. 5259
BACKER HOTWATT, INC.—See NIBE Industrier AB; *Int'l*, pg. 5260
BACKER MARATHON, INC.—See NIBE Industrier AB; *Int'l*, pg. 5260
BACKER OBR SP. Z.O.O.—See NIBE Industrier AB; *Int'l*, pg. 5260
BACKER ROD MANUFACTURING INC.—See Bay Industries Inc.; *U.S. Private*, pg. 493
BACKER-SPRINGFIELD DONGGUAN CO., LTD.—See NIBE Industrier AB; *Int'l*, pg. 5260
BACKER-WILSON ELEMENTS PTY. LTD.—See NIBE Industrier AB; *Int'l*, pg. 5260
BACKER WOLFF GMBH—See NIBE Industrier AB; *Int'l*, pg. 5260
BACKGROUND2 LIMITED—See Dover Corporation; *U.S. Public*, pg. 678
BACKGROUNDCHECKS.COM; *U.S. Private*, pg. 423
BACK IN MOTION PHYSICAL THERAPY—See GPB Capital Holdings, LLC; *U.S. Private*, pg. 1748
BACKJOY ORTHOTICS, LLC; *U.S. Private*, pg. 423
BACKLOGS LIMITED—See HCA Healthcare, Inc.; *U.S. Public*, pg. 991
BACKLOTCARS, INC.—See OPENLANE, Inc.; *U.S. Public*, pg. 1607
BACKNANGSTROM GMBH & CO. KG—See EnBW Energie Baden-Wurttemberg AG; *Int'l*, pg. 2401
BACKOFFICE ASSOCIATES, LLC—See Bridge Growth Partners, LLC; *U.S. Private*, pg. 648
BACK OFFICE SERVICES ESTONIA OU—See Finnair Plc; *Int'l*, pg. 2675
BACKROADS INC.; *U.S. Private*, pg. 423
BACKS GROUP INC.—See Hakuhodo DY Holdings Incorporated; *Int'l*, pg. 3220
BACKSTAGE LLC—See Guggenheim Partners, LLC; *U.S. Private*, pg. 1811
BACKSTAGEPLAY INC.; *Int'l*, pg. 795
BACKSTOP SOLUTIONS GROUP, LLC; *U.S. Private*, pg. 423
BACK TO LIFE SDN. BHD.—See Medi Lifestyle Limited; *Int'l*, pg. 4769
BACK TO NATURE FOODS COMPANY, LLC—See B&G Foods, Inc.; *U.S. Public*, pg. 260
BACKUPIFY, INC.—See Insight Venture Management, LLC; *U.S. Private*, pg. 2090
BACKUP MY INFO!, INC.; *U.S. Private*, pg. 423
BACKUS TURNER INTERNATIONAL; *U.S. Private*, pg. 423
BACKWERK AT GMBH—See Fomento Economico Mexicano, S.A.B. de C.V.; *Int'l*, pg. 2724
BACKWERK NL B.V.—See Fomento Economico Mexicano, S.A.B. de C.V.; *Int'l*, pg. 2724
BACKYARD LEISURE HOLDINGS, INC.—See Aterian Investment Management, L.P.; *U.S. Private*, pg. 366
BACKYARD PRODUCTIONS INC.; *U.S. Private*, pg. 423
BACKYARD VINEYARDS CORP—See Diamond Estates Wines & Spirits, Inc.; *Int'l*, pg. 2105
BAC LIEU FISHERIES JOINT STOCK COMPANY; *Int'l*, pg. 793

BAC MALAYSIA, SDN. BHD.—See AMSTED Industries Incorporated; *U.S. Private*, pg. 267
BAC-MAN GEOTHERMAL INC.—See First Gen Corporation; *Int'l*, pg. 2684
BACO CONSUMER PRODUCTS LTD.—See Pactiv Evergreen Inc.; *U.S. Public*, pg. 1633
BACON COUNTY HEALTH SERVICES, LNC.; *U.S. Private*, pg. 423
BACON GALLERIES INC.; *U.S. Private*, pg. 423
BACON & GRAHAM, INC.—See Wellspring Capital Management LLC; *U.S. Private*, pg. 4477
BACON GROCERY CO., INC.—See Jones Company, Inc.; *U.S. Private*, pg. 2232
BACON INDUSTRIES, INC.—See H.B. Fuller Company; *U.S. Public*, pg. 978
BA CONSULTING GROUP LTD.; *Int'l*, pg. 791
THE BACON VENEER COMPANY; *U.S. Private*, pg. 3990
BACOVA GUILD, LTD.—See Ronile, Inc.; *U.S. Private*, pg. 3478
BACOVA GUILD, LTD.—See Ronile, Inc.; *U.S. Private*, pg. 3478
BACPLAS INC.; *U.S. Private*, pg. 423
BACS BOOTS CO., LTD.—See Autobacs Seven Co., Ltd.; *Int'l*, pg. 726
B.A.C.S. PRIVATE LIMITED—See Zico Holdings Inc.; *Int'l*, pg. 8681
BACTEC CAMBODIA—See Perusa GmbH; *Int'l*, pg. 5821
BACTEC ENVIRONMENTAL CORPORATION; *Int'l*, pg. 795
BACTEC INTERNATIONAL LIMITED—See Perusa GmbH; *Int'l*, pg. 5821
BACTEC LAO LTD—See Perusa GmbH; *Int'l*, pg. 5821
BACTEC MOZAMBIQUE LIMITED—See Perusa GmbH; *Int'l*, pg. 5821
BACTEC SE ASIA PTY. LTD—See Perusa GmbH; *Int'l*, pg. 5821
BACTERIOLOGISCH CONTROLE STATION BV—See Eurofins Scientific S.E.; *Int'l*, pg. 2535
BACTIGUARD HOLDING AB; *Int'l*, pg. 795
BACTIQUANT A/S; *Int'l*, pg. 795
BACTOLAC PHARMACEUTICAL, INC.; *U.S. Private*, pg. 423
BACUI TECHNOLOGIES INTERNATIONAL LTD.; *Int'l*, pg. 795
BACVIET FURNITURE COMPANY LIMITED—See Bacviet Steel JSC; *Int'l*, pg. 795
BACVIET INDUSTRY JOINT STOCK COMPANY—See Bacviet Steel JSC; *Int'l*, pg. 795
BACVIET STEEL JSC; *Int'l*, pg. 795
BACVIET STRUCTURE STEEL BUILDING COMPANY LIMITED—See Bacviet Steel JSC; *Int'l*, pg. 795
BADANAI MOTORS LTD; *Int'l*, pg. 795
BADARO NO.19 SHIP INVESTMENT COMPANY; *Int'l*, pg. 795
BAD BOY FURNITURE WAREHOUSE LIMITED; *Int'l*, pg. 795
BAD BOY RECORDS—See Access Industries, Inc.; *U.S. Private*, pg. 52
BAD BOY RECORDS—See Bad Boy Worldwide Entertainment Group; *U.S. Private*, pg. 423
BAD BOY WORLDWIDE ENTERTAINMENT GROUP; *U.S. Private*, pg. 423
BADCOCK HOME FURNITURE & MORE OF SOUTH FLORIDA; *U.S. Private*, pg. 423
BAD DADDY'S INTERNATIONAL, LLC—See Good Times Restaurants, Inc.; *U.S. Public*, pg. 951
BAD DAWG ACCESSORIES, LLC—See The Toro Company; *U.S. Public*, pg. 2134
BADEA MEDICAL SRL—See MedLife S.A.; *Int'l*, pg. 4784
BADECO ADRIA D.D.; *Int'l*, pg. 795
BADEL 1862 D.D.; *Int'l*, pg. 795
BADEL 1862 D.O.O—See Badel 1862 d.d.; *Int'l*, pg. 795
BADEL D.O.O.E.L—See Badel 1862 d.d.; *Int'l*, pg. 795
BADEL SARAJEVO D.O.O.—See Badel 1862 d.d.; *Int'l*, pg. 795
BADEN GAGE & SCHROEDER, LLC; *U.S. Private*, pg. 424
BADEN WURTTEMBERGISCHE BANK AG—See Landesbank Baden-Wurttemberg; *Int'l*, pg. 4404
BADEN-WURTTEMBERGISCHE EQUITY GESELLSCHAFT MIT BESCHRANKTER HAFTUNG—See Landesbank Baden-Wurttemberg; *Int'l*, pg. 4404
BADEN-WURTTEMBERG L-FINANCE N.V.—See Landesbank Baden-Wurttemberg; *Int'l*, pg. 4404
BADER GMBH; *Int'l*, pg. 795
BADER RUTTER & ASSOCIATES, INC.; *U.S. Private*, pg. 424
BADER RUTTER & ASSOCIATES, INC.—See Bader Rutter & Associates, Inc.; *U.S. Private*, pg. 424
BADGE AGENCY, INC.—See ABRY Partners, LLC; *U.S. Private*, pg. 41
BADGE-A-MINIT LTD—See Malcolm Group Inc.; *U.S. Private*, pg. 2557
BADGEQUO HONG KONG LIMITED—See Warpaint London PLC; *Int'l*, pg. 8345
BADGER ACQUISITION OF ORLANDO LLC—See CVS Health Corporation; *U.S. Public*, pg. 616
BADGER AIR BRUSH COMPANY; *U.S. Private*, pg. 424

BADGER AIR BRUSH COMPANY

BADGER CHEVROLET BUICK, INC.—See Badger Truck and Automotive Group, Inc.; *U.S. Private*, pg. 424
BADGER CORRUGATING COMPANY; *U.S. Private*, pg. 424
BADGER DAYLIGHTING—See Badger Infrastructure Solutions Ltd.; *Int'l*, pg. 796
BADGER EQUIPMENT COMPANY—See Manitex International, Inc.; *U.S. Public*, pg. 1356
BADGER FIRE PROTECTION INC.—See Carrier Global Corporation; *U.S. Public*, pg. 440
BADGER INCORPORATED; *U.S. Private*, pg. 424
BADGER INFRASTRUCTURE SOLUTIONS LTD.; *Int'l*, pg. 796
BADGERLAND SUPPLY, INC.—See GMS Inc.; *U.S. Public*, pg. 947
BADGER LIQUOR CO. INC.; *U.S. Private*, pg. 424
BADGER MAGNETICS, INC.; *U.S. Private*, pg. 424
BADGER METER CZECH REPUBLIC—See Badger Meter, Inc.; *U.S. Public*, pg. 263
BADGER METER DE LAS AMERICAS, S.A. DE C.V.—See Badger Meter, Inc.; *U.S. Public*, pg. 263
BADGER METER DE MEXICO, SA DE CV—See Badger Meter, Inc.; *U.S. Public*, pg. 263
BADGER METER EUROPE, GMBH—See Badger Meter, Inc.; *U.S. Public*, pg. 263
BADGER METER, INC. - RACINE—See Badger Meter, Inc.; *U.S. Public*, pg. 263
BADGER METER, INC.; *U.S. Public*, pg. 263
BADGER METER INTERNATIONAL, INC.—See Badger Meter, Inc.; *U.S. Public*, pg. 263
BADGER METER SLOVAKIA—See Badger Meter, Inc.; *U.S. Public*, pg. 263
BADGER METER SWISS AG—See Badger Meter, Inc.; *U.S. Public*, pg. 263
BADGER MINING CORPORATION; *U.S. Private*, pg. 424
BADGER MURPHY FOODSERVICES; *U.S. Private*, pg. 424
BADGER MUTUAL INSURANCE COMPANY; *U.S. Private*, pg. 424
BADGER PAPER MILLS, INC.; *U.S. Private*, pg. 424
BADGER & PARTNERS, INC.; *U.S. Private*, pg. 424
BADGER PLUG COMPANY; *U.S. Private*, pg. 424
BADGER SHEET METAL WORKS OF GREEN BAY, INC.; *U.S. Private*, pg. 424
BADGER SPORTSWEAR, LLC—See Platinum Equity, LLC; *U.S. Private*, pg. 3207
BADGER STATE ETHANOL LLC; *U.S. Private*, pg. 424
BADGER STATE WESTERN INC.; *U.S. Private*, pg. 424
BADGER TECHNICAL SERVICES, LLC—See Bristol Bay Native Corporation; *U.S. Private*, pg. 655
BADGER TRUCK AND AUTOMOTIVE GROUP, INC.; *U.S. Private*, pg. 424
BADGER WELDING SUPPLIES INC.; *U.S. Private*, pg. 424
BADGER WIRE INC.; *U.S. Private*, pg. 424
BAD HOMBURGER INKASSO GMBH—See DXC Technology Company; *U.S. Public*, pg. 695
BADIA SPICES, INC.; *U.S. Private*, pg. 424
BADILLO SAATCHI & SAATCHI—See Publicis Groupe S.A.; *Int'l*, pg. 6107
BADJAR OGILVY—See WPP plc; *Int'l*, pg. 8484
BADLANDS LEASING, LLC—See Select Water Solutions, Inc.; *U.S. Public*, pg. 1862
BADLANDS POWER FUELS, LLC—See Select Water Solutions, Inc.; *U.S. Public*, pg. 1862
BAD LEONFELDEN HOTELBETRIEBS GESELLSCHAFT MBH—See Erste Group Bank AG; *Int'l*, pg. 2497
BADR INVESTMENT GROUP LLC; *Int'l*, pg. 796
BAECHS CONDITORI A/S—See Orkla ASA; *Int'l*, pg. 5637
BAEKKWANG MINERAL PRODUCTS CO., LTD. - DANYANG 1 FACTORY—See Taekyung BK Co., Ltd.; *Int'l*, pg. 7405
BAEKKWANG MINERAL PRODUCTS CO., LTD. - DANYANG 2 FACTORY—See Taekyung BK Co., Ltd.; *Int'l*, pg. 7405
BAEKKWANG MINERAL PRODUCTS CO., LTD. - GYEONGJU FACTORY—See Taekyung BK Co., Ltd.; *Int'l*, pg. 7405
BAE-NEWPLAN GROUP LIMITED—See AtkinsRealis Group Inc.; *Int'l*, pg. 671
BAER'S FURNITURE CO. INC.; *U.S. Private*, pg. 425
BAERT MARINE INC.; *U.S. Private*, pg. 425
BAE SYSTEMS-ADR—See BAE Systems plc; *Int'l*, pg. 797
BAE SYSTEMS-ANALYTICAL & ORDINANCE SOLUTIONS—See BAE Systems plc; *Int'l*, pg. 797
BAE SYSTEMS APPLIED INTELLIGENCE & SECURITY—See BAE Systems plc; *Int'l*, pg. 796
BAE SYSTEMS APPLIED INTELLIGENCE—See BAE Systems plc; *Int'l*, pg. 798
BAE SYSTEMS APPLIED INTELLIGENCE—See BAE Systems plc; *Int'l*, pg. 796
BAE SYSTEMS APPLIED INTELLIGENCE US CORP; *U.S. Private*, pg. 424
BAE SYSTEMS-APPLIED TECHNOLOGIES—See BAE Systems plc; *Int'l*, pg. 797
BAE SYSTEMS-APPLIED TECHNOLOGIES—See BAE Systems plc; *Int'l*, pg. 797
BAE SYSTEMS-APPLIED TECHNOLOGIES—See BAE Systems plc; *Int'l*, pg. 797

BAE SYSTEMS ARMAMENT SYSTEMS DIVISION—See BAE Systems plc; *Int'l*, pg. 797
BAE SYSTEMS AUSTRALIA LIMITED—See BAE Systems plc; *Int'l*, pg. 796
BAE SYSTEMS C-ITS AB—See BAE Systems plc; *Int'l*, pg. 796
BAE SYSTEMS-COMMUNICATION, NAVIGATION, IDENTIFICATION & RECONNAISSANCE—See BAE Systems plc; *Int'l*, pg. 796
BAE SYSTEMS-COMMUNICATIONS, NAVIGATION, IDENTIFICATION & RECONNAISSANCE—See BAE Systems plc; *Int'l*, pg. 798
BAE SYSTEMS CUSTOMER SOLUTIONS—See BAE Systems plc; *Int'l*, pg. 796
BAE SYSTEMS-ELECTRONICS & INTEGRATED SOLUTIONS—See BAE Systems plc; *Int'l*, pg. 797
BAE SYSTEMS ELECTRONICS LIMITED—See BAE Systems plc; *Int'l*, pg. 796
BAE SYSTEMS ENTERPRISES LIMITED—See BAE Systems plc; *Int'l*, pg. 796
BAE SYSTEMS-FLIGHT SYSTEMS—See BAE Systems plc; *Int'l*, pg. 797
BAE SYSTEMS GROUND SYSTEMS DIVISION—See BAE Systems plc; *Int'l*, pg. 797
BAE SYSTEMS HAGGLUNDS AB—See BAE Systems plc; *Int'l*, pg. 796
BAE SYSTEMS HAWAII SHIPYARDS—See BAE Systems plc; *Int'l*, pg. 797
BAE SYSTEMS IAP RESEARCH, INC.—See BAE Systems plc; *Int'l*, pg. 798
BAE SYSTEMS IMAGING SOLUTIONS—See BAE Systems plc; *Int'l*, pg. 797
BAE SYSTEMS, INC.—See BAE Systems plc; *Int'l*, pg. 796
BAE SYSTEMS INDIA (SERVICES) PVT. LTD—See BAE Systems plc; *Int'l*, pg. 796
BAE SYSTEMS INFORMATION AND ELECTRONIC SYSTEMS INTEGRATION INC.—See BAE Systems plc; *Int'l*, pg. 797
BAE SYSTEMS INFORMATION TECHNOLOGY—See BAE Systems plc; *Int'l*, pg. 797
BAE SYSTEMS INFORMATION TECHNOLOGY—See BAE Systems plc; *Int'l*, pg. 796
BAE SYSTEMS-INFORMATION WARFARE—See BAE Systems plc; *Int'l*, pg. 798
BAE SYSTEMS-INTEGRATED ELECTRONIC SOLUTIONS—See BAE Systems plc; *Int'l*, pg. 797
BAE SYSTEMS-INTEGRATED O & M SOLUTIONS—See BAE Systems plc; *Int'l*, pg. 797
BAE SYSTEMS INTEGRATED SYSTEM TECHNOLOGIES—See BAE Systems plc; *Int'l*, pg. 796
BAE SYSTEMS LAND & ARMAMENTS INC.—See BAE Systems plc; *Int'l*, pg. 797
BAE SYSTEMS (MALAYSIA) SDN BHD—See BAE Systems plc; *Int'l*, pg. 796
BAE SYSTEMS MOBILITY & PROTECTION SYSTEMS—See BAE Systems plc; *Int'l*, pg. 796
BAE SYSTEMS NORFOLK SHIP REPAIR—See BAE Systems plc; *Int'l*, pg. 797
BAE SYSTEMS OMC—See BAE Systems plc; *Int'l*, pg. 796
BAE SYSTEMS (OPERATIONS) LIMITED—See BAE Systems plc; *Int'l*, pg. 796
BAE SYSTEMS-ORDNANCE SYSTEMS—See BAE Systems plc; *Int'l*, pg. 797
BAE SYSTEMS (OVERSEAS HOLDINGS) LIMITED—See BAE Systems plc; *Int'l*, pg. 796
BAE SYSTEMS PERFORMANCE BASED SOLUTIONS—See BAE Systems plc; *Int'l*, pg. 797
BAE SYSTEMS-PLATFORM SOLUTIONS—See BAE Systems plc; *Int'l*, pg. 798
BAE SYSTEMS PLATFORMS & SERVICES—See BAE Systems plc; *Int'l*, pg. 797
BAE SYSTEMS PLC; *Int'l*, pg. 796
BAE SYSTEMS REGIONAL AIRCRAFT—See BAE Systems plc; *Int'l*, pg. 796
BAE SYSTEMS SAN DIEGO SHIP REPAIR—See BAE Systems plc; *Int'l*, pg. 797
BAE SYSTEMS SAUDI ARABIA—See BAE Systems plc; *Int'l*, pg. 796
BAE SYSTEMS SHIP REPAIR—See BAE Systems plc; *Int'l*, pg. 797
BAE SYSTEMS—See BAE Systems plc; *Int'l*, pg. 797
BAE SYSTEMS—See BAE Systems plc; *Int'l*, pg. 797
BAE SYSTEMS—See BAE Systems plc; *Int'l*, pg. 798
BAE SYSTEMS—See BAE Systems plc; *Int'l*, pg. 796
BAE SYSTEMS—See BAE Systems plc; *Int'l*, pg. 796
BAE SYSTEMS—See Puglia Engineering Inc.; *U.S. Private*, pg. 3303
BAE SYSTEMS—See BAE Systems plc; *Int'l*, pg. 797
BAE SYSTEMS—See BAE Systems plc; *Int'l*, pg. 797
BAE SYSTEMS—See BAE Systems plc; *Int'l*, pg. 797
BAE SYSTEMS SOUTHEAST SHIPYARDS ALABAMA, LLC—See BAE Systems plc; *Int'l*, pg. 797
BAE SYSTEMS SOUTHEAST SHIPYARDS AMHC INC.—See BAE Systems plc; *Int'l*, pg. 797
BAE SYSTEMS SOUTHEAST SHIPYARDS JACKSONVILLE, LLC—See BAE Systems plc; *Int'l*, pg. 797

CORPORATE AFFILIATIONS

BAE SYSTEMS SPECTAL LLC—See BAE Systems plc; *Int'l*, pg. 797
BAE SYSTEMS STEEL PRODUCTS DIVISION—See BAE Systems plc; *Int'l*, pg. 797
BAE SYSTEMS SURFACE SHIPS (HOLDINGS) LIMITED—See BAE Systems plc; *Int'l*, pg. 796
BAE SYSTEMS SURVIVABILITY SYSTEMS LLC—See BAE Systems plc; *Int'l*, pg. 796
BAE SYSTEMS-TECHNOLOGY SOLUTIONS & SERVICES SECTOR—See BAE Systems plc; *Int'l*, pg. 797
BAE SYSTEMS TVS INC.—See BAE Systems plc; *Int'l*, pg. 797
BAETA CORP.; *U.S. Private*, pg. 425
BAETE FORSETH INC.; *U.S. Private*, pg. 425
BA EUROLEASE BETEILIGUNGSGESELLSCHAFT M.B.H.—See UniCredit S.p.A.; *Int'l*, pg. 8036
BA EXCHANGE COMPANY (UK) LIMITED—See Bank Asia Limited; *Int'l*, pg. 837
BA EXPRESS USA INC.—See Bank Asia Limited; *Int'l*, pg. 837
BAFANG ELECTRIC SUZHOU CO., LTD.; *Int'l*, pg. 799
B&A FERTILIZERS LIMITED—See AGN Agroindustrial, Projetos e Participacoes Ltda.; *Int'l*, pg. 1204
B&A FERTILIZERS LIMITED—See BTG Pactual Holding S.A.; *Int'l*, pg. 1204
BAFFIN INC.—See Bain Capital, LP; *U.S. Private*, pg. 437
BAFFINLAND IRON MINES CORPORATION—See ArcelorMittal S.A.; *Int'l*, pg. 545
BAFFIN OPTICAL—See Nunasi Corporation; *Int'l*, pg. 5489
BAFGH MINING COMPANY; *Int'l*, pg. 799
BA FINANS AS—See Auchan Holding S.A.; *Int'l*, pg. 699
BAFNA PHARMACEUTICALS LIMITED; *Int'l*, pg. 799
BAFS PIPELINE TRANSPORTATION LTD—See Bangkok Aviation Fuel Services Public Company Limited; *Int'l*, pg. 832
BAF TECHNOLOGIES, INC.—See Westport Fuel Systems Inc.; *Int'l*, pg. 8392
BAGAPROP LIMITED—See ENL Limited; *Int'l*, pg. 2441
BAGAREN OCH KOCKEN AB—See Egmont Fonden; *Int'l*, pg. 2325
BAGATELLE HOTEL OPERATION LIMITED—See ENL Limited; *Int'l*, pg. 2441
BAGATELLE HOTEL OPERATIONS COMPANY LIMITED—See ENL Limited; *Int'l*, pg. 2441
BAGATELLE INTERNATIONAL INC.; *Int'l*, pg. 799
BAGATELLE LITTLE WEST 12TH, LLC—See The ONE Group Hospitality, Inc.; *U.S. Public*, pg. 2118
BAGATTA ASSOCIATES, INC.—See GI Manager L.P.; *U.S. Private*, pg. 1693
BAGATTA ASSOCIATES, INC.—See Summit Partners, L.P.; *U.S. Private*, pg. 3856
BAG BAZAAR LTD.; *U.S. Private*, pg. 425
BAGBY ELEVATOR COMPANY, INC.; *U.S. Private*, pg. 425
B.A.G. CORP.; *U.S. Private*, pg. 420
BAGCRAFT PAPERCORN I, LLC—See Apollo Global Management, Inc.; *U.S. Public*, pg. 153
BAG ELECTRONICS GMBH—See ams AG; *Int'l*, pg. 438
B.A.G. FILMS & MEDIA LIMITED; *Int'l*, pg. 789
BAGGAGE AIRLINE GUEST SERVICES, INC.—See Eldridge Industries LLC; *U.S. Private*, pg. 1351
BAGGALLINI INC.—See Mill Road Capital Management LLC; *U.S. Private*, pg. 2730
BAGGER DAVE'S BURGER TAVERN, INC.; *U.S. Public*, pg. 264
BAGGERMAATSCHAPPIJ BOSKALIS B.V.—See HAL Trust N.V.; *Int'l*, pg. 3224
BAGGERWERKEN DECLOEDT EN ZOON N.V.—See Ackermans & van Haaren NV; *Int'l*, pg. 105
BAGGETT TRANSPORTATION COMPANY; *U.S. Private*, pg. 425
BAGHDAD FOR PACKING MATERIALS; *Int'l*, pg. 799
BAGHDAD MOTOR CARS SERVICING CO.; *Int'l*, pg. 799
BAGHDAD OF IRAQ COMPANY FOR PUBLIC TRANSPORT & REAL ESTATE INVESTMENTS—See Baghdad Soft Drinks Co.; *Int'l*, pg. 799
BAGHDAD SOFT DRINKS CO.; *Int'l*, pg. 799
BA GLASS BULGARIA S.A.—See BA Glass B.V.; *Int'l*, pg. 791
BA GLASS B.V.; *Int'l*, pg. 791
BA GLASS GERMANY GMBH—See BA Glass B.V.; *Int'l*, pg. 791
BA GLASS GREECE , S.A.—See BA Glass B.V.; *Int'l*, pg. 791
BA GLASS I - SERVICOS DE GESTAO E INVESTIMENTOS, S.A.—See BA Glass B.V.; *Int'l*, pg. 791
BA GLASS POLAND SP.Z.O.O.—See BA Glass B.V.; *Int'l*, pg. 791
BA GLASS PORTUGAL S.A.—See BA Glass B.V.; *Int'l*, pg. 791
BA GLASS ROMANIA, S.A.—See Yioula Glassworks S.A.; *Int'l*, pg. 8585
BAGLEY LATINOAMERICA S.A.—See Arcor Sociedad Anonima, Industrial y Comercial; *Int'l*, pg. 550
BAGLEY LATINOAMERICA S.A.—See Danone; *Int'l*, pg. 1965
BAGMASTERS—See CTA Manufacturing, Inc.; *U.S. Private*, pg. 1118
BAG N BAGGAGE; *U.S. Private*, pg. 425

COMPANY NAME INDEX

BAGO GROUP; *Int'l*, pg. 799
BAGS-ENERGOTEHNIKA D.D.; *Int'l*, pg. 799
BAGTRANS GROUP PTY. LTD.—See Singapore Post Limited; *Int'l*, pg. 6941
BAGTRANS PTY. LIMITED—See Singapore Post Limited; *Int'l*, pg. 6941
BAGUIO GREEN GROUP LIMITED; *Int'l*, pg. 799
BAGUIO WASTE MANAGEMENT & RECYCLING LIMITED—See Baguio Green Group Limited; *Int'l*, pg. 799
BA GVG-HOLDING GMBH—See UniCredit S.p.A.; *Int'l*, pg. 8039
BAHAKEL COMMUNICATIONS, LTD.; *U.S. Private*, pg. 425
BAHAMA BREEZE—See Darden Restaurants, Inc.; *U.S. Public*, pg. 632
BAHAMASAIR HOLDINGS LIMITED; *Int'l*, pg. 799
BAHAMAS BILLFISH CHAMPIONSHIP, INC.—See Active Interest Media, Inc.; *U.S. Private*, pg. 69
BAHAMAS CONCIERGE, INC.; *U.S. Private*, pg. 425
BAHAMAS FOOD SERVICES, LTD.—See Sysco Corporation; *U.S. Public*, pg. 1973
BAHAMAS INTERNATIONAL SECURITIES EXCHANGE; *Int'l*, pg. 799
BAHAMAS OIL REFINING COMPANY INTERNATIONAL LIMITED—See Industry Super Holdings Pty. Ltd.; *Int'l*, pg. 3676
THE BAHAMAS TELECOMMUNICATIONS COMPANY LTD.—See Liberty Global plc; *Int'l*, pg. 4485
BAHAMAS UNDERWRITERS SERVICES LIMITED—See National Amusements, Inc.; *U.S. Private*, pg. 2839
BAHEMA EDUCACAO SA; *Int'l*, pg. 799
BAH HOTELANLAGEN AG—See Mahindra & Mahindra Limited; *Int'l*, pg. 4646
BAHIA DE BIZKAIA ELECTRICIDAD S.L.—See BP plc; *Int'l*, pg. 1130
BAHIA DE BIZKAIA ELECTRICIDAD S.L.—See Ente Vasco de la Energia; *Int'l*, pg. 2450
BAHIA DE BIZKAIA GAS, S.L.—See Enagas, S.A.; *Int'l*, pg. 2396
BAHIA DE BIZKAIA GAS, S.L.—See Ente Vasco de la Energia; *Int'l*, pg. 2450
BAHIA LAS MINAS CORP.; *Int'l*, pg. 800
BAHIA PRODUTOS DE MADEIRA S.A.; *Int'l*, pg. 800
BAHIA SUH RESORT S.C—See Banco Bilbao Vizcaya Argentaria, S.A.; *Int'l*, pg. 817
BAHLSEN GMBH & CO. KG; *Int'l*, pg. 800
BAHMAN INVESTMENT COMPANY; *Int'l*, pg. 800
BAHNBAU PETRI HOCH- UND TIEFBAU GESELLSCHAFT M.B.H.—See Swietelsky Baugesellschaft m.b.H.; *Int'l*, pg. 7367
BAHNHOFPLATZ-GESELLSCHAFT STUTTGART AKTIENGESELLSCHAFT—See Landesbank Baden-Wurttemberg; *Int'l*, pg. 4404
BAHNSON HOLDINGS, INC.; *U.S. Private*, pg. 425
BAHNSON, INC.—See Bahnson Holdings, Inc.; *U.S. Private*, pg. 425
BAHNTECHNIK BRAND-ERBISDORF GMBH—See Georgsmarienhutte Holding GmbH; *Int'l*, pg. 2940
BAHN TECHNIK WROCLAW SP. Z O.O.—See Trakcja PRKiI S.A.; *Int'l*, pg. 7891
BA HOLDINGS, INC.—See Luxfer Holdings PLC; *Int'l*, pg. 4588
BAHRAIN ATOMISERS INTERNATIONAL BSC—See Palladium Equity Partners, LLC; *U.S. Private*, pg. 3078
BAHRAIN BOURSE; *Int'l*, pg. 800
BAHRAIN CAR PARK COMPANY B.S.C.; *Int'l*, pg. 800
BAHRAIN CINEMA COMPANY B.S.C.; *Int'l*, pg. 800
BAHRAIN COMMERCIAL FACILITIES COMPANY BSC; *Int'l*, pg. 800
BAHRAIN DISTRICT COOLING COMPANY—See National Central Cooling Company PJSC; *Int'l*, pg. 5155
BAHRAIN DUTY FREE SHOP COMPLEX BSC; *Int'l*, pg. 800
BAHRAIN FAMILY LEISURE COMPANY B.S.C.; *Int'l*, pg. 800
BAHRAIN ISLAMIC BANK; *Int'l*, pg. 800
BAHRAIN KUWAIT INSURANCE COMPANY B.S.C.—See Fairfax Financial Holdings Limited; *Int'l*, pg. 2607
BAHRAIN KUWAIT INSURANCE COMPANY B.S.C.—See Fairfax Financial Holdings Limited; *Int'l*, pg. 2607
BAHRAIN MIDDLE EAST BANK BSC; *Int'l*, pg. 800
BAHRAIN MUMTALAKAT HOLDING COMPANY B.S.C.; *Int'l*, pg. 800
BAHRAIN NATIONAL HOLDING COMPANY BSC; *Int'l*, pg. 800
BAHRAIN NATIONAL INSURANCE COMPANY B.S.C.—See Bahrain National Holding Company BSC; *Int'l*, pg. 800
BAHRAIN NATIONAL LIFE ASSURANCE COMPANY B.S.C.—See Bahrain National Holding Company BSC; *Int'l*, pg. 800
BAHRAIN SHIP REPAIR AND ENGINEERING COMPANY; *Int'l*, pg. 800
BAHRAIN TELECOMMUNICATIONS COMPANY BSC; *Int'l*, pg. 801
BAHRAIN TOURISM COMPANY B.S.C.—See Gulf Hotels Group B.S.C.; *Int'l*, pg. 3180
BAHR BROS MFG, INC.; *U.S. Private*, pg. 425

BAHVEST RESOURCES BERHAD; *Int'l*, pg. 801
BAHWAN CONTRACTING COMPANY—See Suhail Bahwan Group (Holding) LLC; *Int'l*, pg. 7254
BAHWAN ENGINEERING COMPANY L.L.C.—See Suhail Bahwan Group (Holding) LLC; *Int'l*, pg. 7254
BAHWAN FOODS (KHALIJANA) COMPANY L.L.C.—See Suhail Bahwan Group (Holding) LLC; *Int'l*, pg. 7254
BAHWAN IT LLC—See Suhail Bahwan Group (Holding) LLC; *Int'l*, pg. 7254
BAHWAN PROJECTS & TELECOMS LLC—See Suhail Bahwan Group (Holding) LLC; *Int'l*, pg. 7254
BAHWAN TRAVEL AGENCIES—See Suhail Bahwan Group (Holding) LLC; *Int'l*, pg. 7254
BAIADA POULTRY PTY LIMITED; *Int'l*, pg. 801
BAI BRANDS LLC—See JAB Holding Company S.a.r.l.; *Int'l*, pg. 3861
BAIC BLUEPARK NEW ENERGY TECHNOLOGY CO., LTD.; *Int'l*, pg. 801
BAIC MOTOR CORPORATION LTD.—See Beijing Automotive Industry Holding Co., Ltd.; *Int'l*, pg. 945
BAI COMMUNICATIONS PTY LTD; *Int'l*, pg. 801
BAIDA GROUP CO., LTD.; *Int'l*, pg. 801
BAID FINSERV LIMITED; *Int'l*, pg. 801
BAIDU (CHINA) CO., LTD.—See Baidu, Inc.; *Int'l*, pg. 801
BAIDU.COM TIMES TECHNOLOGY (BEIJING) CO., LTD.—See Baidu, Inc.; *Int'l*, pg. 801
BAIDU HOLDINGS LIMITED—See Baidu, Inc.; *Int'l*, pg. 801
BAIDU (HONG KONG) LIMITED—See Baidu, Inc.; *Int'l*, pg. 801
BAIDU, INC.; *Int'l*, pg. 801
BAIDU INTERNATIONAL TECHNOLOGY (SHENZHEN) CO., LTD.—See Baidu, Inc.; *Int'l*, pg. 801
BAIDU JAPAN INC.—See Baidu, Inc.; *Int'l*, pg. 801
BAIDU ONLINE NETWORK TECHNOLOGY (BEIJING) CO. LTD.—See Baidu, Inc.; *Int'l*, pg. 801
BAIER & KOPPEL GMBH & CO. KG—See The Timken Company; *U.S. Public*, pg. 2132
BAIERL AUTOMOTIVE CORPORATION—See Lithia Motors, Inc.; *U.S. Public*, pg. 1321
BAIERL CHEVROLET, INC.—See Lithia Motors, Inc.; *U.S. Public*, pg. 1321
BAIERL TOYOTA—See Lithia Motors, Inc.; *U.S. Public*, pg. 1321
BAIER & MICHELS GMBH & CO. KG—See Wurth Verwaltungsgesellschaft mbH; *Int'l*, pg. 8506
BAIER & MICHELS KFT.—See Wurth Verwaltungsgesellschaft mbH; *Int'l*, pg. 8514
BAIER & MICHELS S.R.L.—See Wurth Verwaltungsgesellschaft mbH; *Int'l*, pg. 8504
BAIER & MICHELS USA INC.—See Wurth Verwaltungsgesellschaft mbH; *Int'l*, pg. 8511
BAIER S.A.R.L.—See Maschinenfabrik OTTO BAIER GmbH; *Int'l*, pg. 4720
BAIERSBRONN FRISCHFASER KARTON GMBH—See Mayr-Melnhof Karton AG; *Int'l*, pg. 4745
BAIERSBRONN FRISCHFASER KARTON VERWALTUNGS GMBH—See Mayr-Melnhof Karton AG; *Int'l*, pg. 4745
BAIER SCANDINAVIA APS—See Maschinenfabrik OTTO BAIER GmbH; *Int'l*, pg. 4721
BAI INC.; *U.S. Private*, pg. 425
BAI, INC.; *U.S. Private*, pg. 425
BAIJIAYUN GROUP LTD; *Int'l*, pg. 801
BAIKALINVESTBANK JSC; *Int'l*, pg. 802
BAIKANG BIOLOGICAL GROUP HOLDINGS LIMITED; *Int'l*, pg. 802
BAIKOWSKI CHIMIE—See PSB Industries SA; *Int'l*, pg. 6014
BAIKOWSKI INTERNATIONAL CORPORATION—See PSB Industries SA; *Int'l*, pg. 6014
BAIKOWSKI MALAKOFF INC.—See PSB Industries SA; *Int'l*, pg. 6014
BAIKOWSKI SAS—See PSB Industries SA; *Int'l*, pg. 6014
BAIKSAN CO., LTD.; *Int'l*, pg. 802
BAILADOR TECHNOLOGY INVESTMENTS LIMITED; *Int'l*, pg. 802
BAILEY & COMPANY BENEFITS GROUP—See Genstar Capital, LLC; *U.S. Private*, pg. 1674
THE BAILEY COMPANY INC.; *U.S. Private*, pg. 3990
BAILEY COMPUTER SERVICES LIMITED—See The Skipton Building Society; *Int'l*, pg. 7686
BAILEY FEED MILL INC.; *U.S. Private*, pg. 425
BAILEY GIBSON BUICK, PONTIAC & GMC, INC.; *U.S. Private*, pg. 425
BAILEY-HARRIS CONSTRUCTION, INC.; *U.S. Private*, pg. 426
BAILEY HATS COMPANY—See Bollman Hat Co.; *U.S. Private*, pg. 611
BAILEY INTERNATIONAL, LLC—See Pfingsten Partners, LLC; *U.S. Private*, pg. 3164
BAILEY KENNEDY LLP; *U.S. Private*, pg. 425
BAILEY LADDERS—See Triton Advisers Limited; *Int'l*, pg. 7935
BAILEY LAUERMAN; *U.S. Private*, pg. 425
BAILEY LAUERMAN—See Bailey Lauerman; *U.S. Private*, pg. 425
BAILEY LUMBER & SUPPLY CO.—See Bain Capital, LP; *U.S. Private*, pg. 450

BAILEY MAINTENANCE SERVICES-NEWCASTLE—See N.G. Bailey & Co. Ltd.; *Int'l*, pg. 5116
BAILEY METAL PROCESSING LIMITED—See Bailey Metal Products Limited; *Int'l*, pg. 802
BAILEY METAL PRODUCTS LIMITED; *Int'l*, pg. 802
BAILEY METAL PRODUCTS LIMITED—See Bailey Metal Products Limited; *Int'l*, pg. 802
BAILEY MORRIS LIMITED—See Indutrade AB; *Int'l*, pg. 3677
BAILEY NURSERIES INC. - SAUVIE IS DIVISION—See Bailey Nurseries Inc.; *U.S. Private*, pg. 426
BAILEY NURSERIES INC.; *U.S. Private*, pg. 425
BAILEY NURSERIES INC. - SUNNYSIDE DIVISION—See Bailey Nurseries Inc.; *U.S. Private*, pg. 426
BAILEY NURSERIES-SHERMAN DIVISION—See Bailey Nurseries Inc.; *U.S. Private*, pg. 426
BAILEY PROPERTIES LLC; *U.S. Private*, pg. 426
BAILEYS FURNITURE OUTLET INC.; *U.S. Private*, pg. 426
BAILEYS GYM, INC.—See Rachas Inc.; *U.S. Private*, pg. 3341
BAILEYS INC.; *U.S. Private*, pg. 426
BAILEY'S MOVING AND STORAGE; *U.S. Private*, pg. 426
BAILEY SOUTHWELL & CO.; *U.S. Private*, pg. 426
BAILEY SQUARE AMBULATORY SURGICAL CENTER, LTD.—See HCA Healthcare, Inc.; *U.S. Public*, pg. 991
BAILEY SQUARE SURGERY CENTER—See HCA Healthcare, Inc.; *U.S. Public*, pg. 991
BAILEY STREET BAKERY, LLC—See Flowers Foods, Inc.; *U.S. Public*, pg. 854
BAILEY TESWAINE LTD.—See N.G. Bailey & Co. Ltd.; *Int'l*, pg. 5116
BAILEY TIRE & AUTO SERVICE; *U.S. Private*, pg. 426
BAILEY WEST INC.—See Bailey Metal Products Limited; *Int'l*, pg. 802
BAILIAN GROUP CO., LTD.; *Int'l*, pg. 802
BAILIAN NANQIAO SHOPPING MALL—See Bailian Group Co., Ltd.; *Int'l*, pg. 802
BAILIAN OUTLETS PLAZA—See Bailian Group Co., Ltd.; *Int'l*, pg. 802
BAILIAN YOUYICHENG SHOPPING MALL—See Bailian Group Co., Ltd.; *Int'l*, pg. 802
THE BAILIWICK COMPANY; *U.S. Private*, pg. 3990
BAILLIE GIFFORD CHINA GROWTH TRUST PLC; *Int'l*, pg. 803
BAILLIE GIFFORD & CO.; *Int'l*, pg. 802
BAILLIE GIFFORD INTERNATIONAL LLC—See Baillie Gifford & Co.; *Int'l*, pg. 803
BAILLIE GIFFORD JAPAN TRUST PLC; *Int'l*, pg. 803
BAILLIE GIFFORD LTD.—See Baillie Gifford & Co.; *Int'l*, pg. 803
BAILLIE GIFFORD LTD.—See The Guardian Life Insurance Company of America; *U.S. Private*, pg. 4040
BAILLIE GIFFORD SHIN NIPPON PLC; *Int'l*, pg. 803
BAILLIE LUMBER CO. INC. - BOONVILLE FACILITY—See Baillie Lumber Co., Inc.; *U.S. Private*, pg. 426
BAILLIE LUMBER CO. INC. - GALION FACILITY—See Baillie Lumber Co., Inc.; *U.S. Private*, pg. 426
BAILLIE LUMBER CO. INC. - LEITCHFIELD FACILITY—See Baillie Lumber Co., Inc.; *U.S. Private*, pg. 426
BAILLIE LUMBER CO. INC. - SMYRNA FACILITY—See Baillie Lumber Co., Inc.; *U.S. Private*, pg. 426
BAILLIE LUMBER CO., INC.; *U.S. Private*, pg. 426
BAILLIE LUMBER CO. INC. - TITUSVILLE FACILITY—See Baillie Lumber Co., Inc.; *U.S. Private*, pg. 426
BAILLIE LUMBER SALES CO. INC.—See Baillie Lumber Co., Inc.; *U.S. Private*, pg. 426
BAILLIO'S INC.; *U.S. Private*, pg. 426
BAIM ENTERPRISES INC.; *U.S. Private*, pg. 426
BAIN ALNAHRAIN INVESTMENT COMPANY; *Int'l*, pg. 803
BAIN ANDALUCIA, S.L.U.—See Borges Agricultural & Industrial Nuts S.A.; *Int'l*, pg. 1114
BAINBRIDGE BANCSHARES, INC.; *U.S. Private*, pg. 453
THE BAINBRIDGE COMPANIES LLC; *U.S. Private*, pg. 3991
BAINBRIDGE INTERNATIONAL INC.; *U.S. Private*, pg. 453
BAINBRIDGE INTERNATIONAL LTD.—See Bainbridge International Inc.; *U.S. Private*, pg. 453
BAINBRIDGE & KNIGHT LABORATORIES; *U.S. Private*, pg. 453
BAIN CAPITAL ADVISORS (CHINA) LTD.—See Bain Capital, LP; *U.S. Private*, pg. 431
BAIN CAPITAL ADVISORS (INDIA) PRIVATE LIMITED—See Bain Capital, LP; *U.S. Private*, pg. 431
BAIN CAPITAL ASIA, LLC—See Bain Capital, LP; *U.S. Private*, pg. 431
BAIN CAPITAL BETEILIGUNGSBERATUNG GMBH—See Bain Capital, LP; *U.S. Private*, pg. 431
BAIN CAPITAL DOUBLE IMPACT, LP—See Bain Capital, LP; *U.S. Private*, pg. 431
BAIN CAPITAL, LP; *U.S. Private*, pg. 428
BAIN CAPITAL LTD.—See Bain Capital, LP; *U.S. Private*, pg. 431

BAIN CAPITAL, LP

BAIN CAPITAL LUXEMBOURG S.A.R.L.—See Bain Capital, LP; *U.S. Private*, pg. 431
BAIN CAPITAL NY, LLC—See Bain Capital, LP; *U.S. Private*, pg. 431
BAIN CAPITAL PRIVATE EQUITY, LP—See Bain Capital, LP; *U.S. Private*, pg. 431
BAIN CAPITAL SPECIALTY FINANCE, INC.; *U.S. Public*, pg. 264
BAIN CAPITAL TECH OPPORTUNITIES, LP—See Bain Capital, LP; *U.S. Private*, pg. 436
BAIN CAPITAL VENTURES, LLC—See Bain Capital, LP; *U.S. Private*, pg. 436
BAIN & COMPANY ARGENTINA S.R.L.—See Bain & Company, Inc.; *U.S. Private*, pg. 427
BAIN & COMPANY BELGIUM, INC.—See Bain & Company, Inc.; *U.S. Private*, pg. 427
BAIN & COMPANY BRAZIL, INC.—See Bain & Company, Inc.; *U.S. Private*, pg. 427
BAIN & COMPANY FINLAND, INC.—See Bain & Company, Inc.; *U.S. Private*, pg. 427
BAIN & COMPANY GERMANY, INC.—See Bain & Company, Inc.; *U.S. Private*, pg. 427
BAIN & COMPANY (HONG KONG)—See Bain & Company, Inc.; *U.S. Private*, pg. 427
BAIN & COMPANY IBERICA, INC.—See Bain & Company, Inc.; *U.S. Private*, pg. 427
BAIN & COMPANY, INC. - NEW YORK—See Bain & Company, Inc.; *U.S. Private*, pg. 427
BAIN & COMPANY, INC. - SAN FRANCISCO—See Bain & Company, Inc.; *U.S. Private*, pg. 428
BAIN & COMPANY, INC.; *U.S. Private*, pg. 426
BAIN & COMPANY, INC. - UNITED KINGDOM—See Bain & Company, Inc.; *U.S. Private*, pg. 428
BAIN & COMPANY INDIA PVT. LTD.—See Bain & Company, Inc.; *U.S. Private*, pg. 427
BAIN & COMPANY ITALY, INC.—See Bain & Company, Inc.; *U.S. Private*, pg. 427
BAIN & COMPANY JAPAN, INC.—See Bain & Company, Inc.; *U.S. Private*, pg. 427
BAIN & COMPANY MEXICO, INC.—See Bain & Company, Inc.; *U.S. Private*, pg. 427
BAIN & COMPANY MIDDLE EAST, INC.—See Bain & Company, Inc.; *U.S. Private*, pg. 427
BAIN & COMPANY NETHERLANDS, LLC—See Bain & Company, Inc.; *U.S. Private*, pg. 427
BAIN & COMPANY RUSSIA, LLC—See Bain & Company, Inc.; *U.S. Private*, pg. 428
BAIN & COMPANY SE ASIA, INC.—See Bain & Company, Inc.; *U.S. Private*, pg. 428
BAIN & COMPANY SOUTH AFRICA, INC.—See Bain & Company, Inc.; *U.S. Private*, pg. 427
BAIN & COMPANY SWITZERLAND, INC.—See Bain & Company, Inc.; *U.S. Private*, pg. 427
BAIN & COMPANY THAILAND, INC.—See Bain & Company, Inc.; *U.S. Private*, pg. 427
BAINE JOHNSTON CORPORATION; *Int'l*, pg. 803
BAINES MANAGEMENT CO.; *U.S. Private*, pg. 453
BAIN ET COMPAGNIE SNC—See Bain & Company, Inc.; *U.S. Private*, pg. 428
BAIN EXTREMADURA, S.L.U.—See Borges Agricultural & Industrial Nuts S.A.; *Int'l*, pg. 1114
BAIN INTERNATIONAL INC. - AUSTRALIA, MAIN OFFICE—See Bain & Company, Inc.; *U.S. Private*, pg. 428
BAINLEA HOUSE (2013) LIMITED—See Arvida Group Limited; *Int'l*, pg. 587
BAIN-MAS COLOM S.L.U.—See Borges Agricultural & Industrial Nuts S.A.; *Int'l*, pg. 1114
BAINOUNAH POWER COMPANY—See Abu Dhabi Water & Electricity Authority; *Int'l*, pg. 73
BAINSWOOD HOUSE REST HOME LIMITED—See Arvida Group Limited; *Int'l*, pg. 587
BA INTERNATIONAL—See Giesecke & Devrient GmbH; *Int'l*, pg. 2969
BAINULTRA INC.; *Int'l*, pg. 803
BAIOO FAMILY INTERACTIVE LIMITED; *Int'l*, pg. 803
BAIP UAB—See INVL Technology AB; *Int'l*, pg. 3790
BAIRAHA FARMS PLC; *Int'l*, pg. 803
BAIRD ADVISORS—See Baird Financial Group, Inc.; *U.S. Private*, pg. 454
BAIRD BROTHERS EXPRESS CAR WASH—See Roark Capital Group Inc.; *U.S. Private*, pg. 3454
BAIRD CAPITAL PARTNERS EUROPE LIMITED—See Baird Financial Group, Inc.; *U.S. Private*, pg. 453
BAIRD CAPITAL PARTNERS—See Baird Financial Group, Inc.; *U.S. Private*, pg. 453
BAIRD FINANCIAL CORPORATION—See Baird Financial Group, Inc.; *U.S. Private*, pg. 454
BAIRD FINANCIAL GROUP, INC.; *U.S. Private*, pg. 453
BAIRD FUNDS, INC.—See Baird Financial Group, Inc.; *U.S. Private*, pg. 454
BAIRD HOME CORPORATION; *U.S. Private*, pg. 454
BAIRD MACGREGOR INSURANCE BROKERS LP; *Int'l*, pg. 803
THE BAIRD MACHINERY CORPORATION; *U.S. Private*, pg. 3991
BAIRD, PATRICK & CO., INC.; *U.S. Private*, pg. 454
BAIRDS MALT LTD.—See GrainCorp Limited; *Int'l*, pg. 3052

BAIRD & WARNER REAL ESTATE, INC.; *U.S. Private*, pg. 453
BAIRD & WARNER—See Baird & Warner Real Estate, Inc.; *U.S. Private*, pg. 453
BAIRESDEV LLC; *U.S. Private*, pg. 454
BAIRONG INC.; *Int'l*, pg. 803
BAIRSTOW LIFTING PRODUCTS CO., INC.—See Altamont Capital Partners; *U.S. Private*, pg. 204
BAISCH & SKINNER INC.; *U.S. Private*, pg. 454
BAISHAN WEIYE GAS CO., LTD.—See Zhongyu Energy Holdings Limited; *Int'l*, pg. 8675
BAI SHA TECHNOLOGY CO., LTD.; *Int'l*, pg. 801
BAIT AL SHIFA PHARMACY LLC—See NMC Health PLC; *Int'l*, pg. 5392
BAIT STUDIO LIMITED—See ITV plc; *Int'l*, pg. 3844
BAIWANG HOLDING CO., LTD.—See Beijing Watertek Information Technology Co., Ltd.; *Int'l*, pg. 960
BAIYANG INVESTMENT GROUP, INC.; *Int'l*, pg. 803
BAIYE TRADING (SHANGHAI) CO., LTD.; *Int'l*, pg. 803
BAIYING HOLDINGS GROUP LIMITED; *Int'l*, pg. 803
BAIYIN NONFERROUS METAL (GROUP) CO., LTD.; *Int'l*, pg. 803
BAIYU HOLDINGS, INC.; *Int'l*, pg. 803
BAIYUN HOTEL, HUANGSHAN TOURISM DEVELOPMENT CO., LTD.—See Huangshan Tourism Development Co., Ltd.; *Int'l*, pg. 3513
BAJA AUTO INSURANCE—See Stone Point Capital LLC; *U.S. Private*, pg. 3818
BAJA CONSTRUCTION CO. INC.; *U.S. Private*, pg. 454
BAJA INTERNATIONAL S.A R.L.—See Camrova Resources Inc.; *Int'l*, pg. 1275
BAJAJ ALLIANZ GENERAL INSURANCE CO. LTD.—See Allianz SE; *Int'l*, pg. 351
BAJAJ ALLIANZ GENERAL INSURANCE CO. LTD.—See Bajaj Auto Ltd.; *Int'l*, pg. 803
BAJAJ ALLIANZ LIFE INSURANCE CO. LTD.—See Allianz SE; *Int'l*, pg. 351
BAJAJ ALLIANZ LIFE INSURANCE CO. LTD.—See Bajaj Auto Ltd.; *Int'l*, pg. 803
BAJAJ AUTO LTD. - AKURDI PLANT—See Bajaj Auto Ltd.; *Int'l*, pg. 803
BAJAJ AUTO LTD.; *Int'l*, pg. 803
BAJAJ AUTO LTD. - WALUJ PLANT—See Bajaj Auto Ltd.; *Int'l*, pg. 804
BAJAJ CONEAGLE LLC—See Bajaj Steel Industries Ltd.; *Int'l*, pg. 804
BAJAJ CONSUMER CARE LIMITED—See Bajaj Hindustan Sugar Limited; *Int'l*, pg. 804
BAJAJ ELECTRICALS LIMITED—See Bajaj Auto Ltd.; *Int'l*, pg. 804
BAJAJ FINANCE LTD.—See Bajaj Auto Ltd.; *Int'l*, pg. 804
BAJAJ FINSERV LIMITED—See Bajaj Auto Ltd.; *Int'l*, pg. 804
BAJAJ GLOBAL LIMITED; *Int'l*, pg. 804
BAJAJ HEALTHCARE LIMITED; *Int'l*, pg. 804
BAJAJ HINDUSTAN SUGAR LIMITED; *Int'l*, pg. 804
BAJAJ HINDUSTHAN LTD. - KINAUNI - SUGAR UNIT—See Bajaj Hindustan Sugar Limited; *Int'l*, pg. 804
BAJAJ HINDUSTHAN LTD. - RUDAULI - SUGAR UNIT—See Bajaj Hindustan Sugar Limited; *Int'l*, pg. 804
BAJAJ HINDUSTHAN SUGAR LTD. - KHAMBHAR KHERA - SUGAR UNIT—See Bajaj Hindustan Sugar Limited; *Int'l*, pg. 804
BAJAJ HOLDINGS & INVESTMENT LIMITED—See Bajaj Auto Ltd.; *Int'l*, pg. 804
BAJAJ STEEL INDUSTRIES LTD.; *Int'l*, pg. 804
BAJA MARINE, INC.—See American Marine Holdings, LLC; *U.S. Private*, pg. 240
BAJAN GROUP, INC.—See Velocity Print Solutions; *U.S. Private*, pg. 4354
BAJA RANCH MARKET; *U.S. Private*, pg. 454
BAJER DESIGN & MARKETING INC.; *U.S. Private*, pg. 454
BAJINOVAC A.D.; *Int'l*, pg. 804
BAJORIA ESTATE PVT. LTD.—See S K Bajoria Group; *Int'l*, pg. 6442
BAJORIA FINANCIAL SERVICES PRIVATE LIMITED—See S K Bajoria Group; *Int'l*, pg. 6442
BAJRANG FINANCE LIMITED—See Remi Group; *Int'l*, pg. 6271
BAJUENERGY WIND GMBH—See BKW AG; *Int'l*, pg. 1054
BAKALARS SAUSAGE COMPANY, INC.; *U.S. Private*, pg. 454
BAKALLAND S.A.—See Innova Capital Sp. z o.o.; *Int'l*, pg. 3711
BAK AMBALAJ SANAYI VE TICARET A.S.; *Int'l*, pg. 804
BAKANLAR MEDYA A.S.; *Int'l*, pg. 804
BAK BATTERY CANADA LTD.—See BAK International Ltd.; *Int'l*, pg. 804
BAK BATTERY LTD.—See BAK International Ltd.; *Int'l*, pg. 804
BAK BATTERY (SHENZHEN) CO., LTD.—See BAK International Ltd.; *Int'l*, pg. 804
BAKBONE SOFTWARE INCORPORATED—See Francisco Partners Management, LP; *U.S. Private*, pg. 1591

CORPORATE AFFILIATIONS

BAKE CRAFTERS FOOD COMPANY; *U.S. Private*, pg. 454
BAKED GAMES S.A.; *Int'l*, pg. 805
BAKEMARK INGREDIENTS-CANADA LTD.—See Rhone Group, LLC; *U.S. Private*, pg. 3423
BAKEMARK USA LLC—See Pamplona Capital Management LLP; *Int'l*, pg. 5711
BAKE 'N JOY FOODS INC.; *U.S. Private*, pg. 454
BAKER/ALTECH—See Justiss Oil Company, Inc.; *U.S. Private*, pg. 2246
BAKER AND PRIEM BULL BARS PTY LIMITED—See Guangzhou Automobile Industry Group Co., Ltd.; *Int'l*, pg. 3164
BAKER & ASSOCIATES ADVERTISING, INC.; *U.S. Private*, pg. 454
BAKER ATLAS - DENVER—See Baker Hughes Company; *U.S. Public*, pg. 264
BAKER ATLAS - PEARLAND—See Baker Hughes Company; *U.S. Public*, pg. 264
BAKER ATLAS—See Baker Hughes Company; *U.S. Public*, pg. 264
BAKER BARRIOS ARCHITECTS, INC.; *U.S. Private*, pg. 455
BAKER BOTTS L.L.P.; *U.S. Private*, pg. 455
BAKER BOYER BANCORP; *U.S. Public*, pg. 264
BAKER-BOYER NATIONAL BANK INC.—See Baker Boyer Bancorp; *U.S. Public*, pg. 264
BAKER BOY; *U.S. Private*, pg. 455
BAKER CAPITAL PARTNERS, LLC; *U.S. Private*, pg. 455
BAKER CHEESE, INC.; *U.S. Private*, pg. 455
THE BAKER CITY HERALD—See Western Communications Inc.; *U.S. Private*, pg. 4491
BAKER COMMODITIES INC.-LOS ANGELES—See Baker Commodities, Inc.; *U.S. Private*, pg. 455
BAKER COMMODITIES, INC.; *U.S. Private*, pg. 455
BAKER COMMUNICATIONS ADVERTISING, MARKETING & PUBLIC RELATIONS; *U.S. Private*, pg. 455
BAKER COMMUNICATIONS, INC.—See Windstream Holdings, Inc.; *U.S. Public*, pg. 2373
THE BAKER COMPANIES; *U.S. Private*, pg. 3991
BAKER COMPANY INC.; *U.S. Private*, pg. 455
BAKER CONCRETE CONSTRUCTION, INC.; *U.S. Private*, pg. 455
BAKERCORP B.V.—See United Rentals, Inc.; *U.S. Public*, pg. 2235
BAKERCORP INTERNATIONAL HOLDINGS, INC.—See United Rentals, Inc.; *U.S. Public*, pg. 2235
BAKER DIALYSIS, LLC—See DaVita Inc.; *U.S. Public*, pg. 636
BAKER DISTRIBUTING COMPANY LLC—See Watsco, Inc.; *U.S. Public*, pg. 2336
BAKER DISTRIBUTING CORP; *U.S. Private*, pg. 456
BAKER DONELSON BEARMAN CALDWELL & BERKOWITZ PC; *U.S. Private*, pg. 456
BAKER DRYWALL CO. INC.; *U.S. Private*, pg. 456
BAKER ELECTRIC SOLAR; *U.S. Private*, pg. 456
BAKER ENERGY INC.; *U.S. Private*, pg. 456
BAKER ENGINEERING PTE. LTD.—See Baker Technology International; *Int'l*, pg. 805
BAKER GROUP; *U.S. Private*, pg. 456
BAKERHICKS AG—See Morgan Sindall Group Plc; *Int'l*, pg. 5044
BAKERHICKS APS—See Morgan Sindall Group Plc; *Int'l*, pg. 5044
BAKERHICKS GMBH—See Morgan Sindall Group Plc; *Int'l*, pg. 5044
BAKER HICKS LIMITED—See Morgan Sindall Group Plc; *Int'l*, pg. 5044
BAKERHICKS S.A.—See Morgan Sindall Group Plc; *Int'l*, pg. 5044
BAKER-HIGHRISE TUNNEL FORM OPERATIONS—See Baker Concrete Construction, Inc.; *U.S. Private*, pg. 455
BAKER & HOSTETLER LLP; *U.S. Private*, pg. 454
BAKER HOUSE APARTMENTS LLC—See Duke Energy Corporation; *U.S. Public*, pg. 690
BAKER HUGHES ASIA PACIFIC LIMITED—See Baker Hughes Company; *U.S. Public*, pg. 264
BAKER HUGHES AUSTRALIA - CANNING VALE—See Baker Hughes Company; *U.S. Public*, pg. 264
BAKER HUGHES AUSTRALIA PTY LIMITED—See Baker Hughes Company; *U.S. Public*, pg. 264
BAKER HUGHES CANADA COMPANY—See Baker Hughes Company; *U.S. Public*, pg. 264
BAKER HUGHES COMPANY; *U.S. Public*, pg. 264
BAKER HUGHES (DEUTSCHLAND) HOLDING GMBH—See Baker Hughes Company; *U.S. Public*, pg. 264
BAKER HUGHES DIGITAL SOLUTIONS GMBH—See Baker Hughes Company; *U.S. Public*, pg. 264
BAKER HUGHES DO BRAZIL LTDA.—See Baker Hughes Company; *U.S. Public*, pg. 264
BAKER HUGHES DRILLING FLUIDS—See Baker Hughes Company; *U.S. Public*, pg. 265
BAKER HUGHES HOLDINGS LLC—See Baker Hughes Company; *U.S. Public*, pg. 264
BAKER HUGHES - HUGHES CHRISTENSEN—See Baker Hughes Company; *U.S. Public*, pg. 264

COMPANY NAME INDEX

BAKER HUGHES INTEQ GMBH—See Baker Hughes Company; *U.S. Public*, pg. 264
BAKER HUGHES INTEQ GMBH—See Baker Hughes Company; *U.S. Public*, pg. 264
BAKER HUGHES INTEQ (M) SDN BHD—See Baker Hughes Company; *U.S. Public*, pg. 265
BAKER HUGHES INTEQ—See Baker Hughes Company; *U.S. Public*, pg. 265
BAKER HUGHES INTERNATIONAL COOPERATIEF U.A.—See Baker Hughes Company; *U.S. Public*, pg. 265
BAKER HUGHES ITALIANA SRL—See Baker Hughes Company; *U.S. Public*, pg. 265
BAKER HUGHES (NEDERLAND) B.V.—See Baker Hughes Company; *U.S. Public*, pg. 264
BAKER HUGHES SINGAPORE PVT—See Baker Hughes Company; *U.S. Public*, pg. 265
BAKER HUGHES SRL—See Baker Hughes Company; *U.S. Public*, pg. 265
BAKER IMPLEMENT CO. INC.; *U.S. Private*, pg. 456
BAKER INDUSTRIES, INC.—See Lincoln Electric Holdings, Inc.; *U.S. Public*, pg. 1317
BAKER INFRASTRUCTURE GROUP, INC.—See Reeves Construction Company; *U.S. Private*, pg. 3384
BAKER INSTALLATIONS INC.; *U.S. Private*, pg. 456
BAKER IRON & METAL CO. INC.—See Cohen Brothers, Inc.; *U.S. Private*, pg. 962
BAKE RITE ROLLS, INC.—See H&S Bakery Inc.; *U.S. Private*, pg. 1823
BAKER KNAPP & TUBBS INC.—See Kohler Company; *U.S. Private*, pg. 2339
BAKER MANUFACTURING COMPANY, INC.; *U.S. Private*, pg. 456
BAKER & MCAULIFFE HOLDINGS PTY LTD—See Hancock & Gore Ltd.; *Int'l*, pg. 3242
BAKER & MCKENZIE LLP; *U.S. Private*, pg. 454
BAKER MCMILLEN CO.; *U.S. Private*, pg. 456
THE BAKER-MEEKINS COMPANY INC.—See Evergreen Advisors, LLC; *U.S. Private*, pg. 1438
BAKER METAL PRODUCTS INC.; *U.S. Private*, pg. 456
BAKER OIL TOOLS GMBH—See Baker Hughes Company; *U.S. Public*, pg. 264
BAKER PERKINS HOLDINGS LIMITED—See Blackstone Inc.; *U.S. Public*, pg. 360
BAKER PERKINS INC.—See Blackstone Inc.; *U.S. Public*, pg. 360
BAKER PETROLITE IBERICA, S.A.—See Baker Hughes Company; *U.S. Public*, pg. 265
BAKER PETROLITE LIMITED—See Baker Hughes Company; *U.S. Public*, pg. 265
BAKER PETROLITE LLC—See Baker Hughes Company; *U.S. Public*, pg. 265
BAKER PETROLITE (MALAYSIA) SDN. BHD.—See Baker Hughes Company; *U.S. Public*, pg. 265
BAKER PETROLITE NORGE—See Baker Hughes Company; *U.S. Public*, pg. 265
BAKER PETROLITE SAUDI ARABIA LTD—See Baker Hughes Company; *U.S. Public*, pg. 265
BAKER PETROLITE—See Baker Hughes Company; *U.S. Public*, pg. 265
BAKER PETROLITE—See Baker Hughes Company; *U.S. Public*, pg. 265
BAKER & PROVAN PTY. LTD.; *Int'l*, pg. 805
BAKER PUBLISHING GROUP; *U.S. Private*, pg. 456
BAKER ROCK CRUSHING CO.; *U.S. Private*, pg. 456
BAKER ROCK RESOURCES—See Baker Rock Crushing Co.; *U.S. Private*, pg. 456
BAKER ROOFING COMPANY; *U.S. Private*, pg. 456
BAKER SALES—See Hindley Manufacturing Company, Inc.; *U.S. Private*, pg. 1948
BAKERS BEST SNACK FOOD CORP.—See J&J Snack Foods Corporation; *U.S. Public*, pg. 1179
BAKERS BEST TROTTER—See J&J Snack Foods Corporation; *U.S. Public*, pg. 1179
THE BAKER'S COTTAGE SDN. BHD.—See Leong Hup International Berhad; *Int'l*, pg. 4461
BAKERSFIELD ARC; *U.S. Private*, pg. 457
THE BAKERSFIELD CALIFORNIAN; *U.S. Private*, pg. 3991
BAKERSFIELD HEART HOSPITAL—See Cardiovascular Care Group, Inc.; *U.S. Private*, pg. 751
BAKERSFIELD MEMORIAL HOSPITAL—See Catholic Health Initiatives; *U.S. Private*, pg. 789
BAKERSFIELD PIPE & SUPPLY; *U.S. Private*, pg. 457
BAKERS INC.; *U.S. Private*, pg. 457
BAKERS MAISON AUSTRALIA PTY LTD—See QAF Limited; *Int'l*, pg. 6131
BAKERS MAISON PTE LTD—See QAF Limited; *Int'l*, pg. 6131
BAKERS MAISON PTY LTD—See QAF Limited; *Int'l*, pg. 6131
BAKERS MANAGEMENT INC.; *U.S. Private*, pg. 457
BAKERS OF PARIS INC.; *U.S. Private*, pg. 457
BAKER & SONS AIR CONDITIONING, INC.; *U.S. Private*, pg. 455
BAKER SPECIALTY & SUPPLY CO; *U.S. Private*, pg. 456
BAKERS PRIDE OVEN COMPANY—See Standex International; *U.S. Public*, pg. 1931

BAKERS SQUARE—See Fidelity National Financial, Inc.; *U.S. Public*, pg. 2107
BAKER'S SUPERMARKETS, INC.—See The Kroger Co.; *U.S. Public*, pg. 2107
BAKER STEEL RESOURCES TRUST LIMITED; *Int'l*, pg. 805
BAKER STREET ADVISORS, LLC—See Affiliated Managers Group, Inc.; *U.S. Public*, pg. 53
BAKER STREET PARTNERS; *U.S. Private*, pg. 456
BAKER & TAYLOR, LLC—See Follett Corporation; *U.S. Private*, pg. 1559
BAKER TECHNOLOGY ASSOCIATES, INC.; *U.S. Private*, pg. 456
BAKER TECHNOLOGY LIMITED; *Int'l*, pg. 805
BAKER THERMAL SOLUTIONS LLC—See The Middleby Corporation; *U.S. Public*, pg. 2113
BAKER TILLY INTERNATIONAL LIMITED; *Int'l*, pg. 805
BAKER TILLY INVESTMENT SOLUTIONS LIMITED—See Baker Tilly UK Holdings Limited; *Int'l*, pg. 805
BAKER TILLY UK AUDIT LLP—See Baker Tilly UK Holdings Limited; *Int'l*, pg. 805
BAKER TILLY UK HOLDINGS LIMITED; *Int'l*, pg. 805
BAKER TILLY US, LLP; *U.S. Private*, pg. 456
BAKERY BARN, INC.; *U.S. Private*, pg. 457
THE BAKERY, CONFECTIONERY, TOBACCO WORKERS AND GRAIN MILLERS INTERNATIONAL UNION; *U.S. Private*, pg. 3991
BAKERY EXPRESS - MID ATLANTIC, INC.; *U.S. Private*, pg. 457
BAKERY FOODS LIMITED—See CapVest Limited; *Int'l*, pg. 1318
THE BAKERY GMBH—See Intershop Communications AG; *Int'l*, pg. 3760
BAKERY VAN DIERMEN BV—See Boboli International, LLC; *U.S. Private*, pg. 607
BAKEWISE BRANDS, INC.—See Yamazaki Baking Co., Ltd.; *Int'l*, pg. 8556
BAKHTAR CABLE; *Int'l*, pg. 805
BAKING TECHNOLOGY SYSTEMS, INC.—See Markel Group Inc.; *U.S. Public*, pg. 1367
BAK INTERNATIONAL LTD.; *Int'l*, pg. 804
BAKKAFROST USA LLC—See P/F Bakkafrost; *Int'l*, pg. 5683
BAKKAVOR EUROPEAN MARKETING BV—See Bakkavor Group plc; *Int'l*, pg. 805
BAKKAVOR FRESH COOK LIMITED—See Bakkavor Group plc; *Int'l*, pg. 805
BAKKAVOR GROUP PLC; *Int'l*, pg. 805
BAKKAVOR HOLDINGS LIMITED—See Bakkavor Group plc; *Int'l*, pg. 805
BAKKAVOR IBERICA S.A.—See Bakkavor Group plc; *Int'l*, pg. 805
BAKKAVOR LIMITED - BAKKAVOR DESSERTS HIGH-BRIDGE FACILITY—See Bakkavor Group plc; *Int'l*, pg. 805
BAKKAVOR LIMITED - BAKKAVOR DESSERTS NEWARK FACILITY—See Bakkavor Group plc; *Int'l*, pg. 805
BAKKAVOR LIMITED - BAKKAVOR MEALS LONDON FACILITY—See Bakkavor Group plc; *Int'l*, pg. 805
BAKKAVOR LIMITED - BAKKAVOR MEALS SUTTON BRIDGE FACILITY—See Bakkavor Group plc; *Int'l*, pg. 805
BAKKAVOR LIMITED - MELROW SALADS FACILITY—See Bakkavor Group plc; *Int'l*, pg. 805
BAKKAVOR LIMITED—See Bakkavor Group plc; *Int'l*, pg. 805
BAKKAVOR LIMITED - TILMANSTONE SALADS FACILITY—See Bakkavor Group plc; *Int'l*, pg. 805
BAKKAVOR LONDON LIMITED—See Bakkavor Group plc; *Int'l*, pg. 805
BAKKAVOR PIZZA—See Bakkavor Group plc; *Int'l*, pg. 805
BAKKAVOR SPALDING LTD—See Bakkavor Group plc; *Int'l*, pg. 805
BAKKAVOR USA INC—See Bakkavor Group plc; *Int'l*, pg. 805
BAKKE EL-INSTALLASJON AS—See Instalco AB; *Int'l*, pg. 3721
BAKKEN ENERGY, LLC; *Int'l*, pg. 806
BAKKEN HUNTER, LLC—See Expand Energy Corporation; *U.S. Public*, pg. 808
BAKKENLINK PIPELINE LLC—See Marathon Petroleum Corporation; *U.S. Public*, pg. 1363
BAKKER BARENDRECHT B.V.—See Greenyard N.V.; *Int'l*, pg. 3077
BAKKER CONTINENTAL B.V.—See Chepri Holding B.V.; *Int'l*, pg. 1471
BAKKINN VORUHOTEL EHF.—See Festi hf; *Int'l*, pg. 2646
BAKKT HOLDINGS, INC.; *U.S. Public*, pg. 265
BAKKT HOLDINGS, INC.—See Intercontinental Exchange, Inc.; *U.S. Public*, pg. 1141
BAKKT, LLC—See Intercontinental Exchange, Inc.; *U.S. Public*, pg. 1141
BAKKT MARKETPLACE, LLC—See Intercontinental Exchange, Inc.; *U.S. Public*, pg. 1141
BAKLAWA MADE BETTER INVESTMENTS LLC—See Agthia Group PJSC; *Int'l*, pg. 222

BALCHEM CORPORATION

BAK LOGISTICS (PRIVATE) LIMITED—See TSL Limited; *Int'l*, pg. 7952
BAKO AS—See Orkla ASA; *Int'l*, pg. 5637
BAKORP L.L.C.—See The Ensign Group, Inc.; *U.S. Public*, pg. 2070
BAKUBUNG MINERALS (PTY) LIMITED—See Wesizwe Platinum Limited; *Int'l*, pg. 8382
BAKUER AMERICAN CO.—See Bakuer S.p.A.; *Int'l*, pg. 806
BAKUER S.P.A.; *Int'l*, pg. 806
BAKUGAN LIMITED—See Sega Sammy Holdings, Inc.; *Int'l*, pg. 6680
BAKU STOCK EXCHANGE; *Int'l*, pg. 806
BALABAN GIDA SANAYI VE TICARET ANONIM SIRKETI—See Nestle S.A.; *Int'l*, pg. 5202
BALACLAVA HOTEL (BMG) PTY LTD—See Woolworths Group Limited; *Int'l*, pg. 8451
BALA INDUSTRIES AND ENTERTAINMENT PVT. LTD.—See Venky's (India) Ltd.; *Int'l*, pg. 8150
BALAI NI FRUITAS INC.; *Int'l*, pg. 806
BALAJI AMINES LIMITED; *Int'l*, pg. 806
BALAJI DISTILLERIES LTD.—See Diageo plc; *Int'l*, pg. 2103
BALAJI MOTION PICTURES LTD—See Balaji Telefilms Ltd.; *Int'l*, pg. 806
BALAJI TELEFILMS LTD.; *Int'l*, pg. 806
BALAKOM SLOVAKIA S.R.O.—See Akzo Nobel N.V.; *Int'l*, pg. 273
BALAKOVO MINERAL FERTILIZERS—See PJSC PhosAgro; *Int'l*, pg. 5883
BALAMARA RESOURCES LIMITED; *Int'l*, pg. 806
BALANCEADOS NOVA SA BALNOVA—See Archer-Daniels-Midland Company; *U.S. Public*, pg. 184
BALANCE AGROTECH CO.—See Balance Labs, Inc.; *U.S. Public*, pg. 265
BALANCED BODY, INC.; *U.S. Private*, pg. 457
BALANCED EQUITY MANAGEMENT PTY. LIMITED—See Franklin Resources, Inc.; *U.S. Public*, pg. 879
BALANCE ERNEUERBARE ENERGIEN GMBH—See EnBW Energie Baden-Wurttemberg AG; *Int'l*, pg. 2400
BALANCE ERVARING OP PROJECTBASIS B.V.—See InterBalance Group B.V.; *U.S. Private*, pg. 3736
BALANCE LABS, INC.; *U.S. Public*, pg. 265
BALANCE POINT CAPITAL ADVISORS, LLC; *U.S. Private*, pg. 457
BALANCEPOINT, INC.; *U.S. Private*, pg. 458
BALANCE RESORT AG—See Erste Group Bank AG; *Int'l*, pg. 2497
BALANCE STAFFING, INC.; *U.S. Private*, pg. 457
BALANCE TECHNOLOGY INC.; *U.S. Private*, pg. 457
BALANCE UK LIMITED—See Quanex Building Products Corp.; *U.S. Public*, pg. 1749
BALARAM PAPERS PVT LTD—See Astron Paper & Board Mill Limited; *Int'l*, pg. 662
BALASA DINVERNO FOLTZ LLC—See CI Financial Corporation; *Int'l*, pg. 1600
BALASORE ALLOYS LIMITED; *Int'l*, pg. 806
BALATACILAR - BALATACILIK SANAYI VE TICARET A.S.; *Int'l*, pg. 806
BALA TECHNO GLOBAL LTD.; *Int'l*, pg. 806
BALATON BUTOR KFT.—See Fotex Holding SE; *Int'l*, pg. 2752
BALATONGAZ KFT. LTD.—See MOL Magyar Olaj- es Gazipari Nyrt.; *Int'l*, pg. 5020
BALAX, INC.—See Sandvik AB; *Int'l*, pg. 6534
BALAXI PHARMACEUTICALS LIMITED; *Int'l*, pg. 807
THE BALBOA BAY CLUB & RESORT—See Eagle Four Equities LLC; *U.S. Private*, pg. 1309
THE BALBOA BAY CLUB & RESORT—See Pacific Hospitality Group, Inc.; *U.S. Private*, pg. 3067
BALBOA CAPITAL CORPORATION; *U.S. Private*, pg. 458
BALBOA FINANCE S.A.—See Alba Grupo March; *Int'l*, pg. 292
BALBOA TRAVEL MANAGEMENT; *U.S. Private*, pg. 458
BAL CARINA IMMOBILIEN LEASING GMBH—See UniCredit S.p.A.; *Int'l*, pg. 8036
BALCHEM BV—See Balchem Corporation; *U.S. Public*, pg. 265
BALCHEM CORPORATION; *U.S. Public*, pg. 265
BALCHEM ITALIA, S.R.L.—See Balchem Corporation; *U.S. Public*, pg. 265
BALCKE-DUERR ITALIANA, S.R.L.—See SPX Technologies, Inc.; *U.S. Public*, pg. 1921
BALCKE-DURR ENGINEERING PRIVATE LTD.—See Mutares SE & Co. KGaA; *Int'l*, pg. 5104
BALCKE-DURR GMBH—See Mutares SE & Co. KGaA; *Int'l*, pg. 5104
BALCKE-DURR ROTHEMUHLE GMBH—See Mutares SE & Co. KGaA; *Int'l*, pg. 5104
BALCKE-DURR TECHNOLOGIES INDIA PRIVATE LTD.—See Mutares SE & Co. KGaA; *Int'l*, pg. 5104
BALCKE-DURR TORINO SRL—See Mutares SE & Co. KGaA; *Int'l*, pg. 5104
BALCO AB—See Segulah Advisor AB; *Int'l*, pg. 6684
BALCO A/S—See Segulah Advisor AB; *Int'l*, pg. 6684
BALCO BALCONY SYSTEMS LTD—See Segulah Advisor AB; *Int'l*, pg. 6684
BALCO BALKONKONSTRUKTIONEN GMBH—See Segulah Advisor AB; *Int'l*, pg. 6684

BALCO BALKONSYSTEMEN B.V.—See Segulah Advisor AB; *Int'l*, pg. 6684
BALCO GROUP AB; *Int'l*, pg. 807
BALCO, INC.—See CSW Industrials, Inc.; *U.S. Public*, pg. 601
THE BALCOM AGENCY; *U.S. Private*, pg. 3991
BALCOM & MOE INC.; *U.S. Private*, pg. 458
BALCONES RECYCLING, INC. - DALLAS FACILITY—See Balcones Recycling, Inc.; *U.S. Private*, pg. 458
BALCONES RECYCLING, INC. - LITTLE ROCK FACILITY—See Balcones Recycling, Inc.; *U.S. Private*, pg. 458
BALCONES RECYCLING, INC.; *U.S. Private*, pg. 458
BALCO SWITZERLAND SAGL—See Time Watch Investments Ltd; *Int'l*, pg. 7751
BALDACCI AB—See Storskogen Group AB; *Int'l*, pg. 7227
BALDAI1 UAB—See BHG Group AB; *Int'l*, pg. 1014
BALDA MEDICAL GMBH & CO. KG—See Stevanato Group S.p.A.; *Int'l*, pg. 7212
BALDA MEDICAL VERWALTUNGSGESELLSCHAFT MBH—See Stevanato Group S.p.A.; *Int'l*, pg. 7212
BAL DEMETER IMMOBILIEN LEASING GMBH—See UniCredit S.p.A.; *Int'l*, pg. 8037
BALDER DANMARK A/S; *Int'l*, pg. 807
BALDER D.O.O.—See Kimberly-Clark Corporation; *U.S. Public*, pg. 1229
BALDER GERMANY GMBH—See Fastighets AB Balder; *Int'l*, pg. 2622
BALDERTON AVIATION HOLDINGS LIMITED—See BlackRock, Inc.; *U.S. Public*, pg. 346
BALDERTON AVIATION HOLDINGS LIMITED—See Blackstone Inc.; *U.S. Public*, pg. 358
BALDERTON AVIATION HOLDINGS LIMITED—See Cascade Investment LLC; *U.S. Private*, pg. 780
BALDERTON CAPITAL; *Int'l*, pg. 807
BALDESSARINI GMBH—See WTW-Beteiligungsgesellschaft mbH; *Int'l*, pg. 8499
BALDINGER BAKING, LP—See The Pritzker Group - Chicago, LLC; *U.S. Private*, pg. 4098
BALDINI ADRIATICA PESCA S.R.L.—See Cremonini S.p.A.; *Int'l*, pg. 1838
BALDOR ELECTRIC CANADA INC.—See ABB Ltd.; *Int'l*, pg. 51
BALDOR ELECTRIC COMPANY DE MEXICO S.A. DE C.V.—See ABB Ltd.; *Int'l*, pg. 51
BALDOR ELECTRIC COMPANY, MANUFACTURING FACILITY—See ABB Ltd.; *Int'l*, pg. 51
BALDOR ELECTRIC COMPANY—See ABB Ltd.; *Int'l*, pg. 51
BALDOR ELECTRIC SWITZERLAND AG—See ABB Ltd.; *Int'l*, pg. 51
BALDOR HOLDINGS INC—See ABB Ltd.; *Int'l*, pg. 51
BALDOR PANAMA S.A—See ABB Ltd.; *Int'l*, pg. 51
BALDOR SPECIALTY FOODS INC.; *U.S. Private*, pg. 458
BALDRICA ADVERTISING & MARKETING; *U.S. Private*, pg. 458
BALDT, INC.; *U.S. Private*, pg. 458
BALDUCCI'S LLC—See Irving Place Capital Management, L.P.; *U.S. Private*, pg. 2141
BALDWIN AMERICAS CORPORATION—See Forsyth Capital Investors LLC; *U.S. Private*, pg. 1573
BALDWIN AMERICAS DO BRASIL LTDA—See Forsyth Capital Investors LLC; *U.S. Private*, pg. 1573
BALDWIN ASIA PACIFIC CORPORATION—See Forsyth Capital Investors LLC; *U.S. Private*, pg. 1573
BALDWIN CONTRACTING COMPANY, INC.—See MDU Resources Group, Inc.; *U.S. Public*, pg. 1410
BALDWIN COUNTY MENTAL HEALTH-MENTAL RETARDATION SERVICES, INC.; *U.S. Private*, pg. 458
BALDWIN CPAS, PLLC; *U.S. Private*, pg. 458
BALDWIN EMC; *U.S. Private*, pg. 458
BALDWIN EUROPE CONSOLIDATED INC.—See Forsyth Capital Investors LLC; *U.S. Private*, pg. 1573
BALDWIN FAMILY HEALTH CARE, INC.; *U.S. Private*, pg. 458
BALDWIN FILTERS (AUST) PTY LIMITED—See Parker Hannifin Corporation; *U.S. Public*, pg. 1640
BALDWIN FILTERS, INC.—See Parker Hannifin Corporation; *U.S. Public*, pg. 1640
BALDWIN FILTERS (PTY) LTD. SA—See Parker Hannifin Corporation; *U.S. Public*, pg. 1641
BALDWIN FRANCE S.A.R.L.—See Forsyth Capital Investors LLC; *U.S. Private*, pg. 1573
BALDWIN GERMANY GMBH—See Forsyth Capital Investors LLC; *U.S. Private*, pg. 1573
BALDWIN GLOBALTEC LTD.—See Forsyth Capital Investors LLC; *U.S. Private*, pg. 1573
BALDWIN GRAPHIC EQUIPMENT PTY.—See Forsyth Capital Investors LLC; *U.S. Private*, pg. 1573
BALDWIN GRAPHIC SYSTEMS, INC.—See Forsyth Capital Investors LLC; *U.S. Private*, pg. 1573
BALDWIN GRAPHIC SYSTEMS—See Forsyth Capital Investors LLC; *U.S. Private*, pg. 1573
BALDWIN HARDWARE CORPORATION—See Spectrum Brands Holdings, Inc.; *U.S. Public*, pg. 1917
BALDWIN HEALTH CENTER INC—See Communicare, Inc.; *U.S. Private*, pg. 988
BALDWIN HOUSE LIMITED—See Workspace Group Plc; *Int'l*, pg. 8456

THE BALDWIN INSURANCE GROUP, INC.; *U.S. Public*, pg. 2035
BALDWIN IVT AB—See Forsyth Capital Investors LLC; *U.S. Private*, pg. 1573
BALDWIN-JAPAN LTD.—See Forsyth Capital Investors LLC; *U.S. Private*, pg. 1573
BALDWIN JIMEK AB—See Forsyth Capital Investors LLC; *U.S. Private*, pg. 1573
BALDWIN KRYSTYN SHERMAN PARTNERS, LLC—See The Baldwin Insurance Group, Inc.; *U.S. Public*, pg. 2035
BALDWIN & OBENAUF, INC.; *U.S. Private*, pg. 458
BALDWIN OXY-DRY AMERICAS—See Forsyth Capital Investors LLC; *U.S. Private*, pg. 1573
BALDWIN PAVING COMPANY INC. - PLANT 1—See Baldwin Paving Company Inc.; *U.S. Private*, pg. 459
BALDWIN PAVING COMPANY INC. - PLANT 2—See Baldwin Paving Company Inc.; *U.S. Private*, pg. 459
BALDWIN PAVING COMPANY INC. - PLANT 3—See Baldwin Paving Company Inc.; *U.S. Private*, pg. 459
BALDWIN PAVING COMPANY INC. - PLANT 4—See Baldwin Paving Company Inc.; *U.S. Private*, pg. 459
BALDWIN PAVING COMPANY INC. - PLANT 5—See Baldwin Paving Company Inc.; *U.S. Private*, pg. 459
BALDWIN PAVING COMPANY INC. - PLANT 6—See Baldwin Paving Company Inc.; *U.S. Private*, pg. 459
BALDWIN PAVING COMPANY INC.; *U.S. Private*, pg. 459
BALDWIN PIANO, INC.—See Gibson Brands, Inc.; *U.S. Private*, pg. 1696
BALDWIN POLE & PILING COMPANY; *U.S. Private*, pg. 459
BALDWIN PRINTING CONTROL EQUIPMENT (BEIJING) COMPANY, LTD.—See Forsyth Capital Investors LLC; *U.S. Private*, pg. 1573
BALDWIN PRINTING CONTROLS LTD.—See Forsyth Capital Investors LLC; *U.S. Private*, pg. 1573
BALDWIN REDI-MIX CO. INC.; *U.S. Private*, pg. 459
BALDWIN RICHARDSON FOODS COMPANY - MACEDON MANUFACTURING FACILITY—See Baldwin Richardson Foods Company; *U.S. Private*, pg. 459
BALDWIN RICHARDSON FOODS COMPANY; *U.S. Private*, pg. 459
BALDWIN RICHARDSON FOODS CORPORATION—See Baldwin Richardson Foods Company; *U.S. Private*, pg. 459
BALDWIN RISK PARTNER'S LLC—See The Baldwin Insurance Group, Inc.; *U.S. Public*, pg. 2036
BALDWIN & SHELL CONSTRUCTION CO. INC. - NORTHEAST ARKANSAS DIVISION—See Baldwin & Shell Construction Co. Inc.; *U.S. Private*, pg. 458
BALDWIN & SHELL CONSTRUCTION CO. INC. - NORTHWEST ARKANSAS DIVISION—See Baldwin & Shell Construction Co. Inc.; *U.S. Private*, pg. 458
BALDWIN & SHELL CONSTRUCTION CO. INC.; *U.S. Private*, pg. 458
BALDWIN SUPPLY COMPANY; *U.S. Private*, pg. 459
BALDWIN SWEDEN HOLDING AB—See Forsyth Capital Investors LLC; *U.S. Private*, pg. 1573
BALDWIN TECHNOLOGY COMPANY, INC.—See Forsyth Capital Investors LLC; *U.S. Private*, pg. 1573
BALDWIN U.K. HOLDING LIMITED—See Forsyth Capital Investors LLC; *U.S. Private*, pg. 1573
BALDWIN (UK) LTD.—See Forsyth Capital Investors LLC; *U.S. Private*, pg. 1573
BALDWIN UV LTD.—See Forsyth Capital Investors LLC; *U.S. Private*, pg. 1573
BALEA ESTIVAL 2002 S.A.; *Int'l*, pg. 807
BA LEASING BSC, LLC—See Bank of America Corporation; *U.S. Public*, pg. 270
BALEA SOFT VERWALTUNGSGESELLSCHAFT MBH—See UniCredit S.p.A.; *Int'l*, pg. 8039
BALE CHEVROLET; *U.S. Private*, pg. 459
BALEKA FREIGHT PROPRIETARY LIMITED—See Super Group Limited; *Int'l*, pg. 7334
BALEMASTER EUROPE BV—See Kadant Inc.; *U.S. Public*, pg. 1212
BALENCIAGA AUSTRIA GMBH—See Kering S.A.; *Int'l*, pg. 4133
BALENCIAGA BELGIUM B.V.—See Kering S.A.; *Int'l*, pg. 4133
BALENCIAGA CZECH REPUBLIC S.R.O.—See Kering S.A.; *Int'l*, pg. 4133
BALENCIAGA DENMARK APS—See Kering S.A.; *Int'l*, pg. 4133
BALENCIAGA NETHERLANDS B.V.—See Kering S.A.; *Int'l*, pg. 4133
BALENCIAGA NEW ZEALAND LTD.—See Kering S.A.; *Int'l*, pg. 4133
BALENCIAGA SA—See Kering S.A.; *Int'l*, pg. 4135
BALENCIAGA UK LTD—See Kering S.A.; *Int'l*, pg. 4133
BALENO KINGDOM LIMITED—See Texwinca Holdings Limited; *Int'l*, pg. 7584
BALE OF KENTUCKY, INC.; *U.S. Private*, pg. 459
BALES CONTINENTAL COMMISSION COMPANY; *U.S. Private*, pg. 459
BALESHWAR KHARAGPUR EXPRESSWAY LIMITED—See Infrastructure Leasing & Financial Services Limited; *Int'l*, pg. 3697
BALES MOTOR COMPANY; *U.S. Private*, pg. 459

BALFORD FARMS—See Milk Industry Management Corp.; *U.S. Private*, pg. 2729
BALFOUR BEATTY BUILDING MANAGEMENT & SERVICES—See Balfour Beatty plc; *Int'l*, pg. 807
BALFOUR BEATTY CAMPUS SOLUTIONS LLC—See Balfour Beatty plc; *Int'l*, pg. 807
BALFOUR BEATTY CAPITAL GROUP INC—See Balfour Beatty plc; *Int'l*, pg. 807
BALFOUR BEATTY CIVIL ENGINEERING LTD—See Balfour Beatty plc; *Int'l*, pg. 807
BALFOUR BEATTY COMMUNITIES LLC—See Balfour Beatty plc; *Int'l*, pg. 807
BALFOUR BEATTY CONSTRUCTION GROUP INC—See Balfour Beatty plc; *Int'l*, pg. 807
BALFOUR BEATTY CONSTRUCTION LIMITED—See Balfour Beatty plc; *Int'l*, pg. 807
BALFOUR BEATTY CONSTRUCTION LLC—See Balfour Beatty plc; *Int'l*, pg. 807
BALFOUR BEATTY CONSTRUCTION LLC—See Balfour Beatty plc; *Int'l*, pg. 807
BALFOUR BEATTY CONSTRUCTION NORTHERN LIMITED—See Balfour Beatty plc; *Int'l*, pg. 807
BALFOUR BEATTY CONSTRUCTION SCOTTISH & SOUTHERN LIMITED—See Balfour Beatty plc; *Int'l*, pg. 807
BALFOUR BEATTY CONSTRUCTION SERVICES UK—See Balfour Beatty plc; *Int'l*, pg. 807
BALFOUR BEATTY-CONSTRUCTION SERVICES UK—See Balfour Beatty plc; *Int'l*, pg. 808
BALFOUR BEATTY ENGINEERING SERVICES LIMITED—See Balfour Beatty plc; *Int'l*, pg. 808
BALFOUR BEATTY GROUND ENGINEERING LTD—See Balfour Beatty plc; *Int'l*, pg. 808
BALFOUR BEATTY GROUP LTD—See Balfour Beatty plc; *Int'l*, pg. 807
BALFOUR BEATTY HOMES LTD.—See Balfour Beatty plc; *Int'l*, pg. 808
BALFOUR BEATTY INFRASTRUCTURE INVESTMENTS LTD—See Balfour Beatty plc; *Int'l*, pg. 808
BALFOUR BEATTY INVESTMENT HOLDINGS LTD—See Balfour Beatty plc; *Int'l*, pg. 808
BALFOUR BEATTY INVESTMENTS INC.—See Balfour Beatty plc; *Int'l*, pg. 808
BALFOUR BEATTY INVESTMENTS LIMITED—See Balfour Beatty plc; *Int'l*, pg. 808
BALFOUR BEATTY PLC; *Int'l*, pg. 807
BALFOUR BEATTY RAIL GMBH—See Vp PLC; *Int'l*, pg. 8312
BALFOUR BEATTY RAIL LTD—See Vp PLC; *Int'l*, pg. 8312
BALFOUR BEATTY RAIL—See Balfour Beatty plc; *Int'l*, pg. 807
BALFOUR LUMBER COMPANY, INC.—See Canfor Corporation; *Int'l*, pg. 1290
BALFOUR TIMBER COMPANY INC.; *U.S. Private*, pg. 459
BALGAS—See UGI Corporation; *U.S. Public*, pg. 2221
B-A-L GERMANY AG; *Int'l*, pg. 784
BAL GLOBAL FINANCE (DEUTSCHLAND) GMBH—See Bank of America Corporation; *U.S. Public*, pg. 270
BALGOPAL COMMERCIAL LIMITED; *Int'l*, pg. 808
BAL HARBOUR SHOPS, LLLP; *U.S. Private*, pg. 457
BAL HESTIA IMMOBILIEN LEASING GMBH—See UniCredit S.p.A.; *Int'l*, pg. 8036
BAL HOLDINGS INC.—See Grupo BAL; *Int'l*, pg. 3121
BAL HORUS IMMOBILIEN LEASING GMBH—See UniCredit S.p.A.; *Int'l*, pg. 8034
BALHOUSIE HOLDINGS LIMITED; *Int'l*, pg. 808
BAL HYPNOS IMMOBILIEN LEASING GMBH—See UniCredit S.p.A.; *Int'l*, pg. 8034
BALIHOO, INC.; *U.S. Private*, pg. 459
BALI LEATHERS INC.; *U.S. Private*, pg. 459
B & A LIMITED; *Int'l*, pg. 783
BALINEAU SA (ANTILLES)—See VINCI S.A.; *Int'l*, pg. 8233
BALINEAU S.A.—See VINCI S.A.; *Int'l*, pg. 8233
BALIRNY DOUWE EGBERTS A.S.—See JAB Holding Company S.a.r.l.; *Int'l*, pg. 3862
BALISE MOTOR SALES CO.; *U.S. Private*, pg. 459
BALKAMP, INC.—See Genuine Parts Company; *U.S. Public*, pg. 932
BALKANCAR ZARYA PLC; *Int'l*, pg. 809
BALKANCERAMIC PLC.—See Synergon Holding PLC; *Int'l*, pg. 7384
BALKAN MINING & MINERALS LIMITED; *Int'l*, pg. 808
BALKAN & SEA PROPERTIES REIT; *Int'l*, pg. 808
BALKAN SERVICES LTD.—See Bulgarian Stock Exchange - Sofia AD; *Int'l*, pg. 1213
BALKAN STAR—See Imperial Brands PLC; *Int'l*, pg. 3632
BALKEMA EXCAVATING INC.; *U.S. Private*, pg. 459
BALKRISHNA INDUSTRIES LIMITED; *Int'l*, pg. 809
BALKRISHNA PAPER MILLS LIMITED; *Int'l*, pg. 809
BAL LABORATORY—See Thielsch Engineering, Inc.; *U.S. Private*, pg. 4144
BALL ADVANCED ALUMINUM TECHNOLOGIES CORP.—See Ball Corporation; *U.S. Public*, pg. 266
BALL AEROCAN CZ S.R.O.—See Ball Corporation; *U.S. Public*, pg. 266

COMPANY NAME INDEX

BALL AEROCAN EUROPE S.A.S.—See Ball Corporation; *U.S. Public*, pg. 266
BALL AEROCAN FRANCE S.A.S—See Ball Corporation; *U.S. Public*, pg. 266
BALL AEROCAN MEXICO S.A. DE C.V.—See Ball Corporation; *U.S. Public*, pg. 266
BALL AEROCAN UK LTD.—See Ball Corporation; *U.S. Public*, pg. 266
BALL AEROSOL PACKAGING INDIA PRIVATE LIMITED—See Ball Corporation; *U.S. Public*, pg. 266
BALL AEROSPACE & TECHNOLOGIES CORP.—See Ball Corporation; *U.S. Public*, pg. 266
BALLANTINE, INC.—See Tsubakimoto Chain Co.; *Int'l*, pg. 7953
THE BALLANTINE PUBLISHING GROUP—See Bertelsmann SE & Co. KGaA; *Int'l*, pg. 991
BALLANTYNE MCKEAN & SULLIVAN LTD.—See BMS Group Ltd.; *Int'l*, pg. 1077
BALLARD COMPANIES, INC.; *U.S. Private*, pg. 460
BALLARD EXPLORATION COMPANY INC; *U.S. Private*, pg. 460
BALLARD MATERIAL PRODUCTS INC.—See Ballard Power Systems, Inc.; *Int'l*, pg. 809
BALLARD PARTNERS, INC.; *U.S. Private*, pg. 460
BALLARD POWER SYSTEMS CORPORATION—See Ballard Power Systems, Inc.; *Int'l*, pg. 809
BALLARD POWER SYSTEMS EUROPE A/S—See Ballard Power Systems, Inc.; *Int'l*, pg. 809
BALLARD POWER SYSTEMS, INC.; *Int'l*, pg. 809
BALLARD REALTY CO INC.; *U.S. Private*, pg. 460
BALLARD SPAHR LLP; *U.S. Private*, pg. 460
BALLARD TECHNOLOGY, INC.—See Astronics Corporation; *U.S. Public*, pg. 217
BALLARD TRUCK CENTER OF WORCESTER; *U.S. Private*, pg. 461
BALLARD UNMANNED SYSTEMS, INC.—See Honeywell International Inc.; *U.S. Public*, pg. 1047
BALLARENA CONSTRUCTION; *U.S. Private*, pg. 461
BALLARPUR INDUSTRIES LIMITED—See Avantha Group; *Int'l*, pg. 735
BALL ASIA PACIFIC LIMITED—See Ball Corporation; *U.S. Public*, pg. 266
BALLAST NEDAM ASFALT B.V.—See Ronesans Holding A.S.; *Int'l*, pg. 6396
BALLAST NEDAM BOUW EN ONTWIKKELING D.V.—See Ronesans Holding A.S.; *Int'l*, pg. 6396
BALLAST NEDAM BOUW EN ONTWIKKELING HOLDING B.V.—See Ronesans Holding A.S.; *Int'l*, pg. 6396
BALLAST NEDAM ENGINEERING B.V.—See Ronesans Holding A.S.; *Int'l*, pg. 6396
BALLAST NEDAM FUNDERINGSTECHNIEKEN B.V.—See Ronesans Holding A.S.; *Int'l*, pg. 6396
BALLAST NEDAM ICT B.V.—See Ronesans Holding A.S.; *Int'l*, pg. 6396
BALLAST NEDAM INFRA BUSINESS DEVELOPMENT B.V.—See Ronesans Holding A.S.; *Int'l*, pg. 6396
BALLAST NEDAM INFRA B.V.—See Ronesans Holding A.S.; *Int'l*, pg. 6396
BALLAST NEDAM INFRA MATERIEEL B.V.—See Ronesans Holding A.S.; *Int'l*, pg. 6396
BALLAST NEDAM INFRA SPECIALITEITEN B.V.—See Ronesans Holding A.S.; *Int'l*, pg. 6396
BALLAST NEDAM INTERNATIONAL PRODUCT MANAGEMENT B.V.—See Ronesans Holding A.S.; *Int'l*, pg. 6396
BALLAST NEDAM INTERNATIONAL PROJECTS B.V.—See Ronesans Holding A.S.; *Int'l*, pg. 6396
BALLAST NEDAM IPM B.V.—See Ronesans Holding A.S.; *Int'l*, pg. 6396
BALLAST NEDAM IPM—See Ronesans Holding A.S.; *Int'l*, pg. 6396
BALLAST NEDAM MILIEUTECHNIEK B.V.—See Ronesans Holding A.S.; *Int'l*, pg. 6396
BALLAST NEDAM N.V.—See Ronesans Holding A.S.; *Int'l*, pg. 6396
BALLAST NEDAM OFFSHORE B.V.—See Ronesans Holding A.S.; *Int'l*, pg. 6396
BALLAST NEDAM ONTWIKKELINGSMAATSCHAPPIJ B.V.—See Ronesans Holding A.S.; *Int'l*, pg. 6396
BALLAST NEDAM SPECIALISTISCH GRONDVERZET B.V.—See Ronesans Holding A.S.; *Int'l*, pg. 6396
BALLAST NEDAM WEST—See Ronesans Holding A.S.; *Int'l*, pg. 6396
BALLAST PHOENIX LTD—See Waterland Private Equity Investments B.V.; *Int'l*, pg. 8357
BALLAST POINT BREWING & SPIRITS, INC.—See Kings & Convicts Brewing Co.; *U.S. Private*, pg. 2311
BALLAST POINT VENTURES LP; *U.S. Private*, pg. 461
BALLAST WISE; *U.S. Private*, pg. 461
BALLATORE CHAMPAGNE CELLARS—See E. & J. Gallo Winery; *U.S. Private*, pg. 1303
BALL BEVERAGE CAN AMERICAS, S.A. DE C.V.—See Ball Corporation; *U.S. Public*, pg. 267
BALL BEVERAGE CAN EGYPT S.A.E.—See Ball Corporation; *U.S. Public*, pg. 267
BALL BEVERAGE CAN SOUTH AMERICA SA—See Ball Corporation; *U.S. Public*, pg. 267
BALL BEVERAGE PACKAGING CZECH REPUBLIC SRO—See Ball Corporation; *U.S. Public*, pg. 267
BALL BEVERAGE PACKAGING EGYPT SAE—See Ball Corporation; *U.S. Public*, pg. 266
BALL BEVERAGE PACKAGING EUROPE LIMITED—See Ball Corporation; *U.S. Public*, pg. 267
BALL BEVERAGE PACKAGING FOSIE AB—See Ball Corporation; *U.S. Public*, pg. 267
BALL BEVERAGE PACKAGING FRANCE SAS—See Ball Corporation; *U.S. Public*, pg. 267
BALL BEVERAGE PACKAGING FREDERICIA A/S—See Ball Corporation; *U.S. Public*, pg. 267
BALL BEVERAGE PACKAGING GELSENKIRCHEN GMBH—See Ball Corporation; *U.S. Public*, pg. 267
BALL BEVERAGE PACKAGING IBERICA SL—See Ball Corporation; *U.S. Public*, pg. 267
BALL BEVERAGE PACKAGING (INDIA) PRIVATE LIMITED—See Ball Corporation; *U.S. Public*, pg. 267
BALL BEVERAGE PACKAGING IRELAND LIMITED—See Ball Corporation; *U.S. Public*, pg. 267
BALL BEVERAGE PACKAGING ITALIA SRL - SAN MARTINO—See Ball Corporation; *U.S. Public*, pg. 267
BALL BEVERAGE PACKAGING ITALIA SRL—See Ball Corporation; *U.S. Public*, pg. 267
BALL BEVERAGE PACKAGING LUDESCH GMBH—See Ball Corporation; *U.S. Public*, pg. 267
BALL BEVERAGE PACKAGING MANTSALA OY—See Ball Corporation; *U.S. Public*, pg. 267
BALL BEVERAGE PACKAGING NARO-FOMINSK LLC—See Ball Corporation; *U.S. Public*, pg. 267
BALL BEVERAGE PACKAGING OSS BV—See Ball Corporation; *U.S. Public*, pg. 267
BALL BEVERAGE PACKAGING UK LTD.—See Ball Corporation; *U.S. Public*, pg. 267
BALL BEVERAGE PACKAGING VSEVOLOZHSK LLC—See Ball Corporation; *U.S. Public*, pg. 267
BALL BEVERAGE PACKAGING WIDNAU GMBH—See Ball Corporation; *U.S. Public*, pg. 267
BALL BEVERAGE TURKEY PAKETLEME SANAYI VE TICARET AS—See Ball Corporation; *U.S. Public*, pg. 267
BALL, BOUNCE & SPORT, INC.; *U.S. Private*, pg. 460
BALL CHAIN MFG CO, INC.; *U.S. Private*, pg. 459
BALL CHILE S.A.—See Ball Corporation; *U.S. Public*, pg. 266
BALL COLEGRAVE LTD—See Ball Horticultural Company; *U.S. Private*, pg. 459
BALL COLOMBIA LTDA.—See Ball Horticultural Company; *U.S. Private*, pg. 459
BALL CORPORATION; *U.S. Public*, pg. 266
BALL DO BRASIL—See Ball Horticultural Company; *U.S. Private*, pg. 460
BALL & DOGGETT GROUP PTY. LTD.—See Japan Pulp and Paper Company Limited; *Int'l*, pg. 3903
BALL & DOGGETT PTY. LTD.—See Japan Pulp and Paper Company Limited; *Int'l*, pg. 3903
BALLE A/S—See Investment AB Latour; *Int'l*, pg. 3782
BALLE A/S—See Investment AB Latour; *Int'l*, pg. 3783
BALLENGER PAVING DIVISION—See CRH plc; *Int'l*, pg. 1846
BALLENISLES COUNTRY CLUB; *U.S. Private*, pg. 461
BALLERINA-KUCHEN H.-E. ELLERSIEK GMBH; *Int'l*, pg. 809
BALLERINA SDN. BHD.—See NPC Resources Berhad; *Int'l*, pg. 5472
BALLESTER HERMANOS INC.; *U.S. Private*, pg. 461
BALLET MAKERS AUSTRALIA PTY LTD—See Capezio Ballet Makers Inc.; *U.S. Private*, pg. 738
BALLET MAKERS EUROPE LTD—See Capezio Ballet Makers Inc.; *U.S. Private*, pg. 738
BALLET THEATRE FOUNDATION, INC.; *U.S. Private*, pg. 461
BALL EUROPE GMBH—See Ball Corporation; *U.S. Public*, pg. 266
BALLEY PACIFIC PETROLEUM; *U.S. Private*, pg. 461
BALL FLORAPLANT—See Ball Horticultural Company; *U.S. Private*, pg. 459
BALL FOUNDATION-NOT FOR PROFIT—See Ball Corporation; *U.S. Public*, pg. 266
BALL GLOBAL BUSINESS SERVICES EUROPE AND AMEA D.O.O. BEOGRAD-NOVI BEOGRAD—See Ball Corporation; *U.S. Public*, pg. 266
BALL GROUP NORGE AS—See Axcel Management A/S; *Int'l*, pg. 762
BALL GROUP SVERIGE AB—See Axcel Management A/S; *Int'l*, pg. 762
BALL HOMES INC.; *U.S. Private*, pg. 459
BALL HORTICULTURAL COMPANY - AUSTRALIA—See Ball Horticultural Company; *U.S. Private*, pg. 460
BALL HORTICULTURAL COMPANY; *U.S. Private*, pg. 459
BALL HORTICULTURAL (KUNMING) CO., LTD.—See Ball Horticultural Company; *U.S. Private*, pg. 460
BALLI GROUP PLC; *Int'l*, pg. 809
BALLI KLOCKNER GMBH—See Balli Group plc; *Int'l*, pg. 809
BALLI KLOCKNER MIDDLE EAST FZE—See Balli Group plc; *Int'l*, pg. 809
BALLIN, INC.; *Int'l*, pg. 809
BALLI STEEL INC—See Balli Group plc; *Int'l*, pg. 809
BALLI STEEL PIPE LLC—See Balli Group plc; *Int'l*, pg. 809

BALLY, CORP.

BALLISTIC RECOVERY SYSTEMS, INC.; *U.S. Public*, pg. 268
BALLI WEST AFRICA LIMITED—See Balli Group plc; *Int'l*, pg. 809
BALL & JEWELL DIVISION—See Harbour Group Industries, Inc.; *U.S. Private*, pg. 1860
BALL METAL BEVERAGE CONTAINER CORP.—See Ball Corporation; *U.S. Public*, pg. 266
BALL METAL BEVERAGE CONTAINER CORP.—See Ball Corporation; *U.S. Public*, pg. 266
BALL METAL BEVERAGE CONTAINER CORP.—See Ball Corporation; *U.S. Public*, pg. 266
BALL METAL BEVERAGE CONTAINER CORP.—See Ball Corporation; *U.S. Public*, pg. 266
BALL METAL FOOD CONTAINER CORP.—See Ball Corporation; *U.S. Public*, pg. 267
BALL METAL FOOD CONTAINER (OAKDALE), LLC—See Ball Corporation; *U.S. Public*, pg. 267
BALL OFFICE PRODUCTS; *U.S. Private*, pg. 460
BALLOONS ARE EVERYWHERE, INC.; *U.S. Private*, pg. 461
BALLOONS ARE EVERYWHERE, INC.—See Balloons Are Everywhere, Inc.; *U.S. Private*, pg. 461
BALLOU CONSTRUCTION COMPANY INCORPORATED; *U.S. Private*, pg. 461
BALLOU PLUM WEALTH ADVISORS, LLC—See EP Wealth Advisors, LLC; *U.S. Private*, pg. 1411
BALL PACKAGING CORP.—See Ball Corporation; *U.S. Public*, pg. 267
BALL PACKAGING EUROPE BIERNE S.A.S.—See Ball Corporation; *U.S. Public*, pg. 267
BALL PACKAGING EUROPE FRANCE S.A.S.—See Ball Corporation; *U.S. Public*, pg. 267
BALL PACKAGING EUROPE GMBH - BRAUNSCHWEIG—See Ball Corporation; *U.S. Public*, pg. 267
BALL PACKAGING EUROPE GMBH—See Ball Corporation; *U.S. Public*, pg. 267
BALL PACKAGING EUROPE HANDELSGES MBH—See Ball Corporation; *U.S. Public*, pg. 267
BALL PACKAGING EUROPE HOLDING B.V.—See Ball Corporation; *U.S. Public*, pg. 267
BALL PACKAGING EUROPE HOLDING GMBH & CO. KG—See Ball Corporation; *U.S. Public*, pg. 267
BALL PACKAGING EUROPE LA CIOTAT S.A.S.—See Ball Corporation; *U.S. Public*, pg. 267
BALL PACKAGING EUROPE LUBLIN SP. Z O.O.—See Ball Corporation; *U.S. Public*, pg. 267
BALL PACKAGING EUROPE RADOMSKO SP.Z O.O.—See Ball Corporation; *U.S. Public*, pg. 267
BALL PACKAGING EUROPE TRADING SP. Z O.O.—See Ball Corporation; *U.S. Public*, pg. 267
BALL PACKAGING PRODUCTS CANADA CORP.—See Ball Corporation; *U.S. Public*, pg. 267
BALL PIPE & SUPPLY INC.—See Yaffe Iron & Metal Company Inc.; *U.S. Private*, pg. 4584
BALL PUBLISHING—See Ball Horticultural Company; *U.S. Private*, pg. 460
BALLREICH SNACK FOOD COMPANY—See Grippo Potato Chip Company, Inc.; *U.S. Private*, pg. 1790
BALL SEED CO.—See Ball Horticultural Company; *U.S. Private*, pg. 460
BALL STATE INNOVATION CORPORATION—See Ball State University; *U.S. Private*, pg. 460
BALL STATE UNIVERSITY; *U.S. Private*, pg. 460
BALLSTON SPA BANCORP INC.; *U.S. Public*, pg. 268
BALL STRAATHOF (PTY) LTD.—See Ball Horticultural Company; *U.S. Private*, pg. 460
BALL TECHNOLOGIES HOLDINGS CORP.—See Ball Corporation; *U.S. Public*, pg. 267
BALL TIRE & GAS INC.; *U.S. Private*, pg. 460
BALL TRADING FRANCE S.A.S.—See Ball Corporation; *U.S. Public*, pg. 266
BALL TRADING GERMANY GMBH—See Ball Corporation; *U.S. Public*, pg. 266
THE BALL TRADING NETHERLANDS B.V.—See Ball Corporation; *U.S. Public*, pg. 266
BALL TRADING POLAND SP. Z O.O.—See Ball Corporation; *U.S. Public*, pg. 266
BALL TRADING UK LTD.—See Ball Corporation; *U.S. Public*, pg. 266
BALL (UK) HOLDINGS, LTD.—See Ball Corporation; *U.S. Public*, pg. 266
BALL VOLVO & G M C TRUCKS; *U.S. Private*, pg. 460
BALL WHOLESALE APS—See Axcel Management A/S; *Int'l*, pg. 762
BALL WINCH, LLC—See L.B. Foster Company; *U.S. Public*, pg. 1278
BALLY AUSTRALIA PTY. LTD.—See JAB Holding Company S.a.r.l.; *Int'l*, pg. 3861
BALLY, CORP.; *Int'l*, pg. 809
BALLY FRANCE SAS—See JAB Holding Company S.a.r.l.; *Int'l*, pg. 3861
BALLY GC RETAIL CO. LIMITED—See JAB Holding Company S.a.r.l.; *Int'l*, pg. 3861
BALLY GMBH—See JAB Holding Company S.a.r.l.; *Int'l*, pg. 3861

BALLY, CORP.

BALLYMORE CO., INC.—See Graycliff Partners LP; *U.S. Private*, pg. 1760
BALLYMORE RESOURCES LIMITED; *Int'l*, pg. 809
BALLY NORTH AMERICA, INC.—See JAB Holding Company S.a.r.l.; *Int'l*, pg. 3861
BALLY REFRIGERATED BOXES, INC.—See United Refrigeration, Inc.; *U.S. Private*, pg. 4296
BALLY RIBBON MILLS; *U.S. Private*, pg. 461
BALLY'S ATLANTIC CITY LLC—See Bally's Corporation; *U.S. Public*, pg. 268
BALLY SCHUHFABRIKEN AG—See JAB Holding Company; *Int'l*, pg. 3861
BALLY'S CORPORATION; *U.S. Public*, pg. 268
BALLY SINGAPORE PTE LTD.—See JAB Holding Company; *Int'l*, pg. 3861
BALLY'S LAKE TAHOE—See Caesars Entertainment, Inc.; *U.S. Public*, pg. 420
BALLY'S LAS VEGAS—See Caesars Entertainment, Inc.; *U.S. Public*, pg. 420
BALLY TECHNOLOGIES AUSTRALIA HOLDINGS I PTY LTD—See Light & Wonder, Inc.; *U.S. Public*, pg. 1314
BALLY TECHNOLOGIES, INC.—See Light & Wonder, Inc.; *U.S. Public*, pg. 1314
BALLY TECHNOLOGIES INDIA PRIVATE LIMITED—See Light & Wonder, Inc.; *U.S. Public*, pg. 1314
BALLY TOTAL FITNESS CORPORATION—See Harbert Management Corporation; *U.S. Private*, pg. 1858
BALLY TOTAL FITNESS HOLDINGS CORPORATION—See Harbert Management Corporation; *U.S. Private*, pg. 1858
BALLY UK SALES LTD.—See JAB Holding Company S.a.r.l.; *Int'l*, pg. 3861
BALLYVESEY FINANCE LTD—See Ballyvesey Holdings Limited; *Int'l*, pg. 809
BALLYVESEY HOLDINGS LIMITED; *Int'l*, pg. 809
BALLYVESEY HOLDINGS POLSKA LTD—See Ballyvesey Holdings Limited; *Int'l*, pg. 809
BALLYVESEY RECYCLING SOLUTIONS LTD—See Ballyvesey Holdings Limited; *Int'l*, pg. 809
BALLYWHOSOCIAL; *U.S. Private*, pg. 461
BALLY WULFF AUTOMATEN GMBH; *Int'l*, pg. 809
BALMAIN CORP.; *Int'l*, pg. 810
BALMAT HOLDINGS CORP.—See Titan Mining Corp.; *Int'l*, pg. 7760
BALMER BUCHERDIENST AG—See Ernst Klett AG; *Int'l*, pg. 2495
BALMER LAWRIE & CO. LTD.; *Int'l*, pg. 810
BALMER LAWRIE INVESTMENTS LTD.; *Int'l*, pg. 810
BAL METALS INTERNATIONAL INC—See Grupo BAL; *Int'l*, pg. 3121
BALMORAL ADVANCED COMPOSITES LIMITED—See Balmoral Group Ltd.; *Int'l*, pg. 810
BALMORAL FUNDS LLC; *U.S. Private*, pg. 461
BALMORAL GROUP LTD.; *Int'l*, pg. 810
BALMORAL INTERNATIONAL LAND HOLDINGS PLC; *Int'l*, pg. 810
BALMORAL INTERNATIONAL LAND LIMITED—See Balmoral International Land Holdings plc; *Int'l*, pg. 810
BALMORAL INTERNATIONAL LAND PROPERTY HOLDINGS BV—See Balmoral International Land Holdings plc; *Int'l*, pg. 810
BALMORAL INTERNATIONAL LAND UK LTD—See Balmoral International Land Holdings plc; *Int'l*, pg. 810
BALMORAL LAND NAUL LTD—See Balmoral International Land Holdings plc; *Int'l*, pg. 810
BALMORAL MARINE LTD.—See Balmoral Group Ltd.; *Int'l*, pg. 810
BALMORAL MOTORS LTD—See Lookers plc; *Int'l*, pg. 4555
BALMORAL TANKS LIMITED—See Balmoral Group Ltd.; *Int'l*, pg. 810
BALMORAL WELLBEING LTD.—See Balmoral Group Ltd.; *Int'l*, pg. 810
BALMUDA, INC.; *Int'l*, pg. 810
BALNEOTERAPIA SATURN SRL—See S.C. TURISM, HOTELURI, RESTAURANTE MAREA NEAGRA S.A.; *Int'l*, pg. 6455
BALNEX 1 A.S—See Warimpex Finanz- und Beteiligungs AG; *Int'l*, pg. 8345
BALNIBARBI CO., LTD.; *Int'l*, pg. 810
BALOCCO S.P.A.; *Int'l*, pg. 810
BALOCHISTAN GLASS LIMITED; *Int'l*, pg. 810
BALOCHISTAN PARTICLE BOARD LIMITED; *Int'l*, pg. 810
BALOG AUCTION SERVICES INC.; *Int'l*, pg. 810
BALOISE ASSET MANAGEMENT INTERNATIONAL AG—See Baloise Holding AG; *Int'l*, pg. 810
BALOISE ASSET MANAGEMENT SCHWEIZ AG—See Baloise Holding AG; *Int'l*, pg. 811
BALOISE ASSURANCES IARD S.A.—See Baloise Holding AG; *Int'l*, pg. 811
BALOISE ASSURANCES LUXEMBOURG S.A.—See Baloise Holding AG; *Int'l*, pg. 811
BALOISE BANK SOBA—See Baloise Holding AG; *Int'l*, pg. 811
BALOISE BELGIUM SA - BRUSSEL—See Baloise Holding AG; *Int'l*, pg. 811
BALOISE BELGIUM SA—See Baloise Holding AG; *Int'l*, pg. 811

BALOISE DELTA HOLDING S.A.R.L.—See Baloise Holding AG; *Int'l*, pg. 811
BALOISE EUROPE VIE SA—See Baloise Holding AG; *Int'l*, pg. 811
BALOISE FUND INVEST ADVICO—See Baloise Holding AG; *Int'l*, pg. 811
BALOISE FUND INVEST—See Baloise Holding AG; *Int'l*, pg. 811
BALOISE HOLDING AG; *Int'l*, pg. 810
BALOISE INSURANCE COMPANY (I.O.M.) LTD.—See Baloise Holding AG; *Int'l*, pg. 811
BALOISE LEBENSVERSICHERUNG AG—See Baloise Holding AG; *Int'l*, pg. 811
BALOISE LIFE (LIECHTENSTEIN) AG—See Baloise Holding AG; *Int'l*, pg. 811
BALOISE LIFE LTD.—See Baloise Holding AG; *Int'l*, pg. 811
BALOISE (LUXEMBOURG) HOLDING S.A.—See Baloise Holding AG; *Int'l*, pg. 810
BALOISE SACHVERSICHERUNG AG—See Baloise Holding AG; *Int'l*, pg. 811
BALOISE VIE LUXEMBOURG S.A—See Baloise Holding AG; *Int'l*, pg. 811
BALO-MOTORTEX GMBH—See Georgsmarienhutte Holding GmbH; *Int'l*, pg. 2940
BALON CORPORATION, *U.S. Private*, pg. 462
BAL PHARMA LTD; *Int'l*, pg. 806
BALQON CORPORATION, *U.S. Private*, pg. 462
BALRAMPUR CHINI MILLS LIMITED; *Int'l*, pg. 811
BALRAMPUR OVERSEAS PVT. LTD.—See Balrampur Chini Mills Limited; *Int'l*, pg. 811
BALSAM BRANDS; *U.S. Private*, pg. 462
BALSAM HILL—See Balsam Brands; *U.S. Private*, pg. 462
BALS CORPORATION; *Int'l*, pg. 811
BAL SEAL ASIA, LTD.—See Arcline Investment Management LP; *U.S. Private*, pg. 314
BAL SEAL ENGINEERING EUROPE BV—See Arcline Investment Management LP; *U.S. Private*, pg. 314
BAL SEAL ENGINEERING, INC.—See Arcline Investment Management LP; *U.S. Private*, pg. 314
BAL SERVICING CORPORATION—See Deutsche Bank Aktiengesellschaft; *Int'l*, pg. 2055
BALS HONG KONG LIMITED—See BALS CORPORATION; *Int'l*, pg. 811
BAL SOBEK IMMOBILIEN LEASING GMBH—See UniCredit S.p.A.; *Int'l*, pg. 8037
BALTA FLOORCOVERING YER DAS, EMELERI SAN.VE TIC A.S.—See Balta Group NV; *Int'l*, pg. 811
BALTA FLOORCOVERING YER DOS, EMELERI SAN.VE TIC A.S.—See Balta Group NV; *Int'l*, pg. 811
BALTA GROUP NV; *Int'l*, pg. 811
BALTA ORIENT TEKSTIL SANAYI VE TICARET A.S.—See Balta Group NV; *Int'l*, pg. 812
BALTA OUDENAARDE NV—See Balta Group NV; *Int'l*, pg. 812
BALTA USA, INC.—See Balta Group NV; *Int'l*, pg. 812
BALTCAP AS; *Int'l*, pg. 812
BALTEC AUSTRALIA TRADING AS TOTAL AIR POLLUTION CONTROL PTY LIMITED—See The Environmental Group Limited; *Int'l*, pg. 7640
BALTEC CORPORATION—See BalTec Maschinenbau AG; *Int'l*, pg. 812
BALTEC IES.PTY LIMITED—See The Environmental Group Limited; *Int'l*, pg. 7640
BALTEC MASCHINENBAU AG; *Int'l*, pg. 812
BALTEC (UK) LTD.—See BalTec Maschinenbau AG; *Int'l*, pg. 812
BALTEK INC.—See Schweiter Technologies AG; *Int'l*, pg. 6645
BALTERM, L.L.P.—See Blue Wolf Capital Partners LLC; *U.S. Private*, pg. 595
BALTER SALES CO. INC.; *U.S. Private*, pg. 462
BALT EXTRUSION SAS—See Bridgepoint Group Plc; *Int'l*, pg. 1154
BALTIA AIR LINES, INC.; *U.S. Private*, pg. 462
BALTIC BRIDGE S.A.; *Int'l*, pg. 812
BALTIC CABLE AB—See E.ON SE; *Int'l*, pg. 2252
BALTIC CABLE AB—See Statkraft SF; *Int'l*, pg. 7185
BALTIC CHAMPS, UAB—See AUGA group, AB; *Int'l*, pg. 703
BALTIC CLASSIFIEDS GROUP PLC; *Int'l*, pg. 812
BALTIC CONTAINER TERMINAL LTD—See International Container Terminal Services, Inc.; *Int'l*, pg. 3746
BALTIC ELEKTRONIK GMBH—See Korber AG; *Int'l*, pg. 4280
THE BALTIC EXCHANGE (ASIA) PTE. LTD.—See Singapore Exchange Limited; *Int'l*, pg. 6940
THE BALTIC EXCHANGE LTD.—See Singapore Exchange Limited; *Int'l*, pg. 6940
BALTIC GREEN CONSTRUCTION SP. Z O.O.—See CEZ, a.s.; *Int'l*, pg. 1426
BALTIC I ACQUISITION CORP.; *Int'l*, pg. 812
BALTIC INTERNATIONAL USA, INC.; *U.S. Public*, pg. 268
BALTIC INVESTMENT BANK PJSC; *Int'l*, pg. 812
BALTIC LEASING LLC—See Central Bank of the Russian Federation; *Int'l*, pg. 1405
BALTIC LINEN COMPANY, INC.; *U.S. Private*, pg. 462

CORPORATE AFFILIATIONS

BALTIC LOGISTIC HOLDING B.V.—See BayWa AG; *Int'l*, pg. 915
BALTIC MARINE CONTRACTORS OU—See Zeppelin GmbH; *Int'l*, pg. 8637
BALTIC MASTER—See Carrier Global Corporation; *U.S. Public*, pg. 441
BALTIC METALLTECHNIK GMBH—See Bader GmbH; *Int'l*, pg. 795
BALTICON SA; *Int'l*, pg. 812
BALTIC REEFERS LTD.; *Int'l*, pg. 812
BALTIC RIM SIA—See SP Group A/S; *Int'l*, pg. 7122
BALTIC SEA PROPERTIES AS; *Int'l*, pg. 812
BALTIC TELEKOM AS; *Int'l*, pg. 812
BALTIC TK—See Tulikivi Corporation; *Int'l*, pg. 7969
BALTIC TRADING LIMITED—See Genco Shipping & Trading Limited; *U.S. Public*, pg. 911
BALTIKA POLAND SP.Z.O.O.—See KJK Capital Oy; *Int'l*, pg. 4197
BALTIKA UKRAINA LTD—See KJK Capital Oy; *Int'l*, pg. 4197
BALTIK IT—See Indra Sistemas, S.A.; *Int'l*, pg. 3660
BALTI MEEDIAMONITOORINGU GRUPP OU—See UP Invest OU; *Int'l*, pg. 8087
BALTIMORE AIRCOIL AUST. PTY.LTD.—See AMSTED Industries Incorporated; *U.S. Private*, pg. 267
BALTIMORE AIRCOIL COMPANY S.A. (PTY) LTD.—See AMSTED Industries Incorporated; *U.S. Private*, pg. 268
BALTIMORE AIRCOIL COMPANY—See AMSTED Industries Incorporated; *U.S. Private*, pg. 267
BALTIMORE AIRCOIL INTERNATIONAL NV—See AMSTED Industries Incorporated; *U.S. Private*, pg. 267
BALTIMORE AIRCOIL ITALIA S.R.L.—See AMSTED Industries Incorporated; *U.S. Private*, pg. 267
BALTIMORE BUSINESS JOURNAL—See Advance Publications, Inc.; *U.S. Private*, pg. 84
BALTIMORE COMMUNITY FOUNDATION, INC.; *U.S. Private*, pg. 462
BALTIMORE COUNTRY CLUB; *U.S. Private*, pg. 462
BALTIMORE COUNTY REVENUE AUTHORITIES; *U.S. Private*, pg. 462
THE BALTIMORE ENDOSCOPY ASC, LLC—See KKR & Co. Inc.; *U.S. Public*, pg. 1247
BALTIMORE EYE PHYSICIANS, LLC—See Centre Partners Management LLC; *U.S. Private*, pg. 828
BALTIMORE FINANCIAL BROKERAGE, INC.—See Baltimore Life Insurance Company Inc.; *U.S. Private*, pg. 462
BALTIMORE FINANCIAL SERVICES CORPORATION—See Baltimore Life Insurance Company Inc.; *U.S. Private*, pg. 462
BALTIMORE FREIGHTLINER; *U.S. Private*, pg. 462
BALTIMORE GAS AND ELECTRIC COMPANY—See Exelon Corporation; *U.S. Public*, pg. 806
BALTIMORE LIFE COMPANY—See Baltimore Life Insurance Company Inc.; *U.S. Private*, pg. 462
BALTIMORE LIFE INSURANCE COMPANY INC.; *U.S. Private*, pg. 462
BALTIMORE MEDICAL SYSTEM INC.; *U.S. Private*, pg. 462
THE BALTIMORE MUSEUM OF ART; *U.S. Private*, pg. 3991
BALTIMORE ORIOLES, L.P.; *U.S. Private*, pg. 462
BALTIMORE RAVENS LIMITED PARTNERSHIP; *U.S. Private*, pg. 462
THE BALTIMORE SUN COMPANY—See Tribune Publishing Company; *U.S. Private*, pg. 4228
BALTIMORE SUN MEDIA GROUP—See Tribune Publishing Company; *U.S. Private*, pg. 4228
BALTIMORE SYMPHONY ORCHESTRA; *U.S. Private*, pg. 463
BALTIMORE WASHINGTON THURGOOD MARSHALL INTERNATIONAL AIRPORT; *U.S. Private*, pg. 463
BALT INTERNATIONAL SAS—See Bridgepoint Group Plc; *Int'l*, pg. 1154
BALTI REHVISEADMETE A/S—See McRolls Oy; *Int'l*, pg. 4761
BALTI UUDISTETALITUSE AS—See UP Invest OU; *Int'l*, pg. 8086
BALTONA SHIPCHANDLERS SP. Z O.O.—See PHZ Baltona S.A.; *Int'l*, pg. 5859
BALTO RESOURCES LTD.; *Int'l*, pg. 812
BALTRANS EXHIBITION & REMOVAL LTD—See Japan Post Holdings Co., Ltd.; *Int'l*, pg. 3900
BALTRANS INTERNATIONAL CARGO LTD—See Japan Post Holdings Co., Ltd.; *Int'l*, pg. 3900
BALTRANS INTERNATIONAL MOVING LTD—See Japan Post Holdings Co., Ltd.; *Int'l*, pg. 3900
BALTRANS LOGISTICS LTD—See Japan Post Holdings Co., Ltd.; *Int'l*, pg. 3900
BALTTRANSSERVIS, OOO—See Globaltrans Investment PLC; *Int'l*, pg. 3004
BAL TURIZM VE GIDA PAZARLAMA A.S.—See Dogus Holding AS; *Int'l*, pg. 2154
THE BALTUS COMPANY; *U.S. Private*, pg. 3991
BALTYCKI TERMINAL DROBNICOWY GDYNIA SP. Z O.O.—See OT Logistics S.A.; *Int'l*, pg. 5655
BALTZ & COMPANY - DENVER—See Baltz & Company; *U.S. Private*, pg. 463
BALTZ & COMPANY; *U.S. Private*, pg. 463

COMPANY NAME INDEX

BALTZ & COMPANY—See Baltz & Company; *U.S. Private*, pg. 463
BALTZINGER SA—See Sonepar S.A.; *Int'l*, pg. 7090
BALUCHISTAN WHEELS LIMITED; *Int'l*, pg. 812
BALU FORGE INDUSTRIES LTD.; *Int'l*, pg. 812
BALURGHAT TECHNOLOGIES LTD.; *Int'l*, pg. 812
BALUSAMY SILVEARS JEWELLERY PRIVATE LIMITED—See Thangamayil Jewellery Limited; *Int'l*, pg. 7608
BALVAC, LTD.—See Balfour Beatty plc; *Int'l*, pg. 807
BALVER ZINN JOSEF JOST GMBH & CO. KG; *Int'l*, pg. 812
BALWIN PROPERTIES LIMITED; *Int'l*, pg. 812
BALYO APAC PTE LTD—See Balyo SA; *Int'l*, pg. 813
BALYO INC.—See Balyo SA; *Int'l*, pg. 813
BALYO SA; *Int'l*, pg. 813
BALZAC CARAVANES; *Int'l*, pg. 813
BALZER INGENIEURE AG—See BKW AG; *Int'l*, pg. 1054
BALZER PACIFIC EQUIPMENT CO.; *U.S. Private*, pg. 463
BALZERS BALINIT DO BRASIL LTDA.—See OC Oerlikon Corporation AG; *Int'l*, pg. 5512
BALZER'S CANADA INC.; *Int'l*, pg. 813
BALZERS KOREA COATING CO., LTD.—See OC Oerlikon Corporation AG; *Int'l*, pg. 5512
BALZERS LTD.—See OC Oerlikon Corporation AG; *Int'l*, pg. 5512
BALZERS REVETEMENTS LA—See OC Oerlikon Corporation AG; *Int'l*, pg. 5512
BALZERS S.A.—See OC Oerlikon Corporation AG; *Int'l*, pg. 5512
BALZERS VERSCHLEISSSCHUTZ GMBH—See OC Oerlikon Corporation AG; *Int'l*, pg. 5512
BAMA AIR, INC.—See Moelis Asset Management LP; *U.S. Private*, pg. 2764
BAMA COMPANIES INC.; *U.S. Private*, pg. 463
BAMA COMPANY; *Int'l*, pg. 813
BAMA CONCRETE BIRMINGHAM, INC.—See Bama Concrete Products Co., Inc.; *U.S. Private*, pg. 463
BAMA CONCRETE PRODUCTS CO., INC.; *U.S. Private*, pg. 463
BAMA FROZEN DOUGH LLC—See Bama Companies Inc.; *U.S. Private*, pg. 463
BAMA-GEVE, S.L.U.—See Alfa-Wassermann S.p.A.; *Int'l*, pg. 314
BAMAG GMBH—See Allied Resource Corporation; *U.S. Private*, pg. 187
BAM AGRICULTURAL SOLUTIONS, INC.—See Zero Gravity Solutions, Inc.; *U.S. Public*, pg. 2403
BAMA GRUPPEN AS; *Int'l*, pg. 813
BAMA INFOTECH PVT. LTD.—See Universal Arts Limited; *Int'l*, pg. 8077
BAMA SEA PRODUCTS INC.; *U.S. Private*, pg. 463
B.A. MASON—See Mason Companies, Inc.; *U.S. Private*, pg. 2602
BAMATEC AG—See Baumann Federn AG; *Int'l*, pg. 895
BAMBACH WIRES & CABLES PTY LTD—See Energy Technologies Limited; *Int'l*, pg. 2423
BAMBACIGNO STEEL COMPANY, INC.; *U.S. Private*, pg. 463
BAMBECK & VEST ASSOCIATES INC.; *U.S. Private*, pg. 463
BAM BELGIUM NV—See Koninklijke BAM Groep N.V.; *Int'l*, pg. 4261
BAMBERGER KALIKO GMBH; *Int'l*, pg. 813
BAMBERGER POLYMERS (CANADA), INC.—See Bamberger Polymers, Inc.; *U.S. Private*, pg. 463
BAMBERGER POLYMERS, INC.; *U.S. Private*, pg. 463
BAMBERGER POLYMERS INTERNATIONAL CORP.—See Bamberger Polymers, Inc.; *U.S. Private*, pg. 463
BAMBI-BANAT AD; *Int'l*, pg. 813
BAMBINO AGRO INDUSTRIES LIMITED; *Int'l*, pg. 813
BAMBOO CAPITAL JSC; *Int'l*, pg. 813
BAMBOO GROVE RECREATIONAL SERVICES LIMITED—See Hysan Development Company Limited; *Int'l*, pg. 3554
BAMBOO MARKETING; *U.S. Private*, pg. 463
BAMBOO PIPELINE, INC.; *U.S. Private*, pg. 463
BAMBOOS EDUCATION- SCHOOL FOR TALENTS LIMITED—See Bamboos Health Care Holdings Limited; *Int'l*, pg. 813
BAMBOOS HEALTH CARE HOLDINGS LIMITED; *Int'l*, pg. 813
BAMBOOS PROFESSIONAL NURSING SERVICES LIMITED—See Bamboos Health Care Holdings Limited; *Int'l*, pg. 813
BAMBORA AB—See Apollo Global Management, Inc.; *U.S. Public*, pg. 151
BAMBORA GROUP AB—See Apollo Global Management, Inc.; *U.S. Public*, pg. 151
BAMBORA INC.—See Apollo Global Management, Inc.; *U.S. Public*, pg. 151
BAM BOUW EN TECHNIEK BV—See Koninklijke BAM Groep N.V.; *Int'l*, pg. 4261
BAM BOUW EN VASTGOED NEDERLAND BV—See Koninklijke BAM Groep N.V.; *Int'l*, pg. 4261
BAMBU AG; *Int'l*, pg. 813
BAMBURI CEMENT PLC—See Amsons Group; *Int'l*, pg. 441

BAMBUSER AB; *Int'l*, pg. 813
BAMCARD D.D.; *Int'l*, pg. 813
BAM CIVIEL B.V.—See Koninklijke BAM Groep N.V.; *Int'l*, pg. 4261
BAMCO CONSTRUCTION, INC.; *U.S. Private*, pg. 463
BAMCO INC.; *U.S. Private*, pg. 463
BAM CONSTRUCTION LIMITED—See Koninklijke BAM Groep N.V.; *Int'l*, pg. 4261
BAM CONSTRUCT UK LTD—See Koninklijke BAM Groep N.V.; *Int'l*, pg. 4261
BAM CONTRACTORS—See Koninklijke BAM Groep N.V.; *Int'l*, pg. 4261
BAM DESIGN LIMITED—See Koninklijke BAM Groep N.V.; *Int'l*, pg. 4261
BAM DEUTSCHLAND STANDORT GOTTINGEN—See Koninklijke BAM Groep N.V.; *Int'l*, pg. 4261
BAM ENTERPRISES, INC.; *U.S. Private*, pg. 463
BA MERCHANT SERVICES, LLC—See Bank of America Corporation; *U.S. Public*, pg. 271
BAMESA ACEROS; *Int'l*, pg. 813
BAMESA CELIK A.S.—See BAMESA Aceros; *Int'l*, pg. 813
BAMESA CELIK MURADIYE DEMIR SANAYI VE TICARET—See BAMESA Aceros; *Int'l*, pg. 813
BAMESA CELIK SERVIS S.V.T.A.S.—See BAMESA Aceros; *Int'l*, pg. 813
BAMESA FRANCE, S.A.—See BAMESA Aceros; *Int'l*, pg. 813
BAMESA OTEL, S.A.—See BAMESA Aceros; *Int'l*, pg. 813
BAM FACILITIES MANAGEMENT LIMITED—See Koninklijke BAM Groep N.V.; *Int'l*, pg. 4261
B&A MINERACAO SA—See AGN Agroindustrial, Projetos e Participacoes Ltda.; *Int'l*, pg. 211
B&A MINERACAO S.A.—See BTG Pactual Holding S.A.; *Int'l*, pg. 1204
BAM INFRACONSULT BV—See Koninklijke BAM Groep N.V.; *Int'l*, pg. 4261
BAM INFRA ENERGIE & WATER BV—See Koninklijke BAM Groep N.V.; *Int'l*, pg. 4261
BAM INFRA RAIL BV—See Koninklijke BAM Groep N.V.; *Int'l*, pg. 4261
BAM INFRA TELECOM BV—See Koninklijke BAM Groep N.V.; *Int'l*, pg. 4261
BAM INTERNATIONAL BV—See Koninklijke BAM Groep N.V.; *Int'l*, pg. 4261
BAMKO, LLC—See Superior Group Of Companies, Inc.; *U.S. Public*, pg. 1966
BAMNI PROTEINS LTD.—See Nitta Gelatin India Limited; *Int'l*, pg. 5383
BAM NUTTALL LTD.—See Koninklijke BAM Groep N.V.; *Int'l*, pg. 4261
BAM PPP B.V.—See Koninklijke BAM Groep N.V.; *Int'l*, pg. 4261
BAM PPP DEUTSCHLAND GMBH—See Koninklijke BAM Groep N.V.; *Int'l*, pg. 4261
BAM PPP IRELAND LTD.—See Koninklijke BAM Groep N.V.; *Int'l*, pg. 4261
BAM PPP NEDERLAND B.V.—See Koninklijke BAM Groep N.V.; *Int'l*, pg. 4261
BAM PPP UK LTD.—See Koninklijke BAM Groep N.V.; *Int'l*, pg. 4261
BAM PROPERTIES LIMITED—See Koninklijke BAM Groep N.V.; *Int'l*, pg. 4261
BAMPSL SECURITIES LIMITED; *Int'l*, pg. 813
BAMPTON (REDBRIDGE) LIMITED—See Centremanor Ltd.; *Int'l*, pg. 1411
BAM STRATEGY; *Int'l*, pg. 813
BAM WONEN BV—See Koninklijke BAM Groep N.V.; *Int'l*, pg. 4261
BAMYAN MEDIA; *U.S. Private*, pg. 464
BANADER HOTELS COMPANY BSC; *Int'l*, pg. 814
BANAH INTERNATIONAL GROUP, INC.; *U.S. Private*, pg. 464
BANA INC.; *U.S. Private*, pg. 464
BANAMEX USA BANCORP—See Citigroup Inc.; *U.S. Public*, pg. 501
BANANA BAY WATERFRONT MOTEL; *U.S. Private*, pg. 464
BANANA IMPORTERS OF IRELAND LIMITED—See Sumitomo Corporation; *Int'l*, pg. 7268
BANANAR EHF.—See Hagar hf.; *Int'l*, pg. 3206
BANANA REPUBLIC—See The Gap, Inc.; *U.S. Public*, pg. 2074
BANANA REPUBLIC—See The Gap, Inc.; *U.S. Public*, pg. 2074
BANANZA AIR MANAGEMENT SYSTEMS, INC.—See Rapid Engineering Inc.; *U.S. Private*, pg. 3355
BANARAS BEADS LIMITED; *Int'l*, pg. 814
BANAS FINANCE LIMITED; *Int'l*, pg. 814
BANAT ESTIVAL 2002 SA; *Int'l*, pg. 814
BANATSKI DESPOTOVAC A.D.; *Int'l*, pg. 814
BANAWI MANE FLAVORS CO., LTD.—See V. Mane Fils SA; *Int'l*, pg. 8105
BANBAO CO., LTD.; *Int'l*, pg. 814
BANC3, INC.; *U.S. Private*, pg. 464
BANCA 24-7 S.P.A.—See Intesa Sanpaolo S.p.A.; *Int'l*, pg. 3766
BANCA ALETTI & C. S.P.A.—See Banco BPM S.p.A.; *Int'l*, pg. 818

BANCA POPOLARE DELL'ETRURIA E DEL LAZIO S.C.

BANCA CABOTO S.P.A.—See Intesa Sanpaolo S.p.A.; *Int'l*, pg. 3764
BANCA CARIGE S.P.A.; *Int'l*, pg. 814
BANCA CATTOLICA S.P.A.—See Credito Valtellinese Societa Cooperativa; *Int'l*, pg. 1837
BANCA CENTRALE DELLA REPUBBLICA DI SAN MARINO; *Int'l*, pg. 814
BANCA CESARE PONTI S.P.A.—See BPER BANCA S.p.A.; *Int'l*, pg. 1132
BANCA COMERCIALA CARPATICA SA; *Int'l*, pg. 814
BANCA COMERCIALA ROMANA CHISINAU S.A.—See B.C. Victoriabank S.A.; *Int'l*, pg. 789
BANCA COMERCIALA ROMANA S.A.—See Erste Group Bank AG; *Int'l*, pg. 2497
BANCA CONSULIA S.P.A.—See Banca Intermobiliare di Investimenti e Gestioni S.p.A.; *Int'l*, pg. 815
BANCA CREDIFARMA S.P.A.—See Banca IFIS S.p.A.; *Int'l*, pg. 815
BANCA C.R. FIRENZE ROMANIA S.A.—See Intesa Sanpaolo S.p.A.; *Int'l*, pg. 3764
BANCA CR FIRENZE S.P.A.—See Intesa Sanpaolo S.p.A.; *Int'l*, pg. 3764
BANCA DE ECONOMII S.A.; *Int'l*, pg. 814
BANCA DELLA CAMPANIA S.P.A.—See BPER BANCA S.p.A.; *Int'l*, pg. 1132
BANCA DELL'ADRIATICO S.P.A.—See Intesa Sanpaolo S.p.A.; *Int'l*, pg. 3765
BANCA DELLA NUOVA TERRA—See BPER BANCA S.p.A.; *Int'l*, pg. 1132
BANCA DEL MEZZOGIORNO-MEDIOCREDITO CENTRALE SPA—See Poste Italiane S.p.A.; *Int'l*, pg. 5939
BANCA DI CIVIDALE S.P.A.; *Int'l*, pg. 814
BANCA D'INTERMEDIAZIONE MOBILIARE IMI S.P.A.—See Intesa Sanpaolo S.p.A.; *Int'l*, pg. 3764
BANCA DI ROMA S.P.A.—See UniCredit S.p.A.; *Int'l*, pg. 8034
BANCA DI SAN GIORGIO S.P.A.—See Intesa Sanpaolo S.p.A.; *Int'l*, pg. 3766
BANCA DI SASSARI S.P.A.—See BPER BANCA S.p.A.; *Int'l*, pg. 1132
BANCA DI TRENTO E BOLZANO S.P.A.—See Intesa Sanpaolo S.p.A.; *Int'l*, pg. 3765
BANCA DI VALLE CAMONICA S.P.A.—See Intesa Sanpaolo S.p.A.; *Int'l*, pg. 3766
BANCADVICE, LLC; *U.S. Private*, pg. 464
BANCA EUROMOBILIARE SPA—See Credito Emiliano S.p.A.; *Int'l*, pg. 1836
BANCA FARMAFACTORING S.P.A.; *Int'l*, pg. 814
BANCA FINNAT EURAMERICA S.P.A.; *Int'l*, pg. 814
BANCA GENERALI S.P.A.—See Assicurazioni Generali S.p.A.; *Int'l*, pg. 643
BANCA GESFID SA—See Unipol Gruppo S.p.A.; *Int'l*, pg. 8056
BANCA HIPOTECARIA—See Banco Bilbao Vizcaya Argentaria, S.A.; *Int'l*, pg. 818
BANCA IFIS S.P.A.; *Int'l*, pg. 815
BANCA IMI SECURITIES CORP.—See Intesa Sanpaolo S.p.A.; *Int'l*, pg. 3764
BANCA IMI—See Intesa Sanpaolo S.p.A.; *Int'l*, pg. 3764
BANCA IMI—See Intesa Sanpaolo S.p.A.; *Int'l*, pg. 3764
BANCA INTERMOBILIARE DI INVESTIMENTI E GESTIONI S.P.A.; *Int'l*, pg. 815
BANCA INTESA JSC; *Int'l*, pg. 815
BANCA INTESA SERVIZI FORMAZIONE—See Intesa Sanpaolo S.p.A.; *Int'l*, pg. 3764
BANCA ITALEASE S.P.A.—See Banco BPM S.p.A.; *Int'l*, pg. 818
BANCA MARCH-LONDON—See Alba Grupo March; *Int'l*, pg. 292
BANCA MARCH S.A.—See Alba Grupo March; *Int'l*, pg. 292
BANCA MEDIOLANUM S.P.A.; *Int'l*, pg. 815
BANCA MONTE DEI PASCHI DI SIENA S.P.A.; *Int'l*, pg. 815
BANCA NATIONALA A MOLDOVEI; *Int'l*, pg. 815
BANCA NAZIONALE DEL LAVORO S.P.A.—See BNP Paribas SA; *Int'l*, pg. 1089
BANCA PER LO SVILUPPO DELLA COOPERAZIONE DI CREDITO S.P.A.—See Iccrea Holding S.p.A.; *Int'l*, pg. 3578
BANCAPERTA S.P.A.—See Credito Valtellinese Societa Cooperativa; *Int'l*, pg. 1837
BANCA POPOLARE DELL'EMILIA ROMAGNA (EUROPE) INTERNATIONAL S.A.—See BPER BANCA (EUROPE); *Int'l*, pg. 1132
BANCA POPOLARE DELL'ETRURIA E DEL LAZIO S.C.; *Int'l*, pg. 815
BANCA POPOLAR E DI ANCONA S.P.A.—See Intesa Sanpaolo S.p.A.; *Int'l*, pg. 3766
BANCA POPOLARE DI APRILIA S.P.A.—See BPER BANCA S.p.A.; *Int'l*, pg. 1132
BANCA POPOLARE DI CREMONA S.P.A.—See Banco BPM S.p.A.; *Int'l*, pg. 819
BANCA POPOLARE DI CROTONE S.P.A.—See BPER BANCA S.p.A.; *Int'l*, pg. 1132
BANCA POPOLARE DI LANCIANO E SULMONA S.P.A.—See BPER BANCA S.p.A.; *Int'l*, pg. 1132
BANCA POPOLARE DI LODI S.P.A.—See Banco BPM S.p.A.; *Int'l*, pg. 819

BANCA POPOLARE DELL'ETRURIA E DEL LAZIO S.C. — CORPORATE AFFILIATIONS

BANCA POPOLARE DI NOVARA S.P.A.—See Banco BPM S.p.A.; *Int'l*, pg. 819
BANCA POPOLARE DI RAVENNA S.P.A.—See BPER BANCA S.p.A; *Int'l*, pg. 1132
BANCA POPOLARE DI SONDRIO S.P.A.; *Int'l*, pg. 815
BANCA POPOLARE DI SONDRIO (SUISSE) S.A.—See Banca Popolare di Sondrio S.p.A.; *Int'l*, pg. 816
BANCA POPOLARE DI SPOLETO S.P.A.; *Int'l*, pg. 816
BANCA POPOLARE DI VERONA - S. GEMINIANO E S. PROSPERO S.P.A.—See Banco BPM S.p.A.; *Int'l*, pg. 819
BANCA POPOLARE PUGLIESE S.C.P.A.; *Int'l*, pg. 816
BANCA PRIVADA D'ANDORRA (PANAMA), S.A.—See Banca Privada D'Andorra, SA; *Int'l*, pg. 816
BANCA PRIVADA D'ANDORRA, SA; *Int'l*, pg. 816
BANCA PROFILO S.P.A.; *Int'l*, pg. 816
BANCA PROGETTO S.P.A.—See Brookfield Corporation; *Int'l*, pg. 1181
BANCA PROSSIMA S.P.A.—See Intesa Sanpaolo S.p.A.; *Int'l*, pg. 3764
BANCA REGIONALE EUROPEA S.P.A.—See Intesa Sanpaolo S.p.A.; *Int'l*, pg. 3766
BANCASAI S.P.A.—See Unipol Gruppo S.p.A.; *Int'l*, pg. 8056
BANCA SELLA HOLDINGS S.P.A.; *Int'l*, pg. 816
BANCA SERFIN, S.A.—See Banco Santander, S.A.; *Int'l*, pg. 826
BANCA SISTEMA S.P.A.; *Int'l*, pg. 816
BANCA TRANSILVANIA S.A.; *Int'l*, pg. 816
BANCA UCB S.P.A.—See BNP Paribas SA; *Int'l*, pg. 1087
BANCA ZARATTINI & CO.—See Lukos SA; *Int'l*, pg. 4576
BANCFIRST CORPORATION; *U.S. Public*, pg. 269
BANCFIRST INSURANCE SERVICES, INC.—See BancFirst Corporation; *U.S. Public*, pg. 269
BANCFIRST—See BancFirst Corporation; *U.S. Public*, pg. 269
THE BANC FUNDS COMPANY LLC; *U.S. Private*, pg. 3991
BANCINDEPENDENT INC.; *U.S. Private*, pg. 464
BANCINSURANCE CORPORATION; *U.S. Private*, pg. 464
BANCLEASING INC.—See BancVue, Ltd.; *U.S. Private*, pg. 464
BANCO ABC BRASIL S.A.—See Arab Banking Corporation B.S.C.; *Int'l*, pg. 529
BANCO ALCALA, SA—See Credit Andorra, S.A.; *Int'l*, pg. 1834
BANCO ALFA DE INVESTIMENTO SA; *Int'l*, pg. 816
BANCO ALIADO, S.A.—See Grupo Aliado S.A.; *Int'l*, pg. 3119
BANCO AZTECA SA—See Grupo Salinas, S.A. de C.V.; *Int'l*, pg. 3135
BANCO B3, S.A—See B3 S.A.; *Int'l*, pg. 791
BANCO BAC DE PANAMA, S.A.; *Int'l*, pg. 816
BANCO BANDEIRANTES—See Itau Unibanco Holding S.A.; *Int'l*, pg. 3830
BANCO BARCLAYS S.A.—See Barclays PLC; *Int'l*, pg. 859
BANCO BBVA ARGENTINA S.A.—See Banco Bilbao Vizcaya Argentaria, S.A.; *Int'l*, pg. 817
BANCO BIC PORTUGUES S.A.; *Int'l*, pg. 816
BANCO BILBAO VIZCAYA ARGENTARIA (PORTUGAL), S.A.—See Banco Bilbao Vizcaya Argentaria, S.A.; *Int'l*, pg. 817
BANCO BILBAO VIZCAYA ARGENTARIA, S.A.; *Int'l*, pg. 816
BANCO BILBAO VIZCAYA ARGENTARIA URUGUAY S.A.—See Banco Bilbao Vizcaya Argentaria, S.A.; *Int'l*, pg. 817
BANCO BMG S.A.; *Int'l*, pg. 818
BANCO BNP PARIBAS BRASIL—See BNP Paribas SA; *Int'l*, pg. 1089
BANCO BNP PARIBAS PERSONAL FINANCE SA—See BNP Paribas SA; *Int'l*, pg. 1089
BANCO BOAVISTA S.A.—See Banco Bradesco S.A.; *Int'l*, pg. 819
BANCO BPI, S.A.—See Lone Star Funds; *U.S. Private*, pg. 2484
BANCO BPM SPA; *Int'l*, pg. 819
BANCO BPM S.A.; *Int'l*, pg. 818
BANCO BRADESCO ARGENTINA S.A.—See Banco Bradesco S.A.; *Int'l*, pg. 819
BANCO BRADESCO EUROPA S.A.—See Banco Bradesco S.A.; *Int'l*, pg. 819
BANCO BRADESCO FINANCIAMENTOS S.A.—See Banco Bradesco S.A.; *Int'l*, pg. 819
BANCO BRADESCO NEW YORK—See Banco Bradesco S.A.; *Int'l*, pg. 819
BANCO BRADESCO S.A.; *Int'l*, pg. 819
BANCO BTG PACTUAL S.A.—See BTG Pactual Holding S.A.; *Int'l*, pg. 1204
BANCO CAIXA GERAL BRASIL, S.A.—See ABANCA CORPORACION BANCARIA, SA; *Int'l*, pg. 48
BANCO CAIXA GERAL, S.A.—See Caixa Geral de Depositos S.A.; *Int'l*, pg. 1260
BANCO CATERPILLAR S.A.—See Caterpillar, Inc.; *U.S. Public*, pg. 449
BANCO CENCOSUD S.A.—See The Bank of Nova Scotia; *Int'l*, pg. 7618
BANCO CENTRAL DE CHILE; *Int'l*, pg. 819

BANCO CENTRAL DE CUBA; *Int'l*, pg. 819
BANCO CENTRAL DE HONDURAS; *Int'l*, pg. 820
BANCO CENTRAL DE LA REPUBLICA ARGENTINA; *Int'l*, pg. 820
BANCO CENTRAL DE LA REPUBLICA DOMINICA; *Int'l*, pg. 820
BANCO CENTRAL DEL ECUADOR; *Int'l*, pg. 820
BANCO CENTRAL DEL PARAGUAY; *Int'l*, pg. 820
BANCO CENTRAL DEL URUGUAY; *Int'l*, pg. 820
BANCO CENTRAL DE RESERVA DE EL SALVADOR; *Int'l*, pg. 820
BANCO CENTRAL DE RESERVA DEL PERU; *Int'l*, pg. 820
BANCO CENTRAL DE VENEZUELA; *Int'l*, pg. 820
BANCO CENTRAL DO BRASIL; *Int'l*, pg. 820
BANCO CETELEM ARGENTINA SA—See BNP Paribas SA; *Int'l*, pg. 1089
BANCO CETELEM S.A.—See BNP Paribas SA; *Int'l*, pg. 1089
BANCO CITIBANK S.A.—See Citigroup Inc.; *U.S. Public*, pg. 501
BANCO CITICARD S.A.—See Itau Unibanco Holding S.A.; *Int'l*, pg. 3830
BANCO CNH CAPITAL S.A.—See CNH Industrial N.V.; *Int'l*, pg. 1674
BANCO COMAFI S.A.; *Int'l*, pg. 820
BANCO COMERCIAL DE MACAU, S.A.—See Dah Sing Financial Holdings Limited; *Int'l*, pg. 1913
BANCO COMERCIAL DO ATLANTICO, S.A.R.L.—See Caixa Geral de Depositos S.A.; *Int'l*, pg. 1260
BANCO COMERCIAL PORTUGUES; *Int'l*, pg. 820
BANCO COMPARTAMOS, S.A., INSTITUCION DE BANCA MULTIPLE—See Gentera, S.A.B. de C.V.; *Int'l*, pg. 2928
BANCO CREDIT SUISSE (BRASIL) S.A.—See UBS Group AG; *Int'l*, pg. 8006
BANCO CREDIT SUISSE (MEXICO), S.A.—See UBS Group AG; *Int'l*, pg. 8005
BANCO CRUZEIRO DO SUL SA; *Int'l*, pg. 820
BANCO DA AMAZONIA S/A; *Int'l*, pg. 820
BANCO DA CHINA BRASIL S.A.—See Bank of China, Ltd.; *Int'l*, pg. 841
BANCO DAVIVIENDA (COSTA RICA) S.A.—See Grupo Bolivar S.A.; *Int'l*, pg. 3123
BANCO DAVIVIENDA HONDURAS, S.A.—See Grupo Bolivar S.A.; *Int'l*, pg. 3123
BANCO DAVIVIENDA S.A.—See Grupo Bolivar S.A.; *Int'l*, pg. 3123
BANCO DAYCOVAL S.A.; *Int'l*, pg. 820
BANCO DE BOGOTA SA; *Int'l*, pg. 820
BANCO DE CHILE—See Quinenco S.A.; *Int'l*, pg. 6163
BANCO DE COMERCIO S.A.; *Int'l*, pg. 820
BANCO DE CREDITO DEL PERU SA—See Credicorp Ltd.; *Int'l*, pg. 1834
BANCO DE CREDITO E INVERSIONES S.A.—See Empresas Juan Yarur S.A.C.; *Int'l*, pg. 2391
BANCO DE ESPANA; *Int'l*, pg. 820
BANCO DE FOMENTO ANGOLA—See Unitel S.A.; *Int'l*, pg. 8074
BANCO DE GALICIA Y BUENOS AIRES S.A.—See Grupo Financiero Galicia S.A.; *Int'l*, pg. 3129
BANCO DE GUATEMALA; *Int'l*, pg. 820
BANCO DE HONDURAS S.A.—See Citigroup Inc.; *U.S. Public*, pg. 501
BANCO DE LA NACION ARGENTINA - NEW YORK—See Banco de la Nacion Argentina; *Int'l*, pg. 820
BANCO DE LA NACION ARGENTINA; *Int'l*, pg. 820
BANCO DE LA NACION ARGENTINA—See Banco de la Nacion Argentina; *Int'l*, pg. 820
BANCO DE LA PROVINCIA DE BUENOS AIRES; *Int'l*, pg. 821
BANCO DE LA REPUBLICA COLOMBIA; *Int'l*, pg. 821
BANCO DEL BAJIO S.A.; *Int'l*, pg. 822
BANCO DEL CARIBE, C.A. BANCO UNIVERSAL; *Int'l*, pg. 822
BANCO DELTA S.A.; *Int'l*, pg. 822
BANCO DE MADRID, S.A.—See Banca Privada D'Andorra, SA; *Int'l*, pg. 816
BANCO DE MOCAMBIQUE; *Int'l*, pg. 821
BANCO DE OCCIDENTE S.A.—See Grupo Aval Acciones y Valores S.A.; *Int'l*, pg. 3121
BANCO DE OCCIDENTE; *Int'l*, pg. 821
BANCO DE ORO SAVINGS BANK INC.—See BDO Unibank, Inc.; *Int'l*, pg. 930
BANCO DE PORTUGAL; *Int'l*, pg. 821
BANCO DEPOSITARIO BBVA, S.A.—See Banco Bilbao Vizcaya Argentaria, S.A.; *Int'l*, pg. 817
BANCO DE SABADELL, S.A.; *Int'l*, pg. 821
BANCO DESIO LAZIO S P A—See Banco Di Desio e Della Brianza S.p.A.; *Int'l*, pg. 822
BANCO DE TOKYO-MITSUBISHI UFJ BRASIL S/A—See Mitsubishi UFJ Financial Group, Inc.; *Int'l*, pg. 4969
BANCO DE VENEZUELA, S.A.—See Banco Santander, S.A.; *Int'l*, pg. 825
BANCO DE VIDA S.A.—See Abbott Laboratories; *U.S. Public*, pg. 19
BANCO DI BRESCIA S.P.A.—See Intesa Sanpaolo S.p.A.; *Int'l*, pg. 3766

BANCO DI CARIBE (ARUBA) N.V.—See Banco di Caribe N.V.; *Int'l*, pg. 822
BANCO DI CARIBE N.V.; *Int'l*, pg. 822
BANCO DI DESIO E DELLA BRIANZA S.P.A.; *Int'l*, pg. 822
BANCO DI SARDEGNA S.P.A.—See BPER BANCA S.p.A; *Int'l*, pg. 1132
BANCO DI SICILIA S.P.A.—See UniCredit S.p.A.; *Int'l*, pg. 8034
BANCO DO BRASIL AG AUSTRIA—See Banco do Brasil S.A.; *Int'l*, pg. 822
BANCO DO BRASIL S.A. - NEW YORK—See Banco do Brasil S.A.; *Int'l*, pg. 822
BANCO DO BRASIL S.A.; *Int'l*, pg. 822
BANCO DO ESTADO DO RIO GRANDE DO SUL SA; *Int'l*, pg. 822
BANCO ECONOMICO S.A.—See Novo Banco, S.A.; *Int'l*, pg. 5462
BANCO ECONOMICO S.A.—See Sociedade Nacional de Combustiveis de Angola, E.P.; *Int'l*, pg. 7033
BANCO EDWARDS DEL BANCO DE CHILE—See Quinenco S.A.; *Int'l*, pg. 6163
BANC OF AMERICA COMMUNITY DEVELOPMENT CORPORATION—See Bank of America Corporation; *U.S. Public*, pg. 270
BANC OF AMERICA CREDIT PRODUCTS, INC.—See Bank of America Corporation; *U.S. Public*, pg. 270
BANC OF AMERICA FSC HOLDINGS, INC.—See Bank of America Corporation; *U.S. Public*, pg. 270
BANC OF AMERICA LEASING & CAPITAL, LLC—See Bank of America Corporation; *U.S. Public*, pg. 270
BANC OF AMERICA PREFERRED FUNDING CORPORATION—See Bank of America Corporation; *U.S. Public*, pg. 270
BANC OF CALIFORNIA, INC.; *U.S. Public*, pg. 268
BANC OF CALIFORNIA, N.A.—See Banc of California, Inc.; *U.S. Public*, pg. 268
BANCO FIBRA S.A.; *Int'l*, pg. 822
BANCO GENERAL (COSTA RICA), S.A.—See Banco General, S.A.; *Int'l*, pg. 822
BANCO GENERAL, S.A.; *Int'l*, pg. 822
BANCO GERDAU—See Metalurgica Gerdau S.A.; *Int'l*, pg. 4849
BANCO GMAC S.A.—See General Motors Company; *U.S. Public*, pg. 925
BANCO GNB COLOMBIA S.A.—See Banco GNB Sudameris S.A.; *Int'l*, pg. 823
BANCO GNB PARAGUAY S.A.—See Banco GNB Sudameris S.A.; *Int'l*, pg. 823
BANCO GNB PERU S.A.—See Banco GNB Sudameris S.A.; *Int'l*, pg. 823
BANCO GNB SUDAMERIS S.A.; *Int'l*, pg. 822
BANCO GUAYAQUIL SA; *Int'l*, pg. 823
BANCO GUIPUZCOANO S.A.—See Banco de Sabadell, S.A.; *Int'l*, pg. 821
BANCO HIPOTECARIO SA; *Int'l*, pg. 823
BANCO HONDA S.A—See Honda Motor Co., Ltd.; *Int'l*, pg. 3460
BANCO HSBC SALVADORENO, S.A.—See HSBC Holdings plc; *Int'l*, pg. 3503
BANCO HSBC S.A.—See HSBC Holdings plc; *Int'l*, pg. 3503
BANCO IBM S.A.—See International Business Machines Corporation; *Int'l*, pg. 1145
BANCO INBURSA S.A.—See Grupo Financiero Inbursa, S.A. de C.V.; *Int'l*, pg. 3129
BANCO INDUSVAL MULTISTOCK - PORTO ALEGRE UNIT—See Banco Master S.A.; *Int'l*, pg. 823
BANCO INDUSVAL MULTISTOCK - RECIFE UNIT—See Banco Master S.A.; *Int'l*, pg. 823
BANCO INDUSVAL MULTISTOCK - RIO DE JANEIRO UNIT—See Banco Master S.A.; *Int'l*, pg. 823
BANCO INDUSVAL MULTISTOCK—See Banco Master S.A.; *Int'l*, pg. 823
BANCO INTERAMERICANO DE FINANZAS SA; *Int'l*, pg. 823
BANCO INTERATLANTICO, S.A.R.L.—See Caixa Geral de Depositos S.A.; *Int'l*, pg. 1260
BANCO INTERNACIONAL DE CABO VERDE—See Novo Banco, S.A.; *Int'l*, pg. 5462
BANCO INTERNACIONAL DE COSTA RICA, S.A.; *Int'l*, pg. 823
BANCO INTERNACIONAL; *Int'l*, pg. 823
BANCO INTER S.A.; *Int'l*, pg. 823
BANCO ITAU ARGENTINA S.A.—See Banco Macro S.A.; *Int'l*, pg. 823
BANCO ITAU BBA S.A.—See Itau Unibanco Holding S.A.; *Int'l*, pg. 3830
BANCO ITAUCARD S.A.—See Itau Unibanco Holding S.A.; *Int'l*, pg. 3830
BANCO ITAU CHILE—See Itau Unibanco Holding S.A.; *Int'l*, pg. 3830
BANCO ITAU EUROPA LUXEMBOURG, S.A.—See Itau Unibanco Holding S.A.; *Int'l*, pg. 3830
BANCO ITAU PARAGUAY S.A.—See Itau Unibanco Holding S.A.; *Int'l*, pg. 3830
BANCO ITAU URUGUAY S.A.—See Itau Unibanco Holding S.A.; *Int'l*, pg. 3830

BANCO JOHN DEERE S.A.—See Deere & Company; *U.S. Public*, pg. 646
BANCO J.P. MORGAN S.A., INSTITUCION DE BANCA MULTIPLE, J.P. MORGAN GRUPO FINANCIERO—See JPMorgan Chase & Co.; *U.S. Public*, pg. 1208
BANCO KEB DO BRASIL S.A.—See Hana Financial Group, Inc.; *Int'l*, pg. 3240
BANCO KEB HANA DO BRASIL S.A.—See Hana Financial Group, Inc.; *Int'l*, pg. 3240
BANCOKLAHOMA MORTGAGE CORPORATION—See BOK Financial Corporation; *U.S. Public*, pg. 367
BANCO LATINOAMERICANO DE COMERCIO EXTERIOR, S.A.; *Int'l*, pg. 823
BANCOLOMBIA CAPITAL LLC—See Bancolombia S.A.; *Int'l*, pg. 828
BANCOLOMBIA PANAMA S.A.—See Bancolombia S.A.; *Int'l*, pg. 828
BANCOLOMBIA PUERTO RICO INTERNACIONAL INC—See Bancolombia S.A.; *Int'l*, pg. 828
BANCOLOMBIA S.A.; *Int'l*, pg. 828
BANCO MACRO S.A.; *Int'l*, pg. 823
BANCO MADESANT - SOCIEDADE UNIPESSOAL, S.A.—See Banco Santander, S.A.; *Int'l*, pg. 825
BANCO MAPFRE, S.A.—See MAPFRE S.A.; *Int'l*, pg. 4683
BANCO MASTER S.A.; *Int'l*, pg. 823
BANCO MEDIOLANUM, S.A.—See Banca Mediolanum S.p.A.; *Int'l*, pg. 815
BANCO MERCANTIL DE INVESTIMENTOS S.A.—See Banco Mercantil do Brasil S.A.; *Int'l*, pg. 823
BANCO MERCANTIL DO BRASIL S.A.; *Int'l*, pg. 823
BANCO MERCEDES-BENZ DO BRASIL S.A.—See Daimler Truck Holding AG; *Int'l*, pg. 1938
BANCOMER TRANSFER SERVICES, INC.—See Banco Bilbao Vizcaya Argentaria, S.A.; *Int'l*, pg. 818
BANCO MODAL S.A.—See XP Inc.; *Int'l*, pg. 8537
BANCO MONEO SA—See Marcopolo S.A.; *Int'l*, pg. 4690
BANCO MONTEPIO GERAL - CABO VERDE, SOCIEDADE UNIPESSOAL, S.A.—See Caixa Economica Montepio Geral; *Int'l*, pg. 1259
BANCO MULTIVA, S.A.—See Grupo Empresarial Angeles, S.A. de C.V.; *Int'l*, pg. 3126
BANCO NACIONAL DE MEXICO, S.A.—See Citigroup Inc.; *U.S. Public*, pg. 504
BANCO NACIONAL DE PANAMA; *Int'l*, pg. 823
BANC ONE CAPITAL HOLDINGS LLC—See JPMorgan Chase & Co.; *U.S. Public*, pg. 1206
BANCO OCCIDENTAL SA—See Banco Bilbao Vizcaya Argentaria, S.A.; *Int'l*, pg. 817
BANCO OPPORTUNITY S/A; *Int'l*, pg. 823
BANCO PAN S.A.—See BTG Pactual Holding S.A.; *Int'l*, pg. 1204
BANCO PARIS S.A.—See Cencosud S.A.; *Int'l*, pg. 1400
BANCO PATAGONIA SUDAMERIS S.A.—See Banco do Brasil S.A.; *Int'l*, pg. 822
BANCO PICHINCHA MIAMI AGENCY; *U.S. Private*, pg. 464
BANCO PINE S.A.; *Int'l*, pg. 824
BANCO POPULAR DE PUERTO RICO—See Popular, Inc.; *U.S. Public*, pg. 1702
BANCO POPULAR DE PUERTO RICO - TRUST DIVISION—See Popular, Inc.; *U.S. Public*, pg. 1702
BANCO POPULAR PUERTO RICO - VIRGIN ISLANDS REGIONAL OFFICE—See Popular, Inc.; *U.S. Public*, pg. 1702
BANCO POPULAR S.A.—See Popular, Inc.; *U.S. Public*, pg. 1702
BANCOPOSTA FONDI SPA—See Poste Italiane S.p.A.; *Int'l*, pg. 5939
BANCO PRIMUS S.A—See Groupe BPCE; *Int'l*, pg. 3092
BANCO PRIMUS SPAIN S.A—See Groupe BPCE; *Int'l*, pg. 3092
BANCO PROCREDIT COLUMBIA S.A.—See Creditos y Ahorro Credifinanciera S.A., Compania de Financiamiento; *Int'l*, pg. 1837
BANCO PROCREDIT S.A.—See ProCredit Holding AG & Co. KGaA; *Int'l*, pg. 5987
BANCO PROCREDIT S.A.—See ProCredit Holding AG & Co. KGaA; *Int'l*, pg. 5987
BANCO PROCREDIT S.A.—See ProCredit Holding AG & Co. KGaA; *Int'l*, pg. 5987
BANCO PRODUCTS (I) LTD.; *Int'l*, pg. 824
BANCO PROVINCIAL OVERSEAS N.V.—See Banco Bilbao Vizcaya Argentaria, S.A.; *Int'l*, pg. 817
BANCO PYME LOS ANDES PROCREDIT S.A.—See ProCredit Holding AG & Co. KGaA; *Int'l*, pg. 5987
BANCO RABOBANK INTERNATIONAL BRASIL S.A.—See Cooperatieve Centrale Raiffeisen-Boerenleenbank B.A.; *Int'l*, pg. 1791
BANCO RIO DE LA PLATA S.A.—See Banco Santander, S.A.; *Int'l*, pg. 825
BANCORP 34, INC.; *U.S. Public*, pg. 269
THE BANCORP BANK—See The Bancorp, Inc.; *U.S. Public*, pg. 2036
THE BANCORP, INC.; *U.S. Public*, pg. 2036
BANCORP OF SOUTHERN INDIANA; *U.S. Public*, pg. 269

BANCORP WEALTH MANAGEMENT NEW ZEALAND LTD.; *Int'l*, pg. 824
BANCO SAFRA S.A.; *Int'l*, pg. 824
BANCO SANTANDER (BRASIL) S.A.—See Banco Santander, S.A.; *Int'l*, pg. 826
BANCO SANTANDER CENTRAL HISPANO (GUERNSEY), LTD.—See Banco Santander, S.A.; *Int'l*, pg. 825
BANCO SANTANDER-CHILE—See Banco Santander, S.A.; *Int'l*, pg. 825
BANCO SANTANDER COLOMBIA, S.A.—See Itau Unibanco Holding S.A.; *Int'l*, pg. 3830
BANCO SANTANDER CONSUMER PORTUGAL, S.A.—See Banco Santander, S.A.; *Int'l*, pg. 825
BANCO SANTANDER DE NEGOCIOS COLOMBIA S.A.—See Banco Santander, S.A.; *Int'l*, pg. 825
BANCO SANTANDER DE NEGOCIOS PORTUGAL, S.A.—See Banco Santander, S.A.; *Int'l*, pg. 825
BANCO SANTANDER INTERNATIONAL—See First BanCorp; *U.S. Public*, pg. 839
BANCO SANTANDER (PANAMA), S.A.—See Banco Santander, S.A.; *Int'l*, pg. 825
BANCO SANTANDER PERU S.A.—See Banco Santander, S.A.; *Int'l*, pg. 825
BANCO SANTANDER PORTUGAL, S.A.—See Banco Santander, S.A.; *Int'l*, pg. 825
BANCO SANTANDER RIO S.A.—See Banco Santander, S.A.; *Int'l*, pg. 825
BANCO SANTANDER, S.A.; *Int'l*, pg. 825
BANCO SANTANDER (SUISSE), S.A.—See Banco Santander, S.A.; *Int'l*, pg. 825
BANCO SANTANDER TOTTA, S.A,—See Banco Santander, S.A.; *Int'l*, pg. 825
BANCO SHINHAN DE MEXICO S.A.—See Shinhan Financial Group Co., Ltd.; *Int'l*, pg. 6843
BANCO SMARTBANK S.A.—See Banco Master S.A.; *Int'l*, pg. 823
BANCO SOCIETE GENERALE BRASIL S.A.—See Societe Generale S.A.; *Int'l*, pg. 7039
BANCO SOFISA S.A.; *Int'l*, pg. 828
BANCO STANDARD TOTTA DE MOZAMBIQUE, SARL—See Standard Chartered PLC; *Int'l*, pg. 7167
BANCO SUMITOMO MITSUI BRASILEIRO S.A.—See Sumitomo Mitsui Financial Group, Inc.; *Int'l*, pg. 7293
BANCO URQUIJO S.A.—See Banco de Sabadell, S.A.; *Int'l*, pg. 821
BANCO VOITER S.A.—See Banco Master S.A.; *Int'l*, pg. 823
BANCO VOLKSWAGEN S.A.—See Porsche Automobil Holding SE; *Int'l*, pg. 5931
BANCO VOLVO (BRASIL) SA—See AB Volvo; *Int'l*, pg. 45
BANCO VOTORANTIM SA—See Votorantim S.A.; *Int'l*, pg. 8309
BANCO VTB AFRICA S.A—See PJSC VTB Bank; *Int'l*, pg. 5886
BANCO WELL LINK, S.A.—See Well Link Group Holdings Ltd.; *Int'l*, pg. 8373
BANCPOST S.A.—See Eurobank Ergasias Services and Holdings S.A.; *Int'l*, pg. 2532
BANCROFT BAG INC.; *U.S. Private*, pg. 464
BANCROFT CONSTRUCTION COMPANY; *U.S. Private*, pg. 464
BANCROFT CONTRACTING CORP.; *U.S. Private*, pg. 464
BANCROFT FUND LTD.—See GAMCO Investors, Inc.; *U.S. Public*, pg. 895
BANCROFT MOTORS LTD; *Int'l*, pg. 828
BANCSABADELL D'ANDORRA, S.A.—See Banco de Sabadell, S.A.; *Int'l*, pg. 821
BANC STATEMENTS, INC. (BSI); *U.S. Private*, pg. 464
BANCTEC, INC.—See Gainline Capital Partners LP; *U.S. Private*, pg. 1635
BANCTEC LTD.—See Gainline Capital Partners LP; *U.S. Private*, pg. 1635
BANCVUE, LTD.; *U.S. Private*, pg. 464
BANCWEST INVESTMENT SERVICES, INC.—See BNP Paribas SA; *Int'l*, pg. 1087
BANDAGES PLUS, INC.—See The Morrissey Group LLC; *U.S. Private*, pg. 4080
BANDAG INCORPORATED—See Bridgestone Corporation; *Int'l*, pg. 1155
BANDAI CHANNEL CO., LTD.—See BANDAI NAMCO Holdings Inc.; *Int'l*, pg. 828
BANDAI CO., LTD.—See BANDAI NAMCO Holdings Inc.; *Int'l*, pg. 828
BANDAI ESPANA S.A.—See BANDAI NAMCO Holdings Inc.; *Int'l*, pg. 828
BANDAI (GUANGZHOU) CO., LTD.—See BANDAI NAMCO Holdings Inc.; *Int'l*, pg. 828
BANDAI (H.K.) CO., LTD.—See BANDAI NAMCO Holdings Inc.; *Int'l*, pg. 828
BANDAI KOREA CO., LTD.—See BANDAI NAMCO Holdings Inc.; *Int'l*, pg. 828
BANDAI LOGIPAL INC.—See BANDAI NAMCO Holdings Inc.; *Int'l*, pg. 828
BANDAI NAMCO AMUSEMENT AMERICA INC.—See BANDAI NAMCO Holdings Inc.; *Int'l*, pg. 829
BANDAI NAMCO AMUSEMENT EUROPE LTD.—See BANDAI NAMCO Holdings Inc.; *Int'l*, pg. 829

BANDAI NAMCO ARTS INC.—See BANDAI NAMCO Holdings Inc.; *Int'l*, pg. 828
BANDAI NAMCO BUSINESS ARC INC.—See BANDAI NAMCO Holdings Inc.; *Int'l*, pg. 829
BANDAI NAMCO ENTERTAINMENT AMERICA INC.—See BANDAI NAMCO Holdings Inc.; *Int'l*, pg. 829
BANDAI NAMCO GAMES FRANCE S.A.S.—See BANDAI NAMCO Holdings Inc.; *Int'l*, pg. 829
BANDAI NAMCO GAMES INC.—See BANDAI NAMCO Holdings Inc.; *Int'l*, pg. 829
BANDAI NAMCO HOLDINGS INC.; *Int'l*, pg. 828
BANDAI NAMCO HOLDINGS UK LTD.—See BANDAI NAMCO Holdings Inc.; *Int'l*, pg. 829
BANDAI NAMCO HOLDINGS (USA) INC.—See BANDAI NAMCO Holdings Inc.; *Int'l*, pg. 829
BANDAI NAMCO ONLINE INC.—See BANDAI NAMCO Holdings Inc.; *Int'l*, pg. 829
BANDAI NAMCO TOYS & COLLECTIBLES AMERICA INC.—See BANDAI NAMCO Holdings Inc.; *Int'l*, pg. 828
BANDA INDUSTRIES SDN. BHD.—See Kerjaya Prospek Property Berhad; *Int'l*, pg. 4136
BANDAI POLSKA SP. Z O.O.—See BANDAI NAMCO Holdings Inc.; *Int'l*, pg. 828
BANDAI S.A.—See BANDAI NAMCO Holdings Inc.; *Int'l*, pg. 828
BANDAI U.K. LTD.—See BANDAI NAMCO Holdings Inc.; *Int'l*, pg. 828
BANDAI VISUAL CO., LTD.—See BANDAI NAMCO Holdings Inc.; *Int'l*, pg. 828
BANDAK GROUP—See Herkules Capital AS; *Int'l*, pg. 3362
BANDANA'S BAR B Q; *U.S. Private*, pg. 465
BANDAR ABBAS ZINC PRODUCTION COMPANY LIMITED—See National Iranian Lead & Zinc Company; *Int'l*, pg. 5160
BANDAR BARU KLANG SPECIALIST HOSPITAL SDN BHD—See KPJ Healthcare Berhad; *Int'l*, pg. 4296
BANDAR BOTANIC RESORT BERHAD—See Gamuda Berhad; *Int'l*, pg. 2879
BANDAR DATO' ONN SPECIALIST HOSPITAL SDN BHD—See KPJ Healthcare Berhad; *Int'l*, pg. 4296
BANDAR KEPALA BATAS SDN. BHD.—See Hunza Properties Berhad; *Int'l*, pg. 3537
BANDAR RAYA DEVELOPMENTS BERHAD; *Int'l*, pg. 829
BANDEIRANTE ENERGIA SA—See EDP - Energias de Portugal, S.A.; *Int'l*, pg. 2314
BANDELIER PIPELINE HOLDING, LLC—See Callon Petroleum Company; *U.S. Public*, pg. 424
BANDEN DEPROOST BV—See Colruyt Group N.V.; *Int'l*, pg. 1705
BANDERA ELECTRIC COOPERATIVE, INC.; *U.S. Private*, pg. 465
BANDERA/LANTANA III, LP—See Forestar Group Inc.; *U.S. Public*, pg. 867
BANDES CONSTRUCTION COMPANY INC.; *U.S. Private*, pg. 465
BANDHAN BANK LIMITED—See Bandhan Financial Services Ltd.; *Int'l*, pg. 830
BANDHAN FINANCIAL HOLDINGS LIMITED—See Bandhan Financial Services Ltd.; *Int'l*, pg. 830
BANDHAN FINANCIAL SERVICES LTD.; *Int'l*, pg. 830
BANDICK CORPORATION—See TOWA Corporation; *Int'l*, pg. 7849
BANDIRMA GUBRE FABRIKALARI A.S.; *Int'l*, pg. 830
BAND-IT CLAMPS (ASIA) PTE., LTD.—See IDEX Corp; *U.S. Public*, pg. 1089
BAND-IT COMPANY LTD.—See IDEX Corp; *U.S. Public*, pg. 1089
BAND-IT-IDEX, INC.—See IDEX Corp; *U.S. Public*, pg. 1089
BANDIT LITES, INC.; *U.S. Private*, pg. 465
BANDIT LITES—See Bandit Lites, Inc.; *U.S. Private*, pg. 465
BAND-IT R.S.A. (PTY) LTD.—See IDEX Corp; *U.S. Public*, pg. 1089
BANDLOCK CORPORATION INC.—See Quanex Building Products Corp.; *U.S. Public*, pg. 1749
BANDMILL COAL CORPORATION—See Alpha Natural Resources, Inc.; *U.S. Private*, pg. 198
BANDO BELT MANUFACTURING(TURKEY), INC.—See Bando Chemical Industries, Ltd.; *Int'l*, pg. 830
BANDO CHEMICAL INDUSTRIES, LTD. - ASHIKAGA PLANT—See Bando Chemical Industries, Ltd.; *Int'l*, pg. 830
BANDO CHEMICAL INDUSTRIES, LTD. - KAKOGAWA PLANT—See Bando Chemical Industries, Ltd.; *Int'l*, pg. 830
BANDO CHEMICAL INDUSTRIES, LTD. - NANKAI PLANT—See Bando Chemical Industries, Ltd.; *Int'l*, pg. 830
BANDO CHEMICAL INDUSTRIES, LTD.; *Int'l*, pg. 830
BANDO CHEMICAL INDUSTRIES, LTD. - WAKAYAMA PLANT—See Bando Chemical Industries, Ltd.; *Int'l*, pg. 830
BANDO ELASTOMER CO., LTD.—See Bando Chemical Industries, Ltd.; *Int'l*, pg. 830

BANDO EUROPE GMBH—See Bando Chemical Industries, Ltd.; *Int'l*, pg. 830
BAND OF CODERS, LP; *U.S. Private*, pg. 464
BANDO IBERICA S.A.—See Bando Chemical Industries, Ltd.; *Int'l*, pg. 830
BANDO (INDIA) PVT. LTD.—See Bando Chemical Industries, Ltd.; *Int'l*, pg. 830
BANDO INDUSTRIAL COMPONENTS & SERVICES, LTD.—See Bando Chemical Industries, Ltd.; *Int'l*, pg. 830
BANDO KOREA CO., LTD.—See Bando Chemical Industries, Ltd.; *Int'l*, pg. 830
BANDO KOSAN CO., LTD.—See Bando Chemical Industries, Ltd.; *Int'l*, pg. 830
BANDO MANUFACTURING (DONGGUAN) CO., LTD.—See Bando Chemical Industries, Ltd.; *Int'l*, pg. 830
BANDO MANUFACTURING (THAILAND) LTD.—See Bando Chemical Industries, Ltd.; *Int'l*, pg. 830
BANDO MANUFACTURING (VIETNAM) CO., LTD.—See Bando Chemical Industries, Ltd.; *Int'l*, pg. 830
BANDON PACIFIC, INC.—See Dulcich, Inc.; *U.S. Private*, pg. 1286
BANDO SAKATA, LTD.—See Bando Chemical Industries, Ltd.; *Int'l*, pg. 830
BANDO-SCHOLTZ CORPORATION—See Bando Chemical Industries, Ltd.; *Int'l*, pg. 830
BANDO (SHANGHAI) MANAGEMENT CO., LTD.—See Bando Chemical Industries, Ltd.; *Int'l*, pg. 830
BANDO SIIX LTD.—See Bando Chemical Industries, Ltd.; *Int'l*, pg. 830
BANDO (SINGAPORE) PTE. LTD.—See Bando Chemical Industries, Ltd.; *Int'l*, pg. 830
BANDO TRADING CO., LTD.—See Bando Chemical Industries, Ltd.; *Int'l*, pg. 830
BANDCO USA, INC.—See Bando Chemical Industries, Ltd.; *Int'l*, pg. 830
BANDO USA, INC.—See Bando Chemical Industries, Ltd.; *Int'l*, pg. 830
BANDPAGE, INC.—See Alphabet Inc.; *U.S. Public*, pg. 84
BAND PRO FILM & DIGITAL INC.; *U.S. Private*, pg. 464
BAND REP MANAGEMENT, INC.; *Int'l*, pg. 828
BANDRICH INC.—See HTC Corporation; *Int'l*, pg. 3508
BANDSTRA TRANSPORTATION SYSTEMS LTD.; *Int'l*, pg. 831
BANDUJO DONKER & BROTHERS; *U.S. Private*, pg. 465
BANDVULC TYRES LTD.; *Int'l*, pg. 831
BANDWAGON BROKERAGE LLC—See Cross Rapids Capital LP; *U.S. Private*, pg. 1105
BANDWAVE SYSTEMS, LLC—See Lingo Management, LLC; *U.S. Private*, pg. 2461
BANDWIDTH INC.; *U.S. Public*, pg. 269
BANDY CARROLL HELLIGE ADVERTISING - INDIANAPOLIS—See Bandy Carroll Hellige Advertising; *U.S. Private*, pg. 465
BANDY CARROLL HELLIGE ADVERTISING; *U.S. Private*, pg. 465
BANEDRIFT AS—See Per Aarsleff Holding A/S; *Int'l*, pg. 5795
BANELCO S.A.—See Banco Macro S.A.; *Int'l*, pg. 823
BANE MACHINERY FORT WORTH, LP—See George P. Bane, Inc.; *U.S. Private*, pg. 1682
BANENG HOLDINGS BHD; *Int'l*, pg. 831
BANERPORTEN AB—See AcadeMedia AB; *Int'l*, pg. 75
BANESCO BANCO UNIVERSAL C.A.; *Int'l*, pg. 831
BANESCO S.A.; *Int'l*, pg. 831
BANESCO USA; *U.S. Private*, pg. 465
BANES GENERAL CONTRACTORS, INC.; *U.S. Private*, pg. 465
BANESTES S.A. BANCO DO ESTADO DO ESPIRITO SANTO; *Int'l*, pg. 831
BANEXI VENTURES PARTNERS—See BNP Paribas SA; *Int'l*, pg. 1089
BANFF HOSPITALITY RESIDENCE LTD.—See Viad Corp.; *U.S. Public*, pg. 2291
BANFIELD CHARITABLE TRUST; *U.S. Private*, pg. 465
BANFI PRODUCT CORP.; *U.S. Private*, pg. 465
BANFI VINTNERS—See Banfi Product Corp.; *U.S. Private*, pg. 465
BANFORA PTE LTD—See RHB Bank Berhad; *Int'l*, pg. 6320
BANGALORE FORT FARMS LIMITED; *Int'l*, pg. 832
BANGALORE INTEGRATED SYSTEM SOLUTIONS PRIVATE LTD—See Illinois Tool Works Inc.; *U.S. Public*, pg. 1101
BANGALORE STOCK EXCHANGE LIMITED; *Int'l*, pg. 832
BANGARANG ENTERPRISES, LLC—See Stran & Company, Inc.; *U.S. Public*, pg. 1953
BANGAS; *Int'l*, pg. 832
THE BANGCHAK BIOFUEL CO., LTD.—See Bangchak Corporation Public Company Limited; *Int'l*, pg. 832
BANGCHAK CORPORATION PUBLIC COMPANY LIMITED; *Int'l*, pg. 832
THE BANGCHAK GREEN NET CO. LTD—See Bangchak Corporation Public Company Limited; *Int'l*, pg. 832
BANGCHAK RETAIL CO.—See Bangchak Corporation Public Company Limited; *Int'l*, pg. 832

BANGDISIDUN (FUJIAN) DRESS DEVELOPMENT CO., LTD.—See Sunbridge Group Limited; *Int'l*, pg. 7310
BANG HOLDINGS CORP.; *U.S. Public*, pg. 269
BANGI PLASTICS SDN. BHD.—See SKP Resources Bhd; *Int'l*, pg. 6991
BANGKOK AGRO-INDUSTRIAL PRODUCTS PUBLIC COMPANY LIMITED—See Charoen Pokphand Foods Public Company Limited; *Int'l*, pg. 1451
BANGKOK AIR AVIATION TRAINING CENTER CO., LTD.—See Bangkok Airways Public Company Limited; *Int'l*, pg. 832
BANGKOK AIR CATERING CO., LTD.—See Bangkok Airways Public Company Limited; *Int'l*, pg. 832
BANGKOK AIR CATERING PHUKET CO., LTD.—See Bangkok Airways Public Company Limited; *Int'l*, pg. 832
BANGKOK AIR CATERING SAMUI CO., LTD.—See Bangkok Airways Public Company Limited; *Int'l*, pg. 832
BANGKOK AIRWAYS GROUND SERVICES CO. LTD.—See Bangkok Airways Public Company Limited; *Int'l*, pg. 832
BANGKOK AIRWAYS PUBLIC COMPANY LIMITED; *Int'l*, pg. 832
BANGKOK AI-TOA CO., LTD—See Iwatani Corporation; *Int'l*, pg. 3850
BANGKOK ART BIENNALE MANAGEMENT CO., LTD.—See Thai Beverage Public Company Limited; *Int'l*, pg. 7589
BANGKOK ATHLETIC CO., LTD.—See Bangkok Rubber Public Co., Ltd.; *Int'l*, pg. 835
BANGKOK AVIATION FUEL SERVICES PUBLIC COMPANY LIMITED; *Int'l*, pg. 832
BANGKOK BANK BERHAD—See Bangkok Bank Public Company Limited; *Int'l*, pg. 833
BANGKOK BANK (CHINA) CO., LTD.—See Bangkok Bank Public Company Limited; *Int'l*, pg. 833
BANGKOK BANK PUBLIC COMPANY LIMITED; *Int'l*, pg. 832
BANGKOK BROADCASTING & TV CO., LTD.; *Int'l*, pg. 833
BANGKOK BUSINESS EQUIPMENT AUTOMATION CO., LTD.; *Int'l*, pg. 833
BANGKOK CAN MANUFACTURING CO., LTD.—See Toyo Seikan Group Holdings, Ltd.; *Int'l*, pg. 7856
BANGKOK CHAIN HOSPITAL PUBLIC COMPANY LIMITED; *Int'l*, pg. 833
BANGKOK CHAYOLIFE COMPANY, LIMITED—See MS&AD Insurance Group Holdings, Inc.; *Int'l*, pg. 5065
BANGKOK CITISMART CO., LTD.—See AP (Thailand) Public Company Limited; *Int'l*, pg. 499
BANGKOK COGENERATION COMPANY LIMITED—See Air Products & Chemicals, Inc.; *U.S. Public*, pg. 66
BANGKOK COIL CENTER CO., LTD. - AMATA NAKORN FACTORY—See Mitsui & Co., Ltd.; *Int'l*, pg. 4973
BANGKOK COIL CENTER CO., LTD.—See Mitsui & Co., Ltd.; *Int'l*, pg. 4973
BANGKOK COLD STORAGE SERVICE LTD.—See Kawasaki Kisen Kaisha, Ltd.; *Int'l*, pg. 4098
BANGKOK COMMERCIAL ASSET MANAGEMENT PUBLIC COMPANY LIMITED; *Int'l*, pg. 833
BANGKOK DEC-CON PUBLIC COMPANY LIMITED; *Int'l*, pg. 833
BANGKOK DUSIT MEDICAL SERVICES PUBLIC COMPANY LIMITED; *Int'l*, pg. 833
BANGKOK ENSHU MACHINERY CO., LTD.—See Enshu Limited; *Int'l*, pg. 2446
THE BANGKOK ENTERTAINMENT CO., LTD.—See BEC World Public Company Limited; *Int'l*, pg. 936
BANGKOK EXHIBITION SERVICES LTD.—See Informa plc; *Int'l*, pg. 3691
BANGKOK EXPRESSWAY AND METRO PUBLIC COMPANY LIMITED—See CH. Karnchang Public Company Limited; *Int'l*, pg. 1435
BANGKOK FOOD PRODUCTS CO., LTD.—See Charoen Pokphand Foods Public Company Limited; *Int'l*, pg. 1451
BANGKOK HELICOPTER SERVICES CO., LTD.—See Bangkok Dusit Medical Services Public Company Limited; *Int'l*, pg. 834
BANGKOK HOSPITAL CHIANGMAI CO., LTD.—See Bangkok Dusit Medical Services Public Company Limited; *Int'l*, pg. 834
BANGKOK HOSPITAL CHIANGRAI CO., LTD.—See Bangkok Dusit Medical Services Public Company Limited; *Int'l*, pg. 834
BANGKOK HOSPITAL HAT YAI CO., LTD.—See Bangkok Dusit Medical Services Public Company Limited; *Int'l*, pg. 834
BANGKOK HOSPITAL MEDICAL CENTER—See Bangkok Dusit Medical Services Public Company Limited; *Int'l*, pg. 834
BANGKOK HOSPITAL PATTAYA CO., LTD.—See Bangkok Dusit Medical Services Public Company Limited; *Int'l*, pg. 834
BANGKOK HOSPITAL PHUKET CO., LTD.—See Bangkok Dusit Medical Services Public Company Limited; *Int'l*, pg. 834

BANGKOK HOSPITAL PRAPADAENG CO., LTD.—See Bangkok Dusit Medical Services Public Company Limited; *Int'l*, pg. 834
BANGKOK HOSPITAL RATCHASIMA CO., LTD.—See Bangkok Dusit Medical Services Public Company Limited; *Int'l*, pg. 834
BANGKOK HOSPITAL SAMUI CO., LTD.—See Bangkok Dusit Medical Services Public Company Limited; *Int'l*, pg. 834
BANGKOK HOSPITAL SURAT CO.—See Bangkok Dusit Medical Services Public Company Limited; *Int'l*, pg. 834
BANGKOK HOSPITAL TRAT CO., LTD.—See Bangkok Dusit Medical Services Public Company Limited; *Int'l*, pg. 834
BANGKOK INDUSTRIAL GAS CO., LTD.—See Air Products & Chemicals, Inc.; *U.S. Public*, pg. 66
BANGKOK INDUSTRIAL GAS CO., LTD.—See Bangkok Bank Public Company Limited; *Int'l*, pg. 833
BANGKOK INSURANCE PUBLIC COMPANY LTD.; *Int'l*, pg. 834
BANGKOK KHON KAEN HOSPITAL CO., LTD.—See Bangkok Dusit Medical Services Public Company Limited; *Int'l*, pg. 834
BANGKOK KOMATSU CO., LTD.—See Komatsu Ltd.; *Int'l*, pg. 4234
BANGKOK KOMATSU FORKLIFT CO., LTD.—See Komatsu Ltd.; *Int'l*, pg. 4235
BANGKOK KOMATSU INDUSTRIES CO., LTD.—See Komatsu Ltd.; *Int'l*, pg. 4235
BANGKOK KOMATSU SALES CO., LTD.—See Komatsu Ltd.; *Int'l*, pg. 4235
BANGKOK LAND AGENCY LIMITED—See Bangkok Land Public Company Limited; *Int'l*, pg. 834
BANGKOK LAND (CAYMAN ISLANDS) LIMITED—See Bangkok Land Public Company Limited; *Int'l*, pg. 834
BANGKOK LAND PUBLIC COMPANY LIMITED; *Int'l*, pg. 834
BANGKOK LIFE ASSURANCE PUBLIC COMPANY LIMITED—See Nippon Life Insurance Company; *Int'l*, pg. 5322
BANGKOK MARKET INC.; *U.S. Private*, pg. 465
BANGKOK MASS TRANSIT SYSTEM PUBLIC COMPANY LIMITED—See BTS Group Holdings Public Company Limited; *Int'l*, pg. 1205
BANGKOK METRO PUBLIC COMPANY LIMITED—See CH. Karnchang Public Company Limited; *Int'l*, pg. 1435
BANGKOK MITSUBISHI HC CAPITAL CO., LTD.—See Mitsubishi HC Capital Inc.; *Int'l*, pg. 4950
BANGKOK MITSUBISHI UFJ LEASE LTD.—See Mitsubishi HC Capital Inc.; *Int'l*, pg. 4950
BANGKOK OA COMS CO., LTD.—See Bangkok Business Equipment Automation Co., Ltd.; *Int'l*, pg. 833
THE BANGKOK ORTHOPEDIC HOSPITAL COMPANY LIMITED—See Srivichaivejvivat Public Company Limited; *Int'l*, pg. 7152
BANGKOK PATTAYA HOSPITAL CO., LTD.—See Bangkok Dusit Medical Services Public Company Limited; *Int'l*, pg. 834
BANGKOK PAYMENT SOLUTIONS CO., LTD.—See BTS Group Holdings Public Company Limited; *Int'l*, pg. 1205
BANGKOK PHUKET HOSPITAL CO., LTD.—See Bangkok Dusit Medical Services Public Company Limited; *Int'l*, pg. 834
BANGKOK POLYETHYLENE PUBLIC COMPANY LIMITED—See PTT Global Chemical Public Company Limited; *Int'l*, pg. 6091
BANGKOK POST PUBLIC COMPANY LIMITED; *Int'l*, pg. 835
BANGKOK PREMIER LIFE INSURANCE BROKER CO., LTD.—See Bangkok Dusit Medical Services Public Company Limited; *Int'l*, pg. 834
BANGKOK PRODUCE MERCHANDISING PLC—See Charoen Pokphand Foods Public Company Limited; *Int'l*, pg. 1451
BANGKOK PRODUCE MERCHANDISING PUBLIC COMPANY LIMITED—See Charoen Pokphand Foods Public Company Limited; *Int'l*, pg. 1451
BANGKOK PR PORTER NOVELLI—See Omnicom Group Inc.; *U.S. Public*, pg. 1590
BANGKOK RANCH PUBLIC COMPANY LIMITED; *Int'l*, pg. 835
BANGKOK RATCHASIMA HOSPITAL CO., LTD.—See Bangkok Dusit Medical Services Public Company Limited; *Int'l*, pg. 834
BANGKOK RAYONG HOSPITAL CO., LTD.—See Bangkok Dusit Medical Services Public Company Limited; *Int'l*, pg. 834
BANGKOK RUBBER PUBLIC CO., LTD.; *Int'l*, pg. 835
BANGKOK RUBBER SAHARATTANA CO., LTD.—See Saha Pathanapibul Public Company Limited; *Int'l*, pg. 6478
BANGKOK SAMUI HOSPITAL CO., LTD.—See Bangkok Dusit Medical Services Public Company Limited; *Int'l*, pg. 834
BANGKOK SATELLITES & TELECOMMUNICATION CO., LTD.—See BEC World Public Company Limited; *Int'l*, pg. 936

COMPANY NAME INDEX

BANGKOK SHEET METAL PUBLIC COMPANY LTD.; *Int'l*, pg. 835
BANGKOK SMARTCARD SYSTEM CO., LTD.—See BTS Group Holdings Public Company Limited; *Int'l*, pg. 1205
BANGKOK SPRING INDUSTRIAL COMPANY LIMITED—See Somboon Advance Technology Public Company Limited; *Int'l*, pg. 7084
BANGKOK STEEL INDUSTRY PUBLIC COMPANY LIMITED; *Int'l*, pg. 835
BANGKOK TELECOM CO., LTD.—See The Furukawa Electric Co., Ltd.; *Int'l*, pg. 7644
BANGKOK TOKYO SOCKS CO., LTD.—See Saha Pathanapibul Public Company Limited; *Int'l*, pg. 6478
BANGKOK TOWER (1999) CO., LTD.—See Saha Pathanapibul Public Company Limited; *Int'l*, pg. 6478
BANGKOK UNION INSURANCE PUBLIC COMPANY LIMITED; *Int'l*, pg. 835
BANGKO SENTRAL NG PILIPINAS; *Int'l*, pg. 832
BANGLADESH AUTOCARS LIMITED; *Int'l*, pg. 835
BANGLADESH BANK; *Int'l*, pg. 835
BANGLADESH BUILDING SYSTEM LTD.; *Int'l*, pg. 835
BANGLADESH EXPORT IMPORT CO. LTD.; *Int'l*, pg. 835
BANGLADESH FINANCE CAPITAL LIMITED—See Bangladesh Finance Limited; *Int'l*, pg. 835
BANGLADESH FINANCE LIMITED; *Int'l*, pg. 835
BANGLADESH FINANCE SECURITIES LIMITED—See Bangladesh Finance Limited; *Int'l*, pg. 835
BANGLADESH GENERAL INSURANCE COMPANY LIMITED; *Int'l*, pg. 835
BANGLADESH HONDA PRIVATE LIMITED—See Honda Motor Co., Ltd.; *Int'l*, pg. 3460
BANGLADESHI MATRIMONY PRIVATE LIMITED—See Matrimony.Com Limited; *Int'l*, pg. 4728
BANGLADESH INDUSTRIAL FINANCE COMPANY LIMITED; *Int'l*, pg. 835
BANGLADESH LAMPS LIMITED; *Int'l*, pg. 836
BANGLADESH NATIONAL INSURANCE CO., LTD.; *Int'l*, pg. 836
BANGLADESH SERVICES LIMITED; *Int'l*, pg. 836
BANGLADESH SHIPPING CO., LTD. BSC; *Int'l*, pg. 836
BANGLADESH STEEL RE-ROLLING MILLS LTD.; *Int'l*, pg. 836
BANGLADESH SUBMARINE CABLE CO., LTD.; *Int'l*, pg. 836
BANGLADESH THAI ALUMINIUM LIMITED; *Int'l*, pg. 836
BANGLADESH WELDING ELECTRODES LIMITED; *Int'l*, pg. 836
BANG & OLUFSEN AG—See Bang & Olufsen a/s; *Int'l*, pg. 831
BANG & OLUFSEN AMERICA, INC.—See Bang & Olufsen a/s; *Int'l*, pg. 831
BANG & OLUFSEN ASIA PTE. LTD.—See Bang & Olufsen a/s; *Int'l*, pg. 831
BANG & OLUFSEN A/S; *Int'l*, pg. 831
BANG & OLUFSEN A/S—See Bang & Olufsen a/s; *Int'l*, pg. 831
BANG & OLUFSEN DANMARK A/S—See Bang & Olufsen a/s; *Int'l*, pg. 831
BANG & OLUFSEN DEUTSCHLAND GMBH—See Bang & Olufsen a/s; *Int'l*, pg. 831
BANG & OLUFSEN ESPANA S.A.—See Bang & Olufsen a/s; *Int'l*, pg. 831
BANG & OLUFSEN EXPANSION A/S—See Bang & Olufsen a/s; *Int'l*, pg. 831
BANG & OLUFSEN FINANCE A/S—See Bang & Olufsen a/s; *Int'l*, pg. 831
BANG & OLUFSEN FRANCE S.A.—See Bang & Olufsen a/s; *Int'l*, pg. 831
BANG & OLUFSEN ICEPOWER A/S—See Bang & Olufsen a/s; *Int'l*, pg. 831
BANG & OLUFSEN ITALIA S.P.A.—See Bang & Olufsen a/s; *Int'l*, pg. 831
BANG & OLUFSEN JAPAN K.K.—See Bang & Olufsen a/s; *Int'l*, pg. 831
BANG & OLUFSEN MEDICOM A/S—See Maj Invest Holding A/S; *Int'l*, pg. 4653
BANG & OLUFSEN N.V./S.A.—See Bang & Olufsen a/s; *Int'l*, pg. 831
BANG & OLUFSEN OPERATIONS A/S—See Bang & Olufsen a/s; *Int'l*, pg. 831
BANG & OLUFSEN SVENSKA AB—See Bang & Olufsen a/s; *Int'l*, pg. 831
BANG & OLUFSEN TELECOM A/S—See Bang & Olufsen a/s; *Int'l*, pg. 831
BANG & OLUFSEN UNITED KINGDOM LTD.—See Bang & Olufsen a/s; *Int'l*, pg. 831
BANGO.NET LIMITED—See Bango Plc; *Int'l*, pg. 836
BANGO PLC; *Int'l*, pg. 836
BANGOR GAS COMPANY—See First Reserve Management, L.P.; *U.S. Private*, pg. 1525
BANGOR HYDRO-ELECTRIC COMPANY-HANCOCK COUNTY DIVISION—See Emera, Inc.; *Int'l*, pg. 2377
BANGOR HYDRO-ELECTRIC COMPANY-NORTHERN DIVISION—See Emera, Inc.; *Int'l*, pg. 2377
BANGOR HYDRO-ELECTRIC COMPANY—See Emera, Inc.; *Int'l*, pg. 2377
BANGOR NATURAL GAS COMPANY—See First Reserve Management, L.P.; *U.S. Private*, pg. 1525
BANGOR PUBLISHING COMPANY; *U.S. Private*, pg. 466

BANGOR SAVINGS BANK; *U.S. Private*, pg. 466
BANG OVERSEAS LTD.; *Int'l*, pg. 831
BANGPA-IN COGENERATION LIMITED—See CH. Karnchang Public Company Limited; *Int'l*, pg. 1435
BANGPA-IN COGENERATION LIMITED—See CK Power Public Company Limited; *Int'l*, pg. 1638
BANGPOO ENVIRONMENTAL COMPLEX LTD.—See Dowa Holdings Co., Ltd.; *Int'l*, pg. 2182
BANGPOO INTERMODAL SYSTEMS CO., LTD.—See Mitsui O.S.K. Lines, Ltd.; *Int'l*, pg. 4989
BANG PRINTING OF OHIO, INC.—See Bang Printing; *U.S. Private*, pg. 465
BANG PRINTING; *U.S. Private*, pg. 465
BANG PRINTING - VALENCIA—See Bang Printing; *U.S. Private*, pg. 465
BANGSAPHAN BARMILL PUBLIC COMPANY LIMITED; *Int'l*, pg. 836
BANG TAI INTERNATIONAL LOGISTICS CO., LIMITED—See Hon Hai Precision Industry Co., Ltd.; *Int'l*, pg. 3456
BANG TAO BEACH LTD.—See Kajima Corporation; *Int'l*, pg. 4053
BANIF-BANCO INTERNACIONAL DO FUNCHAL (BRASIL), SA—See Banco Santander, S.A.; *Int'l*, pg. 825
BANIF BANCO INTERNACIONAL DO FUNCHAL SA—See Banco Santander, S.A.; *Int'l*, pg. 825
BANIJAY ENTERTAINMENT SAS—See LOV Group Invest SAS; *Int'l*, pg. 4563
BANIJAY FINLAND OY—See LOV Group Invest SAS; *Int'l*, pg. 4563
BANIJAY HOLDING SAS—See LOV Group Invest SAS; *Int'l*, pg. 4563
BANIMMO S.A.—See Patronale Life NV; *Int'l*, pg. 5759
BANISTER PIPELINES CONSTRUCTORS CORP.—See Quanta Services, Inc.; *U.S. Public*, pg. 1750
BANISTMO S.A.—See Bancolombia S.A.; *Int'l*, pg. 828
BANJA LAKTASI A.D.; *Int'l*, pg. 836
BANJALUCKA PIVARA A.D., BANJA LUKA—See Altima Partners LLP; *Int'l*, pg. 393
BANJALUKA BERZA HARTIJA OD VRIJEDNOSTI A.D.—See Zagrebacka burza d.d.; *Int'l*, pg. 8619
BANJO CORPORATION—See IDEX Corp; *U.S. Public*, pg. 1089
BANK 34 - ARIZONA DIVISION—See Bancorp 34, Inc.; *U.S. Public*, pg. 269
BANK 34—See Bancorp 34, Inc.; *U.S. Public*, pg. 269
BANK7 CORP.; *U.S. Public*, pg. 274
BANKA BIOLOO LIMITED; *Int'l*, pg. 850
BANKA CELJE D.D.—See Nova Ljubljanska banka d.d.; *Int'l*, pg. 5451
BANKADATI SERVIZI INFORMATICI S.P.A.—See Credito Valtellinese Societa Cooperativa; *Int'l*, pg. 1837
BANK ADMINISTRATION INSTITUTE; *U.S. Private*, pg. 466
BANKA DOMZALE D.D.—See Nova Ljubljanska banka d.d.; *Int'l*, pg. 5451
BANK AGROROS JSC; *Int'l*, pg. 836
BANKA KOPER D.D.—See Intesa Sanpaolo S.p.A.; *Int'l*, pg. 3765
BANK ALBILAD; *Int'l*, pg. 836
BANK AL ETIHAD PSC—See Union Group; *Int'l*, pg. 8052
BANK ALEXANDROVSKY PJSC; *Int'l*, pg. 836
BANK ALFALAH LIMITED—See Abu Dhabi Group; *Int'l*, pg. 71
BANK AL-HABIB LIMITED—See Habib Group of Companies; *Int'l*, pg. 3203
BANK ALJAZIRA; *Int'l*, pg. 836
BANK AL-MAGHRIB; *Int'l*, pg. 836
BANK AL-SHARQ S.A.S; *Int'l*, pg. 836
BANK AL-SHARQ S.A.S.—See Banque Libano-Francaise S.A.L.; *Int'l*, pg. 854
BANK AM BELLEVUE AG—See Bellevue Group AG; *Int'l*, pg. 967
BANKA OTP ALBANIA SHA—See OTP Bank Plc; *Int'l*, pg. 5657
BANKA POSTANSKA STEDIONICA A.D.; *Int'l*, pg. 850
BANKART D.O.O.—See Nova Ljubljanska banka d.d.; *Int'l*, pg. 5451
BANK ASIA LIMITED; *Int'l*, pg. 837
BANK ASIA SECURITIES LIMITED—See Bank Asia Limited; *Int'l*, pg. 837
BANKA SLOVENIJE; *Int'l*, pg. 850
BANKA SOCIETE GENERALE ALBANIA SH.A.—See OTP Bank Plc; *Int'l*, pg. 5657
BANK AUDI FRANCE S.A.—See Bank Audi sal; *Int'l*, pg. 837
BANK AUDI LLC—See Bank Audi sal; *Int'l*, pg. 837
BANK AUDI SAL - JORDAN BRANCHES—See Bank Audi sal; *Int'l*, pg. 837
BANK AUDI SAL; *Int'l*, pg. 837
BANK AUDI S.A.M.—See Bank Audi sal; *Int'l*, pg. 837
BANK AUDI SYRIA SA—See Bank Audi sal; *Int'l*, pg. 837
BANK AUSTRALIA LIMITED; *Int'l*, pg. 837
BANK AUSTRIA CREDITANSTALT D.D. LJUBLJANA—See UniCredit S.p.A.; *Int'l*, pg. 8039
BANK AUSTRIA CREDITANSTALT LEASING IMMOBILIENANLAGEN GMBH—See UniCredit S.p.A.; *Int'l*, pg. 8039

BANK AUSTRIA CREDITANSTALT VERSICHERUNG AG—See Munchener Ruckversicherungs AG; *Int'l*, pg. 5086
BANK AUSTRIA CREDITANSTALT VERSICHERUNGSDIENST GMBH—See Munchener Ruckversicherungs AG; *Int'l*, pg. 5085
BANK AUSTRIA FINANZSERVICE GMBH—See UniCredit S.p.A.; *Int'l*, pg. 8039
BANK AUSTRIA IMMOBILIENSERVICE GMBH—See UniCredit S.p.A.; *Int'l*, pg. 8039
BANK AUSTRIA LEASING ARGO IMMOBILIEN LEASING GMBH—See UniCredit S.p.A.; *Int'l*, pg. 8035
BANK AUSTRIA LEASING HERA IMMOBILIEN LEASING GMBH—See UniCredit S.p.A.; *Int'l*, pg. 8037
BANK AUSTRIA LEASING IKARUS IMMOBILIEN LEASING GESELLSCHAFT M.B.H.—See UniCredit S.p.A.; *Int'l*, pg. 8036
BANK AUSTRIA PRIVATE BANKING AG—See UniCredit S.p.A.; *Int'l*, pg. 8039
BANK AUSTRIA REAL INVEST ASSET MANAGEMENT GMBH—See UniCredit S.p.A.; *Int'l*, pg. 8040
BANK AUSTRIA REAL INVEST CLIENT INVESTMENT GMBH—See UniCredit S.p.A.; *Int'l*, pg. 8040
BANK AUSTRIA REAL INVEST GMBH—See UniCredit S.p.A.; *Int'l*, pg. 8039
BANK AUSTRIA REAL INVEST IMMOBILIEN-KAPITALANLAGE GMBH—See UniCredit S.p.A.; *Int'l*, pg. 8040
BANK AUSTRIA REAL INVEST IMMOBILIENMANAGEMENT GMBH—See UniCredit S.p.A.; *Int'l*, pg. 8033
BANK AUSTRIA WOHNBAUBANK AG—See UniCredit S.p.A.; *Int'l*, pg. 8033
BANKBERATUNG ORGANISATIONSU IT-BERATUNGFUR BANKEN AG—See Diebold Nixdorf, Inc.; *U.S. Public*, pg. 661
BANK BNP LIPPO UTAMA LEASING—See BNP Paribas SA; *Int'l*, pg. 1081
BANK BNP PARIBAS LUXEMBOURG—See BNP Paribas SA; *Int'l*, pg. 1089
BANK BPH S.A.—See General Electric Company; *U.S. Public*, pg. 920
BANK BPH SPOBKA AKCYJNA—See General Electric Company; *U.S. Public*, pg. 916
BANK BTB OJSC; *Int'l*, pg. 837
BANK BUSINESS FACTORY CO., LTD.—See Seven Bank Ltd.; *Int'l*, pg. 6731
BANK CARD COMPANY—See ING Groep N.V.; *Int'l*, pg. 3700
BANKCARD USA MERCHANT SERVICES, INC.; *U.S. Private*, pg. 467
BANK CENTERCREDIT JSC; *Int'l*, pg. 837
BANK CENTRALI TA' MALTA; *Int'l*, pg. 837
BANK CLER AG—See Basler Kantonalbank AG; *Int'l*, pg. 887
BANK COMPUTER SERVICE CORPORATION—See Senshu Ikeda Holdings, Inc.; *Int'l*, pg. 6713
BANK CONSORTIUM TRUST COMPANY LIMITED—See Dah Sing Financial Holdings Limited; *Int'l*, pg. 1913
BANK CONSTANTA—See JSC TBC Bank; *Int'l*, pg. 4012
BANK DELEN N.V.—See Ackermans & van Haaren NV; *Int'l*, pg. 104
BANK DEUTSCHES KRAFTFAHRZEUGGEWERBE GMBH—See Societe Generale S.A.; *Int'l*, pg. 7039
BANK DHOFAR SAOG; *Int'l*, pg. 837
BANKDIRECT—See Texas Capital Bancshares, Inc.; *U.S. Public*, pg. 2025
BANK DOM.RF JSC; *Int'l*, pg. 837
BANKENSERVICE GMBH—See Deutscher Sparkassen- und Giroverband e.V.; *Int'l*, pg. 2085
BANKER EXCHANGE, LLC—See TIC Properties, LLC; *U.S. Private*, pg. 4167
BANKERS BANCORP OF OKLAHOMA, INC.; *U.S. Private*, pg. 467
BANKERS' BANCORPORATION, INC.; *U.S. Private*, pg. 468
BANKERS' BANK—See Bankers' Bancorporation, Inc.; *U.S. Private*, pg. 468
THE BANKERS BANK—See Bankers Bancorp of Oklahoma, Inc.; *U.S. Private*, pg. 467
BANKERS BUSINESS MANAGEMENT SERVICES, INC.; *U.S. Private*, pg. 467
THE BANKERS CLUB, INC.—See BNP Paribas SA; *Int'l*, pg. 1088
BANKERS FIDELITY LIFE INSURANCE COMPANY—See Atlantic American Corporation; *U.S. Public*, pg. 222
BANKERS FINANCIAL CORPORATION—See Bankers International Financial Corporation; *U.S. Private*, pg. 467
BANKERS HEALTHCARE GROUP, LLC - FINANCIAL HEADQUARTERS—See Bankers Healthcare Group, LLC; *U.S. Private*, pg. 467
BANKERS HEALTHCARE GROUP, LLC; *U.S. Private*, pg. 467
BANKERS INSURANCE COMPANY—See Bankers International Financial Corporation; *U.S. Private*, pg. 467
BANKERS INSURANCE GROUP, INC.—See Bankers International Financial Corporation; *U.S. Private*, pg. 467
BANKERS INSURANCE SERVICE, INC.—See Aon plc; *Int'l*, pg. 494

BANKERS INSURANCE SERVICES INC.—See Bankers International Financial Corporation; *U.S. Private*, pg. 467
BANKERS INTERNATIONAL CORPORATION (BRASIL) LTDA.—See Deutsche Bank Aktiengesellschaft; *Int'l*, pg. 2055
BANKERS INTERNATIONAL CORPORATION—See Deutsche Bank Aktiengesellschaft; *Int'l*, pg. 2055
BANKERS INTERNATIONAL FINANCIAL CORPORATION; *U.S. Private*, pg. 467
BANKERS & INVESTORS CO.—See Valley View Bancshares, Inc.; *U.S. Private*, pg. 4336
BANKERS LIFE & CASUALTY COMPANY—See CNO Financial Group, Inc.; *U.S. Public*, pg. 519
BANKERS LIFE HOLDING CORP.—See CNO Financial Group, Inc.; *U.S. Public*, pg. 519
BANKERS LIFE INSURANCE COMPANY—See Bankers International Financial Corporation; *U.S. Private*, pg. 467
BANKERS PETROLEUM LTD.—See Geo-Jade Petroleum Corporation; *Int'l*, pg. 2932
BANKERS STANDARD INSURANCE COMPANY—See Chubb Limited; *Int'l*, pg. 1590
BANKERS SURETY SERVICES—See Bankers International Financial Corporation; *U.S. Private*, pg. 467
BANKER STEEL CO., LLC—See Atlas Holdings, LLC; *U.S. Private*, pg. 376
BANKER'S TOOLBOX, INC.—See The Carlyle Group Inc.; *U.S. Public*, pg. 2045
BANKERS TRUST COMPANY—See BTC Financial Corporation; *U.S. Private*, pg. 675
BANKERS WARRANTY GROUP—See Bankers International Financial Corporation; *U.S. Private*, pg. 468
BANK ESKHATA OJSC; *Int'l*, pg. 837
BANKFIL LIMITED—See Barclays PLC; *Int'l*, pg. 859
BANKFINANCIAL CORPORATION; *U.S. Public*, pg. 274
BANKFINANCIAL, F.S.B.—See BankFinancial Corporation; *U.S. Public*, pg. 274
BANKFIRST CAPITAL CORPORATION; *U.S. Public*, pg. 274
BANK FIRST CORPORATION; *U.S. Public*, pg. 269
BANKFIRST FINANCIAL SERVICES—See BankFirst Capital Corporation; *U.S. Public*, pg. 274
BANK FIRST, N.A.—See Bank First Corporation; *U.S. Public*, pg. 270
BANK FOR INTERNATIONAL SETTLEMENTS; *Int'l*, pg. 837
BANK FOR INVESTMENT & DEVELOPMENT OF CAMBODIA PLC—See Joint Stock Commercial Bank Investment and Development of Vietnam; *Int'l*, pg. 3995
BANK FUR TIROL UND VORARLBERG AG; *Int'l*, pg. 838
BANK GPB INTERNATIONAL S.A.—See Gazprombank JSC; *Int'l*, pg. 2892
BANKGUAM HOLDING COMPANY; *U.S. Public*, pg. 274
BANKGUAM INSURANCE UNDERWRITERS LTD.—See BankGuam Holding Company; *U.S. Public*, pg. 274
BANKHALL SUPPORT SERVICES LIMITED—See Aviva plc; *Int'l*, pg. 746
BANK HANDLOWY W WARSZAWIE S.A.—See Citigroup Inc.; *U.S. Public*, pg. 502
BANK HANDLOWY W WARSZAWIE S.A.—See Citigroup Inc.; *U.S. Public*, pg. 501
BANKHAUS AUGUST LENZ & CO. AG—See Banca Mediolanum S.p.A.; *Int'l*, pg. 815
BANKHAUS BAUER AG—See Raiffeisenbank Reutte reg. Gen.m.b.H.; *Int'l*, pg. 6186
BANKHAUS CARL F. PLUMP & CO.—See M.M. Warburg & Co. KGaA; *Int'l*, pg. 4616
BANKHAUS ERBE JSC; *Int'l*, pg. 850
BANKHAUS HALLBAUM AG & CO. KOMMANDITGESELLSCHAFT—See M.M. Warburg & Co. KGaA; *Int'l*, pg. 4616
BANKHAUS JUNGHOLZ AG—See Alpha RHEINTAL Bank AG; *Int'l*, pg. 369
BANKHAUS LAMPE KG—See Dr. August Oetker KG; *Int'l*, pg. 2190
BANKHAUS NEELMEYER AG—See UniCredit S.p.A.; *Int'l*, pg. 8038
BANKHAUS W. FORTMANN & SOHNE KG—See Allianz SE; *Int'l*, pg. 351
BANKHAUS WOLBERN AG & CO. KG; *Int'l*, pg. 850
BANKIA INVERSIONES FINANCIERAS, S.A.U.—See Lone Star Funds; *U.S. Private*, pg. 2485
BANKIA MAPFRE VIDA, S.A. DE SEGUROS Y REASEGUROS—See Lone Star Funds; *U.S. Private*, pg. 2485
BANKIA MAPFRE VIDA, S.A. DE SEGUROS Y REASEGUROS—See MAPFRE S.A.; *Int'l*, pg. 4683
BANKIA PENSIONES, S.A., E.G.F.P.—See Lone Star Funds; *U.S. Private*, pg. 2485
BANKIA, S.A. - MADRID OPERATIONAL HEADQUARTERS—See Lone Star Funds; *U.S. Private*, pg. 2485
BANKIA, S.A.—See Lone Star Funds; *U.S. Private*, pg. 2484
THE BANK IBA-MOSCOW LLC—See International Bank of Azerbaijan; *Int'l*, pg. 3744
BANK INDEPENDENT—See BancIndependent Inc.; *U.S. Private*, pg. 464

BANK INDONESIA; *Int'l*, pg. 838
BANKING AUTOMATION LTD.—See Sprintquip Pty. Ltd.; *Int'l*, pg. 7145
BANKING COMPUTER SERVICES PRIVATE LIMITED—See Network For Electronic Transfers (Singapore) Pte Ltd.; *Int'l*, pg. 5217
BANKIN KOGYO CO., LTD.—See Press Kogyo Co., Ltd.; *Int'l*, pg. 5964
BANK INSINGER DE BEAUFORT SAFE CUSTODY NV—See BNP Paribas SA; *Int'l*, pg. 1089
BANKINTER CONSULTORIA, ASESORAMIENTO Y ATENCION TELEFONICA, S.A.—See Bankinter, S.A.; *Int'l*, pg. 850
BANKINTER CONSUMER FINANCE, EFC, S.A.—See Bankinter, S.A.; *Int'l*, pg. 850
BANKINTER EMISIONES, S.A.—See Bankinter, S.A.; *Int'l*, pg. 850
BANKINTER GESTAO DE ATIVOS, S.A.—See Bankinter, S.A.; *Int'l*, pg. 850
BANKINTER LUXEMBOURG, S.A.—See Bankinter, S.A.; *Int'l*, pg. 850
BANKINTER, S.A.; *Int'l*, pg. 850
BANKINTER, S.A. - SUCURSAL EM PORTUGAL—See Bankinter, S.A.; *Int'l*, pg. 850
BANKINTER SEGUROS DE VIDA, DE SEGUROS Y REASEGUROS SA—See Bankinter, S.A.; *Int'l*, pg. 850
BANK IOWA CORPORATION; *U.S. Private*, pg. 466
BANK IOWA—See Bank Iowa Corporation; *U.S. Private*, pg. 466
BANKISLAMI PAKISTAN LIMITED; *Int'l*, pg. 850
BANK ISLAM MALAYSIA BERHAD—See Lembaga Tabung Haji; *Int'l*, pg. 4449
BANK J. SAFRA SARASIN AG—See Banco Safra S.A.; *Int'l*, pg. 825
BANK J. SAFRA SARASIN (GIBRALTAR) LTD.—See Banco Safra S.A.; *Int'l*, pg. 825
BANK JULIUS BAER & CO. LTD.—See Julius Baer Group Ltd.; *Int'l*, pg. 4024
BANK JULIUS BAER & CO. LTD.—See Julius Baer Group Ltd.; *Int'l*, pg. 4024
BANK JULIUS BAER EUROPE AG—See Julius Baer Group Ltd.; *Int'l*, pg. 4024
BANK J. VAN BREDA & CO. N.V.—See Ackermans & van Haaren NV; *Int'l*, pg. 104
BANK KERJASAMA RAKYAT MALAYSIA BERHAD; *Int'l*, pg. 838
BANK KUZNECKIY; *Int'l*, pg. 838
BANK LEUMI (JERSEY) LTD.—See Bank Leumi Le-Israel B.M.; *Int'l*, pg. 838
BANK LEUMI LE-ISRAEL B.M.; *Int'l*, pg. 838
BANK LEUMI LE-ISRAEL TRUST CO. LTD.—See Bank Leumi Le-Israel B.M.; *Int'l*, pg. 838
BANK LEUMI (LUXEMBOURG) S.A.—See Bank Leumi Le-Israel B.M.; *Int'l*, pg. 838
BANK LEUMI (UK) PLC—See Bank Leumi Le-Israel B.M.; *Int'l*, pg. 838
BANK LEUMI USA—See Bank Leumi Le-Israel B.M.; *Int'l*, pg. 839
BANK LEUMI USA—See Bank Leumi Le-Israel B.M.; *Int'l*, pg. 839
BANK LEVOBEREZHNY PJSC; *Int'l*, pg. 839
BANK LINTH LLB AG; *Int'l*, pg. 839
BANK MAKRAMAH LIMITED—See Arif Habib Corporation Limited; *Int'l*, pg. 564
BANK MAKRAMAH LIMITED; *Int'l*, pg. 839
BANKMANAGERS CORP.—See Old National Bancorp; *U.S. Public*, pg. 1566
BANK MANDIRI (EUROPE) LIMITED—See PT Bank Mandiri (Persero) Tbk.; *Int'l*, pg. 6026
BANK MASSAD LTD.—See FIBI Holdings Ltd.; *Int'l*, pg. 2652
BANK MELLAT; *Int'l*, pg. 839
BANK MENDES GANS NV—See ING Groep N.V.; *Int'l*, pg. 3700
BANK MIDWEST; *U.S. Private*, pg. 466
BANK MIDWEST—See National Bank Holdings Corporation; *U.S. Public*, pg. 1493
BANK MILLENNIUM S.A.—See Banco Comercial Portugues, S.A.; *Int'l*, pg. 820
BANK MUAMALAT MALAYSIA BERHAD—See DRB-HICOM Berhad; *Int'l*, pg. 2201
BANK MUSCAT SAOG; *Int'l*, pg. 839
BANK NAGELMACKERS NV—See Anbang Insurance Group Co., Ltd.; *Int'l*, pg. 447
THE BANK, NATIONAL ASSOCIATION—See N.B.M. Corporation; *U.S. Private*, pg. 2827
BANK NEGARA INDONESIA—See PT Bank Negara Indonesia (Persero) Tbk; *Int'l*, pg. 6027
BANK NEGARA MALAYSIA; *Int'l*, pg. 839
BANKNEWPORT; *U.S. Private*, pg. 468
BANK NIZWA SAOG; *Int'l*, pg. 839
BANK NORTHWEST—See Caldwell County Bancshares, Inc.; *U.S. Private*, pg. 716
BANKNOTE CAPITAL CORP.; *U.S. Private*, pg. 468
BANK-NOW AG—See UBS Group AG; *Int'l*, pg. 8005
BANK NUSANTARA PARAHYANGAN TBK—See Mitsubishi UFJ Financial Group, Inc.; *Int'l*, pg. 4968
BANK OCHRONY SRODOWISKA S.A.; *Int'l*, pg. 839
BANKO DESIGN LLC; *U.S. Private*, pg. 468

BAN-KOE SYSTEMS COMPANIES; *U.S. Private*, pg. 464
BANK OF AFRICA - BENIN—See BOA Group S.A.; *Int'l*, pg. 1094
BANK OF AFRICA - BURKINA FASO—See BOA Group S.A.; *Int'l*, pg. 1094
BANK OF AFRICA - COTE D'IVOIRE—See BOA Group S.A.; *Int'l*, pg. 1094
BANK OF AFRICA - KENYA LTD.—See BOA Group S.A.; *Int'l*, pg. 1094
BANK OF AFRICA - MADAGASCAR—See BOA Group S.A.; *Int'l*, pg. 1094
BANK OF AFRICA - MALI—See BOA Group S.A.; *Int'l*, pg. 1094
BANK OF AFRICA; *Int'l*, pg. 839
BANK OF AFRICA - TANZANIA LIMITED—See BOA Group S.A.; *Int'l*, pg. 1094
BANK OF AFRICA - UGANDA LTD.—See BOA Group S.A.; *Int'l*, pg. 1094
BANK OF AGRICULTURE & COMMERCE; *U.S. Private*, pg. 466
BANK OF ALBANIA; *Int'l*, pg. 840
BANK OF ALEXANDRIA S.A.E.—See Intesa Sanpaolo S.p.A.; *Int'l*, pg. 3765
BANK OF ALMA; *U.S. Private*, pg. 466
BANK OF AMERICA BUSINESS CAPITAL—See Bank of America Corporation; *U.S. Public*, pg. 270
BANK OF AMERICA BUSINESS CAPITAL—See Bank of America Corporation; *U.S. Public*, pg. 270
BANK OF AMERICA BUSINESS CREDIT—See Bank of America Corporation; *U.S. Public*, pg. 270
BANK OF AMERICA CAPITAL MANAGEMENT COMPANY—See Bank of America Corporation; *U.S. Public*, pg. 270
THE BANK OF AMERICA CHARITABLE FOUNDATION, INC.—See Bank of America Corporation; *U.S. Public*, pg. 272
BANK OF AMERICA CORPORATION; *U.S. Public*, pg. 270
BANK OF AMERICA CUSTODIAL SERVICES (IRELAND) LIMITED—See Bank of America Corporation; *U.S. Public*, pg. 270
BANK OF AMERICA (FRANCE)—See Bank of America Corporation; *U.S. Public*, pg. 270
BANK OF AMERICA GLOBAL CONSUMER & SMALL BUSINESS BANKING—See Bank of America Corporation; *U.S. Public*, pg. 270
BANK OF AMERICA GLOBAL CORPORATE & INVESTMENT BANKING—See Bank of America Corporation; *U.S. Public*, pg. 271
BANK OF AMERICA GLOBAL WEALTH & INVESTMENT MANAGEMENT—See Bank of America Corporation; *U.S. Public*, pg. 271
BANK OF AMERICA HOME LOANS—See Bank of America Corporation; *U.S. Public*, pg. 271
BANK OF AMERICA LEASING CANADA—See Bank of America Corporation; *U.S. Public*, pg. 270
BANK OF AMERICA LEASING—See Bank of America Corporation; *U.S. Public*, pg. 270
BANK OF AMERICA MERRILL LYNCH BANCO MULTIPLO S.A.—See Bank of America Corporation; *U.S. Public*, pg. 270
BANK OF AMERICA MERRILL LYNCH INTERNATIONAL LIMITED—See Bank of America Corporation; *U.S. Public*, pg. 270
BANK OF AMERICA MERRILL LYNCH—See Bank of America Corporation; *U.S. Public*, pg. 270
BANK OF AMERICA MEXICO, S.A., INSTITUCION DE BANCA MULTIPLE—See Bank of America Corporation; *U.S. Public*, pg. 270
BANK OF AMERICA MORTGAGE—See Bank of America Corporation; *U.S. Public*, pg. 271
BANK OF AMERICA, N.A. - CANADA—See Bank of America Corporation; *U.S. Public*, pg. 271
BANK OF AMERICA, N.A.—See Bank of America Corporation; *U.S. Public*, pg. 270
BANK OF AMERICAN FORK—See Glacier Bancorp, Inc.; *U.S. Public*, pg. 938
BANK OF AMERICA SINGAPORE LIMITED—See Bank of America Corporation; *U.S. Public*, pg. 271
BANK OF ANN ARBOR—See Arbor Bancorp, Inc.; *U.S. Private*, pg. 308
BANK OF ASTANA JSC—See Astana Finance, JSC; *Int'l*, pg. 651
BANK OF AUGUSTA—See Pigeon Falls State Bank; *U.S. Private*, pg. 3179
BANK OF AYUDHYA PUBLIC COMPANY LIMITED—See Mitsubishi UFJ Financial Group, Inc.; *Int'l*, pg. 4969
BANK OF BAGHDAD—See Kuwait Projects Company (Holding) K.S.C.P.; *Int'l*, pg. 4346
BANK OF BAKU OJSC; *Int'l*, pg. 840
BANK OF BARODA (BOTSWANA) LTD.—See Bank of Baroda; *Int'l*, pg. 840
BANK OF BARODA (GHANA) LTD.—See Bank of Baroda; *Int'l*, pg. 840
BANK OF BARODA (GUYANA) INC.—See Bank of Baroda; *Int'l*, pg. 840
BANK OF BARODA (KENYA) LTD.—See Bank of Baroda; *Int'l*, pg. 840

BANK OF BARODA (NEW ZEALAND) LTD.—See Bank of Baroda; *Int'l*, pg. 840
BANK OF BARODA; *Int'l*, pg. 840
BANK OF BARODA (TANZANIA) LTD.—See Bank of Baroda; *Int'l*, pg. 840
BANK OF BARODA (TRINIDAD & TOBAGO) LTD.—See Bank of Baroda; *Int'l*, pg. 840
BANK OF BARODA (UGANDA) LTD.—See Bank of Baroda; *Int'l*, pg. 840
BANK OF BARODA (UK) LIMITED—See Bank of Baroda; *Int'l*, pg. 840
BANK OF BEIJING CO., LTD.; *Int'l*, pg. 840
BANK OF BEIRUT S.A.L.; *Int'l*, pg. 840
BANK OF BEIRUT (UK) LTD—See Bank of Beirut S.A.L.; *Int'l*, pg. 840
BANK OF BERMUDA (CAYMAN) LTD.—See HSBC Holdings plc; *Int'l*, pg. 3504
THE BANK OF BERMUDA LTD.—See HSBC Holdings plc; *Int'l*, pg. 3504
BANK OF BILLINGS—See First Miami Bancshares, Inc.; *U.S. Private*, pg. 1521
BANK OF BLUE VALLEY—See Heartland Financial USA, Inc.; *U.S. Public*, pg. 1018
BANK OF BOTETOURT INC.; *U.S. Public*, pg. 272
BANK OF BOTSWANA; *Int'l*, pg. 840
THE BANK OF CANTON; *U.S. Private*, pg. 3991
THE BANK OF CASTILE—See Tompkins Financial Corporation; *U.S. Public*, pg. 2162
BANK OF CENTRAL FLORIDA; *U.S. Private*, pg. 466
BANK OF CEYLON; *Int'l*, pg. 840
BANK OF CEYLON (UK) LIMITED—See Bank of Ceylon; *Int'l*, pg. 840
BANK OF CHANGSHA CO., LTD.; *Int'l*, pg. 841
THE BANK OF CHEJU—See Shinhan Financial Group Co., Ltd.; *Int'l*, pg. 6844
BANK OF CHENGDU CO., LTD.; *Int'l*, pg. 841
BANK OF CHINA (CENTRAL & EASTERN EUROPE) LIMITED—See Bank of China, Ltd.; *Int'l*, pg. 841
BANK OF CHINA CONSUMER FINANCE CO., LTD.—See Bank of China, Ltd.; *Int'l*, pg. 841
BANK OF CHINA (EUROPE) S.A.—See Bank of China, Ltd.; *Int'l*, pg. 841
BANK OF CHINA GROUP INVESTMENT LIMITED—See Bank of China, Ltd.; *Int'l*, pg. 841
BANK OF CHINA (HONG KONG) LIMITED—See Bank of China, Ltd.; *Int'l*, pg. 841
BANK OF CHINA INVESTMENT MANAGEMENT CO., LTD.—See Bank of China, Ltd.; *Int'l*, pg. 841
BANK OF CHINA LIMITED (SINGAPORE)—See Bank of China, Ltd.; *Int'l*, pg. 841
BANK OF CHINA, LTD.; *Int'l*, pg. 841
BANK OF CHINA (LUXEMBOURG) S.A.—See Bank of China, Ltd.; *Int'l*, pg. 841
BANK OF CHINA (MACAU) LIMITED—See Bank of China, Ltd.; *Int'l*, pg. 841
BANK OF CHINA (MALAYSIA) BERHAD—See Bank of China, Ltd.; *Int'l*, pg. 841
BANK OF CHINA (MAURITIUS) LIMITED—See Bank of China, Ltd.; *Int'l*, pg. 841
BANK OF CHINA MEXICO, S.A.—See Bank of China, Ltd.; *Int'l*, pg. 841
BANK OF CHINA-NEW YORK—See Bank of China, Ltd.; *Int'l*, pg. 841
BANK OF CHINA (NEW ZEALAND) LIMITED—See Bank of China, Ltd.; *Int'l*, pg. 841
BANK OF CHINA (PERU) S.A.—See Bank of China, Ltd.; *Int'l*, pg. 841
BANK OF CHINA SRBIJA A.D.—See Bank of China, Ltd.; *Int'l*, pg. 841
BANK OF CHINA (THAI) PUBLIC COMPANY LIMITED—See Bank of China, Ltd.; *Int'l*, pg. 841
BANK OF CHINA TURKEY A.S.—See Bank of China, Ltd.; *Int'l*, pg. 841
BANK OF CHINA (ZAMBIA) LIMITED—See Bank of China, Ltd.; *Int'l*, pg. 841
BANK OF CHONGQING CO., LTD.; *Int'l*, pg. 842
BANK OF CLARENDON; *U.S. Private*, pg. 466
BANK OF CLARKE COUNTY—See Eagle Financial Services, Inc.; *U.S. Public*, pg. 702
BANK OF CLARKSON—See First Breckenridge Bancshares; *U.S. Private*, pg. 1514
BANK OF COLORADO—See Pinnacle Bancorp, Inc.; *U.S. Private*, pg. 3184
BANK OF COMMERCE HOLDINGS; *U.S. Public*, pg. 272
BANK OF COMMERCE INC.; *U.S. Private*, pg. 466
BANK OF COMMERCE—See Southeast Bancshares, Inc.; *U.S. Private*, pg. 3725
BANK OF COMMERCE—See Commerce Bancshares, Inc.; *U.S. Public*, pg. 982
BANK OF COMMERCE & TRUST CO.; *U.S. Private*, pg. 466
BANK OF COMMUNICATIONS CO., LTD.; *Int'l*, pg. 842
BANK OF COMMUNICATIONS TRUSTEE LIMITED—See Bank of Communications, Ltd.; *Int'l*, pg. 842
BANK OF CROCKETT—See Security BanCorp of Tennessee, Inc.; *U.S. Private*, pg. 3595
BANK OF CYPRUS AUSTRALIA PTY LTD—See Bendigo & Adelaide Bank Ltd.; *Int'l*, pg. 970

BANK OF CYPRUS (CHANNEL ISLANDS) LTD—See Bank of Cyprus Holdings Public Limited Company; *Int'l*, pg. 842
BANK OF CYPRUS HOLDINGS PUBLIC LIMITED COMPANY; *Int'l*, pg. 842
BANK OF CYPRUS ROMANIA LTD—See Bank of Cyprus Holdings Public Limited Company; *Int'l*, pg. 842
THE BANK OF DENVER—See Denver Bankshares, Inc.; *U.S. Public*, pg. 656
THE BANK OF EAST ASIA (BVI) LIMITED—See The Bank of East Asia, Limited; *Int'l*, pg. 7615
THE BANK OF EAST ASIA (CHINA) LIMITED—See The Bank of East Asia, Limited; *Int'l*, pg. 7615
THE BANK OF EAST ASIA, LIMITED; *Int'l*, pg. 7615
BANK OF EASTERN OREGON—See BEO Bancorp; *U.S. Public*, pg. 297
THE BANK OF EDWARDSVILLE INC.; *U.S. Private*, pg. 3991
THE BANK OF ELK RIVER; *U.S. Private*, pg. 3991
BANK OF ENGLAND; *Int'l*, pg. 842
BANK OF FARMINGTON—See Farmington Bancorp, Inc.; *U.S. Private*, pg. 1480
THE BANK OF FAYETTE COUNTY—See Moscow Bancshares, Inc.; *U.S. Private*, pg. 2792
THE BANK OF FINCASTLE—See First National Corporation; *U.S. Public*, pg. 846
THE BANK OF FUKUOKA, LTD.—See Fukuoka Financial Group, Inc.; *Int'l*, pg. 2840
BANK OF GANSU CO., LTD.; *Int'l*, pg. 842
BANK OF GEORGIA GROUP PLC; *Int'l*, pg. 843
BANK OF GHANA; *Int'l*, pg. 843
THE BANK OF GLEN BURNIE—See Glen Burnie Bancorp; *U.S. Public*, pg. 940
BANK OF GREECE S.A.; *Int'l*, pg. 843
BANK OF GREELEYVILLE—See Southeastern Bancorp, Inc.; *U.S. Private*, pg. 3727
THE BANK OF GREENE COUNTY—See Greene County Bancorp, Inc.; *U.S. Public*, pg. 964
BANK OF GUAM—See BankGuam Holding Company; *U.S. Public*, pg. 274
BANK OF GUIYANG CO., LTD.; *Int'l*, pg. 843
BANK OF GUIZHOU CO., LTD.; *Int'l*, pg. 843
BANK OF GUYANA; *Int'l*, pg. 843
BANK OF HALLS—See Security BanCorp of Tennessee, Inc.; *U.S. Private*, pg. 3595
BANK OF HANGZHOU CO., LTD.; *Int'l*, pg. 843
BANK OF HAWAII CORPORATION; *U.S. Public*, pg. 272
BANK OF HAWAII—See Bank of Hawaii Corporation; *U.S. Public*, pg. 273
BANK OF HAZLEHURST—See Hazlehurst Investors, Inc.; *U.S. Private*, pg. 1886
BANK OF HEMET; *U.S. Private*, pg. 466
THE BANK OF HIROSHIMA—See The Hiroshima Bank, Ltd.; *Int'l*, pg. 7652
BANK OF HOLLAND—See Holland Bancorp, Inc.; *U.S. Private*, pg. 1964
BANK OF HOPE—See Hope Bancorp, Inc.; *U.S. Public*, pg. 1052
BANK OF IDAHO HOLDING COMPANY; *U.S. Public*, pg. 273
BANK OF IDAHO—See Bank of Idaho Holding Company; *U.S. Public*, pg. 273
BANK OF INDIA (NEW ZEALAND) LTD.—See Bank of India; *Int'l*, pg. 843
BANK OF INDIA; *Int'l*, pg. 843
BANK OF INDIA (TANZANIA) LTD.—See Bank of India; *Int'l*, pg. 843
BANK OF INDIA (UGANDA) LTD.—See Bank of India; *Int'l*, pg. 843
BANK OF INNOVATION, INC.; *Int'l*, pg. 843
BANK OF IRELAND 365—See Bank of Ireland Group plc; *Int'l*, pg. 844
BANK OF IRELAND BUSINESS BANKING UK - BELFAST—See Bank of Ireland Group plc; *Int'l*, pg. 844
BANK OF IRELAND BUSINESS BANKING UK - LONDON—See Bank of Ireland Group plc; *Int'l*, pg. 844
BANK OF IRELAND - BUSINESS ON LINE—See Bank of Ireland Group plc; *Int'l*, pg. 844
BANK OF IRELAND COMMERCIAL FINANCE LTD.—See Bank of Ireland Group plc; *Int'l*, pg. 844
BANK OF IRELAND CONSUMER BANKING UK—See Bank of Ireland Group plc; *Int'l*, pg. 844
BANK OF IRELAND CONSUMER LENDING—See Bank of Ireland Group plc; *Int'l*, pg. 844
BANK OF IRELAND CORPORATE BANKING - BELFAST—See Bank of Ireland Group plc; *Int'l*, pg. 844
BANK OF IRELAND CORPORATE BANKING - FRANKFURT—See Bank of Ireland Group plc; *Int'l*, pg. 844
BANK OF IRELAND CORPORATE BANKING - LONDON—See Bank of Ireland Group plc; *Int'l*, pg. 844
BANK OF IRELAND CORPORATE BANKING—See Bank of Ireland Group plc; *Int'l*, pg. 844
BANK OF IRELAND CREDIT CARD SERVICES—See Bank of Ireland Group plc; *Int'l*, pg. 844

BANK OF IRELAND FINANCE LTD.—See Bank of Ireland Group plc; *Int'l*, pg. 844
BANK OF IRELAND GLOBAL MARKETS - LONDON—See Bank of Ireland Group plc; *Int'l*, pg. 845
BANK OF IRELAND GLOBAL MARKETS - STAMFORD—See Bank of Ireland Group plc; *Int'l*, pg. 845
BANK OF IRELAND GROUP PLC; *Int'l*, pg. 843
BANK OF IRELAND HOME MORTGAGES LIMITED—See Bank of Ireland Group plc; *Int'l*, pg. 844
BANK OF IRELAND INSURANCE & INVESTMENTS LTD.—See Bank of Ireland Group plc; *Int'l*, pg. 844
BANK OF IRELAND INSURANCE SERVICES LTD—See Bank of Ireland Group plc; *Int'l*, pg. 844
BANK OF IRELAND INTERNATIONAL FINANCE LTD.—See Bank of Ireland Group plc; *Int'l*, pg. 844
BANK OF IRELAND (I.O.M.) LIMITED—See Bank of Ireland Group plc; *Int'l*, pg. 844
BANK OF IRELAND LIFE—See Bank of Ireland Group plc; *Int'l*, pg. 844
BANK OF IRELAND MORTGAGE BANK PLC—See Bank of Ireland Group plc; *Int'l*, pg. 844
BANK OF IRELAND PRIVATE BANKING LIMITED—See Bank of Ireland Group plc; *Int'l*, pg. 844
BANK OF IRELAND RETAIL (IRELAND & UK) DIVISION—See Bank of Ireland Group plc; *Int'l*, pg. 844
BANK OF IRELAND—See Bank of Ireland Group plc; *Int'l*, pg. 844
BANK OF IRELAND TRASURY LIMITED—See Bank of Ireland Group plc; *Int'l*, pg. 845
BANK OF IRELAND TREASURY & INTERNATIONAL BANKING LIMITED—See Bank of Ireland Group plc; *Int'l*, pg. 844
BANK OF IRELAND UK FINANCIAL SERVICES—See Bank of Ireland Group plc; *Int'l*, pg. 844
BANK OF IRELAND (UK) PLC—See Bank of Ireland Group plc; *Int'l*, pg. 844
THE BANK OF ISRAEL; *Int'l*, pg. 7615
THE BANK OF IWATE, LTD.; *Int'l*, pg. 7615
BANK OF JACKSON HOLE INC.; *U.S. Private*, pg. 466
THE BANK OF JACKSON—See Security BanCorp of Tennessee, Inc.; *U.S. Private*, pg. 3595
BANK OF JAMAICA; *Int'l*, pg. 845
BANK OF JAPAN; *Int'l*, pg. 845
BANK OF JERUSALEM, LTD.; *Int'l*, pg. 845
BANK OF JIANGSU COMPANY LIMITED; *Int'l*, pg. 845
BANK OF JINZHOU CO., LTD.; *Int'l*, pg. 845
BANK OF JIUJIANG CO., LTD.; *Int'l*, pg. 845
BANK OF JORDAN PLC; *Int'l*, pg. 845
BANK OF JORDAN SYRIA—See Bank of Jordan PLC; *Int'l*, pg. 845
BANK OF KAOHSIUNG CO., LTD.; *Int'l*, pg. 845
BANK OF KATHMANDU LIMITED; *Int'l*, pg. 845
BANK OF KATHMANDU LUMBINI LTD.—See Bank of Kathmandu Limited; *Int'l*, pg. 845
BANK OF KHARTOUM; *Int'l*, pg. 845
THE BANK OF KOCHI LTD.; *Int'l*, pg. 7615
THE BANK OF KOREA; *Int'l*, pg. 7615
THE BANK OF KYOTO, LTD.; *Int'l*, pg. 7615
THE BANK OF KYOTO, LTD. - TREASURY & INVESTMENT DIVISION—See The Bank of Kyoto, Ltd.; *Int'l*, pg. 7616
BANK OF LANZHOU CO., LTD.; *Int'l*, pg. 845
BANK OF LUXEMBURG; *U.S. Private*, pg. 466
THE BANK OF MAHARASHTRA LIMITED; *Int'l*, pg. 7616
BANK OF MALDIVES PLC; *Int'l*, pg. 845
BANK OF MARIN BANCORP; *U.S. Public*, pg. 273
BANK OF MARIN—See Bank of Marin Bancorp; *U.S. Public*, pg. 273
BANK OF MAURITIUS; *Int'l*, pg. 845
THE BANK OF MAUSTON; *U.S. Private*, pg. 3991
THE BANK OF MISSOURI; *U.S. Private*, pg. 3991
THE BANK OF MONGOLIA; *Int'l*, pg. 7616
BANK OF MONTGOMERY—See Grant Bancshares, Inc.; *U.S. Private*, pg. 1756
BANK OF MONTREAL ASSESSORIA E SERVICOS LTDA.—See Bank of Montreal; *Int'l*, pg. 846
BANK OF MONTREAL CAPITAL MARKETS (HOLDINGS) LIMITED—See Bank of Montreal; *Int'l*, pg. 846
BANK OF MONTREAL (CHINA) CO. LTD.—See Bank of Montreal; *Int'l*, pg. 846
BANK OF MONTREAL FINANCE LTD.—See Bank of Montreal; *Int'l*, pg. 846
BANK OF MONTREAL IRELAND PLC—See Bank of Montreal; *Int'l*, pg. 846
BANK OF MONTREAL; *Int'l*, pg. 845
BANK OF MOUNT HOPE; *U.S. Private*, pg. 466
THE BANK OF NAGASAKI, LTD.—See The Nishi-Nippon City Bank, Ltd.; *Int'l*, pg. 7670
THE BANK OF NAGOYA, LTD.; *Int'l*, pg. 7616
BANK OF NAMIBIA; *Int'l*, pg. 847
BANK OF NANJING CO., LTD.; *Int'l*, pg. 847
BANK OF NEVADA—See Western Alliance Bancorporation; *U.S. Public*, pg. 2354
THE BANK OF NEVIS LTD.; *Int'l*, pg. 7616
BANK OF NEW ALBANY; *U.S. Private*, pg. 466
BANK OF NEW HAMPSHIRE—See BNH Financial; *U.S. Private*, pg. 601

BANK OF NEW ALBANY — CORPORATE AFFILIATIONS

THE BANK OF NEW YORK CAPITAL MARKETS, LIMITED—See The Bank of New York Mellon Corporation; *U.S. Public*, pg. 2038

THE BANK OF NEW YORK MELLON CORPORATION; *U.S. Public*, pg. 2036

THE BANK OF NEW YORK MELLON SA/NV—See The Bank of New York Mellon Corporation; *U.S. Public*, pg. 2038

THE BANK OF NEW YORK MELLON TRUST COMPANY, N.A.—See The Bank of New York Mellon Corporation; *U.S. Public*, pg. 2038

THE BANK OF NEW YORK—See The Bank of New York Mellon Corporation; *U.S. Public*, pg. 2038

THE BANK OF NEW YORK—See The Bank of New York Mellon Corporation; *U.S. Public*, pg. 2038

THE BANK OF NEW YORK—See The Bank of New York Mellon Corporation; *U.S. Public*, pg. 2038

BANK OF NEW ZEALAND—See National Australia Bank Limited; *Int'l*, pg. 5151

BANK OF NINGBO CO., LTD.; *Int'l*, pg. 847

BANK OF NORTH DAKOTA; *U.S. Private*, pg. 466

THE BANK OF NOVA SCOTIA - ANTIGUA & BARBUDA—See The Bank of Nova Scotia; *Int'l*, pg. 7619

THE BANK OF NOVA SCOTIA ASIA LIMITED—See The Bank of Nova Scotia; *Int'l*, pg. 7619

THE BANK OF NOVA SCOTIA - ATLANTIC REGION—See The Bank of Nova Scotia; *Int'l*, pg. 7619

THE BANK OF NOVA SCOTIA BERHAD—See The Bank of Nova Scotia; *Int'l*, pg. 7619

THE BANK OF NOVA SCOTIA - BRITISH COLUMBIA & YUKON REGION—See The Bank of Nova Scotia; *Int'l*, pg. 7619

THE BANK OF NOVA SCOTIA - DOMINICAN REPUBLIC—See The Bank of Nova Scotia; *Int'l*, pg. 7619

THE BANK OF NOVA SCOTIA - GUYANA—See The Bank of Nova Scotia; *Int'l*, pg. 7619

THE BANK OF NOVA SCOTIA - HAITI—See The Bank of Nova Scotia; *Int'l*, pg. 7619

THE BANK OF NOVA SCOTIA - INDIA—See The Bank of Nova Scotia; *Int'l*, pg. 7619

THE BANK OF NOVA SCOTIA INTERNATIONAL LIMITED—See The Bank of Nova Scotia; *Int'l*, pg. 7619

THE BANK OF NOVA SCOTIA - JAPAN—See The Bank of Nova Scotia; *Int'l*, pg. 7619

THE BANK OF NOVA SCOTIA - MANITOBA REGION—See The Bank of Nova Scotia; *Int'l*, pg. 7619

THE BANK OF NOVA SCOTIA - ONTARIO REGION—See The Bank of Nova Scotia; *Int'l*, pg. 7619

THE BANK OF NOVA SCOTIA - PANAMA—See The Bank of Nova Scotia; *Int'l*, pg. 7619

THE BANK OF NOVA SCOTIA - PRAIRIE REGION—See The Bank of Nova Scotia; *Int'l*, pg. 7619

THE BANK OF NOVA SCOTIA PROPERTIES INC.—See The Bank of Nova Scotia; *Int'l*, pg. 7619

THE BANK OF NOVA SCOTIA - QUEBEC & EASTERN ONTARIO REGION—See The Bank of Nova Scotia; *Int'l*, pg. 7619

THE BANK OF NOVA SCOTIA; *Int'l*, pg. 7616

THE BANK OF NOVA SCOTIA - SOUTH KOREA—See The Bank of Nova Scotia; *Int'l*, pg. 7619

THE BANK OF NOVA SCOTIA - THAILAND—See The Bank of Nova Scotia; *Int'l*, pg. 7619

THE BANK OF NOVA SCOTIA - TORONTO REGION—See The Bank of Nova Scotia; *Int'l*, pg. 7619

THE BANK OF NOVA SCOTIA TRUST COMPANY (BAHAMAS) LIMITED—See The Bank of Nova Scotia; *Int'l*, pg. 7619

THE BANK OF NOVA SCOTIA TRUST COMPANY (CARIBBEAN) LIMITED—See The Bank of Nova Scotia; *Int'l*, pg. 7618

THE BANK OF NOVA SCOTIA TRUST COMPANY OF NEW YORK—See The Bank of Nova Scotia; *Int'l*, pg. 7618

THE BANK OF N.T. BUTTERFIELD & SON LIMITED; *Int'l*, pg. 7616

BANK OF OAK RIDGE—See Oak Ridge Financial Services, Inc.; *U.S. Public*, pg. 1560

THE BANK OF OKINAWA, LTD.; *Int'l*, pg. 7619

BANK OF PAPUA NEW GUINEA; *Int'l*, pg. 847

BANK OF PONTIAC—See Pontiac Bancorp, Inc.; *U.S. Public*, pg. 1701

BANK OF PUTNAM COUNTY; *U.S. Private*, pg. 466

BANK OF QINGDAO CO., LTD.; *Int'l*, pg. 847

BANK OF QUEENSLAND LIMITED; *Int'l*, pg. 847

THE BANK OF ROMNEY; *U.S. Private*, pg. 3991

BANK OF RUSTON—See Century Next Financial Corporation; *U.S. Public*, pg. 475

THE BANK OF SAGA LTD.; *Int'l*, pg. 7619

THE BANK OF SAN ANTONIO INSURANCE GROUP, INC.—See Southwest Bancshares, Inc.; *U.S. Private*, pg. 3738

BANK OF SAN FRANCISCO; *U.S. Public*, pg. 273

BANK OF SANTA CLARITA—See California BanCorp; *U.S. Public*, pg. 423

BANK OF SCOTLAND CORPORATE BANKING—See Lloyds Banking Group plc; *Int'l*, pg. 4537

BANK OF SCOTLAND PLC—See Lloyds Banking Group plc; *Int'l*, pg. 4536

BANK OF SHANGHAI CO., LTD; *Int'l*, pg. 848

BANK OF SHANGHAI (HONG KONG) LIMITED—See Bank of Shanghai Co., Ltd; *Int'l*, pg. 848

BANK OF SHARJAH P.S.C.; *Int'l*, pg. 848

BANK OF SIERRA LEONE; *Int'l*, pg. 848

BANK OF SINGAPORE LIMITED—See Oversea-Chinese Banking Corporation Limited; *Int'l*, pg. 5671

BANK OF SOUTH CAROLINA CORPORATION; *U.S. Public*, pg. 273

THE BANK OF SOUTH CAROLINA—See Bank of South Carolina Corporation; *U.S. Public*, pg. 273

BANK OF SOUTHSIDE VIRGINIA; *U.S. Private*, pg. 466

BANK OF SPRINGFIELD—See Spring Bancorp, Inc.; *U.S. Private*, pg. 3763

BANK OF STOCKTON—See 1867 Western Financial Corporation; *U.S. Public*, pg. 2

BANK OF ST. VINCENT & THE GRENADINES; *Int'l*, pg. 848

BANK OF SUN PRAIRIE—See BOSP BANCSHARES, INC.; *U.S. Private*, pg. 620

BANK OF SUZHOU CO., LTD.; *Int'l*, pg. 848

BANK OF SYRIA & OVERSEAS S.A.; *Int'l*, pg. 848

THE BANK OF TAMPA—See Tampa Banking Co.; *U.S. Private*, pg. 3928

BANK OF THAILAND; *Int'l*, pg. 848

BANK OF THE FLINT HILLS—See Wamego Bancshares, Inc.; *U.S. Private*, pg. 4435

BANK OF THE JAMES FINANCIAL GROUP, INC.; *U.S. Public*, pg. 273

BANK OF THE JAMES—See Bank of the James Financial Group, Inc.; *U.S. Public*, pg. 273

BANK OF THE LAKES NA; *U.S. Private*, pg. 466

BANK OF THE ORIENT; *U.S. Private*, pg. 467

BANK OF THE OZARKS - MORTGAGE DIVISION—See Bank OZK; *U.S. Public*, pg. 274

BANK OF THE OZARKS—See Bank OZK; *U.S. Public*, pg. 274

THE BANK OF THE PACIFIC—See PACIFIC FINANCIAL CORPORATION; *U.S. Public*, pg. 1631

BANK OF THE PHILIPPINE ISLANDS (EUROPE) PLC—See Bank of the Philippine Islands; *Int'l*, pg. 849

BANK OF THE PHILIPPINE ISLANDS; *Int'l*, pg. 848

BANK OF THE RYUKYUS, LTD.; *Int'l*, pg. 849

BANK OF THE SAN JUANS—See Glacier Bancorp, Inc.; *U.S. Public*, pg. 938

BANK OF THE SIERRA—See Sierra Bancorp; *U.S. Public*, pg. 1877

BANK OF THE WEST—See BNP Paribas SA; *Int'l*, pg. 1087

BANK OF TIANJIN CO., LTD.; *Int'l*, pg. 849

THE BANK OF TIOGA—See Treynor Bancshares, Inc.; *U.S. Private*, pg. 4219

BANK OF TOKYO-MITSUBISHI UFJ (CANADA) LTD.—See Mitsubishi UFJ Financial Group, Inc.; *Int'l*, pg. 4969

BANK OF TOKYO-MITSUBISHI UFJ (CHINA), LTD.—See Mitsubishi UFJ Financial Group, Inc.; *Int'l*, pg. 4969

BANK OF TOKYO-MITSUBISHI UFJ (HOLLAND) N.V. - PRAGUE—See Mitsubishi UFJ Financial Group, Inc.; *Int'l*, pg. 4970

BANK OF TOKYO-MITSUBISHI UFJ (HOLLAND) N.V. - VIENNA—See Mitsubishi UFJ Financial Group, Inc.; *Int'l*, pg. 4970

BANK OF TOKYO-MITSUBISHI UFJ, LTD. - BANGKOK—See Mitsubishi UFJ Financial Group, Inc.; *Int'l*, pg. 4969

BANK OF TOKYO-MITSUBISHI UFJ, LTD. - BRUSSELS—See Mitsubishi UFJ Financial Group, Inc.; *Int'l*, pg. 4969

BANK OF TOKYO-MITSUBISHI UFJ, LTD. - CHICAGO—See Mitsubishi UFJ Financial Group, Inc.; *Int'l*, pg. 4970

BANK OF TOKYO-MITSUBISHI UFJ, LTD. - DUSSELDORF—See Mitsubishi UFJ Financial Group, Inc.; *Int'l*, pg. 4970

THE BANK OF TOKYO-MITSUBISHI UFJ, LTD. - LONDON—See Mitsubishi UFJ Financial Group, Inc.; *Int'l*, pg. 4970

BANK OF TOKYO-MITSUBISHI UFJ, LTD. - LOS ANGELES—See Mitsubishi UFJ Financial Group, Inc.; *Int'l*, pg. 4970

BANK OF TOKYO-MITSUBISHI UFJ, LTD. - MADRID—See Mitsubishi UFJ Financial Group, Inc.; *Int'l*, pg. 4970

BANK OF TOKYO-MITSUBISHI UFJ, LTD. - MILANO—See Mitsubishi UFJ Financial Group, Inc.; *Int'l*, pg. 4970

BANK OF TOKYO-MITSUBISHI UFJ, LTD. - NEW YORK—See Mitsubishi UFJ Financial Group, Inc.; *Int'l*, pg. 4970

BANK OF TOKYO-MITSUBISHI UFJ, LTD. - PARIS—See Mitsubishi UFJ Financial Group, Inc.; *Int'l*, pg. 4970

BANK OF TOKYO-MITSUBISHI UFJ, LTD. - SEOUL—See Mitsubishi UFJ Financial Group, Inc.; *Int'l*, pg. 4970

BANK OF TOKYO-MITSUBISHI UFJ, LTD. - SINGAPORE—See Mitsubishi UFJ Financial Group, Inc.; *Int'l*, pg. 4970

BANK OF TOKYO-MITSUBISHI UFJ, LTD. - SYDNEY—See Mitsubishi UFJ Financial Group, Inc.; *Int'l*, pg. 4970

BANK OF TOKYO-MITSUBISHI UFJ (MALAYSIA) BERHAD—See Mitsubishi UFJ Financial Group, Inc.; *Int'l*, pg. 4969

BANK OF TOKYO-MITSUBISHI UFJ (MEXICO) S.A.—See Mitsubishi UFJ Financial Group, Inc.; *Int'l*, pg. 4969

BANK OF TOKYO-MITSUBISHI UFJ TRUST COMPANY—See Mitsubishi UFJ Financial Group, Inc.; *Int'l*, pg. 4969

BANK OF TOYAMA LTD.; *Int'l*, pg. 849

BANK OF TRAVELERS REST INC.; *U.S. Private*, pg. 467

BANK OF UGANDA; *Int'l*, pg. 849

BANK OF UTAH—See BOU Bancorp, Inc.; *U.S. Private*, pg. 623

BANK OF UTICA; *U.S. Public*, pg. 273

BANK OF VALLETTA P.L.C.; *Int'l*, pg. 849

BANK OF WASHINGTON INC.; *U.S. Private*, pg. 467

BANK OF WEDOWEE; *U.S. Private*, pg. 467

BANK OF WESTERN AUSTRALIA LTD.—See Commonwealth Bank of Australia; *Int'l*, pg. 1719

BANK OF WISCONSIN DELLS; *U.S. Private*, pg. 467

BANK OF WOLCOTT—See Wolcott Bancorp; *U.S. Private*, pg. 4553

BANK OF XIAN CO., LTD.—See Bank of Beijing Co., Ltd.; *Int'l*, pg. 840

THE BANK OF YOKOHAMA, LTD.—See Concordia Financial Group, Ltd.; *Int'l*, pg. 1765

BANK OF YORK; *U.S. Private*, pg. 467

BANK OF ZAMBIA; *Int'l*, pg. 849

BANK OF ZHENGZHOU CO., LTD.; *Int'l*, pg. 849

BANKOH INVESTMENT SERVICES, INC.—See Bank of Hawaii Corporation; *U.S. Public*, pg. 273

BANKOK CHAIN HOSPITAL PLC—See Land & Houses Public Company Limited; *Int'l*, pg. 4403

BANK OTSAR HA-HAYAL LTD.—See FIBI Holdings Ltd.; *Int'l*, pg. 2652

BANK OTSAR HAHAYAL LTD.—See FIBI Holdings Ltd.; *Int'l*, pg. 2652

BANKOWE TOWARZYSTWO KAPITALOWE SA—See PKO Bank Polski SA; *Int'l*, pg. 5887

BANKOWY DOM HIPOTECZNY SP. Z.O.O.—See Commerzbank AG; *Int'l*, pg. 1715

BANK OZK; *U.S. Public*, pg. 273

BANK PASARGAD; *Int'l*, pg. 849

BANKPLUS CORPORATION; *U.S. Private*, pg. 468

BANKPLUS—See BankPlus Corporation; *U.S. Private*, pg. 468

BANK POALEY AGUDAT ISRAEL LTD.—See FIBI Holdings Ltd.; *Int'l*, pg. 2652

BANK POLICY INSTITUTE; *U.S. Private*, pg. 467

BANK POLSKA KASA OPIEKI SPOLKA AKCYJNA; *Int'l*, pg. 849

BANKPOWER GMBH PERSONALDIENSTLEISTUNGEN—See ManpowerGroup Inc.; *U.S. Public*, pg. 1357

BANKPROV; *U.S. Public*, pg. 274

BANKRATE, LLC—See Red Ventures, LLC; *U.S. Private*, pg. 3376

BANK RBK JSC; *Int'l*, pg. 850

BANK RHODE ISLAND—See Brookline Bancorp, Inc.; *U.S. Public*, pg. 395

BANK SADERAT OF IRAN; *Int'l*, pg. 850

BANK SADERAT PLC; *Int'l*, pg. 850

BANK SA—See Westpac Banking Corporation; *Int'l*, pg. 8392

BANKS & ASSOCIATES, LLC—See Seminole Holdings Group, LLC; *U.S. Private*, pg. 3604

BANKS (BARBADOS) BREWERIES LIMITED—See Anheuser-Busch InBev SA/NV; *Int'l*, pg. 464

BANKS BROS. CORPORATION; *U.S. Private*, pg. 468

BANKS.COM, INC.—See Remark Holdings, Inc.; *U.S. Public*, pg. 1782

BANKS ENGINEERING, INC.; *U.S. Private*, pg. 468

BANKSERVE INSURANCE SERVICES LTD.—See BMS Group Ltd.; *Int'l*, pg. 1077

BANKS HARDWOODS, INC. - MENOMONIE FACILITY—See Banks Hardwoods, Inc.; *U.S. Private*, pg. 468

BANKS HARDWOODS, INC. - NEWBERRY FACILITY—See Banks Hardwoods, Inc.; *U.S. Private*, pg. 468

BANKS HARDWOODS, INC.—See Banks Hardwoods, Inc.; *U.S. Private*, pg. 468

BANKS HARDWOODS, INC.—See Banks Hardwoods, Inc.; *U.S. Private*, pg. 468

BANKS HARDWOODS, INC.; *U.S. Private*, pg. 468

BANKS HOLDINGS LIMITED—See Anheuser-Busch InBev SA/NV; *Int'l*, pg. 464

BANK SIAB PJSC; *Int'l*, pg. 850

BANK SINOPAC (CHINA) LTD.—See SinoPac Financial Holdings Company Ltd.; *Int'l*, pg. 6954

BANKS INTEGRATION GROUP, INC.—See The Graham Group, Inc.; *U.S. Private*, pg. 4036

COMPANY NAME INDEX

BANK SNGB JSC—See Surgutneftegas OAO; *Int'l*, pg. 7344
BANKSOFT KFT—See 4iG Nyrt.; *Int'l*, pg. 12
BANK SOYUZ (JSC)—See Ingosstrakh Insurance Company; *Int'l*, pg. 3702
THE BANK STREET GROUP LLC; *U.S. Private*, pg. 3991
BANK TEJARAT; *Int'l*, pg. 850
BANKUNITED, INC.; *U.S. Public*, pg. 274
BANKUNITED, N.A.—See BankUnited, Inc.; *U.S. Public*, pg. 274
BANK URALSIB PAO—See OJSC URALSIB Financial Corporation; *Int'l*, pg. 5543
BANK VAN DE NEDERLANDSE ANTILLEN; *Int'l*, pg. 850
BANKVISTA—See Abdo Investments, Inc.; *U.S. Private*, pg. 37
BANK VON ERNST (LIECHTENSTEIN) AG—See EFG International AG; *Int'l*, pg. 2319
BANK VONTOBEL AG - LUCERNE—See Vontobel Holding AG; *Int'l*, pg. 8306
BANK VONTOBEL AG—See Vontobel Holding AG; *Int'l*, pg. 8306
BANK VONTOBEL EUROPE AG - FRANKFURT—See Vontobel Holding AG; *Int'l*, pg. 8306
BANK VONTOBEL EUROPE AG—See Vontobel Holding AG; *Int'l*, pg. 8306
BANK VONTOBEL OSTERREICH AG—See Vontobel Holding AG; *Int'l*, pg. 8306
BANK VTB (KAZAKHSTAN) JSC—See PJSC VTB Bank; *Int'l*, pg. 5886
BANK VTB NORTH-WEST OJSC—See PJSC VTB Bank; *Int'l*, pg. 5886
BANKWELL BANK—See Bankwell Financial Group, Inc.; *U.S. Public*, pg. 275
BANKWELL FINANCIAL GROUP, INC.; *U.S. Public*, pg. 274
BANKWEST, INC.—See South Dakota Bancshares, Inc.; *U.S. Private*, pg. 3722
BANKY FAMPANDROSOANA VAROTRA SG—See Societe Generale S.A.; *Int'l*, pg. 7039
BANK ZARECHYE JSC; *Int'l*, pg. 850
BANK ZENIT PJSC; *Int'l*, pg. 850
BANLE ENERGY INTERNATIONAL LIMITED—See CBL International Limited; *Int'l*, pg. 1365
BANLE INTERNATIONAL (MALAYSIA) SDN. BHD.—See ODL International Limited; *Int'l*, pg. 1365
BANLE INTERNATIONAL MARKETING LIMITED—See CBL International Limited; *Int'l*, pg. 1365
BAN LEONG CHIN INTER CO., LTD.—See Ban Leong Technologies Limited; *Int'l*, pg. 814
BAN LEONG TECHNOLOGIES LIMITED; *Int'l*, pg. 813
BAN LEONG TECHNOLOGIES SDN BHD—See Ban Leong Technologies Limited; *Int'l*, pg. 814
BAN LOONG HOLDINGS LTD.; *Int'l*, pg. 814
BANMEDICA S.A.—See UnitedHealth Group Incorporated; *U.S. Public*, pg. 2239
BANNARI AMMAN SUGARS LTD.; *Int'l*, pg. 850
BANNEKER PARTNERS, LLC; *U.S. Private*, pg. 468
BANNER ACQUISITION CORP.; *U.S. Public*, pg. 275
BANNER BANK—See Banner Corporation; *U.S. Public*, pg. 275
BANNER BUSINESS SERVICES LIMITED—See Endless LLP; *Int'l*, pg. 2403
BANNER CAPITAL BANK—See Banner County Ban Corporation; *U.S. Private*, pg. 469
BANNER CHEMICALS-BIOCIDES—See Banner Chemicals Limited; *Int'l*, pg. 851
BANNER CHEMICALS-BLUECAT-ADBLUE SOLUTIONS—See Banner Chemicals Limited; *Int'l*, pg. 851
BANNER CHEMICALS-COSMETICS & PERSONAL CARE—See Banner Chemicals Limited; *Int'l*, pg. 851
BANNER CHEMICALS-HYDROCARBON SOLVENTS—See Banner Chemicals Limited; *Int'l*, pg. 851
BANNER CHEMICALS LIMITED; *Int'l*, pg. 851
BANNER CHEMICALS-OIL FIELD APPLICATIONS—See Banner Chemicals Limited; *Int'l*, pg. 851
BANNER CHEMICALS-OXYGENATED SOLVENTS & INTERMEDIATES—See Banner Chemicals Limited; *Int'l*, pg. 851
BANNER CHEMICALS-PHARMACEUTICAL PRODUCTS—See Banner Chemicals Limited; *Int'l*, pg. 851
BANNER CHEMICALS-PRECISION & ELECTRONICS CLEANING—See Banner Chemicals Limited; *Int'l*, pg. 851
BANNER CHEMICALS-SPECIALTY CHEMICALS—See Banner Chemicals Limited; *Int'l*, pg. 851
BANNER CONSTRUCTION LIMITED—See Legal & General Group Plc; *Int'l*, pg. 4442
BANNER CORPORATION; *U.S. Public*, pg. 275
BANNER COUNTY BAN CORPORATION; *U.S. Private*, pg. 469
BANNER ENGINEERING CORP.; *U.S. Private*, pg. 469
BANNER FORD; *U.S. Private*, pg. 469
BANNER FURNACE & FUEL INC.; *U.S. Private*, pg. 469
BANNER-GRAPHIC—See Rust Communications; *U.S. Private*, pg. 3507
BANNER HEALTH SYSTEM; *U.S. Private*, pg. 469

BANNER HEALTH WEST—See Banner Health System; *U.S. Private*, pg. 469
BANNER INDUSTRIES INC.; *U.S. Private*, pg. 469
BANNER LIFE INSURANCE COMPANY—See Legal & General Group Plc; *Int'l*, pg. 4443
BANNER LIFE SCIENCES LLC—See Thermo Fisher Scientific Inc.; *U.S. Public*, pg. 2151
BANNER MANAGEMENT COMPANY INC.—See A&S, Inc.; *U.S. Private*, pg. 21
BANNERMAN ENERGY LTD; *Int'l*, pg. 851
BANNERMAN MINING RESOURCES (NAMIBIA) (PTY.) LTD.—See Bannerman Energy Ltd; *Int'l*, pg. 851
BANNER MATTRESS COMPANY; *U.S. Private*, pg. 469
BANNER MEDICAL INC.—See MiddleGround Management, LP; *U.S. Private*, pg. 2711
BANNER NEWS PUBLISHING CO. INC.—See Wehco Media, Inc.; *U.S. Private*, pg. 4469
BANNER PERSONNEL SERVICE INC.; *U.S. Private*, pg. 469
BANNER PLANT LIMITED—See Henry Boot PLC; *Int'l*, pg. 3354
BANNERS CO., LTD.; *Int'l*, pg. 851
BANNER SERVICE CORPORATION—See MiddleGround Management, LP; *U.S. Private*, pg. 2711
BANNER STAKES LLC—See Bunzl plc; *Int'l*, pg. 1217
BANNER SUPPLY CO.; *U.S. Private*, pg. 469
BANNER SUPPLY CO.; *U.S. Private*, pg. 469
BANNER TRUCK & TRAILER SALES, INC.; *U.S. Private*, pg. 469
BANNER WHOLESALE GROCERS, INC.; *U.S. Private*, pg. 469
BANNIX ACQUISITION CORP.; *U.S. Public*, pg. 275
BANNOCKBURN GLOBAL FOREX, LLC—See First Financial Bancorp.; *U.S. Public*, pg. 843
BANNO, LLC—See Jack Henry & Associates, Inc.; *U.S. Public*, pg. 1182
BANNON DIALYSIS, LLC—See DaVita Inc.; *U.S. Public*, pg. 636
BANNU WOOLLEN MILLS LIMITED; *Int'l*, pg. 851
BANNY COSMIC INTERNATIONAL HOLDINGS, INC.; *Int'l*, pg. 851
BANPONG UTILITIES CO., LTD.—See Electricity Generating Public Co., Ltd.; *Int'l*, pg. 2352
BANPRESTO (H.K.) LTD.—See BANDAI NAMCO Holdings Inc ; *Int'l*, pg. 829
BANPRESTO SALES CO., LTD.—See BANDAI NAMCO Holdings Inc.; *Int'l*, pg. 829
BANPU AUSTRALIA CO., PTY LTD.—See Banpu Public Company Limited; *Int'l*, pg. 852
BANPU COAL POWER LTD.—See Banpu Public Company Limited; *Int'l*, pg. 851
BANPU ENERGY SERVICES (THAILAND) CO., LTD.—See Banpu Public Company Limited; *Int'l*, pg. 851
BANPU INFINERGY CO., LTD.—See Banpu Public Company Limited; *Int'l*, pg. 851
BANPU INTERNATIONAL LTD.—See Banpu Public Company Limited; *Int'l*, pg. 852
BANPU INVESTMENT (CHINA) CO., LTD.—See Banpu Public Company Limited; *Int'l*, pg. 852
BANPU JAPAN K.K.—See Banpu Power PCL; *Int'l*, pg. 851
BANPU MINERALS CO., LTD.—See Banpu Public Company Limited; *Int'l*, pg. 852
BANPU POWER INTERNATIONAL LTD.—See Banpu Public Company Limited; *Int'l*, pg. 852
BANPU POWER INVESTMENT (CHINA) LTD.—See Banpu Public Company Limited; *Int'l*, pg. 852
BANPU POWER (JAPAN) CO., LTD.—See Banpu Power PCL; *Int'l*, pg. 851
BANPU POWER PCL; *Int'l*, pg. 851
BANPU PUBLIC COMPANY LIMITED; *Int'l*, pg. 851
BANPU SINGAPORE PTE. LTD.—See Banpu Public Company Limited; *Int'l*, pg. 851
BANQUE AGF—See Allianz SE; *Int'l*, pg. 342
BANQUE AIG S.A.—See American International Group, Inc.; *U.S. Public*, pg. 104
BANQUE AL BARAKA D'ALGERIE—See Al Baraka Banking Group B.S.C.; *Int'l*, pg. 276
BANQUE AL BARAKA D'ALGERIE S.P.A.—See Al Baraka Banking Group B.S.C.; *Int'l*, pg. 276
BANQUE AUDI (SUISSE) SA—See Bank Audi sal; *Int'l*, pg. 837
BANQUE BANORIENT FRANCE—See BLOM Bank, S.A.L.; *Int'l*, pg. 1064
BANQUE BANORIENT (SWITZERLAND) SA—See BLOM Bank, S.A.L.; *Int'l*, pg. 1064
BANQUE BCP S.A.S.—See Groupe BPCE; *Int'l*, pg. 3097
BANQUE BEMO S.A.L.; *Int'l*, pg. 852
BANQUE BEMO SAUDI FRANSI S.A.; *Int'l*, pg. 852
BANQUE CANTONALE DE GENEVE (FRANCE) SA—See Banque Cantonale de Geneve S.A.; *Int'l*, pg. 852
BANQUE CANTONALE DE GENEVE S.A.; *Int'l*, pg. 852
BANQUE CANTONALE DU JURA S.A.; *Int'l*, pg. 853
BANQUE CANTONALE VAUDOISE; *Int'l*, pg. 853
BANQUE CENTRALE DES COMORES; *Int'l*, pg. 853
BANQUE CENTRALE DES ETATS DE L'AFRIQUE DE L'OUEST; *Int'l*, pg. 853
BANQUE CENTRALE DU LUXEMBOURG; *Int'l*, pg. 853

BANQUE LIBANO-FRANCAISE S.A.L.

BANQUE CENTRALE POPULAIRE S.A.; *Int'l*, pg. 853
BANQUE COMMERCIALE DU BURUNDI S.A.R.L.—See ING Groep N.V.; *Int'l*, pg. 3700
BANQUE COMMERCIALE DU CONGO S.A.R.L.; *Int'l*, pg. 853
BANQUE COVEFI S.A.—See Otto GmbH & Co. KG; *Int'l*, pg. 5663
BANQUE CRAMER & CIE SA—See Norinvest Holding SA; *Int'l*, pg. 5428
BANQUE D'ALGERIE; *Int'l*, pg. 853
BANQUE DE BRETAGNE—See BNP Paribas SA; *Int'l*, pg. 1089
BANQUE DE CHINE (DJIBOUTI) S.A.—See Bank of China, Ltd.; *Int'l*, pg. 842
BANQUE DE COMMERCE ET DE PLACEMENTS S.A.—See Koc Holding A.S.; *Int'l*, pg. 4224
BANQUE DEGROOF LUXEMBOURG S.A.—See Banque Degroof S.A.; *Int'l*, pg. 853
BANQUE DEGROOF S.A.; *Int'l*, pg. 853
BANQUE DE KIGALI S.A.; *Int'l*, pg. 853
BANQUE DE LA POSTE S.A./BANK VAN DE POST N.V.—See BNP Paribas SA; *Int'l*, pg. 1084
BANQUE DE LA POSTE S.A./BANK VAN DE POST N.V.—See bpost NV/SA; *Int'l*, pg. 1133
BANQUE DE LA REUNION SA—See Groupe BPCE; *Int'l*, pg. 3097
BANQUE DE NEUFLIZE OBC S.A.—See ABN AMRO Group N.V.; *Int'l*, pg. 65
BANQUE DE NEUFLIZE—See ABN AMRO Group N.V.; *Int'l*, pg. 65
BANQUE DE NOUVELLE-CALEDONIE SA—See Groupe BPCE; *Int'l*, pg. 3092
BANQUE DE PATRIMOINES PRIVES, SA—See Credit Andorra; *Int'l*, pg. 1834
BANQUE DE POLYNESIE SA—See Societe Generale S.A.; *Int'l*, pg. 7039
BANQUE DE REALISATIONS DE GESTION ET DE FINANCEMENT—See L'Oreal S.A.; *Int'l*, pg. 4378
BANQUE DES TERRITOIRES—See Caisse des Depots et Consignations; *Int'l*, pg. 1257
BANQUE DE TAHITI S.A.—See Bank of Hawaii Corporation; *U.S. Public*, pg. 273
BANQUE DE TUNISIE ET DES EMIRATS; *Int'l*, pg. 853
BANQUE DE WALLIS ET FUTUNA—See BNP Paribas SA; *Int'l*, pg. 1089
BANQUE DU CAIRE; *Int'l*, pg. 853
BANQUE DU LIBAN; *Int'l*, pg. 853
BANQUE ENI SA—See Eni S.p.A.; *Int'l*, pg. 2436
BANQUE ESPIRITO SANTO ET DE LA VENETIE S.A.—See Cerberus Capital Management, L.P.; *U.S. Private*, pg. 839
BANQUE ET CAISSE D'EPARGNE DE L'ETAT; *Int'l*, pg. 853
BANQUE FRANCO LAO LTD.—See Groupe BPCE; *Int'l*, pg. 3092
BANQUE HAVILLAND S.A.—See Blackfish Capital Management Ltd.; *Int'l*, pg. 1060
BANQUE HERITAGE (SUISSE) S.A.; *Int'l*, pg. 853
BANQUE HERITAGE (URUGUAY) S.A.—See Banque Heritage (Suisse) S.A.; *Int'l*, pg. 854
BANQUE INTERNATIONALE A LUXEMBOURG S.A.—See Legend Holdings Corporation; *Int'l*, pg. 4443
BANQUE INTERNATIONALE A LUXEMBOURG (SUISSE) SA—See Legend Holdings Corporation; *Int'l*, pg. 4443
BANQUE INTERNATIONALE ARABE DE TUNISIE; *Int'l*, pg. 854
BANQUE INTERNATIONALE POUR LAFRIQUE AU TOGO SA; *Int'l*, pg. 854
BANQUE INTERNATIONALE POUR LE COMMERCE ET L'INDUSTRIE AU MALI—See BNP Paribas SA; *Int'l*, pg. 1089
BANQUE INTERNATIONALE POUR LE COMMERCE ET L'INDUSTRIE DE LA COTE D'IVOIRE, S.A.—See BNP Paribas SA; *Int'l*, pg. 1089
BANQUE INTERNATIONALE POUR LE COMMERCE ET L'INDUSTRIE DE LA GUINEE—See BNP Paribas SA; *Int'l*, pg. 1089
BANQUE INTERNATIONALE POUR LE COMMERCE ET L'INDUSTRIE DU GABON—See BNP Paribas SA; *Int'l*, pg. 1089
BANQUE INTERNATIONALE POUR LE COMMERCE ET L'INDUSTRIE DU MALI SA—See BNP Paribas SA; *Int'l*, pg. 1089
BANQUE INTERNATIONALE POUR LE COMMERCE ET L'INDUSTRIE DU SENEGAL SA—See BNP Paribas SA; *Int'l*, pg. 1089
BANQUE INTERNATIONALE POUR LE COMMERCE, L'INDUSTRIE ET L'AGRICULTURE DU BURKINA—See BNP Paribas SA; *Int'l*, pg. 1089
BANQUE J. SAFRA SARASIN (MONACO) SA—See Banco Safra S.A.; *Int'l*, pg. 825
BANQUE JULIUS BAER & CIE SA—See Julius Baer Group Ltd.; *Int'l*, pg. 4024
BANQUE LBLUX SA—See Helaba Landesbank Hessen-Thuringen; *Int'l*, pg. 3327
BANQUE LIBANO-FRANCAISE S.A.L.; *Int'l*, pg. 854
BANQUE MAGNETIQUE SAS—See DCC plc; *Int'l*, pg. 1989

BANQUE LIBANO-FRANCAISE S.A.L.
CORPORATE AFFILIATIONS

BANQUE MALGACHE DE L'OCEAN INDIEN—See Banque Centrale Populaire S.A.; *Int'l*, pg. 853
BANQUE MAROCAINE DU COMMERCE ET DE L'INDUSTRIE OFFSHORE—See BNP Paribas SA; *Int'l*, pg. 1089
BANQUE MAROCAINE POUR LE COMMERCE ET L'INDUSTRIE S.A.—See BNP Paribas SA; *Int'l*, pg. 1089
BANQUE MAURITANIENNE POUR LE COMMERCE INTERNATIONAL; *Int'l*, pg. 854
BANQUE MISR; *Int'l*, pg. 854
BANQUE NATIONALE DE BELGIQUE S.A.; *Int'l*, pg. 854
BANQUE NATIONALE DU RWANDA; *Int'l*, pg. 854
BANQUE NOMURA FRANCE—See Nomura Holdings, Inc.; *Int'l*, pg. 5410
BANQUE PALATINE S.A.—See Groupe BPCE; *Int'l*, pg. 3094
BANQUE PIGUET GALLAND & CIE SA—See Banque Cantonale Vaudoise; *Int'l*, pg. 853
BANQUE POPULAIRE ALSACE LORRAINE CHAMPAGNE—See Groupe BPCE; *Int'l*, pg. 3097
BANQUE POPULAIRE AQUITAINE CENTRE ATLANTIQUE SCCV—See Groupe BPCE; *Int'l*, pg. 3092
BANQUE POPULAIRE ATLANTIQUE—See Groupe BPCE; *Int'l*, pg. 3097
BANQUE POPULAIRE AUVERGNE RHONE ALPES SCM—See Groupe BPCE; *Int'l*, pg. 3092
BANQUE POPULAIRE BOURGOGNE FRANCHE-COMTE—See Groupe BPCE; *Int'l*, pg. 3097
BANQUE POPULAIRE CENTRE ATLANTIQUE—See Groupe BPCE; *Int'l*, pg. 3097
BANQUE POPULAIRE COTE D'AZUR—See Groupe BPCE; *Int'l*, pg. 3097
BANQUE POPULAIRE DE L'OUEST—See Groupe BPCE; *Int'l*, pg. 3097
BANQUE POPULAIRE DES ALPES—See Groupe BPCE; *Int'l*, pg. 3097
BANQUE POPULAIRE DU MASSIF CENTRAL—See Groupe BPCE; *Int'l*, pg. 3097
BANQUE POPULAIRE DU NORD—See Groupe BPCE; *Int'l*, pg. 3097
BANQUE POPULAIRE DU SUD-OUEST—See Groupe BPCE; *Int'l*, pg. 3097
BANQUE POPULAIRE DU SUD SCCV—See Groupe BPCE; *Int'l*, pg. 3092
BANQUE POPULAIRE DU SUD—See Groupe BPCE; *Int'l*, pg. 3097
BANQUE POPULAIRE GRAND OUEST SCA—See Groupe BPCE; *Int'l*, pg. 3092
BANQUE POPULAIRE LOIRE ET LYONNAIS—See Groupe BPCE; *Int'l*, pg. 3097
BANQUE POPULAIRE LORRAINE CHAMPAGNE—See Groupe BPCE; *Int'l*, pg. 3097
BANQUE POPULAIRE OCCITANE—See Groupe BPCE; *Int'l*, pg. 3097
BANQUE POPULAIRE PROVENCALE ET CORSE—See Groupe BPCE; *Int'l*, pg. 3097
BANQUE POPULAIRE RIVES DE PARIS—See Groupe BPCE; *Int'l*, pg. 3097
BANQUE POPULAIRE VAL DE FRANCE—See Groupe BPCE; *Int'l*, pg. 3097
BANQUE PRIVEE EDMOND DE ROTHSCHILD EUROPE—See Edmond de Rothschild Holding S.A.; *Int'l*, pg. 2312
BANQUE PRIVEE EDMOND DE ROTHSCHILD S.A.—See Edmond de Rothschild Holding S.A.; *Int'l*, pg. 2312
BANQUE PRIVEE EUROPEENNE—See La Poste S.A.; *Int'l*, pg. 4388
BANQUE PRIVEE SAINT DOMINIQUE—See Groupe BPCE; *Int'l*, pg. 3095
BANQUE PROFIL DE GESTION SA; *Int'l*, pg. 854
BANQUE PSA FINANCE S.A.—See Stellantis N.V.; *Int'l*, pg. 7201
BANQUE PUILAETCO DEWAAY LUXEMBOURG S.A.—See KBL European Private Bankers S.A.; *Int'l*, pg. 4107
BANQUE REGIONALE DE L'AIN—See Confederation Nationale du Credit Mutuel; *Int'l*, pg. 1767
BANQUE RICHELIEU FRANCE—See Societe Generale de Banque au Liban s.a.l.; *Int'l*, pg. 7038
BANQUE RICHELIEU MONACO—See Societe Generale de Banque au Liban s.a.l.; *Int'l*, pg. 7038
BANQUE SAUDI FRANSI; *Int'l*, pg. 854
BANQUE SBA S.A.—See Banque Libano-Francaise S.A.L.; *Int'l*, pg. 854
BANQUE SBM MADAGASCAR SA—See State Bank of Mauritius Ltd.; *Int'l*, pg. 7181
BANQUE SCALBERT DUPONT—See Confederation Nationale du Credit Mutuel; *Int'l*, pg. 1767
BANQUE SOLFEA SA—See ENGIE SA; *Int'l*, pg. 2428
BANQUE SYZ SA—See Financiere SYZ & CO SA; *Int'l*, pg. 2669
BANQUE TRANSATLANTIQUE—See Confederation Nationale du Credit Mutuel; *Int'l*, pg. 1767
BANQUE TRAVELEX S.A.—See Travelex Holdings Limited; *Int'l*, pg. 7907
BANQUE TUNISO KOWEITIENNE SA—See Groupe BPCE; *Int'l*, pg. 3092

BANQUE VONTOBEL SA - GENEVE—See Vontobel Holding AG; *Int'l*, pg. 8306
BANRISUL S.A. CORRETORA DE VM E CAMBIO—See Banco do Estado do Rio Grande do Sul SA; *Int'l*, pg. 822
BANRO CORPORATION; *Int'l*, pg. 854
BANRO SECTIONS LIMITED—See Kingspan Group PLC; *Int'l*, pg. 4176
BANSABADELL CORREDURIA DE SEGUROS SA—See Banco de Sabadell, S.A.; *Int'l*, pg. 821
BANSABADELL FACTURA, S.L.—See Banco de Sabadell, S.A.; *Int'l*, pg. 821
BANSABADELL FINANZIARIA SPA—See Banco de Sabadell, S.A.; *Int'l*, pg. 821
BANSABADELL FINCOM, E.F.C., S.A.—See Banco de Sabadell, S.A.; *Int'l*, pg. 821
BANSABADELL HOLDING, S.L.—See Banco de Sabadell, S.A.; *Int'l*, pg. 821
BANSABADELL INVERSION, S.A., S.G.I.I.C.—See Banco de Sabadell, S.A.; *Int'l*, pg. 821
BANSAL ROOFING PRODUCTS LIMITED; *Int'l*, pg. 854
BANSAMEX, S.A.—See American Express Company; *U.S. Public*, pg. 102
BANSARD BANGLADESH—See Bansard International; *Int'l*, pg. 854
BANSARD INTERNATIONAL; *Int'l*, pg. 854
BANSEI ROYAL RESORTS HIKKADUWA PLC; *Int'l*, pg. 854
BANSEMKO OOO—See Kesko Corporation; *Int'l*, pg. 4141
BAN SENG LEE INDUSTRIES SDN. BHD.—See BSL Corporation Berhad; *Int'l*, pg. 1202
BANSISONS TEA INDUSTRIES LIMITED; *Int'l*, pg. 854
BANSK GROUP LLC; *U.S. Private*, pg. 469
BANSON TOOL HIRE LIMITED—See Frank Key Group Limited; *Int'l*, pg. 2761
BAN SUK SABAI COMPANY LIMITED—See Noble Development Public Company Limited; *Int'l*, pg. 5397
BANSWARA FABRICS LIMITED—See Banswara Syntex Limited; *Int'l*, pg. 855
BANSWARA SYNTEX LIMITED; *Int'l*, pg. 854
BANTA GLOBAL TURNKEY LLC—See Chatham Asset Management, LLC; *U.S. Private*, pg. 862
BANTA GLOBAL TURNKEY LTD. - LIMERICK—See Chatham Asset Management, LLC; *U.S. Private*, pg. 862
BANTA GLOBAL TURNKEY LTD.—See Chatham Asset Management, LLC; *U.S. Private*, pg. 862
BANTA GLOBAL TURNKEY, LTD.—See Chatham Asset Management, LLC; *U.S. Private*, pg. 862
BANTA GLOBAL TURNKEY (SINGAPORE) PTE LTD—See Chatham Asset Management, LLC; *U.S. Private*, pg. 862
BANTA GLOBAL TURNKEY, S.R.O.—See Chatham Asset Management, LLC; *U.S. Private*, pg. 862
BANTAM BAGELS, LLC—See Lancaster Colony Corporation; *U.S. Public*, pg. 1291
BANTAM BOOKS LTD.—See Bertelsmann SE & Co. KGaA; *Int'l*, pg. 991
BANTAM CAPITAL CORP.; *Int'l*, pg. 855
BANTAM DELL CANADA—See Bertelsmann SE & Co. KGaA; *Int'l*, pg. 990
BANTAM DELL PUBLISHING GROUP—See Bertelsmann SE & Co. KGaA; *Int'l*, pg. 990
BANTAM PAPERBACKS UK—See Bertelsmann SE & Co. KGaA; *Int'l*, pg. 991
BANTAM PRESS UK—See Bertelsmann SE & Co KGaA; *Int'l*, pg. 991
BANTAS BANDIRMA AMBALAJ SANAYI VE TICARET AS; *Int'l*, pg. 855
BANTEC, INC.; *U.S. Public*, pg. 275
BANTERRA BANK—See Banterra Corp.; *U.S. Private*, pg. 470
BANTERRA CORP.; *U.S. Private*, pg. 469
BANTON CONSTRUCTION COMPANY; *U.S. Private*, pg. 470
BANTREL CONSTRUCTORS CO.—See Bantrel Co.; *Int'l*, pg. 855
BANTREL CO.; *Int'l*, pg. 855
BANTREL MANAGEMENT SERVICES CO.—See Bantrel Co.; *Int'l*, pg. 855
BANTRY BAY PORT COMPANY LIMITED—See Port of Cork Company Ltd.; *Int'l*, pg. 5933
BANTRY BAY VENTURES-ASIA, LLC; *U.S. Private*, pg. 470
BANVIDA SA; *Int'l*, pg. 855
BANVIT BANDIRMA VITAMINLI YEM SANAYII ANONIM SIRKETI; *Int'l*, pg. 855
BANYAN ACQUISITION CORPORATION; *U.S. Public*, pg. 275
BANYAN AIR SERVICE INC.; *U.S. Private*, pg. 470
BANYAN BIOMARKERS INC.; *U.S. Private*, pg. 470
BANYAN CAPITAL PARTNERS—See Connor, Clark & Lunn Financial Group; *Int'l*, pg. 1769
BANYAN GOLD CORP.; *Int'l*, pg. 855
BANYAN INVESTMENT GROUP; *U.S. Private*, pg. 470
BANYAN MEZZANINE FUND, L.P.; *U.S. Private*, pg. 470
BANYAN SOFTWARE, INC.; *U.S. Private*, pg. 470
BANYAN TECHNOLOGIES GROUP, LLC; *U.S. Private*, pg. 470

BANYAN TREE GALLERY (THAILAND) LIMITED—See Banyan Tree Holdings Ltd.; *Int'l*, pg. 855
BANYAN TREE HOLDINGS LTD.; *Int'l*, pg. 855
BANYAN TREE HOTELS & RESORTS KOREA LIMITED—See Banyan Tree Holdings Ltd.; *Int'l*, pg. 855
BANYAN TREE HOTELS & RESORTS PTE. LTD.—See Banyan Tree Holdings Ltd.; *Int'l*, pg. 855
BANYAN TREE RESORTS & SPAS (THAILAND) COMPANY LIMITED—See Banyan Tree Holdings Ltd.; *Int'l*, pg. 855
BANZ AG—See Poenina Holding AG; *Int'l*, pg. 5903
BAOBAG SAS—See Caisse des Depots et Consignations; *Int'l*, pg. 1258
BAOBAG SAS—See EPIC Bpifrance; *Int'l*, pg. 2460
BAOCHENG FUTURES CO., LTD.—See China Huaneng Group Co., Ltd.; *Int'l*, pg. 1509
BAODEAN SECURITY PRODUCTS CO. LTD—See ASSA ABLOY AB; *Int'l*, pg. 639
BAODING AOZE AUTOMOBILE SALES SERVICES CO., LTD.—See China ZhengTong Auto Services Holdings Limited; *Int'l*, pg. 1566
BAODING DONGLI MACHINERY CO., LTD.; *Int'l*, pg. 855
BAODING GREAT MACHINERY COMPANY LIMITED—See Great Wall Motor Company Limited; *Int'l*, pg. 3065
BAODING INTERNATIONAL PAPER PACKAGING CO., LTD.—See International Paper Company; *U.S. Public*, pg. 1155
BAODING LUCKY INNOVATIVE MATERIALS CO., LTD.; *Int'l*, pg. 855
BAODING NOBO RUBBER PRODUCTION CO., LTD.—See Great Wall Motor Company Limited; *Int'l*, pg. 3066
BAODING NUOBO RUBBER PRODUCTION COMPANY LIMITED—See Great Wall Motor Company Limited; *Int'l*, pg. 3066
BAODING SIFANG SANYI ELECTRIC CO., LTD.—See Beijing Sifang Automation Co., Ltd.; *Int'l*, pg. 957
BAODING TECHNOLOGY CO., LTD.; *Int'l*, pg. 855
BAODING TIANWEI BAOBIAN ELECTRIC CO., LTD.; *Int'l*, pg. 856
BAOFENG GROUP CO., LTD.; *Int'l*, pg. 856
BAOFENG GROUP CO., LTD.; *Int'l*, pg. 856
BAOF INTERNATIONAL LIMITED—See Golden Solar New Energy Technology Holdings Limited; *Int'l*, pg. 3032
BAO ISLAND ENTERPRISES LIMITED—See China Baowu Steel Group Corp., Ltd.; *Int'l*, pg. 1485
BAOJI AEROSPACE POWER PUMP CO., LTD.—See Shaanxi Aerospace Power High-tech Co., Ltd.; *Int'l*, pg. 6746
BAOJIA NACHI ROBOT APPLICATION DEVELOPMENT QINGDAO INC.—See Nachi-Fujikoshi Corp.; *Int'l*, pg. 5121
BAOJI FAST GEAR CO., LTD.—See Shandong Heavy Industry Group Co., Ltd.; *Int'l*, pg. 6753
BAOJI FUFENG BIOTECHNOLOGIES CO., LTD.—See Fufeng Group Limited; *Int'l*, pg. 2804
BAOJI MACHINE TOOL GROUP CO., LTD.—See Qinchuan Machine Tool & Tool Group Share Co., Ltd.; *Int'l*, pg. 6141
BAOJI SHOPPING MALL CO., LTD—See Hainan Traffic Administration Holding Co., Ltd.; *Int'l*, pg. 3213
BAOJI TITANIUM INDUSTRY CO., LTD.; *Int'l*, pg. 856
BAOKU ONLINE TECHNOLOGY LTD.—See Beijing Shiji Information Technology Co., Ltd.; *Int'l*, pg. 956
BAO LAI INVESTMENT JSC—See Vingroup Joint Stock Company; *Int'l*, pg. 8241
BAOLINGBAO BIOLOGY CO., LTD.; *Int'l*, pg. 856
BAOLONG INTERNATIONAL CO., LTD.; *Int'l*, pg. 856
BAO MINH INSURANCE CORPORATION; *Int'l*, pg. 855
BAOSEM—See Sonatrach International Holding Corporation; *Int'l*, pg. 7089
BAOSHAN IRON & STEEL CO., LTD.—See China Baowu Steel Group Corp., Ltd.; *Int'l*, pg. 1485
BAOSHENG MEDIA GROUP HOLDINGS LIMITED; *Int'l*, pg. 856
BAOSHENG SCIENCE & TECHNOLOGY INNOVATION CO., LTD; *Int'l*, pg. 856
BAOSHIDA INTERNATIONAL HOLDING GROUP CO., LTD.; *Int'l*, pg. 856
BAOSHIDA SWISSMETAL LTD.—See Baoshida International Holding Group Co., Ltd.; *Int'l*, pg. 856
BAO SHINN EXPRESS CO., LTD.—See ZZLL Information Technology, Inc.; *Int'l*, pg. 8701
BAO SHINN HOLIDAYS LIMITED—See ZZLL Information Technology, Inc.; *Int'l*, pg. 8701
BAOSHINN INTERNATIONAL EXPRESS LIMITED (BSIE)—See ZZLL Information Technology, Inc.; *Int'l*, pg. 8701
BAOSTEEL AMERICA INC.—See China Baowu Steel Group Corp., Ltd.; *Int'l*, pg. 1485
BAOSTEEL DESHENG STAINLESS STEEL CO., LTD.—See China Baowu Steel Group Corp., Ltd.; *Int'l*, pg. 1485
BAOSTEEL DEVELOPMENT CO., LTD.—See China Baowu Steel Group Corp., Ltd.; *Int'l*, pg. 1485
BAOSTEEL DO BRASIL LTDA.—See China Baowu Steel Group Corp., Ltd.; *Int'l*, pg. 1485

COMPANY NAME INDEX

BAOSTEEL EUROPE GMBH—See China Baowu Steel Group Corp., Ltd.; *Int'l*, pg. 1485
BAOSTEEL GROUP FINANCE CO., LTD.—See China Baowu Steel Group Corp., Ltd.; *Int'l*, pg. 1485
BAOSTEEL GROUP SHANGHAI ERGANG CO., LTD.—See China Baowu Steel Group Corp., Ltd.; *Int'l*, pg. 1485
BAOSTEEL GROUP XINJIANG BAYI IRON & STEEL CO., LTD.—See China Baowu Steel Group Corp., Ltd.; *Int'l*, pg. 1485
BAOSTEEL HITACHI ROLLS (NANTONG) LTD.—See Proterial, Ltd.; *Int'l*, pg. 6005
BAOSTEEL ITALIA DISTRIBUTION CENTER S.P.A.—See China Baowu Steel Group Corp., Ltd.; *Int'l*, pg. 1485
BAOSTEEL METAL CO., LTD.—See China Baowu Steel Group Corp., Ltd.; *Int'l*, pg. 1485
BAOSTEEL-NIPPON STEEL AUTOMOTIVE STEEL SHEETS CO., LTD.—See China Baowu Steel Group Corp., Ltd.; *Int'l*, pg. 1485
BAOSTEEL-NIPPON STEEL AUTOMOTIVE STEEL SHEETS CO., LTD.—See Nippon Steel Corporation; *Int'l*, pg. 5334
BAOSTEEL SINGAPORE PTE. LTD.—See China Baowu Steel Group Corp., Ltd.; *Int'l*, pg. 1485
BAOSTEEL SPECIAL MATERIAL CO., LTD.—See China Baowu Steel Group Corp., Ltd.; *Int'l*, pg. 1485
BAOSTEEL TRADING EUROPE GMBH—See China Baowu Steel Group Corp., Ltd.; *Int'l*, pg. 1485
BAOTAILONG NEW MATERIALS CO., LTD.; *Int'l*, pg. 856
BAOTA INDUSTRY CO., LTD.; *Int'l*, pg. 856
BAOTEK INDUSTRIAL MATERIALS LTD.—See NITTO BOSEKI CO., LTD.; *Int'l*, pg. 5384
BAOTOU DONGBAO BIO-TECH CO., LTD.; *Int'l*, pg. 856
BAOTOU FDK CO., LTD.—See Fujitsu Limited; *Int'l*, pg. 2832
BAOTOU HUAZI INDUSTRY CO., LTD.; *Int'l*, pg. 856
BAOTOU IRON & STEEL (GROUP) COMPANY LIMITED; *Int'l*, pg. 856
BAOTOU LUZE AUTOMOBILE SALES SERVICES CO., LTD.—See China ZhengTong Auto Services Holdings Limited; *Int'l*, pg. 1566
BAOTOU NEW DAMAO RARE EARTH CO., LTD.—See Hongda Xingye Co., Ltd.; *Int'l*, pg. 3470
BAOTOU TOMORROW TECHNOLOGY CO., LTD.; *Int'l*, pg. 857
BAOTOU ZHONGRUI AUTOMOBILE SALES SERVICE CO., LTD.—See China ZhengTong Auto Services Holdings Limited; *Int'l*, pg. 1566
BAO-TRANS ENTERPRISES LTD.—See China Baowu Steel Group Corp., Ltd.; *Int'l*, pg. 1485
BAO VIET COMMERCIAL JOINT STOCK BANK—See Bao Viet Holdings; *Int'l*, pg. 855
BAO VIET FUND MANAGEMENT COMPANY—See Bao Viet Holdings; *Int'l*, pg. 855
BAO VIET HOLDINGS; *Int'l*, pg. 855
BAO VIET INSURANCE CORPORATION—See Bao Viet Holdings; *Int'l*, pg. 855
BAO VIET SECURITIES JOINT STOCK COMPANY—See Bao Viet Holdings; *Int'l*, pg. 855
BAOVIET TOKIO MARINE INSURANCE JOINT VENTURE COMPANY—See Bao Viet Holdings; *Int'l*, pg. 855
BAOVIET TOKIO MARINE INSURANCE JOINT VENTURE COMPANY—See Tokio Marine Holdings, Inc.; *Int'l*, pg. 7782
BAOWU MAGNESIUM TECHNOLOGY CO., LTD.; *Int'l*, pg. 857
BAOXINIAO HOLDING CO., LTD.; *Int'l*, pg. 857
BAOYE DAIWA INDUSTRIALIZED HOUSE MANUFACTURING CO., LTD.—See Daiwa House Industry Co., Ltd.; *Int'l*, pg. 1945
BAOYE GROUP COMPANY LIMITED; *Int'l*, pg. 857
BAOZUN INC.; *Int'l*, pg. 857
B & A PACKAGING INDIA LIMITED; *Int'l*, pg. 783
BAPCOR LIMITED; *Int'l*, pg. 857
BAPCOR NEW ZEALAND LIMITED—See Bapcor Limited; *Int'l*, pg. 857
BAPCOR RETAIL PTY. LTD.—See Bapcor Limited; *Int'l*, pg. 857
BAPI HOANG ANH GIA LAI JOINT STOCK COMPANY—See Hoang Anh Gia Lai Joint Stock Company; *Int'l*, pg. 3436
BAPKO METAL FABRICATORS INC.; *U.S. Private*, pg. 470
BAPRO MANDATOS Y NEGOCIOS S.A.—See Banco de la Provincia de Buenos Aires; *Int'l*, pg. 821
BA PROPERTIES, INC.—See Bank of America Corporation; *U.S. Public*, pg. 270
BAPTISTA'S BAKERY, INC.—See Campbell Soup Company; *U.S. Public*, pg. 427
BAPTIST HEALTH ENTERPRISES—See Baptist Health South Florida, Inc.; *U.S. Private*, pg. 470
BAPTIST HEALTH MEDICAL CENTER; *U.S. Private*, pg. 470
BAPTIST HEALTH SOUTH FLORIDA FOUNDATION—See Baptist Health South Florida, Inc.; *U.S. Private*, pg. 470
BAPTIST HEALTH SOUTH FLORIDA, INC.; *U.S. Private*, pg. 470
BAPTIST HOME HEALTH, LLC—See UnitedHealth Group Incorporated; *U.S. Public*, pg. 2244

THE BAPTIST HOME, INC.; *U.S. Private*, pg. 3991
THE BAPTIST HOME OF PHILADELPHIA; *U.S. Private*, pg. 3991
BAPTIST HOMES SOCIETY; *U.S. Private*, pg. 471
BAPTIST HOSPITAL FOUNDATION INC.—See Ascension Health Alliance; *U.S. Private*, pg. 347
BAPTIST HOSPITAL OF MIAMI—See Baptist Health South Florida, Inc.; *U.S. Private*, pg. 470
BAPTIST HOSPITALS OF SOUTHEAST TEXAS; *U.S. Private*, pg. 471
BAPTIST MEDICAL & DENTAL MISSION INTERNATIONAL, INC.; *U.S. Private*, pg. 471
BAPTIST MEMORIAL HEALTH CARE CORPORATION—See Anderson Regional Health System; *U.S. Private*, pg. 277
BAPTIST MISSIONS INC.; *U.S. Private*, pg. 471
BAPTIST OUTPATIENT SERVICES—See Baptist Health South Florida, Inc.; *U.S. Private*, pg. 470
BAPTIST PLAZA SURGICARE, L.P.—See Tenet Healthcare Corporation; *U.S. Public*, pg. 2009
BAPTIST ST. ANTHONY—See Ventas, Inc.; *U.S. Public*, pg. 2278
BAPTIST SURGERY CENTER, L.P.—See Tenet Healthcare Corporation; *U.S. Public*, pg. 2009
BAQUS GROUP LIMITED; *Int'l*, pg. 857
BAQUS GROUP - OXFORD—See Baqus Group Limited; *Int'l*, pg. 857
BAR 2 LIMITED; *Int'l*, pg. 857
BARABOO BANCORPORATION, INC.; *U.S. Public*, pg. 275
BARABOO MOTORS INC.; *U.S. Private*, pg. 471
THE BARABOO NATIONAL BANK—See Baraboo Bancorporation, Inc.; *U.S. Public*, pg. 275
BARA CHEMICAL CO., LTD—See Sumitomo Chemical Company, Limited; *Int'l*, pg. 7264
BARAFOR LIMITED—See Barclays PLC; *Int'l*, pg. 859
BARAKA FASHIONS LIMITED—See Baraka Power Limited; *Int'l*, pg. 858
BARAKAH OFFSHORE PETROLEUM BERHAD; *Int'l*, pg. 858
BARAKA PATENGA POWER LIMITED—See Baraka Power Limited; *Int'l*, pg. 858
BARAKA POWER LIMITED; *Int'l*, pg. 858
BARAKAT ASSOCIATES, LTD—See Reading Anthracite Company; *U.S. Private*, pg. 3366
BARAK VALLEY CEMENTS LIMITED; *Int'l*, pg. 858
BAR ALE, INC.; *U.S. Private*, pg. 471
BAR-ALL, INC.; *U.S. Private*, pg. 471
BARAMA COMPANY LIMITED—See Samling Strategic Corporation Sdn. Bhd.; *Int'l*, pg. 6507
BARAN CHILE SPA—See Baran Group Ltd.; *Int'l*, pg. 858
BARAN CONSTRUCTION AND INFRASTRUCTURE LTD.—See Baran Group Ltd.; *Int'l*, pg. 858
BARANCORP, LTD.; *U.S. Private*, pg. 471
BARAN ENGINEERING SOUTH AFRICA (PTY) LTD.—See Baran Group Ltd.; *Int'l*, pg. 858
BARAN GROUP LTD.; *Int'l*, pg. 858
BARAN INDUSTRIES (91) LTD.—See Baran Group Ltd.; *Int'l*, pg. 858
BARANMEX, S.A. DE C.V.—See Baran Group Ltd.; *Int'l*, pg. 858
BARAN-OIL & PETROCHEMICAL (1987) PROJECTS LTD.—See Baran Group Ltd.; *Int'l*, pg. 858
BARAN PROJECTS SOUTH AFRICA (PTY) LTD.—See Baran Group Ltd.; *Int'l*, pg. 858
BARAN-ROMANIA LLC—See Baran Group Ltd.; *Int'l*, pg. 858
BARANSKI & ASSOCIATES—See Barancorp, Ltd.; *U.S. Private*, pg. 471
BARANSKI PUBLISHING COMPANY—See Barancorp, Ltd.; *U.S. Private*, pg. 471
BARAN SOUTH EAST ASIA LTD.—See Baran Group Ltd.; *Int'l*, pg. 858
BARAN TELECOM, INC.—See Baran Group Ltd.; *Int'l*, pg. 858
BARAN VIETNAM LTD.—See Baran Group Ltd.; *Int'l*, pg. 858
BARARELAGET KRANCENTER AB—See Peab AB; *Int'l*, pg. 5772
BARARI NATURAL RESOURCES LLC—See Alpha Dhabi Holding PJSC; *Int'l*, pg. 367
BARASTOC STOCKFEEDS PTY. LTD.—See Ridley Corporation Limited; *Int'l*, pg. 6338
BARATZ & ASSOCIATES, PA; *U.S. Private*, pg. 471
BARBADOS BOTTLING CO. LIMITED—See Anheuser-Busch InBev SA/NV; *Int'l*, pg. 464
BARBADOS DAIRY INDUSTRIES LTD.—See Anheuser-Busch InBev SA/NV; *Int'l*, pg. 464
THE BARBADOS LIGHT & POWER COMPANY LIMITED—See Emera, Inc.; *Int'l*, pg. 2377
BARBADOS SHIPPING & TRADING CO. LTD.; *Int'l*, pg. 858
BARBADOS STOCK EXCHANGE INC.; *Int'l*, pg. 858
BARBADOS TOURISM AUTHORITY; *U.S. Private*, pg. 472
BARBARA BUI SA; *Int'l*, pg. 858
BARBARA PERSONNEL INC.; *Int'l*, pg. 858
BARBARAS DEVELOPMENT, INC.; *U.S. Private*, pg. 472

BARCELO ENTERPRISES, INC.

BARBARA THAYER PE ARCH, LANDSCAPE ARCHITECTURE, L S, PC—See PS&S Integrated Services; *U.S. Private*, pg. 3296
THE BARBARIAN GROUP, LLC—See Samsung Group; *Int'l*, pg. 6511
THE BARBARIAN GROUP—See Samsung Group; *Int'l*, pg. 6511
BARBARICUM; *U.S. Private*, pg. 472
BARBAROSSA AND SONS INC.; *U.S. Private*, pg. 472
BARBARY INSURANCE BROKERAGE—See Heffernan Insurance Brokers; *U.S. Private*, pg. 1904
BARBA STATHIS S.A.—See Marfin Investment Group Holdings S.A.; *Int'l*, pg. 4691
BARBEAU-HUTCHINGS ADVERTISING, INC.; *U.S. Private*, pg. 472
BARBEE JACKSON INSURANCE COMPANY; *U.S. Private*, pg. 472
BARBELLA CONSTRUCTION SERVICES, LLC; *U.S. Private*, pg. 472
BARBEN ANALYZER TECHNOLOGY, LLC—See AMETEK, Inc.; *U.S. Public*, pg. 118
BARBEQUE-NATION HOSPITALITY LIMITED—See SAYAJI HOTELS LIMITED; *Int'l*, pg. 6603
BARBEQUES GALORE, INC.—See Grand Hall Enterprise Company Ltd.; *Int'l*, pg. 3055
BARBER AUTO SALES INC.; *U.S. Private*, pg. 472
BARBER BROTHERS CONTRACTING COMPANY - ASPHALT PLANT 1—See Barber Brothers Contracting Company; *U.S. Private*, pg. 472
BARBER BROTHERS CONTRACTING COMPANY - ASPHALT PLANT 6—See Barber Brothers Contracting Company; *U.S. Private*, pg. 472
BARBER BROTHERS CONTRACTING COMPANY; *U.S. Private*, pg. 472
BARBER BROTHERS MOTOR COMPANY; *U.S. Private*, pg. 472
BARBER DAIRIES, INC.—See Dean Foods Company; *U.S. Private*, pg. 1183
BARBERET & BLANC S.A.—See H2 Equity Partners B.V.; *Int'l*, pg. 3199
BARBER FINANCIAL GROUP—See Crestview Partners, L.P.; *U.S. Private*, pg. 1098
BARBER FOODS, LLC—See Tyson Foods, Inc.; *U.S. Public*, pg. 2209
BARBER FORD INC.; *U.S. Private*, pg. 472
BARBER GLASS RETAIL; *Int'l*, pg. 858
BARBERINO BROTHERS, INC.; *U.S. Private*, pg. 472
BARBER MARTIN & ASSOCIATES; *U.S. Private*, pg. 472
BARBER MONUMENTS LTD.—See Family Memorials Inc.; *Int'l*, pg. 2612
BARBER-NICHOLS INC.—See Graham Corporation; *U.S. Public*, pg. 954
BARBER & ROSS COMPANY INC.; *U.S. Private*, pg. 472
BARBER & ROSS MILLWORK COMPANY INC.—See Barber & Ross Company Inc.; *U.S. Private*, pg. 472
BARBER & SONS INVESTMENT CO. INC.; *U.S. Private*, pg. 472
BARBER STEEL FOUNDRY CORP.—See Westinghouse Air Brake Technologies Corporation; *U.S. Public*, pg. 2357
BARBERTON HEALTH SYSTEM, LLC—See Community Health Systems, Inc.; *U.S. Public*, pg. 551
BARBE—See Compagnie de Saint-Gobain SA; *Int'l*, pg. 1722
THE BAR BEVERAGE, INC—See Alliance Global Group, Inc.; *Int'l*, pg. 339
BARBICAN CORPORATE MEMBER LIMITED—See Arch Capital Group Ltd.; *Int'l*, pg. 547
BARBICAN GROUP HOLDINGS LTD.—See Arch Capital Group Ltd.; *Int'l*, pg. 547
BARBICAN REINSURANCE COMPANY LIMITED—See Arch Capital Group Ltd.; *Int'l*, pg. 547
BARBIZON LIGHTING COMPANY; *U.S. Private*, pg. 472
BARBON INSURANCE GROUP LIMITED—See The Carlyle Group Inc.; *U.S. Public*, pg. 2045
BARBOT CM MAXILLY—See FAYAT SAS; *Int'l*, pg. 2624
BARBOT CM—See FAYAT SAS; *Int'l*, pg. 2624
BARBOUR CORPORATION; *U.S. Private*, pg. 472
THE BARBOUR GROUP, LLC; *U.S. Private*, pg. 3991
BARBOUR INTERNATIONAL INC.; *U.S. Private*, pg. 472
BARBOUR STOCKWELL INCORPORATED; *U.S. Private*, pg. 472
BARBOUR WELTING CO.—See Barbour Corporation; *U.S. Private*, pg. 472
BARBRI, INC.—See Francisco Partners Management, LP; *U.S. Private*, pg. 1588
BAR/BRI OF MASSACHUSETTS—See Thomson Reuters Corporation; *Int'l*, pg. 7715
BAR/BRI OF WASHINGTON—See Thomson Reuters Corporation; *Int'l*, pg. 7715
BARC DEVELOPMENTAL SERVICES; *U.S. Private*, pg. 472
BARC ELECTRIC COOPERATIVE; *U.S. Private*, pg. 472
BARCELO CONDAL HOTELES, S.A.—See Barcelo Corporacion Empresarial S.A.; *Int'l*, pg. 859
BARCELO CORPORACION EMPRESARIAL S.A.; *Int'l*, pg. 858
BARCELO ENTERPRISES, INC.; *U.S. Private*, pg. 473

BARCELO ENTERPRISES, INC.

BARCELO GESTION HOTELES ITALIA, SRL—See Barcelo Corporacion Empresarial S.A.; *Int'l*, pg. 859
BARCELONA CARTONBOARD, S.A.U.—See Apollo Global Management, Inc.; *U.S. Public*, pg. 159
BARCELONA SONO; *U.S. Private*, pg. 473
BARCELONESA DE METALES, S.A.—See BAMESA Aceros; *Int'l*, pg. 813
BARCELO PYRAMIDS LLC—See Barcelo Corporacion Empresarial S.A.; *Int'l*, pg. 859
BARCELO SWITZERLAND, S.A—See Barcelo Corporacion Empresarial S.A.; *Int'l*, pg. 859
BARCELO TURIZM OTELCILIK LIMITED—See Barcelo Corporacion Empresarial S.A.; *Int'l*, pg. 859
BARCEL S.A. DE C.V.—See Grupo Bimbo, S.A.B. de C.V.; *Int'l*, pg. 3122
BARCHART.COM, INC.; *U.S. Private*, pg. 473
BARCLAYCARD FUNDING PLC—See Barclays PLC; *Int'l*, pg. 859
BARCLAY DAMON, LLP; *U.S. Private*, pg. 473
BARCLAY DEAN, INC.; *U.S. Private*, pg. 473
BARCLAY DOWNS ASSOCIATES, LP—See Ventas, Inc.; *U.S. Public*, pg. 2278
BARCLAY HEDGE, LTD.—See Backstop Solutions Group, LLC; *U.S. Private*, pg. 423
BARCLAY LEASING LIMITED—See Barclays PLC; *Int'l*, pg. 859
BARCLAY & MATHIESON LTD.—See Stemcor Holdings Limited; *Int'l*, pg. 7206
BARCLAY MEADE LTD.—See Gattaca plc; *Int'l*, pg. 2890
BARCLAY OPERATING CORP.—See InterContinental Hotels Group PLC; *Int'l*, pg. 3737
BARCLAYS ALDERSGATE INVESTMENTS LIMITED—See Barclays PLC; *Int'l*, pg. 859
BARCLAYS ALMA MATER GENERAL PARTNER LIMITED—See Barclays PLC; *Int'l*, pg. 859
BARCLAYS ASIA LIMITED—See Barclays PLC; *Int'l*, pg. 859
BARCLAYS ASSET FINANCE—See Barclays PLC; *Int'l*, pg. 859
BARCLAYS BANK IRELAND PLC—See Barclays PLC; *Int'l*, pg. 859
BARCLAYS BANK - MAURITIUS—See Barclays PLC; *Int'l*, pg. 859
BARCLAYS BANK MEXICO, S.A.—See Barclays PLC; *Int'l*, pg. 860
BARCLAYS BANK OF BOTSWANA LTD.—See Barclays PLC; *Int'l*, pg. 860
BARCLAYS BANK OF GHANA LTD.—See Barclays PLC; *Int'l*, pg. 860
BARCLAYS BANK OF KENYA LTD.—See Barclays PLC; *Int'l*, pg. 860
BARCLAYS BANK OF UGANDA LTD.—See Barclays PLC; *Int'l*, pg. 860
BARCLAYS BANK OF ZAMBIA LTD.—See Barclays PLC; *Int'l*, pg. 860
BARCLAYS BANK PLC—See Barclays PLC; *Int'l*, pg. 859
BARCLAYS BANK PLC - WEALTH & INVESTMENT MANAGEMENT DIVISION—See Barclays PLC; *Int'l*, pg. 860
BARCLAYS BANK (SEYCHELLES) LTD.—See Barclays PLC; *Int'l*, pg. 859
BARCLAYS BANK—See Barclays PLC; *Int'l*, pg. 859
BARCLAYS BANK—See Barclays PLC; *Int'l*, pg. 859
BARCLAYS BANK—See Barclays PLC; *Int'l*, pg. 859
BARCLAYS BANK—See Barclays PLC; *Int'l*, pg. 859
BARCLAYS BANK—See Barclays PLC; *Int'l*, pg. 859
BARCLAYS BANK—See Barclays PLC; *Int'l*, pg. 859
BARCLAYS BANK—See Barclays PLC; *Int'l*, pg. 859
BARCLAYS BANK (SOUTH EAST ASIA) NOMINEES PRIVATE LIMITED—See Barclays PLC; *Int'l*, pg. 859
BARCLAYS BANK TANZANIA LTD.—See Barclays PLC; *Int'l*, pg. 860
BARCLAYS CAPITAL ASIA LIMITED—See Barclays PLC; *Int'l*, pg. 860
BARCLAYS CAPITAL CANADA INC—See Barclays PLC; *Int'l*, pg. 860
BARCLAYS CAPITAL CHARITABLE TRUST—See Barclays PLC; *Int'l*, pg. 860
BARCLAYS CAPITAL ENERGY INC.—See Barclays PLC; *Int'l*, pg. 860
BARCLAYS CAPITAL FINANCE LIMITED—See Barclays PLC; *Int'l*, pg. 860
BARCLAYS CAPITAL GLOBAL SERVICES SINGAPORE PTE. LIMITED—See Barclays PLC; *Int'l*, pg. 861
BARCLAYS CAPITAL INC.—See Barclays PLC; *Int'l*, pg. 860
BARCLAYS CAPITAL JAPAN LIMITED—See Barclays PLC; *Int'l*, pg. 860
BARCLAYS CAPITAL LUXEMBOURG S.A R.L.—See Barclays PLC; *Int'l*, pg. 861
BARCLAYS CAPITAL MARGIN FINANCING LIMITED—See Barclays PLC; *Int'l*, pg. 861
BARCLAYS CAPITAL MARKETS MALAYSIA SDN BHD.—See Barclays PLC; *Int'l*, pg. 861
BARCLAYS CAPITAL PRINCIPAL INVESTMENTS LIMITED—See Barclays PLC; *Int'l*, pg. 861
BARCLAYS CAPITAL SECURITIES LIMITED—See Barclays PLC; *Int'l*, pg. 860
BARCLAYS CAPITAL SERVICES LIMITED—See Barclays PLC; *Int'l*, pg. 861
BARCLAYS CAPITAL—See Barclays PLC; *Int'l*, pg. 860
BARCLAYS CAPITAL—See Barclays PLC; *Int'l*, pg. 860
BARCLAYS CAPITAL STRATEGIC ADVISERS LIMITED—See Barclays PLC; *Int'l*, pg. 861
BARCLAYS CCP FUNDING LLP—See Barclays PLC; *Int'l*, pg. 860
BARCLAYS CENTER—See Onexim Group Limited; *Int'l*, pg. 5581
BARCLAYS COMMERCIAL MORTGAGE SECURITIES LLC—See Barclays PLC; *Int'l*, pg. 860
BARCLAYS CONVERTED INVESTMENTS (NO.2) LIMITED—See Barclays PLC; *Int'l*, pg. 861
BARCLAYS COVERED BOND FUNDING LLP—See Barclays PLC; *Int'l*, pg. 861
BARCLAYS COVERED BONDS LIMITED LIABILITY PARTNERSHIP—See Barclays PLC; *Int'l*, pg. 861
BARCLAYS DARNAY EURO INVESTMENTS LIMITED—See Barclays PLC; *Int'l*, pg. 861
BARCLAYS DIRECTORS LIMITED—See Barclays PLC; *Int'l*, pg. 861
BARCLAYS DIVERSIFICATION SA.—See Barclays PLC; *Int'l*, pg. 861
BARCLAYS DRYROCK ISSUANCE TRUST; *U.S. Private*, pg. 473
BARCLAYS FAMILY S.P.A—See Barclays PLC; *Int'l*, pg. 861
BARCLAYS FIDUCIARY SERVICES (UK) LIMITED—See Barclays PLC; *Int'l*, pg. 861
BARCLAYS FINANCE EUROPE LIMITED—See Barclays PLC; *Int'l*, pg. 861
BARCLAYS FINANCIAL PLANNING LTD—See Barclays PLC; *Int'l*, pg. 861
BARCLAYS FINANCIAL SERVICES ITALIA S.P.A.—See Barclays PLC; *Int'l*, pg. 861
BARCLAYS FINANCIAL SERVICES LIMITED—See Barclays PLC; *Int'l*, pg. 861
BARCLAYS FRANCE SA—See Barclays PLC; *Int'l*, pg. 861
BARCLAYS FUNDS INVESTMENTS LIMITED—See Barclays PLC; *Int'l*, pg. 861
BARCLAYS FUNDS LTD.—See Barclays PLC; *Int'l*, pg. 861
BARCLAYS GBP FUNDING LIMITED—See Barclays PLC; *Int'l*, pg. 861
BARCLAYS GLOBAL INVESTORS CANADA LTD.—See Barclays PLC; *Int'l*, pg. 860
BARCLAYS GLOBAL INVESTORS LIMITED—See Barclays PLC; *Int'l*, pg. 860
BARCLAYS GROUP HOLDINGS LIMITED—See Barclays PLC; *Int'l*, pg. 861
BARCLAYS GROUP PROPERTY SERVICES—See Barclays PLC; *Int'l*, pg. 860
BARCLAYSHARE NOMINEES LIMITED—See Barclays PLC; *Int'l*, pg. 862
BARCLAYS HOLDINGS (ISLE OF MAN) LIMITED—See Barclays PLC; *Int'l*, pg. 861
BARCLAYS HOME FINANCE—See Barclays PLC; *Int'l*, pg. 860
BARCLAYS INFRASTRUCTURE FUNDS MANAGEMENT LIMITED—See 3i Group plc; *Int'l*, pg. 8
BARCLAYS INSURANCE SERVICES CO. LTD.—See Barclays PLC; *Int'l*, pg. 860
BARCLAYS INTERNATIONAL FUND MANAGERS LIMITED—See Barclays PLC; *Int'l*, pg. 861
BARCLAYS INVESTMENTS & LOANS (INDIA) LIMITED—See Barclays PLC; *Int'l*, pg. 860
BARCLAYS LEASING (NO.9) LIMITED—See Barclays PLC; *Int'l*, pg. 861
BARCLAYS LONG ISLAND LIMITED—See Barclays PLC; *Int'l*, pg. 861
BARCLAYS MARLIST LIMITED—See Barclays PLC; *Int'l*, pg. 861
BARCLAYS MERCANTILE BUSINESS FINANCE LIMITED—See Barclays PLC; *Int'l*, pg. 861
BARCLAYS MERCANTILE LIMITED—See Barclays PLC; *Int'l*, pg. 861
BARCLAYS METALS LIMITED—See Barclays PLC; *Int'l*, pg. 861
BARCLAYS PATRIMOINE S.C.S.—See Barclays PLC; *Int'l*, pg. 861
BARCLAYS PHYSICAL TRADING LIMITED—See Barclays PLC; *Int'l*, pg. 861
BARCLAYS PLC; *Int'l*, pg. 859
BARCLAYS PRIVATE BANKING SERVICES LIMITED—See Barclays PLC; *Int'l*, pg. 861
BARCLAYS PRIVATE BANK LTD—See Barclays PLC; *Int'l*, pg. 861
BARCLAYS PRIVATE BANK & TRUST COMPANY—See Barclays PLC; *Int'l*, pg. 860
BARCLAYS PRIVATE BANK & TRUST (ISLE OF MAN) LIMITED—See Barclays PLC; *Int'l*, pg. 861
BARCLAYS PRIVATE BANK & TRUST LTD.—See Barclays PLC; *Int'l*, pg. 860
BARCLAYS PRIVATE TRUST LIMITED—See Barclays PLC; *Int'l*, pg. 861
BARCLAYS SECURED FUNDING (LM) LIMITED—See Barclays PLC; *Int'l*, pg. 861
BARCLAYS SECURED NOTES FINANCE LLP—See Barclays PLC; *Int'l*, pg. 861
BARCLAYS SECURITIES (INDIA) PRIVATE LIMITED—See Barclays PLC; *Int'l*, pg. 860
BARCLAYS (SECURITY REALISATION) LIMITED—See Barclays PLC; *Int'l*, pg. 859
BARCLAYS SERVICES LLC—See Barclays PLC; *Int'l*, pg. 860
BARCLAYS SHAREDEALING LIMITED—See Barclays PLC; *Int'l*, pg. 861
BARCLAYS SHARED SERVICES PRIVATE LIMITED—See Barclays PLC; *Int'l*, pg. 860
BARCLAYS STOCKBROKERS LTD.—See Barclays PLC; *Int'l*, pg. 860
BARCLAYS UNQUOTED INVESTMENTS LIMITED—See Barclays PLC; *Int'l*, pg. 861
BARCLAYS UNQUOTED PROPERTY INVESTMENTS LIMITED—See Barclays PLC; *Int'l*, pg. 861
BARCLAYS VENTURE NOMINEES LIMITED—See Barclays PLC; *Int'l*, pg. 860
BARCLAYS VIE SA—See Barclays PLC; *Int'l*, pg. 861
BARCLAYS WEALTH ASSET MANAGEMENT (MONACO) S.A.M.—See Barclays PLC; *Int'l*, pg. 861
BARCLAYS WEALTH CORPORATE SERVICES (GUERNSEY) LIMITED—See Barclays PLC; *Int'l*, pg. 861
BARCLAYS WEALTH MANAGERS FRANCE SA—See Barclays PLC; *Int'l*, pg. 861
BARCLAYS WEALTH NOMINEES (JERSEY) LIMITED—See Barclays PLC; *Int'l*, pg. 861
BARCLAYS WEALTH NOMINEES LIMITED—See Barclays PLC; *Int'l*, pg. 861
BARCLAYS WEALTH TRUSTEES (GUERNSEY) LIMITED—See Barclays PLC; *Int'l*, pg. 861
BARCLAYS WEALTH TRUSTEES (HONG KONG) LIMITED—See Barclays PLC; *Int'l*, pg. 861
BARCLAYS WEALTH TRUSTEES (INDIA) PRIVATE LIMITED—See Barclays PLC; *Int'l*, pg. 862
BARCLAYS ZIMBABWE NOMINEES (PVT) LIMITED—See Barclays PLC; *Int'l*, pg. 862
BARCLAYTRUST CHANNEL ISLANDS LIMITED—See Barclays PLC; *Int'l*, pg. 862
BARCLAYTRUST INTERNATIONAL (JERSEY) LIMITED—See Barclays PLC; *Int'l*, pg. 862
BARCLAYTRUST (SUISSE) SA—See Barclays PLC; *Int'l*, pg. 862
BARCLAY WATER MANAGEMENT, INC.—See Ecolab Inc.; *U.S. Public*, pg. 712
BARCO COLOMBIA SAS—See Barco N.V.; *Int'l*, pg. 863
BARCO CO., LTD.—See Barco N.V.; *Int'l*, pg. 863
BARCO CONTROL ROOMS—See Barco N.V.; *Int'l*, pg. 863
BARCO COORDINATION CENTER NV—See Barco N.V.; *Int'l*, pg. 863
BAR CODE DIRECT, INC.—See Sole Source Capital LLC; *U.S. Private*, pg. 3708
BARCODES, INC.—See Odyssey Investment Partners, LLC; *U.S. Private*, pg. 2994
BARCODING, INC.—See The Graham Group, Inc.; *U.S. Private*, pg. 4036
BARCO ELECTRONIC SYSTEMS LTD.—See Barco N.V.; *Int'l*, pg. 863
BARCO ELECTRONIC SYSTEMS S.A.—See Barco N.V.; *Int'l*, pg. 863
BARCO ELEKTRONIK SISTEMLERI SAN.TIC. A.S—See Barco N.V.; *Int'l*, pg. 863
BARCO FEDERAL SYSTEMS LLC—See Barco N.V.; *Int'l*, pg. 864
BARCO FREDRIKSTAD AS—See Barco N.V.; *Int'l*, pg. 863
BARCO GMBH—See Barco N.V.; *Int'l*, pg. 863
BARCO, INC.—See Barco N.V.; *Int'l*, pg. 864
BARCOL-AIR B.V.—See SIG plc; *Int'l*, pg. 6906
BARCOL-AIR FRANCE S.A.S.—See Investment AB Latour; *Int'l*, pg. 3780
BARCOL- AIR GROUP AG—See Investment AB Latour; *Int'l*, pg. 3780
BARCOL-AIR ITALIA S.R.L.—See Investment AB Latour; *Int'l*, pg. 3780
BARCOL-AIR PRODUCTION GMBH—See Investment AB Latour; *Int'l*, pg. 3780
BARCO LTDA.—See Barco N.V.; *Int'l*, pg. 863
BARCO LTD.—See Barco N.V.; *Int'l*, pg. 863
BARCO LTD.—See Barco N.V.; *Int'l*, pg. 863
BARCO LTD.—See Barco N.V.; *Int'l*, pg. 863
BARCO LTD.—See Barco N.V.; *Int'l*, pg. 863
BARCO LTD.—See Barco N.V.; *Int'l*, pg. 863
BARCO MANUFACTURING S.R.O.—See Barco N.V.; *Int'l*, pg. 863
BARCO MATERIALS HANDLING LTD.; *Int'l*, pg. 863
BARCOM COMMERCIAL INC.; *U.S. Private*, pg. 473
BARCO N.V.; *Int'l*, pg. 863
BARCO PTE. LTD.—See Barco N.V.; *Int'l*, pg. 863
BARCO S.A.—See Barco N.V.; *Int'l*, pg. 863
BARCO SAS—See Barco N.V.; *Int'l*, pg. 863
BARCOS CO., LTD.; *Int'l*, pg. 864
BARCO SDN BHD—See Barco N.V.; *Int'l*, pg. 863
BARCO SERVICES OOO—See Barco N.V.; *Int'l*, pg. 863
BARCO SILEX N.V.—See Barco N.V.; *Int'l*, pg. 863
BARCO SILEX SAS—See Barco N.V.; *Int'l*, pg. 863
BARCO SIMULATIONS—See Barco N.V.; *Int'l*, pg. 864

COMPANY NAME INDEX

BARCO SINGAPORE PRIVATE LIMITED—See Barco N.V.; *Int'l*, pg. 863
BARCO SP. Z O.O.—See Barco N.V.; *Int'l*, pg. 863
BARCO S.R.L.—See Barco N.V.; *Int'l*, pg. 863
BARCO STAMPING CO; *U.S. Private*, pg. 473
BARCO SVERIGE AB—See Barco N.V.; *Int'l*, pg. 863
BARCO SYSTEMS PTY LTD—See Barco N.V.; *Int'l*, pg. 863
BARCO TRADING (SHANGHAI) CO., LTD.—See Barco N.V.; *Int'l*, pg. 863
BARCO UNIFORMS, INC.; *U.S. Private*, pg. 473
BARCOVIEW AVIONICS—See Barco N.V.; *Int'l*, pg. 864
BARCOVIEW TEXEN SAS—See Barco N.V.; *Int'l*, pg. 864
BARCO VISUAL (BEIJING) ELECTRONICS CO., LTD.—See Barco N.V.; *Int'l*, pg. 863
BARCO VISUAL (BEIJING) TRADING CO., LTD.—See Barco N.V.; *Int'l*, pg. 863
BARCO VISUAL SOLUTIONS, INC.—See Barco N.V.; *Int'l*, pg. 864
BARCO VISUAL SOLUTIONS, LLC—See Barco N.V.; *Int'l*, pg. 864
BARCO VISUAL SOLUTIONS S.A. DE C.V.—See Barco N.V.; *Int'l*, pg. 864
BARCREST GROUP LTD.—See Light & Wonder, Inc.; *U.S. Public*, pg. 1314
BARD ACCESS SYSTEMS, INC.—See Becton, Dickinson & Company; *U.S. Public*, pg. 290
BARDAHL MANUFACTURING CORPORATION - BARDAHL EUROPE DIVISION—See Bardahl Manufacturing Corporation; *U.S. Private*, pg. 474
BARDAHL MANUFACTURING CORPORATION; *U.S. Private*, pg. 473
BARD BENELUX N.V.—See Becton, Dickinson & Company; *U.S. Public*, pg. 290
BARD CANADA INC.—See Becton, Dickinson & Company; *U.S. Public*, pg. 290
BARD CAPITAL GROUP, LLC—See Bard & Company, Inc.; *U.S. Private*, pg. 473
BARD COLOMBIA S.A.S.—See Becton, Dickinson & Company; *U.S. Public*, pg. 290
BARD & COMPANY, INC.; *U.S. Private*, pg. 473
BARD CZECH REPUBLIC S.R.O.—See Becton, Dickinson & Company; *U.S. Public*, pg. 290
BARD DEVICES, INC.—See Becton, Dickinson & Company; *U.S. Public*, pg. 290
BARDELLA S.A. INDUSTRIAS MECANICAS; *Int'l*, pg. 864
BARDEN COMPANIES, INC.; *U.S. Private*, pg. 474
THE BARDEN CORPORATION (UK) LTD.—See INA-Holding Schaeffler GmbH & Co. KG; *Int'l*, pg. 3641
THE BARDEN CORP.—See INA-Holding Schaeffler GmbH & Co. KG; *Int'l*, pg. 3641
BARDEN DEVELOPMENT, INC.—See Barden Companies, Inc.; *U.S. Private*, pg. 474
BARDEN MISSISSIPPI GAMING, LLC—See Majestic Star Casino & Hotel; *U.S. Private*, pg. 2554
THE BARDEN & ROBESON CORPORATION; *U.S. Private*, pg. 3992
BARD FRANCE S.A.S.—See Becton, Dickinson & Company; *U.S. Public*, pg. 290
BARD HELLAS S.A.—See Becton, Dickinson & Company; *U.S. Public*, pg. 290
BARD HOLDING, INC.; *U.S. Private*, pg. 473
BARD HOLDINGS NETHERLANDS BV—See Becton, Dickinson & Company; *U.S. Public*, pg. 290
BARD INDIA HEALTHCARE PVT. LTD.—See Becton, Dickinson & Company; *U.S. Public*, pg. 291
BARD KOREA LIMITED—See Becton, Dickinson & Company; *U.S. Public*, pg. 291
BARD LIMITED—See Becton, Dickinson & Company; *U.S. Public*, pg. 291
BARD MANUFACTURING COMPANY; *U.S. Private*, pg. 473
BARD MEDICAL DIVISION—See Becton, Dickinson & Company; *U.S. Public*, pg. 291
BARD MEDICA S.A.—See Becton, Dickinson & Company; *U.S. Public*, pg. 291
BARDOC GOLD PTY LTD—See St Barbara Limited; *Int'l*, pg. 7157
BARDONS & OLIVER, INC.; *U.S. Private*, pg. 474
BARDON SUPPLIES LIMITED—See Groupe Deschenes Inc.; *Int'l*, pg. 3101
BARDOT PTY. LTD.; *Int'l*, pg. 864
BARD PACIFIC HEALTH CARE COMPANY LTD.—See Becton, Dickinson & Company; *U.S. Public*, pg. 291
BARD PERIPHERAL VASCULAR, INC.—See Becton, Dickinson & Company; *U.S. Public*, pg. 291
BARD POLAND SP. Z.O.O.—See Becton, Dickinson & Company; *U.S. Public*, pg. 291
BARD, RAO + ATHANAS CONSULTING ENGINEERS, LLC - NEW YORK—See Bard, Rao + Athanas Consulting Engineers, LLC; *U.S. Private*, pg. 473
BARD, RAO + ATHANAS CONSULTING ENGINEERS, LLC; *U.S. Private*, pg. 473
BARD SINGAPORE PRIVATE LIMITED—See Becton, Dickinson & Company; *U.S. Public*, pg. 291
BARDSTOWN BOURBON COMPANY, LLC—See The Pritzker Group - Chicago, LLC; *U.S. Private*, pg. 4098

BARD SWEDEN AB—See Becton, Dickinson & Company; *U.S. Public*, pg. 291
BARDWIL INDUSTRIES INC.; *U.S. Private*, pg. 474
BARE BOARD GROUP, INC.—See NCAB Group AB; *Int'l*, pg. 5180
BARE BONES SOFTWARE, INC.; *U.S. Private*, pg. 474
BARED AND SONS INC.; *U.S. Private*, pg. 474
BARE FEET ENTERPRISES, INC.; *U.S. Private*, pg. 474
BAREFOOT BOOKS, INC.; *U.S. Private*, pg. 474
BAREFOOT & COMPANY, LLC—See Builders FirstSource, Inc.; *U.S. Public*, pg. 410
BAREFOOT LODGE & HIKER HOSTEL, LLC—See Barefoot Luxury, Inc.; *U.S. Private*, pg. 474
BAREFOOT LUXURY, INC.; *U.S. Private*, pg. 474
BARE FRUIT LLC; *U.S. Private*, pg. 474
BARE INTERNATIONAL, INC.; *U.S. Private*, pg. 474
BAREKET CAPITAL LTD.; *Int'l*, pg. 864
BAREMAN DAIRY INC.; *U.S. Private*, pg. 474
BARENBRUG BELGIUM NV/SA—See Barenbrug Holding B.V.; *Int'l*, pg. 864
BARENBRUG CHINA R.O.—See Barenbrug Holding B.V.; *Int'l*, pg. 864
BARENBRUG FRANCE S.A.—See Barenbrug Holding B.V.; *Int'l*, pg. 864
BARENBRUG HOLDING B.V.; *Int'l*, pg. 864
BARENBRUG HOLLAND B.V.—See Barenbrug Holding B.V.; *Int'l*, pg. 864
BARENBRUG LUXEMBOURG S.A.—See Barenbrug Holding B.V.; *Int'l*, pg. 864
BARENBRUG POLSKA SP. Z.O.O.—See Barenbrug Holding B.V.; *Int'l*, pg. 864
BARENBRUG RESEARCH USA—See Barenbrug Holding B.V.; *Int'l*, pg. 864
BARENBRUG RESEARCH WOLFHEZE—See Barenbrug Holding B.V.; *Int'l*, pg. 864
BARENBRUG U.K. LTD.—See Barenbrug Holding B.V.; *Int'l*, pg. 864
BARENBRUG USA—See Barenbrug Holding B.V.; *Int'l*, pg. 864
BARENTZ APS—See Cinven Limited; *Int'l*, pg. 1611
BARENTZ ASIA PACIFIC PTE. LTD.—See Cinven Limited; *Int'l*, pg. 1611
BARENTZ B.V.—See Cinven Limited; *Int'l*, pg. 1611
BARENTZ D.O.O.—See Cinven Limited; *Int'l*, pg. 1611
BARENTZ GIDA VE KIMYA TIC. LTD. STI.—See Cinven Limited; *Int'l*, pg. 1611
BARENTZ HUNGARY KFT.—See Cinven Limited; *Int'l*, pg. 1611
BARENTZ INTERNATIONAL B.V.—See Cinven Limited; *Int'l*, pg. 1611
BARENTZ IRELAND LIMITED—See Cinven Limited; *Int'l*, pg. 1611
BARENTZ N.V.—See Cinven Limited; *Int'l*, pg. 1611
BARENTZ (ROMANIA) S.R.L.—See Cinven Limited; *Int'l*, pg. 1611
BARENTZ-SANDER AG—See Cinven Limited; *Int'l*, pg. 1611
BARENTZ SARL—See Cinven Limited; *Int'l*, pg. 1611
BARENTZ SPOL. S.R.O.—See Cinven Limited; *Int'l*, pg. 1611
BARENTZ SPOL. S.R.O.—See Cinven Limited; *Int'l*, pg. 1611
BARENTZ UA LLC—See Cinven Limited; *Int'l*, pg. 1611
BARFIELD, INC.—See Air France-KLM S.A.; *Int'l*, pg. 236
BARFRESH FOOD GROUP INC.; *U.S. Public*, pg. 275
THE BARGAIN BARN INC.—See Gen Cap America, Inc.; *U.S. Private*, pg. 1660
BARGAIN RENT-A-CAR—See AutoNation, Inc.; *U.S. Public*, pg. 233
THE BARGAIN! SHOP HOLDINGS INC.; *Int'l*, pg. 7620
BARGAIN SUPPLY COMPANY; *U.S. Private*, pg. 474
BARGERBURGER INC.; *U.S. Private*, pg. 474
BARGER PACKAGING-IN—See Welch Packaging Group, Inc.; *U.S. Private*, pg. 4473
BARGE WAGGONER SUMNER & CANNON INC.; *U.S. Private*, pg. 474
BAR GMBH—See Watts Water Technologies, Inc.; *U.S. Public*, pg. 2337
BARGREEN-ELLINGSON INC.; *U.S. Private*, pg. 474
BAR HARBOR BANKSHARES; *U.S. Public*, pg. 275
BAR HARBOR BANK & TRUST—See Bar Harbor Bankshares; *U.S. Public*, pg. 275
BAR HARBOR FOODS; *U.S. Private*, pg. 471
BAR HARBOR LOBSTER COMPANY, INC.; *U.S. Private*, pg. 471
BAR HARBOR TRUST SERVICES—See Bar Harbor Bankshares; *U.S. Public*, pg. 275
BARHORST INSURANCE GROUP; *U.S. Private*, pg. 474
BA RIA - VUNG TAU HOUSE DEVELOPMENT JOINT STOCK COMPANY; *Int'l*, pg. 791
BARIBEAU IMPLEMENT COMPANY; *U.S. Private*, pg. 474
BARI COSMETICS LTD; *U.S. Private*, pg. 474
BARIDI BARIDI TANZANIA LTD.—See Daikin Industries, Ltd.; *Int'l*, pg. 1932
BARI-JAY FASHIONS INC.; *U.S. Private*, pg. 474
BARIL CORPORATION—See Clearlake Capital Group, L.P.; *U.S. Private*, pg. 937

BARINGS PRIVATE CREDIT CORPORATION

BARILGA CORPORATION JOINT STOCK COMPANY; *Int'l*, pg. 864
BARILLA AMERICA, INC.—See Barilla Holding S.p.A.; *Int'l*, pg. 865
BARILLA AMERICA N.Y. INC.—See Barilla Holding S.p.A.; *Int'l*, pg. 865
BARILLA AUSTRALIA PTY LTD—See Barilla Holding S.p.A.; *Int'l*, pg. 865
BARILLA AUSTRIA GMBH—See Barilla Holding S.p.A.; *Int'l*, pg. 865
BARILLA CANADA INC.—See Barilla Holding S.p.A.; *Int'l*, pg. 865
BARILLA DANMARK A/S—See Barilla Holding S.p.A.; *Int'l*, pg. 865
BARILLA DEUTSCHLAND GMBH—See Barilla Holding S.p.A.; *Int'l*, pg. 865
BARILLA DO BRASIL LTDA—See Barilla Holding S.p.A.; *Int'l*, pg. 865
BARILLA ESPANA S.L.—See Barilla Holding S.p.A.; *Int'l*, pg. 865
BARILLA FRANCE SAS—See Barilla Holding S.p.A.; *Int'l*, pg. 865
BARILLA GIDA A.S.—See Barilla Holding S.p.A.; *Int'l*, pg. 865
BARILLA HELLAS S.A.—See Barilla Holding S.p.A.; *Int'l*, pg. 865
BARILLA HOLDING S.P.A.; *Int'l*, pg. 865
BARILLA JAPAN K.K.—See Barilla Holding S.p.A.; *Int'l*, pg. 865
BARILLA NETHERLANDS B.V.—See Barilla Holding S.p.A.; *Int'l*, pg. 865
BARILLA NORGE AS—See Barilla Holding S.p.A.; *Int'l*, pg. 865
BARILLA POLAND SP. Z.O.O.—See Barilla Holding S.p.A.; *Int'l*, pg. 865
BARILLA SINGAPORE PTE LTD—See Barilla Holding S.p.A.; *Int'l*, pg. 865
BARILLA SVERIGE AB—See Barilla Holding S.p.A.; *Int'l*, pg. 865
BARILLA SWITZERLAND A.G.—See Barilla Holding S.p.A.; *Int'l*, pg. 865
BARILOCHE TV S.A—See Grupo Clarin S.A.; *Int'l*, pg. 3124
BARINAS ENTERPRISES COMPANY LTD—See Lundin Mining Corporation; *Int'l*, pg. 4583
BAR INDUSTRIESERVICE GMBH—See Bilfinger SE; *Int'l*, pg. 1024
BARING ASSET MANAGEMENT (ASIA) LIMITED—See Massachusetts Mutual Life Insurance Company; *U.S. Private*, pg. 2604
BARING ASSET MANAGEMENT GMBH—See Massachusetts Mutual Life Insurance Company; *U.S. Private*, pg. 2604
BARING ASSET MANAGEMENT (JAPAN) LIMITED—See Massachusetts Mutual Life Insurance Company; *U.S. Private*, pg. 2604
BARING ASSET MANAGEMENT KOREA LIMITED—See Massachusetts Mutual Life Insurance Company; *U.S. Private*, pg. 2604
BARING ASSET MANAGEMENT LTD.—See Massachusetts Mutual Life Insurance Company; *U.S. Private*, pg. 2604
BARING FRANCE SAS—See Massachusetts Mutual Life Insurance Company; *U.S. Private*, pg. 2604
BARING INDUSTRIES, INC.—See Duray/J.F. Duncan Industries, Inc.; *U.S. Private*, pg. 1293
BARING NORTH AMERICA LLC - SAN FRANCISCO OFFICE—See Massachusetts Mutual Life Insurance Company; *U.S. Private*, pg. 2605
BARING NORTH AMERICA LLC—See Massachusetts Mutual Life Insurance Company; *U.S. Private*, pg. 2605
BARING PRIVATE EQUITY ASIA K.K.—See Affiliated Managers Group, Inc.; *U.S. Public*, pg. 54
BARING PRIVATE EQUITY ASIA PTE LIMITED—See Affiliated Managers Group, Inc.; *U.S. Public*, pg. 54
BARINGS BDC, INC.; *U.S. Public*, pg. 276
BARINGS CAPITAL INVESTMENT CORPORATION; *U.S. Private*, pg. 475
BARINGS CORE SPAIN SOCIMI, S.A.; *Int'l*, pg. 865
BARINGS CORPORATE INVESTORS—See Massachusetts Mutual Life Insurance Company; *U.S. Private*, pg. 2605
BARINGS EMERGING EMEA OPPORTUNITIES PLC—See Massachusetts Mutual Life Insurance Company; *U.S. Private*, pg. 2604
BARINGS GLOBAL SHORT DURATION HIGH YIELD FUND—See Massachusetts Mutual Life Insurance Company; *U.S. Private*, pg. 2605
BARING SICE (TAIWAN) LTD—See Massachusetts Mutual Life Insurance Company; *U.S. Private*, pg. 2604
BARINGS LLC—See Massachusetts Mutual Life Insurance Company; *U.S. Private*, pg. 2604
BARINGS PARTICIPATION INVESTORS—See Massachusetts Mutual Life Insurance Company; *U.S. Private*, pg. 2605
BARINGS PRIVATE CREDIT CORPORATION; *U.S. Private*, pg. 475

BARINGS REAL ESTATE ADVISERS LLC—See Massachusetts Mutual Life Insurance Company; *U.S. Private*, pg. 2605
BARINGTON CAPITAL GROUP, L.P.; *U.S. Private*, pg. 475
BARINGTON/HILCO ACQUISITION CORP.; *U.S. Private*, pg. 475
BARING VOSTOK CAPITAL PARTNERS; *Int'l*, pg. 865
BARINTHUS BIOTHERAPEUTICS PLC; *Int'l*, pg. 865
BARISTAS COFFEE COMPANY, INC.; *U.S. Public*, pg. 276
BARISTA SOFTWARE BVBA—See CompuGroup Medical SE & Co. KGaA; *Int'l*, pg. 1755
BARITA INVESTMENTS LIMITED; *Int'l*, pg. 865
BARITS DEVELOPMENT CORPORATION—See Pou Chen Corporation; *Int'l*, pg. 5941
BARKAWI HOLDING GMBH; *Int'l*, pg. 865
BARKAWI MANAGEMENT CONSULTANTS GMBH & CO. KG—See Genpact Limited; *Int'l*, pg. 2926
BARKAWI MANAGEMENT CONSULTANTS GMBH—See Barkawi Holding GmbH; *Int'l*, pg. 865
BARKAWI MANAGEMENT CONSULTANTS, LLC—See Genpact Limited; *Int'l*, pg. 2926
BARKAWI MANAGEMENT CONSULTING (SHANGHAI) CO., LTD.—See Barkawi Holding GmbH; *Int'l*, pg. 865
BARKBOX, INC.—See BARK, Inc.; *U.S. Public*, pg. 276
BARKELL LIMITED—See Modine Manufacturing Company; *U.S. Public*, pg. 1455
BARKER ADVERTISING SPECIALTY COMPANY; *U.S. Private*, pg. 475
BARKER AIR & HYDRAULICS INC.; *U.S. Private*, pg. 475
BARKER/DZP; *U.S. Private*, pg. 475
BARKERGILMORE; *U.S. Private*, pg. 475
BARKER MANUFACTURING CO; *U.S. Private*, pg. 475
BARKER MCCORMAC, OGILVY & MATHER—See WPP plc; *Int'l*, pg. 8484
BARKER MINERALS LTD.; *Int'l*, pg. 865
BARKERS ENGINEERING LTD—See Hill & Smith PLC; *Int'l*, pg. 3391
BARKER STEEL MID-ATLANTIC LLC—See Nucor Corporation; *U.S. Public*, pg. 1553
BARKERVILLE GOLD MINES LTD.—See Osisko Gold Royalties Ltd.; *Int'l*, pg. 5651
BARKEY CORPORATION—See Azenta, Inc.; *U.S. Public*, pg. 257
BARKEY GMBH & CO. KG—See Azenta, Inc.; *U.S. Public*, pg. 257
BARK, INC.; *U.S. Public*, pg. 276
BARKING APPLICATIONS CORPORATION; *Int'l*, pg. 865
THE BARKING DOG, LTD.; *U.S. Private*, pg. 3992
BARKLEY CENTER—See Formation Capital, LLC; *U.S. Private*, pg. 1569
BARKLEY HOLDING COMPANY, INC.; *U.S. Private*, pg. 475
BARKLEY REI—See Barkley; *U.S. Private*, pg. 475
BARKLEY SEED INC.; *U.S. Private*, pg. 475
BARKLEY; *U.S. Private*, pg. 475
BARKLEY—See Barkley; *U.S. Private*, pg. 475
BARKLY INVESTMENTS LTD.—See Deutsche Bank Aktiengesellschaft; *Int'l*, pg. 2055
BARKMAN CONCRETE LTD.; *Int'l*, pg. 865
BARKMAN HONEY, LLC; *U.S. Private*, pg. 475
BARKMAN OIL CO. INC.; *U.S. Private*, pg. 475
BARKO HYDRAULICS LLC—See The Heico Companies, L.L.C.; *U.S. Private*, pg. 4050
BARKSDALE FEDERAL CREDIT UNION; *U.S. Private*, pg. 475
BARKSDALE GMBH—See Crane NXT, Co.; *U.S. Public*, pg. 589
BARKSDALE, INC.—See Crane NXT, Co.; *U.S. Public*, pg. 589
BARKSDALE RESOURCES CORP.; *Int'l*, pg. 865
BARLAGE GMBH; *Int'l*, pg. 866
BARLETTA BOAT COMPANY, LLC—See Winnebago Industries, Inc.; *U.S. Public*, pg. 2374
BARLETTA MATERIALS & CONSTRUCTION; *U.S. Private*, pg. 476
BARLEYCORN'S; *U.S. Private*, pg. 476
BARLEY SNYDER LLC; *U.S. Private*, pg. 476
BARLINEK S.A.; *Int'l*, pg. 866
BARLO PLASTICS CO. INC.; *U.S. Private*, pg. 476
BARLOVENTO, LLC; *U.S. Private*, pg. 476
BARLOW CHEVROLET; *U.S. Private*, pg. 476
BARLOW EDDY JENKINS PA—See Eley Guild Hardy Architects, PA; *U.S. Private*, pg. 1358
BARLOWORLD AUSTRALIA (PTY) LIMITED—See WFM Motors Pty Ltd.; *Int'l*, pg. 8394
BARLOWORLD AUTOMOTIVE (PTY) LIMITED—See Barloworld Ltd.; *Int'l*, pg. 866
BARLOWORLD EQUIPMENT MARTEX—See Barloworld Ltd.; *Int'l*, pg. 866
BARLOWORLD EQUIPMENT (PTY) LIMITED—See Barloworld Ltd.; *Int'l*, pg. 866
BARLOWORLD EQUIPMENT - SOUTHERN AFRICA—See Barloworld Ltd.; *Int'l*, pg. 866
BARLOWORLD EQUIPMENT UK LIMITED—See Barloworld Ltd.; *Int'l*, pg. 866
BARLOWORLD FINANZAUTO—See Barloworld Ltd.; *Int'l*, pg. 866

BARLOWORLD HOLDINGS PLC—See Barloworld Ltd.; *Int'l*, pg. 866
BARLOWORLD INFORMATION SYSTEMS (PTY) LIMITED—See Barloworld Ltd.; *Int'l*, pg. 866
BARLOWORLD LOGISTICS (PTY) LIMITED—See Barloworld Ltd.; *Int'l*, pg. 866
BARLOWORLD LTD.; *Int'l*, pg. 866
BARLOWORLD MERA SA—See Barloworld Ltd.; *Int'l*, pg. 866
BARLOWORLD NETHERLANDS—See Barloworld Ltd.; *Int'l*, pg. 866
BARLOWORLD PLASCON (PTY) LTD.—See Barloworld Ltd.; *Int'l*, pg. 866
BARLOWORLD SIYAKHULA (PTY) LIMITED—See Barloworld Ltd.; *Int'l*, pg. 866
BARLOWORLD SOUTH AFRICA (PTY) LIMITED—See Barloworld Ltd.; *Int'l*, pg. 866
BARMAC (CONSTRUCTION) LIMITED—See Barclays PLC; *Int'l*, pg. 862
BARMAG CZECH REPUBLIC S.R.O.—See OC Oerlikon Corporation AG; *Int'l*, pg. 5514
BARMAG LIEGENSCHAFTEN GMBH & CO. KG—See OC Oerlikon Corporation AG; *Int'l*, pg. 5514
BARMAKIAN JEWELERS; *U.S. Private*, pg. 476
BARMER ENTERPRISES LLC; *U.S. Private*, pg. 476
BAR METHOD INC.—See Self Esteem Brands LLC; *U.S. Private*, pg. 3602
BARMINCO LIMITED—See Perenti Global Limited; *Int'l*, pg. 5798
BARNABAS FOUNDATION; *U.S. Private*, pg. 476
BARNABAS HEALTH, INC.; *U.S. Private*, pg. 476
BARNABAS HEALTH MEDICAL GROUP; *U.S. Private*, pg. 476
BARNA & COMPANY; *U.S. Private*, pg. 476
BARNARD CONSTRUCTION CO. INC.; *U.S. Private*, pg. 477
BARNA STEEL SA—See Celsa Group; *Int'l*, pg. 1395
BARNES AEROSPACE - EAST GRANBY—See Barnes Group Inc.; *U.S. Public*, pg. 276
BARNES AEROSPACE - LANSING—See Barnes Group Inc.; *U.S. Public*, pg. 276
BARNES AEROSPACE—See Barnes Group Inc.; *U.S. Public*, pg. 276
BARNES-BAKER MOTORS INC.; *U.S. Private*, pg. 477
BARNES BULLETS, LLC—See Sierra Bullets LLC; *U.S. Private*, pg. 3646
BARNES, CATMUR & FRIENDS LIMITED—See Dentsu Group Inc.; *Int'l*, pg. 2034
BARNES DE COLOMBIA S.A.—See Corporacion EG S.A.; *Int'l*, pg. 1803
BARNES DISTRIBUTION (CANADA) LTD.—See MSC Industrial Direct Co., Inc.; *U.S. Public*, pg. 1483
BARNES DISTRIBUTION NORTH AMERICA—See MSC Industrial Direct Co., Inc.; *U.S. Public*, pg. 1483
BARNES DISTRIBUTION—See MSC Industrial Direct Co., Inc.; *U.S. Public*, pg. 1483
BARNES GROUP INC.; *U.S. Public*, pg. 276
BARNES GROUP SPAIN SRL—See Barnes Group Inc.; *U.S. Public*, pg. 277
BARNES GROUP (U.K.) LIMITED—See Barnes Group Inc.; *U.S. Public*, pg. 277
BARNES HEALTHCARE SERVICES; *U.S. Private*, pg. 477
BARNES INSURANCE & FINANCIAL SERVICES—See Genstar Capital, LLC; *U.S. Private*, pg. 1674
BARNES INTERNATIONAL, INC.—See Komline-Sanderson Corporation; *U.S. Private*, pg. 2342
BARNES INTERNATIONAL SRL—See Komline-Sanderson Corporation; *U.S. Private*, pg. 2342
BARNES-KASSON HOSPITAL; *U.S. Private*, pg. 477
BARNES KOREA LTD.—See Barnes Group Inc.; *U.S. Public*, pg. 277
BARNESMCINERNEY INC.; *Int'l*, pg. 866
BARNES & NOBLE BOOKSELLERS, INC.—See Elliott Management Corporation; *U.S. Private*, pg. 1364
BARNES & NOBLE COLLEGE BOOKSELLERS, LLC—See Barnes & Noble Education, Inc.; *U.S. Public*, pg. 276
BARNES & NOBLE EDUCATION, INC.; *U.S. Public*, pg. 276
BARNES & NOBLE, INC.—See Elliott Management Corporation; *U.S. Private*, pg. 1364
BARNES NURSERY, INC.; *U.S. Private*, pg. 477
BARNES PAPER COMPANY INCORPORATED; *U.S. Private*, pg. 477
BARNES QUALITY PEST CONTROL, INC.—See Senske Lawn & Tree Care, Inc.; *U.S. Private*, pg. 3608
BARNES & THORNBURG LP; *U.S. Private*, pg. 477
BARNESVILLE HOSPITAL; *U.S. Private*, pg. 477
BARNETT CHRYSLER JEEP KIA; *U.S. Private*, pg. 477
BARNETT COX & ASSOCIATES—See Armanino LLP; *U.S. Private*, pg. 330
BARNETT, DEMROW & ERNST, INC—See Carriage Services, Inc.; *U.S. Public*, pg. 439
BARNETT HARLEY-DAVIDSON; *U.S. Private*, pg. 477
BARNETT IMPLEMENT CO; *U.S. Private*, pg. 477
BARNETT MILLWORKS, INC.; *U.S. Private*, pg. 477
BARNETT & MURPHY, INC; *U.S. Private*, pg. 477

BARNEY ABSTRACT & TITLE CO.—See Nebraska Title Company; *U.S. Private*, pg. 2879
BARNEY & BARNEY, INC.—See Marsh & McLennan Companies, Inc.; *U.S. Public*, pg. 1380
BARNEYS JAPAN CO., LTD.—See Seven & i Holdings Co., Ltd.; *Int'l*, pg. 6730
BARNEYS PUMPS INC.; *U.S. Private*, pg. 477
BARN FURNITURE MART, INC.; *U.S. Private*, pg. 476
BARNHARDT CUSHION-HICKORY PLANT—See Barnhardt Manufacturing Company; *U.S. Private*, pg. 478
BARNHARDT, DAY & HINES; *U.S. Private*, pg. 477
BARNHARDT MANUFACTURING COMPANY; *U.S. Private*, pg. 477
BARNHART CRANE & RIGGING CO.; *U.S. Private*, pg. 478
BARNHART INDUSTRIES, INC.; *U.S. Private*, pg. 478
BARNHART-REESE CONSTRUCTION INC.; *U.S. Private*, pg. 478
BARNHART; *U.S. Private*, pg. 478
BARNHILL CONTRACTING COMPANY; *U.S. Private*, pg. 478
BARNIER ET FILS; *Int'l*, pg. 866
BARNIE'S COFFEE & TEA COMPANY; *U.S. Private*, pg. 478
BARNMASTER INC.; *U.S. Private*, pg. 478
BAR NONE, INC.; *U.S. Private*, pg. 471
BARNSCO FLEET MAINTENANCE, INC.—See Kodiak Building Partners LLC; *U.S. Private*, pg. 2336
BARNSCO INC.—See Kodiak Building Partners LLC; *U.S. Private*, pg. 2336
BARNSCO—See Georgeoo Inc.; *U.S. Private*, pg. 1684
BARNWELL GEOTHERMAL CORPORATION—See Barnwell Industries, Inc.; *U.S. Public*, pg. 278
BARNWELL HAWAIIAN PROPERTIES, INC.—See Barnwell Industries, Inc.; *U.S. Public*, pg. 278
BARNWELL HOUSE OF TIRES INC.; *U.S. Private*, pg. 478
BARNWELL INDUSTRIES, INC.; *U.S. Public*, pg. 278
BARNWELL KONA CORPORATION—See Barnwell Industries, Inc.; *U.S. Public*, pg. 278
BARNWELL MANAGEMENT CO., INC.—See Barnwell Industries, Inc.; *U.S. Public*, pg. 278
BARNWELL OF CANADA LIMITED—See Barnwell Industries, Inc.; *U.S. Public*, pg. 278
BARNWELL OVERSEAS, INC.—See Barnwell Industries, Inc.; *U.S. Public*, pg. 278
BARNWELL SHALLOW OIL, INC.—See Barnwell Industries, Inc.; *U.S. Public*, pg. 278
BARO COMPANIES—See Applied Industrial Technologies, Inc.; *U.S. Public*, pg. 171
BARODA ASSET MANAGEMENT INDIA LTD—See Bank of Baroda; *Int'l*, pg. 840
BARODA EXTRUSION LIMITED; *Int'l*, pg. 866
BARODA GLOBAL SHARED SERVICES LTD.—See Bank of Baroda; *Int'l*, pg. 840
BARODA RAYON CORP LTD.; *Int'l*, pg. 866
BAROID DRILLING FLUIDS DIVISION—See Halliburton Company; *U.S. Public*, pg. 980
BARO LAGERHAUS GMBH & CO. KG—See AGRAVIS Raiffeisen AG; *Int'l*, pg. 215
BAROLIN & SPENCER, INC.; *U.S. Private*, pg. 478
BARON ALI SPA—See Ali Holding S.r.l; *Int'l*, pg. 320
BARONA VALLEY RANCH RESORT & CASINO; *U.S. Private*, pg. 478
BARON BMW—See Group 1 Automotive, Inc.; *U.S. Public*, pg. 970
BARON BROS, INC.; *U.S. Private*, pg. 478
BARON CAPITAL GROUP, INC.; *U.S. Private*, pg. 478
BARON DE LEY, S.A.; *Int'l*, pg. 866
BARON + DOWDLE CONSTRUCTION, LLC.; *U.S. Private*, pg. 478
BARON DRAWN STEEL CORP.—See The Renco Group Inc.; *U.S. Private*, pg. 4104
BARON ENERGY, INC.; *U.S. Public*, pg. 278
BARON GLOBAL FINANCIAL CANADA LTD.—See Hatcher Group Ltd.; *Int'l*, pg. 3284
BARON GROUP LLC; *U.S. Private*, pg. 478
BARONIE CHOCOLATES BELGIUM NV—See Sweet Products Logistics NV; *Int'l*, pg. 7366
BARONIE - DE HEER B.V.—See Sweet Products Logistics NV; *Int'l*, pg. 7366
BARON INDUSTRIES, INC.—See Alta Equipment Group Inc.; *U.S. Public*, pg. 86
BARON INFOTECH LIMITED; *Int'l*, pg. 867
BARON INSULATION PTY LTD—See Fletcher Building Limited; *Int'l*, pg. 2700
BARON LRMS LIMITED—See Heritage Group Ltd.; *Int'l*, pg. 3361
BARON METAL INDUSTRIES INC.—See ASSA ABLOY AB; *Int'l*, pg. 639
BARON MINI—See Group 1 Automotive, Inc.; *U.S. Public*, pg. 970
BARON PARTNERS LIMITED; *Int'l*, pg. 867
BARON SALAZAR & ASSOCIATES—See McCormack Baron Salazar, Inc.; *U.S. Private*, pg. 2630
BARONS AUTOMOTIVE LIMITED—See Group 1 Automotive, Inc.; *U.S. Public*, pg. 970
BARONS AUTOSTAR LIMITED—See Group 1 Automotive, Inc.; *U.S. Public*, pg. 970

COMPANY NAME INDEX

BARONSMEAD SECOND VENTURE TRUST PLC; *Int'l*, pg. 867
BARONSMEAD VENTURE TRUST PLC; *Int'l*, pg. 867
BARONS MOTOR INN—See Northampton Group Inc.; *Int'l*, pg. 5441
BAROQUE JAPAN LIMITED; *Int'l*, pg. 867
BAROQUE (S.W.) LIMITED—See Rollins, Inc.; *U.S. Public*, pg. 1809
BAROUH EATON (CANADA) LTD.—See Ko-Rec-Type Corp.; *U.S. Private*, pg. 2325
BAROYECA GOLD & SILVER INC.; *Int'l*, pg. 867
BAR PACIFIC GROUP HOLDINGS LIMITED; *Int'l*, pg. 857
BARPAX ASSOCIATES LIMITED—See Brown & Brown, Inc.; *U.S. Public*, pg. 397
BARPLAS LIMITED—See Berry Global Group, Inc; *U.S. Public*, pg. 322
BAR PNEUMATISCHE STEUERUNGSSYSTEME GMBH—See Watts Water Technologies, Inc.; *U.S. Public*, pg. 2337
BAR PROCCESSING CORP.; *U.S. Private*, pg. 471
BAR PROCESSING - WICKLIFFE—See Bar Proccessing Corp.; *U.S. Private*, pg. 471
BARRA & ASSOCIATES LLC—See Reliance Global Group, Inc.; *U.S. Public*, pg. 1778
BARRACHD LTD.; *Int'l*, pg. 867
BARRACK MINES PTY. LTD.—See Grange Resources Limited; *Int'l*, pg. 3058
BARRACK'S CATER INN BANQUET CENTER & CATERING; *U.S. Private*, pg. 479
BARRACLOUGH & ASSOCIATES, PC—See Carr, Riggs & Ingram, LLC; *U.S. Private*, pg. 771
BARRACONSULT, LTDA.—See MSCI Inc.; *U.S. Public*, pg. 1483
BARRACUDA LIMITED—See Santos Limited; *Int'l*, pg. 6559
BARRACUDA MSP—See KKR & Co. Inc.; *U.S. Public*, pg. 1241
BARRACUDA MUSIC GMBH—See CTS Eventim AG & Co. KGAA; *Int'l*, pg. 1872
BARRACUDA NETWORKS AG—See KKR & Co. Inc.; *U.S. Public*, pg. 1241
BARRACUDA NETWORKS (HONG KONG) LIMITED—See KKR & Co. Inc.; *U.S. Public*, pg. 1241
BARRACUDA NETWORKS, INC.—See KKR & Co. Inc.; *U.S. Public*, pg. 1241
BARRACUDA NETWORKS (INDIA) PRIVATE LIMITED—See KKR & Co. Inc.; *U.S. Public*, pg. 1241
BARRACUDA NETWORKS JAPAN, K.K.—See KKR & Co. Inc.; *U.S. Public*, pg. 1241
BARRACUDA NETWORKS, LIMITED—See KKR & Co. Inc.; *U.S. Public*, pg. 1241
BARRACUDA NETWORKS SINGAPORE PTE LTD.—See KKR & Co. Inc.; *U.S. Public*, pg. 1241
BARRACUDA NETWORKS TECHNOLOGY CO. LTD.—See KKR & Co. Inc.; *U.S. Public*, pg. 1241
BARRA DO PEIXE MONTAGENS E SERVICOS, LTDA.—See ACS, Actividades de Construccion y Servicios, S.A.; *Int'l*, pg. 110
BARR AIR PATROL, LLC; *U.S. Private*, pg. 479
BARRA JAPAN K.K.—See MSCI Inc.; *U.S. Public*, pg. 1483
BARRA, LLC—See MSCI Inc.; *U.S. Public*, pg. 1483
BARRAMUNDI GROUP LTD.; *Int'l*, pg. 867
BARRAMUNDI LIMITED; *Int'l*, pg. 867
BARRANCA DIAMOND PRODUCTS, INC.—See MK Diamond Products, Inc.; *U.S. Private*, pg. 2753
BARRANCA SURGERY CENTER, LLC—See UnitedHealth Group Incorporated; *U.S. Public*, pg. 2239
BARRATT ASSET MANAGEMENT, LLC; *U.S. Private*, pg. 479
BARRATT BRISTOL LIMITED—See Barratt Developments PLC; *Int'l*, pg. 868
BARRATT CENTRAL LIMITED—See Barratt Developments PLC; *Int'l*, pg. 867
BARRATT CHESTER LIMITED—See Barratt Developments PLC; *Int'l*, pg. 867
BARRATT COMMERCIAL LTD.—See Barratt Developments PLC; *Int'l*, pg. 867
BARRATT CONSTRUCTION LTD.—See Barratt Developments PLC; *Int'l*, pg. 867
BARRATT DEVELOPMENTS PLC; *Int'l*, pg. 867
BARRATT EAST ANGLIA LIMITED—See Barratt Developments PLC; *Int'l*, pg. 868
BARRATT EASTERN COUNTIES LIMITED—See Barratt Developments PLC; *Int'l*, pg. 867
BARRATT EAST MIDLANDS LIMITED—See Barratt Developments PLC; *Int'l*, pg. 867
BARRATT EAST SCOTLAND LIMITED—See Barratt Developments PLC; *Int'l*, pg. 867
BARRATT EXETER—See Barratt Developments PLC; *Int'l*, pg. 868
BARRATT HOMES MERCIA—See Barratt Developments PLC; *Int'l*, pg. 867
BARRATT LONDON LIMITED—See Barratt Developments PLC; *Int'l*, pg. 867
BARRATT MANCHESTER LIMITED—See Barratt Developments PLC; *Int'l*, pg. 867
BARRATT NORTHAMPTON LIMITED—See Barratt Developments PLC; *Int'l*, pg. 868

BARRATT NORTHERN LIMITED—See Barratt Developments PLC; *Int'l*, pg. 868
BARRATT SHEFFIELD—See Barratt Developments PLC; *Int'l*, pg. 867
BARRATT SOUTHAMPTON—See Barratt Developments PLC; *Int'l*, pg. 868
BARRATT SOUTHERN COUNTIES LIMITED—See Barratt Developments PLC; *Int'l*, pg. 868
BARRATT SOUTHERN LIMITED—See Barratt Developments PLC; *Int'l*, pg. 868
BARRATT SOUTH WALES LIMITED—See Barratt Developments PLC; *Int'l*, pg. 868
BARRATT SOUTH WEST LIMITED—See Barratt Developments PLC; *Int'l*, pg. 868
BARRATTS TRADING LIMITED; *Int'l*, pg. 868
BARRATT WEST MIDLANDS LIMITED—See Barratt Developments PLC; *Int'l*, pg. 867
BARRATT WEST SCOTLAND LIMITED—See Barratt Developments PLC; *Int'l*, pg. 868
BARRATT WEST—See Barratt Developments PLC; *Int'l*, pg. 868
BARRATT YORK LIMITED—See Barratt Developments PLC; *Int'l*, pg. 868
BARRAULT; *Int'l*, pg. 868
BARR & BARR, INC.; *U.S. Private*, pg. 479
BARR BROTHERS & CO., INC.; *U.S. Private*, pg. 479
BARR CREDIT SERVICES, INC.; *U.S. Private*, pg. 479
BARRDAY COMPOSITE SOLUTIONS—See Barrday, Inc.; *Int'l*, pg. 869
BARRDAY, INC.; *Int'l*, pg. 868
BARR DO IT BEST LUMBER—See Barr Lumber Co. Inc.; *U.S. Private*, pg. 479
BARREL ACCESSORIES & SUPPLY COMPANY, INC.; *U.S. Private*, pg. 479
BARREL CO., LTD.; *Int'l*, pg. 869
BARREL ENERGY, INC.; *U.S. Public*, pg. 278
BARRELHOUSE CREATIVE—See Yaffe Group; *U.S. Private*, pg. 4584
BARREL O'FUN SNACK FOODS CO.—See KLN Enterprises Inc.; *U.S. Private*, pg. 2320
BARRE LOGISTIQUE SERVICES; *Int'l*, pg. 869
BARRELS UNLIMITED, INC.—See Tonnellerie Francois Freres; *Int'l*, pg. 7810
BARRENETXE S. COOP—See Mondragon Corporation; *Int'l*, pg. 6028
BARR ENGINEERING COMPANY, ANN ARBOR—See Barr Engineering Company; *U.S. Private*, pg. 479
BARR ENGINEERING COMPANY, DULUTH—See Barr Engineering Company; *U.S. Private*, pg. 479
BARR ENGINEERING COMPANY, HIBBING—See Barr Engineering Company; *U.S. Private*, pg. 479
BARR ENGINEERING COMPANY, JEFFERSON CITY—See Barr Engineering Company; *U.S. Private*, pg. 479
BARR ENGINEERING COMPANY; *U.S. Private*, pg. 479
BARREN RIDGE PHYSICAL THERAPY, LIMITED PARTNERSHIP—See U.S. Physical Therapy, Inc.; *U.S. Public*, pg. 2214
BARRETT ASSET MANAGEMENT, LLC—See CI Financial Corporation; *Int'l*, pg. 1600
BARRETT BURSTON MALTING CO. PTY. LTD.—See GrainCorp Limited; *Int'l*, pg. 3052
BARRETT BURSTON MALTING CO. WA PTY. LIMITED—See GrainCorp Limited; *Int'l*, pg. 3052
BARRETT BUSINESS SERVICES, INC.; *U.S. Public*, pg. 278
BARRETT BUSINESS SERVICES—See Barrett Business Services, Inc.; *U.S. Public*, pg. 278
BARRETT CHEVROLET, INC.; *U.S. Private*, pg. 479
BARRETT CORPORATION; *Int'l*, pg. 869
BARRETT DISTRIBUTION CENTERS, INC.; *U.S. Private*, pg. 479
BARRETTE OUTDOOR LIVING, INC.—See CRH plc; *Int'l*, pg. 1845
BARRETT FIREARMS MANUFACTURING, INC.—See NIOA Nominees Pty. Limited; *Int'l*, pg. 5309
BARRETT GRILLO GROUP, INC.; *U.S. Private*, pg. 479
BARRETT HOLDING COMPANY INC.; *U.S. Private*, pg. 479
BARRETT INC.; *U.S. Private*, pg. 479
BARRETT INDUSTRIAL SUPPLY COMPANY; *U.S. Private*, pg. 479
BARRETT INDUSTRIES, INC.; *U.S. Private*, pg. 480
BARRETT-JACKSON AUCTION COMPANY LLC; *U.S. Private*, pg. 480
BARRETT MOTOR CARS; *U.S. Private*, pg. 480
BARRETTS OF BALLINASLOE LIMITED—See Grafton Group plc; *Int'l*, pg. 3050
BARRETT STEEL LIMITED; *Int'l*, pg. 869
BARRETT TUBES DIVISION—See Barrett Steel Limited; *Int'l*, pg. 869
BARRETT TURBINE ENGINE COMPANY—See BlackRock, Inc.; *U.S. Public*, pg. 346
BARRETT TURBINE ENGINE COMPANY—See Blackstone Inc.; *U.S. Public*, pg. 358
BARRETT TURBINE ENGINE COMPANY—See Cascade Investment LLC; *U.S. Private*, pg. 780
BARRHEAD TRAVEL SERVICE LIMITED—See Travel Leaders Group, LLC; *U.S. Private*, pg. 4213

BARRON COLLIER COMPANY, LTD.

BARRICK CHILE LTDA.—See Barrick Gold Corporation; *Int'l*, pg. 869
BARRICK CORTEZ INC.—See Barrick Gold Corporation; *Int'l*, pg. 869
BARRICK ENTERPRISES INC.—See USPP-Tri Lakes, LLC; *U.S. Private*, pg. 4323
BARRICK GOLD AUSTRALIA LIMITED—See Barrick Gold Corporation; *Int'l*, pg. 869
BARRICK GOLD CORP. - DOYON MINE—See Barrick Gold Corporation; *Int'l*, pg. 869
BARRICK GOLD CORPORATION; *Int'l*, pg. 869
BARRICK GOLD EXPLORATION INC.—See Barrick Gold Corporation; *Int'l*, pg. 869
BARRICK GOLD FINANCE COMPANY—See Barrick Gold Corporation; *Int'l*, pg. 869
BARRICK GOLD OF NORTH AMERICA, INC.—See Barrick Gold Corporation; *Int'l*, pg. 869
BARRICK GOLDSTRIKE MINES, INC.—See Barrick Gold Corporation; *Int'l*, pg. 869
BARRICK GOLD U.S. INC.—See Barrick Gold Corporation; *Int'l*, pg. 869
BARRICK (GSM) LTD.—See Barrick Gold Corporation; *Int'l*, pg. 869
BARRICK INTERNATIONAL (BARBADOS) CORP.—See Barrick Gold Corporation; *Int'l*, pg. 869
BARRICK MINING COMPANY (AUSTRALIA) LIMITED—See Barrick Gold Corporation; *Int'l*, pg. 869
BARRICK (NIUGINI) LIMITED—See Barrick Gold Corporation; *Int'l*, pg. 869
BARRICK (PD) AUSTRALIA LIMITED—See Barrick Gold Corporation; *Int'l*, pg. 869
BARRICK (PLUTONIC) LIMITED—See Barrick Gold Corporation; *Int'l*, pg. 869
BARRIE CHRYSLER DODGE JEEP RAM LTD.; *Int'l*, pg. 870
BARRIE & HIBBERT LTD.—See Moody's Corporation; *U.S. Public*, pg. 1466
BARRIE HOUSE COFFEE CO. INC.; *U.S. Private*, pg. 480
BARRIE KNITWEAR LTD.—See Chanel S.A.; *Int'l*, pg. 1441
BARRIER CORP.—See Paul J. Krez Company; *U.S. Private*, pg. 3113
BARRIERE CONSTRUCTION CO. LLC; *U.S. Private*, pg. 480
BARRIERE FRERES S.A.—See Suntory Holdings Limited; *Int'l*, pg. 7326
BARRIER FREE ACCESS, INC.—See SFM Mutual Insurance Company; *U.S. Private*, pg. 3621
BARRIER ISLAND STATION INC.; *U.S. Private*, pg. 480
BARRIERMED GLOVE CO. INC.—See Barriermed Inc.; *U.S. Private*, pg. 480
BARRIERMED INC.; *U.S. Private*, pg. 480
BARRIER MOTOR FUELS INC.; *U.S. Private*, pg. 480
BARRIERSAFE SOLUTIONS INTERNATIONAL INC.—See Ansell Limited; *Int'l*, pg. 478
BARRIER TECHNOLOGY CORP.; *U.S. Private*, pg. 480
BARRINGTON BANK & TRUST COMPANY, N.A.—See Wintrust Financial Corporation; *U.S. Public*, pg. 2374
BARRINGTON CARPETS INC.—See Argand Partners, LP; *U.S. Private*, pg. 319
BARRINGTON CHEMICAL CORP.; *U.S. Private*, pg. 480
BARRINGTON DEVELOPMENT CORP.; *U.S. Private*, pg. 480
BARRINGTON GROUP LTD.; *U.S. Private*, pg. 480
BARRINGTON STOKE LIMITED—See News Corporation; *U.S. Public*, pg. 1518
BARR INTERNATIONAL INC.; *U.S. Private*, pg. 479
BARRIOS DISTRIBUTING; *U.S. Private*, pg. 480
BARRIOS TECHNOLOGY LTD.; *U.S. Private*, pg. 480
BARRIQUAND S.A.S—See VINCI S.A.; *Int'l*, pg. 8212
BARRIQUAND TECHNOLOGIES THERMIQUES SAS - ASET PRODUCTION FACILITY—See Groupe SFPI SA; *Int'l*, pg. 3111
BARRIQUAND TECHNOLOGIES THERMIQUES SAS—See Groupe SFPI SA; *Int'l*, pg. 3111
BARRISTER EXECUTIVE SUITES; *U.S. Private*, pg. 480
BARRISTER GLOBAL SERVICES NETWORK, INC.; *U.S. Private*, pg. 480
BARRISTER REPORTING SERVICE, INC.—See Apax Partners LLP; *Int'l*, pg. 503
BARRISTERS' REPORTING SERVICE, INC.—See Aptus Court Reporting, LLC; *U.S. Private*, pg. 302
BARR LUMBER CO. INC.; *U.S. Private*, pg. 479
BARR-NUNN ENTERPRISES LTD. - OHIO ORIENTATION FACILITY—See Barr-Nunn Enterprises Ltd.; *U.S. Private*, pg. 479
BARR-NUNN ENTERPRISES LTD.; *U.S. Private*, pg. 479
BARR-NUNN LOGISTICS, INC.—See Barr-Nunn Enterprises Ltd.; *U.S. Private*, pg. 479
BARR-NUNN TRANSPORTATION, INC.—See Knight-Swift Transportation Holdings Inc.; *U.S. Public*, pg. 1269
BARRO GROUP PTY LTD; *Int'l*, pg. 870
BARRON BUILDERS & MANAGEMENT COMPANY INC.; *U.S. Private*, pg. 480
BARRON COLLIER COMPANY, LTD.; *U.S. Private*, pg. 480
BARRON COLLIER CORPORATION—See Barron Collier Company, Ltd.; *U.S. Private*, pg. 480

BARRON HEATING & AIR CONDITIONING INC. — CORPORATE AFFILIATIONS

BARRON HEATING & AIR CONDITIONING INC.; *U.S. Private*, pg. 480
BARRON MOTOR INC.; *U.S. Private*, pg. 480
BARRON PRECISION INSTRUMENTS, LLC—See GTCR LLC; *U.S. Private*, pg. 1804
BARRON'S EDUCATIONAL SERIES, INC.; *U.S. Private*, pg. 481
BARRONS ENTERPRISES, INC.—See Bain Capital, LP; *U.S. Private*, pg. 450
BARRON'S—See News Corporation; *U.S. Public*, pg. 1518
BARROW FINE FURNITURE INC.; *U.S. Private*, pg. 481
BARROWGATE LIMITED—See Hysan Development Company Limited; *Int'l*, pg. 3554
BARROW, HANLEY, MEWHINNEY & STRAUSS, LLC—See Perpetual Limited; *Int'l*, pg. 5812
BARROW INDUSTRIES INCORPORATED; *U.S. Private*, pg. 481
BARROW PROPANE GAS—See Ferrellgas Partners, L.P.; *U.S. Public*, pg. 829
BARROWS COAL CO. INC.; *U.S. Private*, pg. 481
&BARR; *U.S. Private*, pg. 1
BARR + WRAY FZE—See Barr + Wray Limited; *Int'l*, pg. 867
BARR + WRAY (H.K.) LIMITED—See Barr + Wray Limited; *Int'l*, pg. 867
BARR + WRAY LIMITED; *Int'l*, pg. 867
BARRY, BETTE & LED DUKE, INC.; *U.S. Private*, pg. 481
BARRY CALLEBAUT AG—See Jacobs Holding AG; *Int'l*, pg. 3865
BARRY CALLEBAUT CANADA INC.—See Jacobs Holding AG; *Int'l*, pg. 3865
BARRY CALLEBAUT FRANCE SAS—See Jacobs Holding AG; *Int'l*, pg. 3865
BARRY CALLEBAUT UK LTD.—See Jacobs Holding AG; *Int'l*, pg. 3865
BARRY CALLEBAUT USA, LLC—See Jacobs Holding AG; *Int'l*, pg. 3865
BARRY CALLEBAUT USA LLC—See Jacobs Holding AG; *Int'l*, pg. 3865
BARRY CALLEBAUT USA LLC—See Jacobs Holding AG; *Int'l*, pg. 3865
BARRY CONTROLS AEROSPACE—See TotalEnergies SE; *Int'l*, pg. 7837
BARRY CONTROLS AEROSPACE—See TotalEnergies SE; *Int'l*, pg. 7837
BARRY CONTROLS INCORPORATED—See TotalEnergies SE; *Int'l*, pg. 7837
BARRY CULLEN CHEVROLET CADILLAC LTD; *Int'l*, pg. 870
BARRY DANMARK APS—See Fortum Oyj; *Int'l*, pg. 2740
BARRY ELECTRIC COOPERATIVE; *U.S. Private*, pg. 481
BARRY & FITZWILLIAM LTD.; *Int'l*, pg. 870
BARRY ISETT & ASSOCIATES INC.; *U.S. Private*, pg. 481
BARRY PONTIAC-BUICK INC.; *U.S. Private*, pg. 481
BARRYROE OFFSHORE ENERGY PLC; *Int'l*, pg. 870
BARRY SALES ENGINEERING INC.; *U.S. Private*, pg. 481
BARRY SALES INC.; *U.S. Private*, pg. 481
BARRY'S CHEVROLET-BUICK, INC.; *U.S. Private*, pg. 481
BARRY SWENSON BUILDER; *U.S. Private*, pg. 481
BARRY-WEHMILLER COMPANIES, INC.; *U.S. Private*, pg. 481
BARRY-WEHMILLER DESIGN GROUP, INC.—See Barry-Wehmiller Companies, Inc.; *U.S. Private*, pg. 481
BARRY-WEHMILLER DESIGN GROUP—See Barry-Wehmiller Companies, Inc.; *U.S. Private*, pg. 481
BARSCO INC.; *U.S. Private*, pg. 482
BARSEBACK KRAFT AB—See Vattenfall AB; *Int'l*, pg. 8136
BARSELE MINERALS CORP.; *Int'l*, pg. 870
BAR-S FOODS CO.—See ALFA, S.A.B. de C.V.; *Int'l*, pg. 314
BARSON COMPOSITES CORP.; *U.S. Private*, pg. 482
BARSPLICE PRODUCTS, INC.—See F.C. Industries Inc.; *U.S. Private*, pg. 1456
BAR'S PRODUCTS, INC.; *U.S. Private*, pg. 471
BARSTEEL CORP; *U.S. Private*, pg. 482
BARSTOW MOTORS INC.; *U.S. Private*, pg. 482
BART & ASSOCIATES INC.; *U.S. Private*, pg. 482
BARTEC AB—See Charterhouse Capital Partners LLP; *Int'l*, pg. 1455
BARTEC BELGIUM NV/SA—See Charterhouse Capital Partners LLP; *Int'l*, pg. 1455
BARTEC DISPENSING TECHNOLOGY INC.—See MAX Automation SE; *Int'l*, pg. 4734
BARTEC ELEKTROTECHNIK GMBH—See Charterhouse Capital Partners LLP; *Int'l*, pg. 1455
BARTEC ENGINEERING LLC—See Baran Group Ltd.; *Int'l*, pg. 858
BARTEC ENGINEERING + SERVICES AG—See Charterhouse Capital Partners LLP; *Int'l*, pg. 1455
BARTEC GMBH—See Charterhouse Capital Partners LLP; *Int'l*, pg. 1455
THE BARTECH GROUP, INC.—See HFBG Holding B.V.; *Int'l*, pg. 3375
BARTECH SYSTEMS INTERNATIONAL INC.; *U.S. Private*, pg. 482

BARTECH TECHNICAL SERVICES OF CANADA LIMITED—See HFBG Holding B.V.; *Int'l*, pg. 3374
BARTEC HUNGARY KFT.—See Charterhouse Capital Partners LLP; *Int'l*, pg. 1455
BARTEC NEDERLAND B.V.—See Charterhouse Capital Partners LLP; *Int'l*, pg. 1455
BARTEC PIXAVI AS—See Charterhouse Capital Partners LLP; *Int'l*, pg. 1455
BARTEC POLSKA SP. Z O.O.—See Charterhouse Capital Partners LLP; *Int'l*, pg. 1455
BARTEC S.A.R.L.—See Charterhouse Capital Partners LLP; *Int'l*, pg. 1455
BARTEC S.A.—See Charterhouse Capital Partners LLP; *Int'l*, pg. 1455
BARTEC S.R.L.—See Charterhouse Capital Partners LLP; *Int'l*, pg. 1455
BARTEC S.R.O.—See Charterhouse Capital Partners LLP; *Int'l*, pg. 1455
BARTEC TECHNOR AS—See Charterhouse Capital Partners LLP; *Int'l*, pg. 1455
BARTEC TOP HOLDING GMBH—See Charterhouse Capital Partners LLP; *Int'l*, pg. 1455
BARTEC UK LTD.—See Charterhouse Capital Partners LLP; *Int'l*, pg. 1455
BARTEC VARNOST, D.O.O.—See Charterhouse Capital Partners LLP; *Int'l*, pg. 1455
BARTEC VODEC LTD.—See Charterhouse Capital Partners LLP; *Int'l*, pg. 1455
THE BARTELL DRUG COMPANY—See New Rite Aid, LLC; *U.S. Private*, pg. 2906
BARTELS LUTHERAN RETIREMENT COMMUNITY; *U.S. Private*, pg. 482
BARTH & DREYFUSS OF CALIFORNIA INC.—See BDK Holdings, Inc.; *U.S. Private*, pg. 500
BARTHEL CONTRACTING COMPANY; *U.S. Private*, pg. 482
BARTH INDUSTRIES, CO. LP—See NESCO, Inc.; *U.S. Private*, pg. 2886
THE BARTHOLOMEW COMPANY, INC.; *U.S. Private*, pg. 3992
BARTHOLOMEW COUNTY RURAL ELECTRIC MEMBERSHIP CORPORATION; *U.S. Private*, pg. 482
BARTIN RECYCLING GROUP S.A.S.—See Derichebourg S.A.; *Int'l*, pg. 2041
BARTLE BOGLE HEGARTY LIMITED—See Publicis Groupe S.A.; *Int'l*, pg. 6097
BARTLE & GIBSON CO. LTD.; *Int'l*, pg. 870
BARTLETT BEARING COMPANY INC.; *U.S. Private*, pg. 483
BARTLETT BEARING COMPANY INC.—See Bartlett Bearing Company Inc.; *U.S. Private*, pg. 483
BARTLETT BRAINARD EACOTT, INC.; *U.S. Private*, pg. 483
BARTLETT CATTLE COMPANY, L.P.—See Bartlett & Company; *U.S. Private*, pg. 483
BARTLETT COCKE, LP; *U.S. Private*, pg. 483
BARTLETT & CO. LLC; *U.S. Private*, pg. 483
BARTLETT-COLLINS CO., INC.—See EveryWare Global, Inc.; *U.S. Private*, pg. 1441
BARTLETT & COMPANY; *U.S. Private*, pg. 483
BARTLETT GRAIN COMPANY, L.P.—See Bartlett & Company; *U.S. Private*, pg. 483
BARTLETT HOLDINGS, INC.—See Bernhard Capital Partners Management, LP; *U.S. Private*, pg. 537
BARTLETT, INC.—See BHI Energy; *U.S. Private*, pg. 549
BARTLETT MANAGEMENT SERVICES; *U.S. Private*, pg. 483
BARTLETT MILLING COMPANY, L.P.—See Bartlett & Company; *U.S. Private*, pg. 483
BARTLETT MITCHELL LTD.—See Westbury Street Holdings Limited; *Int'l*, pg. 8387
BARTLETT TREE SERVICE—See The F.A. Bartlett Tree Expert Company; *U.S. Private*, pg. 4027
BARTON BUSINESS PARK LIMITED—See Blackstone Inc.; *U.S. Public*, pg. 358
BARTON COTTON—See Moore DM Group, LLC; *U.S. Private*, pg. 2780
BARTON COUNTY ELECTRIC COOPERATIVE INC.; *U.S. Private*, pg. 483
BARTON COUNTY IMPLEMENT CO; *U.S. Private*, pg. 483
BARTON ENTERPRISES INC.; *U.S. Private*, pg. 483
BARTON GILANELLI & ASSOCIATES, INC.; *U.S. Private*, pg. 483
BARTON GOLD HOLDINGS LIMITED; *Int'l*, pg. 870
BARTON MALOW COMPANY—See Barton Malow Enterprises, Inc.; *U.S. Private*, pg. 483
BARTON MALOW COMPANY—See Barton Malow Enterprises, Inc.; *U.S. Private*, pg. 483
BARTON MALOW COMPANY—See Barton Malow Enterprises, Inc.; *U.S. Private*, pg. 483
BARTON MALOW COMPANY—See Barton Malow Enterprises, Inc.; *U.S. Private*, pg. 483
BARTON MALOW COMPANY—See Barton Malow Enterprises, Inc.; *U.S. Private*, pg. 483
BARTON MALOW DESIGN—See Barton Malow Enterprises, Inc.; *U.S. Private*, pg. 483
BARTON MALOW ENTERPRISES, INC.; *U.S. Private*, pg. 483
BARTON MALOW YARD—See Barton Malow Enterprises, Inc.; *U.S. Private*, pg. 483

BARTON MINES COMPANY LLC; *U.S. Private*, pg. 483
BARTON NELSON INC.; *U.S. Private*, pg. 483
BARTON SOLVENTS INC.; *U.S. Private*, pg. 483
BARTON STORAGE SYSTEMS LTD.; *Int'l*, pg. 870
BARTOS INDUSTRIES LLC; *U.S. Private*, pg. 484
BARTOW HMA PHYSICIAN MANAGEMENT, LLC—See Community Health Systems, Inc.; *U.S. Public*, pg. 551
BARTOW REGIONAL MEDICAL CENTER INC.—See BayCare Health System Inc.; *U.S. Private*, pg. 495
BART RICH ENTERPRISES INC.; *U.S. Private*, pg. 482
BARTRONICS INDIA LTD.; *Int'l*, pg. 870
BARTSCHER GMBH; *Int'l*, pg. 870
BARUCH SLS, INC.; *U.S. Private*, pg. 484
BARU GOLD CORP.; *Int'l*, pg. 870
BARUM CONTINENTAL SPOL. S.R.O.—See Continental Aktiengesellschaft; *Int'l*, pg. 1782
BARUN ELECTRONICS CO., LTD.; *Int'l*, pg. 870
BARUNSON CO., LTD.; *Int'l*, pg. 870
BARUNSON ENTERTAINMENT & ARTS CORPORATION; *Int'l*, pg. 870
BARVIC; *Int'l*, pg. 870
BARWA BANK GROUP—See The International Bank of Qatar (Q.S.C); *Int'l*, pg. 7656
BARWA CITY REAL ESTATE COMPANY WLL—See Barwa Real Estate Company Q.P.S.C; *Int'l*, pg. 870
BARWANI PETROLEUM SERVICES LLC—See MB Holding Company LLC; *U.S. Private*, pg. 4750
BARWA REAL ESTATE COMPANY Q.P.S.C.; *Int'l*, pg. 870
BARWIL AGENCIES AS—See Wilh. Wilhelmsen Holding ASA; *Int'l*, pg. 8410
BARYTINE DE CHAILLAC S.A.—See Solvay S.A.; *Int'l*, pg. 7077
BARZ, GOWIE, AMON & FULTZ LLC; *U.S. Private*, pg. 484
BAR-ZIV RAVID INSURANCE AGENCY LIMITED—See Howden Group Holdings Limited; *Int'l*, pg. 3493
BASAK TRAKTOR TARIM ZIRAAT VE IS MAKINALARI SANAYI TICARET A.S.—See ASKO Holding A.S.; *Int'l*, pg. 625
BASALITE CONCRETE PRODUCTS, LLC—See Pacific Coast Building Products, Inc.; *U.S. Private*, pg. 3065
BASALT-ACTIEN-GESELLSCHAFT—See Wilh. Werhahn KG; *Int'l*, pg. 8410
BASALT INFRASTRUCTURE PARTNERS LLC—See Colliers International Group Inc.; *Int'l*, pg. 1700
BASALT INFRASTRUCTURE PARTNERS LLP—See Colliers International Group Inc.; *Int'l*, pg. 1700
BASANITE, INC.; *U.S. Public*, pg. 278
BASANITE INDUSTRIES, LLC—See Basanite, Inc.; *U.S. Public*, pg. 279
BASANT AGRO TECH (INDIA) LTD.; *Int'l*, pg. 871
BASA RESOURCES INC.; *U.S. Private*, pg. 484
BAS BROADCASTING, INC.; *U.S. Private*, pg. 484
BAS BROADCASTING - MOUNT VERNON—See BAS Broadcasting, Inc.; *U.S. Private*, pg. 484
BAS BROADCASTING - SANDUSKY—See BAS Broadcasting, Inc.; *U.S. Private*, pg. 484
BAS BUROSYSTEME GMBH—See HP Inc.; *U.S. Public*, pg. 1062
BAS CASTINGS LIMITED; *Int'l*, pg. 871
BASCOGEL; *Int'l*, pg. 871
BASCO MANUFACTURING COMPANY; *U.S. Private*, pg. 484
BASCOM HUNTER TECHNOLOGIES INC.; *U.S. Private*, pg. 484
BASCOM'S CHOP HOUSE; *U.S. Private*, pg. 484
BASE AEROFOTOGRAMETRIA E PROJETOS S.A—See SECOM Co., Ltd.; *Int'l*, pg. 6671
BASEBALL AMERICA, INC.; *U.S. Private*, pg. 484
THE BASEBALL CLUB OF SEATTLE, L.P.; *U.S. Private*, pg. 3992
BASEBALL FACTORY, INC.—See Ripken Baseball, Inc.; *U.S. Private*, pg. 3439
BASEBALL HEAVEN INC.—See Steel Partners Holdings L.P.; *U.S. Public*, pg. 1942
BASEBALLISM, INC.; *U.S. Private*, pg. 484
BASE BRASIL B.I. CORRETORA DE SEGUROS LTDA.—See Alper Consultoria e Corretora de Seguros S.A.; *Int'l*, pg. 366
BASECLICK GMBH—See BASF SE; *Int'l*, pg. 886
BASE COMMERCE, LLC—See Nuvei Corporation; *Int'l*, pg. 5494
BASE CRAFT LLC; *U.S. Private*, pg. 484
BASE DIGITALE GROUP S.R.L.—See Sesa S.p.A.; *Int'l*, pg. 6728
BASE D'INFORMATIONS LEGALES HOLDING S.A.S.; *Int'l*, pg. 871
BASEELAH MECHANICAL WORKS—See Al-Osais International Holding Company; *Int'l*, pg. 287
BASE ENGINEERING INC.; *U.S. Private*, pg. 484
BASEFARM AB—See Orange S.A.; *Int'l*, pg. 5609
BASEFARM AS—See Orange S.A.; *Int'l*, pg. 5609
BASEFARM BV—See Orange S.A.; *Int'l*, pg. 5609
BASE INTELLIGENCE, INC; *U.S. Private*, pg. 484
BASELINE HEALTHCARE, INC.—See The Ensign Group, Inc.; *U.S. Public*, pg. 2070
BASE-LINE, INC.; *U.S. Private*, pg. 484
BASELINE LLC—See Brookfield Corporation; *Int'l*, pg. 1178

BASELINE LLC—See Elliott Management Corporation; *U.S. Private*, pg. 1370
BASELINE-MOCON, INC.—See AMETEK, Inc.; *U.S. Public*, pg. 120
BASELINE—See Ziff Davis Enterprise, Inc.; *U.S. Private*, pg. 4604
BASELINE SPORTS, INC.; *U.S. Private*, pg. 484
BASELL ADVANCED POLYOLEFINS (SUZHOU) CO. LTD.—See LyondellBasell Industries N.V.; *Int'l*, pg. 4607
BASELL ADVANCED POLYOLEFINS (THAILAND) COMPANY LTD.—See LyondellBasell Industries N.V.; *Int'l*, pg. 4607
BASELLANDSCHAFTLICHE KANTONALBANK; *Int'l*, pg. 871
BASELL ARABIE INVESTISSEMENTS SAS—See LyondellBasell Industries N.V.; *Int'l*, pg. 4607
BASELL ASIA PACIFIC CONSULTING (SHANGHAI) CO., LTD.—See LyondellBasell Industries N.V.; *Int'l*, pg. 4607
BASELL ASIA PACIFIC LTD.—See LyondellBasell Industries N.V.; *Int'l*, pg. 4607
BASELL ASIA PACIFIC LTD.—See LyondellBasell Industries N.V.; *Int'l*, pg. 4607
BASELL BAYREUTH CHEMIE GMBH—See LyondellBasell Industries N.V.; *Int'l*, pg. 4607
BASELL BENELUX B.V.—See LyondellBasell Industries N.V.; *Int'l*, pg. 4607
BASELL BRASIL LTD.—See LyondellBasell Industries N.V.; *Int'l*, pg. 4607
BASELL CHEMIE KOLN GMBH—See LyondellBasell Industries N.V.; *Int'l*, pg. 4607
BASELL HOLDINGS MIDDLE EAST GMBH—See LyondellBasell Industries N.V.; *Int'l*, pg. 4607
BASELL INTERNATIONAL TRADING FZE—See LyondellBasell Industries N.V.; *Int'l*, pg. 4607
BASELL ITALIA S.R.L—See LyondellBasell Industries N.V.; *Int'l*, pg. 4607
BASELL ORLEN POLYOLEFINS SP. Z O.O.—See Orlen S.A.; *Int'l*, pg. 5640
BASELL POLIOLEFINAS COMERCIAL ESPAGNOLA S.L.—See LyondellBasell Industries N.V.; *Int'l*, pg. 4607
BASELL POLIOLEFINAS LTDA.—See LyondellBasell Industries N.V.; *Int'l*, pg. 4607
BASELL POLIOLEFINE ITALIA S.R.L.—See LyondellBasell Industries N.V.; *Int'l*, pg. 4607
BASELL POLYOLEFINE GMBH—See LyondellBasell Industries N.V.; *Int'l*, pg. 4607
BASELL POLYOLEFIN ISTANBUL TICARET LIMITED SIRKETI—See LyondellBasell Industries N.V.; *Int'l*, pg. 4607
BASELL POLYOLEFINS COMPANY BVBA—See LyondellBasell Industries N.V.; *Int'l*, pg. 4607
BASELL POLYOLEFINS INDIA PRIVATE LIMITED—See LyondellBasell Industries N.V.; *Int'l*, pg. 4607
BASELL POLYOLEFINS KOREA LTD.—See LyondellBasell Industries N.V.; *Int'l*, pg. 4607
BASELL POLYOLEFINS—See Shell plc; *Int'l*, pg. 6796
BASELL POLYOLEFINS UK LIMITED—See LyondellBasell Industries N.V.; *Int'l*, pg. 4607
BASELL SALES & MARKETING COMPANY B.V.—See LyondellBasell Industries N.V.; *Int'l*, pg. 4607
BASELL (THAILAND) HOLDINGS B.V.—See LyondellBasell Industries N.V.; *Int'l*, pg. 4607
BASELODE ENERGY CORP.; *Int'l*, pg. 871
BASEL REAL ESTATE, OJSC—See Basic Element Company; *Int'l*, pg. 886
BASE METAL TICARET VE SANAYI A.S.—See Viohalco SA/NV; *Int'l*, pg. 8243
BASE ONE INTEGRATED MARKETING SERVICES; *Int'l*, pg. 871
BASEOPS INTERNATIONAL INC.—See World Kinect Corporation; *U.S. Public*, pg. 2380
BASEPOINT BUSINESS CENTRES; *Int'l*, pg. 871
BASEPOINT CENTRES LIMITED—See IWG Plc; *Int'l*, pg. 3850
BASE RESOURCES LIMITED—See Energy Fuels Inc.; *U.S. Public*, pg. 762
BASER FAKTORING A.S.; *Int'l*, pg. 871
BA.SE. SERVICE & CONSULTING GMBH—See Zalaris ASA; *Int'l*, pg. 8621
BASE SPOLKA Z OGRANICZONA ODPOWIEDZIALNOSCIA—See Hellman & Friedman LLC; *U.S. Private*, pg. 1911
BASE SPOLKA Z OGRANICZONA ODPOWIEDZIALNOSCIA—See Permira Advisers LLP; *Int'l*, pg. 5809
BASES—See Brookfield Corporation; *Int'l*, pg. 1180
BASES—See Elliott Management Corporation; *U.S. Private*, pg. 1373
BASE TITANIUM LTD.—See Energy Fuels Inc.; *U.S. Public*, pg. 762
BASE TOLIARA SARL—See Energy Fuels Inc.; *U.S. Public*, pg. 762
BASETROPHY GROUP HOLDINGS LIMITED; *Int'l*, pg. 871
BASEUROPA S.A.—See Vincenzo Zucchi S.p.A.; *Int'l*, pg. 8211

BAS EVANSVILLE, INC.—See Inotiv, Inc.; *U.S. Public*, pg. 1128
BASF 3D PRINTING SOLUTIONS GMBH—See BASF SE; *Int'l*, pg. 871
BASF AB—See BASF SE; *Int'l*, pg. 871
BASF ADMIXTURE SYSTEMS EUROPE—See BASF SE; *Int'l*, pg. 874
BASF AFRIQUE DE L'OUEST S.A.R.L.—See BASF SE; *Int'l*, pg. 872
BASF AGRICULTURAL PRODUCTS DE PUERTO RICO—See BASF SE; *Int'l*, pg. 877
BASF AGRICULTURAL PRODUCTS GROUP CORPORATION—See BASF SE; *Int'l*, pg. 872
BASF AGRICULTURAL RESEARCH FOUNDATION, INC.—See BASF SE; *Int'l*, pg. 877
BASF AGRICULTURAL SOLUTIONS BELGIUM N.V.—See BASF SE; *Int'l*, pg. 872
BASF AGRICULTURAL SPECIALITIES LIMITED—See BASF SE; *Int'l*, pg. 872
BASF AGRI-PRODUCTION S.A.S.—See BASF SE; *Int'l*, pg. 877
BASF AGRO B.V. - ARNHEM (NL)—See BASF SE; *Int'l*, pg. 877
BASF AGRO HELLAS INDUSTRIAL AND COMMERCIAL S.A.—See BASF SE; *Int'l*, pg. 877
BASF AGRO, LTD.—See BASF SE; *Int'l*, pg. 877
BASF AGRO SAS—See BASF SE; *Int'l*, pg. 877
BASF AGRO TRADEMARKS GMBH—See BASF SE; *Int'l*, pg. 872
BASF AKQUISITIONS GMBH—See BASF SE; *Int'l*, pg. 872
BASF AKQUISITIONS- UND OBJEKTVERWERTUNGSGESELLSCHAFT MBH—See BASF SE; *Int'l*, pg. 872
BASF AMERICAS CORPORATION—See BASF SE; *Int'l*, pg. 872
BASF ANTWERPEN N.V.—See BASF SE; *Int'l*, pg. 872
BASF ARGENTINA S.A.—See BASF SE; *Int'l*, pg. 872
BASF ARGENTINA S.A.—See BASF SE; *Int'l*, pg. 872
BASF ASIA PACIFIC (INDIA) PVT. LTD.—See BASF SE; *Int'l*, pg. 877
BASF ASIA-PACIFIC SERVICE CENTRE SDN BHD—See BASF SE; *Int'l*, pg. 878
BASF A/S—See BASF SE; *Int'l*, pg. 871
BASF A/S—See BASF SE; *Int'l*, pg. 874
BASF A/S—See BASF SE; *Int'l*, pg. 871
BASF AS—See BASF SE; *Int'l*, pg. 872
BASF AUSTRALIA LTD.—See BASF SE; *Int'l*, pg. 877
BASF AUXILIARY CHEMICALS CO. LTD.—See BASF SE; *Int'l*, pg. 877
BASF BANGLADESH LIMITED—See BASF SE; *Int'l*, pg. 878
BASF BATTERY TECHNOLOGY INVESTMENT GMBH & CO. KG—See BASF SE; *Int'l*, pg. 872
BASF BAUTECHNIK GMBH—See BASF SE; *Int'l*, pg. 872
BASF BEAUTY CARE SOLUTIONS FRANCE SAS - LYON—See BASF SE; *Int'l*, pg. 878
BASF BEAUTY CARE SOLUTIONS FRANCE SAS—See BASF SE; *Int'l*, pg. 878
BASF BEAUTY CARE SOLUTIONS LLC—See BASF SE; *Int'l*, pg. 879
BASF BELGIUM COORDINATION CENTER COMMV—See BASF SE; *Int'l*, pg. 872
BASF BELGIUM S.A./N.V.—See BASF SE; *Int'l*, pg. 872
BASF BETEILIGUNGSGESELLSCHAFT MBH—See BASF SE; *Int'l*, pg. 872
BASF BIORENEWABLE BETEILIGUNGS GMBH & CO. KG—See BASF SE; *Int'l*, pg. 872
BASF BOLIVIA S.R.L.—See BASF SE; *Int'l*, pg. 872
BASF BULGARIA LTD.—See BASF SE; *Int'l*, pg. 872
BASF CANADA INC.—See BASF SE; *Int'l*, pg. 875
BASF CARE CHEMICALS (SHANGHAI) CO. LTD.—See BASF SE; *Int'l*, pg. 877
BASF CATALYST CANADA ULC—See BASF SE; *Int'l*, pg. 875
BASF CATALYSTS ASIA B.V.—See BASF SE; *Int'l*, pg. 875
BASF CATALYSTS CANADA B.V.—See BASF SE; *Int'l*, pg. 875
BASF CATALYSTS DELAWARE LLC—See BASF SE; *Int'l*, pg. 875
BASF CATALYSTS GERMANY GMBH—See BASF SE; *Int'l*, pg. 875
BASF CATALYSTS GRUNDBESITZ GMBH—See BASF SE; *Int'l*, pg. 872
BASF CATALYSTS (GUILIN) CO. LTD.—See BASF SE; *Int'l*, pg. 875
BASF CATALYSTS HOLDING ASIA B.V.—See BASF SE; *Int'l*, pg. 875
BASF CATALYSTS HOLDING CHINA LLC—See BASF SE; *Int'l*, pg. 875
BASF CATALYSTS INDIA PVT. LTD.—See BASF SE; *Int'l*, pg. 872
BASF CATALYSTS LLC - APPEARANCE & PERFORMANCE TECHNOLOGIES—See BASF SE; *Int'l*, pg. 875
BASF CATALYSTS LLC - EAST WINDSOR—See BASF SE; *Int'l*, pg. 875

BASF CATALYSTS LLC - ENVIRONMENTAL TECHNOLOGIES—See BASF SE; *Int'l*, pg. 875
BASF CATALYSTS LLC - MATERIAL SERVICES—See BASF SE; *Int'l*, pg. 875
BASF CATALYSTS LLC - PAPER PIGMENTS & ADDITIVES—See BASF SE; *Int'l*, pg. 875
BASF CATALYSTS LLC - PROCESS TECHNOLOGIES—See BASF SE; *Int'l*, pg. 875
BASF CATALYSTS LLC - QUINCY—See BASF SE; *Int'l*, pg. 875
BASF CATALYSTS LLC - SEPARATION SYSTEMS & VENTURES—See BASF SE; *Int'l*, pg. 875
BASF CATALYSTS LLC—See BASF SE; *Int'l*, pg. 875
BASF CATALYSTS NL FINANCE C.V.—See BASF SE; *Int'l*, pg. 875
BASF CATALYSTS (SHANGHAI) CO. LTD.—See BASF SE; *Int'l*, pg. 875
BASF CATALYSTS UK HOLDINGS LIMITED—See BASF SE; *Int'l*, pg. 875
BASF CHEMCAT THAILAND LIMITED—See BASF SE; *Int'l*, pg. 872
BASF CHEMICALS (SHANGHAI) CO., LTD.—See BASF SE; *Int'l*, pg. 872
BASF CHEMIKALIEN GMBH—See BASF SE; *Int'l*, pg. 872
BASF CHILE S.A.—See BASF SE; *Int'l*, pg. 872
BASF (CHINA) CO., LTD. - BEIJING—See BASF SE; *Int'l*, pg. 877
BASF (CHINA) CO., LTD. - GUANGZHOU—See BASF SE; *Int'l*, pg. 877
BASF (CHINA) CO., LTD.—See BASF SE; *Int'l*, pg. 877
BASF CHINA LTD.—See BASF SE; *Int'l*, pg. 877
BASF COASTINGS SERVICES SP. Z O.O.—See BASF SE; *Int'l*, pg. 872
BASF COATINGS AG—See BASF SE; *Int'l*, pg. 872
BASF COATINGS A.S.—See BASF SE; *Int'l*, pg. 872
BASF COATINGS AUSTRALIA PTY. LTD.—See BASF SE; *Int'l*, pg. 872
BASF COATINGS DE MEXICO S.A. DE C.V.—See BASF SE; *Int'l*, pg. 873
BASF COATING SERVICES (PTY) LTD.—See BASF SE; *Int'l*, pg. 872
BASF COATING SERVICES S.A.S.—See BASF SE; *Int'l*, pg. 872
BASF COATINGS GMBH—See BASF SE; *Int'l*, pg. 873
BASF COATINGS GMBH—See BASF SE; *Int'l*, pg. 872
BASF COATINGS HOLDING B.V.—See BASF SE; *Int'l*, pg. 872
BASF COATINGS, INC.—See BASF SE; *Int'l*, pg. 873
BASF COATINGS INDIA PRIVATE LTD.—See BASF SE; *Int'l*, pg. 872
BASF COATINGS JAPAN LTD.—See BASF SE; *Int'l*, pg. 872
BASF COATINGS NEDERLAND B.V.—See BASF SE; *Int'l*, pg. 872
BASF COATINGS PRIVATE LTD.—See BASF SE; *Int'l*, pg. 873
BASF COATINGS S.A.—See BASF SE; *Int'l*, pg. 873
BASF COATINGS S.A.S.—See BASF SE; *Int'l*, pg. 873
BASF COATINGS SERVICES AB—See BASF SE; *Int'l*, pg. 873
BASF COATINGS SERVICES AG—See BASF SE; *Int'l*, pg. 873
BASF COATINGS SERVICES B.V.—See BASF SE; *Int'l*, pg. 873
BASF COATINGS SERVICES GMBH—See BASF SE; *Int'l*, pg. 873
BASF COATINGS SERVICES ITALY SRL—See BASF SE; *Int'l*, pg. 879
BASF COATINGS SERVICES ITLAY SRL—See BASF SE; *Int'l*, pg. 873
BASF COATINGS SERVICES PTY. LTD.—See BASF SE; *Int'l*, pg. 873
BASF COATINGS SERVICES S.A./N.V.—See BASF SE; *Int'l*, pg. 873
BASF COATINGS SERVICES S.A.R.L.—See BASF SE; *Int'l*, pg. 873
BASF COATINGS SERVICES S.A.—See BASF SE; *Int'l*, pg. 873
BASF COATINGS SERVICES S.A.S.—See BASF SE; *Int'l*, pg. 873
BASF COATINGS SERVICES S.A.U.—See BASF SE; *Int'l*, pg. 874
BASF COATINGS SERVICES SP. Z O.O.—See BASF SE; *Int'l*, pg. 873
BASF COATINGS SERVICES SP. Z.O.O.—See BASF SE; *Int'l*, pg. 874
BASF COATINGS SERVICES S.R.L.—See BASF SE; *Int'l*, pg. 873
BASF COATINGS SERVICES S.R.O.—See BASF SE; *Int'l*, pg. 873
BASF COATINGS S.P.A.—See BASF SE; *Int'l*, pg. 873
BASF COATINGS, STORITVE ZA AVTOMOBILSKE PREMAZE, D.O.O.—See BASF SE; *Int'l*, pg. 873
BASF COLORS & EFFECTS GMBH—See BASF SE; *Int'l*, pg. 874
BASF COLORS & EFFECTS JAPAN LTD.—See BASF SE; *Int'l*, pg. 874
BASF COLORS & EFFECTS KOREA LTD.—See BASF SE; *Int'l*, pg. 874

BASETROPHY GROUP HOLDINGS LIMITED

CORPORATE AFFILIATIONS

BASF COLORS & EFFECTS SWITZERLAND AG—See BASF SE; *Int'l*, pg. 874
BASF COLOR SOLUTIONS FRANCE S.A.S.—See BASF SE; *Int'l*, pg. 874
BASF COLOR SOLUTIONS GERMANY GMBH—See BASF SE; *Int'l*, pg. 874
BASF COMPANY LTD.—See BASF SE; *Int'l*, pg. 878
BASF CONSTRUCTION ADDITIVES GMBH—See BASF SE; *Int'l*, pg. 874
BASF CONSTRUCTION CANADA HOLDINGS INC.—See BASF SE; *Int'l*, pg. 874
BASF CONSTRUCTION CHEMICALS ALGERIA S.A.R.L.—See BASF SE; *Int'l*, pg. 874
BASF CONSTRUCTION CHEMICALS ASIA/PACIFIC—See BASF SE; *Int'l*, pg. 874
BASF CONSTRUCTION CHEMICALS AUSTRALIA PTY. LTD.—See BASF SE; *Int'l*, pg. 874
BASF CONSTRUCTION CHEMICALS BELGIUM NV—See BASF SE; *Int'l*, pg. 874
BASF CONSTRUCTION CHEMICALS CANADA LTD.—See BASF SE; *Int'l*, pg. 874
BASF CONSTRUCTION CHEMICALS (CHINA) CO. LTD.—See BASF SE; *Int'l*, pg. 874
BASF CONSTRUCTION CHEMICALS ESPANA SA—See BASF SE; *Int'l*, pg. 874
BASF CONSTRUCTION CHEMICALS EUROPE AG—See BASF SE; *Int'l*, pg. 874
BASF CONSTRUCTION CHEMICALS FRANCE S.A.S.—See BASF SE; *Int'l*, pg. 874
BASF CONSTRUCTION CHEMICALS GMBH - FRANKFURT AM MAIN—See BASF SE; *Int'l*, pg. 874
BASF CONSTRUCTION CHEMICALS GMBH—See BASF SE; *Int'l*, pg. 874
BASF CONSTRUCTION CHEMICALS GRUNDBESITZ GMBH & CO. KG—See BASF SE; *Int'l*, pg. 875
BASF CONSTRUCTION CHEMICALS (HONG KONG) LIMITED—See BASF SE; *Int'l*, pg. 874
BASF CONSTRUCTION CHEMICALS ITALIA SPA—See BASF SE; *Int'l*, pg. 874
BASF CONSTRUCTION CHEMICALS, LLC—See BASF SE; *Int'l*, pg. 875
BASF CONSTRUCTION CHEMICALS LTDA.—See BASF SE; *Int'l*, pg. 874
BASF CONSTRUCTION CHEMICALS MALAYSIA SDN BHD—See BASF SE; *Int'l*, pg. 874
BASF CONSTRUCTION CHEMICALS PERU S.A.—See BASF SE; *Int'l*, pg. 874
BASF CONSTRUCTION CHEMICALS (PTY) LTD—See BASF SE; *Int'l*, pg. 874
BASF CONSTRUCTION CHEMICALS (SCHWEIZ) AG—See BASF SE; *Int'l*, pg. 874
BASF CONSTRUCTION CHEMICALS SINGAPORE PTE LTD—See BASF SE; *Int'l*, pg. 874
BASF CONSTRUCTION CHEMICALS SOUTH AFRICA (PTY) LTD.—See BASF SE; *Int'l*, pg. 881
BASF CONSTRUCTION CHEMICALS SWEDEN AB—See BASF SE; *Int'l*, pg. 874
BASF CONSTRUCTION CHEMICALS (TAIWAN) CO., LTD.—See BASF SE; *Int'l*, pg. 874
BASF CONSTRUCTION CHEMICALS UK—See BASF SE; *Int'l*, pg. 874
BASF CONSTRUCTION CHEMICALS VENEZUELA, S.A.—See BASF SE; *Int'l*, pg. 875
BASF CONSTRUCTION SOLUTIONS GMBH—See BASF SE; *Int'l*, pg. 875
BASF CONSTRUCTION SYSTEMS (CHINA) CO. LTD.—See BASF SE; *Int'l*, pg. 875
BASF CONTROLS LTD.—See BASF SE; *Int'l*, pg. 875
BASF COORDINATION CENTER COMM.V.—See BASF SE; *Int'l*, pg. 875
BASF CORP. - AMBLER - CARE CHEMICALS—See BASF SE; *Int'l*, pg. 875
BASF CORP. - APPLETON PLANT—See BASF SE; *Int'l*, pg. 876
BASF CORP. - BEAUMONT AGRICULTURAL PRODUCTS PLANT—See BASF SE; *Int'l*, pg. 877
BASF CORP. - BUILDING SYSTEMS—See BASF SE; *Int'l*, pg. 875
BASF CORP. - CHARLOTTE (CHESAPEAKE) SITE—See BASF SE; *Int'l*, pg. 876
BASF CORP. - CHARLOTTE (STEELE CREEK) TECHNICAL CENTER—See BASF SE; *Int'l*, pg. 876
BASF CORP. - ENGINEERING PLASTICS NAFTA—See BASF SE; *Int'l*, pg. 876
BASF CORP. - EVANS CITY PLANT—See BASF SE; *Int'l*, pg. 876
BASF CORP. - FREEPORT PLANT—See BASF SE; *Int'l*, pg. 876
BASF CORP. - GEISMAR PLANT—See BASF SE; *Int'l*, pg. 876
BASF CORP. - GREENVILLE PLANT—See BASF SE; *Int'l*, pg. 876
BASF CORP. - INDEPENDENCE—See BASF SE; *Int'l*, pg. 876
BASF CORP. - LAGRANGE - NUTRITION & HEALTH—See BASF SE; *Int'l*, pg. 876
BASF CORP. - LIVONIA PLANT—See BASF SE; *Int'l*, pg. 876

BASF CORP. - MONACA POLYMERS PLANT—See BASF SE; *Int'l*, pg. 876
BASF CORP. - NEWPORT PLANT—See BASF SE; *Int'l*, pg. 876
BASF CORPORATION—See BASF SE; *Int'l*, pg. 875
BASF CORP. - PALMYRA (HANNIBAL) AGRICULTURAL PRODUCTS PLANT—See BASF SE; *Int'l*, pg. 877
BASF CORP. - SOUTHFIELD SITE—See BASF SE; *Int'l*, pg. 876
BASF CORP. - SUPERABSORBENTS NORTH AMERICA—See BASF SE; *Int'l*, pg. 876
BASF CORP. - TARRYTOWN RESEARCH FACILITY—See BASF SE; *Int'l*, pg. 876
BASF CORP. - TUCSON - MINING CHEMICALS—See BASF SE; *Int'l*, pg. 876
BASF CORP. - WASHINGTON PLANT—See BASF SE; *Int'l*, pg. 876
BASF CORP. - WEST MEMPHIS PLANT—See BASF SE; *Int'l*, pg. 876
BASF CORP. - WHITE STONE PLANT—See BASF SE; *Int'l*, pg. 876
BASF CORP. - WYANDOTTE PLANT—See BASF SE; *Int'l*, pg. 876
BASF CROATIA D.O.O.—See BASF SE; *Int'l*, pg. 876
BASF CROP PROTECTION DIVISION—See BASF SE; *Int'l*, pg. 877
BASF (CZECH) SPOL. S R.O.—See BASF SE; *Int'l*, pg. 871
BASF DE COSTA RICA S.A.—See BASF SE; *Int'l*, pg. 882
BASF DE EL SALVADOR, S.A. DE C.V.—See BASF SE; *Int'l*, pg. 882
BASF DE GUATEMALA, S.A.—See BASF SE; *Int'l*, pg. 882
BASF DE MEXICO S.A. DE C.V.—See BASF SE; *Int'l*, pg. 876
BASF DE NICARAGUA S.A.—See BASF SE; *Int'l*, pg. 882
BASF DIGITAL FARMING GMBH—See BASF SE; *Int'l*, pg. 877
BASF DOMINICANA S.A.—See BASF SE; *Int'l*, pg. 877
BASF EAST AFRICA LTD.—See BASF SE; *Int'l*, pg. 877
BASF EAST ASIA REGIONAL HEADQUARTERS LTD.—See BASF SE; *Int'l*, pg. 877
BASF ECUATORIANA S.A.—See BASF SE; *Int'l*, pg. 878
BASF ELECTRONIC MATERIALS GMBH—See BASF SE; *Int'l*, pg. 878
BASF ELECTRONIC MATERIALS (SHANGHAI) CO. LTD.—See BASF SE; *Int'l*, pg. 878
BASF ELECTRONIC MATERIALS TAIWAN—See BASF SE; *Int'l*, pg. 878
BASF ENZYMES LLC—See Lallemand, Inc.; *Int'l*, pg. 4399
BASF EOOD—See BASF SE; *Int'l*, pg. 877
BASF ESPANOLA S.L.—See BASF SE; *Int'l*, pg. 878
BASF ESPANOLA S.L.—See BASF SE; *Int'l*, pg. 883
BASF FINANCE EUROPE N.V.—See BASF SE; *Int'l*, pg. 880
BASF FINANCE MALTA GMBH—See BASF SE; *Int'l*, pg. 878
BASF FINA PETROCHEMICALS LP—See BASF SE; *Int'l*, pg. 876
BASF FINE CHEMICALS SWITZERLAND SA—See BASF SE; *Int'l*, pg. 871
BASF FOAM ENTERPRISES—See BASF SE; *Int'l*, pg. 876
BASF FOOD—See BASF SE; *Int'l*, pg. 878
BASF FRANCE S.A.S.—See BASF SE; *Int'l*, pg. 878
BASF FUEL CELL INC.—See BASF SE; *Int'l*, pg. 876
BASF FUTURE BUSINESS GMBH—See BASF SE; *Int'l*, pg. 879
BASF FZE—See BASF SE; *Int'l*, pg. 878
BASF GASTRONOMIE GMBH—See BASF SE; *Int'l*, pg. 879
BASF GRENZACH GMBH—See BASF SE; *Int'l*, pg. 879
BASF HEALTH AND CARE PRODUCTS FRANCE S.A.S.—See BASF SE; *Int'l*, pg. 879
BASF HELLAS INDUSTRIAL AND COMMERCIAL S.A.—See BASF SE; *Int'l*, pg. 879
BASF HELLAS S.A.—See BASF SE; *Int'l*, pg. 879
BASF HOCK MINING CHEMICAL (CHINA) COMPANY LTD.—See BASF SE; *Int'l*, pg. 879
BASF HOLDINGS SOUTH AFRICA (PTY.) LTD.—See BASF SE; *Int'l*, pg. 879
BASF HONG KONG LTD.—See BASF SE; *Int'l*, pg. 879
BASF HUNGARIA KFT.—See BASF SE; *Int'l*, pg. 879
BASF IDEMITSU CO., LTD.—See BASF SE; *Int'l*, pg. 878
BASF IDEMITSU CO., LTD.—See Idemitsu Kosan Co., Ltd.; *Int'l*, pg. 3591
BASF IMMOBILIEN-GESELLSCHAFT MBH—See BASF SE; *Int'l*, pg. 879
BASF IMMOBILIEN PIGMENT GMBH—See BASF SE; *Int'l*, pg. 879
BASF INDIA LTD.—See BASF SE; *Int'l*, pg. 878
BASF INDUSTRIAL METALS LLC—See BASF SE; *Int'l*, pg. 879
BASF INNOVATIONSFONDS GMBH—See BASF SE; *Int'l*, pg. 879
BASF INOAC POLYURETHANES LTD.—See BASF SE; *Int'l*, pg. 879
BASF INOAC POLYURETHANES LTD.—See INOAC Corporation; *Int'l*, pg. 3713

BASF INTERSERVICE SPA—See BASF SE; *Int'l*, pg. 879
BASF INTERSERVICIOS S.A. DE C.V.—See BASF SE; *Int'l*, pg. 879
BASF INTERTRADE AG—See BASF SE; *Int'l*, pg. 871
BASF INTERTRADE CORPORATION—See BASF SE; *Int'l*, pg. 876
BASF IRAN AG—See BASF SE; *Int'l*, pg. 879
BASF IRAN (PJS) CO.—See BASF SE; *Int'l*, pg. 879
BASF IRELAND DAC—See BASF SE; *Int'l*, pg. 879
BASF IRELAND LIMITED—See BASF SE; *Int'l*, pg. 879
BASF ITALIA - CENTRO CUOIO—See BASF SE; *Int'l*, pg. 879
BASF ITALIA - CENTRO RICERCA E SVILUPPO—See BASF SE; *Int'l*, pg. 879
BASF ITALIA - ESPANSI—See BASF SE; *Int'l*, pg. 879
BASF ITALIA - NUTRIZIONE ANIMALE—See BASF SE; *Int'l*, pg. 879
BASF ITALIA S.P.A.—See BASF SE; *Int'l*, pg. 879
BASF IT SERVICES CONSULT GMBH—See BASF SE; *Int'l*, pg. 879
BASF IT SERVICES GMBH—See BASF SE; *Int'l*, pg. 879
BASF IT SERVICES HOLDING GMBH—See BASF SE; *Int'l*, pg. 879
BASF IT SERVICES HOLDING LTD.—See BASF SE; *Int'l*, pg. 879
BASF IT SERVICES LTD.—See BASF SE; *Int'l*, pg. 879
BASF IT SERVICES N.V./S.A. - FRANCE—See BASF SE; *Int'l*, pg. 879
BASF IT SERVICES N.V./S.A.—See BASF SE; *Int'l*, pg. 879
BASF IT SERVICES S.A.—See BASF SE; *Int'l*, pg. 879
BASF IT SERVICES S.P.A.—See BASF SE; *Int'l*, pg. 879
BASF JAPAN LTD. - OSAKA—See BASF SE; *Int'l*, pg. 878
BASF JAPAN LTD.—See BASF SE; *Int'l*, pg. 878
BASF JOBMARKT GMBH—See BASF SE; *Int'l*, pg. 879
BASF KAISTEN AG—See BASF SE; *Int'l*, pg. 871
BASF KANOO GULF FZE—See BASF SE; *Int'l*, pg. 879
BASF KANOO POLYURETHANES LLC—See BASF SE; *Int'l*, pg. 879
BASF KASPIAN YAPI KIMYASALLARI SANAYI MEHUD MESULIYYETLI CEMIYYETI—See BASF SE; *Int'l*, pg. 880
BASF LAMPERTHEIM GMBH—See BASF SE; *Int'l*, pg. 880
BASF-LANKA (PVT.) LTD.—See BASF SE; *Int'l*, pg. 878
BASF LEUNA GMBH—See BASF SE; *Int'l*, pg. 880
BASF LIZENZ GMBH—See BASF SE; *Int'l*, pg. 880
BASF LOGISTICS GMBH—See BASF SE; *Int'l*, pg. 880
BASF LTD.—See BASF SE; *Int'l*, pg. 880
BASF LUDWIGSHAFEN GRUNDBESITZ SE & CO. KG—See BASF SE; *Int'l*, pg. 880
BASF (MALAYSIA) SDN. BHD.—See BASF SE; *Int'l*, pg. 878
BASF MAROC S.A.—See BASF SE; *Int'l*, pg. 880
BASF METAL FORWARDS LIMITED—See BASF SE; *Int'l*, pg. 880
BASF METALS GMBH—See BASF SE; *Int'l*, pg. 880
BASF METALS JAPAN LTD.—See BASF SE; *Int'l*, pg. 880
BASF METALS LTD.—See BASF SE; *Int'l*, pg. 880
BASF METALS RECYCLING LTD.—See BASF SE; *Int'l*, pg. 880
BASF METALS (SHANGHAI) CO. LTD.—See BASF SE; *Int'l*, pg. 880
BASF METASHEEN—See BASF SE; *Int'l*, pg. 880
BASF MEXICANA, S.A. DE C.V.—See BASF SE; *Int'l*, pg. 880
BASF MIDDLE EAST CHEMICALS LLC—See BASF SE; *Int'l*, pg. 880
BASF MINERALS OY—See BASF SE; *Int'l*, pg. 880
BASF MOBILIENLEASING GMBH—See BASF SE; *Int'l*, pg. 880
BASF NEDERLAND B.V., CONSTRUCTION CHEMICALS—See BASF SE; *Int'l*, pg. 874
BASF NEDERLAND B.V.—See BASF SE; *Int'l*, pg. 880
BASF NEDERLAND B.V.—See BASF SE; *Int'l*, pg. 880
BASF NEW BUSINESS GMBH—See BASF SE; *Int'l*, pg. 880
BASF NEW ZEALAND LTD.—See BASF SE; *Int'l*, pg. 877
BASF NUTRITION ANIMALE—See BASF SE; *Int'l*, pg. 880
BASF OPERATIONS B.V.—See BASF SE; *Int'l*, pg. 880
BASF OSTERREICH GMBH—See BASF SE; *Int'l*, pg. 880
BASF OY—See BASF SE; *Int'l*, pg. 880
BASF OY - WOLMAN DIVISION—See BASF SE; *Int'l*, pg. 880
BASF PANAMA S.A.—See BASF SE; *Int'l*, pg. 880
BASF PAPER CHEMICALS (JIANGSU) CO. LTD.—See BASF SE; *Int'l*, pg. 880
BASF PARAGUAYA S.A.—See BASF SE; *Int'l*, pg. 880
BASF PERFORMANCE POLYAMIDES KOREA CO., LTD.—See BASF SE; *Int'l*, pg. 880
BASF PERFORMANCE POLYMERS GMBH—See BASF SE; *Int'l*, pg. 880
BASF PERFORMANCE PRODUCTS FRANCE - GRON PLANT—See BASF SE; *Int'l*, pg. 879
BASF PERFORMANCE PRODUCTS FRANCE SA—See BASF SE; *Int'l*, pg. 879
BASF PERFORMANCE PRODUCTS GMBH—See BASF SE; *Int'l*, pg. 880

COMPANY NAME INDEX

BASF PERFORMANCE PRODUCTS LTD.—See BASF SE; *Int'l*, pg. 880
BASF PERFORMANCE PRODUCTS PLC - BRADFORD PLANT—See BASF SE; *Int'l*, pg. 882
BASF PERFORMANCE PRODUCTS PLC - PAISLEY PLANT—See BASF SE; *Int'l*, pg. 882
BASF PERFORMANCE PRODUCTS PLC - PIGMENTS DIVISION—See BASF SE; *Int'l*, pg. 882
BASF PERFORMANCE PRODUCTS PLC—See BASF SE; *Int'l*, pg. 882
BASF PERSONAL CARE AND NUTRITION GMBH—See BASF SE; *Int'l*, pg. 880
BASF PERUANA S.A.—See BASF SE; *Int'l*, pg. 880
BASF PEST CONTROL SOLUTIONS—See BASF SE; *Int'l*, pg. 882
BASF PETRONAS CHEMICALS SDN. BHD.—See BASF SE; *Int'l*, pg. 878
BASF PETRONAS CHEMICALS SDN. BHD.—See BASF SE; *Int'l*, pg. 878
BASF PETRONAS CHEMICALS SDN. BHD.—See Petroliam Nasional Berhad; *Int'l*, pg. 5829
BASF PHARMA (CALLANISH) LIMITED—See BASF SE; *Int'l*, pg. 882
BASF PHILIPPINES, INC.—See BASF SE; *Int'l*, pg. 880
BASF PIGMENT GMBH—See BASF SE; *Int'l*, pg. 880
BASF-PJPC NEOPENTYLGLYCOL CO. LTD.—See BASF SE; *Int'l*, pg. 882
BASF PLANT SCIENCE COMPANY GMBH—See BASF SE; *Int'l*, pg. 877
BASF PLANT SCIENCE GMBH—See BASF SE; *Int'l*, pg. 877
BASF PLANT SCIENCE LP—See BASF SE; *Int'l*, pg. 877
BASF PLASTIC ADDITIVES MIDDLE EAST S.P.C.—See BASF SE; *Int'l*, pg. 880
BASF PLC—See BASF SE; *Int'l*, pg. 882
BASF POLIURETAN HUNGARIA KFT.—See BASF SE; *Int'l*, pg. 883
BASF POLIURETANI ITALIA SPA—See BASF SE; *Int'l*, pg. 881
BASF POLIURETANOS LTDA.—See BASF SE; *Int'l*, pg. 881
BASF POLIURETANOS S.A.—See BASF SE; *Int'l*, pg. 872
BASF POLIURETANY POLSKA SP. Z O.O.—See BASF SE; *Int'l*, pg. 881
BASF POLSKA SP. Z O. O—See BASF 3E, *Int'l*, pg. 000
BASF POLYURETHANE INDUSTRY AND TRADE CO., LTD. STI—See BASF SE; *Int'l*, pg. 883
BASF POLYURETHANE LICENSING GMBH—See BASF SE; *Int'l*, pg. 881
BASF POLYURETHANES BENELUX B.V.—See BASF SE; *Int'l*, pg. 881
BASF POLYURETHANES (CHINA) CO., LTD.—See BASF SE; *Int'l*, pg. 877
BASF POLYURETHANES (CHONGQING) CO. LTD.—See BASF SE; *Int'l*, pg. 881
BASF POLYURETHANES FRANCE S.A.S.—See BASF SE; *Int'l*, pg. 881
BASF POLYURETHANES GMBH—See BASF SE; *Int'l*, pg. 881
BASF POLYURETHANES (MALAYSIA) SDN. BHD.—See BASF SE; *Int'l*, pg. 878
BASF POLYURETHANES NORDIC AB—See BASF SE; *Int'l*, pg. 881
BASF POLYURETHANES NORTH AMERICA—See BASF SE; *Int'l*, pg. 876
BASF POLYURETHANES PARS (PRIVATE JOINT STOCK) COMPANY—See BASF SE; *Int'l*, pg. 881
BASF POLYURETHANE SPECIALTIES (CHINA) CO. LTD.—See BASF SE; *Int'l*, pg. 881
BASF POLYURETHANES—See BASF SE; *Int'l*, pg. 872
BASF POLYURETHANES SOUTH AFRICA (PTY.) LTD.—See BASF SE; *Int'l*, pg. 881
BASF POLYURETHANES U.K. LTD.—See BASF SE; *Int'l*, pg. 881
BASF PORTUGUESA, LDA.—See BASF SE; *Int'l*, pg. 881
BASF POZZOLITH LTD.—See BASF SE; *Int'l*, pg. 881
BASF PROCESS CATALYSTS GMBH—See BASF SE; *Int'l*, pg. 881
BASF PROPERTIES INC.—See BASF SE; *Int'l*, pg. 881
BASF QTECH INC.—See BASF SE; *Int'l*, pg. 881
BASF QUIMICA COLOMBIANA S.A.—See BASF SE; *Int'l*, pg. 881
BASF RENEWABLE ENERGY GMBH—See BASF SE; *Int'l*, pg. 881
BASF REPRESENTATION BELARUS—See BASF SE; *Int'l*, pg. 881
BASF S.A.—See BASF SE; *Int'l*, pg. 873
BASF SA—See BASF SE; *Int'l*, pg. 881
BASF S.A.—See BASF SE; *Int'l*, pg. 881
BASF SAUDI ARABIA LIMITED COMPANY—See BASF SE; *Int'l*, pg. 881
BASF SCHWARZHEIDE GMBH—See BASF SE; *Int'l*, pg. 883
BASF (SCHWEIZ) AG - BASEL SITE—See BASF SE; *Int'l*, pg. 871
BASF (SCHWEIZ) AG—See BASF SE; *Int'l*, pg. 871
BASF SEE SEN SDN. BHD.—See BASF SE; *Int'l*, pg. 878
BASF SE - EUROPEAN GOVERNMENTAL AFFAIRS—See BASF SE; *Int'l*, pg. 872

BASF SE - LAENDERBEREICH VERTRIEB EUROPE—See BASF SE; *Int'l*, pg. 881
BASF SERVICES EUROPE GMBH—See BASF SE; *Int'l*, pg. 881
BASF SERVICES (MALAYSIA) SDN. BHD.—See BASF SE; *Int'l*, pg. 881
BASF SE; *Int'l*, pg. 871
BASF SHANGHAI COATINGS CO. LTD.—See BASF SE; *Int'l*, pg. 877
BASF, SIA—See BASF SE; *Int'l*, pg. 882
BASF SINGAPORE PTE. LTD.—See BASF SE; *Int'l*, pg. 878
BASF SLOVENIJA D.O.O.—See BASF SE; *Int'l*, pg. 881
BASF SLOVENSKO S.R.O.—See BASF SE; *Int'l*, pg. 881
BASF SONATRACH PROPANCHEM S.A.—See BASF SE; *Int'l*, pg. 878
BASF SONATRACH PROPANCHEM S.A.—See Sonatrach International Holding Corporation; *Int'l*, pg. 7089
BASF SOUTH AFRICA (PTY.) LTD.—See BASF SE; *Int'l*, pg. 881
BASF SOUTH EAST ASIA PTE. LTD.—See BASF SE; *Int'l*, pg. 878
BASF S.P.A.—See BASF SE; *Int'l*, pg. 881
BASF SPOL. S.R.O.—See BASF SE; *Int'l*, pg. 882
BASF SRBIJA D.O.O.—See BASF SE; *Int'l*, pg. 881
BASF S.R.L.—See BASF SE; *Int'l*, pg. 881
BASF STAVEBNI HMOTY CESKA REPUBLIKA S.R.O.—See BASF SE; *Int'l*, pg. 881
BASF SUISSE S.A.—See BASF SE; *Int'l*, pg. 881
BASF TAIWAN B.V.—See BASF SE; *Int'l*, pg. 881
BASF TAIWAN LTD.—See BASF SE; *Int'l*, pg. 878
BASF (THAI) LTD.—See BASF SE; *Int'l*, pg. 878
BASF TODA BATTERY MATERIALS LLC—See BASF SE; *Int'l*, pg. 882
BASF TRADING EGYPT S.A.E.—See BASF SE; *Int'l*, pg. 881
BASF TUERK KIMYA SANAYI VE TICARET LTD. STI.—See BASF SE; *Int'l*, pg. 881
BASF TUERK KIMYA SANAYI VE TICARET LTD. STI.—See BASF SE; *Int'l*, pg. 881
BASF TUNISIE S.A.—See BASF SE; *Int'l*, pg. 881
BASF TURK KIMYA SANAYI VE TICARET LTD. STI.—See BASF SE; *Int'l*, pg. 882
BASF TURK KIMYA SAN. VE TIC. LTD. STI.—See BASF SE; *Int'l*, pg. 881
BASF UAB - LATVIA—See BASF SE; *Int'l*, pg. 882
BASF UAB—See BASF SE; *Int'l*, pg. 882
BASF UK LIMITED—See BASF SE; *Int'l*, pg. 882
BASF URUGUAYA S.A.—See BASF SE; *Int'l*, pg. 882
BASF US VERWALTUNG GMBH—See BASF SE; *Int'l*, pg. 882
BASF VC BETEILIGUNGS- UND MANAGEMENTGESELLSCHAFT—See BASF SE; *Int'l*, pg. 882
BASF VENEZOLANA, S.A.—See BASF SE; *Int'l*, pg. 882
BASF VENEZUELA S.A.—See BASF SE; *Int'l*, pg. 882
BASF VENTURE CAPITAL AMERICA INC.—See BASF SE; *Int'l*, pg. 876
BASF VENTURE CAPITAL GMBH—See BASF SE; *Int'l*, pg. 882
BASF VIETNAM CO. LTD.—See BASF SE; *Int'l*, pg. 882
BASF VITAMINS COMPANY LTD.—See BASF SE; *Int'l*, pg. 882
BASF WALL SYSTEMS, INC.—See BASF SE; *Int'l*, pg. 875
BASF WATERTECHNOLOGIES GMBH & CO. KG—See BASF SE; *Int'l*, pg. 882
BASF WEST AFRICA LTD.—See BASF SE; *Int'l*, pg. 882
BASF WOHNEN + BAUEN GMBH—See BASF SE; *Int'l*, pg. 882
BASF WOLMAN GMBH—See BASF SE; *Int'l*, pg. 882
BASF YAPI KIMYASALLARI SAN A/S—See BASF SE; *Int'l*, pg. 875
BASF-YPC COMPANY LIMITED—See BASF SE; *Int'l*, pg. 877
BASF-YPC COMPANY LIMITED—See China Petrochemical Corporation; *Int'l*, pg. 1539
BASF ZAMBIA LIMITED—See BASF SE; *Int'l*, pg. 882
BASHAS' SUPERMARKETS; *U.S. Private*, pg. 484
BASHKIR HEAT DISTRIBUTION SYSTEM, LLC—See JSC INTER RAO UES; *Int'l*, pg. 4009
BASHOR & LEGENDRE, LLP; *U.S. Private*, pg. 484
BASHUNDHARA PAPER MILLS LTD.; *Int'l*, pg. 886
BASIC ADHESIVES INC.; *U.S. Private*, pg. 484
BASIC AMERICAN FOODS, INC. - MOSES LAKE PROCESSING PLANT—See Basic American Foods, Inc.; *U.S. Private*, pg. 485
BASIC AMERICAN FOODS, INC.; *U.S. Private*, pg. 484
BASIC AMERICAN METAL PRODUCTS—See GF Health Products, Inc.; *U.S. Private*, pg. 1689
BASIC BOOKS—See Vivendi SE; *Int'l*, pg. 8273
BASIC CAPITAL MANAGEMENT CO., LTD.; *Int'l*, pg. 886
BASIC CARBIDE CORP; *U.S. Private*, pg. 485
BASIC COMMERCE AND INDUSTRIES, INC.; *U.S. Private*, pg. 485
BASIC CONSTRUCTION COMPANY - NEW KENT FACILITY—See Basic Construction Company; *U.S. Private*, pg. 485

BASIC CONSTRUCTION COMPANY - OYSTER POINT FACILITY—See Basic Construction Company; *U.S. Private*, pg. 485
BASIC CONSTRUCTION COMPANY; *U.S. Private*, pg. 485
BASIC DIVERSIFIED INDUSTRIAL HOLDINGS, INC—See Basic Energy Corporation; *Int'l*, pg. 886
BASIC ELEMENT COMPANY; *Int'l*, pg. 886
BASIC ENERGY CORPORATION; *Int'l*, pg. 886
BASIC ENERGY SERVICES INC.; *U.S. Public*, pg. 279
BASIC ENERGY SERVICES, L.P.—See Basic Energy Services, Inc.; *U.S. Public*, pg. 279
BASIC-FIT NV; *Int'l*, pg. 886
BASIC FUN, INC.; *U.S. Private*, pg. 485
BASIC GRAIN PRODUCTS INC.; *U.S. Private*, pg. 485
THE BASIC HOUSE(SHANGHAI) CO., LTD.—See TBH Global Co., Ltd.; *Int'l*, pg. 7480
BASIC INDUSTRIES LIMITED—See Pernix Group, Inc.; *U.S. Public*, pg. 1677
BASICITALIA S.R.L.—See BasicNet S.p.A.; *Int'l*, pg. 886
BASIC MATERIALS; *U.S. Private*, pg. 485
BASICNET S.P.A.; *Int'l*, pg. 886
BASIC PETROLEUM SERVICES, INC.—See Permian Resources Corp; *U.S. Public*, pg. 1677
BASIC PROPERTIES B.V.—See BasicNet S.p.A.; *Int'l*, pg. 886
BASIC REMEDIATION COMPANY LLC—See Contran Corporation; *U.S. Private*, pg. 1033
BASIC RESOURCES INC.; *U.S. Private*, pg. 485
BASIC SALES & MARKETING; *U.S. Private*, pg. 485
BASICS GMBH—See Sun Pharmaceutical Industries Ltd.; *Int'l*, pg. 7307
BASICS OFFICE PRODUCTS LTD.; *Int'l*, pg. 886
BASICSOFT INC.—See Leeds Equity Partners, LLC; *U.S. Private*, pg. 2415
BASIC STAINLESS, INC.—See Samuel, Son & Co., Limited; *Int'l*, pg. 6516
BASIC VILLAGE S.P.A.—See BasicNet S.p.A.; *Int'l*, pg. 886
BASIC WATER COMPANY—See Contran Corporation; *U.S. Private*, pg. 1033
BASI HOLDINGS, LLC—See Macquarie Group Limited; *Int'l*, pg. 4627
BASILEA PHARMACEUTICA DEUTSCHLAND GMBH—See Basilea Pharmaceutica Ltd.; *Int'l*, pg. 887
BASILEA PHARMACEUTICA INTERNATIONAL LTD.—See Basilea Pharmaceutica Ltd.; *Int'l*, pg. 887
BASILEA PHARMACEUTICA LTD.; *Int'l*, pg. 887
BASILEA PHARMACEUTICA S.R.L.—See Basilea Pharmaceutica Ltd.; *Int'l*, pg. 887
BASILIC FLY STUDIO LIMITED; *Int'l*, pg. 887
BASIL READ HOLDINGS LIMITED; *Int'l*, pg. 886
BASIL READ (PTY) LIMITED—See Basil Read Holdings Limited; *Int'l*, pg. 886
BASIL STREET PRACTICE LIMITED—See HCA Healthcare, Inc.; *U.S. Public*, pg. 991
BASIN CONTRACTING LIMITED; *Int'l*, pg. 887
BASIN DIALYSIS, LLC—See DaVita Inc.; *U.S. Public*, pg. 636
BASIN ELECTRIC POWER COOPERATIVE; *U.S. Private*, pg. 485
BASIN ENERGY LIMITED; *Int'l*, pg. 887
BASIN ENGINE & PUMP, INC.—See Applied Industrial Technologies, Inc.; *U.S. Public*, pg. 171
BASINGHALL FINANCE PLC.—See Erste Abwicklungsanstalt AoR; *Int'l*, pg. 2497
BASIN HOLDINGS US LLC—See J Fitzgibbons LLC; *U.S. Private*, pg. 2153
BASIN PRECISION MACHINING LLC—See J Fitzgibbons LLC; *U.S. Private*, pg. 2153
BASIN SUPPLY FZCO—See J Fitzgibbons LLC; *U.S. Private*, pg. 2153
BASINTEK LLC—See Riverstone Holdings LLC; *U.S. Private*, pg. 3447
BASIN TELECOMMUNICATION, INC.—See Basin Electric Power Cooperative; *U.S. Private*, pg. 485
BASIN TOOLS, LP—See J Fitzgibbons LLC; *U.S. Private*, pg. 2153
BASIN TRANSLOAD, LLC—See Global Partners LP; *U.S. Public*, pg. 942
BASIN URANIUM CORP.; *Int'l*, pg. 887
BASIN WELL LOGGING WIRELINE SERVICES, INC.—See Steel Partners Holdings L.P.; *U.S. Public*, pg. 1943
BASIN WELL LOGGING WIRELINE SERVICES, INC.—See Steel Partners Holdings L.P.; *U.S. Public*, pg. 1943
BASIS ENGINEERING SRL—See Rosetti Marino S.p.A.; *Int'l*, pg. 6400
BASIS LTD.—See Fuji Media Holdings, Inc.; *Int'l*, pg. 2813
BASITALIA LEASING S.P.A.—See Vincenzo Zucchi S.p.A.; *Int'l*, pg. 8211
BASKETRY BY PHINA, LLC; *U.S. Private*, pg. 485
BASKETRY INC.—See Basketry by Phina, LLC; *U.S. Private*, pg. 485
BASKIN GROUP LIMITED; *U.S. Private*, pg. 485
BASKIN-ROBBINS FRANCHISING LLC—See Roark Capital Group Inc.; *U.S. Private*, pg. 3455

BASKIN-ROBBINS LLC—See Roark Capital Group Inc.; *U.S. Private*, pg. 3455
BASKIN TRUCK & TRACTOR, INC.; *U.S. Private*, pg. 485
BAS KUNDENSERVICE GMBH & CO. KG—See ENGIE SA; *Int'l*, pg. 2429
BAS KUNDENSERVICE GMBH & CO. KG—See E.ON SE; *Int'l*, pg. 2257
BAS KUNDENSERVICE GMBH & CO. KG—See Vattenfall AB; *Int'l*, pg. 8137
BASLER AG; *Int'l*, pg. 887
BASLER ASIA PTE. LTD.—See Basler AG; *Int'l*, pg. 887
BASLER ELECTRIC COMPANY - BASLER ELECTRIC FACILITY—See Basler Electric Company; *U.S. Private*, pg. 485
BASLER ELECTRIC COMPANY - BASLER ELECTRIC FACILITY—See Basler Electric Company; *U.S. Private*, pg. 485
BASLER ELECTRIC COMPANY (SINGAPORE) PTE LTD.—See Basler Electric Company; *U.S. Private*, pg. 485
BASLER ELECTRIC COMPANY; *U.S. Private*, pg. 485
BASLER ELECTRIC FRANCE SAS—See Basler Electric Company; *U.S. Private*, pg. 485
BASLER ELECTRIC (SUZHOU) CO., LTD—See Basler Electric Company; *U.S. Private*, pg. 485
BASLER FRANCE S.A.—See Basler AG; *Int'l*, pg. 887
BASLER HANDELS-GESELLSCHAFT AG—See Welinvest AG; *Int'l*, pg. 8372
BASLER, INC.—See Basler AG; *Int'l*, pg. 887
BASLER JAPAN KK—See Basler AG; *Int'l*, pg. 887
BASLER KANTONALBANK AG; *Int'l*, pg. 887
BASLER KOREA INC.—See Basler AG; *Int'l*, pg. 887
BASLER LEBENSVERSICHERUNGS-AG—See Baloise Holding AG; *Int'l*, pg. 811
BASLER NEUMUNSTER AG—See Basler AG; *Int'l*, pg. 887
BASLER OSIGURANJA - SERBIA—See UNIQA Insurance Group AG; *Int'l*, pg. 8059
BASLER OSIGURANJE ZAGREB D.D—See UNIQA Insurance Group AG; *Int'l*, pg. 8059
BASLER PLASTICS LLC—See Basler Electric Company; *U.S. Private*, pg. 485
BASLER SACHVERSICHERUNGS-AG; *Int'l*, pg. 887
BASLER SECURITAS VERSICHERUNGS-AKTIENGESELLSCHAFT—See Baloise Holding AG; *Int'l*, pg. 811
BASLER TURBO CONVERSIONS, LLC.; *U.S. Private*, pg. 485
BASLER VERSICHERUNGS-GESELLSCHAFT—See Baloise Holding AG; *Int'l*, pg. 811
BASLER VERSICHERUNGS-GESELLSCHAFT—See Baloise Holding AG; *Int'l*, pg. 811
BASLER VISION TECHNOLOGIES TAIWAN INC.—See Basler AG; *Int'l*, pg. 887
BASLER VISION TECHNOLOGY (BEIJING) CO., LTD.—See Basler AG; *Int'l*, pg. 887
BASLER ZEITUNG AG—See TX Group AG; *Int'l*, pg. 7991
BASLINI METALLI S.P.A.—See Baslini S.p.A.; *Int'l*, pg. 887
BASLINI S.P.A.; *Int'l*, pg. 887
BASMAT INC.; *U.S. Private*, pg. 485
BAS OMNISERVIZI SRL—See A2A S.p.A.; *Int'l*, pg. 29
BASO PRECISION OPTICS LTD.—See Eastman Kodak Company; *U.S. Public*, pg. 706
BAS PART SALES LLC—See BAS, Inc.; *U.S. Private*, pg. 484
BASSAC; *Int'l*, pg. 888
BASS AIR CONDITIONING CO, INC.—See DLVA, Inc.; *Int'l*, pg. 1248
BASSANI MANUFACTURING; *U.S. Private*, pg. 486
BASSARI RESOURCES LIMITED; *Int'l*, pg. 888
BASSAT, OGILVY & MATHER COMUNICACION—See WPP plc; *Int'l*, pg. 8489
BASSAT, OGILVY & MATHER COMUNICACION—See WPP plc; *Int'l*, pg. 8489
BASSAT, OGILVY & MATHER COMUNICACION—See WPP plc; *Int'l*, pg. 8490
BASS COMPUTERS INC.; *U.S. Private*, pg. 486
BASS ENGINEERING—See HM International; *U.S. Private*, pg. 1954
BASS ENTERPRISES PRODUCTION CO.—See Keystone Group, L.P.; *U.S. Private*, pg. 2296
BASSET CREEK CAPITAL, INC.; *U.S. Private*, pg. 486
BASSETT DIRECT NC, LLC—See Bassett Furniture Industries, Incorporated; *U.S. Public*, pg. 279
BASSETT DIRECT SC, LLC—See Bassett Furniture Industries, Incorporated; *U.S. Public*, pg. 279
BASSETT FUELS LIMITED—See NWF Group Plc; *Int'l*, pg. 5499
BASSETT FURNITURE CO.—See Bassett Furniture Industries, Incorporated; *U.S. Public*, pg. 279
BASSETT FURNITURE INDUSTRIES, INCORPORATED; *U.S. Public*, pg. 279
BASSETT-HYLAND ENERGY COMPANY; *U.S. Private*, pg. 486
BASSETTI DEUTSCHLAND GMBH—See Vincenzo Zucchi S.p.A.; *Int'l*, pg. 8211
BASSETTI ESPANOLA S.A.—See Vincenzo Zucchi S.p.A.; *Int'l*, pg. 8211
BASSETTI GROUP SAS; *Int'l*, pg. 888

BASSETT INC.—See Omega Enterprises Inc.; *U.S. Private*, pg. 3015
BASSETTI SCHWEIZ A.G.—See Vincenzo Zucchi S.p.A.; *Int'l*, pg. 8211
BASSETTI S.P.A.—See Vincenzo Zucchi S.p.A.; *Int'l*, pg. 8211
BASSETT UPHOLSTERY DIVISION—See Bassett Furniture Industries, Incorporated; *U.S. Public*, pg. 279
BASSETT & WALKER INTERNATIONAL, INC.; *Int'l*, pg. 888
BASS GMBH—See OSG Corporation; *Int'l*, pg. 5648
BASSIAN FARMS, INC.—See The Chefs' Warehouse, Inc.; *U.S. Public*, pg. 2058
BASSI CONSTRUCTION LP—See Fairfax Financial Holdings Limited; *Int'l*, pg. 2607
BASSI ELEKTRO AG—See Burkhalter Holding AG; *Int'l*, pg. 1224
BASSILICHI CEE D.O.O.; *Int'l*, pg. 888
BASSILICHI S.P.A.—See Nexi SpA; *Int'l*, pg. 5244
B.A.S.S., INC.—See The Walt Disney Company; *U.S. Public*, pg. 2138
BASSI S.R.L.—See BorgWarner Inc.; *U.S. Public*, pg. 369
B-ASSIST, INC.—See Bookoff Group Holdings Ltd.; *Int'l*, pg. 1110
BASSMASTER MAGAZINE—See The Walt Disney Company; *U.S. Public*, pg. 2138
BASS OIL LIMITED; *Int'l*, pg. 887
BASSO INDUSTRY CORPORATION - PLASTIC INJECTION PLANT—See Basso Industry Corporation; *Int'l*, pg. 888
BASSO INDUSTRY CORPORATION; *Int'l*, pg. 888
BASSOTECH INC.; *U.S. Private*, pg. 486
BASS PRO GROUP, LLC—See The Great American Outdoors Group LLC; *U.S. Private*, pg. 4037
BASS PRO OUTDOORS ONLINE, LLC—See The Great American Outdoors Group LLC; *U.S. Private*, pg. 4037
BASS PROPERTIES, INC.; *U.S. Private*, pg. 486
BASS PRO SHOPS, INC.—See The Great American Outdoors Group LLC; *U.S. Private*, pg. 4037
BASS SECURITY SERVICES INC.—See Platinum Equity, LLC; *U.S. Private*, pg. 3208
B.A.S.S. TIMES—See The Walt Disney Company; *U.S. Public*, pg. 2138
BASS-UNITED FIRE & SECURITY SYSTEMS, INC.—See The Carlyle Group Inc.; *U.S. Public*, pg. 2053
BASTA FRANCE; *Int'l*, pg. 888
BASTA HOLDINGS, CORP.; *U.S. Private*, pg. 486
BASTAS BASKENT CIMENTO—See Vicat S.A.; *Int'l*, pg. 8185
BASTAS HAZIR BETON SANAYI VE TICARET A.S.—See Vicat S.A.; *Int'l*, pg. 8185
BASTEC AB—See Investment AB Latour; *Int'l*, pg. 3782
BASTEI LUBBE AG; *Int'l*, pg. 888
BASTEI MEDIA GMBH—See Bastei Lubbe AG; *Int'l*, pg. 888
BASTE; *Int'l*, pg. 888
BAST HATFIELD INC.; *U.S. Private*, pg. 486
BASTIAN SOLUTIONS INDIA PVT. LTD.—See Toyota Industries Corporation; *Int'l*, pg. 7866
BASTIAN SOLUTIONS, LLC—See Toyota Industries Corporation; *Int'l*, pg. 7866
BASTIAN SOLUTIONS; *U.S. Private*, pg. 486
BASTIDE DIFFUSION; *Int'l*, pg. 888
BASTIDE LE CONFORT MEDICAL SA; *Int'l*, pg. 888
BASTIDE MANUTENTION; *Int'l*, pg. 888
BASTION MINERALS LIMITED; *Int'l*, pg. 888
BASTI SA; *Int'l*, pg. 888
BAST JSC; *Int'l*, pg. 888
BASTOGI S.P.A.; *Int'l*, pg. 888
BASTY PERE ET FILS; *Int'l*, pg. 888
BAS VAN DER ZEE—See Thames & Hudson Ltd; *Int'l*, pg. 7607
BASWARE AB—See Accel Partners L.P.; *U.S. Private*, pg. 48
BASWARE AB—See KKR & Co. Inc.; *U.S. Public*, pg. 1237
BASWARE AB—See Long Path Partners, LP; *U.S. Private*, pg. 2491
BASWARE A/S—See Accel Partners L.P.; *U.S. Private*, pg. 47
BASWARE AS—See Accel Partners L.P.; *U.S. Private*, pg. 48
BASWARE AS—See KKR & Co. Inc.; *U.S. Public*, pg. 1237
BASWARE A/S—See KKR & Co. Inc.; *U.S. Public*, pg. 1237
BASWARE AS—See Long Path Partners, LP; *U.S. Private*, pg. 2491
BASWARE A/S—See Long Path Partners, LP; *U.S. Private*, pg. 2491
BASWARE BELGIUM NV—See Accel Partners L.P.; *U.S. Private*, pg. 48
BASWARE BELGIUM NV—See KKR & Co. Inc.; *U.S. Public*, pg. 1237
BASWARE BELGIUM NV—See Long Path Partners, LP; *U.S. Private*, pg. 2491
BASWARE B.V.—See Accel Partners L.P.; *U.S. Private*, pg. 48

BASWARE B.V.—See KKR & Co. Inc.; *U.S. Public*, pg. 1237
BASWARE B.V.—See Long Path Partners, LP; *U.S. Private*, pg. 2491
BASWARE CORPORATION—See Accel Partners L.P.; *U.S. Private*, pg. 48
BASWARE CORPORATION—See KKR & Co. Inc.; *U.S. Public*, pg. 1237
BASWARE CORPORATION—See Long Path Partners, LP; *U.S. Private*, pg. 2491
BASWARE GMBH—See Accel Partners L.P.; *U.S. Private*, pg. 48
BASWARE GMBH—See KKR & Co. Inc.; *U.S. Public*, pg. 1237
BASWARE GMBH—See Long Path Partners, LP; *U.S. Private*, pg. 2491
BASWARE HOLDINGS LTD.—See Accel Partners L.P.; *U.S. Private*, pg. 48
BASWARE HOLDINGS LTD.—See KKR & Co. Inc.; *U.S. Public*, pg. 1237
BASWARE HOLDINGS LTD.—See Long Path Partners, LP; *U.S. Private*, pg. 2491
BASWARE, INC.—See Accel Partners L.P.; *U.S. Private*, pg. 48
BASWARE, INC.—See KKR & Co. Inc.; *U.S. Public*, pg. 1238
BASWARE, INC.—See Long Path Partners, LP; *U.S. Private*, pg. 2491
BASWARE INDIA PRIVATE LIMITED—See Accel Partners L.P.; *U.S. Private*, pg. 48
BASWARE INDIA PRIVATE LIMITED—See KKR & Co. Inc.; *U.S. Public*, pg. 1237
BASWARE INDIA PRIVATE LIMITED—See Long Path Partners, LP; *U.S. Private*, pg. 2491
BASWARE OYJ—See Accel Partners L.P.; *U.S. Private*, pg. 47
BASWARE OYJ—See KKR & Co. Inc.; *U.S. Public*, pg. 1237
BASWARE OYJ—See Long Path Partners, LP; *U.S. Private*, pg. 2491
BASWARE PTY LTD—See Accel Partners L.P.; *U.S. Private*, pg. 48
BASWARE PTY LTD—See KKR & Co. Inc.; *U.S. Public*, pg. 1238
BASWARE PTY LTD—See Long Path Partners, LP; *U.S. Private*, pg. 2491
BASWARE RUSSIA—See Accel Partners L.P.; *U.S. Private*, pg. 48
BASWARE RUSSIA—See KKR & Co. Inc.; *U.S. Public*, pg. 1238
BASWARE RUSSIA—See Long Path Partners, LP; *U.S. Private*, pg. 2491
BASWARE SAS—See Accel Partners L.P.; *U.S. Private*, pg. 48
BASWARE SAS—See KKR & Co. Inc.; *U.S. Public*, pg. 1238
BASWARE SAS—See Long Path Partners, LP; *U.S. Private*, pg. 2491
BASWARE UK LTD.—See Accel Partners L.P.; *U.S. Private*, pg. 48
BASWARE UK LTD.—See KKR & Co. Inc.; *U.S. Public*, pg. 1238
BASWARE UK LTD.—See Long Path Partners, LP; *U.S. Private*, pg. 2491
B.A. SWEETIE CANDY COMPANY; *U.S. Private*, pg. 420
BASX, LLC—See AAON, Inc.; *U.S. Public*, pg. 12
BATAILLE MATERIAUX; *Int'l*, pg. 889
BATA INDIA LIMITED; *Int'l*, pg. 889
BATALPHA BOBACH GMBH; *Int'l*, pg. 889
BATAMAS SDN. BHD.—See Mega First Corporation Berhad; *Int'l*, pg. 4792
BA-TAMPTE PICKLE PRODUCTS INCORPORATED; *U.S. Private*, pg. 421
BATANGA, INC.; *U.S. Private*, pg. 486
BATA PAKISTAN LIMITED; *Int'l*, pg. 889
BATA PROPERTIES LIMITED—See Bata India Limited; *Int'l*, pg. 889
BATARD—See Myriad Restaurant Group; *U.S. Private*, pg. 2825
BATA SHOE COMPANY (BANGLADESH) LIMITED; *Int'l*, pg. 889
BATAVIA BIOSCIENCES B.V.—See CJ Corporation; *Int'l*, pg. 1631
BATAVIA BIOSCIENCES INC.—See CJ Corporation; *Int'l*, pg. 1631
BATAVUS B.V.—See Accell Group N.V.; *Int'l*, pg. 80
BAT BLUE CORPORATION—See Fortinet, Inc.; *U.S. Public*, pg. 869
BATCHELDER & COLLINS INC.; *U.S. Private*, pg. 486
BATCHELOR & KIMBALL, INC.—See EMCOR Group, Inc.; *U.S. Public*, pg. 736
BATCHELORS LTD.—See CapVest Limited; *Int'l*, pg. 1318
BATCO MANUFACTURING LTD.—See Ag Growth International Inc.; *Int'l*, pg. 198
B.A.T. (CYPRUS) LTD.—See British American Tobacco plc; *Int'l*, pg. 1165
BATEAUX NANTAIS; *Int'l*, pg. 889
BATEAUX PARISIENS—See Sodexo S.A.; *Int'l*, pg. 7045
BATEG SA—See VINCI S.A.; *Int'l*, pg. 8213

COMPANY NAME INDEX

BATELCO MIDDLE EAST COMPANY SPC—See Bahrain Telecommunications Company BSC; *Int'l*, pg. 801
B&A TELECOM—See Bulley & Andrews, LLC; *U.S. Private*, pg. 685
BATEMAN BROTHERS LUMBER CO., INC.; *U.S. Private*, pg. 486
THE BATEMAN GROUP; *U.S. Private*, pg. 3992
THE BATEMAN GROUP—See The Bateman Group; *U.S. Private*, pg. 3992
BATEMAN-HALL INC; *U.S. Private*, pg. 486
BATEMAN SENIOR MEALS—See Compass Group PLC; *Int'l*, pg. 1750
BATENBURG TECHNIEK N.V.; *Int'l*, pg. 889
BATERO GOLD CORP.; *Int'l*, pg. 889
BATES CARGO-PAK APS—See Illinois Tool Works Inc.; *U.S. Public*, pg. 1101
BATES ENGINEERS/CONTRACTORS INC.; *U.S. Private*, pg. 486
BATES FINANCIAL ADVISORS, INC.—See QCR Holdings, Inc.; *U.S. Public*, pg. 1742
BATES FRANCE—See WPP plc; *Int'l*, pg. 8464
BATES GROUP LLC; *U.S. Private*, pg. 486
BATES/LEE ADVERTISING; *U.S. Private*, pg. 487
BATES NISSAN INC.; *U.S. Private*, pg. 486
BATES RV EXCHANGE; *U.S. Private*, pg. 486
BATES RV; *U.S. Private*, pg. 486
BATES SALES COMPANY INC.; *U.S. Private*, pg. 486
BATES SECURITY, LLC—See Pye-Barker Fire & Safety, LLC; *U.S. Private*, pg. 3309
BATES UNITED—See WPP plc; *Int'l*, pg. 8467
BATESVILLE CANADA LTD.—See Hillenbrand, Inc.; *U.S. Public*, pg. 1035
BATESVILLE CASKET COMPANY, INC.—See LongRange Capital LLC; *U.S. Private*, pg. 2493
BATESVILLE CASKET DE MEXICO, S.A. DE C.V.—See Hillenbrand, Inc.; *U.S. Public*, pg. 1035
BATESVILLE CASKET UK LIMITED—See Hillenbrand, Inc.; *U.S. Public*, pg. 1035
BATESVILLE HMA MEDICAL GROUP, LLC—See Curae Health, Inc.; *U.S. Private*, pg. 1124
BATESVILLE HOLDING UK, LIMITED—See Hillenbrand, Inc.; *U.S. Public*, pg. 1035
BATESVILLE MANUFACTURING, INC.—See Hillenbrand, Inc.; *U.S. Public*, pg. 1035
BATESVILLE SERVICES, INC.—See Hillenbrand, Inc.; *U.S. Public*, pg. 1035
BATESVILLE TOOL & DIE INC.; *U.S. Private*, pg. 487
BATES WHITE, LLC.; *U.S. Private*, pg. 486
BATEY GROUP—See WPP plc; *Int'l*, pg. 8469
BATH AND PORTLAND STONE (HOLDINGS) LIMITED—See Heidelberg Materials AG; *Int'l*, pg. 3308
BATH & BODY WORKS BRAND MANAGEMENT, INC.—See Bath & Body Works, Inc.; *U.S. Public*, pg. 279
BATH & BODY WORKS, INC.; *U.S. Public*, pg. 279
BATH & BODY WORKS, LLC—See Bath & Body Works, Inc.; *U.S. Public*, pg. 279
BATH BUILDING SOCIETY; *Int'l*, pg. 889
BATH BUS COMPANY—See Regie Autonome des Transports Parisiens; *Int'l*, pg. 6253
BATHCLIN CORPORATION—See Earth Corporation; *Int'l*, pg. 2268
BATH COMMUNITY HOSPITAL; *U.S. Private*, pg. 487
BATHCRAFT, INC.—See Investindustrial Advisors Ltd.; *Int'l*, pg. 3779
BATH IRON WORKS CORPORATION—See General Dynamics Corporation; *U.S. Public*, pg. 915
BATH PROPERTY LETTING LIMITED—See Bath Building Society; *Int'l*, pg. 889
BATH SAVER INC.; *U.S. Private*, pg. 487
BATH SAVINGS INSTITUTION; *U.S. Private*, pg. 487
BATHSHOPONLINE LTD.—See Norcros plc; *Int'l*, pg. 5415
THE BATH STONE COMPANY LIMITED—See SigmaRoc Plc; *Int'l*, pg. 6909
BATH STREET CAPITAL LIMITED; *Int'l*, pg. 889
BATHURST METALS CORP.; *Int'l*, pg. 889
BATHURST RESOURCES LIMITED; *Int'l*, pg. 889
BAT IBERICA, S.L.—See BAT S.p.A.; *Int'l*, pg. 888
BATICIM BATI ANADOLU CIMENTO SANAYII A.S.; *Int'l*, pg. 889
BATICIM ENERJI ELEKTRIK URETIM A.S.—See BatiSoke Soke Cimento Sanayii TAS; *Int'l*, pg. 889
BATIC INVESTMENTS & LOGISTICS CO; *Int'l*, pg. 889
BATICOMPOS SPA—See Cevital S.p.A.; *Int'l*, pg. 1425
BATIFOIX SAS—See VINCI S.A.; *Int'l*, pg. 8213
BATIGERE NORD EST; *Int'l*, pg. 889
BATIGROUP DENTAL DIS URUNLERI TICARET AS—See Straumann Holding AG; *Int'l*, pg. 7237
BATIMAP SA—See Groupe BPCE; *Int'l*, pg. 3092
BATIMENTS ET LOGEMENTS RESIDENTIELS; *Int'l*, pg. 889
BATIMETAL S.A.S.—See Owens Corning; *U.S. Public*, pg. 1626
B.A.T. INTERNATIONAL FINANCE P.L.C.—See British American Tobacco plc; *Int'l*, pg. 1165
BAT INVESTMENTS, INC.; *U.S. Private*, pg. 486
BATIROC BRETAGNE PAYS DE LOIRE SA—See Groupe BPCE; *Int'l*, pg. 3092
BATIROC S.A.S.—See Etex SA/NV; *Int'l*, pg. 2521

BATISELF S.A.—See Praktiker AG; *Int'l*, pg. 5954
BATISOKE SOKE CIMENTO SANAYII TAS; *Int'l*, pg. 889
BATIST MEDICAL A.S.—See Interogo Holding AG; *Int'l*, pg. 3754
BATIST MEDICAL SK S.R.O.—See Interogo Holding AG; *Int'l*, pg. 3754
BATISTYL PRODUCTION; *Int'l*, pg. 889
BATIVAL; *Int'l*, pg. 890
BATJER SERVICE; *U.S. Private*, pg. 487
BATLA MINERALS SA; *Int'l*, pg. 890
BATLIBOI LTD.; *Int'l*, pg. 890
BATLINER PAPER STOCK COMPANY, INC.—See Pioneer Industries, Inc.; *U.S. Private*, pg. 3187
BATLINER RECYCLING—See Pioneer Industries, Inc.; *U.S. Private*, pg. 3187
BATM ADVANCED COMMUNICATIONS LTD.; *Int'l*, pg. 890
BATM FRANCE—See BATM Advanced Communications Ltd.; *Int'l*, pg. 890
B.A.T.M. GERMANY GMBH—See BATM Advanced Communications Ltd.; *Int'l*, pg. 890
BATON ROUGE AREA FOUNDATION; *U.S. Private*, pg. 487
BATON ROUGE COCA-COLA BOTTLING COMPANY—See Coca-Cola Bottling Co. United, Inc.; *U.S. Private*, pg. 958
BATON ROUGE FRACTIONATORS LLC—See The Williams Companies, Inc.; *U.S. Public*, pg. 2142
BATON ROUGE JET CENTER LLC; *U.S. Private*, pg. 487
BATON ROUGE TOBACCO CO. INC.; *U.S. Private*, pg. 487
BATON ROUGE TREATMENT CENTER, INC.—See Acadia Healthcare Company, Inc.; *U.S. Public*, pg. 28
BATON ROUGE WATER WORKS COMPANY; *U.S. Private*, pg. 487
BATORY FOODS INC.; *U.S. Private*, pg. 487
BATOT HYDRO POWER LIMITED—See Weizmann Limited; *Int'l*, pg. 8371
BATS GLOBAL MARKETS HOLDINGS, INC.—See Cboe Global Markets, Inc.; *U.S. Public*, pg. 459
BATS GLOBAL MARKETS, INC.—See Cboe Global Markets, Inc.; *U.S. Public*, pg. 459
BATSON-COOK COMPANY—See Kajima Corporation; *Int'l*, pg. 4055
BATSON-COOK DEVELOPMENT COMPANY—See Kajima Corporation; *Int'l*, pg. 4055
BATSON MILL L.L.C.—See Newpark Resources, Inc.; *U.S. Public*, pg. 1517
BAT S.P.A.; *Int'l*, pg. 888
BATS TRADING LIMITED—See Cboe Global Markets, Inc.; *U.S. Public*, pg. 459
B.A.T. SUCURSAL COSTA RICA—See British American Tobacco plc; *Int'l*, pg. 1165
BATTALIA WINSTON INTERNATIONAL; *U.S. Private*, pg. 487
BATTALION OIL CORP.; *U.S. Public*, pg. 279
BATTAT INC.; *U.S. Private*, pg. 487
BATTEA - CLASS ACTION SERVICES, LLC—See SS&C Technologies Holdings, Inc.; *U.S. Public*, pg. 1922
BATTELLE INDIA.—See Battelle Memorial Institute; *U.S. Private*, pg. 487
BATTELLE MEMORIAL INSTITUTE; *U.S. Private*, pg. 487
BATTELLE UK LIMITED—See Battelle Memorial Institute; *U.S. Private*, pg. 487
BATTELLE VENTURES, L.P.—See Battelle Memorial Institute; *U.S. Private*, pg. 487
BATTENFELD-AMERICAN, INC.—See Battenfeld Management Inc.; *U.S. Private*, pg. 488
BATTENFELD GREASE (CANADA) LTD.—See Battenfeld Management Inc.; *U.S. Private*, pg. 488
BATTENFELD GREASE & OIL CORP—See Battenfeld Management Inc.; *U.S. Private*, pg. 488
BATTENFELD MANAGEMENT INC.; *U.S. Private*, pg. 488
BATTENFELD POLSKA INJECTION MOULDING TECHNOLOGY SP. Z O.O.—See Wittmann Kunststoffgerate GmbH; *Int'l*, pg. 8439
BATTENFELD SCHWEIZ AG—See Wittmann Kunststoffgerate GmbH; *Int'l*, pg. 8439
BATTENFELD SVERIGE AB—See Wittmann Kunststoffgerate GmbH; *Int'l*, pg. 8439
BATTENFELD TECHNOLOGIES, INC.—See Smith & Wesson Brands, Inc.; *U.S. Public*, pg. 1896
BATTEN & SHAW, INC.; *U.S. Private*, pg. 488
BATTERIAS HAWKER DE MEXICO S. DE R.L. DE C.V.—See EnerSys; *U.S. Public*, pg. 766
BATTERIES PLUS, LLC—See Freeman Spogli & Co. Incorporated; *U.S. Private*, pg. 1606
BATTERIUNION AB—See Addtech AB; *Int'l*, pg. 132
BATTERSEA REAL ESTATE SRL—See Bank of Cyprus Holdings Public Limited Company; *Int'l*, pg. 842
BATTER UP, LLC; *U.S. Private*, pg. 488
BATTERY ELECTRIC VEHICLE & ELECTRONIC PRODUCTS TESTING CENTER CO., LTD.—See Energy Absolute Public Company Limited; *Int'l*, pg. 2422
BATTERY FUTURE ACQUISITION CORP.; *U.S. Public*, pg. 279
BATTERY MINERAL RESOURCES CORP.; *Int'l*, pg. 890
BATTERY MINERALS LIMITED; *Int'l*, pg. 890

BATTERY POWER INTERNATIONAL PTE LTD.—See EnerSys; *U.S. Public*, pg. 766
BATTERY RECYCLERS OF AMERICA, LLC; *U.S. Private*, pg. 488
BATTERY SALES; *U.S. Private*, pg. 488
BATTERY SHOP, LLC—See HEICO Corporation; *U.S. Public*, pg. 1019
BATTERY SOLUTIONS, INC.—See Heritage Group; *U.S. Private*, pg. 1923
BATTERY SPECIALISTS, INC.—See Auto-Wares, LLC; *U.S. Private*, pg. 398
BATTERY SYSTEMS LLC; *U.S. Private*, pg. 488
BATTERY VENTURES, L.P. - MENLO PARK—See Battery Ventures, L.P.; *U.S. Private*, pg. 488
BATTERY VENTURES, L.P.; *U.S. Private*, pg. 488
BATTERY X METALS INC.; *Int'l*, pg. 890
BATTIKHA SECURITY INC.; *Int'l*, pg. 890
BATTISTELLA ADMINISTRACAO E PARTICIPACOES S.A.; *Int'l*, pg. 890
BATTLE CREEK ENQUIRER—See Gannett Co., Inc.; *U.S. Public*, pg. 897
BATTLE CREEK EQUIPMENT CO.; *U.S. Private*, pg. 489
BATTLE CREEK FARMERS COOP; *U.S. Private*, pg. 489
BATTLE CREEK MUTUAL INSURANCE COMPANY—See Nodak Insurance Company; *U.S. Private*, pg. 2933
BATTLEFIELD FARMS INC.—See Costa Farms, LLC; *U.S. Private*, pg. 1062
BATTLEFIELD - THE CAT RENTAL STORE—See Toromont Industries Ltd.; *Int'l*, pg. 7829
BATTLEGROUND OIL SPECIALTY TERMINAL COMPANY LLC—See Kinder Morgan, Inc.; *U.S. Public*, pg. 1232
BATTLEGROUND RESTAURANT GROUP INC.; *U.S. Private*, pg. 490
BATTLE INVESTMENT GROUP LLC; *U.S. Private*, pg. 489
BATTLE LUMBER COMPANY INC.; *U.S. Private*, pg. 490
BATTLE NORTH GOLD CORPORATION—See Evolution Mining Limited; *Int'l*, pg. 2572
BATTLE RIVER OILFIELD CONSTRUCTION LTD.—See Vertex Resource Group Ltd.; *Int'l*, pg. 8174
BATTLERS CORP.; *Int'l*, pg. 890
BATTLES TRANSPORTATION INC.; *U.S. Private*, pg. 490
BATTLEY HARLEY-DAVIDSON INC.; *U.S. Private*, pg. 490
BATTS INC.; *U.S. Private*, pg. 490
B.A.T (U.K. AND EXPORT) LTD.—See British American Tobacco plc; *Int'l*, pg. 1165
BATU KAWAN BERHAD; *Int'l*, pg. 890
BATUMI AIRPORT LLC—See TAV Havalimanlari Holding A.S.; *Int'l*, pg. 7477
BATUMI INTERNATIONAL CONTAINER TERMINAL LLC—See International Container Terminal Services, Inc.; *Int'l*, pg. 3746
BATUMI OIL TERMINAL LLC—See KazTransOil JSC; *Int'l*, pg. 4103
BATUMI SEA PORT LLC—See KazTransOil JSC; *Int'l*, pg. 4103
BATYS TRANSIT JSC; *Int'l*, pg. 891
BATZER CONSTRUCTION, INC.; *U.S. Private*, pg. 490
BATZNER PEST MANAGEMENT, INC.; *U.S. Private*, pg. 490
BATZ, S. COOP.—See Mondragon Corporation; *Int'l*, pg. 5028
BAUAN INTERNATIONAL PORT, INC—See International Container Terminal Services, Inc.; *Int'l*, pg. 3746
BAUBA RESOURCES LIMITED—See Raubex Group Limited; *Int'l*, pg. 6221
BAUBECON ASSETS GMBH—See Barclays PLC; *Int'l*, pg. 862
BAUBECON BIO GMBH—See Barclays PLC; *Int'l*, pg. 862
BAUBECON HOLDING 1 GMBH—See Barclays PLC; *Int'l*, pg. 862
BAUBECON IMMOBILIEN GMBH—See Barclays PLC; *Int'l*, pg. 862
BAUBLYS LASER GMBH—See Han's Laser Technology Industry Group Co., Ltd.; *Int'l*, pg. 3240
BAUCH ENGINEERING GMBH & CO. KG; *Int'l*, pg. 891
BAUCH POWERTRAIN COMPONENTS CO., LTD.—See BAUCH Engineering GmbH & Co. KG; *Int'l*, pg. 891
BAUDA A/S—See Toyota Motor Corporation; *Int'l*, pg. 7870
BAUDAX BIO, INC.; *U.S. Public*, pg. 280
BAUDOUX CONSTRUCTION METALLIQUES; *Int'l*, pg. 891
BAUDRY AUTOMOBILES; *Int'l*, pg. 891
THE BAUE FUNERAL HOME CO.—See Birch Hill Equity Partners Management Inc.; *Int'l*, pg. 1046
THE BAUE FUNERAL HOME CO.—See Homesteaders Life Co. Inc.; *U.S. Private*, pg. 1974
BAUER AKTIENGESELLSCHAFT; *Int'l*, pg. 891
BAUER AMBIENTE S.R.L.—See BAUER Aktiengesellschaft; *Int'l*, pg. 892
BAUER ANGOLA LDA.—See BAUER Aktiengesellschaft; *Int'l*, pg. 892
BAUER BUILT, INC.; *U.S. Private*, pg. 490
BAUER BUILT TIRE CENTER OF PERRY, IA—See Bauer Built, Inc.; *U.S. Private*, pg. 490
BAUER BULGARIA EOOD.—See BAUER Aktiengesellschaft; *Int'l*, pg. 892

BAUER BUILT, INC.   CORPORATE AFFILIATIONS

BAUER CASINGS MAKINA SANAYI VE TICARET LIMITED SIRKETI—See BAUER Aktiengesellschaft; *Int'l*, pg. 892
THE BAUER COMPANY, INC.—See The Snyder Group, Inc.; *U.S. Private*, pg. 4119
BAUER COMP HOLDING AG; *Int'l*, pg. 894
BAUER COMPRESSEURS S.A.R.L.—See BAUER COMP Holding AG; *Int'l*, pg. 894
BAUER COMPRESSORI S.R.L. UNIPERSONALE—See BAUER COMP Holding AG; *Int'l*, pg. 894
BAUER COMPRESSORS ASIA PTE LTD—See BAUER COMP Holding AG; *Int'l*, pg. 894
BAUER COMPRESSORS CO. LTD.—See BAUER COMP Holding AG; *Int'l*, pg. 894
BAUER COMPRESSORS INC.—See BAUER COMP Holding AG; *Int'l*, pg. 894
BAUER CONSUMER MEDIA LTD.—See Heinrich Bauer Verlag KG; *Int'l*, pg. 3323
BAUER CORPORATE SERVICES PRIVATE LIMITED—See BAUER Aktiengesellschaft; *Int'l*, pg. 891
BAUER CORPORATION; *U.S. Private*, pg. 490
BAUER DIGITAL KG—See Heinrich Bauer Verlag KG; *Int'l*, pg. 3324
BAUER EGYPT S.A.E.—See BAUER Aktiengesellschaft; *Int'l*, pg. 891
BAUER ENGINEERING GHANA LTD.—See BAUER Aktiengesellschaft; *Int'l*, pg. 892
BAUER ENGINEERING INDIA PRIVATE LIMITED—See BAUER Aktiengesellschaft; *Int'l*, pg. 891
BAUER ENVIRO KFT.—See BAUER Aktiengesellschaft; *Int'l*, pg. 891
BAUER EQUIPAMIENTOS DE PANAMA S.A.—See BAUER Aktiengesellschaft; *Int'l*, pg. 892
BAUER EQUIPMENT AMERICA INC.—See BAUER Aktiengesellschaft; *Int'l*, pg. 893
BAUER EQUIPMENT AUSTRALIA PTY. LTD.—See BAUER Aktiengesellschaft; *Int'l*, pg. 893
BAUER EQUIPMENT GULF FZE.—See BAUER Aktiengesellschaft; *Int'l*, pg. 892
BAUER EQUIPMENT HONG KONG LTD.—See BAUER Aktiengesellschaft; *Int'l*, pg. 892
BAUER EQUIPMENT INDIA PRIVATE LIMITED—See BAUER Aktiengesellschaft; *Int'l*, pg. 893
BAUER EQUIPMENT (MALAYASIA) SDN. BHD.—See BAUER Aktiengesellschaft; *Int'l*, pg. 892
BAUER EQUIPMENT (SHANGHAI) CO. LTD.—See BAUER Aktiengesellschaft; *Int'l*, pg. 892
BAUER EQUIPMENT SOUTH ASIA PTE. LTD.—See BAUER Aktiengesellschaft; *Int'l*, pg. 892
BAUER EQUIPMENT UK LIMITED—See BAUER Aktiengesellschaft; *Int'l*, pg. 893
BAUER FONDATIONS SPECIALES EURL—See BAUER Aktiengesellschaft; *Int'l*, pg. 893
BAUER FONDATIONS SPECIALES S.A.S.—See BAUER Aktiengesellschaft; *Int'l*, pg. 892
BAUER FOUNDATION CORP.—See BAUER Aktiengesellschaft; *Int'l*, pg. 891
BAUER FOUNDATIONS AUSTRALIA PTY LTD—See BAUER Aktiengesellschaft; *Int'l*, pg. 891
BAUER FOUNDATIONS CANADA INC.—See BAUER Aktiengesellschaft; *Int'l*, pg. 891
BAUER FOUNDATIONS PHILIPPINES, INC.—See BAUER Aktiengesellschaft; *Int'l*, pg. 891
BAUER FRISCHDIENST GMBH—See J. Bauer GmbH & Co. KG; *Int'l*, pg. 3854
BAUER FUNDACIONES PANAMA S.A.—See BAUER Aktiengesellschaft; *Int'l*, pg. 892
BAUER FUNDERINGSTECHNIEK B.V.—See BAUER Aktiengesellschaft; *Int'l*, pg. 892
BAUER GEAR MOTOR FINLAND OY AB—See Regal Rexnord Corporation; *U.S. Public*, pg. 1772
BAUER GEAR MOTOR LIMITED—See Regal Rexnord Corporation; *U.S. Public*, pg. 1772
BAUER GEORGIA FOUNDATION SPECIALISTS LCC—See BAUER Aktiengesellschaft; *Int'l*, pg. 893
BAUER GEOTECHNICAL SPECIALIZED FOUNDATION LLC—See BAUER Aktiengesellschaft; *Int'l*, pg. 893
BAUER GEOTEKNOLOJI INSAAT ANONIM SIRKETI—See BAUER Aktiengesellschaft; *Int'l*, pg. 893
BAUERHIN-ELEKTRO-WARME GMBH—See Lear Corporation; *U.S. Public*, pg. 1296
BAUER HOCKEY, INC.—See Fairfax Financial Holdings Limited; *Int'l*, pg. 2605
BAUER HOCKEY, INC.—See Power Corporation of Canada; *Int'l*, pg. 5944
BAUER HOLZBAU GMBH; *Int'l*, pg. 894
BAUER HONG KONG LIMITED—See BAUER Aktiengesellschaft; *Int'l*, pg. 894
BAUER INDUSTRIES INC.; *U.S. Private*, pg. 490
BAUER INTERNATIONAL FZE—See BAUER Aktiengesellschaft; *Int'l*, pg. 893
BAUER KOMPRESSOREN AUSTRALIA PTY LTD—See BAUER COMP Holding AG; *Int'l*, pg. 894
BAUER KOMPRESSOREN BEIJING LTD.—See BAUER COMP Holding AG; *Int'l*, pg. 894
BAUER KOMPRESSOREN CHINA LTD.—See BAUER COMP Holding AG; *Int'l*, pg. 894
BAUER KOMPRESSOREN EGYPT LTD.—See BAUER COMP Holding AG; *Int'l*, pg. 894

BAUER KOMPRESSOREN GCC FZE—See BAUER COMP Holding AG; *Int'l*, pg. 894
BAUER KOMPRESSOREN GMBH—See BAUER COMP Holding AG; *Int'l*, pg. 894
BAUER KOMPRESSOREN INDIA PVT. LTD.—See BAUER COMP Holding AG; *Int'l*, pg. 894
BAUER KOMPRESSOREN KOREA LIMITED—See BAUER COMP Holding AG; *Int'l*, pg. 894
BAUER KOMPRESSOREN RUSSIA LTD.—See BAUER COMP Holding AG; *Int'l*, pg. 894
BAUER KOMPRESSOREN SERVICE, S.L.U.—See BAUER COMP Holding AG; *Int'l*, pg. 894
BAUER KOMPRESSOREN SHANGHAI LTD.—See BAUER COMP Holding AG; *Int'l*, pg. 894
BAUER KOMPRESSOREN TURKIYE—See BAUER COMP Holding AG; *Int'l*, pg. 894
BAUER KOMPRESSOREN UK LTD.—See BAUER COMP Holding AG; *Int'l*, pg. 894
BAUER LEBANON FOUNDATION SPECIALISTS S.A.R.L.—See BAUER Aktiengesellschaft; *Int'l*, pg. 893
BAUER MACCHINE ITALIA SRL—See BAUER Aktiengesellschaft; *Int'l*, pg. 893
BAUER MAGYARORSZAG SPECIALIS MELYEPITO KFT.—See BAUER Aktiengesellschaft; *Int'l*, pg. 893
BAUER (MALAYSIA) SDN. BHD.—See BAUER Aktiengesellschaft; *Int'l*, pg. 891
BAUER MANUFACTURING INC.—See BAUER Aktiengesellschaft; *Int'l*, pg. 892
BAUER MASCHINEN GMBH - ARESING PLANT—See BAUER Aktiengesellschaft; *Int'l*, pg. 892
BAUER MASCHINEN GMBH - EDELSHAUSEN PLANT—See BAUER Aktiengesellschaft; *Int'l*, pg. 892
BAUER MASCHINEN GMBH - SCHROBENHAUSEN PLANT—See BAUER Aktiengesellschaft; *Int'l*, pg. 892
BAUER MASCHINEN GMBH.—See BAUER Aktiengesellschaft; *Int'l*, pg. 892
BAUER MASZYNY POLSKA SP.Z.O.O.—See BAUER Aktiengesellschaft; *Int'l*, pg. 893
BAUER MEDIA AB—See Heinrich Bauer Verlag KG; *Int'l*, pg. 3324
BAUER MEDIA APS—See Heinrich Bauer Verlag KG; *Int'l*, pg. 3323
BAUER MEDIA AS—See Heinrich Bauer Verlag KG; *Int'l*, pg. 3323
BAUER MEDIA FRANCE SNC—See Heinrich Bauer Verlag KG; *Int'l*, pg. 3323
BAUER MEDIA GROUP AB—See Heinrich Bauer Verlag KG; *Int'l*, pg. 3323
BAUER MEDIA GROUP—See Heinrich Bauer Verlag KG; *Int'l*, pg. 3323
BAUER MEDIA NEW ZEALAND—See Heinrich Bauer Verlag KG; *Int'l*, pg. 3324
BAUER MEDIA OY—See Heinrich Bauer Verlag KG; *Int'l*, pg. 3323
BAUER MEDIA POLSKA SP. Z O.O.—See Heinrich Bauer Verlag KG; *Int'l*, pg. 3324
BAUER MEDIA SK V.O.S.—See Heinrich Bauer Verlag KG; *Int'l*, pg. 3324
BAUER MEDIA V.O.S.—See Heinrich Bauer Verlag KG; *Int'l*, pg. 3324
BAUER MIETPOOL GMBH.—See BAUER Aktiengesellschaft; *Int'l*, pg. 892
BAUER NIMR LLC—See BAUER Aktiengesellschaft; *Int'l*, pg. 893
BAUER-PILECO INC.—See BAUER Aktiengesellschaft; *Int'l*, pg. 892
BAUER-POSEIDON KOMPRESSOREN GES.M.B.H.—See BAUER COMP Holding AG; *Int'l*, pg. 894
BAUER PRINT CIECHANOW SP. Z O.O.—See Heinrich Bauer Verlag KG; *Int'l*, pg. 3323
BAUER PRINT WYKROTY SP. Z O.O.—See Heinrich Bauer Verlag KG; *Int'l*, pg. 3323
BAUER PUBLISHING USA—See Heinrich Bauer Verlag KG; *Int'l*, pg. 3324
BAUER RADIO LTD.—See Heinrich Bauer Verlag KG; *Int'l*, pg. 3324
BAUER RENEWABLES LIMITED—See BAUER Aktiengesellschaft; *Int'l*, pg. 893
BAUER RESOURCES CANADA LTD.—See BAUER Aktiengesellschaft; *Int'l*, pg. 892
BAUER ROMANIA S.R.L.—See BAUER Aktiengesellschaft; *Int'l*, pg. 892
BAUER SERVICES SINGAPORE PTE. LTD.—See BAUER Aktiengesellschaft; *Int'l*, pg. 892
BAUER SICHUAN CULTURE SERVICE CO.LTD.—See Heinrich Bauer Verlag KG; *Int'l*, pg. 3324
BAUER SPECIAL FOUNDATIONS CAMBODIA CO., LTD.—See BAUER Aktiengesellschaft; *Int'l*, pg. 892
BAUER SPECIALIST MEDIA—See Heinrich Bauer Verlag KG; *Int'l*, pg. 3323
BAUER SPEZIALTIEFBAU GESELLSCHAFT M.B.H.—See BAUER Aktiengesellschaft; *Int'l*, pg. 892
BAUER SPEZIALTIEFBAU GMBH.—See BAUER Aktiengesellschaft; *Int'l*, pg. 892
BAUER SPEZIALTIEFBAU SCHWEIZ AG.—See BAUER Aktiengesellschaft; *Int'l*, pg. 892
BAUER TECHNOLOGIES FAR EAST PTE. LTD.—See BAUER Aktiengesellschaft; *Int'l*, pg. 892

BAUER TECHNOLOGIES LIMITED—See BAUER Aktiengesellschaft; *Int'l*, pg. 892
BAUER TECHNOLOGIES SOUTH AFRICA (PTY) LTD.—See BAUER Aktiengesellschaft; *Int'l*, pg. 892
BAUER TECHNOLOGIES THAILAND CO., LTD.—See BAUER Aktiengesellschaft; *Int'l*, pg. 892
BAUER TIANJIN TECHNOLOGIES CO. LTD.—See BAUER Aktiengesellschaft; *Int'l*, pg. 892
BAUER TRADER MEDIA—See Heinrich Bauer Verlag KG; *Int'l*, pg. 3324
BAUER TRAINING CENTER GMBH—See BAUER Aktiengesellschaft; *Int'l*, pg. 893
BAUER UMWELT GMBH.—See BAUER Aktiengesellschaft; *Int'l*, pg. 892
BAUER VERTRIEBS KG—See Heinrich Bauer Verlag KG; *Int'l*, pg. 3324
BAUER VIETNAM LTD.—See BAUER Aktiengesellschaft; *Int'l*, pg. 892
BAUER-WALSER AG; *Int'l*, pg. 894
BAUGESELLSCHAFT M.B.H. ERHARD MORTL—See PORR AG; *Int'l*, pg. 5922
BAUGHMAN GROUP LTD; *U.S. Private*, pg. 490
BAUGHMAN SEALS INC—See Baughman Group Ltd; *U.S. Private*, pg. 490
BAUGHMAN TILE COMPANY, INC.; *U.S. Private*, pg. 490
BAUGRUND SUD GESELLSCHAFT FUR GEOTHERMIE MBH—See Max Weishaupt GmbH; *Int'l*, pg. 4735
BAUHAUS FURNITURE GROUP, LLC; *U.S. Private*, pg. 490
BAUHAUS INTERNATIONAL (HOLDINGS) LIMITED; *Int'l*, pg. 894
BAUHINIA HOTELS LIMITED—See Century City International Holdings Ltd; *Int'l*, pg. 1417
BAUHINIA PAINTS MANUFACTURING LIMITED—See Yips Chemical Holdings Limited; *Int'l*, pg. 8585
BAU HOLDING BETEILIGUNGS AG—See STRABAG SE; *Int'l*, pg. 7229
BAUKING AG—See CRH plc; *Int'l*, pg. 1843
BAUKNECHT AG—See Whirlpool Corporation; *U.S. Public*, pg. 2367
BAUKNECHT HAUSGERATE GMBH—See Whirlpool Corporation; *U.S. Public*, pg. 2367
BAULANDENTWICKLUNG GDST 1682/8 GMBH & CO OEG—See UniCredit S.p.A.; *Int'l*, pg. 8037
BAULAND GMBH—See BayernLB Holding AG; *Int'l*, pg. 913
BAULDERSTONE PTY LIMITED—See Lendlease Corporation Limited; *Int'l*, pg. 4452
BAULOISE AUTOMOBILES S.A.; *Int'l*, pg. 894
BAUMANN CHRYSLER-JEEP-DODGE; *U.S. Private*, pg. 490
BAUMANN ELECTRO AG—See Burkhalter Holding AG; *Int'l*, pg. 1224
BAUMANN FEDERN AG; *Int'l*, pg. 895
BAUMANN GMBH—See Baumann Federn AG; *Int'l*, pg. 895
BAUMANN KASE AG—See Emmi AG; *Int'l*, pg. 2384
BAUMANN MUELLES S.A.—See Baumann Federn AG; *Int'l*, pg. 895
BAUMANN PROPERTY COMPANY INC.; *U.S. Private*, pg. 490
BAUMANN RESSORTS S.A.—See Baumann Federn AG; *Int'l*, pg. 895
BAUMANN & SONS BUSES, INC.; *U.S. Private*, pg. 490
BAUMANN SPRING CO. (S) PTE. LTD.—See Baumann Federn AG; *Int'l*, pg. 895
BAUMANN SPRINGS & COATING PVT. LTD—See Baumann Federn AG; *Int'l*, pg. 895
BAUMANN SPRINGS LEON S. DE R.L. DEC. V.—See Baumann Federn AG; *Int'l*, pg. 895
BAUMANN SPRINGS & PRESSINGS (UK) LTD.—See Baumann Federn AG; *Int'l*, pg. 895
BAUMANN SPRINGS (SHANGHAI) CO. LTD.—See Baumann Federn AG; *Int'l*, pg. 895
BAUMANN SPRINGS S.R.O.—See Baumann Federn AG; *Int'l*, pg. 895
BAUMANN SPRINGS TEXAS HOLDINGS LLC—See Baumann Federn AG; *Int'l*, pg. 895
BAUMANN SPRINGS TEXAS LTD.—See Baumann Federn AG; *Int'l*, pg. 895
BAUMANN SPRINGS USA, INC.—See Baumann Federn AG; *Int'l*, pg. 895
BAUMAN OIL DISTRIBUTORS INC.; *U.S. Private*, pg. 490
BAU MARKET S.A.—See MATHIOS REFRACTORY S.A.; *Int'l*, pg. 4727
BAUMARKT DIREKT GMBH & CO KG—See Otto GmbH & Co. KG; *Int'l*, pg. 5662
BAUMART HOLDINGS LIMITED; *Int'l*, pg. 895
BAUM BROTHERS IMPORTS INC.; *U.S. Private*, pg. 490
BAUM CAPITAL PARTNERS MANAGEMENT LLC; *U.S. Private*, pg. 490
BAUMEISTER DOO; *Int'l*, pg. 895
BAUMEISTER KARL SEDLMAYER GESELLSCHAFT MIT BESCHRANKTER HAFTUNG—See Swietelsky Baugesellschaft m.b.H.; *Int'l*, pg. 7367
BAUMELER LEITUNGSBAU AG—See BKW AG; *Int'l*, pg. 1055
BAUME & MERCIER, INC.—See Compagnie Financiere Richemont S.A.; *Int'l*, pg. 1741

COMPANY NAME INDEX

BAUME & MERCIER S.A.—See Compagnie Financiere Richemont S.A.; *Int'l*, pg. 1740
BAUMER BETRIEBSHYGIENE VERTRIEBSGESELLSCHAFT MBH—See Bunzl plc; *Int'l*, pg. 1217
BAUMER BOURDON-HAENNI S.A.S.; *Int'l*, pg. 895
BAUMER FOODS INC.; *U.S. Private*, pg. 490
BAUMER HOLDING AG; *Int'l*, pg. 895
BAUMER S.A. - MOGI MIRIM FACTORY—See Baumer S.A.; *Int'l*, pg. 895
BAUMER S.A.; *Int'l*, pg. 895
BAUMERT—See Groupe Gorge S.A.; *Int'l*, pg. 3103
BAUMFOLDER CORPORATION—See Heidelberger Druckmaschinen AG; *Int'l*, pg. 3321
BAUMGARDNER SERVICES INC.—See Applied Industrial Technologies, Inc.; *U.S. Public*, pg. 171
BAUMGARTE BOILER SYSTEMS GMBH—See JFE Holdings, Inc.; *Int'l*, pg. 3935
BAUMGARTEN STAMP CO.—See American Marking Systems, Inc.; *U.S. Private*, pg. 241
BAUMGARTNER & LAMPERSTORFER INSTRUMENTS GMBH.; *Int'l*, pg. 895
BAUMGASSE 131 BAUTRAGER- UND VERWERTUNGSGESELLSCHAFT M.B.H.—See PORR AG; *Int'l*, pg. 5922
BAUMINERAL GMBH HERTEN—See E.ON SE; *Int'l*, pg. 2252
BAUMOT AG—See Baumot Group AG; *Int'l*, pg. 895
BAUMOT GROUP AG; *Int'l*, pg. 895
BAUMOT UK LTD.—See Baumot Group AG; *Int'l*, pg. 895
BAUM TEXTILE MILLS INC.; *U.S. Private*, pg. 490
BAUPERFORMANCE GMBH—See Bilfinger SE; *Int'l*, pg. 1024
THE BAUPOST GROUP LLC; *U.S. Private*, pg. 3992
BAUPRO GMBH—See Etex SA/NV; *Int'l*, pg. 2521
BAUQ PROJEKT GMBH—See Swietelsky Baugesellschaft m.b.H.; *Int'l*, pg. 7367
BAUR OPTIK GESCHAFTSFUHRUNGS-AG—See Fielmann Group AG; *Int'l*, pg. 2656
BAUR OPTIK GMBH RAIN—See Fielmann Group AG; *Int'l*, pg. 2656
BAUR VERSAND (GMBH & CO KG)—See Otto GmbH & Co. KG; *Int'l*, pg. 5662
BAUSCH HEALTH, CANADA INC.—See Bausch Health Companies Inc.; *Int'l*, pg. 897
BAUSCH HEALTH COMPANIES INC.; *Int'l*, pg. 895
BAUSCH HEALTH HELLAS SINGLE-MEMBER PHARMACEUTICALS SA—See Bausch Health Companies Inc.; *Int'l*, pg. 897
BAUSCH HEALTH LIMITED LIABILITY COMPANY—See Bausch Health Companies Inc.; *Int'l*, pg. 897
BAUSCH HEALTH LIMITED LIABILITY COMPANY—See Bausch Health Companies Inc.; *Int'l*, pg. 897
BAUSCH HEALTH LLC—See Bausch Health Companies Inc.; *Int'l*, pg. 897
BAUSCH HEALTH LLP—See Bausch Health Companies Inc.; *Int'l*, pg. 897
BAUSCH HEALTH MAGYARORSZAG KFT—See Bausch Health Companies Inc.; *Int'l*, pg. 897
BAUSCH HEALTH PERU S.R.L.—See Bausch Health Companies Inc.; *Int'l*, pg. 897
BAUSCH HEALTH ROMANIA SRL—See Bausch Health Companies Inc.; *Int'l*, pg. 897
BAUSCH HEALTH SLOVAKIA S.R.O.—See Bausch Health Companies Inc.; *Int'l*, pg. 897
BAUSCH HEALTH TRADING DWC-LLC—See Bausch Health Companies Inc.; *Int'l*, pg. 897
BAUSCH HEALTH UKRAINE LLC—See Bausch Health Companies Inc.; *Int'l*, pg. 897
BAUSCHLINNEMANN NORTH AMERICA, INC.—See Surteco Group SE; *Int'l*, pg. 7344
BAUSCH & LOMB AUSTRALIA PTY. LTD.—See Bausch Health Companies Inc.; *Int'l*, pg. 896
BAUSCH & LOMB B.V.B.A.—See Bausch Health Companies Inc.; *Int'l*, pg. 896
BAUSCH & LOMB B.V.—See Bausch Health Companies Inc.; *Int'l*, pg. 896
BAUSCH & LOMB CANADA, INC.—See Bausch Health Companies Inc.; *Int'l*, pg. 896
BAUSCH + LOMB CORPORATION—See Bausch Health Companies Inc.; *Int'l*, pg. 895
BAUSCH & LOMB ESPANA S.A.—See Bausch Health Companies Inc.; *Int'l*, pg. 896
BAUSCH & LOMB EYECARE (INDIA) PVT LTD.—See Bausch Health Companies Inc.; *Int'l*, pg. 896
BAUSCH & LOMB FRANCE SAS—See Bausch Health Companies Inc.; *Int'l*, pg. 896
BAUSCH & LOMB GESELLSCHAFT M.B.H.—See Bausch Health Companies Inc.; *Int'l*, pg. 897
BAUSCH & LOMB GREECE—See Bausch Health Companies Inc.; *Int'l*, pg. 896
BAUSCH & LOMB (HK) LTD.—See Bausch Health Companies Inc.; *Int'l*, pg. 896
BAUSCH & LOMB INCORPORATED—See Bausch Health Companies Inc.; *Int'l*, pg. 896
BAUSCH & LOMB INDIA PRIVATE LIMITED—See Bausch Health Companies Inc.; *Int'l*, pg. 896
BAUSCH & LOMB INSTRUMENTS—See Bausch Health Companies Inc.; *Int'l*, pg. 896

BAUSCH & LOMB IOM S.P.A.—See Bausch Health Companies Inc.; *Int'l*, pg. 896
BAUSCH & LOMB KOREA, CO. LTD.—See Bausch Health Companies Inc.; *Int'l*, pg. 896
BAUSCH & LOMB MALAYSIA SDN BHD - SURGICAL DIVISION—See Bausch Health Companies Inc.; *Int'l*, pg. 896
BAUSCH & LOMB MEXICO S.A. DE C.V.—See Bausch Health Companies Inc.; *Int'l*, pg. 896
BAUSCH & LOMB (M) SDN BHD—See Bausch Health Companies Inc.; *Int'l*, pg. 896
BAUSCH & LOMB NORDIC AB—See Bausch Health Companies Inc.; *Int'l*, pg. 896
BAUSCH & LOMB NORDIC AKTIEBOLAG—See Bausch Health Companies Inc.; *Int'l*, pg. 896
BAUSCH & LOMB PHARMACEUTICALS, INC.—See Bausch Health Companies Inc.; *Int'l*, pg. 896
BAUSCH & LOMB PHILIPPINES, INC.—See Bausch Health Companies Inc.; *Int'l*, pg. 896
BAUSCH & LOMB POLSKA SP. Z.O.O.—See Bausch Health Companies Inc.; *Int'l*, pg. 896
BAUSCH & LOMB POLSKA SP. Z.O.O.—See Bausch Health Companies Inc.; *Int'l*, pg. 896
BAUSCH & LOMB PUERTO RICO INC.—See Bausch Health Companies Inc.; *Int'l*, pg. 896
BAUSCH & LOMB SAGLIK VE OPTIK URUNLERITIC A.S.—See Bausch Health Companies Inc.; *Int'l*, pg. 896
BAUSCH & LOMB SCOTLAND LIMITED—See Bausch Health Companies Inc.; *Int'l*, pg. 896
BAUSCH & LOMB (SINGAPORE) PRIVATE LIMITED—See Bausch Health Companies Inc.; *Int'l*, pg. 896
BAUSCH & LOMB—See Bausch Health Companies Inc.; *Int'l*, pg. 896
BAUSCH & LOMB SOUTH AFRICA PTY. LTD.—See Bausch Health Companies Inc.; *Int'l*, pg. 896
BAUSCH & LOMB (S) PTE LTD.—See Bausch Health Companies Inc.; *Int'l*, pg. 896
BAUSCH & LOMB SURGICAL CORP.—See Bausch Health Companies Inc.; *Int'l*, pg. 896
BAUSCH & LOMB SURGICAL KOREA—See Bausch Health Companies Inc.; *Int'l*, pg. 896
BAUSCH & LOMB SWISS AG—See Bausch Health Companies Inc.; *Int'l*, pg. 897
BAUSCH & LOMB TAIWAN LTD.—See Bausch Health Companies Inc.; *Int'l*, pg. 896
BAUSCH & LOMB (THAILAND) LTD.—See Bausch Health Companies Inc.; *Int'l*, pg. 896
BAUSCH & LOMB U.K. LIMITED—See Bausch Health Companies Inc.; *Int'l*, pg. 896
BAUSCH & LOMB VENEZUELA S.A.—See Bausch Health Companies Inc.; *Int'l*, pg. 896
BAUSCH PHARMA KAZAKHSTAN LLP—See Bausch Health Companies Inc.; *Int'l*, pg. 897
BAUSCH RUMO LLC—See Bausch Health Companies Inc.; *Int'l*, pg. 897
BAU SHAN LIFE SCIENCE TECHNOLOGY CO., LTD.—See Sino-Life Group Limited; *Int'l*, pg. 6948
BAUSMAN & COMPANY, INC.; *U.S. Private*, pg. 490
BAUSPARKASSE SCHWABISCH HALL AKTIENGESELLSCHAFT - BAUSPARKASSE DER VOLKSBANKEN UND RAIFFEISENBANKEN—See DZ BANK AG Deutsche Zentral-Genossenschaftsbank; *Int'l*, pg. 2243
BAUSTEINWERK BOTT - BLASBERG G.M.B.H. & CO. KOMMANDITGESELLSCHAFT—See Heidelberg Materials AG; *Int'l*, pg. 3308
BAUSTOFF-HANDELS-UNION GMBH & CO. KG—See L. Possehl & Co. mbH; *Int'l*, pg. 4381
BAUSTOFFWERKE DRESDEN GMBH & CO. KG—See Heidelberg Materials AG; *Int'l*, pg. 3316
BAUTECH LABOR GMBH—See PORR AG; *Int'l*, pg. 5922
BAUTECHNIK GESELLSCHAFT M.B.H—See BayWa AG; *Int'l*, pg. 915
BAUTRAGERGESELLSCHAFT OLANDE MBH—See STRABAG SE; *Int'l*, pg. 7229
BAU-UNION POTSDAM GMBH—See Bilfinger SE; *Int'l*, pg. 1024
BAUUNTERNEHMAN ECHTERHOFF GMBH & CO. KG; *Int'l*, pg. 898
BAUUNTERNEHMUNG EHRENFELS GMBH—See VINCI S.A.; *Int'l*, pg. 8236
BAUUNTERNEHMUNG GEBR. ECHTERHOFF GMBH & CO. KG—See Bauunternehman Echterhoff GmbH & Co. KG; *Int'l*, pg. 898
BAUUNTERNEHMUNG KITTELBERGER GMBH I.L—See John Wood Group PLC; *Int'l*, pg. 3983
BAUVAL INC. - BAUVAL SAINTE-SOPHIE DIVISION—See BAUVAL inc.; *Int'l*, pg. 898
BAUVAL INC. - CARRIERE L'ANGE-GARDIEN DIVISION—See BAUVAL inc.; *Int'l*, pg. 898
BAUVAL INC. - LES CARRIERES REGIONALES DIVISION—See BAUVAL inc.; *Int'l*, pg. 898
BAUVAL INC. - SABLES L.G. DIVISION—See BAUVAL inc.; *Int'l*, pg. 899
BAUVAL INC.; *Int'l*, pg. 898
BAU-VEREIN ZU HAMBURG HAUSVERWALTUNGSGESELLSCHAFT MBH—See TAG Immobilien AG; *Int'l*, pg. 7406

BAUVERLAG BV GMBH—See Apax Partners LLP; *Int'l*, pg. 502
BAUVERLAG BV GMBH—See TowerBrook Capital Partners, L.P.; *U.S. Private*, pg. 4195
BAUWERK GROUP AG—See Ernst Gohner Stiftung; *Int'l*, pg. 2495
BAUXITE & NORTHERN RAILWAY COMPANY—See Brookfield Infrastructure Partners L.P.; *Int'l*, pg. 1190
BAUXITE & NORTHERN RAILWAY COMPANY—See GIC Pte. Ltd.; *Int'l*, pg. 2965
BAUZA & ASSOCIATES, LLC; *U.S. Private*, pg. 491
BAVARIA CARBON HOLDINGS GMBH—See Graphite India Ltd; *Int'l*, pg. 3061
BAVARIA CARBON SPECIALITIES GMBH—See Graphite India Ltd; *Int'l*, pg. 3061
BAVARIA ELECTRODES GMBH—See Graphite India Ltd; *Int'l*, pg. 3061
BAVARIA FERNSEHPRODUKTION GMBH—See Bavaria Film GmbH; *Int'l*, pg. 899
BAVARIA FILM GMBH; *Int'l*, pg. 899
BAVARIA FILM INTERACTIVE GMBH—See Bavaria Film GmbH; *Int'l*, pg. 899
BAVARIA FILM- UND FERNSEHSTUDIOS GMBH—See Bavaria Film GmbH; *Int'l*, pg. 899
BAVARIA FILMVERLEIH- UND PRODUKTIONS GMBH—See Bavaria Film GmbH; *Int'l*, pg. 899
BAVARIA IMMOBILIEN-BETEILIGUNGS-GESELLSCHAFT MBH & CO. OBJEKT FURTH KG—See BayernLB Holding AG; *Int'l*, pg. 913
BAVARIA INDUSTRIES GROUP AG; *Int'l*, pg. 899
BAVARIA INTERNATIONAL AIRCRAFT LEASING GMBH & CO. KG—See Schorghuber Stiftung & Co. Holding KG; *Int'l*, pg. 6638
BAVARIA LLOYD REISEBUERO GMBH—See Bayerische Motoren Werke Aktiengesellschaft; *Int'l*, pg. 912
BAVARIA MEDIA ITALIA S.R.L.—See Bavaria Film GmbH; *Int'l*, pg. 899
BAVARIA MEDIA TELEVISION GMBH—See Bavaria Film GmbH; *Int'l*, pg. 899
BAVARIA MOTORS ALGERIE SARL—See Toyota Tsusho Corporation; *Int'l*, pg. 7875
BAVARIAN MEAT PRODUCTS, INC.; *U.S. Private*, pg. 491
BAVARIAN MOTOR TRANSPORT INC.; *U.S. Private*, pg. 491
BAVARIAN NORDIC A/S; *Int'l*, pg. 900
BAVARIAN NORDIC GMBH—See Bavarian Nordic A/S; *Int'l*, pg. 900
BAVARIAN NORDIC, INC.—See Bavarian Nordic A/S; *Int'l*, pg. 900
BAVARIAN SPECIALTY FOODS LLC; *U.S. Private*, pg. 491
BAVARIA PICTURES GMBH—See Bavaria Film GmbH; *Int'l*, pg. 899
BAVARIA PRODUCTION SERVICES GMBH—See Bavaria Film GmbH; *Int'l*, pg. 899
BAVARIA SA - BARRANQUILLA BREWERY PLANT—See Anheuser-Busch InBev SA/NV; *Int'l*, pg. 464
BAVARIA SA—See Anheuser-Busch InBev SA/NV; *Int'l*, pg. 464
BAVARIA SA - TIBITO MALT PLANT—See Anheuser-Busch InBev SA/NV; *Int'l*, pg. 464
BAVARIA SA - TOCANCIPA BREWERY PLANT—See Anheuser-Busch InBev SA/NV; *Int'l*, pg. 464
BAVARIA SA - TROPICAL MALT PLANT—See Anheuser-Busch InBev SA/NV; *Int'l*, pg. 464
BAVARIA SA - VALLE BREWERY PLANT—See Anheuser-Busch InBev SA/NV; *Int'l*, pg. 464
BAVARIA SONOR MUSIKVERLAG UND MERCHANDISING GMBH—See Bavaria Film GmbH; *Int'l*, pg. 899
BAVARIA SPORT & FREIZEIT GMBH—See Schorghuber Stiftung & Co. Holding KG; *Int'l*, pg. 6638
BAVARIA WIRTSCHAFTSAGENTUR GMBH—See Bayerische Motoren Werke Aktiengesellschaft; *Int'l*, pg. 912
BAVELLONI S.P.A.; *Int'l*, pg. 900
BAWAG ALLIANZ MITARBEITERVORSORGEKASSE AG—See Allianz SE; *Int'l*, pg. 351
BAWAG GROUP AG; *Int'l*, pg. 900
BAWAG LEASING & FLEET S.R.O.—See BAWAG Group AG; *Int'l*, pg. 900
BAWAG LEASING & FLEET S.R.O.—See BAWAG Group AG; *Int'l*, pg. 900
BAWAG P.S.K. BANK FUR ARBEIT UND WIRTSCHAFT UND OSTERREICHISCHE POSTSPARKASSE AKTIENGESELLSCHAFT; *Int'l*, pg. 900
BAWAG P.S.K. DATENDIENST GESELLSCHAFT M.B.H.—See BAWAG Group AG; *Int'l*, pg. 900
BAWAG PSK VERSICHERUNG AG—See Assicurazioni Generali S.p.A.; *Int'l*, pg. 645
BAWAN COMPANY; *Int'l*, pg. 900
BAWANG INTERNATIONAL GROUP HOLDING (HK) LIMITED—See BaWang International (Group) Holding Limited; *Int'l*, pg. 900
BAWANG INTERNATIONAL (GROUP) HOLDING LIMITED; *Int'l*, pg. 900
BAWAN WOOD INDUSTRIES CO.—See Bawan Company; *Int'l*, pg. 900
BAWLA CONSULTING INC.; *U.S. Private*, pg. 491
THE BAWMANN GROUP; *U.S. Private*, pg. 3992

THE BAWMANN GROUP — CORPORATE AFFILIATIONS

Company Index

BAXA CORPORATION—See Baxter International Inc.; *U.S. Public*, pg. 280

BAXALTA INCORPORATED—See Takeda Pharmaceutical Company Limited; *Int'l*, pg. 7438

BAXENDALE ADVISORY LIMITED; *Int'l*, pg. 900

BAXI AB—See BDR Thermea Group B.V.; *Int'l*, pg. 930

BAXI A/S—See BDR Thermea Group B.V.; *Int'l*, pg. 930

BAXI BELGIUM SA/NV—See BDR Thermea Group B.V.; *Int'l*, pg. 930

BAXI CALEFACCION, SLU—See BDR Thermea Group B.V.; *Int'l*, pg. 930

BAXI FRANCE—See BDR Thermea Group B.V.; *Int'l*, pg. 930

BAXI GROUP LTD.—See BDR Thermea Group B.V.; *Int'l*, pg. 930

BAXI HEATING (SLOVAKIA) S.R.O—See BDR Thermea Group B.V.; *Int'l*, pg. 930

BAXI INNOTECH GMBH—See BDR Thermea Group B.V.; *Int'l*, pg. 930

BAXI POTTERTON LTD.—See BDR Thermea Group B.V.; *Int'l*, pg. 930

BAXI ROMANIA SA—See BDR Thermea Group B.V.; *Int'l*, pg. 930

BAXI-SENERTEC UK LTD—See BDR Thermea Group B.V.; *Int'l*, pg. 930

BAXI SISTEMAS DE AQUECIMENTO UNIPESSOAL LDA—See BDR Thermea Group B.V.; *Int'l*, pg. 930

BAXI S.P.A.—See BDR Thermea Group B.V.; *Int'l*, pg. 930

BAXTER AG—See Baxter International Inc.; *U.S. Public*, pg. 280

BAXTER ARGENTINA S.A.—See Baxter International Inc.; *U.S. Public*, pg. 280

BAXTER AS—See Baxter International Inc.; *U.S. Public*, pg. 280

BAXTER AUTO GROUP; *U.S. Private*, pg. 491

BAXTER AUTO PARTS INC.; *U.S. Private*, pg. 491

BAXTER BELGIUM SPRL—See Baxter International Inc.; *U.S. Public*, pg. 280

BAXTER BIOSCIENCE DIVISION—See Baxter International Inc.; *U.S. Public*, pg. 280

BAXTER BIOSCIENCE MANUFACTURING SARL—See Baxter International Inc.; *U.S. Public*, pg. 280

THE BAXTER BULLETIN—See Gannett Co., Inc.; *U.S. Public*, pg. 897

BAXTER BUSINESS PTY LTD—See Cleanaway Waste Management Limited; *Int'l*, pg. 1654

BAXTER B.V.—See Baxter International Inc.; *U.S. Public*, pg. 280

BAXTER CARIBE, INC.—See Baxter International Inc.; *U.S. Public*, pg. 280

BAXTER COUNTY NEWSPAPERS, INC.—See Gannett Co., Inc.; *U.S. Public*, pg. 897

BAXTER DEUTSCHLAND GMBH—See Baxter International Inc.; *U.S. Public*, pg. 280

BAXTER DEUTSCHLAND HOLDING GMBH—See Baxter International Inc.; *U.S. Public*, pg. 280

BAXTER DISTRIBUTION CENTER EUROPE SA—See Baxter International Inc.; *U.S. Public*, pg. 280

BAXTER DRUG, INC.—See Walgreens Boots Alliance, Inc.; *U.S. Public*, pg. 2323

BAXTER HEALTHCARE CORPORATION OF PUERTO RICO—See Baxter International Inc.; *U.S. Public*, pg. 280

BAXTER HEALTHCARE CORPORATION—See Baxter International Inc.; *U.S. Public*, pg. 280

BAXTER HEALTHCARE GMBH—See Baxter International Inc.; *U.S. Public*, pg. 281

BAXTER HEALTHCARE (GUANGZHOU) COMPANY LTD—See Baxter International Inc.; *U.S. Public*, pg. 280

BAXTER HEALTHCARE HOLDING GMBH—See Baxter International Inc.; *U.S. Public*, pg. 281

BAXTER HEALTHCARE (HOLDINGS) LIMITED—See Baxter International Inc.; *U.S. Public*, pg. 280

BAXTER HEALTHCARE LIMITED—See Baxter International Inc.; *U.S. Public*, pg. 280

BAXTER HEALTHCARE LIMITED—See Baxter International Inc.; *U.S. Public*, pg. 280

BAXTER HEALTHCARE LIMITED—See Baxter International Inc.; *U.S. Public*, pg. 280

BAXTER HEALTHCARE LIMITED—See Baxter International Inc.; *U.S. Public*, pg. 280

BAXTER HEALTHCARE LIMITED—See Baxter International Inc.; *U.S. Public*, pg. 280

BAXTER HEALTHCARE LIMITED—See Baxter International Inc.; *U.S. Public*, pg. 281

BAXTER HEALTHCARE PTY LTD—See Baxter International Inc.; *U.S. Public*, pg. 280

BAXTER HEALTHCARE SA—See Baxter International Inc.; *U.S. Public*, pg. 280

BAXTER HEALTHCARE (THAILAND) COMPANY LIMITED—See Baxter International Inc.; *U.S. Public*, pg. 280

BAXTER (HELLAS) EPE—See Baxter International Inc.; *U.S. Public*, pg. 280

BAXTER HODELL DONNELLY PRESTON INC.; *U.S. Private*, pg. 491

BAXTER HOLDING B.V.—See Baxter International Inc.; *U.S. Public*, pg. 281

BAXTER HOLDING MEXICO, S. DE R.L. DE C.V.—See Baxter International Inc.; *U.S. Public*, pg. 281

BAXTER HOSPITALAR LTDA.—See Baxter International Inc.; *U.S. Public*, pg. 280

BAXTER (INDIA) PRIVATE LIMITED—See Baxter International Inc.; *U.S. Public*, pg. 280

BAXTER INNOVATIONS GMBH—See Baxter International Inc.; *U.S. Public*, pg. 281

BAXTER INTERNATIONAL INC.; *U.S. Public*, pg. 280

BAXTER LIMITED—See Baxter International Inc.; *U.S. Public*, pg. 281

BAXTER MANUFACTURING S.P.A.—See Takeda Pharmaceutical Company Limited; *Int'l*, pg. 7438

BAXTER MANUFACTURING SP Z O.O.—See Baxter International Inc.; *U.S. Public*, pg. 281

BAXTER MANUFACTURING (THAILAND) CO., LTD.—See Baxter International Inc.; *U.S. Public*, pg. 281

BAXTER MEDICAL AB—See Baxter International Inc.; *U.S. Public*, pg. 280

BAXTER MEDICATION DELIVERY—See Baxter International Inc.; *U.S. Public*, pg. 280

BAXTER MEDICO FAMACEUTICA, LDA.—See Baxter International Inc.; *U.S. Public*, pg. 281

BAXTER ONCOLOGY GMBH—See Baxter International Inc.; *U.S. Public*, pg. 281

BAXTER PHARMACEUTICALS INDIA PVT. LTD.—See Baxter International Inc.; *U.S. Public*, pg. 281

BAXTER PHARMACEUTICAL SOLUTIONS LLC—See Baxter International Inc.; *U.S. Public*, pg. 280

BAXTER POLSKA SP. Z.O.O—See Baxter International Inc.; *U.S. Public*, pg. 281

BAXTER R AND D EUROPE S.C.R.L.—See Baxter International Inc.; *U.S. Public*, pg. 281

BAXTER RECYCLERS PTY LTD—See Cleanaway Waste Management Limited; *Int'l*, pg. 1654

BAXTER RENAL DIVISION—See Baxter International Inc.; *U.S. Public*, pg. 280

BAXTER S.A. DE C.V.—See Baxter International Inc.; *U.S. Public*, pg. 281

BAXTER S.A.—See Baxter International Inc.; *U.S. Public*, pg. 281

BAXTER S.A.S.—See Baxter International Inc.; *U.S. Public*, pg. 281

BAXTER S.L.—See Baxter International Inc.; *U.S. Public*, pg. 281

BAXTER S.P.A.—See Baxter International Inc.; *U.S. Public*, pg. 281

BAXTERS PTY LTD—See Bapcor Limited; *Int'l*, pg. 857

BAY ACQUISITION CORP.; *U.S. Private*, pg. 491

BAYADA HOME HEALTH CARE, INC.; *U.S. Private*, pg. 495

BAY ADVANCED TECHNOLOGIES LLC - AUSTIN—See Bay Advanced Technologies LLC; *U.S. Private*, pg. 491

BAY ADVANCED TECHNOLOGIES LLC; *U.S. Private*, pg. 491

BAYALAG NALAIKH JOINT STOCK COMPANY; *Int'l*, pg. 901

BAY ALARM COMPANY INC.; *U.S. Private*, pg. 491

BAYANAT AI PLC; *Int'l*, pg. 901

BAYANG AT THE QUAY PTE. LTD.—See Katrina Group Ltd.; *Int'l*, pg. 4092

BAYANGOL HOTEL JOINT STOCK COMPANY; *Int'l*, pg. 901

BAYAN INVESTMENT HOLDING COMPANY K.S.C.C.; *Int'l*, pg. 901

BAYANNAOER ZIJIN NON-FERROUS METALS CO., LTD.—See Zijin Mining Group Company Limited; *Int'l*, pg. 8683

BAYAN SULU JSC; *Int'l*, pg. 901

BAYAN TELECOMMUNICATIONS HOLDINGS CORP.—See Deutsche Telekom AG; *Int'l*, pg. 2083

BAYAN TELECOMMUNICATIONS, INC.—See Deutsche Telekom AG; *Int'l*, pg. 2083

BAYANTRADE, INC.—See PLDT Inc.; *Int'l*, pg. 5896

BAYARA FZE LIMITED—See Savola Group; *Int'l*, pg. 6602

BAYARA HOLDING LIMITED—See Savola Group; *Int'l*, pg. 6602

BAYARD ADVERTISING AGENCY, INC.—See Axel Springer SE; *Int'l*, pg. 766

BAYARD ADVERTISING AGENCY, INC—See Axel Springer SE; *Int'l*, pg. 767

BAYARD ADVERTISING AGENCY, INC.—See Axel Springer SE; *Int'l*, pg. 767

BAYARD ADVERTISING AGENCY, INC.—See Axel Springer SE; *Int'l*, pg. 767

BAYARD ADVERTISING AGENCY, INC.—See Axel Springer SE; *Int'l*, pg. 767

BAYARD ADVERTISING AGENCY, INC.—See Axel Springer SE; *Int'l*, pg. 767

BAYARD ADVERTISING AGENCY, INC.—See Axel Springer SE; *Int'l*, pg. 767

BAYARD ADVERTISING AGENCY, INC.—See Axel Springer SE; *Int'l*, pg. 767

BAYARD ADVERTISING AGENCY, INC.—See Axel Springer SE; *Int'l*, pg. 767

BAYARD CANADA, INC.—See Bayard-Presse S.A.; *Int'l*, pg. 901

BAYARD, INC.—See Bayard-Presse S.A.; *Int'l*, pg. 901

BAYARD PRESSE ASIA—See Bayard-Presse S.A.; *Int'l*, pg. 901

BAYARD-PRESSE S.A.; *Int'l*, pg. 901

BAYARD REVISTAS S.A.—See Bayard-Presse S.A.; *Int'l*, pg. 901

BAYARD—See Triton Advisers Limited; *Int'l*, pg. 7934

BAY AREA ADDICTION RESEARCH & TREATMENT, INC.—See Webster Equity Partners, LLC; *U.S. Private*, pg. 4466

BAY AREA ANESTHESIA, LLC—See KKR & Co. Inc.; *U.S. Public*, pg. 1245

BAY AREA BARRICADE SERVICE, INC.—See Investcorp Holdings B.S.C.; *Int'l*, pg. 3776

BAY AREA BARRICADE SERVICE, INC.—See Trilantic Capital Management L.P.; *U.S. Private*, pg. 4231

BAY AREA BUILDING SOLUTIONS, INC.; *U.S. Private*, pg. 491

BAY AREA COMMUNITY HEALTH; *U.S. Private*, pg. 491

BAY AREA COMMUNITY RESOURCES INC.; *U.S. Private*, pg. 491

BAY AREA DERMATOLOGY ASSOCIATES—See Harvest Partners L.P.; *U.S. Private*, pg. 1876

BAY AREA DISTRIBUTING COMPANY; *U.S. Private*, pg. 491

BAY AREA ECONOMICS; *U.S. Private*, pg. 491

BAY AREA GOLD GROUP LIMITED; *Int'l*, pg. 900

BAY AREA HEALTHCARE GROUP, LTD.—See HCA Healthcare, Inc.; *U.S. Public*, pg. 991

BAY AREA HEART CENTER, INC.; *U.S. Private*, pg. 491

BAY AREA HIGH REACH, INC.; *U.S. Private*, pg. 491

BAY AREA HOUSTON ENDOSCOPY CENTER—See HCA Healthcare, Inc.; *U.S. Public*, pg. 991

BAY AREA INDUSTRIAL SERVICES INC.; *U.S. Private*, pg. 491

BAY AREA INSURANCE SERVICES; *U.S. Private*, pg. 491

BAY AREA NEWS GROUP—See Alden Global Capital LLC; *U.S. Private*, pg. 155

BAY AREA OIL SUPPLY INC.; *U.S. Private*, pg. 492

BAY AREA SURGICARE CENTER, INC.—See HCA Healthcare, Inc.; *U.S. Public*, pg. 991

BAY ASSOCIATES INC.; *U.S. Private*, pg. 492

BAY ASSOCIATES WIRE TECHNOLOGIES INC.—See MJM Holdings Inc.; *U.S. Private*, pg. 2753

BAY AUDIOLOGY LTD.—See Amplifon S.p.A.; *Int'l*, pg. 435

BAY AUDIO PTY. LTD.—See Amplifon S.p.A.; *Int'l*, pg. 435

BAYBA FINANCIAL SERVICE LIMITED—See Trust Bank Limited; *Int'l*, pg. 7944

BAY BANKS OF VIRGINIA, INC.—See Blue Ridge Bankshares, Inc.; *U.S. Public*, pg. 364

BAY & BAY TRANSFER COMPANY INC.; *U.S. Private*, pg. 491

BAY BLINDS LIMITED—See Nien Made Enterprise Co., Ltd.; *Int'l*, pg. 5280

BAY BREAD LLC—See Starbucks Corporation; *U.S. Public*, pg. 1938

BAY BREEZE FARMS, INC.—See Agro-Iron, Inc.; *U.S. Private*, pg. 130

BAYBRENT CONSTRUCTION CORP.; *U.S. Private*, pg. 495

BAY BRIDGE FOOD AND PRODUCE COMPANY; *U.S. Private*, pg. 492

BAYBRIDGE PHARMACY CORP.; *U.S. Private*, pg. 495

BAYBRIDGE SENIORS HOUSING INC.—See Ontario Teachers' Pension Plan; *Int'l*, pg. 5587

BAY BULLS MARINE TERMINAL INC.—See Penney Group; *Int'l*, pg. 5787

BAYBUTT CONSTRUCTION CORP.; *U.S. Private*, pg. 495

BAY CAPITAL MORTGAGE CORPORATION; *U.S. Private*, pg. 492

BAY CAPITAL PLC; *Int'l*, pg. 900

BAYCARE ALLIANT HOSPITAL—See BayCare Health System Inc.; *U.S. Private*, pg. 495

BAYCARE HEALTH SYSTEM INC.; *U.S. Private*, pg. 495

BAY CHEVROLET, INC.; *U.S. Private*, pg. 492

BAY CHEVROLET; *U.S. Private*, pg. 492

BAY CITIES APPLIANCE INC.; *U.S. Private*, pg. 492

BAY CITIES AUTO AUCTION—See Cox Enterprises, Inc.; *U.S. Private*, pg. 1076

BAY CITY CABINETS; *U.S. Private*, pg. 492

BAY CITY DIALYSIS CENTER, LLP—See Nautic Partners, LLC; *U.S. Private*, pg. 2869

BAY CLUB AMERICA, INC.—See KKR & Co. Inc.; *U.S. Public*, pg. 1264

BAY CLUB GOLDEN GATEWAY, INC.—See KKR & Co. Inc.; *U.S. Public*, pg. 1264

BAY CLUB MARIN—See KKR & Co. Inc.; *U.S. Public*, pg. 1264

THE BAY CLUBS COMPANY, LLC—See KKR & Co. Inc.; *U.S. Public*, pg. 1264

BAYCOAST BANK—See Narragansett Financial Corp.; *U.S. Private*, pg. 2835

BAYCOAT LTD.—See ArcelorMittal S.A.; *Int'l*, pg. 544

BAY COLONY REALTY, LLC—See iPic Entertainment Inc.; *U.S. Public*, pg. 1167

BAYCOM CORP; *U.S. Public*, pg. 284

294

COMPANY NAME INDEX

BAYCOM, INC.—See OwnersEdge Inc.; *U.S. Private*, pg. 3055
BAY COMMUNICATIONS INC.—See Hankyu Hanshin Holdings Inc.; *Int'l*, pg. 3254
BAYCOM OPTO-ELECTRONICS TECHNOLOGY CO., LTD.—See Tecom Co., Ltd.; *Int'l*, pg. 7519
BAY COMPUTING GROUP; *U.S. Private*, pg. 492
BAY CONVERTING INC.—See Bay Industries Inc.; *U.S. Private*, pg. 493
BAYCORP HOLDINGS, LTD.—See Tavistock Group, Inc.; *U.S. Private*, pg. 3937
BAYCORP HOLDINGS (NZ) LIMITED—See Encore Capital Group, Inc.; *U.S. Public*, pg. 759
BAYCORP (NZ) LIMITED—See Encore Capital Group, Inc.; *U.S. Public*, pg. 759
BAYCORP (WA) PTY LIMITED—See Encore Capital Group, Inc.; *U.S. Public*, pg. 759
BAYCORR PACKAGING INCORPORATED—See Pioneer Packing Inc.; *U.S. Private*, pg. 3187
BAY CORRUGATED CONTAINER INC.; *U.S. Private*, pg. 492
BAY COVE HUMAN SERVICES, INC.; *U.S. Private*, pg. 492
BAY CRANE SERVICE, INC.; *U.S. Private*, pg. 492
BAYCREST SDN BHD—See IOI Corporation Berhad; *Int'l*, pg. 3792
BAYCURRENT CONSULTING, INC.; *Int'l*, pg. 901
BAY DISPOSAL INC.—See Schaubach Holdings Inc.; *U.S. Private*, pg. 3563
BAY-DOVER INC.; *U.S. Private*, pg. 495
BAYEK TEDAVI SAGLIK HIZMETLERI VE ISLETMECILIGI A.S.—See Turkiye Is Bankasi A.S.; *Int'l*, pg. 7976
BAY ELECTRIC COMPANY, INC.; *U.S. Private*, pg. 492
BAY ENGINEERING, INC.—See Atwell, LLC; *U.S. Private*, pg. 384
BAY EQUIPMENT CORP.—See HEICO Corporation; *U.S. Public*, pg. 1019
BAY EQUITY, LLC.; *U.S. Private*, pg. 492
BAYER 04 LEVERKUSEN FUSSBALL GMBH—See Bayer Aktiengesellschaft; *Int'l*, pg. 901
BAYER 04 LEVERKUSEN SPORTFORDERUNG GGMBH—See Bayer Aktiengesellschaft; *Int'l*, pg. 902
BAYER AB—See Bayer Aktiengesellschaft; *Int'l*, pg. 902
BAYER AGCO LIMITED—See Bayer Aktiengesellschaft; *Int'l*, pg. 902
BAYER AGRICULTURE BVBA—See Bayer Aktiengesellschaft; *Int'l*, pg. 902
BAYER AGRICULTURE LIMITED—See Bayer Aktiengesellschaft; *Int'l*, pg. 902
BAYER AKTIENGESELLSCHAFT; *Int'l*, pg. 901
BAYER ALGERIE S.P.A.—See Bayer Aktiengesellschaft; *Int'l*, pg. 902
BAYER ANIMAL HEALTH GMBH—See Elanco Animal Health Incorporated; *U.S. Public*, pg. 722
BAYER ANIMAL HEALTH—See Elanco Animal Health Incorporated; *U.S. Public*, pg. 722
BAYER ANIMAL HEALTH - USA—See Elanco Animal Health Incorporated; *U.S. Public*, pg. 722
BAYER ARGENTINA S.A—See Bayer Aktiengesellschaft; *Int'l*, pg. 902
BAYER AS—See Bayer Aktiengesellschaft; *Int'l*, pg. 902
BAYER A/S—See Bayer Aktiengesellschaft; *Int'l*, pg. 902
BAYER AUSTRALIA LIMITED—See Bayer Aktiengesellschaft; *Int'l*, pg. 902
BAYER AUSTRIA GMBH.—See Bayer Aktiengesellschaft; *Int'l*, pg. 902
BAYER BETEILIGUNGSVERWALTUNG GOSLAR GMBH—See Bayer Aktiengesellschaft; *Int'l*, pg. 902
BAYER BIOSCIENCE GMBH—See Bayer Aktiengesellschaft; *Int'l*, pg. 904
BAYER BIOSCIENCE PVT. LTD.—See Bayer Aktiengesellschaft; *Int'l*, pg. 904
BAYER BITTERFELD GMBH—See Bayer Aktiengesellschaft; *Int'l*, pg. 904
BAYER BOLIVIANA LTDA.—See Bayer Aktiengesellschaft; *Int'l*, pg. 902
BAYER BULGARIA EOOD—See Bayer Aktiengesellschaft; *Int'l*, pg. 902
BAYER BUSINESS SERVICES GMBH—See Bayer Aktiengesellschaft; *Int'l*, pg. 902
BAYER B.V.—See Bayer Aktiengesellschaft; *Int'l*, pg. 902
BAYER CANADIAN HOLDINGS INC.—See Bayer Aktiengesellschaft; *Int'l*, pg. 902
BAYER CAPITAL CORPORATION B.V.—See Bayer Aktiengesellschaft; *Int'l*, pg. 902
BAYER CHEMICALS AG—See Bayer Aktiengesellschaft; *Int'l*, pg. 902
BAYER (CHINA) LIMITED—See Bayer Aktiengesellschaft; *Int'l*, pg. 901
BAYER CO. (MALAYSIA) SDN. BHD.—See Bayer Aktiengesellschaft; *Int'l*, pg. 902
BAYER CONSTRUCTION COMPANY, INC.; *U.S. Private*, pg. 496
BAYER CONSUMER CARE AG—See Bayer Aktiengesellschaft; *Int'l*, pg. 902
BAYER CORPORATION—See Bayer Aktiengesellschaft; *Int'l*, pg. 902
BAYER CROPSCIENCE AG—See Bayer Aktiengesellschaft; *Int'l*, pg. 902

BAYER CROPSCIENCE AUSTRALIA PTY. LTD.—See Bayer Aktiengesellschaft; *Int'l*, pg. 902
BAYER CROPSCIENCE (CHINA) COMPANY LTD.—See Bayer Aktiengesellschaft; *Int'l*, pg. 902
BAYER CROPSCIENCE DEUTSCHLAND GMBH—See Bayer Aktiengesellschaft; *Int'l*, pg. 903
BAYER CROPSCIENCE GUATEMALA, LIMITADA—See Bayer Aktiengesellschaft; *Int'l*, pg. 904
BAYER CROPSCIENCE HOLDING INC.—See Bayer Aktiengesellschaft; *Int'l*, pg. 903
BAYER CROPSCIENCE HOLDING SA—See Bayer Aktiengesellschaft; *Int'l*, pg. 903
BAYER CROPSCIENCE HOLDINGS INC.—See Bayer Aktiengesellschaft; *Int'l*, pg. 903
BAYER CROPSCIENCE HOLDINGS PTY LTD.—See Bayer Aktiengesellschaft; *Int'l*, pg. 903
BAYER CROPSCIENCE INC.—See Bayer Aktiengesellschaft; *Int'l*, pg. 903
BAYER CROPSCIENCE, INC.—See Bayer Aktiengesellschaft; *Int'l*, pg. 903
BAYER CROPSCIENCE K.K.—See Bayer Aktiengesellschaft; *Int'l*, pg. 903
BAYER CROPSCIENCE LIMITED—See Bayer Aktiengesellschaft; *Int'l*, pg. 903
BAYER CROPSCIENCE LIMITED—See Bayer Aktiengesellschaft; *Int'l*, pg. 903
BAYER CROPSCIENCE LP—See Bayer Aktiengesellschaft; *Int'l*, pg. 903
BAYER CROPSCIENCE LTDA.—See Bayer Aktiengesellschaft; *Int'l*, pg. 903
BAYER CROPSCIENCE LTD.—See Bayer Aktiengesellschaft; *Int'l*, pg. 903
BAYER CROPSCIENCE N.V.—See Bayer Aktiengesellschaft; *Int'l*, pg. 903
BAYER CROPSCIENCE (PORTUGAL) PRODUTOS PARA A AGRICULTURA, LDA.—See Bayer Aktiengesellschaft; *Int'l*, pg. 903
BAYER CROPSCIENCE (PRIVATE) LIMITED—See Bayer Aktiengesellschaft; *Int'l*, pg. 903
BAYER CROPSCIENCE PTY LIMITED—See Bayer Aktiengesellschaft; *Int'l*, pg. 903
BAYER CROPSCIENCE RAPS GMBH—See Bayer Aktiengesellschaft; *Int'l*, pg. 903
BAYER CROPSCIENCE S.A.S.—See Bayer Aktiengesellschaft; *Int'l*, pg. 903
BAYER CROPSCIENCE SCHWEIZ AG—See Bayer Aktiengesellschaft; *Int'l*, pg. 904
BAYER CROPSCIENCE, S.L.—See Bayer Aktiengesellschaft; *Int'l*, pg. 903
BAYER CROPSCIENCE—See Bayer Aktiengesellschaft; *Int'l*, pg. 903
BAYER CROPSCIENCE S.R.L.—See Bayer Aktiengesellschaft; *Int'l*, pg. 903
BAYER CROPSCIENCE VERMOGENSVERWALTUNGSGESELLSCHAFT MBH—See Bayer Aktiengesellschaft; *Int'l*, pg. 903
BAYER DE MEXICO, S.A. DE C.V.—See Bayer Aktiengesellschaft; *Int'l*, pg. 906
BAYER DIRECT SERVICES GMBH—See Bayer Aktiengesellschaft; *Int'l*, pg. 902
BAYER D.O.O. SARAJEVO—See Bayer Aktiengesellschaft; *Int'l*, pg. 906
BAYER D.O.O.—See Bayer Aktiengesellschaft; *Int'l*, pg. 906
BAYER D.O.O.—See Bayer Aktiengesellschaft; *Int'l*, pg. 906
BAYER D.O.O.—See Bayer Aktiengesellschaft; *Int'l*, pg. 906
BAYER EAST AFRICA LTD.—See Bayer Aktiengesellschaft; *Int'l*, pg. 904
BAYER FINANCE LTDA.—See Bayer Aktiengesellschaft; *Int'l*, pg. 904
BAYER GASTRONOMIE GMBH—See Bayer Aktiengesellschaft; *Int'l*, pg. 904
BAYER GLOBAL INVESTMENTS B.V.—See Bayer Aktiengesellschaft; *Int'l*, pg. 904
BAYER-HANDELSGESELLSCHAFT MIT BESCHRANKTER HAFTUNG—See Bayer Aktiengesellschaft; *Int'l*, pg. 906
BAYER HEALTHCARE AG - DERMATOLOGY UNIT—See Bayer Aktiengesellschaft; *Int'l*, pg. 904
BAYER HEALTHCARE AG—See Bayer Aktiengesellschaft; *Int'l*, pg. 904
BAYER HEALTHCARE AUSTRALIA—See Bayer Aktiengesellschaft; *Int'l*, pg. 902
BAYER HEALTHCARE BIOLOGICAL PRODUCTS—See Bayer Aktiengesellschaft; *Int'l*, pg. 904
BAYER HEALTHCARE CO. LTD.—See Bayer Aktiengesellschaft; *Int'l*, pg. 904
BAYER HEALTHCARE CONSUMER CARE—See Bayer Aktiengesellschaft; *Int'l*, pg. 904
BAYER HEALTHCARE MANUFACTURING S.R.L.—See Bayer Aktiengesellschaft; *Int'l*, pg. 904
BAYER HEALTHCARE PHARMACEUTICALS CANADA—See Bayer Aktiengesellschaft; *Int'l*, pg. 904
BAYER HEALTHCARE PHARMA—See Bayer Aktiengesellschaft; *Int'l*, pg. 904
BAYERHEALTH CARE—See Bayer Aktiengesellschaft; *Int'l*, pg. 904

BAYER HELLAS AG—See Bayer Aktiengesellschaft; *Int'l*, pg. 905
BAYER HISPANIA SL—See Bayer Aktiengesellschaft; *Int'l*, pg. 905
BAYER HOLDING LTD.—See Bayer Aktiengesellschaft; *Int'l*, pg. 905
BAYER HOLDING (THAILAND) CO., LTD.—See Bayer Aktiengesellschaft; *Int'l*, pg. 905
BAYER HUNGARIA KFT.—See Bayer Aktiengesellschaft; *Int'l*, pg. 905
BAYER INC.—See Bayer Aktiengesellschaft; *Int'l*, pg. 905
BAYER INDUSTRY SERVICES GMBH & CO. OHG—See Bayer Aktiengesellschaft; *Int'l*, pg. 905
BAYER INDUSTRY SERVICES GMBH & CO. OHG—See LANXESS AG; *Int'l*, pg. 4414
BAYER INTELLECTUAL PROPERTY GMBH—See Bayer Aktiengesellschaft; *Int'l*, pg. 905
BAYER INTERNATIONAL TRADE SERVICES CORPORATION—See Bayer Aktiengesellschaft; *Int'l*, pg. 902
BAYERISCHE ASPHALT-MISCHWERKE GMBH & CO.—See STRABAG SE; *Int'l*, pg. 7233
BAYERISCHE BAU UND IMMOBILIEN GMBH & CO. KG—See Schorghuber Stiftung & Co. Holding KG; *Int'l*, pg. 6638
BAYERISCHE BETEILIGUNGSGESELLSCHAFT MBH—See UniCredit S.p.A.; *Int'l*, pg. 8038
BAYERISCHE BORSE AG; *Int'l*, pg. 910
BAYERISCHE FUTTERSAATBAU GMBH—See BayWa AG; *Int'l*, pg. 917
BAYERISCHE HAUSBAU GMBH—See Schorghuber Stiftung & Co. Holding KG; *Int'l*, pg. 6638
BAYERISCHE HAUSBAU IMMOBILIEN GMBH & CO. KG—See Schorghuber Stiftung & Co. Holding KG; *Int'l*, pg. 6639
BAYERISCHE HAUSVERWALTUNG GMBH—See Schorghuber Stiftung & Co. Holding KG; *Int'l*, pg. 6639
BAYERISCHE IMMOBILIEN GMBH & CO. KG—See Schorghuber Stiftung & Co. Holding KG; *Int'l*, pg. 6639
BAYERISCHE LANDESBANK GIROZENTRALE—See BayernLB Holding AG; *Int'l*, pg. 913
BAYERISCHE LANDESBANK IMMOBILIEN-BETEILIGUNGS-GESELLSCHAFT MBH & CO. KG—See BayernLB Holding AG; *Int'l*, pg. 913
BAYERISCHE LANDESBANK INTERNATIONAL S.A.—See BayernLB Holding AG; *Int'l*, pg. 913
BAYERISCHE LANDESBODENKREDITANSTALT—See BayernLB Holding AG; *Int'l*, pg. 913
BAYERISCHE MASINDUSTRIE A. KELLER GMBH; *Int'l*, pg. 910
BAYERISCHE MOTOREN WERKE AKTIENGESELLSCHAFT - BERLIN PLANT—See Bayerische Motoren Werke Aktiengesellschaft; *Int'l*, pg. 912
BAYERISCHE MOTOREN WERKE AKTIENGESELLSCHAFT - LEIPZIG PLANT—See Bayerische Motoren Werke Aktiengesellschaft; *Int'l*, pg. 912
BAYERISCHE MOTOREN WERKE AKTIENGESELLSCHAFT - MUNICH PLANT—See Bayerische Motoren Werke Aktiengesellschaft; *Int'l*, pg. 912
BAYERISCHE MOTOREN WERKE AKTIENGESELLSCHAFT; *Int'l*, pg. 910
BAYERISCHE MOTOREN WERKE AKTIENGESELLSCHAFT - WACKERSDORF PLANT—See Bayerische Motoren Werke Aktiengesellschaft; *Int'l*, pg. 912
BAYERISCHES FILMZENTRUM WIRTSCHAFTS-FORDERUNGS GMBH—See Bavaria Film GmbH; *Int'l*, pg. 899
BAYERISCHE STADTE- UND WOHNUNGSBAU GMBH & CO. KG; *Int'l*, pg. 913
BAYERISCHE WOHNUNGSGESELLSCHAFT FUR HANDEL UND INDUSTRIE, GESELLSCHAFT MIT BESCHRKTER HAFTUNG—See UniCredit S.p.A.; *Int'l*, pg. 8039
BAYER ISRAEL LTD.—See Bayer Aktiengesellschaft; *Int'l*, pg. 905
BAYER JINLING POLYURETHANE CO., LTD.—See Bayer Aktiengesellschaft; *Int'l*, pg. 905
BAYER KOREA LTD.—See Bayer Aktiengesellschaft; *Int'l*, pg. 905
BAYER LIMITED EGYPT LLC—See Bayer Aktiengesellschaft; *Int'l*, pg. 905
BAYER LIMITED—See Bayer Aktiengesellschaft; *Int'l*, pg. 905
BAYER LTD.—See Bayer Aktiengesellschaft; *Int'l*, pg. 905
BAYER (MALAYSIA) SDN. BHD.—See Bayer Aktiengesellschaft; *Int'l*, pg. 901
BAYER MALIBU POLYMERS PRIVATE LIMITED—See Bayer Aktiengesellschaft; *Int'l*, pg. 907
BAYER MATERIALSCIENCE AUSTRALIA—See Bayer Aktiengesellschaft; *Int'l*, pg. 902
BAYER MATERIALSCIENCE (BEIJING) COMPANY LIMITED—See Bayer Aktiengesellschaft; *Int'l*, pg. 907
BAYER MATERIALSCIENCE B.V.—See Bayer Aktiengesellschaft; *Int'l*, pg. 907
BAYER MATERIALSCIENCE (CHINA) COMPANY LIMITED—See Bayer Aktiengesellschaft; *Int'l*, pg. 907
BAYER MATERIALSCIENCE GMBH—See Bayer Aktiengesellschaft; *Int'l*, pg. 907

BAYER MATERIALSCIENCE LTD.—See Bayer Aktiengesellschaft; *Int'l*, pg. 907
BAYER MATERIALSCIENCE LTD.—See Bayer Aktiengesellschaft; *Int'l*, pg. 907
BAYER MATERIALSCIENCE OLDENBURG VERWALTUNGS-GMBH—See Bayer Aktiengesellschaft; *Int'l*, pg. 907
BAYER MATERIALSCIENCE (SHANGHAI) MANAGEMENT COMPANY LIMITED—See Bayer Aktiengesellschaft; *Int'l*, pg. 907
BAYER MATERIALSCIENCE TRADING (SHANGHAI) CO. LTD.—See Bayer Aktiengesellschaft; *Int'l*, pg. 907
BAYER MEDICAL CARE B.V.—See Bayer Aktiengesellschaft; *Int'l*, pg. 905
BAYER MIDDLE EAST FZE—See Bayer Aktiengesellschaft; *Int'l*, pg. 905
BAYER MOTOR CO. INC.; *U.S. Private*, pg. 496
BAYER MOZAMBIQUE, LIMITADA—See Bayer Aktiengesellschaft; *Int'l*, pg. 905
BAYERN BANKETT GASTRONOMIE GMBH—See BayernLB Holding AG; *Int'l*, pg. 913
BAYERN CARD-SERVICES GMBH—See BayernLB Holding AG; *Int'l*, pg. 913
BAYERN-CHEMIE GESELLSCHAFT FUR FLUGCHEMISCHE ANTRIEBE MBH—See Airbus SE; *Int'l*, pg. 247
BAYERN-CHEMIE GESELLSCHAFT FUR FLUGCHEMISCHE ANTRIEBE MBH—See BAE Systems plc; *Int'l*, pg. 798
BAYERN-CHEMIE GESELLSCHAFT FUR FLUGCHEMISCHE ANTRIEBE MBH—See Leonardo S.p.A.; *Int'l*, pg. 4460
BAYERN CONNECT GMBH—See Minds + Machines Group Limited; *Int'l*, pg. 4902
BAYERN CONSULT UNTERNEHMENSBERATUNG GMBH—See Syngroup Management Consulting GmbH; *Int'l*, pg. 7385
BAYERN CORPORATE SERVICES GMBH—See BayernLB Holding AG; *Int'l*, pg. 913
BAYERN NETHERLANDS B.V.—See Bayer Aktiengesellschaft; *Int'l*, pg. 905
BAYER NEW ZEALAND LIMITED—See Bayer Aktiengesellschaft; *Int'l*, pg. 905
BAYERN EXPRESS&P. KUHN BERLIN GMBH—See Deutsche Bahn AG; *Int'l*, pg. 2049
BAYERNGAS ENERGY GMBH—See Stadtwerke Munchen GmbH; *Int'l*, pg. 7161
BAYERNGAS GMBH—See Stadtwerke Munchen GmbH; *Int'l*, pg. 7161
BAYERN GOURMET FOOD COMPANY LIMITED—See Hopewell Holdings Limited; *Int'l*, pg. 3473
BAYERNINVEST KAPITALANLAGEGESELLSCHAFT MBH—See BayernLB Holding AG; *Int'l*, pg. 913
BAYERNINVEST LUXEMBOURG S.A.—See BayernLB Holding AG; *Int'l*, pg. 913
BAYERNLAND EG; *Int'l*, pg. 913
BAYERNLB CAPITAL PARTNER GMBH—See BayernLB Holding AG; *Int'l*, pg. 913
BAYERNLB HOLDING AG; *Int'l*, pg. 913
BAYERNLB—See BayernLB Holding AG; *Int'l*, pg. 913
BAYER NORDIC SE—See Bayer Aktiengesellschaft; *Int'l*, pg. 905
BAYERNUGS GMBH—See Stadtwerke Munchen GmbH; *Int'l*, pg. 7162
BAYERNWERK AG—See E.ON SE; *Int'l*, pg. 2252
BAYER OU—See Bayer Aktiengesellschaft; *Int'l*, pg. 905
BAYER OY—See Bayer Aktiengesellschaft; *Int'l*, pg. 904
BAYER OY—See Bayer Aktiengesellschaft; *Int'l*, pg. 905
BAYER PAKISTAN (PRIVATE) LIMITED—See Bayer Aktiengesellschaft; *Int'l*, pg. 905
BAYER PARSIAN AG—See Bayer Aktiengesellschaft; *Int'l*, pg. 905
BAYER PARSIAN P.J.S. CO.—See Bayer Aktiengesellschaft; *Int'l*, pg. 905
BAYER PHARMA AG—See Bayer Aktiengesellschaft; *Int'l*, pg. 904
BAYER PHARMA AG - WUPPERTAL—See Bayer Aktiengesellschaft; *Int'l*, pg. 905
BAYER PHILIPPINES, INC.—See Bayer Aktiengesellschaft; *Int'l*, pg. 905
BAYER PLC—See Bayer Aktiengesellschaft; *Int'l*, pg. 906
BAYER POLYURETHANES B.V.—See Bayer Aktiengesellschaft; *Int'l*, pg. 905
BAYER PORTUGAL, LDA.—See Bayer Aktiengesellschaft; *Int'l*, pg. 905
BAYER PORTUGAL S.A.—See Bayer Aktiengesellschaft; *Int'l*, pg. 905
BAYER (PROPRIETARY) LIMITED—See Bayer Aktiengesellschaft; *Int'l*, pg. 901
BAYER PUERTO RICO, INC.—See Bayer Aktiengesellschaft; *Int'l*, pg. 902
BAYER REAL ESTATE GMBH—See Bayer Aktiengesellschaft; *Int'l*, pg. 905
BAYER S.A. DE C.V.—See Bayer Aktiengesellschaft; *Int'l*, pg. 906
BAYER SANTE SAS—See Bayer Aktiengesellschaft; *Int'l*, pg. 906
BAYER SA-NV—See Bayer Aktiengesellschaft; *Int'l*, pg. 906
BAYER S.A.—See Bayer Aktiengesellschaft; *Int'l*, pg. 906

BAYER SA—See Bayer Aktiengesellschaft; *Int'l*, pg. 906
BAYER S.A.—See Bayer Aktiengesellschaft; *Int'l*, pg. 905
BAYER S.A.—See Bayer Aktiengesellschaft; *Int'l*, pg. 905
BAYER S.A.—See Bayer Aktiengesellschaft; *Int'l*, pg. 906
BAYER S.A.—See Bayer Aktiengesellschaft; *Int'l*, pg. 906
BAYER S.A.—See Bayer Aktiengesellschaft; *Int'l*, pg. 906
BAYER S.A.—See Bayer Aktiengesellschaft; *Int'l*, pg. 906
BAYER SA—See Bayer Aktiengesellschaft; *Int'l*, pg. 906
BAYER SA—See Bayer Aktiengesellschaft; *Int'l*, pg. 907
BAYER S.A.—See Bayer Aktiengesellschaft; *Int'l*, pg. 906
BAYER S.A.—See Bayer Aktiengesellschaft; *Int'l*, pg. 906
BAYER S.A.S.—See Bayer Aktiengesellschaft; *Int'l*, pg. 906
BAYER SAUDI ARABIA LLC—See Bayer Aktiengesellschaft; *Int'l*, pg. 906
BAYER SCHERING PHARMA AG—See Bayer Aktiengesellschaft; *Int'l*, pg. 904
BAYER (SCHWEIZ) AG—See Bayer Aktiengesellschaft; *Int'l*, pg. 901
BAYER (SICHUAN) ANIMAL HEALTH CO., LTD.—See Bayer Aktiengesellschaft; *Int'l*, pg. 901
BAYER SOUTH AFRICA (PTY.) LTD.—See Bayer Aktiengesellschaft; *Int'l*, pg. 905
BAYER (SOUTH EAST ASIA) PTE LTD.—See Bayer Aktiengesellschaft; *Int'l*, pg. 902
BAYER S.P.A.—See Bayer Aktiengesellschaft; *Int'l*, pg. 904
BAYER S.P.A.—See Bayer Aktiengesellschaft; *Int'l*, pg. 906
BAYER, SPOL. S.R.O.—See Bayer Aktiengesellschaft; *Int'l*, pg. 906
BAYER SP. Z O.O.—See Bayer Aktiengesellschaft; *Int'l*, pg. 906
BAYER S.R.O.—See Bayer Aktiengesellschaft; *Int'l*, pg. 904
BAYER TAIWAN CO., LTD.—See Bayer Aktiengesellschaft; *Int'l*, pg. 906
BAYER TECHNOLOGY & ENGINEERING (SHANGHAI) CO., LTD.—See Bayer Aktiengesellschaft; *Int'l*, pg. 907
BAYER TECHNOLOGY SERVICES AMERICAS—See Bayer Aktiengesellschaft; *Int'l*, pg. 906
BAYER TECHNOLOGY SERVICES GMBH—See Bayer Aktiengesellschaft; *Int'l*, pg. 906
BAYER THAI COMPANY LIMITED—See Bayer Aktiengesellschaft; *Int'l*, pg. 904
BAYER TPU (SHENZHEN) CO. LTD.—See Bayer Aktiengesellschaft; *Int'l*, pg. 906
BAYER TURK KIMYA SANAYI LIMITED SIRKETI—See Bayer Aktiengesellschaft; *Int'l*, pg. 906
BAYER UK LIMITED—See Bayer Aktiengesellschaft; *Int'l*, pg. 906
BAYER-UNTERSTUTZUNGSKASSE GMBH—See Bayer Aktiengesellschaft; *Int'l*, pg. 906
BAYER URETECH LTD.—See Bayer Aktiengesellschaft; *Int'l*, pg. 906
BAYER U.S. LLC—See Bayer Aktiengesellschaft; *Int'l*, pg. 902
BAYER VAPI PRIVATE LIMITED—See Bayer Aktiengesellschaft; *Int'l*, pg. 906
BAYER VIETNAM LTD.—See Bayer Aktiengesellschaft; *Int'l*, pg. 906
BAYER VITAL GMBH—See Bayer Aktiengesellschaft; *Int'l*, pg. 905
BAYER WEIMAR GMBH & CO. KG—See Bayer Aktiengesellschaft; *Int'l*, pg. 906
BAYER WEST-CENTRAL AFRICA S.A.—See Bayer Aktiengesellschaft; *Int'l*, pg. 906
BAYER WR LLC—See Bayer Aktiengesellschaft; *Int'l*, pg. 906
BAYER YAKUHIN, LTD.—See Bayer Aktiengesellschaft; *Int'l*, pg. 906
BAYER ZAMBIA LIMITED—See Bayer Aktiengesellschaft; *Int'l*, pg. 906
BAYER ZIMBABWE (PRIVATE) LIMITED—See Bayer Aktiengesellschaft; *Int'l*, pg. 906
BAYER ZYDUS PHARMA PRIVATE LIMITED—See Bayer Aktiengesellschaft; *Int'l*, pg. 906
BAY FABRICATION INC.—See Bay Industries Inc.; *U.S. Private*, pg. 493
BAYFAIR QUALITY BUILDERS, LLC; *U.S. Private*, pg. 496
BAYFIELD COURT OPERATIONS LIMITED—See Welltower Inc.; *U.S. Public*, pg. 2347
BAYFIRST FINANCIAL CORP.; *U.S. Public*, pg. 284
BAYFIRST NATIONAL BANK—See BayFirst Financial Corp.; *U.S. Public*, pg. 284
BAYFIRST SOLUTIONS, LLC—See Kingswood Capital Management LLC; *U.S. Private*, pg. 2312
BAY FOOD SERVICES CO., LTD.—See Oriental Land Co., Ltd.; *Int'l*, pg. 5625
BAY FOODS INC.; *U.S. Private*, pg. 492
BAYFRONT AMBULATORY SURGICAL CENTER, LLC—See Community Health Systems, Inc.; *U.S. Public*, pg. 551
BAYFRONT HEALTH BROOKSVILLE—See Community Health Systems, Inc.; *U.S. Public*, pg. 551
BAYFRONT HEALTH IMAGING CENTER, LLC—See Community Health Systems, Inc.; *U.S. Public*, pg. 551

BAYFRONT HEALTH PORT CHARLOTTE—See Community Health Systems, Inc.; *U.S. Public*, pg. 551
BAYFRONT HEALTH SPRING HILL—See Community Health Systems, Inc.; *U.S. Public*, pg. 551
BAYFRONT HEALTH ST. PETERSBURG—See Orlando Health, Inc.; *U.S. Private*, pg. 3043
BAYFRONT HEALTH SYSTEM, INC.—See Community Health Systems, Inc.; *U.S. Public*, pg. 551
BAYFRONT HMA CONVENIENT CARE, LLC—See Community Health Systems, Inc.; *U.S. Public*, pg. 551
BAYFRONT HMA MEDICAL CENTER, LLC—See Community Health Systems, Inc.; *U.S. Public*, pg. 551
BAYFRONT HMA PHYSICIAN MANAGEMENT, LLC—See Community Health Systems, Inc.; *U.S. Public*, pg. 551
BAY GAS SERVICE, INC.—See Paraco Gas Corporation; *U.S. Private*, pg. 3089
BAY GROUP HOLDINGS SDN BHD; *Int'l*, pg. 900
BAY GROVE CAPITAL LLC; *U.S. Private*, pg. 492
BAY HARBOR GOLF CLUB INC.—See Boyne USA Resorts Inc.; *U.S. Private*, pg. 629
BAYHEALTH, S.L.—See Bayer Aktiengesellschaft; *Int'l*, pg. 906
BAY HILL CONTRACTING LTD.; *Int'l*, pg. 901
BAYHILL THERAPEUTICS, INC.; *U.S. Private*, pg. 496
BAYHORSE SILVER INC.; *Int'l*, pg. 914
BAY HOSPITAL, INC.—See HCA Healthcare, Inc.; *U.S. Public*, pg. 991
BAY-HOUSTON TOWING CO; *U.S. Private*, pg. 495
BAY HUMAN SERVICES; *U.S. Private*, pg. 493
BAY INDUSTRIES INC. - FABRICATED INSULATION DIVISION—See Bay Industries Inc.; *U.S. Private*, pg. 493
BAY INDUSTRIES INC.; *U.S. Private*, pg. 493
BAYING ECOLOGICAL HOLDING GROUP, INC.; *U.S. Public*, pg. 284
BAY INN, INC.; *U.S. Private*, pg. 493
BAY INSULATION OF ARIZONA INC.—See Bay Industries Inc.; *U.S. Private*, pg. 493
BAY INSULATION OF ILLINOIS INC.—See Bay Industries Inc.; *U.S. Private*, pg. 493
BAY INSULATION OF KANSAS CITY INC.—See Bay Industries Inc.; *U.S. Private*, pg. 493
BAY INSULATION OF MISSOURI INC.—See Bay Industries Inc.; *U.S. Private*, pg. 493
BAY INSULATION OF TENNESSEE INC.—See Bay Industries Inc.; *U.S. Private*, pg. 493
BAY INSULATION OF TEXAS INC.—See Bay Industries Inc.; *U.S. Private*, pg. 493
BAY INSULATION—See Bay Industries Inc.; *U.S. Private*, pg. 493
BAY INSULATION—See Bay Industries Inc.; *U.S. Private*, pg. 493
BAY INSULATION SUPPLY OF COLORADO INC.—See Bay Industries Inc.; *U.S. Private*, pg. 493
BAY INSULATION SUPPLY OF COLUMBUS—See Bay Industries Inc.; *U.S. Private*, pg. 493
BAY INSULATION SUPPLY OF MILWAUKEE—See Bay Industries Inc.; *U.S. Private*, pg. 493
BAY INSULATION SUPPLY OF NEVADA INC—See Bay Industries Inc.; *U.S. Private*, pg. 493
BAY INSULATION SUPPLY OF OHIO—See Bay Industries Inc.; *U.S. Private*, pg. 493
BAY INSULATION SUPPLY OF SAN DIEGO INC.—See Bay Industries Inc.; *U.S. Private*, pg. 493
BAY INSULATION SUPPLY OF SPOKANE—See Bay Industries Inc.; *U.S. Private*, pg. 493
BAY INSULATION SYSTEMS, INC.—See Bay Industries Inc.; *U.S. Private*, pg. 493
BAY INTERNATIONAL CANADA, ULC—See Berry Contracting L.P.; *U.S. Private*, pg. 538
BAYKAZ BETON LLP—See Heidelberg Materials AG; *Int'l*, pg. 3309
BAY KING CHRYSLER DODGE JEEP; *Int'l*, pg. 901
BAY LAKES COOPERATIVE; *U.S. Private*, pg. 494
BAYLAND BUILDINGS, INC.; *U.S. Private*, pg. 496
BAY LEASING & INVESTMENT LIMITED; *Int'l*, pg. 901
BAYLESS ENGINEERING, INC.—See Tide Rock Holdings, LLC; *U.S. Private*, pg. 4167
BAYLEY CONSTRUCTION INC.; *U.S. Private*, pg. 496
BAYLEYS CORPORATION LIMITED; *Int'l*, pg. 914
THE BAYLINE RAILROAD LLC—See Brookfield Infrastructure Partners L.P.; *Int'l*, pg. 1192
THE BAYLINE RAILROAD LLC—See GIC Pte. Ltd.; *Int'l*, pg. 2967
BAYLIN TECHNOLOGIES DO BRAZIL PRODUTOS DE TELECOMMUNICACOES LTDA.—See Baylin Technologies Inc.; *Int'l*, pg. 914
BAYLIN TECHNOLOGIES INC.; *Int'l*, pg. 914
BAYLIS (GLOUCESTER) LIMITED—See General Motors Company; *U.S. Public*, pg. 927
BAYLIS MEDICAL CO. INC.—See Boston Scientific Corporation; *U.S. Public*, pg. 374
BAYLIS MEDICAL COMPANY INC.—See Boston Scientific Corporation; *U.S. Public*, pg. 374
BAYLISS & COOKE LIMITED—See Brown & Brown, Inc.; *U.S. Public*, pg. 397
BAYLOFF STAMPED PRODUCTS DETROIT, INC.—See Bayloff Stamped Products, Inc.; *U.S. Private*, pg. 496

COMPANY NAME INDEX

BAYLOFF STAMPED PRODUCTS, INC.; *U.S. Private*, pg. 496
BAYLOR HEALTH CARE SYSTEM; *U.S. Private*, pg. 496
BAYLOR SCOTT & WHITE HEALTH—See Baylor Scott & White Holdings; *U.S. Private*, pg. 496
BAYLOR SCOTT & WHITE HOLDINGS; *U.S. Private*, pg. 496
BAYLOR SURGICARE AT ENNIS, LLC—See Tenet Healthcare Corporation; *U.S. Public*, pg. 2009
BAYLOR SURGICARE AT GRANBURY, LLC—See Tenet Healthcare Corporation; *U.S. Public*, pg. 2009
BAYLOR SURGICARE AT MANSFIELD, LLC—See Tenet Healthcare Corporation; *U.S. Public*, pg. 2009
BAYLOR SURGICARE AT NORTH DALLAS, LLC—See Tenet Healthcare Corporation; *U.S. Public*, pg. 2009
BAYLOR SURGICARE AT PLANO PARKWAY, LLC—See Tenet Healthcare Corporation; *U.S. Public*, pg. 2009
BAYLOR TRUCKING, INC.—See Werner Enterprises, Inc.; *U.S. Public*, pg. 2349
BAYMAK MAKINA SAN.VE TIC.A.S.—See BDR Thermea Group B.V.; *Int'l*, pg. 930
BAY MANUFACTURED HOMES INC.; *U.S. Private*, pg. 494
BAYMARK HEALTH SERVICES, INC.—See Webster Equity Partners, LLC; *U.S. Private*, pg. 4466
BAYMARK PARTNERS; *U.S. Private*, pg. 496
BAY MECHANICAL INC.; *U.S. Private*, pg. 494
BAY MICROSYSTEMS, INC.; *U.S. Private*, pg. 494
BAY MILL SPECIALTY INSURANCE ADJUSTERS INC.—See Aviva plc; *Int'l*, pg. 746
BAYMINA ENERJI AS—See ENGIE SA; *Int'l*, pg. 2432
BAYMONT MALAYSIA SDN. BHD.—See John Wood Group PLC; *Int'l*, pg. 3982
BAYMOUNT INCORPORATED; *Int'l*, pg. 914
BAY MUTUAL FINANCIAL, LLC; *U.S. Private*, pg. 494
BAYNE MACHINE WORKS, INC.—See Terex Corporation; *U.S. Public*, pg. 2019
BAYNE MINERAL SYSTEMS, INC.—See Crushing Equipment Solutions, LLC; *U.S. Private*, pg. 1114
BAYNES ELECTRIC SUPPLY CO. INC.—See Granite City Electric Supply Co., Inc.; *U.S. Private*, pg. 1755
BAYN EUROPE AB; *Int'l*, pg. 914
BAY NEWS 9—See Charter Communications, Inc.; *U.S. Public*, pg. 483
BAY N GULF INC.; *U.S. Private*, pg. 494
BAYNON INTERNATIONAL CORPORATION—See Henry Schein, Inc.; *U.S. Public*, pg. 1025
BAY OF QUINTE MUTUAL INSURANCE CO.; *Int'l*, pg. 901
BAY OIL COMPANY INC.; *U.S. Private*, pg. 494
BAYONET PLUMBING, HEATING & AIR CONDITIONING, LLC—See IES Holdings, Inc.; *U.S. Public*, pg. 1094
BAYONET POINT SURGERY AND ENDOSCOPY CENTER—See HCA Healthcare, Inc.; *U.S. Public*, pg. 991
BAYONET POINT SURGERY & ENDOSCOPY CENTER—See HCA Healthcare, Inc.; *U.S. Public*, pg. 991
BAYO; *Int'l*, pg. 914
BAYOU BAY DEVELOPMENT SDN. BHD.—See Iskandar Waterfront City Berhad; *Int'l*, pg. 3819
BAYOU CITY EXPLORATION, INC.; *U.S. Private*, pg. 496
BAYOU CITY PUMP COMPANY—See The Gorman-Rupp Company; *U.S. Public*, pg. 2085
BAYOU CONCRETE COMPANY INC.—See Ready Mix USA, Inc.; *U.S. Private*, pg. 3367
BAYOU GOLF CLUB—See Fore Golf Services, LP; *U.S. Private*, pg. 1565
BAYOU HOLZWERKSTOFFE GMBH; *Int'l*, pg. 914
BAYOU STATE OIL CORPORATION; *U.S. Private*, pg. 496
BAYOU STEEL CORPORATION (TENNESSEE)—See Cleveland-Cliffs, Inc.; *U.S. Public*, pg. 514
BAY PARC PLAZA APARTMENTS, L.P.—See Blackstone Inc.; *U.S. Public*, pg. 350
BAYPO II LLC—See Bayer Aktiengesellschaft; *Int'l*, pg. 902
BAYPO I LLC—See Bayer Aktiengesellschaft; *Int'l*, pg. 902
BAYPO LIMITED PARTNERSHIP—See Bayer Aktiengesellschaft; *Int'l*, pg. 902
BAYPORT FIMSA S.A.S—See Bayport Management Limited; *Int'l*, pg. 915
BAYPORT FINANCIAL SERVICES 2010 (PROPRIETARY) LIMITED—See Bayport Management Limited; *Int'l*, pg. 915
BAYPORT FINANCIAL SERVICES GHANA LIMITED—See Bayport Management Limited; *Int'l*, pg. 915
BAYPORT FINANCIAL SERVICES LIMITED—See Bayport Management Limited; *Int'l*, pg. 915
BAYPORT FINANCIAL SERVICES MOZAMBIQUE (MCB), SA—See Bayport Management Limited; *Int'l*, pg. 915
BAYPORT FINANCIAL SERVICES (T) LIMITED—See Bayport Management Limited; *Int'l*, pg. 915
BAYPORT FINANCIAL SERVICES UGANDA LIMITED—See Bayport Management Limited; *Int'l*, pg. 915
BAYPORT INTERNATIONAL HOLDINGS, INC.; *U.S. Public*, pg. 284
BAYPORT MANAGEMENT LIMITED; *Int'l*, pg. 914

BAYPORT MORTGAGE - LAS VEGAS—See The Warmington Group; *U.S. Private*, pg. 4133
BAYPORT MORTGAGE - SACRAMENTO—See The Warmington Group; *U.S. Private*, pg. 4133
BAY PRODUCTS, INC.; *U.S. Private*, pg. 494
BAY RAG CORPORATION; *U.S. Private*, pg. 494
BAYRAK EBT TABAN SANAYI VE TICARET A.S.; *Int'l*, pg. 915
BAY RIDGE AUTOMOTIVE GROUP; *U.S. Private*, pg. 494
BAY RIDGE PREP; *U.S. Private*, pg. 494
BAYRIDGE RESOURCES CORP.; *Int'l*, pg. 915
BAY RIDGE SUBARU; *U.S. Private*, pg. 494
BAY RIDGE VOLVO-AMERICAN INC.; *U.S. Private*, pg. 494
BAYROL DEUTSCHLAND GMBH—See LANXESS AG; *Int'l*, pg. 4415
BAYROL FRANCE S.A.S.—See LANXESS AG; *Int'l*, pg. 4415
BAYROL IBERICA S.L.U.—See LANXESS AG; *Int'l*, pg. 4415
BAYRU LLC; *U.S. Private*, pg. 496
BAYSAVER TECHNOLOGIES, LLC—See Advanced Drainage Systems, Inc.; *U.S. Public*, pg. 46
BAY SHIPBUILDING CO.—See Fincantieri S.p.A.; *Int'l*, pg. 2671
BAY SHIP & YACHT CO; *U.S. Private*, pg. 494
BAYSHORE CENTER AT BIVALVE; *U.S. Private*, pg. 496
BAYSHORE FORD TRUCK SALES INC.; *U.S. Private*, pg. 496
BAYSHORE HEALTH & HOMEMAKER SERVICES, INC.; *U.S. Private*, pg. 496
BAYSHORE INTERNATIONAL TRUCKS; *U.S. Private*, pg. 497
BAY SHORE MALL, LP—See Brookfield Corporation; *Int'l*, pg. 1185
BAYSHORE NETWORKS, LLC—See OPSWAT, Inc.; *U.S. Private*, pg. 3034
BAYSHORE PHARMACEUTICALS LLC—See Ipca Laboratories Ltd.; *Int'l*, pg. 3796
BAYSHORE SOLUTIONS INC.; *U.S. Private*, pg. 497
BAYSHORE SUPPLY & LIGHTS; *U.S. Private*, pg. 497
BAYSHORE TRUCK EQUIPMENT COMPANY—See Illinois Tool Works Inc.; *U.S. Public*, pg. 1101
BAYSIDE CAPITAL, INC.—See H.I.G. Capital, LLC; *U.S. Private*, pg. 1827
BAYSIDE CHRYSLER JEEP DODGE INC.; *U.S. Private*, pg. 497
BAYSIDE CORP.; *U.S. Public*, pg. 284
BAYSIDE DESIGN, INC.—See Socionext Inc.; *Int'l*, pg. 7044
BAYSIDE ENDOSCOPY CENTER, LLC—See Bain Capital, LP; *U.S. Private*, pg. 446
BAYSIDE ENGINEERING, INC.; *U.S. Private*, pg. 497
BAYSIDE FUEL OIL DEPOT CORPORATION; *U.S. Private*, pg. 497
BAYSIDE HEALTHCARE, INC.—See The Ensign Group, Inc.; *U.S. Public*, pg. 2070
BAYSIDE MACHINE CORP.; *U.S. Private*, pg. 497
BAYSIDE MARIN, INC.—See Acadia Healthcare Company, Inc.; *U.S. Public*, pg. 28
BAYSIDE PET RESORT & SPA, INC.; *U.S. Private*, pg. 497
BAYSIDE PHYSICAL THERAPY & SPORTS REHABILITATION, LIMITED PARTNERSHIP—See U.S. Physical Therapy, Inc.; *U.S. Public*, pg. 2214
BAYSIDE SOLUTIONS, INC.; *U.S. Private*, pg. 497
BAYSIDE STREET INCORPORATED—See Omega Healthcare Investors, Inc.; *U.S. Public*, pg. 1571
BAYSIDE VILLAGE ASSOCIATES, L.P.—See Brookfield Corporation; *Int'l*, pg. 1187
BAYSIDE VILLAS, LLC—See INSPIRATO INCORPORATED; *U.S. Public*, pg. 1131
BAYSIDE WEST LIMITED—See ANSA McAl Limited; *Int'l*, pg. 477
THE BAY—See Abrams Capital, LLC; *U.S. Private*, pg. 40
THE BAY—See Rhone Group, LLC; *U.S. Private*, pg. 3424
THE BAY—See WeWork Inc.; *U.S. Public*, pg. 2364
BAY SPRINGS TELEPHONE COMPANY, INC.—See Telephone Electronics Corporation; *U.S. Private*, pg. 3961
BAY STAGE LIGHTING COMPANY, INC.; *U.S. Private*, pg. 494
BAYSTAR HOTEL GROUP, LLC; *U.S. Private*, pg. 497
BAY STATE COLLEGE—See Ambow Education Holding Ltd.; *Int'l*, pg. 415
BAY STATE COMPUTERS INC.; *U.S. Private*, pg. 494
BAY STATE ENVELOPE INC.; *U.S. Private*, pg. 494
BAYSTATE FINANCIAL SERVICES, LLC; *U.S. Private*, pg. 497
BAY STATE GAS COMPANY—See Eversource Energy; *U.S. Public*, pg. 801
BAYSTATE HEALTH SYSTEM, INC.; *U.S. Private*, pg. 497
BAY STATE INSURANCE COMPANY—See The Andover Companies; *U.S. Private*, pg. 3986
BAYSTATE MEDICAL EDUCATION & RESEARCH FOUNDATION INC.—See Baystate Health System, Inc.; *U.S. Private*, pg. 497
BAY STATE MILLING COMPANY; *U.S. Private*, pg. 494
BAY STATE MILLING COMPANY—See Bay State Milling Company; *U.S. Private*, pg. 494

BAYWA AG

BAY STATE PHYSICAL THERAPY; *U.S. Private*, pg. 494
BAY STATE POOL SUPPLIES INC.; *U.S. Private*, pg. 494
BAY STATE SAVINGS BANK; *U.S. Private*, pg. 494
BAYSWATER BROKERAGE MASS. LLC—See Icahn Enterprises L.P.; *U.S. Public*, pg. 1084
BAYSWATER DEVELOPMENT CORPORATION—See The Goldfield Corporation; *U.S. Public*, pg. 2075
BAYSWATER FALLING WATERS LLC—See Icahn Enterprises L.P.; *U.S. Public*, pg. 1084
BAYTACARE PHARMACEUTICAL CO., LTD; *Int'l*, pg. 915
BAY TANK & VESSEL CANADA, LTD.—See Berry Contracting L.P.; *U.S. Private*, pg. 538
BAY TEK GAMES, INC.; *U.S. Private*, pg. 495
BAYTEX ENERGY CORP.; *Int'l*, pg. 915
BAYTEX ENERGY USA, INC.—See Baytex Energy Corp.; *Int'l*, pg. 915
BAYTHERM INSULATION, LLC—See Installed Building Products, Inc.; *U.S. Public*, pg. 1132
BAY TO BAY PROPERTIES, LLC; *U.S. Private*, pg. 495
BAY TOOL & SUPPLY INC.; *U.S. Private*, pg. 495
BAY TREE CENTER—See Formation Capital, LLC; *U.S. Private*, pg. 1569
BAY TREE PRIVATE EQUITY LLP; *Int'l*, pg. 901
BAYU MANUFACTURING SDN. BHD.—See Turbo-Mech Berhad; *Int'l*, pg. 7973
BAY VALLEY FOODS, LLC—See TreeHouse Foods, Inc.; *U.S. Public*, pg. 2187
BAY VALLEY FOODS—See TreeHouse Foods, Inc.; *U.S. Public*, pg. 2187
BAY VALLEY FOODS—See TreeHouse Foods, Inc.; *U.S. Public*, pg. 2187
BAY VALLEY FOODS—See TreeHouse Foods, Inc.; *U.S. Public*, pg. 2187
BAY VALLEY FOODS—See TreeHouse Foods, Inc.; *U.S. Public*, pg. 2187
BAY VALLEY FOODS—See TreeHouse Foods, Inc.; *U.S. Public*, pg. 2187
BAY VALLEY FOODS—See TreeHouse Foods, Inc.; *U.S. Public*, pg. 2187
BAY VALLEY FOODS—See TreeHouse Foods, Inc.; *U.S. Public*, pg. 2187
BAY VALUATION ADVISORS, LLC—See Kelso & Company, L.P.; *U.S. Private*, pg. 2281
BAY-VANGUARD FEDERAL SAVINGS BANK—See Bay-Vanguard, M.H.C.; *U.S. Private*, pg. 495
BAY-VANGUARD, M.H.C.; *U.S. Private*, pg. 495
BAYVIEW ASSET MANAGEMENT, LLC; *U.S. Private*, pg. 497
BAYVIEW CHRYSLER DODGE LTD.; *Int'l*, pg. 915
BAYVIEW CLUB APARTMENTS INDIANA, LLC—See Independence Realty Trust, Inc.; *U.S. Public*, pg. 1115
BAYVIEW ELECTRIC COMPANY, LLC.; *U.S. Private*, pg. 497
BAYVIEW FINANCIAL, L.P.; *U.S. Private*, pg. 497
BAYVIEW FINANCIAL SMALL BUSINESS FUNDING LLC—See Bayview Financial, L.P.; *U.S. Private*, pg. 497
BAY VIEW FOOD PRODUCTS COMPANY; *U.S. Private*, pg. 495
BAYVIEW HOLDING LTD.—See Morgan Stanley; *U.S. Public*, pg. 1471
BAYVIEW INTERNATIONAL SDN. BHD.—See Oriental Holdings Berhad; *Int'l*, pg. 5624
BAYVIEW LIMOUSINE SERVICE, INC.; *U.S. Private*, pg. 497
BAYVIEW PTY LTD—See Seven Group Holdings Limited; *Int'l*, pg. 6732
BAYVIEW QUARRIES PTY LTD—See Seven Group Holdings Limited; *Int'l*, pg. 6733
BAYVIEW TECHNOLOGIES, INC—See AsianLogic Limited; *Int'l*, pg. 619
BAY VILLAGE OF SARASOTA, INC.; *U.S. Private*, pg. 495
BAY VISTA AT MEADOW PARK, L.P.—See PulteGroup, Inc.; *U.S. Public*, pg. 1737
BAYWA AGRARHANDEL GMBH—See BayWa AG; *Int'l*, pg. 916
BAYWA AGRO POLSKA SP. Z O.O.—See BayWa AG; *Int'l*, pg. 916
BAYWA AG; *Int'l*, pg. 915
BAYWA ASSEKURANZ-VERMITTLUNG GMBH—See BayWa AG; *Int'l*, pg. 916
BAYWA BULGARIA EOOD—See BayWa AG; *Int'l*, pg. 916
BAYWA CR SPOL. S.R.O.—See BayWa AG; *Int'l*, pg. 916
BAYWA CS GMBH—See BayWa AG; *Int'l*, pg. 916
BAYWA ENERGIE DIENSTLEISTUNGS GMBH—See BayWa AG; *Int'l*, pg. 916
BAYWA GLOBAL PRODUCE GMBH—See BayWa AG; *Int'l*, pg. 916
BAYWA HANDELS-SYSTEME-SERVICE GMBH—See BayWa AG; *Int'l*, pg. 916
BAYWA INTEROIL MINERALOLHANDELSGESELLSCHAFT MBH—See BayWa AG; *Int'l*, pg. 916
BAY WALK—See The Sembler Company; *U.S. Private*, pg. 4116
BAYWA OBST GMBH & CO. KG—See BayWa AG; *Int'l*, pg. 916
BAYWA R.E. AG—See BayWa AG; *Int'l*, pg. 916

BAYWA AG

CORPORATE AFFILIATIONS

BAYWA R.E. ASSET HOLDING GMBH—See BayWa AG; *Int'l*, pg. 916
BAYWA R.E. ASSET MANAGEMENT GMBH—See BayWa AG; *Int'l*, pg. 916
BAYWA R.E. BIOENERGY GMBH—See BayWa AG; *Int'l*, pg. 916
BAYWA R.E. CLEAN ENERGY SOURCING GMBH—See BayWa AG; *Int'l*, pg. 916
BAYWA R.E. CLEAN ENERGY S.R.L.—See BayWa AG; *Int'l*, pg. 916
BAYWA R.E. ENERGY VENTURES GMBH—See BayWa AG; *Int'l*, pg. 916
BAYWA R.E. ESPANA S.L.U.—See BayWa AG; *Int'l*, pg. 916
BAYWA R.E. FRANCE SAS—See BayWa AG; *Int'l*, pg. 916
BAYWA R.E GMBH—See BayWa AG; *Int'l*, pg. 916
BAYWA R.E. GREEN ENERGY PRODUCTS GMBH—See BayWa AG; *Int'l*, pg. 916
BAYWA R.E. HELLAS MEPE—See BayWa AG; *Int'l*, pg. 916
BAYWA R.E. ITALIA S.R.L.—See BayWa AG; *Int'l*, pg. 916
BAYWA R.E. JAPAN K.K.—See BayWa AG; *Int'l*, pg. 916
BAYWA RE (MALAYSIA) SDN. BHD.—See BayWa AG; *Int'l*, pg. 917
BAYWA R.E. NORDIC AB—See BayWa AG; *Int'l*, pg. 916
BAYWA RENT GMBH—See BayWa AG; *Int'l*, pg. 916
BAYWA R.E. OFFSHORE WIND GMBH—See BayWa AG; *Int'l*, pg. 916
BAYWA R.E. OPERATION SERVICES GMBH—See BayWa AG; *Int'l*, pg. 916
BAYWA R.E. OPERATION SERVICES LIMITED—See BayWa AG; *Int'l*, pg. 916
BAYWA R.E. OPERATION SERVICES S.R.L.—See BayWa AG; *Int'l*, pg. 916
BAYWA R.E. POLSKA SP. Z O.O.—See BayWa AG; *Int'l*, pg. 916
BAYWA R.E. PROGETTI S.R.L.—See BayWa AG; *Int'l*, pg. 916
BAYWA R.E. PROJECTS ESPANA S.L.U.—See BayWa AG; *Int'l*, pg. 916
BAYWA R.E. RENEWABLE ENERGY GMBH—See BayWa AG; *Int'l*, pg. 917
BAYWA R.E. ROMANIA S.R.L.—See BayWa AG; *Int'l*, pg. 916
BAYWA R.E. ROTOR SERVICE GMBH—See BayWa AG; *Int'l*, pg. 916
BAYWA R.E. SCANDINAVIA AB—See BayWa AG; *Int'l*, pg. 916
BAYWA R.E. SOLAR ENERGY SYSTEMS GMBH—See BayWa AG; *Int'l*, pg. 916
BAYWA R.E. SOLAR PROJECTS GMBH—See BayWa AG; *Int'l*, pg. 916
BAYWA R.E. SOLAR PROJECTS LLC—See BayWa AG; *Int'l*, pg. 916
BAYWA R.E. SOLAR PTE. LTD.—See BayWa AG; *Int'l*, pg. 916
BAYWA R.E. SOLARSYSTEME GMBH—See BayWa AG; *Int'l*, pg. 917
BAYWA R.E. SOLARSYSTEMER APS—See BayWa AG; *Int'l*, pg. 917
BAYWA R.E. SOLAR SYSTEMS CO., LTD.—See BayWa AG; *Int'l*, pg. 916
BAYWA R.E. SOLAR SYSTEMS CORPORATION—See BayWa AG; *Int'l*, pg. 916
BAYWA R.E. SOLAR SYSTEMS GMBH—See BayWa AG; *Int'l*, pg. 916
BAYWA R.E. SOLAR SYSTEMS INC.—See BayWa AG; *Int'l*, pg. 916
BAYWA R.E. SOLAR SYSTEMS LLC—See BayWa AG; *Int'l*, pg. 916
BAYWA R.E. SOLAR SYSTEMS PTY. LTD.—See BayWa AG; *Int'l*, pg. 916
BAYWA R.E. SOLAR SYSTEMS S.A R.L.—See BayWa AG; *Int'l*, pg. 916
BAYWA R.E. SOLAR SYSTEMS SAS—See BayWa AG; *Int'l*, pg. 916
BAYWA R.E. SOLAR SYSTEMS S. DE R.L DE C.V.—See BayWa AG; *Int'l*, pg. 916
BAYWA R.E. SOLAR SYSTEMS S.L.U.—See BayWa AG; *Int'l*, pg. 916
BAYWA R.E. SOLAR SYSTEMS SP. Z O. O.—See BayWa AG; *Int'l*, pg. 917
BAYWA R.E. SOLAR SYSTEMS S.R.L.—See BayWa AG; *Int'l*, pg. 916
BAYWA R.E. SOLAR SYSTEMS S.R.O.—See BayWa AG; *Int'l*, pg. 917
BAYWA R.E. (THAILAND) CO., LTD.—See BayWa AG; *Int'l*, pg. 916
BAYWA R.E. UK LIMITED—See BayWa AG; *Int'l*, pg. 917
BAYWA R.E. WIND GMBH—See BayWa AG; *Int'l*, pg. 917
BAYWA R.E. WIND LLC—See BayWa AG; *Int'l*, pg. 917
BAYWA-TANKSTELLEN-GMBH—See BayWa AG; *Int'l*, pg. 917
BAYWA VENTURE GMBH—See BayWa AG; *Int'l*, pg. 916
BAYWA VORARLBERG HANDELSGMBH—See BayWa AG; *Int'l*, pg. 916
BAYWAY LINCOLN-MERCURY INC.; *U.S. Private*, pg. 497

BAY WORX INDUSTRIES, LLC—See Trinity Industries, Inc.; *U.S. Public*, pg. 2193
BAZAAR & NOVELTY LTD.—See Arrow International, Inc.; *U.S. Private*, pg. 335
BAZAARVOICE, INC.—See Marlin Equity Partners, LLC; *U.S. Private*, pg. 2584
BAZAR DE L'HOTEL DE VILLE—See Galeries Lafayette SA; *Int'l*, pg. 2872
BAZAR GROUP INC.; *U.S. Private*, pg. 497
BAZEL INTERNATIONAL LIMITED; *Int'l*, pg. 920
BAZHONG CDB VILLAGE BANK CO., LTD.—See China Development Bank Corporation; *Int'l*, pg. 1497
BAZIAN CEMENT COMPANY LTD.—See Holcim Ltd.; *Int'l*, pg. 3446
BAZI, INC.—See Charlie's Holdings, Inc.; *U.S. Public*, pg. 480
BAZNA HEMIJA D.D.; *Int'l*, pg. 920
BAZOOKA FARMSTAR INC.—See Eldon C. Stutsman Inc.; *U.S. Private*, pg. 1351
BBA AVIATION ENGINE REPAIR & OVERHAUL GROUP—See BlackRock, Inc.; *U.S. Public*, pg. 346
BBA AVIATION ENGINE REPAIR & OVERHAUL GROUP—See Blackstone Inc.; *U.S. Public*, pg. 358
BBA AVIATION ENGINE REPAIR & OVERHAUL GROUP—See Cascade Investment LLC; *U.S. Private*, pg. 780
BBA AVIATION LEGACY SUPPORT GROUP—See BlackRock, Inc.; *U.S. Public*, pg. 346
BBA AVIATION LEGACY SUPPORT GROUP—See Blackstone Inc.; *U.S. Public*, pg. 358
BBA AVIATION LEGACY SUPPORT GROUP—See Cascade Investment LLC; *U.S. Private*, pg. 780
BB ADMINISTRADORA DE CARTOES DE CREDITO S.A.—See Banco do Brasil S.A.; *Int'l*, pg. 822
B&B AIR CONDITIONING & HEATING SERVICE COMPANY; *U.S. Private*, pg. 417
BBAM LLC; *U.S. Private*, pg. 417
B&B APPLIANCE COMPANY INC.; *U.S. Private*, pg. 417
B&B ARMR CORPORATION; *U.S. Private*, pg. 417
BB BACKBONE CORPORATION—See SoftBank Group Corp.; *Int'l*, pg. 7052
BB BANCO DE INVESTIMENTO S.A.—See Banco do Brasil S.A.; *Int'l*, pg. 822
BB BANK ASA—See TF Bank AB; *Int'l*, pg. 7585
BB&B CONSTRUCTION SERVICES OF FLORIDA, INC.; *U.S. Private*, pg. 497
B&B BEST-BUY FOODS INC.; *U.S. Private*, pg. 417
B & B BETRIEBSRESTAURANTS GMBH—See DO & CO Aktiengesellschaft; *Int'l*, pg. 2151
BBB INDUSTRIES LLC—See Clearlake Capital Group, L.P.; *U.S. Private*, pg. 933
BB BIOTECH AG—See Bellevue Group AG; *Int'l*, pg. 967
B&B BUILDERS, INC.; *U.S. Private*, pg. 417
BB CABLE CORPORATION—See SoftBank Group Corp.; *Int'l*, pg. 7052
BBCARLSON—See Aimia Inc.; *Int'l*, pg. 233
B&B CASH GROCERY STORES, INC.—See B&B Corporate Holdings, Inc.; *U.S. Private*, pg. 417
BBC BIOCHEMICAL CORP—See Audax Group, Limited Partnership; *U.S. Private*, pg. 389
BBCC-BUSINESS BELUX-BTC—See BASF SE; *Int'l*, pg. 882
BBCC - EU GOVERNMENT RELATIONS BASF GROUP B.V.—See BASF SE; *Int'l*, pg. 882
BBC CO., LTD.; *Int'l*, pg. 920
BBC FIRE PROTECTION LIMITED—See Marlowe Plc; *U.S. Public*, pg. 4698
BBC GLOBAL NEWS LIMITED—See British Broadcasting Corporation; *Int'l*, pg. 1168
BBC INSURANCE AGENCY, INC.—See Best Buy Co., Inc.; *U.S. Public*, pg. 326
BBC INTERNATIONAL LLC; *U.S. Private*, pg. 498
BBCK ENTERPRISES INC.; *U.S. Private*, pg. 498
B&B CONCRETE COMPANY INC.; *U.S. Private*, pg. 417
B&B CONSTRUCTION CO. OF OHIO—See B&B Contractors & Developers; *U.S. Private*, pg. 417
B&B CONTRACTORS & DEVELOPERS; *U.S. Private*, pg. 417
B&B CORPORATE HOLDINGS, INC.; *U.S. Private*, pg. 417
BBC PROPERTY LIMITED—See British Broadcasting Corporation; *Int'l*, pg. 1168
BBC STEEL CORP.; *U.S. Private*, pg. 498
BBC STUDIOS AFRICA (PTY) LIMITED—See British Broadcasting Corporation; *Int'l*, pg. 1168
BBC STUDIOS AMERICAS INC.—See British Broadcasting Corporation; *Int'l*, pg. 1168
BBC STUDIOS AND POST PRODUCTION LIMITED—See British Broadcasting Corporation; *Int'l*, pg. 1168
BBC STUDIOS AUSTRALIA HOLDINGS PTY LIMITED—See British Broadcasting Corporation; *Int'l*, pg. 1168
BBC STUDIOS CANADA LIMITED—See British Broadcasting Corporation; *Int'l*, pg. 1168
BBC STUDIOS DISTRIBUTION LIMITED—See British Broadcasting Corporation; *Int'l*, pg. 1168
BBC STUDIOS FRANCE SARL—See British Broadcasting Corporation; *Int'l*, pg. 1168

BBC STUDIOS GERMANY GMBH—See British Broadcasting Corporation; *Int'l*, pg. 1168
BBC STUDIOS INDIA PRIVATE LIMITED—See British Broadcasting Corporation; *Int'l*, pg. 1168
BBC STUDIOS INTERMEDIADORA DE PROGRAMADORA ESTANGEIRA LIMITED—See British Broadcasting Corporation; *Int'l*, pg. 1168
BBC STUDIOS JAPAN LIMITED—See British Broadcasting Corporation; *Int'l*, pg. 1168
BBC STUDIOS POLSKA SP. Z O.O.—See British Broadcasting Corporation; *Int'l*, pg. 1168
BBC STUDIOS PRODUCTIONS LIMITED—See British Broadcasting Corporation; *Int'l*, pg. 1168
BBC STUDIOS SINGAPORE PTE. LIMITED—See British Broadcasting Corporation; *Int'l*, pg. 1168
BBC STUDIOWORKS LIMITED—See British Broadcasting Corporation; *Int'l*, pg. 1169
BBC SYMPHONY ORCHESTRA—See British Broadcasting Corporation; *Int'l*, pg. 1169
BBCV RECEIVABLES-Q 2010 LLC—See Hilton Grand Vacations Inc.; *U.S. Public*, pg. 1039
BBC WORLDWIDE AMERICA INC.—See British Broadcasting Corporation; *Int'l*, pg. 1169
BBC WORLDWIDE AUSTRALIA PTY LIMITED—See British Broadcasting Corporation; *Int'l*, pg. 1169
BBC WORLDWIDE LIMITED—See British Broadcasting Corporation; *Int'l*, pg. 1169
BBD ACQUISITION CO—See Breckenridge Holding Company; *U.S. Private*, pg. 644
B.B. DAKOTA INC.—See Steven Madden, Ltd.; *U.S. Public*, pg. 1947
B&B DEPARTMENT STORES SOUTH; *U.S. Private*, pg. 417
BB DEVELOPMENT, LLC—See Churchill Downs, Inc.; *U.S. Public*, pg. 493
B&B DISTRIBUTION LTD.—See Anheuser-Busch InBev SA/NV; *Int'l*, pg. 464
BBDO ARGENTINA—See Omnicom Group Inc.; *U.S. Public*, pg. 1573
BBDO ASIA/PACIFIC—See Omnicom Group Inc.; *U.S. Public*, pg. 1573
BBDO ATHENS—See Omnicom Group Inc.; *U.S. Public*, pg. 1573
BBDO ATLANTA—See Omnicom Group Inc.; *U.S. Public*, pg. 1573
BBDO BANGKOK—See Omnicom Group Inc.; *U.S. Public*, pg. 1573
BBDO BANGLADESH—See Omnicom Group Inc.; *U.S. Public*, pg. 1573
BBDO BUDAPEST—See Omnicom Group Inc.; *U.S. Public*, pg. 1574
BBDO CANADA CORP.—See Omnicom Group Inc.; *U.S. Public*, pg. 1573
BBDO CENTROAMERICA—See Omnicom Group Inc.; *U.S. Public*, pg. 1574
BBDO CHILE—See Omnicom Group Inc.; *U.S. Public*, pg. 1574
BBDO CHINA—See Omnicom Group Inc.; *U.S. Public*, pg. 1574
BBDO CHINA—See Omnicom Group Inc.; *U.S. Public*, pg. 1574
BBDO DUBLIN—See Omnicom Group Inc.; *U.S. Public*, pg. 1574
BBDO DUSSELDORF—See Omnicom Group Inc.; *U.S. Public*, pg. 1574
BBDO EMEA—See Omnicom Group Inc.; *U.S. Public*, pg. 1574
BBDO GUATEMALA—See Omnicom Group Inc.; *U.S. Public*, pg. 1574
BBDO GUERRERO—See Omnicom Group Inc.; *U.S. Public*, pg. 1574
BBDO HONDURAS—See Omnicom Group Inc.; *U.S. Public*, pg. 1574
BBDO INDIA—See Omnicom Group Inc.; *U.S. Public*, pg. 1574
BBDO JAPAN INC.—See Omnicom Group Inc.; *U.S. Public*, pg. 1575
BBDO/J WEST INC. HEADQUARTERS—See Omnicom Group Inc.; *U.S. Public*, pg. 1575
BBDO/J WEST INC. HIROSHIMA BRANCH—See Omnicom Group Inc.; *U.S. Public*, pg. 1575
BBDO/J WEST INC. KITA-KYUSHU BRANCH—See Omnicom Group Inc.; *U.S. Public*, pg. 1575
BBDO/J WEST INC. OKINAWA BRANCH—See Omnicom Group Inc.; *U.S. Public*, pg. 1575
BBDO KOMUNIKA—See Omnicom Group Inc.; *U.S. Public*, pg. 1574
BBDO KOREA—See Omnicom Group Inc.; *U.S. Public*, pg. 1574
BBDO MALAYSIA—See Omnicom Group Inc.; *U.S. Public*, pg. 1574
BBDO MEXICO—See Omnicom Group Inc.; *U.S. Public*, pg. 1574
BBDO MINNEAPOLIS—See Omnicom Group Inc.; *U.S. Public*, pg. 1574
BBDO MOSCOW—See Omnicom Group Inc.; *U.S. Public*, pg. 1574
BBDO NEW YORK—See Omnicom Group Inc.; *U.S. Public*, pg. 1574

COMPANY NAME INDEX

BBDO NICARAGUA—See Omnicom Group Inc.; *U.S. Public*, pg. 1574
BBDO NORTH AMERICA—See Omnicom Group Inc.; *U.S. Public*, pg. 1574
BBDO PANAMA—See Omnicom Group Inc.; *U.S. Public*, pg. 1574
BBDO PORTUGAL—See Omnicom Group Inc.; *U.S. Public*, pg. 1574
BBDO/PROXIMITY SINGAPORE—See Omnicom Group Inc.; *U.S. Public*, pg. 1575
BBDO PUERTO RICO—See Omnicom Group Inc.; *U.S. Public*, pg. 1574
BBDO SAN FRANCISCO—See Omnicom Group Inc.; *U.S. Public*, pg. 1574
BBDO SINGAPORE—See Omnicom Group Inc.; *U.S. Public*, pg. 1574
BBDO—See Omnicom Group Inc.; *U.S. Public*, pg. 1573
BBDO STUTTGART—See Omnicom Group Inc.; *U.S. Public*, pg. 1575
BBDO TAIWAN—See Omnicom Group Inc.; *U.S. Public*, pg. 1575
BBDO TORONTO—See Omnicom Group Inc.; *U.S. Public*, pg. 1575
BBDO WEST—See Omnicom Group Inc.; *U.S. Public*, pg. 1575
BBDO WORLDWIDE INC.—See Omnicom Group Inc.; *U.S. Public*, pg. 1573
BBDO ZAGREB—See Omnicom Group Inc.; *U.S. Public*, pg. 1575
BB ELECTRONICS A/S; *Int'l*, pg. 920
B&B ELECTRONICS MANUFACTURING COMPANY; *U.S. Private*, pg. 417
BB ELECTRONICS SUZHOU CO. LTD.—See BB Electronics A/S; *Int'l*, pg. 920
BBELEMENTS SP. Z.O.O.—See Stroer SE & Co. KGaA; *Int'l*, pg. 7241
B&B ENDEMOL AG—See LOV Group Invest SAS; *Int'l*, pg. 4564
B&B EQUIPMENT & SUPPLY COMPANY INC.—See Begley Company; *U.S. Private*, pg. 514
BBE SOUND INC.; *U.S. Private*, pg. 498
BBEX INC.; *U.S. Private*, pg. 498
B-B-F OIL COMPANY INC.; *U.S. Private*, pg. 419
BBFS ALPHA VERWALTUNGS GMBH—See Bilfinger SE; *Int'l*, pg. 1024
BB GAMMA PPP-PROJEKTGESELLSCHAFT MBH—See Bilfinger SE; *Int'l*, pg. 1024
BBG BAUGERATE GMBH; *Int'l*, pg. 920
BBG COMMUNICATIONS, INC.; *U.S. Private*, pg. 498
B & B GERIG, INC.; *U.S. Private*, pg. 416
BBG GLOBAL AG—See BBG Communications, Inc.; *U.S. Private*, pg. 498
BBGI GLOBAL INFRASTRUCTURE S.A; *Int'l*, pg. 920
BBG INC.; *U.S. Private*, pg. 498
BBGI PUBLIC COMPANY LIMITED—See Bangchak Corporation Public Company Limited; *Int'l*, pg. 832
B&B GLASS, INC.; *U.S. Private*, pg. 417
BB GOVERNMENT SERVICES GMBH—See BAVARIA Industries Group AG; *Int'l*, pg. 899
BB GOVERNMENT SERVICES S.R.L.—See BAVARIA Industries Group AG; *Int'l*, pg. 899
BBGR GMBH—See EssilorLuxottica SA; *Int'l*, pg. 2512
BBGR S.A.—See EssilorLuxottica SA; *Int'l*, pg. 2512
BBGR SKANDINAVISKA AB—See EssilorLuxottica SA; *Int'l*, pg. 2512
BB GRUNDBESITZ GMBH—See Bilfinger SE; *Int'l*, pg. 1024
BBGS SPOLKA Z OGRANICZONA ODPOWIEDZIALNOSCIA—See PORR AG; *Int'l*, pg. 5922
BBH BAHNBUS HOCHSTIFT GMBH—See Deutsche Bahn AG; *Int'l*, pg. 2049
BBHC, INC.; *U.S. Public*, pg. 284
BBH DESIGN—See EwingCole, Inc.; *U.S. Private*, pg. 1444
B&B (H.K.) LIMITED—See Takbo Group Holdings Limited; *Int'l*, pg. 7436
BBH MUMBAI—See Publicis Groupe S.A.; *Int'l*, pg. 6097
BBH NEW YORK—See Publicis Groupe S.A.; *Int'l*, pg. 6097
B.B. HOBBS, INC.; *U.S. Private*, pg. 420
BBH PBMC, LLC—See Tenet Healthcare Corporation; *U.S. Public*, pg. 2001
BBH SBMC, LLC—See Tenet Healthcare Corporation; *U.S. Public*, pg. 2001
BBH SECURITY SERVICES BV—See Koninklijke Volker-Wessels N.V.; *Int'l*, pg. 4271
BBH SINGAPORE—See Publicis Groupe S.A.; *Int'l*, pg. 6097
B B H SOLUTIONS, INC.; *U.S. Private*, pg. 417
BBH WBMC, LLC—See Tenet Healthcare Corporation; *U.S. Public*, pg. 2001
BBI BASIC CANADA INC.—See BBI Life Sciences Corporation; *Int'l*, pg. 920
BBI BURGERLICHES BRAUHAUS IMMOBILIEN AG—See VIB Vermögen AG; *Int'l*, pg. 8184
BBI DETECTION INC.—See Novo Nordisk Fonden; *Int'l*, pg. 5463

BBI DETECTION LIMITED—See Novo Nordisk Fonden; *Int'l*, pg. 5463
BBI DEVELOPMENT SA; *Int'l*, pg. 920
BBI DIAGNOSTICS GROUP LIMITED—See Novo Nordisk Fonden; *Int'l*, pg. 5463
BBI ENZYMES SA (PTY) LIMITED—See Novo Nordisk Fonden; *Int'l*, pg. 5463
BBI ENZYMES (UK) LIMITED—See Novo Nordisk Fonden; *Int'l*, pg. 5463
BBI ENZYMES (USA) LIMITED—See Novo Nordisk Fonden; *Int'l*, pg. 5463
BBIGPLAS POLY PVT LTD.; *Int'l*, pg. 920
THE BBI GROUP—See Novo Nordisk Fonden; *Int'l*, pg. 5463
BBI LIFE SCIENCES CORPORATION; *Int'l*, pg. 920
BB INFRASTRUCTURE SERVICES GMBH—See Bilfinger SE; *Int'l*, pg. 1024
B&B INVESTMENT PARTNERS LLP; *Int'l*, pg. 783
BBI RESEARCH INC.—See Novo Nordisk Fonden; *Int'l*, pg. 5463
BBI SOLUTIONS OEM, LIMITED—See Novo Nordisk Fonden; *Int'l*, pg. 5463
BBIW - BERUFSBILDUNGSWERK BURGHAUSEN—See Wacker Chemie AG; *Int'l*, pg. 8323
BBIX, INC.—See SoftBank Group Corp.; *Int'l*, pg. 7052
B&B JOBBER SERVICES, INC.; *U.S. Private*, pg. 417
BBJ RENTALS INC.; *U.S. Private*, pg. 498
BBK B.S.C.; *Int'l*, pg. 920
BBKO CONSULTING S.A.; *Int'l*, pg. 920
B&B KOREA CORPORATION—See Hitejinro Holdings Co., Ltd.; *Int'l*, pg. 3426
BBL ASSET MANAGEMENT CO., LTD.—See Industrial & Commercial Bank of China Limited; *Int'l*, pg. 3670
BBL BUILDINGS & COMPONENTS, LTD.—See MacArthur Co.; *U.S. Private*, pg. 2534
BBL COMPANY V.O.F.—See N.V. Nederlandse Gasunie; *Int'l*, pg. 5117
BBL DAIDO PRIVATE LIMITED—See Daido Metal Corporation; *Int'l*, pg. 1921
BB LEASING-ARRANDEMENTO MERCANTIL—See Banco do Brasil S.A.; *Int'l*, pg. 822
B. BLEND MAQUINAS E BEBIDAS S.A.—See Whirlpool Corporation; *U.S. Public*, pg. 2367
BB LIGHTCONCEPTS B.V.—See TKH Group N.V.; *Int'l*, pg. 7763
BBMG CORPORATION; *Int'l*, pg. 920
BB MINAQUA AD; *Int'l*, pg. 920
BBM LOGISTICA S.A.—See Stratus Gestao de Carteiras Ltda.; *Int'l*, pg. 7237
BB&M LOWE & PARTNERS—See The Interpublic Group of Companies, Inc.; *U.S. Public*, pg. 2090
BBMS N.V./SA—See Ratos AB; *Int'l*, pg. 6215
BBNED NV—See Deutsche Telekom AG; *Int'l*, pg. 2084
BBN NETWORKS, INC.; *U.S. Private*, pg. 498
B&B OFFICE SYSTEMS, INC.; *U.S. Private*, pg. 417
B&B PHARMACEUTICALS, INC.—See Fagron NV; *Int'l*, pg. 2603
BBPI SENTINEL PTY LTD—See Bilfinger SE; *Int'l*, pg. 1024
B & B PROTECTOR PLANS, INC.—See Brown & Brown, Inc.; *U.S. Public*, pg. 397
BBPS LIMITED—See Brown & Brown, Inc.; *U.S. Public*, pg. 397
BBQ BLUES TEXAS LTD.; *U.S. Private*, pg. 498
BBQ FACTORY PTY. LTD.—See CapitalGroup Limited; *Int'l*, pg. 1314
BBQ GUY'S MANUFACTURING, LLC; *U.S. Private*, pg. 498
BBQ HOLDINGS, INC.—See MTY Food Group Inc.; *Int'l*, pg. 5073
B. BRAUN ADRIA D.O.O.—See B. Braun Melsungen AG; *Int'l*, pg. 786
B.BRAUN AESCULAP DE MEXICO S.A. DE C.V.—See B. Braun Melsungen AG; *Int'l*, pg. 787
B. BRAUN AESCULAP JAPAN CO., LTD.—See B. Braun Melsungen AG; *Int'l*, pg. 786
B.BRAUN AUSTRALIA PTY. LTD.—See B. Braun Melsungen AG; *Int'l*, pg. 787
B. BRAUN AUSTRIA GES. M.B.H.—See B. Braun Melsungen AG; *Int'l*, pg. 786
B. BRAUN AVITUM ANKARA DIYALIZ HIZMETLERI A.S.—See B. Braun Melsungen AG; *Int'l*, pg. 786
B. BRAUN AVITUM AUSTERLITZ S.R.O.—See B. Braun Melsungen AG; *Int'l*, pg. 786
B. BRAUN AVITUM BULOVKA S.R.O.—See B. Braun Melsungen AG; *Int'l*, pg. 786
B. BRAUN AVITUM FRANCE S.A.S.—See B. Braun Melsungen AG; *Int'l*, pg. 786
B. BRAUN AVITUM IRELAND LTD.—See B. Braun Melsungen AG; *Int'l*, pg. 786
B. BRAUN AVITUM ITALY S.P.A.—See B. Braun Melsungen AG; *Int'l*, pg. 786
B.BRAUN AVITUM PHILIPPINES INC.—See B. Braun Melsungen AG; *Int'l*, pg. 787
B. BRAUN AVITUM POLAND SP.Z.O.O.—See B. Braun Melsungen AG; *Int'l*, pg. 786
B. BRAUN AVITUM RUSSLAND OOO—See B. Braun Melsungen AG; *Int'l*, pg. 786

B. BRAUN MELSUNGEN AG

B. BRAUN AVITUM S.A.S.—See B. Braun Melsungen AG; *Int'l*, pg. 786
B. BRAUN AVITUM SAXONIA GMBH—See B. Braun Melsungen AG; *Int'l*, pg. 786
B.BRAUN AVITUM (SHANGHAI) TRADING CO. LTD.—See B. Braun Melsungen AG; *Int'l*, pg. 787
B. BRAUN AVITUM S.R.O.—See B. Braun Melsungen AG; *Int'l*, pg. 786
B. BRAUN AVITUM S.R.O.—See B. Braun Melsungen AG; *Int'l*, pg. 786
B. BRAUN AVITUM TURKEY SANAYI TICARET ANONIM SIRKETI—See B. Braun Melsungen AG; *Int'l*, pg. 786
B. BRAUN AVITUM UAB—See B. Braun Melsungen AG; *Int'l*, pg. 786
B. BRAUN AVITUM ZVOLEN S.R.O.—See B. Braun Melsungen AG; *Int'l*, pg. 786
B. BRAUN DOMINICAN REPUBLIC INC.—See B. Braun Melsungen AG; *Int'l*, pg. 786
B. BRAUN GERMANY GMBH & CO. KG—See B. Braun Melsungen AG; *Int'l*, pg. 786
B. BRAUN HOSPICARE LTD.—See B. Braun Melsungen AG; *Int'l*, pg. 786
B. BRAUN INTERVENTIONAL SYSTEMS INC.—See B. Braun Melsungen AG; *Int'l*, pg. 787
B.BRAUN KOREA CO. LTD.—See B. Braun Melsungen AG; *Int'l*, pg. 787
B. BRAUN LANKA (PRIVATE) LIMITED—See B. Braun Melsungen AG; *Int'l*, pg. 786
B. BRAUN MEDICAL AB—See B. Braun Melsungen AG; *Int'l*, pg. 786
B. BRAUN MEDICAL AG—See B. Braun Melsungen AG; *Int'l*, pg. 786
B. BRAUN MEDICAL A/S—See B. Braun Melsungen AG; *Int'l*, pg. 786
B. BRAUN MEDICAL A/S—See B. Braun Melsungen AG; *Int'l*, pg. 786
B. BRAUN MEDICAL B.V.—See B. Braun Melsungen AG; *Int'l*, pg. 786
B. BRAUN MEDICAL CENTRAL AMERICA & CARIBE, S.A. DE C.V.—See B. Braun Melsungen AG; *Int'l*, pg. 786
B. BRAUN MEDICAL EOOD—See B. Braun Melsungen AG; *Int'l*, pg. 786
B.BRAUN MEDICAL (H.K.) LTD.—See B. Braun Melsungen AG; *Int'l*, pg. 787
B. BRAUN MEDICAL, INC.—See B. Braun Melsungen AG; *Int'l*, pg. 787
B. BRAUN MEDICAL (INDIA) PVT. LTD.—See B. Braun Melsungen AG; *Int'l*, pg. 786
B.BRAUN MEDICAL INDUSTRIES SDN. BHD.—See B. Braun Melsungen AG; *Int'l*, pg. 787
B. BRAUN MEDICAL INTERNATIONAL S.L.—See B. Braun Melsungen AG; *Int'l*, pg. 786
B. BRAUN MEDICAL LDA.—See B. Braun Melsungen AG; *Int'l*, pg. 786
B. BRAUN MEDICAL LLC—See B. Braun Melsungen AG; *Int'l*, pg. 786
B. BRAUN MEDICAL LTD.—See B. Braun Melsungen AG; *Int'l*, pg. 786
B. BRAUN MEDICAL N.V./ S.A.—See B. Braun Melsungen AG; *Int'l*, pg. 786
B. BRAUN MEDICAL OU—See B. Braun Melsungen AG; *Int'l*, pg. 786
B. BRAUN MEDICAL OY—See B. Braun Melsungen AG; *Int'l*, pg. 786
B. BRAUN MEDICAL PARAGUAY S.A—See B. Braun Melsungen AG; *Int'l*, pg. 786
B.BRAUN MEDICAL PERU S.A.—See B. Braun Melsungen AG; *Int'l*, pg. 787
B.BRAUN MEDICAL (PTY) LTD.—See B. Braun Melsungen AG; *Int'l*, pg. 787
B.BRAUN MEDICAL S.A.—See B. Braun Melsungen AG; *Int'l*, pg. 787
B.BRAUN MEDICAL S.A.—See B. Braun Melsungen AG; *Int'l*, pg. 787
B.BRAUN MEDICAL S.A.—See B. Braun Melsungen AG; *Int'l*, pg. 787
B. BRAUN MEDICAL SAS—See B. Braun Melsungen AG; *Int'l*, pg. 786
B. BRAUN MEDICAL SIA—See B. Braun Melsungen AG; *Int'l*, pg. 786
B.BRAUN MEDICAL SPA—See B. Braun Melsungen AG; *Int'l*, pg. 787
B.BRAUN MEDICAL SUPPLIES INC.—See B. Braun Melsungen AG; *Int'l*, pg. 787
B.BRAUN MEDICAL SUPPLIES SDN. BHD.—See B. Braun Melsungen AG; *Int'l*, pg. 787
B.BRAUN MEDICAL (SUZHOU) COMPANY LIMITED—See B. Braun Melsungen AG; *Int'l*, pg. 787
B. BRAUN MEDICAL UAB—See B. Braun Melsungen AG; *Int'l*, pg. 786
B. BRAUN MEDICAL UKRAINE LLC—See B. Braun Melsungen AG; *Int'l*, pg. 786
B. BRAUN MEDIKAL DIS TICARET A.S.—See B. Braun Melsungen AG; *Int'l*, pg. 787
B. BRAUN MELSUNGEN AG; *Int'l*, pg. 785
B. BRAUN MILANO S.P.A.—See B. Braun Melsungen AG; *Int'l*, pg. 787

B. BRAUN NEW ZEALAND PTY LTD—See B. Braun Melsungen AG; *Int'l*, pg. 787
B. BRAUN OF CANADA, LTD.—See B. Braun Melsungen AG; *Int'l*, pg. 787
B.BRAUN PAKISTAN (PRIVATE) LTD.—See B. Braun Melsungen AG; *Int'l*, pg. 787
B. BRAUN PETZOLD GMBH—See B. Braun Melsungen AG; *Int'l*, pg. 787
B. BRAUN PHARMACEUTICALS S.A.—See B. Braun Melsungen AG; *Int'l*, pg. 787
B. BRAUN RSRB D.O.O.—See B. Braun Melsungen AG; *Int'l*, pg. 787
B. BRAUN (SHANDONG) PHARMACEUTICAL MANUFACTURING CO., LTD—See B. Braun Melsungen AG; *Int'l*, pg. 786
B. BRAUN SINGAPORE PTE. LTD.—See B. Braun Melsungen AG; *Int'l*, pg. 787
B. BRAUN STERILOG (BIRMINGHAM) LTD.—See B. Braun Melsungen AG; *Int'l*, pg. 787
B. BRAUN STERILOG (YORKSHIRE) LTD.—See B. Braun Melsungen AG; *Int'l*, pg. 787
B.BRAUN TAIWAN CO. LTD.—See B. Braun Melsungen AG; *Int'l*, pg. 787
B.BRAUN (THAILAND) LTD.—See B. Braun Melsungen AG; *Int'l*, pg. 787
B. BRAUN TRAVACARE GMBH—See B. Braun Melsungen AG; *Int'l*, pg. 787
B.BRAUN VIETNAM CO. LTD.—See B. Braun Melsungen AG; *Int'l*, pg. 787
BBR BANK AG; *Int'l*, pg. 921
BBR CONSTRUCTION SYSTEMS (M) SDN. BHD.—See BBR Holdings (S) Ltd.; *Int'l*, pg. 921
BBR CONSTRUCTION SYSTEMS PTE LTD—See BBR Holdings (S) Ltd.; *Int'l*, pg. 921
BBREAK SYSTEMS CO., LTD.; *Int'l*, pg. 921
B&B REALTY LIMITED; *Int'l*, pg. 783
BBRG FINANCE (UK) LTD.—See NV Bekaert SA; *Int'l*, pg. 5495
BBR HOLDINGS (S) LTD.; *Int'l*, pg. 921
B. BROOKS (NORWICH) LIMITED—See Silver Fern Farms Limited; *Int'l*, pg. 6923
BBR PILING PTE LTD.—See BBR Holdings (S) Ltd.; *Int'l*, pg. 921
BBR SAATCHI & SAATCHI—See Publicis Groupe S.A.; *Int'l*, pg. 6108
B&B RV, INC.—See Camping World Holdings, Inc.; *U.S. Public*, pg. 427
B&B SAAB; *U.S. Private*, pg. 418
BBSA SERVICOS E PARTICIPACOES LIMITADA—See Barclays PLC; *Int'l*, pg. 859
BBS AUTOMATION BLAICHACH GMBH—See Durr AG; *Int'l*, pg. 2230
BBS AUTOMATION CHICAGO INC.—See Durr AG; *Int'l*, pg. 2230
BBS AUTOMATION GMBH—See Durr AG; *Int'l*, pg. 2230
BBS AUTOMATION GUADALAJARA S DE R.L. DE C.V.—See Durr AG; *Int'l*, pg. 2230
BBS AUTOMATION INDIA PRIVATE LTD.—See Durr AG; *Int'l*, pg. 2230
BBS AUTOMATION (KUNSHAN) CO., LTD.—See Durr AG; *Int'l*, pg. 2230
BBS AUTOMATION LIPANY S.R.O.—See Durr AG; *Int'l*, pg. 2230
BBS AUTOMATION PENANG SDN. BHD.—See Durr AG; *Int'l*, pg. 2230
BBS AUTOMATION (SUZHOU) CO., LTD.—See Durr AG; *Int'l*, pg. 2230
BBS AUTOMATION (TIANJIN) CO., LTD.—See Durr AG; *Int'l*, pg. 2230
BBS-BIOACTIVE BONE SUBSTITUTES PLC; *Int'l*, pg. 921
BB'S CAFE SYSTEM PTY LTD—See Retail Food Group Limited; *Int'l*, pg. 6305
BB SECURITIES LTD.—See Banco do Brasil S.A.; *Int'l*, pg. 822
BB SEGURIDADE PARTICIPACOES S/A—See Banco do Brasil S.A.; *Int'l*, pg. 822
BBS I, LLC—See Barrett Business Services, Inc.; *U.S. Public*, pg. 278
BBS JAPAN CO., LTD.—See Maeda Kosen Co., Ltd.; *Int'l*, pg. 4635
BBS KRAFTFAHRZEUGTECHNIK AG; *Int'l*, pg. 921
B&B SMARTWORX LIMITED—See Advantech Co., Ltd.; *Int'l*, pg. 165
BB'S NEW ZEALAND LTD—See Retail Food Group Limited; *Int'l*, pg. 6305
BBS OF AMERICA, INC.—See BBS Kraftfahrzeugtechnik AG; *Int'l*, pg. 921
BB SOFTSERVICE CORP.—See SoftBank Group Corp.; *Int'l*, pg. 7052
BBS OUTSOURCING KUMAMOTO INC.—See Business Brain Showa-Ota Inc.; *Int'l*, pg. 1228
BB S.R.L.—See Poligrafica S. Faustino S.p.A.; *Int'l*, pg. 5909
BBS SCHALUNGSBAU GMBH—See Bilfinger SE; *Int'l*, pg. 1024
BB-STANZ- UND UMFORTECHNIK GMBH—See Wurth Verwaltungsgesellschaft mbH; *Int'l*, pg. 8504
BBS TECHNOLOGIES, INC.; *U.S. Private*, pg. 498

B. B. STUDIO CO., LTD.—See BANDAI NAMCO Holdings Inc.; *Int'l*, pg. 828
B&B SURPLUS, INC.; *U.S. Private*, pg. 418
BBS VERWALTUNGS GMBH—See Accentis SA/NV; *Int'l*, pg. 82
BBS WINDING S.R.L.—See Durr AG; *Int'l*, pg. 2230
BB&T CAPITAL PARTNERS, LLC—See Truist Financial Corporation; *U.S. Public*, pg. 2200
BB&T INSTITUTIONAL INVESTMENT ADVISERS, INC.—See Truist Financial Corporation; *U.S. Public*, pg. 2200
BB&T INSURANCE SERVICES, INC. - BURKEY RISK SERVICES—See Clayton, Dubilier & Rice, LLC; *U.S. Private*, pg. 927
BB&T INSURANCE SERVICES, INC. - BURKEY RISK SERVICES—See Mubadala Investment Company PJSC; *Int'l*, pg. 5076
BB&T INSURANCE SERVICES, INC. - BURKEY RISK SERVICES—See Stone Point Capital LLC; *U.S. Private*, pg. 3826
BB&T INSURANCE SERVICES, INC. - FREDERICK UNDERWRITERS—See Clayton, Dubilier & Rice, LLC; *U.S. Private*, pg. 927
BB&T INSURANCE SERVICES, INC. - FREDERICK UNDERWRITERS—See Mubadala Investment Company PJSC; *Int'l*, pg. 5076
BB&T INSURANCE SERVICES, INC. - FREDERICK UNDERWRITERS—See Stone Point Capital LLC; *U.S. Private*, pg. 3826
BB&T INSURANCE SERVICES, INC.—See Clayton, Dubilier & Rice, LLC; *U.S. Private*, pg. 927
BB&T INSURANCE SERVICES, INC.—See Mubadala Investment Company PJSC; *Int'l*, pg. 5076
BB&T INSURANCE SERVICES, INC.—See Stone Point Capital LLC; *U.S. Private*, pg. 3826
BB&T INSURANCE SERVICES, INC. - TCFC—See Clayton, Dubilier & Rice, LLC; *U.S. Private*, pg. 927
BB&T INSURANCE SERVICES, INC. - TCFC—See Mubadala Investment Company PJSC; *Int'l*, pg. 5076
BB&T INSURANCE SERVICES, INC. - TCFC—See Stone Point Capital LLC; *U.S. Private*, pg. 3826
BB&T INVESTMENT SERVICES, INC.—See Truist Financial Corporation; *U.S. Public*, pg. 2200
BB&T - JOHN BURNHAM INSURANCE SERVICES—See Clayton, Dubilier & Rice, LLC; *U.S. Private*, pg. 927
BB&T - JOHN BURNHAM INSURANCE SERVICES—See Mubadala Investment Company PJSC; *Int'l*, pg. 5076
BB&T - JOHN BURNHAM INSURANCE SERVICES—See Stone Point Capital LLC; *U.S. Private*, pg. 3826
BB&T - J. ROLFE DAVIS INSURANCE—See Clayton, Dubilier & Rice, LLC; *U.S. Private*, pg. 927
BB&T - J. ROLFE DAVIS INSURANCE—See Mubadala Investment Company PJSC; *Int'l*, pg. 5076
BB&T - J. ROLFE DAVIS INSURANCE—See Stone Point Capital LLC; *U.S. Private*, pg. 3826
BB&T - J.V. ARTHUR—See Clayton, Dubilier & Rice, LLC; *U.S. Private*, pg. 927
BB&T - J.V. ARTHUR—See Mubadala Investment Company PJSC; *Int'l*, pg. 5076
BB&T - J.V. ARTHUR—See Stone Point Capital LLC; *U.S. Private*, pg. 3826
BBT NORTH AMERICA CORPORATION—See Robert Bosch GmbH; *Int'l*, pg. 6363
BB TRADE A.D.; *Int'l*, pg. 920
B&B TRADE DISTRIBUTION CENTRE; *Int'l*, pg. 783
BB&T REAL ESTATE FUNDING LLC—See Truist Financial Corporation; *U.S. Public*, pg. 2200
B&B TRIPLEWALL CONTAINERS LIMITED; *Int'l*, pg. 783
BBT THEMOTECHNIK GMBH—See Robert Bosch GmbH; *Int'l*, pg. 6363
BBTV HOLDINGS INC.—See BBTV Holdings Inc.; *Int'l*, pg. 921
BBTV HOLDINGS INC.; *Int'l*, pg. 921
BBTV PRODUCTIONS CO., LTD.—See Bangkok Broadcasting & TV Co., Ltd.; *Int'l*, pg. 833
BBVA BANCOMER AFORE—See Banco Bilbao Vizcaya Argentaria, S.A.; *Int'l*, pg. 818
BBVA BANCO PROVINCIAL, S.A.—See Banco Bilbao Vizcaya Argentaria, S.A.; *Int'l*, pg. 817
BBVA BRASIL BANCO DE INVESTIMENTO SA—See Banco Bilbao Vizcaya Argentaria, S.A.; *Int'l*, pg. 817
BBVA COLOMBIA S.A.—See Banco Bilbao Vizcaya Argentaria, S.A.; *Int'l*, pg. 817
BBVA INFORMATION TECHNOLOGY ESPANA, S.L.—See Banco Bilbao Vizcaya Argentaria, S.A.; *Int'l*, pg. 817
BBVA INSTITUICAO FINANCEIRA DE CREDITO, S.A.—See Banco Bilbao Vizcaya Argentaria, S.A.; *Int'l*, pg. 817
BBVA IRELAND PLC—See Banco Bilbao Vizcaya Argentaria, S.A.; *Int'l*, pg. 817
B+B VAKMEDIANET B.V.—See B+B Vakmedianet Groep B.V.; *Int'l*, pg. 784
B+B VAKMEDIANET GROEP B.V.; *Int'l*, pg. 784
BBVA LEASING MEXICO SA DE CV—See Banco Bilbao Vizcaya Argentaria, S.A.; *Int'l*, pg. 817
BBVA LUXINVEST, S.A.—See Banco Bilbao Vizcaya Argentaria, S.A.; *Int'l*, pg. 817
BBVA PARAGUAY SA—See Banco Bilbao Vizcaya Argentaria, S.A.; *Int'l*, pg. 817

BBVA PROVINCIAL OVERSEAS NV—See Banco Bilbao Vizcaya Argentaria, S.A.; *Int'l*, pg. 817
BBVA SEGUROS COLOMBIA SA—See Banco Bilbao Vizcaya Argentaria, S.A.; *Int'l*, pg. 817
BBVA SEGUROS DE VIDA, S.A.—See The Bank of Nova Scotia; *Int'l*, pg. 7618
BBVA SERVICIOS, S.A.—See Banco Bilbao Vizcaya Argentaria, S.A.; *Int'l*, pg. 817
BBVA SOCIEDAD TITULIZADORA S.A—See Banco Bilbao Vizcaya Argentaria, S.A.; *Int'l*, pg. 817
BBVA (SUIZA) S.A.—See Banco Bilbao Vizcaya Argentaria, S.A.; *Int'l*, pg. 817
BBVA TRANSFER SERVICES INC.—See Banco Bilbao Vizcaya Argentaria, S.A.; *Int'l*, pg. 817
BBVA USA BANCSHARES, INC.—See The PNC Financial Services Group, Inc.; *U.S. Public*, pg. 2119
BBVA USA BANCSHARES, INC.—See The PNC Financial Services Group, Inc.; *U.S. Public*, pg. 2119
BBVA WEALTH SOLUTIONS, INC.—See Banco Bilbao Vizcaya Argentaria, S.A.; *Int'l*, pg. 817
BBV BILBAO—See Banco Bilbao Vizcaya Argentaria, S.A.; *Int'l*, pg. 817
BBV INTERACTIVOS—See Banco Bilbao Vizcaya Argentaria, S.A.; *Int'l*, pg. 817
BBV MADRID—See Banco Bilbao Vizcaya Argentaria, S.A.; *Int'l*, pg. 817
BBV PRIVANZA—See Banco Bilbao Vizcaya Argentaria, S.A.; *Int'l*, pg. 817
BBV SYSTEMS GMBH—See Bilfinger SE; *Int'l*, pg. 1024
BBV SYSTEMS GMBH—See Bilfinger SE; *Int'l*, pg. 1024
BBV SYSTEMS SP. Z O.O.—See Bilfinger SE; *Int'l*, pg. 1024
BB&W ASSOCIATES, INC—See Altas Partners LP; *Int'l*, pg. 387
BB-WERTPAPIERVERWALTUNGSGESELLSCHAFT MBH—See JDC Group AG; *Int'l*, pg. 3925
BBX CAPITAL ASSET MANAGEMENT, LLC—See Hilton Grand Vacations Inc.; *U.S. Public*, pg. 1039
BBX CAPITAL, INC.; *U.S. Public*, pg. 284
BBX CENTROAMERICA LA URUCA—See BBX Minerals Limited; *Int'l*, pg. 921
BBX CHINA CO., LTD—See BBX Minerals Limited; *Int'l*, pg. 921
B.B.X. INC.; *U.S. Private*, pg. 420
BBX MANAGEMENT LTD—See BBX Minerals Limited; *Int'l*, pg. 921
BBX MANAGEMENT PTY. LTD—See BBX Minerals Limited; *Int'l*, pg. 921
BBX MINERALS LIMITED; *Int'l*, pg. 921
BBX SWEET HOLDINGS, LLC—See Hilton Grand Vacations Inc.; *U.S. Public*, pg. 1039
BBYE CORPORATION; *Int'l*, pg. 921
BBZ MITTE GMBH—See ATON GmbH; *Int'l*, pg. 688
BCA BETEILIGUNGS GMBH—See Aurelius Equity Opportunities SE & Co. KGaA; *Int'l*, pg. 707
BC-ABLAKPROFIL KFT.—See Permira Advisers LLP; *Int'l*, pg. 5803
BCA (BRIAN CRONIN & ASSOCIATES INC.); *U.S. Private*, pg. 498
BCA CONSULTANTS PTY LTD.—See VDM Group Limited; *Int'l*, pg. 8142
BCAL DIAGNOSTICS LIMITED; *Int'l*, pg. 925
BCA LOGISTICS LIMITED—See TDR Capital LLP; *Int'l*, pg. 7493
BCA MARKETPLACE PLC—See TDR Capital LLP; *Int'l*, pg. 7493
B*CAPITAL—See BNP Paribas SA; *Int'l*, pg. 1080
B CAPITAL TECHNOLOGY OPPORTUNITIES CORP.; *U.S. Private*, pg. 417
BCAP LLC—See Barclays PLC; *Int'l*, pg. 860
B. CATALANI, INC.; *U.S. Private*, pg. 419
BCA TECHNOLOGIES INC.—See TA Associates, Inc.; *U.S. Private*, pg. 3918
BCB BANCORP, INC.; *U.S. Public*, pg. 285
BCB BERHAD; *Int'l*, pg. 926
BCB COMMUNICATIONS—See Barbados Shipping & Trading Co. Ltd.; *Int'l*, pg. 858
BCB COMMUNITY BANK—See BCB Bancorp, Inc.; *U.S. Public*, pg. 285
BCBG MAX AZRIA GROUP, INC.; *U.S. Private*, pg. 499
THE BCB GROUP, INC.; *U.S. Private*, pg. 3992
BCB HOMES INC.; *U.S. Private*, pg. 498
BCB INTERNATIONAL INC.; *U.S. Private*, pg. 499
BCB MANAGEMENT SDN. BHD.—See BCB Berhad; *Int'l*, pg. 926
B.C. BUNDT, INC.; *U.S. Private*, pg. 420
BC CANNON CO. INC.—See Investcorp Holdings B.S.C.; *Int'l*, pg. 3776
BC CANNON CO. INC.—See Trilantic Capital Management L.P.; *U.S. Private*, pg. 4231
BC CARD CO., LTD.—See KT Corporation; *Int'l*, pg. 4314
BCC ASSICURAZIONI S.P.A.—See Iccrea Holding S.p.A.; *Int'l*, pg. 3578
BCC ASSICURAZIONI S.P.A.—See Societa Cattolica di Assicurazione-Societa Cooperativa; *Int'l*, pg. 7033
BCC BUSINESS COMMUNICATION COMPANY GMBH—See EWE Aktiengesellschaft; *Int'l*, pg. 2575
BCC CORPORATE NV/SA—See American Express Company; *U.S. Public*, pg. 101

COMPANY NAME INDEX

BCC ELECTRO-SPECIAALZAKEN B.V.—See Kingfisher plc; *Int'l*, pg. 4173
BCC ENGINEERING, INC.—See Parsons Corporation; *U.S. Public*, pg. 1650
BCC FACTORING SPA—See Iccrea Holding S.p.A.; *Int'l*, pg. 3578
BCC FINLAND OY—See Atea ASA; *Int'l*, pg. 667
BCC FUBA INDIA LTD.; *Int'l*, pg. 926
BC CHEMICAL CO., LTD.—See Grand Pacific Petrochemical Corporation; *Int'l*, pg. 3055
BCCH, LLC; *U.S. Private*, pg. 499
BCCI CONSTRUCTION COMPANY; *U.S. Private*, pg. 499
BCC INVEST JSC—See Bank CenterCredit JSC; *Int'l*, pg. 837
BCC INVESTMENT CORP.; *U.S. Private*, pg. 499
B.C. CLARK INC.; *U.S. Private*, pg. 420
BCC LEASE SPA—See Iccrea Holding S.p.A.; *Int'l*, pg. 3578
BCCM ADVISORS, LLC—See Air T, Inc.; *U.S. Public*, pg. 67
BCC MID VALLEY OPERATIONS, LLC—See Ventas, Inc.; *U.S. Public*, pg. 2278
BC COMERTBANK SA; *Int'l*, pg. 921
BCC PRODUCTS INC.—See Arsenal Capital Management LP; *U.S. Private*, pg. 339
BC CRAFT SUPPLY CO., LTD.; *Int'l*, pg. 921
BCC RISPARMIO & PREVIDENZA SGRPA—See Iccrea Holding S.p.A.; *Int'l*, pg. 3578
BCC SISTEMI INFORMATICI SPA—See Iccrea Holding S.p.A.; *Int'l*, pg. 3578
BCC SOFTWARE, LLC—See Platinum Equity, LLC; *U.S. Private*, pg. 3202
BCCU INC.; *U.S. Private*, pg. 499
BCC VITA S.P.A.—See Iccrea Holding S.p.A.; *Int'l*, pg. 3578
BCC VITA S.P.A.—See Societa Cattolica di Assicurazione-Societa Cooperativa; *Int'l*, pg. 7033
BCD HOLDINGS N.V.; *Int'l*, pg. 926
BCD MEETINGS & EVENTS GERMANY GMBH—See BCD Holdings N.V.; *Int'l*, pg. 926
BCD MEETINGS & EVENTS LLC—See BCD Holdings N.V.; *Int'l*, pg. 926
BCD MEETINGS & EVENTS SWITZERLAND AG—See BCD Holdings N.V.; *Int'l*, pg. 926
BCD PINPOINT DIRECT MARKETING INC.—See WPP plc; *Int'l*, pg. 8484
BCD POLYMERS SP. Z O.O.—See BRENNTAG SE; *Int'l*, pg. 1146
BCD SEMICONDUCTOR CORP—See Diodes Incorporated; *U.S. Public*, pg. 667
BCD SEMICONDUCTOR LIMITED—See Diodes Incorporated; *U.S. Public*, pg. 667
BCD SEMICONDUCTOR MANUFACTURING LIMITED—See Diodes Incorporated; *U.S. Public*, pg. 667
BCD SEMICONDUCTOR (TAIWAN) COMPANY LIMITED—See Diodes Incorporated; *U.S. Public*, pg. 667
BCD (SHANGHAI) MICRO-ELECTRONICS LIMITED—See Diodes Incorporated; *U.S. Public*, pg. 667
BCD TRAVEL SERVICES B.V.—See BCD Holdings N.V.; *Int'l*, pg. 926
BCD TRAVEL—See BCD Holdings N.V.; *Int'l*, pg. 926
BCD TRAVEL—See BCD Holdings N.V.; *Int'l*, pg. 926
BCDVIDEO; *U.S. Private*, pg. 499
BCE ENGINEERS, INC.—See OceanSound Partners, LP; *U.S. Private*, pg. 2991
BCE FRANCE SAS—See Bertelsmann SE & Co. KGaA; *Int'l*, pg. 990
BCEG ENVIRONMENTAL REMEDIATION CO., LTD.; *Int'l*, pg. 928
BCE INC.; *Int'l*, pg. 926
BCE KRAKOW SP. Z O.O.—See Bjornsen Beratende Ingenieure GmbH; *Int'l*, pg. 1054
BCER ENGINEERING, INC.; *U.S. Private*, pg. 499
BCES—See FAYAT SAS; *Int'l*, pg. 2624
BC EXPO INDIA PVT. LTD. MUMBAI—See Messe Munchen GmbH; *Int'l*, pg. 4841
BC EXPO SOUTH AFRICA PRT. LTD.—See Messe Munchen GmbH; *Int'l*, pg. 4842
BC EXTRUSION HOLDING GMBH—See Nimbus B.V.; *U.S. Private*, pg. 5296
BCF AUSTRALIA PTY LTD—See Super Retail Group Limited; *Int'l*, pg. 7335
BCF MANAGEMENT CONSULTANTS—See Stanwick Management Consultants; *Int'l*, pg. 7172
BCFORWARD; *U.S. Private*, pg. 499
BCF SOLUTIONS, INC.; *U.S. Private*, pg. 499
BCF; *U.S. Private*, pg. 499
BCG COMMUNICATIONS; *Int'l*, pg. 928
BCG ENGINEERING & CONSULTING, INC.—See Littlejohn & Co., LLC; *U.S. Private*, pg. 2469
BCG HOLDINGS INC—See Barington Capital Group, L.P.; *U.S. Private*, pg. 475
BCG PUBLICIDAD & AGRONEGOCIOS S.A.C—See HORIBA Ltd; *Int'l*, pg. 3475
BCH MECHANICAL LLC—See Comfort Systems USA, Inc.; *U.S. Public*, pg. 543

B C HOUSING MANAGEMENT COMMISSION; *Int'l*, pg. 783
B.C. HYDRO; *Int'l*, pg. 789
BCI AIRCRAFT LEASING, INC; *U.S. Private*, pg. 499
BCI ASIA VIETNAM CO, LTD—See Byggfakta Group Nordic HoldCo AB; *Int'l*, pg. 1234
BCI BURKE COMPANY CO—See The Halifax Group LLC; *U.S. Private*, pg. 4042
BCI CENTRAL LTD.—See Byggfakta Group Nordic HoldCo AB; *Int'l*, pg. 1234
BCI CENTRAL SDN BHD.—See Byggfakta Group Nordic HoldCo AB; *Int'l*, pg. 1234
BCI CENTRAL SINGAPORE PTE. LTD.—See Byggfakta Group Nordic HoldCo AB; *Int'l*, pg. 1234
BCI CONSTRUCTION INC.—See The Pike Company Inc.; *U.S. Private*, pg. 4095
BCI GROUP HOLDINGS LIMITED; *Int'l*, pg. 928
BCI HOLDING, INC.; *U.S. Private*, pg. 499
BCII ENTERPRISES, INC.; *U.S. Public*, pg. 285
BCI MATERIALS, INC.—See VINCI S.A.; *Int'l*, pg. 8220
BCI MER ROUGE—See BNP Paribas SA; *Int'l*, pg. 1080
BCI MINERALS LIMITED; *Int'l*, pg. 928
B & C INDUSTRIEHOLDING GMBH—See UniCredit S.p.A.; *Int'l*, pg. 8039
B & C INDUSTRIES LIMITED—See Satu Holdings Limited; *Int'l*, pg. 6587
BCI NEW ZEALAND PTY. LTD.—See Byggfakta Group Nordic HoldCo AB; *Int'l*, pg. 1234
BC INSTITUT D.D. ZAGREB; *Int'l*, pg. 921
BCI PROPERTIES, LLC—See Lennar Corporation; *U.S. Public*, pg. 1305
BCI SEGUROS GENERALES S.A.—See Empresas Juan Yarur S.A.C.; *Int'l*, pg. 2391
BCI SEGUROS VIDA S.A.—See Empresas Juan Yarur S.A.C.; *Int'l*, pg. 2391
BC-KC FORMALIN KFT.—See Permira Advisers LLP; *Int'l*, pg. 5803
B.C LASEPARTNER A/S—See ASSA ABLOY AB; *Int'l*, pg. 639
BCL ENTERPRISES LTD.; *Int'l*, pg. 928
BCL INDUSTRIES LIMITED; *Int'l*, pg. 928
B CLINKSTON & SONS INC.—See Louis Padnos Iron & Metal Company; *U.S. Private*, pg. 2498
DCL LIMITED; *Int'l*, pg. 928
BCLO BRISA PUNTA CANA, BV—See Barcelo Corporacion Empresarial S.A.; *Int'l*, pg. 859
BCLS ACQUISITION CORP.; *U.S. Public*, pg. 285
BCL TECHNOLOGIES—See Thoma Bravo, L.P.; *U.S. Private*, pg. 4146
BCM ALLIANCE BERHAD; *Int'l*, pg. 928
BC MANAGEMENT, INC.—See Resurgens Technology Partners, LLC; *U.S. Private*, pg. 3410
BCM CONSTRUCTION COMPANY INC.; *U.S. Private*, pg. 499
BCM CONTROLS CORPORATION—See Comfort Systems USA, Inc.; *U.S. Public*, pg. 543
BCMEDIA CO., LTD.—See Startia Holdings, Inc.; *Int'l*, pg. 7179
BC MEDICARE SDN. BHD.—See BCM Alliance Berhad; *Int'l*, pg. 928
BCM ENERGY PARTNERS, INC.; *U.S. Private*, pg. 499
BCMGLOBAL ASI LIMITED—See Mitsubishi UFJ Financial Group, Inc.; *Int'l*, pg. 4971
BCMGLOBAL MORTGAGE SERVICES LIMITED—See Mitsubishi UFJ Financial Group, Inc.; *Int'l*, pg. 4971
BC MOLDINDCONBANK S.A.; *Int'l*, pg. 921
BC MOLDOVA AGROINDBANK S.A.; *Int'l*, pg. 922
BC MOLY LTD.; *Int'l*, pg. 922
BCM ONE, INC.—See Thompson Street Capital Manager LLC; *U.S. Private*, pg. 4160
B.C. MOORE & SON INC; *U.S. Private*, pg. 420
BCM RESOURCES CORP.; *Int'l*, pg. 928
BCMZ PRECISION ENGINEERING LIMITED—See Bel Fuse Inc.; *U.S. Public*, pg. 292
BCNC CO., LTD.; *Int'l*, pg. 928
BCNC USA, INC.—See BCnC Co., Ltd.; *Int'l*, pg. 928
BCN DISENOS, S.A. DE C.V—See Industria de Diseno Textil, S.A.; *Int'l*, pg. 3665
BCN DISTRIBUCIONES, S.A.—See Sandmartin International Holdings Limited; *Int'l*, pg. 6526
BCN TECHNICAL SERVICES, INC.—See ANDRITZ AG; *Int'l*, pg. 456
BCO BRASIL S.A.; *Int'l*, pg. 928
BCO BTG PACTUAL S.A.; *Int'l*, pg. 928
BCO ESTADO DO PARA S.A.; *Int'l*, pg. 928
BC-ONGROBAU KFT.—See Permira Advisers LLP; *Int'l*, pg. 5803
BC-ONGROELEKTRO KFT.—See Permira Advisers LLP; *Int'l*, pg. 5803
BC-ONGROPACK KFT.—See Permira Advisers LLP; *Int'l*, pg. 5803
BCO NORDESTE DO BRASIL S.A.; *Int'l*, pg. 928
BC PARTNERS, INC.—See BC Partners LLP; *Int'l*, pg. 923
BC PARTNERS LENDING CORPORATION; *U.S. Private*, pg. 498
BC PARTNERS LLP; *Int'l*, pg. 922
BCP BANK (MAURITIUS) LTD—See Banque Centrale Populaire S.A.; *Int'l*, pg. 853

B. DAZZLE, INC.

BCPG PUBLIC COMPANY LIMITED—See Bangchak Corporation Public Company Limited; *Int'l*, pg. 832
BCP INC.; *U.S. Private*, pg. 499
BCP INGREDIENTS, INC.—See Balchem Corporation; *U.S. Public*, pg. 265
BCPL RAILWAY INFRASTRUCTURE LIMITED; *Int'l*, pg. 929
BCP LTD.; *Int'l*, pg. 929
BC POWER CONTROLS LTD.; *Int'l*, pg. 925
B&C PRIVATSTIFTUNG—See UniCredit S.p.A.; *Int'l*, pg. 8039
BCP TECHNICAL SERVICE, INC.; *U.S. Private*, pg. 499
BCR ASIGURARI DE VIATA VIENNA INSURANCE GROUP S.A.—See Vienna Insurance Group AG Wiener Versicherung Gruppe; *Int'l*, pg. 8194
BCR ENVIRONMENTAL CORPORATION; *U.S. Private*, pg. 499
B.C. RICH GUITARS—See Hanser Holdings International; *U.S. Private*, pg. 1856
BCR PROCESARE SRL—See Erste Group Bank AG; *Int'l*, pg. 2497
BCR SOCIAL FINANCE IFN S.A.—See Erste Group Bank AG; *Int'l*, pg. 2497
BCS AIRPORT SYSTEMS PTY LIMITED—See Daifuku Co., Ltd.; *Int'l*, pg. 1924
BCS BROADCAST SACHSEN GMBH & CO. KG—See Bertelsmann SE & Co. KGaA; *Int'l*, pg. 990
BCS CALLPROCESSING, INC.; *U.S. Private*, pg. 500
BCS DESIGN, INC.—See Butler National Corporation; *U.S. Public*, pg. 413
B.C.S. FINANCIAL CORP.; *U.S. Private*, pg. 420
BCS INFORMATION SYSTEMS PRIVATE LIMITED—See HSBC Holdings plc; *Int'l*, pg. 3503
B.C.S. INSURANCE COMPANY INC.—See B.C.S. Financial Corp.; *U.S. Private*, pg. 420
BCS INTEGRATION SOLUTIONS SDN. BHD.—See Daifuku Co., Ltd.; *Int'l*, pg. 1924
BCS, INC.; *U.S. Public*, pg. 500
BCS MANAGMENT COMPANY—See Vari Corporation; *U.S. Private*, pg. 4346
B&C SPEAKERS BRASIL COMERCIO DE EQUIPAMENTOS DE AUDIO LTDA.—See B&C Speakers SpA; *Int'l*, pg. 783
B&C SPEAKERS NA (USA), LLC—See B&C Speakers SpA; *Int'l*, pg. 783
B&C SPEAKERS SPA; *Int'l*, pg. 783
BCS PROSOFT; *U.S. Private*, pg. 500
BC STEEL BUILDINGS, INC.; *U.S. Private*, pg. 498
BCS WEST LLC; *U.S. Private*, pg. 500
BCT BANK INTERNATIONAL S.A.; *Int'l*, pg. 929
BCT CONSULTING, INC.; *U.S. Private*, pg. 500
BC TECHNICAL, INC.—See Alpha Source, Inc.; *U.S. Private*, pg. 199
BC TECHNOLOGY GROUP LIMITED; *Int'l*, pg. 925
BCT INTERNATIONAL, INC.; *U.S. Private*, pg. 500
B.C. TREE FRUITS LTD.; *Int'l*, pg. 789
BC-USA, INC.—See Savencia Fromage & Dairy; *Int'l*, pg. 6597
B.C. VICTORIABANK S.A.; *Int'l*, pg. 789
BCV ITALIA SRL—See Banque Cantonale Vaudoise; *Int'l*, pg. 853
BCV SOCIAL LLC—See RateGain Technologies Inc.; *U.S. Private*, pg. 3357
BCV TECHNOLOGIES SAS—See Schneider Electric SE; *Int'l*, pg. 6626
BCW GROUP (GOTHIA) LIMITED—See Bertelsmann SE & Co. KGaA; *Int'l*, pg. 996
BCW GROUP HOLDING, INC.; *Int'l*, pg. 929
BCWH, INC.—See Quinn Evans Architects Inc.; *U.S. Private*, pg. 3328
BCWORLD PHARM CO., LTD.; *Int'l*, pg. 929
BCWORLD PHARM CO., LTD. - YEOJU FACTORY—See Bcworld Pharm Co., Ltd.; *Int'l*, pg. 929
BCW V TECH INDIA PRIVATE LIMITED—See L.G. Balakrishnan & Bros. Ltd.; *Int'l*, pg. 4386
B-CYCLE, LLC—See Humana, Inc.; *U.S. Public*, pg. 1069
BD4 TRAVEL GMBH—See The Emirates Group; *Int'l*, pg. 7639
BD AGRO AD; *Int'l*, pg. 929
BD&A REALTY & CONSTRUCTION; *U.S. Private*, pg. 500
B. DAZZLE, INC.; *U.S. Private*, pg. 419
BDB DATA BUREAU (PTY) LTD—See Transaction Capital Limited; *Int'l*, pg. 7894
BDB HOTELS SDN. BHD.—See Bina Darulaman Berhad; *Int'l*, pg. 1032
BDB INFRA SDN. BHD.—See Bina Darulaman Berhad; *Int'l*, pg. 1032
B D & B INVESTMENTS LIMITED—See Barclays PLC; *Int'l*, pg. 859
BD BIOSCIENCES DISCOVERY LABWARE—See Becton, Dickinson & Company; *U.S. Public*, pg. 289
BD BIOSCIENCES PHARMINGEN—See Becton, Dickinson & Company; *U.S. Public*, pg. 289
BDB LAND SDN. BHD.—See Bina Darulaman Berhad; *Int'l*, pg. 1032
BDB LIMITED—See Brown & Brown, Inc.; *U.S. Public*, pg. 397
BDB SYNERGY SDN. BHD.—See Bina Darulaman Berhad; *Int'l*, pg. 1032

BDB (UK) LIMITED—See Brown & Brown, Inc.; *U.S. Public*, pg. 397
B&D BUSINESS SOLUTIONS B.V.—See Munchener Ruckversicherungs AG; *Int'l*, pg. 5085
BD-CAPITAL PARTNERS LIMITED; *Int'l*, pg. 929
BDC DORSCH CONSULT INGENIEURGESELLSCHAFT MBH—See RAG-Stiftung; *Int'l*, pg. 6178
BC CHINE—See Orange S.A.; *Int'l*, pg. 5607
BDCOM ONLINE LIMITED; *Int'l*, pg. 929
BDC VIETNAM INVESTMENT & CONSTRUCTION JSC; *Int'l*, pg. 929
BD DIAGNOSTIC SYSTEMS-INFORMATICS—See Becton, Dickinson & Company; *U.S. Public*, pg. 288
BD DIAGNOSTIC SYSTEMS—See Becton, Dickinson & Company; *U.S. Public*, pg. 288
BD DIESEL PERFORMANCE; *Int'l*, pg. 929
B&D DOORS (NZ) LIMITED—See Nippon Paint Holdings Co., Ltd.; *Int'l*, pg. 5325
BDDP & FILS—See Omnicom Group Inc.; *U.S. Public*, pg. 1596
BDE LAW LIMITED—See Admiral Group plc; *Int'l*, pg. 151
BD ESPANA—See Orange S.A.; *Int'l*, pg. 5607
BDF CENTRO AMERICA S.A.—See maxingvest ag; *Int'l*, pg. 4738
BDF CORPORATIVO, S.A. DE C.V.—See maxingvest ag; *Int'l*, pg. 4738
BDF COSTA RICA, S.A.—See maxingvest ag; *Int'l*, pg. 4738
BDF EL SALVADOR S.A. DE C.V.—See maxingvest ag; *Int'l*, pg. 4738
BD FINANCE CAPITAL HOLDINGS LIMITED—See Bangladesh Finance Limited; *Int'l*, pg. 835
BD FINANCE SECURITIES LIMITED—See Bangladesh Finance Limited; *Int'l*, pg. 835
BDF MEXICO, S.A. DE C.V.—See maxingvest ag; *Int'l*, pg. 4738
BDF NIVEA LTDA.—See maxingvest ag; *Int'l*, pg. 4738
BDF NIVEA S.A.—See maxingvest ag; *Int'l*, pg. 4738
BD FOODS LTD.—See AAK AB; *Int'l*, pg. 32
BDF PANAMA S.A.—See maxingvest ag; *Int'l*, pg. 4738
BDF SPA—See Econocom Group SA; *Int'l*, pg. 2297
BDG ARCHITECTS LLP; *U.S. Private*, pg. 500
BDG MEDIA, INC.; *U.S. Private*, pg. 500
BDH BILISIM DESTEK HIZMETLERI SANAYI VE TICARET A.S.—See Netas Telekomunikasyon Anonim Sirketi; *Int'l*, pg. 5212
BDH INDUSTRIES LTD.; *Int'l*, pg. 929
BD HOLDING S. DE R.L. DE C.V.—See Becton, Dickinson & Company; *U.S. Public*, pg. 288
BDI-BEARING DISTRIBUTORS, INC.; *U.S. Private*, pg. 500
BDI - BIOENERGY INTERNATIONAL AG; *Int'l*, pg. 929
BDI CANADA, INC.—See Forge Industries, Inc.; *U.S. Private*, pg. 1568
BDI. CO., LTD; *Int'l*, pg. 929
BDI DISTRIBUTION WEST INC.—See Apollo Global Management, Inc.; *U.S. Public*, pg. 165
BDI INSULATION OF IDAHO FALLS, INC.—See Installed Building Products, Inc.; *U.S. Public*, pg. 1132
BDI INSULATION OF SALT LAKE, LLC—See Installed Building Products, Inc.; *U.S. Public*, pg. 1132
B&D INDEPENDENCE, LLC—See Investor AB; *Int'l*, pg. 3787
B&D INDUSTRIAL, INC.; *U.S. Private*, pg. 418
BD INDUSTRIEBETEILIGUNGSGESELLSCHAFT MBH—See UniCredit S.p.A.; *Int'l*, pg. 8038
BD ISRAEL LTD.—See Orange S.A.; *Int'l*, pg. 5607
BDK HOLDINGS, INC.; *U.S. Private*, pg. 500
BD KIESTRA BV—See Becton, Dickinson & Company; *U.S. Public*, pg. 288
BDK USA; *U.S. Private*, pg. 500
BDL HOTEL GROUP; *Int'l*, pg. 929
B&D LIFE HEALTH CO.,LTD.; *Int'l*, pg. 784
BD LIFT AB—See Amplex AB; *Int'l*, pg. 434
B&D LITHO OF ARIZONA, INC.—See Ennis, Inc.; *U.S. Public*, pg. 769
BD LUXEMBOURG—See Orange S.A.; *Int'l*, pg. 5608
BD MAROC—See Orange S.A.; *Int'l*, pg. 5608
BD MAURITIUS—See Orange S.A.; *Int'l*, pg. 5608
B&D MHP LLC—See Manufactured Housing Properties Inc.; *U.S. Public*, pg. 1362
BDML CONNECT LIMITED—See Capita plc; *Int'l*, pg. 1308
BDMS SILVER CO., LTD.—See Bangkok Dusit Medical Services Public Company Limited; *Int'l*, pg. 834
BDMS WELLNESS CLINIC CO., LTD.—See Bangkok Dusit Medical Services Public Company Limited; *Int'l*, pg. 833
BD MULTIMEDIA SA; *Int'l*, pg. 929
BD NORGE AS—See Becton, Dickinson & Company; *U.S. Public*, pg. 288
BD-NTWK LONDON; *Int'l*, pg. 929
BD-NTWK SCOTLAND—See BD-NTWK London; *Int'l*, pg. 929
BDO AG WIRTSCHAFTSPRUFUNGSGESELLSCHAFT; *Int'l*, pg. 929
BDO CAPITAL ADVISORS, LLC—See BDO USA, LLP; *U.S. Private*, pg. 501
BDO CAPITAL & INVESTMENT CORPORATION—See BDO Unibank, Inc.; *Int'l*, pg. 930

BDO DIGITAL, LLC—See BDO USA, LLP; *U.S. Private*, pg. 501
BDO DR. LAUTER & FISCHER GMBH WIRTSCHAFTSPRUFUNGS-GESELLSCHAFT—See BDO AG Wirtschaftsprufungsgesellschaft; *Int'l*, pg. 929
BDO DUNWOODY LLP; *Int'l*, pg. 929
BDO ELITE SAVINGS BANK, INC.—See BDO Unibank, Inc.; *Int'l*, pg. 930
BDO INSURANCE BROKERS, INC.—See BDO Unibank, Inc.; *Int'l*, pg. 930
BDO INTERNATIONAL LIMITED; *Int'l*, pg. 930
BDO KENDALLS; *Int'l*, pg. 930
BDO PRIVATE BANK, INC.—See BDO Unibank, Inc.; *Int'l*, pg. 930
BDO PUERTO RICO, P.S.C.; *U.S. Private*, pg. 500
BDO REMIT LIMITED—See BDO Unibank, Inc.; *Int'l*, pg. 930
BDO REMITTANCE (USA) INC.—See BDO Unibank, Inc.; *Int'l*, pg. 930
BDO RENTAL, INC.—See BDO Unibank, Inc.; *Int'l*, pg. 930
BDO SCHLESWIG-HOLSTEINISCHE TREUHANDGESELLSCHAFT MBH WIRTSCHAFTSPRUFUNGSGESELLSCHAFT STEUERBERATUNGSGESELLSCHAFT—See BDO AG Wirtschaftsprufungsgesellschaft; *Int'l*, pg. 929
BDO SCHURMANN & GLASHOFF STEUERBERATUNGSGESELLSCHAFT MBH—See BDO AG Wirtschaftsprufungsgesellschaft; *Int'l*, pg. 929
BDO SECURITIES CORPORATION—See BDO Unibank, Inc.; *Int'l*, pg. 930
BDO SPENCER STEWARD (JOHANNESBURG) INC—See L. Possehl & Co. mbH; *Int'l*, pg. 4381
BDO STRATEGIC HOLDINGS, INC.—See BDO Unibank, Inc.; *Int'l*, pg. 930
BDO UNIBANK, INC.; *Int'l*, pg. 930
BDO USA, LLP; *U.S. Private*, pg. 500
BDO WESTFALEN-REVISION GMBH WIRTSCHAFTSPRUFUNGSGESELLSCHAFT—See BDO AG Wirtschaftsprufungsgesellschaft; *Int'l*, pg. 929
BDP ASIA PACIFIC LIMITED—See BDP International Inc.; *U.S. Private*, pg. 501
BDP ASIA PACIFIC PTE LTD.—See BDP International Inc.; *U.S. Private*, pg. 501
BDP CANADA ULC—See BDP International Inc.; *U.S. Private*, pg. 501
BDP CHILE LTDA.—See BDP International Inc.; *U.S. Private*, pg. 501
BDP GLOBAL LOGISTICS (INDIA) PRIVATE LIMITED—See BDP International Inc.; *U.S. Private*, pg. 501
BDP HOLDINGS LIMITED—See Nippon Koei Co., Ltd.; *Int'l*, pg. 5321
BDP INTERNATIONAL BV—See BDP International Inc.; *U.S. Private*, pg. 501
BDP INTERNATIONAL INC.; *U.S. Private*, pg. 501
BDP INTERNATIONAL LTD.—See BDP International Inc.; *U.S. Private*, pg. 501
BDP INTERNATIONAL MEXICO, S.A. DE C.V.—See BDP International Inc.; *U.S. Private*, pg. 501
BDP INTERNATIONAL NV - AIRFREIGHT DIVISION—See BDP International Inc.; *U.S. Private*, pg. 501
BDP INTERNATIONAL NV—See BDP International Inc.; *U.S. Private*, pg. 501
BDP INTERNATIONAL SPAIN, S.A—See BDP International Inc.; *U.S. Private*, pg. 501
BDP INTERNATIONAL UK LIMITED—See BDP International Inc.; *U.S. Private*, pg. 501
BDP ITALIA S.P.A—See BDP International Inc.; *U.S. Private*, pg. 501
BDP KANOO CHEMICAL LOGISTICS CO. LTD—See BDP International Inc.; *U.S. Private*, pg. 501
BDP LOGISTICS KOREA LIMITED—See BDP International Inc.; *U.S. Private*, pg. 501
BDP (MALAYSIA) SDN BHD—See BDP International Inc.; *U.S. Private*, pg. 501
BD PREANALYTICAL—See Becton, Dickinson & Company; *U.S. Public*, pg. 288
BD PRINT LIMITED—See Ball Corporation; *U.S. Public*, pg. 266
BDP SOUTH AMERICA LTDA.—See BDP International Inc.; *U.S. Private*, pg. 502
BDP TRANSPORT, LLC—See BDP International Inc.; *U.S. Private*, pg. 502
BDR BUILDCON LIMITED; *Int'l*, pg. 930
BDRC AMERICAS INC.—See The BDRC Group; *Int'l*, pg. 7620
BDRC ASIA PTE LTD—See The BDRC Group; *Int'l*, pg. 7620
BDRC CHINA—See The BDRC Group; *Int'l*, pg. 7620
THE BDRC GROUP; *Int'l*, pg. 7620
BDRC JONES DONALD PTY LTD—See The BDRC Group; *Int'l*, pg. 7620
BDR THERMEA (CZECH REPUBLIC) S.R.O.—See BDR Thermea Group B.V.; *Int'l*, pg. 930
BDR THERMEA GROUP B.V.; *Int'l*, pg. 930
BDR THERMEA (TIANJIN) CO. LTD—See BDR Thermea Group B.V.; *Int'l*, pg. 930
BDR TITLE CORPORATION—See Mercedes Homes Inc.; *U.S. Private*, pg. 2668

BDR TRANSPORT, INC.; *U.S. Private*, pg. 502
BD RX INC.—See Becton, Dickinson & Company; *U.S. Public*, pg. 288
B&D SALES & MARKETING, INC.; *U.S. Private*, pg. 418
BDS DESTINATION SERVICES COMPANY—See TUI AG; *Int'l*, pg. 7964
BDS MARKETING, LLC; *U.S. Private*, pg. 502
BDSTAR INFORMATION SERVICE CO., LTD.—See Beijing BDstar Navigation Co., Ltd.; *Int'l*, pg. 946
B & D STRATEGIC HOLDINGS LIMITED; *Int'l*, pg. 783
BD SWITZERLAND SARL—See Becton, Dickinson & Company; *U.S. Public*, pg. 290
BDT BAVARIA DIGITAL TECHNIK GMBH—See AdCapital AG; *Int'l*, pg. 126
BDT CAPITAL PARTNERS, LLC; *U.S. Private*, pg. 502
B&D TECHNOLOGIES—See B&D Industrial, Inc.; *U.S. Private*, pg. 418
BD TECHNOLOGIES—See Becton, Dickinson & Company; *U.S. Public*, pg. 288
BD THAI FOOD & BEVERAGE LTD.; *Int'l*, pg. 929
BDTRONIC BVBA—See MAX Automation SE; *Int'l*, pg. 4734
BDTRONIC GMBH—See MAX Automation SE; *Int'l*, pg. 4734
BDTRONIC ITALY S.R.L.—See MAX Automation SE; *Int'l*, pg. 4734
BDTRONIC LTD.—See MAX Automation SE; *Int'l*, pg. 4734
BDTRONIC S.R.L.—See MAX Automation SE; *Int'l*, pg. 4734
BDTRONIC SUZHOU CO., LTD.—See MAX Automation SE; *Int'l*, pg. 4734
B.DUCK SEMK HOLDINGS INTERNATIONAL LIMITED; *Int'l*, pg. 789
BDU NY, LLC—See Bassett Furniture Industries, Incorporated; *U.S. Public*, pg. 279
BDV BETEILIGUNGEN GMBH & CO. KG—See Hubert Burda Media Holding Kommanditgesellschaft; *Int'l*, pg. 3519
BD VENTURES LLC—See Becton, Dickinson & Company; *U.S. Public*, pg. 288
BDW EAST SCOTLAND LIMITED—See Barratt Developments PLC; *Int'l*, pg. 867
BD WHITE BIRCH PAPER INVESTMENT LLC—See Black Diamond Capital Holdings, LLC; *U.S. Private*, pg. 570
BDW TRADING LIMITED—See Barratt Developments PLC; *Int'l*, pg. 867
BEACH AUTOMOTIVE GROUP; *U.S. Private*, pg. 503
THE BEACHBODY COMPANY, INC.; *U.S. Public*, pg. 2038
BEACHBODY, LLC; *U.S. Private*, pg. 503
BEACHCOMBER HOT TUBS; *Int'l*, pg. 932
BEACH COMMUNITY BANCSHARES, INC.; *U.S. Public*, pg. 285
BEACH COMMUNITY BANK—See Beach Community Bancshares, Inc.; *U.S. Public*, pg. 285
BEACH COMPANY INC.; *U.S. Private*, pg. 503
BEACH ELECTRIC COMPANY INC.—See Railroad Construction Company, Inc.; *U.S. Private*, pg. 3346
BEACH ENERGY LIMITED; *Int'l*, pg. 932
BEACH FORD, INC.; *U.S. Private*, pg. 503
BEACH FORD; *U.S. Private*, pg. 503
BEACH FORD SUFFOLK; *U.S. Private*, pg. 503
BEACH HATCHERY LIMITED; *Int'l*, pg. 932
THE BEACH HOTEL—See Gooderson Leisure Corporation; *Int'l*, pg. 3040
BEACH HOUSE PICTURES PTE LIMITED—See Bertelsmann SE & Co. KGaA; *Int'l*, pg. 994
THE BEACH HOUSE SWIMWEAR, INC.; *U.S. Private*, pg. 3992
BEACH MOLD & TOOL INC.—See NYX Inc.; *U.S. Private*, pg. 2977
BEACH MOLD & TOOL VIRGINIA, INC.—See NYX Inc.; *U.S. Private*, pg. 2977
BEACHNER GRAIN INC.; *U.S. Private*, pg. 503
BEACH OIL COMPANY INC.; *U.S. Private*, pg. 503
BEACH PATROL INC.; *U.S. Private*, pg. 503
BEACH PRODUCTS, INC.; *U.S. Private*, pg. 503
BEACH PROPERTIES OF FLORIDA—See Berkshire Hathaway Inc.; *U.S. Public*, pg. 306
THE BEACH REPORTER—See Alden Global Capital LLC; *U.S. Private*, pg. 158
BEACHSIDE CAPITAL PARTNERS; *U.S. Private*, pg. 503
BEACH STREET CONSULTING, INC.—See InfoTrust Group, Inc.; *U.S. Private*, pg. 2074
BEACH TO BAY CONSTRUCTION INC.; *U.S. Private*, pg. 503
BEACH TOWN CORPORATION—See Renaissance, Inc.; *Int'l*, pg. 6273
BEACON ACQUISITION PARTNERS INC.; *U.S. Private*, pg. 503
BEACON APPLICATION SERVICES CORPORATION; *U.S. Private*, pg. 503
BEACON ASSOCIATES, INC.; *U.S. Private*, pg. 504
BEACON AUTOMATION PTY LTD—See Livestock Improvement Corporation Limited; *Int'l*, pg. 4531
BEACON AVIATION INSURANCE SERVICES, INC.; *U.S. Private*, pg. 504
BEACON BAY AUTO WASH; *U.S. Private*, pg. 504

COMPANY NAME INDEX

BEACON CAPITAL MANAGEMENT, INC.—See Sammons Enterprises, Inc.; *U.S. Private*, pg. 3537
BEACON CAPITAL STRATEGIC L.P.—See Cinven Limited; *Int'l*, pg. 1616
BEACON CAPITAL STRATEGIC L.P.—See Talanx AG; *Int'l*, pg. 7445
BEACON CENTER, LLC—See Saul Centers, Inc.; *U.S. Public*, pg. 1842
BEACON COMMUNICATIONS K.K.—See Publicis Groupe S.A.; *Int'l*, pg. 6100
BEACON COMMUNICATIONS LLC; *U.S. Private*, pg. 504
BEACON COMMUNITIES LLC; *U.S. Private*, pg. 504
BEACON CONSULTING GROUP, LLC—See Accenture plc; *Int'l*, pg. 86
BEACON CONTAINER CORPORATION; *U.S. Private*, pg. 504
BEACON CREDIT UNION; *U.S. Private*, pg. 504
BEACON DRINKS LIMITED—See Nichols Plc; *Int'l*, pg. 5271
BEACON ELECTRIC ASSET HOLDINGS, INC.—See Metro Pacific Investments Corporation; *Int'l*, pg. 4861
BEACON ELECTRIC SUPPLY; *U.S. Private*, pg. 504
BEACON ELECTRONIC ASSOCIATES, INC.; *U.S. Private*, pg. 504
BEACON ENERGY CORPORATION—See EQM Technologies & Energy, Inc.; *U.S. Public*, pg. 784
BEACON ENERGY PLC; *Int'l*, pg. 932
BEACON HEALTH HOLDINGS LLC; *U.S. Private*, pg. 504
BEACON HEALTH OPTIONS OF PENNSYLVANIA, INC.—See Elevance Health, Inc.; *U.S. Public*, pg. 729
BEACON HEALTH STRATEGIES LLC—See Beacon Health Holdings LLC; *U.S. Private*, pg. 504
BEACON HEALTH SYSTEM, INC.; *U.S. Private*, pg. 504
BEACON HILL ASSOCIATES—See Beacon Hill Staffing Group LLC; *U.S. Private*, pg. 504
BEACON HILL FINANCIAL—See Beacon Hill Staffing Group LLC; *U.S. Private*, pg. 504
BEACON HILL FINANCIAL—See Beacon Hill Staffing Group LLC; *U.S. Private*, pg. 504
BEACON HILL HEALTHCARE, INC.—See The Ensign Group, Inc.; *U.S. Public*, pg. 2070
BEACON HILL HR—See Beacon Hill Staffing Group LLC; *U.S. Private*, pg. 504
BEACON HILL LEGAL—See Beacon Hill Staffing Group LLC; *U.S. Private*, pg. 504
BEACON HILL STAFFING GROUP LLC; *U.S. Private*, pg. 504
BEACON HILL TECHNOLOGIES—See Beacon Hill Staffing Group LLC; *U.S. Private*, pg. 504
BEACON HOSPICE, INC.—See Amedisys, Inc.; *U.S. Public*, pg. 93
BEACON INDUSTRIES, INC.; *U.S. Private*, pg. 504
BEACON INTERMODAL LEASING, LLC—See Mitsubishi HC Capital Inc.; *Int'l*, pg. 4950
BEACON INTERNATIONAL LIMITED—See Beacon Lighting Group Ltd; *Int'l*, pg. 932
BEACON INTERNATIONAL SPECIALIST CENTRE SDN. BHD.; *Int'l*, pg. 932
THE BEACON JOURNAL PUBLISHING COMPANY—See Gannett Co., Inc.; *U.S. Public*, pg. 904
BEACON LIGHT BEHAVIORAL HEALTH SYSTEMS—See Children's Home of Bradford, PA; *U.S. Private*, pg. 884
BEACON LIGHTING EUROPE GMBH—See Beacon Lighting Group Ltd; *Int'l*, pg. 932
BEACON LIGHTING GROUP LTD; *Int'l*, pg. 932
BEACON MEDIA GROUP—See Kartoon Studios, Inc.; *U.S. Public*, pg. 1214
BEACON MEDICAL PRODUCTS LLC—See Atlas Copco AB; *Int'l*, pg. 681
BEACON MINERALS LTD.; *Int'l*, pg. 932
BEACON MOBILE, LLC—See Vontier Corporation; *U.S. Public*, pg. 2308
BEACON MOBILITY CORP.—See Audax Group, Limited Partnership; *U.S. Private*, pg. 505
BEACON MOTORS, INC.—See AutoNation, Inc.; *U.S. Public*, pg. 233
BEACON MOTORS, INC.—See AutoNation, Inc.; *U.S. Public*, pg. 233
THE BEACON NEWS—See Chicago Public Media, Inc.; *U.S. Private*, pg. 879
BEACON OCCUPATIONAL HEALTH & SAFETY SERVICES, INC.; *U.S. Private*, pg. 504
BEACON PHARMACEUTICALS LTD.; *Int'l*, pg. 932
BEACON POINTE ADVISORS, LLC—See Beacon Pointe Holdings, LLC; *U.S. Private*, pg. 505
BEACON POINTE HOLDINGS, LLC; *U.S. Private*, pg. 505
BEACON POINTE WEALTH ADVISORS, LLC—See Beacon Pointe Holdings, LLC; *U.S. Private*, pg. 505
BEACON POWER, LLC—See Rockland Capital, LLC; *U.S. Private*, pg. 3467
BEACON RAIL LEASING LTD—See Pamplona Capital Management LLP; *Int'l*, pg. 5711
BEACON RECYCLING INC.—See Beacon Redevelopment Industrial Corp.; *U.S. Public*, pg. 285
BEACON REDEVELOPMENT INDUSTRIAL CORP.; *U.S. Public*, pg. 285
BEACON RESPIRATORY SERVICES, INC.—See AdaptHealth Corp.; *U.S. Public*, pg. 38
BEACON RISE HOLDINGS PLC; *Int'l*, pg. 932

BEACON ROOFING SUPPLY CANADA COMPANY—See Beacon Roofing Supply, Inc.; *U.S. Public*, pg. 285
BEACON ROOFING SUPPLY, INC. - PITTSBURGH—See Beacon Roofing Supply, Inc.; *U.S. Public*, pg. 285
BEACON ROOFING SUPPLY, INC.; *U.S. Public*, pg. 285
BEACON SALES ACQUISITION INC.; *U.S. Private*, pg. 505
BEACONSFIELD FOOTWEAR LIMITED—See Epiris Managers LLP; *Int'l*, pg. 2461
BEACONSMIND AG; *Int'l*, pg. 932
THE BEACON—See Gannett Co., Inc.; *U.S. Public*, pg. 903
BEACON TRUST COMPANY—See Provident Financial Services, Inc.; *U.S. Public*, pg. 1730
THE BEACON-VILLAGER—See Gannett Co., Inc.; *U.S. Public*, pg. 903
BE ACTIVE CORP.; *U.S. Private*, pg. 503
BEADELL RESOURCES LIMITED—See Great Panther Mining Limited; *Int'l*, pg. 3065
BEAD INDUSTRIES INC - BEAD CHAIN DIVISION—See Bead Industries Inc.; *U.S. Private*, pg. 505
BEAD INDUSTRIES INC - BEAD ELECTRONICS DIVISION—See Bead Industries Inc.; *U.S. Private*, pg. 505
BEAD INDUSTRIES INC.; *U.S. Private*, pg. 505
BEADLES COULSDON LIMITED—See Group 1 Automotive, Inc.; *U.S. Public*, pg. 970
BEADLES DARTFORD LIMITED—See Group 1 Automotive, Inc.; *U.S. Public*, pg. 970
BEADLES LUMBER COMPANY, INC.—See Canfor Corporation; *Int'l*, pg. 1290
BEADLES MAIDSTONE LIMITED—See Group 1 Automotive, Inc.; *U.S. Public*, pg. 970
BEADLES MEDWAY LIMITED—See Group 1 Automotive, Inc.; *U.S. Public*, pg. 970
BEADLES SIDCUP LIMITED—See Group 1 Automotive, Inc.; *U.S. Public*, pg. 971
BEA ELEKTROTECHNIK UND AUTOMATION TECHNISCHE DIENSTE LAUSITZ GMBH - DUSSELDORF BUSINESS UNIT—See VINCI S.A.; *Int'l*, pg. 8212
BEA ELEKTROTECHNIK UND AUTOMATION TECHNISCHE DIENSTE LAUSITZ GMBH - EISENHUTTENSTADT FACILITY—See VINCI S.A.; *Int'l*, pg. 8212
BEA ELEKTROTECHNIK UND AUTOMATION TECHNISCHE DIENSTE LAUSITZ GMBH - NOCHTEN/REICHWALDE OPENCAST MINING FACILITY—See VINCI S.A.; *Int'l*, pg. 8213
BEA ELEKTROTECHNIK UND AUTOMATION TECHNISCHE DIENSTE LAUSITZ GMBH - SPREMBERG MINING ENGINEERING BUSINESS UNIT—See VINCI S.A.; *Int'l*, pg. 8213
BEA ELEKTROTECHNIK UND AUTOMATION TECHNISCHE DIENSTE LAUSITZ GMBH - SPREMBERG POWER ENGINEERING BUSINESS UNIT—See VINCI S.A.; *Int'l*, pg. 8213
BEA ELEKTROTECHNIK UND AUTOMATION TECHNISCHE DIENSTE LAUSITZ GMBH - THYSSEN KRUPP NIROSTA KREFELD FACILITY—See VINCI S.A.; *Int'l*, pg. 8213
BEA ELEKTROTECHNIK UND AUTOMATION TECHNISCHE DIENSTE LAUSITZ GMBH - WEST FACILITIES—See VINCI S.A.; *Int'l*, pg. 8213
BEA ELEKTROTECHNIK UND AUTOMATION TECHNISCHE DIENSTE LAUSITZ GMBH - ZEITZ FACILITY—See VINCI S.A.; *Int'l*, pg. 8213
B/E AEROSPACE CANADA COMPANY—See RTX Corporation; *U.S. Public*, pg. 1822
B/E AEROSPACE FISCHER GMBH—See RTX Corporation; *U.S. Public*, pg. 1822
B/E AEROSPACE FISCHER GMBH—See The Boeing Company; *U.S. Public*, pg. 2040
B/E AEROSPACE (GERMANY) GMBH—See RTX Corporation; *U.S. Public*, pg. 1822
B/E AEROSPACE HOLDINGS GMBH—See RTX Corporation; *U.S. Public*, pg. 1822
BE AEROSPACE HOLDINGS (UK) LIMITED—See RTX Corporation; *U.S. Public*, pg. 1822
B/E AEROSPACE, INC.—See RTX Corporation; *U.S. Public*, pg. 1822
B/E AEROSPACE INC.—See RTX Corporation; *U.S. Public*, pg. 1822
B/E AEROSPACE MACHINED PRODUCTS, INC.—See RTX Corporation; *U.S. Public*, pg. 1822
BE AEROSPACE (NETHERLANDS) B.V.—See RTX Corporation; *U.S. Public*, pg. 1822
B/E AEROSPACE SYSTEMS GMBH—See RTX Corporation; *U.S. Public*, pg. 1822
B/E AEROSPACE THERMAL & POWER MANAGEMENT—See RTX Corporation; *U.S. Public*, pg. 1822
BEAGLE AEROSPACE LIMITED—See Monksmead Partnership LLP; *Int'l*, pg. 5034
BEAGLEE, INC.; *Int'l*, pg. 932
BEAGLE WATCH ARMED RESPONSE PROPRIETARY LIMITED—See Prosegur Compania de Seguridad S.A.; *Int'l*, pg. 5999
B.E.A. INC.—See Halma plc; *Int'l*, pg. 3231
THE BEAIRD GROUP; *U.S. Private*, pg. 3992

BEAL BANK INC.—See Beal Financial Corporation; *U.S. Private*, pg. 505
BEAL BANK USA—See Beal Financial Corporation; *U.S. Private*, pg. 505
BEALE LIMITED; *Int'l*, pg. 932
BEAL FINANCIAL CORPORATION; *U.S. Private*, pg. 505
BEAL GROUP; *U.S. Private*, pg. 505
BEALL MANUFACTURING, INC.; *U.S. Private*, pg. 505
BEALL'S DEPT. STORES—See Beall's, Inc.; *U.S. Private*, pg. 505
BEALL'S, INC.; *U.S. Private*, pg. 505
BEALL'S OUTLET INC.—See Beall's, Inc.; *U.S. Private*, pg. 505
BEALL'S WESTGATE CORPORATION—See Beall's, Inc.; *U.S. Private*, pg. 505
BEALS CUNNINGHAM STRATEGIC SERVICES; *U.S. Private*, pg. 505
BEAMAN AUTOMOTIVE GROUP; *U.S. Private*, pg. 506
BEAM A/S—See Bucher Industries AG; *Int'l*, pg. 1207
BEAM AUSTRALIA PTY LTD.—See Suntory Holdings Limited; *Int'l*, pg. 7325
BEAM CANADA INC.—See Suntory Holdings Limited; *Int'l*, pg. 7325
BEAM COMMUNICATIONS PTY. LTD.; *Int'l*, pg. 932
BEAM COMMUNICATIONS PTY LTD.—See Beam Communications Pty. Ltd.; *Int'l*, pg. 932
BEAM CONSTRUCTION CO. INC.; *U.S. Private*, pg. 506
BEAMER & MORE GMBH—See Droege Group AG; *Int'l*, pg. 2205
BEAM GLOBAL; *U.S. Public*, pg. 287
BEAM GLOBAL SPIRITS & WINE LLC—See Suntory Holdings Limited; *Int'l*, pg. 7325
BEAMING AGROTRADE SDN. BHD.—See Emivest Berhad; *Int'l*, pg. 2383
BEAM MACK SALES & SERVICE, INC.; *U.S. Private*, pg. 506
BEAMMWAVE AB; *Int'l*, pg. 932
BEAMR IMAGING LTD.; *Int'l*, pg. 932
BEAMR LTD.; *Int'l*, pg. 932
BEAMS INDUSTRIES, INC.—See TransDigm Group Incorporated; *U.S. Public*, pg. 2182
BEAM STORAGE PTE LTD—See Fatfish Group Ltd.; *Int'l*, pg. 2623
BEAM SUNTORY INC.—See Suntory Holdings Limited; *Int'l*, pg. 7325
BEAM THERAPEUTICS INC.; *U.S. Public*, pg. 287
BEAMTREE HOLDINGS LIMITED; *Int'l*, pg. 932
BEAMZ INTERACTIVE, INC.; *U.S. Public*, pg. 287
BEAN ALLIANCE GROUP PTY. LTD.—See Massimo Zanetti Beverage Group SpA; *Int'l*, pg. 4722
BEAN BOX, INC.; *U.S. Private*, pg. 506
BEAN CHEVROLET BUICK GMC LTD.—See General Motors Company; *U.S. Public*, pg. 923
BEAN CREATIVE, INC.; *U.S. Private*, pg. 506
BEAN DREDGING, L.L.C.—See C.F. Bean, LLC; *U.S. Private*, pg. 707
BEAN DRYWALL, INC.; *U.S. Private*, pg. 506
BEANFIELD TECHNOLOGIES, INC.—See DigitalBridge Group, Inc.; *U.S. Public*, pg. 664
BEAN GROUP; *U.S. Private*, pg. 506
BEAN HORIZON CORP.—See C.F. Bean, LLC; *U.S. Private*, pg. 707
BEAN'S BEST LLC; *U.S. Private*, pg. 506
BEANSTALK NETWORKS, LLC—See Thoma Bravo, L.P.; *U.S. Private*, pg. 4150
BEANSTALK—See Omnicom Group Inc.; *U.S. Public*, pg. 1577
BEA-POLSKA ELEKTROTECHNIKA I AUTOMATYZACJA SP. Z O.O.—See VINCI S.A.; *Int'l*, pg. 8236
BEAR ARCHERY, INC.—See Escalade, Incorporated; *U.S. Public*, pg. 793
BEARBULL INTERNATIONAL LTD—See Banque Degroof S.A.; *Int'l*, pg. 853
BEARCAT TYRES PTY LTD—See Compagnie Generale des Etablissements Michelin SCA; *Int'l*, pg. 1741
BEARCLAW CAPITAL CORP.; *Int'l*, pg. 933
BEARCOM INC. - CLEVELAND—See Bertram Capital Management, LLC; *U.S. Private*, pg. 540
BEARCOM INC.—See Bertram Capital Management, LLC; *U.S. Private*, pg. 540
BEARCOM WIRELESS—See Bertram Capital Management, LLC; *U.S. Private*, pg. 540
BEAR CONSTRUCTION CO., INC.; *U.S. Private*, pg. 506
BEAR CREEK DIALYSIS, L.P.—See DaVita Inc.; *U.S. Public*, pg. 636
BEAR CREEK MINING CORPORATION; *Int'l*, pg. 933
BEAR CREEK MINING INC.—See Bear Creek Mining Corporation; *Int'l*, pg. 933
BEAR CREEK MINING S.A.C.—See Bear Creek Mining Corporation; *Int'l*, pg. 933
BEAR CREEK ORCHARDS, INC.—See 1-800-FLOWERS.COM, Inc.; *U.S. Public*, pg. 1
BEAR CREEK STATION LLC—See Phillips Edison & Company LLC; *U.S. Private*, pg. 3170
BEAR CREEK SURGERY CENTER, LLC—See Tenet Healthcare Corporation; *U.S. Public*, pg. 2001
BEARD ENERGY TRANSITION ACQUISITION CORP.; *U.S. Public*, pg. 287
BEARD EQUIPMENT CO. INC.; *U.S. Private*, pg. 506

BEARD HARDWOODS, INC / CORPORATE AFFILIATIONS

BEARD HARDWOODS, INC; *U.S. Private*, pg. 506
BEARD IMPLEMENT CO.; *U.S. Private*, pg. 506
BEARDOW ADAMS A.B.—See H.B. Fuller Company; *U.S. Public*, pg. 977
BEARDOW ADAMS DO BRASIL ADHESIVES LTDA.—See H.B. Fuller Company; *U.S. Public*, pg. 977
BEARDOW ADAMS GMBH—See H.B. Fuller Company; *U.S. Public*, pg. 977
BEARDOW ADAMS HOT MELT WERK GMBH—See H.B. Fuller Company; *U.S. Public*, pg. 977
BEARDOWADAMS, INC.—See H.B. Fuller Company; *U.S. Public*, pg. 977
BEARDOW ADAMS OY—See H.B. Fuller Company; *U.S. Public*, pg. 977
BEARDOW ADAMS S.A.S.—See H.B. Fuller Company; *U.S. Public*, pg. 977
BEARDOW AND ADAMS (ADHESIVES) LIMITED—See H.B. Fuller Company; *U.S. Public*, pg. 977
BEARDSELL LIMITED; *Int'l*, pg. 933
BEAR ELECTRIC APPLIANCE CO., LTD.; *Int'l*, pg. 933
BEARING DISTRIBUTORS AND DRIVES, INC.—See Applied Industrial Technologies, Inc.; *U.S. Public*, pg. 171
BEARING DISTRIBUTORS, INC.—See Applied Industrial Technologies, Inc.; *U.S. Public*, pg. 171
BEARING ENGINEERS, INC.—See Frontenac Company LLC; *U.S. Private*, pg. 1613
BEARING HEADQUARTERS CO.—See Headco Industries; *U.S. Private*, pg. 1891
BEARING INSPECTION INC.—See The Timken Company; *U.S. Public*, pg. 2132
BEARING LITHIUM CORP.—See Corporacion Nacional del Cobre de Chile; *Int'l*, pg. 1805
BEARING MAN 1955 LIMITED—See Invicta Holdings Limited; *Int'l*, pg. 3788
BEARING MAN (BOTSWANA) (PTY) LTD—See Invicta Holdings Limited; *Int'l*, pg. 3788
BEARING MAN GROUP (PTY) LTD.—See Invicta Holdings Limited; *Int'l*, pg. 3788
BEARING MAN (PTY) LTD.—See Invicta Holdings Limited; *Int'l*, pg. 3788
BEARING MAN (SWAZILAND) (PTY) LTD.—See Invicta Holdings Limited; *Int'l*, pg. 3788
BEARINGPOINT (ASIA PACIFIC) PTE. LTD.—See BearingPoint, Inc.; *U.S. Private*, pg. 507
BEARINGPOINT BELGIUM S.P.R.L.—See BearingPoint Holdings Europe B.V.; *Int'l*, pg. 933
BEARINGPOINT CONSULTING INC.—See BearingPoint Holdings Europe B.V.; *Int'l*, pg. 933
BEARINGPOINT DENMARK AS—See BearingPoint Holdings Europe B.V.; *Int'l*, pg. 933
BEARINGPOINT FINLAND OY—See BearingPoint Holdings Europe B.V.; *Int'l*, pg. 933
BEARINGPOINT FRANCE SAS—See BearingPoint Holdings Europe B.V.; *Int'l*, pg. 933
BEARINGPOINT GMBH—See BearingPoint Holdings Europe B.V.; *Int'l*, pg. 933
BEARINGPOINT GMBH—See BearingPoint Holdings Europe B.V.; *Int'l*, pg. 933
BEARINGPOINT HOLDINGS EUROPE B.V.; *Int'l*, pg. 933
BEARINGPOINT, INC.; *U.S. Private*, pg. 507
BEARINGPOINT INFONOVA GMBH—See BearingPoint Holdings Europe B.V.; *Int'l*, pg. 933
BEARINGPOINT INFORMATION TECHNOLOGIES (SHANGHAI) LTD.—See BearingPoint, Inc.; *U.S. Private*, pg. 507
BEARINGPOINT INFORMATION TECHNOLOGY N.V.—See BearingPoint, Inc.; *U.S. Private*, pg. 507
BEARINGPOINT IRELAND LIMITED—See BearingPoint Holdings Europe B.V.; *Int'l*, pg. 933
BEARINGPOINT ITALY SRL—See BearingPoint Holdings Europe B.V.; *Int'l*, pg. 933
BEARINGPOINT LIMITED—See BearingPoint Holdings Europe B.V.; *Int'l*, pg. 933
BEARINGPOINT MANAGEMENT CONSULTING N.V.—See BearingPoint, Inc.; *U.S. Private*, pg. 507
BEARINGPOINT MAROC—See BearingPoint Holdings Europe B.V.; *Int'l*, pg. 933
BEARING POINT MIDDLE EAST FZ LLC—See BearingPoint Holdings Europe B.V.; *Int'l*, pg. 933
BEARINGPOINT NORWAY A/S—See BearingPoint Holdings Europe B.V.; *Int'l*, pg. 933
BEARINGPOINT OOO—See BearingPoint, Inc.; *U.S. Private*, pg. 507
BEARINGPOINT PTE. LTD.—See BearingPoint, Inc.; *U.S. Private*, pg. 507
BEARINGPOINT (SHANGHAI) ENTERPRISE MANAGEMENT CONSULTING CO. LTD.—See BearingPoint Holdings Europe B.V.; *Int'l*, pg. 933
BEARINGPOINT SOUTH EAST ASIA LLC—See BearingPoint, Inc.; *U.S. Private*, pg. 507
BEARINGPOINT SRL—See BearingPoint, Inc.; *U.S. Private*, pg. 507
BEARINGPOINT SWEDEN AB—See BearingPoint Holdings Europe B.V.; *Int'l*, pg. 933
BEARINGPOINT SWITZERLAND AG—See BearingPoint Holdings Europe B.V.; *Int'l*, pg. 933
BEARING SALES CORPORATION; *U.S. Private*, pg. 506
BEARING SERVICE COMPANY; *U.S. Private*, pg. 506
BEARING SERVICE INC.; *U.S. Private*, pg. 506

BEARING SERVICE & SUPPLY INC.; *U.S. Private*, pg. 506
BEARINGS LIMITED; *U.S. Private*, pg. 507
BEARINGS OF KENTUCKY—See Neill-LaVielle Supply Co.; *U.S. Private*, pg. 2882
BEARINGS & OIL SEALS SPECIALISTS INC.—See Applied Industrial Technologies, Inc.; *U.S. Public*, pg. 171
BEARING SPECIALTY COMPANY INC.; *U.S. Private*, pg. 507
BEARING SUPPLY CO. OF ODESSA; *U.S. Private*, pg. 507
BEAR INSURANCE SERVICE—See First Bancorp; *U.S. Public*, pg. 839
BEAR ISLAND PAPER WB L.P.—See Black Diamond Capital Holdings, LLC; *U.S. Private*, pg. 570
BEARIS ONE CO., LTD.—See Rentracks Co., Ltd.; *Int'l*, pg. 6289
BEARIUM METALS CORPORATION—See MetalTek International; *U.S. Private*, pg. 2682
BEAR MATTRESS LLC—See Cerberus Capital Management, L.P.; *U.S. Private*, pg. 837
BEAR METALLURGICAL COMPANY—See Yildirim Holding Inc.; *Int'l*, pg. 8583
BEAR MOUNTAIN FOREST PRODUCTS, INC.; *U.S. Private*, pg. 506
BEAR NAKED, INC.—See WK Kellogg Co; *U.S. Public*, pg. 2376
BEARN ENVIRONNEMENT SA—See Groupe Seche SAS; *Int'l*, pg. 3110
BEAR REPUBLIC BREWING CO., INC.; *U.S. Private*, pg. 506
BEAR RIDGE MACHINE & FABRICATION, INC.—See Reading Anthracite Company; *U.S. Private*, pg. 3366
BEAR RIVER HEALTHCARE LLC—See The Pennant Group, Inc.; *U.S. Public*, pg. 2118
BEAR RIVER ZEOLITE COMPANY—See United States Antimony Corporation; *U.S. Public*, pg. 2236
BEARSCH COMPEAU KNUDSON, ARCHITECTS & ENGINEERS, PC—See ARCADIS N.V.; *Int'l*, pg. 541
BEARS CO., LTD.—See Vector Inc.; *Int'l*, pg. 8144
BEAR SCOTLAND LIMITED—See Jacobs Engineering Group, Inc.; *U.S. Public*, pg. 1185
BEARSDEN VETS4PETS LIMITED—See Pets at Home Group Plc; *Int'l*, pg. 5833
BEARSKIN LAKE AIR SERVICE LTD.—See Exchange Income Corporation; *Int'l*, pg. 2579
BEARSKIN SERVICES—See Wyandotte Tribal Corporation; *U.S. Private*, pg. 4575
BEAR & SON CUTLERY, INC.; *U.S. Private*, pg. 506
BEAR'S PLUMBING INC.; *U.S. Private*, pg. 506
BEAR STEWART CORPORATION; *U.S. Private*, pg. 506
BEARTOOTH BILLINGS CLINIC; *U.S. Private*, pg. 507
BEARTOOTH MAPPING INC—See Trimble, Inc.; *U.S. Public*, pg. 2190
BEARTRACKS, INC.—See Takeda Pharmaceutical Company Limited; *Int'l*, pg. 7438
BEAR TRANSPORTATION SERVICES, L.P.—See ArcBest Corporation; *U.S. Public*, pg. 180
BEAR VALLEY ELECTRIC SERVICE, INC.—See American States Water Company; *U.S. Public*, pg. 110
BEARWARD ENGINEERING LIMITED—See Westinghouse Air Brake Technologies Corporation; *U.S. Public*, pg. 2357
BEARWARD LIMITED—See Westinghouse Air Brake Technologies Corporation; *U.S. Public*, pg. 2357
BEARWARE, INC.; *U.S. Private*, pg. 507
BEASLEY BROADCAST GROUP, INC. - BOSTON—See Beasley Broadcast Group, Inc.; *U.S. Public*, pg. 287
BEASLEY BROADCAST GROUP, INC. - GREENVILLE—See Beasley Broadcast Group, Inc.; *U.S. Public*, pg. 287
BEASLEY BROADCAST GROUP, INC.; *U.S. Public*, pg. 287
BEASLEY MEDIA GROUP, INC.—See Beasley Broadcast Group, Inc.; *U.S. Public*, pg. 287
BEASLEY MEZZANINE HOLDINGS, LLC—See Beasley Broadcast Group, Inc.; *U.S. Public*, pg. 287
BEASLEY-WILSON, INCORPORATED; *U.S. Private*, pg. 507
BEATLEY GRAVITT COMMUNICATIONS; *U.S. Private*, pg. 507
BEATON BROTHERS FLOORING, INC.; *U.S. Private*, pg. 507
BEATON INC.; *U.S. Private*, pg. 507
BEATPORT, LLC—See LiveStyle, Inc.; *U.S. Private*, pg. 2473
BEATRICE CONCRETE COMPANY INC.—See Nebco Inc.; *U.S. Private*, pg. 2878
BEATS AT SEA, LLC—See Live Nation Entertainment, Inc.; *U.S. Public*, pg. 1328
BEATS ELECTRONICS, LLC—See Apple Inc.; *U.S. Public*, pg. 169
BEATSON CLARK PLC—See Newship Ltd; *Int'l*, pg. 5238
BEATTIE COMMUNICATIONS GROUP; *Int'l*, pg. 933
BEATTIE COMMUNICATIONS GROUP—See Beattie Communications Group; *Int'l*, pg. 933
BEATTIE COMMUNICATIONS GROUP—See Beattie Communications Group; *Int'l*, pg. 933

BEATTIE COMMUNICATIONS GROUP—See Beattie Communications Group; *Int'l*, pg. 933
BEATTIE COMMUNICATIONS GROUP—See Beattie Communications Group; *Int'l*, pg. 933
BEATTIE COMMUNICATIONS GROUP—See Beattie Communications Group; *Int'l*, pg. 933
BEATTIE DODGE CHRYSLER LTD.; *Int'l*, pg. 933
BEATTIE FARMERS UNION COOPERATIVE ASSOCIATION; *U.S. Private*, pg. 507
BEATTIE HOMES LTD; *Int'l*, pg. 933
BEATTIE MCGUINNESS BUNGAY; *Int'l*, pg. 933
BEATTIES BASICS OFFICE PRODUCTS—See Beatties Basics; *Int'l*, pg. 933
BEATTIES BASICS; *Int'l*, pg. 933
BEATTY FLOORS LIMITED; *Int'l*, pg. 934
BEATTY MACHINE & MFG. COMPANY; *U.S. Private*, pg. 507
BE-AT VENUES N.V.—See Live Nation Entertainment, Inc.; *U.S. Public*, pg. 1328
BEATYA ONLINE ENTERTAINMENT P.L.C.—See Novomatic AG; *Int'l*, pg. 5467
BEATY CHEVROLET COMPANY; *U.S. Private*, pg. 507
BEAUBOIS LTEE—See Pomerleau Inc.; *Int'l*, pg. 5917
BEAUCAR ACCESSORIES (M) SDN. BHD.—See MCE Holdings Berhad; *Int'l*, pg. 4758
BEAUCE GOLD FIELDS, INC.; *Int'l*, pg. 934
BEAUCHAMP DISTRIBUTING COMPANY; *U.S. Private*, pg. 508
BEAUCHEM THERMTECH GROUP, INC.—See Max Weishaupt GmbH; *Int'l*, pg. 4735
BEAU DELICIOUS! INTERNATIONAL LLC; *U.S. Private*, pg. 508
BEAUFLOR USA, LLC—See Beaulieu International Group NV; *Int'l*, pg. 934
BEAUFORD MARINE PTE LTD—See Chuan Hup Holdings Limited; *Int'l*, pg. 1589
THE BEAUFORT BONNET COMPANY, LLC—See Oxford Industries, Inc.; *U.S. Public*, pg. 1629
BEAUFORT CAPITAL GMBH; *Int'l*, pg. 934
THE BEAUFORT GAZETTE—See Chatham Asset Management, LLC; *U.S. Private*, pg. 866
BEAUFORT INVESTMENTS COMPANY—See EFG Holding; *Int'l*, pg. 2319
BEAUFORT-JASPER WATER & SEWER AUTHORITY; *U.S. Private*, pg. 508
BEAUFORT PHYSICAL THERAPY, LIMITED PARTNERSHIP—See U.S. Physical Therapy, Inc.; *U.S. Public*, pg. 2214
BEAUFORT UNDERWRITING AGENCY LIMITED—See Cincinnati Financial Corporation; *U.S. Public*, pg. 495
BEAUFOUR IPSEN FARMACEUTICA LTDA—See Ipsen S.A.; *Int'l*, pg. 3798
BEAUFOUR IPSEN (TIANJIN) PHARMACEUTICAL CO., LTD.—See Ipsen S.A.; *Int'l*, pg. 3798
BEAULIEU CANADA—See Beaulieu Group, LLC; *U.S. Private*, pg. 508
BEAULIEU FIBRES INTERNATIONAL TERNI SRL—See Beaulieu International Group NV; *Int'l*, pg. 934
BEAULIEU GROUP, LLC; *U.S. Private*, pg. 508
BEAULIEU INTERNATIONAL GROUP NV BERRY YARNS PLANT—See Beaulieu International Group NV; *Int'l*, pg. 934
BEAULIEU INTERNATIONAL GROUP NV DISTRIPLAST PLANT—See Beaulieu International Group NV; *Int'l*, pg. 934
BEAULIEU INTERNATIONAL GROUP NV HERMOSA PLANT—See Beaulieu International Group NV; *Int'l*, pg. 934
BEAULIEU INTERNATIONAL GROUP NV JUTEKS RU PLANT—See Beaulieu International Group NV; *Int'l*, pg. 934
BEAULIEU INTERNATIONAL GROUP NV KOMEN PLANT—See Beaulieu International Group NV; *Int'l*, pg. 934
BEAULIEU INTERNATIONAL GROUP NV KRUISHOUTEM PLANT—See Beaulieu International Group NV; *Int'l*, pg. 934
BEAULIEU INTERNATIONAL GROUP NV LYNGDAL PLANT—See Beaulieu International Group NV; *Int'l*, pg. 934
BEAULIEU INTERNATIONAL GROUP NV PINNACLE PLANT—See Beaulieu International Group NV; *Int'l*, pg. 934
BEAULIEU INTERNATIONAL GROUP NV; *Int'l*, pg. 934
BEAULIEU INTERNATIONAL GROUP NV TERNI PLANT—See Beaulieu International Group NV; *Int'l*, pg. 934
BEAULIEU INTERNATIONAL GROUP NV WEIHAI PLANT—See Beaulieu International Group NV; *Int'l*, pg. 934
BEAULIEU INTERNATIONAL GROUP NV WIELSBEKE PLANT—See Beaulieu International Group NV; *Int'l*, pg. 934
BEAULIEU OF AUSTRALIA PTY LTD—See Beaulieu International Group NV; *Int'l*, pg. 934
BEAULIEU RIZHAO FLOORCOVERINGS CO. LTD.—See Beaulieu International Group NV; *Int'l*, pg. 934
BEAULIEU TECHNICAL TEXTILES NV—See Beaulieu International Group NV; *Int'l*, pg. 934

COMPANY NAME INDEX

BEAULIEU VINEYARD—See Treasury Wine Estates Limited; *Int'l*, pg. 7909
BEAU MARAIS S.A. (FRANCE)—See McCain Foods Limited; *Int'l*, pg. 4756
BEAUMIER, TROGDON, ORMAN, HURD & VIEGAS, PLLP; *U.S. Private*, pg. 508
BEAUMONT-ARA DIALYSIS LLP—See Nautic Partners, LLC; *U.S. Private*, pg. 2869
BEAUMONT AUTOMOBILES; *Int'l*, pg. 934
BEAUMONT CAPITAL LLP; *Int'l*, pg. 934
BEAUMONT COCA-COLA REFRESHMENTS; *U.S. Private*, pg. 508
BEAUMONT DEVELOPMENT CENTRE HOLDING LTD.—See Accenture plc; *Int'l*, pg. 86
BEAUMONT ENTERPRISE—See The Hearst Corporation; *U.S. Private*, pg. 4047
THE BEAUMONT FOUNDATION—See Beaumont Health; *U.S. Private*, pg. 508
BEAUMONT FREIGHTLINER, STERLING, WESTERN STAR—See Mercedes-Benz Group AG; *Int'l*, pg. 4823
BEAUMONT HEALTH; *U.S. Private*, pg. 508
BEAUMONT HOME MEDICAL EQUIPMENT—See Beaumont Health; *U.S. Private*, pg. 508
BEAUMONT MOBILE MEDICINE—See Beaumont Health; *U.S. Private*, pg. 508
BEAUMONT MOTOR CO.—See Southeast Texas Classic Automotive; *U.S. Private*, pg. 3726
BEAUMONT SELECT CORPORATIONS INC.; *Int'l*, pg. 934
BEAUMONTS INSURANCE BROKERS LIMITED—See Marsh & McLennan Companies, Inc.; *U.S. Public*, pg. 1374
BEAUMONT SURGICAL AFFILIATES, LTD.—See Tenet Healthcare Corporation; *U.S. Public*, pg. 2009
BEA UNION INVESTMENT MANAGEMENT LIMITED—See The Bank of East Asia, Limited; *Int'l*, pg. 7615
BEAU PLAN DEVELOPMENT LTD.—See Terra Mauricia Limited; *Int'l*, pg. 7567
BEAUPRE & CO. PUBLIC RELATIONS INC.—See Omnicom Group Inc.; *U.S. Public*, pg. 1577
BEAUREGARD ELECTRIC COOPERATIVE, INC.; *U.S. Private*, pg. 508
BEAUREGARD EQUIPMENT INC.; *U.S. Private*, pg. 508
BEAU RIVAGE RESORTS, INC—See MGM Resorts International; *U.S. Public*, pg. 1435
BEAU SEVRAN INVEST SCI—See BNP Paribas SA; *Int'l*, pg. 1089
BEAUTECH POWER SYSTEMS, LLC; *U.S. Private*, pg. 508
BEAUTE CREATEURS SAS—See L'Oreal S.A.; *Int'l*, pg. 4378
BEAUTE PRESTIGE INTERNATIONAL S.A.—See Shiseido Company, Limited; *Int'l*, pg. 6854
BEAUTIFUL CHINA HOLDINGS COMPANY LIMITED; *Int'l*, pg. 934
THE BEAUTIFUL GROUP MANAGEMENT, LLC—See Regent, L.P.; *U.S. Private*, pg. 3388
BEAUTIFUL RESTAURANT INC.; *U.S. Private*, pg. 508
BEAUTI-VUE PRODUCTS CORP.; *U.S. Private*, pg. 508
BEAU TOWNSEND FORD INC.; *U.S. Private*, pg. 507
BEAU TOWNSEND FORD LINCOLN, INC.; *U.S. Private*, pg. 507
BEAU TOWNSEND NISSAN, INC.; *U.S. Private*, pg. 508
BEAUTY ALLIANCE, INC.—See L'Oreal S.A.; *Int'l*, pg. 4380
BEAUTY BAKERIE COSMETICS BRAND LLC; *U.S. Private*, pg. 508
BEAUTY BARRAGE, LLC; *U.S. Private*, pg. 508
BEAUTY BAZAR INC.; *U.S. Private*, pg. 508
BEAUTY BIOSCIENCES LLC—See Nu Skin Enterprises, Inc.; *U.S. Public*, pg. 1551
BEAUTY BRANDS INC.; *U.S. Private*, pg. 509
BEAUTY COMMUNITY PUBLIC COMPANY LIMITED; *Int'l*, pg. 935
BEAUTYCOM SAS—See FemTec Health, Inc.; *U.S. Private*, pg. 1494
BEAUTYCOS INTERNATIONAL CO. LTD—See L'Oreal S.A.; *Int'l*, pg. 4378
BEAUTY DRUG SAITO CO., LTD.—See Polaris Capital Group Co., Ltd.; *Int'l*, pg. 5907
BEAUTY ELECTRONIC EMBROIDERING CENTRE SDN. BHD.—See PCCS Group Berhad; *Int'l*, pg. 5767
BEAUTY ENTERPRISES INC.; *U.S. Private*, pg. 509
BEAUTY FARM MEDICAL & HEALTH INDUSTRY INC.; *Int'l*, pg. 935
BEAUTYFIRST INC.—See Regis Corporation; *U.S. Public*, pg. 1777
BEAUTY GARAGE INC.; *Int'l*, pg. 935
BEAUTY GARAGE SINGAPORE PTE. LTD.—See Beauty Garage Inc.; *Int'l*, pg. 935
BEAUTY GARAGE TAIWAN INC.—See Beauty Garage Inc.; *Int'l*, pg. 935
BEAUTYGE BEAUTY GROUP, S.L.—See MacAndrews & Forbes Incorporated; *U.S. Private*, pg. 2533
BEAUTYGE DENMARK A/S—See MacAndrews & Forbes Incorporated; *U.S. Private*, pg. 2533
BEAUTYGE FRANCE SAS—See MacAndrews & Forbes Incorporated; *U.S. Private*, pg. 2533

BEAUTYGE GERMANY GMBH—See MacAndrews & Forbes Incorporated; *U.S. Private*, pg. 2533
BEAUTYGE LOGISTICS SERVICES, S.L.—See MacAndrews & Forbes Incorporated; *U.S. Private*, pg. 2533
BEAUTYGE PARTICIPATIONS, S.L.—See MacAndrews & Forbes Incorporated; *U.S. Private*, pg. 2533
BEAUTYGE PORTUGAL - PRODUTOS COSMETICOS E PROFISSIONAIS LDA.—See MacAndrews & Forbes Incorporated; *U.S. Private*, pg. 2533
BEAUTYGE PROFESSIONAL LIMITED—See MacAndrews & Forbes Incorporated; *U.S. Private*, pg. 2533
THE BEAUTY HEALTH COMPANY; *U.S. Public*, pg. 2038
BEAUTY HEALTH GROUP LIMITED; *Int'l*, pg. 935
BEAUTY IN MOTION SDN. BHD.—See LVMH Moet Hennessy Louis Vuitton SE; *Int'l*, pg. 4590
BEAUTY KADAN CO., LTD.; *Int'l*, pg. 935
BEAUTY MANAGEMENT INCORPORATED; *U.S. Private*, pg. 509
BEAUTY MANUFACTURING SOLUTIONS CORP.; *U.S. Private*, pg. 509
BEAUTY NOW GMBH—See M1 Kliniken AG; *Int'l*, pg. 4617
BEAUTY SKIN CO., LTD.; *Int'l*, pg. 935
THE BEAUTY SOLUTION, LLC—See XCel Brands, Inc.; *U.S. Public*, pg. 2385
BEAUTY SYSTEMS GROUP (CANADA), INC.—See Sally Beauty Holdings, Inc.; *U.S. Public*, pg. 1838
BEAUTY SYSTEMS GROUP LLC—See Sally Beauty Holdings, Inc.; *U.S. Public*, pg. 1838
BEAUX FRERES, LLC—See Maisons & Domaines Henriot France SASU; *Int'l*, pg. 4652
BEAVER AEROSPACE & DEFENSE, INC.—See Heroux-Devtek Inc.; *Int'l*, pg. 3364
BEAVER BUILDERS, INC.; *U.S. Private*, pg. 509
BEAVER CREEK ASSOCIATES, INC.—See Vail Resorts, Inc.; *U.S. Public*, pg. 2271
BEAVER CREEK RESORT—See Vail Resorts, Inc.; *U.S. Public*, pg. 2272
BEAVER DAM COMMUNITY HOSPITALS, INC.; *U.S. Private*, pg. 509
BEAVER ELECTRICAL MACHINERY LTD.; *Int'l*, pg. 935
BEAVER ENTECH LIMITED; *Int'l*, pg. 935
THE BEAVER EXCAVATING COMPANY, INC.; *U.S. Private*, pg. 3002
BEAVER EXPRESS SERVICE, LLC; *U.S. Private*, pg. 509
BEAVER GROUP (HOLDING) COMPANY LIMITED; *Int'l*, pg. 935
BEAVER MACHINE CORPORATION; *Int'l*, pg. 935
BEAVER NEWSPAPERS INC.—See Gannett Co., Inc.; *U.S. Public*, pg. 901
BEAVER STREET FISHERIES, INC.; *U.S. Private*, pg. 509
BEAVERTON TOYOTA COMPANY INC.; *U.S. Private*, pg. 509
BEAVERTOWN BLOCK CO. INC.; *U.S. Private*, pg. 509
BEAVERTOZAN CO., LTD.—See Kohnan Shoji Co., Ltd.; *Int'l*, pg. 4229
BEAVER VALLEY SUPPLY CO. INC.; *U.S. Private*, pg. 509
BEAVER-VISITEC INTERNATIONAL, INC.—See TPG Capital, L.P.; *U.S. Public*, pg. 2169
BEAVEX; *U.S. Private*, pg. 509
BEAZER HOMES CORP.—See Beazer Homes USA, Inc.; *U.S. Public*, pg. 287
BEAZER HOMES INDIANA HOLDINGS CORP.—See Beazer Homes USA, Inc.; *U.S. Public*, pg. 287
BEAZER HOMES INDIANA, LLP—See Beazer Homes USA, Inc.; *U.S. Public*, pg. 287
BEAZER HOMES INVESTMENTS, LLC—See Beazer Homes USA, Inc.; *U.S. Public*, pg. 287
BEAZER HOMES SALES, INC.—See Beazer Homes USA, Inc.; *U.S. Public*, pg. 287
BEAZER HOMES TEXAS, LP—See Beazer Homes USA, Inc.; *U.S. Public*, pg. 288
BEAZER HOMES USA, INC.; *U.S. Public*, pg. 287
BEAZER-INSPIRADA LLC—See Beazer Homes USA, Inc.; *U.S. Public*, pg. 288
BEAZER MORTGAGE CORPORATION—See Beazer Homes USA, Inc.; *U.S. Public*, pg. 288
BEAZER REALTY LOS ANGELES, INC.—See Beazer Homes USA, Inc.; *U.S. Public*, pg. 288
BEAZER REALTY SERVICES, LLC—See Beazer Homes USA, Inc.; *U.S. Public*, pg. 288
BEAZER SPE, LLC—See Beazer Homes USA, Inc.; *U.S. Public*, pg. 288
BEAZLEY DEDICATED LTD.—See Beazley plc; *Int'l*, pg. 935
BEAZLEY DEDICATED NO.2 LIMITED—See Beazley plc; *Int'l*, pg. 935
BEAZLEY FURLONGE HOLDINGS LIMITED—See Beazley plc; *Int'l*, pg. 935
BEAZLEY FURLONGE LIMITED—See Beazley plc; *Int'l*, pg. 935
BEAZLEY GROUP LIMITED—See Beazley plc; *Int'l*, pg. 935
BEAZLEY HOLDINGS, INC.—See Beazley plc; *Int'l*, pg. 935
BEAZLEY INSURANCE DAC—See Beazley plc; *Int'l*, pg. 935

BEAZLEY INVESTMENTS LIMITED—See Beazley plc; *Int'l*, pg. 935
BEAZLEY LIMITED—See Beazley plc; *Int'l*, pg. 935
BEAZLEY PLC; *Int'l*, pg. 935
BEAZLEY PTE. LIMITED—See Beazley plc; *Int'l*, pg. 935
BEAZLEY UNDERWRITING PTY LTD—See Beazley plc; *Int'l*, pg. 936
BEAZLEY UNDERWRITING SERVICES LTD.—See Beazley plc; *Int'l*, pg. 936
BEAZLEY USA SERVICES, INC.—See Beazley plc; *Int'l*, pg. 936
BEBAG BIOENERGIE BATTERKINDEN AG—See BKW AG; *Int'l*, pg. 1054
BE-BE A.D.; *Int'l*, pg. 932
BEBECORD STEMLIFE INTERNATIONAL S.A.—See VITA 34 AG; *Int'l*, pg. 8257
BEBE & CO. SAS—See Dorel Industries, Inc.; *Int'l*, pg. 2176
BEBEK VARLIK YONETYM A.S.—See Deutsche Bank Aktiengesellschaft; *Int'l*, pg. 2055
BEBER SILVERSTEIN GROUP; *U.S. Private*, pg. 509
BEBE STORES, INC.—See B. Riley Financial, Inc.; *U.S. Public*, pg. 262
BEBE STUDIO, INC.—See B. Riley Financial, Inc.; *U.S. Public*, pg. 262
BEBIT INFORMATIONSTECHNIK GMBH—See Bilfinger SE; *Int'l*, pg. 1029
BEBO HEALTH SA; *Int'l*, pg. 936
BEBO, INC.—See Amazon.com, Inc.; *U.S. Public*, pg. 91
BEBOP CHANNEL CORPORATION; *U.S. Public*, pg. 288
BEBUSCH GMBH—See KAP Beteiligungs-AG; *Int'l*, pg. 4076
BEBUSCH HUNGARIA KFT—See KAP Beteiligungs-AG; *Int'l*, pg. 4076
BE-BUSINESS EXCHANGES S.A.—See Eurobank Ergasias Services and Holdings S.A.; *Int'l*, pg. 2532
BECA APPLIED TECHNOLOGIES LTD—See Beca Group Limited; *Int'l*, pg. 936
BECA CARTER HOLLINGS & FERNER LTD—See Beca Group Limited; *Int'l*, pg. 936
BECAFISA S.A. DE C.V—See ED&F Man Holdings Limited; *Int'l*, pg. 2302
BECA GROUP LIMITED; *Int'l*, pg. 936
BECA PTY. LTD.—See Beca Group Limited; *Int'l*, pg. 936
BECAR SRL—See Beghelli S.p.A.; *Int'l*, pg. 941
BEC ASSET CO., LTD.—See BEC World Public Company Limited; *Int'l*, pg. 936
BEC BROADCASTING CENTER CO., LTD.—See BEC World Public Company Limited; *Int'l*, pg. 936
BECCA & BEN LLC; *U.S. Private*, pg. 509
BECCLES H.C.C. LIMITED—See Walgreens Boots Alliance, Inc.; *U.S. Public*, pg. 2322
BECCO CONTRACTORS, INC.; *U.S. Private*, pg. 509
BEC CONSTRUCTION CHAMPAGNE—See FAYAT SAS; *Int'l*, pg. 2624
BEC CONSTRUCTION LANGUEDOC ROUSSILLON—See FAYAT SAS; *Int'l*, pg. 2624
BEC CONSTRUCTION PROVENCE—See FAYAT SAS; *Int'l*, pg. 2624
BECEJSKA PEKARA A.D.; *Int'l*, pg. 936
BECHARD GROUP, INC.; *U.S. Private*, pg. 509
BECHO CO.—See Tutor Perini Corporation; *U.S. Public*, pg. 2205
BECHTEL BETTIS INC.—See Bechtel Group, Inc.; *U.S. Private*, pg. 509
BECHTEL CANADA CO.—See Bechtel Group, Inc.; *U.S. Private*, pg. 509
BECHTEL CHILE LTDA.—See Bechtel Group, Inc.; *U.S. Private*, pg. 510
BECHTEL CIVIL, INC.—See Bechtel Group, Inc.; *U.S. Private*, pg. 510
BECHTEL CONSTRUCTION COMPANY, INC.—See Bechtel Group, Inc.; *U.S. Private*, pg. 510
BECHTEL DESIGNS, INC.; *U.S. Private*, pg. 509
BECHTEL DO BRASIL CONSTRUCOES LTDA.—See Bechtel Group, Inc.; *U.S. Private*, pg. 510
BECHTEL ENTERPRISES, INC.—See Bechtel Group, Inc.; *U.S. Private*, pg. 510
BECHTEL FINANCING SERVICES, INC.—See Bechtel Group, Inc.; *U.S. Private*, pg. 510
BECHTEL GROUP, INC.; *U.S. Private*, pg. 509
BECHTEL HANFORD INC.—See Bechtel Group, Inc.; *U.S. Private*, pg. 510
BECHTEL INDIA PRIVATE LIMITED—See Bechtel Group, Inc.; *U.S. Private*, pg. 510
BECHTEL INTERNATIONAL INC.—See Bechtel Group, Inc.; *U.S. Private*, pg. 510
BECHTEL INTERNATIONAL INC.—See Bechtel Group, Inc.; *U.S. Private*, pg. 510
BECHTEL INTERNATIONAL INC.—See Bechtel Group, Inc.; *U.S. Private*, pg. 510
BECHTEL JACOBS COMPANY LLC—See Bechtel Group, Inc.; *U.S. Private*, pg. 510
BECHTEL LTD.—See Bechtel Group, Inc.; *U.S. Private*, pg. 510
BECHTEL MALAYSIA INC.—See Bechtel Group, Inc.; *U.S. Private*, pg. 510
BECHTEL NATIONAL, INC.—See Bechtel Group, Inc.; *U.S. Private*, pg. 510

BECHTEL GROUP, INC.

BECHTEL POWER CORPORATION—See Bechtel Group, Inc.; *U.S. Private*, pg. 510
BECHTEL SERVICES (AUSTRALIA) PTY LTD—See Bechtel Group, Inc.; *U.S. Private*, pg. 510
BECHTELSVILLE ASPHALT—See Haines & Kibblehouse Inc.; *U.S. Private*, pg. 1840
BECHTLE AG; *Int'l*, pg. 936
BECHTLE BRUSSELS NV—See Bechtle AG; *Int'l*, pg. 937
BECHTLE CLOUDS GMBH—See Bechtle AG; *Int'l*, pg. 937
BECHTLE COMSOFT SAS—See Bechtle AG; *Int'l*, pg. 937
BECHTLE DIRECT AG—See Bechtle AG; *Int'l*, pg. 937
BECHTLE DIRECT B.V.—See Bechtle AG; *Int'l*, pg. 937
BECHTLE DIRECT GMBH—See Bechtle AG; *Int'l*, pg. 937
BECHTLE DIRECT GMBH—See Bechtle AG; *Int'l*, pg. 937
BECHTLE DIRECT KFT.—See Bechtle AG; *Int'l*, pg. 937
BECHTLE DIRECT LIMITED—See Bechtle AG; *Int'l*, pg. 937
BECHTLE DIRECT LTD.—See Bechtle AG; *Int'l*, pg. 937
BECHTLE DIRECT NV—See Bechtle AG; *Int'l*, pg. 937
BECHTLE DIRECT POLSKA SP.Z.O.O—See Bechtle AG; *Int'l*, pg. 937
BECHTLE DIRECT PORTUGAL UNIPESSOAL LDA—See Bechtle AG; *Int'l*, pg. 937
BECHTLE DIRECT SAS—See Bechtle AG; *Int'l*, pg. 937
BECHTLE DIRECT S.L.—See Bechtle AG; *Int'l*, pg. 937
BECHTLE DIRECT S.L.U.—See Bechtle AG; *Int'l*, pg. 937
BECHTLE DIRECT SRL-GMBH—See Bechtle AG; *Int'l*, pg. 937
BECHTLE DIRECT S.R.O.—See Bechtle AG; *Int'l*, pg. 937
BECHTLE FINANCIAL SERVICES AG—See Bechtle AG; *Int'l*, pg. 937
BECHTLE FINANZ- & MARKETINGSERVICES GMBH—See Bechtle AG; *Int'l*, pg. 937
BECHTLE GMBH & CO. KG—See Bechtle AG; *Int'l*, pg. 937
BECHTLE GMBH & CO. KG—See Bechtle AG; *Int'l*, pg. 937
BECHTLE GMBH—See Bechtle AG; *Int'l*, pg. 937
BECHTLE GMBH—See Bechtle AG; *Int'l*, pg. 937
BECHTLE HOSTING & OPERATIONS GMBH & CO. KG—See Bechtle AG; *Int'l*, pg. 937
BECHTLE IT-SYSTEMHAUS GMBH—See Bechtle AG; *Int'l*, pg. 937
BECHTLE NETWORK & SECURITY SOLUTIONS GMBH—See Bechtle AG; *Int'l*, pg. 937
BECHTLE ONSITE SERVICES GMBH—See Bechtle AG; *Int'l*, pg. 937
BECHTLE PRINTING SOLUTIONS AG—See Bechtle AG; *Int'l*, pg. 937
BECHTLE REGENSDORF AG—See Bechtle AG; *Int'l*, pg. 937
BECHTLE REMARKETING GMBH—See Bechtle AG; *Int'l*, pg. 937
BECHTLE STEFFEN SCHWEIZ AG—See Bechtle AG; *Int'l*, pg. 937
BECHTLE ST. GALLEN AG—See Bechtle AG; *Int'l*, pg. 937
BECI CORPORATION CO., LTD.—See BEC World Public Company Limited; *Int'l*, pg. 936
BEC INC.; *U.S. Private*, pg. 509
BECK AG; *U.S. Private*, pg. 510
BECK ARNLEY HOLDINGS LLC—See Apollo Global Management, Inc.; *U.S. Public*, pg. 160
BECK ARNLEY HOLDINGS LLC—See Icahn Enterprises L.P.; *U.S. Public*, pg. 1084
BECK CHEVROLET CO. INC.; *U.S. Private*, pg. 510
BECK & CO. INDUSTRIEBEDARF GMBH & CO. KG—See Salzgitter AG; *Int'l*, pg. 6496
BECK COMPANY; *U.S. Private*, pg. 510
BECK CONSULTING—See TA Associates, Inc.; *U.S. Private*, pg. 3914
BECKENHAM COURTS RETIREMENT VILLAGE LIMITED—See Ryman Healthcare Ltd.; *Int'l*, pg. 6439
BECKER ARENA PRODUCTS INC.—See Fulcrum Capital Partners Inc.; *Int'l*, pg. 2841
BECKER BUICK INC.; *U.S. Private*, pg. 510
BECKER COATING BOYA SANAYI VE TICARET LTD. STI.—See Lindengruppen AB; *Int'l*, pg. 4511
BECKER & CO. GMBH—See ThyssenKrupp AG; *Int'l*, pg. 7723
BECKER COMMUNICATIONS, INC.; *U.S. Private*, pg. 510
BECKER CONVISER PROFESSIONAL REVIEW—See Adtalem Global Education Inc.; *U.S. Public*, pg. 43
BECKER FARBY PRZEMYSLOWE SP. Z.O.O.—See Lindengruppen AB; *Int'l*, pg. 4511
BECKER GLOVE INTERNATIONAL INC.; *U.S. Private*, pg. 511
THE BECKER GROUP, LTD.—See Viad Corp.; *U.S. Public*, pg. 2291
BECKER HOLDING CORPORATION; *U.S. Private*, pg. 511
BECKER INDUSTRIAL COATINGS AB—See Lindengruppen AB; *Int'l*, pg. 4511
BECKER INDUSTRIAL COATINGS (GUANGZHOU) LTD—See Lindengruppen AB; *Int'l*, pg. 4511
BECKER INDUSTRIAL COATINGS (KOREA) LTD—See Lindengruppen AB; *Int'l*, pg. 4511

BECKER INDUSTRIAL COATINGS L.L.C.—See Lindengruppen AB; *Int'l*, pg. 4511
BECKER INDUSTRIAL COATINGS LTD—See Lindengruppen AB; *Int'l*, pg. 4511
BECKER INDUSTRIAL COATINGS (M) SDN BHD—See Lindengruppen AB; *Int'l*, pg. 4510
BECKER INDUSTRIAL COATINGS (PTY) LTD—See Lindengruppen AB; *Int'l*, pg. 4511
BECKER INDUSTRIAL COATINGS (SHANGHAI) LTD—See Lindengruppen AB; *Int'l*, pg. 4511
BECKER INDUSTRIAL COATINGS—See Lindengruppen AB; *Int'l*, pg. 4510
BECKER INDUSTRIAL COATINGS (VIETNAM) CO. LTD—See Lindengruppen AB; *Int'l*, pg. 4511
BECKER INDUSTRIELACK GMBH—See Lindengruppen AB; *Int'l*, pg. 4511
BECKER INDUSTRIE S.A.S.—See Lindengruppen AB; *Int'l*, pg. 4510
BECKER & K LLP; *Int'l*, pg. 938
BECKERLE LUMBER SUPPLY CO., INC.; *U.S. Private*, pg. 511
BECKER LLC; *U.S. Private*, pg. 511
BECKERMAN GROUP; *U.S. Private*, pg. 511
BECKER MARKETING SERVICES INC.; *U.S. Private*, pg. 511
BECKER & MAYER LLC—See The Quarto Group, Inc.; *Int'l*, pg. 7677
THE BECKER MILK COMPANY LIMITED; *Int'l*, pg. 7620
BECKER MOTORS INC.; *U.S. Private*, pg. 511
BECKER & POLIAKOFF, P.A.; *U.S. Private*, pg. 510
BECKERS HIGH PERFORMANCE COATINGS (TIANJIN) LTD—See Lindengruppen AB; *Int'l*, pg. 4511
BECKERS INDUSTRIAL COATINGS ITALIA SPA—See Lindengruppen AB; *Int'l*, pg. 4511
BECKERS INDUSTRIAL COATINGS LTD—See Lindengruppen AB; *Int'l*, pg. 4511
BECKER SPECIALTY CORPORATION—See Lindengruppen AB; *Int'l*, pg. 4511
BECKER'S SCHOOL SUPPLIES, INC.; *U.S. Private*, pg. 511
BECKER STAHL-SERVICE GMBH—See Klockner & Co. SE; *Int'l*, pg. 4201
BECKER TIRE & TREADING INC.; *U.S. Private*, pg. 511
BECKER TREE FARM & NURSERY, INC.—See Becker Holding Corporation; *U.S. Private*, pg. 511
BECKER UNDERWOOD, INC.—See BASF SE; *Int'l*, pg. 877
BECKETT AIR INC.; *U.S. Private*, pg. 511
BECKETT & BECKETT, INC.; *U.S. Private*, pg. 511
BECKETT & BECKETT, INC.—See Beckett & Beckett, Inc.; *U.S. Private*, pg. 511
BECKETT CORPORATION—See General Foam Plastics Corp.; *U.S. Private*, pg. 1665
BECKETT MEDIA LLC; *U.S. Private*, pg. 511
THE BECK GROUP; *U.S. Private*, pg. 3992
BECK & HOFER CONSTRUCTION, INC.; *U.S. Private*, pg. 510
BECKLEY AUTOMALL, INC.; *U.S. Private*, pg. 511
BECKLEY TREATMENT CENTER, LLC—See Acadia Healthcare Company, Inc.; *U.S. Public*, pg. 28
BECKMAN AUSTRALIA APS—See Danaher Corporation; *U.S. Public*, pg. 624
BECKMAN COULTER AB—See Danaher Corporation; *U.S. Public*, pg. 624
BECKMAN COULTER AUSTRALIA PTY. LTD.—See Danaher Corporation; *U.S. Public*, pg. 624
BECKMAN COULTER BIOMEDICAL GMBH—See Danaher Corporation; *U.S. Public*, pg. 624
BECKMAN COULTER BIYOMEDIKAL URUNLER SANAYI VE TICARET LIMITED SIRKETI—See Danaher Corporation; *U.S. Public*, pg. 624
BECKMAN COULTER CANADA, INC.—See Danaher Corporation; *U.S. Public*, pg. 624
BECKMAN COULTER CESKA REPUBLIKA S.R.O.—See Danaher Corporation; *U.S. Public*, pg. 624
BECKMAN COULTER COMMERCIAL ENTERPRISE (CHINA) CO., LTD.—See Danaher Corporation; *U.S. Public*, pg. 624
BECKMAN COULTER DE MEXICO, S.A. DE C.V.—See Danaher Corporation; *U.S. Public*, pg. 625
BECKMAN COULTER DO BRASIL COMERCIO E IMPORTACAO DE PRODUTOS DE LABORATORIO LTDA.—See Danaher Corporation; *U.S. Public*, pg. 625
BECKMAN COULTER D.O.O.—See Danaher Corporation; *U.S. Public*, pg. 625
BECKMAN COULTER ESPANA, S.A.—See Danaher Corporation; *U.S. Public*, pg. 624
BECKMAN COULTER EUROCENTER S.A.—See Danaher Corporation; *U.S. Public*, pg. 624
BECKMAN COULTER FRANCE S.A.—See Danaher Corporation; *U.S. Public*, pg. 624
BECKMAN COULTER GMBH—See Danaher Corporation; *U.S. Public*, pg. 624
BECKMAN COULTER HONG KONG LTD.—See Danaher Corporation; *U.S. Public*, pg. 624
BECKMAN COULTER, INC.—See Danaher Corporation; *U.S. Public*, pg. 624
BECKMAN COULTER INDIA PRIVATE LIMITED—See Danaher Corporation; *U.S. Public*, pg. 624

CORPORATE AFFILIATIONS

BECKMAN COULTER INTERNATIONAL S.A.—See Danaher Corporation; *U.S. Public*, pg. 624
BECKMAN COULTER IRELAND INC.—See Danaher Corporation; *U.S. Public*, pg. 624
BECKMAN COULTER K. K.—See Danaher Corporation; *U.S. Public*, pg. 624
BECKMAN COULTER KOREA LTD.—See Danaher Corporation; *U.S. Public*, pg. 624
BECKMAN COULTER LABORATORY SYSTEMS (SUZHOU) CO. LTD.—See Danaher Corporation; *U.S. Public*, pg. 624
BECKMAN COULTER LIFE SCIENCES—See Danaher Corporation; *U.S. Public*, pg. 624
BECKMAN COULTER LIMITED LIABILITY COMPANY—See Danaher Corporation; *U.S. Public*, pg. 625
BECKMAN COULTER MAGYARORSZAG KFT—See Danaher Corporation; *U.S. Public*, pg. 625
BECKMAN COULTER MISHIMA K.K.—See Danaher Corporation; *U.S. Public*, pg. 625
BECKMAN COULTER NEDERLAND B.V.—See Danaher Corporation; *U.S. Public*, pg. 625
BECKMAN COULTER POLSKA SP. Z.O.O.—See Danaher Corporation; *U.S. Public*, pg. 625
BECKMAN COULTER PUERTO RICO INC.—See Danaher Corporation; *U.S. Public*, pg. 625
BECKMAN COULTER SAUDI ARABIA CO.LTD.—See Danaher Corporation; *U.S. Public*, pg. 624
BECKMAN COULTER SINGAPORE PTE. LTD.—See Danaher Corporation; *U.S. Public*, pg. 625
BECKMAN COULTER SLOVENSKA REPUBLIKA S.R.O.—See Danaher Corporation; *U.S. Public*, pg. 625
BECKMAN COULTER SOUTH AFRICA (PROPRIETARY) LIMITED—See Danaher Corporation; *U.S. Public*, pg. 625
BECKMAN COULTER S.P.A.—See Danaher Corporation; *U.S. Public*, pg. 625
BECKMAN COULTER SRL—See Danaher Corporation; *U.S. Public*, pg. 625
BECKMAN COULTER TAIWAN INC.—See Danaher Corporation; *U.S. Public*, pg. 625
BECKMAN COULTER UNITED KINGDOM LTD.—See Danaher Corporation; *U.S. Public*, pg. 625
BECKMAN & GAST CO. INC.; *U.S. Private*, pg. 511
BECKMANN CONVERTING, INC.; *U.S. Private*, pg. 511
BECKMANN ELEKTRONIK GMBH—See Arlitech Electronic Corp.; *Int'l*, pg. 573
BECKMAN PRODUCTION SERVICES, INC.—See Rock Hill Capital Group, LLC; *U.S. Private*, pg. 3464
BECK & MASTEN AUTOMOTIVE GROUP, INC.—See Group 1 Automotive, Inc.; *U.S. Public*, pg. 971
BECKNELL WHOLESALE I LP; *U.S. Private*, pg. 511
BECK OIL, INC.; *U.S. Private*, pg. 510
BECK & POLLITZER CZECH S.R.O.—See Graphite Capital Management LLP; *Int'l*, pg. 3060
BECK & POLLITZER DEUTSCHLAND GMBH—See Graphite Capital Management LLP; *Int'l*, pg. 3060
BECK & POLLITZER ENGINEERING LTD—See Graphite Capital Management LLP; *Int'l*, pg. 3060
BECK & POLLITZER FRANCE SAS—See Graphite Capital Management LLP; *Int'l*, pg. 3060
BECK & POLLITZER HUNGARY KFT.—See Graphite Capital Management LLP; *Int'l*, pg. 3060
BECK & POLLITZER INDIA PVT. LTD.—See Graphite Capital Management LLP; *Int'l*, pg. 3060
BECK & POLLITZER ITALIA S.R.L.—See Graphite Capital Management LLP; *Int'l*, pg. 3060
BECK & POLLITZER POLSKA SP.Z.O.O—See Graphite Capital Management LLP; *Int'l*, pg. 3060
BECK & POLLITZER ROMANIA SRL—See Graphite Capital Management LLP; *Int'l*, pg. 3060
BECK & POLLITZER TICARET LTD. STI.—See Graphite Capital Management LLP; *Int'l*, pg. 3060
BECK PROPERTIES INC.; *U.S. Private*, pg. 510
BECKS BOOKSTORES INC.; *U.S. Private*, pg. 511
BECK SENSORTECHNIK GMBH—See Indutrade AB; *Int'l*, pg. 3677
BECKS FURNITURE INC.; *U.S. Private*, pg. 511
BECKSTROM ELECTRIC; *U.S. Private*, pg. 511
BECK SUPPLIERS, INC.; *U.S. Private*, pg. 510
BECK TOTAL OFFICE INTERIORS; *U.S. Private*, pg. 510
BECKWITH ELECTRIC CO. INC.; *U.S. Private*, pg. 511
BECKWOOD SERVICES, INC.—See Elbit Systems Limited; *Int'l*, pg. 2344
BECKY'S CARD & GIFTS INC.; *U.S. Private*, pg. 511
BECLE, S.A.B. DE C.V.; *Int'l*, pg. 938
BE CLIMBING, INC.—See TOCCA Life Holdings, Inc.; *U.S. Public*, pg. 2161
BECMAR SPRINKLER SYSTEMS, INC.; *U.S. Private*, pg. 512
BEC MULTIMEDIA CO., LTD.—See BEC World Public Company Limited; *Int'l*, pg. 936
BEC NEWS BUREAU CO., LTD.—See BEC World Public Company Limited; *Int'l*, pg. 936
BECO ENGINEERING COMPANY; *U.S. Private*, pg. 512
BECO HOLDING COMPANY, INC.—See H.I.G. Capital, LLC; *U.S. Private*, pg. 1827

BECOME, INC.—See Symphony Technology Group, LLC; *U.S. Private*, pg. 3900
BECOME RECRUITMENT LIMITED—See Empresaria Group Plc; *Int'l*, pg. 2388
BECOMING INDEPENDENT; *U.S. Private*, pg. 512
BECO PETROLEUM PRODUCTS PLC.; *Int'l*, pg. 938
BECORE; *U.S. Private*, pg. 512
BECORIT GMBH—See Westinghouse Air Brake Technologies Corporation; *U.S. Public*, pg. 2357
BECO STEEL LIMITED; *Int'l*, pg. 938
BECOTEK METAL GROUP AS—See Norvestor Equity AS; *Int'l*, pg. 5447
BECOTEK METAL SRL—See Norvestor Equity AS; *Int'l*, pg. 5447
BECOTEK MFG. INC.—See Norvestor Equity AS; *Int'l*, pg. 5447
BECROMAL S.P.A.—See TDK Corporation; *Int'l*, pg. 7487
BECRYPT LIMITED; *Int'l*, pg. 938
BEC SOUTHWEST, INC.—See Johnson Carlier Inc.; *U.S. Private*, pg. 2227
BEC STUDIO CO., LTD.—See BEC World Public Company Limited; *Int'l*, pg. 936
BEC TECHNOLOGIES INC.—See Billion Electric Co., Ltd.; *Int'l*, pg. 1031
BEC-TERO ARSENAL CO., LTD.—See BEC World Public Company Limited; *Int'l*, pg. 936
BEC TERO ENTERTAINMENT CO., LTD.—See BEC World Public Company Limited; *Int'l*, pg. 936
BEC-TERO ENTERTAINMENT PUBLIC COMPANY LIMITED—See BEC World Public Company Limited; *Int'l*, pg. 936
BEC-TERO EXHIBITIONS CO., LTD.—See BEC World Public Company Limited; *Int'l*, pg. 936
BEC-TERO RADIO CO., LTD.—See BEC World Public Company Limited; *Int'l*, pg. 936
BEC-TERO SASANA CO., LTD.—See BEC World Public Company Limited; *Int'l*, pg. 936
BECTON DICKINSON ADVANCED PEN INJECTION SYSTEMS GMBH—See Becton, Dickinson & Company; *U.S. Public*, pg. 289
BECTON DICKINSON AG—See Becton, Dickinson & Company; *U.S. Public*, pg. 289
BECTON DICKINSON AKTIEBOLAG—See Becton, Dickinson & Company; *U.S. Public*, pg. 289
BECTON DICKINSON ARGENTINA S.R.L.—See Becton, Dickinson & Company; *U.S. Public*, pg. 289
BECTON DICKINSON ASIA LIMITED—See Becton, Dickinson & Company; *U.S. Public*, pg. 289
BECTON DICKINSON A/S—See Becton, Dickinson & Company; *U.S. Public*, pg. 289
BECTON DICKINSON AUSTRIA GMBH—See Becton, Dickinson & Company; *U.S. Public*, pg. 289
BECTON DICKINSON AUSTRIA HOLDINGS GMBH—See Becton, Dickinson & Company; *U.S. Public*, pg. 289
BECTON DICKINSON BENELUX N.V.—See Becton, Dickinson & Company; *U.S. Public*, pg. 289
BECTON DICKINSON BIOSCIENCES, SYSTEMS AND REAGENTS INC.—See Becton, Dickinson & Company; *U.S. Public*, pg. 289
BECTON, DICKINSON B.V.—See Becton, Dickinson & Company; *U.S. Public*, pg. 289
BECTON DICKINSON CANADA INC.—See Becton, Dickinson & Company; *U.S. Public*, pg. 289
BECTON, DICKINSON & COMPANY, LTD.—See Becton, Dickinson & Company; *U.S. Public*, pg. 290
BECTON, DICKINSON & COMPANY - PUERTO RICO—See Becton, Dickinson & Company; *U.S. Public*, pg. 290
BECTON, DICKINSON & COMPANY; *U.S. Public*, pg. 288
BECTON DICKINSON DE COLOMBIA LTDA.—See Becton, Dickinson & Company; *U.S. Public*, pg. 290
BECTON DICKINSON DE MEXICO, S.A. DE C.V.—See Becton, Dickinson & Company; *U.S. Public*, pg. 290
BECTON DICKINSON DISPENSING FRANCE SAS—See Becton, Dickinson & Company; *U.S. Public*, pg. 289
BECTON DICKINSON DISPENSING SPAIN S.L.U.—See Becton, Dickinson & Company; *U.S. Public*, pg. 289
BECTON DICKINSON DISPENSING UK LTD.—See Becton, Dickinson & Company; *U.S. Public*, pg. 289
BECTON DICKINSON DISTRIBUTION CENTER N.V.—See Becton, Dickinson & Company; *U.S. Public*, pg. 289
BECTON DICKINSON FINANCE B.V.—See Becton, Dickinson & Company; *U.S. Public*, pg. 289
BECTON DICKINSON FRANCE S.A.S.—See Becton, Dickinson & Company; *U.S. Public*, pg. 289
BECTON DICKINSON GMBH—See Becton, Dickinson & Company; *U.S. Public*, pg. 289
BECTON DICKINSON HELLAS S.A.—See Becton, Dickinson & Company; *U.S. Public*, pg. 289
BECTON DICKINSON HUNGARY KFT.—See Becton, Dickinson & Company; *U.S. Public*, pg. 289
BECTON DICKINSON INDIA PRIVATE LIMITED—See Becton, Dickinson & Company; *U.S. Public*, pg. 289
BECTON, DICKINSON INDUSTRIAS CIRURGICAS, LTDA.—See Becton, Dickinson & Company; *U.S. Public*, pg. 290
BECTON DICKINSON INFUSION THERAPY AB—See Becton, Dickinson & Company; *U.S. Public*, pg. 289

BECTON DICKINSON INFUSION THERAPY A/S—See Becton, Dickinson & Company; *U.S. Public*, pg. 289
BECTON DICKINSON INFUSION THERAPY B.V.—See Becton, Dickinson & Company; *U.S. Public*, pg. 289
BECTON DICKINSON INFUSION THERAPY GMBH—See Becton, Dickinson & Company; *U.S. Public*, pg. 289
BECTON DICKINSON INFUSION THERAPY HOLDINGS AB—See Becton, Dickinson & Company; *U.S. Public*, pg. 289
BECTON DICKINSON INFUSION THERAPY HOLDINGS UK LIMITED—See Becton, Dickinson & Company; *U.S. Public*, pg. 289
BECTON DICKINSON INFUSION THERAPY SYSTEMS INC., S.A. DE C.V.—See Becton, Dickinson & Company; *U.S. Public*, pg. 289
BECTON DICKINSON INFUSION THERAPY UK—See Becton, Dickinson & Company; *U.S. Public*, pg. 290
BECTON DICKINSON INFUSTION THERAPY AB—See Becton, Dickinson & Company; *U.S. Public*, pg. 289
BECTON DICKINSON INSULIN SYRINGE, LTD.—See Becton, Dickinson & Company; *U.S. Public*, pg. 289
BECTON, DICKINSON ITALIA S.P.A.—See Becton, Dickinson & Company; *U.S. Public*, pg. 290
BECTON DICKINSON KOREA LTD.—See Becton, Dickinson & Company; *U.S. Public*, pg. 289
BECTON DICKINSON LTD.—See Becton, Dickinson & Company; *U.S. Public*, pg. 289
BECTON DICKINSON LTD.—See Becton, Dickinson & Company; *U.S. Public*, pg. 289
BECTON DICKINSON MANAGEMENT GMBH & CO. KG—See Becton, Dickinson & Company; *U.S. Public*, pg. 289
BECTON DICKINSON MEDICAL DEVICES CO. LTD., SUZHOU—See Becton, Dickinson & Company; *U.S. Public*, pg. 290
BECTON DICKINSON MEDICAL DEVICES CO. SHANGHAI LTD.—See Becton, Dickinson & Company; *U.S. Public*, pg. 290
BECTON DICKINSON MEDICAL PRODUCTS PTE. LTD.—See Becton, Dickinson & Company; *U.S. Public*, pg. 290
BECTON DICKINSON MEDICAL—See Becton, Dickinson & Company; *U.S. Public*, pg. 289
BECTON DICKINSON MEDICAL—See Becton, Dickinson & Company; *U.S. Public*, pg. 290
BECTON DICKINSON MEDICAL (S) PTE LTD.—See Becton, Dickinson & Company; *U.S. Public*, pg. 290
BECTON, DICKINSON MEDICAL SURGICAL—See Becton, Dickinson & Company; *U.S. Public*, pg. 290
BECTON DICKINSON NORWAY AS—See Becton, Dickinson & Company; *U.S. Public*, pg. 290
BECTON DICKINSON OY—See Becton, Dickinson & Company; *U.S. Public*, pg. 289
BECTON DICKINSON PAKISTAN (PVT) LTD.—See Becton, Dickinson & Company; *U.S. Public*, pg. 290
BECTON DICKINSON PHILIPPINES, INC.—See Becton, Dickinson & Company; *U.S. Public*, pg. 290
BECTON DICKINSON POLSKA SP.Z.O.O.—See Becton, Dickinson & Company; *U.S. Public*, pg. 290
BECTON DICKINSON PTY. LTD.—See Becton, Dickinson & Company; *U.S. Public*, pg. 290
BECTON DICKINSON (PTY) LTD.—See Becton, Dickinson & Company; *U.S. Public*, pg. 290
BECTON DICKINSON ROWA GERMANY GMBH—See Becton, Dickinson & Company; *U.S. Public*, pg. 290
BECTON DICKINSON ROWA ITALY SRL—See Becton, Dickinson & Company; *U.S. Public*, pg. 290
BECTON DICKINSON (ROYSTON) LIMITED—See Becton, Dickinson & Company; *U.S. Public*, pg. 288
BECTON DICKINSON, S.A.—See Becton, Dickinson & Company; *U.S. Public*, pg. 290
BECTON DICKINSON SDN. BHD.—See Becton, Dickinson & Company; *U.S. Public*, pg. 290
BECTON DICKINSON SWEDEN HOLDINGS AB—See Becton, Dickinson & Company; *U.S. Public*, pg. 290
BECTON DICKINSON SWITZERLAND GLOBAL HOLDINGS SARL—See Becton, Dickinson & Company; *U.S. Public*, pg. 290
BECTON DICKINSON (THAILAND) LIMITED—See Becton, Dickinson & Company; *U.S. Public*, pg. 288
BECTON DICKINSON U.K. LIMITED—See Becton, Dickinson & Company; *U.S. Public*, pg. 290
BECTON DICKINSON VERWALTUNGS GMBH—See Becton, Dickinson & Company; *U.S. Public*, pg. 290
BECUAI INC.; *Int'l*, pg. 938
BEC WORLD PUBLIC COMPANY LIMITED; *Int'l*, pg. 936
BEDAT & CO. SA—See Luxury Concepts Watches & Jewellery Sdn. Bhd.; *Int'l*, pg. 4589
BED BATH & BEYOND CANADA L.P.—See 20230930-DK-Butterfly-1, Inc.; *U.S. Private*, pg. 5
BEDDEN & MATRASSEN B.V.—See Beter Bed Holding N.V.; *Int'l*, pg. 1002
BEDDING GALLERY; *U.S. Private*, pg. 512
THE BEDDING GROUP PTY. LTD.—See Bain Capital, LP; *U.S. Private*, pg. 435
BEDEK AVIATION GROUP - AIRCRAFT DIVISION—See Israel Aerospace Industries Ltd.; *Int'l*, pg. 3822

BEDEK AVIATION GROUP-COMPONENTS DIVISION—See Israel Aerospace Industries Ltd.; *Int'l*, pg. 3822
BEDEK AVIATION GROUP (IAI)—See Israel Aerospace Industries Ltd.; *Int'l*, pg. 3822
BEDELL CRISTIN; *Int'l*, pg. 938
BEDELL DIALYSIS, LLC—See DaVita Inc.; *U.S. Public*, pg. 636
BEDERSON & COMPANY LLP; *U.S. Private*, pg. 512
BEDFORD ADVERTISING INC.; *U.S. Private*, pg. 512
BEDFORD CAPITAL LTD.; *Int'l*, pg. 938
BEDFORD EDUCATION PARTNERSHIP LIMITED—See Bilfinger SE; *Int'l*, pg. 1024
BEDFORD, FREEMAN & WORTH PUBLISHING GROUP LLC—See Verlagsgruppe Georg von Holtzbrinck GmbH; *Int'l*, pg. 8170
BEDFORD FUNDING; *U.S. Private*, pg. 512
BEDFORD HOUSE, LTD.—See Apartment Investment and Management Company; *U.S. Public*, pg. 144
BEDFORD INDUSTRIES, INC.; *U.S. Private*, pg. 512
BEDFORD INSURANCE SERVICES, INC.—See Unico American Corporation; *U.S. Public*, pg. 2225
BEDFORD LOGISTICS, LLC—See Ryder System, Inc.; *U.S. Public*, pg. 1828
BEDFORD METALS CORP.; *Int'l*, pg. 938
BEDFORD MINUTEMAN—See Gannett Co., Inc.; *U.S. Public*, pg. 901
BEDFORD NISSAN INC.; *U.S. Private*, pg. 512
BEDFORD REINFORCED PLASTICS; *U.S. Private*, pg. 512
BEDFORDSHIRE NEWSPAPERS LTD—See JPIMedia Holdings Limited; *Int'l*, pg. 4006
BEDFORD TECHNOLOGY, LLC—See Bedford Industries, Inc.; *U.S. Private*, pg. 512
BEDFORD VALLEY PETROLEUM CORP; *U.S. Private*, pg. 512
BEDFORD WEAVING MILLS INC.; *U.S. Private*, pg. 512
BEDGEAR LLC; *U.S. Private*, pg. 512
BEDMUTHA INDUSTRIES LIMITED; *Int'l*, pg. 938
BEDRIFTSKATALOGEN AS—See Eniro Group AB; *Int'l*, pg. 2439
BEDRIJFSARTSENGROEP HOLDING B.V.—See ASR Nederland N.V.; *Int'l*, pg. 632
BEDROCK AUTOMATION PLATFORMS, INC.—See Analog Devices, Inc.; *U.S. Public*, pg. 135
BED ROCK, INC.—See Daseke, Inc.; *U.S. Public*, pg. 1161
BEDROCK INDUSTRIES GP, LLC; *U.S. Private*, pg. 512
BEDROCK LOGISTICS LLC; *U.S. Private*, pg. 512
BEDROCK QUARRIES, INC.—See Haines & Kibblehouse Inc.; *U.S. Private*, pg. 1840
BEDROCK TECHNOLOGY PARTNERS; *U.S. Private*, pg. 512
BEDROCK TITLE COMPANY, LLC—See Stewart Information Services Corporation; *U.S. Public*, pg. 1947
THE BEDROOM STORE; *U.S. Private*, pg. 3992
BEDSHED FRANCHISING PTY. LTD.—See Joyce Corporation Ltd; *Int'l*, pg. 4004
BED TECHS, INC.—See iMedical Equipment & Services LLC; *U.S. Private*, pg. 2046
BEE AGRICULTURAL COMPANY INC.; *U.S. Private*, pg. 512
BEE-ALIVE INC.; *U.S. Private*, pg. 513
BEEBE MEDICAL CENTER; *U.S. Private*, pg. 513
BEE BRAND MEDICO DENTAL CO., LTD.—See Ono Pharmaceutical Co., Ltd.; *Int'l*, pg. 5582
BEEBY CLARK + MEYLER; *U.S. Private*, pg. 513
BEECH CARE LIMITED—See Sheikh Holdings Group (Investments) Limited; *Int'l*, pg. 6793
BEECHCRAFT CORPORATION—See Textron Inc.; *U.S. Public*, pg. 2028
BEECHCROFT DEVELOPMENTS LTD.; *Int'l*, pg. 939
BEECHER CARLSON HOLDINGS, INC.—See Brown & Brown, Inc.; *U.S. Public*, pg. 397
BEECHER CARLSON MANAGEMENT, LTD.—See Brown & Brown, Inc.; *U.S. Public*, pg. 397
BEECHMONT AUTOMOTIVE GROUP; *U.S. Private*, pg. 513
BEECHMONT FORD INC.; *U.S. Private*, pg. 513
BEECHMONT ISUZU—See Beechmont Automotive Group; *U.S. Private*, pg. 513
BEECHMONT MOTORS, INC; *U.S. Private*, pg. 513
BEECHMONT TOYOTA—See Beechmont Automotive Group; *U.S. Private*, pg. 513
BEECH-NUT NUTRITION CORPORATION—See Hero AG; *Int'l*, pg. 3363
BEECH OVENS PTY LTD.—See The Middleby Corporation; *U.S. Public*, pg. 2113
BEECHUM FINANCIAL CORP.; *U.S. Private*, pg. 513
BEECH UNDERWRITING AGENCIES LIMITED—See Brown & Brown, Inc.; *U.S. Public*, pg. 397
BEECHWOOD CREATIVE, INC.; *U.S. Private*, pg. 513
BEECKEN PETTY O'KEEFE & COMPANY, LLC; *U.S. Private*, pg. 514
BEECRUISE INC.—See BEENOS Inc.; *Int'l*, pg. 939
BEECUBE, INC.—See National Instruments Corporation; *U.S. Public*, pg. 2856
BEE DARLIN', INC.; *U.S. Private*, pg. 512

BEE DARLIN', INC.

BEEDE ELECTRICAL INSTRUMENT CO, INC.—See Faria Beede Instruments, Inc.; *U.S. Private*, pg. 1474
BEEDIE CAPITAL PARTNERS; *Int'l*, pg. 939
BEEDIE INVESTMENTS LTD.—See Beedie Capital Partners; *Int'l*, pg. 939
BEE ELECTRONIC MACHINES LTD.; *Int'l*, pg. 938
BEE EQUIPMENT SALES, LTD.—See SMT Belgium NV; *Int'l*, pg. 7017
BEEF CORPORATION OF AMERICA; *U.S. Private*, pg. 514
BEEF PRODUCERS AUSTRALIA PTY. LTD.—See NH Foods Ltd.; *Int'l*, pg. 5256
BEEGY GMBH—See MVV Energie AG; *Int'l*, pg. 5108
BEEHIVE BRICK & STONE—See Leonard Green & Partners, L.P.; *U.S. Private*, pg. 2429
BEEHIVE COILS LTD; *Int'l*, pg. 939
BEEHIVE COMMUNICATIONS PVT. LTD.—See Publicis Groupe S.A.; *Int'l*, pg. 6097
BEEHIVE DAY NURSERIES LIMITED—See Bain Capital, LP; *U.S. Private*, pg. 437
BEEHIVE INC.—See Henry Crown & Company; *U.S. Private*, pg. 1917
BEEHIVE INSURANCE AGENCY, INC.—See Clyde Companies Inc.; *U.S. Private*, pg. 949
B.E.E. INDUSTRIAL SUPPLY, INC.—See Mallory Safety & Supply LLC; *U.S. Private*, pg. 2558
BEE INSURANCE MANAGEMENT SERVICES LIMITED—See Arthur J. Gallagher & Co.; *U.S. Public*, pg. 203
BEEIO HONEY LTD; *Int'l*, pg. 939
BEE JOO ENVIRONMENTAL PTE. LTD.—See ecoWise Holdings Limited; *Int'l*, pg. 2300
BEE JOO INDUSTRIES PTE. LTD.—See ecoWise Holdings Limited; *Int'l*, pg. 2300
BEEKAY NIRYAT LTD.; *Int'l*, pg. 939
BEEKAY STEEL INDUSTRIES LTD.; *Int'l*, pg. 939
THE BEEKMAN GROUP, LLC; *U.S. Private*, pg. 3992
BEEKMAN MUSIC, INC.—See Theodore Presser Co.; *U.S. Private*, pg. 4141
BEEKS FINANCIAL CLOUD GROUP PLC; *Int'l*, pg. 939
BEELINE.COM, INC.—See Stone Point Capital LLC; *U.S. Private*, pg. 3821
BEE-LINE COMMUNICATIONS; *U.S. Private*, pg. 513
BEE LINE COMPANY—See McLaughlin Body Co.; *U.S. Private*, pg. 2640
BEE LINE CONSTRUCTION L.L.C.—See Bee Line, Inc.; *U.S. Private*, pg. 512
BEE LINE, INC.; *U.S. Private*, pg. 512
BEELINE—See Adecco Group AG; *Int'l*, pg. 141
BEELK HOLDING AG; *Int'l*, pg. 939
BEELMAN TRUCK CO. INC.; *U.S. Private*, pg. 514
BEEMAK PLASTICS, INC.—See Jordan Industries, Inc.; *U.S. Private*, pg. 2235
BEEMA-PAKISTAN COMPANY LIMITED; *Int'l*, pg. 939
BEEM ASIA LIMITED—See The Social Chain AG; *Int'l*, pg. 7687
BEEMER PRECISION, INC.; *U.S. Private*, pg. 514
BEE MINE PRODUCTS INC.; *U.S. Private*, pg. 512
BEENEAR SRL—See Sesa S.p.A.; *Int'l*, pg. 6728
BE ENGINEERING SERVICES INDIA PRIVATE LIMITED—See RTX Corporation; *U.S. Public*, pg. 1822
B&E ENGINEERS INC.—See NJS Co., Ltd.; *Int'l*, pg. 5390
BEENOS INC.; *Int'l*, pg. 939
BEENVERIFIED.COM; *U.S. Private*, pg. 514
BEEOLOGICS INC.—See Bayer Aktiengesellschaft; *Int'l*, pg. 908
BEEPER COMMUNICATIONS ISRAEL LTD.—See Motorola Solutions, Inc.; *U.S. Public*, pg. 1478
BEER CAPITOL DISTRIBUTING, LAKE COUNTRY, LLC; *U.S. Private*, pg. 514
BEER CHANG CO., LTD.—See Thai Beverage Public Company Limited; *Int'l*, pg. 7589
BEERCO LIMITED—See Thai Beverage Public Company Limited; *Int'l*, pg. 7589
BEERENBERG CORP.—See Altrad Investment Authority SAS; *Int'l*, pg. 398
BEERENS O.C. NV—See General Motors Company; *U.S. Public*, pg. 927
BEERE PRECISION PRODUCTS INC.; *U.S. Private*, pg. 514
BEERFEST ASIA PTE. LTD.—See Singapore Press Holdings Ltd.; *Int'l*, pg. 6942
BEER NUTS, INC.; *U.S. Private*, pg. 514
BEERS & HOFFMAN, LTD.; *U.S. Private*, pg. 514
BEER THAI (1991) PCL—See Thai Beverage Public Company Limited; *Int'l*, pg. 7589
BEER THIP BREWERY (1991) CO., LTD.—See Thai Beverage Public Company Limited; *Int'l*, pg. 7589
BEE SALES COMPANY; *U.S. Private*, pg. 513
BEESON HARDWARE CO. INC.; *U.S. Private*, pg. 514
BEESPEED TECHNICAL ENGINEERING CENTER S.R.L.—See ZF Friedrichshafen AG; *Int'l*, pg. 8640
BEE STINGER, LLC—See Vista Outdoor Inc.; *U.S. Public*, pg. 2304
BEES.TRAVEL LIMITED—See Corporate Travel Management Limited; *Int'l*, pg. 1805
BEE STREET HOLDINGS LLC; *U.S. Private*, pg. 513
BEETEL TELETECH LIMITED—See Brightstar Capital Partners, L.P.; *U.S. Private*, pg. 653
BEETLE PLASTICS, LLC—See Midwest Towers Inc.; *U.S. Private*, pg. 2723
BEE VECTORING TECHNOLOGIES INTERNATIONAL INC.; *Int'l*, pg. 939
BEE WINDOW INCORPORATED; *U.S. Private*, pg. 513
BEEYU OVERSEAS LIMITED; *Int'l*, pg. 939
BEEZLEY MANAGEMENT, LLC—See CBRE Group, Inc.; *U.S. Public*, pg. 459
BEFAB ENTREPRENAD MJOLBY AB—See Peab AB; *Int'l*, pg. 5771
BEFAB SCHAKT AB—See Peab AB; *Int'l*, pg. 5771
BEFAR GROUP CO., LTD.; *Int'l*, pg. 939
BEFESA ALUMINIUM GERMANY GMBH—See Befesa S.A.; *Int'l*, pg. 940
BEFESA (CHINA) INVESTMENT CO., LTD.—See Befesa S.A.; *Int'l*, pg. 939
BEFESA MANAGEMENT SERVICES GMBH—See Befesa S.A.; *Int'l*, pg. 940
BEFESA MEDIO AMBIENTE, S.L.—See Befesa S.A.; *Int'l*, pg. 940
BEFESA SALT SLAGS, LTD.—See Befesa S.A.; *Int'l*, pg. 940
BEFESA.S.A.; *Int'l*, pg. 939
BEFESA SCANDUST AB—See Befesa S.A.; *Int'l*, pg. 940
BEFESA SILVERMET ISKENDERUN CELIK TOZU GERI DONUSUMU, A.S.—See Befesa S.A.; *Int'l*, pg. 940
BEFESA STEEL SERVICES GMBH—See Befesa S.A.; *Int'l*, pg. 940
BEFESA VALERA, S.A.S.—See Befesa S.A.; *Int'l*, pg. 940
BEFESA ZINC COMERCIAL, S.A.—See Befesa S.A.; *Int'l*, pg. 940
BEFESA ZINC DUISBURG GMBH—See Befesa S.A.; *Int'l*, pg. 940
BEFESA ZINC FREIBERG GMBH & CO. KG—See Befesa S.A.; *Int'l*, pg. 940
BEFESA ZINC KOREA LTD.—See Befesa S.A.; *Int'l*, pg. 940
BEFESA ZINC OXIDO, S.A.—See Befesa S.A.; *Int'l*, pg. 940
BEFESA ZINC US, INC.—See Befesa S.A.; *Int'l*, pg. 940
BEFIMMO SCA; *Int'l*, pg. 940
BEFOREPAY GROUP LIMITED; *Int'l*, pg. 940
BE FOUND ONLINE; *U.S. Private*, pg. 503
BE FUELCARDS LTD.—See Edenred S.A.; *Int'l*, pg. 2307
BEFUND24 GMBH—See Siemens Aktiengesellschaft; *Int'l*, pg. 6886
BEFUN INC.; *U.S. Private*, pg. 514
BEFUT GLOBAL, INC.; *Int'l*, pg. 940
BEGA CHEESE LTD.; *Int'l*, pg. 940
BEGA CHEESE LTD. - STRATHMERTON PROCESS AND PACKAGING PLANT—See Bega Cheese Ltd.; *Int'l*, pg. 940
BEGA DAIRY AND DRINKS PTY. LTD.—See Bega Cheese Ltd.; *Int'l*, pg. 940
BEGA ELECTROMOTOR SA; *Int'l*, pg. 940
BEGALOM GUSS GMBH—See Unternehmens Invest AG; *Int'l*, pg. 8085
BEGBIES TRAYNOR GROUP PLC; *Int'l*, pg. 940
BEGHELLI ASIA PACIFIC LTD.—See Beghelli S.p.A.; *Int'l*, pg. 941
BEGHELLI CANADA INC.—See Beghelli S.p.A.; *Int'l*, pg. 941
BEGHELLI CHINA CO., LTD.—See Beghelli S.p.A.; *Int'l*, pg. 941
BEGHELLI DE MEXICO, S.A. DE C.V.—See Beghelli S.p.A.; *Int'l*, pg. 941
BEGHELLI ELPLAST A.S.—See Beghelli S.p.A.; *Int'l*, pg. 941
BEGHELLI HUNGARY KFT.—See Beghelli S.p.A.; *Int'l*, pg. 941
BEGHELLI INC.—See Beghelli S.p.A.; *Int'l*, pg. 941
BEGHELLI POLSKA SP. Z O.O.—See Beghelli S.p.A.; *Int'l*, pg. 941
BEGHELLI PRAEZISA GMBH—See Beghelli S.p.A.; *Int'l*, pg. 941
BEGHELLI S.P.A.; *Int'l*, pg. 941
BEGHIN-MEIJI—See Meiji Holdings Co., Ltd.; *Int'l*, pg. 4800
BEGHIN-MEIJI—See Tereos; *Int'l*, pg. 7564
BEGINAGAIN, INC.; *U.S. Private*, pg. 514
BEGISTICS PUBLIC COMPANY LIMITED; *Int'l*, pg. 941
BEGLES DISTRIBUTION SA; *Int'l*, pg. 941
BEGLEY COMPANY; *U.S. Private*, pg. 514
BEGLEY INTERNATIONAL—See Matrix Composites & Engineering Limited; *Int'l*, pg. 4729
BEGLEY LUMBER COMPANY INC.; *U.S. Private*, pg. 514
BEG LIQUID MUD SERVICES CORP.—See Gibson Energy Inc.; *Int'l*, pg. 2963
BE GREEN PACKAGING LLC—See The Riverside Company; *U.S. Private*, pg. 4108
BE GREEN PACKAGING LLC - SOUTH CAROLINA MFG FACILITY—See The Riverside Company; *U.S. Private*, pg. 4108
BE GROUP AB; *Int'l*, pg. 931
BE GROUP AS—See BE Group AB; *Int'l*, pg. 931
B&E GROUP, LLC—See Arlington Capital Partners LLC; *U.S. Private*, pg. 514
BE GROUP OU—See BE Group AB; *Int'l*, pg. 931
BE GROUP OY AB—See BE Group AB; *Int'l*, pg. 931

CORPORATE AFFILIATIONS

BE GROUP SIA—See BE Group AB; *Int'l*, pg. 931
BE GROUP SLOVAKIA S.R.O.—See BE Group AB; *Int'l*, pg. 931
BE GROUP SP. Z O.O.—See BE Group AB; *Int'l*, pg. 931
BE GROUP S.R.O.—See BE Group AB; *Int'l*, pg. 931
BE GROUP SVERIGE AB—See BE Group AB; *Int'l*, pg. 931
BE GROUP UAB—See BE Group AB; *Int'l*, pg. 931
BEHAN COMMUNICATIONS, INC.; *U.S. Private*, pg. 514
BEHARRY AUTOMOTIVE LIMITED—See Edward B. Beharry & Co. Ltd.; *Int'l*, pg. 2316
BEHAR SECURITE SA—See Schneider Electric SE; *Int'l*, pg. 6623
BEHAVIORAL CONNECTIONS OF WOOD COUNTY, INC.—See Harbor Corp.; *U.S. Private*, pg. 1858
BEHAVIORAL CONSULTING OF TAMPA BAY INC.; *U.S. Private*, pg. 514
BEHAVIORAL HEALTHCARE CORPORATION; *U.S. Private*, pg. 515
BEHAVIORAL HEALTHCARE OPTIONS, INC.—See UnitedHealth Group Incorporated; *U.S. Public*, pg. 2252
BEHAVIORAL HEALTHCARE PARTNERS OF CENTRAL OHIO, INC.; *U.S. Private*, pg. 515
BEHAVIORAL HEALTHCARE REALTY, LLC—See AAC Holdings, Inc.; *U.S. Private*, pg. 31
BEHAVIORAL HEALTH CONNECTIONS, INC.—See Universal Health Services, Inc.; *U.S. Public*, pg. 2256
BEHAVIORAL HEALTH GROUP; *U.S. Private*, pg. 514
BEHAVIORAL HEALTH MANAGEMENT, LLC—See Universal Health Services, Inc.; *U.S. Public*, pg. 2256
BEHAVIORAL HEALTH NETWORK, INC.—See Elevance Health, Inc.; *U.S. Public*, pg. 729
BEHAVIORAL HEALTH SERVICES NORTH, INC.; *U.S. Private*, pg. 514
BEHAVIORAL HEALTH SERVICES—See Northwestern Memorial HealthCare; *U.S. Private*, pg. 2962
BEHAVIORAL HEALTH WELLNESS CENTER, LLC—See HCA Healthcare, Inc.; *U.S. Public*, pg. 991
BEHAVIORAL SCIENCE TECHNOLOGY (BST) INC.—See DEKRA e.V.; *Int'l*, pg. 2007
BEHAVIORAL SCIENE TECHNOLOGY CONSULTORES DO BRASIL LTDA.—See DEKRA e.V.; *Int'l*, pg. 2007
BEHAVIOR ANALYSIS CENTER FOR AUTISM—See Gryphon Investors, LLC; *U.S. Private*, pg. 1799
BEHAVIOR TECH COMPUTER CORPORATION - CHUNG LI FACTORY—See Behavior Tech Computer Corporation; *Int'l*, pg. 941
BEHAVIOR TECH COMPUTER CORPORATION; *Int'l*, pg. 941
BEHAVIOR TECH COMPUTER CORPORATION—See Behavior Tech Computer Corporation; *Int'l*, pg. 941
BEHAVIOR TECH COMPUTER EUROPE B.V.—See Behavior Tech Computer Corporation; *Int'l*, pg. 941
BEHAVIOR TECH COMPUTER (US) CORPORATION—See Behavior Tech Computer Corporation; *Int'l*, pg. 941
BEHBAHAN CEMENT COMPANY; *Int'l*, pg. 941
BEHCERAM COMPANY; *Int'l*, pg. 941
BE HEALTH SPA—See Health Biosciences SpA; *Int'l*, pg. 3303
BE HEALTH SPECIALIST LIMITED—See Human Health Holdings Limited; *Int'l*, pg. 3529
BE HEARD GROUP PLC—See OEP Capital Advisors, L.P.; *U.S. Private*, pg. 2999
BEHEERMAATSCHAPPIJ BURG B.V—See China International Marine Containers (Group) Co., Ltd.; *Int'l*, pg. 1511
BE:HERE LIMITED—See Willmott Dixon Limited; *Int'l*, pg. 8419
BE&H EXTRUSION DIES, INC.—See Exco Technologies Limited; *Int'l*, pg. 2580
BEHI-ALDE S. COOP.—See Mondragon Corporation; *Int'l*, pg. 5028
BEHIND THE SCENES, INC; *U.S. Private*, pg. 515
BEHIND THE SCENES MARKETING; *U.S. Private*, pg. 515
BEHLEN CUSTOM FABRICATION—See Behlen Mfg. Co.; *U.S. Private*, pg. 515
BEHLEN INDUSTRIES LP—See WGI Westman Group, Inc.; *Int'l*, pg. 8394
BEHLEN MFG. CO. - BEHLEN BUILDING SYSTEMS UNIT—See Behlen Mfg. Co.; *U.S. Private*, pg. 515
BEHLEN MFG. CO. - BEHLEN COUNTRY DIVISION—See Behlen Mfg. Co.; *U.S. Private*, pg. 515
BEHLEN MFG. CO. - EAST COAST DISTRIBUTION CENTER—See Behlen Mfg. Co.; *U.S. Private*, pg. 515
BEHLEN MFG. CO.; *U.S. Private*, pg. 515
BEHLEN MFG. CO. - WEST COAST PLANT—See Behlen Mfg. Co.; *U.S. Private*, pg. 515
THE BEHLER-YOUNG CO., INC.; *U.S. Private*, pg. 3993
BEHLMAN ELECTRONICS, INC.—See Orbit International Corp.; *U.S. Public*, pg. 1614
BEHNKE NURSERIES CO.; *U.S. Private*, pg. 515
BEHN MEYER AGRICARE, PT.—See Behn Meyer (D) Holding AG & Co.; *Int'l*, pg. 941
BEHN MEYER CHEMICALS (PHILIPPINES) INC.—See Behn Meyer (D) Holding AG & Co.; *Int'l*, pg. 941
BEHN MEYER CHEMICALS (QINGDAO) CO., LTD—See Behn Meyer (D) Holding AG & Co.; *Int'l*, pg. 941

COMPANY NAME INDEX

BEHN MEYER CHEMICALS TAIWAN CO., LTD—See Behn Meyer (D) Holding AG & Co.; *Int'l*, pg. 941
BEHN MEYER CHEMICALS (T) CO., LTD—See Behn Meyer (D) Holding AG & Co.; *Int'l*, pg. 941
BEHN MEYER (D) HOLDING AG & CO.; *Int'l*, pg. 941
BEHN MEYER GROUP MALAYSIA—See Behn Meyer (D) Holding AG & Co.; *Int'l*, pg. 941
BEHN MEYER GROUP SINGAPORE—See Behn Meyer (D) Holding AG & Co.; *Int'l*, pg. 941
BEHN MEYER GROUP VIETNAM—See Behn Meyer (D) Holding AG & Co.; *Int'l*, pg. 941
BEHPAK INDUSTRIAL COMPANY LIMITED—See Behshahr Industrial Development Corp.; *Int'l*, pg. 942
BEHRENS MANUFACTURING, LLC—See Mill City Capital, L.P.; *U.S. Private*, pg. 2730
BEHR-HELLA THERMOCONTROL GMBH—See AUO Corporation; *Int'l*, pg. 706
BEHR HOLDINGS CORPORATION—See Masco Corporation; *U.S. Public*, pg. 1389
BEHRINGER ANLAGENBAU GMBH—See Behringer GmbH; *Int'l*, pg. 941
BEHRINGER EISELE GMBH—See Behringer GmbH; *Int'l*, pg. 941
BEHRINGER FRANCE S.A.R.L.—See SOL S.p.A.; *Int'l*, pg. 7067
BEHRINGER GMBH; *Int'l*, pg. 941
BEHRINGER HARVARD HOLDINGS, LLC; *U.S. Private*, pg. 515
BEHRINGER LTD.—See Behringer GmbH; *Int'l*, pg. 942
BEHRINGER SECURITIES LP—See Behringer Harvard Holdings, LLC; *U.S. Private*, pg. 515
BEHRINGER SRL—See SOL S.p.A.; *Int'l*, pg. 7067
BEHR IRON & STEEL, INC.—See Alter Trading Corporation; *U.S. Private*, pg. 207
BEHRMAN BROTHERS MANAGEMENT CORP.; *U.S. Private*, pg. 515
BEHR PROCESS CANADA LTD.—See Masco Corporation; *U.S. Public*, pg. 1390
BEHR PROCESS CORPORATION—See Masco Corporation; *U.S. Public*, pg. 1390
BEHR PROCESS CORPORATION—See Masco Corporation; *U.S. Public*, pg. 1389
BEHR PROCESS PAINTS (INDIA) PRIVATE LIMITED—See Masco Corporation, *U.S. Public*, pg. 1390
BEH'S CLINIC FOR WOMEN PTE. LTD.—See Singapore O&G Ltd.; *Int'l*, pg. 6941
BEHSHAHR INDUSTRIAL COMPANY—See Savola Group; *Int'l*, pg. 6602
BEHSHAHR INDUSTRIAL DEVELOPMENT CORP.; *Int'l*, pg. 942
BEHSHAHR INDUSTRIAL GROUP INVESTMENT COMPANY; *Int'l*, pg. 942
BEIBU GULF PORT CO., LTD.; *Int'l*, pg. 942
BEI CONSTRUCTION, INC.; *U.S. Private*, pg. 516
BEIER RADIO LLC; *U.S. Private*, pg. 516
BEIERSDORF AB—See maxingvest ag; *Int'l*, pg. 4738
BEIERSDORF AG—See maxingvest ag; *Int'l*, pg. 4738
BEIERSDORF A/S—See maxingvest ag; *Int'l*, pg. 4738
BEIERSDORF A/S—See maxingvest ag; *Int'l*, pg. 4738
BEIERSDORF AUSTRALIA LTD.—See maxingvest ag; *Int'l*, pg. 4738
BEIERSDORF BULGARIA EOOD—See maxingvest ag; *Int'l*, pg. 4738
BEIERSDORF CANADA INC.—See maxingvest ag; *Int'l*, pg. 4738
BEIERSDORF CONSUMER PRODUCTS (PTY.) LTD.—See maxingvest ag; *Int'l*, pg. 4738
BEIERSDORF DAILY CHEMICAL (GUANGZHOU) CO., LTD.—See maxingvest ag; *Int'l*, pg. 4738
BEIERSDORF DAILY CHEMICAL (HUBEI) CO., LTD.—See maxingvest ag; *Int'l*, pg. 4738
BEIERSDORF DAILY CHEMICAL (WUHAN) CO., LTD.—See maxingvest ag; *Int'l*, pg. 4738
BEIERSDORF D.O.O.—See maxingvest ag; *Int'l*, pg. 4739
BEIERSDORF D.O.O.—See maxingvest ag; *Int'l*, pg. 4740
BEIERSDORF D.O.O.—See maxingvest ag; *Int'l*, pg. 4740
BEIERSDORF EAST AFRICA LTD.—See maxingvest ag; *Int'l*, pg. 4738
BEIERSDORF EHF—See maxingvest ag; *Int'l*, pg. 4740
BEIERSDORF GMBH—See maxingvest ag; *Int'l*, pg. 4738
BEIERSDORF HAUTPFLEGE GMBH—See maxingvest ag; *Int'l*, pg. 4738
BEIERSDORF HELLAS AE—See maxingvest ag; *Int'l*, pg. 4738
BEIERSDORF HOLDING B.V.—See maxingvest ag; *Int'l*, pg. 4738
BEIERSDORF INDIA PVT. LTD.—See maxingvest ag; *Int'l*, pg. 4738
BEIERSDORF INDUSTRIA E COMERCIO LTDA.—See maxingvest ag; *Int'l*, pg. 4738
BEIERSDORF IRELAND LTD.—See maxingvest ag; *Int'l*, pg. 4738
BEIERSDORF KAZAKHSTAN LLP—See maxingvest ag; *Int'l*, pg. 4738
BEIERSDORF KFT.—See maxingvest ag; *Int'l*, pg. 4738
BEIERSDORF KIMYA SANAYI VE TICARET A.S.—See maxingvest ag; *Int'l*, pg. 4738
BEIERSDORF KOREA LTD.—See maxingvest ag; *Int'l*, pg. 4739
BEIERSDORF (MALAYSIA) SDN. BHD.—See maxingvest ag; *Int'l*, pg. 4738
BEIERSDORF MANUFACTURING ARGENTONA, S.L.—See maxingvest ag; *Int'l*, pg. 4739
BEIERSDORF MANUFACTURING HAMBURG GMBH—See maxingvest ag; *Int'l*, pg. 4739
BEIERSDORF MANUFACTURING WALDHEIM GMBH—See maxingvest ag; *Int'l*, pg. 4739
BEIERSDORF MAROC S.A.—See maxingvest ag; *Int'l*, pg. 4739
BEIERSDORF MIDDLE EAST FZCO—See maxingvest ag; *Int'l*, pg. 4739
BEIERSDORF NORTH AMERICA INC.—See maxingvest ag; *Int'l*, pg. 4739
BEIERSDORF NV—See maxingvest ag; *Int'l*, pg. 4739
BEIERSDORF OOO—See maxingvest ag; *Int'l*, pg. 4739
BEIERSDORF OU—See maxingvest ag; *Int'l*, pg. 4739
BEIERSDORF OY—See maxingvest ag; *Int'l*, pg. 4739
BEIERSDORF PERSONAL CARE (CHINA) CO., LTD.—See maxingvest ag; *Int'l*, pg. 4739
BEIERSDORF PHILIPPINES INCORPORATED—See maxingvest ag; *Int'l*, pg. 4739
BEIERSDORF PORTUGUESA LDA—See maxingvest ag; *Int'l*, pg. 4739
BEIERSDORF ROMANIA SRL—See maxingvest ag; *Int'l*, pg. 4739
BEIERSDORF S.A.C.—See maxingvest ag; *Int'l*, pg. 4739
BEIERSDORF S.A.—See maxingvest ag; *Int'l*, pg. 4739
BEIERSDORF S.A.—See maxingvest ag; *Int'l*, pg. 4739
BEIERSDORF S.A.—See maxingvest ag; *Int'l*, pg. 4739
BEIERSDORF S.A.—See maxingvest ag; *Int'l*, pg. 4739
BEIERSDORF S.A.—See maxingvest ag; *Int'l*, pg. 4739
BEIERSDORF S.A.—See maxingvest ag; *Int'l*, pg. 4739
BEIERSDORF S.A.—See maxingvest ag; *Int'l*, pg. 4739
BEIERSDORF S.A.—See maxingvest ag; *Int'l*, pg. 4739
BEIERSDORF SHARED SERVICES GMBH—See maxingvest ag; *Int'l*, pg. 4739
BEIERSDORF SINGAPORE PTE. LTD.—See maxingvest ag; *Int'l*, pg. 4739
BEIERSDORF SLOVAKIA, S.R.O.—See maxingvest ag; *Int'l*, pg. 4739
BEIERSDORF SPA—See maxingvest ag; *Int'l*, pg. 4739
BEIERSDORF SPOL. S.R.O.—See maxingvest ag; *Int'l*, pg. 4740
BEIERSDORF S.R.L.—See maxingvest ag; *Int'l*, pg. 4739
BEIERSDORF, SRL—See maxingvest ag; *Int'l*, pg. 4740
BEIERSDORF (THAILAND) CO., LTD.—See maxingvest ag; *Int'l*, pg. 4738
BEIERSDORF THAILAND CO. LTD.—See maxingvest ag; *Int'l*, pg. 4739
BEIERSDORF UAB—See maxingvest ag; *Int'l*, pg. 4739
BEIERSDORF U.K. LIMITED—See maxingvest ag; *Int'l*, pg. 4739
BEIERSDORF UKRAINE LLC—See maxingvest ag; *Int'l*, pg. 4739
BEIERSDORF VIETNAM LLC—See maxingvest ag; *Int'l*, pg. 4739
BEIFANG HELLA AUTOMOTIVE LIGHTING LTD.—See Hella GmbH & Co. KGaA; *Int'l*, pg. 3331
BEIF MANAGEMENT LIMITED—See Barclays PLC; *Int'l*, pg. 859
BEIGENE AUS PTY LTD.—See BeiGene, Ltd.; *Int'l*, pg. 942
BEIGENE (BEIJING) CO., LIMITED—See BeiGene, Ltd.; *Int'l*, pg. 942
BEIGENE, LTD.; *Int'l*, pg. 942
BEIGENE (SHANGHAI) CO., LIMITED—See BeiGene, Ltd.; *Int'l*, pg. 942
BEIGENE (SUZHOU) CO., LIMITED—See BeiGene, Ltd.; *Int'l*, pg. 942
BEIGENE SWITZERLAND GMBH—See BeiGene, Ltd.; *Int'l*, pg. 942
BEIHAI GOFAR CHUANSHAN BIOLOGICAL CO., LTD.; *Int'l*, pg. 942
BEIHAI HOTEL, HUANGSHAN TOURISM DEVELOPMENT CO., LTD.—See Huangshan Tourism Development Co., Ltd.; *Int'l*, pg. 3513
BEIHAI PROLTO SUPPLY CHAIN MANAGEMENT CO., LTD.—See Shenzhen Prolto Supply Chain Management Co., Ltd.; *Int'l*, pg. 6819
BEIHILFE-SERVICE GESELLSCHAFT MBH—See msg group GmbH; *Int'l*, pg. 5067
BEIH-PROPERTY CO., LTD.; *Int'l*, pg. 942
BEIJER ALMA AB; *Int'l*, pg. 942
BEIJER AS—See Beijer Alma AB; *Int'l*, pg. 942
BEIJER ECR IBERICA S.L.—See Beijer Ref AB; *Int'l*, pg. 943
BEIJER ELECTRONICS AS—See Ependion AB; *Int'l*, pg. 2459
BEIJER ELECTRONICS A/S—See Ependion AB; *Int'l*, pg. 2459
BEIJER ELECTRONICS CORP.—See Ependion AB; *Int'l*, pg. 2459
BEIJER ELECTRONICS GMBH & CO. KG—See Ependion AB; *Int'l*, pg. 2459
BEIJER ELECTRONICS INC.—See Ependion AB; *Int'l*, pg. 2459
BEIJER ELECTRONICS KOREA CO., LTD.—See Ependion AB; *Int'l*, pg. 2459
BEIJER ELECTRONICS TRADING (SHANGHAI) CO., LTD.—See Ependion AB; *Int'l*, pg. 2459
BEIJER ELECTRONICS UK LTD.—See Ependion AB; *Int'l*, pg. 2459
BEIJER ELEKTRONIK VE TIC. A.S.—See Ependion AB; *Int'l*, pg. 2459
BEIJER INDUSTRI AB—See Beijer Alma AB; *Int'l*, pg. 942
BEIJER OY—See Beijer Alma AB; *Int'l*, pg. 942
BEIJER REF AB; *Int'l*, pg. 943
BEIJER REF ACADEMY LTD.—See Beijer Ref AB; *Int'l*, pg. 944
BEIJER REF BELGIUM B.V.—See Beijer Ref AB; *Int'l*, pg. 944
BEIJER REF CZECH S.R.O.—See Beijer Ref AB; *Int'l*, pg. 944
BEIJER REF INDIA PVT. LTD.—See Beijer Ref AB; *Int'l*, pg. 944
BEIJER REF LATVIA SIA—See Beijer Ref AB; *Int'l*, pg. 944
BEIJER REF LITHUANIA UAB—See Beijer Ref AB; *Int'l*, pg. 944
BEIJER REF (MAURITIUS) LTD.—See Beijer Ref AB; *Int'l*, pg. 944
BEIJER REF POLSKA SP.Z.O.O.—See Beijer Ref AB; *Int'l*, pg. 944
BEIJER REF SUPPORT NORWAY AS—See Beijer Ref AB; *Int'l*, pg. 944
BEIJER TECH AB—See Beijer Alma AB; *Int'l*, pg. 942
BEIJING 3-D MATRIX INVESTMENT CONSULTING, LTD.—See 3-D Matrix, Ltd.; *Int'l*, pg. 6
BEIJING 58 DAOJIA INFORMATION TECHNOLOGY CO., LTD.—See 58.com Inc.; *Int'l*, pg. 13
BEIJING ABT NETWORKS CO., LTD.; *Int'l*, pg. 945
BEIJING ACOINFO INFORMATION TECHNOLOGY CO. LTD—See Beijing Watertek Information Technology Co., Ltd.; *Int'l*, pg. 960
BEIJING ADIENT AUTOMOTIVE COMPONENTS CO., LTD.—See Adient plc; *Int'l*, pg. 148
BEIJING ADVANCED DIGITAL TECHNOLOGY CO., LTD.—See Green Leader Holdings Group Limited; *Int'l*, pg. 3071
BEIJING ADVANCED VIDEOINFO TECHNOLOGY CO., LTD.—See Cantronic Systems Inc.; *Int'l*, pg. 1299
BEIJING AEROSPACE CHANGFENG CO., LTD.; *Int'l*, pg. 945
BEIJING AEROSPACE GOLDEN CARD CO.—See Aisino Corporation; *Int'l*, pg. 254
BEIJING AEROSPACE SHENZHOU INTELLIGENT EQUIPMENT TECHNOLOGY CO., LTD.; *Int'l*, pg. 945
BEIJING AGIE CHARMILLES INDUSTRIAL ELECTRONICS LTD.—See Georg Fischer AG; *Int'l*, pg. 2934
BEIJING AICHUANG TIANJIE BRAND MANAGEMENT CONSULTING CO., LTD.—See Zhewen Interactive Group Co Ltd; *Int'l*, pg. 8670
BEIJING AIHUA NEW ENTERPRISE LIGHTING APPLIANCE CO., LTD.—See Lightscape Technologies, Inc.; *Int'l*, pg. 4497
BEIJING AILIYANG SOLAR ENERGY TECHNOLOGY CO. LTD.—See China Solar & Clean Energy Solutions, Inc.; *Int'l*, pg. 1552
BEIJING AIRDOC TECHNOLOGY CO., LTD.; *Int'l*, pg. 945
BEIJING AIRPORT FOODS SERVICE CO., LTD.—See Capital Airports Holding Company (CAH); *Int'l*, pg. 1309
BEIJING AIRPORT HIGH-TECH PARK CO., LTD.; *Int'l*, pg. 945
BEIJING ALL ACCESS NOTER COMMUNICATION TECHNOLOGY CO., LIMITED—See China All Access (Holdings) Limited; *Int'l*, pg. 1482
BEIJING ALLFLEX PLASTIC PRODUCTS CO., LTD.—See Merck & Co., Inc.; *U.S. Public*, pg. 1415
BEIJING AMADA MACHINE & TOOLING CO., LTD.—See Amada Holdings Co., Ltd.; *Int'l*, pg. 404
BEIJING AMBOW SHIDA EDUCATION TECHNOLOGY CO.—See Ambow Education Holding Ltd.; *Int'l*, pg. 415
BEIJING ANDAWELL SCIENCE & TECHNOLOGY CO., LTD.; *Int'l*, pg. 945
BEIJING AOSAIKANG PHARMACEUTICAL CO., LTD.; *Int'l*, pg. 945
BEIJING AP BAIF GAS INDUSTRY CO., LTD.—See Air Products & Chemicals, Inc.; *U.S. Public*, pg. 64
BEIJING APPLE KAIXIN FOODS TECH CO., LTD.—See Apple Flavor & Fragrance Group Co., Ltd.; *Int'l*, pg. 520
BEIJING ARITIME INTELLIGENT CONTROL CO., LTD.; *Int'l*, pg. 945
BEIJING ASIACOM INFORMATION TECHNOLOGY CO., LTD.; *Int'l*, pg. 945
BEIJING ASIARAY ADVERTISING—See Asiaray Media Group Limited; *Int'l*, pg. 620
BEIJING ASPIRATION ADVERTISING CO., LTD.—See Zhewen Interactive Group Co Ltd; *Int'l*, pg. 8671
BEIJING ATAS METAL MATERIALS CO., LTD.—See Advanced Technology & Materials Co., Ltd.; *Int'l*, pg. 162

BEIJING ATLANTIC ZEISER TECH CO. LTD.—See Atlantic Zeiser GmbH & Co.; *Int'l*, pg. 676
BEIJING AT&M SIX NINE NEW MATERIALS CO., LTD.—See Advanced Technology & Materials Co., Ltd.; *Int'l*, pg. 162
BEIJING AUCHAN HYPERMARKETS CO., LTD.—See Alibaba Group Holding Limited; *Int'l*, pg. 326
BEIJING AUTELAN TECHNOLOGY CO. LTD.; *Int'l*, pg. 945
BEIJING AUTOMOTIVE INDUSTRY HOLDING CO., LTD.; *Int'l*, pg. 945
BEIJING AUTONICS TECHNOLOGY CO., LTD.—See Zhejiang Shibao Company Limited; *Int'l*, pg. 8663
BEIJING BAINATION PICTURES CO., LTD.; *Int'l*, pg. 946
BEIJING BALANCE MEDICAL TECHNOLOGY CO., LTD.; *Int'l*, pg. 946
BEIJING BANDWISE TECHNOLOGY DEVELOPMENT CO., LTD.—See Jiangsu Skyray Instrument Co., Ltd.; *Int'l*, pg. 3954
BEIJING BAOLANDE SOFTWARE CORP.; *Int'l*, pg. 946
BEIJING BAOZEN BAIWANG AUTOMOBILE SALES AND SERVICES CO., LTD.—See China Yongda Automobiles Services Holdings Limited; *Int'l*, pg. 1564
BEIJING BASHI MEDIA CO., LTD.; *Int'l*, pg. 946
BEIJING BAUSCH & LOMB EYECARE COMPANY, LTD.—See Bausch Health Companies Inc.; *Int'l*, pg. 897
BEIJING BAYI SPACE LCD TECHNOLOGY CO., LTD.; *Int'l*, pg. 946
BEIJING BBMG TIANTAN FURNITURE CO., LTD.—See BBMG Corporation; *Int'l*, pg. 920
BEIJING BDSTAR NAVIGATION CO., LTD.; *Int'l*, pg. 946
BEIJING BEER ASAHI CO., LTD.—See Asahi Group Holdings Ltd.; *Int'l*, pg. 593
BEIJING BEETCH INC.; *Int'l*, pg. 946
BEIJING BEIDA JADE BIRD UNIVERSAL SCI-TECH LIMITED; *Int'l*, pg. 946
BEIJING BEILING SPECIAL AUTOMOBILE CO., LTD.—See Isuzu Motors Limited; *Int'l*, pg. 3825
BEIJING BEILU PHARMACEUTICAL CO., LTD.; *Int'l*, pg. 946
BEIJING BEIMO HIGH-TECH FRICTIONAL MATERIAL CO., LTD.; *Int'l*, pg. 946
BEIJING BEIQI MOULD & PLASTIC TECHNOLOGY CO., LTD.—See Jiangnan Mould & Plastic Technology Co., Ltd.; *Int'l*, pg. 3942
BEIJING BEIREN FUJI PRINTING MACHINERY CO., LTD.—See Beijing Jingcheng Machinery Electric Holding Co., Ltd.; *Int'l*, pg. 953
BEIJING BEIZHONG STEAM TURBINE GENERATOR CO., LTD.—See Beijing Jingcheng Machinery Electric Holding Co., Ltd.; *Int'l*, pg. 953
BEIJING BERNDORF TECHNOLOGY DEVELOPMENT CO., LTD.—See Berndorf AG; *Int'l*, pg. 986
BEIJING BE-WANT FOODS LTD—See Want Want China Holdings Ltd.; *Int'l*, pg. 8342
BEIJING BEWINNER COMMUNICATIONS CO., LTD.; *Int'l*, pg. 946
BEIJING BHD PETROLEUM TECHNOLOGY CO. LTD.—See Recon Technology, Ltd.; *Int'l*, pg. 6238
BEIJING BIG-WANT FOODS LTD—See Want Want China Holdings Ltd.; *Int'l*, pg. 8342
BEIJING BIOSINO-AGIACCU BIOTECHNOLOGY CO., LTD.—See BioSino Bio-technology & Science Inc.; *Int'l*, pg. 1042
BEIJING B. J. ELECTRIC MOTOR CO., LTD.—See Beijing Jingcheng Machinery Electric Holding Co., Ltd.; *Int'l*, pg. 952
BEIJING B.J. ELECTRIC MOTOR CO., LTD.—See Beijing Jingcheng Machinery Electric Holding Co., Ltd.; *Int'l*, pg. 953
BEIJING BOE CHATANI ELECTRONICS CO., LTD.—See BOE Technology Group Co., Ltd.; *Int'l*, pg. 1099
BEIJING BOE DISPLAY TECHNOLOGY CO., LTD.—See BOE Technology Group Co., Ltd.; *Int'l*, pg. 1099
BEIJING BOE ENERGY TECHNOLOGY CO., LTD.—See BOE Technology Group Co., Ltd.; *Int'l*, pg. 1099
BEIJING BOE MARKETING CO., LTD.—See BOE Technology Group Co., Ltd.; *Int'l*, pg. 1099
BEIJING BOE OPTOELECTRONICS TECHNOLOGY CO., LTD.—See BOE Technology Group Co., Ltd.; *Int'l*, pg. 1099
BEIJING BOE REAL ESTATE CO., LTD.—See BOE Technology Group Co., Ltd.; *Int'l*, pg. 1099
BEIJING BOE SENSING TECHNOLOGY CO., LTD.—See BOE Technology Group Co., Ltd.; *Int'l*, pg. 1099
BEIJING BOE SPECIAL DISPLAY TECHNOLOGY CO., LTD.—See BOE Technology Group Co., Ltd.; *Int'l*, pg. 1099
BEIJING BOE VACUUM ELECTRONICS CO., LTD.—See BOE Technology Group Co., Ltd.; *Int'l*, pg. 1099
BEIJING BOE VACUUM TECHNOLOGY CO., LTD.—See BOE Technology Group Co., Ltd.; *Int'l*, pg. 1099
BEIJING BOE VIDEO TECHNOLOGY CO., LTD.—See BOE Technology Group Co., Ltd.; *Int'l*, pg. 1099
BEIJING BOHUI INNOVATION BIOTECHNOLOGY GROUP CO., LTD.; *Int'l*, pg. 946
BEIJING BOHUI SCIENCE & TECHNOLOGY CO., LTD.; *Int'l*, pg. 946

BEIJING BOSSCO ENVIRONMENTAL PROTECTION TECHNOLOGY CO., LTD—See Guangxi Bossco Environmental Protection Technology Co., Ltd.; *Int'l*, pg. 3162
BEIJING BOYU SEMICONDUCTOR VESSEL CRAFT-WORK TECHNOLOGY CO., LTD.—See AXT, Inc.; *U.S. Public*, pg. 256
BEIJING BRAIN CELL SOFTWARE CORPORATION LIMITED—See Fujitsu Limited; *Int'l*, pg. 2833
BEIJING BUILDING MATERIALS IMPORT AND EXPORT CO., LTD.—See BBMG Corporation; *Int'l*, pg. 920
BEIJING BUILDING MATERIALS TESTING ACADEMY CO., LTD.—See BBMG Corporation; *Int'l*, pg. 920
BEIJING CANNY CONSULTING INC.—See Hangzhou Tigermed Consulting Co., Ltd.; *Int'l*, pg. 3251
BEIJING CAPITAL AGRIBUSINESS GROUP CO., LTD.; *Int'l*, pg. 946
BEIJING CAPITAL AIRLINES CO., LTD.—See Hainan Traffic Administration Holding Co., Ltd.; *Int'l*, pg. 3213
BEIJING CAPITAL DEVELOPMENT GROUP CO., LTD.—See Beijing Capital Development Holding Group Co., Ltd; *Int'l*, pg. 947
BEIJING CAPITAL DEVELOPMENT HOLDING GROUP CO., LTD; *Int'l*, pg. 947
BEIJING CAPITAL ECO-ENVIRONMENT PROTECTION GROUP CO., LTD.—See Beijing Capital Group Co., Ltd.; *Int'l*, pg. 947
BEIJING CAPITAL GRAND LIMITED; *Int'l*, pg. 947
BEIJING CAPITAL GROUP CO., LTD.; *Int'l*, pg. 947
BEIJING CAPITAL INTERNATIONAL AIRPORT COMPANY LIMITED; *Int'l*, pg. 947
BEIJING CAPITAL JIAYE PROPERTY SERVICES CO., LIMITED; *Int'l*, pg. 947
BEIJING CAPITAL LAND LTD.; *Int'l*, pg. 947
BEIJING CAPITAL RETAILING GROUP CO., LTD.; *Int'l*, pg. 947
BEIJING CAREER INTERNATIONAL CO., LTD.; *Int'l*, pg. 947
BEIJING CEE TECHNOLOGY CO., LTD.—See Celartem Technology Inc.; *Int'l*, pg. 1391
BEIJING CENTERGATE TECHNOLOGIES (HOLDING) CO., LTD.; *Int'l*, pg. 947
BEIJING CENTURY GSR VENTURES MANAGEMENT CO., LTD.; *Int'l*, pg. 947
BEIJING CENTURY TECHNOLOGY CO., LTD.; *Int'l*, pg. 947
BEIJING CERTIFICATE AUTHORITY CO., LTD.; *Int'l*, pg. 947
BEIJING CHANG CHENG BILFINGER BERGER CONSTRUCTION ENGINEERING CORP. LTD.—See Beijing Construction Engineering (Group) Co., Ltd.; *Int'l*, pg. 948
BEIJING CHANGCHUN AUTOMOTIVE PARTS CO., LTD.—See Jiangsu Changshu Automotive Trim Group Co., Ltd.; *Int'l*, pg. 3945
BEIJING CHANGFENG KEWEI PHOTOELECTRIC CO., LTD.—See Beijing Aerospace Changfeng Co., Ltd.; *Int'l*, pg. 945
BEIJING CHANGJIU LOGISTICS CORP; *Int'l*, pg. 947
BEIJING CHANGYI INFORMATION TECHNOLOGIES CO., LTD.—See Beijing Shiji Information Technology Co., Ltd.; *Int'l*, pg. 956
BEIJING CHANGYUAN LANGHONG TECHNOLOGY CO., LTD.—See Xiangyang Changyuan Donggu Industrial Co., Ltd.; *Int'l*, pg. 8527
BEIJING CHEMSUNNY PROPERTY COMPANY LIMITED—See Sinochem Corporation; *Int'l*, pg. 6949
BEIJING CHIEFTAIN CONTROL ENGINEERING TECHNOLOGY CO., LTD.; *Int'l*, pg. 947
BEIJING CHINASOFT INTERNATIONAL EDUCATION TECHNOLOGY CO., LTD.—See Chinasoft International Ltd.; *Int'l*, pg. 1568
BEIJING CHOSTAR EQUIPMENT ENGINEERING TECHNOLOGY CO., LTD.—See Chori Co., Ltd.; *Int'l*, pg. 1583
BEIJING CHUBB FIRE SECURITY SYSTEMS CO., LIMITED—See Carrier Global Corporation; *U.S. Public*, pg. 440
BEIJING CHUNLIZHENGDA MEDICAL INSTRUMENTS CO., LTD.; *Int'l*, pg. 947
BEIJING CLOUDNET TECHNOLOGY CO., LTD.—See Beijing Watertek Information Technology Co., Ltd.; *Int'l*, pg. 960
BEIJING CM ENVIRONMENT ENGINEERING CORPORATION LIMITED—See Longhua Technology Group Luoyang Co., Ltd.; *Int'l*, pg. 4550
BEIJING C-MER DENNIS LAM EYE HOSPITAL CO., LTD.—See C-Mer Eye Care Holdings Ltd.; *Int'l*, pg. 1239
BEIJING CNG SINGYES GREEN BUILDING TECHNOLOGY CO., LTD.—See China Glass Holdings Limited; *Int'l*, pg. 1504
BEIJING COMENS NEW MATERIALS CO., LTD.; *Int'l*, pg. 948
BEIJING COMPOSITE MATERIAL CO., LTD.—See China National Materials; *Int'l*, pg. 1532
BEIJING COMPUTER TECHNOLOGY CO., LTD.—See Hyosung Corporation; *Int'l*, pg. 3550

BEIJING COMTECH EF DATA EQUIPMENT REPAIR SERVICE, CO., LTD.—See Comtech Telecommunications Corp.; *U.S. Public*, pg. 562
BEIJING CONSEN AUTOMATION CONTROL COMPANY LIMITED—See China Automation Group Limited; *Int'l*, pg. 1483
BEIJING CONST INSTRUMENTS TECHNOLOGY INC.; *Int'l*, pg. 948
BEIJING CONSTRUCTION ENGINEERING (GROUP) CO., LTD.; *Int'l*, pg. 948
BEIJING CONTEC MICROELECTRONICS CORPORATION—See Daifuku Co., Ltd.; *Int'l*, pg. 1924
BEIJING CONTINENT PHARMACEUTICAL CO., LTD.—See GNI Group Ltd.; *Int'l*, pg. 3017
BEIJING CORE SOFTWARE CO., LTD.—See Core Corporation; *Int'l*, pg. 1797
BEIJING COSCO SHIPPING INVESTMENT CO., LTD.—See China COSCO Shipping Corporation Limited; *Int'l*, pg. 1492
BEIJING CREATIVE DISTRIBUTION AUTOMATION CO., LTD.; *Int'l*, pg. 948
BEIJING CSR TIMES LOCOMOTIVE AND ROLLING STOCK MECHANICS CO., LTD.—See CRRC Corporation Limited; *Int'l*, pg. 1858
BEIJING CTJ INFORMATION TECHNO CO., LTD.; *Int'l*, pg. 948
BEIJING CUIWEI TOWER CO.,LTD.; *Int'l*, pg. 948
BEIJING CULTURAL INVESTMENT HOLDINGS CO., LTD.; *Int'l*, pg. 948
BEIJING DABAO COSMETICS CO., LTD.—See Johnson & Johnson; *U.S. Public*, pg. 1194
BEIJING DABEINONG TECHNOLOGY GROUP CO., LTD.; *Int'l*, pg. 948
BEIJING DAEWON ASIA AUTOMOBILE SCIENCE & TECHNOLOGY CO., LTD.—See Daewon Kang Up Co., Ltd.; *Int'l*, pg. 1910
BEIJING DAHAO TECHNOLOGY CORPORATION LIMITED; *Int'l*, pg. 948
BEIJING DAHENG ELECTRIC CO., LTD.—See Daheng New Epoch Technology, Inc.; *Int'l*, pg. 1913
BEIJING DAHENG LASER EQUIPMENT CO., LTD.—See Daheng New Epoch Technology, Inc.; *Int'l*, pg. 1913
BEIJING DAHENG MEDICAL EQUIPMENT CO., LTD.—See Daheng New Epoch Technology, Inc.; *Int'l*, pg. 1913
BEIJING DALONG WEIYE REAL ESTATE DEVELOPMENT CO., LTD.; *Int'l*, pg. 948
BEIJING DANOBAT MACHINERY CO. LTD.—See Mondragon Corporation; *Int'l*, pg. 5028
BEIJING DATA 100 INFORMATION TECHNOLOGY CO., LTD.—See Zhewen Interactive Group Co Ltd; *Int'l*, pg. 8671
BEIJING DATAWAY HORIZON CO., LTD.; *Int'l*, pg. 948
BEIJING DAXING ZHONGFU BEVERAGE CONTAINERS CO. LTD—See Zhuhai Zhongfu Enterprise Co., Ltd.; *Int'l*, pg. 8678
BEIJING DELI SOLAR TECHNOLOGY DEVELOPMENT CO., LTD.—See China Solar & Clean Energy Solutions, Inc.; *Int'l*, pg. 1552
BEIJING DENTSU ADVERTISING CO., LTD.—See Dentsu Group Inc.; *Int'l*, pg. 2035
BEIJING DENTSU ADVERTISING CO., LTD.—See Dentsu Group Inc.; *Int'l*, pg. 2035
BEIJING DENTSU ADVERTISING CO., LTD.—See Dentsu Group Inc.; *Int'l*, pg. 2035
BEIJING DENTSU QINGDAO—See Dentsu Group Inc.; *Int'l*, pg. 2035
BEIJING DESCENTE CO., LTD.—See ITOCHU Corporation; *Int'l*, pg. 3835
BEIJING DIGITAL CHINA LIMITED—See Digital China Holdings Limited; *Int'l*, pg. 2121
BEIJING DIGITAL TELECOM CO., LTD.; *Int'l*, pg. 948
BEIJING DINGHAN TECHNOLOGY GROUP CO., LTD.; *Int'l*, pg. 948
BEIJING DONGJIN SEMICHEM CO., LTD.—See Dongjin Semichem Co., Ltd.; *Int'l*, pg. 2168
BEIJING DOWWAY CULTURAL DEVELOPMENT COMPANY LIMITED—See Dowway Holdings Ltd.; *Int'l*, pg. 2187
BEIJING DT ELECTRONIC TECHNOLOGY CO., LTD.—See Detection Technology Oyj; *Int'l*, pg. 2047
BEIJING DVT TECHNOLOGY CO., LTD.—See Daheng New Epoch Technology, Inc.; *Int'l*, pg. 1913
BEIJING DYNAMIC POWER CO., LTD.; *Int'l*, pg. 948
BEIJING EASPRING MATERIAL TECHNOLOGY CO., LTD.; *Int'l*, pg. 949
BEIJING EAST GATE DEVELOPMENT CO.,LTD—See Silver Grant International Holdings Group Ltd.; *Int'l*, pg. 6923
BEIJING ECOSTAR NANTIAN TECHNOLOGY CO., LTD.—See Yunnan Nantian Electronics Information Co., Ltd.; *Int'l*, pg. 8616
BEIJING EDIMAX SCIENCE & TECHNOLOGY CO., LTD.—See Edimax Technology Co., Ltd.; *Int'l*, pg. 2310
BEIJING EGOVA CO., LTD.; *Int'l*, pg. 949
BEIJING E-HUALU INFORMATION TECHNOLOGY CO., LTD.; *Int'l*, pg. 948
BEIJING ELECTRIC POWER COMPANY—See State Grid Corporation of China; *Int'l*, pg. 7183

COMPANY NAME INDEX

BEIJING ELECTRONIC ZONE HIGH-TECH GROUP CO., LTD.; *Int'l*, pg. 949
BEIJING EMBRACO SNOWFLAKE COMPRESSOR COMPANY LIMITED—See Nidec Corporation; *Int'l*, pg. 5274
BEIJING EMERGING EASTERN AVIATION EQUIPMENT CO., LTD.; *Int'l*, pg. 949
BEIJING ENERGY INTERNATIONAL HOLDING CO., LTD.; *Int'l*, pg. 949
BEIJING ENLIGHT MEDIA CO., LTD.; *Int'l*, pg. 949
BEIJING ENSHU PACKING SERVICE LIMITED COMPANY—See The Sumitomo Warehouse Co. Ltd.; *Int'l*, pg. 7689
BEIJING ENTERPRISES ENVIRONMENT GROUP LIMITED—See Beijing Enterprises Holdings Limited; *Int'l*, pg. 949
BEIJING ENTERPRISES HOLDINGS LIMITED; *Int'l*, pg. 949
BEIJING ENTERPRISES URBAN RESOURCES GROUP LIMITED; *Int'l*, pg. 950
BEIJING ENTERPRISES WATER GROUP LIMITED; *Int'l*, pg. 950
BEIJING ER SHANG-FUKUSHIMA MACHINERY ELECTRIC CO., LTD—See Fukushima Galilei Co. Ltd.; *Int'l*, pg. 2840
BEIJING E-TECHSTAR CO LTD; *Int'l*, pg. 949
BEIJING ETERN ZHIYUAN NETWORK TECHNOLOGY CO., LTD.—See Jiangsu Etern Company Limited; *Int'l*, pg. 3946
BEIJING E-TOWN INTERNATIONAL INVESTMENT & DEVELOPMENT CO., LTD.; *Int'l*, pg. 949
BEIJING FAGOR AUTOMATION EQUIPMENT CO., LTD.—See Mondragon Corporation; *Int'l*, pg. 5028
BEIJING-FANUC MECHATRONICS CO., LTD.—See FANUC Corporation; *Int'l*, pg. 2614
BEIJING FERT TECHNOLOGY CO., LTD.—See PW Medtech Group Limited; *Int'l*, pg. 6126
BEIJING FIDIA MACHINERY & ELECTRONICS CO., LTD.—See FIDIA S.p.A.; *Int'l*, pg. 2654
BEIJING FLINTEC ELECTRONICS AND TECHNOLOGY LTD CO.—See Indutrade AB; *Int'l*, pg. 3678
BEIJING FONGHONG MEDIA LTD.—See Jiangsu Phoenix Publishing & Media Corporation Ltd.; *Int'l*, pg. 3952
BEIJING FOPE JEWELLRY & ARTS, LTD—See Fope O.R.L.; *Int'l*, pg. 2720
BEIJING FOREVER TECHNOLOGY COMPANY LIMITED; *Int'l*, pg. 950
BEIJING FORTUNE DRAEGER SAFETY EQUIPMENT CO., LTD.—See Draegerwerk AG & Co. KGaA; *Int'l*, pg. 2196
BEIJING FRASER SUITES REAL ESTATE MANAGEMENT CO., LTD—See Shanghai Dowell Trading Co. Ltd.; *Int'l*, pg. 6765
BEIJING FRASER SUITES REAL ESTATE MANAGEMENT CO., LTD—See Tishman Speyer Properties LP; *U.S. Private*, pg. 4176
BEIJING FRESENIUS PHARMACEUTICAL CO., LTD.—See Fresenius SE & Co. KGaA; *Int'l*, pg. 2777
BEIJING FUDAN MICROELECTRONICS TECHNOLOGY CO., LTD.—See Shanghai Fudan Microelectronics Group Co., Ltd.; *Int'l*, pg. 6768
BEIJING FUEL TECH ENVIRONMENTAL TECHNOLOGIES CO., LTD.—See Fuel Tech, Inc.; *U.S. Public*, pg. 891
BEIJING FUJITSU SYSTEM ENGINEERING CO., LTD.—See Fujitsu Limited; *Int'l*, pg. 2832
BEIJING FUKUDA DENSHI MEDICAL INSTRUMENTS CO., LTD.—See Fukuda Denshi Co., Ltd.; *Int'l*, pg. 2839
BEIJING FUTONG DONGFANG TECHNOLOGY CO., LTD.—See Futong Technology Development Holdings Limited; *Int'l*, pg. 2852
BEIJING GAINFULL WEALTH INVESTMENT MANAGEMENT CO., LTD.—See Fortune Fountain (Beijing) Holding Group Co., Ltd.; *Int'l*, pg. 2743
BEIJING GALLOPING HORSE FILM & TV PRODUCTION CO., LTD.; *Int'l*, pg. 950
BEIJING GANG YAN DIAMOND PRODUCTS CO., LTD.—See Advanced Technology & Materials Co., Ltd.; *Int'l*, pg. 162
BEIJING GAOCHENG SCIENCE & TECHNOLOGY DEVELOPMENT CO., LTD.—See Beijing E-Hualu Information Technology Co., Ltd.; *Int'l*, pg. 948
BEIJING GAONENG DAHENG ACCELERATOR TECHNOLOGY CO. LTD.—See Daheng New Epoch Technology, Inc.; *Int'l*, pg. 1913
BEIJING GAS BLUE SKY HOLDINGS LIMITED; *Int'l*, pg. 950
BEIJING GDC MEDIA TECHNOLOGIES CO., LTD.—See Global Digital Creations Holdings Limited; *Int'l*, pg. 2994
BEIJING GDF OIL & GAS TECH., INC.—See New Jcm Group Co., Ltd; *Int'l*, pg. 5226
BEIJING GEA ENERGIETECHNIK CO.—See Triton Advisers Limited; *Int'l*, pg. 7930
BEIJING GEHUA CATV NETWORK CO., LTD.; *Int'l*, pg. 950
BEIJING GEHUA CULTURAL DEVELOPMENT GROUP CO., LTD.; *Int'l*, pg. 950

BEIJING GEHUA CULTURE CENTER CO., LTD.—See Beijing Gehua Cultural Development Group Co., Ltd.; *Int'l*, pg. 950
BEIJING GEHUA MEDIA CENTER CO., LTD.—See Beijing Gehua Cultural Development Group Co., Ltd.; *Int'l*, pg. 950
BEIJING GEHUA SCIENCE & TECHNOLOGY CENTER CO., LTD.—See Beijing Gehua Cultural Development Group Co., Ltd.; *Int'l*, pg. 950
BEIJING GEISMAR RAILWAYS EQUIPMENT TRADING CO., LTD.—See Geismar S.A.; *Int'l*, pg. 2912
BEIJING GENETECH PHARMACEUTICAL CO., LIMITED—See Uni-Bio Science Group Ltd; *Int'l*, pg. 8028
BEIJING G.E.O. COFFEE CO., LTD.—See Dynam Japan Holdings, Co., Ltd.; *Int'l*, pg. 2239
BEIJING GEOENVIRON ENGINEERING & TECHNOLOGY, INC.; *Int'l*, pg. 951
BEIJING GLOBAL EXPRESS CO., LTD.—See Mitsubishi Logistics Corporation; *Int'l*, pg. 4962
BEIJING GLOBAL PHARMACEUTICAL RESEARCH CO., LTD.—See EPS Holdings, Inc.; *Int'l*, pg. 2465
BEIJING GLOVIS WAREHOUSING & TRANSPORTATION CO., LTD.—See Hyundai Glovis Co., Ltd.; *Int'l*, pg. 3556
BEIJING GOLDWIN CO., LTD.—See Goldwin, Inc.; *Int'l*, pg. 3035
BEIJING GRAND-CHINA UNIVERSE MEDIA INC.—See Hainan Traffic Administration Holding Co., Ltd.; *Int'l*, pg. 3213
BEIJING GRANT MEMBRANE SEPARATION EQUIPMENT CO., LTD.—See HNAC Technology Co., Ltd.; *Int'l*, pg. 3433
BEIJING GSI HOSIERY CO., LTD.—See GSI Creos Corporation; *Int'l*, pg. 3144
BEIJING GS TECHNOLOGY CO., LTD; *Int'l*, pg. 951
BEIJING GUODU INTERCONNECTION TECHNOLOGY CO., LTD.—See Wutong Holding Group Co., Ltd.; *Int'l*, pg. 8514
BEIJING HAIXIN ENERGY TECHNOLOGY CO., LTD.; *Int'l*, pg. 951
BEIJING HAKUHODO CO., LTD.—See Hakuhodo DY Holdings Incorporated; *Int'l*, pg. 3220
BEIJING HAMAMATSU PHOTON TECHNIQUES INC.—See Hamamatsu Photonics K.K.; *Int'l*, pg. 3235
BEIJING HANBANG TECHNOLOGY CORP.; *Int'l*, pg. 951
BEIJING HANDRUN TECHNOLOGY CO., LTD.—See Beijing Watertek Information Technology Co., Ltd.; *Int'l*, pg. 960
BEIJING HANJIAN HESHAN PIPELINE CO.,LTD.; *Int'l*, pg. 951
BEIJING HANJIAN HESHAN TECHNOLOGY CO., LTD.—See Beijing Hanjian Heshan Pipeline Co.,LTD.; *Int'l*, pg. 951
BEIJING HANMI PHARMACEUTICAL CO., LTD.—See Hanmi Pharmaceutical Co., Ltd.; *Int'l*, pg. 3256
BEIJING HANYI INNOVATION TECHNOLOGY CO., LTD.; *Int'l*, pg. 951
BEIJING HAOHUA ENERGY RESOURCE CO., LTD.; *Int'l*, pg. 951
BEIJING HARMOFINERY TECHNOLOGY CO., LTD.—See Advanced Technology & Materials Co., Ltd.; *Int'l*, pg. 162
BEIJING HEALTH (HOLDINGS) LIMITED; *Int'l*, pg. 951
BEIJING HECHENG R&A VEHICLE PARTS CO., LTD—See Hwaseung Industries Co., Ltd.; *Int'l*, pg. 3542
BEIJING HEIDRICK & STRUGGLES INTERNATIONAL MANAGEMENT CONSULTING COMPANY LIMITED—See Heidrick & Struggles International, Inc.; *U.S. Public*, pg. 1022
BEIJING HENGTAI HENGZHONG INFORMATION SERVICE CO., LTD.—See HengTai Securities CO., LTD; *Int'l*, pg. 3347
BEIJING HENGTAI HONGZE INVESTMENT CO., LTD.—See HengTai Securities CO., LTD; *Int'l*, pg. 3347
BEIJING HENGYU DATACOM AVIATION EQUIPMENT CO., LTD.; *Int'l*, pg. 951
BEIJING HEZONG SCIENCE & TECHNOLOGY CO., LTD.; *Int'l*, pg. 951
BEIJING HIGHLANDER DIGITAL TECHNOLOGY CO., LTD.; *Int'l*, pg. 951
BEIJING HILL CONSTRUCTION CONSULTING CO., LTD.—See Global Infrastructure Solutions, Inc.; *U.S. Private*, pg. 1715
BEIJING HITACHI CONTROL SYSTEMS CO., LTD.—See Hitachi, Ltd.; *Int'l*, pg. 3412
BEIJING HITACHI HUASUN INFORMATION SYSTEMS CO., LTD.—See Hitachi, Ltd.; *Int'l*, pg. 3412
BEIJING HI-VAC ENVIRONMENTAL PROTECTION TECHNOLOGY CO., LTD.—See Hi-Vac Corporation; *U.S. Private*, pg. 1932
BEIJING/H-LINE OGILVY COMMUNICATIONS CO. LTD.—See WPP plc; *Int'l*, pg. 8490
BEIJING HOMYEAR CAPITAL HOLDINGS CO., LTD.; *Int'l*, pg. 951
BEIJING HONGDA NISSIN ELECTRIC CO., LTD.—See Sumitomo Electric Industries, Ltd.; *Int'l*, pg. 7278

BEIJING HONGFA ELECTROACOUSTIC RELAY CO., LTD.—See Hongfa Technology Co Ltd; *Int'l*, pg. 3470
BEIJING HONGGAO CREATIVE CONSTRUCTION DESIGN CO., LTD.; *Int'l*, pg. 951
BEIJING HORIBA METRON INSTRUMENTS CO., LTD.—See HORIBA Ltd; *Int'l*, pg. 3475
BEIJING HORMEL FOODS CO. LTD.—See Hormel Foods Corporation; *U.S. Public*, pg. 1053
BEIJING HOTGEN BIOTECH CO., LTD.; *Int'l*, pg. 951
BEIJING HUAAN MAGNECH BIO-TECH CO., LTD.—See Revvity, Inc.; *U.S. Public*, pg. 1793
BEIJING HUADE HYDRAULIC INDUSTRIAL GROUP CO., LTD.—See Beijing Jingcheng Machinery Electric Holding Co., Ltd.; *Int'l*, pg. 953
BEIJING HUAFENG ELECTRONIC EQUIPMENT CO., LTD.—See Beijing Huafeng Test & Control Technology Co., Ltd.; *Int'l*, pg. 951
BEIJING HUAFENG TEST & CONTROL TECHNOLOGY CO., LTD.; *Int'l*, pg. 951
BEIJING HUALIAN DEPARTMENT STORE CO., LTD.; *Int'l*, pg. 952
BEIJING HUALIAN HYPERMARKET CO., LTD.; *Int'l*, pg. 952
BEIJING HUARU TECHNOLOGY CO., LTD.; *Int'l*, pg. 952
BEIJING HUASUITONG BORING EQUIPMENT CO., LTD.—See JA Solar Technology Co., Ltd.; *Int'l*, pg. 3859
BEIJING HUAYUAN TAIMENG ENERGY-SAVING EQUIPMENT CO., LTD.—See Moon Environment Technology Co., Ltd.; *Int'l*, pg. 5038
BEIJING HUIBAOHANG AUTO SALES & SERVICES CO., LTD.—See China MeiDong Auto Holdings Limited; *Int'l*, pg. 1519
BEIJING HUIHENG ENVIRONMENTAL ENGINEERING CO., LTD.—See WELLE Environmental Group Co., Ltd.; *Int'l*, pg. 8374
BEIJING HUIZUTONG INVESTMENT CONSULTING CO., LTD.—See Zhewen Interactive Group Co Ltd; *Int'l*, pg. 8671
BEIJING HWASHIN AUTOMOBILE PARTS CO., LTD.—See Hwashin Co., Ltd.; *Int'l*, pg. 3543
BEIJING HYF SOFTWARE CO., LTD—See Antenna House, Inc.; *Int'l*, pg. 482
BEIJING HYOSUNG CONTAINER CO., LTD.—See Hyosung Corporation; *Int'l*, pg. 3550
BEIJING HYUNDAI MOBIS AUTOMOTIVE PARTS CO., LTD.—See Hyundai MOBIS Co., Ltd.; *Int'l*, pg. 3558
BEIJING IDEXX LABORATORIES CO. LIMITED—See IDEXX Laboratories, Inc.; *U.S. Public*, pg. 1092
BEIJING IFORCE INTERACTIVE CO., LTD.—See Zhewen Interactive Group Co Ltd; *Int'l*, pg. 8671
BEIJING INFOREFINER TECHNOLOGY CO., LTD.—See PCI Technology Group Co., Ltd; *Int'l*, pg. 5768
BEIJING INFOSEC TECHNOLOGIES CO., LTD.; *Int'l*, pg. 952
BEIJING INFRASTRUCTURE INVESTMENT CO., LTD.; *Int'l*, pg. 952
BEIJING INHAND NETWORKS TECHNOLOGY CO., LTD.; *Int'l*, pg. 952
BEIJING INLAND PORT INTERNATIONAL LOGISTICS CO. LTD.—See Beijing Properties (Holdings) Limited; *Int'l*, pg. 955
BEIJING INTERACT TECHNOLOGY CO., LTD.; *Int'l*, pg. 952
BEIJING INTERNATIONAL CLUB CO. LTD.—See Marriott International, Inc.; *U.S. Public*, pg. 1370
BEIJING IPSOS MARKET CONSULTING LTD.—See Ipsos S.A.; *Int'l*, pg. 3798
BEIJING IRTOUCHSYSTEMS CO., LTD.—See Sansheng Intellectual Education Technology Co., Ltd.; *Int'l*, pg. 6556
BEIJING ITOCHU-HUATANG COMPREHENSIVE PROCESSING CO., LTD.—See ITOCHU Corporation; *Int'l*, pg. 3834
BEIJING JCC MARKETING & SALES COMPANY LIMITED—See Jiangxi Copper Company Limited; *Int'l*, pg. 3958
BEIJING JDA TECHNOLOGIES COMPANY LTD.—See New Mountain Capital, LLC; *U.S. Private*, pg. 2902
BEIJING JETSEN TECHNOLOGY CO., LTD.; *Int'l*, pg. 952
BEIJING JIA AO REAL ESTATE DEVELOPMENT CO. LTD.—See Kerry Group Limited; *Int'l*, pg. 4137
BEIJING JIAMAN DRESS CO., LTD.; *Int'l*, pg. 952
BEIJING JIAODA SIGNAL TECHNOLOGY CO., LTD.; *Int'l*, pg. 952
BEIJING JIAXUN FEIHONG ELECTRICAL CO., LTD.; *Int'l*, pg. 952
BEIJING JIEYUAN NEW ENERGY INVESTMENT CO., LTD.—See Mingyang Smart Energy Group Ltd.; *Int'l*, pg. 4909
BEIJING JINGCHENG ENVIRONMENTAL PROTECTION DEVELOPMENT CO., LTD.—See Beijing Jingcheng Machinery Electric Holding Co., Ltd.; *Int'l*, pg. 953
BEIJING JINGCHENG HEAVY INDUSTRY CO., LTD.—See Beijing Jingcheng Machinery Electric Holding Co., Ltd.; *Int'l*, pg. 953
BEIJING JINGCHENG MACHINERY ELECTRIC CO., LTD.; *Int'l*, pg. 952

BEIJING JINGCHENG MACHINERY ELECTRIC HOLDING CO., LTD. CORPORATE AFFILIATIONS

BEIJING JINGCHENG MACHINERY ELECTRIC HOLDING CO., LTD.; *Int'l*, pg. 952
BEIJING JINGCHENG NEW ENERGY CO., LTD.—See Beijing Jingcheng Machinery Electric Holding Co., Ltd.; *Int'l*, pg. 953
BEIJING JINGCHE SHUANGYANG TRACTION SYSTEM CO., LTD.—See TOYO DENKI SEIZO K.K.; *Int'l*, pg. 7852
BEIJING JINGDONG CENTURY TRADE CO., LTD.—See JD.com, Inc.; *Int'l*, pg. 3924
BEIJING JINGDUN SECOM ELECTRONIC SECURITY CO., LTD.—See SECOM Co., Ltd.; *Int'l*, pg. 6670
BEIJING JINGGHENG COMPRESSOR CO., LTD—See Beijing Jingcheng Machinery Electric Co., Ltd.; *Int'l*, pg. 952
BEIJING JINGKAI INFORMATION STORAGE TECHNOLOGY CO., LTD.—See Amethystum Storage Technology Co., Ltd.; *Int'l*, pg. 424
BEIJING JINGKELONG COMPANY LIMITED; *Int'l*, pg. 953
BEIJING JINGNENG CLEAN ENERGY CO., LTD.; *Int'l*, pg. 953
BEIJING JINGNENG POWER CO., LTD.; *Int'l*, pg. 953
BEIJING JINGNENG THERMAL CO., LTD; *Int'l*, pg. 953
BEIJING JINGXI CULTURE & TOURISM CO., LTD.; *Int'l*, pg. 953
BEIJING JINGYEDA TECHNOLOGY CO., LTD.; *Int'l*, pg. 953
BEIJING JINGYUNTONG TECHNOLOGY CO., LTD.; *Int'l*, pg. 953
BEIJING JIN JIAN TAXI SERVICES CO., LTD.—See ComfortDelGro Corporation Limited; *Int'l*, pg. 1712
BEIJING JIUAN CONSTRUCTION INVESTMENT GROUP CO., LTD.—See Beijing Origin Water Technology Co., Ltd.; *Int'l*, pg. 955
BEIJING JOIN-CHEER SOFTWARE CO., LTD.; *Int'l*, pg. 953
BEIJING JOYFUL JOURNEY TECHNOLOGIES CO., LTD.—See Hainan Traffic Administration Holding Co., Ltd.; *Int'l*, pg. 3213
BEIJING JUYUAN HANYANG HEAT EXCHANGE EQUIPMENT CO., LTD.—See THT Heat Transfer Technology, Inc.; *Int'l*, pg. 7721
BEIJING JWGB SCI. & TECH. CO., LTD.; *Int'l*, pg. 953
BEIJING KAWIN TECHNOLOGY SHARE-HOLDING CO., LTD.; *Int'l*, pg. 953
BEIJING KEHUA HENGSHENG TECHNOLOGY CO., LTD.—See Kehua Data Co., Ltd.; *Int'l*, pg. 4116
BEIJING KER'KANG INSTRUMENT LIMITED COMPANY—See Halma plc; *Int'l*, pg. 3230
BEIJING KINGFORE HV & ENERGY CONSERVATION TECHNOLOGY CO., LTD.; *Int'l*, pg. 954
BEIJING KINGSLEY PROPERTY DEVELOPMENT CO LTD—See Keppel Corporation Limited; *Int'l*, pg. 4130
BEIJING KINGSOFT OFFICE SOFTWARE, INC.; *Int'l*, pg. 954
BEIJING KONRUNS PHARMACEUTICAL CO., LTD.; *Int'l*, pg. 954
BEIJING KOSTER INTERNATIONAL CHEMICAL INDUSTRY CO. LTD.—See Koster Bauchemie AG; *Int'l*, pg. 4291
BEIJING KWS AGRICULTURE TECHNOLOGY CO., LTD.—See KWS SAAT SE & Co. KGaA; *Int'l*, pg. 4352
BEIJING KYUNGDONG NAVIEN HEAT ENERGY EQUIPMENT CO., LTD—See KyungDong Navien Co., Ltd.; *Int'l*, pg. 4367
BEIJING LABTECH INSTRUMENTS CO., LTD.; *Int'l*, pg. 954
BEIJING LANDAUER RADIATION MONITORING TECHNOLOGY CO., LTD.—See Fortive Corporation; *U.S. Public*, pg. 871
BEIJING LANDI RENZO AUTOGAS SYSTEM CO. LTD.—See Landi Renzo S.p.a.; *Int'l*, pg. 4406
BEIJING LEADER & HARVEST ELECTRIC TECHNOLOGIES CO. LTD—See Schneider Electric SE; *Int'l*, pg. 6626
BEIJING LEADMAN BIOCHEMISTRY CO., LTD.; *Int'l*, pg. 954
BEIJING LIANYI HETONG SCIENCE AND TECHNOLOGY CO. LTD.—See Xiamen Anne Corporation Limited; *Int'l*, pg. 8523
BEIJING LI CONTEMPORARY AMPEREX TECHNOLOGY LIMITED—See Contemporary Amperex Technology Co., Ltd.; *Int'l*, pg. 1779
BEIJING LIER HIGH-TEMPERATURE MATERIALS CO., LTD.; *Int'l*, pg. 954
BEIJING LINKHEAD TECHNOLOGIES CO., LTD.—See PacificNet Inc.; *Int'l*, pg. 5692
BEIJING LIONBRIDGE GLOBAL SOLUTIONS TECHNOLOGIES, INC.—See H.I.G. Capital, LLC; *U.S. Private*, pg. 1830
BEIJING LIULIHE CEMENT CO., LTD—See BBMG Corporation; *Int'l*, pg. 920
BEIJING LIVEN TECHNOLOGY CO., LTD.; *Int'l*, pg. 954
BEIJING LOCK&LOCK TRADING CO., LTD.—See Lock&Lock Co., Ltd.; *Int'l*, pg. 4540
BEIJING LONGRUAN TECHNOLOGIES, INC.; *Int'l*, pg. 954

BEIJING LONGYUAN HENGXING URBAN & RURAL PLANNING & DESIGN CO., LTD.—See Long Yuan Construction Group Co., Ltd; *Int'l*, pg. 4549
BEIJING LUFTHANSA CENTER CO. LTD.—See Korea Development Bank; *Int'l*, pg. 4282
BEIJING LURGI ENGINEERING CONSULTING CO. LTD.—See L'Air Liquide S.A.; *Int'l*, pg. 4375
BEIJING LUZHU BIOTECHNOLOGY CO., LTD.; *Int'l*, pg. 954
BEIJING MAPPS-SERI TECHNOLOGY COMPANY LTD.—See L3Harris Technologies, Inc.; *U.S. Public*, pg. 1281
BEIJING MASTER SYSTEMS ENGINEERING CO., LTD—See Johnson Controls International plc; *Int'l*, pg. 3986
BEIJING MEDIA CORPORATION LIMITED; *Int'l*, pg. 954
BEIJING MEDPACE MEDICAL SCIENCE & TECHNOLOGY LTD.—See Cinven Limited; *Int'l*, pg. 1612
BEIJING MED-PHARM CO., LTD.—See Sanofi; *Int'l*, pg. 6547
BEIJING MEHECO BAITAI PHARMACEUTICAL TECHNOLOGY CO., LTD.—See China Meheco Group Co., Ltd.; *Int'l*, pg. 1518
BEIJING MEHECO YONSTRON PHARMACEUTICAL CO., LTD.—See China Meheco Group Co., Ltd.; *Int'l*, pg. 1518
BEIJING MEIZHENG BIO-TECH CO., LTD.—See Revvity, Inc.; *U.S. Public*, pg. 1793
BEIJING MERLIN GREAT WALL COMPUTER ROOM EQUIPMENT & ENGINEERING CO. LTD—See Schneider Electric SE; *Int'l*, pg. 6626
BEIJING MICROVISION TECHNOLOGY CO., LTD.—See Beijing Tongtech Company Limited; *Int'l*, pg. 959
BEIJING MIDEA COMMERCIAL AIR-CONDITIONER SALES CO., LTD—See Midea Group Co., Ltd.; *Int'l*, pg. 4884
BEIJING MINGSHU DATA TECHNOLOGY CO., LTD.—See Long Yuan Construction Group Co., Ltd; *Int'l*, pg. 4549
BEIJING MINHAI BIOTECHNOLOGY CO., LTD.—See Shenzhen Kangtai Biological Products Co., Ltd.; *Int'l*, pg. 6815
BEIJING MOBIS TRANSMISSION CO., LTD.—See Hyundai Motor Company; *Int'l*, pg. 3558
BEIJING MONTAGNE MEDICAL DEVICE CO., LTD.—See Zimmer Biomet Holdings, Inc.; *U.S. Public*, pg. 2405
BEIJING MOTONIC CORPORATION—See MOTONIC CORPORATION; *Int'l*, pg. 5053
BEIJING NAIPU INTERNATIONAL TRADE CO., LTD.—See Naipu Mining Machinery Co., Ltd.; *Int'l*, pg. 5131
BEIJING NANKOU SKF RAILWAY BEARING CO. LTD.—See SKF AB; *Int'l*, pg. 6982
BEIJING NANTIAN INFORMATION ENGINEERING CO., LTD.—See Yunnan Nantian Electronics Information Co., Ltd.; *Int'l*, pg. 8616
BEIJING NANTIAN SOFTWARE CO., LTD.—See Yunnan Nantian Electronics Information Co., Ltd.; *Int'l*, pg. 8616
BEIJING NANTIAN ZHILIAN INFORMATION TECHNOLOGY CO., LTD.—See Yunnan Nantian Electronics Information Co., Ltd.; *Int'l*, pg. 8616
BEIJING NATIONAL RAILWAY RESEARCH & DESIGN INSTITUTE OF SIGNAL & COMMUNICATION CO., LTD.—See China Railway Signal & Communication Corporation Ltd.; *Int'l*, pg. 1544
BEIJING NAURA MICROELECTRONICS EQUIPMENT CO., LTD.—See NAURA Technology Group Co., Ltd.; *Int'l*, pg. 5172
BEIJING NAURA NEW ENERGY TECHNOLOGY CO., LTD.—See NAURA Technology Group Co., Ltd.; *Int'l*, pg. 5172
BEIJING NAURA VACUUM TECHNOLOGY CO., LTD.—See NAURA Technology Group Co., Ltd.; *Int'l*, pg. 5172
BEIJING NAVIGANT CONSULTING CO., LTD.—See Bain Capital, LP; *U.S. Private*, pg. 432
BEIJING NAVISTAR CLOUD SCIENCE & TECHNOLOGY CO., LTD.—See Beijing Watertek Information Technology Co., Ltd.; *Int'l*, pg. 960
BEIJING NETEASE YOUDAO COMPUTER SYSTEM CO., LTD.—See NetEase, Inc.; *Int'l*, pg. 5214
BEIJING NET-INFINITY TECHNOLOGY DEVELOPMENT CO. LTD.—See CK Hutchison Holdings Limited; *Int'l*, pg. 1636
BEIJING NEW BIOLINK TECHNOLOGY DEVELOPMENT CO., LTD.—See Focused Photonics (Hangzhou), Inc.; *Int'l*, pg. 2720
BEIJING NEW BUILDING MATERIALS PUBLIC LIMITED COMPANY—See China National Building Material Group Co., Ltd.; *Int'l*, pg. 1525
BEIJING NEW CHINA FUSHI ASSET MANAGEMENT CO., LTD.—See HengTai Securities CO., LTD; *Int'l*, pg. 3347
BEIJING NEW MEDIA INFORMATION TECHNOLOGY CO. LTD.—See SINA Corporation; *Int'l*, pg. 6935
BEIJING NEWPORT SPECTRA-PHYSICS TECHNOLOGIES CO., LTD.—See MKS Instruments, Inc.; *U.S. Public*, pg. 1453
BEIJING NEW SPACE TECHNOLOGY CO., LTD.; *Int'l*, pg. 954

BEIJING NEWTOUCH JUNYANG INFORMATION TECHNOLOGY CO., LTD.—See Shanghai Newtouch Software Co., Ltd.; *Int'l*, pg. 6776
BEIJING NEW UNIVERSAL ENVIRONMENTAL ENGINEERING & TECHNOLOGY CO., LTD.—See Beijing New Universal Science and Technology Co., Ltd.; *Int'l*, pg. 954
BEIJING NEW UNIVERSAL SCIENCE AND TECHNOLOGY CO., LTD.; *Int'l*, pg. 954
BEIJING NEXGEMO TECHNOLOGY CO., LTD.—See NEXCOM International Co., Ltd.; *Int'l*, pg. 5242
BEIJING NIFCO CO., LTD.—See Nifco Inc.; *Int'l*, pg. 5281
BEIJING NIKON OPHTHALMIC PRODUCTS CO., LTD.—See Nikon Corporation; *Int'l*, pg. 5292
BEIJING NIPPO PRINTING CO., LTD.—See TOPPAN Holdings Inc.; *Int'l*, pg. 7816
BEIJING NO. 1 MACHINE TOOL PLANT—See Beijing Jingcheng Machinery Electric Holding Co., Ltd.; *Int'l*, pg. 953
BEIJING NO.2 MACHINE TOOL WORKS CO., LTD.—See Beijing Jingcheng Machinery Electric Holding Co., Ltd.; *Int'l*, pg. 953
BEIJING NOKIA HANG XING TELECOMMUNICATIONS SYSTEMS CO. LTD—See Nokia Corporation; *Int'l*, pg. 5404
BEIJING NORTHERN CHINA FULL TIN BEVERAGE CO., LTD.—See Zhuhai Zhongfu Enterprise Co., Ltd.; *Int'l*, pg. 8678
BEIJING NORTH STAR COMPANY LIMITED; *Int'l*, pg. 954
BEIJING NORTH VEHICLE GROUP CORPORATION—See China North Industries Group Corporation; *Int'l*, pg. 1535
BEIJING NOVARTIS PHARMA CO., LTD.—See Novartis AG; *Int'l*, pg. 5459
BEIJING NOVEL ENVIRONMENTAL PROTECTION CO LIMITED—See Dongjiang Environmental Company Limited; *Int'l*, pg. 2168
BEIJING NTN-SEOHAN DRIVESHAFT CO., LTD.—See NTN Corporation; *Int'l*, pg. 5481
BEIJING OCEAN HOTEL CO., LTD.—See China COSCO Shipping Corporation Limited; *Int'l*, pg. 1492
BEIJING OMG M2U ADVERTISING COMPANY LIMITED—See Media Chinese International Limited; *Int'l*, pg. 4770
BEIJING ORBIS ELECTRONICS CO., LTD.—See Orbis Systems Oy; *Int'l*, pg. 5614
BEIJING ORG TECHNOLOGY CO., LTD.—See ORG Technology Co., Ltd.; *Int'l*, pg. 5617
BEIJING ORIENTAL JICHENG CO., LTD; *Int'l*, pg. 954
BEIJING ORIENTAL YUHONG WATERPROOF TECHNOLOGY CO., LTD.; *Int'l*, pg. 955
BEIJING ORIENT LANDSCAPE & ENVIRONMENT CO., LTD.; *Int'l*, pg. 954
BEIJING ORIENT NATIONAL COMMUNICATION SCIENCE & TECHNOLOGY CO., LTD.; *Int'l*, pg. 954
BEIJING ORIGIN SEED LIMITED—See Origin Agritech Limited; *Int'l*, pg. 5628
BEIJING ORIGIN STATE HARVEST BIOTECHNOLOGY LIMITED—See Origin Agritech Limited; *Int'l*, pg. 5628
BEIJING ORIGINWATER MEMBRANE TECHNOLOGY CO., LTD.—See Beijing Origin Water Technology Co., Ltd.; *Int'l*, pg. 955
BEIJING ORIGINWATER PURETECH CO., LTD.—See Beijing Origin Water Technology Co., Ltd.; *Int'l*, pg. 955
BEIJING ORIGIN WATER TECHNOLOGY CO., LTD.; *Int'l*, pg. 955
BEIJING OUTSELL HEALTH PRODUCT DEVELOPMENT CO., LTD.; *Int'l*, pg. 955
BEIJING PACIFIC LOGISTICS CO., LTD.—See ITOCHU Corporation; *Int'l*, pg. 3834
BEIJING PANDA FIREWORKS CO., LTD.—See Panda Financial Holding Corp., Ltd.; *Int'l*, pg. 5726
BEIJING PERFECT WORLD GAME SOFTWARE CO., LTD.—See Perfect World Co., Ltd.; *Int'l*, pg. 5799
BEIJING PETROCHEMICAL ENGINEERING CO., LTD.—See Shaanxi Yanchang Petroleum Group Co., Ltd.; *Int'l*, pg. 6747
BEIJING PHADIA DIAGNOSTICS CO LTD—See Thermo Fisher Scientific Inc.; *U.S. Public*, pg. 2145
BEIJING PHILISENSE TECHNOLOGY CO., LTD.; *Int'l*, pg. 955
BEIJING PICO EXHIBITION SERVICES CO., LTD.—See Pico Far East Holdings Limited; *Int'l*, pg. 5860
BEIJING PIZZA HUT CO., LTD.—See Yum China Holdings, Inc.; *U.S. Public*, pg. 2399
BEIJING PLANTYNET CO., LTD.—See Plantynet Co. Ltd.; *Int'l*, pg. 5891
BEIJING PLP CONDUCTOR LINE PRODUCTS, LTD.—See Preformed Line Products Company; *U.S. Public*, pg. 1714
BEIJING POLY ART CENTER CORPORATION LIMITED—See Poly Culture Group Corporation Limited; *Int'l*, pg. 5913
BEIJING POLY ART INVESTMENT MANAGEMENT CORPORATION LIMITED—See Poly Culture Group Corporation Limited; *Int'l*, pg. 5913
BEIJING POLY ARTIST MANAGEMENT CO., LTD.—See China Poly Group Corporation; *Int'l*, pg. 1540

COMPANY NAME INDEX

BEIJING POLY FORBIDDEN CITY THEATRE MANAGEMENT CO., LTD.—See China Poly Group Corporation; *Int'l*, pg. 1540
BEIJING POLY INTERNATIONAL AUCTION CORPORATION LIMITED—See Poly Culture Group Corporation Limited; *Int'l*, pg. 5913
BEIJING POLY PERFORMING ARTS CORPORATION LIMITED—See Poly Culture Group Corporation Limited; *Int'l*, pg. 5913
BEIJING POLYSTAR DIGIDISC CO., LTD.—See China Poly Group Corporation; *Int'l*, pg. 1541
BEIJING POLY THEATRE MANAGEMENT CORPORATION LIMITED—See Poly Culture Group Corporation Limited; *Int'l*, pg. 5913
BEIJING POWER EQUIPMENT GROUP—See State Grid Corporation of China; *Int'l*, pg. 7183
BEIJING PRAXAIR HUASHI CARBON DIOXIDE CO., LTD.—See Linde plc; *Int'l*, pg. 4508
BEIJING PRAXAIR, INC.—See Linde plc; *Int'l*, pg. 4508
BEIJING PRECISE INSTRUMENTS CO., LTD.—See China BPIC Surveying Instruments AG; *Int'l*, pg. 1487
BEIJING PROPERTIES (HOLDINGS) LIMITED; *Int'l*, pg. 955
BEIJING QIAN HU AQUARIUM & PETS CO., LTD.—See Qian Hu Corporation Limited; *Int'l*, pg. 6140
BEIJING QIANJING LANDSCAPE CO., LTD.; *Int'l*, pg. 955
BEIJING QUANSHI WORLD ONLINE NETWORK INFORMATION CO., LTD.; *Int'l*, pg. 955
BEIJING RAILWAY SIGNAL CO., LTD.—See China National Railway Signal & Communication Corp.; *Int'l*, pg. 1534
BEIJING RHODIA EASTERN CHEMICAL CO., LTD—See Solvay S.A.; *Int'l*, pg. 7077
BEIJING RI JIA POWER SUPPLY CO., LTD.—See GS Yuasa Corporation; *Int'l*, pg. 3143
BEIJING RINGIER INTERNATIONAL ADVERTISING CO. LTD.—See Ringier Holding AG; *Int'l*, pg. 6343
BEIJING RISECOMM COMMUNICATION TECHNOLOGY COMPANY LIMITED—See Risecomm Group Holdings Limited; *Int'l*, pg. 6349
BEIJING ROBOROCK TECHNOLOGY CO., LTD.; *Int'l*, pg. 955
BEIJING RONBAY HOLDING INVESTMENT CO., LTD.—See Ningbo Ronbay New Energy Technology Co., Ltd.; *Int'l*, pg. 5305
BEIJING ROSEMOUNT FAR EAST INSTRUMENT CO., LTD.—See Emerson Electric Co.; *U.S. Public*, pg. 742
BEIJING RWS SCIENCE & TECHNOLOGY INFORMATION CONSULTANCY CO. LTD.—See RWS Holdings plc; *Int'l*, pg. 6436
BEIJING SAILHERO ZHONGRUN SCIENCE AND TECHNOLOGY CO., LTD.—See Hebei Sailhero Environmental Protection High-Tech Co., Ltd.; *Int'l*, pg. 3306
BEIJING SANCHONG MIRRORS CO., LTD—See BBMG Corporation; *Int'l*, pg. 921
BEIJING SANFO OUTDOOR PRODUCTS CO., LTD; *Int'l*, pg. 955
BEIJING SANKUANGTONG TECHNOLOGY CO., LTD.—See Shandong Mining Machinery Group Co., Ltd.; *Int'l*, pg. 6756
BEIJING SANKYU LOGISTICS CO., LTD—See Sankyu, Inc.; *Int'l*, pg. 6543
BEIJING SANXIN REFRIGERATION LOGISTICS CO., LTD.—See Nissin Corporation; *Int'l*, pg. 5375
BEIJING SANY HEAVY MACHINERY CO., LTD.—See Sany Group Co., Ltd.; *Int'l*, pg. 6562
BEIJING SANYUAN FOODS CO., LTD.—See Beijing Capital Agribusiness Group Co., Ltd.; *Int'l*, pg. 946
BEIJING SCIENCE SUN PHARMACEUTICAL CO., LTD.; *Int'l*, pg. 955
BEIJING SCITOP BIO-TECH CO., LTD.; *Int'l*, pg. 955
BEIJING SDL TECHNOLOGY CO., LTD.; *Int'l*, pg. 955
BEIJING SEEYON INTERNET SOFTWARE CORP.; *Int'l*, pg. 955
BEIJING SEIKO ELECTRIC GROUP CO., LTD.—See Seiko Electric Co., Ltd.; *Int'l*, pg. 6686
BEIJING SEJONG AUTO PARTS CO., LTD.—See SJG Sejong Co., Ltd.; *Int'l*, pg. 6969
BEIJING SENSETIME TECHNOLOGY DEVELOPMENT CO., LTD.—See SenseTime Group Inc.; *Int'l*, pg. 6713
BEIJING SEPR REFRACORIES CO., LTD.—See Compagnie de Saint-Gobain SA; *Int'l*, pg. 1722
BEIJING SEVENSTAR ELECTRONICS TECHNOLOGY CO., LTD.—See NAURA Technology Group Co., Ltd.; *Int'l*, pg. 5172
BEIJING SEVENSTAR FLOW CO., LTD.—See NAURA Technology Group Co., Ltd.; *Int'l*, pg. 5172
BEIJING-SHANGHAI HIGH SPEED RAILWAY CO., LTD.; *Int'l*, pg. 961
BEIJING SHENGTONG PRINTING CO., LTD.; *Int'l*, pg. 955
BEIJING SHIJI INFORMATION TECHNOLOGY CO., LTD.; *Int'l*, pg. 956
BEIJING SHIJI KUNLUN SOFTWARE CO., LTD.—See Beijing Shiji Information Technology Co., Ltd.; *Int'l*, pg. 956
BEIJING SHIMADZU MEDICAL EQUIPMENT CO., LTD.—See Shimadzu Corporation; *Int'l*, pg. 6831
BEIJING SHIONOGI PHARMACEUTICAL TECHNOLOGY LIMITED—See Shionogi & Co., Ltd.; *Int'l*, pg. 6851
BEIJING SHOUGANG CO., LTD.; *Int'l*, pg. 956
BEIJING SHUNXIN AGRICULTURE CO., LTD.; *Int'l*, pg. 956
BEIJING SHUZHI TECHNOLOGY CO., LTD.; *Int'l*, pg. 957
BEIJING SIEMENS CERBERUS ELECTRONICS LTD.—See Siemens Aktiengesellschaft; *Int'l*, pg. 6886
BEIJING SIFANG AUTOMATION CO., LTD.; *Int'l*, pg. 957
BEIJING SIFANG TONGXING MECHANICAL TECHNOLOGY DEVELOPMENT CO., LTD.—See Beijing New Universal Science and Technology Co., Ltd.; *Int'l*, pg. 954
BEIJING SINBON ELECTRONICS CO., LTD.—See SINBON Electronics Co., Ltd.; *Int'l*, pg. 6936
BEIJING SINNET TECHNOLOGY COMPANY LIMITED; *Int'l*, pg. 957
BEIJING SINODATA TECH CO., LTD.; *Int'l*, pg. 957
BEIJING SINOHYTEC CO., LTD.; *Int'l*, pg. 957
BEIJING SL PHARMACEUTICAL CO., LTD.; *Int'l*, pg. 957
BEIJING SNLN HP NEW SYNTC FBR SER CO LTD; *Int'l*, pg. 957
BEIJING SOGOU TECHNOLOGY DEVELOPMENT CO., LTD.—See SOHU.com Ltd.; *Int'l*, pg. 7060
BEIJING SOHU NEW ERA INFORMATION TECHNOLOGY CO., LTD.—See SOHU.com Ltd.; *Int'l*, pg. 7060
BEIJING SOJO ELECTRIC COMPANY LIMITED; *Int'l*, pg. 957
BEIJING SPC ENVIRONMENT PROTECTION TECH CO., LTD.; *Int'l*, pg. 957
BEIJING SPORTS & ENTERTAINMENT INDUSTRY GROUP LIMITED; *Int'l*, pg. 957
BEIJING SPREADTRUM HIGH-TECH COMMUNICATIONS TECHNOLOGY CO., LTD.—See Tsinghua Holdings Co., Ltd.; *Int'l*, pg. 7951
BEIJING STARBUCKS COFFEE COMPANY LTD.—See Starbucks Corporation; *U.S. Public*, pg. 1938
BEIJING STAR BUILDING MATERIALS CO., LTD—See BBMG Corporation; *Int'l*, pg. 921
BEIJING STARNETO TECHNOLOGY CO.,LTD; *Int'l*, pg. 957
BEIJING STREAMWIDE TECHNOLOGY COMPANY LIMITED—See Streamwide S.A.; *Int'l*, pg. 7239
BEIJING STRONG BIOTECHNOLOGIES, INC.; *Int'l*, pg. 958
BEIJING SUCCEEDER TECHNOLOGY, INC.; *Int'l*, pg. 958
BEIJING SUNDART DECORATION ENGINEERING CO., LTD.—See Sundart Holdings Limited; *Int'l*, pg. 7312
BEIJING SUNGWOO CHE HITECH CO., LTD.—See Sungwoo Hitech Co., Ltd.; *Int'l*, pg. 7315
BEIJING SUNPLUS-EHUE TECH CO., LTD.—See Sunplus Technology Co., Ltd.; *Int'l*, pg. 7320
BEIJING SUNRISING TECHNOLOGY CO., LTD.—See Beijing E-Hualu Information Technology Co., Ltd.; *Int'l*, pg. 948
BEIJING SUN TECHNOLOGY INC.—See Sino Medical Sciences Technology, Inc.; *Int'l*, pg. 6947
BEIJING SUNWAYWORLD SCIENCE AND TECHNOLOGY CO., LTD.—See Abbott Laboratories; *U.S. Public*, pg. 20
BEIJING SUPLET POWER CO., LTD; *Int'l*, pg. 958
BEIJING SWT COMMUNICATIONS CO., LTD.; *Int'l*, pg. 958
BEIJING SWT OPTICAL COMMUNICATIONS TECHNOLOGIES, CO., LTD.—See Beijing SWT Communications Co., Ltd.; *Int'l*, pg. 958
BEIJING SWT OPTICAL COMMUNICATIONS TECHNOLOGIES, CO., LTD.—See Polaray Optoelectronics Co., Ltd.; *Int'l*, pg. 5906
BEIJING SYNNEX INFORMATION TECHNOLOGIES CO , LTD.—See MiTAC International Corp.; *Int'l*, pg. 4923
BEIJING TAKARA SHUZO BREWERY CO., LTD.—See Takara Holdings, Inc.; *Int'l*, pg. 7432
BEIJING TANGRENSHEN MEAT PRODUCT CO., LTD—See Tangrenshen Group Co., Ltd.; *Int'l*, pg. 7458
BEIJING TCMAGES PHARMACEUTICAL CO., LTD.—See Tianjin Chase Sun Pharmaceutical Co., Ltd.; *Int'l*, pg. 7738
BEIJING TCT MEDICAL TECHNOLOGY CO., LTD.—See Hologic, Inc.; *U.S. Public*, pg. 1044
BEIJING TEAMSUN TECHNOLOGY CO., LTD.; *Int'l*, pg. 958
BEIJING TECNATOM NUCLEAR POWER SAFETY TECHNOLOGY SERVICES COMPANY LIMITED—See Enel S.p.A.; *Int'l*, pg. 2411
BEIJING TELECOM NTT ENGINEERING CO., LTD.—See Nippon Telegraph & Telephone Corporation; *Int'l*, pg. 5344
BEIJING TELESOUND ELECTRONICS CO., LTD.; *Int'l*, pg. 958
BEIJING TELESTONE COMMUNICATION TECHNOLOGY CO., LTD.—See Telestone Technologies Corporation; *Int'l*, pg. 7542
BEIJING TELESTONE TECHNOLOGY COMPANY LIMITED—See Telestone Technologies Corporation; *Int'l*, pg. 7542
BEIJING TELESTONE WIRELESS TELECOMMUNICATION CO., LTD.—See Telestone Technologies Corporation; *Int'l*, pg. 7542
BEIJING TELLHOW INTELLIGENT ENGINEERING CO., LTD.—See Beijing Watertek Information Technology Co., Ltd.; *Int'l*, pg. 960
BEIJING TESTOR TECHNOLOGY CO., LTD.—See Beijing Tongtech Company Limited; *Int'l*, pg. 959
BEIJING TEXT 100 CONSULTING SERVICES LIMITED—See Next 15 Group plc; *Int'l*, pg. 5246
BEIJING THUNISOFT CORPORATION LIMITED; *Int'l*, pg. 958
BEIJING TIANHAI CRYOGENIC EQUIPMENT CO., LTD.—See Beijing Jingcheng Machinery Electric Co., Ltd.; *Int'l*, pg. 952
BEIJING TIANHAI INDUSTRY CO., LTD—See Beijing Jingcheng Machinery Electric Co., Ltd.; *Int'l*, pg. 952
BEIJING TIANJUYUAN FERTILIZER CO., LTD.—See China Green Agriculture, Inc.; *Int'l*, pg. 1505
BEIJING TIANTAN BIOLOGICAL PRODUCTS CORPORATION LIMITED—See China National Pharmaceutical Group Corporation; *Int'l*, pg. 1533
BEIJING TIANXINFU MEDICAL APPLIANCE CO., LTD.—See China Biologic Products Holdings, Inc.; *Int'l*, pg. 1486
BEIJING TIANXINGPUXIN BIO-MED SINOPHARM HOLDING CO., LTD.—See Medipal Holdings Corporation; *Int'l*, pg. 4779
BEIJING TIANYISHANGJIA NEW MATERIAL CORP., LTD.; *Int'l*, pg. 958
BEIJING TIANZHONGFANG ENVIRONMENTAL PROTECTION SCIENCE & TECHNOLOGY CO., LTD.—See Beijing New Universal Science and Technology Co., Ltd.; *Int'l*, pg. 954
BEIJING TIEKE SHOUGANG RAILWAY-TECHNOLOGY CO., LTD.; *Int'l*, pg. 958
BEIJING TINAVI MEDICAL TECHNOLOGIES CO., LTD.; *Int'l*, pg. 958
BEIJING TING TONG LOGISTICS CO.—See Tingyi (Cayman Islands) Holding Corp.; *Int'l*, pg. 7754
BEIJING TITAN INSTRUMENT CO., LTD.—See Focused Photonics (Hangzhou), Inc.; *Int'l*, pg. 2720
BEIJING TONGDA REFRACTORY ENGINEERING TECHNOLOGY CO., LTD.—See BBMG Corporation; *Int'l*, pg. 921
BEIJING TONGFANG MICROELECTRONICS CO., LTD.—See Guangdong Leadyo IC Testing Co., Ltd.; *Int'l*, pg. 3158
BEIJING TONGMEI XTAL TECHNOLOGY CO, LTD.—See AXT, Inc.; *U.S. Public*, pg. 256
BEIJING TONG REN TANG (AUCKLAND) COMPANY LIMITED—See Beijing Tong Ren Tang Chinese Medicine Company Limited; *Int'l*, pg. 958
BEIJING TONG REN TANG AUSTRALIA PTY. LTD.—See Beijing Tong Ren Tang Chinese Medicine Company Limited; *Int'l*, pg. 958
BEIJING TONG REN TANG CANADA CO. LTD.—See Beijing Tong Ren Tang Chinese Medicine Company Limited; *Int'l*, pg. 958
BEIJING TONG REN TANG CHINESE MEDICINE COMPANY LIMITED; *Int'l*, pg. 958
BEIJING TONGRENTANG CO., LTD.; *Int'l*, pg. 959
BEIJING TONG REN TANG CZECH REPUBLIC SE—See Tong Ren Tang Technologies Co., Ltd.; *Int'l*, pg. 7806
BEIJING TONG REN TANG GULF FZ-LLC—See Beijing Tong Ren Tang Chinese Medicine Company Limited; *Int'l*, pg. 958
BEIJING TONGRENTANG GULF MEDICAL CLINIC LLC—See Beijing Tong Ren Tang Chinese Medicine Company Limited; *Int'l*, pg. 958
BEIJING TONG REN TANG POLAND SP.ZO.O.—See Beijing Tong Ren Tang Chinese Medicine Company Limited; *Int'l*, pg. 958
BEIJING TONG REN TANG SCIENCE ARTS (SINGAPORE) CO. PTE. LTD.—See Beijing Tong Ren Tang Chinese Medicine Company Limited; *Int'l*, pg. 958
BEIJING TONG REN TANG VANCOUVER HEALTHCARE CENTER CO., LTD.—See Beijing Tong Ren Tang Chinese Medicine Company Limited; *Int'l*, pg. 959
BEIJING TONGTECH COMPANY LIMITED; *Int'l*, pg. 959
BEIJING TONGYIZHONG SPECIALTY FIBER TECHNOLOGY & DEVELOPMENT CO. LTD.—See SDIC Capital Co., Ltd.; *Int'l*, pg. 6658
BEIJING TON YI INDUSTRIAL CO., LTD.—See Uni-President Enterprises Corporation; *Int'l*, pg. 8028
BEIJING TOPNEW INFORMATION & TECHNOLOGY CO., LTD.; *Int'l*, pg. 959
BEIJING TOPPAN DIGITAL PRODUCTS CO., LTD.—See TOPPAN Holdings Inc.; *Int'l*, pg. 7816
BEIJING TOP RESULT PUBLIC TRANSPORTATION ADVERTISING CO., LTD. WUHAN BRANCH—See JCDecaux S.A.; *Int'l*, pg. 3921
BEIJING TOTO CO., LTD.—See Toto Ltd.; *Int'l*, pg. 7846
BEIJING TRANSTRUE TECHNOLOGY INC.; *Int'l*, pg. 959
BEIJING TRICOLOR TECHNOLOGY CO., LTD.; *Int'l*, pg. 959
BEIJING TRS INFORMATION TECHNOLOGY CO., LTD.; *Int'l*, pg. 959

BEIJING TRUSTFAR TECHNOLOGY CO., LTD.; *Int'l*, pg. 959
BEIJING UISF INFORMATION TECHNOLOGY CO., LTD.—See Jiangsu Hoperun Software Co., Ltd.; *Int'l*, pg. 3948
BEIJING ULTRAPOWER SOFTWARE CO., LTD.; *Int'l*, pg. 959
BEIJING UMEONE DIGITAL TEC.CO., LTD.—See HUB Cyber Security Ltd.; *Int'l*, pg. 3516
BEIJING UNISTRONG SCIENCE & TECHNOLOGY CO., LTD.; *Int'l*, pg. 959
BEIJING UNITED FAMILY HOSPITAL CO., LTD.—See Shanghai Fosun Pharmaceutical (Group) Co., Ltd.; *Int'l*, pg. 6767
BEIJING UNITED FAMILY HOSPITAL CO., LTD.—See TPG Capital, L.P.; *U.S. Public*, pg. 2169
BEIJING UNITED FAMILY HOSPITAL MANAGEMENT CO., LTD.—See Shanghai Fosun Pharmaceutical (Group) Co., Ltd.; *Int'l*, pg. 6767
BEIJING UNITED FAMILY HOSPITAL MANAGEMENT CO., LTD.—See TPG Capital, L.P.; *U.S. Public*, pg. 2169
BEIJING UNITED INFORMATION TECHNOLOGY CO., LTD.; *Int'l*, pg. 959
BEIJING UNITIKA TEXTILES TRADING CO., LTD.—See Unitika Ltd.; *Int'l*, pg. 8075
BEIJING URBAN CONSTRUCTION DESIGN & DEVELOPMENT GROUP CO., LTD.; *Int'l*, pg. 959
BEIJING URBAN CONSTRUCTION EXPLORATION & SURVEYING DESIGN RESEARCH INSTITUTE CO., LTD.—See Beijing Urban Construction Design & Development Group Co., Ltd.; *Int'l*, pg. 959
BEIJING URBAN CONSTRUCTION INVESTMENT & DEVELOPMENT CO., LTD.; *Int'l*, pg. 959
BEIJING USCOM CONSULTING CO. LTD.—See USCOM LIMITED; *Int'l*, pg. 8096
BEIJING VANTONE DINGAN PROPERTY SERVICE CO. LTD.—See Vantone Neo Development Group Co., Ltd.; *Int'l*, pg. 8131
BEIJING VASTDATA TECHNOLOGY CO., LTD.; *Int'l*, pg. 959
BEIJING VA TECH WABAG WATER TREATMENT TECHNOLOGY CO., LTD.—See VA TECH WABAG Limited; *Int'l*, pg. 8107
BEIJING VBH CONSTRUCTION HARDWARE CO. LTD.—See VBH Holding AG; *Int'l*, pg. 8139
BEIJING VIASAT SCIENCE & TECHNOLOGY CO., LTD.—See ViaSat, Inc.; *U.S. Public*, pg. 2291
BEIJING VIGOR TIANBAO INTERNATIONAL STUDIOS CO., LTD.—See Hainan Traffic Administration Holding Co., Ltd.; *Int'l*, pg. 3213
BEIJING VITAL RIVER LABORATORY ANIMAL TECHNOLOGY CO., LTD.—See Charles River Laboratories International, Inc.; *U.S. Public*, pg. 479
BEIJING VRV SOFTWARE CORPORATION LIMITED; *Int'l*, pg. 960
BEIJING WABTEC HUAXIA TECHNOLOGY COMPANY LTD.—See Westinghouse Air Brake Technologies Corporation; *U.S. Public*, pg. 2357
BEIJING WALUER INFORMATION TECHNOLOGY CO., LTD.; *Int'l*, pg. 960
BEIJING WANDONG MEDICAL TECHNOLOGY CO., LTD.; *Int'l*, pg. 960
BEIJING WANTAI BIOLOGICAL PHARMACY ENTERPRISE CO., LTD.; *Int'l*, pg. 960
BEIJING WANYUAN-HENNIGES SEALING SYSTEMS CO., LTD.—See China Energine International (Holdings) Limited; *Int'l*, pg. 1500
BEIJING WATER BUSINESS DOCTOR CO., LTD.; *Int'l*, pg. 960
BEIJING WATERTEK FUXI BIG DATA TECHNOLOGY CO., LTD.—See Beijing Watertek Information Technology Co., Ltd.; *Int'l*, pg. 960
BEIJING WATERTEK INFORMATION TECHNOLOGY CO., LTD.; *Int'l*, pg. 960
BEIJING WATERTEK SINDA TECHNOLOGY CO., LTD.—See Beijing Watertek Information Technology Co., Ltd.; *Int'l*, pg. 960
BEIJINGWEST INDUSTRIES INTERNATIONAL LIMITED; *Int'l*, pg. 962
BEIJING WESTMINSTER AIR SERVICE LIMITED—See Corporate Travel Management Limited; *Int'l*, pg. 1805
BEIJING WKW AUTOMOTIVE PARTS CO., LTD.; *Int'l*, pg. 960
BEIJING WOODWORKING FACTORY CO.—See BBMG Corporation; *Int'l*, pg. 921
BEIJING WORLDIA DIAMOND TOOLS CO., LTD.; *Int'l*, pg. 960
BEIJING XIAOCHENG TECHNOLOGY STOCK CO., LTD; *Int'l*, pg. 961
BEIJING XINJIE TECHNOLOGY CO., LTD.—See KONA I Corporation; *Int'l*, pg. 4244
BEIJING XINJINCHENG CO., LTD.—See SK Networks Co., Ltd.; *Int'l*, pg. 6974
BEIJING XINNET CYBER INFORMATION COMPANY LIMITED—See Sino-i Technology Limited; *Int'l*, pg. 6948
BEIJING XINWEI TECHNOLOGY GROUP CO., LTD.; *Int'l*, pg. 961

BEIJING XINYANG TONGLI COMMERCIAL FACILITIES COMPANY LIMITED—See Beijing Jingkelong Company Limited; *Int'l*, pg. 953
BEIJING YANJING BREWERY CO., LTD.—See Beijing Enterprises Holdings Limited; *Int'l*, pg. 950
BEIJING YANLONG IMPORT & EXPORT CO., LTD.—See Beijing Jingcheng Machinery Electric Holding Co., Ltd.; *Int'l*, pg. 953
BEIJING YAXINCHENG MEDICAL INFOTECH CO., LTD.—See Hangzhou Tigermed Consulting Co., Ltd.; *Int'l*, pg. 3251
BEIJING YEE ZHI REAL ESTATE CONSULTANCY CO., LTD.—See Hong Kong Land Holdings Ltd.; *Int'l*, pg. 3466
BEIJING YI KONG PROPERTY MANAGEMENT LTD.—See Taiwan Shin Kong Security Co., Ltd.; *Int'l*, pg. 7424
BEIJING YINGHE CENTURY CO., LTD.—See BOE Technology Group Co., Ltd.; *Int'l*, pg. 1099
BEIJING YJK BUILDING SOFTWARE CO., LTD.; *Int'l*, pg. 961
BEIJING YONG SHENG FENG AMP CO., LTD.—See Public Joint Stock Company Acron; *Int'l*, pg. 6094
BEIJING YOUYU TECHNOLOGIES LIMITED—See Yunfeng Financial Group Limited; *Int'l*, pg. 8613
BEIJING YUANLIU HONGYUAN ELECTRONIC TECHNOLOGY CO., LTD.; *Int'l*, pg. 961
BEIJING YUANLONG YATO CULTURE DISSEMINATION CO., LTD.; *Int'l*, pg. 961
BEIJING YUANZHIMENG ADVERTISING CO., LTD—See HS Ad Inc.; *Int'l*, pg. 3502
BEIJING YURA CORPORATION—See YURATECH Co., Ltd.; *Int'l*, pg. 8617
BEIJING ZHENGTONG BAOZEHANG AUTOMOBILE SALES SERVICES CO., LTD.—See China ZhengTong Auto Services Holdings Limited; *Int'l*, pg. 1566
BEIJING ZHENGTONG DINGWO AUTOMOBILE SALES SERVICES CO., LTD.—See China ZhengTong Auto Services Holdings Limited; *Int'l*, pg. 1566
BEIJING ZHIDEMAI TECHNOLOGY CO., LTD.; *Int'l*, pg. 961
BEIJING ZHIJIE FLOCCULANT—See SNF SAS; *Int'l*, pg. 7027
BEIJING ZHIMEI DIGITAL ANTI-COUNTERFEITING PRINTING CO., LTD.—See Xiamen Anne Corporation Limited; *Int'l*, pg. 8523
BEIJING ZHIYUE NETWORK TECHNOLOGY CO., LTD.—See Zhewen Interactive Group Co Ltd; *Int'l*, pg. 8671
BEIJING ZHONGCHUANG GREEN CITY ENVIRONMENTAL SERVICE CO., LTD.—See Xiamen Zhongchuang Environmental Technology Co., Ltd.; *Int'l*, pg. 8526
BEIJING ZHONGCHUANG TELECOM TEST CO., LTD.—See Beijing Xinwei Technology Group Co., Ltd.; *Int'l*, pg. 961
BEIJING ZHONGFU BEVERAGE CONTAINER CO., LTD.—See Zhuhai Zhongfu Enterprise Co., Ltd.; *Int'l*, pg. 8678
BEIJING ZHONGHENG HENGXIN AUTOMATION EQUIPMENT CO., LTD.—See Rexel, S.A.; *Int'l*, pg. 6316
BEIJING ZHONGKEHAIXUN DIGITAL S & T CO., LTD.; *Int'l*, pg. 961
BEIJING ZHONGKE I/E COMPANY LTD.—See China Science Publishing & Media Ltd.; *Int'l*, pg. 1550
BEIJING ZHONGKE JIAYING SEMICONDUCTOR CO.—See Yunnan Lincang Xinyuan Germanium Industrial Co., Ltd.; *Int'l*, pg. 8615
BEIJING ZHONG KE SAN HUAN HIGH-TECH CO., LTD.; *Int'l*, pg. 961
BEIJING ZHONG KE SAN HUAN INTERNATIONAL TRADING COMPANY—See Beijing Zhong Ke San Huan High-tech Co., Ltd.; *Int'l*, pg. 961
BEIJING ZHONGKE TONGRONG PRIVATE EQUITY INVESTMENT FUND CO., LTD; *Int'l*, pg. 961
BEIJING ZHONGRUAN JINKA INFORMATION TECHNOLOGY CO., LTD.—See Beijing Watertek Information Technology Co., Ltd.; *Int'l*, pg. 960
BEIJING ZHONGSHENG STAR AUTOMOBILE SALES & SERVICE CO., LTD.—See Zhongsheng Group Holdings Limited; *Int'l*, pg. 8674
BEIJING ZHONGYU GAS CO., LTD.—See Zhongyu Energy Holdings Limited; *Int'l*, pg. 8675
BEIJING ZHULI DIANTONG OPTOELECTRONICS TECHNOLOGY CO., LTD.—See Sumitomo Electric Industries, Ltd.; *Int'l*, pg. 7277
BEIJING ZODI INVESTMENT CO., LTD.; *Int'l*, pg. 961
BEIJING ZODNGOC AUTOMATIC TECHNOLOGY CO., LTD.—See Beijing Easpring Material Technology Co., Ltd.; *Int'l*, pg. 949
BEIJING ZOHETEC CO., LTD; *Int'l*, pg. 961
BEIJING ZUOJIANG TECHNOLOGY CO., LTD.; *Int'l*, pg. 961
BEIJING ZZNODE TECHNOLOGIES CO., LTD.; *Int'l*, pg. 961
BEIJING GRINM RS SEMICONDUCTOR MATERIALS CO., LTD.—See RS Technologies Co., Ltd.; *Int'l*, pg. 6419

BEIJIN SONGZ AUTOMOBILE AIR CONDITIONING CO., LTD.—See Songzhi Kallang Automotive Air Conditioning Co., Ltd.; *Int'l*, pg. 7096
BEILUN CDB VILLAGE BANK CO., LTD.—See China Development Bank Corporation; *Int'l*, pg. 1497
BEIMDIEK INSURANCE AGENCY, INC.—See GTCR LLC; *U.S. Private*, pg. 1802
BEING CO., LTD.; *Int'l*, pg. 962
BEING HOLDING CO., LTD.; *Int'l*, pg. 962
BEINGMATE CO., LTD.; *Int'l*, pg. 962
BEING—See Omnicom Group Inc.; *U.S. Public*, pg. 1596
B&E INTERNATIONAL (PTY) LIMITED—See Raubex Group Limited; *Int'l*, pg. 6221
BEI PRECISION SYSTEMS & SPACE COMPANY, INC.—See Arcline Investment Management LP; *U.S. Private*, pg. 313
BEIQI FOTON MOTOR COMPANY LTD.; *Int'l*, pg. 962
BEIRAGAS - COMPANHIA DE GAS DAS BEIRAS, S.A.—See Galp Energia SGPS, S.A.; *Int'l*, pg. 2875
BEIRA GRAIN TERMINAL, S.A.—See Seaboard Corporation; *U.S. Public*, pg. 1850
BEIREN GROUP CORPORATION—See Beijing Jingcheng Machinery Electric Holding Co., Ltd.; *Int'l*, pg. 953
BEIRENS S.A.S.—See Poujoulat SA; *Int'l*, pg. 5942
BEISEN HOLDING LTD.; *Int'l*, pg. 962
BEI SENSORS NORTH AMERICA—See Sensata Technologies Holding plc; *U.S. Public*, pg. 1866
BEI SENSORS SAS—See Sensata Technologies Holding plc; *U.S. Public*, pg. 1865
BEI SERVICES, INC.—See Valsef Group; *Int'l*, pg. 8123
BEISSBARTH AUTOMOTIVE TESTING SOLUTIONS GMBH—See Stargate Capital GmbH; *Int'l*, pg. 7176
BEISSER LUMBER COMPANY; *U.S. Private*, pg. 516
BEISSIER S.A.S.—See Sto SE & Co. KGaA; *Int'l*, pg. 7219
BEISSIER S.A.U.—See Sto SE & Co. KGaA; *Int'l*, pg. 7219
THE BEISTLE COMPANY, INC.; *U.S. Private*, pg. 3993
BEIT DICKSON KSCC—See Gulf Franchising Holding Company K.S.C.C.; *Int'l*, pg. 3180
BEITERS INC.; *U.S. Private*, pg. 516
BEIT GMBH—See Gauselmann AG; *Int'l*, pg. 2890
BEITLER & ASSOCIATES INC.; *U.S. Private*, pg. 516
BEITLER MCKEE COMPANY—See EssilorLuxottica SA; *Int'l*, pg. 2513
BEIT SYSTEMHAUS GMBH—See Gauselmann AG; *Int'l*, pg. 2890
BEITZEL CORPORATION; *U.S. Private*, pg. 516
BEIXIN NEW BUILDING MATERIAL (GROUP) CO., LTD.—See China National Building Material Group Co., Ltd.; *Int'l*, pg. 1525
BEJAC CORPORATION; *U.S. Private*, pg. 516
BEJING BESTPOWER ELECTRICAL TECHNOLOGY CO., LTD.—See Sinosteel Engineering & Technology Co., Ltd.; *Int'l*, pg. 6955
BEJING DAHENG CREATIVE TECHNOLOGY CO., LTD.—See Daheng New Epoch Technology, Inc.; *Int'l*, pg. 1913
BEJO ANDES LTDA.—See Bejo Zaden B.V.; *Int'l*, pg. 962
BEJO BOHEMIA, S.R.O.—See Bejo Zaden B.V.; *Int'l*, pg. 962
BEJO GRAINES FRANCE S.A.R.L.—See Bejo Zaden B.V.; *Int'l*, pg. 962
BEJO IBERICA, S.L.—See Bejo Zaden B.V.; *Int'l*, pg. 962
BEJO ITALIA S.R.L.—See Bejo Zaden B.V.; *Int'l*, pg. 962
BEJO ROMANIA SRL—See Bejo Zaden B.V.; *Int'l*, pg. 962
BEJO SAMEN GMBH—See Bejo Zaden B.V.; *Int'l*, pg. 962
BEJO, S.A.—See Bejo Zaden B.V.; *Int'l*, pg. 962
BEJO SEEDS INC.—See Bejo Zaden B.V.; *Int'l*, pg. 962
BEJO SEEDS PTY LTD—See Bejo Zaden B.V.; *Int'l*, pg. 962
BEJO SEMENTES DO BRASIL LTDA—See Bejo Zaden B.V.; *Int'l*, pg. 962
BEJO SEMILLAS ARGENTINA S.A.—See Bejo Zaden B.V.; *Int'l*, pg. 962
BEJO ZADEN BELGIUM B.V.B.A.—See Bejo Zaden B.V.; *Int'l*, pg. 962
BEJO ZADEN B.V.; *Int'l*, pg. 962
BEJO ZADEN D.O.O.—See Bejo Zaden B.V.; *Int'l*, pg. 962
BEJO ZADEN POLAND SP. Z O.O.—See Bejo Zaden B.V.; *Int'l*, pg. 962
BEKAERT ADVANCED PRODUCTS (SHANGHAI) CO LTD—See NV Bekaert SA; *Int'l*, pg. 5495
BEKAERT ASIA SHANGHAI OFFICE—See NV Bekaert SA; *Int'l*, pg. 5495
BEKAERT A/S—See NV Bekaert SA; *Int'l*, pg. 5495
BEKAERT (AUSTRALIA) PTY. LTD.—See Franz Haniel & Cie. GmbH; *Int'l*, pg. 2762
BEKAERT BENELUX N.V.—See NV Bekaert SA; *Int'l*, pg. 5495
BEKAERT BINJIANG ADVANCED PRODUCTS CO LTD—See NV Bekaert SA; *Int'l*, pg. 5495
BEKAERT BINJIANG STEEL CORD CO LTD—See NV Bekaert SA; *Int'l*, pg. 5495
BEKAERT BRADFORD UK LTD.—See NV Bekaert SA; *Int'l*, pg. 5495
BEKAERT (CHINA) TECHNOLOGY RESEARCH AND DEVELOPMENT CO LTD—See NV Bekaert SA; *Int'l*, pg. 5495

COMPANY NAME INDEX

BEKAERT COMBUSTION TECHNOLOGY BV—See NV Bekaert SA; *Int'l*, pg. 5495
BEKAERT CONTOURS LTD.—See NV Bekaert SA; *Int'l*, pg. 5495
BEKAERT COORDINATIECENTRUM N.V.—See NV Bekaert SA; *Int'l*, pg. 5495
BEKAERT CORPORATION—See NV Bekaert SA; *Int'l*, pg. 5495
BEKAERT CORPORATION—See NV Bekaert SA; *Int'l*, pg. 5495
BEKAERT CORPORATION—See NV Bekaert SA; *Int'l*, pg. 5495
BEKAERT CORPORATION—See NV Bekaert SA; *Int'l*, pg. 5495
BEKAERT DO BRASIL LTDA—See NV Bekaert SA; *Int'l*, pg. 5496
BEKAERT ENGINEERING—See NV Bekaert SA; *Int'l*, pg. 5495
BEKAERT FRANCE S.A.—See NV Bekaert SA; *Int'l*, pg. 5495
BEKAERT GMBH—See NV Bekaert SA; *Int'l*, pg. 5495
BEKAERT GMBH—See NV Bekaert SA; *Int'l*, pg. 5495
BEKAERT GUATEMALA SA—See NV Bekaert SA; *Int'l*, pg. 5495
BEKAERT HEATING TECHNOLOGY (SUZHOU) CO., LTD.—See NV Bekaert SA; *Int'l*, pg. 5495
BEKAERT IBERICA HOLDING SL—See NV Bekaert SA; *Int'l*, pg. 5495
BEKAERT IDEAL SL—See NV Bekaert SA; *Int'l*, pg. 5495
BEKAERT INDUSTRIES PVT LTD—See NV Bekaert SA; *Int'l*, pg. 5496
BEKAERT IZMIT CELIK KORD SANAYI VE TICARET AS—See NV Bekaert SA; *Int'l*, pg. 5496
BEKAERT JAPAN—See NV Bekaert SA; *Int'l*, pg. 5496
BEKAERT-JIANGYIN WIRE PRODUCTS CO LTD—See NV Bekaert SA; *Int'l*, pg. 5496
BEKAERT KOREA LTD—See NV Bekaert SA; *Int'l*, pg. 5496
BEKAERT MANAGEMENT (SHANGHAI) CO LTD—See NV Bekaert SA; *Int'l*, pg. 5496
BEKAERT MUKAND WIRE INDUSTRIES PVT LTD—See NV Bekaert SA; *Int'l*, pg. 5496
BEKAERT NORGE AS—See NV Bekaert SA; *Int'l*, pg. 5496
BEKAERT NORTH AMERICA MANAGEMENT CORPORATION—See NV Bekaert SA; *Int'l*, pg. 5496
BEKAERT POLAND SP. Z O.O.—See NV Bekaert SA; *Int'l*, pg. 5496
BEKAERT PORTUGAL-IMPORTACAO COMERCIALIZACAO DE ARAMES E SEUS DERIVADOS, LTDA.—See NV Bekaert SA; *Int'l*, pg. 5496
BEKAERT (QINGDAO) WIRE PRODUCTS CO LTD—See NV Bekaert SA; *Int'l*, pg. 5495
BEKAERT SARDEGNA SPA—See NV Bekaert SA; *Int'l*, pg. 5496
BEKAERT (SCHWEIZ) AG—See NV Bekaert SA; *Int'l*, pg. 5495
BEKAERT SHAH ALAM SDN. BHD.—See NV Bekaert SA; *Int'l*, pg. 5496
BEKAERT (SHANDONG) TIRE CORD CO LTD—See NV Bekaert SA; *Int'l*, pg. 5495
BEKAERT SINGAPORE PTE. LTD.—See NV Bekaert SA; *Int'l*, pg. 5496
BEKAERT SLOVAKIA SRO—See NV Bekaert SA; *Int'l*, pg. 5496
BEKAERT SPECIALTY FILMS CANADA—See NV Bekaert SA; *Int'l*, pg. 5496
BEKAERT SPECIALTY FILMS LLC—See NV Bekaert SA; *Int'l*, pg. 5495
BEKAERT SPECIALTY FILMS NORDIC AB—See NV Bekaert SA; *Int'l*, pg. 5496
BEKAERT SPECIALTY WIRE PRODUCTS HONG KONG LTD—See NV Bekaert SA; *Int'l*, pg. 5496
BEKAERT SVENSKA A/B—See NV Bekaert SA; *Int'l*, pg. 5496
BEKAERT SVENSKA A/S—See NV Bekaert SA; *Int'l*, pg. 5496
BEKAERT TAIWAN CO., LTD.—See NV Bekaert SA; *Int'l*, pg. 5496
BEKAERT TARAK AKSESUARLARI VE MAKINALARI TICARET AS—See NV Bekaert SA; *Int'l*, pg. 5496
BEKAERT TEXTILES N.V.—See Franz Haniel & Cie. GmbH; *Int'l*, pg. 2762
BEKAERT TEXTILES USA, INC.—See Franz Haniel & Cie. GmbH; *Int'l*, pg. 2762
BEKAERT (THAILAND) CO., LTD.—See NV Bekaert SA; *Int'l*, pg. 5495
BEKAERT TOKO METAL FIBER CO LTD—See NV Bekaert SA; *Int'l*, pg. 5496
BEKAERT TRADE LATIN AMERICA N.V.—See NV Bekaert SA; *Int'l*, pg. 5495
BEKAERT TRADE MEXICO S DE RL DE CV—See NV Bekaert SA; *Int'l*, pg. 5496
BEKA JAPAN CO., LTD.—See The Timken Company; *U.S. Public*, pg. 2132
BEKALAN AIR KIPC SDN BHD—See Petroliam Nasional Berhad; *Int'l*, pg. 5829
BEKALUBE FRANCE S.A.S.—See The Timken Company; *U.S. Public*, pg. 2132

BEKA-LUBE GMBH—See The Timken Company; *U.S. Public*, pg. 2132
BEKALUBE IBERICA, S.L.U.—See The Timken Company; *U.S. Public*, pg. 2132
BEKA-LUBE N.V.—See The Timken Company; *U.S. Public*, pg. 2132
BEKA LUBE PRODUCTS INC.—See The Timken Company; *U.S. Public*, pg. 2132
BEKALUBE S.R.L.—See The Timken Company; *U.S. Public*, pg. 2132
BEKA LUBRICATION SYSTEMS (KUNSHAN) CO., LTD.—See The Timken Company; *U.S. Public*, pg. 2132
BEKASI ASRI PEMULA TBK; *Int'l*, pg. 962
BEKAWORLD SINGAPORE PTE. LTD.—See The Timken Company; *U.S. Public*, pg. 2132
BEK BAUSTOFFE SLOVAKIA S.R.O.—See SIG plc; *Int'l*, pg. 6906
BE&K BUILDING GROUP, LLC - CHARLOTTE—See Pernix Group, Inc.; *U.S. Public*, pg. 1677
BE&K BUILDING GROUP, LLC—See Pernix Group, Inc.; *U.S. Public*, pg. 1677
BEKEM METALS, INC.; *Int'l*, pg. 962
BEKEN CORPORATION; *Int'l*, pg. 962
BEKEY AS—See North Media A/S; *Int'l*, pg. 5440
BEKINS MOVING SOLUTIONS, INC.; *U.S. Private*, pg. 516
BEKINS MOVING & STORAGE CO.; *U.S. Private*, pg. 516
BEKINS VAN LINES, LLC—See Wheaton Van Lines, Inc.; *U.S. Private*, pg. 4505
BEKINTEX N.V.—See NV Bekaert SA; *Int'l*, pg. 5496
BEKKAI UBE CONCRETE CO., LTD.—See UBE Corporation; *Int'l*, pg. 8000
BEKK CONSULTING AS—See TietoEVRY Oyj; *Int'l*, pg. 7745
BEKKIHAYAMI ENVIRONMENT TECHNOLOGY CO., LTD.—See Hitachi Zosen Corporation; *Int'l*, pg. 3410
BEKKOAME INTERNET INC.—See FreeBit Co., Ltd.; *Int'l*, pg. 2769
BEKO A AND NZ PTY LTD.—See Koc Holding A.S.; *Int'l*, pg. 4222
BEKO CESKO S.R.O.—See Koc Holding A.S.; *Int'l*, pg. 4222
BEKO DEUTSCHLAND GMBH—See Koc Holding A.S.; *Int'l*, pg. 4222
BEKO ELECTRONICS ESPANA S.L.—See Koc Holding A.S.; *Int'l*, pg. 4222
BEKO ITALY SRL—See Koc Holding A.S.; *Int'l*, pg. 4222
BEKOMOLD WERKZEUGBAU GMBH—See BERICAP GmbH & Co. KG; *Int'l*, pg. 980
BEKON-KORALLE AG—See Arbonia AG; *Int'l*, pg. 538
BEKO PLC—See Koc Holding A.S.; *Int'l*, pg. 4222
BEKO S.A. CZECH REPUBLIC—See Koc Holding A.S.; *Int'l*, pg. 4222
BEK SYSTEMTECHNIK GMBH & CO.KG—See Rutronik Elektronische Bauelemente GmbH; *Int'l*, pg. 6432
BEKTAS GROUP LLP—See Heidelberg Materials AG; *Int'l*, pg. 3308
BEKUPLAST BENELUX B.V.—See bekuplast GmbH; *Int'l*, pg. 962
BEKUPLAST GMBH; *Int'l*, pg. 962
BEKUPLAST POLSKA SP. Z O.O—See bekuplast GmbH; *Int'l*, pg. 962
BEKY A.S.; *Int'l*, pg. 962
BELA AUTOMOTIVES LIMITED; *Int'l*, pg. 963
BELAGROPROMBANK JSC; *Int'l*, pg. 963
BELAIR BUILDERS INC.; *U.S. Private*, pg. 516
BELAIRBUS SA—See SONACA S.A.; *Int'l*, pg. 7088
BELAIR FENCE LIMITED—See ITOCHU Corporation; *Int'l*, pg. 3838
BELAIR HOUSE SA—See Legend Holdings Corporation; *Int'l*, pg. 4443
BEL AIR INDUSTRIES; *Int'l*, pg. 962
BELAIR INSTRUMENT COMPANY LLC; *U.S. Private*, pg. 516
BEL AIR INTERNET, LLC—See TAC Partners, Inc.; *U.S. Private*, pg. 3920
BEL AIR INVESTMENT ADVISORS LLC—See Fiera Capital Corporation; *Int'l*, pg. 2659
BEL AIR MARKETS—See Raley's Inc.; *U.S. Private*, pg. 3350
BEL AIR OUTBACK, INC.—See Bloomin' Brands, Inc.; *U.S. Public*, pg. 362
BELAIR ROAD SUPPLY COMPANY INC.; *U.S. Private*, pg. 516
BELAIR TIME CORP.—See Selco LLC; *U.S. Private*, pg. 3600
BELAMBRA VVF SNC—See Caravelle SA; *Int'l*, pg. 1320
BELAM INC.; *U.S. Private*, pg. 516
BELANGER, INC.—See Dover Corporation; *U.S. Public*, pg. 678
BELANTARA HOLIDAYS SDN BHD—See Seera Group Holding Co.; *Int'l*, pg. 6679
BEL-ANVIS ANTIVIBRATION SYSTEM (PTY) LTD.—See Sumitomo Riko Company Limited; *Int'l*, pg. 7298
BELAPUR INDUSTRIES LTD.; *Int'l*, pg. 963
BEL-AQUA POOL SUPPLY INC.; *U.S. Private*, pg. 516
BELARAROX LIMITED; *Int'l*, pg. 963

BELARINA ALIMENTOS S.A.—See Seaboard Corporation; *U.S. Public*, pg. 1850
BELARTO GROUP—See HAL Trust N.V.; *Int'l*, pg. 3224
BELARTO LTD—See HAL Trust N.V.; *Int'l*, pg. 3224
BEL-ART PRODUCTS, INC.—See Harbour Group Industries, Inc.; *U.S. Private*, pg. 1861
BELARUSBANK; *Int'l*, pg. 963
BELASCO PETROLEUM CO. INC.; *U.S. Private*, pg. 516
BELAVIA NATSIONALYNAYA VIAKOMPANIYA R.U.P.; *Int'l*, pg. 963
BELA VISTA GERACAO DE ENERGIA S.A.—See Companhia Paranaense de Energia; *Int'l*, pg. 1747
BELAY, INC.; *U.S. Private*, pg. 516
BEL BRANDS USA—See Unibel SA; *Int'l*, pg. 8031
BELCAM INC.; *U.S. Private*, pg. 516
BELCAN LLC—See AE Industrial Partners, LP; *U.S. Private*, pg. 111
BELCANTO FOODS, LLC—See The Chefs' Warehouse, Inc.; *U.S. Public*, pg. 2059
BELCARO GROUP, INC.; *U.S. Private*, pg. 516
BELC CO., LTD.; *Int'l*, pg. 963
BELCHER OIL CO. INC.; *U.S. Private*, pg. 517
BELCHER PHARMACEUTICALS, LLC; *U.S. Private*, pg. 517
BELCHINSKI MINERALNI BANI LTD.—See Synergon Holding PLC; *Int'l*, pg. 7384
BELCO COMMUNITY CREDIT UNION; *U.S. Private*, pg. 517
BELCO, INC.—See NOV, Inc.; *U.S. Public*, pg. 1544
BELCO INDUSTRIES, INC. - FAMCO MACHINE DIVISION—See Belco Industries, Inc.; *U.S. Private*, pg. 517
BELCO INDUSTRIES, INC.; *U.S. Private*, pg. 517
BELCO INDUSTRIES INC.; *U.S. Private*, pg. 517
BELCOLOR AG—See Headlam Group plc; *Int'l*, pg. 3301
BELCOMPANY BV—See Vodafone Group Plc; *Int'l*, pg. 8286
BEL CONNECTOR INC.—See Bel Fuse Inc.; *U.S. Public*, pg. 292
BELCO PACKAGING SYSTEMS INC.; *U.S. Private*, pg. 517
BELCO PROPERTIES LIMITED—See Abengoa S.A.; *Int'l*, pg. 59
BELCO PROPERTIES LIMITED—See Algonquin Power & Utilities Corp.; *Int'l*, pg. 319
BELCORP INC.; *U.S. Private*, pg. 517
BELCO TECHNOLOGIES CORPORATION—See DuPont de Nemours, Inc.; *U.S. Public*, pg. 692
BELDAM CROSSLEY LIMITED—See Indutrade AB; *Int'l*, pg. 3677
BELDEN AB—See Belden, Inc.; *U.S. Public*, pg. 293
THE BELDEN BRICK COMPANY INC.; *U.S. Private*, pg. 3993
THE BELDEN BRICK SALES COMPANY INC.—See The Belden Brick Company Inc.; *U.S. Private*, pg. 3993
BELDEN BRICK & SUPPLY CO. INC.; *U.S. Private*, pg. 517
BELDEN CDT (CANADA) INC.—See Belden, Inc.; *U.S. Public*, pg. 293
BELDEN CDT EUROPEAN SHARED SERVICES B.V.—See Belden, Inc.; *U.S. Public*, pg. 293
BELDEN CEKAN A/S—See Belden, Inc.; *U.S. Public*, pg. 293
BELDEN COMMERCIAL SERVICES B.V.—See Belden, Inc.; *U.S. Public*, pg. 293
BELDEN DEUTSCHLAND GMBH—See Belden, Inc.; *U.S. Public*, pg. 293
BELDEN-DUNA KABEL KFT—See Belden, Inc.; *U.S. Public*, pg. 294
BELDEN ELECTRONICS AMERICAS DIVISION—See Belden, Inc.; *U.S. Public*, pg. 293
BELDEN ELECTRONICS GMBH—See Belden, Inc.; *U.S. Public*, pg. 293
BELDEN EUROPE B.V.—See Belden, Inc.; *U.S. Public*, pg. 293
BELDEN GRASS VALLEY ASIA LIMITED—See Belden, Inc.; *U.S. Public*, pg. 293
BELDEN GRASS VALLEY INDUSTRIA E COMERCIO E SERVICOS LTDA.—See Belden, Inc.; *U.S. Public*, pg. 293
BELDEN & HIRSCHMANN - FRANCE—See Belden, Inc.; *U.S. Public*, pg. 293
BELDEN HIRSCHMANN NETWORKING SYSTEM TRADING (SHANGHAI) CO. LTD.—See Belden, Inc.; *U.S. Public*, pg. 293
BELDEN HIRSCHMANN SOLUTIONS (SHANGHAI) COMPANY LIMITED—See Belden, Inc.; *U.S. Public*, pg. 293
BELDEN & HIRSCHMANN - SPAIN—See Belden, Inc.; *U.S. Public*, pg. 293
BELDEN HOLDINGS, INC.—See Belden, Inc.; *U.S. Public*, pg. 293
BELDEN, INC. - KENTUCKY PLANT—See Belden, Inc.; *U.S. Public*, pg. 294
BELDEN, INC. - PENNSYLVANIA PLANT—See Belden, Inc.; *U.S. Public*, pg. 294
BELDEN, INC.; *U.S. Public*, pg. 293
BELDEN INTERNATIONAL INC. - HONG KONG OFFICE—See Belden, Inc.; *U.S. Public*, pg. 294

BELDEN, INC.

BELDEN POLIRON INDUSTRIA E COMERCIO DE CABOS ESPECIAIS LTDA.—See Belden, Inc.; *U.S. Public*, pg. 294
BELDEN SOLUTIONS ASIA LIMITED—See Belden, Inc.; *U.S. Public*, pg. 294
BELDEN'S SUPER MARKET INC.; *U.S. Private*, pg. 517
BELDEN TRI-STATE BUILDING MATERIALS—See The Belden Brick Company Inc.; *U.S. Private*, pg. 3993
BELDEN VENLO HOLDING B.V.—See Belden, Inc.; *U.S. Public*, pg. 294
BELDEN WIRE & CABLE COMPANY LLC—See Belden, Inc.; *U.S. Public*, pg. 294
BEL DEUTSCHLAND GMBH—See Unibel SA; *Int'l*, pg. 8031
BELDON ENTERPRISES, INC.; *U.S. Private*, pg. 517
BELDON ROOFING COMPANY—See Beldon Enterprises, Inc.; *U.S. Private*, pg. 517
BELEAVE, INC.; *Int'l*, pg. 963
BELECTRIC AUSTRALIA PTY. LIMITED—See RWE AG; *Int'l*, pg. 6433
BELECTRIC CHILE ENERGIA FOTOVOLTAICA LTDA.—See RWE AG; *Int'l*, pg. 6433
BELECTRIC FRANCE S.A.R.L.—See RWE AG; *Int'l*, pg. 6433
BELECTRIC INC.—See RWE AG; *Int'l*, pg. 6433
BELECTRIC ISRAEL LTD.—See RWE AG; *Int'l*, pg. 6433
BELECTRIC ITALIA S.R.L.—See RWE AG; *Int'l*, pg. 6433
BELECTRIC PHOTOVOLTAIC INDIA PRIVATE LIMITED—See RWE AG; *Int'l*, pg. 6433
BELECTRIC PV DACH GMBH—See RWE AG; *Int'l*, pg. 6433
BELECTRIC SOLAR & BATTERY GMBH—See RWE AG; *Int'l*, pg. 6433
BELECTRIC SOLAR LTD.—See RWE AG; *Int'l*, pg. 6433
BELEN ELEKTRIK URETIM A.S.—See Parsan Makina Parcalari Sanayii AS; *Int'l*, pg. 5746
BEL ENGINEERING (UK) LTD—See British Engines Ltd.; *Int'l*, pg. 1171
BELET ACQUISITIONS, INC.—See The Belet Group, Inc.; *U.S. Private*, pg. 3993
THE BELET GROUP, INC.; *U.S. Private*, pg. 3993
BELFAB, INC.—See Enpro Inc.; *U.S. Public*, pg. 774
BELFAIR DIALYSIS, LLC—See DaVita Inc.; *U.S. Public*, pg. 636
BELFAST INTERNATIONAL AIRPORT LTD.—See ACS, Actividades de Construccion y Servicios, S.A.; *Int'l*, pg. 112
BELFEIN SLOVAKIA A.S.—See Hanesbrands Inc.; *U.S. Public*, pg. 982
BELFIUS AUTO LEASE SA/NV—See Belfius Bank SA/NV; *Int'l*, pg. 963
BELFIUS BANK SA/NV; *Int'l*, pg. 963
BELFIUS COMMERCIAL FINANCE—See Belfius Bank SA/NV; *Int'l*, pg. 963
BELFIUS INSURANCE—See Belfius Bank SA/NV; *Int'l*, pg. 963
BELFIUS IRELAND—See Belfius Bank SA/NV; *Int'l*, pg. 963
BELFIUS LEASE SERVICES SA/NV—See Belfius Bank SA/NV; *Int'l*, pg. 963
BELFIUS LEASE—See Belfius Bank SA/NV; *Int'l*, pg. 963
BELFLEX STAFFING NETWORK, LLC—See Elwood Staffing Services, Inc.; *U.S. Private*, pg. 1377
BELFONTE DAIRY DISTRIBUTION INC.; *U.S. Private*, pg. 517
BELFONTE ICE CREAM, INC.—See Belfonte Dairy Distribution Inc.; *U.S. Private*, pg. 517
BELFOR (CANADA) INC.—See BELFOR USA Group, Inc.; *U.S. Private*, pg. 517
BELFOR (CANADA) INC.—See BELFOR USA Group, Inc.; *U.S. Private*, pg. 517
BELFOR USA GROUP, INC.; *U.S. Private*, pg. 517
BELFRUCO NV—See SEA-Invest Group; *Int'l*, pg. 6661
BEL FUSE AMERICA, INC.—See Bel Fuse Inc.; *U.S. Public*, pg. 292
BEL FUSE EUROPE LTD.—See Bel Fuse Inc.; *U.S. Public*, pg. 292
BEL FUSE INC.; *U.S. Public*, pg. 292
BEL FUSE LTD.—See Bel Fuse Inc.; *U.S. Public*, pg. 292
BEL FUSE (MACAO COMMERICAL OFFSHORE) LIMITED—See Bel Fuse Inc.; *U.S. Public*, pg. 292
BELGACOM GROUP INTERNATIONAL SERVICES SA—See Proximus PLC; *Int'l*, pg. 6007
BELGACOM INTERNATIONAL CARRIER SERVICES SA—See Proximus PLC; *Int'l*, pg. 6007
BELGACOM MOBILE S.A—See Proximus PLC; *Int'l*, pg. 6008
BELGARDE ENTERPRISES; *U.S. Private*, pg. 517
BELGAZPROMBANK OJSC—See Gazprombank JSC; *Int'l*, pg. 2892
BELGAZPROMBANK OJSC—See PJSC Gazprom; *Int'l*, pg. 5879
BELGER CARTAGE SERVICE, INC.—See Belcorp Inc.; *U.S. Private*, pg. 517
BELGER REALTY CO. INC.—See Belcorp Inc.; *U.S. Private*, pg. 517
BELGIAN POST INTERNATIONAL SA/NV—See bpost NV/SA; *Int'l*, pg. 1133
BELGIAN SHELL, S.A.—See Shell plc; *Int'l*, pg. 6797

BELGIAN VOLITION SA—See VolitionRX Limited; *U.S. Public*, pg. 2308
BELGIBO N.V.—See Exmar N.V.; *Int'l*, pg. 2585
BELGICA INSURANCE HOLDING S.A.—See Assicurazioni Generali S.p.A.; *Int'l*, pg. 647
BELGICAST INTERNACIONAL, S.L.—See Triton Advisers Limited; *Int'l*, pg. 7934
BELGICAST ITALIA, S.R.L.—See Triton Advisers Limited; *Int'l*, pg. 7934
BELGIOIOSO CHEESE INC.; *U.S. Private*, pg. 517
BELGIOVANE WILLIAMS MACKAY PTY LTD - MELBOURNE—See Dentsu Group Inc.; *Int'l*, pg. 2035
BELGIOVANE WILLIAMS MACKAY PTY LTD—See Dentsu Group Inc.; *Int'l*, pg. 2035
BELGIUM RETAIL 1 N.V.—See Retail Estates N.V.; *Int'l*, pg. 6305
BELGIUM TELEVISION SA—See Groupe AB S.A.; *Int'l*, pg. 3091
BEL GLOBAL RESOURCES HOLDINGS LIMITED; *Int'l*, pg. 962
BELGOLAISE SA—See BNP Paribas SA; *Int'l*, pg. 1089
BELGOMALT S.A.—See Axereal Union de Cooperatives Agricoles; *Int'l*, pg. 767
BELGORODSKY BACON—See Gruppa Kompaniy Rusagro OOO; *Int'l*, pg. 3140
BELGRAVIA HARTFORD CAPITAL INC.; *Int'l*, pg. 963
BELGRAVIUM LIMITED—See TouchStar plc; *Int'l*, pg. 7847
BELHASA ACTIONCRETE INTERNATIONAL—See Belhasa Group of Companies; *Int'l*, pg. 963
BELHASA ANTHONY POOLS CONTRACTING—See Belhasa Group of Companies; *Int'l*, pg. 963
BELHASA AUTOMOTIVE SERVICE CENTER & SPARE PARTS—See Belhasa Group of Companies; *Int'l*, pg. 963
BELHASA BIOTEK SOLUTIONS LLC—See Belhasa Group of Companies; *Int'l*, pg. 964
BELHASA ENGINEERING & CONTRACTING COMPANY—See Belhasa Group of Companies; *Int'l*, pg. 964
BELHASA FOR QUARRIES & CRUSHERS MANAGEMENT L.L.C—See Belhasa Group of Companies; *Int'l*, pg. 964
BELHASA GROUP OF COMPANIES; *Int'l*, pg. 963
BELHASA INTERNATIONAL COMPANY—See Belhasa Group of Companies; *Int'l*, pg. 964
BELHASA JOINERY & DECORATION COMPANY LLC—See Belhasa Group of Companies; *Int'l*, pg. 964
BELHASA MOTORS COMPANY—See Belhasa Group of Companies; *Int'l*, pg. 964
BELHASA PROJECTS LLC—See Belhasa Group of Companies; *Int'l*, pg. 964
BELHASA REAL ESTATE—See Belhasa Group of Companies; *Int'l*, pg. 964
BELHASA REAL ESTATE—See Belhasa Group of Companies; *Int'l*, pg. 964
BELHASA SIX CONSTRUCTION COMPANY—See Belhasa Group of Companies; *Int'l*, pg. 964
BELHASA, TOURISM, TRAVEL & CARGO CO., L.L.C.—See Belhasa Group of Companies; *Int'l*, pg. 964
BELHASA TRADING & DEVELOPMENT COMPANY—See Belhasa Group of Companies; *Int'l*, pg. 964
BELHAVEN BREWERY COMPANY LIMITED—See CK Asset Holdings Limited; *Int'l*, pg. 1635
BELHEALTH INVESTMENT PARTNERS LLC; *U.S. Private*, pg. 517
BELICO HOLDING AB—See AAK AB; *Int'l*, pg. 32
BELIEFNET, INC.—See BN Media LLC; *U.S. Private*, pg. 601
BELIEVE SAS; *Int'l*, pg. 964
BELI MART SDN. BHD.—See MY E.G. Services Berhad; *Int'l*, pg. 5111
BELIMED AG—See Metall Zug AG; *Int'l*, pg. 4846
BELIMED AG—See Miele & Cie KG; *Int'l*, pg. 4889
BELIMED B.V.—See Metall Zug AG; *Int'l*, pg. 4846
BELIMED B.V.—See Miele & Cie KG; *Int'l*, pg. 4890
BELIMED DEUTSCHLAND GMBH—See Metall Zug AG; *Int'l*, pg. 4846
BELIMED DEUTSCHLAND GMBH—See Miele & Cie KG; *Int'l*, pg. 4890
BELIMED D.O.O.—See Metall Zug AG; *Int'l*, pg. 4846
BELIMED D.O.O.—See Miele & Cie KG; *Int'l*, pg. 4890
BELIMED GMBH—See Metall Zug AG; *Int'l*, pg. 4846
BELIMED GMBH—See Miele & Cie KG; *Int'l*, pg. 4890
BELIMED GMBH—See Metall Zug AG; *Int'l*, pg. 4846
BELIMED INC.—See Metall Zug AG; *Int'l*, pg. 4846
BELIMED INC.—See Miele & Cie KG; *Int'l*, pg. 4890
BELIMED INFECTION CONTROL KFT.—See Metall Zug AG; *Int'l*, pg. 4846
BELIMED INFECTION CONTROL KFT.—See Miele & Cie KG; *Int'l*, pg. 4890
BELIMED LIFE SCIENCE AG—See Metall Zug AG; *Int'l*, pg. 4846
BELIMED LIFE SCIENCE AG—See Miele & Cie KG; *Int'l*, pg. 4890
BELIMED LTD.—See Metall Zug AG; *Int'l*, pg. 4846
BELIMED LTD.—See Miele & Cie KG; *Int'l*, pg. 4890

CORPORATE AFFILIATIONS

BELIMED MEDICAL EQUIPMENT (SHANGHAI) CO., LTD—See Metall Zug AG; *Int'l*, pg. 4846
BELIMED MEDICAL EQUIPMENT (SHANGHAI) CO., LTD—See Miele & Cie KG; *Int'l*, pg. 4890
BELIMED SAS—See Metall Zug AG; *Int'l*, pg. 4846
BELIMED SAS—See Miele & Cie KG; *Int'l*, pg. 4890
BELIMED SAUTER AG—See Metall Zug AG; *Int'l*, pg. 4846
BELIMED SAUTER AG—See Miele & Cie KG; *Int'l*, pg. 4890
BELIMED TECHNIK GMBH—See Metall Zug AG; *Int'l*, pg. 4846
BELIMED TECHNIK GMBH—See Miele & Cie KG; *Int'l*, pg. 4890
BELIMO AB—See BELIMO Holding AG; *Int'l*, pg. 964
BELIMO ACTUATORS (INDIA) PVT LTD.—See BELIMO Holding AG; *Int'l*, pg. 964
BELIMO ACTUATORS LTD.—See BELIMO Holding AG; *Int'l*, pg. 964
BELIMO ACTUATORS LTD.—See BELIMO Holding AG; *Int'l*, pg. 964
BELIMO ACTUATORS LTD.—See BELIMO Holding AG; *Int'l*, pg. 964
BELIMO ACTUATORS LTD.—See BELIMO Holding AG; *Int'l*, pg. 964
BELIMO ACTUATORS LTD.—See BELIMO Holding AG; *Int'l*, pg. 964
BELIMO ACTUATORS PTY. LTD.—See BELIMO Holding AG; *Int'l*, pg. 964
BELIMO ACTUATORS (SHANGHAI) TRADING LTD.—See BELIMO Holding AG; *Int'l*, pg. 964
BELIMO AIRCONTROLS (CAN), INC.—See BELIMO Holding AG; *Int'l*, pg. 964
BELIMO AIRCONTROLS (USA), INC.—See BELIMO Holding AG; *Int'l*, pg. 964
BELIMO A/S—See BELIMO Holding AG; *Int'l*, pg. 964
BELIMO AUTOMATION AG—See BELIMO Holding AG; *Int'l*, pg. 964
BELIMO AUTOMATION DEUTSCHLAND GMBH—See BELIMO Holding AG; *Int'l*, pg. 964
BELIMO AUTOMATION FZE—See BELIMO Holding AG; *Int'l*, pg. 964
BELIMO AUTOMATION HANDELSGESELLSCHAFT M.B.H.—See BELIMO Holding AG; *Int'l*, pg. 964
BELIMO AUTOMATION INDIA PRIVATE LIMITED—See BELIMO Holding AG; *Int'l*, pg. 965
BELIMO AUTOMATION MALAYSIA SDN. BHD.—See BELIMO Holding AG; *Int'l*, pg. 964
BELIMO AUTOMATION NORGE A / S—See BELIMO Holding AG; *Int'l*, pg. 964
BELIMO AUTOMATION (SHANGHAI) CO., LTD.—See BELIMO Holding AG; *Int'l*, pg. 965
BELIMO AUTOMATION UK LTD.—See BELIMO Holding AG; *Int'l*, pg. 964
BELIMO BELGIUM B.V.—See BELIMO Holding AG; *Int'l*, pg. 965
BELIMO BRASIL COMERCIO DE AUTOMACAO LTDA.—See BELIMO Holding AG; *Int'l*, pg. 965
BELIMO BULGARIA LTD.—See BELIMO Holding AG; *Int'l*, pg. 965
BELIMO CUSTOMIZATION (USA), INC.—See BELIMO Holding AG; *Int'l*, pg. 965
BELIMO CZ SPOL, S R.O.—See BELIMO Holding AG; *Int'l*, pg. 965
BELIMO FINLAND OY—See BELIMO Holding AG; *Int'l*, pg. 965
BELIMO HOLDING AG; *Int'l*, pg. 964
BELIMO IBERICA DE SERVOMOTORES S.A.—See BELIMO Holding AG; *Int'l*, pg. 965
BELIMO ITALIA S.R.L.—See BELIMO Holding AG; *Int'l*, pg. 965
BELIMO SERVOMOTOREN BV—See BELIMO Holding AG; *Int'l*, pg. 965
BELIMO SERVOMOTORI S.R.L.—See BELIMO Holding AG; *Int'l*, pg. 965
BELIMO SILOWNIKI S.A.—See BELIMO Holding AG; *Int'l*, pg. 965
BELIMO S.R.L.—See BELIMO Holding AG; *Int'l*, pg. 965
BELIMO STELLANTRIEBE VERTRIEBS GMBH—See BELIMO Holding AG; *Int'l*, pg. 965
BELIMO TECHNOLOGY (USA), INC.—See BELIMO Holding AG; *Int'l*, pg. 965
BELIMO TURKEY OTOMASYON A.S.—See BELIMO Holding AG; *Int'l*, pg. 965
BELIMPEX—See Messe Munchen GmbH; *Int'l*, pg. 4841
BELIN & ASSOCIATES, INC.; *U.S. Private*, pg. 518
BELINECO LLC—See Sika AG; *Int'l*, pg. 6914
BELINKA PERKEMIJA, D.O.O.—See Kansai Paint Co., Ltd.; *Int'l*, pg. 4071
BEL INTERNATIONAL LOGISTICS LTD.—See Konoike Transport Co., Ltd.; *Int'l*, pg. 4274
BEL INTERNATIONAL LOGISTICS LTD.—See Konoike Transport Co., Ltd.; *Int'l*, pg. 4274
BEL INTERNATIONAL LOGISTICS VIETNAM COMPANY LTD.—See Konoike Transport Co., Ltd.; *Int'l*, pg. 4274
BELITE BIO, INC.; *U.S. Public*, pg. 294
THE BELIZE BANK LIMITED—See Caribbean Investment Holdings Limited; *Int'l*, pg. 1330

COMPANY NAME INDEX

BELIZE ELECTRIC COMPANY LIMITED—See Fortis Inc.; *Int'l*, pg. 2739
BELIZE TELECOMMUNICATIONS LIMITED; *Int'l*, pg. 965
BELIZE WATER SERVICES LIMITED; *Int'l*, pg. 965
BELK FORD INC.; *U.S. Private*, pg. 518
BELKIN ASIA PACIFIC LIMITED—See Hon Hai Precision Industry Co., Ltd.; *Int'l*, pg. 3456
BELKIN BV—See Hon Hai Precision Industry Co., Ltd.; *Int'l*, pg. 3456
BELK, INC.—See Sycamore Partners Management, LP; *U.S. Private*, pg. 3895
BELKIN GMBH—See Hon Hai Precision Industry Co., Ltd.; *Int'l*, pg. 3456
BELKIN INTERNATIONAL, INC.—See Hon Hai Precision Industry Co., Ltd.; *Int'l*, pg. 3456
BELKIN LIMITED—See Hon Hai Precision Industry Co., Ltd.; *Int'l*, pg. 3456
BELKIN SAS—See Hon Hai Precision Industry Co., Ltd.; *Int'l*, pg. 3456
BELKIN TRADING (SHANGHAI) COMPANY LTD.—See Hon Hai Precision Industry Co., Ltd.; *Int'l*, pg. 3456
BELKITCHEN CORPORATION—See WOOD ONE Co., Ltd.; *Int'l*, pg. 8449
THE BELKNAP WHITE GROUP, LLC; *U.S. Private*, pg. 3993
BELKORP AG, LLC—See Belkorp Industries, Inc.; *Int'l*, pg. 965
BELKORP INDUSTRIES, INC.; *Int'l*, pg. 965
BELL24-CELL PRODUCT, INC.—See CMIC Holdings Co., Ltd.; *Int'l*, pg. 1670
BELLA CASA FASHION & RETAIL LTD.; *Int'l*, pg. 966
BELLA COOLA FISHERIES LTD.; *Int'l*, pg. 966
BELLACOR INC.; *U.S. Private*, pg. 519
BELLA FRESH, LLC; *U.S. Private*, pg. 519
BELLA FRUTTA S.A.—See Orsero S.p.A.; *Int'l*, pg. 5644
BELLAGIO, LLC—See MGM Resorts International; *U.S. Public*, pg. 1435
BELLA GROUP; *U.S. Private*, pg. 519
BELLAIRE OUTPATIENT SURGERY CENTER, L.L.P.—See Tenet Healthcare Corporation; *U.S. Public*, pg. 2009
BELLAIRE SURGICAL HOSPITAL HOLDINGS, LLC—See Nobilis Health Corp.; *U.S. Private*, pg. 2932
BELLAIR EXPEDITING NORTHWEST, INC.—See Bellair Expediting Service Inc.; *U.S. Private*, pg. 519
BELLAIR EXPEDITING SERVICE INC.; *U.S. Private*, pg. 519
BELLAIR VENTURES INC.; *Int'l*, pg. 966
BELL ALIANT INC.—See BCE Inc.; *Int'l*, pg. 926
BELL ALIANT PREFERRED EQUITY INC.—See BCE Inc.; *Int'l*, pg. 926
BELL ALIANT—See BCE Inc.; *Int'l*, pg. 926
BELLAMY'S AUSTRALIA LIMITED—See China Mengniu Dairy Company Limited; *Int'l*, pg. 1520
BELLAMY STRICKLAND CHEVROLET GMC AND PONTIAC INC.; *U.S. Private*, pg. 519
BELLANCA DEVELOPMENTS LTD.—See Dundee Corporation; *Int'l*, pg. 2226
BELL-ANDERSON INSURANCE, INC.; *U.S. Private*, pg. 519
BELL AND MCCOY INC.; *U.S. Private*, pg. 518
BELLARINE PENINSULA COMMUNITY BRANCH LIMITED—See Bendigo & Adelaide Bank Ltd.; *Int'l*, pg. 970
BELLASERA—See SunStream, Inc.; *U.S. Private*, pg. 3873
BELL & ASSOCIATES CONSTRUCTION, LP.; *U.S. Private*, pg. 518
BELLATOR SPORT WORLDWIDE LLC—See National Amusements, Inc.; *U.S. Private*, pg. 2839
BELLAVIA CHEVROLET BUICK; *U.S. Private*, pg. 519
BELL AVIATION INC.; *U.S. Private*, pg. 518
BELLA VISTA GROUP, INC.; *U.S. Private*, pg. 519
BELLAVISTA RESOURCES LTD.; *Int'l*, pg. 966
BELLA VISTA VILLAGE PROPERTY OWNERS ASSOCIATION; *U.S. Private*, pg. 519
BELL & BAIN LTD.; *Int'l*, pg. 965
BELL BCI COMPANY—See Bell Corp. of Rochester; *U.S. Private*, pg. 518
BELL & BELL BUICK PONTIAC GMC ISUZU TRUCKS, INC.; *U.S. Private*, pg. 518
BELL BENELUX N.V.—See Coop-Gruppe Genossenschaft; *Int'l*, pg. 1789
BELLBOY BAR SUPPLY—See Bellboy Corporation; *U.S. Private*, pg. 520
BELLBOY CIGARS—See Bellboy Corporation; *U.S. Private*, pg. 520
BELLBOY CORPORATION; *U.S. Private*, pg. 519
BELL BROTHERS OIL CO. INC.; *U.S. Private*, pg. 518
BELL BUCKLE HOLDINGS, INC.; *U.S. Public*, pg. 294
BELL CANADA—See BCE Inc.; *Int'l*, pg. 926
BELL CARNI S.R.L.—See Cremonini S.p.A.; *Int'l*, pg. 1838
BELL-CARTER FOODS, INC. - CORNING PLANT—See Bell-Carter Foods, Inc.; *U.S. Private*, pg. 519
BELL-CARTER FOODS, INC.; *U.S. Private*, pg. 519
BELL-CARTER PACKAGING—See Bell-Carter Foods, Inc.; *U.S. Private*, pg. 519
BELL & CLEMENTS INC—See Munchener Ruckversicherungs AG; *Int'l*, pg. 5085

BELL & CLEMENTS (LONDON) LTD—See Munchener Ruckversicherungs AG; *Int'l*, pg. 5085
BELL & CLEMENTS UNDERWRITING MANAGERS LTD—See Munchener Ruckversicherungs AG; *Int'l*, pg. 5085
BELLCO CANADA INC.—See Medtronic plc; *Int'l*, pg. 4786
BELLCO DO BRASIL—See Medtronic plc; *Int'l*, pg. 4786
BELLCO DRUG CORP.—See Cencora, Inc.; *U.S. Public*, pg. 467
BELLCO ELECTRICAL (PTY) LIMITED—See The Bidvest Group Limited; *Int'l*, pg. 7621
BELLCO HEALTH CORP.—See Cencora, Inc.; *U.S. Public*, pg. 467
BELLCO HOXEN MEDICAL (SHANGHAI) CO. LTD.—See Medtronic plc; *Int'l*, pg. 4786
BELL CONCRETE INCORPORATED; *U.S. Private*, pg. 518
BELL CONSTRUCTORS INC.—See Bell Corp. of Rochester; *U.S. Private*, pg. 518
BELL COPPER CORPORATION; *Int'l*, pg. 965
BELL CORP. OF ROCHESTER; *U.S. Private*, pg. 518
BELLCO S.R.L.—See Medtronic plc; *Int'l*, pg. 4786
BELL COUNTY COAL CORPORATION—See James River Coal Company; *U.S. Private*, pg. 2185
BELL CREEK EQUIPMENT LLC—See Tym Corporation; *Int'l*, pg. 7994
BELL DEUTSCHLAND HOLDING GMBH—See Coop-Gruppe Genossenschaft; *Int'l*, pg. 1789
BELL DODGE, L.L.C.—See AutoNation, Inc.; *U.S. Public*, pg. 233
BELLEAIR DEVELOPMENT GROUP, INC.; *U.S. Private*, pg. 520
BELLEAIR HOLIDAYS LTD.—See SMS Group Limited; *Int'l*, pg. 7014
BELLE AIR INC.—See NorthCurrent Partners, LLC; *U.S. Private*, pg. 2949
BELLEAIR SURGERY CENTER, LTD.—See HCA Healthcare, Inc.; *U.S. Public*, pg. 991
BELLECAPITAL AG; *Int'l*, pg. 966
BELLECCI & ASSOCIATES, INC.—See Sanderson Bellecci, Inc.; *U.S. Private*, pg. 3543
BELLE CORPORATION; *Int'l*, pg. 966
BELLE CREEK APARTMENTS COLORADO, LLC—See RAIT Financial Trust; *U.S. Private*, pg. 3348
BELLEEK POTTERY LTD.; *Int'l*, pg. 967
BELLE ENGINEERING LTD—See Altrad Investment Authority SAS; *Int'l*, pg. 398
BELLEFAIRE JCB; *U.S. Private*, pg. 520
BELLE FOURCHE PIPELINE CO.—See True Companies; *U.S. Private*, pg. 4247
BELLE GLADE DIALYSIS CENTER, LLC—See Nautic Partners, LLC; *U.S. Private*, pg. 2869
BELLE GROUP INC.—See Altrad Investment Authority SAS; *Int'l*, pg. 398
BELLEGROVE CERAMICS PLC—See QuattroR SGR S.p.A.; *Int'l*, pg. 6157
BELLE INTERNATIONAL HOLDINGS LIMITED—See Hillhouse Investment Management Limited; *Int'l*, pg. 3392
BELL ELECTRICAL CONTRACTORS, INC.—See MDU Resources Group, Inc.; *U.S. Public*, pg. 1410
BELL ELECTRICAL SUPPLY INC.; *U.S. Private*, pg. 518
BELLELI ENERGY CRITICAL PROCESS EQUIPMENT S.R.L.—See Walter Tosto S.p.A.; *Int'l*, pg. 8336
BELLELI ENERGY F.Z.E.—See Enerflex Ltd.; *Int'l*, pg. 2418
BELLEMEAD DEVELOPMENT CORPORATION—See Chubb Limited; *Int'l*, pg. 1590
BELLE OF ORLEANS, LLC—See Boyd Gaming Corporation; *U.S. Public*, pg. 377
BELLE OF SIOUX CITY, L.P.—See PENN Entertainment, Inc.; *U.S. Public*, pg. 1662
BELL EQUIPMENT AUSTRALIA (PTY) LIMITED—See Bell Equipment Limited; *Int'l*, pg. 966
BELL EQUIPMENT COMPANY SA (PTY) LIMITED—See Bell Equipment Limited; *Int'l*, pg. 966
BELL EQUIPMENT COMPANY—See Rotunda Capital Partners LLC; *U.S. Private*, pg. 3488
BELL EQUIPMENT CO SWAZILAND (PROPRIETARY) LIMITED—See Bell Equipment Limited; *Int'l*, pg. 966
BELL EQUIPMENT (DEUTSCHLAND) GMBH—See Bell Equipment Limited; *Int'l*, pg. 966
BELL EQUIPMENT LIMITED; *Int'l*, pg. 965
BELL EQUIPMENT MOZAMBIQUE LIMITADA—See Bell Equipment Limited; *Int'l*, pg. 966
BELL EQUIPMENT RUSSLAND LLC—See Bell Equipment Limited; *Int'l*, pg. 966
BELL EQUIPMENT SALES SOUTH AFRICA LIMITED—See Bell Equipment Limited; *Int'l*, pg. 966
BELL EQUIPMENT (SEA) PTE LIMITED—See Bell Equipment Limited; *Int'l*, pg. 966
BELL EQUIPMENT UK LIMITED—See Bell Equipment Limited; *Int'l*, pg. 966
BELL EQUIPMENT (ZAMBIA) LIMITED—See Bell Equipment Limited; *Int'l*, pg. 966
BELLEROPHON PUBLICATIONS, INC.—See Sandow Media LLC; *U.S. Private*, pg. 3544
BELLEROPHON THERAPEUTICS, INC.; *U.S. Public*, pg. 295
BELLETECH CORP.—See AGC Inc.; *Int'l*, pg. 201

BELLETECH CORP.—See PPG Industries, Inc.; *U.S. Public*, pg. 1707
BELLETETE'S INC.; *U.S. Private*, pg. 520
BELLE TIRE DISTRIBUTOR INC.; *U.S. Private*, pg. 520
BELLE TIRE DISTRIBUTORS, INC.; *U.S. Private*, pg. 520
BELL & EVANS; *U.S. Private*, pg. 518
BELLEVILLE INTELLIGENCER—See Chatham Asset Management, LLC; *U.S. Private*, pg. 861
BELLEVILLE NEWS-DEMOCRAT—See Chatham Asset Management, LLC; *U.S. Private*, pg. 866
BELLEVUE ASSET MANAGEMENT AG—See Bellevue Group AG; *Int'l*, pg. 967
BELLEVUE AUTOMOTIVE, INC.—See AutoNation, Inc.; *U.S. Public*, pg. 233
BELLEVUE BUILDERS SUPPLY - US LBM, LLC—See Bain Capital, LP; *U.S. Private*, pg. 450
BELLEVUE CASH & CARRY LTD.—See Bestway (Holdings) Limited; *Int'l*, pg. 1000
BELLEVUE COLLISION, INC.—See AutoNation, Inc.; *U.S. Public*, pg. 233
BELLEVUE COLLISION, INC.—See AutoNation, Inc.; *U.S. Public*, pg. 233
BELLEVUE DISTRIBUTION SA—See Carrefour SA; *Int'l*, pg. 1343
BELLEVUE GOLD LIMITED; *Int'l*, pg. 967
BELLEVUE GROUP AG; *Int'l*, pg. 967
BELLEVUE HEALTHCARE TRUST PLC; *Int'l*, pg. 967
BELLEVUE HOLDING COMPANY INC.; *U.S. Private*, pg. 520
BELLEVUE LIFE SCIENCES ACQUISITION CORP.; *U.S. Public*, pg. 295
BELLEVUE PHILHARMONIC ORCHESTRA INC.; *U.S. Private*, pg. 520
BELLEVUE SA—See Clariane SE; *Int'l*, pg. 1642
BELLEVUE-S, LLC—See Lithia Motors, Inc.; *U.S. Public*, pg. 1321
BELLEVUE-T, LLC—See Lithia Motors, Inc.; *U.S. Public*, pg. 1321
BELLEVUE TOWERS CONDOMINIUMS, LLC—See Morgan Stanley; *U.S. Public*, pg. 1471
BELLE WORLDWIDE LIMITED—See Hillhouse Investment Management Limited; *Int'l*, pg. 3392
BELL EXPRESSVU, L.P.—See BCE Inc.; *Int'l*, pg. 926
BELL EXPRESSVU—See BCE Inc.; *Int'l*, pg. 926
BELLEZZA CLUB JAPAN INC.—See Brother Industries, Ltd.; *Int'l*, pg. 1196
BELL FINANCIAL GROUP LIMITED; *Int'l*, pg. 966
BELL FLAVORS AND FRAGRANCES DO BRASIL INDUSTRIA—See Bell Flavors & Fragrances, Inc.; *U.S. Private*, pg. 518
BELL FLAVORS & FRAGRANCES DUFT UND AROMA GMBH—See Bell Flavors & Fragrances, Inc.; *U.S. Private*, pg. 518
BELL FLAVORS & FRAGRANCES DUFT UND AROMA GMBH—See Bell Flavors & Fragrances, Inc.; *U.S. Private*, pg. 518
BELL FLAVORS & FRAGRANCES DUFT UND AROMA GMBH—See Bell Flavors & Fragrances, Inc.; *U.S. Private*, pg. 518
BELL FLAVORS & FRAGRANCES, INC. - FRAGRANCE MANUFACTURING FACILITY—See Bell Flavors & Fragrances, Inc.; *U.S. Private*, pg. 518
BELL FLAVORS & FRAGRANCES, INC.; *U.S. Private*, pg. 518
BELL FOOD GROUP AG—See Coop-Gruppe Genossenschaft; *Int'l*, pg. 1789
BELL FOODS, LLC; *U.S. Private*, pg. 518
BELL FORD INC.—See The Berge Group; *U.S. Private*, pg. 3993
BELL FORK LIFT INC.; *U.S. Private*, pg. 518
BELL FRANCE SARL—See Bell Equipment Limited; *Int'l*, pg. 966
BELL-FRUIT GROUP LTD.—See Novomatic AG; *Int'l*, pg. 5467
BELL FUELS INC.; *U.S. Private*, pg. 518
BELL GAS, INC.; *U.S. Private*, pg. 518
BELL HELICOPTER ASIA (PTE) LTD.—See Textron Inc.; *U.S. Public*, pg. 2028
BELL HELICOPTER INDIA INC.—See Textron Inc.; *U.S. Public*, pg. 2028
BELL HELICOPTER MIAMI INC.—See Textron Inc.; *U.S. Public*, pg. 2028
BELL HELICOPTER SUPPLY CENTER N.V.—See Textron Inc.; *U.S. Public*, pg. 2028
BELL HELICOPTER TEXTRON CANADA LIMITED—See Textron Inc.; *U.S. Public*, pg. 2028
BELL HELICOPTER TEXTRON, INC.—See Textron Inc.; *U.S. Public*, pg. 2028
BELL & HOWELL - CANADA—See WestView Capital Partners, L.P.; *U.S. Private*, pg. 4501
BELL & HOWELL, LLC—See WestView Capital Partners, L.P.; *U.S. Private*, pg. 4501
BELL & HOWELL, LLC - WHEELING OFFICE—See WestView Capital Partners, L.P.; *U.S. Private*, pg. 4501
BELLIARD MATERIAUX; *Int'l*, pg. 967
BELLICUM PHARMACEUTICALS, INC.; *U.S. Public*, pg. 295
BELLINDA CESKA REPUBLIKA, S.R.O.—See Hanesbrands Inc.; *U.S. Public*, pg. 982

BELLICUM PHARMACEUTICALS, INC. CORPORATE AFFILIATIONS

BELLINDA HUNGARIA KFT.—See Hanesbrands Inc.; *U.S. Public*, pg. 982
BELLINDA SLOVENSKO S.R.O.—See Hanesbrands Inc.; *U.S. Public*, pg. 982
BELL INDUSTRIES, INC.; *U.S. Public*, pg. 295
BELL-INFO-TEC CORPORATION—See Mitsubishi Corporation; *Int'l*, pg. 4938
BELLINGHAM HERALD PUBLISHING, LLC—See Chatham Asset Management, LLC; *U.S. Private*, pg. 866
THE BELLINGHAM HERALD—See Chatham Asset Management, LLC; *U.S. Private*, pg. 866
BELLINGHAM MARINE INDUSTRIES INC.—See Bellwether Financial Group, Inc.; *U.S. Private*, pg. 520
BELLINGHAM & STANLEY, INC.—See Xylem Inc.; *U.S. Public*, pg. 2395
BELLINGHAM & STANLEY LTD.—See Xylem Inc.; *U.S. Public*, pg. 2395
BELLINGHAM UNDERWRITERS, INC.—See Brown & Brown, Inc.; *U.S. Public*, pg. 397
BELLINI NAUTICA S.P.A.; *Int'l*, pg. 967
BELL I&S CO., LTD.—See Kyongbo Pharmaceutical Co., Ltd.; *Int'l*, pg. 4364
BELLISIO FOODS, INC.—See Charoen Pokphand Foods Public Company Limited; *Int'l*, pg. 1451
BELL IXL INVESTMENTS PTY. LTD.; *Int'l*, pg. 966
BELL LABORATORIES, INC.; *U.S. Private*, pg. 518
BELLMAN OIL CO. INC.; *U.S. Private*, pg. 520
BELL-MARK CORPORATION; *U.S. Private*, pg. 519
BELL MEDIA INC.—See BCE Inc.; *Int'l*, pg. 926
BELL MEDIA RADIO - CALGARY—See BCE Inc.; *Int'l*, pg. 927
BELL MEDIA RADIO—See BCE Inc.; *Int'l*, pg. 927
BELL MEDICAL SOLUTIONS INC.—See Bain Capital, LP; *U.S. Private*, pg. 436
BELL MOBILITY INC.—See BCE Inc.; *Int'l*, pg. 927
BELL MORTGAGE—See State Bankshares, Inc.; *U.S. Private*, pg. 3791
BELL MOTORS, LLC—See AutoNation, Inc.; *U.S. Public*, pg. 233
BELL MTS INC.—See BCE Inc.; *Int'l*, pg. 926
BELL NEDERLAND B.V.—See Coop-Gruppe Genossenschaft; *Int'l*, pg. 1789
BELL NURSERY HOLDINGS, LLC—See Central Garden & Pet Company; *U.S. Public*, pg. 473
BELLOFRAM INSTRUMENTS (INDIA) PVT. LTD.—See Desco Corporation; *U.S. Private*, pg. 1211
BELL'O INTERNATIONAL CORP.—See Z Capital Group, LLC; *U.S. Private*, pg. 4595
BELLONA HOSPITALITY SERVICES LIMITED—See The Phoenix Mills Limited; *Int'l*, pg. 7673
BELLOTA AGRISOLUTIONS & TOOLS USA, LLC—See Ingersoll Tillage Group, Inc.; *Int'l*, pg. 3702
BELLOTA BRASIL, LTDA.—See Ingersoll Tillage Group, Inc.; *Int'l*, pg. 3702
BELLOTA COLOMBIA, S.A.—See Ingersoll Tillage Group, Inc.; *Int'l*, pg. 3702
BELLOTA HERRAMIENTAS S.L.U.—See Ingersoll Tillage Group, Inc.; *Int'l*, pg. 3702
BELLOTA MEXICO, S.A. DE C.V.—See Ingersoll Tillage Group, Inc.; *Int'l*, pg. 3702
BELLOWS FALLS TOWN CRIER—See Alden Global Capital LLC; *U.S. Private*, pg. 155
BELLOWSTECH, LLC—See American Securities LLC; *U.S. Private*, pg. 250
BELL-PARK CO., LTD.; *Int'l*, pg. 966
BELL PARTNERS, INC.; *U.S. Private*, pg. 518
BELL PHYSICIAN PRACTICES, INC.—See Apollo Global Management, Inc.; *U.S. Public*, pg. 154
BELL PLASTICS LIMITED—See Synnovia Plc; *Int'l*, pg. 7386
BELL POLSKA SP. Z O.O—See Coop-Gruppe Genossenschaft; *Int'l*, pg. 1789
BELL POTTER CAPITAL LIMITED—See Bell Financial Group Limited; *Int'l*, pg. 966
BELL POTTER SECURITIES (HK) LIMITED—See Bell Financial Group Limited; *Int'l*, pg. 966
BELL POTTER (US) HOLDINGS INC.—See Bell Financial Group Limited; *Int'l*, pg. 966
BELL PROCESSING INCORPORATED; *U.S. Private*, pg. 519
BELL PRODUCTS, INC.; *U.S. Private*, pg. 519
BELL PUMP SERVICE COMPANY; *U.S. Private*, pg. 519
BELL RACING USA, LLC—See Vista Outdoor Inc.; *U.S. Public*, pg. 2304
BELL RECRUITMENT ADVERTISING; *U.S. Private*, pg. 519
BELLRING BRANDS, INC.—See Post Holdings, Inc.; *U.S. Public*, pg. 1703
BELLRINGER SECURITY, INC.—See Pye-Barker Fire & Safety, LLC; *U.S. Private*, pg. 3309
BELL ROCK CAPITAL, LLC—See WSFS Financial Corporation; *U.S. Public*, pg. 2383
BELL ROSE CAPITAL, INC.; *U.S. Public*, pg. 295
BELL'S BREWERY, INC.; *U.S. Private*, pg. 519
BELL SCHWEIZ AG—See Coop-Gruppe Genossenschaft; *Int'l*, pg. 1789
BELL'S FOOD MARKET INC.; *U.S. Private*, pg. 519

BELLS MARKETING SDN. BHD.—See UNIMECH Group Berhad; *Int'l*, pg. 8049
BELL'S OF ATHENS INC.—See Bell's Food Market Inc.; *U.S. Private*, pg. 519
BELLSOFT, INC.—See Enveric Biosciences, Inc.; *U.S. Public*, pg. 780
BELL SOLUTIONS (PVT) LTD.—See Melstacorp PLC; *Int'l*, pg. 4813
BELL SONS & CO (DRUGGISTS) LIMITED—See Marksans Pharma Ltd; *Int'l*, pg. 4697
BELLSOUTH, LLC—See AT&T Inc.; *U.S. Public*, pg. 219
BELL SPORTS, INC.—See Vista Outdoor Inc.; *U.S. Public*, pg. 2304
BELL STATE BANK & TRUST—See State Bankshares, Inc.; *U.S. Private*, pg. 3791
BELLSTORES INC.—See Lykins Companies, Inc.; *U.S. Private*, pg. 2519
BELL SUPPLY CO.; *U.S. Private*, pg. 519
BELLSYSTEM24 HOLDINGS, INC.; *Int'l*, pg. 967
BELLSYSTEM24, INC.—See Bain Capital, LP; *U.S. Private*, pg. 436
BELL TECHLOGIX—See Bell Industries, Inc.; *U.S. Public*, pg. 295
BELL TECHNICAL SERVICES INC.—See Textron Inc.; *U.S. Public*, pg. 2028
BELL TEXTRON ASIA (PTE) LTD.—See Textron Inc.; *U.S. Public*, pg. 2028
BELL TEXTRON PRAGUE, A.S.—See Textron Inc.; *U.S. Public*, pg. 2028
BELL TRADING INCORPORATED; *U.S. Private*, pg. 519
BELLUNA CO. LTD.; *Int'l*, pg. 967
BELLUSCURA PLC; *Int'l*, pg. 967
BELLUS HEALTH INC.—See GSK plc; *Int'l*, pg. 3145
BELLVANTAGE (PVT) LTD.—See Melstacorp PLC; *Int'l*, pg. 4813
BELLWAY FINANCIAL SERVICES LIMITED—See Bellway plc; *Int'l*, pg. 967
BELLWAY HOMES LIMITED EAST MIDLANDS—See Bellway plc; *Int'l*, pg. 967
BELLWAY HOMES LIMITED ESSEX—See Bellway plc; *Int'l*, pg. 967
BELLWAY HOMES LIMITED MANCHESTER—See Bellway plc; *Int'l*, pg. 967
BELLWAY HOMES LIMITED NORTH EAST—See Bellway plc; *Int'l*, pg. 967
BELLWAY HOMES LIMITED NORTHERN HOME COUNTIES—See Bellway plc; *Int'l*, pg. 968
BELLWAY HOMES LIMITED NORTH LONDON—See Bellway plc; *Int'l*, pg. 968
BELLWAY HOMES LIMITED NORTH WEST—See Bellway plc; *Int'l*, pg. 968
BELLWAY HOMES LIMITED SCOTLAND—See Bellway plc; *Int'l*, pg. 968
BELLWAY HOMES LIMITED—See Bellway plc; *Int'l*, pg. 967
BELLWAY HOMES LIMITED SOUTH EAST—See Bellway plc; *Int'l*, pg. 968
BELLWAY HOMES LIMITED THAMES GATEWAY—See Bellway plc; *Int'l*, pg. 968
BELLWAY HOMES LIMITED WALES—See Bellway plc; *Int'l*, pg. 968
BELLWAY HOMES LIMITED WESSEX—See Bellway plc; *Int'l*, pg. 968
BELLWAY HOMES LIMITED WEST MIDLANDS—See Bellway plc; *Int'l*, pg. 968
BELLWAY HOMES LIMITED YORKSHIRE—See Bellway plc; *Int'l*, pg. 968
BELLWAY HOUSING TRUST LIMITED—See Bellway plc; *Int'l*, pg. 968
BELLWAY PLC; *Int'l*, pg. 967
BELLWAY (SERVICES) LIMITED—See Bellway plc; *Int'l*, pg. 967
BELL WEALTH MANAGEMENT INC.—See Genstar Capital, LLC; *U.S. Private*, pg. 1677
BELL WEALTH MANAGEMENT INC.—See Keystone Group, L.P.; *U.S. Private*, pg. 2298
BELLWEST MANAGEMENT CORPORATION; *U.S. Private*, pg. 520
BELLWETHER ASSET MANAGEMENT, INC.; *U.S. Private*, pg. 520
BELLWETHER COMMUNITY CREDIT UNION; *U.S. Private*, pg. 520
BELLWETHER ENTERPRISE - CHARLOTTE—See Enterprise Community Partners, Inc.; *U.S. Private*, pg. 1403
BELLWETHER ENTERPRISE REAL ESTATE—See Enterprise Community Partners, Inc.; *U.S. Private*, pg. 1403
BELLWETHER FINANCIAL GROUP, INC.; *U.S. Private*, pg. 520
THE BELLWETHER GROUP; *U.S. Private*, pg. 3993
BELLWETHER HOUSING; *U.S. Private*, pg. 520
BELLWYCK PACKAGING SOLUTIONS LTD.; *Int'l*, pg. 968
BELLZONE MINING PLC; *Int'l*, pg. 968
BEL MANUFACTURERA, S.A. DE C.V.—See Hubbell Incorporated; *U.S. Public*, pg. 1066
BELMARK INC.; *U.S. Private*, pg. 520
BELMAR PHARMACY—See Webster Equity Partners, LLC; *U.S. Private*, pg. 4467
BELMAY, INC.; *U.S. Private*, pg. 520

BELMOND CAP JULUCA LTD—See LVMH Moet Hennessy Louis Vuitton SE; *Int'l*, pg. 4590
BELMOND CASTELLO DI CASOLE S.R.L.—See LVMH Moet Hennessy Louis Vuitton SE; *Int'l*, pg. 4590
BELMOND ITALIA S.R.L.—See LVMH Moet Hennessy Louis Vuitton SE; *Int'l*, pg. 4590
BELMOND LTD.—See LVMH Moet Hennessy Louis Vuitton SE; *Int'l*, pg. 4590
BELMOND MANAGEMENT LIMITED—See LVMH Moet Hennessy Louis Vuitton SE; *Int'l*, pg. 4591
BELMOND MOUNT NELSON HOTEL LTD.—See LVMH Moet Hennessy Louis Vuitton SE; *Int'l*, pg. 4591
BELMOND RESERVATION SERVICES INC—See LVMH Moet Hennessy Louis Vuitton SE; *Int'l*, pg. 4591
BELMOND (UK) LIMITED—See LVMH Moet Hennessy Louis Vuitton SE; *Int'l*, pg. 4591
BELMOND USA INC.—See LVMH Moet Hennessy Louis Vuitton SE; *Int'l*, pg. 4591
BELMONT BEHAVIORAL HOSPITAL, LLC—See Acadia Healthcare Company, Inc.; *U.S. Public*, pg. 28
BELMONT CHASE, LLC—See Regency Centers Corporation; *U.S. Public*, pg. 1774
BELMONT CITIZEN-HERALD—See Gannett Co., Inc.; *U.S. Public*, pg. 901
BELMONT COUNTRY CLUB—See Apollo Global Management, Inc.; *U.S. Public*, pg. 149
BELMONT CROSSING, LLC—See Bluerock Residential Growth REIT, Inc.; *U.S. Public*, pg. 366
BELMONT ENTERPRISES, INC.—See Daseke, Inc.; *U.S. Private*, pg. 1161
BELMONT GROUP INC.; *U.S. Private*, pg. 520
BELMONT HOLDINGS CORP.—See RGP Holding, Inc.; *U.S. Private*, pg. 3420
BELMONT HOUSING RESOURCES FOR WNY; *U.S. Private*, pg. 520
BELMONT MEAT PRODUCTS LTD.—See Premium Brands Holdings Corporation; *Int'l*, pg. 5962
BELMONT METALS, INC.; *U.S. Private*, pg. 520
BELMONT NURSING & REHABILITATION CENTER—See Health Dimensions Group; *U.S. Public*, pg. 1893
BELMONT RESOURCES INC.; *Int'l*, pg. 968
BELMONT SOFTWARE SERVICES; *U.S. Private*, pg. 521
BELMONT TAVERN (WA) PTY LTD—See Woolworths Group Limited; *Int'l*, pg. 8451
BELMONT TECHNOLOGY REMARKETING—See Belmont Trading Company; *U.S. Private*, pg. 521
BELMONT TECHNOLOGY REMARKETING—See Belmont Trading Company; *U.S. Private*, pg. 521
BELMONT TECHNOLOGY REMARKETING—See SiPi Metals Corp.; *U.S. Private*, pg. 3671
BELMONT TRADING COMPANY; *U.S. Private*, pg. 521
BELMONT VILLAGE BUFFALO GROVE, L.L.C.—See Welltower Inc.; *U.S. Public*, pg. 2347
BELMONT VILLAGE CAROL STREAM, L.L.C.—See Welltower Inc.; *U.S. Public*, pg. 2347
BELMONT VILLAGE OAK PARK, L.L.C.—See Welltower Inc.; *U.S. Public*, pg. 2348
BELMONT VILLAGE RANCHO PALOS VERDES TENANT, LLC—See Welltower Inc.; *U.S. Public*, pg. 2348
BELMONT VILLAGE SAN JOSE, LLC—See Welltower Inc.; *U.S. Public*, pg. 2348
BELMONT VILLAGE ST. MATTHEWS, L.L.C.—See Welltower Inc.; *U.S. Public*, pg. 2348
BELMONT VILLAGE SUNNYVALE, LLC—See Welltower Inc.; *U.S. Public*, pg. 2348
BELMONT VILLAGE TURTLE CREEK TENANT, LLC—See Welltower Inc.; *U.S. Public*, pg. 2348
BELMONT VILLAGE WEST LAKE HILLS TENANT, LLC—See Welltower Inc.; *U.S. Public*, pg. 2348
BEL NICKEL RESOURCES LIMITED—See BEL Global Resources Holdings Limited; *Int'l*, pg. 963
BELO CORP.—See TEGNA Inc.; *U.S. Public*, pg. 1989
BELO ENTERPRISES, INC.—See DallasNews Corporation; *U.S. Public*, pg. 621
BELO INTERACTIVE, INC.—See DallasNews Corporation; *U.S. Public*, pg. 621
BELOIT BEVERAGE CO. INC.; *U.S. Private*, pg. 521
BELOIT HEALTH SYSTEM, INC.; *U.S. Private*, pg. 521
BELOIT REGIONAL HOSPICE—See Beloit Health System, Inc.; *U.S. Private*, pg. 521
BE-LO MARKETS INC.—See Camellia Food Stores, Inc.; *U.S. Public*, pg. 728
BELONG ACQUISITION CORP.; *U.S. Public*, pg. 295
BEL OPTRONIC DEVICES LTD.—See Bharat Electronics Limited; *Int'l*, pg. 1011
BELORETSK METALLURGICAL PLANT AO—See Mechel PAO; *Int'l*, pg. 4765
BEL-ORO INTERNATIONAL, INC.—See Berkshire Hathaway Inc.; *U.S. Public*, pg. 316
BELORUSNEFT REPUBLICAN UNITARY ENTERPRISE—See Concern Belneftekhim; *Int'l*, pg. 1764
BELO SUN MINING (BARBADOS) CORP—See Belo Sun Mining Corp.; *Int'l*, pg. 968
BELO SUN MINING CORP.; *Int'l*, pg. 968
BELOVO PAPER MILL S.A.; *Int'l*, pg. 968
BELOW THE RADAR LIMITED—See Zinc Media Group plc; *Int'l*, pg. 8684

COMPANY NAME INDEX

BELPARK BV.—See Compagnie des Alpes S.A.; *Int'l*, pg. 1737
BELPHAR LTD.; *Int'l*, pg. 968
BELPOINTE PREP, LLC; *U.S. Public*, pg. 295
BELPOINTE REIT, INC.; *U.S. Public*, pg. 295
BEL POWER EUROPE S.R.L.—See Bel Fuse Inc.; *U.S. Public*, pg. 292
BEL POWER (HANGZHOU) CO. LTD.—See Bel Fuse Inc.; *U.S. Public*, pg. 292
BEL POWER INC.—See Bel Fuse Inc.; *U.S. Public*, pg. 292
BELPOWER INTERNATIONAL S.A.—See Reibel N.V.; *Int'l*, pg. 6256
BEL POWER PRODUCTS INC.—See Bel Fuse Inc.; *U.S. Public*, pg. 293
BEL POWER SOLUTIONS CO. LTD.—See Bel Fuse Inc.; *U.S. Public*, pg. 293
BEL POWER SOLUTIONS GMBH—See Bel Fuse Inc.; *U.S. Public*, pg. 293
BEL POWER SOLUTIONS INC.—See Bel Fuse Inc.; *U.S. Public*, pg. 293
BEL POWER SOLUTIONS IRELAND LIMITED—See Bel Fuse Inc.; *U.S. Public*, pg. 293
BEL POWER SOLUTIONS LIMITED—See Bel Fuse Inc.; *U.S. Public*, pg. 293
BEL POWER SOLUTIONS LTD.—See Bel Fuse Inc.; *U.S. Public*, pg. 293
BEL POWER SOLUTIONS S.R.O.—See Bel Fuse Inc.; *U.S. Public*, pg. 293
BELPOWER S.R.L.—See Reibel N.V.; *Int'l*, pg. 6256
BEL-RAY COMPANY, LLC—See Calumet, Inc.; *U.S. Public*, pg. 425
BELRON CANADA INC.—See s.a. D'Ieteren n.v.; *Int'l*, pg. 6447
BELRON S.A.—See s.a. D'Ieteren n.v.; *Int'l*, pg. 6447
BELSAZAR GMBH—See Diageo plc; *Int'l*, pg. 2101
BELSHAW BROTHERS, INC.—See Ali Holding S.r.l; *Int'l*, pg. 322
BELSHIPS ASA; *Int'l*, pg. 968
BEL SHOWER DOOR CORP.—See Baymark Partners; *U.S. Private*, pg. 496
BEL STEWART CONNECTOR SYSTEMS, INC.—See Bel Fuse Inc.; *U.S. Public*, pg. 293
BEL STEWART S.R.O.—See Bel Fuse Inc.; *U.S. Public*, pg. 293
BEL SUPPLY CHAIN SOLUTION LTD.—See Konoike Transport Co., Ltd.; *Int'l*, pg. 4274
BELTAPHARM S.P.A.—See Strides Pharma Science Limited; *Int'l*, pg. 7240
BELT BROKERS (PTY.) LTD.—See Invicta Holdings Limited; *Int'l*, pg. 3788
BELT COLLINS INTERNATIONAL (HONG KONG) LTD.—See Palm Eco-Town Development Co., Ltd.; *Int'l*, pg. 5709
BELT CONCEPTS OF AMERICA INC.—See The Goodyear Tire & Rubber Company; *U.S. Public*, pg. 2082
BELTERRA RESORT INDIANA, LLC—See Boyd Gaming Corporation; *U.S. Public*, pg. 377
BELTING CO. OF CINCINNATI INC.; *U.S. Private*, pg. 521
BELTING INDUSTRIES CO. INC.; *U.S. Private*, pg. 521
BELTING SUPPLY SERVICES (PTY) LTD—See Hudaco Industries Limited; *Int'l*, pg. 3521
BELTIOS GMBH—See msg group GmbH; *Int'l*, pg. 5067
BELTMANN GROUP INC.; *U.S. Private*, pg. 521
BELTONE ASSET MANAGEMENT—See Chimera Investments LLC; *Int'l*, pg. 1479
BELTONE ELECTRONICS LLC—See GN Store Nord A/S; *Int'l*, pg. 3016
BELTONE ELECTRONICS OF CANADA LTD.—See GN Store Nord A/S; *Int'l*, pg. 3016
BELTONE EUROPE HOLDINGS APS—See GN Store Nord A/S; *Int'l*, pg. 3016
BEL TONE INDIA LIMITED—See GN Store Nord A/S; *Int'l*, pg. 3016
BELTONE INVESTMENT BANKING—See Chimera Investments LLC; *Int'l*, pg. 1479
BELTONE PRIVATE EQUITY—See Chimera Investments LLC; *Int'l*, pg. 1479
BELTONE SECURITIES BROKERAGE—See Chimera Investments LLC; *Int'l*, pg. 1479
BELTON FAMILY PRACTICE CLINIC, LLC—See HCA Healthcare, Inc.; *U.S. Public*, pg. 991
BELTON FINANCIAL HOLDING—See Chimera Investments LLC; *Int'l*, pg. 1479
BELTON INDUSTRIES, INC.; *U.S. Private*, pg. 521
BELTON PUBLISHING COMPANY—See Chatham Asset Management, LLC; *U.S. Private*, pg. 866
BELTON REGIONAL MEDICAL CENTER—See HCA Healthcare, Inc.; *U.S. Public*, pg. 991
BELT POWER LLC—See Platte River Ventures, LLC; *U.S. Private*, pg. 3211
THE BELT RAILWAY COMPANY OF CHICAGO—See Berkshire Hathaway Inc.; *U.S. Public*, pg. 303
BELTRAM EDGE TOOL SUPPLY CORP; *U.S. Private*, pg. 521
BELTRAME LEFFLER ADVERTISING; *U.S. Private*, pg. 521
BELTRAMI ELECTRIC COOPERATIVE, INC.; *U.S. Private*, pg. 521

BEL TRANSFORMER INC.—See Bel Fuse Inc.; *U.S. Public*, pg. 293
BELTSERVICE CORPORATION; *U.S. Private*, pg. 521
BELT TECHNOLOGIES, INC.—See Peter Pan Bus Lines, Inc.; *U.S. Private*, pg. 3159
BELTWAY BUICK INC.; *U.S. Private*, pg. 521
BELTWAY CAPITAL PARTNERS, LLC; *U.S. Private*, pg. 521
BELTWAY INTERNATIONAL TRUCKS, INC.; *U.S. Private*, pg. 521
BELT-WIDE INDUSTRIES, INC.—See Lummus Corporation; *U.S. Private*, pg. 2514
BELTZ IANNI & ASSOCIATES—See Crestview Partners, L.P.; *U.S. Private*, pg. 1098
BELUGA INC.—See Adjmi Apparel Group, Inc.; *U.S. Private*, pg. 79
BELUGA LIMITED—See Hung Hing Printing Group Limited; *Int'l*, pg. 3535
BELUGA NV; *Int'l*, pg. 968
BELUGA VENTURES, LLC; *U.S. Private*, pg. 521
BELUGGAWEB LTD.—See Francoudi & Stephanou Ltd.; *Int'l*, pg. 2761
BEL UK LTD.—See Unibel SA; *Int'l*, pg. 8031
BELUPO D.D.—See Podravka d.d.; *Int'l*, pg. 5902
BELUPO D.O.O.—See Podravka d.d.; *Int'l*, pg. 5902
BELUSA FOODS S.R.O.—See Orkla ASA; *Int'l*, pg. 5637
BEL USA LLC; *U.S. Private*, pg. 516
BELVAC CR, SPOL S.R.O.—See Dover Corporation; *U.S. Public*, pg. 678
BELVAC MIDDLE EAST FZE—See Dover Corporation; *U.S. Public*, pg. 678
BELVAC PRODUCTION MACHINERY, INC.—See Dover Corporation; *U.S. Public*, pg. 679
BEL VALVES LTD—See British Engines Ltd.; *Int'l*, pg. 1171
BELVAROSI KIGYO PATIKA BT.—See PHOENIX Pharmahandel GmbH & Co. KG; *Int'l*, pg. 5854
BELVEDERE CORPORATION; *U.S. Private*, pg. 521
BELVEDERE HOTEL PARTNERSHIP—See Probity International Corporation; *U.S. Private*, pg. 3271
BELVEDERE, LLC; *U.S. Private*, pg. 521
BELVEDERE MARKETING GROUP LLC—See 424 Capital, LLC; *U.S. Private*, pg. 15
BELVEDERE MARKETING GROUP LLC—See HealthEdge Investment Partners, LLC; *U.S. Private*, pg. 1806
BELVEDERE MINING OY—See GlobalBlock Digital Asset Trading Limited; *Int'l*, pg. 3003
BELVEDERE PACIFIC LLC—See Aquiline Capital Partners LLC; *U.S. Private*, pg. 305
BELVEDERE SLOVENSKO, S. R. O.—See Marie Brizard Wine & Spirits S.A.; *Int'l*, pg. 4693
BEL VENTURES INC.—See Bel Fuse Inc.; *U.S. Public*, pg. 293
BELVERON REAL ESTATE PARTNERS, LLC; *U.S. Private*, pg. 521
BELVIDERE SAND & GRAVEL—See Haines & Kibblehouse Inc.; *U.S. Private*, pg. 1840
BELVOIR GROUP PLC—See The Property Franchise Group PLC; *Int'l*, pg. 7676
BELVOIR PROPERTY MANAGEMENT (UK) LIMITED—See The Property Franchise Group PLC; *Int'l*, pg. 7676
BELVOIR PUBLICATIONS INC.; *U.S. Private*, pg. 522
BELWAY INSURANCE SERVICE, INC.—See Belcorp Inc.; *U.S. Private*, pg. 517
BELWITH PRODUCTS, LLC - FIRST WATCH SECURITY DIVISION—See Belwith Products, LLC; *U.S. Private*, pg. 522
BELWITH PRODUCTS, LLC - HICKORY HARDWARE DIVISION—See Belwith Products, LLC; *U.S. Private*, pg. 522
BELWITH PRODUCTS, LLC - KEELER DIVISION—See Belwith Products, LLC; *U.S. Private*, pg. 522
BELWITH PRODUCTS, LLC; *U.S. Private*, pg. 522
BELWOOD FOODS LIMITED—See Argent Group Europe Limited; *Int'l*, pg. 560
BELYA TURIZM INS. ENERJI BLS. SAN. VE TIC. A.S.—See Loras Holding A.S.; *Int'l*, pg. 4557
BELZ ENTERPRISES; *U.S. Private*, pg. 522
BEMAC CONSTRUCTION CORP.—See Bantrel Co.; *Int'l*, pg. 855
BEMAC CORPORATION; *Int'l*, pg. 968
BE.MAINTENANCE—See Ackermans & van Haaren NV; *Int'l*, pg. 105
BEMAP, INC.; *Int'l*, pg. 968
BEM (BURRELL ENGAGEMENT MARKETING)—See FVLCRUM PARTNERS LLC; *U.S. Private*, pg. 1628
BEMCO ASSOCIATES, INC.; *U.S. Private*, pg. 522
BEMCO FLUIDTECHNIK LLP—See BEMCO HYDRAULICS LTD; *Int'l*, pg. 969
BEMCO FULIDTECHNIK LLP—See BEMCO HYDRAULICS LTD; *Int'l*, pg. 969
BEMCO HYDRAULICS LTD; *Int'l*, pg. 968
BEMCO INC.; *U.S. Private*, pg. 522
BEMCOR INC.—See Beatty Machine & Mfg. Company; *U.S. Private*, pg. 507
BEMETALS CORP.; *Int'l*, pg. 969
BEMIDJI CHRYSLER CENTER, LLC; *U.S. Private*, pg. 522

BENARA BEARINGS & PISTONS LTD.

BEMIDJI WOOLEN MILLS; *U.S. Private*, pg. 522
BEMIND A.D.; *Int'l*, pg. 969
BEMIS ASIA PACIFIC SDN BHD—See Amcor plc; *Int'l*, pg. 418
BEMIS ASSOCIATES INC.; *U.S. Private*, pg. 522
BEMIS BRISBANE PTY LTD—See Amcor plc; *Int'l*, pg. 418
BEMIS CLYSAR, INC.—See Amcor plc; *Int'l*, pg. 418
BEMIS COMPANY, INC.—See Amcor plc; *Int'l*, pg. 418
BEMIS COMPANY—See Amcor plc; *Int'l*, pg. 418
BEMIS CUSTOM PRODUCTS—See Amcor plc; *Int'l*, pg. 418
BEMIS DEUTSCHLAND HOLDINGS GMBH—See Amcor plc; *Int'l*, pg. 418
BEMIS ELSHAM LIMITED—See Amcor plc; *Int'l*, pg. 418
BEMIS EUROPE FLEXIBLE PACKAGING—See Amcor plc; *Int'l*, pg. 418
BEMIS FLEXIBLE PACKAGING CANADA LIMITED—See Amcor plc; *Int'l*, pg. 418
BEMIS FLEXIBLE PACKAGING (SUZHOU) CO., LTD.—See Amcor plc; *Int'l*, pg. 418
BEMIS HEALTHCARE PACKAGING IRELAND LIMITED—See Kohlberg & Company, LLC; *U.S. Private*, pg. 2337
BEMIS HONG KONG LTD.—See Bemis Associates Inc.; *U.S. Private*, pg. 522
BEMIS MANUFACTURING COMPANY; *U.S. Private*, pg. 522
BEMIS MAYOR PACKAGING LIMITED—See Amcor plc; *Int'l*, pg. 418
BEMIS MONCEAU S.A.—See Amcor plc; *Int'l*, pg. 418
BEMIS PACKAGING DEUTSCHLAND GMBH—See Amcor plc; *Int'l*, pg. 418
BEMIS PACKAGING MEXICO, S.A. DE C.V.—See Amcor plc; *Int'l*, pg. 418
BEMIS PACKAGING POLSKA SP. Z.O.O.—See Amcor plc; *Int'l*, pg. 418
BEMIS PACKAGING SVERIGE A.B.—See Amcor plc; *Int'l*, pg. 418
BEMIS PACKAGING U.K. LTD.—See Kohlberg & Company, LLC; *U.S. Private*, pg. 2337
BEMIS PERFORMANCE PACKAGING, INC.—See Amcor plc; *Int'l*, pg. 418
BEMIS PIATRA NEAMT—See Amcor plc; *Int'l*, pg. 418
BEMIS SAS—See Amcor plc; *Int'l*, pg. 418
BEMIS (SHANGHAI) TRADING CO., LTD.—See Amcor plc; *Int'l*, pg. 418
BEMISS-JASON—See F.I.L.A. - Fabbrica Italiana Lapis ed Affini S.p.A.; *Int'l*, pg. 2596
BEMIS SWANSEA LTD.—See Kohlberg & Company, LLC; *U.S. Private*, pg. 2337
BEMIS VALKEAKOSKI OY—See Amcor plc; *Int'l*, pg. 418
BEMKA EMAYE BOBIN TELI VE KABLO SAN. TIC. A.S.—See Sarkuysan Elektrolitik Bakir Sanayi Ve Ticaret A.S.; *Int'l*, pg. 6578
BEML BRASIL INDUSTRIAL LTDA—See BEML Limited; *Int'l*, pg. 969
BEML LIMITED - AEROSPACE MANUFACTURING DIVISION—See BEML Limited; *Int'l*, pg. 969
BEML LIMITED - BANGALORE COMPLEX—See BEML Limited; *Int'l*, pg. 969
BEML LIMITED - EARTH MOVING DIVISION—See BEML Limited; *Int'l*, pg. 969
BEML LIMITED - ENGINE DIVISION—See BEML Limited; *Int'l*, pg. 969
BEML LIMITED - HYDRAULICS & POWERLINE (H&P) DIVISION—See BEML Limited; *Int'l*, pg. 969
BEML LIMITED - INTERNATIONAL BUSINESS DIVISION—See BEML Limited; *Int'l*, pg. 969
BEML LIMITED; *Int'l*, pg. 969
BEML LIMITED - TECHNOLOGY DIVISION—See BEML Limited; *Int'l*, pg. 969
BEML LIMITED - TRADING DIVISION—See BEML Limited; *Int'l*, pg. 969
BEML LIMITED - TRUCK DIVISION—See BEML Limited; *Int'l*, pg. 969
BEML (MALAYSIA) SDN.BHD.—See BEML Limited; *Int'l*, pg. 969
BEMMGTSSON MASKIN—See Indutrade AB; *Int'l*, pg. 3677
BEMPFINGER LEBENSMITTEL GMBH—See Hero AG; *Int'l*, pg. 3363
BEMROSEBOOTH PARAGON LIMITED—See Paragon Group Limited; *Int'l*, pg. 5737
BEM SP. Z O.O.—See ASSA ABLOY AB; *Int'l*, pg. 633
BEM SYSTEMS, INC.—See Bernhard Capital Partners Management, LP; *U.S. Private*, pg. 536
BEM SYSTEMS - NEWPORT NEWS—See Bernhard Capital Partners Management, LP; *U.S. Private*, pg. 536
BEM SYSTEMS - ORLANDO—See Bernhard Capital Partners Management, LP; *U.S. Private*, pg. 536
BEM SYSTEMS - PHOENIX—See Bernhard Capital Partners Management, LP; *U.S. Private*, pg. 537
BENAKA, INC.; *U.S. Private*, pg. 523
BENALEC HOLDINGS BERHAD; *Int'l*, pg. 969
BENALEC SDN BHD—See Benalec Holdings Berhad; *Int'l*, pg. 969
BENARA BEARINGS & PISTONS LTD.; *Int'l*, pg. 969
BENARES HOTELS LIMITED—See Tata Sons Limited; *Int'l*, pg. 7468

319

BEN ARNOLD CO., INC.

BEN ARNOLD CO., INC.; *U.S. Private*, pg. 522
THE BEN ARNOLD-SUNBELT BEVERAGE COMPANY OF SOUTH CAROLINA, L.P.—See Breakthru Beverage Group, LLC; *U.S. Private*, pg. 643
BENAROYA RESEARCH INSTITUTE AT VIRGINIA MASON; *U.S. Private*, pg. 523
BENAY-HAT CO.; *U.S. Private*, pg. 523
BEN BAILEY LTD.—See Gladedale Holdings PLC; *Int'l*, pg. 2987
BEN B. BLISS COMPANY, INC.; *U.S. Private*, pg. 522
BENBILT BUILDING SYSTEMS LP—See Woodgrain, Inc.; *U.S. Private*, pg. 4558
THE BEN BRIDGE CORPORATION—See Berkshire Hathaway Inc.; *U.S. Public*, pg. 316
BEN BRIDGE JEWELER, INC.—See Berkshire Hathaway Inc.; *U.S. Public*, pg. 316
BEN BURGESS & COMPANY; *Int'l*, pg. 969
BENCARD A.G.—See ZQ Capital Management Limited; *Int'l*, pg. 8691
BENCARD ALLERGIE (AUSTRIA) GMBH—See ZQ Capital Management Limited; *Int'l*, pg. 8691
BENCARD ALLERGIE GMBH—See ZQ Capital Management Limited; *Int'l*, pg. 8691
BENCHMARC DISPLAY INC.; *U.S. Private*, pg. 523
BENCHMARK ARCHITECTURAL SYSTEMS, INC.—See Metecno S.p.A.; *Int'l*, pg. 4853
BENCHMARK BANKSHARES INC.; *U.S. Public*, pg. 295
BENCHMARK BEHAVIORAL HEALTH SYSTEM, INC.—See Universal Health Services, Inc.; *U.S. Public*, pg. 2256
BENCHMARK - BELEURA PTY LIMITED—See Ramsay Health Care Limited; *Int'l*, pg. 6199
BENCHMARK BRANDS INC.; *U.S. Private*, pg. 523
BENCHMARK BROADCAST SYSTEMS (P) LIMITED—See Benchmark Telecast Integration Pte Ltd; *Int'l*, pg. 970
BENCHMARK BROADCAST SYSTEMS (S) PTE LTD—See Benchmark Telecast Integration Pte Ltd; *Int'l*, pg. 970
BENCHMARK BUILDERS, INC.—See FTE Networks, Inc.; *U.S. Public*, pg. 889
BENCHMARK CAPITAL; *U.S. Private*, pg. 523
BENCHMARK CAPITAL—See Benchmark Capital; *U.S. Private*, pg. 523
BENCHMARK CIVIL ENGINEERING SERVICES INC.; *U.S. Private*, pg. 523
BENCHMARK COMPLETIONS, LLC—See Intervale Capital, LLC; *U.S. Private*, pg. 2127
BENCHMARK CONSTRUCTION COMPANY, INC.; *U.S. Private*, pg. 523
BENCHMARK CONTRACTORS, INC.—See Morley Builders; *U.S. Private*, pg. 2785
BENCHMARK DIGITAL PARTNERS LLC—See Vista Equity Partners, LLC; *U.S. Private*, pg. 4395
BENCHMARK DISPLAYS; *U.S. Private*, pg. 523
BENCHMARK ELECTRONICS INC. - NEW HAMPSHIRE DIVISION—See Benchmark Electronics, Inc.; *U.S. Public*, pg. 295
BENCHMARK ELECTRONICS, INC.; *U.S. Public*, pg. 295
BENCHMARK ELECTRONICS INC.—See Benchmark Electronics, Inc.; *U.S. Public*, pg. 295
BENCHMARK ELECTRONICS INC.—See Benchmark Electronics, Inc.; *U.S. Public*, pg. 295
BENCHMARK ELECTRONICS INC.—See Benchmark Electronics, Inc.; *U.S. Public*, pg. 295
BENCHMARK ELECTRONICS MANUFACTURING SOLUTIONS (MOORPARK), INC.—See Benchmark Electronics, Inc.; *U.S. Public*, pg. 295
BENCHMARK ELECTRONICS NETHERLANDS HOLDING B.V.—See Benchmark Electronics, Inc.; *U.S. Public*, pg. 295
BENCHMARK ENERGY PRODUCTS, LLC—See Select Water Solutions, Inc.; *U.S. Public*, pg. 1862
BENCHMARK FINANCIAL GROUPS, LLC; *U.S. Private*, pg. 523
THE BENCHMARK FINANCIAL GROUP; *U.S. Private*, pg. 3993
BENCHMARK GENETICS NORWAY AS—See Benchmark Holdings Plc; *Int'l*, pg. 970
BENCHMARK HOLDINGS PLC; *Int'l*, pg. 970
BENCHMARK HOMES INC.; *U.S. Private*, pg. 523
BENCHMARK HOSPITALITY INTERNATIONAL INC.; *U.S. Private*, pg. 523
BENCHMARK INDUSTRIAL, INC.; *U.S. Private*, pg. 524
BENCHMARK INDUSTRIES; *U.S. Private*, pg. 524
BENCHMARK INTERNET GROUP, LLC; *U.S. Private*, pg. 524
BENCHMARK LANDSCAPES, LLC—See BrightView Holdings, Inc.; *U.S. Public*, pg. 383
BENCHMARK LOGISTICS, INC.—See ACI Capital Co. LLC; *U.S. Private*, pg. 59
BENCHMARK MANAGEMENT GROUP, INC.—See Community Association Management Specialist, Inc.; *U.S. Private*, pg. 989
BENCHMARK METALS INC.; *Int'l*, pg. 970
BENCHMARK REALTY LLC; *U.S. Private*, pg. 524
BENCHMARK REHAB PARTNERS; *U.S. Private*, pg. 524
BENCHMARK REPORTING AGENCY, INC.—See Apax Partners LLP; *Int'l*, pg. 503

BENCHMARK SENIOR LIVING, LLC; *U.S. Private*, pg. 524
BENCHMARK SERVICES, INC.; *U.S. Private*, pg. 524
BENCHMARK SYSTEMS, INC.—See AntWorks Pte. Ltd.; *Int'l*, pg. 485
BENCHMARK TELECAST INTEGRATION PTE LTD; *Int'l*, pg. 970
BENCHMARK USA; *U.S. Private*, pg. 524
BENCHMARQ MICROELECTRONICS CORPORATION OF SOUTH KOREA—See Texas Instruments Incorporated; *U.S. Public*, pg. 2025
BENCHMARX KITCHENS AND JOINERY LIMITED—See Travis Perkins plc; *Int'l*, pg. 7908
BENCHWORKS, INC.; *U.S. Private*, pg. 524
BENCIS CAPITAL PARTNERS B.V.; *Int'l*, pg. 970
BENCO DENTAL SUPPLY CO. INC.; *U.S. Private*, pg. 524
BENCO INSURANCE HOLDING BV—See Storebrand ASA; *Int'l*, pg. 7226
BENCOM FINANCIAL SERVICES GROUP INC.—See People Corporation; *Int'l*, pg. 5793
BENCOR GLOBAL, INC.—See Keller Group plc; *Int'l*, pg. 4119
BENDALLS ENGINEERING—See Carr's Group PLC; *Int'l*, pg. 1343
BENDA-LUTZ-ALPOCO SP.Z O.O.—See DIC Corporation; *Int'l*, pg. 2109
BENDA-LUTZ CORPORATION—See DIC Corporation; *Int'l*, pg. 2109
BENDA-LUTZ WERKE GMBH—See DIC Corporation; *Int'l*, pg. 2109
BENDA SUNKWANG IND. CO., LTD.; *Int'l*, pg. 970
BEND CABLE COMMUNICATIONS LLC—See Telephone & Data Systems, Inc.; *U.S. Public*, pg. 1997
BENDCARE, LLC; *U.S. Private*, pg. 524
BEND-CDJR, LLC—See Lithia Motors, Inc.; *U.S. Public*, pg. 1321
BENDER GMBH—See Berry Global Group, Inc; *U.S. Public*, pg. 322
BENDER/HELPER IMPACT, INC.—See Dolphin Entertainment, Inc.; *U.S. Public*, pg. 673
BENDER LUMBER COMPANY INC.; *U.S. Private*, pg. 524
BENDER & MODLIN FIRE SPRINKLER, INC.—See Pye-Barker Fire & Safety, LLC; *U.S. Private*, pg. 3309
BENDERSON DEVELOPMENT COMPANY, LLC; *U.S. Private*, pg. 524
BENDER WAREHOUSE CO.; *U.S. Private*, pg. 524
BEND FINANCIAL, INC.—See Webster Financial Corporation; *U.S. Public*, pg. 2341
BENDIGO & ADELAIDE BANK LTD.; *Int'l*, pg. 970
BENDIGO FINANCIAL PLANNING LIMITED—See Bendigo & Adelaide Bank Ltd.; *Int'l*, pg. 970
BENDIGO INVESTMENT SERVICES LIMITED—See Bendigo & Adelaide Bank Ltd.; *Int'l*, pg. 970
BENDIGO PARTNERS, LLC; *U.S. Private*, pg. 524
BENDIGO TELCO LIMITED; *Int'l*, pg. 971
BENDING SPOONS S.P.A.; *Int'l*, pg. 971
BENDING TECHNOLOGIES, INC.—See Activar, Inc.; *U.S. Private*, pg. 68
BENDITO RESOURCES INC.; *U.S. Private*, pg. 524
BENDIX COMMERCIAL VEHICLE SYSTEMS LLC—See Knorr-Bremse AG; *Int'l*, pg. 4210
BENDIX CVS DE MEXICO SA DE CV—See Knorr-Bremse AG; *Int'l*, pg. 4210
BENDIX SPICER FOUNDATION BRAKE LLC—See Knorr-Bremse AG; *Int'l*, pg. 4210
BENDON, INC.—See Irving Place Capital Management, L.P.; *U.S. Private*, pg. 2141
BENDON LIMITED; *Int'l*, pg. 972
BENDON USA INC.—See Bendon Limited; *Int'l*, pg. 972
BEND RESEARCH, INC.—See Lonza Group AG; *Int'l*, pg. 4553
BENDTEC, INC.—See Bernhard Capital Partners Management, LP; *U.S. Private*, pg. 537
BENDURA BANK AG—See Citychamp Watch & Jewellery Group Limited; *Int'l*, pg. 1628
BENDURA FUND MANAGEMENT ALPHA AG—See Valartis Group AG; *Int'l*, pg. 8111
BENDURA FUND MANAGEMENT ALPHA AG—See Citychamp Watch & Jewellery Group Limited; *Int'l*, pg. 1628
BENDURA FUND MANAGEMENT BETA AG—See Citychamp Watch & Jewellery Group Limited; *Int'l*, pg. 1628
BEND WELD ENGINEERING SDN. BHD—See Kobay Technology Bhd.; *Int'l*, pg. 4216
BENE AGERE NORDEN AS—See TPXimpact Holdings PLC; *Int'l*, pg. 7885
BENE BELGIUM BVBA—See Bene GmbH; *Int'l*, pg. 972
BENE BRATISLAVA SPOL.S.R.O,—See Bene GmbH; *Int'l*, pg. 972
BENE BUDAPEST KFT.,—See Bene GmbH; *Int'l*, pg. 972
BENECHIM S.P.R.L.—See PMC Capital Partners, LLC; *U.S. Private*, pg. 3217
BENECKE-KALIKO AG—See Continental Aktiengesellschaft; *Int'l*, pg. 1780
BENECOM INC.—See Relia, Inc.; *Int'l*, pg. 6260
THE BENECON GROUP; *U.S. Private*, pg. 3993
BENECO SYSTEMS, INC.—See Aquiline Capital Partners LLC; *U.S. Private*, pg. 303

CORPORATE AFFILIATIONS

BENECO SYSTEMS, INC.—See Genstar Capital, LLC; *U.S. Private*, pg. 1675
BENEDEK INVESTMENT GROUP, LLC; *U.S. Private*, pg. 524
BENE DEUTSCHLAND GMBH—See Bene GmbH; *Int'l*, pg. 972
BENEDICT ADVERTISING; *U.S. Private*, pg. 525
THE BENEDICT PARTNERSHIP LLP—See inTrust Group of Companies; *Int'l*, pg. 3771
BENEDICT REFRIGERATION SERVICE, INC.; *U.S. Private*, pg. 525
BENEFEX LIMITED; *Int'l*, pg. 972
BENEFIA TU MAJATKOWYCH S.A.—See Vienna Insurance Group AG Wiener Versicherung Gruppe; *Int'l*, pg. 8194
BENEFIA TU NA ZYCIE S.A.—See Vienna Insurance Group AG Wiener Versicherung Gruppe; *Int'l*, pg. 8194
BENEFIA UBEZPIECZENIA SPOLKA Z OGRANICZONA ODPOWIEDZIALNOSCIA—See Vienna Insurance Group AG Wiener Versicherung Gruppe; *Int'l*, pg. 8194
BENEFICIADORA DE CEREAIS MANI LTDA.—See General Mills, Inc.; *U.S. Public*, pg. 921
BENEFICIAL ADVISORS, LLC—See WSFS Financial Corporation; *U.S. Public*, pg. 2384
BENEFICIAL FINANCES—See HSBC Holdings plc; *Int'l*, pg. 3505
BENEFICIAL INSURANCE SERVICES, LLC—See Caisse de Depot et Placement du Quebec; *Int'l*, pg. 1256
BENEFICIAL INSURANCE SERVICES, LLC—See KKR & Co. Inc.; *U.S. Public*, pg. 1265
BENEFICIAL LIFE INSURANCE COMPANY—See Deseret Management Corporation; *U.S. Private*, pg. 1212
BENEFICIAL MANAGEMENT INC.—See HSBC Holdings plc; *Int'l*, pg. 3505
BENEFICIAL NEW MEXICO INC.—See HSBC Holdings plc; *Int'l*, pg. 3505
BENEFICIAL SOUTH CAROLINA INC.—See HSBC Holdings plc; *Int'l*, pg. 3505
BENEFICIAL STANDARD LIFE INSURANCE COMPANY—See CNO Financial Group, Inc.; *U.S. Public*, pg. 519
BENEFICIAL STATE BANCORP, INC.—See Beneficial State Foundation; *U.S. Private*, pg. 525
BENEFICIAL STATE BANK—See Beneficial State Foundation; *U.S. Private*, pg. 525
BENEFICIAL STATE FOUNDATION; *U.S. Private*, pg. 525
BENEFICIAL WASHINGTON INC.—See HSBC Holdings plc; *Int'l*, pg. 3505
BENEFICIENT—See GWG Holdings, Inc.; *U.S. Public*, pg. 975
BENEFICIOS INTEGRALES OPORTUNOS SA—See Marsh & McLennan Companies, Inc.; *U.S. Public*, pg. 1374
BENEFICIOS VOLCAFE S.A.—See ED&F Man Holdings Limited; *Int'l*, pg. 2302
BENEFICKS CORPORATION—See Nihon Kohden Corporation; *Int'l*, pg. 5285
BENE-FIN B.V.—See TomTom N.V.; *Int'l*, pg. 7804
BENEFIS HEALTH SYSTEM; *U.S. Private*, pg. 525
BENEFIT ADMINISTRATION COMPANY LLC; *U.S. Private*, pg. 525
BENEFIT ADMINISTRATION FOR THE SELF EMPLOYED, L.L.C.—See UnitedHealth Group Incorporated; *U.S. Public*, pg. 2239
BENEFIT ADVISORS, INC.; *U.S. Private*, pg. 525
BENEFIT COMMERCE GROUP—See Genstar Capital, LLC; *U.S. Private*, pg. 1674
BENEFIT CONSULTANTS GROUP, INC.—See Horace Mann Educators Corporation; *U.S. Public*, pg. 1053
BENEFIT CONSULTING ALLIANCE, LLC—See Hylant Group Inc.; *U.S. Private*, pg. 2019
BENEFIT CONSULTING GMBH—See JDC Group AG; *Int'l*, pg. 3925
BENEFIT COSMETICS HONG KONG LIMITED—See LVMH Moet Hennessy Louis Vuitton SE; *Int'l*, pg. 4601
BENEFIT COSMETICS LLC—See LVMH Moet Hennessy Louis Vuitton SE; *Int'l*, pg. 4601
BENEFIT COSMETICS SAS—See LVMH Moet Hennessy Louis Vuitton SE; *Int'l*, pg. 4591
BENEFIT COSMETICS SERVICES CANADA INC—See LVMH Moet Hennessy Louis Vuitton SE; *Int'l*, pg. 4591
BENEFIT COSMETICS UK LTD—See LVMH Moet Hennessy Louis Vuitton SE; *Int'l*, pg. 4601
BENEFITED, LLC—See Nelnet, Inc.; *U.S. Public*, pg. 1504
BENEFIT EXPRESS SERVICES, LLC—See WEX, Inc.; *U.S. Public*, pg. 2364
BENEFITFOCUS.COM, INC.—See Voya Financial, Inc.; *U.S. Public*, pg. 2311
BENEFITFOCUS, INC.—See Voya Financial, Inc.; *U.S. Public*, pg. 2311
BENEFIT HOLDING, INC.—See IQVIA Holdings Inc.; *U.S. Public*, pg. 1168
BENEFIT IP SPOLKA Z OGRANICZONA ODPOWIEDZIALNOSCIA SP.K.—See Benefit Systems SA; *Int'l*, pg. 972
BENEFIT JAPAN CO., LTD.; *Int'l*, pg. 972
BENEFIT MANAGEMENT INC.—See Nueterra Capital Management, LLC; *U.S. Private*, pg. 2972

BENEFIT MARKETING SOLUTIONS, L.L.C.—See Aon plc; *Int'l*, pg. 494
BENEFIT ONE INC.—See Pasona Group Inc.; *Int'l*, pg. 5753
BENEFIT ONE SHANGHAI INC.—See Pasona Group Inc.; *Int'l*, pg. 5753
BENEFIT ONE (THAILAND) CO., LTD.—See Pasona Group Inc.; *Int'l*, pg. 5753
BENEFIT ONE USA, INC.—See Pasona Group Inc.; *Int'l*, pg. 5753
BENEFIT PACKING MATERIALS LIMITED—See Perfectech International Holdings Limited; *Int'l*, pg. 5799
BENEFIT PARTNERS INC.—See People Corporation; *Int'l*, pg. 5793
BENEFIT PLANNERS & ASSOCIATES INC.—See Managed Care of America Inc.; *U.S. Private*, pg. 2559
BENEFIT PLANS ADMINISTRATIVE SERVICES, INC.—See Community Bank System, Inc.; *U.S. Public*, pg. 549
BENEFIT RESOURCE GROUP—See GTCR LLC; *U.S. Private*, pg. 1802
BENEFIT RESOURCE, INC.—See ABRY Partners, LLC; *U.S. Private*, pg. 42
BENEFITS ADVISORY GROUP LLC—See Marsh & McLennan Companies, Inc.; *U.S. Public*, pg. 1380
BENEFITS ALLIANCE INSURANCE SERVICES, LLC—See GI Manager L.P.; *U.S. Private*, pg. 1693
BENEFITS ALLIANCE INSURANCE SERVICES, LLC—See Summit Partners, L.P.; *U.S. Private*, pg. 3856
BENEFITS ASSURANCE CO., INC.—See Addus HomeCare Corporation; *U.S. Public*, pg. 40
BENEFIT SERVICES GROUP, INC.—See Wirtz Corporation; *U.S. Private*, pg. 4547
THE BENEFIT SERVICES GROUP, INC.; *U.S. Private*, pg. 3993
BENEFIT SERVICES GROUP—See Aon plc; *Int'l*, pg. 495
BENEFITS & INCENTIVES GROUP, INC.—See Mesirow Financial Holdings, Inc.; *U.S. Private*, pg. 2678
BENEFITS MANAGEMENT CORPORATION—See The Cigna Group; *U.S. Public*, pg. 2060
BENEFITS NETWORK INC.; *U.S. Private*, pg. 525
BENEFITS OF MISSOURI INC.—See Aquilino Capital Partners LLC; *U.S. Private*, pg. 303
BENEFITS OF MISSOURI INC.—See Genstar Capital, LLC; *U.S. Private*, pg. 1675
BENEFIT SOURCE, INC.; *U.S. Private*, pg. 525
BENEFITS S.A.—See ManpowerGroup Inc.; *U.S. Public*, pg. 1357
THE BENEFITS SOLUTION GROUP INC.—See Aon plc; *Int'l*, pg. 497
BENEFIT STREET PARTNERS BDC, INC.—See Franklin Resources, Inc.; *U.S. Public*, pg. 879
BENEFIT STREET PARTNERS LLC—See Franklin Resources, Inc.; *U.S. Public*, pg. 879
BENEFIT SYSTEMS BULGARIA EOOD—See Benefit Systems SA; *Int'l*, pg. 972
BENEFIT SYSTEMS D. O. O.—See Benefit Systems SA; *Int'l*, pg. 972
BENEFIT SYSTEMS GREECE MIKE—See Benefit Systems SA; *Int'l*, pg. 972
BENEFIT SYSTEMS INTERNATIONAL SP. Z O.O.—See Benefit Systems SA; *Int'l*, pg. 972
BENEFIT SYSTEMS SA; *Int'l*, pg. 972
BENEFIT SYSTEMS SLOVAKIA S.R.O.—See Benefit Systems SA; *Int'l*, pg. 972
BENEFITTER INSURANCE SOLUTIONS, INC.—See UnitedHealth Group Incorporated; *U.S. Public*, pg. 2239
BENEFIT TRUST GMBH—See Deutsche Bank Aktiengesellschaft; *Int'l*, pg. 2055
BENEFITWORKS, INC.—See Fulton Financial Corporation; *U.S. Public*, pg. 892
BENEFLEX HR RESOURCES, INC.—See Paylocity Holding Corporation; *U.S. Public*, pg. 1656
BENEFLEX INSURANCE SERVICES, INC.—See New Mountain Capital, LLC; *U.S. Private*, pg. 2901
BENEFYTT TECHNOLOGIES, INC.—See Madison Dearborn Partners, LLC; *U.S. Private*, pg. 2540
BENEGAS B.V.—See DCC plc; *Int'l*, pg. 1990
BENE GMBH; *Int'l*, pg. 972
BENE GMBH—See Bene GmbH; *Int'l*, pg. 972
BEN E. KEITH COMPANY; *U.S. Private*, pg. 522
BEN E. KEITH FOODS OF OKLAHOMA—See Ben E. Keith Company; *U.S. Private*, pg. 522
BENE KYIV TOV—See Bene GmbH; *Int'l*, pg. 972
BENELI AB—See Volati AB; *Int'l*, pg. 8300
BEN ELIAS INDUSTRIES CORP; *U.S. Private*, pg. 522
BENE LJUBLJANA D.O.O.—See Bene GmbH; *Int'l*, pg. 972
BENELLI ARMI S.P.A.—See Fabbrica d'Armi Pietro Beretta S.p.A.; *Int'l*, pg. 2598
BENELLI U.S.A. CORPORATION—See Fabbrica d'Armi Pietro Beretta S.p.A.; *Int'l*, pg. 2598
BENELMAT SA—See Ackermans & van Haaren NV; *Int'l*, pg. 104
BENELUX ASSIST S.A.—See MAPFRE S.A.; *Int'l*, pg. 4685

BENELUX NDT & INSPECTION SUPPLIES B.V.—See TUV Rheinland Berlin-Brandenburg Pfalz e.V.; *Int'l*, pg. 7981
BENE OFFICE FURNITURE IRELAND LTD.—See Bene GmbH; *Int'l*, pg. 972
BENEO-ORAFTI N.V.—See Suddeutsche Zuckerruben-Verwertungs-Genossenschaft eG; *Int'l*, pg. 7252
BENEO-REMY N.V.—See Suddeutsche Zuckerruben-Verwertungs-Genossenschaft eG; *Int'l*, pg. 7252
BENEPLACE, LLC—See Entertainment Benefits Group, LLC; *U.S. Private*, pg. 1404
BENE PLC—See Bene GmbH; *Int'l*, pg. 972
BENE PRAHA SPOL.S.R.O.—See Bene GmbH; *Int'l*, pg. 972
BENE ROMANIA S.R.L.—See Bene GmbH; *Int'l*, pg. 972
BENE RUS OOO—See Bene GmbH; *Int'l*, pg. 972
BENESIS CORPORATION—See Mitsubishi Chemical Group Corporation; *Int'l*, pg. 4935
BENESSE BE STUDIO INC.—See EQT AB; *Int'l*, pg. 2467
BENESSE BUSINESS-MATE, INC.—See EQT AB; *Int'l*, pg. 2467
BENESSE CORPORATION CHINA—See EQT AB; *Int'l*, pg. 2467
BENESSE CORPORATION—See EQT AB; *Int'l*, pg. 2467
BENESSE CORPORATION - TOKYO HEAD OFFICE—See EQT AB; *Int'l*, pg. 2467
BENESSE HOLDINGS, INC.—See EQT AB; *Int'l*, pg. 2467
BENESSE HONG KONG CO., LTD.—See EQT AB; *Int'l*, pg. 2467
BENESSE I-CAREER, CO., LTD.—See EQT AB; *Int'l*, pg. 2467
BENESSE INFOSHELL CO., LTD.—See EQT AB; *Int'l*, pg. 2467
BENESSE MCM CORP.—See EQT AB; *Int'l*, pg. 2467
BENESSE MUSIC PUBLISHING CO.—See EQT AB; *Int'l*, pg. 2467
BENESSE PALETTE CO., LTD.—See EQT AB; *Int'l*, pg. 2467
BENESSERE CAPITAL ACQUISITION CORP.; *U.S. Public*, pg. 296
BENES SERVICE CO.; *U.S. Private*, pg. 525
BENESSE SENIOR SUPPORT CO., LTD.—See EQT AB; *Int'l*, pg. 2467
BENESSE STYLE CARE CO., LTD.—See EQT AB; *Int'l*, pg. 2467
BENESTRA, S. R. O.—See Sandberg Capital správ. spol., a.s.; *Int'l*, pg. 6524
BENESYS, INC.; *U.S. Private*, pg. 525
BENETEAU S.A.; *Int'l*, pg. 972
BENETECH INVESTMENTS CORP; *U.S. Private*, pg. 525
BENETTON ASIA PACIFIC LTD.—See Edizione S.r.l.; *Int'l*, pg. 2311
BENETTON GROUP S.P.A.—See Edizione S.r.l.; *Int'l*, pg. 2311
BENETTON RUGBY TREVISO S.R.L.—See Edizione S.r.l.; *Int'l*, pg. 2311
BENETTON U.S.A. CORPORATION—See Edizione S.r.l.; *Int'l*, pg. 2311
BENEUSA LLC—See Warner Pacific Insurance Services, Inc.; *U.S. Private*, pg. 4442
BENEVA FLOWERS AND GIFTS INC.; *U.S. Private*, pg. 525
BENEV COMPANY, INC.—See ExoCoBio Inc.; *Int'l*, pg. 2586
BENEVIR BIOPHARM, INC.—See Johnson & Johnson; *U.S. Public*, pg. 1196
BENEVOLENTAI SA; *Int'l*, pg. 973
BENE WARSZAWA SP. Z O.O.—See Bene GmbH; *Int'l*, pg. 972
BENEX LTD.—See Becton, Dickinson & Company; *U.S. Public*, pg. 290
BENEXT PARTNERS INC.—See Open Up Group Inc; *Int'l*, pg. 5598
BENEXT SOLUTIONS INC.—See Open Up Group Inc; *Int'l*, pg. 5598
BENEXT TECHNOLOGIES INC.—See Open Up Group Inc; *Int'l*, pg. 5598
BENEXT WITH INC.—See Open Up Group Inc; *Int'l*, pg. 5598
BENEXY CORPORATION—See SANYEI CORPORATION; *Int'l*, pg. 6563
BENFIELD CONTROL & POWER SYSTEMS, INC.—See H.H. Benfield Electric Supply Company Inc.; *U.S. Private*, pg. 1826
BENFIELD ELECTRIC AND ELEVATOR SUPPLY CORP.—See H.H. Benfield Electric Supply Company Inc.; *U.S. Private*, pg. 1826
BENFIELD ELECTRIC COMPANY, INC.; *U.S. Private*, pg. 525
BENFIELD ELECTRIC INTERNATIONAL LTD. INC.—See H.H. Benfield Electric Supply Company Inc.; *U.S. Private*, pg. 1826
BENFIELD ELECTRIC JAPAN CO. LTD.—See H.H. Benfield Electric Supply Company Inc.; *U.S. Private*, pg. 1826
BENFIELD LIGHTING, INC.—See H.H. Benfield Electric Supply Company Inc.; *U.S. Private*, pg. 1826
BENFIELD SANITATION SERVICES, INC.—See Republic Services, Inc.; *U.S. Public*, pg. 1786

BEN FLEET SERVICES GMBH—See EnBW Energie Baden-Wurttemberg AG; *Int'l*, pg. 2398
BEN FOODS (EAST MALAYSIA) SDN BHD—See QAF Limited; *Int'l*, pg. 6131
BEN FOODS (S) PTE LTD.—See QAF Limited; *Int'l*, pg. 6131
BENFORD CAPITAL PARTNERS, LLC; *U.S. Private*, pg. 525
BEN FORTUNE PASTRY MANUFACTURING (M) SDN BHD; *Int'l*, pg. 969
BEN FUNG MACHINERIES & ENGINEERING LTD.—See KONE Oyj; *Int'l*, pg. 4247
BENGAL & ASSAM COMPANY LTD.; *Int'l*, pg. 973
BENGAL ENERGY LTD.; *Int'l*, pg. 973
BENGAL GAS COMPANY LIMITED—See GAIL (India) Limited; *Int'l*, pg. 2869
BENGAL GROUP; *Int'l*, pg. 973
BENGAL MACHINE; *U.S. Private*, pg. 526
BENGAL MOTOR COMPANY, LTD.—See AutoNation, Inc.; *U.S. Public*, pg. 233
BENGAL MOTOR COMPANY, LTD.—See AutoNation, Inc.; *U.S. Public*, pg. 233
BENGAL STEEL INDUSTRIES LTD.; *Int'l*, pg. 973
BENGAL TEA & FABRICS LTD; *Int'l*, pg. 974
BENGAL TIGER LINE LTD.—See Schoeller Holdings Ltd.; *Int'l*, pg. 6637
BENGAL TRANSPORTATION SERVICES, LLC.; *U.S. Private*, pg. 526
BENGAL WINDSOR THERMOPLASTICS LIMITED—See Bengal Group; *Int'l*, pg. 973
BENGANG STEEL PLATES COMPANY LTD.; *Int'l*, pg. 974
BENGARD MARKETING, INC.—See GrubMarket, Inc.; *U.S. Private*, pg. 1797
BENGBU JINHUANGSHAN ROTOGRAVURE PRINTING COMPANY LIMITED—See Litu Holdings Limited; *Int'l*, pg. 4528
BEN-GENERAL CORPORATION—See ITOCHU Corporation; *Int'l*, pg. 3836
BENG HUI MARINE ELECTRICAL PTE LTD—See BH Global Corporation Limited; *Int'l*, pg. 1009
BENG KUANG MARINE (B&Y) PTE. LTD.—See Beng Kuang Marine Limited; *Int'l*, pg. 973
BENG KUANG MARINE LIMITED; *Int'l*, pg. 973
BENGO4.COM, INC.; *Int'l*, pg. 974
BENG SOON MACHINERY HOLDINGS LIMITED; *Int'l*, pg. 973
BENGT LUNDIN AB—See Altor Equity Partners AB; *Int'l*, pg. 396
BENGTSSONS MASKIN AB—See Indutrade AB; *Int'l*, pg. 3677
BENGUETCORP NICKEL MINES, INC.—See Benguet Corporation; *Int'l*, pg. 974
BENGUET CORPORATION; *Int'l*, pg. 974
BENGUET EBARA REAL ESTATE CORP.—See Benguet Corporation; *Int'l*, pg. 974
BENGUET EBARA REAL ESTATE CORP.—See Ebara Corporation; *Int'l*, pg. 2282
BENGUET MANAGEMENT CORPORATION—See Benguet Corporation; *Int'l*, pg. 974
BENGUETRADE, INC—See Benguet Corporation; *Int'l*, pg. 974
BENHAVEN, INC.; *U.S. Private*, pg. 526
BEN HILL GRIFFIN INC.; *U.S. Private*, pg. 522
BEN HUR CONSTRUCTION CO. INC.; *U.S. Private*, pg. 522
BENICIA FOUNDRY & IRON WORKS INC.; *U.S. Private*, pg. 526
BENICIA PORT TERMINAL COMPANY—See AGF Management Limited; *Int'l*, pg. 207
BENICIA PORT TERMINAL COMPANY—See Instar Group Inc.; *Int'l*, pg. 3723
BENICO, LTD.—See Genstar Capital, LLC; *U.S. Private*, pg. 1674
BENICON OPENCAST MINING (PROPRIETARY) LIMITED—See Unicorn Capital Partners Limited; *Int'l*, pg. 8033
BENIC SOLUTION CORPORATION—See Kawasaki Heavy Industries, Ltd.; *Int'l*, pg. 4095
BENIDORM LOCKS S.L.—See Groupe SFPI SA; *Int'l*, pg. 3111
BENIHANA BETHESDA CORP.—See TPG Capital, L.P.; *U.S. Public*, pg. 2167
BENIHANA BROOMFIELD CORP.—See TPG Capital, L.P.; *U.S. Public*, pg. 2167
BENIHANA CARLSBAD CORP.—See TPG Capital, L.P.; *U.S. Public*, pg. 2167
BENIHANA CHANDLER CORP.—See TPG Capital, L.P.; *U.S. Public*, pg. 2167
BENIHANA COLUMBUS CORP.—See TPG Capital, L.P.; *U.S. Public*, pg. 2167
BENIHANA CORAL SPRINGS CORP.—See TPG Capital, L.P.; *U.S. Public*, pg. 2167
BENIHANA ENCINO CORP.—See TPG Capital, L.P.; *U.S. Public*, pg. 2167
BENIHANA INC.—See TPG Capital, L.P.; *U.S. Public*, pg. 2167
BENIHANA LAS COLINAS CORP.—See TPG Capital, L.P.; *U.S. Public*, pg. 2167

BENIHANA LOMBARD CORP.—See TPG Capital, L.P.; U.S. Public, pg. 2167
BENIHANA MARINA CORP.—See TPG Capital, L.P.; U.S. Public, pg. 2167
BENIHANA NATIONAL OF FLORIDA CORP.—See TPG Capital, L.P.; U.S. Public, pg. 2167
BENIHANA OF PUENTE HILLS CORP.—See TPG Capital, L.P.; U.S. Public, pg. 2167
BENIHANA ONTARIO CORP.—See TPG Capital, L.P.; U.S. Public, pg. 2167
BENIHANA ORLANDO CORP.—See TPG Capital, L.P.; U.S. Public, pg. 2167
BENIHANA PLANO CORP.—See TPG Capital, L.P.; U.S. Public, pg. 2167
BENIHANA PLYMOUTH MEETING CORP.—See TPG Capital, L.P.; U.S. Public, pg. 2167
BENIHANA SUNRISE CORP.—See TPG Capital, L.P.; U.S. Public, pg. 2167
BENIHANA WESTBURY CORP.—See TPG Capital, L.P.; U.S. Public, pg. 2167
BENIHANA WHEELING CORP.—See TPG Capital, L.P.; U.S. Public, pg. 2167
BENIHANA WOODLANDS CORP.—See TPG Capital, L.P.; U.S. Public, pg. 2167
BENIN TELECOMS SA; Int'l, pg. 974
BENIN TERMINAL S.A.—See Financiere de L'Odet; Int'l, pg. 2665
BENIREI CORPORATION—See Marubeni Corporation; Int'l, pg. 4705
BENISAF WATER COMPANY, SPA—See ACS, Actividades de Construccion y Servicios, S.A.; Int'l, pg. 110
BENITEC BIOPHARMA INC.; Int'l, pg. 974
BENIX & CO INC.; Int'l, pg. 974
BENIX LIMITED—See Humanica Public Company Limited; Int'l, pg. 3530
BENJAMIN FOODS, LLC.; U.S. Private, pg. 526
BENJAMIN FRANKLIN PLUMBING; U.S. Private, pg. 526
BENJAMIN HORNIGOLD LTD.; Int'l, pg. 974
BENJAMIN MACFARLAND COMPANY, LLC; U.S. Private, pg. 526
BENJAMIN MICHAEL & ASSOCIATES, INC.; U.S. Private, pg. 526
BENJAMIN MOORE & CO.—See Berkshire Hathaway Inc.; U.S. Public, pg. 300
BENJAMIN MOORE & CO.—See Berkshire Hathaway Inc.; U.S. Public, pg. 300
BENJAMIN OBDYKE, INC.; U.S. Private, pg. 526
BENJAMIN STEEL COMPANY INC.; U.S. Private, pg. 526
BENJAMIN TOYS (HK) LTD.—See Benjamin Toys Ltd.; Int'l, pg. 974
BENJAMIN TOYS LTD.; Int'l, pg. 974
BEN & JERRY'S HOMEMADE, INC.—See Unilever PLC; Int'l, pg. 8047
BEN & JERRY'S HOMEMADE LTD.—See Unilever PLC; Int'l, pg. 8047
BEN & JERRY'S HOMEMADE—See Unilever PLC; Int'l, pg. 8047
BENJI INVEST KFT.; Int'l, pg. 974
BENKALA MINING COMPANY JSC; Int'l, pg. 974
BENKO CONSTRUCTION CO., INC.—See Zilber Ltd.; U.S. Private, pg. 4604
BENKO PRODUCTS, INC.; U.S. Private, pg. 526
BEN LEWIS PLUMBING, HEATING & AIR CONDITIONING, INC.; U.S. Private, pg. 522
BEN LOMOND RURAL TELEPHONE CO-OP, INC.; U.S. Private, pg. 523
BEN MACHINE PRODUCTS CO. INC.—See Exchange Income Corporation; Int'l, pg. 2579
BENMARK PTE. LTD.—See FJ Benjamin Holdings Ltd.; Int'l, pg. 2697
BENMAR MARINE ELECTRONICS, INC.; U.S. Private, pg. 526
BEN MEADOWS COMPANY—See The Riverside Company; U.S. Private, pg. 4108
BEN MYNATT MEGASTORE; U.S. Private, pg. 523
BENNER HOLDING GMBH; Int'l, pg. 974
BENNER-NAWMAN INC.; U.S. Private, pg. 526
BENNERT GMBH BETRIEB FUR BAUWERKSICHERUNG—See L. Possehl & Co. mbH; Int'l, pg. 4382
BENNETT AUTOMOTIVE GROUP; U.S. Private, pg. 527
BENNETT AUTO SUPPLY INC.; U.S. Private, pg. 527
BENNETT, BRICKLIN & SALTZBURG LLC; U.S. Private, pg. 527
BENNETT & BROSSEAU ROOFING INC.; U.S. Private, pg. 526
BENNETT BROTHERS, INC.; U.S. Private, pg. 527
BENNETT BROTHERS, INC.—See Bennett Brothers, Inc.; U.S. Private, pg. 527
BENNETT BUICK GMC; U.S. Private, pg. 527
BENNETT BUILDING SYSTEMS, LLC—See Bennett International Group, Inc.; U.S. Private, pg. 527
BENNETT CAPITAL PARTNERS, LLC; U.S. Private, pg. 527
BENNETT CHEVROLET OLDSMOBILE CADILLAC LTD; Int'l, pg. 974
BENNETT, COLEMAN & CO. LTD.; Int'l, pg. 974
BENNETT CONTRACTING, INC.; U.S. Private, pg. 527

BENNETT DISTRIBUTION SERVICES, LLC—See Bennett International Group, Inc.; U.S. Private, pg. 527
BENNETT DUNLOP FORD; Int'l, pg. 974
BENNETT ENTERPRISES INC.; U.S. Private, pg. 527
BENNETT EUBANKS OIL COMPANY; U.S. Private, pg. 527
BENNETT INTERNATIONAL GROUP, INC.; U.S. Private, pg. 527
BENNETT INTERNATIONAL TRANSPORT INC.—See Bennett International Group, Inc.; U.S. Private, pg. 527
BENNETT KUHN VARNER, INC.; U.S. Private, pg. 527
BENNETT LAWRENCE MANAGEMENT, LLC—See Macquarie Group Limited; Int'l, pg. 4624
BENNETT LUMBER COMPANY; U.S. Private, pg. 527
BENNETT MARINE, INC.—See Yamaha Corporation; Int'l, pg. 8550
BENNETT MOTOR EXPRESS INC.—See Bennett International Group, Inc.; U.S. Private, pg. 527
BENNETT PACKAGING OF KANSAS CITY; U.S. Private, pg. 527
BENNETT & PLESS, INC.; U.S. Private, pg. 526
BENNETT PUMP COMPANY—See Hines Corporation; U.S. Private, pg. 1949
BENNETTS OIL CO.; U.S. Private, pg. 528
BENNETT THRASHER; U.S. Private, pg. 527
BENNETT TOYOTA; U.S. Private, pg. 527
BENNETT TRUCK TRANSPORT—See Bennett International Group, Inc.; U.S. Private, pg. 527
BENNING CONSTRUCTION COMPANY INC.; U.S. Private, pg. 528
BENNINGER AG—See Jakob Muller AG; Int'l, pg. 3873
BENNINGER AUTOMATION GMBH—See Jakob Muller AG; Int'l, pg. 3873
BENNINGER INDIA PRIVATE LTD.—See Jakob Muller AG; Int'l, pg. 3873
THE BENNINGTON BANNER—See Alden Global Capital LLC; U.S. Private, pg. 158
BENNINGTON POND LLC—See Independence Realty Trust, Inc.; U.S. Public, pg. 1115
THE BENNINGTON STATE BANK; U.S. Private, pg. 3993
B. EN N. KNAUF EN C-ISOLAVA G.C.V.—See Gebr. Knauf KG; Int'l, pg. 2906
BENNTEC SYSTEMTECHNIK GMBH—See Rheinmetall AG; Int'l, pg. 6321
BENNY'S INC.; U.S. Private, pg. 528
BENOIST BROS. SUPPLY CO. INC.; U.S. Private, pg. 528
BENOIST BROTHERS SUPPLY CO—See Gryphon Investors, LLC; U.S. Private, pg. 1800
BENOIT OILFIELD CONSTRUCTION (1997) LTD.; Int'l, pg. 975
BENOIT PREMIUM THREADING, LLC; U.S. Private, pg. 528
BENOL ENERGIESERVICE GMBH & CO. KG—See Marquard & Bahls AG; Int'l, pg. 4699
BENONE AG—See Lindab International AB; Int'l, pg. 4503
BENO TNR, INC.; Int'l, pg. 975
BENOURE PLUMBING & HEATING INC—See Empowered Ventures, Inc.; U.S. Private, pg. 1387
BENOY MOTOR SALES, INC.; U.S. Private, pg. 528
BENQ AMERICA CORP.—See BenQ Corporation; Int'l, pg. 975
BENQ ASIA PACIFIC CORP.—See Qisda Corporation; Int'l, pg. 6146
BENQ AUSTRALIA PTY. LTD.—See Qisda Corporation; Int'l, pg. 6146
BENQ BENELUX—See BenQ Corporation; Int'l, pg. 975
BENQ CORPORATION; Int'l, pg. 975
BENQ DEUTSCHLAND GMBH—See Qisda Corporation; Int'l, pg. 6146
BENQ DIALYSIS TECHNOLOGY CORP.—See Qisda Corporation; Int'l, pg. 6146
BENQ EUROPE B.V.—See BenQ Corporation; Int'l, pg. 975
BENQ INDIA PRIVATE LTD.—See Qisda Corporation; Int'l, pg. 6146
BENQ LATIN AMERICA CORP.—See BenQ Corporation; Int'l, pg. 975
BENQ MATERIALS CORP.; Int'l, pg. 975
BENQ MATERIAL (WUHU) CO. LTD.—See BenQ Materials Corp.; Int'l, pg. 975
BENQ MEDICAL TECHNOLOGY CORP.; Int'l, pg. 975
BENQ (M.E.) FZE—See Qisda Corporation; Int'l, pg. 6146
BENQ SINGAPORE PTE. LTD.—See Qisda Corporation; Int'l, pg. 6146
THE BENRIACH DISTILLERY CO. LTD.—See Brown-Forman Corporation; U.S. Public, pg. 403
BENSALEM RACING ASSOCIATION, INC.—See International Turf Investment Co., Inc.; U.S. Private, pg. 2121
BEN'S ASPHALT & SEAL COATING INC.; U.S. Private, pg. 523
BENSATA CORPORATION; U.S. Private, pg. 528
BEN SAYERS LIMITED—See Tandem Group PLC; Int'l, pg. 7456
BENSHAW INC.—See Regal Rexnord Corporation; U.S. Public, pg. 1772
BEN SHERMAN LIMITED—See Oxford Industries, Inc.; U.S. Public, pg. 1629
BEN SHERMAN USA—See Oxford Industries, Inc.; U.S. Public, pg. 1629

THE BEN SILVER CORPORATION; U.S. Private, pg. 3993
BEN S. LOEB, INC.; U.S. Private, pg. 523
BENSON AUTOMOTIVE COMPANY; U.S. Private, pg. 528
BENSON CHRYSLER PLYMOUTH INC.; U.S. Private, pg. 528
BENSON HILL HOLDINGS, INC.—See Benson Hills, Inc.; U.S. Public, pg. 296
BENSON HILLS, INC.; U.S. Public, pg. 296
BENSON INDUSTRIES, LLC—See Berkshire Hathaway Inc.; U.S. Public, pg. 312
BENSON LINCOLN MERCURY CORPORATION; U.S. Private, pg. 528
BENSON LINCOLN MERCURY INC.; U.S. Private, pg. 528
BENSON LTD.—See Berkshire Hathaway Inc.; U.S. Public, pg. 312
BENSON LUMBER & HARDWARE INC.; U.S. Private, pg. 528
BENSON MOTORS CORPORATION; U.S. Private, pg. 528
BENSON-QUINN COMMODITIES INC.—See Archer-Daniels-Midland Company; U.S. Public, pg. 181
BENSONS FOR BEDS—See Steinhoff International Holdings N.V.; Int'l, pg. 7195
BENSON'S, INC.; U.S. Private, pg. 528
BENSONS INTERNATIONAL SYSTEMS B.V.—See Ring International Holding AG; Int'l, pg. 6343
BENSONS INTERNATIONAL SYSTEMS, INC.—See Ring International Holding AG; Int'l, pg. 6343
BENSONS INTERNATIONAL SYSTEMS (S) PTE. LTD.—See Ring International Holding AG; Int'l, pg. 6343
BENSON STEEL LIMITED; Int'l, pg. 975
BENSO OIL PALM PLANTATION LIMITED—See Wilmar International Limited; Int'l, pg. 8420
BENSUR CREATIVE MARKETING GROUP; U.S. Private, pg. 528
BENSUSSEN-DEUTSCH & ASSOCIATES INC.; U.S. Private, pg. 528
BENTALLGREENOAK ADVISORS (KOREA) LIMITED—See Sun Life Financial Inc.; Int'l, pg. 7305
BENTALL KENNEDY (CANADA) LIMITED PARTNERSHIP—See Bentall Kennedy LP; Int'l, pg. 975
BENTALL KENNEDY LP; Int'l, pg. 975
BENTALL KENNEDY REAL ESTATE SERVICES LP—See Bentall Kennedy LP; Int'l, pg. 975
BENTALL KENNEDY RETAIL SERVICES LP—See Bentall Kennedy LP; Int'l, pg. 975
BENTALL KENNEDY (U.S.) LIMITED PARTNERSHIP—See Sun Life Financial, Inc.; Int'l, pg. 7305
BEN-TAM, INC.; U.S. Public, pg. 295
BENTA PLANTATIONS (PERAK) SDN BHD—See Pinehill Pacific Berhad; Int'l, pg. 5868
BEN TAYLOR INC.; U.S. Private, pg. 523
BENTEC GMBH—See Pamplona Capital Management LLP; Int'l, pg. 5711
BENTECH INC.; U.S. Private, pg. 528
BENTECH S.A. (PTY) LTD.—See Benetech Investments Corp; U.S. Private, pg. 525
BENTEK ENERGY LLC—See S&P Global Inc.; U.S. Public, pg. 1830
BENTEKK GMBH—See Draegerwerk AG & Co. KGaA; Int'l, pg. 2198
BENTELER ALUMINIUM SYSTEMS DENMARK AS—See Benteler International AG; Int'l, pg. 976
BENTELER ALUMINIUM SYSTEMS FRANCE SNC—See Benteler International AG; Int'l, pg. 976
BENTELER ALUMINIUM SYSTEMS KOREA LTD.—See Benteler International AG; Int'l, pg. 976
BENTELER ALUMINIUM SYSTEMS MICHIGAN, INC—See Benteler International AG; Int'l, pg. 976
BENTELER ALUMINIUM SYSTEMS NORWAY AS—See Benteler International AG; Int'l, pg. 976
BENTELER ALUMINIUM SYSTEMS SWEDEN AB—See Benteler International AG; Int'l, pg. 976
BENTELER AUTOMOBILTECHNIK EISENACH GMBH—See Benteler International AG; Int'l, pg. 976
BENTELER AUTOMOBILTECHNIK NOWGOROD GMBH—See Benteler International AG; Int'l, pg. 975
BENTELER AUTOMOTIVE BELGIUM N.V.—See Benteler International AG; Int'l, pg. 976
BENTELER AUTOMOTIVE (CHANGSHU) COMPANY LIMITED—See Benteler International AG; Int'l, pg. 976
BENTELER AUTOMOTIVE (CHINA) INVESTMENT CO. LTD.—See Benteler International AG; Int'l, pg. 976
BENTELER AUTOMOTIVE (CHONGQING) CO. LTD.—See Benteler International AG; Int'l, pg. 976
BENTELER AUTOMOTIVE (FUZHOU) CO., LTD.—See Benteler International AG; Int'l, pg. 976
BENTELER AUTOMOTIVE INDIA PRIVATE LIMITED—See Benteler International AG; Int'l, pg. 976
BENTELER AUTOMOTIVE INTERNATIONAL GMBH—See Benteler International AG; Int'l, pg. 976
BENTELER AUTOMOTIVE K.K.—See Benteler International AG; Int'l, pg. 976

BENTELER AUTOMOTIVE RUMBURK S.R.O.—See Benteler International AG; *Int'l*, pg. 976
BENTELER AUTOMOTIVE SAS—See Benteler International AG; *Int'l*, pg. 976
BENTELER AUTOMOTIVE (SHANGHAI) CO., LTD.—See Benteler International AG; *Int'l*, pg. 976
BENTELER AUTOMOTIVE SK S.R.O.—See Benteler International AG; *Int'l*, pg. 976
BENTELER AUTOMOTIVE SOUTH AFRICA (PTY) LTD.—See Benteler International AG; *Int'l*, pg. 975
BENTELER AUTOMOTIVE THAILAND LIMITED—See Benteler International AG; *Int'l*, pg. 975
BENTELER AUTOMOTIVE UK LTD.—See Benteler International AG; *Int'l*, pg. 976
BENTELER AUTOMOTIVE VIGO, S.L.—See Benteler International AG; *Int'l*, pg. 975
BENTELER AUTOTECHNIKA KFT—See Benteler International AG; *Int'l*, pg. 976
BENTELER BENELUX B.V—See Benteler International AG; *Int'l*, pg. 976
BENTELER CAPP AUTOMOTIVE SYSTEM (CHANGCHUN) CO., LTD.—See Benteler International AG; *Int'l*, pg. 976
BENTELER COMPONENTES AUTOMOTIVOS LTDA.—See Benteler International AG; *Int'l*, pg. 976
BENTELER CR S.R.O.—See Benteler International AG; *Int'l*, pg. 976
BENTELER DEFENSE GMBH—See Benteler International AG; *Int'l*, pg. 976
BENTELER DISTRIBUCION IBERICA S.L.—See Benteler International AG; *Int'l*, pg. 975
BENTELER DISTRIBUTION AUSTRIA GMBH—See Benteler International AG; *Int'l*, pg. 976
BENTELER DISTRIBUTION BORU SAN. TIC. LTD. STI—See Benteler International AG; *Int'l*, pg. 975
BENTELER DISTRIBUTION BULGARIA S.R.L.—See Benteler International AG; *Int'l*, pg. 976
BENTELER DISTRIBUTION CSO-ES ACELKERESKEDELMI KFT.—See Benteler International AG; *Int'l*, pg. 975
BENTELER DISTRIBUTION CZECH REPUBLIC SPOL. S.R.O.—See Benteler International AG; *Int'l*, pg. 976
BENTELER DISTRIBUTION DEUTSCHLAND GMBH & CO. KG—See Benteler International AG; *Int'l*, pg. 976
BENTELER DISTRIBUTION ESTONIA OU—See Benteler International AG; *Int'l*, pg. 976
BENTELER DISTRIBUTION FRANCE S.A.R.L.—See Benteler International AG; *Int'l*, pg. 976
BENTELER DISTRIBUTION INDIA PRIVATE LIMITED—See Benteler International AG; *Int'l*, pg. 976
BENTELER DISTRIBUTION INTERNATIONAL GMBH—See Benteler International AG; *Int'l*, pg. 976
BENTELER DISTRIBUTION LIMITED—See Benteler International AG; *Int'l*, pg. 976
BENTELER DISTRIBUTION POLAND SP. Z.O.O.—See Benteler International AG; *Int'l*, pg. 976
BENTELER DISTRIBUTION ROMANIA SRL—See Benteler International AG; *Int'l*, pg. 975
BENTELER DISTRIBUTION SINGAPORE PTE LTD—See Benteler International AG; *Int'l*, pg. 976
BENTELER DISTRIBUTION SLOVAKIA S.R.O.—See Benteler International AG; *Int'l*, pg. 976
BENTELER DISTRIBUTION (THAILAND) COMPANY LIMITED—See Benteler International AG; *Int'l*, pg. 975
BENTELER DISTRIBUTION UKRAINE LLC—See Benteler International AG; *Int'l*, pg. 976
BENTELER DISTRIBUZIONE ITALIA S.P.A.—See Benteler International AG; *Int'l*, pg. 976
BENTELER ENGINEERING CHENNAI PRIVATE LIMITED—See Benteler International AG; *Int'l*, pg. 976
BENTELER ESPANA S.A.—See Benteler International AG; *Int'l*, pg. 977
BENTELER FRANCE S.A.S—See Benteler International AG; *Int'l*, pg. 975
BENTELER GLASS PROCESSING GMBH—See Benteler International AG; *Int'l*, pg. 977
BENTELER GOSHEN, INC.—See Benteler International AG; *Int'l*, pg. 977
BENTELER-INDUSTRIA DE COMPONENTES PARA AUTOMOVEIS LDA.—See Benteler International AG; *Int'l*, pg. 977
BENTELER INTERNATIONAL AG; *Int'l*, pg. 975
BENTELER J.I.T. DOUAI S.A.S.—See Benteler International AG; *Int'l*, pg. 976
BENTELER JIT DUSSELDORF GMBH & CO. KG—See Benteler International AG; *Int'l*, pg. 977
BENTELER JIT PAMPLONA, S.L.U.—See Benteler International AG; *Int'l*, pg. 976
BENTELER JIT VITORIA, S.L.U.—See Benteler International AG; *Int'l*, pg. 976
BENTELER MANAGEMENT CONSULTING (SHANGHAI) CO., LTD.—See Benteler International AG; *Int'l*, pg. 977
BENTELER NETHERLANDS HOLDING B.V.—See Benteler International AG; *Int'l*, pg. 977
BENTELER PALENCIA S.L.—See Benteler International AG; *Int'l*, pg. 977
BENTELER ROTHRIST AG—See Benteler International AG; *Int'l*, pg. 977

BENTELER SISTEMAS AUTOMOTIVOS LTDA.—See Benteler International AG; *Int'l*, pg. 977
BENTELER STEEL & TUBE CORPORATION—See Benteler International AG; *Int'l*, pg. 977
BENTELER STEEL/TUBE MANUFACTURING CORPORATION—See Benteler International AG; *Int'l*, pg. 977
BENTELER STEEL/TUBE (NANTONG) CO. LTD.—See Benteler International AG; *Int'l*, pg. 976
BENTELER TRADING INTERNATIONAL GMBH—See Benteler International AG; *Int'l*, pg. 977
BENTELER TRADING (SHANGHAI) CO., LTD.—See Benteler International AG; *Int'l*, pg. 977
BENTELER TRGOVINA D.O.O.—See Benteler International AG; *Int'l*, pg. 977
BENTELER TRGOVINA D.O.O.—See Benteler International AG; *Int'l*, pg. 977
BENTELER TUBOS Y MAQUINARIA S.A.—See Benteler International AG; *Int'l*, pg. 977
BENTELER (U.K.) LTD.—See Benteler International AG; *Int'l*, pg. 976
BENTEL SECURITY S.R.L.—See Johnson Controls International plc; *Int'l*, pg. 3986
BENTEX KIDDIE CORPORATION; *U.S. Private*, pg. 528
BENTHALL BROTHERS, INC.; *U.S. Private*, pg. 528
BEN THANH AUTOMOBILE JSC—See Saigon General Service Corporation; *Int'l*, pg. 6483
BEN THANH RUBBER JOINT STOCK COMPANY; *Int'l*, pg. 969
BEN THANH SERVICE JSC; *Int'l*, pg. 969
BEN THANH TRADING & SERVICE JOINT STOCK COMPANY; *Int'l*, pg. 969
BEN TIRE DISTRIBUTORS LTD. INC.; *U.S. Private*, pg. 523
BENTLEY CANADA, INC.—See Bentley Systems, Inc.; *U.S. Public*, pg. 296
BENTLEY CAPITAL LTD.; *Int'l*, pg. 977
BENTLEY COMMERCIAL ENTERPRISES LIMITED; *Int'l*, pg. 977
BENTLEY FORBES GROUP, LLC; *U.S. Private*, pg. 528
BENTLEY GROUP; *Int'l*, pg. 977
THE BENTLEY HOTEL & BEACH CLUB—See Menin Hotels, Inc.; *U.S. Private*, pg. 2666
BENTLEY LEATHERS, INC.—See Novacap Management Inc.; *Int'l*, pg. 5453
BENTLEY MANUFACTURING INC.—See Playgirl Industries, Inc.; *U.S. Private*, pg. 3212
BENTLEY MOTOR CARS INTERNATIONAL S.A.—See Porsche Automobil Holding SE; *Int'l*, pg. 5932
BENTLEY MOTORS LIMITED—See Porsche Automobil Holding SE; *Int'l*, pg. 5932
BENTLEY MOTORS SERVICES LIMITED—See Porsche Automobil Holding SE; *Int'l*, pg. 5932
BENTLEY PORTER NOVELLI-SHANGHAI—See Omnicom Group Inc.; *U.S. Public*, pg. 1590
BENTLEY PRINCE STREET, INC.—See Dominus Capital, L.P.; *U.S. Private*, pg. 1256
BENTLEY REID & COMPANY LIMITED—See Bentley Reid (Holdings) Limited; *Int'l*, pg. 977
BENTLEY REID (HOLDINGS) LIMITED; *Int'l*, pg. 977
BENTLEY SYSTEMS AUSTRIA GMBH—See Bentley Systems, Inc.; *U.S. Public*, pg. 296
BENTLEY SYSTEMS (BEIJING) CO., LTD.—See Bentley Systems, Inc.; *U.S. Public*, pg. 296
BENTLEY SYSTEMS CO., LTD.—See Bentley Systems, Inc.; *U.S. Public*, pg. 296
BENTLEY SYSTEMS CR S.R.O.—See Bentley Systems, Inc.; *U.S. Public*, pg. 296
BENTLEY SYSTEMS DE MEXICO SA DE CV—See Bentley Systems, Inc.; *U.S. Public*, pg. 296
BENTLEY SYSTEMS EUROPE B.V.—See Bentley Systems, Inc.; *U.S. Public*, pg. 296
BENTLEY SYSTEMS FINLAND OY—See Bentley Systems, Inc.; *U.S. Public*, pg. 296
BENTLEY SYSTEMS FRANCE SARL—See Bentley Systems, Inc.; *U.S. Public*, pg. 296
BENTLEY SYSTEMS GERMANY GMBH—See Bentley Systems, Inc.; *U.S. Public*, pg. 296
BENTLEY SYSTEMS HONG KONG LTD.—See Bentley Systems, Inc.; *U.S. Public*, pg. 296
BENTLEY SYSTEMS IBERICA, S.A.—See Bentley Systems, Inc.; *U.S. Public*, pg. 296
BENTLEY SYSTEMS, INC. - CARLSBAD—See Bentley Systems, Inc.; *U.S. Public*, pg. 297
BENTLEY SYSTEMS, INCORPORATED—See Bentley Systems, Inc.; *U.S. Public*, pg. 297
BENTLEY SYSTEMS, INC.; *U.S. Public*, pg. 296
BENTLEY SYSTEMS INDIA PVT. LTD.—See Bentley Systems, Inc.; *U.S. Public*, pg. 296
BENTLEY SYSTEMS INTERNATIONAL LTD.—See Bentley Systems, Inc.; *U.S. Public*, pg. 296
BENTLEY SYSTEMS ITALIA SRL—See Bentley Systems, Inc.; *U.S. Public*, pg. 296
BENTLEY SYSTEMS KOREA, INC.—See Bentley Systems, Inc.; *U.S. Public*, pg. 296
BENTLEY SYSTEMS PAKISTAN (PVT.) LIMITED—See Bentley Systems, Inc.; *U.S. Public*, pg. 296
BENTLEY SYSTEMS POLSKA SP. Z O.O.—See Bentley Systems, Inc.; *U.S. Public*, pg. 296

BENTLEY SYSTEMS PTY. LTD.—See Bentley Systems, Inc.; *U.S. Public*, pg. 296
BENTLEY SYSTEMS RUSSIA (OOO)—See Bentley Systems, Inc.; *U.S. Public*, pg. 296
BENTLEY SYSTEMS SCANDINAVIA A/S—See Bentley Systems, Inc.; *U.S. Public*, pg. 296
BENTLEY SYSTEMS SCANDINAVIA NUF—See Bentley Systems, Inc.; *U.S. Public*, pg. 296
BENTLEY SYSTEMS SDN. BHD.—See Bentley Systems, Inc.; *U.S. Public*, pg. 296
BENTLEY SYSTEMS SINGAPORE PTE. LTD.—See Bentley Systems, Inc.; *U.S. Public*, pg. 296
BENTLEY SYSTEMS SOUTH AFRICA (PTY) LTD.—See Bentley Systems, Inc.; *U.S. Public*, pg. 296
BENTLEY SYSTEMS SWEDEN AB—See Bentley Systems, Inc.; *U.S. Public*, pg. 296
BENTLEY SYSTEMS SWITZERLAND AG—See Bentley Systems, Inc.; *U.S. Public*, pg. 296
BENTLEY SYSTEMS (UK) LTD.—See Bentley Systems, Inc.; *U.S. Public*, pg. 296
BENTLEY SYSTEMS YAZILIM COZUMLERI LTD.—See Bentley Systems, Inc.; *U.S. Public*, pg. 296
BENTLEY TRUCK SERVICES, INC.; *U.S. Private*, pg. 528
BENTLEY TRUST (MALTA) LIMITED—See Bentley Reid (Holdings) Limited; *Int'l*, pg. 977
BENTLY NEVADA, AUSTRALIA PTY. LTD.—See General Electric Company; *U.S. Public*, pg. 919
BENTLY NEVADA CANADA LTD.—See General Electric Company; *U.S. Public*, pg. 919
BENTLY NEVADA CANADA LTD.—See General Electric Company; *U.S. Public*, pg. 919
BENTLY NEVADA FRANCE S.A.R.L.—See General Electric Company; *U.S. Public*, pg. 919
BENTLY NEVADA, INC.—See General Electric Company; *U.S. Public*, pg. 919
BENTO BOX ENTERTAINMENT, LLC—See Fox Corporation; *U.S. Public*, pg. 875
BENTO & MARTINS, LDA.—See Jeronimo Martins SGPS SA; *Int'l*, pg. 3931
BENTON & BROWN INC.; *U.S. Private*, pg. 528
BENTON CORPORATION SDN. BHD.—See Engtex Group Berhad; *Int'l*, pg. 2436
BENTON COUNTY DAILY RECORD—See Wehco Media, Inc.; *U.S. Private*, pg. 4470
BENTONE AB—See NIBE Industrier AB; *Int'l*, pg. 5260
BENTON ENTERPRISES INCORPORATED; *U.S. Private*, pg. 529
BENTON FINANCIAL CORP.; *U.S. Public*, pg. 297
BENTON-GEORGIA, INC.; *U.S. Private*, pg. 529
BENTON HARBOR LLC—See Blackstone Inc.; *U.S. Public*, pg. 352
BENTONIT A.D.; *Int'l*, pg. 977
BENTON NURSING, LLC—See Regional Health Properties, Inc.; *U.S. Public*, pg. 1775
BENTON & PARKER CO. INC.; *U.S. Private*, pg. 528
BENTON RESOURCES INC.; *Int'l*, pg. 977
BENTON RURAL ELECTRIC ASSOCIATION; *U.S. Private*, pg. 529
BENTON'S EQUIPMENT & CONSTRUCTION, INC.; *U.S. Private*, pg. 529
BENTO PEDROSO CONSTRUCOES S.A.—See Novonor S.A.; *Int'l*, pg. 5469
BENTRE AQUAPRODUCT IMPORT & EXPORT JOINT STOCK COMPANY; *Int'l*, pg. 977
BEN TRE BUILDING MATERIAL JOINT STOCK COMPANY; *Int'l*, pg. 969
BEN TRE PHARMACEUTICAL JSC; *Int'l*, pg. 969
BENTZEL MECHANICAL INC.; *U.S. Private*, pg. 529
BENTZON CARPETS APS—See Egetaepper A/S; *Int'l*, pg. 2324
BENU NEDERLAND B.V.—See PHOENIX Pharmahandel GmbH & Co. KG; *Int'l*, pg. 5854
BENVENUE MEDICAL, INC.—See Kohlberg & Company, LLC; *U.S. Private*, pg. 2337
BENVIC EUROPE IBE SL—See BI-Invest Advisors S.A.; *Int'l*, pg. 1017
BENVIC EUROPE S.A.S.—See BI-Invest Advisors S.A.; *Int'l*, pg. 1017
BENVIC EUROPE S.P.A.—See BI-Invest Advisors S.A.; *Int'l*, pg. 1017
BEN WEITSMAN & SON INC.; *U.S. Private*, pg. 523
BENXI IRON & STEEL GROUP CO. LTD.—See Anshan Iron & Steel Group Corporation; *Int'l*, pg. 479
BENYAN DEVELOPMENT CO. L.L.C.—See Finance House P.J.S.C.; *Int'l*, pg. 2664
BENZ CONNECTION OF NAPLES INC.; *U.S. Private*, pg. 529
BENZEL-BUSCH MOTOR CAR CORP.; *U.S. Private*, pg. 529
BENZER PHARMACY HOLDING LLC; *U.S. Private*, pg. 529
BENZ GMBH WERKZEUGSYSTEME—See Durr AG; *Int'l*, pg. 2232
BENZIGER FAMILY WINERY LLC—See The Wine Group, Inc.; *U.S. Private*, pg. 4137
BENZINA S.R.O.—See Orlen S.A.; *Int'l*, pg. 5641
BENZ INCORPORATED—See Durr AG; *Int'l*, pg. 2232
BENZLER ANTRIEBSTECHNIK G.M.B.H—See Elecon Engineering Company Ltd.; *Int'l*, pg. 2348

BENZER PHARMACY HOLDING LLC

BENZLERS ITALIA S.R.L.—See Elecon Engineering Company Ltd.; *Int'l*, pg. 2348
BENZLERS SYSTEMS AB—See Elecon Engineering Company Ltd.; *Int'l*, pg. 2348
BENZLER TBA B.V.—See Elecon Engineering Company Ltd.; *Int'l*, pg. 2348
BENZLER TRANSMISSION A.S.—See Elecon Engineering Company Ltd.; *Int'l*, pg. 2348
BENZ MINING CORP.; *Int'l*, pg. 977
BENZ OIL INC.—See Amsoil Inc.; *U.S. Private*, pg. 267
BENZ RESEARCH & DEVELOPMENT CORPORATION—See TPG Capital, L.P.; *U.S. Public*, pg. 2169
BEO BANCORP; *U.S. Public*, pg. 297
BEOBANK NV/SA—See Confederation Nationale du Credit Mutuel; *Int'l*, pg. 1767
BEOCARE GROUP, INC.; *U.S. Private*, pg. 529
BEOCIN A.D.; *Int'l*, pg. 978
BEOENTERIJER A.D.; *Int'l*, pg. 978
BEOGAS D.O.O.—See Petrol, Slovenska energetska druzba, d.d.; *Int'l*, pg. 5827
BEOGRAD A.D.; *Int'l*, pg. 978
BEOGRADMONTAZA A.D.; *Int'l*, pg. 978
BEOGRAD PROMET A.D.; *Int'l*, pg. 978
BEOGRADSKA AUTOBUSKA STANICA A.D.; *Int'l*, pg. 978
BEOGRADSKA BERZA A.D.—See Zagrebacka burza d.d.; *Int'l*, pg. 8619
BEOGRADSKA INDUSTRIJA PIVA A.D.; *Int'l*, pg. 978
BEOND GROUP LIMITED—See eEnergy Group Plc; *Int'l*, pg. 2317
BEONE STUTTGART GMBH—See Alten S.A.; *Int'l*, pg. 390
BEOPAN A.D.; *Int'l*, pg. 978
BEOS AG—See Swiss Life Holding; *Int'l*, pg. 7368
BEOTRANS A.D.; *Int'l*, pg. 978
BEO UK LIMITED—See Graham Holdings Company; *U.S. Public*, pg. 954
BEOWULF ENERGY LLC; *U.S. Private*, pg. 529
BEOWULF MINING PLC; *Int'l*, pg. 978
BEOZASTITA A.D.; *Int'l*, pg. 978
BEPCO DEUTSCHLAND GMBH—See Group Thermote & Vanhalst; *Int'l*, pg. 3089
BEPCO IBERICA SA—See Group Thermote & Vanhalst; *Int'l*, pg. 3089
BEPCO, INC.; *U.S. Private*, pg. 529
BEPEX ASIA LIMITED—See Bepex International, LLC; *U.S. Private*, pg. 529
BEPEX INTERNATIONAL, LLC; *U.S. Private*, pg. 529
BEP/LYMAN, LLC—See Bain Capital, LP; *U.S. Private*, pg. 450
BE POLAND THINK, SOLVE & EXECUTE SP Z.O.O—See TAMBURI INVESTMENT PARTNERS S.p.A.; *Int'l*, pg. 7450
BEPPU UOICHI CO., LTD—See Maruha Nichiro Corporation; *Int'l*, pg. 4711
BEPRESS—See RELX plc; *Int'l*, pg. 6268
BEPRONOR - SOCIEDADE DE BETAO PRONTO DO NORDESTE S.A.—See Camargo Correa S.A.; *Int'l*, pg. 1267
B+ EQUIPMENT SAS—See Sealed Air Corporation; *U.S. Public*, pg. 1852
BERACA INGREDIENTES NATURAIS S.A.—See Clariant AG; *Int'l*, pg. 1645
BERAFINA AG.—See Hinduja Group Ltd.; *Int'l*, pg. 3399
BERA HOLDING A.S.; *Int'l*, pg. 978
BERAKAN MAJU SDN BHD—See IJM Corporation Berhad; *Int'l*, pg. 3608
BERALAN S.L.—See Vocento, S.A.; *Int'l*, pg. 8284
BERANEK, INC.—See J & E Precision Tool, LLC; *U.S. Private*, pg. 2152
BERAS CORPORATION SDN BHD—See Padiberas Nasional Berhad; *Int'l*, pg. 5694
BERAT CORPORATION; *U.S. Private*, pg. 529
BERBENS EFFECTENKANTOOR B.V.—See Jyske Bank A/S; *Int'l*, pg. 4037
BERBER FOOD MANUFACTURING INC.; *U.S. Private*, pg. 529
BERBERIAN BROS INC.; *U.S. Private*, pg. 529
BERBERIAN ENTERPRISES INC.; *U.S. Private*, pg. 529
BERCEN INC.—See Cranston Print Works Company; *U.S. Private*, pg. 1086
BERCHER SA PUBLICITE GENERALE—See APG/SGA SA; *Int'l*, pg. 513
BERCHTESGADENER BERGBAHN AG; *Int'l*, pg. 978
BERCHTESGADEN INTERNATIONAL RESORT BETRIEBS GMBH—See BayernLB Holding AG; *Int'l*, pg. 913
BERCHTESGARDENER LAND BAHN GMBH—See Ferrovie dello Stato Italiane S.p.A.; *Int'l*, pg. 2645
BERCHTOLD ASIA SDN BHD—See Stryker Corporation; *U.S. Public*, pg. 1955
BERCHTOLD CHINA LTD—See Stryker Corporation; *U.S. Public*, pg. 1955
BERCHTOLD CONSULTING GMBH—See Stryker Corporation; *U.S. Public*, pg. 1955
BERCHTOLD EQUIPMENT COMPANY; *U.S. Private*, pg. 529

BERCHTOLD ESPANA S.L.—See Stryker Corporation; *U.S. Public*, pg. 1955
BERCHTOLD GMBH & CO KG—See Stryker Corporation; *U.S. Public*, pg. 1955
BERCHTOLD ITALIA SRL—See Stryker Corporation; *U.S. Public*, pg. 1955
BERCHTOLD JAPAN KK—See Stryker Corporation; *U.S. Public*, pg. 1955
BERCHTOLD PACIFIC PTY—See Stryker Corporation; *U.S. Public*, pg. 1955
BERCHTOLD UK LIMITED—See Stryker Corporation; *U.S. Public*, pg. 1955
BERCO BULGARIA EOOD—See ThyssenKrupp AG; *Int'l*, pg. 7731
BERCO DEUTSCHLAND GMBH—See ThyssenKrupp AG; *Int'l*, pg. 7731
BERCO OF AMERICA, INC.—See ThyssenKrupp AG; *Int'l*, pg. 7731
BERCO OF AMERICA INC.—See ThyssenKrupp AG; *Int'l*, pg. 7731
BERCO RESOURCES LLC; *U.S. Private*, pg. 529
BERCO (SHANGHAI) UNDERCARRIAGE TECHNOLOGY CO., LTD.—See ThyssenKrupp AG; *Int'l*, pg. 7723
BERCO (SHANGHAI) UNDERCARRIAGE TRADING CO., LTD.—See ThyssenKrupp AG; *Int'l*, pg. 7723
BERCO S.P.A.—See ThyssenKrupp AG; *Int'l*, pg. 7731
BERCOSUL LTDA.—See ThyssenKrupp AG; *Int'l*, pg. 7723
BERCO (UK) LTD.—See ThyssenKrupp AG; *Int'l*, pg. 7723
BERCO UNDERCARRIAGES (INDIA) PRIVATE LTD.—See ThyssenKrupp AG; *Int'l*, pg. 7723
BERCY HAMMERSON FRANCE—See Hammerson plc; *Int'l*, pg. 3238
BERDON LLP; *U.S. Private*, pg. 529
BEREAN CHRISTIAN STORES—See JMH Capital; *U.S. Private*, pg. 2215
BEREC LAND RESOURCES LNC.—See Benguet Corporation; *Int'l*, pg. 974
BEREKET VARLIK KIRALAMA A.S.; *Int'l*, pg. 978
BEREMA A/S—See Atlas Copco AB; *Int'l*, pg. 681
BEREM PROPERTY MANAGEMENT GMBH—See Swiss Life Holding; *Int'l*, pg. 7368
BERENBERG BANK—See Joh. Berenberg, Gossler & Co.; *Int'l*, pg. 3977
BERENBERG BANK—See Joh. Berenberg, Gossler & Co.; *Int'l*, pg. 3977
BERENBERG CAPITAL MANAGEMENT GMBH—See Joh. Berenberg, Gossler & Co.; *Int'l*, pg. 3977
BERENBERG CAPITAL MARKETS LLC—See Joh. Berenberg, Gossler & Co.; *Int'l*, pg. 3977
BERENBERG CONSULT GMBH—See Joh. Berenberg, Gossler & Co.; *Int'l*, pg. 3977
BERENBERG FINANZANLAGEN—See Joh. Berenberg, Gossler & Co.; *Int'l*, pg. 3977
BERENBERG TREUHAND GMBH—See Joh. Berenberg, Gossler & Co.; *Int'l*, pg. 3977
BERENDSEN FLUID POWER PTY LIMITED; *Int'l*, pg. 978
BERENDSEN GMBH—See Eurazeo SE; *Int'l*, pg. 2528
BERENDSEN LIMITED—See Eurazeo SE; *Int'l*, pg. 2528
BERENDSEN UK LIMITED—See Eurazeo SE; *Int'l*, pg. 2528
BERENSON & COMPANY, INC.; *U.S. Private*, pg. 529
BERENSON & COMPANY, LLC—See Berenson & Company, Inc.; *U.S. Private*, pg. 530
BERENTZEN-GRUPPE AG; *Int'l*, pg. 978
BERESFORD BOX COMPANY INC.; *Int'l*, pg. 979
BERESFORD WILSON & PARTNERS FZ-LLC—See Empresaria Group Plc; *Int'l*, pg. 2388
BE RESOURCES INC.; *Int'l*, pg. 931
BERETTA HOLDING S.P.A.—See Fabbrica d'Armi Pietro Beretta S.p.A.; *Int'l*, pg. 2598
BERETTA U.S.A. CORP.—See Fabbrica d'Armi Pietro Beretta S.p.A.; *Int'l*, pg. 2598
BERETTA VENTURES LTD.; *Int'l*, pg. 979
BEREVA S.R.L.—See BELIMO Holding AG; *Int'l*, pg. 965
BEREXCO INC.; *U.S. Private*, pg. 530
BEREZITOVY RUDNIK LLC—See PAO Severstal; *Int'l*, pg. 5731
BEREZNIKI MECHANICAL WORKS, JSC—See Kovdorskiy GOK JSC; *Int'l*, pg. 4293
BERGAMO TRASPORTI EST S.C.A.R.L.—See Deutsche Bahn AG; *Int'l*, pg. 2049
BERGAN PAULSEN & COMPANY PC; *U.S. Private*, pg. 530
BERGBAHNEN ENGELBERG-TRUBSEE-TITLIS AG; *Int'l*, pg. 979
BERGBAU GOSLAR GMBH—See TUI AG; *Int'l*, pg. 7964
BERG & BERG ENTERPRISES, INC.; *U.S. Private*, pg. 530
BERG & BERG ENTERPRISES, LLC—See Berg & Berg Enterprises, Inc.; *U.S. Private*, pg. 530
BERG & BETONGFORSTARKNING JARL-ERIC MAJQVIST AB—See Nordisk Bergteknik AB; *Int'l*, pg. 5424
BERGBOLAGET I GOTALAND AB—See AF Gruppen ASA; *Int'l*, pg. 184
BERG COMPANY, LLC.; *U.S. Private*, pg. 530
BERGDORF GOODMAN, INC.—See Ares Management Corporation; *U.S. Public*, pg. 190

CORPORATE AFFILIATIONS

BERGDORF GOODMAN, INC.—See Canada Pension Plan Investment Board; *Int'l*, pg. 1281
BERG EARTH CO., LTD.; *Int'l*, pg. 979
BERG EAST IMPORTS INC.; *U.S. Private*, pg. 530
BERGE AUTOMOCION, SL—See Berge y Cia SA; *Int'l*, pg. 979
THE BERGE GROUP; *U.S. Private*, pg. 3993
BERG ELECTRIC CORPORATION; *U.S. Private*, pg. 530
BERGE & MEER TOURISTIK GMBH—See Genui GmbH; *Int'l*, pg. 2930
BERGEN ASSOCIATES PVT. LTD.—See ViTrox Corporation Berhad; *Int'l*, pg. 8262
BERGENBIER S.A.—See Molson Coors Beverage Company; *U.S. Public*, pg. 1459
BERGENBIO ASA; *Int'l*, pg. 979
BERGENBIO LIMITED—See BerGenBio ASA; *Int'l*, pg. 979
BERGEN CABLE TECHNOLOGY, LLC—See Leggett & Platt, Incorporated; *U.S. Public*, pg. 1301
BERGEN CARBON SOLUTIONS AS; *Int'l*, pg. 979
BERGENDAHLS EL GRUPPEN AB—See Storskogen Group AB; *Int'l*, pg. 7227
BERGEN ENERGI AB—See World Kinect Corporation; *U.S. Public*, pg. 2380
BERGEN ENERGI AS—See World Kinect Corporation; *U.S. Public*, pg. 2380
BERGEN ENERGI FRANCE SARL—See World Kinect Corporation; *U.S. Public*, pg. 2380
BERGEN ENERGI NEDERLAND BV—See World Kinect Corporation; *U.S. Public*, pg. 2380
BERGEN ENERGI PORTEFOLJE AS—See World Kinect Corporation; *U.S. Public*, pg. 2380
BERGEN ENGINES INDIA PRIVATE LIMITED—See Rolls-Royce Holdings plc; *Int'l*, pg. 6391
BERGEN GROUP HANOYTANGEN AS—See Endur ASA; *Int'l*, pg. 2409
BERGEN GROUP KIMEK AS—See Endur ASA; *Int'l*, pg. 2409
BERGEN GROUP KIMEK OFFSHORE AS—See Endur ASA; *Int'l*, pg. 2409
BERGEN GROUP SERVICES AS - INDUSTRIAL SERVICE—See Endur ASA; *Int'l*, pg. 2409
BERGEN GROUP SERVICES AS - MARITIME SERVICE—See Endur ASA; *Int'l*, pg. 2409
BERGEN GROUP SERVICES AS—See Endur ASA; *Int'l*, pg. 2409
BERGEN GROUP SKARVELAND AS—See Endur ASA; *Int'l*, pg. 2409
BERGEN LIVE AS—See Live Nation Entertainment, Inc.; *U.S. Public*, pg. 1328
BERGEN PIPE SUPPORTS, INC.—See Hill & Smith PLC; *Int'l*, pg. 3391
BERGEN PIPE SUPPORTS (INDIA) PRIVATE LIMITED—See Hill & Smith PLC; *Int'l*, pg. 3391
BERGEN REGIONAL MEDICAL CENTER; *U.S. Private*, pg. 530
BERGEN SHIPPERS CORP.—See Carl Bennet AB; *Int'l*, pg. 1331
BERGENS RINGEN DA—See Schibsted ASA; *Int'l*, pg. 6616
BERGENS TIDENDE AS—See Schibsted ASA; *Int'l*, pg. 6617
BERG EQUIPMENT CORPORATION; *U.S. Private*, pg. 530
BERGERABAM INC.—See The Louis Berger Group, Inc.; *U.S. Private*, pg. 4073
BERGERABAM—See The Louis Berger Group, Inc.; *U.S. Private*, pg. 4073
BERGER BAU GMBH—See BERGER Holding GmbH; *Int'l*, pg. 979
BERGER BAU POLSKA SP. Z O.O.—See BERGER Holding GmbH; *Int'l*, pg. 979
BERGER BECKER BANGLADESH LIMITED—See Lindengruppen AB; *Int'l*, pg. 4511
BERGER BECKER COATINGS PVT. LTD.—See Lindengruppen AB; *Int'l*, pg. 4511
BERGER BETON GMBH—See BERGER Holding GmbH; *Int'l*, pg. 979
BERGER BROS INC.; *U.S. Private*, pg. 530
BERGER BUILDING PRODUCTS, INC.—See Omnimax Holdings, Inc.; *U.S. Private*, pg. 3017
BERGER CHEVROLET, INC.; *U.S. Private*, pg. 530
BERGER COMPANY; *U.S. Private*, pg. 530
BERGER FAMILY DEALERSHIP; *U.S. Private*, pg. 530
BERGER HOLDING GMBH; *Int'l*, pg. 979
BERGER INTERNATIONAL LTD.—See Asian Paints Limited; *Int'l*, pg. 618
BERGER JENSON & NICHOLSON (NEPAL) PRIVATE LIMITED—See Berger Paints India Limited; *Int'l*, pg. 979
BERGER KAROSSERIE- UND FAHRZEUGBAU GMBH; *Int'l*, pg. 979
BERGER MOTOR SALES INCORPORATED—See Young Automotive Group, Inc.; *U.S. Private*, pg. 4592
BERGERON LAND DEVELOPMENT INC.—See Bergeron Properties & Investment Corp.; *U.S. Private*, pg. 530
BERGERON PROPERTIES & INVESTMENT CORP.; *U.S. Private*, pg. 530
BERGER ORGANIZATION, LLC; *U.S. Private*, pg. 530

COMPANY NAME INDEX

BERGER PAINTS BAHRAIN W.L.L.—See Asian Paints Limited; *Int'l*, pg. 618
BERGER PAINTS BANGLADESH LIMITED; *Int'l*, pg. 979
BERGER PAINTS BARBADOS LTD.—See ANSA McAL Limited; *Int'l*, pg. 476
BERGER PAINTS EMIRATES LIMITED—See Asian Paints Limited; *Int'l*, pg. 618
BERGER PAINTS (HONG KONG) LTD.—See Asian Paints Limited; *Int'l*, pg. 618
BERGER PAINTS INDIA LIMITED; *Int'l*, pg. 979
BERGER PAINTS JAMAICA LIMITED—See ANSA McAL Limited; *Int'l*, pg. 476
BERGER PAINTS NIGERIA PLC.; *Int'l*, pg. 980
BERGER PAINTS NINGBO CO. LTD.—See Asian Paints Limited; *Int'l*, pg. 619
BERGER PAINTS PAKISTAN LIMITED; *Int'l*, pg. 980
BERGER PAINTS SINGAPORE PTE LTD; *Int'l*, pg. 980
BERGER PAINTS (THAILAND) LTD—See Asian Paints Limited; *Int'l*, pg. 618
BERGER SINGERMAN PA.; *U.S. Private*, pg. 530
BERGER TRANSFER & STORAGE, INC.; *U.S. Private*, pg. 530
BERGESEN D.Y. PHILIPPINES, INC.—See BW Group Ltd.; *Int'l*, pg. 1231
BERGESEN WORLDWIDE MEXICO, S.A. DE CV—See BW Offshore Limited; *Int'l*, pg. 1232
BERGE Y CIA SA; *Int'l*, pg. 979
BERGEY'S CHEVROLET—See Bergeys Inc.; *U.S. Private*, pg. 531
BERGEYS INC.; *U.S. Private*, pg. 531
BERG FASHION LIBRARY LIMITED—See Bloomsbury Publishing Plc; *Int'l*, pg. 1065
BERGFREUNDE GMBH—See Decathlon SA; *Int'l*, pg. 1999
BERGGRUEN HOLDINGS, INC.; *U.S. Private*, pg. 531
BERGGRUEN HOLDINGS, LTD.—See Berggruen Holdings, Inc.; *U.S. Private*, pg. 531
BERGHOEF GMBH—See Mohawk Industries, Inc.; *U.S. Public*, pg. 1457
BERGHOEF-HOUT B.V.—See Mohawk Industries, Inc.; *U.S. Public*, pg. 1457
BERGHORST FOODS SERVICES INC.; *U.S. Private*, pg. 531
BERGIO INTERNATIONAL, INC.; *U.S. Public*, pg. 297
BERGKAMP INC.; *U.S. Private*, pg. 531
BERG LACQUER CO.—See Matissart Nord SA; *Int'l*, pg. 4728
BERGLAND GMBH—See Bayernland eG; *Int'l*, pg. 913
BERGLUND CONSTRUCTION COMPANY; *U.S. Private*, pg. 531
BERGLUND OAK RIDGE TOYOTA; *U.S. Private*, pg. 531
BERGMAN ASSOCIATES; *U.S. Private*, pg. 531
BERGMAN AS—See Addtech AB; *Int'l*, pg. 132
BERGMAN & BEVING AB; *Int'l*, pg. 980
BERGMAN & BEVING DEVELOPMENT AB—See Bergman & Beving AB; *Int'l*, pg. 980
BERGMAN & BEVING FASTIGHETER AB—See Bergman & Beving AB; *Int'l*, pg. 980
BERGMAN & BEVING INVEST AB—See Bergman & Beving AB; *Int'l*, pg. 980
BERGMAN & BEVING SAFETY AB—See Bergman & Beving AB; *Int'l*, pg. 980
BERGMAN DIAGNOSTIKA AS—See Addtech AB; *Int'l*, pg. 132
BERGMANLABORA AB—See Addtech AB; *Int'l*, pg. 132
BERGMANN ASSOCIATES, ARCHITECTS, ENGINEERS, LANDSCAPE ARCHITECTS & SURVEYORS, D.P.C.; *U.S. Private*, pg. 531
BERGMANN AUTOMOTIVE GMBH—See ECM Equity Capital Management GmbH; *Int'l*, pg. 2291
BERGMANN'S CLEANING INC.—See Bergmann's Inc.; *U.S. Private*, pg. 531
BERGMANN'S INC.; *U.S. Private*, pg. 531
BERG MILL SUPPLY COMPANY INC.; *U.S. Private*, pg. 530
BERGMOEN AS—See Kistefos AS; *Int'l*, pg. 4192
BERGOS AG; *Int'l*, pg. 980
THE BERGQUIST COMPANY - BIGFORK FACILITY—See GGI Solutions; *Int'l*, pg. 2957
THE BERGQUIST COMPANY - CANNON FALLS FACILITY—See Henkel AG & Co. KGaA; *Int'l*, pg. 3353
THE BERGQUIST COMPANY GMBH—See Henkel AG & Co. KGaA; *Int'l*, pg. 3353
THE BERGQUIST COMPANY KOREA, LTD.—See Henkel AG & Co. KGaA; *Int'l*, pg. 3353
THE BERGQUIST COMPANY SHENZHEN LTD.—See Henkel AG & Co. KGaA; *Int'l*, pg. 3354
THE BERGQUIST COMPANY—See Henkel AG & Co. KGaA; *Int'l*, pg. 3353
THE BERGQUIST COMPANY ZHUHAI LTD.—See Henkel AG & Co. KGaA; *Int'l*, pg. 3354
BERGSALA AB—See Thunderful Group AB; *Int'l*, pg. 7722
BERGSALA AS—See Thunderful Group AB; *Int'l*, pg. 7722
BERGSON HOLDING B.V.—See Sopra Steria Group S.A.; *Int'l*, pg. 7109
BERGSON SOFTWARE FACTORY SERVICES B.V.—See Sopra Steria Group S.A.; *Int'l*, pg. 7109
BERGSON TECHNICAL AUTOMATION B.V.—See Sopra Steria Group S.A.; *Int'l*, pg. 7109
BERGS SKOG AB—See Norvik hf; *Int'l*, pg. 5448
BERG STEEL CORP.—See UPG Enterprises LLC; *U.S. Private*, pg. 4311
BERG STEEL PIPE CORPORATION—See Salzgitter AG; *Int'l*, pg. 6496
BERGS TIMBER AB—See Norvik hf; *Int'l*, pg. 5448
BERGS TIMBER BITUS AB—See Norvik hf; *Int'l*, pg. 5448
BERGS TIMBER MORLUNDA AB—See Norvik hf; *Int'l*, pg. 5448
BERGS TIMBER PRODUCTION AB—See Norvik hf; *Int'l*, pg. 5448
BERGS TIMBER (UK) LTD.—See Norvik hf; *Int'l*, pg. 5448
BERGSTROM CADILLAC OF MADISON—See Bergstrom Corp.; *U.S. Private*, pg. 531
BERGSTROM CORP.; *U.S. Private*, pg. 531
BERGSTROM ELECTRIC INC.; *U.S. Private*, pg. 531
BERGSTROM INC.; *U.S. Private*, pg. 531
BERGSUNDET HERRESATET AB—See Samhallsbyggnadsbolaget I Norden AB; *Int'l*, pg. 6504
BERGVIK KOPET 3 K.B.—See Eurocommercial Properties N.V.; *Int'l*, pg. 2534
BERICAP ASIA PTE. LTD.—See BERICAP GmbH & Co. KG; *Int'l*, pg. 980
BERICAP ASIA PTE. LTD.—See BERICAP GmbH & Co. KG; *Int'l*, pg. 980
BERICAP BENELUX B.V.—See BERICAP GmbH & Co. KG; *Int'l*, pg. 980
BERICAP DO BRASIL LTDA.—See BERICAP GmbH & Co. KG; *Int'l*, pg. 981
BERICAP D.O.O.—See BERICAP GmbH & Co. KG; *Int'l*, pg. 981
BERICAP EAST AFRICA LTD.—See BERICAP GmbH & Co. KG; *Int'l*, pg. 980
BERICAP EGYPT JSC—See BERICAP GmbH & Co. KG; *Int'l*, pg. 980
BERICAP GMBH & CO. KG; *Int'l*, pg. 980
BERICAP INDIA PVT. LTD.—See BERICAP GmbH & Co. KG; *Int'l*, pg. 980
BERICAP KAPAK SANAYI A.S.—See BERICAP GmbH & Co. KG; *Int'l*, pg. 980
BERICAP KAZAKHSTAN LTD.—See BERICAP GmbH & Co. KG; *Int'l*, pg. 980
BERICAP (KUNSHAN) CO. LTD—See BERICAP GmbH & Co. KG; *Int'l*, pg. 980
BERICAP, LLC—See Amcor plc; *Int'l*, pg. 417
BERICAP, LLC—See BERICAP GmbH & Co. KG; *Int'l*, pg. 981
BERICAP MALAYSIA SDN. BHD.—See BERICAP GmbH & Co. KG; *Int'l*, pg. 980
BERICAP MEXICO, S. DE R.L. DE C.V.—See BERICAP GmbH & Co. KG; *Int'l*, pg. 980
BERICAP MIDDLE EAST FZE—See BERICAP GmbH & Co. KG; *Int'l*, pg. 980
BERICAP NORTH AMERICA, INC.—See Amcor plc; *Int'l*, pg. 417
BERICAP NORTH AMERICA, INC.—See BERICAP GmbH & Co. KG; *Int'l*, pg. 980
BERICAP POLSKA SP. Z O.O.—See BERICAP GmbH & Co. KG; *Int'l*, pg. 981
BERICAP ROMANIA S.R.L.—See BERICAP GmbH & Co. KG; *Int'l*, pg. 981
BERICAP S.A. - BUENOS AIRES PLANT—See BERICAP GmbH & Co. KG; *Int'l*, pg. 981
BERICAP SARL—See BERICAP GmbH & Co. KG; *Int'l*, pg. 981
BERICAP S.A.—See BERICAP GmbH & Co. KG; *Int'l*, pg. 981
BERICAP S.A.U.—See BERICAP GmbH & Co. KG; *Int'l*, pg. 981
BERICAP SC LLC—See Amcor plc; *Int'l*, pg. 417
BERICAP SC LLC—See BERICAP GmbH & Co. KG; *Int'l*, pg. 981
BERICAP SINGAPORE PTE LTD—See BERICAP GmbH & Co. KG; *Int'l*, pg. 981
BERICAP S.R.L.—See BERICAP GmbH & Co. KG; *Int'l*, pg. 981
BERICAP UK LTD.—See BERICAP GmbH & Co. KG; *Int'l*, pg. 981
BERICAP ZARODASTECHNIKAI B.T.—See BERICAP GmbH & Co. KG; *Int'l*, pg. 981
BERICAP ZHUHAI CO., LTD.—See BERICAP GmbH & Co. KG; *Int'l*, pg. 981
BERICE LLC—See Charoen Pokphand Foods Public Company Limited; *Int'l*, pg. 1451
BERICO HEATING AND AIR CONDITIONING, INC.; *U.S. Private*, pg. 531
BERICO TECHNOLOGIES LLC; *U.S. Private*, pg. 531
BERINGER ASSOCIATES, INC.; *U.S. Private*, pg. 532
BERINGER CAPITAL; *Int'l*, pg. 981
BERING HOME CENTER INC.; *U.S. Private*, pg. 532
BERING MARINE CORPORATION—See Lynden Incorporated; *U.S. Private*, pg. 2521
BERING SEA ECCOTECH INC.—See Tanadgusix Corp.; *U.S. Private*, pg. 3930
BERING STRAITS NATIVE CORPORATION; *U.S. Private*, pg. 532
BERITA HARIAN SDN BERHAD—See Media Prima Berhad; *Int'l*, pg. 4771
BERITA INFORMATION SYSTEM SDN BHD—See Media Prima Berhad; *Int'l*, pg. 4771
BERJAYA 2ND HOMES (MM2H) SDN BHD—See Berjaya Corporation Berhad; *Int'l*, pg. 982
BERJAYA AIR SDN BHD—See Berjaya Corporation Berhad; *Int'l*, pg. 982
BERJAYA ASSETS BERHAD; *Int'l*, pg. 981
BERJAYA BEAU VALLON BAY BEACH RESORT LIMITED—See Berjaya Corporation Berhad; *Int'l*, pg. 982
BERJAYA BOOKS SDN BHD—See Berjaya Corporation Berhad; *Int'l*, pg. 982
BERJAYA BRILLIANCE AUTO SDN BHD—See Berjaya Corporation Berhad; *Int'l*, pg. 984
BERJAYA CAPITAL BERHAD—See Berjaya Corporation Berhad; *Int'l*, pg. 982
BERJAYA (CHINA) GREAT MALL CO. LTD—See Berjaya Corporation Berhad; *Int'l*, pg. 982
BERJAYA CHINA MOTOR SDN BHD—See Berjaya Corporation Berhad; *Int'l*, pg. 982
BERJAYA CORPORATION BERHAD; *Int'l*, pg. 982
BERJAYA CORPORATION (S) PTE LTD—See Berjaya Corporation Berhad; *Int'l*, pg. 982
BERJAYA ENERGIES SDN BHD—See Naza Corporation Holdings Sdn Bhd; *Int'l*, pg. 5178
BERJAYA FOOD BERHAD—See Berjaya Corporation Berhad; *Int'l*, pg. 982
BERJAYA FOOD SUPREME SDN BHD—See Berjaya Corporation Berhad; *Int'l*, pg. 982
BERJAYA FOOD TRADING SDN BHD—See Berjaya Corporation Berhad; *Int'l*, pg. 982
BERJAYA GOLF RESORT BERHAD—See Berjaya Corporation Berhad; *Int'l*, pg. 983
BERJAYA GROUP BERHAD—See Berjaya Corporation Berhad; *Int'l*, pg. 982
BERJAYA HIGHER EDUCATION SDN BHD—See Berjaya Corporation Berhad; *Int'l*, pg. 982
BERJAYA HILLS BERHAD—See Berjaya Corporation Berhad; *Int'l*, pg. 982
BERJAYA HOLDINGS (HK) LIMITED—See Berjaya Corporation Berhad; *Int'l*, pg. 984
BERJAYA HOSPITALITY SERVICES SDN BHD—See Berjaya Corporation Berhad; *Int'l*, pg. 983
BERJAYA HOTELS & RESORTS (M) SDN BHD—See Berjaya Corporation Berhad; *Int'l*, pg. 984
BERJAYA HOTELS & RESORTS (SINGAPORE) PTE LTD—See Berjaya Corporation Berhad; *Int'l*, pg. 983
BERJAYA HOTELS & RESORTS VIETNAM SDN BHD—See Berjaya Corporation Berhad; *Int'l*, pg. 982
BERJAYA KRISPY KREME DOUGHNUTS MALAYSIASDN BHD—See Berjaya Corporation Berhad; *Int'l*, pg. 984
BERJAYA LAND BERHAD—See Berjaya Corporation Berhad; *Int'l*, pg. 982
BERJAYA LAND DEVELOPMENT SDN BHD—See Berjaya Corporation Berhad; *Int'l*, pg. 982
BERJAYA LANGKAWI BEACH RESORT SDN BHD—See Berjaya Corporation Berhad; *Int'l*, pg. 983
BERJAYA LOTTERY MANAGEMENT (HK) LTD.—See Berjaya Corporation Berhad; *Int'l*, pg. 983
BERJAYA MEDIA BERHAD—See Berjaya Corporation Berhad; *Int'l*, pg. 983
BERJAYA MOUNT ROYAL BEACH HOTEL LIMITED—See Berjaya Corporation Berhad; *Int'l*, pg. 982
BERJAYA PENANG HOTEL SDN BHD.—See Berjaya Corporation Berhad; *Int'l*, pg. 983
BERJAYA PHARMACY DISTRIBUTION SDN BHD—See Berjaya Corporation Berhad; *Int'l*, pg. 984
BERJAYA PHARMACY SDN BHD—See Berjaya Corporation Berhad; *Int'l*, pg. 984
BERJAYA PHILIPPINES, INC.—See Berjaya Corporation Berhad; *Int'l*, pg. 983
BERJAYA PIZZA COMPANY SDN BHD—See Berjaya Corporation Berhad; *Int'l*, pg. 982
BERJAYA PRASLIN LIMITED—See Berjaya Corporation Berhad; *Int'l*, pg. 984
BERJAYA RESORT MANAGEMENT SERVICES SDN BHD—See Berjaya Corporation Berhad; *Int'l*, pg. 983
BERJAYA ROASTERS (M) SDN BHD—See Berjaya Corporation Berhad; *Int'l*, pg. 984
BERJAYA SOMPO INSURANCE BERHAD—See Sompo Holdings, Inc.; *Int'l*, pg. 7086
BERJAYA STARBUCKS COFFEE COMPANY SDN. BHD.—See Berjaya Corporation Berhad; *Int'l*, pg. 982
BERJAYA STARBUCKS COFFEE COMPANY SDN. BHD.—See Starbucks Corporation; *U.S. Public*, pg. 1938
BERJAYA TIMES SQUARE SDN. BHD.—See Berjaya Assets Berhad; *Int'l*, pg. 981
BERJAYA TIMES SQUARE THEME PARK SDN BHD—See Berjaya Assets Berhad; *Int'l*, pg. 981
BERJAYA VACATION CLUB BERHAD—See Berjaya Corporation Berhad; *Int'l*, pg. 983
BERJAYA WATERFRONT SDN. BHD.—See Berjaya Assets Berhad; *Int'l*, pg. 981
BERKADIA COMMERCIAL MORTGAGE LLC; *U.S. Private*, pg. 532
BERKAT SETIA SDN. BHD.—See NPC Resources Berhad; *Int'l*, pg. 5472

BERKEL & COMPANY CONTRACTORS INC.

BERKEL & COMPANY CONTRACTORS INC.; *U.S. Private*, pg. 532
BERKELEY ADVANCED BIOMATERIALS, INC.—See GNI Group Ltd.; *Int'l*, pg. 3017
BERKELEY ASPHALT COMPANY; *U.S. Private*, pg. 532
THE BERKELEY ASSOCIATES CORPORATION—See The Judge Group, Inc.; *U.S. Private*, pg. 4064
BERKELEY COMMERCIAL DEVELOPMENTS LTD.—See The Berkeley Group Holdings plc; *Int'l*, pg. 7620
BERKELEY CONTRACT PACKAGING LLC—See Summit Container Corporation; *U.S. Private*, pg. 3854
BERKELEY COUNTY WATER & SANITATION AUTHORITY; *U.S. Private*, pg. 532
BERKELEY ELECTRIC COOPERATIVE INC.; *U.S. Private*, pg. 532
BERKELEY ENERGIA LIMITED; *Int'l*, pg. 985
BERKELEY EXPLORATION ESPANA S.L.U.—See Berkeley Energia Limited; *Int'l*, pg. 985
BERKELEY FARMS, LLC—See Dean Foods Company; *U.S. Private*, pg. 1183
BERKELEY FIRST LIMITED—See The Berkeley Group Holdings plc; *Int'l*, pg. 7620
BERKELEY FLORIST SUPPLY CO, INC.; *U.S. Private*, pg. 532
BERKELEY FORGE & TOOL INC.; *U.S. Private*, pg. 532
THE BERKELEY GROUP HOLDINGS PLC; *Int'l*, pg. 7620
THE BERKELEY GROUP PLC—See The Berkeley Group Holdings plc; *Int'l*, pg. 7621
BERKELEY HEARTLAB, INC.—See Quest Diagnostics, Inc.; *U.S. Public*, pg. 1755
BERKELEY HOMES (CENTRAL LONDON) LIMITED—See The Berkeley Group Holdings plc; *Int'l*, pg. 7620
BERKELEY HOMES (EASTERN COUNTIES) LIMITED—See The Berkeley Group Holdings plc; *Int'l*, pg. 7620
BERKELEY HOMES (EASTERN COUNTIES) LIMITED—See The Berkeley Group Holdings plc; *Int'l*, pg. 7620
BERKELEY HOMES (EASTERN) LIMITED—See The Berkeley Group Holdings plc; *Int'l*, pg. 7620
BERKELEY HOMES (EAST THAMES) LIMITED—See The Berkeley Group Holdings plc; *Int'l*, pg. 7620
BERKELEY HOMES (HAMPSHIRE) LIMITED—See The Berkeley Group Holdings plc; *Int'l*, pg. 7620
BERKELEY HOMES (KENT) LIMITED—See The Berkeley Group Holdings plc; *Int'l*, pg. 7620
BERKELEY HOMES (OXFORD & CHILTERN) LIMITED—See The Berkeley Group Holdings plc; *Int'l*, pg. 7620
BERKELEY HOMES PLC—See The Berkeley Group Holdings plc; *Int'l*, pg. 7620
BERKELEY HOMES (SOUTHALL) LIMITED—See The Berkeley Group Holdings plc; *Int'l*, pg. 7620
BERKELEY HOMES (SOUTH EAST LONDON) LIMITED—See The Berkeley Group Holdings plc; *Int'l*, pg. 7620
BERKELEY HOMES (SOUTHERN) LIMITED—See The Berkeley Group Holdings plc; *Int'l*, pg. 7620
BERKELEY HOMES (URBAN RENAISSANCE) LIMITED—See The Berkeley Group Holdings plc; *Int'l*, pg. 7620
BERKELEY HOMES (WEST LONDON) LIMITED—See The Berkeley Group Holdings plc; *Int'l*, pg. 7620
BERKELEY HOMES (WEST THAMES) LIMITED—See The Berkeley Group Holdings plc; *Int'l*, pg. 7620
THE BERKELEY HOTEL LIMITED—See Maybourne Hotels Limited; *Int'l*, pg. 4743
BERKELEY INSURANCE GROUP LIMITED—See Brown & Brown, Inc.; *U.S. Public*, pg. 397
BERKELEY INSURANCE GROUP UK LIMITED—See Brown & Brown, Inc.; *U.S. Public*, pg. 397
BERKELEY MINERA ESPANA, S.A.—See Berkeley Energia Limited; *Int'l*, pg. 985
BERKELEY MORGAN GROUP LIMITED—See Personal Group Holdings plc; *Int'l*, pg. 5820
BERKELEY MORGAN LIMITED—See Personal Group Holdings plc; *Int'l*, pg. 5820
BERKELEY NUCLEONICS CORP.; *U.S. Private*, pg. 532
BERKELEY PARTNERSHIP HOMES LIMITED—See The Berkeley Group Holdings plc; *Int'l*, pg. 7620
BERKELEY POINT CAPITAL, LLC—See Newmark Group, Inc.; *U.S. Public*, pg. 1515
BERKELEY PROPERTIES LIMITED—See The Berkeley Group Holdings plc; *Int'l*, pg. 7620
BERKELEY RESEARCH GROUP LLC; *U.S. Private*, pg. 532
BERKELEY SANITARY SERVICE, INC.—See Republic Services, Inc.; *U.S. Public*, pg. 1786
BERKELEY SCOTT LIMITED—See The Kellan Group Plc; *Int'l*, pg. 7662
BERKELEY SDN. BHD.—See Paramount Corporation Berhad; *Int'l*, pg. 5738
BERKELEYS FRANCHISE SERVICES PTY. LTD.—See Downer EDI Limited; *Int'l*, pg. 2185
BERKELEY STRATEGIC LAND LIMITED—See The Berkeley Group Holdings plc; *Int'l*, pg. 7620
BERKELEY SYMPHONY ORCHESTRA; *U.S. Private*, pg. 532

BERKELEY URBAN RENAISSANCE LIMITED—See The Berkeley Group Holdings plc; *Int'l*, pg. 7620
BERKEL (IRELAND) LIMITED—See Illinois Tool Works Inc.; *U.S. Public*, pg. 1101
BERKEMPLAST SAN. VE TIC. LTD. STI.—See Bischof + Klein GmbH & Co. KG; *Int'l*, pg. 1048
BERKERY, NOYES & CO., LLC; *U.S. Private*, pg. 533
BERKHOF VALKENSWAARD BV—See VDL Groep B.V.; *Int'l*, pg. 8141
BERKHOUT LANGEVELD BV—See What's Cooking Group NV; *Int'l*, pg. 8396
BERKH UUL JOINT STOCK COMPANY; *Int'l*, pg. 985
BERKIM CONSTRUCTION INC.; *Int'l*, pg. 985
BERKLEY ACCIDENT & HEALTH LLC—See W.R. Berkley Corporation; *U.S. Public*, pg. 2316
BERKLEY ALLIANCE MANAGERS, LLC—See W.R. Berkley Corporation; *U.S. Public*, pg. 2316
BERKLEY ARGENTINA DE REASEGUROS S.A.—See W.R. Berkley Corporation; *U.S. Public*, pg. 2316
BERKLEY ASSET PROTECTION UNDERWRITERS, LLC—See W.R. Berkley Corporation; *U.S. Public*, pg. 2316
BERKLEY AVIATION, LLC—See W.R. Berkley Corporation; *U.S. Public*, pg. 2316
BERKLEY CAPITAL INVESTORS, LP—See W.R. Berkley Corporation; *U.S. Public*, pg. 2316
BERKLEY CAPITAL, LLC—See W.R. Berkley Corporation; *U.S. Public*, pg. 2316
BERKLEY CUSTOM INSURANCE MANAGERS, LLC—See W.R. Berkley Corporation; *U.S. Public*, pg. 2316
BERKLEY DEAN & COMPANY, INC.—See W.R. Berkley Corporation; *U.S. Public*, pg. 2316
BERKLEY EAST SOLAR, LLC—See Duke Energy Corporation; *U.S. Public*, pg. 690
BERKLEY FINSECURE, LLC—See W.R. Berkley Corporation; *U.S. Public*, pg. 2316
BERKLEY HEALTHCARE PROFESSIONAL INSURANCE SERVICES, LLC—See W.R. Berkley Corporation; *U.S. Public*, pg. 2316
BERKLEY INSURANCE COMPANY—See W.R. Berkley Corporation; *U.S. Public*, pg. 2318
BERKLEY INTERNATIONAL ARGENTINA, S.A.—See W.R. Berkley Corporation; *U.S. Public*, pg. 2316
BERKLEY INTERNATIONAL DO BRASIL SEGUROS S. A.—See W.R. Berkley Corporation; *U.S. Public*, pg. 2317
BERKLEY INTERNATIONAL LATINOAMERICA S. A.—See W.R. Berkley Corporation; *U.S. Public*, pg. 2316
BERKLEY INTERNATIONAL LIFE INSURANCE COMPANY, INC.—See W.R. Berkley Corporation; *U.S. Public*, pg. 2316
BERKLEY INTERNATIONAL, LLC—See W.R. Berkley Corporation; *U.S. Public*, pg. 2317
BERKLEY INTERNATIONAL SEGUROS COLOMBIA S.A.—See W.R. Berkley Corporation; *U.S. Public*, pg. 2316
BERKLEY INTERNATIONAL SEGUROS, S. A.—See W.R. Berkley Corporation; *U.S. Public*, pg. 2316
BERKLEY INTERNATIONAL SEGUROS, S. A.—See W.R. Berkley Corporation; *U.S. Public*, pg. 2316
BERKLEY LIFE SCIENCES, LLC—See W.R. Berkley Corporation; *U.S. Public*, pg. 2317
BERKLEY LS INSURANCE SOLUTIONS, LLC—See W.R. Berkley Corporation; *U.S. Public*, pg. 2317
BERKLEY MEDICAL RESOURCES INC.; *U.S. Private*, pg. 533
BERKLEY MEDICAL RESOURCES INC.—See Berkley Medical Resources Inc.; *U.S. Private*, pg. 533
BERKLEY MID-ATLANTIC GROUP—See W.R. Berkley Corporation; *U.S. Public*, pg. 2318
BERKLEY NET UNDERWRITERS L.L.C.—See W.R. Berkley Corporation; *U.S. Public*, pg. 2317
BERKLEY NORTH PACIFIC GROUP, LLC—See W.R. Berkley Corporation; *U.S. Public*, pg. 2317
BERKLEY OFFSHORE UNDERWRITING MANAGERS, LLC—See W.R. Berkley Corporation; *U.S. Public*, pg. 2317
BERKLEY OFFSHORE UNDERWRITING MANAGERS UK, LIMITED—See W.R. Berkley Corporation; *U.S. Public*, pg. 2317
BERKLEY OIL & GAS SPECIALTY SERVICES, LLC—See W.R. Berkley Corporation; *U.S. Public*, pg. 2317
BERKLEY PROFESSIONAL LIABILITY, LLC—See W.R. Berkley Corporation; *U.S. Public*, pg. 2317
BERKLEY PROGRAM SPECIALISTS, LLC—See W.R. Berkley Corporation; *U.S. Public*, pg. 2317
BERKLEY PUBLIC ENTITY MANAGERS, LLC—See W.R. Berkley Corporation; *U.S. Public*, pg. 2317
BERKLEY RE AMERICA, LLC—See W.R. Berkley Corporation; *U.S. Public*, pg. 2317
BERKLEY REGIONAL SPECIALTY INSURANCE COMPANY—See W.R. Berkley Corporation; *U.S. Public*, pg. 2317
BERKLEY RENEWABLES INC.; *Int'l*, pg. 985
BERKLEY RE SOLUTIONS—See W.R. Berkley Corporation; *U.S. Public*, pg. 2317
BERKLEY RE UK LIMITED—See W.R. Berkley Corporation; *U.S. Public*, pg. 2317

CORPORATE AFFILIATIONS

BERKLEY RISK ADMINISTRATORS COMPANY, LLC—See W.R. Berkley Corporation; *U.S. Public*, pg. 2317
BERKLEY RISK MANAGERS—See W.R. Berkley Corporation; *U.S. Public*, pg. 2317
BERKLEY RISK SOLUTIONS, INC.—See W.R. Berkley Corporation; *U.S. Public*, pg. 2317
BERKLEY SELECT, LLC—See W.R. Berkley Corporation; *U.S. Public*, pg. 2317
BERKLEY SOUTHEAST INSURANCE GROUP, LLC—See W.R. Berkley Corporation; *U.S. Public*, pg. 2317
BERKLEY SPECIALTY UNDERWRITING MANAGERS, LLC—See W.R. Berkley Corporation; *U.S. Public*, pg. 2317
BERKLEY SURETY GROUP, INC.—See W.R. Berkley Corporation; *U.S. Public*, pg. 2317
BERKLEY TECHNOLGY SERVICES—See W.R. Berkley Corporation; *U.S. Public*, pg. 2317
BERKLEY TECHNOLOGY UNDERWRITERS, LLC—See W.R. Berkley Corporation; *U.S. Public*, pg. 2317
BERKLY ENTERPRISES INC.; *U.S. Private*, pg. 533
BERKMANNS ANTRIEBE GMBH—See Groschopp AG; *Int'l*, pg. 3088
BERKOSAN YALITIM VE TECRIT MADDELERI URETIM VE TICARET A.S.; *Int'l*, pg. 985
BERKOT LTD. INC.; *U.S. Private*, pg. 533
BERKOWITZ DEVELOPMENT GROUP, INC.; *U.S. Private*, pg. 533
BERKOWITZ POLLACK BRANT; *U.S. Private*, pg. 533
BERKS COUNTY CENTER FOR INDEPENDENT LIVING; *U.S. Private*, pg. 533
BERKS GROUP—See News-Press & Gazette Company; *U.S. Private*, pg. 2917
BERKSHIRE AGENCY, INC.—See ABRY Partners, LLC; *U.S. Private*, pg. 41
BERKSHIRE ASSET MANAGEMENT, LLC; *U.S. Private*, pg. 533
BERKSHIRE ASSOCIATES, LLC.—See Levine Leichtman Capital Partners, LLC; *U.S. Private*, pg. 2436
BERKSHIRE BANCORP INC.; *U.S. Public*, pg. 533
THE BERKSHIRE BANK—See Berkshire Bancorp Inc.; *U.S. Private*, pg. 533
BERKSHIRE BANK—See Berkshire Hills Bancorp, Inc.; *U.S. Public*, pg. 320
BERKSHIRE BLANKET INCORPORATED—See China National Machinery Industry Corporation; *Int'l*, pg. 1531
THE BERKSHIRE EAGLE—See Alden Global Capital LLC; *U.S. Private*, pg. 158
BERKSHIRE FARM CENTER AND SERVICES FOR YOUTH; *U.S. Private*, pg. 533
BERKSHIRE FASHIONS INC.; *U.S. Private*, pg. 533
BERKSHIRE FINANCIAL SERVICES, INC.; *U.S. Private*, pg. 533
THE BERKSHIRE GAS COMPANY—See Iberdrola, S.A.; *Int'l*, pg. 3571
BERKSHIRE GREY, INC.—See SoftBank Group Corp.; *Int'l*, pg. 7051
BERKSHIRE GROUP, LLC; *U.S. Private*, pg. 533
BERKSHIRE HATHAWAY AUTOMOTIVE INC.—See Berkshire Hathaway Inc.; *U.S. Public*, pg. 300
BERKSHIRE HATHAWAY CREDIT CORPORATION—See Berkshire Hathaway Inc.; *U.S. Public*, pg. 300
BERKSHIRE HATHAWAY ENERGY COMPANY—See Berkshire Hathaway Inc.; *U.S. Public*, pg. 300
BERKSHIRE HATHAWAY HOMESERVICES FOX & ROACH, REALTORS—See Berkshire Hathaway Inc.; *U.S. Public*, pg. 306
BERKSHIRE HATHAWAY HOMESERVICES NEW ENGLAND PROPERTIES—See Berkshire Hathaway Inc.; *U.S. Public*, pg. 306
BERKSHIRE HATHAWAY HOMESTATE INSURANCE COMPANY—See Berkshire Hathaway Inc.; *U.S. Public*, pg. 301
BERKSHIRE HATHAWAY INC.; *U.S. Public*, pg. 297
BERKSHIRE HATHAWAY INTERNATIONAL INSURANCE LIMITED—See Berkshire Hathaway Inc.; *U.S. Public*, pg. 301
BERKSHIRE HATHAWAY LIFE INSURANCE COMPANY OF NEBRASKA—See Berkshire Hathaway Inc.; *U.S. Public*, pg. 301
BERKSHIRE HILLS BANCORP, INC.; *U.S. Public*, pg. 319
BERKSHIRE INCOME REALTY LLC—See Berkshire Group, LLC; *U.S. Private*, pg. 533
BERKSHIRE INSURANCE GROUP, INC.—See Berkshire Hills Bancorp, Inc.; *U.S. Public*, pg. 320
BERKSHIRE LIFE INSURANCE COMPANY OF AMERICA—See The Guardian Life Insurance Company of America; *U.S. Private*, pg. 4040
BERKSHIRE MANUFACTURED PRODUCTS, INC.—See Waverly Partners Inc.; *U.S. Private*, pg. 4458
BERKSHIRE MOUNTAIN SPRING WATER; *U.S. Private*, pg. 533
BERKSHIRE PARTNERS LLC; *U.S. Private*, pg. 534
BERKSHIRE TACONIC COMMUNITY FOUNDATION, INC.; *U.S. Private*, pg. 535
BERKSHIRE-WESTWOOD GRAPHICS GROUP; *U.S. Private*, pg. 535
BERKS HOME DESIGN BUILD; *U.S. Private*, pg. 533

COMPANY NAME INDEX

BERK-TEK ELECTRONICS DIVISION—See Leviton Manufacturing Company, Inc.; *U.S. Private*, pg. 2436
BERK-TEK FIBER OPTIC DIVISION—See Leviton Manufacturing Company, Inc.; *U.S. Private*, pg. 2436
BERK-TEK LLC—See Leviton Manufacturing Company, Inc.; *U.S. Private*, pg. 2436
BERK WIPER CONVERTING & PACKAGING, LLC; *U.S. Private*, pg. 532
BERK WIPER INTERNATIONAL LLC; *U.S. Private*, pg. 532
BERLACK GMBH—See Burelle S.A.; *Int'l*, pg. 1223
BERLANDS INC.; *U.S. Private*, pg. 535
BERLI DYNAPLAST CO., LTD.—See PT Dynaplast Tbk.; *Int'l*, pg. 6037
BERLI JUCKER CELLOX LIMITED—See Berli Jucker Public Co. Ltd.; *Int'l*, pg. 985
BERLI JUCKER FOODS LIMITED—See Berli Jucker Public Co. Ltd.; *Int'l*, pg. 985
BERLI JUCKER LOGISTICS LIMITED—See Berli Jucker Public Co. Ltd.; *Int'l*, pg. 985
BERLI JUCKER PUBLIC CO. LTD.; *Int'l*, pg. 985
BERLI JUCKER SPECIALTIES LTD.—See Berli Jucker Public Co. Ltd.; *Int'l*, pg. 985
BERLIMED - ESPECIALIDADES FARMACEUTICAS LDA.—See Bayer Aktiengesellschaft; *Int'l*, pg. 907
BERLIMED-PRODUCTOS QUIMICOS FARMACEUTICOS E BIOLOGICOS LTDA.—See Bayer Aktiengesellschaft; *Int'l*, pg. 904
BERLIMED, S.A.—See Bayer Aktiengesellschaft; *Int'l*, pg. 904
BERLINA PTE. LTD.—See PT. Berlina Tbk; *Int'l*, pg. 6085
BERLIN-BECHSTEIN SHANGHAI CO., LTD.—See Samick Musical Instrument Co., Ltd.; *Int'l*, pg. 6505
BERLIN CAMERON UNITED—See WPP plc; *Int'l*, pg. 8467
BERLIN CAPITAL FUND GMBH—See Triginta Capital; *Int'l*, pg. 7921
BERLIN-CHEMIE AG—See A Menarini Industrie Farmaceutiche Riunite Srl; *Int'l*, pg. 18
BERLIN CITY AUTO GROUP—See Booth Creek Management Corporation; *U.S. Private*, pg. 617
BERLIN CITY FORD, INC.—See Booth Creek Management Corporation; *U.S. Private*, pg. 617
BERLIN CITY'O OF CHEVROLET BUICK, INC.—See Booth Creek Management Corporation; *U.S. Private*, pg. 617
BERLIN DIVISION—See American Litho Inc.; *U.S. Private*, pg. 240
BERLINER BANK AG & CO. KG—See Deutsche Bank Aktiengesellschaft; *Int'l*, pg. 2055
BERLINER EFFEKTENGESELLSCHAFT AG; *Int'l*, pg. 986
BERLINER PRESSE VERTRIEB GMBH & CO. KG—See Bertelsmann SE & Co. KGaA; *Int'l*, pg. 994
BERLINER RUNDFUNK—See Bertelsmann SE & Co. KGaA; *Int'l*, pg. 994
BERLINER SPECIALTY DISTRIBUTORS, INC.; *U.S. Private*, pg. 535
BERLINER VERMOGENSVERWALTUNG GMBH—See Siemens Aktiengesellschaft; *Int'l*, pg. 6886
BERLINER VOLKSBANK EG; *Int'l*, pg. 986
BERLINE; *U.S. Private*, pg. 535
BERLING S.A.; *Int'l*, pg. 986
BERLINGSKE MEDIA A/S—See DPG Media Group NV; *Int'l*, pg. 2188
BERLIN HYP AG—See Deutscher Sparkassen- und Giroverband e.V.; *Int'l*, pg. 2085
BERLIN HYP AG - WARSAW OFFICE—See Deutscher Sparkassen- und Giroverband e.V.; *Int'l*, pg. 2085
BERLIN HYP IMMOBILIEN GMBH—See Deutscher Sparkassen- und Giroverband e.V.; *Int'l*, pg. 2085
BERLIN LUMBER COMPANY, INC.—See Your Building Centers, Inc.; *U.S. Private*, pg. 4594
BERLIN METALS LLC—See Olympic Steel Inc.; *U.S. Public*, pg. 1570
BERLINOVO IMMOBILIEN GESELLSCHAFT MBH; *Int'l*, pg. 986
BERLIN PACKAGING - FORT LEE—See Keystone Group, L.P.; *U.S. Private*, pg. 2296
BERLIN PACKAGING LLC—See Keystone Group, L.P.; *U.S. Private*, pg. 2296
BERLIN PACKAGING - PITTSBURGH—See Keystone Group, L.P.; *U.S. Private*, pg. 2297
BERLIN PACKAGING - RANCHO CUCAMONGA—See Keystone Group, L.P.; *U.S. Private*, pg. 2297
BERLIN ROSEN LTD.—See O2 Investment Partners, LLC; *U.S. Private*, pg. 2982
THE BERLIN STEEL CONSTRUCTION COMPANY - BERLIN STEEL BALTIMORE/WASHINGTON DIVISION—See The Berlin Steel Construction Company; *U.S. Private*, pg. 3994
THE BERLIN STEEL CONSTRUCTION COMPANY - BERLIN STEEL MID-ATLANTIC DIVISION—See The Berlin Steel Construction Company; *U.S. Private*, pg. 3994
THE BERLIN STEEL CONSTRUCTION COMPANY - MA DIVISION—See The Berlin Steel Construction Company; *U.S. Private*, pg. 3994
THE BERLIN STEEL CONSTRUCTION COMPANY; *U.S. Private*, pg. 3993

BERLINWASSER METITO TECHNICAL DEVELOPMENT LTD—See Metito Holdings Ltd.; *Int'l*, pg. 4854
BERLIS AG—See Bayer Aktiengesellschaft; *Int'l*, pg. 901
BERLISS BEARING CO.—See FICODIS Inc.; *Int'l*, pg. 2653
BERLITZ CORPORATION—See Quad Partners, LLC; *U.S. Private*, pg. 3314
BERLUTI HONG KONG COMPANY LTD—See LVMH Moet Hennessy Louis Vuitton SE; *Int'l*, pg. 4592
BERLUTI ITALIA—See LVMH Moet Hennessy Louis Vuitton SE; *Int'l*, pg. 4592
BERLUTI JAPAN—See LVMH Moet Hennessy Louis Vuitton SE; *Int'l*, pg. 4592
BERLUTI LLC—See LVMH Moet Hennessy Louis Vuitton SE; *Int'l*, pg. 4592
BERLUTI S.A.—See LVMH Moet Hennessy Louis Vuitton SE; *Int'l*, pg. 4592
BERLUTI UK—See LVMH Moet Hennessy Louis Vuitton SE; *Int'l*, pg. 4592
BERMAS L.T.D.A.—See Rino Mastrotto Group S.p.A.; *Int'l*, pg. 6345
BERMAS SA; *Int'l*, pg. 986
BERMAX CONSTRUCTION; *Int'l*, pg. 986
BERMAZ AUTO BERHAD—See Berjaya Corporation Berhad; *Int'l*, pg. 983
BERMAZ MOTOR SDN BHD—See Berjaya Corporation Berhad; *Int'l*, pg. 984
BERMCO ALUMINUM; *U.S. Private*, pg. 535
BERMELE PLC; *Int'l*, pg. 986
BERMIL INDUSTRIES CORP.; *U.S. Private*, pg. 535
BERMO ENTERPRISES INC.; *U.S. Private*, pg. 535
BERMO INCORPORATED; *U.S. Private*, pg. 535
BERMONT DEVELOPMENT SDN. BHD; *Int'l*, pg. 986
BERMO SCOTLAND, LTD.—See Bermo Incorporated; *U.S. Private*, pg. 535
BERMUDA.COM LIMITED—See MediaHouse Limited; *Int'l*, pg. 4772
BERMUDA COMMERCIAL BANK LTD.—See ICM Limited; *Int'l*, pg. 3582
BERMUDA COMPUTER SERVICES LTD.—See International Business Machines Corporation; *U.S. Public*, pg. 1145
BERMUDA DIGITAL COMMUNICATIONS, LTD.—See One Communications Ltd.; *Int'l*, pg. 5575
BERMUDA ELECTRIC LIGHT COMPANY LIMITED—See Abengoa S.A.; *Int'l*, pg. 59
BERMUDA ELECTRIC LIGHT COMPANY LIMITED—See Algonquin Power & Utilities Corp.; *Int'l*, pg. 319
BERMUDA INTERNATIONAL FINANCE LTD.—See HSBC Holdings plc; *Int'l*, pg. 3504
BERMUDA INTERNATIONAL INVESTMENT MANAGEMENT LTD.—See HSBC Holdings plc; *Int'l*, pg. 3504
BERMUDA MONETARY AUTHORITY; *Int'l*, pg. 986
BERMUDA PAINT COMPANY LIMITED—See Devonshire Industries Limited; *Int'l*, pg. 2089
BERMUDA SKYPORT CORPORATION LIMITED—See Aecon Group Inc.; *Int'l*, pg. 172
BERMUDA STOCK EXCHANGE—See Miami International Holdings, Inc.; *U.S. Private*, pg. 2697
BERMUDA SUN LIMITED—See MediaHouse Limited; *Int'l*, pg. 4772
THE BERMUDA TELEPHONE COMPANY LIMITED—See Digicel Group Ltd.; *Int'l*, pg. 2119
BERMUDA TRUST COMPANY LTD.—See The Bank of N.T. Butterfield & Son Limited; *Int'l*, pg. 7616
BERMUDA TRUST (HONG KONG) LTD.—See HSBC Holdings plc; *Int'l*, pg. 3504
BERMUDA YELLOW PAGES LIMITED—See One Communications Ltd.; *Int'l*, pg. 5575
BERMULLER & CO. GMBH; *Int'l*, pg. 986
BERNABE COTE D'IVOIRE; *Int'l*, pg. 986
BERNA BIOTECH KOREA CORP.—See Johnson & Johnson; *U.S. Public*, pg. 1194
BERNAFON AG—See Demant A/S; *Int'l*, pg. 2023
BERNAFON A/S—See Demant A/S; *Int'l*, pg. 2023
BERNAFON AUSTRALIA PTY. LTD.—See Demant A/S; *Int'l*, pg. 2023
BERNAFON CANADA LTD.—See Demant A/S; *Int'l*, pg. 2023
BERNAFON HORGERATE GMBH—See Demant A/S; *Int'l*, pg. 2023
BERNAFON IBERICA S.L.U.—See Demant A/S; *Int'l*, pg. 2023
BERNAFON, LLC—See Demant A/S; *Int'l*, pg. 2023
BERNAFON NEDERLAND B.V.—See Demant A/S; *Int'l*, pg. 2023
BERNAFON NEW ZEALAND LTD.—See Demant A/S; *Int'l*, pg. 2023
BERNAFON S.R.L.—See Demant A/S; *Int'l*, pg. 2023
BERNAFON (UK) LTD.—See Demant A/S; *Int'l*, pg. 2023
BERNAL, LLC—See Auxo Investment Partners, LLC; *U.S. Private*, pg. 402
BERNAM ADVISORY SERVICES SDN. BHD.—See United Plantations Berhad; *Int'l*, pg. 8072
BERNAM AGENCIES SDN. BHD.—See United Plantations Berhad; *Int'l*, pg. 8072
BERNAM BAKERY SDN BHD—See United Plantations Berhad; *Int'l*, pg. 8072

BERNER KANTONALBANK AG

BERNAN PRESS—See The Rowman & Littlefield Publishing Group, Inc.; *U.S. Private*, pg. 4112
BERN AQUA—See Archer-Daniels-Midland Company; *U.S. Public*, pg. 184
BERNARD ATHLETIC KNIT LTD.; *Int'l*, pg. 986
BERNARDAUD S.A.; *Int'l*, pg. 986
BERNARDAUD—See Bernardaud S.A.; *Int'l*, pg. 986
BERNARD BUILDING CENTER INC.; *U.S. Private*, pg. 535
BERNARD CHAUS, INC.; *U.S. Private*, pg. 535
BERNARD DUMAS S.A.S.—See Hokuetsu Corporation; *Int'l*, pg. 3443
BERNARD FOOD INDUSTRIES INC.; *U.S. Private*, pg. 536
BERNARD FRANCE SAS—See The RAJA Group; *Int'l*, pg. 7678
BERNARDI AUTOMALL TRUST; *U.S. Private*, pg. 536
BERNARDI HONDA; *U.S. Private*, pg. 536
BERNARDI ITALIAN FOODS—See Ajinomoto Company, Inc.; *Int'l*, pg. 257
BERNARDIN LTD.—See Newell Brands Inc.; *U.S. Public*, pg. 1513
BERNARDI'S HONDA; *U.S. Private*, pg. 536
BERNARD KARCHER INVESTMENTS INC.; *U.S. Private*, pg. 536
BERNARD KLEIN INC.; *U.S. Private*, pg. 536
BERNARD KRIEF CONSULTANTS SA; *Int'l*, pg. 986
BERNARD LOISEAU SA; *Int'l*, pg. 986
BERNARD MATTHEWS FOODS LTD.—See Boparan Holdings Limited; *Int'l*, pg. 1111
BERNARD MATTHEWS OLDENBURG GMBH—See Sprehe Geflugel- und Tiefkuhlfeinkost Handels GmbH & Co. KG; *Int'l*, pg. 7144
BERNARD PAYSAGE & ENVIRONNEMENT—See FAYAT SAS; *Int'l*, pg. 2624
BERNARD ROBINSON & COMPANY, L.L.P.; *U.S. Private*, pg. 536
BERNARD R. WOLFE & ASSOCIATES INC.—See Aon plc; *Int'l*, pg. 495
BERNARDS BROS, INC.; *U.S. Private*, pg. 536
BERNARDS BROTHERS, INC.; *U.S. Private*, pg. 536
BERNARD & SONS INC.; *U.S. Private*, pg. 535
BERNARD WELDING—See Illinois Tool Works Inc.; *U.S. Public*, pg. 1101
BERNARD WILLIAMS & CO.; *U.S. Private*, pg. 536
BERNATELLOS PIZZA INC.; *U.S. Private*, pg. 536
BERND GROUP INC.; *U.S. Private*, pg. 536
BERND LINDECKE WERKZEUGBAU GMBH—See Xin Point Holdings Limited; *Int'l*, pg. 8528
BERNDORF AG; *Int'l*, pg. 986
BERNDORF BADERBAU DEUTSCHLAND GMBH—See Berndorf AG; *Int'l*, pg. 986
BERNDORF BADERBAU SCHWEIZ AG—See Berndorf AG; *Int'l*, pg. 986
BERNDORF BADERBAU SK S.R.O.—See Berndorf AG; *Int'l*, pg. 987
BERNDORF BADERBAU SP. Z O.O—See Berndorf AG; *Int'l*, pg. 987
BERNDORF BADERBAU SRL—See Berndorf AG; *Int'l*, pg. 987
BERNDORF BADERBAU S.R.O.—See Berndorf AG; *Int'l*, pg. 987
BERNDORF BAND ENGINEERING GMBH—See Berndorf AG; *Int'l*, pg. 987
BERNDORF BAND GMBH—See Berndorf AG; *Int'l*, pg. 986
BERNDORF BAND LATINOAMERICA S.A.S.—See Berndorf AG; *Int'l*, pg. 987
BERNDORF BELT TECHNOLOGY INC.—See Berndorf AG; *Int'l*, pg. 987
BERNDORF METALL- UND BADERBAU AG—See Berndorf AG; *Int'l*, pg. 987
BERNDORF METALL- UND BADERBAU GMBH—See Berndorf AG; *Int'l*, pg. 987
BERNDORF METALLWAREN GMBH—See Berndorf AG; *Int'l*, pg. 987
BERNDORF STEEL BELT SYSTEMS CO. LTD.—See Berndorf AG; *Int'l*, pg. 987
BERND RICHTER GMBH—See Amphenol Corporation; *U.S. Public*, pg. 129
BERND RICHTER U.S.A., INC.—See Amphenol Corporation; *U.S. Public*, pg. 129
BERNDT GMBH—See RETHMANN AG & Co. KG; *Int'l*, pg. 6306
THE BERNDT GROUP LTD.—See Valtech SE; *Int'l*, pg. 8123
BERNE APPAREL CORP; *U.S. Private*, pg. 536
BERNECKER + RAINER INDUSTRIE ELEKTRONIK GMBH—See ABB Ltd.; *Int'l*, pg. 56
BERNE COOPERATIVE ASSOCIATION INC.; *U.S. Private*, pg. 536
BERNER EAZYMATIC AG—See Hormann KG Verkaufsgesellschaft; *Int'l*, pg. 3480
BERNER EESTI OY—See Berner Oy; *Int'l*, pg. 988
BERNER INTERNATIONAL CO. LTD.—See Munters AB; *Int'l*, pg. 5705
BERNER KANTONALBANK AG; *Int'l*, pg. 988
BERNER OY - HEINAVESI PLANT—See Berner Oy; *Int'l*, pg. 988

BERNER OY

BERNER OY; *Int'l*, pg. 988
BERNER SE; *Int'l*, pg. 988
BERNER TORANTRIEBE KG—See Hormann KG Verkaufsgesellschaf; *Int'l*, pg. 3480
BERNETT S.R.L.—See Indena S.p.A.; *Int'l*, pg. 3649
BERNE UNION LIMITED—See Jordan Loan Guarantee Corporation; *Int'l*, pg. 3998
BERNEY OFFICE SOLUTIONS, LLC—See Xerox Holdings Corporation; *U.S. Public*, pg. 2387
BERNHARD BROTHERS MECHANICAL CONTRACTORS, LLC.; *U.S. Private*, pg. 536
BERNHARD CAPITAL PARTNERS MANAGEMENT, LP; *U.S. Private*, pg. 536
BERNHARD, LLC—See DIF Management Holding B.V.; *Int'l*, pg. 2117
BERNHARD SCHULTE SHIPMANAGEMENT (CHINA) COMPANY LIMITED—See Bernhard Schulte Shipmanagement (Cyprus) Ltd.; *Int'l*, pg. 988
BERNHARD SCHULTE SHIPMANAGEMENT (CYPRUS) LTD.; *Int'l*, pg. 988
BERNHARD SCHULTE SHIPMANAGEMENT (DEUTSCHLAND) GMBH & CO. KG—See Bernhard Schulte Shipmanagement (Cyprus) Ltd.; *Int'l*, pg. 988
BERNHARD SCHULTE SHIPMANAGEMENT (HELLAS) SPLLC.—See Bernhard Schulte Shipmanagement (Cyprus) Ltd.; *Int'l*, pg. 988
BERNHARD SCHULTE SHIPMANAGEMENT (HONG KONG) LTD.—See Bernhard Schulte Shipmanagement (Cyprus) Ltd.; *Int'l*, pg. 988
BERNHARD SCHULTE SHIPMANAGEMENT (INDIA) PVT. LIMITED—See Bernhard Schulte Shipmanagement (Cyprus) Ltd.; *Int'l*, pg. 988
BERNHARD SCHULTE SHIPMANAGEMENT (ISLE OF MAN) LTD.—See Bernhard Schulte Shipmanagement (Cyprus) Ltd.; *Int'l*, pg. 988
BERNHARD SCHULTE SHIPMANAGEMENT (POLAND) LTD.—See Bernhard Schulte Shipmanagement (Cyprus) Ltd.; *Int'l*, pg. 988
BERNHARD SCHULTE SHIPMANAGEMENT (SINGAPORE) PTE. LTD.—See Bernhard Schulte Shipmanagement (Cyprus) Ltd.; *Int'l*, pg. 989
BERNHARD SCHULTE SHIPMANAGEMENT (UK) LTD.—See Bernhard Schulte Shipmanagement (Cyprus) Ltd.; *Int'l*, pg. 989
BERNHARDT FURNITURE COMPANY - BERNHARDT HOSPITALITY DIVISION—See Bernhardt Furniture Company; *U.S. Private*, pg. 537
BERNHARDT FURNITURE COMPANY; *U.S. Private*, pg. 537
BERNICK COMPANIES - BEMIDJI PLANT—See Bernick Companies; *U.S. Private*, pg. 537
BERNICK COMPANIES - BRAINERD PLANT—See Bernick Companies; *U.S. Private*, pg. 537
BERNICK COMPANIES - DRESSER PLANT—See Bernick Companies; *U.S. Private*, pg. 537
BERNICK COMPANIES - DULUTH PLANT—See Bernick Companies; *U.S. Private*, pg. 537
BERNICK COMPANIES; *U.S. Private*, pg. 537
BERNICK COMPANIES - TWIN CITIES PLANT—See Bernick Companies; *U.S. Private*, pg. 537
BERNICK COMPANIES - WILLMAR PLANT—See Bernick Companies; *U.S. Private*, pg. 537
BERNICKS PEPSICOLA INC.—See Bernick Companies; *U.S. Private*, pg. 537
BERNIER CONNECT SAS—See HEICO Corporation; *U.S. Public*, pg. 1020
BERNINA INTERNATIONAL AG—See Bernina Schweiz AG; *Int'l*, pg. 989
BERNINA OF AMERICA INC.—See Bernina Schweiz AG; *Int'l*, pg. 989
BERNINA SCHWEIZ AG; *Int'l*, pg. 989
BERNING MARKETING, LLC; *U.S. Private*, pg. 537
BERNINI INC.; *U.S. Private*, pg. 537
BERNIS—See SNCF; *Int'l*, pg. 7025
BERNIS TRANSPORT—See SNCF; *Int'l*, pg. 7025
BERNOULLI ENTERPRISE, INC.—See Francisco Partners Management, LP; *U.S. Private*, pg. 1589
BERNSTEIN AUTONOMOUS LLP—See Equitable Holdings, Inc.; *U.S. Public*, pg. 789
THE BERNSTEIN COMPANIES; *U.S. Private*, pg. 3994
BERNSTEIN MANAGEMENT CORPORATION; *U.S. Private*, pg. 538
BERNSTEIN-REIN ADVERTISING, INC.; *U.S. Private*, pg. 538
BERNTSEN BRASS & ALUMINUM FOUNDRY INC.; *U.S. Private*, pg. 538
BERNZOMATIC—See Worthington Industries, Inc.; *U.S. Public*, pg. 2382
BERONI BIOTECH INC.—See Beroni Group Limited; *Int'l*, pg. 989
BERONI GROUP LIMITED; *Int'l*, pg. 989
BERONI JAPAN INC.—See Beroni Group Limited; *Int'l*, pg. 989
BERONIO LUMBER CO; *U.S. Private*, pg. 538
BERONI USA CORPORATION—See Beroni Group Limited; *Int'l*, pg. 989
BERRENDA MESA WATER DISTRICT; *U.S. Private*, pg. 538

BERRETT MORTGAGE SERVICES—See Xcel Financial LLC; *U.S. Private*, pg. 4580
BERRICLE LLC; *U.S. Private*, pg. 538
BERRIDGE MANUFACTURING COMPANY INC.; *U.S. Private*, pg. 538
BERRIEHILL RESEARCH CORPORATION—See Applied Research Associates, Inc.; *U.S. Private*, pg. 299
BERRIMA COAL PTY LIMITED—See Banpu Public Company Limited; *Int'l*, pg. 852
BERRY ACE PACKAGING (JIAXING) COMPANY LIMITED—See Berry Global Group, Inc; *U.S. Public*, pg. 320
BERRYALLOC NV—See Beaulieu International Group NV; *Int'l*, pg. 934
BERRY AVIATION INC.—See Acorn Growth Companies, LC; *U.S. Private*, pg. 63
BERRY BROS. & RUDD LIMITED; *Int'l*, pg. 989
BERRY BROS & RUDD SINGAPORE PTE. LTD.—See Berry Bros. & Rudd Limited; *Int'l*, pg. 989
BERRY COMPANIES, INC.; *U.S. Private*, pg. 538
THE BERRY COMPANY LLC - CINCINNATI—See The Berry Company LLC; *U.S. Private*, pg. 3994
THE BERRY COMPANY LLC - INGLEWOOD—See The Berry Company LLC; *U.S. Private*, pg. 3994
THE BERRY COMPANY LLC; *U.S. Private*, pg. 3994
BERRY CONTRACT INC.; *U.S. Private*, pg. 538
BERRY CONTRACTING L.P. - BELLE CHASSE FACILITY—See Berry Contracting L.P.; *U.S. Private*, pg. 538
BERRY CONTRACTING L.P. - COLOMBIA FACILITY—See Berry Contracting L.P.; *U.S. Private*, pg. 538
BERRY CONTRACTING L.P. - HOUSTON FACILITY—See Berry Contracting L.P.; *U.S. Private*, pg. 538
BERRY CONTRACTING L.P. - MEXICO FACILITY—See Berry Contracting L.P.; *U.S. Private*, pg. 538
BERRY CONTRACTING L.P. - MONTANA FACILITY—See Berry Contracting L.P.; *U.S. Private*, pg. 538
BERRY CONTRACTING L.P. - MORGAN CITY FACILITY—See Berry Contracting L.P.; *U.S. Private*, pg. 538
BERRY CONTRACTING L.P. - REDFISH BAY TERMINAL FACILITY—See Berry Contracting L.P.; *U.S. Private*, pg. 538
BERRY CONTRACTING L.P; *U.S. Private*, pg. 538
BERRY CORPORATION (BRY); *U.S. Public*, pg. 320
BERRY ECKE ASSOCIATES; *U.S. Private*, pg. 538
BERRY ENTERPRISES INC.; *U.S. Private*, pg. 538
BERRY GENOMICS CO., LTD.; *Int'l*, pg. 989
BERRY GLOBAL GROUP, INC; *U.S. Public*, pg. 320
BERRY GLOBAL, INC—See Berry Global Group, Inc; *U.S. Public*, pg. 321
BERRY GLOBAL, INC.—See Berry Global Group, Inc; *U.S. Public*, pg. 321
BERRY GLOBAL, INC—See Berry Global Group, Inc; *U.S. Public*, pg. 321
BERRY GLOBAL INDIA PRIVATE LIMITED—See Berry Global Group, Inc; *U.S. Public*, pg. 320
BERRY INVESTMENTS INC.; *U.S. Private*, pg. 538
BERRY IOWA, LLC—See Berry Global Group, Inc; *U.S. Public*, pg. 321
BERRYMAN PRODUCTS, INC.; *U.S. Private*, pg. 538
BERRY MATERIAL HANDLING, INC.—See Berry Companies, Inc.; *U.S. Private*, pg. 538
BERRYNE CO., LTD.—See Chudenko Corporation; *Int'l*, pg. 1594
BERRY NETWORK, INC.—See Thryv Holdings, Inc.; *U.S. Public*, pg. 2157
BERRY PACK INC.—See Goldberg Lindsay & Co., LLC; *U.S. Private*, pg. 1729
BERRY PETROLEUM COMPANY, LLC—See Berry Corporation (Bry); *U.S. Public*, pg. 320
BERRY PLASTICS CORP. - ANAHEIM—See Berry Global Group, Inc; *U.S. Public*, pg. 321
BERRY PLASTICS CORP. - BALTIMORE—See Berry Global Group, Inc; *U.S. Public*, pg. 321
BERRY PLASTICS CORP. - CHICAGO—See Berry Global Group, Inc; *U.S. Public*, pg. 321
BERRY PLASTICS CORP. - CRANBURY—See Berry Global Group, Inc; *U.S. Public*, pg. 321
BERRY PLASTICS CORP. - EVANSVILLE—See Berry Global Group, Inc; *U.S. Public*, pg. 321
BERRY PLASTICS CORP. - FLEXIBLE PACKAGING, SCHAUMBERG PLANT—See Berry Global Group, Inc; *U.S. Public*, pg. 321
BERRY PLASTICS CORP. - HENDERSON—See Berry Global Group, Inc; *U.S. Public*, pg. 321
BERRY PLASTICS CORP. - LANCASTER—See Berry Global Group, Inc; *U.S. Public*, pg. 321
BERRY PLASTICS CORPORATION—See Berry Global Group, Inc; *U.S. Public*, pg. 320
BERRY PLASTICS CORP. - SARASOTA—See Berry Global Group, Inc; *U.S. Public*, pg. 321
BERRY PLASTICS CORP. - SUFFOLK—See Berry Global Group, Inc; *U.S. Public*, pg. 321
BERRY PLASTICS CORP. - TUBED PRODUCTS DIVISION—See Berry Global Group, Inc; *U.S. Public*, pg. 321

CORPORATE AFFILIATIONS

BERRY PLASTICS FILMCO, INC.—See Berry Global Group, Inc; *U.S. Public*, pg. 321
BERRY PLASTICS SP, INC.—See Berry Global Group, Inc; *U.S. Public*, pg. 321
BERRY SUPERFOS BESANCON SAS—See Berry Global Group, Inc; *U.S. Public*, pg. 321
BERRY SUPERFOS DEVENTER B.V.—See Berry Global Group, Inc; *U.S. Public*, pg. 321
BERRY SUPERFOS PAMPLONA SA—See Berry Global Group, Inc; *U.S. Public*, pg. 321
BERRY SYSTEMS—See Hill & Smith PLC; *Int'l*, pg. 3391
BERRY TRACTOR & EQUIPMENT CO—See Berry Companies, Inc.; *U.S. Private*, pg. 538
BERRYVILLE GRAPHICS INC.—See Bertelsmann SE & Co. KGaA; *Int'l*, pg. 990
BERSATU SAGO INDUSTRIES (MUKAH) SDN BHD—See EKA Noodles Berhad; *Int'l*, pg. 2337
BERSATU SAGO INDUSTRIES SDN BHD—See EKA Noodles Berhad; *Int'l*, pg. 2337
BERSCHAUER PHILLIPS CONSTRUCTION CO; *U.S. Private*, pg. 539
BERSHKA BELGIQUE S.A.—See Industria de Diseno Textil, S.A.; *Int'l*, pg. 3665
BERSHKA BSK ESPANA S.A.—See Industria de Diseno Textil, S.A.; *Int'l*, pg. 3665
BERSHKA BULGARIA, LTD.—See Industria de Diseno Textil, S.A.; *Int'l*, pg. 3665
BERSHKA CESKA REPUBLICA S.R.O.—See Industria de Diseno Textil, S.A.; *Int'l*, pg. 3665
BERSHKA CIS, LTD.—See Industria de Diseno Textil, S.A.; *Int'l*, pg. 3665
BERSHKA COMMERCIAL (SHANGHAI) CO. LTD.—See Industria de Diseno Textil, S.A.; *Int'l*, pg. 3665
BERSHKA DEUTSCHLAND B.V. & CO. KG—See Industria de Diseno Textil, S.A.; *Int'l*, pg. 3665
BERSHKA DISENO, S.L.—See Industria de Diseno Textil, S.A.; *Int'l*, pg. 3665
BERSHKA FRANCE, S.A.R.L.—See Industria de Diseno Textil, S.A.; *Int'l*, pg. 3665
BERSHKA GIYIM ITHALAT IHRACAT VE TIC. LTD.—See Industria de Diseno Textil, S.A.; *Int'l*, pg. 3665
BERSHKA HELLAS, S.A.—See Industria de Diseno Textil, S.A.; *Int'l*, pg. 3665
BERSHKA HONG KONG LIMITED—See Industria de Diseno Textil, S.A.; *Int'l*, pg. 3665
BERSHKA IRELAND LTD.—See Industria de Diseno Textil, S.A.; *Int'l*, pg. 3665
BERSHKA ITALIA S.R.L.—See Industria de Diseno Textil, S.A.; *Int'l*, pg. 3665
BERSHKA JAPAN, LTD.—See Industria de Diseno Textil, S.A.; *Int'l*, pg. 3665
BERSHKA KOREA, LTD.—See Industria de Diseno Textil, S.A.; *Int'l*, pg. 3665
BERSHKA LOGISTICA, S.A.—See Industria de Diseno Textil, S.A.; *Int'l*, pg. 3665
BERSHKA MAGYAROSZAG KFT.—See Industria de Diseno Textil, S.A.; *Int'l*, pg. 3665
BERSHKA MEXICO, S.A. DE C.V.—See Industria de Diseno Textil, S.A.; *Int'l*, pg. 3665
BERSHKA NEDERLAND B.V.—See Industria de Diseno Textil, S.A.; *Int'l*, pg. 3665
BERSHKA OSTERREICH CLOTHING GMBH—See Industria de Diseno Textil, S.A.; *Int'l*, pg. 3665
BERSHKA POLSKA SP Z O.O.—See Industria de Diseno Textil, S.A.; *Int'l*, pg. 3665
BERSHKA PORTUGAL CONF. SOC. UNIP. SA—See Industria de Diseno Textil, S.A.; *Int'l*, pg. 3665
BERSHKA SERBIA, D.O.O.—See Industria de Diseno Textil, S.A.; *Int'l*, pg. 3665
BERSHKA SLOVAKIA, S.R.O.—See Industria de Diseno Textil, S.A.; *Int'l*, pg. 3665
BERSHKA SUISSE S.A.R.L.—See Industria de Diseno Textil, S.A.; *Int'l*, pg. 3665
BERSHKA U.K., LTD.—See Industria de Diseno Textil, S.A.; *Int'l*, pg. 3665
BERSIN BY DELOITTE—See Deloitte LLP; *U.S. Private*, pg. 1198
BERSIN BY DELOITTE—See Deloitte Touche Tohmatsu Limited; *Int'l*, pg. 2014
BERSON MILIEUTECHNIEK B.V.—See Halma plc; *Int'l*, pg. 3232
BERTAGNI 1882 SPA—See Ebro Foods S.A.; *Int'l*, pg. 2286
BERTAKO S.L.U.—See DS Smith Plc; *Int'l*, pg. 2207
BERTAM ALLIANCE BERHAD; *Int'l*, pg. 989
BERTAM DEVELOPMENT SDN. BHD.—See Bertam Alliance Berhad; *Int'l*, pg. 989
BERTANI DOMAINS S.R.L.—See Angelini ACRAF S.p.A.; *Int'l*, pg. 460
BERTA SERVICES SDN. BHD.—See United Plantations Berhad; *Int'l*, pg. 8072
BERTCH CABINET MANUFACTURING INC.; *U.S. Private*, pg. 539
THE BERT COMPANY—See Caisse de Depot et Placement du Quebec; *Int'l*, pg. 1256
THE BERT COMPANY—See KKR & Co. Inc.; *U.S. Public*, pg. 1265
BERTECH-KELEX, INC.; *U.S. Private*, pg. 539
BERTELKAMP AUTOMATION INC.; *U.S. Private*, pg. 539

COMPANY NAME INDEX

BERTEL O. STEEN AS; *Int'l*, pg. 989
BERTELSMANN AVIATION GMBH—See Bertelsmann SE & Co. KGaA; *Int'l*, pg. 994
BERTELSMANN CORPORATE SERVICES INDIA PRIVATE LIMITED—See Bertelsmann SE & Co. KGaA; *Int'l*, pg. 990
BERTELSMANN DATA SERVICES GMBH—See Bertelsmann SE & Co. KGaA; *Int'l*, pg. 990
BERTELSMANN GLOBAL BUSINESS SERVICES GMBH—See Bertelsmann SE & Co. KGaA; *Int'l*, pg. 990
BERTELSMANN INC.—See Bertelsmann SE & Co. KGaA; *Int'l*, pg. 990
BERTELSMANN LEXIKOTHEK VERLAG GMBH—See Bertelsmann SE & Co. KGaA; *Int'l*, pg. 991
BERTELSMANN SE & CO. KGAA; *Int'l*, pg. 989
BERTELSON BROTHERS, INC.—See The ODP Corporation; *U.S. Public*, pg. 2117
BERT HAZEKAMP & SON, INC.; *U.S. Private*, pg. 539
BERTHEAS & CIE—See Cheynet S.A.S; *Int'l*, pg. 1474
BERTHEL FISHER & CO. FINANCIAL SERVICES—See Berthel Fisher & Company Inc.; *U.S. Private*, pg. 539
BERTHEL FISHER & CO LEASING—See Berthel Fisher & Company Inc.; *U.S. Private*, pg. 539
BERTHEL FISHER & CO. MANAGEMENT CORP.—See Berthel Fisher & Company Inc.; *U.S. Private*, pg. 539
BERTHEL FISHER & COMPANY INC.; *U.S. Private*, pg. 539
BERTHEL FISHER INVESTMENTS INC—See Berthel Fisher & Company Inc.; *U.S. Private*, pg. 539
BERTHOD MOTORS INC.; *U.S. Private*, pg. 539
BERTHOLD FARMERS ELEVATOR CO.; *U.S. Private*, pg. 539
BERTHOLD FRANCE SAS—See BERTHOLD TECHNOLOGIES GmbH & Co. KG; *Int'l*, pg. 997
BERTHOLD ITALIA S.R.L—See BERTHOLD TECHNOLOGIES GmbH & Co. KG; *Int'l*, pg. 997
BERTHOLD TECHNOLOGIES (BELGIUM) NV/SA—See BERTHOLD TECHNOLOGIES GmbH & Co. KG; *Int'l*, pg. 997
BERTHOLD TECHNOLOGIES GMBH & CO. KG; *Int'l*, pg. 997
BERTHOLD TECHNOLOGIES GMBH—See BERTHOLD TECHNOLOGIES GmbH & Co. KG; *Int'l*, pg. 997
BERTHOLD TECHNOLOGIES (SCHWEIZ) OMBH—See BERTHOLD TECHNOLOGIES GmbH & Co. KG; *Int'l*, pg. 997
BERTHOLD TECHNOLOGIES (U.K.) LTD.—See BERTHOLD TECHNOLOGIES GmbH & Co. KG; *Int'l*, pg. 997
BERTHOLD TECHNOLOGIES U.S.A. LLC—See BERTHOLD TECHNOLOGIES GmbH & Co. KG; *Int'l*, pg. 997
BERTHOUD AGRICOLE SAS—See Exel Industries SA; *Int'l*, pg. 2582
BERTHOUD SPRAYERS LTD—See Exel Industries SA; *Int'l*, pg. 2582
BERTIN IT SAS—See CNIM Constructions Industrielles de la Mediterranee SA; *Int'l*, pg. 1677
BERTIN PHARMA SAS—See CT Ingenieros AAISL; *Int'l*, pg. 1868
BERTIN TECHNOLOGIES SAS—See CNIM Constructions Industrielles de la Mediterranee SA; *Int'l*, pg. 1677
BERTKE INVESTMENTS, INC.; *U.S. Private*, pg. 539
BERTLING LOGISTICS INC.; *U.S. Private*, pg. 539
BERTMARK MEDIA AB—See Sanoma Oyj; *Int'l*, pg. 6553
BERTMARKS FORLAG AB—See Sanoma Oyj; *Int'l*, pg. 6553
BERT NASH COMMUNITY MENTAL HEALTH CENTER, INC.; *U.S. Private*, pg. 539
BERTOLOTTI S.P.A.—See LKQ Corporation; *U.S. Public*, pg. 1334
BERTOLUCCI SA—See Dickson Concepts (International) Limited; *Int'l*, pg. 2112
BERTRAM ASSOCIATES; *U.S. Private*, pg. 539
BERTRAM CAPITAL MANAGEMENT, LLC; *U.S. Private*, pg. 539
BERTRAM CORPORATION; *U.S. Private*, pg. 540
BERTRAM & GRAF GMBH—See Steel Partners Holdings L.P.; *U.S. Public*, pg. 1943
BERTRAM GROUP LTD.—See Aurelius Equity Opportunities SE & Co. KGaA; *Int'l*, pg. 707
BERTRAM'S GMBH—See Intek Group S.p.A.; *Int'l*, pg. 3732
BERTRAND-PUMA—See Ali Holding S.r.l; *Int'l*, pg. 320
BERTRANDT AG; *Int'l*, pg. 997
BERTRANDT CESKA REPUBLIKA ENGINEERING TECHNOLOGIES S.R.O.—See Bertrandt AG; *Int'l*, pg. 997
BERTRANDT ENGINEERING SHANGHAI CO., LTD.—See Bertrandt AG; *Int'l*, pg. 997
BERTRANDT FAHRERPROBUNG SUD GMBH—See Bertrandt AG; *Int'l*, pg. 997
BERTRANDT PROJEKTGESELLSCHAFT MBH—See Bertrandt AG; *Int'l*, pg. 998
BERTRANDT SAS BETRIEBSSTATTE—See Bertrandt AG; *Int'l*, pg. 998
BERTRANDT S.A.S.—See Bertrandt AG; *Int'l*, pg. 998
BERTRANDT UK LTD.—See Bertrandt AG; *Int'l*, pg. 998
BERTRANDT US INC.—See Bertrandt AG; *Int'l*, pg. 998
BERTRANDT VERWALTUNGS GMBH—See Bertrandt AG; *Int'l*, pg. 998
BERT R HUNCILMAN & SON INC.; *U.S. Private*, pg. 539
BERT SMITH AUTOMOTIVE; *U.S. Private*, pg. 539
BERT SMITH OLDSMOBILE, INC.; *U.S. Private*, pg. 539
BERTUCCI CONTRACTING CORPORATION; *U.S. Private*, pg. 540
BERTUCCI'S CORPORATION—See Earl Enterprises; *U.S. Private*, pg. 1312
BERT WOLFE AUTOMOTIVE GROUP; *U.S. Private*, pg. 539
BERT WOLFE FORD; *U.S. Private*, pg. 539
BERU EICHENAUER GMBH—See BorgWarner Inc.; *U.S. Public*, pg. 369
BERUFSBILDUNGSGESELLSCHAFT GEORGSMARIENHUTTE MBH—See Georgsmarienhutte Holding GmbH; *Int'l*, pg. 2940
BERU ITALIA S.R.L.—See BorgWarner Inc.; *U.S. Public*, pg. 369
BERU MEXICO S.A. DE C.V.—See BorgWarner Inc.; *U.S. Public*, pg. 369
BERVIN INVESTMENT & LEASING LIMITED; *Int'l*, pg. 998
BERWICK ELECTRIC CO.; *U.S. Private*, pg. 540
BERWICK HOSPITAL COMPANY, LLC—See Community Health Systems, Inc.; *U.S. Public*, pg. 551
BERWICK OFFRAY, LLC—See IG Design Group Plc; *Int'l*, pg. 3600
BERWIND CORPORATION; *U.S. Private*, pg. 540
BERWIND NATURAL RESOURCES CORPORATION—See Berwind Corporation; *U.S. Private*, pg. 540
BERWIND PROPERTY GROUP, LTD.—See Berwind Corporation; *U.S. Private*, pg. 541
BERWIN GROUP LIMITED—See HEXPOL AB; *Int'l*, pg. 3371
BERWIN INC.; *U.S. Private*, pg. 540
BERWIN INDUSTRIAL POLYMERS LIMITED—See HEXPOL AB; *Int'l*, pg. 3371
THE BERYL COMPANIES; *U.S. Private*, pg. 3994
BERYL CORPORATION; *U.S. Private*, pg. 541
BERYL DRUGS LTD.; *Int'l*, pg. 998
BERYL SECURITIES LIMITED; *Int'l*, pg. 998
BERZACK BROTHERS (JHB) (PTY) LIMITED—See The Bidvest Group Limited; *Int'l*, pg. 7621
BERZACK BROTHERS (PTY) LIMITED—See The Bidvest Group Limited; *Int'l*, pg. 7621
BESALCO S.A.; *Int'l*, pg. 998
BESAM AUTOMATIC DOOR SYSTEMS TRADING CO. LTD.—See ASSA ABLOY AB; *Int'l*, pg. 634
BESAM BELGIE N.V.—See ASSA ABLOY AB; *Int'l*, pg. 634
BESAM ENTRANCE SOLUTIONS INC—See ASSA ABLOY AB; *Int'l*, pg. 634
BESAM GMBH—See ASSA ABLOY AB; *Int'l*, pg. 634
BESAM IBERICA SA—See ASSA ABLOY AB; *Int'l*, pg. 634
BESAM LIMITED—See ASSA ABLOY AB; *Int'l*, pg. 634
BESAM (MANUFACTURING) PTE. LTD.—See ASSA ABLOY AB; *Int'l*, pg. 634
BESAM MASCHINENHANDELS GMBH—See ASSA ABLOY AB; *Int'l*, pg. 634
BESAM NEDERLAND BV—See ASSA ABLOY AB; *Int'l*, pg. 634
BESAM OY—See ASSA ABLOY AB; *Int'l*, pg. 634
BESAM POLSKA SP. Z.O.O.—See ASSA ABLOY AB; *Int'l*, pg. 634
BESAM SA—See ASSA ABLOY AB; *Int'l*, pg. 634
BESAM S.P.A.—See ASSA ABLOY AB; *Int'l*, pg. 634
BESAM SPOL.S.R.O.—See ASSA ABLOY AB; *Int'l*, pg. 634
BESAM US INC.—See ASSA ABLOY AB; *Int'l*, pg. 634
BESANA UK LIMITED; *Int'l*, pg. 998
BESCAST, INC.; *U.S. Private*, pg. 541
BESCHE OIL COMPANY, INC.; *U.S. Private*, pg. 541
BESCHICHTUNGSWERK WYHLEN GMBH—See Muehlhan AG; *Int'l*, pg. 5077
BESCONN EMEA, S.R.O.—See Korea Electric Terminal Co., Ltd.; *Int'l*, pg. 4284
BESEL S.A.—See Cantoni Motor S.A.; *Int'l*, pg. 1299
BE SEMICONDUCTOR INDUSTRIES N.V.; *Int'l*, pg. 931
BES ENGINEERING CORPORATION; *Int'l*, pg. 998
BE SHAPING THE FUTURE - FINANCIAL INDUSTRY SOLUTIONS AG—See TAMBURI INVESTMENT PARTNERS S.p.A; *Int'l*, pg. 7450
BE SHAPING THE FUTURE S.P.A.—See TAMBURI INVESTMENT PARTNERS S.p.A; *Int'l*, pg. 7450
BESHENICH MUIR & ASSOCIATES, LLC; *U.S. Private*, pg. 541
BESHORE & KOLLER INC.; *U.S. Private*, pg. 541
BESI APAC SDN. BHD.—See BE Semiconductor Industries N.V.; *Int'l*, pg. 931
BESI AUSTRIA GMBH—See BE Semiconductor Industries N.V.; *Int'l*, pg. 931
BESI AUSTRIA GMBH—See BE Semiconductor Industries N.V.; *Int'l*, pg. 931
BESI JAPAN CO. LTD.—See BE Semiconductor Industries N.V.; *Int'l*, pg. 931
BESI KOREA LTD.—See BE Semiconductor Industries N.V.; *Int'l*, pg. 931
BESIKTA BILPROVNING I SVERIGE AB—See Volati AB; *Int'l*, pg. 8300
BESIKTAS FUTBOL YATIRIMLARI SANAYI VE TICARET AS; *Int'l*, pg. 998
BESI LESHAN CO., LTD.—See BE Semiconductor Industries N.V.; *Int'l*, pg. 931
BESIN AMBOISE SA—See Packaging Corporation of America; *U.S. Public*, pg. 1633
BESI NORTH AMERICA, INC.—See BE Semiconductor Industries N.V.; *Int'l*, pg. 931
BESI PHILIPPINES, INC.—See BE Semiconductor Industries N.V.; *Int'l*, pg. 931
BESI (SHANGHAI) TRADING CO., LTD.—See BE Semiconductor Industries N.V.; *Int'l*, pg. 931
BESI SINGAPORE PTE. LTD.—See BE Semiconductor Industries N.V.; *Int'l*, pg. 931
BESI (THAI) S&S LTD.—See BE Semiconductor Industries N.V.; *Int'l*, pg. 931
BESI USA, INC.—See BE Semiconductor Industries N.V.; *Int'l*, pg. 931
BESIX GROUP SA—See Orascom Construction PLC; *Int'l*, pg. 5612
BESIX INFRA N.V.—See Orascom Construction PLC; *Int'l*, pg. 5612
BESLER GIDA VE KIMYA SAN. VE TIC. A.S.—See Yildiz Holding AS; *Int'l*, pg. 8583
THE BESL TRANSFER CO. INC.—See CRST International, Inc.; *U.S. Private*, pg. 1113
B.E. SMITH, INC.—See AMN Healthcare Services, Inc.; *U.S. Public*, pg. 125
B. E. SMITH, LLC—See AMN Healthcare Services, Inc.; *U.S. Public*, pg. 125
BESPAK EUROPE LTD. - INJECTABLES—See Recipharm AB; *Int'l*, pg. 6236
BESPAK EUROPE LTD.—See Recipharm AB; *Int'l*, pg. 6236
THE BESPOKE BRICK COMPANY LIMITED—See Brickability Group plc; *Int'l*, pg. 1151
BESPOKE CAPITAL PARTNERS, LLC—See Global Leisure Partners LLP; *Int'l*, pg. 2998
BESPOKE EXTRACTS, INC.; *U.S. Public*, pg. 326
BESPOON SAS—See TRUMPF SE + Co. KG; *Int'l*, pg. 7942
BESQAB AB; *Int'l*, pg. 998
BESRA GOLD INC.; *Int'l*, pg. 998
BESSAC ANDINA SA—See VINCI S.A.; *Int'l*, pg. 8213
BESSE FOREST PRODUCTS GROUP, CO.—See The Hoffmann Family of Companies; *U.S. Private*, pg. 4053
BESSE FOREST PRODUCTS GROUP - THE BARAGA LUMBER DIVISION—See The Hoffmann Family of Companies; *U.S. Private*, pg. 4053
BESSE LUMBER COMPANY—See The Hoffmann Family of Companies; *U.S. Private*, pg. 4053
BESSE MEDICAL SUPPLY—See Cencora, Inc.; *U.S. Public*, pg. 466
THE BESSEMER GROUP, INCORPORATED - NEW YORK OFFICE—See The Bessemer Group, Incorporated; *U.S. Private*, pg. 3994
THE BESSEMER GROUP, INCORPORATED; *U.S. Private*, pg. 3994
BESSEMER GROUP TRUST COMPANY OF FLORIDA - MIAMI—See The Bessemer Group, Incorporated; *U.S. Private*, pg. 3994
BESSEMER GROUP TRUST COMPANY OF FLORIDA - NAPLES—See The Bessemer Group, Incorporated; *U.S. Private*, pg. 3994
BESSEMER GROUP TRUST COMPANY OF FLORIDA—See The Bessemer Group, Incorporated; *U.S. Private*, pg. 3994
BESSEMER GROUP UK LTD.—See The Bessemer Group, Incorporated; *U.S. Private*, pg. 3994
BESSEMER INVESTMENT PARTNERS LLC; *U.S. Private*, pg. 541
BESSEMER INVESTORS LLC—See Bessemer Investment Partners LLC; *U.S. Private*, pg. 541
BESSEMER TRUST CO. - ATLANTA—See The Bessemer Group, Incorporated; *U.S. Private*, pg. 3994
BESSEMER TRUST CO. - CHICAGO—See The Bessemer Group, Incorporated; *U.S. Private*, pg. 3994
BESSEMER TRUST COMPANY (CAYMAN) LIMITED—See The Bessemer Group, Incorporated; *U.S. Private*, pg. 3994
BESSEMER TRUST COMPANY, N.A.—See The Bessemer Group, Incorporated; *U.S. Private*, pg. 3994
BESSEMER TRUST COMPANY OF CALIFORNIA - LOS ANGELES—See The Bessemer Group, Incorporated; *U.S. Private*, pg. 3994
BESSEMER TRUST COMPANY OF CALIFORNIA, N.A.—See The Bessemer Group, Incorporated; *U.S. Private*, pg. 3994
BESSEMER TRUST COMPANY—See The Bessemer Group, Incorporated; *U.S. Private*, pg. 3994
BESSEMER TRUST CO. - WASHINGTON, DC—See The Bessemer Group, Incorporated; *U.S. Private*, pg. 3994
BESSEMER VENTURE PARTNERS; *U.S. Private*, pg. 541
BESSER COMPANY; *U.S. Private*, pg. 542
BESSER CO.—See Besser Company; *U.S. Private*, pg. 542

BESSER COMPANY

BESSER PRONEQ, INC.—See Besser Company; *U.S. Private*, pg. 542
BESSER QUINN MACHINE & FOUNDRY—See Besser Company; *U.S. Private*, pg. 542
BESSETTE DEVELOPMENT CORPORATION; *U.S. Private*, pg. 542
BESSEY MOTOR SALES, INC.; *U.S. Private*, pg. 542
BESSO GRIMME INSURANCE BROKERSGMBH—See BGC Group, Inc.; *U.S. Public*, pg. 328
BESSO INSURANCE GROUP LIMITED—See BGC Group, Inc.; *U.S. Public*, pg. 328
BESSOLO DESIGN GROUP, INC.; *U.S. Private*, pg. 542
BESSO RE BRASIL CORRETORA DE RESSEGUROS LTDA.—See BGC Group, Inc.; *U.S. Public*, pg. 328
BESSOR MINERALS INC.; *Int'l*, pg. 998
BESSO SIGORTA VE REASURANS BROKERLIGI LTD.—See BGC Group, Inc.; *U.S. Public*, pg. 328
BEST2SERVE B.V.—See Hainan Traffic Administration Holding Co., Ltd.; *Int'l*, pg. 3214
BESTAC ADVANCED MATERIAL CO., LTD.—See San Fang Chemical Industrial Co., Ltd.; *Int'l*, pg. 6520
BESTACT SOLUTIONS INC.—See Yaskawa Electric Corporation; *Int'l*, pg. 8569
BEST AGROLIFE LTD.; *Int'l*, pg. 998
BESTA INTERNATIONAL TRADING PTE. LTD.—See Inventec Besta Co., Ltd.; *Int'l*, pg. 3773
BEST-ANNIVERSARY INC.—See Tsukada Global Holdings Inc.; *Int'l*, pg. 7956
BESTAR INC.—See Novacap Management Inc.; *Int'l*, pg. 5453
BEST AVIATION—See Fieldale Farms Corporation; *U.S. Private*, pg. 1504
BEST - BANCO ELECTRONICO DE SERVICO TOTAL, S.A.—See Novo Banco, S.A.; *Int'l*, pg. 5462
BEST BAR PTY, LTD.—See Tata Sons Limited; *Int'l*, pg. 7468
BEST-BLU CONSULTING WITH ENERGY GMBH—See EWE Aktiengesellschaft; *Int'l*, pg. 2576
BEST BRANDS BEVERAGE INC.—See The United Group; *U.S. Private*, pg. 4129
BEST BRIDAL HAWAII, INC.—See Tsukada Global Holdings Inc.; *Int'l*, pg. 7956
BEST BRIDAL INC.—See Tsukada Global Holdings Inc.; *Int'l*, pg. 7956
BEST BRIDAL KOREA INC.—See Tsukada Global Holdings Inc.; *Int'l*, pg. 7956
BEST BRIDAL SINGAPORE PTE. LTD.—See Tsukada Global Holdings Inc.; *Int'l*, pg. 7956
BESTBRIGHT ELECTRONICS CO., LTD.—See Brightking Holdings Limited; *Int'l*, pg. 1162
BEST BUILT INC.—See VHC Inc.; *U.S. Private*, pg. 4375
BEST BUY CANADA LTD.—See Best Buy Co., Inc.; *U.S. Public*, pg. 326
BEST BUY CO., INC.; *U.S. Public*, pg. 326
BESTBUY.COM, LLC—See Best Buy Co., Inc.; *U.S. Public*, pg. 326
BEST BUY ENTERPRISES, S. DE R.L. DE C.V.—See Best Buy Co., Inc.; *U.S. Public*, pg. 326
BEST BUYS INTERNATIONAL AS—See Altia Oyj; *Int'l*, pg. 392
BEST BUY STORES L.P.—See Best Buy Co., Inc.; *U.S. Public*, pg. 326
BEST BUY STORES, S. DE R.L. DE C.V.—See Best Buy Co., Inc.; *U.S. Public*, pg. 326
BEST BUY TIRE CENTER, INC.; *U.S. Private*, pg. 542
BESTCAN FOOD TECHNOLOGICAL INDUSTRIAL SDN BHD—See Far East Organization Pte. Ltd.; *Int'l*, pg. 2616
BEST CAPITAL ITALY S.R.L.—See BEST S.A.; *Int'l*, pg. 999
BEST CARBIDE CUTTING TOOLS, INC.—See PLANSEE Holding AG; *Int'l*, pg. 5890
BEST CARTAGE INC.—See Best Logistics Group, Inc.; *U.S. Private*, pg. 543
BEST CAST IT LTD; *Int'l*, pg. 998
BEST CATERING PTE. LTD.—See Neo Group Limited; *Int'l*, pg. 5196
BEST CELLARS, INC.—See The Great Atlantic & Pacific Tea Company, Inc.; *U.S. Private*, pg. 4038
BEST CHAIRS INC.; *U.S. Private*, pg. 542
BEST CHANCE PROPERTIES PTE LTD—See Second Chance Properties Ltd.; *Int'l*, pg. 6672
BEST CHEM, LTD.—See Momar, Inc.; *U.S. Private*, pg. 2767
BEST CHEVROLET INC.; *U.S. Private*, pg. 542
BEST CHIPS CO., LTD.; *Int'l*, pg. 998
BESTCO, INC.—See Tamanda Holdings USA Inc.; *U.S. Private*, pg. 3928
BEST COLD CHAIN CO., LTD.—See Nissin Corporation; *Int'l*, pg. 5375
BESTCOM INFOTECH CORP.—See Synnex Technology International Corporation; *Int'l*, pg. 7385
THE BEST CONNECTION GROUP LIMITED; *Int'l*, pg. 7621
BEST CONTRACTING SERVICES INC.; *U.S. Private*, pg. 542
BEST COURIER & DELIVERY SERVICE—See NewSpring Capital LLC; *U.S. Private*, pg. 2918

BESTCRETE AGGREGATES LIMITED—See ANSA McAL Limited; *Int'l*, pg. 477
BEST & CROMPTON ENGG. LTD.; *Int'l*, pg. 998
BEST CUT LIMITED; *Int'l*, pg. 999
BEST CUTTING DIE CO.; *U.S. Private*, pg. 542
BEST DEAL FOOD COMPANY, INC.; *U.S. Private*, pg. 542
BEST DEAL FOOD COMPANY INC.—See Best Deal Food Company, Inc.; *U.S. Private*, pg. 542
BEST DEAL PROPERTIES HOLDING PLC; *Int'l*, pg. 999
BEST DEAL SPRING INC.—See American Securities LLC; *U.S. Private*, pg. 248
BEST DENKI MALAYSIA SDN. BHD.—See Yamada Holdings Co., Ltd.; *Int'l*, pg. 8548
BEST DISTRIBUTION; *U.S. Private*, pg. 542
BEST DOCTORS CANADA INC.—See Teladoc Health, Inc.; *U.S. Public*, pg. 1992
BEST DOCTORS, INC.—See Teladoc Health, Inc.; *U.S. Public*, pg. 1992
BEST DOCTORS PORTUGAL LTD.—See Teladoc Health, Inc.; *U.S. Public*, pg. 1992
BEST DOORS AUSTRALIA PTY. LTD.—See dormakaba Holding AG; *Int'l*, pg. 2177
BEST DRIVERS; *U.S. Private*, pg. 542
BEST EASTERN HOTELS LTD.; *Int'l*, pg. 999
BESTEC ELECTRONICS USA—See Bestec Power Electronics Co., Ltd.; *Int'l*, pg. 1000
BESTECHNIC SHANGHAI CO., LTD.; *Int'l*, pg. 1000
BESTEC POWER ELECTRONICS CO., LTD.; *Int'l*, pg. 1000
BEST EDGE SEO, INC.; *U.S. Private*, pg. 542
BEST EFFORTS BANK PJSC; *Int'l*, pg. 999
BEST EINDHOVEN BV—See Best N.V.; *Int'l*, pg. 999
BEST ENVIRONMENTAL SYSTEMS TECHNOLOGY, INC.—See EMP Management, LLC; *U.S. Private*, pg. 1384
BEST EQUIPMENT SERVICE & SALES COMPANY, LLC—See DXP Enterprises, Inc.; *U.S. Public*, pg. 697
BESTERRA CO., LTD.; *Int'l*, pg. 1000
BEST EXPRESS FOODS, INC.; *U.S. Private*, pg. 542
BEST FACILITY SERVICES; *U.S. Private*, pg. 542
BEST FENCING GROUP B.V.; *Int'l*, pg. 999
BEST FINANCE COMPANY LIMITED; *Int'l*, pg. 999
BEST FOOD HOLDING COMPANY LIMITED; *Int'l*, pg. 999
BEST FRIENDS ANIMAL SOCIETY; *U.S. Private*, pg. 542
BEST GLOBAL, INC.—See Tsukada Global Holdings Inc.; *Int'l*, pg. 7956
BEST GLOBAL LOGISTICS CO., LTD.—See Senko Group Holdings Co., Ltd.; *Int'l*, pg. 6709
BESTGOFER INC.; *U.S. Private*, pg. 544
BESTGUM SP. Z O.O.—See PGE Polska Grupa Energetyczna S.A.; *Int'l*, pg. 5837
BEST HEALTH, INC.; *U.S. Private*, pg. 542
BESTHIDES GMBH—See Darling Ingredients Inc.; *U.S. Public*, pg. 633
BESTHIRE, LLC—See SHL; *Int'l*, pg. 6856
BEST HOME CARE LP—See Encompass Health Corporation; *U.S. Public*, pg. 754
BEST HOMES TITLE AGENCY, LLC; *U.S. Private*, pg. 543
BEST HOSPITALITY NETWORK CORPORATION—See Tsukada Global Holdings Inc.; *Int'l*, pg. 7956
BEST HOTEL PROPERTIES A.S.; *Int'l*, pg. 999
BESTIGE HOLDINGS LLC; *U.S. Private*, pg. 544
BEST IMPRESSIONS CATALOG COMPANY—See Malcolm Group Inc.; *U.S. Private*, pg. 2557
BEST IN CLASS TECHNOLOGY SERVICES, LLC—See Investcorp Holdings B.S.C.; *Int'l*, pg. 3775
BEST INC.; *Int'l*, pg. 999
BESTINET HEALTHCARE SDN BHD—See G3 Global Berhad; *Int'l*, pg. 2866
BEST-IN OY—See Atria Plc; *Int'l*, pg. 694
BEST INSTRUMENTS CO., LTD.—See A&D Co., Ltd.; *Int'l*, pg. 19
BEST INTERIORS INC.; *U.S. Private*, pg. 543
BESTINVER, S.A.—See Acciona, S.A.; *Int'l*, pg. 90
BEST IPRODUCTS.COM LLC; *U.S. Private*, pg. 543
BEST ITALIA S.R.L.—See BEST S.A.; *Int'l*, pg. 999
BESTIT CORP.; *U.S. Private*, pg. 543
BEST LABEL COMPANY INC.—See Ares Management Corporation; *U.S. Public*, pg. 190
BEST & LESS PTY. LIMITED—See Steinhoff International Holdings N.V.; *Int'l*, pg. 7195
BESTLIFE 3 INTERNATIONAL GMBH & CO. KG—See BayernLB Holding AG; *Int'l*, pg. 913
BEST LIFE STYLE INC.—See Tsukada Global Holdings Inc.; *Int'l*, pg. 7956
BEST LIGHTING PRODUCTS, INC.—See Harlow Aerostructures, LLC; *U.S. Private*, pg. 1865
BEST LINE LEASING INC.; *U.S. Private*, pg. 543
BEST LINKAGE (MACAO COMMERCIAL OFFSHORE) LIMITED—See Victory City International Holdings Limited; *Int'l*, pg. 8189
BEST LINK INC.—See Vision, Inc; *Int'l*, pg. 8253
BEST LINKING GROUP HOLDINGS LIMITED; *Int'l*, pg. 999
BEST LOCKERS, LLC—See ASSA ABLOY AB; *Int'l*, pg. 640

CORPORATE AFFILIATIONS

BEST LOGISTICS GROUP, INC.; *U.S. Private*, pg. 543
BEST LOGISTICS TECHNOLOGIES (CHINA) CO., LTD.—See BEST Inc.; *Int'l*, pg. 999
BEST LUBRICANT BLENDING LIMITED—See Yips Chemical Holdings Limited; *Int'l*, pg. 8585
BEST MANUFACTURING-FAYETTE—See Showa Glove Co.; *Int'l*, pg. 6861
BEST MANUFACTURING GROUP LLC—See GHCL Limited; *Int'l*, pg. 2959
BEST MANUFACTURING, INC.—See Reliance Steel & Aluminum Co.; *U.S. Public*, pg. 1779
BESTMARK, INC.—See Generation Growth Capital, Inc.; *U.S. Private*, pg. 1668
BEST MART 360 HOLDINGS LIMITED; *Int'l*, pg. 999
BEST MASONRY & TOOL SUPPLY, INC.—See CRH plc; *Int'l*, pg. 1846
BEST MATERIALS, LLC—See The Sterling Group, L.P.; *U.S. Private*, pg. 4122
BEST MAYFLOWER—See UniGroup, Inc.; *U.S. Private*, pg. 4283
BEST MEDICAL CANADA, LTD.—See Best Medical International, Inc.; *U.S. Private*, pg. 543
BEST MEDICAL CO., LTD.—See Hulic Co., Ltd.; *Int'l*, pg. 3528
BEST MEDICAL INTERNATIONAL, INC.; *U.S. Private*, pg. 543
BESTMED RESPIRATORY, INC.—See AdaptHealth Corp.; *U.S. Public*, pg. 38
BEST MODULES CORP.—See Holtek Semiconductor Inc.; *Int'l*, pg. 3453
BEST MOULDING CORP; *U.S. Private*, pg. 543
BEST MOUNTAIN DEUTSCHLAND HOLZWIRTSCHAFT GMBH; *Int'l*, pg. 999
BESTNEST, INC,; *U.S. Private*, pg. 544
BEST NOMOS RADIATION ONCOLOGY—See Best Medical International, Inc.; *U.S. Private*, pg. 543
BEST N.V.; *Int'l*, pg. 999
BESTODECK LTD.; *Int'l*, pg. 999
BEST ODOUR CO., LTD.—See R&B Food Supply Public Company Limited; *Int'l*, pg. 6168
BEST OF 52 LLC—See INSPIRATO INCORPORATED; *U.S. Public*, pg. 1131
BESTOFMEDIA, LLC—See Purch Group, Inc.; *U.S. Private*, pg. 3305
BEST OF THE BEST PLC; *Int'l*, pg. 999
BEST OIL COMPANY; *U.S. Private*, pg. 543
BESTOLIFE CORPORATION—See Quexco Incorporated; *U.S. Private*, pg. 3326
BESTONE.COM CO., LTD.; *Int'l*, pg. 1000
BEST ONE TIRE & SERVICE OF MID AMERICA, INC.; *U.S. Private*, pg. 543
BESTON GLOBAL FOOD COMPANY LIMITED; *Int'l*, pg. 1000
BESTON TECHNOLOGIES PTY LTD—See Beston Global Food Company Limited; *Int'l*, pg. 1000
BESTOP, INC.—See Kinderhook Industries, LLC; *U.S. Private*, pg. 2306
BESTORE CO., LTD.; *Int'l*, pg. 1000
BESTOW, INC.; *U.S. Private*, pg. 544
BEST PACIFIC INTERNATIONAL HOLDINGS LIMITED; *Int'l*, pg. 999
BESTPARK INTERNATIONAL LIMITED; *Int'l*, pg. 1000
BEST PARTY CONCEPTS, LLC—See Vinco Ventures, Inc.; *U.S. Public*, pg. 2298
BESTPASS, INC.; *U.S. Private*, pg. 544
BEST PERSONALIZED BOOKS, INC.; *U.S. Private*, pg. 543
BESTPHONE, S.A. DE C.V.—See Grupo Televisa, S.A.B.; *Int'l*, pg. 3136
BEST PLANNING, INC.—See Tsukada Global Holdings Inc.; *Int'l*, pg. 7956
BEST PLUMBING TILE & STONE INC.; *U.S. Private*, pg. 543
BEST PLUMBING TILE & STONE INC.—See Best Plumbing Tile & Stone Inc.; *U.S. Private*, pg. 543
BEST PLUMBING TILE & STONE INC.—See Best Plumbing Tile & Stone Inc.; *U.S. Private*, pg. 543
BEST PRACTICE ASSOCIATES, L.L.C.—See Sagewind Capital LLC; *U.S. Private*, pg. 3527
BEST PRACTICE IFA GROUP LIMITED—See Schroders plc; *Int'l*, pg. 6639
BESTPRACTICES, INC.—See KKR & Co. Inc.; *U.S. Public*, pg. 1249
BEST PROPERTY CO., LTD.—See Biken Techno Corporation Ltd.; *Int'l*, pg. 1023
BEST PROVISION CO., INC.; *U.S. Private*, pg. 543
BESTRANS CO., LTD.—See Warabeya Nichiyo Holdings Co., Ltd.; *Int'l*, pg. 8344
BEST RATE INSURANCE AGENCY, INC.—See Stone Point Capital LLC; *U.S. Private*, pg. 3818
BEST RATE REFERRALS—See Digital Media Solutions, Inc.; *U.S. Public*, pg. 663
BEST RESTAURANT EQUIPMENT & DESIGN CO.; *U.S. Private*, pg. 543
BEST RESULT CLEANING SERVICES LIMITED—See Tsim Sha Tsui Properties Limited; *Int'l*, pg. 7951
BEST SAND CORPORATION—See Covia Holdings Corporation; *U.S. Private*, pg. 1072
BEST S.A.; *Int'l*, pg. 999

COMPANY NAME INDEX

BEST SEATING SYSTEMS GMBH—See Addtech AB; *Int'l*, pg. 132
BESTSELLER A/S; *Int'l*, pg. 1000
BESTSERVE FINANCIAL LIMITED—See Sun Life Financial Inc.; *Int'l*, pg. 7305
BEST SOLUTIONS LLC—See WH Group Limited; *Int'l*, pg. 8395
BEST SOLUTION TECHNOLOGY INC.—See Holtek Semiconductor Inc.; *Int'l*, pg. 3453
BEST S.P.A.—See Melrose Industries PLC; *Int'l*, pg. 4813
BEST SPIRITS COMPANY LIMITED—See Thai Beverage Public Company Limited; *Int'l*, pg. 7589
BESTSUN ENERGY CO., LTD.; *Int'l*, pg. 1000
BEST TAIWAN INC.—See Action Electronics Co., Ltd.; *Int'l*, pg. 119
BEST TECH & ENGINEERING LIMITED—See BT Wealth Industries Public Company Limited; *Int'l*, pg. 1204
BESTTECHNICA EOOD—See Besttechnica TM - Radomir; *Int'l*, pg. 1000
BESTTECHNICA TM - RADOMIR; *Int'l*, pg. 1000
BEST TEXTILES ACQUISITION, LLC—See GHCL Limited; *Int'l*, pg. 2959
BEST TEXTILES ACQUISITION, LLC—See Patriarch Partners, LLC; *U.S. Private*, pg. 3109
BEST TFI S.A.—See BEST S.A.; *Int'l*, pg. 999
BEST TOURS ITALIA S.P.A.—See Alessandro Rosso Group S.p.A.; *Int'l*, pg. 306
BEST TOURS S.P.A.—See Alessandro Rosso Group S.p.A.; *Int'l*, pg. 306
BEST TRANSPORT AB—See Valedo Partners AB; *Int'l*, pg. 8112
BEST TRANSPORTATION OF ST. LOUIS; *U.S. Private*, pg. 543
BESTTRANSPORT.COM, INC.—See The Descartes Systems Group Inc.; *Int'l*, pg. 7636
BESTTRAVEL DORTMUND GMBH—See Borussia Dortmund GmbH & Co. KGaA; *Int'l*, pg. 1115
BEST UNIFORMS, LLC—See Charlesbank Capital Partners, LLC; *U.S. Private*, pg. 855
BEST UPON REQUEST CORPORATE, INC.; *U.S. Private*, pg. 543
BEST VALUE TECHNOLOGY, INC. (BVTI); *U.S. Private*, pg. 543
BEST VASCULAR, INC.—See Best Medical International, Inc., *U.S. Private*, pg. 540
BEST-WADE PETROLEUM INC.—See Litco Petroleum Inc.; *U.S. Private*, pg. 2467
BEST-WADE—See Litco Petroleum Inc.; *U.S. Private*, pg. 2467
BEST WAREHOUSING & TRANSPORTATION CENTER INC.—See Bluejay Capital Partners, LLC; *U.S. Private*, pg. 597
BEST WATER TECHNOLOGY (IRELAND) LTD.—See BWT Aktiengesellschaft; *Int'l*, pg. 1233
BESTWAY AUSTRALIA PTY. LTD.—See Bestway Global Holding Inc.; *Int'l*, pg. 1001
BESTWAY CEMENT LIMITED—See Bestway (Holdings) Limited; *Int'l*, pg. 1001
BESTWAY CENTRAL & SOUTH AMERICA LTDA.—See Bestway Global Holding Inc.; *Int'l*, pg. 1001
BESTWAY DEUTSCHLAND GMBH—See Bestway Global Holding Inc.; *Int'l*, pg. 1001
BESTWAY EASTERN EUROPE SP. Z O.O.—See Bestway Global Holding Inc.; *Int'l*, pg. 1001
BESTWAY ENTERPRISES INC.; *U.S. Private*, pg. 544
BESTWAY (EUROPE) S.R.L.—See Bestway Global Holding Inc.; *Int'l*, pg. 1001
BESTWAY FRANCE S.R.L.—See Bestway Global Holding Inc.; *Int'l*, pg. 1001
BESTWAY GLOBAL HOLDING INC.; *Int'l*, pg. 1001
BESTWAY (HOLDINGS) LIMITED; *Int'l*, pg. 1000
BESTWAY (HONG KONG) INTERNATIONAL LIMITED—See Bestway Global Holding Inc.; *Int'l*, pg. 1001
BESTWAY, INC.; *U.S. Private*, pg. 544
BESTWAY ITALY S.R.L.—See Bestway Global Holding Inc.; *Int'l*, pg. 1001
BEST WAY MECHANTRONIC CO.—See Awea Mechantronic Co., Ltd.; *Int'l*, pg. 753
BEST-WAY MOTOR LINES INC.; *U.S. Private*, pg. 544
BEST WAY OF INDIANA INC.; *U.S. Private*, pg. 543
BESTWAY OF NEW ENGLAND, INC.—See Bestway Enterprises Inc.; *U.S. Private*, pg. 544
BESTWAY OF PENNSYLVANIA, INC.—See Bestway Enterprises Inc.; *U.S. Private*, pg. 544
BESTWAY PANACEA HOLDINGS LTD—See Bestway (Holdings) Limited; *Int'l*, pg. 1001
BESTWAY RECYCLING COMPANY INC.; *U.S. Private*, pg. 544
BESTWAY REFRIGERATED SERVICE, INC.; *U.S. Private*, pg. 544
BESTWAY SOUTH, INC.—See Bestway Enterprises Inc.; *U.S. Private*, pg. 544
BESTWAY SYSTEMS, INC. - MEMPHIS DIVISION—See RJW, Inc.; *U.S. Private*, pg. 3450
BESTWAY SYSTEMS, INC.—See RJW, Inc.; *U.S. Private*, pg. 3449
BESTWAY (USA), INC.—See Bestway Global Holding Inc.; *Int'l*, pg. 1001

BESTWAY WHOLESALE LIMITED—See Bestway (Holdings) Limited; *Int'l*, pg. 1001
BESTWEB CORPORATION—See Antin Infrastructure Partners SAS; *Int'l*, pg. 483
BEST WELL SERVICES, LLC (BWS); *U.S. Private*, pg. 544
BEST WESTERN - DENVER INTERNATIONAL AIRPORT—See Stonebridge Realty Advisors, Inc.; *U.S. Private*, pg. 3827
BEST WESTERN INTERNATIONAL, INC.; *U.S. Private*, pg. 544
BEST WESTERN—See Northampton Group Inc.; *Int'l*, pg. 5441
BEST WESTERN—See Northampton Group Inc.; *Int'l*, pg. 5441
BEST WESTERN VILLAGE PARK INN; *Int'l*, pg. 999
BEST WILSON BUCKLEY FAMILY LAW PTY. LTD.—See Shine Justice Ltd.; *Int'l*, pg. 6842
BEST WONDERS SCIENCE & TECHNOLOGY CO., LTD—See Beijing Watertek Information Technology Co., Ltd.; *Int'l*, pg. 960
BEST WORLD INTERNATIONAL LTD.; *Int'l*, pg. 999
BEST WORLD LIFESTYLE (HK) COMPANY LIMITED—See Best World International Ltd.; *Int'l*, pg. 1000
BEST WORLD LIFESTYLE PTE LTD—See Best World International Ltd.; *Int'l*, pg. 1000
BEST WORLD LIFESTYLE SDN. BHD.—See Best World International Ltd.; *Int'l*, pg. 1000
BEST WORLD VIETNAM COMPANY LIMITED—See Best World International Ltd.; *Int'l*, pg. 1000
BESTWORTH-ROMMEL, INC.—See OneAccord Capital LLC; *U.S. Private*, pg. 3024
BEST YET MARKET INCORPORATED; *U.S. Private*, pg. 544
BESUNYEN HOLDINGS COMPANY LIMITED; *Int'l*, pg. 1001
BET365 GROUP LIMITED; *Int'l*, pg. 1001
BETABEIRAS - BETOES DA BEIRA S.A.—See Camargo Correa S.A.; *Int'l*, pg. 1267
BETA CAPITAL CORP.—See Security National Financial Corporation; *U.S. Public*, pg. 1856
BETA CAPITAL MANAGEMENT LP—See Credit Andorra, S.A.; *Int'l*, pg. 1834
BETACOM S.A.; *Int'l*, pg. 1002
BETA DB LINDSELL LIMITED S.C.S.—See Deutsche Bank Aktiengesellschaft; *Int'l*, pg. 2055
BETA DRUGS LIMITED; *Int'l*, pg. 1001
BETA ENGINEERING LLC—See Crest Industries, LLC; *U.S. Private*, pg. 1096
BETAFENCE DEUTSCHLAND GMBH—See CVC Capital Partners SICAV-FIS S.A.; *Int'l*, pg. 1885
BETAFENCE FRANCE SA—See CVC Capital Partners SICAV-FIS S.A.; *Int'l*, pg. 1885
BETAFENCE NV—See CVC Capital Partners SICAV-FIS S.A.; *Int'l*, pg. 1885
BETAFENCE—See CVC Capital Partners SICAV-FIS S.A.; *Int'l*, pg. 1885
BETAFENCE SP ZOO—See CVC Capital Partners SICAV-FIS S.A.; *Int'l*, pg. 1885
BETA FIRE PROTECTION LIMITED—See London Security PLC; *Int'l*, pg. 4547
BETA FUELING SYSTEMS, LLC—See Alfons Haar Maschinenbau GmbH & Co. KG; *Int'l*, pg. 315
BETAGRO PUBLIC COMPANY LIMITED; *Int'l*, pg. 1002
BETAGRO SCIENCE CENTER COMPANY LIMITED—See Betagro Public Company Limited; *Int'l*, pg. 1002
BETAGRO-THAI LUXE HOLDING COMPANY LIMITED—See PP Prime Public Company Limited; *Int'l*, pg. 5950
BETA HEALTHCARE INTERNATIONAL LTD—See Aspen Pharmacare Holdings Limited; *Int'l*, pg. 629
BETA HEALTHCARE (UGANDA) LIMITED—See Aspen Pharmacare Holdings Limited; *Int'l*, pg. 629
BETA INSTITUT FOR SOZIAIMEDIZINISCHE FORSCHUNG AND ENTWICKLUNG GMBH—See Dr. Reddy's Laboratories Limited; *Int'l*, pg. 2195
BETA INTERNATIONAL & AFFILIATES; *U.S. Private*, pg. 544
BETA LASERMIKE, INC.—See Spectris Plc; *Int'l*, pg. 7130
BETALLIC LLC—See Centric Group LLC; *U.S. Private*, pg. 830
BETAMEK BERHAD; *Int'l*, pg. 1002
BETA MUSIC GROUP, INC.; *U.S. Private*, pg. 545
BETANCOURT SPORTS NUTRITION, LLC—See B. Riley Financial, Inc.; *U.S. Public*, pg. 261
BETANCOURT SPORTS NUTRITION, LLC—See Irradiant Partners, LP; *U.S. Private*, pg. 2141
BETANN SYSTEMS AB—See SPARTA AG; *Int'l*, pg. 7127
BETAO LIZ S.A.—See Camargo Correa S.A.; *Int'l*, pg. 1267
BETAPART PARTICIPACOES S/A; *Int'l*, pg. 1002
BETAPHARM ARZNEIMITTEL GMBH—See Dr. Reddy's Laboratories Limited; *Int'l*, pg. 2195
BETA PLASTICS CORPORATION—See Alpha Industries, Inc.; *U.S. Private*, pg. 197
BETA RAVEN INC.—See Gilbert Global Equity Partners; *U.S. Private*, pg. 1698
BETA SA BUZAU; *Int'l*, pg. 1001

BETA SECURITIZADORA S.A.; *Int'l*, pg. 1002
BETASEED FRANCE S.A.R.L.—See KWS SAAT SE & Co. KGaA; *Int'l*, pg. 4352
BETASEED GMBH—See KWS SAAT SE & Co. KGaA; *Int'l*, pg. 4352
BETASEED, INC.—See KWS SAAT SE & Co. KGaA; *Int'l*, pg. 4352
BETASENZE DEUSTCHLAND GMBH—See NV Bekaert SA; *Int'l*, pg. 5496
BETA SOFT SYSTEMS, INC.; *U.S. Private*, pg. 545
BETA SQUARED LITHOGRAPHY, INC.; *U.S. Private*, pg. 545
BETA SQUARED LITHOGRAPHY SINGAPORE PTE LTD.—See Beta Squared Lithography, Inc.; *U.S. Private*, pg. 545
BETA STEEL—See MNP Corporation; *U.S. Private*, pg. 2756
BETA SYSTEMS DCI SOFTWARE AG—See SPARTA AG; *Int'l*, pg. 7127
BETA SYSTEMS EDV SOFTWARE GES.M.B.H.—See SPARTA AG; *Int'l*, pg. 7127
BETA SYSTEMS OF NORTH AMERICA, INC.—See SPARTA AG; *Int'l*, pg. 7127
BETA SYSTEMS SOFTWARE AG—See SPARTA AG; *Int'l*, pg. 7126
BETA SYSTEMS SOFTWARE ESPANA, S.L.—See SPARTA AG; *Int'l*, pg. 7127
BETA SYSTEMS SOFTWARE FRANCE S.A.R.L.—See SPARTA AG; *Int'l*, pg. 7127
BETA SYSTEMS SOFTWARE LTD.—See SPARTA AG; *Int'l*, pg. 7127
BETA SYSTEMS SOFTWARE OF CANADA, INC.—See SPARTA AG; *Int'l*, pg. 7127
BETA SYSTEMS SOFTWARE SPRL.—See SPARTA AG; *Int'l*, pg. 7127
BETA SYSTEMS SOFTWARE SRL—See SPARTA AG; *Int'l*, pg. 7127
BETATECH GMBH—See steep GmbH; *Int'l*, pg. 7190
BETATECHNIC SDN BHD—See Kuala Lumpur Kepong Berhad; *Int'l*, pg. 4318
BET-AT-HOME.COM AG; *Int'l*, pg. 1001
BET-AT-HOME.COM ENTERTAINMENT GMBH—See bet-at-home.com AG; *Int'l*, pg. 1001
BET-AT-HOME.COM ENTERTAINMENT LTD.—See bet-at-home.com AG; *Int'l*, pg. 1001
BETA TRANSFORMER TECHNOLOGY CORPORATION—See TransDigm Group Incorporated; *U.S. Public*, pg. 2182
BETBULL HOLDING SE; *Int'l*, pg. 1002
BETC DIGITAL SAS—See Vivendi SE; *Int'l*, pg. 8265
BETCO CORPORATION; *U.S. Private*, pg. 545
BETCO INC.; *U.S. Private*, pg. 545
BETCOZA ONLINE (RF) PROPRIETARY LIMITED—See Niveus Investments Limited; *Int'l*, pg. 5389
BETC—See Vivendi SE; *Int'l*, pg. 8268
BETDIGITAL LTD.—See Light & Wonder, Inc.; *U.S. Public*, pg. 1314
BE TEAM S.R.L.—See Devoteam SA; *Int'l*, pg. 2089
BETECH A/S—See Addtech AB; *Int'l*, pg. 132
BETECH DATA A/S—See Lagercrantz Group AB; *Int'l*, pg. 4393
BETE FOG NOZZLE INC.; *U.S. Private*, pg. 545
BETEILIGUNGSVERWALTUNGSGESELLSCHAFT DER BANK AUSTRIA CREDITANSTALT LEASING GMBH—See UniCredit S.p.A.; *Int'l*, pg. 8036
BETEK BERGBAU- UND HARTMETALLTECHNIK KARL-HEINZ SIMON GMBH & CO. KG—See INDUS Holding AG; *Int'l*, pg. 3662
BETEK BOYA VE KIMYA SANAYI ANONIM SIRKETI—See Nippon Paint Holdings Co., Ltd.; *Int'l*, pg. 5325
BETEK GMBH & CO. KG—See INDUS Holding AG; *Int'l*, pg. 3662
BETEK TOOLS, INC.—See INDUS Holding AG; *Int'l*, pg. 3662
BETEK TOOLS TAICANG LTD.—See INDUS Holding AG; *Int'l*, pg. 3662
BETEO GMBH & CO KG—See LISI S.A.; *Int'l*, pg. 4524
BETEO GMBH—See LISI S.A.; *Int'l*, pg. 4523
BETER BED B.V.—See Beter Bed Holding N.V.; *Int'l*, pg. 1002
BETER BED HOLDING N.V.; *Int'l*, pg. 1002
BETER BEHEER B.V.—See Beter Bed Holding N.V.; *Int'l*, pg. 1002
BETER HOREN BV—See Amplifon S.p.A.; *Int'l*, pg. 435
BE-TERNA BUSINESS SOLUTIONS GMBH—See Telefonica, S.A.; *Int'l*, pg. 7535
BE-TERNA ENHANCEMENT GMBH—See Telefonica, S.A.; *Int'l*, pg. 7535
BE-TERNA GMBH—See DPE Deutsche Private Equity GmbH; *Int'l*, pg. 2187
BE-TERNA INDUSTRY SOLUTIONS GMBH—See Telefonica, S.A.; *Int'l*, pg. 7535
THE BETESH GROUP, INC.; *U.S. Private*, pg. 3994
BETEX INDIA LIMITED; *Int'l*, pg. 1002
BETFAIR GROUP LIMITED—See Flutter Entertainment plc; *Int'l*, pg. 2715
BETFAIR HOLDING (MALTA) LIMITED—See Flutter Entertainment plc; *Int'l*, pg. 2715

BETFAIR LIMITED—See Flutter Entertainment plc; *Int'l*, pg. 2715
BETHANNA INC.; *U.S. Private*, pg. 545
BETHANY CHRISTIAN SERVICES; *U.S. Private*, pg. 545
BETHANY FOR CHILDREN & FAMILIES; *U.S. Private*, pg. 545
BETHANY HOME SOCIETY OF SAN JOAQUIN COUNTY, INC.; *U.S. Private*, pg. 545
BETHANY HOSPICE AND PALLIATIVE CARE—See Apollo Global Management, Inc.; *U.S. Public*, pg. 156
BETHANY HOUSE PUBLISHERS—See Baker Publishing Group; *U.S. Private*, pg. 456
BETHANY ST. JOSEPH CORPORATION; *U.S. Private*, pg. 545
BETHEL AUTOMOTIVE SAFETY SYSTEMS CO., LTD.; *Int'l*, pg. 1002
BETHEL-ECKERT ENTERPRISES INC.; *U.S. Private*, pg. 545
BETHEL MILLS, INC.; *U.S. Private*, pg. 545
BETHEL MILLS KITCHEN & BATH—See Bethel Mills, Inc.; *U.S. Private*, pg. 545
BETHEL WOODS CENTER FOR THE ARTS, INC.; *U.S. Private*, pg. 545
BETHESDA ANESTHESIA ASSOCIATES, INC.—See KKR & Co. Inc.; *U.S. Public*, pg. 1245
BETHESDA CHEVY CHASE SURGERY CENTER, LLC—See Tenet Healthcare Corporation; *U.S. Public*, pg. 2001
BETHESDA COUNTRY CLUB; *U.S. Private*, pg. 545
BETHESDA FOUNDATION; *U.S. Private*, pg. 545
BETHESDA HEALTHCARE INC.—See Catholic Health Initiatives; *U.S. Private*, pg. 790
BETHESDA HOSPITAL—See Fairview Health Services; *U.S. Private*, pg. 1464
BETHESDA INVESTMENT HOLDING CO., INC.; *U.S. Private*, pg. 546
BETHESDA LUXURY IMPORTS, LLC—See AutoNation, Inc.; *U.S. Public*, pg. 233
BETHESDA MINISTRIES; *U.S. Private*, pg. 546
BETHESDA OUTPATIENT SURGERY CENTER, LLC—See KKR & Co. Inc.; *U.S. Public*, pg. 1245
BETHESDA SOFTWORKS, LLC—See Microsoft Corporation; *U.S. Public*, pg. 1443
BETH ISRAEL CEMETERY ASSOCIATION OF WOODBRIDGE—See Axar Capital Management L.P.; *U.S. Private*, pg. 411
BETH ISRAEL DEACONESS MEDICAL CENTER—See CareGroup, Inc.; *U.S. Private*, pg. 753
BETH ISRAEL LAHEY HEALTH INC; *U.S. Private*, pg. 545
BETHLEHEM ADVANCED TECHNOLOGIES CO., LTD.—See Aiphone Co., Ltd.; *Int'l*, pg. 235
BETHLEHEM CONSTRUCTION INC.; *U.S. Private*, pg. 546
THE BETHLEHEM CORPORATION; *U.S. Private*, pg. 3994
BETHLEHEM COUNTRY CLUB VILLAGE LIMITED—See Arvida Group Limited; *Int'l*, pg. 587
BETHLEHEM ENDOSCOPE CENTER; *U.S. Private*, pg. 546
BETHLEHEM HAVEN—See Pittsburgh Mercy Health System, Inc.; *U.S. Private*, pg. 3191
BETHLEHEM INTL. SALES CORP.—See The Bethlehem Corporation; *U.S. Private*, pg. 3994
BETHLEHEM WM TRENCHING LTD—See Sentrex Communications Inc.; *Int'l*, pg. 6715
BETHLEN HOME OF THE HUNGARIAN REFORMED FEDERATION OF AMERICA; *U.S. Private*, pg. 546
BETHMANN BANK AG—See ABN AMRO Group N.V.; *Int'l*, pg. 65
BET HOLDINGS LLC—See National Amusements, Inc.; *U.S. Private*, pg. 2839
BETH SHOLOM LIFECARE COMMUNITY; *U.S. Private*, pg. 545
BETHUNE NONWOVENS, INC.—See Suominen Oyj; *Int'l*, pg. 7334
BETHYL LABORATORIES, INC.—See Fortis Life Sciences; *U.S. Private*, pg. 1576
BETI D.D.; *Int'l*, pg. 1002
BET INFORMATION SYSTEMS, INC.—See Trax Technology Solutions Pte Ltd.; *Int'l*, pg. 7908
BETINOKS TURKEY—See Acerinox, S.A.; *Int'l*, pg. 100
BET INTERACTIVE, LLC—See National Amusements, Inc.; *U.S. Private*, pg. 2839
BETINTERNET.COM (IOM) LIMITED—See Webis Holdings Plc; *Int'l*, pg. 8366
BETI PREJA D.O.O.—See Beti d.d.; *Int'l*, pg. 1002
BETLAN DOS S.A.; *Int'l*, pg. 1002
BETLEM SERVICE CORPORATION—See EMCOR Group, Inc.; *U.S. Public*, pg. 737
BETMAKERS TECHNOLOGY GROUP LTD.; *Int'l*, pg. 1002
BETMAR HATS, INC.—See Bollman Hat Co.; *U.S. Private*, pg. 611
BETOCIM SA—See Camargo Correa S.A.; *Int'l*, pg. 1267
BETOMAX KUNSTSTOFF- UND METALLWARENFABRIK GMBH & CO. KG—See INDUS Holding AG; *Int'l*, pg. 3662

BETOMAX SYSTEMS GMBH & CO. KG—See INDUS Holding AG; *Int'l*, pg. 3662
BETON 06 SA—See Chequers SA; *Int'l*, pg. 1471
BETON 6 CORPORATION; *Int'l*, pg. 1002
BETON A.D.; *Int'l*, pg. 1002
BETON AG BASEL—See Vicat S.A.; *Int'l*, pg. 8185
BETON AG INTERLAKEN—See Vicat S.A.; *Int'l*, pg. 8185
BETON BELANGER INC.—See Beton Provincial Ltee; *Int'l*, pg. 1002
BETON BRUNSWICK LTEE—See Beton Provincial Ltee; *Int'l*, pg. 1002
BETON CATALAN S.A.—See CRH plc; *Int'l*, pg. 1843
BETON CHANTIERS DE BRETAGNE S.A.S.—See Holcim Ltd.; *Int'l*, pg. 3449
BETON CONTROLE COTE D—See Vicat S.A.; *Int'l*, pg. 8185
BETON DE LIEGE SA—See Heidelberg Materials AG; *Int'l*, pg. 3309
BETON DU RIED S.A.S.—See Buzzi SpA; *Int'l*, pg. 1230
BETONGINDUSTRI AB—See Heidelberg Materials AG; *Int'l*, pg. 3315
BETONG OST AS—See Heidelberg Materials AG; *Int'l*, pg. 3309
BETONG PREMIX SDN. BHD.—See Cahya Mata Sarawak Berhad; *Int'l*, pg. 1251
BETON GRANULATS IDF—See Vicat S.A.; *Int'l*, pg. 8185
BETONGRUPPEN RBR A/S—See CRH plc; *Int'l*, pg. 1843
BETONG SOR AS—See Heidelberg Materials AG; *Int'l*, pg. 3309
BETON HI-TECH INC.—See Beton Provincial Ltee; *Int'l*, pg. 1002
BETONIKA UAB—See Bain Capital, LP; *U.S. Private*, pg. 438
BETONJERKA A.D.; *Int'l*, pg. 1003
BETONJERKA A.D.; *Int'l*, pg. 1003
BETON MANUFACTURE DE VITRE—See Compagnie de Saint-Gobain SA; *Int'l*, pg. 1722
BETONMAST AS—See AF Gruppen ASA; *Int'l*, pg. 184
BETONMAST BUSKERUD-VESTFOLD AS—See AF Gruppen ASA; *Int'l*, pg. 184
BETONMAST INNLANDET AS—See AF Gruppen ASA; *Int'l*, pg. 184
BETONMAST OSTFOLD AS—See AF Gruppen ASA; *Int'l*, pg. 184
BETONMAST RINGERIKE AS—See AF Gruppen ASA; *Int'l*, pg. 184
BETONMAST ROMERIKE AS—See AF Gruppen ASA; *Int'l*, pg. 184
BETONMAST ROSAND AS—See AF Gruppen ASA; *Int'l*, pg. 184
BETONMAST TELEMARK AS—See AF Gruppen ASA; *Int'l*, pg. 184
BETONMAST TRONDELAG AS—See AF Gruppen ASA; *Int'l*, pg. 184
BETON MISTRAL LTEE—See Beton Provincial Ltee; *Int'l*, pg. 1002
BETONMORTEL CENTRALE GRONINGEN (B.C.G.) B.V.—See Buzzi SpA; *Int'l*, pg. 1230
BETON MOULE INDUSTRIEL S.A.—See CRH plc; *Int'l*, pg. 1843
BETON PROVINCIAL LTEE; *Int'l*, pg. 1002
BETONPUMPEN OBERLAND AG—See Vicat S.A.; *Int'l*, pg. 8185
BETON REGIONAL INC.—See Beton Provincial Ltee; *Int'l*, pg. 1002
BETON RHONE ALPES—See Vicat S.A.; *Int'l*, pg. 8185
BETON RIVE-NORD INC.—See Beton Provincial Ltee; *Int'l*, pg. 1002
BETONS GRANULATS DU CENTRE—See Vicat S.A.; *Int'l*, pg. 8185
BETONSKI PROIZVODI A.D.; *Int'l*, pg. 1003
BETONSTAHL LEIPZIG GMBH; *Int'l*, pg. 1003
BETON-STIP; *Int'l*, pg. 1003
BETONS TRIO INC.—See Beton Provincial Ltee; *Int'l*, pg. 1003
BETONTIR S.P.A.—See Heidelberg Materials AG; *Int'l*, pg. 3309
BETON TRAVAUX—See Vicat S.A.; *Int'l*, pg. 8185
BETON- UND MONIERBAU GESELLSCHAFT M.B.H.—See ALPINE Bau GmbH; *Int'l*, pg. 371
BETONUT CONSTRUCTII S.R.L.—See Betonut Szolgaltato es Epito Rt.; *Int'l*, pg. 1003
BETONUT SZOLGALTATO ES EPITO RT.; *Int'l*, pg. 1003
BETON VICAT—See Vicat S.A.; *Int'l*, pg. 8185
BETOP STAFF, LTD.—See Brother Industries, Ltd.; *Int'l*, pg. 1196
BETOTECH BAUSTOFFLABOR GMBH—See Heidelberg Materials AG; *Int'l*, pg. 3309
BETOTECH GMBH—See Heidelberg Materials AG; *Int'l*, pg. 3309
BETOTECH MUNCHEN VERWALTUNGS GMBH—See Heidelberg Materials AG; *Int'l*, pg. 3321
BETOTECH, S.R.O.—See Heidelberg Materials AG; *Int'l*, pg. 3308
BETOTECH VERWALTUNGS-GMBH—See Heidelberg Materials AG; *Int'l*, pg. 3309
BETPREF SP. Z O.O.—See Dekpol S.A.; *Int'l*, pg. 2006
BETRACO STAHL VERTRIEBS GMBH—See Georgsmarienhutte Holding GmbH; *Int'l*, pg. 2940

BETRANS SP. Z O.O.—See PGE Polska Grupa Energetyczna S.A.; *Int'l*, pg. 5837
BETRAS USA, INC.; *U.S. Private*, pg. 546
BETREND CORPORATION; *Int'l*, pg. 1003
BETRIEBSGESELLSCHAFT PFORTNERHAUS MBH—See Fielmann Group AG; *Int'l*, pg. 2656
BETRIEBS- UND BAUGESELLSCHAFT MBH—See RHI Magnesita N.V.; *Int'l*, pg. 6325
BETRIUM NR 53 VERMOGENSVERWALTUNGS-GMBH—See MK-Kliniken AG; *Int'l*, pg. 5001
BET SERVICES, INC.—See National Amusements, Inc.; *U.S. Private*, pg. 2839
BET SHEMESH ENGINES HOLDINGS (1997) LTD.; *Int'l*, pg. 1001
BET SHEMESH ENGINES LTD.—See Bet Shemesh Engines Holdings (1997) Ltd.; *Int'l*, pg. 1001
BETSILL BROTHERS CONSTRUCTION, INC.; *U.S. Private*, pg. 546
BETSON ENTERPRISES—See H. Betti Industries, Inc.; *U.S. Private*, pg. 1824
BETSSON AB; *Int'l*, pg. 1003
BETSTAL SP. Z O.O.—See Bowim S.A.; *Int'l*, pg. 1124
BETSY & ADAM LTD.; *U.S. Private*, pg. 546
BETSY ANN CANDIES, INC.; *U.S. Private*, pg. 546
BETTA PHARMACEUTICALS CO., LTD.; *Int'l*, pg. 1003
BETT-A-WAY TRAFFIC SYSTEMS, INC.; *U.S. Private*, pg. 546
BETTCHER INDUSTRIES INC.—See KKR & Co. Inc.; *U.S. Public*, pg. 1241
BETTE & CRING, LLC; *U.S. Private*, pg. 546
BETTEN AUTO CENTER, INC.; *U.S. Private*, pg. 546
BETTENDORF ENTERPRISES INC.; *U.S. Private*, pg. 546
BETTENHAUSEN AUTOMOTIVE; *U.S. Private*, pg. 546
BETTEN IMPORTS; *U.S. Private*, pg. 546
BETTER BACKERS INC.; *U.S. Private*, pg. 546
BETTER BAKED FOODS, INC.; *U.S. Private*, pg. 546
BETTER BATHROOMS UK LIMITED; *Int'l*, pg. 1003
THE BETTER BEING CO.; *U.S. Public*, pg. 2038
BETTER BEVERAGES, INC.; *U.S. Private*, pg. 546
BETTER BRANDS SOUTH GEORGIA LLP—See J & L Ventures LLC; *U.S. Private*, pg. 2152
BETTER CAPITAL LLP—See Heritage Group Ltd.; *Int'l*, pg. 3361
BETTER CAPITAL PCC LIMITED; *Int'l*, pg. 1003
BETTER CHANCE PROPERTIES PTE LTD—See Second Chance Properties Ltd.; *Int'l*, pg. 6672
BETTER CHOICE COMPANY, INC.; *U.S. Public*, pg. 326
BETTER CHOICE HOME LOANS PTY LTD—See BNK Banking Corporation Limited; *Int'l*, pg. 1079
BETTER COLLECTIVE A/S; *Int'l*, pg. 1003
BETTER COLLECTIVE D.O.O.—See Better Collective A/S; *Int'l*, pg. 1003
BETTER COLLECTIVE GREECE P.C.—See Better Collective A/S; *Int'l*, pg. 1003
BETTER COLLECTIVE SAS—See Better Collective A/S; *Int'l*, pg. 1003
BETTER COMMUNICATIONS, INC—See The Ariel Group LLC; *U.S. Private*, pg. 3988
BETTER ENVIRONMENT CONCEPTS, INC.; *U.S. Public*, pg. 326
BETTER FOOD SYSTEMS INCORPORATION; *U.S. Private*, pg. 546
BETTER FOR YOU WELLNESS, INC.; *U.S. Public*, pg. 326
BETTER HEADS LLC; *U.S. Private*, pg. 546
BETTER HEALTH; *U.S. Private*, pg. 546
BETTER HOME & FINANCE HOLDING COMPANY; *U.S. Public*, pg. 326
BETTER HOMES & GARDENS BOOKS—See Meredith Corporation; *U.S. Public*, pg. 1422
BETTER HOMES & GARDENS REAL ESTATE LLC—See Anywhere Real Estate Inc.; *U.S. Public*, pg. 140
BETTER LIFE COMMERCIAL CHAIN SHARE CO., LTD.; *Int'l*, pg. 1003
BETTERLIFE HOLDING LIMITED; *Int'l*, pg. 1003
BETTERLIFE PHARMA INC.; *Int'l*, pg. 1004
BETTER LIFE TECHNOLOGY, LLC—See Century Park Capital Partners, LLC; *U.S. Private*, pg. 833
BETTER LIVING INC.; *U.S. Private*, pg. 546
BETTER MADE SNACK FOODS INC.; *U.S. Private*, pg. 546
BETTERMENT LLC; *U.S. Public*, pg. 547
BETTER MERCHANT RATES INC.; *U.S. Private*, pg. 547
BETTERMOO(D) FOOD CORPORATION; *Int'l*, pg. 1004
BETTER MORTGAGE CORPORATION—See Better Home & Finance Holding Company; *U.S. Public*, pg. 327
BETTEROADS ASPHALT CORP; *U.S. Private*, pg. 547
BETTER PACKAGES, INC.—See Clearlake Capital Group, L.P.; *U.S. Private*, pg. 935
BETTER PLANT SCIENCES INC.; *Int'l*, pg. 1003
BETTER PROSPECTS SDN. BHD.—See NPC Resources Berhad; *Int'l*, pg. 5472
BETTER ROADS INC.; *U.S. Private*, pg. 547
BETTER SOFTWARE GROUP S.A.—See Spyrosoft S.A.; *Int'l*, pg. 7146
BETTER SOURCING WORLDWIDE LIMITED—See Kiu Hung International Holdings Limited; *Int'l*, pg. 4197
BETTER THERAPEUTICS, INC.; *U.S. Public*, pg. 327

COMPANY NAME INDEX

BETTERU EDUCATION CORP.—See Varshney Capital Corp.; *Int'l*, pg. 8133
BETTERWARE DE MEXICO S.A.P.I. DE C.V.; *Int'l*, pg. 1004
BETTER WORLD BOOKS; *U.S. Private*, pg. 547
BETTER WORLD GREEN PUBLIC COMPANY LIMITED; *Int'l*, pg. 1003
BETTERWORLD TELECOM, LLC; *U.S. Private*, pg. 547
BETTINEHOEVE B.V.—See Emmi AG; *Int'l*, pg. 2384
BETTING COMPANY S.A.—See INTRALOT S.A.; *Int'l*, pg. 3768
BETTIOL FUEL SERVICE INC.; *U.S. Private*, pg. 547
BETTIS CANADA LTD.—See Emerson Electric Co.; *U.S. Public*, pg. 746
BETTS GROUP PTY. LTD.; *Int'l*, pg. 1004
BETTS INDUSTRIES INC.; *U.S. Private*, pg. 547
BETTS SPRING COMPANY, INC.; *U.S. Private*, pg. 547
BETTWORK INDUSTRIES, INC.; *U.S. Public*, pg. 327
BETTY BARCLAY KLEIDERFABRIK GMBH; *Int'l*, pg. 1004
BETTY BOSSI VERLAG AG—See Ringier Holding AG; *Int'l*, pg. 6343
BETTY CROCKER PRODUCTS—See General Mills, Inc.; *U.S. Public*, pg. 921
THE BETTY FORD CENTER—See Hazelden Betty Ford Foundation; *U.S. Private*, pg. 1886
BETTY JEAN KERR PEOPLES HEALTH CENTERS; *U.S. Private*, pg. 547
BETTY LOU'S, INC.; *U.S. Private*, pg. 547
THE BETTY MILLS COMPANY, INC.; *U.S. Private*, pg. 3994
BETTY TV LIMITED—See Liberty Global plc; *Int'l*, pg. 4484
BETTY TV LIMITED—See Warner Bros. Discovery, Inc.; *U.S. Public*, pg. 2326
BETTZEIT GMBH; *Int'l*, pg. 1004
BETULA CARS S.L.—See General Motors Company; *U.S. Public*, pg. 927
BETUMAT QUIMICA LTDA.—See RPM International Inc.; *U.S. Public*, pg. 1816
THE BETZ COMPANIES; *U.S. Private*, pg. 3994
BEUCKMAN FORD INC.; *U.S. Private*, pg. 547
BEUERMAN MILLER FITZGERALD, INC.; *U.S. Private*, pg. 547
BEUTEL, GOODMAN & COMPANY LTD.—See Affiliated Managers Group, Inc.; *U.S. Public*, pg. 54
BEUTLER HEATING & AIR CONDITIONING INC.; *U.S. Private*, pg. 547
BEUTLER & LANG SCHALUNGS- UND BEHALTER-BAU GMBH; *Int'l*, pg. 1004
BEUTLER NOVA AG—See ANDRITZ AG; *Int'l*, pg. 456
BEUTLICH PHARMACEUTICALS LP; *U.S. Private*, pg. 547
BEUTTER PRAZISIONS-KOMPONENTEN GMBH & CO. KG; *Int'l*, pg. 1004
BE VACCINES SAS—See Biological E. Limited; *Int'l*, pg. 1039
BEVAN SECURITY SYSTEMS INC.—See Pye-Barker Fire & Safety, LLC; *U.S. Private*, pg. 3309
BEVCANNA ENTERPRISES, INC.; *Int'l*, pg. 1004
BEV CAP PTY. LTD.—See Pro-Pac Packaging Limited; *Int'l*, pg. 5985
BEVCO AB—See Altia Oyj; *Int'l*, pg. 392
BEVCO LIMITED—See Thai Beverage Public Company Limited; *Int'l*, pg. 7589
BEVCORP, LLC—See John Bean Technologies Corporation; *U.S. Public*, pg. 1191
BEVCO SALES, INC.—See National Beverage Corp.; *U.S. Public*, pg. 1493
BEVERAGE-AIR CO.—See Haier Smart Home Co., Ltd.; *Int'l*, pg. 3210
BEVERAGE BRANDS (UK) LTD—See SHS Group, Ltd.; *Int'l*, pg. 6867
BEVERAGE CAPITAL CORPORATION—See Pepsi-Cola & National Brand Beverages, Ltd.; *U.S. Private*, pg. 3145
BEVERAGE CORPORATION INTERNATIONAL, INC.—See National Beverage Corp.; *U.S. Public*, pg. 1494
BEVERAGE DISTRIBUTION CENTER, INC.—See Pepsi-Cola & National Brand Beverages, Ltd.; *U.S. Private*, pg. 3145
BEVERAGE DISTRIBUTORS COMPANY, LLC—See Breakthru Beverage Group, LLC; *U.S. Private*, pg. 643
BEVERAGE MARKETING CORPORATION; *U.S. Private*, pg. 547
BEVERAGE MARKETING USA INC.; *U.S. Private*, pg. 547
BEVERAGE PLASTICS LTD.—See Indorama Ventures Public Company Limited; *Int'l*, pg. 3658
BEVERAGES, FOODS & SERVICE INDUSTRIES, INC.—See PepsiCo, Inc.; *U.S. Public*, pg. 1668
BEVERAGES & MORE INC.—See goBrands, Inc.; *U.S. Private*, pg. 1724
BEVERAGE WORKS NY INC.; *U.S. Private*, pg. 547
BEVERLEY BUILDING SOCIETY; *Int'l*, pg. 1004
BEVERLY BANK & TRUST COMPANY, N.A. - OAK LAWN BANK & TRUST—See Wintrust Financial Corporation; *U.S. Public*, pg. 2374
BEVERLY BANK & TRUST COMPANY, N.A.—See Wintrust Financial Corporation; *U.S. Public*, pg. 2374
BEVERLY CAPITAL LLC; *U.S. Private*, pg. 547
BEVERLY CITIZEN—See Gannett Co., Inc.; *U.S. Public*, pg. 902
BEVERLY-HANKS & ASSOCIATES INC.—See Hanna Holdings, Inc.; *U.S. Private*, pg. 1854
BEVERLY HILLS DIALYSIS PARTNERSHIP—See DaVita Inc.; *U.S. Public*, pg. 636
THE BEVERLY HILLS HOTEL—See Dorchester Group of Companies; *Int'l*, pg. 2175
BEVERLY HILLS SHOE CO.; *U.S. Private*, pg. 547
BEVERLY HILLS TEDDY BEAR COMPANY; *U.S. Private*, pg. 547
BEVERLY HILLS TRANSFER & STORAGE CO.; *U.S. Private*, pg. 547
BEVERLY J. SEARLES FOUNDATION; *U.S. Private*, pg. 547
BEVESTOR GMBH—See DekaBank; *Int'l*, pg. 2005
BEVI CHINA—See Addtech AB; *Int'l*, pg. 132
BEVI DANMARK A/S—See Addtech AB; *Int'l*, pg. 132
BEVI ELECTRIC SHANGHAI CO., LTD.—See Addtech AB; *Int'l*, pg. 132
BEVI EST OU—See Addtech AB; *Int'l*, pg. 132
BEVI FINLAND OY—See Addtech AB; *Int'l*, pg. 132
BEVILACQUA-KNIGHT, INC.—See Gas Technology Institute; *U.S. Private*, pg. 1647
BEVILACQUA RESEARCH CORPORATION; *U.S. Private*, pg. 548
BEVING ELEKTRONIK AB—See Addtech AB; *Int'l*, pg. 132
BEVI NORD AB—See Addtech AB; *Int'l*, pg. 132
BEVI NORGE AS—See Addtech AB; *Int'l*, pg. 132
BEVI TEKNIK & SERVICE AB—See Addtech AB; *Int'l*, pg. 132
BEVI UAB—See Addtech AB; *Int'l*, pg. 132
BEVO FARMS LTD—See SNDL Inc.; *Int'l*, pg. 7027
BEVOLUTION GROUP—See Highlander Partners, LP; *U.S. Private*, pg. 1939
BEVPAC COMPANY LIMITED—See BERICAP GmbH & Co. KG; *Int'l*, pg. 981
BEVPAK (NIGERIA) LIMITED—See Indorama Ventures Public Company Limited; *Int'l*, pg. 3658
BEVSOURCE, INC.; *U.S. Private*, pg. 548
BEVTECH CO., LTD.—See Thai Beverage Public Company Limited; *Int'l*, pg. 7589
BEWATEC CONNECTED.CARE GMBH—See Phoenix Mecano AG; *Int'l*, pg. 5851
BEWATEC KOMMUNIKATIONSTECHNIK GMBH—See Phoenix Mecano AG; *Int'l*, pg. 5851
BE WATER S.A.—See Beijing Enterprises Water Group Limited; *Int'l*, pg. 950
BEWEHRTE ERDE GMBH—See VINCI S.A.; *Int'l*, pg. 8231
BEWETEC AG—See Klockner & Co. SE; *Int'l*, pg. 4202
BEWG (M) SDN BHD—See Beijing Enterprises Water Group Limited; *Int'l*, pg. 950
BEWHERE HOLDINGS INC.; *Int'l*, pg. 1004
BEWI ASA; *Int'l*, pg. 1004
BEWI NORPLASTA AS—See BEWI Produkter AS; *Int'l*, pg. 1004
BEWI PRODUKTER AS; *Int'l*, pg. 1004
BEWITAL GMBH & CO. KG; *Int'l*, pg. 1004
BEWITH, INC.—See Pasona Group Inc.; *Int'l*, pg. 5753
BEWLEY'S LTD.—See Campbells/Bewley Group; *Int'l*, pg. 1274
BEWLEY'S ORIENTAL CAFES LIMITED—See Campbells/Bewley Group; *Int'l*, pg. 1274
BEW NETZE GMBH—See RWE AG; *Int'l*, pg. 6433
B.E. WRIGHT, INC.—See Wright Wisner Distributing Corp.; *U.S. Private*, pg. 4573
BEXAR VENTURES, INC.; *Int'l*, pg. 1004
BEXCELLENT GROUP HOLDINGS LIMITED; *Int'l*, pg. 1004
BEXCO N.V.—See Exmar N.V.; *Int'l*, pg. 2585
BEXEL CORPORATION—See The Carlyle Group Inc.; *U.S. Public*, pg. 2049
BEXEMA GMBH—See HORIBA Ltd; *Int'l*, pg. 3475
BEXHILL UK LIMITED—See Orchard Funding Group PLC; *Int'l*, pg. 5615
BEXIL CORPORATION; *U.S. Public*, pg. 327
BEXIMCO ENGINEERING LTD.—See Bangladesh Export Import Co. Ltd.; *Int'l*, pg. 835
BEXIMCO PHARMACEUTICALS LIMITED; *Int'l*, pg. 1005
BEXIMCO SYNTHETICS LIMITED; *Int'l*, pg. 1005
BEXITY GMBH—See Mutares SE & Co. KGaA; *Int'l*, pg. 5104
BEXTEX LIMITED—See Bangladesh Export Import Co. Ltd.; *Int'l*, pg. 835
BEYAZ FILO OTO KIRALAMA A.S.; *Int'l*, pg. 1005
BEYELER MASCHINENBAU GMBH—See Bystronic AG; *Int'l*, pg. 1236
BEYER BROS. CORP.; *U.S. Private*, pg. 548
BEYER CONSTRUCTION LTD.; *U.S. Private*, pg. 548
BEYERDYNAMIC GMBH & CO KG; *Int'l*, pg. 1005
BEYER MECHANICAL, LTD.; *U.S. Private*, pg. 548
BEYKOZ GAYRIMENKUL YATIRIM INSAAT TURIZM SANAYI VE TICARET A.S.—See Allianz SE; *Int'l*, pg. 351

BEYOND THE OFFICE DOOR, LLC

BEYKOZ TANKERCILIK A.S.—See Koc Holding A.S.; *Int'l*, pg. 4223
BEYNON SPORTS SURFACES, INC.—See Tarkett S.A.; *Int'l*, pg. 7463
BEYON3D LTD.; *Int'l*, pg. 1005
BEYOND4 SDN. BHD.—See Censof Holdings Berhad; *Int'l*, pg. 1401
BEYOND AIR, INC.; *U.S. Public*, pg. 327
BEYOND BREAD; *U.S. Private*, pg. 548
BEYOND CLOTHING, LLC—See Compass Diversified Holdings; *U.S. Public*, pg. 559
BEYOND.COM, INC.; *U.S. Private*, pg. 548
BEYOND COMMERCE, INC.; *U.S. Public*, pg. 327
BEYOND COMMUNICATIONS LIMITED—See Writtle Holdings Limited; *Int'l*, pg. 8495
BEYOND COMPONENTS OF MASS INC.; *U.S. Private*, pg. 548
BEYOND CORPORATION LIMITED—See Next 15 Group plc; *Int'l*, pg. 5246
BEYOND DISTRIBUTION PTY LTD—See LOV Group Invest SAS; *Int'l*, pg. 4563
BEYOND ENTERTAINMENT PTY LTD—See LOV Group Invest SAS; *Int'l*, pg. 4563
BEYONDEXPECT S.L.—See Beyondsoft Corporation; *Int'l*, pg. 1005
BEYOND FILMS LIMITED—See LOV Group Invest SAS; *Int'l*, pg. 4563
BEYOND FRAMES ENTERTAINMENT AB; *Int'l*, pg. 1005
BEYOND HOME ENTERTAINMENT PTY LTD—See LOV Group Invest SAS; *Int'l*, pg. 4563
BEYOND HOME PRODUCTIONS; *U.S. Private*, pg. 548
BEYOND_I CO., LTD.—See Chemtronics Co., Ltd.; *Int'l*, pg. 1464
BEYOND, INC.,; *U.S. Public*, pg. 327
BEYOND INTERNATIONAL LIMITED—See LOV Group Invest SAS; *Int'l*, pg. 4563
BEYOND LIMITS, INC.; *U.S. Private*, pg. 548
BEYOND LITHIUM INC.; *Int'l*, pg. 1005
BEYOND MEAT, INC.; *U.S. Public*, pg. 327
BEYOND MEDICAL TECHNOLOGIES INC.; *Int'l*, pg. 1005
BEYONDPAY INC.—See CBIZ, Inc.; *U.S. Public*, pg. 456
BEYOND PRODUCTIONS PTY LTD—See LOV Group Invest SAS; *Int'l*, pg. 4563
BEYOND PROPERTIES PTY LTD—See LOV Group Invest SAS; *Int'l*, pg. 4564
BEYOND PTY LTD—See LOV Group Invest SAS; *Int'l*, pg. 4564
BEYOND RATINGS, S.A.S.—See London Stock Exchange Group plc; *Int'l*, pg. 4547
BEYONDROI, LLC; *U.S. Private*, pg. 548
BEYOND SECURITY, INC.—See HGGC, LLC; *U.S. Private*, pg. 1929
BEYONDSOFT CONSULTING INC.—See Beyondsoft Corporation; *Int'l*, pg. 1005
BEYONDSOFT CORPORATION; *Int'l*, pg. 1005
BEYONDSOFT CORPORATION—See Beyondsoft Corporation; *Int'l*, pg. 1005
BEYONDSOFT CORPORATION—See Beyondsoft Corporation; *Int'l*, pg. 1005
BEYONDSOFT CORPORATION—See Beyondsoft Corporation; *Int'l*, pg. 1005
BEYONDSOFT CORPORATION—See Beyondsoft Corporation; *Int'l*, pg. 1005
BEYONDSOFT CORPORATION—See Beyondsoft Corporation; *Int'l*, pg. 1005
BEYONDSOFT CORPORATION—See Beyondsoft Corporation; *Int'l*, pg. 1005
BEYONDSOFT CORPORATION—See Beyondsoft Corporation; *Int'l*, pg. 1005
BEYONDSOFT CORPORATION—See Beyondsoft Corporation; *Int'l*, pg. 1005
BEYONDSOFT CORPORATION—See Beyondsoft Corporation; *Int'l*, pg. 1005
BEYONDSOFT CORPORATION—See Beyondsoft Corporation; *Int'l*, pg. 1005
BEYONDSOFT CORPORATION—See Beyondsoft Corporation; *Int'l*, pg. 1005
BEYONDSOFT JAPAN CO., LTD.—See Beyondsoft Corporation; *Int'l*, pg. 1005
BEYONDSOFT JIZHI TECH CO., LTD.—See Beyondsoft Corporation; *Int'l*, pg. 1005
BEYONDSOFT SOLUTIONS CORP—See Beyondsoft Corporation; *Int'l*, pg. 1005
BEYOND SOLUTION CO., LTD.—See YMT Co., Ltd.; *Int'l*, pg. 8590
BEYOND SPOTS & DOTS INC.; *U.S. Private*, pg. 548
BEYONDSPRING INC.; *U.S. Public*, pg. 327
BEYOND THE OFFICE DOOR, LLC; *U.S. Private*, pg. 548
BEYONDTRUST SOFTWARE, INC.—See Francisco Partners Management, LP; *U.S. Private*, pg. 1589
BEYONICS ADVANCED MANUFACTURING PTE LTD—See ShawKwei & Partners Ltd.; *Int'l*, pg. 6792
BEYONICS INTERNATIONAL PTE LTD—See ShawKwei & Partners Ltd.; *Int'l*, pg. 6792
BEYONICS PRECISION ENGINEERING PTE LTD—See ShawKwei & Partners Ltd.; *Int'l*, pg. 6792

BEYOND THE OFFICE DOOR, LLC

BEYONICS PRECISION MACHINING SDN BHD—See ShawKwei & Partners Ltd.; *Int'l*, pg. 6792
BEYONICS PRECISION STAMPINGS PTE LTD—See ShawKwei & Partners Ltd.; *Int'l*, pg. 6792
BEYONICS TECHNOLOGY ELECTRONICS (CHANGSHU) CO., LTD.—See ShawKwei & Partners Ltd.; *Int'l*, pg. 6792
BEYONICS TECHNOLOGY ELECTRONICS (SUZHOU) CO., LTD.—See ShawKwei & Partners Ltd.; *Int'l*, pg. 6792
BEYONICS TECHNOLOGY (KL) SDN BHD—See ShawKwei & Partners Ltd.; *Int'l*, pg. 6792
BEYONICS TECHNOLOGY LIMITED—See ShawKwei & Partners Ltd.; *Int'l*, pg. 6792
BEYONICS TECHNOLOGY (SENAI) SDN BHD - SENAI CAMPUS—See ShawKwei & Partners Ltd.; *Int'l*, pg. 6792
BEYONICS TECHNOLOGY (SENAI) SDN BHD—See ShawKwei & Partners Ltd.; *Int'l*, pg. 6792
BEYONICS TECHNOLOGY (THAILAND) CO., LTD.—See ShawKwei & Partners Ltd.; *Int'l*, pg. 6792
BEZAC EQUIPMENT CO.—See Johnson-Lancaster & Associates, Inc.; *U.S. Private*, pg. 2229
BEZAIRE ELECTRIC INC.; *U.S. Private*, pg. 548
BEZANT RESOURCES PLC; *Int'l*, pg. 1006
BEZDAN POLJOPRIVREDNO PREDUZECE A.D.; *Int'l*, pg. 1006
BEZEMA BUICK CORPORATION; *U.S. Private*, pg. 548
BEZEQ - THE ISRAEL TELECOMMUNICATION CORP. LIMITED; *Int'l*, pg. 1006
BEZHITSA-BANK—See PJSC VTB Bank; *Int'l*, pg. 5886
BEZIER LIMITED—See H.I.G. Capital, LLC; *U.S. Private*, pg. 1828
BEZIERS POLYGONE SARL—See Guess? Inc.; *U.S. Public*, pg. 974
BF1 MOTORSPORT HOLDINGS LTD.; *Int'l*, pg. 1006
BF1SYSTEMS LTD.—See BF1 Motorsport Holdings Ltd.; *Int'l*, pg. 1006
BFA EDUCATIONAL MEDIA—See The Phoenix Learning Group, Inc.; *U.S. Private*, pg. 4095
BFA TENEDORA DE ACCIONES, S.A.U.; *Int'l*, pg. 1006
B+F BETON- UND FERTIGTEILGESELLSCHAFT MBH LAUCHHAMMER—See General Atomics; *U.S. Private*, pg. 1663
BF BIOSCIENCES LIMITED—See Ferozsons Laboratories Limited; *Int'l*, pg. 2639
BF BOLTHOUSE HOLDCO LLC—See Campbell Soup Company; *U.S. Public*, pg. 426
B&F CAPITAL MARKETS, INC.—See Stifel Financial Corp.; *U.S. Public*, pg. 1949
B&F CAPITAL MARKETS, LLC—See Stifel Financial Corp.; *U.S. Public*, pg. 1949
BF CO., LTD.—See Hokuetsu Corporation; *Int'l*, pg. 3443
B+F DORSTEN GMBH; *Int'l*, pg. 784
BFE INSTITUT FUR ENERGIE UND UMWELT GMBH.—See MVV Energie AG; *Int'l*, pg. 5108
BF ENGINE PARTS LLC—See Rheinmetall AG; *Int'l*, pg. 6321
BF ENTERPRISES, INC.; *U.S. Private*, pg. 548
B FERNANDEZ & HNOS INC.; *U.S. Private*, pg. 417
B!FERRAZ; *Int'l*, pg. 783
BFFI GROUP INC.; *Int'l*, pg. 1006
B&F FINANCE CORP.; *U.S. Private*, pg. 418
BFFT GESELLSCHAFT FUR FAHRZEUGTECHNIK MBH—See ATON GmbH; *Int'l*, pg. 688
BFG FEINGUSS NIEDERRHEIN GMBH—See Impro Precision Industries Limited; *Int'l*, pg. 3637
BF&G INSURANCE LIMITED—See Arthur J. Gallagher & Co.; *U.S. Public*, pg. 204
BFG MARKETING, LLC—See Eastport Holdings, Inc.; *U.S. Private*, pg. 1322
BFG SUPPLY CO., LLC - GRAND RAPIDS—See Pamplona Capital Management LLP; *Int'l*, pg. 5711
BFG SUPPLY CO., LLC—See Pamplona Capital Management LLP; *Int'l*, pg. 5711
BFI-BETEILIGUNGSGESELLSCHAFT FUR INDUSTRIEWERTE MBH—See Deutsche Bank Aktiengesellschaft; *Int'l*, pg. 2055
BFI (BIG SCREEN) LIMITED—See British Film Institute; *Int'l*, pg. 1171
BFIL FINANCE LIMITED—See ITC Limited; *Int'l*, pg. 3831
BF INVESTMENT LIMITED; *Int'l*, pg. 1006
BFI TRANSFER SYSTEMS OF GEORGIA, LLC—See Republic Services, Inc.; *U.S. Public*, pg. 1786
BFI WASTE SYSTEMS OF GEORGIA, LLC—See Republic Services, Inc.; *U.S. Public*, pg. 1786
BFI WASTE SYSTEMS OF KENTUCKY, LLC—See Republic Services, Inc.; *U.S. Public*, pg. 1786
BFI WASTE SYSTEMS OF VIRGINIA, LLC—See Republic Services, Inc.; *U.S. Public*, pg. 1786
BFK FRANCHISE COMPANY, LLC—See DriveItAway Holdings, Inc.; *U.S. Public*, pg. 688
BFLABS CO.,LTD.; *Int'l*, pg. 1006
BFL ASSET FINVEST LIMITED; *Int'l*, pg. 1006
BFL BETEILIGUNGSGESELLSCHAFT FUR FLUGZEUGLEASING MBH—See UniCredit S.p.A.; *Int'l*, pg. 8038
B-FLEXION GROUP HOLDINGS SA; *Int'l*, pg. 785
BFL FABRICATORS LTD.—See Bird Construction Inc.; *Int'l*, pg. 1046

BFL LEASING GMBH—See BAWAG Group AG; *Int'l*, pg. 900
B.F. LORENZETTI & ASSOCIATES; *Int'l*, pg. 789
BF&M (CANADA) LIMITED—See BF&M Limited; *Int'l*, pg. 1006
BF&M LIMITED; *Int'l*, pg. 1006
B.F. MODARABA; *Int'l*, pg. 789
B.F. MYERS FURNITURE COMPANY, INC.; *U.S. Private*, pg. 420
B FOOD SCIENCE CO., LTD.—See Mitsui & Co., Ltd.; *Int'l*, pg. 4973
BFP BETEILIGUNGSGESELLSCHAFT FUR PROJEKTE MBH—See Bilfinger SE; *Int'l*, pg. 1024
BFP BETONFERTIGTEILE PULHEIM GMBH—See Zech Group SE; *Int'l*, pg. 8628
BFPE INTERNATIONAL INC.; *U.S. Private*, pg. 548
BFP GMBH—See Bonduelle SAS; *Int'l*, pg. 1106
BFP WHOLESALE LTD.; *Int'l*, pg. 1006
B.F. RICH CO. INC.; *U.S. Private*, pg. 420
BFS ABRECHNUNGS GMBH—See ECM Equity Capital Management GmbH; *Int'l*, pg. 2291
BFS BUSINESS PRINTING INC.; *U.S. Private*, pg. 548
BFS CARGO DMK CO., LTD.—See Bangkok Airways Public Company Limited; *Int'l*, pg. 832
BFS DIVERSIFIED PRODUCTS, LLC—See Bridgestone Corporation; *Int'l*, pg. 1156
BFS FINANCE GMBH—See Bertelsmann SE & Co. KGaA; *Int'l*, pg. 993
BFS FINANCE MUNSTER GMBH—See Bertelsmann SE & Co. KGaA; *Int'l*, pg. 993
BFS FOODS INC.—See Bruceton Farm Service, Inc.; *U.S. Private*, pg. 671
BFSG, LLC—See Clayton, Dubilier & Rice, LLC; *U.S. Private*, pg. 923
BFSG, LLC—See Stone Point Capital LLC; *U.S. Private*, pg. 3824
BFS GROUP LIMITED—See The Bidvest Group Limited; *Int'l*, pg. 7621
THE B. F. SHAW PRINTING COMPANY; *U.S. Private*, pg. 3990
BFS HEALTH FINANCE GMBH—See Bertelsmann SE & Co. KGaA; *Int'l*, pg. 993
BF SOUTH INC.; *U.S. Private*, pg. 548
BF SPA; *Int'l*, pg. 1006
BFT ADRIA D.O.O.—See Somfy SA; *Int'l*, pg. 7084
BFT ANTRIEBSSYSTEME GMBH—See Somfy SA; *Int'l*, pg. 7084
BFT AUTO GATE & DOOR (SHANGHAI) CO. LTD.—See Somfy SA; *Int'l*, pg. 7084
BFT AUTOMATION AUSTRALIA PTY. LTD.—See Somfy SA; *Int'l*, pg. 7084
BFT AUTOMATION LTD.—See Somfy SA; *Int'l*, pg. 7084
BFT AUTOMATION NEW ZEALAND LTD.—See Somfy SA; *Int'l*, pg. 7084
BFT AUTOMATION (SOUTH) LTD.—See Somfy SA; *Int'l*, pg. 7084
BFT AUTOMATION SYSTEMS PTL—See Somfy SA; *Int'l*, pg. 7084
BFT AUTOMATION UK LIMITED—See Somfy SA; *Int'l*, pg. 7084
BFT BENELUX S.A.—See Somfy SA; *Int'l*, pg. 7085
BFT CZ SRO—See Somfy SA; *Int'l*, pg. 7084
BFT GMBH—See Dr. Aichhorn GmbH; *Int'l*, pg. 2190
BFT GROUP ITALIBERICA DE AUTOMATISMOS S.L.—See Somfy SA; *Int'l*, pg. 7085
BFT LANGUEDOC S.A.S.—See Somfy SA; *Int'l*, pg. 7084
BFT MIDDLE EAST FZO—See Somfy SA; *Int'l*, pg. 7084
BFT PIEMONTE S.R.L.—See Somfy SA; *Int'l*, pg. 7084
BFT POLSKA SP. Z.O.O.—See Somfy SA; *Int'l*, pg. 7085
BFT PORTUGAL S.A.—See Somfy SA; *Int'l*, pg. 7085
BFT S.P.A.—See Somfy SA; *Int'l*, pg. 7084
BFT TORANTRIEBSSYSTEME GMBH—See Somfy SA; *Int'l*, pg. 7085
BFT U.S. INC.—See Somfy SA; *Int'l*, pg. 7085
BF UTILITIES LTD.; *Int'l*, pg. 1006
BFW LIEGENSCHAFTEN AG; *Int'l*, pg. 1006
BG AGRI SALES & SERVICE INC.—See Mid Valley Agricultural Services, Inc.; *U.S. Private*, pg. 2706
BG AGRO JSC; *Int'l*, pg. 1006
BGA INSURANCE AGENCY, INC.—See Cross Financial Corporation; *U.S. Private*, pg. 1104
BG AMIA SP. Z. O.O.—See Endur ASA; *Int'l*, pg. 2409
B GAON HOLDINGS LTD.; *Int'l*, pg. 783
BGB GIOVANNI BOZZETTO, S.A.—See Aimia Inc.; *Int'l*, pg. 233
BGC (AUSTRALIA) PTY. LTD.; *Int'l*, pg. 1007
BGC BROKERS L.P.—See BGC Group, Inc.; *U.S. Public*, pg. 328
BGC CAPITAL MARKETS & FOREIGN EXCHANGE BROKER (KOREA) LTD.—See BGC Group, Inc.; *U.S. Public*, pg. 328
BGC CAPITAL MARKETS (HONG KONG) LTD.—See BGC Group, Inc.; *U.S. Public*, pg. 328
BGC CAPITAL MARKETS (JAPAN), LLC—See BGC Group, Inc.; *U.S. Public*, pg. 328
BGC CAPITAL MARKETS (SWITZERLAND) LLC—See BGC Group, Inc.; *U.S. Public*, pg. 328
BGC ENVIRONMENTAL BROKERAGE SERVICES, L.P.—See BGC Group, Inc.; *U.S. Public*, pg. 328

CORPORATE AFFILIATIONS

BGC FINANCIAL GROUP, INC.—See BGC Group, Inc.; *U.S. Public*, pg. 328
BGC GLASS SOLUTION CO., LTD.—See BG Container Glass Public Company Limited; *Int'l*, pg. 1006
BGC GROUP (HK) LIMITED—See Omnibridge Holdings Limited; *Int'l*, pg. 5564
BGC GROUP, INC.; *U.S. Public*, pg. 327
BGC GROUP PTE. LTD.—See Omnibridge Holdings Limited; *Int'l*, pg. 5564
BGC INTERNATIONAL, L.P.—See BGC Group, Inc.; *U.S. Public*, pg. 328
BGC INTERNATIONAL—See BGC Group, Inc.; *U.S. Public*, pg. 328
BGC LIQUIDEZ DISTRIBUIDORA DE TITULOS E VALORES MOBILIARIOS LTDA.—See BGC Group, Inc.; *U.S. Public*, pg. 328
BGC MARKET DATA, L.P.—See BGC Group, Inc.; *U.S. Public*, pg. 328
BG CONTAINER GLASS PUBLIC COMPANY LIMITED; *Int'l*, pg. 1006
BGC PACKAGING CO., LTD.—See BG Container Glass Public Company Limited; *Int'l*, pg. 1006
BGC PARTNERS (AUSTRALIA) PTY. LTD.—See BGC Group, Inc.; *U.S. Public*, pg. 328
BGC PARTNERS CIS LLC—See BGC Group, Inc.; *U.S. Public*, pg. 328
BGC PARTNERS MENKUL DEGERLER A.S.—See BGC Group, Inc.; *U.S. Public*, pg. 328
BGC PARTNERS (SINGAPORE) LIMITED—See BGC Group, Inc.; *U.S. Public*, pg. 328
B&G CRANE SERVICE, LLC—See Apollo Global Management, Inc.; *U.S. Public*, pg. 153
BGC SA FINANCIAL BROKERS (PTY) LIMITED—See BGC Group, Inc.; *U.S. Public*, pg. 328
BGC SECURITIES (HONG KONG) LLC—See BGC Group, Inc.; *U.S. Public*, pg. 328
BGC SECURITIES SARL—See BGC Group, Inc.; *U.S. Public*, pg. 328
BGC SHOKEN KAISHA LIMITED—See BGC Group, Inc.; *U.S. Public*, pg. 328
BGC USA, L.P.—See BGC Group, Inc.; *U.S. Public*, pg. 328
BGD BODENGESUNDHEITSDIENST GMBH—See Suddeutsche Zuckerruben-Verwertungs-Genossenschaft eG; *Int'l*, pg. 7252
B&G DIVERSIFIED CONCEPTS LLC—See B&G Food Enterprises Inc.; *U.S. Private*, pg. 418
BGE ELEKTROTECHNIK GMBH; *Int'l*, pg. 1007
BGE HOME PRODUCTS & SERVICES, LLC—See Constellation Energy Corporation; *U.S. Public*, pg. 571
B&G ELECTRICAL CONTRACTORS OF NY—See B&G Industries, Ltd.; *U.S. Private*, pg. 418
B & G EQUIPMENT, INC.; *U.S. Private*, pg. 417
B.G.E. SERVICE & SUPPLY LTD.; *Int'l*, pg. 789
BGF CO., LTD.; *Int'l*, pg. 1007
BGFECOMATERIALS CO., LTD.;
BGF ECOMATERIALS, CO. LTD.—See BGF Co., Ltd.; *Int'l*, pg. 1007
BGF GROUP PLC; *Int'l*, pg. 1007
BG FIDUCIARIA SIM S.P.A.—See Assicurazioni Generali S.p.A.; *Int'l*, pg. 643
BGF INDUSTRIES INC.—See Groupe Porcher Industries; *Int'l*, pg. 3109
B&G FOOD ENTERPRISES INC.; *U.S. Private*, pg. 418
B&G FOOD ENTERPRISES TEXAS LLC—See B&G Food Enterprises Inc.; *U.S. Private*, pg. 418
B&G FOODS, INC.; *U.S. Public*, pg. 260
B&G FOODS NORTH AMERICA, INC.—See B&G Foods, Inc.; *U.S. Public*, pg. 260
B&G FOODS SNACKS, INC.—See B&G Foods, Inc.; *U.S. Public*, pg. 260
BGF RETAIL CO. LTD.; *Int'l*, pg. 1007
BG GAS SERVICES LIMITED—See Shell plc; *Int'l*, pg. 6794
BG GROUP LIMITED—See Shell plc; *Int'l*, pg. 6795
BGH CAPITAL PTY LTD; *Int'l*, pg. 1007
BGI AMERICAS CORPORATION—See BGI-Shenzhen; *Int'l*, pg. 1008
BGI AVIATION TECHNICAL SERVICES (OVERSEAS) LIMITED.—See Bristow Group, Inc.; *U.S. Public*, pg. 387
BGI CHINA—See BGI-Shenzhen; *Int'l*, pg. 1008
BGI GENOMICS CO., LTD.; *Int'l*, pg. 1008
BGI GROUP AD; *Int'l*, pg. 1008
BGI GROUP JSC—See Vietnam Construction Stock Corporation; *Int'l*, pg. 8197
BGI HONG KONG CO, LIMITED—See BGI-Shenzhen; *Int'l*, pg. 1008
BGI INVESTMENTS (1961) LTD.; *Int'l*, pg. 1008
BGI JAPAN—See BGI-Shenzhen; *Int'l*, pg. 1008
BGIL FILMS & TECHNOLOGIES LTD.; *Int'l*, pg. 1008
B&G INDUSTRIES, LTD.; *U.S. Private*, pg. 418
BG INVESTMENT SERVICES, INC.—See BankGuam Holding Company; *U.S. Public*, pg. 274
BGI OF BRANDYWINE, INC.—See Acadia Healthcare Company, Inc.; *U.S. Public*, pg. 28
BGIS GLOBAL INTEGRATED SOLUTIONS CANADA LP—See Johnson Controls International plc; *Int'l*, pg. 3985

COMPANY NAME INDEX

BGI-SHENZHEN; *Int'l*, pg. 1008
BGI USA, INC.; *U.S. Private*, pg. 548
B&G JAPAN CO., LTD.—See Cofco Biotechnology Co., Ltd.; *Int'l*, pg. 1691
B&G JAPAN CO., LTD.—See Finasucre S.A.; *Int'l*, pg. 2670
B. GJERDE—See Bridgestone Corporation; *Int'l*, pg. 1158
BGK FINISHING SYSTEMS—See Carlisle Companies Incorporated; *U.S. Public*, pg. 436
BGL BNP PARIBAS S.A.—See BNP Paribas SA; *Int'l*, pg. 1084
BGL GROUP LIMITED; *Int'l*, pg. 1008
BGL LUXEMBOURG—See BNP Paribas SA; *Int'l*, pg. 1084
BGLOBAL METERING LIMITED—See Astatine Investment Partners LLC; *U.S. Private*, pg. 360
B&G MANUFACTURING CO. INC.; *U.S. Private*, pg. 418
BGMC INTERNATIONAL LIMITED; *Int'l*, pg. 1008
B-G MECHANICAL, INC.—See Bouygues S.A.; *Int'l*, pg. 1121
B-G MECHANICAL SERVICE, INC.—See Bouygues S.A.; *Int'l*, pg. 1121
BG MEDICINE, INC.; *U.S. Public*, pg. 327
BGN INDUSTRIAL TYRE (PVT) LTD.—See Richard Pieris & Co. Ltd.; *Int'l*, pg. 6330
BG PARTNERS INC.—See Beauty Garage Inc.; *Int'l*, pg. 935
BGP CORP.—See BGP Corp.; *U.S. Private*, pg. 549
BGP CORP.; *U.S. Private*, pg. 549
BG PICTURES LLC; *U.S. Private*, pg. 548
B&G PLASTICS, INC.; *U.S. Private*, pg. 418
BGP PRODUCTS APS—See Viatris Inc.; *U.S. Public*, pg. 2293
BGP PRODUCTS GMBH—See Viatris Inc.; *U.S. Public*, pg. 2293
BGP PRODUCTS OPERATIONS GMBH—See Viatris Inc.; *U.S. Public*, pg. 2293
BG PRODUCTS, INC.; *U.S. Private*, pg. 548
BGR ANNAPOLIS, LLC—See Sonnet BioTherapeutics Holdings, Inc.; *U.S. Public*, pg. 1904
BGR BOILERS PRIVATE LIMITED—See BGR Energy Systems Limited; *Int'l*, pg. 1008
BGR COLUMBIA, LLC—See Sonnet BioTherapeutics Holdings, Inc.; *U.S. Public*, pg. 1904
B. GREEN & CO., *U.S. Private*, pg. 410
BGR ENERGY SYSTEMS LIMITED - AIR FIN COOLER DIVISION—See BGR Energy Systems Limited; *Int'l*, pg. 1008
BGR ENERGY SYSTEMS LIMITED - CAPTIVE POWER DIVISION—See BGR Energy Systems Limited; *Int'l*, pg. 1008
BGR ENERGY SYSTEMS LIMITED - ELECTRICAL PROJECTS DIVISION—See BGR Energy Systems Limited; *Int'l*, pg. 1008
BGR ENERGY SYSTEMS LIMITED - ENVIRONMENT ENGINEERING DIVISION—See BGR Energy Systems Limited; *Int'l*, pg. 1008
BGR ENERGY SYSTEMS LIMITED - INFRASTRUCTURE DIVISION—See BGR Energy Systems Limited; *Int'l*, pg. 1008
BGR ENERGY SYSTEMS LIMITED - OIL & GAS EQUIPMENT DIVISION—See BGR Energy Systems Limited; *Int'l*, pg. 1009
BGR ENERGY SYSTEMS LIMITED - POWER PROJECTS DIVISION—See BGR Energy Systems Limited; *Int'l*, pg. 1009
BGR ENERGY SYSTEMS LIMITED; *Int'l*, pg. 1008
B.GRIMM AIR CONDITIONING LIMITED—See B. Grimm Group; *Int'l*, pg. 788
B.GRIMM ALMA LINK BUILDING CO., LTD.—See B. Grimm Group; *Int'l*, pg. 788
B. GRIMM CARRIER (THAILAND) LIMITED—See Carrier Global Corporation; *U.S. Public*, pg. 440
B. GRIMM & CO., R.O.P.—See Electricity Generating Public Co., Ltd.; *Int'l*, pg. 2352
B. GRIMM & CO. R.O.P.—See B. Grimm Group; *Int'l*, pg. 788
B.GRIMM DR. GERHARD LINK BUILDING CO., LTD.—See B. Grimm Group; *Int'l*, pg. 788
B. GRIMM GROUP; *Int'l*, pg. 788
B. GRIMM GROUP—See B. Grimm Group; *Int'l*, pg. 788
B. GRIMM HEALTHCARE CO., LTD.—See B. Grimm Group; *Int'l*, pg. 788
B. GRIMM HOLDING CO., LTD.—See B. Grimm Group; *Int'l*, pg. 788
B. GRIMM INTERNATIONAL SERVICE CO., LTD.—See B. Grimm Group; *Int'l*, pg. 788
B.GRIMM JOINT VENTURE HOLDING LTD.—See B. Grimm Group; *Int'l*, pg. 788
B. GRIMM MBM METALWORKS LIMITED—See B. Grimm Group; *Int'l*, pg. 788
B.GRIMM POWER (LAEM CHABANG) 1 LIMITED—See B. Grimm Group; *Int'l*, pg. 788
BGRIMM SCIENCE & TECHNOLOGY CO., LTD.; *Int'l*, pg. 1009
B. GRIMM TRADING COMPANY—See B. Grimm Group; *Int'l*, pg. 788
B.GRIMM TRADING CORPORATION LIMITED—See B. Grimm Group; *Int'l*, pg. 788

B. GRIMM TRANSPORT LTD.—See B. Grimm Group; *Int'l*, pg. 788
BGR INC.; *U.S. Private*, pg. 549
BGR MEDIA, LLC—See Penske Media Corporation; *U.S. Private*, pg. 3139
BGR MOSAIC, LLC—See Sonnet BioTherapeutics Holdings, Inc.; *U.S. Public*, pg. 1904
BGR OPERATIONS, LLC—See Sonnet BioTherapeutics Holdings, Inc.; *U.S. Public*, pg. 1904
BGR TURBINES COMPANY PRIVATE LIMITED—See BGR Energy Systems Limited; *Int'l*, pg. 1009
BGR TYSONS, LLC—See Sonnet BioTherapeutics Holdings, Inc.; *U.S. Public*, pg. 1904
BGR TYSONS, LLC—See Sonnet BioTherapeutics Holdings, Inc.; *U.S. Public*, pg. 1904
BGR WASHINGTONIAN, LLC—See Sonnet BioTherapeutics Holdings, Inc.; *U.S. Public*, pg. 1904
BGS ACQUISITION CORP.; *Int'l*, pg. 1009
BGSF, INC.; *U.S. Public*, pg. 330
BG SPORTS EUROPE SARL—See Fenway Partners, LLC; *U.S. Private*, pg. 1495
BGS SVENSSON AB—See Nordisk Bergteknik AB; *Int'l*, pg. 5424
BG T&A CO.; *Int'l*, pg. 1007
BGT CORPORATION PUBLIC COMPANY LIMITED; *Int'l*, pg. 1009
BGT GROUP CO., LTD.; *Int'l*, pg. 1009
BG VENTURES INC.—See Beauty Garage Inc.; *Int'l*, pg. 935
BGW CPA, PLLC; *U.S. Private*, pg. 549
B & G WHOLESALE DISTRIBUTING, INC.; *U.S. Private*, pg. 417
B&G WHOLESALE DISTRIBUTING INC.; *U.S. Private*, pg. 418
BGZ BNPP FAKTORING SPOLKA Z O.O.—See BNP Paribas SA; *Int'l*, pg. 1080
BGZ FONDSVERWALTUNG GMBH—See PNE AG; *Int'l*, pg. 5900
BHA ALTAIR, LLC—See Parker Hannifin Corporation; *U.S. Public*, pg. 1640
BHAGAWATI OXYGEN LIMITED; *Int'l*, pg. 1009
BHAGERIA INDUSTRIES LIMITED; *Int'l*, pg. 1009
BHAGIRADHA CHEMICALS & INDUSTRIES LTD.; *Int'l*, pg. 1009
BHAGWAN MARINE; *Int'l*, pg. 1009
BHAGWATI AUTOCAST LTD.—See TGB Banquets & Hotels Limited; *Int'l*, pg. 7587
BHAGWATI SYNDICATE PVT. LTD.; *Int'l*, pg. 1010
BHAGYALAXMI DAIRY FARMS PRIVATE LIMITED—See Parag Milk Foods Ltd; *Int'l*, pg. 5735
BHAGYANAGAR GREEN ENERGY PRIVATE LIMITED—See Surana Telecom and Power Limited; *Int'l*, pg. 7342
BHAGYANAGAR INDIA LIMITED; *Int'l*, pg. 1010
BHAGYANAGAR PROPERTIES LIMITED; *Int'l*, pg. 1010
B.H. AIRCRAFT CO., INC.; *U.S. Private*, pg. 420
BHAKA BHUMI DEVELOPMENT CO., LTD.—See Italian-Thai Development pcl; *Int'l*, pg. 3829
BHAKTI GEMS & JEWELLERY LIMITED; *Int'l*, pg. 1010
BHALCHANDRAM CLOTHING LIMITED; *Int'l*, pg. 1010
BHANDARI HOSIERY EXPORTS LTD.; *Int'l*, pg. 1010
BHANDERI INFRACON LIMITED; *Int'l*, pg. 1010
BHANERO TEXTILE MILLS LIMITED; *Int'l*, pg. 1010
B. HANEY & SONS, INC.—See The Davey Tree Expert Company; *U.S. Private*, pg. 4018
BHANG INC.; *Int'l*, pg. 1010
BHANSALI ENGINEERING POLYMERS LIMITED; *Int'l*, pg. 1010
BHARAT AGRI FERT & REALTY LIMITED; *Int'l*, pg. 1010
BHARAT ALUMINIUM COMPANY LIMITED—See Vedanta Resources Ltd; *Int'l*, pg. 8146
BHARAT BHUSHAN FINANCE & COMMODITY BROKERS LTD.; *Int'l*, pg. 1010
BHARAT BIJLEE LTD - DRIVES DIVISION—See Bharat Bijlee Ltd; *Int'l*, pg. 1010
BHARAT BIJLEE LTD; *Int'l*, pg. 1010
BHARAT CERTIS AGRISCIENCE LTD.—See Nippon Soda Co., Ltd.; *Int'l*, pg. 5334
BHARAT COKING COAL LIMITED—See Coal India Limited; *Int'l*, pg. 1680
BHARAT DYNAMICS LIMITED; *Int'l*, pg. 1010
BHARAT ELECTRONICS LIMITED; *Int'l*, pg. 1010
BHARAT FIH LIMITED—See Hon Hai Precision Industry Co., Ltd.; *Int'l*, pg. 3456
BHARAT FINANCIAL INCLUSION LIMITED—See IndusInd Bank Ltd.; *Int'l*, pg. 3665
BHARAT FORGE AMERICA INC—See Kalyani Group; *Int'l*, pg. 4058
BHARAT FORGE LIMITED - CAPITAL GOODS DIVISION—See Kalyani Group; *Int'l*, pg. 4058
BHARAT FORGE LTD.—See Kalyani Group; *Int'l*, pg. 4058
BHARAT GEARS LIMITED; *Int'l*, pg. 1011
BHARAT HEAVY ELECTRICALS LIMITED; *Int'l*, pg. 1011
BHARAT HEAVY PLATES & VESSELS LIMITED—See Bharat Heavy Electricals Limited; *Int'l*, pg. 1011
BHARATHI CEMENT CORPORATION PRIVATE LTD—See Vicat S.A.; *Int'l*, pg. 8185
BHARAT HIGHWAYS INVIT.; *Int'l*, pg. 1011

BHARATI DEFENCE AND INFRASTRUCTURE LIMITED; *Int'l*, pg. 1011
BHARAT IMMUNOLOGICALS AND BIOLOGICALS CORPORATION LIMITED; *Int'l*, pg. 1011
BHARAT IT SERVICES LIMITED—See Digilife Technologies Limited; *Int'l*, pg. 2119
BHARATIYA GLOBAL INFOMEDIA LTD.; *Int'l*, pg. 1011
BHARATIYA RESERVE BANK NOTE MUDRAN PVT. LTD.—See Reserve Bank of India; *Int'l*, pg. 6295
BHARAT OMAN REFINERIES LIMITED—See Bharat Petroleum Corporation Limited; *Int'l*, pg. 1011
BHARAT OMAN REFINERIES LIMITED—See OQ S.A.O.C.; *Int'l*, pg. 5607
BHARAT PARENTERALS LIMITED; *Int'l*, pg. 1011
BHARAT PETROLEUM CORPORATION LIMITED - KOCHI REFINERY—See Bharat Petroleum Corporation Limited; *Int'l*, pg. 1011
BHARAT PETROLEUM CORPORATION LIMITED; *Int'l*, pg. 1011
BHARAT PETRO RESOURCES LTD.—See Bharat Petroleum Corporation Limited; *Int'l*, pg. 1011
BHARAT RASAYAN LIMITED; *Int'l*, pg. 1011
BHARAT REFRIGERATIONS PRIVATE LIMITED—See Ice Make Refrigeration Ltd.; *Int'l*, pg. 3579
BHARAT ROAD NETWORK LTD.; *Int'l*, pg. 1011
BHARAT SEATS LIMITED; *Int'l*, pg. 1011
BHARAT SERUMS & VACCINES LIMITED—See Mankind Pharma Ltd.; *Int'l*, pg. 4673
BHARAT SHELL LIMITED—See Bharat Petroleum Corporation Limited; *Int'l*, pg. 1011
BHARAT SHELL LIMITED—See Shell plc; *Int'l*, pg. 6796
BHARAT TELECOM LTD.; *Int'l*, pg. 1011
BHARAT WIRE ROPES LIMITED; *Int'l*, pg. 1011
BHARCAP ACQUISITION CORP.; *U.S. Private*, pg. 549
BHARCAP PARTNERS, LLC; *U.S. Private*, pg. 549
BHARGAV BIKASH BANK LIMITED; *Int'l*, pg. 1011
BHARTIA BACHAT LIMITED; *Int'l*, pg. 1011
BHARTI AIRTEL (FRANCE) SAS—See Bharti Enterprises Limited; *Int'l*, pg. 1013
BHARTI AIRTEL INTERNATIONAL (NETHERLANDS) B.V.—See Bharti Enterprises Limited; *Int'l*, pg. 1013
BHARTI AIRTEL LANKA (PRIVATE) LIMITED—See Bharti Enterprises Limited; *Int'l*, pg. 1013
BHARTI AIRTEL LIMITED—See Bharti Enterprises Limited; *Int'l*, pg. 1012
BHARTI AIRTEL SERVICES LIMITED—See Bharti Enterprises Limited; *Int'l*, pg. 1013
BHARTI AIRTEL (UK) LIMITED—See Bharti Enterprises Limited; *Int'l*, pg. 1013
BHARTI ENTERPRISES LIMITED; *Int'l*, pg. 1011
BHARTI INTERNATIONAL (SINGAPORE) PTE. LTD—See Bharti Enterprises Limited; *Int'l*, pg. 1013
BHARTI REALTY LIMITED—See Bharti Enterprises Limited; *Int'l*, pg. 1013
BHARTI RESOURCES LTD.—See Bharti Enterprises Limited; *Int'l*, pg. 1013
BHARTIYA INTERNATIONAL LTD.; *Int'l*, pg. 1013
BHASKAR AGROCHEMICALS LTD.; *Int'l*, pg. 1013
BHASKARI ELECTRICAL SYSTEMS PVT. LTD.—See Annapurna Bhaskari Group; *Int'l*, pg. 473
BHATIA BROTHERS GROUP - BHATIA BROTHERS-AUTOMOTIVE DIVISION—See Bhatia Brothers Group; *Int'l*, pg. 1013
BHATIA BROTHERS GROUP; *Int'l*, pg. 1013
BHATIA BROTHERS LLC - AUTOMOTIVE & INDUSTRIAL CHEMICALS—See Bhatia Brothers Group; *Int'l*, pg. 1013
BHATIA BROTHERS LLC - INDUSTRIAL SUPPLIES DIVISION—See Bhatia Brothers Group; *Int'l*, pg. 1013
BHATIA BROTHERS & PARTNERS L.L.C—See Bhatia Brothers Group; *Int'l*, pg. 1013
BHATIA COLD STORAGE & TRADING CO., LLC—See Bhatia Brothers Group; *Int'l*, pg. 1013
BHATIA COLOUR CHEM LIMITED; *Int'l*, pg. 1014
BHATIA COMMUNICATION & RETAIL (INDIA) LIMITED; *Int'l*, pg. 1014
BHAWANA CAPITAL PRIVATE LIMITED—See Multitude SE; *Int'l*, pg. 5084
B&H BAG COMPANY—See Apollo Global Management, Inc.; *U.S. Public*, pg. 153
BHB BRAUHOLDING BAYERN-MITTE AG; *Int'l*, pg. 1014
BHB INC.; *U.S. Private*, pg. 549
BH BOTSWANA (PTY) LTD.; *Int'l*, pg. 1009
B.H. BUNN COMPANY; *U.S. Private*, pg. 420
BHC ALHAMBRA HOSPITAL, INC.—See Universal Health Services, Inc.; *U.S. Public*, pg. 2256
BH CAPITAL PARTNERS, LLC; *U.S. Private*, pg. 549
BHC BELMONT PINES HOSPITAL, INC.—See Universal Health Services, Inc.; *U.S. Public*, pg. 2256
BHCC CONSTRUCTION PTE. LTD.—See BHCC Holding Limited; *Int'l*, pg. 1014
BHCC HOLDING LIMITED; *Int'l*, pg. 1014
BHC FAIRFAX HOSPITAL, INC.—See Universal Health Services, Inc.; *U.S. Public*, pg. 2256
BHC FOX RUN HOSPITAL, INC.—See Universal Health Services, Inc.; *U.S. Public*, pg. 2256
BHC FREMONT HOSPITAL, INC.—See Universal Health Services, Inc.; *U.S. Public*, pg. 2256

BHCC HOLDING LIMITED

BHC GUMMI-METALL GMBH—See Rupf Industries GmbH; *Int'l*, pg. 6428
BHC HEALTH SERVICES OF NEVADA, INC.—See Universal Health Services, Inc.; *U.S. Public*, pg. 2256
BHC HERITAGE OAKS HOSPITAL, INC.—See Universal Health Services, Inc.; *U.S. Public*, pg. 2256
BHC INTERMOUNTAIN HOSPITAL, INC.—See Universal Health Services, Inc.; *U.S. Public*, pg. 2256
BHC MANAGEMENT SERVICES OF STREAMWOOD, LLC—See Universal Health Services, Inc.; *U.S. Public*, pg. 2256
BHCMC, LLC—See Butler National Corporation; *U.S. Public*, pg. 413
BHC MESILLA VALLEY HOSPITAL, LLC—See Universal Health Services, Inc.; *U.S. Public*, pg. 2256
BH CO., LTD.; *Int'l*, pg. 1009
B&H CONSULTING SERVICES, INC.—See Voisin Consulting, Inc.; *U.S. Private*, pg. 4409
BH COSMETICS, LLC—See Revolution Beauty Group Plc; *Int'l*, pg. 6313
BHC PINNACLE POINTE HOSPITAL, INC.—See Universal Health Services, Inc.; *U.S. Public*, pg. 2256
B. H. CRAIG CONSTRUCTION COMPANY; *U.S. Private*, pg. 419
BHC SIERRA VISTA HOSPITAL, INC.—See Universal Health Services, Inc.; *U.S. Public*, pg. 2256
BHC STREAMWOOD HOSPITAL, INC.—See Universal Health Services, Inc.; *U.S. Public*, pg. 2256
BHDT GMBH—See Dr. Aichhorn GmbH; *Int'l*, pg. 2190
B&H EDUCATION, INC.; *U.S. Private*, pg. 418
BHEEMA CEMENTS LTD.; *Int'l*, pg. 1014
BHEL ELECTRICAL MACHINES LIMITED—See Bharat Heavy Electricals Limited; *Int'l*, pg. 1011
B+H EQUIMAR SINGAPORE PTE. LTD.—See B+H Ocean Carriers Ltd.; *Int'l*, pg. 784
BHE RENEWABLES, LLC—See Berkshire Hathaway Inc.; *U.S. Public*, pg. 300
BHF-BANK (SCHWEIZ) AG—See ODDO BHF SCA; *Int'l*, pg. 5524
BHF IMMOBILIEN-GMBH—See ODDO BHF SCA; *Int'l*, pg. 5524
B&H FOTO & ELECTRONIC CORP.; *U.S. Private*, pg. 418
BHF PRIVATE EQUITY MANAGEMENT GMBH—See ODDO BHF SCA; *Int'l*, pg. 5524
BHF PRIVATE EQUITY TREUHAND- UND BERATUNGSGESELLSCHAFT MBH—See ODDO BHF SCA; *Int'l*, pg. 5524
BHFS ONE LIMITED—See Bain Capital, LP; *U.S. Private*, pg. 436
BHF TRUST MANAGEMENT GESELLSCHAFT FUR VERMOGENSVERWALTUNG MBH—See ODDO BHF SCA; *Int'l*, pg. 5524
BHF ZURICH FAMILY OFFICE AG—See ODDO BHF SCA; *Int'l*, pg. 5525
BHG BETEILIGUNGSMANAGEMENT UND HOLDING GMBH—See Raiffeisenlandesbank Oberosterreich Aktiengesellschaft; *Int'l*, pg. 6187
BHG BITUMENHANDELSGESELLSCHAFT MBH—See STRABAG SE; *Int'l*, pg. 7229
BHG CZ S.R.O.—See STRABAG SE; *Int'l*, pg. 7229
BHG GROUP AB; *Int'l*, pg. 1014
BH GLOBAL CORPORATION LIMITED; *Int'l*, pg. 1009
BHG RETAIL TRUST MANAGEMENT PTE. LTD.; *Int'l*, pg. 1015
BHG S.A. - BRAZIL HOSPITALITY GROUP—See GTIS Partners LP; *U.S. Private*, pg. 1807
BHG SP. Z O.O.—See STRABAG SE; *Int'l*, pg. 7229
BHH AFFILIATES, LLC—See Berkshire Hathaway Inc.; *U.S. Public*, pg. 299
BHHH COMPANIES INC.; *U.S. Private*, pg. 549
BHH MIKROMED SP. Z O.O.—See Acciaierie Valbruna S.p.A.; *Int'l*, pg. 89
BHIC BOFORS ASIA SDN. BHD.—See Boustead Heavy Industries Corporation Berhad; *Int'l*, pg. 1120
BHI CO., LTD.; *Int'l*, pg. 1015
B/HI COMMUNICATIONS, INC.—See Dolphin Entertainment, Inc.; *U.S. Public*, pg. 673
BHI ENERGY I POWER SERVICES LLC—See Bernhard Capital Partners Management, LP; *U.S. Private*, pg. 537
BHI ENERGY I SPECIALTY SERVICES LLC—See Bernhard Capital Partners Management, LP; *U.S. Private*, pg. 537
BHI ENERGY; *U.S. Private*, pg. 549
BHI HOLDINGS INC.; *Int'l*, pg. 1015
BHILAI ENGINEERING CORP LTD.; *Int'l*, pg. 1015
BHILAI JAYPEE CEMENT LIMITED—See Jaiprakash Associates Limited; *Int'l*, pg. 3872
BHILWARA SPINNERS LIMITED; *Int'l*, pg. 1015
BHILWARA TECHNICAL TEXTILES LIMITED; *Int'l*, pg. 1015
BHIMA RIDDHI INFOTAINMENT PRIVATE LIMITED—See Hinduja Global Solutions Ltd.; *Int'l*, pg. 3398
B & H INSURANCE, LLC—See GTCR LLC; *U.S. Private*, pg. 1802
BHIRA INVESTMENTS LTD.—See Tata Power Company Limited; *Int'l*, pg. 7468
BHIRAJ OFFICE LEASEHOLD REIT; *Int'l*, pg. 1015
BHI SENIOR LIVING, INC.; *U.S. Private*, pg. 549

BHIVPURI INVESTMENTS LTD.—See Tata Power Company Limited; *Int'l*, pg. 7468
BHJ A/S—See Lauridsen Group Inc.; *U.S. Private*, pg. 2399
BHJ BALTIC UAB—See Lauridsen Group Inc.; *U.S. Private*, pg. 2399
BHJ CANADA MEAT PRODUCTS INC.—See Lauridsen Group Inc.; *U.S. Private*, pg. 2399
BHJ FARUTEX SP. ZO.O.—See Lauridsen Group Inc.; *U.S. Private*, pg. 2399
BHJ FINLAND OY AB—See Lauridsen Group Inc.; *U.S. Private*, pg. 2399
BHJ KALINO FOOD AB—See Lauridsen Group Inc.; *U.S. Private*, pg. 2399
BHJ ROMANIA SRL—See Lauridsen Group Inc.; *U.S. Private*, pg. 2399
BHJ UK FOOD LTD.—See Lauridsen Group Inc.; *U.S. Private*, pg. 2399
BHJ UK PROTEIN FOODS LTD.—See Lauridsen Group Inc.; *U.S. Private*, pg. 2399
BHJ UK SEAFOODS LTD.—See Lauridsen Group Inc.; *U.S. Private*, pg. 2400
BHJ USA, INC.—See Lauridsen Group Inc.; *U.S. Private*, pg. 2400
BHK INSURANCE SERVICES LIMITED—See Brown & Brown, Inc.; *U.S. Public*, pg. 397
BHLDN LLC—See Urban Outfitters, Inc.; *U.S. Public*, pg. 2265
BH MACRO LTD.; *Int'l*, pg. 1009
B&H MAINTENANCE & CONSTRUCTION INC.; *U.S. Private*, pg. 418
B+H MANAGEMENT LTD.—See B+H Ocean Carriers Ltd.; *Int'l*, pg. 784
BH MANAGEMENT SERVICES, LLC; *U.S. Private*, pg. 549
B&H MANUFACTURING COMPANY; *U.S. Private*, pg. 418
BHM CAPITAL FINANCIAL SERVICES PSC; *Int'l*, pg. 1015
BH MEDIA GROUP INC.—See Lee Enterprises, Incorporated; *U.S. Public*, pg. 1298
BH MEDIA GROUP—See Lee Enterprises, Incorporated; *U.S. Public*, pg. 1298
BHMS INVESTMENTS LP; *U.S. Private*, pg. 549
BHNA HOLDINGS INC.—See Bristow Group, Inc.; *U.S. Public*, pg. 387
B+H OCEAN CARRIERS LTD.; *Int'l*, pg. 784
BHOME MORTGAGE, LLC—See Green Brick Partners, Inc.; *U.S. Public*, pg. 962
BHOPAL DHULE TRANSMISSION COMPANY LIMITED—See India Grid Trust; *Int'l*, pg. 3651
BHORUKA ALUMINIUM LTD.; *Int'l*, pg. 1015
BHORUKA EXTRUSIONS PVT LTD.—See YKK Corporation; *Int'l*, pg. 8589
BHORUKA FABCONS PRIVATE LIMITED—See Bhoruka Aluminium Ltd.; *Int'l*, pg. 1015
BHORUKA SPECIALTY GASES PRIVATE LTD.—See SOL S.p.A.; *Int'l*, pg. 7067
BHPA, INC.; *U.S. Public*, pg. 330
BH PARTNERS, LLC—See Platinum Equity, LLC; *U.S. Private*, pg. 3209
BHP BILLITON (BOLIVIA), INC.—See BHP Group Limited; *Int'l*, pg. 1015
BHP BILLITON CHINA—See BHP Group Limited; *Int'l*, pg. 1015
BHP BILLITON INTERNATIONAL TRADING (SHANGHAI) CO. LTD.—See BHP Group Limited; *Int'l*, pg. 1015
BHP BILLITON IRON ORE PTY. LTD.—See BHP Group Limited; *Int'l*, pg. 1016
BHP BILLITON NICKEL WEST PTY. LTD.—See BHP Group Limited; *Int'l*, pg. 1016
BHP BILLITON PETROLEUM (AMERICAS) INC.—See BHP Group Limited; *Int'l*, pg. 1015
BHP BILLITON PETROLEUM PTY. LTD.—See BHP Group Limited; *Int'l*, pg. 1015
BHP COAL PTY. LTD.—See BHP Group Limited; *Int'l*, pg. 1016
BHP GROUP LIMITED; *Int'l*, pg. 1015
BHP GROUP PLC—See BHP Group Limited; *Int'l*, pg. 1015
BHP MINERALS—See BHP Group Limited; *Int'l*, pg. 1016
BHP NEW ZEALAND STEEL LTD.—See BlueScope Steel Limited; *Int'l*, pg. 1073
BHP PETROLEUM PTY. LTD.—See Woodside Energy Group Ltd; *Int'l*, pg. 8450
BHP PETROLEUM PTY, LTD.—See Woodside Energy Group Ltd; *Int'l*, pg. 8450
BHP SHARED SERVICES MALAYSIA SDN. BHD.—See BHP Group Limited; *Int'l*, pg. 1016
BHP SHARED SERVICES PHILIPPINES INC.—See BHP Group Limited; *Int'l*, pg. 1016
BHP TITANIUM MINERALS—See BHP Group Limited; *Int'l*, pg. 1016
BHR HOCHDRUCK-ROHRLEITUNGSBAU GMBH—See Bilfinger SE; *Int'l*, pg. 1027
BHR LUXEMBOURG S.A.R.L.—See InterContinental Hotels Group PLC; *Int'l*, pg. 3736
BHR OVERSEAS (FINANCE) B.V.—See InterContinental Hotels Group PLC; *Int'l*, pg. 3736

CORPORATE AFFILIATIONS

BHR PACIFIC HOLDINGS, INC.—See InterContinental Hotels Group PLC; *Int'l*, pg. 3737
BHR PIPING SYSTEMS (PTY) LTD.—See Bilfinger SE; *Int'l*, pg. 1027
BHS BOOK PRINTING SDN BHD—See Nextgreen Global Berhad; *Int'l*, pg. 5249
BHSF, INC.—See Berkshire Hathaway Inc.; *U.S. Public*, pg. 299
BH SHOE HOLDINGS, INC.—See Berkshire Hathaway Inc.; *U.S. Public*, pg. 299
BHS SPECIALTY CHEMICALS; *U.S. Private*, pg. 549
BHS TABLETOP AG—See Serafin Unternehmensgruppe GmbH; *Int'l*, pg. 6720
BH TELECOM D.D.; *Int'l*, pg. 1009
B.H.T. ELECTRONICS PURCHASING INC.; *U.S. Private*, pg. 420
BHT HYGIENETECHNIK GMBH—See STERIS plc; *Int'l*, pg. 7208
BH TRANS COMPANY, LLC—See Community Health Systems, Inc.; *U.S. Public*, pg. 551
B-H TRANSFER CO; *U.S. Private*, pg. 419
BH TRAVEL RETAIL POLAND SP. Z O.O—See PHZ Baltona S.A.; *Int'l*, pg. 5859
BHTT ENTERTAINMENT, INC.—See J.H. Whitney & Co., LLC; *U.S. Private*, pg. 2166
BHUB HOLDINGS SDN. BHD.—See TSR Capital Berhad; *Int'l*, pg. 7952
BHUDEVI INFRA PROJECTS LTD.; *Int'l*, pg. 1016
BHUMI RESOURCES (SINGAPORE) PTE LIMITED.—See The Braj Binani Group; *Int'l*, pg. 7627
BHUTAN NATIONAL BANK LIMITED; *Int'l*, pg. 1016
BHVT MOTORS INC.; *U.S. Private*, pg. 549
BHW BAUSPARKASSE AG—See Deutsche Post AG; *Int'l*, pg. 2079
BHW (COMPONENTS) LIMITED—See a2e Venture Catalysts Limited; *Int'l*, pg. 30
BHW - GESELLSCHAFT FUR WOHNUNGSWIRTSCHAFT MBH & CO. IMMOBILIENVERWALTUNGS KG—See Deutsche Bank Aktiengesellschaft; *Int'l*, pg. 2055
BHW - GESELLSCHAFT FUR WOHNUNGSWIRTSCHAFT MBH—See Deutsche Bank Aktiengesellschaft; *Int'l*, pg. 2055
BHW IMMOBILIEN GMBH—See Deutsche Post AG; *Int'l*, pg. 2079
BHW SHEET METAL COMPANY; *U.S. Private*, pg. 549
BHX INC.; *U.S. Private*, pg. 549
BH-ZACD (TUAS BAY) DEVELOPMENT PTE. LTD.—See CNQC International Holdings Ltd.; *Int'l*, pg. 1678
BIA ACQUISITION LTD—See Grupo Posadas S.A.B. de C.V.; *Int'l*, pg. 3134
BIA AUTOMATION S.R.L.—See THK CO., LTD., *Int'l*, pg. 7711
BIA BURKINA SARL—See BIA Overseas S.A.; *Int'l*, pg. 1017
BIA B.V./S.A.—See BIA Overseas S.A.; *Int'l*, pg. 1017
BIA CAMEROON—See BIA Overseas S.A.; *Int'l*, pg. 1017
BIA COTE D'IVOIRE—See BIA Overseas S.A.; *Int'l*, pg. 1017
BI ACQUISITION CORP.; *U.S. Private*, pg. 549
BIA DANILO S.R.L.—See THK CO., LTD.; *Int'l*, pg. 7711
BIAFO INDUSTRIES LIMITED; *Int'l*, pg. 1017
BIAGGIS RISTORANTE ITALIANO; *U.S. Private*, pg. 550
BIAGI BROS INC.; *U.S. Private*, pg. 550
BIA GUINEE S.A—See BIA Overseas S.A.; *Int'l*, pg. 1017
BIA-HAZLETON—See Barry Isett & Associates Inc.; *U.S. Private*, pg. 481
BIALETTI INDUSTRIE S.P.A.; *Int'l*, pg. 1017
BIAMEDITEK SP. Z O. O.—See Indutrade AB; *Int'l*, pg. 3677
BIAMP SYSTEMS, LLC—See AMETEK, Inc.; *U.S. Public*, pg. 118
BIANCAMANO S.P.A.; *Int'l*, pg. 1017
BIANCHI CAFE & CYCLES SVERIGE AB—See Grimaldi Industri AB; *Int'l*, pg. 3085
B IANCHI & CO. (1916) LTD.—See Albert Ballin KG; *Int'l*, pg. 294
BIANCHI HONDA; *U.S. Private*, pg. 550
BIANCHI INTERNATIONAL INC.—See BAE Systems plc; *Int'l*, pg. 796
BIANCHI LAND CO.; *U.S. Private*, pg. 550
BIANCHI PUBLIC RELATIONS INC.; *U.S. Private*, pg. 550
BIANCHI—See Sonepar S.A.; *Int'l*, pg. 7090
BIANCHI U.S.A., INC.; *U.S. Private*, pg. 550
BIANCHI VINEYARDS—See Modern Development Company; *U.S. Private*, pg. 2760
BIANCO—See FAYAT SAS; *Int'l*, pg. 2624
BIANOR HOLDING AD; *Int'l*, pg. 1017
BIANTE PTY LIMITED—See Hancock & Gore Ltd.; *Int'l*, pg. 3242
BIA N.V./S.A.—See BIA Overseas S.A.; *Int'l*, pg. 1017
BIAO-COTE D'IVOIRE; *Int'l*, pg. 1017
BIA OVERSEAS S.A.; *Int'l*, pg. 1017
BIA-PHILLIPSBURG—See Barry Isett & Associates Inc.; *U.S. Private*, pg. 481
BIA-PHOENIXVILLE—See Barry Isett & Associates Inc.; *U.S. Private*, pg. 481
BIA POINTE NOIRE—See BIA Overseas S.A.; *Int'l*, pg. 1017
BIARRITZ OCEAN SAS—See VINCI S.A.; *Int'l*, pg. 8213

COMPANY NAME INDEX

BIAS CORPORATION—See Deloitte LLP; *U.S. Private*, pg. 1198
BIAS CORPORATION—See Deloitte Touche Tohmatsu Limited; *Int'l*, pg. 2014
BIA TOGO—See BIA Overseas S.A.; *Int'l*, pg. 1017
B&I AUTO SUPPLIES INC.; *U.S. Private*, pg. 418
BIAWAR PRODUKCJA SP Z.O.O—See NIBE Industrier AB; *Int'l*, pg. 5260
BIAXIS OY, LTD.—See Sojitz Corporation; *Int'l*, pg. 7061
BIAXPLEN K LLC—See OAO SIBUR Holding; *Int'l*, pg. 5507
BIAXPLEN LLC—See OAO SIBUR Holding; *Int'l*, pg. 5507
BIAXPLEN M LLC—See OAO SIBUR Holding; *Int'l*, pg. 5507
BIAXPLEN NK LLC—See OAO SIBUR Holding; *Int'l*, pg. 5507
BIA ZAMBIA—See BIA Overseas S.A.; *Int'l*, pg. 1017
BIBANCA S.P.A.—See BPER BANCA S.p.A; *Int'l*, pg. 1132
BIBAO EDITORIAL PRODUCENTES, S.L.—See Vocento, S.A.; *Int'l*, pg. 8284
BIBBERO SYSTEMS INC.; *U.S. Private*, pg. 550
BIBBINSTRUMENTS AB; *Int'l*, pg. 1017
BIBBY AGRICULTURE LIMITED—See Carr's Group PLC; *Int'l*, pg. 1343
BIBBY AGRICULTURE LIMITED—See Wynnstay Group Plc; *Int'l*, pg. 8517
BIBBY DISTRIBUTION LIMITED—See Endless LLP; *Int'l*, pg. 2403
BIBBY FACTOR FRANCE S.A.—See Bibby Line Group Limited; *Int'l*, pg. 1017
BIBBY FACTORING SERVICES (MALAYSIA) SDN BHD—See Bibby Line Group Limited; *Int'l*, pg. 1017
BIBBY FACTORING SLOVAKIA A.S.—See Bibby Line Group Limited; *Int'l*, pg. 1018
BIBBY FINANCIAL SERVICES AB—See Bibby Line Group Limited; *Int'l*, pg. 1018
BIBBY FINANCIAL SERVICES (ASIA) LIMITED—See Bibby Line Group Limited; *Int'l*, pg. 1018
BIBBY FINANCIAL SERVICES A.S.—See Bibby Line Group Limited; *Int'l*, pg. 1018
BIBBY FINANCIAL SERVICES (CA), INC—See Bibby Line Group Limited; *Int'l*, pg. 1018
BIBBY FINANCIAL SERVICES (CANADA), INC—See Bibby Line Group Limited; *Int'l*, pg. 1018
BIBBY FINANCIAL SERVICES GMDI I—See Bibby Line Group Limited; *Int'l*, pg. 1018
BIBBY FINANCIAL SERVICES (HOLDINGS) INC—See Global Merchant Fund Corp.; *U.S. Private*, pg. 1716
BIBBY FINANCIAL SERVICES (INDIA) PVT LIMITED—See Bibby Line Group Limited; *Int'l*, pg. 1018
BIBBY FINANCIAL SERVICES (IRELAND) LIMITED—See Bibby Line Group Limited; *Int'l*, pg. 1018
BIBBY FINANCIAL SERVICES LIMITED—See Bibby Line Group Limited; *Int'l*, pg. 1017
BIBBY FINANCIAL SERVICES (SINGAPORE) PTE LIMITED—See Bibby Line Group Limited; *Int'l*, pg. 1018
BIBBY FINANCIAL SERVICES S.P. Z.O.O.—See Bibby Line Group Limited; *Int'l*, pg. 1018
BIBBY HOLDINGS LIMITED—See Bibby Line Group Limited; *Int'l*, pg. 1018
BIBBY LINE GROUP LIMITED; *Int'l*, pg. 1017
BIBBY LINE LIMITED—See Bibby Line Group Limited; *Int'l*, pg. 1018
BIBBY LINE LIMITED—See Bibby Line Group Limited; *Int'l*, pg. 1018
BIBBY MARINE LIMITED—See Bibby Line Group Limited; *Int'l*, pg. 1018
BIBBY MARITIME LIMITED—See Bibby Line Group Limited; *Int'l*, pg. 1018
BIBBY MARITIME LIMITED—See Bibby Line Group Limited; *Int'l*, pg. 1018
BIBBY OFFSHORE AS—See HAL Trust N.V.; *Int'l*, pg. 3226
BIBBY OFFSHORE LIMITED—See HAL Trust N.V.; *Int'l*, pg. 3226
BIBENDUM AB—See Altia Oyj; *Int'l*, pg. 392
BIBENDUM AS—See Altia Oyj; *Int'l*, pg. 392
BIBENDUM WINE LIMITED; *Int'l*, pg. 1018
BIBETTE (PTY) LTD.—See E Media Holdings Limited; *Int'l*, pg. 2246
BIBICA CORPORATION—See The Pan Group Joint Stock Company; *Int'l*, pg. 7672
BIBLE BROADCASTING NETWORK; *U.S. Private*, pg. 550
BIBLE STUDY FELLOWSHIP; *U.S. Private*, pg. 550
BIBLIOLABS, LLC—See LYRASIS Inc.; *U.S. Private*, pg. 2522
BIBLIU LTD.; *Int'l*, pg. 1018
BIBOJEE SERVICES PRIVATE LIMITED; *Int'l*, pg. 1018
BIBUN CORPORATION—See NICHIMO CO. LTD.; *Int'l*, pg. 5269
BIBUS ITALIA SRL—See Daikin Industries, Ltd.; *Int'l*, pg. 1932
BIC AMAZONIA SA—See Societe BIC S.A.; *Int'l*, pg. 7036
BICAPITAL CORPORATION; *Int'l*, pg. 1018
BIC ARGENTINA SA—See Societe BIC S.A.; *Int'l*, pg. 7036

BIC AUSTRALIA PTY. LTD.—See Societe BIC S.A.; *Int'l*, pg. 7036
BIC (AUSTRIA) VERTRIEBSGESELLSCHAFT MBH—See Societe BIC S.A.; *Int'l*, pg. 7036
BIC BELGIUM SPRL—See Societe BIC S.A.; *Int'l*, pg. 7036
BIC BENELUX S.A.—See Societe BIC S.A.; *Int'l*, pg. 7036
BIC BRED (SUISSE) SA—See Groupe BPCE; *Int'l*, pg. 3092
BIC CAMERA INC.; *Int'l*, pg. 1018
BIC CLICHY SAS—See Societe BIC S.A.; *Int'l*, pg. 7036
BIC CONSUMER PRODUCTS MANUFACTURING CO. INC.—See Societe BIC S.A.; *Int'l*, pg. 7036
BIC CORPORATION—See Societe BIC S.A.; *Int'l*, pg. 7036
BIC DE GUATEMALA—See Societe BIC S.A.; *Int'l*, pg. 7036
BIC DEUTSCHLAND GMBH & CO.—See Societe BIC S.A.; *Int'l*, pg. 7036
BICECORP SA; *Int'l*, pg. 1018
BI-CEMENT LLP—See Build Investments Group JSC; *Int'l*, pg. 1212
BICENT POWER LLC—See Beowulf Energy LLC; *U.S. Private*, pg. 529
BICENT POWER LLC—See NGP Energy Capital Management, LLC; *U.S. Private*, pg. 2923
BICESTER VETS4PETS LIMITED—See Pets at Home Group Plc; *Int'l*, pg. 5833
BIC GMBH—See Societe BIC S.A.; *Int'l*, pg. 7036
BIC GRAPHIC BRASIL LTDA.—See Societe BIC S.A.; *Int'l*, pg. 7036
BIC GRAPHIC EUROPE SA—See Societe BIC S.A.; *Int'l*, pg. 7036
BIC GRAPHIC FRANCE SASU—See Societe BIC S.A.; *Int'l*, pg. 7036
BICHAMP CUTTING TECHNOLOGY (HUNAN) CO., LTD; *Int'l*, pg. 1018
BICI-BAIL DE COTE D'IVOIRE—See BNP Paribas SA; *Int'l*, pg. 1080
BIC IBERIA SA—See Societe BIC S.A.; *Int'l*, pg. 7036
BIC (IRELAND) LTD.—See Societe BIC S.A.; *Int'l*, pg. 7036
BIC ITALIA SPA—See Societe BIC S.A.; *Int'l*, pg. 7036
BIC JAPAN KK—See Societe BIC S.A.; *Int'l*, pg. 7036
BICK CO.; *U.S. Private*, pg. 550
BICKEL'S SNACK FOODS, INC.—See Hanover Foods Corporation; *U.S. Public*, pg. 984
BICKERDIKE REDEVELOPMENT CORPORATION; *U.S. Private*, pg. 550
BICKFORD AT MISSION SPRINGS I, L.L.C.—See National Health Investors, Inc.; *U.S. Public*, pg. 1495
BICKFORD OF ALPHARETTA, LLC—See Bickford Senior Living Group, LLC; *U.S. Private*, pg. 550
BICKFORD OF CARMEL, LLC—See National Health Investors, Inc.; *U.S. Public*, pg. 1495
BICKFORD OF MIDDLETOWN, LLC—See National Health Investors, Inc.; *U.S. Public*, pg. 1495
BICKFORD OF OVERLAND PARK, L.L.C.—See National Health Investors, Inc.; *U.S. Public*, pg. 1495
BICKFORD SENIOR LIVING GROUP, LLC; *U.S. Private*, pg. 550
BICKFORD'S FAMILY RESTAURANTS; *U.S. Private*, pg. 550
BICK GROUP, INC.; *U.S. Private*, pg. 550
BICKLEYLAKE LIMITED—See Heidelberg Materials AG; *Int'l*, pg. 3309
BIC MAROC SARL—See Societe BIC S.A.; *Int'l*, pg. 7036
BIC NETHERLANDS BV—See Societe BIC S.A.; *Int'l*, pg. 7036
BIC NORDIC AB—See Societe BIC S.A.; *Int'l*, pg. 7036
BIC (NZ) LTD.—See Societe BIC S.A.; *Int'l*, pg. 7036
BICO AKRON INC.—See The Burger Iron Company; *U.S. Private*, pg. 4003
BICOASTAL MEDIA - ALBANY—See Bicoastal Media, LLC; *U.S. Private*, pg. 550
BICOASTAL MEDIA - CENTRALIA—See Bicoastal Media, LLC; *U.S. Private*, pg. 550
BICOASTAL MEDIA - CRESCENT CITY—See Bicoastal Media, LLC; *U.S. Private*, pg. 550
BICOASTAL MEDIA - EUREKA—See Bicoastal Media, LLC; *U.S. Private*, pg. 551
BICOASTAL MEDIA, LLC; *U.S. Private*, pg. 550
BICOASTAL MEDIA - MEDFORD—See Bicoastal Media, LLC; *U.S. Private*, pg. 551
BICOASTAL MEDIA - UKIAH-LAKEPORT—See Bicoastal Media, LLC; *U.S. Private*, pg. 551
BICO DRILLING TOOLS INC.—See Schoeller-Bleckmann Oilfield Equipment AG; *Int'l*, pg. 6637
BICO FASTER DRILLING TOOLS INC.—See Schoeller-Bleckmann Oilfield Equipment AG; *Int'l*, pg. 6637
BICO GROUP AB; *Int'l*, pg. 1018
BICO MICHIGAN INC.—See The Burger Iron Company; *U.S. Private*, pg. 4003
BI-CON SERVICES, INC.; *U.S. Private*, pg. 549
BI CONSULTING GROUP; *U.S. Private*, pg. 549
B & I CONTRACTORS, INC.; *U.S. Private*, pg. 417
BICO SOUTH INC.—See The Burger Iron Company; *U.S. Private*, pg. 4003

BIC PAZARLAMA LTD.—See Societe BIC S.A.; *Int'l*, pg. 7036
BIC POLSKA SP ZOO—See Societe BIC S.A.; *Int'l*, pg. 7036
BIC PORTUGAL SA—See Societe BIC S.A.; *Int'l*, pg. 7036
BIC PRODUCT (ASIA) PTE. LTD.—See Societe BIC S.A.; *Int'l*, pg. 7036
BIC PRODUCT (KOREA) LTD.—See Societe BIC S.A.; *Int'l*, pg. 7036
BIC PRODUCT (SINGAPORE) PTE. LTD.—See Societe BIC S.A.; *Int'l*, pg. 7036
BIC PRODUCT (THAILAND) LTD.—See Societe BIC S.A.; *Int'l*, pg. 7036
BIC (ROMANIA) MARKETING & DISTRIBUTION SRL—See Societe BIC S.A.; *Int'l*, pg. 7036
BICRON PRODUCTS PPL—See Compagnie de Saint-Gobain SA; *Int'l*, pg. 1730
BIC (SHANGHAI) STATIONERY MANUFACTURING CO. LTD.—See Societe BIC S.A.; *Int'l*, pg. 7036
BICS LLC—See Tomra Systems ASA; *Int'l*, pg. 7803
BIC (SOUTH AFRICA) PTY. LTD.—See Societe BIC S.A.; *Int'l*, pg. 7036
BIC SPORT NORTH AMERICA, INC.—See Societe BIC S.A.; *Int'l*, pg. 7036
BIC STATIONERY (SHANGHAI) CO. LTD.—See Societe BIC S.A.; *Int'l*, pg. 7036
BIC TECHNOLOGIES SA—See Societe BIC S.A.; *Int'l*, pg. 7036
BIC UK LTD.—See Societe BIC S.A.; *Int'l*, pg. 7036
BIC USA INC.—See Societe BIC S.A.; *Int'l*, pg. 7037
BIC VERWALTUNGS GMBH—See Societe BIC S.A.; *Int'l*, pg. 7037
BIC VIOLEX SA—See Societe BIC S.A.; *Int'l*, pg. 7037
BICYCLE CASINO; *U.S. Private*, pg. 551
THE BICYCLE MUSIC COMPANY—See Massachusetts Mutual Life Insurance Company; *U.S. Private*, pg. 2605
BICYCLE THERAPEUTICS PLC; *Int'l*, pg. 1019
BID2WIN SOFTWARE, INC.—See Trimble, Inc.; *U.S. Public*, pg. 2190
BID4ASSETS, INC.; *U.S. Private*, pg. 551
BID4FLOORS.COM; *U.S. Private*, pg. 551
BIDACHEM S.P.A.—See C.H. Boehringer Sohn AG & Co. KG; *Int'l*, pg. 1242
BIDAIR CARGO—See The Bidvest Group Limited; *Int'l*, pg. 7621
BIDAIR SERVICES (PTY) LIMITED—See The Bidvest Group Limited; *Int'l*, pg. 7621
BIDCLERK, INC.—See Roper Technologies, Inc.; *U.S. Public*, pg. 1810
BIDCO OIL REFINERIES LIMITED; *Int'l*, pg. 1019
BIDCORP LIMITED—See The Bidvest Group Limited; *Int'l*, pg. 7621
BIDDINGFORGOOD INC.; *U.S. Private*, pg. 551
BIDDLE INSURANCE SERVICES, INC.—See GTCR LLC; *U.S. Private*, pg. 1802
BIDDLE SAWYER CORPORATION; *U.S. Private*, pg. 551
BIDELEK SAREAK, A.I.E.—See Iberdrola, S.A.; *Int'l*, pg. 3571
BIDELL EQUIPMENT LP—See Total Energy Services Inc.; *Int'l*, pg. 7834
BIDELL GAS COMPRESSION INC.—See Total Energy Services Inc.; *Int'l*, pg. 7834
BIDENERGY INC.—See Optima Technology Group Limited; *Int'l*, pg. 5604
BIDENERGY LIMITED—See Optima Technology Group Limited; *Int'l*, pg. 5604
BIDFOOD B.V.—See Koninklijke Ahold Delhaize N.V.; *Int'l*, pg. 4260
BID FOOD INGREDIENTS (PTY) LIMITED—See The Bidvest Group Limited; *Int'l*, pg. 7621
BIDFOOD TECHNOLOGIES (PTY) LIMITED—See The Bidvest Group Limited; *Int'l*, pg. 7621
BIDFREIGHT INTERMODAL (PTY) LIMITED—See The Bidvest Group Limited; *Int'l*, pg. 7622
BIDFREIGHT MANAGEMENT SERVICES—See The Bidvest Group Limited; *Int'l*, pg. 7622
BIDFREIGHT PORT OPERATIONS (PTY) LIMITED—See The Bidvest Group Limited; *Int'l*, pg. 7622
BIDFREIGHT TERMINALS (PTY) LIMITED—See The Bidvest Group Limited; *Int'l*, pg. 7622
BID GROUP LTD.; *Int'l*, pg. 1019
BID INFORMATION EXCHANGE (PTY) LIMITED—See The Bidvest Group Limited; *Int'l*, pg. 7621
BI DOLYNA DEVELOPMENT LLC—See Dragon Ukrainian Properties & Development Plc; *Int'l*, pg. 2199
BIDPAL, INC.; *U.S. Private*, pg. 551
BIDPROCURE (PTY) LIMITED—See The Bidvest Group Limited; *Int'l*, pg. 7622
BID SERVICES DIVISION (UK) LIMITED—See The Bidvest Group Limited; *Int'l*, pg. 7621
BIDSERV INDUSTRIAL PRODUCTS (PTY) LIMITED—See The Bidvest Group Limited; *Int'l*, pg. 7621
BIDSPOTTER, INC.—See Mobeus Equity Partners LLP; *Int'l*, pg. 5008
BIDSTACK GROUP PLC; *Int'l*, pg. 1019
BIDSYNC INC.—See KKR & Co. Inc.; *U.S. Public*, pg. 1267
BIDTRAVEL (PTY) LIMITED—See The Bidvest Group Limited; *Int'l*, pg. 7622

BIDV BAC BO INSURANCE COMPANY—See BIDV Insurance Corporation; *Int'l*, pg. 1019
BIDV BAC TAY NGUYEN INSURANCE COMPANY—See BIDV Insurance Corporation; *Int'l*, pg. 1019
BIDV BAC TRUNG BO INSURANCE COMPANY—See BIDV Insurance Corporation; *Int'l*, pg. 1019
BIDV BINH DINH INSURANCE COMPANY—See BIDV Insurance Corporation; *Int'l*, pg. 1019
BIDV BINH DUONG INSURANCE COMPANY—See BIDV Insurance Corporation; *Int'l*, pg. 1019
BIDV DA NANG INSURANCE COMPANY—See BIDV Insurance Corporation; *Int'l*, pg. 1019
BIDV DONG BAC INSURANCE COMPANY—See BIDV Insurance Corporation; *Int'l*, pg. 1019
BIDVEST ADVISORY SERVICES PROPRIETARY LIMITED—See The Bidvest Group Limited; *Int'l*, pg. 7622
BIDVEST AFCOM PROPRIETARY LIMITED—See The Bidvest Group Limited; *Int'l*, pg. 7622
BIDVEST AUSTRALIA LIMITED—See The Bidvest Group Limited; *Int'l*, pg. 7622
BIDVEST BANK HOLDINGS LIMITED—See The Bidvest Group Limited; *Int'l*, pg. 7622
BIDVEST BANK LIMITED—See The Bidvest Group Limited; *Int'l*, pg. 7622
BIDVEST BRANDED PRODUCTS HOLDINGS PROPRIETARY LIMITED—See The Bidvest Group Limited; *Int'l*, pg. 7623
BIDVEST BUFFALO TAPES PROPRIETARY LIMITED—See The Bidvest Group Limited; *Int'l*, pg. 7623
BIDVEST CAPITAL (PTY) LIMITED—See The Bidvest Group Limited; *Int'l*, pg. 7623
BIDVEST CATERING SERVICES PROPRIETARY LIMITED—See The Bidvest Group Limited; *Int'l*, pg. 7623
BIDVEST COMMERCIAL PRODUCTS HOLDINGS PROPRIETARY LIMITED—See The Bidvest Group Limited; *Int'l*, pg. 7623
BIDVEST CZECH REPUBLIC S.R.O.—See The Bidvest Group Limited; *Int'l*, pg. 7622
BIDVEST DATA—See The Bidvest Group Limited; *Int'l*, pg. 7623
BIDVEST DATA—See The Bidvest Group Limited; *Int'l*, pg. 7623
BIDVEST FACILITIES MANAGEMENT PROPRIETARY LIMITED—See The Bidvest Group Limited; *Int'l*, pg. 7623
BIDVEST FOODSERVICE GEELONG—See The Bidvest Group Limited; *Int'l*, pg. 7622
BIDVEST FOODSERVICE INTERNATIONAL LIMITED—See The Bidvest Group Limited; *Int'l*, pg. 7623
THE BIDVEST GROUP LIMITED; *Int'l*, pg. 7621
BIDVEST INSURANCE LIMITED—See The Bidvest Group Limited; *Int'l*, pg. 7623
BIDVEST INTERNATIONAL LIMITED—See The Bidvest Group Limited; *Int'l*, pg. 7623
BIDVEST MAGNUM GROUP PTY LTD—See The Bidvest Group Limited; *Int'l*, pg. 7623
BIDVEST MAGNUM GROUP PTY LTD—See The Bidvest Group Limited; *Int'l*, pg. 7623
BIDVEST MATERIALS HANDLING PROPRIETARY LIMITED—See The Bidvest Group Limited; *Int'l*, pg. 7623
BIDVEST MCCARTHY BRANDS PROPRIETARY LIMITED—See The Bidvest Group Limited; *Int'l*, pg. 7623
BIDVEST MERCHANT SERVICES PROPRIETARY LIMITED—See The Bidvest Group Limited; *Int'l*, pg. 7623
BIDVEST NAMIBIA COMMERCIAL & INDUSTRIAL SERVICES & PRODUCTS PROPRIETARY LIMITED—See The Bidvest Group Limited; *Int'l*, pg. 7623
BIDVEST NAMIBIA LIMITED—See The Bidvest Group Limited; *Int'l*, pg. 7623
BIDVEST NEW ZEALAND LIMITED—See The Bidvest Group Limited; *Int'l*, pg. 7623
BIDVEST NOONAN (ROI) LIMITED—See The Bidvest Group Limited; *Int'l*, pg. 7623
BIDVEST NOONAN (UK) LIMITED—See The Bidvest Group Limited; *Int'l*, pg. 7623
BIDVEST NOONAN (UK) LTD.—See The Bidvest Group Limited; *Int'l*, pg. 7623
BIDVEST (N.S.W) LIMITED—See The Bidvest Group Limited; *Int'l*, pg. 7622
BIDVEST PANALPINA LOGISTICS—See DSV A/S; *Int'l*, pg. 2214
BIDVEST PRESTIGE GROUP—See The Bidvest Group Limited; *Int'l*, pg. 7623
BIDVEST PROTEA COIN PROPRIETARY LIMITED—See The Bidvest Group Limited; *Int'l*, pg. 7623
BIDVEST SERVICES—See The Bidvest Group Limited; *Int'l*, pg. 7623
BIDVEST STEINER NAMIBIA PTY. LTD.—See The Bidvest Group Limited; *Int'l*, pg. 7623
BIDVEST TANK TERMINALS—See The Bidvest Group Limited; *Int'l*, pg. 7623

BIDVEST (UK) LIMITED—See The Bidvest Group Limited; *Int'l*, pg. 7622
BIDVEST (VICTORIA) (PTY) LIMITED—See The Bidvest Group Limited; *Int'l*, pg. 7622
BIDVEST (WA) (PTY) LIMITED—See The Bidvest Group Limited; *Int'l*, pg. 7622
BIDVEST WITS UNIVERSITY FOOTBALL CLUB (PTY) LIMITED—See The Bidvest Group Limited; *Int'l*, pg. 7623
BIDV HAI DUONG INSURANCE COMPANY—See BIDV Insurance Corporation; *Int'l*, pg. 1019
BIDV HAI PHONG INSURANCE COMPANY—See BIDV Insurance Corporation; *Int'l*, pg. 1019
BIDV HA NOI INSURANCE COMPANY—See BIDV Insurance Corporation; *Int'l*, pg. 1019
BIDV HO CHI MINH INSURANCE COMPANY—See BIDV Insurance Corporation; *Int'l*, pg. 1019
BIDV INSURANCE CORPORATION; *Int'l*, pg. 1019
BIDV METLIFE LIFE INSURANCE LIMITED LIABILITY COMPANY—See MetLife, Inc.; *U.S. Public*, pg. 1429
BIDV MIEN DONG BIDV INSURANCE COMPANY—See BIDV Insurance Corporation; *Int'l*, pg. 1019
BIDV MIEN TAY INSURANCE COMPANY—See BIDV Insurance Corporation; *Int'l*, pg. 1019
BIDV QUANG NINH INSURANCE COMPANY—See BIDV Insurance Corporation; *Int'l*, pg. 1019
BIDV SAI GON INSURANCE COMPANY—See BIDV Insurance Corporation; *Int'l*, pg. 1019
BIDV SECURITIES JOINT STOCK COMPANY; *Int'l*, pg. 1019
BIDV TAY BAC INSURANCE COMPANY—See BIDV Insurance Corporation; *Int'l*, pg. 1019
BIDV TAY NGUYEN INSURANCE COMPANY—See BIDV Insurance Corporation; *Int'l*, pg. 1019
BIDV THAI NGUYEN INSURANCE COMPANY—See BIDV Insurance Corporation; *Int'l*, pg. 1019
BIDV THANG LONG INSURANCE COMPANY—See BIDV Insurance Corporation; *Int'l*, pg. 1019
BIDV VUNG TAU INSURANCE COMPANY—See BIDV Insurance Corporation; *Int'l*, pg. 1019
BIDWELL DIALYSIS, LLC—See DaVita Inc.; *U.S. Public*, pg. 636
BIDWELL HENDERSON COSTS CONSULTANTS LIMITED—See Frenkel Topping Group plc; *Int'l*, pg. 2773
BIDWELL INDUSTRIAL GROUP, INC.; *U.S. Private*, pg. 551
BIEDERMANN MANUFACTURING INDUSTRIES; *U.S. Private*, pg. 551
BIEDERMANN PUBLICIDAD S.A.—See The Interpublic Group of Companies, Inc.; *U.S. Public*, pg. 2099
BIEDERMANN & SONS, INC.; *U.S. Private*, pg. 551
BIE EXECUTIVE LIMITED—See Barclays PLC; *Int'l*, pg. 859
BIEFFE CONTAINER LOGISTIC S.R.L.—See Deutsche Post AG; *Int'l*, pg. 2071
BIEFFE MEDITAL NEDERLAND N.V.—See Baxter International Inc.; *U.S. Public*, pg. 281
BIEFFE MEDITAL S.P.A.—See Baxter International Inc.; *U.S. Public*, pg. 280
BIEGELAAR BV; *Int'l*, pg. 1020
BIEGLER & ASSOCIATES, P.C.—See Kositzka & Wicks Co.; *U.S. Private*, pg. 2344
BIEHL & CO. L.P.—See Biehl International Corporation; *U.S. Private*, pg. 551
BIEHL INTERNATIONAL CORPORATION; *U.S. Private*, pg. 551
BIELY & SHOAF CO.; *U.S. Private*, pg. 551
BIEM.L .FDLKK GARMENT CO., LTD.; *Int'l*, pg. 1020
BIEN CO., LTD.—See Onward Holdings Co., Ltd.; *Int'l*, pg. 5592
BIENER AUTO GROUP, INC.; *U.S. Private*, pg. 551
BIEN HOA PACKAGING COMPANY; *Int'l*, pg. 1020
BIEN HOA SUGAR JSC; *Int'l*, pg. 1020
BIEN SPAREBANK A.S.A.; *Int'l*, pg. 1020
BIENVENIDO A SCHOTT MUSIC S.L.—See Schott Music GmbH & Co. KG; *Int'l*, pg. 6639
BIENVENIDOS; *U.S. Private*, pg. 551
BIENVIVIR SENIOR HEALTH SERVICES; *U.S. Private*, pg. 551
BIEN-ZENKER GMBH—See Equistone Partners Europe Limited; *Int'l*, pg. 2486
BIERHAKE GMBH & CO. KG; *Int'l*, pg. 1020
BIERI ELEKTROTECHNIK AG—See Burkhalter Holding AG; *Int'l*, pg. 1224
BIERLEIN COMPANIES INCORPORATED; *U.S. Private*, pg. 551
BIERSCHBACH EQUIPMENT & SUPPLY CO.; *U.S. Private*, pg. 551
BIESSE AMERICA, INC.—See Biesse S.p.A.; *Int'l*, pg. 1020
BIESSE ASIA PTE LTD.—See Biesse S.p.A.; *Int'l*, pg. 1020
BIESSE CANADA INC.—See Biesse S.p.A.; *Int'l*, pg. 1020
BIESSE GROUP AUSTRALIA PTY LTD—See Biesse S.p.A.; *Int'l*, pg. 1020
BIESSE GROUP DEUTSCHLAND GMBH—See Biesse S.p.A.; *Int'l*, pg. 1020

BIESSE GROUP FRANCE SARL—See Biesse S.p.A.; *Int'l*, pg. 1020
BIESSE GROUP UK LTD.—See Biesse S.p.A.; *Int'l*, pg. 1020
BIESSE MANUFACTURING CO. PVT. LTD.—See Biesse S.p.A.; *Int'l*, pg. 1020
BIESSERVICE SCANDINAVIA AB—See Biesse S.p.A.; *Int'l*, pg. 1020
BIESSE S.P.A.; *Int'l*, pg. 1020
BIFFA GROUP LIMITED; *Int'l*, pg. 1020
BIFFA LEICESTER LIMITED—See Biffa Group Limited; *Int'l*, pg. 1020
BIFFA WASTE SERVICES LIMITED—See Biffa Group Limited; *Int'l*, pg. 1020
BIFFI ITALIA S.R.L.—See Emerson Electric Co.; *U.S. Public*, pg. 742
BIFFIN PTY. LIMITED—See ARN Media Limited; *Int'l*, pg. 576
BIFIDO CO., LTD.; *Int'l*, pg. 1020
BIFIRE S.P.A.; *Int'l*, pg. 1020
BIFLEX INTIMATE GROUP, LLC; *U.S. Private*, pg. 552
BIFOLD FLUIDPOWER LIMITED—See Rotork Plc; *Int'l*, pg. 6405
BIG 2 TOYOTA; *U.S. Private*, pg. 552
BIG 3 PRECISION MOLD SERVICES, LLC—See The Eastern Company; *U.S. Public*, pg. 2069
BIG 3 PRECISION PRODUCTS, INC.—See The Eastern Company; *U.S. Public*, pg. 2069
BIG 5 CORPORATION DISTRIBUTION CENTER—See Big 5 Sporting Goods Corporation; *U.S. Public*, pg. 330
BIG 5 SPORTING GOODS CORPORATION; *U.S. Public*, pg. 330
BIG 8 SPLIT, INC.; *Int'l*, pg. 1020
BIG-A COMPANY, INC.—See AEON Co., Ltd.; *Int'l*, pg. 177
B.I.G.A. D.O.O.—See Securitas AB; *Int'l*, pg. 6675
BIGAIR GROUP PTY LTD—See Superloop Limited; *Int'l*, pg. 7338
BIGAL CO., LTD.—See MIT Holdings Co., Ltd.; *Int'l*, pg. 4923
BIG' ANT (M) SDN. BHD.—See K-One Technology Berhad; *Int'l*, pg. 4042
BIG APPLE CAR INC.; *U.S. Private*, pg. 552
BI.GARAGE, INC.—See Dentsu Group Inc.; *Int'l*, pg. 2034
BIG ARROW CONSULTING GROUP, LLC; *U.S. Private*, pg. 552
BIG BANC SPLIT CORP.; *Int'l*, pg. 1021
BIG BANG, D.O.O.—See Merkur, d.d.; *Int'l*, pg. 4837
BIG BANK PRODUCTIONS, INC.; *U.S. Private*, pg. 552
BIG BARN HARLEY-DAVIDSON, INC.; *U.S. Private*, pg. 552
BIG BAZAAR—See Future Corporate Resources Limited; *Int'l*, pg. 2853
BIG BEAM EMERGENCY SYSTEMS, INC.; *U.S. Private*, pg. 552
BIG BEAR A/C & HEATING, LLC—See Coltala Holdings, LLC; *U.S. Private*, pg. 976
BIGBEAR.AI HOLDINGS LLC—See AE Industrial Partners, LP; *U.S. Private*, pg. 112
BIG BEAR GROUP LIMITED—See Raisio PLC; *Int'l*, pg. 6190
BIG BEAR MOUNTAIN RESORT—See KSL Capital Partners, LLC; *U.S. Private*, pg. 2354
BIG BEAR STORES INC.; *U.S. Private*, pg. 552
BIGBEE STEEL & TANK COMPANY; *U.S. Private*, pg. 555
BIG BELL GOLD OPERATIONS PTY LTD—See Harmony Gold Mining Company Limited; *Int'l*, pg. 3278
BIG BEND ELECTRIC COOPERATIVE, INC.; *U.S. Private*, pg. 552
BIG BEND HOME CARE SERVICES, LLC—See Community Health Systems, Inc.; *U.S. Public*, pg. 551
BIG BEND TELEPHONE COMPANY, INC.; *U.S. Private*, pg. 552
BIGBEN INTERACTIVE SA; *Int'l*, pg. 1022
BIG BEN REALTY, INC.; *U.S. Private*, pg. 552
BIGBLOC CONSTRUCTION LIMITED; *Int'l*, pg. 1022
BIG BLOCKCHAIN INTELLIGENCE GROUP INC.; *Int'l*, pg. 1021
BIGBLU BROADBAND GROUP PLC; *Int'l*, pg. 1022
BIG B LUMBERTERIA; *U.S. Private*, pg. 552
BIG BOY JAPAN, INC.—See Zensho Holdings Co., Ltd.; *Int'l*, pg. 8634
BIG BOY RESTAURANTS INTERNATIONAL, LLC; *U.S. Private*, pg. 552
BIG BRAND TIRE & SERVICE; *U.S. Private*, pg. 552
BIG BREAK PRODUCTIONS, INC.—See Bertelsmann SE & Co. KGaA; *Int'l*, pg. 991
BIG BROTHERS BIG SISTERS OF AMERICA; *U.S. Private*, pg. 552
BIG BUCK BREWERY & STEAKHOUSE, INC.; *U.S. Private*, pg. 552
BIG BUDDHA, INC.—See Steven Madden, Ltd.; *U.S. Public*, pg. 1947
BIGBY COMPANIES; *U.S. Private*, pg. 555
BIG CAMERA CORPORATION PCL; *Int'l*, pg. 1021
BIG CAT ADVERTISING; *U.S. Private*, pg. 552
BIG CAT RESCUE CORP.; *U.S. Private*, pg. 552
BIG C CORPORATION; *U.S. Private*, pg. 552

COMPANY NAME INDEX

BIG CEDAR LODGE; *U.S. Private*, pg. 552
BIG C FAIRY LIMITED—See Berli Jucker Public Co. Ltd.; *Int'l*, pg. 985
BIG CHIEF DISTRIBUTING CO. INC.; *U.S. Private*, pg. 552
BIG CHIEF INC.—See Gryphon Investors, LLC; *U.S. Private*, pg. 1799
BIG CHILL DISTRIBUTION LIMITED—See Freightways Group Limited; *Int'l*, pg. 2771
BIG CITY ACCESS, INC.—See Brand Industrial Services, Inc.; *U.S. Private*, pg. 636
BIG CITY INSULATION, INC.—See Installed Building Products, Inc.; *U.S. Public*, pg. 1132
BIG CITY INSULATION OF IDAHO, INC.—See Installed Building Products, Inc.; *U.S. Public*, pg. 1132
BIG C LUMBER CO. INC.; *U.S. Private*, pg. 552
BIGCOMMERCE HOLDINGS, INC.; *U.S. Public*, pg. 331
BIGCOMMERCE, INC.; *U.S. Private*, pg. 555
BIG COMMUNICATIONS LTD.—See The Mission Group Public Limited Company; *Int'l*, pg. 7667
BIG COUNTRY ELECTRIC COOP; *U.S. Private*, pg. 552
BIG COUNTRY ENERGY SERVICES LLC—See MasTec, Inc.; *U.S. Public*, pg. 1393
BIG CREEK CONSTRUCTION, LTD.; *U.S. Private*, pg. 553
BIG CREEK LUMBER CO. INC.; *U.S. Private*, pg. 553
BIG C SUPERCENTER PUBLIC COMPANY LIMITED—See Berli Jucker Public Co. Ltd.; *Int'l*, pg. 985
BIG DATA HEALTHCARE LLC—See Fifth Third Bancorp; *U.S. Public*, pg. 833
BIG DATA LDN—See RELX plc; *Int'l*, pg. 6266
BIG-D CONSTRUCTION CORPORATION; *U.S. Private*, pg. 555
BIG DEE AUTO SALES INC.; *U.S. Private*, pg. 553
BIG E DRILLING CO.—See Eastham Enterprises Inc.; *U.S. Private*, pg. 1321
BIG E ENTERPRISES INC.; *U.S. Private*, pg. 553
BIGELOW HOMES, LLC.; *U.S. Private*, pg. 555
BIGELOW LABORATORY FOR OCEAN SCIENCES; *U.S. Private*, pg. 555
BIGEON CORP.; *Int'l*, pg. 1022
BIG E TRANSPORTATION LLC—See Estes Express Lines, Inc.; *U.S. Private*, pg. 1429
BIGEYES AUTO PARTS CO., LTD.—3ee WCDG OO., LTD.; *Int'l*, pg. 8367
BIG FISH GAMES, INC.—See Aristocrat Leisure Limited; *Int'l*, pg. 566
BIGFIX, INC.—See HCL Technologies Ltd.; *Int'l*, pg. 3298
BIG FLOORCOVERINGS NV—See Beaulieu International Group NV; *Int'l*, pg. 934
BIGFOOT BIOMEDICAL, INC.—See Abbott Laboratories; *U.S. Public*, pg. 19
BIGFORK CUSTOM WOODWORKS—See Martel Construction, Inc.; *U.S. Private*, pg. 2593
BIG FREIGHT SYSTEMS INC.—See Daseke, Inc.; *U.S. Private*, pg. 1161
BIG FRESH MEDIA, INC.; *U.S. Private*, pg. 553
BIG FUEL COMMUNICATIONS LLC—See Publicis Groupe S.A.; *Int'l*, pg. 6097
BIG GAIN INC.; *U.S. Private*, pg. 553
BIGGE CRANE AND RIGGING CO.—See Bigge Crane & Rigging Company; *U.S. Private*, pg. 555
BIGGE CRANE & RIGGING COMPANY; *U.S. Private*, pg. 555
BIGGE DEVELOPMENT CORPORATION—See Bigge Crane & Rigging Company; *U.S. Private*, pg. 555
BIGGE EQUIPMENT CO.—See Bigge Crane & Rigging Company; *U.S. Private*, pg. 555
BIGGE POWER CONSTRUCTORS—See Bigge Crane & Rigging Company; *U.S. Private*, pg. 555
BIGGER MITSUBISHI; *U.S. Private*, pg. 555
BIG GEYSER INC.; *U.S. Private*, pg. 553
BIG GOLD INC.; *Int'l*, pg. 1021
BIG GREEN SURGICAL COMPANY PTY LIMITED—See Diploma PLC; *Int'l*, pg. 2128
BIGG'S HYPER SHOPPES, INC.—See United Natural Foods, Inc.; *U.S. Public*, pg. 2231
BIGGS PONTIAC; *U.S. Private*, pg. 555
BIGHAM BROTHERS, INC.—See Andrew W. Byrd & Co., LLC; *U.S. Private*, pg. 280
BIGHAM CABLE CONSTRUCTION INC.; *U.S. Private*, pg. 555
BIGHAM CABLE CONSTRUCTION, INC.—See Dycom Industries, Inc.; *U.S. Public*, pg. 698
BIGHAND LTD.—See Levine Leichtman Capital Partners, LLC; *U.S. Private*, pg. 2435
BIG H AUTO AUCTION SERVICES, INC.—See Cox Enterprises, Inc.; *U.S. Private*, pg. 1076
BIG HEART PET BRANDS - BLOOMSBURG PLANT—See The J.M. Smucker Company; *U.S. Public*, pg. 2107
BIG HEART PET BRANDS—See The J.M. Smucker Company; *U.S. Public*, pg. 2106
BIG HONKIN' IDEAS (B.H.I.); *U.S. Private*, pg. 553
BIG HORN COOPERATIVE MARKETING ASSOCIATION; *U.S. Private*, pg. 553
BIG I ADVANTAGE, INC.—See Independent Insurance Agents & Brokers of America, Inc.; *U.S. Private*, pg. 2059

BIG IDEA, INC.; *U.S. Private*, pg. 553
BIG IDEA TECHNOLOGY, LLC; *U.S. Private*, pg. 553
BIG IMAGINATION GROUP; *U.S. Private*, pg. 553
BIG-IMMOBILIEN GESELLSCHAFT MIT BESCHRANKTER HAFTUNG—See DZ BANK AG Deutsche Zentral-Genossenschaftsbank; *Int'l*, pg. 2243
B.I.G. INDUSTRIAL GAS SDN. BHD.—See B.I.G. Industries Berhad; *Int'l*, pg. 790
B.I.G. INDUSTRIES BERHAD; *Int'l*, pg. 789
BIG INK PR & MARKETING; *U.S. Private*, pg. 553
BIG INNOVATION COMPANY LTD.—See Hon Hai Precision Industry Co., Ltd.; *Int'l*, pg. 3456
BIG INSURANCE LIMITED—See Brown & Brown, Inc.; *U.S. Public*, pg. 397
BIG ISLAND TOYOTA INC—See David S. De Luz Sr Enterprises; *U.S. Private*, pg. 1171
BIGI S.P.A.—See Cantine Riunite & CIV S.C.Agr.; *Int'l*, pg. 1299
BIG J ENTERPRISES LLC; *U.S. Private*, pg. 553
BIG LAKE KIDNEY CENTER LLC—See Nautic Partners, LLC; *U.S. Private*, pg. 2869
BIG LAKE LUMBER, INC.; *U.S. Private*, pg. 553
BIG LAKE SERVICES LLC—See Rock Hill Capital Group, LLC; *U.S. Private*, pg. 3464
BIG LANGUAGE SOLUTIONS LLC—See MSouth Equity Partners, LLC; *U.S. Private*, pg. 2808
BIGLARI HOLDINGS INC.; *U.S. Public*, pg. 331
BIG L CORPORATION; *U.S. Private*, pg. 553
BIG LEAGUE FOODS, INC.—See Verus International, Inc.; *U.S. Public*, pg. 2290
BIGLER, LP; *U.S. Private*, pg. 555
BIGLIFT SHIPPING B.V.—See Spliethoff's Bevrachtingskantoor B.V.; *Int'l*, pg. 7141
BIGLIFT SHIPPING FZE—See Spliethoff's Bevrachtingskantoor B.V.; *Int'l*, pg. 7141
BIGLIFT SHIPPING INC—See Spliethoff's Bevrachtingskantoor B.V.; *Int'l*, pg. 7141
BIG LOTS, INC.; *U.S. Public*, pg. 330
BIG LOTS STORES, INC.—See Big Lots, Inc.; *U.S. Public*, pg. 330
BIGL TECHNOLOGIES (CHONGQING) CO., LTD.—See Broadway Industrial Group Limited; *Int'l*, pg. 1172
BIGL TECHNOLOGIES (SHENZHEN) CO., LTD.—See Broadway Industrial Group Limited; *Int'l*, pg. 1172
BIGL TECHNOLOGIES (THAILAND) CO., LTD.—See Broadway Industrial Group Limited; *Int'l*, pg. 1172
BIGL TECHNOLOGIES (WUXI) CO., LTD.—See Broadway Industrial Group Limited; *Int'l*, pg. 1172
BIG MACHINE DESIGN LLC—See Roger TV; *U.S. Private*, pg. 3471
BIG MAGAZINES LIMITED PARTNERSHIP—See GVIC Communications Corp.; *Int'l*, pg. 3189
BIG M. AGENCY—See Grinnell Mutual Reinsurance Company Inc.; *U.S. Private*, pg. 1790
B.I.G. MARKETING SDN. BHD.—See B.I.G. Industries Berhad; *Int'l*, pg. 790
BIG M FORD LINCOLN LTD.; *Int'l*, pg. 1021
BIG M, INC.; *U.S. Private*, pg. 553
BIG M ON DIXIE, LLC.; *U.S. Private*, pg. 553
BIG NERD RANCH, LLC—See Amdocs Limited; *Int'l*, pg. 420
BIG NIGHT ENTERTAINMENT GROUP; *U.S. Private*, pg. 553
BIG O TIRES, INC.—See Sumitomo Corporation; *Int'l*, pg. 7274
THE BIG PARTNERSHIP GROUP LIMITED; *Int'l*, pg. 7627
BIG PASS S.A.—See Edenred S.A.; *Int'l*, pg. 2307
BIG PHARMACY HEALTHCARE SDN. BHD; *Int'l*, pg. 1021
BIG PHARMA SPLIT CORP.; *Int'l*, pg. 1021
BIG PLANET, INC.—See Nu Skin Enterprises, Inc.; *U.S. Public*, pg. 1551
BIGPOINT GMBH—See Youzu Interactive Co., Ltd.; *Int'l*, pg. 8605
B.I.G. PRAGUE—See WPP plc; *Int'l*, pg. 8477
BIG QUILL RESOURCES INC.—See Compass Minerals International, Inc.; *U.S. Private*, pg. 560
BIG RED DOG, INC.—See Wantman Group, Inc.; *U.S. Private*, pg. 4436
BIG RED EXPRESS TRUCKING LLC; *U.S. Private*, pg. 553
BIG RED FASTENERS, INC.; *U.S. Private*, pg. 553
BIG RED INC.; *U.S. Private*, pg. 553
BIG RED KENO LTD.; *U.S. Private*, pg. 553
BIG RED LTD.—See Court Square Capital Partners, L.P.; *U.S. Private*, pg. 1068
BIG RED MINING CORPORATION; *Int'l*, pg. 1021
BIG RED ROOSTER, INC.—See Jones Lang LaSalle Incorporated; *U.S. Public*, pg. 1201
BIG RED/SEVEN UP BOTTLING GROUP—See JAB Holding Company S.a.r.l.; *Int'l*, pg. 3861
BIG RED/SEVEN UP BOTTLING GROUP—See JAB Holding Company S.a.r.l.; *Int'l*, pg. 3861
BIG RED SPORTS IMPORTS, INC.; *U.S. Private*, pg. 554
BIGRENTZ, INC.; *U.S. Private*, pg. 555
BIG RIDGE GOLD CORP.; *Int'l*, pg. 1021
BIG RIVER CYPRESS & HARDWOOD, INC.; *U.S. Private*, pg. 554

BIG THREE RESTAURANTS, INC.

BIG RIVER GOLD LIMITED—See Northwestern Enterprises Ltd.; *Int'l*, pg. 5447
BIG RIVER GROUP PTY. LTD.—See Anacacia Capital Pty Ltd; *Int'l*, pg. 445
BIG RIVER INDUSTRIES, INC.—See CRH plc; *Int'l*, pg. 1845
BIG RIVER INDUSTRIES LIMITED; *Int'l*, pg. 1021
BIG RIVER OIL COMPANY INC.; *U.S. Private*, pg. 554
BIG RIVER PROPANE SERVICE LLC—See Big River Oil Company Inc.; *U.S. Private*, pg. 554
BIG RIVER RESOURCES WEST BURLINGTON, LLC; *U.S. Private*, pg. 554
BIG RIVERS ELECTRIC CORPORATION; *U.S. Private*, pg. 554
BIG RIVER STEEL LLC—See United States Steel Corporation; *U.S. Public*, pg. 2236
BIG RIVER TELEPHONE COMPANY LLC; *U.S. Private*, pg. 554
BIG ROCK 2005 PTY LTD—See Eagers Automotive Limited; *Int'l*, pg. 2263
BIG ROCK BREWERY INC.; *Int'l*, pg. 1021
BIG ROCK PTY LTD—See Eagers Automotive Limited; *Int'l*, pg. 2263
BIG ROCK RESOURCES INC.; *Int'l*, pg. 1021
BIG ROCK SPORTS, LLC—See Peak Global Holdings, LLC; *U.S. Private*, pg. 3123
BIG ROCK TRANSPORTATION, LLC—See Roadrunner Transportation Systems, Inc.; *U.S. Public*, pg. 1802
BI GROUP PLC—See National Industries Group Holding S.A.K.; *Int'l*, pg. 5159
BIG SANDY FURNITURE INC.; *U.S. Private*, pg. 554
BIG SANDY RECC; *U.S. Private*, pg. 554
BIG SAVINGS INSURANCE AGENCY INC.—See Dowling Capital Management, LLC; *U.S. Private*, pg. 1268
BIG SAVINGS INSURANCE AGENCY INC.—See Keystone Group, L.P.; *U.S. Private*, pg. 2298
BIG SCREEN ENTERTAINMENT GROUP, INC.; *U.S. Public*, pg. 331
BIG SCREEN ENTERTAINMENT PVT. LIMITED—See Eros International Plc; *Int'l*, pg. 2496
BIG SEA COMPANY LIMITED—See Prima Marine PCL; *Int'l*, pg. 5975
BIG SEA, INC.; *U.S. Private*, pg. 554
BIG SHOPPING CENTERS LTD.; *Int'l*, pg. 1021
BIG SHOT BEVERAGES, INC.—See National Beverage Corp.; *U.S. Public*, pg. 1494
BIG SHOULDERS CAPITAL LLC; *U.S. Private*, pg. 554
BIG SKY CARVERS INC.—See Thompson Street Capital Manager LLC; *U.S. Private*, pg. 4161
BIG SKY COMMUNICATIONS, INC.; *U.S. Private*, pg. 554
BIG SKY GOLF AND COUNTRY CLUB—See Belkorp Industries, Inc.; *Int'l*, pg. 965
BIG SKY GROWTH PARTNERS, INC.; *U.S. Private*, pg. 554
BIG SKY LASER TECHNOLOGIES, INC.—See Lumibird Group; *Int'l*, pg. 4578
BIG SKY PUBLISHING CO. INC.—See Pioneer Newspapers Inc.; *U.S. Private*, pg. 3187
BIG SKY RESORT—See Boyne USA Resorts Inc.; *U.S. Private*, pg. 629
BIG SKY TECHNOLOGIES INC.—See Fortive Corporation; *U.S. Public*, pg. 872
BIG SKY WESTERN BANK—See Glacier Bancorp, Inc.; *U.S. Public*, pg. 938
BIG SOFA TECHNOLOGIES GROUP PLC; *Int'l*, pg. 1021
BIG SPRING HOSPITAL CORPORATION—See Quorum Health Corporation; *U.S. Private*, pg. 3329
BIG SPRINGS INC.; *U.S. Private*, pg. 554
BIG STATE ELECTRIC LTD.; *U.S. Private*, pg. 554
BIGSTON CORPORATION USA; *U.S. Private*, pg. 556
BIG STONE PUBLISHING, INC.—See Pocket Outdoor Media, Inc.; *U.S. Private*, pg. 3219
BIG STREET CONSTRUCTION, INC.; *U.S. Private*, pg. 554
BIG SUNSHINE CO., LTD.; *Int'l*, pg. 1021
BIGSUPERSEARCH.COM, INC.; *U.S. Public*, pg. 331
BIG SUR TECHNOLOGIES, INC.; *U.S. Private*, pg. 554
BIG SWITCH NETWORKS, INC.—See Arista Networks, Inc.; *U.S. Public*, pg. 192
BIG SYNERGY MEDIA LTD.—See Reliance - ADA Group Limited; *Int'l*, pg. 6263
BIG TALK PRODUCTIONS LIMITED—See ITV plc; *Int'l*, pg. 3844
BIG TECHNOLOGIES PLC; *Int'l*, pg. 1021
BIGTECH SOFTWARE PRIVATE LIMITED—See Enveric Biosciences, Inc.; *U.S. Public*, pg. 780
BIG TEN ACADEMIC ALLIANCE; *U.S. Private*, pg. 554
BIG TEN CONFERENCE; *U.S. Private*, pg. 554
BIG TEN NETWORK, LLC—See Fox Corporation; *U.S. Public*, pg. 875
BIG TEX TRAILER MANUFACTURING, INC.—See Bain Capital, LP; *U.S. Private*, pg. 436
BIG TEX TRAILER WORLD, INC. - HOUSTON—See Bain Capital, LP; *U.S. Private*, pg. 436
BIG TEX TRAILER WORLD, INC.—See Bain Capital, LP; *U.S. Private*, pg. 436
BIG TEX TRAILER WORLD, INC. - TUCSON—See Bain Capital, LP; *U.S. Private*, pg. 436
BIG THREE RESTAURANTS, INC.; *U.S. Private*, pg. 554

BIG TICKET PICTURES INC.—See National Amusements, Inc.; *U.S. Private*, pg. 2839
BIG TICKET PRODUCTIONS INC.—See National Amusements, Inc.; *U.S. Private*, pg. 2839
BIG TIME HOLDINGS, INC.; *U.S. Public*, pg. 331
BIG TIME PRODUCTS, LLC—See Hillman Solutions Corp.; *U.S. Public*, pg. 1038
BIGTIME SOFTWARE, INC.—See Vista Equity Partners, LLC; *U.S. Private*, pg. 4395
BIGTINCAN HOLDINGS LIMITED; *U.S. Public*, pg. 331
BIG TOP, LLC—See Constellation Energy Corporation; *U.S. Public*, pg. 571
BIG TOURS S.L.—See CTS Eventim AG & Co. KGAA; *Int'l*, pg. 1872
BIGTOYS, INC.—See Court Square Capital Partners, L.P.; *U.S. Private*, pg. 1069
BIG TRADING CO., LTD.—See Gun Ei Chemical Industry Co., Ltd.; *Int'l*, pg. 3183
BIG TREE CARBON INC.; *Int'l*, pg. 1021
BIG TREE CLOUD HOLDINGS LIMITED; *Int'l*, pg. 1022
BIG TREE GROUP, INC.; *U.S. Private*, pg. 554
BIG TREE GROUP INC.; *Int'l*, pg. 1022
BIG TREE ORGANIC FARMS, INC.—See Once Again Nut Butter Collective Inc.; *U.S. Private*, pg. 3019
BIG TREE OUTDOOR SDN BHD—See Media Prima Berhad; *Int'l*, pg. 4771
BIG TRUCK RENTAL, LLC; *U.S. Private*, pg. 554
BIG VALLEY, INC.—See Chatham Asset Management, LLC; *U.S. Private*, pg. 866
BIG VALLEY RANCHERIA; *U.S. Private*, pg. 555
THE BIG VIEW; *U.S. Private*, pg. 3995
BIGVISIBLE SOLUTIONS, INC.; *U.S. Private*, pg. 556
BIG V SUPERMARKET INC.; *U.S. Private*, pg. 555
BIG V WHOLESALE CO. INC.—See Vaughan Furniture Company Inc.; *U.S. Private*, pg. 4348
BIG WEST OIL, LLC—See FJ Management, Inc.; *U.S. Private*, pg. 1538
BIG WING CO., LTD.—See Japan Airport Terminal Co., Ltd.; *Int'l*, pg. 3885
BIGWORLD PTY LIMITED—See Wargaming Public Company Limited; *Int'l*, pg. 8344
BIGWORLD PTY. LTD. - DEVELOPMENT STUDIO—See Wargaming Public Company Limited; *Int'l*, pg. 8344
BIG YELLOW (BATTERSEA) LIMITED—See Big Yellow Group plc; *Int'l*, pg. 1022
BIG YELLOW GROUP PLC; *Int'l*, pg. 1022
BIG YELLOW SELF STORAGE COMPANY 6 LIMITED—See Big Yellow Group plc; *Int'l*, pg. 1022
BIG YELLOW SELF STORAGE COMPANY 8 LIMITED—See Big Yellow Group plc; *Int'l*, pg. 1022
BIG YELLOW SELF STORAGE COMPANY LIMITED—See Big Yellow Group plc; *Int'l*, pg. 1022
BIG YELLOW SELF STORAGE (GP) LIMITED—See Big Yellow Group plc; *Int'l*, pg. 1022
BIG Y FOODS, INC.; *U.S. Private*, pg. 555
BIGZ PUBLISHING A.D.; *Int'l*, pg. 1022
BIHACKA PIVOVARA D.D.; *Int'l*, pg. 1022
BIHAR SPONGE IRON LIMITED; *Int'l*, pg. 1022
BIHATEAM D.O.O.—See OBB-Holding AG; *Int'l*, pg. 5509
BIH HEATERS MALAYSIA SDN BHD—See Boustead Singapore Limited; *Int'l*, pg. 1120
BIHLERFLEX, LLC—See Otto Bihler Maschinenfabrik GmbH & Co. KG; *Int'l*, pg. 5662
BIHLER MACHINERY CO., LTD.—See Otto Bihler Maschinenfabrik GmbH & Co. KG; *Int'l*, pg. 5662
BIHLER OF AMERICA INC.—See Otto Bihler Maschinenfabrik GmbH & Co. KG; *Int'l*, pg. 5662
B.I. INCORPORATED (CO)—See The GEO Group, Inc.; *U.S. Public*, pg. 2075
BI INCORPORATED—See The GEO Group, Inc.; *U.S. Public*, pg. 2075
B.I. INTERNATIONAL LIMITED—See UniCredit S.p.A.; *Int'l*, pg. 8034
BI-INVEST ADVISORS S.A.; *Int'l*, pg. 1016
BII RAILWAY TRANSPORTATION TECHNOLOGY HOLDINGS COMPANY LIMITED—See Beijing Infrastructure Investment Co., Ltd.; *Int'l*, pg. 952
BIJELJINA PUT AD—See Grupa Fortis d.o.o. Banja Luka; *Int'l*, pg. 3116
BIJLEE TEXTILES LIMITED; *Int'l*, pg. 1022
BIJOU BRIGITTE MODISCHE ACCESSOIRES AG; *Int'l*, pg. 1022
BIJOUTERIE ADLER SA; *Int'l*, pg. 1022
BIJOUX INTERNATIONAL INC.; *U.S. Private*, pg. 556
BIJOUX TERNER, INC.; *U.S. Private*, pg. 556
BIJUR LUBRICATING CORPORATION—See Summa Holdings, Inc.; *U.S. Private*, pg. 3852
BIKAJI FOODS INTERNATIONAL LIMITED; *Int'l*, pg. 1022
BIKAM PHARMACEUTICALS, INC.—See Takeda Pharmaceutical Company Limited; *Int'l*, pg. 7438
BIK BOUWPRODUKTEN B.V.—See H2 Equity Partners B.V.; *Int'l*, pg. 3199
BIKE24 GMBH—See Bike24 Holding AG; *Int'l*, pg. 1023
BIKE24 HOLDING AG; *Int'l*, pg. 1022
BIKE AMERICA, INC.—See Barmer Enterprises LLC; *U.S. Private*, pg. 476
BIKE BROS. INC.—See PROTO CORPORATION; *Int'l*, pg. 6006

THE BIKE COOPERATIVE—See CCA Global Partners, Inc.; *U.S. Private*, pg. 799
BIKEEXCHANGE AUSTRALIA PTY. LTD.—See BikeExchange Limited; *Int'l*, pg. 1023
BIKEEXCHANGE COLOMBIA S.A.S.—See BikeExchange Limited; *Int'l*, pg. 1023
BIKEEXCHANGE DE VERTRIEBS GMBH—See BikeExchange Limited; *Int'l*, pg. 1023
BIKEEXCHANGE LIMITED; *Int'l*, pg. 1023
BIKE GROUP S.A.—See Giant Manufacturing Co., Ltd.; *Int'l*, pg. 2961
BIKEN TECHNO CORPORATION LTD.; *Int'l*, pg. 1023
BIKE O & COMPANY LTD.; *Int'l*, pg. 1022
BIKINI.COM—See Always Summer LLC; *U.S. Private*, pg. 214
BIKINI—See WPP plc; *Int'l*, pg. 8472
BIKINIS SPORTS BAR & GRILL; *U.S. Private*, pg. 556
BIKUREY HASADE HOLDINGS LTD; *Int'l*, pg. 1023
BILAD OMAN LLC—See Suhail Bahwan Group (Holding) LLC; *Int'l*, pg. 7254
BILAL FIBRES LIMITED; *Int'l*, pg. 1023
BILANDER ACQUISITION CORP.; *U.S. Public*, pg. 331
BILAN SERVICES S.N.C.—See Allianz SE; *Int'l*, pg. 351
BILANZ DEUTSCHLAND WIRTSCHAFTSMAGAZIN GMBH—See Axel Springer SE; *Int'l*, pg. 766
BIL AUSTRALIA PTY LIMITED—See Hong Leong Investment Holdings Pte. Ltd.; *Int'l*, pg. 3468
BILBAO, COMPANIA ANONIMA DE SEGUROS Y REASEGUROS—See Grupo Catalana Occidente, S.A.; *Int'l*, pg. 3124
BILBAO HIPOTECARIA, S.A., E.F.C.—See Grupo Catalana Occidente, S.A.; *Int'l*, pg. 3124
BILBAO VIDA Y GESTORES FINANCIEROS, S.A.—See Grupo Catalana Occidente, S.A.; *Int'l*, pg. 3124
BILCARE LIMITED; *Int'l*, pg. 1023
BILCARE LTD.—See Bilcare Limited; *Int'l*, pg. 1023
BILCARE MARKETING AMERICA LATINA LTDA.—See Bilcare Limited; *Int'l*, pg. 1023
BILCARE RESEARCH GMBH—See Bilcare Limited; *Int'l*, pg. 1023
BILCARE SINGAPORE PTE. LTD.—See Bilcare Limited; *Int'l*, pg. 1023
BILCARE TECHNOLOGIES SINGAPORE PTE. LTD.—See Bilcare Limited; *Int'l*, pg. 1023
BILCIRKELN MALMO AB—See General Motors Company; *U.S. Public*, pg. 926
THE BILCO COMPANY—See Quanex Building Products Corp.; *U.S. Public*, pg. 1750
BILCO UK LTD.—See Quanex Building Products Corp.; *U.S. Public*, pg. 1749
BILD & COMPANY; *U.S. Private*, pg. 556
BILDCO CEMENT PRODUCTS LLC—See Abu Dhabi National Company for Building Material; *Int'l*, pg. 72
BILDCO REINFORCING STEEL SERVICES—See Abu Dhabi National Company for Building Material; *Int'l*, pg. 72
BILDEMONTERING I HELSINGBORG AV—See LKQ Corporation; *U.S. Public*, pg. 1334
BILDERGARTEN ENTERTAINMENT GMBH—See ITV plc; *Int'l*, pg. 3844
BILDUNGSVERLAG EINS GMBH—See SHV Holdings N.V.; *Int'l*, pg. 6871
BILDUNGSZENTRUM ENERGIE GMBH—See RWE AG; *Int'l*, pg. 6436
BILEKO TIRES AB—See MEKO AB; *Int'l*, pg. 4805
BILENDI AB—See Bilendi SA; *Int'l*, pg. 1023
BILENDI A/S—See Bilendi SA; *Int'l*, pg. 1023
BILENDI GMBH—See Bilendi SA; *Int'l*, pg. 1023
BILENDI LIMITED—See Bilendi SA; *Int'l*, pg. 1023
BILENDI OY—See Bilendi SA; *Int'l*, pg. 1023
BILENDI SA; *Int'l*, pg. 1023
BILENDI SA—See Bilendi SA; *Int'l*, pg. 1023
BIL ENERGY SYSTEMS LIMITED; *Int'l*, pg. 1023
BILESU PARADIZE SIA—See AS Ekspress Grupp; *Int'l*, pg. 589
BILETIX BILET DAGITIM BASIM VE TICARET AS—See Live Nation Entertainment, Inc.; *U.S. Public*, pg. 1328
BILETIX BILET DAGITIM VE BASIM TIC AS—See Koc Holding A.S.; *Int'l*, pg. 4223
BILFINGER ARNHOLDT GMBH—See Bilfinger SE; *Int'l*, pg. 1026
BILFINGER BERGER A1 MOBIL GMBH—See Bilfinger SE; *Int'l*, pg. 1024
BILFINGER BERGER AG-CIVIL—See Bilfinger SE; *Int'l*, pg. 1024
BILFINGER BERGER AG-HOCHBAU—See Bilfinger SE; *Int'l*, pg. 1024
BILFINGER BERGER AMBIENTE S.R.L.—See Bilfinger SE; *Int'l*, pg. 1024
BILFINGER BERGER BAUGESELLSCHAFT MBH—See Bilfinger SE; *Int'l*, pg. 1024
BILFINGER BERGER BELGIUM S.A.—See Bilfinger SE; *Int'l*, pg. 1025
BILFINGER BERGER BUDOWNICTWO S.A.—See Bilfinger SE; *Int'l*, pg. 1025
BILFINGER BERGER BUILDING POLSKA SP. Z O.O.—See Bilfinger SE; *Int'l*, pg. 1025
BILFINGER BERGER (CANADA) INC.—See Bilfinger SE; *Int'l*, pg. 1024

BILFINGER BERGER CONSTRUCTION, LLC—See Bilfinger SE; *Int'l*, pg. 1024
BILFINGER BERGER EMIRATES CONSTRUCTION B.V.—See Bilfinger SE; *Int'l*, pg. 1025
BILFINGER BERGER ENTSORGUNG GMBH—See Bilfinger SE; *Int'l*, pg. 1025
BILFINGER BERGER INDUSTRIAL SERVICES GMBH—See Bilfinger SE; *Int'l*, pg. 1025
BILFINGER BERGER INDUSTRIAL SERVICES SPAIN S.A.—See Bilfinger SE; *Int'l*, pg. 1026
BILFINGER BERGER INGENIEURBAU GMBH—See Bilfinger SE; *Int'l*, pg. 1024
BILFINGER BERGER INSTANDSETZUNG GMBH—See Bilfinger SE; *Int'l*, pg. 1024
BILFINGER BERGER PARKING GMBH—See Bilfinger SE; *Int'l*, pg. 1024
BILFINGER BERGER PI CORPORATE SERVICES GMBH—See Bilfinger SE; *Int'l*, pg. 1026
BILFINGER BERGER PI INTERNATIONAL HOLDING GMBH—See Bilfinger SE; *Int'l*, pg. 1026
BILFINGER BERGER POLSKA S.A.—See Bilfinger SE; *Int'l*, pg. 1026
BILFINGER BERGER POWER HOLDINGS (PTY) LTD.—See Bilfinger SE; *Int'l*, pg. 1026
BILFINGER BERGER PROJECT INVESTMENTS GMBH—See Bilfinger SE; *Int'l*, pg. 1026
BILFINGER BERGER PROJECT INVESTMENTS INC.—See Bilfinger SE; *Int'l*, pg. 1026
BILFINGER BERGER PROJECTS S.A.R.L.—See Bilfinger SE; *Int'l*, pg. 1026
BILFINGER BERGER REGIOBAU GMBH—See Bilfinger SE; *Int'l*, pg. 1026
BILFINGER BERGER SPEZIALTIEFBAU GMBH—See Bilfinger SE; *Int'l*, pg. 1026
BILFINGER BERGER STAVEBNI PRAHA, S.R.O.—See Bilfinger SE; *Int'l*, pg. 1027
BILFINGER BERGER (THAI) CONSTRUCTION CO., LTD.—See Bilfinger SE; *Int'l*, pg. 1024
BILFINGER BERGER UK LIMITED—See Bilfinger SE; *Int'l*, pg. 1024
BILFINGER BERGER UMWELTTECHNIK GMBH—See Bilfinger SE; *Int'l*, pg. 1026
BILFINGER BOHR- UND ROHRTECHNIK GMBH—See Bilfinger SE; *Int'l*, pg. 1027
BILFINGER BRABANT MOBIEL B.V.—See Bilfinger SE; *Int'l*, pg. 1027
BILFINGER CHEMSERV GMBH—See Bilfinger SE; *Int'l*, pg. 1026
BILFINGER DANMARK A/S—See Bilfinger SE; *Int'l*, pg. 1027
BILFINGER EMS GMBH—See Bilfinger SE; *Int'l*, pg. 1026
BILFINGER EMV B.V.—See Bilfinger SE; *Int'l*, pg. 1027
BILFINGER ENGINEERING & MAINTENANCE GMBH—See Bilfinger SE; *Int'l*, pg. 1027
BILFINGER ENGINEERING & MAINTENANCE NORDICS AB—See Bilfinger SE; *Int'l*, pg. 1027
BILFINGER ENGINEERING & MAINTENANCE NORDICS AS—See Bilfinger SE; *Int'l*, pg. 1027
BILFINGER ENGINEERING & MAINTENANCE NORDICS OY—See Bilfinger SE; *Int'l*, pg. 1027
BILFINGER GERBER GMBH—See Bilfinger SE; *Int'l*, pg. 1027
BILFINGER HEIGHT SPECIALISTS B.V.—See Bilfinger SE; *Int'l*, pg. 1027
BILFINGER INDUSTRIAL AUTOMATION SERVICES LTD.—See Bilfinger SE; *Int'l*, pg. 1027
BILFINGER INDUSTRIAL AUTOMATION SERVICES LTD.—See Bilfinger SE; *Int'l*, pg. 1026
BILFINGER INDUSTRIAL SERVICES AUSTRIA GMBH—See Bilfinger SE; *Int'l*, pg. 1027
BILFINGER INDUSTRIAL SERVICES BELGIE N.V.—See Bilfinger SE; *Int'l*, pg. 1027
BILFINGER INDUSTRIAL SERVICES BETEILIGUNGS GMBH—See Bilfinger SE; *Int'l*, pg. 1027
BILFINGER INDUSTRIAL SERVICES GERMANY GMBH—See Bilfinger SE; *Int'l*, pg. 1027
BILFINGER INDUSTRIAL SERVICES INC.—See Bilfinger SE; *Int'l*, pg. 1026
BILFINGER INDUSTRIAL SERVICES NEDERLAND B.V.—See Bilfinger SE; *Int'l*, pg. 1027
BILFINGER INDUSTRIAL SERVICES NORWAY AS—See Bilfinger SE; *Int'l*, pg. 1026
BILFINGER INDUSTRIAL SERVICES POLSKA SP. Z O.O.—See Bilfinger SE; *Int'l*, pg. 1027
BILFINGER INDUSTRIAL SERVICES SCHWEIZ AG—See Bilfinger SE; *Int'l*, pg. 1026
BILFINGER INDUSTRIAL SERVICES SWITZERLAND AG—See Bilfinger SE; *Int'l*, pg. 1027
BILFINGER LIFE SCIENCE AUTOMATION GMBH—See Bilfinger SE; *Int'l*, pg. 1026
BILFINGER LIFE SCIENCE GMBH—See Bilfinger SE; *Int'l*, pg. 1026
BILFINGER LTM INDUSTRIE SAS—See Bilfinger SE; *Int'l*, pg. 1027
BILFINGER MASCHINENBAU GMBH & CO KG—See Bilfinger SE; *Int'l*, pg. 1027
BILFINGER NORDICS AS—See Bilfinger SE; *Int'l*, pg. 1027

COMPANY NAME INDEX BIL-RAY GROUP
Company Index

BILFINGER NORTH AMERICA INC.—See Bilfinger SE; *Int'l*, pg. 1027
BILFINGER NUCLEAR & ENERGY TRANSITION GMBH—See Bilfinger SE; *Int'l*, pg. 1027
BILFINGER PERSONALSERVICE OSTERREICH GMBH—See Bilfinger SE; *Int'l*, pg. 1027
BILFINGER PETERS ENGINEERING SAS—See Bilfinger SE; *Int'l*, pg. 1027
BILFINGER POWER SYSTEMS GMBH—See Bilfinger SE; *Int'l*, pg. 1027
BILFINGER REAL ESTATE BV—See Bilfinger SE; *Int'l*, pg. 1027
BILFINGER REAL ESTATE GESERV GMBH—See Bilfinger SE; *Int'l*, pg. 1027
BILFINGER REAL ESTATE GMBH—See Bilfinger SE; *Int'l*, pg. 1027
BILFINGER REAL ESTATE INSERV GMBH—See Bilfinger SE; *Int'l*, pg. 1027
BILFINGER ROB N.V.—See Bilfinger SE; *Int'l*, pg. 1027
BILFINGER ROTRING ENGINEERING GMBH—See Bilfinger SE; *Int'l*, pg. 1027
BILFINGER SALAMIS UK LIMITED—See Bilfinger SE; *Int'l*, pg. 1026
BILFINGER SCHEVEN GMBH—See Bilfinger SE; *Int'l*, pg. 1026
BILFINGER SE; *Int'l*, pg. 1023
BILFINGER SHARED SERVICES GMBH—See Bilfinger SE; *Int'l*, pg. 1027
BILFINGER TEBODIN BELGIUM NV—See Bilfinger SE; *Int'l*, pg. 1027
BILFINGER TEBODIN HUNGARY KFT.—See Bilfinger SE; *Int'l*, pg. 1028
BILFINGER TEBODIN NETHERLANDS B.V.—See Bilfinger SE; *Int'l*, pg. 1028
BILFINGER TEBODIN ROMANIA S.R.L.—See Bilfinger SE; *Int'l*, pg. 1028
BILFINGER TEBODIN—See Bilfinger SE; *Int'l*, pg. 1026
BILFINGER UK LIMITED—See Bilfinger SE; *Int'l*, pg. 1026
BILFINGER WOLFFERTS GEBAUDETECHNIK GMBH—See Bilfinger SE; *Int'l*, pg. 1028
BILGIN ENERJI YATIRIM HOLDING A.S.; *Int'l*, pg. 1029
BILGLASCENTRALEN AB—See MEKO AB; *Int'l*, pg. 4805
BILGUN TEKSTIL A.S—See Bilici Yatirim Sanayi ve Ticaret A.S.; *Int'l*, pg. 1029
BILIA AB; *Int'l*, pg. 1029
BILIA BMU AB—See Bilia AB; *Int'l*, pg. 1029
BILIA EMOND LUXEMBOURG SA—See Bilia AB; *Int'l*, pg. 1029
BILIA FORDON AB—See Bilia AB; *Int'l*, pg. 1029
BILIA GROUP GOTEBORG AB—See Bilia AB; *Int'l*, pg. 1029
BILIA PERSONBILAR AB—See Bilia AB; *Int'l*, pg. 1029
BILIA PERSONBIL AS—See Bilia AB; *Int'l*, pg. 1029
BILIA VERSTRAETEN NV—See Bilia AB; *Int'l*, pg. 1029
BILIBILI CO., LTD.—See Bilibili Inc.; *Int'l*, pg. 1029
BILIBILI INC.; *Int'l*, pg. 1029
BILICI YATIRIM SANAYI VE TICARET A.S.; *Int'l*, pg. 1029
BIL IMMOBILIEN FONDS GMBH—See UniCredit S.p.A.; *Int'l*, pg. 8034
BIL INDUSTRIEMETALLE GMBH & CO. 886 KG—See Rheinmetall AG; *Int'l*, pg. 6321
BI-LINK METAL SPECIALTIES INC.; *U.S. Private*, pg. 550
BIL-JAC FOODS INC.; *U.S. Private*, pg. 556
BIL-JAX, INC.—See Haulotte Group SA; *Int'l*, pg. 3285
BILKOM AS—See Koc Holding A.S.; *Int'l*, pg. 4223
BILKOM BILISIM HIZMETLERI A.S.—See Koc Holding A.S.; *Int'l*, pg. 4222
BILLA AG—See REWE-Zentral-Aktiengesellschaft; *Int'l*, pg. 6314
BILLABONG INTERNATIONAL LIMITED—See Leonard Green & Partners, L.P.; *U.S. Private*, pg. 2424
BILLAG AG—See Swisscom AG; *Int'l*, pg. 7373
BILL ALEXANDER FORD LINCOLN MERCURY, INC.; *U.S. Private*, pg. 556
BILL AYARES CHEVROLET, LLC—See AutoNation, Inc.; *U.S. Public*, pg. 233
BILL BAILEY MEAT PACKING CO INC.—See Square-H Brands Inc.; *U.S. Private*, pg. 3766
BILL BARNES; *U.S. Private*, pg. 556
BILL BARTH FORD, INC.; *U.S. Private*, pg. 556
BILL BARTMANN ENTERPRISES; *U.S. Private*, pg. 556
BILL BLACK CHEVROLET CADILLAC INC.; *U.S. Private*, pg. 556
BILL BLASS GROUP, LLC; *U.S. Private*, pg. 556
BILLBOARD CENTRAL; *U.S. Private*, pg. 559
BILLBOARD CONNECTION; *U.S. Private*, pg. 559
BILLBOARD JSC; *Int'l*, pg. 1030
BILLBOARD—See Valence Media Group; *U.S. Private*, pg. 4330
BILL BRITT MAZDA; *U.S. Private*, pg. 556
BILL BROWN FORD INC.—See Penske Automotive Group, Inc.; *U.S. Public*, pg. 1664
BILL BUCK CHEVROLET INC.; *U.S. Private*, pg. 556
BILL BUCKLE AUTOS PTY LTD—See Eagers Automotive Limited; *Int'l*, pg. 2264
BILL BUCKLE HOLDINGS PTY LTD—See Eagers Automotive Limited; *Int'l*, pg. 2264
BILL BUTLER CHRYSLER DODGE PLYMOUTH JEEP, INC.; *U.S. Private*, pg. 556
BILL CLARK HOMES LLC; *U.S. Private*, pg. 556
BILLCO MOTORS INC.; *U.S. Private*, pg. 559
BILL CURRIE FORD INC.; *U.S. Private*, pg. 556
BILL DELORD AUTOCENTER INC.; *U.S. Private*, pg. 556
BILL DE NOON LUMBER CO.; *U.S. Private*, pg. 556
BILL DODGE AUTO GROUP; *U.S. Private*, pg. 556
BILL DORAN COMPANY; *U.S. Private*, pg. 557
BIL LEASE S.A.—See Legend Holdings Corporation; *Int'l*, pg. 4443
BILL EDWARDS PRESENTS, INC.; *U.S. Private*, pg. 557
BILLEO, INC; *U.S. Private*, pg. 559
BILLERICA MINUTEMAN—See Gannett Co., Inc.; *U.S. Public*, pg. 902
BILLER REINHART STRUCTURAL GROUP INC.; *U.S. Private*, pg. 559
BILLERUD AB; *Int'l*, pg. 1030
BILLERUD AMERICAS CORPORATION—See Billerud AB; *Int'l*, pg. 1030
BILLERUD BEETHAM LTD—See Billerud AB; *Int'l*, pg. 1030
BILLERUD FRANCE S.A—See Billerud AB; *Int'l*, pg. 1030
BILLERUD GULF—See Billerud AB; *Int'l*, pg. 1030
BILLERUD IBERICA S.L—See Billerud AB; *Int'l*, pg. 1030
BILLERUD KARLSBORG AB—See Billerud AB; *Int'l*, pg. 1030
BILLERUDKORSNAS FINLAND OY—See Billerud AB; *Int'l*, pg. 1030
BILLERUDKORSNAS LATVIA SIA—See Billerud AB; *Int'l*, pg. 1030
BILLERUDKORSNAS MANAGED PACKAGING AB—See Billerud AB; *Int'l*, pg. 1030
BILLERUDKORSNAS SKARBLACKA AB—See Billerud AB; *Int'l*, pg. 1030
BILLERUD SCANDINAVIA—See Billerud AB; *Int'l*, pg. 1030
BILLERUD SKARBLACKA AB—See Billerud AB; *Int'l*, pg. 1030
BILLERUD SKOG AB—See Billerud AB; *Int'l*, pg. 1030
BILLERUD S.R.L.—See Billerud AB; *Int'l*, pg. 1030
BILLERUD TENOVA BIOPLASTICS AB—See Billerud AB; *Int'l*, pg. 1030
BILLERUD TRADING (SHANGHAI) CO. LTD—See Billerud AB; *Int'l*, pg. 1030
BILLETLUGEN A/S—See Egmont Fonden; *Int'l*, pg. 2325
BILLETNET AS—See Live Nation Entertainment, Inc.; *U.S. Public*, pg. 1329
BILLET SAS; *Int'l*, pg. 1030
BILLETTSERVICE AS—See Live Nation Entertainment, Inc.; *U.S. Public*, pg. 1330
BILL FAIR & CO.; *U.S. Private*, pg. 557
BILL GATTON ACURA MAZDA SATURN; *U.S. Private*, pg. 557
BILL GRAY VOLVO; *U.S. Private*, pg. 557
BILLGUARD, INC.—See Prosper Marketplace, Inc.; *U.S. Private*, pg. 3288
BILL HANKS LUMBER CO.; *U.S. Private*, pg. 557
BILL HEARD ENTERPRISES, INC.; *U.S. Private*, pg. 557
BILL HESSER ENTERPRISES INC.; *U.S. Private*, pg. 557
BILL HOLDINGS, INC.; *U.S. Public*, pg. 331
BILL HOOD FORD INC.; *U.S. Private*, pg. 557
BILL HOUSTON FORD LTD.; *Int'l*, pg. 1030
BILL HOWICH CHRYSLER LTD.; *Int'l*, pg. 1030
BILL HUDSON & ASSOCIATES, INC., ADVERTISING & PUBLIC RELATIONS; *U.S. Private*, pg. 557
BILLIAN PUBLISHING INC.; *U.S. Private*, pg. 559
BILLIE, INC.—See Edgewell Personal Care Company; *U.S. Public*, pg. 718
BILLING CENTER LAKE POINTE MEDICAL, L.L.C.—See Tenet Healthcare Corporation; *U.S. Public*, pg. 2006
BILLING COMPONENTS GMBH—See Sobha Renaissance Information Technologies Pvt Ltd; *Int'l*, pg. 7030
BILLINGORCHARD—See Payscape Advisors; *U.S. Private*, pg. 3117
BILLING SERVICES GROUP, LLC; *U.S. Private*, pg. 559
BILLING SERVICES, INC.—See Fellow Health Partners, Inc.; *U.S. Private*, pg. 1494
THE BILLINGS GAZETTE—See Lee Enterprises, Incorporated; *U.S. Public*, pg. 1300
BILLINGSLEY RANCH OUTFITTERS; *U.S. Private*, pg. 559
BILLING SYSTEM CORP.; *Int'l*, pg. 1031
BILLINGTON CARTMELL; *Int'l*, pg. 1031
BILLINGTON HOLDINGS PLC; *Int'l*, pg. 1031
BILLINGTON STRUCTURES LIMITED—See Billington Holdings Plc; *Int'l*, pg. 1031
BILLION CC, INC.—See Billion Motors, Inc.; *U.S. Private*, pg. 559
BILLION ELECTRIC CO., LTD.; *Int'l*, pg. 1031
BILLION HOLDING INC.; *Int'l*, pg. 1031
BILLION HONDA OF IOWA CITY—See Billion Motors, Inc.; *U.S. Private*, pg. 559
BILLION INDUSTRIAL HOLDINGS LIMITED; *Int'l*, pg. 1031
BILLION MOTORS - CHRYSLER DODGE JEEP FIAT—See Billion Motors, Inc.; *U.S. Private*, pg. 559
BILLION MOTORS - GMC BUICK KIA—See Billion Motors, Inc.; *U.S. Private*, pg. 559
BILLION MOTORS, INC.; *U.S. Private*, pg. 559
BILLIONS CO., LTD.; *Int'l*, pg. 1031
BILLION SOUTHTOWN, INC.—See Billion Motors, Inc.; *U.S. Private*, pg. 559
BILLIONTON SYSTEMS INC.; *Int'l*, pg. 1031
BILLION WATTS TECHNOLOGIES CO., LTD.—See Billion Electric Co., Ltd.; *Int'l*, pg. 1031
BILLITON BASE METALS—See BHP Group Limited; *Int'l*, pg. 1016
BILL JACKSON, INC.; *U.S. Private*, pg. 557
BILL JACOBS MOTORSPORT INC.; *U.S. Private*, pg. 557
BILL JARRETT FORD, INC.; *U.S. Private*, pg. 557
BILL JOHNSONS RESTAURANT; *U.S. Private*, pg. 557
BILL L. DOVER INC.; *U.S. Private*, pg. 557
BILL LEWIS MOTORS INC.; *U.S. Private*, pg. 557
BILL LUKE CHRYSLER JEEP & DODGE, INC.; *U.S. Private*, pg. 557
BILL LYNCH ASSOCIATES, LLC; *U.S. Private*, pg. 557
BILL MACINTYRE CHEVROLET BUICK; *U.S. Private*, pg. 557
BILL MARKVE & ASSOCIATES GROUP; *U.S. Private*, pg. 557
BILL MARSH AUTO MALL; *U.S. Private*, pg. 557
BILLMATRIX CORPORATION—See Fiserv, Inc.; *U.S. Public*, pg. 850
BILL MCCURLEY CHEVROLET; *U.S. Private*, pg. 557
BILL ME LATER, INC.—See PayPal Holdings, Inc.; *U.S. Public*, pg. 1656
BILL MILLER EQUIPMENT SALES; *U.S. Private*, pg. 557
BILL NAITO COMPANY; *U.S. Private*, pg. 558
BILLOWS ELECTRIC SUPPLY CO.—See Sonepar S.A.; *Int'l*, pg. 7093
BILL PAGE HONDA; *U.S. Private*, pg. 558
BILL PAGE IMPORTS INC.; *U.S. Private*, pg. 558
BILL PEARCE MOTORS INC.; *U.S. Private*, pg. 558
BILL PENNEY TOYOTA; *U.S. Private*, pg. 558
BILL PLEMMONS INC.; *U.S. Private*, pg. 558
BILL RAPP SUPERSTORE; *U.S. Private*, pg. 558
BILL RAY NISSAN, INC.; *U.S. Private*, pg. 558
BILL ROBERTSON & SONS INCORPORATED; *U.S. Private*, pg. 558
BILLSAVE UK LIMITED; *Int'l*, pg. 1031
BILL SEIDLE AUTOMOTIVE GROUP; *U.S. Private*, pg. 558
BILLS ELECTRIC, INC.; *U.S. Private*, pg. 559
BILL SELIG FORD, INC.; *U.S. Private*, pg. 558
BILL SHULTZ CHEVROLET, INC.; *U.S. Private*, pg. 558
BILLS KHAKIS—See NEJ, Inc.; *U.S. Private*, pg. 2882
BILL SMITH INCORPORATED; *U.S. Private*, pg. 558
BILL SNETHKAMP INC.; *U.S. Private*, pg. 558
BILL SNETHKAMP LANSING DODGE—See Bill Snethkamp Inc.; *U.S. Private*, pg. 558
BILL SPURLOCK DODGE INC.; *U.S. Private*, pg. 558
BILLS SWEEPING SERVICE, INC.—See Warburg Pincus LLC; *U.S. Private*, pg. 4440
BILL STASEK CHEVROLET; *U.S. Private*, pg. 558
BILLSTROM RIEMER ANDERSSON AB—See Veidekke ASA; *Int'l*, pg. 8148
BILL TERPENING INC.; *U.S. Private*, pg. 558
BILLUPS, INC.; *U.S. Private*, pg. 559
BILL UTTER FORD; *U.S. Private*, pg. 558
BILL WALSH AUTOMOTIVE GROUP; *U.S. Private*, pg. 558
BILL WALSH CHEVROLET—See Bill Walsh Automotive Group; *U.S. Private*, pg. 558
BILL WALSH FORD LINCOLN MERCURY KIA—See Bill Walsh Automotive Group; *U.S. Private*, pg. 558
BILL WHITE VOLKSWAGEN AUDI INC.; *U.S. Private*, pg. 558
BILL WILLIAMS TIRE CENTER; *U.S. Private*, pg. 558
BILLWIN INDUSTRIES LIMITED; *Int'l*, pg. 1031
BILL WRIGHT TOYOTA; *U.S. Private*, pg. 558
BILLY BENDER CHEVROLET INC.; *U.S. Private*, pg. 559
BILLY GENE IS MARKETING, INC.; *U.S. Private*, pg. 559
BILLY GOAT INDUSTRIES, INC.—See Briggs & Stratton Corporation; *U.S. Private*, pg. 650
BILLY GRAHAM EVANGELISTIC ASSOCIATION; *U.S. Private*, pg. 559
BILLY HOWELL FORD-LINCOLN; *U.S. Private*, pg. 559
BILLY MOORE CORRECTIONAL CENTER—See Management & Training Corporation; *U.S. Private*, pg. 2560
BILLY REID, INC.; *U.S. Private*, pg. 559
BILMAR BEACH RESORT; *U.S. Private*, pg. 559
BIL MARKEDET APS—See eBay Inc.; *U.S. Public*, pg. 709
BILOKALNIK-IPA D.D.—See DS Smith Plc; *Int'l*, pg. 2207
BI-LO, LLC—See Aldi Einkauf SE & Co. oHG; *Int'l*, pg. 304
BILOTTA CONSTRUCTION CORP.; *U.S. Private*, pg. 559
BILOXI HMA, INC.—See Community Health Systems, Inc.; *U.S. Public*, pg. 551
BILOXI MARSH LANDS CORP.; *U.S. Public*, pg. 331
BILPARTNER AB—See Amplex AB; *Int'l*, pg. 433
BILPOWER LIMITED - BARODA UNIT—See Bilpower Limited; *Int'l*, pg. 1031
BILPOWER LIMITED; *Int'l*, pg. 1031
BILPOWER LTD - KANCHAD PLANT—See Bilpower Limited; *Int'l*, pg. 1031
BILPOWER LTD - UTTRANCHAL PLANT—See Bilpower Limited; *Int'l*, pg. 1031
BIL-RAY GROUP; *U.S. Private*, pg. 556
BIL-RAY HOME IMPROVEMENTS—See Bil-Ray Group; *U.S. Private*, pg. 556

BIL-RAY GROUP

CORPORATE AFFILIATIONS

BILSALONGEN AS—See Bilia AB; *Int'l*, pg. 1029
BILSTEIN & SIEKERMANN COLD FORMING (TAICANG) CO., LTD.—See INDUS Holding AG; *Int'l*, pg. 3662
BILSTEIN & SIEKERMANN GMBH + CO. KG—See INDUS Holding AG; *Int'l*, pg. 3662
BILTECH BUILDING ELEMENTS LIMITED—See Avantha Group; *Int'l*, pg. 735
BILTMORE APARTMENTS, LTD.—See Apartment Investment and Management Company; *U.S. Public*, pg. 144
BILTMORE CAPITAL ADVISORS LLC—See Merit Financial Group, LLC; *U.S. Private*, pg. 2674
BILTMORE CONSTRUCTION CO. INC.; *U.S. Private*, pg. 559
BILTMORE ESTATE WINE COMPANY; *U.S. Private*, pg. 560
BILTMORE HOLDING ARIZONA L.L.C.; *U.S. Private*, pg. 560
BILTMORE (M) SDN BHD—See S P Setia Berhad; *Int'l*, pg. 6443
BILTMORE TRADING CORPORATION—See HCI Equity Management, L.P.; *U.S. Private*, pg. 1889
BILTON PLC—See SEGRO plc; *Int'l*, pg. 6683
THE BILTRITE CORPORATION; *U.S. Private*, pg. 3995
BILT RITE SCAFFOLD CO; *U.S. Private*, pg. 559
BILUTSTYR ARENDAL AS—See MEKO AB; *Int'l*, pg. 4805
BILXTRA AUTOGARDEN KONGSBERG AS—See MEKO AB; *Int'l*, pg. 4805
BILXTRA KRISTIANSUND AS—See MEKO AB; *Int'l*, pg. 4805
BILXTRA SKOYEN AS—See MEKO AB; *Int'l*, pg. 4805
BIMA 83 SASU—See Societe BIC S.A.; *Int'l*, pg. 7037
BIM AD; *Int'l*, pg. 1031
BIMAL D.D.; *Int'l*, pg. 1032
BIMAN BANGLADESH AIRLINES; *Int'l*, pg. 1032
BIMAN FLIGHT CATERING CENTRE LTD—See Biman Bangladesh Airlines; *Int'l*, pg. 1032
BIMAN POULTRY COMPLEX LTD—See Biman Bangladesh Airlines; *Int'l*, pg. 1032
BIMAR S.R.L.—See Garofalo Health Care SpA; *Int'l*, pg. 2886
BI-MART ACQUISITION CORP.; *U.S. Private*, pg. 550
BI-MART CORPORATION—See Bi-Mart Acquisition Corp.; *U.S. Private*, pg. 550
BIMATEC SORALUCE ZERSPANUNGSTECHNOLOGIE GMBH—See Mondragon Corporation; *Int'l*, pg. 5031
BIMATEX GMBH—See Dierig Holding AG; *Int'l*, pg. 2115
BIMAX, INC.—See Mitsubishi Chemical Group Corporation; *Int'l*, pg. 4932
BIMBADGEN ESTATE PTY LIMITED—See Mulpha International Bhd.; *Int'l*, pg. 5081
BIMBA MANUFACTURING COMPANY, INC.—See IMI plc; *Int'l*, pg. 3624
BIMB HOLDINGS BERHAD—See Lembaga Tabung Haji; *Int'l*, pg. 4449
BIM BIRLESIK MAGAZALAR A.S.; *Int'l*, pg. 1031
BIMBO BAKERIES USA INC. - EARTH CITY—See Grupo Bimbo, S.A.B. de C.V.; *Int'l*, pg. 3122
BIMBO BAKERIES USA INC. - FORT WORTH—See Grupo Bimbo, S.A.B. de C.V.; *Int'l*, pg. 3122
BIMBO BAKERIES USA INC. - FREDERICK—See Grupo Bimbo, S.A.B. de C.V.; *Int'l*, pg. 3122
BIMBO BAKERIES USA INC. - GASTONIA—See Grupo Bimbo, S.A.B. de C.V.; *Int'l*, pg. 3122
BIMBO BAKERIES USA INC. - GRAND RAPIDS—See Grupo Bimbo, S.A.B. de C.V.; *Int'l*, pg. 3122
BIMBO BAKERIES USA INC. - KNOXVILLE—See Grupo Bimbo, S.A.B. de C.V.; *Int'l*, pg. 3122
BIMBO BAKERIES USA INC. - LA CROSSE—See Grupo Bimbo, S.A.B. de C.V.; *Int'l*, pg. 3122
BIMBO BAKERIES USA INC. - MADISON—See Grupo Bimbo, S.A.B. de C.V.; *Int'l*, pg. 3122
BIMBO BAKERIES USA INC. - MILWAUKEE—See Grupo Bimbo, S.A.B. de C.V.; *Int'l*, pg. 3122
BIMBO BAKERIES USA INC. - MONTEBELLO—See Grupo Bimbo, S.A.B. de C.V.; *Int'l*, pg. 3122
BIMBO BAKERIES USA INC. - OCONOMOWOC—See Grupo Bimbo, S.A.B. de C.V.; *Int'l*, pg. 3122
BIMBO BAKERIES USA INC. - SAINT PAUL—See Grupo Bimbo, S.A.B. de C.V.; *Int'l*, pg. 3122
BIMBO BAKERIES USA INC.—See Grupo Bimbo, S.A.B. de C.V.; *Int'l*, pg. 3122
BIMBO-MARTINEZ COMERCIAL, S.L.—See Grupo Bimbo, S.A.B. de C.V.; *Int'l*, pg. 3123
BIMBOSAN AG—See HOCHDORF Holding AG; *Int'l*, pg. 3437
BIMBO S.A.—See Grupo Bimbo, S.A.B. de C.V.; *Int'l*, pg. 3123
BIM DISTRIBUZIONE S.R.L.—See Wild Bunch AG; *Int'l*, pg. 8409
BIMECO GARNHANDEL GMBH & CO. KG; *Int'l*, pg. 1032
BIMECO GROUP INC.; *U.S. Private*, pg. 560
BIMEDA, INC.; *U.S. Private*, pg. 560
BI MEDICAL, INC.—See Bellsystem24 holdings, Inc.; *Int'l*, pg. 967
BIMEKS BILGI ISLEM VE DIS TICARET A.S.; *Int'l*, pg. 1032
BIMETAL BEARINGS LTD—See Daido Metal Corporation; *Int'l*, pg. 1921

BI METALLURGICAL SPECIALTIES, INC.—See Joint Holdings/Basic Metal Industries, Inc.; *U.S. Private*, pg. 2230
BIMI INTERNATIONAL MEDICAL INC.; *Int'l*, pg. 1032
BIM IMMOBILIARE SRL—See Banca Intermobiliare di Investimenti e Gestioni S.p.A.; *Int'l*, pg. 815
BIMINI CAPITAL MANAGEMENT, INC.; *U.S. Public*, pg. 331
BIMINI TECHNOLOGIES, LLC; *U.S. Private*, pg. 560
BIM INSURANCE BROKER SPA—See Banca Intermobiliare di Investimenti e Gestioni S.p.A.; *Int'l*, pg. 815
BIM ITALIA S.R.L.—See GPI S.p.A.; *Int'l*, pg. 3046
BIMOBJECT AB; *Int'l*, pg. 1032
BIMOTION GMBH—See Mensch und Maschine Software SE; *Int'l*, pg. 4818
BIMSA ULUSLARARASI IS, BILGI VE YONETIM SISTEMLERI A.S.—See Haci Omer Sabanci Holding A.S.; *Int'l*, pg. 3203
BIM SHARK APS—See Byggfakta Group Nordic HoldCo AB; *Int'l*, pg. 1234
BIMSON CEMENT JOINT STOCK COMPANY; *Int'l*, pg. 1033
BINA ADVANCED CONCRETE PRODUCTS COMPANY—See Bawan Company; *Int'l*, pg. 900
BINA ALAM BERSATU SDN BHD—See KUB Malaysia Berhad; *Int'l*, pg. 4319
BINA DARULAMAN BERHAD; *Int'l*, pg. 1032
BINAFIKIR SDN. BHD.—See Malayan Banking Berhad; *Int'l*, pg. 4659
BINANI CEMENT FACTORY LLC—See The Braj Binani Group; *Int'l*, pg. 7627
BINANI CEMENT LIMITED—See The Aditya Birla Group; *Int'l*, pg. 7611
BINANI ENERGY PVT. LTD—See The Braj Binani Group; *Int'l*, pg. 7627
BINANI INDUSTRIES LIMITED—See The Braj Binani Group; *Int'l*, pg. 7627
BINANI METALS LTD.—See The Braj Binani Group; *Int'l*, pg. 7627
BINANI ZINC LIMITED—See The Braj Binani Group; *Int'l*, pg. 7627
BINA PURI (B) SDN BHD—See Bina Puri Holdings Bhd; *Int'l*, pg. 1032
BINA PURI CONSTRUCTION SDN BHD—See Bina Puri Holdings Bhd; *Int'l*, pg. 1032
BINA PURI HOLDINGS BHD; *Int'l*, pg. 1032
BINA PURI PAKISTAN (PRIVATE) LTD.—See Bina Puri Holdings Bhd; *Int'l*, pg. 1032
BINA PURI PROPERTIES SDN BHD—See Bina Puri Holdings Bhd; *Int'l*, pg. 1032
BINA PURI SDN BHD—See Bina Puri Holdings Bhd; *Int'l*, pg. 1032
BINA READY-MIX CONCRETE PRODUCTS COMPANY—See Bawan Company; *Int'l*, pg. 900
BINAR ELEKTRONIK AB—See Pomona-Gruppen AB; *Int'l*, pg. 5918
BINAR HANDLING GMBH—See Pomona-Gruppen AB; *Int'l*, pg. 5918
BINAR HANDLING SUD GMBH—See Pomona-Gruppen AB; *Int'l*, pg. 5918
BINARI SONORI AMERICA INC.—See Canada Pension Plan Investment Board; *Int'l*, pg. 1280
BINARI SONORI AMERICA INC.—See EQT AB; *Int'l*, pg. 2482
BINARI SONORI AMERICA INC.—See Temasek Holdings (Private) Limited; *Int'l*, pg. 7548
BINARI SONORI S.R.L.—See Canada Pension Plan Investment Board; *Int'l*, pg. 1280
BINARI SONORI S.R.L.—See EQT AB; *Int'l*, pg. 2482
BINARI SONORI S.R.L.—See Temasek Holdings (Private) Limited; *Int'l*, pg. 7548
BINAR OLOFSTROM AB—See Pomona-Gruppen AB; *Int'l*, pg. 5918
BINAR QUICK-LIFT SYSTEMS AB—See Pomona-Gruppen AB; *Int'l*, pg. 5918
BINARY DEFENSE SYSTEMS, LLC; *U.S. Private*, pg. 560
BINARY FOUNTAIN INC.—See Ares Management Corporation; *U.S. Public*, pg. 190
BINARY FOUNTAIN INC.—See Leonard Green & Partners, L.P.; *U.S. Private*, pg. 2427
BINARY GROUP, INC.—See Cybergy Holdings, Inc.; *U.S. Private*, pg. 1133
BINARY NETWORKS PTY. LTD.—See Comms Group Ltd; *Int'l*, pg. 1720
BINARY TREE, INC.; *U.S. Private*, pg. 560
BINASAT COMMUNICATIONS BERHAD; *Int'l*, pg. 1033
BINAS D.D.; *Int'l*, pg. 1033
BINATONE COMMUNICATIONS EUROPE—See Binatone Electronics International Ltd.; *Int'l*, pg. 1033
BINATONE ELECTRONICS INTERNATIONAL LTD.; *Int'l*, pg. 1033
BINATONE GLOBAL ELECTRONICS (SHENZHEN) CO. LIMITED—See Binatone Electronics International Ltd.; *Int'l*, pg. 1033
BINATONE NORTH AMERICA INC.—See Binatone Electronics International Ltd.; *Int'l*, pg. 1033
BINATONE TELECOMMUNICATION PVT LIMITED—See Binatone Electronics International Ltd.; *Int'l*, pg. 1033

BINATONE TELECOM PLC—See Binatone Electronics International Ltd.; *Int'l*, pg. 1033
BINAWANI SDN BHD—See Ekovest Berhad; *Int'l*, pg. 2339
BINA WAREHOUSE SDN. BHD.; *Int'l*, pg. 1033
BINAYAK TEX PROCESSORS LIMITED; *Int'l*, pg. 1033
BIN CHUAN ENTERPRISE CORP.; *Int'l*, pg. 1032
BINCKBANK N.V.—See Zhejiang Geely Holding Group Co., Ltd.; *Int'l*, pg. 8653
BINDAGRAPHICS INC.; *U.S. Private*, pg. 560
BINDAGRAPHICS SOUTH, INC.—See Bindagraphics Inc.; *U.S. Private*, pg. 560
BINDAL EXPORTS LIMITED; *Int'l*, pg. 1033
BINDAREE BEEF PTY. LIMITED; *Int'l*, pg. 1033
BINDAR TRADING & INVESTMENT CO. PLC; *Int'l*, pg. 1033
BINDER ASIA PTE. LTD.—See MTQ Corporation Limited; *Int'l*, pg. 5071
BINDER+CO AG; *Int'l*, pg. 1033
BINDER GROUP PTY. LTD.—See MTQ Corporation Limited; *Int'l*, pg. 5071
BINDERHOLZ GMBH; *Int'l*, pg. 1033
BINDERHOLZ NORDIC OY—See Binderholz GmbH; *Int'l*, pg. 1033
BINDERLESS COAL BRIQUETTING COMPANY PTY. LTD—See White Energy Company Limited; *Int'l*, pg. 8398
BINDEV SDN. BHD.—See OSK Holdings Berhad; *Int'l*, pg. 5651
BINDI METALS LIMITED; *Int'l*, pg. 1033
THE BINDING SITE BENELUX B.V.—See Thermo Fisher Scientific Inc.; *U.S. Public*, pg. 2152
THE BINDING SITE BRASIL COMERCIO DE PRODUTOS PARA LABORATORIO LTDA.—See Thermo Fisher Scientific Inc.; *U.S. Public*, pg. 2152
THE BINDING SITE CORPORATION LIMITED—See Thermo Fisher Scientific Inc.; *U.S. Public*, pg. 2152
THE BINDING SITE FRANCE S.A.S.—See Thermo Fisher Scientific Inc.; *U.S. Public*, pg. 2152
THE BINDING SITE GMBH—See Thermo Fisher Scientific Inc.; *U.S. Public*, pg. 2152
THE BINDING SITE PORTUGAL, SPECIALIST PROTEIN COMPANY, UNIP LDA.—See Thermo Fisher Scientific Inc.; *U.S. Public*, pg. 2152
THE BINDING SITE PTE LTD.—See Thermo Fisher Scientific Inc.; *U.S. Public*, pg. 2152
THE BINDING SITE PTY LIMITED—See Thermo Fisher Scientific Inc.; *U.S. Public*, pg. 2152
THE BINDING SITE SPAIN (SPECIALIST PROTEIN COMPANY) S.L.—See Thermo Fisher Scientific Inc.; *U.S. Public*, pg. 2152
THE BINDING SITE S.R.L.—See Thermo Fisher Scientific Inc.; *U.S. Public*, pg. 2152
THE BINDING SITE S.R.O.—See Thermo Fisher Scientific Inc.; *U.S. Public*, pg. 2152
BINDTECH LLC; *U.S. Private*, pg. 560
BINET SA—See What's Cooking Group NV; *Int'l*, pg. 8396
BINEX CO., LTD.; *Int'l*, pg. 1033
BINEX INTERNATIONAL COMPANY FOR BUILDING MATERIALS LTD.—See Xenel Industries Ltd.; *Int'l*, pg. 8521
BINEX LINE CORP.; *U.S. Private*, pg. 560
BINGAMAN & SON LUMBER, INC.; *U.S. Private*, pg. 560
BING CONSTRUCTION COMPANY INC.; *U.S. Private*, pg. 560
BING ENERGY INTERNATIONAL, LLC; *U.S. Private*, pg. 560
BINGGRAE CO., LTD.; *Int'l*, pg. 1033
BINGHAM COOPERATIVE INC.; *U.S. Private*, pg. 560
BINGHAM GREENEBAUM DOLL LLP; *U.S. Private*, pg. 560
BINGHAM MEMORIAL HOSPITAL; *U.S. Private*, pg. 560
BINGHAMTON MATERIAL HANDLING, INC.—See Win Win, Inc.; *U.S. Private*, pg. 4532
BINGO EXPRESS CO., LTD.—See Nippon Express Holdings, Inc.; *Int'l*, pg. 5314
BINGO GROUP HOLDINGS LIMITED; *Int'l*, pg. 1033
BINGO INDUSTRIES LIMITED—See Macquarie Group Limited; *Int'l*, pg. 4626
BINGO KING COMPANY—See Arrow International, Inc.; *U.S. Private*, pg. 335
BINGO NATION, INC.; *U.S. Private*, pg. 561
BING POWER ORIGIN KFT.—See BING Power Systems GmbH; *Int'l*, pg. 1033
BING POWER SYSTEMS GMBH; *Int'l*, pg. 1033
BINGSHAN REFRIGERATION & HEAT TECHNOLOGIES CO., LTD.; *Int'l*, pg. 1033
BINHAI INVESTMENT COMPANY LIMITED; *Int'l*, pg. 1034
BINH CHANH CONSTRUCTION INVESTMENT JOINT STOCK COMPANY; *Int'l*, pg. 1034
BINH DIEN FERTILIZERS JOINT STOCK COMPANY—See Masan Consumer Corp.; *Int'l*, pg. 4719
BINH DINH BOOK & EQUIPMENT JOINT STOCK COMPANY; *Int'l*, pg. 1034
BINH DINH MINERALS JOINT STOCK COMPANY; *Int'l*, pg. 1034

COMPANY NAME INDEX

BINH DINH TOYOTA CO., LTD.—See Phu Tai Joint Stock Company; *Int'l*, pg. 5857
BINH DUONG MINERAL & CONSTRUCTION JSC; *Int'l*, pg. 1034
BINH DUONG PORT CORPORATION—See Gemadept Corporation; *Int'l*, pg. 2915
BINH DUONG WATER ENVIRONMENT JSC; *Int'l*, pg. 1034
BINH HIEP JOINT STOCK COMPANY—See DongNai Plastic JSC; *Int'l*, pg. 2169
BINH MINH PLASTICS JOINT STOCK COMPANY; *Int'l*, pg. 1034
BINH SON REFINING AND PETROCHEMICAL COMPANY LIMITED—See Vietnam Oil and Gas Group; *Int'l*, pg. 8202
BINH THANH IMPORT - EXPORT PRODUCTION & TRADE JSC; *Int'l*, pg. 1034
BINH THUAN BOOK & EQUIPMENT JOINT STOCK COMPANY; *Int'l*, pg. 1034
BINH TIEN DONG NAI IMEX CORP., PTE., LTD—See Binh Tien Imex Corp. Pte. Ltd.; *Int'l*, pg. 1034
BINH TIEN IMEX CORP. PTE. LTD.; *Int'l*, pg. 1034
BINJIANG SERVICE GROUP CO., LTD.; *Int'l*, pg. 1034
BINKELMAN CORPORATION; *U.S. Private*, pg. 561
BINKERT AG—See Nicolas Correa S.A.; *Int'l*, pg. 5272
BINKLEY & OBER INC.—See CRH plc; *Int'l*, pg. 1847
BINKS—See Illinois Tool Works Inc.; *U.S. Public*, pg. 1102
BINNINGTON COPELAND & ASSOCIATES (PTY.) LTD.—See Global Infrastructure Solutions, Inc.; *U.S. Private*, pg. 1715
BINNY LIMITED; *Int'l*, pg. 1034
BINNY MILLS LIMITED; *Int'l*, pg. 1034
BINNY'S INC.—See Gold Standard Enterprises Inc.; *U.S. Private*, pg. 1728
BINOL AB—See Quaker Chemical Corporation; *U.S. Public*, pg. 1745
BINOPTICS CORP.—See MACOM Technology Solutions Holdings, Inc.; *U.S. Public*, pg. 1352
BINOVI TECHNOLOGIES CORP.; *Int'l*, pg. 1034
BINS CORPORATION; *U.S. Private*, pg. 561
BINSONS HOSPITAL SUPPLIES INC.; *U.S. Private*, pg. 561
BINSWANGER BROOKER (THAILAND) LIMITED—See The Brooker Group Public Company Limited; *Int'l*, pg. 7630
BINSWANGER ENTERPRISES, LLC—See Wingate Partners, LLP; *U.S. Private*, pg. 4541
BINSWANGER INTERNATIONAL LTD.—See Binswanger Management Corp.; *U.S. Private*, pg. 561
BINSWANGER MANAGEMENT CORP.; *U.S. Private*, pg. 561
BINTAI KINDEN CORPORATION BERHAD—See Kinden Corporation; *Int'l*, pg. 4165
BINTAI KINDENKO PTE. LTD.—See Kinden Corporation; *Int'l*, pg. 4165
BINTANG SERIBU SDN. BHD.—See Can-One Berhad; *Int'l*, pg. 1276
BINTAN OFFSHORE FABRICATORS PTE LTD—See Keppel Corporation Limited; *Int'l*, pg. 4130
BINTAN RESORT FERRIES PRIVATE LIMITED—See Gallant Venture Ltd.; *Int'l*, pg. 2874
BINTAN RESORTS INTERNATIONAL PTE. LTD.—See Gallant Venture Ltd.; *Int'l*, pg. 2874
BINTER CANARIAS, S.A.; *Int'l*, pg. 1034
BINTER & CO PTE. LTD.—See Bridgestone Corporation; *Int'l*, pg. 1155
BINTERSISTEMAS—See Binter Canarias, S.A.; *Int'l*, pg. 1034
BINTERSWIFT—See Binter Canarias, S.A.; *Int'l*, pg. 1034
BINTERTECHNIC—See Binter Canarias, S.A.; *Int'l*, pg. 1034
BIN TO BOTTLE, LLC; *U.S. Private*, pg. 560
BINTULU EDIBLE OILS SDN BHD—See Wilmar International Limited; *Int'l*, pg. 8421
BINTULU PORT HOLDINGS BERHAD; *Int'l*, pg. 1034
BINTULU PORT SDN. BHD.—See Bintulu Port Holdings Berhad; *Int'l*, pg. 1034
BI NUTRACEUTICALS ASIA PACIFIC—See The Zuellig Group Inc.; *Int'l*, pg. 7705
B INVESTMENTS HOLDING SAE; *Int'l*, pg. 783
BINYL RECORDS INC.—See Avex Inc.; *Int'l*, pg. 740
BINZAGR BARWIL MARITIME TRANSPORT CO. LTD.—See Wilh. Wilhelmsen Holding ASA; *Int'l*, pg. 8410
BINZAGR COMPANY; *Int'l*, pg. 1035
BINZAGR FACTORY FOR INSULATION MATERIALS LTD.—See Binzagr Company; *Int'l*, pg. 1035
BINZAGR INDUSTRIAL CLEANING SERVICES—See Binzagr Company; *Int'l*, pg. 1035
BINZAGR UNILEVER CO.—See Unilever PLC; *Int'l*, pg. 8044
BIO3DMODEL S.R.L.—See Solid World S.p.A.; *Int'l*, pg. 7072
BIOACTIVE FOODS AS—See Zinzino AB; *Int'l*, pg. 8685
BIOACTIVE TECHNOLOGIES INTERNATIONAL LIMITED—See New Image Group Limited; *Int'l*, pg. 5225
BIOADAPTIVES, INC.; *U.S. Public*, pg. 334

BIOAFFINITY TECHNOLOGIES, INC.; *U.S. Public*, pg. 334
THE BIO AGENCY LTD.—See Mahindra & Mahindra Limited; *Int'l*, pg. 4648
BIOAGILYTIX LABS, LLC—See Cobepa S.A.; *Int'l*, pg. 1683
BIOAGRI AB—See Lantmannen ek for; *Int'l*, pg. 4413
BIOALGAE S.A.—See Abbott Laboratories; *U.S. Public*, pg. 19
BIOALPHA HOLDINGS BERHAD; *Int'l*, pg. 1036
BIOAMBER INC.; *Int'l*, pg. 1036
BIO-AMD, INC.; *Int'l*, pg. 1035
BIO-AMERICA, INC.; *Int'l*, pg. 1035
BIOANALYTICA AG—See Sonic Healthcare Limited; *Int'l*, pg. 7096
BIOARCTIC AB; *Int'l*, pg. 1036
BIOARRAY SOLUTIONS, LTD.—See Werfen Life Group, S.A.U.; *Int'l*, pg. 8379
BIOARTIGAS—See Ente Vasco de la Energia; *Int'l*, pg. 2450
BIOASIS TECHNOLOGIES INC.; *U.S. Public*, pg. 335
BIOATLA, INC; *U.S. Public*, pg. 335
BIOAUTHORIZE HOLDINGS, INC.; *U.S. Private*, pg. 561
BIOBASE CORPORATION—See Incyte Corporation; *U.S. Public*, pg. 1115
BIO BASIC CANADA INC.—See BBI Life Sciences Corporation; *Int'l*, pg. 920
BIOBE AS—See BEWi ASA; *Int'l*, pg. 1004
BIOBEST S.A.—See Floridienne SA; *Int'l*, pg. 2708
BIOBLOCKS, INC.—See Genesis Biotechnology Group, LLC; *U.S. Private*, pg. 1669
BIO-BLOOD COMPONENTS, INC.—See Grifols, S.A.; *Int'l*, pg. 3085
BIO-BRIDGE SCIENCE, INC.; *U.S. Public*, pg. 332
BIOBRIDGES LLC—See Adecco Group AG; *Int'l*, pg. 141
BIOCANCELL THERAPEUTICS ISRAEL LTD.—See Chemomab Therapeutics Ltd.; *Int'l*, pg. 1463
BIOCARDIA, INC.; *U.S. Public*, pg. 335
BIOCARDIA LIFESCIENCES, INC.—See BioCardia, Inc.; *U.S. Public*, pg. 335
BIOCARE EUROPE S.R.L.—See FUJIFILM Holdings Corporation; *Int'l*, pg. 2821
BIOCARE LIMITED—See Elder Pharmaceuticals Ltd.; *Int'l*, pg. 2346
BIOCARE MEDICAL, LLC; *U.S. Private*, pg. 561
BIOCARE TECHNOLOGY COMPANY LIMITED—See Fresenius Medical Care AG; *Int'l*, pg. 2775
BIOCARTIS GROUP NV; *Int'l*, pg. 1036
BIOCARTIS US INC.—See Biocartis Group NV; *Int'l*, pg. 1036
BIOCATALYSTS LTD.—See BRAIN Biotech AG; *Int'l*, pg. 1137
BIOCAT GMBH—See AddLife AB; *Int'l*, pg. 129
BIO C' BON JAPON CO., LTD.—See AEON Co., Ltd.; *Int'l*, pg. 177
BIOCELL TECHNOLOGY LIMITED—See China Regenerative Medicine International Co., Ltd.; *Int'l*, pg. 1547
BIOCELTIX S.A.; *Int'l*, pg. 1036
BIOCENTRIC ENERGY HOLDINGS, INC.; *U.S. Public*, pg. 335
BIOCENTRIC HEALTH INC.; *U.S. Private*, pg. 561
BIOCEPT, INC.; *U.S. Public*, pg. 335
BIOCERES CROP SOLUTIONS CORP.—See Bioceres S.A.; *Int'l*, pg. 1036
BIOCERES S.A.; *Int'l*, pg. 1036
BIOCEVAL GMBH & CO. KG—See RETHMANN AG & Co. KG; *Int'l*, pg. 6306
BIOCHECK, INC.—See OriGene Technologies, Inc.; *U.S. Private*, pg. 3042
BIO-CHEM FLUIDICS INC.—See Halma plc; *Int'l*, pg. 3231
BIO-CHEM TECHNOLOGY (HK) LIMITED—See Global Bio-chem Technology Group Company Limited; *Int'l*, pg. 2993
BIOCHROM GMBH—See Merck KGaA; *Int'l*, pg. 4830
BIOCHROM LTD.—See Harvard Bioscience, Inc.; *U.S. Public*, pg. 987
BIOCHROM US, INC.—See Harvard Bioscience, Inc.; *U.S. Public*, pg. 987
BIO-CIDE INTERNATIONAL, INC.—See Kemin Industries, Inc.; *U.S. Private*, pg. 2281
BIO CLEAN ENVIRONMENTAL SERVICES—See Lone Star Global Acquisitions, LLC; *U.S. Private*, pg. 2487
BIO-CLEAN INTERNATIONAL, INC.; *U.S. Public*, pg. 332
BIOCLEANSE LTD.—See Getinge AB; *Int'l*, pg. 2949
BIOCLINICA, INC.—See Astorg Partners S.A.S.; *Int'l*, pg. 657
BIOCLINICA, INC.—See Nordic Capital AB; *Int'l*, pg. 5421
BIOCLINICA, INC.—See Novo Nordisk Fonden; *Int'l*, pg. 5465
BIOCNG, LLC—See Tetra Tech, Inc.; *U.S. Public*, pg. 2022
BIOCODEX AB—See Biocodex SA; *Int'l*, pg. 1036
BIOCODEX, INC.—See Biocodex SA; *Int'l*, pg. 1036
BIOCODEX OY—See Biocodex SA; *Int'l*, pg. 1036
BIOCODEX SA; *Int'l*, pg. 1036
BIOCODEX SIA—See Biocodex SA; *Int'l*, pg. 1036
BIOCODEX UAB—See Biocodex SA; *Int'l*, pg. 1036
BIOCOMPATIBLES INC.—See Boston Scientific Corporation; *U.S. Public*, pg. 373

BIOETHICS, LTD.

BIOCOMPATIBLES UK LIMITED—See Boston Scientific Corporation; *U.S. Public*, pg. 373
BIOCOMPOSITES LTD.—See TA Associates, Inc.; *U.S. Private*, pg. 3914
BIOCON 1, LLC—See Nephros, Inc.; *U.S. Public*, pg. 1506
BIOCON ACADEMY PVT. LTD.—See Biocon Ltd.; *Int'l*, pg. 1036
BIOCON BIOLOGICS LIMITED—See Eris Lifesciences Limited; *Int'l*, pg. 2493
BIOCON BIOPHARMACEUTICALS PRIVATE LIMITED—See Biocon Ltd.; *Int'l*, pg. 1036
BIO-CONCEPT LABORATORIES, INC—See Leonard Green & Partners, L.P.; *U.S. Private*, pg. 2426
BIOCON LTD.; *Int'l*, pg. 1036
BIOCON SDN. BHD.—See Biocon Ltd.; *Int'l*, pg. 1036
BIOCORE B.V.—See BayWa AG; *Int'l*, pg. 917
BIOCORP SA—See Novo Nordisk Fonden; *Int'l*, pg. 5463
BIOCORRX INC.; *U.S. Public*, pg. 335
BIOCOSMETIQUES S.A.—See Intercos S.p.A.; *Int'l*, pg. 3739
BIOCRATES LIFE SCIENCES AG; *Int'l*, pg. 1036
BIOCRUDE TECHNOLOGIES INC.; *Int'l*, pg. 1037
BIOCRUDE TECHNOLOGIES USA, INC.; *Int'l*, pg. 1037
BIOCRYST PHARMACEUTICALS, INC.; *U.S. Public*, pg. 335
BIOCSL (NZ) LTD—See CSL Limited; *Int'l*, pg. 1867
BIOCYCLING GMBH—See Veolia Environnement S.A.; *Int'l*, pg. 8153
BIOCYTOGEN BOSTON CORP.—See Biocytogen Pharmaceuticals (Beijing) Co., Ltd.; *Int'l*, pg. 1037
BIOCYTOGEN PHARMACEUTICALS (BEIJING) CO., LTD.; *Int'l*, pg. 1037
BIODAROU PLC—See Grifols, S.A.; *Int'l*, pg. 3084
BIODELIVERY SCIENCES INTERNATIONAL, INC.—See Collegium Pharmaceutical, Inc.; *U.S. Public*, pg. 533
BIODERM INC.; *U.S. Private*, pg. 561
BIODESIX, INC.; *U.S. Public*, pg. 335
BIO-DETEK, INC.—See Asahi Kasei Corporation; *Int'l*, pg. 597
BIODEXA PHARMACEUTICALS PLC; *Int'l*, pg. 1037
BIODEX MEDICAL SYSTEMS, INC.—See Mirion Technologies, Inc.; *U.S. Public*, pg. 1450
BIODIEM LIMITED; *Int'l*, pg. 1037
BIODIESEL OF LAS VEGAS INC.—See New-Com Inc.; *U.S. Private*, pg. 2913
BIODIESEL OKAYAMA CO,. LTD.—See Dowa Holdings Co., Ltd.; *Int'l*, pg. 2183
BIODIRECT INC.—See Copia Scientific, Inc.; *U.S. Private*, pg. 1044
BIODISCOVERY, INC.—See Bionano Genomics, Inc.; *U.S. Public*, pg. 338
BIO-DISTRIFRAIS AUBAGNE—See PAI Partners S.A.S.; *Int'l*, pg. 5700
BIO-DISTRIFRAIS-CHANTENAT SAS—See PAI Partners S.A.S.; *Int'l*, pg. 5700
BIOD,LLC—See Integra LifeSciences Holdings Corporation; *U.S. Public*, pg. 1135
BIODOT, INC.—See ATS Corporation; *Int'l*, pg. 695
BIODTECH, INC.; *U.S. Private*, pg. 561
BIODUE S.P.A; *Int'l*, pg. 1037
BIODURO LLC—See Advent International Corporation; *U.S. Private*, pg. 98
BIODYNE CO., LTD.; *Int'l*, pg. 1037
BIOEKO GRUPA TAURON SP. Z O.O.—See Tauron Polska Energia S.A.; *Int'l*, pg. 7476
BIOELECTRONICS CORP.; *U.S. Public*, pg. 335
BIOELEKTROWNIA HYDROPOL-4 SP. Z O.O.—See Synthos S.A.; *Int'l*, pg. 7387
BIOELEMENTS, INC.; *U.S. Private*, pg. 561
BIOELIFE CORP.; *U.S. Public*, pg. 335
BIO ENERGIA GUARCINO S.R.L.—See Neodecortech S.p.A.; *Int'l*, pg. 5196
BIOENERGIE AHLEN GMBH & CO. KG—See Biogas Nord AG; *Int'l*, pg. 1038
BIOENERGIE ELBE-ELSTER GMBH & CO. KG—See Munchener Ruckversicherungs AG; *Int'l*, pg. 5085
BIOENERGIE MERZIG GMBH—See E.ON SE; *Int'l*, pg. 2251
BIOENERGIE TAUFKIRCHEN GMBH & CO. KG—See Stadtwerke Munchen GmbH; *Int'l*, pg. 7162
BIOENERGIE VERWALTUNGS-GMBH—See Munchener Ruckversicherungs AG; *Int'l*, pg. 5085
BIO-ENGINEERED SUPPLEMENTS & NUTRITION, INC.—See Glanbia Co-Operative Society Limited; *Int'l*, pg. 2987
THE BIOENGINEERING GROUP, INC.; *U.S. Private*, pg. 3995
BIO-EN HOLDINGS CORP.; *U.S. Public*, pg. 332
BIOENZYMES PTY LTD.; *Int'l*, pg. 1037
BIOEPIDERM GMBH—See Bio-Gate AG; *Int'l*, pg. 1035
BIOERA S.P.A.; *Int'l*, pg. 1037
BIOERDGAS HALLERTAU GMBH—See E.ON SE; *Int'l*, pg. 2251
BIO ESSENCE CORP.; *U.S. Public*, pg. 332
BIO ESSENCE HERBAL ESSENTIALS INC.; *U.S. Private*, pg. 561
BIOETHICS, LTD.; *U.S. Public*, pg. 335
BIOEUROPE GMBH—See Biomerica, Inc.; *U.S. Public*, pg. 337

BIOETHICS, LTD.
CORPORATE AFFILIATIONS

BIOEXAM AG—See Sonic Healthcare Limited; *Int'l*, pg. 7096
BIOEXTRAX AB; *Int'l*, pg. 1037
BIOFARMA SRL—See Ardian SAS; *Int'l*, pg. 555
BIOFARM SRL—See SIF Banat-Crisana S.A.; *Int'l*, pg. 6905
BIO FD&C CO., LTD.; *Int'l*, pg. 1035
BIOFERMIN PHARMACEUTICAL CO., LTD.—See Taisho Pharmaceutical Holdings Co., Ltd; *Int'l*, pg. 7417
BIOFERMS GMBH—See Viessmann Werke GmbH & Co. KG; *Int'l*, pg. 8196
BIOFIL CHEMICALS & PHARMACEUTICALS LIMITED; *Int'l*, pg. 1037
BIOFILM, INC.—See Combe Incorporated; *U.S. Private*, pg. 980
BIOFINA, INC.; *U.S. Private*, pg. 561
BIOFIN HOLDING INTERNATIONAL BV—See DiaSorin S.p.A.; *Int'l*, pg. 2106
BIOFISH HOLDING AS; *Int'l*, pg. 1037
BIO-FLEX SOLUTIONS, L.L.C.—See Repligen Corporation; *U.S. Public*, pg. 1784
BIOFLEX S.R.L.—See Recticel S.A.; *Int'l*, pg. 6241
BIOFOCUS DPI AG—See Charles River Laboratories International, Inc.; *U.S. Public*, pg. 480
BIOFOCUS DPI (HOLDINGS) LIMITED—See Charles River Laboratories International, Inc.; *U.S. Public*, pg. 480
BIOFOCUS DPI—See Charles River Laboratories International, Inc.; *U.S. Public*, pg. 480
BIOFOCUS, INC.—See Charles River Laboratories International, Inc.; *U.S. Public*, pg. 480
BIOFORCE NANOSCIENCES HOLDINGS, INC.; *U.S. Public*, pg. 335
BIOFOREST PTE LTD—See Samko Timber Limited; *Int'l*, pg. 6506
BIOFORTIS, INC.—See IQVIA Holdings Inc.; *U.S. Public*, pg. 1168
BIOFRONTERA AG; *Int'l*, pg. 1037
BIOFRONTERA INC.; *U.S. Public*, pg. 335
BIOFUEL ENERGY SYSTEMS, LLC—See Rentech, Inc.; *U.S. Private*, pg. 3400
BIOFUEL RESEARCH PTE LTD—See USP Group Limited; *Int'l*, pg. 8099
BIOFUELS ENERGY, LLC; *U.S. Private*, pg. 561
BIOFUELS MARKETING, INC.—See Aemetis, Inc.; *U.S. Public*, pg. 52
BIOFUELS POWER CORP.; *U.S. Private*, pg. 561
BIOGAIA AB; *Int'l*, pg. 1037
BIOGAIA JAPAN INC.—See Biogaia AB; *Int'l*, pg. 1037
BIOGAIA PHARMA AB—See Biogaia AB; *Int'l*, pg. 1038
BIOGAS DUCHEROW GMBH—See E.ON SE; *Int'l*, pg. 2251
BIOGAS ENERGY SOLUTIONS, LLC; *U.S. Private*, pg. 561
BIOGAS FRIEDLAND GMBH & CO. KG—See EnviTec Biogas AG; *Int'l*, pg. 2455
BIOGAS HERZBERG GMBH & CO. KG—See EnviTec Biogas AG; *Int'l*, pg. 2455
BIOGAS NEU KOSENOW GMBH & CO KG—See Alpiq Holding AG; *Int'l*, pg. 372
BIOGAS NIEHEIM GMBH & CO. KG—See EnviTec Biogas AG; *Int'l*, pg. 2455
BIOGAS NORD AG; *Int'l*, pg. 1038
BIOGAS NORD ANLAGENBAU GMBH—See Biogas Nord AG; *Int'l*, pg. 1038
BIOGAS NORD POLSKA SP.Z O.O.—See Biogas Nord AG; *Int'l*, pg. 1038
BIOGAS NORD UK LTD.—See Biogas Nord AG; *Int'l*, pg. 1038
BIOGASPARK NV; *Int'l*, pg. 1038
BIO-GATE AG; *Int'l*, pg. 1035
BIOGAZ FEJLESZTO KFT.—See AGRANA Beteiligungs-AG; *Int'l*, pg. 214
BIOGEMMA S.A.S.—See Avril SCA; *Int'l*, pg. 750
BIOGEMMA S.A.S.—See Euralis Coop; *Int'l*, pg. 2527
BIOGEMMA S.A.S.—See Groupe Limagrain Holding SA; *Int'l*, pg. 3107
BIOGEN (ARGENTINA) SRL—See Biogen Inc.; *U.S. Public*, pg. 336
BIOGEN AUSTRALIA PTY LTD—See Biogen Inc.; *U.S. Public*, pg. 336
BIOGEN BELGIUM N.V./S.A.—See Biogen Inc.; *U.S. Public*, pg. 336
BIOGEN BRASIL PRODUTOS FARMACEUTICOS LTDA—See Biogen Inc.; *U.S. Public*, pg. 336
BIOGEN CANADA INC.—See Biogen Inc.; *U.S. Public*, pg. 336
BIOGEN (CZECH REPUBLIC) S.R.O.—See Biogen Inc.; *U.S. Public*, pg. 336
BIOGEN (DENMARK) A/S—See Biogen Inc.; *U.S. Public*, pg. 336
BIOGEN (DENMARK) A/S—See Biogen Inc.; *U.S. Public*, pg. 336
BIOGEND THERAPEUTICS CO., LTD.; *Int'l*, pg. 1038
BIOGENE PHARMA LTD.—See Mauna Kea Technologies SA; *Int'l*, pg. 4732
BIOGENESIS BAGO S.A.—See Bago Group; *Int'l*, pg. 799
BIOGEN ESTONIA OU—See Biogen Inc.; *U.S. Public*, pg. 336
BIO-GENE TECHNOLOGY LIMITED; *Int'l*, pg. 1035

BIOGENETICS CO.,LTD. - CHINA FACTORY—See Billions Co., Ltd.; *Int'l*, pg. 1031
BIOGENETICS CO.,LTD. - JEUNGPYOUNG FACTORY—See Billions Co., Ltd.; *Int'l*, pg. 1031
BIOGEN FINLAND OY—See Biogen Inc.; *U.S. Public*, pg. 336
BIOGEN FRANCE S.A.S.—See Biogen Inc.; *U.S. Public*, pg. 336
BIOGEN GMBH—See Biogen Inc.; *U.S. Public*, pg. 336
BIOGEN HEMOPHILIA INC.—See Biogen Inc.; *U.S. Public*, pg. 336
BIOGEN HONG KONG LIMITED—See Biogen Inc.; *U.S. Public*, pg. 336
BIOGEN HUNGARY KFT—See Biogen Inc.; *U.S. Public*, pg. 336
BIOGEN IDEC BELGIUM S.A./N.V.—See Biogen Inc.; *U.S. Public*, pg. 336
BIOGEN IDEC (DENMARK) MANUFACTURING APS—See Biogen Inc.; *U.S. Public*, pg. 336
BIOGEN IDEC FRANCE—See Biogen Inc.; *U.S. Public*, pg. 336
BIOGEN IDEC GMBH—See Biogen Inc.; *U.S. Public*, pg. 336
BIOGEN IDEC GMBH—See Biogen Inc.; *U.S. Public*, pg. 336
BIOGEN IDEC IBERIA—See Biogen Inc.; *U.S. Public*, pg. 336
BIOGEN IDEC INTERNATIONAL B.V.—See Biogen Inc.; *U.S. Public*, pg. 336
BIOGEN IDEC INTERNATIONAL GMBH—See Biogen Inc.; *U.S. Public*, pg. 336
BIOGEN IDEC (IRELAND) LTD.—See Biogen Inc.; *U.S. Public*, pg. 336
BIOGEN IDEC JAPAN LTD.—See Biogen Inc.; *U.S. Public*, pg. 336
BIOGEN IDEC LIMITED—See Biogen Inc.; *U.S. Public*, pg. 336
BIOGEN IDEC MA INC.—See Biogen Inc.; *U.S. Public*, pg. 336
BIOGEN IDEC PORTUGAL SOCIEDADE FARMACEUTICA, UNIPESSOAL, LDA.—See Biogen Inc.; *U.S. Public*, pg. 336
BIOGEN IDEC RESEARCH & CORPORATE CAMPUS—See Biogen Inc.; *U.S. Public*, pg. 336
BIOGEN IDEC (SINGAPORE) PTE LTD—See Biogen Inc.; *U.S. Public*, pg. 336
BIOGEN IDEC SWEDEN AB—See Biogen Inc.; *U.S. Public*, pg. 336
BIOGEN INC.; *U.S. Public*, pg. 335
BIOGEN INTERNATIONAL GMBH—See Biogen Inc.; *U.S. Public*, pg. 336
BIOGEN ITALIA SRL—See Biogen Inc.; *U.S. Public*, pg. 336
BIOGEN JAPAN LTD.—See Biogen Inc.; *U.S. Public*, pg. 336
BIOGEN KOREA—See Biogen Inc.; *U.S. Public*, pg. 336
BIOGEN LATVIA SIA—See Biogen Inc.; *U.S. Public*, pg. 336
BIOGEN LIMITED; *Int'l*, pg. 1038
BIOGEN LITHUANIA UAB—See Biogen Inc.; *U.S. Public*, pg. 336
BIOGEN NETHERLANDS B.V.—See Biogen Inc.; *U.S. Public*, pg. 336
BIOGEN NEW VENTURES INC.—See Biogen Inc.; *U.S. Public*, pg. 336
BIOGEN NORWAY AS—See Biogen Inc.; *U.S. Public*, pg. 336
BIOGEN NZ BIOPHARMA LTD—See Biogen Inc.; *U.S. Public*, pg. 336
BIOGENOMICS LTD.—See MB Holding Company LLC; *Int'l*, pg. 4750
BIOGEN PHARMA D.O.O.—See Biogen Inc.; *U.S. Public*, pg. 336
BIOGEN PHARMA, FARMACEVTSKA IN BIOTEHNOLOSKA DRUZBA D.O.O—See Biogen Inc.; *U.S. Public*, pg. 336
BIOGEN POLAND SP. Z.O.O—See Biogen Inc.; *U.S. Public*, pg. 336
BIOGEN PORTUGAL SOCIEDADE FARMACEUTICA, UNIPESSOAL, LDA.—See Biogen Inc.; *U.S. Public*, pg. 337
BIOGEN SLOVAKIA S.R.O.—See Biogen Inc.; *U.S. Public*, pg. 337
BIOGEN SPAIN, S.L.—See Biogen Inc.; *U.S. Public*, pg. 337
BIOGEN SWEDEN AB—See Biogen Inc.; *U.S. Public*, pg. 337
BIOGEN SWITZERLAND AG—See Biogen Inc.; *U.S. Public*, pg. 337
BIOGEN U.S. CORPORATION—See Biogen Inc.; *U.S. Public*, pg. 337
BIOGLAN AB—See Reig Jofre Group; *Int'l*, pg. 6257
BIOGRAN S.L.—See PAI Partners S.A.S.; *Int'l*, pg. 5700
THE BIOGRAPHY CHANNEL—See The Hearst Corporation; *U.S. Private*, pg. 4045
THE BIOGRAPHY CHANNEL—See The Walt Disney Company; *U.S. Public*, pg. 2137
BIO GREEN ENERGY TECH PUBLIC COMPANY; *Int'l*, pg. 1035

BIO GREEN PAPERS LIMITED; *Int'l*, pg. 1035
BIO GREEN PAPERS LIMITED - SRIKAKULAM FACILITY—See Bio Green Papers Limited; *Int'l*, pg. 1035
BIOGROUPUSA, INC.; *U.S. Private*, pg. 562
BIO HABITAT SAS—See Beneteau S.A; *Int'l*, pg. 972
BIOHABITATS, INC.; *U.S. Private*, pg. 562
BIOHARVEST SCIENCES INC.; *Int'l*, pg. 1038
BIOHAVEN LTD.; *U.S. Public*, pg. 337
BIOHAVEN PHARMACEUTICAL HOLDING COMPANY LTD.—See Pfizer Inc.; *U.S. Public*, pg. 1679
BIOHELP - BIOLOGISCHER PFLANZENSCHUTZ-NUTZLINGSPRODUKTIONS-, HANDELS- UND BERATUNGS GMBH—See BayWa AG; *Int'l*, pg. 919
BIOHIT BIOTECH (SUZHOU) CO. LTD.—See Sartorius AG; *Int'l*, pg. 6578
BIOHIT FRANCE S.A.S.—See Sartorius AG; *Int'l*, pg. 6578
BIOHIT OOO—See Sartorius AG; *Int'l*, pg. 6578
BIOHORIZONS CAMLOG ITALIA SRL—See Henry Schein, Inc.; *U.S. Public*, pg. 1025
BIOHORIZONS, INC.—See Henry Schein, Inc.; *U.S. Public*, pg. 1025
BIOIASIS JSC; *Int'l*, pg. 1038
BIOINFRA LIFE SCIENCE INC; *Int'l*, pg. 1038
BIOINGENIERIA DEHNER S.R.L.; *Int'l*, pg. 1038
BIOINVENT INTERNATIONAL AB; *Int'l*, pg. 1038
BIO-ITECH B.V.—See Eppendorf AG; *Int'l*, pg. 2464
BIOIVT, LLC; *U.S. Private*, pg. 562
BIO-JOURDENESS COSMETIC CO. (MY) SDN. BHD.—See Jourdeness Group Limited; *Int'l*, pg. 4003
BIOKARPET BULGARIA E.O.O.D.—See Biokarpet S.A.; *Int'l*, pg. 1038
BIOKARPET ROMANIA S.R.L.—See Biokarpet S.A.; *Int'l*, pg. 1038
BIOKARPET S.A.; *Int'l*, pg. 1038
BIO-KEY HONG KONG LIMITED—See BIO-key International, Inc.; *U.S. Public*, pg. 332
BIO-KEY INTERNATIONAL, INC.; *U.S. Public*, pg. 332
BIOKIRCH GMBH—See Dermapharm Holding SE; *Int'l*, pg. 2043
BIOKIT S.A.—See Werfen Life Group, S.A.U.; *Int'l*, pg. 8378
BIOKLEEN MILJOKEMI AB—See OrganoClick AB; *Int'l*, pg. 5619
BIOKOSMES SRL—See Venture Life Group PLC; *Int'l*, pg. 8152
BIOKRAFT INTERNATIONAL AB; *Int'l*, pg. 1038
BIOKRAFT NATURBRENNSTOFFE GMBH.—See MVV Energie AG; *Int'l*, pg. 5108
BIOKYOWA INC.—See Kirin Holdings Company, Limited; *Int'l*, pg. 4188
BIOLAB ARABIA LTD. - JUBAIL FACTORY—See Al-Hejailan Group; *Int'l*, pg. 286
BIOLAB ARABIA LTD.—See Al-Hejailan Group; *Int'l*, pg. 286
BIOLAB, INC.—See Centerbridge Partners, L.P.; *U.S. Private*, pg. 815
BIOLAC GMBH & CO. KG—See Arla Foods amba; *Int'l*, pg. 572
BIOLAND CO., LTD - ANSAN PLANT—See Hyundai Bioland Co., Ltd.; *Int'l*, pg. 3555
BIOLAND CO., LTD - OCHANG PLANT—See Hyundai Bioland Co., Ltd.; *Int'l*, pg. 3555
BIOLAND CO., LTD - OSONG PLANT—See Hyundai Bioland Co., Ltd.; *Int'l*, pg. 3555
BIOLARGO ENGINEERING, SCIENCE & TECHNOLOGIES, LLC—See BioLargo, Inc.; *U.S. Public*, pg. 337
BIOLARGO, INC.; *U.S. Public*, pg. 337
BIOLARGO WATER, INC.—See BioLargo, Inc.; *U.S. Public*, pg. 337
BIOLASCO TAIWAN CO., LTD.; *Int'l*, pg. 1038
BIOLASE EUROPE GMBH—See BIOLASE, Inc.; *U.S. Public*, pg. 337
BIOLASE, INC.; *U.S. Public*, pg. 337
BIOLCHIM S.P.A.—See Chequers SA; *Int'l*, pg. 1471
BIOLCHIM S.P.A.—See Neuberger Berman Group LLC; *U.S. Private*, pg. 2890
BIOLEADERS CORPORATION; *Int'l*, pg. 1038
BIOLECTRIC NV—See Ackermans & van Haaren NV; *Int'l*, pg. 104
BIOLEGEND, INC.—See Revvity, Inc.; *U.S. Public*, pg. 1793
BIOLIDICS LIMITED; *Int'l*, pg. 1038
BIOLIFE, LLC; *U.S. Private*, pg. 562
BIO-LIFE MARKETING SDN. BHD.—See Mega Lifesciences Public Company Limited; *Int'l*, pg. 4792
BIOLIFE REMEDIES, INC.; *Int'l*, pg. 1039
BIOLIFE SOLUTIONS, INC.; *U.S. Public*, pg. 337
BIOLIGHT LIFE SCIENCES LTD.; *Int'l*, pg. 1039
BIOLINE GMBH—See Meridian Bioscience Inc.; *U.S. Public*, pg. 1424
BIOLINE INNOVATIONS JERUSALEM—See BioLineRX Ltd.; *Int'l*, pg. 1039
BIOLINE LTD.—See Meridian Bioscience Inc.; *U.S. Public*, pg. 1424
BIOLINE REAGENTS LTD.—See Meridian Bioscience Inc.; *U.S. Public*, pg. 1424
BIOLINERX LTD.; *Int'l*, pg. 1039

COMPANY NAME INDEX

BIOLINE USA INC.—See Meridian Bioscience Inc.; *U.S. Public*, pg. 1424
BIOLINKER S.A.—See Abbott Laboratories; *U.S. Public*, pg. 19
BIOLIN SCIENTIFIC AB—See AddLife AB; *Int'l*, pg. 129
BIOLIN SCIENTIFIC LIMITED—See AddLife AB; *Int'l*, pg. 129
BIOLIN SCIENTIFIC OY—See AddLife AB; *Int'l*, pg. 129
BIOLITEC AG; *Int'l*, pg. 1039
BIOLITEC ITALIA SRL—See biolitec AG; *Int'l*, pg. 1039
BIOLITEC (M) SDN. BHD.—See biolitec AG; *Int'l*, pg. 1039
BIOLITEC PHARMA (IRELAND) LTD.—See biolitec AG; *Int'l*, pg. 1039
BIOLOG DEVICE CO., LTD; *Int'l*, pg. 1039
BIOLOGICAL E. LIMITED; *Int'l*, pg. 1039
BIOLOGICAL - GESTAO DE RESIDUOS INDUSTRIAIS, LDA.—See SODIM, SGPS, SA; *Int'l*, pg. 7049
BIOLOGICAL MEDIATION SYSTEMS, LLC—See Worth Investment Group, LLC; *U.S. Private*, pg. 4570
BIOLOGICAL SPECIALTY COMPANY LLC—See BioIVT, LLC; *U.S. Private*, pg. 562
BIOLOGICI ITALIA LABORATORIES S.R.L.—See Recipharm AB; *Int'l*, pg. 6235
BIOLOGICS DEVELOPMENT SERVICES, LLC; *U.S. Private*, pg. 562
BIOLOGICS, INC.—See McKesson Corporation; *U.S. Public*, pg. 1407
BIOLOGISCHE HEILMITTEL HEEL GMBH—See Delton AG; *Int'l*, pg. 2021
BIOLUMIX, INC.—See Neogen Corporation; *U.S. Public*, pg. 1505
BIOMAGNETICS DIAGNOSTICS CORP.; *U.S. Public*, pg. 337
BIOMAR A/S—See Aktieselskabet Schouw & Co.; *Int'l*, pg. 265
BIOMAR AS—See Aktieselskabet Schouw & Co.; *Int'l*, pg. 265
BIOMAR CHILE SA—See Aktieselskabet Schouw & Co.; *Int'l*, pg. 265
BIOMAR GROUP A/S—See Aktieselskabet Schouw & Co.; *Int'l*, pg. 265
BIOMAR HELLENIC SA—See Aktieselskabet Schouw & Co.; *Int'l*, pg. 265
BIOMAR IBERIA S.A.—See Aktieselskabet Schouw & Co.; *Int'l*, pg. 265
BIOMARIN BRASIL FARMACEUTICA LTDA.—See BioMarin Pharmaceutical Inc.; *U.S. Public*, pg. 337
BIOMARIN INTERNATIONAL LTD—See BioMarin Pharmaceutical Inc.; *U.S. Public*, pg. 337
BIOMARIN LEIDEN HOLDING BV—See BioMarin Pharmaceutical Inc.; *U.S. Public*, pg. 337
BIOMARIN PHARMACEUTICAL INC.; *U.S. Public*, pg. 337
BIOMARK DIAGNOSTICS INC.; *Int'l*, pg. 1039
BIOMARKETING SERVICES (M) SDN BHD—See HORIBA Ltd; *Int'l*, pg. 3475
BIOMARK, INC.; *U.S. Private*, pg. 562
BIOMAR LTD.—See Aktieselskabet Schouw & Co.; *Int'l*, pg. 265
BIOMAR OOO—See Aktieselskabet Schouw & Co.; *Int'l*, pg. 265
BIOMAR S.A.S.—See Aktieselskabet Schouw & Co.; *Int'l*, pg. 265
BIOMAR SP. Z.O.O.—See Aktieselskabet Schouw & Co.; *Int'l*, pg. 265
BIOMAR SRL—See Aktieselskabet Schouw & Co.; *Int'l*, pg. 265
BIOMASSEANLAGE ESSENHEIM GMBH—See Veolia Environnement S.A.; *Int'l*, pg. 8153
BIOMASSEHEIZKRAFTWERK EMDEN GMBH—See E.ON SE; *Int'l*, pg. 2251
BIOMASS ENERGY CORPORATION—See Pine Capital Group Limited; *Int'l*, pg. 5867
BIOMASSEN-HEIZKRAFTWERK ALTENSTADT GMBH.—See MVV Energie AG; *Int'l*, pg. 5108
BIOMASS HEATING SOLUTIONS LTD.; *Int'l*, pg. 1039
BIOMASS HOLDINGS S.A R.L.—See Deutsche Bank Aktiengesellschaft; *Int'l*, pg. 2055
BIOMASS SECURE POWER INC.; *Int'l*, pg. 1039
BIOMASTER, INC.—See Kaneka Corporation; *Int'l*, pg. 4066
BIOMATRICA, INC.—See Exact Sciences Corporation; *U.S. Public*, pg. 805
BIO-MATRIX SCIENTIFIC GROUP, INC.; *U.S. Public*, pg. 332
BIOMATRIX SPECIALTY PHARMACY, LLC—See Frazier Management, LLC; *U.S. Private*, pg. 1600
BIOMAT, S.A.—See Grifols, S.A.; *Int'l*, pg. 3084
BIOMAT USA - ALTAMONTE SPRINGS—See Grifols, S.A.; *Int'l*, pg. 3084
BIOMAT USA, INC.—See Grifols, S.A.; *Int'l*, pg. 3084
BIOMAT USA - VAN NUYS—See Grifols, S.A.; *Int'l*, pg. 3084
BIOMAX ENVIRONMENTAL TECHNOLOGY (BEIJING) LIMITED—See Capital Environment Holdings Limited; *Int'l*, pg. 1310
BIOMAX ENVIRONMENTAL TECHNOLOGY (SHANGHAI) COMPANY LIMITED—See Capital Environment Holdings Limited; *Int'l*, pg. 1310

BIOMAX RUBBER INDUSTRIES LIMITED; *Int'l*, pg. 1039
BIOMEA FUSION, INC.; *U.S. Public*, pg. 337
BIOME AUSTRALIA LIMITED; *Int'l*, pg. 1039
BIOME BIOPLASTICS LIMITED—See Biome Technologies plc; *Int'l*, pg. 1039
BIOMED DIAGNOSTICS, INC.—See Diagnostic Consulting Network, Inc.; *U.S. Private*, pg. 1222
BIOMEDICA ARGENTINA S.A.—See Biotronik GmbH & Co.; *Int'l*, pg. 1044
BIOMEDICA BULGARIA OOD—See AddLife AB; *Int'l*, pg. 129
BIOMEDICA CS S.R.O.—See AddLife AB; *Int'l*, pg. 129
BIOMEDICA DIJAGNOSTIKA DOO—See AddLife AB; *Int'l*, pg. 129
BIOMEDICA D.O.O.—See AddLife AB; *Int'l*, pg. 129
BIOMEDICA HUNGARIA KFT.—See AddLife AB; *Int'l*, pg. 129
BIOMEDICA INC.—See Oxford Biomedica Plc; *Int'l*, pg. 5674
BIOMEDICA ITALIA S.R.L.—See AddLife AB; *Int'l*, pg. 129
BIOMEDICAL ENTERPRISES, INC.—See Johnson & Johnson; *U.S. Public*, pg. 1195
BIOMEDICAL RESEARCH FOUNDATION OF NORTHWEST LOUISIANA; *U.S. Private*, pg. 562
BIOMEDICAL RESEARCH INSTITUTE OF NEW MEXICO; *U.S. Private*, pg. 562
BIOMEDICAL RESEARCH MODELS, INC.—See Joinn Laboratories (China) Co., Ltd; *Int'l*, pg. 3995
BIOMEDICAL SYSTEMS CORP.—See Astorg Partners S.A.S.; *Int'l*, pg. 657
BIOMEDICAL SYSTEMS CORP.—See Nordic Capital AB; *Int'l*, pg. 5421
BIOMEDICAL SYSTEMS CORP.—See Novo Nordisk Fonden; *Int'l*, pg. 5465
BIOMEDICAL SYSTEMS PTY LIMITED—See CVC Limited; *Int'l*, pg. 1889
BIOMEDICA MEDIZINPRODUKTE GMBH—See AddLife AB; *Int'l*, pg. 129
BIOMEDICA MEDIZINPRODUKTE ROMANIA SRL—See AddLife AB; *Int'l*, pg. 129
BIOMEDICA MP D.O.O.—See AddLife AB; *Int'l*, pg. 129
BIOMEDICA POLAND SP. Z O.O.—See AddLife AB; *Int'l*, pg. 129
BIOMEDICA SLOVAKITA S.R.O.—See AddLife AB; *Int'l*, pg. 129
BIO MEDIC CORPORATION; *U.S. Private*, pg. 561
BIO MEDIC DATA SYSTEMS INC—See Bio Medic Corporation; *U.S. Private*, pg. 561
BIOMED LABORATORIES INC.—See Mativ Holdings, Inc.; *U.S. Public*, pg. 1396
BIOMED-LUBLIN WYTWORNIA SUROWIC I SZCZEPIONEK S.A.; *Int'l*, pg. 1039
BIOMED REALTY, L.P.—See Blackstone Inc.; *U.S. Public*, pg. 350
BIOMEDSKLO PJSC—See Yioula Glassworks S.A.; *Int'l*, pg. 8585
BIOME GROW, INC.; *Int'l*, pg. 1039
BIOME GROW INC.; *Int'l*, pg. 1039
BIOME MAKERS INC.; *U.S. Private*, pg. 562
BIOMENOVO RESEARCH PRIVATE LIMITED—See Ningbo Menovo Pharmaceutical Co., Ltd.; *Int'l*, pg. 5304
BIOMERICA, INC.; *U.S. Public*, pg. 337
BIOMERICS, LLC—See Wasatch Advantage Group, LLC; *U.S. Private*, pg. 4445
BIOMERIEUX, INC.—See Institut Merieux; *Int'l*, pg. 3724
BIOMERIEUX S.A.—See Institut Merieux; *Int'l*, pg. 3723
BIOMET 3I AUSTRALIA PTY. LTD.—See Zimmer Biomet Holdings, Inc.; *U.S. Public*, pg. 2405
BIOMET 3I BELGIUM N.V.—See Zimmer Biomet Holdings, Inc.; *U.S. Public*, pg. 2405
BIOMET 3I CANADA, INC.—See Zimmer Biomet Holdings, Inc.; *U.S. Public*, pg. 2405
BIOMET 3I DE BRASIL LTDA.—See Zimmer Biomet Holdings, Inc.; *U.S. Public*, pg. 2405
BIOMET 3I DENTAL IBERICA SL—See Zimmer Biomet Holdings, Inc.; *U.S. Public*, pg. 2405
BIOMET 3I DO BRASIL COMERCIO DE APARELHOS MEDICOS LTDA.—See Zimmer Biomet Holdings, Inc.; *U.S. Public*, pg. 2405
BIOMET 3I FRANCE SAS—See Zimmer Biomet Holdings, Inc.; *U.S. Public*, pg. 2405
BIOMET 3I, LLC—See Zimmer Biomet Holdings, Inc.; *U.S. Public*, pg. 2405
BIOMET 3I NETHERLANDS B.V.—See Zimmer Biomet Holdings, Inc.; *U.S. Public*, pg. 2405
BIOMET 3I NORDIC AB—See Zimmer Biomet Holdings, Inc.; *U.S. Public*, pg. 2405
BIOMET ARGENTINA SA—See Zimmer Biomet Holdings, Inc.; *U.S. Public*, pg. 2405
BIOMET AUSTRALIA PTY. LTD.—See Zimmer Biomet Holdings, Inc.; *U.S. Public*, pg. 2405
BIOMET AUSTRIA GMBH—See Zimmer Biomet Holdings, Inc.; *U.S. Public*, pg. 2405
BIOMET BIOLOGICS, LLC—See Zimmer Biomet Holdings, Inc.; *U.S. Public*, pg. 2405
BIOMET CEMENTING TECHNOLOGIES AB—See Zimmer Biomet Holdings, Inc.; *U.S. Public*, pg. 2405

BIONIK LABORATORIES CORP.

BIOMET CHILE SA—See Zimmer Biomet Holdings, Inc.; *U.S. Public*, pg. 2405
BIOMET CHINA CO., LTD.—See Zimmer Biomet Holdings, Inc.; *U.S. Public*, pg. 2405
BIOMET DEUTSCHLAND GMBH—See Zimmer Biomet Holdings, Inc.; *U.S. Public*, pg. 2405
BIOME TECHNOLOGIES PLC; *Int'l*, pg. 1039
BIOMET EL SALVADOR SA DE CV—See Zimmer Biomet Holdings, Inc.; *U.S. Public*, pg. 2405
BIOMET EUROPE B.V.—See Zimmer Biomet Holdings, Inc.; *U.S. Public*, pg. 2405
BIOMET FAIR LAWN LLC—See Zimmer Biomet Holdings, Inc.; *U.S. Public*, pg. 2406
BIOMET FRANCE SARL—See Zimmer Biomet Holdings, Inc.; *U.S. Public*, pg. 2405
BIOMET GLOBAL SUPPLY CHAIN CENTER B.V.—See Zimmer Biomet Holdings, Inc.; *U.S. Public*, pg. 2406
BIO METHANOL CHEMIE NEDERLAND BV; *Int'l*, pg. 1035
BIOMET HELLAS SA—See Zimmer Biomet Holdings, Inc.; *U.S. Public*, pg. 2406
BIOMETICS INTERNATIONAL, INC.; *U.S. Private*, pg. 562
BIOMET, INC.—See Zimmer Biomet Holdings, Inc.; *U.S. Public*, pg. 2406
BIOMET MEDIKAL DRUNJER DADYTYM PAZARLAMA YHRACAT VE DYS TICARET LTD. STI.—See Zimmer Biomet Holdings, Inc.; *U.S. Public*, pg. 2406
BIOMET MEXICO S.A. DE C.V.—See Zimmer Biomet Holdings, Inc.; *U.S. Public*, pg. 2406
BIOMET ORTHOPAEDIC INDIA PRIVATE LIMITED—See Zimmer Biomet Holdings, Inc.; *U.S. Public*, pg. 2406
BIOMET ORTHOPAEDICS SWITZERLAND GMBH—See Zimmer Biomet Holdings, Inc.; *U.S. Public*, pg. 2406
BIOMET ORTHOPEDICS PUERTO RICO, INC.—See Zimmer Biomet Holdings, Inc.; *U.S. Public*, pg. 2406
BIOMETRA GMBH—See Endress+Hauser (International) Holding AG; *Int'l*, pg. 2405
BIOMETRIC ALBANIA SH.P.K.—See HORIBA Ltd; *Int'l*, pg. 3475
BIO-METRICS, LIMITED—See Bio-Rad Laboratories, Inc.; *U.S. Public*, pg. 332
BIOMETRICS LTD—See Bio-Rad Laboratories, Inc.; *U.S. Public*, pg. 333
BIOMET SPAIN ORTHOPAEDICS, S.L.—See Zimmer Biomet Holdings, Inc.; *U.S. Public*, pg. 2405
BIOMET SPORTS MEDICINE, LLC—See Zimmer Biomet Holdings, Inc.; *U.S. Public*, pg. 2406
BIOMET TRAUMA, LLC—See Zimmer Biomet Holdings, Inc.; *U.S. Public*, pg. 2406
BIOMET UK LIMITED—See Zimmer Biomet Holdings, Inc.; *U.S. Public*, pg. 2405
BIOMET UK LIMITED - SWINDON—See Zimmer Biomet Holdings, Inc.; *U.S. Public*, pg. 2405
BIOMET US INC—See Zimmer Biomet Holdings, Inc.; *U.S. Public*, pg. 2406
BIOMICROLAB, INC.—See SPT Labtech Limited; *U.S. Private*, pg. 3765
BIO MILK LTD.; *Int'l*, pg. 1035
BIOMIMIX, INC.; *U.S. Public*, pg. 338
BIOMIND LABS INC.; *Int'l*, pg. 1040
BIOMM S. A.; *Int'l*, pg. 1040
BIOMNIS EMPREINTES GENETIQUES SAS—See Eurofins Scientific S.E.; *Int'l*, pg. 2535
BIOMONTAN GMBH—See SNF SAS; *Int'l*, pg. 7027
BIOMX INC; *Int'l*, pg. 1040
BIONAL NEDERLAND BV—See Perrigo Company plc; *Int'l*, pg. 5813
BIONANO GENOMICS, INC.; *U.S. Public*, pg. 338
BIONEER CORPORATION; *Int'l*, pg. 1040
BIONEER, INC.—See Bioneer Corporation; *Int'l*, pg. 1040
BION ENVIRONMENTAL TECHNOLOGIES, INC.; *U.S. Public*, pg. 338
BIONESS, INC.—See Bioventus Inc.; *U.S. Public*, pg. 339
BIONET CORP.; *Int'l*, pg. 1040
THE BIONETICS CORPORATION; *U.S. Private*, pg. 3995
BIONEUTRA GLOBAL CORPORATION; *Int'l*, pg. 1040
BIONEUTRAL GROUP, INC.; *U.S. Private*, pg. 562
BIONEUTRA NORTH AMERICA INC.—See BioNeutra Global Corporation; *Int'l*, pg. 1040
BIONEXUS GENE LAB CORP.; *Int'l*, pg. 1040
BIONICHE ANIMAL HEALTH A/ASIA PTY. LTD.—See Vetoquinol S.A.; *Int'l*, pg. 8181
BIONICHE ANIMAL HEALTH USA, INC.—See Vetoquinol S.A.; *Int'l*, pg. 8181
BIONIC MEDIZINTECHNIK GMBH—See JMS Co., Ltd.; *Int'l*, pg. 3975
BIONIC PRODUCTION GMBH—See Hamburger Hafen und Logistik AG; *Int'l*, pg. 3236
BIONIC PRODUCTIONS LIMITED—See NBA Quantum PLC; *Int'l*, pg. 5179
BIONICS CORPORATION LTD.—See Transition Evergreen; *Int'l*, pg. 7900
BIONI CS GMBH FZE—See Bioni CS GmbH; *Int'l*, pg. 1040
BIONI CS GMBH; *Int'l*, pg. 1040
BIONICS INSTRUMENT CO., LTD.—See DKK-TOA Corporation; *Int'l*, pg. 2139
BIONIC SOLUTION LLC—See Accenture plc; *Int'l*, pg. 86
BIONIK LABORATORIES CORP.; *Int'l*, pg. 1040

BIONIK LABORATORIES CORP.

BIONIME AUSTRALIA PTY LIMITED—See Bionime Corporation; *Int'l*, pg. 1040
BIONIME CORPORATION; *Int'l*, pg. 1040
BIONIME GMBH—See Bionime Corporation; *Int'l*, pg. 1040
BIONIME (MALAYSIA) SDN. BHD.—See Bionime Corporation; *Int'l*, pg. 1040
BIONIME (PINGTAN) CO., LTD.—See Bionime Corporation; *Int'l*, pg. 1040
BIONIME USA CORPORATION—See Bionime Corporation; *Int'l*, pg. 1040
BIONI SYSTEM GMBH—See Bioni CS GmbH; *Int'l*, pg. 1040
BIONITROGEN HOLDINGS CORP.; *U.S. Public*, pg. 338
BIONI USA AND AMERICAS LLC.—See Bioni CS GmbH; *Int'l*, pg. 1040
BIO-NOMIC SERVICES, INC.—See Carylon Corporation; *U.S. Private*, pg. 777
BIONOMICS INC—See Bionomics Limited; *Int'l*, pg. 1040
BIONOMICS LIMITED; *Int'l*, pg. 1040
BIONORDIKA BERGMAN AS—See AddLife AB; *Int'l*, pg. 129
BIONORDIKA (DENMARK) A/S—See AddLife AB; *Int'l*, pg. 129
BIONORDIKA (SWEDEN) AB—See AddLife AB; *Int'l*, pg. 129
BIONOR HOLDING AS; *Int'l*, pg. 1040
BIONOR IMMUNO AS—See Bionor Holding AS; *Int'l*, pg. 1040
BIONOSTICS INC.—See Bio-Techne Corporation; *U.S. Public*, pg. 334
BIONOTE, INC.—See Abbott Laboratories; *U.S. Public*, pg. 19
BIONOVA HOLDING CORPORATION—See Pulsar Internacional S.A. de C.V.; *Int'l*, pg. 6116
BIONOVATE TECHNOLOGIES CORP; *U.S. Private*, pg. 562
BIONOV SA—See Robertet S.A.; *Int'l*, pg. 6369
BIONTECH DELIVERY TECHNOLOGIES GMBH—See BioNTech SE; *Int'l*, pg. 1041
BIONTECH EUROPE GMBH—See BioNTech SE; *Int'l*, pg. 1041
BIONTECH INNOVATIVE MANUFACTURING SERVICES GMBH—See BioNTech SE; *Int'l*, pg. 1041
BIONTECH MANUFACTURING MARBURG GMBH—See BioNTech SE; *Int'l*, pg. 1041
BIONTECH SE; *Int'l*, pg. 1040
BIONTECH US INC.—See BioNTech SE; *Int'l*, pg. 1041
BIONUMERIK PHARMACEUTICALS, INC.; *U.S. Private*, pg. 562
BIONUTRITIONAL RESEARCH GROUP, INC.; *U.S. Private*, pg. 562
BIONXT SOLUTIONS INC.; *Int'l*, pg. 1041
BIOONE; *U.S. Private*, pg. 562
BIO-OPTRONICS, INC.—See Genstar Capital, LLC; *U.S. Private*, pg. 1673
BIOOREGON PROTEIN, INC.—See Dulcich, Inc.; *U.S. Private*, pg. 1286
BIOO SCIENTIFIC CORPORATION—See Revvity, Inc.; *U.S. Public*, pg. 1793
BIOPALMA DA AMAZONIA S.A - REFLORESTAMENTO, INDUSTRIA E COMERCIO—See Vale S.A.; *Int'l*, pg. 8111
BIO PAPPEL, S.A.B. DE C.V.; *Int'l*, pg. 1035
BIO PAPPEL SCRIBE, S.A. DE C.V.—See Bio Pappel, S.A.B. de C.V.; *Int'l*, pg. 1035
BIOPARK, S.R.O.—See CPI Property Group, S.A.; *Int'l*, pg. 1825
BIO-PATH HOLDINGS, INC.; *U.S. Public*, pg. 332
BIOPHAN TECHNOLOGIES, INC.; *U.S. Public*, pg. 338
BIOPHARMA CREDIT PLC; *Int'l*, pg. 1041
BIOPHARMA MANUFACTURING SOLUTIONS, INC.; *U.S. Private*, pg. 562
BIOPHARM COMMUNICATIONS, LLC—See Omnicom Group Inc.; *U.S. Public*, pg. 1577
BIOPHARM ENGINEERING AD—See Sopharma AD; *Int'l*, pg. 7108
BIOPHYTIS SA; *Int'l*, pg. 1041
BIO-PLANET N.V.—See Colruyt Group N.V.; *Int'l*, pg. 1705
BIOPLUS ACQUISITION CORP.; *U.S. Public*, pg. 338
BIOPLUS CO., LTD.; *Int'l*, pg. 1041
BIOPLUS LIFE CORP.; *Int'l*, pg. 1041
BIOPLUS SPECIALTY PHARMACY SERVICES, LLC; *U.S. Private*, pg. 562
BIOPOLIS, S.L.—See Archer-Daniels-Midland Company; *U.S. Public*, pg. 184
BIOPORTO A/S; *Int'l*, pg. 1041
BIOPORTO DIAGNOSTICS INC.—See BioPorto A/S; *Int'l*, pg. 1041
BIOPOWER KATSUTA CO., LTD.—See Takuma Co., Ltd.; *Int'l*, pg. 7442
BIOPREMIER - INOVACAO E SERVICOS EM BIOTECNOLOGIA S.A.; *Int'l*, pg. 1041
BIOPROD BIOMEDICINSKI PRODUKTI D.O.O.—See Baxter International Inc.; *U.S. Public*, pg. 281
BIO-PROTECH INC; *Int'l*, pg. 1035
BIOPROTECTION SYSTEMS CORPORATION—See Lumos Pharma, Inc.; *U.S. Public*, pg. 1348
BIOPSY SCIENCES, LLC; *U.S. Private*, pg. 562

BIOPTIGEN, INC.—See Danaher Corporation; *U.S. Public*, pg. 628
BIOPTIK TECHNOLOGY, INC.; *Int'l*, pg. 1041
BIOPURE TECHNOLOGY LTD.—See Spirax-Sarco Engineering plc; *Int'l*, pg. 7137
BIOQUAL INC.; *U.S. Public*, pg. 338
BIOQUANTA SA; *Int'l*, pg. 1041
BIOQUELL ASIA PACIFIC PTE LTD—See Ecolab Inc.; *U.S. Public*, pg. 712
BIOQUELL GLOBAL LOGISTICS (IRELAND) LTD.—See Ecolab Inc.; *U.S. Public*, pg. 712
BIOQUELL GMBH—See Ecolab Inc.; *U.S. Public*, pg. 712
BIOQUELL INC.—See Ecolab Inc.; *U.S. Public*, pg. 712
BIOQUELL PLC—See Ecolab Inc.; *U.S. Public*, pg. 712
BIOQUELL SAS—See Ecolab Inc.; *U.S. Public*, pg. 712
BIOQUELL TECHNOLOGY (SHENZHEN) LTD.—See Ecolab Inc.; *U.S. Public*, pg. 712
BIOQUELL UK LIMITED—See Ecolab Inc.; *U.S. Public*, pg. 712
BIOQUERCY S.A.S.—See TotalEnergies SE; *Int'l*, pg. 7835
BIOQUEST CORP.; *U.S. Public*, pg. 338
BIOQUEST, INC.—See Diversified Search, LLC; *U.S. Private*, pg. 1243
BIORA AB—See Straumann Holding AG; *Int'l*, pg. 7237
BIO-RAD ABD SEROTEC GMBH—See Bio-Rad Laboratories, Inc.; *U.S. Public*, pg. 332
BIO-RAD ABD SEROTEC LTD—See Bio-Rad Laboratories, Inc.; *U.S. Public*, pg. 332
BIO-RAD DENMARK APS—See Bio-Rad Laboratories, Inc.; *U.S. Public*, pg. 332
BIO-RAD FINLAND OY—See Bio-Rad Laboratories, Inc.; *U.S. Public*, pg. 332
BIO-RAD FRANCE HOLDING—See Bio-Rad Laboratories, Inc.; *U.S. Public*, pg. 332
BIO-RAD FRANCE—See Bio-Rad Laboratories, Inc.; *U.S. Public*, pg. 332
BIO-RAD HAIFA LTD.—See Bio-Rad Laboratories, Inc.; *U.S. Public*, pg. 332
BIO-RAD HUNGARY TRADING LTD.—See Bio-Rad Laboratories, Inc.; *U.S. Public*, pg. 332
BIO-RAD KOREA LIMITED—See Bio-Rad Laboratories, Inc.; *U.S. Public*, pg. 332
BIO-RAD LABORATORIES AB—See Bio-Rad Laboratories, Inc.; *U.S. Public*, pg. 333
BIO-RAD LABORATORIES AG—See Bio-Rad Laboratories, Inc.; *U.S. Public*, pg. 333
BIO-RAD LABORATORIES-APARELHOS E REAGENTES PARA LABORATORIOS, LDA—See Bio-Rad Laboratories, Inc.; *U.S. Public*, pg. 333
BIO-RAD LABORATORIES B.V.—See Bio-Rad Laboratories, Inc.; *U.S. Public*, pg. 333
BIO-RAD LABORATORIES (CANADA) LTD.—See Bio-Rad Laboratories, Inc.; *U.S. Public*, pg. 332
BIO-RAD LABORATORIES E.P.E.—See Bio-Rad Laboratories, Inc.; *U.S. Public*, pg. 333
BIO-RAD LABORATORIES EUROPE LIMITED—See Bio-Rad Laboratories, Inc.; *U.S. Public*, pg. 333
BIO-RAD LABORATORIES, GES.M.B.H.—See Bio-Rad Laboratories, Inc.; *U.S. Public*, pg. 333
BIO-RAD LABORATORIES GMBH—See Bio-Rad Laboratories, Inc.; *U.S. Public*, pg. 333
BIO-RAD LABORATORIES, INC. - CLINICAL DIAGNOSTICS—See Bio-Rad Laboratories, Inc.; *U.S. Public*, pg. 333
BIO-RAD LABORATORIES, INC. - LIFE SCIENCE GROUP—See Bio-Rad Laboratories, Inc.; *U.S. Public*, pg. 333
BIO-RAD LABORATORIES, INC.; *U.S. Public*, pg. 332
BIO-RAD LABORATORIES, INC.—See Bio-Rad Laboratories, Inc.; *U.S. Public*, pg. 333
BIO-RAD LABORATORIES, INC. - SPECTROSCOPY PRODUCTS—See Bio-Rad Laboratories, Inc.; *U.S. Public*, pg. 333
BIO-RAD LABORATORIES (INDIA) PVT. LTD.—See Bio-Rad Laboratories, Inc.; *U.S. Public*, pg. 332
BIO-RAD LABORATORIES ISRAEL (1996) LTD.—See Bio-Rad Laboratories, Inc.; *U.S. Public*, pg. 333
BIO-RAD LABORATORIES K.K.—See Bio-Rad Laboratories, Inc.; *U.S. Public*, pg. 333
BIO-RAD LABORATORIES LIMITED—See Bio-Rad Laboratories, Inc.; *U.S. Public*, pg. 333
BIO-RAD LABORATORIES LTD.—See Bio-Rad Laboratories, Inc.; *U.S. Public*, pg. 333
BIO-RAD LABORATORIES M E.P.E.—See Bio-Rad Laboratories, Inc.; *U.S. Public*, pg. 333
BIO-RAD LABORATORIES PTY. LIMITED—See Bio-Rad Laboratories, Inc.; *U.S. Public*, pg. 333
BIO-RAD LABORATORIES S.A.—See Bio-Rad Laboratories, Inc.; *U.S. Public*, pg. 333
BIO-RAD LABORATORIES S.A.—See Bio-Rad Laboratories, Inc.; *U.S. Public*, pg. 333
BIO-RAD LABORATORIES S.A.S.—See Bio-Rad Laboratories, Inc.; *U.S. Public*, pg. 333
BIO-RAD LABORATORIES (SHANGHAI) CO., LTD.—See Bio-Rad Laboratories, Inc.; *U.S. Public*, pg. 332
BIO-RAD LABORATORIES (SINGAPORE) PTE. LIMITED—See Bio-Rad Laboratories, Inc.; *U.S. Public*, pg. 333

CORPORATE AFFILIATIONS

BIO-RAD LABORATORIES—See Bio-Rad Laboratories, Inc.; *U.S. Public*, pg. 332
BIO-RAD LABORATORIES S.R.L.—See Bio-Rad Laboratories, Inc.; *U.S. Public*, pg. 333
BIO-RAD LABORATORII—See Bio-Rad Laboratories, Inc.; *U.S. Public*, pg. 333
BIO-RAD LABORATORII OOO—See Bio-Rad Laboratories, Inc.; *U.S. Public*, pg. 333
BIO-RAD LABORATORIOS BRASIL LTDA.—See Bio-Rad Laboratories, Inc.; *U.S. Public*, pg. 333
BIO-RAD LABORATORIOS BRASIL LTDA.—See Bio-Rad Laboratories, Inc.; *U.S. Public*, pg. 333
BIO-RAD LTD.—See Bio-Rad Laboratories, Inc.; *U.S. Public*, pg. 333
BIO-RAD MEDICAL DIAGNOSTICS GMBH—See Biotest AG; *Int'l*, pg. 1043
BIO-RAD NEW ZEALAND—See Bio-Rad Laboratories, Inc.; *U.S. Public*, pg. 333
BIO-RAD PACIFIC LTD.—See Bio-Rad Laboratories, Inc.; *U.S. Public*, pg. 333
BIO-RAD POLSKA SP. Z O.O.—See Bio-Rad Laboratories, Inc.; *U.S. Public*, pg. 333
BIO-RAD QSD DIVISION—See Bio-Rad Laboratories, Inc.; *U.S. Public*, pg. 333
BIO RAD S.A.—See Bio-Rad Laboratories, Inc.; *U.S. Public*, pg. 333
BIO-RAD SERVICES UK LIMITED—See Bio-Rad Laboratories, Inc.; *U.S. Public*, pg. 333
BIO-RAD SNC—See Bio-Rad Laboratories, Inc.; *U.S. Public*, pg. 333
BIO-RAD—See Bio-Rad Laboratories, Inc.; *U.S. Public*, pg. 332
BIO-RAD SPOL. SR.O—See Bio-Rad Laboratories, Inc.; *U.S. Public*, pg. 333
BIO-RAD VERDOT—See Bio-Rad Laboratories, Inc.; *U.S. Public*, pg. 332
BIORA THERAPEUTICS, INC.; *U.S. Public*, pg. 338
BIO-REFERENCE LABORATORIES, INC.—See OPKO Health, Inc.; *U.S. Public*, pg. 1608
BIOREGENX, INC.; *U.S. Public*, pg. 338
BIORELIANCE CORPORATION—See Merck KGaA; *Int'l*, pg. 4832
BIORELIANCE KK—See Merck KGaA; *Int'l*, pg. 4832
BIORELIANCE LTD.—See Merck KGaA; *Int'l*, pg. 4832
BIOREM ENVIRONMENTAL INC.—See Tsinghua Holdings Co., Ltd.; *Int'l*, pg. 7951
BIOREM INC.—See Tsinghua Holdings Co., Ltd.; *Int'l*, pg. 7951
BIOREM TECHNOLOGIES INC.—See Tsinghua Holdings Co., Ltd.; *Int'l*, pg. 7951
BIORESOURCE INTERNATIONAL, INC.—See Mitsui & Co., Ltd.; *Int'l*, pg. 4979
BIORESTORATIVE THERAPIES, INC.; *U.S. Public*, pg. 338
BIORETEC LTD.; *Int'l*, pg. 1041
BIORIGINAL EUROPE/ASIA B.V.—See Cooke, Inc.; *Int'l*, pg. 1788
BIORIGINAL FOOD & SCIENCE CORPORATION—See Cooke, Inc.; *Int'l*, pg. 1788
BIORIGIN EUROPE N.V.—See Zilor Energia e Alimentos Ltda.; *Int'l*, pg. 8683
BIORIGIN USA, LLC—See Zilor Energia e Alimentos Ltda.; *Int'l*, pg. 8683
BIORIVER CO., LTD.—See BioLASCO Taiwan Co., Ltd.; *Int'l*, pg. 1038
BIOR MEDICA S.R.L.—See STERIS plc; *Int'l*, pg. 7208
BIORRECICLAJE DE CADIZ, S.A.—See GS Holdings Corp.; *Int'l*, pg. 3142
BIOSAFE SYSTEMS, LLC; *U.S. Private*, pg. 562
BIOSAFETY RESEARCH CENTER INC.—See Trans Genic Inc.; *Int'l*, pg. 7894
BIOSAR AMERICA LLC—See ELLAKTOR S.A.; *Int'l*, pg. 2364
BIOSAR AUSTRALIA PTY LTD—See ELLAKTOR S.A.; *Int'l*, pg. 2364
BIOSAR BRASIL - ENERGIA RENOVAVEL LTDA—See ELLAKTOR S.A.; *Int'l*, pg. 2365
BIOSAR CHILE SPA—See ELLAKTOR S.A.; *Int'l*, pg. 2365
BIOSAR ENERGY (UK) LTD.—See ELLAKTOR S.A.; *Int'l*, pg. 2365
BIOSAR HOLDINGS LTD.—See ELLAKTOR S.A.; *Int'l*, pg. 2365
BIOSAR PANAMA INC.—See ELLAKTOR S.A.; *Int'l*, pg. 2365
BIOSAUDE - PRODUTOS FARMACEUTICOS, LDA.—See Alfa-Wassermann S.p.A.; *Int'l*, pg. 314
BIO.S BIOGAS VERWALTUNGS GMBH—See Biogas Nord AG; *Int'l*, pg. 1038
BIOSCIENCE BRANDS LIMITED; *Int'l*, pg. 1041
BIOSCIENCE NEUTRACEUTICALS, INC.; *U.S. Public*, pg. 338
BIOSCIENCE RESEARCH REAGENTS—See Merck KGaA; *Int'l*, pg. 4830
BIO-SCIENCES LTD.—See Thermo Fisher Scientific Inc.; *U.S. Public*, pg. 2145
BIOSCIENTIA HEALTHCARE GMBH—See Sonic Healthcare Limited; *Int'l*, pg. 7096

COMPANY NAME INDEX

BIOSCIENTIA INSTITUT FUR MEDIZINISCHE DIAGNOSTIK GMBH LABOR JENA—See Sonic Healthcare Limited; *Int'l*, pg. 7096
BIOSCIENTIA INSTITUT FUR MEDIZINISCHE DIAGNOSTIK GMBH—See Sonic Healthcare Limited; *Int'l*, pg. 7096
BIOSCIENTIA MVZ SAARBRUCKEN GMBH—See Sonic Healthcare Limited; *Int'l*, pg. 7096
BIOSCREEN TECHNOLOGIES SRL—See Balchem Corporation; *U.S. Public*, pg. 265
BIOSCRIP INFUSION SERVICES, LLC—See Option Care Health, Inc.; *U.S. Public*, pg. 1609
BIOSCRIP MEDICAL SUPPLY SERVICES, LLC—See Option Care Health, Inc.; *U.S. Public*, pg. 1609
BIOSCRIP NURSING SERVICES, LLC—See Option Care Health, Inc.; *U.S. Public*, pg. 1609
BIOSCRIP PBM SERVICES, LLC—See Option Care Health, Inc.; *U.S. Public*, pg. 1609
BIOSCRIP PHARMACY, INC.—See Option Care Health, Inc.; *U.S. Public*, pg. 1609
BIOSCRIP PHARMACY SERVICES, INC.—See Option Care Health, Inc.; *U.S. Public*, pg. 1609
BIO SEARCH (N.I.) LIMITED—See Eurofins Scientific S.E.; *Int'l*, pg. 2535
BIOSEARCH S.A.—See Kerry Group plc; *Int'l*, pg. 4138
BIOSECTOR 2; *U.S. Private*, pg. 563
BIOSEED RESEARCH INDIA PRIVATE LIMITED—See DCM Shriram Limited; *Int'l*, pg. 1992
BIOSEED RESEARCH PHILIPPINES INC—See DCM Shriram Limited; *Int'l*, pg. 1992
BIOSEED VIETNAM LIMITED—See DCM Shriram Limited; *Int'l*, pg. 1992
BIOSEEK LLC—See DiscoveRx Corp.; *U.S. Private*, pg. 1237
BIOSENSE TECHNOLOGIES PVT. LTD.—See Revvity, Inc.; *U.S. Public*, pg. 1795
BIOSENSE WEBSTER INC.—See Johnson & Johnson; *U.S. Public*, pg. 1194
BIOSENSE WEBSTER (ISRAEL) LTD.—See Johnson & Johnson; *U.S. Public*, pg. 1194
BIOSENSING INSTRUMENT INC.—See Level Biotechnology, Inc.; *Int'l*, pg. 4470
BIOSENSORS B.V.—See Biosensors International Group, Ltd.; *Int'l*, pg. 1041
BIOSENSORS EUROPE SA—See Biosensors International Group, Ltd.; *Int'l*, pg. 1041
BIOSENSORS INTERNATIONAL GROUP, LTD.; *Int'l*, pg. 1041
BIOSENSORS INTERNATIONAL PTE LTD—See Biosensors International Group, Ltd.; *Int'l*, pg. 1041
BIOSENSORS INTERNATIONAL USA—See Biosensors International Group, Ltd.; *Int'l*, pg. 1041
BIOSENSORS INTERVENTIONAL TECHNOLOGIES PTE LTD—See Biosensors International Group, Ltd.; *Int'l*, pg. 1041
BIOSENSORS JAPAN CO., LTD.—See Biosensors International Group, Ltd.; *Int'l*, pg. 1042
BIOSERGEN AB; *Int'l*, pg. 1042
BIO-SERV CORPORATION; *U.S. Private*, pg. 561
BIOSERVE BIOTECHNOLOGIES (INDIA) PRIVATE LIMITED—See ReproCELL Inc.; *Int'l*, pg. 6292
BIO-SERVICES CONGO SARL—See HORIBA Ltd; *Int'l*, pg. 3475
BIOSEV S.A. - CONTINENTAL UNIT—See Raizen S.A.; *Int'l*, pg. 6191
BIOSEV S.A. - CRESCIUMAL UNIT—See Raizen S.A.; *Int'l*, pg. 6192
BIOSEV S.A. - ESTIVAS UNIT—See Raizen S.A.; *Int'l*, pg. 6192
BIOSEV S.A. - GIASA UNIT—See Raizen S.A.; *Int'l*, pg. 6192
BIOSEV S.A. - LAGOA DA PRATA UNIT—See Raizen S.A.; *Int'l*, pg. 6192
BIOSEV S.A. - MARACAJU UNIT—See Raizen S.A.; *Int'l*, pg. 6192
BIOSEV S.A. - MB UNIT—See Raizen S.A.; *Int'l*, pg. 6192
BIOSEV S.A. - PASSA TEMPO UNIT—See Raizen S.A.; *Int'l*, pg. 6192
BIOSEV S.A. - RIO BRILHANTE UNIT—See Raizen S.A.; *Int'l*, pg. 6192
BIOSEV S.A. - SANTELISA UNIT—See Raizen S.A.; *Int'l*, pg. 6192
BIOSEV S.A.—See Raizen S.A.; *Int'l*, pg. 6191
BIOSEV S.A. - VALE DO ROSARIO UNIT—See Raizen S.A.; *Int'l*, pg. 6192
BIOSHAFT WATER TECHNOLOGY, INC.; *U.S. Public*, pg. 338
BIOSIGMA C.A.—See HORIBA Ltd; *Int'l*, pg. 3475
BIOSIGMA S.A.—See Corporacion Nacional del Cobre de Chile; *Int'l*, pg. 1804
BIOSIGMA S.A.—See ENEOS Holdings, Inc.; *Int'l*, pg. 2415
BIOSIGMA S.R.L.—See Dominique Dutscher SAS; *Int'l*, pg. 2161
BIOSIGN TECHNOLOGIES INC.; *Int'l*, pg. 1042
BIOSIG TECHNOLOGIES, INC.; *U.S. Public*, pg. 338
BIOS, INC.—See SECOM Co., Ltd.; *Int'l*, pg. 6670
BIOSINO BIO-TECHNOLOGY & SCIENCE INC.; *Int'l*, pg. 1042

BIOSKIN GMBH—See Eurofins Scientific S.E.; *Int'l*, pg. 2552
BIO SLYM S.R.L.—See PAI Partners S.A.S.; *Int'l*, pg. 5700
BIOSMART CO. LTD.; *Int'l*, pg. 1042
BIO SOIL ENHANCERS, INC.; *U.S. Private*, pg. 561
BIOSOLUTION CO., LTD.; *Int'l*, pg. 1042
BIO SOLUTIONS INTERNATIONAL CO. LTD.—See Virbac S.A.; *Int'l*, pg. 8246
BIOSPACE, INC.—See Ziff Davis, Inc.; *U.S. Public*, pg. 2404
BIOSPACIFIC, INC.—See Bio-Techne Corporation; *U.S. Public*, pg. 334
BIOSPAN CONTAMINATION CONTROL SOLUTIONS PVT. LTD.—See Span Divergent Ltd.; *Int'l*, pg. 7124
BIOSPECIFICS TECHNOLOGIES CORP.—See Endo International plc; *Int'l*, pg. 2403
BIOSPECTRA INC.; *U.S. Private*, pg. 563
BIOSPHERE MEDICAL EMEA & INDIA—See Merit Medical Systems, Inc.; *U.S. Public*, pg. 1425
BIOSPHERE MEDICAL, INC.—See Merit Medical Systems, Inc.; *U.S. Public*, pg. 1425
BIOSPLICE THERAPEUTICS, INC.; *U.S. Private*, pg. 563
BIO SPRINGER ASIA—See Compagnie des Levures Lesaffre SA; *Int'l*, pg. 1738
BIOSPRINGER GUANGXI YIPINXIAN CO. LTD—See Compagnie des Levures Lesaffre SA; *Int'l*, pg. 1738
BIO SPRINGER PACIFIC—See Compagnie des Levures Lesaffre SA; *Int'l*, pg. 1738
BIO SPRINGER S.A.—See Compagnie des Levures Lesaffre SA; *Int'l*, pg. 1738
BIO SPRINGER S.A. - YEAST EXTRACTS FACTORY—See Compagnie des Levures Lesaffre SA; *Int'l*, pg. 1738
BIO SPRINGER SOUTH AMERICA—See Compagnie des Levures Lesaffre SA; *Int'l*, pg. 1738
BIOSSOL CONSTRUCTION TOOLS S.A.—See Unibios Holdings S.A.; *Int'l*, pg. 8031
BIOS S.P.A.; *Int'l*, pg. 1041
BIOSTAR ANGEL STEM CELL CORPORATION; *U.S. Private*, pg. 563
BIOSTAR BIOMEDIKAL MUHENDISLIK ANONIM SIRKETI—See Medtronic plc; *Int'l*, pg. 4788
BIOSTAR MICROTECH INTERNATIONAL CORP.; *Int'l*, pg. 1042
BIOSTAR MICROTECH (U.S.A) CORP—See Biostar Microtech International Corp.; *Int'l*, pg. 1042
BIOSTAR PHARMACEUTICALS, INC.; *Int'l*, pg. 1042
BIOSTAT INTERNATIONAL, INC.; *U.S. Private*, pg. 563
BIOSTEM TECHNOLOGIES, INC.; *U.S. Public*, pg. 338
BIOSTIME HONG KONG LIMITED—See Health and Happiness (H&H) International Holdings Limited; *Int'l*, pg. 3303
BIOSTOCK CORPORATION—See Nippon Telegraph & Telephone Corporation; *Int'l*, pg. 5340
BIOSTORAGE TECHNOLOGIES ASIA PACIFIC PTE. LTD.—See Azenta, Inc.; *U.S. Public*, pg. 257
BIOSTORAGE TECHNOLOGIES GMBH—See Azenta, Inc.; *U.S. Public*, pg. 257
BIOSTORAGE TECHNOLOGIES, INC—See Azenta, Inc.; *U.S. Public*, pg. 257
BIOSTRATEGIES GROUP, INC.—See CRA International, Inc.; *U.S. Public*, pg. 588
BIOSTRIDE, INC.—See DevCo Partners Oy; *Int'l*, pg. 2086
BIOSTYLE CO., LTD.—See Keihan Holdings Co., Ltd.; *Int'l*, pg. 4116
BIOSUN BIOCHEMICALS, INC.—See BRAIN Biotech AG; *Int'l*, pg. 1137
BIOSURPLUS, INC.—See Copia Scientific, Inc.; *U.S. Private*, pg. 1044
BIOSYENT INC.; *Int'l*, pg. 1042
BIOSYMM PTY LTD.—See Madison Dearborn Partners, LLC; *U.S. Private*, pg. 2540
BIOSYN ARZNEIMITTEL GMBH; *Int'l*, pg. 1042
BIOSYN CORPORATION—See biosyn Arzneimittel GmbH; *Int'l*, pg. 1042
BIO-SYNECTICS; *Int'l*, pg. 1035
BIOSYNERGIE SARL—See HORIBA Ltd; *Int'l*, pg. 3475
BIOSYNERGY, INC.—See Harbour Group Industries, Inc.; *U.S. Private*, pg. 1861
BIOSYNEX SA; *Int'l*, pg. 1042
BIOTAGE AB; *Int'l*, pg. 1042
BIOTAGE GB LTD.—See Biotage AB; *Int'l*, pg. 1042
BIOTAGE KOREA CO., LTD.—See Biotage AB; *Int'l*, pg. 1042
BIOTAGE LLC—See Biotage AB; *Int'l*, pg. 1042
BIOTAGE SINGAPORE PTE. LTD.—See Biotage AB; *Int'l*, pg. 1042
BIOTAGE—See Biotage AB; *Int'l*, pg. 1042
BIOTAGE SWEDEN AB—See Biotage AB; *Int'l*, pg. 1042
BIOTAGE TRADING (SHANGHAI) CO., LTD.—See Biotage AB; *Int'l*, pg. 1042
BIOTALYS NV; *Int'l*, pg. 1042
BIOTA SCIENTIFIC MANAGEMENT PTY. LTD.—See Vaxart, Inc.; *U.S. Public*, pg. 2276
BIOTAY S.A.—See Phibro Animal Health Corporation; *U.S. Public*, pg. 1685
BIOTEC BIOLOGISCHE NATURVERPACKUNGEN GMBH & CO. KG—See Sphere SA; *Int'l*, pg. 7134
BIOTECH ACQUISITION COMPANY; *U.S. Public*, pg. 339

BIOTECH DENTAL PROSTHETICS, INC.—See Cerberus Capital Management, L.P.; *U.S. Private*, pg. 839
BIOTECH GROUP ACQUISITION CORPORATION; *U.S. Public*, pg. 339
THE BIOTECH GROWTH TRUST PLC; *Int'l*, pg. 7627
BIOTECH INVESTMENT GROUP LLC; *U.S. Private*, pg. 563
BIOTECH LABORATORIES PTY LIMITED—See Sonic Healthcare Limited; *Int'l*, pg. 7096
BIOTECH LABORATORIES (PTY.) LTD.—See JB Chemicals & Pharmaceuticals Ltd.; *Int'l*, pg. 3917
BIOTECHLOGIC, INC.—See Dark Horse Consulting; *U.S. Private*, pg. 1159
BIOTECH MEDICAL, INC.—See Suarez Corporation Industries; *U.S. Private*, pg. 3846
BIOTECH MEDICS, INC.; *U.S. Public*, pg. 339
BIO-TECHNE CORPORATION; *U.S. Public*, pg. 334
BIO-TECHNE LTD.—See Bio-Techne Corporation; *U.S. Public*, pg. 334
BIO-TECHNICAL RESOURCES—See Arkion Life Sciences L.L.C.; *U.S. Private*, pg. 326
BIOTECHNOLOGIES—See Informa plc; *Int'l*, pg. 3692
BIO-TECHNOLOGY GENERAL (ISRAEL) LTD.—See Ferring Holding SA; *Int'l*, pg. 2642
BIOTECHPROGRESS SCIENTIFIC RESEARCH & PRODUCTION CO. ZAO; *Int'l*, pg. 1043
BIOTECHSOL SRL—See SOL S.p.A.; *Int'l*, pg. 7067
BIOTECNET I MAS D S.A.—See FAES Farma, S.A.; *Int'l*, pg. 2601
BIOTECNOLOGIA APLICADA AL SANEAMIENTO AMBIENTAL, S.A. DE C.V.—See Promotora Ambiental S.A.B de C.V.; *Int'l*, pg. 5995
BIOTE CORP.; *U.S. Public*, pg. 339
BIOTECTOR ANALYTICAL SYSTEMS LTD—See Danaher Corporation; *U.S. Public*, pg. 625
BIOTEK INSTRUMENTS GMBH—See Agilent Technologies, Inc.; *U.S. Public*, pg. 61
BIOTEK INSTRUMENTS, INC.—See Agilent Technologies, Inc.; *U.S. Public*, pg. 61
BIOTEK INSTRUMENTS (I) PVT. LTD.—See Agilent Technologies, Inc.; *U.S. Public*, pg. 61
BIOTEK INSTRUMENTS LIMITED—See Agilent Technologies, Inc.; *U.S. Public*, pg. 61
BIOTEK INSTRUMENTS SAS—See Agilent Technologies, Inc.; *U.S. Public*, pg. 61
BIOTEK INSTRUMENTS SOUTH KOREA LTD.—See Agilent Technologies, Inc.; *U.S. Public*, pg. 62
BIOTEK INSTRUMENTS (SWITZERLAND) GMBH—See Agilent Technologies, Inc.; *U.S. Public*, pg. 61
BIOTEK INSTRUMENTS TAIWAN, INC.—See Agilent Technologies, Inc.; *U.S. Public*, pg. 62
BIOTEKNO; *Int'l*, pg. 1043
BIOTEK SERVICES, INC.—See Transcat, Inc.; *U.S. Public*, pg. 2179
BIOTELEMETRY, INC.—See Koninklijke Philips N.V.; *Int'l*, pg. 4267
BIOTEQ ARIZONA, INC.—See BQE Water Inc.; *Int'l*, pg. 1133
BIOTER S.A.; *Int'l*, pg. 1043
BIOTEST AG; *Int'l*, pg. 1043
BIOTEST AUSTRIA GMBH—See Biotest AG; *Int'l*, pg. 1043
BIOTEST FARMACEUTICA LTDA.—See Biotest AG; *Int'l*, pg. 1043
BIOTEST FRANCE SARL—See Biotest AG; *Int'l*, pg. 1043
BIOTEST GRUNDSTUCKSVERWALTUNGS GMBH—See Biotest AG; *Int'l*, pg. 1043
BIOTEST HELLAS M.E.P.E.—See Biotest AG; *Int'l*, pg. 1043
BIOTEST HUNGARIA KFT.—See Biotest AG; *Int'l*, pg. 1043
BIOTEST ITALIA S.R.L.—See Biotest AG; *Int'l*, pg. 1043
BIOTEST K.K.—See Biotest AG; *Int'l*, pg. 1043
BIOTEST LABORATORIES, INC.—See STERIS plc; *Int'l*, pg. 7209
BIOTEST MEDICAL, S.L.U.—See Biotest AG; *Int'l*, pg. 1043
BIOTEST MED SRL—See MedLife S.A.; *Int'l*, pg. 4784
BIOTEST PHARMACEUTICALS CORPORATION—See Biotest AG; *Int'l*, pg. 1043
BIOTEST PHARMA GMBH—See Biotest AG; *Int'l*, pg. 1043
BIOTEST (SCHWEIZ) AG—See Biotest AG; *Int'l*, pg. 1043
BIOTEST (UK) LTD.—See Biotest AG; *Int'l*, pg. 1043
BIOTHERA HOLDING CORP.; *U.S. Private*, pg. 563
BIOTHERA, INC.—See Biothera Holding Corp.; *U.S. Private*, pg. 563
BIOTHERANOSTICS, INC.—See Hologic, Inc.; *U.S. Public*, pg. 1044
BIO-THERA SOLUTIONS LTD.; *Int'l*, pg. 1035
BIOTIKA, A.S.—See Fiera Capital Corporation; *Int'l*, pg. 2660
BIOTIKA BOHEMIA SPOL. S R.O.; *Int'l*, pg. 1043
BIOTIX INC.; *U.S. Private*, pg. 563
BIOTON S.A.; *Int'l*, pg. 1043
BIOTOXTECH CO., LTD.; *Int'l*, pg. 1043
BIOTRAN INC.—See ProMed Waste Solutions LLC; *U.S. Private*, pg. 3282

BIOTREND CEVRE VE ENERJI YATIRIMLARI A.S.

BIOTREND CEVRE VE ENERJI YATIRIMLARI A.S.; *Int'l*, pg. 1043
BIOTRICITY INC.; *U.S. Public*, pg. 339
BIOTROL INTERNATIONAL—See The Jordan Company, L.P.; *U.S. Private*, pg. 4063
BIOTRON HEALTHCARE (INDIA) P. LTD.—See Seegene, Inc.; *Int'l*, pg. 6678
BIOTRONIK AG—See Biotronik GmbH & Co.; *Int'l*, pg. 1044
BIOTRONIK APS—See Biotronik GmbH & Co.; *Int'l*, pg. 1044
BIOTRONIK ARGENTINA S.R.L.—See Biotronik GmbH & Co.; *Int'l*, pg. 1044
BIOTRONIK ASIA PACIFIC PTE LTD.—See Biotronik GmbH & Co.; *Int'l*, pg. 1044
BIOTRONIK AUSTRALIA PTY. LTD.—See Biotronik GmbH & Co.; *Int'l*, pg. 1044
BIOTRONIK BALTIJA SIA—See Biotronik GmbH & Co.; *Int'l*, pg. 1044
BIOTRONIK (BEIJING) MEDICAL DEVICES LTD.—See Biotronik GmbH & Co.; *Int'l*, pg. 1044
BIOTRONIK BELGIUM S.A.—See Biotronik GmbH & Co.; *Int'l*, pg. 1044
BIOTRONIK BIYOMEDIKAL TEKNOLOJILER LTD. STI.—See Biotronik GmbH & Co.; *Int'l*, pg. 1044
BIOTRONIK BULGARIA LTD—See Biotronik GmbH & Co.; *Int'l*, pg. 1044
BIOTRONIK CANADA INC.—See Biotronik GmbH & Co.; *Int'l*, pg. 1044
BIOTRONIK COMERCIAL MEDICA LTDA.—See Biotronik GmbH & Co.; *Int'l*, pg. 1044
BIOTRONIK D.O.O.—See Biotronik GmbH & Co.; *Int'l*, pg. 1044
BIOTRONIK FRANCE S.A.S.—See Biotronik GmbH & Co.; *Int'l*, pg. 1044
BIOTRONIK GMBH & CO.; *Int'l*, pg. 1044
BIOTRONIK GMBH & CO.—See Biotronik GmbH & Co.; *Int'l*, pg. 1044
BIOTRONIK GMBH & CO. VERTRIEBS KG—See Biotronik GmbH & Co.; *Int'l*, pg. 1044
BIOTRONIK HELLAS SINGLE MEMBER LTD.—See Biotronik GmbH & Co.; *Int'l*, pg. 1044
BIOTRONIK HONG KONG LIMITED—See Biotronik GmbH & Co.; *Int'l*, pg. 1044
BIOTRONIK HUNGARIA KFT—See Biotronik GmbH & Co.; *Int'l*, pg. 1044
BIOTRONIK INC.—See Biotronik GmbH & Co.; *Int'l*, pg. 1044
BIOTRONIK ITALIA S.P.A.—See Biotronik GmbH & Co.; *Int'l*, pg. 1044
BIOTRONIK JAPAN, INC.—See Biotronik GmbH & Co.; *Int'l*, pg. 1044
BIOTRONIK KAZAKHSTAN GMBH—See Biotronik GmbH & Co.; *Int'l*, pg. 1044
BIOTRONIK KOREA CO., LTD.—See Biotronik GmbH & Co.; *Int'l*, pg. 1044
BIOTRONIK MEDICAL DEVICES INDIA PRIVATE LIMITED.—See Biotronik GmbH & Co.; *Int'l*, pg. 1044
BIOTRONIK MEDICAL DEVICES (MALAYSIA) SDN BHD—See Biotronik GmbH & Co.; *Int'l*, pg. 1044
BIOTRONIK NEDERLAND B.V.—See Biotronik GmbH & Co.; *Int'l*, pg. 1044
BIOTRONIK OY—See Biotronik GmbH & Co.; *Int'l*, pg. 1044
BIOTRONIK POLSKA SP. Z.O.O—See Biotronik GmbH & Co.; *Int'l*, pg. 1044
BIOTRONIK PORTUGAL UNIPESSOAL LDA.—See Biotronik GmbH & Co.; *Int'l*, pg. 1044
BIOTRONIK PRAHA SPOL. S.R.O.—See Biotronik GmbH & Co.; *Int'l*, pg. 1044
BIOTRONIK SA (PTY) LTD.—See Biotronik GmbH & Co.; *Int'l*, pg. 1044
BIOTRONIK SCHWEIZ AG—See Biotronik GmbH & Co.; *Int'l*, pg. 1044
BIOTRONIK SLOVENSKO, S.R.O.—See Biotronik GmbH & Co.; *Int'l*, pg. 1044
BIOTRONIK (THAILAND) CO., LTD.—See Biotronik GmbH & Co.; *Int'l*, pg. 1044
BIOTRONIK UK LTD.—See Biotronik GmbH & Co.; *Int'l*, pg. 1044
BIOTRONIK VERTRIEBS-GMBH—See Biotronik GmbH & Co.; *Int'l*, pg. 1044
BIOTRON LIMITED; *Int'l*, pg. 1043
BIOTROPICS MALAYSIA BERHAD—See Khazanah Nasional Berhad; *Int'l*, pg. 4152
BIOTTA AG—See Orior AG; *Int'l*, pg. 5633
BIOURJA TRADING, LLC; *U.S. Private*, pg. 563
BIO-UV GROUP; *Int'l*, pg. 1036
BIOU (ZHEJIANG) FOOD INDUSTRY CO., LTD.—See Apple Flavor & Fragrance Group Co., Ltd.; *Int'l*, pg. 520
BIOVACCINES NIGERIA LIMITED—See May & Baker Nigeria Plc.; *Int'l*, pg. 4743
BIOVAIL PHARMACEUTICALS CANADA—See Bausch Health Companies Inc.; *Int'l*, pg. 898
BIOVAIL TECHNOLOGIES LTD.—See Bausch Health Companies Inc.; *Int'l*, pg. 898
BIOVAXYS TECHNOLOGY CORP.; *Int'l*, pg. 1044
BIOVECTRA INC.—See Agilent Technologies, Inc.; *U.S. Public*, pg. 62

BIOVENTIX PLC; *Int'l*, pg. 1045
BIOVENTURE CENTRE PTE. LTD.—See Becton, Dickinson & Company; *U.S. Public*, pg. 290
BIOVENTURE CENTRE PTE. LTD.—See Johns Hopkins University; *U.S. Private*, pg. 2226
BIOVENTUS COOPERATIEF U.A.—See Bioventus Inc.; *U.S. Public*, pg. 339
BIOVENTUS INC.; *U.S. Public*, pg. 339
BIOVENTUS LLC; *U.S. Private*, pg. 563
BIOVER NV—See Perrigo Company plc; *Int'l*, pg. 5812
BIOVET I.K.E.—See Swedencare AB; *Int'l*, pg. 7365
BIO-VET, INC.—See Anpario plc; *Int'l*, pg. 475
BIOVET JSC—See Huvepharma EOOD; *Int'l*, pg. 3540
BIO VETO TEST SAS—See Virbac S.A.; *Int'l*, pg. 8246
BIOVICA INC.—See Biovica International AB; *Int'l*, pg. 1045
BIOVICA INTERNATIONAL AB; *Int'l*, pg. 1045
BIOVIE, INC.; *U.S. Public*, pg. 339
BIO VIEW LTD; *Int'l*, pg. 1035
BIOVILL CO., LTD.; *Int'l*, pg. 1045
BIOVIS DIAGNOSTIK MVZ GMBH—See Sonic Healthcare Limited; *Int'l*, pg. 7096
BIOVISION, INC.—See Danaher Corporation; *U.S. Public*, pg. 624
BIOWA, INC.—See Kirin Holdings Company, Limited; *Int'l*, pg. 4188
BIOWARE AUSTIN LLC—See Electronic Arts Inc.; *U.S. Public*, pg. 723
BIOWARE ULC—See Electronic Arts Inc.; *U.S. Public*, pg. 723
BIOWIND GROUP S.A. - MANUFACTURING PLANT—See Biowind Group S.A.; *Int'l*, pg. 1045
BIOWIND GROUP S.A.; *Int'l*, pg. 1045
BIOWISDOM LTD.—See ArchiMed SAS; *Int'l*, pg. 548
BIOWORKSHOPS LIMITED—See CSPC Pharmaceutical Group Limited; *Int'l*, pg. 1867
BIOWORKS, INC.—See Floridienne SA; *Int'l*, pg. 2708
BIO-WORKS TECHNOLOGIES AB; *Int'l*, pg. 1036
BIOWORLD MERCHANDISING, INC.; *U.S. Private*, pg. 563
BIOXCEL THERAPEUTICS, INC.; *U.S. Public*, pg. 339
BIOXYNE INTERNATIONAL MALAYSIA SDN BHD—See Bioxyne Limited; *Int'l*, pg. 1045
BIOXYNE LIMITED; *Int'l*, pg. 1045
BIOXYTRAN, INC.; *U.S. Public*, pg. 339
BIOZYME HOLDINGS LIMITED—See Abbott Laboratories; *U.S. Public*, pg. 19
BIOZYME INCORPORATED; *U.S. Private*, pg. 563
BIPADOSA SA; *Int'l*, pg. 1045
BIPAR SCIENCES, INC.—See Sanofi; *Int'l*, pg. 6552
BIPARTISAN POLICY CENTER; *U.S. Private*, pg. 563
BIP - BUSINESS INTEGRATION PARTNERS S.P.A.—See CVC Capital Partners SICAV-FIS S.A.; *Int'l*, pg. 1882
BI-PETRO, INC.; *U.S. Private*, pg. 550
BIPHA CORPORATION—See Mitsubishi Chemical Group Corporation; *Int'l*, pg. 4935
BI-PHASE TECHNOLOGIES, LLC—See Power Solutions International, Inc.; *U.S. Public*, pg. 1705
BIPIEMME VITA S.P.A.—See Banco BPM S.p.A.; *Int'l*, pg. 819
BIP INVESTMENT PARTNERS S.A.; *Int'l*, pg. 1045
BIPL SECURITIES LTD.; *Int'l*, pg. 1045
BI-PMB WASTE MANAGEMENT SDN. BHD.—See Press Metal Aluminium Holdings Bhd; *Int'l*, pg. 5965
BIPONEN LIMITED—See Navana Group of Companies; *Int'l*, pg. 5173
BIP OPPORTUNITIES FUND, LP; *U.S. Private*, pg. 563
BIPORT BULKERS SDN. BHD.—See Bintulu Port Holdings Berhad; *Int'l*, pg. 1034
BIPROGY INC.; *Int'l*, pg. 1045
BIPSO GMBH—See Bracco S.p.A.; *Int'l*, pg. 1134
BI PURE WATER INC.; *Int'l*, pg. 1016
BIP VENTURES EVERGREEN BDC; *U.S. Private*, pg. 563
BIRAL AG—See The Poul Due Jensen Foundation; *Int'l*, pg. 7674
BIRAL GMBH—See The Poul Due Jensen Foundation; *Int'l*, pg. 7674
BIRCHBOX, INC.—See FemTec Health, Inc.; *U.S. Private*, pg. 1494
BIRCH BRANCH ACQUISITION CORP.; *Int'l*, pg. 1046
BIRCHCLIFF ENERGY LTD; *Int'l*, pg. 1046
BIRCH COMMUNICATIONS, INC.—See Fusion Connect, Inc.; *U.S. Private*, pg. 1625
BIRCH DIALYSIS, LLC—See DaVita Inc.; *U.S. Public*, pg. 636
BIRCH FAMILY SERVICES, INC.; *U.S. Private*, pg. 564
BIRCHFIELD VENTURES, LLC—See SNDL Inc.; *Int'l*, pg. 7027
BIRCH HILL EQUITY PARTNERS MANAGEMENT INC.; *Int'l*, pg. 1046
BIRCHLAND PLYWOOD-VENEER LIMITED; *Int'l*, pg. 1046
BIRCHLAWN BURIAL PARK LLC—See Axar Capital Management LP; *U.S. Private*, pg. 411
BIRCH SWING CAPITAL LLC; *U.S. Private*, pg. 564
BIRCHTREE INVESTMENTS LTD.; *Int'l*, pg. 1046
BIRCHWOOD AUTOMOTIVE GROUP LTD.—See The Megill-Stephenson Company Ltd.; *Int'l*, pg. 7666

BIRCHWOOD FOODS—See Kenosha Beef International Ltd. Inc.; *U.S. Private*, pg. 2287
BIRCHWOOD FOODS—See Kenosha Beef International Ltd. Inc.; *U.S. Private*, pg. 2287
BIRCHWOOD FORD—See The Megill-Stephenson Company Ltd.; *Int'l*, pg. 7666
BIRCHWOOD LIGHTING, INC.—See Leviton Manufacturing Company, Inc.; *U.S. Private*, pg. 2436
BIRCHWOOD MALL, LLC—See Brookfield Corporation; *Int'l*, pg. 1185
BIRCHWOOD MANUFACTURING COMPANY—See The Hoffmann Family of Companies; *U.S. Private*, pg. 4053
BIRCHWOOD OMNIA LIMITED—See Heidelberg Materials AG; *Int'l*, pg. 3309
THE BIRCHWOOD; *U.S. Private*, pg. 3995
BIRCHWOOD TRANSPORT INC.—See Kenosha Beef International Ltd. Inc.; *U.S. Private*, pg. 2287
BIRDAIR, INC.—See Taiyo Kogyo Corporation; *Int'l*, pg. 7425
BIRDAIR MEXICO, S.A.DE C.V.—See Taiyo Kogyo Corporation; *Int'l*, pg. 7425
BIRD B GONE, INC.—See Lloyds Banking Group plc; *Int'l*, pg. 4537
BIRD B GONE, INC.—See Pelsis Holding (UK) Limited; *Int'l*, pg. 5784
BIRD & BIRD LLP; *Int'l*, pg. 1046
BIRDBRAIN, INC.; *U.S. Private*, pg. 564
BIRD CONSTRUCTION COMPANY, INC.; *U.S. Private*, pg. 564
BIRD CONSTRUCTION INC.; *Int'l*, pg. 1046
BIRD & CRONIN, LLC—See Dynatronics Corporation; *U.S. Public*, pg. 700
BIRDDOG SOFTWARE CORPORATION; *U.S. Private*, pg. 564
BIRDDOG SOLUTIONS, INC.; *U.S. Private*, pg. 564
BIRDDOG TECHNOLOGY LIMITED; *Int'l*, pg. 1047
BIRDEYE, INC.; *U.S. Private*, pg. 564
BIRD GLOBAL, INC.; *U.S. Public*, pg. 339
BIRDHI CHAND PANNALAL AGENCIES LIMITED; *Int'l*, pg. 1047
BIRDIE WIN CORPORATION; *Int'l*, pg. 1047
BIRDMAN, INC.; *Int'l*, pg. 1047
BIRD PACKAGING LIMITED; *Int'l*, pg. 1047
BIRD RIVER RESOURCES INC.; *Int'l*, pg. 1047
BIRD ROCK SYSTEMS, INC.; *U.S. Private*, pg. 564
BIRDSALL INTERACTIVE, INC.; *U.S. Private*, pg. 564
BIRDS BARBERSHOP; *U.S. Private*, pg. 564
BIRDSBORO MATERIALS—See Haines & Kibblehouse Inc.; *U.S. Private*, pg. 1840
BIRDS EYE FOODS LLC—See Conagra Brands, Inc.; *U.S. Public*, pg. 564
BIRDS EYE IRELAND LIMITED—See Nomad Foods Limited; *Int'l*, pg. 5408
BIRDSONG CORPORATION; *U.S. Private*, pg. 564
BIRDSONG GREGORY INC.; *U.S. Private*, pg. 564
BIRDSTEP TECHNOLOGY LTD—See Techstep ASA; *Int'l*, pg. 7512
BIRDS TRANSPORT & LOGISTICS LTD—See Ballyvesey Holdings Limited; *Int'l*, pg. 809
BIRD TECHNOLOGIES GROUP INC.; *U.S. Private*, pg. 564
BIRDY FUEL CELLS LLC—See Abalance Ltd.; *Int'l*, pg. 48
BIREPO A/S—See Addtech AB; *Int'l*, pg. 132
BIR FINANCIAL LIMITED; *Int'l*, pg. 1045
BIRGER BOSTAD AB—See Fabege AB; *Int'l*, pg. 2598
BIR HOLDINGS, LLC; *U.S. Private*, pg. 563
BIRIKIM VARLIK YONETIM A.S.; *Int'l*, pg. 1047
BI-RITE COMPANY INC.; *U.S. Private*, pg. 550
BI-RITE SERVICE FOOD CO.; *U.S. Private*, pg. 550
BIRKENSTOCK HOLDING PLC; *Int'l*, pg. 1047
BIRKENSTOCK USA, LP; *U.S. Private*, pg. 564
BIRKETT CUTMASTER LIMITED—See Carclo plc; *Int'l*, pg. 1321
THE BIRKETT MILLS; *U.S. Private*, pg. 3995
BIRKEY'S FARM STORE INC.; *U.S. Private*, pg. 564
BIRKITT ENVIRONMENTAL SERVICES, INC.; *U.S. Private*, pg. 564
BIRK MANUFACTURING, INC.; *U.S. Private*, pg. 564
BIRKO BIRLESIK KOYUNLULULAR MENSUCATTI- CARET VE SANAYI AS; *Int'l*, pg. 1047
BIRKO CORPORATION—See Platinum Equity, LLC; *U.S. Private*, pg. 3204
BIRKS GROUP INC.; *Int'l*, pg. 1047
BIRLA ACCUCAST LIMITED—See The Yash Birla Group; *Int'l*, pg. 7701
BIRLA ART LIFESTYLE PVT. LTD.—See The Yash Birla Group; *Int'l*, pg. 7701
BIRLA CABLE LTD.—See Birla Corporation Ltd.; *Int'l*, pg. 1047
BIRLA CARBON ALEXANDRIA CARBON BLACK CO. SAE—See The Aditya Birla Group; *Int'l*, pg. 7610
BIRLA CARBON COLUMBIAN CARBON EUROPA SRL.—See The Aditya Birla Group; *Int'l*, pg. 7610
BIRLA CARBON COLUMBIAN CARBON SPAIN S.L.—See The Aditya Birla Group; *Int'l*, pg. 7610
BIRLA CARBON COLUMBIAN CHEMICALS BRAZIL LTDA—See The Aditya Birla Group; *Int'l*, pg. 7610

COMPANY NAME INDEX

BIRLA CARBON COLUMBIAN CHEMICALS CO.—See The Aditya Birla Group; *Int'l*, pg. 7610
BIRLA CARBON COLUMBIAN CHEMICALS DEUTSCHLAND GMBH—See The Aditya Birla Group; *Int'l*, pg. 7610
BIRLA CARBON COLUMBIAN CHEMICALS KOREA CO. LTD.—See The Aditya Birla Group; *Int'l*, pg. 7610
BIRLA CARBON COLUMBIAN CHEMICALS WEIFANG CO. LTD.—See The Aditya Birla Group; *Int'l*, pg. 7610
BIRLA CARBON COLUMBIAN TISZAI CARBON LLC—See The Aditya Birla Group; *Int'l*, pg. 7610
BIRLA CARBON COMPANY LIMITED - BIRLA CARBON HI-TECH CARBON INDIA UNIT—See The Aditya Birla Group; *Int'l*, pg. 7610
BIRLA CARBON COMPANY LIMITED—See The Aditya Birla Group; *Int'l*, pg. 7610
BIRLA CARBON (THAILAND) PUBLIC COMPANY LIMITED—See The Aditya Birla Group; *Int'l*, pg. 7612
BIRLA CARBON U.S.A., INC.—See The Aditya Birla Group; *Int'l*, pg. 7610
BIRLA CENTURY EXPORTS PRIVATE LIMITED—See Century Textiles and Industries Limited; *Int'l*, pg. 1419
BIRLA CORPORATION LTD. - AUTOTRIM DIVISION I—See Birla Corporation Ltd.; *Int'l*, pg. 1047
BIRLA CORPORATION LTD. - DURGAPUR CEMENT WORKS—See Birla Corporation Ltd.; *Int'l*, pg. 1047
BIRLA CORPORATION LTD. - JUTE DIVISION—See Birla Corporation Ltd.; *Int'l*, pg. 1047
BIRLA CORPORATION LTD. - RAEBARELI CEMENT WORKS—See Birla Corporation Ltd.; *Int'l*, pg. 1047
BIRLA CORPORATION LTD. - SATNA CEMENT WORKS—See Birla Corporation Ltd.; *Int'l*, pg. 1047
BIRLA CORPORATION LTD.; *Int'l*, pg. 1047
BIRLA CORPORATION LTD. - VINDHYACHAL STEEL FOUNDRY—See Birla Corporation Ltd.; *Int'l*, pg. 1047
BIRLA COTSYN (INDIA) LIMITED—See The Yash Birla Group; *Int'l*, pg. 7701
BIRLA EDUTECH LTD.—See The Yash Birla Group; *Int'l*, pg. 7702
BIRLA ELECTRICALS LTD.—See The Yash Birla Group; *Int'l*, pg. 7702
BIRLA ESTATES PRIVATE LIMITED—See Century Textiles and Industries Limited; *Int'l*, pg. 1419
BIRLA FINANCIAL SERVICES INDIA PVT. LTD.—See The Yash Birla Group; *Int'l*, pg. 7702
BIRLA FURUKAWA FIBRE OPTICS LIMITED—See The Furukawa Electric Co., Ltd.; *Int'l*, pg. 7644
BIRLA LIFESTYLE PVT. LTD—See Zenith Birla India Ltd; *Int'l*, pg. 8633
BIRLA PACIFIC MEDSPA LTD—See The Yash Birla Group; *Int'l*, pg. 7702
BIRLA POWER SOLUTIONS LIMITED—See The Yash Birla Group; *Int'l*, pg. 7702
BIRLA PRECISION TECHNOLOGIES LIMITED—See The Yash Birla Group; *Int'l*, pg. 7702
BIRLASOFT LTD.; *Int'l*, pg. 1048
BIRLASOFT SOLUTIONS FRANCE SAS—See Birlasoft Ltd.; *Int'l*, pg. 1048
BIRLASOFT SOLUTIONS GMBH—See Birlasoft Ltd.; *Int'l*, pg. 1048
BIRLASOFT SOLUTIONS LIMITED—See Birlasoft Ltd.; *Int'l*, pg. 1048
BIRLASOFT SOLUTIONS LTDA.—See Birlasoft Ltd.; *Int'l*, pg. 1048
BIRLASOFT SOLUTIONS ME FZE—See Birlasoft Ltd.; *Int'l*, pg. 1048
BIRLA SUN LIFE INSURANCE COMPANY LIMITED; *Int'l*, pg. 1047
BIRLA TYRES LIMITED; *Int'l*, pg. 1048
BIRLA VIKAS CEMENT—See Birla Corporation Ltd.; *Int'l*, pg. 1047
BIRLA VIKING TRAVELS LTD.—See The Yash Birla Group; *Int'l*, pg. 7702
BIRLESIK DIS TICARET A.S.—See Yildiz Holding AS; *Int'l*, pg. 8583
BIRLESIK MOTOR SANAYI VE TICARET AS—See Koc Holding A.S.; *Int'l*, pg. 4223
BIRLESIK ODEME HIZMETLERI A.S.—See Fibabanka A.S.; *Int'l*, pg. 2651
BIRLIK MENSUCAT TICARET VE SANAYI ISLETMESI A.S.; *Int'l*, pg. 1048
BIRMAN WOOD & HARDWARE LTD.; *Int'l*, pg. 1048
BIRMIND AUTOMACAO E SERVICOS S.A.—See WEG S.A.; *Int'l*, pg. 8367
BIRMINGHAM BARONS, LLC; *U.S. Private*, pg. 564
BIRMINGHAM BEVERAGE COMPANY INC.—See Adams Beverages, Inc.; *U.S. Private*, pg. 73
BIRMINGHAM CITY FOOTBALL CLUB PLC—See Birmingham Sports Holdings Limited; *Int'l*, pg. 1048
BIRMINGHAM COCA-COLA BOTTLING COMPANY—See Coca-Cola Bottling Co. United, Inc.; *U.S. Private*, pg. 958
BIRMINGHAM FASTENER & SUPPLY INC. - B-FAST BOLT & SUPPLY DIVISION—See Birmingham Fastener & Supply Inc.; *U.S. Private*, pg. 564
BIRMINGHAM FASTENER & SUPPLY INC.; *U.S. Private*, pg. 564

BIRMINGHAM HIDE & TALLOW COMPANY INC. - ABERDEEN DIVISION—See Birmingham Hide & Tallow Company Inc.; *U.S. Private*, pg. 565
BIRMINGHAM HIDE & TALLOW COMPANY INC. - ARLEY DIVISION—See Birmingham Hide & Tallow Company Inc.; *U.S. Private*, pg. 565
BIRMINGHAM HIDE & TALLOW COMPANY INC. - BESSEMER DIVISION—See Birmingham Hide & Tallow Company Inc.; *U.S. Private*, pg. 565
BIRMINGHAM HIDE & TALLOW COMPANY INC. - HUNTSVILLE DIVISION—See Birmingham Hide & Tallow Company Inc.; *U.S. Private*, pg. 565
BIRMINGHAM HIDE & TALLOW COMPANY INC. - LOXLEY DIVISION—See Birmingham Hide & Tallow Company Inc.; *U.S. Private*, pg. 565
BIRMINGHAM HIDE & TALLOW COMPANY INC. - MONTGOMERY DIVISION—See Birmingham Hide & Tallow Company Inc.; *U.S. Private*, pg. 565
BIRMINGHAM HIDE & TALLOW COMPANY INC. - PANAMA CITY DIVISION—See Birmingham Hide & Tallow Company Inc.; *U.S. Private*, pg. 565
BIRMINGHAM HIDE & TALLOW COMPANY INC. - RINGGOLD DIVISION—See Birmingham Hide & Tallow Company Inc.; *U.S. Private*, pg. 565
BIRMINGHAM HIDE & TALLOW COMPANY INC.; *U.S. Private*, pg. 564
BIRMINGHAM HOLDINGS, LLC—See Community Health Systems, Inc.; *U.S. Public*, pg. 551
BIRMINGHAM HOME CARE SERVICES, LLC—See Community Health Systems, Inc.; *U.S. Public*, pg. 551
BIRMINGHAM INTERNATIONAL FOREST PRODUCTS, LLC—See Forest City Trading Group, LLC; *U.S. Private*, pg. 1566
BIRMINGHAM JEFFERSON CONVENTION COMPLEX; *U.S. Private*, pg. 565
BIRMINGHAM MIDSHIRES FINANCIAL SERVICES LTD.—See Lloyds Banking Group plc; *Int'l*, pg. 4536
BIRMINGHAM MIDSHIRES—See Lloyds Banking Group plc; *Int'l*, pg. 4537
BIRMINGHAM NEWS—See Advance Publications, Inc.; *U.S. Private*, pg. 85
BIRMINGHAM ORTHOPEDICS & SPORTS SPECIALISTS, LLC—See Community Health Systems, Inc.; *U.S. Public*, pg. 551
BIRMINGHAM OUTPATIENT SURGERY CENTER, LTD.—See UnitedHealth Group Incorporated; *U.S. Public*, pg. 2239
BIRMINGHAM RAIL LOCOMOTIVE CO.; *U.S. Private*, pg. 565
BIRMINGHAM SPECIALITIES LTD.—See Indutrade AB; *Int'l*, pg. 3677
BIRMINGHAM SPORTS HOLDINGS LIMITED; *Int'l*, pg. 1048
BIRMINGHAM SURGERY CENTER, LLC—See Bain Capital, LP; *U.S. Private*, pg. 446
BIRMINGHAM TERMINAL RAILWAY—See Kinder Morgan, Inc.; *U.S. Public*, pg. 1233
BIRMINGHAM VENDING COMPANY; *U.S. Private*, pg. 565
BIRNBACH COMMUNICATIONS, INC.; *U.S. Private*, pg. 565
BIRNER DENTAL MANAGEMENT SERVICES, INC.—See New Mountain Capital, LLC; *U.S. Private*, pg. 2904
BIRN SERBIA; *Int'l*, pg. 1048
BIRNS TELECOMMUNICATIONS INC.; *U.S. Private*, pg. 565
BIROTEHNA D.O.O.—See Avtotehna, d.d.; *Int'l*, pg. 751
BIRRA PERONI S.R.L.—See Asahi Group Holdings Ltd.; *Int'l*, pg. 593
BIRSECK HYDRO AG—See Kleinkraftwerk Birseck AG (KKB); *Int'l*, pg. 4200
BIRSE GROUP SERVICES—See Balfour Beatty plc; *Int'l*, pg. 807
BIRSE GROUP—See Balfour Beatty plc; *Int'l*, pg. 807
BIRSE METRO LIMITED—See Balfour Beatty plc; *Int'l*, pg. 807
BIRSE PROCESS ENGINEERING LIMITED—See Balfour Beatty plc; *Int'l*, pg. 807
BIRST, INC.—See Koch Industries, Inc.; *U.S. Private*, pg. 2330
BIRS WASSERKRAFT AG—See Alpiq Holding AG; *Int'l*, pg. 373
THE BIRTH COMPANY LIMITED—See HCA Healthcare, Inc.; *U.S. Public*, pg. 1011
BIRTHDAYEXPRESS.COM—See Rubie's Costume Company Inc.; *U.S. Private*, pg. 3500
BIRTLEY BUILDING PRODUCTS LTD—See Hill & Smith PLC; *Int'l*, pg. 3391
BIRTLEY GROUP LIMITED—See Hill & Smith PLC; *Int'l*, pg. 3391
BIRWELCO USA INC.—See Boustead Singapore Limited; *Int'l*, pg. 1120
BIRZ ASSOCIATION LTD.—See Onward Holdings Co., Ltd.; *Int'l*, pg. 5592
BIRZEIT PHARMACEUTICAL COMPANY; *Int'l*, pg. 1048
BISALLOY STEEL GROUP LTD.; *Int'l*, pg. 1048
BISALLOY STEELS PTY LIMITED—See Bisalloy Steel Group Ltd.; *Int'l*, pg. 1048

BISIL PLAST LIMITED

BISALLOY (THAILAND) CO LIMITED—See Bisalloy Steel Group Ltd.; *Int'l*, pg. 1048
BIS BETEILIGUNGSVERWALTUNGS GMBH—See Bilfinger SE; *Int'l*, pg. 1025
BIS BLOHM + VOSS INSPECTION SERVICE GMBH—See ThyssenKrupp AG; *Int'l*, pg. 7723
BIS BRABANT MOBIEL B.V.—See Bilfinger SE; *Int'l*, pg. 1025
BISCA MATERIAUX SARL; *Int'l*, pg. 1048
BISCAYNE CONTRACTORS INCORPORATED; *U.S. Private*, pg. 565
BISCAYNE ENGINEERING COMPANY, INC.—See Atwell, LLC; *U.S. Private*, pg. 384
BISCHOF GESELLSCHAFT MBH.—See Deutsche Bahn AG; *Int'l*, pg. 2049
BISCHOF HANDELS-GMBH—See Nayax Ltd.; *Int'l*, pg. 5178
BISCHOF + KLEIN ASIA PTE. LTD.—See Bischof + Klein GmbH & Co. KG; *Int'l*, pg. 1048
BISCHOF + KLEIN FRANCE SAS—See Bischof + Klein GmbH & Co. KG; *Int'l*, pg. 1048
BISCHOF + KLEIN GMBH & CO. KG; *Int'l*, pg. 1048
BISCHOF + KLEIN MIDDLE EAST CO.—See Bischof + Klein GmbH & Co. KG; *Int'l*, pg. 1048
BISCHOF + KLEIN (SHANGHAI) TRADING CO. LTD.—See Bischof + Klein GmbH & Co. KG; *Int'l*, pg. 1048
BISCHOF & KLEIN (U.K.) LTD.—See Bischof + Klein GmbH & Co. KG; *Int'l*, pg. 1048
BISCHOFSZELL FOODS AG—See The Federation of Migros Cooperatives; *Int'l*, pg. 7642
BISCO INDUSTRIES, INC.—See EACO Corporation; *U.S. Public*, pg. 701
BISCOMERICA CORP.; *U.S. Private*, pg. 565
BISCOMISR—See Kellanova; *U.S. Public*, pg. 1217
BISCUITS LECLERC LTD.; *Int'l*, pg. 1049
BISCUITVILLE, INC.; *U.S. Private*, pg. 565
BIS CZECH S.R.O.—See Bilfinger SE; *Int'l*, pg. 1025
BIS DIGITAL, INC.; *U.S. Private*, pg. 565
BIS ENTECH GMBH—See Bilfinger SE; *Int'l*, pg. 1025
BIS FRUCON INDUSTRIAL SERVICES INC.—See Bilfinger SE; *Int'l*, pg. 1026
BIS GERATETECHNIK DEUTSCHLAND GMBH—See Bilfinger SE; *Int'l*, pg. 1025
BIS GERATETECHNIK GMBH—See Bilfinger SE; *Int'l*, pg. 1025
BISHARA ESTABLISHMENT LLC—See Omar Zawawi Establishment LLC; *Int'l*, pg. 5561
BISHOP & ASSOCIATES, INC.; *U.S. Private*, pg. 565
BISHOP AUCKLAND VETS4PETS LIMITED—See Pets at Home Group Plc; *Int'l*, pg. 5833
BISHOP & BROGDON, INC.; *U.S. Private*, pg. 565
BISHOP BROTHERS AUTO AUCTION—See Cox Enterprises, Inc.; *U.S. Private*, pg. 1077
BISHOP BUSINESS EQUIPMENT CO.; *U.S. Private*, pg. 565
BISHOP CAPITAL CORP/WYOMING; *U.S. Public*, pg. 339
BISHOP DISTRIBUTING CO.; *U.S. Private*, pg. 565
BISHOP ENERGY SERVICES, L.L.C.; *U.S. Private*, pg. 565
BISHOP FIXTURE AND MILLWORK; *U.S. Private*, pg. 565
BISHOP INTERNATIONAL, INC.; *U.S. Private*, pg. 565
BISHOP LIFTING PRODUCTS, INC.—See Altamont Capital Partners; *U.S. Private*, pg. 204
BISHOP MUSEUM; *U.S. Private*, pg. 565
BISHOP ROSEN & CO. INC.; *U.S. Private*, pg. 565
BISHOPS MEAD (LYDNEY) MANAGEMENT COMPANY LIMITED—See Persimmon plc; *Int'l*, pg. 5815
BISHOP STEERING TECHNOLOGY PTY LTD—See Georgsmarienhutte Holding GmbH; *Int'l*, pg. 2940
BISHOP STREET CAPITAL MANAGEMENT CORPORATION—See BNP Paribas SA; *Int'l*, pg. 1088
BISHOP & WACHHOLZ INC.—See Minnesota Ag Group Inc.; *U.S. Private*, pg. 2743
BISHRELT INDUSTRIAL JOINT STOCK COMPANY; *Int'l*, pg. 1049
BISH'S RV, INC.; *U.S. Private*, pg. 565
BISHU KOSAN CO., LTD.—See Mino Ceramic Co., Ltd.; *Int'l*, pg. 4910
BIS HUNGARY KFT.—See Bilfinger SE; *Int'l*, pg. 1025
BISICHI PLC; *Int'l*, pg. 1049
BIS IKF GMBH—See Bilfinger SE; *Int'l*, pg. 1025
BISIL PLAST LIMITED; *Int'l*, pg. 1049
BIS INDUSTRIAL SERVICES BELGIE N.V.—See Bilfinger SE; *Int'l*, pg. 1025
BIS INDUSTRIAL SERVICES NEDERLAND B.V.—See Bilfinger SE; *Int'l*, pg. 1025
BIS INDUSTRIAL SERVICES OSTERREICH GMBH—See Bilfinger SE; *Int'l*, pg. 1025
BIS INDUSTRIAL SERVICES SWEDEN AB—See Bilfinger SE; *Int'l*, pg. 1025
BIS INDUSTRIER AS—See Bilfinger SE; *Int'l*, pg. 1025
BIS INDUSTRIER DANMARK A/S—See Bilfinger SE; *Int'l*, pg. 1025
BIS INDUSTRIES LIMITED—See KKR & Co. Inc.; *U.S. Public*, pg. 1239
BIS INSPECTION SERVICE GMBH—See Zeppelin GmbH; *Int'l*, pg. 8637

BIS INSULATION B.V.—See Bilfinger SE; *Int'l*, pg. 1025
BIS INTERNATIONAL CONSTRUCTION AND TRADING N.V.—See Bilfinger SE; *Int'l*, pg. 1025
BIS ISENTA AB—See Bilfinger SE; *Int'l*, pg. 1025
BIS ISENTA NORR AB—See Bilfinger SE; *Int'l*, pg. 1025
BIS ISOLIERTECHNIK NORD GMBH—See Bilfinger SE; *Int'l*, pg. 1025
BIS IZOMAR SP. Z O.O.—See Bilfinger SE; *Int'l*, pg. 1025
BISK EDUCATION, INC.; *U.S. Private*, pg. 566
BISKON YAPI A.S.—See Kiler Holding A.S.; *Int'l*, pg. 4161
BISKOT BISKUVI GIDA SANAYI VE TICARET A.S.—See Yildiz Holding AS; *Int'l*, pg. 8583
BISLEY & COMPANY PTY. LTD.; *Int'l*, pg. 1049
BIS MAINSERV SP. Z O.O.—See Bilfinger SE; *Int'l*, pg. 1025
BIS MAINTENANCE NORD GMBH—See Bilfinger SE; *Int'l*, pg. 1025
BIS MAINTENANCE SUDWEST GMBH—See Bilfinger SE; *Int'l*, pg. 1025
BISMARCK HONDA NISSAN HYUNDAI; *U.S. Private*, pg. 566
THE BISMARCK TRIBUNE—See Lee Enterprises, Incorporated; *U.S. Public*, pg. 1300
BIS MIXAB AB—See Bilfinger SE; *Int'l*, pg. 1025
BIS MULTISERWIS SP. Z O.O.—See Bilfinger SE; *Int'l*, pg. 1025
BISNETT INSURANCE, INC.—See Kelso & Company, L.P.; *U.S. Private*, pg. 2279
BISNODE AB—See Ratos AB; *Int'l*, pg. 6215
BISNODE AUSTRIA GMBH—See Ratos AB; *Int'l*, pg. 6215
BISNODE AUSTRIA HOLDING GMBH—See Ratos AB; *Int'l*, pg. 6215
BISNODE BELGIUM SA—See Ratos AB; *Int'l*, pg. 6215
BISNODE BUSINESS & MARKET INFORMATION A/S—See Ratos AB; *Int'l*, pg. 6216
BISNODE CENTRAL INVEST AB—See Ratos AB; *Int'l*, pg. 6216
BISNODE CESKA REPUBLIKA, A.S.—See Ratos AB; *Int'l*, pg. 6216
BISNODE DANMARK A/S—See Ratos AB; *Int'l*, pg. 6216
BISNODE D&B MAGYAYORSZAG KFT.—See Ratos AB; *Int'l*, pg. 6216
BISNODE D&B SCHWEIZ AG—See Ratos AB; *Int'l*, pg. 6216
BISNODE DEUTSCHLAND GMBH—See Ratos AB; *Int'l*, pg. 6216
BISNODE D.O.O.—See Ratos AB; *Int'l*, pg. 6216
BISNODE FINLAND OY—See Ratos AB; *Int'l*, pg. 6216
BISNODE FRANCE, S.A.S.—See Ratos AB; *Int'l*, pg. 6216
BISNODE GRUNDBESITZ DARMSTADT GMBH—See Ratos AB; *Int'l*, pg. 6216
BISNODE HUNGARY LTD.—See Ratos AB; *Int'l*, pg. 6216
BISNODE INFODATA HOLDING AB—See Ratos AB; *Int'l*, pg. 6216
BISNODE INFORMATICS AUSTRIA GMBH—See Ratos AB; *Int'l*, pg. 6216
BISNODE INFORMATICS, DENMARK A/S—See Ratos AB; *Int'l*, pg. 6216
BISNODE INFORMATICS SWEDEN AB—See Ratos AB; *Int'l*, pg. 6216
BISNODE LTD.—See Ratos AB; *Int'l*, pg. 6216
BISNODE NORGE AS—See Ratos AB; *Int'l*, pg. 6216
BISNODE NORWAY AS—See Ratos AB; *Int'l*, pg. 6216
BISNODE POLSKA SP.Z.O.O.—See Ratos AB; *Int'l*, pg. 6216
BISNODE SCHWEIZ AG—See Ratos AB; *Int'l*, pg. 6216
BISNODE SLOVENSKO, S.R.O.—See Ratos AB; *Int'l*, pg. 6216
BISNODE SVERIGE AB—See Ratos AB; *Int'l*, pg. 6216
BISNODE UK HOLDINGS LTD.—See Ratos AB; *Int'l*, pg. 6216
BISNOW LLC—See The Wicks Group of Companies, LLC; *U.S. Private*, pg. 4135
BIS NYHAMMAR VAST AB—See Bilfinger SE; *Int'l*, pg. 1025
BISOL VALLARTA, S.A. DE C.V.—See Melia Hotels International, S.A.; *Int'l*, pg. 4809
BISON BANK, S.A; *Int'l*, pg. 1049
BISON BASEBALL, INC.—See Rich Holdings, Inc.; *U.S. Private*, pg. 3426
BISON BUILDING MATERIALS LTD.—See Builders FirstSource, Inc.; *U.S. Public*, pg. 409
BISON CAPITAL ASSET MANAGEMENT, LLC; *U.S. Private*, pg. 566
BISON ENERGY SERVICES PLC; *Int'l*, pg. 1049
BISON FINANCE GROUP LIMITED—See Xynomic Pharmaceuticals Holdings, Inc.; *Int'l*, pg. 8542
BISON GEAR & ENGINEERING CORPORATION—See AMETEK, Inc.; *U.S. Public*, pg. 120
BISON INSURANCE AGENCY—See Duke Energy Corporation; *U.S. Public*, pg. 690
BISON INVESTMENTS INC.; *U.S. Private*, pg. 566
BISON OPTICAL DISC INC.; *U.S. Private*, pg. 566
BISON PIPELINE LLC—See TC Energy Corporation; *Int'l*, pg. 7482
BISON TRANSPORT, INC.—See James Richardson & Sons, Limited; *Int'l*, pg. 3878
BIS PLETTAC SP. Z O.O.—See Bilfinger SE; *Int'l*, pg. 1026

BIS PREFAL - ISOLAMENTOS TERMICOS LDA.—See Bilfinger SE; *Int'l*, pg. 1025
BIS PRODUCTION PARTNER AB—See Bilfinger SE; *Int'l*, pg. 1025
BIS PRODUCTION PARTNER IPEC AS—See Bilfinger SE; *Int'l*, pg. 1025
BIS PROZESSTECHNIK GMBH—See Bilfinger SE; *Int'l*, pg. 1025
BIS ROB ZEELAND B.V.—See Bilfinger SE; *Int'l*, pg. 1025
BIS ROHRBAU GRENZACH GMBH—See Bilfinger SE; *Int'l*, pg. 1025
BIS ROHRLEITUNGSBAU GMBH—See Bilfinger SE; *Int'l*, pg. 1025
BIS SALAMIS INC.—See Bilfinger SE; *Int'l*, pg. 1026
BIS SALAMIS INTERNATIONAL LIMITED—See Bilfinger SE; *Int'l*, pg. 1026
BISSELL AUSTRALIA PTY LTD—See Bissell Homecare, Inc.; *U.S. Private*, pg. 566
BISSELL CANADA CORP.—See Bissell Homecare, Inc.; *U.S. Private*, pg. 566
BISSELL HOMECARE, INC.; *U.S. Private*, pg. 566
BISSELL HOMECARE (OVERSEAS) INC.—See Bissell Homecare, Inc.; *U.S. Private*, pg. 566
BISSETT EQUIPMENT CORP.—See SiteOne Landscape Supply, Inc.; *U.S. Public*, pg. 1889
BISSETT NURSERY CORP.—See SiteOne Landscape Supply, Inc.; *U.S. Public*, pg. 1889
BIS SHARED SERVICES B.V.—See Bilfinger SE; *Int'l*, pg. 1026
BIS SHARED SERVICES OSTERREICH GMBH—See Bilfinger SE; *Int'l*, pg. 1026
BI-STATE PACKAGING INCORPORATED—See Group O Inc.; *U.S. Private*, pg. 1794
BI-STATE PROFESSIONAL SERVICES, INC.—See Beecken Petty O'Keefe & Company, LLC; *U.S. Private*, pg. 514
BI-STATE PROPANE, INC.—See UGI Corporation; *U.S. Public*, pg. 2221
BIS TEPSCO INC.—See Bilfinger SE; *Int'l*, pg. 1026
BISTOS CO., LTD.; *Int'l*, pg. 1049
BISTRO ASIA CO., LTD.—See Thai Beverage Public Company Limited; *Int'l*, pg. 7589
BISTRO MANAGEMENT; *U.S. Private*, pg. 566
BISTROMD, INC.—See Marley Spoon Group SE; *Int'l*, pg. 4698
BISTRO SOUPS, LTD.—See Vienna Sausage Mfg. Co.; *U.S. Private*, pg. 4381
BIS TSG INDUSTRIESERVICE GMBH—See Bilfinger SE; *Int'l*, pg. 1026
BIS VAM ANLAGENTECHNIK GMBH—See Bilfinger SE; *Int'l*, pg. 1026
BIS WILLICH GMBH—See Bilfinger SE; *Int'l*, pg. 1026
BIT8 LTD.—See INTRALOT S.A.; *Int'l*, pg. 3768
BIT9, INC.; *U.S. Private*, pg. 566
BITAC MAP S.L.U.—See IQVIA Holdings Inc.; *U.S. Public*, pg. 1168
BIT ANALYTICAL INSTRUMENTS GMBH—See MEC Holding GmbH; *Int'l*, pg. 4764
BITAUTO HOLDINGS LIMITED; *Int'l*, pg. 1049
BIT BROKERS INTERNATIONAL, LTD.; *U.S. Private*, pg. 566
BIT BROTHER LIMITED; *Int'l*, pg. 1049
BITBURGER BRAUEREI TH. SIMON GMBH—See Bitburger Braugruppe GmbH; *Int'l*, pg. 1049
BITBURGER BRAUGRUPPE GMBH; *Int'l*, pg. 1049
BITBURGER HOLDING GMBH; *Int'l*, pg. 1049
BITCENTRALCOM INC.—See Bitcentral Inc.; *U.S. Private*, pg. 567
BITCENTRAL INC.; *U.S. Private*, pg. 566
BITCO CORPORATION—See Old Republic International Corporation; *U.S. Public*, pg. 1567
BITCOIN BRANDS INC.; *U.S. Private*, pg. 567
BITCOIN DEPOT INC.; *U.S. Public*, pg. 339
BITCOIN GROUP SE; *Int'l*, pg. 1049
BITCOIN SERVICES, INC.; *U.S. Public*, pg. 339
BIT COMPUTER CO., LTD.; *Int'l*, pg. 1049
BITDEFENDER LLC—See BitDefender S.R.L.; *Int'l*, pg. 1049
BITDEFENDER S.R.L.; *Int'l*, pg. 1049
BIT DIGITAL, INC.; *U.S. Public*, pg. 339
BITE ACQUISITION CORP.—See Above Food Ingredients Inc.; *Int'l*, pg. 67
BITEBACK PUBLISHING LTD.; *Int'l*, pg. 1050
BI TECHNOLOGIES CORPORATION SDN BHD—See TT Electronics plc; *Int'l*, pg. 7958
BI TECHNOLOGIES ECD—See TT Electronics plc; *Int'l*, pg. 7959
BI TECHNOLOGIES JAPAN LTD—See TT Electronics plc; *Int'l*, pg. 7959
BI TECHNOLOGIES LTD—See TT Electronics plc; *Int'l*, pg. 7959
BI TECHNOLOGIES MCD—See TT Electronics plc; *Int'l*, pg. 7959
BI TECHNOLOGIES PTE LTD—See TT Electronics plc; *Int'l*, pg. 7959
BITECH TECHNOLOGIES CORPORATION; *U.S. Public*, pg. 339
BITEC INC.; *U.S. Private*, pg. 567

BITE COMMUNICATIONS GROUP LIMITED—See Next 15 Group plc; *Int'l*, pg. 5246
BITE COMMUNICATIONS LTD.—See Next 15 Group plc; *Int'l*, pg. 5246
BITE COMMUNICATIONS LTD., UK FILIAL—See Next 15 Group plc; *Int'l*, pg. 5246
BITE COMMUNICATIONS—See Next 15 Group plc; *Int'l*, pg. 5246
BITE COMMUNICATIONS—See Next 15 Group plc; *Int'l*, pg. 5246
BITE COMMUNICATIONS—See Next 15 Group plc; *Int'l*, pg. 5246
BITEK PTY LTD.; *Int'l*, pg. 1050
BITEKS IPLIK A.S.—See Bilici Yatirim Sanayi ve Ticaret A.S.; *Int'l*, pg. 1030
BITE MARKETING CONSULTING PTY LIMITED—See Next 15 Group plc; *Int'l*, pg. 5246
BIT FLOW INC.—See Advantech Co., Ltd.; *Int'l*, pg. 165
BITFUFU INC.; *Int'l*, pg. 1050
BITGLASS, INC.—See Francisco Partners Management, LP; *U.S. Private*, pg. 1588
BITHEADS, INC.; *Int'l*, pg. 1050
BITIBA GMBH—See zooplus AG; *Int'l*, pg. 8690
BIT JAPAN LTD.—See MEC Holding GmbH; *Int'l*, pg. 4764
BITMAMA S.R.L.—See Armando Testa S.p.A.; *Int'l*, pg. 574
BITMAMA S.R.L.—See Reply S.p.A.; *Int'l*, pg. 6290
BIT MEDTECH, LLC—See MEC Holding GmbH; *Int'l*, pg. 4764
BIT MINING LTD.; *Int'l*, pg. 1049
BITMIS CORP.; *Int'l*, pg. 1050
BITNER GOODMAN; *U.S. Private*, pg. 567
BITNER HENNESSY—See Bitner Goodman; *U.S. Private*, pg. 567
BITNER TOOLING TECHNOLOGIES—See L Squared Capital Management LP; *U.S. Private*, pg. 2362
BITNIX, INC.—See Bit Computer Co., Ltd.; *Int'l*, pg. 1049
BITOPI ADVERTISING LTD.—See Publicis Groupe S.A.; *Int'l*, pg. 6100
BITOR AMERICA CORP.—See Petroleos de Venezuela S.A.; *Int'l*, pg. 5828
BITPIPE, INC.—See TechTarget, Inc.; *U.S. Public*, pg. 1989
BITROS CONSTRUCTION S.A.—See Bitros Holding S.A.; *Int'l*, pg. 1050
BITROS HOLDING S.A.; *Int'l*, pg. 1050
BITROS REBAR CENTER S.A.—See Bitros Holding S.A.; *Int'l*, pg. 1050
BITROS STEEL S.A.—See Bitros Holding S.A.; *Int'l*, pg. 1050
BITRUSH CORP.; *Int'l*, pg. 1050
BITS FROM BYTES, LTD.—See 3D Systems Corporation; *U.S. Public*, pg. 4
BITS LTD.; *Int'l*, pg. 1050
BITS PRIVATE LIMITED; *Int'l*, pg. 1050
BITSQUID AB—See Autodesk, Inc.; *U.S. Public*, pg. 229
BIT SYSTEMS, INC.—See CACI International Inc.; *U.S. Public*, pg. 418
BITTER CREEK PIPELINES, LLC—See MDU Resources Group, Inc.; *U.S. Public*, pg. 1410
BITTERFELDER FERNWARME GMBH—See Stadtwerke Hannover AG; *Int'l*, pg. 7161
BITTERROOT INTERNATIONAL SYSTEMS, LTD.; *U.S. Private*, pg. 567
BITTERROOT RESOURCES LTD.; *Int'l*, pg. 1050
BITTIUM BIOSIGNALS LTD.—See Bittium Oyj; *Int'l*, pg. 1050
BITTIUM GERMANY GMBH—See Bittium Oyj; *Int'l*, pg. 1050
BITTIUM MEXICO S.A. DE C.V.—See Bittium Oyj; *Int'l*, pg. 1050
BITTIUM OYJ; *Int'l*, pg. 1050
BITTIUM SAFEMOVE OY—See Bittium Oyj; *Int'l*, pg. 1050
BITTIUM SINGAPORE PTE. LTD.—See Bittium Oyj; *Int'l*, pg. 1050
BITTIUM USA, INC.—See Bittium Oyj; *Int'l*, pg. 1050
BITTIUM WIRELESS OY—See Bittium Oyj; *Int'l*, pg. 1050
BITTNER VENDING, INC.; *U.S. Private*, pg. 567
BITTNET SYSTEMS SA BUCURESTI; *Int'l*, pg. 1050
BITTUBE INTERNATIONAL SE; *Int'l*, pg. 1050
BITTWARE, INC.—See Koch Industries, Inc.; *U.S. Private*, pg. 2333
BITU - BAU GESELLSCHAFT M.B.H.—See PORR AG; *Int'l*, pg. 5922
BITUBULK PTE LTD—See Tower Capital Asia Pte. Ltd.; *Int'l*, pg. 7850
BITUMA CORPORATION—See Gencor Industries, Inc.; *U.S. Public*, pg. 911
BITUMA-STOR, INC.—See Gencor Industries, Inc.; *U.S. Public*, pg. 911
BITUMENES ORINOCO, S.A.—See Petroleos de Venezuela S.A.; *Int'l*, pg. 5828
BITUMEN HANDELSGESELLSCHAFT M.B.H. & CO KG—See STRABAG SE; *Int'l*, pg. 7229
BITUMENKA D.D.; *Int'l*, pg. 1050
BITUMINA INDUSTRIES LTD.; *Int'l*, pg. 1050
BITUMINEX COCHIN PVT LTD—See Agarwal Industrial Corporation Ltd.; *Int'l*, pg. 200
BITUMINOUS CASUALTY CORPORATION—See Old Republic International Corporation; *U.S. Public*, pg. 1567

COMPANY NAME INDEX

BITUMINOUS FIRE AND MARINE INSURANCE COMPANY—See Old Republic International Corporation; *U.S. Public*, pg. 1567
BITUMINOUS ROADWAYS, INC. - INVER GROVE HEIGHTS PLANT—See Bituminous Roadways, Inc.; *U.S. Private*, pg. 567
BITUMINOUS ROADWAYS, INC. - MINNEAPOLIS PLANT—See Bituminous Roadways, Inc.; *U.S. Private*, pg. 567
BITUMINOUS ROADWAYS, INC. - SHAKOPEE PLANT—See Bituminous Roadways, Inc.; *U.S. Private*, pg. 567
BITUMINOUS ROADWAYS, INC.; *U.S. Private*, pg. 567
BITUMIX (CHILE) LTDA.—See VINCI S.A.; *Int'l*, pg. 8218
BITUMIX GRANITE SDN BHD—See Heidelberg Materials AG; *Int'l*, pg. 3309
BITUMIX S.A.—See VINCI S.A.; *Int'l*, pg. 8213
BITUNO VA BAUSTOFFTECHNIK GESELLSCHAFT M.B.H—See STRABAG SE; *Int'l*, pg. 7229
BITUNOVA GMBH & CO. KG—See STRABAG SE; *Int'l*, pg. 7229
BITUNOVA KFT.—See STRABAG SE; *Int'l*, pg. 7229
BITUNOVA SPOL. S.R.O.—See STRABAG SE; *Int'l*, pg. 7229
BITUNOVA SP. Z O.O.—See STRABAG SE; *Int'l*, pg. 7229
BITWALLET, INC.—See Rakuten Group, Inc.; *Int'l*, pg. 6196
BITWISE BITCOIN ETP TRUST; *U.S. Private*, pg. 567
BIT-WIZARDS INFORMATION TECHNOLOGY SOLUTIONS, INC.; *U.S. Private*, pg. 566
BITZER ANDINA SPA—See BITZER SE; *Int'l*, pg. 1051
BITZER AUSTRALIA PTY LIMITED—See BITZER SE; *Int'l*, pg. 1051
BITZER AUSTRIA GMBH—See BITZER SE; *Int'l*, pg. 1051
BITZER BENELUX BVBA—See BITZER SE; *Int'l*, pg. 1051
BITZER CANADA INC.—See BITZER SE; *Int'l*, pg. 1051
BITZER CIS LTD.—See BITZER SE; *Int'l*, pg. 1051
BITZER COMPRESSORES LTDA—See BITZER SE; *Int'l*, pg. 1051
BITZER COMPRESSORES S.A.—See BITZER SE; *Int'l*, pg. 1051
BITZER COMPRESSORS (BEIJING) LTD.—See BITZER SE; *Int'l*, pg. 1051
BITZER ELECTRONICS A/S—See BITZER SE; *Int'l*, pg. 1051
BITZER FRANCE S.A.R.L.—See BITZER SE; *Int'l*, pg. 1051
BITZER INDIA PRIVATE LIMITED—See BITZER SE; *Int'l*, pg. 1051
BITZER INDUSTRIAL EQUIPMENT (BEIJING) CO., LTD.—See BITZER SE; *Int'l*, pg. 1051
BITZER INVERTERTECHNOLOGIE GMBH—See BITZER SE; *Int'l*, pg. 1051
BITZER ITALIA S.R.L.—See BITZER SE; *Int'l*, pg. 1051
BITZER JAPAN K.K.—See BITZER SE; *Int'l*, pg. 1051
BITZER KENYA LTD.—See BITZER SE; *Int'l*, pg. 1051
BITZER KOREA CO., LTD.—See BITZER SE; *Int'l*, pg. 1051
BITZER KUHLMASCHINENBAU GMBH—See BITZER SE; *Int'l*, pg. 1051
BITZER KUHLMASCHINENBAU (S.A.) (PROPRIETARY) LTD.—See BITZER SE; *Int'l*, pg. 1051
BITZER KUHLMASCHINENBAU SCHKEUDITZ GMBH—See BITZER SE; *Int'l*, pg. 1051
BITZER MEXICO, S. DE R.L. DE C.V.—See BITZER SE; *Int'l*, pg. 1051
BITZER NEW ZEALAND PTY. LTD.—See BITZER SE; *Int'l*, pg. 1051
BITZER (PORTUGAL) COMPRESSORES PARA FRIO, S.A.—See BITZER SE; *Int'l*, pg. 1051
BITZER REFRIGERATION ASIA LIMITED—See BITZER SE; *Int'l*, pg. 1051
BITZER REFRIGERATION ASIA PTE., LTD.—See BITZER SE; *Int'l*, pg. 1051
BITZER REFRIGERATION ASIA PTE. LTD.—See BITZER SE; *Int'l*, pg. 1051
BITZER REFRIGERATION ASIA PTE LTD—See BITZER SE; *Int'l*, pg. 1051
BITZER REFRIGERATION TECHNOLOGY (CHINA) CO. LTD.—See BITZER SE; *Int'l*, pg. 1051
BITZER SA—See BITZER SE; *Int'l*, pg. 1051
BITZER SCROLL, INC.—See BITZER SE; *Int'l*, pg. 1052
BITZER SE—See BITZER SE; *Int'l*, pg. 1052
BITZER SE; *Int'l*, pg. 1051
BITZER SL—See BITZER SE; *Int'l*, pg. 1052
BITZER (SOUTH EAST ASIA) SDN. BHD.—See BITZER SE; *Int'l*, pg. 1051
BITZER UK LIMITED—See BITZER SE; *Int'l*, pg. 1052
BITZER US, INC.—See BITZER SE; *Int'l*, pg. 1052
BIURO CENTRUM SP. Z O.O.—See Stalexport Autostrady S.A.; *Int'l*, pg. 7164
BIURO FORBO FLOORING POLAND—See Forbo Holding Ltd.; *Int'l*, pg. 2729
BIURO INWESTYCJI KAPITALOWYCH S.A.; *Int'l*, pg. 1052
BIURO INZYNIERSKIE ATECHEM SP. Z O.O.—See Introl S.A.; *Int'l*, pg. 3769
BIURO PROJEKTOW KOMUNIKACYJNYCH W POZNANIU SP. Z O.O.—See ZUE S.A.; *Int'l*, pg. 8692

BIURO STUDIOW I PROJEKTOW GAZOWNICTWA GAZOPROJEKT SA—See Polskie Gornictwo Naftowe i Gazownictwo S.A.; *Int'l*, pg. 5912
BIURRARENA S. COOP.—See Mondragon Corporation; *Int'l*, pg. 5028
BIVARUS, INC.—See Ares Management Corporation; *U.S. Public*, pg. 190
BIVARUS, INC.—See Leonard Green & Partners, L.P.; *U.S. Private*, pg. 2427
BI-VENT AB—See Instalco AB; *Int'l*, pg. 3721
BIVICTRIX THERAPEUTICS PLC; *Int'l*, pg. 1052
BIVOL-UTILIDADES, EQUIPAMENTOS E INVEST. IMOBILIARIOS, LDA.—See Jeronimo Martins SGPS SA; *Int'l*, pg. 3931
BIWAKO KISEN STEAMSHIP CO., LTD.—See Keihan Holdings Co., Ltd.; *Int'l*, pg. 4116
BIWATER AEWT, INC.—See Biwater Holdings Limited; *Int'l*, pg. 1052
BIWATER ALGERIE SPA—See Biwater Holdings Limited; *Int'l*, pg. 1052
BIWATER CONSTRUCTION LIMITED—See Biwater Holdings Limited; *Int'l*, pg. 1052
BIWATER CONTRACTING B.V.—See Biwater Holdings Limited; *Int'l*, pg. 1052
BIWATER HOLDINGS LIMITED; *Int'l*, pg. 1052
BIWATER INTERNATIONAL LIMITED (PANAMA)—See Biwater Holdings Limited; *Int'l*, pg. 1052
BIWATER INTERNATIONAL LIMITED—See Biwater Holdings Limited; *Int'l*, pg. 1052
BIWATER INTERNATIONAL LIMITED—See Biwater Holdings Limited; *Int'l*, pg. 1052
BIWATER INTERNATIONAL LIMITED—See Biwater Holdings Limited; *Int'l*, pg. 1052
BIWATER LEISURE PLC—See Biwater Holdings Limited; *Int'l*, pg. 1052
BIWATER (MALAYSIA) SDN BHD—See Biwater Holdings Limited; *Int'l*, pg. 1052
BIWATER MAN LEE LIMITED—See Sun Fook Kong Group; *Int'l*, pg. 7303
BIWATER MAROC SA—See Biwater Holdings Limited; *Int'l*, pg. 1052
BIWATER (NIGERIA) LIMITED—See Biwater Holdings Limited; *Int'l*, pg. 1052
BIWATER PHILIPPINES INC.—See Biwater Holdings Limitod; *Int'l*, pg. 1052
BIWATER (PTY) LIMITED—See Biwater Holdings Limited; *Int'l*, pg. 1052
BIWATER S.A.—See Biwater Holdings Limited; *Int'l*, pg. 1052
BIWATER USA INC.—See Biwater Holdings Limited; *Int'l*, pg. 1052
BIW BUSINESS PARK DEVELOPMENT COMPANY WLL—See Inovest BSC; *Int'l*, pg. 3715
BIXBY INTERNATIONAL CORP.; *U.S. Private*, pg. 567
BIXOLON AMERICA INC.—See Bixolon Co Ltd; *Int'l*, pg. 1052
BIXOLON CO LTD; *Int'l*, pg. 1052
BIXOLON EUROPE GMBH—See Bixolon Co Ltd; *Int'l*, pg. 1052
BIXOLON MIDDLE EAST & AFRICA CO., LTD.—See Bixolon Co Ltd; *Int'l*, pg. 1052
BIYO BRIGHT CO., LTD.—See Mino Ceramic Co., Ltd.; *Int'l*, pg. 4910
BIZ-ALLIANZ INTERNATIONAL (M) SDN. BHD.—See OCB Berhad; *Int'l*, pg. 5515
BIZBASH MEDIA INC.; *U.S. Private*, pg. 567
BIZBUYSELL.COM—See CoStar Group, Inc.; *U.S. Public*, pg. 586
BIZCENTRAL USA, INC.; *U.S. Private*, pg. 567
BIZCHAIR.COM; *U.S. Private*, pg. 567
BIZCOM ELECTRONICS, INC.—See Compal Electronics, Inc.; *Int'l*, pg. 1746
BIZCOM WEB SERVICES, INC.; *U.S. Private*, pg. 567
BIZCONF TELECOM CO., LTD.; *Int'l*, pg. 1052
BIZCONN INT'L CORP.—See BizLink Holding Inc.; *Int'l*, pg. 1053
BIZ-CORE—See Data Core Systems Inc.; *U.S. Private*, pg. 1162
BIZERBA CANADA INC.; *Int'l*, pg. 1053
BIZER INC.—See Persol Holdings Co., Ltd.; *Int'l*, pg. 5818
BIZEX CORPORATION—See ASKUL Corporation; *Int'l*, pg. 625
BIZFILINGS—See Wolters Kluwer n.v.; *Int'l*, pg. 8444
BIZIBLE INC.—See Adobe Inc.; *U.S. Public*, pg. 42
BIZIMGAZ SANAYI VE TICARET A.S.—See SHV Holdings N.V.; *Int'l*, pg. 6872
BIZIM HESAP A.S.—See Fibabanka A.S.; *Int'l*, pg. 2651
BIZIM TOPTAN SATIS MAGAZALARI A.S.; *Int'l*, pg. 1053
BIZIT SYSTEMS (M) SDN. BHD.—See Aimflex Berhad; *Int'l*, pg. 233
BIZIT SYSTEMS & SOLUTIONS PTE. LTD.—See Aimflex Berhad; *Int'l*, pg. 233
BIZJET INTERNATIONAL SALES & SUPPORT, INC.—See Deutsche Lufthansa AG; *Int'l*, pg. 2069
BIZJOURNALS.COM—See Advance Publications, Inc.; *U.S. Private*, pg. 84
BIZLAB, INC.; *U.S. Private*, pg. 567
BIZLINK ELOCAB GMBH—See BizLink Holding Inc.; *Int'l*, pg. 1053

BIZLINK ELOCAB LTD.—See BizLink Holding Inc.; *Int'l*, pg. 1053
BIZLINK HOLDING INC.; *Int'l*, pg. 1053
BIZLINK INDUSTRY CZECH S.R.O.—See BizLink Holding Inc.; *Int'l*, pg. 1053
BIZLINK INDUSTRY SLOVAKIA SPOL. S.R.O.—See BizLink Holding Inc.; *Int'l*, pg. 1053
BIZLINK INTI CORP.—See BizLink Holding Inc.; *Int'l*, pg. 1053
BIZLINK ROBOTIC SOLUTIONS GERMANY GMBH—See BizLink Holding Inc.; *Int'l*, pg. 1053
BIZLINK SILITHERM S.R.L.—See BizLink Holding Inc.; *Int'l*, pg. 1053
BIZLINK SPECIAL CABLES (CHANGZHOU) CO., LTD.—See BizLink Holding Inc.; *Int'l*, pg. 1053
BIZLINK SPECIAL CABLES GERMANY GMBH—See BizLink Holding Inc.; *Int'l*, pg. 1053
BIZLINK TAILOR-MADE CABLE UK LIMITED—See LEONI AG; *Int'l*, pg. 4462
BIZLINK TECHNOLOGY (SLOVAKIA) S.R.O.—See BizLink Holding Inc.; *Int'l*, pg. 1053
BIZMATES, INC.; *Int'l*, pg. 1053
BIZMATICA SPA—See Econocom Group SA; *Int'l*, pg. 2297
BIZMATICS INC.—See Constellation Software Inc.; *Int'l*, pg. 1773
BIZMO CO., LTD.—See ZIGExN Co., Ltd.; *Int'l*, pg. 8682
BIZNESS APPS, INC.—See Buildfire, Inc.; *U.S. Private*, pg. 682
BIZNET CORPORATION—See PLUS Corporation; *Int'l*, pg. 5898
BIZOTIC COMMERCIAL LIMITED; *Int'l*, pg. 1053
BIZRATE.COM; *U.S. Private*, pg. 567
BIZRATE INSIGHTS INC.—See Meredith Corporation; *U.S. Public*, pg. 1422
BIZRIGHT TECHNOLOGY, INC.—See Ecomic Co Ltd; *Int'l*, pg. 2296
BIZ SHARE CORPORATION—See Konami Group Corporation; *Int'l*, pg. 4245
BIZSPACE LTD.—See Sirius Real Estate Limited; *Int'l*, pg. 6962
BIZSTREAM, INC.; *U.S. Private*, pg. 567
BIZ TECHNOLOGY SOLUTIONS, INC.—See Oval Partners; *U.S. Private*, pg. 3052
BIZTECH SOLUTIONS; *U.S. Private*, pg. 567
BIZTILES ITALIA S.P.A.—See QuattroR SGR S.p.A.; *Int'l*, pg. 6157
BIZVIZ AUDIENCE ANALYTICS, INC.; *U.S. Private*, pg. 567
BIXCHANGE INCORPORATED; *U.S. Private*, pg. 568
BIZZACK, INC.—See CRH plc; *Int'l*, pg. 1847
BIZZOOM INC.; *U.S. Private*, pg. 568
BIZZTOOLS GMBH—See Swiss Life Holding; *Int'l*, pg. 7368
BIZZUKA, INC.; *U.S. Private*, pg. 568
BJ ACQUISITION LLC—See Steven Madden, Ltd.; *U.S. Public*, pg. 1947
B.J. ALAN COMPANY; *U.S. Private*, pg. 420
B.J. BALDWIN ELECTRIC INC.; *U.S. Private*, pg. 420
BJ BALL GROUP LTD.—See Maui Capital Ltd.; *Int'l*, pg. 4731
BJ BALL PTY. LTD.—See Maui Capital Ltd.; *Int'l*, pg. 4731
BJ BALL—See Maui Capital Ltd.; *Int'l*, pg. 4731
BJ BALL—See Maui Capital Ltd.; *Int'l*, pg. 4731
BJB CAREER EDUCATION COMPANY, LIMITED; *Int'l*, pg. 1053
BJB CO., LTD.—See BJB GMBH & CO. KG; *Int'l*, pg. 1053
BJB ELECTRIC DONGGUAN LTD.—See BJB GMBH & CO. KG; *Int'l*, pg. 1053
BJB ELECTRIC L.P.—See BJB GMBH & CO. KG; *Int'l*, pg. 1053
BJB ELECTRIC TAIWAN CORPORATION—See BJB GMBH & CO. KG; *Int'l*, pg. 1053
BJB GMBH & CO. KG; *Int'l*, pg. 1053
BJB PROCESA S.A.—See BJB GMBH & CO. KG; *Int'l*, pg. 1053
BJB S.P.A.—See BJB GMBH & CO. KG; *Int'l*, pg. 1053
B&J BUILDER'S SUPPLY & SERVICE; *U.S. Private*, pg. 418
BJB (UK) LTD.—See BJB GMBH & CO. KG; *Int'l*, pg. 1053
BJCC, INC.—See Bank of America Corporation; *U.S. Public*, pg. 270
B.J. CECIL TRUCKING INC.; *U.S. Private*, pg. 420
BJC ENGINEERING COMPANY LIMITED—See Berli Jucker Public Co. Ltd.; *Int'l*, pg. 985
BJC FOODS (MALAYSIA) SDN. BHD.—See Berli Jucker Public Co. Ltd.; *Int'l*, pg. 985
BJC/HEALTHSOUTH REHABILITATION CENTER, L.L.C.—See Encompass Health Corporation; *U.S. Public*, pg. 754
BJC HEALTH SYSTEM; *U.S. Private*, pg. 568
BJC HEAVY INDUSTRIES PUBLIC COMPANY LIMITED; *Int'l*, pg. 1053
BJC INDUSTRIAL AND TRADING CO., LTD.—See Berli Jucker Public Co. Ltd.; *Int'l*, pg. 985
BJC INTERNATIONAL CO., LTD.—See Berli Jucker Public Co. Ltd.; *Int'l*, pg. 985
BJC INTERNATIONAL HOLDING PTE. LTD.—See Berli Jucker Public Co. Ltd.; *Int'l*, pg. 985

BJC HEAVY INDUSTRIES PUBLIC COMPANY LIMITED — CORPORATE AFFILIATIONS

BJC MARKETING COMPANY LIMITED—See Berli Jucker Public Co. Ltd.; *Int'l*, pg. 985
BJC SPECIALTIES CO., LTD.—See Berli Jucker Public Co. Ltd.; *Int'l*, pg. 985
BJC TRADING COMPANY LIMITED—See Berli Jucker Public Co. Ltd.; *Int'l*, pg. 985
BJ ELECTRIC SUPPLY, INC.; *U.S. Private*, pg. 568
BJERKE & LUTHER AS—See DBAY Advisors Limited; *Int'l*, pg. 1987
BJG ELECTRONICS, INC.—See Audax Group, Limited Partnership; *U.S. Private*, pg. 387
BJJ COMPANY INC.; *U.S. Private*, pg. 568
BJK INDUSTRIES INC.; *U.S. Private*, pg. 568
BJL GROUP LIMITED—See Dentsu Group Inc.; *Int'l*, pg. 2035
BJM AND ASSOCIATES INC.; *U.S. Private*, pg. 568
B & J MARINE PTE. LTD.—See Beng Kuang Marine Limited; *Int'l*, pg. 973
B.J. MCGLONE CO. INC.; *U.S. Private*, pg. 420
B J MCGLONE CO—See B.J. McGlone Co. Inc.; *U.S. Private*, pg. 420
B&J MUSIC LIMITED—See TPG Capital, L.P.; *U.S. Public*, pg. 2173
BJOORN KLICKGOLV PA NATET AB—See Valinge Invest AB; *Int'l*, pg. 8116
BJORGUN EHF—See Heidelberg Materials AG; *Int'l*, pg. 3309
BJORKA MINERAL AB—See Omya (Schweiz) AG; *Int'l*, pg. 5570
BJORN BORG AB; *Int'l*, pg. 1053
BJORN BORG BRANDS AB—See Bjorn Borg AB; *Int'l*, pg. 1053
BJORN BORG CLOTHING AB—See Bjorn Borg AB; *Int'l*, pg. 1054
BJORN BORG FINLAND OY—See Bjorn Borg AB; *Int'l*, pg. 1054
BJORN BORG FOOTWEAR AB—See Bjorn Borg AB; *Int'l*, pg. 1054
BJORN BORG RETAIL AB—See Bjorn Borg AB; *Int'l*, pg. 1054
BJORN BORG SWEDEN AB—See Bjorn Borg AB; *Int'l*, pg. 1054
BJORN BORG UK LIMITED—See Bjorn Borg AB; *Int'l*, pg. 1054
BJORN BYGG AS—See Peab AB; *Int'l*, pg. 5771
BJORNDALEN PANORAMA AS—See Storebrand ASA; *Int'l*, pg. 7226
BJORNSEN BERATENDE INGENIEURE GMBH; *Int'l*, pg. 1054
BJORNSEN CONSULTING ENGINEERING ERFURT GMBH—See Bjornsen Beratende Ingenieure GmbH; *Int'l*, pg. 1054
B.J. PETRUSO AGENCY & ASSOCIATES, INC.—See Northwest Bancshares, Inc.; *U.S. Public*, pg. 1542
B&J PHOTO, INC.; *U.S. Private*, pg. 418
BJ PROCESS & PIPELINE SERVICES CO.—See Baker Hughes Company; *U.S. Public*, pg. 264
BJ'S CHARITABLE FOUNDATION INC.—See Leonard Green & Partners, L.P.; *U.S. Private*, pg. 2425
BJ SERVICES COMPANY ITALIA S.R.L.—See Baker Hughes Company; *U.S. Public*, pg. 264
BJ SERVICES COMPANY—See Baker Hughes Company; *U.S. Public*, pg. 264
BJ SERVICES CO. (SINGAPORE) PTE LTD—See Baker Hughes Company; *U.S. Public*, pg. 264
BJ SERVICES, INC.; *U.S. Private*, pg. 568
B J S, INC.—See Pettus Office Products, Inc.; *U.S. Private*, pg. 3163
BJ'S RESTAURANT OPERATIONS COMPANY—See BJ'S RESTAURANTS, INC.; *U.S. Public*, pg. 340
BJ'S RESTAURANTS, INC.; *U.S. Public*, pg. 340
BJ'S WHOLESALE CLUB HOLDINGS, INC.; *U.S. Public*, pg. 340
BJ'S WHOLESALE CLUB, INC.—See Leonard Green & Partners, L.P.; *U.S. Private*, pg. 2425
BJT INC.; *U.S. Private*, pg. 568
BJ TUBULAR SERVICES B.V.—See Baker Hughes Company; *U.S. Public*, pg. 264
BJ TUBULAR SERVICES LIMITED—See Baker Hughes Company; *U.S. Public*, pg. 264
B.J. UNDERWOOD PTY. LTD.—See Nutrien Ltd.; *Int'l*, pg. 5492
BJURENWALL LAUREA AB—See Lagercrantz Group AB; *Int'l*, pg. 4393
B.J. VINES INC.; *U.S. Private*, pg. 420
BK ARGENTINA SERVICIOS, S.A.—See Restaurant Brands International Inc.; *Int'l*, pg. 6304
BKB AQUA ENGINEERING PTY. LTD.—See The Poul Due Jensen Foundation; *Int'l*, pg. 7674
BKB BUILDING SOLUTIONS PTY. LTD—See The Poul Due Jensen Foundation; *Int'l*, pg. 7674
B+K BETEILIGUNGEN GMBH—See Bischof + Klein GmbH & Co. KG; *Int'l*, pg. 1048
B.K.B. EUROPA SARL—See Kuala Lumpur Kepong Berhad; *Int'l*, pg. 4318
B.K.B. HEVEA PRODUCTS SDN BHD—See Kuala Lumpur Kepong Berhad; *Int'l*, pg. 4318
B&K COMPONENTS LTD.; *U.S. Private*, pg. 418

B-K CONCRETE PRODUCTS INC.—See K-Five Construction Corporation; *U.S. Private*, pg. 2251
B&K CONSTRUCTION CO. INC.; *U.S. Private*, pg. 418
BKCV SDN BHD—See Chin Hin Group Berhad; *Int'l*, pg. 1480
BKCW, L.P.; *U.S. Private*, pg. 568
BKD BELLE MEADE, LLC—See Brookdale Senior Living Inc.; *U.S. Public*, pg. 393
BKD COLLEGE PLACE, LLC—See Brookdale Senior Living Inc.; *U.S. Public*, pg. 393
BKD CORPORATE FINANCE, LLC—See BKD, LLP; *U.S. Private*, pg. 568
BKD INSURANCE, LLC—See BKD, LLP; *U.S. Private*, pg. 568
BKD JONES FARM, LLC—See Brookdale Senior Living Inc.; *U.S. Public*, pg. 393
BKD LAWRENCEVILLE, LLC—See Brookdale Senior Living Inc.; *U.S. Public*, pg. 393
BKD, LLP - INDIANAPOLIS—See BKD, LLP; *U.S. Private*, pg. 568
BKD, LLP; *U.S. Private*, pg. 568
BKD LODI, LLC—See Brookdale Senior Living Inc.; *U.S. Public*, pg. 393
BKD MURRAY, LLC—See Brookdale Senior Living Inc.; *U.S. Public*, pg. 393
BKD NEWNAN, LLC—See Brookdale Senior Living Inc.; *U.S. Public*, pg. 393
BKD NORTH GILBERT, LLC—See Brookdale Senior Living Inc.; *U.S. Public*, pg. 393
BKD NORTH GLENDALE, LLC—See Brookdale Senior Living Inc.; *U.S. Public*, pg. 393
BKD OAK PARK, LLC—See Brookdale Senior Living Inc.; *U.S. Public*, pg. 393
BKD PARKPLACE, LLC—See Brookdale Senior Living Inc.; *U.S. Public*, pg. 393
BKD SOUTH BAY, LLC—See Brookdale Senior Living Inc.; *U.S. Public*, pg. 393
BKD TANQUE VERDE, LLC—See Brookdale Senior Living Inc.; *U.S. Public*, pg. 393
BKD TULLAHOMA, LLC—See Brookdale Senior Living Inc.; *U.S. Public*, pg. 393
BKD WEALTH ADVISORS, LLC—See BKD, LLP; *U.S. Private*, pg. 568
BKD WEKIWA SPRINGS, LLC—See Brookdale Senior Living Inc.; *U.S. Public*, pg. 393
BKD WILSONVILLE, LLC—See Brookdale Senior Living Inc.; *U.S. Public*, pg. 393
B&K ELECTRIC WHOLESALE; *U.S. Private*, pg. 418
BK-ELECTRONIC GMBH—See Resideo Technologies, Inc.; *U.S. Public*, pg. 1790
BK ENERGIA ITACOATIARA LTDA.—See Precious Woods Holding AG; *Int'l*, pg. 5956
B&K ENTERPRISES INC.; *U.S. Private*, pg. 419
BKEP MANAGEMENT, INC.—See Ergon, Inc.; *U.S. Private*, pg. 1418
BKEP MATERIALS LLC—See Ergon, Inc.; *U.S. Private*, pg. 1418
BKEP MATERIALS LLC—See Ergon, Inc.; *U.S. Private*, pg. 1418
BKEP OPERATING, L.L.C.—See Ergon, Inc.; *U.S. Private*, pg. 1418
BKEP SERVICES LLC—See Ergon, Inc.; *U.S. Private*, pg. 1418
BKE SHELF LTD.—See Eurasia Drilling Company Limited; *Int'l*, pg. 2527
BKF CAPITAL GROUP, INC.; *U.S. Public*, pg. 340
BKF-KLIMA A/S—See Beijer Ref AB; *Int'l*, pg. 944
BKGM INDUSTRIES SDN BHD—See Chin Hin Group Berhad; *Int'l*, pg. 1480
BK HOLDINGS CO., LTD; *Int'l*, pg. 1054
BKI GABON S.A.—See HAL Trust N.V.; *Int'l*, pg. 3224
BKI INVESTMENT COMPANY LIMITED; *Int'l*, pg. 1054
BK IMMOBILIEN VERWALTUNG GMBH—See DIC Asset AG; *Int'l*, pg. 2107
BK IMMO VORSORGE GMBH—See Capital Bank - GRAWE Gruppe AG; *Int'l*, pg. 1310
BKI—See Standex International; *U.S. Public*, pg. 1930
B&K, LLC—See Mueller Industries, Inc.; *U.S. Public*, pg. 1484
B&K MANUFACTURING—See Byrnes & Kiefer Company; *U.S. Private*, pg. 701
BKM CAPITAL PARTNERS, L.P.; *U.S. Private*, pg. 569
B-K MEDICAL AB—See Altaris Capital Partners, LLC; *U.S. Private*, pg. 205
BK MEDICAL APS—See Altaris Capital Partners, LLC; *U.S. Private*, pg. 205
BK MEDICAL AUSTRALIA PTY LTD.—See GE HealthCare Technologies Inc.; *U.S. Public*, pg. 908
BK MEDICAL AUSTRIA GMBH—See GE HealthCare Technologies Inc.; *U.S. Public*, pg. 908
BK MEDICAL FRANCE SAS—See GE HealthCare Technologies Inc.; *U.S. Public*, pg. 908
BK MEDICAL HOLDING COMPANY, INC.—See GE HealthCare Technologies Inc.; *U.S. Public*, pg. 908
BK MEDICAL ITALIA S.R.L.—See GE HealthCare Technologies Inc.; *U.S. Public*, pg. 908
BK MEDICAL MEDIZINISCHE SYSTEME GMBH—See Altaris Capital Partners, LLC; *U.S. Private*, pg. 205

BK MEDICAL SCHWEIZ GMBH—See GE HealthCare Technologies Inc.; *U.S. Public*, pg. 908
BK MEDICAL SWEDEN AB—See GE HealthCare Technologies Inc.; *U.S. Public*, pg. 908
B-K MEDICAL SYSTEMS, INC.—See Altaris Capital Partners, LLC; *U.S. Private*, pg. 205
BK MEDICAL TECHNOLOGY SHANGHAI CO., LTD.—See GE HealthCare Technologies Inc.; *U.S. Public*, pg. 908
BK MEDICAL UK LIMITED—See GE HealthCare Technologies Inc.; *U.S. Public*, pg. 908
B.K. MILLER CO., INC.; *U.S. Private*, pg. 420
BKM INDUSTRIES LIMITED—See Manaksia Ltd; *Int'l*, pg. 4667
BKM MANAGEMENT LIMITED; *Int'l*, pg. 1054
BKM OF CALIFORNIA—See bkm OfficeWorks; *U.S. Private*, pg. 569
BKM OFFICEWORKS; *U.S. Private*, pg. 569
BKM TOTAL OFFICE TEXAS LP; *U.S. Private*, pg. 569
BKN BIOSTROM AG; *Int'l*, pg. 1054
BK PLASTICS INDUSTRY, INC.; *U.S. Private*, pg. 568
B+K POLSKA GMBH SP.K.—See Bischof + Klein GmbH & Co. KG; *Int'l*, pg. 1048
BKR CR, S.R.O.—See VKR Holding A/S; *Int'l*, pg. 8281
BKS BANK AG—See Bank fur Tirol und Vorarlberg Ag; *Int'l*, pg. 838
BK SECURITIES LIMITED—See Banque de Kigali S.A.; *Int'l*, pg. 853
BKS-IMMOBILIENLEASING GESELLSCHAFT MBH—See Bank fur Tirol und Vorarlberg Ag; *Int'l*, pg. 838
BKS IMMOBILIEN-SERVICE GESELLSCHAFT MBH—See Bank fur Tirol und Vorarlberg Ag; *Int'l*, pg. 838
BKS-LEASING GESELLSCHAFT MBH—See Bank fur Tirol und Vorarlberg Ag; *Int'l*, pg. 838
BKS SURVEYS LTD—See Amalgamated Metal Corporation PLC; *Int'l*, pg. 408
BKS ZENTRALE-ERRICHTUNGS- U. VERMIETUNGSGESELLSCHAFT. MBH—See Bank fur Tirol und Vorarlberg Ag; *Int'l*, pg. 838
BK TECHNOLOGIES CORPORATION; *U.S. Public*, pg. 340
BKT ENTERPRISES INC.; *U.S. Private*, pg. 569
BK ULTRASOUND LIMITED—See Altaris Capital Partners, LLC; *U.S. Private*, pg. 205
BKV TELLOS, INC.; *U.S. Private*, pg. 569
BKW AEK CONTRACTING AG—See BKW AG; *Int'l*, pg. 1054
BKW AG; *Int'l*, pg. 1054
BKW ENERGIE AG—See BKW AG; *Int'l*, pg. 1054
BKW ENVIRONMENTAL SERVICES, LLC—See Ridgemont Partners Management LLC; *U.S. Private*, pg. 3432
BK WERKSTOFFTECHNIKPRUFSTELLE FUR WERKSTOFFE, GMBH—See I Squared Capital Advisors (US) LLC; *U.S. Private*, pg. 2022
BK WERKSTOFFTECHNIKPRUFSTELLE FUR WERKSTOFFE, GMBH—See TDR Capital LLP; *Int'l*, pg. 7491
BKW FMB ENERGIE AG—See E.ON SE; *Int'l*, pg. 2251
BKW ITALIA S.P.A.—See BKW AG; *Int'l*, pg. 1054
BKW SMART ENERGY & MOBILITY AG—See BKW AG; *Int'l*, pg. 1054
BKY-GARDNER USA—See SKion GmbH; *Int'l*, pg. 6987
BLAACANKA A.D.; *Int'l*, pg. 1056
BLACH CONSTRUCTION; *U.S. Private*, pg. 569
BLACHLY-LANE COUNTY COOPERATIVE ELECTRIC ASSOCIATION; *U.S. Private*, pg. 569
BLACKALL ASSOCIATES INC.; *U.S. Private*, pg. 573
BLACK AND DECKER, S.A. DE C.V.—See Stanley Black & Decker, Inc.; *U.S. Public*, pg. 1936
BLACKARCH PARTNERS LP.—See Regions Financial Corporation; *U.S. Public*, pg. 1776
BLACK BALLOON PUBLISHING, LLC; *U.S. Private*, pg. 569
BLACKBAUD CANADA, INC.—See Blackbaud, Inc.; *U.S. Public*, pg. 341
BLACKBAUD EUROPE LTD.—See Blackbaud, Inc.; *U.S. Public*, pg. 341
BLACKBAUD, INC.; *U.S. Public*, pg. 341
BLACKBAUD PACIFIC PTY. LTD.—See Blackbaud, Inc.; *U.S. Public*, pg. 341
BLACK BEAR MEDICAL, INC.—See Quipt Home Medical Corp.; *U.S. Public*, pg. 1757
BLACK BEAR SPORTS GROUP, INC.—See Blackstreet Capital Holdings LLC; *U.S. Private*, pg. 576
BLACK BELT SOLUTIONS LLC; *U.S. Private*, pg. 569
BLACKBERN PARTNERS LLC; *U.S. Private*, pg. 573
BLACKBERRY AUSTRALIA PTY LIMITED—See BlackBerry Limited; *Int'l*, pg. 1060
BLACKBERRY AUSTRIA GMBH—See BlackBerry Limited; *Int'l*, pg. 1060
BLACKBERRY CORPORATION—See BlackBerry Limited; *Int'l*, pg. 1060
BLACKBERRY LIMITED; *Int'l*, pg. 1060
BLACKBERRY LTD. - WATERLOO MANUFACTURING FACILITY—See BlackBerry Limited; *Int'l*, pg. 1060
BLACKBERRY MOBILE SOUTH AFRICA (PROPRIETARY) LIMITED—See BlackBerry Limited; *Int'l*, pg. 1060
BLACKBERRY SINGAPORE PTE. LIMITED—See BlackBerry Limited; *Int'l*, pg. 1060

COMPANY NAME INDEX

BLACKBERRY UK LIMITED—See BlackBerry Limited; *Int'l*, pg. 1060
BLACK BIRD BIOTECH, INC.; *U.S. Public*, pg. 340
BLACKBIRD DATA SYSTEMS LTD—See Panasonic Holdings Corporation; *Int'l*, pg. 5725
BLACKBIRD HERITAGE MOTORWORKS LIMITED—See CCT Fortis Holdings Limited; *Int'l*, pg. 1369
BLACKBIRD PLC; *Int'l*, pg. 1060
BLACKBIRD TECHNOLOGIES, INC.—See RTX Corporation; *U.S. Public*, pg. 1824
BLACKBIXON SDN. BHD.—See Ni Hsin Group Berhad; *Int'l*, pg. 5259
BLACKBOARD (AUSTRALIA) PTY LTD.—See Class Technologies Inc.; *U.S. Private*, pg. 915
BLACKBOARD COLLABORATE—See Class Technologies Inc.; *U.S. Private*, pg. 915
BLACKBOARD CZECH S.R.O.—See Class Technologies Inc.; *U.S. Private*, pg. 915
BLACKBOARD EDUCATIONAL (CANADA) CORPORATION—See Class Technologies Inc.; *U.S. Private*, pg. 915
BLACKBOARD GERMANY GMBH—See Class Technologies Inc.; *U.S. Private*, pg. 915
BLACKBOARD INC.—See Class Technologies Inc.; *U.S. Private*, pg. 915
BLACKBOARD INC.—See Class Technologies Inc.; *U.S. Private*, pg. 915
BLACKBOARD INTERNATIONAL B.V.—See Class Technologies Inc.; *U.S. Private*, pg. 915
BLACKBOARD JAPAN K.K.—See Class Technologies Inc.; *U.S. Private*, pg. 915
BLACKBOARD STUDENT SERVICES—See Class Technologies Inc.; *U.S. Private*, pg. 915
BLACK BOOK MARKET RESEARCH LLC; *U.S. Private*, pg. 569
BLACK BOX AB—See Black Box Limited; *Int'l*, pg. 1056
BLACK BOX A/S—See Black Box Limited; *Int'l*, pg. 1056
BLACK BOX CANADA CORP.—See Black Box Limited; *Int'l*, pg. 1058
BLACK BOX CHILE S.A.—See Black Box Limited; *Int'l*, pg. 1056
BLACK BOX COMUNICACIONES, S.A.—See Black Box Limited; *Int'l*, pg. 1057
BLACK BOX CORPORATION—See Black Box Limited; *Int'l*, pg. 1056
BLACK BOX DATACOM B.V.—See Black Box Limited; *Int'l*, pg. 1057
BLACK BOX DE MEXICO S.A. DE C.V.—See Black Box Limited; *Int'l*, pg. 1058
BLACK BOX DEUTSCHLAND GMBH—See Black Box Limited; *Int'l*, pg. 1057
BLACK BOX DO BRASIL INDUSTRIA E COMERCIO LTDA—See Black Box Limited; *Int'l*, pg. 1058
BLACK BOX FINLAND OY—See Black Box Limited; *Int'l*, pg. 1057
BLACK BOX FRANCE—See Black Box Limited; *Int'l*, pg. 1057
BLACK BOX GMBH—See Black Box Limited; *Int'l*, pg. 1057
BLACK BOX INTERNATIONAL B.V.—See Black Box Limited; *Int'l*, pg. 1057
BLACK BOX ITALIA S.R.L.—See Black Box Limited; *Int'l*, pg. 1057
BLACK BOX LIMITED; *Int'l*, pg. 1056
BLACK BOX NETWORK PRODUCTS NV—See Black Box Limited; *Int'l*, pg. 1057
BLACK BOX NETWORK SERVICES AB—See Black Box Limited; *Int'l*, pg. 1057
BLACK BOX NETWORK SERVICES AG—See Black Box Limited; *Int'l*, pg. 1057
BLACK BOX NETWORK SERVICES AUSTRALIA PTY LTD—See Black Box Limited; *Int'l*, pg. 1057
BLACK BOX NETWORK SERVICES B.V.—See Black Box Limited; *Int'l*, pg. 1058
BLACK BOX NETWORK SERVICES CORPORATION—See Black Box Limited; *Int'l*, pg. 1058
BLACK BOX NETWORK SERVICES - GOVERNMENT SOLUTIONS—See Black Box Limited; *Int'l*, pg. 1058
BLACK BOX NETWORK SERVICES HONG KONG LIMITED—See Black Box Limited; *Int'l*, pg. 1058
BLACK BOX NETWORK SERVICES, INC. - GOVERNMENT SOLUTIONS—See Black Box Limited; *Int'l*, pg. 1058
BLACK BOX NETWORK SERVICES INDIA PRIVATE LIMITED—See Black Box Limited; *Int'l*, pg. 1058
BLACK BOX NETWORK SERVICES NEW ZEALAND LIMITED—See Black Box Limited; *Int'l*, pg. 1058
BLACK BOX NETWORK SERVICES NV—See Black Box Limited; *Int'l*, pg. 1058
BLACK BOX NETWORK SERVICES SDN. BHD.—See Black Box Limited; *Int'l*, pg. 1058
BLACK BOX NETWORK SERVICES SINGAPORE PTE LTD—See Black Box Limited; *Int'l*, pg. 1058
BLACK BOX NETWORK SERVICES—See Black Box Limited; *Int'l*, pg. 1057
BLACK BOX NETWORK SERVICES—See Black Box Limited; *Int'l*, pg. 1057
BLACK BOX NETWORK SERVICES—See Black Box Limited; *Int'l*, pg. 1057
BLACK BOX NETWORK SERVICES—See Black Box Limited; *Int'l*, pg. 1057
BLACK BOX NETWORK SERVICES—See Black Box Limited; *Int'l*, pg. 1057
BLACK BOX NETWORK SERVICES—See Black Box Limited; *Int'l*, pg. 1057
BLACK BOX NETWORK SERVICES—See Black Box Limited; *Int'l*, pg. 1057
BLACK BOX NETWORK SERVICES—See Black Box Limited; *Int'l*, pg. 1058
BLACK BOX NETWORK SERVICES—See Black Box Limited; *Int'l*, pg. 1057
BLACK BOX NETWORK SERVICES—See Black Box Limited; *Int'l*, pg. 1057
BLACK BOX NETWORK SERVICES—See Black Box Limited; *Int'l*, pg. 1057
BLACK BOX NETWORK SERVICES—See Black Box Limited; *Int'l*, pg. 1057
BLACK BOX NETWORK SERVICES—See Black Box Limited; *Int'l*, pg. 1057
BLACK BOX NETWORK SERVICES—See Black Box Limited; *Int'l*, pg. 1057
BLACK BOX NETWORK SERVICES—See Black Box Limited; *Int'l*, pg. 1057
BLACK BOX NETWORK SERVICES—See Black Box Limited; *Int'l*, pg. 1057
BLACK BOX NETWORK SERVICES—See Black Box Limited; *Int'l*, pg. 1057
BLACK BOX NETWORK SERVICES—See Black Box Limited; *Int'l*, pg. 1057
BLACK BOX NETWORK SERVICES—See Black Box Limited; *Int'l*, pg. 1057
BLACK BOX NETWORK SERVICES—See Black Box Limited; *Int'l*, pg. 1057
BLACK BOX NETWORK SERVICES—See Black Box Limited; *Int'l*, pg. 1057
BLACK BOX NETWORK SERVICES—See Black Box Limited; *Int'l*, pg. 1057
BLACK BOX NETWORK SERVICES—See Black Box Limited; *Int'l*, pg. 1057
BLACK BOX NETWORK SERVICES S.R.L.—See Black Box Limited; *Int'l*, pg. 1058
BLACK BOX NETWORK SERVICES (UK) LTD.—See Black Box Limited; *Int'l*, pg. 1057
BLACK BOX NETWORK SERVICES-VOICE SERVICES CANADA—See Black Box Limited; *Int'l*, pg. 1058
BLACK BOX NORGE AS—See Black Box Limited; *Int'l*, pg. 1058
BLACK BOX PHILADELPHIA—See Black Box Limited; *Int'l*, pg. 1058
BLACK BOX P.R. CORP.—See Black Box Limited; *Int'l*, pg. 1058
BLACK BOX RESALE SERVICES—See Black Box Limited; *Int'l*, pg. 1058
BLACK BOX SERVICES RESEAUX MEDITERRANEE—See Black Box Limited; *Int'l*, pg. 1058
BLACKBOXSTOCKS INC.; *U.S. Public*, pg. 341
BLACKBOX TECHNOLOGIES INTERNATIONAL LLC—See Quanta Services, Inc.; *U.S. Public*, pg. 1750
BLACKBRUSH OIL & GAS, L.P.—See Ares Management Corporation; *U.S. Public*, pg. 188
BLACKBURN RADIO INC; *Int'l*, pg. 1060
BLACKBURN-RUSSELL CO. INC.; *U.S. Private*, pg. 573
BLACKBURN'S PHYSICIANS PHARMACY, INC.; *U.S. Private*, pg. 573
BLACK CABS COMBINED PTY LTD—See ComfortDelGro Corporation Limited; *Int'l*, pg. 1712
BLACK CANYON CAPITAL LLC; *U.S. Private*, pg. 569
BLACK CANYON LIMITED; *Int'l*, pg. 1059
BLACK CAT BLADES LTD.; *Int'l*, pg. 1059
BLACK CAT FIREWORKS LIMITED—See Li & Fung Limited; *Int'l*, pg. 4479
BLACK CAT SYNDICATE LIMITED; *Int'l*, pg. 1059
BLACKCIRCLES.COM LIMITED—See Compagnie Generale des Etablissements Michelin SCA; *Int'l*, pg. 1741
BLACK COACH NETWORK, INC.; *U.S. Private*, pg. 570
BLACK & COMPANY; *U.S. Private*, pg. 569
BLACK CONSTRUCTION CORPORATION—See Tutor Perini Corporation; *U.S. Public*, pg. 2206
BLACK CONTRACTORS ASSOCIATION OF SAN DIEGO, INC.; *U.S. Private*, pg. 570
BLACKCRAFT CULT, INC.; *U.S. Private*, pg. 573
BLACK CREEK CAPITAL MARKETS, LLC—See Black Creek Group, LLC; *U.S. Private*, pg. 570
BLACK CREEK GROUP, LLC; *U.S. Private*, pg. 570

BLACK CREEK INTEGRATED SYSTEMS CORPORATION; *U.S. Private*, pg. 570
BLACK CREEK MEDICAL CONSULTANTS LLC—See Community Health Systems, Inc.; *U.S. Public*, pg. 551
BLACK DAVIS & SHUE AGENCY INC.; *U.S. Private*, pg. 570
BLACK & DECKER AG—See Stanley Black & Decker, Inc.; *U.S. Public*, pg. 1936
BLACK & DECKER AKTIEBOLAG—See Stanley Black & Decker, Inc.; *U.S. Public*, pg. 1936
BLACK & DECKER ARGENTINA S.A.—See Stanley Black & Decker, Inc.; *U.S. Public*, pg. 1936
BLACK & DECKER ASIA PACIFIC PTE. LTD.—See Stanley Black & Decker, Inc.; *U.S. Public*, pg. 1936
BLACK & DECKER (BELGIUM) N.V.—See Stanley Black & Decker, Inc.; *U.S. Public*, pg. 1936
THE BLACK & DECKER CORPORATION—See Stanley Black & Decker, Inc.; *U.S. Public*, pg. 1936
BLACK & DECKER CZECH SRO—See Stanley Black & Decker, Inc.; *U.S. Public*, pg. 1936
BLACK & DECKER DE COLOMBIA S.A.—See Stanley Black & Decker, Inc.; *U.S. Public*, pg. 1936
BLACK & DECKER DE ESPANA S.A.—See Stanley Black & Decker, Inc.; *U.S. Public*, pg. 1936
BLACK & DECKER DO BRASIL LTDA.—See Stanley Black & Decker, Inc.; *U.S. Public*, pg. 1936
BLACK & DECKER EUROPE—See Stanley Black & Decker, Inc.; *U.S. Public*, pg. 1932
BLACK & DECKER GMBH—See Stanley Black & Decker, Inc.; *U.S. Public*, pg. 1936
BLACK & DECKER (HELLAS) SA—See Stanley Black & Decker, Inc.; *U.S. Public*, pg. 1936
BLACK & DECKER HOLDINGS GMBH; *Int'l*, pg. 1056
BLACK & DECKER IBERICA S.COM POR A.—See Stanley Black & Decker, Inc.; *U.S. Public*, pg. 1936
BLACK & DECKER INTERNATIONAL—See Stanley Black & Decker, Inc.; *U.S. Public*, pg. 1936
BLACK & DECKER (IRELAND)—See Stanley Black & Decker, Inc.; *U.S. Public*, pg. 1936
BLACK & DECKER ITALY S.P.A.—See Stanley Black & Decker, Inc.; *U.S. Public*, pg. 1936
BLACK & DECKER MACAO—See Stanley Black & Decker, Inc.; *U.S. Public*, pg. 1936
BLACK & DECKER (NEDERLAND) B.V.—See Stanley Black & Decker, Inc.; *U.S. Public*, pg. 1936
BLACK & DECKER (OVERSEAS) AG—See Stanley Black & Decker, Inc.; *U.S. Public*, pg. 1936
BLACK & DECKER POLSKA SP.Z.O.O.—See Stanley Black & Decker, Inc.; *U.S. Public*, pg. 1932
BLACK & DECKER PUERTO RICO—See Stanley Black & Decker, Inc.; *U.S. Public*, pg. 1936
BLACK & DECKER SSC CO., LTD.—See Stanley Black & Decker, Inc.; *U.S. Public*, pg. 1936
BLACK & DECKER SUZHOU POWER TOOLS CO. LTD.—See Stanley Black & Decker, Inc.; *U.S. Public*, pg. 1936
BLACK & DECKER (THAILAND) LIMITED—See Stanley Black & Decker, Inc.; *U.S. Public*, pg. 1936
BLACK & DECKER (U.S.) INC.—See Stanley Black & Decker, Inc.; *U.S. Public*, pg. 1932
BLACK & DEW; *U.S. Private*, pg. 569
BLACK DIAMOND ASSOCIATES, LLC; *U.S. Private*, pg. 570
BLACK DIAMOND CAPITAL HOLDINGS, LLC; *U.S. Private*, pg. 570
BLACK DIAMOND CAPITAL MANAGEMENT LIMITED—See Black Diamond Capital Holdings, LLC; *U.S. Private*, pg. 570
BLACK DIAMOND CAPITAL MANAGEMENT, LLC - GREENWICH OFFICE—See Black Diamond Capital Holdings, LLC; *U.S. Private*, pg. 570
BLACK DIAMOND CAPITAL MANAGEMENT, LLC—See Black Diamond Capital Holdings, LLC; *U.S. Private*, pg. 570
BLACK DIAMOND ENERGY HOLDINGS LLC—See Legend Oil and Gas, Ltd.; *U.S. Public*, pg. 1301
BLACK DIAMOND ENERGY, INC.; *U.S. Public*, pg. 571
BLACK DIAMOND ENERGY SERVICES INC.—See Black Diamond Group Limited; *Int'l*, pg. 1059
BLACK DIAMOND EQUIPMENT AG—See Clarus Corporation; *U.S. Public*, pg. 508
BLACK DIAMOND EQUIPMENT EUROPE GMBH—See Clarus Corporation; *U.S. Public*, pg. 508
BLACK DIAMOND EQUIPMENT LTD.—See Clarus Corporation; *U.S. Public*, pg. 508
BLACK DIAMOND FINANCIAL GROUP, LLC; *U.S. Private*, pg. 571
BLACK DIAMOND GROUP, INC.; *U.S. Private*, pg. 571
BLACK DIAMOND GROUP LIMITED; *Int'l*, pg. 1059
BLACK DIAMOND LIMITED PARTNERSHIP—See Black Diamond Group Limited; *Int'l*, pg. 1059
BLACK DIAMOND MEDIA; *U.S. Private*, pg. 571
BLACK DIAMOND PERFORMANCE REPORTING, LLC—See SS&C Technologies Holdings, Inc.; *U.S. Public*, pg. 1922
BLACK DIAMOND PLUMBING & MECHANICAL, INC.; *U.S. Private*, pg. 571
BLACK DIAMOND RANCH—See Escalante Golf, Inc.; *U.S. Private*, pg. 1424

BLACK DIAMONDS STRUCTURES, LLC—See Saudi Basic Industries Corporation; *Int'l*, pg. 6590
BLACK DIAMOND THERAPEUTICS, INC.; *U.S. Public*, pg. 340
BLACK DIAMOND VIDEO, INC.—See STERIS plc; *Int'l*, pg. 7209
BLACKDOWN HORTICULTURAL CONSULTANTS LIMITED—See The Alumasc Group plc; *Int'l*, pg. 7613
BLACK DRAGON CAPITAL LLC; *U.S. Private*, pg. 571
BLACK DRAGON GOLD CORP.; *Int'l*, pg. 1059
BLACK DRAGON RESOURCE COMPANIES, INC.; *U.S. Public*, pg. 340
BLACK DUCK SOFTWARE, INC.—See Synopsys, Inc.; *U.S. Public*, pg. 1970
BLACK EAGLE CONSULTING, INC.—See OceanSound Partners, LP; *U.S. Private*, pg. 2991
BLACK EAGLE LLC—See HF Sinclair Corporation; *U.S. Public*, pg. 1033
BLACKEAGLE PARTNERS, LLC; *U.S. Private*, pg. 573
BLACK EARTH TELEPHONE CO.—See Telephone & Data Systems, Inc.; *U.S. Public*, pg. 1998
BLACK ELECTRICAL SUPPLY; *U.S. Private*, pg. 571
BLACK ELECTRIC, INC.—See Hull Street Energy, LLC; *U.S. Private*, pg. 2005
BLACK ELK ENERGY OFFSHORE OPERATIONS, LLC; *U.S. Private*, pg. 572
BLACK ELK ENERGY; *U.S. Private*, pg. 572
BLACK ENTERTAINMENT TELEVISION, LLC—See National Amusements, Inc.; *U.S. Private*, pg. 2839
BLACK EQUIPMENT CO. INC.; *U.S. Private*, pg. 572
BLACK-EYED PEA RESTAURANTS INC.—See Dynamic Management Company LLC; *U.S. Private*, pg. 1298
BLACK FAMILY DEVELOPMENT, INC.; *U.S. Private*, pg. 572
BLACKFIN CAPITAL PARTNERS SAS; *Int'l*, pg. 1060
BLACKFINCH SPRING VCT PLC; *Int'l*, pg. 1060
BLACKFIN MARKETING GROUP; *U.S. Private*, pg. 573
BLACKFISH CAPITAL MANAGEMENT LTD.; *Int'l*, pg. 1060
BLACKFOOT COMMUNICATIONS INC.—See Blackfoot Telephone Cooperative, Inc.; *U.S. Private*, pg. 573
BLACKFOOT MOTORCYCLES LTD.; *Int'l*, pg. 1061
BLACKFOOT TELEPHONE COOPERATIVE, INC.; *U.S. Private*, pg. 573
BLACKFORD ANALYSIS LIMITED—See Bayer Aktiengesellschaft; *Int'l*, pg. 907
BLACKFORD CAPITAL LLC; *U.S. Private*, pg. 574
BLACK FOREST BUILDING COMPANY; *U.S. Private*, pg. 572
BLACK FOREST DISTILLERS GMBH—See Pernod Ricard S.A.; *Int'l*, pg. 5810
BLACK FOREST INDUSTRIES; *U.S. Private*, pg. 572
BLACKFRIARS CORP.; *U.S. Private*, pg. 574
BLACKGOLD NATURAL RESOURCES LTD.; *Int'l*, pg. 1061
BLACK GOLD POTATO SALES INC.; *U.S. Private*, pg. 572
BLACK-HAAK HEATING, INC.; *U.S. Private*, pg. 573
BLACK HAWK ACQUISITION CORPORATION; *U.S. Public*, pg. 340
BLACKHAWK BANCORP INC.—See First Mid Bancshares, Inc.; *U.S. Public*, pg. 846
BLACKHAWK BROADCASTING LLC - KSWT-DT—See Northwest Broadcasting, Inc.; *U.S. Private*, pg. 2959
BLACKHAWK BROADCASTING LLC - KYMA-DT—See Northwest Broadcasting, Inc.; *U.S. Private*, pg. 2959
BLACKHAWK BROADCASTING LLC—See Northwest Broadcasting, Inc.; *U.S. Private*, pg. 2959
BLACKHAWK CAPITAL, LLP; *Int'l*, pg. 1061
BLACKHAWK COUNTRY CLUB; *U.S. Private*, pg. 575
BLACK HAWK ENERGY SERVICES, INC.—See Steel Partners Holdings L.P.; *U.S. Public*, pg. 1943
BLACKHAWK ENGINEERING, INC.—See Cie Automotive S.A.; *Int'l*, pg. 1604
BLACKHAWK GOLF CLUB—See OnCourse Strategies; *U.S. Private*, pg. 3019
BLACKHAWK GROWTH CORP.; *Int'l*, pg. 1061
BLACKHAWK INC.—See Sagewind Capital LLC; *U.S. Private*, pg. 3528
BLACKHAWK INDUSTRIAL DISTRIBUTION, INC.—See TruArc Partners, L.P.; *U.S. Private*, pg. 4244
BLACKHAWK INDUSTRIAL - OMAHA—See TruArc Partners, L.P.; *U.S. Private*, pg. 4244
BLACKHAWK INDUSTRIAL - PEORIA—See TruArc Partners, L.P.; *U.S. Private*, pg. 4244
BLACKHAWK INDUSTRIAL - SPRINGFIELD—See TruArc Partners, L.P.; *U.S. Private*, pg. 4244
BLACKHAWK MANUFACTURING, INC.—See Green Automotive Company; *U.S. Private*, pg. 1771
BLACKHAWK MINING, LLC—See JMP Coal Holdings, LLC; *U.S. Private*, pg. 2216
BLACKHAWK MODIFICATIONS INC.; *U.S. Private*, pg. 575
BLACKHAWK MOLDING CO. INC.; *U.S. Private*, pg. 575
BLACKHAWK NEFF INC.; *U.S. Private*, pg. 575
BLACKHAWK NETWORK (AUSTRALIA) PTY LTD.—See P2 Capital Partners, LLC; *U.S. Private*, pg. 3061
BLACKHAWK NETWORK (AUSTRALIA) PTY LTD.—See Silver Lake Group, LLC; *U.S. Private*, pg. 3656
BLACKHAWK NETWORK CALIFORNIA, INC.—See P2 Capital Partners, LLC; *U.S. Private*, pg. 3061
BLACKHAWK NETWORK CALIFORNIA, INC.—See Silver Lake Group, LLC; *U.S. Private*, pg. 3656
BLACKHAWK NETWORK HOLDINGS, INC.—See P2 Capital Partners, LLC; *U.S. Private*, pg. 3061
BLACKHAWK NETWORK HOLDINGS, INC.—See Silver Lake Group, LLC; *U.S. Private*, pg. 3656
BLACKHAWK S.A.S.—See Snap-on Incorporated; *U.S. Public*, pg. 1897
BLACKHAWK SPECIALTY TOOLS, LLC—See Expro Group Holdings N.V.; *Int'l*, pg. 2591
BLACKHAWK STATE BANK—See First Mid Bancshares, Inc.; *U.S. Public*, pg. 846
BLACKHAWK STEEL CORP; *U.S. Private*, pg. 576
BLACKHAWK TRANSPORT INC.—See Hendricks Holding Company, Inc.; *U.S. Private*, pg. 1915
BLACKHAWK WASTE DISPOSAL CO., INC.—See Watts Trucking Service, Inc.; *U.S. Private*, pg. 4456
BLACKHEATH & BROMLEY HARRIERS AC; *Int'l*, pg. 1061
BLACK HILLS BENTONITE LLP; *U.S. Private*, pg. 572
BLACK HILLS/COLORADO ELECTRIC UTILITY COMPANY, LP—See Black Hills Corporation; *U.S. Public*, pg. 340
BLACK HILLS/COLORADO UTILITY COMPANY, LLC—See Black Hills Corporation; *U.S. Public*, pg. 340
BLACK HILLS CORPORATION; *U.S. Public*, pg. 340
BLACK HILLS ELECTRIC GENERATION, LLC—See Black Hills Corporation; *U.S. Public*, pg. 340
BLACK HILLS ENERGY SERVICES COMPANY—See Black Hills Corporation; *U.S. Public*, pg. 340
BLACK HILLS ESTATE WINERY INC.—See Andrew Peller Limited; *Int'l*, pg. 451
BLACK HILLS EXPLORATION & PRODUCTION, INC.—See Black Hills Corporation; *U.S. Public*, pg. 340
BLACK HILLS GAS, LLC—See Black Hills Corporation; *U.S. Public*, pg. 340
BLACK HILLS/IOWA GAS UTILITY COMPANY, LLC—See Black Hills Corporation; *U.S. Public*, pg. 340
BLACK HILLS/KANSAS GAS UTILITY COMPANY, LLC—See Black Hills Corporation; *U.S. Public*, pg. 340
BLACK HILLS/NEBRASKA GAS UTILITY COMPANY, LLC—See Black Hills Corporation; *U.S. Public*, pg. 341
BLACK HILLS POWER, INC.—See Black Hills Corporation; *U.S. Public*, pg. 340
BLACK HILLS SURGICAL HOSPITAL—See Medical Facilities Corporation; *Int'l*, pg. 4775
BLACK HILLS TRUCKING CO.—See True Companies; *U.S. Private*, pg. 4247
BLACK HILLS TRUCK & TRAILER INC.—See North American Truck & Trailer, Inc.; *U.S. Private*, pg. 2941
BLACK HORSE LIMITED—See Lloyds Banking Group plc; *Int'l*, pg. 4536
BLACK HORSE LLC—See Caterpillar, Inc.; *U.S. Public*, pg. 449
BLACK HORSE OFFSHORE LTD.—See Lloyds Banking Group plc; *Int'l*, pg. 4536
BLACKICE ENTERPRISE RISK MANAGEMENT INC.; *Int'l*, pg. 1061
BLACKIE MCDONALD - MELBOURNE—See WPP plc; *Int'l*, pg. 8469
BLACK IPO, INC.; *U.S. Private*, pg. 572
BLACK IRON INC.; *Int'l*, pg. 1059
BLACK ISLE RESOURCES CORP.; *Int'l*, pg. 1059
BLACK KNIGHT, INC.—See Intercontinental Exchange, Inc.; *U.S. Public*, pg. 1141
BLACK KNIGHT INFOSERV, LLC—See Intercontinental Exchange, Inc.; *U.S. Public*, pg. 1141
BLACK KNIGHT SPORTS ARENA LLC—See Black Knight Sports & Entertainment LLC; *U.S. Private*, pg. 572
BLACK KNIGHT SPORTS & ENTERTAINMENT LLC; *U.S. Private*, pg. 572
BLACK LAB, LLC—See Covia Holdings Corporation; *U.S. Private*, pg. 1072
BLACK LAKE CAPITAL, LLC; *U.S. Private*, pg. 572
BLACK LETTER DISCOVERY, INC.—See Milestone Partners Ltd.; *U.S. Private*, pg. 2728
BLACKLIDGE EMULSIONS, INC.; *U.S. Private*, pg. 576
BLACKLINE, INC.; *U.S. Public*, pg. 341
BLACKLINE SAFETY CORP.; *Int'l*, pg. 1061
BLACKLINE SAFETY EUROPE LTD.—See Blackline Safety Corp.; *Int'l*, pg. 1061
BLACKLINE SYSTEMS GERMANY GMB H—See BlackLine, Inc.; *U.S. Public*, pg. 341
BLACKLINE SYSTEMS LIMITED—See BlackLine, Inc.; *U.S. Public*, pg. 342
BLACKLINE SYSTEMS, LTD.—See BlackLine, Inc.; *U.S. Public*, pg. 342
BLACKLINE SYSTEMS PTE. LTD.—See BlackLine, Inc.; *U.S. Public*, pg. 342
BLACKLINE SYSTEMS S.A.R.L.—See BlackLine, Inc.; *U.S. Public*, pg. 342
BLACKLINE SYSTEMS; *U.S. Private*, pg. 576
BLACK LOTUS COMMUNICATIONS; *U.S. Private*, pg. 572
BLACK LUMBER CO. INC.; *U.S. Private*, pg. 572
BLACKMAGIC DESIGN PTY. LTD.; *Int'l*, pg. 1061
BLACK MAMMOTH METALS CORPORATION; *Int'l*, pg. 1059
BLACKMAN PLUMBING SUPPLY CO. INC., MINEOLA BRANCH—See Blackman Plumbing Supply Co. Inc.; *U.S. Private*, pg. 576
BLACKMAN PLUMBING SUPPLY CO. INC.; *U.S. Private*, pg. 576
BLACKMAN PLUMBING SUPPLY CO. INC.—See Blackman Plumbing Supply Co. Inc.; *U.S. Private*, pg. 576
BLACKMAN PLUMBING SUPPLY CO. INC.—See Blackman Plumbing Supply Co. Inc.; *U.S. Private*, pg. 576
BLACKMAN PLUMBING SUPPLY CO. INC.—See Blackman Plumbing Supply Co. Inc.; *U.S. Private*, pg. 576
BLACKMAN PLUMBING SUPPLY CO. INC.—See Blackman Plumbing Supply Co. Inc.; *U.S. Private*, pg. 576
BLACKMAN PLUMBING SUPPLY CO. INC.—See Blackman Plumbing Supply Co. Inc.; *U.S. Private*, pg. 576
BLACKMAN PLUMBING SUPPLY CO. INC.—See Blackman Plumbing Supply Co. Inc.; *U.S. Private*, pg. 576
BLACKMAN PLUMBING SUPPLY CO. INC.—See Blackman Plumbing Supply Co. Inc.; *U.S. Private*, pg. 576
BLACKMAN PLUMBING SUPPLY CO. INC.—See Blackman Plumbing Supply Co. Inc.; *U.S. Private*, pg. 576
BLACKMAN PLUMBING SUPPLY CO. INC.—See Blackman Plumbing Supply Co. Inc.; *U.S. Private*, pg. 576
BLACKMAN PLUMBING SUPPLY CO. INC.—See Blackman Plumbing Supply Co. Inc.; *U.S. Private*, pg. 576
BLACK MARLIN PIPELINE LLC—See The Williams Companies, Inc.; *U.S. Public*, pg. 2142
BLACK & MCDONALD BERMUDA LIMITED—See Black & McDonald Limited; *Int'l*, pg. 1056
BLACK & MCDONALD LIMITED; *Int'l*, pg. 1056
BLACKMER PUMP—See Dover Corporation; *U.S. Public*, pg. 679
BLACK MILLWORK CO., INC.; *U.S. Private*, pg. 572
BLACKMORE & BUCKNER ROOFING, LLC.—See Altas Partners LP; *U.S. Private*, pg. 386
BLACKMORES CHINA CO. LIMITED—See Blackmores Limited; *Int'l*, pg. 1061
BLACKMORES INDIA PRIVATE LIMITED—See Blackmores Limited; *Int'l*, pg. 1061
BLACKMORES INTERNATIONAL PTE. LIMITED—See Blackmores Limited; *Int'l*, pg. 1061
BLACKMORES KOREA LIMITED—See Blackmores Limited; *Int'l*, pg. 1061
BLACKMORES LIMITED; *Int'l*, pg. 1061
BLACKMORES (MALAYSIA) SDN BHD—See Blackmores Limited; *Int'l*, pg. 1061
BLACKMORES (NEW ZEALAND) LIMITED—See Blackmores Limited; *Int'l*, pg. 1061
BLACKMORES (SINGAPORE) PTE LIMITED—See Blackmores Limited; *Int'l*, pg. 1061
BLACKMORES (TAIWAN) LIMITED—See Blackmores Limited; *Int'l*, pg. 1061
BLACKMORES (THAILAND) LIMITED—See Blackmores Limited; *Int'l*, pg. 1061
BLACKMORES VIETNAM CO. LIMITED—See Blackmores Limited; *Int'l*, pg. 1061
BLACK MOUNTAIN ACQUISITION CORP.; *U.S. Public*, pg. 341
BLACK MOUNTAIN MINING (PROPRIETARY) LIMITED—See Vedanta Resources Ltd; *Int'l*, pg. 8145
BLACK MOUNTAIN NEWS—See Gannett Co., Inc.; *U.S. Public*, pg. 897
BLACK MOUNTAIN PHYSICAL THERAPY LLC—See Audax Group, Limited Partnership; *U.S. Private*, pg. 389
BLACK MOUNTAIN RESOURCES LIMITED; *Int'l*, pg. 1059
BLACK MOUNTAIN RESOURCES LLC—See Alpha Natural Resources, Inc.; *U.S. Private*, pg. 199
BLACK MOUNTAIN SOFTWARE, LLC; *U.S. Private*, pg. 572
BLACK MOUNTAIN SYSTEMS, LLC—See Vista Equity Partners, LLC; *U.S. Private*, pg. 4395
BLACK OAK SECURITY SP. Z O.O.—See Impel S.A.; *Int'l*, pg. 3631
BLACKOUT MEDIA CORP.; *Int'l*, pg. 1061
BLACKOUT PRODUCTIONS INC.—See National Amusements, Inc.; *U.S. Private*, pg. 2842
BLACK PAGE CONCESSIONS, LLC—See Live Nation Entertainment, Inc.; *U.S. Public*, pg. 1328
BLACKPEARL RESOURCES INC.—See Lundin Group of Companies; *Int'l*, pg. 4583
BLACK PEARL S.A.; *Int'l*, pg. 1059
BLACK PEONY (GROUP) CO., LTD.; *Int'l*, pg. 1059
THE BLACK PHOENIX GROUP; *U.S. Private*, pg. 3995
BLACKPOINT IT SERVICES, INC.; *U.S. Private*, pg. 576
BLACKPOOL GAZETTE & HERALD LTD—See JPIMedia Holdings Limited; *Int'l*, pg. 4006
BLACKPOOL PLEASURE BEACH LTD.; *Int'l*, pg. 1061
BLACKPOOL WARBRECK VETS4PETS LIMITED—See Pets at Home Group Plc; *Int'l*, pg. 5833
BLACK PRESS GROUP LTD.; *Int'l*, pg. 1059
BLACKRAPID, INC.; *U.S. Private*, pg. 576
BLACK RED WHITE SA; *Int'l*, pg. 1059
BLACK RETAIL; *U.S. Private*, pg. 572
BLACK RIFLE COFFEE COMPANY LLC—See BRC Inc.; *U.S. Public*, pg. 380
BLACK RIVER ASSET MANAGEMENT LLC—See Cargill, Inc.; *U.S. Private*, pg. 754

COMPANY NAME INDEX

BLACK RIVER COMPUTER, LLC; *U.S. Private*, pg. 572
BLACK RIVER ELECTRIC CO-OP., INC.; *U.S. Private*, pg. 572
BLACK RIVER ELECTRIC CO-OP; *U.S. Private*, pg. 572
BLACK RIVER MEMORIAL HOSPITAL; *U.S. Private*, pg. 573
BLACKROCK 2022 GLOBAL INCOME OPPORTUNITY TRUST; *U.S. Public*, pg. 342
BLACKROCK ARGENTINA ASESORIAS LTDA.—See BlackRock, Inc.; *U.S. Public*, pg. 344
BLACK ROCK ARTS FOUNDATION—See Burning Man Project; *U.S. Private*, pg. 689
BLACKROCK ASSET MANAGEMENT CANADA LIMITED—See BlackRock, Inc.; *U.S. Public*, pg. 344
BLACKROCK ASSET MANAGEMENT NORTH ASIA LIMITED—See BlackRock, Inc.; *U.S. Public*, pg. 344
BLACKROCK ASSET MANAGEMENT (SCHWEIZ) AG—See BlackRock, Inc.; *U.S. Public*, pg. 344
BLACKROCK CAPITAL INVESTMENT CORPORATION; *U.S. Public*, pg. 342
BLACKROCK CAPITAL MANAGEMENT, INC.—See BlackRock, Inc.; *U.S. Public*, pg. 345
BLACKROCK (CHANNEL ISLANDS) LIMITED—See BlackRock, Inc.; *U.S. Public*, pg. 344
BLACKROCK COLOMBIA INFRAESTRUCTURA S.A.S.—See BlackRock, Inc.; *U.S. Public*, pg. 345
BLACKROCK COLOMBIA SAS—See BlackRock, Inc.; *U.S. Public*, pg. 345
BLACKROCK CORE BOND TRUST; *U.S. Public*, pg. 342
BLACKROCK CORPORATE HIGH YIELD FUND, INC.; *U.S. Public*, pg. 342
BLACKROCK CREDIT ALLOCATION INCOME TRUST; *U.S. Public*, pg. 342
BLACKROCK DEBT STRATEGIES FUND, INC.; *U.S. Public*, pg. 342
BLACKROCK ENERGY & RESOURCES—See BlackRock, Inc.; *U.S. Public*, pg. 345
BLACKROCK ENHANCED CAPITAL & INCOME FUND, INC.; *U.S. Public*, pg. 342
BLACKROCK ENHANCED EQUITY DIVIDEND TRUST; *U.S. Public*, pg. 342
BLACKROCK ENHANCED GLOBAL DIVIDEND TRUST; *U.S. Public*, pg. 342
BLACKROCK ENHANCED GOVERNMENT FUND, INC.; *U.S. Public*, pg. 342
BLACKROCK ENHANCED INTERNATIONAL DIVIDEND TRUST; *U.S. Public*, pg. 342
BLACKROCK FINANCE EUROPE LIMITED—See BlackRock, Inc.; *U.S. Public*, pg. 345
BLACKROCK FINANCIAL MANAGEMENT, INC.—See BlackRock, Inc.; *U.S. Public*, pg. 345
BLACKROCK FLOATING RATE INCOME STRATEGIES FUND, INC.; *U.S. Public*, pg. 342
BLACKROCK FLOATING RATE INCOME TRUST; *U.S. Public*, pg. 342
BLACKROCK FRONTIERS INVESTMENT TRUST PLC; *Int'l*, pg. 1061
BLACKROCK GREATER EUROPE INVESTMENT TRUST PLC; *Int'l*, pg. 1061
BLACKROCK HUNGARY KFT—See BlackRock, Inc.; *U.S. Public*, pg. 345
BLACKROCK INCOME & GROWTH INVESTMENT TRUST PLC; *Int'l*, pg. 1062
BLACKROCK INCOME TRUST, INC.; *U.S. Public*, pg. 342
BLACKROCK, INC.; *U.S. Public*, pg. 344
BLACKROCK INTERNATIONAL LIMITED—See BlackRock, Inc.; *U.S. Public*, pg. 345
BLACKROCK INVESTMENT MANAGEMENT (AUSTRALIA) LIMITED—See BlackRock, Inc.; *U.S. Public*, pg. 345
BLACKROCK INVESTMENT MANAGEMENT INTERNATIONAL LIMITED—See BlackRock, Inc.; *U.S. Public*, pg. 345
BLACKROCK INVESTMENT MANAGEMENT, LLC—See BlackRock, Inc.; *U.S. Public*, pg. 345
BLACKROCK INVESTMENT MANAGEMENT (TAIWAN) LIMITED—See BlackRock, Inc.; *U.S. Public*, pg. 345
BLACKROCK INVESTMENT MANAGEMENT (UK) LIMITED—See BlackRock, Inc.; *U.S. Public*, pg. 345
BLACKROCK INVESTMENT QUALITY MUNI TR; *U.S. Public*, pg. 342
BLACKROCK INVESTMENTS CANADA, INC.—See BlackRock, Inc.; *U.S. Public*, pg. 345
BLACKROCK JAPAN CO., LTD.—See BlackRock, Inc.; *U.S. Public*, pg. 345
BLACKROCK LATIN AMERICAN INVESTMENT TRUST PLC; *Int'l*, pg. 1062
BLACKROCK LIMITED DURATION INCOME TRUST; *U.S. Public*, pg. 342
BLACKROCK LONG-TERM MUNICIPAL ADTGTRUST; *U.S. Public*, pg. 342
BLACKROCK (LUXEMBOURG) S.A.—See BlackRock, Inc.; *U.S. Public*, pg. 344
BLACKROCK MARYLAND MUNICIPAL BOND TRUST; *U.S. Public*, pg. 342
BLACKROCK MASSACHUSETTS TAX-EXEMPT TRUST; *U.S. Public*, pg. 342
BLACK ROCK MINING LIMITED; *Int'l*, pg. 1060

BLACKROCK MUNIASSETS FUND, INC.; *U.S. Public*, pg. 342
BLACKROCK MUNICIPAL 2030 TARGET TERM TRUST; *U.S. Public*, pg. 343
BLACKROCK MUNICIPAL INCOME FUND, INC.; *U.S. Public*, pg. 343
BLACKROCK MUNICIPAL INCOME INVESTMENT QUALITY TRUST; *U.S. Public*, pg. 343
BLACKROCK MUNICIPAL INCOME INVESTMENT TRUST; *U.S. Public*, pg. 343
BLACKROCK MUNICIPAL INCOME QUALITY TRUST; *U.S. Public*, pg. 343
BLACKROCK MUNICIPAL INCOME TRUST II; *U.S. Public*, pg. 343
BLACKROCK MUNICIPAL INCOME TRUST; *U.S. Public*, pg. 343
BLACKROCK MUNIENHANCED FUND, INC.; *U.S. Public*, pg. 343
BLACKROCK MUNIHOLDINGS CALIFORNIA QUALITY FUND, INC.; *U.S. Public*, pg. 343
BLACKROCK MUNIHOLDINGS FUND II, INC.; *U.S. Public*, pg. 343
BLACKROCK MUNIHOLDINGS FUND, INC.; *U.S. Public*, pg. 343
BLACKROCK MUNIHOLDINGS INVESTMENT QUALITY FUND; *U.S. Public*, pg. 343
BLACKROCK MUNIHOLDINGS NEW JERSEY QUALITY FUND, INC.; *U.S. Public*, pg. 343
BLACKROCK MUNIHOLDINGS QUALITY FUND II, INC.; *U.S. Public*, pg. 343
BLACKROCK MUNIHOLDINGS QUALITY FUND, INC.; *U.S. Public*, pg. 343
BLACKROCK MUNI NEW YORK INTERMEDIATE DURATION FUND, INC.; *U.S. Public*, pg. 342
BLACKROCK MUNIVEST FUND II, INC.; *U.S. Public*, pg. 343
BLACKROCK MUNIYIELD ARIZONA FUND, INC.; *U.S. Public*, pg. 343
BLACKROCK MUNIYIELD CALIFORNIA FUND, INC.; *U.S. Public*, pg. 343
BLACKROCK MUNIYIELD CALIFORNIA QUALITY FUND, INC.; *U.S. Public*, pg. 343
BLACKROCK MUNIYIELD FUND, INC.; *U.S. Public*, pg. 343
BLACKROCK MUNIYIELD INVESTMENT QUALITY FUND; *U.S. Public*, pg. 343
BLACKROCK MUNIYIELD INVSTMT FD; *U.S. Public*, pg. 343
BLACKROCK MUNIYIELD MICHIGAN QUALITY FUND, INC.; *U.S. Public*, pg. 343
BLACKROCK MUNIYIELD NEW JERSEY FUND, INC.; *U.S. Public*, pg. 344
BLACKROCK MUNIYIELD PENNSYLVANIA QUALITY FUND; *U.S. Public*, pg. 344
BLACKROCK MUNIYIELD QUALITY FUND II; *U.S. Public*, pg. 344
BLACKROCK MUNIYIELD QUALITY FUND, INC.; *U.S. Public*, pg. 344
BLACKROCK (NETHERLANDS) B.V.—See BlackRock, Inc.; *U.S. Public*, pg. 344
BLACKROCK NEW YORK MUNICIPAL BOND TRUST; *U.S. Public*, pg. 344
BLACKROCK NEW YORK MUNICIPAL INCOME QUALITY TRUST; *U.S. Public*, pg. 344
BLACKROCK OIL CORPORATION; *Int'l*, pg. 1062
BLACKROCK PERU ASESORIAS S.A.—See BlackRock, Inc.; *U.S. Public*, pg. 345
BLACKROCK RESOURCES & COMMODITIES STRATEGY TRUST; *U.S. Public*, pg. 344
BLACKROCK SAUDI ARABIA—See BlackRock, Inc.; *U.S. Public*, pg. 345
BLACKROCK SCIENCE & TECHNOLOGY TRUST; *U.S. Public*, pg. 344
BLACKROCK SERVICES INDIA PRIVATE LIMITED—See BlackRock, Inc.; *U.S. Public*, pg. 345
BLACKROCK (SHANGHAI) CO., LTD.—See BlackRock, Inc.; *U.S. Public*, pg. 344
BLACKROCK SILVER CORP.; *Int'l*, pg. 1062
BLACKROCK (SINGAPORE HOLDCO) PTE. LIMITED—See BlackRock, Inc.; *U.S. Public*, pg. 344
BLACKROCK (SINGAPORE) LIMITED—See BlackRock, Inc.; *U.S. Public*, pg. 344
BLACKROCK SMALLER COMPANIES TRUST PLC; *Int'l*, pg. 1062
BLACKROCK STRATEGIC MUNICIPAL TRUST; *U.S. Public*, pg. 344
BLACKROCK SUSTAINABLE AMERICAN INCOME TRUST PLC; *Int'l*, pg. 1062
BLACKROCK TAXABLE MUNICIPAL BOND TRUST; *U.S. Public*, pg. 344
BLACKROCK TCP CAPITAL CORP.; *U.S. Public*, pg. 344
BLACKROCK THROGMORTON TRUST PLC; *Int'l*, pg. 1062
BLACKROCK UK HOLDCO LIMITED—See BlackRock, Inc.; *U.S. Public*, pg. 344
BLACKROCK UTILITIES, INFRASTRUCTURE & POWER OPPORTUNITIES TRUST; *U.S. Public*, pg. 344
BLACKROCK VIRGINIA MUNICIPAL BOND TRUST; *U.S. Public*, pg. 344

BLACKROCK WORLD MINING TRUST PLC; *Int'l*, pg. 1062
BLACK ROSE INDUSTRIES LTD.; *Int'l*, pg. 1060
BLACK RUBBER PTY. LTD.—See National Tyre & Wheel Limited; *Int'l*, pg. 5164
BLACK SABLE ENERGY, LLC—See Pass Creek Resources LLC; *U.S. Private*, pg. 3104
BLACKSANDS PETROLEUM, INC.; *U.S. Private*, pg. 576
BLACK SEA PROPERTY AS; *Int'l*, pg. 1060
BLACKSKY TECHNOLOGY INC.; *U.S. Public*, pg. 347
BLACKSMITH APPLICATIONS, INC—See TELUS CORPORATION; *Int'l*, pg. 7546
BLACKSMITH JACKS PTY LTD—See Wesfarmers Limited; *Int'l*, pg. 8381
BLACKSMITHS DEPOT—See Kayne & Son Custom Hardware Inc.; *U.S. Private*, pg. 2266
BLACKS OUTDOOR RETAIL LIMITED—See Pentland Group Limited; *Int'l*, pg. 5792
BLACK SPADE ACQUISITION CO.; *Int'l*, pg. 1060
BLACK SPECTACLES, LLC; *U.S. Private*, pg. 573
BLACK STALLION OIL AND GAS, INC.; *U.S. Public*, pg. 341
BLACKSTAR ENTERPRISE GROUP, INC; *U.S. Public*, pg. 347
BLACK STAR NETWORKS, INC.; *U.S. Private*, pg. 573
BLACK STAR PETROLEUM LIMITED; *Int'l*, pg. 1060
BLACKSTEEL ENERGY INC.; *Int'l*, pg. 1062
BLACKSTONE ADVISORS INDIA PRIVATE LIMITED—See Blackstone Inc.; *U.S. Public*, pg. 360
BLACKSTONE ADVISORY PARTNERS L.P.—See Blackstone Inc.; *U.S. Public*, pg. 348
BLACKSTONE ALTERNATIVE ASSET MANAGEMENT L.P.—See Blackstone Inc.; *U.S. Public*, pg. 348
BLACKSTONE ALTERNATIVE CREDIT ADVISORS LP—See Blackstone Inc.; *U.S. Public*, pg. 348
BLACKSTONE ASSESSORIA EM INVESTIMENTOS LTDA—See Blackstone Inc.; *U.S. Public*, pg. 349
BLACKSTONE AUDIO, INC.; *U.S. Private*, pg. 576
BLACKSTONE CALLING CARD, INC.; *U.S. Private*, pg. 576
BLACKSTONE CAPITAL PARTNERS—See Blackstone Inc.; *U.S. Public*, pg. 349
BLACKSTONE DEBT ADVISORS L.P.—See Blackstone Inc.; *U.S. Public*, pg. 349
BLACK STONE ENERGY COMPANY, LLC—See Black Stone Minerals, L.P.; *U.S. Public*, pg. 341
THE BLACKSTONE GROUP DENMARK APS—See Blackstone Inc.; *U.S. Public*, pg. 359
THE BLACKSTONE GROUP GERMANY GMBH—See Blackstone Inc.; *U.S. Public*, pg. 361
THE BLACKSTONE GROUP (HK) LIMITED—See Blackstone Inc.; *U.S. Public*, pg. 360
THE BLACKSTONE GROUP INTERNATIONAL LIMITED—See Blackstone Inc.; *U.S. Public*, pg. 359
THE BLACKSTONE GROUP INTERNATIONAL PARTNERS LLP—See Blackstone Inc.; *U.S. Public*, pg. 361
THE BLACKSTONE GROUP JAPAN K.K.—See Blackstone Inc.; *U.S. Public*, pg. 361
BLACKSTONE GROUP TECHNOLOGIES PVT LIMITED—See SEPC Limited; *Int'l*, pg. 6718
BLACKSTONE / GSO STRATEGIC CREDIT FUND—See Blackstone Inc.; *U.S. Public*, pg. 348
BLACKSTONE INC.; *U.S. Public*, pg. 347
BLACKSTONE IRELAND LIMITED—See Blackstone Inc.; *U.S. Public*, pg. 349
BLACKSTONE LONG-SHORT CREDIT INCOME FUND; *U.S. Public*, pg. 361
BLACK STONE MINERALS COMPANY, L.P.—See Black Stone Minerals, L.P.; *U.S. Public*, pg. 341
BLACKSTONE MINERALS LIMITED; *Int'l*, pg. 1062
BLACK STONE MINERALS, L.P.; *U.S. Public*, pg. 341
BLACKSTONE MORTGAGE TRUST, INC.—See Blackstone Inc.; *U.S. Public*, pg. 349
BLACKSTONE NEY ULTRASONICS INC.—See Alpha Capital Partners, Ltd.; *U.S. Private*, pg. 197
BLACK STONE OPERATIONS, LLC—See UnitedHealth Group Incorporated; *U.S. Public*, pg. 2243
BLACKSTONE/OTR, LLC—See OTR Wheel Engineering, Inc.; *U.S. Private*, pg. 3049
BLACKSTONE PRIVATE CREDIT FUND—See Blackstone Inc.; *U.S. Public*, pg. 349
BLACKSTONE PROPERTY MANAGEMENT LIMITED—See Blackstone Inc.; *U.S. Public*, pg. 360
BLACKSTONE REAL ESTATE ADVISORS—See Blackstone Inc.; *U.S. Public*, pg. 349
BLACKSTONE REAL ESTATE ASIA PTE. LTD.—See Blackstone Inc.; *U.S. Public*, pg. 350
BLACKSTONE REAL ESTATE INCOME TRUST, INC.—See Blackstone Inc.; *U.S. Public*, pg. 351
BLACKSTONE RESOURCES AG; *Int'l*, pg. 1062
BLACKSTONE RESOURCES MANAGEMENT AG—See Blackstone Resources AG; *Int'l*, pg. 1062
BLACKSTONE SENFINA ADVISORS LLC—See Blackstone Inc.; *U.S. Public*, pg. 352
BLACKSTONE SENIOR FLOATING RATE 2027 TERM FUND; *U.S. Public*, pg. 361
BLACKSTONE SINGAPORE PTE. LTD.—See Blackstone Inc.; *U.S. Public*, pg. 352

BLACKSTONE SENIOR FLOATING RATE 2027 TERM FUND CORPORATE AFFILIATIONS

BLACKSTONE VALLEY OFFICE SYSTEMS—See Xerox Holdings Corporation; *U.S. Public*, pg. 2389
BLACKSTRATUS, INC.; *U.S. Private*, pg. 576
BLACKSTREET CAPITAL HOLDINGS LLC; *U.S. Private*, pg. 576
BLACKSTREET CAPITAL MANAGEMENT, LLC; *U.S. Private*, pg. 577
BLACKTECH OTOMOTIV SANAYI VE TICARET A.S.—See Freudenberg SE; *Int'l*, pg. 2782
BLACKTHORNE PARTNERS LTD.; *U.S. Private*, pg. 577
BLACK TIE LIMOUSINE INC.—See Grace Limousine, LLC; *U.S. Private*, pg. 1749
BLACKTIE LLC; *U.S. Private*, pg. 577
BLACKTIE-SAN ANTONIO—See Blacktie LLC; *U.S. Private*, pg. 577
BLACK TIE TRANSPORTATION LLC; *U.S. Private*, pg. 573
BLACKTON, INC.; *U.S. Private*, pg. 577
BLACKTON INTERIORS OF ORLANDO—See Blackton, Inc.; *U.S. Private*, pg. 577
BLACKTOP CREATIVE—See Barkley; *U.S. Private*, pg. 475
BLACK TUSK RESOURCES, INC.; *Int'l*, pg. 1060
BLACK & VEATCH CONSTRUCTION, INC—See Black & Veatch Holding Company; *U.S. Private*, pg. 569
BLACK & VEATCH CORPORATION—See Black & Veatch Holding Company; *U.S. Private*, pg. 569
BLACK & VEATCH HOLDING COMPANY; *U.S. Private*, pg. 569
BLACK & VEATCH INTERNATIONAL COMPANY—See Black & Veatch Holding Company; *U.S. Private*, pg. 569
BLACK & VEATCH LTD.—See Black & Veatch Holding Company; *U.S. Private*, pg. 569
BLACKWALL FUND SERVICES LIMITED—See BlackWall Limited; *Int'l*, pg. 1062
BLACKWALL LIMITED; *Int'l*, pg. 1062
BLACKWALL MANAGEMENT SERVICES PTY LTD—See BlackWall Limited; *Int'l*, pg. 1062
BLACK WARRIOR METHANE CORP.—See Atlas Energy Group, LLC; *U.S. Public*, pg. 223
BLACK WARRIOR METHANE CORP.—See Warrior Met Coal, Inc; *U.S. Public*, pg. 2329
BLACK WARRIOR TRANSMISSION CORP.—See Atlas Energy Group, LLC; *U.S. Public*, pg. 223
BLACK WARRIOR TRANSMISSION CORP.—See Warrior Met Coal, Inc; *U.S. Public*, pg. 2329
BLACKWATCH INTERNATIONAL CORP.; *U.S. Private*, pg. 577
BLACKWATER GEORGIA, LLC—See ArcLight Capital Holdings, LLC; *U.S. Private*, pg. 312
BLACKWATER MIDSTREAM CORP.—See ArcLight Capital Holdings, LLC; *U.S. Private*, pg. 312
BLACKWATER NEW ORLEANS, LLC—See ArcLight Capital Holdings, LLC; *U.S. Private*, pg. 312
BLACKWAVE SPORTS INVESTMENT COMPANY LLC—See Vivendi SE; *Int'l*, pg. 8276
BLACKWELL 3D CONSTRUCTION CORP; *U.S. Public*, pg. 361
BLACKWELL CAPITAL GROUP LLC; *U.S. Private*, pg. 577
BLACKWELL CO-OP; *U.S. Private*, pg. 577
BLACKWELL GLOBAL CONSULTING LLC—See CGN & Associates Inc.; *U.S. Private*, pg. 844
BLACKWELL HMA, LLC—See Community Health Systems, Inc.; *U.S. Public*, pg. 551
BLACKWELL LAND, LLC; *U.S. Private*, pg. 577
BLACKWELL LTD.—See Elliott Management Corporation; *U.S. Private*, pg. 1365
BLACKWELL MUNKSGAARD—See John Wiley & Sons, Inc.; *U.S. Public*, pg. 1193
BLACKWELL'S NORTH AMERICA INC—See Elliott Management Corporation; *U.S. Private*, pg. 1365
BLACKWELL VERLAG GMBH—See John Wiley & Sons, Inc.; *U.S. Public*, pg. 1192
BLACK & WHITE ADVERTISING, INC.; *U.S. Private*, pg. 569
BLACK & WHITE SPORTSWEAR CO., LTD.—See Goldwin, Inc.; *Int'l*, pg. 3035
BLACKWOLF COPPER & GOLD LTD.—See NexGold Mining Corp.; *Int'l*, pg. 5243
BLACKWOLF INC.; *U.S. Private*, pg. 577
BLACKWOLF ADVISORY PTY. LTD.—See Azimut Holding SpA; *Int'l*, pg. 779
BLACKWOOD BUILDING CENTRE LTD.; *Int'l*, pg. 1062
BLACKWOOD COMMUNICATIONS GROUP—See Publicis Groupe S.A.; *Int'l*, pg. 6100
BLACKWOOD COMMUNICATIONS—See Blackfoot Telephone Cooperative, Inc.; *U.S. Private*, pg. 573
BLACKWOOD HODGE (ZIMBABWE) PRIVATE LIMITED—See Tata Sons Limited; *Int'l*, pg. 7470
BLACKWOOD INDUSTRIES, INC.—See Organizacion Corona SA; *Int'l*, pg. 5618
BLACKWOOD SEVEN A/S; *Int'l*, pg. 1062
BLADCENTRALEN ANS—See Egmont Fonden; *Int'l*, pg. 2325
BLADCENTRALENS EIENDOMSSELSKAP AS—See Egmont Fonden; *Int'l*, pg. 2325
BLADE AIR MOBILITY, INC.; *U.S. Public*, pg. 361

BLADE CHEVROLET; *U.S. Private*, pg. 577
THE BLADE CO.—See Block Communications, Inc.; *U.S. Private*, pg. 582
BLADE ENERGY PARTNERS, LTD.; *U.S. Private*, pg. 577
BLADE HQ, LLC; *U.S. Private*, pg. 577
BLADE NETWORK TECHNOLOGIES, INC.—See International Business Machines Corporation; *U.S. Public*, pg. 1148
BLADERANGER LTD.; *Int'l*, pg. 1062
BLADES CO. INC.; *U.S. Private*, pg. 577
BLADES MACHINERY CO INC—See Blades Co. Inc.; *U.S. Private*, pg. 577
BLADES OF GREEN, INC.—See Senske Lawn & Tree Care, Inc.; *U.S. Private*, pg. 3608
BLADES TECHNOLOGY LTD.—See RTX Corporation; *U.S. Public*, pg. 1821
BLADE-TECH INDUSTRIES, INC.; *U.S. Private*, pg. 577
BLADE URBAN AIR MOBILITY, INC.—See Blade Air Mobility, Inc.; *U.S. Public*, pg. 361
BLADEX REPRESENTACAO LTDA.—See Banco Latinoamericano de Comercio Exterior, S.A.; *Int'l*, pg. 823
BLADKOMPANIET AS—See Schibsted ASA; *Int'l*, pg. 6616
BLAGDON PUMP HOLDINGS LTD.—See IDEX Corp; *U.S. Public*, pg. 1089
BLAGOEVGRAD-BT AD—See Bulgarian Investment Holding; *Int'l*, pg. 1213
BLAINE CONSTRUCTION CORPORATION—See W.G. Yates & Sons Construction Company; *U.S. Private*, pg. 4420
BLAINE CONVENTION SERVICES; *U.S. Private*, pg. 577
THE BLAINE GROUP; *U.S. Private*, pg. 3995
BLAINE JENSEN RV CENTERS, LLC—See Camping World Holdings, Inc.; *U.S. Public*, pg. 427
BLAINE LABS, INC.—See Alternate Health Corp.; *Int'l*, pg. 391
BLAINE LARSEN FARMS INC.; *U.S. Private*, pg. 578
BLAINE MN MULTI-SPECIALTY ASC, LLC—See KKR & Co. Inc.; *U.S. Public*, pg. 1245
BLAINE WARREN ADVERTISING LLC; *U.S. Private*, pg. 578
BLAIN SUPPLY, INC.; *U.S. Private*, pg. 577
THE BLAIR AGENCY, INC.—See LTC Global, Inc.; *U.S. Private*, pg. 2509
BLAIR & ASSOCIATES, LTD.; *U.S. Private*, pg. 578
BLAIR ATHOL COAL PTY LTD—See Rio Tinto plc; *Int'l*, pg. 6347
BLAIR BUILDING MATERIALS INC.—See GMS Inc.; *U.S. Public*, pg. 947
BLAIR COMPANIES, INC.; *U.S. Private*, pg. 578
BLAIR CONSTRUCTION INC.; *U.S. Private*, pg. 578
BLAIREX LABORATORIES, INC.; *U.S. Private*, pg. 578
BLAIR INDUSTRIES, INC.—See Magnaghi Aeronautica S.p.A.; *Int'l*, pg. 4640
BLAIR, LLC—See Bluestem Brands, Inc.; *U.S. Private*, pg. 598
BLAIRMHOR LIMITED—See Thai Beverage Public Company Limited; *Int'l*, pg. 7589
BLAIR PARK SERVICES, LLC—See Dycom Industries, Inc.; *U.S. Public*, pg. 698
BLAIR RUBBER COMPANY—See IKO Enterprises Ltd.; *Int'l*, pg. 3612
BLAIR SERVICES OF AMERICA INC.; *U.S. Private*, pg. 578
BLAISE OF COLOR—See LKQ Corporation; *U.S. Public*, pg. 1336
BLAISTEN SA—See Cencosud S.A.; *Int'l*, pg. 1400
BLAKE ELEARNING PTY. LTD.—See 3P Learning Limited; *Int'l*, pg. 9
BLAKE EQUIPMENT COMPANY INC.; *U.S. Private*, pg. 578
BLAKEFORD AT GREEN HILLS; *U.S. Private*, pg. 578
BLAKE H BROWN INC.; *U.S. Private*, pg. 578
BLAKE HOLDINGS LIMITED; *Int'l*, pg. 1062
BLAKE INTERNATIONAL USA RIGS, LLC; *U.S. Private*, pg. 578
BLAKELY PRODUCTS COMPANY—See ShoreView Industries, LLC; *U.S. Private*, pg. 3642
BLAKE MEDICAL CENTER—See HCA Healthcare, Inc.; *U.S. Public*, pg. 991
BLAKEMORE CONSTRUCTION CORP.; *U.S. Private*, pg. 578
BLAKE OIL COMPANY—See Conserv FS Inc.; *U.S. Private*, pg. 1019
BLAKE & PENDLETON INC.; *U.S. Private*, pg. 578
BLAKE REAL ESTATE, INC.; *U.S. Private*, pg. 578
BLAKE & SANYU—See Joseph J. Blake Associates, Inc.; *U.S. Private*, pg. 2236
BLAKESLEE ADVERTISING - PARK CITY—See Blakeslee Advertising; *U.S. Private*, pg. 578
BLAKESLEE ADVERTISING; *U.S. Private*, pg. 578
BLAKESLEE ARPAIA CHAPMAN INC.; *U.S. Private*, pg. 578
BLAKESLEE PRESTRESS INC.; *U.S. Private*, pg. 578
BLAKE'S LOTABURGER LLC; *U.S. Private*, pg. 578
BLAKEWAY PRODUCTIONS LIMITED—See Zinc Media Group plc; *Int'l*, pg. 8684
BLAKE WILLSON GROUP, LLC; *U.S. Private*, pg. 578
BLAKLEY CORPORATION; *U.S. Private*, pg. 578
BLALOCK WALTERS P.A.; *U.S. Private*, pg. 578

BLAMMO WORLDWIDE; *Int'l*, pg. 1062
BLANC AERO INDUSTRIES S.A.—See LISI S.A.; *Int'l*, pg. 4524
BLANC AERO INDUSTRIES UK LTD.—See LISI S.A.; *Int'l*, pg. 4523
BLANC AERO TECHNOLOGIES S.A.—See LISI S.A.; *Int'l*, pg. 4524
BLANCCO AUSTRALASIA PTY LTD—See Francisco Partners Management, LP; *U.S. Private*, pg. 1588
BLANCCO CENTRAL EUROPE GMBH—See Francisco Partners Management, LP; *U.S. Private*, pg. 1588
BLANCCO FRANCE SAS—See Francisco Partners Management, LP; *U.S. Private*, pg. 1588
BLANCCO JAPAN INC.—See Francisco Partners Management, LP; *U.S. Private*, pg. 1588
BLANCCO LLC—See Francisco Partners Management, LP; *U.S. Private*, pg. 1588
BLANCCO OY LTD—See Francisco Partners Management, LP; *U.S. Private*, pg. 1588
BLANCCO SEA SDN BHD—See Francisco Partners Management, LP; *U.S. Private*, pg. 1588
BLANCCO SWEDEN SFO—See Francisco Partners Management, LP; *U.S. Private*, pg. 1588
BLANCCO TECHNOLOGY GROUP PLC—See Francisco Partners Management, LP; *U.S. Private*, pg. 1588
BLANCCO UK LTD—See Francisco Partners Management, LP; *U.S. Private*, pg. 1588
BLANCETT—See Badger Meter, Inc.; *U.S. Public*, pg. 263
BLANCHARD EQUIPMENT CO. INC.; *U.S. Private*, pg. 579
BLANCHARD INVESTMENTS, INC.—See WRB Enterprises, Inc.; *U.S. Private*, pg. 4572
BLANCHARD SCHAEFER ADVERTISING & PUBLIC RELATIONS; *U.S. Private*, pg. 579
BLANCHARD SYSTEMS, INC.; *U.S. Private*, pg. 579
BLANCHARD VALLEY FARMERS CO-OP; *U.S. Private*, pg. 579
BLANCHARD VALLEY HEALTH SYSTEM; *U.S. Private*, pg. 579
BLANCHARDVILLE COOP OIL ASSOCIATION; *U.S. Private*, pg. 579
BLANC INDUSTRIES, INC.; *U.S. Private*, pg. 579
BLANC & OTUS PUBLIC RELATIONS—See WPP plc; *Int'l*, pg. 8477
BLANC & OTUS PUBLIC RELATIONS—See WPP plc; *Int'l*, pg. 8477
BLANC & OTUS PUBLIC RELATIONS—See WPP plc; *Int'l*, pg. 8477
BLANCO Y NEGRO SA; *Int'l*, pg. 1062
BLANCPAIN LES BOUTIQUES SA—See The Swatch Group Ltd.; *Int'l*, pg. 7691
BLANCPAIN S.A.—See The Swatch Group Ltd.; *Int'l*, pg. 7691
BLANC RESTAURANTS LTD.—See LVMH Moet Hennessy Louis Vuitton SE; *Int'l*, pg. 4591
BLANC SAS—See Bunzl plc; *Int'l*, pg. 1217
BLAND FARMS; *U.S. Private*, pg. 579
BLANDIN PAPER CO.—See UPM-Kymmene Corporation; *Int'l*, pg. 8092
BLANK CANVAS STUDIOS (AUS) PTY LTD—See Vection Technologies Ltd.; *Int'l*, pg. 8143
BLANKENSHIP ASSOCIATES, INC.—See Bain Capital, LP; *U.S. Private*, pg. 431
BLANKINSHIP & ASSOCIATES, INC.—See Bowman Consulting Group Ltd.; *U.S. Public*, pg. 376
BLANK ROME LLP; *U.S. Private*, pg. 579
BLANSKI PETER KRONLAGE & ZACH, P.A.—See Smith Schafer and Associates, Ltd.; *U.S. Private*, pg. 3695
BLANTON & ASSOCIATES, INC.—See ICF International, Inc.; *U.S. Public*, pg. 1085
BLANTON CONSTRUCTION; *U.S. Private*, pg. 579
BLANVALET VERLAG GMBH—See Bertelsmann SE & Co. KGaA; *Int'l*, pg. 992
BLASCHAK ANTHRACITE CORPORATION; *U.S. Private*, pg. 579
BLASCHKO COMPUTERS, INC.—See Open Systems, Inc.; *U.S. Private*, pg. 3030
BLASE MANUFACTURING COMPANY; *U.S. Private*, pg. 579
BLASER DIE CASTING CO.; *U.S. Private*, pg. 579
BLASER JAGDWAFFEN GMBH—See SAN Swiss Arms AG; *Int'l*, pg. 6521
BLASER'S USA, INC.; *U.S. Private*, pg. 579
BLASER USA, INC.—See SAN Swiss Arms AG; *Int'l*, pg. 6521
BLA SERVICIOS, S.A.—See Bunge Limited; *U.S. Public*, pg. 410
BLASI GMBH—See ASSA ABLOY AB; *Int'l*, pg. 638
BLASSINGER GMBH—See THK CO., LTD.; *Int'l*, pg. 7711
BLASS MARKETING; *U.S. Private*, pg. 579
BLAST DEFLECTORS, INC.—See Hanover Partners, Inc.; *U.S. Public*, pg. 1855
BLASTECH ABRASIVES PTE LTD—See Sembcorp Industries Ltd.; *Int'l*, pg. 6703
BLASTERPRODUKTER I KOPING AB—See Addtech AB; *Int'l*, pg. 132
BLASTERS, INC.—See Federal Signal Corporation; *U.S. Public*, pg. 826

COMPANY NAME INDEX

BLAST ! FILMS LIMITED—See Comcast Corporation; *U.S. Public*, pg. 537
BLASTING & EXCAVATING (PTY) LIMITED—See Basil Read Holdings Limited; *Int'l*, pg. 887
BLASTING SOLUTIONS INC.—See Argosy Capital Group, LLC; *U.S. Private*, pg. 321
BLASTMASTER PTY. LTD.—See INDUS Holding AG; *Int'l*, pg. 3664
BLASTRAC NA, INC.—See Bard & Company, Inc.; *U.S. Private*, pg. 473
BLAST RADIUS HAMBURG—See WPP plc; *Int'l*, pg. 8467
BLAST RADIUS—See WPP plc; *Int'l*, pg. 8467
BLAST RADIUS TORONTO—See WPP plc; *Int'l*, pg. 8467
BLAST RADIUS VANCOUVER—See WPP plc; *Int'l*, pg. 8467
BLAST RESOURCES INC.; *Int'l*, pg. 1063
BLASTWORKS INC.—See Gaming Realms plc; *Int'l*, pg. 2878
BLATT BILLIARDS CORP.; *U.S. Private*, pg. 579
BLATT CONSTRUCTION INC.—See Blatt Group; *U.S. Private*, pg. 580
BLATT GROUP; *U.S. Private*, pg. 580
BLATT INDUSTRIAL SERVICES INC.—See Blatt Group; *U.S. Private*, pg. 580
BLATTNER ENERGY, LLC—See Quanta Services, Inc.; *U.S. Public*, pg. 1750
BLATTNER HOLDING COMPANY, LLC—See Quanta Services, Inc.; *U.S. Public*, pg. 1750
BLATT WELDING AND FABRICATION, INC.—See Blatt Group; *U.S. Private*, pg. 580
BLAUER MANUFACTURING COMPANY, INC.; *U.S. Private*, pg. 580
BLAUPUNKT AUDIOVISION GMBH & CO. KG—See Aurelius Equity Opportunities SE & Co. KGaA; *Int'l*, pg. 707
BLAUPUNKT CAR AUDIO SYSTEMS GMBH & CO. KG—See Aurelius Equity Opportunities SE & Co. KGaA; *Int'l*, pg. 708
BLAUPUNKT INTERNATIONAL GMBH & CO. KG—See Aurelius Equity Opportunities SE & Co. KGaA; *Int'l*, pg. 707
BLAUPUNKT INTERNATIONAL SERVICES AG—See Aurelius Equity Opportunities SE & Co. KGaA; *Int'l*, pg. 708
BL AUTOTEC, LTD.—See Bando Chemical Industries, Ltd.; *Int'l*, pg. 830
BLAUWHOED HOLDING B.V.; *Int'l*, pg. 1063
BLAXTAIR INC.—See Arcure; *Int'l*, pg. 552
BLAYLOCK ROBERT VAN LLC; *U.S. Private*, pg. 580
BLAYLOCK ROBERT VAN LLC—See Blaylock Robert Van LLC; *U.S. Private*, pg. 580
BLAYLOCK, THREET, PHILLIPS & ASSOCIATES, INC.; *U.S. Private*, pg. 580
BLAZE CORPORATION—See MTG Co., Ltd.; *Int'l*, pg. 5070
BLAZE KING INDUSTRIES CANADA LTD.—See Decisive Dividend Corporation; *Int'l*, pg. 2001
BLAZE KING INDUSTRIES INC.—See Decisive Dividend Corporation; *Int'l*, pg. 2001
BLAZE MINERALS LIMITED; *Int'l*, pg. 1063
BLAZE PORTFOLIO SYSTEMS LLC—See LPL Financial Holdings Inc.; *U.S. Public*, pg. 1343
BLAZE PRODUCTS CORPORATION—See BCP Inc.; *U.S. Private*, pg. 499
BLAZE RECYCLING & METALS LLC—See Newell Recycling Southeast, LLC; *U.S. Private*, pg. 2914
BLAZER ELECTRIC SUPPLY COMPANY OF COLORADO SPRINGS—See Graybar Electric Company, Inc.; *U.S. Private*, pg. 1760
BLAZER INDUSTRIES INC.; *U.S. Private*, pg. 580
BLB CONSULTING GMBH—See Norddeutsche Landesbank Girozentrale; *Int'l*, pg. 5416
BLB IMMOBILIEN GMBH—See Norddeutsche Landesbank Girozentrale; *Int'l*, pg. 5416
BLB LEASING GMBH—See Norddeutsche Landesbank Girozentrale; *Int'l*, pg. 5416
BLB LTD; *Int'l*, pg. 1063
B&L BOLT, INC.—See Audax Group, Limited Partnership; *U.S. Private*, pg. 387
BLB RESOURCES, INC.; *U.S. Private*, pg. 580
B&L BROKERAGE SERVICES, INC.—See The Progressive Corporation; *U.S. Public*, pg. 2125
BLC ATRIUM-JACKSONVILLE, LLC—See Brookdale Senior Living Inc.; *U.S. Public*, pg. 393
BLC BANK SAL; *Int'l*, pg. 1063
BLC COMMUNITY BANK—See Independent Bancorp., Limited; *U.S. Private*, pg. 2058
BLC COSMETICS PTY LTD—See Hancock & Gore Ltd.; *Int'l*, pg. 3242
BLC FINANCE SAL—See BLC Bank SAL; *Int'l*, pg. 1063
BLC FOXWOOD SPRINGS LLC—See Brookdale Senior Living Inc.; *U.S. Public*, pg. 393
BLC GABLES MONROVIA LP—See Brookdale Senior Living Inc.; *U.S. Public*, pg. 393
BLC INVEST SAL—See BLC Bank SAL; *Int'l*, pg. 1063
BLCP POWER LTD.—See Banpu Public Company Limited; *Int'l*, pg. 851
BLCP POWER LTD.—See Electricity Generating Public Co., Ltd.; *Int'l*, pg. 2352

BLC RAMSEY LLC—See Brookdale Senior Living Inc.; *U.S. Public*, pg. 393
BLC TAMPA GC LLC—See Brookdale Senior Living Inc.; *U.S. Public*, pg. 393
BLD ASSET MANAGEMENT EAD—See AG Capital; *Int'l*, pg. 197
BLDD ARCHITECTS, INC.; *U.S. Private*, pg. 580
BLDG MANAGEMENT INC.; *U.S. Private*, pg. 580
BLDG.WORKS-USA, INC.; *U.S. Private*, pg. 580
BLD PLANTATION BHD; *Int'l*, pg. 1063
BLDY CO., LTD.—See Bain Capital, LP; *U.S. Private*, pg. 444
BLEACHER REPORT, INC.—See Warner Bros. Discovery, Inc.; *U.S. Public*, pg. 2328
BLEACHER RESTORATORS OF COLORADO, LLC; *U.S. Private*, pg. 580
BLEACHER SALES COMPANY INC.; *U.S. Private*, pg. 580
BLEACH GROUP, INC.; *U.S. Private*, pg. 580
BLEACH INC.; *Int'l*, pg. 1063
BLEDINA SA—See Danone; *Int'l*, pg. 1965
BLEDSOE COAL CORPORATION—See James River Coal Company; *U.S. Private*, pg. 2185
BLEDSOE COAL LEASING COMPANY—See James River Coal Company; *U.S. Private*, pg. 2185
BLEDSOE TELEPHONE COOPERATIVE CORPORATION; *U.S. Private*, pg. 580
BLEECKER SA; *Int'l*, pg. 1063
BLEES-KOLLING-BAU GMBH—See STRABAG SE; *Int'l*, pg. 7229
BLEIGH CONSTRUCTION CO. INC.; *U.S. Private*, pg. 580
BLEI S.P.A.—See RCS MediaGroup S.p.A.; *Int'l*, pg. 6229
BLE KEDROS REAL ESTATE INVESTMENT COMPANY SA; *Int'l*, pg. 1063
BLENCOWE RESOURCES PLC; *Int'l*, pg. 1063
BLENDER AS—See Umoe Gruppen AS; *Int'l*, pg. 8026
BLENDER FINANCIAL TECHNOLOGIES LTD.; *Int'l*, pg. 1063
BLENDE SILVER CORP.; *Int'l*, pg. 1063
BLENDEX COMPANY; *U.S. Private*, pg. 580
BLEND IMAGES, LLC; *U.S. Private*, pg. 580
BLEND LABS, INC.; *U.S. Public*, pg. 361
BLEND & PACK PTY. LTD.—See Mason Group Holdings Limited; *Int'l*, pg. 4722
BLENHEIM BOTTLERS INC.—See The Schafer Company Inc.; *U.S. Private*, pg. 4114
BLENKO GLASS COMPANY INC.; *U.S. Private*, pg. 580
BLE OR—See Groupe Limagrain Holding SA; *Int'l*, pg. 3107
BLEP HOLDING GMBH—See Bausch Health Companies Inc.; *Int'l*, pg. 896
BLESBERGER G.M.B.H.—See London Security PLC; *Int'l*, pg. 4547
BLESSED TEXTILES LIMITED; *Int'l*, pg. 1063
BLESSTON PRINTING AND ASSOCIATES (PTY) LIMITED—See The Bidvest Group Limited; *Int'l*, pg. 7623
BLESS YOU INC.—See Dentsu Group Inc.; *Int'l*, pg. 2040
BLETEC SOFTWARE GMBH—See MEDIQON Group AG; *Int'l*, pg. 4780
BLETHEN CORPORATION; *U.S. Private*, pg. 580
BLETHEN, GAGE & KRAUSE, PLLP; *U.S. Private*, pg. 581
BLEUACACIA LTD.; *U.S. Public*, pg. 361
BLEU OCEANE; *Int'l*, pg. 1063
BLEU RESIDENCE LORMONT SCI—See Groupe BPCE; *Int'l*, pg. 3092
BLEVINS FRANKS FINANCIAL MANAGEMENT LIMITED; *Int'l*, pg. 1063
BLEVINS FRANKS TAX LIMITED—See Blevins Franks Financial Management Limited; *Int'l*, pg. 1063
BLEVINS INC.; *U.S. Private*, pg. 581
BLEVINS WORK SHOP INC.; *U.S. Private*, pg. 581
BLEWETT & ASSOCIATES INC.—See Munchener Ruckversicherungs AG; *Int'l*, pg. 5085
BLEWETT'S FOOD, INC.; *U.S. Private*, pg. 581
BLEYHL FARM SERVICE INC.; *U.S. Private*, pg. 581
BLG AUTOTERMINAL BREMERHAVEN GMBH & CO. KG.—See Bremer Lagerhaus-Gesellschaft; *Int'l*, pg. 1145
BLG AUTOTERMINAL GDANSK SP. Z O. O.—See Bremer Lagerhaus-Gesellschaft; *Int'l*, pg. 1145
BLG HYPOTHEEKBANK N.V.—See SNS Bank N.V.; *Int'l*, pg. 7029
BLG LOGISTICS AUTOMOBILE SPB—See Bremer Lagerhaus-Gesellschaft; *Int'l*, pg. 1145
BLG LOGISTICS GROUP AG & CO. KG—See Bremer Lagerhaus-Gesellschaft; *Int'l*, pg. 1145
BLG LOGISTICS INC.—See Bremer Lagerhaus-Gesellschaft; *Int'l*, pg. 1145
BLG LOGISTICS SOLUTIONS ITALIA S.R.L.—See Bremer Lagerhaus-Gesellschaft; *Int'l*, pg. 1145
BL GRUNDVANDSAENKNING A/S—See Per Aarsleff Holding A/S; *Int'l*, pg. 5795
B.L. HARBERT INTERNATIONAL, LLC; *U.S. Private*, pg. 420
BLH BAUELEMENTE FUR LUFTTECHNIK HENNEN GMBH—See SIG plc; *Int'l*, pg. 6906
BLH SAS; *Int'l*, pg. 1063

BLI CAPITAL LIMITED—See Bay Leasing & Investment Limited; *Int'l*, pg. 901
BLICKMAN HEALTH INDUSTRIES, INC.; *U.S. Private*, pg. 581
BLICNET D.O.O.—See Telekomunikacije Republike Srpske a.d.; *Int'l*, pg. 7538
BLIFFERT LUMBER & FUEL CO. INC.; *U.S. Private*, pg. 581
BLIGH RESOURCES LIMITED—See Northern Star Resources Ltd; *Int'l*, pg. 5444
B-LIGHT CO., LTD.—See AB&Company Co., Ltd.; *Int'l*, pg. 47
BLIGHT OIL COMPANY; *U.S. Private*, pg. 581
BLI LEGACY, INC.—See New Water Capital, L.P.; *U.S. Private*, pg. 2907
BLILEY TECHNOLOGIES INC.—See KYOCERA Corporation; *Int'l*, pg. 4359
BLIMPIE INTERNATIONAL INC.; *U.S. Private*, pg. 581
BLIMPIE SUBS & SALADS—See Blimpie International Inc.; *U.S. Private*, pg. 581
BLINC INC.; *U.S. Private*, pg. 581
BLIND INDUSTRIES & SERVICES OF MARYLAND; *U.S. Private*, pg. 581
BLINDINGQUEEN PROPERTIES SRL—See Bank of Cyprus Holdings Public Limited Company; *Int'l*, pg. 842
BLINDLIGHT LLC—See Canada Pension Plan Investment Board; *Int'l*, pg. 1280
BLINDLIGHT LLC—See EQT AB; *Int'l*, pg. 2482
BLINDLIGHT LLC—See Temasek Holdings (Private) Limited; *Int'l*, pg. 7548
BLINDS CHALET; *U.S. Private*, pg. 581
BLINDS.COM; *U.S. Private*, pg. 581
BLINDS TO GO (CANADA) INC.—See Blinds To Go Inc.; *U.S. Private*, pg. 581
BLINDS TO GO INC.; *U.S. Private*, pg. 581
BLIND SUPPLY, LLC; *U.S. Private*, pg. 581
BL INDUSTRIA OTICA, LTDA.—See Bausch Health Companies Inc.; *Int'l*, pg. 896
B-LINE APPAREL, INC.; *U.S. Private*, pg. 419
BLINI S.A.—See Alfesca hf.; *Int'l*, pg. 315
BLINKBONNY QUARRY (BORDERS) LIMITED—See Breedon Group plc; *Int'l*, pg. 1144
BLINK CHARGING CO.; *U.S. Public*, pg. 361
BLINK INTERACTIVE, INC.—See Blackstone Inc.; *U.S. Public*, pg. 356
BLINK MOBILITY, LLC—See Blink Charging Co.; *U.S. Public*, pg. 361
BLINK PRODUCTIONS LTD.—See Zhejiang Talent Television & Film Company Limited; *Int'l*, pg. 8664
BLINKX, INC.—See Nexxen International Ltd.; *Int'l*, pg. 5251
BLINNPR; *U.S. Private*, pg. 581
BLIP SYSTEMS A/S—See Gentrack Group Limited; *Int'l*, pg. 2929
BLISH-MIZE CO.; *U.S. Private*, pg. 581
BLISS-BRET A.S.—See Haco N.V.; *Int'l*, pg. 3204
BLISSCO CANNABIS CORP.—See Canopy Growth Corporation; *Int'l*, pg. 1298
BLISS COMMUNICATIONS, INC.—See Adams Publishing Group, LLC; *U.S. Private*, pg. 74
BLISS DIALYSIS, LLC—See DaVita Inc.; *U.S. Public*, pg. 636
BLISS GVS PHARMA LTD.; *Int'l*, pg. 1063
BLISS INTEGRATED COMMUNICATION; *U.S. Private*, pg. 582
BLISS INTELLIGENCE PUBLIC COMPANY LIMITED; *Int'l*, pg. 1063
BLISSPR—See Bliss Integrated Communication; *U.S. Private*, pg. 582
BLISS REFRIGERATION LTD.—See GEA Group Aktiengesellschaft; *Int'l*, pg. 2897
BLISS UNLIMITED LLC—See HumanCo LLC; *U.S. Private*, pg. 2006
BLIS TECHNOLOGIES LIMITED; *Int'l*, pg. 1063
BLISTEX, INC.; *U.S. Private*, pg. 582
BLISTEX LIMITED—See Blistex, Inc.; *U.S. Private*, pg. 582
B. LITTLE & COMPANY INC.; *U.S. Private*, pg. 419
BLITZ AGENCY; *U.S. Private*, pg. 582
BLITZ COMMUNICATIONS GROUP LIMITED—See Viad Corp.; *U.S. Public*, pg. 2290
BLITZ DDB—See Omnicom Group Inc.; *U.S. Public*, pg. 1579
BLITZ MEDIA-DIRECT—See The Linick Group, Inc.; *U.S. Private*, pg. 4070
BLITZ MEDIA, INC.; *U.S. Private*, pg. 582
BLITZWAY CO., LTD.; *Int'l*, pg. 1064
BLIVEX ENERGY TECHNOLOGY CO., LTD.; *Int'l*, pg. 1064
BLIXT GROUP LIMITED; *Int'l*, pg. 1064
BLI ZAMBIA LTD—See Boart Longyear Ltd.; *Int'l*, pg. 1094
BLIZZARD ENTERTAINMENT S.A.S.—See Microsoft Corporation; *U.S. Public*, pg. 1438
BLIZZARD ENTERTAINMENT—See Microsoft Corporation; *U.S. Public*, pg. 1438
BLIZZARD INDUSTRIAL SUPPLY—See Raleigh Mine & Industrial Supply, Inc.; *U.S. Private*, pg. 3349
B.L.J. COMPANY LTD.—See Bausch Health Companies Inc.; *Int'l*, pg. 896
B L KASHYAP & SONS LIMITED; *Int'l*, pg. 783

BLK SISTEMAS FINANCEIROS LTDA.—See B3 S.A.; *Int'l*, pg. 791
B.L.L. HOLDINGS LTD; *Int'l*, pg. 790
BLME HOLDINGS PLC; *Int'l*, pg. 1064
THE BLM GROUP, INC.; *Int'l*, pg. 7627
BLOCH & LEVITAN (PTY) LIMITED—See The Bidvest Group Limited; *Int'l*, pg. 7623
BLOCH S.A.—See Trelleborg AB; *Int'l*, pg. 7910
BLOCK47 EATS LLP—See Global Food Creators Co., Ltd.; *Int'l*, pg. 2997
BLOCKADE MEDICAL LLC—See Bridgepoint Group Plc; *Int'l*, pg. 1154
THE BLOCK AGENCY, INC., *U.S. Private*, pg. 3995
BLOCKBUSTER AUSTRALIA PTY. LTD.—See Franchise Entertainment Group Pty Ltd.; *Int'l*, pg. 2760
BLOCKBUSTER DE MEXICO, S.A. DE C.V.—See Grupo Salinas, S.A. de C.V.; *Int'l*, pg. 3135
BLOCKBUSTER ENTERTAINMENT LIMITED—See Gordon Brothers Group, LLC; *U.S. Private*, pg. 1742
BLOCK CAPITAL CORP; *U.S. Public*, pg. 361
BLOCKCHAIN GROUP COMPANY LIMITED; *Int'l*, pg. 1064
THE BLOCKCHAIN GROUP; *Int'l*, pg. 7627
BLOCKCHAINK2 CORP.; *Int'l*, pg. 1064
BLOCKCHAIN MOON ACQUISITION CORP.; *U.S. Public*, pg. 362
BLOCKCHAIN OF THINGS, INC.; *U.S. Private*, pg. 583
BLOCKCHAINS, LLC; *U.S. Private*, pg. 583
BLOCKCHAIN SOLUTIONS INC.; *U.S. Private*, pg. 583
BLOCKCHAIN VENTURE CAPITAL INC.; *Int'l*, pg. 1064
BLOCK COMMUNICATIONS, INC.; *U.S. Private*, pg. 582
BLOCK & COMPANY, INC.; *U.S. Private*, pg. 582
BLOCK & DECORSO; *U.S. Private*, pg. 582
BLOCK ELECTRIC CO. INC.; *U.S. Private*, pg. 582
BLOCK ENERGY PLC; *Int'l*, pg. 1064
BLOCK GRAPHICS, INC.—See Ennis, Inc.; *U.S. Public*, pg. 769
BLOCKHOLD CAPITAL CORPORATION; *U.S. Public*, pg. 362
BLOCKHOUSE COMPANY, INC.; *U.S. Private*, pg. 583
BLOCK IMAGING PARTS & SERVICE, LLC—See Siemens Aktiengesellschaft; *Int'l*, pg. 6886
BLOCK, INC.; *U.S. Public*, pg. 361
BLOCK INDUSTRIES INC.; *U.S. Private*, pg. 582
BLOCK INSTITUTE; *U.S. Private*, pg. 583
BLOCKLEYS BRICK LTD.—See Michelmersh Brick Holdings PLC; *Int'l*, pg. 4875
BLOCKLINE INC.—See Sumitomo Mitsui Financial Group, Inc.; *Int'l*, pg. 7293
BLOCKMATE VENTURES, INC.; *Int'l*, pg. 1064
BLOCKMINT TECHNOLOGIES, INC.; *Int'l*, pg. 1064
BLOCK SOLUTIONS LTD.; *Int'l*, pg. 1064
BLOCKSOM & CO.; *U.S. Private*, pg. 583
BLOCK USA ALABAMA DIVISION LLC—See Ready Mix USA, Inc.; *U.S. Private*, pg. 3367
BLOCK WATNE AS—See OBOS BBL; *Int'l*, pg. 5512
BLODGETT COMBI—See The Middleby Corporation; *U.S. Public*, pg. 2113
BLODGETT OIL COMPANY, INC.; *U.S. Private*, pg. 583
BLODGETT OVEN COMPANY INC—See The Middleby Corporation; *U.S. Public*, pg. 2113
BLODGETT SUPPLY CO. INC.—See SPL Associates Inc.; *U.S. Private*, pg. 3759
BLO DISTRIBUTION—See Carrefour SA; *Int'l*, pg. 1343
BLOEDORN LUMBER COMPANY INC.; *U.S. Private*, pg. 583
BLOGHER INC.—See Great Hill Partners, L.P.; *U.S. Private*, pg. 1763
BLOGWATCHER INC.—See Dentsu Group Inc.; *Int'l*, pg. 2034
BLOHM JUNG GMBH—See United Grinding Group AG; *Int'l*, pg. 8067
BLOHM + VOSS B.V & CO. KG—See Fr. Lurssen Werft GmbH & Co. KG; *Int'l*, pg. 2758
BLOHM + VOSS EL DJAZAIR S.A.R.L.—See ThyssenKrupp AG; *Int'l*, pg. 7724
BLOHM + VOSS INDUSTRIES (SINGAPORE) PTE. LTD.—See ThyssenKrupp AG; *Int'l*, pg. 7724
BLOHM + VOSS (KOREA) LTD.—See ThyssenKrupp AG; *Int'l*, pg. 7724
BLOHM + VOSS MARINE SYSTEMS GMBH—See ThyssenKrupp AG; *Int'l*, pg. 7724
BLOHM + VOSS NAVAL GMBH—See ThyssenKrupp AG; *Int'l*, pg. 7724
BLOHM + VOSS OIL TOOLS GMBH—See Forum Energy Technologies, Inc.; *U.S. Public*, pg. 873
BLOHM + VOSS OIL TOOLS, LLC—See ThyssenKrupp AG; *Int'l*, pg. 7724
BLOHM + VOSS REPAIR GMBH—See STAR Capital Partners Limited; *Int'l*, pg. 7173
BLOHM + VOSS SHIPYARDS & SERVICES GMBH—See ThyssenKrupp AG; *Int'l*, pg. 7724
BLOK TECHNOLOGIES, INC.; *Int'l*, pg. 1064
BLOM AEROFILMS LTD.—See Cyient Limited; *Int'l*, pg. 1895
BLOM ASSET MANAGEMENT COMPANY S.A.L.—See BLOM Bank, S.A.L.; *Int'l*, pg. 1064
BLOM BANK EGYPT S.A.E.—See BLOM Bank, S.A.L.; *Int'l*, pg. 1064

BLOM BANK QATAR LLC—See BLOM Bank, S.A.L.; *Int'l*, pg. 1064
BLOM BANK, S.A.L.; *Int'l*, pg. 1064
BLOMBERGER HOLZINDUSTRIE B. HAUSMANN GMBH & CO. KG—See Delignit AG; *Int'l*, pg. 2013
BLOMBERGER HOLZINDUSTRIE GMBH—See MBB SE; *Int'l*, pg. 4751
BLOMBERG WERKE GMBH—See Koç Holding A.S.; *Int'l*, pg. 4222
BLOM CGR S.P.A.—See NRC Group ASA; *Int'l*, pg. 5473
BLOM CZECH REPUBLIC—See NRC Group ASA; *Int'l*, pg. 5473
BLOM DATA AS—See NRC Group ASA; *Int'l*, pg. 5473
BLOM DEUTSCHLAND GMBH—See NRC Group ASA; *Int'l*, pg. 5473
BLOM DEVELOPMENT BANK S.A.L.—See BLOM Bank, S.A.L.; *Int'l*, pg. 1064
BLOM EGYPT INVESTMENT S.A.E.—See BLOM Bank, S.A.L.; *Int'l*, pg. 1065
BLOM EGYPT SECURITIES S.A.E.—See BLOM Bank, S.A.L.; *Int'l*, pg. 1065
BLOMENBURG HOLDING GMBH—See Asklepios Kliniken GmbH & Co. KGaA; *Int'l*, pg. 623
BLOMESYSTEM GMBH—See GUS Group AG & Co KG; *Int'l*, pg. 3188
BLOMINVEST BANK SAL—See BLOM Bank, S.A.L.; *Int'l*, pg. 1064
BLOMINVEST BANK SAUDI ARABIA COMPANY—See BLOM Bank, S.A.L.; *Int'l*, pg. 1065
BLOMMER CHOCOLATE COMPANY - CALIFORNIA PLANT—See Fuji Oil Holdings Inc.; *Int'l*, pg. 2815
BLOMMER CHOCOLATE COMPANY - CHICAGO PLANT—See Fuji Oil Holdings Inc.; *Int'l*, pg. 2815
BLOMMER CHOCOLATE COMPANY - PENNSYLVANIA PLANT—See Fuji Oil Holdings Inc.; *Int'l*, pg. 2815
BLOMMER CHOCOLATE COMPANY—See Fuji Oil Holdings Inc.; *Int'l*, pg. 2815
BLOMMER CHOCOLATE MANUFACTURING (SHANGHAI) COMPANY LTD.—See Fuji Oil Company, Ltd.; *Int'l*, pg. 2815
BLOM PORTUGAL LDA.—See NRC Group ASA; *Int'l*, pg. 5473
BLOMQUIST ANNONSBYRA AB; *Int'l*, pg. 1065
BLOMSTERLANDET AB—See STENA AB; *Int'l*, pg. 7206
BLOMSTERLANDET AB—See STENA AB; *Int'l*, pg. 7206
BLONDE DIGITAL LTD.—See Arsenal Capital Management LP; *U.S. Private*, pg. 338
BLONDER TONGUE INTERNATIONAL INC.—See Blonder Tongue Laboratories, Inc.; *U.S. Public*, pg. 362
BLONDER TONGUE LABORATORIES, INC.; *U.S. Public*, pg. 362
BLOOD BANK OF HAWAII; *U.S. Private*, pg. 583
BLOOD-HORSE PUBLICATIONS; *U.S. Private*, pg. 583
BLOOD HOUND, LLC—See USIC, LLC; *U.S. Private*, pg. 4323
THE BLOOD & TISSUE CENTER OF CENTRAL TEXAS; *U.S. Private*, pg. 3995
BLOOMAGE BIOTECHNOLOGY CORPORATION LIMITED; *Int'l*, pg. 1065
BLOOMBERG BUSINESSWEEK—See Bloomberg L.P.; *U.S. Private*, pg. 583
BLOOMBERG CONSULTING, INC.—See YOUNG & Associates; *U.S. Private*, pg. 4592
BLOOMBERG L.P.; *U.S. Private*, pg. 583
BLOOMBERG TELEVISION—See Bloomberg L.P.; *U.S. Private*, pg. 583
BLOOMBERG TRADEBOOK LLC—See Bloomberg L.P.; *U.S. Private*, pg. 583
BLOOMBERRY RESORTS CORPORATION; *Int'l*, pg. 1065
BLOOMCHEER LIMITED—See Cafe de Coral Holdings Limited; *Int'l*, pg. 1249
BLOOM COMBUSTION (INDIA) PRIVATE LTD.—See Caledonia Investments plc; *Int'l*, pg. 1262
BLOOM DEKOR LIMITED; *Int'l*, pg. 1065
BLOOM ELECTRIC SERVICES, INC.; *U.S. Private*, pg. 583
BLOOM ENERGY CORPORATION; *U.S. Public*, pg. 362
BLOOM ENERGY (INDIA) PUT. LTD.—See Bloom Energy Corporation; *U.S. Public*, pg. 362
BLOOM ENERGY (INDIA) PVT. LTD.—See Bloom Energy Corporation; *U.S. Public*, pg. 362
BLOOM ENGINEERING CO. INC.—See Caledonia Investments plc; *Int'l*, pg. 1262
BLOOM ENGINEERING (EUROPA) GMBH—See Caledonia Investments plc; *Int'l*, pg. 1262
BLOOM EQUITY PARTNERS MANAGEMENT, LLC; *U.S. Private*, pg. 583
BLOOMERANG, LLC; *U.S. Private*, pg. 584
BLOOMER CANDY CO.; *U.S. Private*, pg. 584
BLOOMER PLASTICS, INC.; *U.S. Private*, pg. 584
BLOOMFIELD COLLEGE—See Montclair State University; *U.S. Private*, pg. 2775
BLOOMFIELD ENGINEERING COMPANY INC.—See Caledonia Investments plc; *Int'l*, pg. 1262
BLOOMFIELD HOMES—See Sumitomo Forestry Co., Ltd.; *Int'l*, pg. 7286
THE BLOOMFIELD MANUFACTURING CO., INC.; *U.S. Private*, pg. 3995

BLOOM HOLDCO LLC; *U.S. Private*, pg. 583
BLOOMIN' BRANDS, INC.; *U.S. Public*, pg. 362
BLOOM INDUSTRIES LIMITED; *Int'l*, pg. 1065
BLOOMING COLOR, INC.; *U.S. Private*, pg. 584
BLOOMINGDALES.COM—See Macy's, Inc.; *U.S. Public*, pg. 1353
BLOOMINGDALE'S, INC.—See Macy's, Inc.; *U.S. Public*, pg. 1353
BLOOMING GLEN CONTRACTORS INC.—See Haines & Kibblehouse Inc.; *U.S. Private*, pg. 1840
BLOOMING GLEN QUARRY—See Haines & Kibblehouse Inc.; *U.S. Private*, pg. 1840
BLOOMINGTON COMPENSATION INSURANCE COMPANY—See State Automobile Mutual Insurance Company; *U.S. Private*, pg. 3791
BLOOMINGTON MEADOWS, GENERAL PARTNERSHIP—See Universal Health Services, Inc.; *U.S. Public*, pg. 2256
BLOOMINGTON-NORMAL SEATING COMPANY—See Magna International Inc.; *Int'l*, pg. 4640
BLOOMINGTON-NORMAL SEATING COMPANY—See Namba Press Works Co., Ltd.; *Int'l*, pg. 5135
BLOOMINGTON OFFSET PROCESS; *U.S. Private*, pg. 584
BLOOM INVESTMENT COUNSEL, INC.; *Int'l*, pg. 1065
BLOOMIOS, INC.; *U.S. Public*, pg. 363
BLOOM MEDIA (UK) LTD.—See Jaywing PLC; *Int'l*, pg. 3916
BLOOMNATION, INC.; *U.S. Private*, pg. 584
BLOOM NO.2 LIMITED—See Bloomin' Brands, Inc.; *U.S. Public*, pg. 362
BLOOMREACH B.V.—See BloomReach, Inc.; *U.S. Private*, pg. 584
BLOOMREACH, INC.; *U.S. Private*, pg. 584
BLOOMSBURG CARPET INDUSTRIES INC.; *U.S. Private*, pg. 584
BLOOMSBURG MILLS INC.; *U.S. Private*, pg. 584
BLOOMSBURY BOOK PUBLISHING COMPANY LIMITED—See Bloomsbury Publishing Plc; *Int'l*, pg. 1065
BLOOMSBURY INDIA UK LIMITED—See Bloomsbury Publishing Plc; *Int'l*, pg. 1065
BLOOMSBURY INFORMATION LIMITED—See Bloomsbury Publishing Plc; *Int'l*, pg. 1065
BLOOMSBURY PROFESSIONAL LIMITED—See Bloomsbury Publishing Plc; *Int'l*, pg. 1065
BLOOMSBURY PUBLISHING INC.—See Bloomsbury Publishing Plc; *Int'l*, pg. 1065
BLOOMSBURY PUBLISHING INDIA PVT LIMITED—See Bloomsbury Publishing Plc; *Int'l*, pg. 1065
BLOOMSBURY PUBLISHING PLC; *Int'l*, pg. 1065
BLOOMSBURY PUBLISHING PTY LTD.—See Bloomsbury Publishing Plc; *Int'l*, pg. 1065
BLOOM SELECT INCOME FUND—See Bloom Investment Counsel, Inc.; *Int'l*, pg. 1065
BLOOM THAT, INC.—See FTD Companies, Inc.; *U.S. Private*, pg. 1619
BLOOM & WAKE LTD; *Int'l*, pg. 1065
THE BLOSSAN COMPANIES INC.; *U.S. Private*, pg. 3995
BLOSSMAN GAS INC.—See The Blossman Companies Inc.; *U.S. Private*, pg. 3995
BLOSSOM FARM PRODUCTS CO.; *U.S. Private*, pg. 584
BLOSSOM GLORY LIMITED—See IT Ltd; *Int'l*, pg. 3827
BLOSSOMS HEALTHCARE LLP—See HCA Healthcare, Inc.; *U.S. Public*, pg. 991
BLOSSOM TIME SDN. BHD.—See Atlan Holdings Berhad; *Int'l*, pg. 673
B-LOT CO., LTD.; *Int'l*, pg. 785
B-LOT SINGAPORE PTE., LTD.—See b-lot Co., Ltd.; *Int'l*, pg. 785
BLOUNT CANADA LTD.—See American Securities LLC; *U.S. Private*, pg. 247
BLOUNT CANADA LTD.—See P2 Capital Partners, LLC; *U.S. Private*, pg. 3062
BLOUNT EUROPE, S.A.—See American Securities LLC; *U.S. Private*, pg. 247
BLOUNT EUROPE, S.A.—See P2 Capital Partners, LLC; *U.S. Private*, pg. 3061
BLOUNT FINE FOODS CORPORATION; *U.S. Private*, pg. 584
BLOUNT GMBH—See American Securities LLC; *U.S. Private*, pg. 247
BLOUNT GMBH—See P2 Capital Partners, LLC; *U.S. Private*, pg. 3061
BLOUNT, INC.—See American Securities LLC; *U.S. Private*, pg. 247
BLOUNT, INC.—See P2 Capital Partners, LLC; *U.S. Private*, pg. 247
BLOUNT INDUSTRIAL LTDA.—See American Securities LLC; *U.S. Private*, pg. 247
BLOUNT INDUSTRIAL LTDA.—See P2 Capital Partners, LLC; *U.S. Private*, pg. 3061
BLOUNT INTERNATIONAL, INC.—See American Securities LLC; *U.S. Private*, pg. 247
BLOUNT INTERNATIONAL, INC.—See P2 Capital Partners, LLC; *U.S. Private*, pg. 3061
BLOUNT JAPAN, INC.—See American Securities LLC; *U.S. Private*, pg. 247

COMPANY NAME INDEX

BLOUNT JAPAN, INC.—See P2 Capital Partners, LLC; *U.S. Private*, pg. 3062
BLOUNT SMALL SHIP ADVENTURES, INC.; *U.S. Private*, pg. 584
BLOUNT UK LTD.—See American Securities LLC; *U.S. Private*, pg. 247
BLOUNT UK LTD.—See P2 Capital Partners, LLC; *U.S. Private*, pg. 3062
BLOW BROS.—See Casella Waste Systems, Inc.; *U.S. Public*, pg. 445
BLOWER APPLICATION COMPANY, INC.—See Valesco Industries, Inc; *U.S. Private*, pg. 4331
BLOWER DEMPSAY CORPORATION; *U.S. Private*, pg. 584
BLOW IN BLANKET, LLC—See Masco Corporation; *U.S. Public*, pg. 1391
THE BLOWING ROCKET—See Adams Publishing Group, LLC; *U.S. Private*, pg. 75
BLOWING ROCK INVESTMENT PROPERTIES, INC.—See Hanna Holdings, Inc.; *U.S. Private*, pg. 1854
BLOWTHERM S.P.A.; *Int'l*, pg. 1065
BLOWUP MEDIA BENELUX B.V.—See Stroer SE & Co. KGaA; *Int'l*, pg. 7242
BLOWUP MEDIA ESPANA S.A.—See Stroer SE & Co. KGaA; *Int'l*, pg. 7242
BLOWUP MEDIA GMBH—See Stroer SE & Co. KGaA; *Int'l*, pg. 7243
BLOX, INC.; *U.S. Public*, pg. 363
BLOXWICH (MALAYSIA) SDN. BHD.—See Mega First Corporation Berhad; *Int'l*, pg. 4792
BLOYALTY SDN BHD—See Berjaya Corporation Berhad; *Int'l*, pg. 982
BL - PEGSON LIMITED—See Terex Corporation; *U.S. Public*, pg. 2020
BL PHARMTECH CORP; *Int'l*, pg. 1056
B&L PIPECO SERVICES INC.—See Sumitomo Corporation; *Int'l*, pg. 7268
BL PRODUCTS AB—See Indutrade AB; *Int'l*, pg. 3677
BLP TRAINING & SERVICES PTY. LTD.; *Int'l*, pg. 1065
BLR AEROSPACE, LLC—See Ducommun Incorporated; *U.S. Public*, pg. 689
BL RESTAURANT OPERATIONS, LLC—See Sun Capital Partners, Inc.; *U.S. Private*, pg. 3858
BLR/FURTHER; *U.S. Private*, pg. 505
BLRT GRUPP AS; *Int'l*, pg. 1065
BLSA INDUSTRIES (PTY) LTD.—See Centerbridge Partners, L.P.; *U.S. Private*, pg. 815
B.L.S. AUFZUGSERVICE GMBH—See ThyssenKrupp AG; *Int'l*, pg. 7723
BLS INFOTECH LIMITED; *Int'l*, pg. 1066
BLS INTERNATIONAL SERVICES BELARUS INC.—See BLS International Services Limited; *Int'l*, pg. 1066
BLS INTERNATIONAL SERVICES CANADA INC.—See BLS International Services Limited; *Int'l*, pg. 1066
BLS INTERNATIONAL SERVICES CHINA INC.—See BLS International Services Limited; *Int'l*, pg. 1066
BLS INTERNATIONAL SERVICES DOMINICAN REPUBLIC INC.—See BLS International Services Limited; *Int'l*, pg. 1066
BLS INTERNATIONAL SERVICES EGYPT INC.—See BLS International Services Limited; *Int'l*, pg. 1066
BLS INTERNATIONAL SERVICES GHANA INC.—See BLS International Services Limited; *Int'l*, pg. 1066
BLS INTERNATIONAL SERVICES INDONESIA INC.—See BLS International Services Limited; *Int'l*, pg. 1066
BLS INTERNATIONAL SERVICES JORDAN INC.—See BLS International Services Limited; *Int'l*, pg. 1066
BLS INTERNATIONAL SERVICES KAZAKHSTAN INC.—See BLS International Services Limited; *Int'l*, pg. 1066
BLS INTERNATIONAL SERVICES KUWAIT INC.—See BLS International Services Limited; *Int'l*, pg. 1067
BLS INTERNATIONAL SERVICES LEBANON INC.—See BLS International Services Limited; *Int'l*, pg. 1066
BLS INTERNATIONAL SERVICES LIMITED; *Int'l*, pg. 1066
BLS INTERNATIONAL SERVICES LIMITED—See BLS International Services Limited; *Int'l*, pg. 1066
BLS INTERNATIONAL SERVICES LIMITED—See BLS International Services Limited; *Int'l*, pg. 1066
BLS INTERNATIONAL SERVICES LIMITED—See BLS International Services Limited; *Int'l*, pg. 1066
BLS INTERNATIONAL SERVICES LTD.—See BLS International Services Limited; *Int'l*, pg. 1066
BLS INTERNATIONAL SERVICES MAURITANIA INC.—See BLS International Services Limited; *Int'l*, pg. 1066
BLS INTERNATIONAL SERVICES NIGERIA INC.—See BLS International Services Limited; *Int'l*, pg. 1066
BLS INTERNATIONAL SERVICES NORWAY AS—See BLS International Services Limited; *Int'l*, pg. 1066
BLS INTERNATIONAL SERVICES OMAN INC.—See BLS International Services Limited; *Int'l*, pg. 1066
BLS INTERNATIONAL SERVICES PAKISTAN INC.—See BLS International Services Limited; *Int'l*, pg. 1066
BLS INTERNATIONAL SERVICES PHILIPPINES INC.—See BLS International Services Limited; *Int'l*, pg. 1066
BLS INTERNATIONAL SERVICES QATAR INC.—See BLS International Services Limited; *Int'l*, pg. 1066
BLS INTERNATIONAL SERVICES REPUBLIC OF COTE D'IVOIRE INC.—See BLS International Services Limited; *Int'l*, pg. 1066
BLS INTERNATIONAL SERVICES RUSSIA INC.—See BLS International Services Limited; *Int'l*, pg. 1066
BLS INTERNATIONAL SERVICES SAUDIARABIA INC.—See BLS International Services Limited; *Int'l*, pg. 1066
BLS INTERNATIONAL SERVICES SENEGAL INC.—See BLS International Services Limited; *Int'l*, pg. 1066
BLS INTERNATIONAL SERVICES SINGAPORE PTE LTD—See BLS International Services Limited; *Int'l*, pg. 1066
BLS INTERNATIONAL SERVICES SOUTH AFRICA INC.—See BLS International Services Limited; *Int'l*, pg. 1066
BLS INTERNATIONAL SERVICES TURKEY INC.—See BLS International Services Limited; *Int'l*, pg. 1066
BLS INTERNATIONAL SERVICES UAE INC.—See BLS International Services Limited; *Int'l*, pg. 1066
BLS INTERNATIONAL SERVICES UKRAINE INC.—See BLS International Services Limited; *Int'l*, pg. 1066
BLS INTERNATIONAL SERVICES UNITED KINGDOM INC.—See BLS International Services Limited; *Int'l*, pg. 1067
BLS INTERNATIONAL SERVICES VIETNAM INC.—See BLS International Services Limited; *Int'l*, pg. 1067
BLS INTERNATIONAL (THAILAND) LTD.—See BLS International Services Limited; *Int'l*, pg. 1066
BLS LIMOUSINE SERVICE; *U.S. Private*, pg. 585
B.L. SPILLE CONSTRUCTION, INC.; *U.S. Private*, pg. 421
BLT BAULOGISTIK UND TRANSPORT GMBH—See STRABAG SE; *Int'l*, pg. 7229
BLT BRANDENBURGER LANDTECHNIK GMBH—See Claas KGaA mbH; *Int'l*, pg. 1641
BLT BURGER (HK) LIMITED—See Life Concepts Holdings Limited; *Int'l*, pg. 4492
B&L TELEPHONE LLC—See Fortran Corporation; *U.S. Public*, pg. 872
BLT ENTERPRISES; *U.S. Private*, pg. 585
BLU3, INC.—See Brownie's Marine Group, Inc.; *U.S. Public*, pg. 403
BLU-ALLIANCE LIFESCIENCE; *U.S. Private*, pg. 585
BLU A/S—See Bertelsmann SE & Co. KGaA; *Int'l*, pg. 994
BLUBECKERS LIMITED—See Apollo Global Management, Inc.; *U.S. Public*, pg. 164
BLUBERI GAMING TECHNOLOGIES INC.—See Callidus Capital Corporation; *Int'l*, pg. 1265
BLUBUZZARD, INC.; *U.S. Public*, pg. 363
BLUCHER (AUSTRALIA) PTY. LTD.—See E&A Limited; *Int'l*, pg. 2246
BLUCHER SWEDEN AB—See Watts Water Technologies, Inc.; *U.S. Public*, pg. 2337
BLUCHER UK LTD—See Watts Water Technologies, Inc.; *U.S. Public*, pg. 2337
BLUCOM VINA CO., LTD.—See Bluecom Co., Ltd.; *Int'l*, pg. 1071
BLUDAU FABRICATION INC.; *U.S. Private*, pg. 585
BLU DOT DESIGN & MANUFACTURING, INC.; *U.S. Private*, pg. 585
BLUDOT INC.—See 3 Rivers Capital, LLC; *U.S. Private*, pg. 7
BLUDWORTH MARINE, LLC; *U.S. Private*, pg. 585
BLUE1USA, LLC; *U.S. Private*, pg. 596
BLUE4IT PROFESSIONALS B.V.—See adesso SE; *Int'l*, pg. 144
BLUE ACORN, LLC—See Beringer Capital; *Int'l*, pg. 981
BLUE AEROSPACE LLC—See HEICO Corporation; *U.S. Public*, pg. 1021
BLUEAIR AB—See Unilever PLC; *Int'l*, pg. 8044
BLUEAIR ASIA LIMITED—See Unilever PLC; *Int'l*, pg. 8044
BLUEAIR INDIA PVT. LIMITED—See Unilever PLC; *Int'l*, pg. 8044
BLUEAIR SHANGHAI SALES CO. LIMITED—See Unilever PLC; *Int'l*, pg. 8044
BLUEALLY TECHNOLOGY SOLUTIONS, LLC—See Source Capital, LLC; *U.S. Private*, pg. 3717
BLUE ANT MEDIA, INC.; *Int'l*, pg. 1067
BLUE ANT MEDIA NZ LIMITED; *Int'l*, pg. 1067
BLUEAPPLE DENTAL & IMPLANT TEAM LIMITED—See The British United Provident Association Limited; *Int'l*, pg. 7629
BLUE APRON HOLDINGS, INC.—See Wonder Group, Inc.; *U.S. Private*, pg. 4556
BLUE ARMOR SECURITY SERVICES, INC.; *U.S. Private*, pg. 585
BLUE ARROW LTD.—See HFBG Holding B.V.; *Int'l*, pg. 3374
BLUE ARROW RECRUITMENT SOLUTIONS LTD.—See HFBG Holding B.V.; *Int'l*, pg. 3374
BLUE & ASSOCIATES, INC.; *U.S. Private*, pg. 585
BLUE ATLANTIC TRADING—See Oceana Group Limited; *Int'l*, pg. 5517
BLUE BAKER; *U.S. Private*, pg. 585
BLUEBAND FINANCING LIMITED; *Int'l*, pg. 1070
BLUEBAY ASSET MANAGEMENT LLP—See Royal Bank of Canada; *Int'l*, pg. 6410
BLUEBAY ASSET MANAGEMENT (SERVICES) LTD.—See Royal Bank of Canada; *Int'l*, pg. 6410
BLUE BAY TRAVEL GROUP LTD.—See Lloyds Banking Group plc; *Int'l*, pg. 4536
BLUE BEACON INTERNATIONAL, INC.; *U.S. Private*, pg. 585
BLUE BEACON TRUCK WUSHEA—See Blue Beacon International, Inc.; *U.S. Private*, pg. 585
BLUEBEAM AB—See Nemetschek SE; *Int'l*, pg. 5194
BLUEBEAM GMBH—See Nemetschek SE; *Int'l*, pg. 5194
BLUEBEAM LIMITED UK, LTD.—See Nemetschek SE; *Int'l*, pg. 5194
BLUE BELL ADVERTISING ASSOCIATES; *U.S. Private*, pg. 585
BLUE BELL BIO-MEDICAL—See Kennedy Manufacturing Company; *U.S. Private*, pg. 2285
BLUE BELL CREAMERIES, L.P.; *U.S. Private*, pg. 585
BLUE BELL CREAMERIES—See Blue Bell Creameries, L.P.; *U.S. Private*, pg. 585
BLUE BELL CREAMERIES—See Blue Bell Creameries, L.P.; *U.S. Private*, pg. 585
BLUEBELL ENERGY SUPPLY LIMITED—See Inspired PLC; *Int'l*, pg. 3720
BLUEBELL SAWMILLS LIMITED—See Grafton Group plc; *Int'l*, pg. 3050
BLUE BENEFITS CONSULTING INC.; *U.S. Private*, pg. 585
BLUEBERRIES MEDICAL CORP.; *Int'l*, pg. 1070
BLUEBERRY FORD MERCURY INC.; *U.S. Private*, pg. 596
BLUEBERRY HILL HEALTHCARE NURSING HOME—See Apollo Global Management, Inc.; *U.S. Public*, pg. 156
BLUEBERRY THERAPEUTICS LIMITED—See China Medical System Holdings Ltd.; *Int'l*, pg. 1518
BLUEBET HOLDINGS LTD.; *Int'l*, pg. 1070
BLUE BIOFUELS, INC.; *U.S. Public*, pg. 364
BLUEBIRD BIO GREECE SINGLE MEMBER, L.L.C.—See bluebird bio, Inc.; *U.S. Public*, pg. 365
BLUEBIRD BIO, INC.; *U.S. Public*, pg. 365
BLUEBIRD CONTRACTING SERVICES—See Trotter & Morton Ltd.; *Int'l*, pg. 7939
BLUE BIRD CORPORATION—See American Securities LLC; *U.S. Private*, pg. 247
BLUEBIRD EXPRESS, LLC—See Cryoport, Inc.; *U.S. Public*, pg. 600
BLUEBIRD FOODS LIMITED—See PepsiCo, Inc.; *U.S. Public*, pg. 1668
BLUEBIRD FOODS LIMITED—See PepsiCo, Inc.; *U.S. Public*, pg. 1668
BLUEBIRD INTERACTIVE; *U.S. Private*, pg. 596
BLUEBIRD NETWORK, LLC—See Macquarie Group Limited; *Int'l*, pg. 4628
BLUE BLENDS (INDIA) LIMITED - DENIM DIVISION—See Blue Blends (India) Limited; *Int'l*, pg. 1067
BLUE BLENDS (INDIA) LIMITED; *Int'l*, pg. 1067
BLUEBLOOD VENTURES LIMITED; *Int'l*, pg. 1070
BLUEBONNET ELECTRIC CO-OP, INC.; *U.S. Private*, pg. 596
BLUEBONNET LIFE INSURANCE COMPANY—See Blue Cross & Blue Shield of Mississippi; *U.S. Private*, pg. 587
BLUEBONNET NUTRITION, CORP.; *U.S. Private*, pg. 596
BLUEBONNET PROPERTIES, LLC—See Security National Financial Corporation; *U.S. Public*, pg. 1856
BLUE BOTTLE COFFEE, INC.—See Nestle S.A.; *Int'l*, pg. 5202
BLUE BOX AIR ENGINEERING (INDIA) PVT. LTD—See Investment AB Latour; *Int'l*, pg. 3783
BLUE BOX GROUP S.R.l—See Investment AB Latour; *Int'l*, pg. 3783
BLUE BUFFALO CO., LTD.—See General Mills, Inc.; *U.S. Public*, pg. 921
BLUE BUFFALO COMPANY, LTD.—See General Mills, Inc.; *U.S. Public*, pg. 921
BLUE BUG INC.—See Clayton, Dubilier & Rice, LLC; *U.S. Private*, pg. 930
BLUE BYTE GMBH—See Ubisoft Entertainment S.A.; *Int'l*, pg. 8003
BLUE BYTE GMBH—See Ubisoft Entertainment S.A.; *Int'l*, pg. 8003
BLUE CABOOSE INC.; *U.S. Private*, pg. 585
BLUE CALYPSO, INC.; *U.S. Public*, pg. 364
BLUE CANOE BODYWEAR; *U.S. Private*, pg. 585
BLUE CANOPY GROUP, LLC—See Jacobs Engineering Group, Inc.; *U.S. Public*, pg. 1183
BLUE CANOPY, INC.; *U.S. Private*, pg. 585
BLUE CANYON HOLDINGS AB—See GTCR LLC; *U.S. Private*, pg. 1804
BLUE CANYON PARTNERS, INC.; *U.S. Private*, pg. 585
BLUE CANYON TECHNOLOGIES LLC; *U.S. Private*, pg. 586
BLUE CAP AG; *Int'l*, pg. 1067
BLUE CAPITAL EUROPA IMMOBILIEN GMBH & CO. ACHTE OBJEKTE GROBRITANNIEN KG—See UniCredit S.p.A.; *Int'l*, pg. 8041
BLUECARE AG—See Zur Rose Group AG; *Int'l*, pg. 8696

BLUE CAP AG

BLUE CARE NETWORK OF MICHIGAN—See Blue Cross Blue Shield of Michigan; *U.S. Private*, pg. 587
BLUE CASA COMMUNICATIONS, INC.; *U.S. Private*, pg. 586
BLUE CAST DENIM CO. INC.; *U.S. Private*, pg. 586
BLUECAT JAPAN CO., LTD.—See Madison Dearborn Partners, LLC; *U.S. Private*, pg. 2540
BLUECAT NETWORKS, INC.—See Madison Dearborn Partners, LLC; *U.S. Private*, pg. 2540
BLUECAVA, INC.; *U.S. Private*, pg. 596
BLUECHARGE PTE. LTD.—See TotalEnergies SE; *Int'l*, pg. 7835
BLUECHIP LIMITED; *Int'l*, pg. 1070
BLUECHIP AGENTUR FOR PUBLIC RELATIONS & STRATEGY GMBH.—See Dentsu Group Inc.; *Int'l*, pg. 2035
BLUE CHIP BROADCASTING, LTD.—See Urban One, Inc.; *U.S. Public*, pg. 2265
BLUE CHIP CAPITAL GROUP, INC.; *U.S. Private*, pg. 586
BLUE CHIP CASINO, LLC—See Boyd Gaming Corporation; *U.S. Public*, pg. 377
BLUE CHIP INDIA LTD.; *Int'l*, pg. 1067
BLUECHIP STOCKSPIN LIMITED; *Int'l*, pg. 1070
BLUE CHIP SURGICAL CENTER PARTNERS, LLC—See Nueterra Capital Management, LLC; *U.S. Private*, pg. 2972
BLUE CHIP TEX INDUSTRIES LTD.; *Int'l*, pg. 1067
BLUE CHIP VENTURE COMPANY, LTD; *U.S. Private*, pg. 586
BLUE CHOICE HEALTH PLAN—See Blue Cross & Blue Shield of South Carolina; *U.S. Private*, pg. 587
BLUECIELO ECM SOLUTIONS B.V.—See Fortive Corporation; *U.S. Public*, pg. 870
BLUE CIRCLE BV—See Bertelsmann SE & Co. KGaA; *Int'l*, pg. 994
BLUE CIRCLE ENGINEERING LIMITED—See HELLENiQ ENERGY Holdings S.A; *Int'l*, pg. 3334
BLUE CIRCLE SERVICES LIMITED; *Int'l*, pg. 1067
BLUECITY HOLDINGS LIMITED—See Newborn Town, Inc.; *Int'l*, pg. 5233
BLUECITY UK LTD.—See Financiere de L'Odet; *Int'l*, pg. 2666
BLUECLAW MEDIA LTD.—See XLMedia PLC; *Int'l*, pg. 8536
BLUE C, LLC—See Comfort Systems USA, Inc.; *U.S. Public*, pg. 543
BLUE CLOUD SOFTECH SOLUTIONS LTD.; *Int'l*, pg. 1067
BLUE CLOVER; *U.S. Private*, pg. 586
BLUE COAST HOTELS LIMITED; *Int'l*, pg. 1067
BLUE COD TECHNOLOGIES, INC.; *U.S. Private*, pg. 586
BLUE COLIBRI AG; *Int'l*, pg. 1067
BLUE & CO. LLC; *U.S. Private*, pg. 585
BLUECOM CO., LTD.; *Int'l*, pg. 1071
BLUE COMPACTOR SERVICES, LLC—See Waste Connections, Inc.; *Int'l*, pg. 8352
BLUE-CON CONSTRUCTION; *Int'l*, pg. 1070
BLUE CONTINENT PRODUCTS (PTY) LTD.—See Oceana Group Limited; *Int'l*, pg. 5517
BLUE CORONA; *U.S. Private*, pg. 586
BLUECOTTON, INC.; *U.S. Private*, pg. 596
BLUE CREEK INVESTMENT PARTNERS; *U.S. Private*, pg. 586
BLUE CREEK WIND FARM, LLC—See Iberdrola, S.A.; *Int'l*, pg. 3570
BLUECREST CAPITAL FINANCE CORP.; *U.S. Private*, pg. 596
BLUE CROSS (ASIA-PACIFIC) INSURANCE LIMITED—See The Bank of East Asia, Limited; *Int'l*, pg. 7615
BLUE CROSS & BLUE SHIELD ASSOCIATION GOVERNMENT RELATIONS—See Blue Cross & Blue Shield Association; *U.S. Private*, pg. 586
BLUE CROSS & BLUE SHIELD ASSOCIATION; *U.S. Private*, pg. 586
BLUE CROSS BLUE SHIELD HEALTHCARE PLAN OF GEORGIA, INC.—See Elevance Health, Inc.; *U.S. Public*, pg. 729
BLUE CROSS & BLUE SHIELD OF ALABAMA; *U.S. Private*, pg. 586
BLUE CROSS & BLUE SHIELD OF ARIZONA, INC.; *U.S. Private*, pg. 586
BLUE CROSS & BLUE SHIELD OF FLORIDA, INC.—See GuideWell Mutual Holding Corporation; *U.S. Private*, pg. 1813
BLUE CROSS & BLUE SHIELD OF ILLINOIS—See Health Care Service Corporation; *U.S. Private*, pg. 1892
BLUE CROSS & BLUE SHIELD OF KANSAS CITY, INC.; *U.S. Private*, pg. 586
BLUE CROSS & BLUE SHIELD OF MASSACHUSETTS, INC.; *U.S. Private*, pg. 587
BLUE CROSS BLUE SHIELD OF MICHIGAN FOUNDATION—See Blue Cross Blue Shield of Michigan; *U.S. Private*, pg. 588
BLUE CROSS BLUE SHIELD OF MICHIGAN; *U.S. Private*, pg. 587
BLUE CROSS & BLUE SHIELD OF MISSISSIPPI; *U.S. Private*, pg. 587

BLUE CROSS & BLUE SHIELD OF NEBRASKA; *U.S. Private*, pg. 587
BLUE CROSS & BLUE SHIELD OF NEW MEXICO—See Health Care Service Corporation; *U.S. Private*, pg. 1892
BLUE CROSS & BLUE SHIELD OF NORTH CAROLINA INC; *U.S. Private*, pg. 587
BLUE CROSS & BLUE SHIELD OF RHODE ISLAND; *U.S. Private*, pg. 587
BLUE CROSS & BLUE SHIELD OF SOUTH CAROLINA; *U.S. Private*, pg. 587
BLUE CROSS & BLUE SHIELD OF TEXAS, INC.—See Health Care Service Corporation; *U.S. Private*, pg. 1892
BLUE CROSS BLUE SHIELD OF WISCONSIN—See Elevance Health, Inc.; *U.S. Public*, pg. 729
BLUE CROSS-BLUE SHIELD WYOMING; *U.S. Private*, pg. 588
BLUE CROSS COMPLETE OF MICHIGAN; *U.S. Private*, pg. 588
BLUE CROSS LABORATORIES; *U.S. Private*, pg. 588
BLUE CROSS LIFE & HEALTH INSURANCE COMPANY—See Elevance Health, Inc.; *U.S. Public*, pg. 729
BLUE CROSS OF CALIFORNIA—See Elevance Health, Inc.; *U.S. Public*, pg. 729
BLUE CROWN B.V.—See Air France-KLM S.A.; *Int'l*, pg. 236
BLUE CUBE BELGIUM BVBA—See Olin Corporation; *U.S. Public*, pg. 1570
BLUE CUBE CHEMICALS FZE—See Olin Corporation; *U.S. Public*, pg. 1570
BLUE CUBE COLOMBIA LTDA.—See Olin Corporation; *U.S. Public*, pg. 1570
BLUE CUBE PORTABLE COLD STORES LIMITED—See Turner & Co. (Glasgow) Limited; *Int'l*, pg. 7978
BLUECUB SAS—See Financiere de L'Odet; *Int'l*, pg. 2666
BLUECURRENT HONG KONG—See Omnicom Group Inc.; *U.S. Public*, pg. 1583
BLUECURRENT JAPAN—See Omnicom Group Inc.; *U.S. Public*, pg. 1583
BLUE DAISY MEDIA; *U.S. Private*, pg. 588
BLUE DANUBE INCORPORATED; *U.S. Private*, pg. 588
BLUE DART AVIATION LTD.—See Deutsche Post AG; *Int'l*, pg. 2071
BLUE DART EXPRESS LIMITED; *Int'l*, pg. 1067
BLUE DECK CO., LTD.—See Ananda Development Public Company Limited; *Int'l*, pg. 447
BLUE DELTA CAPITAL PARTNERS LLC; *U.S. Private*, pg. 588
BLUE DIAMOND GROWERS - GLOBAL INGREDIENTS DIVISION—See Blue Diamond Growers; *U.S. Private*, pg. 588
BLUE DIAMOND GROWERS; *U.S. Private*, pg. 588
BLUE DIAMOND INDUSTRIES LLC—See Hexatronic Group AB; *Int'l*, pg. 3370
BLUE DIAMOND RESORTS, INC—See Sunwing Travel Group, Inc.; *Int'l*, pg. 7331
BLUE DIAMONDS JEWELLERY WORLDWIDE PLC—See Hayleys PLC; *Int'l*, pg. 3291
BLUE DIAMOND VENTURES, INC.; *U.S. Public*, pg. 364
BLUE DINOSAUR PTY. LTD.—See Forbidden Foods Limited; *Int'l*, pg. 2729
BLUE DOG BUSINESS SERVICES, LLC—See Fortis Payment Systems LLC; *U.S. Private*, pg. 1576
BLUE DOG LLC—See Equity CommonWealth; *U.S. Public*, pg. 790
BLUE DOLPHIN ENERGY COMPANY; *U.S. Public*, pg. 364
BLUE DOLPHIN EXPLORATION COMPANY—See Blue Dolphin Energy Company; *U.S. Public*, pg. 364
BLUE DOLPHIN PETROLEUM COMPANY—See Blue Dolphin Energy Company; *U.S. Public*, pg. 364
BLUE DOLPHIN SERVICES CO.—See Blue Dolphin Energy Company; *U.S. Public*, pg. 364
BLUEDON INFORMATION SECURITY TECHNOLOGIES CO., LTD.; *Int'l*, pg. 1071
BLUEDOOR, LLC—See Tophatmonocle Corp.; *Int'l*, pg. 7816
BLUEDOT COMMUNICATIONS; *U.S. Private*, pg. 596
BLUEDOT MEDICAL, INC.; *U.S. Private*, pg. 596
BLUE EAGLE LITHIUM INC.; *U.S. Private*, pg. 588
BLUE EARTH DIAGNOSTICS LIMITED—See Syncona Ltd.; *Int'l*, pg. 7382
BLUE EARTH FOODS LIMITED—See Seafresh Industry Public Company Limited; *Int'l*, pg. 6663
BLUE EARTH JAPAN CO., LTD.—See Senko Group Holdings Co., Ltd.; *Int'l*, pg. 6709
BLUE EARTH-NICOLLET COOPERATIVE ELECTRIC ASSOCIATION; *U.S. Private*, pg. 588
BLUE EARTH VALLEY COMMUNICATIONS; *U.S. Private*, pg. 588
BLUE EARTH VALLEY COMMUNICATIONS—See Blue Earth Valley Communications; *U.S. Private*, pg. 588
BLUE ENERGY LIMITED; *Int'l*, pg. 1068
BLUE ENGINEERING S.R.L.—See CRRC Corporation Limited; *Int'l*, pg. 1858
BLUE ENGINE MESSAGE & MEDIA, LLC; *U.S. Private*, pg. 588

CORPORATE AFFILIATIONS

BLUE ENSIGN TECHNOLOGIES LIMITED; *Int'l*, pg. 1068
BLUE ENTERTAINMENT LTD.—See Swisscom AG; *Int'l*, pg. 7373
BLUE EQUITY, LLC; *U.S. Private*, pg. 588
BLUE EXPRESS INTL S.A.—See LATAM Airlines Group S.A.; *Int'l*, pg. 4422
BLUEFACE ITALIA S.R.L.—See Comcast Corporation; *U.S. Public*, pg. 537
BLUEFACE LTD.—See Comcast Corporation; *U.S. Public*, pg. 537
BLUE FALLS MANUFACTURING LTD.; *Int'l*, pg. 1068
BLUEFIELD CLINIC COMPANY, LLC—See Community Health Systems, Inc.; *U.S. Public*, pg. 551
BLUEFIELD HBP MEDICAL GROUP, LLC—See Community Health Systems, Inc.; *U.S. Public*, pg. 551
BLUEFIELD HOSPITAL COMPANY, LLC—See Princeton Community Hospital; *U.S. Private*, pg. 3264
BLUEFIELD SOLAR INCOME FUND; *Int'l*, pg. 1071
BLUEFIN ADVISORY SERVICES LIMITED—See AXA S.A.; *Int'l*, pg. 759
BLUE FINANCIAL COMMUNICATION S.P.A.; *Int'l*, pg. 1068
BLUEFIN GROUP LIMITED—See AXA S.A.; *Int'l*, pg. 758
BLUEFIN IMAGING GROUP, LLC—See BVK, Inc.; *U.S. Private*, pg. 700
BLUEFIN, LLC—See O2 Investment Partners, LLC; *U.S. Private*, pg. 2982
BLUEFIN PAYMENT SYSTEMS; *U.S. Private*, pg. 596
BLUEFIN RESOURCES PTY. LIMITED—See Bain Capital, LP; *U.S. Private*, pg. 433
BLUEFIN SEAFOOD CORP; *U.S. Private*, pg. 596
BLUEFIN SOLUTIONS LTD.—See Larsen & Toubro Limited; *Int'l*, pg. 4419
BLUEFIN UNDERWRITING LIMITED—See Marsh & McLennan Companies, Inc.; *U.S. Public*, pg. 1374
BLUEFIRE EQUIPMENT CORP.; *U.S. Private*, pg. 596
BLUEFIRE RENEWABLES, INC.; *U.S. Private*, pg. 365
BLUE FLAME PROPANE, INC.—See Foster Blue Water Oil, LLC; *U.S. Private*, pg. 1578
BLUE FLAME THINKING; *U.S. Private*, pg. 588
BLUE FLINT ETHANOL LLC—See Great River Energy; *U.S. Private*, pg. 1767
BLUEFLY, INC.—See Clearlake Capital Group, L.P.; *U.S. Private*, pg. 933
BLUEFOCUS INTELLIGENT COMMUNICATIONS GROUP CO., LTD.; *Int'l*, pg. 1071
BLUEFOCUS INTERNATIONAL LIMITED—See Bluefocus Intelligent Communications Group Co., Ltd.; *Int'l*, pg. 1071
BLUE FORCE TECHNOLOGIES, INC.—See Anduril Industries, Inc.; *U.S. Private*, pg. 280
BLUEFORS OY—See DevCo Partners Oy; *Int'l*, pg. 2086
BLUE FOUNDRY BANCORP; *U.S. Public*, pg. 364
BLUE FOUNTAIN MEDIA INC.—See China Electronics Corporation; *Int'l*, pg. 1499
BLUE FOX TACKLE CO.—See Rapala VMC Oyj; *Int'l*, pg. 6210
BLUEFRONT B.V.—See adesso SE; *Int'l*, pg. 144
BLUE FUNNEL ANGOLA—See Albert Ballin KG; *Int'l*, pg. 294
BLUEGAME S.R.L.—See Sanlorenzo S.p.A.; *Int'l*, pg. 6546
BLUE GECKO, LLC; *U.S. Private*, pg. 588
BLUEGEM CAPITAL PARTNERS LLP; *Int'l*, pg. 1071
BLUEGLASS INTERACTIVE AG—See BlueGlass Interactive, Inc.; *U.S. Private*, pg. 596
BLUEGLASS INTERACTIVE, INC.; *U.S. Private*, pg. 596
BLUEGLASS INTERACTIVE UK LTD.—See BlueGlass Interactive, Inc.; *U.S. Private*, pg. 596
BLUE GLOBAL MEDIA; *U.S. Private*, pg. 588
BLUE & GOLD FLEET INC.—See PIER 39 L.P.; *U.S. Private*, pg. 3178
BLUEGOLF, LLC—See Clubessential Holdings, LLC; *U.S. Private*, pg. 949
BLUE GOOSE GROWERS, LLC; *U.S. Private*, pg. 589
BLUE-GRACE LOGISTICS, LLC; *U.S. Private*, pg. 596
BLUEGRANITE, INC.—See Gryphon Investors, LLC; *U.S. Private*, pg. 1798
BLUEGRASS COCA COLA BOTTLING COMPANY—See The Coca-Cola Company; *U.S. Public*, pg. 2064
BLUE GRASS COMMUNITY FOUNDATION; *U.S. Private*, pg. 589
BLUEGRASS DAIRY AND FOOD, INC.—See Dubilier & Company, Inc.; *U.S. Private*, pg. 1283
BLUE GRASS DAIRY & FOOD LLC; *U.S. Private*, pg. 589
BLUE-GRASS ENERGY COOPERATIVE; *U.S. Private*, pg. 596
BLUEGRASS MATERIALS COMPANY, LLC—See Martin Marietta Materials, Inc.; *U.S. Public*, pg. 1389
BLUEGRASS.ORG, INC.; *U.S. Private*, pg. 597
BLUEGRASS OXYGEN, INC.—See AdaptHealth Corp.; *U.S. Public*, pg. 38
BLUE GRASS PROVISION COMPANY; *U.S. Private*, pg. 589
BLUE GRASS SHOWS, INC.; *U.S. Private*, pg. 589
BLUEGRASS SUPPLY CHAIN SERVICES; *U.S. Private*, pg. 596
BLUEGRASS TOOL WAREHOUSE INC.; *U.S. Private*, pg. 596

COMPANY NAME INDEX

BLUEGREEN/BIG CEDAR VACATIONS, LLC—See Hilton Grand Vacations Inc.; *U.S. Public*, pg. 1039
BLUEGREEN COMMUNITIES, LLC—See Hilton Grand Vacations Inc.; *U.S. Public*, pg. 1039
BLUEGREEN VACATIONS CORPORATION—See Hilton Grand Vacations Inc.; *U.S. Public*, pg. 1039
BLUEGREEN VACATIONS HOLDING CORPORATION—See Hilton Grand Vacations Inc.; *U.S. Public*, pg. 1039
BLUEGREEN VACATIONS UNLIMITED, INC.—See Hilton Grand Vacations Inc.; *U.S. Public*, pg. 1039
BLUE & GREY TRANSPORTATION—See US 1 Industries, Inc.; *U.S. Private*, pg. 4317
BLUEGROUND US INC; *U.S. Private*, pg. 597
BLUEHALO, LLC—See Arlington Capital Partners LLC; *U.S. Private*, pg. 327
BLUEHARBOR BANK; *U.S. Public*, pg. 365
BLUE HARBOR RESORT & CONVENTION CENTER—See Centerbridge Partners, L.P.; *U.S. Private*, pg. 814
BLUE HARBOUR GROUP, L.P.; *U.S. Private*, pg. 589
BLUE HARVEST FISHERIES, LLC—See COFRA Holding AG; *Int'l*, pg. 1694
BLUE HARVEST FOODS, LLC - FLEET DIVISION—See COFRA Holding AG; *Int'l*, pg. 1694
BLUE HARVEST FOODS, LLC - HYGRADE DIVISION—See COFRA Holding AG; *Int'l*, pg. 1694
BLUE HARVEST FOODS, LLC—See COFRA Holding AG; *Int'l*, pg. 1694
BLUE HAT INTERACTIVE ENTERTAINMENT TECHNOLOGY; *Int'l*, pg. 1068
BLUE HAVEN POOLS NATIONAL INC.; *U.S. Private*, pg. 589
BLUE HERON BIOTECH, LLC—See Eurofins Scientific S.E.; *Int'l*, pg. 2535
BLUE HIGHWAY SERVICE K.K.—See Mitsui O.S.K. Lines, Ltd.; *Int'l*, pg. 4989
BLUE HILL DATA SERVICES, INC.; *U.S. Private*, pg. 589
BLUE HOLDING S.P.A.—See Green Holding S.p.A.; *Int'l*, pg. 3071
BLUEHONE SECURED ASSETS LIMITED; *Int'l*, pg. 1071
BLUE HORIZON SOFTWARE HOLDINGS LLC; *U.S. Private*, pg. 589
BLUE HORSESHOE SOLUTIONS, INC.; *U.S. Private*, pg. 589
BLUEHOST INC.—See Clearlake Capital Group, L.P.; *U.S. Private*, pg. 934
BLUEHOST INC.—See Siris Capital Group, LLC; *U.S. Private*, pg. 3673
BLUE HUB VENTURES B.V.—See Anadolu Efes Biracilik ve Malt Sanayii A.S.; *Int'l*, pg. 445
BLUE ICEBERG, LLC; *U.S. Private*, pg. 589
BLUE INC.; *Int'l*, pg. 1068
BLUEINGREEN, LLC—See Chart Industries, Inc.; *U.S. Public*, pg. 481
BLUE INNOVATION CO., LTD.; *Int'l*, pg. 1068
BLUE INSURANCE LIMITED—See Hillhouse Investment Management Limited; *Int'l*, pg. 3393
BLUE INTERACTIVE AGENCY; *U.S. Private*, pg. 589
BLUE INTERACTIVE MARKETING PTE. LTD.—See WPP plc; *Int'l*, pg. 8483
BLUE INTERACTIVE MARKETING—See WPP plc; *Int'l*, pg. 8483
BLUE ISLAND CLINIC COMPANY, LLC—See Quorum Health Corporation; *U.S. Private*, pg. 3329
BLUE ISLAND HOME CARE SERVICES, LLC—See Community Health Systems, Inc.; *U.S. Public*, pg. 551
BLUE ISLAND PLC; *Int'l*, pg. 1068
BLUEJAY CAPITAL PARTNERS, LLC; *U.S. Private*, pg. 597
BLUE JAY CONSULTING, LLC—See Koninklijke Philips N.V.; *Int'l*, pg. 4269
BLUEJAY DIAGNOSTICS, INC.; *U.S. Public*, pg. 365
BLUEJAY HOLDINGS LLC—See PepsiCo, Inc.; *U.S. Public*, pg. 1668
BLUEJAY MINING PLC; *Int'l*, pg. 1071
BLUE JEANS NETWORK, INC.—See Verizon Communications Inc.; *U.S. Public*, pg. 2284
BLUE JET HEALTHCARE LIMITED; *Int'l*, pg. 1068
BLUE KAI, INC.—See Oracle Corporation; *U.S. Public*, pg. 1610
BLUE KEY TECHNOLOGY LLC—See GadellNet Consulting Services, LLC; *U.S. Private*, pg. 1633
BLUEKNIGHT ENERGY PARTNERS, L.P.—See Ergon, Inc.; *U.S. Private*, pg. 1418
BLUE LABEL DISTRIBUTION PROPRIETARY LIMITED—See Blue Label Telecoms Limited; *Int'l*, pg. 1068
BLUE LABEL MEXICO S.A. DE C.V.—See Grupo Bimbo, S.A.B. de C.V.; *Int'l*, pg. 3123
BLUE LABEL TELECOMS LIMITED; *Int'l*, pg. 1068
BLUE LAGOON CRUISES HOLDINGS PTE LIMITED—See Fijian Holdings Limited; *Int'l*, pg. 2662
BLUE LAGOON RESOURCES, INC.; *Int'l*, pg. 1068
BLUE LAKE FINE ARTS CAMP; *U.S. Private*, pg. 589
BLUELAKE MINERAL AB; *Int'l*, pg. 1072
BLUELIB SAS—See Financiere de L'Odet; *Int'l*, pg. 2666
BLUELIFE LTD.; *Int'l*, pg. 1072
BLUELIGHT GMBH—See Per Aarsleff Holding A/S; *Int'l*, pg. 5795
BLUELINEA SA; *Int'l*, pg. 1072
BLUE LINE DISTRIBUTING—See Ilitch Holdings, Inc.; *U.S. Private*, pg. 2042
BLUELINE PARTNERS, LLC; *U.S. Private*, pg. 597
BLUE LINE PROTECTION GROUP, INC.; *U.S. Public*, pg. 364
BLUELINE RENTAL, LLC—See United Rentals, Inc.; *U.S. Public*, pg. 2235
BLUELINE RENTAL—See The Pape Group, Inc.; *U.S. Private*, pg. 4090
BLUELINE; *U.S. Private*, pg. 597
BLUELINK INTERNATIONAL AUSTRALIA PTY. LTD.—See Air France-KLM S.A.; *Int'l*, pg. 237
BLUELINK INTERNATIONAL CHILE SPA.—See Air France-KLM S.A.; *Int'l*, pg. 237
BLUELINK INTERNATIONAL CZ S. R. O.—See Air France-KLM S.A.; *Int'l*, pg. 237
BLUELINK INTERNATIONAL STRASBOURG SA—See Air France-KLM S.A.; *Int'l*, pg. 237
BLUELINK—See Air France-KLM S.A.; *Int'l*, pg. 237
BLUELINX BUILDING PRODUCTS CANADA LTD.—See Cerberus Capital Management, L.P.; *U.S. Private*, pg. 837
BLUELINX CORPORATION—See Cerberus Capital Management, L.P.; *U.S. Private*, pg. 837
BLUELINX FLORIDA LP—See Cerberus Capital Management, L.P.; *U.S. Private*, pg. 837
BLUELINX HOLDINGS, INC.—See Cerberus Capital Management, L.P.; *U.S. Private*, pg. 837
BLUE LNG SP. Z O.O—See Unimot SA; *Int'l*, pg. 8050
BLUE LOTUS COMMUNICATIONS (BANGALORE)—See Blue Lotus Communications Consultancy; *Int'l*, pg. 1068
BLUE LOTUS COMMUNICATIONS (CHENNAI)—See Blue Lotus Communications Consultancy; *Int'l*, pg. 1068
BLUE LOTUS COMMUNICATIONS CONSULTANCY; *Int'l*, pg. 1068
BLUE LOTUS COMMUNICATIONS (HYDERBAD)—See Blue Lotus Communications Consultancy; *Int'l*, pg. 1068
BLUE LOTUS COMMUNICATIONS (KOLKATA)—See Blue Lotus Communications Consultancy; *Int'l*, pg. 1068
BLUE LOTUS COMMUNICATIONS (NEW DELHI)—See Blue Lotus Communications Consultancy; *Int'l*, pg. 1068
BLUE LOTUS COMMUNICATIONS (PUNE)—See Blue Lotus Communications Consultancy; *Int'l*, pg. 1069
BLUE LYNX MEDIA, LLC—See Tribune Publishing Company; *U.S. Private*, pg. 4227
BLUELY SAS—See Financiere de L'Odet; *Int'l*, pg. 2666
BLUE MAN PRODUCTIONS, INC.—See TPG Capital, L.P.; *U.S. Public*, pg. 2169
BLUE MARBLE BRANDS, LLC—See United Natural Foods, Inc.; *U.S. Public*, pg. 2231
BLUE MARBLE MEDIA INC.; *U.S. Private*, pg. 589
BLUE MAX BANNER LIMITED; *Int'l*, pg. 1069
BLUE MEDIUM, INC.; *U.S. Private*, pg. 589
BLUEMERCURY, INC.—See Macy's, Inc.; *U.S. Public*, pg. 1353
BLUE META S.P.A.—See Ascopiave S.p.A.; *Int'l*, pg. 603
BLUE MICROPHONES, LLC—See Transom Capital Group, LLC; *U.S. Private*, pg. 4209
BLUE MOON GROUP HOLDINGS LIMITED; *Int'l*, pg. 1069
BLUE MOONLIGHT PROPERTIES 215 (PTY) LTD—See Miranda Minerals Holdings Limited; *Int'l*, pg. 4918
BLUE MOON METALS INC.; *Int'l*, pg. 1069
BLUE MOON WORKS, INC.; *U.S. Private*, pg. 589
BLUE MOOSE OF BOULDER, INC.—See Sartori Company; *U.S. Private*, pg. 3551
BLUE MOUNTAIN AGRI SUPPORT, INC.—See AGCO Corporation; *U.S. Public*, pg. 58
BLUEMOUNTAIN CAPITAL MANAGEMENT, LLC—See Affiliated Managers Group, Inc.; *U.S. Public*, pg. 54
BLUEMOUNTAIN CAPITAL PARTNERS (LONDON) LLP—See Affiliated Managers Group, Inc.; *U.S. Public*, pg. 54
BLUE MOUNTAIN CHRYSLER; *Int'l*, pg. 1069
BLUEMOUNTAIN CLO MANAGEMENT, LLC—See Assured Guaranty Ltd.; *Int'l*, pg. 650
BLUE MOUNTAIN ECO TOURS INC.; *Int'l*, pg. 1069
BLUE MOUNTAIN EQUIPMENT RENTAL CORPORATION—See United Rentals, Inc.; *U.S. Public*, pg. 2235
BLUE MOUNTAIN MIDSTREAM LLC—See Citizen Energy Operating LLC; *U.S. Private*, pg. 902
BLUE MOUNTAIN POWER COMPANY INC.,—See Alternative Earth Resources Inc.; *U.S. Public*, pg. 391
BLUE MOUNTAIN PRODUCTION CO.—See Oil-Dri Corporation of America; *U.S. Public*, pg. 1565
BLUE MOUNTAIN RESORTS LIMITED PARTNERSHIP—See KSL Capital Partners, LLC; *U.S. Private*, pg. 2354
BLUE MOUNTAINS TRANSIT PTY. LTD.—See ComfortDelGro Corporation Limited; *Int'l*, pg. 1713
BLUE MOUNTAIN WALLCOVERINGS, INC.; *Int'l*, pg. 1069
BLUENICA CORPORATION—See Digi International Inc.; *U.S. Public*, pg. 662
BLUE NILE, INC.—See Bain Capital, LP; *U.S. Private*, pg. 436
BLUE NILE MAHSREG BANK; *Int'l*, pg. 1069
BLUENORD ASA; *Int'l*, pg. 1072
THE BLUE NOTE LABEL GROUP—See Universal Music Group N.V.; *Int'l*, pg. 8079
BLUE NOTE SPA—See Casta Diva Group; *Int'l*, pg. 1355
BLUENRGY GROUP LIMITED; *Int'l*, pg. 1072
BLUENRGY, LLC—See BlueNRGY Group Limited; *Int'l*, pg. 1072
BLUE OAK ENERGY, INC.—See TRC Companies, Inc.; *U.S. Public*, pg. 4215
BLUE OCEAN ACQUISITION CORP.; *U.S. Public*, pg. 364
BLUE OCEAN ENTERTAINMENT AG—See Hubert Burda Media Holding Kommanditgesellschaft; *Int'l*, pg. 3519
BLUE OCEAN PRESS, INC.; *U.S. Private*, pg. 589
BLUE OCEAN TECHNOLOGIES LLC—See Oceaneering International, Inc.; *U.S. Public*, pg. 1562
BLUE OCEAN TECHNOLOGIES, LLC—See Beyond, Inc.,; *U.S. Public*, pg. 327
BLUEONE CARD, INC.; *U.S. Public*, pg. 365
BLUE ONE CO., LTD.—See TAEYOUNG Engineering & Construction Co., Ltd.; *Int'l*, pg. 7406
BLUE ORTHO SAS—See TPG Capital, L.P.; *U.S. Public*, pg. 2173
BLUE OVAL HOLDINGS LIMITED—See Ford Motor Company; *U.S. Public*, pg. 865
BLUE OWL CAPITAL CORPORATION III—See Blue Owl Capital Inc.; *U.S. Public*, pg. 364
BLUE OWL CAPITAL CORPORATION II—See Blue Owl Capital Inc.; *U.S. Public*, pg. 364
BLUE OWL CAPITAL CORPORATION—See Blue Owl Capital Inc.; *U.S. Public*, pg. 364
BLUE OWL CAPITAL INC.; *U.S. Public*, pg. 364
BLUE OWL CREDIT INCOME CORP.; *U.S. Private*, pg. 589
BLUE OWL TECHNOLOGY FINANCE CORP.; *U.S. Private*, pg. 589
BLUE PACIFIC TOURS—See Air New Zealand Limited; *Int'l*, pg. 239
BLUEPAY CANADA, ULC—See Fiserv, Inc.; *U.S. Public*, pg. 850
BLUEPAY PROCESSING, LLC—See Fiserv, Inc.; *U.S. Public*, pg. 850
BLUEPEAK TECHNOLOGY SOLUTIONS, LLC; *U.S. Private*, pg. 597
BLUEPEARL VETERINARY PARTNERS LLC; *U.S. Private*, pg. 597
BLUE PHOENIX MEDIA, INC.; *U.S. Private*, pg. 590
BLUEPHOENIX SOLUTIONS ITALIA—See Advanced Business Software & Solutions Ltd.; *Int'l*, pg. 157
BLUEPHOENIX SOLUTIONS NORDIC APS—See Advanced Business Software & Solutions Ltd.; *Int'l*, pg. 157
BLUEPLANET ENVIRONMENTAL INC.; *Int'l*, pg. 1072
BLUE PLANET FOODS, INC.—See McKee Foods Corporation; *U.S. Private*, pg. 2637
BLUE PLANET INVESTMENT TRUST PLC; *Int'l*, pg. 1069
BLUE PLANET—See Ciena Corporation; *U.S. Public*, pg. 494
BLUE PLANET WORLDWIDE FINANCIALS INVESTMENT TRUST PLC; *Int'l*, pg. 1069
BLUE PLATE CATERING, LTD.; *U.S. Private*, pg. 590
BLUE POINT BREWING COMPANY, INC.—See Anheuser-Busch InBev SA/NV; *Int'l*, pg. 465
BLUE POINT CAPITAL PARTNERS, LLC; *U.S. Private*, pg. 590
BLUEPOINT DATA, INC.; *U.S. Private*, pg. 597
BLUE POINT LONDON LTD.—See Financiere de L'Odet; *Int'l*, pg. 2665
BLUE POINT TOOL & SUPPLY CO, INC.—See FICODIS Inc.; *Int'l*, pg. 2653
BLUEPOOL GMBH; *Int'l*, pg. 1072
BLUE PRAIRIE GROUP LLC—See Genstar Capital, LLC; *U.S. Private*, pg. 1676
BLUEPRINT FINANCIAL LLC—See Lightyear Capital LLC; *U.S. Private*, pg. 2454
BLUEPRINT FINANCIAL LLC—See Ontario Teachers' Pension Plan; *Int'l*, pg. 5586
BLUEPRINT GAMING LTD.—See Gauselmann AG; *Int'l*, pg. 2890
BLUEPRINT GENETICS OY—See Quest Diagnostics, Inc.; *U.S. Public*, pg. 1755
BLUEPRINT GROUP PTY LTD—See Navis Capital Partners Limited; *Int'l*, pg. 5176
BLUEPRINT HEALTH MERGER CORP.; *U.S. Private*, pg. 597
THE BLUE PRINT INDEPENDENCE—See ARC DOCUMENT SOLUTIONS, INC.; *U.S. Public*, pg. 179
BLUEPRINT MEDICINES CORPORATION; *U.S. Public*, pg. 366
BLUEPRINT PRODUCTS N.V.—See Heidelberger Druckmaschinen AG; *Int'l*, pg. 3321
BLUEPRINT TECHNOLOGIES, INC.; *U.S. Public*, pg. 366
BLUE PRINT TECHNOLOGIES (PTY) LTD.—See Current Water Technologies Inc.; *U.S. Public*, pg. 1879
BLUEPRINT VENTURES, LLC; *U.S. Private*, pg. 597

BLUEPRINT VENTURES, LLC

BLUE PRISM AB—See SS&C Technologies Holdings, Inc.; *U.S. Public*, pg. 1923
BLUE PRISM GMBH—See SS&C Technologies Holdings, Inc.; *U.S. Public*, pg. 1923
BLUE PRISM GROUP PLC—See SS&C Technologies Holdings, Inc.; *U.S. Public*, pg. 1922
BLUE PRISM INDIA PVT. LTD.—See SS&C Technologies Holdings, Inc.; *U.S. Public*, pg. 1923
BLUE PRISM K.K.—See SS&C Technologies Holdings, Inc.; *U.S. Public*, pg. 1923
BLUE PRISM LIMITED—See SS&C Technologies Holdings, Inc.; *U.S. Public*, pg. 1923
BLUE PRISM PTE. LTD.—See SS&C Technologies Holdings, Inc.; *U.S. Public*, pg. 1923
BLUE PRISM PTY. LTD.—See SS&C Technologies Holdings, Inc.; *U.S. Public*, pg. 1923
BLUE PRISM SARL—See SS&C Technologies Holdings, Inc.; *U.S. Public*, pg. 1923
BLUE PRISM SOFTWARE INC.—See SS&C Technologies Holdings, Inc.; *U.S. Public*, pg. 1923
BLUE RACER MIDSTREAM, LLC—See The Williams Companies, Inc.; *U.S. Public*, pg. 2143
BLUE RAVEN SOLAR, LLC—See SunPower Corporation; *U.S. Public*, pg. 1965
BLUE REPLY S.R.L.—See Reply S.p.A.; *Int'l*, pg. 6290
BLUE RHINO GLOBAL SOURCING, INC.—See Ferrellgas Partners, L.P.; *U.S. Public*, pg. 829
BLUE RIBBON FARM DAIRY INC.; *U.S. Private*, pg. 591
BLUE RIBBON INCOME FUND; *Int'l*, pg. 1069
BLUE RIBBON, LP—See Altamont Capital Partners; *U.S. Private*, pg. 205
BLUE RIBBON MEATS INC.; *U.S. Private*, pg. 591
BLUE RIBBON SOFTWARE MALTA LIMITED—See DraftKings Inc.; *U.S. Public*, pg. 687
BLUE RIBBON TRANSPORT, INC.; *U.S. Private*, pg. 591
BLUE RIDGE ACQUISITION CO. LLC; *U.S. Private*, pg. 591
BLUERIDGE ANALYTICS INC.—See Bentley Systems, Inc.; *U.S. Public*, pg. 296
BLUE RIDGE ARSENAL INC.; *U.S. Private*, pg. 591
BLUE RIDGE ATLANTIC, LLC—See Watts Water Technologies, Inc.; *U.S. Public*, pg. 2337
BLUE RIDGE BANCSHARES INC.; *U.S. Private*, pg. 591
BLUE RIDGE BANK AND TRUST CO.—See Blue Ridge Bancshares Inc.; *U.S. Private*, pg. 591
BLUE RIDGE BANKSHARES, INC.; *U.S. Public*, pg. 364
BLUE RIDGE BANK—See Blue Ridge Bankshares, Inc.; *U.S. Public*, pg. 365
BLUE RIDGE BEHAVIORAL HEALTHCARE; *U.S. Private*, pg. 591
BLUE RIDGE BEVERAGE COMPANY INCORPORATED; *U.S. Private*, pg. 591
BLUE RIDGE CAPITAL, LLC; *U.S. Private*, pg. 591
BLUE RIDGE CHINA; *Int'l*, pg. 1069
THE BLUE RIDGE/CLEMSON ORTHOPAEDIC ASC, LLC—See KKR & Co. Inc.; *U.S. Public*, pg. 1247
BLUE RIDGE ELECTRIC COOPERATIVE INC.; *U.S. Private*, pg. 591
BLUE RIDGE ELECTRIC MEMBERSHIP CORPORATION; *U.S. Private*, pg. 591
BLUE RIDGE ENERGIES, INC.—See Blue Ridge Electric Membership Corporation; *U.S. Private*, pg. 591
BLUE RIDGE FIBERBOARD, INC. - LISBON FALLS—See W. R. Meadows, Inc.; *U.S. Private*, pg. 4418
BLUE RIDGE FIBERBOARD, INC.—See W. R. Meadows, Inc.; *U.S. Private*, pg. 4418
BLUERIDGE FILMS INC.—See Arkema S.A.; *Int'l*, pg. 570
BLUE RIDGE FOODS LLC.; *U.S. Private*, pg. 591
BLUE RIDGE GROUP INC.; *U.S. Private*, pg. 591
BLUERIDGE GROUP—See Blue Ridge Group Inc.; *U.S. Private*, pg. 591
BLUE RIDGE HARLEY-DAVIDSON—See Scott Fischer Enterprises LLC; *U.S. Private*, pg. 3577
BLUE RIDGE HOSPICE; *U.S. Private*, pg. 591
BLUE RIDGE INDEMNITY COMPANY—See QBE Insurance Group Limited; *Int'l*, pg. 6136
BLUE RIDGE INDUSTRIES, INC.; *U.S. Private*, pg. 592
BLUE RIDGE KNIVES, INC.; *U.S. Private*, pg. 592
BLUE RIDGE LOG CABINS, LLC; *U.S. Private*, pg. 592
BLUE RIDGE LUMBER INC.—See West Fraser Timber Co., Ltd.; *Int'l*, pg. 8383
BLUE RIDGE MOUNTAIN RECOVERY CENTER, LLC—See Acadia Healthcare Company, Inc.; *U.S. Public*, pg. 28
BLUE RIDGE MOUNTAIN RESOURCES, INC.—See Expand Energy Corporation; *U.S. Public*, pg. 808
BLUE RIDGE MOUNTAIN SPORTS LTD; *U.S. Private*, pg. 592
BLUE RIDGE PRESSURE CASTINGS, INC.; *U.S. Private*, pg. 592
BLUE RIDGE PRINTING CO., INC.; *U.S. Private*, pg. 592
BLUE RIDGE REAL ESTATE COMPANY; *U.S. Public*, pg. 365
BLUE RIDGE RESCUE SUPPLIERS, INC.—See Platte River Ventures, LLC; *U.S. Private*, pg. 3211
BLUE RIDGE SECURITY SYSTEMS—See Blue Ridge Electric Cooperative Inc.; *U.S. Private*, pg. 591
BLUE RIDGE SURGERY CENTER—See HCA Healthcare, Inc.; *U.S. Public*, pg. 1007
BLUE RIDGE SURGICAL CENTER, LLC—See Bain Capital, LP; *U.S. Private*, pg. 445
BLUE RIDGE TELEPHONE CO.—See Telephone & Data Systems, Inc.; *U.S. Public*, pg. 1998
BLUE RIDGE TEXTILE MANUFACTURING, INC.—See Coyne International Enterprises Corp.; *U.S. Private*, pg. 1079
BLUERIVER ACQUISITION CORP.; *U.S. Public*, pg. 366
BLUE RIVER GROUP, LLC.; *U.S. Private*, pg. 592
BLUE RIVER PARTNERS LLC—See IQ EQ Luxembourg SA; *Int'l*, pg. 3803
BLUE RIVER RESOURCES LTD.; *Int'l*, pg. 1069
BLUE RIVER TECHNOLOGY, INC.—See Deere & Company; *U.S. Public*, pg. 646
BLUE ROAD MANAGEMENT, L.P.; *U.S. Private*, pg. 592
BLUEROCK DIAMONDS PLC; *Int'l*, pg. 1072
BLUEROCK ENERGY, INC.; *U.S. Private*, pg. 597
BLUE ROCK OF MAINE; *U.S. Private*, pg. 592
BLUE ROCK PARTNERS, LLC; *U.S. Private*, pg. 592
BLUEROCK RESIDENTIAL GROWTH REIT, INC.; *U.S. Public*, pg. 366
BLUEROCK THERAPEUTICS LP—See Bayer Aktiengesellschaft; *Int'l*, pg. 907
BLUEROCK VENTURES CORP.; *Int'l*, pg. 1072
BLUERUN VENTURES; *U.S. Private*, pg. 597
BLUERUSH DIGITAL MEDIA CORP.—See BlueRush Inc.; *Int'l*, pg. 1072
BLUERUSH INC.; *Int'l*, pg. 1072
BLUE SAFARI GROUP ACQUISITION CORP.; *Int'l*, pg. 1069
BLUE SAGE CAPITAL, L.P.; *U.S. Private*, pg. 592
BLUE SAIL MEDICAL CO., LTD.; *Int'l*, pg. 1069
BLUE SALON ESTABLISHMENT; *Int'l*, pg. 1069
BLUESCAPE OPPORTUNITIES ACQUISITION CORP.; *U.S. Public*, pg. 366
BLUESCOPE ACIER NOUVELLE CALEDONIE SA—See BlueScope Steel Limited; *Int'l*, pg. 1072
BLUESCOPE BUILDINGS (GUANGZHOU) LTD.—See BlueScope Steel Limited; *Int'l*, pg. 1072
BLUESCOPE BUILDINGS NORTH AMERICA ENGINEERING (MICHIGAN) LLC—See BlueScope Steel Limited; *Int'l*, pg. 1072
BLUESCOPE BUILDINGS NORTH AMERICA INC.—See BlueScope Steel Limited; *Int'l*, pg. 1073
BLUESCOPE BUILDINGS (VIETNAM) LIMITED—See BlueScope Steel Limited; *Int'l*, pg. 1072
BLUESCOPE BUILDING SYSTEMS (XI'AN) CO., LTD.—See BlueScope Steel Limited; *Int'l*, pg. 1072
BLUESCOPE COATED PRODUCTS LLC—See BlueScope Steel Limited; *Int'l*, pg. 1072
BLUESCOPE CONSTRUCTION INC.—See BlueScope Steel Limited; *Int'l*, pg. 1073
BLUESCOPE DISTRIBUTION PTY LTD.—See BlueScope Steel Limited; *Int'l*, pg. 1072
BLUESCOPE LYSAGHT (BRUNEI) SDN BHD—See BlueScope Steel Limited; *Int'l*, pg. 1072
BLUESCOPE LYSAGHT (CHENGDU) LTD.—See BlueScope Steel Limited; *Int'l*, pg. 1072
BLUESCOPE LYSAGHT FIJI LTD.—See BlueScope Steel Limited; *Int'l*, pg. 1073
BLUESCOPE LYSAGHT (SABAH) SDN BHD—See BlueScope Steel Limited; *Int'l*, pg. 1072
BLUESCOPE LYSAGHT (SHANGHAI) LTD.—See BlueScope Steel Limited; *Int'l*, pg. 1072
BLUESCOPE LYSAGHT (SINGAPORE) PTE. LTD.—See BlueScope Steel Limited; *Int'l*, pg. 1073
BLUESCOPE LYSAGHT SINGAPORE PTE. LTD.—See BlueScope Steel Limited; *Int'l*, pg. 1073
BLUESCOPE LYSAGHT TAIWAN LTD.—See BlueScope Steel Limited; *Int'l*, pg. 1072
BLUESCOPE LYSAGHT (THAILAND) LTD.—See BlueScope Steel Limited; *Int'l*, pg. 1072
BLUESCOPE LYSAGHT (VANUATU) LTD.—See BlueScope Steel Limited; *Int'l*, pg. 1073
BLUESCOPE PROPERTIES GROUP LLC—See BlueScope Steel Limited; *Int'l*, pg. 1073
BLUESCOPE PTY LTD.—See BlueScope Steel Limited; *Int'l*, pg. 1073
BLUESCOPE RECYCLING AND MATERIALS LLC—See BlueScope Steel Limited; *Int'l*, pg. 1073
BLUESCOPE STEEL (AIS) PTY LTD—See BlueScope Steel Limited; *Int'l*, pg. 1073
BLUESCOPE STEEL AMERICAS LLC—See BlueScope Steel Limited; *Int'l*, pg. 1073
BLUESCOPE STEEL ASIA HOLDINGS PTY LTD.—See BlueScope Steel Limited; *Int'l*, pg. 1073
BLUESCOPE STEEL ASIA PTE LTD—See BlueScope Steel Limited; *Int'l*, pg. 1073
BLUESCOPE STEEL (FINANCE) LTD.—See BlueScope Steel Limited; *Int'l*, pg. 1073
BLUESCOPE STEEL INTERNATIONAL TRADING (SHANGHAI) CO.,LTD.—See BlueScope Steel Limited; *Int'l*, pg. 1073
BLUESCOPE STEEL INVESTMENT MANAGEMENT (SHANGHAI) LTD.—See BlueScope Steel Limited; *Int'l*, pg. 1073
BLUESCOPE STEEL LIMITED; *Int'l*, pg. 1072
BLUESCOPE STEEL LOGISTICS CO PTY LTD.—See BlueScope Steel Limited; *Int'l*, pg. 1073

CORPORATE AFFILIATIONS

BLUESCOPE STEEL NORTH AMERICA CORPORATION—See BlueScope Steel Limited; *Int'l*, pg. 1073
BLUESCOPE STEEL NORTH ASIA LTD—See BlueScope Steel Limited; *Int'l*, pg. 1073
BLUESCOPE STEEL PHILIPPINES INC—See BlueScope Steel Limited; *Int'l*, pg. 1073
BLUESCOPE STEEL—See BlueScope Steel Limited; *Int'l*, pg. 1073
BLUESCOPE STEEL SOUTHERN AFRICA (PTY) LTD.—See BlueScope Steel Limited; *Int'l*, pg. 1073
BLUESCOPE STEEL (SUZHOU) LTD—See BlueScope Steel Limited; *Int'l*, pg. 1073
BLUESCOPE STEEL (THAILAND) LTD.—See BlueScope Steel Limited; *Int'l*, pg. 1073
BLUESCOPE STEEL TRADING NZ LTD.—See BlueScope Steel Limited; *Int'l*, pg. 1073
BLUESCOPE STEEL VIETNAM LIMITED.—See BlueScope Steel Limited; *Int'l*, pg. 1073
BLUESCOPE WATER PTY LTD.—See BlueScope Steel Limited; *Int'l*, pg. 1073
BLUE SEA CAPITAL MANAGEMENT LLC; *U.S. Private*, pg. 592
THE BLUE SEA COMPANY W.L.L.—See POSCO Holdings Inc.; *Int'l*, pg. 5938
BLUE SEAL LIMITED—See Ali Holding S.r.l; *Int'l*, pg. 321
BLUE SEA SYSTEMS—See Brunswick Corporation; *U.S. Public*, pg. 408
BLUE SERVICE S.R.I—See Investment AB Latour; *Int'l*, pg. 3783
BLUESG PTE. LTD.—See Goldbell Corporation; *Int'l*, pg. 3027
BLUE SHIELD OF CALIFORNIA - LARGE GROUP BUSINESS UNIT—See Blue Shield of California; *U.S. Private*, pg. 593
BLUE SHIELD OF CALIFORNIA LIFE & HEALTH INSURANCE COMPANY—See Blue Shield of California; *U.S. Private*, pg. 593
BLUE SHIELD OF CALIFORNIA; *U.S. Private*, pg. 592
BLUE SHIELD OF CALIFORNIA—See Blue Shield of California; *U.S. Private*, pg. 593
THE BLUESHIRT GROUP LLC - NEW YORK—See Next 15 Group plc; *Int'l*, pg. 5247
THE BLUESHIRT GROUP LLC—See Next 15 Group plc; *Int'l*, pg. 5247
BLUESIGHT, INC.—See Thoma Bravo, L.P.; *U.S. Private*, pg. 4146
BLUE SKY AGENCY; *U.S. Private*, pg. 593
BLUE SKY ALTERNATIVE INVESTMENTS LIMITED; *Int'l*, pg. 1069
BLUE SKY BIOTECH, INC.—See LakePharma, Inc.; *U.S. Private*, pg. 2376
BLUE SKY DATA CORP.—See OTC Markets Group Inc.; *U.S. Public*, pg. 1622
BLUESKY DIGITAL ASSETS CORP.; *Int'l*, pg. 1074
BLUESKY.ENERGY GMBH; *Int'l*, pg. 1074
BLUE SKY ENERGY INC.; *Int'l*, pg. 1069
BLUE SKY ENERGY; *U.S. Private*, pg. 593
BLUE SKY ENVIRONMENTAL TECHNOLOGY (SHENZHEN) LIMITED—See Global Token Limited; *Int'l*, pg. 3001
BLUE SKY EXHIBITS; *U.S. Private*, pg. 593
BLUE SKY FINANCIAL GROUP—See ING Groep N.V.; *Int'l*, pg. 3699
BLUE SKY GROUP HOLDINGS, INC.; *U.S. Private*, pg. 593
BLUE SKY HOSTING LTD; *Int'l*, pg. 1069
BLUESKY HOTELS & RESORTS INC.; *Int'l*, pg. 1074
BLUE SKY INDUSTRIES, INC.—See Audax Group, Limited Partnership; *U.S. Private*, pg. 388
BLUESKY INTERNATIONAL LTD.; *Int'l*, pg. 1074
BLUE SKY IT PARTNERS CORPORATION; *U.S. Private*, pg. 593
BLUE SKY MD; *U.S. Private*, pg. 593
BLUE SKY MD—See Blue Sky MD; *U.S. Private*, pg. 593
BLUE SKY NATURAL BEVERAGE CO.—See Monster Beverage Corporation; *U.S. Public*, pg. 1465
BLUE SKY NETWORK, LLC; *U.S. Private*, pg. 593
BLUESKY ONLINE SERVICES LIMITED—See Tomizone Limited; *Int'l*, pg. 7800
BLUESKY RESOURCE SOLUTIONS, LLC; *U.S. Private*, pg. 597
BLUE SKY REUNION SAS—See ENL Limited; *Int'l*, pg. 2441
BLUESKY SAMOA LTD.—See Fiji National Provident Fund; *Int'l*, pg. 2661
BLUE SKY SCRUBS LLC; *U.S. Private*, pg. 593
BLUESKY SECURITIES JOINT STOCK COMPANY; *Int'l*, pg. 1074
BLUE SKY STUDIOS INC.—See The Walt Disney Company; *U.S. Public*, pg. 2140
BLUE SKY TOWERS PTY LTD—See American Tower Corporation; *U.S. Public*, pg. 111
BLUE SKY URANIUM CORP.; *Int'l*, pg. 1069
BLUE SLATE SOLUTIONS, LLC—See ExlService Holdings, Inc.; *U.S. Public*, pg. 807
BLUESNAP, INC.; *U.S. Private*, pg. 597
BLUE SOFTWARE LLC—See Danaher Corporation; *U.S. Public*, pg. 625

COMPANY NAME INDEX

BLUE SOLUTIONS LIMITED; *Int'l*, pg. 1069
BLUE SOLUTIONS S.A.—See Financiere de L'Odet; *Int'l*, pg. 2666
BLUE SOMBRERO, LLC—See Genstar Capital, LLC; *U.S. Private*, pg. 1678
BLUESOURCE LTD.; *Int'l*, pg. 1074
BLUESPACE SOFTWARE CORP—See Sterling Computers; *U.S. Private*, pg. 3805
BLUESPED FRANCE SARL—See Die Schweizerische Post AG; *Int'l*, pg. 2112
BLUESPED LOGISTICS SARL—See Die Schweizerische Post AG; *Int'l*, pg. 2112
BLUESPHERE ADVISORS LLC; *U.S. Private*, pg. 597
BLUE SPHERE CORPORATION; *U.S. Public*, pg. 365
BLUE SPHERE SOLUTIONS, INC.—See Conway, Dierking & Hillman, Inc.; *U.S. Private*, pg. 1037
BLUESPIRE, INC. - MONTVALE—See High Road Capital Partners, LLC; *U.S. Private*, pg. 1936
BLUESPIRE, INC.—See High Road Capital Partners, LLC; *U.S. Private*, pg. 1936
BLUE SPRIG PEDIATRICS, INC.; *U.S. Private*, pg. 593
BLUESPRING WEALTH PARTNERS LLC—See Warburg Pincus LLC; *U.S. Private*, pg. 4439
BLUE SQUARE LTD.—See Flutter Entertainment plc; *Int'l*, pg. 2715
BLUESQUARE RESOLUTIONS, LLC.; *U.S. Private*, pg. 597
BLUES SEAFOOD RESTAURANT LLC—See DAMAC Group; *Int'l*, pg. 1955
BLUESTAR ADISSEO COMPANY LIMITED; *Int'l*, pg. 1074
BLUESTAR ALLIANCE LLC; *U.S. Private*, pg. 597
BLUESTAR (BEIJING) CHEMICAL MACHINERY CO., LTD.—See Bluestar Adisseo Company Limited; *Int'l*, pg. 1074
BLUE STAR BUSINESS SOLUTIONS LIMITED—See Manx Financial Group PLC; *Int'l*, pg. 4680
BLUE STAR BUS SALES, LTD.—See A-Z Bus Sales, Inc.; *U.S. Private*, pg. 22
BLUE STAR CAPITAL PLC; *Int'l*, pg. 1069
BLUE STAR DESIGN & ENGINEERING LTD.—See Blue Star Limited; *Int'l*, pg. 1070
BLUESTAR DISTRIBUTION INC.—See Apollo Global Management, Inc.; *U.S. Public*, pg. 165
BLUE STAR ENGINEERING & ELECTRONICS LTD.—See Blue Star Limited; *Int'l*, pg. 1070
BLUESTAR EXCHANGE LIMITED—See Giordano International Limited; *Int'l*, pg. 2977
BLUE STAR FOODS CORP.; *U.S. Public*, pg. 365
BLUE STAR FORD LINCOLN SALES LTD; *Int'l*, pg. 1069
BLUE STAR GAS; *U.S. Private*, pg. 593
BLUE STAR GOLD CORP.; *Int'l*, pg. 1069
BLUE STAR GROWERS INC.; *U.S. Private*, pg. 593
BLUESTAR HARBIN PETROCHEMICAL CORPORATION—See Bluestar Adisseo Company Limited; *Int'l*, pg. 1074
BLUE STAR HELIUM LTD.; *Int'l*, pg. 1070
BLUESTAR INDUSTRIES, LLC; *U.S. Private*, pg. 598
BLUE STAR INTERNATIONAL FZCO—See Blue Star Limited; *Int'l*, pg. 1070
BLUE STAR JETS, INC.; *U.S. Private*, pg. 593
BLUE STAR LIMITED; *Int'l*, pg. 1070
BLUE STAR LIMITED - THANE FACILITY—See Blue Star Limited; *Int'l*, pg. 1070
BLUE STAR LTD.—See Blue Star Limited; *Int'l*, pg. 1070
BLUE STAR LTD.—See Blue Star Limited; *Int'l*, pg. 1070
BLUE STAR LTD.—See Blue Star Limited; *Int'l*, pg. 1070
BLUE STAR LTD.—See Blue Star Limited; *Int'l*, pg. 1070
BLUE STAR MARITIME S.A.—See Attica Group; *Int'l*, pg. 696
BLUESTAR MARKETING, INC.; *U.S. Private*, pg. 598
BLUE STAR M & E ENGINEERING SDN BHD—See Amcorp Group Berhad; *Int'l*, pg. 418
BLUE STAR NORTH AMERICA INC—See Blue Star Limited; *Int'l*, pg. 1070
BLUE STAR OPPORTUNITIES CORP.; *U.S. Public*, pg. 365
BLUESTAR OPTIONS INC.—See Microsoft Corporation; *U.S. Public*, pg. 1442
BLUE STAR PARTNERS LLC; *U.S. Private*, pg. 593
BLUE STAR PRINT GROUP LIMITED—See CHAMP Private Equity Pty. Ltd.; *Int'l*, pg. 1439
BLUE STAR PROPERTIES, INC.—See Banner Corporation; *U.S. Public*, pg. 275
BLUE STAR QATAR WLL—See Blue Star Limited; *Int'l*, pg. 1070
BLUESTAR RESORT & GOLF LLC—See J.F. Shea Co., Inc.; *U.S. Private*, pg. 2164
BLUESTAR SECUTECH INC.; *Int'l*, pg. 1074
BLUESTAR SILICON MATERIAL CO. LTD.—See Bluestar Adisseo Company Limited; *Int'l*, pg. 1074
BLUE STAR WEBBING CORP.; *U.S. Private*, pg. 593
BLUESTAR WUXI PETROCHEMICAL CO LTD—See Bluestar Adisseo Company Limited; *Int'l*, pg. 1074
BLUE STATE DIGITAL—See WPP plc; *Int'l*, pg. 8467
BLUE STEC GMBH—See Orbis SE; *Int'l*, pg. 5614
BLUESTEM BRANDS, INC.; *U.S. Private*, pg. 598
BLUESTEM EQUITY, LTD.; *U.S. Private*, pg. 598
BLUESTEM FARM & RANCH SUPPLY, INC.; *U.S. Private*, pg. 598

BLUESTEM GAS SERVICES, L.L.C.—See The Williams Companies, Inc.; *U.S. Public*, pg. 2143
BLUESTEM GROUP INC.; *U.S. Public*, pg. 366
BLUESTONE GLOBAL LIMITED; *Int'l*, pg. 1074
BLUESTONE INDUSTRIES, INC.—See Mechel Bluestone Inc.; *U.S. Private*, pg. 2649
BLUESTONE INVESTMENT PARTNERS, LLC; *U.S. Private*, pg. 598
BLUESTONE PARTNERS LLC; *U.S. Private*, pg. 598
BLUESTONE PAYMENTS, LLC—See PCP Enterprise, L.P.; *U.S. Private*, pg. 3121
BLUESTONE RESOURCES INC.; *Int'l*, pg. 1075
BLUE STREAK FINISHERS, LTD.—See Coast Plating, Inc.; *U.S. Private*, pg. 954
BLUE STREAK-HYGRADE MOTOR PRODUCTS LTD.—See Standard Motor Products, Inc.; *U.S. Public*, pg. 1929
BLUESTREAM PROFESSIONAL SERVICES, LLC—See KGP Telecommunications, Inc.; *U.S. Private*, pg. 2301
BLUE SUN BIODIESEL; *U.S. Private*, pg. 593
BLUESWORD INTELLIGENT TECHNOLOGY CO., LTD.; *Int'l*, pg. 1075
BLUE TECH, INC.; *U.S. Private*, pg. 593
BLUE TEE CORPORATION; *U.S. Private*, pg. 594
BLUE THUNDER MINING, INC.; *Int'l*, pg. 1070
BLUE TOMATO DEUTSCHLAND GMBH—See Zumiez Incorporated; *U.S. Public*, pg. 2411
BLUE TOMATO NETHERLANDS B.V.—See Zumiez Incorporated; *U.S. Public*, pg. 2411
BLUE TORCH CAPITAL, LP; *U.S. Private*, pg. 594
BLUE TORCH FINANCE LLC—See Blue Torch Capital, LP; *U.S. Private*, pg. 594
BLUETORINO SRL—See Financiere de L'Odet; *Int'l*, pg. 2666
BLUE TOWER GMBH—See Concord Blue Engineering GmbH; *Int'l*, pg. 1764
BLUE TREE SYSTEMS GMBH—See ORBCOMM, Inc.; *U.S. Public*, pg. 1614
BLUE TREE SYSTEMS INC.—See ORBCOMM, Inc.; *U.S. Public*, pg. 1614
BLUE TREE SYSTEMS LTD.—See ORBCOMM, Inc.; *U.S. Public*, pg. 1614
BLUE TREE SYSTEMS SARL—See ORBCOMM, Inc.; *U.S. Public*, pg. 1614
BLUE TRIANGLE HARDWOODS, LLC—See Baillie Lumber Co., Inc.; *U.S. Private*, pg. 426
BLUETRITON BRANDS, INC.—See Metropoulos & Co.; *U.S. Private*, pg. 2690
BLUETRITON BRANDS, INC.—See One Rock Capital Partners, LLC; *U.S. Private*, pg. 3021
BLUE VALLEY BAN CORP.—See Heartland Financial USA, Inc.; *U.S. Public*, pg. 1018
THE BLUE VENTURE FUND; *U.S. Private*, pg. 3995
BLUE VICTORY HOLDINGS, INC.; *U.S. Private*, pg. 594
BLUE VILLAGE FRANKLIN MOBIL GMBH—See MVV Energie AG; *Int'l*, pg. 5108
BLUE VISION A/S; *Int'l*, pg. 1070
BLUEWARE, INC.; *U.S. Private*, pg. 598
BLUEWATER AB; *Int'l*, pg. 1075
BLUEWATER ACQUISITION CORP.; *Int'l*, pg. 1075
BLUEWATER CREEK MANAGEMENT CO.—See Deutsche Bank Aktiengesellschaft; *Int'l*, pg. 2055
BLUEWATER DEFENSE, INC.; *U.S. Private*, pg. 598
BLUEWATER EDITIONS—See Southeastern Printing Company Inc.; *U.S. Private*, pg. 3728
BLUE WATER ENERGY LLP; *Int'l*, pg. 1070
BLUE WATER ENERGY SOLUTIONS, LLC—See GreenHunter Resources, Inc.; *U.S. Private*, pg. 1778
BLUEWATER FEDERAL SOLUTIONS, INC.—See Tetra Tech, Inc.; *U.S. Public*, pg. 2022
BLUE WATER FINANCIAL TECHNOLOGIES HOLDING COMPANY, LLC—See Voxtur Analytics Corp.; *Int'l*, pg. 8311
BLUE WATER GLOBAL GROUP, INC.; *Int'l*, pg. 1070
BLUEWATER MEDIA LLC; *U.S. Private*, pg. 598
BLUE WATER PETROLEUM CORP.; *U.S. Private*, pg. 594
BLUEWATER POWER DISTRIBUTION CORPORATION; *Int'l*, pg. 1075
BLUEWATER SEAFOODS, INC.—See Nissui Corporation; *Int'l*, pg. 5377
BLUE WATER SHIELD LLC; *U.S. Private*, pg. 594
BLUEWATER TECHNOLOGIES INC.; *U.S. Private*, pg. 598
BLUEWATER THERMAL PROCESSION, LLC—See Blackstone Inc.; *U.S. Public*, pg. 352
BLUEWATER TRADING INC.; *U.S. Private*, pg. 599
BLUE WATER VACCINES, INC.; *U.S. Public*, pg. 365
BLUE WAVE COMMUNICATIONS, LLC—See Dosal Capital, LLC; *U.S. Private*, pg. 1264
BLUEWAVE COMPUTING LLC; *U.S. Private*, pg. 599
BLUEWAVE CORPORATION—See ORIX Corporation; *Int'l*, pg. 5633
BLUE WAVE MICRO; *U.S. Private*, pg. 594
BLUEWAVE TECHNOLOGY GROUP, LLC; *U.S. Private*, pg. 599
BLUEWELL CORPORATION—See Sumitomo Corporation; *Int'l*, pg. 7268
BLUEWELL INSURANCE BROKERS LTD.—See Sumitomo Corporation; *Int'l*, pg. 7268

BLUE WHALE WATER TECHNOLOGIES CORPORATION—See Continental Holdings Corp.; *Int'l*, pg. 1784
BLUE WHALE WEB SOLUTIONS, INC.; *U.S. Private*, pg. 594
BLUE-WHITE INDUSTRIES LTD; *U.S. Private*, pg. 596
BLUE WOLF CAPITAL MANAGEMENT LLC—See Blue Wolf Capital Partners LLC; *U.S. Private*, pg. 594
BLUE WOLF CAPITAL PARTNERS LLC; *U.S. Private*, pg. 594
BLUEWOLF, INC.; *U.S. Private*, pg. 599
BLUEWOLF UK—See Bluewolf, Inc.; *U.S. Private*, pg. 599
BLUE WORLD ACQUISITION CORPORATION; *U.S. Public*, pg. 365
BLUE WORLDWIDE—See Daniel J. Edelman, Inc.; *U.S. Private*, pg. 1154
BLUEWORX—See Waterfield Technologies, Inc.; *U.S. Private*, pg. 4453
BLUE ZEN MEMORIAL PARKS INC.; *Int'l*, pg. 1070
BLUE ZONES, LLC—See Adventist Health System; *U.S. Private*, pg. 108
BLUFERRIES S.R.L.—See Ferrovie dello Stato Italiane S.p.A.; *Int'l*, pg. 2645
BLUFF CITY BEER COMPANY; *U.S. Private*, pg. 599
BLUFF CITY DISTRIBUTING CO., INC.; *U.S. Private*, pg. 599
BLUFF EQUIPMENT, INC.; *U.S. Private*, pg. 599
BLUFF HOLDING COMPANY, LLC—See Churchill Downs, Inc.; *U.S. Public*, pg. 493
BLUFF MANUFACTURING, INC.—See Wincove Private Holdings, LP; *U.S. Private*, pg. 4533
BLUFF POINT ASSOCIATES CORP.; *U.S. Private*, pg. 599
BLUFFS AT HIGHLANDS RANCH LLC—See Sares-Regis Group; *U.S. Private*, pg. 3550
BLUFFTON HEALTH SYSTEM, LLC—See Community Health Systems, Inc.; *U.S. Public*, pg. 551
BLUFFTON MOTOR WORKS—See WEG S.A.; *Int'l*, pg. 8367
BLUFFTON OKATIE PRIMARY CARE, L.L.C.—See Tenet Healthcare Corporation; *U.S. Public*, pg. 2007
BLUFFTON OKATIE SURGERY CENTER, L.L.C.—See Tenet Healthcare Corporation; *U.S. Public*, pg. 2005
BLUGLASS LIMITED; *Int'l*, pg. 1075
BLU GREY—See WPP plc; *Int'l*, pg. 8469
BLU HOMES, INC—See Dvele, Inc.; *U.S. Private*, pg. 1295
BLU INC MEDIA (CHINA) LIMITED.—See Singapore Press Holdings Ltd.; *Int'l*, pg. 6942
BLU INC MEDIA SDN. BHD—See Singapore Press Holdings Ltd.; *Int'l*, pg. 6942
BLU INC MEDIA SINGAPORE PTE LTD—See Singapore Press Holdings Ltd.; *Int'l*, pg. 6942
BLUJAY SOLUTIONS LTD.—See Francisco Partners Management, LP; *U.S. Private*, pg. 1589
BLU JET S.R.L.—See Ferrovie dello Stato Italiane S.p.A.; *Int'l*, pg. 2645
BLUMAR S. A.; *Int'l*, pg. 1075
BLUMARTIN GMBH—See Investment AB Latour; *Int'l*, pg. 3784
BLUMAUERPLATZ BETEILIGUNGS-HOLDING GMBH—See Fresenius SE & Co. KGaA; *Int'l*, pg. 2777
BLUMBERGEXCELSIOR INC.; *U.S. Private*, pg. 599
BLUMBERG INDUSTRIES INC.; *U.S. Private*, pg. 599
BLUM CAPITAL PARTNERS, L.P.; *U.S. Private*, pg. 599
BLUMEL SRL—See Wurth Verwaltungsgesellschaft mbH; *Int'l*, pg. 8504
BLUMENTHAL PERFORMING ARTS; *U.S. Private*, pg. 599
BLUME STAHLSERVICE GMBH—See Tata Sons Limited; *Int'l*, pg. 7471
BLUME STAHLSERVICE POLSKA SP.Z.O.O—See Tata Sons Limited; *Int'l*, pg. 7471
BLUME TREE SERVICES, INC.—See Asplundh Tree Expert Co.; *U.S. Private*, pg. 353
BLUMETRIC ENVIRONMENTAL INC.; *Int'l*, pg. 1075
BLUM, SHAPIRO & COMPANY, P.C.; *U.S. Private*, pg. 599
BLUNDELL SEAFOODS LTD.; *Int'l*, pg. 1075
BLUNDEN CONSTRUCTION LTD.; *Int'l*, pg. 1075
BLUNT ENTERPRISES LLC; *U.S. Private*, pg. 599
BLUO SICAV-SIF; *Int'l*, pg. 1075
BLU-RAY DIV—See Bidwell Industrial Group, Inc.; *U.S. Private*, pg. 551
BLURB, INC.—See Reischling Press, Inc.; *U.S. Private*, pg. 3392
BLUSDESIGN B.V.—See London Security PLC; *Int'l*, pg. 4547
BLUSKY RESTORATION CONTRACTORS, LLC—See Kohlberg & Company, LLC; *U.S. Private*, pg. 2337
BLUSKY RESTORATION CONTRACTORS, LLC—See Partners Group Holding AG; *Int'l*, pg. 5749
BLUSOLAR PTY LTD—See BluGlass Limited; *Int'l*, pg. 1075
BLUTIP POWER TECHNOLOGIES LTD.; *Int'l*, pg. 1075
BLUWARE, INC.—See Computer Modelling Group Ltd.; *Int'l*, pg. 1760
BLVD COMPANIES; *U.S. Private*, pg. 600

BLVD SUITES CORPORATE HOUSING, INC. — *U.S. Private*, pg. 600
BLV LICHT-UND VAKUUMTECHNIK GMBH—See Ushio, Inc.; *Int'l*, pg. 8097
BLV VERSICHERUNGSMANAGEMENT GMBH—See Benteler International AG; *Int'l*, pg. 976
B&L WHOLESALE SUPPLY INC.; *U.S. Private*, pg. 419
BLYNCSY, INC.—See Bentley Systems, Inc.; *U.S. Public*, pg. 297
BLYTHE AMBULANCE SERVICE—See KKR & Co. Inc.; *U.S. Public*, pg. 1251
BLYTHECO, LLC; *U.S. Private*, pg. 600
BLYTHE CONSTRUCTION, INC. - CHARLOTTE PLANT—See VINCI S.A.; *Int'l*, pg. 8220
BLYTHE CONSTRUCTION, INC. - CONCORD PLANT—See VINCI S.A.; *Int'l*, pg. 8220
BLYTHE CONSTRUCTION, INC. - MATTHEWS PLANT—See VINCI S.A.; *Int'l*, pg. 8220
BLYTHE CONSTRUCTION, INC. - PINEVILLE PLANT—See VINCI S.A.; *Int'l*, pg. 8220
BLYTHE CONSTRUCTION, INC.—See VINCI S.A.; *Int'l*, pg. 8220
BLYTHEDALE CHILDREN'S HOSPITAL; *U.S. Private*, pg. 600
BLYTHE DEVELOPMENT CO.; *U.S. Private*, pg. 600
BLYTHE ENERGY, LLC—See AltaGas Ltd.; *Int'l*, pg. 384
BLYTHE VALLEY INNOVATION CENTRE LTD.—See Prologis, Inc.; *U.S. Public*, pg. 1727
BLYTHEWOOD OIL CO. INC.; *U.S. Private*, pg. 600
BLYTH S.R.O.—See Bunzl plc; *Int'l*, pg. 1217
BMAC LIMITED—See Methode Electronics, Inc.; *U.S. Public*, pg. 1428
B M AGENCY SERVICES LIMITED—See Personal Group Holdings plc; *Int'l*, pg. 5820
B. MAIER ZERKLEINERUNGSTECHNIK GMBH—See Dieffenbacher Holding GmbH & Co. KG; *Int'l*, pg. 2114
B. MASON & SONS LTD.—See Wieland-Werke AG; *Int'l*, pg. 8402
BM BANK, JSC—See PJSC VTB Bank; *Int'l*, pg. 5886
BMB DINING SERVICES (STEMMONS), INC.—See RCI Hospitality Holdings, Inc.; *U.S. Public*, pg. 1767
BMB ENTERPRISES; *U.S. Private*, pg. 600
BMB GESTION DOCUMENTAL CANARIAS S.L.—See Indra Sistemas, S.A.; *Int'l*, pg. 3660
BMB INTERNATIONAL CORP.—See Brother Industries, Ltd.; *Int'l*, pg. 1196
BMB MOTT MACDONALD—See Mott MacDonald Group Ltd.; *Int'l*, pg. 5054
BMB MUSIC & MAGNETICS LIMITED; *Int'l*, pg. 1076
BMB OCEL S.R.O.—See Benteler International AG; *Int'l*, pg. 976
BMB PROPERTY SERVICES—See Bahrain Middle East Bank BSC; *Int'l*, pg. 800
BMB (SHANGHAI) INTERNATIONAL CORP.—See Brother Industries, Ltd.; *Int'l*, pg. 1196
BMB STEERING INNOVATION GMBH—See ThyssenKrupp AG; *Int'l*, pg. 7723
BMC ADVERTISING; *U.S. Private*, pg. 600
BMC ADVIES B.V.—See Randstad N.V.; *Int'l*, pg. 6201
BM CARPENTERIE OIL & GAS S.R.L.; *Int'l*, pg. 1075
BMC BOLSA MERCANTIL DE COLOMBIA SA; *Int'l*, pg. 1076
BMC CAPITAL, INC.; *U.S. Private*, pg. 600
BMC DONGGUAN LIMITED—See LyondellBasell Industries N.V.; *Int'l*, pg. 4607
BMC EAST, LLC—See Builders FirstSource, Inc.; *U.S. Public*, pg. 409
BMCE CAPITAL BOURSE—See Bank of Africa; *Int'l*, pg. 839
BMCE CAPITAL CONSEIL—See Bank of Africa; *Int'l*, pg. 839
BMCE CAPITAL GESTION—See Bank of Africa; *Int'l*, pg. 839
BMCE CAPITAL—See Bank of Africa; *Int'l*, pg. 839
BMCE INTERNATIONAL, S.A.U.—See Bank of Africa; *Int'l*, pg. 839
BMC ENTERPRISES, INC.—See Breedon Group plc; *Int'l*, pg. 1144
BMC FAR EAST LIMITED—See LyondellBasell Industries N.V.; *Int'l*, pg. 4607
BMC FORESTRY CORPORATION—See Benguet Corporation; *Int'l*, pg. 974
BMC GROEP B.V.—See Randstad N.V.; *Int'l*, pg. 6201
BMCH TENNESSEE, LLC—See Century Communities, Inc.; *U.S. Public*, pg. 475
BMC MEDICAL CO., LTD.; *Int'l*, pg. 1076
BMC SELECT - ABILENE TRUSS PLANT—See Builders FirstSource, Inc.; *U.S. Public*, pg. 409
BMC SELECT - EVERETT TRUSS PLANT—See Builders FirstSource, Inc.; *U.S. Public*, pg. 409
BMC SELECT - HELENA TRUSS PLANT—See Builders FirstSource, Inc.; *U.S. Public*, pg. 409
BMC SELECT - IDAHO FALLS TRUSS PLANT—See Builders FirstSource, Inc.; *U.S. Public*, pg. 409
BMC SELECT - INDIO TRUSS AND PANEL PLANT—See Builders FirstSource, Inc.; *U.S. Public*, pg. 409
BMC SELECT - KALISPELL TRUSS PLANT—See Builders FirstSource, Inc.; *U.S. Public*, pg. 409
BMC SELECT - MISSOULA TRUSS PLANT—See Builders FirstSource, Inc.; *U.S. Public*, pg. 409
BMC SELECT - NEW BRAUNFELS TRUSS AND PANEL PLANT—See Builders FirstSource, Inc.; *U.S. Public*, pg. 409
BMC SELECT - WEST JORDAN TRUSS PLANT—See Builders FirstSource, Inc.; *U.S. Public*, pg. 410
BMC SOFTWARE AB—See KKR & Co. Inc.; *U.S. Public*, pg. 1240
BMC SOFTWARE ASIA PACIFIC PTE. LTD.—See KKR & Co. Inc.; *U.S. Public*, pg. 1240
BMC SOFTWARE ASIA SDN BHD—See KKR & Co. Inc.; *U.S. Public*, pg. 1240
BMC SOFTWARE A/S—See KKR & Co. Inc.; *U.S. Public*, pg. 1239
BMC SOFTWARE AS—See KKR & Co. Inc.; *U.S. Public*, pg. 1240
BMC SOFTWARE (AUSTRALIA) PTY. LTD.—See KKR & Co. Inc.; *U.S. Public*, pg. 1239
BMC SOFTWARE (AUSTRALIA) PTY. LTD.—See KKR & Co. Inc.; *U.S. Public*, pg. 1239
BMC SOFTWARE BELGIUM NV—See KKR & Co. Inc.; *U.S. Public*, pg. 1240
BMC SOFTWARE CANADA, INC.—See KKR & Co. Inc.; *U.S. Public*, pg. 1240
BMC SOFTWARE CANADA—See KKR & Co. Inc.; *U.S. Public*, pg. 1240
BMC SOFTWARE (CHINA) LIMITED—See KKR & Co. Inc.; *U.S. Public*, pg. 1239
BMC SOFTWARE CHINA—See KKR & Co. Inc.; *U.S. Public*, pg. 1239
BMC SOFTWARE DE ARGENTINA S.A.—See KKR & Co. Inc.; *U.S. Public*, pg. 1240
BMC SOFTWARE DE MEXICO, S.A. DE C.V.—See KKR & Co. Inc.; *U.S. Public*, pg. 1240
BMC SOFTWARE DISTRIBUTION B.V.—See KKR & Co. Inc.; *U.S. Public*, pg. 1240
BMC SOFTWARE DO BRASIL LTDA.—See KKR & Co. Inc.; *U.S. Public*, pg. 1240
BMC SOFTWARE EUROPE—See KKR & Co. Inc.; *U.S. Public*, pg. 1240
BMC SOFTWARE FRANCE SAS—See KKR & Co. Inc.; *U.S. Public*, pg. 1240
BMC SOFTWARE GMBH—See KKR & Co. Inc.; *U.S. Public*, pg. 1240
BMC SOFTWARE GMBH—See KKR & Co. Inc.; *U.S. Public*, pg. 1240
BMC SOFTWARE GMBH—See KKR & Co. Inc.; *U.S. Public*, pg. 1240
BMC SOFTWARE GMBH—See KKR & Co. Inc.; *U.S. Public*, pg. 1240
BMC SOFTWARE GMBH—See KKR & Co. Inc.; *U.S. Public*, pg. 1240
BMC SOFTWARE (HONG KONG) LIMITED—See KKR & Co. Inc.; *U.S. Public*, pg. 1239
BMC SOFTWARE, INC.—See KKR & Co. Inc.; *U.S. Public*, pg. 1239
BMC SOFTWARE INDIA PRIVATE LIMITED—See KKR & Co. Inc.; *U.S. Public*, pg. 1240
BMC SOFTWARE INVESTMENT, L.L.C.—See KKR & Co. Inc.; *U.S. Public*, pg. 1240
BMC SOFTWARE IRELAND LIMITED—See KKR & Co. Inc.; *U.S. Public*, pg. 1240
BMC SOFTWARE ISRAEL LTD.—See KKR & Co. Inc.; *U.S. Public*, pg. 1240
BMC SOFTWARE K.K.—See KKR & Co. Inc.; *U.S. Public*, pg. 1240
BMC SOFTWARE KOREA, LTD.—See KKR & Co. Inc.; *U.S. Public*, pg. 1240
BMC SOFTWARE LIMITED—See KKR & Co. Inc.; *U.S. Public*, pg. 1240
BMC SOFTWARE (NEW ZEALAND) LTD.—See KKR & Co. Inc.; *U.S. Public*, pg. 1239
BMC SOFTWARE OY—See KKR & Co. Inc.; *U.S. Public*, pg. 1240
BMC SOFTWARE SALES (POLAND) SP. O.O.—See KKR & Co. Inc.; *U.S. Public*, pg. 1240
BMC SOFTWARE S.A.—See KKR & Co. Inc.; *U.S. Public*, pg. 1240
BMC SOFTWARE S.A.—See KKR & Co. Inc.; *U.S. Public*, pg. 1240
BMC SOFTWARE S.R.L.—See KKR & Co. Inc.; *U.S. Public*, pg. 1240
BMC SOFTWARE S.R.L.—See KKR & Co. Inc.; *U.S. Public*, pg. 1240
BMC SOFTWARE (THAILAND) LIMITED—See KKR & Co. Inc.; *U.S. Public*, pg. 1239
BMC, SPOL. S.R.O.—See Agrofert Holding, a.s.; *Int'l*, pg. 219
BMC STOCK HOLDINGS, INC.—See Builders FirstSource, Inc.; *U.S. Public*, pg. 409
BMC TRANSPORTATION CO.—See Behlen Mfg. Co.; *U.S. Private*, pg. 515
BMC WEST CORPORATION—See Builders FirstSource, Inc.; *U.S. Public*, pg. 410
BMDI TUTA HEALTHCARE PTY LTD—See ICU Medical, Inc.; *U.S. Public*, pg. 1087
BMD PRIVATE LIMITED—See Seiren Co., Ltd.; *Int'l*, pg. 6691
BME CLEARING SAU—See SIX Group AG; *Int'l*, pg. 6966
BMEC (MALAYSIA) SDN. BHD.—See Boustead Singapore Limited; *Int'l*, pg. 1120
BMEC PTE. LTD.—See Boustead Singapore Limited; *Int'l*, pg. 1120
B MEDICAL SYSTEMS INDIA PRIVATE LIMITED—See Azenta, Inc.; *U.S. Public*, pg. 257
B MEDICAL SYSTEMS NORTH AMERICA LLC—See Azenta, Inc.; *U.S. Public*, pg. 257
B MEDICAL SYSTEMS S.A.R.L.—See Azenta, Inc.; *U.S. Public*, pg. 257
BME LIFT LTD.—See Schindler Holding AG; *Int'l*, pg. 6618
B. METZLER SEEL. SOHN & CO. HOLDING AG; *Int'l*, pg. 788
B. METZLER SEEL. SOHN & CO. KGAA—See B. Metzler seel. Sohn & Co. Holding AG; *Int'l*, pg. 788
B&M EUROPEAN VALUE RETAIL S.A.; *Int'l*, pg. 784
BMEX GOLD, INC.; *Int'l*, pg. 1076
BMEYE B.V.—See Edwards Lifesciences Corporation; *U.S. Public*, pg. 720
BMF ADVERTISING PTY LIMITED—See Enero Group Limited; *Int'l*, pg. 2423
BMF—See Enero Group Limited; *Int'l*, pg. 2423
BM&F USA INC.—See B3 S.A.; *Int'l*, pg. 791
BMG ARIOLA MUSICA S.P.A.—See Universal Music Group N.V.; *Int'l*, pg. 8081
BMG ARIOLA MUSIC LTDA.—See Universal Music Group N.V.; *Int'l*, pg. 8081
BMG ARIOLA, S.A.—See Universal Music Group N.V.; *Int'l*, pg. 8081
BMGB CAPITAL CORP.; *Int'l*, pg. 1076
BMG METALS, INC.; *U.S. Private*, pg. 600
BMG MUSIC PUBLISHING LTD.—See Universal Music Group N.V.; *Int'l*, pg. 8081
BMG MUSIC PUBLISHING—See Universal Music Group N.V.; *Int'l*, pg. 8081
BMG/MUSIC—See Universal Music Group N.V.; *Int'l*, pg. 8081
BMG PRODUCTION MUSIC (FRANCE) SAS—See Bertelsmann SE & Co. KGaA; *Int'l*, pg. 990
BMG PRODUCTION MUSIC (GERMANY) GMBH—See Bertelsmann SE & Co. KGaA; *Int'l*, pg. 990
BMG PRODUCTION MUSIC, INC.—See Bertelsmann SE & Co. KGaA; *Int'l*, pg. 990
BM GREENTECH BHD; *Int'l*, pg. 1075
BMG RESOURCES LIMITED; *Int'l*, pg. 1076
BMG RIGHTS MANAGEMENT (EUROPE) GMBH—See Bertelsmann SE & Co. KGaA; *Int'l*, pg. 994
BMG RIGHTS MANAGEMENT GMBH—See Bertelsmann SE & Co. KGaA; *Int'l*, pg. 990
BMG RIGHTS MANAGEMENT SERVICES (UK) LIMITED—See Bertelsmann SE & Co. KGaA; *Int'l*, pg. 990
BMG RIGHTS MANAGEMENT (US) LLC—See Bertelsmann SE & Co. KGaA; *Int'l*, pg. 990
BMG US - NEW YORK—See Universal Music Group N.V.; *Int'l*, pg. 8081
BM H BETEILIGUNGS MANAGEMENTGESELLSCHAFT HESSEN MBH—See Helaba Landesbank Hessen-Thuringen; *Int'l*, pg. 3327
BMH CORP.; *U.S. Private*, pg. 600
BMH INVESTMENT GROUP, LLC—See U.S. Financial Services, LLC; *U.S. Private*, pg. 4270
BMHIOL INDUSTRIES—See Hiolle Industries S.A.; *Int'l*, pg. 3401
BMH LTD.; *Int'l*, pg. 1076
B.M.H. SYSTEMS INC.—See Astec Industries, Inc.; *U.S. Public*, pg. 216
BMH TECHNOLOGY AB—See BMH Technology Oy; *Int'l*, pg. 1076
BMH TECHNOLOGY OY; *Int'l*, pg. 1076
BMH TECHNOLOGY OY—See BMH Technology Oy; *Int'l*, pg. 1076
BMH TECHNOLOGY SP. Z O.O.—See BMH Technology Oy; *Int'l*, pg. 1076
BMH WOOD TECHNOLOGY AB—See BMH Technology Oy; *Int'l*, pg. 1076
BMI BANK BSC—See Al Salam Bank-Bahrain B.S.C.; *Int'l*, pg. 282
BMI BENEFITS, L.L.C.—See Aon plc; *Int'l*, pg. 495
BMI ELITE, INC.; *U.S. Private*, pg. 600
BMI FINANCIAL GROUP, INC.; *U.S. Private*, pg. 600
BMI HEALTHCARE LIMITED—See Centene Corporation; *U.S. Public*, pg. 468
BMI HOLDINGS CO., LTD.—See ITOCHU Corporation; *Int'l*, pg. 3834
BMI IMAGING SYSTEMS INC.; *U.S. Private*, pg. 600
BMI LTD.—See Mapal Communications Ltd.; *Int'l*, pg. 4681
B&M INDUSTRIAL, INC.; *U.S. Private*, pg. 419
B+M INFORMATIK AG—See Allgeier SE; *Int'l*, pg. 338
BM INNOTECH INDUSTRY COMPANY LIMITED—See Bangkok Sheet Metal Public Company Ltd.; *Int'l*, pg. 835
BMI SOUTHEND PRIVATE HOSPITAL LTD.—See Centene Corporation; *U.S. Public*, pg. 468
BMI S.P.A.—See Stellantis N.V.; *Int'l*, pg. 7196
BMI SPORTS INFO PROPRIETARY LIMITED—See Caxton and CTP Publishers and Printers Ltd.; *Int'l*, pg. 1363

BMI SYON CLINIC LTD.—See Centene Corporation; *U.S. Public*, pg. 468
BMI SYSTEMS CORPORATION; *U.S. Private*, pg. 600
BMI THE EDGBASTON HOSPITAL—See Centene Corporation; *U.S. Public*, pg. 468
BMI THE HUDDERSFIELD HOSPITAL—See Centene Corporation; *U.S. Public*, pg. 468
BMI THE LANCASTER HOSPITAL—See Centene Corporation; *U.S. Public*, pg. 468
BMIT TECHNOLOGIES PLC—See Tunisie Telecom; *Int'l*, pg. 7972
B-MIX BETON NV—See SigmaRoc Plc; *Int'l*, pg. 6908
BMJ FOODS PR INC.; *U.S. Private*, pg. 601
BMK TURIZM VE OTELCILIK HIZMETLERI A.S.—See Dogus Holding AS; *Int'l*, pg. 2154
BMK UAB—See Atea ASA; *Int'l*, pg. 667
BMK & ZANATPRODUKT A.D.; *Int'l*, pg. 1076
B.M. LAWRENCE & CO.; *U.S. Private*, pg. 421
BML FOOD SCIENCE SOLUTIONS, INC.—See BML, Inc.; *Int'l*, pg. 1076
BML FUKUSHIMA, INC.—See BML, Inc.; *Int'l*, pg. 1076
BML HOLDINGS PTY. LTD.—See Grange Resources Limited; *Int'l*, pg. 3058
BML, INC.; *Int'l*, pg. 1076
BML LIFE SCIENCE HOLDINGS, INC.—See BML, Inc.; *Int'l*, pg. 1076
BML MEDICAL WORKS, INC.—See BML, Inc.; *Int'l*, pg. 1076
B&M METALS LP; *U.S. Private*, pg. 419
BM MIAMI INC.; *U.S. Private*, pg. 600
BMMI B.S.C.; *Int'l*, pg. 1076
BMMI DJIBOUTI—See BMMI B.S.C.; *Int'l*, pg. 1076
BMM, INC.—See Ingersoll Rand Inc.; *U.S. Public*, pg. 1120
BM MOBILITY LTD.; *Int'l*, pg. 1075
BMN MSI CO., LTD.—See BioLASCO Taiwan Co., Ltd.; *Int'l*, pg. 1038
B&M NV—See Mohawk Industries, Inc.; *U.S. Public*, pg. 1457
BMO ASSET MANAGEMENT CORP.—See Bank of Montreal; *Int'l*, pg. 846
BMO CAPITAL MARKETS CORP.—See Bank of Montreal; *Int'l*, pg. 846
BMO CAPITAL MARKETS EQUITY GROUP (U.S.), INC.—See Bank of Montreal; *Int'l*, pg. 846
BMO CAPITAL MARKETS LIMITED—See Bank of Montreal; *Int'l*, pg. 846
BMO CAPITAL MARKETS—See Bank of Montreal; *Int'l*, pg. 846
BMO CAPITAL TRUST—See Bank of Montreal; *Int'l*, pg. 846
BMO ENTREPRENOR AS—See Endur ASA; *Int'l*, pg. 2409
BMO FINANCE COMPANY I, S.A R.L.—See Bank of Montreal; *Int'l*, pg. 846
BMO FINANCIAL CORP.—See Bank of Montreal; *Int'l*, pg. 846
B-MOGEN BIOTECHNOLOGIES INC.—See Bio-Techne Corporation; *U.S. Public*, pg. 334
BMO GLOBAL ASSET MANAGEMENT (EMEA)—See Bank of Montreal; *Int'l*, pg. 846
BMO GLOBAL ASSET MANAGEMENT—See Bank of Montreal; *Int'l*, pg. 846
BMO GLOBAL WATER SOLUTIONS TACTIC FUND—See Bank of Montreal; *Int'l*, pg. 846
BMO GROUP RETIREMENT SERVICES INC.—See Bank of Montreal; *Int'l*, pg. 846
BMO HARRIS BANK N.A.—See Bank of Montreal; *Int'l*, pg. 846
BMO HARRIS EQUIPMENT FINANCE COMPANY—See Bank of Montreal; *Int'l*, pg. 846
BMO HARRIS FINANCIAL ADVISORS, INC.—See Bank of Montreal; *Int'l*, pg. 846
BMO HARRIS FINANCING, INC.—See Bank of Montreal; *Int'l*, pg. 846
B&M OIL COMPANY, INC.—See BRENNTAG SE; *Int'l*, pg. 1146
BMO INVESTORLINE, INC.—See Bank of Montreal; *Int'l*, pg. 846
BMO LIFE ASSURANCE COMPANY—See Bank of Montreal; *Int'l*, pg. 846
BMO LIFE INSURANCE COMPANY—See Bank of Montreal; *Int'l*, pg. 846
BMO NESBITT BURNS INC.—See Bank of Montreal; *Int'l*, pg. 846
BMO PRIVATE EQUITY (CANADA) INC.—See Bank of Montreal; *Int'l*, pg. 846
BMO REAL ESTATE PARTNERS GMBH & CO. KG—See Bank of Montreal; *Int'l*, pg. 847
BMO REAL ESTATE PARTNERS LLP—See Bank of Montreal; *Int'l*, pg. 847
BMO REINSURANCE LIMITED—See Bank of Montreal; *Int'l*, pg. 846
B. MOSS CLOTHING COMPANY LTD.; *U.S. Private*, pg. 419
BMO TRUST COMPANY—See Bank of Montreal; *Int'l*, pg. 846
B & M PAINTING CO., INC.—See ATL Partners, LLC; *U.S. Private*, pg. 369
B & M PAINTING CO., INC.—See British Columbia Investment Management Corp.; *Int'l*, pg. 1170

BMP BETEILIGUNGSMANAGEMENT AG; *Int'l*, pg. 1076
BMP GREENGAS GMBH—See EnBW Energie Baden-Wurttemberg AG; *Int'l*, pg. 2401
BMP METALS INC.; *Int'l*, pg. 1076
BMP POLYCO LTD.; *Int'l*, pg. 1075
BMP PHARMA TRADING AG; *Int'l*, pg. 1076
B&M RETAIL LIMITED—See Clayton, Dubilier & Rice, LLC; *U.S. Private*, pg. 920
B&M ROOFING OF COLORADO. INC.; *U.S. Private*, pg. 419
BMS ASIA INTERMEDIARIES LTD.—See BMS Group Ltd.; *Int'l*, pg. 1077
BMS ASIA INTER-MEDIARIES PTE., LTD.—See BMS Group Ltd.; *Int'l*, pg. 1077
BMS ASSOCIATES LTD.—See BMS Group Ltd.; *Int'l*, pg. 1077
BMS BERMUDA LTD.—See BMS Group Ltd.; *Int'l*, pg. 1077
BMS BVBA—See Alpha Associes Conseil SAS; *Int'l*, pg. 366
BMS CAT, INC.; *U.S. Private*, pg. 601
BMS CORPORATE SERVICES LIMITED—See Salcon Berhad; *Int'l*, pg. 6492
BMS ENTERPRISES INC.; *U.S. Private*, pg. 601
BMS FACULTATIVE LTD.—See BMS Group Ltd.; *Int'l*, pg. 1077
BMS FINANCE AB LIMITED—See Sancus Lending Group Limited; *Int'l*, pg. 6524
BMS GROUP LTD.; *Int'l*, pg. 1077
BMS HARRIS & DIXON LTD.—See BMS Group Ltd.; *Int'l*, pg. 1077
BMS HARRIS & DIXON MARINE LTD.—See BMS Group Ltd.; *Int'l*, pg. 1077
BMS HARRIS & DIXON REINSURANCE BROKERS LTD.—See BMS Group Ltd.; *Int'l*, pg. 1077
BMS HOLDINGS SPAIN, S.L.—See Bristol-Myers Squibb Company; *U.S. Public*, pg. 384
BMS INTERNATIONAL INTERMEDIARIES LTD.—See BMS Group Ltd.; *Int'l*, pg. 1077
BMS.K—See KMW Inc.; *Int'l*, pg. 4205
BMS MANAGEMENT SERVICES LTD.—See BMS Group Ltd.; *Int'l*, pg. 1077
BMS PHARMACEUTICAL KOREA LIMITED—See Bristol-Myers Squibb Company; *U.S. Public*, pg. 384
BMS RE LTD.—See BMS Group Ltd.; *Int'l*, pg. 1077
BMS SPECIAL RISK SERVICES LTD.—See BMS Group Ltd.; *Int'l*, pg. 1077
BMSVISION LLC—See Alpha Associes Conseil SAS; *Int'l*, pg. 366
BMS VISION LTD.—See Alpha Associes Conseil SAS; *Int'l*, pg. 366
BMS VISION RE LTD.—See BMS Group Ltd.; *Int'l*, pg. 1077
BMT ARGOSS B.V.—See BMT Group Limited; *Int'l*, pg. 1077
BMT ARGOSS LIMITED—See BMT Group Limited; *Int'l*, pg. 1077
BMT ASIA PACIFIC LTD.—See BMT Group Limited; *Int'l*, pg. 1077
BMT ASIA PACIFIC PTE. LTD.—See BMT Group Limited; *Int'l*, pg. 1077
BMTC GROUP INC.; *Int'l*, pg. 1078
BMT CO., LTD.; *Int'l*, pg. 1077
BMT CO., LTD. - YANGSAN FACTORY—See BMT Co., Ltd.; *Int'l*, pg. 1077
BMT COMMODITY CORPORATION; *U.S. Private*, pg. 601
BMT CONSULTANTS (INDIA) PVT. LTD.—See BMT Group Limited; *Int'l*, pg. 1077
BMT CORDAH LIMITED—See BMT Group Limited; *Int'l*, pg. 1077
BMT DE BEER BV—See BMT Group Limited; *Int'l*, pg. 1077
BMT DEFENCE SERVICES (AUSTRALIA) PTY. LTD.—See BMT Group Limited; *Int'l*, pg. 1077
BMT DEFENCE SERVICES LTD.—See BMT Group Limited; *Int'l*, pg. 1077
BMT DESIGNERS & PLANNERS, INC.—See BMT Group Limited; *Int'l*, pg. 1077
BMT DESIGN & TECHNOLOGY PTY LTD—See BMT Group Limited; *Int'l*, pg. 1077
BM TECHNOLOGIES, INC.; *U.S. Public*, pg. 366
BMT ENERGY AND ENVIRONMENT—See BMT Group Limited; *Int'l*, pg. 1077
BMT ENERGY—See BMT Group Limited; *Int'l*, pg. 1077
BMT FLEET TECHNOLOGY LIMITED—See BMT Group Limited; *Int'l*, pg. 1077
BMT FLEET TECHNOLOGY LIMITED—See BMT Group Limited; *Int'l*, pg. 1077
BMT FLEET TECHNOLOGY LIMITED—See BMT Group Limited; *Int'l*, pg. 1078
BMT FLEET TECHNOLOGY LIMITED—See BMT Group Limited; *Int'l*, pg. 1078
BMT FLUID MECHANICS LIMITED—See BMT Group Limited; *Int'l*, pg. 1078
BMT GMBH LABORPRODUKTE—See Thermo Fisher Scientific Inc.; *U.S. Public*, pg. 2153
BMT GROUP LIMITED; *Int'l*, pg. 1077
BMT HI-Q SIGMA LTD—See BMT Group Limited; *Int'l*, pg. 1078

BMTI CR S.R.O.—See STRABAG SE; *Int'l*, pg. 7229
BMT INSURANCE ADVISORS INC.—See Bryn Mawr Bank Corporation; *U.S. Public*, pg. 408
BMTI POLSKA SP.Z.O.O.—See STRABAG SE; *Int'l*, pg. 7229
BMT ISIS LTD—See BMT Group Limited; *Int'l*, pg. 1078
BMT JFA CONSULTANTS PTY LTD—See BMT Group Limited; *Int'l*, pg. 1078
BMT NIGEL GEE LTD—See BMT Group Limited; *Int'l*, pg. 1078
BMT OCEANICA PTY LTD.—See BMT Group Limited; *Int'l*, pg. 1078
BMT RELIABILITY CONSULTANTS LTD.—See BMT Group Limited; *Int'l*, pg. 1078
BMT SCIENTIFIC MARINE SERVICES INC—See BMT Group Limited; *Int'l*, pg. 1078
BMT SCIENTIFIC MARINE SERVICES LTDA—See BMT Group Limited; *Int'l*, pg. 1078
BMT SMART LTD—See BMT Group Limited; *Int'l*, pg. 1078
BMT SURVEYS (AMSTERDAM) B.V.—See BMT Group Limited; *Int'l*, pg. 1078
BMT SURVEYS (ANTWERP) NV—See BMT Group Limited; *Int'l*, pg. 1078
BMT SURVEYS (LONDON) LIMITED—See BMT Group Limited; *Int'l*, pg. 1078
BMT SURVEYS (ROTTERDAM) B.V.—See BMT Group Limited; *Int'l*, pg. 1078
BMT SYNTEK TECHNOLOGIES, INC.—See BMT Group Limited; *Int'l*, pg. 1078
BMT WBM INC.—See BMT Group Limited; *Int'l*, pg. 1078
BMT WBM PTY. LTD.—See BMT Group Limited; *Int'l*, pg. 1078
BM VALLA EHF—See Heidelberg Materials AG; *Int'l*, pg. 3308
BMW AUSTRALIA FINANCE LTD.—See Bayerische Motoren Werke Aktiengesellschaft; *Int'l*, pg. 911
BMW AUSTRALIA LTD.—See Bayerische Motoren Werke Aktiengesellschaft; *Int'l*, pg. 911
BMW AUSTRIA BANK GMBH—See Bayerische Motoren Werke Aktiengesellschaft; *Int'l*, pg. 911
BMW AUSTRIA GESELLSCHAFT M.B.H.—See Bayerische Motoren Werke Aktiengesellschaft; *Int'l*, pg. 911
BMW AUSTRIA LEASING GMBH—See Bayerische Motoren Werke Aktiengesellschaft; *Int'l*, pg. 911
BMW AUTOMOTIVE (IRELAND) LTD.—See Bayerische Motoren Werke Aktiengesellschaft; *Int'l*, pg. 911
BMW BANK GMBH—See Bayerische Motoren Werke Aktiengesellschaft; *Int'l*, pg. 911
BMW BANK OF NORTH AMERICA INC.—See Bayerische Motoren Werke Aktiengesellschaft; *Int'l*, pg. 912
BMW BRILLIANCE AUTOMOTIVE LTD.—See Bayerische Motoren Werke Aktiengesellschaft; *Int'l*, pg. 911
BMW BRILLIANCE AUTOMOTIVE LTD.—See Brilliance China Automotive Holdings Limited; *Int'l*, pg. 1163
BMW CANADA INC.—See Bayerische Motoren Werke Aktiengesellschaft; *Int'l*, pg. 912
BMW CAR IT GMBH—See Bayerische Motoren Werke Aktiengesellschaft; *Int'l*, pg. 911
BMWC CONSTRUCTORS, INC. - SEATTLE—See BMWC Group Inc.; *U.S. Private*, pg. 601
BMWC CONSTRUCTORS, INC.—See BMWC Group Inc.; *U.S. Private*, pg. 601
BMWC GROUP INC.; *U.S. Private*, pg. 601
BMW CHINA AUTOMOTIVE TRADING LTD—See Bayerische Motoren Werke Aktiengesellschaft; *Int'l*, pg. 911
BMW CREDIT (MALAYSIA) SDN BHD—See Bayerische Motoren Werke Aktiengesellschaft; *Int'l*, pg. 911
BMW DANMARK A/S—See Bayerische Motoren Werke Aktiengesellschaft; *Int'l*, pg. 911
BMW DE ARGENTINA S.A.—See Bayerische Motoren Werke Aktiengesellschaft; *Int'l*, pg. 910
BMW DE MEXICO, S. A. DE C. V.—See Bayerische Motoren Werke Aktiengesellschaft; *Int'l*, pg. 912
BMW FAHRZEUGTECHNIK GMBH—See Bayerische Motoren Werke Aktiengesellschaft; *Int'l*, pg. 911
BMW FINANCE S.N.C.—See Bayerische Motoren Werke Aktiengesellschaft; *Int'l*, pg. 911
BMW FINANCIAL SERVICES B.V.—See Bayerische Motoren Werke Aktiengesellschaft; *Int'l*, pg. 911
BMW FINANCIAL SERVICES DE MEXICO S.A. DE C.V.—See Bayerische Motoren Werke Aktiengesellschaft; *Int'l*, pg. 911
BMW FINANCIAL SERVICES DENMARK A/S—See Bayerische Motoren Werke Aktiengesellschaft; *Int'l*, pg. 911
BMW FINANCIAL SERVICES (GB) LTD—See Bayerische Motoren Werke Aktiengesellschaft; *Int'l*, pg. 911
BMW FINANCIAL SERVICES GMBH—See Bayerische Motoren Werke Aktiengesellschaft; *Int'l*, pg. 911
BMW FINANCIAL SERVICES (IRELAND) DAC—See Bayerische Motoren Werke Aktiengesellschaft; *Int'l*, pg. 911
BMW FINANCIAL SERVICES KOREA CO. LTD.—See Bayerische Motoren Werke Aktiengesellschaft; *Int'l*, pg. 911
BMW FINANCIAL SERVICES NA, LLC—See Bayerische Motoren Werke Aktiengesellschaft; *Int'l*, pg. 912
BMW FINANCIAL SERVICES NEW ZEALAND LTD.—See Bayerische Motoren Werke Aktiengesellschaft; *Int'l*, pg. 911

BMWC GROUP INC.

BMW FINANCIAL SERVICES SINGAPORE PTE. LTD.—See Bayerische Motoren Werke Aktiengesellschaft; *Int'l*, pg. 911
BMW FINANCIAL SERVICES (SOUTH AFRICA) (PTY) LTD.—See Bayerische Motoren Werke Aktiengesellschaft; *Int'l*, pg. 911
BMW FINANZ VERWALTUNGS GMBH—See Bayerische Motoren Werke Aktiengesellschaft; *Int'l*, pg. 911
BMW FRANCE S.A.—See Bayerische Motoren Werke Aktiengesellschaft; *Int'l*, pg. 911
BMW (GB) LTD.—See Bayerische Motoren Werke Aktiengesellschaft; *Int'l*, pg. 910
BMW HAMS HALL MOTOREN GMBH—See Bayerische Motoren Werke Aktiengesellschaft; *Int'l*, pg. 911
BMW HOLDING B.V.—See Bayerische Motoren Werke Aktiengesellschaft; *Int'l*, pg. 911
BMW HUNGARY KFT.—See Bayerische Motoren Werke Aktiengesellschaft; *Int'l*, pg. 911
BMW IBERICA S.A.—See Bayerische Motoren Werke Aktiengesellschaft; *Int'l*, pg. 911
BMW INDIA FINANCIAL SERVICES PRIVATE LTD.—See Bayerische Motoren Werke Aktiengesellschaft; *Int'l*, pg. 911
BMW INDIA PRIVATE LIMITED—See Bayerische Motoren Werke Aktiengesellschaft; *Int'l*, pg. 911
BMW INDUSTRIES LIMITED; *Int'l*, pg. 1078
BMW INGENIEUR ZENTRUM GMBH & CO.—See Bayerische Motoren Werke Aktiengesellschaft; *Int'l*, pg. 911
BMW INSURANCE SERVICES KOREA CO., LTD.—See Bayerische Motoren Werke Aktiengesellschaft; *Int'l*, pg. 911
BMW ITALIA S.P.A.—See Bayerische Motoren Werke Aktiengesellschaft; *Int'l*, pg. 911
BMW JAPAN CORP.—See Bayerische Motoren Werke Aktiengesellschaft; *Int'l*, pg. 911
BMW KOREA CO. LTD.—See Bayerische Motoren Werke Aktiengesellschaft; *Int'l*, pg. 910
BMW KUNDENBETREUUNG—See Bayerische Motoren Werke Aktiengesellschaft; *Int'l*, pg. 911
BMW LEASE (MALAYSIA) SDN. BHD.—See Bayerische Motoren Werke Aktiengesellschaft; *Int'l*, pg. 911
BMW LEASING CORP.—See Bayerische Motoren Werke Aktiengesellschaft; *Int'l*, pg. 912
BMW LEASING GMBH—See Bayerische Motoren Werke Aktiengesellschaft; *Int'l*, pg. 912
BMW MADRID S.L.—See Bayerische Motoren Werke Aktiengesellschaft; *Int'l*, pg. 912
BMW MALAYSIA SDN BHD—See Bayerische Motoren Werke Aktiengesellschaft; *Int'l*, pg. 910
BMW MALTA LTD.—See Bayerische Motoren Werke Aktiengesellschaft; *Int'l*, pg. 912
BMW MANUFACTURING CO., LLC—See Bayerische Motoren Werke Aktiengesellschaft; *Int'l*, pg. 912
BMW MANUFACTURING INDUSTRIA DE MOTOS DA AMAZONIA LTDA.—See Bayerische Motoren Werke Aktiengesellschaft; *Int'l*, pg. 912
BMW MANUFACTURING (THAILAND) CO., LTD.—See Bayerische Motoren Werke Aktiengesellschaft; *Int'l*, pg. 912
BMW MASCHINENFABRIK SPANDAU GMBH—See Bayerische Motoren Werke Aktiengesellschaft; *Int'l*, pg. 912
BMW M GMBH GESELLSCHAFT FUR INDIVIDUELLE AUTOMOBILE—See Bayerische Motoren Werke Aktiengesellschaft; *Int'l*, pg. 912
BMW M GMBH—See Bayerische Motoren Werke Aktiengesellschaft; *Int'l*, pg. 912
BMW MOTOREN GES.M.B.H.—See Bayerische Motoren Werke Aktiengesellschaft; *Int'l*, pg. 911
BMW MOTOREN GMBH—See Bayerische Motoren Werke Aktiengesellschaft; *Int'l*, pg. 910
BMW NEDERLAND B.V.—See Bayerische Motoren Werke Aktiengesellschaft; *Int'l*, pg. 912
BMW NEW ZEALAND LTD.—See Bayerische Motoren Werke Aktiengesellschaft; *Int'l*, pg. 912
BMW NORGE AS—See Bayerische Motoren Werke Aktiengesellschaft; *Int'l*, pg. 912
BMW NORTHERN EUROPE AB—See Bayerische Motoren Werke Aktiengesellschaft; *Int'l*, pg. 912
BMW NORTHWEST INC.; *U.S. Private*, pg. 601
BMW OF AUSTIN; *U.S. Private*, pg. 601
BMW OF BAYSIDE; *U.S. Private*, pg. 601
BMW OF DARIEN; *U.S. Private*, pg. 601
BMW OF EL PASO—See Group 1 Automotive, Inc.; *U.S. Public*, pg. 970
BMW OF ESCONDIDO; *U.S. Private*, pg. 601
BMW OF MACON; *U.S. Private*, pg. 601
BMW OF MANHATTAN INC.—See Bayerische Motoren Werke Aktiengesellschaft; *Int'l*, pg. 912
BMW OF NORTH AMERICA, LLC—See Bayerische Motoren Werke Aktiengesellschaft; *Int'l*, pg. 912
BMW OF SILVER SPRING—See Atlantic Automotive Corp.; *U.S. Private*, pg. 371
BMW OF STRATHAM—See Group 1 Automotive, Inc.; *U.S. Public*, pg. 970
BMW OVERSEAS ENTERPRISES N. V.—See Bayerische Motoren Werke Aktiengesellschaft; *Int'l*, pg. 912
BMW PORTUGAL LDA—See Bayerische Motoren Werke Aktiengesellschaft; *Int'l*, pg. 912

BMW SA/NV—See Bayerische Motoren Werke Aktiengesellschaft; *Int'l*, pg. 912
BMW (SCHWEIZ) AG—See Bayerische Motoren Werke Aktiengesellschaft; *Int'l*, pg. 910
BMW SLOVENSKA REPUBLIKA S.R.O.—See Bayerische Motoren Werke Aktiengesellschaft; *Int'l*, pg. 912
BMW (SOUTH AFRICA) PTY. LTD. - ROSSLYN PLANT—See Bayerische Motoren Werke Aktiengesellschaft; *Int'l*, pg. 911
BMW (SOUTH AFRICA) PTY. LTD.—See Bayerische Motoren Werke Aktiengesellschaft; *Int'l*, pg. 910
BMW SVERIGE AB—See Bayerische Motoren Werke Aktiengesellschaft; *Int'l*, pg. 912
BMW SYDNEY PTY. LTD.—See Bayerische Motoren Werke Aktiengesellschaft; *Int'l*, pg. 912
BMW (THAILAND) CO. LTD.—See Bayerische Motoren Werke Aktiengesellschaft; *Int'l*, pg. 911
BMW TORONTO; *Int'l*, pg. 1078
BMW (UK) CAPITAL PLC—See Bayerische Motoren Werke Aktiengesellschaft; *Int'l*, pg. 911
BMW (UK) LTD. - HAMS HALL PLANT—See Bayerische Motoren Werke Aktiengesellschaft; *Int'l*, pg. 911
BMW (UK) LTD—See Bayerische Motoren Werke Aktiengesellschaft; *Int'l*, pg. 911
BMW US CAPITAL, LLC—See Bayerische Motoren Werke Aktiengesellschaft; *Int'l*, pg. 912
BMW (US) HOLDING CORPORATION—See Bayerische Motoren Werke Aktiengesellschaft; *Int'l*, pg. 912
BN AEROCOMPONENTS LTD—See B-N Group Limited; *Int'l*, pg. 785
BN AEROSYSTEMS LTD—See B-N Group Limited; *Int'l*, pg. 785
BNA INC.—See Sysmex Corporation; *Int'l*, pg. 7388
BNA INSURANCE & INVESTMENTS, INC.—See Bank of New Albany; *U.S. Private*, pg. 466
BNA INTERNATIONAL INC.—See Bloomberg L.P.; *U.S. Private*, pg. 584
B NANJI ENTERPRISES LIMITED; *Int'l*, pg. 783
BNA NUROL BAE SYSTEMS AIR SYSTEMS INC.—See Nurol Holding A.S.; *Int'l*, pg. 5490
BNA PLUS—See Bloomberg L.P.; *U.S. Private*, pg. 584
BNA SOFTWARE—See Bloomberg L.P.; *U.S. Private*, pg. 584
BN AVIATION LTD—See B-N Group Limited; *Int'l*, pg. 785
BN BANK ASA—See SpareBank 1 Gruppen AS; *Int'l*, pg. 7125
B & N BASE OILS LTD.—See FUCHS SE; *Int'l*, pg. 2803
BNB BANK—See Financial Services Corp.; *U.S. Private*, pg. 1508
BNBM PNG LIMITED—See China National Building Material Group Co., Ltd.; *Int'l*, pg. 1525
BNBS, INC.—See Deluxe Corporation; *U.S. Public*, pg. 652
BNBUILDERS, INC.; *U.S. Private*, pg. 601
BNC COMPANY CO., LTD.; *Int'l*, pg. 1078
BNCCORP, INC.; *U.S. Public*, pg. 366
BNC INSURANCE AGENCY, INC.; *U.S. Private*, pg. 601
BNC KOREA CO., LTD.; *Int'l*, pg. 1078
B&N CLEARING AND ENVIRONMENTAL, LLC—See Quanta Services, Inc.; *U.S. Public*, pg. 1750
BNC NATIONAL BANK—See BNCCORP, Inc.; *U.S. Public*, pg. 366
BNC REAL ESTATE; *U.S. Private*, pg. 601
BN DEFENCE LTD—See B-N Group Limited; *Int'l*, pg. 785
BND ELEKTRIK URETIM A.S.—See Isiklar Holding A.S.; *Int'l*, pg. 3818
BNDES PARTICIPACOES SA; *Int'l*, pg. 1078
BNDT PRUFTECHNIK GMBH—See TUV Rheinland Berlin-Brandenburg Pfalz e.V.; *Int'l*, pg. 7981
BNE LAND & DEVELOPMENT CO.—See Boddie-Noell Enterprises, Inc.; *U.S. Private*, pg. 607
BNET MEDIA GROUP, INC.; *U.S. Public*, pg. 366
BNG BANK N.V.; *Int'l*, pg. 1078
BNG CAPITAL MANAGEMENT B.V.—See BNG Bank N.V.; *Int'l*, pg. 1078
BNG CONSULTANCY SERVICES B.V.—See BNG Bank N.V.; *Int'l*, pg. 1078
BNG GEBIEDSONTWIKKELING BV—See BNG Bank N.V.; *Int'l*, pg. 1078
BNG MANAGEMENT SERVICES B.V.—See BNG Bank N.V.; *Int'l*, pg. 1079
B-N GROUP LIMITED; *Int'l*, pg. 785
BNG SPECIALIZED ENGINEERING SERVICES LTD—See Tetra Tech, Inc.; *U.S. Public*, pg. 2022
BNG VASTGOEDONTWIKKELING B.V.—See BNG Bank N.V.; *Int'l*, pg. 1079
BNG VERMOGENSBEHEER BV—See BNG Bank N.V.; *Int'l*, pg. 1079
BNH FINANCIAL; *U.S. Private*, pg. 601
BNH MEDICAL CENTER CO., LTD.—See Bangkok Dusit Medical Services Public Company Limited; *Int'l*, pg. 833
BNI COAL, LTD.—See ALLETE, Inc.; *U.S. Public*, pg. 79
BNI ENERGY, INC.—See ALLETE, Inc.; *U.S. Public*, pg. 79
BNI PUBLICATIONS, INC.; *U.S. Private*, pg. 602
BNI REMITTANCE LIMITED—See PT Bank Negara Indonesia (Persero) Tbk; *Int'l*, pg. 6027
BNI SECURITIES PTE. LTD.—See PT Bank Negara Indonesia (Persero) Tbk; *Int'l*, pg. 6027

CORPORATE AFFILIATIONS

BNK ADVISORY GROUP, INC.—See Asplundh Tree Expert Co.; *U.S. Private*, pg. 353
BNK ASSET MANAGEMENT CO., LTD.—See BNK Financial Group Inc.; *Int'l*, pg. 1079
BNK BANKING CORPORATION LIMITED; *Int'l*, pg. 1079
BNK CAPITAL CO., LTD.—See BNK Financial Group Inc.; *Int'l*, pg. 1079
BNKC (CAMBODIA) MFI PLC—See BNK Financial Group Inc.; *Int'l*, pg. 1079
BNK COMMODITIES PVT LTD.—See Quest Capital Markets Ltd.; *Int'l*, pg. 6160
BNK CREDIT INFORMATION CO., LTD.—See BNK Financial Group Inc.; *Int'l*, pg. 1079
BNK FINANCIAL GROUP INC.; *Int'l*, pg. 1079
BNK PETROLEUM INC.; *U.S. Public*, pg. 366
BNK SAVINGS BANK CO., LTD.—See BNK Financial Group Inc.; *Int'l*, pg. 1079
BNK SECURITIES CO., LTD.—See BNK Financial Group Inc.; *Int'l*, pg. 1079
BNK SYSTEM CO., LTD.—See BNK Financial Group Inc.; *Int'l*, pg. 1079
BNK VENTURE CAPITAL CO., LTD.—See BNK Financial Group Inc.; *Int'l*, pg. 1079
BNL EUROLENS SA—See EssilorLuxottica SA; *Int'l*, pg. 2512
BNL FINANCE SPA—See BNP Paribas SA; *Int'l*, pg. 1080
BNL (JAPAN) INC—See Synnovia Plc; *Int'l*, pg. 7386
BNL TECHNOLOGIES INC.; *U.S. Private*, pg. 602
BNL (UK) LIMITED—See Synnovia Plc; *Int'l*, pg. 7385
BNL (US) INC—See Synnovia Plc; *Int'l*, pg. 7386
BN MEDIA LLC; *U.S. Private*, pg. 601
BNM STENSTRUP A/S—See Dr. Ing. K. Busch GmbH; *Int'l*, pg. 2192
BNN TECHNOLOGY PLC; *Int'l*, pg. 1079
BNNT TECHNOLOGY LIMITED—See PPK Group Limited; *Int'l*, pg. 5951
BNP COMMODITY FUTURES INC.—See BNP Paribas SA; *Int'l*, pg. 1087
BNP COOPER-NEFF GROUP—See BNP Paribas SA; *Int'l*, pg. 1087
BNP FACTOR - PORTUGAL—See BNP Paribas SA; *Int'l*, pg. 1080
BNP JERSEY TRUST CORP. LIMITED—See BNP Paribas SA; *Int'l*, pg. 1081
BNP LEASE GROUP S.P.A.—See BNP Paribas SA; *Int'l*, pg. 1087
BNP MEDIA, INC.; *U.S. Private*, pg. 602
BNP MEDIA—See BNP Media, Inc;; *U.S. Private*, pg. 602
BNP PACIFIC (AUSTRALIA) LTD.—See BNP Paribas SA; *Int'l*, pg. 1081
BNP PARIBAS ABU DHABI—See BNP Paribas SA; *Int'l*, pg. 1081
BNP PARIBAS ANDES—See BNP Paribas SA; *Int'l*, pg. 1081
BNP PARIBAS ANTILLES GUYANE SA—See BNP Paribas SA; *Int'l*, pg. 1081
BNP PARIBAS ARBITRAGE—See BNP Paribas SA; *Int'l*, pg. 1081
BNP PARIBAS ARGENTINA—See BNP Paribas SA; *Int'l*, pg. 1081
BNP PARIBAS ASIA PRIVATE BANKING—See BNP Paribas SA; *Int'l*, pg. 1081
BNP PARIBAS ASSET MANAGEMENT HOLDING SA—See BNP Paribas SA; *Int'l*, pg. 1081
BNP PARIBAS ASSET MANAGEMENT INC.—See BNP Paribas SA; *Int'l*, pg. 1082
BNP PARIBAS ASSET MANAGEMENT INDIA PRIVATE LTD—See BNP Paribas SA; *Int'l*, pg. 1082
BNP PARIBAS ASSET MANAGEMENT LUXEMBOURG S.A.—See BNP Paribas SA; *Int'l*, pg. 1082
BNP PARIBAS ASSET MANAGEMENT S.A.S.—See BNP Paribas SA; *Int'l*, pg. 1082
BNP PARIBAS ASSET MANAGEMENT SGR SPA—See BNP Paribas SA; *Int'l*, pg. 1087
BNP PARIBAS ASSET MANAGEMENT SINGAPORE LIMITED—See BNP Paribas SA; *Int'l*, pg. 1082
BNP PARIBAS ASSET MANAGEMENT—See BNP Paribas SA; *Int'l*, pg. 1082
BNP PARIBAS ATHENS BRANCH—See BNP Paribas SA; *Int'l*, pg. 1082
BNP PARIBAS BANGKOK—See BNP Paribas SA; *Int'l*, pg. 1081
BNP PARIBAS BANK JSC—See BNP Paribas SA; *Int'l*, pg. 1082
BNP PARIBAS BANK N.V.—See BNP Paribas SA; *Int'l*, pg. 1086
BNP PARIBAS BANK POLSKA SA—See BNP Paribas SA; *Int'l*, pg. 1082
BNP PARIBAS BDDI PARTICIPATIONS—See BNP Paribas SA; *Int'l*, pg. 1082
BNP PARIBAS BEIJING—See BNP Paribas SA; *Int'l*, pg. 1081
BNP PARIBAS BROKERAGE SERVICES, INC—See BNP Paribas SA; *Int'l*, pg. 1087
BNP PARIBAS-BRUSSELS BRANCH—See BNP Paribas SA; *Int'l*, pg. 1087
BNP PARIBAS BULGARIA EAD—See BNP Paribas SA; *Int'l*, pg. 1082

COMPANY NAME INDEX

BNP PARIBAS (CANADA) INC.—See BNP Paribas SA; *Int'l*, pg. 1081
BNP PARIBAS CANADA-QUEBEC—See BNP Paribas SA; *Int'l*, pg. 1082
BNP PARIBAS CANADA—See BNP Paribas SA; *Int'l*, pg. 1082
BNP PARIBAS (CANADA)—See BNP Paribas SA; *Int'l*, pg. 1081
BNP PARIBAS CANADA-TORONTO—See BNP Paribas SA; *Int'l*, pg. 1082
BNP PARIBAS CAPITAL (ASIA PACIFIC) LTD.—See BNP Paribas SA; *Int'l*, pg. 1083
BNP PARIBAS CAPITAL INVESTMENTS LTD.—See BNP Paribas SA; *Int'l*, pg. 1083
BNP PARIBAS CAPITAL (SINGAPORE) LTD.—See BNP Paribas SA; *Int'l*, pg. 1083
BNP PARIBAS CAPSTAR PARTNERS INC.—See BNP Paribas SA; *Int'l*, pg. 1087
BNP PARIBAS CARDIF EMEKLILIK ANONIM SIRKETI—See BNP Paribas SA; *Int'l*, pg. 1083
BNP PARIBAS CARDIF - PORTUGAL—See BNP Paribas SA; *Int'l*, pg. 1083
BNP PARIBAS CARDIF SA—See BNP Paribas SA; *Int'l*, pg. 1083
BNP PARIBAS CARDIF TCB LIFE INSURANCE CO., LTD.—See Taiwan Cooperative Financial Holding Co., Ltd.; *Int'l*, pg. 7419
BNP PARIBAS-CHICAGO—See BNP Paribas SA; *Int'l*, pg. 1087
BNP PARIBAS CHINA GROUP—See BNP Paribas SA; *Int'l*, pg. 1081
BNP PARIBAS (CHINA) LTD.—See BNP Paribas SA; *Int'l*, pg. 1081
BNP PARIBAS CMG LTD.—See BNP Paribas SA; *Int'l*, pg. 1082
BNP PARIBAS COLUMBIA—See BNP Paribas SA; *Int'l*, pg. 1083
BNP PARIBAS COMMERCIAL FINANCE LTD.—See BNP Paribas SA; *Int'l*, pg. 1084
BNP PARIBAS COMMODITY FUTURES LTD.—See BNP Paribas SA; *Int'l*, pg. 1083
BNP PARIBAS-DALLAS—See BNP Paribas SA; *Int'l*, pg. 1087
BNP PARIBAS DEVELOPPEMENT SA—See BNP Paribas SA; *Int'l*, pg. 1083
BNP PARIBAS DUBAI—See BNP Paribas SA; *Int'l*, pg. 1083
BNP PARIBAS DUBLIN—See BNP Paribas SA; *Int'l*, pg. 1083
BNP PARIBAS E & B LTD.—See BNP Paribas SA; *Int'l*, pg. 1083
BNP PARIBAS EL DJAZAIR S.P.A.—See BNP Paribas SA; *Int'l*, pg. 1083
BNP PARIBAS ENERGY TRADING CANADA CORP—See BNP Paribas SA; *Int'l*, pg. 1083
BNP PARIBAS EQUITY STRATEGIES S.N.C.—See BNP Paribas SA; *Int'l*, pg. 1083
BNP PARIBAS ESPANA S.A.—See BNP Paribas SA; *Int'l*, pg. 1083
BNP PARIBAS FACTOR ASIA LTD.—See BNP Paribas SA; *Int'l*, pg. 1084
BNP PARIBAS FACTOR A/S—See BNP Paribas SA; *Int'l*, pg. 1084
BNP PARIBAS FACTOR GMBH—See BNP Paribas SA; *Int'l*, pg. 1084
BNP PARIBAS FACTOR, SA SUCURSAL EN ESPANA—See BNP Paribas SA; *Int'l*, pg. 1084
BNP PARIBAS FACTOR—See BNP Paribas SA; *Int'l*, pg. 1083
BNP PARIBAS FIN AMS—See BNP Paribas SA; *Int'l*, pg. 1084
BNP PARIBAS FINANCE (HONG-KONG) LTD.—See BNP Paribas SA; *Int'l*, pg. 1084
BNP PARIBAS FINANCE PLC—See BNP Paribas SA; *Int'l*, pg. 1084
BNP PARIBAS FINANCIAL SERVICES LLC—See BNP Paribas SA; *Int'l*, pg. 1087
BNP PARIBAS FLEET HOLDINGS LTD.—See BNP Paribas SA; *Int'l*, pg. 1084
BNP PARIBAS FORTIS FACTOR NV/SA—See BNP Paribas SA; *Int'l*, pg. 1084
BNP PARIBAS FORTIS FUNDING SA—See BNP Paribas SA; *Int'l*, pg. 1084
BNP PARIBAS FORTIS MERCHANT BANKING—See BNP Paribas SA; *Int'l*, pg. 1084
BNP PARIBAS FORTIS SA/NV—See BNP Paribas SA; *Int'l*, pg. 1084
BNP PARIBAS FORTIS YATIRIMLAR HOLDING A.S.—See BNP Paribas SA; *Int'l*, pg. 1084
BNP PARIBAS FRANKFURT BRANCH—See BNP Paribas SA; *Int'l*, pg. 1084
BNP PARIBAS FUND SERVICES AUSTRALASIA LTD.—See BNP Paribas SA; *Int'l*, pg. 1084
BNP PARIBAS FUND SERVICES DUBLIN LTD.—See BNP Paribas SA; *Int'l*, pg. 1085
BNP PARIBAS GUANGZHOU—See BNP Paribas SA; *Int'l*, pg. 1081
BNP PARIBAS GUYANE—See BNP Paribas SA; *Int'l*, pg. 1085

BNP PARIBAS HOME LOAN SFH—See BNP Paribas SA; *Int'l*, pg. 1085
BNP PARIBAS HONG KONG—See BNP Paribas SA; *Int'l*, pg. 1081
BNP PARIBAS-HOUSTON—See BNP Paribas SA; *Int'l*, pg. 1087
BNP PARIBAS HUNGARIA BANK RT—See BNP Paribas SA; *Int'l*, pg. 1085
BNP PARIBAS IMMOBILIER PROMOTION IMMOBILIER D'ENTREPRISE—See BNP Paribas SA; *Int'l*, pg. 1085
BNP PARIBAS IMMOBILIER RESIDENTIEL PROMOTION MEDITERRANEE—See BNP Paribas SA; *Int'l*, pg. 1085
BNP PARIBAS IMMOBILIER RESIDENTIEL RESIDENCES SERVICES BSA—See BNP Paribas SA; *Int'l*, pg. 1085
BNP PARIBAS IMMOBILIER RESIDENTIEL RESIDENCES SERVICES SOFIANE—See BNP Paribas SA; *Int'l*, pg. 1085
BNP PARIBAS IMMOBILIER RESIDENTIEL S.A.S.—See BNP Paribas SA; *Int'l*, pg. 1085
BNP PARIBAS IMMOBILIER RESIDENTIEL TRANSACTION & CONSEIL—See BNP Paribas SA; *Int'l*, pg. 1085
BNP PARIBAS INDIA SOLUTIONS PRIVATE LTD.—See BNP Paribas SA; *Int'l*, pg. 1085
BNP PARIBAS INVESTMENT PARTNERS ASIA LIMITED—See BNP Paribas SA; *Int'l*, pg. 1082
BNP PARIBAS INVESTMENT PARTNERS ASIA LTD—See BNP Paribas SA; *Int'l*, pg. 1085
BNP PARIBAS INVESTMENT PARTNERS (AUSTRALIA) LTD—See BNP Paribas SA; *Int'l*, pg. 1085
BNP PARIBAS INVESTMENT PARTNERS BELGIUM SA—See BNP Paribas SA; *Int'l*, pg. 1085
BNP PARIBAS INVESTMENT PARTNERS - BOSTON—See BNP Paribas SA; *Int'l*, pg. 1082
BNP PARIBAS INVESTMENT PARTNERS BSC—See BNP Paribas SA; *Int'l*, pg. 1085
BNP PARIBAS INVESTMENT PARTNERS (HONG KONG) LIMITED—See BNP Paribas SA; *Int'l*, pg. 1082
BNP PARIBAS INVESTMENT PARTNERS JAPAN LTD.—See BNP Paribas SA; *Int'l*, pg. 1082
BNP PARIBAS INVESTMENT PARTNERS LUXEMBOURG SA—See BNP Paribas SA; *Int'l*, pg. 1085
BNP PARIBAS INVESTMENT PARTNERS NETHERLANDS NV—See BNP Paribas SA; *Int'l*, pg. 1085
BNP PARIBAS INVESTMENT PARTNERS NL HOLDING NV—See BNP Paribas SA; *Int'l*, pg. 1085
BNP PARIBAS INVESTMENT PARTNERS SINGAPORE LIMITED—See BNP Paribas SA; *Int'l*, pg. 1085
BNP PARIBAS INVESTMENT PARTNERS UK LTD—See BNP Paribas SA; *Int'l*, pg. 1085
BNP PARIBAS ISLAMIC ISSUANCE BV—See BNP Paribas SA; *Int'l*, pg. 1085
BNP PARIBAS ISSUANCE B.V.—See BNP Paribas SA; *Int'l*, pg. 1085
BNP PARIBAS ISTANBUL—See BNP Paribas SA; *Int'l*, pg. 1085
BNP PARIBAS (JAPAN) LIMITED—See BNP Paribas SA; *Int'l*, pg. 1081
BNP PARIBAS LEASE GROUP BELGIUM SA—See BNP Paribas SA; *Int'l*, pg. 1085
BNP PARIBAS LEASE GROUP GMBH & CO KG—See BNP Paribas SA; *Int'l*, pg. 1085
BNP PARIBAS LEASE GROUP IFN S.A.—See BNP Paribas SA; *Int'l*, pg. 1085
BNP PARIBAS LEASE GROUP LIZING RT—See BNP Paribas SA; *Int'l*, pg. 1085
BNP PARIBAS LEASE GROUP LUXEMBOURG SA—See BNP Paribas SA; *Int'l*, pg. 1085
BNP PARIBAS LEASE GROUP (RENTALS) LTD.—See BNP Paribas SA; *Int'l*, pg. 1085
BNP PARIBAS LEASE GROUP SA EFC—See BNP Paribas SA; *Int'l*, pg. 1085
BNP PARIBAS LEASE GROUP S.A.—See BNP Paribas SA; *Int'l*, pg. 1085
BNP PARIBAS LEASE GROUP SP. Z O.O.—See BNP Paribas SA; *Int'l*, pg. 1085
BNP PARIBAS LEASING CORPORATION—See BNP Paribas SA; *Int'l*, pg. 1087
BNP PARIBAS LEASING SOLUTIONS (BELGIUM) S.A.—See BNP Paribas SA; *Int'l*, pg. 1085
BNP PARIBAS LEASING SOLUTIONS LIMITED—See BNP Paribas SA; *Int'l*, pg. 1085
BNP PARIBAS LEASING SOLUTIONS N.V.—See BNP Paribas SA; *Int'l*, pg. 1085
BNP PARIBAS LEASING SOLUTIONS NV—See BNP Paribas SA; *Int'l*, pg. 1086
BNP PARIBAS LEASING SOLUTIONS—See BNP Paribas SA; *Int'l*, pg. 1085
BNP PARIBAS LEASING SOLUTIONS SPA—See BNP Paribas SA; *Int'l*, pg. 1086
BNP PARIBAS LEASING SOLUTIONS SP. Z O.O.—See BNP Paribas SA; *Int'l*, pg. 1085
BNP PARIBAS LEASING SOLUTIONS ZRT—See BNP Paribas SA; *Int'l*, pg. 1086
BNP PARIBAS LE CAIRE—See BNP Paribas SA; *Int'l*, pg. 1085
BNP PARIBAS MACAU—See BNP Paribas SA; *Int'l*, pg. 1081

BNP PARIBAS-MANAMA BRANCH—See BNP Paribas SA; *Int'l*, pg. 1088
BNP PARIBAS-MANILA OFFSHORE BRANCH—See BNP Paribas SA; *Int'l*, pg. 1081
BNP PARIBAS MARTINIQUE—See BNP Paribas SA; *Int'l*, pg. 1086
BNP PARIBAS - MEXICO REPRESENTATIVE OFFICE—See BNP Paribas SA; *Int'l*, pg. 1081
BNP PARIBAS MORTGAGE CORPORATION—See BNP Paribas SA; *Int'l*, pg. 1087
BNP PARIBAS MUMBAI BRANCH—See BNP Paribas SA; *Int'l*, pg. 1086
BNP PARIBAS NETHERLANDS—See BNP Paribas SA; *Int'l*, pg. 1086
BNP PARIBAS NEW DELHI BRANCH—See BNP Paribas SA; *Int'l*, pg. 1086
BNP PARIBAS-NEW YORK—See BNP Paribas SA; *Int'l*, pg. 1087
BNP PARIBAS NOUVELLE CALEDONIE—See BNP Paribas SA; *Int'l*, pg. 1086
BNP PARIBAS PANAMA—See BNP Paribas SA; *Int'l*, pg. 1086
BNP PARIBAS PEREGRINE—See BNP Paribas SA; *Int'l*, pg. 1081
BNP PARIBAS PEREGRINE—See BNP Paribas SA; *Int'l*, pg. 1081
BNP PARIBAS PEREGRINE THAILAND—See BNP Paribas SA; *Int'l*, pg. 1081
BNP PARIBAS PERSONAL FINANCE BV—See BNP Paribas SA; *Int'l*, pg. 1086
BNP PARIBAS PERSONAL FINANCE EAD—See Eurobank Ergasias Services and Holdings S.A.; *Int'l*, pg. 2532
BNP PARIBAS PERSONAL FINANCE SPA—See BNP Paribas SA; *Int'l*, pg. 1086
BNP PARIBAS PERSONAL INVESTORS—See BNP Paribas SA; *Int'l*, pg. 1090
BNP PARIBAS PORTUGAL—See BNP Paribas SA; *Int'l*, pg. 1086
BNP PARIBAS PRIME BROKERAGE INC.—See BNP Paribas SA; *Int'l*, pg. 1087
BNP PARIBAS PRINCIPAL INVESTMENTS JAPAN LTD.—See BNP Paribas SA; *Int'l*, pg. 1086
BNP PARIBAS PRIVATE BANK PLC—See BNP Paribas SA; *Int'l*, pg. 1086
BNP PARIBAS PRIVATE BANK SWITZERLAND S.A.—See BNP Paribas SA; *Int'l*, pg. 1086
BNP PARIBAS PRIVATE EQUITY—See BNP Paribas SA; *Int'l*, pg. 1082
BNP PARIBAS QATAR—See BNP Paribas SA; *Int'l*, pg. 1086
BNP PARIBAS RCC, INC.—See BNP Paribas SA; *Int'l*, pg. 1087
BNP PARIBAS REAL ESTATE ADVISORY BELGIUM SA—See BNP Paribas SA; *Int'l*, pg. 1086
BNP PARIBAS REAL ESTATE ADVISORY ITALY SPA—See BNP Paribas SA; *Int'l*, pg. 1086
BNP PARIBAS REAL ESTATE ADVISORY & PROPERTY MANAGEMENT LUXEMBOURG SA—See BNP Paribas SA; *Int'l*, pg. 1086
BNP PARIBAS REAL ESTATE ADVISORY SPAIN SA—See BNP Paribas SA; *Int'l*, pg. 1086
BNP PARIBAS REAL ESTATE CONSULT FRANCE—See BNP Paribas SA; *Int'l*, pg. 1086
BNP PARIBAS REAL ESTATE CONSULT GMBH—See BNP Paribas SA; *Int'l*, pg. 1086
BNP PARIBAS REAL ESTATE FACILITIES MANAGEMENT LTD.—See BNP Paribas SA; *Int'l*, pg. 1086
BNP PARIBAS REAL ESTATE FINANCIAL PARTNER—See BNP Paribas SA; *Int'l*, pg. 1086
BNP PARIBAS REAL ESTATE GMBH—See BNP Paribas SA; *Int'l*, pg. 1086
BNP PARIBAS REAL ESTATE HOLDING GMBH—See BNP Paribas SA; *Int'l*, pg. 1086
BNP PARIBAS REAL ESTATE INVESTMENT MANAGEMENT GERMANY GMBH—See BNP Paribas SA; *Int'l*, pg. 1086
BNP PARIBAS REAL ESTATE INVESTMENT MANAGEMENT LTD.—See BNP Paribas SA; *Int'l*, pg. 1086
BNP PARIBAS REAL ESTATE INVESTMENT MANAGEMENT LUXEMBOURG SA—See BNP Paribas SA; *Int'l*, pg. 1086
BNP PARIBAS REAL ESTATE INVESTMENT MANAGEMENT—See BNP Paribas SA; *Int'l*, pg. 1086
BNP PARIBAS REAL ESTATE JERSEY LTD.—See BNP Paribas SA; *Int'l*, pg. 1086
BNP PARIBAS REAL ESTATE PROPERTY DEVELOPPEMENT UK LTD.—See BNP Paribas SA; *Int'l*, pg. 1086
BNP PARIBAS REAL ESTATE PROPERTY MANAGEMENT BELGIUM SA—See BNP Paribas SA; *Int'l*, pg. 1086
BNP PARIBAS REAL ESTATE PROPERTY MANAGEMENT GMBH—See BNP Paribas SA; *Int'l*, pg. 1086
BNP PARIBAS REAL ESTATE, S.A.—See BNP Paribas SA; *Int'l*, pg. 1086
BNP PARIBAS REAL ESTATE—See BNP Paribas SA; *Int'l*, pg. 1086
BNP PARIBAS REAL ESTATE TRANSACTION FRANCE S.A.—See BNP Paribas SA; *Int'l*, pg. 1086

BNP PARIBAS REUNION—See BNP Paribas SA; *Int'l*, pg. 1086
BNP PARIBAS SAE—See BNP Paribas SA; *Int'l*, pg. 1087
BNP PARIBAS-SAN FRANCISCO—See BNP Paribas SA; *Int'l*, pg. 1087
BNP PARIBAS SA; *Int'l*, pg. 1079
BNP PARIBAS SECURITIES (ASIA) LTD.—See BNP Paribas SA; *Int'l*, pg. 1087
BNP PARIBAS SECURITIES CORP.—See BNP Paribas SA; *Int'l*, pg. 1087
BNP PARIBAS SECURITIES (JAPAN) LIMITED—See BNP Paribas SA; *Int'l*, pg. 1081
BNP PARIBAS SECURITIES KOREA COMPANY LTD.—See BNP Paribas SA; *Int'l*, pg. 1087
BNP PARIBAS SECURITIES SERVICES (HOLDINGS) LTD.—See BNP Paribas SA; *Int'l*, pg. 1087
BNP PARIBAS SECURITIES SERVICES—See BNP Paribas SA; *Int'l*, pg. 1087
BNP PARIBAS SECURITIES (SINGAPORE) PTE LTD.—See BNP Paribas SA; *Int'l*, pg. 1087
BNP PARIBAS SECURITIES (TAIWAN) CO LTD.—See BNP Paribas SA; *Int'l*, pg. 1087
BNP PARIBAS SERVICES (HONG KONG) LTD.—See BNP Paribas SA; *Int'l*, pg. 1087
BNP PARIBAS SHANGHAI—See BNP Paribas SA; *Int'l*, pg. 1081
BNP PARIBAS (SINGAPORE) PTE. LTD.—See BNP Paribas SA; *Int'l*, pg. 1081
BNP PARIBAS - SOUTH EAST ASIA—See BNP Paribas SA; *Int'l*, pg. 1081
BNP PARIBAS SOUTH KOREA—See BNP Paribas SA; *Int'l*, pg. 1081
BNP PARIBAS SUCCURSALE ITALIA—See BNP Paribas SA; *Int'l*, pg. 1087
BNP PARIBAS-SUCCURSALE ITALIA—See BNP Paribas SA; *Int'l*, pg. 1087
BNP PARIBAS SUISSE S.A.—See BNP Paribas SA; *Int'l*, pg. 1081
BNP PARIBAS (SUISSE) SA—See BNP Paribas SA; *Int'l*, pg. 1081
BNP PARIBAS SYDNEY—See BNP Paribas SA; *Int'l*, pg. 1081
BNP PARIBAS TAIWAN—See BNP Paribas SA; *Int'l*, pg. 1081
BNP PARIBAS TEL-AVIV—See BNP Paribas SA; *Int'l*, pg. 1087
BNP PARIBAS TRUST COMPANY (GUERNESEY) LTD.—See BNP Paribas SA; *Int'l*, pg. 1087
BNP PARIBAS UK TREASURY LTD.—See BNP Paribas SA; *Int'l*, pg. 1087
BNP PARIBAS URUGUAY S.A.—See BNP Paribas SA; *Int'l*, pg. 1088
BNP PARIBAS USA, INC.—See BNP Paribas SA; *Int'l*, pg. 1087
BNP PARIBAS WEALTH MANAGEMENT MONACO—See BNP Paribas SA; *Int'l*, pg. 1088
BNP PARIBAS WEALTH MANAGEMENT—See BNP Paribas SA; *Int'l*, pg. 1088
BNP PARIBAS WEALTH MANAGEMENT—See BNP Paribas SA; *Int'l*, pg. 1088
BNP PARIBAS ZAO—See BNP Paribas SA; *Int'l*, pg. 1088
BNPP ASSET MANAGEMENT ASIA LTD.—See BNP Paribas SA; *Int'l*, pg. 1088
BNPP ASSET MANAGEMENT BRASIL LTDA—See BNP Paribas SA; *Int'l*, pg. 1088
BNPP ASSET MANAGEMENT JAPAN LTD.—See BNP Paribas SA; *Int'l*, pg. 1088
BNPP ASSET MANAGEMENT NEDERLAND NV—See BNP Paribas SA; *Int'l*, pg. 1088
BNPP ASSET MANAGEMENT USA INC.—See BNP Paribas SA; *Int'l*, pg. 1087
BNPP CARDIF COMPANIA DE SEGUROS Y REASEGUROS SA—See BNP Paribas SA; *Int'l*, pg. 1088
BNPP CARDIF GENERAL INSURANCE CO., LTD.—See BNP Paribas SA; *Int'l*, pg. 1088
BNPP CARDIF POJISTOVNA AS—See BNP Paribas SA; *Int'l*, pg. 1088
BNPP CARDIF SEGUROS DE VIDA SA—See BNP Paribas SA; *Int'l*, pg. 1088
BNPP COLOMBIA CORPORACION FINANCIERA SA—See BNP Paribas SA; *Int'l*, pg. 1088
BNPP FACTOR NV—See BNP Paribas SA; *Int'l*, pg. 1088
BNPP FINANSAL KIRALAMA AS—See BNP Paribas SA; *Int'l*, pg. 1088
BNPP GLOBAL SECURITIES OPERATIONS PRIVATE LTD.—See BNP Paribas SA; *Int'l*, pg. 1088
BNPP LEASING SERVICES SP. Z O.O.—See BNP Paribas SA; *Int'l*, pg. 1088
BNPP LEASING SOLUTIONS SUISSE SA—See BNP Paribas SA; *Int'l*, pg. 1088
BNPP MALAYSIA BERHAD—See BNP Paribas SA; *Int'l*, pg. 1088
BNPP PERSONAL FINANCE SA—See BNP Paribas SA; *Int'l*, pg. 1088
BNPP REAL ESTATE ADVISORY NETHERLANDS BV—See BNP Paribas SA; *Int'l*, pg. 1088
BNPP REAL ESTATE ADVISORY & PROPERTY MANAGEMENT IRELAND LTD.—See BNP Paribas SA; *Int'l*, pg. 1088
BNPP REAL ESTATE APM CR SRO—See BNP Paribas SA; *Int'l*, pg. 1088
BNPP REAL ESTATE POLAND SP. Z O.O.—See BNP Paribas SA; *Int'l*, pg. 1088
BNPP RENTAL SOLUTIONS LTD.—See BNP Paribas SA; *Int'l*, pg. 1088
BNP PRIME PEREGRINE (SECURITIES) PTE LTD.—See BNP Paribas SA; *Int'l*, pg. 1081
BNPP SECURITIES INDIA PRIVATE LTD.—See BNP Paribas SA; *Int'l*, pg. 1088
BNPP YATIRIMLAR HOLDING AS—See BNP Paribas SA; *Int'l*, pg. 1088
BN PRODUCTIONS INC.—See National Amusements, Inc.; *U.S. Private*, pg. 2842
B N RATHI COMTRADE PRIVATE LIMITED—See B N Rathi Securities Ltd.; *Int'l*, pg. 783
B N RATHI SECURITIES LTD.; *Int'l*, pg. 783
BNR UDYOG LTD.; *Int'l*, pg. 1093
BNS ASIA LIMITED—See The Bank of Nova Scotia; *Int'l*, pg. 7616
BNS EESTI OU—See UP Invest OU; *Int'l*, pg. 8086
BNSF LOGISTICS INTERNATIONAL—See Berkshire Hathaway Inc.; *U.S. Public*, pg. 303
BNSF LOGISTICS, LLC—See Berkshire Hathaway Inc.; *U.S. Public*, pg. 303
BNSF LOGISTICS, LLC—See Berkshire Hathaway Inc.; *U.S. Public*, pg. 303
BNSF RAILWAY COMPANY—See Berkshire Hathaway Inc.; *U.S. Public*, pg. 303
BNS INTERNATIONAL (BARBADOS) LIMITED—See The Bank of Nova Scotia; *Int'l*, pg. 7618
BNS INVESTMENTS INC.—See The Bank of Nova Scotia; *Int'l*, pg. 7616
BNS NUCLEAR SERVICES LIMITED—See Babcock International Group PLC; *Int'l*, pg. 792
BNS SPLIT CORP II; *Int'l*, pg. 1093
BNS UAB—See UP Invest OU; *Int'l*, pg. 8086
BNT CHEMICALS GMBH—See IBU-Tec Advanced Materials AG; *Int'l*, pg. 3577
BNT HIDRAULIKA D.D. NOVI TRAVNIK; *Int'l*, pg. 1093
BNT HOLDING D.D.; *Int'l*, pg. 1093
BNT POSLOVNI SUSTAV D.D.; *Int'l*, pg. 1094
BNX SHIPPING INC.; *U.S. Private*, pg. 602
BNY FUND SERVICES (IRELAND) LTD.—See The Bank of New York Mellon Corporation; *U.S. Public*, pg. 2036
BNY INTERNATIONAL FINANCING CORPORATION—See The Bank of New York Mellon Corporation; *U.S. Public*, pg. 2036
BNY MELLON-ALCENTRA MEZZANINE PARTNERS—See Franklin Resources, Inc.; *U.S. Public*, pg. 879
BNY MELLON ARX INVESTIMENTOS LTDA.—See The Bank of New York Mellon Corporation; *U.S. Public*, pg. 2036
BNY MELLON ASSET MANAGEMENT JAPAN LIMITED—See The Bank of New York Mellon Corporation; *U.S. Public*, pg. 2036
BNY MELLON ASSET SERVICING B.V.—See The Bank of New York Mellon Corporation; *U.S. Public*, pg. 2037
BNY MELLON CAPITAL MARKETS, LLC—See The Bank of New York Mellon Corporation; *U.S. Public*, pg. 2037
BNY MELLON FUND MANAGEMENT (LUXEMBOURG) SA—See The Bank of New York Mellon Corporation; *U.S. Public*, pg. 2037
BNY MELLON FUND MANAGERS LIMITED—See The Bank of New York Mellon Corporation; *U.S. Public*, pg. 2037
BNY MELLON HIGH YIELD STRATEGIES FUND; *U.S. Public*, pg. 366
BNY MELLON-HONG KONG—See The Bank of New York Mellon Corporation; *U.S. Public*, pg. 2037
BNY MELLON INTERNATIONAL ASSET MANAGEMENT GROUP LIMITED—See The Bank of New York Mellon Corporation; *U.S. Public*, pg. 2037
BNY MELLON INTERNATIONAL OPERATIONS (INDIA) PRIVATE LIMITED—See The Bank of New York Mellon Corporation; *U.S. Public*, pg. 2037
BNY MELLON INVESTMENT MANAGEMENT EMEA LIMITED—See The Bank of New York Mellon Corporation; *U.S. Public*, pg. 2037
BNY MELLON INVESTMENT SERVICING (INTERNATIONAL) LIMITED—See The Bank of New York Mellon Corporation; *U.S. Public*, pg. 2037
BNY MELLON INVESTMENT SERVICING (US) INC.—See The Bank of New York Mellon Corporation; *U.S. Public*, pg. 2037
BNY MELLON MUNICIPAL INCOME, INC.; *U.S. Public*, pg. 366
BNY MELLON, NATIONAL ASSOCIATION—See The Bank of New York Mellon Corporation; *U.S. Public*, pg. 2037
BNY MELLON (POLAND) SP. Z O.O.—See The Bank of New York Mellon Corporation; *U.S. Public*, pg. 2036
BNY MELLON SECURITIES SERVICES (IRELAND) LIMITED—See The Bank of New York Mellon Corporation; *U.S. Public*, pg. 2037
BNY MELLON SINGAPORE—See The Bank of New York Mellon Corporation; *U.S. Public*, pg. 2037
BNY MELLON STRATEGIC MUNICIPAL BOND FUND, INC.; *U.S. Public*, pg. 366
BNY MELLON STRATEGIC MUNICIPALS, INC.; *U.S. Public*, pg. 366
BNY MELLON TRUST COMPANY OF ILLINOIS—See The Bank of New York Mellon Corporation; *U.S. Public*, pg. 2037
BNY MELLON TRUST OF DELAWARE—See The Bank of New York Mellon Corporation; *U.S. Public*, pg. 2037
BNY MELLON WEALTH MANAGEMENT - MENLO PARK—See The Bank of New York Mellon Corporation; *U.S. Public*, pg. 2037
BNY MELLON WEALTH MANAGEMENT—See The Bank of New York Mellon Corporation; *U.S. Public*, pg. 2037
BNZ INTERNATIONAL FUNDING LIMITED—See National Australia Bank Limited; *Int'l*, pg. 5151
BNZ MATERIALS, INC. - BILLERICA PLANT—See BNZ Materials, Inc.; *U.S. Private*, pg. 602
BNZ MATERIALS, INC. - INSULATING FIRE BRICK PLANT—See BNZ Materials, Inc.; *U.S. Private*, pg. 602
BNZ MATERIALS, INC.; *U.S. Private*, pg. 602
BNZ S.A.—See BNZ Materials, Inc.; *U.S. Private*, pg. 602
BOA ACQUISITION CORP.—See Selina Hospitality PLC; *Int'l*, pg. 6701
BOAB METALS LIMITED; *Int'l*, pg. 1094
BOA CONCEPT SA; *Int'l*, pg. 1094
BOADICEA RESOURCES LIMITED; *Int'l*, pg. 1094
BOA GROUP S.A.; *Int'l*, pg. 1094
BOA HOLDINGS INC.—See Compass Diversified Holdings; *U.S. Public*, pg. 560
BOAI NKY MEDICAL HOLDINGS LTD.; *Int'l*, pg. 1094
BOAN CONTRACTING CO. INC.; *U.S. Private*, pg. 602
BOA OFFSHORE AS—See Taubatkompaniet AS; *Int'l*, pg. 7476
BOARDMAN DIALYSIS CENTER LLC—See Nautic Partners, LLC; *U.S. Private*, pg. 2869
BOARDMAN FOODS INC.; *U.S. Private*, pg. 602
BOARDMAN INDUSTRIES INC.; *U.S. Private*, pg. 602
THE BOARD OF TRADE OF KANSAS CITY, MISSOURI, INC.—See CME Group, Inc.; *U.S. Public*, pg. 518
BOARDRIDERS CLUB BRATISLAVA S.R.O.—See Leonard Green & Partners, L.P.; *U.S. Private*, pg. 2424
BOARDRIDERS, INC.—See Leonard Green & Partners, L.P.; *U.S. Private*, pg. 2424
BOARDRIDERS JAPAN CO., LTD.—See Leonard Green & Partners, L.P.; *U.S. Private*, pg. 2424
BOARDROOM BUSINESS SOLUTIONS PTE. LTD.—See G. K. Goh Holdings Limited; *Int'l*, pg. 2864
BOARDROOM.COM SDN. BHD.—See Aldrich Resources Bhd; *Int'l*, pg. 305
BOARDROOM CORPORATE SERVICES (HK) LIMITED—See G. K. Goh Holdings Limited; *Int'l*, pg. 2864
BOARDROOM CORPORATE SERVICES (JOHOR) SDN BHD—See G. K. Goh Holdings Limited; *Int'l*, pg. 2864
BOARDROOM CORPORATE SERVICES (PENANG) SDN BHD—See G. K. Goh Holdings Limited; *Int'l*, pg. 2864
BOARDROOM INCORPORATED; *U.S. Private*, pg. 602
BOARDROOM LIMITED—See G. K. Goh Holdings Limited; *Int'l*, pg. 2864
BOARDROOM LSC BEIJING LIMITED—See G. K. Goh Holdings Limited; *Int'l*, pg. 2864
BOARDROOM LSC CHINA LIMITED—See G. K. Goh Holdings Limited; *Int'l*, pg. 2864
BOARDROOM PTY LIMITED—See G. K. Goh Holdings Limited; *Int'l*, pg. 2864
BOARDTEK ELECTRONICS CORP.—See Zhen Ding Technology Holding Limited; *Int'l*, pg. 8669
BOARDVANTAGE, INC.—See Nasdaq, Inc.; *U.S. Public*, pg. 1491
BOARDWALK ACQUISITION COMPANY, LLC—See Loews Corporation; *U.S. Public*, pg. 1339
THE BOARDWALK COMPANY; *U.S. Private*, pg. 3995
BOARDWALK FIELD SERVICES, LLC—See Loews Corporation; *U.S. Public*, pg. 1339
BOARDWALK INC.—See Dentsu Group Inc.; *Int'l*, pg. 2034
BOARDWALK OPERATING GP, LLC—See Loews Corporation; *U.S. Public*, pg. 1339
BOARDWALK PIPELINE PARTNERS, LP—See Loews Corporation; *U.S. Public*, pg. 1339
BOARDWALK PIPELINES, LP—See Loews Corporation; *U.S. Public*, pg. 1339
BOARDWALK REAL ESTATE INVESTMENT TRUST; *Int'l*, pg. 1094
BOARDWALK STORAGE COMPANY, LLC—See Loews Corporation; *U.S. Public*, pg. 1339
BOARDWALKTECH, INC.—See Boardwalktech Software Corp.; *U.S. Public*, pg. 366
BOARDWALKTECH SOFTWARE CORP.; *U.S. Public*, pg. 366
BOARDWALK VOLKSWAGEN; *U.S. Private*, pg. 602
BOARDWARE INFORMATION SYSTEM LIMITED—See BoardWare Intelligence Technology Limited; *Int'l*, pg. 1094
BOARDWARE INTELLIGENCE TECHNOLOGY LIMITED; *Int'l*, pg. 1094
BOARMAN KROOS VOGEL GROUP INC.; *U.S. Private*, pg. 602
BOAR'S HEAD PROVISIONS CO., INC.—See Frank Brunckhorst Co., LLC; *U.S. Private*, pg. 1593

COMPANY NAME INDEX

BOART LONGYEAR ALBERTA LIMITED—See Boart Longyear Ltd.; *Int'l*, pg. 1094
BOART LONGYEAR AUSTRALIA PTY LTD—See Boart Longyear Ltd.; *Int'l*, pg. 1094
BOART LONGYEAR BV—See Boart Longyear Ltd.; *Int'l*, pg. 1094
BOART LONGYEAR CANADA—See Boart Longyear Ltd.; *Int'l*, pg. 1095
BOART LONGYEAR COMPANY INC.—See Boart Longyear Ltd.; *Int'l*, pg. 1095
BOART LONGYEAR DRILLING PRODUCTS COMPANY (WUXI) LTD—See Boart Longyear Ltd.; *Int'l*, pg. 1095
BOART LONGYEAR DRILLING SERVICES—See Boart Longyear Ltd.; *Int'l*, pg. 1095
BOART LONGYEAR EMEA COOPERATIEF U.A—See Boart Longyear Ltd.; *Int'l*, pg. 1094
BOART LONGYEAR GMBH & CO. KG—See Boart Longyear Ltd.; *Int'l*, pg. 1094
BOART LONGYEAR INC.—See Boart Longyear Ltd.; *Int'l*, pg. 1095
BOART LONGYEAR INTERNATIONAL BV—See Boart Longyear Ltd.; *Int'l*, pg. 1094
BOART LONGYEAR INTERNATIONAL HOLDINGS INC.—See Boart Longyear Ltd.; *Int'l*, pg. 1094
BOART LONGYEAR INVESTMENTS PTY LTD—See Boart Longyear Ltd.; *Int'l*, pg. 1095
BOART LONGYEAR LIMITED—See Boart Longyear Ltd.; *Int'l*, pg. 1095
BOART LONGYEAR LTDA.—See Boart Longyear Ltd.; *Int'l*, pg. 1095
BOART LONGYEAR LTD.; *Int'l*, pg. 1094
BOART LONGYEAR MANAGEMENT PTY LTD—See Boart Longyear Ltd.; *Int'l*, pg. 1095
BOART LONGYEAR NETHERLANDS BV—See Boart Longyear Ltd.; *Int'l*, pg. 1095
BOART LONGYEAR SAC - LIMA, PERU—See Boart Longyear Ltd.; *Int'l*, pg. 1095
BOART LONGYEAR S.A.—See Boart Longyear Ltd.; *Int'l*, pg. 1095
BOASSO AMERICA - CHANNELVIEW—See Apax Partners LLP; *Int'l*, pg. 505
BOASSO AMERICA - CHARLESTON—See Apax Partners LLP; *Int'l*, pg. 505
BOASSO AMERICA - CHESAPEAKE—See Apax Partners LLP; *Int'l*, pg. 505
BOASSO AMERICA - CHICAGO—See Apax Partners LLP; *Int'l*, pg. 505
BOASSO AMERICA CORPORATION—See Apax Partners LLP; *Int'l*, pg. 505
BOASSO AMERICA - DETROIT—See Apax Partners LLP; *Int'l*, pg. 505
BOASSO AMERICA - GARDEN CITY—See Apax Partners LLP; *Int'l*, pg. 505
BOASSO AMERICA - JACKSONVILLE—See Apax Partners LLP; *Int'l*, pg. 505
BOASSO AMERICA - WEST MEMPHIS—See Apax Partners LLP; *Int'l*, pg. 505
BOASSO GLOBAL, INC.—See KKR & Co. Inc.; *U.S. Public*, pg. 1241
BOAT AMERICA CORPORATION—See Berkshire Hathaway Inc.; *U.S. Public*, pg. 303
BOATARAMA INC.; *U.S. Private*, pg. 602
BOATECHNOLOGY GMBH—See Compass Diversified Holdings; *U.S. Public*, pg. 559
BOA TECHNOLOGY INC.—See Compass Diversified Holdings; *U.S. Public*, pg. 560
BOA TECHNOLOGY JAPAN INC.—See Compass Diversified Holdings; *U.S. Public*, pg. 559
BOA TECHNOLOGY KOREA INC—See Compass Diversified Holdings; *U.S. Public*, pg. 559
BOA TECHNOLOGY (SHENZEN) LTD.—See Compass Diversified Holdings; *U.S. Public*, pg. 559
BOATHOUSE CAPITAL MANAGEMENT, LLC; *U.S. Private*, pg. 603
BOATHOUSE GROUP INC.; *U.S. Private*, pg. 603
THE BOATHOUSE RESTAURANTS OF CANADA, INC.—See Fertitta Entertainment, Inc.; *U.S. Private*, pg. 1499
BOATIM, INC.; *U.S. Public*, pg. 366
BOATING GEAR CENTER, LLC—See MarineMax, Inc.; *U.S. Public*, pg. 1366
BOATNER CONSTRUCTION CO INC.; *U.S. Private*, pg. 603
BOATRACS LLC; *U.S. Private*, pg. 603
BOATRIGHT RAILROAD COMPANIES, INC.; *U.S. Private*, pg. 603
BOAT ROCKER MEDIA; *Int'l*, pg. 1095
BOAT S.P.A.—See Boero Bartolomeo S.p.A.; *Int'l*, pg. 1100
BOAT TREE INC.; *U.S. Private*, pg. 602
BOATZON HOLDINGS, LLC—See MarineMax, Inc.; *U.S. Public*, pg. 1366
BOA VISTA ENERGIA S.A.—See Oliveira Energia Geracao e Servicos Ltda.; *Int'l*, pg. 5553
BOAVISTA GOLF & SPA RESORT EMPREENDIMENTOS TUR ISTICOS, SA—See Emerson Developments (Holdings) Limited; *Int'l*, pg. 2379
BOBACK COMMERCIAL GROUP; *U.S. Private*, pg. 606
BOBAK SAUSAGE COMPANY; *U.S. Private*, pg. 606

BOB ALLEN-CHRYSLER PLYMOUTH DODGE; *U.S. Private*, pg. 603
BOB ALLEN FORD; *U.S. Private*, pg. 603
BOB ALLEN MOTOR MALL; *U.S. Private*, pg. 603
BOBAR AUTOSEMBERIJA—See Kompanija BOBAR d.o.o.; *Int'l*, pg. 4244
BOBAR BOBEX DOO—See Kompanija BOBAR d.o.o.; *Int'l*, pg. 4244
BOBAR INZENJERING DQO—See Kompanija BOBAR d.o.o.; *Int'l*, pg. 4244
BOBAR OSIGURANJE DD—See Kompanija BOBAR d.o.o.; *Int'l*, pg. 4244
BOBAR RADIO DOO—See Kompanija BOBAR d.o.o.; *Int'l*, pg. 4244
BOBAR SPEDICIJA I TRANSPORT—See Kompanija BOBAR d.o.o.; *Int'l*, pg. 4244
BOBAR TOURS—See Kompanija BOBAR d.o.o.; *Int'l*, pg. 4244
BOB BAKER AUTO GROUP; *U.S. Private*, pg. 603
BOB BARBOUR, INC.; *U.S. Private*, pg. 603
BOB BARKER COMPANY, INC.; *U.S. Private*, pg. 603
BOBB AUTOMOTIVE INC.; *U.S. Private*, pg. 606
BOB BAY & SONS INC.; *U.S. Private*, pg. 603
BOBBI BROWN PROFESSIONAL COSMETICS—See The Estee Lauder Companies Inc.; *U.S. Public*, pg. 2073
BOBBIE BABY, INC.; *U.S. Private*, pg. 606
BOB BOAST VOLKSWAGEN; *U.S. Private*, pg. 603
BOB-BOYD FORD MAZDA DODGE INC.—See Bob-Boyd Lincoln of Columbus; *U.S. Private*, pg. 606
BOB-BOYD LINCOLN OF COLUMBUS; *U.S. Private*, pg. 606
BOB BRADY DODGE INC.; *U.S. Private*, pg. 603
BOB BRANDI STATIONS, INC.—See Applegreen Plc; *Int'l*, pg. 521
BOB BROCKLAND BUICK GMC; *U.S. Private*, pg. 603
BOB BROWN CHEVROLET INC.; *U.S. Private*, pg. 603
BOBBY&CARL GMBH—See ThyssenKrupp AG; *Int'l*, pg. 7724
BOBBY COX COMPANIES, INC.; *U.S. Private*, pg. 606
BOBBY DODD INSTITUTE; *U.S. Private*, pg. 606
BOBBY FORD INC.—See Sonic Automotive, Inc.; *U.S. Public*, pg. 1902
BOBBY HENARD TIRE SERVICE; *U.S. Private*, pg. 606
BOBBY LAYMAN CADILLAC GMC, INC ; *U.S. Private*, pg. 606
BOBBY MURRAY TOYOTA; *U.S. Private*, pg. 606
BOBBY RAHAL AUTO GROUP; *U.S. Private*, pg. 606
BOBBY RAHAL HONDA; *U.S. Private*, pg. 606
BOBBY TAYLOR OIL COMPANY, INC.—See Parker Holding Company, Inc.; *U.S. Private*, pg. 3097
BOB CALDWELL CHRYSLER JEEP DODGE RAM; *U.S. Private*, pg. 603
BOB CAPITAL MARKETS LTD.—See Bank of Baroda; *Int'l*, pg. 840
BOBCAT BENSHEIM GMBH—See Doosan Corporation; *Int'l*, pg. 2172
BOBCAT COMPANY—See HD Hyundai Infracore Co., Ltd.; *Int'l*, pg. 3300
BOBCAT ENTERPRISES INC.; *U.S. Private*, pg. 606
BOBCAT EQUIPMENT LTD.—See Doosan Corporation; *Int'l*, pg. 2172
BOBCAT OF BOSTON, INC.; *U.S. Private*, pg. 606
BOBCAT OF CONNECTICUT INC.; *U.S. Private*, pg. 606
BOBCAT OF HOUSTON, INC.—See Berry Companies, Inc.; *U.S. Private*, pg. 538
BOBCAT OF NEW YORK INC.; *U.S. Private*, pg. 606
BOBCAT OF THE ROCKIES, LLC—See Berry Companies, Inc.; *U.S. Private*, pg. 538
BOBCATS BASKETBALL CENTER, LLC—See MJ Basketball Holdings, LLC; *U.S. Private*, pg. 2752
BOBCAT WEST—See The Pape Group, Inc.; *U.S. Private*, pg. 4090
BOBCO INC.; *U.S. Private*, pg. 606
BOB DAVIDSON FORD LINCOLN; *U.S. Private*, pg. 604
BOB DEAN SUPPLY, INC.; *U.S. Private*, pg. 604
BOB DEAN SUPPLY INC.—See Bob Dean Supply, Inc.; *U.S. Private*, pg. 604
BOB DUNN HYUNDAI SUBARU; *U.S. Private*, pg. 604
BOBER SP.Z.O.O.—See Zeidler & Wimmel Verwaltungs-GmbH; *Int'l*, pg. 8631
BOB EVANS FARMS, LLC—See Post Holdings, Inc.; *U.S. Public*, pg. 1703
BOB EVANS RESTAURANTS, LLC—See Golden Gate Capital Management II, LLC; *U.S. Private*, pg. 1731
BOB FINANCIAL SOLUTIONS LIMITED—See Bank of Baroda; *Int'l*, pg. 840
BOB FISHER CHEVROLET, INC.; *U.S. Private*, pg. 604
BOB FOWLER & ASSOCIATES; *U.S. Private*, pg. 604
BOB GOLD & ASSOCIATES; *U.S. Private*, pg. 604
BOB GRIMM CHEVROLET INC.; *U.S. Private*, pg. 604
BOB HALL INC.; *U.S. Private*, pg. 604
BOB HEMBREE MOTOR COMPANY INC.; *U.S. Private*, pg. 604
BOB HOOK CHEVROLET; *U.S. Private*, pg. 604
BOB HOOK OF SHELBYVILLE; *U.S. Private*, pg. 604
BOB HOPE AIRPORT; *U.S. Private*, pg. 604
BOB HOWARD AUTOMOTIVE-EAST, INC.—See Group 1 Automotive, Inc.; *U.S. Public*, pg. 971

BOB HOWARD CHEVROLET, INC.—See Group 1 Automotive, Inc.; *U.S. Public*, pg. 971
BOB HOWARD DODGE, INC.—See Group 1 Automotive, Inc.; *U.S. Public*, pg. 971
BOB HOWARD DOWNTOWN DODGE INC.; *U.S. Public*, pg. 604
BOB HOWARD MOTORS, INC.—See Group 1 Automotive, Inc.; *U.S. Public*, pg. 971
BOB HOWARD NISSAN, INC.—See Group 1 Automotive, Inc.; *U.S. Public*, pg. 971
BOBIJA A.D.; *Int'l*, pg. 1095
BOBITAG INC.—See Realtek Semiconductor Corp.; *Int'l*, pg. 6234
BOBIT BUSINESS MEDIA INC.; *U.S. Private*, pg. 607
BOB KING AUTO MALL; *U.S. Private*, pg. 604
BOB KING, INC.; *U.S. Private*, pg. 604
BOB, LLC—See Windstream Holdings, Inc.; *U.S. Public*, pg. 2373
BOB MASSIE TOYOTA; *U.S. Private*, pg. 604
BOB MAXEY FORD, INC-BOB MAXEY LINCOLN MERCURY—See Bob Maxey Ford, Inc.; *U.S. Private*, pg. 604
BOB MAXEY FORD, INC.; *U.S. Private*, pg. 604
BOB MICKLER'S, INC.—See Timberfence Capital Partners, LLC; *U.S. Private*, pg. 4171
BOB MILLS FURNITURE CO. INC.; *U.S. Private*, pg. 604
BOB MOORE CADILLAC INC.; *U.S. Private*, pg. 604
BOB MOORE DODGE, LLC; *U.S. Private*, pg. 604
BOB NEILL INC.; *U.S. Private*, pg. 604
BOB NOVICK AUTO MALL; *U.S. Private*, pg. 604
BOBOLI INTERNATIONAL, LLC; *U.S. Private*, pg. 607
BOB OWENS RETIREMENT VILLAGE LIMITED—See Ryman Healthcare Ltd.; *Int'l*, pg. 6439
BOB PARKS REALTY LLC; *U.S. Private*, pg. 604
BOB PARRETT CONSTRUCTION INC.; *U.S. Private*, pg. 605
BOB POPP BUILDING SERVICES, INC.—See Osceola Capital Management, LLC; *U.S. Private*, pg. 3047
BOB PROPHETER CONSTRUCTION LLC; *U.S. Private*, pg. 605
BOB RICHARDS, INC.; *U.S. Private*, pg. 605
BOBRICK WASHROOM EQUIPMENT, INC.; *U.S. Private*, pg. 607
BOBRICK WASHROOM EQUIPMENT LIMITED—See Bobrick Washroom Equipment, Inc.; *U.S. Private*, pg. 607
BOB RIDINGS FORD INC.; *U.S. Private*, pg. 605
BOB ROHRMAN MOTORS INCORPORATED; *U.S. Private*, pg. 605
BOB ROSS BUICK, INC.; *U.S. Private*, pg. 605
BOBRUISK MACHINE BUILDING PLANT OJSC—See HMS Hydraulic Machines & Systems Group plc; *Int'l*, pg. 3432
BOB SAKS BUICK—See Farmington Hills Holding Company; *U.S. Private*, pg. 1480
BOB'S BARRICADES INC.; *U.S. Private*, pg. 605
BOB SCHMITT HOMES INC.; *U.S. Private*, pg. 605
BOB SCOTT RETIREMENT VILLAGE LIMITED—See Ryman Healthcare Ltd.; *Int'l*, pg. 6439
BOB'S DISCOUNT FURNITURE INC.—See Bain Capital, LP; *U.S. Private*, pg. 436
BOB'S DISCOUNT INC.; *U.S. Private*, pg. 605
BOBSHELL ELECTRODES LIMITED; *Int'l*, pg. 1095
BOB SIGHT FORD INC.; *U.S. Private*, pg. 605
BOB'S KWIK SHOP FOODS CO; *U.S. Private*, pg. 605
BOB'S MARKETS INC.; *U.S. Private*, pg. 605
BOB'S OVERHEAD DOOR REPAIR & SERVICE, INC.—See On-Point Group, LLC; *U.S. Private*, pg. 3018
BOB'S PROCESSING, INC.; *U.S. Private*, pg. 605
BOB'S RED MILL NATURAL FOODS, INC.; *U.S. Private*, pg. 606
BOB'S STORES, LLC—See GoDigital Media Group, LLC; *U.S. Private*, pg. 1724
BOB'S SUPER SAVER INC; *U.S. Private*, pg. 606
BOBST (AFRICA & MIDDLE EAST) LTD.—See Bobst Group S.A.; *Int'l*, pg. 1095
BOB STALL CHEVROLET; *U.S. Private*, pg. 605
BOBST BENELUX NV—See Bobst Group S.A.; *Int'l*, pg. 1095
BOBST BIELEFELD GMBH—See Bobst Group S.A.; *Int'l*, pg. 1095
BOBST BRASIL LTDA.—See Bobst Group S.A.; *Int'l*, pg. 1095
BOBST CENTRAL EUROPE LIMITED—See Bobst Group S.A.; *Int'l*, pg. 1095
BOBST (CHANGZHOU) LTD.—See Bobst Group S.A.; *Int'l*, pg. 1095
BOBST CIS LLC—See Bobst Group S.A.; *Int'l*, pg. 1095
BOBST FIRENZE S.R.L.—See Bobst Group S.A.; *Int'l*, pg. 1095
BOBST GRENCHEN AG—See Bobst Group S.A.; *Int'l*, pg. 1095
BOBST GRENCHEN AG—See Bobst Group S.A.; *Int'l*, pg. 1095
BOBST GROUP BENELUX N.V.—See Bobst Group S.A.; *Int'l*, pg. 1095
BOBST GROUP CENTRAL EUROPE SPOL. S R.O.—See Bobst Group S.A.; *Int'l*, pg. 1095

BOBST GROUP DEUTSCHLAND GMBH—See Bobst Group S.A.; *Int'l*, pg. 1095
BOBST GROUP IBERICA, S.L.—See Bobst Group S.A.; *Int'l*, pg. 1095
BOBST GROUP ITALIA S.P.A.—See Bobst Group S.A.; *Int'l*, pg. 1095
BOBST GROUP LATINOAMERICA NORTE S.A. DE CV.—See Bobst Group S.A.; *Int'l*, pg. 1095
BOBST GROUP NORTH AMERICA, INC.—See Bobst Group S.A.; *Int'l*, pg. 1095
BOBST GROUP POLSKA SP. Z O.O.—See Bobst Group S.A.; *Int'l*, pg. 1096
BOBST GROUP S.A.; *Int'l*, pg. 1095
BOBST GROUP SINGAPORE PTE LTD—See Bobst Group S.A.; *Int'l*, pg. 1096
BOBST GROUP THAILAND LTD—See Bobst Group S.A.; *Int'l*, pg. 1096
BOBST GROUP VOSTOK LLC—See Bobst Group S.A.; *Int'l*, pg. 1096
BOBST IBERICA, S.L.—See Bobst Group S.A.; *Int'l*, pg. 1096
BOBST INDIA PRIVATE LTD.—See Bobst Group S.A.; *Int'l*, pg. 1096
BOBST ISTANBUL AMBALAJ A.S.—See Bobst Group S.A.; *Int'l*, pg. 1096
BOBST ITALIA SPA—See Bobst Group S.A.; *Int'l*, pg. 1096
BOBST ITALIA SPA—See Bobst Group S.A.; *Int'l*, pg. 1096
BOBST JAPAN LTD.—See Bobst Group S.A.; *Int'l*, pg. 1096
BOBST LAGOS LTD.—See Bobst Group S.A.; *Int'l*, pg. 1096
BOBST LATINOAMERICA DO SUL LTDA—See Bobst Group S.A.; *Int'l*, pg. 1096
BOBST (LATINOAMERICA NORTE Y CARIBE) S.A. DE C.V.—See Bobst Group S.A.; *Int'l*, pg. 1095
BOBST LYON SAS—See Bobst Group S.A.; *Int'l*, pg. 1096
BOBST MALAYSIA SDN. BHD.—See Bobst Group S.A.; *Int'l*, pg. 1096
BOBST MANCHESTER LTD.—See Bobst Group S.A.; *Int'l*, pg. 1096
BOBST MANCHESTER LTD.—See Bobst Group S.A.; *Int'l*, pg. 1096
BOBST MEERBUSCH GMBH—See Bobst Group S.A.; *Int'l*, pg. 1096
BOBST MEX SA—See Bobst Group S.A.; *Int'l*, pg. 1096
BOBST PARIS SAS—See Bobst Group S.A.; *Int'l*, pg. 1096
BOBST POLSKA SP. Z O.O.—See Bobst Group S.A.; *Int'l*, pg. 1096
BOB'S TRANSPORT STORAGE CO; *U.S. Private*, pg. 606
BOBST S.A.—See Bobst Group S.A.; *Int'l*, pg. 1096
BOBST SCANDINAVIA APS—See Bobst Group S.A.; *Int'l*, pg. 1096
BOBST SCANDINAVIA APS—See Bobst Group S.A.; *Int'l*, pg. 1096
BOBST (SEA) PTE LTD—See Bobst Group S.A.; *Int'l*, pg. 1095
BOBST (SHANGHAI) LTD—See Bobst Group S.A.; *Int'l*, pg. 1095
BOBST STUTTGART GMBH—See Bobst Group S.A.; *Int'l*, pg. 1096
BOBST (TAIWAN) LTD.—See Bobst Group S.A.; *Int'l*, pg. 1095
BOBST UK HOLDINGS LTD—See Bobst Group S.A.; *Int'l*, pg. 1096
BOBST UK & IRELAND LTD.—See Bobst Group S.A.; *Int'l*, pg. 1096
BOBST UK & IRELAND LTD.—See Bobst Group S.A.; *Int'l*, pg. 1096
BOBST VIETNAM CO. LTD.—See Bobst Group S.A.; *Int'l*, pg. 1096
BOB SUMEREL TIRE CO., INC.; *U.S. Private*, pg. 605
BOB SWOPE FORD, INC.; *U.S. Private*, pg. 605
BOB TAYLOR CHEVROLET INC.; *U.S. Private*, pg. 605
BOB TOMES FORD, INC.; *U.S. Private*, pg. 605
BOB TRACEY INC.; *U.S. Private*, pg. 605
B.O.B. TRAILERS, INC.—See Nordic Capital AB; *Int'l*, pg. 5419
BOB UTTER FORD; *U.S. Private*, pg. 605
BOB WAGNER'S MILL CARPET INC.; *U.S. Private*, pg. 605
BOB WARD & SONS INCORPORATED; *U.S. Private*, pg. 605
BOB WONDRIES FORD; *U.S. Private*, pg. 605
BOB WOODRUFF FOUNDATION; *U.S. Private*, pg. 605
BOB ZIMMERMAN FORD INC.; *U.S. Private*, pg. 605
BOCA ANESTHESIA SERVICE, INC.—See KKR & Co. Inc.; *U.S. Public*, pg. 1245
BOCA ENTERPRISE MANAGEMENT (SHANGHAI) CO., LTD.—See Korn Ferry; *U.S. Public*, pg. 1272
BOCA FOODS COMPANY—See 3G Capital Inc.; *U.S. Private*, pg. 10
BOCA FOODS COMPANY—See Berkshire Hathaway Inc.; *U.S. Public*, pg. 317
BOCAGREENMD, INC.—See TherapeuticsMD, Inc.; *U.S. Public*, pg. 2145
THE BOCA RATON OPHTHALMOLOGY ASC, LLC—See KKR & Co. Inc.; *U.S. Public*, pg. 1247

BOCA RATON REGIONAL HOSPITAL, INC.—See Baptist Health South Florida, Inc.; *U.S. Private*, pg. 470
BOCA RATON TRAVEL & CRUISES, INC.; *U.S. Private*, pg. 607
BOCA RESORTS, INC.—See Blackstone Inc.; *U.S. Public*, pg. 352
BOC ASSET MANAGEMENT LTD.—See Bank of Cyprus Holdings Public Limited Company; *Int'l*, pg. 842
BOCA SYSTEMS, INC.; *U.S. Private*, pg. 607
BOCA THEATER & AUTOMATION, INC.; *U.S. Private*, pg. 607
BOC AUSTRALIA—See Linde plc; *Int'l*, pg. 4506
BOC AVIATION—See Bank of China, Ltd.; *Int'l*, pg. 841
BOCA WEST COUNTRY CLUB INC.; *U.S. Private*, pg. 607
BOC BUSINESS OBJECTIVES CONSULTING IBERICA S.L.U.—See BOC Information Technologies Consulting AG; *Int'l*, pg. 1096
BOCCHI LABORATORIES, INC.—See Aterian Investment Management, L.P.; *U.S. Private*, pg. 366
BOC (CHINA) HOLDINGS CO., LTD.—See Linde plc; *Int'l*, pg. 4506
BOC FINANCIAL ASSET INVESTMENT COMPANY, LIMITED—See Bank of China, Ltd.; *Int'l*, pg. 841
BOC FINANCIAL LEASING CO., LTD.—See Bank of China, Ltd.; *Int'l*, pg. 841
BOC FINANCIAL TECHNOLOGY CO., LTD.—See Bank of China, Ltd.; *Int'l*, pg. 841
BOC FULLERTON COMMUNITY BANK CO., LTD.—See Bank of China, Ltd.; *Int'l*, pg. 841
BOC GASES ARUBA NV—See Linde plc; *Int'l*, pg. 4507
BOC GASES FIJI LTD.—See Linde plc; *Int'l*, pg. 4507
BOC GASES FINANCE LIMITED—See Linde plc; *Int'l*, pg. 4506
BOC GASES IRELAND LTD.—See Linde plc; *Int'l*, pg. 4507
BOC GASES MOZAMBIQUE LIMITED—See Linde plc; *Int'l*, pg. 4507
BOC GASES (NANJING) COMPANY LIMITED—See Linde plc; *Int'l*, pg. 4507
BOC GASES NIGERIA PLC—See Linde plc; *Int'l*, pg. 4507
BOC GASES PAPUA NEW GUINEA PTY. LTD.—See Linde plc; *Int'l*, pg. 4507
BOC GASES SOLOMON ISLANDS LIMITED—See Linde plc; *Int'l*, pg. 4507
BOC GASES (SUZHOU) CO., LTD.—See Linde plc; *Int'l*, pg. 4507
BOC GASES (TIANJIN) COMPANY LIMITED—See Linde plc; *Int'l*, pg. 4507
BOC GASES (WUHAN) CO., LTD.—See Linde plc; *Int'l*, pg. 4507
BOC GAS & GEAR—See Linde plc; *Int'l*, pg. 4504
BOC GROUP LIFE ASSURANCE CO., LTD.—See Bank of China, Ltd.; *Int'l*, pg. 841
THE BOC GROUP LIMITED—See Linde plc; *Int'l*, pg. 4506
BO CHEMICAL CO., LTD.—See Dai Nippon Toryo Co., Ltd.; *Int'l*, pg. 1916
BOC HONG KONG (HOLDINGS) LIMITED—See Bank of China, Ltd.; *Int'l*, pg. 841
BOCHUMER VEREIN VERKEHRSTECHNIK GMBH; *Int'l*, pg. 1097
BOCHUM PERSPEKTIVE 2022 GMBH—See General Motors Company; *U.S. Public*, pg. 926
BOCIMAR BELGIUM NV—See Compagnie Maritime Belge S.A.; *Int'l*, pg. 1745
BOCIMAR HONG KONG LIMITED—See Compagnie Maritime Belge S.A.; *Int'l*, pg. 1746
BOCIMAR INTERNATIONAL N.V.—See Compagnie Maritime Belge S.A.; *Int'l*, pg. 1746
BOCIMAR NV—See Compagnie Maritime Belge S.A.; *Int'l*, pg. 1746
BOC INFORMATION SYSTEMS GMBH—See BOC Information Technologies Consulting AG; *Int'l*, pg. 1096
BOC INFORMATION TECHNOLOGIES CONSULTING AG; *Int'l*, pg. 1096
BOC INFORMATION TECHNOLOGIES CONSULTING GMBH—See BOC Information Technologies Consulting AG; *Int'l*, pg. 1096
BOC INFORMATION TECHNOLOGIES CONSULTING LTD.—See BOC Information Technologies Consulting AG; *Int'l*, pg. 1096
BOC INFORMATION TECHNOLOGIES CONSULTING SP. Z O.O.—See BOC Information Technologies Consulting AG; *Int'l*, pg. 1096
BOC INTERNATIONAL CHINA CO., LTD.; *Int'l*, pg. 1096
BOC INTERNATIONAL HOLDINGS LIMITED—See Bank of China, Ltd.; *Int'l*, pg. 841
BOC INTERNATIONAL, INC.; *U.S. Private*, pg. 607
BOC INTRESSENTER AB—See Linde plc; *Int'l*, pg. 4507
BOC INVESTMENT HOLDINGS LIMITED—See Linde plc; *Int'l*, pg. 4507
BOC INVESTMENTS NO.1 LIMITED—See Linde plc; *Int'l*, pg. 4507
BOC INVESTMENTS NO.5 LIMITED—See Linde plc; *Int'l*, pg. 4507
BOCK AUSTRALIA PTY. LTD.—See GEA Group Aktiengesellschaft; *Int'l*, pg. 2897
BOCK & CLARK CORPORATION—See NV5 Global, Inc.; *U.S. Public*, pg. 1557

BOCK COMMUNICATIONS, INC.; *U.S. Private*, pg. 607
BOCK COMPRESSORS (HANGZHOU) CO., LTD.—See NORD Holding Unternehmensbeteiligungsgesellschaft mbH; *Int'l*, pg. 5416
BOCK COMPRESSOR TECHNOLOGY (THAILAND) CO., LTD.—See NORD Holding Unternehmensbeteiligungsgesellschaft mbH; *Int'l*, pg. 5416
BOCK CONSTRUCTION, INC.; *U.S. Private*, pg. 607
BOC KENYA PLC—See Linde plc; *Int'l*, pg. 4507
BOCKER CHEVROLET BUICK GMC CADILLAC; *U.S. Private*, pg. 607
BOCK (INDIA) PVT. LTD.—See NORD Holding Unternehmensbeteiligungsgesellschaft mbH; *Int'l*, pg. 5416
BOCKINGFOLD SOLAR LIMITED—See Voltalia S.A.; *Int'l*, pg. 8303
BOCKSTAEL CONSTRUCTION LIMITED; *Int'l*, pg. 1097
BOCLH INDUSTRIAL GASES (SHANGHAI) CO., LTD.—See Linde plc; *Int'l*, pg. 4507
BOCLH INDUSTRIAL GASES (SONGJIANG) CO., LTD.—See Linde plc; *Int'l*, pg. 4507
BOCLH INDUSTRIAL GASES (XIAMEN) CO., LTD.—See Linde plc; *Int'l*, pg. 4507
BOC LIENHWA INDUSTRIAL GASES CO. LTD.—See Linde plc; *Int'l*, pg. 4507
BOC LIEN HWA INDUSTRIAL GASES CORP.—See MiTAC International Corp.; *Int'l*, pg. 4923
BOC LIMITED—See Linde plc; *Int'l*, pg. 4507
BOCM PAULS LTD.—See Agricola Group Ltd; *Int'l*, pg. 216
BOC NEW ZEALAND LTD.—See Linde plc; *Int'l*, pg. 4507
BOCOM INTERNATIONAL HOLDINGS CO., LTD.—See Bank of Communications Co., Ltd.; *Int'l*, pg. 842
BOCOMMLIFE INSURANCE COMPANY LIMITED—See Bank of Communications Co., Ltd.; *Int'l*, pg. 842
BOCOM MSIG LIFE INSURANCE COMPANY LIMITED—See Bank of Communications Co., Ltd.; *Int'l*, pg. 842
BOCONCEPT HOLDING A/S—See 3i Group plc; *Int'l*, pg. 8
BOC OPHTHALMIC INSTRUMENTS PTY LTD—See Hancock & Gore Ltd.; *Int'l*, pg. 3242
BOCO ROCK WIND FARM PTY. LTD.—See Electricity Generating Public Co., Ltd.; *Int'l*, pg. 2352
BOC PROPERTY DEVELOPMENT & MANAGEMENT (PVT) LTD—See Bank of Ceylon; *Int'l*, pg. 840
BOC-SAMSUNG LIFE INSURANCE CO., LTD.—See Bank of China, Ltd.; *Int'l*, pg. 841
BOCS BREMEN OVERSEAS CHARTERING AND SHIPPING GMBH; *Int'l*, pg. 1097
BOC TANZANIA LIMITED—See Linde plc; *Int'l*, pg. 4507
BOC (TRADING) LIMITED—See Linde plc; *Int'l*, pg. 4506
BOC TRAVELS (PRIVATE) LIMITED—See Bank of Ceylon; *Int'l*, pg. 840
BOC UNTERNEHMENSBERATUNG GMBH—See BOC Information Technologies Consulting AG; *Int'l*, pg. 1096
BOC WEALTH MANAGEMENT CO., LTD.—See Bank of China, Ltd.; *Int'l*, pg. 841
BOC ZIMBABWE (PVT) LIMITED—See Linde plc; *Int'l*, pg. 4507
BODAK-CAMERON ENGINEERING—See Cameron Engineering & Associates, LLP; *U.S. Private*, pg. 728
BODAL CHEMICALS LTD.; *Int'l*, pg. 1097
BODARD CONSTRUCTION MODULAIRE; *Int'l*, pg. 1097
BODDEN PARTNERS; *U.S. Private*, pg. 607
BODDIE-NOELL ENTERPRISES, INC.; *U.S. Private*, pg. 607
BODDINGTON LUMBER CO; *U.S. Private*, pg. 607
BODEANS BAKING COMPANY LLC; *U.S. Private*, pg. 607
BODEANS WAFER COMPANY, LLC; *U.S. Private*, pg. 607
BODE BYG A/S—See Hojgaard Holding A/S; *Int'l*, pg. 3442
BODE CELLMARK FORENSICS, INC.—See Laboratory Corporation of America Holdings; *U.S. Public*, pg. 1285
BODE CHEMIE GMBH & CO.—See PAUL HARTMANN AG; *Int'l*, pg. 5760
BODE CONCRETE, LLC—See Vulcan Materials Company; *U.S. Public*, pg. 2313
BODE DESIGN GMBH—See Inspecs Group Plc; *Int'l*, pg. 3719
BODE ENERGY EQUIPMENT CO., LTD.; *Int'l*, pg. 1097
BODEGA CHANDON ARGENTINA S.A.—See LVMH Moet Hennessy Louis Vuitton SE; *Int'l*, pg. 4599
BODEGA LATINA CORPORATION—See Grupo Comercial Chedraui S.A.B. de C.V.; *Int'l*, pg. 3125
BODEGAS BILBAINAS, S.A.—See The Carlyle Group Inc.; *U.S. Public*, pg. 2045
BODEGAS BVBA—See Colruyt Group N.V.; *Int'l*, pg. 1705
BODEGAS CHANDON ARGENTINA SA—See LVMH Moet Hennessy Louis Vuitton SE; *Int'l*, pg. 4599
BODEGAS RIOJANAS, S.A.; *Int'l*, pg. 1097
BODEGAS TERRAZAS DE LOS ANDES—See LVMH Moet Hennessy Louis Vuitton SE; *Int'l*, pg. 4599
BODE GRAVEL CO.—See Vulcan Materials Company; *U.S. Public*, pg. 2313
BODE KOREA CO., LTD.—See The Carlyle Group Inc.; *U.S. Public*, pg. 2053
BODELL CONSTRUCTION COMPANY INC. - HAWAII DIVISION—See Bodell Construction Company; *U.S. Private*, pg. 608

COMPANY NAME INDEX BODY WISE INTERNATIONAL INC.

Company Index

BODELL CONSTRUCTION COMPANY INC.; *U.S. Private*, pg. 608
BODEN BRUSSELS NV—See General Motors Company; *U.S. Public*, pg. 923
BODENHAUS GMBH—See Hornbach Holding AG & Co. KGaA; *Int'l*, pg. 3481
BODE NORTH AMERICA INC.—See The Carlyle Group Inc.; *U.S. Public*, pg. 2053
BODENSTEINER IMPLEMENT COMPANY; *U.S. Private*, pg. 608
BODEN STORE FIXTURES INC.; *U.S. Private*, pg. 608
BODHI TREE MULTIMEDIA LIMITED; *Int'l*, pg. 1097
BODHTREE CONSULTING LTD.; *Int'l*, pg. 1097
BODILY RV, INC.—See Camping World Holdings, Inc.; *U.S. Public*, pg. 427
BODIM PORT OY—See Aurelius Equity Opportunities SE & Co. KGaA; *Int'l*, pg. 709
BODIN CONCRETE LP; *U.S. Private*, pg. 608
BODINE ALUMINUM INC.—See Toyota Motor Corporation; *Int'l*, pg. 7874
BODINE AND COMPANY, LLC; *U.S. Private*, pg. 608
BODINE ELECTRIC COMPANY; *U.S. Private*, pg. 608
BODINE GROUP HOLDING COMPANY INC.—See Signify N.V.; *Int'l*, pg. 6912
BOD INTERNATIONAL PTY. LIMITED—See Eu Yan Sang International Ltd.; *Int'l*, pg. 2525
BODIS, LLC; *U.S. Private*, pg. 608
BODITECH MED, INC.; *Int'l*, pg. 1097
BODITSE (PTY) LIMITED—See Alviva Holdings Limited; *Int'l*, pg. 401
BODKIN ASSOCIATES, INC.; *U.S. Private*, pg. 608
BODMIN VETS4PETS LIMITED—See Pets at Home Group Plc; *Int'l*, pg. 5833
BODON INDUSTRIES INC.; *U.S. Private*, pg. 608
BODONI SYSTEMS—See Agfa-Gevaert N.V.; *Int'l*, pg. 208
BOD SCIENCE LIMITED; *Int'l*, pg. 1097
BODWELL CHRYSLER-JEEP-DODGE; *U.S. Private*, pg. 608
BODY ACTION ENTERPRISE CO., LTD.; *Int'l*, pg. 1097
BODY AND MIND INC.; *Int'l*, pg. 1097
BODY ART AUSTRALIA PTY LIMITED—See PVH Corp.; *U.S. Public*, pg. 1739
BODY BASICS FITNESS EQUIPMENT; *U.S. Private*, pg. 608
BODY BASICS, INC.; *U.S. Private*, pg. 608
BODYBUILDING.COM, LLC—See Qurate Retail, Inc.; *U.S. Public*, pg. 1757
BODY CENTRAL CORP.—See WestView Capital Partners, L.P.; *U.S. Private*, pg. 4501
BODY CENTRAL STORES, INC.—See WestView Capital Partners, L.P.; *U.S. Private*, pg. 4501
BODY CONTOURS PTE LTD—See Fitgenes Australia Pty Ltd.; *Int'l*, pg. 2695
BODY CORPORATE BROKERS PTY LTD—See Steadfast Group Limited; *Int'l*, pg. 7187
BODYCOTE ARGENTINA SA—See Bodycote plc; *Int'l*, pg. 1097
BODYCOTE BRASIMET PROCESSAMENTO TERMICO S.A.—See Bodycote plc; *Int'l*, pg. 1097
BODYCOTE COATING CENTRUM BV—See Bodycote plc; *Int'l*, pg. 1097
BODYCOTE FRANCE—See Bodycote plc; *Int'l*, pg. 1097
BODYCOTE HARDIFF B.V.—See Bodycote plc; *Int'l*, pg. 1098
BODYCOTE HARDIFF GMBH—See Bodycote plc; *Int'l*, pg. 1098
BODYCOTE HARDINGSCENTRUM BV—See Bodycote plc; *Int'l*, pg. 1098
BODYCOTE HEAT TREATMENTS LTD.—See Bodycote plc; *Int'l*, pg. 1098
BODYCOTE HEISS-ISOSTATISCHES PRESSEN GMBH—See Bodycote plc; *Int'l*, pg. 1098
BODYCOTE HIP GMBH—See Bodycote plc; *Int'l*, pg. 1097
BODYCOTE H.I.P. LTD.—See Bodycote plc; *Int'l*, pg. 1097
BODYCOTE HIP N.V.—See Bodycote plc; *Int'l*, pg. 1097
BODYCOTE HOKEZELO KFT—See Bodycote plc; *Int'l*, pg. 1098
BODYCOTE HOT ISOSTATIC PRESSING AB—See Bodycote plc; *Int'l*, pg. 1098
BODYCOTE HOT ISOSTATIC PRESSING—See Bodycote plc; *Int'l*, pg. 1098
BODYCOTE HT S.R.O—See Bodycote plc; *Int'l*, pg. 1098
BODYCOTE IMT INC.—See Bodycote plc; *Int'l*, pg. 1098
BODYCOTE INTERNATIONAL INC.—See Bodycote plc; *Int'l*, pg. 1098
BODYCOTE ISTAS ISIL ISLEM SANAYI VE TICARET AS—See Bodycote plc; *Int'l*, pg. 1098
BODYCOTE ITALIA SRL—See Bodycote plc; *Int'l*, pg. 1098
BODYCOTE JAPAN K.K.—See Bodycote plc; *Int'l*, pg. 1098
BODYCOTE K-TECH, INC.—See Bodycote plc; *Int'l*, pg. 1098
BODYCOTE LAMPOKASITTELY OY—See Bodycote plc; *Int'l*, pg. 1098
BODYCOTE METALLURGICAL COATINGS LTD.—See Bodycote plc; *Int'l*, pg. 1098
BODYCOTE (NINGBO) HEAT TREATMENT CO. LIMITED—See Bodycote plc; *Int'l*, pg. 1097
BODYCOTE PLC; *Int'l*, pg. 1097
BODYCOTE POLSKA SP Z.O.O—See Bodycote plc; *Int'l*, pg. 1098
BODYCOTE RHEINTAL WARMEBEHANDLUNG AG—See Bodycote plc; *Int'l*, pg. 1098
BODYCOTE SAS—See Bodycote plc; *Int'l*, pg. 1098
BODYCOTE SCHWEIZ WARMEBEHANDLUNG AG—See Bodycote plc; *Int'l*, pg. 1098
BODYCOTE SINGAPORE PTE LTD—See Bodycote plc; *Int'l*, pg. 1098
BODYCOTE SLOVAKIA S.R.O.—See Bodycote plc; *Int'l*, pg. 1098
BODYCOTE SURFACE TECHNOLOGY WARTBURG, INC.—See Bodycote plc; *Int'l*, pg. 1098
BODYCOTE THERMAL PROCESSING CANADA, INC.—See Bodycote plc; *Int'l*, pg. 1098
BODYCOTE THERMAL PROCESSING—See Bodycote plc; *Int'l*, pg. 1098
BODYCOTE THERMAL PROCESSING—See Bodycote plc; *Int'l*, pg. 1098
BODYCOTE TRATAMENTE TERMICE SRL—See Bodycote plc; *Int'l*, pg. 1098
BODYCOTE TRATTAMENTI TERMICI SPA—See Bodycote plc; *Int'l*, pg. 1098
BODYCOTE VARMEBEHANDLING AB—See Bodycote plc; *Int'l*, pg. 1098
BODYCOTE VARMEBEHANDLING A/S—See Bodycote plc; *Int'l*, pg. 1098
BODYCOTE WARMEBEHANDLUNG GMBH—See Bodycote plc; *Int'l*, pg. 1098
BODYCOTE WARMEBEHANDLUNG GMBH—See Bodycote plc; *Int'l*, pg. 1098
BODYCOTE WARMEBEHANDLUNG MARCHTRENK GMBH—See Bodycote plc; *Int'l*, pg. 1098
BODYCOTE WARMEBEHANDLUNG WIEN GMBH—See Bodycote plc; *Int'l*, pg. 1098
BODYCOTE WUXI TECHNOLOGY CO. LIMITED—See Bodycote plc; *Int'l*, pg. 1098
BODYCOTE YTBEHANDLING AB—See Bodycote plc; *Int'l*, pg. 1098
BODY GLOVE INTERNATIONAL, LLC—See Marquee Brands LLC; *U.S. Private*, pg. 2586
BODY GLOVE(M) SDN. BHD.—See BGT Corporation Public Company Limited; *Int'l*, pg. 1009
BODYGUARD LIFESCIENCES PTY. LTD.—See Wellfully Limited; *Int'l*, pg. 8374
BODYGUARD WORKWEAR LIMITED—See Bunzl plc; *Int'l*, pg. 1217
BODYGUARDZ; *U.S. Private*, pg. 608
BODYHEALTH.COM LLC; *U.S. Private*, pg. 608
BODYMEDIA, INC.—See AliphCom; *U.S. Private*, pg. 168
BODYNET LTD—See HeiTech Padu Berhad; *Int'l*, pg. 3326
BODY ONE S.A.; *Int'l*, pg. 1097
BODYPOWER SPORTS PLC; *Int'l*, pg. 1099
THE BODY SHOP A ISLANDI—See Aurelius Equity Opportunities SE & Co. KGaA; *Int'l*, pg. 710
THE BODY SHOP BETEILIGUNGS-GMBH—See Aurelius Equity Opportunities SE & Co. KGaA; *Int'l*, pg. 710
BODYSHOPBIDS, INC.; *U.S. Private*, pg. 608
THE BODY SHOP CANADA LIMITED—See Aurelius Equity Opportunities SE & Co. KGaA; *Int'l*, pg. 710
THE BODY SHOP (FRANCE) SARL—See Aurelius Equity Opportunities SE & Co. KGaA; *Int'l*, pg. 710
THE BODY SHOP GERMANY GMBH—See Aurelius Equity Opportunities SE & Co. KGaA; *Int'l*, pg. 710
THE BODY SHOP INTERNATIONAL INC.—See Aurelius Equity Opportunities SE & Co. KGaA; *Int'l*, pg. 710
THE BODY SHOP INTERNATIONAL LIMITED—See Aurelius Equity Opportunities SE & Co. KGaA; *Int'l*, pg. 709
THE BODY SHOP INTERNATIONAL (PTE) LTD.—See Aurelius Equity Opportunities SE & Co. KGaA; *Int'l*, pg. 710
BODY SHOP OF AMERICA, INC.—See WestView Capital Partners, L.P.; *U.S. Private*, pg. 4501
THE BODY SHOP (SINGAPORE) PTE LTD—See Aurelius Equity Opportunities SE & Co. KGaA; *Int'l*, pg. 710
THE BODY SHOP SVENSKA AB—See Aurelius Equity Opportunities SE & Co. KGaA; *Int'l*, pg. 710
THE BODY SHOP SWITZERLAND AG—See Aurelius Equity Opportunities SE & Co. KGaA; *Int'l*, pg. 710
BODYTECHNICS LIMITED—See Berjaya Corporation Berhad; *Int'l*, pg. 984
BODYTEL GMBH—See InhaleRx Limited; *Int'l*, pg. 3703
BODY WAVES INC.; *U.S. Private*, pg. 608
BODY WISE INTERNATIONAL INC.; *U.S. Private*, pg. 608
BOECKMANS BELGIE NV—See Banco Safra S.A.; *Int'l*, pg. 824
BOECKMANS BELGIE NV—See Sucocitrico Cutrale Ltda.; *Int'l*, pg. 7251
BOECKMANS NEDERLAND B.V.—See Banco Safra S.A.; *Int'l*, pg. 824
BOECKMANS NEDERLAND B.V.—See Sucocitrico Cutrale Ltda.; *Int'l*, pg. 7251
BOECORE, INC.—See Enlightenment Capital LLC; *U.S. Private*, pg. 1400
BOEFLY, INC.—See ConnectOne Bancorp, Inc.; *U.S. Public*, pg. 567
BOE HEALTHCARE INVESTMENT & MANAGEMENT CO., LTD.—See BOE Technology Group Co., Ltd.; *Int'l*, pg. 1099
BOE (HEBEI) MOBILE TECHNOLOGY CO., LTD.—See BOE Technology Group Co., Ltd.; *Int'l*, pg. 1099
THE BOEHM PRESSED STEEL CO.—See Validor Capital LLC; *U.S. Private*, pg. 4332
BOEHRINGER INGELHEIM AB—See C.H. Boehringer Sohn AG & Co. KG; *Int'l*, pg. 1241
BOEHRINGER INGELHEIM ANIMAL HEALTH AUSTRALIA PTY. LTD.—See C.H. Boehringer Sohn AG & Co. KG; *Int'l*, pg. 1241
BOEHRINGER INGELHEIM ANIMAL HEALTH BELGIUM S.A.—See C.H. Boehringer Sohn AG & Co. KG; *Int'l*, pg. 1241
BOEHRINGER INGELHEIM ANIMAL HEALTH DO BRASIL LTDA.—See C.H. Boehringer Sohn AG & Co. KG; *Int'l*, pg. 1241
BOEHRINGER INGELHEIM ANIMAL HEALTH JAPAN CO., LTD.—See C.H. Boehringer Sohn AG & Co. KG; *Int'l*, pg. 1241
BOEHRINGER INGELHEIM ANIMAL HEALTH NETHERLANDS B.V.—See C.H. Boehringer Sohn AG & Co. KG; *Int'l*, pg. 1241
BOEHRINGER INGELHEIM ANIMAL HEALTH NEW ZEALAND LIMITED—See C.H. Boehringer Sohn AG & Co. KG; *Int'l*, pg. 1241
BOEHRINGER INGELHEIM ANIMAL HEALTH SOUTH AFRICA PTY. LTD.—See C.H. Boehringer Sohn AG & Co. KG; *Int'l*, pg. 1241
BOEHRINGER INGELHEIM AUSTRIA GMBH—See C.H. Boehringer Sohn AG & Co. KG; *Int'l*, pg. 1241
BOEHRINGER INGELHEIM BH D.O.O—See C.H. Boehringer Sohn AG & Co. KG; *Int'l*, pg. 1241
BOEHRINGER INGELHEIM B.V.—See C.H. Boehringer Sohn AG & Co. KG; *Int'l*, pg. 1241
BOEHRINGER INGELHEIM (CANADA) LTD.—See C.H. Boehringer Sohn AG & Co. KG; *Int'l*, pg. 1240
BOEHRINGER INGELHEIM C.A.—See C.H. Boehringer Sohn AG & Co. KG; *Int'l*, pg. 1241
BOEHRINGER INGELHEIM CHEMICALS, INC.—See C.H. Boehringer Sohn AG & Co. KG; *Int'l*, pg. 1241
BOEHRINGER INGELHEIM CORP.—See C.H. Boehringer Sohn AG & Co. KG; *Int'l*, pg. 1241
BOEHRINGER INGELHEIM DANMARK A/S—See C.H. Boehringer Sohn AG & Co. KG; *Int'l*, pg. 1241
BOEHRINGER INGELHEIM DEL ECUADOR CIA. LTDA.—See C.H. Boehringer Sohn AG & Co. KG; *Int'l*, pg. 1242
BOEHRINGER INGELHEIM DO BRASIL QUIMICA E FARMACEUTICA LTDA.—See C.H. Boehringer Sohn AG & Co. KG; *Int'l*, pg. 1242
BOEHRINGER INGELHEIM ELLAS AE—See C.H. Boehringer Sohn AG & Co. KG; *Int'l*, pg. 1241
BOEHRINGER INGELHEIM ESPANA, S.A.—See C.H. Boehringer Sohn AG & Co. KG; *Int'l*, pg. 1241
BOEHRINGER INGELHEIM EUROPE GMBH—See C.H. Boehringer Sohn AG & Co. KG; *Int'l*, pg. 1241
BOEHRINGER INGELHEIM FINLAND KY—See C.H. Boehringer Sohn AG & Co. KG; *Int'l*, pg. 1241
BOEHRINGER INGELHEIM FRANCE S.A.S.—See C.H. Boehringer Sohn AG & Co. KG; *Int'l*, pg. 1241
BOEHRINGER INGELHEIM FREMONT, INC.—See C.H. Boehringer Sohn AG & Co. KG; *Int'l*, pg. 1241
BOEHRINGER INGELHEIM GMBH—See C.H. Boehringer Sohn AG & Co. KG; *Int'l*, pg. 1242
BOEHRINGER INGELHEIM (HONG KONG) LTD.—See C.H. Boehringer Sohn AG & Co. KG; *Int'l*, pg. 1241
BOEHRINGER INGELHEIM ILAC TICARET A.S.—See C.H. Boehringer Sohn AG & Co. KG; *Int'l*, pg. 1242
BOEHRINGER INGELHEIM INDIA PRIVATE LTD.—See C.H. Boehringer Sohn AG & Co. KG; *Int'l*, pg. 1242
BOEHRINGER INGELHEIM INTERNATIONAL TRADING (SHANGHAI) CO. LTD.—See C.H. Boehringer Sohn AG & Co. KG; *Int'l*, pg. 1242
BOEHRINGER INGELHEIM ISRAEL LTD—See C.H. Boehringer Sohn AG & Co. KG; *Int'l*, pg. 1242
BOEHRINGER INGELHEIM ITALIA S.P.A.—See C.H. Boehringer Sohn AG & Co. KG; *Int'l*, pg. 1242
BOEHRINGER INGELHEIM KOREA LTD.—See C.H. Boehringer Sohn AG & Co. KG; *Int'l*, pg. 1242
BOEHRINGER INGELHEIM LTDA.—See C.H. Boehringer Sohn AG & Co. KG; *Int'l*, pg. 1242
BOEHRINGER INGELHEIM LTDA.—See C.H. Boehringer Sohn AG & Co. KG; *Int'l*, pg. 1242
BOEHRINGER INGELHEIM LTD.—See C.H. Boehringer Sohn AG & Co. KG; *Int'l*, pg. 1242
BOEHRINGER INGELHEIM MICROPARTS GMBH—See C.H. Boehringer Sohn AG & Co. KG; *Int'l*, pg. 1242
BOEHRINGER INGELHEIM NORWAY KS—See C.H. Boehringer Sohn AG & Co. KG; *Int'l*, pg. 1241
BOEHRINGER INGELHEIM (N.Z.) LIMITED—See C.H. Boehringer Sohn AG & Co. KG; *Int'l*, pg. 1241
BOEHRINGER INGELHEIM PERU S.A.C.—See C.H. Boehringer Sohn AG & Co. KG; *Int'l*, pg. 1242
BOEHRINGER INGELHEIM PHARMACEUTICALS, INC.—See C.H. Boehringer Sohn AG & Co. KG; *Int'l*, pg. 1241

BOEHRINGER INGELHEIM PHARMA GES.M.B.H.—See C.H. Boehringer Sohn AG & Co. KG; *Int'l*, pg. 1241
BOEHRINGER INGELHEIM PHARMA GES MBH—See C.H. Boehringer Sohn AG & Co. KG; *Int'l*, pg. 1242
BOEHRINGER INGELHEIM PHARMA GMBH & CO. KG—See C.H. Boehringer Sohn AG & Co. KG; *Int'l*, pg. 1242
BOEHRINGER INGELHEIM (PHILIPPINES) INC.—See C.H. Boehringer Sohn AG & Co. KG; *Int'l*, pg. 1241
BOEHRINGER INGELHEIM PROMECO, S.A. DE C.V.—See C.H. Boehringer Sohn AG & Co. KG; *Int'l*, pg. 1242
BOEHRINGER INGELHEIM PTY. LTD.—See C.H. Boehringer Sohn AG & Co. KG; *Int'l*, pg. 1242
BOEHRINGER INGELHEIM (PTY.) LTD.—See C.H. Boehringer Sohn AG & Co. KG; *Int'l*, pg. 1241
BOEHRINGER INGELHEIM S.A./N.V.—See C.H. Boehringer Sohn AG & Co. KG; *Int'l*, pg. 1242
BOEHRINGER INGELHEIM S.A.—See C.H. Boehringer Sohn AG & Co. KG; *Int'l*, pg. 1242
BOEHRINGER INGELHEIM S.A.—See C.H. Boehringer Sohn AG & Co. KG; *Int'l*, pg. 1242
BOEHRINGER INGELHEIM (SCHWEIZ) GMBH—See C.H. Boehringer Sohn AG & Co. KG; *Int'l*, pg. 1241
BOEHRINGER INGELHEIM SEIYAKU CO., LTD.—See C.H. Boehringer Sohn AG & Co. KG; *Int'l*, pg. 1243
BOEHRINGER INGELHEIM SERBIA D.O.O.—See C.H. Boehringer Sohn AG & Co. KG; *Int'l*, pg. 1242
BOEHRINGER INGELHEIM SHANGHAI PHARMACEUTICALS CO., LTD.—See C.H. Boehringer Sohn AG & Co. KG; *Int'l*, pg. 1242
BOEHRINGER INGELHEIM SPOL. S R.O.—See C.H. Boehringer Sohn AG & Co. KG; *Int'l*, pg. 1242
BOEHRINGER INGELHEIM SP. Z O.O.—See C.H. Boehringer Sohn AG & Co. KG; *Int'l*, pg. 1241
BOEHRINGER INGELHEIM S.R.O.—See C.H. Boehringer Sohn AG & Co. KG; *Int'l*, pg. 1241
BOEHRINGER INGELHEIM TAIWAN LTD.—See C.H. Boehringer Sohn AG & Co. KG; *Int'l*, pg. 1242
BOEHRINGER INGELHEIM (THAI) LTD.—See C.H. Boehringer Sohn AG & Co. KG; *Int'l*, pg. 1241
BOEHRINGER INGELHEIM VENTURE FUND GMBH—See C.H. Boehringer Sohn AG & Co. KG; *Int'l*, pg. 1242
BOEHRINGER INGELHEIM VETERINARY RESEARCH CENTER GMBH & CO. KG—See C.H. Boehringer Sohn AG & Co. KG; *Int'l*, pg. 1242
BOEHRINGER INGELHEIM VETMEDICA GMBH—See C.H. Boehringer Sohn AG & Co. KG; *Int'l*, pg. 1242
BOEHRINGER INGELHEIM VETMEDICA, INC.—See C.H. Boehringer Sohn AG & Co. KG; *Int'l*, pg. 1241
BOEHRINGER INGELHEIM VETMEDICA JAPAN—See C.H. Boehringer Sohn AG & Co. KG; *Int'l*, pg. 1243
BOEHRINGER INGELHEIM VETMEDICA KOREA LTD.—See C.H. Boehringer Sohn AG & Co. KG; *Int'l*, pg. 1242
BOEHRINGER INGELHEIM VETMEDICA S.A. DE C.V.—See C.H. Boehringer Sohn AG & Co. KG; *Int'l*, pg. 1242
BOEHRINGER INGELHEIM ZAGREB D.O.O.—See C.H. Boehringer Sohn AG & Co. KG; *Int'l*, pg. 1242
BOE HYUNDAI LCD (BEIJING) DISPLAY TECHNOLOGY CO., LTD.—See BOE Technology Group Co., Ltd.; *Int'l*, pg. 1099
BOEING ADVANCED INFORMATION SYSTEMS-MARYLAND OPERATIONS—See The Boeing Company; *U.S. Public*, pg. 2039
BOEING AEROSPACE OPERATIONS, INC.—See The Boeing Company; *U.S. Public*, pg. 2039
BOEING AEROSTRUCTURES AUSTRALIA PTY LTD.—See The Boeing Company; *U.S. Public*, pg. 2040
BOEING AUSTRALIA HOLDINGS PROPRIETARY LIMITED—See The Boeing Company; *U.S. Public*, pg. 2040
BOEING CANADA OPERATIONS LTD.—See The Boeing Company; *U.S. Public*, pg. 2040
BOEING CAPITAL CORPORATION—See The Boeing Company; *U.S. Public*, pg. 2039
BOEING CAPITAL LOAN CORPORATION—See The Boeing Company; *U.S. Public*, pg. 2039
THE BOEING CO. - 777 PROGRAM—See The Boeing Company; *U.S. Public*, pg. 2039
THE BOEING CO. - ANAHEIM—See The Boeing Company; *U.S. Public*, pg. 2040
THE BOEING CO. - ELECTRONIC SYSTEMS—See The Boeing Company; *U.S. Public*, pg. 2040
THE BOEING CO. - EL PASO—See The Boeing Company; *U.S. Public*, pg. 2040
THE BOEING CO. - HELICOPTER DIVISION—See The Boeing Company; *U.S. Public*, pg. 2039
THE BOEING CO. - HUNTSVILLE—See The Boeing Company; *U.S. Public*, pg. 2040
THE BOEING CO. - LONG BEACH—See The Boeing Company; *U.S. Public*, pg. 2041
BOEING COMMERCIAL AIRPLANE GROUP - EVERETT—See The Boeing Company; *U.S. Public*, pg. 2039
BOEING COMMERCIAL AIRPLANE GROUP - SEATTLE—See The Boeing Company; *U.S. Public*, pg. 2039
BOEING COMMERCIAL AIRPLANE GROUP—See The Boeing Company; *U.S. Public*, pg. 2039
BOEING COMMERCIAL AVIATION SERVICES—See The Boeing Company; *U.S. Public*, pg. 2039
THE BOEING COMPANY; *U.S. Public*, pg. 2038
THE BOEING CO. - OAK RIDGE—See The Boeing Company; *U.S. Public*, pg. 2040
THE BOEING CO. - RIDLEY PARK—See The Boeing Company; *U.S. Public*, pg. 2041
THE BOEING CO. - SEATTLE—See The Boeing Company; *U.S. Public*, pg. 2041
BOEING DEFENCE AUSTRALIA LTD—See The Boeing Company; *U.S. Public*, pg. 2040
BOEING DEFENCE UK LIMITED—See The Boeing Company; *U.S. Public*, pg. 2041
BOEING DEFENSE, SPACE & SECURITY GROUP—See The Boeing Company; *U.S. Public*, pg. 2039
BOEING DEUTSCHLAND GMBH—See The Boeing Company; *U.S. Public*, pg. 2040
BOEING DISTRIBUTION, INC.—See The Boeing Company; *U.S. Public*, pg. 2039
BOEING DISTRIBUTION SERVICES GMBH—See The Boeing Company; *U.S. Public*, pg. 2040
BOEING DISTRIBUTION SERVICES II GMBH—See The Boeing Company; *U.S. Public*, pg. 2040
BOEING DISTRIBUTION SERVICES II LIMITED—See The Boeing Company; *U.S. Public*, pg. 2040
BOEING DISTRIBUTION SERVICES, INC.-PARAMUS—See The Boeing Company; *U.S. Public*, pg. 2040
BOEING DISTRIBUTION SERVICES INC.—See The Boeing Company; *U.S. Public*, pg. 2040
BOEING DISTRIBUTION SERVICES INC.—See The Boeing Company; *U.S. Public*, pg. 2040
BOEING DISTRIBUTION SERVICES SAS—See The Boeing Company; *U.S. Public*, pg. 2040
BOEING DISTRIBUTION SERVICES—See The Boeing Company; *U.S. Public*, pg. 2040
BOEING DISTRIBUTION SERVICES SP Z.O.O—See RTX Corporation; *U.S. Public*, pg. 1822
BOEING DISTRIBUTION SERVICES - TOULOUSE—See The Boeing Company; *U.S. Public*, pg. 2040
BOEING INTELLECTUAL PROPERTY LICENSING COMPANY—See The Boeing Company; *U.S. Public*, pg. 2040
BOEING INTELLIGENCE & ANALYTICS, INC.—See The Boeing Company; *U.S. Public*, pg. 2039
BOEING INTERNATIONAL B.V. & CO. HOLDING KGAA—See The Boeing Company; *U.S. Public*, pg. 2040
BOEING INTERNATIONAL CORP. - AUSTRALIA—See The Boeing Company; *U.S. Public*, pg. 2040
BOEING INTERNATIONAL CORP. - FRANCE—See The Boeing Company; *U.S. Public*, pg. 2040
BOEING INTERNATIONAL CORPORATION—See The Boeing Company; *U.S. Public*, pg. 2040
BOEING JAPAN CO., LTD.—See The Boeing Company; *U.S. Public*, pg. 2040
BOEING LAUNCH SERVICES, INC.—See The Boeing Company; *U.S. Public*, pg. 2041
BOEING MILITARY AIRCRAFT DIVISION—See The Boeing Company; *U.S. Public*, pg. 2039
BOEING NETHERLANDS B.V.—See The Boeing Company; *U.S. Public*, pg. 2040
BOEING NEVADA, INC.—See The Boeing Company; *U.S. Public*, pg. 2041
BOEING NORTH AMERICAN SERVICES INC.—See The Boeing Company; *U.S. Public*, pg. 2041
BOEING REALTY CORPORATION—See The Boeing Company; *U.S. Public*, pg. 2041
BOEING SATELLITE SYSTEMS INTERNATIONAL, INC.—See The Boeing Company; *U.S. Public*, pg. 2039
BOEING SINGAPORE TRAINING AND FLIGHT SERVICES PTE. LTD.—See The Boeing Company; *U.S. Public*, pg. 2040
BOEING TRAINING & FLIGHT SERVICES AUSTRALIA PTY LTD—See The Boeing Company; *U.S. Public*, pg. 2040
BOEING TRAINING & FLIGHT SERVICES—See The Boeing Company; *U.S. Public*, pg. 2039
BOEING UK LTD. - HOUNSLOW—See The Boeing Company; *U.S. Public*, pg. 2041
BOEING UNITED KINGDOM LIMITED—See The Boeing Company; *U.S. Public*, pg. 2041
BOEING WINNIPEG—See The Boeing Company; *U.S. Public*, pg. 2041
BOEKEL INDUSTRIES INC.; *U.S. Private*, pg. 608
BOE (KOREA) CO., LTD.—See BOE Technology Group Co., Ltd.; *Int'l*, pg. 1099
BOE LAND CO., LTD.—See BOE Technology Group Co., Ltd.; *Int'l*, pg. 1099
BOELS TOPHOLDING B.V.; *Int'l*, pg. 1099
THE BOELTER COMPANIES INC.; *U.S. Private*, pg. 3995
THE BOELTER COMPANIES INC.—See The Boelter Companies Inc.; *U.S. Private*, pg. 3995

BOELTER + LINCOLN MARKETING COMMUNICATIONS; *U.S. Private*, pg. 608
BOEMER RENTAL SERVICES GROUP—See Egeria Capital Management B.V.; *Int'l*, pg. 2323
BOENNING & SCATTERGOOD, INC.; *U.S. Private*, pg. 608
BOE OPTICAL SCIENCE & TECHNOLOGY CO., LTD.—See BOE Technology Group Co., Ltd.; *Int'l*, pg. 1099
BOE (PTY) LIMITED—See Nedbank Group Limited; *Int'l*, pg. 5187
BOERLIND GESELLSCHAFT FUER ERZEUGNISSE MBH; *Int'l*, pg. 1099
BOERNER TRUCK CENTER; *U.S. Private*, pg. 609
BOERO BARTOLOMEO S.P.A.; *Int'l*, pg. 1100
BOERO COLORI FRANCE S.A.R.L—See Boero Bartolomeo S.p.A.; *Int'l*, pg. 1100
BOER POWER HOLDINGS LIMITED; *Int'l*, pg. 1099
BOERSE BERLIN AG—See Deutsche Borse AG; *Int'l*, pg. 2065
BOER (SHANGHAI) SWITCH APPARATUS CO., LTD.—See Boer Power Holdings Limited; *Int'l*, pg. 1099
BOE SEMI-CONDUCTOR CO., LTD.—See BOE Technology Group Co., Ltd.; *Int'l*, pg. 1099
BOE SMART TECHNOLOGY CO., LTD.—See BOE Technology Group Co., Ltd.; *Int'l*, pg. 1099
BOE TECHNOLOGY GROUP CO., LTD.; *Int'l*, pg. 1099
BOETGER ACQUISITION CORP.—See Northwest Bancshares, Inc.; *U.S. Public*, pg. 1542
BOE VARITRONIX LIMITED—See BOE Technology Group Co., Ltd.; *Int'l*, pg. 1099
BOFA AMERICAS INC.—See Donaldson Company, Inc.; *U.S. Public*, pg. 675
BOFA CANADA BANK—See Bank of America Corporation; *U.S. Public*, pg. 271
BOFA INTERNATIONAL LTD.—See Donaldson Company, Inc.; *U.S. Public*, pg. 675
BOFA SECURITIES INDIA LIMITED—See Bank of America Corporation; *U.S. Public*, pg. 271
BOFA SECURITIES JAPAN CO., LTD.—See Bank of America Corporation; *U.S. Public*, pg. 271
BOFEX BEOGRAD, D.O.O.—See Merkur, d.d.; *Int'l*, pg. 4837
BOFEX, D.O.O.—See Merkur, d.d.; *Int'l*, pg. 4837
BOFOAM S.R.O.—See Recticel S.A.; *Int'l*, pg. 6241
BOFORS MISSILES AB—See Saab AB; *Int'l*, pg. 6459
BOGACHIEL DIALYSIS, LLC—See DaVita Inc.; *U.S. Public*, pg. 636
BOGALA GRAPHITE LANKA PLC—See AMG Critical Materials N.V.; *Int'l*, pg. 425
BOG'ART BUILDING MANAGEMENT SRL—See Bog'Art S.R.L.; *Int'l*, pg. 1100
BOG'ART FASHION SRL—See Bog'Art S.R.L.; *Int'l*, pg. 1100
BOG'ART S.R.L.; *Int'l*, pg. 1100
BOG'ART STEEL SRL—See Bog'Art S.R.L.; *Int'l*, pg. 1100
BOGATI URNS COMPANY; *U.S. Private*, pg. 609
BOGAWANTALAWA TEA CEYLON (PVT) LTD.—See Bogawantalawa Tea Estates PLC; *Int'l*, pg. 1100
BOGAWANTALAWA TEA ESTATES PLC; *Int'l*, pg. 1100
BOGAZ ENDUSTRI VE MADENCILIK LTD.—See Holcim Ltd.; *Int'l*, pg. 3446
BOGAZICI VARLIK YONETIM A.S.; *Int'l*, pg. 1100
BOGDANA CORPORATION; *U.S. Private*, pg. 609
BOGDAN CORPORATION; *Int'l*, pg. 1100
BOGEN COMMUNICATIONS, INC.—See Bogen Communications International Inc.; *U.S. Public*, pg. 367
BOGEN COMMUNICATIONS INTERNATIONAL INC.; *U.S. Public*, pg. 367
BOGEN CORPORATION—See Bogen Communications International Inc.; *U.S. Public*, pg. 367
BOGER CONCRETE; *U.S. Private*, pg. 609
BOGESUNDS EL & TELE AB—See Instalco AB; *Int'l*, pg. 3721
BOGEY HOLDING COMPANY SPAIN S.L.—See Metalurgica Gerdau S.A.; *Int'l*, pg. 4849
BOGGABRI COAL PTY LIMITED—See Idemitsu Kosan Co., Ltd.; *Int'l*, pg. 3590
BOGGY CREEK PTY LIMITED—See Linde plc; *Int'l*, pg. 4504
BOGLE AND TIMMS LIMITED—See W.W. Grainger, Inc.; *U.S. Public*, pg. 2319
BOGLIOLI S.P.A.—See PHI Asset Management Partners SGEIC S.A.; *Int'l*, pg. 5843
BOGLIOLI USA CORPORATION—See PHI Asset Management Partners SGEIC S.A.; *Int'l*, pg. 5843
BOGNER CONSTRUCTION COMPANY; *U.S. Private*, pg. 609
BOGO CO., LTD.—See Daeyang Electric Co., Ltd.; *Int'l*, pg. 1911
BOGO-MEDELLIN MILLING COMPANY, INC.; *Int'l*, pg. 1100
BOGOPA ENTERPRISES INC.; *U.S. Private*, pg. 609
BOGOTA FINANCIAL CORP.; *U.S. Public*, pg. 367
BOGOTA LATIN BISTRO; *U.S. Private*, pg. 609
BOGOTA SAVINGS BANK; *U.S. Private*, pg. 609
BOGRAD BROTHERS INC.; *U.S. Private*, pg. 609
BOGSTRAND AS—See Peab AB; *Int'l*, pg. 5771

COMPANY NAME INDEX

BOGUCHANSKY LPK LLC—See RusForest AB; *Int'l*, pg. 6429
BOHAE BREWERY CO., LTD.; *Int'l*, pg. 1100
BOHAI ALUMINIUM INDUSTRIES LTD.—See CITIC Group Corporation; *Int'l*, pg. 1619
BOHAI AUTOMOTIVE SYSTEMS CO., LTD.; *Int'l*, pg. 1100
BOHAI FERRY GROUP CO., LTD.; *Int'l*, pg. 1100
BOHAI FERRY (QINGDAO) INTERNATIONAL TRAVEL SERVICE CO., LTD.—See Bohai Ferry Group Co., Ltd.; *Int'l*, pg. 1100
BOHAI INDUSTRIAL INVESTMENT FUND MANAGEMENT COMPANY LTD.; *Int'l*, pg. 1100
BOHAI LEASING CO., LTD.—See Hainan Traffic Administration Holding Co., Ltd.; *Int'l*, pg. 3213
BOHAI PHARMACEUTICALS GROUP, INC.; *Int'l*, pg. 1100
BOHAI STEEL GROUP CO., LTD.; *Int'l*, pg. 1100
BOHAI TRIMET AUTOMOTIVE HOLDING GMBH—See TRIMET Aluminium SE; *Int'l*, pg. 7923
BOHAI WATER INDUSTRY CO., LTD.; *Int'l*, pg. 1100
BOH BROS. CONSTRUCTION CO., LLC; *U.S. Private*, pg. 609
BOHEMIA ASFALT , S.R.O.—See STRABAG SE; *Int'l*, pg. 7229
BOHEMIA BITUNOVA, SPOL S.R.O.—See STRABAG SE; *Int'l*, pg. 7229
BOHEMIA FAKTORING, A.S.; *Int'l*, pg. 1100
BOHEMIA INTERACTIVE SIMULATIONS K.S.—See BAE Systems plc; *Int'l*, pg. 798
BOHEN-KASEI CO., LTD.—See Astena Holdings Co., Ltd.; *Int'l*, pg. 653
BOHLASIA STEELS SDN. BHD.—See voestalpine AG; *Int'l*, pg. 8288
BOHL CRANE INC.; *U.S. Private*, pg. 609
BOHLE AG; *Int'l*, pg. 1100
THE BOHLE COMPANY; *U.S. Private*, pg. 3995
BOHL EQUIPMENT CO.; *U.S. Private*, pg. 609
BOHLER BLECHE GMBH—See voestalpine AG; *Int'l*, pg. 8287
BOHLER BV—See voestalpine AG; *Int'l*, pg. 8291
BOHLER EDELSTAHL GMBH & CO KG—See voestalpine AG; *Int'l*, pg. 8287
BOHLER EDELSTAHL GMBH—See voestalpine AG; *Int'l*, pg. 8287
BOHLER GRUNDSTUCKS BETEILIGUNGS GMBH—See voestalpine AG; *Int'l*, pg. 8292
BOHLER GRUNDSTUCKS GMBH & CO. KG—See voestalpine AG; *Int'l*, pg. 8292
BOHLER HIGH PERFORMANCE METALS PRIVATE LIMITED—See voestalpine AG; *Int'l*, pg. 8288
BOHLER INTERNATIONAL GMBH—See voestalpine AG; *Int'l*, pg. 8291
BOHLER KERESKEDALMI KFT—See voestalpine AG; *Int'l*, pg. 8291
BOHLER LASTECHNIEK GROEP NEDERLAND B.V.—See voestalpine AG; *Int'l*, pg. 8288
BOHLER SCHMIEDETECHNIK GMBH & CO KG—See voestalpine AG; *Int'l*, pg. 8288
BOHLER SCHMIEDETECHNIK GMBH—See voestalpine AG; *Int'l*, pg. 8291
BOHLER SCHWEISSTECHNIK AUSTRIA GMBH—See voestalpine AG; *Int'l*, pg. 8291
BOHLER SCHWEISSTECHNIK DEUTSCHLAND GMBH—See voestalpine AG; *Int'l*, pg. 8288
BOHLER SOLDADURAS S.A. DE C.V.—See voestalpine AG; *Int'l*, pg. 8288
BOHLER SPECIAL STEELS (SHANGHAI) CO., LTD.—See voestalpine AG; *Int'l*, pg. 8288
BOHLERSTAHL VERTRIEBSGESELLSCHAFT M.B.H.—See voestalpine AG; *Int'l*, pg. 8291
BOHLER TECNICA DE SOLDAGEM LTDA.—See voestalpine AG; *Int'l*, pg. 8288
BOHLER THYSSEN WELDING S.A.—See voestalpine AG; *Int'l*, pg. 8291
BOHLER UDDEHOLM AFRICA (PTY) LTD—See voestalpine AG; *Int'l*, pg. 8287
BOHLER-UDDEHOLM (AUSTRALIA) PTY LTD.—See voestalpine AG; *Int'l*, pg. 8291
BOHLER-UDDEHOLM B.V.—See voestalpine AG; *Int'l*, pg. 8288
BOHLER-UDDEHOLM COLOMBIA S.A.—See voestalpine AG; *Int'l*, pg. 8291
BOHLER-UDDEHOLM CORPORATION—See voestalpine AG; *Int'l*, pg. 8291
BOHLER UDDEHOLM CZ S.R.O.—See voestalpine AG; *Int'l*, pg. 8288
BOHLER-UDDEHOLM FRANCE S.A.S—See voestalpine AG; *Int'l*, pg. 8291
BOHLER-UDDEHOLM IBERICA S.A.—See voestalpine AG; *Int'l*, pg. 8291
BOHLER-UDDEHOLM KK—See voestalpine AG; *Int'l*, pg. 8288
BOHLER-UDDEHOLM LIMITED—See voestalpine AG; *Int'l*, pg. 8291
BOHLER-UDDEHOLM LTD.—See voestalpine AG; *Int'l*, pg. 8288
BOHLER-UDDEHOLM LTD. - THERMAL PROCESSING FACILITY—See voestalpine AG; *Int'l*, pg. 8288

BOHLER UDDEHOLM POLSKA SP. Z O.O.—See voestalpine AG; *Int'l*, pg. 8287
BOHLER UDDEHOLM PRECISION STEEL AB—See voestalpine AG; *Int'l*, pg. 8291
BOHLER UDDEHOLM PRECISION STRIP AB—See voestalpine AG; *Int'l*, pg. 8292
BOHLER-UDDEHOLM PRECISION STRIP GMBH & CO KG—See voestalpine AG; *Int'l*, pg. 8291
BOHLER UDDEHOLM PRECISION STRIP LLC—See voestalpine AG; *Int'l*, pg. 8291
BOHLER UDDEHOLM PRECISION STRIP TRADING (SUZHOU) CO., LTD—See voestalpine AG; *Int'l*, pg. 8291
BOHLER UDDEHOLM ROMANIA S.R.L.—See voestalpine AG; *Int'l*, pg. 8287
BOHLER-UDDEHOLM SAW STEEL AB—See voestalpine AG; *Int'l*, pg. 8292
BOHLER UDDEHOLM SCHWEIZ AS—See voestalpine AG; *Int'l*, pg. 8292
BOHLER UDDEHOLM SERVICE CENTER AB—See voestalpine AG; *Int'l*, pg. 8291
BOHLER UDDEHOLM SLOVAKIA, S.R.O.—See voestalpine AG; *Int'l*, pg. 8288
BOHLER-UDDEHOLM SPECIALTY METALS, LLC—See voestalpine AG; *Int'l*, pg. 8291
BOHLER-UDDEHOLM (UK) LIMITED—See voestalpine AG; *Int'l*, pg. 8287
BOHLER-UDDEHOLM UKRAINE LLC—See voestalpine AG; *Int'l*, pg. 8287
BOHLER-UDDEHOLM ZAGREB D.O.O.—See voestalpine AG; *Int'l*, pg. 8287
BOHLER-UDDENHOLM DEUTSCHLAND GMBH—See voestalpine AG; *Int'l*, pg. 8292
BOHLER WARMEBEHANDLUNG GMBH—See voestalpine AG; *Int'l*, pg. 8287
BOHLER WELDING GROUP CANADA LTD.—See voestalpine AG; *Int'l*, pg. 8288
BOHLER WELDING GROUP CENTRAL EASTERN EUROPE GMBH—See voestalpine AG; *Int'l*, pg. 8288
BOHLER WELDING GROUP GREECE S.A.—See voestalpine AG; *Int'l*, pg. 8288
BOHLER WELDING GROUP INDIA PRIVATE LIMITED—See voestalpine AG; *Int'l*, pg. 8288
BOHLER WELDING GROUP ITALIA S.P.A.—See voestalpine AG; *Int'l*, pg. 8288
BOHLER WELDING GROUP MIDDLE EAST FZE—See voestalpine AG; *Int'l*, pg. 8288
BOHLER WELDING GROUP NORDIC AB—See voestalpine AG; *Int'l*, pg. 8291
BOHLER WELDING GROUP SCHWEIZ AG—See voestalpine AG; *Int'l*, pg. 8288
BOHLER WELDING GROUP SRL—See voestalpine AG; *Int'l*, pg. 8288
BOHLER WELDING GROUP UK LIMITED—See voestalpine AG; *Int'l*, pg. 8288
BOHLER WELDING GROUP USA INC.—See voestalpine AG; *Int'l*, pg. 8291
BOHLER WELDING HOLDING GMBH—See voestalpine AG; *Int'l*, pg. 8288
BOHLER WELDING TRADING (SHANGHAI) CO., LTD.—See voestalpine AG; *Int'l*, pg. 8288
BOHLER-YBBSTAL PROFIL GMBH—See voestalpine AG; *Int'l*, pg. 8288
BOHME; *U.S. Private*, pg. 609
BOHM+KELLENERS GMBH—See Palladius AG; *Int'l*, pg. 5708
BOHM STADTBAUMEISTER & GEBAUDETECHNIK GMBH—See STRABAG SE; *Int'l*, pg. 7229
BOHN BROTHERS TOYOTA; *U.S. Private*, pg. 609
BOHNERT INTERNATIONAL, INC.—See Wolter Group LLC; *Int'l*, pg. 4554
THE BOHN ZONE; *U.S. Private*, pg. 3995
BOHRA INDUSTRIES LTD.; *Int'l*, pg. 1101
BOHREN'S MOVING & STORAGE INC.; *U.S. Private*, pg. 609
BO HSING ENTERPRISE CO., LTD.—See Kwong Lung Enterprise Co., Ltd.; *Int'l*, pg. 4351
BOHUS BERGSPRANGNING AB—See Nordisk Bergteknik AB; *Int'l*, pg. 5424
BOIARDI PRODUCTS CORPORATION—See Q.E.P. Co., Inc.; *U.S. Public*, pg. 1741
BOI CARLSBAD LLC—See Brandywine Realty Trust; *U.S. Public*, pg. 380
BOICE ENTERPRISES, INC.; *U.S. Private*, pg. 609
BOIES SCHILLER FLEXNER LLP; *U.S. Private*, pg. 609
BOIE-TAKEDA CHEMICALS, INC.—See Takeda Pharmaceutical Company Limited; *Int'l*, pg. 7439
THE BOILER INSPECTION AND INSURANCE COMPANY OF CANADA—See Munchener Ruckversicherungs AG; *Int'l*, pg. 5090
BOILERMECH SDN BHD—See BM GreenTech Bhd; *Int'l*, pg. 1075
BOILERROOM EQUIPMENT, INC.—See Thermal Energy International Inc.; *Int'l*, pg. 7707
BOILER TUBE COMPANY OF AMERICA—See Babcock Power, Inc.; *U.S. Private*, pg. 422
BOILERWORKS A/S—See Thermax Limited; *Int'l*, pg. 7707
BOILING SPRINGS SAVINGS BANK INC.; *U.S. Private*, pg. 609

BOILLAT LES BOIS S.A.—See Citychamp Watch & Jewellery Group Limited; *Int'l*, pg. 1629
BOILL HEALTHCARE HOLDINGS LIMITED; *Int'l*, pg. 1101
BOI MERCHANT BANKERS LTD.—See Bank of India; *Int'l*, pg. 843
BOINGO LIMITED—See DigitalBridge Group, Inc.; *U.S. Public*, pg. 664
BOINGO WIRELESS, INC.—See DigitalBridge Group, Inc.; *U.S. Public*, pg. 664
BOING S.P.A.—See Mediaset S.p.A.; *Int'l*, pg. 4773
BOING US HOLDCO, INC.—See Roark Capital Group Inc.; *U.S. Private*, pg. 3454
BOIRON ASIA LIMITED—See Boiron Group; *Int'l*, pg. 1101
BOIRON BG EOOD—See Boiron Group; *Int'l*, pg. 1101
BOIRON CANADA INC.—See Boiron Group; *Int'l*, pg. 1101
BOIRON CZ S.R.O—See Boiron Group; *Int'l*, pg. 1101
BOIRON GROUP; *Int'l*, pg. 1101
BOIRON (HANGZHOU) TRADING CO., LTD.—See Boiron Group; *Int'l*, pg. 1101
BOIRON HUNGARIA KFT—See Boiron Group; *Int'l*, pg. 1101
BOIRON INC—See Boiron Group; *Int'l*, pg. 1101
BOIRON MEDICAMENTOS HOMEOPATICOS LTDA—See Boiron Group; *Int'l*, pg. 1101
BOIRON PORTUGAL LTDA—See Boiron Group; *Int'l*, pg. 1101
BOIRON RO SRL—See Boiron Group; *Int'l*, pg. 1101
BOIRON RUSSIE O.O.O—See Boiron Group; *Int'l*, pg. 1101
BOIRON SA—See Boiron Group; *Int'l*, pg. 1101
BOIRON SAS—See VINCI S.A.; *Int'l*, pg. 8213
BOIRON SK S.R.O—See Boiron Group; *Int'l*, pg. 1101
BOIRON SOCIEDAD IBERICA DE HOMEOPATIA—See Boiron Group; *Int'l*, pg. 1101
BOIRON SP Z.O.O—See Boiron Group; *Int'l*, pg. 1101
BOIRON SRL—See Boiron Group; *Int'l*, pg. 1101
BOIRON SUISSE SA—See Boiron Group; *Int'l*, pg. 1101
BOIRON TN SARL—See Boiron Group; *Int'l*, pg. 1101
BOIRON USA INC.—See Boiron Group; *Int'l*, pg. 1101
BOISE HOUSING CORPORATION; *U.S. Private*, pg. 609
BOISE OFFICE EQUIPMENT, INC.—See Xerox Holdings Corporation; *U.S. Public*, pg. 2387
BOISE PAPER - IDAHO—See Packaging Corporation of America; *U.S. Public*, pg. 1632
BOISE PETERBILT, INC.; *U.S. Private*, pg. 609
BOISERIE LUSSIER—See Richelieu Hardware Ltd.; *Int'l*, pg. 6330
BOISERIES RAYMOND INC; *Int'l*, pg. 1101
BOISE SALES CO; *U.S. Private*, pg. 609
BOIS ET CHIFFONS INTERNATIONAL SA; *Int'l*, pg. 1101
BOISE WHITE PAPER, LLC—See Packaging Corporation of America; *U.S. Public*, pg. 1633
BOI SHAREHOLDING LIMITED—See Bank of India; *Int'l*, pg. 843
BOIS ROUGE—See Tereos; *Int'l*, pg. 7564
BOISSET, LA FAMILLE DES GRANDS VINS; *Int'l*, pg. 1101
BOISSIERE FINANCE SNC—See Schneider Electric SE; *Int'l*, pg. 6626
BOISSY; *Int'l*, pg. 1101
BOJANGLES', INC.—See Durational Capital Management, LP; *U.S. Private*, pg. 1293
BOJANGLES', INC.—See The Jordan Company, L.P.; *U.S. Private*, pg. 4060
BOJANGLES' RESTAURANTS, INC.—See Durational Capital Management, LP; *U.S. Private*, pg. 1293
BOJANGLES' RESTAURANTS, INC.—See The Jordan Company, L.P.; *U.S. Private*, pg. 4060
BOJAY M&E (SUZHOU) CO., LTD.—See Zhuhai Bojay Electronics Co., Ltd.; *Int'l*, pg. 8677
BOJAY TECHNOLOGIES INC.—See Zhuhai Bojay Electronics Co., Ltd.; *Int'l*, pg. 8677
BOJI MEDICAL TECHNOLOGY CO., LTD.; *Int'l*, pg. 1101
BOJNOURD CEMENT CO.—See Fars & Khuzestan Cement Co.; *Int'l*, pg. 2620
BOJUN AGRICULTURE HOLDINGS LIMITED; *Int'l*, pg. 1101
BOJUN EDUCATION COMPANY LIMITED; *Int'l*, pg. 1102
BOKARA RUG CO., INC.; *U.S. Private*, pg. 609
BOKELA GMBH—See Tsukishima Holdings Co., Ltd.; *Int'l*, pg. 7956
BOK FINANCIAL ASSET MANAGEMENT, INC.—See BOK Financial Corporation; *U.S. Public*, pg. 367
BOK FINANCIAL CORPORATION; *U.S. Public*, pg. 367
BOK FINANCIAL EQUIPMENT FINANCE, INC.—See BOK Financial Corporation; *U.S. Public*, pg. 367
BOK FINANCIAL INSURANCE, INC.—See Caisse de Depot et Placement du Quebec; *Int'l*, pg. 1256
BOK FINANCIAL INSURANCE, INC.—See KKR & Co. Inc.; *U.S. Public*, pg. 1265
BOK FINANCIAL PRIVATE WEALTH, INC.—See BOK Financial Corporation; *U.S. Public*, pg. 367
BOK FINANCIAL SECURITIES, INC.—See BOK Financial Corporation; *U.S. Public*, pg. 367
BOKF, N.A. - BANK OF ALBUQUERQUE—See BOK Financial Corporation; *U.S. Public*, pg. 367
BOKF, N.A. - BANK OF ARIZONA—See BOK Financial Corporation; *U.S. Public*, pg. 367

BOK FINANCIAL CORPORATION

BOKF, N.A. - BANK OF ARKANSAS—See BOK Financial Corporation; *U.S. Public*, pg. 367
BOKF, N.A. - BANK OF TEXAS, HOUSTON REGIONAL OFFICE—See BOK Financial Corporation; *U.S. Public*, pg. 367
BOKF, N.A. - BANK OF TEXAS—See BOK Financial Corporation; *U.S. Public*, pg. 367
BOKF, N.A. - COLORADO STATE BANK & TRUST—See BOK Financial Corporation; *U.S. Public*, pg. 367
BOKF, N.A. - MOBANK—See BOK Financial Corporation; *U.S. Public*, pg. 367
BOKF, NATIONAL ASSOCIATION—See BOK Financial Corporation; *U.S. Public*, pg. 367
BOKHANDELSGRUPPEN I SVERIGE AB—See Volati AB; *Int'l*, pg. 8300
BOKIL GOLWILKAR METROPOLIS HEALTHCARE PRIVATE LIMITED—See Metropolis Healthcare Ltd.; *Int'l*, pg. 4863
BOKOMO FOODS (UK) LTD - PETERBOROUGH FACTORY—See PepsiCo, Inc.; *U.S. Public*, pg. 1672
BOKRETA MANAGEMENT KFT.—See Vonovia SE; *Int'l*, pg. 8305
BOKSIT A.D.; *Int'l*, pg. 1102
BOKSIT A.D.; *Int'l*, pg. 1102
BOKU, INC.; *U.S. Private*, pg. 610
BOKUS AB—See Volati AB; *Int'l*, pg. 8300
BOKWANG HI-TECH CO., LTD—See Bokwang TS Co.; *Int'l*, pg. 1102
BOKWANG INDUSTRY CO.,LTD; *Int'l*, pg. 1102
BOKWANG TS CO.; *Int'l*, pg. 1102
BOLAITE (SHANGHAI) COMPRESSOR CO., LTD.—See Atlas Copco AB; *Int'l*, pg. 681
BOLAK COMPANY LIMITED; *Int'l*, pg. 1102
BOLAN CASTINGS LIMITED; *Int'l*, pg. 1102
BOLAND MALONEY ENTERPRISES INC; *U.S. Private*, pg. 610
BOLAND-MALONEY LUMBER COMPANY INC.—See Boland Maloney Enterprises Inc.; *U.S. Private*, pg. 610
BOLAND-MALONEY REALTY CO.—See Boland Maloney Enterprises Inc.; *U.S. Private*, pg. 610
BOLAND TRANE SERVICES INC.; *U.S. Private*, pg. 610
BOLA WEBINFORMATION GMBH—See Better Collective A/S; *Int'l*, pg. 1003
BOL BANCSHARES, INC.; *U.S. Public*, pg. 367
BOLCOF-PORT POLYMERS—See Ravago Holding S.A.; *Int'l*, pg. 6222
BOL.COM B.V.—See Koninklijke Ahold Delhaize N.V.; *Int'l*, pg. 4261
BOLDATA TECHNOLOGY, INC.; *U.S. Private*, pg. 610
BOLDER BIOPATH, INC.—See Inotiv, Inc.; *U.S. Public*, pg. 1128
BOLDER OUTREACH SOLUTIONS, LLC—See Cognizant Technology Solutions Corporation; *U.S. Public*, pg. 523
BOLDFACE GROUP, INC.; *U.S. Private*, pg. 610
BOLD HARDWARE CO.; *U.S. Private*, pg. 610
BOLD INTERNATIONAL SA—See Devoteam SA; *Int'l*, pg. 2089
BOLD INVESTMENT CO., LTD.; *Int'l*, pg. 1102
BOLD OGILVY GREECE—See WPP plc; *Int'l*, pg. 8484
BOLDON JAMES LTD.—See QinetiQ Group plc; *Int'l*, pg. 6141
BOLD ORANGE COMPANY, LLC; *U.S. Private*, pg. 610
BOLD STROKE VENTURES INC.; *Int'l*, pg. 1102
THE BOLDT COMPANY—See The Boldt Group Inc.; *U.S. Private*, pg. 3996
BOLDT CONSULTING SERVICES—See The Boldt Group Inc.; *U.S. Private*, pg. 3995
THE BOLDT GROUP INC.; *U.S. Private*, pg. 3995
BOLD THINKING, LLC—See The Boldt Group Inc.; *U.S. Private*, pg. 3996
BOLDT TECHNICAL SERVICES—See The Boldt Group Inc.; *U.S. Private*, pg. 3996
BOLDUC LEROUX INC.; *Int'l*, pg. 1102
BOLD VENTURES INC.; *Int'l*, pg. 1102
BOLDYN NETWORKS GLOBAL LTD.; *Int'l*, pg. 1102
BOLEK INC.; *U.S. Private*, pg. 610
THE BOLER COMPANY; *U.S. Private*, pg. 3996
BOLER VENTURES LLC; *U.S. Private*, pg. 610
BOLEY CENTERS, INC.; *U.S. Private*, pg. 610
BOLEY-FEATHERSTON-HUFFMAN & DEAL CO.—See Arthur J. Gallagher & Co.; *U.S. Public*, pg. 204
BOLEY TOOL & MACHINE WORKS; *U.S. Private*, pg. 610
BOLGER ADVERTISING; *U.S. Private*, pg. 610
BOLGER & ASSOCIATES, INC.; *U.S. Private*, pg. 610
BOLIDEN AB; *Int'l*, pg. 1102
BOLIDEN BERGSOE AS—See Boliden AB; *Int'l*, pg. 1102
BOLIDEN COMMERCIAL AB—See Boliden AB; *Int'l*, pg. 1102
BOLIDEN HARJAVALTA OY - COPPER REFINERY—See Boliden AB; *Int'l*, pg. 1102
BOLIDEN HARJAVALTA OY—See Boliden AB; *Int'l*, pg. 1102
BOLIDEN KOKKOLA OY—See Boliden AB; *Int'l*, pg. 1102
BOLIDEN TARA MINES LIMITED—See Boliden AB; *Int'l*, pg. 1102
BOLIGA GRUPPEN A/S; *Int'l*, pg. 1102
BOLIGMANAGER APS—See North Media A/S; *Int'l*, pg. 5440

BOLIG- OG NAERINGSKREDITT ASA—See SpareBank 1 Gruppen AS; *Int'l*, pg. 7125
BOLIGPORTAL.DK APS—See North Media A/S; *Int'l*, pg. 5441
BOLINA HOLDING CO., LTD.; *Int'l*, pg. 1102
BOLIN AUTO & TRUCK PARTS CO., INC.—See American Securities LLC; *U.S. Private*, pg. 248
BOLIN MARKETING & ADVERTISING; *U.S. Private*, pg. 610
BOLIVAR ENERGY COLOMBIA INC.—See NG Energy International Corp.; *Int'l*, pg. 5253
BOLIVAR FARMERS EXCHANGE; *U.S. Private*, pg. 610
BOLIVAR INSULATION CO—See Quad-C Management, Inc.; *U.S. Private*, pg. 3315
BOLIVAR MEDICAL CENTER—See Apollo Global Management, Inc.; *U.S. Public*, pg. 154
BOLIVAR MINING CORP.; *U.S. Private*, pg. 610
BOLIVAR READY MIX & MATERIAL, INC.; *U.S. Private*, pg. 610
BOLIX S.A.—See Berger Paints India Limited; *Int'l*, pg. 980
BOLIX UKRAINA SP. Z O.O.—See Berger Paints India Limited; *Int'l*, pg. 980
BOLKAN PROPERTY INSTRUMENTS REIT; *Int'l*, pg. 1102
BOLKE HANDEL GMBH—See BayWa AG; *Int'l*, pg. 917
BOLL & BRANCH LLC; *U.S. Private*, pg. 610
BOLLE AUSTRALIA PTY LTD—See Alvarez & Marsal, Inc.; *U.S. Private*, pg. 212
BOLLE BRANDS SAS—See Alvarez & Marsal, Inc.; *U.S. Private*, pg. 212
BOLLE (N.Z.) LIMITED—See Alvarez & Marsal, Inc.; *U.S. Private*, pg. 212
BOLLER CONSTRUCTION COMPANY, INC.; *U.S. Private*, pg. 610
BOLLES MOTORS, INC.; *U.S. Private*, pg. 610
BOLLINGER ALGIERS LLC—See Bollinger Shipyards, Inc.; *U.S. Private*, pg. 611
BOLLINGER AMELIA REPAIR, LLC—See Bollinger Shipyards, Inc.; *U.S. Private*, pg. 611
BOLLINGER DIALYSIS, LLC—See DaVita Inc.; *U.S. Public*, pg. 636
BOLLINGER FOURCHON, LLC—See Bollinger Shipyards, Inc.; *U.S. Private*, pg. 611
BOLLINGER INDUSTRIES, INC.; *U.S. Public*, pg. 367
BOLLINGER MARINE FABRICATORS, LLC—See Bollinger Shipyards, Inc.; *U.S. Private*, pg. 611
BOLLINGER MORGAN CITY, LLC—See Bollinger Shipyards, Inc.; *U.S. Private*, pg. 611
BOLLINGER QUICK REPAIR—See Bollinger Shipyards, Inc.; *U.S. Private*, pg. 611
BOLLINGER RGS—See Bollinger Shipyards, Inc.; *U.S. Private*, pg. 611
BOLLINGER SHIPYARD LOCKPORT, LLC—See Bollinger Shipyards, Inc.; *U.S. Private*, pg. 611
BOLLINGER SHIPYARDS, INC.; *U.S. Private*, pg. 610
BOLLINGER TEXAS CITY, LP—See Bollinger Shipyards, Inc.; *U.S. Private*, pg. 611
BOLLIN GROUP LTD.; *Int'l*, pg. 1102
BOLLMAN HAT CO.; *U.S. Private*, pg. 611
BOLLO CONSTRUCTION, INC.; *U.S. Private*, pg. 611
BOLLORE AFRICA LOGISTICS ANGOLA LIMITADA—See Financiere de L'Odet; *Int'l*, pg. 2666
BOLLORE AFRICA LOGISTICS MAROC SA—See Financiere de L'Odet; *Int'l*, pg. 2666
BOLLORE AFRICA LOGISTICS SAS—See Mediterranean Shipping Company, S.A.; *Int'l*, pg. 4781
BOLLORE AFRICA LOGISTICS (SL) LTD.—See Financiere de L'Odet; *Int'l*, pg. 2666
BOLLORE ENERGIE—See Financiere de L'Odet; *Int'l*, pg. 2667
BOLLORE INTERMEDIA—See Financiere de L'Odet; *Int'l*, pg. 2667
BOLLORE LOGISTICS ARGENTINA SA—See Financiere de L'Odet; *Int'l*, pg. 2666
BOLLORE LOGISTICS ASIA-PACIFIC CORPORATE PTE. LTD.—See Financiere de L'Odet; *Int'l*, pg. 2666
BOLLORE LOGISTICS AUSTRALIA PTY. LTD.—See Financiere de L'Odet; *Int'l*, pg. 2666
BOLLORE LOGISTICS BELGIUM NV—See Financiere de L'Odet; *Int'l*, pg. 2666
BOLLORE LOGISTICS BRAZIL LTDA—See Financiere de L'Odet; *Int'l*, pg. 2666
BOLLORE LOGISTICS (CAMBODIA) LTD.—See Financiere de L'Odet; *Int'l*, pg. 2666
BOLLORE LOGISTICS CANADA INC.—See Financiere de L'Odet; *Int'l*, pg. 2666
BOLLORE LOGISTICS CHILE SA—See Financiere de L'Odet; *Int'l*, pg. 2666
BOLLORE LOGISTICS CHINA CO. LTD.—See Financiere de L'Odet; *Int'l*, pg. 2666
BOLLORE LOGISTICS CZECH REPUBLIC S.R.O.—See Financiere de L'Odet; *Int'l*, pg. 2666
BOLLORE LOGISTICS GERMANY GMBH—See Financiere de L'Odet; *Int'l*, pg. 2666
BOLLORE LOGISTICS GUADELOUPE SAS—See Financiere de L'Odet; *Int'l*, pg. 2666
BOLLORE LOGISTICS HONG KONG LTD.—See Financiere de L'Odet; *Int'l*, pg. 2666

CORPORATE AFFILIATIONS

BOLLORE LOGISTICS INDIA LTD.—See Financiere de L'Odet; *Int'l*, pg. 2666
BOLLORE LOGISTICS JAPAN KK—See Financiere de L'Odet; *Int'l*, pg. 2666
BOLLORE LOGISTICS KOREA CO. LTD.—See Financiere de L'Odet; *Int'l*, pg. 2666
BOLLORE LOGISTICS LAO LTD.—See Financiere de L'Odet; *Int'l*, pg. 2666
BOLLORE LOGISTICS LLC—See The Emirates Group; *Int'l*, pg. 7639
BOLLORE LOGISTICS LUXEMBOURG SA—See Financiere de L'Odet; *Int'l*, pg. 2666
BOLLORE LOGISTICS MARTINIQUE SAS—See Financiere de L'Odet; *Int'l*, pg. 2666
BOLLORE LOGISTICS MAYOTTE SARL—See Financiere de L'Odet; *Int'l*, pg. 2666
BOLLORE LOGISTICS MEXICO, SA DE CV—See Financiere de L'Odet; *Int'l*, pg. 2666
BOLLORE LOGISTICS NETHERLANDS BV—See Financiere de L'Odet; *Int'l*, pg. 2666
BOLLORE LOGISTICS NEW ZEALAND LTD.—See Financiere de L'Odet; *Int'l*, pg. 2666
BOLLORE LOGISTICS NORWAY AS—See Financiere de L'Odet; *Int'l*, pg. 2666
BOLLORE LOGISTICS NOUVELLE-CALEDONIE SA—See Financiere de L'Odet; *Int'l*, pg. 2666
BOLLORE LOGISTICS POLAND SP. Z.O.O.—See Financiere de L'Odet; *Int'l*, pg. 2666
BOLLORE LOGISTICS POLYNESIE SAS—See Financiere de L'Odet; *Int'l*, pg. 2666
BOLLORE LOGISTICS PORTUGAL LDA—See Financiere de L'Odet; *Int'l*, pg. 2666
BOLLORE LOGISTICS REUNION SAS—See Financiere de L'Odet; *Int'l*, pg. 2666
BOLLORE LOGISTICS (SHANGHAI) CO. LTD.—See Financiere de L'Odet; *Int'l*, pg. 2666
BOLLORE LOGISTICS SINGAPORE PTE. LTD.—See Financiere de L'Odet; *Int'l*, pg. 2666
BOLLORE LOGISTICS TAIWAN LTD.—See Financiere de L'Odet; *Int'l*, pg. 2666
BOLLORE LOGISTICS TANGER MED SA—See Financiere de L'Odet; *Int'l*, pg. 2666
BOLLORE LOGISTICS UK LTD.—See Financiere de L'Odet; *Int'l*, pg. 2666
BOLLORE LOGISTICS VIETNAM CO. LTD.—See Financiere de L'Odet; *Int'l*, pg. 2666
BOLLORE MEDIA REGIE SA—See Financiere de L'Odet; *Int'l*, pg. 2666
BOLLORE PLASTIC FILM DIVISION—See Financiere de L'Odet; *Int'l*, pg. 2667
BOLLORE S.A.—See Financiere de L'Odet; *Int'l*, pg. 2666
BOLLORE TRANSPORT & LOGISTICS BOTSWANA (PTY) LTD.—See Financiere de L'Odet; *Int'l*, pg. 2667
BOLLORE TRANSPORT & LOGISTICS BURUNDI SA—See Financiere de L'Odet; *Int'l*, pg. 2667
BOLLORE TRANSPORT & LOGISTICS CAMEROUN SA—See Financiere de L'Odet; *Int'l*, pg. 2667
BOLLORE TRANSPORT & LOGISTICS CENTRAFRIQUE SA—See Financiere de L'Odet; *Int'l*, pg. 2667
BOLLORE TRANSPORT & LOGISTICS CONGO SA—See Financiere de L'Odet; *Int'l*, pg. 2667
BOLLORE TRANSPORT LOGISTICS CORPORATE SAS—See Financiere de L'Odet; *Int'l*, pg. 2667
BOLLORE TRANSPORT & LOGISTICS COTE D'IVOIRE SA—See Financiere de L'Odet; *Int'l*, pg. 2667
BOLLORE TRANSPORT & LOGISTICS GAMBIA LTD.—See Financiere de L'Odet; *Int'l*, pg. 2667
BOLLORE TRANSPORT & LOGISTICS GUINEE SA—See Financiere de L'Odet; *Int'l*, pg. 2667
BOLLORE TRANSPORT & LOGISTICS KENYA LTD.—See Financiere de L'Odet; *Int'l*, pg. 2667
BOLLORE TRANSPORT & LOGISTICS LEKKI FZE—See Financiere de L'Odet; *Int'l*, pg. 2667
BOLLORE TRANSPORT & LOGISTICS MADAGASCAR—See Financiere de L'Odet; *Int'l*, pg. 2667
BOLLORE TRANSPORT & LOGISTICS MALAWI LTD.—See Financiere de L'Odet; *Int'l*, pg. 2667
BOLLORE TRANSPORT & LOGISTICS MALI—See Financiere de L'Odet; *Int'l*, pg. 2667
BOLLORE TRANSPORT & LOGISTICS MAROC SA—See Financiere de L'Odet; *Int'l*, pg. 2667
BOLLORE TRANSPORT & LOGISTICS MOCAMBIQUE SA—See Financiere de L'Odet; *Int'l*, pg. 2667
BOLLORE TRANSPORT & LOGISTICS NAMIBIA PROPRIETARY LTD.—See Financiere de L'Odet; *Int'l*, pg. 2667
BOLLORE TRANSPORT & LOGISTICS NIGERIA LTD.—See Financiere de L'Odet; *Int'l*, pg. 2667
BOLLORE TRANSPORT & LOGISTICS RDC SA—See Financiere de L'Odet; *Int'l*, pg. 2667
BOLLORE TRANSPORT & LOGISTICS RWANDA LTD.—See Financiere de L'Odet; *Int'l*, pg. 2667
BOLLORE TRANSPORT & LOGISTICS (SL) LTD.—See Financiere de L'Odet; *Int'l*, pg. 2667
BOLLORE TRANSPORT & LOGISTICS SOUTH AFRICA (PTY.) LTD.—See Financiere de L'Odet; *Int'l*, pg. 2667
BOLLORE TRANSPORT LOGISTICS SPAIN SA—See Financiere de L'Odet; *Int'l*, pg. 2667

COMPANY NAME INDEX

BOLLORE TRANSPORT & LOGISTICS TANZANIA LTD.—See Financiere de L'Odet; *Int'l*, pg. 2667
BOLLORE TRANSPORT & LOGISTICS TOGO CO., LTD.—See Financiere de L'Odet; *Int'l*, pg. 2667
BOLLORE TRANSPORT & LOGISTICS TUNISIE SA—See Financiere de L'Odet; *Int'l*, pg. 2667
BOLLORE TRANSPORT & LOGISTICS UGANDA LTD.—See Financiere de L'Odet; *Int'l*, pg. 2667
BOLLORE TRANSPORT & LOGISTICS ZAMBIA LTD.—See Financiere de L'Odet; *Int'l*, pg. 2667
BOLLORE TRANSPORT & LOGISTICS ZIMBABWE (PRIVATE) LTD.—See Financiere de L'Odet; *Int'l*, pg. 2667
BOLOCO; *U.S. Private*, pg. 611
BOLOGNESI EMPREENDIMENTOS LTDA.; *Int'l*, pg. 1103
BOLOGNUE HOLDINGS INC.; *U.S. Private*, pg. 611
BOLONIA REAL ESTATE SL—See Enel S.p.A.; *Int'l*, pg. 2411
BOLSA DE BARCELONA—See SIX Group AG; *Int'l*, pg. 6966
BOLSA DE BILBAO—See SIX Group AG; *Int'l*, pg. 6966
BOLSA DE COMERCIO DE BUENOS AIRES; *Int'l*, pg. 1103
BOLSA DE COMERCIO DE SANTIAGO, BOLSA DE VALORES; *Int'l*, pg. 1103
BOLSA DE VALORES DE CARACAS; *Int'l*, pg. 1103
BOLSA DE VALORES DE LIMA S.A.; *Int'l*, pg. 1103
BOLSA DE VALORES DE PANAMA S.A.; *Int'l*, pg. 1103
BOLSA MEXICANA DE VALORES, S.A.B. DE C.V.; *Int'l*, pg. 1103
BOLSA NACIONAL DE VALORES, S.A.; *Int'l*, pg. 1103
BOLSAN COMPANY, INC.—See Inflexion Private Equity Partners LLP; *Int'l*, pg. 3688
BOLSAS Y MERCADOS ARGENTINOS S.A. (BYMA)—See Bolsa de Comercio de Buenos Aires; *Int'l*, pg. 1103
BOLSAS Y MERCADOS ESPANOLES, SOCIEDAD HOLDING DE MERCADOS SISTEMAS FINANCIEROS, S.A.—See SIX Group AG; *Int'l*, pg. 6966
BOLSENA HOLDING GMBH & CO. KG—See Deutsche Bank Aktiengesellschaft; *Int'l*, pg. 2055
BOLS HUNGARY, KFT—See CJSC Russian Standard Corporation; *Int'l*, pg. 1634
BOLS MOTOREN B.V.—See LKQ Corporation; *U.S. Public*, pg. 1334
BOLSONES VERFT AS—See Havila Holding AS; *Int'l*, pg. 3287
BOLSONES VERFT AS—See Vision Ridge Partners, LLC; *U.S. Private*, pg. 4391
BOLT BIOTHERAPEUTICS, INC.; *U.S. Public*, pg. 368
BOLT BUS—See Peter Pan Bus Lines, Inc.; *U.S. Private*, pg. 3159
BOLTECH SP. Z O.O—See Stalprodukt S.A.; *Int'l*, pg. 7164
BOLTEK HOLDINGS LIMITED; *Int'l*, pg. 1103
BOLTEX INC.; *U.S. Private*, pg. 611
BOLT EXPRESS LLC; *U.S. Private*, pg. 611
BOLTHOUSE FARMS JAPAN YK—See Campbell Soup Company; *U.S. Public*, pg. 426
BOLTHOUSE INVESTMENT COMPANY—See Campbell Soup Company; *U.S. Public*, pg. 426
BOLTHOUSE JUICE PRODUCTS, LLC—See Campbell Soup Company; *U.S. Public*, pg. 426
BOLT METALS CORP.; *Int'l*, pg. 1103
BOLT MOBILITY CORP.; *U.S. Private*, pg. 611
BOLTON AEROSPACE, INC.—See The Carlyle Group Inc.; *U.S. Public*, pg. 2054
BOLTON CENTRAL VETS4PETS LIMITED—See Pets at Home Group Plc; *Int'l*, pg. 5833
BOLTON & COMPANY—See IMA Financial Group, Inc.; *U.S. Private*, pg. 2043
BOLTON CONDUCTIVE SYSTEMS, LLC—See Stoneridge, Inc.; *U.S. Public*, pg. 1951
BOLTON EMERSON AMERICAS, LLC; *U.S. Private*, pg. 611
BOLTON FOOTWEAR (PTY) LTD.; *Int'l*, pg. 1103
BOLTON FORD INC.; *U.S. Private*, pg. 611
BOLTON FURNITURE INC.—See Bertram Capital Management, LLC; *U.S. Private*, pg. 540
BOLTON GATE SERVICES LTD.—See Sanwa Holdings Corporation; *Int'l*, pg. 6560
BOLTON MEDICAL ESPANA S.L.U.—See Werfen Life Group, S.A.U.; *Int'l*, pg. 8378
BOLTON MEDICAL, INC.—See Terumo Corporation; *Int'l*, pg. 7569
BOLTON MEDICAL S.P.A—See Werfen Life Group, S.A.U.; *Int'l*, pg. 8378
BOLTON & MENK, INC.; *U.S. Private*, pg. 611
BOLTON MILLS RETIREMENT COMMUNITY INC.—See Extendicare Inc.; *Int'l*, pg. 2591
BOLTON OIL CO. LTD; *U.S. Private*, pg. 611
BOLTON PEREZ & ASSOCIATES, INC.—See Colliers International Group Inc.; *Int'l*, pg. 1700
BOLTON PRINT PTY LTD—See IVE Group Limited; *Int'l*, pg. 3846
BOLTON SARL—See Derichebourg S.A.; *Int'l*, pg. 2042
BOLT ON TECHNOLOGY, LLC—See Performant Management Company, LLC; *U.S. Private*, pg. 3150
BOLT SOLUTIONS, INC.—See CVC Capital Partners SICAV-FIS S.A.; *Int'l*, pg. 1885
BOLTTECH MANNINGS, INC.—See Grey Mountain Partners, LLC; *U.S. Private*, pg. 1784
BOLT UNDERWATER SERVICES, INC.—See Volkert, Inc.; *U.S. Private*, pg. 4410
BOLU CIMENTO SANAYII A.S.; *Int'l*, pg. 1103
BOLUO FENG CHING MAGNET WIRE MANUFACTURING CO., LTD.—See Feng Ching Metal Corp.; *Int'l*, pg. 2634
BOLZONI AURAMO AB—See Hyster-Yale Materials Handling, Inc.; *U.S. Public*, pg. 1080
BOLZONI AURAMO BV—See Hyster-Yale Materials Handling, Inc.; *U.S. Public*, pg. 1080
BOLZONI AURAMO CANADA LTD—See Hyster-Yale Materials Handling, Inc.; *U.S. Public*, pg. 1080
BOLZONI AURAMO GMBH—See Hyster-Yale Materials Handling, Inc.; *U.S. Public*, pg. 1080
BOLZONI AURAMO INC.—See Hyster-Yale Materials Handling, Inc.; *U.S. Public*, pg. 1080
BOLZONI AURAMO POLSKA SP ZOO—See Hyster-Yale Materials Handling, Inc.; *U.S. Public*, pg. 1080
BOLZONI AURAMO (PTY) LTD—See Hyster-Yale Materials Handling, Inc.; *U.S. Public*, pg. 1079
BOLZONI AURAMO S.A.R.L.—See Hyster-Yale Materials Handling, Inc.; *U.S. Public*, pg. 1080
BOLZONI AURAMO S.L.—See Hyster-Yale Materials Handling, Inc.; *U.S. Public*, pg. 1080
BOLZONI AURAMO (WUXI) FORKLIFT TRUCK ATTACHMENT CO. LTD.—See Hyster-Yale Materials Handling, Inc.; *U.S. Public*, pg. 1079
BOLZONI CAPITAL HOLDING B.V.—See Hyster-Yale Materials Handling, Inc.; *U.S. Public*, pg. 1079
BOLZONI (HEBEI) FORKS—See Hyster-Yale Materials Handling, Inc.; *U.S. Public*, pg. 1079
BOLZONI ITALIA SRL—See Hyster-Yale Materials Handling, Inc.; *U.S. Public*, pg. 1079
BOLZONI LIMITED—See Hyster-Yale Materials Handling, Inc.; *U.S. Public*, pg. 1080
BOLZONI SARL—See Hyster-Yale Materials Handling, Inc.; *U.S. Public*, pg. 1080
BOLZONI SOUTH AMERICA LTDA.—See Hyster-Yale Materials Handling, Inc.; *U.S. Public*, pg. 1080
BOLZONI S.P.A.—See Hyster-Yale Materials Handling, Inc.; *U.S. Public*, pg. 1079
BOMAC INC.; *U.S. Private*, pg. 611
BOMA EQUIPMENT—See FAYAT SAS; *Int'l*, pg. 2624
BOMAG AMERICAS, INC.—See FAYAT SAS; *Int'l*, pg. 2624
BOMAG BRESIL—See FAYAT SAS; *Int'l*, pg. 2624
BOMAG CHEMNITZ—See FAYAT SAS; *Int'l*, pg. 2624
BOMAG (CHINA) CONSTRUCTION MACHINERY CO., LTD—See FAYAT SAS; *Int'l*, pg. 2624
BOMAG FRANCE S.A.S.—See FAYAT SAS; *Int'l*, pg. 2624
BOMAG GMBH—See FAYAT SAS; *Int'l*, pg. 2624
BOMAG (GREAT BRITAIN) LTD—See FAYAT SAS; *Int'l*, pg. 2624
BOMAG ITALIA SRL.—See FAYAT SAS; *Int'l*, pg. 2624
BOMAG MARINI LATIN AMERICA—See FAYAT SAS; *Int'l*, pg. 2624
BOMAG MASCHINENHANDELSGESELLSCHAFT M.B.H.—See FAYAT SAS; *Int'l*, pg. 2624
BOMAG PAVING PRODUCTS INC—See FAYAT SAS; *Int'l*, pg. 2624
BOMAG SINGAPORE—See FAYAT SAS; *Int'l*, pg. 2624
BOMAN KEMP BASEMENT WINDOW SYSTEMS; *U.S. Private*, pg. 611
BOMAR CRYSTAL COMPANY—See BOMAR EXO LLC; *U.S. Private*, pg. 612
BOMAR EXO LLC; *U.S. Private*, pg. 612
BOMARKO, INC.; *U.S. Private*, pg. 612
BOMAR PNEUMATICS, INC.—See Blue Sea Capital Management LLC; *U.S. Private*, pg. 592
BOMAT, INC.—See RPM International Inc.; *U.S. Public*, pg. 1816
BOMAY ELECTRIC INDUSTRIES CO.—See STABILIS SOLUTIONS, INC.; *U.S. Public*, pg. 1924
BOMBARD ELECTRIC, LLC—See MDU Resources Group, Inc.; *U.S. Public*, pg. 1409
BOMBARDIER AEROSPACE BELFAST—See Bombardier Inc.; *Int'l*, pg. 1103
BOMBARDIER AEROSPACE—See Bombardier Inc.; *Int'l*, pg. 1103
BOMBARDIER AEROSPACE—See Bombardier Inc.; *Int'l*, pg. 1103
BOMBARDIER AEROSPACE—See Bombardier Inc.; *Int'l*, pg. 1103
BOMBARDIER CAPITAL INCORPORATED—See Bombardier Inc.; *Int'l*, pg. 1104
BOMBARDIER CAPITAL INTERNATIONAL B.V.—See Bombardier Inc.; *Int'l*, pg. 1104
BOMBARDIER CORP.—See Bombardier Inc.; *Int'l*, pg. 1104
BOMBARDIER CREDIT RECEIVABLES CORPORATION—See Bombardier Inc.; *Int'l*, pg. 1104
BOMBARDIER EUROPEAN HOLDINGS, S.L.U.—See Bombardier Inc.; *Int'l*, pg. 1104
BOMBARDIER EUROPEAN INVESTMENTS, S.L.—See Bombardier Inc.; *Int'l*, pg. 1104
BOMBARDIER INC. - REAL ESTATE SERVICES—See Bombardier Inc.; *Int'l*, pg. 1104
BOMBARDIER INC.; *Int'l*, pg. 1103
BOMBARDIER - LEARJET—See Bombardier Inc.; *Int'l*, pg. 1103
BOMBARDIER - LEARJET—See Bombardier Inc.; *Int'l*, pg. 1103
BOMBARDIER MASS TRANSIT CORPORATION—See Alstom S.A.; *Int'l*, pg. 382
BOMBARDIER (MAURITIUS) LTD—See Bombardier Inc.; *Int'l*, pg. 1103
BOMBARDIER MEXICO, S.A. DE C.V.—See Alstom S.A.; *Int'l*, pg. 382
BOMBARDIER MOTOR CORPORATION OF AMERICA—See Bain Capital, LP; *U.S. Private*, pg. 431
BOMBARDIER MOTOR CORPORATION OF AMERICA—See Bain Capital, LP; *U.S. Private*, pg. 431
BOMBARDIER MOTOR CORPORATION OF AMERICA—See Bain Capital, LP; *U.S. Private*, pg. 431
BOMBARDIER MOTOR CORPORATION OF AMERICA—See Bain Capital, LP; *U.S. Private*, pg. 431
BOMBARDIER RECREATIONAL PRODUCTS INC.—See Bain Capital, LP; *U.S. Private*, pg. 431
BOMBARDIER RECREATIONAL PRODUCTS, INC.—See Bain Capital, LP; *U.S. Private*, pg. 431
BOMBARDIER RECREATIONAL PRODUCTS - JOHNSON & EVINRUDE—See Bain Capital, LP; *U.S. Private*, pg. 431
BOMBARDIER TRANSIT CORPORATION—See Alstom S.A.; *Int'l*, pg. 382
BOMBARDIER TRANSPAORTATION ISRAEL LTD.—See Alstom S.A.; *Int'l*, pg. 381
BOMBARDIER TRANSPORTATION AB—See Alstom S.A.; *Int'l*, pg. 382
BOMBARDIER TRANSPORTATION AG—See Alstom S.A.; *Int'l*, pg. 382
BOMBARDIER TRANSPORTATION AUSTRALIA PTY. LTD.—See Alstom S.A.; *Int'l*, pg. 382
BOMBARDIER TRANSPORTATION AUSTRIA GMBH—See Alstom S.A.; *Int'l*, pg. 382
BOMBARDIER TRANSPORTATION (BAHNTECHNOLOGIE) GERMANY GMBH—See Alstom S.A.; *Int'l*, pg. 382
BOMBARDIER TRANSPORTATION BELGIUM—See Alstom S.A.; *Int'l*, pg. 382
BOMBARDIER TRANSPORTATION BRASIL LTDA.—See Alstom S.A.; *Int'l*, pg. 382
BOMBARDIER TRANSPORTATION CANADA—See Alstom S.A.; *Int'l*, pg. 382
BOMBARDIER TRANSPORTATION CANADA - TRANSIT SYSTEMS—See Alstom S.A.; *Int'l*, pg. 382
BOMBARDIER TRANSPORTATION (CHINA) LTD.—See Alstom S.A.; *Int'l*, pg. 382
BOMBARDIER TRANSPORTATION CZECH REPUBLIC A/S—See Alstom S.A.; *Int'l*, pg. 382
BOMBARDIER TRANSPORTATION DENMARK A/S—See Alstom S.A.; *Int'l*, pg. 382
BOMBARDIER TRANSPORTATION EQUIPMENT (SUZHOU) CO., LTD.—See Alstom S.A.; *Int'l*, pg. 382
BOMBARDIER TRANSPORTATION GMBH—See Alstom S.A.; *Int'l*, pg. 381
BOMBARDIER TRANSPORTATION HOLDINGS (THAILAND) LTD.—See Alstom S.A.; *Int'l*, pg. 382
BOMBARDIER TRANSPORTATION (HOLDINGS) UK LTD.—See Alstom S.A.; *Int'l*, pg. 382
BOMBARDIER TRANSPORTATION (HOLDINGS) USA INC.—See Alstom S.A.; *Int'l*, pg. 382
BOMBARDIER TRANSPORTATION HUNGARY KFT.—See Alstom S.A.; *Int'l*, pg. 382
BOMBARDIER TRANSPORTATION KOREA LTD.—See Alstom S.A.; *Int'l*, pg. 382
BOMBARDIER TRANSPORTATION (MALAYSIA) SDN. BHD.—See Alstom S.A.; *Int'l*, pg. 382
BOMBARDIER TRANSPORTATION (NETHERLAND) B.V.—See Alstom S.A.; *Int'l*, pg. 382
BOMBARDIER TRANSPORTATION NORTH AMERICA INC.—See Alstom S.A.; *Int'l*, pg. 382
BOMBARDIER TRANSPORTATION NORWAY AS—See Alstom S.A.; *Int'l*, pg. 382
BOMBARDIER TRANSPORTATION (OBSLUGA KLIENTA) POLSKA SP. Z.O.O.—See Alstom S.A.; *Int'l*, pg. 382
BOMBARDIER TRANSPORTATION POLSKA SP. Z.O.O.—See Alstom S.A.; *Int'l*, pg. 383
BOMBARDIER TRANSPORTATION PORTUGAL, S.A.—See Alstom S.A.; *Int'l*, pg. 383
BOMBARDIER TRANSPORTATION (PROPULSION & CONTROLS) GERMANY GMBH—See Alstom S.A.; *Int'l*, pg. 382
BOMBARDIER TRANSPORTATION (RAIL ENGINEERING) POLSKA SP. Z O.O—See Alstom S.A.; *Int'l*, pg. 382
BOMBARDIER TRANSPORTATION (ROLLING STOCK) UK LTD—See Alstom S.A.; *Int'l*, pg. 382
BOMBARDIER TRANSPORTATION ROMANIA SRL—See Alstom S.A.; *Int'l*, pg. 383
BOMBARDIER TRANSPORTATION SA—See Alstom S.A.; *Int'l*, pg. 383
BOMBARDIER TRANSPORTATION (SHARED SERVICES) PHILIPPINES INC.—See Alstom S.A.; *Int'l*, pg. 382
BOMBARDIER TRANSPORTATION SHARED SERVICES ROMANIA SRL—See Alstom S.A.; *Int'l*, pg. 383

BOMBARDIER INC.

BOMBARDIER TRANSPORTATION (SIGNAL) GERMANY GMBH—See Alstom S.A.; *Int'l*, pg. 382
BOMBARDIER TRANSPORTATION—See Alstom S.A.; *Int'l*, pg. 382
BOMBARDIER TRANSPORTATION SOUTH AFRICA (PTY.) LTD—See Alstom S.A.; *Int'l*, pg. 383
BOMBARDIER TRANSPORTATION (SWITZERLAND) LTD.—See Alstom S.A.; *Int'l*, pg. 383
BOMBARDIER TRANSPORTATION UK LTD.—See Alstom S.A.; *Int'l*, pg. 383
BOMBARDIER TRANSPORTATION (ZWUS) POLSKA SP. Z O.O.—See Alstom S.A.; *Int'l*, pg. 382
BOMBARDIER TRANSPORT FRANCE S.A.S. - SERVICES DIVISION—See Alstom S.A.; *Int'l*, pg. 382
BOMBARDIER TRANSPORT FRANCE S.A.S.—See Alstom S.A.; *Int'l*, pg. 381
BOMBARDIER-WIEN SCHIENENFAHRZEUGE AG—See Alstom S.A.; *Int'l*, pg. 383
BOMBARD MECHANICAL, LLC—See MDU Resources Group, Inc.; *U.S. Public*, pg. 1409
BOMBAS BORNEMANN S.R.L.—See ITT Inc.; *U.S. Public*, pg. 1177
BOMBAS BOYSER, S.L.—See ProMinent Dosiertechnik GmbH; *Int'l*, pg. 5994
BOMBAS GOULDS DE MEXICO S. DE R.L. DE C.V.—See ITT Inc.; *U.S. Public*, pg. 1177
BOMBAS GOULDS S.A.—See ITT Inc.; *U.S. Public*, pg. 1177
BOMBAS GRUNDFOS DE ARGENTINA S.A.—See The Poul Due Jensen Foundation; *Int'l*, pg. 7674
BOMBAS GRUNDFOS DE MEXICO MANUFACTURING S.A. DE C.V.—See The Poul Due Jensen Foundation; *Int'l*, pg. 7674
BOMBAS GRUNDFOS DE MEXICO S.A. DE C.V.—See The Poul Due Jensen Foundation; *Int'l*, pg. 7674
BOMBAS GRUNDFOS DO BRASIL LTDA—See The Poul Due Jensen Foundation; *Int'l*, pg. 7674
BOMBAS GRUNDFOS ESPANA S.A.U.—See The Poul Due Jensen Foundation; *Int'l*, pg. 7674
BOMBAS GRUNDFOS (PORTUGAL) S.A.—See The Poul Due Jensen Foundation; *Int'l*, pg. 7674
BOMBAS LEAO SA—See Franklin Electric Co., Inc.; *U.S. Public*, pg. 878
THE BOMBAY BURMAH TRADING CORPORATION LIMITED; *Int'l*, pg. 7627
BOMBAY CYCLE & MOTOR AGENCY LIMITED; *Int'l*, pg. 1104
BOMBAY DYEING & MANUFACTURING COMPANY LTD. - PSF PLANT—See The Wadia Group; *Int'l*, pg. 7698
BOMBAY DYEING & MANUFACTURING COMPANY LTD.—See The Wadia Group; *Int'l*, pg. 7698
BOMBAY DYEING & MANUFACTURING COMPANY LTD. - TEXTILE PROCESSING UNIT—See The Wadia Group; *Int'l*, pg. 7698
BOMBAY METRICS SUPPLY CHAIN LIMITED; *Int'l*, pg. 1104
BOMBAY OXYGEN INVESTMENTS LTD.; *Int'l*, pg. 1104
BOMBAY PALACE COMPANY; *U.S. Private*, pg. 612
BOMBAY POTTERIES & TILES LIMITED; *Int'l*, pg. 1104
BOMBAY RAYON FASHIONS LIMITED; *Int'l*, pg. 1104
BOMBAY REALTY—See The Wadia Group; *Int'l*, pg. 7698
BOMBAY STOCK EXCHANGE LIMITED; *Int'l*, pg. 1104
BOMBAY SUPER HYBRID SEEDS LTD.; *Int'l*, pg. 1104
BOMBAY WIRE ROPES LIMITED; *Int'l*, pg. 1104
BOMBAYWORKS AB—See Storskogen Group AB; *Int'l*, pg. 7227
BOMBERGERS STORE INC.; *U.S. Private*, pg. 612
BOMBRIL S.A.; *Int'l*, pg. 1104
BOMBSHELL ACCESSORIES INC.; *U.S. Private*, pg. 612
BOMC PTE. LTD.—See Qube Holdings Limited; *Int'l*, pg. 6158
BOMEK CONSULTING AS—See Multiconsult ASA; *Int'l*, pg. 5083
BOMEL CONSTRUCTION CO. INC.; *U.S. Private*, pg. 612
BOMESC OFFSHORE ENGINEERING COMPANY LIMITED; *Int'l*, pg. 1104
BOMFORD TURNER LIMITED—See Alamo Group Inc.; *U.S. Public*, pg. 70
BOMFORD TURNER LIMITED—See Alamo Group Inc.; *U.S. Public*, pg. 70
BOMGAARS SUPPLY INC.; *U.S. Private*, pg. 612
BOMGAR CORPORATION—See Francisco Partners Management, LP; *U.S. Private*, pg. 1589
BOMI ITALIA S.P.A.—See United Parcel Service, Inc.; *U.S. Public*, pg. 2233
BOMIN BUNKER HOLDING GMBH & CO. KG—See Marquard & Bahls AG; *Int'l*, pg. 4699
BOMIN BUNKER OIL LTD.—See Marquard & Bahls AG; *Int'l*, pg. 4699
BOMIN ELECTRONICS CO., LTD.; *Int'l*, pg. 1104
BOMINFLOT BUNKERGESELLSCHAFT FUR MINERALOWLE MBH & CO. KG—See Marquard & Bahls AG; *Int'l*, pg. 4699
BOMINFLOT DO BRASIL COMERCIO LTDA.—See Marquard & Bahls AG; *Int'l*, pg. 4699
BOMINFLOT FUJAIRAH L.L.C.—See Marquard & Bahls AG; *Int'l*, pg. 4699
BOMINFLOT (GIBRALTAR) LIMITED—See Marquard & Bahls AG; *Int'l*, pg. 4699

BOMINFLOT GREECE S. A.—See Marquard & Bahls AG; *Int'l*, pg. 4699
BOMIN LINDE LNG GMBH & CO. KG—See Marquard & Bahls AG; *Int'l*, pg. 4699
BOMIN OIL PVT. LTD.—See Marquard & Bahls AG; *Int'l*, pg. 4699
BOMIN TANKLAGER KIEL GMBH & CO. KG—See Marquard & Bahls AG; *Int'l*, pg. 4699
BOMMARITO AUTOMOTIVE GROUP; *U.S. Private*, pg. 612
BOMMARITO CHEVROLET MAZDA INC.; *U.S. Private*, pg. 612
BOMMER INDUSTRIES, INC. - GAFFNEY PLANT—See Bommer Industries, Inc.; *U.S. Private*, pg. 612
BOMMER INDUSTRIES, INC.; *U.S. Private*, pg. 612
BOMSOWA CO. LTD.; *Int'l*, pg. 1105
BONACCORD CAPITAL PARTNERS LLC—See P10, Inc.; *U.S. Public*, pg. 1630
BON ACCORD CASPIAN—See Groupe BPCE; *Int'l*, pg. 3095
BONADENT DENTAL LABORATORIES; *U.S. Private*, pg. 613
BONADIO & CO. LLP; *U.S. Private*, pg. 613
BONAFARMA PRODUTOS FARMACEUTICOS S.A.—See Recordati S.p.A.; *Int'l*, pg. 6238
BONA FILM GROUP LIMITED; *Int'l*, pg. 1105
BON-AIRE INDUSTRIES INC.; *U.S. Private*, pg. 613
BONAIRE SOFTWARE SOLUTIONS, LLC—See Broadridge Financial Solutions, Inc.; *U.S. Public*, pg. 391
BONAL INTERNATIONAL, INC.; *U.S. Public*, pg. 368
BONAL TECHNOLOGIES, INC.—See Bonal International, Inc.; *U.S. Public*, pg. 368
BONAMOUR, INC.; *U.S. Private*, pg. 613
BONANDER PONTIAC INC.; *U.S. Private*, pg. 613
BONANZA CO., LTD.—See Noevir Holdings Co., Ltd.; *Int'l*, pg. 5399
BONANZA CREEK ENERGY OPERATING COMPANY LLC—See Civitas Resources, Inc.; *U.S. Public*, pg. 507
BONANZA CREEK ENERGY RESOURCES, LLC—See Civitas Resources, Inc.; *U.S. Public*, pg. 507
BONANZA FOODS & PROVISIONS INC.; *U.S. Private*, pg. 613
BONANZA MINING CORPORATION; *Int'l*, pg. 1105
BONANZA OIL AND GAS, INC.; *U.S. Private*, pg. 613
BONANZA RESOURCES CORP.; *Int'l*, pg. 1105
BONANZA RESTAURANTS—See Fog Cutter Capital Group Inc.; *U.S. Private*, pg. 1557
BON APPETIT MAGAZINE—See Advance Publications, Inc.; *U.S. Private*, pg. 85
BON APPETIT MANAGEMENT CO—See Compass Group PLC; *Int'l*, pg. 1750
BONAR GMBH & CO. KG—See Freudenberg SE; *Int'l*, pg. 2789
BONARKA CITY CENTER SP. Z O.O.—See NEPI Rockcastle N.V.; *Int'l*, pg. 5200
BON ARTISAN CO., LTD.—See Di-Nikko Engineering Co., Ltd.; *Int'l*, pg. 2101
BONAR YARNS & FABRICS LIMITED—See Freudenberg SE; *Int'l*, pg. 2789
BONASUDDEN HOLDING AB; *Int'l*, pg. 1105
BONA TECHNOLOGY INC.—See Serial System Ltd.; *Int'l*, pg. 6723
BONATLA PROPERTY HOLDINGS LIMITED; *Int'l*, pg. 1105
BONATRANS GROUP A.S.; *Int'l*, pg. 1105
BONATRANS INDIA PRIVATE LIMITED—See Jupiter Wagons Limited; *Int'l*, pg. 4030
BONAVA AB; *Int'l*, pg. 1105
BONAVA DANMARK A/S—See Bonava AB; *Int'l*, pg. 1105
BONAVA EESTI OU—See Bonava AB; *Int'l*, pg. 1105
BONAVA LATVIJA SIA—See Bonava AB; *Int'l*, pg. 1105
BONAVA NORGE AS—See Bonava AB; *Int'l*, pg. 1105
BONAVA SUOMI OY—See Bonava AB; *Int'l*, pg. 1105
BONAVENTURA SERVICES GMBH—See Groupe Egis S.A.; *Int'l*, pg. 3102
BONAVENTURE CAPITAL LLC; *U.S. Private*, pg. 613
BONAVENTURE CO, LLC; *U.S. Private*, pg. 613
BONAVIA FOODS LLC; *U.S. Private*, pg. 613
BONA VIDA, INC.—See Better Choice Company, Inc.; *U.S. Public*, pg. 326
BONAVISTA DE BONMONT SL—See Pierre & Vacances SA; *Int'l*, pg. 5864
BONAVISTA ENERGY CORPORATION—See Tourmaline Oil Corp.; *Int'l*, pg. 7848
BONA VISTA PROGRAMS, INC.; *U.S. Private*, pg. 613
BON BELTA CO., LTD.—See AEON Co., Ltd.; *Int'l*, pg. 177
BONCAFE (CAMBODIA) LTD—See Segafredo Zanetti S.p.A.; *Int'l*, pg. 6681
BONCAFE CHINA LIMITED—See Massimo Zanetti Beverage Group SpA; *Int'l*, pg. 4722
BONCAFE (EAST MALAYSIA) SDN BHD—See Segafredo Zanetti S.p.A.; *Int'l*, pg. 6681
BONCAFE (HONG KONG) LIMITED—See Segafredo Zanetti S.p.A.; *Int'l*, pg. 6681
BONCAFE INTERNATIONAL PTE LTD—See Segafredo Zanetti S.p.A.; *Int'l*, pg. 6681
BONCAFE MALAYSIA SDN BHD—See Segafredo Zanetti S.p.A.; *Int'l*, pg. 6681

CORPORATE AFFILIATIONS

BONCAFE MIDDLE EAST LLC—See Segafredo Zanetti S.p.A.; *Int'l*, pg. 6681
BONCAFE (THAILAND) LTD—See Segafredo Zanetti S.p.A.; *Int'l*, pg. 6681
BONCAFE VIETNAM COMPANY LIMITED—See Massimo Zanetti Beverage Group SpA; *Int'l*, pg. 4722
BON CHEF INC.; *U.S. Private*, pg. 612
BON CLINICAL LABORATORIES—See Schryver Medical Sales; *U.S. Private*, pg. 3570
BONCO IRONMONGERY LIMITED—See E. Bon Holdings Ltd; *Int'l*, pg. 2249
BONDALTI CAPITAL, S.A.—See Jose de Mello, SGPS, S.A.; *Int'l*, pg. 4001
BOND AUTO PARTS INC.; *U.S. Private*, pg. 613
BOND BRAND LOYALTY INC.; *Int'l*, pg. 1105
BOND COMMUNITY HEALTH CENTER, INC.; *U.S. Private*, pg. 613
BONDCOTE PERFORMANCE TEXTILES, LLC.—See XFS Global LLC; *U.S. Private*, pg. 4581
BONDDESK GROUP LLC—See Tradeweb Markets Inc.; *U.S. Public*, pg. 2178
BOND DRUG COMPANY OF ILLINOIS, LLC—See Walgreens Boots Alliance, Inc.; *U.S. Public*, pg. 2323
BONDED BUILDERS INSURANCE SERVICES—See Bankers International Financial Corporation; *U.S. Private*, pg. 468
BONDED BUILDERS WARRANTY GROUP—See Bankers International Financial Corporation; *U.S. Private*, pg. 468
BONDED CARRIERS INC.; *U.S. Private*, pg. 613
BONDED SERVICES GROUP LIMITED—See The Wicks Group of Companies, LLC; *U.S. Private*, pg. 4135
BONDED SERVICES (INTERNATIONAL) B.V.—See Iron Mountain Incorporated; *U.S. Public*, pg. 1172
BONDED SERVICES INTERNATIONAL LIMITED—See Iron Mountain Incorporated; *U.S. Public*, pg. 1172
BONDED SERVICES LIMITED—See Iron Mountain Incorporated; *U.S. Public*, pg. 1172
BOND ELECTRONIC EXCHANGE—See The Stock Exchange of Thailand; *Int'l*, pg. 7688
BONDEXCEL (PTY) LTD—See Finbond Group Limited; *Int'l*, pg. 2670
BONDEX SUPPLY CHAIN MANAGEMENT CO., LTD.; *Int'l*, pg. 1105
BONDFIELD CONSTRUCTION COMPANY LIMITED; *Int'l*, pg. 1105
BOND FLUIDAIRE INC.—See Exotic Automation & Supply, Inc.; *U.S. Private*, pg. 1449
BOND FLUIDAIRE INC.—See Exotic Automation & Supply, Inc.; *U.S. Private*, pg. 1449
BOND FLUIDAIRE INC.—See Exotic Automation & Supply, Inc.; *U.S. Private*, pg. 1449
BOND FLUIDAIRE, INC. - WESTSIDE—See Exotic Automation & Supply, Inc.; *U.S. Private*, pg. 1449
BONDING INSURANCE AGENCY & INSURANCE FACTORS—See Vinet Holdings Inc.; *U.S. Private*, pg. 4385
BOND INTERNATIONAL JAPAN K.K.—See Symphony Technology Group, LLC; *U.S. Private*, pg. 3900
BOND INTERNATIONAL SOFTWARE CHINA LIMITED—See Symphony Technology Group, LLC; *U.S. Private*, pg. 3900
BOND INTERNATIONAL SOFTWARE, INC. - MINNEAPOLIS OFFICE—See Symphony Technology Group, LLC; *U.S. Private*, pg. 3900
BOND INTERNATIONAL SOFTWARE, INC.—See Symphony Technology Group, LLC; *U.S. Private*, pg. 3900
BOND INTERNATIONAL SOFTWARE (UK) LIMITED—See Symphony Technology Group, LLC; *U.S. Private*, pg. 3900
BONDIOLI I PAVESI UKRAINE L.L.C.—See Bondioli & Pavesi S.p.A.; *Int'l*, pg. 1106
BONDIOLI & PAVESI-FRANCE S.A.—See Bondioli & Pavesi S.p.A.; *Int'l*, pg. 1106
BONDIOLI & PAVESI GMBH DEUTSCHLAND—See Bondioli & Pavesi S.p.A.; *Int'l*, pg. 1106
BONDIOLI & PAVESI GS.M.B.H—See Bondioli & Pavesi S.p.A.; *Int'l*, pg. 1106
BONDIOLI & PAVESI HYDRAULIC AND MECHANICAL COMPONENT (HANGZHOU) CO., LTD—See Bondioli & Pavesi S.p.A.; *Int'l*, pg. 1105
BONDIOLI & PAVESI INC.—See Bondioli & Pavesi S.p.A.; *Int'l*, pg. 1106
BONDIOLI & PAVESI INDIA PVT. LTD.—See Bondioli & Pavesi S.p.A.; *Int'l*, pg. 1105
BONDIOLI & PAVESI LTD.—See Bondioli & Pavesi S.p.A.; *Int'l*, pg. 1105
BONDIOLI & PAVESI S.P.A.; *Int'l*, pg. 1105
BONDIOLI & PAVESI SP.ZO.O.—See Bondioli & Pavesi S.p.A.; *Int'l*, pg. 1106
BONDIOLI Y PAVESI IBERICA S.A.—See Bondioli & Pavesi S.p.A.; *Int'l*, pg. 1106
BOND-LAMINATES GMBH—See LANXESS AG; *Int'l*, pg. 4414
BONDPARTNERS SA; *Int'l*, pg. 1106
BOND PHARMACY, INC.; *U.S. Private*, pg. 613
BOND PLUMBING SUPPLY INCORPORATED; *U.S. Private*, pg. 613
BOND RESOURCES, INC.; *Int'l*, pg. 1105

COMPANY NAME INDEX

BOND, SCHOENECK & KING, PLLC; *U.S. Private*, pg. 613
BONDS COMPANY, INC.; *U.S. Private*, pg. 613
BONDS, INC.—See Kelso & Company, L.P.; *U.S. Private*, pg. 2279
BOND SOLON TRAINING LIMITED—See Wilmington plc; *Int'l*, pg. 8422
BONDSPOT S.A.—See Gielda Papierow Wartosciowych w Warszawie S.A.; *Int'l*, pg. 2968
BONDSTRAND LTD.—See NOV, Inc.; *U.S. Public*, pg. 1544
BONDSTRAND LTD.—See Saudi Arabian Amiantit Company; *Int'l*, pg. 6588
BOND TACT INDUSTRIAL LIMITED—See Phoenix Mecano AG; *Int'l*, pg. 5852
BOND TURNER LIMITED—See Anexo Group Plc; *Int'l*, pg. 459
BONDUELLE DEUTSCHLAND GMBH—See Bonduelle SAS; *Int'l*, pg. 1106
BONDUELLE EUROPE LONG LIFE SAS—See Bonduelle SAS; *Int'l*, pg. 1106
BONDUELLE IBERICA SAU—See Bonduelle SAS; *Int'l*, pg. 1106
BONDUELLE NORTHERN EUROPE NV—See Bonduelle SAS; *Int'l*, pg. 1106
BONDUELLE POLSKA S.A.—See Bonduelle SAS; *Int'l*, pg. 1106
BONDUELLE SAS; *Int'l*, pg. 1106
BONDUELLE USA INC.—See Bonduelle SAS; *Int'l*, pg. 1106
BONDY A/S—See THK CO., LTD.; *Int'l*, pg. 7711
BONDY CENTRUM, S.R.O.—See Raiffeisen Bank International AG; *Int'l*, pg. 6182
BONDY LMT A/S—See Addtech AB; *Int'l*, pg. 132
BONDYS FORD INC.; *U.S. Private*, pg. 613
BONEAL INCORPORATED; *U.S. Private*, pg. 614
THE BONE AND JOINT CENTRE PTE. LTD.—See Livingstone Health Holdings Limited; *Int'l*, pg. 4533
BONE BIOLOGICS, CORP.; *U.S. Public*, pg. 368
BONEFISH/CENTREVILLE, LIMITED PARTNERSHIP—See Bloomin' Brands, Inc.; *U.S. Public*, pg. 362
BONEFISH/CRESCENT SPRINGS, LIMITED PARTNERSHIP—See Bloomin' Brands, Inc.; *U.S. Public*, pg. 362
BONEFISH/FREDERICKSBURG, LIMITED PARTNERSHIP—See Bloomin' Brands, Inc.; *U.S. Public*, pg. 362
BONEFISH/GREENSBORO, LIMITED PARTNERSHIP—See Bloomin' Brands, Inc.; *U.S. Public*, pg. 362
BONEFISH GRILL, LLC—See Bloomin' Brands, Inc.; *U.S. Public*, pg. 362
BONEFISH GRILL OF FLORIDA, LLC—See Bloomin' Brands, Inc.; *U.S. Public*, pg. 362
BONEFISH HOLDINGS, LLC—See Bloomin' Brands, Inc.; *U.S. Public*, pg. 362
BONEFISH/HYDE PARK, LIMITED PARTNERSHIP—See Bloomin' Brands, Inc.; *U.S. Public*, pg. 362
BONEFISH/NEWPORT NEWS, LIMITED PARTNERSHIP—See Bloomin' Brands, Inc.; *U.S. Public*, pg. 362
BONEFISH OF BEL AIR, LLC—See Bloomin' Brands, Inc.; *U.S. Public*, pg. 362
BONEFISH OF GAITHERSBURG, INC.—See Bloomin' Brands, Inc.; *U.S. Public*, pg. 362
BONEFISH/RICHMOND, LIMITED PARTNERSHIP—See Bloomin' Brands, Inc.; *U.S. Public*, pg. 362
BONEFISH/TALLAHASSEE, LIMITED PARTNERSHIP—See Bloomin' Brands, Inc.; *U.S. Public*, pg. 362
BONEFISH/VIRGINIA, LIMITED PARTNERSHIP—See Bloomin' Brands, Inc.; *U.S. Public*, pg. 363
BONE FRONTIER COMPANY—See Grey Mountain Partners, LLC; *U.S. Private*, pg. 1784
BONEI HATICHON CIVIL ENGINEERING & INFRASTRUCTURES LTD.; *Int'l*, pg. 1106
BONEL BUILDING CORPORATION INC.; *U.S. Private*, pg. 614
BONELLI ENTERPRISES—See Pella Corporation; *U.S. Private*, pg. 3131
BONE MCALLESTER NORTON PLLC—See Spencer Fane LLP; *U.S. Private*, pg. 3755
THE BONER GROUP, INC./ANN K. SAVAGE—See The Boner Group, Inc.; *U.S. Private*, pg. 3996
THE BONER GROUP, INC.; *U.S. Private*, pg. 3996
BONERTS (PTY) LTD—See Combined Motor Holdings Limited; *Int'l*, pg. 1709
BONES TOYOTA, INC.; *U.S. Private*, pg. 614
BONESUPPORT HOLDING AB; *Int'l*, pg. 1106
BONE THERAPEUTICS SA; *Int'l*, pg. 1106
BONETTI CANADA INC.—See ANDRITZ AG; *Int'l*, pg. 455
BONEYARD BEER LLC—See Deschutes Brewery Inc.; *U.S. Private*, pg. 1211
BONEY'S FARM STORE, INC.; *U.S. Private*, pg. 614
BON FAME CO., LTD.; *Int'l*, pg. 1105
BONFARE MARKETS INC.—See Kapoor Enterprises; *U.S. Private*, pg. 2261

BONFIGLIOLI FRANCE SA—See Bonfiglioli Riduttori S.p.A.; *Int'l*, pg. 1106
BONFIGLIOLI ITALIA S.P.A.—See Bonfiglioli Riduttori S.p.A.; *Int'l*, pg. 1106
BONFIGLIOLI RIDUTTORI S.P.A.; *Int'l*, pg. 1106
BONFIGLIOLI USA, INC.—See Bonfiglioli Riduttori S.p.A.; *Int'l*, pg. 1106
BONFIGLIOLI VECTRON GMBH—See Brd. Klee A/S; *Int'l*, pg. 1143
BONFIRE MARKETING COMPANY—See Thesis, Inc.; *U.S. Private*, pg. 4143
BON-FOOD PTE LTD—See Bonvests Holdings Limited; *Int'l*, pg. 1110
BONFRESH PTE LTD—See Bonvests Holdings Limited; *Int'l*, pg. 1110
BONG AB; *Int'l*, pg. 1106
BONGARD S.A.—See Ali Holding S.r.l; *Int'l*, pg. 322
BONGARDS CREAMERIES; *U.S. Private*, pg. 614
BONGARDS SOUTH LLC.—See Bongards Creameries; *U.S. Private*, pg. 614
BONG BELGIUM S.A.—See Bong AB; *Int'l*, pg. 1106
BONG CALY SWIAT KOPERT SP Z O.O.—See Bong AB; *Int'l*, pg. 1106
BONG DANMARK A/S—See Bong AB; *Int'l*, pg. 1106
BONG DENMARK A/S—See Bong AB; *Int'l*, pg. 1106
BONG EESTI OU—See Bong AB; *Int'l*, pg. 1106
BONG ENVELO SRL—See Bong AB; *Int'l*, pg. 1106
BONG GMBH—See Bong AB; *Int'l*, pg. 1106
BONG GMBH—See Bong AB; *Int'l*, pg. 1107
BONGIORNO SRL—See SEMIKRON International GmbH; *Int'l*, pg. 6705
BONG LATVIJA SIA—See Bong AB; *Int'l*, pg. 1107
BONG LJUNGDAHL SVERIGE AB—See Bong AB; *Int'l*, pg. 1107
BONG NETHERLANDS BV—See Bong AB; *Int'l*, pg. 1107
BONG NORGE AS—See Bong AB; *Int'l*, pg. 1107
BONG NORGE AS—See Bong AB; *Int'l*, pg. 1107
BONGO JAVA ROASTING CO.; *U.S. Private*, pg. 614
BONG PACKAGING S.R.L.—See Bong AB; *Int'l*, pg. 1107
BONG POLSKA S.P. Z.O.O.—See Bong AB; *Int'l*, pg. 1107
BONGRAIN EUROPE SAS—See Savencia Fromage & Dairy; *Int'l*, pg. 6597
BONGRAIN-GERARD SAS—See Savencia Fromage & Dairy; *Int'l*, pg. 6597
BONGRAIN INTERNATIONAL—See Savencia Fromage & Dairy; *Int'l*, pg. 6597
BONG RETAIL SOLUTIONS AB—See Bong AB; *Int'l*, pg. 1107
BONG RETAIL SOLUTIONS N.V.—See Bong AB; *Int'l*, pg. 1107
BONG S.A.S.—See Bong AB; *Int'l*, pg. 1107
BONG SCHWEIZ AG—See Bong AB; *Int'l*, pg. 1107
BONG SECURITY SOLUTIONS S.A.—See Bong AB; *Int'l*, pg. 1107
BONG SUOMI OY—See Bong AB; *Int'l*, pg. 1107
BONG SVERIGE AB—See Bong AB; *Int'l*, pg. 1107
BONHAMS 1793 LTD.—See Epiris Managers LLP; *Int'l*, pg. 2460
BONHAMS & BUTTERFIELDS—See Epiris Managers LLP; *Int'l*, pg. 2460
BONHEUR ASA—See Fred. Olsen & Co.; *Int'l*, pg. 2768
BONHEURE CO., LTD.—See Uchiyama Holdings Co., Ltd.; *Int'l*, pg. 8013
BONHILL GROUP PLC; *Int'l*, pg. 1107
BONIA CORPORATION BERHAD; *Int'l*, pg. 1107
BONIAL INTERNATIONAL GMBH—See Axel Springer SE; *Int'l*, pg. 766
BONIAL SAS—See Axel Springer SE; *Int'l*, pg. 766
BONIDE PRODUCTS, INC.—See China National Chemical Corporation; *Int'l*, pg. 1526
BONIFACE ENGINEERING, LTD.—See Miller Industries, Inc.; *U.S. Public*, pg. 1446
BONIFACE-HIERS INSURANCE AGENCY, INC.; *U.S. Private*, pg. 614
BONIFACIO COMMUNICATIONS CORPORATION—See PLDT Inc.; *Int'l*, pg. 5895
BONIFAZ KOHLER GMBH—See Hochland SE; *Int'l*, pg. 3437
BONIFICHE FERRARESI S.P.A.; *Int'l*, pg. 1107
BONITA BANNER—See Gannett Co., Inc.; *U.S. Public*, pg. 898
BONITA BAY CLUB; *U.S. Private*, pg. 614
BONITA BAY MARINA—See Bonita Bay Properties, Inc.; *U.S. Private*, pg. 614
BONITA BAY PROPERTIES, INC.; *U.S. Private*, pg. 614
BONITA LAKES MALL LIMITED PARTNERSHIP—See CBL & Associates Properties, Inc.; *U.S. Public*, pg. 457
BONITAS INTERNATIONAL LLC; *U.S. Private*, pg. 614
BONITASOFT, S.A.—See Fortino Capital Partners; *Int'l*, pg. 2739
BONITA SPRINGS UTILITIES INC.; *U.S. Private*, pg. 614
BONITZ CONTRACTING COMPANY, INC.—See Bonitz Inc.; *U.S. Private*, pg. 614
BONITZ CONTRACTING COMPANY—See Bonitz Inc.; *U.S. Private*, pg. 614
BONITZ FLOORING GROUP, INC.—See Bonitz Inc.; *U.S. Private*, pg. 614
BONITZ INC. - ROOFING SYSTEMS DIVISION—See Bonitz Inc.; *U.S. Private*, pg. 614

BONITZ INC.; *U.S. Private*, pg. 614
BONITZ INSULATION COMPANY, INC.—See Bonitz Inc.; *U.S. Private*, pg. 614
BONJOUR BAKERY PTE LTD.—See QAF Limited; *Int'l*, pg. 6131
BON JOUR CAPITAL; *U.S. Private*, pg. 612
BONJOUR HOLDINGS LIMITED; *Int'l*, pg. 1107
BON JOUR INTERNATIONAL LICENSING DIVISION—See Bon Jour Capital; *U.S. Private*, pg. 612
BON L ALUMINUM LLC—See Tredegar Corporation; *U.S. Public*, pg. 2187
BONLAND INDUSTRIES, INC.; *U.S. Private*, pg. 614
BONLON INDUSTRIES LIMITED; *Int'l*, pg. 1107
BON MANAGEMENT INC.; *U.S. Private*, pg. 612
BONMARCHE HOLDINGS PLC; *Int'l*, pg. 1107
BONNA ESTATES COMPANY LIMITED—See Hang Lung Group Limited; *Int'l*, pg. 3244
BONNASSE LYONNAISE DE BANQUE—See Confederation Nationale du Credit Mutuel; *Int'l*, pg. 1767
BONNA TERRA B.V.—See HZPC Holland B.V.; *Int'l*, pg. 3561
BONNA TUNISIA—See Bain Capital, LP; *U.S. Private*, pg. 438
BON NATURAL LIFE LIMITED; *Int'l*, pg. 1105
BONNAVILLA—See Chief Industries, Inc.; *U.S. Private*, pg. 881
BONNE CO., LTD.; *Int'l*, pg. 1107
BONNELL ALUMINUM (CLEARFIELD), INC.—See Tredegar Corporation; *U.S. Public*, pg. 2187
BONNELL ALUMINUM (ELKHART), INC.—See Tredegar Corporation; *U.S. Public*, pg. 2187
BONNELL ALUMINUM (ELKHART), INC.—See Tredegar Corporation; *U.S. Public*, pg. 2187
BONNELL ALUMINUM (NILES), LLC—See Tredegar Corporation; *U.S. Public*, pg. 2187
BONNER CHEVROLET CO. INC.; *U.S. Private*, pg. 614
BONNER FOODS INC.; *U.S. Private*, pg. 614
BONNETERRE ET COMPAGNIE S.A.S.—See PAI Partners S.A.S.; *Int'l*, pg. 5700
BONNETTE PAGE & STONE CORP.; *U.S. Private*, pg. 614
BONNEVILLE BILLING & COLLECTIONS; *U.S. Private*, pg. 615
BONNEVILLE CANNING COCA COLA; *U.S. Private*, pg. 615
BONNEVILLE COMMUNICATIONS; *U.S. Private*, pg. 615
BONNEVILLE INTERNATIONAL CORPORATION—See Deseret Management Corporation; *U.S. Private*, pg. 1212
BONNEVILLE INTERNATIONAL CORP. - PHOENIX—See Deseret Management Corporation; *U.S. Private*, pg. 1212
BONNEVILLE INTERNATIONAL CORP. - SACRAMENTO—See Deseret Management Corporation; *U.S. Private*, pg. 1212
BONNEVILLE INTERNATIONAL CORP. - SAN FRANCISCO—See Deseret Management Corporation; *U.S. Private*, pg. 1212
BONNEVILLE POWER ADMINISTRATION; *U.S. Private*, pg. 615
BONNEVILLE & SON INC.; *U.S. Private*, pg. 614
BONNEY FORGE CORPORATION - RP & C VALVE DIVISION—See Bonney Forge Corporation; *U.S. Private*, pg. 615
BONNEY FORGE CORPORATION; *U.S. Private*, pg. 615
BONNEY LAKE FOOD BANK; *U.S. Private*, pg. 615
BONNIE INTERNATIONAL—See Golden Touch Imports, Inc.; *U.S. Private*, pg. 1734
BONNIE PLANT FARM—See Alabama Farmers Cooperative, Inc.; *U.S. Private*, pg. 148
BONNIE PLANTS, LLC—See The Scotts Miracle-Gro Company; *U.S. Public*, pg. 2126
BONNIER AB; *Int'l*, pg. 1108
BONNIER ACTIVE MEDIA, INC.—See Bonnier AB; *Int'l*, pg. 1108
BONNIER ANNONS AB—See Bonnier AB; *Int'l*, pg. 1108
BONNIER BOOKS AB—See Bonnier AB; *Int'l*, pg. 1108
BONNIER BUSINESS FORUM OY—See Bonnier AB; *Int'l*, pg. 1108
BONNIER BUSINESS MEDIA SWEDEN AB—See Bonnier AB; *Int'l*, pg. 1108
BONNIER BUSINESS PRESS AB—See Bonnier AB; *Int'l*, pg. 1108
BONNIER BUSINESS PRESS, ZAO—See Bonnier AB; *Int'l*, pg. 1108
BONNIER CORPORATION—See Bonnier AB; *Int'l*, pg. 1108
BONNIER ENTERTAINMENT AB—See Telia Company AB; *Int'l*, pg. 7543
BONNIERFORLAGEN AB—See Bonnier AB; *Int'l*, pg. 1108
BONNIER MAGAZINE GROUP AB—See Bonnier AB; *Int'l*, pg. 1108
BONNIER MEDIA DEUTSCHLAND GMBH—See Bonnier AB; *Int'l*, pg. 1108
BONNIER NEWSPAPERS—See Bonnier AB; *Int'l*, pg. 1109
BONNY COLART CO LTD—See Lindengruppen AB; *Int'l*, pg. 4510
BONNY INTERNATIONAL HOLDING LTD.; *Int'l*, pg. 1109

BONNY WORLDWIDE LIMITED; *Int'l*, pg. 1109
BONOBOS, INC.—See WHP Global; *U.S. Private*, pg. 4515
BONPACK CO., LTD.—See ITOCHU Corporation; *Int'l*, pg. 3834
BONPRIX HANDELSGESELLSCHAFT MBH—See Otto GmbH & Co. KG; *Int'l*, pg. 5663
BON PRIX SP. Z.O.O.—See Otto GmbH & Co. KG; *Int'l*, pg. 5663
BONREE DATA TECHNOLOGY CO., LTD.; *Int'l*, pg. 1109
BONSAI INVESTMENT AG—See Deutsche Bank Aktiengesellschaft; *Int'l*, pg. 2055
BONSAI OUTLET; *U.S. Private*, pg. 615
BONSAL AMERICAN, INC.—See CRH plc; *Int'l*, pg. 1845
BONSALL SHAFFERMAN ARCHITECTS AND SPACE PLANNERS, PC—See Serfass Construction Company Inc.; *U.S. Private*, pg. 3613
BON SECOUR BOATS INC.—See Bon Secour Fisheries Inc.; *U.S. Private*, pg. 612
BON SECOUR FISHERIES INC.; *U.S. Private*, pg. 612
BON SECOUR MARINE SUPPLY INC.—See Bon Secour Fisheries Inc.; *U.S. Private*, pg. 612
BON SECOURS HEALTH SYSTEM, INC.—See Bon Secours Mercy Health, Inc.; *U.S. Private*, pg. 612
BON SECOURS HEALTH SYSTEM LTD—See Bon Secours Mercy Health, Inc.; *U.S. Private*, pg. 612
BON SECOURS MERCY HEALTH, INC.; *U.S. Private*, pg. 612
BON SECOURS SURGERY CENTER AT HARBOUR VIEW, LLC—See Tenet Healthcare Corporation; *U.S. Public*, pg. 2009
BON SECOURS SURGERY CENTER AT VIRGINIA BEACH, LLC—See Tenet Healthcare Corporation; *U.S. Public*, pg. 2009
BONSET AMERICA CORPORATION—See ITOCHU Corporation; *Int'l*, pg. 3834
BONSET LATIN AMERICA S.A.—See ITOCHU Corporation; *Int'l*, pg. 3834
BONSO ELECTRONICS INTERNATIONAL INC.; *Int'l*, pg. 1109
BONSO ELECTRONICS LIMITED—See Bonso Electronics International Inc.; *Int'l*, pg. 1109
BONSO ELECTRONICS (SHENZHEN) CO. LIMITED—See Bonso Electronics International Inc.; *Int'l*, pg. 1109
BONSOIR OF LONDON LTD.; *Int'l*, pg. 1109
BON SWEETS WLL—See Gulf Franchising Holding Company K.S.C.C.; *Int'l*, pg. 3180
THE BONTE INC.—See AEON Co., Ltd.; *Int'l*, pg. 178
BONTERRA BUILDERS, LLC—See Brookfield Corporation; *Int'l*, pg. 1183
BONTERRA CONSULTING; *U.S. Private*, pg. 615
BONTERRA ENERGY CORP; *Int'l*, pg. 1109
BONTERRA LTD.—See Hayleys PLC; *Int'l*, pg. 3291
BONTERRA RESOURCES INC.; *Int'l*, pg. 1109
BONTEX (ASIA) HOLDING COMPANY LIMITED—See Bontex, Inc.; *U.S. Public*, pg. 368
BONTEX DE MEXICO, S.A. DE C.V.—See Bontex, Inc.; *U.S. Public*, pg. 368
BONTEXGEO NV—See Waterland Private Equity Investments B.V.; *Int'l*, pg. 8357
BONTEX, INC.; *U.S. Public*, pg. 368
BONTEX KOREA—See Bontex, Inc.; *U.S. Public*, pg. 368
THE BON-TON DEPARTMENT STORES, INC.—See The Bon Ton Stores, Inc.; *U.S. Public*, pg. 2041
THE BON-TON GIFTCO, INC.—See The Bon Ton Stores, Inc.; *U.S. Public*, pg. 2041
THE BON TON STORES, INC.; *U.S. Public*, pg. 2041
BON TOOL COMPANY; *U.S. Private*, pg. 612
BONTRONIC GMBH—See Gerard Perrier Industrie S.A.; *Int'l*, pg. 2942
BONUM ANLAGE-UND BETEILIGUNGSGESELLSCHAFT MBH—See UniCredit S.p.A.; *Int'l*, pg. 8038
BONUM HEALTH, LLC—See Scienture Holdings, Inc.; *U.S. Public*, pg. 1849
BONUM PUBLICUM GD UAB—See Siauliu bankas AB; *Int'l*, pg. 6876
BONUS BIOGROUP LTD.; *Int'l*, pg. 1109
BONUS CROP FERTILIZER, INC.; *U.S. Private*, pg. 615
BONUSKAD LOYALTY SDN BHD—See AMMB Holdings Berhad; *Int'l*, pg. 429
BON VENT DE L EBRE, S.L.—See EDP - Energias de Portugal, S.A.; *Int'l*, pg. 2314
BONVER AB; *Int'l*, pg. 1109
BONVESTS HOLDINGS LIMITED; *Int'l*, pg. 1109
BONVITO GMBH—See Shift4 Payments, Inc.; *U.S. Public*, pg. 1875
BONWORTH INC.; *U.S. Private*, pg. 615
BONYAD PP FIBER PROD CO.; *Int'l*, pg. 1110
BONZI TECHNOLOGY INC.; *U.S. Private*, pg. 615
BOODAI AVIATION AGENCIES CO WLL—See City Group Company KSCP; *Int'l*, pg. 1626
BOODAI AVIATION CO. WLL—See City Group Company KSCP; *Int'l*, pg. 1626
BOOFORGE STEEL AB—See Toyota Industries Corporation; *Int'l*, pg. 7868
BOOHOO.COM UK LIMITED—See Boohoo Group Plc; *Int'l*, pg. 1110
BOOHOO GROUP PLC; *Int'l*, pg. 1110

BOOJ, LLC—See RE/MAX Holdings, Inc.; *U.S. Public*, pg. 1768
BOOK4GOLF (PTY) LTD—See Primedia Limited; *Int'l*, pg. 5978
BOOKANDSMILE GMBH—See Heinrich Bauer Verlag KG; *Int'l*, pg. 3324
BOOKATABLE GMBH & CO. KG.—See TripAdvisor, Inc.; *U.S. Public*, pg. 2195
BOOKAZINE COMPANY, INC.; *U.S. Private*, pg. 615
BOOK & CLAIM LTD.—See AAK AB; *Int'l*, pg. 32
BOOK CLUB ASSOCIATES LTD.—See Bertelsmann SE & Co. KGaA; *Int'l*, pg. 992
BOOK COUNTRY LLC—See Pearson plc; *Int'l*, pg. 5777
BOOKCYPRUS.COM—See Francoudi & Stephanou Ltd.; *Int'l*, pg. 2761
THE BOOK DEPOT LIMITED—See The Warehouse Group Limited; *Int'l*, pg. 7699
BOOKE & COMPANY, INC.; *U.S. Private*, pg. 615
BOOKER CASH & CARRY LTD.—See Tesco PLC; *Int'l*, pg. 7571
BOOKER DIRECT LIMITED—See Tesco PLC; *Int'l*, pg. 7571
BOOKER GROUP LIMITED—See Tesco PLC; *Int'l*, pg. 7571
BOOKER INDIA PRIVATE LIMITED—See Trent Limited; *Int'l*, pg. 7916
BOOKER LIMITED—See Tesco PLC; *Int'l*, pg. 7571
BOOKER RETAIL PARTNERS (GB) LIMITED—See Tesco PLC; *Int'l*, pg. 7571
BOOKER SOFTWARE, INC.—See Vista Equity Partners, LLC; *U.S. Private*, pg. 4398
BOOKER TATE LTD.—See Remgro Limited; *Int'l*, pg. 6271
BOOKER TRANSPORTATION SERVICES, INC.; *U.S. Private*, pg. 615
BOOKING.COM BRASIL SERVICOS DE RESERVA DE HOTEIS LTDA—See Booking Holdings, Inc.; *U.S. Public*, pg. 368
BOOKING.COM B.V.—See Booking Holdings, Inc.; *U.S. Public*, pg. 368
BOOKING HOLDINGS, INC.; *U.S. Public*, pg. 368
BOOKIT B.V.—See Cox & Kings Limited; *Int'l*, pg. 1822
BOOKKEEPERS.COM, LLC; *U.S. Private*, pg. 615
BOOKLET CO., LTD.—See Onward Holdings Co., Ltd.; *Int'l*, pg. 5592
BOOK MAKER CO., LTD.—See Bangkok Broadcasting & TV Co., Ltd.; *Int'l*, pg. 833
BOOKMARQUE—See Chevrillon Philippe Industrie; *Int'l*, pg. 1474
BOOK NETWORK INTERNATIONAL LIMITED—See Ingram Industries, Inc.; *U.S. Private*, pg. 2076
BOOKOFF GROUP HOLDINGS LTD.; *Int'l*, pg. 1110
BOOKOFF WITH CO., LTD.—See Bookoff Group Holdings Ltd.; *Int'l*, pg. 1110
BOOK-OF-THE-MONTH CLUB, INC.—See Bertelsmann SE & Co. KGaA; *Int'l*, pg. 992
BOOKOOK SECURITIES CO., LTD.; *Int'l*, pg. 1110
BOOKOOK STEEL CO., LTD.; *Int'l*, pg. 1110
BOOKPAL, L.L.C.; *U.S. Private*, pg. 615
BOOKPOINT LTD—See Vivendi SE; *Int'l*, pg. 8273
BOOKRAGS, INC.; *U.S. Private*, pg. 615
BOOKS24X7.COM, INC.—See Charterhouse Capital Partners LLP; *Int'l*, pg. 1456
BOOKS-A-MILLION, INC.; *U.S. Private*, pg. 615
BOOKS.COM CO., LTD.—See Uni-President Enterprises Corporation; *Int'l*, pg. 8028
THE BOOK SERVICE LIMITED—See Bertelsmann SE & Co. KGaA; *Int'l*, pg. 996
BOOKS INCORPORATED; *U.S. Private*, pg. 615
BOOKS ON TAPE, INC.—See Bertelsmann SE & Co. KGaA; *Int'l*, pg. 991
THE BOOKSOURCE INC.—See GL Group, Inc.; *U.S. Private*, pg. 1704
BOOKSPAN, LLC—See Bertelsmann SE & Co. KGaA; *Int'l*, pg. 992
BOOKSTORE1SARASOTA; *U.S. Private*, pg. 616
BOOKSY INC.; *U.S. Private*, pg. 616
BOOKTOPIA PTY. LTD.; *Int'l*, pg. 1110
BOOKWALKER TAIWAN CO. LTD.—See Kadokawa Corporation; *Int'l*, pg. 4047
BOOKWELL OY—See Sanoma Oyj; *Int'l*, pg. 6553
BOOK WORLD INC.; *U.S. Private*, pg. 615
THE BOOKYARD LIMITED—See Restore plc; *Int'l*, pg. 6304
BOOM BATTLE BAR CARDIFF LIMITED—See XP Factory Plc; *Int'l*, pg. 8537
BOOMBIT S. A.; *Int'l*, pg. 1110
BOOM CYMRU TV LTD.—See ITV plc; *Int'l*, pg. 3844
BOOMERANG COMMERCE, INC.—See Lowe's Companies, Inc.; *U.S. Public*, pg. 1343
BOOMERANG COMMUNICATION—See WPP plc; *Int'l*, pg. 8484
BOOMERANG DIRECT MARKETING, LLC; *U.S. Private*, pg. 616
BOOMERANGER BOATS OY—See International Golden Group PJSC; *Int'l*, pg. 3749
BOOMERANG LABORATORIES, INC.—See Centre Partners Management LLC; *U.S. Private*, pg. 828
BOOMERANG PLUS PLC; *Int'l*, pg. 1110

BOOMERANG-REISEN GMBH—See TUI AG; *Int'l*, pg. 7964
BOOMERANG REISEN - PACIFIC TOURS AG—See TUI AG; *Int'l*, pg. 7964
BOOMERANG SYSTEMS, INC.; *U.S. Private*, pg. 616
BOOMERANG TV SA—See Vivendi SE; *Int'l*, pg. 8271
BOOM EXTREME PUBLISHING LIMITED—See Boomerang Plus plc; *Int'l*, pg. 1110
BOOM FILMS LIMITED—See Boomerang Plus plc; *Int'l*, pg. 1110
BOOM FREESPORTS LIMITED—See Boomerang Plus plc; *Int'l*, pg. 1110
BOOMI, INC.—See Dell Technologies Inc.; *U.S. Public*, pg. 649
BOOMI INTERNATIONAL OY; *Int'l*, pg. 1110
BOOMING GMBH—See Blackwood Seven A/S; *Int'l*, pg. 1062
BOOM LOGISTICS LIMITED; *Int'l*, pg. 1110
BOOM MARKETING INC.—See Stagwell, Inc.; *U.S. Public*, pg. 1926
BOOMM MARKETING & COMMUNICATIONS; *U.S. Private*, pg. 616
BOOM POWER ELECTRONICS (SU ZHOU) CO. LTD.—See Coretronic Corporation; *Int'l*, pg. 1800
BOOMSENSE TECHNOLOGY CO., LTD.; *Int'l*, pg. 1111
BOOMSET, INC.—See Bending Spoons S.p.A.; *Int'l*, pg. 971
BOOM TALENT LIMITED—See Boomerang Plus plc; *Int'l*, pg. 1110
BOOMTOWN, LLC; *U.S. Private*, pg. 616
BOOMTOWN, LLC—See PENN Entertainment, Inc.; *U.S. Public*, pg. 1662
BOOMWORKS PTY. LTD.; *Int'l*, pg. 1111
BOONE BANK AND TRUST CO.—See Ames National Corporation; *U.S. Public*, pg. 115
THE BOONE COUNTY NATIONAL BANK OF COLUMBIA—See Central Bancompany, Inc.; *U.S. Public*, pg. 473
BOON EDAM B.V.; *Int'l*, pg. 1111
BOON EDAM THOMPSON INC—See Boon Edam B.V.; *Int'l*, pg. 1111
BOONE & DARR, INC.; *U.S. Private*, pg. 616
BOONE DELEON COMMUNICATIONS, INC.; *U.S. Private*, pg. 616
BOONE EAST DEVELOPMENT CO.—See Alpha Natural Resources, Inc.; *U.S. Private*, pg. 198
BOONE FORD LINCOLN MERCURY, INC.; *U.S. Private*, pg. 616
BOONE MEMORIAL HOSPITAL; *U.S. Private*, pg. 616
BOONEOAKLEY; *U.S. Private*, pg. 616
BOONE PLUMBING & HEATING SUPPLY INC.—See Groupe Deschenes Inc.; *Int'l*, pg. 3101
BOONE & SONS INC.; *U.S. Private*, pg. 616
BOON, INC.—See Tomy Company, Ltd.; *Int'l*, pg. 7804
BOON KOON FLEET MANAGEMENT SDN BHD—See Chin Hin Group Berhad; *Int'l*, pg. 1480
BOON KOON SERVICES & PARTS SDN BHD—See Chin Hin Group Berhad; *Int'l*, pg. 1480
BOON KOON VEHICLES INDUSTRIES SDN BHD—See Chin Hin Group Berhad; *Int'l*, pg. 1480
BOON RAWD BREWERY CO, LTD—See Asahi Group Holdings Ltd.; *Int'l*, pg. 593
BOON SIEW (BORNEO) SENDIRIAN BERHAD—See Oriental Holdings Berhad; *Int'l*, pg. 5624
BOON SIEW HONDA SDN. BHD.—See Honda Motor Co., Ltd.; *Int'l*, pg. 3460
BOONTON ELECTRONICS CORP.—See Artemis Capital Partners Management Co., LLC; *U.S. Private*, pg. 341
BOOQ SOFTWARE B.V.—See Metro AG; *Int'l*, pg. 4856
BOORT GRAIN COOPERATIVE LTD—See CHS INC.; *U.S. Public*, pg. 491
BOORTMALT N.V.—See Axereal Union de Cooperatives Agricoles; *Int'l*, pg. 767
BOOSE CHEVROLET CO., INC.; *U.S. Private*, pg. 616
BOOSEY & HAWKES BOTE & BOCK GMBH & CO.—See HgCapital Trust plc; *Int'l*, pg. 3376
BOOSEY & HAWKES, INC.—See HgCapital Trust plc; *Int'l*, pg. 3376
BOOSEY & HAWKES LIMITED—See HgCapital Trust plc; *Int'l*, pg. 3376
BOOSEY & HAWKES MUSIC PUBLISHERS LTD.—See HgCapital Trust plc; *Int'l*, pg. 3376
BOOSH PLANT-BASED BRANDS INC.; *Int'l*, pg. 1111
BOOST CONTROLLED PERFORMANCE INC.—See HKS CO., LTD.; *Int'l*, pg. 3429
BOOSTER CO., LTD.; *Int'l*, pg. 1111
BOOSTHEAT SAS; *Int'l*, pg. 1111
BOOST MOBILE, LLC—See EchoStar Corporation; *U.S. Public*, pg. 711
BOOST NUTRITION C.V.—See Ebro Foods S.A.; *Int'l*, pg. 2287
BOOST NUTRITION S.C./C.V.—See Ebro Foods S.A.; *Int'l*, pg. 2286
BOOST PAYMENT SOLUTIONS, INC.; *U.S. Private*, pg. 616
BOOST REWARDS—See Boost Technologies, LLC; *U.S. Private*, pg. 616
BOOST TECHNOLOGIES, LLC; *U.S. Private*, pg. 616
BOOT BARN HOLDINGS, INC.; *U.S. Public*, pg. 368

COMPANY NAME INDEX

BOOT BARN, INC.—See Boot Barn Holdings, Inc.; *U.S. Public*, pg. 368
BOOTCAMP EDUCATION, INC.—See Graham Holdings Company; *U.S. Public*, pg. 955
BOOT CREEK ROYALTY LTD.; *U.S. Private*, pg. 616
BOOTHAM CRESCENT (YORK) RESIDENTS MANAGEMENT COMPANY LIMITED—See Persimmon plc; *Int'l*, pg. 5815
BOOTH & ASSOCIATES LLC—See VINCI S.A.; *Int'l*, pg. 8213
BOOTH CREEK MANAGEMENT CORPORATION; *U.S. Private*, pg. 616
BOOTH CREEK SKI HOLDINGS, INC.—See Booth Creek Management Corporation; *U.S. Private*, pg. 616
BOOTHEEL PETROLEUM COMPANY; *U.S. Private*, pg. 617
BOOTH INDUSTRIES LTD.—See Avingtrans plc; *Int'l*, pg. 743
BOOTH & LADUKE MOTORS, INC.; *U.S. Private*, pg. 616
BOOTH NEWSPAPERS, INC.—See Advance Publications, Inc.; *U.S. Private*, pg. 85
BOOTH NEWSPAPERS—See Advance Publications, Inc.; *U.S. Private*, pg. 85
BOOTH NEWSPAPERS—See Advance Publications, Inc.; *U.S. Private*, pg. 85
BOOTH SECURITIES LTD.; *Int'l*, pg. 1111
BOOTH WALTZ ENTERPRISES, INC.; *U.S. Private*, pg. 617
BOOT RANCH CIRCLE LLC—See Terra Verde Group, LLC; *U.S. Private*, pg. 3970
BOOT RANCH CIRCLE LLC—See Wheelock Street Capital L.L.C.; *U.S. Private*, pg. 4506
BOOTS APOTEK AS—See Walgreens Boots Alliance, Inc.; *U.S. Public*, pg. 2323
BOOTS CHARITABLE TRUST—See Walgreens Boots Alliance, Inc.; *U.S. Public*, pg. 2322
THE BOOTS COMPANY PLC—See Walgreens Boots Alliance, Inc.; *U.S. Public*, pg. 2323
BOOTS HEARINGCARE LIMITED—See Walgreens Boots Alliance, Inc.; *U.S. Public*, pg. 2322
BOOTS NEDERLAND B.V.—See Walgreens Boots Alliance, Inc.; *U.S. Public*, pg. 2322
BOOTS OPTICIANS LTD—See Walgreens Boots Alliance, Inc.; *U.S. Public*, pg. 2323
BOOTS OPTICIANS PROFESSIONAL SERVICES LIMITED—See Walgreens Boots Alliance, Inc.; *U.S. Public*, pg. 2322
BOOTS RETAIL (IRELAND) LIMITED—See Walgreens Boots Alliance, Inc.; *U.S. Public*, pg. 2322
BOOTS RETAIL USA INC.—See Walgreens Boots Alliance, Inc.; *U.S. Public*, pg. 2322
BOOTS SMITH OILFIELD SERVICES, LLC; *U.S. Private*, pg. 617
BOOTSTRAP SOFTWARE PARTNERS, LLC; *U.S. Private*, pg. 617
BOOTS UK LIMITED—See Walgreens Boots Alliance, Inc.; *U.S. Public*, pg. 2323
BOOTT HYDROPOWER INC—See Enel S.p.A.; *Int'l*, pg. 2411
BOOTZ MANUFACTURING COMPANY; *U.S. Private*, pg. 617
THE BOOYAH AGENCY—See Booyah Networks, Inc.; *U.S. Private*, pg. 617
BOOYAH NETWORKS, INC.; *U.S. Private*, pg. 617
BOOZ ALLEN HAMILTON HOLDING CORPORATION; *U.S. Public*, pg. 368
BOOZ ALLEN HAMILTON INC.—See Booz Allen Hamilton Holding Corporation; *U.S. Public*, pg. 369
BOOZT AB; *Int'l*, pg. 1111
BOOZT BALTICS UAB—See Boozt AB; *Int'l*, pg. 1111
BOOZT FASHION AB—See Boozt AB; *Int'l*, pg. 1111
BOOZT TECHNOLOGY BALTICS UAB—See Boozt AB; *Int'l*, pg. 1111
BOP 1801 CALIFORNIA STREET LLC—See Brookfield Corporation; *Int'l*, pg. 1186
BOP 650 MASS LLC—See Brookfield Corporation; *Int'l*, pg. 1186
BOPARAN HOLDINGS LIMITED; *Int'l*, pg. 1111
BOPLA GEHAUSE SYSTEME GMBH—See Phoenix Mecano AG; *Int'l*, pg. 5852
BOPP DEL ECUADOR S.A.—See Oben Holding Group SAC; *Int'l*, pg. 5510
BOPP & REUTHER VALVES GMBH—See IMI plc; *Int'l*, pg. 3624
B.O.P. PRODUCTS, LLC.; *U.S. Private*, pg. 421
THE BOPPY COMPANY, LLC.—See BI-Invest Advisors S.A.; *Int'l*, pg. 1017
BOQ EQUIPMENT FINANCE LIMITED—See Bank of Queensland Limited; *Int'l*, pg. 848
BOQ FINANCE (AUST) LIMITED—See Bank of Queensland Limited; *Int'l*, pg. 848
BOQII HOLDING LIMITED; *Int'l*, pg. 1112
BORA BORA INC.; *U.S. Private*, pg. 617
BORA BORA RESOURCES LIMITED; *Int'l*, pg. 1112
BORAC A.D.; *Int'l*, pg. 1112
BORAC EXPORT-IMPORT D.D.; *Int'l*, pg. 1112
BORAC H & H A.D.; *Int'l*, pg. 1112
BORA CORPORATION; *Int'l*, pg. 1112
BORA KECIC ATP A.D.; *Int'l*, pg. 1112

BORAL BRICKS PTY. LTD.—See Seven Group Holdings Limited; *Int'l*, pg. 6732
BORAL BUILDING MATERIALS PTY LTD—See Seven Group Holdings Limited; *Int'l*, pg. 6732
BORAL BUILDING PRODUCTS INC.—See Seven Group Holdings Limited; *Int'l*, pg. 6733
BORAL BUILDING PRODUCTS LTD—See Seven Group Holdings Limited; *Int'l*, pg. 6732
BORAL CONCRETE PRODUCTS PTY. LTD.—See Seven Group Holdings Limited; *Int'l*, pg. 6732
BORAL CONCRETE (THAILAND) LTD—See Seven Group Holdings Limited; *Int'l*, pg. 6732
BORAL CONSTRUCTION MATERIALS LLC—See Brannan Sand & Gravel Co. LLC; *U.S. Private*, pg. 639
BORAL CONSTRUCTION MATERIALS LTD—See Seven Group Holdings Limited; *Int'l*, pg. 6732
BORAL CONTRACTING PTY LTD—See Seven Group Holdings Limited; *Int'l*, pg. 6732
BORALEX INC.; *Int'l*, pg. 1112
BORALEX POWER INC.—See Boralex Inc.; *Int'l*, pg. 1112
BORALEX S.A.S.—See Boralex Inc.; *Int'l*, pg. 1112
BORAL INDUSTRIES INC.—See Seven Group Holdings Limited; *Int'l*, pg. 6732
BORAL INTERNATIONAL PTY LTD—See Seven Group Holdings Limited; *Int'l*, pg. 6732
BORAL INVESTMENTS PTY LTD—See Seven Group Holdings Limited; *Int'l*, pg. 6732
BORAL INVESTMENTS—See Seven Group Holdings Limited; *Int'l*, pg. 6732
BORAL LIFETILE INC.—See Seven Group Holdings Limited; *Int'l*, pg. 6732
BORAL LIMITED—See Seven Group Holdings Limited; *Int'l*, pg. 6732
BORAL MASONRY LTD—See Seven Group Holdings Limited; *Int'l*, pg. 6732
BORAL MATERIALS LLC—See Seven Group Holdings Limited; *Int'l*, pg. 6733
BORAL RECYCLING PTY LTD—See Seven Group Holdings Limited; *Int'l*, pg. 6732
BORAL RESOURCES LTD.—See Seven Group Holdings Limited; *Int'l*, pg. 6732
BORAL RESOURCES (QLD) PTY LTD—See Seven Group Holdings Limited; *Int'l*, pg. 6732
BORAL RESOURCES (SA) LTD—See Seven Group Holdings Limited; *Int'l*, pg. 6732
BORAL RESOURCES (VIC) PTY LTD—See Seven Group Holdings Limited; *Int'l*, pg. 6732
BORAL ROOFING LLC—See Seven Group Holdings Limited; *Int'l*, pg. 6732
BORAL SHARED BUSINESS SERVICES PTY LTD—See Seven Group Holdings Limited; *Int'l*, pg. 6732
BORAL TIMBER INC—See Seven Group Holdings Limited; *Int'l*, pg. 6732
BORAL WINDOWS SYSTEMS LTD—See Seven Group Holdings Limited; *Int'l*, pg. 6732
BORAN CRAIG BARBER ENGEL CONSTRUCTION CO., INC.; *U.S. Private*, pg. 617
BORAN MESRUBAT SANAYI VE TICARET A.S.—See Derluks Yatirim Holding A.S; *Int'l*, pg. 2042
BORA PHARMACEUTICALS CO., LTD.; *Int'l*, pg. 1112
BORAS ELHANDEL AB—See Vattenfall AB; *Int'l*, pg. 8136
BORA TIAL CO., LTD.; *Int'l*, pg. 1112
BORATT AB—See JM AB; *Int'l*, pg. 3974
BORAX ARGENTINA S.A.; *Int'l*, pg. 1112
BORAX ESPANA S.A.—See Rio Tinto plc; *Int'l*, pg. 6348
BORAX FRANCAIS S.A.—See Rio Tinto plc; *Int'l*, pg. 6348
BORAX MORARJI (EUROPE) GMBH—See Borax Morarji Limited; *Int'l*, pg. 1112
BORAX MORARJI LIMITED; *Int'l*, pg. 1112
BORAX PAPER PRODUCTS—See Bain Capital, LP; *U.S. Private*, pg. 440
BORAX SOUTH AMERICA—See Rio Tinto plc; *Int'l*, pg. 6348
BORBET ALABAMA INC.—See BORBET GmbH; *Int'l*, pg. 1112
BORBET AUSTRIA GMBH—See BORBET GmbH; *Int'l*, pg. 1112
BORBET GMBH; *Int'l*, pg. 1112
BORBET SACHSEN GMBH—See BORBET GmbH; *Int'l*, pg. 1112
BORBET SOLINGEN GMBH—See BORBET GmbH; *Int'l*, pg. 1112
BORBET SOUTH AFRICA (PTY) LTD.—See BORBET GmbH; *Int'l*, pg. 1112
BORBET THURINGEN GMBH—See BORBET GmbH; *Int'l*, pg. 1112
BORBET VERTRIEBS GMBH—See BORBET GmbH; *Int'l*, pg. 1112
BORBONESE SPA; *Int'l*, pg. 1112
BORCHERDING BUICK GMC, INC.; *U.S. Private*, pg. 617
BORCHERDT CONCRETE PRODUCTS LIMITED—See OSCO Construction Group; *Int'l*, pg. 5648
BORCHERS SAS—See The Jordan Company, L.P.; *U.S. Private*, pg. 4060
BORCH TEXTILE GROUP A/S; *Int'l*, pg. 1113
BORDEAUX DEVELOPMENTS CORPORATION; *Int'l*, pg. 1113
BORDEAUX INDEX (HONG KONG) LTD.—See Bordeaux Index Ltd.; *Int'l*, pg. 1113

BORDEAUX INDEX LTD.; *Int'l*, pg. 1113
BORDEAUX INDEX (SINGAPORE) LTD.—See Bordeaux Index Ltd.; *Int'l*, pg. 1113
BORDEAUX INDEX US INC.—See Bordeaux Index Ltd.; *Int'l*, pg. 1113
THE BORDEN AGENCY; *U.S. Private*, pg. 3996
BORDEN DAIRY COMPANY OF FLORIDA—See Capitol Peak Partners, LLC; *U.S. Public*, pg. 744
BORDEN DAIRY COMPANY OF FLORIDA—See KKR & Co. Inc.; *U.S. Public*, pg. 1241
BORDEN DAIRY COMPANY—See Capitol Peak Partners, LLC; *U.S. Private*, pg. 744
BORDEN DAIRY COMPANY—See KKR & Co. Inc.; *U.S. Public*, pg. 1241
BORDEN MILK PRODUCTS—See Capitol Peak Partners, LLC; *U.S. Private*, pg. 744
BORDEN MILK PRODUCTS—See KKR & Co. Inc.; *U.S. Public*, pg. 1242
THE BORDEN-PERLMAN INSURANCE AGENCY, INC.; *U.S. Private*, pg. 3996
BORDEN PERLMAN INSURANCE AGENCY, INC.—See CBIZ, Inc.; *U.S. Public*, pg. 456
BORDER CHEMICAL CO., LTD.; *Int'l*, pg. 1113
BORDER CONSTRUCTION SPECIALTIES, LLC—See The Sterling Group, L.P.; *U.S. Private*, pg. 4122
THE BORDER COURT INC.—See The Schafer Company Inc.; *U.S. Private*, pg. 4114
BORDER FOODS, INC.; *U.S. Private*, pg. 617
BORDERFREE, INC.—See Global-E Online Ltd.; *Int'l*, pg. 3003
BORDERFREE LIMITED—See Pitney Bowes Inc.; *U.S. Public*, pg. 1694
BORDER GRILL; *U.S. Private*, pg. 617
BORDERGURU GMBH—See Otto GmbH & Co. KG; *Int'l*, pg. 5662
BORDER INSURANCE SERVICES, INC.—See Marsh & McLennan Companies, Inc.; *U.S. Public*, pg. 1380
BORDER INTERNATIONAL; *U.S. Private*, pg. 617
BORDER INTERNATIONAL TRUCKS; *U.S. Private*, pg. 617
BORDERLAND INVESTMENTS LIMITED—See MetLife, Inc.; *U.S. Public*, pg. 1430
BORDERLESS HOLDINGS, INC.; *U.S. Private*, pg. 618
BORDERLINK, INC.—See Will Group, Inc.; *Int'l*, pg. 8412
BORDER MAIL PRINTING PTY LTD—See Rural Press Pty Limited; *Int'l*, pg. 6429
THE BORDER MORNING MAIL PTY LTD—See Nine Entertainment Co. Holdings Limited; *Int'l*, pg. 5299
BORDER PETROLEUM LIMITED; *Int'l*, pg. 1113
BORDERPLEX REALTY LLC; *U.S. Private*, pg. 618
BORDER PROPERTIES, INC.—See PepsiCo, Inc.; *U.S. Public*, pg. 1668
BORDERS PERRIN NORRANDER INC.; *U.S. Private*, pg. 618
BORDERS & SOUTHERN PETROLEUM PLC; *Int'l*, pg. 1113
BORDER STATES COOPERATIVES—See CHS INC.; *U.S. Public*, pg. 491
BORDER STATES ELECTRIC SUPPLY LLC—See Border States Industries, Inc.; *U.S. Private*, pg. 617
BORDER STATES INDUSTRIES, INC.; *U.S. Private*, pg. 617
BORDER STATES INDUSTRIES, INC.—See Border States Industries, Inc.; *U.S. Private*, pg. 617
BORDER STATES INDUSTRIES, INC. - UTILICOR DIVISION—See Border States Industries, Inc.; *U.S. Private*, pg. 617
BORDER STATES PAVING, INC.; *U.S. Private*, pg. 618
BORDER TIMBERS LIMITED; *Int'l*, pg. 1113
BORDER VALLEY TRADING LTD; *U.S. Private*, pg. 618
BORDEX PACKAGING B.V.; *Int'l*, pg. 1113
BORD GAIS ENERGY LIMITED—See Centrica plc; *Int'l*, pg. 1413
BORDIER'S NURSERY INC; *U.S. Private*, pg. 618
BORD NA MONA ENERGY TECH/ADMIN—See Bord na Mona Plc; *Int'l*, pg. 1113
BORD NA MONA ENVIRONMENTAL LIMITED—See Bord na Mona Plc; *Int'l*, pg. 1113
BORD NA MONA FUELS LIMITED—See Bord na Mona Plc; *Int'l*, pg. 1113
BORD NA MONA HORTICULTURE LIMITED—See Bord na Mona Plc; *Int'l*, pg. 1113
BORD NA MONA PLC; *Int'l*, pg. 1113
BORDO ELK. ENERJISI TOPTAN SATIS A.S.—See Parsan Makina Parcalari Sanayii AS; *Int'l*, pg. 5747
BORDO ENERJI A.S.—See Parsan Makina Parcalari Sanayii AS; *Int'l*, pg. 5747
BORDON HILL NURSERIES LTD.—See Ball Horticultural Company; *U.S. Private*, pg. 460
BORDURE LIMITED—See Camellia Plc; *Int'l*, pg. 1271
BOREA ASSET MANAGEMENT AS—See Borea AS; *Int'l*, pg. 1113
BOREA AS; *Int'l*, pg. 1113
BOREA CONSTRUCTION ULC—See Pomerleau Inc.; *Int'l*, pg. 5917
BOREAL INTERNATIONAL CORPORATION—See Watsco, Inc.; *U.S. Public*, pg. 2336
BOREALIS AB—See OMV Aktiengesellschaft; *Int'l*, pg. 5568

BOREALIS AG MOSCOW—See OMV Aktiengesellschaft; *Int'l*, pg. 5568
BOREALIS AGROLINZ MELAMINE DEUTSCHLAND GMBH—See OMV Aktiengesellschaft; *Int'l*, pg. 5568
BOREALIS AGROLINZ MELAMINE GMBH—See OMV Aktiengesellschaft; *Int'l*, pg. 5568
BOREALIS AG—See OMV Aktiengesellschaft; *Int'l*, pg. 5568
BOREALIS ANTWERPEN COMPOUNDING N.V.—See OMV Aktiengesellschaft; *Int'l*, pg. 5569
BOREALIS A/S—See OMV Aktiengesellschaft; *Int'l*, pg. 5568
BOREALIS BRASIL S.A.—See OMV Aktiengesellschaft; *Int'l*, pg. 5568
BOREALIS CHILE SPA—See OMV Aktiengesellschaft; *Int'l*, pg. 5567
BOREALIS CHIMIE S.A.S. - GRANDPUITS PLANT—See OMV Aktiengesellschaft; *Int'l*, pg. 5569
BOREALIS CHIMIE S.A.S. - GRAND-QUEVILLY PLANT—See OMV Aktiengesellschaft; *Int'l*, pg. 5569
BOREALIS CHIMIE S.A.S.—See OMV Aktiengesellschaft; *Int'l*, pg. 5569
BOREALIS COLOMBIA S.A.S.—See OMV Aktiengesellschaft; *Int'l*, pg. 5567
BOREALIS COMPOUNDS INC.—See OMV Aktiengesellschaft; *Int'l*, pg. 5569
BOREALIS EXPLORATION LIMITED; *Int'l*, pg. 1113
BOREALIS FINANCIAL SERVICES N.V.—See OMV Aktiengesellschaft; *Int'l*, pg. 5569
BOREALIS FOODS INC.; *Int'l*, pg. 1114
BOREALIS FRANCE S.A.S.—See OMV Aktiengesellschaft; *Int'l*, pg. 5568
BOREALIS GROUP SERVICES AS—See OMV Aktiengesellschaft; *Int'l*, pg. 5568
BOREALIS ITALIA S.P.A.—See OMV Aktiengesellschaft; *Int'l*, pg. 5569
BOREALIS KALLO N.V.—See OMV Aktiengesellschaft; *Int'l*, pg. 5569
BOREALIS L.A.T BEOGRAD D.O.O.—See OMV Aktiengesellschaft; *Int'l*, pg. 5569
BOREALIS L.A.T BULGARIA EOOD—See OMV Aktiengesellschaft; *Int'l*, pg. 5569
BOREALIS L.A.T CZECH REPUBLIC SPOL. S.R.O.—See OMV Aktiengesellschaft; *Int'l*, pg. 5569
BOREALIS L.A.T D.O.O. ZA TRGOVINU—See OMV Aktiengesellschaft; *Int'l*, pg. 5569
BOREALIS L.A.T FRANCE S.A.S.—See OMV Aktiengesellschaft; *Int'l*, pg. 5567
BOREALIS L.A.T HRVATSKA D.O.O.—See OMV Aktiengesellschaft; *Int'l*, pg. 5567
BOREALIS L.A.T HUNGARY KFT.—See OMV Aktiengesellschaft; *Int'l*, pg. 5569
BOREALIS L.A.T ITALIA S.R.L.—See OMV Aktiengesellschaft; *Int'l*, pg. 5567
BOREALIS L.A.T POLSKA SP. Z O.O.—See OMV Aktiengesellschaft; *Int'l*, pg. 5567
BOREALIS L.A.T ROMANIA S.R.L.—See OMV Aktiengesellschaft; *Int'l*, pg. 5569
BOREALIS L.A.T SLOVAKIA S.R.O.—See OMV Aktiengesellschaft; *Int'l*, pg. 5569
BOREALIS L.A.T. SOBELAGRO S.A.S.—See OMV Aktiengesellschaft; *Int'l*, pg. 5569
BOREALIS PEC-RHIN SAS—See OMV Aktiengesellschaft; *Int'l*, pg. 5569
BOREALIS PLASTICOS S.A. DE C.V.—See OMV Aktiengesellschaft; *Int'l*, pg. 5569
BOREALIS PLASTIK VE KIMYASAL MADDELER TICARET LIMITED SIRKETI—See OMV Aktiengesellschaft; *Int'l*, pg. 5569
BOREALIS PLASTOMERS B.V.—See OMV Aktiengesellschaft; *Int'l*, pg. 5569
BOREALIS POLSKA SP Z O.O.—See OMV Aktiengesellschaft; *Int'l*, pg. 5569
BOREALIS POLYMERE GMBH—See OMV Aktiengesellschaft; *Int'l*, pg. 5569
BOREALIS POLYMERS N.V.—See OMV Aktiengesellschaft; *Int'l*, pg. 5569
BOREALIS POLYMERS OY—See OMV Aktiengesellschaft; *Int'l*, pg. 5569
BOREALIS POLYOLEFINE GMBH—See OMV Aktiengesellschaft; *Int'l*, pg. 5569
BOREALIS PRODUITS ET RESINES CHIMIQUES DU RHIN S.A.S.—See OMV Aktiengesellschaft; *Int'l*, pg. 5567
BOREALMAGIC UNIPESSOAL, LDA.—See BERICAP GmbH & Co. KG; *Int'l*, pg. 981
BOREAL NORGE AS—See Caisse des Depots et Consignations; *Int'l*, pg. 1259
BOREAL RIDGE CORP—See Powdr Corp.; *U.S. Private*, pg. 3236
BOREAL S.R.L.—See Viva! Group; *Int'l*, pg. 8265
BOREA OPPORTUNITY MANAGEMENT AS—See Borea AS; *Int'l*, pg. 1113
BOREHAMWOOD VETS4PETS LIMITED—See Pets at Home Group Plc; *Int'l*, pg. 5833
BOREINVEST AB—See Bore Tech AB; *Int'l*, pg. 1113
BOREK CONSTRUCTION, LTD.; *Int'l*, pg. 1114
BORELLI TEA HOLDINGS LIMITED—See McLeod Russel India Limited; *Int'l*, pg. 4759

BORE LTD.—See Spliethoff's Bevrachtingskantoor B.V.; *Int'l*, pg. 7141
BORE-MAX CORP.—See Golden Gate Capital Management II, LLC; *U.S. Private*, pg. 1732
BORENSTEIN CATERERS, INC.—See El Al Airlines Ltd.; *Int'l*, pg. 2340
THE BORENSTEIN GROUP, INC.; *U.S. Private*, pg. 3996
BOREO OYJ—See Preato Capital AB; *Int'l*, pg. 5955
BORE TECH AB; *Int'l*, pg. 1113
BORE TECH UTILITIES & MAINTENANCE INC.; *U.S. Private*, pg. 618
BORETS INTERNATIONAL LTD.—See Tangent Fund Management LLC; *U.S. Private*, pg. 3930
BORETS-WEATHERFORD DO BRASIL LTDA.—See Tangent Fund Management LLC; *U.S. Private*, pg. 3930
BOREUS GMBH—See WIIT SpA; *Int'l*, pg. 8408
B-ORGANIZED INSULATION, LLC—See Installed Building Products, Inc.; *U.S. Public*, pg. 1132
BORGATA HOTEL CASINO & SPA, LLC—See MGM Resorts International; *U.S. Public*, pg. 1435
BORG AUTOMOTIVE A/S—See Aktieselskabet Schouw & Co.; *Int'l*, pg. 265
BORG AUTOMOTIVE REMAN SPAIN S.L.U.—See Aktieselskabet Schouw & Co.; *Int'l*, pg. 265
BORG AUTOMOTIVE SPAIN S.L.U.—See Aktieselskabet Schouw & Co.; *Int'l*, pg. 265
BORG AUTOMOTIVE SP.Z.O.O.—See Aktieselskabet Schouw & Co.; *Int'l*, pg. 265
BORG AUTOMOTIVE UK LTD.—See Aktieselskabet Schouw & Co.; *Int'l*, pg. 265
BORG COMPRESSED STEELE; *U.S. Private*, pg. 618
BORGERS SE & CO. KGAA—See Autoneum Holding Ltd.; *Int'l*, pg. 731
BORGES AGRICULTURAL & INDUSTRIAL NUTS S.A.; *Int'l*, pg. 1114
BORGES OF CALIFORNIA, INC.—See Borges Agricultural & Industrial Nuts S.A.; *Int'l*, pg. 1114
BORGESS HEALTH ALLIANCE, INC.—See Ascension Health Alliance; *U.S. Private*, pg. 346
BORGESS MEDICAL CENTER—See Ascension Health Alliance; *U.S. Private*, pg. 346
BORGESTAD ASA; *Int'l*, pg. 1114
BORGESTAD POLAND SP.Z.O.O—See Borgestad ASA; *Int'l*, pg. 1114
BORGHESE, INC.; *U.S. Private*, pg. 618
BORGHESI BUILDING & ENGINEERING CO., INC.; *U.S. Private*, pg. 618
BORG INDAK INC.; *U.S. Private*, pg. 618
BORGMAN CAPITAL LLC; *U.S. Private*, pg. 618
BORGMAN FORD MAZDA; *U.S. Private*, pg. 618
BORG MANUFACTURING PTY LTD.; *Int'l*, pg. 1114
BORGO 21 SA—See Giorgio Armani S.p.A.; *Int'l*, pg. 2978
BORGO 21 S.P.A.—See Giorgio Armani S.p.A.; *Int'l*, pg. 2978
BORGOSESIA S.P.A; *Int'l*, pg. 1114
BORGSTENA TEXTILE PORTUGAL, LDA—See Seiren Co., Ltd.; *Int'l*, pg. 6691
BORGUN HF; *Int'l*, pg. 1114
BORGWALDT FLAVOR GMBH—See Korber AG; *Int'l*, pg. 4280
BORGWALDT KC GMBH—See Korber AG; *Int'l*, pg. 4280
BORGWALDT KC, INC.—See Korber AG; *Int'l*, pg. 4280
BORGWARNER AFTERMARKET EUROPE GMBH—See BorgWarner Inc.; *U.S. Public*, pg. 369
BORGWARNER ARDEN LLC—See BorgWarner Inc.; *U.S. Public*, pg. 369
BORGWARNER AUTOMOTIVE COMPONENTS (NINGBO) CO., LTD.—See BorgWarner Inc.; *U.S. Public*, pg. 369
BORGWARNER AUTOMOTIVE SYSTEMS SINGAPORE INVESTMENTS PTE. LTD.—See Aptiv PLC; *U.S. Public*, pg. 524
BORG-WARNER AUTOMOTIVE TAIWAN CO., LTD.—See Enstar Group Limited; *Int'l*, pg. 2448
BORGWARNER BERU SYSTEMS GMBH—See BorgWarner Inc.; *U.S. Public*, pg. 369
BORGWARNER BERU SYSTEMS KANDEL GMBH—See BorgWarner Inc.; *U.S. Public*, pg. 369
BORGWARNER BRASIL, LTDA.—See BorgWarner Inc.; *U.S. Public*, pg. 369
BORGWARNER CANADA INC.—See BorgWarner Inc.; *U.S. Public*, pg. 369
BORGWARNER CHUNGJU LTD.—See BorgWarner Inc.; *U.S. Public*, pg. 369
BORGWARNER COOLING SYSTEMS GMBH—See BorgWarner Inc.; *U.S. Public*, pg. 370
BORGWARNER COOLING SYSTEMS (INDIA) PRIVATE LIMITED—See BorgWarner Inc.; *U.S. Public*, pg. 370
BORGWARNER COOLING SYSTEMS KOREA, INC.—See BorgWarner Inc.; *U.S. Public*, pg. 370
BORGWARNER DRIVETRAIN DE MEXICO S.A. DE C.V.—See BorgWarner Inc.; *U.S. Public*, pg. 370
BORGWARNER DRIVETRAIN ENGINEERING GMBH—See BorgWarner Inc.; *U.S. Public*, pg. 370
BORGWARNER DRIVETRAIN MANAGEMENT SERVICES DE MEXICO S.A. DE C.V.—See BorgWarner Inc.; *U.S. Public*, pg. 369
BORGWARNER EMISSIONS SYSTEMS LTDA.—See BorgWarner Inc.; *U.S. Public*, pg. 369

BORGWARNER EMISSIONS SYSTEMS OF MICHIGAN INC.—See BorgWarner Inc.; *U.S. Public*, pg. 369
BORGWARNER EMISSIONS SYSTEMS PORTUGAL UNIPESSOAL LDA.—See BorgWarner Inc.; *U.S. Public*, pg. 369
BORGWARNER EMISSIONS SYSTEMS SPAIN S.L.—See BorgWarner Inc.; *U.S. Public*, pg. 369
BORGWARNER EMISSIONS TALEGAON PRIVATE LIMITED—See BorgWarner Inc.; *U.S. Public*, pg. 369
BORGWARNER EMOBILITY POLAND SP. Z O.O.—See BorgWarner Inc.; *U.S. Public*, pg. 369
BORGWARNER ENGINEERING SERVICES SWITZERLAND AG—See BorgWarner Inc.; *U.S. Public*, pg. 369
BORGWARNER ESSLINGEN GMBH—See BorgWarner Inc.; *U.S. Public*, pg. 369
BORGWARNER EUROPE GMBH—See BorgWarner Inc.; *U.S. Public*, pg. 369
BORGWARNER FRANCE S.A.S.—See BorgWarner Inc.; *U.S. Public*, pg. 369
BORGWARNER GATESHEAD LIMITED—See BorgWarner Inc.; *U.S. Public*, pg. 369
BORGWARNER GERMANY GMBH—See BorgWarner Inc.; *U.S. Public*, pg. 369
BORGWARNER HEIDELBERG II RE GMBH & CO. KG—See BorgWarner Inc.; *U.S. Public*, pg. 369
BORGWARNER HOLDINGS LIMITED—See BorgWarner Inc.; *U.S. Public*, pg. 371
BORGWARNER INC.; *U.S. Public*, pg. 369
BORGWARNER IT SERVICES EUROPE GMBH—See BorgWarner Inc.; *U.S. Public*, pg. 369
BORGWARNER IT SERVICES GROUP GMBH—See BorgWarner Inc.; *U.S. Public*, pg. 369
BORGWARNER KFT.—See BorgWarner Inc.; *U.S. Public*, pg. 369
BORGWARNER LIMITED—See BorgWarner Inc.; *U.S. Public*, pg. 371
BORGWARNER LUDWIGSBURG GMBH—See BorgWarner Inc.; *U.S. Public*, pg. 369
BORGWARNER MASSACHUSETTS INC.—See BorgWarner Inc.; *U.S. Public*, pg. 369
BORGWARNER MORSE SYSTEMS INDIA PRIVATE LIMITED—See BorgWarner Inc.; *U.S. Public*, pg. 370
BORGWARNER MORSE SYSTEMS ITALY S.R.L.—See BorgWarner Inc.; *U.S. Public*, pg. 370
BORGWARNER MORSE SYSTEMS JAPAN K.K.—See BorgWarner Inc.; *U.S. Public*, pg. 370
BORGWARNER MORSE TEC JAPAN K.K.—See Enstar Group Limited; *Int'l*, pg. 2448
BORGWARNER MORSE TEC KOREA LTD.—See Enstar Group Limited; *Int'l*, pg. 2448
BORGWARNER MORSE TEC, LLC—See Enstar Group Limited; *Int'l*, pg. 2448
BORGWARNER MORSE TEC MEXICO, S.A. DE C.V.—See Enstar Group Limited; *Int'l*, pg. 2448
BORGWARNER NEW ENERGY (XIANGYANG) CO., LTD.—See BorgWarner Inc.; *U.S. Public*, pg. 370
BORGWARNER NOBLESVILLE LLC—See BorgWarner Inc.; *U.S. Public*, pg. 370
BORGWARNER OCHANG INC.—See BorgWarner Inc.; *U.S. Public*, pg. 370
BORGWARNER OROSZLANY KFT.—See BorgWarner Inc.; *U.S. Public*, pg. 370
BORGWARNER PDS BEIJING CO. LTD.—See BorgWarner Inc.; *U.S. Public*, pg. 370
BORGWARNER PDS BRASIL PRODUTOS AUTOMOTIVOS LTDA.—See BorgWarner Inc.; *U.S. Public*, pg. 370
BORGWARNER PDS (CHANGNYEONG) INC.—See BorgWarner Inc.; *U.S. Public*, pg. 370
BORGWARNER PDS (OCHANG) INC.—See BorgWarner Inc.; *U.S. Public*, pg. 370
BORGWARNER PDS TECHNOLOGIES, L.L.C.—See BorgWarner Inc.; *U.S. Public*, pg. 370
BORGWARNER PDS (USA) INC.—See BorgWarner Inc.; *U.S. Public*, pg. 370
BORGWARNER POWDERED METALS INC.—See BorgWarner Inc.; *U.S. Public*, pg. 370
BORGWARNER PYONGTAEK LLC—See BorgWarner Inc.; *U.S. Public*, pg. 370
BORGWARNER REYNOSA S DE R.L. DE C.V.L—See BorgWarner Inc.; *U.S. Public*, pg. 370
BORGWARNER SALTILLO S. DE R.L. DE C.V.—See BorgWarner Inc.; *U.S. Public*, pg. 370
BORGWARNER SHENGLONG (NINGBO) CO. LTD.—See BorgWarner Inc,; *U.S. Public*, pg. 370
BORGWARNER SLP S. DE R.L. DE C.V.—See BorgWarner Inc.; *U.S. Public*, pg. 370
BORGWARNER SOUTHBOROUGH INC.—See BorgWarner Inc.; *U.S. Public*, pg. 370
BORGWARNER STUTTGART GMBH—See BorgWarner Inc.; *U.S. Public*, pg. 370
BORGWARNER SWEDEN AB—See BorgWarner Inc.; *U.S. Public*, pg. 370
BORGWARNER SYSTEMS LUGO S.R.L.—See BorgWarner Inc.; *U.S. Public*, pg. 370
BORGWARNER (THAILAND) LIMITED—See BorgWarner Inc.; *U.S. Public*, pg. 369
BORGWARNER THERMAL SYSTEMS INC.—See BorgWarner Inc.; *U.S. Public*, pg. 370

COMPANY NAME INDEX

BORGWARNER TORQTRANSFER SYSTEMS AB—See BorgWarner Inc.; *U.S. Public*, pg. 370
BORGWARNER TRALEE LTD.—See BorgWarner Inc.; *U.S. Public*, pg. 370
BORGWARNER TRANSMISSION SYSTEMS ARNSTADT GMBH—See BorgWarner Inc.; *U.S. Public*, pg. 370
BORGWARNER TRANSMISSION SYSTEMS GMBH—See BorgWarner Inc.; *U.S. Public*, pg. 370
BORGWARNER TRANSMISSION SYSTEMS INC.—See BorgWarner Inc.; *U.S. Public*, pg. 370
BORGWARNER TRANSMISSION SYSTEMS KOREA LTD.—See BorgWarner Inc.; *U.S. Public*, pg. 370
BORGWARNER TRANSMISSION SYSTEMS MONACO S.A.M.—See BorgWarner Inc.; *U.S. Public*, pg. 370
BORGWARNER TRANSMISSION SYSTEMS TULLE S.A.S.—See BorgWarner Inc.; *U.S. Public*, pg. 371
BORGWARNER TTS, S. DE R.L. DE C.V.—See BorgWarner Inc.; *U.S. Public*, pg. 370
BORGWARNER TURBO & EMISSIONS SYSTEMS FRANCE S.A.S.—See BorgWarner Inc.; *U.S. Public*, pg. 371
BORGWARNER TURBO SYSTEMS ALKATRESZGYARTO KFT.—See BorgWarner Inc.; *U.S. Public*, pg. 371
BORGWARNER TURBO SYSTEMS ENGINEERING GMBH—See BorgWarner Inc.; *U.S. Public*, pg. 371
BORGWARNER TURBO SYSTEMS GMBH—See BorgWarner Inc.; *U.S. Public*, pg. 371
BORGWARNER TURBO SYSTEMS INC.—See BorgWarner Inc.; *U.S. Public*, pg. 371
BORGWARNER TURBO SYSTEMS POLAND SP.Z.O.O—See BorgWarner Inc.; *U.S. Public*, pg. 371
BORGWARNER TURBO SYSTEMS WORLDWIDE HEADQUARTERS GMBH—See BorgWarner Inc.; *U.S. Public*, pg. 371
BORGWARNER VERTRIEBS UND VERWALTUNGS GMBH—See BorgWarner Inc.; *U.S. Public*, pg. 370
BORGWARNER WREXHAM LIMITED—See BorgWarner Inc.; *U.S. Public*, pg. 371
BORIANA JSC—See Stara Planina Hold Plc; *Int'l*, pg. 7175
BORICI A.D.; *Int'l*, pg. 1114
BORID ENERGY (M) SDN BHD—See Hup Soon Global Corporation Limited; *Int'l*, pg. 3538
BORING BUSINESS SYSTEMS, INC., *U.S. Private*, pg. 618
BORING & TUNNELING CO. OF AMERICA; *U.S. Private*, pg. 618
BORINQUEN CONTAINER CORP.; *U.S. Private*, pg. 618
BORINQUEN FIBER DRUMS—See Borinquen Container Corp.; *U.S. Private*, pg. 618
BORIS FX, INC.; *U.S. Private*, pg. 618
BORISOFF INSURANCE SERVICES, INC.—See Hellman & Friedman LLC; *U.S. Private*, pg. 1909
BORISOV PLASTIC PRODUCTS PLANT OPEN JOINT-STOCK COMPANY—See Concern Belneftekhim; *Int'l*, pg. 1764
BORKHOLDER CORPORATION; *U.S. Private*, pg. 618
BORLAND AUSTRALIA PTY LTD.—See Micro Focus International plc; *Int'l*, pg. 4876
BORLAND BENEFIELD, P.C.; *U.S. Private*, pg. 618
BORLAND CANADA, INC.—See Micro Focus International plc; *Int'l*, pg. 4876
BORLAND GMBH—See Micro Focus International plc; *Int'l*, pg. 4876
BORLAND (SINGAPORE) PTE. LTD.—See Micro Focus International plc; *Int'l*, pg. 4876
BORLAND SOFTWARE CORPORATION—See Micro Focus International plc; *Int'l*, pg. 4876
BORLANGE HANDELSSTAL AB—See SSAB AB; *Int'l*, pg. 7153
BORLIN SENDIRIAN BERHAD—See Ta Ann Holdings Berhad; *Int'l*, pg. 7398
BORMAN LIGHTING S.R.L.—See Dexelance S.p.A.; *Int'l*, pg. 2092
BORMAN MOTOR COMPANY; *U.S. Private*, pg. 619
BORMIOLI PHARMA S.P.A.—See Triton Advisers Limited; *Int'l*, pg. 7934
BORMIOLI ROCCO GLASS CO. INC.—See Banco BPM S.p.A.; *Int'l*, pg. 819
BORMIOLI ROCCO S.P.A.—See Vision Capital, LLP; *Int'l*, pg. 8251
BORN BRILLEN OPTIK GMBH & CO. OHG—See Fielmann Group AG; *Int'l*, pg. 2656
BORNEMANN EXZENTERSCHNECKENPUMPEN GMBH—See ITT Inc.; *U.S. Public*, pg. 1177
BORNEMANN INC.—See ITT Inc.; *U.S. Public*, pg. 1177
BORNEMANN MIDDLE EAST FZE—See ITT Inc.; *U.S. Public*, pg. 1177
BORNEMANN PUMPS ASIA PTE. LTD.—See ITT Inc.; *U.S. Public*, pg. 1177
BORNEMANN PUMPS & SYSTEMS CO. LTD—See ITT Inc.; *U.S. Public*, pg. 1177
BORNEMANN S.A. DE C.V.—See ITT Inc.; *U.S. Public*, pg. 1177
BORNEO GEOTECHNIC SDN. BHD.—See CSC Holdings Limited; *Int'l*, pg. 1862
BORNEO GRANITE SDN. BHD.—See Cahya Mata Sarawak Berhad; *Int'l*, pg. 1251

BORNEO HIGHLANDS HORNBILL GOLF & JUNGLE CLUB BERHAD—See Country Heights Holdings Berhad; *Int'l*, pg. 1819
BORNEO MOTORS (SINGAPORE) PTE LTD—See Inchcape plc; *Int'l*, pg. 3647
BORNEO OIL BERHAD; *Int'l*, pg. 1114
BORNEO RESOURCE INVESTMENTS LTD.; *Int'l*, pg. 1114
BORNEO TECHNICAL CO. (M) SDN. BHD.—See Solid Automotive Berhad; *Int'l*, pg. 7071
BORNEO TREE SEEDS & SEEDLINGS SUPPLIES SENDIRIAN BERHAD—See Ta Ann Holdings Berhad; *Int'l*, pg. 7398
BORN HEATERS CANADA, ULC—See Primoris Services Corporation; *U.S. Public*, pg. 1718
BORN INC.; *U.S. Public*, pg. 371
BORNQUIST INC.; *U.S. Private*, pg. 619
BORNS GROUP, INC.; *U.S. Private*, pg. 619
BORNSTEIN SEAFOODS INC.; *U.S. Private*, pg. 619
BORO CONSTRUCTION; *U.S. Private*, pg. 619
BOROMIR PROD SA BUZAU; *Int'l*, pg. 1114
BORON MOLECULAR PTY. LIMITED—See Welvic Australia Pty. Ltd.; *Int'l*, pg. 8375
BORON PRODUCTS, LLC—See 3M Company; *U.S. Public*, pg. 8
BOROSIL RENEWABLES LIMITED; *Int'l*, pg. 1114
BOROTREX SA—See REHAU Verwaltungszentrale AG; *Int'l*, pg. 6255
BOROUGE AUSTRALIA PTY LTD—See Abu Dhabi National Oil Company; *Int'l*, pg. 73
BOROUGE HONG KONG LTD—See Abu Dhabi National Oil Company; *Int'l*, pg. 73
BOROUGE LTD—See Abu Dhabi National Oil Company; *Int'l*, pg. 73
BOROUGE PLC—See Abu Dhabi National Oil Company; *Int'l*, pg. 73
BOROUGE PTE. LTD.—See Abu Dhabi National Oil Company; *Int'l*, pg. 73
BOROUGE PVT LTD—See Abu Dhabi National Oil Company; *Int'l*, pg. 73
BOROUGE SALES AND MARKETING CO. LTD—See Abu Dhabi National Oil Company; *Int'l*, pg. 73
BOROWIAK'S IGA FOODLINER, INC.; *U.S. Private*, pg. 619
BORO WIDE RECYCLING CORP.; *U.S. Private*, pg. 619
BORQS INTERNATIONAL HOLDING CORP.—See BORQS Technologies, Inc.; *Int'l*, pg. 1114
BORQS TECHNOLOGIES, INC.; *Int'l*, pg. 1114
BORRACHAS E EQUIPAMENTOS ELGI LTDA—See Elgi Rubber Company Limited; *Int'l*, pg. 2360
BORRACHAS VIPAL SA; *Int'l*, pg. 1114
BORR COMPANY; *Int'l*, pg. 1114
BORR DRILLING LIMITED; *Int'l*, pg. 1114
BORR DRILLING MANAGEMENT AS—See Borr Drilling Limited; *Int'l*, pg. 1114
BORR DRILLING MANAGEMENT DMCC—See Borr Drilling Limited; *Int'l*, pg. 1114
BORR DRILLING MANAGEMENT (UK) LTD.—See Borr Drilling Limited; *Int'l*, pg. 1114
BORREGAARD ASA; *Int'l*, pg. 1115
BORREGO SOLAR SYSTEM INC. LTD.—See Walsin Lihwa Corporation; *Int'l*, pg. 8334
BORREGO SOLAR SYSTEMS, INC.—See Walsin Lihwa Corporation; *Int'l*, pg. 8334
BORRELL ELECTRIC CO INC.; *U.S. Private*, pg. 619
BORRMANN METAL CENTER, INC.—See Triple-S Steel Holdings Inc.; *U.S. Private*, pg. 4237
BORROWMONEY.COM, INC.; *U.S. Public*, pg. 371
BORSA DE BARCELONA; *Int'l*, pg. 1115
BORSA INSTANBUL A.S.; *Int'l*, pg. 1115
BORSA ITALIANA S.P.A.—See London Stock Exchange Group plc; *Int'l*, pg. 4547
BORSE DUBAI LIMITED—See Investment Corporation of Dubai; *Int'l*, pg. 3785
BORSENMEDIEN AG; *Int'l*, pg. 1115
BORSHEIM JEWELRY COMPANY, INC.—See Berkshire Hathaway Inc.; *U.S. Public*, pg. 303
BORSIG GMBH—See KNM Group Berhad; *Int'l*, pg. 4209
BORSIG MEMBRANE TECHNOLOGY GMBH—See KNM Group Berhad; *Int'l*, pg. 4209
BORSIG ZM COMPRESSION GMBH—See KNM Group Berhad; *Int'l*, pg. 4209
BORSODCHEM MCHZ, S.R.O.—See Permira Advisers LLP; *Int'l*, pg. 5803
BORSODCHEM NYRT.—See Permira Advisers LLP; *Int'l*, pg. 5803
BORSODI SORGYAR KORLATOLT FELELOSSEGU TARSASAG—See Molson Coors Beverage Company; *U.S. Public*, pg. 1459
BORSODI SORGYAR ZRT.—See Molson Coors Beverage Company; *U.S. Public*, pg. 1459
BOR S.R.O.—See BayWa AG; *Int'l*, pg. 915
BORTEK INDUSTRIES INC.; *U.S. Private*, pg. 619
BORTEK, LLC—See Liberty Broadband Corporation; *U.S. Public*, pg. 1310
BORTEX GLOBAL LIMITED; *Int'l*, pg. 1115
BORTEX GROUP FINANCE PLC; *Int'l*, pg. 1115
BORTON-LAWSON ENGINEERING, INC.—See Sterling Investment Partners, L.P.; *U.S. Private*, pg. 3806

BORTON, LC; *U.S. Private*, pg. 619
BORTON & SON'S INC.—See Altafresh LLC; *U.S. Private*, pg. 204
BORTON VOLVO, INC.; *U.S. Private*, pg. 619
BORUJERD TEXTILE CO (PUBLIC JOINT STOCK); *Int'l*, pg. 1115
BORUSAN BIRLESIK BORU FABRIKALARI SANAYI VE TICARET AS; *Int'l*, pg. 1115
BORUSAN MANNESMANN BORU YATIRIM HOLDING A.S.—See Salzgitter AG; *Int'l*, pg. 6496
BORUSAN YATIRIM VE PAZARLAMA AS; *Int'l*, pg. 1115
BORUSSIA DORTMUND GMBH & CO. KGAA; *Int'l*, pg. 1115
BORUTA-ZACHEM SA; *Int'l*, pg. 1115
BORYEONG LNG TERMINAL CO., LTD.—See GS Holdings Corp.; *Int'l*, pg. 3141
BORYEONG LNG TERMINAL CO., LTD.—See SK Innovation Co., Ltd.; *Int'l*, pg. 6973
BORYSZEW S.A.; *Int'l*, pg. 1115
BORYUNG CO., LTD. - ANSAN FACTORY—See Medience Co., Ltd.; *Int'l*, pg. 4777
BORYUNG CO., LTD.—See Medience Co., Ltd.; *Int'l*, pg. 4776
BORYUNG PHARMACEUTICAL - ANSAN FACTORY—See Boryung Pharmaceutical; *Int'l*, pg. 1115
BORYUNG PHARMACEUTICAL; *Int'l*, pg. 1115
BORZA TA' MALTA; *Int'l*, pg. 1115
BORZEN, D.O.O.—See Elektro Slovenia d.o.o.; *Int'l*, pg. 2357
BOS AGENCY INC—See Uwharrie Capital Corp.; *U.S. Public*, pg. 2268
BOSAK MOTORS OF HIGHLAND INC.; *U.S. Private*, pg. 619
BOSAL AFRICA (PTY) LTD.—See Bosal International NV; *Int'l*, pg. 1116
BOSAL AUTOMOTIVE & INDUSTRIAL COMPONENTS LTD—See Bosal International NV; *Int'l*, pg. 1116
BOSAL GERMANY GMBH—See Bosal International NV; *Int'l*, pg. 1116
BOSAL INTERNATIONAL - GEORGIA—See Bosal International NV; *Int'l*, pg. 1116
BOSAL INTERNATIONAL NORTH AMERICA—See Bosal International NV; *Int'l*, pg. 1116
BOSAL INTERNATIONAL NV; *Int'l*, pg. 1116
BOSAL IRELAND LTD—See Bosal International NV; *Int'l*, pg. 1116
BOSAL MEXICO AM—See Bosal International NV; *Int'l*, pg. 1116
BOSAL MIMAYSAN A.S.—See Bosal International NV; *Int'l*, pg. 1116
BOSAL NEDERLAND BV—See Bosal International NV; *Int'l*, pg. 1116
BOSAL USA, INC.—See Bosal International NV; *Int'l*, pg. 1116
BOSANAC D.D.; *Int'l*, pg. 1116
BOSA PROPERTIES INC.; *Int'l*, pg. 1116
BOSA TECHNOLOGY HOLDINGS LTD.; *Int'l*, pg. 1116
B.O.S. BETTER ONLINE SOLUTIONS LTD.; *Int'l*, pg. 790
BOS BROTHERS FRUIT AND VEGETABLES BV—See Clayton, Dubilier & Rice, LLC; *U.S. Private*, pg. 930
BOSC AGENCY, INC.—See BOK Financial Corporation; *U.S. Public*, pg. 367
BOSC AGENCY, INC.—See BOK Financial Corporation; *U.S. Public*, pg. 367
BOSCH ACCESS SYSTEMS GMBH—See Robert Bosch GmbH; *Int'l*, pg. 6359
BOSCH AUTOMOTIVE DIESEL SYSTEMS CO., LTD.—See Robert Bosch GmbH; *Int'l*, pg. 6362
BOSCH AUTOMOTIVE ELECTRONICS INDIA PRIVATE LTD.—See Robert Bosch GmbH; *Int'l*, pg. 6362
BOSCH AUTOMOTIVE SERVICE SOLUTIONS CORPORATION—See Robert Bosch GmbH; *Int'l*, pg. 6363
BOSCH AUTOMOTIVE SERVICE SOLUTIONS GMBH—See Robert Bosch GmbH; *Int'l*, pg. 6363
BOSCH AUTOMOTIVE SERVICE SOLUTIONS LLC—See Robert Bosch GmbH; *Int'l*, pg. 6363
BOSCH AUTOMOTIVE SERVICE SOLUTIONS LTD.—See Robert Bosch GmbH; *Int'l*, pg. 6362
BOSCH AUTOMOTIVE SERVICE SOLUTIONS PTY. LTD.—See Robert Bosch GmbH; *Int'l*, pg. 6362
BOSCH AUTOMOTIVE SERVICE SOLUTIONS S.A. DE C.V.—See Robert Bosch GmbH; *Int'l*, pg. 6362
BOSCH AUTOMOTIVE SERVICE SOLUTIONS S.R.L.—See Robert Bosch GmbH; *Int'l*, pg. 6362
BOSCH AUTOMOTIVE SERVICE SOLUTIONS (SUZHOU) CO., LTD.—See Robert Bosch GmbH; *Int'l*, pg. 6362
BOSCH AUTOMOTIVE SYSTEMS CORPORATION—See Robert Bosch GmbH; *Int'l*, pg. 6362
BOSCH AUTOMOTIVE THAILAND CO. LTD.—See Robert Bosch GmbH; *Int'l*, pg. 6362
BOSCH BAUGESELLSCHAFT M.B.H.—See PORR AG; *Int'l*, pg. 5922
BOSCH BKK—See Robert Bosch GmbH; *Int'l*, pg. 6359
BOSCH CAR MULTIMEDIA PORTUGAL, S.A.—See Robert Bosch GmbH; *Int'l*, pg. 6362
BOSCH CHASSIS SYSTEMS AUSTRALIA—See Robert Bosch GmbH; *Int'l*, pg. 6362

BOSCH CHASSIS SYSTEMS INDIA LTD.—See Robert Bosch GmbH; *Int'l*, pg. 6359
BOSCH (CHINA) INVESTMENT LTD.—See Robert Bosch GmbH; *Int'l*, pg. 6359
BOSCH COMMUNICATION CENTER MAGDEBURG GMBH—See Robert Bosch GmbH; *Int'l*, pg. 6359
BOSCH COMMUNICATION CENTER S.R.L.—See Robert Bosch GmbH; *Int'l*, pg. 6359
BOSCH COMMUNICATIONS CENTER B.V.—See Robert Bosch GmbH; *Int'l*, pg. 6359
BOSCH CONNECTED DEVICES AND SOLUTIONS GMBH—See Robert Bosch GmbH; *Int'l*, pg. 6359
BOSCH CORPORATION - HIGASHIMATSUYAMA PLANT—See Robert Bosch GmbH; *Int'l*, pg. 6359
BOSCH CORPORATION - MUSASHI PLANT—See Robert Bosch GmbH; *Int'l*, pg. 6359
BOSCH CORPORATION - OTA PLANT—See Robert Bosch GmbH; *Int'l*, pg. 6359
BOSCH CORPORATION - TOCHIGI PLANT—See Robert Bosch GmbH; *Int'l*, pg. 6359
BOSCH CORPORATION - YORII PLANT—See Robert Bosch GmbH; *Int'l*, pg. 6359
BOSCH DIESEL S.R.O.—See Robert Bosch GmbH; *Int'l*, pg. 6359
BOSCH ELECTRICAL DRIVES CO., LTD.—See Robert Bosch GmbH; *Int'l*, pg. 6359
BOSCH ELECTRICAL DRIVES INDIA PRIVATE LTD.—See Robert Bosch GmbH; *Int'l*, pg. 6359
BOSCH ELECTRONIC SERVICE KFT.—See Robert Bosch GmbH; *Int'l*, pg. 6359
BOSCH EMISSION SYSTEMS GMBH & CO. KG—See Robert Bosch GmbH; *Int'l*, pg. 6359
BOSCH ENERGY AND BUILDING SOLUTIONS GMBH—See Robert Bosch GmbH; *Int'l*, pg. 6359
BOSCH ENERGY AND BUILDING SOLUTIONS ITALY S.R.L.—See Robert Bosch GmbH; *Int'l*, pg. 6359
BOSCH ENGINEERING K.K.—See Robert Bosch GmbH; *Int'l*, pg. 6359
BOSCH FINANCIAL SOFTWARE GMBH—See Robert Bosch GmbH; *Int'l*, pg. 6359
BOSCH FREN SISTEMLERI SANAYI VE TICARET A.S.—See Robert Bosch GmbH; *Int'l*, pg. 6359
BOSCH GENERAL AVIATION TECHNOLOGY GMBH—See Robert Bosch GmbH; *Int'l*, pg. 6359
BOSCH HEALTHCARE SOLUTIONS GMBH—See Robert Bosch GmbH; *Int'l*, pg. 6359
BOSCH HUAYU STEERING SYSTEMS CO., LTD.—See Robert Bosch GmbH; *Int'l*, pg. 6359
BOSCH HUAYU STEERING SYSTEMS (NANJING) CO., LTD.—See Robert Bosch GmbH; *Int'l*, pg. 6359
BOSCH HUAYU STEERING SYSTEMS (WUHAN) CO., LTD.—See Robert Bosch GmbH; *Int'l*, pg. 6359
BOSCH HUAYU STEERING SYSTEMS (YANTAI) CO., LTD.—See Robert Bosch GmbH; *Int'l*, pg. 6359
BOSCH INDUSTRIEKESSEL AUSTRIA GMBH—See Robert Bosch GmbH; *Int'l*, pg. 6359
BOSCH INDUSTRIEKESSEL GMBH—See Robert Bosch GmbH; *Int'l*, pg. 6359
BOSCH INSPECTION TECHNOLOGY GMBH—See CVC Capital Partners SICAV-FIS S.A.; *Int'l*, pg. 1884
BOSCH INSPECTION TECHNOLOGY INC.—See CVC Capital Partners SICAV-FIS S.A.; *Int'l*, pg. 1884
BOSCH INSPECTION TECHNOLOGY (SHANGHAI) CO., LTD.—See CVC Capital Partners SICAV-FIS S.A.; *Int'l*, pg. 1884
BOSCH K.K.—See Robert Bosch GmbH; *Int'l*, pg. 6359
BOSCH KWK SYSTEME GMBH—See Robert Bosch GmbH; *Int'l*, pg. 6359
BOSCH LASER EQUIPMENT (DONGGUAN) LIMITED—See Robert Bosch GmbH; pg. 6360
BOSCH LIMITED; *Int'l*, pg. 1116
BOSCH LIMITED—See Robert Bosch GmbH; *Int'l*, pg. 6360
BOSCH MANAGEMENT SUPPORT GMBH—See Robert Bosch GmbH; *Int'l*, pg. 6360
BOSCH MOTORS; *U.S. Private*, pg. 619
BOSCH PACKAGING SERVICES AG—See Robert Bosch GmbH; *Int'l*, pg. 6360
BOSCH PACKAGING SERVICES S.A.R.L.—See Robert Bosch GmbH; *Int'l*, pg. 6360
BOSCH PACKAGING SERVICES—See CVC Capital Partners SICAV-FIS S.A.; *Int'l*, pg. 1884
BOSCH PACKAGING SYSTEMS AG—See CVC Capital Partners SICAV-FIS S.A.; *Int'l*, pg. 1884
BOSCH PACKAGING SYSTEMS GMBH—See Robert Bosch GmbH; *Int'l*, pg. 6360
BOSCH PACKAGING SYSTEMS KFT.—See CVC Capital Partners SICAV-FIS S.A.; *Int'l*, pg. 1884
BOSCH PACKAGING TECHNOLOGY B.V.—See CVC Capital Partners SICAV-FIS S.A.; *Int'l*, pg. 1884
BOSCH PACKAGING TECHNOLOGY (CHENGDU) CO., LTD.—See CVC Capital Partners SICAV-FIS S.A.; *Int'l*, pg. 1884
BOSCH PACKAGING TECHNOLOGY (HANGZHOU) CO., LTD.—See CVC Capital Partners SICAV-FIS S.A.; *Int'l*, pg. 1884
BOSCH PACKAGING TECHNOLOGY, INC.—See CVC Capital Partners SICAV-FIS S.A.; *Int'l*, pg. 1884
BOSCH PACKAGING TECHNOLOGY K.K.—See CVC Capital Partners SICAV-FIS S.A.; *Int'l*, pg. 1884
BOSCH PACKAGING TECHNOLOGY K.K.—See CVC Capital Partners SICAV-FIS S.A.; *Int'l*, pg. 1884
BOSCH PACKAGING TECHNOLOGY LTD.—See CVC Capital Partners SICAV-FIS S.A.; *Int'l*, pg. 1884
BOSCH PACKAGING TECHNOLOGY LTD.—See CVC Capital Partners SICAV-FIS S.A.; *Int'l*, pg. 1884
BOSCH PACKAGING TECHNOLOGY SA—See CVC Capital Partners SICAV-FIS S.A.; *Int'l*, pg. 1884
BOSCH PACKAGING TECHNOLOGY SAS—See CVC Capital Partners SICAV-FIS S.A.; *Int'l*, pg. 1884
BOSCH PACKAGING TECHNOLOGY (SINGAPORE) PTE. LTD.—See CVC Capital Partners SICAV-FIS S.A.; *Int'l*, pg. 1884
BOSCH PACKAGING TECHNOLOGY—See CVC Capital Partners SICAV-FIS S.A.; *Int'l*, pg. 1884
BOSCH PENSIONSFONDS AG—See Robert Bosch GmbH; *Int'l*, pg. 6360
BOSCH POWER TEC GMBH—See Robert Bosch GmbH; *Int'l*, pg. 6360
BOSCH POWER TOOLS ENGINEERING SDN. BHD.—See Robert Bosch GmbH; *Int'l*, pg. 6360
BOSCH REXROTH AB—See Robert Bosch GmbH; *Int'l*, pg. 6365
BOSCH REXROTH AG - ELCHINGEN—See Robert Bosch GmbH; *Int'l*, pg. 6365
BOSCH REXROTH AG - INDUSTRIAL HYDRAULICS—See Robert Bosch GmbH; *Int'l*, pg. 6365
BOSCH REXROTH AG - LOHR AM MAIN—See Robert Bosch GmbH; *Int'l*, pg. 6365
BOSCH REXROTH AG—See Robert Bosch GmbH; *Int'l*, pg. 6365
BOSCH REXROTH A/S—See Robert Bosch GmbH; *Int'l*, pg. 6365
BOSCH REXROTH AS—See Robert Bosch GmbH; *Int'l*, pg. 6365
BOSCH REXROTH (BEIJING) HYDRAULIC CO., LTD.—See Robert Bosch GmbH; *Int'l*, pg. 6365
BOSCH REXROTH BV—See Robert Bosch GmbH; *Int'l*, pg. 6365
BOSCH REXROTH CANADA—See Robert Bosch GmbH; *Int'l*, pg. 6365
BOSCH REXROTH (CHANGZHOU) CO., LTD.—See Robert Bosch GmbH; *Int'l*, pg. 6365
BOSCH REXROTH (CHINA) LTD.—See Robert Bosch GmbH; *Int'l*, pg. 6365
BOSCH REXROTH CO. LTD.—See Robert Bosch GmbH; *Int'l*, pg. 6365
BOSCH REXROTH CORPORATION—See Robert Bosch GmbH; *Int'l*, pg. 6365
BOSCH REXROTH CORPORATION—See Robert Bosch GmbH; *Int'l*, pg. 6365
BOSCH REXROTH CORPORATION—See Robert Bosch GmbH; *Int'l*, pg. 6365
BOSCH REXROTH DSI S.A.S.—See Robert Bosch GmbH; *Int'l*, pg. 6365
BOSCH REXROTH GHANA LTD.—See Robert Bosch GmbH; *Int'l*, pg. 6360
BOSCH REXROTH GMBH—See Robert Bosch GmbH; *Int'l*, pg. 6365
BOSCH REXROTH (INDIA) LTD.—See Robert Bosch GmbH; *Int'l*, pg. 6365
BOSCH REXROTH INTERLIT GMBH—See Robert Bosch GmbH; *Int'l*, pg. 6365
BOSCH REXROTH KENYA LTD.—See Robert Bosch GmbH; *Int'l*, pg. 6360
BOSCH REXROTH KFT.—See Robert Bosch GmbH; *Int'l*, pg. 6365
BOSCH REXROTH KOREA LTD.—See Robert Bosch GmbH; *Int'l*, pg. 6365
BOSCH REXROTH LIMITED—See Robert Bosch GmbH; *Int'l*, pg. 6365
BOSCH REXROTH LTDA—See Robert Bosch GmbH; *Int'l*, pg. 6366
BOSCH REXROTH LTD.—See Robert Bosch GmbH; *Int'l*, pg. 6366
BOSCH REXROTH LTD.—See Robert Bosch GmbH; *Int'l*, pg. 6366
BOSCH REXROTH MELLANSEL AB—See Robert Bosch GmbH; *Int'l*, pg. 6366
BOSCH REXROTH MEXICO SA DE CV—See Robert Bosch GmbH; *Int'l*, pg. 6366
BOSCH REXROTH MOROCCO S.A.R.L.—See Robert Bosch GmbH; *Int'l*, pg. 6360
BOSCH REXROTH N.V.—See Robert Bosch GmbH; *Int'l*, pg. 6366
BOSCH REXROTH OIL CONTROL S.P.A.—See Robert Bosch GmbH; *Int'l*, pg. 6366
BOSCH REXROTH OTOMASYON SAN.VE TIC A.S.—See Robert Bosch GmbH; *Int'l*, pg. 6366
BOSCH REXROTH OY—See Robert Bosch GmbH; *Int'l*, pg. 6366
BOSCH REXROTH PNEUMATIC AG—See Robert Bosch GmbH; *Int'l*, pg. 6366
BOSCH REXROTH PTE. LTD.—See Robert Bosch GmbH; *Int'l*, pg. 6366
BOSCH REXROTH PTY. LTD.—See Robert Bosch GmbH; *Int'l*, pg. 6366
BOSCH REXROTH, S.A. DE C.V.—See Robert Bosch GmbH; *Int'l*, pg. 6366
BOSCH REXROTH S.A.I.C.—See Robert Bosch GmbH; *Int'l*, pg. 6366
BOSCH REXROTH SA—See Robert Bosch GmbH; *Int'l*, pg. 6366
BOSCH REXROTH SA—See Robert Bosch GmbH; *Int'l*, pg. 6366
BOSCH REXROTH S.A.—See Robert Bosch GmbH; *Int'l*, pg. 6366
BOSCH REXROTH S.A.—See Robert Bosch GmbH; *Int'l*, pg. 6366
BOSCH REXROTH S.A.S.—See Robert Bosch GmbH; *Int'l*, pg. 6366
BOSCH REXROTH S.A.S.—See Robert Bosch GmbH; *Int'l*, pg. 6366
BOSCH REXROTH SCHWEIZ AG—See Robert Bosch GmbH; *Int'l*, pg. 6366
BOSCH REXROTH SDN. BHD.—See Robert Bosch GmbH; *Int'l*, pg. 6366
BOSCH REXROTH SERVICES BV—See Robert Bosch GmbH; *Int'l*, pg. 6365
BOSCH REXROTH, S.L.—See Robert Bosch GmbH; *Int'l*, pg. 6366
BOSCH REXROTH—See Robert Bosch GmbH; *Int'l*, pg. 6365
BOSCH REXROTH SPA.—See Robert Bosch GmbH; *Int'l*, pg. 6366
BOSCH REXROTH, SPOL. S.R.O.—See Robert Bosch GmbH; *Int'l*, pg. 6366
BOSCH REXROTH SP.ZOO—See Robert Bosch GmbH; *Int'l*, pg. 6366
BOSCH REXROTH S.R.L.—See Robert Bosch GmbH; *Int'l*, pg. 6366
BOSCH REXROTH TECHNIQUE AB—See Robert Bosch GmbH; *Int'l*, pg. 6365
BOSCH REXROTH TEKNIK AB—See Robert Bosch GmbH; *Int'l*, pg. 6365
BOSCH REXROTH (XI'AN) ELECTRIC DRIVES AND CONTROLS CO., LTD.—See Robert Bosch GmbH; *Int'l*, pg. 6365
BOSCH SANAYI VE TICARET A.S.—See Robert Bosch GmbH; *Int'l*, pg. 6360
BOSCH SECURITY SYSTEMS B.V.—See Robert Bosch GmbH; *Int'l*, pg. 6363
BOSCH SECURITY SYSTEMS, INC.—See Robert Bosch GmbH; *Int'l*, pg. 6363
BOSCH SECURITY SYSTEMS LTD.—See Robert Bosch GmbH; *Int'l*, pg. 6363
BOSCH SECURITY SYSTEMS LTD.—See Robert Bosch GmbH; *Int'l*, pg. 6363
BOSCH SECURITY SYSTEMS LTD.—See Robert Bosch GmbH; *Int'l*, pg. 6363
BOSCH SECURITY SYSTEMS PTY. LTD.—See Robert Bosch GmbH; *Int'l*, pg. 6363
BOSCH SECURITY SYSTEMS S.A.—See Robert Bosch GmbH; *Int'l*, pg. 6363
BOSCH SECURITY SYSTEMS, S.A.—See Robert Bosch GmbH; *Int'l*, pg. 6360
BOSCH SECURITY SYSTEMS—See Robert Bosch GmbH; *Int'l*, pg. 6363
BOSCH SECURITY SYSTEMS S.P.A.—See Robert Bosch GmbH; *Int'l*, pg. 6363
BOSCH SENSORTEC GMBH—See Robert Bosch GmbH; *Int'l*, pg. 6360
BOSCH SERVICE SOLUTIONS CORPORATION—See Robert Bosch GmbH; *Int'l*, pg. 6360
BOSCH SERVICE SOLUTIONS GMBH—See Robert Bosch GmbH; *Int'l*, pg. 6360
BOSCH SERVICE SOLUTIONS, INC.—See Robert Bosch GmbH; *Int'l*, pg. 6360
BOSCH SERVICE SOLUTIONS LTD.—See Robert Bosch GmbH; *Int'l*, pg. 6360
BOSCH SERVICE SOLUTIONS MAGDEBURG GMBH—See Robert Bosch GmbH; *Int'l*, pg. 6360
BOSCH SERVICE SOLUTIONS, S.A.U.—See Robert Bosch GmbH; *Int'l*, pg. 6360
BOSCH SERVICE SOLUTIONS S.R.L.—See Robert Bosch GmbH; *Int'l*, pg. 6360
BOSCH SICHERHEITSSYSTEME ENGINEERING GMBH—See Robert Bosch GmbH; *Int'l*, pg. 6360
BOSCH SICHERHEITSSYSTEME GMBH—See Robert Bosch GmbH; *Int'l*, pg. 6363
BOSCH SICHERHEITSSYSTEME MONTAGE UND SERVICE GMBH—See Robert Bosch GmbH; *Int'l*, pg. 6360
BOSCH SILICON TRADING GMBH—See Robert Bosch GmbH; *Int'l*, pg. 6360
BOSCH SOFTTEC GMBH—See Robert Bosch GmbH; *Int'l*, pg. 6360
BOSCH SOFTWARE INNOVATIONS CORP.—See Robert Bosch GmbH; *Int'l*, pg. 6366
BOSCH SOFTWARE INNOVATIONS GMBH—See Robert Bosch GmbH; *Int'l*, pg. 6360
BOSCH SOLAR ENERGY AG—See Robert Bosch GmbH; *Int'l*, pg. 6360
BOSCH SOLAR SERVICES GMBH—See Robert Bosch GmbH; *Int'l*, pg. 6360

COMPANY NAME INDEX

BOSCH SOLARTHERMIE GMBH—See Robert Bosch GmbH; *Int'l*, pg. 6360
BOSCH SYSTEMS—See Robert Bosch GmbH; *Int'l*, pg. 6363
BOSCH TECHNOLOGY LICENSING ADMINISTRATION GMBH—See Robert Bosch GmbH; *Int'l*, pg. 6360
BOSCH TERMOTECHNOLOGIA, S.A.—See Robert Bosch GmbH; *Int'l*, pg. 6363
BOSCH TERMOTECNOLOGIA LTDA.—See Robert Bosch GmbH; *Int'l*, pg. 6363
BOSCH TERMOTEKNIK SANAYI VE TICARET A.S.—See Robert Bosch GmbH; *Int'l*, pg. 6363
BOSCH THERMOTECHNIEK B.V.—See Robert Bosch GmbH; *Int'l*, pg. 6363
BOSCH THERMOTECHNIKA S.R.O.—See Robert Bosch GmbH; *Int'l*, pg. 6363
BOSCH THERMOTECHNIK GMBH FHP MANUFACTURING PLANT—See Robert Bosch GmbH; *Int'l*, pg. 6363
BOSCH THERMOTECHNIK GMBH LOLLAR PLANT—See Robert Bosch GmbH; *Int'l*, pg. 6363
BOSCH THERMOTECHNIK GMBH—See Robert Bosch GmbH; *Int'l*, pg. 6363
BOSCH THERMOTECHNIK GMBH WERNAU PLANT—See Robert Bosch GmbH; *Int'l*, pg. 6363
BOSCH THERMOTECHNOLOGY (BEIJING) CO., LTD.—See Robert Bosch GmbH; *Int'l*, pg. 6364
BOSCH THERMOTECHNOLOGY CORP.—See Robert Bosch GmbH; *Int'l*, pg. 6366
BOSCH THERMOTECHNOLOGY LTD.—See Robert Bosch GmbH; *Int'l*, pg. 6364
BOSCH THERMOTECHNOLOGY N.V. / S.A.—See Robert Bosch GmbH; *Int'l*, pg. 6364
BOSCH THERMOTECHNOLOGY (SHANDONG) CO., LTD.—See Robert Bosch GmbH; *Int'l*, pg. 6364
BOSCH THERMOTECHNOLOGY (WUHAN) CO., LTD.—See Robert Bosch GmbH; *Int'l*, pg. 6364
BOSCH THERMOTEKNIK AB—See Robert Bosch GmbH; *Int'l*, pg. 6364
BOSCH TRADING (SHANGHAI) CO., LTD.—See Robert Bosch GmbH; *Int'l*, pg. 6360
BOSCH TRANSMISSION TECHNOLOGY B.V.—See Robert Bosch GmbH; *Int'l*, pg. 6360
BOSCH VIETNAM CO., LTD.—See Robert Bosch GmbH; *Int'l*, pg. 6360
BOSCH WATER HEATING—See Robert Bosch GmbH; *Int'l*, pg. 6363
BOSCH (ZHUHAI) SECURITY SYSTEMS CO., LTD.—See Robert Bosch GmbH; *Int'l*, pg. 6359
BOSC INTERNATIONAL COMPANY LIMITED—See Bank of Shanghai Co., Ltd; *Int'l*, pg. 848
BOSCOGEN INC—See Standard Chem. & Pharm. Co., Ltd.; *Int'l*, pg. 7168
BOSCO OIL, INC.; *U.S. Private*, pg. 619
BOSCOV'S DEPARTMENT STORE, LLC—See Boscov's Inc.; *U.S. Private*, pg. 619
BOSCOV'S INC.; *U.S. Private*, pg. 619
BOSC REALTY ADVISORS; *U.S. Private*, pg. 619
BOSCUS CANADA INC; *Int'l*, pg. 1116
BOSE AG—See Bose Corporation; *U.S. Private*, pg. 619
BOSE A/S - NORWAY REPRESENTATIVE OFFICE—See Bose Corporation; *U.S. Private*, pg. 619
BOSE A/S—See Bose Corporation; *U.S. Private*, pg. 619
BOSE A/S - SWEDEN REPRESENTATIVE OFFICE—See Bose Corporation; *U.S. Private*, pg. 619
BOSE B.V.—See Bose Corporation; *U.S. Private*, pg. 619
BOSE CORPORATION INDIA PRIVATE LIMITED—See Bose Corporation; *U.S. Private*, pg. 619
BOSE CORPORATION; *U.S. Private*, pg. 619
BOSE ELECTRONICS (SHANGHAI) CO. LIMITED—See Bose Corporation; *U.S. Private*, pg. 619
BOSE GES.M.B.H.—See Bose Corporation; *U.S. Private*, pg. 620
BOSE GMBH - CONSUMER DIRECT DIVISION—See Bose Corporation; *U.S. Private*, pg. 620
BOSE GMBH—See Bose Corporation; *U.S. Private*, pg. 620
BOSE K.K.—See Bose Corporation; *U.S. Private*, pg. 620
BOSE LIMITED—See Bose Corporation; *U.S. Private*, pg. 620
BOSE LTD.—See Bose Corporation; *U.S. Private*, pg. 620
BOSE N.V.—See Bose Corporation; *U.S. Private*, pg. 620
BOSE PTY. LTD.—See Bose Corporation; *U.S. Private*, pg. 620
BOS EQUIPEMENT HOTELIER; *Int'l*, pg. 1115
BOSE S.A. DE C.V.—See Bose Corporation; *U.S. Private*, pg. 620
BOSE S.A.R.L.—See Bose Corporation; *U.S. Private*, pg. 620
BOSE S.P.A.—See Bose Corporation; *U.S. Private*, pg. 620
BOSE SP. Z O.O.—See Bose Corporation; *U.S. Private*, pg. 620
BOSE SYSTEMS CORPORATION - ELECTROFORCE SYSTEMS GROUP—See Bose Corporation; *U.S. Private*, pg. 620
BOSE SYSTEMS CORPORATION—See Bose Corporation; *U.S. Private*, pg. 620
BOSE UAE TRADING LLC—See Bose Corporation; *U.S. Private*, pg. 620

BOSE U.K., LTD.—See Bose Corporation; *U.S. Private*, pg. 620
BOSFA PTY. LTD.—See NV Bekaert SA; *Int'l*, pg. 5495
BO'S FOOD STORES; *U.S. Private*, pg. 602
BOSFOR TOURISM MANAGEMENT INC.—See Nurol Holding A.S.; *Int'l*, pg. 5490
BOSFOR TURIZM ISLETMECILIK A.S.—See Nurol Holding A.S.; *Int'l*, pg. 5490
BOS GLOBAL HOLDINGS LIMITED; *Int'l*, pg. 1115
BOSHART INDUSTRIES INC.; *Int'l*, pg. 1116
BOSH GLOBAL SERVICES, INC.—See MAG DS Corp.; *U.S. Private*, pg. 2545
BOSHIWA INTERNATIONAL HOLDING LIMITED; *Int'l*, pg. 1116
BOSHOKU AUTOMOTIVE (THAILAND) CO., LTD.—See Toyota Boshoku Corporation; *Int'l*, pg. 7863
BOS HOMOGENISERS B.V.—See GEA Group Aktiengesellschaft; *Int'l*, pg. 2897
BOSIDENG INTERNATIONAL HOLDINGS LIMITED; *Int'l*, pg. 1116
BOSIG BAUKUNSTSTOFFE GMBH—See BOSIG Holding GmbH & Co. KG; *Int'l*, pg. 1116
BOSIG GMBH—See BOSIG Holding GmbH & Co. KG; *Int'l*, pg. 1116
BOSIG HOLDING GMBH & CO. KG; *Int'l*, pg. 1116
BOSIG INC.—See BOSIG Holding GmbH & Co. KG; *Int'l*, pg. 1116
BOSIG POLSKA SP. Z O.O.—See BOSIG Holding GmbH & Co. KG; *Int'l*, pg. 1116
BOS INCASSO B.V.—See Munchener Ruckversicherungs AG; *Int'l*, pg. 5085
BOS INC.—See Vision, Inc; *Int'l*, pg. 8253
BOSIO D.O.O.—See Berndorf AG; *Int'l*, pg. 987
BOSKALIS ARGENTINA—See HAL Trust N.V.; *Int'l*, pg. 3224
BOSKALIS AUSTRALIA PTY LTD—See HAL Trust N.V.; *Int'l*, pg. 3225
BOSKALIS B.V.—See HAL Trust N.V.; *Int'l*, pg. 3225
BOSKALIS DO BRASIL DRAGAGEM E SERVICOS MARITIMOS LTDA.—See HAL Trust N.V.; *Int'l*, pg. 3225
BOSKALIS DOLMAN B.V.—See HAL Trust N.V.; *Int'l*, pg. 3225
BOSKALIS DREDGING INDIA PVT. LTD.—See HAL Trust N.V.; *Int'l*, pg. 3225
BOSKALIS ENVIRONMENTAL B.V.—See HAL Trust N.V.; *Int'l*, pg. 3225
BOSKALIS GERMANY HOLDING GMBH—See HAL Trust N.V.; *Int'l*, pg. 3225
BOSKALIS GUYANA INC.—See HAL Trust N.V.; *Int'l*, pg. 3225
BOSKALIS INFRA B.V.—See HAL Trust N.V.; *Int'l*, pg. 3224
BOSKALIS INTERNATIONAL (S) PTE LTD—See HAL Trust N.V.; *Int'l*, pg. 3225
BOSKALIS INTERNATIONAL URUGUAY S.A.—See HAL Trust N.V.; *Int'l*, pg. 3225
BOSKALIS ITALIA S.R.L.—See HAL Trust N.V.; *Int'l*, pg. 3225
BOSKALIS MARITIME INVESTMENTS B.V.—See HAL Trust N.V.; *Int'l*, pg. 3225
BOSKALIS NEDERLAND B.V.—See HAL Trust N.V.; *Int'l*, pg. 3225
BOSKALIS NEDERLAND INFRA B.V.—See HAL Trust N.V.; *Int'l*, pg. 3225
BOSKALIS OFFSHORE B.V.—See HAL Trust N.V.; *Int'l*, pg. 3225
BOSKALIS OFFSHORE CONTRACTING B.V.—See HAL Trust N.V.; *Int'l*, pg. 3225
BOSKALIS OFFSHORE GMBH—See HAL Trust N.V.; *Int'l*, pg. 3225
BOSKALIS OFFSHORE HEAVY MARINE TRANSPORT B.V.—See HAL Trust N.V.; *Int'l*, pg. 3225
BOSKALIS OFFSHORE MARINE SERVICES B.V.—See HAL Trust N.V.; *Int'l*, pg. 3225
BOSKALIS OFFSHORE SUBSEA CONTRACTING AZERBAIJAN LLC—See HAL Trust N.V.; *Int'l*, pg. 3225
BOSKALIS OFFSHORE TRANSPORT SERVICES N.V.—See HAL Trust N.V.; *Int'l*, pg. 3225
BOSKALIS PANAMA S.A.—See HAL Trust N.V.; *Int'l*, pg. 3225
BOSKALIS POLSKA SP. Z O.O.—See HAL Trust N.V.; *Int'l*, pg. 3225
BOSKALIS SMIT INDIA LLP—See HAL Trust N.V.; *Int'l*, pg. 3225
BOSKALIS SOUTH AFRICA (PTY) LTD—See HAL Trust N.V.; *Int'l*, pg. 3225
BOSKALIS S.R.L.—See HAL Trust N.V.; *Int'l*, pg. 3225
BOSKALIS SWEDEN AB—See HAL Trust N.V.; *Int'l*, pg. 3225
BOSKALIS TRANSPORT B.V.—See HAL Trust N.V.; *Int'l*, pg. 3225
BOSKALIS WESTMINSTER CONTRACTING LIMITED—See HAL Trust N.V.; *Int'l*, pg. 3225
BOSKALIS WESTMINSTER DREDGING LTD.—See HAL Trust N.V.; *Int'l*, pg. 3225
BOSKALIS WESTMINSTER LTD.—See HAL Trust N.V.; *Int'l*, pg. 3225
BOSKALIS WESTMINSTER MIDDLE EAST LTD.—See HAL Trust N.V.; *Int'l*, pg. 3225

BOSS HOLDINGS, INC.

BOSKALIS WESTMINSTER SHIPPING B.V.—See HAL Trust N.V.; *Int'l*, pg. 3225
BOSKALIS ZINKCON LTD.—See HAL Trust N.V.; *Int'l*, pg. 3225
BOSKA RK A.D.; *Int'l*, pg. 1116
BOSKOVICH FARMS INC.; *U.S. Private*, pg. 620
BOSLEY MEDICAL—See Aderans Co., Ltd.; *Int'l*, pg. 143
THE BOSMA GROUP, PC; *U.S. Private*, pg. 3997
BOSNALIJEK D.D.; *Int'l*, pg. 1116
BOSNAMONTAZA A.D.; *Int'l*, pg. 1116
BOSNAPLAST D.O.O.; *Int'l*, pg. 1116
BOSNA REOSIGURANJE D.D.; *Int'l*, pg. 1116
BOSNA TRGOVINA A.D.; *Int'l*, pg. 1116
BOSO COMPUTER SERVICE CO., LTD.—See K&O Energy Group Inc.; *Int'l*, pg. 4038
BOSO OIL & FAT CO., LTD.—See Showa Sangyo Co., Ltd.; *Int'l*, pg. 6861
BO'S PALLETS, INC.—See Audax Group, Limited Partnership; *U.S. Private*, pg. 386
BOSP BANCSHARES, INC.; *U.S. Private*, pg. 620
BOSQUE MEDICAL CENTER S.A.—See UnitedHealth Group Incorporated; *U.S. Public*, pg. 2239
BOSQUE RIVER PHYSICAL THERAPY & REHABILITATION, LIMITED PARTNERSHIP—See U.S. Physical Therapy, Inc.; *U.S. Public*, pg. 2214
BOSSARD AEROSPACE GERMANY GMBH—See Bossard Holding AG; *Int'l*, pg. 1117
BOSSARD AEROSPACE, INC.—See Bossard Holding AG; *Int'l*, pg. 1117
BOSSARD AEROSPACE SWITZERLAND AG—See Bossard Holding AG; *Int'l*, pg. 1117
BOSSARD AUSTRALIA PTY LTD—See Bossard Holding AG; *Int'l*, pg. 1117
BOSSARD CANADA INC.—See Bossard Holding AG; *Int'l*, pg. 1117
BOSSARD CZ S.R.O.—See Bossard Holding AG; *Int'l*, pg. 1117
BOSSARD DENMARK A/S—See Bossard Holding AG; *Int'l*, pg. 1117
BOSSARD DEUTSCHLAND GMBH—See Bossard Holding AG; *Int'l*, pg. 1117
BOSSARD FRANCE SAS—See Bossard Holding AG; *Int'l*, pg. 1117
BOSSARD HOLDING AG; *Int'l*, pg. 1117
BOSSARD, INC.—See Bossard Holding AG; *Int'l*, pg. 1117
BOSSARD ITALIA S.R.L.—See Bossard Holding AG; *Int'l*, pg. 1117
BOSSARD (KOREA) LTD.—See Bossard Holding AG; *Int'l*, pg. 1117
BOSSARD LTD.—See Bossard Holding AG; *Int'l*, pg. 1117
BOSSARD M SDN. BHD.—See Bossard Holding AG; *Int'l*, pg. 1117
BOSSARD NEDERLAND B.V.—See Bossard Holding AG; *Int'l*, pg. 1117
BOSSARD NORTH AMERICA, INC. - MILWAUKEE—See Bossard Holding AG; *Int'l*, pg. 1117
BOSSARD NORTH AMERICA, INC.—See Bossard Holding AG; *Int'l*, pg. 1117
BOSSARD NORWAY AS—See Bossard Holding AG; *Int'l*, pg. 1117
BOSSARD ONTARIO INC.—See Bossard Holding AG; *Int'l*, pg. 1117
BOSSARD POLAND SP. Z O.O.—See Bossard Holding AG; *Int'l*, pg. 1117
BOSSARD SOUTH AFRICA (PTY) LTD.—See Bossard Holding AG; *Int'l*, pg. 1117
BOSSARD SPAIN SA—See Bossard Holding AG; *Int'l*, pg. 1117
BOSSARD SWEDEN AB—See Bossard Holding AG; *Int'l*, pg. 1117
BOSSARD THAILAND LTD.—See Bossard Holding AG; *Int'l*, pg. 1117
BOSSA TICARET VE SANAYI ISLETMELERI TAS; *Int'l*, pg. 1117
BOSS BALLOON COMPANY—See Boss Holdings, Inc.; *U.S. Public*, pg. 371
BOSS CANADA, INC.—See Boss Holdings, Inc.; *U.S. Public*, pg. 371
BOSS CHAIR, INC.; *U.S. Private*, pg. 620
BOSS CREATIVE; *U.S. Private*, pg. 620
BOSS DESIGN LTD.; *Int'l*, pg. 1117
BOSSDOM DIGIINNOVATION CO., LTD.; *Int'l*, pg. 1118
BOSSDORF & KERSTAN GMBH—See Havelländische Eisenbahn AG; *Int'l*, pg. 3286
BOSSELMAN ENERGY INC.; *U.S. Private*, pg. 620
BOSSE MATTINGLY CONSTRUCTORS, INC.; *U.S. Private*, pg. 620
BOSS ENERGY LIMITED; *Int'l*, pg. 1117
BOSS ENTERPRISES INC.; *U.S. Private*, pg. 620
BOSS GROUP LTD.—See Drake New Zealand Ltd.; *Int'l*, pg. 2200
BOSSHARDT REALTY SERVICES, INC.; *U.S. Private*, pg. 620
BOSS HOLDINGS, INC.; *U.S. Public*, pg. 371
BOSSIER CASINO VENTURE, LLC—See PENN Entertainment, Inc.; *U.S. Public*, pg. 1662
BOSSINI FASHION GMBH—See Li & Fung Limited; *Int'l*, pg. 4479

BOSS HOLDINGS, INC.

BOSSINI INTERNATIONAL HOLDINGS LIMITED—See Viva Goods Company Limited; *Int'l*, pg. 8264
BOSS MANUFACTURING COMPANY—See Boss Holdings, Inc.; *U.S. Public*, pg. 371
BOSS OFFICE PRODUCTS; *U.S. Private*, pg. 620
BOS SOLUTIONS LTD.—See Advent International Corporation; *U.S. Private*, pg. 98
BOSSON ET PILLET S.A.—See Romande Energie Holding S.A.; *Int'l*, pg. 6394
BOSSONG HOSIERY MILLS, INC.; *U.S. Private*, pg. 620
BOSS PET PRODUCTS, INC.—See Boss Holdings, Inc.; *U.S. Public*, pg. 371
BOSS SYSTEMS LIMITED—See China Trends Holdings Limited; *Int'l*, pg. 1561
BOS STAFFING; *U.S. Private*, pg. 619
BOSTA BETON SP. Z O.O.—See CRH plc; *Int'l*, pg. 1843
BOST IBERICA S.L.—See Knorr-Bremse AG; *Int'l*, pg. 4210
BOSTIK AB—See Arkema S.A.; *Int'l*, pg. 570
BOSTIK AEROSOLS GMBH—See Arkema S.A.; *Int'l*, pg. 570
BOSTIK ARGENTINA S.A.—See Arkema S.A.; *Int'l*, pg. 570
BOSTIK A/S—See Arkema S.A.; *Int'l*, pg. 570
BOSTIK BELUX S.A. - N.V.—See Arkema S.A.; *Int'l*, pg. 570
BOSTIK B.V. CONSTRUCTION DIVISION—See Arkema S.A.; *Int'l*, pg. 570
BOSTIK B.V. INDUSTRIAL DIVISION—See Arkema S.A.; *Int'l*, pg. 570
BOSTIK CANADA LTD.—See Arkema S.A.; *Int'l*, pg. 570
BOSTIK EGYPT FOR PRODUCTION OF ADHESIVES S.A.E—See Arkema S.A.; *Int'l*, pg. 570
BOSTIK FINDLEY CHINA CO., LTD.—See Arkema S.A.; *Int'l*, pg. 570
BOSTIK FINDLEY (MALAYSIA) SDN. BHD.—See Arkema S.A.; *Int'l*, pg. 570
BOSTIK GMBH—See Arkema S.A.; *Int'l*, pg. 570
BOSTIK HELLAS S.A.—See Arkema S.A.; *Int'l*, pg. 570
BOSTIK HOLDING S.A.—See TotalEnergies SE; *Int'l*, pg. 7835
BOSTIK, INC. - BOSTON—See Arkema S.A.; *Int'l*, pg. 570
BOSTIK, INC. - CONYERS—See Arkema S.A.; *Int'l*, pg. 570
BOSTIK, INC. - GREENVILLE—See Arkema S.A.; *Int'l*, pg. 570
BOSTIK, INC. - LOUISVILLE—See Arkema S.A.; *Int'l*, pg. 570
BOSTIK, INC.—See Arkema S.A.; *Int'l*, pg. 570
BOSTIK, INC. - TEMECULA—See Arkema S.A.; *Int'l*, pg. 570
BOSTIK INDIA PRIVATE LTD.—See Arkema S.A.; *Int'l*, pg. 570
BOSTIK INDUSTRIES LIMITED—See Arkema S.A.; *Int'l*, pg. 570
BOSTIK KIMYA SANAYI VE TICARET A.S.—See Arkema S.A.; *Int'l*, pg. 570
BOSTIK L.L.C.—See Arkema S.A.; *Int'l*, pg. 570
BOSTIK LTD—See Arkema S.A.; *Int'l*, pg. 570
BOSTIK MEXICANA S.A. DE C.V.—See Arkema S.A.; *Int'l*, pg. 570
BOSTIK NETHERLAND B.V.—See Arkema S.A.; *Int'l*, pg. 570
BOSTIK NEW ZEALAND LTD.—See Arkema S.A.; *Int'l*, pg. 570
BOSTIK-NITTA CO., LTD.—See Arkema S.A.; *Int'l*, pg. 570
BOSTIK OY—See Arkema S.A.; *Int'l*, pg. 570
BOSTIK PHILIPPINES INC.—See Arkema S.A.; *Int'l*, pg. 570
BOSTIK ROMANIA S.R.L.—See Arkema S.A.; *Int'l*, pg. 570
BOSTIK SA—See Arkema S.A.; *Int'l*, pg. 570
BOSTIK (SHANGHAI) MANAGEMENT CO., LTD.—See Arkema S.A.; *Int'l*, pg. 570
BOSTIK SP Z.O.O.—See Arkema S.A.; *Int'l*, pg. 570
BOSTIK TECHNOLOGY GMBH—See Arkema S.A.; *Int'l*, pg. 570
BOSTIK (THAILAND) CO., LTD.—See Arkema S.A.; *Int'l*, pg. 570
BOSTIK UAB—See Arkema S.A.; *Int'l*, pg. 570
BOST, INC.; *U.S. Private*, pg. 620
BOSTLEMAN CORP.; *U.S. Private*, pg. 621
BOSTOCK COMPANY, INC.; *U.S. Private*, pg. 621
BOSTON ACOUSTICS, INC.—See Bain Capital, LP; *U.S. Private*, pg. 438
BOSTON ADVISORS LLC—See Equitable Holdings, Inc.; *U.S. Public*, pg. 790
BOSTON AGREX INC.; *U.S. Private*, pg. 621
BOSTONAIR LTD; *Int'l*, pg. 1118
BOSTON ATHLETIC ASSOCIATION; *U.S. Private*, pg. 621
BOSTON BALLET INC.; *U.S. Private*, pg. 621
BOSTON BARRICADE CO., INC.—See Mosaic Capital Partners; *U.S. Private*, pg. 2792
BOSTON BASKETBALL PARTNERS LLC; *U.S. Private*, pg. 621
BOSTONBEAN COFFEE CO., INC.; *U.S. Private*, pg. 622
THE BOSTON BEER COMPANY, INC.; *U.S. Public*, pg. 2041
BOSTON BENEFIT PARTNERS, LLC; *U.S. Private*, pg. 621

BOSTON BIOCHEM, INC.—See Bio-Techne Corporation; *U.S. Public*, pg. 334
BOSTON BIOMEDICAL ASSOCIATES LLC—See Factory CRO BV; *Int'l*, pg. 2601
BOSTON BRACE INTERNATIONAL, INC.—See OrthoPediatrics Corp.; *U.S. Public*, pg. 1619
BOSTON BREWING COMPANY, INC.—See The Boston Beer Company, Inc.; *U.S. Public*, pg. 2041
BOSTON BUSINESS JOURNAL—See Advance Publications, Inc.; *U.S. Private*, pg. 84
BOSTON CAR SERVICE, INC.; *U.S. Private*, pg. 621
BOSTON CELTICS LIMITED PARTNERSHIP—See Boston Basketball Partners LLC; *U.S. Private*, pg. 621
BOSTON CENTERLESS INC.; *U.S. Private*, pg. 621
BOSTONCOACH—See Marcou Transportation Group LLC; *U.S. Private*, pg. 2572
BOSTON COMMON ASSET MANAGEMENT, LLC; *U.S. Private*, pg. 621
THE BOSTON CONSULTING GROUP AB—See The Boston Consulting Group, Inc.; *U.S. Private*, pg. 3997
THE BOSTON CONSULTING GROUP - ABU DHABI—See The Boston Consulting Group, Inc.; *U.S. Private*, pg. 3997
THE BOSTON CONSULTING GROUP - ATHENS—See The Boston Consulting Group, Inc.; *U.S. Private*, pg. 3997
THE BOSTON CONSULTING GROUP - BANGKOK—See The Boston Consulting Group, Inc.; *U.S. Private*, pg. 3997
THE BOSTON CONSULTING GROUP - BARCELONA—See The Boston Consulting Group, Inc.; *U.S. Private*, pg. 3997
THE BOSTON CONSULTING GROUP - BEIJING—See The Boston Consulting Group, Inc.; *U.S. Private*, pg. 3997
THE BOSTON CONSULTING GROUP - BRUSSELS—See The Boston Consulting Group, Inc.; *U.S. Private*, pg. 3997
THE BOSTON CONSULTING GROUP - BUDAPEST—See The Boston Consulting Group, Inc.; *U.S. Private*, pg. 3997
THE BOSTON CONSULTING GROUP - BUENOS AIRES—See The Boston Consulting Group, Inc.; *U.S. Private*, pg. 3997
THE BOSTON CONSULTING GROUP B.V.—See The Boston Consulting Group, Inc.; *U.S. Private*, pg. 3997
THE BOSTON CONSULTING GROUP - CASABLANCA—See The Boston Consulting Group, Inc.; *U.S. Private*, pg. 3997
THE BOSTON CONSULTING GROUP - DUBAI—See The Boston Consulting Group, Inc.; *U.S. Private*, pg. 3997
THE BOSTON CONSULTING GROUP GMBH - BERLIN—See The Boston Consulting Group, Inc.; *U.S. Private*, pg. 3997
THE BOSTON CONSULTING GROUP GMBH - COLOGNE—See The Boston Consulting Group, Inc.; *U.S. Private*, pg. 3997
THE BOSTON CONSULTING GROUP GMBH—See The Boston Consulting Group, Inc.; *U.S. Private*, pg. 3997
THE BOSTON CONSULTING GROUP - HONG KONG—See The Boston Consulting Group, Inc.; *U.S. Private*, pg. 3997
THE BOSTON CONSULTING GROUP, INC. - ATLANTA—See The Boston Consulting Group, Inc.; *U.S. Private*, pg. 3998
THE BOSTON CONSULTING GROUP, INC. - CHICAGO—See The Boston Consulting Group, Inc.; *U.S. Private*, pg. 3998
THE BOSTON CONSULTING GROUP, INC. - DALLAS—See The Boston Consulting Group, Inc.; *U.S. Private*, pg. 3998
THE BOSTON CONSULTING GROUP, INC. - HOUSTON—See The Boston Consulting Group, Inc.; *U.S. Private*, pg. 3998
THE BOSTON CONSULTING GROUP, INC.; *U.S. Private*, pg. 3997
THE BOSTON CONSULTING GROUP, INC. - WASHINGTON, D.C.—See The Boston Consulting Group, Inc.; *U.S. Private*, pg. 3998
THE BOSTON CONSULTING GROUP - JAKARTA—See The Boston Consulting Group, Inc.; *U.S. Private*, pg. 3997
THE BOSTON CONSULTING GROUP - KUALA LUMPUR—See The Boston Consulting Group, Inc.; *U.S. Private*, pg. 3997
THE BOSTON CONSULTING GROUP - MADRID—See The Boston Consulting Group, Inc.; *U.S. Private*, pg. 3997
THE BOSTON CONSULTING GROUP NORDIC AB - COPENHAGEN—See The Boston Consulting Group, Inc.; *U.S. Private*, pg. 3997
THE BOSTON CONSULTING GROUP NORDIC AB - HELSINKI—See The Boston Consulting Group, Inc.; *U.S. Private*, pg. 3997
THE BOSTON CONSULTING GROUP NORDIC AB - OSLO—See The Boston Consulting Group, Inc.; *U.S. Private*, pg. 3997

CORPORATE AFFILIATIONS

THE BOSTON CONSULTING GROUP PTY. LTD. - CANBERRA—See The Boston Consulting Group, Inc.; *U.S. Private*, pg. 3998
THE BOSTON CONSULTING GROUP PTY. LTD. - NEW ZEALAND—See The Boston Consulting Group, Inc.; *U.S. Private*, pg. 3998
THE BOSTON CONSULTING GROUP PTY. LTD.—See The Boston Consulting Group, Inc.; *U.S. Private*, pg. 3998
THE BOSTON CONSULTING GROUP PTY. LTD. - SYDNEY—See The Boston Consulting Group, Inc.; *U.S. Private*, pg. 3998
THE BOSTON CONSULTING GROUP RSA PTY. LTD.—See The Boston Consulting Group, Inc.; *U.S. Private*, pg. 3998
THE BOSTON CONSULTING GROUP - SHANGHAI—See The Boston Consulting Group, Inc.; *U.S. Private*, pg. 3997
THE BOSTON CONSULTING GROUP SINGAPORE PTE. LTD.—See The Boston Consulting Group, Inc.; *U.S. Private*, pg. 3998
THE BOSTON CONSULTING GROUP - TAIPEI—See The Boston Consulting Group, Inc.; *U.S. Private*, pg. 3997
THE BOSTON CONSULTING GROUP - TOKYO—See The Boston Consulting Group, Inc.; *U.S. Private*, pg. 3997
BOSTON DYNAMICS INC.—See Hyundai Motor Company; *Int'l*, pg. 3558
BOSTON ENDOSCOPY CENTER, LLC—See KKR & Co. Inc.; *U.S. Public*, pg. 1245
BOSTON ENDO-SURGICAL TECHNOLOGIES LLC—See NN, Inc.; *U.S. Public*, pg. 1531
BOSTON ENERGY TRADING AND MARKETING LLC—See Mitsubishi Corporation; *Int'l*, pg. 4938
BOSTON FINANCIAL INVESTMENT MANAGEMENT, LP—See ORIX Corporation; *Int'l*, pg. 5633
BOSTON FINANCIAL MANAGEMENT, INC.; *U.S. Private*, pg. 621
BOSTON GEAR—See Regal Rexnord Corporation; *U.S. Public*, pg. 1772
BOSTON GLOBE ELECTRONIC PUBLISHING LLC—See NE Media Group, Inc.; *U.S. Private*, pg. 2877
THE BOSTON GLOBE—See NE Media Group, Inc.; *U.S. Private*, pg. 2877
THE BOSTON GROUP, INC.—See Isovera, LLC; *U.S. Private*, pg. 2146
BOSTON HARBOR CRUISES; *U.S. Private*, pg. 621
BOSTON HARLEY-DAVIDSON; *U.S. Private*, pg. 621
BOSTON HEALTHCARE ASSOCIATES, INC.—See Veranex; *U.S. Private*, pg. 4359
BOSTON HEALTH CARE FOR THE HOMELESS PROGRAM; *U.S. Private*, pg. 621
BOSTON HEART DIAGNOSTICS CORPORATION—See Eurofins Scientific S.E.; *Int'l*, pg. 2535
BOSTON HERALD INC.—See Alden Global Capital LLC; *U.S. Private*, pg. 155
THE BOSTON HOME, INC.; *U.S. Private*, pg. 3998
BOSTON HOMES—See Gannett Co., Inc.; *U.S. Public*, pg. 902
BOSTON HOTEL COMPANY, L.L.C.—See Hyatt Hotels Corporation; *U.S. Public*, pg. 1076
THE BOSTONIAN GROUP INSURANCE AGENCY, INC.—See Marsh & McLennan Companies, Inc.; *U.S. Public*, pg. 1382
BOSTONIAN WHOLESALE DIVISION—See C&J Clark Limited; *Int'l*, pg. 1239
BOSTON INC.; *U.S. Private*, pg. 621
BOSTON INTERIORS INC.—See Castle Island Partners LLC; *U.S. Private*, pg. 785
BOSTON INTERNATIONAL HOLDINGS PLC; *Int'l*, pg. 1118
BOSTON IRRIGATION SUPPLY CO; *U.S. Private*, pg. 621
BOSTON IT SOLUTIONS PVT. LTD.—See 2Crsi SA; *Int'l*, pg. 4
BOSTON KITCHEN DIST. INC; *U.S. Private*, pg. 621
BOSTON LAWNMOWER COMPANY—See The Crandall-Hicks Company, Inc.; *U.S. Private*, pg. 4016
BOSTON LEASING & FINANCE LTD.; *Int'l*, pg. 1118
BOSTON LIMITED—See Cerberus Capital Management, L.P.; *U.S. Private*, pg. 839
BOSTON MANAGEMENT AND RESEARCH—See Morgan Stanley; *U.S. Public*, pg. 1472
BOSTON MARKET CORPORATION; *U.S. Private*, pg. 621
BOSTON METAL PRODUCTS CORPORATION, HOME CENTER MERCHANDISING DIVISION—See Boston Metal Products Corporation; *U.S. Private*, pg. 622
BOSTON METAL PRODUCTS CORPORATION; *U.S. Private*, pg. 621
BOSTON MUTUAL LIFE INSURANCE COMPANY; *U.S. Private*, pg. 622
BOSTON NATIONAL TITLE AGENCY, LLC—See Incenter, LLC; *U.S. Private*, pg. 2053
BOSTON OMAHA CORPORATION; *U.S. Public*, pg. 371
BOSTON ORGANICS LLC—See GrubMarket, Inc.; *U.S. Private*, pg. 1797
BOSTON OUT-PATIENT SURGICAL SUITES, L.L.C.—See KKR & Co. Inc.; *U.S. Public*, pg. 1245
BOSTON PIANO GMBH—See Paulson & Co. Inc.; *U.S. Private*, pg. 3114

BOSTON PIZZA INTERNATIONAL, INC.; *Int'l*, pg. 1118
BOSTON PIZZA ROYALTIES INCOME FUND; *Int'l*, pg. 1118
BOSTON PRIVATE BANK & TRUST COMPANY—See Boston Private Financial Holdings, Inc.; *U.S. Public*, pg. 372
BOSTON PRIVATE BANK & TRUST CO. - SAN FRANCISCO BAY AREA DIVISION—See Boston Private Financial Holdings, Inc.; *U.S. Public*, pg. 372
BOSTON PRIVATE BANK & TRUST CO. - SOUTHERN CALIFORNIA DIVISION—See Boston Private Financial Holdings, Inc.; *U.S. Public*, pg. 372
BOSTON PRIVATE FINANCIAL HOLDINGS, INC.; *U.S. Public*, pg. 372
BOSTON PROFESSIONAL HOCKEY ASSOCIATION, INC.; *U.S. Private*, pg. 622
BOSTON PROPER LLC—See Brentwood Associates; *U.S. Private*, pg. 645
BOSTON PROPERTIES, INC.; *U.S. Public*, pg. 372
BOSTON PROPERTIES LIMITED PARTNERSHIP—See Boston Properties, Inc.; *U.S. Public*, pg. 372
BOSTON PROPERTIES SERVICES, LLC—See Boston Properties, Inc.; *U.S. Public*, pg. 373
BOSTON RED SOX BASEBALL CLUB LIMITED PARTNERSHIP—See Fenway Sports Group Holdings, LLC; *U.S. Private*, pg. 1496
BOSTON RESTAURANT ASSOCIATES, INC.; *U.S. Private*, pg. 622
BOSTON SAND & GRAVEL COMPANY; *U.S. Public*, pg. 373
BOSTON SCIENTIFIC - ARDEN HILLS/SAINT PAUL—See Boston Scientific Corporation; *U.S. Public*, pg. 374
BOSTON SCIENTIFIC ASIA PACIFIC PTE. LTD.—See Boston Scientific Corporation; *U.S. Public*, pg. 374
BOSTON SCIENTIFIC CARDIAC DIAGNOSTICS, INC.—See Boston Scientific Corporation; *U.S. Public*, pg. 374
BOSTON SCIENTIFIC CLONMEL (CRM)—See Boston Scientific Corporation; *U.S. Public*, pg. 374
BOSTON SCIENTIFIC COLOMBIA LIMITADA—See Boston Scientific Corporation; *U.S. Public*, pg. 374
BOSTON SCIENTIFIC CORK LIMITED—See Boston Scientific Corporation; *U.S. Public*, pg. 374
BOSTON SCIENTIFIC CORPORATION; *U.S. Public*, pg. 373
BOSTON SCIENTIFIC DEL CARRIBE, INC.—See Boston Scientific Corporation; *U.S. Public*, pg. 375
BOSTON SCIENTIFIC DE MEXICO, S.A. DE C.V.—See Boston Scientific Corporation; *U.S. Public*, pg. 375
BOSTON SCIENTIFIC - ELECTROPHYSIOLOGY - LOWELL—See Boston Scientific Corporation; *U.S. Public*, pg. 374
BOSTON SCIENTIFIC - FREMONT—See Boston Scientific Corporation; *U.S. Public*, pg. 374
BOSTON SCIENTIFIC GESELLSCHAFT M.B.H.—See Boston Scientific Corporation; *U.S. Public*, pg. 374
BOSTON SCIENTIFIC GROUP PLC—See Boston Scientific Corporation; *U.S. Public*, pg. 374
BOSTON SCIENTIFIC HELLAS S.A.—See Boston Scientific Corporation; *U.S. Public*, pg. 374
BOSTON SCIENTIFIC HONG KONG LIMITED—See Boston Scientific Corporation; *U.S. Public*, pg. 374
BOSTON SCIENTIFIC INTERNATIONAL B.V.—See Boston Scientific Corporation; *U.S. Public*, pg. 374
BOSTON SCIENTIFIC INTERNATIONAL S.A.—See Boston Scientific Corporation; *U.S. Public*, pg. 374
BOSTON SCIENTIFIC JAPAN K.K.—See Boston Scientific Corporation; *U.S. Public*, pg. 374
BOSTON SCIENTIFIC LATIN AMERICA B.V.—See Boston Scientific Corporation; *U.S. Public*, pg. 374
BOSTON SCIENTIFIC LEBANON SAL—See Boston Scientific Corporation; *U.S. Public*, pg. 374
BOSTON SCIENTIFIC LIMITED—See Boston Scientific Corporation; *U.S. Public*, pg. 374
BOSTON SCIENTIFIC - MAPLE GROVE—See Boston Scientific Corporation; *U.S. Public*, pg. 374
BOSTON SCIENTIFIC MEDIZINTECHNIK GMBH—See Boston Scientific Corporation; *U.S. Public*, pg. 374
BOSTON SCIENTIFIC NEDERLAND B.V.—See Boston Scientific Corporation; *U.S. Public*, pg. 374
BOSTON SCIENTIFIC NEUROMODULATION CORPORATION—See Boston Scientific Corporation; *U.S. Public*, pg. 374
BOSTON SCIENTIFIC NEW ZEALAND LIMITED—See Boston Scientific Corporation; *U.S. Public*, pg. 374
BOSTON SCIENTIFIC NORDIC AB—See Boston Scientific Corporation; *U.S. Public*, pg. 375
BOSTON SCIENTIFIC PHILIPPINES, INC.—See Boston Scientific Corporation; *U.S. Public*, pg. 375
BOSTON SCIENTIFIC - PLYMOUTH TECHNOLOGY CENTER—See Boston Scientific Corporation; *U.S. Public*, pg. 374
BOSTON SCIENTIFIC POLSKA SP. Z O.O.—See Boston Scientific Corporation; *U.S. Public*, pg. 375
BOSTON SCIENTIFIC PTY. LTD.—See Boston Scientific Corporation; *U.S. Public*, pg. 375
BOSTON SCIENTIFIC - SAN JOSE—See Boston Scientific Corporation; *U.S. Public*, pg. 374

BOSTON SCIENTIFIC S.A.S.—See Boston Scientific Corporation; *U.S. Public*, pg. 375
BOSTON SCIENTIFIC SCIMED, INC.—See Boston Scientific Corporation; *U.S. Public*, pg. 375
BOSTON SCIENTIFIC (SOUTH AFRICA) PROPRIETARY LIMITED—See Boston Scientific Corporation; *U.S. Public*, pg. 374
BOSTON SCIENTIFIC SPA—See Boston Scientific Corporation; *U.S. Public*, pg. 375
BOSTON SCIENTIFIC - SPENCER—See Boston Scientific Corporation; *U.S. Public*, pg. 374
BOSTON SCIENTIFIC SVERIGE AB—See Boston Scientific Corporation; *U.S. Public*, pg. 375
BOSTON SCIENTIFIC (THAILAND) LTD.—See Boston Scientific Corporation; *U.S. Public*, pg. 374
BOSTON SCIENTIFIC - VIENNA—See Boston Scientific Corporation; *U.S. Public*, pg. 374
BOSTON SEMI EQUIPMENT LLC; *U.S. Private*, pg. 622
BOSTON SERVER & STORAGE SOLUTIONS GMBH—See 2Crsi SA; *Int'l*, pg. 4
BOSTON SERVICE COMPANY, INC.—See Truist Financial Corporation; *U.S. Public*, pg. 2199
BOSTON SWORD & TUNA INC.—See Investcorp Holdings B.S.C.; *Int'l*, pg. 3776
BOSTON TAPES S.P.A.—See Chargeurs SA; *Int'l*, pg. 1449
BOSTON TECHNOLOGIES, INC.; *U.S. Private*, pg. 622
BOSTON TECHNOLOGY CORPORATION; *U.S. Private*, pg. 622
BOSTON TEKNOWSYS (INDIA) LIMITED; *Int'l*, pg. 1118
BOSTON TRADE INTERIOR SOLUTIONS—See Blackford Capital LLC; *U.S. Private*, pg. 574
BOSTON VA RESEARCH INSTITUTE, INC.; *U.S. Private*, pg. 622
BOSTON WHALER, INC.—See Brunswick Corporation; *U.S. Public*, pg. 407
BOSTON WHARF COMPANY—See Dubai World Corporation; *Int'l*, pg. 2220
BOST - STROJE, S.R.O.—See Quaser Machine Tools, Inc.; *Int'l*, pg. 6156
BOSTWICK-BRAUN COMPANY; *U.S. Private*, pg. 622
BOSTWICK LABORATORIES, INC.—See Poplar Healthcare, PLLC; *U.S. Private*, pg. 3228
BOSUN CO LTD; *Int'l*, pg. 1118
BOSUNG POWER TECHNOLOGY CO., LTD.; *Int'l*, pg. 1118
BOSUN TOOLS INC.—See Bosun Co Ltd; *Int'l*, pg. 1118
BOSWELL ENGINEERING; *U.S. Private*, pg. 622
BOSWELL ENGINEERING—See Boswell Engineering; *U.S. Private*, pg. 622
BOSWELL MCCLAVE ENGINEERING—See Boswell Engineering; *U.S. Private*, pg. 622
BOSWELL PROPERTIES INC.—See J.G. Boswell Co., Inc.; *U.S. Private*, pg. 2165
BOSWELL UNDERWATER ENGINEERING—See Boswell Engineering; *U.S. Private*, pg. 622
BOSWORTH GMBH—See Music Sales Corporation; *U.S. Private*, pg. 2817
BOSWORTH PAPERS INC.; *U.S. Private*, pg. 622
BOSWORTH STEEL ERECTORS, INC.; *U.S. Private*, pg. 622
BOTA BIO CO., LTD.; *Int'l*, pg. 1118
BOTAI TECHNOLOGY LIMITED; *Int'l*, pg. 1118
BOTALA ENERGY LIMITED; *Int'l*, pg. 1118
BOTANECO SPECIALTY INGREDIENTS INC.—See AVAC, Ltd.; *Int'l*, pg. 733
BOTANICA INTERNATIONAL FLORIST, INC.; *U.S. Private*, pg. 622
BOTANICAL FOOD COMPANY, INC.—See McCormick & Company, Incorporated; *U.S. Public*, pg. 1404
BOTANICAL FOOD COMPANY PTY. LTD.—See McCormick & Company, Incorporated; *U.S. Public*, pg. 1404
BOTANIX PHARMACEUTICALS LIMITED; *Int'l*, pg. 1118
THE BOTANTIST, INC.—See Acreage Holdings, Inc.; *U.S. Public*, pg. 36
BOTANY BAY IMPORTS & EXPORTS PTY LTD—See EBOS Group Limited; *Int'l*, pg. 2285
BOTEC BONCOURT S.A.—See Die Schweizerische Post AG; *Int'l*, pg. 2112
BO TECHNOLOGY INCORPORATED; *U.S. Private*, pg. 602
BOTEC SARL—See Die Schweizerische Post AG; *Int'l*, pg. 2112
BOT ELEKTROWINA TUROW SA—See Elektrownia Belchatow S.A.; *Int'l*, pg. 2357
BOT GORNICTWO I ENERGETYKA SA—See Elektrownia Belchatow S.A.; *Int'l*, pg. 2357
BOTHRA METALS & ALLOYS LTD; *Int'l*, pg. 1118
BO TIAN SUGAR INDUSTRY COMPANY LIMITED—See The Garfield Weston Foundation; *Int'l*, pg. 7648
BOTIM BUSINESS MANAGEMENT & TRADING INC.—See Nurol Holding A.S.; *Int'l*, pg. 5490
BOTJ INVESTMENT GROUP, INC.—See Bank of the James Financial Group, Inc.; *U.S. Public*, pg. 273
BOTKIN LUMBER COMPANY, INC.; *U.S. Private*, pg. 622
BOT LEASE CO., LTD.—See Mitsubishi UFJ Financial Group, Inc.; *Int'l*, pg. 4968
BOTNIA EXPLORATION HOLDINGS AB; *Int'l*, pg. 1118
BOTNIATAG AB—See Deutsche Bahn AG; *Int'l*, pg. 2049

BOTSFORD & GOODFELLOW, INC.; *U.S. Private*, pg. 623
BOTS INC.; *U.S. Public*, pg. 375
BOTSWANA DEVELOPMENT CORPORATION LIMITED; *Int'l*, pg. 1118
BOTSWANA DIAMONDS PLC; *Int'l*, pg. 1118
BOTSWANA INSURANCE COMPANY (PTY) LTD—See Masawara PLC; *Int'l*, pg. 4719
BOTSWANA INSURANCE HOLDINGS LIMITED—See Sanlam Limited; *Int'l*, pg. 6545
BOTSWANA OXYGEN COMPANY (PTY) LIMITED—See Linde plc; *Int'l*, pg. 4504
BOTSWANA STOCK EXCHANGE; *Int'l*, pg. 1118
BOTTCHER ENERGIE GMBH & CO. KG—See Marquard & Bahls AG; *Int'l*, pg. 4699
BOTTE FONDATIONS—See VINCI S.A.; *Int'l*, pg. 8213
BOTTEGA VENETA (CHINA) TRADING LTD—See Kering S.A.; *Int'l*, pg. 4135
BOTTEGA VENETA ESPANA SL—See Kering S.A.; *Int'l*, pg. 4135
BOTTEGA VENETA FRANCE SAS—See Kering S.A.; *Int'l*, pg. 4135
BOTTEGA VENETA GERMANY GMBH—See Kering S.A.; *Int'l*, pg. 4135
BOTTEGA VENETA GREECE S.A.—See Kering S.A.; *Int'l*, pg. 4133
BOTTEGA VENETA HONG KONG LIMITED—See Kering S.A.; *Int'l*, pg. 4135
BOTTEGA VENETA IRELAND LTD.—See Kering S.A.; *Int'l*, pg. 4133
BOTTEGA VENETA MALAYSIA SDN BHD—See Kering S.A.; *Int'l*, pg. 4135
BOTTEGA VENETA SRL—See Kering S.A.; *Int'l*, pg. 4135
BOTTEGA VENETA SWEDEN AB—See Kering S.A.; *Int'l*, pg. 4133
BOTTINI FUEL COMPANY; *U.S. Private*, pg. 623
BOTTLECUBE INC.—See CYBIRD Holdings Co., Ltd.; *Int'l*, pg. 1894
BOTTLECYCLER AUSTRALIA PTY. LTD.—See Tomra Systems ASA; *Int'l*, pg. 7802
BOTTLEGREEN DRINKS LTD—See SHS Group, Ltd.; *Int'l*, pg. 6867
BOTTLE GREEN LIMITED—See DCC plc; *Int'l*, pg. 1989
BOTTLE LAB TECHNOLOGIES PRIVATE LIMITED—See Compass Group PLC; *Int'l*, pg. 1750
BOTTLE ROCK POWER, LLC—See AltaRock Energy Inc.; *U.S. Private*, pg. 206
BOTTLERS NEPAL LIMITED; *Int'l*, pg. 1119
BOTTLERS NEPAL (TERAI) LIMITED—See Bottlers Nepal Limited; *Int'l*, pg. 1119
BOTTO FILA S.P.A.—See M&C S.p.A.; *Int'l*, pg. 4610
BOTTOM LINE AVIATION, LLC—See Nexstar Media Group, Inc.; *U.S. Public*, pg. 1524
BOTTOM LINE EQUIPMENT, L.L.C.; *U.S. Private*, pg. 623
BOTTOM LINE FOOD PROCESSORS, INC.—See Advent International Corporation; *U.S. Private*, pg. 98
BOTTOM LINE MARKETING & PUBLIC RELATIONS, INC.—See Michael, Best & Friedrich LLP; *U.S. Private*, pg. 2699
BOTTOM-LINE PERFORMANCE, INC.—See Tier 1 Performance Solutions, LLC; *U.S. Private*, pg. 4168
BOTTOM LINE PROCESS TECHNOLOGIES, INC.; *U.S. Private*, pg. 623
BOTTOM LINE SERVICES, LLC—See MasTec, Inc.; *U.S. Public*, pg. 1393
BOTTOMLINE TECHNOLOGIES INC.—See Thoma Bravo, L.P.; *U.S. Private*, pg. 4146
BOTT RADIO NETWORK; *U.S. Private*, pg. 623
BOU BANCORP, INC.; *U.S. Private*, pg. 623
BOUBLOK (PTY) LIMITED—See Afrimat Limited; *Int'l*, pg. 192
BOUBYAN BANK K.S.C.—See National Bank of Kuwait S.A.K.; *Int'l*, pg. 5153
BOUBYAN PETROCHEMICAL CO. KSC; *Int'l*, pg. 1119
BOUCART MEDICAL SRL—See Creo Medical Group PLC; *Int'l*, pg. 1839
BOUCHARA RECORDATI S.A.S.—See Recordati S.p.A.; *Int'l*, pg. 6238
BOUCHER AND JONES FUELS; *Int'l*, pg. 1119
BOUCHER CHEVROLET, INC.; *U.S. Private*, pg. 623
THE BOUCHER GROUP, INC.; *U.S. Private*, pg. 3998
BOUCHER & MUIR PTY LIMITED—See ADVANZ PHARMA Corp. Limited; *Int'l*, pg. 166
BOUCHERON RUSSIA OOO—See Kering S.A.; *Int'l*, pg. 4133
BOUCHERON SAM—See Kering S.A.; *Int'l*, pg. 4133
BOUCHERON SAS—See Kering S.A.; *Int'l*, pg. 4133
BOUCHERON (SUISSE) SA—See Kering S.A.; *Int'l*, pg. 4133
BOUCHERON TAIWAN CO., LTD.—See Kering S.A.; *Int'l*, pg. 4133
BOUCHERON TIMEPIECES S.A.—See Kering S.A.; *Int'l*, pg. 4133
BOUCHONS PRIOUX SARL—See CORTICEIRA AMORIM, S.G.P.S., S.A.; *Int'l*, pg. 1807
BOUCKAERT INDUSTRIAL TEXTILES, INC.—See Hyman Brickle & Son, Inc.; *U.S. Private*, pg. 2019
BOUCLAIR INC.; *Int'l*, pg. 1119

BOUGAINVILLE COPPER LIMITED—See Rio Tinto plc; *Int'l*, pg. 6346
BOUGHEY DISTRIBUTION LIMITED—See NWF Group Plc; *Int'l*, pg. 5499
BOU KHALIL SOCIETE MODERNE SARL; *Int'l*, pg. 1119
BOULCOTT HOSPITAL LIMITED—See Evolution Healthcare Pty. Ltd.; *Int'l*, pg. 2572
BOULDER CHEVROLET BUICK, INC.; *U.S. Private*, pg. 623
BOULDER CITY HOSPITAL; *U.S. Private*, pg. 623
THE BOULDER COMPANY—See Bertram Capital Management, LLC; *U.S. Private*, pg. 540
BOULDER CREEK APARTMENTS LP—See Edison International; *U.S. Public*, pg. 719
BOULDER CREEK BUILDERS; *U.S. Private*, pg. 623
BOULDER DAM CREDIT UNION; *U.S. Private*, pg. 623
BOULDER ENERGY LTD.—See Highwood Asset Management Ltd.; *Int'l*, pg. 3389
BOULDER GROWTH & INCOME FUND INC.; *U.S. Public*, pg. 375
BOULDER IONICS CORPORATION—See Molson Coors Beverage Company; *U.S. Public*, pg. 1459
BOULDER MEDIA LIMITED—See Hasbro, Inc.; *U.S. Public*, pg. 987
BOULDER PHILHARMONIC ORCHESTRA; *U.S. Private*, pg. 623
BOULDERS AMBULATORY SURGERY CENTER—See HCA Healthcare, Inc.; *U.S. Public*, pg. 991
BOULDER SCIENTIFIC COMPANY; *U.S. Private*, pg. 623
BOULDER SPINE CENTER, LLC—See Bain Capital, LP; *U.S. Private*, pg. 445
BOULDERS RESORT & GOLDEN DOOR SPA—See Blackstone Inc.; *U.S. Public*, pg. 351
BOULDINCORP.; *U.S. Private*, pg. 623
BOULD OPPORTUNITIES PLC; *Int'l*, pg. 1119
BOULE DIAGNOSTICS AB; *Int'l*, pg. 1119
BOULE MEDICAL AB—See Boule Diagnostics AB; *Int'l*, pg. 1119
BOULE MEDICAL (BEIJING) CO. LTD—See Boule Diagnostics AB; *Int'l*, pg. 1119
BOULE MEDICAL LLC—See Boule Diagnostics AB; *Int'l*, pg. 1119
BOULEVARD ACQUISITION CORP. II; *U.S. Public*, pg. 375
BOULEVARD AUTO SALES INC.; *U.S. Private*, pg. 623
BOULEVARD BREWING CO.—See Fibemi NV; *Int'l*, pg. 2651
BOULEVARD HOLDINGS, INC.; *Int'l*, pg. 1119
BOULEVARD MALL, LLC—See Brookfield Corporation; *Int'l*, pg. 1185
BOULEVARD MANOR NURSING CENTER—See Sava Senior Care LLC; *U.S. Private*, pg. 3555
BOULEVARD MOTEL CORP.—See Sunburst Hospitality Corporation; *U.S. Private*, pg. 3865
BOULEVARD RESIDENTIAL, LLC—See MetLife, Inc.; *U.S. Public*, pg. 1429
BOULEVARD SHOPPING BELEM S.A—See Allos SA; *Int'l*, pg. 359
BOUMA CORPORATION; *U.S. Private*, pg. 623
BOUMATIC LLC—See Madison One Holdings; *U.S. Private*, pg. 2544
THE BOUNCE AGENCY; *U.S. Private*, pg. 3998
BOUNCE ENERGY, INC.—See NRG Energy, Inc.; *U.S. Public*, pg. 1549
BOUNCE LOGISTICS, INC.—See XPO, Inc.; *U.S. Public*, pg. 2392
BOUNDARY BEND LIMITED; *Int'l*, pg. 1119
BOUNDARY DEVICES, LLC.—See Audax Group, Limited Partnership; *U.S. Private*, pg. 388
BOUNDARY GOLD AND COPPER MINING LTD.; *Int'l*, pg. 1119
BOUNDARY SYSTEMS, LTD; *U.S. Private*, pg. 623
BOUNDARY WATERS BANK—See Highland Bankshares Inc.; *U.S. Private*, pg. 1938
BOUNDLESS IMMIGRATION INC.; *U.S. Private*, pg. 623
BOUNDLESS NETWORK; *U.S. Private*, pg. 623
BOUNDLESS TECHNOLOGIES, INC.—See Video Display Corporation; *U.S. Public*, pg. 2297
BOUND TO STAY BOUND BOOKS INC.; *U.S. Private*, pg. 623
BOUND TREE MEDICAL, LLC—See Investor AB; *Int'l*, pg. 3787
BOUNTEOUS, INC.; *U.S. Private*, pg. 624
THE BOUNTIFUL COMPANY—See KKR & Co. Inc.; *U.S. Public*, pg. 1264
BOUNTIFUL SURGERY CENTER, LLC—See HCA Healthcare, Inc.; *U.S. Public*, pg. 991
BOUNTY BRANDS PTY LTD.; *Int'l*, pg. 1119
BOUNTY HOLDINGS INC—See Anam Inc.; *U.S. Private*, pg. 271
BOUNTYJOBS INC.; *U.S. Private*, pg. 624
BOUNTYLAND PETROLEUM INC.; *U.S. Private*, pg. 624
BOUNTY OIL & GAS NL; *Int'l*, pg. 1119
BOUNTY SERVICES PTY LTD.—See Apax Partners LLP; *Int'l*, pg. 507
BOUNTY SERVICES PTY LTD.—See The Scott Trust Limited; *Int'l*, pg. 7681
BOUNTY UK LTD.; *Int'l*, pg. 1120
BOUQUET COLLECTION, INC.; *U.S. Private*, pg. 624

BOURBON AUTOMOTIVE PLASTIC SA—See Plastiques du Val de Loire S.A.; *Int'l*, pg. 5892
BOURBON AUTOMOTIVE PLASTICS GMBH—See Plastiques du Val de Loire S.A.; *Int'l*, pg. 5892
BOURBON AUTOMOTIVE PLASTICS MARINHA GRANDE, S.A.—See Plastiques du Val de Loire S.A.; *Int'l*, pg. 5892
BOURBON COMMUNITY HOSPITAL, LLC—See Apollo Global Management, Inc.; *U.S. Public*, pg. 154
BOURBON CORPORATION; *Int'l*, pg. 1120
BOURBON FOODS USA CORPORATION—See Bourbon Corporation; *Int'l*, pg. 1120
BOURBON; *Int'l*, pg. 1120
BOURBON VANILLA LTD—See Taylor Smith Group; *Int'l*, pg. 7478
BOURDARIOS SAS—See VINCI S.A.; *Int'l*, pg. 8234
BOURDEAUS BROS OF MIDDLEBURY; *U.S. Private*, pg. 624
BOURGEOIS SAS—See VINCI S.A.; *Int'l*, pg. 8213
BOURGEOIS—See Compagnie de Saint-Gobain SA; *Int'l*, pg. 1722
BOURGET BROS. BUILDING MATERIALS; *U.S. Private*, pg. 624
BOURGEY MONTREUIL—See SNCF; *Int'l*, pg. 7025
BOURGOGNE HYGIENE ENTRETIEN SAS—See Bunzl plc; *Int'l*, pg. 1217
BOURJOIS LIMITED—See JAB Holding Company S.a.r.l.; *Int'l*, pg. 3860
BOURJOIS S.A.R.L.—See JAB Holding Company S.a.r.l.; *Int'l*, pg. 3860
BOURKE STREET CLINIC PTY LTD—See Healius Limited; *Int'l*, pg. 3302
BOURLAND & LEVERICH HOLDING COMPANY; *U.S. Private*, pg. 624
BOURLAND & LEVERICH SUPPLY CO. INC.—See Bourland & Leverich Holding Company; *U.S. Private*, pg. 624
BOURNE LEISURE GROUP LTD.—See Blackstone Inc.; *U.S. Public*, pg. 352
BOURNEMOUTH INTERNATIONAL AIRPORT LIMITED—See Rigby Group (RG) PLC; *Int'l*, pg. 6340
THE BOURNEMOUTH NUFFIELD HOSPITAL—See Nuffield Health; *Int'l*, pg. 5487
BOURNE PREPARED PRODUCE—See Bakkavor Group plc; *Int'l*, pg. 805
BOURNE STIR FRY—See Bakkavor Group plc; *Int'l*, pg. 806
BOURNE TEXTILE SERVICES LIMITED—See Johnson Service Group PLC; *Int'l*, pg. 3993
BOURNIVAL INC.; *U.S. Private*, pg. 624
BOURN & KOCH FELLOWS SERVICES GROUP—See Berkshire Hathaway Inc.; *U.S. Public*, pg. 298
BOURN & KOCH, INC.-REPLACEMENT PARTS DIVISION—See Berkshire Hathaway Inc.; *U.S. Public*, pg. 298
BOURN & KOCH, INC.—See Berkshire Hathaway Inc.; *U.S. Public*, pg. 298
BOURNS AG—See Bourns, Inc.; *U.S. Private*, pg. 624
BOURNS ASIA PACIFIC INC.—See Bourns, Inc.; *U.S. Private*, pg. 624
BOURNS DE MEXICO, S. DE R.L. DE C.V. - AUTOMOTIVE DIVISION—See Bourns, Inc.; *U.S. Private*, pg. 624
BOURNS DE MEXICO S DE RL DE CV—See Bourns, Inc.; *U.S. Private*, pg. 624
BOURNS ELECTRONICS, LTD.—See Bourns, Inc.; *U.S. Private*, pg. 624
BOURNS ELECTRONICS (TAIWAN) LTD.—See Bourns, Inc.; *U.S. Private*, pg. 624
BOURNS, INC. - AUTOMOTIVE DIVISION—See Bourns, Inc.; *U.S. Private*, pg. 624
BOURNS, INC. - CIRCUIT PROTECTION DIVISION—See Bourns, Inc.; *U.S. Private*, pg. 624
BOURNS, INC.; *U.S. Private*, pg. 624
BOURNS KFT.—See Bourns, Inc.; *U.S. Private*, pg. 624
BOURNS LTD.—See Bourns, Inc.; *U.S. Private*, pg. 624
BOURNS SENSORS GMBH—See Bourns, Inc.; *U.S. Private*, pg. 624
BOURNS TRADING (SHANGHAI) CO., LTD.—See Bourns, Inc.; *U.S. Private*, pg. 624
BOURNS (XIAMEN) LTD.—See Bourns, Inc.; *U.S. Private*, pg. 624
BOURQUE INDUSTRIES, INC.; *U.S. Public*, pg. 375
BOURSE DATA PTY. LTD.—See Sequoia Financial Group Limited; *Int'l*, pg. 6719
BOURSE DIRECT ET BOURSE DISCOUNT SA; *Int'l*, pg. 1120
BOURSE REGIONALE DES VALEURS MOBILIERS; *Int'l*, pg. 1120
BOURSORAMA S.A.—See Societe Generale S.A.; *Int'l*, pg. 7039
BOURY ENTERPRISES; *U.S. Private*, pg. 624
BOUSSARD & GAVAUDAN ASSET MANAGEMENT, LP—See Boussard & Gavaudan Holding Limited; *Int'l*, pg. 1120
BOUSSARD & GAVAUDAN GESTION S.A.S.—See Boussard & Gavaudan Holding Limited; *Int'l*, pg. 1120
BOUSSARD & GAVAUDAN HOLDING LIMITED; *Int'l*, pg. 1120

BOUSTEAD CRUISE CENTRE SDN BHD—See Lembaga Tabung Angkatan Tentera; *Int'l*, pg. 4448
BOUSTEAD HEAVY INDUSTRIES CORPORATION BERHAD; *Int'l*, pg. 1120
BOUSTEAD HOLDINGS BERHAD—See Lembaga Tabung Angkatan Tentera; *Int'l*, pg. 4448
BOUSTEAD INFORMATION TECHNOLOGY PTE LTD—See Boustead Singapore Limited; *Int'l*, pg. 1120
BOUSTEAD INFRASTRUCTURES PTE. LTD.—See Boustead Singapore Limited; *Int'l*, pg. 1120
BOUSTEAD INTERNATIONAL HEATERS CANADA LIMITED—See Boustead Singapore Limited; *Int'l*, pg. 1120
BOUSTEAD INTERNATIONAL HEATERS LIMITED—See Boustead Singapore Limited; *Int'l*, pg. 1120
BOUSTEAD LANGKAWI SHIPYARD SDN BHD—See Lembaga Tabung Angkatan Tentera; *Int'l*, pg. 4448
BOUSTEAD MAXITHERM ENERGY PTE LTD—See Boustead Singapore Limited; *Int'l*, pg. 1120
BOUSTEAD MEDICAL CARE HOLDINGS PTE. LTD.—See Boustead Singapore Limited; *Int'l*, pg. 1120
BOUSTEAD PLANTATIONS BERHAD—See Lembaga Tabung Angkatan Tentera; *Int'l*, pg. 4448
BOUSTEAD PROJECTS INVESTMENTS PTE LTD—See Boustead Singapore Limited; *Int'l*, pg. 1120
BOUSTEAD PROJECTS LTD.—See Boustead Singapore Limited; *Int'l*, pg. 1120
BOUSTEAD SALCON PTE LTD—See Boustead Singapore Limited; *Int'l*, pg. 1120
BOUSTEAD SALCON WATER SOLUTIONS PTE LTD—See Boustead Singapore Limited; *Int'l*, pg. 1120
BOUSTEAD SDN. BHD.—See Nissan Motor Co., Ltd.; *Int'l*, pg. 5367
BOUSTEAD SHIPPING AGENCIES SDN BHD—See Lembaga Tabung Angkatan Tentera; *Int'l*, pg. 4448
BOUSTEAD SINGAPORE LIMITED; *Int'l*, pg. 1120
BOUSTEAD TRAVEL SERVICES SDN BHD—See Lembaga Tabung Angkatan Tentera; *Int'l*, pg. 4448
BOUSTEAD WAVEFRONT INC.; *Int'l*, pg. 1121
BOUTER B.V.—See Sligro Food Group N.V.; *Int'l*, pg. 6997
BOUTHILLETTE PARIZEAU; *Int'l*, pg. 1121
BOUTIQUE COLLECTIVE INVESTMENTS (RF) (PTY) LTD—See Apex Fund Services Holdings Ltd.; *Int'l*, pg. 510
BOUTIQUE CORPORATION PUBLIC COMPANY LIMITED; *Int'l*, pg. 1121
BOUTIQUE FITNESS, LLC—See Town Sports International Holdings, Inc.; *U.S. Private*, pg. 4197
BOUTIQUE HOTEL MANAGEMENT GROUP, LLC; *U.S. Private*, pg. 624
BOUTIQUE JACOB INC.; *Int'l*, pg. 1121
BOUTIQUE LA VIE EN ROSE, INC.; *Int'l*, pg. 1121
BOUTIQUE NEWCITY PUBLIC COMPANY LIMITED; *Int'l*, pg. 1121
BOUTIQUES, INC.; *Int'l*, pg. 1121
BOUTIQUE TERE, INC.; *U.S. Private*, pg. 624
BOUTWELL OWENS & CO. INC.; *U.S. Private*, pg. 624
BOUVERAT INDUSTRIES, S.A.S.—See NN, Inc.; *U.S. Public*, pg. 1530
BOUVET ASA; *Int'l*, pg. 1121
BOUVET LADUBAY SA; *Int'l*, pg. 1121
BOUVET STOCKHOLM AB—See Bouvet ASA; *Int'l*, pg. 1121
BOUVET SVERIGE AB—See Bouvet ASA; *Int'l*, pg. 1121
BOUVET SYD AB—See Bouvet ASA; *Int'l*, pg. 1121
BOUWBORG B.V.—See Friso Bouwgroep B.V.; *Int'l*, pg. 2793
BOUWCOMBINATIE INTERMEZZO V.O.F.—See Heijmans N.V.; *Int'l*, pg. 3322
BOUWCOMBINATIE KOHNSTAMMLOCATIE V.O.F.—See Ronesans Holding A.S.; *Int'l*, pg. 6396
BOUWFONDS INVESTMENT MANAGEMENT B.V.; *Int'l*, pg. 1121
BOUWFONDS PROPERTY DEVELOPMENT B.V.—See Cooperatieve Centrale Raiffeisen-Boerenleenbank B.A.; *Int'l*, pg. 1791
BOUWONTWIKKELING JONGEN BV—See Koninklijke VolkerWessels N.V.; *Int'l*, pg. 4271
BOUYER LEROUX SA; *Int'l*, pg. 1121
BOUYER MANUTENTION S.A.—See Konecranes Plc; *Int'l*, pg. 4251
BOUYGUES BATIMENT ILE-DE-FRANCE—See Bouygues S.A.; *Int'l*, pg. 1121
BOUYGUES BATIMENT INTERNATIONAL—See Bouygues S.A.; *Int'l*, pg. 1122
BOUYGUES CONSTRUCTION—See Bouygues S.A.; *Int'l*, pg. 1121
BOUYGUES ENERGIES & SERVICES GABON—See Bouygues S.A.; *Int'l*, pg. 1122
BOUYGUES ENERGIES & SERVICES SAS—See Bouygues S.A.; *Int'l*, pg. 1122
BOUYGUES ENTREPRISES FRANCE-EUROPE—See Bouygues S.A.; *Int'l*, pg. 1122
BOUYGUES E&S CONTRACTING UK LIMITED—See Bouygues S.A.; *Int'l*, pg. 1122
BOUYGUES E&S FM UK LIMITED—See Bouygues S.A.; *Int'l*, pg. 1122
BOUYGUES E&S INFRASTRUCTURE UK LIMITED—See Bouygues S.A.; *Int'l*, pg. 1122

COMPANY NAME INDEX

BOUYGUES E&S INTEC AG—See Bouygues S.A.; *Int'l*, pg. 1123
BOUYGUES E&S INTEC ITALIA S.P.A.—See Bouygues S.A.; *Int'l*, pg. 1123
BOUYGUES E&S INTEC ITALIA SPA—See Bouygues S.A.; *Int'l*, pg. 1123
BOUYGUES E&S INTEC SCHWEIZ AG—See Bouygues S.A.; *Int'l*, pg. 1123
BOUYGUES E&S INTEC SCHWEIZ AG—See Bouygues S.A.; *Int'l*, pg. 1123
BOUYGUES E&S INTEC SCHWEIZ AG—See Bouygues S.A.; *Int'l*, pg. 1123
BOUYGUES E&S INTEC SWITZERLAND LTD—See Bouygues S.A.; *Int'l*, pg. 1123
BOUYGUES E&S PROZESSAUTOMATION AG—See Bouygues S.A.; *Int'l*, pg. 1123
BOUYGUES E&S UK LTD.—See Bouygues S.A.; *Int'l*, pg. 1122
BOUYGUES IMMOBILIER—See Bouygues S.A.; *Int'l*, pg. 1122
BOUYGUES INMOBILIARIA S.A.—See Bouygues S.A.; *Int'l*, pg. 1122
BOUYGUES S.A.; *Int'l*, pg. 1121
BOUYGUES TELECOM SA—See Bouygues S.A.; *Int'l*, pg. 1122
BOUYGUES TRAVAUX PUBLICS—See Bouygues S.A.; *Int'l*, pg. 1122
BOUYGUES (UK) LTD.—See Bouygues S.A.; *Int'l*, pg. 1121
BOUYOUD DISTRIBUTION—See Tonnellerie Francois Freres; *Int'l*, pg. 7810
BOVACO—See Omnicom Group Inc.; *U.S. Public*, pg. 1596
BOVA FRANCE; *Int'l*, pg. 1123
BOVA SPECIALS UK LTD.—See Vimian Group AB; *Int'l*, pg. 8208
BOV ASSET MANAGEMENT LIMITED—See Bank of Valletta p.l.c.; *Int'l*, pg. 849
BOVEC SAS—See Genus Plc; *Int'l*, pg. 2930
BOVEDA INC.; *U.S. Private*, pg. 624
BOV FUND SERVICES LTD.—See Bank of Valletta p.l.c.; *Int'l*, pg. 849
BOVIE CANADA ULC—See Apyx Medical Corporation; *U.S. Public*, pg. 175
BOVIET SOLAR TECHNOLOGY CO., LTD.—See Ningbo Powerway Alloy Materials Co., Ltd.; *Int'l*, pg. 5305
BOVIET SOLAR USA LTD.—See Ningbo Powerway Alloy Materials Co., Ltd.; *Int'l*, pg. 5305
BOVIL APS—See SP Group A/S; *Int'l*, pg. 7122
BOVIL DDB—See Omnicom Group Inc.; *U.S. Public*, pg. 1579
BOVIS HOMES LIMITED—See Vistry Group PLC; *Int'l*, pg. 8255
BOVISION AB—See Alma Media Corporation; *Int'l*, pg. 362
BOVIS LEND LEASE A.S.—See Lendlease Corporation Limited; *Int'l*, pg. 4451
BOVIS LEND LEASE BAU GMBH—See Lendlease Corporation Limited; *Int'l*, pg. 4451
BOVIS LEND LEASE BV—See Lendlease Corporation Limited; *Int'l*, pg. 4451
BOVIS LEND LEASE CONSTRUCTION & PROJECT MANAGEMENT LTD—See Lendlease Corporation Limited; *Int'l*, pg. 4451
BOVIS LEND LEASE CORP—See Lendlease Corporation Limited; *Int'l*, pg. 4451
BOVIS LEND LEASE GENERAL CONSTRUCTION L.L.C.—See Lendlease Corporation Limited; *Int'l*, pg. 4451
BOVIS LEND LEASE GMBH—See Lendlease Corporation Limited; *Int'l*, pg. 4451
BOVIS LEND LEASE (HK) LTD.—See Lendlease Corporation Limited; *Int'l*, pg. 4451
BOVIS LEND LEASE INC.—See Lendlease Corporation Limited; *Int'l*, pg. 4451
BOVIS LEND LEASE IRELAND—See Lendlease Corporation Limited; *Int'l*, pg. 4451
BOVIS LEND LEASE JAPAN INC.—See Lendlease Corporation Limited; *Int'l*, pg. 4451
BOVIS LEND LEASE KFT—See Lendlease Corporation Limited; *Int'l*, pg. 4451
BOVIS LEND LEASE LMB—See Lendlease Corporation Limited; *Int'l*, pg. 4451
BOVIS LEND LEASE PHARMACEUTICAL DIVISION—See Lendlease Corporation Limited; *Int'l*, pg. 4451
BOVIS LEND LEASE PORTUGAL LDA.—See Lendlease Corporation Limited; *Int'l*, pg. 4451
BOVIS LEND LEASE PTE LTD—See Lendlease Corporation Limited; *Int'l*, pg. 4451
BOVIS LEND LEASE, S.A. DE C.V.—See Lendlease Corporation Limited; *Int'l*, pg. 4451
BOVIS LEND LEASE SA—See Lendlease Corporation Limited; *Int'l*, pg. 4451
BOVIS LEND LEASE SA—See Lendlease Corporation Limited; *Int'l*, pg. 4451
BOVIS LEND LEASE—See Lendlease Corporation Limited; *Int'l*, pg. 4451
BOVIS LEND LEASE—See Lendlease Corporation Limited; *Int'l*, pg. 4451

BOVIS LEND LEASE SP. Z O.O—See Lendlease Corporation Limited; *Int'l*, pg. 4451
BOWA-ELECTRONIC GMBH & CO. KG; *Int'l*, pg. 1123
BOWA INTERNATIONAL SP. Z O.O. SP. K.—See BOWA-electronic GmbH & Co. KG; *Int'l*, pg. 1123
BOW AND ARROW MANOR INC.; *U.S. Private*, pg. 625
BOWATER BUILDING PRODUCTS LTD.; *Int'l*, pg. 1123
BOW-BOECK ENTERPRISES LLC; *U.S. Private*, pg. 625
BOW CYCLE & MOTOR COMPANY LTD.; *Int'l*, pg. 1123
BOWDEN FORD LINCOLN MERCURY, INC.; *U.S. Private*, pg. 625
BOWDEN OIL COMPANY, INC.—See Majors Management, LLC; *U.S. Private*, pg. 2555
BOWDENS SILVER PTY. LIMITED—See Silver Mines Limited; *Int'l*, pg. 6924
BOWDITCH MARINE, INC.—See Lovell Minnick Partners LLC; *U.S. Private*, pg. 2502
THE BOWDOIN GROUP, INC.; *U.S. Private*, pg. 3998
BOWE CARDTEC GMBH—See BOWE SYSTEC AG; *Int'l*, pg. 1123
BOWE INDUSTRIES INC.; *U.S. Private*, pg. 625
BOWEN ACQUISITION CORP.; *U.S. Public*, pg. 376
BOWEN AGENCY INC.; *U.S. Private*, pg. 625
BOWEN BUILDING, L.P.—See Vornado Realty Trust; *U.S. Public*, pg. 2310
THE BOWEN CONSULTING GROUP, INC.; *U.S. Private*, pg. 3998
BOWEN ENERGY LTD.—See Tata Sons Limited; *Int'l*, pg. 7471
BOWEN ENGINEERING CORPORATION; *U.S. Private*, pg. 625
BOWEN INDUSTRIAL CONTRACTORS; *U.S. Private*, pg. 625
BOWEN JUICES INTERNATIONAL; *U.S. Private*, pg. 625
BOWEN, MICLETTE & BRITT, INC.; *U.S. Private*, pg. 625
BOWEN PETROLEUM INC.; *U.S. Private*, pg. 625
BOWEN & POMEROY PTY. LTD.; *Int'l*, pg. 1124
BOWEN SCARFF FORD SALES, INC.; *U.S. Private*, pg. 625
BOWENS INTERNATIONAL LTD.—See Aurelius Equity Opportunities SE & Co. KGaA; *Int'l*, pg. 708
BOWEN TRAVEL SERVICES INC.; *U.S. Private*, pg. 625
BOWERS ENTERPRISES, LLC; *U.S. Private*, pg. 625
BOWERS ENVELOPE COMPANY, INC.—See Supremex Inc.; *Int'l*, pg. 7341
BOWERS FIBERS INC.; *U.S. Private*, pg. 625
BOWERSOX INSURANCE AGENCY COMPANY—See Keystone Agency Investors LLC; *U.S. Private*, pg. 2295
THE BOWERSTON SHALE COMPANY; *U.S. Private*, pg. 3998
THE BOWERY PRESENTS, LLC—See The Anschutz Corporation; *U.S. Private*, pg. 3987
BOWERY RESIDENTS' COMMITTEE, INC.; *U.S. Private*, pg. 625
BOWES CONSTRUCTION, INC.; *U.S. Private*, pg. 625
BOWE SYSTEC AB—See L. Possehl & Co. mbH; *Int'l*, pg. 4382
BOWE SYSTEC AG; *Int'l*, pg. 1123
BOWE SYSTEC AUSTRIA GMBH—See L. Possehl & Co. mbH; *Int'l*, pg. 4382
BOWE SYSTEC, CEE, S.A.—See BOWE SYSTEC AG; *Int'l*, pg. 1123
BOWE SYSTEC COMERCIO DE EQUIPAMENTOS PARA ESCRITORIO S.A.—See L. Possehl & Co. mbH; *Int'l*, pg. 4382
BOWE SYSTEC (IR) LTD.—See L. Possehl & Co. mbH; *Int'l*, pg. 4382
BOWE SYSTEC JAPAN LTD.—See L. Possehl & Co. mbH; *Int'l*, pg. 4382
BOWE SYSTEC LTD.—See L. Possehl & Co. mbH; *Int'l*, pg. 4382
BOWE SYSTEC NEDERLAND B.V.—See L. Possehl & Co. mbH; *Int'l*, pg. 4382
BOWE SYSTEC NORTH-AMERICA INC.—See L. Possehl & Co. mbH; *Int'l*, pg. 4382
BOWE SYSTEC S.A.—See L. Possehl & Co. mbH; *Int'l*, pg. 4382
BOWE SYSTEC S.A.S.—See L. Possehl & Co. mbH; *Int'l*, pg. 4382
BOWE SYSTEC (SCHWEIZ) AG—See L. Possehl & Co. mbH; *Int'l*, pg. 4382
BOWE SYSTEC S.P.A.—See L. Possehl & Co. mbH; *Int'l*, pg. 4382
BOWFLEX INC.—See Johnson Health Tech. Co., Ltd.; *Int'l*, pg. 3991
BOWHEAD MANUFACTURING COMPANY, LLC—See Ukpeagvik Inupiat Corporation; *U.S. Private*, pg. 4275
BOWHUNTER MAGAZINE—See InterMedia Advisors, LLC; *U.S. Private*, pg. 2112
BOWIE MALL COMPANY, LLC—See Washington Prime Group Inc.; *U.S. Private*, pg. 4448
BOWIE RESOURCES LLC; *U.S. Private*, pg. 625
BOWIE-SIMS-PRANGE INC.; *U.S. Private*, pg. 625
BOWIE-SIMS-PRANGE TREATING CORP.—See Bowie-Sims-Prange Inc.; *U.S. Private*, pg. 625
BOWIM-PODKARPACIE SP. Z O.O.—See Bowim S.A.; *Int'l*, pg. 1124
BOWIM S.A.; *Int'l*, pg. 1124
BOWKER BLACKBURN LTD.; *Int'l*, pg. 1124

BOWL AMERICA INCORPORATED—See Bowlero Corp; *U.S. Public*, pg. 376
BOWL AMERICA SHIRLEY INC.—See Bowlero Corp; *U.S. Public*, pg. 376
BOWLEN SPORTS, INC.; *U.S. Private*, pg. 625
BOWLER METCALF LIMITED; *Int'l*, pg. 1124
BOWLER MOTORS LIMITED—See Tata Motors Limited; *Int'l*, pg. 7466
BOWLERO CORP; *U.S. Public*, pg. 376
BOWLES CORPORATE SERVICES INC.; *U.S. Private*, pg. 626
BOWLEVEN PLC; *Int'l*, pg. 1124
BOWLING GREEN FREIGHT INC.; *U.S. Private*, pg. 626
BOWLING GREEN INN OF PENSACOLA, INC.—See Acadia Healthcare Company, Inc.; *U.S. Public*, pg. 28
BOWLING GREEN INN OF SOUTH DAKOTA, INC.—See Acadia Healthcare Company, Inc.; *U.S. Public*, pg. 28
BOWLING PORTFOLIO MANAGEMENT LLC—See CI Financial Corporation; *Int'l*, pg. 1600
THE BOWLIN GROUP LLC; *U.S. Private*, pg. 3998
BOWLIN TRAVEL CENTERS, INC.; *U.S. Public*, pg. 376
BOWL NEW ENGLAND INC.; *U.S. Private*, pg. 626
BOWMAN ANDROS PRODUCTS, LLC; *U.S. Private*, pg. 626
BOWMAN CONSTRUCTORS, INC.; *U.S. Private*, pg. 626
BOWMAN CONSULTING GROUP LTD.; *U.S. Public*, pg. 376
BOWMAN DEVELOPMENT CORPORATION—See Bowman Group LLP; *U.S. Private*, pg. 626
BOWMAN ENTERPRISES INC.; *U.S. Private*, pg. 626
BOWMAN FARMS INC.—See Bowman Enterprises Inc.; *U.S. Private*, pg. 626
BOWMAN GROUP LLP; *U.S. Private*, pg. 626
BOWMAN HOLLIS MANUFACTURING CO., INC. - LAGRANGE—See Bowman Hollis Manufacturing, Inc.; *U.S. Private*, pg. 626
BOWMAN HOLLIS MANUFACTURING, INC.; *U.S. Private*, pg. 626
BOWMAN INC.; *U.S. Private*, pg. 626
BOWMAN & KEMP REBAR—See Boman Kemp Basement Window Systems; *U.S. Private*, pg. 611
BOWMAN & KEMP STEEL & SUPPLY COMPANY—See Boman Kemp Basement Window Systems; *U.S. Private*, pg. 611
BOWMAN LOGISTICS—See Bowman Group LLP; *U.S. Private*, pg. 626
BOWMAN POWER GROUP LTD; *Int'l*, pg. 1124
BOWMAN PROMOTIONAL SPECIALTIES INC.—See Target Print & Mail; *U.S. Private*, pg. 3933
BOWMAN SALES & EQUIPMENT INC.—See Bowman Group LLP; *U.S. Private*, pg. 626
BOWMAN SYSTEMS, L.L.C.—See Leonard Green & Partners, L.P.; *U.S. Private*, pg. 2430
BOWMAN SYSTEMS, L.L.C.—See TPG Capital, L.P.; *U.S. Public*, pg. 2177
BOWMAN TOOL & MACHINING INC.—See Polaris, Inc.; *U.S. Public*, pg. 1701
BOWMAN TRUCK LEASING, LLC—See Bowman Group LLP; *U.S. Private*, pg. 626
BOWMARK CAPITAL LLP; *Int'l*, pg. 1124
BOWMO, INC.; *U.S. Public*, pg. 377
BOWNE INTERNATIONAL LTD.—See Chatham Asset Management, LLC; *U.S. Private*, pg. 862
BOWON LIGHT METAL CO., LTD.—See NICE Holdings Co., Ltd.; *Int'l*, pg. 5264
BOW PHYSICAL THERAPY & SPINE CENTER, LIMITED PARTNERSHIP—See U.S. Physical Therapy, Inc.; *U.S. Public*, pg. 2214
BOW PLANNING GROUP INC; *Int'l*, pg. 1123
BOWRAL MANAGEMENT COMPANY PTY LIMITED—See Ramsay Health Care Limited; *Int'l*, pg. 6199
BOWRING MARSH (BERMUDA) LTD.—See Marsh & McLennan Companies, Inc.; *U.S. Public*, pg. 1374
BOWRING MARSH (DUBLIN) LIMITED—See Marsh & McLennan Companies, Inc.; *U.S. Public*, pg. 1374
BOWRING MARSH LIMITED—See Marsh & McLennan Companies, Inc.; *U.S. Public*, pg. 1374
BOW RIVER ASSET MANAGEMENT CORP.; *U.S. Private*, pg. 625
BOWSPRIT CAPITAL CORP. LTD—See OUE Limited; *Int'l*, pg. 5665
BOW STREET, LLC; *U.S. Private*, pg. 625
BOWTHORPE-HELLERMANN DISTRIBUTORS—See Spirent Communications plc; *Int'l*, pg. 7139
BOW TIE CINEMAS, LLC; *U.S. Private*, pg. 625
BOWTIE PRESS—See Fancy Publications Inc.; *U.S. Private*, pg. 1472
BOWX ACQUISITION CORP.; *U.S. Public*, pg. 377
BOXABL INC.; *U.S. Private*, pg. 626
BOXAL NETHERLANDS B.V.—See Ontario Teachers' Pension Plan; *Int'l*, pg. 5589
BOXAL (SUISSE) SA—See Ontario Teachers' Pension Plan; *Int'l*, pg. 5589
BOX BOARD PRODUCTS, INC.—See Greif Inc.; *U.S. Public*, pg. 965
THE BOXBORO GROUP—See Bischof + Klein GmbH & Co. KG; *Int'l*, pg. 1049
BOXCEIPTS.COM, INC.; *U.S. Private*, pg. 626

BOXCEIPTS.COM, INC.

CORPORATE AFFILIATIONS

BOX CHARTER CO., LTD.—See Seino Holdings Co., Ltd.; *Int'l*, pg. 6690
BOXCLEVER—See ITV plc; *Int'l*, pg. 3845
BOX.COM (UK) LTD—See Box, Inc.; *U.S. Public*, pg. 377
BOXED, INC.—See MSG Distributors, Inc.; *U.S. Private*, pg. 2807
BOXERCRAFT INCORPORATED; *U.S. Private*, pg. 626
BOXER CREATIVE—See The Marketing Store; *U.S. Private*, pg. 4075
BOXER PROPERTY MANAGEMENT CORPORATION; *U.S. Private*, pg. 626
BOXER SUPERSTORES (PTY) LIMITED—See Pink n Pay Holdings Limited RF; *Int'l*, pg. 5870
BOXES ETC. II, LLC—See Monomoy Capital Partners LLC; *U.S. Private*, pg. 2772
BOXHOLM MEJERI AB—See Arla Foods amba; *Int'l*, pg. 572
BOXHOLM STAL AB—See Swiss Steel Holding AG; *Int'l*, pg. 7372
BOX, INC.; *U.S. Public*, pg. 377
BOXLEY MATERIALS COMPANY—See Summit Materials, Inc.; *U.S. Public*, pg. 1960
BOXLIGHT CORPORATION; *U.S. Public*, pg. 377
BOXLIGHT INC.; *U.S. Private*, pg. 626
THE BOXMAKER INC.; *U.S. Private*, pg. 3998
THE BOXMAKER INC.—See The Boxmaker Inc.; *U.S. Private*, pg. 3998
THE BOXMAKER INC.—See The Boxmaker Inc.; *U.S. Private*, pg. 3998
BOX MANUFACTURING COMPANY LIMITED—See ENL Limited; *Int'l*, pg. 2441
BOX MANUFACTURING CO—See ENL Limited; *Int'l*, pg. 2441
BOXOFFICETICKETSALES.COM; *U.S. Private*, pg. 626
BOX-PAK (HANOI) CO., LTD.—See Can-One Berhad; *Int'l*, pg. 1276
BOX-PAK (MALAYSIA) BERHAD—See Can-One Berhad; *Int'l*, pg. 1276
BOX-PAK (VIETNAM) CO., LTD.—See Can-One Berhad; *Int'l*, pg. 1276
BOXPLAN GMBH & CO. KG—See Bobst Group S.A.; *Int'l*, pg. 1096
BOX SHIPS, INC.; *Int'l*, pg. 1124
BOX TELEVISION LTD.—See Channel Four Television Corporation; *Int'l*, pg. 1446
BOX TELEVISION LTD.—See Heinrich Bauer Verlag KG; *Int'l*, pg. 3323
BOX TV LIMITED—See DCD Media plc; *Int'l*, pg. 1991
BOX UK LIMITED; *Int'l*, pg. 1124
BOX UK LIMITED—See Box UK Limited; *Int'l*, pg. 1124
BOXUNION HOLDINGS LLC; *U.S. Private*, pg. 627
BOXWOOD PARTNERS LLC; *U.S. Private*, pg. 627
BOXX MODULAR INC. - DENVER OFFICE—See Black Diamond Group Limited; *Int'l*, pg. 1059
BOXX MODULAR INC.—See Black Diamond Group Limited; *Int'l*, pg. 1059
BOXX TECHNOLOGIES, LLC—See Craftsman Capital Partners, LLC; *U.S. Private*, pg. 1082
BOXY CHARM, INC.; *U.S. Private*, pg. 627
BOYAA INTERACTIVE INTERNATIONAL LTD; *Int'l*, pg. 1124
BOYALIFE GROUP; *Int'l*, pg. 1124
BOYAUDERIE ORLEANAISE SA—See Danish Crown AmbA; *Int'l*, pg. 1964
BOYAUX BRESSANS SA—See Danish Crown AmbA; *Int'l*, pg. 1964
BOYCE LUMBER CO.; *U.S. Private*, pg. 627
BOYD AUTOMOTIVE; *U.S. Private*, pg. 627
BOYD BILOXI, LLC—See Boyd Gaming Corporation; *U.S. Public*, pg. 377
BOYD BROS. TRANSPORTATION INC.—See Daseke, Inc.; *U.S. Private*, pg. 1161
BOYD CHEVROLET INC.; *U.S. Private*, pg. 627
BOYD COFFEE COMPANY—See Farmer Brothers Co.; *U.S. Public*, pg. 821
BOYD COUNTY FORD; *U.S. Private*, pg. 627
BOYDEN WORLD CORPORATION; *U.S. Private*, pg. 627
BOYDEN & YOUNGBLUTT ADVERTISING & MARKETING; *U.S. Private*, pg. 627
BOYD EXPLORATION CONSULTANTS LIMITED—See RPS Group plc; *Int'l*, pg. 6415
BOYD FLOTATION, INC—See The Bedroom Store; *U.S. Private*, pg. 3992
BOYD GAMING CORPORATION; *U.S. Public*, pg. 377
THE BOYD GROUP INC.—See Boyd Group Services Inc.; *Int'l*, pg. 1124
BOYD GROUP SERVICES INC.; *Int'l*, pg. 1124
THE BOYD GROUP (U.S.) INC.—See Boyd Group Services Inc.; *Int'l*, pg. 1124
BOYD INDUSTRIES, INC.—See Salt Creek Capital Management, LLC; *U.S. Private*, pg. 3533
BOYD INSURANCE & INVESTMENT SERVICES, INC.; *U.S. Private*, pg. 627
BOYD LIGHTING; *U.S. Private*, pg. 627
BOYD LOGISTICS, LLC—See Daseke, Inc.; *U.S. Private*, pg. 1161
BOYD MANAGEMENT; *U.S. Private*, pg. 627
BOYD METALS, INC.; *U.S. Private*, pg. 627

BOYD METALS OF JOPLIN, INC—See Boyd Metals, Inc.; *U.S. Private*, pg. 627
BOYD PROPERTIES, LLC—See Pye-Barker Fire & Safety, LLC; *U.S. Private*, pg. 3309
BOYD RACING, L.L.C.—See Boyd Gaming Corporation; *U.S. Public*, pg. 377
THE BOYDS COLLECTION, LTD.—See Enesco, LLC; *U.S. Private*, pg. 1397
BOYD SHARED SERVICES INC.—See Boyd Gaming Corporation; *U.S. Public*, pg. 377
BOYDS MEN'S STORE; *U.S. Private*, pg. 628
BOYDS MILLS PRESS, INC.—See Highlights for Children, Inc.; *U.S. Private*, pg. 1940
BOYD'S TIRE & SERVICE—See Greenbriar Equity Group, L.P.; *U.S. Private*, pg. 1776
BOYD TAMNEY CROSS INC.; *U.S. Private*, pg. 627
BOYD THERMAL SYSTEMS TAIWAN INC.—See The Goldman Sachs Group, Inc.; *U.S. Public*, pg. 2080
BOYD TUNICA, INC.—See Boyd Gaming Corporation; *U.S. Public*, pg. 377
BOYD WATTERSON ASSET MANAGEMENT, LLC—See TAMCO Holdings, LLC; *U.S. Private*, pg. 3928
BOYER AND RITTER LLC; *U.S. Private*, pg. 628
BOYER CANDY COMPANY INC.; *U.S. Private*, pg. 628
THE BOYER COMPANY, LLC; *U.S. Private*, pg. 3999
BOYERS & CO. LIMITED—See Arnotts Ltd.; *Int'l*, pg. 577
BOYER'S FOOD MARKETS INC.; *U.S. Private*, pg. 628
BOYERTOWN FOUNDRY COMPANY—See Mestek, Inc.; *U.S. Private*, pg. 1426
BOYETT CONSTRUCTION INC.; *U.S. Private*, pg. 628
BOYETT PETROLEUM; *U.S. Private*, pg. 628
BOYKIN CONTRACTING, INC.; *U.S. Private*, pg. 628
BOYKIN MANAGEMENT COMPANY, LLC; *U.S. Private*, pg. 628
BOYLAND HONDA; *U.S. Private*, pg. 628
BOYLAN SALES INC.; *U.S. Private*, pg. 628
BOYLE BANCORP INC.; *U.S. Public*, pg. 378
BOYLE BUICK GMC; *U.S. Private*, pg. 628
BOYLE CONSTRUCTION INC.; *U.S. Private*, pg. 628
BOYLE INVESTMENT COMPANY; *U.S. Private*, pg. 628
BOYLES MOTOR SALES INCORPORATED; *U.S. Private*, pg. 628
BOYLE TRANSPORTATION INC.; *U.S. Private*, pg. 628
BOYNE CAPITAL MANAGEMENT, LLC; *U.S. Private*, pg. 628
BOYNE HIGHLANDS RESORT—See Boyne USA Resorts Inc.; *U.S. Private*, pg. 629
BOYNE MOUNTAIN RESORT—See Boyne USA Resorts Inc.; *U.S. Private*, pg. 629
BOYNER BUYUK MAGAZACILIK A.S.; *Int'l*, pg. 1125
BOYNE SMELTERS LIMITED—See Rio Tinto plc; *Int'l*, pg. 6346
BOYNE USA RESORTS INC.; *U.S. Private*, pg. 629
BOYNTON BEACH EFL IMAGING CENTER, LLC—See HCA Healthcare, Inc.; *U.S. Public*, pg. 991
BOYNTON BEACH MALL, LLC—See Washington Prime Group Inc.; *U.S. Private*, pg. 4448
BOYNTON PLATINUM (PTY) LTD.—See Sedibelo Platinum Mines Limited; *Int'l*, pg. 6677
BOY SCOUTS OF AMERICA; *U.S. Private*, pg. 627
BOYSEN AEROSPACE U.S., INC.—See Bossard Holding AG; *Int'l*, pg. 1117
BOYSEN GMBH—See Bossard Holding AG; *Int'l*, pg. 1117
BOYS & GIRLS CLUBS OF BOSTON; *U.S. Private*, pg. 629
BOYS' LIFE MAGAZINE—See Boy Scouts of America; *U.S. Private*, pg. 627
BOYUAN CONSTRUCTION GROUP, INC.; *Int'l*, pg. 1125
BOYUAN HOLDINGS LIMITED; *Int'l*, pg. 1125
BOZARD FORD CO.; *U.S. Private*, pg. 629
BOZ ELECTRICAL CONTRACTORS, INC.; *U.S. Private*, pg. 629
BOZELL & JACOBS, LLC; *U.S. Private*, pg. 629
BOZEMAN FORD; *U.S. Private*, pg. 629
BOZEMAN TREE SERVICE, INC.—See Apax Partners LLP; *Int'l*, pg. 506
THE BOZ GROUP—See Publicis Groupe S.A.; *Int'l*, pg. 6109
BOZHON PRECISION INDUSTRY TECHNOLOGY CO., LTD.; *Int'l*, pg. 1125
BOZHOU LIPENG CAPS MAKING CO., LTD.—See Shandong Chiway Industry Development Co., Ltd.; *Int'l*, pg. 6752
BOZLU HOLDING; *Int'l*, pg. 1125
BOZ PARIS—See Publicis Groupe S.A.; *Int'l*, pg. 6097
BOZZETO KIMYA SA. VE TIC. A.S.—See Aimia Inc.; *Int'l*, pg. 233
BOZZETTO GMBH—See Aimia Inc.; *Int'l*, pg. 233
BOZZETTO INC.—See Aimia Inc.; *Int'l*, pg. 234
BOZZETTO KIMYA SAN.VE TIC . A.S.—See Aimia Inc.; *Int'l*, pg. 234
BOZZETTO POLSKA SP. Z O.O.—See Aimia Inc.; *Int'l*, pg. 234
BOZZUTO CONSTRUCTION COMPANY—See The Bozzuto Group; *U.S. Private*, pg. 3999
BOZZUTO DEVELOPMENT CO. INC—See The Bozzuto Group; *U.S. Private*, pg. 3999
THE BOZZUTO GROUP; *U.S. Private*, pg. 3999

BOZZUTO HOMES—See The Bozzuto Group; *U.S. Private*, pg. 3999
BOZZUTO LAND SERVICES—See The Bozzuto Group; *U.S. Private*, pg. 3999
BOZZUTO MANAGEMENT COMPANY—See The Bozzuto Group; *U.S. Private*, pg. 3999
BOZZUTO'S INC.; *U.S. Private*, pg. 629
BPA ASSEGURANCES, SA—See Banca Privada D'Andorra, SA; *Int'l*, pg. 816
B. PACORINI S.P.A.; *Int'l*, pg. 788
BPA CORPORATE FACILITATION LTD.—See Verint Systems Inc.; *U.S. Public*, pg. 2281
BP ADVERTISING (SHANGHAI) COMPANY LIMITED—See Nikkei Inc.; *Int'l*, pg. 5289
BPA FINANCIAL GROUP LTD.—See People Corporation; *Int'l*, pg. 5793
BPA FONS, SA—See Banca Privada D'Andorra, SA; *Int'l*, pg. 816
BPA FREIZEIT- UND UNTERHALTUNGSBETRIEBE GMBH—See Novomatic AG; *Int'l*, pg. 5467
BPA GESTIO, SA—See Banca Privada D'Andorra, SA; *Int'l*, pg. 816
BPA INTERNATIONAL; *U.S. Private*, pg. 629
BPA IPWM (SUISSE), S.A.—See Banca Privada D'Andorra, SA; *Int'l*, pg. 816
BP ALGERIA—See BP plc; *Int'l*, pg. 1126
BP ALTERNATIVE ENERGY INTERNATIONAL LTD.—See BP plc; *Int'l*, pg. 1126
BP ALTERNATIVE ENERGY NORTH AMERICA, INC.—See BP plc; *Int'l*, pg. 1126
BP AMERICA, INC. - COOPER RIVER PLANT—See BP plc; *Int'l*, pg. 1126
BP AMERICA, INC.—See BP plc; *Int'l*, pg. 1126
BP AMERICA PRODUCTION CO.—See BP plc; *Int'l*, pg. 1126
BP AMERICA PRODUCTION CO.—See BP plc; *Int'l*, pg. 1126
BP AMERICA PRODUCTION CO.—See BP plc; *Int'l*, pg. 1126
BP AMERICA PRODUCTION CO.—See BP plc; *Int'l*, pg. 1126
BP AMERICA PRODUCTION CO.—See BP plc; *Int'l*, pg. 1126
BP AMERICA PRODUCTION CO.—See BP plc; *Int'l*, pg. 1126
BP AMERICA - WEST—See BP plc; *Int'l*, pg. 1126
BP AMOCO CHEMICAL COMPANY—See BP plc; *Int'l*, pg. 1126
BP ANGOLA—See BP plc; *Int'l*, pg. 1128
BPA SERVEIS, SA—See Banca Privada D'Andorra, SA; *Int'l*, pg. 816
BP ASIA PACIFIC (MALAYSIA)—See BP plc; *Int'l*, pg. 1128
BPATH PTY LIMITED—See Sonic Healthcare Limited; *Int'l*, pg. 7096
BPATT LLC—See Agital Holdings, LLC; *U.S. Private*, pg. 128
BP AUSTRALIA CAPITAL MARKETS LIMITED—See BP plc; *Int'l*, pg. 1128
BP AUSTRALIA PTY. LTD.—See BP plc; *Int'l*, pg. 1128
BP AUSTRIA AKTIENGESELLSCHAFT—See BP plc; *Int'l*, pg. 1128
BP AUSTRIA MARKETING GMBH—See BP plc; *Int'l*, pg. 1128
BPA WORLDWIDE, INC.—See Alliance for Audited Media; *U.S. Private*, pg. 182
BP AZERBAIJAN—See BP plc; *Int'l*, pg. 1128
B+P BEATMUNGSPRODUKTE GMBH—See COLTENE Holding AG; *Int'l*, pg. 1706
BP BELGIUM NV/SA—See BP plc; *Int'l*, pg. 1128
BP BERAU LTD.—See BP plc; *Int'l*, pg. 1128
BPB GYPROC—See Compagnie de Saint-Gobain SA; *Int'l*, pg. 1725
BPB GYPSUM BV—See Compagnie de Saint-Gobain SA; *Int'l*, pg. 1722
BPB GYPSUM (PTY) LTD.—See Compagnie de Saint-Gobain SA; *Int'l*, pg. 1725
BPB GYPSUM URETIM VE TICARET LTD. STI (TRADING)—See Compagnie de Saint-Gobain SA; *Int'l*, pg. 1725
BPB HOLDINGS S.A.—See Barclays PLC; *Int'l*, pg. 859
BPB IBERPLACO SA—See Compagnie de Saint-Gobain SA; *Int'l*, pg. 1725
BP BIOFUELS LOUISIANA LLC—See BP plc; *Int'l*, pg. 1126
BP BIOFUELS NORTH AMERICA LLC—See BP plc; *Int'l*, pg. 1126
BPB ITALIA SPA—See Compagnie de Saint-Gobain SA; *Int'l*, pg. 1725
BPB LIMITADA—See Compagnie de Saint-Gobain SA; *Int'l*, pg. 1725
BPB NETHERLANDS B.V.—See Compagnie de Saint-Gobain SA; *Int'l*, pg. 1725
BPB PLACO S.A.—See Compagnie de Saint-Gobain SA; *Int'l*, pg. 1722
BPB PLC—See Compagnie de Saint-Gobain SA; *Int'l*, pg. 1725
BP BRASIL LTDA—See BP plc; *Int'l*, pg. 1128
BP CANADA ENERGY COMPANY—See BP plc; *Int'l*, pg. 1126

COMPANY NAME INDEX

B. P. CAPITAL LIMITED; *Int'l*, pg. 788
BP CAPITAL MARKETS PLC—See BP plc; *Int'l*, pg. 1128
BP CARSON REFINERY—See BP plc; *Int'l*, pg. 1126
BP CASTROL CONSUMER NORTH AMERICA INC.—See BP plc; *Int'l*, pg. 1127
BP CASTROL K.K.—See BP plc; *Int'l*, pg. 1130
BP - CASTROL (THAILAND) LIMITED—See BP plc; *Int'l*, pg. 1126
BP CASTROL (THAILAND) LIMITED—See BP plc; *Int'l*, pg. 1129
BPCE CAR LEASE SASU—See Groupe BPCE; *Int'l*, pg. 3092
BPCE FACTOR SA—See Groupe BPCE; *Int'l*, pg. 3092
BPCE INFOGERANCE & TECHNOLOGIES EIG—See Groupe BPCE; *Int'l*, pg. 3092
BPCE LEASE MADRID SE—See Groupe BPCE; *Int'l*, pg. 3092
BPCE LEASE SA—See Groupe BPCE; *Int'l*, pg. 3092
BPCE S.A.—See Groupe BPCE; *Int'l*, pg. 3094
BP CHEMBEL N.V.—See BP plc; *Int'l*, pg. 1128
BP CHEMICALS INC.—See BP plc; *Int'l*, pg. 1126
BP CHEMICALS, INC.—See BP plc; *Int'l*, pg. 1126
BP CHEMICALS LTD.—See BP plc; *Int'l*, pg. 1128
BP CHEMICALS MALAYSIA SDN. BHD.—See Reliance - ADA Group Limited; *Int'l*, pg. 6262
BP CHEMICAL TRELLEBORG AB—See BP plc; *Int'l*, pg. 1128
BP (CHINA) HOLDINGS LIMITED—See BP plc; *Int'l*, pg. 1126
BPCL-KIAL FUEL FARM PRIVATE LIMITED—See Bharat Petroleum Corporation Limited; *Int'l*, pg. 1011
BP COMPANY NORTH AMERICA INC.—See BP plc; *Int'l*, pg. 1128
BP COMPONENTES HIDRAULICOS E MECANICOS LTDA.—See Bondioli & Pavesi S.p.A.; *Int'l*, pg. 1106
BP CONSTRUCTION—See FAYAT SAS; *Int'l*, pg. 2624
BP CORPORATION NORTH AMERICA INC.—See BP plc; *Int'l*, pg. 1126
BP CORPORATION NORTH AMERICA INC.—See BP plc; *Int'l*, pg. 1126
BP CORPORATION NORTH AMERICA INC.—See BP plc; *Int'l*, pg. 1126
BP CORPORATION NORTH AMERICA INC.—See BP plc; *Int'l*, pg. 1126
BPC SA/NV—See Ackermans & van Haaren NV; *Int'l*, pg. 104
BP DANMARK A/S—See BP plc; *Int'l*, pg. 1128
BPD INDUSTRIAL REAL ESTATE FUND REIT; *Int'l*, pg. 1131
BPEA EQT LIMITED—See EQT AB; *Int'l*, pg. 2469
BP EGYPT—See BP plc; *Int'l*, pg. 1128
BP ENERGY COMPANY—See BP plc; *Int'l*, pg. 1127
BP ENERGY COMPANY-TRINIDAD & TOBAGO—See BP plc; *Int'l*, pg. 1128
BP ENERGY CO.—See BP plc; *Int'l*, pg. 1127
BP ENERGY DO BRAZIL LTDA—See BP plc; *Int'l*, pg. 1130
BP ENERGY MARKETING B.V.—See BP plc; *Int'l*, pg. 1129
BP ENERGY PARTNERS, LLC; *U.S. Private*, pg. 629
BPER BANCA S.P.A; *Int'l*, pg. 1131
BPER BANK LUXEMBOURG S.A.—See BPER BANCA S.p.A; *Int'l*, pg. 1132
BPER EUROPE ISRAEL—See Edmond de Rothschild Holding S.A.; *Int'l*, pg. 2312
BPER FACTOR S.P.A.—See BPER BANCA S.p.A; *Int'l*, pg. 1132
BP ERGO LIMITED—See HNI Corporation; *U.S. Public*, pg. 1042
BPER SERVICES S.C.P.A.—See BPER BANCA S.p.A; *Int'l*, pg. 1132
BP ESPANA S.A.U.—See BP plc; *Int'l*, pg. 1128
BPE SRL—See Dana Incorporated; *U.S. Public*, pg. 621
BPE UNTERNEHMENS BETEILIGUNGEN GMBH; *Int'l*, pg. 1131
BP EUROPA SE ODDZIAL W POLSCE—See BP plc; *Int'l*, pg. 1128
BP EUROPA SE—See BP plc; *Int'l*, pg. 1131
BP EUROPA SE ZWEIGNIEDERLASSUNG BP AUSTRIA AG—See BP plc; *Int'l*, pg. 1128
BP EUROPA SE ZWEIGNIEDERLASSUNG BP GAS AUSTRIA—See BP plc; *Int'l*, pg. 1128
BP EXPLORATION (ALASKA) INC.—See BP plc; *Int'l*, pg. 1127
BP EXPLORATION (ALPHA) LIMITED—See BP plc; *Int'l*, pg. 1128
BP EXPLORATION AND PRODUCTION EGYPT LLC—See BP plc; *Int'l*, pg. 1128
BP EXPLORATION (CASPIAN SEA) LTD—See BP plc; *Int'l*, pg. 1128
BP EXPLORATION COMPANY LIMITED—See BP plc; *Int'l*, pg. 1129
BP EXPLORATION (FAROES) LIMITED—See BP plc; *Int'l*, pg. 1129
BP EXPLORATION OPERATING CO LTD—See BP plc; *Int'l*, pg. 1128
BP EXPLORATION OPERATING COMPANY LIMITED—See BP plc; *Int'l*, pg. 1128

BPF MEXICO S.A. DE CV—See Stellantis N.V.; *Int'l*, pg. 7201
B.P. FOOD PRODUCTS CO., LTD.—See Charoen Pokphand Foods Public Company Limited; *Int'l*, pg. 1451
BPF PAZARLAMA ACENTELIK HIZMETLERI A.S.—See Stellantis N.V.; *Int'l*, pg. 7201
BP FRANCE LUBRIFIANTS INDUSTRIELS & SERVICES—See BP plc; *Int'l*, pg. 1130
BP FRANCE SA—See BP plc; *Int'l*, pg. 1129
BP FUELS & LUBRICANTS—See BP plc; *Int'l*, pg. 1130
BP FUJIAN LIMITED—See China Resources (Holdings) Co., Ltd.; *Int'l*, pg. 1548
BP GAS AUSTRIA GMBH NFG. OHG—See BP plc; *Int'l*, pg. 1128
BP GAS ESPANA S.A.—See BP plc; *Int'l*, pg. 1128
BPG BUILDING PARTNERS GROUP GMBH—See Aurelius Equity Opportunities SE & Co. KGaA; *Int'l*, pg. 707
B+P GERUSTBAU GMBH—See Aurelius Equity Opportunities SE & Co. KGaA; *Int'l*, pg. 707
B+P GERUSTBAU HAMBURG GMBH—See Aurelius Equity Opportunities SE & Co. KGaA; *Int'l*, pg. 707
BP GLOBAL INVESTMENT SALALAH & CO LLC—See BP plc; *Int'l*, pg. 1129
BP GLOBAL INVESTMENTS LTD.—See BP plc; *Int'l*, pg. 1129
BPG REAL ESTATE SERVICES LLC—See The Buccini/Pollin Group, Inc.; *U.S. Private*, pg. 4002
BPG RESIDENTIAL SERVICES, LLC—See The Buccini/Pollin Group, Inc.; *U.S. Private*, pg. 4002
BPGS CONSTRUCTION LLC—See The Buccini/Pollin Group, Inc.; *U.S. Private*, pg. 4002
BPH ENERGY LIMITED; *Int'l*, pg. 1132
BPH EQUIPMENT LIMITED—See Balfour Beatty plc; *Int'l*, pg. 807
BP HONG KONG LIMITED—See BP plc; *Int'l*, pg. 1129
BP HUNGARY LTD—See BP plc; *Int'l*, pg. 1129
BP HUSKY REFINERY—See BP plc; *Int'l*, pg. 1127
BP HUSKY REFINERY—See Cenovus Energy Inc.; *Int'l*, pg. 1401
BPI AIA LIFE ASSURANCE CORPORATION—See AIA Group Limited; *Int'l*, pg. 227
BPI ASSET MANAGEMENT—See Bank of the Philippine Islands; *Int'l*, pg. 848
BPI BY PRODUCT INDUSTRIES; *U.S. Private*, pg. 629
BPI CAPITAL CORPORATION—See Bank of the Philippine Islands; *Int'l*, pg. 848
BPI CARD CORPORATION—See Bank of the Philippine Islands; *Int'l*, pg. 848
BPI CENTURY TOKYO LEASE & FINANCE CORPORATION—See Bank of the Philippine Islands; *Int'l*, pg. 848
BPI CENTURY TOKYO LEASE & FINANCE CORPORATION—See Tokyo Century Corporation; *Int'l*, pg. 7788
BPI COMPUTER SYSTEMS CORP—See Bank of the Philippine Islands; *Int'l*, pg. 848
BPI DIRECT BANKO INC.—See Bank of the Philippine Islands; *Int'l*, pg. 848
BPI DIRECT SAVINGS BANK—See Bank of the Philippine Islands; *Int'l*, pg. 848
BPI EUROPE B V—See Berry Global Group, Inc; *U.S. Public*, pg. 322
BPI EXPRESS REMITTANCE CORP.—See Bank of the Philippine Islands; *Int'l*, pg. 848
BPI EXPRESS REMITTANCE SPAIN S.A—See Bank of the Philippine Islands; *Int'l*, pg. 848
BPI FAMILY SAVINGS BANK, INC.—See Bank of the Philippine Islands; *Int'l*, pg. 848
BPI FINANCIAL GROUP LIMITED—See Theme International Holdings Limited; *Int'l*, pg. 7706
BPI FOREX CORPORATION—See Bank of the Philippine Islands; *Int'l*, pg. 848
BPI FOUNDATION, INC.—See Bank of the Philippine Islands; *Int'l*, pg. 848
BPIFRANCE FINANCEMENT—See Caisse des Depots et Consignations; *Int'l*, pg. 1258
BPIFRANCE FINANCEMENT—See EPIC Bpifrance; *Int'l*, pg. 2460
BPIFRANCE INVESTISSEMENT SAS—See Caisse des Depots et Consignations; *Int'l*, pg. 1258
BPIFRANCE INVESTISSEMENT SAS—See EPIC Bpifrance; *Int'l*, pg. 2460
BPIFRANCE PARTICIPATIONS—See Caisse des Depots et Consignations; *Int'l*, pg. 1258
BPIFRANCE PARTICIPATIONS—See EPIC Bpifrance; *Int'l*, pg. 2460
BPI (INDIA) PRIVATE LIMITED—See S Chand & Company Limited; *Int'l*, pg. 6442
BPI INFORMATION SYSTEMS OF OHIO, INC.; *U.S. Private*, pg. 629
BPI LEASING CORPORATION—See Bank of the Philippine Islands; *Int'l*, pg. 848
BPI/MS INSURANCE CORPORATION—See Bank of the Philippine Islands; *Int'l*, pg. 848
BPI/MS INSURANCE CORPORATION—See MS&AD Insurance Group Holdings, Inc.; *Int'l*, pg. 5066
BP INC.—See UnitedHealth Group Incorporated; *U.S. Public*, pg. 2239

BP INDIA SERVICES PVT. LTD—See BP plc; *Int'l*, pg. 1129
BP INTERNATIONAL LTD.—See BP plc; *Int'l*, pg. 1129
BPI OPERATIONS MANAGEMENT CORPORATION—See Bank of the Philippine Islands; *Int'l*, pg. 848
BPI-PHILAM LIFE ASSURANCE CORPORATION—See AIA Group Limited; *Int'l*, pg. 227
BPI-PHILAM LIFE ASSURANCE CORPORATION—See Bank of the Philippine Islands; *Int'l*, pg. 848
BPI PHILAM LIFE ASSURANCE CORPORATION—See Bank of the Philippine Islands; *Int'l*, pg. 848
BPI PLC—See Berry Global Group, Inc; *U.S. Public*, pg. 322
BPI REPRO, LLC—See ARC DOCUMENT SOLUTIONS, INC.; *U.S. Public*, pg. 179
BPI SA/NV—See Ackermans & van Haaren NV; *Int'l*, pg. 104
BPI SECURITIES CORPORATION—See Bank of the Philippine Islands; *Int'l*, pg. 848
BPI (SUISSE) S.A.—See Lone Star Funds; *U.S. Private*, pg. 2484
BP ITALIA SPA—See BP plc; *Int'l*, pg. 1129
BPI WEALTH HONG KONG LIMITED—See Bank of the Philippine Islands; *Int'l*, pg. 848
BP JAPAN KK—See BP plc; *Int'l*, pg. 1129
BP KINGSTOWNE OFFICE BUILDING T LLC—See Boston Properties, Inc.; *U.S. Public*, pg. 372
BP KOREA LTD.—See BP plc; *Int'l*, pg. 1130
BP KOREA MARKETING LTD.—See BP plc; *Int'l*, pg. 1130
BP KUWAIT LIMITED—See BP plc; *Int'l*, pg. 1129
BPLATS, INC.; *Int'l*, pg. 1132
BPLI HOLDINGS INC.; *Int'l*, pg. 1132
BPL LIMITED; *Int'l*, pg. 1132
BPL MEDICAL TECHNOLOGIES PRIVATE LTD.—See The Goldman Sachs Group, Inc.; *U.S. Public*, pg. 2076
BP LOGIX, INC.—See Finrock Growth Partners, LLC; *U.S. Private*, pg. 1511
BP LUBRICANTS A/S—See BP plc; *Int'l*, pg. 1128
BP LUBRICANTS USA INC.—See BP plc; *Int'l*, pg. 1127
BP LUBRICANTS USA INC.—See BP plc; *Int'l*, pg. 1127
B PLUS L TECHNOLOGIES INC.; *U.S. Private*, pg. 417
BP LUXEMBOURG S.A.—See BP plc; *Int'l*, pg. 1129
BP MAGYARORSZAG KFT—See BP plc; *Int'l*, pg. 1129
BP MALAWI LIMITED—See BP plc; *Int'l*, pg. 1129
BP MAI AWI I IMITED—See Sociedade Nacional de Combustiveis de Angola, E.P.; *Int'l*, pg. 7033
BP MALAWI LIMITED—See Trafigura Beheer B.V.; *Int'l*, pg. 7890
BP MANAGEMENT, L.P.—See Boston Properties, Inc.; *U.S. Public*, pg. 372
B&P MANUFACTURING; *U.S. Private*, pg. 419
BP MARINE LIMITED—See BP plc; *Int'l*, pg. 1129
BP MARINE—See BP plc; *Int'l*, pg. 1129
BP MARKETING EGYPT LTD—See BP plc; *Int'l*, pg. 1128
B.P. MARSH & PARTNERS PLC; *Int'l*, pg. 790
BPM BROADCAST & PROFESSIONAL MEDIA GMBH—See Avemio AG; *Int'l*, pg. 738
BP MEXICO S.A. DE C.V.—See BP plc; *Int'l*, pg. 1129
BP MICROSYSTEMS, L.P.; *U.S. Private*, pg. 629
BP MIDDLE EAST LTD.—See BP plc; *Int'l*, pg. 1129
BP MIDSTREAM PARTNERS LP; *U.S. Public*, pg. 378
BPM INC.; *U.S. Private*, pg. 629
BPM MEDIA (MIDLANDS) LTD.—See Reach PLC; *Int'l*, pg. 6231
BPM MINERALS LIMITED; *Int'l*, pg. 1133
BP MOZAMBIQUE LIMITED—See BP plc; *Int'l*, pg. 1129
BP MPAK SDN. BHD.—See Can-One Berhad; *Int'l*, pg. 1276
BP NEDERLAND B.V.—See BP plc; *Int'l*, pg. 1129
BP NEDERLAND HOLDINGS B.V.—See BP plc; *Int'l*, pg. 1129
BPN TRANSMISSOES LTDA.—See Bondioli & Pavesi S.p.A.; *Int'l*, pg. 1106
BPO COLLECTIONS LTD.—See Everyday People Financial Corp.; *Int'l*, pg. 2570
BPO HOLDCO COOPERATIEF U.A.—See TD Synnex Corp; *U.S. Public*, pg. 1983
BPO HOUSE—See Alna AB; *Int'l*, pg. 364
BP OIL AUSTRALIA PTY. LTD.—See BP plc; *Int'l*, pg. 1129
BP OIL COMPANY—See BP plc; *Int'l*, pg. 1127
BP OIL CO.—See BP plc; *Int'l*, pg. 1127
BP OIL ESPANA S.A.—See BP plc; *Int'l*, pg. 1128
BP OIL HELLENIC SA—See BP plc; *Int'l*, pg. 1129
BP OIL NEW ZEALAND LIMITED—See BP plc; *Int'l*, pg. 1129
BP OIL PIPELINE—See BP plc; *Int'l*, pg. 1127
BP OIL REFINERIA DE CASTELLON, S.A.U.—See BP plc; *Int'l*, pg. 1128
BP OIL SHIPPING COMPANY—See BP plc; *Int'l*, pg. 1127
BP OIL SHIPPING COMPANY USA—See BP plc; *Int'l*, pg. 1127
BP OIL SHIPPING COMPANY USA—See BP plc; *Int'l*, pg. 1127
BP OIL SUPPLY COMPANY INC.—See BP plc; *Int'l*, pg. 1128
BP OIL SUPPLY COMPANY INC.—See BP plc; *Int'l*, pg. 1128
BP OIL THAILAND—See BP plc; *Int'l*, pg. 1129
BP OIL U.K.—See BP plc; *Int'l*, pg. 1129

BPOST NV/SA; *Int'l*, pg. 1133
BPO SYSTEMS INC.; *U.S. Private*, pg. 630
BPO TECHNICAL SERVICES LLC—See The Carlyle Group Inc; *U.S. Public*, pg. 2054
B & P OUTDOOR BV—See Clear Channel Outdoor Holdings, Inc.; *U.S. Public*, pg. 511
BPP ACTUARIAL EDUCATION LTD.—See TDR Capital LLP; *Int'l*, pg. 7493
BPP BAUTECHNIK GMBH—See PORR AG; *Int'l*, pg. 5925
BPP (CI) LIMITED—See TDR Capital LLP; *Int'l*, pg. 7493
BP PETROCHINA JIANGMEN FUELS CO. LTD.—See BP plc; *Int'l*, pg. 1129
BP PETROCHINA JIANGMEN FUELS CO. LTD.—See China National Petroleum Corporation; *Int'l*, pg. 1533
BP PETROLLERI A.S.—See BP plc; *Int'l*, pg. 1129
BP PETRONAS ACETYLS SDN BHD—See BP plc; *Int'l*, pg. 1128
BP PETRONAS ACETYLS SDN BHD—See Petroliam Nasional Berhad; *Int'l*, pg. 5829
BPP HOLDINGS LIMITED—See TDR Capital LLP; *Int'l*, pg. 7493
BP PIPELINES (ALASKA) INC.—See BP plc; *Int'l*, pg. 1127
BP PIPELINES NORTH AMERICA INC.—See BP plc; *Int'l*, pg. 1126
BP PIPELINES NORTH AMERICA INC.—See BP plc; *Int'l*, pg. 1126
BP PIPELINES NORTH AMERICA INC.—See BP plc; *Int'l*, pg. 1127
BP PIPELINES NORTH AMERICA INC.—See BP plc; *Int'l*, pg. 1127
BP PIPELINES NORTH AMERICA INC.—See BP plc; *Int'l*, pg. 1127
BP PLASTICS HOLDING BHD.; *Int'l*, pg. 1125
BP PLC; *Int'l*, pg. 1131
BP PLC; *Int'l*, pg. 1125
BPP LEARNING MEDIA LIMITED—See TDR Capital LLP; *Int'l*, pg. 7493
BPPL HOLDINGS PLC; *Int'l*, pg. 1133
BPP NEDERLAND BV—See TDR Capital LLP; *Int'l*, pg. 7493
BP POLSKA SP. Z O.O.—See BP plc; *Int'l*, pg. 1129
BPP PROFESSIONAL EDUCATION LIMITED—See TDR Capital LLP; *Int'l*, pg. 7494
BPP PROFESSIONAL EDUCATION SP Z.O.O.—See TDR Capital LLP; *Int'l*, pg. 7494
BPP RENEWABLE INVESTMENT (CHINA) CO., LTD.—See Banpu Public Company Limited; *Int'l*, pg. 851
BP PRODUCTS NORTH AMERICA INC.—See BP plc; *Int'l*, pg. 1127
BP PRODUCTS NORTH AMERICA INC.—See BP plc; *Int'l*, pg. 1127
BP PRODUCTS NORTH AMERICA INC.—See BP plc; *Int'l*, pg. 1127
BP PRODUCTS NORTH AMERICA INC.—See BP plc; *Int'l*, pg. 1127
BP PRODUCTS NORTH AMERICA INC.—See BP plc; *Int'l*, pg. 1127
BP PRODUCTS NORTH AMERICA INC.—See BP plc; *Int'l*, pg. 1127
BP PRODUCTS NORTH AMERICA INC.—See BP plc; *Int'l*, pg. 1127
BP PRUDHOE BAY ROYALTY TRUST; *U.S. Public*, pg. 378
BPP UNIVERSITY LIMITED—See TDR Capital LLP; *Int'l*, pg. 7494
BPR-BATIMENT INC.—See Tetra Tech, Inc.; *U.S. Public*, pg. 2022
BPR CSO SOLUTIONS INC.—See Tetra Tech, Inc.; *U.S. Public*, pg. 2022
BP REALTY, LLC—See United Natural Foods, Inc.; *U.S. Public*, pg. 2231
BP REFINING & PETROCHEMICALS GMBH—See BP plc; *Int'l*, pg. 1131
BPR-ENERGIE INC.—See Tetra Tech, Inc.; *U.S. Public*, pg. 2022
BPREX BRAZIL HOLDING INC.—See Berry Global Group, Inc; *U.S. Public*, pg. 321
BPREX CLOSURES, LLC—See Berry Global Group, Inc; *U.S. Public*, pg. 321
BPREX DELTA, INC.—See Berry Global Group, Inc; *U.S. Public*, pg. 321
BPR GROUPE-CONSEIL, S.E.N.C.—See Tetra Tech, Inc.; *U.S. Public*, pg. 2022
BPR-INFRASTRUCTURE INC.—See Tetra Tech, Inc.; *U.S. Public*, pg. 2022
BPRL VENTURES BV—See Bharat Petroleum Corporation Limited; *Int'l*, pg. 1011
BPR-RICO EQUIPMENT INC.; *U.S. Private*, pg. 630
BPR-TRIAX INC.—See Tetra Tech, Inc.; *U.S. Public*, pg. 2022
BPS ASSOCIATES LTD.—See Teleperformance SE; *Int'l*, pg. 7540
BP SCHMIERSTOFFE GMBH NFG. OHG—See BP plc; *Int'l*, pg. 1128

BPS CONTACT CENTRE SERVICES—See Teleperformance SE; *Int'l*, pg. 7540
BPS COOPERATIEF U.A.—See Bel Fuse Inc.; *U.S. Public*, pg. 292
BP SHANGHAI TRADING CO. LTD.—See BP plc; *Int'l*, pg. 1129
B.P. SHORT & SON PAVING CO.; *U.S. Private*, pg. 421
BP SINGAPORE PTE. LIMITED—See BP plc; *Int'l*, pg. 1129
BP SOLAR ESPANA, S.A.U.—See BP plc; *Int'l*, pg. 1128
BP—See BP plc; *Int'l*, pg. 1128
BP SOUTHEAST ASIA LTD.—See BP plc; *Int'l*, pg. 1129
BP SOUTHERN AFRICA PTY LTD.—See BP plc; *Int'l*, pg. 1129
BP SOUTHERN AFRICA (PTY). LTD.—See BP plc; *Int'l*, pg. 1130
BP SOUTH-WEST PACIFIC LIMITED—See BP plc; *Int'l*, pg. 1129
BPS-SBERBANK OJSC; *Int'l*, pg. 1133
BPS SPEDITIONS-SERVICE AG—See Die Schweizerische Post AG; *Int'l*, pg. 2112
BPS SPEDITIONS-SERVICE BASEL AG—See Die Schweizerische Post AG; *Int'l*, pg. 2112
BP SWAZILAND (PTY) LIMITED—See BP plc; *Int'l*, pg. 1129
BP SWITZERLAND—See BP plc; *Int'l*, pg. 1130
BP TAIWAN MARKETING LIMITED—See BP plc; *Int'l*, pg. 1130
BP TANZANIA LIMITED—See BP plc; *Int'l*, pg. 1130
BP TANZANIA LIMITED—See Sociedade Nacional de Combustiveis de Angola, E.P.; *Int'l*, pg. 7033
BP TANZANIA LIMITED—See Trafigura Beheer B.V.; *Int'l*, pg. 7890
BPTG CO., LTD.—See PTG Energy Public Company Limited; *Int'l*, pg. 6090
BPT LIMITED—See Grainger plc; *Int'l*, pg. 3052
BPTP LIMITED; *Int'l*, pg. 1133
BP TRINIDAD AND TOBAGO LLC—See BP plc; *Int'l*, pg. 1130
BPU INGENIEURUNTERNEHMUNG AG—See BKW AG; *Int'l*, pg. 1054
BPV ENVIRONMENTAL—See Pestell Nutrition Inc.; *Int'l*, pg. 5823
BP WEST COAST PRODUCTS LLC—See BP plc; *Int'l*, pg. 1126
BP WHITING REFINERY—See BP plc; *Int'l*, pg. 1127
BP WIND ENERGY NORTH AMERICA INC.—See BP plc; *Int'l*, pg. 1126
BPW INSURANCE SERVICES LIMITED—See Brown & Brown, Inc.; *U.S. Public*, pg. 397
BPX ENERGY INC.—See BP plc; *Int'l*, pg. 1130
BP ZHUHAI CHEMICAL COMPANY LIMITED—See BP plc; *Int'l*, pg. 1130
BP ZIMBABWE (PVT) LIMITED—See BP plc; *Int'l*, pg. 1130
BQE SOFTWARE, INC.; *U.S. Private*, pg. 630
BQE WATER INC.; *Int'l*, pg. 1133
B&Q LIMITED—See Kingfisher plc; *Int'l*, pg. 4173
B&Q PROPERTIES LIMITED—See Kingfisher plc; *Int'l*, pg. 4173
BQT SOLUTIONS (AUSTRALIA) PTY. LTD.—See Ava Risk Group Limited; *Int'l*, pg. 733
BQT SOLUTIONS (NZ) LTD.—See Ava Risk Group Limited; *Int'l*, pg. 733
BQT SOLUTIONS (UK) LTD.—See Ava Risk Group Limited; *Int'l*, pg. 733
B-QUIK CO., LTD.—See Marubeni Corporation; *Int'l*, pg. 4705
B-R 31 ICE CREAM CO., LTD.; *Int'l*, pg. 785
BRAAS COMPANY—See Genuine Parts Company; *U.S. Public*, pg. 933
BRAAS MONIER BUILDING GROUP SERVICES GMBH; *Int'l*, pg. 1133
BRAAS SCHWEIZ AG—See PAI Partners S.A.S.; *Int'l*, pg. 5701
BRAATHENS AVIATION—See Braganza AS; *Int'l*, pg. 1136
BRAAVOS, INC.; *U.S. Private*, pg. 630
BRABAMIJ INFRA BV—See Solutions 30 SE; *Int'l*, pg. 7076
BRABANK ASA; *Int'l*, pg. 1133
BRABANT ALUCAST INTERNATIONAL B.V.—See Endless LLP; *Int'l*, pg. 2403
BRABANTS DAGBLAD BV—See DPG Media Group NV; *Int'l*, pg. 2189
BRABENDERCOX, LLC - PITTSBURGH—See Brabender-Cox, LLC; *U.S. Private*, pg. 630
BRABENDERCOX, LLC; *U.S. Private*, pg. 630
BRABHAM OIL CO. INC.; *U.S. Private*, pg. 630
BRABNER & HOLLON, INC.; *U.S. Private*, pg. 630
BRABO ROBOTICS & AUTOMATION LIMITED—See Tata Motors Limited; *Int'l*, pg. 7466
BRA BYGG AB—See Veidekke ASA; *Int'l*, pg. 8148
BRACALENTE MANUFACTURING CO., INC.; *U.S. Private*, pg. 630
BRAC BANK LIMITED—See BRAC; *Int'l*, pg. 1134
BRACCO DIAGNOSTICS INC.—See Bracco S.p.A.; *Int'l*, pg. 1134
BRACCO-EISAI CO., LTD.—See Bracco S.p.A.; *Int'l*, pg. 1134

BRACCO-EISAI CO., LTD.—See Eisai Co., Ltd.; *Int'l*, pg. 2334
BRACCO FAR EAST LTD.—See Bracco S.p.A.; *Int'l*, pg. 1134
BRACCO IMAGING DEUTSCHLAND GMBH—See Bracco S.p.A.; *Int'l*, pg. 1134
BRACCO IMAGING EUROPE BV—See Bracco S.p.A.; *Int'l*, pg. 1134
BRACCO IMAGING FRANCE SA—See Bracco S.p.A.; *Int'l*, pg. 1134
BRACCO IMAGING ITALIA S.R.L.—See Bracco S.p.A.; *Int'l*, pg. 1134
BRACCO IMAGING KOREA, LTD.—See Bracco S.p.A.; *Int'l*, pg. 1134
BRACCO IMAGING POLSKA SP.Z.O.O.—See Bracco S.p.A.; *Int'l*, pg. 1134
BRACCO IMAGING SCANDINAVIA AB—See Bracco S.p.A.; *Int'l*, pg. 1134
BRACCO IMAGING S.P.A.—See Bracco S.p.A.; *Int'l*, pg. 1134
BRACCO INTERNATIONAL B.V.—See Bracco S.p.A.; *Int'l*, pg. 1134
BRACCO OSTERREICH GMBH—See Bracco S.p.A.; *Int'l*, pg. 1134
BRACCO RESEARCH USA INC.—See Bracco S.p.A.; *Int'l*, pg. 1134
BRACCO S.P.A.; *Int'l*, pg. 1134
BRACCO SUISSE S.A.—See Bracco S.p.A.; *Int'l*, pg. 1134
BRACCO UK LTD.—See Bracco S.p.A.; *Int'l*, pg. 1134
BRACE INDUSTRIAL GROUP, INC.—See Brand Industrial Services, Inc.; *U.S. Private*, pg. 636
BRACELL; *Int'l*, pg. 1134
BRACE SHOP, LLC—See VeriTeQ Corporation; *U.S. Private*, pg. 4366
BRACEWELL & GIULIANI LLP; *U.S. Private*, pg. 630
BRACEY'S SUPERMARKET INC.; *U.S. Private*, pg. 630
BRACHE DIALYSIS, LLC—See DaVita Inc.; *U.S. Public*, pg. 636
BRACHT, DECKERS & MACKELBERT N.V.—See The Hartford Financial Services Group, Inc.; *U.S. Public*, pg. 2088
BRACING SYSTEMS INC.; *U.S. Private*, pg. 630
BRACK CAPITAL PROPERTIES NV—See ADLER Group SA; *Int'l*, pg. 150
BRACK CAPITAL REAL ESTATE; *Int'l*, pg. 1134
BRACKE HAYES MILLER MAHON, ARCHITECTS LLP—See Bray Associates Architects Inc.; *U.S. Private*, pg. 641
BRACKEN ENGINEERING, INC; *U.S. Private*, pg. 630
BRACKER AG—See Rieter Holding Ltd.; *Int'l*, pg. 6338
BRACKER GMBH INNOVATIVER MASCHINENBAU—See Blackstone Inc.; *U.S. Public*, pg. 360
BRACKER S.A.S.—See Rieter Holding Ltd.; *Int'l*, pg. 6338
BRACKET GLOBAL LLC—See Genstar Capital, LLC; *U.S. Private*, pg. 1675
BRACKET GLOBAL, S.R.O.—See Genstar Capital, LLC; *U.S. Private*, pg. 1675
BRACKNELL ROOFING LTD.—See Avonside Group Services Limited; *Int'l*, pg. 750
BRACKNELL VETS4PETS LIMITED—See Pets at Home Group Plc; *Int'l*, pg. 5833
BRACNET LTD.—See KDDI Corporation; *Int'l*, pg. 4111
BRAC; *Int'l*, pg. 1133
BRACY TUCKER BROWN & VALANZANO; *U.S. Private*, pg. 630
BRADAVERSE EDUCATION (INT'L) INVESTMENTS GROUP LIMITED.; *Int'l*, pg. 1134
BRAD!BRYAN MULTIMEDIA INC.; *U.S. Private*, pg. 631
BRADBURN PLUMBING CO. INC.—See Bryant-Durham Electric Co., Inc.; *U.S. Private*, pg. 674
BRADBURY COMPANY, INC.; *U.S. Private*, pg. 631
BRADBURY STAMM CONSTRUCTION, INC.; *U.S. Private*, pg. 631
BRADCO INC.; *U.S. Private*, pg. 631
BRAD COLE CONSTRUCTION COMPANY, INCORPORATED—See Arctic Slope Regional Corporation; *U.S. Private*, pg. 316
BRADCO SUPPLY CORPORATION—See Hendricks Holding Company, Inc.; *U.S. Private*, pg. 1914
BRADDA HEAD LITHIUM LIMITED; *Int'l*, pg. 1134
BRAD DEERY MOTORS, INC.; *U.S. Private*, pg. 630
BRADDOCK CARIBE METALLURGICAL, CORP—See Braddock Metallurgical, Inc.; *U.S. Private*, pg. 631
BRADDOCK HEAT TREATING CO., INC.—See Braddock Metallurgical, Inc.; *U.S. Private*, pg. 631
BRADDOCKMATTHEWSBARRETT, LLC; *U.S. Private*, pg. 631
BRADDOCK METALLURGICAL AEROSPACE - BOYNTON BEACH—See Braddock Metallurgical, Inc.; *U.S. Private*, pg. 631
BRADDOCK METALLURGICAL - ATLANTA—See Braddock Metallurgical, Inc.; *U.S. Private*, pg. 631
BRADDOCK METALLURGICAL - DAYTONA—See Braddock Metallurgical, Inc.; *U.S. Private*, pg. 631
BRADDOCK METALLURGICAL, INC.; *U.S. Private*, pg. 631
BRADDOCK METALLURGICAL - JACKSONVILLE—See Braddock Metallurgical, Inc.; *U.S. Private*, pg. 631

COMPANY NAME INDEX

BRADDOCK METALLURGICAL - TAMPA—See Braddock Metallurgical, Inc.; *U.S. Private*, pg. 631
BRADENBURG INDUSTRIAL SERVICE COMPANY INC.-BETHLEHEM, PA—See Brandenburg Industrial Service Company Inc.; *U.S. Private*, pg. 637
BRADEN-EUROPE B.V.—See TriWest Capital Management Corp.; *Int'l*, pg. 7937
BRADEN MANUFACTURING, LLC—See TriWest Capital Management Corp.; *Int'l*, pg. 7937
BRADEN MANUFACTURING SA DE CV—See The Toronto-Dominion Bank; *Int'l*, pg. 7696
BRADEN PARTNERS L.P; *U.S. Private*, pg. 631
THE BRADEN SUTPHIN INK COMPANY; *U.S. Private*, pg. 3999
BRADENTON DIALYSIS CENTER LLC—See Nautic Partners, LLC; *U.S. Private*, pg. 2869
BRADENTON FUEL OIL; *U.S. Private*, pg. 631
THE BRADENTON HERALD—See Chatham Asset Management, LLC; *U.S. Private*, pg. 866
BRADENTON OUTPATIENT SERVICES, LLC—See HCA Healthcare, Inc.; *U.S. Public*, pg. 991
BRADESCO ARGENTINA DE SEGUROS S.A—See Banco Bradesco S.A.; *Int'l*, pg. 819
BRADESCO AUTO/RE COMPANHIA DE SEGUROS—See Banco Bradesco S.A.; *Int'l*, pg. 819
BRADESCO CAPITALIZACAO S.A.—See Banco Bradesco S.A.; *Int'l*, pg. 819
BRADESCO CORRETORA T.V.M.—See Banco Bradesco S.A.; *Int'l*, pg. 819
BRADESCO DENTAL SA—See Odontoprev S.A.; *Int'l*, pg. 5527
BRADESCO LEASING S.A. ARRENDAMENTO MERCANTIL—See Banco Bradesco S.A.; *Int'l*, pg. 819
BRADESCO SAUDE S.A.—See Banco Bradesco S.A.; *Int'l*, pg. 819
BRADESCO SECURITIES, INC.,—See Banco Bradesco S.A.; *Int'l*, pg. 819
BRADESCO VIDA E PREVIDENCIA S.A.—See Banco Bradesco S.A.; *Int'l*, pg. 819
BRADESPAR S.A.; *Int'l*, pg. 1134
BRAD FOOTE GEAR WORKS, INC.—See Broadwind, Inc.; *U.S. Public*, pg. 392
BRADFORD BANCORP, INC.; *U.S. Private*, pg. 631
BRADFORD COMPANY; *U.S. Private*, pg. 631
BRADFORD DE MEXICO, S. DE R.L. DE C.V.—See Bradford Company; *U.S. Private*, pg. 631
BRADFORD ENGINEERING B.V.—See Moog Inc.; *U.S. Public*, pg. 1470
BRADFORD EQUITIES MANAGEMENT, LLC; *U.S. Private*, pg. 631
BRADFORD FAIRWAY SALES & LEASING INC.; *U.S. Private*, pg. 631
BRADFORD FOREST, INC.—See Danzer AG; *Int'l*, pg. 1970
BRADFORD & GALT INC.—See ManpowerGroup Inc.; *U.S. Public*, pg. 1362
BRADFORD GREENHOUSES LTD.; *Int'l*, pg. 1134
THE BRADFORD GROUP; *U.S. Private*, pg. 3999
BRADFORD INDUSTRIAL SUPPLY; *U.S. Private*, pg. 631
BRADFORD INDUSTRIES, INC.—See Wembly Enterprises LLC; *U.S. Private*, pg. 4480
BRADFORD MACHINE CO—See HC Private Investments LLC; *U.S. Private*, pg. 1888
BRADFORD MARINE, INC.; *U.S. Private*, pg. 631
THE BRADFORD NATIONAL BANK OF GREENVILLE—See Bradford Bancorp, Inc.; *U.S. Private*, pg. 631
BRADFORD OIL COMPANY, INC.; *U.S. Private*, pg. 631
BRADFORD PRODUCTS, LLC.; *U.S. Private*, pg. 632
BRADFORDS BUILDING SUPPLIES LTD.; *Int'l*, pg. 1134
BRADFORD SQUARE NURSING, LLC—See Formation Capital, LLC; *U.S. Private*, pg. 1569
BRADFORD SUPPLY COMPANY; *U.S. Private*, pg. 632
BRADFORD SYSTEMS MALAYSIA SDN. BHD.—See Bradford Company; *U.S. Private*, pg. 631
BRADFORD VETS4PETS LIMITED—See Pets at Home Group Plc; *Int'l*, pg. 5833
BRADFORD-WHITE CORPORATION; *U.S. Private*, pg. 632
BRADGATE BAKERY—See Samworth Brothers Ltd.; *Int'l*, pg. 6519
BRADINGTON-YOUNG LLC—See Hooker Furnishings Corporation; *U.S. Public*, pg. 1052
BRADKEN-ENGINEERED PRODUCTS—See Hitachi, Ltd.; *Int'l*, pg. 3415
BRADKEN HOLDINGS PTY LIMITED—See Hitachi, Ltd.; *Int'l*, pg. 3415
BRADKEN, INC.—See Hitachi, Ltd.; *Int'l*, pg. 3415
BRADKEN, INC.—See Hitachi, Ltd.; *Int'l*, pg. 3415
BRADKEN, INC.—See Hitachi, Ltd.; *Int'l*, pg. 3415
BRADKEN-LONDON LTD.—See Hitachi, Ltd.; *Int'l*, pg. 3415
BRADKEN LTD.—See Hitachi, Ltd.; *Int'l*, pg. 3415
BRADKEN RESOURCES WUNDOWIE FOUNDRY PTY. LTD.—See Hitachi, Ltd.; *Int'l*, pg. 3415
BRADKEN UK LIMITED—See Hitachi, Ltd.; *Int'l*, pg. 3415
BRADKE SYNERGIES SDN. BHD.—See PT Selamat Sempurna Tbk; *Int'l*, pg. 6071
BRAD LANIER OIL CO. INC.; *U.S. Private*, pg. 631

BRADLEE DANVERS LLC—See UDR, Inc.; *U.S. Public*, pg. 2218
BRADLEY ARANT BOULT CUMMINGS LLP; *U.S. Private*, pg. 632
BRADLEY BANCORP, INC.; *U.S. Private*, pg. 632
BRADLEY BANCSHARES, INC.; *U.S. Private*, pg. 632
BRADLEY BARTON VIEW MANAGEMENT COMPANY LIMITED—See Persimmon plc; *Int'l*, pg. 5815
BRADLEY CALDWELL, INC.; *U.S. Private*, pg. 632
BRADLEY CHEVROLET INC.; *U.S. Private*, pg. 632
BRADLEY COATING INC.; *U.S. Private*, pg. 632
BRADLEY CORPORATION - FIXTURES DIVISION—See Watts Water Technologies, Inc.; *U.S. Public*, pg. 2337
BRADLEY CORPORATION—See Watts Water Technologies, Inc.; *U.S. Public*, pg. 2337
BRADLEY COUNTY MEDICAL CENTER; *U.S. Private*, pg. 632
BRADLEY DIRECT SERVICES—See W.C. Bradley Co.; *U.S. Private*, pg. 4419
BRADLEY EXCAVATING, INC.; *U.S. Private*, pg. 632
BRADLEY HARDWARE INC.; *U.S. Private*, pg. 633
BRADLEY INSURANCE AGENCY.—See Marsh & McLennan Companies, Inc.; *U.S. Public*, pg. 1380
BRADLEY INVESTMENTS, INC.; *U.S. Private*, pg. 633
BRADLEY LIFTING CORPORATION—See Xtek, Inc.; *U.S. Private*, pg. 4583
THE BRADLEY MARKETING GROUP; *U.S. Private*, pg. 3999
BRADLEY & MONTGOMERY ADVERTISING; *U.S. Private*, pg. 632
BRADLEY MORRIS INC.—See Thompson Street Capital Manager LLC; *U.S. Private*, pg. 4160
BRADLEY REPRESENTATIVES; *U.S. Private*, pg. 633
BRADLEY SERVICES, INC.—See Wind Point Advisors LLC; *U.S. Private*, pg. 4534
BRADLEY WASHROOM ACCESSORIES DIV—See Watts Water Technologies, Inc.; *U.S. Public*, pg. 2337
BRADMAN LAKE CHINA—See Langley Holdings Plc; *Int'l*, pg. 4409
BRADMAN LAKE INC—See Langley Holdings Plc; *Int'l*, pg. 4409
BRADMAN LAKE LTD—See Langley Holdings Plc; *Int'l*, pg. 4409
BRADMAN LAKE RUSSIA—See Langley Holdings Plc; *Int'l*, pg. 4409
BRADMARK TECHNOLOGIES INC.; *U.S. Private*, pg. 633
THE BRADNAM GROUP; *Int'l*, pg. 7627
BRADSBY GROUP; *U.S. Private*, pg. 633
BRADSHAW ADVERTISING; *U.S. Private*, pg. 633
BRADSHAW AUTOMOTIVE GROUP, INC.; *U.S. Private*, pg. 633
BRADSHAW CONSTRUCTION CORP; *U.S. Private*, pg. 633
BRADSHAW, FOWLER, PROCTOR & FAIRGRAVE, PC—See Dickinson, Mackaman, Tyler & Hagen, P.C.; *U.S. Private*, pg. 1227
BRADSHAW INTERNATIONAL, INC.; *U.S. Private*, pg. 633
BRADSHAW MEDICAL, INC.—See In'Tech Medical SAS; *Int'l*, pg. 3639
BRAD SYSTEMS, INC.—See Lawrence Paper Company; *U.S. Private*, pg. 2401
BRADVIN TRAILER SALES LTD.; *Int'l*, pg. 1134
BRADY AB—See Brady Corporation; *U.S. Public*, pg. 378
BRADY A/S—See Brady Corporation; *U.S. Public*, pg. 378
BRADY AUSTRALIA PTY. LTD.—See Brady Corporation; *U.S. Public*, pg. 378
BRADY (BEIJING) CO. LTD.—See Brady Corporation; *U.S. Public*, pg. 378
BRADY B.V.—See Brady Corporation; *U.S. Public*, pg. 378
THE BRADY COMPANIES; *U.S. Private*, pg. 3999
BRADY COMPANY/CENTRAL CALIFORNIA, INC.—See The Brady Companies; *U.S. Private*, pg. 3999
BRADY COMPANY INDIA PRIVATE LIMITED—See Brady Corporation; *U.S. Public*, pg. 378
BRADY COMPANY/LOS ANGELES, INC.—See The Brady Companies; *U.S. Private*, pg. 3999
BRADY COMPANY/SAN DIEGO, INC.—See The Brady Companies; *U.S. Private*, pg. 3999
BRADY CORPORATION ASIA PACIFIC PTE. LTD.—See Brady Corporation; *U.S. Public*, pg. 378
BRADY CORPORATION ASIA PTE. LTD.—See Brady Corporation; *U.S. Public*, pg. 378
BRADY CORPORATION HONG KONG LIMITED—See Brady Corporation; *U.S. Public*, pg. 378
BRADY CORPORATION LTD.—See Brady Corporation; *U.S. Public*, pg. 378
BRADY CORPORATION LTD.—See Brady Corporation; *U.S. Public*, pg. 378
BRADY CORPORATION; *U.S. Public*, pg. 378
BRADY DISTRIBUTING COMPANY INC.; *U.S. Private*, pg. 633
BRADY ENERGY AG—See Brady plc; *Int'l*, pg. 1135
BRADY ENERGY CANADA, INC.—See Brady plc; *Int'l*, pg. 1135
BRADY ENERGY NORWAY AS—See Brady plc; *Int'l*, pg. 1135
BRADY ENERGY US, INC.—See Brady plc; *Int'l*, pg. 1135
BRADY ENTERPRISES, INC.; *U.S. Private*, pg. 633

BRADY ETIKET VE ISARETLEME TICARET LTD. SIRKETI—See Brady Corporation; *U.S. Public*, pg. 378
BRADY FARMS INC.; *U.S. Private*, pg. 633
BRADY GMBH—See Brady Corporation; *U.S. Public*, pg. 378
BRADY GROUPE S.A.S—See Brady Corporation; *U.S. Public*, pg. 378
BRADY IDENTIFICACION S.L.U.—See Brady Corporation; *U.S. Public*, pg. 378
BRADY INDUSTRIES INC.—See Kelso & Company, L.P.; *U.S. Private*, pg. 2279
BRADY INDUSTRIES INC.—See Warburg Pincus LLC; *U.S. Private*, pg. 4436
BRADY ITALIA, S.R.L.—See Brady Corporation; *U.S. Public*, pg. 378
BRADY KOREA LLP—See Brady Corporation; *U.S. Public*, pg. 378
BRADY LLC—See Brady Corporation; *U.S. Public*, pg. 379
BRADY MARKETING COMPANY; *U.S. Private*, pg. 633
BRADY MEXICO, S. DE R.L. DE C.V.—See Brady Corporation; *U.S. Public*, pg. 379
BRADY & MORRIS ENGINEERING CO. LTD.; *Int'l*, pg. 1135
BRADY PLC; *Int'l*, pg. 1135
BRADY POLSKA SP. Z.O.O.—See Brady Corporation; *U.S. Public*, pg. 379
BRADY RISK MANAGEMENT, INC.—See Hellman & Friedman LLC; *U.S. Private*, pg. 1908
BRADY SERVICES PVT. LTD.—See W. H. Brady & Co. Ltd.; *Int'l*, pg. 8321
BRADY S.R.O.—See Brady Corporation; *U.S. Public*, pg. 379
BRADY SWITZERLAND SA—See Brady plc; *Int'l*, pg. 1135
BRADY TECHNOLOGIES (THAILAND) CO. LTD.—See Brady Corporation; *U.S. Public*, pg. 379
BRADY TECHNOLOGY SDN. BHD.—See Brady Corporation; *U.S. Public*, pg. 379
BRADY/TISCOR, INC.—See Brady Corporation; *U.S. Public*, pg. 379
BRADY TRANE SERVICE, INC.; *U.S. Private*, pg. 633
BRADY USA, INC.—See Brady plc; *Int'l*, pg. 1135
BRADY VIETNAM COMPANY LIMITED—See Brady Corporation; *U.S. Public*, pg. 379
BRADY WARE & SCHOENFELD INC.; *U.S. Private*, pg. 633
BRADY WORLDWIDE, INC.—See Brady Corporation; *U.S. Public*, pg. 379
BRAEBURN ALLOY STEEL—See Compagnie de Saint-Gobain SA; *Int'l*, pg. 1730
BRAE BURN CONSTRUCTION, CO.—See Welty Building Company, Ltd.; *U.S. Private*, pg. 4480
BRAEBURN INC.; *U.S. Private*, pg. 633
BRAEDT, S. A.—See ALFA, S.A.B. de C.V.; *Int'l*, pg. 313
BRAEGER CHEVROLET INC.—See Braeger Company of Wisconsin Inc.; *U.S. Private*, pg. 633
BRAEGER COMPANY OF WISCONSIN INC.; *U.S. Private*, pg. 633
BRAEGER FORD INC.—See Braeger Company of Wisconsin Inc.; *U.S. Private*, pg. 633
BRAEMAR ACM SHIPBROKING PTY LIMITED—See Braemar PLC; *Int'l*, pg. 1135
BRAEMAR ACM SHIPBROKING (USA) INC.—See Braemar PLC; *Int'l*, pg. 1135
BRAEMAR ADJUSTING PTE LTD—See Braemar PLC; *Int'l*, pg. 1135
BRAEMAR COUNTRY CLUB—See Apollo Global Management, Inc.; *U.S. Public*, pg. 149
BRAEMAR ESTATES LIMITED—See Rendall & Rittner Ltd.; *Int'l*, pg. 6275
BRAEMAR FALCONER PTE LIMITED—See Braemar PLC; *Int'l*, pg. 1135
BRAEMAR FALCONER PTY LIMITED—See Braemar PLC; *Int'l*, pg. 1135
BRAEMAR FALCONER (SHANGHAI) PTE LTD—See Braemar PLC; *Int'l*, pg. 1135
BRAEMAR FALCONER—See Braemar PLC; *Int'l*, pg. 1135
BRAEMAR FALCONER VIETNAM CO LIMITED—See Braemar PLC; *Int'l*, pg. 1135
BRAEMAR GROUP LIMITED—See Brooks Macdonald Group plc; *Int'l*, pg. 1194
BRAEMAR HOLDINGS (USA) INC.—See Braemar PLC; *Int'l*, pg. 1135
BRAEMAR HOTELS & RESORTS, INC.; *U.S. Public*, pg. 379
BRAEMAR MANUFACTURING, LLC—See Koninklijke Philips N.V.; *Int'l*, pg. 4267
BRAEMAR NAVES CORPORATE FINANCE LIMITED—See Braemar PLC; *Int'l*, pg. 1135
BRAEMAR PLC; *Int'l*, pg. 1135
BRAEMAR QUINCANNON PTE LIMITED—See Braemar PLC; *Int'l*, pg. 1135
BRAEMAR QUINCANNON PTE LIMITED—See Quincannon Associates, Inc.; *U.S. Private*, pg. 3327
BRAEMAR SEASCOPE (DRY CARGO) PTE LIMITED—See Braemar PLC; *Int'l*, pg. 1135
BRAEMAR SEASCOPE INDIA PRIVATE LIMITED—See Braemar PLC; *Int'l*, pg. 1135

BRAEMAR PLC

BRAEMAR SEASCOPE ITALIA SRL—See Braemar PLC; *Int'l*, pg. 1135
BRAEMAR SEASCOPE LIMITED—See Braemar PLC; *Int'l*, pg. 1135
BRAEMAR SEASCOPE PTY LIMITED—See Braemar PLC; *Int'l*, pg. 1135
BRAEMAR SEASCOPE (SHANGHAI) LIMITED—See Braemar PLC; *Int'l*, pg. 1135
BRAEMAR STEEGE CANADA LIMITED—See ABL Group ASA; *Int'l*, pg. 62
BRAEMAR STEEGE INC—See ABL Group ASA; *Int'l*, pg. 62
BRAEMAR STEEGE, LLC—See ABL Group ASA; *Int'l*, pg. 62
BRAEMAR STEEGE PTE. LTD.—See Braemar PLC; *Int'l*, pg. 1135
BRAEMAR STEEGE RIO DE JANEIRO—See ABL Group ASA; *Int'l*, pg. 62
BRAEMAR STEEGE SHANGHAI—See ABL Group ASA; *Int'l*, pg. 62
BRAEMAR TECHNICAL SERVICED (OFFSHORE) SDN BHD—See Braemar PLC; *Int'l*, pg. 1136
BRAEMAR TECHNICAL SERVICES (OFFSHORE) INDIA PVT LTD—See Braemar PLC; *Int'l*, pg. 1135
BRAEMAR WAVESPEC USA INC.—See Braemar PLC; *Int'l*, pg. 1136
BRAEMONT CAPITAL MANAGEMENT LLC; *U.S. Private*, pg. 633
BRAEMORE RESOURCES PLC—See Jubilee Metals Group plc; *Int'l*, pg. 4021
BRAES CAPITAL LLC; *U.S. Private*, pg. 633
BRAFTON, INCORPORATED; *U.S. Private*, pg. 633
BRAGANZA AS; *Int'l*, pg. 1136
BRAG FZ-LLC—See Live Nation Entertainment, Inc.; *U.S. Public*, pg. 1328
BRAGG CRANE & RIGGING; *U.S. Private*, pg. 634
BRAGG CRANE & RIGGING—See Bragg Investment Company, Inc.; *U.S. Private*, pg. 634
BRAGG CRANE SERVICE—See Bragg Investment Company, Inc.; *U.S. Private*, pg. 634
BRAGG GAMING GROUP INC.; *Int'l*, pg. 1136
BRAGG GROUP OF COMPANIES; *Int'l*, pg. 1136
BRAGG INVESTMENT COMPANY, INC.; *U.S. Private*, pg. 634
BRAGG LIVE FOOD PRODUCTS, LLC—See Swander Pace Capital, LLC; *U.S. Private*, pg. 3889
BRAHIM'S HOLDINGS BERHAD; *Int'l*, pg. 1136
BRAHMA GROUP, INC.—See Terra Millenium Corporation; *U.S. Private*, pg. 3970
BRAHMANAND HIMGHAR LIMITED; *Int'l*, pg. 1136
BRAHMAPUTRA CRACKER AND POLYMER LTD.—See GAIL (India) Limited; *Int'l*, pg. 2869
BRAHMAPUTRA INFRASTRUCTURE LIMITED; *Int'l*, pg. 1136
BRAHMIN LEATHER WORKS, LLC—See Markel Group Inc.; *U.S. Public*, pg. 1367
B.R.A.H.M.S. AUSTRIA GMBH—See Thermo Fisher Scientific Inc.; *U.S. Public*, pg. 2154
B.R.A.H.M.S. BIOTECH GMBH—See Thermo Fisher Scientific Inc.; *U.S. Public*, pg. 2154
B.R.A.H.M.S GMBH—See Thermo Fisher Scientific Inc.; *U.S. Public*, pg. 2145
B.R.A.H.M.S. GMBH—See Thermo Fisher Scientific Inc.; *U.S. Public*, pg. 2154
BRAHMSQ OBJEKT GMBH & CO. KG—See Allianz SE; *Int'l*, pg. 351
BRAHO BRANDPREVENTIE B.V.—See London Security PLC; *Int'l*, pg. 4547
BRAI-COST S.P.A.; *Int'l*, pg. 1136
BRAIFORM GROUP PTY LTD.—See Pacific Equity Partners Pty. Limited; *Int'l*, pg. 5688
BRAIFORM (U.K.) LTD—See Pacific Equity Partners Pty. Limited; *Int'l*, pg. 5688
BRAILLE BATTERIES UK—See Braille Energy Systems Inc.; *Int'l*, pg. 1136
BRAILLE BATTERY INC.—See Braille Energy Systems Inc.; *Int'l*, pg. 1136
BRAILLE ENERGY SYSTEMS INC.; *Int'l*, pg. 1136
BRAILLE INSTITUTE OF AMERICA; *U.S. Private*, pg. 634
BRAILSFORD & DUNLAVEY; *U.S. Private*, pg. 634
BRAIME ELEVATOR COMPONENTS LIMITED—See Braime Group Plc; *Int'l*, pg. 1136
BRAIME GROUP PLC; *Int'l*, pg. 1136
BRAIME PRESSINGS LIMITED—See Braime Group Plc; *Int'l*, pg. 1136
BRAINARD AIRPORT SERVICES, INC.—See Macquarie Group Limited; *Int'l*, pg. 4627
BRAINARD RIVET COMPANY—See Fastener Industries Inc.; *U.S. Private*, pg. 1482
BRAIN BIOTECH AG; *Int'l*, pg. 1137
BRAINBITS LLC—See Thompson Street Capital Manager LLC; *U.S. Private*, pg. 4161
BRAIN BOX—See Omnicom Group Inc.; *U.S. Public*, pg. 1596
BRAIN CAPITAL GMBH—See BRAIN Biotech AG; *Int'l*, pg. 1137
BRAINCHIP HOLDINGS LTD.; *Int'l*, pg. 1137
BRAINCHIP RESEARCH INSTITUTE PTY LTD—See Brainchip Holdings Ltd.; *Int'l*, pg. 1137

BRAINCOOL AB; *Int'l*, pg. 1137
BRAIN CORPORATION—See Kowa Co., Ltd.; *Int'l*, pg. 4293
BRAINERD COMMUNICATORS, INC.; *U.S. Private*, pg. 634
BRAINERD DISPATCH—See Forum Communications Company; *U.S. Private*, pg. 1577
BRAINERD INTERNATIONAL RACEWAY—See BIR Holdings, LLC; *U.S. Private*, pg. 564
BRAIN FORCE B.V.—See Cegeka Groep NV; *Int'l*, pg. 1390
BRAIN FORCE GMBH—See Cegeka Groep NV; *Int'l*, pg. 1391
BRAIN FORCE SOFTWARE S.R.O.—See Cegeka Groep NV; *Int'l*, pg. 1391
BRAIN FORCE S.P.A.—See Cegeka Groep NV; *Int'l*, pg. 1390
BRAINGRID LTD.; *Int'l*, pg. 1137
BRAINHOLE TECHNOLOGY LIMITED; *Int'l*, pg. 1137
BRAININ-ADVANCE INDUSTRIES, LLC—See NN, Inc.; *U.S. Public*, pg. 1531
BRAININ DE MEXICO S.A. DE C.V.—See NN, Inc.; *U.S. Public*, pg. 1531
BRAININ (FOSHAN) PRECISION ENGINEERED PRODUCTS, CO. LTD—See NN, Inc.; *U.S. Public*, pg. 1531
BRAINIUM INC.; *U.S. Private*, pg. 634
BRAINLAB AG—See Intel Corporation; *U.S. Public*, pg. 1138
BRAINLAB FRANCE—See BrainLAB Inc.; *U.S. Private*, pg. 634
BRAINLAB INC.; *U.S. Private*, pg. 634
BRAIN LABS DIGITAL LTD.; *Int'l*, pg. 1137
BRAINPAD INC.; *Int'l*, pg. 1137
BRAINPOOL TV GMBH—See LOV Group Invest SAS; *Int'l*, pg. 4563
BRAINPOOL TV GMBH—See National Amusements, Inc.; *U.S. Private*, pg. 2839
BRAINPOP LLC—See Kirkbi A/S; *Int'l*, pg. 4189
BRAIN POWER INC.; *U.S. Private*, pg. 634
BRAIN POWER INTERNATIONAL LTD.—See Brain Power Inc.; *U.S. Private*, pg. 634
BRAIN SCIENTIFIC, INC.—See Piezo Motion Corp.; *U.S. Private*, pg. 3179
BRAINSELLERS.COM CORP.—See Tecnos Japan Inc.; *Int'l*, pg. 7517
BRAINSELL TECHNOLOGIES, LLC; *U.S. Private*, pg. 634
BRAINSHARK, INC.—See Bigtincan Holdings Limited; *U.S. Public*, pg. 331
BRAINS II INC.; *Int'l*, pg. 1137
BRAINS ON FIRE, INC. - LOS ANGELES—See Brains on Fire, Inc.; *U.S. Private*, pg. 634
BRAINS ON FIRE, INC.; *U.S. Private*, pg. 634
BRAIN SOURCE CO., LTD.—See Samart Corporation Public Company Limited; *Int'l*, pg. 6501
BRAINS TECHNOLOGY, INC.; *Int'l*, pg. 1137
BRAINSTORM CELL THERAPEUTICS INC.; *U.S. Public*, pg. 379
BRAINSTORM CELL THERAPEUTICS LTD.—See BrainStorm Cell Therapeutics Inc.; *U.S. Public*, pg. 380
BRAINSTORM CORPORATION; *U.S. Private*, pg. 634
BRAINSTORMUSA LLC; *U.S. Private*, pg. 634
BRAINSWAY LTD.; *Int'l*, pg. 1137
BRAINTREE ELECTRIC LIGHT DEPARTMENT; *U.S. Private*, pg. 634
BRAINTREE FORUM—See Gannett Co., Inc.; *U.S. Public*, pg. 902
BRAINTREE, INC.—See PayPal Holdings, Inc.; *U.S. Public*, pg. 1656
BRAINTREE PAYMENT SOLUTIONS, LLC—See PayPal Holdings, Inc.; *U.S. Public*, pg. 1656
BRAINWARE, INC.; *U.S. Private*, pg. 634
BRAINZCOMPANY CO., LTD.; *Int'l*, pg. 1137
BRAISHFIELD ASSOCIATES, INC.—See Brown & Brown, Inc.; *U.S. Public*, pg. 397
BRAIT INTERNATIONAL LTD.—See Brait S.E.; *Int'l*, pg. 1137
BRAIT MAURITIUS LIMITED—See Brait S.E.; *Int'l*, pg. 1137
BRAITRIM (DEUTSCHLAND) GMBH—See Pacific Equity Partners Pty. Limited; *Int'l*, pg. 5688
BRAITRIM INDIA (PRIVATE) LTD.—See Pacific Equity Partners Pty. Limited; *Int'l*, pg. 5688
BRAITRIM (LANKA) PVT LTD.—See Pacific Equity Partners Pty. Limited; *Int'l*, pg. 5688
BRAITRIM PLASTI-FORM (MIDDLE EAST) FZCO—See Pacific Equity Partners Pty. Limited; *Int'l*, pg. 5688
BRAITRIM PLASTI-FORM SOUTH AFRICA (PTY) LIMITED—See Pacific Equity Partners Pty. Limited; *Int'l*, pg. 5688
BRAITRIM (SCANDINAVIA) AB—See Pacific Equity Partners Pty. Limited; *Int'l*, pg. 5688
BRAIT S.E.; *Int'l*, pg. 1137
BRAIT SOUTH AFRICA LIMITED—See Brait S.E.; *Int'l*, pg. 1137
THE BRAJ BINANI GROUP; *Int'l*, pg. 7627
BRAKE BROS FOODSERVICE LIMITED—See Sysco Corporation; *U.S. Public*, pg. 1973
BRAKE BROS LIMITED—See Sysco Corporation; *U.S. Public*, pg. 1973

CORPORATE AFFILIATIONS

BRAKE BROS LTD. - ASHFORD HEAD OFFICE—See Sysco Corporation; *U.S. Public*, pg. 1973
BRAKE BROS LTD. - THORPE DEPOT—See Sysco Corporation; *U.S. Public*, pg. 1973
BRAKEBUSH BROTHERS INC.; *U.S. Private*, pg. 635
BRAKE FORCE ONE GMBH—See ZF Friedrichshafen AG; *Int'l*, pg. 8641
BRAKELEY PARK CENTER—See Formation Capital, LLC; *U.S. Private*, pg. 1569
BRAKE-O-RAMA INC.; *U.S. Private*, pg. 634
BRAKE-O-RAMA—See Brake-O-Rama Inc.; *U.S. Private*, pg. 635
BRAKE PARTS INC LLC—See Torque Capital Group, LLC; *U.S. Private*, pg. 4189
BRAKEQUIP, LLC; *U.S. Private*, pg. 635
BRAKES AUTO (INDIA) LIMITED; *Int'l*, pg. 1137
BRAKES CATERING EQUIPMENT—See Sysco Corporation; *U.S. Public*, pg. 1973
BRAKES FOODSERVICE NI LIMITED—See Sysco Corporation; *U.S. Public*, pg. 1973
BRAKES FOODSERVICE NI LIMITED—See Sysco Corporation; *U.S. Public*, pg. 1973
BRAKES INDIA LTD.—See ZF Friedrichshafen AG; *Int'l*, pg. 8645
BRAKES PLUS CORPORATION; *U.S. Private*, pg. 635
BRAKE SUPPLY CO.—See Koch Enterprises, Inc.; *U.S. Private*, pg. 2326
BRAKE SYSTEMS, INC.—See Enstar Group Limited; *Int'l*, pg. 2448
BRAKE & TRANSMISSION NZ LIMITED—See Bapcor Limited; *Int'l*, pg. 857
BRAKING-SUNSTAR S.P.A.—See Sunstar Suisse S.A.; *Int'l*, pg. 7323
BRALCO METALS (AUSTRALIA) PTY LTD.—See Reliance Steel & Aluminum Co.; *U.S. Public*, pg. 1779
BRALCO METALS—See Reliance Steel & Aluminum Co.; *U.S. Public*, pg. 1779
THE BRALEY & WELLINGTON INSURANCE AGENCY CORPORATION—See Workers' Credit Union; *U.S. Private*, pg. 4563
BRAL RESTSTOFF-BEARBEITUNGS GMBH—See Alba SE; *Int'l*, pg. 293
BRAMAC DACHSYSTEME INTERNATIONAL GMBH—See PAI Partners S.A.S.; *Int'l*, pg. 5700
BRAMAC DACHSYSTEME INTERNATIONAL GMBH—See Wienerberger AG; *Int'l*, pg. 8404
BRAMAC KFT.—See PAI Partners S.A.S.; *Int'l*, pg. 5700
BRAMAC KFT.—See Wienerberger AG; *Int'l*, pg. 8404
BRAMAC POKROVNI SISTEMI D.O.O.—See PAI Partners S.A.S.; *Int'l*, pg. 5700
BRAMAC POKROVNI SISTEMI D.O.O.—See Wienerberger AG; *Int'l*, pg. 8404
BRAMAC STRESNI SISTEMI D.O.O.—See PAI Partners S.A.S.; *Int'l*, pg. 5700
BRAMAC STRESNI SISTEMI D.O.O.—See Wienerberger AG; *Int'l*, pg. 8404
BRAMAC STRESNI SYSTEMY SPOL. S R.O.—See PAI Partners S.A.S.; *Int'l*, pg. 5700
BRAMAC STRESNI SYSTEMY SPOL. S R.O.—See Wienerberger AG; *Int'l*, pg. 8405
BRAMAN CADILLAC INC.—See Braman Motors, Inc.; *U.S. Private*, pg. 635
BRAMAN IMPORTS, INC.; *U.S. Private*, pg. 635
BRAMAN MOTORS, INC.; *U.S. Private*, pg. 635
BRAMBLE RISE (HETTON) MANAGEMENT COMPANY LIMITED—See Persimmon plc; *Int'l*, pg. 5815
BRAMBLES ENTERPRISES LIMITED—See Brambles Limited; *Int'l*, pg. 1138
BRAMBLES LIMITED; *Int'l*, pg. 1138
BRAMBLES USA INC.—See Brambles Limited; *Int'l*, pg. 1138
BRAMCO INC. - CERTIFIED RENTAL DIVISION—See Bramco Inc.; *U.S. Private*, pg. 635
BRAMCO INC.; *U.S. Private*, pg. 635
BRAMCO-MPS—See Bramco Inc.; *U.S. Private*, pg. 635
BRAMER CORPORATION LIMITED—See British American Investment Co. (Mtius) Ltd.; *Int'l*, pg. 1165
BRAME SPECIALTY COMPANY INC.; *U.S. Private*, pg. 635
BRAMHULTS JUICE AB—See Eckes AG; *Int'l*, pg. 2290
BRAM INDUSTRIES LTD.; *Int'l*, pg. 1138
BRAMLEY VETS4PETS LIMITED—See Pets at Home Group Plc; *Int'l*, pg. 5833
BRAMMER BIO, LLC—See Thermo Fisher Scientific Inc.; *U.S. Public*, pg. 2145
BRAMMER CZECH A.S.—See THK CO., LTD.; *Int'l*, pg. 7711
BRAMMER ENGINEERING INC.; *U.S. Private*, pg. 635
BRAMMER FRANCE—See Advent International Corporation; *U.S. Private*, pg. 98
BRAMMER IBERIA SA—See THK CO., LTD.; *Int'l*, pg. 7711
BRAMMER MAGYARORSZAG KFT.—See THK CO., LTD.; *Int'l*, pg. 7711
BRAMMER PLC—See Advent International Corporation; *U.S. Private*, pg. 98
BRAMMER SLOVAKIA S.R.O.—See THK CO., LTD.; *Int'l*, pg. 7711

COMPANY NAME INDEX

BRAMMERTZ INGENIEROS S.A.—See Hydac International GmbH; *Int'l*, pg. 3544
BRAMMING PLAST-INDUSTRI A/S—See Indutrade AB; *Int'l*, pg. 3677
B.R. AMON & SONS INC.; *U.S. Private*, pg. 421
BRAMPTON BRICK INC—See Brampton Brick Limited; *Int'l*, pg. 1139
BRAMPTON BRICK LIMITED; *Int'l*, pg. 1139
BRAMPTON ISLAND PTY LIMITED—See GPT Group; *Int'l*, pg. 3047
BRAMPTON RENOLD SA—See Renold plc; *Int'l*, pg. 6284
BRAMTON COMPANY INC.—See NCH Corporation; *U.S. Private*, pg. 2875
BRANAGH INC.; *U.S. Private*, pg. 635
BRANAM FASTENING SYSTEMS INC.—See MSD Capital, L.P.; *U.S. Private*, pg. 2807
BRANCE KRACHY COMPANY, INC.; *U.S. Private*, pg. 635
BRANCH & ASSOCIATES, INC. - RICHMOND DIVISION—See The Branch Group, Inc.; *U.S. Private*, pg. 3999
BRANCH & ASSOCIATES, INC.—See The Branch Group, Inc.; *U.S. Private*, pg. 3999
BRANCH CAPITAL PARTNERS LP; *U.S. Private*, pg. 635
THE BRANCH GROUP, INC.; *U.S. Private*, pg. 3999
BRANCH HIGHWAYS, INC.—See The Branch Group, Inc.; *U.S. Private*, pg. 3999
BRANCHOUT FOOD INC.; *U.S. Public*, pg. 380
BRANCH PROPERTIES, INC.; *U.S. Private*, pg. 635
BRANCHSERV SYSTEMS INTEGRATION LLC—See Custom Vault Corp; *U.S. Private*, pg. 1130
BRANCO ENTERPRISES INC.; *U.S. Private*, pg. 635
BRANCO MOTORES LTDA.—See Briggs & Stratton Corporation; *U.S. Private*, pg. 650
BRAND ADDITION GMBH—See Caisse de Depot et Placement du Quebec; *Int'l*, pg. 1254
BRAND ADDITION GMBH—See Generation Investment Management LLP; *Int'l*, pg. 2920
BRAND ADDITION LIMITED—See Elysian Capital LLP; *Int'l*, pg. 2372
BRAND ADVANTAGE GROUP—See Deluxe Corporation; *U.S. Public*, pg. 652
THE BRAND AGENCY-MELBOURNE—See The Brand Agency Pty. Ltd.; *Int'l*, pg. 7627
THE BRAND AGENCY PTY. LTD., *Int'l*, pg. 7627
BRANDALLEY UK LIMITED; *Int'l*, pg. 1139
BRAND ARCHITECTURE INTERNATIONAL—See Omnicom Group Inc.; *U.S. Public*, pg. 1598
BRAND ARCHITEKTS GROUP PLC; *Int'l*, pg. 1139
BRANDBANK (HUNGARY) KFT.—See Brookfield Corporation; *Int'l*, pg. 1178
BRANDBANK (HUNGARY) KFT.—See Elliott Management Corporation; *U.S. Private*, pg. 1370
BRAND BANKING COMPANY; *U.S. Private*, pg. 635
BRANDBANK (IRELAND) LIMITED.—See Brookfield Corporation; *Int'l*, pg. 1178
BRANDBANK (IRELAND) LIMITED.—See Elliott Management Corporation; *U.S. Private*, pg. 1370
BRANDBANK LIMITED—See Brookfield Corporation; *Int'l*, pg. 1178
BRANDBANK LIMITED—See Elliott Management Corporation; *U.S. Private*, pg. 1370
BRANDBANK (NETHERLANDS) B .V.—See Brookfield Corporation; *Int'l*, pg. 1178
BRANDBANK (NETHERLANDS) B .V.—See Elliott Management Corporation; *U.S. Private*, pg. 1370
BRANDBANK (POLAND) SP. Z .O.O.—See Brookfield Corporation; *Int'l*, pg. 1178
BRANDBANK (POLAND) SP. Z .O.O.—See Elliott Management Corporation; *U.S. Private*, pg. 1370
BRANDBANK (SLOVAKIA) S.R.O.—See Brookfield Corporation; *Int'l*, pg. 1178
BRANDBANK (SLOVAKIA) S.R.O.—See Elliott Management Corporation; *U.S. Private*, pg. 1370
BRANDBEE HOLDING AB; *Int'l*, pg. 1139
BRANDBUCKET MEDIA & TECHNOLOGY LIMITED; *Int'l*, pg. 1139
BRANDBUZZ—See WPP plc; *Int'l*, pg. 8491
BRAND CHAIN GMBH—See The Social Chain AG; *Int'l*, pg. 7687
BRAND CLOUD.INC.—See Vector Inc.; *Int'l*, pg. 8144
BRAND COLLECTIVE PTY LTD—See Anchorage Capital Partners Pty. Limited; *Int'l*, pg. 448
BRAND CONCEPTS LIMITED; *Int'l*, pg. 1139
BRAND CONNECTIONS, LLC—See Advantage Sales & Marketing, LLC; *U.S. Private*, pg. 95
BRAND COOL MARKETING INC.—See Butler/Till Media Services, Inc.; *U.S. Private*, pg. 697
BRAND DATA BANK INC.—See Bain Capital, LP; *U.S. Private*, pg. 442
BRANDDELI C.V.—See Bertelsmann SE & Co. KGaA; *Int'l*, pg. 995
BRAND DEVELOPMENT COMPANY LIMITED; *Int'l*, pg. 1139
BRANDED CITIES NETWORK, LLC—See Shamrock Capital Advisors, LLC; *U.S. Private*, pg. 3624
BRANDED ENTERTAINMENT NETWORK, INC. - NEW YORK OFFICE—See Branded Entertainment Network, Inc.; *U.S. Private*, pg. 637

BRANDED ENTERTAINMENT NETWORK, INC.; *U.S. Private*, pg. 637
BRANDED GROUP, INC.; *U.S. Private*, pg. 637
BRANDED LIMITED—See Writtle Holdings Limited; *Int'l*, pg. 8495
BRANDED ONLINE INC.—See Nogin, Inc.; *U.S. Public*, pg. 1532
BRANDED PRODUCTIONS, INC.—See National Amusements, Inc.; *U.S. Private*, pg. 2839
BRANDEIS MACHINERY & SUPPLY COMPANY—See Bramco Inc.; *U.S. Private*, pg. 635
BRANDENBURG ENERGY CORP.; *Int'l*, pg. 1139
BRANDENBURG INDUSTRIAL SERVICE COMPANY INC.; *U.S. Private*, pg. 637
BRANDENBURG PROPERTIES; *U.S. Private*, pg. 637
BRANDENBURG TELEPHONE COMPANY; *U.S. Private*, pg. 637
BRAND ENERGY & INFRASTRUCTURE SERVICES AUSTRALIA PTY LTD—See Brand Industrial Services, Inc.; *U.S. Private*, pg. 636
BRAND ENERGY & INFRASTRUCTURE SERVICES B.V.—See Brand Industrial Services, Inc.; *U.S. Private*, pg. 636
BRAND ENERGY & INFRASTRUCTURE SERVICES (GLADSTONE) PTY. LTD.—See Brand Industrial Services, Inc.; *U.S. Private*, pg. 636
BRAND ENERGY & INFRASTRUCTURE SERVICES GMBH—See Brand Industrial Services, Inc.; *U.S. Private*, pg. 636
BRAND ENERGY & INFRASTRUCTURE SERVICES-HAZEL CREST—See Brand Industrial Services, Inc.; *U.S. Private*, pg. 636
BRAND ENERGY & INFRASTRUCTURE SERVICES (HUNTER VALLEY) PTY. LTD.—See Brand Industrial Services, Inc.; *U.S. Private*, pg. 636
BRAND ENERGY & INFRASTRUCTURE SERVICES NV/SA—See Brand Industrial Services, Inc.; *U.S. Private*, pg. 636
BRAND ENERGY & INFRASTRUCTURE SERVICES—See Brand Industrial Services, Inc.; *U.S. Private*, pg. 636
BRAND ENERGY SOLUTIONS—See Brand Industrial Services, Inc.; *U.S. Private*, pg. 636
BRAND ENGAGEMENT NETWORK, INC.; *U.S. Public*, pg. 380
BRANDERS.COM INC.—See BEL USA LLC; *U.S. Private*, pg. 516
BRANDEX EUROPE C.V.—See Abbott Laboratories; *U.S. Public*, pg. 19
BRANDEXTRACT, LLC; *U.S. Private*, pg. 637
BRANDFIELD B.V.—See The Platform Group AG; *Int'l*, pg. 7674
BRAND FRANCE S.A.S.—See Brand Industrial Services, Inc.; *U.S. Private*, pg. 636
BRAND FX BODY COMPANY; *U.S. Private*, pg. 635
BRANDFX BODY COMPANY—See Stonebridge Partners, LLC; *U.S. Private*, pg. 3827
BRANDHOUSE RETAILS LTD; *Int'l*, pg. 1139
BRANDIA CENTRAL; *Int'l*, pg. 1139
BRANDICORP; *U.S. Private*, pg. 637
BRANDIFY, INC.—See SOCi, Inc.; *U.S. Private*, pg. 3702
BRANDIMAGE BELGIQUE HOLDINGS SA—See Matthews International Corporation; *U.S. Public*, pg. 1400
BRANDIMAGE DESGRIPPES AND LAGA SAS—See Matthews International Corporation; *U.S. Public*, pg. 1400
BRANDIMAGE DESGRIPPES & LAGA; *U.S. Private*, pg. 637
BRAND INDUSTRIAL SERVICES, INC.; *U.S. Private*, pg. 635
THE BRANDING AGENCY, LLC; *U.S. Private*, pg. 3999
BRANDING ENGINEER CO., LTD.; *Int'l*, pg. 1140
BRANDING TECHNOLOGY, INC.; *Int'l*, pg. 1140
BRAND INNOVATION GROUP; *U.S. Private*, pg. 637
BRAND INSULATION SERVICES—See Brand Industrial Services, Inc.; *U.S. Private*, pg. 636
BRAND INTEGRITY, INC.—See Edenred S.A.; *Int'l*, pg. 2308
BRANDISH LIMITED—See General Motors Company; *U.S. Public*, pg. 927
BRAND ITALIA S.P.A.—See Brand Industrial Services, Inc.; *U.S. Private*, pg. 636
BRANDITO, LLC—See Monroe Street Partners LLC; *U.S. Private*, pg. 2774
BRAND LEADERS INCOME FUND—See Harvest Portfolios Group Inc.; *Int'l*, pg. 3281
BRAND LEARNING LLC—See Accenture plc; *Int'l*, pg. 87
BRAND LOUNGE; *Int'l*, pg. 1139
BRAND LOYALTY BV—See Bread Financial Holdings Inc.; *U.S. Public*, pg. 381
BRAND LOYALTY FRANCE SARL—See Bread Financial Holdings Inc.; *U.S. Public*, pg. 381
BRAND LOYALTY JAPAN KK—See Bread Financial Holdings Inc.; *U.S. Public*, pg. 381
BRAND LOYALTY LIMITED—See Bread Financial Holdings Inc.; *U.S. Public*, pg. 381
BRANDMAN CENTERS FOR SENIOR CARE; *U.S. Private*, pg. 637
BRANDMARK CREATIVE INC.—See Winbrook Inc.; *U.S. Private*, pg. 4533

BRAND MARKETING TEAM LTD.—See Providence Equity Partners L.L.C.; *U.S. Private*, pg. 3291
BRANDMARK INTERNATIONAL HOLDING B.V.—See Matthews International Corporation; *U.S. Public*, pg. 1400
BRAND MARVEL WORLDWIDE CONSUMER PRODUCTS CORPORATION; *Int'l*, pg. 1139
BRAND MEDIA SOLUTIONS GMBH—See Hubert Burda Media Holding Kommanditgesellschaft; *Int'l*, pg. 3519
BRANDMIND; *U.S. Private*, pg. 637
BRANDMUSCLE, INC.; *U.S. Private*, pg. 638
BRAND MUSCLE, INC.—See The Riverside Company; *U.S. Private*, pg. 4108
BRAND NETWORKS, LLC—See Augeo Affinity Marketing, Inc.; *U.S. Private*, pg. 391
BRAND NEW LIVE BV—See Live Nation Entertainment, Inc.; *U.S. Public*, pg. 1328
BRAND NEW VINTAGE LIMITED; *Int'l*, pg. 1139
BRAND-NU LABORATORIES INC.; *U.S. Private*, pg. 637
BRANDOM CABINETS; *U.S. Private*, pg. 638
BRANDON AB—See Kering S.A.; *Int'l*, pg. 4133
BRANDON ADVERTISING, INC.; *U.S. Private*, pg. 638
BRANDON AMBULATORY SURGERY CENTER, LLC—See UnitedHealth Group Incorporated; *U.S. Public*, pg. 2239
BRANDON CAPITAL PARTNERS PTY LTD.; *Int'l*, pg. 1140
BRANDON & CLARK INC.; *U.S. Private*, pg. 638
BRANDON COMPANY; *U.S. Private*, pg. 638
BRANDON CONSTRUCTION COMPANY, INC.; *U.S. Private*, pg. 638
BRANDON GERMANY GMBH—See Kering S.A.; *Int'l*, pg. 4133
BRANDON HIRE LIMITED—See Vp PLC; *Int'l*, pg. 8312
BRANDON HMA, LLC—See Community Health Systems, Inc.; *U.S. Public*, pg. 551
BRANDON HONDA—See Morgan Auto Group, LLC; *U.S. Private*, pg. 2783
BRANDON INTERNATIONAL; *U.S. Private*, pg. 638
BRANDON PHYSICIAN MANAGEMENT, LLC—See Community Health Systems, Inc.; *U.S. Public*, pg. 551
BRANDON REGIONAL HOSPITAL—See HCA Healthcare, Inc.; *U.S. Public*, pg. 991
BRAND & OPPENHEIMER CO., INC.—See Praesidian Capital Corp.; *U.S. Private*, pg. 3241
BRANDORCHARD; *U.S. Private*, pg. 638
BRANDPACK CONSULTING GMBH—See Graphic Packaging Holding Company; *U.S. Public*, pg. 958
BRAND PARTNERSHIP LTD.; *Int'l*, pg. 1139
BRAND PHARM—See Publicis Groupe S.A.; *Int'l*, pg. 6097
BRANDPOINT SERVICES, INC.; *U.S. Private*, pg. 638
BRANDPREVENTIE GROEP B.V.—See London Security PLC; *Int'l*, pg. 4547
BRANDPROJEKTING SVERIGE AB—See Storskogen Group AB; *Int'l*, pg. 7227
BRANDPROTECT INC.; *Int'l*, pg. 1140
BRAND REALTY SERVICES LTD.; *Int'l*, pg. 1139
BRANDRILL LIMITED—See Perenti Global Limited; *Int'l*, pg. 5798
BRAND SCAFFOLDING SERVICES—See Brand Industrial Services, Inc.; *U.S. Private*, pg. 636
BRANDS EUROPEAN SHOE TRADE; *Int'l*, pg. 1140
BRANDS & FASHION NV—See Frasers Group plc; *Int'l*, pg. 2765
BRANDSHELTER INC.—See Team Internet Group plc; *Int'l*, pg. 7500
BRANDS IN SPACE PTY LIMITED—See M&C Saatchi plc; *Int'l*, pg. 4611
BRANDS, LLC; *U.S. Private*, pg. 638
BRANDSMART USA; *U.S. Private*, pg. 638
BRANDS ON FIRE, LLC—See Level Equity Management, LLC; *U.S. Private*, pg. 2434
BRANDSPA LLC; *U.S. Private*, pg. 638
BRANDSPINS, LLC; *U.S. Private*, pg. 638
BRANDSPRING SOLUTIONS LLC; *U.S. Private*, pg. 638
BRAND STORY EXPERTS INC.; *U.S. Private*, pg. 637
BRANDS WITHIN REACH, LLC—See Zachert Private Equity GmbH; *Int'l*, pg. 8619
BRANDT BOX & PAPER CO INC; *U.S. Private*, pg. 638
BRANDT CO., INC.; *U.S. Private*, pg. 638
THE BRANDT COMPANIES, LLC—See Southland Industries; *U.S. Private*, pg. 3737
BRANDT CONSOLIDATED, INC.; *U.S. Private*, pg. 638
THE BRANDT CO.; *U.S. Private*, pg. 4000
BRANDT & HILL INC.; *U.S. Private*, pg. 638
BRANDT HOLDINGS COMPANY; *U.S. Private*, pg. 638
BRANDT INDUSTRIES LTD.; *Int'l*, pg. 1140
BRANDT INFORMATION SERVICES, INC.; *U.S. Private*, pg. 639
BRANDT KANTENTECHNIK GMBH—See Durr AG; *Int'l*, pg. 2232
BRANDT OILFIELD SERVICES—See NOV, Inc.; *U.S. Public*, pg. 1544
BRAND TRADING (INDIA) PVT. LIMITED—See Retail Holdings N.V.; *Int'l*, pg. 6305
BRANDTRUST, INC.; *U.S. Private*, pg. 639
BRANDT TRACTOR LTD.—See Brandt Industries Ltd.; *Int'l*, pg. 1140
BRANDT TRUCK LINE INC.; *U.S. Private*, pg. 639

BRANDT & WALTHER GMBH

BRANDT & WALTHER GMBH; *Int'l*, pg. 1140
THE BRAND UNION AB—See WPP plc; *Int'l*, pg. 8466
THE BRAND UNION COMPANY, INC.—See WPP plc; *Int'l*, pg. 8466
BRAND UP, LLC; *U.S. Private*, pg. 637
BRANDVAULT GLOBAL SERVICES LTD.—See Strax AB; *Int'l*, pg. 7239
BRAND VELOCITY ACQUISITION CORP.; *U.S. Private*, pg. 637
BRAND VELOCITY PARTNERS; *U.S. Private*, pg. 637
BRANDVIA ALLIANCE, INC.; *U.S. Private*, pg. 639
BRANDVISION K.K.—See ad-comm Co., Ltd.; *Int'l*, pg. 123
BRANDWELLS CONSTRUCTION; *Int'l*, pg. 1140
BRANDWIDTH GROUP LIMITED—See Next 15 Group plc; *Int'l*, pg. 5246
BRANDWIZARD—See Omnicom Group Inc.; *U.S. Public*, pg. 1577
BRAND X CO., LTD.; *Int'l*, pg. 1139
BRANDYWINE AUTO PARTS INC.; *U.S. Private*, pg. 639
BRANDYWINE COACH WORKS, INC.—See Susquehanna International Group, LLP; *U.S. Private*, pg. 3885
BRANDYWINE COMMUNICATIONS, INC.—See Cache Creek Industries, LLC; *U.S. Private*, pg. 712
BRANDYWINE COMMUNICATIONS, INC.—See Rockmont Capital Partners Ltd.; *U.S. Private*, pg. 3467
THE BRANDYWINE COMPANIES, LLC; *U.S. Private*, pg. 4000
BRANDYWINE CONSTRUCTION & MANAGEMENT; *U.S. Private*, pg. 639
BRANDYWINE FINANCIAL SERVICES CORPORATION—See The Brandywine Companies, LLC; *U.S. Private*, pg. 4000
BRANDYWINEGLOBAL - GLOBAL INCOME OPPORTUNITIES FUND INC.; *U.S. Public*, pg. 380
BRANDYWINE GLOBAL INVESTMENT MANAGEMENT (EUROPE) LIMITED—See Franklin Resources, Inc.; *U.S. Public*, pg. 881
BRANDYWINE GLOBAL INVESTMENT MANAGEMENT, LLC—See Franklin Resources, Inc.; *U.S. Public*, pg. 881
BRANDYWINE HALL CARE CENTER—See Formation Capital, LLC; *U.S. Private*, pg. 1569
BRANDYWINE OPERATING PARTNERSHIP, L.P.—See Brandywine Realty Trust; *U.S. Public*, pg. 380
BRANDYWINE REAL ESTATE MANAGEMENT SERVICES CORPORATION—See The Brandywine Companies, LLC; *U.S. Private*, pg. 4000
BRANDYWINE REALTY SERVICES CORPORATION—See Brandywine Realty Trust; *U.S. Public*, pg. 380
BRANDYWINE REALTY TRUST; *U.S. Public*, pg. 380
BRANDYWINE SPORTS, INC.; *U.S. Private*, pg. 639
BRANER USA, INC.—See Holleway Capital Partners LLC; *U.S. Private*, pg. 1964
BRANFORD CASTLE, INC.; *U.S. Private*, pg. 639
BRANFORD CASTLE PARTNERS, L.P.—See Branford Castle, Inc.; *U.S. Private*, pg. 639
BRANGISTA, INC.—See Nexyz.Group Corporation; *Int'l*, pg. 5251
BRANHAM CORP.—See LKCM Headwater Investments; *U.S. Private*, pg. 2475
BRANHAVEN CHRYSLER JEEP DODGE RAM; *U.S. Private*, pg. 639
BRANKAMP GMBH—See Marposs S.p.A.; *Int'l*, pg. 4698
BRANKO A.S.; *Int'l*, pg. 1140
BRAN & LUEBBE GMBH—See SPX Technologies, Inc.; *U.S. Public*, pg. 1920
BRANNAN PAVING COMPANY, LTD.; *U.S. Private*, pg. 639
BRANNAN SAND & GRAVEL CO. LLC; *U.S. Private*, pg. 639
BRANNEN BANK SERVICES INC.—See Brannen Banks of Florida, Inc.; *U.S. Private*, pg. 640
BRANNEN BANKS OF FLORIDA, INC.; *U.S. Private*, pg. 640
BRANNEN BANK—See Brannen Banks of Florida, Inc.; *U.S. Private*, pg. 640
BRANNON STEEL; *Int'l*, pg. 1140
BRANOM INSTRUMENT CO. INC.; *U.S. Private*, pg. 640
BRANSCUM CONSTRUCTION COMPANY, INC.; *U.S. Private*, pg. 640
BRANSHAW PARK (KEIGHLEY) MANAGEMENT COMPANY LIMITED—See Persimmon plc; *Int'l*, pg. 5815
BRANSON DE MEXICO, S.A. DE C.V.—See Emerson Electric Co.; *U.S. Public*, pg. 742
BRANSON MACHINERY LLC—See Dongkuk Steel Mill Co., Ltd.; *Int'l*, pg. 2169
BRANSON TRACTORS LIMITED—See Tym Corporation; *Int'l*, pg. 7994
BRANSON ULTRASONICS CORPORATION—See Emerson Electric Co.; *U.S. Public*, pg. 750
BRANSON ULTRASONICS (SHANGHAI) CO., LTD.—See Emerson Electric Co.; *U.S. Public*, pg. 742
BRANTANO RETAIL LIMITED—See Alteri Partners LLP; *Int'l*, pg. 391
THE BRANTFORD EXPOSITOR—See Chatham Asset Management, LLC; *U.S. Private*, pg. 861

BRANTFORD LIMITED—See TCC Concepts Ltd; *Int'l*, pg. 7483
BRANT PUBLICATIONS, INC.; *U.S. Private*, pg. 640
BRANTRIDGE MANAGEMENT LIMITED—See Intercorp Group; *Int'l*, pg. 3739
BRANWELL GRAPHITE LTD.—See AMG Critical Materials N.V.; *Int'l*, pg. 425
BRAN-ZAN CO. INC.; *U.S. Private*, pg. 635
BRAPENTA ELETRONICA LTDA.—See Illinois Tool Works Inc.; *U.S. Public*, pg. 1102
BRASADA CAPITAL MANAGEMENT LP; *U.S. Private*, pg. 640
BRASALPLA AMAZONIA INDUSTRIA DE EMBALAGENS LTDA.—See Alpla-Werke Alwin Lehner GmbH & Co. KG; *Int'l*, pg. 374
BRASALPLA BRASIL INDUSTRIA DE EMBALAGENS LTDA.—See Alpla-Werke Alwin Lehner GmbH & Co. KG; *Int'l*, pg. 374
BRASALPLA PERNAMBUCO - INDUSTRIA DE EMBALAGENS LTDA.—See Alpla-Werke Alwin Lehner GmbH & Co. KG; *Int'l*, pg. 374
BRASA MIDDLE EAST FZE—See Marcopolo S.A.; *Int'l*, pg. 4690
BRASBAUER EQUIPAMENTOS DE PERFURACAO LTDA.—See BAUER Aktiengesellschaft; *Int'l*, pg. 893
BRASCABOS COMPONENTES ELETRICOS E ELETRONICOS LIMITADA—See Solartech International Holdings Limited; *Int'l*, pg. 7070
BRASCITI INDUSTRIA E COMERCIO DE RELOGIOS DA AMAZONIA, S.A.—See Citizen Watch Co., Ltd.; *Int'l*, pg. 1623
BRASCO LOGISTICA OFFSHORE LTDA.—See Ocean Wilsons Holdings Limited; *Int'l*, pg. 5517
BRASELTON ENDOSCOPY CENTER, LLC—See Tenet Healthcare Corporation; *U.S. Public*, pg. 2001
BRASELTON HOMES, INC.—See D.R. Horton, Inc.; *U.S. Public*, pg. 619
BRASFIELD & GORRIE, LLC; *U.S. Private*, pg. 640
BRASFLEX TUBOS FLEXIVEIS LTDA.—See TechnipFMC plc; *Int'l*, pg. 7507
BRASHE ADVERTISING, INC.; *U.S. Private*, pg. 640
BRASILAGRO-CIA BRAS DE PROP AGRICOLAS; *Int'l*, pg. 1140
BRASILAGRO - COMPANHIA BRASILEIRA DE PROPRIEDADES AGRICOLAS; *Int'l*, pg. 1140
BRASIL BROKERS PARTICIPACOES S.A.; *Int'l*, pg. 1140
BRASIL DE IMOVEIS E PARTICIPACOES LTDA.—See Allianz SE; *Int'l*, pg. 351
BRASILIAN AMERICAN MERCHANT BANK—See Banco do Brasil S.A.; *Int'l*, pg. 822
BRASILIT SA—See Compagnie de Saint-Gobain SA; *Int'l*, pg. 1722
BRASIL KIRIN PARTICIPACOES E REPRESENTACOES S.A.—See Kirin Holdings Company, Limited; *Int'l*, pg. 4186
BRASIL PLURAL S.A. BANCO MULTIPLO; *Int'l*, pg. 1140
BRASILPREV PREVIDENCIA PRIVADA S.A.—See Principal Financial Group, Inc.; *U.S. Public*, pg. 1719
BRASILPREV SEGUROS E PREVIDENCIA S.A.—See Banco do Brasil S.A.; *Int'l*, pg. 822
BRASKEM AMERICA, INC.—See Novonor S.A.; *Int'l*, pg. 5469
BRASKEM S.A.—See Novonor S.A.; *Int'l*, pg. 5469
BRASMOTOR S.A.—See Whirlpool Corporation; *U.S. Public*, pg. 2368
BRA SMYTH OF CALIFORNIA, INC.; *U.S. Private*, pg. 630
BRAS N THINGS PTY. LIMITED—See Hanesbrands Inc.; *U.S. Public*, pg. 982
BRASPAG TECNO. EM PAGTO. LTDA.—See Cielo S.A.; *Int'l*, pg. 1605
BRASPETRO OIL SERVICES CO. - BRASOIL—See Retroleo Brasileiro S.A. - PETROBRAS; *Int'l*, pg. 5827
BRASS AGENCY LTD.; *Int'l*, pg. 1140
BRASS ARMADILLO INC.; *U.S. Private*, pg. 640
BRASS CO., LTD.; *Int'l*, pg. 1140
BRASSCRAFT CANADA LTD.—See Masco Corporation; *U.S. Public*, pg. 1390
BRASSCRAFT MANUFACTURING COMPANY—See Masco Corporation; *U.S. Public*, pg. 1390
BRASSCRAFT MANUFACTURING COMPANY—See Masco Corporation; *U.S. Public*, pg. 1390
BRASSCRAFT MANUFACTURING COMPANY—See Masco Corporation; *U.S. Public*, pg. 1390
BRASSELER CANADA, INC.—See Carousel Capital Partners; *U.S. Private*, pg. 769
BRASSELER USA, INC.—See Carousel Capital Partners; *U.S. Private*, pg. 769
BRASSERIE D'ACHOUFFE NV—See Fibemi NV; *Int'l*, pg. 2651
BRASSERIE DE LUXEMBOURG MOUSEL - DIEKIRCH SA—See Anheuser-Busch InBev SA/NV; *Int'l*, pg. 465
BRASSERIE DE TAHITI SA; *Int'l*, pg. 1140
BRASSERIES DU LOGONE S.A.—See L'Arche Green N.V.; *Int'l*, pg. 4376
BRASSERIES ET LIMONADERIES DU BURUNDI BRARUDI S.A.—See L'Arche Green N.V.; *Int'l*, pg. 4376

CORPORATE AFFILIATIONS

BRASSERIES ET LIMONADERIES DU RWANDA BRALIRWA S.A.—See L'Arche Green N.V.; *Int'l*, pg. 4376
BRASSERIES KRONENBOURG—See Carlsberg A/S; *Int'l*, pg. 1339
BRASSERIES, LIMONADERIES ET MALTERIES BRALIMA S.A.R.L.—See L'Arche Green N.V.; *Int'l*, pg. 4376
BRASSEUR S.A.—See Accell Group N.V.; *Int'l*, pg. 80
BRASSEUR TRANSPORT INC.; *Int'l*, pg. 1140
BRASS MEDIA INC.; *U.S. Private*, pg. 640
BR ASSOCIATES, INC.; *U.S. Private*, pg. 630
BRASSO NISSAN; *Int'l*, pg. 1140
B.R.A.S.S. PARTNERSHIP IN COMMENDAM—See UnitedHealth Group Incorporated; *U.S. Public*, pg. 2239
BRASS RING CAPITAL INC.; *U.S. Private*, pg. 640
BRASSTECH, INC.—See Masco Corporation; *U.S. Public*, pg. 1390
BRASTER S.A.; *Int'l*, pg. 1140
BRASTILE INC.; *U.S. Private*, pg. 640
BRASWELL FOODS—See Braswell Milling Company; *U.S. Private*, pg. 640
BRASWELL MILLING COMPANY; *U.S. Private*, pg. 640
BRASWELL OFFICE SYSTEMS INC.—See Sentinel Capital Partners, L.L.C.; *U.S. Private*, pg. 3609
BRATACO, PT; *Int'l*, pg. 1140
BRATNEY EQUIPMENT COMPANY INC—See K.B.C. Group Inc.; *U.S. Private*, pg. 2251
BRATSK FERROALLOY PLANT OOO—See Mechel PAO; *Int'l*, pg. 4765
BRATSTVO A.D.; *Int'l*, pg. 1141
BRATTAIN INTERNATIONAL TRUCKS, INC.; *U.S. Private*, pg. 640
BRATTLEBORO REFORMER—See Alden Global Capital LLC; *U.S. Public*, pg. 155
BRATTLEBORO RETREAT; *U.S. Private*, pg. 640
BRATTON CORPORATION; *U.S. Private*, pg. 640
BRATTON MASONRY INC.; *U.S. Private*, pg. 640
BRAUEREI BECK GMBH & CO. KG—See Anheuser-Busch InBev SA/NV; *Int'l*, pg. 465
BRAUEREI DIEBELS GMBH & CO. KG—See Anheuser-Busch InBev SA/NV; *Int'l*, pg. 465
BRAUEREI FOHRENBURG GMBH & CO KG; *Int'l*, pg. 1141
BRAUEREI MAX LEIBINGER GMBH; *Int'l*, pg. 1141
BRAUEREI ZOLLER-HOF GRAF-FLEISCHHUT GMBH & CO.KG; *Int'l*, pg. 1141
BRAUERGILDE HANNOVER AG—See Anheuser-Busch InBev SA/NV; *Int'l*, pg. 465
BRAUER MATERIAL HANDLING SYSTEMS, INC.; *U.S. Private*, pg. 640
BRAUER SUPPLY COMPANY; *U.S. Private*, pg. 640
BRAU HOLDING INTERNATIONAL GMBH & CO. KGAA—See L'Arche Green N.V.; *Int'l*, pg. 4376
BRAU HOLDING INTERNATIONAL GMBH & CO. KGAA—See Schorghuber Stiftung & Co. Holding KG; *Int'l*, pg. 6639
BRAUM'S ICE CREAM & DAIRY STORES INC.; *U.S. Private*, pg. 640
THE BRAUN AGENCY, INC.; *U.S. Private*, pg. 4000
BRAUN AIDUN (SHANGHAI) TRADING CO., LTD.—See B. Braun Melsungen AG; *Int'l*, pg. 787
BRAUN & BUTLER CONSTRUCTION, INC.; *U.S. Private*, pg. 641
THE BRAUN CORPORATION—See Investor AB; *Int'l*, pg. 3787
BRAUN ELECTRIC COMPANY INCORPORATED; *U.S. Private*, pg. 641
BRAUN-GILLETTE IMMOBILIEN GMBH & CO. KG—See The Procter & Gamble Company; *U.S. Public*, pg. 2124
BRAUN GMBH—See The Procter & Gamble Company; *U.S. Public*, pg. 2124
BRAUN INDUSTRIES, INC.—See Caisse de Depot et Placement du Quebec; *Int'l*, pg. 1254
BRAUN INDUSTRIES, INC.—See Clearspring Capital Partners; *U.S. Private*, pg. 1657
BRAUN INTERTEC CORPORATION; *U.S. Private*, pg. 641
BRAUN MEDICAL (SHANDONG) CO., LTD.—See B. Braun Melsungen AG; *Int'l*, pg. 787
BRAUN MEDICAL (SHANGHAI) INTERNATIONAL TRADE CO., LTD.—See B. Braun Melsungen AG; *Int'l*, pg. 787
BRAUN NORTH AMERICA—See The Procter & Gamble Company; *U.S. Public*, pg. 2124
BRAUNSCHWEIGER BROS., INC.; *U.S. Private*, pg. 641
BRAUNSCHWEIGER NETZ GMBH—See Veolia Environnement S.A.; *Int'l*, pg. 8153
BRAUNSCHWEIGER VERSORGUNGS - AG & CO.KG—See Veolia Environnement S.A.; *Int'l*, pg. 8153
BRAUNS EXPRESS INC.; *U.S. Private*, pg. 641
BRAUN (SHANGHAI) CO. LTD.—See The Procter & Gamble Company; *U.S. Public*, pg. 2124
BRAUNS ONLINE MEDIA INC.; *U.S. Private*, pg. 641
BRAUN THYSSENKRUPP ELEVATOR, LLC—See Advent International Corporation; *U.S. Private*, pg. 106
BRAUN THYSSENKRUPP ELEVATOR, LLC—See Cinven Limited; *Int'l*, pg. 1614
BRAUN THYSSENKRUPP ELEVATOR, LLC—See RAG-Stiftung; *Int'l*, pg. 6179

COMPANY NAME INDEX

BRAUSSE EUROPE BV—See Bobst Group S.A.; *Int'l*, pg. 1096
B&R AUTOMACAO INDUSTRIAL LTDA.—See ABB Ltd.; *Int'l*, pg. 56
B+R AUTOMATIZACE, SPOL. S R.O.—See ABB Ltd.; *Int'l*, pg. 56
B&R AUTOMATYKA PRZEMYSLOWA SP. Z.O.O.—See ABB Ltd.; *Int'l*, pg. 56
B&R AUTOMAZIONE INDUSTRIALE S.R.L.—See ABB Ltd.; *Int'l*, pg. 56
BRAU UNION AG—See L'Arche Green N.V.; *Int'l*, pg. 4377
BRAU UNION AUSTRIA GMBH—See L'Arche Green N.V.; *Int'l*, pg. 4377
BRAU-UNION INTERNATIONAL GMBH—See L'Arche Green N.V.; *Int'l*, pg. 4377
BRAU UNION OSTERREICH AG—See L'Arche Green N.V.; *Int'l*, pg. 4377
BRAVADA GOLD CORPORATION; *Int'l*, pg. 1141
BRAVADA INTERNATIONAL, LTD.; *U.S. Public*, pg. 380
BRAVA HOME, INC.—See The Middleby Corporation; *U.S. Public*, pg. 2113
BRAVAS LLC—See Presidio Investors LLC; *U.S. Private*, pg. 3255
BRAVAS MINNEAPOLIS—See Presidio Investors LLC; *U.S. Private*, pg. 3255
BRAVATEK SOLUTIONS, INC.; *U.S. Public*, pg. 380
BRAVE ASSET MANAGEMENT INC.; *U.S. Private*, pg. 641
BRAVE BISON ASIA PACIFIC PTE. LTD.—See Brave Bison Group plc; *Int'l*, pg. 1141
BRAVE BISON GROUP PLC; *Int'l*, pg. 1141
BRAVE BISON LIMITED—See Brave Bison Group plc; *Int'l*, pg. 1141
BRAVE C&H SUPPLY CO., LTD.; *Int'l*, pg. 1141
BRAVE DRAGON LTD—See Wing Tai Holdings Limited; *Int'l*, pg. 8427
BRAVEHEART INVESTMENT GROUP PLC; *Int'l*, pg. 1141
BRAVEHEART RESOURCES INC.; *Int'l*, pg. 1141
BRAVE, INC.—See Faith, Inc.; *Int'l*, pg. 2609
BRAVENETMEDIA.COM; *Int'l*, pg. 1141
BRAVE NEW WORLD; *U.S. Private*, pg. 641
BRAVE PRECISION MFG. SUZHOU CO., LTD.—See Brave C&H Supply Co., Ltd.; *Int'l*, pg. 1141
BRAVERA BANK—See American Bancor, Ltd.; *U.S. Private*, pg. 223
BRAVERN VENTURES LTD.; *Int'l*, pg. 1141
BRAVE; *Int'l*, pg. 1141
BRAVE SPIRITS LLC; *U.S. Private*, pg. 641
BRAVES PRODUCTIONS LLC—See Atlanta Braves Holdings, Inc.; *U.S. Public*, pg. 222
BRAVE TECHNOLOGY (CHENGDU) CO., LTD.—See Brave C&H Supply Co., Ltd.; *Int'l*, pg. 1141
BRAVIA CAPITAL HONG KONG LIMITED; *Int'l*, pg. 1141
BRAVIA CAPITAL PARTNERS, INC.—See Bravia Capital Hong Kong Limited; *Int'l*, pg. 1141
BRAVIA CAPITAL SERVICES INDIA PVT. LTD.—See Bravia Capital Hong Kong Limited; *Int'l*, pg. 1141
BRAVIDA AB—See Bravida Holding AB; *Int'l*, pg. 1142
BRAVIDA DANMARK AS—See Bravida Holding AB; *Int'l*, pg. 1142
BRAVIDA FINLAND OY—See Bravida Holding AB; *Int'l*, pg. 1142
BRAVIDA HOLDING AB; *Int'l*, pg. 1141
BRAVIDA NORGE 4 AS—See Bravida Holding AB; *Int'l*, pg. 1142
BRAVIDA NORGE AS—See Bravida Holding AB; *Int'l*, pg. 1142
BRAVIDA PRENAD AB—See Bravida Holding AB; *Int'l*, pg. 1142
BRAVIDA SVERIGE AB - NORTH DIVISION—See Bravida Holding AB; *Int'l*, pg. 1142
BRAVIDA SVERIGE AB—See Bravida Holding AB; *Int'l*, pg. 1142
BRAVIDA SVERIGE AB - SOUTH DIVISION—See Bravida Holding AB; *Int'l*, pg. 1142
BRAVOBUS S.R.L.—See Accel Partners L.P.; *U.S. Private*, pg. 48
BRAVOBUS S.R.L.—See KKR & Co. Inc.; *U.S. Public*, pg. 1238
BRAVO CHEVROLET CADILLAC; *U.S. Private*, pg. 641
BRAVOFLY RUMBO GROUP N.V.; *Int'l*, pg. 1142
THE BRAVO GROUP HQ—See WPP plc; *Int'l*, pg. 8493
THE BRAVO GROUP—See WPP plc; *Int'l*, pg. 8493
THE BRAVO GROUP—See WPP plc; *Int'l*, pg. 8493
BRAVO HEALTH, LLC—See The Cigna Group; *U.S. Public*, pg. 2060
BRAVO HEALTH OF PENNSYLVANIA, INC.—See The Cigna Group; *U.S. Public*, pg. 2060
BRAVO INNS LIMITED—See NewRiver Retail Ltd; *Int'l*, pg. 5237
BRAVO, LLC—See Alvarez & Marsal, Inc.; *U.S. Private*, pg. 212
BRAVO MEDIA LLC—See Comcast Corporation; *U.S. Public*, pg. 539
BRAVO MULTINATIONAL INCORPORATED; *U.S. Public*, pg. 380
BRAVO PASSENGER SOLUTION PTE LIMITED; *Int'l*, pg. 1142
BRAVO RESTAURANTS INC.; *U.S. Private*, pg. 641

BRAVOSOLUTION BENELUX B.V.—See Accel Partners L.P.; *U.S. Private*, pg. 48
BRAVOSOLUTION BENELUX B.V.—See KKR & Co. Inc.; *U.S. Public*, pg. 1238
BRAVOSOLUTION CHINA CO. LTD—See Accel Partners L.P.; *U.S. Private*, pg. 48
BRAVOSOLUTION CHINA CO. LTD—See KKR & Co. Inc.; *U.S. Public*, pg. 1238
BRAVOSOLUTION ESPANA S.A.—See Accel Partners L.P.; *U.S. Private*, pg. 48
BRAVOSOLUTION ESPANA S.A.—See KKR & Co. Inc.; *U.S. Public*, pg. 1238
BRAVOSOLUTION FRANCE S.A.S.—See Accel Partners L.P.; *U.S. Private*, pg. 48
BRAVOSOLUTION FRANCE S.A.S.—See KKR & Co. Inc.; *U.S. Public*, pg. 1238
BRAVOSOLUTION GMBH—See Accel Partners L.P.; *U.S. Private*, pg. 48
BRAVOSOLUTION GMBH—See KKR & Co. Inc.; *U.S. Public*, pg. 1238
BRAVOSOLUTION MEXICO S.R.L. DE C.V.—See Accel Partners L.P.; *U.S. Private*, pg. 48
BRAVOSOLUTION MEXICO S.R.L. DE C.V.—See KKR & Co. Inc.; *U.S. Public*, pg. 1238
BRAVOSOLUTION SOFTWARE, INC.—See Accel Partners L.P.; *U.S. Private*, pg. 48
BRAVOSOLUTION SOFTWARE, INC.—See KKR & Co. Inc.; *U.S. Public*, pg. 1238
BRAVOSOLUTION S.P.A.—See Accel Partners L.P.; *U.S. Private*, pg. 48
BRAVOSOLUTION S.P.A.—See KKR & Co. Inc.; *U.S. Public*, pg. 1238
BRAVOSOLUTION TECHNOLOGIES LTD—See Accel Partners L.P.; *U.S. Private*, pg. 48
BRAVOSOLUTION TECHNOLOGIES LTD—See KKR & Co. Inc.; *U.S. Public*, pg. 1238
BRAVOSOLUTION UK LTD—See Accel Partners L.P.; *U.S. Private*, pg. 48
BRAVOSOLUTION UK LTD—See KKR & Co. Inc.; *U.S. Public*, pg. 1238
BRAVO SPORTS CORPORATION—See Transom Capital Group, LLC; *U.S. Private*, pg. 4209
BRAVO TANGO ADVERTISING FIRM INC.; *Int'l*, pg. 1142
BRAVO WELLNESS, LLC—See Medical Mutual of Ohio; *U.S. Private*, pg 2655
BRAVURA INC.—See The Walt Disney Company; *U.S. Public*, pg. 2140
BRAVURA SECURITY, INC.—See Constellation Software Inc.; *Int'l*, pg. 1775
BRAVURA SOFTWARE SOLUTIONS (SA) (PROPRIETARY) LIMITED—See Ironbridge Capital; *Int'l*, pg. 3810
BRAVURA SOLUTIONS (HK) LIMITED—See Ironbridge Capital; *Int'l*, pg. 3810
BRAVURA SOLUTIONS LIMITED—See Ironbridge Capital; *Int'l*, pg. 3810
BRAVURA SOLUTIONS LUXEMBOURG HOLDINGS S.A.R.L.—See Ironbridge Capital; *Int'l*, pg. 3810
BRAVURA SOLUTIONS (NZ) LIMITED—See Ironbridge Capital; *Int'l*, pg. 3810
BRAVURA SOLUTIONS POLSKA SP. Z OO—See Ironbridge Capital; *Int'l*, pg. 3810
BRAVURA SOLUTIONS SERVICES (UK) LIMITED—See Ironbridge Capital; *Int'l*, pg. 3810
BRAVURA SOLUTIONS (THAILAND) COMPANY LIMITED—See Ironbridge Capital; *Int'l*, pg. 3810
BRAVURA SOLUTIONS (UK) LTD.—See Ironbridge Capital; *Int'l*, pg. 3810
BRAWER BROS INC.; *U.S. Private*, pg. 641
BRAWN BIOTECH LTD.; *Int'l*, pg. 1142
BRAWN OF CALIFORNIA, INC.—See Chelsey Direct, LLC; *U.S. Private*, pg. 870
BRAXIA SCIENTIFIC CORP.; *Int'l*, pg. 1142
BRAXTON RESOURCES INC.; *U.S. Private*, pg. 641
BRAXTON STRATEGIC GROUP; *U.S. Private*, pg. 641
BRAXTON TECHNOLOGIES, LLC—See Parsons Corporation; *U.S. Public*, pg. 1650
BRAY ASSOCIATES ARCHITECTS INC.; *U.S. Private*, pg. 641
BRAYBAR PUMPS (PROPRIETARY) LIMITED—See Kirloskar Brothers Limited; *Int'l*, pg. 4191
BRAY CONTROLS ANDINA LTDA.—See Bray International, Inc.; *U.S. Private*, pg. 641
BRAY CONTROLS CANADA CORPORATION—See Bray International, Inc.; *U.S. Private*, pg. 641
BRAY CONTROLS FRANCE S.A.R.L—See Bray International, Inc.; *U.S. Private*, pg. 641
BRAY CONTROLS PACIFIC PTY. LTD.—See Bray International, Inc.; *U.S. Private*, pg. 641
BRAY CONTROLS PERU S.A.C—See Bray International, Inc.; *U.S. Private*, pg. 641
BRAY CONTROLS S.A.—See Bray International, Inc.; *U.S. Private*, pg. 641
BRAY CONTROLS SOUTHEAST ASIA PTE LTD—See Bray International, Inc.; *U.S. Private*, pg. 641
BRAY CONTROLS (UK) LTD.—See Bray International, Inc.; *U.S. Private*, pg. 641
BRAY CONTROLS VIETNAM COMPANY LTD.—See Bray International, Inc.; *U.S. Private*, pg. 641

BRAY INTERNATIONAL, INC. - BRAY CONTROLS BENELUX DIVISION—See Bray International, Inc.; *U.S. Private*, pg. 641
BRAY INTERNATIONAL, INC. - BRAY CONTROLS INDONESIA DIVISION—See Bray International, Inc.; *U.S. Private*, pg. 642
BRAY INTERNATIONAL, INC. - BRAY CONTROLS POLAND DIVISION—See Bray International, Inc.; *U.S. Private*, pg. 642
BRAY INTERNATIONAL, INC. - BRAY CONTROLS S. KOREA DIVISION—See Bray International, Inc.; *U.S. Private*, pg. 642
BRAY INTERNATIONAL, INC.; *U.S. Private*, pg. 641
BRAY LEINO LIMITED—See The Mission Group Public Limited Company; *Int'l*, pg. 7667
BRAY LEINO SINGAPORE PTE. LTD.—See The Mission Group Public Limited Company; *Int'l*, pg. 7667
BRAY LEINO SPLASH SDN. BHD.—See The Mission Group Public Limited Company; *Int'l*, pg. 7667
BRAYMAN CONSTRUCTION CORPORATION; *U.S. Private*, pg. 642
BRAYMAN FOUNDATIONS LLC—See Brayman Construction Corporation; *U.S. Private*, pg. 642
BRAY MEDIA, LLC; *U.S. Private*, pg. 642
BRAY SALES SOUTHERN CALIFORNIA INC.—See Bray International, Inc.; *U.S. Private*, pg. 642
BRAY & SCARFF INC.; *U.S. Private*, pg. 641
BRAY TECHNICAL SERVICES INDIA PVT. LTD.—See Bray International, Inc.; *U.S. Private*, pg. 642
BRAYTON & HUGHES DESIGN STUDIO—See DLR Holding, LLC; *U.S. Private*, pg. 1247
BRAY TRUCKING INC.; *U.S. Private*, pg. 642
BRAY VALVULAS DE MEXICO S.A. DE C.V.—See Bray International, Inc.; *U.S. Private*, pg. 642
BRAZAURO RECURSOS MINERAIS SA—See Eldorado Gold Corporation; *Int'l*, pg. 2347
BRAZCOT LTDA.—See Unitika Ltd.; *Int'l*, pg. 8074
BRAZE, INC.; *U.S. Public*, pg. 380
BRAZEWAY INC.; *U.S. Private*, pg. 642
BRAZI BITES LLC—See San Francisco Equity Partners; *U.S. Private*, pg. 3540
BRAZIL FAST FOOD CORP.; *Int'l*, pg. 1142
BRAZILIAN FINANCE & REAL ESTATE S.A.; *Int'l*, pg. 1143
BRAZILIAN RESOURCES MINERACAO LTDA—See Talon Metals Corp.; *Int'l*, pg. 7448
BRAZIL IOWA FARMS, LLC—See BXR Group B.V.; *Int'l*, pg. 1233
BRAZIL PHARMA S.A.; *Int'l*, pg. 1142
BRAZIL PLANTRONICS TELECOMMUNICACOES LTDA.—See HP Inc.; *U.S. Public*, pg. 1064
THE BRAZIL TIMES—See Rust Communications; *U.S. Private*, pg. 3507
BRAZONICS, INC.—See RTX Corporation; *U.S. Public*, pg. 1822
BRAZORIA TELEPHONE CO; *U.S. Private*, pg. 642
BRAZOS ELECTRIC POWER COOPERATIVE, INC.; *U.S. Private*, pg. 642
BRAZOS HIGHER EDUCATION SERVICE CORPORATION; *U.S. Private*, pg. 642
BRAZOS PRIVATE EQUITY PARTNERS, LLC; *U.S. Private*, pg. 642
BRAZOS VALLEY LONGHORN, L.L.C.—See Expand Energy Corporation; *U.S. Public*, pg. 808
BRAZOS VALLEY PHYSICAL THERAPY, LIMITED PARTNERSHIP—See U.S. Physical Therapy, Inc.; *U.S. Public*, pg. 2214
BRB - ADMINISTRADORA E CORRETORA DE SEGUROS S.A.—See BRB BCO DE BRASILIA S.A.; *Int'l*, pg. 1143
BR BAUHANDEL AG—See CRH plc; *Int'l*, pg. 1843
BRB BANCO DE BRASILIA SA; *Int'l*, pg. 1143
BRB BCO DE BRASILIA S.A.; *Int'l*, pg. 1143
BRB CONTRACTORS, INC.; *U.S. Private*, pg. 642
BRB - DISTRIBUIDORA DE TITULOS E VALORES MOBILIARIOS S.A.—See BRB BCO DE BRASILIA S.A.; *Int'l*, pg. 1143
BRC ACOUSTICS & AUDIOVISUAL DESIGN—See Coffman Engineers, Inc.; *U.S. Private*, pg. 961
BR&C AGENTS PTY. LTD.—See Nutrien Ltd.; *Int'l*, pg. 5492
BRC ASIA LIMITED; *Int'l*, pg. 1143
BRCCA SERVICES PRIVATE LIMITED; *Int'l*, pg. 1143
B.R. CHEMICALS CO., LTD.—See Black Rose Industries Ltd.; *Int'l*, pg. 1060
BRCH HOME HEALTH SERVICE INC.—See BRRH Corporation; *U.S. Private*, pg. 670
BRC INC.; *U.S. Public*, pg. 380
BRC INVESTOR SERVICES S.A.—See S&P Global Inc.; *U.S. Public*, pg. 1830
B.R. COHN WINERY—See Vintage Wine Estates, Inc.; *U.S. Public*, pg. 2298
BRC PREFAB HOLDINGS SDN. BHD.—See BRC Asia Limited; *Int'l*, pg. 1143
BRC RUBBER & PLASTICS INC.; *U.S. Private*, pg. 642
BRCS (BUILDING CONTROL) LIMITED—See CEPS PLC; *Int'l*, pg. 1420
BRC SEHER A.D.; *Int'l*, pg. 1143

BRC SEHER A.D.

BRC S.R.L.—See Westport Fuel Systems Inc.; *Int'l*, pg. 8392
BRD ASSET MANAGEMENT SAI SA—See Societe Generale S.A.; *Int'l*, pg. 7039
BRD FINANCE IFN S.A.—See Societe Generale S.A.; *Int'l*, pg. 7039
BRD - GROUPE SOCIETE GENERALE S.A.—See Societe Generale S.A.; *Int'l*, pg. 7039
BRD. KLEE A/S; *Int'l*, pg. 1143
BRDR. LEMBCKE A/S—See Dole plc; *Int'l*, pg. 2158
BREA ATLANTA COURT LLC—See Brookdale Senior Living Inc.; *U.S. Public*, pg. 393
BREA BOYNTON BEACH LLC—See Brookdale Senior Living Inc.; *U.S. Public*, pg. 393
BREA DENVER LLC—See Brookdale Senior Living Inc.; *U.S. Public*, pg. 393
BREAD FINANCIAL HOLDINGS INC.; *U.S. Public*, pg. 380
BREADTALK CONCEPT HONG KONG LIMITED—See BreadTalk Group Pte Ltd.; *Int'l*, pg. 1143
BREADTALK GROUP PTE LTD.; *Int'l*, pg. 1143
BREADTALK INTERNATIONAL PTE. LTD.—See BreadTalk Group Pte Ltd.; *Int'l*, pg. 1143
BREADTALK PTE LTD—See BreadTalk Group Pte Ltd.; *Int'l*, pg. 1143
BREADWINNER FOODS LIMITED—See Greencore Group plc; *Int'l*, pg. 3074
BREA EAST MESA LLC—See Brookdale Senior Living Inc.; *U.S. Public*, pg. 393
BREAKAWAY COMMUNICATIONS LLC; *U.S. Private*, pg. 642
BREAKAWAY COMMUNICATIONS LLC—See Breakaway Communications LLC; *U.S. Private*, pg. 642
BREAKAWAY HOLDINGS, LLC—See Insight Venture Management, LLC; *U.S. Private*, pg. 2088
BREAKAWAY HOLDINGS, LLC—See Stone Point Capital LLC; *U.S. Private*, pg. 3822
BREAKAWAY HONDA; *U.S. Private*, pg. 642
BREAKER ELECTRICAL PTY. LTD.—See Mitsubishi Heavy Industries, Ltd.; *Int'l*, pg. 4953
BREAKER GLASS CO INC.—See s.a. D'Ieteren n.v.; *Int'l*, pg. 6448
BREAKER RESOURCES NL; *Int'l*, pg. 1144
BREAKERS PALM BEACH INC.—See Flagler System Inc.; *U.S. Private*, pg. 1539
BREAKERS UNLIMITED INC.; *U.S. Private*, pg. 642
BREAKERS UNLIMITED—See Breakers Unlimited Inc.; *U.S. Private*, pg. 642
BREAKERS WEST DEVELOPMENT CORP.—See Flagler System Inc.; *U.S. Private*, pg. 1539
BREAKER TECHNOLOGY, INC.—See Astec Industries, Inc.; *U.S. Public*, pg. 216
BREAKER TECHNOLOGY LTD—See Astec Industries, Inc.; *U.S. Public*, pg. 216
BREAK-FREE—See BAE Systems plc; *Int'l*, pg. 796
BREAKOUT KINGS PRODUCTIONS LLC—See The Walt Disney Company; *U.S. Public*, pg. 2140
BREAKTHROUGH MANAGEMENT GROUP, INC.; *U.S. Private*, pg. 642
BREAKTHROUGH PHYSICAL THERAPY MARKETING LLC; *U.S. Private*, pg. 643
BREAKTHROUGH T1D; *U.S. Private*, pg. 643
BREAKTHRU BEVERAGE GROUP, LLC; *U.S. Private*, pg. 643
BREAKTHRU BEVERAGE ILLINOIS—See Breakthru Beverage Group, LLC; *U.S. Private*, pg. 643
BREAKTHRU BEVERAGE MINNESOTA—See Breakthru Beverage Group, LLC; *U.S. Private*, pg. 643
BREAKTHRU BEVERAGE NEVADA—See Breakthru Beverage Group, LLC; *U.S. Private*, pg. 643
BREAKTHRU BEVERAGE WISCONSIN—See Breakthru Beverage Group, LLC; *U.S. Private*, pg. 643
BREAKWATER ISLAND LIMITED—See The Star Entertainment Group Limited; *Int'l*, pg. 7688
BREAL CAPITAL LTD.; *Int'l*, pg. 1144
BREA PEORIA LLC—See Brookdale Senior Living Inc.; *U.S. Public*, pg. 393
BREA RENO LLC—See Brookdale Senior Living Inc.; *U.S. Public*, pg. 393
BREA ROANOKE LLC—See Brookdale Senior Living Inc.; *U.S. Public*, pg. 393
BREA SARASOTA LLC—See Brookdale Senior Living Inc.; *U.S. Public*, pg. 393
BREAS MEDICAL AB—See Shanghai Fosun Pharmaceutical (Group) Co., Ltd.; *Int'l*, pg. 6767
BREAS MEDICAL GMBH—See Shanghai Fosun Pharmaceutical (Group) Co., Ltd.; *Int'l*, pg. 6767
BREAS MEDICAL LIMITED—See Shanghai Fosun Pharmaceutical (Group) Co., Ltd.; *Int'l*, pg. 6767
BREAS MEDICAL SARL—See Shanghai Fosun Pharmaceutical (Group) Co., Ltd.; *Int'l*, pg. 6767
BREAS MEDICAL S.R.L.—See Shanghai Fosun Pharmaceutical (Group) Co., Ltd.; *Int'l*, pg. 6767
THE BREAST CANCER CHARITIES OF AMERICA; *U.S. Private*, pg. 4000
THE BREAST CANCER SOCIETY, INC.; *U.S. Private*, pg. 4000
THE BREAST CLINIC PTE. LTD.—See Singapore Medical Group Limited; *Int'l*, pg. 6941

BREAST DIAGNOSTICS OF NORTH TEXAS, P.A—See Solis Women's Health, Inc.; *U.S. Private*, pg. 3709
BREATEC B.V.—See BRAIN Biotech AG; *Int'l*, pg. 1137
BREATHABLEBABY, LLC—See Transom Capital Group, LLC; *U.S. Private*, pg. 4209
BREATHE FREE LANKA (PRIVATE) LIMITED—See Cipla Ltd.; *Int'l*, pg. 1616
BREATHE GRACE MEDICAL SUPPLY, LLC—See AdaptHealth Corp.; *U.S. Public*, pg. 38
BREATHOMETER, INC.; *U.S. Private*, pg. 643
BREATHRESEARCH INC.—See AireHealth, LLC; *U.S. Private*, pg. 141
BREATHTECH CORPORATION—See Astrotech Corporation; *U.S. Public*, pg. 218
BREAUX MART INC.; *U.S. Private*, pg. 643
BREA WEST ORANGE LLC—See Brookdale Senior Living Inc.; *U.S. Public*, pg. 393
BREAZEALE, SACHSE & WILSON, LLP.; *U.S. Private*, pg. 643
BRECHBUHLER SCALES INC.; *U.S. Private*, pg. 644
B & R ECKEL'S TRANSPORT LTD.—See Mullen Group Ltd.; *Int'l*, pg. 5079
THE BRECKENRIDGE AMERICAN—See Alden Global Capital LLC; *U.S. Private*, pg. 156
BRECKENRIDGE BREWERY—See Anheuser-Busch InBev SA/NV; *Int'l*, pg. 466
BRECKENRIDGE BUILDING CENTER, INC.—See Bain Capital, LP; *U.S. Private*, pg. 450
BRECKENRIDGE HOLDING COMPANY; *U.S. Private*, pg. 644
BRECKENRIDGE INSURANCE GROUP, INC.—See W.R. Berkley Corporation; *U.S. Public*, pg. 2317
BRECKENRIDGE INSURANCE SERVICES—See Breckenridge IS, Inc.; *U.S. Private*, pg. 644
BRECKENRIDGE IS, INC.; *U.S. Private*, pg. 644
BRECKENRIDGE MATERIAL COMPANY—See Breedon Group plc; *Int'l*, pg. 1144
BRECKENRIDGE SKI RESORT—See Vail Resorts, Inc.; *U.S. Public*, pg. 2272
BRECKINRIDGE HEALTH, INC.; *U.S. Private*, pg. 644
BRECKNELL WILLIS & CO., LIMITED—See Westinghouse Air Brake Technologies Corporation; *U.S. Public*, pg. 2358
BRECKNELL WILLIS COMPOSITES LTD.—See Westinghouse Air Brake Technologies Corporation; *U.S. Public*, pg. 2358
BRECKNELL WILLIS (TAIWAN) CO., LIMITED—See Westinghouse Air Brake Technologies Corporation; *U.S. Public*, pg. 2358
BRECKNELL WILLIS (TIANJIN) ELECTRIFICATION SYSTEMS, CO., LTD—See Westinghouse Air Brake Technologies Corporation; *U.S. Public*, pg. 2357
BRECK OPERATING CORP.—See States Unlimited; *U.S. Private*, pg. 3793
BRECLAV PRODUCTION S.R.O.—See Priema Metaalwarenfabriek BV; *Int'l*, pg. 5973
BRECO ANTRIEBSTECHNIK BREHER GMBH & CO. KG; *Int'l*, pg. 1144
BRECO HOLDINGS, INC; *U.S. Private*, pg. 644
BRECO INTERNATIONAL INC.—See Arcline Investment Management LP; *U.S. Private*, pg. 313
BREÇONCHERRY LTD.—See GEA Group Aktiengesellschaft; *Int'l*, pg. 2897
BREDBAND2 I SKANDINAVIEN AB; *Int'l*, pg. 1144
BRED BANK CAMBODIA PLC—See Groupe BPCE; *Int'l*, pg. 3092
BRED BANK FIJI LTD.—See Groupe BPCE; *Int'l*, pg. 3092
BRED BANQUE POPULAIRE—See Groupe BPCE; *Int'l*, pg. 3097
BREDEL HOSE PUMPS B.V.—See Spirax-Sarco Engineering plc; *Int'l*, pg. 7139
BREDEMANN CHEVROLET INC.; *U.S. Private*, pg. 644
BREDERODE S.A.; *Int'l*, pg. 1144
BREDERO SHAW LTD.—See ShawCor Ltd.; *Int'l*, pg. 6791
BREDERO SHAW MIDDLE EAST LIMITED—See ShawCor Ltd.; *Int'l*, pg. 6791
BREDERO SHAW NORWAY AS—See ShawCor Ltd.; *Int'l*, pg. 6791
BREDERO SHAW (SINGAPORE) PTE. LTD.—See ShawCor Ltd.; *Int'l*, pg. 6791
BRE DIAMOND HOTEL LLC—See Blackstone Inc.; *U.S. Public*, pg. 350
BRED I.T. THAILAND LTD.—See Groupe BPCE; *Int'l*, pg. 3092
BRED VANUATU LTD.—See Groupe BPCE; *Int'l*, pg. 3092
BREED & CO. INC.; *U.S. Private*, pg. 644
BREEDING RESEARCH INSTITUTE—See Dongbu Group; *Int'l*, pg. 2165
BREEDLINK BV—See Cellnex Telecom, S.A.; *Int'l*, pg. 1394
BREEDON AGGREGATES ENGLAND LIMITED—See Breedon Group plc; *Int'l*, pg. 1144
BREEDON AGGREGATES SCOTLAND LIMITED—See Breedon Group plc; *Int'l*, pg. 1144
BREEDON BOW HIGHWAYS LIMITED—See Breedon Group plc; *Int'l*, pg. 1144
BREEDON GROUP PLC; *Int'l*, pg. 1144
BREEN INTERNATIONAL (HK) CO LTD—See Breen International Pte. Ltd.; *Int'l*, pg. 1144

CORPORATE AFFILIATIONS

BREEN INTERNATIONAL PTE. LTD.; *Int'l*, pg. 1144
BREEN INTERNATIONAL SDN BHD—See Breen International Pte. Ltd.; *Int'l*, pg. 1144
BREEN'S MARKET, INC.; *U.S. Private*, pg. 644
THE BREEZE CORPORATION—See The Nutting Company, Inc.; *U.S. Private*, pg. 4086
BREEZE-EASTERN LLC—See TransDigm Group Incorporated; *U.S. Public*, pg. 2182
BREEZE HOLDINGS ACQUISITION CORP.; *U.S. Public*, pg. 381
BREEZE UNDERWRITING LIMITED—See PSC Insurance Group Limited; *Int'l*, pg. 6015
BREEZE UNDERWRITING PTY LTD—See PSC Insurance Group Limited; *Int'l*, pg. 6015
BREEZWAY AUSTRALIA PTY LTD—See ONEX Corporation; *Int'l*, pg. 5579
BREEZWAY (MALAYSIA) SDN BHD.—See ONEX Corporation; *Int'l*, pg. 5579
BREEZWAY NORTH AMERCIA—See ONEX Corporation; *Int'l*, pg. 5579
BREEZY POINT INTERNATIONAL, INC.—See Whitebirch Enterprises, Inc.; *U.S. Private*, pg. 4511
BREEZY POINT LP; *U.S. Private*, pg. 644
BREEZY POLAND SP. Z.O.O.—See ASBISc Enterprises Plc; *Int'l*, pg. 600
BRE FAKTORING S.A.—See Commerzbank AG; *Int'l*, pg. 1719
BREGAL CAPITAL LLP—See COFRA Holding AG; *Int'l*, pg. 1693
BREGAL FRESHSTREAM LLP—See COFRA Holding AG; *Int'l*, pg. 1693
BREGAL INVESTMENTS, INC.—See COFRA Holding AG; *Int'l*, pg. 1694
BREGAL INVESTMENTS LLP—See COFRA Holding AG; *Int'l*, pg. 1693
BREGAL MILESTONE LLP; *Int'l*, pg. 1144
BREGAL PARTNERS, L.P.—See COFRA Holding AG; *Int'l*, pg. 1694
BREGAL SAGEMOUNT—See COFRA Holding AG; *Int'l*, pg. 1694
BREGAVA D.D.; *Int'l*, pg. 1144
BREG, INC.—See Water Street Healthcare Partners, LLC; *U.S. Private*, pg. 4452
BREGMAN & COMPANY, PC—See Fiondella, Milone & LaSaracina LLP; *U.S. Private*, pg. 1511
BREGUET LES BOUTIQUES SA—See The Swatch Group Ltd.; *Int'l*, pg. 7691
BREHM COMMUNICATIONS INC. - GOLD COUNTRY PRINTING DIVISION—See Brehm Communications Inc.; *U.S. Private*, pg. 644
BREHM COMMUNICATIONS INC.; *U.S. Private*, pg. 644
BREHOB CORPORATION; *U.S. Private*, pg. 644
BREHOB NURSERY INC.—See DCA Outdoor, Inc.; *U.S. Private*, pg. 1179
BRE HOLDING SP. Z O.O.—See Commerzbank AG; *Int'l*, pg. 1719
BREIHOLZ CONSTRUCTION CO; *U.S. Private*, pg. 644
BREIJN B.V.—See Heijmans N.V.; *Int'l*, pg. 3322
BREINING MASCHINEN-UND FAHRZEUGBAU GMBH—See FAYAT SAS; *Int'l*, pg. 2624
BREITBURN FLORIDA LLC—See Maverick Natural Resources, LLC; *U.S. Private*, pg. 2616
BREITBURN MANAGEMENT COMPANY, LLC—See Maverick Natural Resources, LLC; *U.S. Private*, pg. 2616
BREITBURN OPERATING L.P.—See Maverick Natural Resources, LLC; *U.S. Private*, pg. 2616
BREITBURN TRANSPETCO LP LLC—See Maverick Natural Resources, LLC; *U.S. Private*, pg. 2616
BREITENER ENERGETICA S/A—See Skanska AB; *Int'l*, pg. 6978
BREITLING CHINA LIMITED—See CVC Capital Partners SICAV-FIS S.A.; *Int'l*, pg. 1883
BREITLING ENERGY CORPORATION; *U.S. Private*, pg. 644
BREITLING FRANCE S.A.R.L.—See CVC Capital Partners SICAV-FIS S.A.; *Int'l*, pg. 1883
BREITLING ITALIA SRL—See CVC Capital Partners SICAV-FIS S.A.; *Int'l*, pg. 1883
BREITLING JAPAN LTD—See CVC Capital Partners SICAV-FIS S.A.; *Int'l*, pg. 1883
BREITLING S.A.—See CVC Capital Partners SICAV-FIS S.A.; *Int'l*, pg. 1882
BREITLING USA INC.—See CVC Capital Partners SICAV-FIS S.A.; *Int'l*, pg. 1883
BREKOM GMBH—See EWE Aktiengesellschaft; *Int'l*, pg. 2575
BREL-COM SP. Z O. O.—See Commerzbank AG; *Int'l*, pg. 1717
BRE LEASING SP. Z O.O.—See Commerzbank AG; *Int'l*, pg. 1717
BRELET TRANSPORT SAS—See Groupement FLO; *Int'l*, pg. 3112
BRELIAN, INC.; *U.S. Private*, pg. 644
BRE.LOCUM S.A.—See Commerzbank AG; *Int'l*, pg. 1719
BREMA GROUP S.P.A—See Hoshizaki Corporation; *Int'l*, pg. 3483
BREMAR CONSTRUCTION LTD.—See Aecon Group Inc.; *Int'l*, pg. 172

COMPANY NAME INDEX

BRE.M.A. WARMWALZ—See Marcegaglia S.p.A.; *Int'l*, pg. 4688
BREMBO DO BRASIL LTDA.—See Brembo S.p.A.; *Int'l*, pg. 1145
BREMBO JAPAN CO. LTD.—See Brembo S.p.A.; *Int'l*, pg. 1145
BREMBO NORTH AMERICA, INC.—See Brembo S.p.A.; *Int'l*, pg. 1145
BREMBO NORTH AMERICA, INC.—See Brembo S.p.A.; *Int'l*, pg. 1145
BREMBO RASSINI S.A. DE C.V.—See Brembo S.p.A.; *Int'l*, pg. 1145
BREMBO SCANDINAVIA A.B.—See Brembo S.p.A.; *Int'l*, pg. 1145
BREMBO SGL CARBON CERAMIC BRAKES S.P.A.—See Brembo S.p.A.; *Int'l*, pg. 1145
BREMBO S.P.A.; *Int'l*, pg. 1144
BREMEDIA PRODUKTION GMBH—See Bavaria Film GmbH; *Int'l*, pg. 899
BREMEN-BOWDON INVESTMENT CO; *U.S. Private*, pg. 645
BREMEN CASTINGS, INC.; *U.S. Private*, pg. 645
BREMEN CORPORATION—See Industrial Opportunity Partners, LLC; *U.S. Private*, pg. 2067
BREMER AUTHENTIC INGREDIENTS—See Spectral Enterprises, Inc.; *U.S. Private*, pg. 3751
BREMER BANK, N.A.—See Bremer Financial Corporation; *U.S. Private*, pg. 645
BREMER BUSINESS FINANCE CORPORATION—See Bremer Financial Corporation; *U.S. Private*, pg. 645
BREMER FINANCIAL CORPORATION; *U.S. Private*, pg. 645
BREMER FINANCIAL SERVICES, INC.—See Bremer Financial Corporation; *U.S. Private*, pg. 645
BREMER GALVANISIERUNGS GMBH—See ArcelorMittal S.A.; *Int'l*, pg. 543
BREMER INSURANCE AGENCIES, INC.—See Bremer Financial Corporation; *U.S. Private*, pg. 645
BREMER KREDITBANK AG—See Apollo Global Management, Inc.; *U.S. Public*, pg. 148
BREMER KREDITBANK AG—See Grovepoint Capital LLP; *Int'l*, pg. 3112
BREMER KREDITBANK AG—See Teacher Retirement System of Texas; *U.S. Private*, pg. 3944
BREMER LAGERHAUS-GESELLSCHAFT, *Int'l*, pg. 1145
BREMER LANDESBANK CAPITAL MARKETS PLC—See Norddeutsche Landesbank Girozentrale; *Int'l*, pg. 5416
BREMER LANDESBANK KREDITANSTALT OLDENBURG—See Norddeutsche Landesbank Girozentrale; *Int'l*, pg. 5416
BREMER & LEGUIL GMBH—See FUCHS SE; *Int'l*, pg. 2802
BREMER PHARMA GMBH—See SeQuent Scientific Limited; *Int'l*, pg. 6719
BREMER STAHL SERVICE GMBH; *Int'l*, pg. 1145
BREMFIELD SDN. BHD.—See Mewah International Inc.; *Int'l*, pg. 4868
BREM HOLDING BERHAD; *Int'l*, pg. 1144
BREMNERDUKE MCKINNEY DEVELOPMENT I, LLC—See Prologis, Inc.; *U.S. Public*, pg. 1726
BREMNER FOOD GROUP, INC.—See Conagra Brands, Inc.; *U.S. Public*, pg. 563
BREMWORTH CARPETS AND RUGS LIMITED—See Bremworth Limited; *Int'l*, pg. 1145
BREMWORTH LIMITED; *Int'l*, pg. 1145
BRENCAL CONTRACTORS INC.—See BEC Inc.; *U.S. Private*, pg. 509
BRENCO, INC.—See AMSTED Industries Incorporated; *U.S. Private*, pg. 268
BRENCO MARKETING CORP; *U.S. Private*, pg. 645
BRENDAN TECHNOLOGIES, INC.; *U.S. Private*, pg. 645
BRENDEN THEATRE CORPORATION; *U.S. Private*, pg. 645
BRENDERUP A/S—See Storskogen Group AB; *Int'l*, pg. 7227
BRENDERUP GROUP AB—See Storskogen Group AB; *Int'l*, pg. 7227
BR ENDUSTRIYEL OTOMASYON SANAYI VE TICARET LIMITED—See ABB Ltd.; *Int'l*, pg. 56
BRENHAM BANCSHARES, INC.; *U.S. Private*, pg. 645
BRENHAM CHRYSLER JEEP DODGE; *U.S. Private*, pg. 645
THE BRENHAM NATIONAL BANK—See Brenham Bancshares, Inc.; *U.S. Private*, pg. 645
THE BRENLIN GROUP, LLC; *U.S. Private*, pg. 4000
BRENMILLER ENERGY LTD.; *Int'l*, pg. 1145
BRENNAN & ASSOCIATES RISK MANAGEMENT & INSURANCE SERVICES, INC.—See Aon plc; *Int'l*, pg. 495
BRENNAN BEER GORMAN ARCHITECTS LLP; *U.S. Private*, pg. 645
BRENNAN ELECTRIC, LLC—See Area Energy & Electric, Inc.; *U.S. Private*, pg. 317
BRENNAN INDUSTRIES INC.; *U.S. Private*, pg. 645
BRENNAN INVESTMENT GROUP, LLC; *U.S. Private*, pg. 645
BRENNAN IT PTY. LIMITED; *Int'l*, pg. 1145
BRENNER MILLS (PTY) LTD. - BRENNCO FEED MILLS—See Brenner Mills (Pty) Ltd.; *Int'l*, pg. 1146

BRENNER MILLS (PTY) LTD.; *Int'l*, pg. 1145
BRENNER MILLS (PTY) LTD. - TSWANA MILL—See Brenner Mills (Pty) Ltd.; *Int'l*, pg. 1146
BRENNER MILLS (PTY) LTD. - WARMBATHS MILL—See Brenner Mills (Pty) Ltd.; *Int'l*, pg. 1146
BRENNER MILLS (PTY) LTD. - ZOUTPANSBERG MILL—See Brenner Mills (Pty) Ltd.; *Int'l*, pg. 1146
BRENNER OIL COMPANY INC.; *U.S. Private*, pg. 645
BRENNTAG AMSTERDAM B.V.—See BRENNTAG SE; *Int'l*, pg. 1147
BRENNTAG ARGENTINA S.A.—See BRENNTAG SE; *Int'l*, pg. 1147
BRENNTAG AUSTRALIA PTY. LTD.—See BRENNTAG SE; *Int'l*, pg. 1146
BRENNTAG AUSTRIA GMBH—See BRENNTAG SE; *Int'l*, pg. 1146
BRENNTAG AUSTRIA HOLDING GMBH—See BRENNTAG SE; *Int'l*, pg. 1146
BRENNTAG BANGLADESH LTD.—See BRENNTAG SE; *Int'l*, pg. 1146
BRENNTAG BETEILIGUNGS GMBH—See BRENNTAG SE; *Int'l*, pg. 1146
BRENNTAG BOLIVIA SRL—See BRENNTAG SE; *Int'l*, pg. 1147
BRENNTAG BRASIL LTDA.—See BRENNTAG SE; *Int'l*, pg. 1147
BRENNTAG BULGARIA LTD—See BRENNTAG SE; *Int'l*, pg. 1146
BRENNTAG CANADA INC.—See BRENNTAG SE; *Int'l*, pg. 1146
BRENNTAG CARIBE S.A.—See BRENNTAG SE; *Int'l*, pg. 1147
BRENNTAG CEE GMBH—See BRENNTAG SE; *Int'l*, pg. 1146
BRENNTAG CHEMICAL DISTRIBUTION (IRELAND) LTD.—See BRENNTAG SE; *Int'l*, pg. 1146
BRENNTAG CHEMICALS DISTRIBUTION (IRELAND) LIMITED—See BRENNTAG SE; *Int'l*, pg. 1146
BRENNTAG CHEMICALS MALAYSIA SDN. BHD.—See BRENNTAG SE; *Int'l*, pg. 1146
BRENNTAG CHEMICALS NIGERIA LIMITED—See BRENNTAG SE; *Int'l*, pg. 1146
BRENNTAG CHILE COMERCIAL E INDUSTRIAL LTDA.—See BRENNTAG SE; *Int'l*, pg. 1146
BRENNTAG CHILE LTDA.—See BRENNTAG SE; *Int'l*, pg. 1147
BRENNTAG COLOMBIA S. A.—See BRENNTAG SE; *Int'l*, pg. 1147
BRENNTAG COLOURS LTD.—See BRENNTAG SE; *Int'l*, pg. 1146
BRENNTAG COOPERATIEF U.A.—See BRENNTAG SE; *Int'l*, pg. 1147
BRENNTAG CR S.R.O.—See BRENNTAG SE; *Int'l*, pg. 1146
BRENNTAG DUTCH C.V.—See BRENNTAG SE; *Int'l*, pg. 1147
BRENNTAG ECUADOR S. A.—See BRENNTAG SE; *Int'l*, pg. 1147
BRENNTAG EL SALVADOR S.A. DE C.V.—See BRENNTAG SE; *Int'l*, pg. 1147
BRENNTAG EUROPEAN SERVICES GMBH & CO. KG—See BRENNTAG SE; *Int'l*, pg. 1147
BRENNTAG EXPORT SARL—See BRENNTAG SE; *Int'l*, pg. 1147
BRENNTAG FOREIGN HOLDING GMBH—See BRENNTAG SE; *Int'l*, pg. 1147
BRENNTAG FRANCE HOLDING SAS—See BRENNTAG SE; *Int'l*, pg. 1147
BRENNTAG GERMANY HOLDING GMBH—See BRENNTAG SE; *Int'l*, pg. 1147
BRENNTAG GMBH—See BRENNTAG SE; *Int'l*, pg. 1147
BRENNTAG GMBH—See BRENNTAG SE; *Int'l*, pg. 1147
BRENNTAG GMBH—See BRENNTAG SE; *Int'l*, pg. 1147
BRENNTAG GMBH—See BRENNTAG SE; *Int'l*, pg. 1147
BRENNTAG GREAT LAKES, LLC—See BRENNTAG SE; *Int'l*, pg. 1148
BRENNTAG GUATEMALA S. A.—See BRENNTAG SE; *Int'l*, pg. 1147
BRENNTAG (HOLDING) B.V.—See BRENNTAG SE; *Int'l*, pg. 1146
BRENNTAG HOLDING GMBH—See BRENNTAG SE; *Int'l*, pg. 1147
BRENNTAG HOLDING S.P.A.—See BRENNTAG SE; *Int'l*, pg. 1146
BRENNTAG HONG KONG LIMITED—See BRENNTAG SE; *Int'l*, pg. 1147
BRENNTAG HRVATSKA D.O.O.—See BRENNTAG SE; *Int'l*, pg. 1146
BRENNTAG HUNGARIA KFT.—See BRENNTAG SE; *Int'l*, pg. 1147
BRENNTAG INDIA PRIVATE LTD.—See BRENNTAG SE; *Int'l*, pg. 1147
BRENNTAG INGREDIENTS INC.—See BRENNTAG SE; *Int'l*, pg. 1147
BRENNTAG INGREDIENTS (INDIA) PRIVATE LIMITED—See BRENNTAG SE; *Int'l*, pg. 1147
BRENNTAG INGREDIENTS (THAILAND) PUBLIC COMPANY LTD.—See BRENNTAG SE; *Int'l*, pg. 1147

BRENNTAG INORGANIC CHEMICALS (THETFORD) LTD.—See BRENNTAG SE; *Int'l*, pg. 1147
BRENNTAG INTERNATIONAL CHEMICALS GMBH—See BRENNTAG SE; *Int'l*, pg. 1146
BRENNTAG KENYA LIMITED—See BRENNTAG SE; *Int'l*, pg. 1147
BRENNTAG KIMYA TICARET LIMITED SIRKETI—See BRENNTAG SE; *Int'l*, pg. 1147
BRENNTAG KOREA CO., LTD.—See BRENNTAG SE; *Int'l*, pg. 1147
BRENNTAG LANKA (PRIVATE) LIMITED—See BRENNTAG SE; *Int'l*, pg. 1147
BRENNTAG LATIN AMERICA, INC.—See BRENNTAG SE; *Int'l*, pg. 1147
BRENNTAG LJUBLJANA D.O.O.—See BRENNTAG SE; *Int'l*, pg. 1147
BRENNTAG LUBRICANTS, LLC—See BRENNTAG SE; *Int'l*, pg. 1147
BRENNTAG LUBRICANTS (THAILAND) CO., LTD.—See BRENNTAG SE; *Int'l*, pg. 1147
BRENNTAG MAGHREB SAS—See BRENNTAG SE; *Int'l*, pg. 1147
BRENNTAG MALAYSIA SDN. BHD.—See BRENNTAG SE; *Int'l*, pg. 1147
BRENNTAG MAROC S.A.R.L.—See BRENNTAG SE; *Int'l*, pg. 1147
BRENNTAG MEXICO, S. A. DE C. V.—See BRENNTAG SE; *Int'l*, pg. 1147
BRENNTAG MID-SOUTH, INC.—See BRENNTAG SE; *Int'l*, pg. 1148
BRENNTAG NEDERLAND B.V.—See BRENNTAG SE; *Int'l*, pg. 1147
BRENNTAG NEW ZEALAND LIMITED—See BRENNTAG SE; *Int'l*, pg. 1147
BRENNTAG NICARAGUA, S.A.—See BRENNTAG SE; *Int'l*, pg. 1147
BRENNTAG NORDIC AB—See BRENNTAG SE; *Int'l*, pg. 1147
BRENNTAG NORDIC AS—See BRENNTAG SE; *Int'l*, pg. 1146
BRENNTAG NORDIC A/S—See BRENNTAG SE; *Int'l*, pg. 1147
BRENNTAG NORDIC OY—See BRENNTAG SE; *Int'l*, pg. 1146
BRENNTAG NORTH AMERICA, INC.—See BRENNTAG SE; *Int'l*, pg. 1148
BRENNTAG NORTHEAST, INC.—See BRENNTAG SE; *Int'l*, pg. 1148
BRENNTAG N.V.—See BRENNTAG SE; *Int'l*, pg. 1147
BRENNTAG PACIFIC, INC. - FAIRBANKS—See BRENNTAG SE; *Int'l*, pg. 1148
BRENNTAG PACIFIC, INC.—See BRENNTAG SE; *Int'l*, pg. 1148
BRENNTAG PACIFIC, INC. - SOUTH GATE—See BRENNTAG SE; *Int'l*, pg. 1148
BRENNTAG PANAMA S.A.—See BRENNTAG SE; *Int'l*, pg. 1148
BRENNTAG PERU A. C.—See BRENNTAG SE; *Int'l*, pg. 1147
BRENNTAG PHILIPPINES INC.—See BRENNTAG SE; *Int'l*, pg. 1148
BRENNTAG POLSKA SP. Z O.O.—See BRENNTAG SE; *Int'l*, pg. 1146
BRENNTAG PORTUGAL LDA.—See BRENNTAG SE; *Int'l*, pg. 1148
BRENNTAG PORTUGAL-PRODUTOS QUIMICOS LDA.—See BRENNTAG SE; *Int'l*, pg. 1146
BRENNTAG PTE. LTD.—See BRENNTAG SE; *Int'l*, pg. 1148
BRENNTAG PTY. LTD.—See BRENNTAG SE; *Int'l*, pg. 1148
BRENNTAG PUERTO RICO, INC.—See BRENNTAG SE; *Int'l*, pg. 1148
BRENNTAG QUIMICA BRASIL LTDA.—See BRENNTAG SE; *Int'l*, pg. 1148
BRENNTAG QUIMICA S.A.—See BRENNTAG SE; *Int'l*, pg. 1146
BRENNTAG REAL ESTATE GMBH—See BRENNTAG SE; *Int'l*, pg. 1148
BRENNTAG S.A.—See BRENNTAG SE; *Int'l*, pg. 1148
BRENNTAG SCHWEIZERHALL AG—See BRENNTAG SE; *Int'l*, pg. 1148
BRENNTAG SE; *Int'l*, pg. 1146
BRENNTAG (SHANGHAI) CHEMICAL TRADING CO., LIMITED—See BRENNTAG SE; *Int'l*, pg. 1146
BRENNTAG (SHANGHAI) ENTERPRISE MANAGEMENT CO., LTD.—See BRENNTAG SE; *Int'l*, pg. 1146
BRENNTAG SINGAPORE PTE. LTD.—See BRENNTAG SE; *Int'l*, pg. 1146
BRENNTAG SLOVAKIA S.R.O.—See BRENNTAG SE; *Int'l*, pg. 1146
BRENNTAG SOUTHEAST, INC.—See BRENNTAG SE; *Int'l*, pg. 1148
BRENNTAG SOUTHWEST, INC. - BORGER—See BRENNTAG SE; *Int'l*, pg. 1148
BRENNTAG SOUTHWEST, INC. - LANCASTER—See BRENNTAG SE; *Int'l*, pg. 1148
BRENNTAG SOUTHWEST, INC.—See BRENNTAG SE; *Int'l*, pg. 1148

BRENNTAG SE

BRENNTAG S.P.A.—See BRENNTAG SE; *Int'l*, pg. 1146
BRENNTAG SPECIALTIES, INC.—See BRENNTAG SE; *Int'l*, pg. 1148
BRENNTAG SPECIALTIES—See BRENNTAG SE; *Int'l*, pg. 1148
BRENNTAG S.R.L.—See BRENNTAG SE; *Int'l*, pg. 1148
BRENNTAG (TAIWAN) CO. LTD.—See BRENNTAG SE; *Int'l*, pg. 1146
BRENNTAG TANZANIA LIMITED—See BRENNTAG SE; *Int'l*, pg. 1148
BRENNTAG (THAILAND) CO. LTD.—See BRENNTAG SE; *Int'l*, pg. 1146
BRENNTAG TUNISIE S.A.R.L.—See BRENNTAG SE; *Int'l*, pg. 1148
BRENNTAG UGANDA LIMITED—See BRENNTAG SE; *Int'l*, pg. 1148
BRENNTAG UK AND IRELAND LIMITED—See BRENNTAG SE; *Int'l*, pg. 1148
BRENNTAG (UK) LTD.—See BRENNTAG SE; *Int'l*, pg. 1146
BRENNTAG UKRAINE LTD—See BRENNTAG SE; *Int'l*, pg. 1148
BRENNTAG VASTGOED B.V.—See BRENNTAG SE; *Int'l*, pg. 1148
BRENNTAG VIETNAM COMPANY LIMITED—See BRENNTAG SE; *Int'l*, pg. 1148
BREN SECURITY (PVT) LTD—See Securitas AB; *Int'l*, pg. 6675
BRENTHAVEN; *U.S. Private*, pg. 645
BRENT INDUSTRIES, INC.; *U.S. Private*, pg. 645
BRENTON, LLC.—See Leonard Green & Partners, L.P.; *U.S. Private*, pg. 2427
BRENTRIDGE FORD SALES; *Int'l*, pg. 1150
BRENT RUN LANDFILL, INC.—See Waste Connections, Inc.; *Int'l*, pg. 8353
BRENT SCARBROUGH & COMPANY, INC.; *U.S. Private*, pg. 645
BRENTWOOD ACQUISITION, INC.—See Universal Health Services, Inc.; *U.S. Public*, pg. 2256
BRENTWOOD ASSOCIATES; *U.S. Private*, pg. 645
BRENTWOOD BANK; *U.S. Private*, pg. 646
BRENTWOOD-BENSON MUSIC PUBLISHING, INC.—See Sony Group Corporation; *Int'l*, pg. 7103
BRENTWOOD BIOMEDICAL RESEARCH INSTITUTE, INC.; *U.S. Private*, pg. 646
BRENTWOOD CORP.—See Quanex Building Products Corp.; *U.S. Public*, pg. 1750
BRENTWOOD HOSPITAL—See Universal Health Services, Inc.; *U.S. Public*, pg. 2256
BRENTWOOD INDUSTRIES INC. - NRG PRODUCTS DIVISION—See Brentwood Industries Inc.; *U.S. Private*, pg. 646
BRENTWOOD INDUSTRIES INC; *U.S. Private*, pg. 646
BRENTWOOD SURGERY CENTER, LLC—See Bain Capital, LP; *U.S. Private*, pg. 445
BRENTWOOD VENTURE MANAGEMENT, LLC; *U.S. Private*, pg. 646
BRENT WOODWARD, INC.—See Quanta Services, Inc.; *U.S. Public*, pg. 1750
BRENWOOD PARK SENIOR LIVING, INC.—See The Ensign Group, Inc.; *U.S. Public*, pg. 2070
BRE/PEARLRIDGE, LLC—See Washington Prime Group Inc.; *U.S. Private*, pg. 4448
BRE PROPERTIES, INC.—See Essex Property Trust, Inc.; *U.S. Public*, pg. 795
BRE PROPERTY PARTNER SP. Z O.O.—See Commerzbank AG; *Int'l*, pg. 1719
BRERA HOLDINGS PLC; *Int'l*, pg. 1150
BRE RETAIL CENTERS CORP—See Blackstone Inc.; *U.S. Public*, pg. 350
BRESCOME BARTON INC.—See Quaker Equities Ltd., Inc.; *U.S. Private*, pg. 3316
BRESDI S.A.S.—See LDC SA; *Int'l*, pg. 4430
BRESLER & REINER, INC.; *U.S. Public*, pg. 381
BRESNAN COMMUNICATIONS, INC.—See Charter Communications, Inc.; *U.S. Public*, pg. 483
B RESOURCE, INC.; *U.S. Private*, pg. 417
BRESSLERGROUP, INC.—See Trinity Hunt Management, L.P.; *U.S. Private*, pg. 4234
BRESSNER TECHNOLOGY GMBH—See One Stop Systems, Inc.; *U.S. Public*, pg. 1602
BRETECHE INDUSTRIE SAS—See Equistone Partners Europe Limited; *Int'l*, pg. 2486
BRETFORD MANUFACTURING INC.; *U.S. Private*, pg. 646
THE BRETHREN HOME COMMUNITY; *U.S. Private*, pg. 4000
BRETHREN HOME COMMUNITY WINDBER; *U.S. Private*, pg. 646
BRETHREN RETIREMENT COMMUNITY; *U.S. Private*, pg. 646
BRETHREN VILLAGE; *U.S. Private*, pg. 646
BRETMOR HEADWEAR, INC.; *U.S. Private*, pg. 646
BRET SA—See Haco N.V.; *Int'l*, pg. 3204
BRETSCHNEIDER VERPACKUNGEN GMBH—See DS Smith Plc; *Int'l*, pg. 2207
BRETT HARVEY CONSTRUCTIONS PTY. LIMITED—See MAAS Group Holdings Limited; *Int'l*, pg. 4618

BRETTING DEVELOPMENT CORP., INC.—See C. G. Bretting Manufacturing Co., Inc.; *U.S. Private*, pg. 705
BRETZ CAPITAL SPORTS SALES, INC.—See Bretz, Inc.; *U.S. Private*, pg. 646
BRETZ, INC.; *U.S. Private*, pg. 646
BREUER GMBH—See Horst Wellness GmbH & Co. KG; *Int'l*, pg. 3482
BREUNING GMBH; *Int'l*, pg. 1150
BREUNING INC.—See Breuning GmbH; *Int'l*, pg. 1150
BREVARD FAMILY PARTNERSHIP; *U.S. Private*, pg. 646
BREVARD HMA HOME HEALTH, LLC—See Community Health Systems, Inc.; *U.S. Public*, pg. 551
BREVARD HMA HOSPICE, LLC—See Community Health Systems, Inc.; *U.S. Public*, pg. 551
BREVARD HMA NURSING HOME, LLC—See Community Health Systems, Inc.; *U.S. Public*, pg. 551
BREVE TUFVASSONS SP. Z O.O.—See Addtech AB; *Int'l*, pg. 132
BREVILLE GROUP LIMITED; *Int'l*, pg. 1150
BREVILLE MEXICO, S.A. DE C.V.—See Breville Group Limited; *Int'l*, pg. 1150
BREVILLE NEW ZEALAND LIMITED—See Breville Group Limited; *Int'l*, pg. 1150
BREVILLE PTY LIMITED—See Breville Group Limited; *Int'l*, pg. 1150
BREVILLE USA, INC.—See Breville Group Limited; *Int'l*, pg. 1150
BREVINI AUSTRALIA PTY LTD—See Dana Incorporated; *U.S. Public*, pg. 621
BREVINI CANADA LIMITED—See Dana Incorporated; *U.S. Public*, pg. 621
BREVINI ESPANA S.A—See Dana Incorporated; *U.S. Public*, pg. 621
BREVINI FINLAND OY—See Dana Incorporated; *U.S. Public*, pg. 621
BREVINI FLUID POWER BEIJING CO. LTD.—See Dana Incorporated; *U.S. Public*, pg. 621
BREVINI FLUID POWER DISTRIBUTION S.R.L.—See Dana Incorporated; *U.S. Public*, pg. 621
BREVINI FLUID POWER FRANCE SAS—See Dana Incorporated; *U.S. Public*, pg. 621
BREVINI FLUID POWER GMBH—See Dana Incorporated; *U.S. Public*, pg. 621
BREVINI FLUID POWER UK LIMITED—See Dana Incorporated; *U.S. Public*, pg. 621
BREVINI FLUID POWER VENETO S.R.L.—See Dana Incorporated; *U.S. Public*, pg. 621
BREVINI INDIA LTD—See Dana Incorporated; *U.S. Public*, pg. 621
BREVINI IRELAND LIMITED—See Dana Incorporated; *U.S. Public*, pg. 621
BREVINI JAPAN LTD—See Dana Incorporated; *U.S. Public*, pg. 621
BREVINI KOREA CO., LTD.—See Dana Incorporated; *U.S. Public*, pg. 621
BREVINI LATINO-AMERICANA IND. & CO. LTD.—See Dana Incorporated; *U.S. Public*, pg. 622
BREVINI NEW ZEALAND LIMITED—See Dana Incorporated; *U.S. Public*, pg. 622
BREVINI NORGE AS—See Dana Incorporated; *U.S. Public*, pg. 622
BREVINI POWER TRANSMISSION FRANCE—See Dana Incorporated; *U.S. Public*, pg. 622
BREVINI POWER TRANSMISSION REDUKTOR SANAYI VE TICARED LIMITED SIRTEKI—See Dana Incorporated; *U.S. Public*, pg. 622
BREVINI SVENSKA AB—See Dana Incorporated; *U.S. Public*, pg. 622
BREVINI THAILAND CO. LTD.—See Dana Incorporated; *U.S. Public*, pg. 622
BREVINI USA INC.—See Dana Incorporated; *U.S. Public*, pg. 622
BREVINI YANCHENG PLANETARY DRIVES CO. LTD.—See Dana Incorporated; *U.S. Public*, pg. 622
BREW-BEV—See Neal H. Knapp, LLC; *U.S. Private*, pg. 2877
BREWBILT BREWING COMPANY; *U.S. Public*, pg. 381
BREWBILT MANUFACTURING, INC.; *U.S. Public*, pg. 381
BRE WEALTH MANAGEMENT S.A.—See Commerzbank AG; *Int'l*, pg. 1719
BREWER & BUNNEY LTD.—See NIBE Industrier AB; *Int'l*, pg. 5260
BREWER & COMPANY OF WEST VIRGINIA, INC.; *U.S. Private*, pg. 647
THE BREWER COMPANY; *U.S. Private*, pg. 4000
THE BREWER COMPANY; *U.S. Private*, pg. 4000
BREWER DIRECT, INC.; *U.S. Private*, pg. 647
BREWER ELECTRIC & UTILITIES—See Reilly Electrical Contractors; *U.S. Public*, pg. 3391
BREWER ENTERPRISES INC—See Savino Del Bene S.p.A.; *Int'l*, pg. 6600
BREWER-GARRETT CO; *U.S. Private*, pg. 647
BREWER-HENDLEY OIL CO; *U.S. Private*, pg. 647
BREWER OIL CO.; *U.S. Private*, pg. 647
BREWER SCIENCE, INC.; *U.S. Private*, pg. 647
BREWER SCIENCE, INC.—See Brewer Science, Inc.; *U.S. Private*, pg. 647
BREWER SCIENCE, INC.—See Brewer Science, Inc.; *U.S. Private*, pg. 647

CORPORATE AFFILIATIONS

BREWER SCIENCE, INC.—See Brewer Science, Inc.; *U.S. Private*, pg. 647
BREWER SCIENCE JAPAN, G.K.—See Brewer Science, Inc.; *U.S. Private*, pg. 647
BREWER SCIENCE LIMITED—See Brewer Science, Inc.; *U.S. Private*, pg. 647
BREWER SEWING SUPPLIES CO; *U.S. Private*, pg. 647
BREWERS RETAIL INC.; *Int'l*, pg. 1150
BREWIN DOLPHIN CAPITAL & INVESTMENTS (IRELAND) LIMITED—See Brewin Dolphin Holdings PLC; *Int'l*, pg. 1150
BREWIN DOLPHIN HOLDINGS PLC; *Int'l*, pg. 1150
BREWIN DOLPHIN SECURITIES—See Brewin Dolphin Holdings PLC; *Int'l*, pg. 1150
BREWIN NOMINEES LIMITED—See Brewin Dolphin Holdings PLC; *Int'l*, pg. 1150
BREWMASTER, INC.—See Full Circle Brewing Co., Ltd.; *U.S. Private*, pg. 1620
BREW MEDIA RELATIONS—See Publicis Groupe S.A.; *Int'l*, pg. 6099
BREW; *U.S. Private*, pg. 646
BREWSTER CHARTER SERVICES—See Viad Corp.; *U.S. Public*, pg. 2291
BREWSTER DAIRY INC.; *U.S. Private*, pg. 647
BREWSTER INC.—See Viad Corp.; *U.S. Public*, pg. 2291
BREWSTER'S FRANCHISE CORPORATION—See BAB, Inc.; *U.S. Public*, pg. 262
BREWSTER TRAVEL CANADA INC.—See Viad Corp.; *U.S. Public*, pg. 2291
BREWSTER WALLCOVERING INTERNATIONAL TRADE (SHANGHAI) LTD.—See Brewster Wallpaper Corp.; *U.S. Private*, pg. 647
BREWSTER WALLPAPER CORP.; *U.S. Private*, pg. 647
BREWSTER WHOLESALER COMPANY—See The RMR Group Inc.; *U.S. Public*, pg. 2126
BREXIA GOLDPLATA PERU S.A.C.—See Auplata SAS; *Int'l*, pg. 706
BREZELBACKEREI DITSCH GMBH—See Fomento Economico Mexicano, S.A.B. de C.V.; *Int'l*, pg. 2724
BREZELKONIG AG—See Fomento Economico Mexicano, S.A.B. de C.V.; *Int'l*, pg. 2724
BREZILLON SA—See Bouygues S.A.; *Int'l*, pg. 1122
BREZZA LIVING SDN. BHD.—See Lorenzo International Limited; *Int'l*, pg. 4558
BRF BRASIL FOODS PTE LTD.—See BRF S.A.; *Int'l*, pg. 1151
BRF B.V.—See BRF S.A.; *Int'l*, pg. 1150
BRF GERMANY GMBH—See BRF S.A.; *Int'l*, pg. 1150
BRF HOLIDAYS PTE LTD—See Gallant Venture Ltd.; *Int'l*, pg. 2873
BRF S.A.; *Int'l*, pg. 1150
B.R. FUNSTEN & CO., INC.; *U.S. Private*, pg. 421
BRG APPLIANCES LIMITED—See Breville Group Limited; *Int'l*, pg. 1150
BRG GROUP JOINT STOCK CO.; *Int'l*, pg. 1151
BRG INTERNATIONAL, LLC—See Jones Lang LaSalle Incorporated; *U.S. Public*, pg. 1201
BRGM—See Bureau de Recherches Geologiques et Miniere; *Int'l*, pg. 1221
BRG PETROLEUM CORPORATION; *U.S. Private*, pg. 647
BRG SPORTS, INC.—See Fenway Partners, LLC; *U.S. Private*, pg. 1495
BRG SPORTS MEXICO, S.A. DE C.V.—See Fenway Partners, LLC; *U.S. Private*, pg. 1495
BRH & ASSOCIATES; *U.S. Private*, pg. 647
BRH GARVER CONSTRUCTION, L.P.—See Kidd & Company LLC; *U.S. Private*, pg. 2302
BR. HOLDINGS CORPORATION; *Int'l*, pg. 1133
B.R. HOLDINGS SIA—See Africa Israel Investments Ltd.; *Int'l*, pg. 190
BR HOMEBUILDING GROUP, L.P.; *U.S. Private*, pg. 630
BRH VIABUS GMBH—See Metropolitan European Transport Limited; *Int'l*, pg. 4864
BRIABE MEDIA INC.; *U.S. Private*, pg. 647
BRIACELL THERAPEUTICS CORP. - BERKELEY BRANCH—See BriaCell Therapeutics Corp.; *Int'l*, pg. 1151
BRIACELL THERAPEUTICS CORP.; *Int'l*, pg. 1151
THE BRIAD GROUP; *U.S. Private*, pg. 4000
BRIAN BEMIS AUTOMOTIVE GROUP, LTD.; *U.S. Private*, pg. 647
BRIAN BEMIS AUTO WORLD, INC.—See Brian Bemis Automotive Group, Ltd.; *U.S. Private*, pg. 647
BRIAN BEMIS, INC.—See Brian Bemis Automotive Group, Ltd.; *U.S. Private*, pg. 647
BRIAN CORK HUMAN CAPITAL; *U.S. Private*, pg. 647
BRIANFID-LUX S A—See Banco Di Desio e Della Brianza S.p.A.; *Int'l*, pg. 822
BRIAN KURTZ TRUCKING LTD.; *Int'l*, pg. 1151
BRIAN TAYLOR INTERNATIONAL LLC; *U.S. Private*, pg. 647
BRIAN TRADING CO. INC.; *U.S. Private*, pg. 647
BRIAN UNLIMITED DISTRIBUTION COMPANY, INC.; *U.S. Private*, pg. 647
BRIAR CHEMICALS LTD.—See Safex Chemicals (India) Limited; *Int'l*, pg. 6471
BRIARCLIFF AMBULATORY SURGERY CENTER, L.P.—See Tenet Healthcare Corporation; *U.S. Public*, pg. 2009

COMPANY NAME INDEX

BRIARCLIFFE COLLEGE—See Perdoceo Education Corporation; *U.S. Public*, pg. 1673
BRIAR FOREST-ELDRIDGE MEDICAL CENTER LLC—See Adeptus Health Inc.; *U.S. Private*, pg. 78
BRIARPATCH INC.—See University Games Corporation; *U.S. Private*, pg. 4307
BRIARWOOD CONTINUING CARE RETIREMENT COMMUNITY; *U.S. Private*, pg. 648
BRIARWOOD FORD, INC.; *U.S. Private*, pg. 648
BRI BIOPHARMACEUTICAL RESEARCH INC.—See Hangzhou Tigermed Consulting Co., Ltd.; *Int'l*, pg. 3251
BRIBUS B.V.—See Nobia AB; *Int'l*, pg. 5395
BRICARD S.A.—See Ingersoll Rand Inc.; *U.S. Public*, pg. 1120
BRICE BUILDING COMPANY, INC.—See Tutor Perini Corporation; *U.S. Public*, pg. 2206
BRICE ENVIRONMENTAL SERVICES CORPORATION; *U.S. Private*, pg. 648
BRICFRUIT SAS—See Britvic plc; *Int'l*, pg. 1171
BRI-CHEM CORP.; *Int'l*, pg. 1151
BRI-CHEM SUPPLY LTD.—See Bri-Chem Corp.; *Int'l*, pg. 1151
BRICKABILITY GROUP PLC; *Int'l*, pg. 1151
BRICK-ABILITY LTD.—See Brickability Group plc; *Int'l*, pg. 1151
BRICK AND TILE CORP. OF LAWRENCEVILLE; *U.S. Private*, pg. 648
BRICKELL BANK; *U.S. Private*, pg. 648
BRICKELL GLOBAL MARKETS, INC.—See Brickell Bank; *U.S. Private*, pg. 648
BRICKELL TRAVEL MANAGEMENT, LLC—See Talma Travel and Tours Ltd.; *Int'l*, pg. 7448
BRICKFIELD PROPERTIES LIMITED—See Centremanor Ltd.; *Int'l*, pg. 1411
BRICK HAND & REHABILITATIVE SERVICES, LIMITED PARTNERSHIP—See U.S. Physical Therapy, Inc.; *U.S. Public*, pg. 2214
BRICKHOUSE SECURITY; *U.S. Private*, pg. 648
BRICK INVESTMENT PARTNERS LLC; *U.S. Private*, pg. 648
BRICKLE REALTY GROUP—See Hyman Brickle & Son, Inc.; *U.S. Private*, pg. 2019
BRICK-LINK LIMITED—See Brickability Group plc; *Int'l*, pg. 1151
THE BRICK LTD.—See Leon's Furniture Limited; *Int'l*, pg. 4457
BRICKMONGERS (WESSEX) LTD.—See Brickability Group plc; *Int'l*, pg. 1151
BRICKNER CHRYSLER CENTER—See Brickner Motors, Inc.; *U.S. Private*, pg. 648
BRICKNER MOTORS, INC.; *U.S. Private*, pg. 648
BRICKNERS OF ANTIGO—See Brickner Motors, Inc.; *U.S. Private*, pg. 648
BRICKNER—See Brickner Motors, Inc.; *U.S. Private*, pg. 648
BRICKPACK AB—See Investment AB Latour; *Int'l*, pg. 3782
BRICK SERVICES LIMITED—See Brickability Group plc; *Int'l*, pg. 1151
THE BRICK SLIP BUSINESS LIMITED—See Brickability Group plc; *Int'l*, pg. 1151
BRICKS NEWCO LIMITED; *Int'l*, pg. 1151
BRICKSTREET INSURANCE; *U.S. Private*, pg. 648
BRICKTOWN RESTAURANT GROUP, INC.; *U.S. Private*, pg. 648
BRICKWORKS BUILDING PRODUCTS PTY LTD—See Brickworks Limited; *Int'l*, pg. 1152
BRICKWORKS LIMITED; *Int'l*, pg. 1151
BRICKWORKS SUPPLY LLC—See Brickworks Limited; *Int'l*, pg. 1152
BRICKYARD BANCORP; *U.S. Private*, pg. 648
BRICKYARD BANK—See Brickyard Bancorp; *U.S. Private*, pg. 648
BRICO DEPOT ROMANIA—See Kingfisher plc; *Int'l*, pg. 4173
BRICO DEPOT SAS—See Kingfisher plc; *Int'l*, pg. 4173
BRICOLAJE BRICOMAN S.L.U.—See Groupe Adeo S.A.; *Int'l*, pg. 3091
BRICOMAN ITALIA S.R.L.—See Groupe Adeo S.A.; *Int'l*, pg. 3091
BRICOMAN POLAND SP. Z O.O.—See Groupe Adeo S.A.; *Int'l*, pg. 3091
BRICOMAN S.A.—See Groupe Adeo S.A.; *Int'l*, pg. 3091
BRICON AG—See CENTROTEC SE; *Int'l*, pg. 1414
BRICORAMA S.A.; *Int'l*, pg. 1152
BRIDAS CORPORATION; *Int'l*, pg. 1152
BRIDEX AUSTRALIA PTY. LIMITED—See Fuji Electric Co., Ltd.; *Int'l*, pg. 2812
BRIDEX ELECTRIC PHILIPPINES, INC.—See Osaki Electric Co., Ltd.; *Int'l*, pg. 5647
BRIDEX SINGAPORE PTE LTD.—See Fuji Electric Co., Ltd.; *Int'l*, pg. 2812
BRIDGE ABSTRACT LLC—See Dime Community Bancshares, Inc.; *U.S. Public*, pg. 666
BRIDGE AGRI PARTNERS, INC.—See The Andersons Incorporated; *U.S. Public*, pg. 2034
BRIDGE ALUMINIUM LIMITED—See Caparo Group Ltd.; *Int'l*, pg. 1301

BRIDGEBIO PHARMA, INC.; *U.S. Public*, pg. 381
BRIDGE BIOTHERAPEUTICS, INC.; *Int'l*, pg. 1152
BRIDGE CITY STATE BANK—See AmTex Bancshares Inc.; *U.S. Private*, pg. 268
BRIDGECOM LLC; *U.S. Public*, pg. 649
BRIDGE COMMERCIAL REAL ESTATE LLC—See Bridge Investment Group Holdings Inc.; *U.S. Public*, pg. 381
BRIDGE CONSULTING GROUP INC.; *Int'l*, pg. 1152
BRIDGE CORE LLC—See NewSpring Capital LLC; *U.S. Private*, pg. 2917
BRIDGEDALE OUTDOOR LTD—See Bollin Group Ltd.; *Int'l*, pg. 1102
BRIDGE DESIGN, INC.—See SV Health Investors, LLP; *U.S. Private*, pg. 3888
BRIDGE ENERGY GROUP, INC.—See Accenture plc; *Int'l*, pg. 86
BRIDGEFIELD CASUALTY INSURANCE COMPANY—See American Financial Group, Inc.; *U.S. Public*, pg. 102
BRIDGEFIELD EMPLOYERS INSURANCE COMPANY—See American Financial Group, Inc.; *U.S. Public*, pg. 103
BRIDGEFIELD PTY. LTD.—See Santos Limited; *Int'l*, pg. 6559
BRIDGE FUNDING GROUP, INC.—See BankUnited, Inc.; *U.S. Public*, pg. 274
BRIDGEGATE PICTURES CORPORATION; *U.S. Public*, pg. 382
BRIDGE GLOBAL STRATEGIES, LLC—See Didit.com, Inc.; *U.S. Private*, pg. 1227
BRIDGE GROWTH PARTNERS, LLC; *U.S. Private*, pg. 648
BRIDGE HOLDINGS USA, LLC; *U.S. Private*, pg. 649
THE BRIDGE INC.; *U.S. Private*, pg. 4000
BRIDGE INTERNATIONAL CORP.; *Int'l*, pg. 1152
BRIDGE INVESTMENT GROUP HOLDINGS INC.; *U.S. Public*, pg. 381
BRIDGELINE DIGITAL, INC.; *U.S. Public*, pg. 382
BRIDGELINE DIGITAL, INC. - TAMPA—See Bridgeline Digital, Inc.; *U.S. Public*, pg. 382
BRIDGE LOGISTICS, INC.; *U.S. Private*, pg. 649
BRIDGELUX, INC.—See China Electronics Corporation; *Int'l*, pg. 1499
BRIDGEMAN'S RESTAURANTS INC.; *U.S. Private*, pg. 640
BRIDGEMARQ REAL ESTATE SERVICES INC.; *Int'l*, pg. 1153
BRIDGEMERE UK PLC; *Int'l*, pg. 1153
BRIDGENET INTERNATIONAL—See Tetra Tech, Inc.; *U.S. Public*, pg. 2022
BRIDGENEXT, INC.—See Kelso & Company, L.P.; *U.S. Private*, pg. 2277
THE BRIDGE OF CENTRAL MASSACHUSETTS, INC.; *U.S. Private*, pg. 4000
BRIDGE OF WEIR LEATHER COMPANY LIMITED—See Scottish Leather Group Ltd.; *Int'l*, pg. 6653
BRIDGE PARTNERS CONSULTING; *U.S. Private*, pg. 649
BRIDGEPOINT AB—See Bridgepoint Group Plc; *Int'l*, pg. 1153
BRIDGEPOINT ADVISERS GROUP LIMITED—See Bridgepoint Group Plc; *Int'l*, pg. 1153
BRIDGEPOINT ADVISERS LIMITED—See Bridgepoint Group Plc; *Int'l*, pg. 1153
BRIDGEPOINT ADVISERS UK LIMITED—See Bridgepoint Group Plc; *Int'l*, pg. 1153
BRIDGEPOINT CONSULTING LLC—See Odyssey Investment Partners, LLC; *U.S. Private*, pg. 2994
BRIDGEPOINT DEVELOPMENT CAPITAL LIMITED—See Bridgepoint Group Plc; *Int'l*, pg. 1153
BRIDGEPOINTE TECHNOLOGIES, INC—See Charlesbank Capital Partners, LLC; *U.S. Private*, pg. 854
BRIDGEPOINT GMBH—See Bridgepoint Group Plc; *Int'l*, pg. 1154
BRIDGEPOINT GROUP PLC; *Int'l*, pg. 1153
BRIDGEPOINT INVESTMENT CONSULTANTS (SHANGHAI) CO., LTD.—See Bridgepoint Group Plc; *Int'l*, pg. 1155
BRIDGEPOINT, LLC—See Bridgepoint Group Plc; *Int'l*, pg. 1155
BRIDGEPOINT LTD. STI.—See Bridgepoint Group Plc; *Int'l*, pg. 1154
BRIDGEPOINT NETHERLANDS B.V.—See Bridgepoint Group Plc; *Int'l*, pg. 1155
BRIDGEPOINT S.A.—See Bridgepoint Group Plc; *Int'l*, pg. 1154
BRIDGEPOINT S.A.S.—See Bridgepoint Group Plc; *Int'l*, pg. 1154
BRIDGEPOINT S.P.A.—See Bridgepoint Group Plc; *Int'l*, pg. 1155
BRIDGEPOINT SP. Z O.O.—See Bridgepoint Group Plc; *Int'l*, pg. 1155
BRIDGEPOINT SYSTEMS; *U.S. Private*, pg. 649
BRIDGEPOINT TECHNOLOGIES; *U.S. Private*, pg. 649
BRIDGEPORT BENEFITS—See GI Manager L.P.; *U.S. Private*, pg. 1693
BRIDGEPORT BENEFITS—See Summit Partners, L.P.; *U.S. Private*, pg. 3856
BRIDGEPORT BUILDING CENTERS—See Nation's Best Holdings, LLC; *U.S. Private*, pg. 2839

BRIDGE SECURITIES LIMITED

BRIDGEPORT CAPITAL MANAGEMENT PTY LTD; *Int'l*, pg. 1155
BRIDGEPORT EQUIPMENT & TOOL; *U.S. Private*, pg. 649
BRIDGEPORT FITTINGS, INC.—See Odyssey Investment Partners, LLC; *U.S. Private*, pg. 2995
BRIDGEPORT NETWORKS, INC.—See Alianza Inc.; *U.S. Private*, pg. 167
BRIDGEPORT NEWS—See Hersam Acorn Newspapers LLC; *U.S. Private*, pg. 1926
BRIDGEPORT PARTNERS LP; *U.S. Private*, pg. 649
BRIDGE PRINTING OFFICE PTY LIMITED—See Nine Entertainment Co. Holdings Limited; *Int'l*, pg. 5298
BRIDGE PRIVATE LENDING, LP; *U.S. Private*, pg. 649
BRIDGE PUBLICATIONS INC.; *U.S. Private*, pg. 649
BRIDGEQUEST, INC.—See Advanced Business Software & Solutions Ltd.; *Int'l*, pg. 157
BRIDGER AEROSPACE GROUP HOLDINGS, INC.; *U.S. Public*, pg. 382
BRIDGER AEROSPACE GROUP HOLDINGS, LLC—See Bridger Aerospace Group Holdings, Inc.; *U.S. Public*, pg. 382
BRIDGER AEROSPACE, LLC—See Bridger Aerospace Group Holdings, Inc.; *U.S. Public*, pg. 382
BRIDGER BIOMED, INC.—See Becton, Dickinson & Company; *U.S. Public*, pg. 291
BRIDGER COAL COMPANY; *U.S. Private*, pg. 649
BRIDGER FOREST PRODUCTS—See OrePac Holding Company Inc.; *U.S. Private*, pg. 3041
BRIDGER INSURANCE AGENCY, INC.; *U.S. Private*, pg. 649
BRIDGER, LLC; *U.S. Private*, pg. 649
BRIDGER PHOTONICS, INC.; *U.S. Private*, pg. 649
BRIDGER VALLEY ELECTRIC ASSOCIATION, INC.; *U.S. Private*, pg. 649
BRIDGE SAAS LIMITED; *Int'l*, pg. 1152
THE BRIDGES AT RANCHO SANTA FE SALES COMPANY, INC.—See Lennar Corporation; *U.S. Public*, pg. 1307
BRIDGES & COMPANY, INC.; *U.S. Private*, pg. 649
BRIDGES CONSULTING, INC.—See CACI International Inc.; *U.S. Public*, pg. 417
BRIDGE SECURITIES LIMITED; *Int'l*, pg. 1152
BRIDGES FINANCIAL SERVICES PTY LIMITED—See Insignia Financial Ltd.; *Int'l*, pg. 3719
BRIDGE SHINE COFFEE EQUIPMENT (SHANGHAI) CO., LTD.—See Investcorp Holdings B.S.C.; *Int'l*, pg. 3777
BRIDGE SHINE COFFEE (SHANGHAI) CO., LTD.—See Investcorp Holdings B.S.C.; *Int'l*, pg. 3777
BRIDGE SOLUTIONS GROUP CORP.—See Pivotree Inc.; *Int'l*, pg. 5876
THE BRIDGE S.P.A.—See Piquadro SpA; *Int'l*, pg. 5873
BRIDGESTATE FOUNDRY CORPORATION—See Campbell Foundry Company; *U.S. Private*, pg. 730
BRIDGESTONE AIRCRAFT TIRE COMPANY (ASIA) LIMITED—See Bridgestone Corporation; *Int'l*, pg. 1156
BRIDGESTONE AIRCRAFT TIRE COMPANY (CHINA) LIMITED—See Bridgestone Corporation; *Int'l*, pg. 1156
BRIDGESTONE AIRCRAFT TIRE (EUROPE) S.A.—See Bridgestone Corporation; *Int'l*, pg. 1158
BRIDGESTONE AIRCRAFT TIRE (USA), INC.—See Bridgestone Corporation; *Int'l*, pg. 1156
BRIDGESTONE AMERICAS CENTER FOR RESEARCH AND TECHNOLOGY, LLC—See Cox Enterprises, Inc.; *U.S. Private*, pg. 1075
BRIDGESTONE AMERICAS, INC. - AKRON—See Cox Enterprises, Inc.; *U.S. Private*, pg. 1075
BRIDGESTONE AMERICAS, INC. - BUSINESS TECHNOLOGY GROUP DIVISION—See Cox Enterprises, Inc.; *U.S. Private*, pg. 1075
BRIDGESTONE AMERICAS, INC. - CENTER FOR RESEARCH & TECHNOLOGY—See Bridgestone Corporation; *Int'l*, pg. 1156
BRIDGESTONE AMERICAS, INC.—See Bridgestone Corporation; *Int'l*, pg. 1156
BRIDGESTONE AMERICAS TIRE OPERATIONS, LLC - ABILENE MANUFACTURING FACILITY—See Cox Enterprises, Inc.; *U.S. Private*, pg. 1075
BRIDGESTONE AMERICAS TIRE OPERATIONS, LLC - AGRICULTURAL TIRE, U.S. & CANADA COMMERCIAL TIRE SALES DIVISION—See Cox Enterprises, Inc.; *U.S. Private*, pg. 1075
BRIDGESTONE AMERICAS TIRE OPERATIONS, LLC - AIKEN COUNTY MANUFACTURING FACILITY—See Cox Enterprises, Inc.; *U.S. Private*, pg. 1075
BRIDGESTONE AMERICAS TIRE OPERATIONS, LLC - AKRON MANUFACTURING FACILITY—See Cox Enterprises, Inc.; *U.S. Private*, pg. 1075
BRIDGESTONE AMERICAS TIRE OPERATIONS, LLC - AKRON TECHNICAL CENTER DIVISION—See Cox Enterprises, Inc.; *U.S. Private*, pg. 1075
BRIDGESTONE AMERICAS TIRE OPERATIONS, LLC - BLOOMINGTON-NORMAL MANUFACTURING FACILITY—See Cox Enterprises, Inc.; *U.S. Private*, pg. 1075
BRIDGESTONE AMERICAS TIRE OPERATIONS, LLC - BRIDGESTONE BANDAG TIRE SOLUTIONS DIVISION—See Cox Enterprises, Inc.; *U.S. Private*, pg. 1075

BRIDGE SECURITIES LIMITED

CORPORATE AFFILIATIONS

BRIDGESTONE AMERICAS TIRE OPERATIONS, LLC - DES MOINES MANUFACTURING FACILITY—See Cox Enterprises, Inc.; *U.S. Private*, pg. 1075
BRIDGESTONE AMERICAS TIRE OPERATIONS, LLC - DES MOINES—See Cox Enterprises, Inc.; *U.S. Private*, pg. 1075
BRIDGESTONE AMERICAS TIRE OPERATIONS, LLC - GRIFFIN MANUFACTURING FACILITY—See Cox Enterprises, Inc.; *U.S. Private*, pg. 1075
BRIDGESTONE AMERICAS TIRE OPERATIONS, LLC - JOLIETTE MANUFACTURING FACILITY—See Cox Enterprises, Inc.; *U.S. Private*, pg. 1075
BRIDGESTONE AMERICAS TIRE OPERATIONS, LLC - LAVERGNE MANUFACTURING FACILITY—See Cox Enterprises, Inc.; *U.S. Private*, pg. 1075
BRIDGESTONE AMERICAS TIRE OPERATIONS, LLC - LONG BEACH MANUFACTURING FACILITY—See Cox Enterprises, Inc.; *U.S. Private*, pg. 1075
BRIDGESTONE AMERICAS TIRE OPERATIONS, LLC - MUSCATINE MANUFACTURING FACILITY—See Cox Enterprises, Inc.; *U.S. Private*, pg. 1075
BRIDGESTONE AMERICAS TIRE OPERATIONS, LLC - OFF ROAD TIRE, U.S. & CANADA TIRE SALES DIVISION—See Cox Enterprises, Inc.; *U.S. Private*, pg. 1075
BRIDGESTONE AMERICAS TIRE OPERATIONS, LLC - ORIGINAL EQUIPMENT, U.S. & CANADA CONSUMER TIRE SALES DIVISION—See Cox Enterprises, Inc.; *U.S. Private*, pg. 1075
BRIDGESTONE AMERICAS TIRE OPERATIONS, LLC - OXFORD MANUFACTURING FACILITY—See Cox Enterprises, Inc.; *U.S. Private*, pg. 1075
BRIDGESTONE AMERICAS TIRE OPERATIONS, LLC - REPLACEMENT TIRE SALES, U.S. & CANADA CONSUMER TIRE SALES DIVISION—See Cox Enterprises, Inc.; *U.S. Private*, pg. 1075
BRIDGESTONE AMERICAS TIRE OPERATIONS, LLC - SAO PAULO FACILITY—See Cox Enterprises, Inc.; *U.S. Private*, pg. 1075
BRIDGESTONE AMERICAS TIRE OPERATIONS, LLC—See Cox Enterprises, Inc.; *U.S. Private*, pg. 1075
BRIDGESTONE AMERICAS TIRE OPERATIONS, LLC - TEXAS PROVING GROUND DIVISION—See Cox Enterprises, Inc.; *U.S. Private*, pg. 1075
BRIDGESTONE AMERICAS TIRE OPERATIONS, LLC - WARREN COUNTY MANUFACTURING FACILITY—See Cox Enterprises, Inc.; *U.S. Private*, pg. 1075
BRIDGESTONE AMERICAS TIRE OPERATIONS, LLC - WILSON MANUFACTURING FACILITY—See Cox Enterprises, Inc.; *U.S. Private*, pg. 1075
BRIDGESTONE APM COMPANY—See Bridgestone Corporation; *Int'l*, pg. 1156
BRIDGESTONE ARGENTINA S.A.I.C.—See Bridgestone Corporation; *Int'l*, pg. 1156
BRIDGESTONE ASIA PACIFIC PTE. LTD. - INDORE PLANT—See Bridgestone Corporation; *Int'l*, pg. 1157
BRIDGESTONE ASIA PACIFIC PTE. LTD.—See Bridgestone Corporation; *Int'l*, pg. 1157
BRIDGESTONE ASIA PACIFIC TECHNICAL CENTER CO., LTD.—See Bridgestone Corporation; *Int'l*, pg. 1157
BRIDGESTONE AUSTRALIA LTD.—See Bridgestone Corporation; *Int'l*, pg. 1158
BRIDGESTONE AUSTRIA GMBH—See Bridgestone Corporation; *Int'l*, pg. 1158
BRIDGESTONE BALTICS, SIA—See Bridgestone Corporation; *Int'l*, pg. 1158
BRIDGESTONE BELUX NV/SA—See Bridgestone Corporation; *Int'l*, pg. 1158
BRIDGESTONE BENELUX B.V.—See Bridgestone Corporation; *Int'l*, pg. 1158
BRIDGESTONE CANADA, INC.—See Bridgestone Corporation; *Int'l*, pg. 1156
BRIDGESTONE CHILE, S.A.—See Bridgestone Corporation; *Int'l*, pg. 1156
BRIDGESTONE (CHINA) INVESTMENT CO., LTD.—See Bridgestone Corporation; *Int'l*, pg. 1157
BRIDGESTONE (CHINA) RESEARCH & DEVELOPMENT CO., LTD.—See Bridgestone Corporation; *Int'l*, pg. 1155
BRIDGESTONE (CHINA) TIRE ASSESSMENT & DEVELOPMENT CO., LTD.—See Bridgestone Corporation; *Int'l*, pg. 1155
BRIDGESTONE CORPORATION - AMAGI PLANT—See Bridgestone Corporation; *Int'l*, pg. 1158
BRIDGESTONE CORPORATION - HOFU PLANT—See Bridgestone Corporation; *Int'l*, pg. 1158
BRIDGESTONE CORPORATION - KUMAMOTO PLANT—See Bridgestone Corporation; *Int'l*, pg. 1158
BRIDGESTONE CORPORATION - KUROISO PLANT—See Bridgestone Corporation; *Int'l*, pg. 1158
BRIDGESTONE CORPORATION - KURUME PLANT—See Bridgestone Corporation; *Int'l*, pg. 1158
BRIDGESTONE CORPORATION - NASU PLANT—See Bridgestone Corporation; *Int'l*, pg. 1158
BRIDGESTONE CORPORATION - SEKI PLANT—See Bridgestone Corporation; *Int'l*, pg. 1158
BRIDGESTONE CORPORATION - SHIMONOSEKI PLANT—See Bridgestone Corporation; *Int'l*, pg. 1158
BRIDGESTONE CORPORATION; *Int'l*, pg. 1155
BRIDGESTONE CORPORATION - TOCHIGI PLANT—See Bridgestone Corporation; *Int'l*, pg. 1158
BRIDGESTONE CORPORATION - TOKYO PLANT—See Bridgestone Corporation; *Int'l*, pg. 1158
BRIDGESTONE CORPORATION - TOSU PLANT—See Bridgestone Corporation; *Int'l*, pg. 1158
BRIDGESTONE CORPORATION - YOKOHAMA PLANT—See Bridgestone Corporation; *Int'l*, pg. 1158
BRIDGESTONE CR, S.R.O.—See Bridgestone Corporation; *Int'l*, pg. 1158
BRIDGESTONE CYCLE CO., LTD. - AGEO PLANT—See Bridgestone Corporation; *Int'l*, pg. 1158
BRIDGESTONE CYCLE CO., LTD. - ASAHI PLANT—See Bridgestone Corporation; *Int'l*, pg. 1158
BRIDGESTONE CYCLE CO., LTD.—See Bridgestone Corporation; *Int'l*, pg. 1158
BRIDGESTONE CYCLE EAST JAPAN SALES CO., LTD.—See Bridgestone Corporation; *Int'l*, pg. 1158
BRIDGESTONE CYCLE WEST JAPAN SALES CO., LTD.—See Bridgestone Corporation; *Int'l*, pg. 1158
BRIDGESTONE DE COLOMBIA, S.A.S—See Bridgestone Corporation; *Int'l*, pg. 1158
BRIDGESTONE DE COSTA RICA, S.A.—See Bridgestone Corporation; *Int'l*, pg. 1158
BRIDGESTONEDE MEXICO, S.A. DE C.V.—See Bridgestone Corporation; *Int'l*, pg. 1157
BRIDGESTONE DE MEXICO, S.A.DE C.V.—See Bridgestone Corporation; *Int'l*, pg. 1157
BRIDGESTONE DENMARK A/S—See Bridgestone Corporation; *Int'l*, pg. 1158
BRIDGESTONE DEUTSCHLAND GMBH—See Bridgestone Corporation; *Int'l*, pg. 1158
BRIDGESTONE DIVERSIFIED CHEMICAL PRODUCTS CO., LTD.—See Bridgestone Corporation; *Int'l*, pg. 1158
BRIDGESTONE DIVERSIFIED PRODUCTS (CHINA) CO., LTD.—See Bridgestone Corporation; *Int'l*, pg. 1158
BRIDGESTONE DIVERSIFIED PRODUCTS EAST CO., LTD.—See Bridgestone Corporation; *Int'l*, pg. 1158
BRIDGESTONE DIVERSIFIED PRODUCTS EAST CO., LTD.—See Bridgestone Corporation; *Int'l*, pg. 1158
BRIDGESTONE DIVERSIFIED PRODUCTS WEST CO., LTD.—See Bridgestone Corporation; *Int'l*, pg. 1158
BRIDGESTONE DO BRASIL INDUSTRIA E COMERCIO LTDA. - SAO PAULO PLANT—See Bridgestone Corporation; *Int'l*, pg. 1157
BRIDGESTONE DO BRASIL INDUSTRIA E COMERCIO LTDA.—See Bridgestone Corporation; *Int'l*, pg. 1158
BRIDGESTONE EARTHMOVER TYRES PTY. LTD.—See Bridgestone Corporation; *Int'l*, pg. 1158
BRIDGESTONE ENGINEERED PRODUCTS OF ASIA, SDN BHD.—See Bridgestone Corporation; *Int'l*, pg. 1158
BRIDGESTONE EUROPE NV/SA—See Bridgestone Corporation; *Int'l*, pg. 1158
BRIDGESTONE FINANCE CORPORATION—See Bridgestone Corporation; *Int'l*, pg. 1159
BRIDGESTONE FINLAND OY—See Bridgestone Corporation; *Int'l*, pg. 1158
BRIDGESTONE/FIRESTONE CANADA, INC.—See Bridgestone Corporation; *Int'l*, pg. 1157
BRIDGESTONE/FIRESTONE CHILE, S.A.—See Bridgestone Corporation; *Int'l*, pg. 1157
BRIDGESTONE/FIRESTONE CREDIT CARD DIVISION—See Bridgestone Corporation; *Int'l*, pg. 1157
BRIDGESTONE/FIRESTONE DE COSTA RICA, S.A.—See Bridgestone Corporation; *Int'l*, pg. 1157
BRIDGESTONE/FIRESTONE DO BRASIL INDUSTRIA E COMERCIO LTDA—See Bridgestone Corporation; *Int'l*, pg. 1157
BRIDGESTONE/FIRESTONE INFORMATION SERVICES COMPANY—See Bridgestone Corporation; *Int'l*, pg. 1157
BRIDGESTONE/FIRESTONE OFF ROAD TIRE DIVISION—See Cox Enterprises, Inc.; *U.S. Private*, pg. 1075
BRIDGESTONE/FIRESTONE ORIGINAL EQUIPMENT DIVISION—See Cox Enterprises, Inc.; *U.S. Private*, pg. 1075
BRIDGESTONE FLOWTECH CORPORATION—See Bridgestone Corporation; *Int'l*, pg. 1159
BRIDGESTONE FRANCE S.A.S - BETHUNE PLANT—See Bridgestone Corporation; *Int'l*, pg. 1158
BRIDGESTONE FRANCE S.A.—See Bridgestone Corporation; *Int'l*, pg. 1158
BRIDGESTONE GOLF, INC.—See Bridgestone Corporation; *Int'l*, pg. 1159
BRIDGESTONE HISPANIA S.A - BILBAO PLANT—See Bridgestone Corporation; *Int'l*, pg. 1159
BRIDGESTONE HISPANIA S.A - BURGOS PLANT—See Bridgestone Corporation; *Int'l*, pg. 1159
BRIDGESTONE HISPANIA S.A.—See Bridgestone Corporation; *Int'l*, pg. 1159
BRIDGESTONE HOSEPOWER - ARIZONA—See Bridgestone Corporation; *Int'l*, pg. 1156
BRIDGESTONE HOSEPOWER, LLC—See Bridgestone Corporation; *Int'l*, pg. 1156
BRIDGESTONE (HUIZHOU) TIRE CO., LTD.—See Bridgestone Corporation; *Int'l*, pg. 1155
BRIDGESTONE INDIA PRIVATE LIMITED—See Bridgestone Corporation; *Int'l*, pg. 1159
BRIDGESTONE INDUSTRIAL LTD.—See Bridgestone Corporation; *Int'l*, pg. 1159
BRIDGESTONE IRELAND LTD.—See Bridgestone Corporation; *Int'l*, pg. 1158
BRIDGESTONE ITALIA SALES S.R.L.—See Bridgestone Corporation; *Int'l*, pg. 1159
BRIDGESTONE ITALIA S.P.A.—See Bridgestone Corporation; *Int'l*, pg. 1159
BRIDGESTONE LIVING LLC—See The Ensign Group, Inc.; *U.S. Public*, pg. 2070
BRIDGESTONE MAGYARORSZAG KFT.—See Bridgestone Corporation; *Int'l*, pg. 1159
BRIDGESTONE MIDDLE EAST & AFRICA FZE.—See Bridgestone Corporation; *Int'l*, pg. 1159
BRIDGESTONE MINING SOLUTIONS AUSTRALIA PTY. LTD.—See Bridgestone Corporation; *Int'l*, pg. 1159
BRIDGESTONE MULTIMEDIA GROUP; *U.S. Private*, pg. 649
BRIDGESTONE NATURAL RUBBER (THAILAND) CO., LTD.—See Bridgestone Corporation; *Int'l*, pg. 1159
BRIDGESTONE NEDERLAND B.V.—See Bridgestone Corporation; *Int'l*, pg. 1159
BRIDGESTONE NEW ZEALAND LTD.—See Bridgestone Corporation; *Int'l*, pg. 1159
BRIDGESTONE OFF-THE-ROAD TIRE LATIN AMERICA S.A.—See Bridgestone Corporation; *Int'l*, pg. 1156
BRIDGESTONE OFF-THE-ROAD TIRE PERU S.A.C.—See Bridgestone Corporation; *Int'l*, pg. 1156
BRIDGESTONE PORTUGAL LDA.—See Bridgestone Corporation; *Int'l*, pg. 1159
BRIDGESTONE POZNAN SP. Z.O.O.—See Bridgestone Corporation; *Int'l*, pg. 1159
BRIDGESTONE RETAIL OPERATIONS, LLC—See Bridgestone Corporation; *Int'l*, pg. 1156
BRIDGESTONE RIHGA, LTD.—See Bridgestone Corporation; *Int'l*, pg. 1155
BRIDGESTONE ROMANIA S.R.L.—See Bridgestone Corporation; *Int'l*, pg. 1159
BRIDGESTONE SALES POLSKA SP. Z O.O.—See Bridgestone Corporation; *Int'l*, pg. 1159
BRIDGESTONE SALES (THAILAND) CO., LTD.—See Mitsubishi Corporation; *Int'l*, pg. 4938
BRIDGESTONE (SCHWEIZ) AG—See Bridgestone Corporation; *Int'l*, pg. 1158
BRIDGESTONE (SHENYANG) TIRE CO., LTD.—See Bridgestone Corporation; *Int'l*, pg. 1157
BRIDGESTONE SINGAPORE PTE. LTD.—See Bridgestone Corporation; *Int'l*, pg. 1159
BRIDGESTONE SLOVAKIA S.R.O.—See Bridgestone Corporation; *Int'l*, pg. 1159
BRIDGESTONE SOUTH AFRICA HOLDINGS (PTY) LTD.—See Bridgestone Corporation; *Int'l*, pg. 1159
BRIDGESTONE SOUTH AFRICA (PTY) LTD.—See Bridgestone Corporation; *Int'l*, pg. 1159
BRIDGESTONE SPORTS CO., LTD.—See Bridgestone Corporation; *Int'l*, pg. 1159
BRIDGESTONE STARGARD SP. Z.O.O—See Bridgestone Corporation; *Int'l*, pg. 1159
BRIDGESTONE SWEDEN AB—See Bridgestone Corporation; *Int'l*, pg. 1159
BRIDGESTONE TAIWAN CO., LTD.—See Bridgestone Corporation; *Int'l*, pg. 1159
BRIDGESTONE (TIANJIN) TIRE CO., LTD.—See Bridgestone Corporation; *Int'l*, pg. 1157
BRIDGESTONE TIRE MANUFACTURING (THAILAND) CO., LTD.—See Bridgestone Corporation; *Int'l*, pg. 1159
BRIDGESTONE TIRE MANUFACTURING VIETNAM LIMITED LIABILITY COMPANY—See Bridgestone Corporation; *Int'l*, pg. 1159
BRIDGESTONE TIRE SALES KOREA LTD.—See Bridgestone Corporation; *Int'l*, pg. 1159
BRIDGESTONE TYRE SALES (MALAYSIA) SDN. BHD.—See Bridgestone Corporation; *Int'l*, pg. 1159
BRIDGESTONE TYRE SALES SINGAPORE PTE. LTD.—See Bridgestone Corporation; *Int'l*, pg. 1155
BRIDGESTONE TYRE SALES VIETNAM LLC—See Bridgestone Corporation; *Int'l*, pg. 1159
BRIDGESTONE TYRES (P.N.G) PTY. LTD—See Bridgestone Corporation; *Int'l*, pg. 1155
BRIDGESTONE U.K. LTD.—See Bridgestone Corporation; *Int'l*, pg. 1159
BRIDGESTONE (WUXI) TIRE CO., LTD.—See Bridgestone Corporation; *Int'l*, pg. 1156
BRIDGES TRANSITIONS INC.—See Xap Corporation; *U.S. Private*, pg. 4580
BRIDGESTREET ACCOMMODATIONS LONDON LTD.—See Independence Capital Partners, LLC; *U.S. Private*, pg. 2057
BRIDGESTREET WORLDWIDE INC.—See Independence Capital Partners, LLC; *U.S. Private*, pg. 2057
BRIDGES VENTURES LLP; *Int'l*, pg. 1155
BRIDGETEC CORP.; *Int'l*, pg. 1160

COMPANY NAME INDEX

BRIDGE TECHNICAL SOLUTIONS; *U.S. Private*, pg. 649
BRIDGE TECHNOLOGIES—See Raya Holding Company; *Int'l*, pg. 6223
BRIDGE TECHNOLOGY INC; *U.S. Private*, pg. 649
BRIDGETEX PIPELINE COMPANY, LLC—See ONEOK, Inc.; *U.S. Public*, pg. 1603
BRIDGETEX PIPELINE COMPANY, LLC—See Ontario Municipal Employees Retirement System; *Int'l*, pg. 5584
BRIDGETEX PIPELINE COMPANY, LLC—See Plains All American Pipeline, L.P.; *U.S. Public*, pg. 1696
BRIDGETOWER MEDIA, LLC—See Transom Capital Group, LLC; *U.S. Private*, pg. 4209
BRIDGETOWN 3 HOLDINGS LIMITED; *Int'l*, pg. 1160
BRIDGETOWN HOLDINGS LIMITED; *Int'l*, pg. 1160
BRIDGETOWN PRINTING CO.—See Chatham Asset Management, LLC; *U.S. Private*, pg. 862
BRIDGEVIEW BANCORP, INC.—See Old National Bancorp; *U.S. Public*, pg. 1567
BRIDGEVIEW BANK GROUP—See Old National Bancorp; *U.S. Public*, pg. 1567
BRIDGEVIEW CAPITAL SOLUTIONS, LLC—See Old National Bancorp; *U.S. Public*, pg. 1567
BRIDGEVIEW COMMUNITY MENTAL HEALTH CENTER—See Bethany for Children & Families; *U.S. Private*, pg. 545
BRIDGEVIEW MANAGEMENT CO. INC.—See Grupo Mexico, S.A.B. de C.V.; *Int'l*, pg. 3132
BRIDGEVINE, INC.; *U.S. Private*, pg. 649
BRIDGEWATER BANCSHARES, INC.; *U.S. Public*, pg. 382
BRIDGEWATER BANK—See Bridgewater Bancshares, Inc.; *U.S. Public*, pg. 382
THE BRIDGEWATER CANDLE COMPANY, LLC—See Grace Management Group, LLC; *U.S. Private*, pg. 1749
BRIDGEWATER CHEVROLET, INC.—See General Motors Company; *U.S. Public*, pg. 923
BRIDGEWATER EQUITY RELEASE LIMITED—See Grainger plc; *Int'l*, pg. 3052
BRIDGEWATER GROUP, LLC—See Field Pros Direct LLC; *U.S. Private*, pg. 1504
BRIDGEWATER LUMBER CO—See Chelsea Lumber Company; *U.S. Private*, pg. 870
BRIDGEWATER OFFSHORE PTE. LTD.—See Kim Heng Limited; *Int'l*, pg. 4162
BRIDGEWATER RESOURCES CORPORATION; *U.S. Private*, pg. 650
BRIDGEWATER SAVINGS BANK; *U.S. Private*, pg. 650
BRIDGEWATER TENANCIES LIMITED—See Grainger plc; *Int'l*, pg. 3052
BRIDGEWATER WEALTH & FINANCIAL MANAGEMENT LLC—See Clayton, Dubilier & Rice, LLC; *U.S. Private*, pg. 923
BRIDGEWATER WEALTH & FINANCIAL MANAGEMENT LLC—See Stone Point Capital LLC; *U.S. Private*, pg. 3824
BRIDGEWATER WHOLESALERS, INC.—See Owens Corning; *U.S. Public*, pg. 1626
BRIDGEWAY HEALTH SERVICES, LLC—See Merit Capital Partners; *U.S. Private*, pg. 2674
BRIDGEWAY HEALTH SOLUTIONS OF ARIZONA LLC—See Centene Corporation; *U.S. Public*, pg. 468
THE BRIDGEWAY HOSPITAL—See Universal Health Services, Inc.; *U.S. Public*, pg. 2260
BRIDGEWAY NATIONAL CORP.; *U.S. Public*, pg. 382
BRIDGEWAY REHABILITATION SERVICES; *U.S. Private*, pg. 650
BRIDGEWELL INCOME TRUST INC.; *U.S. Private*, pg. 650
BRIDGEWELL INC.; *U.S. Private*, pg. 650
BRIDGEWEST GROUP, INC.; *U.S. Private*, pg. 650
BRIDGFORD FOOD PROCESSING CORPORATION—See Bridgford Foods Corporation; *U.S. Public*, pg. 382
BRIDGFORD FOOD PROCESSING OF TEXAS, L.P.—See Bridgford Foods Corporation; *U.S. Public*, pg. 382
BRIDGFORD FOODS CORPORATION; *U.S. Public*, pg. 382
BRIDGFORD MARKETING COMPANY—See Bridgford Foods Corporation; *U.S. Public*, pg. 382
BRIDGFORD & SONS LIMITED—See Co-operative Group Limited; *Int'l*, pg. 1679
BRIDGING THE GAP PHYSICAL THERAPY LLC—See HealthLynked Corp.; *U.S. Public*, pg. 1016
BRIDGNORTH ALUMINIUM LIMITED—See Viohalco SA/NV; *Int'l*, pg. 8243
BRIDGTON HOSPITAL; *U.S. Private*, pg. 650
BRIDLINGTON VETS4PETS LIMITED—See Pets at Home Group Plc; *Int'l*, pg. 5833
BRIDON AMERICAN CORPORATION—See Ontario Teachers' Pension Plan; *Int'l*, pg. 5587
BRIDON CORDAGE LLC—See Universal Cooperatives, Inc.; *U.S. Private*, pg. 4304
BRIDON HANGZHOU ROPES CO. LTD.—See Ontario Teachers' Pension Plan; *Int'l*, pg. 5587
BRIDON HONG KONG LTD.—See Ontario Teachers' Pension Plan; *Int'l*, pg. 5587

BRIDON INTERNATIONAL GMBH—See Ontario Teachers' Pension Plan; *Int'l*, pg. 5587
BRIDON INTERNATIONAL LIMITED—See Ontario Teachers' Pension Plan; *Int'l*, pg. 5587
BRIDON INTERNATIONAL MOSCOW—See Ontario Teachers' Pension Plan; *Int'l*, pg. 5587
BRIDON MIDDLE EAST—See Ontario Teachers' Pension Plan; *Int'l*, pg. 5587
BRIDON NEW ZEALAND LIMITED—See Ontario Teachers' Pension Plan; *Int'l*, pg. 5587
BRIDON SINGAPORE (PTE) LTD.—See Ontario Teachers' Pension Plan; *Int'l*, pg. 5587
BRIDOON TRADE AND INVEST 197 (PTY) LIMITED—See Reunert Limited; *Int'l*, pg. 6311
BRIDOR FRANCE—See Holding Le Duff SA; *Int'l*, pg. 3450
BRIDOR INC.—See Holding Le Duff SA; *Int'l*, pg. 3450
BRIDPORT ERIE AVIATION, INC.—See TransDigm Group Incorporated; *U.S. Public*, pg. 2182
BRIECHLE-FERNANDEZ MARKETING SERVICES INC.; *U.S. Private*, pg. 650
BRIEFING.COM, INC.; *U.S. Private*, pg. 650
BRIEFING MEDIA LTD.—See Horizon Capital LLP; *Int'l*, pg. 3479
BRIEFLY STATED HOLDINGS, INC.—See Li & Fung Limited; *Int'l*, pg. 4480
BRIEFLY STATED, INC.—See Li & Fung Limited; *Int'l*, pg. 4480
THE BRIEN CENTER; *U.S. Private*, pg. 4000
BRIEN MOTORS INC.; *U.S. Private*, pg. 650
BRIER CREEK COUNTRY CLUB—See Apollo Global Management, Inc.; *U.S. Public*, pg. 149
BRIERLEY EUROPE LIMITED—See Capillary Technologies International Pte Ltd.; *Int'l*, pg. 1308
BRIERLEY HOLDINGS LIMITED—See Hong Leong Investment Holdings Pte. Ltd.; *Int'l*, pg. 3468
BRIERLEY & PARTNERS, INC.—See Capillary Technologies International Pte Ltd.; *Int'l*, pg. 1307
BRIERLEY+PARTNERS JAPAN, INC.—See Capillary Technologies International Pte Ltd.; *Int'l*, pg. 1308
BRIERLEY & PARTNERS - LOS ANGELES—See Capillary Technologies International Pte Ltd.; *Int'l*, pg. 1308
BRIERTY LTD.; *Int'l*, pg. 1160
BRIESS MALT & INGREDIENTS CO.; *U.S. Private*, pg. 650
BRIGADE CAPITAL MANAGEMENT, LLC; *U.S. Private*, pg. 650
BRIGADE ENTERPRISES LTD.; *Int'l*, pg. 1160
BRIGADE HOSPITALITY SERVICES LIMITED—See Brigade Enterprises Ltd.; *Int'l*, pg. 1160
BRIGANDI & ASSOCIATES, INC. MARKETING COMMUNICATIONS; *U.S. Private*, pg. 650
BRIGANTINE ACQUISITION CORP.; *U.S. Private*, pg. 650
THE BRIGANTINE RESTAURANT CORP.; *U.S. Private*, pg. 4000
BRIGGS ADVERTISING, INC.—See CD&M Communications; *U.S. Private*, pg. 802
BRIGGS & CALDWELL; *U.S. Private*, pg. 650
BRIGGS CORP.; *U.S. Private*, pg. 651
BRIGGS ELECTRIC INC.; *U.S. Private*, pg. 651
BRIGGS EQUIPMENT, INC.—See Sammons Enterprises, Inc.; *U.S. Private*, pg. 3537
BRIGGS EQUIPMENT S.A. DE C.V.—See Sammons Enterprises, Inc.; *U.S. Private*, pg. 3537
BRIGGS EQUIPMENT UK LIMITED—See Sammons Enterprises, Inc.; *U.S. Private*, pg. 3537
BRIGGS EQUIPMENT UK LIMITED—See Sammons Enterprises, Inc.; *U.S. Private*, pg. 3537
BRIGGS HEALTHCARE—See Briggs Corp.; *U.S. Private*, pg. 651
BRIGGS INC.; *U.S. Private*, pg. 651
BRIGGS INDUSTRIAL FOOTWEAR LTD.—See Superhouse Limited; *Int'l*, pg. 7337
BRIGGS INDUSTRIES, INC.—See Ceramica Lima S.A.; *Int'l*, pg. 1421
BRIGGS INTERNATIONAL, INC.—See Sammons Enterprises, Inc.; *U.S. Private*, pg. 3537
BRIGGS NEW YORK CORP.—See Sun Capital Partners, Inc.; *U.S. Private*, pg. 3859
BRIGGS & RILEY TRAVELWARE—See United States Luggage Company, LLC; *U.S. Private*, pg. 4299
BRIGGS & STRATTON AUSTRALIA PTY. LIMITED—See Briggs & Stratton Corporation; *U.S. Private*, pg. 650
BRIGGS & STRATTON CANADA INC.—See Briggs & Stratton Corporation; *U.S. Private*, pg. 651
BRIGGS & STRATTON CORPORATION; *U.S. Private*, pg. 650
BRIGGS & STRATTON CZ, S.R.O.—See Briggs & Stratton Corporation; *U.S. Private*, pg. 651
BRIGGS & STRATTON FRANCE S.A.R.L.—See Briggs & Stratton Corporation; *U.S. Private*, pg. 651
BRIGGS & STRATTON GERMANY GMBH—See Briggs & Stratton Corporation; *U.S. Private*, pg. 651
BRIGGS & STRATTON INDIA PRIVATE LIMITED—See Briggs & Stratton Corporation; *U.S. Private*, pg. 651
BRIGGS & STRATTON INTERNATIONAL HOLDING BV—See Briggs & Stratton Corporation; *U.S. Private*, pg. 651

BRIGGS & STRATTON INTERNATIONAL SALES—See Briggs & Stratton Corporation; *U.S. Private*, pg. 651
BRIGGS & STRATTON JAPAN KK—See Briggs & Stratton Corporation; *U.S. Private*, pg. 651
BRIGGS & STRATTON (MALAYSIA) SDN. BHD.—See Briggs & Stratton Corporation; *U.S. Private*, pg. 650
BRIGGS & STRATTON NETHERLANDS B.V.—See Briggs & Stratton Corporation; *U.S. Private*, pg. 651
BRIGGS & STRATTON NEW ZEALAND LIMITED—See Briggs & Stratton Corporation; *U.S. Private*, pg. 651
BRIGGS & STRATTON POWER PRODUCTS GROUP, LLC - MCDONOUGH—See Briggs & Stratton Corporation; *U.S. Private*, pg. 651
BRIGGS & STRATTON POWER PRODUCTS GROUP, LLC—See Briggs & Stratton Corporation; *U.S. Private*, pg. 651
BRIGGS & STRATTON REPRESENTACAO DE MOTORES E PRODUCTOS DE FORCA DO BRASIL LTDA.—See Briggs & Stratton Corporation; *U.S. Private*, pg. 651
BRIGGS & STRATTON RSA (PROPRIETARY) LIMITED—See Briggs & Stratton Corporation; *U.S. Private*, pg. 651
BRIGGS & STRATTON (SHANGHAI) INTERNATIONAL TRADING CO., LTD.—See Briggs & Stratton Corporation; *U.S. Private*, pg. 650
BRIGGS & STRATTON SWEDEN AB—See Briggs & Stratton Corporation; *U.S. Private*, pg. 651
BRIGGS & STRATTON U.K. LIMITED—See Briggs & Stratton Corporation; *U.S. Private*, pg. 651
BRIGGS & VESELKA CO.; *U.S. Private*, pg. 651
BRIGHAM CITY COMMUNITY HOSPITAL, INC.—See HCA Healthcare, Inc.; *U.S. Public*, pg. 991
BRIGHAM MINERALS, INC.—See Sitio Royalties Corp.; *U.S. Public*, pg. 1889
BRIGHAM RESOURCES LLC—See Sitio Royalties Corp.; *U.S. Public*, pg. 1889
THE BRIGHAM & WOMEN'S FAULKNER HOSPITAL—See Partners HealthCare System, Inc.; *U.S. Private*, pg. 3102
THE BRIGHAM & WOMEN'S HOSPITAL—See Partners HealthCare System, Inc.; *U.S. Private*, pg. 3102
BRIGHAM & WOMEN'S PHYSICIANS ORGANIZATION—See Partners HealthCare System, Inc.; *U.S. Private*, pg. 3102
BRIGHOLME INTERIORS GROUP; *Int'l*, pg. 1161
BRIGHT & ASSOCIATES, INC.—See Brown & Brown, Inc.; *U.S. Public*, pg. 397
BRIGHT AUTOPLAST PVT. LTD.—See Sintex Industries, Ltd.; *Int'l*, pg. 6957
BRIGHT & BEAUTIFUL UK LIMITED—See Harvest Partners L.P.; *U.S. Private*, pg. 1877
BRIGHT BLUE FOODS LIMITED—See Stage Capital LLP; *Int'l*, pg. 7163
BRIGHTBOX, INC.; *U.S. Private*, pg. 651
BRIGHT BRICKS LIMITED—See Live Company Group Plc; *Int'l*, pg. 4530
BRIGHT BROTHERS LIMITED; *Int'l*, pg. 1161
BRIGHTCLAIM, INC.—See Genpact Limited; *Int'l*, pg. 2926
BRIGHTCOM GROUP LTD.; *Int'l*, pg. 1162
BRIGHTCOVE FZ-LLC—See Brightcove, Inc.; *U.S. Public*, pg. 383
BRIGHTCOVE, INC.; *U.S. Public*, pg. 383
BRIGHTCOVE INDIA PTE. LTD.—See Brightcove, Inc.; *U.S. Public*, pg. 383
BRIGHTCOVE KK—See Transcosmos Inc.; *Int'l*, pg. 7898
BRIGHTCOVE KOREA—See Brightcove, Inc.; *U.S. Public*, pg. 383
BRIGHTCOVE SINGAPORE PTE. LTD.—See Brightcove, Inc.; *U.S. Public*, pg. 383
BRIGHTCOVE UK LTD—See Brightcove, Inc.; *U.S. Public*, pg. 383
BRIGHT CRYSTAL COMPANY LIMITED—See Bright Led Electronics Corp.; *Int'l*, pg. 1161
BRIGHT DAIRY & FOOD CO., LTD.—See Bright Food (Group) Co., Ltd.; *Int'l*, pg. 1161
BRIGHTEDGE TECHNOLOGIES, INC.; *U.S. Private*, pg. 651
BRIGHTEK OPTOELECTRONIC CO., LTD.; *Int'l*, pg. 1162
BRIGHTEN OPTIX CORPORATION; *Int'l*, pg. 1162
BRIGHTEN SWITCHBOARD BUILDERS (M) SDN BHD—See Fuji Electric Co., Ltd.; *Int'l*, pg. 2812
BRIGHT EQUIPMENT INC.; *U.S. Private*, pg. 651
BRIGHTERION, INC.—See Mastercard Incorporated; *U.S. Public*, pg. 1394
BRIGHTER PICTURES LTD—See LOV Group Invest SAS; *Int'l*, pg. 4564
BRIGHTFIELDS, INC.; *U.S. Private*, pg. 652
BRIGHTFISH NV—See Kinepolis Group N.V.; *Int'l*, pg. 4166
BRIGHTFLOW.AI, INC.; *U.S. Private*, pg. 652
BRIGHTFOCUS FOUNDATION; *U.S. Private*, pg. 652
BRIGHT FOOD (GROUP) CO., LTD.; *Int'l*, pg. 1161
BRIGHT FUTURE INTERNATIONAL LIMITED—See Bang & Olufsen a/s; *Int'l*, pg. 831
BRIGHT FUTURE TECHNOLOGY HOLDINGS LTD.; *Int'l*, pg. 1161
BRIGHTGENE BIO-MEDICAL TECHNOLOGY CO., LTD.; *Int'l*, pg. 1162

BRIGHTGENE BIO-MEDICAL TECHNOLOGY CO., LTD.

BRIGHTGENE FERMENTATION TECHNOLOGY CO. LTD.—See BrightGene Bio-Medical Technology Co., Ltd.; *Int'l*, pg. 1162
BRIGHTGENE FINE CHEMICAL CO. LTD.—See Bright-Gene Bio-Medical Technology Co., Ltd.; *Int'l*, pg. 1162
BRIGHTGENE PHARMACEUTICAL CO. LTD.—See BrightGene Bio-Medical Technology Co., Ltd.; *Int'l*, pg. 1162
BRIGHT GREEN CORPORATION; *U.S. Public*, pg. 382
BRIGHT GREY—See The Royal London Mutual Insurance Society Limited; *Int'l*, pg. 7679
BRIGHT HEALTH MANAGEMENT, INC.—See NeueHealth, Inc.; *U.S. Public*, pg. 1510
BRIGHT HORIZONS CHILDREN'S CENTERS LLC—See Bain Capital, LP; *U.S. Private*, pg. 437
BRIGHT HORIZONS FAMILY SOLUTIONS CALIFORNIA REGIONAL OFFICE—See Bain Capital, LP; *U.S. Private*, pg. 436
BRIGHT HORIZONS FAMILY SOLUTIONS CHICAGO REGIONAL OFFICE—See Bain Capital, LP; *U.S. Private*, pg. 436
BRIGHT HORIZONS FAMILY SOLUTIONS FLORIDA REGIONAL OFFICE—See Bain Capital, LP; *U.S. Private*, pg. 436
BRIGHT HORIZONS FAMILY SOLUTIONS, INC.—See Bain Capital, LP; *U.S. Private*, pg. 436
BRIGHT HORIZONS FAMILY SOLUTIONS IRELAND—See Bain Capital, LP; *U.S. Private*, pg. 436
BRIGHT HORIZONS FAMILY SOLUTIONS LIMITED—See Bain Capital, LP; *U.S. Private*, pg. 437
BRIGHT HORIZONS FAMILY SOLUTIONS LLC—See Bain Capital, LP; *U.S. Private*, pg. 436
BRIGHT HORIZONS FAMILY SOLUTIONS MARYLAND REGIONAL OFFICE—See Bain Capital, LP; *U.S. Private*, pg. 437
BRIGHT HORIZONS FAMILY SOLUTIONS NASHVILLE REGIONAL OFFICE—See Bain Capital, LP; *U.S. Private*, pg. 437
BRIGHT HORIZONS FAMILY SOLUTIONS SCOTLAND REGIONAL OFFICE—See Bain Capital, LP; *U.S. Private*, pg. 437
BRIGHT HORIZONS FAMILY SOLUTIONS TEXAS REGIONAL OFFICE—See Bain Capital, LP; *U.S. Private*, pg. 437
BRIGHT HORIZONS FAMILY SOLUTIONS UNITED KINGDOM—See Bain Capital, LP; *U.S. Private*, pg. 437
BRIGHT HORIZONS LIVINGSTON LTD.—See Bain Capital, LP; *U.S. Private*, pg. 437
BRIGHT HORIZONS LLC—See Bain Capital, LP; *U.S. Private*, pg. 436
BRIGHTHOUSE FINANCIAL, INC.; *U.S. Public*, pg. 383
BRIGHTHOUSE GROUP PLC; *Int'l*, pg. 1162
BRIGHTHOUSE LIFE INSURANCE COMPANY—See MetLife, Inc.; *U.S. Public*, pg. 1430
BRIGHT INSURANCE AGENCY, INC.—See Sun Communities, Inc.; *U.S. Public*, pg. 1961
BRIGHT INTERNATIONAL, LLC—See Aterian Investment Management, L.P.; *U.S. Private*, pg. 366
BRIGHT KEY; *U.S. Private*, pg. 651
BRIGHT KINDLE RESOURCES AND INVESTMENTS INC.—See Philippine Business Bank Inc.; *Int'l*, pg. 5845
BRIGHTKING (BEIJING) CO., LTD.—See Brightking Holdings Limited; *Int'l*, pg. 1163
BRIGHTKING ELECTRONICS CO., LTD.—See Brightking Holdings Limited; *Int'l*, pg. 1162
BRIGHTKING ELECTRONICS INC.—See Brightking Holdings Limited; *Int'l*, pg. 1162
BRIGHTKING ENTERPRISE (H.K) CO., LTD—See Brightking Holdings Limited; *Int'l*, pg. 1163
BRIGHTKING HOLDINGS LIMITED; *Int'l*, pg. 1162
BRIGHTKING (SHANGAI) CO., LTD.—See Brightking Holdings Limited; *Int'l*, pg. 1163
BRIGHTKING (SHENZHEN) CO., LTD.—See Brightking Holdings Limited; *Int'l*, pg. 1163
BRIGHTLANE ACQUISITION CORP.; *U.S. Private*, pg. 652
BRIGHTLANE.COM, INC.—See DLH Holdings Corp.; *U.S. Public*, pg. 670
BRIGHTLANE CORP.—See Brightlane Acquisition Corp.; *U.S. Private*, pg. 652
BRIGHT LED ELECTRONICS CORP. - CHINA FACTORY—See Bright Led Electronics Corp.; *Int'l*, pg. 1161
BRIGHT LED ELECTRONICS CORP.; *Int'l*, pg. 1161
BRIGHT LED EUROPE GMBH—See Bright Led Electronics Corp.; *Int'l*, pg. 1161
BRIGHT LIGHTS ACQUISITION CORP.; *U.S. Public*, pg. 382
BRIGHTLITE NOMINEES PROPRIETARY LIMITED; *Int'l*, pg. 1163
BRIGHTLY SOFTWARE AUSTRALIA PTY. LTD.—See Siemens Aktiengesellschaft; *Int'l*, pg. 6886
BRIGHT MARKET, LLC; *U.S. Private*, pg. 651
BRIGHT MINDS BIOSCIENCES INC.; *U.S. Public*, pg. 383
BRIGHTMINE—See RELX plc; *Int'l*, pg. 6266
BRIGHT MOUNTAIN MEDIA, INC.; *U.S. Public*, pg. 383

BRIGHTNET OKLAHOMA—See Chickasaw Holding Company; *U.S. Private*, pg. 880
BRIGHT OCEANS INTER-TELECOM CO., LTD.; *Int'l*, pg. 1161
BRIGHTOIL PETROLEUM HOLDINGS LIMITED; *Int'l*, pg. 1163
BRIGHTON AGENCY, INC.; *U.S. Private*, pg. 652
BRIGHTON BANK; *U.S. Private*, pg. 652
BRIGHTON-BEST INTERNATIONAL, INC.; *U.S. Private*, pg. 652
BRIGHTON COLLECTIBLES, INC.; *U.S. Private*, pg. 652
BRIGHTON CO., LTD.—See Oriental Land Co., Ltd.; *Int'l*, pg. 5625
BRIGHTON COMMERCIAL TRAINING CENTRE PTE LTD.—See AEC Education plc; *Int'l*, pg. 171
BRIGHTON COMMUNITY HOSPITAL ASSOCIATION; *U.S. Private*, pg. 652
BRIGHTON CORPORATION—See Enerfab, Inc.; *U.S. Private*, pg. 1393
BRIGHTON CROMWELL, LLC—See AE Industrial Partners, LP; *U.S. Private*, pg. 112
BRIGHTONE GMBH—See Aurelius Equity Opportunities SE & Co. KGaA; *Int'l*, pg. 710
BRIGHTONE HEALTHCARE SOLUTIONS B.V.—See Aurelius Equity Opportunities SE & Co. KGaA; *Int'l*, pg. 710
BRIGHTON FORD-MERCURY INC.; *U.S. Private*, pg. 652
BRIGHTON HOMES LTD.; *U.S. Private*, pg. 652
BRIGHTON HOMES; *U.S. Private*, pg. 652
BRIGHTON HOTEL (WA) PTY LTD—See Woolworths Group Limited; *Int'l*, pg. 8451
BRIGHTON & HOVE BUS & COACH COMPANY LIMITED—See GLOBALVIA Inversiones, S.A.U.; *Int'l*, pg. 3005
BRIGHTON & HOVE BUS & COACH COMPANY LIMITED—See Kinetic Group Services Pty Ltd.; *Int'l*, pg. 4167
BRIGHTON MANAGEMENT LLC; *U.S. Private*, pg. 652
BRIGHTON MAZDA; *U.S. Private*, pg. 652
BRIGHTON MINING GROUP LIMITED; *Int'l*, pg. 1163
BRIGHTON PARK CAPITAL MANAGEMENT, L.P.; *U.S. Private*, pg. 652
BRIGHTON PARTNERS, LLC; *U.S. Private*, pg. 652
THE BRIGHTON PIER GROUP PLC; *Int'l*, pg. 7627
BRIGHTON SKI RESORT—See Boyne USA Resorts Inc.; *U.S. Private*, pg. 629
BRIGHTON SURGICENTER, LLC—See HCA Healthcare, Inc.; *U.S. Public*, pg. 991
BRIGHTON TRU-EDGE HEADS—See Enerfab, Inc.; *U.S. Private*, pg. 1393
BRIGHTON VETS4PETS LIMITED—See Pets at Home Group Plc; *Int'l*, pg. 5833
BRIGHT ORIENT (HOLDING) LTD.; *Int'l*, pg. 1161
BRIGHT OUTDOOR MEDIA LIMITED; *Int'l*, pg. 1161
BRIGHT PACKAGING INDUSTRY BERHAD; *Int'l*, pg. 1161
BRIGHTPATH BIOTHERAPEUTICS CO., LTD.; *Int'l*, pg. 1163
BRIGHTPATH EARLY LEARNING INC.—See Ontario Teachers' Pension Plan; *Int'l*, pg. 5587
BRIGHT PLASTICS, INC.—See Thunderbird LLC; *U.S. Private*, pg. 4166
BRIGHTPOINT HEALTH, INC.—See Hudson River HealthCare, Inc.; *U.S. Private*, pg. 2002
BRIGHT POINT INTERNATIONAL FINANCIAL (UK) LTD.—See Theme International Holdings Limited; *Int'l*, pg. 7706
BRIGHT POINT INTERNATIONAL FUTURES (SG) PTE. LTD.—See Theme International Holdings Limited; *Int'l*, pg. 7706
BRIGHTPOINT NZ LIMITED—See Hainan Traffic Administration Holding Co., Ltd.; *Int'l*, pg. 3215
BRIGHTPOOL LIMITED—See IG Group Holdings plc; *Int'l*, pg. 3601
B-RIGHT REAL ESTATE LIMITED; *Int'l*, pg. 785
BRIGHTREE LLC—See ResMed Inc.; *U.S. Public*, pg. 1790
BRIGHTREE PATIENT COLLECTIONS LLC—See ResMed Inc.; *U.S. Public*, pg. 1790
BRIGHTREE SERVICES LLC—See ResMed Inc.; *U.S. Public*, pg. 1790
BRIGHTROCK GOLD CORP.; *U.S. Private*, pg. 652
BRIGHT SCHOLAR EDUCATION HOLDINGS LIMITED; *Int'l*, pg. 1161
BRIGHT SHEET METAL COMPANY, INC.; *U.S. Private*, pg. 651
BRIGHT SHELAND INTERNATIONAL CO., LTD.; *Int'l*, pg. 1162
BRIGHTSIDE GROUP PLC—See AnaCap Financial Partners LLP; *Int'l*, pg. 445
BRIGHT SMART SECURITIES & COMMODITIES GROUP LIMITED; *Int'l*, pg. 1162
BRIGHT SMILE DENTAL SURGERY (BUANGKOK MRT) PTE. LTD.—See Q&M Dental Group (Singapore) Limited; *Int'l*, pg. 6129
BRIGHT SMILE DENTAL SURGERY PTE. LTD.—See Q&M Dental Group (Singapore) Limited; *Int'l*, pg. 6129
BRIGHT SOLAR LTD.; *Int'l*, pg. 1162
BRIGHTSOLID—See D.C. Thomson & Co. Ltd.; *Int'l*, pg. 1900

CORPORATE AFFILIATIONS

BRIGHTSOURCE ENERGY, INC.; *U.S. Private*, pg. 652
BRIGHTSOURCE LIMITED—See Arsenal Capital Management LP; *U.S. Private*, pg. 338
BRIGHTSPARK CAPITOL CORP.; *U.S. Public*, pg. 383
BRIGHTSPARK TRAVEL—See TUI AG; *Int'l*, pg. 7964
BRIGHTSPARK TRAVEL—See TUI AG; *Int'l*, pg. 7964
BRIGHTSPHERE INTERNATIONAL, LTD.—See BrightSphere Investment Group Inc.; *U.S. Public*, pg. 383
BRIGHTSPHERE INVESTMENT GROUP INC.; *U.S. Public*, pg. 383
BRIGHTSPIRE CAPITAL, INC.; *U.S. Public*, pg. 383
BRIGHTSTAR 20:20 MOBILE—See Brightstar Capital Partners, L.P.; *U.S. Private*, pg. 653
BRIGHTSTAR 20:20 MOBILE—See Brightstar Capital Partners, L.P.; *U.S. Private*, pg. 653
BRIGHTSTAR ARGENTINA, S.A.—See Brightstar Capital Partners, L.P.; *U.S. Private*, pg. 653
BRIGHTSTAR CAPITAL PARTNERS, L.P.; *U.S. Private*, pg. 652
BRIGHTSTAR COLOMBIA LTDA.—See Brightstar Capital Partners, L.P.; *U.S. Private*, pg. 653
BRIGHTSTAR CORPORATION; *U.S. Private*, pg. 653
BRIGHTSTAR CORP.—See Brightstar Capital Partners, L.P.; *U.S. Private*, pg. 653
BRIGHTSTAR DOMINICANA S.A.—See Brightstar Capital Partners, L.P.; *U.S. Private*, pg. 653
BRIGHT STAR FIREWORKS LTD.—See Panda Financial Holding Corp., Ltd.; *Int'l*, pg. 5726
BRIGHT STAR FOOTWEAR, INC.—See Iconix Acquisition LLC; *U.S. Private*, pg. 2032
BRIGHTSTAR FOX PRODUCTIONS LLC—See The Walt Disney Company; *U.S. Public*, pg. 2140
BRIGHTSTAR FRANCHISING, LLC; *U.S. Private*, pg. 653
BRIGHT STAR, INC.—See Berkshire Hathaway Inc.; *U.S. Public*, pg. 310
BRIGHTSTAR LOGISTICS PTY. LTD.—See Brightstar Capital Partners, L.P.; *U.S. Private*, pg. 653
BRIGHTSTAR MEXICO S.A. DE C.V.—See Brightstar Capital Partners, L.P.; *U.S. Private*, pg. 653
BRIGHTSTAR PARAGUAY S.R.L.—See Brightstar Capital Partners, L.P.; *U.S. Private*, pg. 653
BRIGHTSTAR PARTNERS, INC.—See Avnet, Inc.; *U.S. Public*, pg. 252
BRIGHTSTAR PROCEEDOR DE SOLUCIONES TECNOLOGICAS S.A.—See Brightstar Capital Partners, L.P.; *U.S. Private*, pg. 653
BRIGHTSTAR PUERTO RICO, INC.—See Brightstar Capital Partners, L.P.; *U.S. Private*, pg. 653
BRIGHTSTAR RESOURCES LIMITED; *Int'l*, pg. 1163
BRIGHTTALK INC.—See TechTarget, Inc.; *U.S. Public*, pg. 1989
BRIGHTTALK LIMITED—See TechTarget, Inc.; *U.S. Public*, pg. 1989
BRIGHTTECH INC.—See Danaher Corporation; *U.S. Public*, pg. 625
BRIGHTVIEW HOLDINGS, INC.; *U.S. Public*, pg. 383
BRIGHTVIEW LANDSCAPES, LLC—See KKR & Co. Inc.; *U.S. Public*, pg. 1242
BRIGHT VIEW TECHNOLOGIES CORPORATION—See Tredegar Corporation; *U.S. Public*, pg. 2187
BRIGHTWAVE MARKETING, LLC—See Ansira Partners, Inc.; *U.S. Private*, pg. 285
BRIGHTWAY INSURANCE, INC.; *U.S. Private*, pg. 653
BRIGHTWAY VISION LTD.—See Koito Manufacturing Co., Ltd.; *Int'l*, pg. 4230
BRIGHTWELL PAYMENTS, INC.—See Navigation Capital Partners, Inc.; *U.S. Private*, pg. 2873
BRIGHTWHISTLE, INC.—See Vestar Capital Partners, LLC; *U.S. Private*, pg. 4372
BRIGHTWING; *U.S. Private*, pg. 653
BRIGHTWOOD CAPITAL ADVISORS, LLC; *U.S. Private*, pg. 653
BRIGHTWOOD CAREER INSTITUTE—See Education Corporation of America; *U.S. Public*, pg. 1338
BRIGHT WOOD CORP.; *U.S. Private*, pg. 651
BRIGHTWORK REAL ESTATE, INC.; *U.S. Private*, pg. 654
BRIGHTWORKS SUSTAINABILITY LLC; *U.S. Private*, pg. 654
BRIGHTYIELD SDN. BHD.—See Milux Corporation Berhad; *Int'l*, pg. 4897
BRIGITTE FRANCE; *Int'l*, pg. 1163
BRIGL & BERGMEISTER GMBH—See Roxcel Handelsges.m.b.H.; *Int'l*, pg. 6408
BRIGTPET NUTRITION GROUP, LLC—See Alvarez & Marsal, Inc.; *U.S. Private*, pg. 212
BRII BIOSCIENCES LIMITED; *Int'l*, pg. 1163
BRI INC.; *U.S. Private*, pg. 647
BRIJLAXMI LEASING & FINANCE LIMITED; *Int'l*, pg. 1163
BRIJU S.A.; *Int'l*, pg. 1163
BRIKOR LIMITED—See Nikkel Trading 392 Proprietary Limited; *Int'l*, pg. 5290
B. RILEY ALTERNATIVES GP, LLC—See B. Riley Financial, Inc.; *U.S. Public*, pg. 260
B. RILEY CAPITAL MANAGEMENT, LLC—See B. Riley Financial, Inc.; *U.S. Public*, pg. 260
B. RILEY & CO., LLC—See B. Riley Financial, Inc.; *U.S. Public*, pg. 260

COMPANY NAME INDEX

B. RILEY FBR, INC.—See B. Riley Financial, Inc.; *U.S. Public*, pg. 260
B. RILEY FBR, INC.—See B. Riley Financial, Inc.; *U.S. Public*, pg. 260
B. RILEY FINANCIAL, INC.; *U.S. Public*, pg. 260
B. RILEY WEALTH MANAGEMENT, INC.—See B. Riley Financial, Inc.; *U.S. Public*, pg. 260
B. RILEY WEALTH MANAGEMENT, INC.—See B. Riley Financial, Inc.; *U.S. Public*, pg. 260
BRILLANTE ENTRETENIMIENTO, INC.—See LOV Group Invest SAS; *Int'l*, pg. 4565
BRILLANTE ILUMINACION SA DE CV—See A.A.G. STUCCHI s.r.l.; *Int'l*, pg. 22
BRILLCAST INC.—See Decorative Castings Inc.; *U.S. Private*, pg. 1188
BRILLEN-BUNZEL GMBH—See Fielmann Group AG; *Int'l*, pg. 2656
BRILLEN MULLER GMBH & CO. OHG—See Fielmann Group AG; *Int'l*, pg. 2656
BRILLIANCE-BEA AUTO FINANCE CO., LTD.—See Brilliance China Automotive Holdings Limited; *Int'l*, pg. 1163
BRILLIANCE CHINA AUTOMOTIVE HOLDINGS LIMITED; *Int'l*, pg. 1163
BRILLIANCE PUBLISHING, INC—See Amazon.com, Inc.; *U.S. Public*, pg. 90
BRILLIANCE TECHNOLOGY CO LTD; *Int'l*, pg. 1163
BRILLIANT ACQUISITION CORPORATION—See Nukkleus Inc.; *U.S. Public*, pg. 1555
BRILLIANT AG—See The National Lighting Company Ltd.; *Int'l*, pg. 7670
BRILLIANT BIO PHARMA PRIVATE LIMITED—See TGV Sraac Limited; *Int'l*, pg. 7588
BRILLIANT COLD STORAGE MANAGEMENT LIMITED—See Daido Group Ltd; *Int'l*, pg. 1920
BRILLIANT DIGITAL ENTERTAINMENT, INC.; *U.S. Private*, pg. 654
BRILLIANT EARTH GROUP, INC.; *U.S. Public*, pg. 384
BRILLIANT ENVIRONMENTAL SERVICES, LLC; *U.S. Private*, pg. 654
BRILLIANT FUTURE AB; *Int'l*, pg. 1163
BRILLIANT LAVENDER SDN BHD—See Momar, Inc.; *U.S. Private*, pg. 2767
BRILLIANT LIGHT POWER, INC.—See Exelon Corporation; *U.S. Public*, pg. 807
BRILLIANT MEDIA; *Int'l*, pg. 1163
BRILLIANT MEDIA—See Brilliant Media; *Int'l*, pg. 1163
BRILLIANT MEDIA—See Brilliant Media; *Int'l*, pg. 1163
BRILLIANT N.E.V. CORP; *Int'l*, pg. 1163
BRILLIANT PORTFOLIOS LIMITED; *Int'l*, pg. 1163
BRILLIANT TELECOMMUNICATIONS, INC.; *U.S. Private*, pg. 654
BRILLIANT TIME LIMITED—See SinoCloud Group Limited; *Int'l*, pg. 6951
BRILLIANT TOP IN LOGISTICS LIMITED—See Daido Group Ltd; *Int'l*, pg. 1920
BRILLIENT CORPORATION; *U.S. Private*, pg. 654
BRILLOCA LIMITED—See Hindware Home Innovation Limited; *Int'l*, pg. 3400
BRILL SHOE INDUSTRIES LTD.; *Int'l*, pg. 1163
BRILLSTEIN ENTERTAINMENT PARTNERS, LLC—See Wasserman Media Group, LLC; *U.S. Private*, pg. 4450
BRILONER LEUCHTEN GMBH; *Int'l*, pg. 1164
BRIM AB—See Arthur J. Gallagher & Co.; *U.S. Public*, pg. 204
BRIMAG DIGITAL AGE LTD.; *Int'l*, pg. 1164
BRIMAR WOOD INNOVATIONS, INC.; *U.S. Private*, pg. 654
BRIMCO, S. DE R.L. DE C.V.—See Deutsche Bank Aktiengesellschaft; *Int'l*, pg. 2059
BRIMMER, BUREK & KEELAN, LLP; *U.S. Private*, pg. 654
BRIMROSE-ACOUSTO OPTIC COMPONENTS DIVISION—See Brimrose Corporation of America; *U.S. Private*, pg. 654
BRIMROSE CORPORATION OF AMERICA; *U.S. Private*, pg. 654
BRIMROSE-NIR PROCESS ANALYSIS DIVISION—See Brimrose Corporation of America; *U.S. Private*, pg. 654
BRIMSTONE ACQUISITION HOLDINGS CORP.; *U.S. Private*, pg. 654
BRIMSTONE INVESTMENT CORPORATION LTD.; *Int'l*, pg. 1164
BRIMTEK, INC.—See Digital Barriers plc; *Int'l*, pg. 2120
BRINADD INTERNATIONAL COMPANY INC.—See United Salt Corporation; *U.S. Private*, pg. 4297
BRINCH AGENCY, LLC—See Inszone Insurance Services, LLC; *U.S. Private*, pg. 2096
BRINCKERHOFF & NEUVILLE, INC.—See Rhinebeck Bank; *U.S. Private*, pg. 3421
BRINDAVAN ROLLER FLOUR MILLS LIMITED—See Sunil Agro Foods Limited; *Int'l*, pg. 7316
BRINDERSON CONSTRUCTORS, INC.—See New Mountain Capital, LLC; *U.S. Private*, pg. 2899
BRINDERSON L.P.—See New Mountain Capital, LLC; *U.S. Private*, pg. 2899
BRINDERSON SERVICES, LLC—See New Mountain Capital, LLC; *U.S. Private*, pg. 2899

BRINDLE PARK (BAMBER BRIDGE) MANAGEMENT COMPANY LIMITED—See Persimmon plc; *Int'l*, pg. 5815
BRINDLEY ADVERTISING LTD.; *Int'l*, pg. 1164
BRINDLEY BEACH VACATIONS & SALES; *U.S. Private*, pg. 654
BRINDLEY CONSTRUCTION, LLC.; *U.S. Private*, pg. 654
B&R INDUSTRIAL AUTOMATION A/S—See ABB Ltd.; *Int'l*, pg. 56
B&R INDUSTRIAL AUTOMATION CO., LTD.—See ABB Ltd.; *Int'l*, pg. 56
B&R INDUSTRIAL AUTOMATION CO. LTD.—See ABB Ltd.; *Int'l*, pg. 56
B&R INDUSTRIAL AUTOMATION CORP.—See ABB Ltd.; *Int'l*, pg. 56
B&R INDUSTRIAL AUTOMATION INC.—See ABB Ltd.; *Int'l*, pg. 56
B&R INDUSTRIAL AUTOMATION LTD.—See ABB Ltd.; *Int'l*, pg. 56
B&R INDUSTRIAL AUTOMATION, OOO—See ABB Ltd.; *Int'l*, pg. 56
B&R INDUSTRIAL AUTOMATION PTE LTD—See ABB Ltd.; *Int'l*, pg. 56
B&R INDUSTRIAL AUTOMATION PVT. LTD.—See ABB Ltd.; *Int'l*, pg. 56
B&R INDUSTRIAL AUTOMATION—See ABB Ltd.; *Int'l*, pg. 56
B&R INDUSTRIAUTOMATION AB—See ABB Ltd.; *Int'l*, pg. 56
B&R INDUSTRIE-AUTOMATION AG—See ABB Ltd.; *Int'l*, pg. 56
B&R INDUSTRIE-ELEKTRONIK GMBH—See ABB Ltd.; *Int'l*, pg. 56
B&R INDUSTRIELE AUTOMATISIERUNG B.V.—See ABB Ltd.; *Int'l*, pg. 56
B&R INDUSTRIELLE AUTOMATISERING BV—See ABB Ltd.; *Int'l*, pg. 56
BR INDUSTRIER AS; *Int'l*, pg. 1133
BRINE, INC.—See New Balance Athletic Shoe, Inc.; *U.S. Private*, pg. 2892
BRINEY TOOLING SYSTEMS, INC.—See Gemini Group, Inc.; *U.S. Private*, pg. 1657
BRIN FINANCIAL CORPORATION; *U.S. Private*, pg. 654
BRING CARGO/BRING FRIGO—See Posten Norge AS; *Int'l*, pg. 5939
BRING FRIGOSCANDIA AB—See Posten Norge AS; *Int'l*, pg. 5939
BRING FRIGOSCANDIA A/S—See Posten Norge AS; *Int'l*, pg. 5940
BRING FRIGOSCANDIA—See Posten Norge AS; *Int'l*, pg. 5939
BRING LOGISTICS NETHERLANDS B.V.—See Posten Norge AS; *Int'l*, pg. 5940
BRINGSPRING SCIENCE & TECHNOLOGY CO., LTD.; *Int'l*, pg. 1164
BRING TRANSPORT INDUSTRIES PTY LTD—See CTI Logistics Limited; *Int'l*, pg. 1871
BRING UP CO.,LTD.—See Cybozu Inc.; *Int'l*, pg. 1894
BRINKAB AB—See Veidekke ASA; *Int'l*, pg. 8148
BRINK CLIMATE SYSTEMS B.V.—See CENTROTEC SE; *Int'l*, pg. 1414
BRINK CLIMATE SYSTEMS DEUTSCHLAND GMBH—See CENTROTEC SE; *Int'l*, pg. 1414
BRINK CLIMATE SYSTEMS FRANCE S.A.S.—See CENTROTEC SE; *Int'l*, pg. 1414
BRINK CONSTRUCTORS, INC.; *U.S. Private*, pg. 654
BRINKER CAPITAL HOLDINGS INC.; *U.S. Private*, pg. 654
BRINKER INTERNATIONAL, INC.; *U.S. Public*, pg. 384
BRINKER LOUISIANA, INC.—See Brinker International, Inc.; *U.S. Public*, pg. 384
BRINKER RESTAURANT CORPORATION—See Brinker International, Inc.; *U.S. Public*, pg. 384
BRINK FOREST PRODUCTS LTD.—See Brink Group of Companies; *Int'l*, pg. 1164
BRINK GROUP OF COMPANIES; *Int'l*, pg. 1164
BRINK-INNOSOURCE GMBH—See CENTROTEC SE; *Int'l*, pg. 1414
BRINKLEY FINANCIAL GROUP; *U.S. Private*, pg. 655
BRINKMAN INTERNATIONAL GROUP, INC.; *U.S. Private*, pg. 655
BRINKMANN CORP.; *U.S. Private*, pg. 655
BRINKMANN INSTRUMENTS (CANADA), LTD.—See Eppendorf AG; *Int'l*, pg. 2464
BRINKMANN INSTRUMENTS, INC.—See Eppendorf AG; *Int'l*, pg. 2464
BRINKMAN PRODUCTS INC—See Brinkman International Group, Inc.; *U.S. Private*, pg. 655
BRINKMERE CAPITAL PARTNERS LLC; *U.S. Private*, pg. 655
BRINK'S ARGENTINA S.A.—See The Brink's Company; *U.S. Public*, pg. 2042
BRINK'S AUSTRALIA PTY. LTD—See The Brink's Company; *U.S. Public*, pg. 2042
BRINK'S BETEILIGUNGSGESELLSCHAFT MBH—See The Brink's Company; *U.S. Public*, pg. 2042
BRINK'S BOLIVIA S.A.—See The Brink's Company; *U.S. Public*, pg. 2042

THE BRINK'S COMPANY

BRINK'S CANADA LIMITED—See The Brink's Company; *U.S. Public*, pg. 2042
BRINK'S CASH SERVICES (IRELAND) LIMITED—See The Brink's Company; *U.S. Public*, pg. 2042
BRINK'S CASH & VALUABLE SERVICES S.A.—See The Brink's Company; *U.S. Public*, pg. 2041
BRINK'S CHILE, S.A.—See The Brink's Company; *U.S. Public*, pg. 2042
BRINK'S C.L. HUNGARIA LIMITED—See The Brink's Company; *U.S. Public*, pg. 2042
THE BRINK'S COMPANY; *U.S. Public*, pg. 2041
BRINK'S CYPRUS (PRIVATE SECURITY SERVICES) LIMITED—See The Brink's Company; *U.S. Public*, pg. 2042
BRINK'S DIAMOND & JEWELLERY SERVICES (INTERNATIONAL) LTD.—See The Brink's Company; *U.S. Public*, pg. 2042
BRINK'S DIAMOND & JEWELRY SERVICES BVBA—See The Brink's Company; *U.S. Public*, pg. 2042
BRINK'S EMEA SAS—See The Brink's Company; *U.S. Public*, pg. 2042
BRINK'S FAR EAST LIMITED—See The Brink's Company; *U.S. Public*, pg. 2042
BRINK'S GLOBAL HOLDINGS B.V.—See The Brink's Company; *U.S. Public*, pg. 2042
BRINK'S GLOBAL SERVICES ANTWERP BVBA—See The Brink's Company; *U.S. Public*, pg. 2042
BRINK'S GLOBAL SERVICES (BGS) BOTSWANA (PROPRIETARY) LIMITED—See The Brink's Company; *U.S. Public*, pg. 2042
BRINK'S GLOBAL SERVICES DEUTSCHLAND GMBH—See The Brink's Company; *U.S. Public*, pg. 2042
BRINK'S GLOBAL SERVICES FZE—See The Brink's Company; *U.S. Public*, pg. 2042
BRINK'S GLOBAL SERVICES INTERNATIONAL, INC.—See The Brink's Company; *U.S. Public*, pg. 2042
BRINK'S GLOBAL SERVICES KOREA LIMITED—See The Brink's Company; *U.S. Public*, pg. 2042
BRINK'S GLOBAL SERVICES KOREA LIMITED - YUNAN HOESA BRINK'S GLOBAL—See The Brink's Company; *U.S. Public*, pg. 2042
BRINK'S GLOBAL SERVICES POLAND SP.ZO.O.—See The Brink's Company; *U.S. Public*, pg. 2042
BRINK'S GLOBAL SERVICES—See The Brink's Company; *U.S. Public*, pg. 2042
BRINK'S GLOBAL SERVICES S.R.L.—See The Brink's Company; *U.S. Public*, pg. 2042
BRINK'S GUVENLIK HIZMETLERI ANONIM SIRKETI—See The Brink's Company; *U.S. Public*, pg. 2042
BRINK'S HONG KONG LIMITED—See The Brink's Company; *U.S. Public*, pg. 2042
BRINK'S, INCORPORATED—See The Brink's Company; *U.S. Public*, pg. 2042
BRINK'S INDIA PRIVATE LIMITED—See The Brink's Company; *U.S. Public*, pg. 2042
BRINK'S INTERNATIONAL HOLDINGS AG—See The Brink's Company; *U.S. Public*, pg. 2042
BRINK'S IRELAND LIMITED—See The Brink's Company; *U.S. Public*, pg. 2042
BRINK'S (ISRAEL) LIMITED—See The Brink's Company; *U.S. Public*, pg. 2042
BRINK'S JAPAN LIMITED—See The Brink's Company; *U.S. Public*, pg. 2042
BRINK'S LIMITED (BAHRAIN) EC—See The Brink's Company; *U.S. Public*, pg. 2042
BRINK'S LUXEMBOURG S.A.—See The Brink's Company; *U.S. Public*, pg. 2042
BRINKS MONGOLIA LLC—See The Brink's Company; *U.S. Public*, pg. 2043
BRINK'S NEDERLAND B.V.—See The Brink's Company; *U.S. Public*, pg. 2042
BRINK'S PUERTO RICO, INC.—See The Brink's Company; *U.S. Public*, pg. 2042
BRINK'S SECURITY INTERNATIONAL, INC.—See The Brink's Company; *U.S. Public*, pg. 2042
BRINK'S SECURITY SERVICES, B.V.—See The Brink's Company; *U.S. Public*, pg. 2042
BRINK'S SECURITY TRANSPORTATION (SHANGHAI) COMPANY LIMITED—See The Brink's Company; *U.S. Public*, pg. 2043
BRINK'S SINGAPORE PTE LTD.—See The Brink's Company; *U.S. Public*, pg. 2042
BRINK'S SOUTHERN AFRICA PTY LTD.—See The Brink's Company; *U.S. Public*, pg. 2043
BRINK'S TAIWAN SECURITY LIMITED—See The Brink's Company; *U.S. Public*, pg. 2043
BRINKSTER COMMUNICATIONS CORPORATION—See Trapp Technology, Inc.; *U.S. Private*, pg. 4212
BRINK'S (UK) LIMITED—See The Brink's Company; *U.S. Public*, pg. 2042
BRINK'S U.S.—See The Brink's Company; *U.S. Public*, pg. 2043
BRINK'S VIETNAM, INCORPORATED—See The Brink's Company; *U.S. Public*, pg. 2043
BRINK'S WORLDBRIDGE SECURE LOGISTICS CO., LTD.—See The Brink's Company; *U.S. Public*, pg. 2042

BRINLEY'S GRADING SERVICE, INC.

BRINLEY'S GRADING SERVICE, INC.; *U.S. Private*, pg. 655
BRINNO, INC.; *Int'l*, pg. 1164
BRIN NORTHWESTERN GLASS COMPANY INC.; *U.S. Private*, pg. 654
BRINOVA FASTIGHETER AB; *Int'l*, pg. 1164
BRINSON AUTO GROUP; *U.S. Private*, pg. 655
BRINTON MANOR, INC.—See Welltower Inc.; *U.S. Public*, pg. 2348
BRINTONS CARPETS ASIA PVT LTD.—See Argand Partners, LP; *U.S. Private*, pg. 319
BRINTONS CARPETS LIMITED—See Argand Partners, LP; *U.S. Private*, pg. 319
BRINTONS FRANCE S.A.R.L.—See Argand Partners, LP; *U.S. Private*, pg. 319
BRINTONS INDUSTRIA DE ALCATIFAS LDA.—See Argand Partners, LP; *U.S. Private*, pg. 319
BRINTONS PTY LTD—See Argand Partners, LP; *U.S. Private*, pg. 319
BRINTONS U.S. AXMINSTER, INC.—See Argand Partners, LP; *U.S. Private*, pg. 319
BRINVEST NV—See Ackermans & van Haaren NV; *Int'l*, pg. 104
BRINX RESOURCES LTD.; *U.S. Private*, pg. 655
BRINY MARINE SERVICES SDN BHD—See Keppel Corporation Limited; *Int'l*, pg. 4130
BRIO BENEFIT CONSULTING, INC.—See Genstar Capital, LLC; *U.S. Private*, pg. 1674
BRIOCHE DOREE—See Holding Le Duff SA; *Int'l*, pg. 3450
BRIO FREEHOLD, LLC—See GP Investments, Ltd.; *Int'l*, pg. 3045
BRIO MARLTON, LLC—See GP Investments, Ltd.; *Int'l*, pg. 3045
BRIONI SPA—See Kering S.A.; *Int'l*, pg. 4134
BRION TECHNOLOGIES, INC—See ASML Holding N.V.; *Int'l*, pg. 627
BRION TECHNOLOGIES KK—See ASML Holding N.V.; *Int'l*, pg. 627
BRION TECHNOLOGIES (SHENZHEN) CO., LTD.—See ASML Holding N.V.; *Int'l*, pg. 627
BRIO RETIREMENT LIVING (CHAPELTON) LIMITED—See Places for People Group Limited; *Int'l*, pg. 5888
BRIO RETIREMENT LIVING (HOLDINGS) LIMITED—See Places for People Group Limited; *Int'l*, pg. 5888
BRIOSCHI FINANZIARIA S.P.A.—See Bastogi S.p.A.; *Int'l*, pg. 888
BRIOSCHI INTERNATIONAL CORP.—See Brioschi Pharmaceuticals International, LLC; *U.S. Private*, pg. 655
BRIOSCHI PHARMACEUTICALS INTERNATIONAL, LLC; *U.S. Private*, pg. 655
BRIOTIX HEALTH, LIMITED PARTNERSHIP—See U.S. Physical Therapy, Inc.; *U.S. Public*, pg. 2214
BRIO TUSCAN GRILLE OF CHEROKEE, LLC—See GP Investments, Ltd.; *Int'l*, pg. 3045
BRIO TUSCAN GRILLE OF MARYLAND, INC—See GP Investments, Ltd.; *Int'l*, pg. 3045
BRIOVARX INFUSION SERVICES 101, INC.—See UnitedHealth Group Incorporated; *U.S. Public*, pg. 2239
BRIOVARX INFUSION SERVICES 102, LLC—See UnitedHealth Group Incorporated; *U.S. Public*, pg. 2239
BRIOVARX INFUSION SERVICES 103, LLC—See UnitedHealth Group Incorporated; *U.S. Public*, pg. 2239
BRIOVARX INFUSION SERVICES 200, INC.—See UnitedHealth Group Incorporated; *U.S. Public*, pg. 2239
BRIOVARX INFUSION SERVICES 201, INC.—See UnitedHealth Group Incorporated; *U.S. Public*, pg. 2239
BRIOVARX INFUSION SERVICES 202, INC.—See UnitedHealth Group Incorporated; *U.S. Public*, pg. 2239
BRIOVARX INFUSION SERVICES 203, INC.—See UnitedHealth Group Incorporated; *U.S. Public*, pg. 2239
BRIOVARX INFUSION SERVICES 207, INC.—See UnitedHealth Group Incorporated; *U.S. Public*, pg. 2239
BRIOVARX INFUSION SERVICES 208, INC.—See UnitedHealth Group Incorporated; *U.S. Public*, pg. 2239
BRIOVARX INFUSION SERVICES 302, LLC—See UnitedHealth Group Incorporated; *U.S. Public*, pg. 2239
BRIOVARX INFUSION SERVICES 308, LLC—See UnitedHealth Group Incorporated; *U.S. Public*, pg. 2239
BRIOVARX INFUSION SERVICES 402, LLC—See UnitedHealth Group Incorporated; *U.S. Public*, pg. 2239
BRIOVARX INFUSION SERVICES 403, LLC—See UnitedHealth Group Incorporated; *U.S. Public*, pg. 2239
BRIOVARX INFUSION SERVICES 404, LLC—See UnitedHealth Group Incorporated; *U.S. Public*, pg. 2239
BRIOVARX, LLC—See UnitedHealth Group Incorporated; *U.S. Public*, pg. 2239
BRIOVARX OF CALIFORNIA, INC.—See UnitedHealth Group Incorporated; *U.S. Public*, pg. 2239
BRIOVARX OF FLORIDA, INC.—See UnitedHealth Group Incorporated; *U.S. Public*, pg. 2239
BRIOVARX OF INDIANA, LLC—See UnitedHealth Group Incorporated; *U.S. Public*, pg. 2239
BRIOVARX OF LOUISIANA, INC.—See UnitedHealth Group Incorporated; *U.S. Public*, pg. 2239
BRIOVARX OF MAINE, INC.—See UnitedHealth Group Incorporated; *U.S. Public*, pg. 2247
BRIOVARX OF MASSACHUSETTS, LLC—See UnitedHealth Group Incorporated; *U.S. Public*, pg. 2239
BRIOVARX OF NEVADA, LLC—See UnitedHealth Group Incorporated; *U.S. Public*, pg. 2239
BRIOVARX OF NEW YORK, INC.—See UnitedHealth Group Incorporated; *U.S. Public*, pg. 2239
BRIOVARX OF TEXAS, INC.—See UnitedHealth Group Incorporated; *U.S. Public*, pg. 2239
BRIOX AB; *Int'l*, pg. 1164
BRIPANEL INDUSTRIES SDN. BHD.—See Dominant Enterprise Berhad; *Int'l*, pg. 2161
BRIQ PROPERTIES REIC; *Int'l*, pg. 1164
BRI REMITTANCE CO. LTD.—See PT Bank Rakyat Indonesia (Persero) Tbk; *Int'l*, pg. 6028
BRISA ASSISTENCIA RODOVIARIA, S.A.—See APG Asset Management NV; *Int'l*, pg. 512
BRISA ASSISTENCIA RODOVIARIA, S.A.—See National Pension Service of Korea; *Int'l*, pg. 5162
BRISA ASSISTENCIA RODOVIARIA, S.A.—See Swiss Life Holding; *Int'l*, pg. 7369
BRISA AUTO-ESTRADAS DE PORTUGAL, S.A.—See APG Asset Management NV; *Int'l*, pg. 512
BRISA AUTO-ESTRADAS DE PORTUGAL, S.A.—See National Pension Service of Korea; *Int'l*, pg. 5162
BRISA AUTO-ESTRADAS DE PORTUGAL, S.A.—See Swiss Life Holding; *Int'l*, pg. 7369
BRISA BRIDGESTONE SABANCI LASTIK SANAYI VE TICARET A.S.—See Bridgestone Corporation; *Int'l*, pg. 1159
BRISA BRIDGESTONE SABANCI LASTIK SANAYI VE TICARET A.S.—See Haci Omer Sabanci Holding A.S.; *Int'l*, pg. 3203
BRISA GROUP S.A.—See Jose de Mello, SGPS, S.A.; *Int'l*, pg. 4001
BRISA INTERNACIONAL, SGPS, S.A.—See APG Asset Management NV; *Int'l*, pg. 512
BRISA INTERNACIONAL, SGPS, S.A.—See National Pension Service of Korea; *Int'l*, pg. 5162
BRISA INTERNACIONAL, SGPS, S.A.—See Swiss Life Holding; *Int'l*, pg. 7369
BRISA NORTH AMERICA, INC—See APG Asset Management NV; *Int'l*, pg. 512
BRISA NORTH AMERICA, INC—See National Pension Service of Korea; *Int'l*, pg. 5162
BRISA NORTH AMERICA, INC—See Swiss Life Holding; *Int'l*, pg. 7369
BRISA O&M, S.A.—See APG Asset Management NV; *Int'l*, pg. 512
BRISA O&M, S.A.—See National Pension Service of Korea; *Int'l*, pg. 5162
BRISA O&M, S.A.—See Swiss Life Holding; *Int'l*, pg. 7369
BRISA - SERVICOS VIARIOS, SGPS, S.A.—See APG Asset Management NV; *Int'l*, pg. 512
BRISA - SERVICOS VIARIOS, SGPS, S.A.—See National Pension Service of Korea; *Int'l*, pg. 5162
BRISA - SERVICOS VIARIOS, SGPS, S.A.—See Swiss Life Holding; *Int'l*, pg. 7369
BRISA—See Arcus Infrastructure Partners LLP; *Int'l*, pg. 552
BRISA UNITED STATES, LLC—See APG Asset Management NV; *Int'l*, pg. 512
BRISA UNITED STATES, LLC—See National Pension Service of Korea; *Int'l*, pg. 5162
BRISA UNITED STATES, LLC—See Swiss Life Holding; *Int'l*, pg. 7369
BRISBANE AIRPORT FUEL SERVICES PTY LTD—See Ampol Limited; *Int'l*, pg. 436
BRISBANE BMW BODYSHOP PTY. LTD.—See Sime Darby Berhad; *Int'l*, pg. 6928
BRISBANE BRONCOS LIMITED—See News Corporation; *U.S. Public*, pg. 1520
BRISBANE BRONCOS MANAGEMENT CORPORATION PTY. LTD.—See News Corporation; *U.S. Public*, pg. 1520
BRISBANE BRONCOS RUGBY LEAGUE CLUB PTY. LTD.—See News Corporation; *U.S. Public*, pg. 1520
BRISBANE LODGING, L.P.—See Stonebridge Realty Advisors, Inc.; *U.S. Private*, pg. 3827
BRISBANE PRIVATE HOSPITAL PTY. LTD.—See Brookfield Corporation; *Int'l*, pg. 1176
BRISBANE WATERS ADMINISTRATION PTY. LTD.—See Brookfield Corporation; *Int'l*, pg. 1176
BRISBANE WATERS EQUITIES PTY. LTD.—See Brookfield Corporation; *Int'l*, pg. 1176
BRISCO APPAREL CO. INC.; *U.S. Private*, pg. 655
BRISCOE GROUP LIMITED; *Int'l*, pg. 1164
BRISCOE PROPERTIES LIMITED—See R. T. Briscoe (Nigeria) Plc; *Int'l*, pg. 6170
BRISCOE PROTECTIVE SYSTEMS, INC.—See Pye-Barker Fire & Safety, LLC; *U.S. Private*, pg. 3309
BRISCOES (NEW ZEALAND) LIMITED—See Briscoe Group Limited; *Int'l*, pg. 1164
BRISCOE TIMBER LIMITED—See EAC Invest AS; *Int'l*, pg. 2261
BRISCON ELECTRIC MANUFACTURING CORPORATION—See nVent Electric plc; *Int'l*, pg. 5498
BRISKHEAT CORPORATION HK LIMITED—See NIBE Industrier AB; *Int'l*, pg. 5260
BRISKHEAT CORPORATION—See NIBE Industrier AB; *Int'l*, pg. 5260
BRISKHEAT SHENZHEN TRADING COMPANY LIMITED—See NIBE Industrier AB; *Int'l*, pg. 5260
BRISKHEAT TECHNOLOGY COMPANY CO. LTD.—See NIBE Industrier AB; *Int'l*, pg. 5260
BRISK WATERPROOFING COMPANY—See Western Construction Group; *U.S. Private*, pg. 4492
BRISSET BEER INTERNATIONAL, INC.; *Int'l*, pg. 1164
BRISTAN GROUP LTD.—See Masco Corporation; *U.S. Public*, pg. 1391
BRI-STEEL CORPORATION—See Bri-Chem Corp.; *Int'l*, pg. 1151
BRISTILE GUARDIANS PTY LTD.—See Brickworks Limited; *Int'l*, pg. 1152
BRISTILE LTD.—See Brickworks Limited; *Int'l*, pg. 1152
BRISTILE OPERATIONS PTY LTD.—See Brickworks Limited; *Int'l*, pg. 1152
BRISTILE ROOFING (EAST COAST) PTY LTD.—See Brickworks Limited; *Int'l*, pg. 1152
BRISTILE ROOFING PTY. LTD.—See Brickworks Limited; *Int'l*, pg. 1152
BRISTLECONE ADVISORS; *U.S. Private*, pg. 655
BRISTLECONE GMBH—See Mahindra & Mahindra Limited; *Int'l*, pg. 4645
BRISTLECONE INC—See Mahindra & Mahindra Limited; *Int'l*, pg. 4645
BRISTLECONE INDIA LIMITED—See Mahindra & Mahindra Limited; *Int'l*, pg. 4645
BRISTLECONE INTERNATIONAL AG—See Mahindra & Mahindra Limited; *Int'l*, pg. 4645
BRISTLECONE LIMITED—See Mahindra & Mahindra Limited; *Int'l*, pg. 4645
BRISTLECONE (MALAYSIA) SDN BHD—See Mahindra & Mahindra Limited; *Int'l*, pg. 4645
BRISTLECONE (SINGAPORE) PTE. LIMITED—See Mahindra & Mahindra Limited; *Int'l*, pg. 4645
BRISTLECONE (UK) LIMITED—See Mahindra & Mahindra Limited; *Int'l*, pg. 4645
BRISTOL AEROSPACE LIMITED—See Magellan Aerospace Corporation; *Int'l*, pg. 4637
BRISTOL AIRPORT LIMITED—See Ontario Teachers' Pension Plan; *Int'l*, pg. 5587
BRISTOL BABCOCK AB—See Emerson Electric Co.; *U.S. Public*, pg. 748
BRISTOL BAY ECONOMIC DEVELOPMENT CORPORATION; *U.S. Private*, pg. 655
BRISTOL BAY NATIVE CORPORATION; *U.S. Private*, pg. 655
BRISTOL BAY PRODUCTIONS, LLC—See The Anschutz Corporation; *U.S. Private*, pg. 3987
BRISTOL BAY RESOURCE SOLUTIONS, LLC—See Bristol Bay Native Corporation; *U.S. Private*, pg. 655
BRISTOL BROADCASTING CO. INC.; *U.S. Private*, pg. 656
BRISTOL COMMUNITY ORGANIZATION, INC.—See Human Resources Agency of New Britain, Inc.; *U.S. Private*, pg. 2006
BRISTOL COMPRESSORS INTERNATIONAL, INC.—See Garrison Investment Group LP; *U.S. Private*, pg. 1645
BRISTOL COUNTY SAVINGS BANK; *U.S. Private*, pg. 656
BRISTOL DEVELOPMENT LLC; *U.S. Private*, pg. 656
BRISTOL ENVIRONMENTAL ENGINEERING SERVICES CORPORATION—See Bristol Bay Native Corporation; *U.S. Private*, pg. 655
BRISTOL EXCHANGE—See Koninklijke KPN N.V.; *Int'l*, pg. 4267
BRISTOL FIBERLITE INDUSTRIES; *U.S. Private*, pg. 656
BRISTOL FUEL SYSTEMS, LLC—See Bristol Bay Native Corporation; *U.S. Private*, pg. 656
BRISTOL GENERAL CONTRACTORS, LLC—See Bristol Bay Native Corporation; *U.S. Private*, pg. 656
BRISTOL GROUP - HALIFAX—See Bristol Group; *Int'l*, pg. 1164
BRISTOL GROUP; *Int'l*, pg. 1164
BRISTOL HERALD COURIER—See Lee Enterprises, Incorporated; *U.S. Public*, pg. 1298
BRISTOL HONDA—See Honda Motor Co., Ltd.; *Int'l*, pg. 3462
BRISTOL HOSPICE, LLC—See Webster Equity Partners, LLC; *U.S. Private*, pg. 4467
BRISTOL ID TECHNOLOGIES, INC.; *U.S. Private*, pg. 656
BRISTOL INDUSTRIES LLC—See Tinicum Enterprises, Inc.; *U.S. Private*, pg. 4174
BRISTOL INVESTMENTS, LTD.; *U.S. Private*, pg. 656
BRISTOL MANAGEMENT CENTRE LIMITED—See KBR, Inc.; *U.S. Public*, pg. 1215
BRISTOL METALS, LLC—See Ascent Industries Co.; *U.S. Public*, pg. 210
BRISTOL MOTOR SPEEDWAY—See Sonic Financial Corporation; *U.S. Private*, pg. 3713
BRISTOL-MYERS DE VENEZUELA, S.A.—See Bristol-Myers Squibb Company; *U.S. Public*, pg. 384
BRISTOL-MYERS K.K.—See Bristol-Myers Squibb Company; *U.S. Public*, pg. 384
BRISTOL-MYERS PHARMACEUTICAL—See Bristol-Myers Squibb Company; *U.S. Public*, pg. 384

COMPANY NAME INDEX

BRISTOL-MYERS SQUIBB AB—See Bristol-Myers Squibb Company; *U.S. Public*, pg. 384
BRISTOL-MYERS SQUIBB AG—See Bristol-Myers Squibb Company; *U.S. Public*, pg. 385
BRISTOL-MYERS SQUIBB AKTIEBOLAG—See Bristol-Myers Squibb Company; *U.S. Public*, pg. 385
BRISTOL-MYERS SQUIBB ARGENTINA S.R.L.—See Bristol-Myers Squibb Company; *U.S. Public*, pg. 385
BRISTOL-MYERS SQUIBB AUSTRALIA PTY. LTD.—See Bristol-Myers Squibb Company; *U.S. Public*, pg. 385
BRISTOL-MYERS SQUIBB BELGIUM S.A.—See Bristol-Myers Squibb Company; *U.S. Public*, pg. 385
BRISTOL-MYERS SQUIBB BUSINESS SERVICES LIMITED—See Bristol-Myers Squibb Company; *U.S. Public*, pg. 385
BRISTOL-MYERS SQUIBB B.V.—See Bristol-Myers Squibb Company; *U.S. Public*, pg. 385
BRISTOL-MYERS SQUIBB CANADA CO.—See Bristol-Myers Squibb Company; *U.S. Public*, pg. 385
BRISTOL-MYERS SQUIBB CANADA INTERNATIONAL LIMITED—See Bristol-Myers Squibb Company; *U.S. Public*, pg. 385
BRISTOL-MYERS SQUIBB COMPANY - LAWRENCEVILLE R&D FACILITY—See Bristol-Myers Squibb Company; *U.S. Public*, pg. 385
BRISTOL-MYERS SQUIBB COMPANY; *U.S. Public*, pg. 384
BRISTOL-MYERS SQUIBB COMPANY - WALLINGFORD R&D FACILITY—See Bristol-Myers Squibb Company; *U.S. Public*, pg. 385
BRISTOL-MYERS SQUIBB DE GUATEMALA, S.A.—See Bristol-Myers Squibb Company; *U.S. Public*, pg. 385
BRISTOL-MYERS SQUIBB DENMARK FILIAL OF BRISTOL-MYERS SQUIBB AB—See Bristol-Myers Squibb Company; *U.S. Public*, pg. 385
BRISTOL-MYERS SQUIBB DENMARK—See Bristol-Myers Squibb Company; *U.S. Public*, pg. 385
BRISTOL-MYERS SQUIBB FARMACEUTICA LTDA—See Bristol-Myers Squibb Company; *U.S. Public*, pg. 385
BRISTOL-MYERS SQUIBB FARMACEUTICA PORTUGUESA S.A.—See Bristol-Myers Squibb Company; *U.S. Public*, pg. 385
BRISTOL-MYERS SQUIBB GES. M.B.H.—See Bristol-Myers Squibb Company; *U.S. Public*, pg. 385
BRISTOL-MYERS SQUIBB GESMBH.—See Bristol-Myers Squibb Company; *U.S. Public*, pg. 385
BRISTOL-MYERS SQUIBB GMBH—See Bristol-Myers Squibb Company; *U.S. Public*, pg. 385
BRISTOL-MYERS SQUIBB HOLDINGS GERMANY VERWALTUNGS GMBH—See Bristol-Myers Squibb Company; *U.S. Public*, pg. 385
BRISTOL-MYERS SQUIBB (HONG KONG) LIMITED—See Bristol-Myers Squibb Company; *U.S. Public*, pg. 384
BRISTOL-MYERS SQUIBB ILACLARI, INC.—See Bristol-Myers Squibb Company; *U.S. Public*, pg. 385
BRISTOL-MYERS SQUIBB INDIA PVT. LTD.—See Bristol-Myers Squibb Company; *U.S. Public*, pg. 385
BRISTOL-MYERS SQUIBB (ISRAEL) LTD—See Bristol-Myers Squibb Company; *U.S. Public*, pg. 384
BRISTOL-MYERS SQUIBB K.K.—See Bristol-Myers Squibb Company; *U.S. Public*, pg. 385
BRISTOL-MYERS SQUIBB LIMITED LIABILITY COMPANY—See Bristol-Myers Squibb Company; *U.S. Public*, pg. 385
BRISTOL-MYERS SQUIBB MARKETING SERVICES S.R.L.—See Bristol-Myers Squibb Company; *U.S. Public*, pg. 385
BRISTOL-MYERS SQUIBB MARKETING SERVICES S.R.L.—See Bristol-Myers Squibb Company; *U.S. Public*, pg. 385
BRISTOL-MYERS SQUIBB MIDDLE EAST & AFRICA FZ-LLC—See Bristol-Myers Squibb Company; *U.S. Public*, pg. 385
BRISTOL-MYERS SQUIBB NORWAY LTD.—See Bristol-Myers Squibb Company; *U.S. Public*, pg. 385
BRISTOL-MYERS SQUIBB (NZ) LIMITED—See Bristol-Myers Squibb Company; *U.S. Public*, pg. 384
BRISTOL-MYERS SQUIBB PERU S.A.—See Bristol-Myers Squibb Company; *U.S. Public*, pg. 385
BRISTOL-MYERS SQUIBB PHARMACEUTICALS LIMITED—See Bristol-Myers Squibb Company; *U.S. Public*, pg. 385
BRISTOL-MYERS SQUIBB PHARMACEUTICALS UNLIMITED COMPANY—See Bristol-Myers Squibb Company; *U.S. Public*, pg. 385
BRISTOL-MYERS SQUIBB PHARMA (THAILAND) CO. LTD.—See Bristol-Myers Squibb Company; *U.S. Public*, pg. 385
BRISTOL-MYERS SQUIBB POLSKA SP.Z.O.O.—See Bristol-Myers Squibb Company; *U.S. Public*, pg. 385
BRISTOL-MYERS SQUIBB PUERTO RICO, INC. - HUMACAO PLANT—See Bristol-Myers Squibb Company; *U.S. Public*, pg. 385
BRISTOL-MYERS SQUIBB PUERTO RICO, INC. - MANATI PLANT—See Bristol-Myers Squibb Company; *U.S. Public*, pg. 385
BRISTOL-MYERS SQUIBB SARL—See Bristol-Myers Squibb Company; *U.S. Public*, pg. 385

BRISTOL-MYERS SQUIBB S.A.—See Bristol-Myers Squibb Company; *U.S. Public*, pg. 385
BRISTOL-MYERS SQUIBB SA—See Bristol-Myers Squibb Company; *U.S. Public*, pg. 385
BRISTOL-MYERS SQUIBB, S.A.U.—See Bristol-Myers Squibb Company; *U.S. Public*, pg. 385
BRISTOL-MYERS SQUIBB SERVICES SP. Z O.O.—See Bristol-Myers Squibb Company; *U.S. Public*, pg. 385
BRISTOL-MYERS SQUIBB (SINGAPORE) PTE. LIMITED—See Bristol-Myers Squibb Company; *U.S. Public*, pg. 384
BRISTOL-MYERS SQUIBB SPOL. S R.O.—See Bristol-Myers Squibb Company; *U.S. Public*, pg. 385
BRISTOL-MYERS SQUIBB S.R.L.—See Bristol-Myers Squibb Company; *U.S. Public*, pg. 385
BRISTOL-MYERS SQUIBB (TAIWAN) LTD.—See Bristol-Myers Squibb Company; *U.S. Public*, pg. 384
BRISTOL-MYERS SQUIBB TRUSTEES LTD.—See Bristol-Myers Squibb Company; *U.S. Public*, pg. 385
THE BRISTOL NUFFIELD HOSPITAL—See Nuffield Health; *Int'l*, pg. 5487
THE BRISTOL NUFFIELD HOSPITAL—See Nuffield Health; *Int'l*, pg. 5487
BRISTOL OAKBROOK TENANT COMPANY—See InterContinental Hotels Group PLC; *Int'l*, pg. 3737
BRISTOL OFFICE SUPPLY INC.—See R.J. Young Co., Inc.; *U.S. Private*, pg. 3337
BRISTOL SPINE CENTER, LLC—See Bain Capital, LP; *U.S. Private*, pg. 445
BRISTOL STREET GROUP LIMITED—See Vertu Motors plc; *Int'l*, pg. 8175
BRISTOL TOOL & GAUGE INTERNATIONAL GMBH—See Absolent Air Care Group AB; *Int'l*, pg. 70
BRISTOL VIRGINIA UTILITIES; *U.S. Private*, pg. 657
BRISTOL WATER PLC—See Pennon Group PLC; *Int'l*, pg. 5787
BRISTOL WEST INSURANCE GROUP—See Zurich Insurance Group Limited; *Int'l*, pg. 8698
BRISTOW ACADEMY, INC.—See Bristow Group, Inc.; *U.S. Public*, pg. 387
BRISTOW CARIBBEAN LTD.—See Bristow Group, Inc.; *U.S. Public*, pg. 387
BRISTOW GROUP, INC.; *U.S. Public*, pg. 387
BRISTOW HELICOPTER GROUP LIMITED—See Bristow Group, Inc.; *U.S. Public*, pg. 387
BRISTOW HELICOPTERS (AUSTRALIA PTY.) LTD—See Bristow Group, Inc.; *U.S. Public*, pg. 387
BRISTOW HOLDINGS U.S. INC.—See Bristow Group, Inc.; *U.S. Public*, pg. 387
BRISTOW MANAGEMENT SERVICES PTY LIMITED—See Bristow Group, Inc.; *U.S. Public*, pg. 387
BRISTOW NORWAY AS—See Bristow Group, Inc.; *U.S. Public*, pg. 387
BRISTOW TRAVEL PROPRIETARY LIMITED—See Bristow Group, Inc.; *U.S. Public*, pg. 387
BRISTOW U.S. LLC—See Bristow Group, Inc.; *U.S. Public*, pg. 387
BRITAIN CHEVROLET, INC.—See General Motors Company; *U.S. Public*, pg. 923
BRIT AIR—See Air France-KLM S.A.; *Int'l*, pg. 237
BRITAM ASSET MANAGERS (KENYA) LIMITED—See Britam Holdings Plc; *Int'l*, pg. 1164
BRITAM COMPANHIA DE SEGUROS DE MOCAMBIQUE SA—See Britam Holdings Plc; *Int'l*, pg. 1164
BRITAM - COMPANHIA DE SEGUROS DE MOZAMBIQUE S.A.—See Britam Holdings Plc; *Int'l*, pg. 1164
BRITAM GENERAL INSURANCE COMPANY (KENYA) LIMITED—See Britam Holdings Plc; *Int'l*, pg. 1164
BRITAM HOLDINGS PLC; *Int'l*, pg. 1164
BRITAM INSURANCE COMPANY LIMITED—See Britam Holdings Plc; *Int'l*, pg. 1165
BRITAM INSURANCE COMPANY LIMITED—See Britam Holdings Plc; *Int'l*, pg. 1165
BRITAM INSURANCE COMPANY (RWANDA) LIMITED—See Britam Holdings Plc; *Int'l*, pg. 1165
BRITAM INSURANCE COMPANY (TANZANIA) LIMITED—See Britam Holdings Plc; *Int'l*, pg. 1165
BRITAM INSURANCE COMPANY (UGANDA) LIMITED—See Britam Holdings Plc; *Int'l*, pg. 1165
BRITAM INSURANCE (TANZANIA) LIMITED—See Britam Holdings Plc; *Int'l*, pg. 1164
BRITANNIA CONSTRUCTION LIMITED—See Walter Lilly & Co Ltd.; *Int'l*, pg. 8336
BRITANNIA INDUSTRIES LTD.—See The Wadia Group; *Int'l*, pg. 7698
BRITANNIA JINKY JERSEY LIMITED—See Northern Trust Group Ltd.; *Int'l*, pg. 5445
BRITANNIA KITCHEN VENTILATION LIMITED—See The Middleby Corporation; *U.S. Public*, pg. 2115
BRITANNIA LIFE SCIENCES INC.; *Int'l*, pg. 1165
BRITANNIA LIMITED—See Deutsche Bank Aktiengesellschaft; *Int'l*, pg. 2055
BRITANNIA MINING INC.; *U.S. Public*, pg. 388
BRITANNIA MUSIC COMPANY LTD.—See Universal Music Group N.V.; *Int'l*, pg. 8079
BRITANNIA PHARMACEUTICALS LTD.—See Bain Capital, LP; *U.S. Private*, pg. 443

BRITANNIA PHARMACEUTICALS LTD.—See Cinven Limited; *Int'l*, pg. 1613
BRITANNIA REFINED METALS LIMITED—See Glencore plc; *Int'l*, pg. 2990
BRITANNIA SUPERFINE LTD.; *Int'l*, pg. 1165
BRITA (USA), INC.—See The Clorox Company; *U.S. Public*, pg. 2062
BRITAX AUTOMOTIVE EQUIPMENT PTY—See Ecco Safety Group; *U.S. Private*, pg. 1326
BRITAX AUTOZUBEHOR GMBH—See Ecco Safety Group; *U.S. Private*, pg. 1326
BRITAX CHILDCARE HONG KONG LTD.—See Nordic Capital AB; *Int'l*, pg. 5419
BRITAX CHILDCARE LTD.—See Nordic Capital AB; *Int'l*, pg. 5419
BRITAX CHILDCARE NZ LTD.—See Nordic Capital AB; *Int'l*, pg. 5419
BRITAX CHILDCARE PTY. LTD.—See Nordic Capital AB; *Int'l*, pg. 5419
BRITAX CHILD SAFETY, INC.—See Nordic Capital AB; *Int'l*, pg. 5419
BRITAX EXCELSIOR LIMITED—See Nordic Capital AB; *Int'l*, pg. 5419
BRITAX NORDISKA BARN AB—See Nordic Capital AB; *Int'l*, pg. 5419
BRITAX PMG LIMITED—See Ecco Safety Group; *U.S. Private*, pg. 1326
BRITAX POHJOLAN LAPSET OY—See Nordic Capital AB; *Int'l*, pg. 5419
BRITAX PSV WYPERS LTD.—See Ecco Safety Group; *U.S. Private*, pg. 1326
BRITAX ROEMER KINDERSICHERHEIT GMBH—See Nordic Capital AB; *Int'l*, pg. 5419
BRITAX SIGNALISATION SAS—See Ecco Safety Group; *U.S. Private*, pg. 1326
BRITCON; *Int'l*, pg. 1165
BRITE:BILL EMPLOYMENT COMPANY LIMITED—See Amdocs Limited; *Int'l*, pg. 420
BRITE:BILL GROUP LIMITED—See Amdocs Limited; *Int'l*, pg. 420
BRITE:BILL LIMITED—See Amdocs Limited; *Int'l*, pg. 420
BRITECH, INC.—See Cerberus Capital Management, L.P.; *U.S. Private*, pg. 838
BRITF COMPUTERS; *U.S. Private*, pg. 657
BRITE-LINE TECHNOLOGIES, INC.—See Independence Capital Partners, LLC; *U.S. Private*, pg. 2057
BRITEPAK TRADING (PTY) LTD—See Transpaco Ltd.; *Int'l*, pg. 7904
BRITESKIES, LLC; *U.S. Private*, pg. 657
BRITE-STRIKE TACTICAL ILLUMINATION PRODUCTS, INC.; *U.S. Public*, pg. 388
BRITE-TECH BERHAD; *Int'l*, pg. 1165
BRITE-TECH CORPORATION SDN. BERHAD—See Brite-Tech Berhad; *Int'l*, pg. 1165
BRIT GROUP SERVICES LIMITED—See Fairfax Financial Holdings Limited; *Int'l*, pg. 2606
BRITHOL MICHCOMA MOZAMBIQUE LIMITED; *Int'l*, pg. 1165
BRIT INSURANCE LIMITED—See Fairfax Financial Holdings Limited; *Int'l*, pg. 2606
BRITISH AMERICAN TOBACCO HOLDINGS (THE NETHERLANDS) B.V.—See British American Tobacco plc; *Int'l*, pg. 1165
BRITISH AGRICULTURAL SERVICES LIMITED—See Heidelberg Materials AG; *Int'l*, pg. 3309
BRITISH AIRWAYS - AUSTRALIA OFFICE—See International Consolidated Airlines Group S.A.; *Int'l*, pg. 3745
BRITISH AIRWAYS - GERMANY OFFICE—See International Consolidated Airlines Group S.A.; *Int'l*, pg. 3745
BRITISH AIRWAYS HOLIDAYS LIMITED—See International Consolidated Airlines Group S.A.; *Int'l*, pg. 3745
BRITISH AIRWAYS INTERIOR ENGINEERING LIMITED—See International Consolidated Airlines Group S.A.; *Int'l*, pg. 3745
BRITISH AIRWAYS MAINTENANCE CARDIFF LTD—See International Consolidated Airlines Group S.A.; *Int'l*, pg. 3745
BRITISH AIRWAYS PENSION TRUSTEES (NO 2) LIMITED—See International Consolidated Airlines Group S.A.; *Int'l*, pg. 3745
BRITISH AIRWAYS PLC—See International Consolidated Airlines Group S.A.; *Int'l*, pg. 3745
BRITISH AIRWAYS - US OFFICE—See International Consolidated Airlines Group S.A.; *Int'l*, pg. 3745
BRITISH AMERICAN INVESTMENT CO. (MTIUS) LTD.; *Int'l*, pg. 1165
BRITISH & AMERICAN INVESTMENT TRUST PLC; *Int'l*, pg. 1165
BRITISH AMERICAN TOBACCO - ALBANIA SH.P.K.—See British American Tobacco plc; *Int'l*, pg. 1166
BRITISH AMERICAN TOBACCO (ALGERIE) S.P.A.—See British American Tobacco plc; *Int'l*, pg. 1166
BRITISH AMERICAN TOBACCO ARGENTINA S.A.I.C.Y F.—See British American Tobacco plc; *Int'l*, pg. 1166
BRITISH AMERICAN TOBACCO AUSTRALASIA LTD.—See British American Tobacco plc; *Int'l*, pg. 1166
BRITISH AMERICAN TOBACCO AUSTRALIA LTD.—See British American Tobacco plc; *Int'l*, pg. 1166

BRITISH & AMERICAN INVESTMENT TRUST PLC

BRITISH AMERICAN TOBACCO (AUSTRIA) GMBH—See British American Tobacco plc; *Int'l*, pg. 1166
BRITISH AMERICAN TOBACCO BANGLADESH CO. LTD.—See British American Tobacco plc; *Int'l*, pg. 1166
BRITISH AMERICAN TOBACCO-B.A.T. ANGOLA, LIMITADA—See British American Tobacco plc; *Int'l*, pg. 1167
BRITISH AMERICAN TOBACCO BELGIUM SA/NV—See British American Tobacco plc; *Int'l*, pg. 1166
BRITISH AMERICAN TOBACCO BOTSWANA (PTY) LIMITED—See British American Tobacco plc; *Int'l*, pg. 1166
BRITISH AMERICAN TOBACCO (BRANDS) LTD.—See British American Tobacco plc; *Int'l*, pg. 1166
BRITISH AMERICAN TOBACCO (CAMBODIA) LIMITED—See British American Tobacco plc; *Int'l*, pg. 1166
BRITISH AMERICAN TOBACCO CAMEROUN S.A.—See British American Tobacco plc; *Int'l*, pg. 1166
BRITISH AMERICAN TOBACCO CHILE OPERACIONES S.A.—See British American Tobacco plc; *Int'l*, pg. 1166
BRITISH AMERICAN TOBACCO COLOMBIA S.A.S.—See British American Tobacco plc; *Int'l*, pg. 1166
BRITISH AMERICAN TOBACCO (CZECH REPUBLIC), S.R.O.—See British American Tobacco plc; *Int'l*, pg. 1166
BRITISH AMERICAN TOBACCO DEL PERU HOLDINGS S.A.—See British American Tobacco plc; *Int'l*, pg. 1167
BRITISH AMERICAN TOBACCO DENMARK—See British American Tobacco plc; *Int'l*, pg. 1166
BRITISH AMERICAN TOBACCO EGYPT LLC—See British American Tobacco plc; *Int'l*, pg. 1166
BRITISH AMERICAN TOBACCO ESPANA, S.A.—See British American Tobacco plc; *Int'l*, pg. 1166
BRITISH AMERICAN TOBACCO ESTONIA AS—See British American Tobacco plc; *Int'l*, pg. 1166
BRITISH AMERICAN TOBACCO (FIJI) MARKETING PTE LIMITED—See British American Tobacco plc; *Int'l*, pg. 1166
BRITISH AMERICAN TOBACCO FINANCE BV—See British American Tobacco plc; *Int'l*, pg. 1165
BRITISH AMERICAN TOBACCO FINLAND OY—See British American Tobacco plc; *Int'l*, pg. 1166
BRITISH AMERICAN TOBACCO FRANCE SAS—See British American Tobacco plc; *Int'l*, pg. 1166
BRITISH-AMERICAN TOBACCO (GERMANY) GMBH—See British American Tobacco plc; *Int'l*, pg. 1167
BRITISH AMERICAN TOBACCO (GLP) LTD.—See British American Tobacco plc; *Int'l*, pg. 1166
BRITISH AMERICAN TOBACCO HELLAS S.A.—See British American Tobacco plc; *Int'l*, pg. 1166
BRITISH-AMERICAN TOBACCO (HOLDINGS) LTD.—See British American Tobacco plc; *Int'l*, pg. 1167
BRITISH AMERICAN TOBACCO HOLDINGS SOUTH AFRICA (PTY) LTD.—See British American Tobacco plc; *Int'l*, pg. 1166
BRITISH AMERICAN TOBACCO HOLDINGS (THE NETHERLANDS) B.V.—See British American Tobacco plc; *Int'l*, pg. 1166
BRITISH AMERICAN TOBACCO (HONG KONG) LTD.—See British American Tobacco plc; *Int'l*, pg. 1166
BRITISH AMERICAN TOBACCO (INDUSTRIE) GMBH—See British American Tobacco plc; *Int'l*, pg. 1166
BRITISH AMERICAN TOBACCO INTERNATIONAL LTD.—See British American Tobacco plc; *Int'l*, pg. 1166
BRITISH AMERICAN TOBACCO (INVESTMENTS) LTD.—See British American Tobacco plc; *Int'l*, pg. 1166
BRITISH AMERICAN TOBACCO ITALIA S.P.A.—See British American Tobacco plc; *Int'l*, pg. 1166
BRITISH AMERICAN TOBACCO JAPAN, LTD.—See British American Tobacco plc; *Int'l*, pg. 1166
BRITISH AMERICAN TOBACCO KAZAKHSTAN TRADING LLP—See British American Tobacco plc; *Int'l*, pg. 1166
BRITISH AMERICAN TOBACCO KENYA PLC—See British American Tobacco plc; *Int'l*, pg. 1166
BRITISH AMERICAN TOBACCO KOREA LTD.—See British American Tobacco plc; *Int'l*, pg. 1167
BRITISH AMERICAN TOBACCO KOREA MANUFACTURING LTD.—See British American Tobacco plc; *Int'l*, pg. 1167
BRITISH AMERICAN TOBACCO KOSOVO SH.P.K.—See British American Tobacco plc; *Int'l*, pg. 1167
BRITISH AMERICAN TOBACCO (MALAWI) LIMITED—See British American Tobacco plc; *Int'l*, pg. 1166
BRITISH AMERICAN TOBACCO (MALAYSIA) BERHAD—See British American Tobacco plc; *Int'l*, pg. 1166
BRITISH AMERICAN TOBACCO (MALTA) LIMITED—See British American Tobacco plc; *Int'l*, pg. 1166
BRITISH AMERICAN TOBACCO MARKETING NIGERIA LIMITED—See British American Tobacco plc; *Int'l*, pg. 1167
BRITISH AMERICAN TOBACCO ME DMCC—See British American Tobacco plc; *Int'l*, pg. 1167
BRITISH AMERICAN TOBACCO MEXICO—See British American Tobacco plc; *Int'l*, pg. 1167

BRITISH AMERICAN TOBACCO-MOLDOVA S.R.L.—See British American Tobacco plc; *Int'l*, pg. 1167
BRITISH AMERICAN TOBACCO MOZAMBIQUE LIMITADA—See British American Tobacco plc; *Int'l*, pg. 1167
BRITISH AMERICAN TOBACCO MYANMAR LIMITED—See British American Tobacco plc; *Int'l*, pg. 1167
BRITISH AMERICAN TOBACCO NAMIBIA (PTY) LIMITED—See British American Tobacco plc; *Int'l*, pg. 1167
BRITISH AMERICAN TOBACCO NEDERLAND B.V.—See British American Tobacco plc; *Int'l*, pg. 1167
BRITISH AMERICAN TOBACCO (NEW ZEALAND) LTD.—See British American Tobacco plc; *Int'l*, pg. 1166
BRITISH AMERICAN TOBACCO NORWAY AS—See British American Tobacco plc; *Int'l*, pg. 1167
BRITISH AMERICAN TOBACCO PLC; *Int'l*, pg. 1165
BRITISH-AMERICAN TOBACCO POLSKA S.A.—See British American Tobacco plc; *Int'l*, pg. 1167
BRITISH AMERICAN TOBACCO POLSKA TRADING SP. Z.O.O.—See British American Tobacco plc; *Int'l*, pg. 1167
BRITISH AMERICAN TOBACCO RCI SARL—See British American Tobacco plc; *Int'l*, pg. 1167
BRITISH AMERICAN TOBACCO RESEARCH & DEVELOPMENT—See British American Tobacco plc; *Int'l*, pg. 1167
BRITISH AMERICAN TOBACCO (ROMANIA) TRADING SRL—See British American Tobacco plc; *Int'l*, pg. 1166
BRITISH AMERICAN TOBACCO SERVICES CONGO SARL—See British American Tobacco plc; *Int'l*, pg. 1167
BRITISH-AMERICAN TOBACCO (SINGAPORE) PTE. LTD.—See British American Tobacco plc; *Int'l*, pg. 1167
BRITISH AMERICAN TOBACCO SOUTH AFRICA—See British American Tobacco plc; *Int'l*, pg. 1167
BRITISH AMERICAN TOBACCO SWEDEN AB—See British American Tobacco plc; *Int'l*, pg. 1167
BRITISH AMERICAN TOBACCO SWITZERLAND SA—See British American Tobacco plc; *Int'l*, pg. 1167
BRITISH AMERICAN TOBACCO THE NETHERLANDS B.V.—See British American Tobacco plc; *Int'l*, pg. 1165
BRITISH-AMERICAN TOBACCO TRADING COMPANY FOREIGN PRIVATE TRADING UNITARY ENTERPRISE—See British American Tobacco plc; *Int'l*, pg. 1167
BRITISH AMERICAN TOBACCO TRADING EOOD—See British American Tobacco plc; *Int'l*, pg. 1167
BRITISH AMERICAN TOBACCO TUTUN MAMULLERI SANAYI VE TICARET A.S.—See British American Tobacco plc; *Int'l*, pg. 1167
BRITISH AMERICAN TOBACCO (UGANDA) LTD.—See British American Tobacco plc; *Int'l*, pg. 1166
BRITISH AMERICAN TOBACCO UK LTD.—See British American Tobacco plc; *Int'l*, pg. 1167
BRITISH AMERICAN TOBACCO VIETNAM LTD.—See British American Tobacco plc; *Int'l*, pg. 1167
BRITISH AMERICAN TOBACCO VRANJE A.D.—See British American Tobacco plc; *Int'l*, pg. 1167
BRITISH AMERICAN TOBACCO (ZAMBIA) PLC—See British American Tobacco plc; *Int'l*, pg. 1166
BRITISH AMERICAN TOBACCO ZIMBABWE (HOLDINGS) LIMITED—See British American Tobacco plc; *Int'l*, pg. 1167
BRITISH ARAB COMMERCIAL BANK LIMITED; *Int'l*, pg. 1168
BRITISH AVIATION INSURANCE COMPANY LIMITED—See Intact Financial Corporation; *Int'l*, pg. 3726
BRITISH AVIATION INSURANCE COMPANY LIMITED—See Tryg A/S; *Int'l*, pg. 7946
BRITISH BROADCASTING CORPORATION; *Int'l*, pg. 1168
BRITISH CAR AUCTIONS LIMITED—See TDR Capital LLP; *Int'l*, pg. 7493
BRITISH COLUMBIA FERRY SERVICES INC; *Int'l*, pg. 1169
BRITISH COLUMBIA INVESTMENT MANAGEMENT CORP.; *Int'l*, pg. 1169
BRITISH COLUMBIA LIFE AND CASUALTY COMPANY—See PBC Health Benefits Society; *Int'l*, pg. 5765
BRITISH COLUMBIA TRANSIT; *Int'l*, pg. 1171
BRITISH CONVERTING SOLUTIONS, LTD.; *Int'l*, pg. 1171
BRITISH ENGINES LTD.; *Int'l*, pg. 1171
BRITISH FILM INSTITUTE; *Int'l*, pg. 1171
BRITISH GAS SERVICES LIMITED—See Centrica plc; *Int'l*, pg. 1413
BRITISH GYPSUM-ISOVER LTD.—See Compagnie de Saint-Gobain SA; *Int'l*, pg. 1725
BRITISH GYPSUM LTD.—See Compagnie de Saint-Gobain SA; *Int'l*, pg. 1725
BRITISH INDUSTRIAL GASES LIMITED—See Linde plc; *Int'l*, pg. 4504
THE BRITISH INTERNATIONAL SCHOOL BRATISLAVA—See Canada Pension Plan Investment Board; *Int'l*, pg. 1281

CORPORATE AFFILIATIONS

THE BRITISH INTERNATIONAL SCHOOL BRATISLAVA—See EQT AB; *Int'l*, pg. 2470
THE BRITISH INTERNATIONAL SCHOOL BUDAPEST—See Canada Pension Plan Investment Board; *Int'l*, pg. 1281
THE BRITISH INTERNATIONAL SCHOOL BUDAPEST—See EQT AB; *Int'l*, pg. 2470
BRITISH INTERNATIONAL SCHOOL OF TBILISI LLC—See Georgia Capital PLC; *Int'l*, pg. 2939
THE BRITISH INTERNATIONAL SCHOOL SHANGHAI—See Canada Pension Plan Investment Board; *Int'l*, pg. 1281
THE BRITISH INTERNATIONAL SCHOOL SHANGHAI—See EQT AB; *Int'l*, pg. 2470
THE BRITISH LAND COMPANY PLC; *Int'l*, pg. 7628
THE BRITISH LAND CORPORATION LTD.—See The British Land Company PLC; *Int'l*, pg. 7628
BRITISH LAND DEVELOPMENTS LTD.—See The British Land Company PLC; *Int'l*, pg. 7628
BRITISH LAND FINANCING LTD.—See The British Land Company PLC; *Int'l*, pg. 7628
BRITISH LAND INVESTMENTS NETHERLANDS BV—See The British Land Company PLC; *Int'l*, pg. 7628
BRITISH LAND PROPERTIES LTD.—See The British Land Company PLC; *Int'l*, pg. 7628
BRITISH LAND RETAIL WAREHOUSES LIMITED—See The British Land Company PLC; *Int'l*, pg. 7628
THE BRITISH LIBRARY; *Int'l*, pg. 7628
BRITISH & MALAYAN TRUSTEES LIMITED; *Int'l*, pg. 1165
BRITISH MARINE MANAGERS LIMITED—See QBE Insurance Group Limited; *Int'l*, pg. 6136
BRITISH METAL CORPORATION (INDIA) PTE LTD—See Amalgamated Metal Corporation PLC; *Int'l*, pg. 408
BRITISH METAL TREATMENTS LIMITED—See Camellia Plc; *Int'l*, pg. 1271
BRITISH MIDLAND REGIONAL LTD.—See Sector Aviation Holdings Ltd. (SAH); *Int'l*, pg. 6673
BRITISH MOHAIR SPINNERS LIMITED—See Dewavrin Groupe; *Int'l*, pg. 2091
BRITISH MOTOR CAR DISTRIBUTORS LTD.; *U.S. Private*, pg. 657
BRITISH PAINTS CO., LTD.—See TOA Group Holding Co., Ltd.; *Int'l*, pg. 7769
BRITISH PATHE PLC—See Daily Mail & General Trust plc; *Int'l*, pg. 1937
THE BRITISH PEPPER & SPICE COMPANY LTD—See SHS Group, Ltd.; *Int'l*, pg. 6867
BRITISH PIPELINE AGENCY LTD.—See BP plc; *Int'l*, pg. 1129
BRITISH PIPELINE AGENCY LTD.—See Shell plc; *Int'l*, pg. 6799
BRITISH PIPE SUPPORTS (JINGJIANG) LIMITED—See Hill & Smith PLC; *Int'l*, pg. 3391
THE BRITISH PLASTICS FEDERATION; *Int'l*, pg. 7628
BRITISH POLAR ENGINES LIMITED—See Associated British Engineering plc; *Int'l*, pg. 648
BRITISH POLYTHENE INDUSTRIES LIMITED—See Berry Global Group, Inc; *U.S. Public*, pg. 322
BRITISH POLYTHENE LIMITED—See Berry Global Group, Inc; *U.S. Public*, pg. 322
BRITISH POTATO COUNCIL; *Int'l*, pg. 1171
BRITISH ROTOTHERM COMPANY LTD.; *Int'l*, pg. 1171
BRITISH SALT LTD.—See Tata Sons Limited; *Int'l*, pg. 7469
THE BRITISH SCHOOL SP. Z O.O.—See Canada Pension Plan Investment Board; *Int'l*, pg. 1281
THE BRITISH SCHOOL SP. Z O.O.—See EQT AB; *Int'l*, pg. 2470
BRITISH SMALLER COMPANIES VCT PLC; *Int'l*, pg. 1171
BRITISH STANDARDS INSTITUTION GROUP IBERIA SAU—See The British Standards Institution; *Int'l*, pg. 7629
THE BRITISH STANDARDS INSTITUTION; *Int'l*, pg. 7628
BRITISH STEEL LIMITED—See Jingye Group; *Int'l*, pg. 3968
BRITISH SUGAR PLC—See The Garfield Weston Foundation; *Int'l*, pg. 7648
BRITISH TELECOM B.V.—See Koninklijke KPN N.V.; *Int'l*, pg. 4267
BRITISH TELECOMMUNICATIONS PLC—See BT Group plc; *Int'l*, pg. 1203
BRITISH TRAVEL CENTRE AB—See VisitBritain; *Int'l*, pg. 8253
BRITISH TRIMMINGS LTD.—See Conso International Corporation; *U.S. Private*, pg. 1020
THE BRITISH UNITED PROVIDENT ASSOCIATION LIMITED; *Int'l*, pg. 7629
BRITISH VITA GROUP SOCIETE A RESPONSAIBILITE LIMITEE—See TPG Capital, L.P.; *U.S. Public*, pg. 2175
BRIT LIMITED—See Fairfax Financial Holdings Limited; *Int'l*, pg. 2606
BRIT MEDIA, INC.; *U.S. Private*, pg. 657
BRITON EMS LIMITED—See OSI Systems, Inc.; *U.S. Public*, pg. 1621
BRITON ENGINEERING DEVELOPMENTS LTD.—See Doppelmayr Group; *Int'l*, pg. 2174

BRIT SYNDICATES LIMITED—See Fairfax Financial Holdings Limited; *Int'l*, pg. 2606
BRIT SYSTEMS, LLC—See KKR & Co. Inc.; *U.S. Public*, pg. 1249
BRITTAIN MACHINE, INC.—See Berkshire Hathaway Inc.; *U.S. Public*, pg. 313
BRITTANICA HOME FASHIONS INC.; *U.S. Private*, pg. 657
BRITTANY CORPORATION—See Vista Land & Lifescapes, Inc.; *Int'l*, pg. 8254
BRITTANY DYEING & PRINTING CORPORATION; *U.S. Private*, pg. 657
BRITTANY FARMING CO.—See Smith Frozen Foods, Inc.; *U.S. Private*, pg. 3694
BRITTANY STAMPING, LLC; *U.S. Private*, pg. 657
BRITTEN-NORMAN AIRCRAFT LTD—See B-N Group Limited; *Int'l*, pg. 785
BRITTEN-NORMAN INC—See B-N Group Limited; *Int'l*, pg. 785
BRITTEN-NORMAN PTY LTD—See B-N Group Limited; *Int'l*, pg. 785
BRITTINGHAM & HIXON LUMBER CO.—See Alexander Lumber Co., Inc.; *U.S. Private*, pg. 163
BRITT METAL PROCESSING, INC.—See Jets MRO, LLC; *U.S. Private*, pg. 2204
BRITT MOBILE HOMES INC.; *U.S. Private*, pg. 657
BRITTON-DECFOLEX LTD.—See Sun Capital Partners, Inc.; *U.S. Private*, pg. 3861
BRITTON GROUP HOLDINGS LTD.—See Sun Capital Partners, Inc.; *U.S. Private*, pg. 3861
BRITTON TACO LTD.—See Sun Capital Partners, Inc.; *U.S. Private*, pg. 3861
BRITT RICE ELECTRIC LP.; *U.S. Private*, pg. 657
BRITT'S HOME FURNISHINGS, INC.; *U.S. Private*, pg. 657
BRITT SHOP—See Grupo Britt N.V.; *Int'l*, pg. 3123
BRITUS INTERNATIONAL SCHOOL FOR SPECIAL EDUCATION W.L.L.—See GFH Financial Group B.S.C.; *Int'l*, pg. 2956
BRIT UW LIMITED—See Fairfax Financial Holdings Limited; *Int'l*, pg. 2606
BRITVIC AQUA LIBRA CO LIMITED—See Britvic plc; *Int'l*, pg. 1171
BRITVIC IRELAND—See Britvic plc; *Int'l*, pg. 1171
BRITVIC NORTH AMERICA LLC—See Britvic plc; *Int'l*, pg. 1171
BRITVIC PLC; *Int'l*, pg. 1171
BRITVIC SOFT DRINKS LTD.—See Britvic plc; *Int'l*, pg. 1171
BRITWIND LTD.—See Ecotricity Group Ltd.; *Int'l*, pg. 2300
BRITZ & COMPANY; *U.S. Private*, pg. 657
BRIVAIS VILNIS AS; *Int'l*, pg. 1171
BRIVANT LIMITED—See Integer Holdings Corporation; *U.S. Public*, pg. 1134
BRIVIS CLIMATE SYSTEMS PTY. LTD.—See Rinnai Corporation; *Int'l*, pg. 6344
BRIVO SYSTEMS, LLC; *U.S. Private*, pg. 657
BRIX CORPORATION; *U.S. Private*, pg. 657
BRIXEY & MEYER CAPITAL LLC—See Brixey & Meyer, Inc.; *U.S. Private*, pg. 658
BRIXEY & MEYER, INC.; *U.S. Private*, pg. 658
THE BRIX GROUP INC.; *U.S. Private*, pg. 4000
BRIXHAM MARINE SERVICES LTD—See Damen Shipyards Group; *Int'l*, pg. 1956
BRIX HOLDINGS, LLC; *U.S. Private*, pg. 657
BRIXMOR LLC- SOUTHWEST—See Blackstone Inc.; *U.S. Public*, pg. 352
BRIXMOR OPERATING PARTNERSHIP LP—See Blackstone Inc.; *U.S. Public*, pg. 352
BRIXMOR PROPERTY GROUP INC. - CONSHOHOCKEN—See Blackstone Inc.; *U.S. Public*, pg. 352
BRIXMOR PROPERTY GROUP INC.—See Blackstone Inc.; *U.S. Public*, pg. 352
BRIXTON GROUP INC.; *U.S. Private*, pg. 658
BRIXTON METALS CORPORATION; *Int'l*, pg. 1171
BRIXTON USA CORPORATION—See Brixton Metals Corporation; *Int'l*, pg. 1171
B.R. JOHNSON, LLC—See Regional Brands Inc.; *U.S. Public*, pg. 1775
BRK BRANDS, INC.—See Resideo Technologies, Inc.; *U.S. Public*, pg. 1789
BRK FINANCIAL GROUP S.A.; *Int'l*, pg. 1171
BRK, INC.; *U.S. Private*, pg. 658
B&R K.K.—See ABB Ltd.; *Int'l*, pg. 56
BRK SPECIALIS MELYEPITO KFT.—See BAUER Aktiengesellschaft; *Int'l*, pg. 892
BRL LANDHOLDINGS PTY LTD.—See Sandon Capital Investments Limited; *Int'l*, pg. 6526
BRL RAIFFEISEN-IMMOBILIEN-LEASING GESELLSCHAFT M.B.H.—See Raiffeisen Bank International AG; *Int'l*, pg. 6182
BRL TRUST SERVICOS FIDUCIARIOS E PARTICIPACOES LTDA.—See Apex Fund Services Holdings Ltd.; *Int'l*, pg. 510
BR MALLS PARTICIPACOES S.A.—See Allos SA; *Int'l*, pg. 359
BR MALLS SERVICOS COMPARTILHADOS LTDA.—See Allos SA; *Int'l*, pg. 359

BR MEDICAL SUITES FZ LLC—See NMC Health PLC; *Int'l*, pg. 5392
BRMI; *U.S. Private*, pg. 658
B&R MOLL, INC.; *U.S. Private*, pg. 419
BROACH & COMPANY; *U.S. Private*, pg. 658
BROAD ACRES NURSING HOME ASSOCIATION; *U.S. Private*, pg. 658
BROADATA COMMUNICATIONS INC—See Mercury Systems, Inc.; *U.S. Public*, pg. 1422
BROADBAND ACCESS LIMITED—See Nippon Telegraph & Telephone Corporation; *Int'l*, pg. 5340
BROADBAND ACCESS NETWORKING GROUP, INC.; *U.S. Private*, pg. 658
BROADBAND CS CO., LTD.—See SK Telecom Co., Ltd.; *Int'l*, pg. 6976
BROADBAND ENTERPRISES, INC.—See Specific Media Inc.; *U.S. Private*, pg. 3751
BROADBAND MEDIA CO., LTD.—See SK Telecom Co., Ltd.; *Int'l*, pg. 6976
BROADBAND NETWORKS INC.—See Sierra Wireless, Inc.; *Int'l*, pg. 6904
BROADBAND SECURITY, INC.; *Int'l*, pg. 1172
BROADBAND SPECIALIST; *U.S. Private*, pg. 658
BROADBAND TELCOM POWER, INC.—See E.ON SE; *Int'l*, pg. 2258
BROADBAND TOWER, INC.; *Int'l*, pg. 1172
BROADBANDTV CORPORATION—See BBTV Holdings Inc.; *Int'l*, pg. 921
BROADBEAN INC.—See Veritone, Inc.; *U.S. Public*, pg. 2283
BROAD CAPITAL ACQUISITION CORP.; *U.S. Public*, pg. 388
BROADCAST ELECTRONICS, INC.; *U.S. Private*, pg. 658
BROADCAST ELECTRONICS, INC.—See Audax Group, Limited Partnership; *U.S. Private*, pg. 386
BROADCASTER, INC.; *U.S. Private*, pg. 659
THE BROADCASTER—See Yankton Media, Inc.; *U.S. Private*, pg. 4586
BROADCAST HUNGARY KFT.—See Transition Evergreen; *Int'l*, pg. 7901
BROADCASTING CENTER EUROPE SA—See Bertelsmann SE & Co. KGaA; *Int'l*, pg. 994
BROADCASTING COMMUNICATIONS, LLC—See Northwest Broadcasting, Inc.; *U.S. Private*, pg. 4000
BROADCAST INTERACTIVE MEDIA, LLC—See Benedek Investment Group, LLC; *U.S. Private*, pg. 524
BROADCASTLE LTD.—See Siemens Aktiengesellschaft; *Int'l*, pg. 6886
BROADCAST MARKETING GROUP, INC.; *U.S. Public*, pg. 388
BROADCASTMED, INC.; *U.S. Private*, pg. 659
BROADCAST MICROWAVE SERVICES EUROPE GMBH—See Vislink Technologies Inc.; *U.S. Public*, pg. 2304
BROADCAST MICROWAVE SERVICES, INC.—See Vislink Technologies Inc.; *U.S. Public*, pg. 2304
BROADCAST MUSIC INC.—See New Mountain Capital, LLC; *U.S. Private*, pg. 2900
BROADCAST SOFTWARE INTERNATIONAL INC.—See Cumulus Media Inc.; *U.S. Public*, pg. 609
BROADCAST SPORTS INTERNATIONAL, LLC—See The Carlyle Group Inc.; *U.S. Public*, pg. 2049
BROADCASTSTORE.COM; *U.S. Private*, pg. 659
BROADCAST SUPPLY WORLDWIDE, INC.; *U.S. Private*, pg. 659
BROADCAST TIME, INC.; *U.S. Private*, pg. 659
BROADCOM CORPORATION—See Broadcom Inc.; *U.S. Public*, pg. 388
BROADCOM INC.; *U.S. Public*, pg. 388
BROADCOM SINGAPORE PTE. LTD.—See Broadcom Inc.; *U.S. Public*, pg. 388
BROADCOM UK LTD.—See Broadcom Inc.; *U.S. Public*, pg. 388
BROAD CONSTRUCTION SERVICES PTY LTD—See ACS, Actividades de Construccion y Servicios, S.A.; *Int'l*, pg. 110
BROADDUS & ASSOCIATES, INC.; *U.S. Private*, pg. 659
BROADEX TECHNOLOGIES CO., LTD.; *Int'l*, pg. 1172
BROADEX TECHNOLOGIES UK LTD.—See Broadex Technologies Co., Ltd.; *Int'l*, pg. 1172
BROADFIELD DISTRIBUTING INC.; *U.S. Private*, pg. 659
BROADGATE ESTATES LTD.—See The British Land Company PLC; *Int'l*, pg. 7628
BROADGATE INC; *U.S. Private*, pg. 659
BROADGRAIN COMMODITIES INC.; *Int'l*, pg. 1172
BROADHEAD + CO., INC.; *U.S. Private*, pg. 659
BROADHURST ENVIRONMENTAL, INC.—See Republic Services, Inc.; *U.S. Public*, pg. 1786
BROADLAND RADIATORS AND HEAT EXCHANGERS LIMITED—See Caterpillar, Inc.; *U.S. Public*, pg. 449
BROADLEAF CO., LTD.; *Int'l*, pg. 1172
THE BROADLEAF GROUP, LLC; *U.S. Private*, pg. 4000
BROADLINE COMPONENTS, LLC; *U.S. Private*, pg. 659
BROADMARK PRIVATE REIT MANAGEMENT, LLC—See Waterfall Asset Management LLC; *U.S. Private*, pg. 4453
BROADMARK REALTY CAPITAL INC.—See Waterfall Asset Management LLC; *U.S. Private*, pg. 4453
BROADMEDIA CORPORATION; *Int'l*, pg. 1172

BROAD-MINDED CO., LTD.; *Int'l*, pg. 1171
BROADMOOR HOTEL, INC.—See The Anschutz Corporation; *U.S. Private*, pg. 3987
BROAD NET MUX CORPORATION—See Sumitomo Electric Industries, Ltd.; *Int'l*, pg. 7277
BROADNET TELESERVICES; *U.S. Private*, pg. 659
BROAD OAK HOMES LIMITED—See Barratt Developments PLC; *Int'l*, pg. 868
BROADPLEX LLC—See Court Square Capital Partners, L.P.; *U.S. Private*, pg. 1068
BROADPOINT, INC.—See Velosio, LLC; *U.S. Private*, pg. 4355
BROADPOINT, LLC—See MTPCS, LLC; *U.S. Private*, pg. 2809
BROADPOINT TECHNOLOGIES, INC.—See Velosio, LLC; *U.S. Private*, pg. 4355
BROAD REACH ENGINEERING COMPANY—See Moog Inc.; *U.S. Public*, pg. 1470
BROADREACH MEDICAL RESOURCES, INC.; *U.S. Private*, pg. 659
BROADRIDGE BUSINESS PROCESS OUTSOURCING, LLC—See Broadridge Financial Solutions, Inc.; *U.S. Public*, pg. 391
BROADRIDGE CORPORATE ISSUER SOLUTIONS, INC.—See Broadridge Financial Solutions, Inc.; *U.S. Public*, pg. 391
BROADRIDGE FINANCIAL SOLUTIONS, INC. - JERSEY CITY—See Broadridge Financial Solutions, Inc.; *U.S. Public*, pg. 391
BROADRIDGE FINANCIAL SOLUTIONS, INC.—See Automatic Data Processing, Inc.; *U.S. Public*, pg. 230
BROADRIDGE FINANCIAL SOLUTIONS, INC.; *U.S. Public*, pg. 391
BROADRIDGE FINANCIAL SOLUTIONS LIMITED—See Broadridge Financial Solutions, Inc.; *U.S. Public*, pg. 391
BROADRIDGE FX & LIQUIDITY SOLUTIONS, LLC—See Broadridge Financial Solutions, Inc.; *U.S. Public*, pg. 391
BROADRIDGE INVESTOR COMMUNICATIONS CORPORATION—See Broadridge Financial Solutions, Inc.; *U.S. Public*, pg. 391
BROADRIDGE (JAPAN) LTD.—See Broadridge Financial Solutions, Inc.; *U.S. Public*, pg. 391
BROADRIDGE MANAGED SOLUTIONS, INC.—See Broadridge Financial Solutions, Inc.; *U.S. Public*, pg. 391
BROADRIDGE (SINGAPORE) PRIVATE LIMITED—See Broadridge Financial Solutions, Inc.; *U.S. Public*, pg. 391
BROADRIVER COMMUNICATIONS CORPORATION—See Integracore, Inc.; *U.S. Private*, pg. 2098
BROAD RIVER PRIMARY CARE, L.L.C.—See Tenet Healthcare Corporation; *U.S. Public*, pg. 2007
BROADSCALE ACQUISITION CORP.; *U.S. Public*, pg. 392
BROADSHORE CAPITAL PARTNERS LLC—See The Guardian Life Insurance Company of America; *U.S. Private*, pg. 4040
BROADSIGHT SYSTEMS INC.—See CBC Co., Ltd.; *Int'l*, pg. 1365
BROAD SKY NETWORKS, LLC—See IntelliSite Corporation; *U.S. Private*, pg. 2106
BROADSMART GLOBAL, INC.—See Ooma, Inc.; *U.S. Public*, pg. 1605
BROADSOFT HOSPITALITY, INC.—See Cisco Systems, Inc.; *U.S. Public*, pg. 497
BROADSOFT, INC.—See Cisco Systems, Inc.; *U.S. Public*, pg. 497
BROADSOFT JAPAN KK—See Cisco Systems, Inc.; *U.S. Public*, pg. 497
BROADSOFT TECHNOLOGIES PRIVATE LIMITED—See Cisco Systems, Inc.; *U.S. Public*, pg. 497
BROADSOUND CORPORATION—See Maywufa Company Limited; *Int'l*, pg. 4748
BROADSPECTRUM (AUSTRALIA) PTY. LTD.—See Apollo Global Management, Inc.; *U.S. Public*, pg. 166
BROADSPECTRUM AUSTRALIA (QLD) PTY LIMITED—See Apollo Global Management, Inc.; *U.S. Public*, pg. 166
BROADSPECTRUM (NEW ZEALAND) LIMITED—See Apollo Global Management, Inc.; *U.S. Public*, pg. 166
BROADSPECTRUM PTY. LTD.—See Apollo Global Management, Inc.; *U.S. Public*, pg. 166
BROADSPECTRUM (WA) PTY LIMITED—See Apollo Global Management, Inc.; *U.S. Public*, pg. 166
BROADSPIRE SERVICES, INC.—See Crawford & Company; *U.S. Public*, pg. 592
BROADSTEP BEHAVIORAL HEALTH—See Bain Capital, LP; *U.S. Private*, pg. 431
BROADSTONE ACQUISITION CORP.; *Int'l*, pg. 1172
THE BROADSTONE GROUP, LLC; *U.S. Private*, pg. 4000
BROADSTONE NET LEASE, INC.; *U.S. Public*, pg. 392
BROADSTONE REAL ESTATE, LLC; *U.S. Private*, pg. 659
BROAD STREET GLOBAL ADVISORS LLC—See Prudential Financial, Inc.; *U.S. Public*, pg. 1731
BROAD STREET MEDIA, LLC - CHERRY HILL—See Broad Street Media, LLC; *U.S. Private*, pg. 658

BROAD STREET MEDIA, LLC

BROAD STREET MEDIA, LLC; *U.S. Private*, pg. 658
BROADSTREET PRODUCTIONS, LLC; *U.S. Private*, pg. 659
BROAD STREET REALTY, INC.—See Broad Street Realty, LLC; *U.S. Private*, pg. 658
BROAD STREET REALTY, LLC; *U.S. Private*, pg. 658
BROADTEAM ELECTRONICS (GUANGZHOU) INC.—See FIC Global, INC; *Int'l*, pg. 2653
BROAD TECHNOLOGY (GUANGZHOU) INC.—See FIC Global, INC; *Int'l*, pg. 2653
BROAD TECHNOLOGY INCORPORATED—See FIC Global, INC; *Int'l*, pg. 2653
BROADTEC TV R&D CENTER SDN. BHD.—See Funai Electric Co., Ltd.; *Int'l*, pg. 2844
BROADTREE PARTNERS, LLC; *U.S. Private*, pg. 659
BROADUS OIL CORP. OF ILLINOIS; *U.S. Private*, pg. 659
BROADVIEW ENERGY PRIME II, LLC—See Macquarie Group Limited; *Int'l*, pg. 4624
BROADVIEW GROUP HOLDINGS, LLC; *U.S. Private*, pg. 660
BROADVIEW HOLDING B.V.—See HAL Trust N.V.; *Int'l*, pg. 3223
BROADVIEW INDUSTRIES AG—See HAL Trust N.V.; *Int'l*, pg. 3223
BROADVIEW NETWORKS HOLDINGS, INC.—See Windstream Holdings, Inc.; *U.S. Public*, pg. 2373
BROADVIEW NETWORKS, INC.—See Windstream Holdings, Inc.; *U.S. Public*, pg. 2373
BROADVIEW PRESS INC.; *Int'l*, pg. 1172
BROADVISION DEUTSCHLAND GMBH—See ESW Capital, LLC; *U.S. Private*, pg. 1429
BROADVISION FRANCE, S.A.—See ESW Capital, LLC; *U.S. Private*, pg. 1430
BROADVISION, INC.—See ESW Capital, LLC; *U.S. Private*, pg. 1429
BROADVISION, INC.—See ESW Capital, LLC; *U.S. Private*, pg. 1430
BROADVISION JAPAN K.K.—See ESW Capital, LLC; *U.S. Private*, pg. 1430
BROADVISION SYSTEM PVT LTD.—See ESW Capital, LLC; *U.S. Private*, pg. 1430
BROADVISION UK, LTD.—See ESW Capital, LLC; *U.S. Private*, pg. 1430
BROADVOICE, INC.; *U.S. Private*, pg. 660
BROADVOX LLC—See Sinch AB; *Int'l*, pg. 6937
BROADWAY ACROSS AMERICA - MINNEAPOLIS—See Key Brand Entertainment, Inc.; *U.S. Private*, pg. 2292
BROADWAY ACROSS AMERICA - SALT LAKE CITY—See Key Brand Entertainment, Inc.; *U.S. Private*, pg. 2292
BROADWAY ACROSS AMERICA - SEATTLE—See Key Brand Entertainment, Inc.; *U.S. Private*, pg. 2292
BROADWAY ACROSS AMERICA—See Key Brand Entertainment, Inc.; *U.S. Private*, pg. 2292
BROADWAY ASSET MANAGEMENT, INC.—See Synovus Financial Corp.; *U.S. Public*, pg. 1971
BROADWAY AUTOMOTIVE-GREEN BAY, INC.—See Broadway Enterprises, Inc.; *U.S. Private*, pg. 660
BROADWAY BANCSHARES, INC.; *U.S. Private*, pg. 660
BROADWAY ELECTRIC SERVICE CORPORATION; *U.S. Private*, pg. 660
BROADWAY ELITE LLC—See Shanghai Construction Group Co., Ltd.; *Int'l*, pg. 6763
BROADWAY ENTERPRISES, INC.; *U.S. Private*, pg. 660
BROADWAY FEDERAL BANK, F.S.B.—See Broadway Financial Corporation; *U.S. Public*, pg. 392
BROADWAY FINANCIAL CORPORATION; *U.S. Public*, pg. 392
BROADWAY FLOORS, INC.—See Bid4floors.com; *U.S. Private*, pg. 551
BROADWAY & FRAME PREMIX CONCRETE PTY LTD—See Holcim Ltd.; *Int'l*, pg. 3446
BROADWAY INDUSTRIAL GROUP LIMITED; *Int'l*, pg. 1172
BROADWAY NATIONAL BANK—See Broadway Bancshares, Inc.; *U.S. Private*, pg. 660
BROADWAY RENTAL CARS, INC.—See Broadway Enterprises, Inc.; *U.S. Private*, pg. 660
BROADWAY SERVICES, INC.; *U.S. Private*, pg. 660
BROADWAY SOUND—See Broadway Video Inc.; *U.S. Private*, pg. 660
BROADWAY STORAGE SOLUTIONS, L.L.C.—See National Storage Affiliates Trust; *U.S. Public*, pg. 1498
BROADWAY SYSTEMS & TECHNOLOGY CO., LTD.—See Platinum Equity, LLC; *U.S. Private*, pg. 3201
BROADWAY TECHNOLOGY, LLC—See Bloomberg L.P.; *U.S. Private*, pg. 583
BROADWAY TRUCK CENTERS; *U.S. Private*, pg. 660
BROADWAY VIDEO INC.; *U.S. Private*, pg. 660
BROADWIND HEAVY FABRICATIONS, INC.—See Broadwind, Inc.; *U.S. Public*, pg. 392
BROADWIND, INC.; *U.S. Public*, pg. 392
BROADWIND SERVICES, LLC—See Broadwind, Inc.; *U.S. Public*, pg. 392
BROADWING COMMUNICATIONS, INC.; *U.S. Private*, pg. 660
BROAN-NUTONE, LLC—See Melrose Industries PLC; *Int'l*, pg. 4813

BROASTER COMPANY LLC—See Broaster Company; *U.S. Private*, pg. 660
BROASTER COMPANY; *U.S. Private*, pg. 660
B ROBERT'S FOODS LLC—See Bakkavor Group plc; *Int'l*, pg. 805
BROCACEF B.V.—See PHOENIX Pharmahandel GmbH & Co. KG; *Int'l*, pg. 5854
BROCACEF GROEP N.V.—See PHOENIX Pharmahandel GmbH & Co. KG; *Int'l*, pg. 5854
BROCA & WERNICKE INTEGRATED HEALTHCARE COMMUNICATIONS—See WPP plc; *Int'l*, pg. 8492
BROCCOLI CO., LTD.; *Int'l*, pg. 1172
BROCCOLINI CONSTRUCTION INC.; *Int'l*, pg. 1172
BROCE MANUFACTURING CO. INC.; *U.S. Private*, pg. 660
BROCK CANADA INC.—See AIP, LLC; *U.S. Private*, pg. 134
BROCK & COMPANY INC.; *U.S. Private*, pg. 660
BROCK ELECTRONICS LTD.—See Fuji Corporation; *Int'l*, pg. 2809
BROCK ENTERPRISES, LLC—See AIP, LLC; *U.S. Private*, pg. 134
BROCK FORD SALES; *Int'l*, pg. 1172
BROCKHAUS PRIVATE EQUITY GMBH; *Int'l*, pg. 1172
BROCKHAUS TECHNOLOGIES AG—See Brockhaus Private Equity GmbH; *Int'l*, pg. 1172
BROCK HOLDINGS III, INC.—See Goldberg Lindsay & Co., LLC; *U.S. Private*, pg. 1729
BROCKHOUSE GROUP LIMITED—See Original Steel Services Limited; *Int'l*, pg. 5630
BROCK INSURANCE AGENCY; *U.S. Private*, pg. 660
BROCK INVESTMENTS INC.; *U.S. Private*, pg. 660
BROCKMAN ENGINEERING PTY LTD—See EVZ Limited; *Int'l*, pg. 2574
BROCKMAN IRON PTY. LTD.—See Brockman Mining Limited; *Int'l*, pg. 1173
BROCKMAN MINING LIMITED; *Int'l*, pg. 1173
BROCKMAN MINING (MANAGEMENT) LIMITED—See Brockman Mining Limited; *Int'l*, pg. 1173
BROCK-MCVEY COMPANY—See A.Y. McDonald Manufacturing Co.; *U.S. Private*, pg. 29
BROCK SERVICES, LLC—See AIP, LLC; *U.S. Private*, pg. 134
BROCKS PLYWOOD SALES, INC.—See Hammond Lumber Company; *U.S. Private*, pg. 1850
BROCKTON DIALYSIS CENTER, LLC—See Nautic Partners, LLC; *U.S. Private*, pg. 2869
BROCKTON HEALTHCARE CLINIC, LLC—See Nautic Partners, LLC; *U.S. Private*, pg. 2869
BROCKTON NEIGHBORHOOD HEALTH CENTER; *U.S. Private*, pg. 660
BROCKTON VISITING NURSE ASSOCIATION; *U.S. Private*, pg. 660
BROCKWAY MORAN & PARTNERS, INC.; *U.S. Private*, pg. 661
BROCK WHITE COMPANY LLC—See The Sterling Group, L.P.; *U.S. Private*, pg. 4122
BROCO, INC.; *U.S. Private*, pg. 661
BRODA CONSTRUCTION LNC.—See Bird Construction Inc.; *Int'l*, pg. 1046
BRODA ENTERPRISES, INC.—See Sorenson Capital Partners; *U.S. Private*, pg. 3715
BRODART CO. - BOOKS & LIBRARY SERVICES DIVISION—See Brodart Co.; *U.S. Private*, pg. 661
BRODART CO. - CONTRACT FURNITURE DIVISION—See Brodart Co.; *U.S. Private*, pg. 661
BRODART COMPANY—See Brodart Co.; *U.S. Private*, pg. 661
BRODART CO.; *U.S. Private*, pg. 661
BRODART CO. - SUPPLIES & FURNISHINGS DIVISION—See Brodart Co.; *U.S. Private*, pg. 661
BRODER BROS., CO.—See Bain Capital, LP; *U.S. Private*, pg. 437
BRODERICK BROS. LIMITED; *Int'l*, pg. 1173
BRODERNA ANDERSSONS GRUS AB—See Nordisk Bergteknik AB; *Int'l*, pg. 5424
BRODERNA BERNER HANDELS AB—See Berner Oy; *Int'l*, pg. 988
BRODERNA BOURGHARDT AB—See SP Group A/S; *Int'l*, pg. 7122
BRODERNA INGEMAR OCH BO MEKANISKA AB—See CTT Systems AB; *Int'l*, pg. 1874
BRODERSON MANUFACTURING CORP.—See Lanco International Inc.; *U.S. Private*, pg. 2382
BRODEUR BRAZIL—See Omnicom Group Inc.; *U.S. Public*, pg. 1577
BRODEUR CARVELL INC.; *U.S. Private*, pg. 661
BRODEUR MARTEC—See Omnicom Group Inc.; *U.S. Public*, pg. 1577
BRODEUR PARTNERS—See Omnicom Group Inc.; *U.S. Public*, pg. 1577
BRODEUR PARTNERS—See Omnicom Group Inc.; *U.S. Public*, pg. 1578
BRODEUR PARTNERS—See Omnicom Group Inc.; *U.S. Public*, pg. 1578
BRODEUR PARTNERS—See Omnicom Group Inc.; *U.S. Public*, pg. 1578
BRODIE BUICK MITSUBISHI KIA; *U.S. Private*, pg. 661

CORPORATE AFFILIATIONS

BRODIE CONTRACTORS INC.; *U.S. Private*, pg. 661
BRODIE MELROSE DRYSDALE & CO. LTD.—See Massimo Zanetti Beverage Group SpA; *Int'l*, pg. 4722
BRODIES MELROSE DRYSDALE & CO. LTD.—See Segafredo Zanetti S.p.A.; *Int'l*, pg. 6681
BRODIE TOYOTA-LIFT; *U.S. Private*, pg. 661
BRO-DIL, A.D.—See Pozavarovalnica Sava, d.d.; *Int'l*, pg. 5949
BRODOGRADILISTE VIKTOR LENAC D.D.—See Palumbo Group S.P.A.; *Int'l*, pg. 5710
BRODOMERKUR DD; *Int'l*, pg. 1173
BRODOS AG; *Int'l*, pg. 1173
BRODOS ROMANIA SRL—See Euronet Worldwide, Inc.; *U.S. Public*, pg. 797
BRODRENE A & O JOHANSEN A/S; *Int'l*, pg. 1173
BRODRENE DAHL A/S—See Compagnie de Saint-Gobain SA; *Int'l*, pg. 1733
BRODRENE DAHL A/S—See Compagnie de Saint-Gobain SA; *Int'l*, pg. 1733
BRODRENE HARTMANN A/S—See Thornico A/S; *Int'l*, pg. 7719
BRODRENE HEDEGAARD A/S—See Per Aarsleff Holding A/S; *Int'l*, pg. 5795
THE BROE COMPANIES, INC.; *U.S. Private*, pg. 4000
BROEN A/S—See Aalberts N.V.; *Int'l*, pg. 33
BROENDBYERNES IF FODBOLD A/S; *Int'l*, pg. 1173
BROEN FINLAND OY—See Aalberts N.V.; *Int'l*, pg. 33
BROEN, INC.—See Aalberts N.V.; *Int'l*, pg. 33
BROEN LTD.—See Aalberts N.V.; *Int'l*, pg. 33
BROEN MALAYSIA SDN. BHD.—See Aalberts N.V.; *Int'l*, pg. 33
BROEN RAUFOSS AB—See Aalberts N.V.; *Int'l*, pg. 33
BROEN S.A.—See Aalberts N.V.; *Int'l*, pg. 33
BROEN SEI SRL—See Aalberts N.V.; *Int'l*, pg. 33
BROEN SINGAPORE PTE LTD—See Aalberts N.V.; *Int'l*, pg. 33
BROEN VALVES (BEIJING) CO., LTD.—See Aalberts N.V.; *Int'l*, pg. 33
BROEN VALVES LTD.—See Aalberts N.V.; *Int'l*, pg. 33
BROEN-ZAWGAZ SP. Z.O.O.—See Aalberts N.V.; *Int'l*, pg. 33
BROETJE ORCHARDS; *U.S. Private*, pg. 661
BROGAN & PARTNERS CONVERGENCE MARKETING; *U.S. Private*, pg. 661
BROGAN & PARTNERS CONVERGENCE MARKETING—See Brogan & Partners Convergence Marketing; *U.S. Private*, pg. 661
BROGAN TENNYSON GROUP, INC.; *U.S. Private*, pg. 661
BROGAN TENNYSON—See Brogan Tennyson Group, Inc.; *U.S. Private*, pg. 661
BROGENT TECHNOLOGIES, INC.; *Int'l*, pg. 1173
BROHL & APPELL INC.—See Rexel, S.A.; *Int'l*, pg. 6316
THE BROHN GROUP LLC—See Berkshire Hathaway Inc.; *U.S. Public*, pg. 304
BROKELMANN ALUTEC GMBH + CO. KG—See Knauf Interfer SE; *Int'l*, pg. 4205
BROKELMANN POLSKA SP. Z.O.O.—See Knauf Interfer SE; *Int'l*, pg. 4205
BROKEN ARROW COMMUNICATIONS, INC.—See QualTek Services Inc.; *U.S. Public*, pg. 1748
BROKEN ARROW ELECTRIC SUPPLY INC.; *U.S. Private*, pg. 661
BROKEN ARROW INCORPORATED; *U.S. Private*, pg. 661
BROKEN ARROW INSURANCE AGENCY, INC.—See Stone Point Capital LLC; *U.S. Private*, pg. 3818
BROKEN BOW WIND, LLC—See NRG Energy, Inc.; *U.S. Public*, pg. 1549
BROKEN DRUM INSULATION VISALIA, INC.—See Installed Building Products, Inc.; *U.S. Public*, pg. 1132
BROKEN DRUM OF BAKERSFIELD, INC.—See Installed Building Products, Inc.; *U.S. Public*, pg. 1132
BROKEN HILL OPERATIONS PTY LTD; *Int'l*, pg. 1173
BROKEN SOUND CLUB, INC.; *U.S. Private*, pg. 661
BROKERAGE CONCEPTS INC.; *U.S. Private*, pg. 662
BROKERBAY INC.—See Carrier Global Corporation; *U.S. Public*, pg. 440
THE BROKER FORUM INC.—See KKR & Co. Inc.; *U.S. Public*, pg. 1267
BROKER GENIUS, INC.; *U.S. Private*, pg. 661
BROKER INS LTD.—See Alfa Finance Holding AD; *Int'l*, pg. 307
BROKERLINK INC.—See Intact Financial Corporation; *Int'l*, pg. 3726
BROKER ONLINE EXCHANGE LLC; *U.S. Private*, pg. 661
BROKERSCLUB AG; *Int'l*, pg. 1173
BROKERS CONSOLIDATED, INC.; *U.S. Private*, pg. 662
BROKERS INTERNATIONAL, LTD.—See Integrity Marketing Group LLC; *U.S. Public*, pg. 2103
BROKERS LOGISTICS, LTD.; *U.S. Private*, pg. 662
BROKER SOLUTIONS, INC.; *U.S. Private*, pg. 661
BROKERS RISK PLACEMENT SERVICE, INC.—See One80 Intermediaries LLC; *U.S. Private*, pg. 3024
BROKERS' SERVICE MARKETING GROUP—See Hellman & Friedman LLC; *U.S. Private*, pg. 1909
BROKERS TITLE, LLC—See Stewart Information Services Corporation; *U.S. Public*, pg. 1947

COMPANY NAME INDEX

BROKERS TRUST INSURANCE GROUP INC.; *Int'l*, pg. 1173

BROKERS UNION SP. Z.O.O.—See Impel S.A.; *Int'l*, pg. 3631

BROKERSXPRESS, LLC—See The Charles Schwab Corporation; *U.S. Public*, pg. 2058

BROKER TECHNOLOGY SOLUTIONS LLC—See Anywhere Real Estate Inc.; *U.S. Public*, pg. 142

BROKERTEC—See CME Group, Inc.; *U.S. Public*, pg. 517

BROKK AB—See Carl Bennet AB; *Int'l*, pg. 1332

BROKK, INC.—See Carl Bennet AB; *Int'l*, pg. 1332

BROLI FINANCE PTY. LTD.—See Australia Finance Group Ltd; *Int'l*, pg. 720

BROLLO SONEPAR—See Sonepar S.A.; *Int'l*, pg. 7092

BROMANCO BJORKGREN AB—See Amplex AB; *Int'l*, pg. 434

BROMBERGS BOKFORLAG; *Int'l*, pg. 1173

BROMBOROUGH VETS4PETS LIMITED—See Pets at Home Group Plc; *Int'l*, pg. 5833

BROME LAKE DUCKS LTD; *Int'l*, pg. 1173

BROMFORD INDUSTRIES LIMITED - LEICESTER FACILITY—See Bromford Industries Limited; *Int'l*, pg. 1173

BROMFORD INDUSTRIES LIMITED; *Int'l*, pg. 1173

BROMFORD IRON & STEEL COMPANY LTD.—See Original Steel Services Limited; *Int'l*, pg. 5630

BROMFORD TECHNOLOGIES - ALCESTER FACILITY—See Bromford Industries Limited; *Int'l*, pg. 1173

BROMIDE TECHNOLOGIES (PTY) LTD—See EOH HOLDINGS LIMITED; *Int'l*, pg. 2457

BROMI MASKIN AB; *Int'l*, pg. 1173

BROMIUM, INC.; *U.S. Private*, pg. 662

BROMIUM UK LIMITED—See HP Inc.; *U.S. Public*, pg. 1062

BROMLEY COMMUNICATIONS, LLC—See Publicis Groupe S.A.; *Int'l*, pg. 6097

BROMLEY PROPERTY INVESTMENTS LIMITED—See Grainger plc; *Int'l*, pg. 3052

BROMMA (MALAYSIA) SDN. BHD.—See Cargotec Corporation; *Int'l*, pg. 1326

BROMPTON FUNDS LIMITED; *Int'l*, pg. 1173

BROMPTON HEIGHTS, INC.—See The Hamister Group, Inc.; *U.S. Private*, pg. 4042

BROMPTON HOMES LIMITED—See Co-operative Group Limited; *Int'l*, pg. 1679

BROMPTON LIFECO SPLIT CORP.; *Int'l*, pg. 1174

BROMPTON OIL SPLIT CORP.; *Int'l*, pg. 1174

BROMPTON SPLIT BANC CORP.—See Brompton Funds Limited; *Int'l*, pg. 1173

BROMWELL FINANCIAL FUND, LIMITED PARTNERSHIP; *U.S. Private*, pg. 662

BRONBERGER & KESSLER HANDELSGESELLSCHAFT GMBH—See Eni S.p.A.; *Int'l*, pg. 2437

BRONCO BILLY CO., LTD.; *Int'l*, pg. 1174

BRONCO CREEK EXPLORATION, INC.—See EMX Royalty Corporation; *Int'l*, pg. 2395

BRONCO MANUFACTURING LLC—See Akastor ASA; *Int'l*, pg. 260

BRONCO MOTORS INC.; *U.S. Private*, pg. 662

BRONCO PACKAGING CORP.—See Orora Limited; *Int'l*, pg. 5642

BRONCO WINE COMPANY; *U.S. Private*, pg. 662

BRONCUS MEDICAL, INC; *U.S. Private*, pg. 662

BRONDBY DYREKLINIK APS—See Vimian Group AB; *Int'l*, pg. 8208

BRONDES FORD TOLEDO; *U.S. Private*, pg. 662

BRONDOW, INC.; *U.S. Private*, pg. 662

BRONER GLOVE COMPANY INC.; *U.S. Private*, pg. 662

BRONIEC ASSOCIATES INC.; *U.S. Private*, pg. 662

BRONNER BROTHERS; *U.S. Private*, pg. 662

BRONNUM APS—See NoHo Partners Plc; *Int'l*, pg. 5400

BRONSON AND JACOBS (H.K.) LIMITED—See Keppel Corporation Limited; *Int'l*, pg. 4131

BRONSON ATHLETIC CLUB—See Bronson Healthcare Group, Inc.; *U.S. Private*, pg. 662

BRONSON BATTLE CREEK HOSPITAL—See Bronson Healthcare Group, Inc.; *U.S. Private*, pg. 662

BRONSON & BRATTON INC; *U.S. Private*, pg. 662

BRONSON HEALTHCARE GROUP, INC.; *U.S. Private*, pg. 662

BRONSON & JACOBS PTY LTD—See Keppel Corporation Limited; *Int'l*, pg. 4131

BRONSON & JACOBS (S.E. ASIA) PTE LIMITED—See Keppel Corporation Limited; *Int'l*, pg. 4131

BRONSSTADET AB; *Int'l*, pg. 1174

BRONSWOOD CEMETERY, INC.—See Axar Capital Management L.P.; *U.S. Private*, pg. 411

BRON TAPES LLC—See Rotunda Capital Partners LLC; *U.S. Private*, pg. 3488

BRONTO SKYLIFT OY AB—See Morita Holdings Corporation; *Int'l*, pg. 5048

BRONTO SOFTWARE, LLC—See Oracle Corporation; *U.S. Public*, pg. 1611

BRONX HONDA; *U.S. Private*, pg. 662

BRONZE HEADQUARTERS, INC.—See Headco Industries; *U.S. Private*, pg. 1891

BRONZE INFRA-TECH LIMITED; *Int'l*, pg. 1174

BROODSTOCK CAPITAL AS; *Int'l*, pg. 1174

BROOKCOURT SOLUTIONS LIMITED—See Shearwater Group plc; *Int'l*, pg. 6792

BROOK CROMPTON HOLDINGS LTD.—See Wolong Holding Group Co., Ltd.; *Int'l*, pg. 8443

BROOK CROMPTON LTD.—See Wolong Holding Group Co., Ltd.; *Int'l*, pg. 8443

BROOK CROMPTON MOTORS INC—See Wolong Holding Group Co., Ltd.; *Int'l*, pg. 8443

BROOK CROMPTON UK LIMITED—See Wolong Holding Group Co., Ltd.; *Int'l*, pg. 8443

BROOKDALE BEND OR, LLC—See Brookdale Senior Living Inc.; *U.S. Public*, pg. 393

BROOKDALE CASTLE HILLS, LLC—See Brookdale Senior Living Inc.; *U.S. Public*, pg. 393

BROOKDALE EAU GALLIE—See Brookdale Senior Living Inc.; *U.S. Public*, pg. 393

BROOKDALE GARDENS INC—See Brookdale Senior Living Inc.; *U.S. Public*, pg. 394

THE BROOKDALE GROUP LLC; *U.S. Private*, pg. 4001

BROOKDALE HOME HEALTH—See Brookdale Senior Living Inc.; *U.S. Public*, pg. 394

BROOKDALE LEAWOOD—See Brookdale Senior Living Inc.; *U.S. Public*, pg. 394

BROOKDALE LIVING COMMUNITIES OF NEW JERSEY, LLC—See Ventas, Inc.; *U.S. Public*, pg. 2278

BROOKDALE LIVING COMMUNITIES OF NORTH CAROLINA, INC.—See Brookdale Senior Living Inc.; *U.S. Public*, pg. 394

BROOKDALE MCMINNVILLE WESTSIDE, LLC—See Brookdale Senior Living Inc.; *U.S. Public*, pg. 394

BROOKDALE MOTOR SALES INC—See Luther Holding Company; *U.S. Private*, pg. 5204

BROOKDALE PLACE AT FALL CREEK, LLC—See Brookdale Senior Living Inc.; *U.S. Public*, pg. 394

BROOKDALE PLACE AT KENWOOD, LLC—See Brookdale Senior Living Inc.; *U.S. Public*, pg. 394

BROOKDALE PLACE AT OAKWOOD, LLC—See Brookdale Senior Living Inc.; *U.S. Public*, pg. 394

BROOKDALE PLACE AT WILLOW LAKE, LLC—See Brookdale Senior Living Inc.; *U.S. Public*, pg. 394

BROOKDALE PLACE OF ANN ARBOR, LLC—See Brookdale Senior Living Inc.; *U.S. Public*, pg. 394

BROOKDALE PLACE OF AUGUSTA, LLC—See Brookdale Senior Living Inc.; *U.S. Public*, pg. 394

BROOKDALE PLACE OF BATH, LLC—See Brookdale Senior Living Inc.; *U.S. Public*, pg. 394

BROOKDALE PLACE OF ENGLEWOOD, LLC—See Brookdale Senior Living Inc.; *U.S. Public*, pg. 394

BROOKDALE PLACE OF WEST HARTFORD, LLC—See Brookdale Senior Living Inc.; *U.S. Public*, pg. 394

BROOKDALE PLACE OF WILTON, LLC—See Brookdale Senior Living Inc.; *U.S. Public*, pg. 394

BROOKDALE PLACE OF WOOSTER, LLC—See Brookdale Senior Living Inc.; *U.S. Public*, pg. 394

BROOKDALE PLASTICS, INC.—See Placon Corporation; *U.S. Private*, pg. 3194

BROOKDALE REALTY SERVICE, LLC—See The Brookdale Group LLC; *U.S. Private*, pg. 4001

BROOKDALE SENIOR LIVING INC. - JACKSONVILLE—See Brookdale Senior Living Inc.; *U.S. Public*, pg. 394

BROOKDALE SENIOR LIVING INC.; *U.S. Public*, pg. 392

BROOKDALE SENIOR LIVING, INC.—See Brookdale Senior Living Inc.; *U.S. Public*, pg. 394

BROOKDALE ST. AUGUSTINE LLC—See Brookdale Senior Living Inc.; *U.S. Public*, pg. 394

BROOKDALE WELLINGTON, INC.—See Brookdale Senior Living Inc.; *U.S. Public*, pg. 394

BROOKDALE YORKTOWNE—See Brookdale Senior Living Inc.; *U.S. Public*, pg. 394

BROOK DIALYSIS, LLC—See DaVita Inc.; *U.S. Public*, pg. 636

BROOKE ASIA LTD—See Rhong Khen International Berhad; *Int'l*, pg. 6327

BROOKE CHASE ASSOCIATES, INC.; *U.S. Private*, pg. 663

BROOKE DISTRIBUTORS INC.; *U.S. Private*, pg. 663

BROOK ELECTRICAL SUPPLY COMPANY—See Sonepar S.A.; *Int'l*, pg. 7093

BROOKE PRIVATE EQUITY ASSOCIATES MANAGEMENT LLC; *U.S. Private*, pg. 663

THE BROOKER GROUP PUBLIC COMPANY LIMITED; *Int'l*, pg. 7630

BROOKES & GATEHOUSE, LTD.—See Brunswick Corporation; *U.S. Public*, pg. 408

THE BROOKESIDE GROUP, INC.; *U.S. Private*, pg. 4001

BROOKESIDE VENTURES INC.; *U.S. Private*, pg. 663

BROOKFIDELD RENEWABLE POWER PREFERRED EQUALITY INC.—See Brookfield Renewable Corporation; *U.S. Public*, pg. 395

BROOKFIELD AUTO WRECKERS INC.; *U.S. Private*, pg. 663

BROOKFIELD BRASIL, S.A.—See Brookfield Corporation; *Int'l*, pg. 1175

BROOKFIELD BRIDGE LENDING FUND INC—See Brookfield Corporation; *Int'l*, pg. 1175

BROOKFIELD BUSINESS CORPORATION; *Int'l*, pg. 1174

BROOKFIELD BUSINESS PARTNERS L.P.—See Brookfield Corporation; *Int'l*, pg. 1175

BROOKFIELD CANADA OFFICE PROPERTIES—See Brookfield Corporation; *Int'l*, pg. 1186

BROOKFIELD CORPORATION; *Int'l*, pg. 1174

BROOKFIELD DTLA FUND OFFICE TRUST INVESTOR, INC.; *U.S. Public*, pg. 395

BROOKFIELD ENGINEERING LABORATORIES, INC.—See AMETEK, Inc.; *U.S. Public*, pg. 120

BROOKFIELD FINANCIAL PROPERTIES, L.P.—See Brookfield Corporation; *Int'l*, pg. 1186

BROOKFIELD GLOBAL INFRASTRUCTURE SECURITIES INCOME FUND; *Int'l*, pg. 1189

BROOKFIELD GLOBAL RELOCATION SERVICES—See Brookfield Corporation; *Int'l*, pg. 1181

BROOKFIELD HOMES ONTARIO LTD.—See Brookfield Corporation; *Int'l*, pg. 1187

BROOKFIELD INCORPORACOES S.A.—See Brookfield Corporation; *Int'l*, pg. 1175

BROOKFIELD INFRASTRUCTURE CORPORATION—See Brookfield Infrastructure Partners L.P.; *Int'l*, pg. 1189

BROOKFIELD INFRASTRUCTURE L.P.—See Brookfield Infrastructure Partners L.P.; *Int'l*, pg. 1190

BROOKFIELD INFRASTRUCTURE PARTNERS L.P.; *Int'l*, pg. 1189

BROOKFIELD INVESTMENT MANAGEMENT INC.—See Brookfield Corporation; *Int'l*, pg. 1181

BROOKFIELD INVESTMENT PARTNERS, LLC—See Nicolet Bankshares, Inc.; *U.S. Public*, pg. 1528

BROOKFIELD INVESTMENTS CORPORATION—See Brookfield Corporation; *Int'l*, pg. 1184

BROOKFIELD MULTIPLEX CAPITAL LIMITED—See Brookfield Corporation; *Int'l*, pg. 1185

BROOKFIELD MULTIPLEX DEVELOPMENTS—See Brookfield Corporation; *Int'l*, pg. 1185

BROOKFIELD MULTIPLEX GROUP LIMITED—See Brookfield Corporation; *Int'l*, pg. 1185

BROOKFIELD OAKTREE HOLDINGS, LLC—See Brookfield Corporation; *Int'l*, pg. 1181

BROOKFIELD OFFICE PROPERTIES INC.—See Brookfield Corporation; *Int'l*, pg. 1186

BROOKFIELD PROPERTIES, INC.—See Brookfield Corporation; *Int'l*, pg. 1186

BROOKFIELD PROPERTIES MANAGEMENT CORPORATION—See Brookfield Corporation; *Int'l*, pg. 1186

BROOKFIELD PROPERTIES MANAGEMENT LLC—See Brookfield Corporation; *Int'l*, pg. 1186

BROOKFIELD PROPERTIES RETAIL INC.—See Brookfield Corporation; *Int'l*, pg. 1185

BROOKFIELD PROPERTY GROUP—See Brookfield Corporation; *Int'l*, pg. 1185

BROOKFIELD PROPERTY PARTNERS L.P.—See Brookfield Corporation; *Int'l*, pg. 1185

BROOKFIELD PROPERTY REIT INC.—See Brookfield Corporation; *Int'l*, pg. 1186

BROOKFIELD RAIL PTY. LTD.—See Brookfield Infrastructure Partners L.P.; *Int'l*, pg. 1190

BROOKFIELD REAL ASSETS INCOME FUND INC.—See Brookfield Corporation; *Int'l*, pg. 1184

BROOKFIELD REINSURANCE LTD.; *Int'l*, pg. 1193

BROOKFIELD RENEWABLE CORPORATION; *U.S. Public*, pg. 395

BROOKFIELD RENEWABLE PARTNERS L.P.—See Brookfield Corporation; *Int'l*, pg. 1186

BROOKFIELD RENEWABLE POWER PREFERRED EQUITY INC.—See Brookfield Corporation; *Int'l*, pg. 1186

BROOKFIELD RESIDENTIAL (ALBERTA) LP—See Brookfield Corporation; *Int'l*, pg. 1187

BROOKFIELD RESIDENTIAL PROPERTIES INC.—See Brookfield Corporation; *Int'l*, pg. 1187

BROOKFIELD RESIDENTIAL SERVICES LTD.—See Brookfield Corporation; *Int'l*, pg. 1187

BROOKFIELD SQUARE PARCEL, LLC—See CBL & Associates Properties, Inc.; *U.S. Public*, pg. 457

BROOKFIELD VILLAGE MANAGEMENT PTY LTD—See Lifestyle Communities Limited; *Int'l*, pg. 4494

BROOKFIELD VISCOMETERS, LTD.—See AMETEK, Inc.; *U.S. Public*, pg. 120

BROOK FURNITURE RENTAL, INC.; *U.S. Private*, pg. 663

BROOKHAVEN COUNTRY CLUB—See Apollo Global Management, Inc.; *U.S. Public*, pg. 149

BROOKHAVEN HOSPITAL, INC.—See Vizion Health LLC; *U.S. Private*, pg. 4407

BROOKHAVEN MEDICAL, INC.; *U.S. Private*, pg. 663

BROOKHILL GROUP INC.; *U.S. Private*, pg. 663

BROOKHOLLOW CORPORATION—See Martin Marietta Materials, Inc.; *U.S. Public*, pg. 1389

BROOKHURST, INC.; *U.S. Private*, pg. 663

THE BROOKINGS INSTITUTION; *U.S. Private*, pg. 4001

BROOKINGS NEWSPAPERS LLC—See News Media Corporation; *U.S. Private*, pg. 2916

BROOK LANE; *U.S. Private*, pg. 663

BROOK LAPPING PRODUCTIONS LIMITED—See Zinc Media Group plc; *Int'l*, pg. 8684

BROOKLAWN INC.; *U.S. Private*, pg. 663

BROOKLAWN INSURANCE AGENCY, INC.—See Kaplansky Insurance Agency, Inc.; *U.S. Private*, pg. 2261

BROOK LEDGE INC—See Gotwals Inc.; *U.S. Private*, pg. 1745

BROOKLINE BANCORP, INC.

BROOKLINE BANCORP, INC.; *U.S. Public*, pg. 395
BROOKLINE BANK—See Brookline Bancorp, Inc.; *U.S. Public*, pg. 396
BROOKLINE FURNITURE CO, LLC—See Heartwood Partners, LLC; *U.S. Private*, pg. 1901
BROOKLINE PUBLIC RELATIONS INC.; *Int'l*, pg. 1194
BROOKLIN MEDICAL CENTRE—See WELL Health Technologies Corp.; *Int'l*, pg. 8372
BROOKLYN ACADEMY OF MUSIC, INC.; *U.S. Private*, pg. 663
BROOKLYN BEDDING LLC—See Cerberus Capital Management, L.P.; *U.S. Private*, pg. 837
BROOKLYN BOTANIC GARDEN CORPORATION; *U.S. Private*, pg. 663
BROOKLYN BOTTLING CO. OF MILTON, NY; *U.S. Private*, pg. 663
BROOKLYN BOWL LAS VEGAS, LLC—See Live Nation Entertainment, Inc.; *U.S. Public*, pg. 1328
BROOKLYN BREWERY CORPORATION; *U.S. Private*, pg. 663
THE BROOKLYN BROTHERS LIMITED—See The Interpublic Group of Companies, Inc.; *U.S. Public*, pg. 2094
BROOKLYN CHILDREN'S MUSEUM INC.; *U.S. Private*, pg. 663
BROOKLYN ELEVATOR INC.; *U.S. Private*, pg. 663
BROOKLYN FORD; *U.S. Private*, pg. 663
BROOKLYN INDUSTRIES; *U.S. Private*, pg. 663
BROOKLYN INSTITUTE OF ARTS AND SCIENCES; *U.S. Private*, pg. 664
BROOKLYN NETS—See Onexim Group Limited; *Int'l*, pg. 5581
BROOKLYN UNDERWRITING PTY LIMITED—See AXA S.A.; *Int'l*, pg. 760
BROOKMAN-FELS ASSOCIATES INCORPORATED; *U.S. Private*, pg. 664
BROOKMAY PROPERTIES (PTY) LIMITED—See Esor Limited; *Int'l*, pg. 2504
BROOK MAYS MUSIC COMPANY INC.; *U.S. Private*, pg. 663
BROOK MOTORS LTD—See Wolong Holding Group Co., Ltd.; *Int'l*, pg. 8443
BROOKRIDGE FUNDING CORP.; *U.S. Private*, pg. 664
BROOKS ASSOCIATES INC.; *U.S. Private*, pg. 664
BROOKS AUTOMATION AG—See Azenta, Inc.; *U.S. Public*, pg. 258
BROOKS AUTOMATION FRANCE SAS—See Azenta, Inc.; *U.S. Public*, pg. 257
BROOKS AUTOMATION (GERMANY) GMBH - MISTELGAU—See Azenta, Inc.; *U.S. Public*, pg. 257
BROOKS AUTOMATION (GERMANY) GMBH—See Azenta, Inc.; *U.S. Public*, pg. 257
BROOKS AUTOMATION, INC. CTI-CRYOGENICS PRODUCTS CENTER—See Atlas Copco AB; *Int'l*, pg. 682
BROOKS AUTOMATION, INC.—See Azenta, Inc.; *U.S. Public*, pg. 257
BROOKS AUTOMATION ISRAEL, LTD.—See Azenta, Inc.; *U.S. Public*, pg. 257
BROOKS AUTOMATION KOREA, LTD.—See Azenta, Inc.; *U.S. Public*, pg. 257
BROOKS AUTOMATION LUXEMBOURG SARL—See Azenta, Inc.; *U.S. Public*, pg. 257
BROOKS AUTOMATION (SINGAPORE), PTE LTD.—See Azenta, Inc.; *U.S. Public*, pg. 257
BROOKS AUTOMATION TAIWAN COMPANY LTD.—See Azenta, Inc.; *U.S. Public*, pg. 257
BROOKS AUTO SUPPLY INC.; *U.S. Private*, pg. 664
BROOKS BIDDLE AUTOMOTIVE; *U.S. Private*, pg. 664
BROOKS & BROOKS SERVICES INC.; *U.S. Private*, pg. 664
BROOKS BROTHERS, INC.; *U.S. Private*, pg. 664
BROOKS CCS GMBH—See Azenta, Inc.; *U.S. Public*, pg. 257
BROOKS CCS JAPAN KK—See Azenta, Inc.; *U.S. Public*, pg. 257
BROOKS CCS RS AG—See Azenta, Inc.; *U.S. Public*, pg. 257
BROOKS CONSTRUCTION COMPANY; *U.S. Private*, pg. 664
BROOKS ELECTRONICS INC.—See Legrand S.A.; *Int'l*, pg. 4446
BROOKS EQUIPMENT COMPANY, LLC—See H.I.G. Capital, LLC; *U.S. Private*, pg. 1827
BROOKS FORGINGS LTD.; *Int'l*, pg. 1194
BROOKS & FREUND, LLC; *U.S. Private*, pg. 664
BROOKS GROUP INSURANCE AGENCY, LLC.—See CCP Fund III Management LLC; *U.S. Private*, pg. 801
BROOKSHIRE BROTHERS, LTD.; *U.S. Private*, pg. 664
BROOKSHIRE GROCERY COMPANY; *U.S. Private*, pg. 664
BROOKSIDE CAPITAL, INC.; *U.S. Private*, pg. 665
BROOKSIDE CAPITAL, LLC—See Bain Capital, LP; *U.S. Private*, pg. 437
BROOKSIDE CAPITAL PARTNERS FUND, L.P.—See Bain Capital, LP; *U.S. Private*, pg. 437
BROOKSIDE ENTERPRISES, LLC; *U.S. Private*, pg. 665
BROOKSIDE EQUIPMENT SALES; *U.S. Private*, pg. 665
BROOKSIDE EQUITY PARTNERS LLC—See Brookside International Incorporated; *U.S. Private*, pg. 665

BROOKSIDE INTERNATIONAL INCORPORATED; *U.S. Private*, pg. 665
BROOKSIDE LUMBER COMPANY; *U.S. Private*, pg. 665
BROOKSIDE METAL COMPANY LTD—See Amalgamated Metal Corporation PLC; *Int'l*, pg. 408
BROOKSIDE VILLAGE MOBILE HOME PARK, LLC—See Sun Communities, Inc.; *U.S. Public*, pg. 1961
BROOKS INCORPORATED; *U.S. Private*, pg. 664
BROOKS INSTITUTE—See Perdoceo Education Corporation; *U.S. Public*, pg. 1673
BROOKS INSTRUMENT B.V.—See Illinois Tool Works Inc.; *U.S. Public*, pg. 1102
BROOKS INSTRUMENT GMBH—See Illinois Tool Works Inc.; *U.S. Public*, pg. 1102
BROOKS INSTRUMENT INDIA PRIVATE LIMITED—See Illinois Tool Works Inc.; *U.S. Public*, pg. 1102
BROOKS INSTRUMENT KFT—See Illinois Tool Works Inc.; *U.S. Public*, pg. 1102
BROOKS INSTRUMENT K.K.—See Illinois Tool Works Inc.; *U.S. Public*, pg. 1102
BROOKS INSTRUMENT KOREA, LTD.—See Illinois Tool Works Inc.; *U.S. Public*, pg. 1102
BROOKS INSTRUMENT, LLC—See Illinois Tool Works Inc.; *U.S. Public*, pg. 1102
BROOKS INSTRUMENT SINGAPORE PTE, LTD.—See Illinois Tool Works Inc.; *U.S. Public*, pg. 1102
BROOKS JAPAN K.K.—See Azenta, Inc.; *U.S. Public*, pg. 257
BROOKS LABORATORIES LIMITED; *Int'l*, pg. 1194
BROOKS LIFE SCIENCES—See Azenta, Inc.; *U.S. Public*, pg. 258
BROOKS LIFE SCIENCE SYSTEMS—See Azenta, Inc.; *U.S. Public*, pg. 257
BROOKS LIFE SCIENCE SYSTEMS—See Azenta, Inc.; *U.S. Public*, pg. 257
BROOKS MACDONALD ASSET MANAGEMENT LIMITED—See Brooks Macdonald Group plc; *Int'l*, pg. 1194
BROOKS MACDONALD ASSET MANAGEMENT (TUNBRIDGE WELLS) LIMITED—See Brooks Macdonald Group plc; *Int'l*, pg. 1194
BROOKS MACDONALD FUNDS LIMITED—See Brooks Macdonald Group plc; *Int'l*, pg. 1194
BROOKS MACDONALD GROUP PLC; *Int'l*, pg. 1194
BROOKS MEMORIAL HOSPITAL; *U.S. Private*, pg. 664
BROOKS MUFFLER & BRAKE CENTER; *U.S. Private*, pg. 664
BROOKS PEANUT COMPANY, INC.—See Temasek Holdings (Private) Limited; *Int'l*, pg. 7549
BROOKS RESOURCES CORPORATION; *U.S. Private*, pg. 664
BROOKS RESOURCES SALES CORP.—See Brooks Resources Corporation; *U.S. Private*, pg. 664
BROOKS RESTAURANTS INC.; *U.S. Private*, pg. 664
BROOKS RUN MINING COMPANY, LLC—See Alpha Natural Resources, Inc.; *U.S. Private*, pg. 199
BROOKS SPORTS INC.—See Berkshire Hathaway Inc.; *U.S. Public*, pg. 305
BROOKS TECHNOLOGY (SHANGHAI) LIMITED—See Azenta, Inc.; *U.S. Public*, pg. 258
BROOKSTONE COMPANY, INC.—See Bluestar Alliance LLC; *U.S. Private*, pg. 598
BROOKSTONE COMPANY, INC.—See B. Riley Financial, Inc.; *U.S. Public*, pg. 262
BROOKSTONE HOLDINGS, INC.; *U.S. Private*, pg. 665
BROOKS TRACTOR INCORPORATED—See Brooks Incorporated; *U.S. Private*, pg. 664
BROOK STREET BUREAU PLC—See ManpowerGroup Inc.; *U.S. Public*, pg. 1359
BROOK STREET (UK) LIMITED—See ManpowerGroup Inc.; *U.S. Public*, pg. 1359
BROOKS UTILITY PRODUCTS GROUP—See Bertram Capital Management, LLC; *U.S. Private*, pg. 540
BROOKS UTILITY PRODUCTS GROUP—See Crimson Investment; *U.S. Private*, pg. 1100
BROOKSVILLE HMA PHYSICIAN MANAGEMENT, LLC—See Community Health Systems, Inc.; *U.S. Public*, pg. 551
BROOKVALE INTERNATIONAL CORPORATION—See California Cartage Company LLC; *U.S. Private*, pg. 718
BROOKVIEW LP—See UMH Properties, Inc.; *U.S. Public*, pg. 2224
BROOKVILLE CARRIERS FLATBED LP—See TFI International Inc.; *Int'l*, pg. 7585
BROOKVILLE CARRIERS VAN LP—See TFI International Inc.; *Int'l*, pg. 7585
BROOKVILLE GLOVE MANUFACTURING COMPANY, INC.—See BSI Diversified LLC; *U.S. Private*, pg. 675
BROOK & WHITTLE LIMITED—See Genstar Capital, LLC; *U.S. Private*, pg. 1676
BROOKWOOD BAPTIST IMAGING, LLC—See Tenet Healthcare Corporation; *U.S. Public*, pg. 2001
BROOKWOOD CENTER DEVELOPMENT CORPORATION—See Tenet Healthcare Corporation; *U.S. Public*, pg. 2007
BROOKWOOD COMPANIES INC.—See Hallwood Group, LLC; *U.S. Private*, pg. 1845
BROOKWOOD HEALTH SERVICES, INC.—See Tenet Healthcare Corporation; *U.S. Public*, pg. 2008

CORPORATE AFFILIATIONS

BROOKWOOD HOME HEALTH, LLC—See Tenet Healthcare Corporation; *U.S. Public*, pg. 2008
BROOKWOOD - MATERNAL FETAL MEDICINE, L.L.C.—See Tenet Healthcare Corporation; *U.S. Public*, pg. 2002
BROOKWOOD MEDICAL PARTNERS - ENT, L.L.C.—See Tenet Healthcare Corporation; *U.S. Public*, pg. 2002
BROOKWOOD PRIMARY CARE CAHABA HEIGHTS, L.L.C.—See Tenet Healthcare Corporation; *U.S. Public*, pg. 2002
BROOKWOOD PRIMARY CARE - GRAND RIVER, L.L.C.—See Tenet Healthcare Corporation; *U.S. Public*, pg. 2001
BROOKWOOD PRIMARY CARE HOOVER, L.L.C.—See Tenet Healthcare Corporation; *U.S. Public*, pg. 2002
BROOKWOOD PRIMARY CARE - INVERNESS, L.L.C.—See Tenet Healthcare Corporation; *U.S. Public*, pg. 2002
BROOKWOOD PRIMARY CARE - MOUNTAIN BROOK, L.L.C.—See Tenet Healthcare Corporation; *U.S. Public*, pg. 2002
BROOKWOOD PRIMARY CARE - OAK MOUNTAIN, L.L.C.—See Tenet Healthcare Corporation; *U.S. Public*, pg. 2002
BROOKWOOD PRIMARY CARE THE NARROWS, L.L.C.—See Tenet Healthcare Corporation; *U.S. Public*, pg. 2002
BROOKWOOD SPECIALTY CARE - ENDOCRINOLOGY, L.L.C.—See Tenet Healthcare Corporation; *U.S. Public*, pg. 2002
BROOKWOOD SPORTS AND ORTHOPEDICS, L.L.C.—See Tenet Healthcare Corporation; *U.S. Public*, pg. 2003
BROOKWOOD WOMEN'S CARE, L.L.C.—See Tenet Healthcare Corporation; *U.S. Public*, pg. 2003
BROOKWOOD WOMEN'S DIAGNOSTIC CENTER, LLC—See Tenet Healthcare Corporation; *U.S. Public*, pg. 2009
BROO LIMITED; *Int'l*, pg. 1174
BROOME OLDSMOBILE CADILLAC INC.; *U.S. Private*, pg. 665
BROOMFIELD ENTERPRISE—See Alden Global Capital LLC; *U.S. Private*, pg. 157
BROOMFIELD LABORATORIES INC.; *U.S. Private*, pg. 665
BROPFS CORPORATION; *U.S. Private*, pg. 665
BROPLAST S.A.R.L—See Aurea, S.A.; *Int'l*, pg. 707
BRO RETAIL GROUP INC.; *U.S. Private*, pg. 658
BROSA DESIGN PTY. LTD.—See Kogan.com Ltd; *Int'l*, pg. 4228
BROS EASTERN CO., LTD.; *Int'l*, pg. 1195
BROSE AUNDE FAHRZEUGITSZE GMBH—See Brose Fahrzeugteile GmbH & Co. KG; *Int'l*, pg. 1195
BROSE AUTOMOTIVE LA SUZE S.A.S.—See Brose Fahrzeugteile GmbH & Co. KG; *Int'l*, pg. 1195
BROSE BEIJING AUTOMOTIVE SYSTEMS CO., LTD.—See Brose Fahrzeugteile GmbH & Co. KG; *Int'l*, pg. 1195
BROSE BELVIDERE INC.—See Brose Fahrzeugteile GmbH & Co. KG; *Int'l*, pg. 1195
BROSE BRATISLAVA, SPOL. S R.O.—See Brose Fahrzeugteile GmbH & Co. KG; *Int'l*, pg. 1195
BROSE CANADA INC—See Brose Fahrzeugteile GmbH & Co. KG; *Int'l*, pg. 1195
BROSE CHANGCHUN AUTOMOTIVE SYSTEMS CO., LTD.—See Brose Fahrzeugteile GmbH & Co. KG; *Int'l*, pg. 1195
BROSE CHICAGO, INC.—See Brose Fahrzeugteile GmbH & Co. KG; *Int'l*, pg. 1195
BROSE CHINA CO., LTD.—See Brose Fahrzeugteile GmbH & Co. KG; *Int'l*, pg. 1195
BROSE CHONGQING AUTOMOTIVE SYSTEMS CO., LTD.—See Brose Fahrzeugteile GmbH & Co. KG; *Int'l*, pg. 1195
BROSE CZ SPOL. S R.O.—See Brose Fahrzeugteile GmbH & Co. KG; *Int'l*, pg. 1195
BROSE DELLOYD AUTOMOTIVE CO., LTD.—See Brose Fahrzeugteile GmbH & Co. KG; *Int'l*, pg. 1195
BROSE DO BRASIL LTDA.—See Brose Fahrzeugteile GmbH & Co. KG; *Int'l*, pg. 1196
BROSE FAHRZEUGTEILE GMBH & CO. KG; *Int'l*, pg. 1195
BROSE FAHRZEUGTEILE GMBH—See Brose Fahrzeugteile GmbH & Co. KG; *Int'l*, pg. 1195
BROSE FRANCE S.A.S.—See Brose Fahrzeugteile GmbH & Co. KG; *Int'l*, pg. 1195
BROSE GENT BVBA—See Brose Fahrzeugteile GmbH & Co. KG; *Int'l*, pg. 1195
BROSE GUANGZHOU AUTOMOTIVE SYSTEMS CO., LTD.—See Brose Fahrzeugteile GmbH & Co. KG; *Int'l*, pg. 1195
BROSE HUNGARY AUTOMOTIVE KFT.—See Brose Fahrzeugteile GmbH & Co. KG; *Int'l*, pg. 1195
BROSE INDIA AUTOMOTIVE SYSTEMS PVT LTD.—See Brose Fahrzeugteile GmbH & Co. KG; *Int'l*, pg. 1195
BROSE ITALIA S.R.L.—See Brose Fahrzeugteile GmbH & Co. KG; *Int'l*, pg. 1195
BROSE JAPAN LTD.—See Brose Fahrzeugteile GmbH & Co. KG; *Int'l*, pg. 1195

COMPANY NAME INDEX

BROSE JEFFERSON, INC.—See Brose Fahrzeugteile GmbH & Co. KG; *Int'l*, pg. 1195
BROSE KOREA LTD.—See Brose Fahrzeugteile GmbH & Co. KG; *Int'l*, pg. 1195
BROSE LIMITED—See Brose Fahrzeugteile GmbH & Co. KG; *Int'l*, pg. 1195
BROSE MELFI AUTOMOTIVE S.R.L.—See Brose Fahrzeugteile GmbH & Co. KG; *Int'l*, pg. 1195
BROSE MEXICO, S.A. DE C. V.—See Brose Fahrzeugteile GmbH & Co. KG; *Int'l*, pg. 1195
BROSE NEW BOSTON, INC.—See Brose Fahrzeugteile GmbH & Co. KG; *Int'l*, pg. 1195
BROSE NORTH AMERICA, INC.—See Brose Fahrzeugteile GmbH & Co. KG; *Int'l*, pg. 1195
BROSE PRIEVIDZA SPOL. S.R.O.—See Brose Fahrzeugteile GmbH & Co. KG; *Int'l*, pg. 1195
BROSE PUEBLA, S.A. DE C.V.—See Brose Fahrzeugteile GmbH & Co. KG; *Int'l*, pg. 1195
BROSE QUERETARO S.A. DE C.V.—See Brose Fahrzeugteile GmbH & Co. KG; *Int'l*, pg. 1195
BROSE RUSSLAND LLC—See Brose Fahrzeugteile GmbH & Co. KG; *Int'l*, pg. 1195
BROSE S. A.—See Brose Fahrzeugteile GmbH & Co. KG; *Int'l*, pg. 1195
BROSE SCHLIESSSYSTEME GMBH & CO., KG—See Brose Fahrzeugteile GmbH & Co. KG; *Int'l*, pg. 1195
BROSE SHANGHAI AUTOMOTIVE SYSTEMS CO., LTD.—See Brose Fahrzeugteile GmbH & Co. KG; *Int'l*, pg. 1195
BROSE SHENYANG AUTOMOTIVE SYSTEMS CO., LTD.—See Brose Fahrzeugteile GmbH & Co. KG; *Int'l*, pg. 1195
BROSE SISTEMAS DE FECHADURAS PARA AUTO-MOVEIS, UNIPESSOAL LDA.—See Brose Fahrzeugteile GmbH & Co. KG; *Int'l*, pg. 1196
BROSE SPARTANBURG, INC.—See Brose Fahrzeugteile GmbH & Co. KG; *Int'l*, pg. 1196
BROSE SWEDEN AB—See Brose Fahrzeugteile GmbH & Co. KG; *Int'l*, pg. 1196
BROSE TAICANG AUTOMOTIVE SYSTEMS CO., LTD.—See Brose Fahrzeugteile GmbH & Co. KG; *Int'l*, pg. 1196
BROSE (THAILAND) CO., LTD.—See Brose Fahrzeugteile GmbH & Co. KG; *Int'l*, pg. 1195
BROSE TOGLIATTI AUTOMOTIVE LLC—See Brose Fahrzeugteile GmbH & Co. KG; *Int'l*, pg. 1196
BROSE TUSCALOOSA, INC.—See Brose Fahrzeugteile GmbH & Co. KG; *Int'l*, pg. 1195
BROSE WUHAN AUTOMOTIVE SYSTEMS CO., LTD.—See Brose Fahrzeugteile GmbH & Co. KG; *Int'l*, pg. 1196
BROS HOLDING LTD.—See Bros Eastern Co., Ltd.; *Int'l*, pg. 1195
BROS MANAGEMENT INC.; *U.S. Private*, pg. 665
BROSPOWER CO., LTD.—See P-Duke Technology Co., Ltd.; *Int'l*, pg. 5681
BROSSETTE SAS—See Compagnie de Saint-Gobain SA; *Int'l*, pg. 1724
BROSSE USA INC.—See Zignago Vetro S.p.A.; *Int'l*, pg. 8682
BROS SPINNING (SHENZHEN) CO., LTD.—See Bros Eastern Co., Ltd.; *Int'l*, pg. 1195
BROSTROM AB—See A.P. Moller-Maersk A/S; *Int'l*, pg. 26
BROSTROM HOLDING BV—See A.P. Moller-Maersk A/S; *Int'l*, pg. 26
BROSTROM TANKERS AB—See A.P. Moller-Maersk A/S; *Int'l*, pg. 26
BROSTROM TANKERS SAS—See A.P. Moller-Maersk A/S; *Int'l*, pg. 26
BROTEX (VIETNAM) CO., LTD—See Bros Eastern Co., Ltd.; *Int'l*, pg. 1195
BROTHER CENTRAL AND EASTERN EUROPE GMBH—See Brother Industries, Ltd.; *Int'l*, pg. 1196
BROTHER (CHINA) LTD.—See Brother Industries, Ltd.; *Int'l*, pg. 1196
BROTHER COMMERCIAL (THAILAND) LTD.—See Brother Industries, Ltd.; *Int'l*, pg. 1196
BROTHER CORPORATION (ASIA) LTD.—See Brother Industries, Ltd.; *Int'l*, pg. 1196
BROTHER ENTERPRISE, LTD.—See Brother Industries, Ltd.; *Int'l*, pg. 1196
BROTHER ENTERPRISES HOLDING CO., LTD.; *Int'l*, pg. 1196
BROTHER FINANCE (JAPAN), LTD.—See Brother Industries, Ltd.; *Int'l*, pg. 1196
BROTHER FINANCE (U.K.) PLC—See Brother Industries, Ltd.; *Int'l*, pg. 1196
BROTHER HOLDING (EUROPE) LTD.—See Brother Industries, Ltd.; *Int'l*, pg. 1196
BROTHERHOOD BANCSHARES INC.; *U.S. Public*, pg. 396
BROTHERHOOD BANK & TRUST CO—See Brotherhood Bancshares Inc.; *U.S. Public*, pg. 396
BROTHERHOOD'S RELIEF AND COMPENSATION FUND; *U.S. Private*, pg. 665
BROTHER IBERIA, S.L.U.—See Brother Industries, Ltd.; *Int'l*, pg. 1196
BROTHER INDUSTRIAL PRINTING (JAPAN), LTD.—See Brother Industries, Ltd.; *Int'l*, pg. 1197

BROTHER INDUSTRIES, LTD.; *Int'l*, pg. 1196
BROTHER INDUSTRIES (PHILIPPINES), INC.—See Brother Industries, Ltd.; *Int'l*, pg. 1197
BROTHER INDUSTRIES (SHENZHEN) LTD.—See Brother Industries, Ltd.; *Int'l*, pg. 1197
BROTHER INDUSTRIES (SLOVAKIA) S.R.O.—See Brother Industries, Ltd.; *Int'l*, pg. 1197
BROTHER INDUSTRIES TECHNOLOGY (MALAYSIA) SDN. BHD.—See Brother Industries, Ltd.; *Int'l*, pg. 1197
BROTHER INDUSTRIES TECHNOLOGY (M) SDN. BHD.—See Brother Industries, Ltd.; *Int'l*, pg. 1197
BROTHER INDUSTRIES (U.K.) LTD.—See Brother Industries, Ltd.; *Int'l*, pg. 1197
BROTHER INDUSTRIES (U.S.A.), INC.—See Brother Industries, Ltd.; *Int'l*, pg. 1197
BROTHER INDUSTRIES (VIETNAM) LTD.—See Brother Industries, Ltd.; *Int'l*, pg. 1197
BROTHER INTERNATIONAL CORPORATION (CANADA) LTD.—See Brother Industries, Ltd.; *Int'l*, pg. 1197
BROTHER INTERNATIONAL CORPORATION DE ARGENTINA S.R.L.—See Brother Industries, Ltd.; *Int'l*, pg. 1197
BROTHER INTERNATIONAL CORPORATION DO BRAZIL, LTDA.—See Brother Industries, Ltd.; *Int'l*, pg. 1197
BROTHER INTERNATIONAL CORPORATION - USA—See Brother Industries, Ltd.; *Int'l*, pg. 1197
BROTHER INTERNATIONAL DE CHILE, LTDA.—See Brother Industries, Ltd.; *Int'l*, pg. 1197
BROTHER INTERNATIONAL DEL PERU S.A.C.—See Brother Industries, Ltd.; *Int'l*, pg. 1196
BROTHER INTERNATIONAL DE MEXICO, S.A. DE C.V.—See Brother Industries, Ltd.; *Int'l*, pg. 1197
BROTHER INTERNATIONAL KOREA CO., LTD.—See Brother Industries, Ltd.; *Int'l*, pg. 1196
BROTHER INTERNATIONAL TAIWAN LTD.—See Brother Industries, Ltd.; *Int'l*, pg. 1197
BROTHER LIVING CO., LTD.—See Brother Industries, Ltd.; *Int'l*, pg. 1197
BROTHER LOGITEC LTD.—See Brother Industries, Ltd.; *Int'l*, pg. 1196
BROTHER MACHINERY (ASIA) LTD.—See Brother Industries, Ltd.; *Int'l*, pg. 1197
BROTHER MACHINERY SHANGHAI LTD.—See Brother Industries, Ltd.; *Int'l*, pg. 1197
BROTHER MACHINERY XIAN CO., LTD.—See Brother Industries, Ltd.; *Int'l*, pg. 1197
BROTHER MOBILE SOLUTIONS, INC.—See Brother Industries, Ltd.; *Int'l*, pg. 1197
BROTHER NORDIC A/S—See Brother Industries, Ltd.; *Int'l*, pg. 1197
BROTHER POLSKA SP. Z O.O—See Brother Industries, Ltd.; *Int'l*, pg. 1196
BROTHER REAL ESTATE, LTD.—See Brother Industries, Ltd.; *Int'l*, pg. 1197
BROTHERS AIR & HEAT, INC.—See Del-Air Heating, Air Conditioning & Refrigeration Corp.; *U.S. Private*, pg. 1193
BROTHER SALES, LTD.—See Brother Industries, Ltd.; *Int'l*, pg. 1197
BROTHERS AUTO SALVAGE YARD, INC.—See Stellex Capital Management LP; *U.S. Private*, pg. 3800
BROTHER'S BROTHER FOUNDATION; *U.S. Private*, pg. 665
BROTHERS & CO.; *U.S. Private*, pg. 665
BROTHER SEWING MACHINES EUROPE GMBH—See Brother Industries, Ltd.; *Int'l*, pg. 1196
BROTHER SEWING MACHINE (SHANGHAI) CO., LTD.—See Brother Industries, Ltd.; *Int'l*, pg. 1197
BROTHERS INTERNATIONAL CORP; *U.S. Private*, pg. 665
BROTHERS INTERNATIONAL DESSERTS, INC.; *U.S. Private*, pg. 665
BROTHER SOFTWARE DEVELOPMENT (HANGZHOU) LTD.—See Brother Industries, Ltd.; *Int'l*, pg. 1196
BROTHERS PROPERTY CORPORATION—See American Financial Group, Inc.; *U.S. Public*, pg. 103
BROTHERS & SISTERS SVERIGE AB—See Coala-Life Group AB; *Int'l*, pg. 1640
BROTHERS TEXTILE MILLS LIMITED; *Int'l*, pg. 1198
BROTHERS TRADING CO. INC.; *U.S. Private*, pg. 665
BROTHER SYSTEM TECHNOLOGY DEVELOPMENT (HANGZHOU) LTD.—See Brother Industries, Ltd.; *Int'l*, pg. 1197
BROTHER TECHNOLOGY (SHENZHEN) LTD.—See Brother Industries, Ltd.; *Int'l*, pg. 1196
BROTJE AUTOMATION GMBH—See Claas KGaA mbH; *Int'l*, pg. 1640
BROTMAN WINTER FRIED COMMUNICATIONS; *U.S. Private*, pg. 665
BROTOMATIC S.L.; *Int'l*, pg. 1198
BROUGHTON FOODS LLC—See Dean Foods Company; *U.S. Private*, pg. 1183
BROUGHTONS OF CHELTENHAM LTD—See Berjaya Corporation Berhad; *Int'l*, pg. 983
BROULIMS SUPER MARKET INC.; *U.S. Private*, pg. 665
BROUSSARD PARTNERS & ASSOCIATES—See Guggenheim Partners, LLC; *U.S. Private*, pg. 1812

BROUSSARD POCHE LEWIS BREAUX LLC; *U.S. Private*, pg. 665
BROUWERIJ BELAME LTD—See Fibemi NV; *Int'l*, pg. 2651
BROUWERIJ DE KONINCK NV—See Fibemi NV; *Int'l*, pg. 2651
BROUWERIJ VAN HOEGAARDEN N.V.—See Anheuser-Busch InBev SA/NV; *Int'l*, pg. 466
BROUWERS EQUIPMENT B.V.—See GEA Group Aktiengesellschaft; *Int'l*, pg. 2897
BROWALLIA AB—See Bronsstadet AB; *Int'l*, pg. 1174
BROWARD BEHAVIORAL HEALTH COALITION, INC.; *U.S. Private*, pg. 666
BROWARD HEALTH; *U.S. Private*, pg. 666
BROWARD NEUROSURGEONS, LLC—See HCA Healthcare, Inc.; *U.S. Public*, pg. 992
BROWARD ONCOLOGY ASSOCIATES, P.A.—See The Oncology Institute, Inc.; *U.S. Public*, pg. 2118
BROWAVE CORPORATION; *Int'l*, pg. 1198
BROWER EQUIPMENT—See Hawkeye Steel Products, Inc.; *U.S. Private*, pg. 1882
THE BROWER GLASS TINTING COMPANY—See Solar Art Window Film, Inc.; *U.S. Private*, pg. 3707
BROWN ADVISORY US SMALLER COMPANIES PLC; *Int'l*, pg. 1198
BROWN AEROSPACE MFG. SYSTEMS, LLC—See AIP, LLC; *U.S. Private*, pg. 133
BROWN AND CALDWELL; *U.S. Private*, pg. 666
BROWN APPLIANCE PARTS COMPANY; *U.S. Private*, pg. 666
BROWN AUTOMOTIVE GROUP, INC.; *U.S. Private*, pg. 666
BROWN & BIGELOW, INC.; *U.S. Private*, pg. 666
BROWNBOOTS INTERACTIVE, INC.; *U.S. Private*, pg. 669
BROWN BROS. CADILLAC, INC.; *U.S. Private*, pg. 666
BROWN BROS FORD LINCOLN SALES & SERVICE; *Int'l*, pg. 1198
BROWN BROTHERS DISTRIBUTION LIMITED—See PPG Industries, Inc.; *U.S. Public*, pg. 1707
BROWN BROTHERS DISTRIBUTION LIMITED—See Brown Brothers Harriman & Co.; *U.S. Private*, pg. 666
BROWN BROTHERS HARRIMAN & CO.; *U.S. Private*, pg. 666
BROWN BROTHERS HARRIMAN FUND ADMINISTRATION SERVICES (IRELAND) LIMITED—See Brown Brothers Harriman & Co.; *U.S. Private*, pg. 667
BROWN BROTHERS HARRIMAN (HONG KONG) LTD.—See Brown Brothers Harriman & Co.; *U.S. Private*, pg. 666
BROWN BROTHERS HARRIMAN INVESTORS SERVICES INCORPORATED—See Brown Brothers Harriman & Co.; *U.S. Private*, pg. 667
BROWN BROTHERS HARRIMAN (LUXEMBOURG) S.A.—See Brown Brothers Harriman & Co.; *U.S. Private*, pg. 666
BROWN BROTHERS HARRIMAN (POLAND) SP. Z O.O.—See Brown Brothers Harriman & Co.; *U.S. Private*, pg. 667
BROWN BROTHERS HARRIMAN SECURITIES (JAPAN) INC.—See Brown Brothers Harriman & Co.; *U.S. Private*, pg. 667
BROWN BROTHERS HARRIMAN SERVICES AG—See Brown Brothers Harriman & Co.; *U.S. Private*, pg. 667
BROWN BROTHERS HARRIMAN TRUST CO. (CAYMAN) LTD.—See Brown Brothers Harriman & Co.; *U.S. Private*, pg. 667
BROWN BROTHERS HARRIMAN TRUST CO., LLC—See Brown Brothers Harriman & Co.; *U.S. Private*, pg. 667
BROWN BROTHERS HARRIMAN TRUST COMPANY, N. A.—See Brown Brothers Harriman & Co.; *U.S. Private*, pg. 667
BROWN BROTHERS HARRIMAN TRUST COMPANY OF DELAWARE, N. A.—See Brown Brothers Harriman & Co.; *U.S. Private*, pg. 667
BROWN BROTHERS HARRIMAN TRUSTEE SERVICES (IRELAND) LIMITED—See Brown Brothers Harriman & Co.; *U.S. Private*, pg. 667
BROWN & BROWN ABSENCE SERVICES GROUP, LLC—See Brown & Brown, Inc.; *U.S. Public*, pg. 397
BROWN & BROWN AGENCY OF INSURANCE PROFESSIONALS, INC.—See Brown & Brown, Inc.; *U.S. Public*, pg. 397
BROWN & BROWN BENEFIT ADVISORS, INC.—See Brown & Brown, Inc.; *U.S. Public*, pg. 397
BROWN & BROWN CHEVROLET, INC.—See AutoNation, Inc.; *U.S. Public*, pg. 233
BROWN & BROWN CHEVROLET - SUPERSTITION SPRINGS, LLC—See AutoNation, Inc.; *U.S. Public*, pg. 233
BROWN & BROWN DISASTER RELIEF FOUNDATION, INC.—See Brown & Brown, Inc.; *U.S. Public*, pg. 397
BROWN & BROWN (EUROPE) LIMITED—See Brown & Brown, Inc.; *U.S. Public*, pg. 397
BROWN & BROWN, INC.; *U.S. Public*, pg. 396
BROWN & BROWN, INC. - TAMPA CORPORATE OFFICE—See Brown & Brown, Inc.; *U.S. Public*, pg. 400

BROWN & BROWN, INC.

CORPORATE AFFILIATIONS

BROWN & BROWN INSURANCE AGENCY OF VIRGINIA, INC.—See Brown & Brown, Inc.; *U.S. Public*, pg. 397
BROWN & BROWN INSURANCE BROKERS OF SACRAMENTO, INC.—See Brown & Brown, Inc.; *U.S. Public*, pg. 397
BROWN & BROWN INSURANCE OF ARIZONA, INC. - PRESCOTT—See Brown & Brown, Inc.; *U.S. Public*, pg. 398
BROWN & BROWN INSURANCE OF ARIZONA, INC.—See Brown & Brown, Inc.; *U.S. Public*, pg. 398
BROWN & BROWN INSURANCE OF GEORGIA, INC.—See Brown & Brown, Inc.; *U.S. Public*, pg. 398
BROWN & BROWN INSURANCE OF NEVADA, INC.—See Brown & Brown, Inc.; *U.S. Public*, pg. 398
BROWN & BROWN INSURANCE SERVICES OF CALIFORNIA, INC.—See Brown & Brown, Inc.; *U.S. Public*, pg. 398
BROWN & BROWN INSURANCE SERVICES OF SAN ANTONIO, INC.—See Brown & Brown, Inc.; *U.S. Public*, pg. 398
BROWN & BROWN INSURANCE SERVICES OF TEXAS, INC.—See Brown & Brown, Inc.; *U.S. Public*, pg. 398
BROWN & BROWN INSURANCE—See Brown & Brown, Inc.; *U.S. Public*, pg. 398
BROWN & BROWN LONE STAR INSURANCE SERVICES, INC.—See Brown & Brown, Inc.; *U.S. Public*, pg. 398
BROWN & BROWN METRO, INC. - MOUNT LAUREL—See Brown & Brown, Inc.; *U.S. Public*, pg. 398
BROWN & BROWN METRO, INC.—See Brown & Brown, Inc.; *U.S. Public*, pg. 398
BROWN & BROWN NISSAN, INC.—See AutoNation, Inc.; *U.S. Public*, pg. 233
BROWN & BROWN NISSAN, INC.—See AutoNation, Inc.; *U.S. Public*, pg. 233
BROWN & BROWN NISSAN MESA, LLC—See AutoNation, Inc.; *U.S. Public*, pg. 233
BROWN & BROWN NISSAN MESA, LLC—See AutoNation, Inc.; *U.S. Public*, pg. 233
BROWN & BROWN OF ARKANSAS, INC.—See Brown & Brown, Inc.; *U.S. Public*, pg. 398
BROWN & BROWN OF BARTLESVILLE, INC.—See Brown & Brown, Inc.; *U.S. Public*, pg. 398
BROWN & BROWN OF CENTRAL MICHIGAN, INC.—See Brown & Brown, Inc.; *U.S. Public*, pg. 398
BROWN & BROWN OF CENTRAL OKLAHOMA, INC.—See Brown & Brown, Inc.; *U.S. Public*, pg. 398
BROWN & BROWN OF COLORADO, INC.—See Brown & Brown, Inc.; *U.S. Public*, pg. 398
BROWN & BROWN OF CONNECTICUT, INC.—See Brown & Brown, Inc.; *U.S. Public*, pg. 398
BROWN & BROWN OF DELAWARE, INC.—See Brown & Brown, Inc.; *U.S. Public*, pg. 398
BROWN & BROWN OF DETROIT, INC.—See Brown & Brown, Inc.; *U.S. Public*, pg. 398
BROWN & BROWN OF FLORIDA, INC. - BREVARD—See Brown & Brown, Inc.; *U.S. Public*, pg. 398
BROWN & BROWN OF FLORIDA, INC. - BROOKSVILLE—See Brown & Brown, Inc.; *U.S. Public*, pg. 398
BROWN & BROWN OF FLORIDA, INC. - FT. LAUDERDALE—See Brown & Brown, Inc.; *U.S. Public*, pg. 398
BROWN & BROWN OF FLORIDA, INC. - FT. MYERS—See Brown & Brown, Inc.; *U.S. Public*, pg. 398
BROWN & BROWN OF FLORIDA, INC. - JACKSONVILLE—See Brown & Brown, Inc.; *U.S. Public*, pg. 398
BROWN & BROWN OF FLORIDA, INC. - LEESBURG—See Brown & Brown, Inc.; *U.S. Public*, pg. 398
BROWN & BROWN OF FLORIDA, INC. - MIAMI—See Brown & Brown, Inc.; *U.S. Public*, pg. 398
BROWN & BROWN OF FLORIDA, INC. - MONTICELLO—See Brown & Brown, Inc.; *U.S. Public*, pg. 398
BROWN & BROWN OF FLORIDA, INC. - NAPLES—See Brown & Brown, Inc.; *U.S. Public*, pg. 398
BROWN & BROWN OF FLORIDA, INC. - ORLANDO—See Brown & Brown, Inc.; *U.S. Public*, pg. 398
BROWN & BROWN OF FLORIDA, INC. - SARASOTA—See Brown & Brown, Inc.; *U.S. Public*, pg. 398
BROWN & BROWN OF FLORIDA, INC.—See Brown & Brown, Inc.; *U.S. Public*, pg. 398
BROWN & BROWN OF FLORIDA, INC. - TAMPA—See Brown & Brown, Inc.; *U.S. Public*, pg. 398
BROWN & BROWN OF FLORIDA, INC. - WEST PALM BEACH—See Brown & Brown, Inc.; *U.S. Public*, pg. 398
BROWN & BROWN OF GARDEN CITY, INC.—See Brown & Brown, Inc.; *U.S. Public*, pg. 399
BROWN & BROWN OF ILLINOIS, INC.—See Brown & Brown, Inc.; *U.S. Public*, pg. 399
BROWN & BROWN OF INDIANA, INC.—See Brown & Brown, Inc.; *U.S. Public*, pg. 399
BROWN & BROWN OF KENTUCKY, INC.—See Brown & Brown, Inc.; *U.S. Public*, pg. 399
BROWN & BROWN OF LEHIGH VALLEY, INC.—See Brown & Brown, Inc.; *U.S. Public*, pg. 399
BROWN & BROWN OF LOUISIANA, INC.—See Brown & Brown, Inc.; *U.S. Public*, pg. 399
BROWN & BROWN OF MASSACHUSETTS, LLC—See Brown & Brown, Inc.; *U.S. Public*, pg. 399
BROWN & BROWN OF MICHIGAN, INC.—See Brown & Brown, Inc.; *U.S. Public*, pg. 399
BROWN & BROWN OF MINNESOTA, INC. - RETAIL DIVISION—See Brown & Brown, Inc.; *U.S. Public*, pg. 399
BROWN & BROWN OF MINNESOTA, INC.—See Brown & Brown, Inc.; *U.S. Public*, pg. 399
BROWN & BROWN OF MISSISSIPPI, LLC—See Brown & Brown, Inc.; *U.S. Public*, pg. 399
BROWN & BROWN OF MISSOURI, INC.—See Brown & Brown, Inc.; *U.S. Public*, pg. 399
BROWN & BROWN OF NEW JERSEY, LLC—See Brown & Brown, Inc.; *U.S. Public*, pg. 399
BROWN & BROWN OF NEW MEXICO, INC. - ALBUQUERQUE—See Brown & Brown, Inc.; *U.S. Public*, pg. 399
BROWN & BROWN OF NEW MEXICO, INC.—See Brown & Brown, Inc.; *U.S. Public*, pg. 399
BROWN & BROWN OF NEW YORK, INC.—See Brown & Brown, Inc.; *U.S. Public*, pg. 399
BROWN & BROWN OF NEW YORK, INC. - SYRACUSE—See Brown & Brown, Inc.; *U.S. Public*, pg. 399
BROWN & BROWN OF NORTHERN CALIFORNIA, INC.—See Brown & Brown, Inc.; *U.S. Public*, pg. 399
BROWN & BROWN OF NORTHERN ILLINOIS, INC.—See Brown & Brown, Inc.; *U.S. Public*, pg. 399
BROWN & BROWN OF OHIO, INC.—See Brown & Brown, Inc.; *U.S. Public*, pg. 399
BROWN & BROWN OF OKLAHOMA, INC.—See Brown & Brown, Inc.; *U.S. Public*, pg. 399
BROWN & BROWN OF OREGON, LLC—See Brown & Brown, Inc.; *U.S. Public*, pg. 399
BROWN & BROWN OF PENNSYLVANIA, INC.—See Brown & Brown, Inc.; *U.S. Public*, pg. 399
BROWN & BROWN OF SOUTH CAROLINA, INC.—See Brown & Brown, Inc.; *U.S. Public*, pg. 399
BROWN & BROWN OF SOUTHWEST INDIANA, INC.—See Brown & Brown, Inc.; *U.S. Public*, pg. 400
BROWN & BROWN OF TENNESSEE, INC.—See Brown & Brown, Inc.; *U.S. Public*, pg. 400
BROWN & BROWN OF WASHINGTON, INC. - LYNDEN-SSK—See Brown & Brown, Inc.; *U.S. Public*, pg. 400
BROWN & BROWN OF WASHINGTON, INC. - SEATTLE—See Brown & Brown, Inc.; *U.S. Public*, pg. 400
BROWN & BROWN OF WASHINGTON, INC.—See Brown & Brown, Inc.; *U.S. Public*, pg. 400
BROWN & BROWN OF WISCONSIN, INC.—See Brown & Brown, Inc.; *U.S. Public*, pg. 400
BROWN & BROWN PACIFIC INSURANCE SERVICES, INC.—See Brown & Brown, Inc.; *U.S. Public*, pg. 398
BROWN BUILDERS INC.; *U.S. Private*, pg. 667
BROWNBUILT METAL SECTIONS—See Tiso Blackstar Group SE; *Int'l*, pg. 7759
BROWNBUILT PTY LIMITED—See Arrowcrest Group Pty. Ltd.; *Int'l*, pg. 580
BROWN-CAMPBELL COMPANY; *U.S. Private*, pg. 669
BROWN CHEMICAL CO., INC.; *U.S. Private*, pg. 667
BROWN CHEVROLET CO. INC.; *U.S. Private*, pg. 667
THE BROWN & CHURCH COMPANY—See Individualized Apparel Group; *U.S. Private*, pg. 2064
BROWN CITY BANNER—See JAMS Media LLC; *U.S. Private*, pg. 2186
BROWN & CO INSURANCE SERVICES LP—See Galiot Insurance Services, Inc.; *U.S. Private*, pg. 1638
BROWN COLLEGE—See Perdoceo Education Corporation; *U.S. Public*, pg. 1673
BROWN COMMUNICATIONS GROUP; *Int'l*, pg. 1198
BROWN COMMUNICATIONS GROUP—See Brown Communications Group; *Int'l*, pg. 1198
BROWN CORPORATION OF MOBERLY INC.—See Matcor-Matsu Group Inc.; *Int'l*, pg. 4726
BROWN COUNTY DEMOCRAT—See Home News Enterprises, LLC; *U.S. Private*, pg. 1971
BROWN CRAIG TURNER; *U.S. Private*, pg. 667
BROWN-DAUB INC.; *U.S. Private*, pg. 669
BROWN DERBY STORES INC.; *U.S. Private*, pg. 667
BROWN DISTRIBUTING COMPANY, INCORPORATED; *U.S. Private*, pg. 667
BROWN DISTRIBUTING COMPANY; *U.S. Private*, pg. 667
BROWNE & CO.; *Int'l*, pg. 1198
BROWNELL & COMPANY, INC.; *U.S. Private*, pg. 669
BROWN ENTERPRISES; *U.S. Private*, pg. 667
BROWNES FOODS OPERATIONS PTY. LTD.—See Shanghai Milkground Food Tech Co., Ltd.; *Int'l*, pg. 6775
BROWN EUROPE SAS—See Eramet SA; *Int'l*, pg. 2488
BROWN EYED BOY (VICIOUS) LIMITED—See LOV Group Invest SAS; *Int'l*, pg. 4565
BROWNFIELD OIL COMPANY, INC.—See MFA Oil Company; *U.S. Private*, pg. 2693
BROWN FOODSERVICE, INC.; *U.S. Private*, pg. 667
BROWN-FORMAN AUSTRALIA PTY. LTD.—See Brown-Forman Corporation; *U.S. Public*, pg. 403
BROWN-FORMAN BEVERAGES AUSTRALIA PTY LTD.—See Brown-Forman Corporation; *U.S. Public*, pg. 403
BROWN-FORMAN BEVERAGES EUROPE, LTD.—See Brown-Forman Corporation; *U.S. Public*, pg. 403
BROWN-FORMAN BEVERAGES NORTH ASIA, LLC—See Brown-Forman Corporation; *U.S. Public*, pg. 403
BROWN-FORMAN BEVERAGES—See Brown-Forman Corporation; *U.S. Public*, pg. 403
BROWN-FORMAN COOPERAGE—See Brown-Forman Corporation; *U.S. Public*, pg. 403
BROWN-FORMAN CORP. - LOUISVILLE DISTILLERY—See Brown-Forman Corporation; *U.S. Public*, pg. 403
BROWN-FORMAN CORPORATION; *U.S. Public*, pg. 403
BROWN-FORMAN DEUTSCHLAND GMBH—See Brown-Forman Corporation; *U.S. Public*, pg. 403
BROWN-FORMAN FINLAND OY—See Brown-Forman Corporation; *U.S. Public*, pg. 403
BROWN-FORMAN KOREA LTD.—See Brown-Forman Corporation; *U.S. Public*, pg. 403
BROWN-FORMAN LJUBLJANA MARKETING, D.O.O—See Brown-Forman Corporation; *U.S. Public*, pg. 403
BROWN-FORMAN MEDIA SERVICES—See Brown-Forman Corporation; *U.S. Public*, pg. 403
BROWN-FORMAN RO S.R.L.—See Brown-Forman Corporation; *U.S. Public*, pg. 403
BROWN-FORMAN RUS L.L.C.—See Brown-Forman Corporation; *U.S. Public*, pg. 403
BROWN-FORMAN SPAIN, S.L.—See Brown-Forman Corporation; *U.S. Public*, pg. 403
BROWN-FORMAN WORLDWIDE (SHANGHAI) CO., LTD.—See Brown-Forman Corporation; *U.S. Public*, pg. 403
BROWN & GAY ENGINEERS, INC.; *U.S. Private*, pg. 666
BROWN, GIBBONS, LANG & COMPANY, LLC; *U.S. Private*, pg. 669
BROWN & HALEY; *U.S. Private*, pg. 666
BROWN HARRIS STEVENS, LLC - COCONUT GROVE OFFICE—See Brown Harris Stevens, LLC; *U.S. Private*, pg. 667
BROWN HARRIS STEVENS, LLC; *U.S. Private*, pg. 667
BROWNIE BRITTLE, LLC—See CapVest Limited; *Int'l*, pg. 1318
BROWNIE BROWN INC.—See Nintendo Co., Ltd.; *Int'l*, pg. 5308
BROWNIE'S MARINE GROUP, INC.; *U.S. Public*, pg. 403
BROWNIE SPECIAL PRODUCTS CO. INC.—See Chattanooga Bakery Inc.; *U.S. Private*, pg. 868
BROWN IMPORTS INC.; *U.S. Private*, pg. 667
BROWN INDUSTRIES, INC.; *U.S. Private*, pg. 667
BROWNING CHEVROLET; *U.S. Private*, pg. 667
BROWNING INTERNATIONAL S.A.—See Herstal, S.A.; *Int'l*, pg. 3364
BROWNING MAZDA—See Dick Browning, Inc.; *U.S. Private*, pg. 1225
BROWNING PRODUCTIONS & ENTERTAINMENT, INC.; *U.S. Private*, pg. 669
BROWNING VIANA FABRICA DE ARMAS E ARTIGOS DE DESPORTO SA—See Herstal, S.A.; *Int'l*, pg. 3364
BROWN INTEGRITY, LLC—See Cypress Environmental Partners, L.P.; *U.S. Public*, pg. 618
BROWN INTERNATIONAL CORP.; *U.S. Private*, pg. 668
BROWN JORDAN INTERNATIONAL INC.—See Littlejohn & Co., LLC; *U.S. Private*, pg. 2470
BROWN & JOSEPH LTD.; *U.S. Private*, pg. 666
BROWNLEE AGENCY, INC.—See Brown & Brown, Inc.; *U.S. Public*, pg. 400
BROWNLEE APPRAISAL SERVICES INC.—See Starrex International Ltd.; *Int'l*, pg. 7179
BROWNLEE JEWELERS OF THE CAROLINAS; *U.S. Private*, pg. 669
BROWN LUMBER SALES COMPANY; *U.S. Private*, pg. 668
BROWN LUMBER & SUPPLY COMPANY; *U.S. Private*, pg. 668
BROWN MACHINE GROUP—See Tenex Capital Management, L.P.; *U.S. Private*, pg. 3966
BROWN MACHINE, LLC—See Tenex Capital Management, L.P.; *U.S. Private*, pg. 3966
BROWN MACKIE COLLEGE-ALBUQUERQUE LLC—See Dream Center Foundation, a California Nonprofit Corp.; *U.S. Private*, pg. 1273
BROWN MACKIE COLLEGE - ATLANTA/COLLEGE PARK, INC.—See Dream Center Foundation, a California Nonprofit Corp.; *U.S. Private*, pg. 1273
BROWN MACKIE COLLEGE-BIRMINGHAM LLC—See Dream Center Foundation, a California Nonprofit Corp.; *U.S. Private*, pg. 1273
BROWN MACKIE COLLEGE - BOISE, INC.—See Dream Center Foundation, a California Nonprofit Corp.; *U.S. Private*, pg. 1273

COMPANY NAME INDEX

BROWN MACKIE COLLEGE - DALLAS/ FT. WORTH LLC—See Dream Center Foundation, a California Nonprofit Corp.; *U.S. Private*, pg. 1273
BROWN MACKIE COLLEGE-FORT WAYNE—See Dream Center Foundation, a California Nonprofit Corp.; *U.S. Private*, pg. 1273
BROWN MACKIE COLLEGE-GREENVILLE, INC.—See Dream Center Foundation, a California Nonprofit Corp.; *U.S. Private*, pg. 1273
BROWN MACKIE COLLEGE-KANSAS CITY LLC—See Dream Center Foundation, a California Nonprofit Corp.; *U.S. Private*, pg. 1273
BROWN MACKIE COLLEGE - MIAMI, INC.—See Dream Center Foundation, a California Nonprofit Corp.; *U.S. Private*, pg. 1273
BROWN MACKIE COLLEGE-OKLAHOMA CITY LLC—See Dream Center Foundation, a California Nonprofit Corp.; *U.S. Private*, pg. 1273
BROWN MACKIE COLLEGE-PHOENIX, INC.—See Dream Center Foundation, a California Nonprofit Corp.; *U.S. Private*, pg. 1273
BROWN MACKIE COLLEGE-SALINA LLC—See Dream Center Foundation, a California Nonprofit Corp.; *U.S. Private*, pg. 1273
BROWN MACKIE COLLEGE - SAN ANTONIO LLC—See Dream Center Foundation, a California Nonprofit Corp.; *U.S. Private*, pg. 1273
BROWN MACKIE COLLEGE-ST. LOUIS, INC.—See Dream Center Foundation, a California Nonprofit Corp.; *U.S. Private*, pg. 1273
BROWN MACKIE COLLEGE-TUCSON, INC.—See Dream Center Foundation, a California Nonprofit Corp.; *U.S. Private*, pg. 1273
BROWN MACKIE COLLEGE - TULSA, INC.—See Dream Center Foundation, a California Nonprofit Corp.; *U.S. Private*, pg. 1273
BROWN MACKIE EDUCATION CORPORATION—See Dream Center Foundation, a California Nonprofit Corp.; *U.S. Private*, pg. 1273
BROWNMED, INC.; *U.S. Private*, pg. 669
BROWN METALS COMPANY; *U.S. Private*, pg. 668
BROWN-MINNEAPOLIS-ROCKY MOUNTAIN, LLC—See Brown-Minneapolis Tank, Co.; *U.S. Private*, pg. 669
BROWN-MINNEAPOLIS TANK, CO.; *U.S. Private*, pg. 669
BROWN, MITCHELL & ALEXANDER, INC., *U.S. Private*, pg. 669
BROWN MOTORS, INC.; *U.S. Private*, pg. 668
BROWN MOTORS INC.; *U.S. Private*, pg. 668
BROWN & NEWIRTH LTD.; *Int'l*, pg. 1198
BROWN OIL CO.; *U.S. Private*, pg. 668
BROWN PACKAGING; *U.S. Private*, pg. 668
BROWN PACKING CO., INC.; *U.S. Private*, pg. 668
BROWN PACKING COMPANY INC.; *U.S. Private*, pg. 668
BROWN PALACE HOTEL ASSOCIATES L.P.; *U.S. Private*, pg. 668
BROWN PAPER COMPANY INC.; *U.S. Private*, pg. 668
BROWN PAPER GOODS COMPANY; *U.S. Private*, pg. 668
BROWN PAPER TICKETS LLC—See Events.com, Inc.; *U.S. Private*, pg. 1437
BROWN PARKER & DEMARINIS ADVERTISING INC.; *U.S. Private*, pg. 668
BROWN PONTIAC AUTOMOTIVE GROUP LP; *U.S. Private*, pg. 668
BROWN ROAD SENIOR HOUSING LLC—See The Ensign Group, Inc.; *U.S. Public*, pg. 2070
BROWN & ROOT INDUSTRIAL SERVICES, LLC—See Bernhard Capital Partners Management, LP; *U.S. Private*, pg. 537
BROWN & ROOT INDUSTRIAL SERVICES, LLC—See KBR, Inc.; *U.S. Public*, pg. 1216
BROWN RUDNICK LLP; *U.S. Private*, pg. 668
BROWN & SAENGER; *U.S. Private*, pg. 666
BROWN'S AUTOMOTIVE GROUP LTD—See Safford Automotive Group; *U.S. Private*, pg. 3525
BROWNS BEACH HOTELS PLC; *Int'l*, pg. 1198
BROWNS BROOKLAWN INC.; *U.S. Private*, pg. 669
BROWNS CAPITAL PLC; *Int'l*, pg. 1199
BROWNS CHELTENHAM LLC—See Browns Super Stores Inc.; *U.S. Private*, pg. 670
BROWNS' CHEVROLET; *Int'l*, pg. 1199
BROWN'S CHICKEN & PASTA, INC.; *U.S. Private*, pg. 669
BROWNS ELECTRICAL SUPPLY CO.; *U.S. Private*, pg. 669
BROWN-SERVICE FUNERAL HOMES CO. INC.—See Globe Life Inc.; *U.S. Public*, pg. 946
BROWN'S FAIRFAX NISSAN; *U.S. Private*, pg. 669
BROWN & SHARPE INC—See Hexagon AB; *Int'l*, pg. 3367
BROWN & SHARPE QIANSHAO—See Hexagon AB; *Int'l*, pg. 3367
BROWN, SHIPLEY & CO. LIMITED—See KBL European Private Bankers S.A.; *Int'l*, pg. 4107
THE BROWN SHIPLEY PENSION PORTFOLIO LIMITED—See KBL European Private Bankers S.A.; *Int'l*, pg. 4107
BROWN'S HONDA CITY—See Safford Automotive Group; *U.S. Private*, pg. 3525

BROWNS JEEP EAGLE CHRYSLER PLYMOUTH; *U.S. Private*, pg. 669
BROWN'S MEDICAL IMAGING, LLC—See Atlantic Street Capital Management LLC; *U.S. Private*, pg. 374
BROWN SMITH WALLACE LLC; *U.S. Private*, pg. 668
BROWN SPRINKLER CORPORATION; *U.S. Private*, pg. 669
BROWN'S RICHMOND VOLKSWAGEN—See Safford Automotive Group; *U.S. Private*, pg. 3525
BROWNS SALES & LEASING INC.; *U.S. Private*, pg. 670
BROWNS SUPER STORES INC.; *U.S. Private*, pg. 670
BROWNSTEIN GROUP; *U.S. Private*, pg. 670
THE BROWNSTEIN GROUP—See Brownstein Group; *U.S. Private*, pg. 670
BROWNSTEIN HYATT FARBER SCHRECK, LLP.; *U.S. Private*, pg. 670
BROWN STEVENS ELMORE & SPARRE; *U.S. Private*, pg. 669
THE BROWNSTONE SCHOOL; *U.S. Private*, pg. 4001
BROWNSTOWN ELECTRIC SUPPLY CO. INC.; *U.S. Private*, pg. 670
BROWN'S TOYOTA—See Safford Automotive Group; *U.S. Private*, pg. 3525
BROWN-STRAUSS STEEL—See Blue Tee Corporation; *U.S. Private*, pg. 594
BROWN SUGAR BAKERY & CAFE, INC.; *U.S. Private*, pg. 669
BROWNSVILLE CARE ASSOCIATES, INC.—See The Ensign Group, Inc.; *U.S. Public*, pg. 2070
THE BROWNSVILLE HERALD—See AIM Media Texas, LLC; *U.S. Private*, pg. 132
BROWNSVILLE HOSPITAL CORPORATION—See Community Health Systems, Inc.; *U.S. Public*, pg. 551
BROWNSVILLE KIDNEY CENTER, LTD—See DaVita Inc.; *U.S. Public*, pg. 636
BROWNSVILLE PUBLIC UTILITIES BOARD; *U.S. Private*, pg. 670
BROWNSVILLE SURGICAL SPECIALISTS, PLLC—See HCA Healthcare, Inc.; *U.S. Public*, pg. 992
BROWN TRANSFER COMPANY; *U.S. Private*, pg. 669
BROWN TRUCK LEASING CORP; *U.S. Private*, pg. 669
BROWN & WATSON INTERNATIONAL PTY LTD—See Amotiv Limited; *Int'l*, pg. 431
BROWN & WHITE, INC.—See Bain Capital, LP; *U.S. Private*, pg. 441
BROWN-WILBERT INC.; *U.S. Private*, pg. 669
BROWN WINDOW CORPORATION; *Int'l*, pg. 1198
BROWNWOOD ACRES FOODS, INC.; *U.S. Private*, pg. 670
BROWNWOOD HOSPITAL, L.P.—See Community Health Systems, Inc.; *U.S. Public*, pg. 551
BROWN & WOOD, INC.; *U.S. Private*, pg. 666
BROWNWOOD IRON & METAL CO—See M. Lipsitz & Co., Ltd.; *U.S. Private*, pg. 2527
BROWNWOOD MEDICAL CENTER, LLC—See Community Health Systems, Inc.; *U.S. Public*, pg. 551
BROWNWOOD NEWSPAPERS, INC.—See American Consolidated Media LP; *U.S. Private*, pg. 228
BROWN WOOD PRESERVING COMPANY INC.—See Koppers Holdings Inc.; *U.S. Public*, pg. 1272
BROWSERSOFT INC.—See Lightbeam Health Solutions LLC; *U.S. Private*, pg. 2452
BROX INDUSTRIES INC.; *U.S. Private*, pg. 670
BROYHILL FURNITURE INDUSTRIES, INC.—See Heritage Home Group, Inc.; *U.S. Private*, pg. 1924
BRP - FINLAND OY—See Bain Capital, LP; *U.S. Private*, pg. 431
BRP HANNIBAL, INC.—See Anhui Zhongding Holding (Group) Co., Ltd.; *Int'l*, pg. 471
BRPH COMPANIES, INC.; *U.S. Private*, pg. 670
BRP INC.—See Bain Capital, LP; *U.S. Private*, pg. 430
BRP INC.—See Bain Capital, LP; *U.S. Private*, pg. 431
BRP LEASING, LLC—See Jefferies Financial Group Inc.; *U.S. Public*, pg. 1188
BR PRINTERS, INC.; *U.S. Private*, pg. 630
BR PROPERTIES S.A.—See GP Investments, Ltd.; *Int'l*, pg. 3045
BRP-ROTAX GMBH & CO. KG—See Bain Capital, LP; *U.S. Private*, pg. 431
BRP US INC. - OUTBOARD ENGINE DIVISION—See Bain Capital, LP; *U.S. Private*, pg. 431
BRQ SOLUCOES EM INFORMATICA S.A.; *Int'l*, pg. 1199
B.R.R. GUARDIAN MODARABA; *Int'l*, pg. 790
BRRH CORPORATION; *U.S. Private*, pg. 670
B/R/S GROUP INC.; *U.S. Private*, pg. 421
BRS LTD—See AB Volvo; *Int'l*, pg. 42
BRS MEDIA INC.; *U.S. Private*, pg. 670
BRS RESOURCES LTD.; *Int'l*, pg. 1199
B&R STORES INC.; *U.S. Private*, pg. 419
B&R SUPERMARKET INC.; *U.S. Private*, pg. 419
BRS VENTURES INVESTMENT LTD; *Int'l*, pg. 1199
BRT APARTMENTS CORP.; *U.S. Public*, pg. 403
BRT INC.; *U.S. Private*, pg. 670
BRTRC FEDERAL SOLUTIONS, INC.—See Serco Group plc; *Int'l*, pg. 6721
BRTUV AVALIACOES DA QUALIDADE S.A.—See TUV NORD AG; *Int'l*, pg. 7979
BRUBAKER GRAIN & CHEMICAL INC.; *U.S. Private*, pg. 670

BRUBAKER, INC.; *U.S. Private*, pg. 670
BRUBAKER TOOL CORPORATION—See Talbot Holdings Inc.; *U.S. Private*, pg. 3925
BRUBIN PUMPS (PTY) LTD—See Set Point Group Limited; *Int'l*, pg. 6730
BRUCE AEROSPACE, INC.—See TransDigm Group Incorporated; *U.S. Public*, pg. 2182
BRUCE ASHLEY GROUP INC.—See Royal Unibrew A/S; *Int'l*, pg. 6414
BRUCE CAVENAUGH'S AUTOMART; *U.S. Private*, pg. 670
BRUCE CLAY AUSTRALIA PTY LTD—See Bruce Clay, Inc.; *U.S. Private*, pg. 670
BRUCE CLAY EUROPE—See Bruce Clay, Inc.; *U.S. Private*, pg. 670
BRUCE CLAY, INC.; *U.S. Private*, pg. 670
BRUCE CLAY INDIA PVT LTD—See Bruce Clay, Inc.; *U.S. Private*, pg. 670
BRUCE CLAY JAPAN, INC.—See Bruce Clay, Inc.; *U.S. Private*, pg. 671
BRUCE COMPANY OF WISCONSIN, INC.; *U.S. Private*, pg. 671
BRUCE FOODS CORPORATION; *U.S. Private*, pg. 671
BRUCE FOX INC.; *U.S. Private*, pg. 671
BRUCE LOWRIE CHEVROLET INC.; *U.S. Private*, pg. 671
BRUCE MAU DESIGN INC.—See Stagwell, Inc.; *U.S. Public*, pg. 1926
BRUCE MAU HOLDINGS LTD.—See Stagwell, Inc.; *U.S. Public*, pg. 1926
BRUCE MCLAREN RETIREMENT VILLAGE LIMITED—See Ryman Healthcare Ltd.; *Int'l*, pg. 6439
BRUCE POWER, INC.—See Ontario Municipal Employees Retirement System; *Int'l*, pg. 5583
BRUCE-ROGERS COMPANY—See Ferguson plc; *Int'l*, pg. 2637
BRUCE R SMITH LIMITED; *Int'l*, pg. 1199
BRUCE SUPPLY CORP.—See Ferguson plc; *Int'l*, pg. 2637
BRUCE TECHNOLOGIES EUROPE GMBH—See Amtech Systems, Inc.; *U.S. Public*, pg. 133
BRUCE TECHNOLOGIES, INC—See Amtech Systems, Inc.; *U.S. Public*, pg. 133
BRUCE-TERMINIX COMPANY, INC.—See Rentokil Initial plc; *Int'l*, pg. 6289
BRUCETON AG-SERVICES INC.—See Bruceton Farm Service, Inc.; *U.S. Private*, pg. 671
BRUCETON FARM SERVICE, INC.; *U.S. Private*, pg. 671
BRUCETON PETROLEUM CO. INC.—See Bruceton Farm Service, Inc.; *U.S. Private*, pg. 671
BRUCE WILLIAMS HOMES, INC.; *U.S. Private*, pg. 671
BRU-CHEVRON NV—See S.A. Spadel N.V.; *Int'l*, pg. 6448
BRUCKENBAU PLAUEN GMBH—See GEA Group Aktiengesellschaft; *Int'l*, pg. 2897
BRUCKMANN, ROSSER, SHERRILL & CO., LLC; *U.S. Private*, pg. 671
BRUCKNER GROUP GMBH; *Int'l*, pg. 1199
BRUCKNER LEASING CO. INC.—See Bruckner Truck Sales, Inc.; *U.S. Private*, pg. 671
BRUCKNER SUPPLY CO., INC.—See WESCO International, Inc.; *U.S. Public*, pg. 2351
BRUCKNER TRUCK SALES, INC.; *U.S. Private*, pg. 671
BRUCKNER TRUCK SALES—See Bruckner Truck Sales, Inc.; *U.S. Private*, pg. 671
BRUDERMAN & CO., LLC; *U.S. Private*, pg. 671
BRUDER MANNESMANN AG; *Int'l*, pg. 1199
BRUECKNER GROUP USA, INC. - FRASER—See Bruckner Group GmbH; *Int'l*, pg. 1199
BRUECKNER GROUP USA, INC.—See Bruckner Group GmbH; *Int'l*, pg. 1199
BRUEGGER'S ENTERPRISES—See Holding Le Duff SA; *Int'l*, pg. 3450
BRUEL & KJAER—See Spectris Plc; *Int'l*, pg. 7130
BRUEL & KJAER SOUND & VIBRATION MEASUREMENT A/S—See Spectris Plc; *Int'l*, pg. 7130
BRUEL & KJAER SOUND & VIBRATION—See Spectris Plc; *Int'l*, pg. 7130
BRUEL & KJAER UK LTD—See Spectris Plc; *Int'l*, pg. 7130
BRUEL & KJAER VIBRO—See Spectris Plc; *Int'l*, pg. 7130
BRUGAL & CO., S.A.—See The Edrington Group; *Int'l*, pg. 7637
BRUGMAN C.V.—See Vorwerk & Co. KG; *Int'l*, pg. 8307
BRUGMAN FABRYKA GRZEJNIKOW SP. Z O.O.—See Vaessen Industries nv; *Int'l*, pg. 8108
BRUGMAN INTERNATIONAL B.V.—See Vaessen Industries nv; *Int'l*, pg. 8108
BRUGMAN KEUKENS & BADKAMERS B.V.—See Vorwerk & Co. KG; *Int'l*, pg. 8307
BRUGMAN RADIATORENFABRIEK B.V.—See Vaessen Industries nv; *Int'l*, pg. 8108
BRUIL INFRA BV—See Koninklijke VolkerWessels N.V.; *Int'l*, pg. 4271
BRUIN CAPITAL HOLDINGS, LLC; *U.S. Private*, pg. 671
BRUIN EXPRESS INTERMODAL LLC—See US 1 Industries, Inc.; *U.S. Private*, pg. 4317
BRUINHOF BV—See The Carlyle Group Inc.; *U.S. Public*, pg. 2046
BRUIN PLASTICS COMPANY, INC.; *U.S. Private*, pg. 671

BRUINS SPORTS CAPITAL, LLC

BRUINS SPORTS CAPITAL, LLC; *U.S. Private*, pg. 671
BRUKER AUSTRIA GMBH—See Bruker Corporation; *U.S. Public*, pg. 404
BRUKER AXS ANALYTICAL INSTRUMENTS PVT. LTD.—See Bruker Corporation; *U.S. Public*, pg. 404
BRUKER AXS GMBH—See Bruker Corporation; *U.S. Public*, pg. 404
BRUKER AXS HANDHELD INC.—See Bruker Corporation; *U.S. Public*, pg. 404
BRUKER AXS, INC.—See Bruker Corporation; *U.S. Public*, pg. 404
BRUKER AXS K.K.—See Bruker Corporation; *U.S. Public*, pg. 404
BRUKER AXS NORDIC AB—See Bruker Corporation; *U.S. Public*, pg. 404
BRUKER AXS PTE LTD—See Bruker Corporation; *U.S. Public*, pg. 404
BRUKER BELGIUM SA/NV—See Bruker Corporation; *U.S. Public*, pg. 404
BRUKER BIOSCIENCES KOREA CO., LTD.—See Bruker Corporation; *U.S. Public*, pg. 404
BRUKER BIOSPIN AG—See Bruker Corporation; *U.S. Public*, pg. 404
BRUKER BIOSPIN CORPORATION—See Bruker Corporation; *U.S. Public*, pg. 404
BRUKER BIOSPIN INTERNATIONAL AG—See Bruker Corporation; *U.S. Public*, pg. 404
BRUKER BIOSPIN INTERNATIONAL AG - THAILAND OFFICE—See Bruker Corporation; *U.S. Public*, pg. 404
BRUKER BIOSPIN K.K.—See Bruker Corporation; *U.S. Public*, pg. 404
BRUKER BIOSPIN KOREA CO. LTD.—See Bruker Corporation; *U.S. Public*, pg. 405
BRUKER BIOSPIN MRI GMBH—See Bruker Corporation; *U.S. Public*, pg. 405
BRUKER BIOSPIN MRI INC.—See Bruker Corporation; *U.S. Public*, pg. 405
BRUKER BIOSPIN PTE. LTD.—See Bruker Corporation; *U.S. Public*, pg. 404
BRUKER BIOSPIN S.A. / N.V.—See Bruker Corporation; *U.S. Public*, pg. 405
BRUKER BIOSPIN S.A.—See Bruker Corporation; *U.S. Public*, pg. 405
BRUKER BIOSPIN SCANDINAVIA AB—See Bruker Corporation; *U.S. Public*, pg. 405
BRUKER CELLULAR ANALYSIS, INC.—See Bruker Corporation; *U.S. Public*, pg. 405
BRUKER CHEMICAL & APPLIED MARKETS—See Bruker Corporation; *U.S. Public*, pg. 405
BRUKER CORPORATION; *U.S. Public*, pg. 403
BRUKER DALTONICS INC.—See Bruker Corporation; *U.S. Public*, pg. 405
BRUKER DALTONICS, INC.—See Bruker Corporation; *U.S. Public*, pg. 405
BRUKER DALTONICS K.K.—See Bruker Corporation; *U.S. Public*, pg. 405
BRUKER DALTONICS LTD.—See Bruker Corporation; *U.S. Public*, pg. 405
BRUKER DALTONICS LTD.—See Bruker Corporation; *U.S. Public*, pg. 405
BRUKER DALTONICS PTE. LTD.—See Bruker Corporation; *U.S. Public*, pg. 405
BRUKER DALTONICS PTY LTD—See Bruker Corporation; *U.S. Public*, pg. 405
BRUKER DALTONICS SCANDINAVIA AB—See Bruker Corporation; *U.S. Public*, pg. 405
BRUKER DALTONICS SCANDINAVIA AB—See Bruker Corporation; *U.S. Public*, pg. 405
BRUKER DALTONICS SPRL/BVBA—See Bruker Corporation; *U.S. Public*, pg. 405
BRUKER DALTONICS S.R.L.—See Bruker Corporation; *U.S. Public*, pg. 405
BRUKER DALTONICS S.R.O.—See Bruker Corporation; *U.S. Public*, pg. 405
BRUKER DALTONIK GMBH—See Bruker Corporation; *U.S. Public*, pg. 405
BRUKER DALTONIK GMBH—See Bruker Corporation; *U.S. Public*, pg. 405
BRUKER DETECTION CORPORATION—See Bruker Corporation; *U.S. Public*, pg. 406
BRUKER DO BRASIL LTDA.—See Bruker Corporation; *U.S. Public*, pg. 404
BRUKER ELEMENTAL GMBH—See Bruker Corporation; *U.S. Public*, pg. 404
BRUKER ESPANOLA S.A.—See Bruker Corporation; *U.S. Public*, pg. 405
BRUKER FINANCE B.V.—See Bruker Corporation; *U.S. Public*, pg. 405
BRUKER FRANCE S.A.S—See Bruker Corporation; *U.S. Public*, pg. 405
BRUKER FRANCE S.A.S.—See Bruker Corporation; *U.S. Public*, pg. 405
BRUKER INDIA SCIENTIFIC PVT. LTD.—See Bruker Corporation; *U.S. Public*, pg. 405
BRUKER ITALIA S.R.L.—See Bruker Corporation; *U.S. Public*, pg. 405
BRUKER JV ISRAEL LTD.—See Bruker Corporation; *U.S. Public*, pg. 405

BRUKER JV UK LTD.—See Bruker Corporation; *U.S. Public*, pg. 405
BRUKER KOREA CO., LTD.—See Bruker Corporation; *U.S. Public*, pg. 406
BRUKER KOREA CO. LTD.—See Bruker Corporation; *U.S. Public*, pg. 405
BRUKER LTD.—See Bruker Corporation; *U.S. Public*, pg. 405
BRUKER (MALAYSIA) SDN BHD—See Bruker Corporation; *U.S. Public*, pg. 404
BRUKER MEXICANA, S.A. DE C.V.—See Bruker Corporation; *U.S. Public*, pg. 404
BRUKER MICROCT N.V.—See Bruker Corporation; *U.S. Public*, pg. 404
BRUKER NANO GMBH—See Bruker Corporation; *U.S. Public*, pg. 404
BRUKER NANO, INC.—See Bruker Corporation; *U.S. Public*, pg. 404
BRUKER NANO, INC.—See Bruker Corporation; *U.S. Public*, pg. 404
BRUKER NEDERLAND B.V.—See Bruker Corporation; *U.S. Public*, pg. 405
BRUKER OPTICS AB—See Bruker Corporation; *U.S. Public*, pg. 405
BRUKER OPTICS GMBH—See Bruker Corporation; *U.S. Public*, pg. 405
BRUKER OPTICS INC.—See Bruker Corporation; *U.S. Public*, pg. 405
BRUKER OPTICS K.K.—See Bruker Corporation; *U.S. Public*, pg. 406
BRUKER OPTICS LTD—See Bruker Corporation; *U.S. Public*, pg. 406
BRUKER OPTICS SCANDINAVIA AB—See Bruker Corporation; *U.S. Public*, pg. 406
BRUKER OPTICS TAIWAN LTD.—See Bruker Corporation; *U.S. Public*, pg. 406
BRUKER OPTICS UKRAINE—See Bruker Corporation; *U.S. Public*, pg. 406
BRUKER OPTIK ASIA PACIFIC LIMITED—See Bruker Corporation; *U.S. Public*, pg. 406
BRUKER OPTIK GMBH—See Bruker Corporation; *U.S. Public*, pg. 406
BRUKER OPTIQUE SA—See Bruker Corporation; *U.S. Public*, pg. 406
BRUKER PHYSIK GMBH—See Bruker Corporation; *U.S. Public*, pg. 405
BRUKER POLSKA SP. Z O.O.—See Bruker Corporation; *U.S. Public*, pg. 404
BRUKER PORTUGAL UNIPESSOAL LDA—See Bruker Corporation; *U.S. Public*, pg. 406
BRUKER PTY. LTD.—See Bruker Corporation; *U.S. Public*, pg. 405
BRUKER PTY. LTD.—See Bruker Corporation; *U.S. Public*, pg. 406
BRUKER SCIENTIFIC INSTRUMENTS HONG KONG CO., LTD.—See Bruker Corporation; *U.S. Public*, pg. 406
BRUKER SCIENTIFIC ISRAEL LTD.—See Bruker Corporation; *U.S. Public*, pg. 406
BRUKER SCIENTIFIC LLC—See Bruker Corporation; *U.S. Public*, pg. 406
BRUKER SINGAPORE PTE. LTD.—See Bruker Corporation; *U.S. Public*, pg. 404
BRUKER SOUTH AFRICA PTY LTD—See Bruker Corporation; *U.S. Public*, pg. 404
BRUKER SWITZERLAND AG—See Bruker Corporation; *U.S. Public*, pg. 406
BRUKER TAIWAN CO. LTD.—See Bruker Corporation; *U.S. Public*, pg. 406
BRUKS SIWERTELL GROUP AB—See JCE Group AB; *Int'l*, pg. 3923
BRULERIE DES CAFES CORSICA S.A.S.—See Segafredo Zanetti S.p.A.; *Int'l*, pg. 6681
THE BRULIN CORPORATION; *U.S. Public*, pg. 4001
BRUMA MACHINEHANDEL B.V.—See TRUMPF SE + Co. KG; *Int'l*, pg. 7942
BRUMBY'S BAKERIES (NZ) LTD—See Retail Food Group Limited; *Int'l*, pg. 6305
BRUMFIELD OIL COMPANY INC.; *U.S. Private*, pg. 672
BRUMFIELD & PETERS INSURANCE SERVICES, INC.—See Inszone Insurance Services, LLC; *U.S. Private*, pg. 2096
BRUMIT OIL CO. INC.; *U.S. Private*, pg. 672
BRUMIT RESTAURANT GROUP; *U.S. Private*, pg. 672
BRUMMEL KANEPI PIRITA—See Omnicom Group Inc.; *U.S. Public*, pg. 1592
BRUNA BROS IMPLEMENT LLC; *U.S. Private*, pg. 672
THE BRUNA CORPORATION—See Genstar Capital, LLC; *U.S. Private*, pg. 1679
BRUNDAGE ASSOCIATES INCORPORATED; *U.S. Private*, pg. 672
BRUNDAGE-BONE CONCRETE PUMPING, INC.—See Peninsula Pacific Strategic Partners, LLC; *U.S. Private*, pg. 3133
BRUNDAGE MANAGEMENT COMPANY; *U.S. Private*, pg. 672
BRUNDER DYREHOSPITAL APS—See Vimian Group AB; *Int'l*, pg. 8208
BRUNEI LNG SDN. BHD.—See Mitsubishi Corporation; *Int'l*, pg. 4938

CORPORATE AFFILIATIONS

BRUNEI LNG SDN. BHD.—See Shell plc; *Int'l*, pg. 6797
BRUNEI METHANOL COMPANY SDN. BHD.—See Mitsubishi Gas Chemical Company, Inc.; *Int'l*, pg. 4948
BRUNEI SHELL PETROLEUM CO. SDN. BHD.—See Mitsubishi Corporation; *Int'l*, pg. 4938
BRUNEI SHELL PETROLEUM CO. SDN. BHD.—See Shell plc; *Int'l*, pg. 6797
BRUNEL AUSTRIA GMBH—See Brunel International N.V.; *Int'l*, pg. 1199
BRUNEL BELGIUM N.V.—See Brunel International N.V.; *Int'l*, pg. 1199
BRUNEL CANADA LTD—See Brunel International N.V.; *Int'l*, pg. 1199
BRUNEL CAR SYNERGIES GMBH—See Brunel International N.V.; *Int'l*, pg. 1199
BRUNEL CZ S.R.O.—See Brunel International N.V.; *Int'l*, pg. 1199
BRUNEL ENERGY CANADA INC—See Brunel International N.V.; *Int'l*, pg. 1199
BRUNEL ENERGY EUROPE BV—See Brunel International N.V.; *Int'l*, pg. 1199
BRUNEL ENERGY HOLDING BV—See Brunel International N.V.; *Int'l*, pg. 1199
BRUNEL ENERGY INC.—See Brunel International N.V.; *Int'l*, pg. 1199
BRUNEL ENERGY JAPAN KK—See Brunel International N.V.; *Int'l*, pg. 1199
BRUNEL ENERGY KOREA LTD.—See Brunel International N.V.; *Int'l*, pg. 1199
BRUNEL ENERGY KUWAIT W.L.L.—See Brunel International N.V.; *Int'l*, pg. 1199
BRUNEL ENERGY L.L.C.—See Brunel International N.V.; *Int'l*, pg. 1199
BRUNEL ENERGY MALAYSIA SDN BHD—See Brunel International N.V.; *Int'l*, pg. 1199
BRUNEL ENERGY NIGERIA LTD—See Brunel International N.V.; *Int'l*, pg. 1199
BRUNEL ENERGY PTY LTD—See Brunel International N.V.; *Int'l*, pg. 1199
BRUNEL ENERGY QATAR W.L.L.—See Brunel International N.V.; *Int'l*, pg. 1199
BRUNEL ENGINEERING CONSULTANTS NV—See Brunel International N.V.; *Int'l*, pg. 1199
BRUNEL GMBH—See Brunel International N.V.; *Int'l*, pg. 1199
BRUNEL HEALTHCARE MANUFACTURING LIMITED—See Elder Pharmaceuticals Ltd.; *Int'l*, pg. 2346
BRUNEL ICT NV—See Brunel International N.V.; *Int'l*, pg. 1199
BRUNEL INDIA PRIVATE LTD.—See Brunel International N.V.; *Int'l*, pg. 1200
BRUNEL INTERNATIONAL FRANCE SARL—See Brunel International N.V.; *Int'l*, pg. 1200
BRUNEL INTERNATIONAL N.V.; *Int'l*, pg. 1199
BRUNEL INTERNATIONAL SOUTH EAST ASIA PTE LTD—See Brunel International N.V.; *Int'l*, pg. 1200
BRUNEL INTERNATIONAL UK LTD—See Brunel International N.V.; *Int'l*, pg. 1200
BRUNELLO CUCINELLI AUSTRIA GMBH—See Brunello Cucinelli S.p.A.; *Int'l*, pg. 1200
BRUNELLO CUCINELLI BRASIL LTDA—See Brunello Cucinelli S.p.A.; *Int'l*, pg. 1200
BRUNELLO CUCINELLI DENMARK APS—See Brunello Cucinelli S.p.A.; *Int'l*, pg. 1200
BRUNELLO CUCINELLI HELLAS SA—See Brunello Cucinelli S.p.A.; *Int'l*, pg. 1200
BRUNELLO CUCINELLI KUWAIT FOR READYMADE & NOVELTY CLOTHES RETAIL WLL—See Brunello Cucinelli S.p.A.; *Int'l*, pg. 1200
BRUNELLO CUCINELLI-MIDDLE EAST LLC—See Brunello Cucinelli S.p.A.; *Int'l*, pg. 1200
BRUNELLO CUCINELLI NETHERLANDS B.V.—See Brunello Cucinelli S.p.A.; *Int'l*, pg. 1200
BRUNELLO CUCINELLI RETAIL SPAIN SL—See Brunello Cucinelli S.p.A.; *Int'l*, pg. 1200
BRUNELLO CUCINELLI (SICHUAN) FASHION CO., LTD.—See Brunello Cucinelli S.p.A.; *Int'l*, pg. 1200
BRUNELLO CUCINELLI S.P.A.; *Int'l*, pg. 1200
BRUNELLO CUCINELLI SUISSE SA—See Brunello Cucinelli S.p.A.; *Int'l*, pg. 1200
BRUNEL NEDERLAND BV—See Brunel International N.V.; *Int'l*, pg. 1200
BRUNEL OIL & GAS SERVICES WLL—See Brunel International N.V.; *Int'l*, pg. 1200
BRUNEL RECRUITMENT KAZAKHSTAN LLP—See Brunel International N.V.; *Int'l*, pg. 1200
BRUNEL STREET WORKS ENERGY SERVICES LIMITED—See Vistry Group PLC; *Int'l*, pg. 8255
BRUNEL SURINAME N.V.—See Brunel International N.V.; *Int'l*, pg. 1200
BRUNEL SWITZERLAND AG—See Brunel International N.V.; *Int'l*, pg. 1200
BRUNEL TECHNICAL SERVICES PTE LTD—See Brunel International N.V.; *Int'l*, pg. 1200
BRUNEL TECHNICAL SERVICES PTY LTD—See Brunel International N.V.; *Int'l*, pg. 1200
BRUNEL TECHNICAL SERVICES (THAILAND) LIMITED—See Brunel International N.V.; *Int'l*, pg. 1200

BRUNEL VIETNAM COMPANY LTD.—See Brunel International N.V.; *Int'l*, pg. 1200
BRUNER AUTO GROUP—See Bruner Motors, Inc.; *U.S. Private*, pg. 672
BRUNER MOTORS, INC.; *U.S. Private*, pg. 672
BRUNET-GARCIA ADVERTISING, INC.—See Fors Marsh Group LLC.; *U.S. Private*, pg. 1573
BRUNING GRAIN & FEED CO. INC; *U.S. Private*, pg. 672
BRUNK INDUSTRIES, INC.; *U.S. Private*, pg. 672
BRUNNER INSURANCE, INC.—See Lacher & Associates Insurance Agency, Inc.; *U.S. Private*, pg. 2371
BRUNNER INVESTMENT TRUST PLC; *Int'l*, pg. 1200
BRUNNER MANUFACTURING CO. INC.; *U.S. Private*, pg. 672
BRUNNER MOND GENERATION COMPANY LIMITED—See Tata Sons Limited; *Int'l*, pg. 7469
BRUNNER MOND GROUP LIMITED—See Tata Sons Limited; *Int'l*, pg. 7468
BRUNNER; *U.S. Private*, pg. 672
BRUNNER—See Brunner; *U.S. Private*, pg. 672
BRUNN GMBH—See LKQ Corporation; *U.S. Public*, pg. 1334
BRUNNING AND PRICE LIMITED—See Apollo Global Management, Inc.; *U.S. Public*, pg. 164
BRUNO DIALYSIS, LLC—See The Ensign Group, Inc.; *U.S. Public*, pg. 2070
BRUNO, DIBELLO & CO., LLC; *U.S. Private*, pg. 672
BRUNO,INC.—See RIZAP GROUP, Inc.; *Int'l*, pg. 6354
BRUNO INDEPENDENT LIVING AIDS, INC.; *U.S. Private*, pg. 672
BRUNO SAINT HILAIRE SAS; *Int'l*, pg. 1200
BRUNO'S CONTRACTING (THUNDER BAY) LTD.; *Int'l*, pg. 1200
BRUNSCHWIG & FILS, INC.—See Kravet, Inc.; *U.S. Private*, pg. 2350
BRUNS, CONNELL, VOLLMAR & ARMSTRONG, LLC; *U.S. Private*, pg. 672
BRUNSELL BROTHERS LTD.; *U.S. Private*, pg. 672
BRUNS-PAK INC.; *U.S. Private*, pg. 672
BRUNSWICK AUTO MART, INC.; *U.S. Private*, pg. 672
BRUNSWICK BANCORP—See Mid Penn Bancorp, Inc.; *U.S. Public*, pg. 1444
BRUNSWICK BOAT GROUP—See Brunswick Corporation; *U.S. Public*, pg. 407
BRUNSWICK BOWLING & BILLIARDS CORPORATION—See Brunswick Corporation; *U.S. Public*, pg. 407
BRUNSWICK CELLULOSE—See Koch Industries, Inc.; *U.S. Private*, pg. 2328
BRUNSWICK COCA-COLA BOTTLING COMPANY—See Coca-Cola Bottling Co. United, Inc.; *U.S. Private*, pg. 958
BRUNSWICK COMMERCIAL & GOVERNMENT PRODUCTS, INC.—See Brunswick Corporation; *U.S. Public*, pg. 407
BRUNSWICK CORPORATION; *U.S. Public*, pg. 407
BRUNSWICK ELECTRIC MEMBERSHIP CORPORATION; *U.S. Private*, pg. 672
BRUNSWICK EXPLORATION INC.; *Int'l*, pg. 1200
BRUNSWICK GMBH—See Brunswick Corporation; *U.S. Public*, pg. 407
BRUNSWICK GROUP (BEIJING) CO., LTD.—See Brunswick Group Limited; *Int'l*, pg. 1200
BRUNSWICK GROUP GMBH—See Brunswick Group Limited; *Int'l*, pg. 1200
BRUNSWICK GROUP (HK) CO., LTD.—See Brunswick Group Limited; *Int'l*, pg. 1200
BRUNSWICK GROUP LIMITED; *Int'l*, pg. 1200
BRUNSWICK GROUP LLC—See Brunswick Group Limited; *Int'l*, pg. 1201
BRUNSWICK GROUP NV/SA—See Brunswick Group Limited; *Int'l*, pg. 1201
BRUNSWICK GROUP (PTY) LTD.—See Brunswick Group Limited; *Int'l*, pg. 1200
BRUNSWICK GROUP—See Brunswick Group Limited; *Int'l*, pg. 1200
BRUNSWICK GROUP—See Brunswick Group Limited; *Int'l*, pg. 1201
BRUNSWICK GULF LTD.—See Brunswick Group Limited; *Int'l*, pg. 1201
BRUNSWICK HAW PAR HOLDINGS PTE LTD.—See Haw Par Corporation Limited; *Int'l*, pg. 3287
BRUNSWICK HUNGARY MANUFACTURING AND TRADING LIMITED LIABILITY COMPANY—See Brunswick Corporation; *U.S. Public*, pg. 407
BRUNSWICK INDOOR RECREATION GROUP—See Brunswick Corporation; *U.S. Public*, pg. 407
BRUNSWICK INTERNATIONAL GMBH—See Brunswick Corporation; *U.S. Public*, pg. 407
BRUNSWICK INTERNATIONAL LIMITED—See Brunswick Corporation; *U.S. Public*, pg. 407
BRUNSWICK LEISURE BOAT COMPANY, LLC—See Brunswick Corporation; *U.S. Public*, pg. 407
BRUNSWICK MARINE IN EMEA, INC.—See Brunswick Corporation; *U.S. Public*, pg. 408
BRUNSWICK MEDIA SERVICES LLC; *U.S. Private*, pg. 672

BRUNSWICK NETHERLANDS B.V.—See Brunswick Corporation; *U.S. Public*, pg. 407
BRUNSWICK NEWS, INC.—See Chatham Asset Management, LLC; *U.S. Private*, pg. 860
BRUNSWICK POINT NORTH CAROLINA, LLC—See Independence Realty Trust, Inc.; *U.S. Public*, pg. 1115
BRUNSWICK RESOURCES INC.; *Int'l*, pg. 1201
BRUNSWICK SQUARE MALL, LLC—See Washington Prime Group Inc.; *U.S. Private*, pg. 4448
BRUNTONS AERO PRODUCTS LIMITED—See Carclo plc; *Int'l*, pg. 1321
BRUNTON SHAW UK LIMITED—See Usha Martin Limited; *Int'l*, pg. 8096
BRUNTON WIRE ROPES FZCO—See Usha Martin Limited; *Int'l*, pg. 8096
BRUSH BARCLAY LTD.—See Westinghouse Air Brake Technologies Corporation; *U.S. Public*, pg. 2357
BRUSH ELECTRICAL MACHINES LTD.—See OEP Capital Advisors, L.P.; *U.S. Private*, pg. 2998
BRUSHFIRE, INC.—See Marketsmith, Inc.; *U.S. Private*, pg. 2581
BRUSHFOIL—See Nicolet Capital Partners, LLC; *U.S. Private*, pg. 2926
BRUSH HMA B.V.—See Melrose Industries PLC; *Int'l*, pg. 4812
BRUSH MASTERS, INC.; *U.S. Private*, pg. 672
BRUSH NEWS TRIBUNE—See Alden Global Capital LLC; *U.S. Private*, pg. 157
BRUSH RESEARCH MANUFACTURING COMPANY; *U.S. Private*, pg. 673
BRUSH SEM S.R.O.—See Melrose Industries PLC; *Int'l*, pg. 4812
BRUSH SWITCHGEAR LIMITED—See Melrose Industries PLC; *Int'l*, pg. 4812
BRUSH TRACTION LTD.—See Westinghouse Air Brake Technologies Corporation; *U.S. Public*, pg. 2357
BRUSH TRANSFORMERS LTD.—See Melrose Industries PLC; *Int'l*, pg. 4812
THE BRUSS COMPANY—See Tyson Foods, Inc.; *U.S. Public*, pg. 2527
BRUSSELS AUTO GROUP GROOT-BIJGAARDEN N.V.—See s.a. D'Ieteren n.v.; *Int'l*, pg. 6448
BRUSSELS AUTO GROUP TERNAT B.V.—See s.a. D'Ieteren n.v.; *Int'l*, pg. 6448
BRUSSELS CO., LTD.—See Amuse Inc.; *Int'l*, pg. 442
BRUSTER'S REAL ICE CREAM, INC.; *U.S. Private*, pg. 673
BRUTGER EQUITIES, INC.; *U.S. Private*, pg. 673
BRUTOCO ENGINEERING & CONSTRUCTION, INC.; *U.S. Private*, pg. 673
BRUTUS MEDIA GMBH—See Yoc AG; *Int'l*, pg. 8591
BRUUN S GALLERI AS—See BNP Paribas SA; *Int'l*, pg. 1089
BRUUSH ORAL CARE, INC.; *Int'l*, pg. 1201
BRUXELAS EMPREENDIMENTOS IMOBILIARIOS SPE LTDA—See PDG Realty S.A. Empreendimentos e Participacoes; *Int'l*, pg. 5770
BRUYNZEEL STORAGE SYSTEMS B.V.—See Gilde Equity Management (GEM) Benelux Partners B.V.; *Int'l*, pg. 2975
BRUZZONE SHIPPING, INC.; *U.S. Private*, pg. 673
BRVENIK A.D.; *Int'l*, pg. 1201
BRVZ BAU-, RECHEN- UND VERWALTUNGSZENTRUM AG—See STRABAG SE; *Int'l*, pg. 7229
BRVZ BAU- RECHEN- U. VERWALTUNGSZENTRUM GESELLSCHAFT M.B.H.—See STRABAG SE; *Int'l*, pg. 7229
BRVZ CENTER ZA RACUNOVODSTVO IN UPRAVLJANJE D.O.O.—See STRABAG SE; *Int'l*, pg. 7229
BRVZ S.R.O.—See STRABAG SE; *Int'l*, pg. 7229
BRW PAPER CO., INC.—See Gould Paper Corporation; *U.S. Private*, pg. 1745
BRYAH RESOURCES LIMITED; *Int'l*, pg. 1201
BRYAN BUSH CONSTRUCTION COMPANY, INC.; *U.S. Private*, pg. 673
BRYAN CAVE LLP; *U.S. Private*, pg. 673
BRYAN CHEVROLET INC.; *U.S. Private*, pg. 673
BRYAN-COLLEGE STATION COMMUNICATIONS, INC.—See Berkshire Hathaway Inc.; *U.S. Public*, pg. 303
BRYAN CONSTRUCTION COMPANY; *U.S. Private*, pg. 673
BRYAN DONKIN VALVES LTD.—See AVK Holding A/S; *Int'l*, pg. 747
BRYAN EASLER TOYOTA; *U.S. Private*, pg. 673
BRYAN HONDA-FAYETTEVILLE; *U.S. Private*, pg. 673
BRYAN IMPORTS INC.; *U.S. Private*, pg. 673
BRYAN IRON & METAL, LTD.—See M. Lipsitz & Co., Ltd.; *U.S. Private*, pg. 2527
BRYAN LGH MEDICAL CENTER INC.; *U.S. Private*, pg. 673
BRYAN METALS, LLC—See Wieland-Werke AG; *Int'l*, pg. 8403
BRYAN MILLS IRADESSO CORP.—See Stagwell, Inc.; *U.S. Private*, pg. 1926
BRYAN, PENDLETON, SWATS & MCALLISTER, LLC—See Wells Fargo & Company; *U.S. Public*, pg. 2343

BRYAN STEAM LLC—See Burnham Holdings, Inc.; *U.S. Public*, pg. 412
BRYANT BOATS, INC.—See Correct Craft, Inc.; *U.S. Private*, pg. 1058
BRYANT DISTRIBUTING COMPANY; *U.S. Private*, pg. 673
BRYANT-DURHAM ALARM CO. INC.—See Bryant-Durham Electric Co., Inc.; *U.S. Private*, pg. 674
BRYANT-DURHAM ELECTRIC CO., INC. - EASTERN DIVISION—See Bryant-Durham Electric Co., Inc.; *U.S. Private*, pg. 674
BRYANT-DURHAM ELECTRIC CO., INC.; *U.S. Private*, pg. 673
BRYANT-DURHAM SERVICES INC.—See Bryant-Durham Electric Co., Inc.; *U.S. Private*, pg. 674
BRYANT ELECTRIC COMPANY—See Hubbell Incorporated; *U.S. Public*, pg. 1066
BRYANT ELECTRIC SUPPLY COMPANY INC.—See Nautic Partners, LLC; *U.S. Private*, pg. 2872
BRYANT ELECTRIC SUPPLY COMPANY INC.—See Nautic Partners, LLC; *U.S. Private*, pg. 2872
BRYANT RESTAURANTS INC.; *U.S. Private*, pg. 673
BRYANT RUBBER CORP; *U.S. Private*, pg. 673
BRYANT SUGAR HOUSE—See United States Sugar Corporation; *U.S. Private*, pg. 4300
BRYANT & WELBORN L.L.P.; *U.S. Private*, pg. 673
BRYAST-D JSC; *Int'l*, pg. 1201
BRYCE CORPORATION; *U.S. Private*, pg. 674
BRYCON CORP; *U.S. Private*, pg. 674
BRYDENS BUSINESS SOLUTIONS INC.—See ANSA McAL Limited; *Int'l*, pg. 476
BRYDENS INSURANCE INC.—See ANSA McAL Limited; *Int'l*, pg. 476
BRYDENS RETAIL INC.—See ANSA McAL Limited; *Int'l*, pg. 476
BRYDEN STOKES LIMITED—See ANSA McAL Limited; *Int'l*, pg. 476
BRYDENS XPRESS (OFFICE SUPPLIES) INC.—See ANSA McAL Limited; *Int'l*, pg. 476
THE BRYDON GROUP LLC; *U.S. Private*, pg. 4001
BRYEN & LANGLEY LTD.; *Int'l*, pg. 1201
BRYGGEN VEJLE AS—See BNP Paribas SA; *Int'l*, pg. 1089
BRYMOR CONTRACTORS LTD.; *Int'l*, pg. 1201
THE BRYNAVON GROUP, INC.; *U.S. Private*, pg. 4001
BRYN MAWR BANK CORPORATION; *U.S. Public*, pg. 408
BRYN MAWR BROKERAGE CO., INC.—See Bryn Mawr Bank Corporation; *U.S. Public*, pg. 408
BRYN MAWR CAPITAL MANAGEMENT, INC.—See WSFS Financial Corporation; *U.S. Public*, pg. 2383
THE BRYN MAWR TRUST COMPANY OF DELAWARE—See Bryn Mawr Bank Corporation; *U.S. Public*, pg. 408
THE BRYN MAWR TRUST COMPANY—See Bryn Mawr Bank Corporation; *U.S. Public*, pg. 408
BRYNN MARR HOSPITAL, INC.—See Universal Health Services, Inc.; *U.S. Public*, pg. 2256
BRYN RESOURCES, INC.; *U.S. Public*, pg. 408
BRYNWOOD PARTNERS MANAGEMENT LLC; *U.S. Private*, pg. 674
BRYSTAR CONTRACTING, INC.; *U.S. Private*, pg. 674
BRYTE INSURANCE COMPANY LTD.—See Fairfax Financial Holdings Limited; *Int'l*, pg. 2606
BRYTEX BUILDING SYSTEMS INC.; *Int'l*, pg. 1201
BRYTON MARINE GROUP; *Int'l*, pg. 1201
BRZ INVESTIMENTOS S.A.; *Int'l*, pg. 1201
BRZZ GEAR LLC; *U.S. Private*, pg. 674
BSA ADVANCED PROPERTY SOLUTIONS (ACT) PTY LTD—See BSA Limited; *Int'l*, pg. 1201
BSA ADVANCED PROPERTY SOLUTIONS (NT) PTY LTD—See BSA Limited; *Int'l*, pg. 1201
BSA ADVANCED PROPERTY SOLUTIONS (VIC) PTY LTD—See BSA Limited; *Int'l*, pg. 1201
BSA COMMUNICATIONS & UTILITY INFRASTRUCTURE PTY LTD—See BSA Limited; *Int'l*, pg. 1201
B SAFE INC.—See Pye-Barker Fire & Safety, LLC; *U.S. Private*, pg. 3309
BSAFE SYSTEMS AS—See Bergman & Beving AB; *Int'l*, pg. 980
BSA INDIA FOOD INGR. PVT. LTD.—See International Flavors & Fragrances Inc.; *U.S. Public*, pg. 1151
BSA INDUSTRIES, INC.—See EssilorLuxottica SA; *Int'l*, pg. 2513
BSA LIMITED; *Int'l*, pg. 1201
BS AUTO PRAHA SRO—See General Motors Company; *U.S. Public*, pg. 926
B+S BANKSYSTEME AG; *Int'l*, pg. 784
B+S BANKSYSTEME AKTIENGESELLSCHAFT—See B+S Banksysteme AG; *Int'l*, pg. 784
B+S BANKSYSTEME AKTIENGESELLSCHAFT—See B+S Banksysteme AG; *Int'l*, pg. 784
B+S BANKSYSTEME DEUTSCHLAND GMBH—See B+S Banksysteme AG; *Int'l*, pg. 784
B+S BANKSYSTEME SCHWEIZ AG—See B+S Banksysteme AG; *Int'l*, pg. 784
BS BAUFACHHANDEL BRANDS & SCHNITZLER GMBH & CO. KG—See BayWa AG; *Int'l*, pg. 919

BS BAUFACHHANDEL BRANDS & SCHNITZLER VERWALTUNGS-GMBH—See BayWa AG; *Int'l*, pg. 920
BSB BAU- UND SPEZIALGERUSTBAU GMBH—See Aurelius Equity Opportunities SE & Co. KGaA; *Int'l*, pg. 707
BS&B MID ATLANTIC—See BS&B Safety Systems, LLC; *U.S. Private*, pg. 674
BS&B PRESSURE SAFETY MANAGEMENT, L.L.C.—See BS&B Safety Systems, LLC; *U.S. Private*, pg. 674
BS&B SAFETY SYSTEMS (INDIA) LTD.—See BS&B Safety Systems, LLC; *U.S. Private*, pg. 674
BS&B SAFETY SYSTEMS (INDIA) LTD.—See Sanmar Holdings Ltd.; *Int'l*, pg. 6546
BS&B SAFETY SYSTEMS, LLC; *U.S. Private*, pg. 674
BSB SA; *Int'l*, pg. 1202
B-SCADA, INC.; *U.S. Private*, pg. 419
BSC AMERICA; *U.S. Private*, pg. 674
BS CAPITAL CO., LTD.—See BNK Financial Group Inc.; *Int'l*, pg. 1079
BSC DRUKARNIA OPAKOWAN SA—See CVC Capital Partners SICAV-FIS S.A.; *Int'l*, pg. 1881
B SCENE ADVERTISING AGENCY; *U.S. Private*, pg. 417
BSC FILTERS—See Dover Corporation; *U.S. Public*, pg. 678
BSC GROUP, INC.; *U.S. Private*, pg. 674
B. SCHOENBERG & CO. INC.; *U.S. Private*, pg. 419
BSC MANAGEMENT SEAFARER RECRUITMENT COMPANY LIMITED—See Prima Marine PCL; *Int'l*, pg. 5974
BSC STEEL INC.; *U.S. Private*, pg. 674
B.S.D. CROWN LTD.; *Int'l*, pg. 790
BS DENMARK A/S—See Aurelius Equity Opportunities SE & Co. KGaA; *Int'l*, pg. 709
BSD MEDICAL CORPORATION—See Scion Medical Technologies, LLC; *U.S. Private*, pg. 3574
BSEC S.A.—See Banque BEMO S.A.L.; *Int'l*, pg. 852
BSE INDUSTRIAL CONTRACTORS; *U.S. Private*, pg. 674
B&S ELECTRIC SUPPLY CO. INC.; *U.S. Private*, pg. 419
B+S ELEKTRO TELEMATIK AG—See BKW AG; *Int'l*, pg. 1056
BSEL INFRASTRUCTURE REALTY FZE—See BSEL Infrastructure Realty Limited; *Int'l*, pg. 1202
BSEL INFRASTRUCTURE REALTY LIMITED; *Int'l*, pg. 1202
BS ENERGIE—See Veolia Environnement S.A.; *Int'l*, pg. 8153
BSE PV LLC—See Robert Bosch GmbH; *Int'l*, pg. 6366
BSE—See BSE Industrial Contractors; *U.S. Private*, pg. 675
BSF-ARBORS RIVER OAKS—See Independence Realty Trust, Inc.; *U.S. Public*, pg. 1115
BSF ENTERPRISE PLC; *Int'l*, pg. 1202
B&S FRAGRANCES & COSMETICS INC.; *U.S. Private*, pg. 419
BSG CONSTRUCTION MALAYSIA SDN BHD—See VINCI S.A.; *Int'l*, pg. 8231
BSG CRAFTBREWING—See Rahr Corporation; *U.S. Private*, pg. 3346
B&S GROUP S.A.; *Int'l*, pg. 784
BSG WIRELESS LIMITED—See GI Manager L.P.; *U.S. Private*, pg. 1694
B-SHARP MUSICAL PRODUCTIONS; *U.S. Private*, pg. 419
BSH BRAUNSCHWEIGER SCHROTTHANDEL GMBH—See Salzgitter AG; *Int'l*, pg. 6496
BSH CONTINENTAL ELETRODOMESTICOS LTDA.—See Robert Bosch GmbH; *Int'l*, pg. 6358
BSH DRIVES & PUMPS S.R.O.—See Robert Bosch GmbH; *Int'l*, pg. 6358
BSH ELECTROCASNICE S.R.L.—See Robert Bosch GmbH; *Int'l*, pg. 6358
BSH ELECTRODOMESTICOS ESPANA, S.A.—See Robert Bosch GmbH; *Int'l*, pg. 6358
BSH ELECTRODOMESTICOS S.A.C.—See Robert Bosch GmbH; *Int'l*, pg. 6358
BSH ELETTRODOMESTICI S.P.A.—See Robert Bosch GmbH; *Int'l*, pg. 6360
BSH EV ALETLERI SANAYI VE TICARET A.S.—See Robert Bosch GmbH; *Int'l*, pg. 6358
BSH HAUSGERATE AG—See Robert Bosch GmbH; *Int'l*, pg. 6358
BSH HAUSGERATE GESELLSCHAFT MBH—See Robert Bosch GmbH; *Int'l*, pg. 6358
BSH HAUSGERATE GMBH—See Robert Bosch GmbH; *Int'l*, pg. 6358
BSH HAZTARTASI KESZULEK KERESKEDELMI KFT.—See Robert Bosch GmbH; *Int'l*, pg. 6358
BSH HISNI APARATI D.O.O.—See Robert Bosch GmbH; *Int'l*, pg. 6358
BSH HOME APPLIANCES AB—See Robert Bosch GmbH; *Int'l*, pg. 6358
BSH HOME APPLIANCES CO., LTD.—See Robert Bosch GmbH; *Int'l*, pg. 6358
BSH HOME APPLIANCES CORPORATION—See Robert Bosch GmbH; *Int'l*, pg. 6358
BSH HOME APPLIANCES FZE—See Robert Bosch GmbH; *Int'l*, pg. 6358
BSH HOME APPLIANCES HOLDING (CHINA) CO., LTD.—See Robert Bosch GmbH; *Int'l*, pg. 6358
BSH HOME APPLIANCES LTD.—See Robert Bosch GmbH; *Int'l*, pg. 6358
BSH HOME APPLIANCES LTD.—See Robert Bosch GmbH; *Int'l*, pg. 6359
BSH HOME APPLIANCES LTD.—See Robert Bosch GmbH; *Int'l*, pg. 6359
BSH HOME APPLIANCES LTD.—See Robert Bosch GmbH; *Int'l*, pg. 6359
BSH HOME APPLIANCES LTD.—See Robert Bosch GmbH; *Int'l*, pg. 6359
BSH HOME APPLIANCES PTE. LTD.—See Robert Bosch GmbH; *Int'l*, pg. 6359
BSH HOME APPLIANCES (PTY.) LTD.—See Robert Bosch GmbH; *Int'l*, pg. 6358
BSH HOME APPLIANCES PTY. LTD.—See Robert Bosch GmbH; *Int'l*, pg. 6359
BSH HOME APPLIANCES SDN. BHD.—See Robert Bosch GmbH; *Int'l*, pg. 6359
BSH HOUSEHOLD APPLIANCES MANUFACTURING PRIVATE LIMITED—See Robert Bosch GmbH; *Int'l*, pg. 6359
BSH HUISHOUDAPPARATEN B.V.—See Robert Bosch GmbH; *Int'l*, pg. 6359
BSH HVIDEVARER A/S—See Robert Bosch GmbH; *Int'l*, pg. 6359
BSH IT SOLUTIONS GMBH—See Allgeier SE; *Int'l*, pg. 337
BSH KODINKONEET OY—See Robert Bosch GmbH; *Int'l*, pg. 6359
BSH SPRZET GOSPODARSTWA DOMOWEGO SP. Z O.O.—See Robert Bosch GmbH; *Int'l*, pg. 6359
B&S HTG B.V.—See B&S Group S.A.; *Int'l*, pg. 784
BSI AMERICA PROFESSIONAL SERVICES INC.—See The British Standards Institution; *Int'l*, pg. 7629
BSI ASSURANCE UK LIMITED—See The British Standards Institution; *Int'l*, pg. 7628
BSI BRASIL SISTEMAS DE GESTAO LTDA—See The British Standards Institution; *Int'l*, pg. 7628
BSI BRASIL—See The British Standards Institution; *Int'l*, pg. 7628
BSI CONSTRUCTORS, INC.; *U.S. Private*, pg. 675
BSI CYBERSECURITY AND INFORMATION RESILIENCE (UK) LIMITED—See The British Standards Institution; *Int'l*, pg. 7628
BSI CYBERSECURITY & INFORMATION RESILIENCE (IRELAND) LIMITED—See The British Standards Institution; *Int'l*, pg. 7628
BSI DIVERSIFIED LLC; *U.S. Private*, pg. 675
BSI ENGINEERING, INC.; *U.S. Private*, pg. 675
BSI GROUP (AUSTRALIA AND NEW ZEALAND) PTY LTD—See The British Standards Institution; *Int'l*, pg. 7628
BSI GROUP CANADA INC—See The British Standards Institution; *Int'l*, pg. 7628
BSI GROUP DEUTSCHLAND GMBH—See The British Standards Institution; *Int'l*, pg. 7628
BSI GROUP EURASIA BELGELENDIRRME HIZMETLERI LIMITED SIRKETI—See The British Standards Institution; *Int'l*, pg. 7628
BSI GROUP EURASIA CERTIFICATION SERVICES CO. LTD—See The British Standards Institution; *Int'l*, pg. 7628
BSI GROUP FRANCE SARL—See The British Standards Institution; *Int'l*, pg. 7628
BSI GROUP INDIA PRIVATE LTD—See The British Standards Institution; *Int'l*, pg. 7628
BSI GROUP ITALIA SRL—See The British Standards Institution; *Int'l*, pg. 7628
BSI GROUP JAPAN KK—See The British Standards Institution; *Int'l*, pg. 7628
BSI GROUP KOREA LTD—See The British Standards Institution; *Int'l*, pg. 7628
BSI GROUP LIMITED—See Capita plc; *Int'l*, pg. 1308
BSI GROUP MEXICO S DR RL DE CV—See The British Standards Institution; *Int'l*, pg. 7628
BSI GROUP PHILIPPINES, INC.—See The British Standards Institution; *Int'l*, pg. 7628
BSI GROUP POLSKA SPOLKA Z.O.O.—See The British Standards Institution; *Int'l*, pg. 7628
BSI GROUP SINGAPORE PTE LTD—See The British Standards Institution; *Int'l*, pg. 7628
BSI GROUP SOUTH AFRICA (PTY) LIMITED—See The British Standards Institution; *Int'l*, pg. 7628
BSI GROUP (THAILAND) CO., LTD—See The British Standards Institution; *Int'l*, pg. 7628
BSI GROUP THE NETHERLANDS BV—See The British Standards Institution; *Int'l*, pg. 7629
BSI HEALTHCARE SAUDI ARABIA—See The British Standards Institution; *Int'l*, pg. 7629
BSI INC.—See The British Standards Institution; *Int'l*, pg. 7629
BSI LIMITED—See The British Standards Institution; *Int'l*, pg. 7629
BSI LLC—See Levine Leichtman Capital Partners, LLC; *U.S. Private*, pg. 2435
BSI MANAGEMENT SYSTEMS CERTIFICATION (BEIJING) CO. LTD.—See The British Standards Institution; *Int'l*, pg. 7629
BSI MANAGEMENT SYSTEMS CIS LLC—See The British Standards Institution; *Int'l*, pg. 7629
B & S INTERNATIONAL HOLDINGS LTD.; *Int'l*, pg. 783
BSI PACIFIC LIMITED—See The British Standards Institution; *Int'l*, pg. 7629
BSI (PANAMA) S.A.—See EFG International AG; *Int'l*, pg. 2320
BSI SEMICONDUCTOR KOREA CO., LTD.—See WT Microelectronics Co., Ltd.; *Int'l*, pg. 8498
BSI SERVICES (ASIA PACIFIC) SDN BHD—See The British Standards Institution; *Int'l*, pg. 7629
BSI SERVICES MALAYSIA SDN. BHD.—See The British Standards Institution; *Int'l*, pg. 7629
BSI SERVICES & SOLUTIONS (NYC) INC.—See The British Standards Institution; *Int'l*, pg. 7629
BSI STEEL LIMITED; *Int'l*, pg. 1202
BSI TRUST CORPORATION (MALTA) LIMITED—See EFG International AG; *Int'l*, pg. 2320
BSI VIETNAM CO., LTD—See The British Standards Institution; *Int'l*, pg. 7629
BS JAPAN CORPORATION—See TV TOKYO Holdings Corporation; *Int'l*, pg. 7987
BSJ BANCSHARES, INC.; *U.S. Private*, pg. 675
BSK ARKITEKTER AB—See Veidekke ASA; *Int'l*, pg. 8148
BSK CORPORATION—See Ilshin Spinning Co., Ltd.; *Int'l*, pg. 3616
BSKE, GMBH—See Industria de Diseno Textil, S.A.; *Int'l*, pg. 3665
BSLC II; *U.S. Private*, pg. 675
BSL CORPORATION BERHAD; *Int'l*, pg. 1202
BSL ECO ENERGY SDN. BHD.—See BSL Corporation Berhad; *Int'l*, pg. 1202
BSL ELECTRONICS & TECHNOLOGIES SDN. BHD.—See BSL Corporation Berhad; *Int'l*, pg. 1202
BSL FREIGHT SOLUTION PRIVATE LIMITED—See Shreyas Shipping & Logistics Limited; *Int'l*, pg. 6865
BS LIMITED; *Int'l*, pg. 1201
B&S LINK CO., LTD.—See Test-Rite International Co., Ltd.; *Int'l*, pg. 7575
BSL INSURANCE CORPORATION—See UNIVA Oak Holdings Limited; *Int'l*, pg. 8076
BSL LEASING CO., LTD.—See Bangkok Bank Public Company Limited; *Int'l*, pg. 833
BSL LIMITED; *Int'l*, pg. 1202
BSL MANUFACTURING SDN. BHD.—See BSL Corporation Berhad; *Int'l*, pg. 1202
B&S LOGGING INC.; *U.S. Private*, pg. 419
BSL UNIFY PTE. LTD.—See BSL Corporation Berhad; *Int'l*, pg. 1202
BSM BANKINGSYSTEME UND MANAGEMENTBERATUNG GMBH—See msg group GmbH; *Int'l*, pg. 5067
BSM CHEMICAL CO., LTD.; *Int'l*, pg. 1202
BSM CREW SERVICE CENTRE (CROATIA) LTD.—See Bernhard Schulte Shipmanagement (Cyprus) Ltd.; *Int'l*, pg. 988
BSM CREW SERVICE CENTRE (ESTONIA) LTD.—See Bernhard Schulte Shipmanagement (Cyprus) Ltd.; *Int'l*, pg. 988
BSM CREW SERVICE CENTRE (LATVIA) LTD.—See Bernhard Schulte Shipmanagement (Cyprus) Ltd.; *Int'l*, pg. 988
BSM CREW SERVICE CENTRE (MYANMAR) LTD.—See Bernhard Schulte Shipmanagement (Cyprus) Ltd.; *Int'l*, pg. 988
BSM CREW SERVICE CENTRE (ROMANIA) SRL—See Bernhard Schulte Shipmanagement (Cyprus) Ltd.; *Int'l*, pg. 988
BSM CREW SERVICE CENTRE (VENEZUELA) C.A.—See Bernhard Schulte Shipmanagement (Cyprus) Ltd.; *Int'l*, pg. 988
BSM GROUP LIMITED; *Int'l*, pg. 1202
BS MICRO ELECTRONICS (S) PTE LTD.—See STMicroelectronics N.V.; *Int'l*, pg. 7217
B. SMITH ENTERPRISES LTD.; *U.S. Private*, pg. 420
BSM TECHNOLOGIES INC.—See Geotab, Inc.; *Int'l*, pg. 2941
BSN GASSPACK FRANCE—See O-I Glass, Inc.; *U.S. Public*, pg. 1559
BSN GLASSPACK SPAIN—See O-I Glass, Inc.; *U.S. Public*, pg. 1559
BS NIPPON CORPORATION—See Nippon Television Holdings Inc.; *Int'l*, pg. 5356
BSN-JOBST GMBH—See Svenska Cellulosa Aktiebolaget SCA; *Int'l*, pg. 7356
BSN MEDIA HOLDINGS, INC.; *Int'l*, pg. 1202
BSN MEDICAL GMBH—See Svenska Cellulosa Aktiebolaget SCA; *Int'l*, pg. 7356
BSN MEDICAL, INC.—See Svenska Cellulosa Aktiebolaget SCA; *Int'l*, pg. 7356
BSN RADIANTE SAS—See Essity Aktiebolag; *Int'l*, pg. 2516
BSN SPORTS, LLC—See Bain Capital, LP; *U.S. Private*, pg. 451
B-SOFT CO., LTD.; *Int'l*, pg. 785
BSOFT S.R.L.—See Biesse S.p.A.; *Int'l*, pg. 1020

COMPANY NAME INDEX

B.S. OIL PALM PLANTATIONS SDN BHD—See Far East Holdings Berhad; *Int'l*, pg. 2616
BSP ACQUISITION CORP.; *U.S. Private*, pg. 675
BSP - BIOLOGICAL SIGNAL PROCESSING LTD.; *Int'l*, pg. 1202
BSP CAPITAL LIMITED—See BSP Financial Group Limited; *Int'l*, pg. 1202
BSP CONVERTIBLE NOTES LIMITED—See BSP Financial Group Limited; *Int'l*, pg. 1202
BSP FINANCIAL GROUP LIMITED; *Int'l*, pg. 1202
BSP INTERNATIONAL FOUNDATIONS LIMITED—See Tex Holdings Plc; *Int'l*, pg. 7582
BSP LIFE (FIJI) LIMITED—See BSP Financial Group Limited; *Int'l*, pg. 1202
BSP LIFE (PNG) LIMITED—See BSP Financial Group Limited; *Int'l*, pg. 1202
BSP MARKETING INC.; *U.S. Private*, pg. 675
BSP (SHANGHAI) INC.—See UNIRITA Inc.; *Int'l*, pg. 8060
BSP SOFTWARE LLC; *U.S. Private*, pg. 675
BSP TRANSPORTATION INC.; *U.S. Private*, pg. 675
BSQUARE CORPORATION—See Kontron AG; *Int'l*, pg. 4277
BSQUARE EMEA LIMITED—See Kontron AG; *Int'l*, pg. 4277
BSQUARE KK—See Kontron AG; *Int'l*, pg. 4277
BSQUARE TAIWAN CORPORATION—See Kontron AG; *Int'l*, pg. 4277
BSRM STEELS LIMITED; *Int'l*, pg. 1202
BSR REAL ESTATE INVESTMENT TRUST; *U.S. Public*, pg. 409
BSS AUDIO—See Samsung Group; *Int'l*, pg. 6512
BS SAVINGS BANK CO., LTD.—See BNK Financial Group Inc.; *Int'l*, pg. 1079
BS SECURITIES CO., LTD.—See BNK Financial Group Inc.; *Int'l*, pg. 1079
BSS GROUP LTD—See Travis Perkins plc; *Int'l*, pg. 7908
BSS&M REAL ESTATE AG—See Mobimo Holding AG; *Int'l*, pg. 5012
BSSW ARCHITECTS, INC.—See Bernhard Capital Partners Management, LP; *U.S. Private*, pg. 537
BS SYSTEM INFORMATION CO., LTD.—See BNK Financial Group Inc.; *Int'l*, pg. 1079
B-STAFF CO., LTD.—See Tomoku Co., Ltd.; *Int'l*, pg. 7801
BST & CO. CPA LLP; *U.S. Private*, pg. 075
BST CONSULTANTS PTE. LTD.—See DEKRA e.V.; *Int'l*, pg. 2007
BST ELTROMAT INTERNATIONAL GMBH—See SMS Holding GmbH; *Int'l*, pg. 7015
BST INTERNATIONAL GMBH—See SMS Holding GmbH; *Int'l*, pg. 7016
BST NANOCARBON LLC; *U.S. Private*, pg. 675
BST NORTH AMERICA, INC.—See SMS Holding GmbH; *Int'l*, pg. 7016
BS TV TOKYO CORPORATION—See TV TOKYO Holdings Corporation; *Int'l*, pg. 7987
BSV SARL—See Cegedim S.A.; *Int'l*, pg. 1390
BSWIFT LLC—See Francisco Partners Management, LP; *U.S. Private*, pg. 1593
BSWIFT RESOURCES LLC—See CVS Health Corporation; *U.S. Public*, pg. 616
BSW MACHINERY HANDELS-GMBH—See Windmoeller & Hoelscher KG; *Int'l*, pg. 8425
BSW TIMBER LTD.—See Endless LLP; *Int'l*, pg. 2403
BSX SERVICES PTY LIMITED—See NSX Limited; *Int'l*, pg. 5481
BTA BALTIC INSURANCE COMPANY AAS—See Vienna Insurance Group AG Wiener Versicherung Gruppe; *Int'l*, pg. 8194
BTA BANK JSC; *Int'l*, pg. 1204
BT AMERICAS INC.—See BT Group plc; *Int'l*, pg. 1203
BTA OIL PRODUCERS INC.; *U.S. Private*, pg. 675
BT ASIA MARKETING & ENGINEERING PTE LTDBT ASIA MARKETING & ENGINEERING PTE LTD—See Beng Kuang Marine Limited; *Int'l*, pg. 973
BT ASSET MANAGEMENT SAI S.A.—See Banca Transilvania S.A.; *Int'l*, pg. 816
BT AUSTRALASIA PTY LIMITED—See BT Group plc; *Int'l*, pg. 1203
BTB-BLOCKHEIZKRAFTWERKS, TRAGER- UND BETREIBERGESELLSCHAFT MBH—See RWE AG; *Int'l*, pg. 6433
BT BILISIM HIZMETLERI ANONIM SIRKETI—See BT Group plc; *Int'l*, pg. 1202
BT BRANDS, INC.; *U.S. Public*, pg. 409
BTB REAL ESTATE INVESTMENT TRUST; *Int'l*, pg. 1204
B-T BROKERAGE INC.—See The Decker Companies Inc.; *U.S. Private*, pg. 4019
BT BROKERAGE, INC.—See BT Trucking, Inc.; *U.S. Private*, pg. 675
B.T.C. ACTIVEWEAR LTD.—See New Wave Group AB; *Int'l*, pg. 5229
BT CAPITAL PARTNERS S.A.—See Banca Transilvania S.A.; *Int'l*, pg. 816
BTC BILISIM HIZMETLERI A.S.—See EWE Aktiengesellschaft; *Int'l*, pg. 2575
BTC BUSINESS TECHNOLOGY CONSULTING AG—See EWE Aktiengesellschaft; *Int'l*, pg. 2575
BTC DIGITAL LTD.; *Int'l*, pg. 1204

BTC ELECTRONIC COMPONENTS, INC.—See Audax Group, Limited Partnership; *U.S. Private*, pg. 388
BTC EMBEDDED SYSTEMS AG—See EWE Aktiengesellschaft; *Int'l*, pg. 2575
BTC EUROPE GMBH—See BASF SE; *Int'l*, pg. 882
BTC FINANCIAL CORPORATION; *U.S. Private*, pg. 675
BTC HEALTH LIMITED; *Int'l*, pg. 1204
BTC HOLDINGS INC.—See Blackfoot Telephone Cooperative, Inc.; *U.S. Private*, pg. 573
BTC INDUSTRIBATTERIER AB—See Addtech AB; *Int'l*, pg. 132
BTC IT SERVICES GMBH—See EWE Aktiengesellschaft; *Int'l*, pg. 2575
BT COMMUNICATIONS DO BRASIL LIMITADA—See BT Group plc; *Int'l*, pg. 1203
BT COMMUNICATIONS IRELAND LIMITED—See BT Group plc; *Int'l*, pg. 1203
BT COMPONENTS A/S—See VKR Holding A/S; *Int'l*, pg. 8281
BT COMPOSITES LIMITED—See The Braj Binani Group; *Int'l*, pg. 7627
BT CONFERENCING, INC.—See BT Group plc; *Int'l*, pg. 1203
BT CONFERENCING—See BT Group plc; *Int'l*, pg. 1203
BT CONVERGENT SOLUTIONS LIMITED—See BT Group plc; *Int'l*, pg. 1203
BTCS INC.; *U.S. Public*, pg. 409
BTC SOFTWARE SYSTEMS SP. Z O.O.—See EWE Aktiengesellschaft; *Int'l*, pg. 2575
BTC SOFTWARE TECHNOLOGY (SHANGHAI) CO., LTD.—See EWE Aktiengesellschaft; *Int'l*, pg. 2575
BTC SOLUTIONS LIMITED—See Snap-on Incorporated; *U.S. Public*, pg. 1897
BT DIRECT IFN S.A.—See Banca Transilvania S.A.; *Int'l*, pg. 816
BTD MANUFACTURING, INC.—See Otter Tail Corporation; *U.S. Public*, pg. 1624
B-TEAM CONSULT AND SERVICES SRL—See 2G Energy AG; *Int'l*, pg. 5
B TECH INDUSTRY CO. LTD.—See Top Glove Corporation Bhd.; *Int'l*, pg. 7812
BT ENIA TELECOMUNICAZIONI S.P.A.—See BT Group plc; *Int'l*, pg. 1203
B.T. EQUIPMENT CO., INC.—See Hallamore Corporation; *U.S. Private*, pg. 1844
BT EQUIPMENT PTY LIMITED—See Affirma Capital Limited; *Int'l*, pg. 187
BT ESPANA S.A.—See BT Group plc; *Int'l*, pg. 1203
B&T EXACT GMBH; *Int'l*, pg. 784
B&T EXPRESS INC.; *U.S. Private*, pg. 675
BT FINANCE PTY LIMITED—See Westpac Banking Corporation; *Int'l*, pg. 8391
BT FINANCIAL GROUP PTY LTD—See Westpac Banking Corporation; *Int'l*, pg. 8391
BT FLEET LIMITED—See Aurelius Equity Opportunities SE & Co. KGaA; *Int'l*, pg. 707
BT FRANCE S.A.R.L—See Toyota Industries Corporation; *Int'l*, pg. 7867
BT FRONTLINE PTE. LTD.—See BT Group plc; *Int'l*, pg. 1203
BT FUNDS MANAGEMENT (NZ) LIMITED—See Westpac Banking Corporation; *Int'l*, pg. 8391
BTG AUSTRALASIA PTY LIMITED—See Boston Scientific Corporation; *U.S. Public*, pg. 373
B.T.G. BELGISCHE TECHNISCHE GASSEN BVBA/SPRL—See SOL S.p.A.; *Int'l*, pg. 7067
BTG ECLEPENS SA—See Voith GmbH & Co. KGaA; *Int'l*, pg. 8297
BT (GERMANY) GMBH & CO. OHG—See BT Group plc; *Int'l*, pg. 1203
BTG GLOBAL ADVISORY LIMITED—See Begbies Traynor Group plc; *Int'l*, pg. 940
BTG HOTELS GROUP CO., LTD.; *Int'l*, pg. 1204
BTG INTELLIGENCE LIMITED—See Begbies Traynor Group plc; *Int'l*, pg. 940
BTG INTERNATIONAL (HOLDINGS) LTD—See Boston Scientific Corporation; *U.S. Public*, pg. 373
BTG INTERNATIONAL INC.—See Boston Scientific Corporation; *U.S. Public*, pg. 373
BTG INTERNATIONAL LTD.—See Boston Scientific Corporation; *U.S. Public*, pg. 373
BT GLOBAL COMMUNICATIONS INDIA PRIVATE LIMITED—See BT Group plc; *Int'l*, pg. 1203
BT GLOBAL SERVICES—See BT Group plc; *Int'l*, pg. 1203
BT GLOBENET NOMINEES LIMITED—See Deutsche Bank Aktiengesellschaft; *Int'l*, pg. 2055
BTG PACTUAL ARGENTINA S.A.—See BCO BTG PACTUAL S.A.; *Int'l*, pg. 928
BTG PACTUAL ASIA LIMITED—See BCO BTG PACTUAL S.A.; *Int'l*, pg. 928
BTG PACTUAL CASA DE BOLSA, S.A. DE C.V.—See BCO BTG PACTUAL S.A.; *Int'l*, pg. 928
BTG PACTUAL EUROPE LLP—See BCO BTG PACTUAL S.A.; *Int'l*, pg. 928
BTG PACTUAL HOLDING S.A.; *Int'l*, pg. 1204
BTG PACTUAL NY CORPORATION—See BCO BTG PACTUAL S.A.; *Int'l*, pg. 928
BTG PACTUAL; *Int'l*, pg. 1204

BTG PLC—See Boston Scientific Corporation; *U.S. Public*, pg. 373
BT GROUP PLC; *Int'l*, pg. 1202
BTHC X, INC.; *Int'l*, pg. 1204
BT HOLDING AG; *Int'l*, pg. 1204
BT HONG KONG LIMITED—See BT Group plc; *Int'l*, pg. 1203
BTI BANK COMPANY—See Al Baraka Banking Group B.S.C.; *Int'l*, pg. 276
BTI BEFESTIGUNGSTECHNIK GMBH & CO. KG—See Berner SE; *Int'l*, pg. 988
BTIC AMERICA CORPORATION—See Beijing Jingcheng Machinery Electric Co., Ltd.; *Int'l*, pg. 952
BTICINO CHILE LTDA—See Legrand S.A.; *Int'l*, pg. 4445
BTICINO CHILE S.A.—See Legrand S.A.; *Int'l*, pg. 4445
BTICINO CHINA—See Legrand S.A.; *Int'l*, pg. 4445
BTICINO DE MEXICO SA DE CV—See Legrand S.A.; *Int'l*, pg. 4445
BTICINO SPA—See Legrand S.A.; *Int'l*, pg. 4445
BTI CONSULTANTS HONG KONG LIMITED—See Kelly Services, Inc.; *U.S. Public*, pg. 1219
BTI CONSULTANTS (INDIA) PRIVATE LIMITED—See Kelly Services, Inc.; *U.S. Public*, pg. 1219
BTI CONSULTANTS PTE. LTD.—See Kelly Services, Inc.; *U.S. Public*, pg. 1218
BTI EXECUTIVE PLACEMENT (THAILAND) CO.—See Kelly Services, Inc.; *U.S. Public*, pg. 1219
BT IGNITE—See BT Group plc; *Int'l*, pg. 1203
BTI GROUP; *U.S. Private*, pg. 675
B.T.I. INVESTMENTS INC.—See Deutsche Bank Aktiengesellschaft; *Int'l*, pg. 2055
BT INCORPORATED; *U.S. Private*, pg. 675
B-T INC.—See The Decker Companies Inc.; *U.S. Private*, pg. 4019
BT INFONET—See BT Group plc; *Int'l*, pg. 1203
BT INVESTMENT MANAGEMENT LIMITED—See Westpac Banking Corporation; *Int'l*, pg. 8391
BT INVESTMENTS S.R.L.—See Banca Transilvania S.A.; *Int'l*, pg. 816
BTI STUDIOS AB—See The Carlyle Group Inc.; *U.S. Public*, pg. 2045
BTI STUDIOS - ROMANIA—See The Carlyle Group Inc.; *U.S. Public*, pg. 2045
BTI STUDIOS SP. Z O.O—See The Carlyle Group Inc.; *U.S. Public*, pg. 2045
BT ITALIA SPA—See BT Group plc; *Int'l*, pg. 1203
BT IT SERVICES LIMITED—See BT Group plc; *Int'l*, pg. 1203
BT LATAM BRASIL LTDA—See BT Group plc; *Int'l*, pg. 1203
BT LEASING MD SRL—See Banca Transilvania S.A.; *Int'l*, pg. 816
BT LEASING TRANSILVANIA IFN S.A.—See Banca Transilvania S.A.; *Int'l*, pg. 816
BTL S.A.—See L'Air Liquide S.A.; *Int'l*, pg. 4375
B.T. MANCINI CO., INC.; *U.S. Private*, pg. 421
BTM BAUSTOFF-TECHNIK + MISCHWERKE GMBH—See VINCI S.A.; *Int'l*, pg. 8213
BTM COMPANY, LLC—See CapitalSouth Corp.; *U.S. Private*, pg. 742
BTM CO.; *U.S. Private*, pg. 675
BTME GROUP LTD.—See Investor AB; *Int'l*, pg. 3787
BTM ENGINEERING INC.—See Bowman Consulting Group Ltd.; *U.S. Public*, pg. 376
B&T METALS CO.; *U.S. Private*, pg. 419
BTM MARKETING & TRADING SDN. BHD.—See BTM Resources Berhad; *Int'l*, pg. 1205
BTM RESOURCES BERHAD; *Int'l*, pg. 1204
BTMU LEASE (DEUTSCHLAND) GMBH—See Mitsubishi UFJ Financial Group, Inc.; *Int'l*, pg. 4968
BTMU LEASING & FINANCE, INC.—See Mitsubishi UFJ Financial Group, Inc.; *Int'l*, pg. 4969
BTMU PARTICIPATION (THAILAND) CO., LTD.—See Mitsubishi UFJ Financial Group, Inc.; *Int'l*, pg. 4968
BT MURITZ GMBH—See Deutsche Bank Aktiengesellschaft; *Int'l*, pg. 2055
BTN BARAN TELECOM NETWORKS GMBH—See Baran Group Ltd.; *Int'l*, pg. 858
BTN, LLC—See PENN Entertainment, Inc.; *U.S. Public*, pg. 1662
BTN TURBOCHARGER SERVICE LIMITED—See Blackstone Inc.; *U.S. Public*, pg. 359
BT NYLOPLAST GMBH—See Tessenderlo Group NV; *Int'l*, pg. 7573
BT NYLOPLAST KFT—See Tessenderlo Group NV; *Int'l*, pg. 7573
BTOB—See Crain Communications, Inc.; *U.S. Private*, pg. 1084
B TO D GROUP—See WPP plc; *Int'l*, pg. 8467
B-TOHIN MACHINE (JIANGSU) CO., LTD.—See Nippon Steel Corporation; *Int'l*, pg. 5337
BTOMORROW VENTURES LIMITED—See British American Tobacco plc; *Int'l*, pg. 1165
BT OPERATIONAL LEASING SA—See Banca Transilvania S.A.; *Int'l*, pg. 816
BTP BANQUE SA—See Groupe BPCE; *Int'l*, pg. 3092
BTP CAPITAL CONSEIL SAS—See Groupe BPCE; *Int'l*, pg. 3092

BTM RESOURCES BERHAD

BT POZNAN SP. Z.O.O.—See Heidelberg Materials AG; *Int'l*, pg. 3308
BT PRODUCTS AB—See Toyota Industries Corporation; *Int'l*, pg. 7867
BT PROPERTY LTD.—See BT Group plc; *Int'l*, pg. 1203
BTQ TECHNOLOGIES CORP; *Int'l*, pg. 1205
BTR CAPITAL MANAGEMENT INC.—See TA Associates, Inc.; *U.S. Private*, pg. 3919
BT REDCARE GROUP—See BT Group plc; *Int'l*, pg. 1203
BT REDCARE—See BT Group plc; *Int'l*, pg. 1203
BTREN MANTENIMIENTO FERROVIARIO S.A.—See Alstom S.A.; *Int'l*, pg. 383
BT RETAIL—See BT Group plc; *Int'l*, pg. 1203
BTR FARMERS CO-OP; *U.S. Private*, pg. 675
BTR INCORPORATED; *U.S. Private*, pg. 675
BTRS HOLDINGS INC.—See EQT AB; *Int'l*, pg. 2472
BT SABLE, L.L.C.—See Deutsche Bank Aktiengesellschaft; *Int'l*, pg. 2055
BTS ALLIANCE, LLC—See AvidXchange Holdings, Inc.; *U.S. Public*, pg. 246
BTS ASIA PACIFIC PTE. LTD.—See BTS Group AB; *Int'l*, pg. 1205
BTS AUSTRALASIA—See BTS Group AB; *Int'l*, pg. 1205
BTS BILBAO—See BTS Group AB; *Int'l*, pg. 1205
BTS BRUSSELS NV—See BTS Group AB; *Int'l*, pg. 1205
BTS BUSINESS CONSULTING (THAILAND) CO.,LTD.—See BTS Group AB; *Int'l*, pg. 1205
BTS CHICAGO LIMITED—See BTS Group AB; *Int'l*, pg. 1205
BTS CONSULTING (SHANGHAI) CO., LTD.—See BTS Group AB; *Int'l*, pg. 1205
BT SECURITIES S.A.—See Banca Transilvania S.A.; *Int'l*, pg. 816
BTS GROUP AB; *Int'l*, pg. 1205
BTS GROUP HOLDINGS PUBLIC COMPANY LIMITED; *Int'l*, pg. 1205
BTS IN AMSTERDAM BV—See BTS Group AB; *Int'l*, pg. 1205
BT SINGAPORE PTE LTD—See BT Group plc; *Int'l*, pg. 1203
BTS LIMITED—See Abengoa S.A.; *Int'l*, pg. 59
BTS LIMITED—See Algonquin Power & Utilities Corp.; *Int'l*, pg. 319
BTS LONDON—See BTS Group AB; *Int'l*, pg. 1205
BTS MANAGEMENT SA—See BTS Group AB; *Int'l*, pg. 1205
BTS MEXICO—See BTS Group AB; *Int'l*, pg. 1205
BTS PHILADELPHIA—See BTS Group AB; *Int'l*, pg. 1205
BTSR INTERNATIONAL S.P.A.; *Int'l*, pg. 1206
BTS SCOTTSDALE—See BTS Group AB; *Int'l*, pg. 1205
BTS SEOUL—See BTS Group AB; *Int'l*, pg. 1205
BTS SOUTH AFRICA—See BTS Group AB; *Int'l*, pg. 1205
BTS SP. Z O.O.; *Int'l*, pg. 1206
BTS STAMFORD—See BTS Group AB; *Int'l*, pg. 1205
BTS STOCKHOLM—See BTS Group AB; *Int'l*, pg. 1205
BTS SVERIGE AB—See BTS Group AB; *Int'l*, pg. 1205
BTS TAIPEI—See BTS Group AB; *Int'l*, pg. 1205
BTS TOKYO—See BTS Group AB; *Int'l*, pg. 1205
BTS UNITED STATES—See BTS Group AB; *Int'l*, pg. 1205
BTS USA, INC.—See BTS Group AB; *Int'l*, pg. 1205
BT SWITZERLAND AG—See BT Group plc; *Int'l*, pg. 1203
BT TELEKOM HIZMETLERI ANONIM SIRKETI—See BT Group plc; *Int'l*, pg. 1203
BT TRUCKING, INC.; *U.S. Private*, pg. 675
BT-TWISS TRANSPORT LLC—See Bulova Technologies Group, Inc.; *U.S. Private*, pg. 685
BTU ANALYTICS, LLC—See FactSet Research Systems Inc.; *U.S. Public*, pg. 819
BTU EUROPE LTD.—See Amtech Systems, Inc.; *U.S. Public*, pg. 133
BTU (FRANCE)—See Amtech Systems, Inc.; *U.S. Public*, pg. 133
BTU INTERNATIONAL, INC.—See Amtech Systems, Inc.; *U.S. Public*, pg. 133
BTU LTD.—See Amtech Systems, Inc.; *U.S. Public*, pg. 133
BTU METALS CORP.; *Int'l*, pg. 1206
BTU OVERSEAS, LTD.—See Amtech Systems, Inc.; *U.S. Public*, pg. 133
BTV ANLAGENLEASING 2 GMBH—See Bank fur Tirol und Vorarlberg Ag; *Int'l*, pg. 838
BTV ANLAGENLEASING 3 GMBH—See Bank fur Tirol und Vorarlberg Ag; *Int'l*, pg. 838
BTV CROWN EQUITIES, INC.; *U.S. Private*, pg. 676
BTV LEASING DEUTSCHLAND GMBH—See Bank fur Tirol und Vorarlberg Ag; *Int'l*, pg. 838
BTV LEASING GMBH—See Bank fur Tirol und Vorarlberg Ag; *Int'l*, pg. 838
BTV LEASING SCHWEIZ AG—See Bank fur Tirol und Vorarlberg Ag; *Int'l*, pg. 838
BTV MOBILIEN LEASING GMBH—See Bank fur Tirol und Vorarlberg Ag; *Int'l*, pg. 838
B.T. VORDERTAUNUS (LUXEMBOURG), S.A R.L.—See Deutsche Bank Aktiengesellschaft; *Int'l*, pg. 2055
BTV REAL-LEASING GMBH—See Bank fur Tirol und Vorarlberg Ag; *Int'l*, pg. 838
BTV REAL-LEASING I GMBH—See Bank fur Tirol und Vorarlberg Ag; *Int'l*, pg. 838

BTV REAL-LEASING II GMBH—See Bank fur Tirol und Vorarlberg Ag; *Int'l*, pg. 838
BTV REAL-LEASING III NACHFOLGE GMBH AND CO KG—See Bank fur Tirol und Vorarlberg Ag; *Int'l*, pg. 838
BT WEALTH INDUSTRIES PUBLIC COMPANY LTD.; *Int'l*, pg. 1204
BT WHOLESALE—See BT Group plc; *Int'l*, pg. 1203
BTX GROUP A/S—See Sun Capital Partners, Inc.; *U.S. Private*, pg. 3861
BTX—See Harvard Bioscience, Inc.; *U.S. Public*, pg. 987
BUA CEMENT PLC; *Int'l*, pg. 1206
BUALI INVESTMENT COMPANY; *Int'l*, pg. 1206
BUALUANG OFFICE LEASEHOLD REIT; *Int'l*, pg. 1206
BUALUANG SECURITIES PUBLIC COMPANY LIMITED—See Bangkok Bank Public Company Limited; *Int'l*, pg. 833
BUALUANG VENTURES LTD.—See Bangkok Bank Public Company Limited; *Int'l*, pg. 833
BUBALUS RESOURCES LIMITED; *Int'l*, pg. 1206
BUBBA GUMP SHRIMP CO. RESTAURANTS, INC.—See Fertitta Entertainment, Inc.; *U.S. Private*, pg. 1499
BUBBA OUSTALET INC.; *U.S. Private*, pg. 676
BUBBIES HOMEMADE ICE CREAM & DESSERTS, INC.—See Kenex Holdings LLC; *U.S. Private*, pg. 2284
BUBBLES BAKING CO.—See Surge Private Equity LLC; *U.S. Private*, pg. 3884
BUBBLES INTERGROUP LTD; *Int'l*, pg. 1206
BUBBLEUP, LTD; *U.S. Private*, pg. 676
BUBBLR, INC.; *Int'l*, pg. 1206
BUBCHEN-WERK EWALD HERMES PHARMAZEUTISCHE FABRIK GMBH—See Nestle S.A.; *Int'l*, pg. 5202
BU BETEILIGUNGS-UND VERMOGENSVERWALTUNG GMBH—See voestalpine AG; *Int'l*, pg. 8287
BUBLITZ MATERIAL HANDLING, INC.; *U.S. Private*, pg. 676
BUBNY DEVELOPMENT S.R.O.; *Int'l*, pg. 1206
BUBS AUSTRALIA LIMITED; *Int'l*, pg. 1206
BUCA DI BEPPO MINNEAPOLIS—See Planet Hollywood International, Inc.; *U.S. Private*, pg. 3196
BUCA, INC.—See Planet Hollywood International, Inc.; *U.S. Private*, pg. 3196
BUCCANEER GOLD CORP.; *Int'l*, pg. 1206
BUCCANEER LANDSCAPE MANAGEMENT CORPORATION; *U.S. Private*, pg. 676
BUCCANEERS LIMITED PARTNERSHIP; *U.S. Private*, pg. 676
BUCCELLATI HOLDING ITALIA S.P.A.—See Compagnie Financiere Richemont S.A.; *Int'l*, pg. 1741
THE BUCCINI/POLLIN GROUP, INC.; *U.S. Private*, pg. 4002
BUCHA GLASSWORKS S.A.—See Yioula Glassworks S.A.; *Int'l*, pg. 8585
BUCHALTER, NEMER, FIELDS & YOUNGER LLP; *U.S. Private*, pg. 676
BUCHANAN COMMUNICATIONS LTD.—See WPP plc; *Int'l*, pg. 8462
BUCHANAN & EDWARDS INC.; *U.S. Private*, pg. 676
BUCHANAN FOREST PRODUCTS, LTD.; *Int'l*, pg. 1206
BUCHANAN HARDWOODS INC.; *U.S. Private*, pg. 676
BUCHANAN INGERSOLL & ROONEY PC; *U.S. Private*, pg. 676
BUCHANAN OIL CORPORATION; *U.S. Private*, pg. 676
BUCHANAN SALES CO INC; *U.S. Private*, pg. 676
BUCHANAN STREET PARTNERS, INC.; *U.S. Private*, pg. 676
BUCHANAN TECHNOLOGIES, INC.—See Lightview Capital LLC; *U.S. Private*, pg. 2453
BUCHANG PHARMACEUTICAL,INC; *Int'l*, pg. 1206
BUCHAN TECHNICAL SERVICES LIMITED—See James Fisher & Sons Public Limited Company; *Int'l*, pg. 3875
BUCHART HORN INC.—See Pace Resources, Inc.; *U.S. Private*, pg. 3064
BUCHART HORN INC—See Pace Resources, Inc.; *U.S. Private*, pg. 3064
BUCHBINDER TUNICK & COMPANY LLP; *U.S. Private*, pg. 676
BUCH.CH—See Orell Fussli Holding AG; *Int'l*, pg. 5616
BUCH.CH—See Thalia Bucher GmbH; *Int'l*, pg. 7607
BUCHER AEROSPACE CORP.—See Bucher Leichtbau AG; *Int'l*, pg. 1209
BUCHER-ALIMENTECH LTD—See Bucher Industries AG; *Int'l*, pg. 1208
BUCHER AUTOMATION AG—See Bucher Industries AG; *Int'l*, pg. 1206
BUCHER AUTOMATION HUNGARY KFT.—See Bucher Industries AG; *Int'l*, pg. 1206
BUCHER AUTOMATION TETTNANG GMBH—See Bucher Industries AG; *Int'l*, pg. 1206
BUCHER BETEILIGUNGEN GMBH—See Bucher Industries AG; *Int'l*, pg. 1207
BUCHER DENWEL, SPOL. S R.O.—See Bucher Industries AG; *Int'l*, pg. 1207
BUCHERER AG; *Int'l*, pg. 1209
BUCHER EXZEL, S.L.—See Bucher Industries AG; *Int'l*, pg. 1207
BUCHER-GUYER AG FOOD TECH—See Bucher Industries AG; *Int'l*, pg. 1208

CORPORATE AFFILIATIONS

BUCHER-GUYER AG MUNICIPAL VEHICLES—See Bucher Industries AG; *Int'l*, pg. 1208
BUCHER-GUYER AG—See Bucher Industries AG; *Int'l*, pg. 1208
BUCHER HIDRAULICA LTDA.—See Bucher Industries AG; *Int'l*, pg. 1207
BUCHER HIDROLIK SISTEMLERI TIC. LTD.—See Bucher Industries AG; *Int'l*, pg. 1207
BUCHER HYDRAULICS AG FRUTIGEN—See Bucher Industries AG; *Int'l*, pg. 1207
BUCHER HYDRAULICS AG—See Bucher Industries AG; *Int'l*, pg. 1207
BUCHER HYDRAULICS CO., LTD.—See Bucher Industries AG; *Int'l*, pg. 1207
BUCHER HYDRAULICS CORPORATION—See Bucher Industries AG; *Int'l*, pg. 1207
BUCHER HYDRAULICS CORP—See Bucher Industries AG; *Int'l*, pg. 1207
BUCHER HYDRAULICS DACHAU GMBH—See Bucher Industries AG; *Int'l*, pg. 1207
BUCHER HYDRAULICS ERDING GMBH—See Bucher Industries AG; *Int'l*, pg. 1207
BUCHER HYDRAULICS FRUHGEN AG—See Bucher Industries AG; *Int'l*, pg. 1207
BUCHER HYDRAULICS GMBH—See Bucher Industries AG; *Int'l*, pg. 1207
BUCHER HYDRAULICS KK—See Bucher Industries AG; *Int'l*, pg. 1207
BUCHER HYDRAULICS LTD—See Bucher Industries AG; *Int'l*, pg. 1207
BUCHER HYDRAULICS PVT LTD.—See Bucher Industries AG; *Int'l*, pg. 1207
BUCHER HYDRAULICS REMSCHEID GMBH—See Bucher Industries AG; *Int'l*, pg. 1207
BUCHER HYDRAULICS SAS—See Bucher Industries AG; *Int'l*, pg. 1207
BUCHER HYDRAULICS—See Bucher Industries AG; *Int'l*, pg. 1207
BUCHER HYDRAULICS—See Bucher Industries AG; *Int'l*, pg. 1207
BUCHER HYDRAULICS S.P.A.—See Bucher Industries AG; *Int'l*, pg. 1207
BUCHER HYDRAULICS SUZHOU CO., LTD.—See Bucher Industries AG; *Int'l*, pg. 1207
BUCHER HYDRAULICS (WUXI) CO., LTD.—See Bucher Industries AG; *Int'l*, pg. 1207
BUCHER IBERICA SL—See Bucher Industries AG; *Int'l*, pg. 1207
BUCHER INDUSTRIES AG; *Int'l*, pg. 1206
BUCHER INTERIORS GMBH—See Bucher Leichtbau AG; *Int'l*, pg. 1209
BUCHER LANDTECHNIK AG—See Bucher Industries AG; *Int'l*, pg. 1208
BUCHER LEICHTBAU AG; *Int'l*, pg. 1209
BUCHER MANAGEMENT AG—See Bucher Industries AG; *Int'l*, pg. 1207
BUCHER MERK PROCESS GMBH—See Bucher Industries AG; *Int'l*, pg. 1207
BUCHER MUNICIPAL AG—See Bucher Industries AG; *Int'l*, pg. 1208
BUCHER MUNICIPAL A/S—See Bucher Industries AG; *Int'l*, pg. 1207
BUCHER MUNICIPAL COUDES SARL—See Bucher Industries AG; *Int'l*, pg. 1207
BUCHER MUNICIPAL GMBH—See Bucher Industries AG; *Int'l*, pg. 1207
BUCHER MUNICIPAL LLC—See Bucher Industries AG; *Int'l*, pg. 1207
BUCHER MUNICIPAL LTD.—See Bucher Industries AG; *Int'l*, pg. 1207
BUCHER MUNICIPAL NORTH AMERICA—See Bucher Industries AG; *Int'l*, pg. 1207
BUCHER MUNICIPAL PTY LTD—See Bucher Industries AG; *Int'l*, pg. 1207
BUCHER MUNICIPAL S.A.S.—See Bucher Industries AG; *Int'l*, pg. 1207
BUCHER MUNICIPAL SIA—See Bucher Industries AG; *Int'l*, pg. 1207
BUCHER MUNICIPAL WERNBERG GMBH—See Bucher Industries AG; *Int'l*, pg. 1207
BUCHER-SCHOERLING GMBH—See Bucher Industries AG; *Int'l*, pg. 1208
BUCHER SCHORLING AG—See Bucher Industries AG; *Int'l*, pg. 1207
BUCHER SCHORLING KOREA LTD—See Bucher Industries AG; *Int'l*, pg. 1207
BUCHER UNIPEKTIN AG—See Bucher Industries AG; *Int'l*, pg. 1208
BUCHER UNIPEKTIN CO. LTD.—See Bucher Industries AG; *Int'l*, pg. 1208
BUCHER UNIPEKTIN LTD—See Bucher Industries AG; *Int'l*, pg. 1208
BUCHER UNIPEKTIN SP. Z O.O.—See Bucher Industries AG; *Int'l*, pg. 1208
BUCHER VASLIN MS SA—See Bucher Industries AG; *Int'l*, pg. 1208
BUCHER VASLIN NORTH AMERICA, INC—See Bucher Industries AG; *Int'l*, pg. 1208

COMPANY NAME INDEX

BUCHER VASLIN SA—See Bucher Industries AG; *Int'l*, pg. 1208
BUCHER VASLIN S.R.L.—See Bucher Industries AG; *Int'l*, pg. 1208
BUCHER VASLIN SUDAMERICA—See Bucher Industries AG; *Int'l*, pg. 1208
BUCHGEMEINSCHAFT DONAULAND KREMAYR & SCHERIAU KG—See Bertelsmann SE & Co. KGaA; *Int'l*, pg. 992
BUCHHEIT INC.; *U.S. Private*, pg. 676
BUCHLER GRAFINO AG—See TX Group AG; *Int'l*, pg. 7991
BUCH & MEDIEN GMBH—See Thalia Bucher GmbH; *Int'l*, pg. 7606
BUCH UND KUNST GMBH & CO. KG—See Thalia Bucher GmbH; *Int'l*, pg. 7606
BUCH- UND PRESSE-GROSSVERTRIEB HAMBURG GMBH & CO. KG—See Axel Springer SE; *Int'l*, pg. 766
BUCHVERTRIEB BLANK GMBH—See Bonnier AB; *Int'l*, pg. 1108
BUCK-CHEMIE GMBH; *Int'l*, pg. 1209
BUCK CONSULTANTS (ADMINISTRATION & INVESTMENT) LIMITED—See Arthur J. Gallagher & Co.; *U.S. Public*, pg. 204
BUCK CONSULTANTS BV—See Arthur J. Gallagher & Co.; *U.S. Public*, pg. 204
BUCK CONSULTANTS (HEALTHCARE) LIMITED—See Arthur J. Gallagher & Co.; *U.S. Public*, pg. 204
BUCK CONSULTANTS LIMITED—See Arthur J. Gallagher & Co.; *U.S. Public*, pg. 204
BUCK CONSULTANTS NV/SA—See Arthur J. Gallagher & Co.; *U.S. Public*, pg. 204
BUCKELEW'S FOOD SERVICE EQUIPMENT CO.; *U.S. Private*, pg. 677
BUCKET STUDIO CO., LTD.; *Int'l*, pg. 1209
BUCKEYE BOXES INC.; *U.S. Private*, pg. 677
BUCKEYE CABLEVISION—See Block Communications, Inc.; *U.S. Private*, pg. 582
BUCKEYE CHECK CASHING INC.; *U.S. Private*, pg. 677
BUCKEYE COMMUNITY HEALTH PLAN INC.—See Centene Corporation; *U.S. Public*, pg. 468
BUCKEYE CONTAINER—See Buckeye Corrugated Inc.; *U.S. Private*, pg. 677
BUCKEYE CORRUGATED INC.; *U.S. Private*, pg. 677
BUCKEYE DRUGS; *U.S. Private*, pg. 677
BUCKEYE FASTENERS INC.—See Fastener Industries Inc.; *U.S. Private*, pg. 1482
BUCKEYE FIRE EQUIPMENT COMPANY; *U.S. Private*, pg. 677
BUCKEYE FORD, INC.; *U.S. Private*, pg. 677
BUCKEYE GP LLC—See Industry Super Holdings Pty. Ltd.; *Int'l*, pg. 3676
BUCKEYE HEATING AND COOLING SERVICES, INC.—See Leonard Green & Partners, L.P.; *U.S. Private*, pg. 2430
BUCKEYE INDUSTRIAL SUPPLY CO.—See MSC Industrial Direct Co., Inc.; *U.S. Public*, pg. 1483
BUCKEYE INTERNATIONAL INC.; *U.S. Private*, pg. 677
BUCKEYE NISSAN INC.; *U.S. Private*, pg. 677
BUCKEYE PACIFIC, LLC—See Forest City Trading Group, LLC; *U.S. Private*, pg. 1566
BUCKEYE PARTNERS, L.P.—See Industry Super Holdings Pty. Ltd.; *Int'l*, pg. 3676
BUCKEYE POWER SALES COMPANY INC; *U.S. Private*, pg. 677
BUCKEYE PUMPS INC.—See Genstar Capital, LLC; *U.S. Private*, pg. 1678
BUCKEYE READY-MIX LLC; *U.S. Private*, pg. 677
BUCKEYE RESOURCES, INC.—See CRH plc; *Int'l*, pg. 1845
BUCKEYE RUBBER & PACKING CO.; *U.S. Private*, pg. 677
BUCKEYES HOTEL OWNER LP—See Pebblebrook Hotel Trust; *U.S. Public*, pg. 1660
BUCKEYE STATE BANCSHARES, INC.; *U.S. Private*, pg. 677
BUCKEYE STATE BANK—See Buckeye State Bancshares, Inc.; *U.S. Private*, pg. 677
BUCKEYE STATE MUTUAL INSURANCE CO.; *U.S. Private*, pg. 677
BUCKEYE SWEEPING, INC.—See Warburg Pincus LLC; *U.S. Private*, pg. 4440
BUCKEYE TELESYSTEM, INC.—See Block Communications, Inc.; *U.S. Private*, pg. 582
BUCK GLOBAL LLC—See Arthur J. Gallagher & Co.; *U.S. Public*, pg. 204
BUCKHEAD BEEF COMPANY—See Sysco Corporation; *U.S. Public*, pg. 1973
BUCKHEAD BEEF NORTHEAST—See Sysco Corporation; *U.S. Public*, pg. 1973
BUCKHEAD MEAT COMPANY—See Sysco Corporation; *U.S. Public*, pg. 1973
BUCKHEAD MEAT MIDWEST, INC.—See Sysco Corporation; *U.S. Public*, pg. 1973
BUCKHEAD MEAT OF DALLAS, INC.—See Sysco Corporation; *U.S. Public*, pg. 1973
BUCKHEAD MEAT OF DENVER, INC.—See Sysco Corporation; *U.S. Public*, pg. 1973
BUCKHEAD MEAT OF SAN ANTONIO, LP—See Sysco Corporation; *U.S. Public*, pg. 1973
BUCKHEAD MEAT & SEAFOOD OF HOUSTON, INC.—See Sysco Corporation; *U.S. Public*, pg. 1973
BUCK HILL FALLS CO.; *U.S. Public*, pg. 409
BUCKHORN ENERGY SERVICES, LLC—See Blackstone Inc.; *U.S. Public*, pg. 359
BUCKHORN INC.—See Myers Industries, Inc.; *U.S. Public*, pg. 1488
BUCKHORN SERVICES, INC.—See Myers Industries, Inc.; *U.S. Public*, pg. 1488
BUCKINGHAM ASSET MANAGEMENT, LLC—See Clayton, Dubilier & Rice, LLC; *U.S. Private*, pg. 923
BUCKINGHAM ASSET MANAGEMENT, LLC—See Stone Point Capital LLC; *U.S. Private*, pg. 3824
BUCKINGHAM BADLER ASSOCIATES, INC.—See Scottish American Capital LLC; *U.S. Private*, pg. 3578
BUCKINGHAM CAPITAL, LLC; *U.S. Private*, pg. 677
BUCKINGHAM CAPITAL MANAGEMENT, INC.—See Buckingham & Company; *U.S. Private*, pg. 677
BUCKINGHAM COAL COMPANY, LLC—See Westmoreland Coal Company; *U.S. Private*, pg. 4499
BUCKINGHAM & COMPANY; *U.S. Private*, pg. 677
BUCKINGHAM FINANCIAL GROUP, INC.—See Buckingham & Company; *U.S. Private*, pg. 677
BUCKINGHAM FOUNDATION; *U.S. Private*, pg. 677
BUCKINGHAM FOUNTAIN LP; *U.S. Private*, pg. 678
BUCKINGHAM'S CHICAGO, LLC—See Park Hotels & Resorts Inc.; *U.S. Public*, pg. 1638
BUCKINGHAMSHIRE BUILDING SOCIETY; *Int'l*, pg. 1210
BUCKINGHAMSHIRE GOLF COMPANY, LTD.—See Arora Hotels Limited; *Int'l*, pg. 577
BUCKINGHAM STRATEGIC PARTNERS, LLC—See Clayton, Dubilier & Rice, LLC; *U.S. Private*, pg. 923
BUCKINGHAM STRATEGIC PARTNERS, LLC—See Stone Point Capital LLC; *U.S. Private*, pg. 3824
BUCKING HORSE ENERGY INC.; *Int'l*, pg. 1209
BUCK KNIVES, INC.; *U.S. Private*, pg. 676
BUCK & KNOBBY EQUIPMENT CO.; *U.S. Private*, pg. 676
BUCKLAND CUSTOMS BROKERS LTD.; *Int'l*, pg. 1210
BUCK LA; *U.S. Private*, pg. 676
BUCKLE AGENCY LLC; *U.S. Private*, pg. 678
THE BUCKLE, INC.; *U.S. Public*, pg. 2043
BUCKLES-SMITH ELECTRIC COMPANY—See Rexel, S.A.; *Int'l*, pg. 6317
BUCKLEY ASSOCIATES INC.; *U.S. Private*, pg. 678
BUCKLEY & COMPANY INC.; *U.S. Private*, pg. 678
BUCKLEY HEALTHCARE CENTER, LLC—See National HealthCare Corporation; *U.S. Public*, pg. 1495
BUCKLEY INDUSTRIES INC.; *U.S. Private*, pg. 678
BUCKLEY & KALDENBACH; *U.S. Private*, pg. 678
BUCKLEY OIL COMPANY INC.; *U.S. Private*, pg. 678
BUCKLEY POWDER CO.; *U.S. Private*, pg. 678
BUCKLEYSANDLER LLP.; *U.S. Private*, pg. 678
THE BUCKLIN TRACTOR & IMPLEMENT CO; *U.S. Private*, pg. 4002
BUCKMAN LABORATORIES (ASIA) PTE LTD.—See Bulab Holdings, Inc.; *U.S. Private*, pg. 683
BUCKMAN LABORATORIES, INC.—See Bulab Holdings, Inc.; *U.S. Private*, pg. 683
BUCKMAN LABORATORIES (INDIA) PRIVATE LIMITED—See Bulab Holdings, Inc.; *U.S. Private*, pg. 683
BUCKMAN LABORATORIES INTERNATIONAL, INC.—See Bulab Holdings, Inc.; *U.S. Private*, pg. 683
BUCKMAN LABORATORIES, K.K.—See Bulab Holdings, Inc.; *U.S. Private*, pg. 683
BUCKMAN LABORATORIES, N.V.—See Bulab Holdings, Inc.; *U.S. Private*, pg. 684
BUCKMAN LABORATORIES OF CANADA, LTD.—See Bulab Holdings, Inc.; *U.S. Private*, pg. 683
BUCKMAN LABORATORIES PTY LTD.—See Bulab Holdings, Inc.; *U.S. Private*, pg. 683
BUCKMAN LABORATORIES PTY. LTD.—See Bulab Holdings, Inc.; *U.S. Private*, pg. 683
BUCKMAN LABORATORIES, S.A. DE C.V.—See Bulab Holdings, Inc.; *U.S. Private*, pg. 684
BUCKMAN LABORATORIES (SHANGHAI) CHEMICALS CO., LTD.—See Bulab Holdings, Inc.; *U.S. Private*, pg. 683
BUCKMAN LABORATORIOS CHILE LTDA.—See Bulab Holdings, Inc.; *U.S. Private*, pg. 683
BUCKMAN-MITCHELL, INC.—See Arthur J. Gallagher & Co.; *U.S. Public*, pg. 204
BUCKMAN'S INC.; *U.S. Private*, pg. 678
THE BUCKNER COMPANY, INC.—See RiskProNet International Inc.; *U.S. Private*, pg. 3441
BUCKNER HEAVYLIFT CRANES, LLC—See Markel Group Inc.; *U.S. Public*, pg. 1367
BUCKNER'S HEATING & COOLING CO.—See Heartland Homecare Services, Inc.; *U.S. Private*, pg. 1900
BUCK NY—See Buck LA; *U.S. Private*, pg. 676
BUCKO'S INC.; *U.S. Private*, pg. 678
BUCKS COUNTY COFFEE COMPANY; *U.S. Private*, pg. 678
BUCKS COUNTY FREE LIBRARY; *U.S. Private*, pg. 678
BUCKS COUNTY WATER & SEWER AUTHORITY; *U.S. Private*, pg. 678
THE BUCKS HERALD—See JPIMedia Holdings Limited; *Int'l*, pg. 4007
BUCK'S INC.; *U.S. Private*, pg. 676
BUCKSKIN MINING COMPANY—See Peter Kiewit Sons', Inc.; *U.S. Private*, pg. 3158
BUCKSWOOD INTERNATIONAL SCHOOL - TBILISI, LLC—See Georgia Capital PLC; *Int'l*, pg. 2939
BUCKTHORN PARTNERS LLP; *Int'l*, pg. 1210
BUCKWOLD WESTERN LTD.; *Int'l*, pg. 1210
BUCOVINA SA; *Int'l*, pg. 1210
BUCYRUS AMERICA, INC.—See Caterpillar, Inc.; *U.S. Public*, pg. 450
BUCYRUS EQUIPMENT LLC—See Caterpillar, Inc.; *U.S. Public*, pg. 449
BUCYRUS EUROPE GMBH—See Caterpillar, Inc.; *U.S. Public*, pg. 450
BUCYRUS INTERNATIONAL, INC.—See Caterpillar, Inc.; *U.S. Public*, pg. 450
BUCYRUS (LANGFANG) MINING MACHINERY CO. LTD.—See Caterpillar, Inc.; *U.S. Public*, pg. 450
BUCYRUS MINING AUSTRALIA PTY. LTD.—See Caterpillar, Inc.; *U.S. Public*, pg. 449
BUCYRUS TELEGRAPH-FORUM—See Gannett Co., Inc.; *U.S. Public*, pg. 897
BUDAMAR LOGISTICS AS; *Int'l*, pg. 1210
BUD ANTLE, INC.—See Dole plc; *Int'l*, pg. 2157
BUDAOWENG FOODS CO., LTD.—See Ottogi Corporation; *Int'l*, pg. 5665
BUDAPEST BANK—See MBH Bank Nyrt.; *Int'l*, pg. 4752
BUDAPESTI ELEKTROMOS MUVEK ZRT.—See RWE AG; *Int'l*, pg. 6433
BUDAPESTI EROMU ZRT—See Energeticky a Prumyslovy Holding, a.s.; *Int'l*, pg. 2419
BUDAPESTI ERTEKTOZSDE ZRT.—See Magyar Nemzeti Bank; *Int'l*, pg. 4643
BUDAPESTI INGATLAN NYRT; *Int'l*, pg. 1210
BUDAPEST PROPERTY UTILIZATION AND DEVELOPMENT PLC.; *Int'l*, pg. 1210
BUD BROWN VOLKSWAGEN; *U.S. Private*, pg. 678
BUDCAN HOLDINGS INC.—See ThyssenKrupp AG; *Int'l*, pg. 7724
BUD CLARY CHEVROLET CADILLAC INC.; *U.S. Private*, pg. 679
BUD CLARY TOYOTA OF YAKIMA; *U.S. Private*, pg. 679
BUDCO CREATIVE SERVICES; *U.S. Private*, pg. 679
BUDCO GROUP, INC.; *U.S. Private*, pg. 679
BUDCO, INC.; *U.S. Private*, pg. 679
BUD COMERCIO DE ELETRODOMESTICOS LTDA.—See Whirlpool Corporation; *U.S. Public*, pg. 2368
BUD DAVIS CADILLAC, INC.; *U.S. Private*, pg. 679
BUDD BAER; *U.S. Private*, pg. 679
BUDDE FORDERTECHNIK GMBH—See INDUS Holding AG; *Int'l*, pg. 3662
BUDDERFLY LLC—See Partners Group Holding AG; *Int'l*, pg. 5749
THE BUDD GROUP INC. - CHARLOTTE OFFICE—See The Budd Group Inc.; *U.S. Private*, pg. 4002
THE BUDD GROUP INC. - DURHAM OFFICE—See The Budd Group Inc.; *U.S. Private*, pg. 4002
THE BUDD GROUP INC. - GREENSBORO OFFICE—See The Budd Group Inc.; *U.S. Private*, pg. 4002
THE BUDD GROUP INC. - GREENVILLE/SPARTANBURG, SC OFFICE—See The Budd Group Inc.; *U.S. Private*, pg. 4002
THE BUDD GROUP INC. - ORLANDO OFFICE—See The Budd Group Inc.; *U.S. Private*, pg. 4002
THE BUDD GROUP INC.; *U.S. Private*, pg. 4002
THE BUDD GROUP INC. - TAMPA OFFICE—See The Budd Group Inc.; *U.S. Private*, pg. 4002
BUDDHA AIR PVT. LTD.; *Int'l*, pg. 1210
BUDDI LIMITED—See Big Technologies Plc; *Int'l*, pg. 1021
BUDDI US LLC—See Big Technologies Plc; *Int'l*, pg. 1021
BUDDS' BMW; *Int'l*, pg. 1210
BUDD VAN LINES, INC.; *U.S. Private*, pg. 679
BUDDY GREGG MOTOR HOMES INC.—See Lazydays Holdings, Inc.; *U.S. Public*, pg. 1294
BUDDY MEDIA, INC.—See Salesforce, Inc.; *U.S. Public*, pg. 1836
BUDDY MOORE TRUCKING, INC.—See OEP Capital Advisors, L.P.; *U.S. Private*, pg. 2999
BUDDY PLATFORM, INC.—See Buddy Platform Ltd.; *Int'l*, pg. 1211
BUDDY PLATFORM LTD.; *Int'l*, pg. 1210
BUDDY'S CARPET AND FLOORING LLC; *U.S. Private*, pg. 679
BUDDY'S KITCHEN, INC.—See Premium Brands Holdings Corporation; *Int'l*, pg. 5962
BUDDY'S MINI MARTS, INC.—See Pipeline Oil Sales Inc.; *U.S. Private*, pg. 679
BUDDY SQUIRREL, LLC; *U.S. Private*, pg. 679
BUDDYTV; *U.S. Private*, pg. 679
BUDELCO BV—See Nyrstar NV; *Int'l*, pg. 5501
BUDENHEIM USA, INC.—See Dr. August Oetker KG; *Int'l*, pg. 2190
BUDERIM GINGER AMERICA, INC.—See Health and Plant Protein Group Limited; *Int'l*, pg. 3303
BUDERIM GINGER (OVERSEAS) HOLDINGS PTY LTD—See Health and Plant Protein Group Limited; *Int'l*, pg. 3303

BUDDYTV

BUDERIM MACADAMIAS PTY LTD—See Health and Plant Protein Group Limited; *Int'l*, pg. 3303
BUDERUS EDELSTAHL GMBH—See voestalpine AG; *Int'l*, pg. 8288
BUDERUS GUSS GMBH—See Robert Bosch GmbH; *Int'l*, pg. 6360
BUDERUS HEIZTECHNIK AG—See Robert Bosch GmbH; *Int'l*, pg. 6360
BUDERUS HYDRONIC SYSTEMS—See Robert Bosch GmbH; *Int'l*, pg. 6363
BUDERUS IMMOBILIEN GMBH—See Robert Bosch GmbH; *Int'l*, pg. 6360
BUDETTAN AB—See Storskogen Group AB; *Int'l*, pg. 7227
BUDEXPO SP. Z O.O.—See Polski Holding Nieruchomosci S.A.; *Int'l*, pg. 5912
BUD-GAZ SP. Z O.O.—See Polskie Gornictwo Naftowe i Gazownictwo S.A.; *Int'l*, pg. 5912
BUDGE BUDGE COMPANY LTD.; *Int'l*, pg. 1211
BUDGE BUDGE FLOORCOVERINGS LIMITED—See Birla Corporation Ltd.; *Int'l*, pg. 1047
BUDGE INDUSTRIES INC.; *U.S. Private*, pg. 679
BUDGET AUTO PARTS U-PULL-IT, INC.—See LKQ Corporation; *U.S. Public*, pg. 1334
BUDGET BINS LIMITED—See Capital Environment Holdings Limited; *Int'l*, pg. 1310
BUDGET BLINDS, INC.—See JM Family Enterprises Inc.; *U.S. Private*, pg. 2214
BUDGET INSURANCE COMPANY LIMITED—See BGL Group Limited; *Int'l*, pg. 1008
BUDGET INTERNATIONAL, INC.—See Avis Budget Group, Inc.; *U.S. Public*, pg. 249
BUDGET LIGHTING INC.; *U.S. Private*, pg. 679
BUDGET LOANS LTD—See Cynotech Holdings Limited; *Int'l*, pg. 1896
BUDGET MOTELS INC.; *U.S. Private*, pg. 679
BUDGET NATIONAL FINANCE CO.; *U.S. Private*, pg. 679
BUDGET RENT A CAR AUSTRALIA PTY. LTD.—See Avis Budget Group, Inc.; *U.S. Public*, pg. 249
BUDGET RENT A CAR LICENSOR, LLC—See Avis Budget Group, Inc.; *U.S. Public*, pg. 249
BUDGET RENT-A-CAR OF B.C. LTD; *Int'l*, pg. 1211
BUDGET RENT A CAR SYSTEM, INC.—See Avis Budget Group, Inc.; *U.S. Public*, pg. 249
BUDGET TRUCK RENTAL LLC—See Avis Budget Group, Inc.; *U.S. Public*, pg. 249
BUDI IMPIAN SDN BHD—See Berjaya Corporation Berhad; *Int'l*, pg. 983
BUDIMEX BAU GMBH—See Ferrovial S.A.; *Int'l*, pg. 2644
BUDIMEX S.A.—See Ferrovial S.A.; *Int'l*, pg. 2644
BUD INDUSTIES—See Bud Industries, Inc.; *U.S. Private*, pg. 679
BUD INDUSTRIES, INC.; *U.S. Private*, pg. 679
BUD-INZ SP.Z O O.—See VINCI S.A.; *Int'l*, pg. 8213
BUD KOUTS CHEVROLET COMPANY; *U.S. Private*, pg. 679
BUDLEX SP ZOO; *Int'l*, pg. 1211
BUDNEY INDUSTRIES; *U.S. Private*, pg. 679
BUDREX SP. Z O.O.—See UNIBEP S.A.; *Int'l*, pg. 8031
BUD'S BEST COOKIES, INC.; *U.S. Private*, pg. 679
BUD SHELL FORD INC.; *U.S. Private*, pg. 679
BUDSOFT SP. Z O.O.—See Addnode Group AB; *Int'l*, pg. 130
BUDUCNOST A.D.; *Int'l*, pg. 1211
BUDUCNOST A.D.; *Int'l*, pg. 1211
BUDUCNOST HLADENJE SLAP A.D.; *Int'l*, pg. 1211
BUDUCNOST JAGODINA A.D.; *Int'l*, pg. 1211
BUDUCNOST NOVI SAD A.D.; *Int'l*, pg. 1211
BUDVAR CENTRUM SA; *Int'l*, pg. 1211
BUDWAY ENTERPRISES INC.; *U.S. Private*, pg. 679
BUDWEISER BREWING COMPANY APAC LIMITED; *Int'l*, pg. 1211
BUDWEISER WUHAN INTERNATIONAL BREWING COMPANY LIMITED—See Anheuser-Busch InBev SA/NV; *Int'l*, pg. 465
BUDWORTH PROPERTIES LIMITED; *Int'l*, pg. 1211
BUDZAR INDUSTRIES INC.—See Shelburne Corp.; *U.S. Private*, pg. 3630
BUECHEL STONE CORPORATION; *U.S. Private*, pg. 680
BUECHER.DE GMBH & CO. KG—See Thalia Bucher GmbH; *Int'l*, pg. 7606
BUECHL HANDELS-UND BETEILIGUNGS-KG; *Int'l*, pg. 1211
BUEHLER FOOD MARKETS INC.; *U.S. Private*, pg. 680
BUEHLER GMBH—See Illinois Tool Works Inc.; *U.S. Public*, pg. 1102
BUEHLER LTD., IRVINE—See Illinois Tool Works Inc.; *U.S. Public*, pg. 1102
BUEHLER, LTD.—See Illinois Tool Works Inc.; *U.S. Public*, pg. 1102
BUEHLER MOTOR INC.; *U.S. Private*, pg. 680
BUEHLER—See Illinois Tool Works Inc.; *U.S. Public*, pg. 1102
BUENA PARK LUXURY IMPORTS, INC.—See AutoNation, Inc.; *U.S. Public*, pg. 233
BUENA PARK SUITE HOSPITALITY LLC—See InnSuites Hospitality Trust; *U.S. Public*, pg. 1128
BUENA VIDA CONTINUING CARE & REHABILITATION CENTER; *U.S. Private*, pg. 680

BUENA VISTA CARNEROS WINERY INC.—See Boisset, La Famille des Grands Vins; *Int'l*, pg. 1101
BUENAVISTA DEL COBRE, S.A DE C.V.—See Grupo Mexico, S.A.B. de C.V.; *Int'l*, pg. 3133
BUENA VISTA HOME ENTERTAINMENT, INC.—See The Walt Disney Company; *U.S. Public*, pg. 2138
BUENA VISTA HOSPICE CARE, INC.—See The Ensign Group, Inc.; *U.S. Public*, pg. 2070
BUENA VISTA HOSPITALITY GROUP; *U.S. Private*, pg. 680
BUENA VISTA INTERNATIONAL, INC.—See The Walt Disney Company; *U.S. Public*, pg. 2138
BUENA VISTA PALACE—See Blackstone Inc.; *U.S. Public*, pg. 351
BUENA VISTA TELEVISION, LLC—See The Walt Disney Company; *U.S. Public*, pg. 2138
BUENA VISTA THEATRICAL GROUP LLC—See The Walt Disney Company; *U.S. Public*, pg. 2138
BUENO OF CALIFORNIA INC.; *U.S. Private*, pg. 680
BUERKLE AUTOMOTIVE GROUP; *U.S. Private*, pg. 680
BUERKLE HONDA—See Buerkle Automotive Group; *U.S. Private*, pg. 680
BUERKLE HYUNDAI—See Buerkle Automotive Group; *U.S. Private*, pg. 680
BUESCHER INTERESTS LP; *U.S. Private*, pg. 680
BUESO & FORMAN, INC.; *U.S. Private*, pg. 680
BUETTNER S.A. INDUSTRIA E COMERCIO; *Int'l*, pg. 1211
BUFAB AB—See Nordic Capital AB; *Int'l*, pg. 5419
BUFA COMPOSITES BALTIC OU—See BUFA GmbH & Co. KG; *Int'l*, pg. 1211
BUFA COMPOSITES GMBH & CO. KG—See BUFA GmbH & Co. KG; *Int'l*, pg. 1211
BUFA COMPOSITE SYSTEMS GMBH & CO. KG—See BUFA GmbH & Co. KG; *Int'l*, pg. 1211
BUFA GMBH & CO. KG; *Int'l*, pg. 1211
BUFFALO ABRASIVES—See SAK Industries Pvt Ltd; *Int'l*, pg. 6486
BUFFALO AIR HANDLING—See Ampco-Pittsburgh Corporation; *U.S. Public*, pg. 126
BUFFALO AND ERIE COUNTY WORKFORCE DEVELOPMENT CONSORTIUM, INC.; *U.S. Private*, pg. 680
BUFFALO BATT & FELT, LLC—See Leggett & Platt, Incorporated; *U.S. Public*, pg. 1301
BUFFALO BAYOU PARTNERSHIP, INC.; *U.S. Private*, pg. 680
BUFFALO BILL MEMORIAL ASSOCIATION; *U.S. Private*, pg. 680
BUFFALO BILLS, INC.; *U.S. Private*, pg. 680
BUFFALO CHINA, INC.—See EveryWare Global, Inc.; *U.S. Private*, pg. 1441
BUFFALO COAL CORP.; *Int'l*, pg. 1211
BUFFALO CO., LTD.; *Int'l*, pg. 1211
BUFFALO CRUSHED STONE, INC. - ALFRED SAND AND GRAVEL PLANT—See New Enterprise Stone & Lime Co.; *U.S. Private*, pg. 2895
BUFFALO CRUSHED STONE, INC. - BARTON ROAD BLACKTOP PLANT—See New Enterprise Stone & Lime Co., Inc.; *U.S. Private*, pg. 2895
BUFFALO CRUSHED STONE, INC. - COMO PARK BLACKTOP PLANT—See New Enterprise Stone & Lime Co., Inc.; *U.S. Private*, pg. 2895
BUFFALO CRUSHED STONE, INC. - FRANKLINVILLE SAND AND GRAVEL PLANT—See New Enterprise Stone & Lime Co., Inc.; *U.S. Private*, pg. 2895
BUFFALO CRUSHED STONE, INC. - OLEAN BLACKTOP PLANT—See New Enterprise Stone & Lime Co., Inc.; *U.S. Private*, pg. 2895
BUFFALO CRUSHED STONE, INC.—See New Enterprise Stone & Lime Co., Inc.; *U.S. Private*, pg. 2895
BUFFALO DAVID BITTON; *Int'l*, pg. 1211
BUFFALO DENTAL MANUFACTURING CO., INC.; *U.S. Private*, pg. 680
BUFFALO DIRECT INC.—See Melco Holdings Inc.; *Int'l*, pg. 4807
BUFFALO ENVELOPE INC.—See Supremex Inc.; *Int'l*, pg. 7341
BUFFALO EU B.V.—See Melco Holdings Inc.; *Int'l*, pg. 4808
BUFFALO EXCHANGE LTD.; *U.S. Private*, pg. 680
BUFFALO EXECUTAPE (PTY) LIMITED—See The Bidvest Group Limited; *Int'l*, pg. 7623
BUFFALO EXTERMINATING CO., INC.—See Rentokil Initial plc; *Int'l*, pg. 6288
BUFFALO FEDERAL SAVINGS BANK—See Crazy Woman Creek Bancorp, Inc.; *U.S. Public*, pg. 593
BUFFALO FILTER LLC—See CONMED Corporation; *U.S. Public*, pg. 567
THE BUFFALO FINE ARTS ACADEMY; *U.S. Private*, pg. 4002
BUFFALO FUEL CORP.; *U.S. Private*, pg. 680
BUFFALO GAMES, LLC—See Mason Wells, Inc.; *U.S. Private*, pg. 2602
BUFFALO GAP INSTRUMENTATION & ELECTRICAL CO., INC.—See Sunland Construction Inc.; *U.S. Private*, pg. 3868
BUFFALO GRILL S.A.—See ABENEX Capital S.A.; *Int'l*, pg. 59

CORPORATE AFFILIATIONS

BUFFALO GROUPE LLC—See Troon Golf L.L.C.; *U.S. Private*, pg. 4242
THE BUFFALO GROUP, LLC—See Jacobs Engineering Group, Inc.; *U.S. Public*, pg. 1186
BUFFALO HOSPITAL SUPPLY CO., INC.; *U.S. Private*, pg. 680
BUFFALO HOTEL SUPPLY COMPANY, INC.—See Lorraine Capital LLC; *U.S. Private*, pg. 2496
BUFFALO INC.—See Melco Holdings Inc.; *Int'l*, pg. 4808
BUFFALO IT SOLUTIONS INC.—See Melco Holdings Inc.; *Int'l*, pg. 4808
BUFFALO LAW JOURNAL—See Advance Publications, Inc.; *U.S. Private*, pg. 84
BUFFALO LEASE INC.—See Melco Holdings Inc.; *Int'l*, pg. 4808
BUFFALO LODGING ASSOCIATES, LLC; *U.S. Private*, pg. 680
BUFFALO LOGISTICS INC.—See Melco Holdings Inc.; *Int'l*, pg. 4808
BUFFALO LUMBER CO; *U.S. Private*, pg. 681
BUFFALO LUMBER & TIE CO.—See Midwest Hardwood Corporation; *U.S. Private*, pg. 2721
THE BUFFALO NEWS—See Lee Enterprises, Incorporated; *U.S. Public*, pg. 1300
BUFFALO NIAGARA MEDICAL CAMPUS; *U.S. Private*, pg. 681
BUFFALO OPTICAL COMPANY INC.; *U.S. Private*, pg. 681
BUFFALO & PITTSBURGH RAILROAD, INC.—See Brookfield Infrastructure Partners L.P.; *Int'l*, pg. 1190
BUFFALO & PITTSBURGH RAILROAD, INC.—See GIC Pte. Ltd.; *Int'l*, pg. 2965
BUFFALO & PITTSBURGH RAILROAD, INC.—See Brookfield Infrastructure Partners L.P.; *Int'l*, pg. 1190
BUFFALO & PITTSBURGH RAILROAD, INC.—See GIC Pte. Ltd.; *Int'l*, pg. 2965
BUFFALO PUMPS, INC.—See Ampco-Pittsburgh Corporation; *U.S. Public*, pg. 126
BUFFALO ROCK COMPANY; *U.S. Private*, pg. 681
BUFFALO'S EXPERT SERVICE TECHNICIANS, INC.; *U.S. Private*, pg. 681
BUFFALO'S FRANCHISE CONCEPTS, INC.—See Fog Cutter Capital Group Inc.; *U.S. Private*, pg. 1556
BUFFALO TECHNOLOGY (TAIWAN) INC.—See Melco Holdings Inc.; *Int'l*, pg. 4808
BUFFALO TECHNOLOGY (USA) INC.—See Melco Holdings Inc.; *Int'l*, pg. 4808
BUFFALO TRUCK CENTER; *U.S. Private*, pg. 681
BUFFALO TUNGSTEN, INC.—See Sandvik AB; *Int'l*, pg. 6528
BUFFALO WHEELCHAIR, INC.—See AdaptHealth Corp.; *U.S. Public*, pg. 38
BUFFALO WILD WINGS, INC.—See Roark Capital Group Inc.; *U.S. Private*, pg. 3455
BUFFALO WIRE WORKS CO., INC.; *U.S. Private*, pg. 681
BUFFELEN WOODWORKING COMPANY; *U.S. Private*, pg. 681
BUFFELSHOEK TRANSPORT SA PROPRIETARY LIMITED—See OneLogix Group Limited; *Int'l*, pg. 5576
BUFFET CRAMPON DEUTSCHLAND GMBH—See Fondations Capital SA; *Int'l*, pg. 2725
BUFFET CRAMPON HOLDINGS SAS—See Fondations Capital SA; *Int'l*, pg. 2725
BUFFET CRAMPON S.A.S.—See Fondations Capital SA; *Int'l*, pg. 2725
BUFFET GROUP CHINA—See Fondations Capital SA; *Int'l*, pg. 2725
BUFFET GROUP DISTRIBUTION GERMANY GMBH—See Fondations Capital SA; *Int'l*, pg. 2725
BUFFET GROUP JAPAN—See Fondations Capital SA; *Int'l*, pg. 2725
BUFFET GROUP USA, INC.—See Fondations Capital SA; *Int'l*, pg. 2725
BUFFET PARTNERS HOLDING COMPANY, LLC—See Food Management Partners, Inc.; *U.S. Private*, pg. 1561
BUFF WHELAN CHEVROLET & GEO, INC.; *U.S. Private*, pg. 680
BUFKOR, INC.—See Sigma S.A. de C.V.; *Int'l*, pg. 6908
BUFORD DIALYSIS, LLC—See DaVita Inc.; *U.S. Public*, pg. 636
BUFORD ROAD IMAGING, L.L.C.—See HCA Healthcare, Inc.; *U.S. Public*, pg. 992
BUFORD WHITE LUMBER COMPANY; *U.S. Private*, pg. 681
BUG-ALUTECHNIC GMBH—See STRABAG SE; *Int'l*, pg. 7229
BUG BUSTERS, INC.; *U.S. Private*, pg. 681
BUG BUSTERS USA, INC.; *U.S. Private*, pg. 681
BUGGSI, INC.; *U.S. Private*, pg. 681
BUGGY BUS INC.—See Historic Tours of America Inc.; *U.S. Private*, pg. 1952
BUGMASTER TERMITE & PEST CONTROL—See Arrow Exterminators Inc.; *U.S. Private*, pg. 335
BUGOJNOPROMET D.D.; *Int'l*, pg. 1211
BUG OUT SERVICE, INC.—See Rentokil Initial plc; *Int'l*, pg. 6286
BUGSENSE INC.—See Cisco Systems, Inc.; *U.S. Public*, pg. 500

COMPANY NAME INDEX

BUHLER AEROGLIDE—See Buhler AG; *Int'l*, pg. 1211
BUHLER AEROGLIDE U.K.—See Buhler AG; *Int'l*, pg. 1211
BUHLER AG; *Int'l*, pg. 1211
BUHLER BARTH GMBH—See Buhler AG; *Int'l*, pg. 1212
BUHLER (CANADA) INC.—See Buhler AG; *Int'l*, pg. 1211
BUHLER DODGE, INC.; *U.S. Private*, pg. 681
BUHLER FARMILA VIETNAM LTD.—See Buhler AG; *Int'l*, pg. 1212
BUHLER GMBH—See Buhler AG; *Int'l*, pg. 1212
BUHLER INC.—See Buhler AG; *Int'l*, pg. 1212
BUHLER INDUSTRIES INC.—See ASKO Holding A.S.; *Int'l*, pg. 625
BUHLER LIMITED—See Buhler AG; *Int'l*, pg. 1212
BUHLER LTD.—See Buhler AG; *Int'l*, pg. 1212
BUHLER LTD.—See Buhler AG; *Int'l*, pg. 1212
BUHLER PAKISTAN (PVT.) LTD.—See Buhler AG; *Int'l*, pg. 1212
BUHLER P.J.S.C—See Buhler AG; *Int'l*, pg. 1212
BUHLER SA—See Buhler AG; *Int'l*, pg. 1212
BUHLER SORTEX INC.—See Buhler AG; *Int'l*, pg. 1212
BUHLER VIETNAM COMPANY LIMITED—See Buhler AG; *Int'l*, pg. 1212
BUHL INDUSTRIES INC.; *U.S. Private*, pg. 681
BU HOLDINGS, LLC—See Tregaron Management, LLC; *U.S. Private*, pg. 4217
BUHRMANN-UBBENS PAPIER BV—See KPP Group Holdings Co., Ltd.; *Int'l*, pg. 4298
BUICK GMC OF BEAVERTON—See Lithia Motors, Inc.; *U.S. Public*, pg. 1321
BUIKEMAS ACE HARDWARE HOME CENTER; *U.S. Private*, pg. 681
BUILD-A-BEAR RETAIL MANAGEMENT, INC.—See Build-A-Bear Workshop, Inc.; *U.S. Public*, pg. 409
BUILD-A-BEAR WORKSHOP DENMARK APS—See Build-A-Bear Workshop, Inc.; *U.S. Public*, pg. 409
BUILD-A-BEAR WORKSHOP, INC.; *U.S. Public*, pg. 409
BUILD-A-BEAR WORKSHOP UK HOLDINGS LTD.—See Build-A-Bear Workshop, Inc.; *U.S. Public*, pg. 409
BUILD ACQUISITION CORP.; *U.S. Public*, pg. 409
BUILDASIGN.COM; *U.S. Private*, pg. 681
BUILD A SIGN LLC—See Cimpress plc; *Int'l*, pg. 1609
BUILDBASE LIMITED—See Grafton Group plc; *Int'l*, pg. 3050
BUILD CREATIVEHAUS INC.—See Dentsu Group Inc.; *Int'l*, pg. 2034
BUILDDESK POLSKA SP. Z.O.O.—See ROCKWOOL A/S; *Int'l*, pg. 6379
BUILDERFUSION, INC.—See Greenridge Investment Partners; *U.S. Private*, pg. 1779
BUILDER HOMESITE, INC.; *U.S. Private*, pg. 681
BUILDER MEDIA SOLUTIONS, LLC—See Tribune Publishing Company; *U.S. Private*, pg. 4227
BUILDERMT, INC.—See Berkshire Hathaway Inc.; *U.S. Public*, pg. 312
BUILDERS ALLIANCE LLC—See The Sterling Group, L.P.; *U.S. Private*, pg. 4122
BUILDERS BEST DEWITT CENTERS INC.—See Bestway Enterprises Inc.; *U.S. Private*, pg. 544
BUILDERS BOX (INDIA) PVT. LTD—See BuilderSmart Public Company Limited; *Int'l*, pg. 1212
BUILDERS CAPITAL MORTGAGE CORP.; *Int'l*, pg. 1212
BUILDERS CARPET INC.; *U.S. Private*, pg. 681
THE BUILDERS CENTRE (SHEFFIELD) LIMITED—See Frank Key Group Limited; *Int'l*, pg. 2761
BUILDERS CHOICE PRODUCTS LTD.—See Kenroc Building Materials Co. Ltd.; *Int'l*, pg. 4128
BUILDERS CONCRETE INC.—See Vicat S.A.; *Int'l*, pg. 8185
BUILDERS CONCRETE SERVICES LLC; *U.S. Private*, pg. 682
BUILDERS DESIGN & LEASING INC.; *U.S. Private*, pg. 682
BUILDERS DEVELOPMENT INC.—See Builders Inc.; *U.S. Private*, pg. 682
BUILDERS FENCE COMPANY INC.; *U.S. Private*, pg. 682
BUILDERS FIRSTSOURCE - FLORIDA, LLC—See Builders FirstSource, Inc.; *U.S. Public*, pg. 410
BUILDERS FIRSTSOURCE, INC.; *U.S. Public*, pg. 409
BUILDERS FIRSTSOURCE - MBS, LLC—See Builders FirstSource, Inc.; *U.S. Public*, pg. 410
BUILDERS FIRSTSOURCE OF GREENVILLE—See Builders FirstSource, Inc.; *U.S. Public*, pg. 410
BUILDERS FIRSTSOURCE OF HIGH POINT—See Builders FirstSource, Inc.; *U.S. Public*, pg. 410
BUILDERS FIRSTSOURCE OF SOUTHPORT—See Builders FirstSource, Inc.; *U.S. Public*, pg. 410
BUILDERS FIRSTSOURCE OF SUMTER—See Builders FirstSource, Inc.; *U.S. Public*, pg. 410
BUILDERS FIRSTSOURCE - SOUTHEAST GROUP, LLC—See Builders FirstSource, Inc.; *U.S. Public*, pg. 410
BUILDERS GENERAL SUPPLY COMPANY; *U.S. Private*, pg. 682
BUILDERS GYPSUM SUPPLY—See Beacon Roofing Supply, Inc.; *U.S. Public*, pg. 285
BUILDERS HARDWARE, INC.—See Wynnchurch Capital, L.P.; *U.S. Private*, pg. 4578

BUILDERS' HARDWARE & SPECIALTY CO.—See Platinum Equity, LLC; *U.S. Private*, pg. 3208
BUILDERS' HARDWARE & SUPPLY CO.; *U.S. Private*, pg. 682
BUILDERS INC.; *U.S. Private*, pg. 682
BUILDERS INSTALLED PRODUCTS OF VERMONT, LLC—See Installed Building Products, Inc.; *U.S. Public*, pg. 1132
BUILDERS INSURANCE SERVICES, LLC—See Stone Point Capital LLC; *U.S. Private*, pg. 3820
BUILDERSMART PUBLIC COMPANY LIMITED; *Int'l*, pg. 1212
BUILDERSMART (VIETNAM) LIMITED—See BuilderSmart Public Company Limited; *Int'l*, pg. 1212
BUILDERS MATERIAL COMPANY—See E.C. Barton & Company; *U.S. Private*, pg. 1304
BUILDERS SAND & CEMENT CO., INC.; *U.S. Private*, pg. 682
BUILDERS SHOP PTE. LTD.—See Lorenzo International Limited; *Int'l*, pg. 4558
BUILDERS SPECIALTIES & HARDWARE; *U.S. Private*, pg. 682
BUILDERS SUPPLY COMPANY INC.; *U.S. Private*, pg. 682
BUILDERS SURPLUS, INC.; *U.S. Private*, pg. 682
BUILDERS & TRADESMEN'S INSURANCE SERVICES, INC.—See Stone Point Capital LLC; *U.S. Private*, pg. 3820
BUILDERS TRANSPORTATION CO., LLC—See Daseke, Inc.; *U.S. Private*, pg. 1161
BUILDERS TRUSS INC; *U.S. Private*, pg. 682
BUILDERTREND SOLUTIONS INC.; *U.S. Private*, pg. 682
BUILDEX, LLC—See Summit Materials, Inc.; *U.S. Public*, pg. 1959
BUILDEX VENTURE CAPITAL CORPORATION; *Int'l*, pg. 1212
BUILDFAX, INC.—See Verisk Analytics, Inc.; *U.S. Public*, pg. 2282
BUILDFIRE, INC.; *U.S. Private*, pg. 682
BUILD GROUP, INC.; *U.S. Private*, pg. 681
BUILDING AIR SERVICES, INC.—See Ares Management Corporation; *U.S. Public*, pg. 189
BUILDING BOOK CENTER CO., LTD.—See Kadokawa Corporation; *Int'l*, pg. 4047
THE BUILDING CENTER, INC.; *U.S. Private*, pg. 4002
BUILDING CHEMICAL SUPPLIES LIMITED—See New Mountain Capital, LLC; *U.S. Private*, pg. 2899
BUILDING CHOICES LIMITED—See Fletcher Building Limited; *Int'l*, pg. 2699
THE BUILDING COMPANY PROPRIETARY LIMITED—See Capitalworks Investment Partners (Pty) Ltd; *Int'l*, pg. 1314
BUILDING COMPONENT SOLUTIONS COMPANY LIMITED—See Zamil Industrial Investment Company; *Int'l*, pg. 8624
BUILDING CONSTRUCTION LOGISTICS GMBH—See Implenia AG; *Int'l*, pg. 3636
BUILDING CONTROLS & SOLUTIONS; *U.S. Private*, pg. 682
BUILDING CRAFTS INC.; *U.S. Private*, pg. 682
BUILDING DREAMSTAR TECHNOLOGY INC.; *Int'l*, pg. 1212
BUILDING ENGINES, INC.; *U.S. Private*, pg. 682
BUILDING EQUITY SOONER FOR TOMORROW; *U.S. Private*, pg. 682
BUILDING ERECTION SERVICES CO.; *U.S. Private*, pg. 682
BUILDING EXTERIOR SOLUTIONS—See Terracon Consultants, Inc.; *U.S. Private*, pg. 3970
BUILDING FASTENERS OF MINNESOTA INC.; *U.S. Private*, pg. 682
BUILDING INDUSTRY PARTNERS LLC; *U.S. Private*, pg. 682
BUILDING INFORMATION SYSTEMS LLC—See CBRE Group, Inc.; *U.S. Public*, pg. 459
BUILDINGIQ, INC.; *Int'l*, pg. 1212
BUILDING MAINTENANCE SERVICE LLC—See Vornado Realty Trust; *U.S. Public*, pg. 2310
BUILDING MAINTENANCE & SUPPLY; *U.S. Private*, pg. 683
BUILDING MATERIAL DISTRIBUTORS; *U.S. Private*, pg. 683
BUILDING MATERIALS CORPORATION OF AMERICA—See GAF Materials Corporation; *U.S. Private*, pg. 1633
BUILDING MATERIALS FINANCE, INC.—See Installed Building Products, Inc.; *U.S. Public*, pg. 1132
BUILDINGMINDS GMBH—See Schindler Holding AG; *Int'l*, pg. 6618
BUILDING PLASTICS, INC.; *U.S. Private*, pg. 683
BUILDINGPOINT DEUTSCHLAND NORD GMBH—See Trimble, Inc.; *U.S. Public*, pg. 2190
BUILDING PRODUCTS CORP.; *U.S. Private*, pg. 683
BUILDING PRODUCTS INC. OF IOWA—See Building Products, Inc.; *U.S. Private*, pg. 683
BUILDING PRODUCTS INC. OF S.D.—See Building Products, Inc.; *U.S. Private*, pg. 683
BUILDING PRODUCTS INC.; *U.S. Private*, pg. 683

BUILDING PRODUCTS OF CANADA CORP.—See Compagnie de Saint-Gobain SA; *Int'l*, pg. 1722
BUILDING SECURITY SERVICES, INC.; *U.S. Private*, pg. 683
BUILDING SERVICE INDUSTRIAL SUPPLY CO.; *U.S. Private*, pg. 683
BUILDING SOLUTIONS, LLC; *U.S. Private*, pg. 683
BUILDING SPECIALTIES COMPANY, INC.—See Platinum Equity, LLC; *U.S. Private*, pg. 3208
BUILDINGSTARS; *U.S. Private*, pg. 683
BUILDING SYSTEMS DESIGN INC.—See Schneider Electric SE; *Int'l*, pg. 6624
BUILDING SYSTEMS TRANSPORTATION CO.; *U.S. Private*, pg. 683
BUILDING TECHNOLOGY ENGINEERS, INC.—See EMCOR Group, Inc.; *U.S. Public*, pg. 737
BUILDING TEMPERATURE SOLUTIONS, LLC—See Comfort Systems USA, Inc.; *U.S. Public*, pg. 543
BUILD INVESTMENTS GROUP JSC - ASTANA MDU DIVISION—See Build Investments Group JSC; *Int'l*, pg. 1212
BUILD INVESTMENTS GROUP JSC - CONSTRUCTION MATERIALS PRODUCTION DIVISION—See Build Investments Group JSC; *Int'l*, pg. 1212
BUILD INVESTMENTS GROUP JSC; *Int'l*, pg. 1212
BUILDIUM, LLC—See Thoma Bravo, L.P.; *U.S. Private*, pg. 4152
BUILD KING HOLDINGS LIMITED; *Int'l*, pg. 1212
BUILD LLC; *U.S. Private*, pg. 681
BUILDMAX AGGREGATES AND QUARRIES (PTY) LIMITED—See Vuwa Investments (Pty) Ltd; *Int'l*, pg. 8318
BUILDMAX LIMITED—See Vuwa Investments (Pty) Ltd; *Int'l*, pg. 8318
BUILDMAX MANAGEMENT SERVICES (PTY) LIMITED—See Vuwa Investments (Pty) Ltd; *Int'l*, pg. 8318
BUILDOUT, INC.—See The Riverside Company; *U.S. Private*, pg. 4108
BUILDPAY LLC—See Marsh & McLennan Companies, Inc.; *U.S. Public*, pg. 1374
BUILDPOINT CORPORATION; *U.S. Private*, pg. 683
BUILNET CO., LTD.—See Kyoritsu Maintenance Co., Ltd.; *Int'l*, pg. 4365
BUIMA ENERGY INC.—See Buima Group, Inc.; *Int'l*, pg. 1212
BUIMA GROUP, INC.; *Int'l*, pg. 1212
BUITEN & ASSOCIATES, LLC—See Brown & Brown, Inc.; *U.S. Public*, pg. 399
BUITONI NORTH AMERICA—See Nestle S.A.; *Int'l*, pg. 5208
BUJAGALI ENERGY LIMITED—See Scatec ASA; *Int'l*, pg. 6613
BUJIAS NGK DE MEXICO S.A. DE C.V.—See Niterra Co., Ltd.; *Int'l*, pg. 5379
BUKA INVESTMENTS LIMITED; *Int'l*, pg. 1212
BUKALAPAK.COM PT TBK; *Int'l*, pg. 1212
BUKE TURIZM VE LOKANTACILIK TICARET A.S.—See Dogus Holding AS; *Int'l*, pg. 2154
BUKIT BATOK DRIVING CENTRE LTD.—See Honda Motor Co., Ltd.; *Int'l*, pg. 3460
BUKIT GAMBANG RESORT CITY—See Sentoria Group Berhad; *Int'l*, pg. 6715
BUKIT HITAM DEVELOPMENT SDN. BHD.—See AYER Holdings Berhad; *Int'l*, pg. 775
BUKIT INDAH (JOHOR) SDN BHD—See S P Setia Berhad; *Int'l*, pg. 6443
BUKIT KIARA RESORT BERHAD—See Berjaya Corporation Berhad; *Int'l*, pg. 983
BUKIT MERAH RESORT SDN. BHD.—See M K Land Holdings Berhad; *Int'l*, pg. 4610
BUKIT SELIM SDN. BHD.—See Hua Yang Berhad; *Int'l*, pg. 3510
BUKIT SEMBAWANG ESTATES LTD; *Int'l*, pg. 1213
BUKIT SEMBAWANG RUBBER COMPANY LIMITED—See Bukit Sembawang Estates Ltd; *Int'l*, pg. 1213
BUKIT SEMBAWANG VIEW PTE LTD—See Bukit Sembawang Estates Ltd; *Int'l*, pg. 1213
BUKIT UNGGUL COUNTRY CLUB BHD.—See Nagacorp Ltd.; *Int'l*, pg. 5124
BUKO MINING CO., LTD.—See Taiheiyo Cement Corporation; *Int'l*, pg. 7411
BUKWANG MEDICAL INC.—See Bukwang Pharmaceutical Co., Ltd.; *Int'l*, pg. 1213
BUKWANG PHARMACEUTICAL CO., LTD.; *Int'l*, pg. 1213
BULAB HOLDINGS, INC.; *U.S. Private*, pg. 683
BULAB REALTY OF MISSOURI, LLC—See Bulab Holdings, Inc.; *U.S. Private*, pg. 684
BULAB REALTY OF TENNESSEE, LLC—See Bulab Holdings, Inc.; *U.S. Private*, pg. 684
BULACHGUSS AG—See Allreal Holding AG; *Int'l*, pg. 360
BULBMAN INC; *U.S. Private*, pg. 684
BULBROKERS AD—See Alfa Finance Holding AD; *Int'l*, pg. 307
BULBS.COM INCORPORATED; *U.S. Private*, pg. 684
BULBTRONICS INC.; *U.S. Private*, pg. 684
BULBULOGLU VINC SANAYII VE TICARET A.S.—See FAYAT SAS; *Int'l*, pg. 2624

BULDAN TEKSTIL TIC. SAN. LTD. STI.; *Int'l*, pg. 1213
BULGAR CZECH INVEST HOLDING AD; *Int'l*, pg. 1213
BULGARIA AIR AD—See Chimimport AD; *Int'l*, pg. 1479
BULGARIA HOLDING CO AD-SOFIA; *Int'l*, pg. 1213
BULGARIAN AMERICAN CREDIT BANK AD; *Int'l*, pg. 1213
BULGARIAN INVESTMENT GROUP REIT; *Int'l*, pg. 1213
BULGARIAN INVESTMENT HOLDING; *Int'l*, pg. 1213
BULGARIAN LAND DEVELOPMENT EAD—See AG Capital; *Int'l*, pg. 197
BULGARIAN LAND DEVELOPMENT EAD—See CLS Holdings plc; *Int'l*, pg. 1663
BULGARIAN LAND DEVELOPMENT EAD—See Laxey Partners Ltd.; *Int'l*, pg. 4426
BULGARIAN MINT EAD—See Bulgarian National Bank; *Int'l*, pg. 1213
BULGARIAN NATIONAL BANK; *Int'l*, pg. 1213
BULGARIAN PETROLEUM REFINERY LTD—See Chimimport AD; *Int'l*, pg. 1479
BULGARIAN REAL ESTATE FUND; *Int'l*, pg. 1213
BULGARIAN REGISTER OF SHIPPING AD—See Industrial Holding Bulgaria AD; *Int'l*, pg. 3672
BULGARIAN RIVER SHIPPING J.S.CO.; *Int'l*, pg. 1213
BULGARIAN ROSE PLC; *Int'l*, pg. 1213
BULGARIAN ROSE SEVTOPOLIS AD—See Sopharma AD; *Int'l*, pg. 7108
BULGARIAN STOCK EXCHANGE - SOFIA AD; *Int'l*, pg. 1213
BULGARIAN TELECOMMUNICATIONS COMPANY EAD—See BC Partners LLP; *Int'l*, pg. 923
BULGARI ASIA PACIFIC LTD.—See LVMH Moet Hennessy Louis Vuitton SE; *Int'l*, pg. 4592
BULGARI AUSTRALIA PTY LTD—See LVMH Moet Hennessy Louis Vuitton SE; *Int'l*, pg. 4592
BULGARI BELGIUM S.A.—See LVMH Moet Hennessy Louis Vuitton SE; *Int'l*, pg. 4592
BULGARI CORPORATION OF AMERICA—See LVMH Moet Hennessy Louis Vuitton SE; *Int'l*, pg. 4592
BULGARI DEUTSCHLAND GMBH—See LVMH Moet Hennessy Louis Vuitton SE; *Int'l*, pg. 4592
BULGARI ESPANA S.A. UNIPERSONAL—See LVMH Moet Hennessy Louis Vuitton SE; *Int'l*, pg. 4592
BULGARI FRANCE SAS—See LVMH Moet Hennessy Louis Vuitton SE; *Int'l*, pg. 4591
BULGARI GIOIELLI SPA—See LVMH Moet Hennessy Louis Vuitton SE; *Int'l*, pg. 4592
BULGARI GLOBAL OPERATIONS SA—See LVMH Moet Hennessy Louis Vuitton SE; *Int'l*, pg. 4592
BULGARI HORLOGERIE SA—See LVMH Moet Hennessy Louis Vuitton SE; *Int'l*, pg. 4602
BULGARI HOTELS AND RESORTS MILANO, S.R.L.—See Marriott International, Inc.; *U.S. Public*, pg. 1370
BULGARI ITALIA SPA—See LVMH Moet Hennessy Louis Vuitton SE; *Int'l*, pg. 4592
BULGARI JAPAN LTD—See LVMH Moet Hennessy Louis Vuitton SE; *Int'l*, pg. 4592
BULGARI KOREA LTD—See LVMH Moet Hennessy Louis Vuitton SE; *Int'l*, pg. 4593
BULGARI SA—See LVMH Moet Hennessy Louis Vuitton SE; *Int'l*, pg. 4591
BULGARI SOUTH ASIAN OPERATIONS PTE LTD—See LVMH Moet Hennessy Louis Vuitton SE; *Int'l*, pg. 4593
BULGARI S.P.A.—See LVMH Moet Hennessy Louis Vuitton SE; *Int'l*, pg. 4592
BULGARI (TAIWAN) LTD.—See LVMH Moet Hennessy Louis Vuitton SE; *Int'l*, pg. 4592
BULGARI (THAILAND) LTD.—See LVMH Moet Hennessy Louis Vuitton SE; *Int'l*, pg. 4592
BULGARI UK LIMITED—See LVMH Moet Hennessy Louis Vuitton SE; *Int'l*, pg. 4593
BULGARSKA ZAHAR AD; *Int'l*, pg. 1213
BULGARSKI TRANSPORTEN HOLDING AD; *Int'l*, pg. 1213
BULGARTABAC-TRADING AD—See Bulgarian Investment Holding; *Int'l*, pg. 1213
BULIGO CAPITAL ORD SHS; *Int'l*, pg. 1214
BULILD SJC—See Build Group, Inc.; *U.S. Private*, pg. 681
BULK CEMENT CORPORATION (INDIA) LIMITED—See ACC Limited; *Int'l*, pg. 79
BULK CHEMICAL SERVICES, LLC - SANDERSVILLE PLANT—See Bulk Chemical Services, LLC; *U.S. Private*, pg. 684
BULK CHEMICAL SERVICES, LLC; *U.S. Private*, pg. 684
BULK CONNECTIONS (PTY) LIMITED—See The Bidvest Group Limited; *Int'l*, pg. 7623
BULK INVEST ASA—See Kistefos AS; *Int'l*, pg. 4192
BULKLEY DUNTON, INC.—See Clayton, Dubilier & Rice, LLC; *U.S. Private*, pg. 928
BULK LOGISTICS INC.—See Tankstar USA, Inc.; *U.S. Private*, pg. 3931
BULK MATERIALS INTERNATIONAL CO.; *U.S. Private*, pg. 684
BULKMATIC TRANSPORT COMPANY INC.; *U.S. Private*, pg. 684
BULK MOLDING COMPOUNDS DO BRAZIL LTDA.—See LyondellBasell Industries N.V.; *Int'l*, pg. 4607
BULK MOLDING COMPOUNDS INC.—See LyondellBasell Industries N.V.; *Int'l*, pg. 4607
BULK-PACK INC.; *U.S. Private*, pg. 684

BULK PARTNERS (BERMUDA) LTD.—See Pangaea Logistics Solutions Ltd.; *U.S. Public*, pg. 1635
BULK PLUS LOGISTICS—See Trimac Transportation Ltd.; *Int'l*, pg. 7923
BULK REEF SUPPLY; *U.S. Private*, pg. 684
BULK STORAGE SOFTWARE, INC.; *U.S. Private*, pg. 684
BULK TRANSIT CORPORATION; *U.S. Private*, pg. 684
BULK TRANSPORTATION; *U.S. Private*, pg. 684
BULK TRANSPORT COMPANY—See TFI International Inc.; *Int'l*, pg. 7586
BULK TRANSPORT COMPANY WEST, INC.—See TFI International Inc.; *Int'l*, pg. 7585
BULKTRANS PTY LIMITED—See K&S Corporation Limited; *Int'l*, pg. 4039
BULL ALGERIE—See Atos SE; *Int'l*, pg. 691
BULLAND INVESTMENTS REIT; *Int'l*, pg. 1214
BULLARD CONSTRUCTION INC.; *U.S. Private*, pg. 684
BULLARD RESTAURANTS INC.; *U.S. Private*, pg. 684
BULL BROS., INC.; *U.S. Private*, pg. 684
BULL COTE D'IVOIRE SA—See Atos SE; *Int'l*, pg. 691
BULL CYPRUS LTD—See Atos SE; *Int'l*, pg. 691
BULL DO BRASIL SISTEMAS DE INFORMACAO LTDA—See Atos SE; *Int'l*, pg. 692
BULLDOG AUTOMATION, LLC—See Huizenga Manufacturing Group, Inc.; *U.S. Private*, pg. 2004
BULLDOG BATTERY CORPORATION; *U.S. Private*, pg. 684
BULLDOG DRUMMOND, INC.; *U.S. Private*, pg. 684
BULLDOG HARDWARE CO.—See Nova Capital Management Limited; *Int'l*, pg. 5450
BULLDOG HIWAY EXPRESS INC.—See Daseke, Inc.; *U.S. Private*, pg. 1161
BULLDOG HIWAY LOGISTICS, LLC—See Daseke, Inc.; *U.S. Private*, pg. 1161
BULLDOG MARINE; *U.S. Private*, pg. 684
BULLDOG MEDIA GROUP, INC.; *U.S. Private*, pg. 684
BULLDOG MOVERS, INC.; *U.S. Private*, pg. 685
BULLDOG OFFICE PRODUCTS INC.; *U.S. Private*, pg. 685
BULL-DOG SAUCE CO., LTD.; *Int'l*, pg. 1214
BULLDOG SOLUTIONS EUROPE—See AEA Investors LP; *U.S. Private*, pg. 114
BULLDOG SOLUTIONS, INC.—See AEA Investors LP; *U.S. Private*, pg. 114
BULLDOG VSI—See Nova Capital Management Limited; *Int'l*, pg. 5450
BULL ENGINEERED PRODUCTS, INC.; *U.S. Private*, pg. 684
BULLEN MIDWEST INC.—See Hospeco Brands Group; *U.S. Private*, pg. 1985
BULLERBEKAMPAREN AB—See Christian Berner Tech Trade AB; *Int'l*, pg. 1586
BULLER ELECTRICITY LTD.; *Int'l*, pg. 1214
BULLET EXPLORATION INC.; *Int'l*, pg. 1214
BULLETIN RESOURCES LIMITED; *Int'l*, pg. 1214
THE BULLETIN—See Gannett Co., Inc.; *U.S. Public*, pg. 904
THE BULLETIN—See Western Communications Inc.; *U.S. Private*, pg. 4491
BULLET—See Next 15 Group plc; *Int'l*, pg. 5246
BULLEX, INC.—See Lakeland Industries, Inc.; *U.S. Public*, pg. 1288
BULLEY & ANDREWS CONCRETE RESTORATION—See Bulley & Andrews, LLC; *U.S. Private*, pg. 685
BULLEY & ANDREWS, LLC; *U.S. Private*, pg. 685
BULLFROG AI HOLDINGS, INC.; *U.S. Public*, pg. 410
BULLFROG MINES LLC—See Augusta Gold Corp.; *Int'l*, pg. 703
BULL GABON—See Atos SE; *Int'l*, pg. 691
BULL GMBH—See Atos SE; *Int'l*, pg. 691
BULL GROUP CO., LTD.; *Int'l*, pg. 1214
BULLHEAD CITY CLINIC CORP.—See Community Health Systems, Inc.; *U.S. Public*, pg. 551
BULLHEAD CITY HOSPITAL CORPORATION—See Community Health Systems, Inc.; *U.S. Public*, pg. 551
BULLHEAD FREEDOM STORAGE, L.L.C.—See National Storage Affiliates Trust; *U.S. Public*, pg. 1498
BULL HEAD PRODUCTS INC.—See Ilustrato Pictures International Inc.; *Int'l*, pg. 3616
BULLHORN, INC.—See Insight Venture Management, LLC; *U.S. Private*, pg. 2087
BULL INDIAN OCEAN LTD.—See Atos SE; *Int'l*, pg. 692
BULL INFORMATION SYSTEMS CO. LIMITED (BEIJING)—See Atos SE; *Int'l*, pg. 692
BULL INFORMATION SYSTEMS (HONG KONG) LTD.—See Atos SE; *Int'l*, pg. 692
BULL INFORMATION SYSTEMS IRELAND—See Atos SE; *Int'l*, pg. 692
BULLION GOLD RESOURCES CORP.; *Int'l*, pg. 1214
BULLIVANTS NATURAL HEALTH PRODUCTS (INTERNATIONAL) PTY LTD—See Sanofi; *Int'l*, pg. 6547
BULLIVANTS PTY LIMITED—See Wesfarmers Limited; *Int'l*, pg. 8381
BULL MADAGASCAR S.A.—See Atos SE; *Int'l*, pg. 692
BULLMAN MINERALS INC.; *Int'l*, pg. 1214
BULL MOOSE TUBE COMPANY - CASA GRANDE PLANT—See Caparo Group Ltd.; *Int'l*, pg. 1301

BULL MOOSE TUBE COMPANY - CHICAGO HEIGHTS PLANT—See Caparo Group Ltd.; *Int'l*, pg. 1301
BULL MOOSE TUBE COMPANY - GERALD PLANT—See Caparo Group Ltd.; *Int'l*, pg. 1301
BULL MOOSE TUBE COMPANY - MASURY PLANT—See Caparo Group Ltd.; *Int'l*, pg. 1301
BULL MOOSE TUBE COMPANY—See Caparo Group Ltd.; *Int'l*, pg. 1301
BULL MOOSE TUBE COMPANY - TRENTON PLANT—See Caparo Group Ltd.; *Int'l*, pg. 1301
BULL MOOSE TUBES LTD.—See Caparo Group Ltd.; *Int'l*, pg. 1301
BULL MOOSE TUBES—See Caparo Group Ltd.; *Int'l*, pg. 1301
BULL MOROCCO—See Atos SE; *Int'l*, pg. 692
BULL MOTORS, LLC—See AutoNation, Inc.; *U.S. Public*, pg. 233
BULLNOSE LIMITED—See Providence Equity Partners L.L.C.; *U.S. Private*, pg. 3291
BULLOCH & BULLOCH, INC.; *U.S. Private*, pg. 685
BULLOCK & LEES (CHRISTCHURCH) LIMITED—See The Skipton Building Society; *Int'l*, pg. 7686
BULLOCKS EXPRESS TRANSPORTATION; *U.S. Private*, pg. 685
BULLOCK TICE ASSOCIATES, INC.—See Bernhard Capital Partners Management, LP; *U.S. Private*, pg. 537
BULLPAK LTD.—See Nampak Ltd.; *Int'l*, pg. 5136
BULLPEN PARLAY ACQUISITION COMPANY; *U.S. Public*, pg. 410
BULL POLSKA SP. Z.O.O.—See Atos SE; *Int'l*, pg. 692
BULL SAL—See Atos SE; *Int'l*, pg. 692
BULL S.A.—See Atos SE; *Int'l*, pg. 691
BULL SAS—See Prologue S.A.; *Int'l*, pg. 5992
BULL SENEGAL SARL—See Atos SE; *Int'l*, pg. 692
BULLSEYE DATABASE MARKETING LLC; *U.S. Private*, pg. 685
BULLSEYE MINING LIMITED—See Emerald Resources NL; *Int'l*, pg. 2378
BULLSEYE TELECOM INC.—See Lingo Management, LLC; *U.S. Private*, pg. 2461
BULL TRADING AND INVESTMENTS LTD.; *Int'l*, pg. 1214
BULL URUGUAY SA—See Atos SE; *Int'l*, pg. 692
BULL WEALTH MANAGEMENT GROUP INC.—See EFG International AG; *Int'l*, pg. 2319
BULLWELL TRAILER SOLUTIONS LIMITED—See Ryder System, Inc.; *U.S. Public*, pg. 1828
BULL WILL CO., LTD.; *Int'l*, pg. 1214
BULLYAN TRAILER SALES INC.; *U.S. Private*, pg. 685
BULMA XXI S.L.U.—See Kuriyama Holdings Corporation; *Int'l*, pg. 4341
BULMER HARVEST LIMITED—See Treasury Wine Estates Limited; *Int'l*, pg. 7909
BULMERS LTD—See C&C Group Plc; *Int'l*, pg. 1238
BULOVA CORPORATION—See Citizen Watch Co., Ltd.; *Int'l*, pg. 1623
BULOVA DE MEXICO, SRL—See Citizen Watch Co., Ltd.; *Int'l*, pg. 1623
BULOVA TECHNOLOGIES GROUP, INC.; *U.S. Private*, pg. 685
BULOVA TECHNOLOGIES MACHINERY LLC—See Bulova Technologies Group, Inc.; *U.S. Private*, pg. 685
BULPROS CONSULTING AD; *Int'l*, pg. 1214
BULSTRAD LIFE VIENNA INSURANCE GROUP JOINT STOCK COMPANY—See Vienna Insurance Group AG Wiener Versicherung Gruppe; *Int'l*, pg. 8194
BULSTRAD VIENNA INSURANCE GROUP—See Vienna Insurance Group AG Wiener Versicherung Gruppe; *Int'l*, pg. 8194
BULTEN AB; *Int'l*, pg. 1214
BULTEN FASTENERS AB—See Bulten AB; *Int'l*, pg. 1214
BULTEN FASTENERS (TIANJIN) CO., LTD.—See Bulten AB; *Int'l*, pg. 1214
BULTEN GMBH—See Bulten AB; *Int'l*, pg. 1214
BULTEN HALLSTAHAMMAR AB—See Bulten AB; *Int'l*, pg. 1214
BULTEN LTD.—See Bulten AB; *Int'l*, pg. 1214
BULTEN NORTH AMERICA LLC—See Bulten AB; *Int'l*, pg. 1214
BULTEN POLSKA S.A.—See Bulten AB; *Int'l*, pg. 1214
BULTEN SWEDEN AB—See Bulten AB; *Int'l*, pg. 1214
BULTHAUP GMBH & CO.—See Toto Ltd.; *Int'l*, pg. 7845
BULVARIA HOLDING EAD—See Eurohold Bulgaria AD; *Int'l*, pg. 2553
BULVARIA VARNA EOOD—See Eurohold Bulgaria AD; *Int'l*, pg. 2553
BULVESTA HOLDING AD; *Int'l*, pg. 1215
BUM BETON- UND MONIERBAU GMBH; *Int'l*, pg. 1215
BUMBLEBEE ECO SOLUTIONS SDN. BHD.—See YBS International Berhad; *Int'l*, pg. 8574
BUMBLE BEE FOODS LLC—See FCF Co., Ltd.; *Int'l*, pg. 2627
BUMBLE BEE PUERTO RICO—See FCF Co., Ltd.; *Int'l*, pg. 2627
BUMBLE BEE SEAFOODS LLC—See FCF Co., Ltd.; *Int'l*, pg. 2627
BUMBLE, INC.; *U.S. Public*, pg. 410
BUMCITY SDN. BHD.—See Asia Brands Berhad; *Int'l*, pg. 610

BUMECH SA; *Int'l*, pg. 1215
BUMGARNER OIL CO. INC.; *U.S. Private*, pg. 685
BUMHAN INDUSTRIES CO., LTD.; *Int'l*, pg. 1215
BUMI ARMADA BERHAD; *Int'l*, pg. 1215
BUMI ARMADA CASPIAN LLC—See Bumi Armada Berhad; *Int'l*, pg. 1215
BUMI ARMADA ENGINEERING SDN BHD—See Bumi Armada Berhad; *Int'l*, pg. 1215
BUMI ARMADA NAVIGATION LABUAN LIMITED—See Bumi Armada Berhad; *Int'l*, pg. 1215
BUMI ARMADA NAVIGATION SDN. BHD.—See Bumi Armada Berhad; *Int'l*, pg. 1215
BUMI ARMADA (SINGAPORE) PTE. LTD.—See Bumi Armada Berhad; *Int'l*, pg. 1215
BUMI ARMADA UK LIMITED—See Bumi Armada Berhad; *Int'l*, pg. 1215
BUMI SEGAR INDAH SDN. BHD.—See Ann Joo Resources Berhad; *Int'l*, pg. 473
BUMITAMA AGRI LTD.; *Int'l*, pg. 1215
BUMPERDOC INC.; *U.S. Private*, pg. 685
BUMRUNGRAD HEALTH NETWORK CO., LTD.—See Bumrungrad Hospital Public Company Limited; *Int'l*, pg. 1215
BUMRUNGRAD HOSPITAL PUBLIC COMPANY LIMITED; *Int'l*, pg. 1215
BUMRUNGRAD MEDICAL CENTER LTD. (BMC)—See Bumrungrad Hospital Public Company Limited; *Int'l*, pg. 1215
BUMRUNGRAD MONGOLIA LLC—See Bumrungrad Hospital Public Company Limited; *Int'l*, pg. 1215
BUMRUNGRAD MYANMAR CO., LTD.—See Bumrungrad Hospital Public Company Limited; *Int'l*, pg. 1215
BUMYANG CONSTRUCTION CO., LTD.; *Int'l*, pg. 1215
BUNCEE, LLC—See Coughlan Companies, Inc.; *U.S. Private*, pg. 1064
BUNCHBALL, INC.—See Schoeneckers Inc.; *U.S. Private*, pg. 3567
THE BUNCHER COMPANY; *U.S. Private*, pg. 4002
BUNCH TRANSPORT INC.; *U.S. Private*, pg. 685
BUNDABERG BROADCASTERS PTY LTD—See Nine Entertainment Co. Holdings Limited; *Int'l*, pg. 5298
BUNDABERG DISTILLING COMPANY PTY. LIMITED—See Diageo plc; *Int'l*, pg. 2101
BUNDABERG SUGAR GROUP LTD.—See Finasucre S.A.; *Int'l*, pg. 2669
BUNDABERG SUGAR LTD.—See Finasucre S.A.; *Int'l*, pg. 2670
BUNDABERG WALKERS ENGINEERING LTD.—See Finasucre S.A.; *Int'l*, pg. 2670
BUND CENTER INVESTMENT LTD.; *Int'l*, pg. 1215
BUNDELKHAND SAUR URJA LIMITED—See NHPC Ltd.; *Int'l*, pg. 5259
BUNDESDRUCKEREI GMBH; *Int'l*, pg. 1215
BUNDY AMERICAN CORPORATION—See JJF Management Services, Inc.; *U.S. Private*, pg. 2211
BUNDY KFT—See Sun Capital Partners, Inc.; *U.S. Private*, pg. 3861
BUNDY REFRIGERACAO BRASIL IND E COMERCIO—See Sun Capital Partners, Inc.; *U.S. Private*, pg. 3861
BUNDY REFRIGERATION INTERNATIONAL HOLDING B.V.—See Sun Capital Partners, Inc.; *U.S. Private*, pg. 3861
BUNDY REFRIGERATION SP. ZO.O.—See Sun Capital Partners, Inc.; *U.S. Private*, pg. 3861
BUNDY REFRIGERATION S.R.L.—See Sun Capital Partners, Inc.; *U.S. Private*, pg. 3861
BUNES FRYSELAGER AS—See TINE SA; *Int'l*, pg. 7753
BUNGA DEVELOPMENT SDN. BHD.—See OSK Holdings Berhad; *Int'l*, pg. 5651
BUNGE AGRIBUSINESS AUSTRALIA PTY. LTD.—See Bunge Limited; *U.S. Public*, pg. 411
BUNGE AGRIBUSINESS SINGAPORE PTE. LTD.—See Bunge Limited; *U.S. Public*, pg. 411
BUNGE AGRITRADE S.A.—See Bunge Limited; *U.S. Public*, pg. 411
BUNGE ARGENTINA S.A.—See Bunge Limited; *U.S. Public*, pg. 411
BUNGE ARGENTINA—See Bunge Limited; *U.S. Public*, pg. 411
BUNGE ASIA PTE. LTD.—See Bunge Limited; *U.S. Public*, pg. 411
BUNGE CANADA—See Bunge Limited; *U.S. Public*, pg. 411
BUNGE COLOMBIA S.A.S.—See Bunge Limited; *U.S. Public*, pg. 411
BUNGE COMERCIALIZADORA DE ENERGIA LTDA.—See Bunge Limited; *U.S. Public*, pg. 411
BUNGE CORPORATION LTD.—See Bunge Limited; *U.S. Public*, pg. 411
BUNGE CORPORATION—See Bunge Limited; *U.S. Public*, pg. 411
BUNGE DEUTSCHLAND G.M.B.H.—See Bunge Limited; *U.S. Public*, pg. 411
BUNGE ETGO L.P.—See Bunge Limited; *U.S. Public*, pg. 411
BUNGE FERTILIZANTES S.A.—See Bunge Limited; *U.S. Public*, pg. 411
BUNGE FINANCE B.V.—See Bunge Limited; *U.S. Public*, pg. 411
BUNGE GLOBAL MARKETS, INC.—See Bunge Limited; *U.S. Public*, pg. 411
BUNGE HOLDINGS FRANCE S.A.S.—See Bunge Limited; *U.S. Public*, pg. 411
BUNGE IBERICA PORTUGAL, S.A.—See Bunge Limited; *U.S. Public*, pg. 411
BUNGE INVESTMENT IBERICA S.L.U.—See Bunge Limited; *U.S. Public*, pg. 411
BUNGE ITALIA S.P.A.—See Bunge Limited; *U.S. Public*, pg. 411
BUNGE LIMITED; *U.S. Public*, pg. 410
BUNGE LODERS CROKLAAN (GHANA) LTD.—See Bunge Limited; *U.S. Public*, pg. 411
BUNGE LODERS CROKLAAN GROUP B.V.—See Bunge Limited; *U.S. Public*, pg. 411
BUNGE LODERS CROKLAAN OILS B.V.—See Bunge Limited; *U.S. Public*, pg. 411
BUNGE LODERS CROKLAAN OILS SDN BHD—See Bunge Limited; *U.S. Public*, pg. 411
BUNGE LODERS CROKLAAN (SHANGHAI) TRADING CO. LTD.—See Bunge Limited; *U.S. Public*, pg. 411
BUNGE LODERS (XIAMEN) OILS TECHNOLOGY, CO. LTD.—See Bunge Limited; *U.S. Public*, pg. 411
BUNGE MEXICO HOLDINGS, INC.—See Bunge Limited; *U.S. Public*, pg. 411
BUNGE MILLING, INC.—See Bunge Limited; *U.S. Public*, pg. 411
BUNGE MILLING, LLC—See Bunge Limited; *U.S. Public*, pg. 411
BUNGE MILLING (SOUTHWEST), INC.—See Bunge Limited; *U.S. Public*, pg. 411
BUNGE - MORRISTOWN GRAIN COMPANY—See Bunge Limited; *U.S. Public*, pg. 411
BUNGE N.A. FINANCE L.P.—See Bunge Limited; *U.S. Public*, pg. 411
BUNGE (NANJING) GRAIN AND OILS CO.,LTD.—See Bunge Limited; *U.S. Public*, pg. 411
BUNGE NORTH AMERICA EAST—See Bunge Limited; *U.S. Public*, pg. 411
BUNGE NORTH AMERICA, INC.—See Bunge Limited; *U.S. Public*, pg. 411
BUNGER & FRESE GMBH—See Maytronics Ltd.; *Int'l*, pg. 4747
BUNGE S.A.—See Bunge Limited; *U.S. Public*, pg. 411
BUNGE-SCF GRAIN, LLC—See Bunge Limited; *U.S. Public*, pg. 411
BUNGE (THAILAND) LTD.—See Bunge Limited; *U.S. Public*, pg. 411
BUNG LODERS CROKLAAN B.V.—See Bunge Limited; *U.S. Public*, pg. 411
BUNGOBOX; *U.S. Private*, pg. 685
BUNIM/MURRAY PRODUCTIONS, INC.—See LOV Group Invest SAS; *Int'l*, pg. 4563
BUNKAKOBO, INC.—See TV Asahi Holdings Corporation; *Int'l*, pg. 7986
BUNKA KOUGEI CO., LTD.—See Bunka Shutter Co., Ltd.; *Int'l*, pg. 1216
BUNKA PANEL KOGYO CO., LTD.—See Bunka Shutter Co., Ltd.; *Int'l*, pg. 1216
BUNKA SHUTTER CO., LTD.; *Int'l*, pg. 1216
BUNKA SHUTTER SERVICE CO., LTD.—See Bunka Shutter Co., Ltd.; *Int'l*, pg. 1216
BUNK CAMPERS LTD.—See Tourism Holdings Limited; *Int'l*, pg. 7848
BUNKEIDO CO., LTD.; *Int'l*, pg. 1216
BUNKER CORPORATION; *U.S. Private*, pg. 685
BUNKERFUELS CORPORATION—See World Kinect Corporation; *U.S. Public*, pg. 2380
BUNKER HILL CAPITAL LP; *U.S. Private*, pg. 685
BUNKER HILL INSURANCE CASUALTY COMPANY—See The Plymouth Rock Co.; *U.S. Private*, pg. 4097
BUNKER HILL INSURANCE COMPANY—See The Plymouth Rock Co.; *U.S. Private*, pg. 4097
BUNKER HILL MINING CORP.; *Int'l*, pg. 1216
BUNKER INDUSTRIA FARMACEUTICA LTDA.—See Bausch Health Companies Inc.; *Int'l*, pg. 897
BUNKER PROPERTIES INC.—See PBI/Gordon Corporation; *U.S. Private*, pg. 3118
BUNKHOUSE GROUP LLC—See Hyatt Hotels Corporation; *U.S. Public*, pg. 1078
BUNKOFF GENERAL CONTRACTORS; *U.S. Private*, pg. 685
BUNKYODO GROUP HOLDINGS CO., LTD.; *Int'l*, pg. 1216
BUNNINGS JOONDALUP PTY LTD—See Wesfarmers Limited; *Int'l*, pg. 8381
BUNNINGS LIMITED—See Wesfarmers Limited; *Int'l*, pg. 8382
BUNNINGS MANAGEMENT SERVICES PTY LTD—See Wesfarmers Limited; *Int'l*, pg. 8382
BUNNINGS PTY., LTD.—See Wesfarmers Limited; *Int'l*, pg. 8382
BUNN-O-MATIC CORP. OF CANADA LTD.—See Bunn-O-Matic Corporation; *U.S. Private*, pg. 685
BUNN-O-MATIC CORPORATION; *U.S. Private*, pg. 685
BUNNY'S LIMITED; *Int'l*, pg. 1216
BUN PENNY INC.; *U.S. Private*, pg. 685
BUNRI CO., LTD.—See Gakken Holdings Co., Ltd.; *Int'l*, pg. 2869
BUNTE VERLAG GMBH—See Hubert Burda Media Holding Kommanditgesellschaft; *Int'l*, pg. 3519
BUNTING BEARINGS CORP.; *U.S. Private*, pg. 686
BUNTING CONSTRUCTION CORPORATION; *U.S. Private*, pg. 686
BUNTING DOOR & HARDWARE CO., INC.—See Platinum Equity, LLC; *U.S. Private*, pg. 3208
BUNTING MAGNETICS CO.—See Bunting Magnetics Co.; *U.S. Private*, pg. 686
BUNTING MAGNETICS CO.; *U.S. Private*, pg. 686
BUNTING MAGNETICS EUROPE LIMITED—See Bunting Magnetics Co.; *U.S. Private*, pg. 686
BUNTING MANAGEMENT GROUP, INC.; *U.S. Private*, pg. 686
THE BUNTIN GROUP; *U.S. Private*, pg. 4002
BUNTIN OUT-OF-HOME MEDIA—See The Buntin Group; *U.S. Private*, pg. 4002
BUNTMETALL AMSTETTEN GES.M.B.H.—See Wieland-Werke AG; *Int'l*, pg. 8404
BUNZL AUSTRALASIA LTD—See Bunzl plc; *Int'l*, pg. 1217
BUNZL & BIACH GES.M.B.H—See Heinzel Holding GmbH; *Int'l*, pg. 3325
BUNZL & BIACH GES.M.B.H—See Svenska Cellulosa Aktiebolaget SCA; *Int'l*, pg. 7357
BUNZL CANADA, INC.—See Bunzl plc; *Int'l*, pg. 1217
BUNZL CATERING SUPPLIES LIMITED—See Bunzl plc; *Int'l*, pg. 1217
BUNZL CS S.R.O.—See Bunzl plc; *Int'l*, pg. 1217
BUNZL DE MEXICO S.A. DE C.V—See Bunzl plc; *Int'l*, pg. 1218
BUNZL DISTRIBUTIE SRL—See Bunzl plc; *Int'l*, pg. 1217
BUNZL DISTRIBUTION DANMARK A/S—See Bunzl plc; *Int'l*, pg. 1217
BUNZL DISTRIBUTION OKLAHOMA, INC.—See Bunzl plc; *Int'l*, pg. 1217
BUNZL DISTRIBUTION SPAIN, S.A.U.—See Bunzl plc; *Int'l*, pg. 1217
BUNZL DISTRIBUTION USA, LLC—See Bunzl plc; *Int'l*, pg. 1217
BUNZL GROSSHANDEL GMBH—See Bunzl plc; *Int'l*, pg. 1217
BUNZL HEALTHCARE GMBH—See Bunzl plc; *Int'l*, pg. 1217
BUNZL HIGIENE E LIMPEZA LTDA.—See Bunzl plc; *Int'l*, pg. 1217
BUNZL HOLDING GMBH—See Bunzl plc; *Int'l*, pg. 1217
BUNZL IRELAND LIMITED—See Bunzl plc; *Int'l*, pg. 1217
BUNZL MAGYARORSZAG KFT—See Bunzl plc; *Int'l*, pg. 1217
BUNZL MINNEAPOLIS, LLC—See Bunzl plc; *Int'l*, pg. 1217
BUNZL OUTSOURCING SERVICES BV—See Bunzl plc; *Int'l*, pg. 1217
BUNZL PLC; *Int'l*, pg. 1216
BUNZL RETAIL, LLC—See Bunzl plc; *Int'l*, pg. 1217
BUNZL ROMANIA SRL—See Bunzl plc; *Int'l*, pg. 1217
BUNZL UK LTD—See Bunzl plc; *Int'l*, pg. 1217
BUNZL USA HOLDINGS LLC—See Bunzl plc; *Int'l*, pg. 1217
BUNZL USA, LLC—See Bunzl plc; *Int'l*, pg. 1217
BUNZL VERPACKUNGEN GMBH—See Bunzl plc; *Int'l*, pg. 1218
BUONGIORNO DEUTSCHLAND GMBH—See Nippon Telegraph & Telephone Corporation; *Int'l*, pg. 5349
BUONGIORNO FRANCE S.A.S.—See Nippon Telegraph & Telephone Corporation; *Int'l*, pg. 5349
BUONGIORNO HELLAS LTD—See Nippon Telegraph & Telephone Corporation; *Int'l*, pg. 5349
BUONGIORNO MYALERT BRASIL SERVICIOS CELULARES LTDA.—See Nippon Telegraph & Telephone Corporation; *Int'l*, pg. 5349
BUONGIORNO MYALERT S.A.—See Nippon Telegraph & Telephone Corporation; *Int'l*, pg. 5349
BUONGIORNO SOUTH AFRICA (PTY) LIMITED—See Nippon Telegraph & Telephone Corporation; *Int'l*, pg. 5349
BUONGIORNO S.P.A.—See Nippon Telegraph & Telephone Corporation; *Int'l*, pg. 5349
BUONGIORNO UK LTD—See Nippon Telegraph & Telephone Corporation; *Int'l*, pg. 5349
BUOY LABS, INC.—See Resideo Technologies, Inc.; *U.S. Public*, pg. 1789
BUPA ACIBADEM SIGORTA A.S.—See The British United Provident Association Limited; *Int'l*, pg. 7629
BUPA ARABIA FOR COOPERATIVE INSURANCE COMPANY; *Int'l*, pg. 1220
BUPA (ASIA) LIMITED—See The British United Provident Association Limited; *Int'l*, pg. 7629
BUPA AUSTRALIA PTY LIMITED—See The British United Provident Association Limited; *Int'l*, pg. 7629
BUPA CARE HOMES (BNH) LIMITED—See The British United Provident Association Limited; *Int'l*, pg. 7629
BUPA CARE HOMES (CFG) PLC—See The British United Provident Association Limited; *Int'l*, pg. 7629
BUPA CARE SERVICES LIMITED—See The British United Provident Association Limited; *Int'l*, pg. 7629

BUPA ARABIA FOR COOPERATIVE INSURANCE COMPANY

CORPORATE AFFILIATIONS

BUPA CARE VILLAGES AUSTRALIA PTY LTD.—See The British United Provident Association Limited; *Int'l*, pg. 7629
BUPA DOMINICANA, S.A.—See The British United Provident Association Limited; *Int'l*, pg. 7629
BUPA GUATEMALA, COMPANIA DE SEGUROS, S.A.—See The British United Provident Association Limited; *Int'l*, pg. 7629
BUPA HEALTHCARE NEW ZEALAND LIMITED—See The British United Provident Association Limited; *Int'l*, pg. 7629
BUPA HI PTY LTD.—See The British United Provident Association Limited; *Int'l*, pg. 7629
BUPA OCCUPATIONAL HEALTH LIMITED—See The British United Provident Association Limited; *Int'l*, pg. 7629
BUPA OPTICAL PTY LTD.—See The British United Provident Association Limited; *Int'l*, pg. 7629
BUPA REHABILITATION LIMITED—See The British United Provident Association Limited; *Int'l*, pg. 7629
BUPA SERVICIOS DE SALUD SPA—See The British United Provident Association Limited; *Int'l*, pg. 7629
BUQUET DISTRIBUTING COMPANY, INC.; *U.S. Private*, pg. 686
BUQUET & LEBLANC CONTRACTORS, INC.; *U.S. Private*, pg. 686
BUQUET & LE BLANC INC.; *U.S. Private*, pg. 686
BURBAGE IRON CRAFT LTD.—See ARGENT INDUSTRIAL LIMITED; *Int'l*, pg. 560
BURBAGE IRON CRAFT SERVICES LIMITED—See ARGENT INDUSTRIAL LIMITED; *Int'l*, pg. 560
BURBANK AUSTRALIA PTY LTD; *Int'l*, pg. 1220
BURBANK LEADER—See Los Angeles Times Communications, LLC; *U.S. Private*, pg. 2497
THE BURBANK OPHTHALMOLOGY ASC, L.P.—See KKR & Co. Inc.; *U.S. Public*, pg. 1247
BURBERRY ANTWERP NV—See Burberry Group plc; *Int'l*, pg. 1220
BURBERRY (AUSTRIA) GMBH—See Burberry Group plc; *Int'l*, pg. 1220
BURBERRY CZECH REP S.R.O.—See Burberry Group plc; *Int'l*, pg. 1220
BURBERRY (DEUTSCHLAND) GMBH—See Burberry Group plc; *Int'l*, pg. 1220
BURBERRY GROUP PLC; *Int'l*, pg. 1220
BURBERRY LIMITED—See Burberry Group plc; *Int'l*, pg. 1220
BURBERRY (SHANGHAI) TRADING CO., LTD.—See Burberry Group plc; *Int'l*, pg. 1220
BURBERRY (SUISSE) SA—See Burberry Group plc; *Int'l*, pg. 1220
BURCAP PLASTICS (PTY) LTD.—See Nampak Ltd.; *Int'l*, pg. 5136
BURCELIK BURSA CELIK DOKUM SANAYI AS; *Int'l*, pg. 1220
BURCELIK VANA SANAYI VE TICARET A.S.; *Int'l*, pg. 1220
THE BURCHFIELD GROUP, INC.—See Aon plc; *Int'l*, pg. 495
BURCH FOOD SERVICE INC.; *U.S. Private*, pg. 686
BURCH MANAGEMENT CO., INC.; *U.S. Private*, pg. 686
BURCH MATERIALS CO., INC.—See PennSpring Capital, LLC; *U.S. Private*, pg. 3136
BURCKHARDT COMPRESSION AG—See Burckhardt Compression Holding AG; *Int'l*, pg. 1220
BURCKHARDT COMPRESSION (BRASIL) LTDA.—See Burckhardt Compression Holding AG; *Int'l*, pg. 1220
BURCKHARDT COMPRESSION (CANADA) INC.—See Burckhardt Compression Holding AG; *Int'l*, pg. 1220
BURCKHARDT COMPRESSION (DEUTSCHLAND) GMBH—See Burckhardt Compression Holding AG; *Int'l*, pg. 1220
BURCKHARDT COMPRESSION (ESPANA) S.A.—See Burckhardt Compression Holding AG; *Int'l*, pg. 1220
BURCKHARDT COMPRESSION (FRANCE) S.A.S—See Burckhardt Compression Holding AG; *Int'l*, pg. 1220
BURCKHARDT COMPRESSION HOLDING AG; *Int'l*, pg. 1220
BURCKHARDT COMPRESSION (INDIA) PVT. LTD.—See Burckhardt Compression Holding AG; *Int'l*, pg. 1220
BURCKHARDT COMPRESSION (ITALIA) S.R.L.—See Burckhardt Compression Holding AG; *Int'l*, pg. 1220
BURCKHARDT COMPRESSION (JAPAN) LTD.—See Burckhardt Compression Holding AG; *Int'l*, pg. 1220
BURCKHARDT COMPRESSION KOREA BUSAN LTD.—See Burckhardt Compression Holding AG; *Int'l*, pg. 1220
BURCKHARDT COMPRESSION KOREA LTD.—See Burckhardt Compression Holding AG; *Int'l*, pg. 1221
BURCKHARDT COMPRESSION (MIDDLE EAST) FZE—See Burckhardt Compression Holding AG; *Int'l*, pg. 1220
BURCKHARDT COMPRESSION (NETHERLANDS) BV—See Burckhardt Compression Holding AG; *Int'l*, pg. 1220
BURCKHARDT COMPRESSION (SAUDI ARABIA) LLC—See Burckhardt Compression Holding AG; *Int'l*, pg. 1220

BURCKHARDT COMPRESSION (SHANGHAI) CO. LTD.—See Burckhardt Compression Holding AG; *Int'l*, pg. 1220
BURCKHARDT COMPRESSION SINGAPORE PTE LTD.—See Burckhardt Compression Holding AG; *Int'l*, pg. 1221
BURCKHARDT COMPRESSION SOUTH AFRICA (PTY) LTD.—See Burckhardt Compression Holding AG; *Int'l*, pg. 1221
BURCKHARDT COMPRESSION (UK) LTD.—See Burckhardt Compression Holding AG; *Int'l*, pg. 1220
BURCKHARDT COMPRESSION (US) INC.—See Burckhardt Compression Holding AG; *Int'l*, pg. 1220
BURCKHARDT KOMPRESOR SAN. VE TIC. LTD.—See Burckhardt Compression Holding AG; *Int'l*, pg. 1221
BURCO APPLIANCES LTD.—See The Glen Dimplex Group; *Int'l*, pg. 7649
BURCON NUTRASCIENCE CORPORATION; *Int'l*, pg. 1221
BURCON NUTRASCIENCE (MB) CORP.—See Burcon NutraScience Corporation; *Int'l*, pg. 1221
BURDA COMMUNICATIONS SP. Z O.O.—See Hubert Burda Media Holding Kommanditgesellschaft; *Int'l*, pg. 3519
BURDA COMMUNITY NETWORK GMBH—See Hubert Burda Media Holding Kommanditgesellschaft; *Int'l*, pg. 3519
BURDA DRUCK NURNBERG GMBH & CO. KG—See Hubert Burda Media Holding Kommanditgesellschaft; *Int'l*, pg. 3519
BURDA PRAHA SPOL. S.R.O.—See Hubert Burda Media Holding Kommanditgesellschaft; *Int'l*, pg. 3519
BURDA PUBLICATIONS, INC.—See Hubert Burda Media Holding Kommanditgesellschaft; *Int'l*, pg. 3519
BURDA SERVICE AG—See Hubert Burda Media Holding Kommanditgesellschaft; *Int'l*, pg. 3519
BURDA SERVICES GMBH—See Hubert Burda Media Holding Kommanditgesellschaft; *Int'l*, pg. 3519
BURDA SINGAPORE PTE. LTD.—See Hubert Burda Media Holding Kommanditgesellschaft; *Int'l*, pg. 3520
BURDA TAIWAN CO. LTD.—See Hubert Burda Media Holding Kommanditgesellschaft; *Int'l*, pg. 3520
BURDA (THAILAND) CO., LTD.—See Hubert Burda Media Holding Kommanditgesellschaft; *Int'l*, pg. 3519
BURDEN SALES COMPANY; *U.S. Private*, pg. 686
BURD & FLETCHER COMPANY; *U.S. Private*, pg. 686
BURDICK PLUMBING & HEATING CO; *U.S. Private*, pg. 686
BURDICK TOYOTA; *U.S. Private*, pg. 686
BURDITCH MARKETING COMMUNICATIONS; *U.S. Private*, pg. 686
BUREAU D'ASSURANCES ET DEPRETS—See Apollo Global Management, Inc.; *U.S. Public*, pg. 147
BUREAU D'ELECTRONIQUE APPLIQUEE S.A.—See Halma plc; *Int'l*, pg. 3230
BUREAU DE LIAISON DOHLER FRANCE S.A.R.L.—See Dohler GmbH; *Int'l*, pg. 2155
BUREAU DE PROJETOS E CONSULTORIA LTDA.—See TUV SUD AG; *Int'l*, pg. 7984
BUREAU DE RECHERCHES GEOLOGIQUES ET MINIERE; *Int'l*, pg. 1221
BUREAU DE WIT BV—See Eurofins Scientific S.E.; *Int'l*, pg. 2535
BUREAU D'EXPERTISES DESPRETZ S.A.—See Allianz SE; *Int'l*, pg. 351
THE BUREAU OF ENGRAVING, INC.; *U.S. Private*, pg. 4002
THE BUREAU OF NATIONAL AFFAIRS, INC.—See Bloomberg L.P.; *U.S. Private*, pg. 583
BUREAU VAN DIJK EDITIONS ELECTRONIQUES S.A.—See Moody's Corporation; *U.S. Public*, pg. 1467
BUREAU VAN DIJK EDITIONS ELECTRONIQUES SAS—See Moody's Corporation; *U.S. Public*, pg. 1467
BUREAU VAN DIJK EDIZIONI ELETTRONICHE SPA—See Moody's Corporation; *U.S. Public*, pg. 1467
BUREAU VAN DIJK ELECTRONIC PUBLISHING AB—See Moody's Corporation; *U.S. Public*, pg. 1467
BUREAU VAN DIJK ELECTRONIC PUBLISHING APS—See Moody's Corporation; *U.S. Public*, pg. 1467
BUREAU VAN DIJK ELECTRONIC PUBLISHING (BEIJING) CO. LIMITED—See Moody's Corporation; *U.S. Public*, pg. 1467
BUREAU VAN DIJK ELECTRONIC PUBLISHING BV—See Moody's Corporation; *U.S. Public*, pg. 1467
BUREAU VAN DIJK ELECTRONIC PUBLISHING GMBH—See Moody's Corporation; *U.S. Public*, pg. 1467
BUREAU VAN DIJK ELECTRONIC PUBLISHING HONG KONG LIMITED—See Moody's Corporation; *U.S. Public*, pg. 1467
BUREAU VAN DIJK ELECTRONIC PUBLISHING INC.—See Moody's Corporation; *U.S. Public*, pg. 1467
BUREAU VAN DIJK ELECTRONIC PUBLISHING KK—See Moody's Corporation; *U.S. Public*, pg. 1467
BUREAU VAN DIJK ELECTRONIC PUBLISHING LLC—See Moody's Corporation; *U.S. Public*, pg. 1467
BUREAU VAN DIJK ELECTRONIC PUBLISHING LTD—See Moody's Corporation; *U.S. Public*, pg. 1467

BUREAU VAN DIJK ELECTRONIC PUBLISHING PTE LTD—See Moody's Corporation; *U.S. Public*, pg. 1467
BUREAU VAN DIJK ELECTRONIC PUBLISHING PTY LIMITED—See Moody's Corporation; *U.S. Public*, pg. 1467
BUREAU VAN DIJK ELECTRONIC PUBLISHING SA DE CV—See Moody's Corporation; *U.S. Public*, pg. 1467
BUREAU VAN DIJK ELECTRONIQ PUBLISHING SA (PTY) LTD.—See Moody's Corporation; *U.S. Public*, pg. 1467
BUREAU VAN DIJK E.P. DMCC—See Moody's Corporation; *U.S. Public*, pg. 1466
BUREAU VAN DIJK PUBLICACAO ELECTRONICA LTDA—See Moody's Corporation; *U.S. Public*, pg. 1467
BUREAU VAN DIJK PUBLICACIONES ELECTRONICAS SA—See Moody's Corporation; *U.S. Public*, pg. 1467
BUREAU VERITAS ASSET INTEGRITY & RELIABILITY SERVICES PTY. LTD.—See Bureau Veritas S.A.; *Int'l*, pg. 1221
BUREAU VERITAS AUSTRALIA PTY. LTD.—See Bureau Veritas S.A.; *Int'l*, pg. 1221
BUREAU VERITAS CONSUMER PRODUCTS SERVICES, INC.—See Bureau Veritas S.A.; *Int'l*, pg. 1221
BUREAU VERITAS INTERNATIONAL TRADE AUSTRALIA PTY. LTD.—See Bureau Veritas S.A.; *Int'l*, pg. 1221
BUREAU VERITAS NORTH AMERICA, INC. - COSTA MESA—See Bureau Veritas S.A.; *Int'l*, pg. 1221
BUREAU VERITAS NORTH AMERICA, INC.—See Bureau Veritas S.A.; *Int'l*, pg. 1221
BUREAU VERITAS S.A.; *Int'l*, pg. 1221
BUREAU VERITAS UK LIMITED—See Bureau Veritas S.A.; *Int'l*, pg. 1222
BUREAUX A PARTACER SAS—See Nexity SA; *Int'l*, pg. 5244
BURE EQUITY AB; *Int'l*, pg. 1221
BURELLE S.A.; *Int'l*, pg. 1222
BURELLESLUCE—See Burrelle's Information Services LLC; *U.S. Private*, pg. 691
BURESKI HOLDINGS, INC.—See Advanced Pavement Group Corp.; *U.S. Private*, pg. 91
BURFORD BAKERY SOLUTIONS LIMITED—See The Middleby Corporation; *U.S. Public*, pg. 2113
BURFORD CAPITAL LIMITED; *Int'l*, pg. 1223
BURFORD CAPITAL LLC; *U.S. Private*, pg. 686
BURFORD CORP.—See The Middleby Corporation; *U.S. Public*, pg. 2113
BURGAD AG—See Eczacibasi Holding A.S.; *Int'l*, pg. 2301
BURGAN BANK AS—See Kuwait Projects Company (Holding) K.S.C.P.; *Int'l*, pg. 4346
BURGAN BANK S.A.K.—See Kuwait Projects Company (Holding) K.S.C.P.; *Int'l*, pg. 4346
BURGAN COMPANY FOR WELL DRILLING, TRADING & MAINTENANCE KSCC; *Int'l*, pg. 1223
BURGARELLO ALARM INC.—See Fire Protection Services Corp.; *U.S. Private*, pg. 2518
BURGBAD AKTIENGESELLSCHAFT; *Int'l*, pg. 1223
BURG CARROSSERIE B.V.—See China International Marine Containers (Group) Co., Ltd.; *Int'l*, pg. 1511
BURGEE-HENSS-SEITZ FUNERAL HOME, INC.—See Service Corporation International; *U.S. Public*, pg. 1869
BURGEL BETEILIGUNGS GMBH—See Allianz SE; *Int'l*, pg. 351
BURGEL ERFURT BETEILIGUNGSGESELLSCHAFT MBH—See Allianz SE; *Int'l*, pg. 351
BURGEL ERFURT GMBH & CO. KG—See Allianz SE; *Int'l*, pg. 351
BURGEL INTERNATIONALE INKASSOGESELLSCHAFT GMBH—See Allianz SE; *Int'l*, pg. 351
BURGEL WIRTSCHAFTSINFORMATIONEN GMBH & CO. KG—See Allianz SE; *Int'l*, pg. 351
BURGEL WIRTSCHAFTSINFORMATIONEN VERWALTUNGS-GMBH—See Allianz SE; *Int'l*, pg. 351
BURGENCIO S.A. DE C.V.—See Tocvan Ventures Corp.; *Int'l*, pg. 7772
BURGENLAND HOLDING AG—See EVN AG; *Int'l*, pg. 2570
BURGERBUSTERS INC.; *U.S. Private*, pg. 686
BURGER CHRYSLER-JEEP; *U.S. Private*, pg. 686
BURGERFI INTERNATIONAL, INC.; *U.S. Public*, pg. 412
THE BURGER IRON COMPANY; *U.S. Private*, pg. 4003
BURGER KING A.B.—See Restaurant Brands International Inc.; *Int'l*, pg. 6304
BURGER KING CORPORATION—See Restaurant Brands International Inc.; *Int'l*, pg. 6304
BURGER KING ESPANA S.L.U.—See Restaurant Brands International Inc.; *Int'l*, pg. 6304
BURGER KING FRANCE SAS—See Groupe Bertrand SARL; *Int'l*, pg. 3092
BURGER KING HOLDINGS, INC.—See Restaurant Brands International Inc.; *Int'l*, pg. 6304
BURGER KING LIMITED—See Restaurant Brands International Inc.; *Int'l*, pg. 6304
BURGER KING NEDERLAND SERVICES B.V.—See Restaurant Brands International Inc.; *Int'l*, pg. 6304
BURGER KING (UK) LIMITED—See Restaurant Brands International Inc.; *Int'l*, pg. 6304
BURGER KING WORLDWIDE, INC.—See Restaurant Brands International Inc.; *Int'l*, pg. 6304

COMPANY NAME INDEX

BURGER PHILLIPS BUILDING, LLC—See Synovus Financial Corp.; *U.S. Public*, pg. 1971
BURGER PHILLIPS BUILDING, LLC—See Synovus Financial Corp.; *U.S. Public*, pg. 1972
BURGERS ERGON B.V.—See Heijmans N.V.; *Int'l*, pg. 3322
BURGER STREET INCORPORATED; *U.S. Private*, pg. 686
BURGERVILLE USA—See The Holland, Inc.; *U.S. Private*, pg. 4054
BURGESS-AARDING—See CECO Environmental Corp.; *U.S. Public*, pg. 464
BURGESS ARCHITECTURAL PRODUCTS LIMITED; *Int'l*, pg. 1223
BURGESS CARRIAGE HOUSE INC.; *U.S. Private*, pg. 687
BURGESS CIVIL, LLC; *U.S. Private*, pg. 687
BURGESS COMPUTER DECISIONS, INC.; *U.S. Private*, pg. 687
THE BURGESS GROUP, LLC—See Blackstone Inc.; *U.S. Public*, pg. 354
BURGESS LIGHTING & DISTRIBUTING CO.; *U.S. Private*, pg. 687
BURGESS & NIPLE, INC. - CHANTILLY—See Burgess & Niple, Inc.; *U.S. Private*, pg. 687
BURGESS & NIPLE, INC. - FORTH WORTH—See Burgess & Niple, Inc.; *U.S. Private*, pg. 687
BURGESS & NIPLE, INC. - PAINESVILLE—See Burgess & Niple, Inc.; *U.S. Private*, pg. 687
BURGESS & NIPLE, INC.; *U.S. Private*, pg. 687
BURGESS & NIPLE, INC.—See Burgess & Niple, Inc.; *U.S. Private*, pg. 687
BURGESS-NORTON MANUFACTURING COMPANY—See AMSTED Industries Incorporated; *U.S. Private*, pg. 268
BURGESS PIGMENT COMPANY—See Burgess Pigment Company; *U.S. Private*, pg. 687
BURGESS PIGMENT COMPANY; *U.S. Private*, pg. 687
BURGESS STEEL PRODUCTS CORP; *U.S. Private*, pg. 687
THE BURGGRAF CORPORATION; *U.S. Private*, pg. 4003
THE BURGISS GROUP, LLC—See MSCI Inc.; *U.S. Public*, pg. 1483
BURGMANN DALIAN CO., LTD.—See Freudenberg SE; *Int'l*, pg. 2783
BURGMANN INDUSTRIES HOLDING GMBH—See Freudenberg SE; *Int'l*, pg. 2783
BURGMANN PACKINGS GMBH—See Freudenberg SE; *Int'l*, pg. 2783
BURGMANN SEALING MATERIALS CO., LTD. CIXI—See Freudenberg SE; *Int'l*, pg. 2783
BURGMANN SHANGHAI CO., LTD.—See Freudenberg SE; *Int'l*, pg. 2783
BURGO ARDENNES SA—See Burgo Group S.p.A.; *Int'l*, pg. 1223
BURGO BENELUX SA—See Burgo Group S.p.A.; *Int'l*, pg. 1223
BURGO CENTRAL EUROPE GMBH—See Burgo Group S.p.A.; *Int'l*, pg. 1223
BURGO DEUTSCHLAND GMBH—See Burgo Group S.p.A.; *Int'l*, pg. 1223
BURGO DISTRIBUZIONE SRL—See Burgo Group S.p.A.; *Int'l*, pg. 1223
BURGO EASTERN EUROPE SP. Z O.O.—See Burgo Group S.p.A.; *Int'l*, pg. 1223
BURGO ENERGIA SRL—See Burgo Group S.p.A.; *Int'l*, pg. 1223
BURGO FACTOR SPA—See Burgo Group S.p.A.; *Int'l*, pg. 1223
BURGO FRANCE SARL—See Burgo Group S.p.A.; *Int'l*, pg. 1224
BURGO GROUP S.P.A.; *Int'l*, pg. 1223
BURGO IBERICA PAPEL SA—See Burgo Group S.p.A.; *Int'l*, pg. 1224
BURGO INC.—See Kerry Group Limited; *Int'l*, pg. 4137
BURGO NORTH AMERICA INC—See Burgo Group S.p.A.; *Int'l*, pg. 1224
BURGO POLASKA SP Z O O—See Burgo Group S.p.A.; *Int'l*, pg. 1224
BURGOS GROUP LLC—See Prairie Band Potawatomi Nation; *U.S. Private*, pg. 3242
BURGO UK LTD—See Burgo Group S.p.A.; *Int'l*, pg. 1224
BURG SERVICE B.V.—See China International Marine Containers (Group) Co., Ltd.; *Int'l*, pg. 1511
BURG TRAILER SERVICE B.V.—See CIMC Vehicle (Group) Co., Ltd.; *Int'l*, pg. 1608
BURGUNDY DIAMOND MINES LIMITED; *Int'l*, pg. 1224
BURGUNDY TECHNOLOGY ACQUISITION CORPORATION; *Int'l*, pg. 1224
BURG-WACHTER KG; *Int'l*, pg. 1223
BURG-WAECHTER S.A.R.L.—See Burg-Wachter KG; *Int'l*, pg. 1223
BURGWEDEL BIOTECH GMBH—See Merck & Co., Inc.; *U.S. Public*, pg. 1415
BURIEN TOYOTA; *U.S. Private*, pg. 687
BURIRAM SUGAR PUBLIC COMPANY LIMITED; *Int'l*, pg. 1224
BURK ADVERTISING & MARKETING; *U.S. Private*, pg. 687

BURKE AIR PTY LIMITED - KALGOORLIE DIVISION—See BSA Limited; *Int'l*, pg. 1201
BURKE AIR PTY LIMITED—See BSA Limited; *Int'l*, pg. 1201
BURKE BROTHERS INC.; *U.S. Private*, pg. 688
BURKE CORPORATION—See Hormel Foods Corporation; *U.S. Public*, pg. 1053
BURKE ENGINEERING COMPANY; *U.S. Private*, pg. 688
BURKE E. PORTER MACHINERY COMPANY—See China Everbright Group Limited; *Int'l*, pg. 1501
BURKE FLOORING PRODUCTS DIVISION—See Mannington Mills, Inc.; *U.S. Private*, pg. 2565
BURKE FLOORING PRODUCTS—See Mannington Mills, Inc.; *U.S. Private*, pg. 2565
BURKE FOUNDATION; *U.S. Private*, pg. 688
BURKE FUEL & HEATING CO.—See Star Group, L.P.; *U.S. Public*, pg. 1937
THE BURKE GROUP, INC.; *U.S. Private*, pg. 4003
BURKE HANDLING SYSTEMS, INC.; *U.S. Private*, pg. 688
BURKE & HERBERT BANK & TRUST COMPANY; *U.S. Private*, pg. 687
BURKE & HERBERT FINANCIAL SERVICES CORP.—See Burke & Herbert Bank & Trust Company; *U.S. Private*, pg. 687
BURKE INC.; *U.S. Private*, pg. 688
BURKE INC.; *U.S. Private*, pg. 688
BURKE INDUSTRIES, INC. - BURKELINE ROOFING SYSTEMS DIVISION—See Mannington Mills, Inc.; *U.S. Private*, pg. 2565
BURKE INDUSTRIES, INC. - CUSTOM PROCESS—See Mannington Mills, Inc.; *U.S. Private*, pg. 2565
BURKE INDUSTRIES, INC.—See Mannington Mills, Inc.; *U.S. Private*, pg. 2565
BURKE INSURANCE GROUP, LLC—See Kelso & Company, L.P.; *U.S. Private*, pg. 2279
BURKE MARKETING CORPORATION; *U.S. Private*, pg. 688
BURKE NEWCO S.L.—See Alten S.A.; *Int'l*, pg. 390
BURKE OIL CO., INC.; *U.S. Private*, pg. 688
THE BURKE-PARSONS-BOWLBY CORPORATION—See Stella-Jones, Inc.; *Int'l*, pg. 7196
BURKE PEST CONTROL, INC.—See Rentokil Initial plc; *Int'l*, pg. 6280
THE BURKE PORTER GROUP; *U.S. Private*, pg. 4003
BURKE REHABILITATION HOSPITAL—See The Winifred Masterson Burke Rehabilitation Hospital, Inc.; *U.S. Private*, pg. 4137
BURKE RUBBER CO.—See Mannington Mills, Inc.; *U.S. Private*, pg. 2566
BURKE'S OUTLET STORES—See Beall's, Inc.; *U.S. Private*, pg. 505
BURKE SUPPLY COMPANY INC.; *U.S. Private*, pg. 688
BURKES WESTGATE CORPORATION—See Beall's, Inc.; *U.S. Private*, pg. 505
BURKE TRADING, INC.—See Hecla Mining Company; *U.S. Public*, pg. 1019
BURKETTEUA—See Eppstein Uhen Architects, Inc.; *U.S. Private*, pg. 1414
BURKETT RESTAURANT EQUIPMENT, CO.; *U.S. Private*, pg. 688
BURKEY CONSTRUCTION CO. INC.; *U.S. Private*, pg. 688
BURKHALTER AUTOMATION AG—See Burkhalter Holding AG; *Int'l*, pg. 1224
BURKHALTER ELEKTROTECHNIK AG—See Burkhalter Holding AG; *Int'l*, pg. 1224
BURKHALTER HOLDING AG; *Int'l*, pg. 1224
BURKHALTER SERVICES AG—See Burkhalter Holding AG; *Int'l*, pg. 1224
BURKHALTER TECHNICS AG—See Burkhalter Holding AG; *Int'l*, pg. 1224
BURKHARDT DISTRIBUTING COMPANY—See Mitchell Companies; *U.S. Private*, pg. 2750
BURKHARDT EXCAVATING; *U.S. Private*, pg. 688
BURKHARDT LTD.; *U.S. Private*, pg. 688
BURKHARDT+WEBER FERTIGUNGSSYSTEME GMBH—See Industrias Romi S.A.; *Int'l*, pg. 3674
BURKHARDT + WEBER LLC—See Industrias Romi S.A.; *Int'l*, pg. 3674
BURKHARDT + WEBER / ROMI (SHANGHAI) CO., LTD.—See Industrias Romi S.A.; *Int'l*, pg. 3674
BURKHART DENTAL SUPPLY CO. INC.; *U.S. Private*, pg. 688
BURKHOLDER'S HEATING & AIR CONDITIONING, INC.; *U.S. Private*, pg. 688
BURKINA LOGISTICS & MINING SERVICES SA—See Financiere de L'Odet; *Int'l*, pg. 2667
BURKI VERPACKUNGSTECHNIK AG; *Int'l*, pg. 1226
BURKLAND INC.—See Wolverine Capital Partners LLC; *U.S. Private*, pg. 4555
BURKLUND DISTRIBUTORS INC.—See AMCON Distributing Company; *U.S. Public*, pg. 92
BURKMANN INDUSTRIES INC.; *U.S. Private*, pg. 688
BURK ROYALTY CO.; *U.S. Private*, pg. 687
BURLAGE HOTEL ASSOCIATES LLC; *U.S. Private*, pg. 688
BURLAN CORPORATION; *U.S. Private*, pg. 688

BURLEIGH MARR DISTRIBUTIONS (PTY) LIMITED—See The Bidvest Group Limited; *Int'l*, pg. 7623
BURLEN CORP.—See GMM Capital LLC; *U.S. Private*, pg. 1722
BURLESON CONSULTING, INC.—See Terracon Consultants, Inc.; *U.S. Private*, pg. 3970
BURLESON'S INC.; *U.S. Private*, pg. 688
BURLESON STAR—See Alden Global Capital LLC; *U.S. Private*, pg. 156
BURLEY MINERALS LTD.; *Int'l*, pg. 1226
BURLINGAME INDUSTRIES, INCORPORATED; *U.S. Private*, pg. 688
BURLINGTON AUTOMATION CORPORATION—See Lincoln Electric Holdings, Inc.; *U.S. Public*, pg. 1317
BURLINGTON BASKET CO.; *U.S. Private*, pg. 688
BURLINGTON BAY RESIDENTIAL MORTGAGE SECURITIES LLC—See Two Harbors Investment Corp.; *U.S. Public*, pg. 2207
BURLINGTON CAPITAL LLC; *U.S. Private*, pg. 689
BURLINGTON CAPITAL PARTNERS, LLC; *U.S. Private*, pg. 689
BURLINGTON CHEMICAL COMPANY INC.; *U.S. Private*, pg. 689
BURLINGTON COAT FACTORY INVESTMENTS HOLDINGS, INC.—See Bain Capital, LP; *U.S. Private*, pg. 437
BURLINGTON DRUG COMPANY, INC.—See J.M. Smith Corporation; *U.S. Private*, pg. 2169
BURLINGTON FREE PRESS—See Gannett Co., Inc.; *U.S. Public*, pg. 897
BURLINGTON HEALTHCARE PROVIDERS, INC.; *U.S. Private*, pg. 689
THE BURLINGTON INSURANCE COMPANY—See IFG Companies; *U.S. Private*, pg. 2038
BURLINGTON MANOR, LLC—See Brookdale Senior Living Inc.; *U.S. Public*, pg. 394
BURLINGTON MATTRESS CO. LLC—See Tempur Sealy International, Inc.; *U.S. Public*, pg. 1999
BURLINGTON MEDICAL LLC—See Fox Three Partners LLC; *U.S. Private*, pg. 1585
BURLINGTON MEDICAL LLC—See Peninsula Capital Partners LLC; *U.S. Private*, pg. 3133
BURLINGTON MOTORS, INC.; *U.S. Private*, pg. 689
BURLINGTON NORTHERN (MANITOBA) LIMITED—See Berkshire Hathaway Inc.; *U.S. Public*, pg. 303
BURLINGTON NORTHERN SANTA FE, LLC—See Berkshire Hathaway Inc.; *U.S. Public*, pg. 303
THE BURLINGTON RECORD—See Alden Global Capital LLC; *U.S. Private*, pg. 157
BURLINGTON RIVER APARTMENTS, LIMITED PARTNERSHIP—See Apartment Investment and Management Company; *U.S. Public*, pg. 144
BURLINGTON STORES, INC.—See Bain Capital, LP; *U.S. Private*, pg. 437
BURLINGTON TIMBER—See Burlington Basket Co.; *U.S. Private*, pg. 688
BURLINGTON TIMES, INC.—See Gannett Co., Inc.; *U.S. Public*, pg. 901
BURLINGTON UNION—See Gannett Co., Inc.; *U.S. Public*, pg. 902
BURLINGTON VERMONT CITY ELECTRIC; *U.S. Private*, pg. 689
BURLINGTON WOODS CARE CENTER—See Formation Capital, LLC; *U.S. Private*, pg. 1570
BURLINGTON WOODS CONVALESCENT CENTER, INC.—See Welltower Inc.; *U.S. Public*, pg. 2348
BURLINGTON WORLDWIDE INC.—See Platinum Equity, LLC; *U.S. Private*, pg. 3203
BURLODGE CANADA LTD.—See Ali Holding S.r.l; *Int'l*, pg. 320
BURLODGE LTD.—See Ali Holding S.r.l; *Int'l*, pg. 320
BURLODGE SAS—See Ali Holding S.r.l; *Int'l*, pg. 320
BURLODGE S.R.L.—See Ali Holding S.r.l; *Int'l*, pg. 320
BURLODGE USA INC.—See Ali Holding S.r.l; *Int'l*, pg. 320
BURLOV CENTRE FASTIGHETS A.B.—See Eurocommercial Properties N.V.; *Int'l*, pg. 2534
THE BURLY CORPORATION OF NORTH AMERICA, INC.—See Mueller Inc.; *U.S. Private*, pg. 2810
BURMA BIBAS INC.; *U.S. Private*, pg. 689
BURMAC MACHINERY LTD.—See ANSA McAL Limited; *Int'l*, pg. 477
BURMAH CASTROL AUSTRALIA PTY LTD.—See BP plc; *Int'l*, pg. 1130
BURMATEX LIMITED—See AIREA PLC; *Int'l*, pg. 247
BURMATEX SP. Z.O.O.—See AIREA PLC; *Int'l*, pg. 247
BURMAX COMPANY INC.; *U.S. Private*, pg. 689
BURMEISTER & WAIN ENERGY A/S—See STF S.p.A; *Int'l*, pg. 7213
BURMEISTER & WAIN SCANDINAVIAN CONTRACTOR A/S—See Mitsui E&S Holdings Co., Ltd.; *Int'l*, pg. 4984
BURNAC CORPORATION; *Int'l*, pg. 1226
BURNAM HOLDING COMPANIES INC; *U.S. Private*, pg. 689
BURNBRIDGE GLASS PTY LIMITED—See CSR Limited; *Int'l*, pg. 1867
BURN BRITE LIGHTS PTY. LTD.—See Washington H. Soul Pattinson & Company Limited; *Int'l*, pg. 8351
BURNCO COLORADO, LLC—See Burnco Rock Products Ltd; *Int'l*, pg. 1226

BURNCO ROCK PRODUCTS LTD

BURNCO ROCK PRODUCTS LTD; *Int'l*, pg. 1226
BURNDY CANADA INC.—See Hubbell Incorporated; *U.S. Public*, pg. 1066
BURNDY DO BRASIL INDUSTRIA, COMERCIO, IMPORTACAO E EXPORTACAO DE CONECTORES LTDA.—See Hubbell Incorporated; *U.S. Public*, pg. 1066
BURNDY LLC—See Hubbell Incorporated; *U.S. Public*, pg. 1066
BURNDY PRODUCTS MEXICO, S.A. DE C.V.—See Hubbell Incorporated; *U.S. Public*, pg. 1066
BURNED MEDIA LTD.; *U.S. Public*, pg. 412
BURNES GROUP—See Cerberus Capital Management, L.P.; *U.S. Private*, pg. 837
BURNESS, CORLETT THREE QUAYS LTD.—See Oceanic Investment Corporation; *Int'l*, pg. 5518
BURNETT & CO. INC.; *U.S. Private*, pg. 689
THE BURNETT COMPANIES CONSOLIDATED INC.; *U.S. Private*, pg. 4003
BURNETT DAIRY COOP ASSOCIATION; *U.S. Private*, pg. 689
BURNETTE FOODS INC.; *U.S. Private*, pg. 689
BURNET TITLE LLC—See Anywhere Real Estate Inc.; *U.S. Public*, pg. 142
BURNET TITLE OF INDIANA, LLC—See Anywhere Real Estate Inc.; *U.S. Public*, pg. 142
BURNETT MEDICAL CENTER; *U.S. Private*, pg. 689
BURNEY DIALYSIS, LLC—See DaVita Inc.; *U.S. Public*, pg. 636
BURNHAM ASSET MANAGEMENT CORP.; *U.S. Private*, pg. 689
BURNHAM BENEFIT ADVISORS—See Genstar Capital, LLC; *U.S. Private*, pg. 1674
BURNHAM BENEFITS INSURANCE SERVICES, INC.; *U.S. Private*, pg. 689
BURNHAM HOLDINGS, INC.; *U.S. Public*, pg. 412
BURNHAM INDUSTRIAL CONTRACTORS INC.; *U.S. Private*, pg. 689
BURNHAM INSULATION SALES, INC.—See Dunes Point Capital, LLC; *U.S. Private*, pg. 1289
BURNHAM RICHARDS ADVERTISING; *U.S. Private*, pg. 689
BURNHAM WORLD FORWARDERS INC.—See Stevens Group, Inc.; *U.S. Private*, pg. 3809
BURNING MAN PROJECT; *U.S. Private*, pg. 689
BURNING ROCK BIOTECH LIMITED; *Int'l*, pg. 1226
BURNIPS EQUIPMENT COMPANY; *U.S. Private*, pg. 689
BURNISHINE PRODUCTS—See TA Associates, Inc.; *U.S. Private*, pg. 3919
BURNISHINE PRODUCTS—See The Carlyle Group Inc.; *U.S. Public*, pg. 2057
BURNPUR CEMENT LIMITED; *Int'l*, pg. 1226
BURNS360; *U.S. Private*, pg. 691
BURNS BROS. CONTRACTORS, INC.; *U.S. Private*, pg. 690
BURNS BROS., INC.; *U.S. Private*, pg. 690
BURNS BUICK-GMC-HYUNDAI-HONDA; *U.S. Private*, pg. 691
BURNS CONTROLS COMPANY; *U.S. Private*, pg. 691
BURNS FORD INC.; *U.S. Private*, pg. 691
BURNSIDE RV CENTERS, LLC—See Camping World Holdings, Inc.; *U.S. Public*, pg. 427
BURNSIDE WAR MEMORIAL HOSPITAL INC.; *Int'l*, pg. 1226
BURNS INDUSTRIAL EQUIPMENT, INC.; *U.S. Private*, pg. 691
BURNS & MCBRIDE INC.—See Morgan Stanley; *U.S. Public*, pg. 1474
BURNS MCCLELLAN, INC.; *U.S. Private*, pg. 691
BURNS & MCDONNELL, INC.; *U.S. Private*, pg. 689
BURNS MECHANICAL, INC.—See Riverstone Holdings LLC; *U.S. Private*, pg. 3447
BURNS MOTOR FREIGHT INC.; *U.S. Private*, pg. 691
BURN; *Int'l*, pg. 1226
BURNS & SCALO NORTH CAROLINA, INC.—See Burns & Scalo Roofing Co., Inc.; *U.S. Private*, pg. 690
BURNS & SCALO OHIO, INC.—See Burns & Scalo Roofing Co., Inc.; *U.S. Private*, pg. 690
BURNS & SCALO ROOFING CO., INC.; *U.S. Private*, pg. 690
BURNSTAD BROTHERS, INC.; *U.S. Private*, pg. 691
BURNSTEAD CONSTRUCTION COMPANY; *U.S. Private*, pg. 691
BURNS TIMES-HERALD—See Survival Media LLC; *U.S. Private*, pg. 3885
BURNSVILLE SANITARY LANDFILL, INC.—See Waste Management, Inc.; *U.S. Public*, pg. 2330
BURNS & WILCOX CANADA—See H.W. Kaufman Financial Group, Inc.; *U.S. Private*, pg. 1836
BURNS & WILCOX LIMITED—See Arch Capital Group Ltd.; *Int'l*, pg. 547
BURNS & WILCOX LTD.—See H.W. Kaufman Financial Group, Inc.; *U.S. Private*, pg. 1836
BURNS & WILCOX LTD.—See H.W. Kaufman Financial Group, Inc.; *U.S. Private*, pg. 1836
BURNS & WILCOX OF SAN FRANCISCO—See H.W. Kaufman Financial Group, Inc.; *U.S. Private*, pg. 1836
BURNS & WILCOX—See H.W. Kaufman Financial Group, Inc.; *U.S. Private*, pg. 1836

BURNS & WILCOX—See H.W. Kaufman Financial Group, Inc.; *U.S. Private*, pg. 1836
BURNT CHURCH PRIMARY & URGENT CARE, L.L.C.—See Tenet Healthcare Corporation; *U.S. Public*, pg. 2008
BURNT STORE MARINA, INC.—See PGI Incorporated; *U.S. Public*, pg. 1684
BURNWELL GAS OF CANADA LTD.—See Superior Plus Corp.; *Int'l*, pg. 7338
BURN & WILCOX LTD.—See H.W. Kaufman Financial Group, Inc.; *U.S. Private*, pg. 1836
BUROGEBAUDE DARMSTADTER LANDSTRASSE GMBH & CO. KG—See Helaba Landesbank Hessen-Thuringen; *Int'l*, pg. 3327
BURO HAPPOLD APS—See Buro Happold Engineers Limited; *Int'l*, pg. 1226
BURO HAPPOLD CONSULTING ENGINEERS (BEIJING) LIMITED—See Buro Happold Engineers Limited; *Int'l*, pg. 1226
BURO HAPPOLD CONSULTING ENGINEERS, INC.—See Buro Happold Engineers Limited; *Int'l*, pg. 1226
BURO HAPPOLD CONSULTING ENGINEERS LIMITED—See Buro Happold Engineers Limited; *Int'l*, pg. 1226
BURO HAPPOLD ENGINEERS INDIA PVT. LTD.—See Buro Happold Engineers Limited; *Int'l*, pg. 1226
BURO HAPPOLD ENGINEERS LIMITED; *Int'l*, pg. 1226
BURO HAPPOLD INTERNATIONAL (HONG KONG) LIMITED—See Buro Happold Engineers Limited; *Int'l*, pg. 1226
BURO HAPPOLD LIMITED—See Buro Happold Engineers Limited; *Int'l*, pg. 1226
BURO HAPPOLD & PARTNER FOR ENGINEERING CONSULTANCY CO—See Buro Happold Engineers Limited; *Int'l*, pg. 1226
BURO HAPPOLD POLSKA SP. Z O.O.—See Buro Happold Engineers Limited; *Int'l*, pg. 1226
BURO SCANDINAVIA B.V.—See STENA AB; *Int'l*, pg. 7207
BUROSITZMOBELFABRIK FRIEDRICH- W. DAUPHIN GMBH & CO. KG—See Dauphin HumanDesign Group GmbH & Co. KG; *Int'l*, pg. 1982
BUROTECH LIMITED—See Samson Paper Holdings Limited; *Int'l*, pg. 6509
BURRELL CENTER; *U.S. Private*, pg. 691
BURRELL COLOUR INC.—See Jasco Tools Inc.; *U.S. Private*, pg. 2189
BURRELL COMMUNICATIONS GROUP, LLC - ATLANTA—See FVLCRUM PARTNERS LLC; *U.S. Private*, pg. 1628
BURRELL COMMUNICATIONS GROUP, LLC—See FVLCRUM PARTNERS LLC; *U.S. Private*, pg. 1628
BURRELLE'S INFORMATION SERVICES LLC; *U.S. Private*, pg. 691
BURRELL MINING PRODUCTS INC.; *U.S. Private*, pg. 691
BURRELL MINING PRODUCTS INC. UTAH—See Burrell Mining Products Inc.; *U.S. Private*, pg. 691
BURREN ENERGY—See Eni S.p.A.; *Int'l*, pg. 2437
BURR & FORMAN LLP; *U.S. Private*, pg. 691
BURRIEL NAVARRO S.L.—See Wartsila Corporation; *Int'l*, pg. 8346
BURRIS EQUIPMENT CO—See Alta Equipment Group Inc.; *U.S. Public*, pg. 86
BURRIS LOGISTICS; *U.S. Private*, pg. 691
BURROAKCOMMONSPLUS, LLC—See Welltower Inc.; *U.S. Public*, pg. 2348
BURROUGHS & CHAPIN CO. INC.; *U.S. Private*, pg. 692
BURROUGHS, INC.—See Marlin Equity Partners, LLC; *U.S. Private*, pg. 2584
BURROUGHS WELLCOME (INDIA) LTD.—See GSK plc; *Int'l*, pg. 3145
BURROW GLOBAL, LLC; *U.S. Private*, pg. 692
BURROWS NETHERLANDS B.V.—See Burrows Paper Corporation; *U.S. Private*, pg. 692
BURROWS PAPER CORPORATION; *U.S. Private*, pg. 692
BURROWS SHENFIELD—See WPP plc; *Int'l*, pg. 8478
BURR, PILGER & MAYER LLP; *U.S. Private*, pg. 691
BURRTEC WASTE INDUSTRIES, INC.; *U.S. Private*, pg. 692
BURRUS INVESTMENT GROUP INC.; *U.S. Private*, pg. 692
BURRUS & MATTHEWS, INC.; *U.S. Private*, pg. 692
BURRY FOODS; *U.S. Private*, pg. 692
BURSA ARES CEVRE VE ENERJI TEKNOLOJILERI SANAYI VE TICARET A.S.—See Bursa Cimento Fabrikasi A.S.; *Int'l*, pg. 1226
BURSA BETON A.S.—See Bursa Cimento Fabrikasi A.S.; *Int'l*, pg. 1226
BURSA BETON SANAYI TICARET A.S.—See Bursa Cimento Fabrikasi A.S.; *Int'l*, pg. 1226
BURSA CIMENTO FABRIKASI A.S.; *Int'l*, pg. 1226
BURSA DE VALORI BUCURESTI; *Int'l*, pg. 1227
BURSAGAZ BURSA SEHIRICI DOGALGAZ DAGITIM TICARET VE TAAHHUT A.S.—See EWE Aktiengesellschaft; *Int'l*, pg. 2575
BURSA MALAYSIA BERHAD; *Int'l*, pg. 1227

CORPORATE AFFILIATIONS

BURSA MALAYSIA DERIVATIVES BERHAD—See Bursa Malaysia Berhad; *Int'l*, pg. 1227
BURSA MALAYSIA INFORMATION SDN BHD—See Bursa Malaysia Berhad; *Int'l*, pg. 1227
BURSA MALAYSIA IT SDN BHD—See Bursa Malaysia Berhad; *Int'l*, pg. 1227
BURSA MALAYSIA PROPERTY SDN BHD—See Bursa Malaysia Berhad; *Int'l*, pg. 1227
BURSCH TRAVEL AGENCY, INC.; *U.S. Private*, pg. 692
BURSCH TRAVEL - SHERIDAN—See Bursch Travel Agency, Inc.; *U.S. Private*, pg. 692
BURSEI DE VALORI A MOLDOVEI; *Int'l*, pg. 1227
BURSERYDS BRUK AB—See Illinois Tool Works Inc.; *U.S. Public*, pg. 1102
BURSICH ASSOCIATES, INC.—See Bursich Associates, Inc.; *U.S. Private*, pg. 692
BURSICH ASSOCIATES, INC.; *U.S. Private*, pg. 692
BURSON COHN & WOLFE AG—See WPP plc; *Int'l*, pg. 8467
BURSON COHN & WOLFE AG- ZWEIGNIEDERLASSUNG BERN—See WPP plc; *Int'l*, pg. 8467
BURSON COHN & WOLFE—See WPP plc; *Int'l*, pg. 8467
BURSON-MARSTELLER AB—See WPP plc; *Int'l*, pg. 8468
BURSON-MARSTELLER AG - GENEVA—See WPP plc; *Int'l*, pg. 8467
BURSON-MARSTELLER A/S—See WPP plc; *Int'l*, pg. 8468
BURSON-MARSTELLER - CHICAGO—See WPP plc; *Int'l*, pg. 8468
BURSON-MARSTELLER GMBH - BERLIN—See WPP plc; *Int'l*, pg. 8468
BURSON-MARSTELLER GMBH—See WPP plc; *Int'l*, pg. 8468
BURSON-MARSTELLER (HONG KONG) LIMITED—See WPP plc; *Int'l*, pg. 8468
BURSON-MARSTELLER, LLC—See WPP plc; *Int'l*, pg. 8467
BURSON-MARSTELLER LLC—See WPP plc; *Int'l*, pg. 8468
BURSON-MARSTELLER, LTDA.—See WPP plc; *Int'l*, pg. 8468
BURSON-MARSTELLER LTD.—See WPP plc; *Int'l*, pg. 8468
BURSON-MARSTELLER MEXICO, S.A. DE C.V.—See WPP plc; *Int'l*, pg. 8468
BURSON-MARSTELLER PTY. LTD. - MELBOURNE—See WPP plc; *Int'l*, pg. 8468
BURSON-MARSTELLER PTY. LTD.—See WPP plc; *Int'l*, pg. 8468
BURSON-MARSTELLER S.A./N.V.—See WPP plc; *Int'l*, pg. 8468
BURSON-MARSTELLER, S.A.—See WPP plc; *Int'l*, pg. 8468
BURSON-MARSTELLER, S.A.—See WPP plc; *Int'l*, pg. 8468
BURSON-MARSTELLER (SEA) PTE. LTD.—See WPP plc; *Int'l*, pg. 8468
BURSON-MARSTELLER—See WPP plc; *Int'l*, pg. 8467
BURSON-MARSTELLER—See WPP plc; *Int'l*, pg. 8467
BURSON-MARSTELLER—See WPP plc; *Int'l*, pg. 8467
BURSON-MARSTELLER—See WPP plc; *Int'l*, pg. 8467
BURSON-MARSTELLER—See WPP plc; *Int'l*, pg. 8467
BURSON-MARSTELLER—See WPP plc; *Int'l*, pg. 8467
BURSON-MARSTELLER—See WPP plc; *Int'l*, pg. 8467
BURSON-MARSTELLER—See WPP plc; *Int'l*, pg. 8467
BURSON-MARSTELLER—See WPP plc; *Int'l*, pg. 8468
BURSON-MARSTELLER—See WPP plc; *Int'l*, pg. 8467
BURSON-MARSTELLER—See WPP plc; *Int'l*, pg. 8467
BURSON-MARSTELLER—See WPP plc; *Int'l*, pg. 8468
BURSON-MARSTELLER—See WPP plc; *Int'l*, pg. 8467
BURSON-MARSTELLER S.R.L.—See WPP plc; *Int'l*, pg. 8468
BURSON-MARSTELLER S.R.L.—See WPP plc; *Int'l*, pg. 8468
BURSON-MARSTELLER - WASHINGTON—See WPP plc; *Int'l*, pg. 8468
BURST COMMUNICATIONS INC.; *U.S. Private*, pg. 692
BURST MEDIA CORPORATION LTD.—See Nexxen International Ltd.; *Int'l*, pg. 5251
BURST MEDIA CORPORATION—See Nexxen International Ltd.; *Int'l*, pg. 5251
BURSTNER GMBH & CO. KG—See Thor Industries, Inc.; *U.S. Public*, pg. 2156
BURT BOULTON & HAYWOOD LTD.—See Iivari Mononen Oy; *Int'l*, pg. 3608
BURT BROTHERS TIRE & SERVICE, INC.; *U.S. Private*, pg. 692
BURT-BURNETT, INC.—See Fiat Incorporated; *U.S. Private*, pg. 1501
BURTCO, INC.; *U.S. Private*, pg. 692
BURTECH ACQUISITION CORP.; *U.S. Public*, pg. 412
BURTECK LLC—See Ningbo Tianlong Electronics Co., Ltd.; *Int'l*, pg. 5306
BURTEK ENTERPRISES, INC.—See Stone River Capital Partners, LLC; *U.S. Private*, pg. 3826
BURTEK ENTERPRISES, INC.—See Wynnchurch Capital, L.P.; *U.S. Private*, pg. 4577

COMPANY NAME INDEX

BURTIS MOTOR COMPANY, INC.; *U.S. Private*, pg. 692
BURT LEWIS INTERNATIONAL CORP; *U.S. Private*, pg. 692
BURTNESS CHEVROLET, INC.; *U.S. Private*, pg. 692
BURTNESS CHEVROLET OF WHITEWATER—See Burtness Chevrolet, Inc.; *U.S. Private*, pg. 692
BURTON BANCSHARES, INC.; *U.S. Private*, pg. 693
BURTON BROTHERS GENERAL CONTRACTORS LC; *U.S. Private*, pg. 693
BURTON CAROL MANAGEMENT, LLC; *U.S. Private*, pg. 693
BURTON COAL PTY LTD—See Peabody Energy Corporation; *U.S. Public*, pg. 1659
BURTON ENERGY GROUP; *U.S. Private*, pg. 693
BURTON F CLARK INC.; *U.S. Private*, pg. 693
THE BURTON FOUNDATION; *U.S. Private*, pg. 4003
BURTON INDUSTRIES INC.; *U.S. Private*, pg. 693
BURTON LUMBER CORP.; *U.S. Private*, pg. 693
BURTON LUMBER & HARDWARE CO.; *U.S. Private*, pg. 693
BURTON MCCALL LIMITED—See Bollin Group Ltd.; *Int'l*, pg. 1103
BURTON MEDICAL PRODUCTS CORPORATION—See Koninklijke Philips N.V.; *Int'l*, pg. 4269
BURTON'S FOODS LTD.—See Ontario Teachers' Pension Plan; *Int'l*, pg. 5587
BURTON SIGNWORKS, INC.; *U.S. Private*, pg. 693
BURTONS INC.; *U.S. Private*, pg. 693
BURTON SNOWBOARD COMPANY; *U.S. Private*, pg. 693
BURTON STATE BANK—See Burton Bancshares, Inc.; *U.S. Private*, pg. 693
BURT PROCESS EQUIPMENT INC.; *U.S. Private*, pg. 692
BURTRONICS BUSINESS SYSTEMS, INC.; *U.S. Private*, pg. 693
BURT'S BEES INC.—See The Clorox Company; *U.S. Public*, pg. 2062
BURU ENERGY LIMITED; *Int'l*, pg. 1227
BURU FITZROY PTY LIMITED—See Buru Energy Limited; *Int'l*, pg. 1227
BURUJ COOPERATIVE INSURANCE COMPANY; *Int'l*, pg. 1227
BURWILL HOLDINGS LIMITED; *Int'l*, pg. 1227
BURWILL RESOURCES LIMITED—See Burwill Holdings Limited; *Int'l*, pg. 1227
BURWILL STEEL PIPES LIMITED—See Burwill Holdings Limited; *Int'l*, pg. 1227
BURWOOD GROUP INC.; *U.S. Private*, pg. 693
BURWOOD MAZDA PTY. LIMITED—See Peter Warren Automotive Holdings Ltd.; *Int'l*, pg. 5824
BURZA CENNYCH PAPIEROV V BRATISLAVE, A.S.; *Int'l*, pg. 1227
BURZA CENNYCH PAPIRU PRAHA, A.S.—See CEESEG AG; *Int'l*, pg. 1389
BURZYNSKI RESEARCH INSTITUTE, INC.; *U.S. Public*, pg. 412
BUSAN BANK, LTD.—See BNK Financial Group Inc.; *Int'l*, pg. 1079
BUSAN CITY GAS CO., LTD.—See SK Innovation Co., Ltd.; *Int'l*, pg. 6973
BUSAN CREDIT & INFORMATION CO., LTD.—See BNK Financial Group Inc.; *Int'l*, pg. 1079
BUSAN INDUSTRIAL CO., LTD.; *Int'l*, pg. 1227
BUSAN JUNGKWAN ENERGY CO., LTD.—See SK Inc.; *Int'l*, pg. 6971
BUSBAR SYSTEMS (INDIA) LIMITED—See Godrej & Boyce Mfg. Co. Ltd.; *Int'l*, pg. 3020
BUSBY WEB SOLUTIONS PTY. LTD.—See Hire Intelligence International Limited; *Int'l*, pg. 3404
BUSCANDO RESOURCES CORP.; *Int'l*, pg. 1227
BUSCAR CO.; *U.S. Public*, pg. 413
BUSCH AGRICULTURAL RESOURCES, INC.—See Anheuser-Busch InBev SA/NV; *Int'l*, pg. 465
BUSCH AG—See Dr. Ing. K. Busch GmbH; *Int'l*, pg. 2192
BUSCH ARGENTINA S.R.L.—See Dr. Ing. K. Busch GmbH; *Int'l*, pg. 2192
BUSCH AUSTRALIA PTY. LTD.—See Dr. Ing. K. Busch GmbH; *Int'l*, pg. 2192
BUSCH AUSTRIA GMBH—See Dr. Ing. K. Busch GmbH; *Int'l*, pg. 2193
BUSCH B.V.—See Dr. Ing. K. Busch GmbH; *Int'l*, pg. 2192
BUSCH CHILE S.A.—See Dr. Ing. K. Busch GmbH; *Int'l*, pg. 2192
BUSCH CLEAN AIR S.A.—See Dr. Ing. K. Busch GmbH; *Int'l*, pg. 2192
BUSCH COLOMBIA SAS—See Dr. Ing. K. Busch GmbH; *Int'l*, pg. 2192
BUSCH DISTRIBUTORS INC.; *U.S. Private*, pg. 693
BUSCH DO BRASIL LTDA.—See Dr. Ing. K. Busch GmbH; *Int'l*, pg. 2193
BUSCHE PERFORMANCE GROUP, INC.; *U.S. Private*, pg. 693
BUSCHE SOUTHFIELD, INC.—See Busche Performance Group, Inc.; *U.S. Private*, pg. 693
BUSCH FRANCE S.A.S.—See Dr. Ing. K. Busch GmbH; *Int'l*, pg. 2192
BUSCH GARDENS TAMPA BAY—See United Parks & Resorts Inc.; *U.S. Public*, pg. 2234
BUSCH GARDENS WILLIAMSBURG—See United Parks & Resorts Inc.; *U.S. Public*, pg. 2234
BUSCH GVT LTD.—See Dr. Ing. K. Busch GmbH; *Int'l*, pg. 2192
BUSCH IRELAND LTD.—See Dr. Ing. K. Busch GmbH; *Int'l*, pg. 2193
BUSCH ISRAEL LTD.—See Dr. Ing. K. Busch GmbH; *Int'l*, pg. 2193
BUSCH ITALIA S.R.L.—See Dr. Ing. K. Busch GmbH; *Int'l*, pg. 2193
BUSCH-JAEGER ELEKTRO GMBH—See ABB Ltd.; *Int'l*, pg. 50
BUSCHJOST GMBH—See IMI plc; *Int'l*, pg. 3624
BUSCH KOREA LTD.—See Dr. Ing. K. Busch GmbH; *Int'l*, pg. 2193
BUSCH LBERICA S.A.—See Dr. Ing. K. Busch GmbH; *Int'l*, pg. 2193
BUSCH LLC - MORGAN HILL—See Dr. Ing. K. Busch GmbH; *Int'l*, pg. 2193
BUSCH LLC—See Dr. Ing. K. Busch GmbH; *Int'l*, pg. 2193
BUSCH MALAYSIA SDN BHD—See Dr. Ing. K. Busch GmbH; *Int'l*, pg. 2193
BUSCH MANUFACTURING KOREA LTD.—See Dr. Ing. K. Busch GmbH; *Int'l*, pg. 2193
BUSCH MANUFACTURING LLC—See Dr. Ing. K. Busch GmbH; *Int'l*, pg. 2193
BUSCH NEW ZEALAND LTD.—See Dr. Ing. K. Busch GmbH; *Int'l*, pg. 2193
BUSCH N.V.—See Dr. Ing. K. Busch GmbH; *Int'l*, pg. 2193
BUSCH PERU SRL—See Dr. Ing. K. Busch GmbH; *Int'l*, pg. 2193
BUSCH POLSKA SP. Z O.O.—See Dr. Ing. K. Busch GmbH; *Int'l*, pg. 2193
BUSCH PROPERTIES, INC.—See Anheuser-Busch InBev SA/NV; *Int'l*, pg. 465
BUSCHS INC.; *U.S. Private*, pg. 693
BUSCH TAIWAN CORPORATION—See Dr. Ing. K. Busch GmbH; *Int'l*, pg. 2193
BUSCH (UK) LTD.—See Dr. Ing. K. Busch GmbH; *Int'l*, pg. 2192
BUSCH VACUUM FZE—See Dr. Ing. K. Busch GmbH; *Int'l*, pg. 2193
BUSCH VACUUM INDIA PVT LTD.—See Dr. Ing. K. Busch GmbH; *Int'l*, pg. 2193
BUSCH VACUUM KFT.—See Dr. Ing. K. Busch GmbH; *Int'l*, pg. 2193
BUSCH VACUUM MEXICO S DE R.L. DE C.V—See Dr. Ing. K. Busch GmbH; *Int'l*, pg. 2193
BUSCH VACUUM RUSSIA OOO—See Dr. Ing. K. Busch GmbH; *Int'l*, pg. 2193
BUSCH VACUUM (SHANGHAI) CO. LTD.—See Dr. Ing. K. Busch GmbH; *Int'l*, pg. 2193
BUSCH VACUUM SINGAPORE PTE. LTD.—See Dr. Ing. K. Busch GmbH; *Int'l*, pg. 2193
BUSCH VACUUM SOUTH AFRICA (PTY) LTD.—See Dr. Ing. K. Busch GmbH; *Int'l*, pg. 2193
BUSCH VACUUM TECHNICS INC.—See Dr. Ing. K. Busch GmbH; *Int'l*, pg. 2193
BUSCH VACUUM (THAILAND) CO. LTD.—See Dr. Ing. K. Busch GmbH; *Int'l*, pg. 2193
BUSCH VAKUUM S.R.O.—See Dr. Ing. K. Busch GmbH; *Int'l*, pg. 2193
BUSCH VAKUUMTEKNIK AB—See Dr. Ing. K. Busch GmbH; *Int'l*, pg. 2193
BUSCH VAKUUMTEKNIK AS—See Dr. Ing. K. Busch GmbH; *Int'l*, pg. 2193
BUSCH VAKUUMTEKNIK OY—See Dr. Ing. K. Busch GmbH; *Int'l*, pg. 2193
BUSCO INC.; *U.S. Private*, pg. 693
BUS COMMUNICATIONS PTY LTD—See CSE Global Ltd.; *Int'l*, pg. 1863
BUSCOTRADE D.O.O.—See Quaser Machine Tools, Inc.; *Int'l*, pg. 6156
THE BUS DEPOT, INC.—See GTJ REIT, Inc.; *U.S. Private*, pg. 1807
BUSEY BANK—See First Busey Corporation; *U.S. Public*, pg. 840
BUSEY CAPITAL MANAGEMENT, INC.—See First Busey Corporation; *U.S. Public*, pg. 840
THE BUSEY GROUP; *U.S. Private*, pg. 4003
BUSEY WEALTH MANAGEMENT, INC.—See First Busey Corporation; *U.S. Public*, pg. 840
BUS FOCUS LTD.—See Xynomic Pharmaceuticals Holdings, Inc.; *Int'l*, pg. 8542
BUSH AND ROE FINANCIAL, INC.—See Madison County Financial, Inc.; *U.S. Public*, pg. 1353
BUSH AUSTRALIA PTY LIMITED—See Harvard International Inc.; *Int'l*, pg. 3280
BUSH AUTO PLACE INC.; *U.S. Private*, pg. 693
BUSH BOAKE ALLEN DO BRASIL INDUSTRIA E COMERCIO LTDA.—See International Flavors & Fragrances Inc.; *U.S. Public*, pg. 1151
BUSHBREAKS & MORE PROPRIETARY LIMITED—See The Bidvest Group Limited; *Int'l*, pg. 7623
BUSH BROTHERS & COMPANY PLANT—See Bush Brothers & Company; *U.S. Private*, pg. 694
BUSH BROTHERS & COMPANY; *U.S. Private*, pg. 693
BUSH COMMUNICATIONS, LLC; *U.S. Private*, pg. 694

BUSINESS CENTRIC SERVICES GROUP

BUSH & COMPANY REHABILITATION LIMITED—See NAHL Group plc; *Int'l*, pg. 5130
THE BUSH COMPANY; *U.S. Private*, pg. 4003
BUSH CONSTRUCTION COMPANY, INC.—See McCarthy Bush Corporation; *U.S. Private*, pg. 2626
BUSH EQUITIES; *U.S. Private*, pg. 694
BUSH EUROPE LTD.—See Novacap Management Inc.; *Int'l*, pg. 5453
BUSH HOG, INC.—See Alamo Group Inc.; *U.S. Public*, pg. 71
BUSH INC.; *U.S. Private*, pg. 694
BUSH INDUSTRIES INC.—See Novacap Management Inc.; *Int'l*, pg. 5453
BUSHIROAD CREATIVE, INC.—See Bushiroad, Inc.; *Int'l*, pg. 1227
BUSHIROAD, INC.; *Int'l*, pg. 1227
BUSHIROAD INTERNATIONAL PTE. LTD.—See Bushiroad, Inc.; *Int'l*, pg. 1227
BUSHIROAD MEDIA, INC.—See Bushiroad, Inc.; *Int'l*, pg. 1227
BUSHIROAD MUSIC, INC.—See Bushiroad, Inc.; *Int'l*, pg. 1227
BUSHIROAD USA INC.—See Bushiroad, Inc.; *Int'l*, pg. 1227
BUSHLANDS GAME LODGE—See Gooderson Leisure Corporation; *Int'l*, pg. 3039
BUSHMASTER EXPLORATION SERVICES (2007) LTD.—See Triumph Gold Corp.; *Int'l*, pg. 7936
BUSHNELL CORPORATION OF CANADA—See Vista Outdoor Inc.; *U.S. Public*, pg. 2304
BUSHNELL OUTDOOR PRODUCTS, INC.—See Vista Outdoor Inc.; *U.S. Public*, pg. 2304
BUSHNELL OUTDOOR PRODUCTS JAPAN LIMITED—See Vista Outdoor Inc.; *U.S. Public*, pg. 2304
BUSHNELL OUTDOOR PRODUCTS SAS—See Vista Outdoor Inc.; *U.S. Public*, pg. 2304
BUSHNELL OUTDOOR PRODUCTS SPAIN, S.A.U.—See Vista Outdoor Inc.; *U.S. Public*, pg. 2304
BUSHNELL PERFORMANCE OPTICS ASIA LIMITED—See Vista Outdoor Inc.; *U.S. Public*, pg. 2305
BUSHNELL PERFORMANCE OPTICS GERMANY GMBH—See Vista Outdoor Inc.; *U.S. Public*, pg. 2305
BUSHNELL PERFORMANCE OPTICS ITALY S.R.L.—See Vista Outdoor Inc.; *U.S. Public*, pg. 2305
BUSHNELL PERFORMANCE OPTICS MEXICO S.A. DE C.V.—See Vista Outdoor Inc.; *U.S. Public*, pg. 2305
BUSHNELL PERFORMANCE OPTICS UK LIMITED—See Vista Outdoor Inc.; *U.S. Public*, pg. 2305
BUSH O'DONNELL & CO., INC.; *U.S. Private*, pg. 694
BUSH O'DONNELL INVESTMENT ADVISORS, INC.—See Bush O'Donnell & Co., Inc.; *U.S. Private*, pg. 694
BUSH SUPPLY COMPANY—See Border States Industries, Inc.; *U.S. Private*, pg. 618
BUSHU DISTRIBUTION CO., LTD.—See Lion Corporation; *Int'l*, pg. 4517
BUSHU PHARMACEUTICALS LTD. - MISATO PLANT—See EQT AB; *Int'l*, pg. 2469
BUSHU PHARMACEUTICALS LTD.—See EQT AB; *Int'l*, pg. 2469
BUSHVELD ENERGY COMPANY (PTY) LIMITED—See Bushveld Minerals Limited; *Int'l*, pg. 1228
BUSHVELD MINERALS LIMITED; *Int'l*, pg. 1228
BUSHWICK METALS LLC - BINGHAMTON DIVISION—See Berkshire Hathaway Inc.; *U.S. Public*, pg. 309
BUSHWICK METALS, LLC—See Berkshire Hathaway Inc.; *U.S. Public*, pg. 309
BUSHWICK STUYVESANT HEIGHTS HOME ATTENDANTS, INC.; *U.S. Private*, pg. 694
BUSICA LTD.—See Forval Corporation; *Int'l*, pg. 2745
BUSI GROUP S.R.L.; *Int'l*, pg. 1228
BUSINESS ACTIVE—See Publicis Groupe S.A.; *Int'l*, pg. 6108
BUSINESS ADVERTISING GMBH—See Stroer SE & Co. KGaA; *Int'l*, pg. 7241
BUSINESS ADVISORY SERVICE LIMITED—See Smarter Business Limited; *Int'l*, pg. 7002
BUSINESS ALIGNMENT PUBLIC COMPANY LIMITED; *Int'l*, pg. 1228
BUSINESS ALLIANCE JSC; *Int'l*, pg. 1228
BUSINESS ANCHOR CORPORATION—See Chori Co., Ltd.; *Int'l*, pg. 1583
BUSINESS ASPECT (ACT) PTY LTD—See Data#3 Limited; *Int'l*, pg. 1977
BUSINESS ASPECT PTY LTD—See Data#3 Limited; *Int'l*, pg. 1977
THE BUSINESS BACKER, LLC—See Enova International, Inc.; *U.S. Public*, pg. 770
BUSINESS BRAIN SHOWA-OTA INC.; *Int'l*, pg. 1228
BUSINESS BREAKTHROUGH, INC.; *Int'l*, pg. 1228
BUSINESS BROKERS OF SAN ANTONIO; *U.S. Private*, pg. 694
BUSINESS CARD SERVICE INC.; *U.S. Private*, pg. 694
BUSINESS CAROLINA, INC.—See United Community Banks, Inc.; *U.S. Public*, pg. 2230
BUSINESS CENTRIC SERVICES GROUP; *Int'l*, pg. 1228

BUSINESS CENTRIC SERVICES GROUP / CORPORATE AFFILIATIONS

BUSINESSCLICK SP. Z O.O.—See Wirtualna Polska Holding S.A.; *Int'l*, pg. 8434
BUSINESS COMMUNICATIONS, INC.; *U.S. Private*, pg. 694
BUSINESS COMMUNICATIONS MANAGEMENT, INC; *U.S. Private*, pg. 694
BUSINESS COMMUNICATIONS SYSTEMS, INC.—See Center For Computer Resources, LLC; *U.S. Private*, pg. 810
BUSINESS CONNEXION COMMUNICATIONS (PTY) LIMITED—See Business Connexion Group Limited; *Int'l*, pg. 1228
BUSINESS CONNEXION GROUP LIMITED; *Int'l*, pg. 1228
BUSINESS CONNEXION LIMITED—See Business Connexion Group Limited; *Int'l*, pg. 1228
BUSINESS CONNEXION MOZAMBIQUE LIMITADA—See Business Connexion Group Limited; *Int'l*, pg. 1228
BUSINESS CONNEXION NAMIBIA (PTY) LIMITED—See Business Connexion Group Limited; *Int'l*, pg. 1228
BUSINESS CONNEXION NETWORKS (NIGERIA) LIMITED—See Business Connexion Group Limited; *Int'l*, pg. 1228
BUSINESS CONNEXION (PTY) LIMITED—See Business Connexion Group Limited; *Int'l*, pg. 1228
BUSINESS CONNEXION TANZANIA LIMITED—See Business Connexion Group Limited; *Int'l*, pg. 1228
BUSINESS CONNEXION TECHNOLOGY HOLDINGS (PTY) LIMITED—See Business Connexion Group Limited; *Int'l*, pg. 1228
BUSINESS CONSULTING GROUP, INC.; *U.S. Private*, pg. 694
BUSINESS CONTROL SYSTEMS LP; *U.S. Private*, pg. 694
BUSINESS DATA LTD.—See The Interpublic Group of Companies, Inc.; *U.S. Public*, pg. 2092
BUSINESS & DECISION AG—See Orange S.A.; *Int'l*, pg. 5608
BUSINESS & DECISION BENELUX SA—See Orange S.A.; *Int'l*, pg. 5608
BUSINESS & DECISION NETHERLANDS BV—See Orange S.A.; *Int'l*, pg. 5608
BUSINESS & DECISION SA—See Orange S.A.; *Int'l*, pg. 5607
BUSINESS & DECISION SOFTWARE INDIA (P) LTD—See Orange S.A.; *Int'l*, pg. 5608
BUSINESS DEVELOPMENT ASIA LLC; *U.S. Private*, pg. 694
BUSINESS DEVELOPMENT BANK OF CANADA; *Int'l*, pg. 1228
BUSINESS DEVELOPMENT CORPORATION OF SOUTH CAROLINA—See Wells Fargo & Company; *U.S. Public*, pg. 2343
BUSINESS DEVELOPMENT SALES; *U.S. Private*, pg. 694
BUSINESS ELECTRONICS CORP.—See R.J. Young Co., Inc.; *U.S. Private*, pg. 3337
BUSINESS ELECTRONICS SOLDERING TECHNOLOGIES; *U.S. Private*, pg. 694
BUSINESS ELEMENTS GROUP B.V.—See Reply S.p.A.; *Int'l*, pg. 6290
BUSINESS ENGINEERING CORPORATION—See Toyo Engineering Corporation; *Int'l*, pg. 7852
BUSINESS EQUIPMENT UNLIMITED—See Xerox Holdings Corporation; *U.S. Public*, pg. 2387
BUSINESS EXPERT INC.—See Nippon Telegraph & Telephone Corporation; *Int'l*, pg. 5349
BUSINESS EXPERT KANSAI, INC.—See Nippon Telegraph & Telephone Corporation; *Int'l*, pg. 5349
BUSINESS EXPERT KYUSHU, INC.—See Nippon Telegraph & Telephone Corporation; *Int'l*, pg. 5349
BUSINESS EXPERT TOKAI INC.—See Nippon Telegraph & Telephone Corporation; *Int'l*, pg. 5349
THE BUSINESS FINANCE STORE—See The Finance Store; *U.S. Private*, pg. 4028
BUSINESS FIRST BANCSHARES, INC.; *U.S. Public*, pg. 413
BUSINESSFIRST INSURANCE COMPANY—See American Financial Group, Inc.; *U.S. Public*, pg. 103
BUSINESS FIRST OF COLUMBUS—See Advance Publications, Inc.; *U.S. Private*, pg. 84
BUSINESS FIRST OF LOUISVILLE—See Advance Publications, Inc.; *U.S. Private*, pg. 84
BUSINESS FURNITURE, INC.; *U.S. Private*, pg. 694
BUSINESS FURNITURE LLC; *U.S. Private*, pg. 694
BUSINESS GRAND WORKS, CO., LTD.—See Nojima Corporation; *Int'l*, pg. 5401
BUSINESS GROWTH FUND LIMITED—See BGF Group PLC; *Int'l*, pg. 1007
BUSINESS GROWTH FUND PLC - MIDLANDS—See BGF Group PLC; *Int'l*, pg. 1007
BUSINESS GROWTH FUND PLC - NORTH, NORTHEAST & IRELAND—See BGF Group PLC; *Int'l*, pg. 1007
BUSINESS GROWTH FUND PLC - SCOTLAND—See BGF Group PLC; *Int'l*, pg. 1007
BUSINESS IMMO S.A.S.—See CoStar Group, Inc.; *U.S. Public*, pg. 585
BUSINESS IMPACT GROUP LLC; *U.S. Private*, pg. 694
BUSINESS & INDUSTRIAL INSURANCE COMPANY LTD.; *Int'l*, pg. 1228

BUSINESS INDUSTRIAL NETWORK; *U.S. Private*, pg. 694
BUSINESS INFORMATION SYSTEMS, INC.—See i3 Verticals, Inc.; *U.S. Public*, pg. 1081
BUSINESS INFORMATION TECHNOLOGY SOLUTIONS, INC.—See Accenture plc; *Int'l*, pg. 85
BUSINESS INSIGHTS LTD.—See Informa plc; *Int'l*, pg. 3692
BUSINESS INSURANCE—See Crain Communications, Inc.; *U.S. Private*, pg. 1084
BUSINESS INTEGRA TECHNOLOGY SOLUTIONS, INC.; *U.S. Private*, pg. 695
BUSINESS INTEGRATORS INC.; *U.S. Private*, pg. 695
BUSINESS INTELLIGENCE ASSOCIATES, INC.—See Quad-C Management, Inc.; *U.S. Private*, pg. 3315
BUSINESS INTERACTIONS, LLC—See Novacap Management Inc.; *U.S. Private*, pg. 5453
BUSINESS INTERIORS INC.; *U.S. Private*, pg. 695
BUSINESS INTERIORS OF SEATTLE NORTH WEST INC.; *U.S. Private*, pg. 695
BUSINESS INTERNATIONAL GROUP LLC—See HORIBA Ltd; *Int'l*, pg. 3475
BUSINESS IT SOURCE, INC.—See Computacenter plc; *Int'l*, pg. 1758
THE BUSINESS JOURNAL OF PORTLAND, INC.—See Advance Publications, Inc.; *U.S. Private*, pg. 85
BUSINESS KEEPER GMBH—See Thoma Bravo, L.P.; *U.S. Private*, pg. 4147
BUSINESS LEADER MEDIA; *U.S. Private*, pg. 695
BUSINESS & LEGAL RESOURCES INC.; *U.S. Private*, pg. 694
BUSINESS LENDERS, LLC—See Bank of America Corporation; *U.S. Public*, pg. 272
BUSINESS LOGISTICS (THAILAND) CO., LTD.—See Oki Electric Industry Co., Ltd.; *Int'l*, pg. 5548
BUSINESS MANAGEMENT DAILY—See Capitol Information Group, Inc.; *U.S. Private*, pg. 744
BUSINESS MARKETERS GROUP, INC.—See Halma plc; *Int'l*, pg. 3230
BUSINESS MARKETING ASSOCIATION, INC.—See Association of National Advertisers, Inc.; *U.S. Private*, pg. 358
BUSINESSMART CORPORATION—See ASKUL Corporation; *Int'l*, pg. 625
BUSINESS MENS INSURANCE CORPORATION—See BMI Financial Group, Inc.; *U.S. Private*, pg. 600
BUSINESS MONITOR INTERNATIONAL LTD.—See The Hearst Corporation; *U.S. Private*, pg. 4044
THE BUSINESS MORTGAGE COMPANY LIMITED—See Paragon Banking Group PLC; *Int'l*, pg. 5736
THE BUSINESS MORTGAGE COMPANY SERVICES LIMITED—See Paragon Banking Group PLC; *Int'l*, pg. 5736
BUSINESS NETWORK CONSULTING, LTD.; *U.S. Private*, pg. 695
BUSINESSNOW COPENHAGEN APS—See DXC Technology Company; *U.S. Public*, pg. 694
BUSINESS OBJECTS S.A.—See SAP SE; *Int'l*, pg. 6566
BUSINESS OBJECTS SOFTWARE LIMITED—See SAP SE; *Int'l*, pg. 6566
BUSINESS OBJECTS SOFTWARE (SHANGHAI) CO., LTD.—See SAP SE; *Int'l*, pg. 6566
BUSINESS OBJECTS (UK) LIMITED—See SAP SE; *Int'l*, pg. 6567
BUSINESS OBSERVER—See Observer Media Group, Inc.; *U.S. Private*, pg. 2988
BUSINESS OFFICE SUITE SERVICES, INC.; *U.S. Private*, pg. 695
BUSINESS OFFICE SYSTEMS INC.; *U.S. Private*, pg. 695
BUSINESSON COMMUNICATION CO., LTD.; *Int'l*, pg. 1229
BUSINESSONLINE INC.; *U.S. Private*, pg. 695
BUSINESS ONLINE PUBLIC COMPANY LIMITED; *Int'l*, pg. 1229
BUSINESS OWNERS LIABILITY TEAM LLC—See CVC Capital Partners SICAV-FIS S.A.; *Int'l*, pg. 1885
BUSINESS PARK VARNA AD—See Africa Israel Investments Ltd.; *Int'l*, pg. 190
BUSINESS PARTNERS CO., LTD.—See Dynam Japan Holdings, Co., Ltd.; *Int'l*, pg. 2239
BUSINESS PEOPLE CO., LTD.—See Kimura-Unity Co., Ltd.; *Int'l*, pg. 4163
BUSINESS PLUS INC.—See Relia, Inc.; *Int'l*, pg. 6260
BUSINESS PROFESSIONAL SOLUTIONS RECRUITMENTS CO., LTD.—See PTT Public Company Limited; *Int'l*, pg. 6092
BUSINESS RECORDS MANAGEMENT, INC.; *U.S. Private*, pg. 695
BUSINESS RESERVATIONS CENTRE HOLLAND B.V.—See Cox & Kings Limited; *Int'l*, pg. 1822
BUSINESS RESOURCE SOLUTIONS LLC—See Bristol Bay Native Corporation; *U.S. Private*, pg. 656
THE BUSINESS REVIEW—See Advance Publications, Inc.; *U.S. Private*, pg. 85
BUSINESS SEARCH TECHNOLOGIES CORPORATION—See Geniee, Inc.; *Int'l*, pg. 2923
BUSINESS SECURITY CONSULTANTS, INC.; *U.S. Private*, pg. 695
BUSINESS SENSE SOLUTIONS; *U.S. Private*, pg. 695

BUSINESS SOFT SERVICE CO., LTD.—See Computer Institute of Japan Ltd.; *Int'l*, pg. 1759
BUSINESS SOFTWARE, INC.; *U.S. Private*, pg. 695
BUSINESS SOLUTIONS BUILDERS (BELGIUM) SA—See BSB SA; *Int'l*, pg. 1202
BUSINESS SOLUTIONS S.P.A.—See Stellantis N.V.; *Int'l*, pg. 7196
BUSINESS SPECTATOR PTY LTD—See News Corporation; *U.S. Public*, pg. 1518
BUSINESS STRATEGIES & BEYOND LLC; *U.S. Private*, pg. 695
BUSINESS-SUPPLY.COM, INC.—See LoanSource Inc.; *U.S. Private*, pg. 2477
BUSINESS SUPPORT CENTER CO., LTD.—See Toyota Motor Corporation; *Int'l*, pg. 7870
BUSINESS SUPPORT SOLUTION S.A.—See CEPD N.V.; *Int'l*, pg. 1420
BUSINESS SYSTEMS HOLDINGS GROUP PLC—See Vista Equity Partners, LLC; *U.S. Private*, pg. 4394
BUSINESS TALENT GROUP, LLC—See Heidrick & Struggles International, Inc.; *U.S. Public*, pg. 1022
BUSINESS TECHNOLOGY SERVICES, INC.; *U.S. Private*, pg. 695
BUSINESS-TO-BUSINESS MARKETING COMMUNICATIONS; *U.S. Private*, pg. 695
BUSINESS TRAINING LIBRARY; *U.S. Private*, pg. 695
BUSINESS TRAINING SOLUTIONS S.L.—See BTS Group AB; *Int'l*, pg. 1205
BUSINESS UNDERWRITERS ASSOCIATES, LLC—See Hellman & Friedman LLC; *U.S. Private*, pg. 1909
BUSINESS VISION S.A.—See MercadoLibre, Inc.; *Int'l*, pg. 4819
BUSINESS WATCH INTERNATIONAL INC.—See Leadsonline LLC; *U.S. Private*, pg. 2407
BUSINESS WIRE, INC.—See Berkshire Hathaway Inc.; *U.S. Public*, pg. 303
BUSINESSWISE SOLUTIONS LIMITED—See Inspired PLC; *Int'l*, pg. 3720
BUSINESSWORLD PUBLISHING CORPORATION—See PLDT Inc.; *Int'l*, pg. 5896
BUSITALIA CAMPANIA S.P.A.—See Ferrovie dello Stato Italiane S.p.A.; *Int'l*, pg. 2645
BUSITALIA RAIL SERVICE S.R.L.—See Ferrovie dello Stato Italiane S.p.A.; *Int'l*, pg. 2645
BUSITALIA VENETO S.P.A.—See Ferrovie dello Stato Italiane S.p.A.; *Int'l*, pg. 2645
BUSKE LINES, INC.—See Fourshore Capital LLC; *U.S. Private*, pg. 1583
BUSLINK ALICE SPRINGS PTY. LTD.—See ComfortDelGro Corporation Limited; *Int'l*, pg. 1712
BUSLINK BROKEN HILL PTY. LTD.—See ComfortDelGro Corporation Limited; *Int'l*, pg. 1712
BUSLINK GLADSTONE PTY. LTD.—See ComfortDelGro Corporation Limited; *Int'l*, pg. 1712
BUSLINK MEDIA; *U.S. Private*, pg. 695
BUSLINK NT PTY. LTD.—See ComfortDelGro Corporation Limited; *Int'l*, pg. 1712
BUSLINK SUNRAYSIA PTY. LTD.—See ComfortDelGro Corporation Limited; *Int'l*, pg. 1712
BUSLINK SUNSHINE COAST PTY. LTD.—See ComfortDelGro Corporation Limited; *Int'l*, pg. 1712
BUS-PLUS SERVICES PTE. LTD.—See Temasek Holdings (Private) Limited; *Int'l*, pg. 7550
BUSS AG—See Fabrel AG; *Int'l*, pg. 2599
BUSSAN FOOD MATERIALS CO., LTD.—See Mitsui & Co., Ltd.; *Int'l*, pg. 4973
BUSSAN LOGISTICS SOLUTIONS CO., LTD.—See Mitsui & Co., Ltd.; *Int'l*, pg. 4973
BUSSAN REAL ESTATE CO., LTD.—See Mitsui & Co., Ltd.; *Int'l*, pg. 4973
BUSSAN SUMISHO CARBON ENERGY CO., LTD.—See Mitsui & Co., Ltd.; *Int'l*, pg. 4973
BUSSEN QUARRIES, INC. - JEFFERSON BARRACKS QUARRY—See Bussen Quarries, Inc.; *U.S. Private*, pg. 696
BUSSEN QUARRIES, INC.; *U.S. Private*, pg. 696
BUSSEN QUARRIES, INC. - TRAUTMAN QUARRY—See Bussen Quarries, Inc.; *U.S. Private*, pg. 696
BUSSE/SJI—See Arrowhead Conveyor Corporation, Inc.; *U.S. Private*, pg. 336
BUSSETO FOODS, INC.—See Cremonini S.p.A.; *Int'l*, pg. 1838
BUSSEYS AND SABBERTON BROS. LTD.; *Int'l*, pg. 1229
BUSS FORD LLC; *U.S. Private*, pg. 696
BUSS FORD SALES; *U.S. Private*, pg. 696
BUSSMANN DO BRASIL LTDA.—See Eaton Corporation plc; *Int'l*, pg. 2277
BUSSMANN, S. DE R.L. DE C.V.—See Eaton Corporation plc; *Int'l*, pg. 2279
BUS SPORT AG—See Fenix Outdoor International AG; *Int'l*, pg. 2634
BUSS-SMS-CANZLER GMBH; *Int'l*, pg. 1229
BUS STOP CO., LTD.—See Onward Holdings Co., Ltd.; *Int'l*, pg. 5592
BUS SUPPLY COMPANY, INC.; *U.S. Private*, pg. 693
BUSTAMI & SAHEB TRADING CO., LTD.—See Nissan Motor Co., Ltd.; *Int'l*, pg. 5367
BUSTELO COFFEE ROASTING CO.—See The J.M. Smucker Company; *U.S. Public*, pg. 2107

COMPANY NAME INDEX

BUSVERKEHR MARKISCH-ODERLAND GMBH—See Deutsche Bahn AG; *Int'l*, pg. 2049
BUSVERKEHR ODER-SPREE GMBH—See Deutsche Bahn AG; *Int'l*, pg. 2049
BUSWAYS TRAVEL SERVICES LTD.—See Stagecoach Group Plc; *Int'l*, pg. 7163
BUSY BEAVER BUILDING CENTERS, INC.; *U.S. Private*, pg. 696
BUSY BEE CABINETS, INC.; *U.S. Private*, pg. 696
BUSY BEE CLEANING SERVICES LTD.; *Int'l*, pg. 1229
BUSY BEES EARLY LEARNING AUSTRALIA PTY. LTD.—See Ontario Teachers' Pension Plan; *Int'l*, pg. 5587
BUSY BEES HOLDINGS LIMITED—See Ontario Teachers' Pension Plan; *Int'l*, pg. 5587
BUSY BODY FITNESS IN MOTION; *U.S. Private*, pg. 696
BUSYBUSY, INC.—See Toolwatch Corp.; *U.S. Private*, pg. 4186
BUTAGAZ SAS—See DCC plc; *Int'l*, pg. 1989
BUTANE INDUSTRIAL COMPANY; *Int'l*, pg. 1229
BUTANO DIALYSIS, LLC—See DaVita Inc.; *U.S. Public*, pg. 636
BUTAN PLIN D.D.—See SHV Holdings N.V.; *Int'l*, pg. 6872
BUTAN PLIN D.O.O.—See SHV Holdings N.V.; *Int'l*, pg. 6872
BUTCHER & BAECKER CONSTRUCTION CO., INC.; *U.S. Private*, pg. 696
BUTCHER DISTRIBUTORS INC.; *U.S. Private*, pg. 696
THE BUTCHER ENGINEERING ENTERPRISES LIMITED; *Int'l*, pg. 7630
BUTCHER'S PET CARE LTD.; *Int'l*, pg. 1229
BUTCHER'S PET CARE SP.Z.O.O—See Butcher's Pet Care Ltd.; *Int'l*, pg. 1229
BUTCHER VENTURE CAPITAL COMPANY; *U.S. Private*, pg. 696
BUTCH OUSTALET CHEVROLET CADILLAC; *U.S. Private*, pg. 696
BUTCH OUSTALET FORD LINCOLN; *U.S. Private*, pg. 696
BUTCOMBE BREWERY LTD.—See Caledonia Investments plc; *Int'l*, pg. 1262
BUTECH BLISS; *U.S. Private*, pg. 696
BUTERA FINER FOODS INC.; *U.S. Private*, pg. 696
BUTIMOVE—See Crown Holdings, Inc.; *U.S. Public*, pg. 597
BUTINA A/S—See Marel hf; *Int'l*, pg. 4690
BUTLER AMERICA AEROSPACE LLC—See HCL Technologies Ltd.; *Int'l*, pg. 3298
BUTLER AMERICA, INC.; *U.S. Private*, pg. 696
BUTLER ANIMAL HEALTH HOLDING COMPANY, LLC—See Clayton, Dubilier & Rice, LLC; *U.S. Private*, pg. 921
BUTLER ANIMAL HEALTH HOLDING COMPANY, LLC—See TPG Capital, L.P.; *U.S. Public*, pg. 2170
BUTLER ANIMAL HEALTH SUPPLY—See Clayton, Dubilier & Rice, LLC; *U.S. Private*, pg. 921
BUTLER ANIMAL HEALTH SUPPLY—See TPG Capital, L.P.; *U.S. Public*, pg. 2170
BUTLER-ARA, LLC—See Nautic Partners, LLC; *U.S. Private*, pg. 2869
BUTLER AUTOMATIC, INC.; *U.S. Private*, pg. 696
BUTLER AUTOMOTIVE GROUP INC.; *U.S. Private*, pg. 697
BUTLER AUTO SALES AND PARTS, INC.—See Stellex Capital Management LP; *U.S. Private*, pg. 3800
BUTLER AVIONICS, INC.—See Butler National Corporation; *U.S. Public*, pg. 413
BUTLER BROS, INC.; *U.S. Private*, pg. 697
BUTLER & BUTLER INVESTMENTS; *U.S. Private*, pg. 696
BUTLER CAPITAL PARTNERS; *Int'l*, pg. 1229
BUTLER CARPET COMPANY INC.; *U.S. Private*, pg. 697
BUTLER COUNTY LANDFILL, INC.—See Waste Connections, Inc.; *Int'l*, pg. 8353
BUTLER DESIGN SERVICES, INC.—See Butler America, Inc.; *U.S. Private*, pg. 696
BUTLER DIRECT LTD.—See Informa plc; *Int'l*, pg. 3692
BUTLER ENGINEERING & MARKETING S.P.A—See Dover Corporation; *U.S. Public*, pg. 678
BUTLER ENTERPRISES; *U.S. Private*, pg. 697
BUTLER FLEET SERVICES, INC.—See Butler America, Inc.; *U.S. Private*, pg. 696
BUTLER FOODS OF PENSACOLA INC.; *U.S. Private*, pg. 697
BUTLER HOME PRODUCTS, INC.; *U.S. Private*, pg. 697
BUTLER INDUSTRIES INC.; *U.S. Private*, pg. 697
BUTLER-JOHNSON CORPORATION; *U.S. Private*, pg. 697
BUTLER MACHINERY COMPANY; *U.S. Private*, pg. 697
BUTLER MANUFACTURING COMPANY—See BlueScope Steel Limited; *Int'l*, pg. 1073
BUTLER MERCHANDISING SOLUTIONS, INC.—See Presence From Innovation, LLC; *U.S. Private*, pg. 3254
BUTLER NATIONAL CORPORATION; *U.S. Public*, pg. 413
BUTLER PETROLEUM CORPORATION; *U.S. Private*, pg. 697
BUTLER REFRIGERATED MEATS, INC.—See Giant Eagle, Inc.; *U.S. Private*, pg. 1694

BUTLER RESEARCH LTD.—See Informa plc; *Int'l*, pg. 3692
BUTLER'S ELECTRIC SUPPLY; *U.S. Private*, pg. 697
BUTLER SERVICE GROUP, INC.—See Butler America, Inc.; *U.S. Private*, pg. 696
BUTLER SERVICE GROUP - U.K. LTD.—See Butler America, Inc.; *U.S. Private*, pg. 696
BUTLER (SHANGHAI), INC.—See BlueScope Steel Limited; *Int'l*, pg. 1073
BUTLER, SHINE, STERN & PARTNERS; *U.S. Private*, pg. 697
BUTLER SNOW LLP; *U.S. Private*, pg. 697
BUTLER SUPPLY INC.; *U.S. Private*, pg. 697
BUTLER TECHNICAL SERVICES INDIA PRIVATE LIMITED—See Butler America, Inc.; *U.S. Private*, pg. 696
BUTLER TECHNOLOGY SOLUTIONS, INC.—See Butler America, Inc.; *U.S. Private*, pg. 696
BUTLER (TIANJIN) INC.—See BlueScope Steel Limited; *Int'l*, pg. 1073
BUTLER/TILL MEDIA SERVICES, INC.; *U.S. Private*, pg. 697
BUTLER TIRE COMPANY INCORPORATED; *U.S. Private*, pg. 697
BUTLER TRUCKING COMPANY; *U.S. Private*, pg. 697
BUTLER UTILITY SERVICE, INC.—See Butler America, Inc.; *U.S. Private*, pg. 696
BUTLER WHOLESALE PRODUCTS, INC.; *U.S. Private*, pg. 697
BUTLIN'S LIMITED—See Blackstone Inc.; *U.S. Public*, pg. 352
BUTMAC PTY LTD—See Eagers Automotive Limited; *Int'l*, pg. 2263
BUTN LIMITED; *Int'l*, pg. 1229
BUT'ONE INFORMATION CORPORATION; *Int'l*, pg. 1229
BUTRA HEIDELBERGCEMENT SDN. BHD.—See Heidelberg Materials AG; *Int'l*, pg. 3309
BUT SAS—See Clayton, Dubilier & Rice, LLC; *U.S. Private*, pg. 920
BUT SAS—See XXXLutz KG; *Int'l*, pg. 8542
BUTSURYU 24, INC.—See Medipal Holdings Corporation; *Int'l*, pg. 4779
BUTTE COUNTY RICE GROWERS ASSOCIATION; *U.S. Private*, pg. 699
BUTTE ENERGY INC.; *Int'l*, pg. 1229
BUTTE GLASS; *U.S. Private*, pg. 698
BUTTERBALL, LLC—See Maxwell Foods, LLC; *U.S. Private*, pg. 2619
BUTTERBALL, LLC—See Maxwell Foods, LLC; *U.S. Private*, pg. 2619
BUTTERBALL, LLC—See Maxwell Foods, LLC; *U.S. Private*, pg. 2619
BUTTERBALL, LLC—See Seaboard Corporation; *U.S. Public*, pg. 1850
BUTTERBALL, LLC—See Seaboard Corporation; *U.S. Public*, pg. 1850
BUTTERBALL, LLC—See Seaboard Corporation; *U.S. Public*, pg. 1850
BUTTER BUDS FOOD INGREDIENTS—See Cumberland Packing Corp.; *U.S. Private*, pg. 1122
BUTTERCUP LEYS (BOULTON MOOR) RESIDENTIAL MANAGEMENT COMPANY LIMITED—See Persimmon plc; *Int'l*, pg. 5815
BUTTERFIELD ASSET MANAGEMENT LIMITED—See The Bank of N.T. Butterfield & Son Limited; *Int'l*, pg. 7616
BUTTERFIELD BANK (CAYMAN) LIMITED—See The Bank of N.T. Butterfield & Son Limited; *Int'l*, pg. 7616
BUTTERFIELD BANK (GUERNSEY) LTD.—See The Bank of N.T. Butterfield & Son Limited; *Int'l*, pg. 7616
BUTTERFIELD BANK (JERSEY) LIMITED—See The Bank of N.T. Butterfield & Son Limited; *Int'l*, pg. 7616
BUTTERFIELD COLOR, INC.—See Sika AG; *Int'l*, pg. 6914
BUTTERFIELD HOLDINGS (UK) LIMITED—See The Bank of N.T. Butterfield & Son Limited; *Int'l*, pg. 7616
BUTTERFIELD MORTGAGES LIMITED—See The Bank of N.T. Butterfield & Son Limited; *Int'l*, pg. 7616
BUTTERFIELD PROPERTIES LLC—See PulteGroup, Inc.; *U.S. Public*, pg. 1737
BUTTERFIELD SECURITIES (BERMUDA) LIMITED—See The Bank of N.T. Butterfield & Son Limited; *Int'l*, pg. 7616
BUTTERFIELD TRAIL VILLAGE, INC.; *U.S. Private*, pg. 698
BUTTERFIELD TRUST (ASIA) LIMITED—See The Bank of N.T. Butterfield & Son Limited; *Int'l*, pg. 7616
BUTTERFIELD TRUST (BAHAMAS) LIMITED—See The Bank of N.T. Butterfield & Son Limited; *Int'l*, pg. 7616
BUTTERFIELD TRUST (BERMUDA) LIMITED—See The Bank of N.T. Butterfield & Son Limited; *Int'l*, pg. 7616
BUTTERFIELD TRUST (CAYMAN) LIMITED—See The Bank of N.T. Butterfield & Son Limited; *Int'l*, pg. 7616
BUTTERFIELD TRUST (GUERNSEY) LIMITED—See The Bank of N.T. Butterfield & Son Limited; *Int'l*, pg. 7616
BUTTERFIELD TRUST (SWITZERLAND) LIMITED—See The Bank of N.T. Butterfield & Son Limited; *Int'l*, pg. 7616

BUTTERFIELD YOUTH SERVICES, INC.—See Great Circle; *U.S. Private*, pg. 1762
BUTTERFLY CORPORATION—See Sega Sammy Holdings, Inc.; *Int'l*, pg. 6680
BUTTERFLY EFFECTS INC; *U.S. Private*, pg. 698
BUTTERFLY EQUITY LP; *U.S. Private*, pg. 698
BUTTERFLY GANDHIMATHI APPLIANCES LIMITED—See Crompton Greaves Consumer Electricals Limited; *Int'l*, pg. 1853
BUTTERFLY LIVING LLC—See Kids2, Inc.; *U.S. Private*, pg. 2303
BUTTERFLY NETWORK, INC.; *U.S. Public*, pg. 413
BUTTERFLY S.R.L.—See TXT e-Solutions S.p.A.; *Int'l*, pg. 7993
BUTTER KRUST BAKING COMPANY; *U.S. Private*, pg. 698
BUTTER LONDON LLC—See Astral Brands, Inc.; *U.S. Private*, pg. 361
BUTTERWORTH BULKING INSTALLATION SDN. BHD.—See United Plantations Berhad; *Int'l*, pg. 8072
BUTTIKOFER AG—See Bystronic AG; *Int'l*, pg. 1236
BUTTNER ENERGIE- UND TROCKNUNGSTECHNIK GMBH—See G. Siempelkamp GmbH & Co. KG; *Int'l*, pg. 2864
BUTTON MOTORS, INC.; *U.S. Private*, pg. 698
BUTTON TRANSPORTATION INC.; *U.S. Private*, pg. 698
BUTTONWILLOW WAREHOUSE CO., INC.—See Tech Agricultural, Inc.; *U.S. Private*, pg. 3951
BUTTS FOODS INC.—See Palladium Equity Partners, LLC; *U.S. Private*, pg. 3078
BUTWAL POWER COMPANY LIMITED; *Int'l*, pg. 1229
BUTZ ENTERPRISES, INC.; *U.S. Private*, pg. 698
BUUDAIN TSATSAL JOINT STOCK COMPANY; *Int'l*, pg. 1229
BUU LONG INDUSTRY & INVESTMENT JOINT STOCK COMPANY—See The Siam Cement Public Company Limited; *Int'l*, pg. 7682
BUURMA FARMS INC.; *U.S. Private*, pg. 698
BUURTWINKELS OKAY NV—See Colruyt Group N.V.; *Int'l*, pg. 1705
BUUTTI OY—See Netum Group Plc; *Int'l*, pg. 5216
BUVIHIR KFT—See Vivendi SE; *Int'l*, pg. 8275
BUWOG AG—See Vonovia SE; *Int'l*, pg. 8304
BUWOG- BAUEN UND WOHNEN GESELLSCHAFT MRH—See Vonovia SE; *Int'l*, pg. 8304
BUWOG BAUTRAGER GMBH—See Vonovia SE; *Int'l*, pg. 8304
BUWOG-LINDENSTRASSE DEVELOPMENT GMBH—See Vonovia SE; *Int'l*, pg. 8304
BUWOG SUD GMBH—See Vonovia SE; *Int'l*, pg. 8304
BUWON MOTORS CO., LTD.—See Bridgestone Corporation; *Int'l*, pg. 1159
BUXBAUM AUTOMATION GMBH—See Softing AG; *Int'l*, pg. 7055
BUXBAUM GROUP; *U.S. Private*, pg. 698
BUXLY PAINTS LIMITED; *Int'l*, pg. 1229
BUXTON ACQUISITION CO., LLC; *U.S. Private*, pg. 698
BUXTON OIL CO. INC.; *U.S. Private*, pg. 698
BUXTON RESOURCES LIMITED; *Int'l*, pg. 1230
BUY ADS DIRECT; *U.S. Private*, pg. 698
BUYANG INTERNATIONAL HOLDING INC.; *Int'l*, pg. 1230
BUYATAB ONLINE INC.—See Corpay, Inc.; *U.S. Public*, pg. 579
BUYATIMESHARE.COM; *U.S. Private*, pg. 698
BUY BUY BABY, INC.—See 20230930-DK-Butterfly-1, Inc.; *U.S. Private*, pg. 5
BUYCASTINGS.COM; *U.S. Private*, pg. 699
BUYCOSTUMES.COM—See Rubie's Costume Company Inc.; *U.S. Private*, pg. 3500
BUY EFFICIENT, LLC—See Sunstone Hotel Investors, Inc.; *U.S. Private*, pg. 1966
BUYER ADVERTISING, INC.; *U.S. Private*, pg. 699
BUYERQUEST HOLDINGS INC.—See The ODP Corporation; *U.S. Public*, pg. 2117
BUYERS EDGE PLATFORM LLC; *U.S. Private*, pg. 699
BUYERS LABORATORY LLC—See SFW Capital Partners LLC; *U.S. Private*, pg. 3622
BUYERS VEHICLE PROTECTION PLAN, INC.—See Credit Acceptance Corporation; *U.S. Public*, pg. 593
BUYERZONE.COM LLC—See Purch Group, Inc.; *U.S. Private*, pg. 3305
BUY & EZ SELL RECYCLER CORPORATION—See Digital Air Strike Inc.; *U.S. Private*, pg. 1230
BUY GOLD AND SILVER CORP.—See A-Mark Precious Metals, Inc.; *U.S. Public*, pg. 10
BUY HAPPIER, LLC; *U.S. Private*, pg. 698
BUYITDIRECT.COM N.V.—See Bechtle AG; *Int'l*, pg. 937
BUY-LO QUALITY FOOD STORES; *U.S. Private*, pg. 698
BUY-LOW FOODS LTD.—See The Jim Pattison Group; *Int'l*, pg. 7660
BUYMALL SERVICES SDN. BHD.—See Revenue Group Bhd; *Int'l*, pg. 6312
BUYMETAL.COM, INC.—See Scope Metals Group Ltd.; *Int'l*, pg. 6650
BUYMYTRONICS.COM; *U.S. Private*, pg. 699
BUY NOW ASIA SDN. BHD.—See MY E.G. Services Berhad; *Int'l*, pg. 5111
BUYONLINENOW.COM; *U.S. Private*, pg. 699

BUYONLINENOW.COM

CORPORATE AFFILIATIONS

BUY-OUT CENTRAL EUROPE II BETEILIGUNGS-INVEST AG—See Global Equity Partners Beteiligungs-Management AG; *Int'l*, pg. 2996
BUYRITE CLUB CORP.; *U.S. Private*, pg. 699
BUY-RITE FOODS INC.; *U.S. Private*, pg. 698
BUYSEASONS ENTERPRISES, LLC—See Rubie's Costume Company Inc.; *U.S. Private*, pg. 3500
BUYSELL TECHNOLOGIES CO.; *Int'l*, pg. 1230
BUYSMETAL N.V.—See Klockner & Co. SE; *Int'l*, pg. 4202
BUY TO LET DIRECT LIMITED—See Paragon Banking Group PLC; *Int'l*, pg. 5735
BUZBUZ CAPITAL CORP.; *Int'l*, pg. 1230
BUZEN KUBOTA KAIUN CO., LTD.—See Azuma Shipping Co., Ltd.; *Int'l*, pg. 782
BUZICK CONSTRUCTION INC.; *U.S. Private*, pg. 699
BUZIL ROSSARI PRIVATE LIMITED—See Rossari Biotech Limited; *Int'l*, pg. 6401
BUZTRONICS, INC.; *U.S. Private*, pg. 699
BUZZ CAPITAL 2, INC.; *Int'l*, pg. 1230
BUZZ CAPITAL, INC.; *Int'l*, pg. 1230
BUZZFEED, INC.—See BuzzFeed, Inc.; *U.S. Public*, pg. 413
BUZZFEED, INC.; *U.S. Public*, pg. 413
BUZZI SPA; *Int'l*, pg. 1230
BUZZI UNICEM USA INC.—See Buzzi SpA; *Int'l*, pg. 1230
BUZZI UNICEM USA—See Buzzi SpA; *Int'l*, pg. 1230
BUZZMAN SAS—See Vivendi SE; *Int'l*, pg. 8267
BUZZ OATES COMPANIES; *U.S. Private*, pg. 699
BUZZ OATES CONSTRUCTION, LP—See Buzz Oates Companies; *U.S. Private*, pg. 699
BUZZ PRODUCTS, INC.; *U.S. Private*, pg. 699
BUZZSAW ADVERTISING & DESIGN INC.; *U.S. Private*, pg. 699
BUZZTABLE INC.; *U.S. Private*, pg. 699
BUZZ TECHNOLOGIES, INC.; *Int'l*, pg. 1230
BUZZTIME ENTERTAINMENT, INC—See Eterna Therapeutics Inc.; *U.S. Public*, pg. 797
BUZZWIT CO., LTD.—See Adastria Co., Ltd.; *Int'l*, pg. 126
B.V. ALGEMENE HOLDING EN FINANCIERINGS MAATSCHAPPIJ—See Assicurazioni Generali S.p.A.; *Int'l*, pg. 645
B.V. ARROW ELECTRONICS DLC—See Arrow Electronics, Inc.; *U.S. Public*, pg. 198
BVBA KME BENELUX SPRL—See Intek Group S.p.A.; *Int'l*, pg. 3732
BVBA SWEDISH ORPHAN BIOVITRUM—See Swedish Orphan Biovitrum AB; *Int'l*, pg. 7365
BVB BETEILIGUNGS-GMBH—See Borussia Dortmund GmbH & Co. KGaA; *Int'l*, pg. 1115
B.V. BETONCENTRALE BEMA—See Heidelberg Materials AG; *Int'l*, pg. 3308
B.V. BETONCENTRALE DE SCHELDE—See Heidelberg Materials AG; *Int'l*, pg. 3308
BVB EVENT & CATERING GMBH—See Borussia Dortmund GmbH & Co. KGaA; *Int'l*, pg. 1115
BVB GENERAL CONTRACTORS, LLC; *U.S. Private*, pg. 700
BVB MERCHANDISING GMBH—See Borussia Dortmund GmbH & Co. KGaA; *Int'l*, pg. 1115
B.V. BOUWGRONDSTOFFEN A.G.M.—See Heidelberg Materials AG; *Int'l*, pg. 3308
BVB PROPERTIES; *U.S. Private*, pg. 700
BVB STADION GMBH—See Borussia Dortmund GmbH & Co. KGaA; *Int'l*, pg. 1115
BVB STADION HOLDING GMBH—See Borussia Dortmund GmbH & Co. KGaA; *Int'l*, pg. 1115
BVB STADIONMANAGEMENT GMBH—See Borussia Dortmund GmbH & Co. KGaA; *Int'l*, pg. 1115
B.V. CTH GROEP—See Darling Ingredients Inc.; *U.S. Public*, pg. 633
B.V. DELI-HTL TABAK MAATSCHAPPIJ—See Blackstone Inc.; *U.S. Public*, pg. 356
B & V DELITZSCH GMBH—See Duroc AB; *Int'l*, pg. 2229
BVE HOLDING SE; *Int'l*, pg. 1231
BV. ELSPEC—See TKH Group N.V.; *Int'l*, pg. 7765
B.V. EXPLOITATIEMAATSCHAPPIJ GELREDOME—See Live Nation Entertainment, Inc.; *U.S. Public*, pg. 1328
BV FINANCIAL, INC.—See Bay-Vanguard, M.H.C.; *U.S. Private*, pg. 495
BVG BERGEDORFER VERSICHERUNGSVERMITTLUNG GMBH—See Korber AG; *Int'l*, pg. 4280
BV GRUNDSTUCKSENTWICKLUNGSGMBH & CO. SCHLOSSBERGPROJEKTEN—See UniCredit S.p.A.; *Int'l*, pg. 8034
BV HOLDING AG; *Int'l*, pg. 1231
BVI DOUBLE DRIVE-THRU INC.; *U.S. Private*, pg. 700
BV INVESTMENT PARTNERS LLC; *U.S. Private*, pg. 699
BVK DIRECT, INC.—See BVK, Inc.; *U.S. Private*, pg. 700
BVK, INC.; *U.S. Private*, pg. 700
B.V. KONINKLIJKE VAN KEMPEN & BEGEER—See Koninklijke Delftsch Aardewerkfabriek N.V.; *Int'l*, pg. 4262
BV LEASING - ARRENDAMENTO MERCANTIL S.A.—See Votorantim S.A.; *Int'l*, pg. 8309
B.V. LEERDAM CRYSTAL—See Koninklijke Delftsch Aardewerkfabriek N.V.; *Int'l*, pg. 4262
BV LIFE JOINT STOCK COMPANY—See Vietnam Construction Stock Corporation; *Int'l*, pg. 8197

B.V. MORTEL INSTALLATIE ASSEN—See Heidelberg Materials AG; *Int'l*, pg. 3308
B.V.'NEDEXIMPO' NEDERLANDSE EXPORT- EN IMPORTMAATSCHAPPIJ—See ThyssenKrupp AG; *Int'l*, pg. 7723
BVO BUSVERKEHR OSTWESTFALEN GMBH—See Deutsche Bahn AG; *Int'l*, pg. 2049
BVR BUSVERKEHR RHEINLAND GMBH—See Deutsche Bahn AG; *Int'l*, pg. 2049
B.V. ROYAL DELFT ONROEREND GOED—See Koninklijke Delftsch Aardewerkfabriek N.V.; *Int'l*, pg. 4262
BVR TECHNOLOGIES CO.—See Kaney Aerospace, Inc.; *U.S. Private*, pg. 2260
BVS ENTERTAINMENT, INC.—See The Walt Disney Company; *U.S. Public*, pg. 2138
BV SNIJ-UNIE HIFI—See Saudi Basic Industries Corporation; *Int'l*, pg. 6590
BVT DYNIV GMBH—See VINCI S.A.; *Int'l*, pg. 8231
BV TEKNIK A/S—See Addtech AB; *Int'l*, pg. 132
B.V. TWENTSCHE KABELFABRIEK—See TKH Group N.V.; *Int'l*, pg. 7763
BV VAN VLIET GROEP MILIEU-DIENSTVERLENERS—See Renewi plc; *Int'l*, pg. 6279
B.V. VEGA MEET- EN REGELTECHNIEK—See Grieshaber Holding GmbH; *Int'l*, pg. 3083
B.V. WEEKENDJEWEG.NL—See Cox & Kings Limited; *Int'l*, pg. 1822
BVZ HOLDING AG; *Int'l*, pg. 1231
BWAB, INC.; *U.S. Private*, pg. 700
B-W ADVERTISING AGENCY, INC.—See Best Western International, Inc.; *U.S. Private*, pg. 544
BWA GROUP PLC; *Int'l*, pg. 1232
BWA JAPAN LTD.—See Sumitomo Corporation; *Int'l*, pg. 7268
BWAY CORP. - CINCINNATI PLANT—See Stone Canyon Industries, LLC; *U.S. Private*, pg. 3817
BWAY CORP. - ELK GROVE VILLAGE PLANT—See Stone Canyon Industries, LLC; *U.S. Private*, pg. 3817
BWAY CORP. - LAGRANGE PLANT—See Stone Canyon Industries, LLC; *U.S. Private*, pg. 3817
BWAY CORP. - LANGLEY PLANT—See Stone Canyon Industries, LLC; *U.S. Private*, pg. 3817
BWAY CORP. - MANSFIELD PLANT—See Stone Canyon Industries, LLC; *U.S. Private*, pg. 3817
BWAY CORP. - OAKVILLE PLANT—See Stone Canyon Industries, LLC; *U.S. Private*, pg. 3817
BWAY CORPORATION—See Stone Canyon Industries, LLC; *U.S. Private*, pg. 3817
BWAY CORP. - SPRINGHILL PLANT—See Stone Canyon Industries, LLC; *U.S. Private*, pg. 3817
BWAY CORP. - TRENTON PLANT—See Stone Canyon Industries, LLC; *U.S. Private*, pg. 3817
BWAY CORP. - YORK PLANT—See Stone Canyon Industries, LLC; *U.S. Private*, pg. 3817
BWAY.NET, INC.; *U.S. Private*, pg. 700
BWB PARTNERS P/S; *Int'l*, pg. 1232
BWB SUNBELT HOME HEALTH SERVICES, LLC—See Apollo Global Management, Inc.; *U.S. Public*, pg. 156
BW CAPITAL MARKETS INC—See Landesbank Baden-Wurttemberg; *Int'l*, pg. 4404
BWC TERMINALS LLC; *U.S. Private*, pg. 700
BWE-BAU FERTIGTEILWERK GMBH—See Zech Group SE; *Int'l*, pg. 8628
BWE ENERGY INDIA PVT. LTD.—See STF S.p.A; *Int'l*, pg. 7213
BWE INTERNATIONAL B.V.—See STF S.p.A; *Int'l*, pg. 7213
BW ELECTRICAL SERVICES LLC—See Charge Enterprises, Inc.; *U.S. Public*, pg. 478
B.W. ELLIOTT MANUFACTURING COMPANY, LLC—See Enerpac Tool Group Corp.; *U.S. Public*, pg. 765
BW ENERGY GABON SA—See BW Offshore Limited; *Int'l*, pg. 1231
BW ENERGY LIMITED; *Int'l*, pg. 1231
BW EPIC KOSAN LTD.; *Int'l*, pg. 1231
BW FLEET MANAGEMENT PTE LTD—See BW Group Ltd.; *Int'l*, pg. 1231
BW GAS ASA—See BW Group Ltd.; *Int'l*, pg. 1231
BW GAS & CONVENIENCE HOLDINGS, LLC; *U.S. Private*, pg. 700
BWG HOLDINGS I CORP—See AEA Investors LP; *U.S. Private*, pg. 113
BWG HOMES AB—See OBOS BBL; *Int'l*, pg. 5512
BWG HOMES ASA—See OBOS BBL; *Int'l*, pg. 5511
BW GROUP LTD.; *Int'l*, pg. 1231
B&W GROUP (SCHWEIZ) GMBH—See Masimo Corporation; *U.S. Public*, pg. 1392
BWG STRATEGY LLC—See Infinedi Partners LP; *U.S. Private*, pg. 2070
BWI COMPANIES INC; *U.S. Private*, pg. 700
BWI CZECH REPUBLIC S.R.O.—See BeijingWest Industries International Limited; *Int'l*, pg. 962
BWI DENMARK, INC.—See Best Western International, Inc.; *U.S. Private*, pg. 544
BW IDEOL AS; *Int'l*, pg. 1231
BWI EAGLE, INC.—See Harbour Group Industries, Inc.; *U.S. Private*, pg. 1860
BWI, INC.; *U.S. Private*, pg. 700
BWIN LATAM S.A.S.—See Entain PLC; *Int'l*, pg. 2449

BWISE BEHEER B.V.—See EQT AB; *Int'l*, pg. 2471
BWISE B.V.—See EQT AB; *Int'l*, pg. 2471
BWISE DEVELOPMENT B.V.—See EQT AB; *Int'l*, pg. 2471
BWISE GERMANY GMBH—See EQT AB; *Int'l*, pg. 2471
BWISE INTERNAL CONTROL INC.—See EQT AB; *Int'l*, pg. 2471
BWI TECH S.R.L.—See Wowjoint Holdings Limited; *Int'l*, pg. 8460
BWK GMBH UNTERNEHMENS BETEILIGUNGSGESELLSCHAFT; *Int'l*, pg. 1232
BWL HEALTH & SCIENCES, INC.—See Best World International Ltd.; *Int'l*, pg. 1000
BWL KOREA CO., LTD.—See Best World International Ltd.; *Int'l*, pg. 1000
BWL LIMITED; *Int'l*, pg. 1232
BW LPG LIMITED—See BW Group Ltd.; *Int'l*, pg. 1231
BW MARITIME PTE LTD.—See BW Group Ltd.; *Int'l*, pg. 1231
B & W MECHANICAL CONTRACTORS, INC.; *U.S. Private*, pg. 417
BWM OUTCOMES, LLC—See Hammond, Kennedy, Whitney & Company, Inc.; *U.S. Private*, pg. 1850
B.W.O.C. LIMITED—See Marquard & Bahls AG; *Int'l*, pg. 4699
BW OFFSHORE CHINA LTD.—See BW Offshore Limited; *Int'l*, pg. 1231
BW OFFSHORE CYPRUS LTD—See BW Offshore Limited; *Int'l*, pg. 1231
BW OFFSHORE DO BRASIL LTDA—See BW Offshore Limited; *Int'l*, pg. 1232
BW OFFSHORE LIMITED; *Int'l*, pg. 1231
BW OFFSHORE MANAGEMENT B.V.—See BW Offshore Limited; *Int'l*, pg. 1231
BW OFFSHORE NIGERIA LTD.—See BW Offshore Limited; *Int'l*, pg. 1231
BW OFFSHORE NORWAY AS—See BW Offshore Limited; *Int'l*, pg. 1231
BW OFFSHORE SHIPHOLDING CYPRUS LIMITED—See BW Offshore Limited; *Int'l*, pg. 1231
BW OFFSHORE SINGAPORE PTE. LTD.—See BW Offshore Limited; *Int'l*, pg. 1232
BW OFFSHORE (UK) LIMITED—See BW Offshore Limited; *Int'l*, pg. 1231
BW OFFSHORE USA, LLC—See BW Offshore Limited; *Int'l*, pg. 1232
BW OFFSHORE USA MANAGEMENT, INC.—See BW Offshore Limited; *Int'l*, pg. 1232
BWP ASSOCIATES, LTD.—See Tenet Healthcare Corporation; *U.S. Public*, pg. 2008
BWP MANAGEMENT LIMITED—See Wesfarmers Limited; *Int'l*, pg. 8381
B&W PRESS, INC.; *U.S. Private*, pg. 419
BWP TRANSPORT, INC.—See Wind Point Advisors LLC; *U.S. Private*, pg. 4535
BWP TRUST; *Int'l*, pg. 1232
BW REAL ESTATE, INC.—See Western Alliance Bancorporation; *U.S. Public*, pg. 2354
BWR EXPLORATION, INC.; *Int'l*, pg. 1232
B/W/R—See WPP plc; *Int'l*, pg. 8483
B/W/R—See WPP plc; *Int'l*, pg. 8483
BWSC LANKA (PRIVATE) LTD.—See Mitsui E&S Holdings Co., Ltd.; *Int'l*, pg. 4984
BWSC MALTA LTD.—See Mitsui E&S Holdings Co., Ltd.; *Int'l*, pg. 4984
BWSC (MAURITIUS) LTD.—See Mitsui E&S Holdings Co., Ltd.; *Int'l*, pg. 4984
BWSC MINDANAO INC—See Mitsui E&S Holdings Co., Ltd.; *Int'l*, pg. 4984
BW SHIPPING PHILIPPINES INC.—See BW Group Ltd.; *Int'l*, pg. 1231
BW SPORTS PRACTICE, LLC—See Tenet Healthcare Corporation; *U.S. Public*, pg. 2001
BWT AKTIENGESELLSCHAFT; *Int'l*, pg. 1232
BWT AQUA AG—See BWT Aktiengesellschaft; *Int'l*, pg. 1232
BWT AUSTRIA GMBH—See BWT Aktiengesellschaft; *Int'l*, pg. 1232
BWT BELGIUM N.V.—See BWT Aktiengesellschaft; *Int'l*, pg. 1232
BWT-BETEILIGUNGSGESELLSCHAFT FUR DEN WIRTSCHAFTSAUFBAU THURINGENS MBH—See Helaba Landesbank Hessen-Thuringen; *Int'l*, pg. 3327
BWT CESKA REPUBLIKA S.R.O.—See BWT Aktiengesellschaft; *Int'l*, pg. 1232
BWT FRANCE SAS—See BWT Aktiengesellschaft; *Int'l*, pg. 1232
BWT HUNGARIA KFT—See BWT Aktiengesellschaft; *Int'l*, pg. 1232
BWT INTERNATIONAL TRADING LTD—See BWT Aktiengesellschaft; *Int'l*, pg. 1232
BWT MALTA HOLDINGS LTD.—See BWT Aktiengesellschaft; *Int'l*, pg. 1232
BWT NEDERLAND BV—See BWT Aktiengesellschaft; *Int'l*, pg. 1232
BWT PHARMA & BIOTECH AB—See BWT Aktiengesellschaft; *Int'l*, pg. 1233
BWT PHARMA & BIOTECH GMBH—See BWT Aktiengesellschaft; *Int'l*, pg. 1233

COMPANY NAME INDEX

BWT PHARMA & BIOTECH LTD.—See BWT Aktiengesellschaft; *Int'l*, pg. 1232
BWT POLSKA SP. Z.O.O.—See BWT Aktiengesellschaft; *Int'l*, pg. 1232
BWT UK LIMITED—See BWT Aktiengesellschaft; *Int'l*, pg. 1233
BWT UKRAINE LTD.—See BWT Aktiengesellschaft; *Int'l*, pg. 1232
BWT WASSERTECHNIK GMBH—See BWT Aktiengesellschaft; *Int'l*, pg. 1232
BWT WATER AND MORE IBERICA S.L.—See BWT Aktiengesellschaft; *Int'l*, pg. 1232
BWT WATER+MORE DEUTSCHLAND GMBH—See BWT Aktiengesellschaft; *Int'l*, pg. 1232
BWT WATER + MORE GMBH—See BWT Aktiengesellschaft; *Int'l*, pg. 1233
BWT WATER+MORE ITALIA SRL—See BWT Aktiengesellschaft; *Int'l*, pg. 1233
BWT WATER TECHNOLOGY (SHANGHAI) CO. LTD.—See BWT Aktiengesellschaft; *Int'l*, pg. 1233
BW WATER PTE. LTD.—See BW Group Ltd.; *Int'l*, pg. 1231
B.W. WILSON PAPER COMPANY INCORPORATED; *U.S. Private*, pg. 421
BWX LIMITED; *Int'l*, pg. 1233
BWXT CANADA LTD.—See BWX Technologies, Inc.; *U.S. Public*, pg. 413
BWX TECHNOLOGIES, INC.; *U.S. Public*, pg. 413
BWXT GOVERNMENT GROUP, INC.—See BWX Technologies, Inc.; *U.S. Public*, pg. 413
BWXT NUCLEAR ENERGY CANADA INC.—See BWX Technologies, Inc.; *U.S. Public*, pg. 413
BWXT NUCLEAR ENERGY, INC.—See Electricite de France S.A.; *Int'l*, pg. 2351
BWXT NUCLEAR OPERATIONS GROUP, INC.—See Electricite de France S.A.; *Int'l*, pg. 2351
BWXT TECHNICAL SERVICES GROUP, INC.—See BWX Technologies, Inc.; *U.S. Public*, pg. 413
BWXT Y-12, LLC—See BWX Technologies, Inc.; *U.S. Public*, pg. 413
BW YEE SENG HARDWARE TRADING SDN. BHD.—See IJM Corporation Berhad; *Int'l*, pg. 3608
BX AIWA INSURANCE SERVICE CO., LTD.—See Bunka Shutter Co., Ltd.; *Int'l*, pg. 1216
BX ASAHI KENZAI OO., LTD.—See Bunka Shutter Co., Ltd.; *Int'l*, pg. 1216
BX BUNKA AUSTRALIA PTY LTD—See Bunka Shutter Co., Ltd.; *Int'l*, pg. 1216
BX BUNKA KOUGEI CO., LTD.—See Bunka Shutter Co., Ltd.; *Int'l*, pg. 1216
BX BUNKA PANEL CO., LTD.—See Bunka Shutter Co., Ltd.; *Int'l*, pg. 1216
BX BUNKA VIETNAM CO., LTD.—See Bunka Shutter Co., Ltd.; *Int'l*, pg. 1216
B-XI BEDFORD LLC—See Welltower Inc.; *U.S. Public*, pg. 2347
B-XII BILLERICA LLC—See Welltower Inc.; *U.S. Public*, pg. 2347
B-XII SHREWSBURY LLC—See Welltower Inc.; *U.S. Public*, pg. 2347
BXI—See Ontario Municipal Employees Retirement System; *Int'l*, pg. 5584
BX KANESHIN CO., LTD.—See Bunka Shutter Co., Ltd.; *Int'l*, pg. 1216
BX KENSEI CO., LTD.—See Bunka Shutter Co., Ltd.; *Int'l*, pg. 1216
BX KOUN CO., LTD.—See Bunka Shutter Co., Ltd.; *Int'l*, pg. 1216
BXM INSURANCE SERVICES, INC.—See W.R. Berkley Corporation; *U.S. Public*, pg. 2316
BX NISHIYAMA TETSUMOU CO., LTD.—See Bunka Shutter Co., Ltd.; *Int'l*, pg. 1216
B-X NORTH ANDOVER LLC—See Welltower Inc.; *U.S. Public*, pg. 2347
B-X NORTH CHELMSFORD LLC—See Welltower Inc.; *U.S. Public*, pg. 2347
BX OKINAWA BUNKA SHUTTER CO., LTD—See Bunka Shutter Co., Ltd.; *Int'l*, pg. 1216
BXP 601 & 651 GATEWAY CENTER LP—See Boston Properties, Inc.; *U.S. Public*, pg. 372
B-X PROVIDENCE LLC—See Welltower Inc.; *U.S. Public*, pg. 2347
B-X QUINCY LLC—See Welltower Inc.; *U.S. Public*, pg. 2347
BXR GROUP B.V.; *Int'l*, pg. 1233
BX ROOTES CO., LTD.—See Bunka Shutter Co., Ltd.; *Int'l*, pg. 1216
BXR PARTNERS KFT—See BXR Group B.V.; *Int'l*, pg. 1233
BXR PARTNERS LLP—See BXR Group B.V.; *Int'l*, pg. 1233
BXR PARTNERS PTE. LTD.—See BXR Group B.V.; *Int'l*, pg. 1233
BX SHINSEI SEIKI CO., LTD.—See Bunka Shutter Co., Ltd.; *Int'l*, pg. 1216
BX TETSUYA CO., LTD.—See Bunka Shutter Co., Ltd.; *Int'l*, pg. 1216
BX TOHOKU TETSUYA CO., LTD.—See Bunka Shutter Co., Ltd.; *Int'l*, pg. 1216

BX TOSHO CO., LTD.—See Bunka Shutter Co., Ltd.; *Int'l*, pg. 1216
BX TR CO., LTD.—See Bunka Shutter Co., Ltd.; *Int'l*, pg. 1216
B-X TRUMBULL LLC—See Welltower Inc.; *U.S. Public*, pg. 2347
B-X YARMOUTH LLC—See Welltower Inc.; *U.S. Public*, pg. 2347
BX YUTORI FORM CO., LTD.—See Bunka Shutter Co., Ltd.; *Int'l*, pg. 1216
BYALLACCOUNTS, INC.—See Morningstar, Inc.; *U.S. Public*, pg. 1476
BY APPOINTMENT ONLY, INC.; *U.S. Private*, pg. 700
BYARS-WRIGHT, INC.—See Galiot Insurance Services, Inc.; *U.S. Private*, pg. 1638
BYBLOS BANK AFRICA LTD.—See Byblos Bank S.A.L.; *Int'l*, pg. 1233
BYBLOS BANK ARMENIA CJSC—See Byblos Bank S.A.L.; *Int'l*, pg. 1233
BYBLOS BANK EUROPE S.A.—See Byblos Bank S.A.L.; *Int'l*, pg. 1233
BYBLOS BANK INVEST S.A.L—See Byblos Bank S.A.L.; *Int'l*, pg. 1233
BYBLOS BANK S.A.L; *Int'l*, pg. 1233
BYBLOS BANK SYRIA S.A.—See Byblos Bank S.A.L.; *Int'l*, pg. 1233
BYBON GROUP COMPANY LIMITED; *Int'l*, pg. 1234
BYC CO., LTD.; *Int'l*, pg. 1234
BYCO ISOMERISATION PAKISTAN (PRIVATE) LIMITED—See Byco Petroleum Pakistan Limited; *Int'l*, pg. 1234
BYCO PETROLEUM PAKISTAN LIMITED; *Int'l*, pg. 1234
BYD AMERICA CORPORATION—See BYD Company Limited; *Int'l*, pg. 1234
BYD AUSTRALIA PTY. LTD.—See BYD Company Limited; *Int'l*, pg. 1234
BYD CHILE S.P.A.—See BYD Company Limited; *Int'l*, pg. 1234
BYD COMPANY LIMITED - HUIZHOU PLANT 2—See BYD Company Limited; *Int'l*, pg. 1234
BYD COMPANY LIMITED; *Int'l*, pg. 1234
BYD ELECTRONIC HUNGARY KFT—See BYD Company Limited; *Int'l*, pg. 1234
BYD ELECTRONIC INTERNATIONAL CO. LTD.—See BYD Company Limited; *Int'l*, pg. 1234
BYD E-MOTORS ECUADOR S.A—See BYD Company Limited; *Int'l*, pg. 1234
BYDESIGN, INC.—See The BCB Group, Inc.; *U.S. Private*, pg. 3992
BY DESIGN LLC; *U.S. Private*, pg. 700
BY DESIGN PUBLISHING—See CARDON Group Inc.; *Int'l*, pg. 1323
BYD EUROPEAN B.V.—See BYD Company Limited; *Int'l*, pg. 1234
BYD EUROPE B.V.—See BYD Company Limited; *Int'l*, pg. 1234
BYD (H.K.) CO., LIMITED—See BYD Company Limited; *Int'l*, pg. 1234
BYD JAPAN CO., LTD.—See BYD Company Limited; *Int'l*, pg. 1234
BYD KOREA COMPANY LTD.—See BYD Company Limited; *Int'l*, pg. 1234
BYD MALAYSIA SDN. BHD.—See BYD Company Limited; *Int'l*, pg. 1234
BYD MOTOR COLOMBIA SAS—See BYD Company Limited; *Int'l*, pg. 1234
BYD MOTORS INC.—See BYD Company Limited; *Int'l*, pg. 1234
BYD MOTORS PERU S.A.C.—See BYD Company Limited; *Int'l*, pg. 1234
BYER CALIFORNIA - LOS ANGELES FACTORY—See Byer California; *U.S. Private*, pg. 700
BYER CALIFORNIA; *U.S. Private*, pg. 700
BYERLY FORD-NISSAN INC.; *U.S. Private*, pg. 700
BYERLY'S INC.—See Lund Food Holdings, Inc.; *U.S. Private*, pg. 2515
BYERS ENGINEERING COMPANY; *U.S. Private*, pg. 700
BYGDANYTT AS—See Schibsted ASA; *Int'l*, pg. 6616
BYGGEFAKTA A/S—See Byggfakta Group Nordic HoldCo AB; *Int'l*, pg. 1234
BYGGFAKTA DOCU AS—See Byggfakta Group Nordic HoldCo AB; *Int'l*, pg. 1234
BYGGFAKTA GROUP NORDIC HOLDCO AB; *Int'l*, pg. 1234
BYGGFAKTA GROUP—See Stirling Square Capital Partners LLP; *Int'l*, pg. 7216
BYGGHEMMA BUTIK I STHLM AB—See BHG Group AB; *Int'l*, pg. 1014
BYGGHEMMA SVERIGE AB—See BHG Group AB; *Int'l*, pg. 1014
BYGGHJEMME NORGE AS—See BHG Group AB; *Int'l*, pg. 1014
BYGGLET AB—See SmartCraft ASA; *Int'l*, pg. 7002
BYGGMA ASA; *Int'l*, pg. 1235
BYGGMAKKER HANDEL AS—See Kesko Corporation; *Int'l*, pg. 4141
BYGGMAKKER NORGE AS—See Kesko Corporation; *Int'l*, pg. 4141

BYGGMASTARE ANDERS J AHLSTROM HOLDING AB; *Int'l*, pg. 1235
BYGGMAX GROUP AB—See Altor Equity Partners AB; *Int'l*, pg. 394
BYGGNADS AB FORSSTROM RAKENNUS OY—See YIT Corporation; *Int'l*, pg. 8586
BYGGPARTNER AS—See Kingspan Group PLC; *Int'l*, pg. 4178
BYGGPARTNER GRUPPEN AB; *Int'l*, pg. 1235
BYGGSERVICE & VEDLIKEHOLD AS—See Peab AB; *Int'l*, pg. 5771
BYGHJEMME.DK APS—See BHG Group AB; *Int'l*, pg. 1014
BYJC-OKUMA (BEIJING) MACHINE TOOL CORPORATION—See Okuma Corporation; *Int'l*, pg. 5550
BYJUNO AG—See Intrum AB; *Int'l*, pg. 3770
BYK ADDITIVES GMBH—See SKion GmbH; *Int'l*, pg. 6989
BYK ADDITIVES INC.—See SKion GmbH; *Int'l*, pg. 6989
BYK ADDITIVES INC.—See SKion GmbH; *Int'l*, pg. 6989
BYK ADDITIVES LTD.—See SKion GmbH; *Int'l*, pg. 6989
BYK ADDITIVES (SHANGHAI) CO., LTD.—See SKion GmbH; *Int'l*, pg. 6989
BYK ASIA PACIFIC PTE. LTD.—See SKion GmbH; *Int'l*, pg. 6989
BYK-CERA B.V.—See SKion GmbH; *Int'l*, pg. 6986
BYK-CHEMIE GMBH—See SKion GmbH; *Int'l*, pg. 6986
BYK-CHEMIE JAPAN KK—See SKion GmbH; *Int'l*, pg. 6986
BYK-CHEMIE USA, INC.—See SKion GmbH; *Int'l*, pg. 6986
THE BYKE HOSPITALITY LIMITED; *Int'l*, pg. 7630
BYK-GARDNER GMBH—See SKion GmbH; *Int'l*, pg. 6987
BYK JAPAN KK—See SKion GmbH; *Int'l*, pg. 6986
BYK KOREA LLC—See SKion GmbH; *Int'l*, pg. 6989
BYKO EHF—See Einhell Germany AG; *Int'l*, pg. 2332
BYK (TONGLING) CO., LTD.—See SKion GmbH; *Int'l*, pg. 6989
BY LIGHT PROFESSIONAL IT SERVICES, LLC—See Sagewind Capital LLC; *U.S. Private*, pg. 3527
BYLINE BANCORP, INC.; *U.S. Public*, pg. 413
BYLINE BANK—See Byline Bancorp, Inc.; *U.S. Public*, pg. 414
BYLOG GROUP CORP.; *Int'l*, pg. 1235
BY-LO MARKETS INC.; *U.S. Private*, pg. 700
BY-LO OIL COMPANY INC.; *U.S. Private*, pg. 700
BY MALENE BIRGER A/S—See Friheden Invest A/S; *Int'l*, pg. 2792
BYMANPOWER, S.L.U.—See ManpowerGroup Inc.; *U.S. Public*, pg. 1357
BYMAX CORP.; *Int'l*, pg. 1235
BYNAS CO., LTD—See CDS Co., Ltd.; *Int'l*, pg. 1371
THE BYNE GROUP—See GMLV-Global Marketing With A Local Vision; *U.S. Private*, pg. 1722
BYNET DATA COMMUNICATIONS LTD.—See RAD Group; *Int'l*, pg. 6172
BYNET ELECTRONICS LTD.—See RAD Group; *Int'l*, pg. 6172
BYNET SOFTWARE SYSTEMS LTD.—See RAD Group; *Int'l*, pg. 6172
BYNET SYSTEMS APPLICATIONS LTD.—See RAD Group; *Int'l*, pg. 6172
BYNORDIC ACQUISITION CORPORATION; *Int'l*, pg. 1235
BYON CO., LTD.; *Int'l*, pg. 1235
BYOTROL CONSUMER PRODUCTS LIMITED—See Byotrol Limited; *Int'l*, pg. 1235
BYOTROL INC.—See Byotrol Limited; *Int'l*, pg. 1235
BYOTROL LIMITED; *Int'l*, pg. 1235
BYOTROL TECHNOLOGY LIMITED—See Byotrol Limited; *Int'l*, pg. 1235
BYPASS POWER COMPANY—See Enel S.p.A.; *Int'l*, pg. 2411
BYRAM CONCRETE & SUPPLY LLC—See Peckham Industries, Inc.; *U.S. Private*, pg. 3127
BYRAM HEALTHCARE CENTERS, INC.—See Owens & Minor, Inc.; *U.S. Public*, pg. 1625
BYRAM HEALTHCARE CENTERS, INC.—See Owens & Minor, Inc.; *U.S. Public*, pg. 1625
BYRAM HEALTHCARE, INC.—See Advent International Corporation; *U.S. Private*, pg. 104
BYRD COOKIE CO.; *U.S. Private*, pg. 700
BYRDS MOBILE HOME SALES INC.; *U.S. Private*, pg. 700
BYRIDER FINANCE, LLC—See Altamont Capital Partners; *U.S. Private*, pg. 205
BYRIDER SALES OF INDIANA, LLC—See Altamont Capital Partners; *U.S. Private*, pg. 205
BYRNA TECHNOLOGIES INC.; *U.S. Public*, pg. 414
BYRNE DAIRY INC.; *U.S. Private*, pg. 701
BYRNE ELECTRICAL SPECIALISTS, INC.; *U.S. Private*, pg. 701
BYRNE GROUP LIMITED—See Wilson Bayly Holmes-Ovcon Limited; *Int'l*, pg. 8422
BYRNE, RICE & TURNER, INC.; *U.S. Private*, pg. 701
BYRNES CONSULTING, LLC; *U.S. Private*, pg. 701
BYRNES & KIEFER COMPANY; *U.S. Private*, pg. 701
BYRNE TOOL & DIE INC.—See Byrne Electrical Specialists, Inc.; *U.S. Private*, pg. 701

BYRON ENERGY LIMITED; *Int'l*, pg. 1235
BYRON E. TALBOT CONTRACTOR; *U.S. Private*, pg. 701
BYSSCO LIMITED—See Big Yellow Group plc; *Int'l*, pg. 1022
BYSTROBANK PJSC; *Int'l*, pg. 1235
BYSTRONIC AG; *Int'l*, pg. 1235
BYSTRONIC ASIA PTE. LTD.—See Bystronic AG; *Int'l*, pg. 1236
BYSTRONIC AUSTRIA GMBH—See Bystronic AG; *Int'l*, pg. 1236
BYSTRONIC BENELUX B.V.—See Bystronic AG; *Int'l*, pg. 1236
BYSTRONIC DEUTSCHLAND GMBH—See Bystronic AG; *Int'l*, pg. 1236
BYSTRONIC DO BRASIL LTDA—See Bystronic AG; *Int'l*, pg. 1236
BYSTRONIC FRANCE SAS—See Bystronic AG; *Int'l*, pg. 1236
BYSTRONIC GLASS UK LTD.—See Bystronic AG; *Int'l*, pg. 1236
BYSTRONIC IBERICA S.A.—See Bystronic AG; *Int'l*, pg. 1236
BYSTRONIC INC.—See Bystronic AG; *Int'l*, pg. 1236
BYSTRONIC LASER AG—See Bystronic AG; *Int'l*, pg. 1236
BYSTRONIC MASCHINEN AG—See Glaston Oyj Abp; *Int'l*, pg. 2989
BYSTRONIC POLSKA SP. Z O.O.—See Bystronic AG; *Int'l*, pg. 1236
BYSTRONIC SALES AG—See Bystronic AG; *Int'l*, pg. 1236
BYSTRONIC SCANDINAVIA AB—See Bystronic AG; *Int'l*, pg. 1236
BYSTRONIC (TIANJIN) MACHINERY CO, LTD.—See Bystronic AG; *Int'l*, pg. 1236
BYSTRONIC UK LTD.—See Bystronic AG; *Int'l*, pg. 1236
BYSTRONIC UK LTD.—See Bystronic AG; *Int'l*, pg. 1236
BYT BIL NORDIC AB—See Schibsted ASA; *Int'l*, pg. 6616
BYTE BULGARIA LTD.—See Ideal Group S.A.; *Int'l*, pg. 3589
BYTE COMPUTER SA—See Ideal Group S.A.; *Int'l*, pg. 3589
BYTEGRID HOLDINGS LLC—See Lincoln Property Company; *U.S. Private*, pg. 2458
BYTE IT SRL—See Ideal Group S.A.; *Int'l*, pg. 3589
BYTEK AUTOMOBILES INC.; *Int'l*, pg. 1237
BYTEK S.R.L.—See Datrix S.p.A.; *Int'l*, pg. 1982
BYTEMARK INC.—See Siemens Aktiengesellschaft; *Int'l*, pg. 6889
BYTEMARK LIMITED—See iomart Group plc; *Int'l*, pg. 3792
BYTEMOBILE EUROPEAN DEVELOPMENT CENTER MEPE—See Elliott Management Corporation; *U.S. Private*, pg. 1366
BYTEMOBILE EUROPEAN DEVELOPMENT CENTER MEPE—See Vista Equity Partners, LLC; *U.S. Private*, pg. 4395
BYTE POWER GROUP LIMITED; *Int'l*, pg. 1236
BYTE POWER (HONG KONG) LIMITED—See Byte Power Group Limited; *Int'l*, pg. 1236
BYTE POWER PTY LTD—See Byte Power Group Limited; *Int'l*, pg. 1237
BYTE POWER TECHNOLOGIES PTY LTD—See Byte Power Group Limited; *Int'l*, pg. 1237
BYTE SOFTWARE HOUSE S.P.A.; *Int'l*, pg. 1237
BYTES TECHNOLOGY GROUP (PROPRIETARY) LIMITED—See Altron Limited; *Int'l*, pg. 399
BYTEST S.R.L.—See TUV SUD AG; *Int'l*, pg. 7985
BYTEWISE MEASUREMENT SYSTEMS—See Middle-Ground Management, LP; *U.S. Private*, pg. 2713
BY THE BAY HEALTH—See University of California San Francisco Medical Center; *U.S. Private*, pg. 4308
BYT HOLDINGS LTD.; *Int'l*, pg. 1236
BYTOM S.A.—See VRG SA; *Int'l*, pg. 8313
BYUCKSAN AMERICA INC.—See Byucksan Engineering & Construction Co., Ltd.; *Int'l*, pg. 1237
BYUCKSAN CORPORATION - HUNA PLANT 1—See Byucksan Corporation; *Int'l*, pg. 1237
BYUCKSAN CORPORATION - HUNA PLANT 2—See Byucksan Corporation; *Int'l*, pg. 1237
BYUCKSAN CORPORATION; *Int'l*, pg. 1237
BYUCKSAN ENGINEERING & CONSTRUCTION CO., LTD.; *Int'l*, pg. 1237
BYUCKSAN PAINT & COATINGS CO., LTD.—See Byucksan Corporation; *Int'l*, pg. 1237
BYWATERS LTD; *Int'l*, pg. 1237
BY WORD OF MOUTH LIMITED—See Aramark; *U.S. Public*, pg. 178
BZAM LTD.; *Int'l*, pg. 1237
BZ BANK AKTIENGESELLSCHAFT; *Int'l*, pg. 1237
BZ FUND MANAGEMENT AKTIENGESELLSCHAFT—See BZ Bank Aktiengesellschaft; *Int'l*, pg. 1237
BZGRAF S.A.—See Przedsiebiorstwo Produkcyjno Handlowe Kompap S.A.; *Int'l*, pg. 6014
BZ LANGENTHALER TAGBLATT—See TX Group AG; *Int'l*, pg. 7991
BZL-BILDUNGSZENTRUM LENZING GMBH—See Lenzing Aktiengesellschaft; *Int'l*, pg. 4455

BZ WBK ASSET MANAGEMENT S.A.—See Banco Santander, S.A.; *Int'l*, pg. 826
BZ WBK FINANSE & LEASING S.A.—See Banco Santander, S.A.; *Int'l*, pg. 826
BZW LIEGENSCHAFTSVERWALTUNGS GMBH—See PORR AG; *Int'l*, pg. 5922
BZZAGENT, INC.—See Battery Ventures, L.P.; *U.S. Private*, pg. 488

C

C1000—See Jumbo Supermarkten B.V.; *Int'l*, pg. 4026
C10 COMMUNICATIONS PTY LTD.—See Casa Systems, Inc.; *U.S. Private*, pg. 778
C21 INVESTMENTS INC.; *Int'l*, pg. 1244
C29 METALS LIMITED; *Int'l*, pg. 1245
C2 BLOCKCHAIN, INC.; *U.S. Public*, pg. 415
C2CE PTY, LTD.—See Westinghouse Air Brake Technologies Corporation; *U.S. Public*, pg. 2357
C2C METALS CORP.; *Int'l*, pg. 1245
C 2 CONCERTS GMBH—See DEAG Deutsche Entertainment AG; *Int'l*, pg. 1997
C2C OUTDOOR; *U.S. Private*, pg. 709
C2 CREATIVE—See Omnicom Group Inc.; *U.S. Public*, pg. 1578
C2C SAS—See VINCI S.A.; *Int'l*, pg. 8213
C2C SERVICES LIMITED—See Severn Trent Plc; *Int'l*, pg. 6735
C2C SOLUTIONS, INC.; *U.S. Private*, pg. 709
C2 DESIGN AUTOMATION—See Cadence Design Systems, Inc.; *U.S. Public*, pg. 418
C2DESIGN; *U.S. Private*, pg. 709
C2E ENERGY, INC.; *U.S. Public*, pg. 415
C2F, INC.; *U.S. Private*, pg. 709
C2 IMAGING, LLC-CHICAGO—See Vomela Specialty Company; *U.S. Private*, pg. 4412
C2 IMAGING, LLC-ENGLEWOOD—See Vomela Specialty Company; *U.S. Private*, pg. 4412
C2 IMAGING, LLC - GAITHERSBURG—See Vomela Specialty Company; *U.S. Private*, pg. 4412
C2 IMAGING, LLC-HOUSTON—See Vomela Specialty Company; *U.S. Private*, pg. 4412
C2 IMAGING, LLC-NEW YORK—See Vomela Specialty Company; *U.S. Private*, pg. 4412
C2 IMAGING, LLC—See Vomela Specialty Company; *U.S. Private*, pg. 4412
C2 OPTIONS EXCHANGE, INCORPORATED—See Cboe Global Markets, Inc.; *U.S. Public*, pg. 459
C2SNOW; *U.S. Private*, pg. 709
C2 SOFTWARE LIMITED—See BGF Group PLC; *Int'l*, pg. 1007
C2 SOLUTIONS GROUP, INC.; *U.S. Private*, pg. 709
C2 TECHNOLOGIES, INC.; *U.S. Private*, pg. 709
C2 THERAPEUTICS, INC.—See Hoya Corporation; *Int'l*, pg. 3495
C-2 UTILITY CONTRACTORS, LLC—See Dycom Industries, Inc.; *U.S. Public*, pg. 698
C3.AI, INC.; *U.S. Public*, pg. 415
C3 BANCORP; *U.S. Private*, pg. 710
C3BANK, NATIONAL ASSOCIATION—See C3 Bancorp; *U.S. Private*, pg. 710
C3 CAPITAL PARTNERS, LP; *U.S. Private*, pg. 710
C3 CO., LTD.—See Cresco, Ltd.; *Int'l*, pg. 1840
C3 COMPUTER CORPORATION; *U.S. Private*, pg. 710
C3 CONSULTING LLC; *U.S. Private*, pg. 710
C3 CUSTOMER CONTACT CHANNELS & HOLDINGS L.P.; *U.S. Private*, pg. 710
C3 EVENT MANAGEMENT, INC.; *U.S. Private*, pg. 710
C3G, L.P.; *U.S. Private*, pg. 710
C3I, INC.—See HCL Technologies Ltd.; *Int'l*, pg. 3299
C3-ILEX LLC—See L3Harris Technologies, Inc.; *U.S. Public*, pg. 1281
C3 INTEGRATED SOLUTIONS INC.; *U.S. Private*, pg. 710
C3I SUPPORT SERVICES PRIVATE LIMITED—See Merck & Co., Inc.; *U.S. Public*, pg. 1415
C3 LIMITED—See BlackRock, Inc.; *U.S. Public*, pg. 345
C3 LIMITED—See Canada Pension Plan Investment Board; *Int'l*, pg. 1279
C3 LIMITED—See China Investment Corporation; *Int'l*, pg. 1513
C3 LIMITED—See Port of Tauranga Limited; *Int'l*, pg. 5933
C3 LIMITED—See Qube Holdings Limited; *Int'l*, pg. 6157
C3, LLC—See Constellation Energy Corporation; *U.S. Public*, pg. 571
C3 METALS INC.; *Int'l*, pg. 1245
C3 PRESENTS, LLC—See Live Nation Entertainment, Inc.; *U.S. Public*, pg. 1328
C4 GLOBAL CO., LTD.—See Tapaco Public Company Limited; *Int'l*, pg. 7461
C4 HUS AB—See Tapaco Public Company Limited; *Int'l*, pg. 7461
C4 INCORPORATED; *U.S. Private*, pg. 710
C4 THERAPEUTICS, INC.; *U.S. Public*, pg. 416
C4X DISCOVERY HOLDINGS PLC; *Int'l*, pg. 1245
C5 ACQUISITION CORPORATION; *U.S. Public*, pg. 416
C5 WEALTH MANAGEMENT, LLC; *U.S. Private*, pg. 710
CAA CLUB GROUP; *Int'l*, pg. 1245
CAANES, LLC.; *U.S. Private*, pg. 710

CA ARABIA FZ-LLC—See Broadcom Inc.; *U.S. Public*, pg. 388
CAASE GROUP BV—See Insight Enterprises, Inc.; *U.S. Public*, pg. 1129
CAA SPORTS—See TPG Capital, L.P.; *U.S. Public*, pg. 2170
CAA SPORTS—See TPG Capital, L.P.; *U.S. Public*, pg. 2170
CAB AGUAS DE PARANAGUA S.A.—See Igua Saneamento SA; *Int'l*, pg. 3603
CAB AID LIMITED—See ZIGUP plc; *Int'l*, pg. 8682
CABALETTA BIO, INC.; *U.S. Public*, pg. 416
CABANA GRILL, INC.—See Garnett Station Partners, LLC; *U.S. Private*, pg. 1645
THE CABANA GROUP, LLC; *U.S. Private*, pg. 4003
CABANA HOLDINGS LLC; *U.S. Private*, pg. 710
CABARAN MINDA SDN. BHD.—See HPI Resources Berhad; *Int'l*, pg. 3500
CABARAN PERSPEKTIF SDN. BHD.—See HPI Resources Berhad; *Int'l*, pg. 3500
CABARET EAST—See RCI Hospitality Holdings, Inc.; *U.S. Public*, pg. 1767
CABASSE GROUP; *Int'l*, pg. 1245
CABASSE S.A.—See Cabasse Group; *Int'l*, pg. 1245
CABB AG—See Permira Advisers LLP; *Int'l*, pg. 5803
CABBEEN FASHION LIMITED; *Int'l*, pg. 1245
CABB GMBH—See Permira Advisers LLP; *Int'l*, pg. 5803
CABB OY—See Permira Advisers LLP; *Int'l*, pg. 5803
CAB CAKARAN CORPORATION BERHAD; *Int'l*, pg. 1245
CAB CANARANA LTDA.—See Igua Saneamento SA; *Int'l*, pg. 3603
CABCHARGE PAYMENTS PTY. LTD.—See ComfortDelGro Corporation Limited; *Int'l*, pg. 1712
CAB COLIDER LTDA.—See Igua Saneamento SA; *Int'l*, pg. 3603
CAB COMODORO LTDA.—See Igua Saneamento SA; *Int'l*, pg. 3603
CAB EAST LLC—See Ford Motor Company; *U.S. Public*, pg. 865
CABELA'S CREDIT CARD MASTER NOTE TRUST; *U.S. Private*, pg. 710
CABELA'S LLC—See The Great American Outdoors Group LLC; *U.S. Private*, pg. 4038
CABELA'S MASTER CREDIT CARD TRUST; *U.S. Private*, pg. 710
CABELA'S RETAIL CANADA, INC.—See The Great American Outdoors Group LLC; *U.S. Private*, pg. 4038
CABELA'S RETAIL IL, INC.—See The Great American Outdoors Group LLC; *U.S. Private*, pg. 4038
CABELA'S RETAIL MO, LLC—See The Great American Outdoors Group LLC; *U.S. Private*, pg. 4038
C&A BELGIE COMM. V.—See COFRA Holding AG; *Int'l*, pg. 1694
CA BELGIUM BVBA—See Broadcom Inc.; *U.S. Public*, pg. 388
CA BELGIUM SA—See Broadcom Inc.; *U.S. Public*, pg. 389
CABELL HUNTINGTON HOSPITAL, INC.; *U.S. Private*, pg. 710
CAB FINANCIAL CORPORATION—See Park National Corporation; *U.S. Public*, pg. 1638
CAB GUARATINGUETA S.A.—See Igua Saneamento SA; *Int'l*, pg. 3603
CABIC CO., LTD.—See Bain Capital, LP; *U.S. Private*, pg. 433
CABI DEVELOPERS, LLC; *U.S. Private*, pg. 710
CABIN CO., LTD.—See Fast Retailing Co., Ltd.; *Int'l*, pg. 2621
CAB INCORPORATED; *U.S. Private*, pg. 710
CAB INCORPORATED - TEXAS MFG. & DISTR. FACILITY—See CAB Incorporated; *U.S. Private*, pg. 710
CABINDA PARTICIPACOES S.A.; *Int'l*, pg. 1245
CABINET D'EXPERTISE R.TANFERRI S.A.S.—See DEKRA e.V.; *Int'l*, pg. 2007
CABINET DISCOUNTERS INC.; *U.S. Private*, pg. 710
CABINETRY BY KARMAN—See Wellborn Cabinet, Inc.; *U.S. Private*, pg. 4474
CABINETRY DIVISION—See Zurn Elkay Water Solutions Corporation; *U.S. Public*, pg. 2412
CABINETWERKS DESIGN STUDIO, LLC.; *U.S. Private*, pg. 711
CABIN PLAZA CO., LTD.—See Dynam Japan Holdings, Co., Ltd.; *Int'l*, pg. 2239
CABINS FOR YOU, LLC; *U.S. Private*, pg. 711
CABIO BIOTECH WUHAN CO., LTD.; *Int'l*, pg. 1245
CABI S.A.—See CRH plc; *Int'l*, pg. 1844
CABI S.R.L.—See Biesse S.p.A.; *Int'l*, pg. 1020
CABKA GMBH & CO. KG—See CABKA Group GmbH; *Int'l*, pg. 1245
CABKA GROUP GMBH; *Int'l*, pg. 1245
CABKA NORTH AMERICA, INC.—See CABKA Group GmbH; *Int'l*, pg. 1245
CABKA N.V.; *Int'l*, pg. 1245
CABKA SPAIN S.L.U.—See CABKA Group GmbH; *Int'l*, pg. 1245

COMPANY NAME INDEX

CABLE ACCESSORIES (AUSTRALIA) PTY LTD—See Adamantem Capital Management Pty Limited; *Int'l*, pg. 123
CABLEAMERICA CORPORATION; *U.S. Private*, pg. 711
CABLE BAHAMAS LTD.; *Int'l*, pg. 1246
CABLECAM, LLC—See Kroenke Sports & Entertainment, LLC; *U.S. Private*, pg. 2352
CABLE CAR CAPITAL LLC; *U.S. Private*, pg. 711
THE CABLE CENTER; *U.S. Private*, pg. 4003
CABLE/CISCO—See The Carpenter Group; *U.S. Private*, pg. 4005
CABLECLIX USA, INC.; *U.S. Public*, pg. 416
CABLE CO. LTD.—See One Communications Ltd.; *Int'l*, pg. 5575
CABLECOM GMBH—See Liberty Global plc; *Int'l*, pg. 4484
CABLECOM KABELKOMMUNIKATION GMBH—See Liberty Global plc; *Int'l*, pg. 4484
CABLECOM, LLC—See Dycom Industries, Inc.; *U.S. Public*, pg. 698
CABLECOM OF CALIFORNIA, INC.—See Dycom Industries, Inc.; *U.S. Public*, pg. 698
CABLE CONNECTORS, LLC—See Dycom Industries, Inc.; *U.S. Public*, pg. 698
CABLE CORPORATION OF INDIA LTD. - MALEGAON PLANT—See Cable Corporation of India Ltd.; *Int'l*, pg. 1246
CABLE CORPORATION OF INDIA LTD. - NASHIK PLANT—See Cable Corporation of India Ltd.; *Int'l*, pg. 1246
CABLE CORPORATION OF INDIA LTD.; *Int'l*, pg. 1246
CABLECO—See The Carpenter Group; *U.S. Private*, pg. 4005
CABLECRAFT LIMITED—See Diploma PLC; *Int'l*, pg. 2128
CABLECRAFT MOTION CONTROLS LLC—See Torque Capital Group, LLC; *U.S. Private*, pg. 4189
CABLECRAFT MOTION CONTROLS LLC—See Torque Capital Group, LLC; *U.S. Private*, pg. 4189
CABLE DEVICES INCORPORATED—See CommScope Holding Company, Inc.; *U.S. Public*, pg. 548
CABLE ENTERPRISES INC.; *U.S. Private*, pg. 711
CABLEL WIRES S.A.—See Viohalco SA/NV; *Int'l*, pg. 8243
CABLE MANAGEMENT PRODUCTS LTD.—See ABB Ltd.; *Int'l*, pg. 52
CABLE MANUFACTURING, INC., *U.S. Private*, pg. 711
CABLEMAS, S.A. DE C.V.—See Grupo Televisa, S.A.B.; *Int'l*, pg. 3136
CABLENA DO BRASIL LTDA—See Grupo Carso, S.A.B. de C.V.; *Int'l*, pg. 3123
CABLENA DO BRASIL LTDA - TELECOM PLANT—See Grupo Carso, S.A.B. de C.V.; *Int'l*, pg. 3123
CABLENA, S.A.—See Grupo Carso, S.A.B. de C.V.; *Int'l*, pg. 3123
CABLENET, S.A.—See America Movil, S.A.B. de C.V.; *Int'l*, pg. 421
CABLENET SERVICES UNLIMITED, LLC—See Resilience Capital Partners, LLC; *U.S. Private*, pg. 3405
CABLE NEWS NETWORK, INC.—See Warner Bros. Discovery, Inc.; *U.S. Public*, pg. 2328
CABLE ONDA, S.A.—See Millicom International Cellular S.A.; *Int'l*, pg. 4896
CABLE ONE, INC.; *U.S. Public*, pg. 416
CABLEORGANIZER.COM, INC.; *U.S. Private*, pg. 711
CABLE PLUS INC.; *U.S. Private*, pg. 711
CABLEPRICE (NZ) LTD.—See Hitachi, Ltd.; *Int'l*, pg. 3415
CABLE PRINT B.V.B.A.—See Diebold Nixdorf, Inc.; *U.S. Public*, pg. 659
CABLEREADY CORPORATION; *U.S. Private*, pg. 711
CABLERIES DE VALENCIENNES SAS—See Prysmian S.p.A.; *Int'l*, pg. 6010
CABLE RUNNER AUSTRIA GMBH & CO. KG—See America Movil, S.A.B. de C.V.; *Int'l*, pg. 421
CABLE RUNNER IBERICA S.L.—See America Movil, S.A.B. de C.V.; *Int'l*, pg. 421
CABLESANDKITS.COM; *U.S. Private*, pg. 711
CABLESCAN B.V.—See Amphenol Corporation; *U.S. Public*, pg. 129
CABLESCAN LIMITED—See Amphenol Corporation; *U.S. Public*, pg. 129
THE CABLESHOPPE INC.; *Int'l*, pg. 7630
CABLE SISTEMA DE VICTORIA, S.A. DE C.V.—See Grupo Televisa, S.A.B.; *Int'l*, pg. 3136
CABLE SOLUTIONS & ELECTRICAL (SEA) PTE LTD.—See Sonepar S.A.; *Int'l*, pg. 7090
CABLE SOLUTIONS (SEA) PTE. LTD.—See KVC Industrial Supplies Sdn. Bhd.; *Int'l*, pg. 4349
CABLE SOLUTIONS (THAILAND) CO. LTD.—See Sonepar S.A.; *Int'l*, pg. 7090
CABLES PLUS LLC; *U.S. Private*, pg. 711
CABLES TO GO—See Legrand S.A.; *Int'l*, pg. 4445
CABLES TO GO—See Legrand S.A.; *Int'l*, pg. 4445
CABLES UNLIMITED, INC.—See RF Industries, Ltd.; *U.S. Public*, pg. 1796
CABLES Y ESLINGAS, S.A.—See Axel Johnson Gruppen AB; *Int'l*, pg. 763
CABLE SYSTEM CONSTRUCTION CO., LTD.—See SYNCLAYER INC.; *Int'l*, pg. 7382
CABLE SYSTEMS, INC.—See Altice USA, Inc.; *U.S. Public*, pg. 87

CABLE TECH, LTD.—See Kobelco Wire Co Ltd; *Int'l*, pg. 4221
CABLETEC INTERCONNECT COMPONENTS SYSTEMS LIMITED—See Diploma PLC; *Int'l*, pg. 2128
CABLE TELEVISION LABORATORIES, INC.; *U.S. Private*, pg. 711
CABLE TELEVISION TOKYO, LTD.—See KDDI Corporation; *Int'l*, pg. 4111
CABLE TELEVISION TSUYAMA CO., LTD.—See TOKAI Holdings Corporation; *Int'l*, pg. 7779
CABLEUROPA, S.A.U.—See Banco Santander, S.A.; *Int'l*, pg. 825
CABLEVISION HOLDING S.A.; *Int'l*, pg. 1246
CABLEVISION LIGHTPATH, LLC—See Altice USA, Inc.; *U.S. Public*, pg. 87
CABLEVISION OF MONMOUTH, INC.—See Altice USA, Inc.; *U.S. Public*, pg. 87
CABLEVISION S.A.—See Cablevision Holding S.A.; *Int'l*, pg. 1246
CABLEVISION SYSTEMS CORPORATION—See Altice USA, Inc.; *U.S. Public*, pg. 87
CABLEVISION SYSTEMS WESTCHESTER CORPORATION—See Altice USA, Inc.; *U.S. Public*, pg. 87
CABLEWAY AG—See Teleste Corporation; *Int'l*, pg. 7541
CABLEWAY CYBER OPTIC GMBH & CO. KG—See Teleste Corporation; *Int'l*, pg. 7541
CABLEWAY MITTE GMBH—See Teleste Corporation; *Int'l*, pg. 7541
CABLEWAY NORD GMBH—See Teleste Corporation; *Int'l*, pg. 7541
CABLEWAY SUD GMBH—See Teleste Corporation; *Int'l*, pg. 7541
CABLEWHOLESALE.COM; *U.S. Private*, pg. 711
CABLE & WIRELESS (BARBADOS) LTD.—See Liberty Global plc; *Int'l*, pg. 4485
CABLE & WIRELESS COMMUNICATIONS LIMITED—See Liberty Global plc; *Int'l*, pg. 4485
CABLE & WIRELESS PANAMA S.A.—See Liberty Global plc; *Int'l*, pg. 4485
CABLE & WIRELESS (SEYCHELLES) LTD.; *Int'l*, pg. 1246
CABLE & WIRELESS UK HOLDINGS LIMITED—See Vodafone Group Plc; *Int'l*, pg. 8284
CABLE & WIRELESS WORLDWIDE PLC—See Vodafone Group Plc; *Int'l*, pg. 8284
CABLEX LTD.—See Swisscom AG; *Int'l*, pg. 7373
CABLEX METAL MATERIAL (ANFU) CO., LTD.—See Copartner Technology Corporation; *Int'l*, pg. 1793
CABLEXPRESS CORPORATION—See H.I.G. Capital, LLC; *U.S. Private*, pg. 1829
CABLEX WIRE & CABLE (KUNSHAN) MFG. LIMITED—See Copartner Technology Corporation; *Int'l*, pg. 1793
CABLEX WIRE (SHENZHEN) MFG CO., LTD.—See Copartner Technology Corporation; *Int'l*, pg. 1793
CABLOFIL INC.—See Legrand S.A.; *Int'l*, pg. 4445
CABLO METALL-RECYCLING UND HANDEL GMBH—See Aurubis AG; *Int'l*, pg. 715
CABLOSWISS S.P.A—See Nexans S.A.; *Int'l*, pg. 5241
CAB MARINE RESOURCES SDN. BHD.—See Cab Cakaran Corporation Berhad; *Int'l*, pg. 1245
CAB MT PARTICIPACOES LTDA—See Igua Saneamento SA; *Int'l*, pg. 3603
CABNET HOLDING BERHAD; *Int'l*, pg. 1246
CABNET M&E SDN. BHD.—See Cabnet Holding Berhad; *Int'l*, pg. 1246
CABO DRILLING (ATLANTIC) CORP—See Cabo Drilling Corp.; *Int'l*, pg. 1246
CABO DRILLING CORP.; *Int'l*, pg. 1246
CABO DRILLING (INTERNATIONAL) INC.—See Cabo Drilling Corp.; *Int'l*, pg. 1246
CABO DRILLING (ONTARIO) CORP.—See Cabo Drilling Corp.; *Int'l*, pg. 1246
CABO DRILLING (PACIFIC) CORP.—See Cabo Drilling Corp.; *Int'l*, pg. 1246
CABO DRILLING (PANAMA) CORP.—See Cabo Drilling Corp.; *Int'l*, pg. 1246
CABOOLTURE HOSPITAL PTY LIMITED—See Ramsay Health Care Limited; *Int'l*, pg. 6199
CABOT ACTIVATED CARBON B.V.—See Cabot Corporation; *U.S. Public*, pg. 416
CABOT ADVANCED BATTERY MATERIALS (TIANJIN) CO., LTD.—See Cabot Corporation; *U.S. Public*, pg. 416
CABOT AEROGEL GMBH—See Cabot Corporation; *U.S. Public*, pg. 416
CABOT ARGENTINA S.A.I.C.—See Cabot Corporation; *U.S. Public*, pg. 416
CABOT BRASIL INDUSTRIA E COMERCIO LTDA.—See Cabot Corporation; *U.S. Public*, pg. 416
CABOT B.V.—See Cabot Corporation; *U.S. Public*, pg. 416
CABOT CANADA LTD.—See Cabot Corporation; *U.S. Public*, pg. 416
CABOT CARBON LIMITED—See Cabot Corporation; *U.S. Public*, pg. 416
CABOT (CHINA) LIMITED—See Cabot Corporation; *U.S. Public*, pg. 416
CABOT COACH BUILDER INC.; *U.S. Private*, pg. 711

CABOT COLOMBIANA S.A.—See Cabot Corporation; *U.S. Public*, pg. 416
CABOT CORPORATION - BUSINESS & TECHNOLOGY CENTER—See Cabot Corporation; *U.S. Public*, pg. 416
CABOT CORPORATION CARBON BLACK DIVISION—See Cabot Corporation; *U.S. Public*, pg. 416
CABOT CORPORATION; *U.S. Public*, pg. 416
CABOT CREAMERY CO-OPERATIVE INC.—See Agri-Mark, Inc.; *U.S. Private*, pg. 129
CABOT CREDIT MANAGEMENT GROUP LIMITED—See Encore Capital Group, Inc.; *U.S. Public*, pg. 759
CABOT CREDIT MANAGEMENT LIMITED—See Encore Capital Group, Inc.; *U.S. Public*, pg. 759
CABOT ENERGY PLC; *Int'l*, pg. 1246
CABOT FINANCIAL (EUROPE) LIMITED—See Encore Capital Group, Inc.; *U.S. Public*, pg. 759
CABOT FINANCIAL FRANCE—See Encore Capital Group, Inc.; *U.S. Public*, pg. 759
CABOT FINANCIAL GROUP LIMITED—See AnaCap Financial Partners LLP; *Int'l*, pg. 445
CABOT FINANCIAL (IRELAND) LIMITED—See AnaCap Financial Partners LLP; *Int'l*, pg. 445
CABOT FINANCIAL (MARLIN) LIMITED—See Encore Capital Group, Inc.; *U.S. Public*, pg. 759
CABOT GMBH—See Cabot Corporation; *U.S. Public*, pg. 416
CABOT INDIA LIMITED—See Cabot Corporation; *U.S. Public*, pg. 416
CABOT INTERNATIONAL GMBH—See Cabot Corporation; *U.S. Public*, pg. 417
CABOT INVESTMENT TECHNOLOGY, INC.—See FactSet Research Systems Inc.; *U.S. Public*, pg. 819
CABOT LODGE SECURITIES, LLC; *U.S. Private*, pg. 711
CABOT MALAYSIA SDN. BHD.—See Cabot Corporation; *U.S. Public*, pg. 417
CABOT MICROELECTRONICS JAPAN K.K.—See Entegris, Inc.; *U.S. Public*, pg. 776
CABOT MICROELECTRONICS POLISHING CORPORATION—See Entegris, Inc.; *U.S. Public*, pg. 776
CABOT MICROELECTRONICS SINGAPORE PTE. LTD.—See Entegris, Inc.; *U.S. Public*, pg. 776
CABOT NORIT AMERICAS, INC.—See Cabot Corporation; *U.S. Public*, pg. 417
CABOT NORIT ITALIA S.P.A.—See Cabot Corporation; *U.S. Public*, pg. 417
CABOT NORIT JAPAN CO. LTD.—See Cabot Corporation; *U.S. Public*, pg. 417
CABOT NORIT NEDERLAND B.V.—See Cabot Corporation; *U.S. Public*, pg. 417
CABOT NORIT SINGAPORE PTE. LTD.—See Cabot Corporation; *U.S. Public*, pg. 417
CABOT PERFORMANCE MATERIALS NETHERLANDS B.V.—See Cabot Corporation; *U.S. Public*, pg. 417
CABOT PERFORMANCE MATERIALS (ZHUHAI) CO., LTD.—See Cabot Corporation; *U.S. Public*, pg. 417
CABOT PETROLEUM NORTH SEA LIMITED—See Coterra Energy Inc.; *U.S. Public*, pg. 587
CABOT PLASTICS BELGIUM S.A.—See Cabot Corporation; *U.S. Public*, pg. 417
CABOT PLASTICS CANADA LP—See Cabot Corporation; *U.S. Public*, pg. 417
CABOT PLASTICS HONG KONG LIMITED—See Cabot Corporation; *U.S. Public*, pg. 417
CABOT PROPERTIES, INC.; *U.S. Private*, pg. 711
CABOT RHEINFELDEN GMBH & CO. KG—See Cabot Corporation; *U.S. Public*, pg. 417
CABOT SANMAR LTD.—See Cabot Corporation; *U.S. Public*, pg. 417
CABOT SANMAR LTD.—See Sanmar Holdings Ltd.; *Int'l*, pg. 6546
CABOT SECURITY MATERIALS INC.—See SICPA Holding SA; *Int'l*, pg. 6882
CABOT SINGAPORE PTE. LTD.—See Cabot Corporation; *U.S. Public*, pg. 417
CABOT SPECIALTY CHEMICALS COORDINATION CENTER—See Cabot Corporation; *U.S. Public*, pg. 417
CABOT SPECIALTY CHEMICALS, INC.—See Cabot Corporation; *U.S. Public*, pg. 417
CABOT SPECIALTY CHEMICALS MEXICO S.A.P.I. DE C.V.—See Cabot Corporation; *U.S. Public*, pg. 417
CABOT SPECIALTY FLUIDS INC.—See Sinomine Resource Group Co., Ltd.; *Int'l*, pg. 6953
CABOT SQUARE CAPITAL LLP; *Int'l*, pg. 1246
CABOT SUPERMETALS K.K.—See Cabot Corporation; *U.S. Public*, pg. 417
CABOT SWITZERLAND GMBH—See Cabot Corporation; *U.S. Public*, pg. 417
CABO VERDE, S.A.R.L.—See Caixa Geral de Depositos S.A.; *Int'l*, pg. 1260
CABO VERDE TELECOM S.A.—See Altice Europe N.V.; *Int'l*, pg. 392
CAB PIQUETE S.A.—See Igua Saneamento SA; *Int'l*, pg. 3603
CABRAL GOLD INC.; *Int'l*, pg. 1246

CABRAL WESTERN MOTORS, INC.; U.S. Private, pg. 711
CABRERA SERVICES, INC.—See The Toronto-Dominion Bank; Int'l, pg. 7695
CABRINHAKITES, INC.—See Shriro Pacific Ltd.; Int'l, pg. 6866
CABRINI HEALTH LIMITED; Int'l, pg. 1246
CABRINI TECHNOLOGY SERVICES—See Cabrini Health Limited; Int'l, pg. 1246
CABS NURSING HOME COMPANY INC.; U.S. Private, pg. 711
CABTEC THAI CO., LTD.—See Komatsu Ltd.; Int'l, pg. 4235
CABUS & RAULOT SA—See Sonepar S.A.; Int'l, pg. 7090
CAC AMERICA CORPORATION—See CAC Corporation; Int'l, pg. 1247
CACCO, INC.; Int'l, pg. 1247
CAC CORPORATION; Int'l, pg. 1246
CAC CROIT CORPORATION—See CAC Holdings Corporation; Int'l, pg. 1247
CACDO CO., LTD.—See Dentsu Group Inc.; Int'l, pg. 2034
CACESA-COMPANIA AUXILIAR AL CARGO EXPRESS, S.A.—See International Consolidated Airlines Group S.A.; Int'l, pg. 3745
CAC EUROPE LIMITED—See CAC Corporation; Int'l, pg. 1247
CAC-FLORIDA MEDICAL CENTERS, LLC—See Humana, Inc.; U.S. Public, pg. 1069
CACHE CREEK FOODS, LLC.; U.S. Private, pg. 711
CACHE CREEK INDUSTRIES, LLC; U.S. Private, pg. 711
CACHEMATRIX HOLDINGS, LLC—See BlackRock, Inc.; U.S. Public, pg. 345
CACHENDO LLC—See SpeedCast International Limited; Int'l, pg. 7132
CACHE RIVER VALLEY SEED, LLC; U.S. Private, pg. 712
CACHET INDUSTRIES INC.; U.S. Private, pg. 712
CACHET PHARMACEUTICAL CO., LTD.; Int'l, pg. 1247
CACHET PHARMACEUTICALS PRIVATE LIMITED—See Alkem Laboratories Ltd.; Int'l, pg. 330
CACHE VALLEY BANKING COMPANY; U.S. Private, pg. 712
CACHE VALLEY BANK—See Cache Valley Banking Company; U.S. Private, pg. 712
CACHE VALLEY ELECTRIC COMPANY INC. - AVTEC SYSTEMS INTEGRATOR DIVISION—See Cache Valley Electric Company Inc.; U.S. Private, pg. 712
CACHE VALLEY ELECTRIC COMPANY INC.; U.S. Private, pg. 712
CACHE VALLEY ELECTRIC COMPANY INC.—See Cache Valley Electric Company Inc.; U.S. Private, pg. 712
CACHE VALLEY PUBLISHING COMPANY—See Pioneer Newspapers Inc.; U.S. Private, pg. 3187
C&A (CHINA) CO., LTD—See COFRA Holding AG; Int'l, pg. 1694
CAC HOLDINGS CORPORATION; Int'l, pg. 1247
CACI DYNAMIC SYSTEMS, INC.—See CACI International Inc.; U.S. Public, pg. 417
C.A. CIGARRERA BIGOTT SUCS—See British American Tobacco plc; Int'l, pg. 1167
CACI, INC.-FEDERAL—See CACI International Inc.; U.S. Public, pg. 417
CACI INTERNATIONAL INC.; U.S. Public, pg. 417
CACI-ISS, INC.—See CACI International Inc.; U.S. Public, pg. 417
CACI LIMITED—See CACI International Inc.; U.S. Public, pg. 417
CAC INDIA PRIVATE LIMITED—See CAC Holdings Corporation; Int'l, pg. 1247
CAC INDUSTRIES INC.; U.S. Private, pg. 711
CACI N.V.—See CACI International Inc.; U.S. Public, pg. 417
CACI PREMIER TECHNOLOGY, INC.—See CACI International Inc.; U.S. Public, pg. 417
CACIQUE, INC.; U.S. Private, pg. 712
CACI TECHNOLOGIES, INC—See CACI International Inc.; U.S. Public, pg. 417
CACI-WGI, INC.—See CACI International Inc.; U.S. Public, pg. 417
CAC KNOWLEDGE CO., LTD.—See Yuasa Trading Co., Ltd.; Int'l, pg. 8609
CAC LLC—See Berkshire Hathaway Inc.; U.S. Public, pg. 298
CAC MARUHA NICHIRO SYSTEMS CORPORATION—See CAC Corporation; Int'l, pg. 1247
CAC MARUHA NICHIRO SYSTEMS LTD.—See CAC Corporation; Int'l, pg. 1247
CAC MEDICAL CENTER HOLDINGS, INC.—See Humana, Inc.; U.S. Public, pg. 1069
CACONDE PARTICIPACOES S.A.; Int'l, pg. 1247
CA CONSULTING SA—See ComArch S.A.; Int'l, pg. 1707
CAC ORBIS CORPORATION—See CAC Corporation; Int'l, pg. 1247
CAC SHANGHAI CORPORATION—See CAC Corporation; Int'l, pg. 1247
CACTUS ADVERTISING & MARKETING ETHIOPIA—See WPP plc; Int'l, pg. 8484
CACTUS COATINGS, INC.—See Marck & Associates, Inc.; U.S. Private, pg. 2571

CACTUS CO., LTD.—See NOF Corporation; Int'l, pg. 5399
CACTUS COMMUNICATIONS, INC.; U.S. Private, pg. 712
CACTUS FEEDERS, INC.; U.S. Private, pg. 712
CACTUS IMAGING LIMITED—See OPUS Group Limited; Int'l, pg. 5606
CACTUS, INC.; U.S. Public, pg. 418
CACTUS PETE'S, LLC—See PENN Entertainment, Inc.; U.S. Public, pg. 1662
CACTUS; U.S. Private, pg. 712
CA CULTURAL TECHNOLOGY GROUP LIMITED; Int'l, pg. 1245
C. A. CURTZE COMPANY INC.; U.S. Private, pg. 704
CADAC EUROPE B.V.—See Dometic Group AB; Int'l, pg. 2160
CADAC GROUP B.V.—See Cadac Group Holding B.V.; Int'l, pg. 1247
CADAC GROUP HOLDING B.V.; Int'l, pg. 1247
CADAGUA S.A.—See Ferrovial S.A.; Int'l, pg. 2644
CADAM BV—See Carrefour SA; Int'l, pg. 1344
CADAM S.A.—See IMin Partners, L.P.; U.S. Private, pg. 2047
CADARET, GRANT & CO., INC.—See Lee Equity Partners LLC; U.S. Private, pg. 2412
CADBURY ADAMS MEXICO, S. DE R.L. DE C.V.—See Mondelez International, Inc.; U.S. Public, pg. 1460
CADBURY ADAMS MIDDLE EAST S.A.L.—See Mondelez International, Inc.; U.S. Public, pg. 1460
CADBURY ADAMS (THAILAND) LIMITED—See Mondelez International, Inc.; U.S. Public, pg. 1460
CADBURY CONFECTIONERY MALAYSIA SDN BHD—See Mondelez International, Inc.; U.S. Public, pg. 1460
CADBURY CONFECTIONERY SALES (M) SDN, BHD.—See Mondelez International, Inc.; U.S. Public, pg. 1460
CADBURY EIGHT LLP—See Mondelez International, Inc.; U.S. Public, pg. 1460
CADBURY ENTERPRISES PTE. LTD.—See Mondelez International, Inc.; U.S. Public, pg. 1460
CADBURY FOOD CO. LTD.—See Mondelez International, Inc.; U.S. Public, pg. 1460
CADBURY FRANCE SAS—See Mondelez International, Inc.; U.S. Public, pg. 1460
CADBURY GHANA LTD.—See Mondelez International, Inc.; U.S. Public, pg. 1460
CADBURY INDIA LIMITED—See Mondelez International, Inc.; U.S. Public, pg. 1460
CADBURY IRELAND LTD.—See Mondelez International, Inc.; U.S. Public, pg. 1460
CADBURY JAPAN LTD.—See Mondelez International, Inc.; U.S. Public, pg. 1460
CADBURY KENYA LIMITED—See Mondelez International, Inc.; U.S. Public, pg. 1461
CADBURY LIMITED—See Mondelez International, Inc.; U.S. Public, pg. 1460
CADBURY LTD.—See Mondelez International, Inc.; U.S. Public, pg. 1461
CADBURY MARKETING SERVICES PTY LIMITED—See Mondelez International, Inc.; U.S. Public, pg. 1461
CADBURY NIGERIA PLC—See Mondelez International, Inc.; U.S. Public, pg. 1461
CADBURY PAKISTAN LIMITED—See Mondelez International, Inc.; U.S. Public, pg. 1461
CADBURY SINGAPORE PTE. LTD.—See Mondelez International, Inc.; U.S. Public, pg. 1461
CADBURY SOUTH AFRICA (PTY) LTD.—See Mondelez International, Inc.; U.S. Public, pg. 1461
CADBURY SOUTH AFRICA—See Mondelez International, Inc.; U.S. Public, pg. 1461
CADBURY STANI ADAMS ARGENTINA S.A.—See Mondelez International, Inc.; U.S. Public, pg. 1461
CADBURY (SWAZILAND) (PTY) LIMITED—See Mondelez International, Inc.; U.S. Public, pg. 1460
CADBURY TRADING HONG KONG LTD.—See Mondelez International, Inc.; U.S. Public, pg. 1461
CADBURY UK LIMITED—See Mondelez International, Inc.; U.S. Public, pg. 1461
CADCENTRE PROPERTY LIMITED—See Schneider Electric SE; Int'l, pg. 6623
CADD EDGE INC.; U.S. Private, pg. 712
CADDELL CONSTRUCTION CO., INC.; U.S. Private, pg. 712
CADDEN CROWE (QUEENSLAND) PTY LIMITED—See Rubicor Group Limited; Int'l, pg. 6422
CADDEN CROWE (VICTORIA) PTY LIMITED—See Rubicor Group Limited; Int'l, pg. 6422
CADDOCK ELECTRONICS, INC.; U.S. Private, pg. 712
CADDOCK NETWORK DIVISION—See Caddock Electronics, Inc.; U.S. Private, pg. 712
CADDO CREEK RESOURCES CO., LLC—See NACCO Industries, Inc.; U.S. Public, pg. 1490
CADDO ELECTRIC COOPERATIVE; U.S. Private, pg. 712
CADDO ENTERPRISES, LIMITED—See Hang Lung Group Limited; Int'l, pg. 3244
CADDO HOLDING COMPANY, LLC—See ALLETE, Inc.; U.S. Public, pg. 79
CADDPLUS INC—See MGS Manufacturing Group, Inc.; U.S. Private, pg. 2695

CADDY CORPORATION OF AMERICA; U.S. Private, pg. 712
CADECI INTERNATIONAL CORPORATION; U.S. Private, pg. 712
CADELER A/S; Int'l, pg. 1247
CADELTA GROUP—See Lendlease Corporation Limited; Int'l, pg. 4451
CADE, LTD.; U.S. Private, pg. 712
CADEMO CORPORATION—See SBM Offshore N.V.; Int'l, pg. 6607
CADENA CONTRACTING, INC.; U.S. Private, pg. 712
CADENCE AEROSPACE, LLC—See Arlington Capital Partners LLC; U.S. Private, pg. 327
CADENCE AMS DESIGN INDIA PRIVATE LIMITED—See Cadence Design Systems, Inc.; U.S. Public, pg. 418
CADENCE CAPITAL LIMITED; Int'l, pg. 1247
CADENCE CAPITAL MANAGEMENT LLC—See Pacific Mutual Holding Company; U.S. Private, pg. 3069
CADENCE DESIGN (ISRAEL) II LTD.—See Cadence Design Systems, Inc.; U.S. Public, pg. 418
CADENCE DESIGN SERVICES TYK—See Cadence Design Systems, Inc.; U.S. Public, pg. 418
CADENCE DESIGN SYSTEMS AB—See Cadence Design Systems, Inc.; U.S. Public, pg. 418
CADENCE DESIGN SYSTEMS DO BRASIL MICRO-ELETRONICA LTDA.—See Cadence Design Systems, Inc.; U.S. Public, pg. 418
CADENCE DESIGN SYSTEMS GMBH—See Cadence Design Systems, Inc.; U.S. Public, pg. 418
CADENCE DESIGN SYSTEMS, INC.; U.S. Public, pg. 418
CADENCE DESIGN SYSTEMS (INDIA) PRIVATE LTD.—See Cadence Design Systems, Inc.; U.S. Public, pg. 418
CADENCE DESIGN SYSTEMS (IRELAND) LIMITED—See Cadence Design Systems, Inc.; U.S. Public, pg. 418
CADENCE DESIGN SYSTEMS (ISRAEL) LIMITED—See Cadence Design Systems, Inc.; U.S. Public, pg. 418
CADENCE DESIGN SYSTEMS (JAPAN) B.V.—See Cadence Design Systems, Inc.; U.S. Public, pg. 418
CADENCE DESIGN SYSTEMS KFT.—See Cadence Design Systems, Inc.; U.S. Public, pg. 418
CADENCE DESIGN SYSTEMS LIMITED—See Cadence Design Systems, Inc.; U.S. Public, pg. 418
CADENCE DESIGN SYSTEMS MANAGEMENT (SHANGHAI) CO., LTD.—See Cadence Design Systems, Inc.; U.S. Public, pg. 418
CADENCE DESIGN SYSTEMS S.A.S.—See Cadence Design Systems, Inc.; U.S. Public, pg. 418
CADENCE DESIGN SYSTEMS (S) PTE LTD.—See Cadence Design Systems, Inc.; U.S. Public, pg. 418
CADENCE, INC.—See Kohlberg & Company, LLC; U.S. Private, pg. 2337
CADENCE INSURANCE, INC.—See Arthur J. Gallagher & Co.; U.S. Public, pg. 204
CADENCE KOREA LTD.—See Cadence Design Systems, Inc.; U.S. Public, pg. 418
CADENCE MCSHANE CORPORATION; U.S. Private, pg. 713
CADENCE MINERALS PLC; Int'l, pg. 1247
CADENCE PHARMACEUTICALS, INC.—See Mallinckrodt Public Limited Company; Int'l, pg. 4663
CADENCE RESEARCH & CONSULTING; U.S. Private, pg. 713
CADENSWORTH FZE—See Redington (India) Limited; Int'l, pg. 6247
CADENSWORTH (INDIA) PVT LIMITED.—See Redington (India) Limited; Int'l, pg. 6247
CADENT ENERGY PARTNERS, LLC; U.S. Private, pg. 713
CAD ENTERPRISES, INC.—See Crawford United Corporation; U.S. Public, pg. 592
CADENT, LLC—See Novacap Management Inc.; Int'l, pg. 5453
CADENT TECHNOLOGY, INC.—See Cross Mediaworks, Inc.; U.S. Private, pg. 1105
C.A. DE SEGUROS AMERICAN INTERNATIONAL—See American International Group, Inc.; U.S. Public, pg. 106
CA DESIGN, INC.—See CyberAgent, Inc.; Int'l, pg. 1892
C A DESIGN SERVICES LTD—See HAL Trust N.V.; Int'l, pg. 3226
CADES STUDEC TECHNOLOGIES (INDIA) PRIVATE LIMITED—See Axiscades Technologies Ltd.; Int'l, pg. 770
CA DEUTSCHLAND GMBH—See Broadcom Inc.; U.S. Public, pg. 389
CADEX ELECTRONICS GMBH—See Cadex Electronics Inc.; Int'l, pg. 1248
CADEX ELECTRONICS INC.; Int'l, pg. 1248
CADIA HOLDINGS PTY LTD—See Newmont Corporation; U.S. Public, pg. 1517
CADIA MINES PTY LTD—See Newmont Corporation; U.S. Public, pg. 1517
CADIENT, INC.—See Cognizant Technology Solutions Corporation; U.S. Public, pg. 523
CADIE PRODUCTS CORP.; U.S. Private, pg. 713
CADILLAC COFFEE COMPANY; U.S. Private, pg. 713
CADILLAC EUROPE GMBH—See General Motors Company; U.S. Public, pg. 923

COMPANY NAME INDEX

THE CADILLAC FAIRVIEW CORPORATION LIMITED; *Int'l*, pg. 7630
CADILLAC JACK, INC.—See Flutter Entertainment plc; *Int'l*, pg. 2715
CADILLAC OF ARLINGTON—See Group 1 Automotive, Inc.; *U.S. Public*, pg. 971
CADILLAC OF GREENWICH, INC.—See General Motors Company; *U.S. Public*, pg. 923
CADILLAC OF PORTLAND LLOYD CENTER, LLC—See Lithia Motors, Inc.; *U.S. Public*, pg. 1321
CADILLAC PLASTIC FRANCE S.A.S.—See ThyssenKrupp AG; *Int'l*, pg. 7729
CADILLAC POLANCO, S.A. DE C.V.—See General Motors Company; *U.S. Public*, pg. 923
CADILLAC PRODUCTS, INC.; *U.S. Private*, pg. 713
CADILLAC PRODUCTS PACKAGING COMPANY - DALLAS PLANT—See Cadillac Products, Inc.; *U.S. Private*, pg. 713
CADILLAC PRODUCTS PACKAGING COMPANY - PARIS PLANT—See Cadillac Products, Inc.; *U.S. Private*, pg. 713
CADILLAC RENEWABLE ENERGY LLC—See I Squared Capital Advisors (US) LLC; *U.S. Private*, pg. 2025
CADILLAC UNIFORM & LINEN SUPPLY; *U.S. Private*, pg. 713
CADILLAC VENTURES HOLDINGS INC.—See Cadillac Ventures Inc.; *Int'l*, pg. 1248
CADILLAC VENTURES INC.; *Int'l*, pg. 1248
CADINI S.R.L.—See Siyaram Silk Mills Limited; *Int'l*, pg. 6968
CADISTA HOLDINGS INC.—See Jubilant Bhartia Group; *Int'l*, pg. 4020
CAD IT S.P.A.; *Int'l*, pg. 1247
CADIZ ASSET MANAGEMENT (PTY) LTD—See Stellar Capital Partners Limited; *Int'l*, pg. 7204
CADIZ HOLDINGS (PTY) LTD—See Stellar Capital Partners Limited; *Int'l*, pg. 7204
CADIZ INC.; *U.S. Public*, pg. 419
CAD-KOMPAGNIET A/S—See Lagercrantz Group AB; *Int'l*, pg. 4393
CADLAB INC.—See Zuken, Inc.; *Int'l*, pg. 8694
THE CADLE COMPANY INC.; *U.S. Private*, pg. 4003
CADLOG GMBH—See Sesa S.p.A.; *Int'l*, pg. 6728
CADLOG GROUP SRL—See Sesa S.p.A.; *Int'l*, pg. 6728
CADLOG S.A.S.—See Sesa S.p.A.; *Int'l*, pg. 6728
CADLOG S.L.—See Sesa S.p.A.; *Int'l*, pg. 6728
CADMAN (BLACK DIAMOND), INC.—See Heidelberg Materials AG; *Int'l*, pg. 3309
CADMAN, INC.—See Heidelberg Materials AG; *Int'l*, pg. 3313
CADMAN (ROCK), INC.—See Heidelberg Materials AG; *Int'l*, pg. 3309
CADMAN (SEATTLE), INC.—See Heidelberg Materials AG; *Int'l*, pg. 3309
CADMES FRANCE S.A.S.—See Bechtle AG; *Int'l*, pg. 937
CADMIN SERVICES, INC.—See Addnode Group AB; *Int'l*, pg. 131
CADMUS COMMUNICATIONS - HURLOCK—See Cenveo, Inc.; *U.S. Private*, pg. 834
THE CADMUS GROUP, INC. - PORTLAND—See CI Capital Partners LLC; *U.S. Private*, pg. 896
THE CADMUS GROUP, LLC—See CI Capital Partners LLC; *U.S. Private*, pg. 895
CADMUS JOURNAL SERVICES, INC.—See Cenveo, Inc.; *U.S. Private*, pg. 834
CADMUS PAYMENT SOLUTIONS PTY LIMITED—See SmartPay Holdings Limited; *Int'l*, pg. 7002
CADNUM S.A.R.L.—See Pennar Industries Limited; *Int'l*, pg. 5786
CADOGAN BITLYANSKE BV—See Cadogan Energy Solutions plc; *Int'l*, pg. 1248
CADOGAN ENERGY SOLUTIONS PLC; *Int'l*, pg. 1248
CADOGAN MANAGEMENT, LLC; *U.S. Private*, pg. 713
CADOGAN PETROLEUM HOLDINGS BV—See Cadogan Energy Solutions plc; *Int'l*, pg. 1248
CADOGAN PETROLEUM HOLDINGS LTD—See Cadogan Energy Solutions plc; *Int'l*, pg. 1248
CADON PLATING COMPANY; *U.S. Private*, pg. 713
CADOOZ GMBH—See Euronet Worldwide, Inc.; *U.S. Public*, pg. 798
CADOOZ REWARDS GMBH—See Euronet Worldwide, Inc.; *U.S. Public*, pg. 798
CAD QUALITY A/S—See Addnode Group AB; *Int'l*, pg. 130
CAD-QUALITY FINLAND OY—See Addnode Group AB; *Int'l*, pg. 130
CAD-QUALITY SVERIGE AB—See Addnode Group AB; *Int'l*, pg. 130
CADRE AS; *Int'l*, pg. 1248
CADRE HOLDINGS, INC.; *U.S. Public*, pg. 419
CADRENAL THERAPEUTICS, INC.; *U.S. Public*, pg. 419
CADRE PROPPANTS - VOCA PLANT—See Apollo Global Management, Inc.; *U.S. Public*, pg. 164
CADRE SERVICES INC.—See Apollo Global Management, Inc.; *U.S. Public*, pg. 164
CADREX MANUFACTURING SOLUTIONS—See CORE Industrial Partners, LLC; *U.S. Private*, pg. 1048
CAD SERVICES LTD.—See Facilities by ADF Plc; *Int'l*, pg. 2600
CAD S.R.L.—See CAD IT S.p.A.; *Int'l*, pg. 1247

CADSTAR FRANCE, S. A.—See Melia Hotels International, S.A.; *Int'l*, pg. 4809
CADSYS (INDIA) LTD.; *Int'l*, pg. 1248
CADSYS TECHNOLOGIES LLC—See Cadsys (India) Ltd.; *Int'l*, pg. 1248
CAD TECHNOLOGY CENTER—See Addnode Group AB; *Int'l*, pg. 130
CADUCEUS SOFTWARE SYSTEMS CORP.; *Int'l*, pg. 1248
CADU INMOBILIARIA S.A DE C.V.; *Int'l*, pg. 1248
CADUM INTERNATIONAL SA—See L'Oreal S.A.; *Int'l*, pg. 4378
CADWALADER, WICKERSHAM & TAFT LLP; *U.S. Private*, pg. 713
CADY CHEESE FACTORY, INC.; *U.S. Private*, pg. 713
CADY LIFTERS—See Columbus McKinnon Corporation; *U.S. Public*, pg. 535
CAE AUSTRALIA PTY LTD—See CAE Inc.; *Int'l*, pg. 1248
CAE AUTOMOTIVE GMBH; *Int'l*, pg. 1248
CAE AVIATION TRAINING PERU S.A.—See CAE Inc.; *Int'l*, pg. 1248
CAE BRUNEI MULTI PURPOSE TRAINING CENTRE SDN BHD—See CAE Inc.; *Int'l*, pg. 1248
CAE CENTER BRUSSELS N.V.—See CAE Inc.; *Int'l*, pg. 1248
CAE CENTRE COPENHAGEN A/S—See CAE Inc.; *Int'l*, pg. 1248
CAE CENTRE HONG KONG LIMITED—See CAE Inc.; *Int'l*, pg. 1248
CAE CENTRE OSLO AS—See CAE Inc.; *Int'l*, pg. 1248
CAE CENTRE STOCKHOLM AB—See CAE Inc.; *Int'l*, pg. 1248
CAE CIVIL AVIATION TRAINING SOLUTION, INC.; *U.S. Private*, pg. 713
CAE COLOMBIA FLIGHT TRAINING S.A.S.—See CAE Inc.; *Int'l*, pg. 1248
CAE DATA SAS—See TKH Group N.V.; *Int'l*, pg. 7763
CAE DEVELOPMENT APS—See Schneider Electric SE; *Int'l*, pg. 6624
CAE DOSS AVIATION, INC.—See CAE Inc.; *Int'l*, pg. 1248
CAE ELEKTRONIK GMBH—See CAE Inc.; *Int'l*, pg. 1248
CAE FLIGHT TRAINING CENTER MEXICO, S.A. DE C.V.—See CAE Inc.; *Int'l*, pg. 1248
CAE FLIGHT TRAINING (INDIA) PRIVATE LIMITED—See CAE Inc.; *Int'l*, pg. 1248
CAE HEALTHCARE, INC.—See CAE Inc.; *Int'l*, pg. 1248
CAE HEALTHCARE INC.—See Madison Industries Holdings LLC; *U.S. Private*, pg. 2543
CAE ICELANDAIR FLIGHT TRAINING EHF.—See Icelandair Group hf.; *Int'l*, pg. 3579
CAE INC.; *Int'l*, pg. 1248
CAE INDIA PRIVATE LIMITED—See CAE Inc.; *Int'l*, pg. 1248
CAE KUALA LUMPUR SDN BHD—See CAE Inc.; *Int'l*, pg. 1249
CAELUM CO., LTD.; *Int'l*, pg. 1249
CAELUM RESEARCH CORPORATION; *U.S. Private*, pg. 713
CAELUS ENERGY ALASKA LLC—See Caelus Energy LLC; *U.S. Private*, pg. 714
CAELUS ENERGY LLC; *U.S. Private*, pg. 713
CAE NORTH EAST TRAINING INC.—See CAE Inc.; *Int'l*, pg. 1249
CAE OXFORD AVIATION ACADEMY PHOENIX INC.—See CAE Inc.; *Int'l*, pg. 1249
CAERUS CORPORATION; *U.S. Private*, pg. 714
CAESAR PAC CARTON & PAPER PRODUCTS CO.—See Caesars Group; *Int'l*, pg. 1249
CAESARS CARGO CO. W.L.L.—See Caesars Group; *Int'l*, pg. 1249
CAESARS ENTERTAINMENT, INC.; *U.S. Public*, pg. 419
CAESARS ENTERTAINMENT OPERATING COMPANY, INC.—See Caesars Entertainment, Inc.; *U.S. Public*, pg. 419
CAESARS ENTERTAINMENT UK LTD.—See Caesars Entertainment, Inc.; *U.S. Public*, pg. 420
CAESARS ENTERTAINMENT WINDSOR HOLDING INC.—See Caesars Entertainment, Inc.; *U.S. Public*, pg. 420
CAESARS GENERAL TRADING AND CONTRACTING COMPANY W.L.L.—See Caesars Group; *Int'l*, pg. 1249
CAESARS GROUP; *Int'l*, pg. 1249
CAESARS GROWTH BALLY'S LV, LLC—See Caesars Entertainment, Inc.; *U.S. Public*, pg. 420
CAESARS GROWTH PARTNERS, LLC—See Caesars Entertainment, Inc.; *U.S. Public*, pg. 420
CAESARS HOLDINGS, INC.—See Caesars Entertainment, Inc.; *U.S. Public*, pg. 419
CAESARS HOLIDAYS—See Caesars Group; *Int'l*, pg. 1249
CAESARS INTERACTIVE ENTERTAINMENT, LLC—See Caesars Entertainment, Inc.; *U.S. Public*, pg. 420
CAESARS INT'L SHIPPING & LOGISTICS CO. W.L.L.—See Caesars Group; *Int'l*, pg. 1249
CAESARS NEW JERSEY, INC.—See Caesars Entertainment, Inc.; *U.S. Public*, pg. 419
CAESARS PALACE CORPORATION—See Caesars Entertainment, Inc.; *U.S. Public*, pg. 419

CAESARS RIVERBOAT CASINO, LLC—See Caesars Entertainment, Inc.; *U.S. Public*, pg. 419
CAESARSTONE AUSTRALIA PTY LTD—See Caesarstone Ltd.; *Int'l*, pg. 1249
CAESARSTONE CANADA INC.—See Caesarstone Ltd.; *Int'l*, pg. 1249
CAESARSTONE LTD.; *Int'l*, pg. 1249
CAESARSTONE SOUTH EAST ASIA PTE LTD—See Caesarstone Ltd.; *Int'l*, pg. 1249
CAESARSTONE US—See Caesarstone Ltd.; *Int'l*, pg. 1249
CAESARS TRAVEL COMPANY—See Caesars Group; *Int'l*, pg. 1249
CAESARS TRAVEL GROUP—See Caesars Group; *Int'l*, pg. 1249
CAE SINGAPORE (S.E.A.) PTE LTD.—See CAE Inc.; *Int'l*, pg. 1249
CAETANO AUTO, S.A.—See Toyota Caetano Portugal S.A.; *Int'l*, pg. 7865
CAETANOBUS - FABRICACAO DE CARROCARIAS, S.A.—See Toyota Caetano Portugal S.A.; *Int'l*, pg. 7865
CAETEC GMBH—See INDUS Holding AG; *Int'l*, pg. 3663
CAETECH INTERNATIONAL, INC.; *U.S. Private*, pg. 714
CAE TECHNOLOGY INDIA PRIVATE LIMITED—See CAE Inc.; *Int'l*, pg. 1249
CAE TRAINING & SERVICES UK LTD.—See CAE Inc.; *Int'l*, pg. 1249
CAE UK PLC—See CAE Inc.; *Int'l*, pg. 1249
C&A - EUROPE HEAD OFFICE—See COFRA Holding AG; *Int'l*, pg. 1694
CAE USA, INC.—See CAE Inc.; *Int'l*, pg. 1249
C.A. FABRICA NACIONAL DE CEMENTOS, S.A.C.A.; *Int'l*, pg. 1240
CAF ARGELIA EURL—See Construcciones y Auxiliar de Ferrocarriles S.A.; *Int'l*, pg. 1776
THE CAFARO CO.; *U.S. Private*, pg. 4003
CAF BRASIL INDUSTRIA E COMERCIO, S.A.—See Construcciones y Auxiliar de Ferrocarriles S.A.; *Int'l*, pg. 1776
CAF-CAF INC.—See Compass Group PLC; *Int'l*, pg. 1750
CAFCA LIMITED; *Int'l*, pg. 1249
CAF CHILE, S.A.—See Construcciones y Auxiliar de Ferrocarriles S.A.; *Int'l*, pg. 1776
CAF DEUTSCHLAND GMBH—See Construcciones y Auxiliar de Ferrocarriles S.A.; *Int'l*, pg. 1776
CAFE24 CORP.; *Int'l*, pg. 1250
CAFE BRITT CHILE LTDA.—See Grupo Britt N.V.; *Int'l*, pg. 3123
CAFE BRITT PERU S.A.C.—See Grupo Britt N.V.; *Int'l*, pg. 3123
CAFE BRITT—See Grupo Britt N.V.; *Int'l*, pg. 3123
CAFE BRITT USA—See Grupo Britt N.V.; *Int'l*, pg. 3123
CAFE CAPRIS S.A.—See ED&F Man Holdings Limited; *Int'l*, pg. 2302
CAFE CENTRO—See Delaware North Companies, Inc.; *U.S. Private*, pg. 1195
CAFECO ARMAZENS GERAIS LTDA—See B. Pacorini S.p.A.; *Int'l*, pg. 789
CAFE+CO INTERNATIONAL HOLDING GMBH—See Raiffeisen-Holding Niederosterreich-Wien reg. Gen.m.b.H.; *Int'l*, pg. 6185
CAFE DE CORAL FAST FOOD LIMITED—See Cafe de Coral Holdings Limited; *Int'l*, pg. 1250
CAFE DE CORAL GROUP LIMITED—See Cafe de Coral Holdings Limited; *Int'l*, pg. 1250
CAFE DE CORAL HOLDINGS LIMITED; *Int'l*, pg. 1249
CAFE ENTERPRISES, INC.—See Milestone Partners Ltd.; *U.S. Private*, pg. 2728
CAFE EXPRESS LLC; *U.S. Private*, pg. 714
CAFEL INVERSIONES 2008, S.L.—See Assicurazioni Generali S.p.A.; *Int'l*, pg. 643
CAFE PINOT—See Delaware North Companies, Inc.; *U.S. Private*, pg. 1195
CAFEPRESS, INC.—See Claranova SA; *Int'l*, pg. 1642
CAFE RIO, INC.; *U.S. Private*, pg. 714
CAFES DE ESPECIALIDAD DE CHIAPAS, S.A.P.I. DE C.V.—See Ecom Agroindustrial Corporation Ltd.; *Int'l*, pg. 2296
CAFE SOLUVEL BRASILIA SA; *Int'l*, pg. 1250
CAFESTORE, S.A.—See Sacyr, S.A.; *Int'l*, pg. 6465
CAFETALERA AMAZONICA SAC—See Ecom Agroindustrial Corporation Ltd.; *Int'l*, pg. 2296
CAFETALERA DEL PACIFICO S.A DE C.V.—See Ecom Agroindustrial Corporation Ltd.; *Int'l*, pg. 2296
CAFE VALLEY INC.—See Swander Pace Capital, LLC; *U.S. Private*, pg. 3889
CAFFAREL S.P.A.—See Chocoladefabriken Lindt & Sprungli AG; *Int'l*, pg. 1577
CAFFEINE—See Mascola Advertising; *U.S. Private*, pg. 2601
CAFFE NERO GROUP LTD.; *Int'l*, pg. 1250
CAFFINO INC.; *U.S. Private*, pg. 714
CAF FRANCIA, S.A.S.—See Construcciones y Auxiliar de Ferrocarriles S.A.; *Int'l*, pg. 1776
CAFFYNS PLC; *Int'l*, pg. 1250
CAFG AUSTRALEASE PTY. LTD.; *Int'l*, pg. 1250
CAF HUNGARY KFT.—See Construcciones y Auxiliar de Ferrocarriles S.A.; *Int'l*, pg. 1776

CA FINANCIAL APPOINTMENTS (PTY) LTD.—See ADvTECH Limited; *Int'l*, pg. 168
CAF INDIA PRIVATE LIMITED—See Construcciones y Auxiliar de Ferrocarriles S.A.; *Int'l*, pg. 1776
CAFINTER S.A.—See Ecom Agroindustrial Corporation Ltd.; *Int'l*, pg. 2296
CAF ISRAEL RAILS LTD.—See Construcciones y Auxiliar de Ferrocarriles S.A.; *Int'l*, pg. 1776
CAF ITALIA, S.R.L.—See Construcciones y Auxiliar de Ferrocarriles S.A.; *Int'l*, pg. 1776
CAF LLC; *U.S. Public*, pg. 714
CAF MEXICO, S.A. DE C.V.—See Construcciones y Auxiliar de Ferrocarriles S.A.; *Int'l*, pg. 1776
CAFO, INC.—See Truist Financial Corporation; *U.S. Public*, pg. 2201
CAFOM SA; *Int'l*, pg. 1250
C A FORTUNE & COMPANY—See Carlin O'Brien Inc.; *U.S. Private*, pg. 763
CAF POWER & AUTOMATION, S.L.U.—See Construcciones y Auxiliar de Ferrocarriles S.A.; *Int'l*, pg. 1776
CAF RAIL AUSTRALIA PTY LTD—See Construcciones y Auxiliar de Ferrocarriles S.A.; *Int'l*, pg. 1776
CAF RAIL UK LIMITED—See Construcciones y Auxiliar de Ferrocarriles S.A.; *Int'l*, pg. 1776
CAF SIGNALLING, S.L.U.—See Construcciones y Auxiliar de Ferrocarriles S.A.; *Int'l*, pg. 1776
CAF TURNKEY & ENGINEERING, S.L.U.—See Construcciones y Auxiliar de Ferrocarriles S.A.; *Int'l*, pg. 1776
CAF USA, INC.—See Construcciones y Auxiliar de Ferrocarriles S.A.; *Int'l*, pg. 1777
CAFU VERMOEGENSVERWALTUNG GMBH & CO OG—See UniCredit S.p.A.; *Int'l*, pg. 8040
CAGAYAN DE ORO COLLEGE, INC.—See PHINMA Corporation; *Int'l*, pg. 5848
CAGE INC.—See Ross & Baruzzini, Inc.; *U.S. Private*, pg. 3485
CAGGIATI FRANCE SARL—See Matthews International Corporation; *U.S. Public*, pg. 1400
CAG HOLDING GMBH; *Int'l*, pg. 1250
CAGLES DIALYSIS, LLC—See DaVita Inc.; *U.S. Public*, pg. 636
CAGLIARI CRUISE PORT SRL—See Global Yatirim Holding A.S.; *Int'l*, pg. 3002
CA GLOBAL FINANCE (PTY) LTD.—See ADvTECH Limited; *Int'l*, pg. 169
CA GLOBAL HEADHUNTERS (PTY) LTD.—See ADvTECH Limited; *Int'l*, pg. 169
CA GLOBAL PROPERTY INTERNATIONALE IMMOBILIEN AG—See Assicurazioni Generali S.p.A.; *Int'l*, pg. 645
CAGNES SUR MER STATIONNEMENT SA—See Indigo Group S.A.S.; *Int'l*, pg. 3655
CAGUAS MECHANICAL CONTRACTOR, INC.; *U.S. Private*, pg. 714
CAGWIN & DORWARD; *U.S. Private*, pg. 714
CAHABA ORTHOPEDICS, LLC—See Community Health Systems, Inc.; *U.S. Public*, pg. 552
CAHABA TIMBER, INC.—See Stella-Jones, Inc.; *Int'l*, pg. 7196
CA HEALTHCARE ACQUISITION CORP.; *U.S. Public*, pg. 416
CAHILL GORDON & REINDEL LLP; *U.S. Private*, pg. 714
CAHILL MAY ROBERTS LTD.—See Uniphar Plc; *Int'l*, pg. 8056
CA (HONG KONG) LIMITED—See Broadcom Inc.; *U.S. Public*, pg. 388
CAHYA MATA ALAM SDN. BHD.—See Cahya Mata Sarawak Berhad; *Int'l*, pg. 1251
CAHYA MATA CEMENT SDN. BHD.—See Cahya Mata Sarawak Berhad; *Int'l*, pg. 1251
CAHYA MATA DEVELOPMENT SDN. BHD.—See Cahya Mata Sarawak Berhad; *Int'l*, pg. 1251
CAHYA MATA PHOSPHATE INDUSTRIES SDN. BHD.—See Cahya Mata Sarawak Berhad; *Int'l*, pg. 1251
CAHYA MATA ROADS SDN. BHD.—See Cahya Mata Sarawak Berhad; *Int'l*, pg. 1251
CAHYA MATA SARAWAK BERHAD; *Int'l*, pg. 1251
CAHYA SURIA ENERGY SDN. BHD.—See Annica Holdings Limited; *Int'l*, pg. 474
CAIAC FUND MANAGEMENT AG; *Int'l*, pg. 1252
CAIANO AS; *Int'l*, pg. 1252
CA IB CORPORATE FINANCE LTD.—See UniCredit S.p.A.; *Int'l*, pg. 8034
CAICA DIGITAL INC.; *Int'l*, pg. 1252
CAI CANADA INC—See Computer Aid, Inc.; *U.S. Private*, pg. 1004
CAI CAPITAL MANAGEMENT INC.—See CAI Private Equity; *Int'l*, pg. 1252
CAI CAPITAL MANAGEMENT INC.—See CAI Private Equity; *Int'l*, pg. 1252
CAI-CHARLESTON—See CAI International, Inc.; *U.S. Public*, pg. 421
CAI CHILE S.P.A—See CAI International, Inc.; *U.S. Public*, pg. 421
CAIDAO CAPITAL LIMITED; *Int'l*, pg. 1252
CAIDA SECURITIES CO., LTD.; *Int'l*, pg. 1252
CAID INDUSTRIES, INC.—See Samuel, Son & Co., Limited; *Int'l*, pg. 6516

CAI INTERNATIONAL GMBH—See CAI International, Inc.; *U.S. Public*, pg. 421
CAI INTERNATIONAL, INC.; *U.S. Public*, pg. 421
CAI LAY VETERINARY PHARMACEUTICAL JOINT STOCK COMPANY; *Int'l*, pg. 1252
CAILLAUD LAMELLE—See VINCI S.A.; *Int'l*, pg. 8213
CAI LOGISTICS INC.—See CAI International, Inc.; *U.S. Public*, pg. 421
CAIMAN CONSULTING, CORP.—See Sia Partners & Company; *Int'l*, pg. 6874
CA IMMO ASSET MANAGEMENT GMBH—See Starwood Capital Group Global I, LLC; *U.S. Private*, pg. 3788
CA IMMOBILIEN ANLAGEN AG—See Starwood Capital Group Global I, LLC; *U.S. Private*, pg. 3788
CA IMMOBILIEN ANLAGEN BETEILIGUNGS GMBH & CO FINANZIERUNGS OEG—See Starwood Capital Group Global I, LLC; *U.S. Private*, pg. 3789
CA IMMOBILIEN ANLAGEN BETEILIGUNGS GMBH—See Starwood Capital Group Global I, LLC; *U.S. Private*, pg. 3789
CA IMMO BIP LIEGENSCHAFTSVERWALTUNG GMBH—See Starwood Capital Group Global I, LLC; *U.S. Private*, pg. 3789
CA IMMO CZECH REPUBLIC—See Starwood Capital Group Global I, LLC; *U.S. Private*, pg. 3789
CA IMMO DEUTSCHLAND GMBH—See Starwood Capital Group Global I, LLC; *U.S. Private*, pg. 3789
CA IMMO DEUTSCHLAND GMBH—See Starwood Capital Group Global I, LLC; *U.S. Private*, pg. 3789
CA IMMO GALLERIA LIEGENSCHAFTSVERWALTUNG GMBH—See Starwood Capital Group Global I, LLC; *U.S. Private*, pg. 3789
CA IMMO REAL ESTATE MANAGEMENT HUNGARY KFT.—See Starwood Capital Group Global I, LLC; *U.S. Private*, pg. 3789
CA IMMO REAL ESTATE MANAGEMENT POLAND SP. Z O.O.—See Starwood Capital Group Global I, LLC; *U.S. Private*, pg. 3789
CA IMMO REAL ESTATE MANAGEMENT ROMANIA SRL—See Starwood Capital Group Global I, LLC; *U.S. Private*, pg. 3789
CA IMMO RENNWEG 16 GMBH—See Starwood Capital Group Global I, LLC; *U.S. Private*, pg. 3789
CAIN ACQUISITION CORPORATION; *U.S. Private*, pg. 714
CAINA TECHNOLOGY CO., LTD.; *Int'l*, pg. 1252
CAIN BROTHERS & COMPANY, LLC—See KeyCorp; *U.S. Public*, pg. 1226
CAIN & BULTMAN, INC.; *U.S. Private*, pg. 714
CA, INC.—See Broadcom Inc.; *U.S. Public*, pg. 388
CA (INDIA) TECHNOLOGIES PRIVATE LIMITED—See Broadcom Inc.; *U.S. Public*, pg. 388
C&A INDUSTRIES INC.—See TPG Capital, L.P.; *U.S. Public*, pg. 2176
CAIN ELECTRICAL SUPPLY CORP.; *U.S. Private*, pg. 714
CAIN INTERNATIONAL LIMITED; *Int'l*, pg. 1252
CAINS FOODS, L.P.—See TreeHouse Foods, Inc.; *U.S. Public*, pg. 2187
CAINS INCORPORATED; *U.S. Private*, pg. 714
CAIN'S PIPELINE & INDUSTRIAL SERVICES, LLC.; *U.S. Private*, pg. 714
CAIN TOYOTA; *U.S. Private*, pg. 714
CA INVESTMENT HOLDING, INC.—See Broadcom Inc.; *U.S. Public*, pg. 389
CAI PRIVATE EQUITY; *Int'l*, pg. 1252
CAIRE INC.—See Niterra Co., Ltd.; *Int'l*, pg. 5379
CAIRN CAPITAL LIMITED—See Mediobanca-Banca de Credito Finanziario S.p.A.; *Int'l*, pg. 4778
CAIRN ENERGY GROUP HOLDINGS B.V.—See Vedanta Resources Ltd; *Int'l*, pg. 8146
CAIRN ENERGY HYDROCARBONS LIMITED—See Capricorn Energy PLC; *Int'l*, pg. 1316
CAIRN ENERGY INDIA PTY. LIMITED—See Vedanta Resources Ltd; *Int'l*, pg. 8146
CAIRN ENERGY LUMBINI LIMITED—See Capricorn Energy PLC; *Int'l*, pg. 1316
CAIRN ENERGY NETHERLANDS HOLDINGS B.V.—See Vedanta Resources Ltd; *Int'l*, pg. 8146
CAIRNFIELD SDN. BHD.—See W T K Holdings Berhad; *Int'l*, pg. 8320
CAIRN HOMES PLC; *Int'l*, pg. 1252
CAIRN INDIA LIMITED—See Vedanta Resources Ltd; *Int'l*, pg. 8146
CAIRN UK HOLDINGS LIMITED—See Capricorn Energy PLC; *Int'l*, pg. 1316
CAIRO AIRPORT COMPANY—See Fraport AG; *Int'l*, pg. 2764
CAIRO & ALEXANDRIA STOCK EXCHANGES; *Int'l*, pg. 1253
CAIRO AMMAN BANK; *Int'l*, pg. 1253
CAIRO COMMUNICATION S.P.A.; *Int'l*, pg. 1253
CAIRO COOPERATIVE EQUITY EXCHANGE; *U.S. Private*, pg. 714
CAIRO DEVELOPMENT & INVESTMENT, (S.A.E.); *Int'l*, pg. 1253
CAIRO EDITORE S.P.A.—See Cairo Communication S.p.A.; *Int'l*, pg. 1253

CAIRO ELECRTRICAL GROUP—See A.A.G. STUCCHI s.r.l.; *Int'l*, pg. 22
CAIRO FOODS INDUSTRIES SAE—See 3G Capital Inc.; *U.S. Private*, pg. 9
CAIRO FOODS INDUSTRIES SAE—See Berkshire Hathaway Inc.; *U.S. Public*, pg. 317
CAIRO INVESTMENT & REAL ESTATE DEVELOPMENT; *Int'l*, pg. 1253
CAIRO MEZZ PLC; *Int'l*, pg. 1253
CAIRO OIL & SOAP COMPANY; *Int'l*, pg. 1253
CAIRO POULTRY COMPANY—See Adeptio LLC; *Int'l*, pg. 143
CAIRO PUBBLICITA S.P.A—See Cairo Communication S.p.A.; *Int'l*, pg. 1253
CAIRO PUBLISHING SRL—See Cairo Communication S.p.A.; *Int'l*, pg. 1253
CAIRO RESOURCES INC.; *Int'l*, pg. 1253
CAIRO SPORT SRL—See Cairo Communication S.p.A.; *Int'l*, pg. 1253
CAIRO THREE A GROUP; *Int'l*, pg. 1253
CAI SOFTWARE, LLC—See Symphony Technology Group, LLC; *U.S. Private*, pg. 3902
CAISSA TOSUN DEVELOPMENT CO., LTD.; *Int'l*, pg. 1253
CAISSE CENTRALE DE REESCOMPTE, S.A.—See UBS Group AG; *Int'l*, pg. 8007
CAISSE DE DEPOT ET PLACEMENT DU QUEBEC; *Int'l*, pg. 1253
CAISSE D'EPARGNE AQUITAINE POITOU-CHARENTES SCA—See Groupe BPCE; *Int'l*, pg. 3093
CAISSE D'EPARGNE BRETAGNE PAYS DE LOIRE SCA—See Groupe BPCE; *Int'l*, pg. 3093
CAISSE D'EPARGNE COTE D'AZUR S.A.—See Groupe BPCE; *Int'l*, pg. 3093
CAISSE D'EPARGNE D'AUVERGNE ET DU LIMOUSIN SCA—See Groupe BPCE; *Int'l*, pg. 3093
CAISSE D'EPARGNE DE BOURGOGNE FRANCHE-COMTE SAS—See Groupe BPCE; *Int'l*, pg. 3093
CAISSE D'EPARGNE DE MIDI-PYRENEES S.A.—See Groupe BPCE; *Int'l*, pg. 3093
CAISSE D'EPARGNE ET DE PREVOYANCE DE RHONE ALPES—See Groupe BPCE; *Int'l*, pg. 3097
CAISSE D'EPARGNE ET DE PREVOYANCE ILE-DE-FRANCE—See Groupe BPCE; *Int'l*, pg. 3097
CAISSE D'EPARGNE ET DE PREVOYANCE PROVENCE-ALPES-CORSE—See Groupe BPCE; *Int'l*, pg. 3097
CAISSE D'EPARGNE GRAND EST EUROPE SCA—See Groupe BPCE; *Int'l*, pg. 3093
CAISSE D'EPARGNE HAUTS DE FRANCE SAS—See Groupe BPCE; *Int'l*, pg. 3093
CAISSE D'EPARGNE LANGUEDOC-ROUSSILLON SCA—See Groupe BPCE; *Int'l*, pg. 3093
CAISSE D'EPARGNE LOIRE-CENTRE SCA—See Groupe BPCE; *Int'l*, pg. 3093
CAISSE D'EPARGNE LOIRE DROME ARDECHE SCA—See Groupe BPCE; *Int'l*, pg. 3093
CAISSE D'EPARGNE NORMANDIE SAS—See Groupe BPCE; *Int'l*, pg. 3093
CAISSE D'EPARGNE RHONE ALPES SCA—See Groupe BPCE; *Int'l*, pg. 3093
CAISSE DES DEPOTS ET CONSIGNATIONS - BANKING SERVICES—See Caisse des Depots et Consignations; *Int'l*, pg. 1257
CAISSE DES DEPOTS ET CONSIGNATIONS - LOCAL & REGIONAL DEVELOPMENT—See Caisse des Depots et Consignations; *Int'l*, pg. 1257
CAISSE DES DEPOTS ET CONSIGNATIONS; *Int'l*, pg. 1257
CAISSE FRANCAISE DE FINANCEMENT LOCAL; *Int'l*, pg. 1259
CAISSE REGIONALE DE CREDIT AGRICOLE MUTUEL ATLANTIQUE VENDEE SC; *Int'l*, pg. 1259
CAISSE REGIONALE DE CREDIT AGRICOLE MUTUEL BRIE PICARDIE SCA; *Int'l*, pg. 1259
CAISSE REGIONALE DE CREDIT AGRICOLE MUTUEL DE LA TOURAINE ET DU POITOU SCACV; *Int'l*, pg. 1259
CAISSE REGIONALE DE CREDIT AGRICOLE MUTUEL DE NORD DE FRANCE SC; *Int'l*, pg. 1259
CAISSE REGIONALE DE CREDIT AGRICOLE MUTUEL DE NORMANDIE SEINE SC; *Int'l*, pg. 1259
CAISSE REGIONALE DE CREDIT AGRICOLE MUTUEL DE PARIS ET D'ILE DE FRANCE SC; *Int'l*, pg. 1259
CAISSE REGIONALE DE CREDIT AGRICOLE MUTUEL D'ILLE-ET-VILLAINE SC; *Int'l*, pg. 1259
CAISSE REGIONALE DE CREDIT AGRICOLE MUTUEL SUD RHONE ALPES; *Int'l*, pg. 1259
CAISSE REGIONALE DE CREDIT AGRICOLE TOULOUSE 31; *Int'l*, pg. 1259
CAISSE SOLIDAIRE SCCV—See Groupe BPCE; *Int'l*, pg. 3093
CAISSON INTERVENTIONAL, LLC—See LivaNova PLC; *Int'l*, pg. 4529
CAITHNESS ENERGY, LLC; *U.S. Private*, pg. 714
CA IT INFRASTRUCTURE SOLUTIONS SDN BHD—See Omesti Berhad; *Int'l*, pg. 5562
CAITO FISHERIES INC.—See Prospect Enterprises Inc.; *U.S. Private*, pg. 3287
CAITO FOODS SERVICE INC.; *U.S. Private*, pg. 714

COMPANY NAME INDEX

CAITONG SECURITIES CO., LTD.; *Int'l*, pg. 1259
CAIXA - BANCO DE INVESTIMENTO, S.A.—See Caixa Geral de Depositos S.A.; *Int'l*, pg. 1260
CAIXABANK, S.A.—See Lone Star Funds; *U.S. Private*, pg. 2484
CAIXA ECONOMICA FEDERAL; *Int'l*, pg. 1259
CAIXA ECONOMICA MONTEPIO GERAL; *Int'l*, pg. 1259
CAIXA GERAL DE DEPOSITOS (FRANCE)—See Caixa Geral de Depositos S.A.; *Int'l*, pg. 1260
CAIXA GERAL DE DEPOSITOS S.A.; *Int'l*, pg. 1259
CAIXA GESTAO DE ATIVOS, SGOIC, SA—See Caixa Geral de Depositos S.A.; *Int'l*, pg. 1260
CAIXA-IMOBILIARIO-SOCIEDADE DE GESTAO E INVESTIMENTO IMOBILIARIO S.A.—See Caixa Geral de Depositos S.A.; *Int'l*, pg. 1260
CAIXA LEASING & FACTORING, IFIC, SA—See Caixa Geral de Depositos S.A.; *Int'l*, pg. 1260
CAIXA SEGUROS—See CNP Assurances SA; *Int'l*, pg. 1678
CAJA BV—See VDL Groep B.V.; *Int'l*, pg. 8140
CAJA DE SEGUROS S.A.—See Assicurazioni Generali S.p.A.; *Int'l*, pg. 643
CAJANUKSENTIENKOTI OY—See Humana AB; *Int'l*, pg. 3529
CA JAPAN, LTD.—See Broadcom Inc.; *U.S. Public*, pg. 389
CAJAS Y EMPAQUES DE GUATEMALA, S.A.—See Sigma S.A. de C.V.; *Int'l*, pg. 6908
CAJAVEC A.D.; *Int'l*, pg. 1260
CAJAVEC-MEGA A.D.; *Int'l*, pg. 1260
CAJAVEC SIP A.D.; *Int'l*, pg. 1260
CAJAVEC USLUZNE DJELATNOSTI A.D.—See Cajavec SIP a.d.; *Int'l*, pg. 1260
CAJOLEBEN INC.; *U.S. Private*, pg. 714
CAJUN COMPANY; *U.S. Private*, pg. 714
CAJUN CONSTRUCTORS INC.; *U.S. Private*, pg. 714
CAJUN INDUSTRIES, L.L.C.; *U.S. Private*, pg. 714
CAJUN OUTBOARDS INC.; *U.S. Private*, pg. 715
CAKE BOX HOLDINGS PLC; *Int'l*, pg. 1260
CAKE DECOR LTD.—See Orkla ASA; *Int'l*, pg. 5637
CAKEWALK, INC.; *U.S. Private*, pg. 715
CA KOREA INC.—See Broadcom Inc.; *U.S. Public*, pg. 389
CAKOVECKI MLINOVI D.D.; *Int'l*, pg. 1260
CALABRESE CONSULTING, LLC; *U.S. Private*, pg. 715
CALABRESE HUFF, *U.S. Private*, pg. 715
CALABRIO, INC.—See Thoma Bravo, L.P.; *U.S. Private*, pg. 4146
CALACHEM LTD.—See Aurelius Equity Opportunities SE & Co. KGaA; *Int'l*, pg. 708
CALA CO.—See The Kroger Co.; *U.S. Public*, pg. 2107
CALAC TRUCKING LTD.; *Int'l*, pg. 1261
CALA FORMENTOR, S.A. DE C.V.—See Melia Hotels International, S.A.; *Int'l*, pg. 4809
CALA GROUP LIMITED—See Legal & General Group Plc; *Int'l*, pg. 4442
CALA HOMES (CHILTERN) LIMITED—See Legal & General Group Plc; *Int'l*, pg. 4442
CALA HOMES (EAST) LIMITED—See Legal & General Group Plc; *Int'l*, pg. 4442
CALA HOMES (MIDLANDS) LIMITED—See Legal & General Group Plc; *Int'l*, pg. 4442
CALA HOMES (NORTH HOME COUNTIES) LIMITED—See Legal & General Group Plc; *Int'l*, pg. 4442
CALA HOMES (SCOTLAND) LIMITED—See Legal & General Group Plc; *Int'l*, pg. 4442
CALA HOMES (SOUTH HOME COUNTIES) LIMITED—See Legal & General Group Plc; *Int'l*, pg. 4443
CALA HOMES (SOUTH) LIMITED—See Legal & General Group Plc; *Int'l*, pg. 4442
CALA HOMES (THAMES) LIMITED—See Legal & General Group Plc; *Int'l*, pg. 4443
CALA HOMES (WEST) LIMITED—See Legal & General Group Plc; *Int'l*, pg. 4442
CALAIS REGIONAL HOSPITAL; *U.S. Private*, pg. 716
CALAMARI FISHING (PTY) LIMITED—See Oceana Group Limited; *Int'l*, pg. 5517
CALAMOS ASSET MANAGEMENT, INC.; *U.S. Private*, pg. 716
CALAMOS CONVERTIBLE & HIGH INCOME FUND; *U.S. Public*, pg. 421
CALAMOS CONVERTIBLE OPPRTNTY & INCOME; *U.S. Public*, pg. 421
CALAMOS DYNAMIC CONVERTIBLE AND INCOME FUND; *U.S. Public*, pg. 421
CALAMOS FINANCIAL SERVICES LLC—See Calamos Asset Management, Inc.; *U.S. Private*, pg. 716
CALAMOS GLOBAL DYNAMIC INCOME FUND; *U.S. Public*, pg. 421
CALAMOS GLOBAL TOTAL RETURN FUND; *U.S. Public*, pg. 421
CALAMOS INVESTMENTS LLC—See Calamos Asset Management, Inc.; *U.S. Private*, pg. 716
CALAMOS INVESTMENTS LLP—See Calamos Asset Management, Inc.; *U.S. Private*, pg. 716
CALAMOS STRATEGIC TOTAL RETURN FUND; *U.S. Public*, pg. 421
CALAMP CORP.; *U.S. Public*, pg. 422

CALANBAU BRANDSCHUTZANLAGEN GMBH—See VINCI S.A.; *Int'l*, pg. 8238
CALANBAU BRANDSCHUTZ AUSTRIA GMBH—See VINCI S.A.; *Int'l*, pg. 8236
CALANBAU GFA FEUERSCHUTZ GMBH—See VINCI S.A.; *Int'l*, pg. 8238
CALANCASCA AG—See Axpo Holding AG; *Int'l*, pg. 771
CALANCE CORPORATION; *Int'l*, pg. 1261
CALANDROS SUPERMARKET, INC.; *U.S. Private*, pg. 716
CALAR BELGIUM S.A./N.V.—See Euroclear S.A./N.V.; *Int'l*, pg. 2534
CAL-ARK INC.; *U.S. Private*, pg. 715
CALASTONE LIMITED; *Int'l*, pg. 1261
CALATA CORPORATION; *Int'l*, pg. 1261
CALATLANTIC GROUP, INC.—See Lennar Corporation; *U.S. Public*, pg. 1305
CALATLANTIC HOMES OF TEXAS, INC.—See Lennar Corporation; *U.S. Public*, pg. 1305
CALATLANTIC TITLE AGENCY, LLC—See Lennar Corporation; *U.S. Public*, pg. 1306
CALATRAVA CAPITAL S.A.; *Int'l*, pg. 1261
CALAVERAS MATERIALS INC. - CENTRAL AVENUE PLANT—See Heidelberg Materials AG; *Int'l*, pg. 3313
CALAVERAS MATERIALS INC. - HUGHSON PLANT—See Heidelberg Materials AG; *Int'l*, pg. 3313
CALAVERAS MATERIALS INC. - LATHROP PLANT—See Heidelberg Materials AG; *Int'l*, pg. 3313
CALAVERAS MATERIALS INC. - RIVER ROCK PLANT—See Heidelberg Materials AG; *Int'l*, pg. 3314
CALAVERAS MATERIALS INC. - SAN ANDREAS PLANT—See Heidelberg Materials AG; *Int'l*, pg. 3314
CALAVERAS MATERIALS INC.—See Heidelberg Materials AG; *Int'l*, pg. 3313
CALAVERAS MATERIALS INC. - THORNE AVENUE PLANT—See Heidelberg Materials AG; *Int'l*, pg. 3314
CALAVERAS STANDARD MATERIALS—See Heidelberg Materials AG; *Int'l*, pg. 3309
CALAVO FOODS, INC.—See Calavo Growers, Inc.; *U.S. Public*, pg. 422
CALAVO GROWERS, INC.; *U.S. Public*, pg. 422
CALAWAY TRADING, INC.—See Pacific Ag, LLC; *U.S. Private*, pg. 3065
THE C.A. LAWTON COMPANY; *U.S. Private*, pg. 4003
CALBAG METALS CO.; *U.S. Private*, pg. 716
CALBAG METALS CO. - TACOMA—See Calbag Metals Co.; *U.S. Private*, pg. 716
CALBANK PLC; *Int'l*, pg. 1261
CAL-BAY INTERNATIONAL, INC.; *U.S. Public*, pg. 421
CALBEE AMERICA, INC.—See Calbee, Inc.; *Int'l*, pg. 1261
CALBEE GROUP (UK) LIMITED—See Calbee, Inc.; *Int'l*, pg. 1261
CALBEE (HANGZHOU) FOODS CO., LTD.—See Calbee, Inc.; *Int'l*, pg. 1261
CALBEE, INC.; *Int'l*, pg. 1261
CALBEE LOGISTICS, INC.—See Calbee, Inc.; *Int'l*, pg. 1261
CALBEE MOH SENG PTE., LTD.—See Calbee, Inc.; *Int'l*, pg. 1261
CALBEE NORTH AMERICA, LLC—See Calbee, Inc.; *Int'l*, pg. 1261
CALBEE POTATO, INC.—See Calbee, Inc.; *Int'l*, pg. 1261
CALBEE TANAWAT CO., LTD.—See Calbee, Inc.; *Int'l*, pg. 1261
CALBERSON MEDITERRANEE-NICE—See SNCF; *Int'l*, pg. 7025
CALBERSON MONTPELLIER—See SNCF; *Int'l*, pg. 7025
CALBERSON NORMANDIE AGENCE DEVREUX—See SNCF; *Int'l*, pg. 7025
CALBERSON RHONE ALPES—See SNCF; *Int'l*, pg. 7025
CALBERSON ROUSSILLON—See SNCF; *Int'l*, pg. 7025
CALBERSON SAS—See SNCF; *Int'l*, pg. 7025
CALBERSON (SNTR) SUD OUEST-AGEN—See SNCF; *Int'l*, pg. 7025
CALBERSON—See SNCF; *Int'l*, pg. 7025
CALBERSON SUD OUEST-TOULOUSE—See SNCF; *Int'l*, pg. 7025
CALB GROUP CO., LTD.; *Int'l*, pg. 1261
CALBIOTECH, INC.—See Transasia Bio-Medicals Ltd.; *Int'l*, pg. 7896
CALCEMENTI JONICI S.R.L.—See Heidelberg Materials AG; *Int'l*, pg. 3316
CALCESTRUZZI S.P.A—See Heidelberg Materials AG; *Int'l*, pg. 3316
CAL-CHLOR CORPORATION; *U.S. Private*, pg. 715
CALCIALIMENT; *Int'l*, pg. 1262
CALCIMEDICA, INC.; *U.S. Public*, pg. 422
CALCIMEDICA SUBSIDIARY, INC.—See CalciMedica, Inc.; *U.S. Public*, pg. 422
CALCIMIN COMPANY; *Int'l*, pg. 1262
CALCITECH LTD.; *Int'l*, pg. 1262
CAL-CLEVE LIMITED; *U.S. Private*, pg. 715
CAL COAST CARPET WAREHOUSE, INC—See Live Ventures Incorporated; *U.S. Public*, pg. 1332
CAL-COAST MACHINERY, INC.; *U.S. Private*, pg. 715
CALCO INTERNATIONAL, INC.—See Itoham Yonekyu Holdings Inc.; *Int'l*, pg. 3842
CALCOM ESI SA—See Keysight Technologies, Inc.; *U.S. Public*, pg. 1226

CALDWELL INDUSTRIES INC.

CAL-COMP AUTOMATION AND INDUSTRIAL 4.0 SERVICE (THAILAND) CO., LTD.—See Cal-Comp Electronics (Thailand) pcl; *Int'l*, pg. 1260
CAL-COMP ELECTRONICS AND COMMUNICATIONS COMPANY LIMITED—See Cal-Comp Electronics (Thailand) pcl; *Int'l*, pg. 1261
CAL-COMP ELECTRONICS - MAHACHAI—See Cal-Comp Electronics (Thailand) pcl; *Int'l*, pg. 1260
CAL-COMP ELECTRONICS - PETCHABURI—See Cal-Comp Electronics (Thailand) pcl; *Int'l*, pg. 1260
CAL-COMP ELECTRONICS (SUZHOU) COMPANY LIMITED—See Cal-Comp Electronics (Thailand) pcl; *Int'l*, pg. 1260
CAL-COMP ELECTRONICS (THAILAND) PCL; *Int'l*, pg. 1260
CAL-COMP ELECTRONICS (USA) CO., LTD.—See Cal-Comp Electronics (Thailand) pcl; *Int'l*, pg. 1260
CAL-COMP INDUSTRIA E COMERCIO DE ELETRONICOS E INFORMATICA LTD.—See Cal-Comp Electronics (Thailand) pcl; *Int'l*, pg. 1261
CAL-COMP OPTICAL ELECTRONICS (SUZHOU) COMPANY LIMITED—See Cal-Comp Electronics (Thailand) pcl; *Int'l*, pg. 1261
CAL-COMP OPTICAL ELECTRONICS (YUEYANG) CO., LTD.—See Cal-Comp Electronics (Thailand) pcl; *Int'l*, pg. 1261
CAL-COMP PRECISION HOLDING CO., LTD.—See Cal-Comp Electronics (Thailand) pcl; *Int'l*, pg. 1261
CAL-COMP PRECISION (THAILAND) LIMITED—See Cal-Comp Electronics (Thailand) pcl; *Int'l*, pg. 1261
CAL-COMP PRECISION (YUEYANG) CO., LTD.—See Cal-Comp Electronics (Thailand) pcl; *Int'l*, pg. 1261
CALCOM VISION LTD.; *Int'l*, pg. 1262
CALCON CONSTRUCTORS, INC.; *U.S. Private*, pg. 716
CALCON DEUTSCHLAND GMBH—See Advent International Corporation; *U.S. Private*, pg. 96
CALCON DEUTSCHLAND GMBH—See Centerbridge Partners, L.P.; *U.S. Private*, pg. 812
CALCORP LIMITED; *Int'l*, pg. 1262
CALCOT, LTD.; *U.S. Private*, pg. 716
CALCOT, LTD. - THE GLENDALE FACILITY—See Calcot, Ltd.; *U.S. Private*, pg. 716
CALCULAGRAPH CO.; *U.S. Private*, pg. 716
CALCULUS VCT PLC; *Int'l*, pg. 1262
CALCUTTA STOCK EXCHANGE ASSOCIATION LTD.; *Int'l*, pg. 1262
CALDARO AB—See Addtech AB; *Int'l*, pg. 132
CALDARO INC.—See Addtech AB; *Int'l*, pg. 132
CALDAS GOLD CORP.; *Int'l*, pg. 1262
CALDERA, INC.—See Dover Corporation; *U.S. Public*, pg. 678
CALDER DEVELOPMENT ASSOCIATES, INC.; *U.S. Private*, pg. 716
CALDER GMBH—See Flowserve Corporation; *U.S. Public*, pg. 855
CALDER GRANGE (DEWSBURY) MANAGEMENT COMPANY LIMITED—See Persimmon plc; *Int'l*, pg. 5815
CALDER IMMEDIATE CARE, PLLC—See HCA Healthcare, Inc.; *U.S. Public*, pg. 992
CALDER RACE COURSE, INC.—See Churchill Downs, Inc.; *U.S. Public*, pg. 493
CALDER URGENT CARE, PLLC—See HCA Healthcare, Inc.; *U.S. Public*, pg. 992
CALDERYS AUSTRIA GMBH—See Groupe Bruxelles Lambert SA; *Int'l*, pg. 3099
CALDERYS BELGIUM SA/NV—See Groupe Bruxelles Lambert SA; *Int'l*, pg. 3099
CALDERYS FRANCE SAS—See Groupe Bruxelles Lambert SA; *Int'l*, pg. 3099
CALDERYS ITALIA SRL—See Groupe Bruxelles Lambert SA; *Int'l*, pg. 3099
CALDERYS MAGYARORSZAG KFT—See Groupe Bruxelles Lambert SA; *Int'l*, pg. 3099
CALDERYS NORDIC AB—See Groupe Bruxelles Lambert SA; *Int'l*, pg. 3099
CALDERYS SOUTH AFRICA PTY LTD—See Groupe Bruxelles Lambert SA; *Int'l*, pg. 3099
CAL DEVELOPMENT INC.; *U.S. Private*, pg. 715
CALDIC B.V.; *Int'l*, pg. 1262
CALDIC NEW ZEALAND LTD.—See Caldic B.V.; *Int'l*, pg. 1262
CALDIC USA INC.—See Caldic B.V.; *Int'l*, pg. 1262
CALDURAN KALKZANDSTEEN B.V.—See CRH plc; *Int'l*, pg. 1844
CALDWELL-AIR, LLC—See Lithia Motors, Inc.; *U.S. Public*, pg. 1321
CALDWELL COUNTY BANCSHARES, INC.; *U.S. Private*, pg. 716
CALDWELL COUNTY HOSPITAL, INC.; *U.S. Private*, pg. 716
CALDWELL FREIGHT LINES INC.—See CF Holding Company, Inc.; *U.S. Private*, pg. 843
CALDWELL HARDWARE, LTD—See ASSA ABLOY AB; *Int'l*, pg. 639
CALDWELL IMPLEMENT COMPANY; *U.S. Private*, pg. 716
CALDWELL IMPORTS INC.; *U.S. Private*, pg. 716
CALDWELL INDUSTRIES INC.; *U.S. Private*, pg. 716

CALDWELL INDUSTRIES INC.

CALDWELL INTERIM EXECUTIVES INC.—See The Caldwell Partners International Inc.; *Int'l*, pg. 7630
CALDWELL LESLIE & PROCTOR PC—See Boies Schiller Flexner LLP; *U.S. Private*, pg. 609
CALDWELL MANUFACTURING COMPANY NORTH AMERICA, LLC—See ASSA ABLOY AB; *Int'l*, pg. 639
CALDWELL MARINE INTERNATIONAL, LLC (CMI)—See Northeast Remsco Construction, Inc.; *U.S. Private*, pg. 2951
CALDWELL MILLING CO. INC.; *U.S. Private*, pg. 716
THE CALDWELL PARTNERS INTERNATIONAL INC.; *Int'l*, pg. 7630
CALDWELL PLUMBING CO., INC.; *U.S. Private*, pg. 716
CALDWELL TANKS, INC. - ATLANTA—See Caldwell Tanks, Inc.; *U.S. Private*, pg. 716
CALDWELL TANKS, INC.; *U.S. Private*, pg. 716
CALDWELL TRUST COMPANY—See Trust Companies of America, Inc.; *U.S. Private*, pg. 4250
CAL-DYNASTY INTERNATIONAL, INC.—See China Airlines Ltd.; *Int'l*, pg. 1481
CALDYNE AUTOMATICS LIMITED—See EXIDE INDUSTRIES LIMITED; *Int'l*, pg. 2585
CALEA LTD.—See Fresenius SE & Co. KGaA; *Int'l*, pg. 2777
CALE AMERICA, INC.—See Mellby Gard Holding AB; *Int'l*, pg. 4811
CA-LEASING SENIOREN PARK GMBH—See UniCredit S.p.A.; *Int'l*, pg. 8036
CA-LEASING YPSILON INGATLANHASZNOSITO KORLATOLT FELELOSSEGU TARSASAG—See UniCredit S.p.A.; *Int'l*, pg. 8036
CALE AS—See Mellby Gard Holding AB; *Int'l*, pg. 4811
CALE AUSTRALIA PTY. LTD.—See Astorg Partners S.A.S.; *Int'l*, pg. 656
CALEB BRETT - ITS TESTING SERVICES UK LTD.—See Intertek Group plc; *Int'l*, pg. 3762
CALEB HALEY & CO. INC.; *U.S. Private*, pg. 716
CALE BRIPARC LTD—See Mellby Gard Holding AB; *Int'l*, pg. 4811
CALE DANMARK A/S—See Mellby Gard Holding AB; *Int'l*, pg. 4811
CALE DEUTSCHLAND GMBH—See Mellby Gard Holding AB; *Int'l*, pg. 4811
CALEDON COAL PTY. LTD.—See Guangdong Rising Assets Management Co., Ltd.; *Int'l*, pg. 3159
CALEDONIA FARMERS ELEVATOR COMPANY INC.; *U.S. Private*, pg. 717
CALEDONIA GROUP SERVICES LTD—See Caledonia Investments plc; *Int'l*, pg. 1262
CALEDONIA HOLDINGS ZIMBABWE (LIMITED)—See Caledonia Mining Corporation Plc; *Int'l*, pg. 1262
CALEDONIA HOLDINGS ZIMBABWE (PRIVATE) LIMITED—See Caledonia Mining Corporation Plc; *Int'l*, pg. 1262
CALEDONIA INVESTMENTS PLC; *Int'l*, pg. 1262
CALEDONIA MINING CORPORATION PLC; *Int'l*, pg. 1262
CALEDONIAN ALLOYS GROUP LIMITED—See Berkshire Hathaway Inc.; *U.S. Public*, pg. 313
CALEDONIAN ALLOYS LIMITED—See Berkshire Hathaway Inc.; *U.S. Public*, pg. 314
CALEDONIAN BOTTLERS PLC—See SHS Group, Ltd.; *Int'l*, pg. 6867
CALEDONIAN CITY DEVELOPMENTS LTD.—See Caledonian Trust PLC; *Int'l*, pg. 1263
CALEDONIAN INSURANCE GROUP, INC.—See Truist Financial Corporation; *U.S. Public*, pg. 2200
CALEDONIAN PETROLEUM SERVICES LTD.—See Global Energy (Holdings) Ltd.; *Int'l*, pg. 2995
CALEDONIAN PRODUCE—See Bakkavor Group plc; *Int'l*, pg. 806
CALEDONIAN PROPERTIES LIMITED—See Derwent London plc; *Int'l*, pg. 2043
CALEDONIAN PROPERTY INVESTMENTS LIMITED—See Derwent London plc; *Int'l*, pg. 2043
CALEDONIAN SCOTTISH DEVELOPMENTS LTD.—See Caledonian Trust PLC; *Int'l*, pg. 1263
CALEDONIAN TOWAGE LTD—See Global Energy (Holdings) Ltd.; *Int'l*, pg. 2995
CALEDONIAN TRUST PLC; *Int'l*, pg. 1263
CALEDONIA (PRIVATE) INVESTMENTS PTY. LTD.; *Int'l*, pg. 1262
CALEDONIA TREASURY LTD—See Caledonia Investments plc; *Int'l*, pg. 1262
CALEFFI ARMATUREN GMBH—See Caleffi S.p.A.; *Int'l*, pg. 1263
CALEFFI FRANCE CONSULTING—See Caleffi S.p.A.; *Int'l*, pg. 1263
CALEFFI INTERNATIONA N.V.—See Caleffi S.p.A.; *Int'l*, pg. 1263
CALEFFI LDA.—See Caleffi S.p.A.; *Int'l*, pg. 1263
CALEFFI NORTH AMERICA, INC.—See Caleffi S.p.A.; *Int'l*, pg. 1263
CALEFFI - S.P.A.; *Int'l*, pg. 1263
CALEFFI S.P.A.; *Int'l*, pg. 1263
CALE GROUP AB—See Mellby Gard Holding AB; *Int'l*, pg. 4811
CALEIDO GROUP S.P.A.; *Int'l*, pg. 1263

CALENDAR CLUB LLC—See Specialty Retail Ventures LLC; *U.S. Private*, pg. 3750
CALE NETHERLANDS BV—See Mellby Gard Holding AB; *Int'l*, pg. 4811
CAL ENGINEERING & GEOLOGY INC—See Haley & Aldrich Inc.; *U.S. Private*, pg. 1842
CALENIA ENERGIA S.P.A.—See Axpo Holding AG; *Int'l*, pg. 771
CALENTADORES CINSA, S.A. DE C.V.—See Grupo Industrial Saltillo S.A. de C.V.; *Int'l*, pg. 3130
CALEO, S.A.—See Reditus SGPS S.A.; *Int'l*, pg. 6248
CALE PARKING IBERICA SL—See Astorg Partners S.A.S.; *Int'l*, pg. 656
CALEPPIOVINIL S.P.A.—See Solvay S.A.; *Int'l*, pg. 7077
CALERA CAPITAL MANAGEMENT, INC.; *U.S. Private*, pg. 717
CALERES CANADA, INC.—See Caleres, Inc.; *U.S. Public*, pg. 422
CALERES, INC.; *U.S. Public*, pg. 422
CALERES ITALY S.R.L.—See Caleres, Inc.; *U.S. Public*, pg. 422
CALERIS, INC.—See Iowa Network Services Inc.; *U.S. Private*, pg. 2135
CALERO SOFTWARE, LLC—See Riverside Partners, LLC; *U.S. Private*, pg. 3445
CALESA MOTORS INC.; *U.S. Private*, pg. 717
CALE SAS—See Mellby Gard Holding AB; *Int'l*, pg. 4811
CALESCO FOIL AB—See NIBE Industrier AB; *Int'l*, pg. 5260
CALE SYSTEMS INC—See Mellby Gard Holding AB; *Int'l*, pg. 4811
CALETHOS, INC.; *U.S. Public*, pg. 423
CALEX EXPRESS INC—See Calex Logistics Corp.; *U.S. Private*, pg. 717
CALEX LOGISTICS CORP.; *U.S. Private*, pg. 717
CALEX TRUCK SALES INC—See Calex Logistics Corp.; *U.S. Private*, pg. 717
THE CALEY GROUP LIMITED—See Berkshire Hathaway Inc.; *U.S. Public*, pg. 315
CALEY LTD.—See HSBC Holdings plc; *Int'l*, pg. 3503
CALEY LTD.—See Lloyds Banking Group plc; *Int'l*, pg. 4536
CALFEE COMPANY OF DALTON, INC.; *U.S. Private*, pg. 717
CALFRAC WELL SERVICES (ARGENTINA) S.A.—See Calfrac Well Services Ltd.; *Int'l*, pg. 1263
CALFRAC WELL SERVICES CORP.—See Calfrac Well Services Ltd.; *Int'l*, pg. 1263
CALFRAC WELL SERVICES CORP.—See Calfrac Well Services Ltd.; *Int'l*, pg. 1263
CALFRAC WELL SERVICES LTD.; *Int'l*, pg. 1263
CALG 307 MOBILIEN LEASING GMBH—See UniCredit S.p.A.; *Int'l*, pg. 8036
CALG 443 GRUNDSTUCKVERWALTUNG GMBH—See UniCredit S.p.A.; *Int'l*, pg. 8036
CALG 445 GRUNDSTUCKVERWALTUNG GMBH—See UniCredit S.p.A.; *Int'l*, pg. 8037
CALG 451 GRUNDSTUCKVERWALTUNG GMBH—See UniCredit S.p.A.; *Int'l*, pg. 8037
CALG ALPHA GRUNDSTUCKVERWALTUNG GMBH—See UniCredit S.p.A.; *Int'l*, pg. 8034
CALG ANLAGEN LEASING GMBH—See UniCredit S.p.A.; *Int'l*, pg. 8037
CALGARY CO-OPERATIVE ASSOCIATION LIMITED; *Int'l*, pg. 1263
CALGARY CO-OP HOME HEALTH CARE LIMITED—See Calgary Co-operative Association Limited; *Int'l*, pg. 1263
CALGARY FLAMES LIMITED PARTNERSHIP; *Int'l*, pg. 1263
CALGARY HERALD—See Chatham Asset Management, LLC; *U.S. Private*, pg. 861
CALGARY METAL RECYCLING INC.; *Int'l*, pg. 1263
THE CALGARY SUN—See Chatham Asset Management, LLC; *U.S. Private*, pg. 861
CALGARY TENT & AWNING LTD.; *Int'l*, pg. 1263
CALGAZ INTERNATIONAL LLC—See L'Air Liquide S.A.; *Int'l*, pg. 4374
CALG GAMMA GRUNDSTUCKVERWALTUNG GMBH—See UniCredit S.p.A.; *Int'l*, pg. 8037
CALG GRUNDSTUCKVERWALTUNG GMBH—See UniCredit S.p.A.; *Int'l*, pg. 8037
CALG IMMOBILIEN LEASING GMBH & CO 1050 WIEN, SIEBENBRUNNENGASSE 10-21 OG—See UniCredit S.p.A.; *Int'l*, pg. 8037
CALG IMMOBILIEN LEASING GMBH & CO 1120 WIEN, SCHONBRUNNER SCHLOSS-STRASSE 38-42 OG—See UniCredit S.p.A.; *Int'l*, pg. 8037
CALG IMMOBILIEN LEASING GMBH & CO PROJEKT VIER OG—See UniCredit S.p.A.; *Int'l*, pg. 8037
CALG IMMOBILIEN LEASING GMBH—See UniCredit S.p.A.; *Int'l*, pg. 8037
CALGON CARBON CORPORATION—See Kuraray Co., Ltd.; *Int'l*, pg. 4336
CALGRO M3 HOLDINGS LIMITED; *Int'l*, pg. 1263
CAL HOTEL CO. LTD.—See China Airlines Ltd.; *Int'l*, pg. 1482
CALHOUN AGENCY, INC.—See World Insurance Associates LLC; *U.S. Private*, pg. 4565

CORPORATE AFFILIATIONS

CALHOUN APPAREL INC.; *U.S. Private*, pg. 717
CALHOUN ASPHALT COMPANY, INC.—See Vulcan Materials Company; *U.S. Public*, pg. 2313
CALHOUN BUILDERS INC.; *U.S. Private*, pg. 717
CALHOUN COUNTY ROAD COMMISSION; *U.S. Private*, pg. 717
CALHOUN ENTERPRISES INC.; *U.S. Private*, pg. 717
CALHOUN INTERNATIONAL, LLC; *U.S. Private*, pg. 717
CALHOUN LIBERTY HOSPITAL; *U.S. Private*, pg. 717
CALIAN GROUP LTD.; *Int'l*, pg. 1263
CALIAN LTD. - SED SYSTEMS DIVISION—See Calian Group Ltd.; *Int'l*, pg. 1264
CALIAN LTD.—See Calian Group Ltd.; *Int'l*, pg. 1263
CALIAN LTD. - TORONTO—See Calian Group Ltd.; *Int'l*, pg. 1264
CALI BAMBOO LLC—See High Road Capital Partners, LLC; *U.S. Private*, pg. 1936
CALIBER BODYWORKS OF TEXAS, INC.—See Hellman & Friedman LLC; *U.S. Private*, pg. 1907
CALIBERCOS, INC.; *U.S. Public*, pg. 423
CALIBER HOME LOANS, INC.—See Rithm Capital Corp.; *U.S. Public*, pg. 1799
CALIBER POINT BUSINESS SOLUTIONS—See EQT AB; *Int'l*, pg. 2470
CALIBRACIER SAS—See Jacquet Metal Service SA; *Int'l*, pg. 3866
CALIBRA MEDICAL, INC.—See Johnson & Johnson; *U.S. Public*, pg. 1194
CALIBRATED FORMS CO., INC.—See Ennis, Inc.; *U.S. Public*, pg. 769
CALIBRATION TECHNOLOGIES—See Transcat, Inc.; *U.S. Public*, pg. 2179
CALIBRATION TECHNOLOGY LTD.—See Eppendorf AG; *Int'l*, pg. 2464
CALIBRE GROUP LTD; *Int'l*, pg. 1264
CALIBRE MINING CORP.; *Int'l*, pg. 1264
CALIBRE NATURE (M) SDN. BHD.—See Charoen Pokphand Foods Public Company Limited; *Int'l*, pg. 1452
CALIBRE SCIENTIFIC, INC.—See StoneCalibre, LLC; *U.S. Private*, pg. 3827
CALIBRE SYSTEMS INC.; *U.S. Private*, pg. 717
CALIBURN INTERNATIONAL CORPORATION; *U.S. Private*, pg. 717
CALICO CORNERS—See Everfast Inc.; *U.S. Private*, pg. 1438
CALI'CO HARDWOODS INC.—See Wynnchurch Capital, L.P.; *U.S. Private*, pg. 4578
CALICO LLC—See Alphabet Inc.; *U.S. Public*, pg. 82
CALICO PRECISION MOLDING, LLC; *U.S. Private*, pg. 717
CALICO TAG & LABEL INC—See AFE Industries, Inc.; *U.S. Private*, pg. 121
CALIDA AG—See Calida Holding AG; *Int'l*, pg. 1264
CALIDA GROUP DIGITAL GMBH—See Calida Holding AG; *Int'l*, pg. 1264
CALIDA HOLDING AG; *Int'l*, pg. 1264
CALIDI BIOTHERAPEUTICS, INC.; *U.S. Public*, pg. 423
CALIDI BIOTHERAPEUTICS (NEVADA), INC.—See Calidi Biotherapeutics, Inc.; *U.S. Public*, pg. 423
CALIDUS HOLDINGS, LLC—See Benjamin Macfarland Company, LLC; *U.S. Private*, pg. 526
CALIENDO SAVIO ENTERPRISES, INC.—See TPG Capital, L.P.; *U.S. Public*, pg. 2176
CALIFONE INTERNATIONAL, INC.—See School Specialty, Inc.; *U.S. Public*, pg. 1848
CALIFON PRODUCTIONS, INC.—See Sony Group Corporation; *Int'l*, pg. 7105
CALIFORNIA ACRYLIC INDUSTRIES, INC.; *U.S. Private*, pg. 717
CALIFORNIA AMERICAN WATER COMPANY—See American Water Works Company, Inc.; *U.S. Public*, pg. 112
CALIFORNIA AMFORGE CORP.—See Wynnchurch Capital, L.P.; *U.S. Private*, pg. 4578
CALIFORNIA AMMONIA CO.; *U.S. Private*, pg. 717
CALIFORNIA AMPLIFIER S.A.R.L—See CalAmp Corp.; *U.S. Public*, pg. 422
CALIFORNIA ANALYTICAL INSTRUMENTS, INC.—See The Carlyle Group Inc.; *U.S. Public*, pg. 2046
CALIFORNIA ASBESTOS MONOFILL, INC.—See Waste Management, Inc.; *U.S. Public*, pg. 2330
CALIFORNIA ASSOCIATION OF FOOD BANKS; *U.S. Private*, pg. 717
CALIFORNIA ASSOCIATION OF REALTORS; *U.S. Private*, pg. 717
CALIFORNIA AUTOMOBILE INSURANCE COMPANY—See Mercury General Corporation; *U.S. Public*, pg. 1421
CALIFORNIA BACKYARD INC.; *U.S. Private*, pg. 718
CALIFORNIA BANCORP; *U.S. Public*, pg. 423
CALIFORNIA BANK OF COMMERCE, N.A.—See California BanCorp; *U.S. Public*, pg. 423
CALIFORNIA BANK & TRUST—See Zions Bancorporation, National Association; *U.S. Public*, pg. 2408
CALIFORNIA BANQUET CORPORATION; *U.S. Private*, pg. 718
CALIFORNIA BEACH RESTAURANTS; *U.S. Private*, pg. 718

COMPANY NAME INDEX

CALIFORNIA BENEFITS DENTAL PLAN—See Sun Life Financial Inc.; *Int'l*, pg. 7305
CALIFORNIA BRAZING COMPANY—See Trive Capital Inc.; *U.S. Private*, pg. 4240
CALIFORNIA BROADCAST CENTER, LLC—See AT&T Inc.; *U.S. Public*, pg. 220
CALIFORNIA BUSINESS BANK; *U.S. Public*, pg. 423
CALIFORNIA CAFE; *U.S. Private*, pg. 718
CALIFORNIA CARTAGE COMPANY LLC; *U.S. Private*, pg. 718
CALIFORNIA CASUALTY MANAGEMENT COMPANY; *U.S. Private*, pg. 718
CALIFORNIA CEDAR PRODUCTS COMPANY - PALOMINO BRANDS DIVISION—See California Cedar Products Company; *U.S. Private*, pg. 718
CALIFORNIA CEDAR PRODUCTS COMPANY; *U.S. Private*, pg. 718
CALIFORNIA CHOICE BENEFIT ADMINISTRATORS, INC.—See Word & Brown, Insurance Administrators, Inc.; *U.S. Private*, pg. 4562
CALIFORNIA CHURROS CORP.—See J&J Snack Foods Corporation; *U.S. Public*, pg. 1179
CALIFORNIA CIDER CO., INC.—See Vintage Wine Estates, Inc.; *U.S. Public*, pg. 2298
CALIFORNIA CITIES WATER COMPANY, INC.—See American States Water Company; *U.S. Public*, pg. 110
CALIFORNIA CLOSET COMPANY, INC.—See FirstService Corporation; *Int'l*, pg. 2691
CALIFORNIA COASTAL COMMUNITIES, INC.; *U.S. Private*, pg. 718
CALIFORNIA COAST CREDIT UNION; *U.S. Private*, pg. 718
CALIFORNIA CODE CHECK, INC.—See Bureau Veritas S.A.; *Int'l*, pg. 1222
CALIFORNIA COMMERCIAL ASPHALT CORP.; *U.S. Private*, pg. 718
CALIFORNIA COMMUNICATIONS ACCESS FOUNDATION; *U.S. Private*, pg. 718
CALIFORNIA COMMUNITY NEWS CORPORATION—See Tribune Publishing Company; *U.S. Private*, pg. 4227
CALIFORNIA CREDIT UNION; *U.S. Private*, pg. 718
CALIFORNIA CRYOBANK LLC—See GI Manager L.P.; *U.S. Private*, pg. 1691
CALIFORNIA CRYOBANK STEM CELL SERVICES LLC—See Longitude Capital Management Co., LLC; *U.S. Private*, pg. 2492
CALIFORNIA CUSTOM SHAPES INC; *U.S. Private*, pg. 718
CALIFORNIA DAIRIES, INC. - FRESNO PLANT—See California Dairies, Inc.; *U.S. Private*, pg. 718
CALIFORNIA DAIRIES, INC. - LOS BANOS PLANT—See California Dairies, Inc.; *U.S. Private*, pg. 718
CALIFORNIA DAIRIES, INC.; *U.S. Private*, pg. 718
CALIFORNIA DAIRIES, INC. - TIPTON PLANT—See California Dairies, Inc.; *U.S. Private*, pg. 718
CALIFORNIA DAIRIES, INC. - TURLOCK PLANT—See California Dairies, Inc.; *U.S. Private*, pg. 718
CALIFORNIA DELUXE WINDOWS; *U.S. Private*, pg. 718
CALIFORNIA DEMOCRAT—See Wehco Media, Inc.; *U.S. Private*, pg. 4469
CALIFORNIA DENTAL ASSOCIATION; *U.S. Private*, pg. 719
CALIFORNIA DEPARTMENT OF CONSERVATION; *U.S. Private*, pg. 719
CALIFORNIA DIGITAL INC.; *U.S. Private*, pg. 719
CALIFORNIA DROP FORGE, INC.—See HBD Industries, Inc.; *U.S. Private*, pg. 1887
CALIFORNIA EASTERN LABORATORIES, INC.; *U.S. Private*, pg. 719
CALIFORNIA EMERGENCY FOODLINK; *U.S. Private*, pg. 719
CALIFORNIA-ENGELS MINING CO; *U.S. Public*, pg. 424
CALIFORNIA EXPANDED METAL PRODUCTS COMPANY; *U.S. Private*, pg. 719
CALIFORNIA FACTORS & FINANCE LP; *U.S. Private*, pg. 719
CALIFORNIA FAMILY HEALTH COUNCIL; *U.S. Private*, pg. 719
CALIFORNIA FAMILY HEALTH LLC—See Perpetual Capital, LLC; *U.S. Private*, pg. 3152
CALIFORNIA FARM BUREAU FEDERATION; *U.S. Private*, pg. 719
CALIFORNIA FAST FOODS SERVICES INC.; *U.S. Private*, pg. 719
CALIFORNIA FAUCETS INC.; *U.S. Private*, pg. 719
CALIFORNIA FINANCIAL PARTNERS, INC.; *U.S. Private*, pg. 719
CALIFORNIA FIRST NATIONAL BANCORP; *U.S. Private*, pg. 719
CALIFORNIA FORENSIC MEDICAL GROUP, INC.; *U.S. Private*, pg. 719
CALIFORNIA FRINGE BENEFIT AND INSURANCE MARKETING CORPORATION—See Lincoln National Corporation; *U.S. Public*, pg. 1319
CALIFORNIA GENERAL UNDERWRITERS INSURANCE COMPANY, INC.—See Mercury General Corporation; *U.S. Public*, pg. 1421
CALIFORNIA GOLD MINING INC.—See Stratabound Minerals Corp.; *Int'l*, pg. 7235

CALIFORNIA GRILL LLC—See RCI Hospitality Holdings, Inc.; *U.S. Public*, pg. 1767
CALIFORNIA HARDWARE COMPANY—See Amarillo Hardware Company; *U.S. Private*, pg. 216
CALIFORNIA HEALTHCARE MEDICAL BILLING, LLC—See Veradigm Inc.; *U.S. Public*, pg. 2280
CALIFORNIA HEALTH & WELLNESS PLAN—See Centene Corporation; *U.S. Public*, pg. 468
CALIFORNIA HEAVY OIL, INC.—See Occidental Petroleum Corporation; *U.S. Public*, pg. 1561
CALIFORNIA HOSPITAL MEDICAL CENTER—See Catholic Health Initiatives; *U.S. Private*, pg. 789
CALIFORNIA HOTEL & CASINO—See Boyd Gaming Corporation; *U.S. Public*, pg. 377
CALIFORNIA HYDRONICS CORPORATION; *U.S. Private*, pg. 719
CALIFORNIA INDEPENDENT SYSTEMS OPERATOR; *U.S. Private*, pg. 719
CALIFORNIA INDUSTRIAL RUBBER COMPANY; *U.S. Private*, pg. 719
CALIFORNIA INSTITUTE OF TECHNOLOGY; *U.S. Private*, pg. 719
CALIFORNIA INSTRUMENTS CORPORATION—See AMETEK, Inc.; *U.S. Public*, pg. 118
CALIFORNIA INSURANCE COMPANY—See Berkshire Hathaway Inc.; *U.S. Public*, pg. 304
CALIFORNIA INTERNATIONAL BANK; *U.S. Public*, pg. 423
CALIFORNIA LIFE & HEALTH INSURANCE GUARANTEE ASSOCIATION; *U.S. Private*, pg. 719
CALIFORNIA LIGHTING SALES INCORPORATED; *U.S. Private*, pg. 719
CALIFORNIA MANUFACTURING CO., INC.—See Ajinomoto Company, Inc.; *Int'l*, pg. 257
CALIFORNIA MANUFACTURING CO. INC.; *U.S. Private*, pg. 719
CALIFORNIA MARKETING ASSOCIATES, INC.—See Ivystone Group, LLC; *U.S. Private*, pg. 2152
CALIFORNIA MEDICAL INNOVATIONS—See Arsenal Capital Management LP; *U.S. Private*, pg. 339
CALIFORNIA MEDICAL LABORATORIES, INC.—See LivaNova PLC; *Int'l*, pg. 4530
CALIFORNIA MENTOR FAMILY HOME AGENCY, LLC—See Centerbridge Partners, L.P.; *U.S. Private*, pg. 813
THE CALIFORNIA MUSHROOM FARM, INC.—See Modern Mushroom Farms, Inc.; *U.S. Private*, pg. 2761
CALIFORNIA MUSTANG SALES & PARTS, INC.—See Classic Industries Corp; *U.S. Private*, pg. 916
CALIFORNIA NANOTECHNOLOGIES CORP.; *U.S. Private*, pg. 719
CALIFORNIA NATURAL PRODUCTS, INC.—See Wind Point Advisors LLC; *U.S. Private*, pg. 4534
CALIFORNIA-NEVADA METHODIST HOMES—See Pacifica Companies, LLC; *U.S. Private*, pg. 3072
CALIFORNIA NEWSPAPERS PARTNERSHIP—See Alden Global Capital LLC; *U.S. Public*, pg. 155
CALIFORNIA NORTHERN RAILROAD COMPANY—See Brookfield Infrastructure Partners L.P.; *Int'l*, pg. 1191
CALIFORNIA NORTHERN RAILROAD COMPANY—See GIC Pte. Ltd.; *Int'l*, pg. 2965
CALIFORNIANS AGAINST HIGHER HEALTHCARE COSTS; *U.S. Private*, pg. 720
CALIFORNIA NUMISMATIC INVESTMENTS INC.; *U.S. Private*, pg. 720
CALIFORNIA NURSES ASSOCIATION; *U.S. Private*, pg. 720
CALIFORNIA OFFSET PRINTERS, INC.—See COP Communications; *U.S. Private*, pg. 1044
CALIFORNIA OLIVE RANCH INC.; *U.S. Private*, pg. 720
CALIFORNIA ORCHARDS CO.; *U.S. Public*, pg. 423
CALIFORNIA OREGON BROADCASTING INC.; *U.S. Private*, pg. 720
CALIFORNIA OUTDOOR ADVERTISING; *U.S. Private*, pg. 720
CALIFORNIA PACIFIC HOMES INC.; *U.S. Private*, pg. 720
CALIFORNIA PACIFIC MEDICAL CENTER—See Sutter Health; *U.S. Private*, pg. 3887
CALIFORNIA PACIFIC RESEARCH, INC.; *U.S. Private*, pg. 720
CALIFORNIA PANEL & VENEER COMPANY; *U.S. Private*, pg. 720
CALIFORNIA PARKING COMPANY, INC.—See Propark, Inc.; *U.S. Private*, pg. 3284
CALIFORNIA PAVEMENT MAINTENANCE CO., INC.; *U.S. Private*, pg. 720
CALIFORNIA PELLET MILL CO.—See Gilbert Global Equity Partners; *U.S. Private*, pg. 1699
CALIFORNIA PIZZA KITCHEN, INC.—See Golden Gate Capital Management II, LLC; *U.S. Private*, pg. 1731
CALIFORNIA PORTLAND CEMENT COMPANY-COLTON CEMENT PLANT—See Taiheiyo Cement Corporation; *Int'l*, pg. 7412
CALIFORNIA PORTLAND CEMENT COMPANY-MOJAVE CEMENT PLANT—See Taiheiyo Cement Corporation; *Int'l*, pg. 7412

CALIFORNIA WASTE SOLUTIONS

CALIFORNIA PORTLAND CEMENT COMPANY-RILLITO CEMENT PLANT—See Taiheiyo Cement Corporation; *Int'l*, pg. 7412
CALIFORNIA PORTLAND CEMENT COMPANY—See Taiheiyo Cement Corporation; *Int'l*, pg. 7412
CALIFORNIA PRETZEL COMPANY—See Conagra Brands, Inc.; *U.S. Public*, pg. 564
CALIFORNIA PRODUCTS CORPORATION—See Audax Group, Limited Partnership; *U.S. Private*, pg. 388
CALIFORNIA PRODUCTS CORP. - PAINT DIVISION—See Audax Group, Limited Partnership; *U.S. Private*, pg. 388
CALIFORNIA PRODUCTS CORP. - RECREATIONAL PRODUCTS DIVISION—See Audax Group, Limited Partnership; *U.S. Private*, pg. 388
CALIFORNIA PROPERTY HOLDINGS III LLC—See Abbott Laboratories; *U.S. Public*, pg. 19
CALIFORNIA PUBLIC EMPLOYEES' RETIREMENT SYSTEM; *U.S. Private*, pg. 720
CALIFORNIA PV ENERGY, LLC—See Constellation Energy Corporation; *U.S. Public*, pg. 571
CALIFORNIA RAIL BUILDERS, LLC—See Ferrovial S.A.; *Int'l*, pg. 2644
CALIFORNIA REHABILITATION INSTITUTE, LLC—See Select Medical Holdings Corporation; *U.S. Public*, pg. 1857
CALIFORNIA RESOURCES CORPORATION; *U.S. Public*, pg. 423
CALIFORNIA RESOURCES ELK HILLS, LLC—See California Resources Corporation; *U.S. Public*, pg. 423
CALIFORNIA RESOURCES LONG BEACH, INC.—See California Resources Corporation; *U.S. Public*, pg. 423
CALIFORNIA RESOURCES PRODUCTION CORPORATION—See California Resources Corporation; *U.S. Public*, pg. 423
CALIFORNIA RURAL INDIAN HEALTH BOARD, INC.; *U.S. Private*, pg. 720
CALIFORNIA SAFETY & SUPPLY CO.—See Mallory Safety & Supply LLC; *U.S. Private*, pg. 2558
CALIFORNIA SCENTS, INC.—See Energizer Holdings, Inc.; *U.S. Public*, pg. 760
CALIFORNIA SCHOOL EMPLOYEES ASSOCIATION; *U.S. Private*, pg. 720
CALIFORNIA SCREW PRODUCTS CORP.—See Inflexion Private Equity Partners LLP; *Int'l*, pg. 3688
CALIFORNIA SERVICE TOOL INC.; *U.S. Private*, pg. 720
CALIFORNIA SHELLFISH COMPANY; *U.S. Private*, pg. 720
CALIFORNIA SHINGLE & SHAKE CO.; *U.S. Private*, pg. 720
CALIFORNIA SOFTWARE COMPANY LTD.; *Int'l*, pg. 1264
CALIFORNIA STATE EMPLOYEES ASSOCIATION; *U.S. Private*, pg. 720
CALIFORNIA STEEL INDUSTRIES, INC.—See JFE Holdings, Inc.; *Int'l*, pg. 3934
CALIFORNIA STEEL INDUSTRIES, INC.—See Nucor Corporation; *U.S. Public*, pg. 1553
CALIFORNIA STEEL & ORNAMENTAL SUPPLIES, INC.; *U.S. Private*, pg. 720
CALIFORNIA STYLE PALMS, INC.; *U.S. Public*, pg. 423
CALIFORNIA SUITES INC.; *U.S. Private*, pg. 720
CALIFORNIA SULLIVAN'S, INC.—See Catterton Management Company, LLC; *U.S. Private*, pg. 793
CALIFORNIA SUN DRY FOODS, INC.—See Benford Capital Partners, LLC; *U.S. Private*, pg. 526
CALIFORNIA SUPERMARKET INC.; *U.S. Private*, pg. 720
CALIFORNIA SUPPLY, INC.; *U.S. Private*, pg. 720
CALIFORNIA SUPPLY, INC. - UNION CITY—See California Supply, Inc.; *U.S. Private*, pg. 720
CALIFORNIA SUPPRESSION SYSTEMS INC.; *U.S. Private*, pg. 721
CALIFORNIA SURVEYING & DRAFTING SUPPLY, INC.—See Cansel Survey Equipment, Ltd.; *Int'l*, pg. 1298
CALIFORNIA TANK LINES INC.—See Chemical Transfer Company; *U.S. Private*, pg. 871
CALIFORNIA TEACHING FELLOWS FOUNDATION; *U.S. Private*, pg. 721
CALIFORNIA TECHNOLOGY VENTURES, LLC; *U.S. Private*, pg. 721
CALIFORNIA TELESERVICES INC.; *U.S. Private*, pg. 721
CALIFORNIA TITLE COMPANY—See Orange Coast Title Company Inc.; *U.S. Private*, pg. 3036
CALIFORNIA TOMATO MACHINERY—See Westside Equipment Co.; *U.S. Private*, pg. 4500
CALIFORNIA TOOL & WELDING SUPPLIES; *U.S. Private*, pg. 721
CALIFORNIA TRANSPLANT DONOR NETWORK; *U.S. Private*, pg. 721
CALIFORNIA TREATMENT SERVICES—See Acadia Healthcare Company, Inc.; *U.S. Public*, pg. 28
CALIFORNIA TRUSFRAME, LLC—See Builders FirstSource, Inc.; *U.S. Public*, pg. 410
CALIFORNIA WASTE SOLUTIONS; *U.S. Private*, pg. 721
CALIFORNIA WATER SERVICE COMPANY—See California Water Service Group; *U.S. Public*, pg. 423
CALIFORNIA WATER SERVICE COMPANY—See California Water Service Group; *U.S. Public*, pg. 423

CALIFORNIA WATER SERVICE COMPANY—See California Water Service Group; *U.S. Public*, pg. 423
CALIFORNIA WATER SERVICE COMPANY—See California Water Service Group; *U.S. Public*, pg. 423
CALIFORNIA WATER SERVICE COMPANY—See California Water Service Group; *U.S. Public*, pg. 424
CALIFORNIA WATER SERVICE COMPANY—See California Water Service Group; *U.S. Public*, pg. 424
CALIFORNIA WATER SERVICE COMPANY—See California Water Service Group; *U.S. Public*, pg. 424
CALIFORNIA WATER SERVICE COMPANY—See California Water Service Group; *U.S. Public*, pg. 424
CALIFORNIA WATER SERVICE COMPANY—See California Water Service Group; *U.S. Public*, pg. 424
CALIFORNIA WATER SERVICE GROUP; *U.S. Public*, pg. 423
CALIGOR PHARMACY—See Henry Schein, Inc.; *U.S. Public*, pg. 1025
CALIGOR RX, INC.—See Diversis Capital, LLC; *U.S. Private*, pg. 1244
CALIHAN PORK PROCESSORS, INC.—See Rosens Diversified, Inc.; *U.S. Private*, pg. 3484
CALIMA ENERGY INC.—See Calima Energy Limited; *Int'l*, pg. 1264
CALIMA ENERGY LIMITED; *Int'l*, pg. 1264
CALIMMUNE INC.—See CSL Limited; *Int'l*, pg. 1865
C.A. LINDMAN INC.; *U.S. Private*, pg. 705
CALINGTON LIMITED—See Pabrik Kertas Tjiwi Kimia Tbk; *Int'l*, pg. 5684
CAL INSPECTION BUREAU, INC.—See XPT Group LLC; *U.S. Private*, pg. 4582
CALIN TECHNOLOGY CO., LTD.; *Int'l*, pg. 1265
CAL INVESTMENTS LIMITED—See CalBank PLC; *Int'l*, pg. 1261
CALIPER BUILDING SYSTEMS, LLC—See UFP Industries, Inc.; *U.S. Public*, pg. 2218
CALIPER CORPORATION—See Educational Testing Service Inc.; *U.S. Private*, pg. 1340
CALIPER LIFE SCIENCES, INC.—See Revvity, Inc.; *U.S. Public*, pg. 1793
CALIPSO S.A—See SIF Banat-Crisana S.A.; *Int'l*, pg. 6905
CALIPSO SPA—See Banca Finnat Euramerica S.p.A.; *Int'l*, pg. 814
CALIQUA AG—See ENGIE SA; *Int'l*, pg. 2429
CALIQUA ANLAGENTECHNIK GMBH—See Alpiq Holding AG; *Int'l*, pg. 372
CALIQUA POWERTEC GMBH—See ENGIE SA; *Int'l*, pg. 2429
CALISE PARTNERS, LLC; *U.S. Private*, pg. 721
CALISE & SEDEI; *U.S. Private*, pg. 721
CALISE & SONS BAKERY INC.; *U.S. Private*, pg. 721
CALISSIO RESOURCES GROUP INC.; *U.S. Public*, pg. 424
CALITHERA BIOSCIENCES, INC.; *U.S. Public*, pg. 424
C.A. LITZLER CO., INC.; *U.S. Private*, pg. 705
CALIX INC. - DEVELOPMENT CENTER—See Calix Inc.; *U.S. Public*, pg. 424
CALIX INC.; *U.S. Public*, pg. 424
CALIX LIMITED; *Int'l*, pg. 1265
CALIX—See Calix Inc.; *U.S. Public*, pg. 424
CALJAN AS—See Investment AB Latour; *Int'l*, pg. 3781
CALJAN GMBH—See Investment AB Latour; *Int'l*, pg. 3781
CALJAN LIMITED—See Investment AB Latour; *Int'l*, pg. 3781
CALJAN RITE-HITE APS—See Investment AB Latour; *Int'l*, pg. 3781
CALJAN RITE-HITE BENELUX BV—See Investment AB Latour; *Int'l*, pg. 3781
CALJAN RITE-HITE GMBH—See Investment AB Latour; *Int'l*, pg. 3781
CALJAN RITE-HITE LATVIA SIA—See Investment AB Latour; *Int'l*, pg. 3781
CALJAN RITE-HITE LTD.—See Investment AB Latour; *Int'l*, pg. 3781
CALJAN RITE-HITE S.A.R.L—See Investment AB Latour; *Int'l*, pg. 3781
CALJAN S.A.R.L.—See Investment AB Latour; *Int'l*, pg. 3781
CALKIN COMPANIES INC.; *U.S. Private*, pg. 721
CALKINS GMC; *U.S. Private*, pg. 721
CALL-2 B.V.—See Koninklijke KPN N.V.; *Int'l*, pg. 4267
CALL2RECYCLE, INC; *U.S. Private*, pg. 721
CALLAGHEN INNOVATION RESEARCH LIMITED; *Int'l*, pg. 1265
CALLAHAN CAPITAL PARTNERS; *U.S. Private*, pg. 722
CALLAHAN CHEMICAL COMPANY; *U.S. Private*, pg. 722
CALLAHAN CREEK, INC.—See Barkley; *U.S. Private*, pg. 475
CALLAHAN CREEK—See Barkley; *U.S. Private*, pg. 475
CALLAHAN FINANCIAL PLANNING COMPANY; *U.S. Private*, pg. 722
CALLAHAN, INC.; *U.S. Private*, pg. 722
CALLAHAN'S GENERAL STORE; *U.S. Private*, pg. 722
CALLANAN INDUSTRIES, INC.—See CRH plc; *Int'l*, pg. 1847
CALLAWAY CAPITAL MANAGEMENT, LLC; *U.S. Private*, pg. 722
CALLAWAY ELECTRIC COOPERATIVE; *U.S. Private*, pg. 722

CALLAWAY GOLF BALL OPERATIONS, INC.—See Topgolf Callaway Brands Corp.; *U.S. Public*, pg. 2164
CALLAWAY GOLF CANADA LTD.—See Topgolf Callaway Brands Corp.; *U.S. Public*, pg. 2164
CALLAWAY GOLF EUROPE LTD.—See Topgolf Callaway Brands Corp.; *U.S. Public*, pg. 2164
CALLAWAY GOLF INTERACTIVE, INC.—See Topgolf Callaway Brands Corp.; *U.S. Public*, pg. 2164
CALLAWAY GOLF KABUSHIKI KAISHA—See Topgolf Callaway Brands Corp.; *U.S. Public*, pg. 2164
CALLAWAY GOLF KOREA LTD.—See Topgolf Callaway Brands Corp.; *U.S. Public*, pg. 2164
CALLAWAY GOLF MALAYSIA SDN. BHD.—See Topgolf Callaway Brands Corp.; *U.S. Public*, pg. 2164
CALLAWAY GOLF SALES COMPANY—See Topgolf Callaway Brands Corp.; *U.S. Public*, pg. 2164
CALLAWAY GOLF SOUTH PACIFIC PTY LTD.—See Topgolf Callaway Brands Corp.; *U.S. Public*, pg. 2164
CALLAWAY JONES FUNERAL HOME—See Birch Hill Equity Partners Management Inc.; *Int'l*, pg. 1046
CALLAWAY JONES FUNERAL HOME—See Homesteaders Life Co. Inc.; *U.S. Private*, pg. 1974
CALLAWAY SAFETY EQUIPMENT CO., INC.—See Littlejohn & Co., LLC; *U.S. Private*, pg. 2472
CALLAWAY TEMECULA LIMITED PARTNERSHIP; *U.S. Private*, pg. 722
CALLAWAY VINEYARD & WINERY—See Callaway Temecula Limited Partnership; *U.S. Private*, pg. 722
CALL CATERLINK LTD.—See Orkla ASA; *Int'l*, pg. 5638
CALL CENTER HELLAS S.A—See NEWSPHONE HELLAS S.A.; *Int'l*, pg. 5238
CALL CENTRE TECHNOLOGY LIMITED—See Capita plc; *Int'l*, pg. 1308
CALLCOPY, INC.; *U.S. Private*, pg. 722
CALLCREDIT LIMITED—See GTCR LLC; *U.S. Private*, pg. 1804
CALLCREDIT MARKETING LIMITED—See GTCR LLC; *U.S. Private*, pg. 1804
CALL DIRECT VERSICHERUNGEN AG—See UNIQA Insurance Group AG; *Int'l*, pg. 8057
CALLDRIP LLC; *U.S. Private*, pg. 722
CALLE & COMPANY; *U.S. Private*, pg. 722
CALLEJA LTD.—See A.A.G. STUCCHI s.r.l.; *Int'l*, pg. 22
CALLEJA S.A. DE C.V.; *Int'l*, pg. 1265
CALL-EM-ALL LLC; *U.S. Private*, pg. 721
CALLEN DIE CASTING LLC—See Callen Manufacturing Corporation; *U.S. Private*, pg. 722
CALLEN MANUFACTURING CORPORATION; *U.S. Private*, pg. 722
CALL EXPERTS; *U.S. Private*, pg. 721
CALLFIRE; *U.S. Private*, pg. 722
CALL HENRY, INC.; *U.S. Private*, pg. 721
CALLIANCE GESTION—See ENGIE SA; *Int'l*, pg. 2428
CALLICO METALS, INC.; *U.S. Private*, pg. 722
CALLICOTTE RANCH HOA, LLC—See BOK Financial Corporation; *U.S. Public*, pg. 367
CALLIDEN GROUP LIMITED—See Steadfast Group Limited; *Int'l*, pg. 7187
CALLIDITAS THERAPEUTICS AB—See Asahi Kasei Corporation; *Int'l*, pg. 596
CALLIDUS CAPITAL CORPORATION; *Int'l*, pg. 1265
CALLIDUS CORPORATION; *U.S. Private*, pg. 722
CALLIDUS SOFTWARE INC.—See SAP SE; *Int'l*, pg. 6567
CALLIDUS SOFTWARE LTD.—See SAP SE; *Int'l*, pg. 6567
CAL-LIFT, INC.; *U.S. Private*, pg. 715
CALLIGARIS S.P.A.—See Alpha Associes Conseil SAS; *Int'l*, pg. 366
CALLI GHANA LTD—See Element Solutions Inc.; *U.S. Public*, pg. 725
CALLIGRAPHEN AB—See HAL Trust N.V.; *Int'l*, pg. 3224
CALLIGRAPHEN APS—See HAL Trust N.V.; *Int'l*, pg. 3224
CALLIGRAPHEN OY—See HAL Trust N.V.; *Int'l*, pg. 3224
CALLINEX MINES INC.; *Int'l*, pg. 1265
CALLISONRTKL, INC.—See ARCADIS N.V.; *Int'l*, pg. 541
CALLISONRTKL, INC.—See ARCADIS N.V.; *Int'l*, pg. 541
CALLISONRTKL—See ARCADIS N.V.; *Int'l*, pg. 541
CALLISONRTKL-UK LTD.—See ARCADIS N.V.; *Int'l*, pg. 541
CALLISTA INDUSTRIES LTD.; *Int'l*, pg. 1265
CALLISTA PRIVATE EQUITY GMBH & CO. KG; *Int'l*, pg. 1265
CALLISTUS BLINDS MIDDLE EAST (FZC)—See Marvel Decor Ltd.; *Int'l*, pg. 4716
CALLISTUS UK LTD.—See Marvel Decor Ltd.; *Int'l*, pg. 4716
CALLITAS HEALTH INC.; *U.S. Private*, pg. 722
CALLITAS THERAPEUTICS, INC.—See Callitas Health Inc.; *U.S. Private*, pg. 722
CALL-IT BELGIUM NV—See Koramic Real Estate NV; *Int'l*, pg. 4280
CALLITECH LIMITED—See ECI Partners LLP; *Int'l*, pg. 2289
CALL-IT INTERNATIONAL B.V.—See Koramic Real Estate NV; *Int'l*, pg. 4280
CALLIVOIRE SGFD SA—See Element Solutions Inc.; *U.S. Public*, pg. 725
CALL MANAGEMENT PRODUCTS INC.; *U.S. Private*, pg. 721

CALLMEWINE S.R.L.—See Italmobiliare S.p.A.; *Int'l*, pg. 3829
CALLMINER, INC.; *U.S. Private*, pg. 722
CALLMINER UK—See CallMiner, Inc.; *U.S. Private*, pg. 722
CALLMOBILE GMBH—See freenet AG; *Int'l*, pg. 2770
CALL NORWEGIAN AS—See Norwegian Air Shuttle ASA; *Int'l*, pg. 5448
CALL NOW, INC.; *U.S. Private*, pg. 721
CALLODINE ACQUISITION CORPORATION; *U.S. Public*, pg. 424
CALLODINE GROUP, LLC—See Callodine Acquisition Corporation; *U.S. Public*, pg. 424
CALLOGIX, INC.; *U.S. Private*, pg. 722
CALL ONE, INC.—See Synergy Communications Management; *U.S. Private*, pg. 3904
CALLONE; *U.S. Private*, pg. 722
CALLON OFFSHORE PRODUCTION—See Callon Petroleum Company; *U.S. Public*, pg. 424
CALLON PETROLEUM COMPANY; *U.S. Public*, pg. 424
CALLON PETROLEUM OPERATING COMPANY—See Callon Petroleum Company; *U.S. Public*, pg. 424
CALLOWAY CREEK SURGERY CENTER, L.P.—See HCA Healthcare, Inc.; *U.S. Public*, pg. 992
CALLOWAY'S NURSERY, INC.; *U.S. Private*, pg. 723
CALLPOINTE.COM, INC.—See Apollo Global Management, Inc.; *U.S. Public*, pg. 152
CALLSCRIPTER LIMITED—See The Yonder Digital Group Limited; *Int'l*, pg. 7705
CALL SERVICES LTD.—See Mauritius Telecom Ltd.; *Int'l*, pg. 4732
CALLSOURCE, INC.; *U.S. Private*, pg. 723
CALLTEC PTY. LTD.—See Azure Healthcare Limited; *Int'l*, pg. 782
CALLTOWER INC.; *U.S. Private*, pg. 723
CALLTOWER NET LTD.—See One Software Technologies Ltd.; *Int'l*, pg. 5575
CALL US ASSISTANCE INTERNATIONAL GMBH—See AXA S.A.; *Int'l*, pg. 754
CALMAC CORP.—See Trane Technologies Plc; *Int'l*, pg. 7891
CAL-MAINE FOODS, INC.; *U.S. Public*, pg. 421
CAL-MAINE FOODS—See Cal-Maine Foods, Inc.; *U.S. Public*, pg. 421
CALM AIR INTERNATIONAL LTD.—See Exchange Income Corporation; *Int'l*, pg. 2579
CALMANN LEVY S.A.—See Vivendi SE; *Int'l*, pg. 8272
CALMARE THERAPEUTICS INCORPORATED; *U.S. Public*, pg. 425
CALMARK SWEDEN AB; *Int'l*, pg. 1265
CALMENA ENERGY SERVICES INC.; *Int'l*, pg. 1265
THE CALMER CO INTERNATIONAL LIMITED; *Int'l*, pg. 7630
CALMET SERVICES INC.; *U.S. Private*, pg. 723
CAL MICRO RECYCLING—See Tide Rock Holdings, LLC; *U.S. Private*, pg. 4167
CALMON ABACUS TEXTILES PTE. LTD.—See Duroc AB; *Int'l*, pg. 2229
CALMONT LEASING LTD; *Int'l*, pg. 1265
CALMONT TRUCK CENTRE LTD.—See Calmont Leasing Ltd; *Int'l*, pg. 1265
CALMUND & RIEMER GMBH—See MEDIQON Group AG; *Int'l*, pg. 4780
CALNAC CO., LTD.—See Calbee, Inc.; *Int'l*, pg. 1261
CALNET, INC. OF SAN DIEGO—See CALNET, Inc.; *U.S. Private*, pg. 723
CAL.NET, INC.; *U.S. Private*, pg. 715
CALNET, INC.; *U.S. Private*, pg. 723
CALNETIX TECHNOLOGIES, LLC.; *U.S. Private*, pg. 723
CAL NET TECHNOLOGY GROUP; *U.S. Private*, pg. 715
CALNEX AMERICAS CORPORATION—See Calnex Solutions Plc; *Int'l*, pg. 1265
CALNEX SOLUTIONS PLC; *Int'l*, pg. 1265
CALNUTRI, INC.; *U.S. Private*, pg. 723
CALOFIC CORPORATION—See Wilmar International Limited; *Int'l*, pg. 8420
CALOLYMPIC GLOVE & SAFETY CO, INC.; *U.S. Private*, pg. 723
CALOOSA BELLE—See Independent Newspapers, Inc.; *U.S. Private*, pg. 2060
CALORE SA—See Azienda Elettrica Ticinese; *Int'l*, pg. 778
CALOREX HEAT PUMPS LTD—See Procuritas Partners AB; *Int'l*, pg. 5987
CALOR GAS LTD.—See SHV Holdings N.V.; *Int'l*, pg. 6872
CALOR GAS NORTHERN IRELAND LTD.—See SHV Holdings N.V.; *Int'l*, pg. 6872
CALOR GROUP—See SHV Holdings N.V.; *Int'l*, pg. 6872
CALORIC ANLAGENBAU GMBH; *Int'l*, pg. 1265
CALOR S.A.S.—See SEB S.A.; *Int'l*, pg. 6667
CALOR TEORANTA—See SHV Holdings N.V.; *Int'l*, pg. 6872
CAL PACIFIC PRODUCTS INC.; *U.S. Private*, pg. 715
CAL PACIFIC SPECIALTY FOODS; *U.S. Private*, pg. 715
CALPAM MINERALOL GMBH—See Financiere de L'Odet; *Int'l*, pg. 2667
CALPANA BUSINESS CONSULTING GMBH—See Kapsch-Group Beteiligungs GmbH; *Int'l*, pg. 4077
CALPE INSURANCE COMPANY LIMITED—See Berkshire Hathaway Inc.; *U.S. Public*, pg. 299

COMPANY NAME INDEX

CALPINE BOSQUE ENERGY CENTER, LLC—See Energy Capital Partners Management, LP; *U.S. Private*, pg. 1394
CALPINE CONTAINERS INC.—See Rainier Partners LP; *U.S. Private*, pg. 3348
CALPINE CORPORATION - DUBLIN—See Energy Capital Partners Management, LP; *U.S. Private*, pg. 1394
CALPINE CORPORATION - MIDDLETOWN—See Energy Capital Partners Management, LP; *U.S. Private*, pg. 1394
CALPINE CORPORATION—See Energy Capital Partners Management, LP; *U.S. Private*, pg. 1394
CALPINE ENERGY SERVICES—See Energy Capital Partners Management, LP; *U.S. Private*, pg. 1394
CALPINE GUADALUPE GP, LLC—See Energy Capital Partners Management, LP; *U.S. Private*, pg. 1394
CALPINE HIDALGO ENERGY CENTER, L.P.—See Energy Capital Partners Management, LP; *U.S. Private*, pg. 1394
CALPINE MERCHANT SERVICES COMPANY—See Energy Capital Partners Management, LP; *U.S. Private*, pg. 1394
CALPINE TURBINE MAINTENANCE GROUP—See Energy Capital Partners Management, LP; *U.S. Private*, pg. 1394
CALPIS BEVERAGES CO., LTD.—See Asahi Group Holdings Ltd.; *Int'l*, pg. 593
CALPIS CO., LTD.—See Asahi Group Holdings Ltd.; *Int'l*, pg. 593
CALPIS FOODS SERVICE CO., LTD.—See Asahi Group Holdings Ltd.; *Int'l*, pg. 593
CALPIS U.S.A. INC.—See Asahi Group Holdings Ltd.; *Int'l*, pg. 593
CAL POLY CORPORATION; *U.S. Private*, pg. 715
CAL POLY POMONA FOUNDATION, INC.; *U.S. Private*, pg. 715
CALPOP.COM, INC.; *U.S. Private*, pg. 723
CALPORTLAND CEMENT COMPANY—See Taiheiyo Cement Corporation; *Int'l*, pg. 7412
CALPORTLAND CEMENT COMPANY—See Taiheiyo Cement Corporation; *Int'l*, pg. 7412
CALPORTLAND CONCRETE PRODUCTS—See Taiheiyo Cement Corporation; *Int'l*, pg. 7412
CALPRIVATE BANK—See Private Bancorp of America, Inc.; *U.S. Public*, pg. 1722
CALRAM, INC.—See Insight Equity Holdings LLC; *U.S. Private*, pg. 2086
C-A-L RANCH STORES; *U.S. Private*, pg. 704
CAL RIPKEN, SR. FOUNDATION; *U.S. Private*, pg. 715
CAL SDI, INC.; *U.S. Private*, pg. 715
CAL SHEETS, LLC—See Goldberg Lindsay & Co., LLC; *U.S. Private*, pg. 1729
CAL SIERRA DISPOSAL—See Waste Management, Inc.; *U.S. Public*, pg. 2330
CALS LOGISTICS, INC.—See A-Sonic Aerospace Limited; *Int'l*, pg. 21
CALSOFT LABS UK PRIVATE LTD.—See Alten S.A.; *Int'l*, pg. 390
CALSONIC KANSEI (GUANGZHOU) CORP.—See KKR & Co. Inc.; *U.S. Public*, pg. 1260
CALSONIC KANSEI (HAIMEN) CAR AIR-CONDITIONING COMPRESSOR CORPORATION—See KKR & Co. Inc.; *U.S. Public*, pg. 1260
CALSONIC KANSEI KOREA CORPORATION—See KKR & Co. Inc.; *U.S. Public*, pg. 1260
CALSONIC KANSEI (MALAYSIA) SDN.BHD.—See KKR & Co. Inc.; *U.S. Public*, pg. 1260
CALSONIC KANSEI MEXICANA, S.A. DE R.L. DE C.V.—See KKR & Co. Inc.; *U.S. Public*, pg. 1260
CALSONIC KANSEI MOTHERSON AUTO PRODUCTS PRIVATE LIMITED—See KKR & Co. Inc.; *U.S. Public*, pg. 1260
CALSONIC KANSEI (SHANGHAI) CORP.—See KKR & Co. Inc.; *U.S. Public*, pg. 1260
CALSONIC KANSEI (WUXI) CORPORATION—See KKR & Co. Inc.; *U.S. Public*, pg. 1260
CALSPAN AERO SYSTEMS ENGINEERING, INC.—See Calspan Technology Holding Corporation; *U.S. Private*, pg. 723
CALSPAN AIR SERVICES, LLC—See TransDigm Group Incorporated; *U.S. Public*, pg. 2180
CALSPAN CORP.—See TransDigm Group Incorporated; *U.S. Public*, pg. 2180
CALSPAN SYSTEMS CORPORATION—See TransDigm Group Incorporated; *U.S. Public*, pg. 2180
CALSPAN TECHNOLOGY HOLDING CORPORATION; *U.S. Private*, pg. 723
CAL SPAS, INC.; *U.S. Private*, pg. 715
CALS REFINERIES LIMITED; *Int'l*, pg. 1265
CALSTAR MOTORS INC—See Parkley Holding Inc.; *U.S. Private*, pg. 3098
CALSTAR PROPERTIES LLC; *U.S. Private*, pg. 723
CAL-STATE AUTO PARTS, INC.; *U.S. Private*, pg. 715
CAL-STATE STEEL CORP.; *U.S. Private*, pg. 715
CAL-STEAM, INC.—See Ferguson plc; *Int'l*, pg. 2637
CALSTONE, CO.—See CRH plc; *Int'l*, pg. 1845
CALSTORES PTY LTD—See Ampol Limited; *Int'l*, pg. 436
CALSTRIP INDUSTRIES INC.; *U.S. Private*, pg. 723

CALSTRIP STEEL CORPORATION—See Calstrip Industries Inc.; *U.S. Private*, pg. 723
CALTAGIRONE EDITORE S.P.A.; *Int'l*, pg. 1265
CALTECH SOFTWARE SYSTEMS, LLC—See Frontenac Company LLC; *U.S. Private*, pg. 1613
CALTECH SURVEYS LTD.; *Int'l*, pg. 1266
CAL TEC LABS, INC.—See Medical Technology Associates, LLC; *U.S. Public*, pg. 2656
CALTEX AUSTRALIA CUSTODIANS PTY LTD—See Ampol Limited; *Int'l*, pg. 436
CALTEX AUSTRALIA FINANCE PTY LTD—See Ampol Limited; *Int'l*, pg. 436
CALTEX AUSTRALIA INVESTMENTS PTY LTD—See Ampol Limited; *Int'l*, pg. 436
CALTEX AUSTRALIA MANAGEMENT PTY LTD—See Ampol Limited; *Int'l*, pg. 436
CALTEX AUSTRALIA PETROLEUM PTY LTD—See Ampol Limited; *Int'l*, pg. 436
CALTEX LUBRICATING OIL REFINERY PTY LTD.—See Ampol Limited; *Int'l*, pg. 436
CALTEX PETROLEUM SERVICES PTY LTD—See Ampol Limited; *Int'l*, pg. 436
CALTEX PETROLEUM (VICTORIA) PTY LTD—See Ampol Limited; *Int'l*, pg. 436
CAL-TEX PROTECTIVE COATINGS INC.—See Cornell Capital LLC; *U.S. Private*, pg. 1051
CALTHERM CORPORATION—See Magnum Corporation; *U.S. Private*, pg. 2549
CAL THERMOPLASTICS, INC.; *U.S. Private*, pg. 715
CALTH INC.; *Int'l*, pg. 1266
CALTHORPE ASSOCIATES, INC.—See HDR, Inc.; *U.S. Private*, pg. 1890
CALTIUS CAPITAL MANAGEMENT, L.P.; *U.S. Private*, pg. 723
CALTIUS MEZZANINE PARTNERS—See Caltius Capital Management, L.P.; *U.S. Private*, pg. 723
CALTIUS PRIVATE EQUITY PARTNERS I, L.P.—See Caltius Capital Management, L.P.; *U.S. Private*, pg. 723
CALTON & ASSOCIATES, INC.; *U.S. Private*, pg. 723
CALTRAX INC.—See Sojitz Corporation; *Int'l*, pg. 7061
CALTROL, INC. - ESS DIVISION—See Caltrol, Inc.; *U.S. Private*, pg. 724
CALTROL, INC.; *U.S. Private*, pg. 723
CALTROL—See Caltrol, Inc.; *U.S. Private*, pg. 724
CALTRON CASE COMPANY; *U.S. Private*, pg. 724
CALTRONICS BUSINESS SYSTEMS; *U.S. Private*, pg. 724
CALTROP CORPORATION—See TRC Companies, Inc.; *U.S. Private*, pg. 4215
CALTY DESIGN RESEARCH, INC.—See Toyota Motor Corporation; *Int'l*, pg. 7874
CALUMET ARMATURE & ELECTRIC, LLC—See IES Holdings, Inc.; *U.S. Public*, pg. 1094
CALUMET BANCORPORATION, INC.; *U.S. Private*, pg. 724
CALUMET BRANDED PRODUCTS, LLC—See Calumet, Inc.; *U.S. Public*, pg. 425
CALUMET CARTON COMPANY; *U.S. Private*, pg. 724
CALUMET COTTON VALLEY REFINING, LLC—See Calumet, Inc.; *U.S. Public*, pg. 425
CALUMET DICKINSON REFINING, LLC—See Calumet, Inc.; *U.S. Public*, pg. 425
CALUMET DIVERSIFIED MEATS INC.; *U.S. Private*, pg. 724
CALUMET, INC.; *U.S. Public*, pg. 425
CALUMET KARNS CITY REFINING, LLC—See Calumet, Inc.; *U.S. Public*, pg. 425
CALUMET MISSOURI, LLC—See Calumet, Inc.; *U.S. Public*, pg. 425
CALUMET OPERATING, LLC—See Calumet, Inc.; *U.S. Public*, pg. 425
CALUMET PACKAGING, LLC—See Calumet, Inc.; *U.S. Public*, pg. 425
CALUMET PARALOGICS, INC.—See Calumet, Inc.; *U.S. Public*, pg. 425
CALUMET PHOTOGRAPHIC BV—See Aurelius Equity Opportunities SE & Co. KGaA; *Int'l*, pg. 708
CALUMET PHOTOGRAPHIC GMBH—See Aurelius Equity Opportunities SE & Co. KGaA; *Int'l*, pg. 708
CALUMET PHOTOGRAPHIC LTD.—See Aurelius Equity Opportunities SE & Co. KGaA; *Int'l*, pg. 708
CALUMET PRINCETON REFINING, LLC—See Calumet, Inc.; *U.S. Public*, pg. 425
CALUMET REFINING, LLC—See Calumet, Inc.; *U.S. Public*, pg. 425
CALUMET SAN ANTONIO REFINING, LLC—See Calumet, Inc.; *U.S. Public*, pg. 425
CALUMET SHREVEPORT REFINING, LLC—See Calumet, Inc.; *U.S. Public*, pg. 425
CALUMET SPECIALTY PRODUCTS PARTNERS, L.P.—See Calumet, Inc.; *U.S. Public*, pg. 425
CALUMITE LIMITED—See Heidelberg Materials AG; *Int'l*, pg. 3309
CALUMITE S.R.O.—See Heidelberg Materials AG; *Int'l*, pg. 3309
CALVADA SALES COMPANY INC.; *U.S. Private*, pg. 724
CALVALLEY ENERGY LTD.; *Int'l*, pg. 1266
CALVALLEY PETROLEUM (CYPRUS) LTD.—See Calvalley Energy Ltd.; *Int'l*, pg. 1266

CALYPSO ST. BARTH INC.

CALVARY CENTER, INC.—See Universal Health Services, Inc.; *U.S. Public*, pg. 2256
CALVARY FELLOWSHIP HOMES; *U.S. Private*, pg. 724
CALVARY HOSPITAL, INC.; *U.S. Private*, pg. 724
CALVATEC LIMITED—See Analog Devices, Inc.; *U.S. Public*, pg. 135
CALVATIS ASIA PACIFIC CO., LTD—See Calvatis GmbH; *Int'l*, pg. 1266
CALVATIS B.V.—See Calvatis GmbH; *Int'l*, pg. 1266
CALVATIS GMBH; *Int'l*, pg. 1266
CALVATIS GMBH—See Calvatis GmbH; *Int'l*, pg. 1266
CALVATIS HIJYEN SAN. VE DS TIC. LTD. STI.—See Calvatis GmbH; *Int'l*, pg. 1266
CALVATIS OOO—See Calvatis GmbH; *Int'l*, pg. 1266
CALVATIS SRL—See Calvatis GmbH; *Int'l*, pg. 1266
CALVATIS SRL—See Calvatis GmbH; *Int'l*, pg. 1266
CALVATIS UAB—See Calvatis GmbH; *Int'l*, pg. 1266
CALVERLEY SUPPLY CO. INC.; *U.S. Private*, pg. 724
CALVERT ADMINISTRATIVE SERVICES COMPANY—See Ameritas Mutual Holding Company; *U.S. Private*, pg. 261
CALVERT ASSET MANAGEMENT COMPANY, INC.—See Ameritas Mutual Holding Company; *U.S. Private*, pg. 261
CALVERT CO. INC.—See Western Forest Products Inc.; *Int'l*, pg. 8388
THE CALVERT COMPANY—See AZZ, Inc.; *U.S. Public*, pg. 260
THE CALVERT COUNTY NURSING CENTER, INC.; *U.S. Private*, pg. 4003
CALVERT DISTRIBUTORS, INC.—See Ameritas Mutual Holding Company; *U.S. Private*, pg. 261
CALVERT HOLDINGS, INC.; *U.S. Private*, pg. 724
CALVERT INVESTMENTS, INC.—See Ameritas Mutual Holding Company; *U.S. Private*, pg. 261
CALVERT LABORATORIES, INC.—See Altasciences Company Inc.; *U.S. Private*, pg. 387
CALVERT RESEARCH, LLC—See Calvert Holdings, Inc.; *U.S. Private*, pg. 724
CALVERT SHAREHOLDER SERVICES, INC.—See Ameritas Mutual Holding Company; *U.S. Private*, pg. 261
CALVERT STREET CAPITAL PARTNERS; *U.S. Private*, pg. 724
CALVERT'S WALK LLC—See UDR, Inc.; *U.S. Public*, pg. 2218
CALVERT WIRE & CABLE CORPORATION; *U.S. Private*, pg. 724
CALVETON UK LTD; *Int'l*, pg. 1266
CALVETTI FERGUSON, P.C.; *U.S. Private*, pg. 724
CALVIAS GMBH—See DPE Deutsche Private Equity GmbH; *Int'l*, pg. 2187
CALVI HOLDING S.R.L.; *Int'l*, pg. 1266
CALVIN B. TAYLOR BANKSHARES, INC.; *U.S. Public*, pg. 425
CALVIN, GIORDANO & ASSOCIATES, INC.; *U.S. Private*, pg. 724
CALVIN GROUP; *U.S. Private*, pg. 724
CALVIN KLEIN, INC.—See PVH Corp.; *U.S. Public*, pg. 1739
CALVIN L. WADSWORTH CONSTRUCTION CO.; *U.S. Private*, pg. 724
CALVISTA AUSTRALIA PTY LTD.—See Moab Minerals Limited; *Int'l*, pg. 5007
CALVISTA NEW ZEALAND LIMITED—See Moab Minerals Limited; *Int'l*, pg. 5007
CALVO ENTERPRISES, INC.; *U.S. Private*, pg. 725
CALWEST COMPRESS & WAREHOUSE CO., INC.—See ITOCHU Corporation; *Int'l*, pg. 3838
CAL-X INCORPORATED—See CORE Industrial Partners, LLC; *U.S. Private*, pg. 1049
CALYPSO COMMUNICATIONS LLC—See Matter Communications Inc.; *U.S. Private*, pg. 2613
CALYPSO COMMUNICATIONS—See Matter Communications Inc.; *U.S. Private*, pg. 2613
CALYPSO GMBH—See DZ BANK AG Deutsche Zentral-Genossenschaftsbank; *Int'l*, pg. 2243
CALYPSO PLAZA MANAGEMENT PTY. LTD.—See Minor International PCL; *Int'l*, pg. 4913
CALYPSO REEF CHARTERS PTY. LTD.—See Experience Co Limited; *Int'l*, pg. 2588
CALYPSO SOFT DRINKS LIMITED—See KKR & Co. Inc.; *U.S. Public*, pg. 1263
CALYPSO—See Allianz SE; *Int'l*, pg. 342
CALYPSO ST. BARTH INC.; *U.S. Private*, pg. 725
CALYPSO TECHNOLOGY DEUTSCHLAND GMBH—See Thoma Bravo, L.P.; *U.S. Private*, pg. 4146
CALYPSO TECHNOLOGY, INC.—See Thoma Bravo, L.P.; *U.S. Private*, pg. 4146
CALYPSO TECHNOLOGY K.K.—See Thoma Bravo, L.P.; *U.S. Private*, pg. 4146
CALYPSO TECHNOLOGY LTD—See Thoma Bravo, L.P.; *U.S. Private*, pg. 4146
CALYPSO TECHNOLOGY PRIVATE LIMITED—See Thoma Bravo, L.P.; *U.S. Private*, pg. 4146
CALYPSO TECHNOLOGY PTY LTD—See Thoma Bravo, L.P.; *U.S. Private*, pg. 4146
CALYPSO TECHNOLOGY S.A.—See Thoma Bravo, L.P.; *U.S. Private*, pg. 4146

CALYPTE BIOMEDICAL CORPORATION; U.S. Private, pg. 725
CALYSTENE; Int'l, pg. 1266
CALYX & COROLLA, INC.—See The Mustang Group, LLC; U.S. Private, pg. 4081
CALYXO GMBH—See TS Group GmbH; Int'l, pg. 7947
CALYX TECHNOLOGY, INC. - SALES, SUPPORT & TRAINING CENTER—See Calyx Technology, Inc.; U.S. Private, pg. 725
CALYX TECHNOLOGY, INC.; U.S. Private, pg. 725
CALYX VENTURES INC.; Int'l, pg. 1266
CALZADOS AZALEIA PERU S.A.—See Vulcabras Azaleia S.A.; Int'l, pg. 8318
CALZONE CASE CO., LTD.—See Caltron Case Company; U.S. Private, pg. 724
CAM2 SRL—See FARO Technologies, Inc.; U.S. Public, pg. 823
CAMACC SYSTEMS INC.—See Stanley Black & Decker, Inc.; U.S. Public, pg. 1932
CAMAC DEVELOPMENT SERVICES PTY. LTD.—See CA-MAC International Corporation; U.S. Private, pg. 725
CAMAC INTERNATIONAL CORPORATION; U.S. Private, pg. 725
CAMAC INTERNATIONAL LIMITED—See CAMAC International Corporation; U.S. Private, pg. 725
CAMAC INTERNATIONAL (UK) LTD.—See CAMAC International Corporation; U.S. Private, pg. 725
CAMAC NIGERIA LIMITED—See CAMAC International Corporation; U.S. Private, pg. 725
CAMACO LLC—See P&C Group, Inc.; U.S. Private, pg. 3058
CAMACO LORAIN MANUFACTURING—See P&C Group, Inc.; U.S. Private, pg. 3058
CAMAC TRADING, LLC—See CAMAC International Corporation; U.S. Private, pg. 725
CAMALCO SA—See Canyon Resources Ltd; Int'l, pg. 1300
CAMALLOY, INC.—See Republic Financial Corporation; U.S. Private, pg. 3402
CAM ALTERNATIVES GMBH; Int'l, pg. 1266
CAMANCHACA S.A.; Int'l, pg. 1267
CAMARA CHILENO-ALEMANA DE COMERCIO E INDUSTRIA—See Messe Munchen GmbH; Int'l, pg. 4841
CAMARA DE COMERCIO E INDUSTRIA BOLIVIANO-ALEMANA—See Messe Munchen GmbH; Int'l, pg. 4841
CAMARA DE COMERCIO E INDUSTRIA PERUANO-ALEMANA—See Messe Munchen GmbH; Int'l, pg. 4841
CAMARA DE COMERCIO E INDUSTRIA VENEZOLANO-ALEMANA—See Messe Munchen GmbH; Int'l, pg. 4841
CAMARA DE INDUSTRIA Y COMERCIO ARGENTINO-ALEMANA—See Messe Munchen GmbH; Int'l, pg. 4841
CAMARA/TBWA—See Omnicom Group Inc.; U.S. Public, pg. 1594
CAMARENA HEALTH; U.S. Private, pg. 725
CAMARES COMMUNICATIONS INC.; U.S. Private, pg. 725
CAMARGOCOPELAND ARCHITECTS, LLP; U.S. Private, pg. 725
CAMARGO CORREA S.A.; Int'l, pg. 1267
CAMARGUE UNDERWRITING MANAGERS (PTY) LIMITED—See Hollard Insurance Company Ltd; Int'l, pg. 3451
CAMARICO INVESTMENT GROUP LTD.; Int'l, pg. 1268
CAMARILLO COMMUNITY CARE, INC.—See The Ensign Group, Inc.; U.S. Public, pg. 2070
CA MARKETING CORPORATION—See Broadcom Inc.; U.S. Public, pg. 389
C&A MARKETING, INC. - RITZ CAMERA & IMAGE DIVISION—See C&A Marketing, Inc.; U.S. Private, pg. 702
C&A MARKETING, INC.; U.S. Private, pg. 702
CAMARK S.A.—See STERIS plc; Int'l, pg. 7209
CAMAU TRADING JOINT STOCK COMPANY; Int'l, pg. 1268
CAMBA; U.S. Private, pg. 725
CAMBECK PETROLEUM CORP.; U.S. Private, pg. 725
CAMBELLA LIMITED—See Tai Sang Land Development Ltd; Int'l, pg. 7408
CAMBER CORPORATION—See Huntington Ingalls Industries, Inc.; U.S. Public, pg. 1072
CAMBER ENERGY, INC.; U.S. Public, pg. 425
CAMBERLEY ENTERPRISES LIMITED—See Li & Fung Limited; Int'l, pg. 4479
CAMBER TECHNICAL SERVICES LLC—See Huntington Ingalls Industries, Inc.; U.S. Public, pg. 1072
CAMBEX CORPORATION; U.S. Public, pg. 425
CAMBEY & WEST, INC.; U.S. Private, pg. 725
CAMBIA HEALTH SOLUTIONS, INC.; U.S. Private, pg. 725
CAMBIAN ANSEL LIMITED—See Sheikh Holdings Group (Investments) Limited; Int'l, pg. 6793
CAMBIAN GROUP PLC—See Sheikh Holdings Group (Investments) Limited; Int'l, pg. 6793
CAMBIAR INVESTORS LLC; U.S. Private, pg. 726

CAMBI ASA; Int'l, pg. 1268
CAMBIE ROOFING & DRAINAGE CONTRACTORS LTD.; Int'l, pg. 1268
CAMBI GROUP AS—See Cambi ASA; Int'l, pg. 1268
CAMBIO HEALTHCARE SYSTEMS AB—See Investcorp Holdings B.S.C.; Int'l, pg. 3775
CAMBION ELECTRONICS LIMITED—See Yanlord Land Group Limited; Int'l, pg. 8562
CAMBIUM BIO LIMITED; Int'l, pg. 1268
CAMBIUM EDUCATION, INC.—See Veritas Capital Fund Management, LLC; U.S. Private, pg. 4361
CAMBIUM GLOBAL TIMBERLAND LIMITED; Int'l, pg. 1269
CAMBIUM LEARNING GROUP, INC.—See Veritas Capital Fund Management, LLC; U.S. Private, pg. 4361
CAMBIUM NETWORKS CORPORATION; U.S. Public, pg. 425
CAMBODIA AIR TRAFFIC SERVICES CO., LTD.—See Samart Corporation Public Company Limited; Int'l, pg. 6501
CAMBODIA LIFE INSURANCE PLC—See Royal Group of Companies Ltd.; Int'l, pg. 6412
CAMBODIAN COMMERCIAL BANK LTD.—See Siam Commercial Bank Public Company Limited; Int'l, pg. 6875
CAMBODIAN PUBLIC BANK LIMITED—See Public Bank Berhad; Int'l, pg. 6094
CAMBODIA - VIETNAM INSURANCE PLC.—See Joint Stock Commercial Bank Investment and Development of Vietnam; Int'l, pg. 3995
CAMBRAY MUTUAL HOLDING COMPANY; U.S. Private, pg. 726
CAMBREX CHARLES CITY, INC.—See Permira Advisers LLP; Int'l, pg. 5803
CAMBREX CORPORATION—See Permira Advisers LLP; Int'l, pg. 5803
CAMBREX HIGH POINT, INC.—See Permira Advisers LLP; Int'l, pg. 5803
CAMBREX IEP, GMBH—See Permira Advisers LLP; Int'l, pg. 5803
CAMBREX KARLSKOGA AB—See Permira Advisers LLP; Int'l, pg. 5803
CAMBREX MIRABEL—See Permira Advisers LLP; Int'l, pg. 5803
CAMBREX PROFARMACO MILANO S.R.L.—See Permira Advisers LLP; Int'l, pg. 5803
CAMBREX WHIPPANY—See Permira Advisers LLP; Int'l, pg. 5803
CAMBRIA AFRICA PLC; Int'l, pg. 1269
CAMBRIA AUTOMOBILES PLC; Int'l, pg. 1269
CAMBRIA AUTOMOTIVE COMPANIES; U.S. Private, pg. 726
CAMBRIA COGEN INC.—See Ontario Teachers' Pension Plan; Int'l, pg. 5590
CAMBRIA COGEN INC.—See UBS Group AG; Int'l, pg. 8008
CAMBRIA CONSULTING INC.—See SSI (U.S.) Inc.; U.S. Private, pg. 3769
CAMBRIAN COAL CORPORATION—See Wright Management Company, LLC; U.S. Private, pg. 4573
CAMBRIAN CONSULTANTS (CC) AMERICA INC—See RPS Group plc; Int'l, pg. 6415
CAMBRIAN FORD SALES INC; Int'l, pg. 1269
CAMBRIAN WIND ENERGY LTD—See Falck S.p.A.; Int'l, pg. 2610
CAMBRIA SOLUTIONS, INC.; U.S. Private, pg. 726
CAMBRIC CONSULTING SRL—See Tata Sons Limited; Int'l, pg. 7469
CAMBRIC CORPORATION—See Tata Sons Limited; Int'l, pg. 7468
CAMBRICON TECHNOLOGIES CORPORATION LIMITED; Int'l, pg. 1269
CAMBRIDGE ADVISORY GROUP, INC.—See Kelso & Company, L.P.; U.S. Private, pg. 2279
THE CAMBRIDGE AERO CLUB LIMITED—See Marshall of Cambridge (Holdings) Limited; Int'l, pg. 4702
CAMBRIDGE AGGREGATES INC.—See Heidelberg Materials AG; Int'l, pg. 3317
CAMBRIDGE ARCHITECTURAL—See Zurn Elkay Water Solutions Corporation; U.S. Public, pg. 2412
CAMBRIDGE ARIZONA INSURANCE COMPANY; U.S. Private, pg. 726
CAMBRIDGE ARTS & SCIENCE LIMITED—See Bright Scholar Education Holdings Limited; Int'l, pg. 1161
CAMBRIDGE ASSOCIATES LLC; U.S. Private, pg. 726
CAMBRIDGE BANCORP; U.S. Public, pg. 425
CAMBRIDGE BIOMARKETING GROUP, LLC—See Clayton, Dubilier & Rice, LLC; U.S. Private, pg. 927
CAMBRIDGE BIOMEDICAL INC.—See Cobepa S.A.; Int'l, pg. 1683
CAMBRIDGE BIZSERVE INC.—See Cambridge Technology Enterprises Ltd.; Int'l, pg. 1269
CAMBRIDGE BRANDS, INC.—See Tootsie Roll Industries, Inc.; U.S. Public, pg. 2163
CAMBRIDGE BRASS—See A.Y. McDonald Manufacturing Co.; U.S. Private, pg. 29
CAMBRIDGE BROADBAND NETWORKS LIMITED; Int'l, pg. 1269
CAMBRIDGE BUILDING SOCIETY; Int'l, pg. 1269

CAMBRIDGE CAPITAL ACQUISITION CORPORATION; U.S. Private, pg. 726
CAMBRIDGE CAPITAL HOLDINGS, INC.; U.S. Public, pg. 426
CAMBRIDGE CENTER NORTH TRUST—See Boston Properties, Inc.; U.S. Public, pg. 373
CAMBRIDGE CHRONICLE—See Gannett Co., Inc.; U.S. Public, pg. 902
CAMBRIDGE COGNITION HOLDINGS PLC; Int'l, pg. 1269
CAMBRIDGE CONSTRUCTION MANAGEMENT, INC.—See Accenture plc; Int'l, pg. 86
CAMBRIDGE CONSULTANTS, INC.—See Capgemini SE; Int'l, pg. 1305
CAMBRIDGE CONSULTANTS LTD—See Capgemini SE; Int'l, pg. 1305
CAMBRIDGE CREDIT COUNSELING CORP.; U.S. Private, pg. 726
CAMBRIDGE DISPLAY TECHNOLOGY LTD.—See Sumitomo Chemical Company, Limited; Int'l, pg. 7266
CAMBRIDGE EDUCATION LIMITED—See Mott MacDonald Group Ltd.; Int'l, pg. 5054
CAMBRIDGE EDUCATION LLC—See Mott MacDonald Group Ltd.; Int'l, pg. 5054
CAMBRIDGE ENGINEERED SOLUTIONS—See Zurn Elkay Water Solutions Corporation; U.S. Public, pg. 2412
CAMBRIDGE ENGLISH FOR LIFE SDN. BHD.—See Paramount Corporation Berhad; Int'l, pg. 5738
CAMBRIDGE FINANCIAL GROUP, INC.; U.S. Private, pg. 726
CAMBRIDGE FLUID SYSTEMS LIMITED—See Ultra Clean Holdings, Inc.; U.S. Public, pg. 2223
THE CAMBRIDGE GROUP, INC.—See Brookfield Corporation; Int'l, pg. 1180
THE CAMBRIDGE GROUP, INC.—See Elliott Management Corporation; U.S. Private, pg. 1372
CAMBRIDGE HEALTH ALLIANCE; U.S. Public, pg. 727
CAMBRIDGE HEALTHTECH INSTITUTE; U.S. Private, pg. 727
CAMBRIDGE HEALTHTECH MEDIA GROUP—See Cambridge Healthtech Institute; U.S. Private, pg. 727
CAMBRIDGE HEIGHTS APARTMENTS LIMITED PARTNERSHIP—See Apartment Investment and Management Company; U.S. Public, pg. 144
CAMBRIDGE INDUSTRIES GROUP, LTD.—See CIG Shanghai Co., Ltd.; Int'l, pg. 1606
CAMBRIDGE INDUSTRIES USA, INC.—See CIG Shanghai Co., Ltd.; Int'l, pg. 1607
CAMBRIDGE INFORMATION GROUP, INC.; U.S. Private, pg. 727
CAMBRIDGE INTERNATIONAL, INC.—See Zurn Elkay Water Solutions Corporation; U.S. Public, pg. 2412
CAMBRIDGE INVESTMENT GROUP, INC.; U.S. Private, pg. 727
CAMBRIDGE INVESTMENT RESEARCH, INC.—See Cambridge Investment Group, Inc.; U.S. Private, pg. 727
CAMBRIDGE ISOTOPE LABORATORIES, INC.—See Otsuka Holdings Co., Ltd.; Int'l, pg. 5659
CAMBRIDGE-LEE CANADA LTD.—See Cambridge-Lee Industries, Inc.; U.S. Private, pg. 727
CAMBRIDGE-LEE (EUROPE) LTD.—See Cambridge-Lee Industries, Inc.; U.S. Private, pg. 727
CAMBRIDGE-LEE INDUSTRIES, INC.; U.S. Private, pg. 727
CAMBRIDGE LIFE SCIENCES LTD.; Int'l, pg. 1269
CAMBRIDGE MANAGEMENT SERVICES, INC.—See LeCesse Development Corporation; U.S. Private, pg. 2409
CAMBRIDGE MERCANTILE (AUSTRALIA) PTY. LTD.—See Corpay, Inc.; U.S. Public, pg. 579
CAMBRIDGE MERCANTILE CORP.—See Corpay, Inc.; U.S. Public, pg. 579
CAMBRIDGE MERCANTILE CORP. (U.K.) LTD.—See Corpay, Inc.; U.S. Public, pg. 579
CAMBRIDGE MERCANTILE CORP. (U.S.A.)—See Corpay, Inc.; U.S. Public, pg. 579
CAMBRIDGE METALS & PLASTICS, INC.—See Wind Point Advisors LLC; U.S. Private, pg. 4534
CAMBRIDGE MUTUAL FIRE INSURANCE COMPANY; U.S. Private, pg. 727
CAMBRIDGE NUTRITIONAL SCIENCES LIMITED—See Cambridge Nutritional Sciences Plc; Int'l, pg. 1269
CAMBRIDGE NUTRITIONAL SCIENCES PLC; Int'l, pg. 1269
CAMBRIDGE PACKING CO., INC.—See The Chefs' Warehouse, Inc.; U.S. Public, pg. 2058
CAMBRIDGE PERNE ROAD VETS4PETS LIMITED—See Pets at Home Group Plc; Int'l, pg. 5833
CAMBRIDGE PLYMOUTH CHRYSLER LTD; Int'l, pg. 1269
CAMBRIDGE PRO FAB INC. - PLANT 2—See Cambridge Pro Fab Inc.; Int'l, pg. 1269
CAMBRIDGE PRO FAB INC. - PLANT 3—See Cambridge Pro Fab Inc.; Int'l, pg. 1269
CAMBRIDGE PRO FAB INC. - PLANT 4—See Cambridge Pro Fab Inc.; Int'l, pg. 1269
CAMBRIDGE PRO FAB INC.; Int'l, pg. 1269

COMPANY NAME INDEX

CAMBRIDGE REAL ESTATE DEVELOPMENT, LLC—See Restaurant Brands International Inc.; *Int'l*, pg. 6304
CAMBRIDGE RUSKIN INTERNATIONAL COLLEGE LIMITED—See Navitas Limited; *Int'l*, pg. 5176
CAMBRIDGE SAVINGS BANK—See Cambridge Financial Group, Inc.; *U.S. Private*, pg. 726
CAMBRIDGE SCHOOL OF VISUAL & PERFORMING ARTS LIMITED—See Bright Scholar Education Holdings Limited; *Int'l*, pg. 1161
CAMBRIDGE SHARPE, INC.; *U.S. Private*, pg. 727
CAMBRIDGE SILVERSMITHS LTD., INC.—See Centre Lane Partners, LLC; *U.S. Private*, pg. 827
CAMBRIDGE SOUND MANAGEMENT INC.—See AMETEK, Inc.; *U.S. Public*, pg. 118
CAMBRIDGE SOUNDWORKS, INC.—See Creative Technology Ltd.; *Int'l*, pg. 1833
CAMBRIDGE STREET METAL CO.; *U.S. Private*, pg. 727
CAMBRIDGE TECHNOLOGY ENTERPRISES LTD.; *Int'l*, pg. 1269
CAMBRIDGE TECHNOLOGY INC.—See Cambridge Technology Enterprises Ltd.; *Int'l*, pg. 1269
CAMBRIDGE TECHNOLOGY INVESTMENTS PTE. LTD.—See Cambridge Technology Enterprises Ltd.; *Int'l*, pg. 1269
CAMBRIDGE TECHNOLOGY PARTNERS, LTD.—See BIPROGY Inc.; *Int'l*, pg. 1045
CAMBRIDGE TRUST COMPANY OF NEW HAMPSHIRE, INC.—See Cambridge Bancorp; *U.S. Public*, pg. 426
CAMBRIDGE TRUST COMPANY—See Cambridge Bancorp; *U.S. Public*, pg. 425
CAMBRIDGE UNDERWRITERS LIMITED; *U.S. Private*, pg. 727
CAMBRIDGE UNIVERSITY PRESS INDIA PRIVATE LIMITED—See Cambridge University Press; *Int'l*, pg. 1270
CAMBRIDGE UNIVERSITY PRESS JAPAN K.K.—See Cambridge University Press; *Int'l*, pg. 1270
CAMBRIDGE UNIVERSITY PRESS, NORTH AMERICA—See Cambridge University Press; *Int'l*, pg. 1270
CAMBRIDGE UNIVERSITY PRESS; *Int'l*, pg. 1269
CAMBRIDGE VACUUM ENGINEERING INC—See Aquasium Technology Limited; *Int'l*, pg. 528
CAMBRIDGE VACUUM ENGINEERING LIMITED—See Aquasium Technology Limited; *Int'l*, pg. 528
CAMBRIDGE VISCOSITY, INC—See Roper Technologies, Inc.; *U.S. Public*, pg. 1810
CAMBRIDGE WATER PLC—See Arjun Infrastructure Partners Limited; *Int'l*, pg. 568
CAMBRIO ACQUISITION, LLC—See Sandvik AB; *Int'l*, pg. 6528
CAMBRO MANUFACTURING COMPANY; *U.S. Private*, pg. 727
CAMBUCI S.A.; *Int'l*, pg. 1270
CAMBUHY INVESTIMENTOS LTDA.; *Int'l*, pg. 1270
CAMBUS LIMITED—See Stagecoach Group plc; *Int'l*, pg. 7163
CAMBUS TEORANTA LTD.—See Freudenberg SE; *Int'l*, pg. 2782
CAM CAPITAL, S.A.U.—See Banco de Sabadell, S.A.; *Int'l*, pg. 821
CAMCARE HEALTH CORPORATION; *U.S. Private*, pg. 727
CAMCASTING SRL—See Camozzi Group; *Int'l*, pg. 1273
CAMC CANCER CENTERS, LLC—See Akumin, Inc.; *U.S. Public*, pg. 70
CAM CLARK FORD; *Int'l*, pg. 1266
CAMCO ACURA; *Int'l*, pg. 1270
CAMCO ADVISORY SERVICES (TANZANIA) LIMITED—See Invinity Energy Systems plc; *Int'l*, pg. 3789
CAMCO CHEMICAL COMPANY INC.; *U.S. Private*, pg. 727
CAMCO INTERNATIONAL CARBON ASSETS INFORMATION CONSULTING (BEIJING) CO. LIMITED—See Invinity Energy Systems plc; *Int'l*, pg. 3789
CAMCO INTERNATIONAL GROUP INCORPORATED; *U.S. Private*, pg. 727
CAMCO MANUFACTURING INC.; *U.S. Private*, pg. 727
CAM COMMERCE SOLUTIONS, INC.—See Celerant Technology Corp.; *U.S. Private*, pg. 806
CAM CONNECTIONS, INC.—See Apollo Global Management, Inc.; *U.S. Public*, pg. 146
CAM CONSULTANTS, INC.; *U.S. Private*, pg. 725
CAMCO RECYCLING INC.—See Tomra Systems ASA; *Int'l*, pg. 7803
CAMCOR INC.; *U.S. Private*, pg. 727
CAMCORP INC—See Camrost-Felcorp Inc.; *Int'l*, pg. 1275
CAMCORP MANUFACTURING, INC.—See Camrost-Felcorp Inc.; *Int'l*, pg. 1275
CAMCO SERVICES (UK) LIMITED—See Invinity Energy Systems plc; *Int'l*, pg. 3789
CAMCO VENTURES (CHINA) LIMITED—See Invinity Energy Systems plc; *Int'l*, pg. 3789
CAMCO VENTURES LIMITED—See Invinity Energy Systems plc; *Int'l*, pg. 3789
CAMCRAFT INC.; *U.S. Private*, pg. 728
CAMDEN COUNTY ENERGY RECOVERY ASSOCIATES, L.P.—See EQT AB; *Int'l*, pg. 2473

CAMDEN HOMECARE, LLC—See UnitedHealth Group Incorporated; *U.S. Public*, pg. 2244
CAMDEN IRON & METAL INC.; *U.S. Private*, pg. 728
THE CAMDEN NATIONAL BANK—See Camden National Corporation; *U.S. Public*, pg. 426
CAMDEN NATIONAL CORPORATION; *U.S. Public*, pg. 426
CAMDEN NEWS PUBLISHING COMPANY—See Wehco Media, Inc.; *U.S. Private*, pg. 4469
CAMDEN OPERATING, L.P.—See Camden Property Trust; *U.S. Public*, pg. 426
CAMDEN PARTNERS HOLDINGS, LLC; *U.S. Private*, pg. 728
CAMDEN PROPERTY TRUST; *U.S. Public*, pg. 426
CAMDEN RESOURCE RECOVERY FACILITY—See EQT AB; *Int'l*, pg. 2473
CAMDEN SUMMIT, INC.—See Camden Property Trust; *U.S. Public*, pg. 426
CAMDEN TELEPHONE & TELEGRAPH COMPANY, INC.—See Telephone & Data Systems, Inc.; *U.S. Public*, pg. 1998
CAMDON CONSTRUCTION LTD; *Int'l*, pg. 1270
CAMECA GMBH—See AMETEK, Inc.; *U.S. Public*, pg. 117
CAMECA INSTRUMENTS, INC.—See AMETEK, Inc.; *U.S. Public*, pg. 117
CAMECA S.A.S.—See AMETEK, Inc.; *U.S. Public*, pg. 117
CAMECA TAIWAN CORP. LTD.—See AMETEK, Inc.; *U.S. Public*, pg. 117
CAMEC (NZ) LIMITED—See Fleetwood Limited; *Int'l*, pg. 2699
CAMECO AUSTRALIA PTY. LTD.—See Cameco Corporation; *Int'l*, pg. 1270
CAMECO CORPORATION; *Int'l*, pg. 1270
CAMECO FUEL MANUFACTURING INC—See Cameco Corporation; *Int'l*, pg. 1270
CAMEC PTY LTD—See Fleetwood Limited; *Int'l*, pg. 2699
CAME DANMARK A/S—See Lagercrantz Group AB; *Int'l*, pg. 4394
CAMELBACK COLONNADE ASSOCIATES LIMITED PARTNERSHIP—See The Macerich Company; *U.S. Public*, pg. 2109
CAMELBACK COUNTRY CLUB INC.—See Marriott International, Inc.; *U.S. Public*, pg. 1370
CAMELBACK FORD; *U.S. Private*, pg. 728
CAMELBACK SKI CORPORATION; *U.S. Private*, pg. 728
CAMELBAK PRODUCTS LLC—See Vista Outdoor Inc.; *U.S. Public*, pg. 2305
CAMELEON B.V.—See E.ON SE; *Int'l*, pg. 2251
CAMELEON SOFTWARE SA—See PROS Holdings, Inc.; *U.S. Public*, pg. 1728
CAMELEON SOFTWARE USA, INC.—See PROS Holdings, Inc.; *U.S. Public*, pg. 1728
CAMEL GROUP CO., LTD.; *Int'l*, pg. 1270
CAMELLIA FOOD STORES, INC.; *U.S. Private*, pg. 728
CAMELLIA LINE CO., LTD.—See Nippon Yusen Kabushiki Kaisha; *Int'l*, pg. 5357
CAMELLIA MEMORIAL LAWN, INC.—See Service Corporation International; *U.S. Public*, pg. 1869
CAMELLIA PLC; *Int'l*, pg. 1270
CAMELLIA TROPICANA SDN. BHD.—See WCT Holdings Berhad; *Int'l*, pg. 8362
CAMELOT CARE CENTERS, INC—See ATAR Capital, LLC; *U.S. Private*, pg. 364
CAMELOT COMMUNICATIONS LTD.—See PMG Worldwide LLC; *U.S. Private*, pg. 3218
CAMELOT COMMUNITY CARE, INC.—See ModivCare, Inc.; *U.S. Public*, pg. 1455
CAMELOT ELECTRONIC TECHNOLOGY CO., LTD.; *Int'l*, pg. 1271
CAMELOT GHANA LIMITED; *Int'l*, pg. 1271
CAMELOT INFORMATIK UND CONSULTING GESELL-SCHAFT M.B.H.—See Vienna Insurance Group AG Wiener Versicherung Gruppe; *Int'l*, pg. 8194
CAMELOT INFORMATION SYSTEMS INC.; *Int'l*, pg. 1271
CAMELOT LANDFILL TX, LP—See Republic Services, Inc.; *U.S. Public*, pg. 1786
CAMELOT MANAGEMENT CONSULTANTS AG; *Int'l*, pg. 1271
CAMELOT MANAGEMENT CONSULTANTS INC.—See Camelot Management Consultants AG; *Int'l*, pg. 1271
CAMELOT MANAGEMENT CONSULTANTS MIDDLE EAST DMCC—See Camelot Management Consultants AG; *Int'l*, pg. 1271
CAMELOT SECURITY SOLUTIONS LIMITED—See Camelot Ghana Limited; *Int'l*, pg. 1271
CAMELOT UK LOTTERIES LIMITED—See KKCG Group; *Int'l*, pg. 4198
CAMEL POWER TRADING SDN. BHD.—See Camel Group Co., Ltd.; *Int'l*, pg. 1270
CAM ELYAF SANAYII A.S.—See Turkiye Sise ve Cam Fabrikalari A.S.; *Int'l*, pg. 7977
CAMEN INTERNATIONAL TRADING, INC.—See ALFA, S.A.B. de C.V.; *Int'l*, pg. 313
CAMEO COMMUNICATION, INC.; *Int'l*, pg. 1271
CAMEO INSURANCE SERVICES, INC.—See Inszone Insurance Services, LLC; *U.S. Private*, pg. 2096
CAMEO SOLUTIONS—See New Era Technology, Inc.; *U.S. Private*, pg. 2896
THE CAMERA COMPANY; *U.S. Private*, pg. 4003

CAMERA CORNER INC.; *U.S. Private*, pg. 728
CAMERA CORPS LTD.—See Videndum plc; *Int'l*, pg. 8190
CAMERA HOUSE LIMITED—See FUJIFILM Holdings Corporation; *Int'l*, pg. 2821
CAMERA REPAIR INSTRUMENT SERVICE; *U.S. Private*, pg. 728
THE CAMERA STORE LIMITED—See Videndum plc; *Int'l*, pg. 8191
CAMERFIRMA COLOMBIA S.A.S.—See Tinexta S.p.A.; *Int'l*, pg. 7753
CAMERICAN INTERNATIONAL, INC.—See Gellert Global Group; *U.S. Private*, pg. 1656
CAMERIT AG; *Int'l*, pg. 1271
CAMERON ARGENTINA S.A.I.C.—See Schlumberger Limited; *U.S. Public*, pg. 1843
CAMERON ASHLEY BUILDING PRODUCTS, INC.—See Pacific Avenue Capital Partners, LLC; *U.S. Private*, pg. 3065
CAMERON BALLOONS LTD.; *Int'l*, pg. 1271
CAMERON BALLOONS U.S.—See Cameron Balloons Ltd.; *Int'l*, pg. 1271
CAMERON CARE, LLC—See Jackson House; *U.S. Private*, pg. 2177
CAMERON COMMUNICATION LLC—See Madison Dearborn Partners, LLC; *U.S. Private*, pg. 2540
CAMERON & COMPANY, INC.; *U.S. Private*, pg. 728
CAMERON DEL PACIFICO, S. DE R.L. DE C.V.—See Playa Hotels & Resorts N.V.; *U.S. Public*, pg. 5894
CAMERON ENGINEERING & ASSOCIATES, LLP; *U.S. Private*, pg. 728
CAMERON FLOW CONTROL TECHNOLOGY (UK) LIMITED—See Schlumberger Limited; *U.S. Public*, pg. 1843
CAMERON GENERAL CORPORATION; *U.S. Private*, pg. 728
CAMERON HIGHLANDS RESORT SDN. BHD.—See YTL Corporation Berhad; *Int'l*, pg. 8606
CAMERON HOLDINGS CORPORATION; *U.S. Private*, pg. 728
CAMERON HOLDINGS CORPORATION - ST. LOUIS OFFICE—See Cameron Holdings Corporation; *U.S. Private*, pg. 728
CAMERON HUGHES WINE—See Vintage Wine Estates, Inc.; *U.S. Public*, pg. 2298
CAMERON INTERNATIONAL CORPORATION—See Schlumberger Limited; *U.S. Public*, pg. 1843
CAMERON INVESTORS TRUST PLC—See STS Global Income & Growth Trust plc; *Int'l*, pg. 7244
CAMERON MITCHELL RESTAURANTS, LLC; *U.S. Private*, pg. 729
CAMERON NORGE AS—See Schlumberger Limited; *U.S. Public*, pg. 1843
CAMERON NORGE HOLDING AS—See Schlumberger Limited; *U.S. Public*, pg. 1843
CAMERON OFFICE PRODUCTS, LLC—See Xerox Holdings Corporation; *U.S. Public*, pg. 2387
CAMERON PETROLEUM (UK) LIMITED—See Schlumberger Limited; *U.S. Public*, pg. 1843
CAMERON REAL ESTATE SERVICES, INC.; *U.S. Private*, pg. 729
CAMERON RIG SOLUTIONS LLC—See Schlumberger Limited; *U.S. Public*, pg. 1843
CAMERONS BREWERY LTD.; *Int'l*, pg. 1272
CAMERON SEARCH & STAFFING LLC; *U.S. Private*, pg. 729
CAMERON SENSE AS—See Schlumberger Limited; *U.S. Public*, pg. 1843
CAMERON SERVICES INTERNATIONAL PTY LTD—See Schlumberger Limited; *U.S. Public*, pg. 1843
CAMERON—See The Stratford-Cambridge Group Co.; *U.S. Private*, pg. 4123
CAMERON SYSTEMS LIMITED—See Schlumberger Limited; *U.S. Public*, pg. 1843
CAMERON SYSTEMS (VIC) PTY LTD—See Nordic Capital AB; *Int'l*, pg. 5420
CAMERONTEC AB—See Nordic Capital AB; *Int'l*, pg. 5420
CAMERONTEC AMERICAS, INC.—See Nordic Capital AB; *Int'l*, pg. 5420
CAMERON TELEPHONE COMPANY INC—See Madison Dearborn Partners, LLC; *U.S. Private*, pg. 2540
CAMERON THOMSON ENTERTAINMENT LTD.—See Cameron Thomson Group Ltd.; *Int'l*, pg. 1272
CAMERON THOMSON GROUP LTD.; *Int'l*, pg. 1272
CAMERON TOOL CORP.—See Tool Tech, Inc.; *U.S. Private*, pg. 4185
CAMERON VALVES & MEASUREMENT - LITTLE ROCK—See Schlumberger Limited; *U.S. Public*, pg. 1844
CAMERON VALVES & MEASUREMENT—See Schlumberger Limited; *U.S. Public*, pg. 1843
CAMERON WEST COAST INC.—See Schlumberger Limited; *U.S. Public*, pg. 1844
CAMEROON AIRLINES SA; *Int'l*, pg. 1272
CAMEROON MOTORS INDUSTRIES S.A.—See Toyota Tsusho Corporation; *Int'l*, pg. 7875
CAMESA, INC.—See ONEX Corporation; *Int'l*, pg. 5580
CAMETA CAMERA; *U.S. Private*, pg. 729
CAMETOR S.L.—See Siemens Energy AG; *Int'l*, pg. 6902

CAMETA CAMERA

CAMEX EQUIPMENT SALES & RENTALS LTD.—See Brandt Industries Ltd.; *Int'l*, pg. 1140
C&A MEXICO S. DE R.L.—See COFRA Holding AG; *Int'l*, pg. 1694
CAMEXIP S.A.; *Int'l*, pg. 1272
CAMEX LIMITED; *Int'l*, pg. 1272
CAMEX MACHINERY INC.—See Quaser Machine Tools, Inc.; *Int'l*, pg. 6156
CAMFAUD CONCRETE PUMPS LIMITED—See Concrete Pumping Holdings, Inc.; *U.S. Public*, pg. 566
CAMFIL AB; *Int'l*, pg. 1272
CAMFIL AG—See Camfil AB; *Int'l*, pg. 1272
CAMFIL AIRFILTER SDN. BHD.—See Camfil AB; *Int'l*, pg. 1272
CAMFIL A/S—See Camfil AB; *Int'l*, pg. 1272
CAMFIL AUSTRALIA PTY LTD—See Camfil AB; *Int'l*, pg. 1272
CAMFIL AUSTRIA GMBH—See Camfil AB; *Int'l*, pg. 1272
CAMFIL BV—See Camfil AB; *Int'l*, pg. 1272
CAMFIL CANADA INC.—See Camfil AB; *Int'l*, pg. 1272
CAMFIL ESPANA SA—See Camfil AB; *Int'l*, pg. 1272
CAMFIL INDIA PVT. LTD.—See Camfil AB; *Int'l*, pg. 1272
CAMFIL (IRL) LTD—See Camfil AB; *Int'l*, pg. 1272
CAMFIL LTD.—See Camfil AB; *Int'l*, pg. 1272
CAMFIL NEW ZEALAND LIMITED—See Camfil AB; *Int'l*, pg. 1272
CAMFIL NORGE AS—See Camfil AB; *Int'l*, pg. 1272
CAMFIL OY—See Camfil AB; *Int'l*, pg. 1272
CAMFIL POLSKA SP. Z O.O.—See Camfil AB; *Int'l*, pg. 1272
CAMFIL SA—See Camfil AB; *Int'l*, pg. 1272
CAMFIL SPA—See Camfil AB; *Int'l*, pg. 1272
CAMFIL S.R.O.—See Camfil AB; *Int'l*, pg. 1272
CAMFIL UAE—See Camfil AB; *Int'l*, pg. 1272
CAMFIL USA, INC.—See Camfil AB; *Int'l*, pg. 1272
CAMFIN S.P.A.; *Int'l*, pg. 1272
CAMFOUR, INC.—See Peter Pan Bus Lines, Inc.; *U.S. Private*, pg. 3159
CAMGESTION—See BNP Paribas SA; *Int'l*, pg. 1089
CAMGIAN MICROSYSTEMS, INC.; *U.S. Private*, pg. 729
CAM GROUP, INC.; *Int'l*, pg. 1266
CAMICO MUTUAL INSURANCE COMPANY; *U.S. Private*, pg. 729
CAMIF COLLECTIVITES-ENTREPRISES SA—See Manutan International SA; *Int'l*, pg. 4679
CAMIL ALIMENTOS S.A.; *Int'l*, pg. 1272
CAMILLA PECAN COMPANY; *U.S. Private*, pg. 729
CAMILLE BAUER AG—See METRAWATT International GmbH; *Int'l*, pg. 4855
CAMILLERI STOCKFEEDS PTY LTD—See Ridley Corporation Limited; *Int'l*, pg. 6338
CAMILLUS HOUSE, INC.; *U.S. Private*, pg. 729
CAMIMEX GROUP JOINT STOCK COMPANY; *Int'l*, pg. 1272
CAM IMMOBILIARE S.P.A.—See Camfin S.p.A.; *Int'l*, pg. 1272
CAMIN CARGO CONTROL INC.—See Metalmark Capital Holdings LLC; *U.S. Private*, pg. 2681
CA MINING (RTY) LTD.—See ADvTECH Limited; *Int'l*, pg. 169
CAMINO AGAVE INC.; *U.S. Private*, pg. 729
CAMINO MINERALS CORPORATION; *Int'l*, pg. 1273
CAMINO REAL CHEVROLET; *U.S. Private*, pg. 729
CAMINO REAL ENVIRONMENTAL CENTER, INC.—See Waste Connections, Inc.; *Int'l*, pg. 8353
CAMINO REAL FOODS, INC.—See Nissin Foods Holdings Co., Ltd.; *Int'l*, pg. 5376
CAMINO REAL FUELS, LLC—See NACCO Industries, Inc.; *U.S. Public*, pg. 1490
CAMINO ROJO S.A. DE C.V.—See Newmont Corporation; *U.S. Public*, pg. 1516
CAMINOS DE LAS SIERRAS S.A.; *Int'l*, pg. 1273
CAMINOS Y CARRETERAS DEL MAYAB, S.A.P.I. DE C.V.—See Empresas ICA S.A.B. de C.V.; *Int'l*, pg. 2390
CAMIONNAGE G.H.L. INC—See TFI International Inc.; *Int'l*, pg. 7585
CAMIRA FABRICS GMBH—See Camira Fabrics Ltd.; *Int'l*, pg. 1273
CAMIRA FABRICS LTD. - LITHUANIA MANUFACTURING FACILITY—See Camira Fabrics Ltd.; *Int'l*, pg. 1273
CAMIRA FABRICS LTD. - MELTHAM MANUFACTURING FACILITY—See Camira Fabrics Ltd.; *Int'l*, pg. 1273
CAMIRA FABRICS LTD.; *Int'l*, pg. 1273
CAMIRA FABRICS SHANGHAI LTD—See Camira Fabrics Ltd.; *Int'l*, pg. 1273
CAMIRA GROUP, INC—See Camira Fabrics Ltd.; *Int'l*, pg. 1273
CAM IRON S.A.—See Sundance Resources Limited; *Int'l*, pg. 7311
CAMIS AMBALAJ SANAYI A.S. - ESKISEHIR PLANT—See Turkiye Sise ve Cam Fabrikalari A.S.; *Int'l*, pg. 7977
CAMIS AMBALAJ SANAYI A.S.—See Turkiye Sise ve Cam Fabrikalari A.S.; *Int'l*, pg. 7977
CAMIS EGYPT MINING LTD. CO.—See Turkiye Sise ve Cam Fabrikalari A.S.; *Int'l*, pg. 7977
CAMIS LIMITED—See Turkiye Sise ve Cam Fabrikalari A.S.; *Int'l*, pg. 7977

CAMLAB, LTD.—See StoneCalibre, LLC; *U.S. Private*, pg. 3827
CAMLINE DRESDEN GMBH—See Elisa Corporation; *Int'l*, pg. 2362
CAMLINE GMBH—See Elisa Corporation; *Int'l*, pg. 2362
CAMLINE PTE. LTD.—See Elisa Corporation; *Int'l*, pg. 2362
CAMLINE USA INC.—See Elisa Corporation; *Int'l*, pg. 2362
CAMLIN FINE SCIENCES LTD.; *Int'l*, pg. 1273
CAM LOGISTICS, LLC—See US 1 Industries, Inc.; *U.S. Private*, pg. 4317
CAM MEDIA CREATIVE WORKS SP. Z O.O.; *Int'l*, pg. 1266
CAMMSYS CO., LTD; *Int'l*, pg. 1273
CAMMSYS GLOBAL CO., LTD.—See CAMMSYS Co., LTD; *Int'l*, pg. 1273
CAMMSYS VINA CO., LTD.—See CAMMSYS Co., LTD; *Int'l*, pg. 1273
CA MOBILE LTD.—See CyberAgent, Inc.; *Int'l*, pg. 1892
C&A MODAS S.A.; *Int'l*, pg. 1238
C&A MODA TRGOVINA D.O.O.—See COFRA Holding AG; *Int'l*, pg. 1694
C&A MODE AG—See COFRA Holding AG; *Int'l*, pg. 1694
C&A MODE GMBH & CO. KG—See COFRA Holding AG; *Int'l*, pg. 1694
C&A MODE S.A.—See COFRA Holding AG; *Int'l*, pg. 1694
CAMOLA APS—See BHG Group AB; *Int'l*, pg. 1014
CA MONTESSORI CHILDREN'S CENTER, INC.—See Broadcom Inc.; *U.S. Public*, pg. 389
CA MONTESSORI CHILDREN'S CENTER, INC.—See Broadcom Inc.; *U.S. Public*, pg. 389
CA MONTESSORI CHILDREN'S CENTER, INC.—See Broadcom Inc.; *U.S. Public*, pg. 389
CA MONTESSORI CHILDREN'S CENTER, INC.—See Broadcom Inc.; *U.S. Public*, pg. 389
CAMO SOFTWARE, INC.; *U.S. Private*, pg. 729
CAMOS TECHNOLOGIES CO.,LTD.—See AAC Technologies Holdings Inc.; *Int'l*, pg. 31
CAMOSY CONSTRUCTION; *U.S. Private*, pg. 729
CAMOSY, INC.; *U.S. Private*, pg. 729
CAMOTION, INC.—See Pohlad Companies; *U.S. Private*, pg. 3220
CAMOUFLAGE B.V.—See TalkPool AG; *Int'l*, pg. 7447
CAMOZZI ADVANCED MANUFACTURING S.P.A.—See Camozzi Group; *Int'l*, pg. 1273
CAMOZZI APS—See Camozzi Group; *Int'l*, pg. 1273
CAMOZZI AUTOMATION AB—See Camozzi Group; *Int'l*, pg. 1273
CAMOZZI AUTOMATION APS—See Camozzi Group; *Int'l*, pg. 1273
CAMOZZI AUTOMATION AS—See Camozzi Group; *Int'l*, pg. 1273
CAMOZZI AUTOMATION B.V.—See Camozzi Group; *Int'l*, pg. 1273
CAMOZZI AUTOMATION GMBH—See Camozzi Group; *Int'l*, pg. 1273
CAMOZZI AUTOMATION GMBH—See Camozzi Group; *Int'l*, pg. 1273
CAMOZZI AUTOMATION LTD.—See Camozzi Group; *Int'l*, pg. 1273
CAMOZZI AUTOMATION OU—See Camozzi Group; *Int'l*, pg. 1273
CAMOZZI AUTOMATION SARL—See Camozzi Group; *Int'l*, pg. 1273
CAMOZZI AUTOMATION S.P.A.—See Camozzi Group; *Int'l*, pg. 1273
CAMOZZI AUTOMATION SP. Z O.O.—See Camozzi Group; *Int'l*, pg. 1273
CAMOZZI BENELUX B.V.—See Camozzi Group; *Int'l*, pg. 1273
CAMOZZI DIGITAL S.R.L.—See Camozzi Group; *Int'l*, pg. 1273
CAMOZZI DO BRASIL LTDA.—See Camozzi Group; *Int'l*, pg. 1274
CAMOZZI GMBH—See Camozzi Group; *Int'l*, pg. 1273
CAMOZZI GMBH—See Camozzi Group; *Int'l*, pg. 1273
CAMOZZI GROUP - LUMEZZANE PLANT—See Camozzi Group; *Int'l*, pg. 1273
CAMOZZI GROUP - POLPENAZZE PLANT—See Camozzi Group; *Int'l*, pg. 1273
CAMOZZI GROUP; *Int'l*, pg. 1273
CAMOZZI IBERICA SL—See Camozzi Group; *Int'l*, pg. 1273
CAMOZZI INDIA PRIVATE LIMITED—See Camozzi Group; *Int'l*, pg. 1273
CAMOZZI MALAYSIA SDN. BHD.—See Camozzi Group; *Int'l*, pg. 1273
CAMOZZI MANUFACTURING SRL—See Camozzi Group; *Int'l*, pg. 1274
CAMOZZI NEUMATICA S.A. DE C.V.—See Camozzi Group; *Int'l*, pg. 1274
CAMOZZI NEUMATICA S.A.—See Camozzi Group; *Int'l*, pg. 1274
CAMOZZI OTOMASYON A.S.—See Camozzi Group; *Int'l*, pg. 1274
CAMOZZI PNEUMATIC KAZAKHSTAN LLP—See Camozzi Group; *Int'l*, pg. 1274
CAMOZZI PNEUMATIC LLC—See Camozzi Group; *Int'l*, pg. 1274

CORPORATE AFFILIATIONS

CAMOZZI PNEUMATICS INC—See Camozzi Group; *Int'l*, pg. 1274
CAMOZZI PNEUMATICS LTD.—See Camozzi Group; *Int'l*, pg. 1274
CAMOZZI PNEUMATIK AB—See Camozzi Group; *Int'l*, pg. 1274
CAMOZZI PNEUMATIQUE SARL—See Camozzi Group; *Int'l*, pg. 1274
CAMOZZI R.O.—See Camozzi Group; *Int'l*, pg. 1274
CAMOZZI S.R.O.—See Camozzi Group; *Int'l*, pg. 1274
CAMOZZI TECHNOPOLYMERS S.R.L.—See Camozzi Group; *Int'l*, pg. 1274
CAMOZZI VENEZUELA S.A.—See Camozzi Group; *Int'l*, pg. 1274
CAMPAGNANI BBDO—See Omnicom Group Inc.; *U.S. Public*, pg. 1575
CAMPAIGN CONSULTATION, INC.; *U.S. Private*, pg. 730
CAMPAIGNERCRM—See Ziff Davis, Inc.; *U.S. Public*, pg. 2403
CAMPAIGN MAIL & DATA, INC.; *U.S. Private*, pg. 730
CAMPAIGN MONITOR PTY LTD; *Int'l*, pg. 1274
CAMPAIGNS & GREY—See WPP plc; *Int'l*, pg. 8469
CAMPAIGNTRACK PTY. LTD.—See Nine Entertainment Co. Holdings Limited; *Int'l*, pg. 5298
CAMP AMERICA—See American Institute for Foreign Study, Inc.; *U.S. Private*, pg. 237
CAMPANIA HOLDING COMPANY, INC.—See The Hanover Insurance Group, Inc.; *U.S. Public*, pg. 2087
CAMPAP MAREKETING SDN. BHD.—See CWG Holdings Berhad; *Int'l*, pg. 1890
CAMPAP MARKETING SDN. BHD.—See CWG Holdings Berhad; *Int'l*, pg. 1890
CAMPARI AMERICA LLC—See Alicros S.p.A.; *Int'l*, pg. 327
CAMPARI S.P.A.—See Alicros S.p.A.; *Int'l*, pg. 327
CAM PARTECIPAZIONI S.P.A.—See Camfin S.p.A.; *Int'l*, pg. 1272
CAMP AUTOMOTIVE, INC.—See Lithia Motors, Inc.; *U.S. Public*, pg. 1321
CAMPBELL ALTERNATIVE ASSET TRUST—See Reverence Capital Partners LLC; *U.S. Private*, pg. 3415
CAMPBELL ARNOTTS LIMITED—See Campbell Soup Company; *U.S. Public*, pg. 426
CAMPBELL CATERING (BELFAST) LTD.—See Aramark; *U.S. Public*, pg. 177
CAMPBELL CATERING LIMITED—See Campbells/Bewley Group; *Int'l*, pg. 1274
CAMPBELL CHEONG CHAN MALAYSIA SDN BHD—See Campbell Soup Company; *U.S. Public*, pg. 426
CAMPBELL CHRYSLER JEEP DODGE RAM; *U.S. Private*, pg. 730
CAMPBELL CLINIC ORTHOPAEDICS; *U.S. Private*, pg. 730
CAMPBELL & COMPANY, INC.—See Reverence Capital Partners LLC; *U.S. Private*, pg. 3415
CAMPBELL COMPANY OF CANADA LTD—See Campbell Soup Company; *U.S. Public*, pg. 426
CAMPBELL CONCRETE & MATERIALS, L.P.—See Heidelberg Materials AG; *Int'l*, pg. 3313
CAMPBELL CONSTRUCTION INC.; *U.S. Private*, pg. 730
CAMPBELL COUNTY HMA, LLC—See Community Health Systems, Inc.; *U.S. Public*, pg. 552
CAMPBELL-EWALD COMPANY—See The Interpublic Group of Companies, Inc.; *U.S. Public*, pg. 2090
CAMPBELL-EWALD DETROIT—See The Interpublic Group of Companies, Inc.; *U.S. Public*, pg. 2090
CAMPBELL-EWALD LOS ANGELES—See The Interpublic Group of Companies, Inc.; *U.S. Public*, pg. 2090
CAMPBELL-EWALD SAN ANTONIO—See The Interpublic Group of Companies, Inc.; *U.S. Public*, pg. 2090
CAMPBELL-EWALD—See The Interpublic Group of Companies, Inc.; *U.S. Public*, pg. 2090
CAMPBELL & FETTER BANK; *U.S. Private*, pg. 730
CAMPBELL FITTINGS, INC.—See TruArc Partners, L.P.; *U.S. Private*, pg. 4245
CAMPBELL FOODS BELGIUM N.V/S.A.—See Campbell Soup Company; *U.S. Public*, pg. 426
CAMPBELL FOODSERVICE COMPANY—See Campbell Soup Company; *U.S. Public*, pg. 426
CAMPBELL FORD; *Int'l*, pg. 1274
CAMPBELL FOUNDRY COMPANY; *U.S. Private*, pg. 730
CAMPBELL FREIGHT AGENCIES LIMITED—See DSV A/S; *Int'l*, pg. 2211
CAMPBELL GLOBAL, LLC—See JPMorgan Chase & Co.; *U.S. Public*, pg. 1208
CAMPBELL GLOBAL, LLC—See BrightSphere Investment Group Inc.; *U.S. Public*, pg. 383
CAMPBELL HAUSFELD—See Berkshire Hathaway Inc.; *U.S. Public*, pg. 299
CAMPBELL, HENRY & CALVIN, INC.; *U.S. Private*, pg. 731
CAMPBELL-HOGUE & ASSOCIATES; *U.S. Private*, pg. 731
CAMPBELL JAPAN INCORPORATED—See Campbell Soup Company; *U.S. Public*, pg. 426
CAMPBELL LODGING INC.; *U.S. Private*, pg. 730
CAMPBELL MANUFACTURING INC.; *U.S. Private*, pg. 730

COMPANY NAME INDEX CAMST-COOPERATIVA ALBERGO

Company Index

CAMPBELL NELSON VOLKSWAGEN; *U.S. Private*, pg. 730
CAMPBELL NORTH AMERICA—See Campbell Soup Company; *U.S. Public*, pg. 426
CAMPBELL OIL & GAS COMPANY; *U.S. Private*, pg. 730
CAMPBELL OIL, INC.—See Lykins Companies, Inc.; *U.S. Private*, pg. 2519
CAMPBELL POOLS INC.; *Int'l*, pg. 1274
CAMPBELL SALES COMPANY—See Campbell Soup Company; *U.S. Public*, pg. 427
CAMPBELLS/BEWLEY GROUP; *Int'l*, pg. 1274
CAMPBELLS CAKE COMPANY LTD.—See DBAY Advisors Limited; *Int'l*, pg. 1986
CAMPBELL SCIENTIFIC AFRICA (PTY) LTD.—See Campbell Scientific, Inc.; *U.S. Private*, pg. 730
CAMPBELL SCIENTIFIC AUSTRALIA PTY LTD—See Campbell Scientific, Inc.; *U.S. Private*, pg. 730
CAMPBELL SCIENTIFIC CANADA CORP.—See Campbell Scientific, Inc.; *U.S. Private*, pg. 730
CAMPBELL SCIENTIFIC DO BRASIL, LTDA.—See Campbell Scientific, Inc.; *U.S. Private*, pg. 730
CAMPBELL SCIENTIFIC, INC.; *U.S. Private*, pg. 730
CAMPBELL SCIENTIFIC SPAIN, S.L.—See Campbell Scientific, Inc.; *U.S. Private*, pg. 730
CAMPBELL SLEEP, LLC—See Mattress Direct, Inc.; *U.S. Private*, pg. 2614
CAMPBELL & SONS OIL COMPANY, INC.; *U.S. Private*, pg. 730
CAMPBELL SOUP ASIA LIMITED—See Campbell Soup Company; *U.S. Public*, pg. 427
CAMPBELL SOUP COMPANY; *U.S. Public*, pg. 426
CAMPBELL SOUP CO. - PARIS PLANT—See Campbell Soup Company; *U.S. Public*, pg. 427
CAMPBELL SOUP FINLAND OY—See Campbell Soup Company; *U.S. Public*, pg. 427
CAMPBELL SOUP SUPPLY COMPANY L.L.C.—See Campbell Soup Company; *U.S. Public*, pg. 427
CAMPBELL SOUP SWEDEN AB—See Campbell Soup Company; *U.S. Public*, pg. 427
CAMPBELL SOUP TRADING (SHANGHAI) COMPANY LIMITED—See Campbell Soup Company; *U.S. Public*, pg. 427
CAMPBELL SOUTHEAST ASIA SDN BHD—See Campbell Soup Company; *U.S. Public*, pg. 427
CAMPBELLSPORT BUILDING SUPPLY; *U.S. Private*, pg. 731
CAMPBELL SUPPLY COMPANY; *U.S. Private*, pg. 730
CAMPBELL SUPPLY CO.—See Campbell Supply Company; *U.S. Private*, pg. 730
CAMPBELLSVILLE APPAREL COMPANY, LLC; *U.S. Private*, pg. 731
CAMPBELL SWIRE (HK) LTD—See Campbell Soup Company; *U.S. Public*, pg. 427
CAMPBELL TOOL & METAL SUPPLY, INC.—See Industrial Metal Supply Company; *U.S. Private*, pg. 2067
CAMPBELLTOWN MRI PTY LTD—See Healius Limited; *Int'l*, pg. 3302
CAMPBELL TRACTOR & IMPLEMENT CO.; *U.S. Private*, pg. 730
CAMPBELL WHOLESALE COMPANY, INC.; *U.S. Private*, pg. 731
CAMPBELL WRAPPER CORPORATION; *U.S. Private*, pg. 731
CAMP BOW WOW-BROOMFIELD; *U.S. Private*, pg. 729
CAMPE BILDUNGSZENTRUM HANNOVER GGMBH—See Ernst Klett AG; *Int'l*, pg. 2495
CAMPELLO BANCORP, INC.; *U.S. Private*, pg. 731
CAMPENON BERNARD CONSTRUCTION—See VINCI S.A.; *Int'l*, pg. 8213
CAMPENON BERNARD DAUPHINE ARDECHE SAS—See VINCI S.A.; *Int'l*, pg. 8234
CAMPENON BERNARD REGIONS SAS—See VINCI S.A.; *Int'l*, pg. 8234
CAMPENON BERNARD TP COTE D'AZUR SAS—See VINCI S.A.; *Int'l*, pg. 8234
CAMPENON SAIGON BUILDERS LTD—See VINCI S.A.; *Int'l*, pg. 8235
CAMPER CLINIC, INC.; *U.S. Private*, pg. 731
CAMPER COUNTRY RV—See Redwood Capital Investments, LLC; *U.S. Private*, pg. 3380
CAMPER & NICHOLSONS MARINA INVST. LTD.; *Int'l*, pg. 1274
CAMPER & NICHOLSONS MARINAS LTD.—See Camper & Nicholsons Marina Invst. Ltd.; *Int'l*, pg. 1274
CAMPER & NICHOLSONS USA, INC.—See Camper & Nicholsons Marina Invst. Ltd.; *Int'l*, pg. 1274
CAMPERS INN HOLDING CORP.; *U.S. Private*, pg. 731
CAMPERS INN OF KINGSTON INC—See Campers Inn Holding Corp.; *U.S. Private*, pg. 731
CAMPERS INN OF RAYNHAM INC—See Campers Inn Holding Corp.; *U.S. Private*, pg. 731
CAM PETROLI S.R.L.—See Camfin S.p.A.; *Int'l*, pg. 1272
CAM PETROLI S.R.L.—See Eni S.p.A.; *Int'l*, pg. 2436
CAMP EUROPE SAS—See The Hearst Corporation; *U.S. Private*, pg. 4044
CAMPFIRE INTERACTIVE, INC.; *U.S. Private*, pg. 731
CAMPFIRE; *U.S. Private*, pg. 731
CAMPGROUP LLC; *U.S. Private*, pg. 731
CAMPHOR TECHNOLOGIES, INC.; *U.S. Private*, pg. 731
CAMPI ALIMENTOS, S.A. DE C.V.—See Industrias Bachoco S.A.B. de C.V.; *Int'l*, pg. 3673
CAMPINE FRANCE S.A.S—See Campine N.V.; *Int'l*, pg. 1275
CAMPINE N.V.; *Int'l*, pg. 1275
CAMPINE RECYCLED POLYMERS S.A.S.—See Campine N.V.; *Int'l*, pg. 1275
CAMPING GAZ CS S.R.O.—See Newell Brands Inc.; *U.S. Public*, pg. 1513
CAMPING GAZ (DEUTSCHLAND) GMBH—See Newell Brands Inc.; *U.S. Public*, pg. 1515
CAMPING GAZ (SCHWEIZ) AG—See Newell Brands Inc.; *U.S. Public*, pg. 1515
CAMPING IN COMFORT B.V.—See Cox & Kings Limited; *Int'l*, pg. 1822
CAMPING WORLD HOLDINGS, INC.; *U.S. Public*, pg. 427
CAMPING WORLD, INC.—See Camping World Holdings, Inc.; *U.S. Public*, pg. 427
CAMPING WORLD OF DAVENPORT—See Camping World Holdings, Inc.; *U.S. Public*, pg. 427
CAMPING WORLD RV SALES, LLC—See Camping World Holdings, Inc.; *U.S. Public*, pg. 427
CAMPION AMBULANCE SERVICE, INC.; *U.S. Private*, pg. 731
CAMPIONI ENTERPRISES INC.; *U.S. Private*, pg. 731
CAMPION INSURANCE INC.—See Maury, Donnelly & Parr, Inc.; *U.S. Private*, pg. 2615
CAMPION MARINE INC.; *Int'l*, pg. 1275
CAMPI SRL; *Int'l*, pg. 1274
CAMP KAZ PRODUCTIONS INC.—See AOI TYO Holdings Inc.; *Int'l*, pg. 488
CAM PLASTIC INDUSTRY SDN. BHD.—See CAM Resources Berhad; *Int'l*, pg. 1267
CAMP LEJEUNE RAILROAD COMPANY—See Norfolk Southern Corporation; *U.S. Public*, pg. 1535
CAMPLIFY HOLDINGS LIMITED; *Int'l*, pg. 1275
CAMP LOWELL SURGERY CENTER, L.L.C.—See Tenet Healthcare Corporation; *U.S. Public*, pg. 2009
CAMP MANAGEMENT INC.; *U.S. Private*, pg. 729
CAMPMED CASUALTY & INDEMNITY COMPANY, INC.—See The Hanover Insurance Group, Inc.; *U.S. Public*, pg. 2087
CAMPMOR INC.; *U.S. Private*, pg. 731
CAMPOFRIO FOOD GROUPE FRANCE HOLDING SAS—See ALFA, S.A.B. de C.V.; *Int'l*, pg. 314
CAMPOFRIO FOOD GROUP, S.A. - MANUFACTURING PITESTI—See ALFA, S.A.B. de C.V.; *Int'l*, pg. 314
CAMPOFRIO FOOD GROUP, S.A. - MANUFACTURING TULCEA—See ALFA, S.A.B. de C.V.; *Int'l*, pg. 314
CAMPOFRIO FOOD GROUP, S.A.—See ALFA, S.A.B. de C.V.; *Int'l*, pg. 313
CAMPOFRIO PORTUGAL, S.A.—See ALFA, S.A.B. de C.V.; *Int'l*, pg. 314
CAMPO GRANDE PARKING LTDA.—See Allos SA; *Int'l*, pg. 359
CAMPONA SHOPPING CENTER KFT.—See CPI Property Group, S.A.; *Int'l*, pg. 1825
CAMPO OIL COMPANY INC.; *U.S. Private*, pg. 731
CAMPORA INC.; *U.S. Private*, pg. 731
CAMPORA WHOLESALE PROPANE—See Campora Inc.; *U.S. Private*, pg. 731
CAMPO RECYCLE PLAZA CO., LTD.—See Takuma Co., Ltd.; *Int'l*, pg. 7442
CAMPOS CREATIVE WORKS, INC.; *U.S. Private*, pg. 731
CAMPOS, INC.; *U.S. Private*, pg. 732
CAMPOSOL HOLDING PLC; *Int'l*, pg. 1275
CAMPOSTANO GROUP S.P.A.; *Int'l*, pg. 1275
CAMP-OUT, INC.; *U.S. Private*, pg. 730
THE CAMP RECOVERY CENTER, LLC—See Acadia Healthcare Company, Inc.; *U.S. Public*, pg. 30
THE CAMP RECOVERY CENTERS, L.P.—See Acadia Healthcare Company, Inc.; *U.S. Public*, pg. 30
CAMPRESS SRL—See Camozzi Group; *Int'l*, pg. 1274
CAMP RICHARD CAMPERS ASSOCIATION, INC.; *U.S. Private*, pg. 729
CAMPSIE VETERINARY CENTRE LIMITED—See CVS Group Plc; *Int'l*, pg. 1890
CAMP SYSTEMS INTERNATIONAL, INC.—See The Hearst Corporation; *U.S. Private*, pg. 4044
CAMP SYSTEMS INTERNATIONAL, INC. - WICHITA—See The Hearst Corporation; *U.S. Private*, pg. 4044
CAMP THREE SIGNS (YINGKOU) FINE CHEMICAL CO., LTD.—See Tsaker New Energy Tech Co., Limited; *Int'l*, pg. 7949
CAMPUS ACTIVEWEAR LIMITED; *Int'l*, pg. 1275
CAMPUS BOOK RENTALS, INC.; *U.S. Private*, pg. 732
CAMPUSCLARITY—See EverFi, Inc.; *U.S. Private*, pg. 1438
CAMPUS CREST COMMUNITIES, INC.—See Colliers International Group Inc.; *Int'l*, pg. 1701
CAMPUS DOOR HOLDINGS INC.—See Incenter, LLC; *U.S. Private*, pg. 2053
CAMPU SECURITIES PLC—See Public Bank Berhad; *Int'l*, pg. 6094
CAMPUS ELITIS PHARMA INC.—See KDA Group, Inc.; *Int'l*, pg. 4111
CAMPUS-FOYER APOTHEKE GMBH—See Johnson & Johnson; *U.S. Public*, pg. 1194
CAMPUS LIVING VILLAGES, CENTURY; *U.S. Private*, pg. 732
CAMPUSLOGIC, INC.—See e.Bricks Ventures; *Int'l*, pg. 2251
CAMPUS MEDIA GROUP, LLC; *U.S. Private*, pg. 732
CAMPUS PARTNERS; *U.S. Private*, pg. 732
CAMPUS RESEARCH CORPORATION; *U.S. Private*, pg. 732
THE CAMPUS SPECIAL, LLC—See Chegg Inc.; *U.S. Public*, pg. 483
CAMPUS SURGERY CENTER, LLC—See KKR & Co. Inc.; *U.S. Public*, pg. 1245
CAMPUS USA CREDIT UNION; *U.S. Private*, pg. 732
CAMP VENTURE, INC.; *U.S. Private*, pg. 730
CAMP WAHANOWIN; *Int'l*, pg. 1274
CAMRADATA ANALYTICAL SERVICES LTD—See Punter Southall Group Limited; *Int'l*, pg. 6120
CAM RANH INTERNATIONAL AIRPORT SERVICES JSC; *Int'l*, pg. 1266
CAM/RB INC—See CAM Consultants, Inc.; *U.S. Private*, pg. 725
CAM RESOURCES BERHAD; *Int'l*, pg. 1267
CAMRIS INTERNATIONAL, LLC—See Henry M. Jackson Foundation for the Advance; *U.S. Private*, pg. 1919
CAMRON PUBLIC RELATIONS LIMITED—See Pico Far East Holdings Limited; *Int'l*, pg. 5860
CAMROST-FELCORP INC.; *Int'l*, pg. 1275
CAMROVA RESOURCES INC.; *Int'l*, pg. 1275
CAMS BLUEWIRE TECHNOLOGY, LLC; *U.S. Private*, pg. 732
CAMS FINANCIAL INFORMATION SERVICES PRIVATE LIMITED—See Computer Age Management Services Limited; *Int'l*, pg. 1758
CAMSING GLOBAL, LLC; *U.S. Private*, pg. 732
CAMSING HEALTHCARE LIMITED; *Int'l*, pg. 1275
CAMSING INTERNATIONAL HOLDING LIMITED; *Int'l*, pg. 1275
CAMS INSURANCE REPOSITORY SERVICES LIMITED—See Computer Age Management Services Limited; *Int'l*, pg. 1759
CAMSO CIS LLC—See Compagnie Generale des Etablissements Michelin SCA; *Int'l*, pg. 1741
CAMSO DEUTSCHLAND GMBH—See Compagnie Generale des Etablissements Michelin SCA; *Int'l*, pg. 1741
CAMSO DISTRIBUCION MEXICO, S.A. DE C.V.—See Compagnie Generale des Etablissements Michelin SCA; *Int'l*, pg. 1741
CAMSO DISTRIBUTION CANADA INC.—See Compagnie Generale des Etablissements Michelin SCA; *Int'l*, pg. 1742
CAMSO FRANCE SAS—See Compagnie Generale des Etablissements Michelin SCA; *Int'l*, pg. 1742
CAMSO HOLDING BRASIL LTDA—See Compagnie Generale des Etablissements Michelin SCA; *Int'l*, pg. 1742
CAMSO INC.—See Compagnie Generale des Etablissements Michelin SCA; *Int'l*, pg. 1742
CAMSO INDUSTRIELLE HUNGARY KFT.—See Compagnie Generale des Etablissements Michelin SCA; *Int'l*, pg. 1742
CAMSO INTERNATIONAL S.A.R.L.—See Compagnie Generale des Etablissements Michelin SCA; *Int'l*, pg. 1742
CAMSO ITALY S.P.A.—See Compagnie Generale des Etablissements Michelin SCA; *Int'l*, pg. 1742
CAMSO JAPAN CO., LTD.—See Compagnie Generale des Etablissements Michelin SCA; *Int'l*, pg. 1742
CAMSO LASTIK TICARET LIMITED SIRKETI—See Compagnie Generale des Etablissements Michelin SCA; *Int'l*, pg. 1742
CAMSO NEDERLAND B.V.—See Compagnie Generale des Etablissements Michelin SCA; *Int'l*, pg. 1742
CAMSO NEW ZEALAND LIMITED—See Compagnie Generale des Etablissements Michelin SCA; *Int'l*, pg. 1742
CAMSON SEEDS LTD.; *Int'l*, pg. 1275
CAMSO POLSKA S.A.—See Compagnie Generale des Etablissements Michelin SCA; *Int'l*, pg. 1742
CAMSO SCHWEIZ AG—See Compagnie Generale des Etablissements Michelin SCA; *Int'l*, pg. 1742
CAMSO SPAIN, S.L.—See Compagnie Generale des Etablissements Michelin SCA; *Int'l*, pg. 1742
CAMSO TAERYUK LTD.—See Compagnie Generale des Etablissements Michelin SCA; *Int'l*, pg. 1742
CAMSO UK LIMITED—See Compagnie Generale des Etablissements Michelin SCA; *Int'l*, pg. 1742
CAMSO VIETNAM CO., LTD.—See Compagnie Generale des Etablissements Michelin SCA; *Int'l*, pg. 1742
CAM SPECIALTY PRODUCTS, INC.—See Riverstone Holdings LLC; *U.S. Private*, pg. 3448
CAM SRL—See Group Thermote & Vanhalst; *Int'l*, pg. 3089
CAMST-COOPERATIVA ALBERGO; *Int'l*, pg. 1275
CAM SYSTEMS GMBH—See Certina Holding AG; *Int'l*, pg. 1423
CAMTEK EUROPE SA—See Priortech Ltd.; *Int'l*, pg. 5981
CAMTEK HONG KONG LTD.—See Priortech Ltd.; *Int'l*, pg. 5981

CAMST-COOPERATIVA ALBERGO

CAMTEK IMAGING TECHNOLOGY (SUZHOU) CO., LTD—See Priortech Ltd.; *Int'l*, pg. 5982
CAMTEK JAPAN LTD.—See Priortech Ltd.; *Int'l*, pg. 5982
CAMTEK KOREA CO., LTD.—See Priortech Ltd.; *Int'l*, pg. 5982
CAMTEK LTD.—See Priortech Ltd.; *Int'l*, pg. 5981
CAMTEK SOUTH EAST ASIA PTE LTD.—See Priortech Ltd.; *Int'l*, pg. 5982
CAMTEK TAIWAN LTD.—See Priortech Ltd.; *Int'l*, pg. 5982
CAMTEK USA, INC.—See Priortech Ltd.; *Int'l*, pg. 5982
CAM-TEL CO. INC.—See Wehco Media, Inc.; *U.S. Private*, pg. 4469
CAMTERRA RESOURCES PARTNERS; *U.S. Private*, pg. 732
CAMTOR COMMERCIAL REAL ESTATE LENDING, L.P.; *U.S. Private*, pg. 732
CAM TRANSPORT, LLC—See US 1 Industries, Inc.; *U.S. Private*, pg. 4317
C.A. MUER CORPORATION—See Fertitta Entertainment, Inc.; *U.S. Private*, pg. 1499
CAMUNA ENERGIA S.R.L.—See A2A S.p.A.; *Int'l*, pg. 29
C.A. MURREN & SONS COMPANY; *U.S. Private*, pg. 706
CAMURUS AB; *Int'l*, pg. 1275
CAMURUS GMBH—See Camurus AB; *Int'l*, pg. 1275
CAMURUS LTD.—See Camurus AB; *Int'l*, pg. 1275
CAMURUS PTY. LTD.—See Camurus AB; *Int'l*, pg. 1275
CAMUTO LLC—See Schottenstein Stores Corporation; *U.S. Private*, pg. 3569
CAMUZZI GAS PAMPEANA S.A.; *Int'l*, pg. 1275
CAMX POWER LLC—See TIAX LLC; *U.S. Private*, pg. 4166
CAN2 TERMIK A.S.; *Int'l*, pg. 1277
CANAAN INC.; *Int'l*, pg. 1277
CANAAN PARTNERS; *U.S. Private*, pg. 732
CANACCORD GENUITY ASIA (BEIJING) LIMITED—See Canaccord Genuity Group Inc.; *Int'l*, pg. 1277
CANACCORD GENUITY (AUSTRALIA) LIMITED—See Canaccord Genuity Group Inc.; *Int'l*, pg. 1277
CANACCORD GENUITY CORP.—See Canaccord Genuity Group Inc.; *Int'l*, pg. 1277
CANACCORD GENUITY (DUBAI) LTD.—See Canaccord Genuity Group Inc.; *Int'l*, pg. 1277
CANACCORD GENUITY FINANCIAL LIMITED—See Canaccord Genuity Group Inc.; *Int'l*, pg. 1277
CANACCORD GENUITY GROUP INC.; *Int'l*, pg. 1277
CANACCORD GENUITY HAWKPOINT LIMITED—See Canaccord Genuity Group Inc.; *Int'l*, pg. 1277
CANACCORD GENUITY (HONG KONG) LIMITED—See Canaccord Genuity Group Inc.; *Int'l*, pg. 1277
CANACCORD GENUITY INC.—See Canaccord Genuity Group Inc.; *Int'l*, pg. 1277
CANACCORD GENUITY LIMITED—See Canaccord Genuity Group Inc.; *Int'l*, pg. 1277
CANACCORD GENUITY MANAGEMENT COMPANY LIMITED—See Canaccord Genuity Group Inc.; *Int'l*, pg. 1277
CANACCORD GENUITY SAS—See Canaccord Genuity Group Inc.; *Int'l*, pg. 1277
CANACCORD GENUITY SECURITIES LLC—See Canaccord Genuity Group Inc.; *Int'l*, pg. 1277
CANACCORD GENUITY SG PTE. LTD.—See Canaccord Genuity Group Inc.; *Int'l*, pg. 1277
CANACCORD GENUITY WEALTH (INTERNATIONAL) LIMITED—See Canaccord Genuity Group Inc.; *Int'l*, pg. 1277
CANAC KITCHENS—See Kohler Company; *U.S. Private*, pg. 2339
CANACOL ENERGY LTD.; *Int'l*, pg. 1277
CANACRE LTD.—See Quanta Services, Inc.; *U.S. Public*, pg. 1750
CANADABIS CAPITAL, INC.; *Int'l*, pg. 1282
CANADA BREAD COMPANY LTD.—See Grupo Bimbo, S.A.B. de C.V.; *Int'l*, pg. 3123
CANADA CARBON INC.; *Int'l*, pg. 1277
CANADA CARTAGE CORPORATION.; *Int'l*, pg. 1277
CANADA COAL INC.; *Int'l*, pg. 1277
CANADA COMPUTATIONAL UNLIMITED CORP.; *Int'l*, pg. 1277
CANADA CORDAGE, INC.; *Int'l*, pg. 1277
CANADA CULVERT INC.—See WGI Westman Group, Inc.; *Int'l*, pg. 8394
CANADA DRUGS LTD.; *Int'l*, pg. 1278
CANADA DRY BOTTLING COMPANY OF NEW YORK, L.P.—See Pepsi-Cola & National Brand Beverages, Ltd.; *U.S. Private*, pg. 3145
CANADA DRY DELAWARE VALLEY BOTTLING COMPANY—See Pepsi-Cola & National Brand Beverages, Ltd.; *U.S. Private*, pg. 3145
CANADA DRY MOTT'S INC.—See JAB Holding Company S.a.r.l.; *Int'l*, pg. 3862
CANADA ENERGY PARTNERS INC.; *Int'l*, pg. 1278
CANADA FLUORSPAR INC.—See African Minerals Exploration & Development SICAR SCA; *Int'l*, pg. 192
CANADA FORGINGS INC.; *Int'l*, pg. 1278
CANADA GARDENWORKS LTD.; *Int'l*, pg. 1278
CANADA GLOBAL (T.R) LTD; *Int'l*, pg. 1278
CANADA GOLD COLOMBIA S.A.S.—See South Star Battery Metals Corp.; *Int'l*, pg. 7117

CANADA GOOSE HOLDINGS INC.—See Bain Capital, LP; *U.S. Private*, pg. 437
CANADA GOOSE INC.—See Bain Capital, LP; *U.S. Private*, pg. 437
CANADA HOUSE WELLNESS GROUP INC.; *Int'l*, pg. 1278
CANADA IRON INC.; *Int'l*, pg. 1278
CANADA LAND LIMITED; *Int'l*, pg. 1278
CANADA LANDS COMPANY LIMITED; *Int'l*, pg. 1278
THE CANADA LIFE ASSURANCE COMPANY—See Power Corporation of Canada; *Int'l*, pg. 5943
THE CANADA LIFE ASSURANCE COMPANY (U.K.) LIMITED—See Power Corporation of Canada; *Int'l*, pg. 5944
THE CANADA LIFE GROUP (U.K.) LIMITED—See Power Corporation of Canada; *Int'l*, pg. 5944
CANADA LIFE LIMITED—See Power Corporation of Canada; *Int'l*, pg. 5944
CANADA LIFE MANAGEMENT (U.K.) LIMITED—See Power Corporation of Canada; *Int'l*, pg. 5944
CANADA LIFE TRUSTEE LIMITED—See Power Corporation of Canada; *Int'l*, pg. 5944
CANADA LIFE (U.K.) LIMITED—See Power Corporation of Canada; *Int'l*, pg. 5944
CANADA MALTING CO LIMITED—See GrainCorp Limited; *Int'l*, pg. 3052
CANADA MOLD TECHNOLOGY, INC.—See Nagase & Co., Ltd.; *Int'l*, pg. 5126
CANADA MORTGAGE & HOUSING CORPORATION; *Int'l*, pg. 1278
CANADA NICKEL COMPANY, INC.; *Int'l*, pg. 1278
CANADA OIL SANDS CO., LTD.—See Japan Petroleum Exploration Co. Ltd.; *Int'l*, pg. 3900
CANADA ONE MINING CORP.; *Int'l*, pg. 1278
CANADA PENSION PLAN INVESTMENT BOARD; *Int'l*, pg. 1278
CANADA PIPE CO. LTD.—See McWane, Inc.; *U.S. Private*, pg. 2645
CANADA PIPE CO. LTD.—See McWane, Inc.; *U.S. Private*, pg. 2645
CANADA PIPE CO. LTD.—See McWane, Inc.; *U.S. Private*, pg. 2645
CANADA POST CORPORATION; *Int'l*, pg. 1282
CANADA POST INTERNATIONAL LTD.—See Canada Post Corporation; *Int'l*, pg. 1282
CANADA POWER TECHNOLOGY LIMITED; *Int'l*, pg. 1282
CANADA RARE EARTH CORP.; *Int'l*, pg. 1282
CANADA RENEWABLE BIOENERGY CORP.; *Int'l*, pg. 1282
CANADA ROYAL MILK ULC—See China Feihe Limited; *Int'l*, pg. 1502
CANADA SAFEWAY LIMITED—See Empire Company Limited; *Int'l*, pg. 2387
CANADA SILVER COBALT WORKS INC.; *Int'l*, pg. 1282
CANADA SINOMINE RESOURCES INC.—See Sinomine Resource Group Co., Ltd.; *Int'l*, pg. 6953
CANADA'S ISLAND GARDENS, INC.—See Pyxus International, Inc.; *U.S. Public*, pg. 1740
CANADA'S OUTDOOR SHOWS LIMITED PARTNERSHIP—See GVIC Communications Corp.; *Int'l*, pg. 3189
CANADA SQUARE OPERATIONS LIMITED—See Citigroup Inc.; *U.S. Public*, pg. 502
CANADA'S WONDERLAND COMPANY—See Six Flags Entertainment Corporation; *U.S. Public*, pg. 1890
CANADA TOOLS & MOLDING SUPPLIES, INC.—See Season Group International Co., Ltd.; *Int'l*, pg. 6666
CANA-DATUM MOULDS LTD.; *Int'l*, pg. 1277
CANADA TUNGSTEN (CAYMAN) INC.—See Teck Resources Limited; *Int'l*, pg. 7514
CANADA UNLIMITED INC.—See Messe Munchen GmbH; *Int'l*, pg. 4841
CANADA WEST HARVEST CENTRE INC.—See Claas KGaA mbH; *Int'l*, pg. 1640
CANADAY & COMPANY; *U.S. Private*, pg. 732
CANADEAN LIMITED—See GlobalData Plc; *Int'l*, pg. 3003
CANADELLE L.P.—See Hanesbrands Inc.; *U.S. Public*, pg. 982
CANADIAN ADVANCED TECHNOLOGY ALLIANCE; *Int'l*, pg. 1282
CANADIAN AIR-CRANE LTD—See Erickson Incorporated; *U.S. Private*, pg. 1419
CANADIAN AMERICAN STANDARD HEMP INC.—See Real Brands, Inc.; *U.S. Public*, pg. 1768
CANADIAN APARTMENT PROPERTIES REAL ESTATE INVESTMENT TRUST; *Int'l*, pg. 1282
CANADIAN ART PRINTS, INC.—See Encore Art Group; *Int'l*, pg. 2402
CANADIAN ASSOCIATION OF INTERNET PROVIDERS—See Canadian Advanced Technology Alliance; *Int'l*, pg. 1282
CANADIAN BACK INSTITUTE LIMITED PARTNERSHIP; *Int'l*, pg. 1282
CANADIAN BANC CORP.—See Quadravest Capital Management Inc.; *Int'l*, pg. 6149
CANADIAN BANK NOTE COMPANY LIMITED; *Int'l*, pg. 1282

CORPORATE AFFILIATIONS

CANADIAN BANK NOTE DESIGN INC.—See Canadian Bank Note Company Limited; *Int'l*, pg. 1282
CANADIAN BENEFIT ADMINISTRATORS LTD.—See NexgenRx Inc.; *Int'l*, pg. 5243
CANADIAN BRINE LTD.—See K+S Aktiengesellschaft; *Int'l*, pg. 4039
THE CANADIAN BROADCASTING CORPORATION; *Int'l*, pg. 7630
CANADIAN BROADCAST SALES—See Corus Entertainment Inc.; *Int'l*, pg. 1808
CANADIAN BROADCAST SALES—See Rogers Communications Inc.; *Int'l*, pg. 6383
CANADIAN CANNABIS CORP.; *Int'l*, pg. 1283
CANADIAN CHEMICAL CLEANING SERVICES INC.—See AIP, LLC; *U.S. Private*, pg. 135
CANADIAN CLUB CANADA INC.—See Suntory Holdings Limited; *Int'l*, pg. 7325
CANADIAN COMMERCIAL CORPORATION; *Int'l*, pg. 1283
CANADIAN COMMERCIAL VEHICLES CORPORATION—See The Eastern Company; *U.S. Public*, pg. 2069
CANADIAN CONSULTING GROUP LIMITED—See Bird Construction Inc.; *Int'l*, pg. 1046
THE CANADIAN DEPOSITORY FOR SECURITIES LIMITED—See TMX Group Limited; *Int'l*, pg. 7767
CANADIAN DERIVATIVES CLEARING CORPORATION—See TMX Group Limited; *Int'l*, pg. 7767
CANADIAN DEWATERING L.P.—See Mullen Group Ltd.; *Int'l*, pg. 5079
CANADIAN DIRECT FINANCIAL—See Canadian Western Bank; *Int'l*, pg. 1286
CANADIAN DIRECT INSURANCE INCORPORATED—See Intact Financial Corporation; *Int'l*, pg. 3726
CANADIAN ELECTROLYTIC ZINC LIMITED—See Glencore plc; *Int'l*, pg. 2990
CANADIAN ENTERPRISE GAS PRODUCTS, LTD.—See Enterprise Products Partners L.P.; *U.S. Public*, pg. 778
CANADIAN FAMILY—See St. Joseph Communications Inc.; *Int'l*, pg. 7159
CANADIAN FERRO REFRACTORIES; *Int'l*, pg. 1283
CANADIAN FISH EXPORTERS, INC.; *U.S. Private*, pg. 732
CANADIAN FISHING COMPANY - RICHMOND PLANT—See The Jim Pattison Group; *Int'l*, pg. 7660
CANADIAN FISHING COMPANY—See The Jim Pattison Group; *Int'l*, pg. 7660
CANADIAN FOREST PRODUCTS - CHETWYND—See Canfor Corporation; *Int'l*, pg. 1290
CANADIAN FOREST PRODUCTS - CLEAR LAKE—See Canfor Corporation; *Int'l*, pg. 1290
CANADIAN FOREST PRODUCTS - ENGLEWOOD LOGGING—See Canfor Corporation; *Int'l*, pg. 1290
CANADIAN FOREST PRODUCTS - GRANDE PRAIRIE—See Canfor Corporation; *Int'l*, pg. 1290
CANADIAN FOREST PRODUCTS - ISLE PIERRE—See Canfor Corporation; *Int'l*, pg. 1290
CANADIAN FOREST PRODUCTS LTD.—See Canfor Corporation; *Int'l*, pg. 1290
CANADIAN FOREST PRODUCTS - PRINCE GEORGE PULP & PAPER MILLS—See Canfor Corporation; *Int'l*, pg. 1290
CANADIANFOREX LIMITED—See OFX Group Limited; *Int'l*, pg. 5531
CANADIAN FREIGHTWAYS LTD.—See TFI International Inc.; *Int'l*, pg. 7585
CANADIAN GENERAL FILTERS LIMITED—See General Filters, Inc.; *U.S. Private*, pg. 1665
CANADIAN GENERAL INVESTMENTS, LIMITED—See Morgan Meighen & Associates Limited; *Int'l*, pg. 5044
CANADIAN GENERAL TOWER LIMITED; *Int'l*, pg. 1283
CANADIAN GOLDCAMPS CORP.; *Int'l*, pg. 1283
CANADIAN GOLD SEAFOOD COMPANY; *Int'l*, pg. 1283
CANADIAN HEARING CARE—See Audiotech Healthcare Corporation; *Int'l*, pg. 702
CANADIAN HELICOPTERS LIMITED—See PHI, Inc.; *U.S. Private*, pg. 3168
CANADIAN HIGHWAYS INFRASTRUCTURE CORPORATION—See Aecon Group Inc.; *Int'l*, pg. 172
CANADIAN HIGH YIELD FOCUS FUND—See Fiera Capital Corporation; *Int'l*, pg. 2659
CANADIAN HOSPITAL SPECIALTIES LIMITED; *Int'l*, pg. 1283
CANADIAN HYDROVAC LTD.—See Mullen Group Ltd.; *Int'l*, pg. 5080
CANADIAN IMPERIAL BANK OF COMMERCE; *Int'l*, pg. 1283
CANADIAN IMPERIAL GINSENG ONTARIO LTD.—See Imperial Ginseng Products Ltd.; *Int'l*, pg. 3634
CANADIAN IMPERIAL HOLDINGS INC.—See Canadian Imperial Bank of Commerce; *Int'l*, pg. 1283
CANADIAN KAWASAKI MOTORS, INC.—See Kawasaki Heavy Industries, Ltd.; *Int'l*, pg. 4095
CANADIAN LIFE COMPANIES SPLIT CORP.—See Quadravest Capital Management Inc.; *Int'l*, pg. 6149
CANADIAN LINEN & UNIFORM SERVICE CO.; *Int'l*, pg. 1284

COMPANY NAME INDEX

CANADIAN LOCKER CO., LTD.—See American Locker Group Incorporated; *U.S. Private*, pg. 240
CANADIAN LOCKER COMPANY OF CANADA, LTD.—See American Locker Group Incorporated; *U.S. Private*, pg. 240
CANADIAN MALARTIC CORPORATION—See Agnico Eagle Mines Limited; *Int'l*, pg. 212
CANADIAN MALARTIC PARTNERSHIP—See Agnico Eagle Mines Limited; *Int'l*, pg. 212
CANADIAN MANGANESE COMPANY INC.; *Int'l*, pg. 1284
CANADIAN METALS INC.; *Int'l*, pg. 1284
CANADIAN MIST DISTILLERS LIMITED—See Brown-Forman Corporation; *U.S. Public*, pg. 403
CANADIAN NATIONAL RAILWAY COMPANY; *Int'l*, pg. 1284
CANADIAN NATIONAL RAILWAY COMPANY—See Canadian National Railway Company; *Int'l*, pg. 1284
CANADIAN NATIONAL RAILWAY COMPANY—See Canadian National Railway Company; *Int'l*, pg. 1284
CANADIAN NATURAL RESOURCES LTD.; *Int'l*, pg. 1284
CANADIAN NET REAL ESTATE INVESTMENT TRUST; *Int'l*, pg. 1284
CANADIAN NEXUS TEAM VENTURES CORP.; *Int'l*, pg. 1285
CANADIAN NIAGARA POWER INC. - EASTERN ONTARIO POWER DIVISION—See Fortis Inc.; *Int'l*, pg. 2739
CANADIAN NIAGARA POWER INC.—See Fortis Inc.; *Int'l*, pg. 2739
CANADIAN NORTHERN SHIELD INSURANCE COMPANY—See Intact Financial Corporation; *Int'l*, pg. 3727
CANADIAN NORTHERN SHIELD INSURANCE COMPANY—See Tryg A/S; *Int'l*, pg. 7947
CANADIAN NORTH RESOURCES INC.; *Int'l*, pg. 1285
CANADIAN OIL RECOVERY & REMEDIATION ENTERPRISES LIMITED; *Int'l*, pg. 1285
CANADIAN OVERSEAS PETROLEUM LIMITED; *Int'l*, pg. 1285
CANADIAN PACIFIC KANSAS CITY LIMITED; *Int'l*, pg. 1285
CANADIAN PALLADIUM RESOURCES, INC.; *Int'l*, pg. 1285
CANADIAN PREFERRED SHARE TRUST; *Int'l*, pg. 1285
CANADIAN PREMIUM SAND INC.; *Int'l*, pg. 1285
CANADIAN PUREGAS EQUIPMENT LIMITED; *Int'l*, pg. 1285
CANADIAN RESOURCES INCOME TRUST; *Int'l*, pg. 1285
CANADIAN RESOURCES INSURANCE SOLUTIONS INC.—See Hellman & Friedman LLC; *U.S. Private*, pg. 1909
CANADIAN RIVER MUNICIPAL WATER AUTHORITY; *U.S. Private*, pg. 732
CANADIAN ROYALTIES INC.—See Jilin Horoc Nonferrous Metal Group Co., Ltd.; *Int'l*, pg. 3963
THE CANADIAN SALT CO. LTD.—See K+S Aktiengesellschaft; *Int'l*, pg. 4041
THE CANADIAN SALT CO. LTD.—See K+S Aktiengesellschaft; *Int'l*, pg. 4041
CANADIAN SALT FINANCE COMPANY—See K+S Aktiengesellschaft; *Int'l*, pg. 4039
CANADIAN SILVER HUNTER INC.; *Int'l*, pg. 1285
CANADIAN SOLAR (AUSTRALIA) PTY., LTD.—See Canadian Solar Inc.; *Int'l*, pg. 1286
CANADIAN SOLAR CONSTRUCTION S.R.L.—See Canadian Solar Inc.; *Int'l*, pg. 1286
CANADIAN SOLAR EMEA GMBH—See Canadian Solar Inc.; *Int'l*, pg. 1286
CANADIAN SOLAR INC.; *Int'l*, pg. 1285
CANADIAN SOLAR INFRASTRUCTURE FUND, INC.; *Int'l*, pg. 1286
CANADIAN SOLAR JAPAN K.K.—See Canadian Solar Inc.; *Int'l*, pg. 1286
CANADIAN SOLAR MANUFACTURING (SUZHOU) INC.—See Canadian Solar Inc.; *Int'l*, pg. 1286
CANADIAN SOLAR PROJECTS K.K.—See Canadian Solar Inc.; *Int'l*, pg. 1286
CANADIAN SOLAR SOUTH AFRICA (PTY) LTD.—See Canadian Solar Inc.; *Int'l*, pg. 1286
CANADIAN SOLAR (USA) INC.—See Canadian Solar Inc.; *Int'l*, pg. 1286
CANADIAN SPIRIT RESOURCES INC.; *Int'l*, pg. 1286
CANADIAN STANDARDS ASSOCIATION (FAR EAST OPERATIONS) LTD.—See CSA Group; *Int'l*, pg. 1861
CANADIAN STANDARDS ASSOCIATION—See CSA Group; *Int'l*, pg. 1861
CANADIAN THERMOS PRODUCTS, INC.—See Thermos L.L.C.; *U.S. Private*, pg. 4143
CANADIAN TIMKEN LTD.—See The Timken Company; *U.S. Public*, pg. 2132
CANADIAN TIRE BANK—See Canadian Tire Corporation Limited; *Int'l*, pg. 1286
CANADIAN TIRE CENTRE—See Capital Sports Group of Companies; *Int'l*, pg. 1312
CANADIAN TIRE CORPORATION LIMITED; *Int'l*, pg. 1286
CANADIAN TODS LIMITED—See Lamar Advertising Company; *U.S. Public*, pg. 1290

CANADIAN TRAFFIC NETWORK—See GTCR LLC; *U.S. Private*, pg. 1805
CANADIAN ULTRAMAR COMPANY—See Valero Energy Corporation; *U.S. Public*, pg. 2272
CANADIAN UNIVERSITIES TRAVEL SERVICE LIMITED; *Int'l*, pg. 1286
CANADIAN UTILITIES LIMITED—See ATCO Ltd.; *Int'l*, pg. 666
CANADIAN UTILITIES & TELECOM INCOME FUND; *Int'l*, pg. 1286
CANADIAN UTILITY CONSTRUCTION LIMITED—See Quanta Services, Inc.; *U.S. Public*, pg. 1750
CANADIAN VALLEY ELECTRIC CO-OP; *U.S. Private*, pg. 732
CANADIAN WESTERN BANK; *Int'l*, pg. 1286
CANADIAN WESTERN TRUST—See Canadian Western Bank; *Int'l*, pg. 1286
CANADIAN WILLAMETTE INDUSTRIES, INC.—See The Willamette Valley Company; *U.S. Private*, pg. 4136
CANADIAN WORLD FUND LIMITED—See Morgan Meighen & Associates Limited; *Int'l*, pg. 5044
CANADREAM CORPORATION—See Tourism Holdings Limited; *Int'l*, pg. 7848
CANAFARMA HEMP PRODUCTS CORP.; *Int'l*, pg. 1287
CANAF-CLAL FINANCE MANAGEMENT LTD.—See IDB Development Corporation Ltd.; *Int'l*, pg. 3588
CANAF INVESTMENTS INC.; *Int'l*, pg. 1287
CANAG DIAGNOSTICS (BEIJING) CO., LTD.—See H.U. Group Holdings, Inc.; *Int'l*, pg. 3196
CANAGOLD RESOURCES LTD.; *Int'l*, pg. 1287
CANA INC.—See Patrick Industries, Inc.; *U.S. Public*, pg. 1652
CANALASKA URANIUM LTD.; *Int'l*, pg. 1287
CANAL BANK, S.A.; *Int'l*, pg. 1287
CANAL BARGE COMPANY INC.; *U.S. Private*, pg. 732
CANAL+ BELGIUM—See Vivendi SE; *Int'l*, pg. 8265
CANAL+ CALEDONIE—See Vivendi SE; *Int'l*, pg. 8266
CANAL+ CAMEROUN—See Vivendi SE; *Int'l*, pg. 8266
CANAL CAPITAL MANAGEMENT LLC; *U.S. Private*, pg. 732
CANAL CHIP, LLC—See Canal Wood LLC; *U.S. Private*, pg. 733
CANAL CORPORATION; *U.S. Private*, pg. 733
CANAL+ CYFROWY SP. Z OO—See Vivendi SE; *Int'l*, pg. 8265
CANAL DIGITAL AS—See Telenor ASA; *Int'l*, pg. 7538
CANAL DIGITAL—See Vivendi SE; *Int'l*, pg. 8265
CANAL+ DISTRIBUTION S.A.S.—See Vivendi SE; *Int'l*, pg. 8266
CANALE COMMUNICATIONS INC.—See Clayton, Dubilier & Rice, LLC; *U.S. Private*, pg. 927
CANAL+ FINLAND—See Vivendi SE; *Int'l*, pg. 8266
CANAL+ FLANDERS—See Vivendi SE; *Int'l*, pg. 8266
CANAL+ FRANCE—See Vivendi SE; *Int'l*, pg. 8265
CANAL GLOBE, LTD.—See BIPROGY Inc.; *Int'l*, pg. 1045
CANAL+ GROUP—See Vivendi SE; *Int'l*, pg. 8265
CANALI S.P.A.; *Int'l*, pg. 1287
CANALI USA INC.—See Canali S.p.A.; *Int'l*, pg. 1287
CANAL JIMMY—See Vivendi SE; *Int'l*, pg. 8266
CANAL J—See Metropole Television SA; *Int'l*, pg. 4863
CANAL+ MADAGASCAR—See Vivendi SE; *Int'l*, pg. 8266
CANAL MARINE & INDUSTRIAL INC.—See Upper Lakes Group Inc.; *Int'l*, pg. 8093
CANAL MUNDO RADIO CATALUNA S.L.—See RCS MediaGroup S.p.A.; *Int'l*, pg. 6229
CANAL+ NORWAY—See Vivendi SE; *Int'l*, pg. 8266
CANAL+ OVERSEAS PRODUCTIONS—See Vivendi SE; *Int'l*, pg. 8266
CANAL+ OVERSEAS S.A.S.—See Vivendi SE; *Int'l*, pg. 8266
CANAL PARTNERS, LLC; *U.S. Private*, pg. 733
CANAL PAYMENT SERVICE, LTD.—See BIPROGY Inc.; *Int'l*, pg. 1045
CANAL+ REGIE—See Vivendi SE; *Int'l*, pg. 8266
CANAL RURAL SATELITAL S.A.—See Grupo Clarin S.A.; *Int'l*, pg. 3125
CANAL+ SA—See Vivendi SE; *Int'l*, pg. 8266
CANAL SATELITE DIGITAL S.L—See Vivendi SE; *Int'l*, pg. 8265
CANAL+ SENEGAL—See Vivendi SE; *Int'l*, pg. 8266
CANAL+ SWEDEN—See Vivendi SE; *Int'l*, pg. 8266
CANAL VENTURES, LTD.—See BIPROGY Inc.; *Int'l*, pg. 1045
CANAL WALK SHOPPING CENTRE—See Hyprop Investments Limited; *Int'l*, pg. 3554
CANAL WOOD LLC; *U.S. Private*, pg. 733
CANAL WOOD LLC—See Canal Wood LLC; *U.S. Private*, pg. 733
CANAL WOOD LLC—See Canal Wood LLC; *U.S. Private*, pg. 733
CANALWORKS ADVERTISING; *U.S. Private*, pg. 733
CANAMAX ENERGY LTD.—See Edge Natural Resources LLC; *U.S. Private*, pg. 1334
CANAM-BRIDGE—See AIP, LLC; *U.S. Private*, pg. 134
CANAM-BRIDGE—See Placements CMI Inc.; *Int'l*, pg. 5887
CANAM COAL CORP.; *Int'l*, pg. 1287
CAN-AM COMMUNICATIONS, INC.—See Dycom Industries, Inc.; *U.S. Public*, pg. 698

CAN CAPITAL, INC.

CANAMERA ENERGY METALS CORP.; *Int'l*, pg. 1287
CAN-AMERI AGRI CO. INC.; *Int'l*, pg. 1276
CANAMEX GOLD CORP.; *Int'l*, pg. 1287
CANAM GROUP INC.—See AIP, LLC; *U.S. Private*, pg. 134
CANAM GROUP INC.—See Placements CMI Inc.; *Int'l*, pg. 5887
CANAM STEEL CORPORATION—See AIP, LLC; *U.S. Private*, pg. 134
CANAM STEEL CORPORATION—See Placements CMI Inc.; *Int'l*, pg. 5887
THE CANANDAIGUA NATIONAL BANK & TRUST COMPANY—See Canandaigua National Corporation; *U.S. Public*, pg. 428
CANANDAIGUA NATIONAL CORPORATION; *U.S. Public*, pg. 428
CANAN KOZMETIK SANAYI VE TICARET A.S.—See L'Oreal S.A.; *Int'l*, pg. 4378
CANAN TUKETIM URUNLERI PAZARLAMA A.S.—See L'Oreal S.A.; *Int'l*, pg. 4378
CANAQUEST MEDICAL CORP; *Int'l*, pg. 1287
CANARA BANK SECURITIES LTD.—See Canara Bank; *Int'l*, pg. 1287
CANARA BANK; *Int'l*, pg. 1287
CANARA BANK (TANZANIA) LTD.—See Canara Bank; *Int'l*, pg. 1287
CANARA ROBECCO ASSET MANAGEMENT COMPANY LTD.—See Canara Bank; *Int'l*, pg. 1287
CANARC RESOURCES CORP.; *Int'l*, pg. 1287
CANARE CORPORATION OF AMERICA—See Canare Electric Co., Ltd.; *Int'l*, pg. 1288
CANARE CORPORATION OF KOREA—See Canare Electric Co., Ltd.; *Int'l*, pg. 1288
CANARE CORPORATION OF TAIWAN—See Canare Electric Co., Ltd.; *Int'l*, pg. 1288
CANARE CORPORATION—See Canare Electric Co., Ltd.; *Int'l*, pg. 1288
CANARE ELECTRIC CO., LTD.; *Int'l*, pg. 1288
CANARE ELECTRIC CORPORATION OF TIANJIN CO., LTD.—See Canare Electric Co., Ltd.; *Int'l*, pg. 1288
CANARE ELECTRIC INDIA PRIVATE LIMITED—See Canare Electric Co., Ltd.; *Int'l*, pg. 1288
CANARE ELECTRIC (SHANGHAI) CO., LTD.—See Canare Electric Co., Ltd.; *Int'l*, pg. 1288
CANARE EUROPE GMBH—See Canare Electric Co., Ltd.; *Int'l*, pg. 1288
CANARE FRANCE SAS—See Canare Electric Co., Ltd.; *Int'l*, pg. 1288
CANARE MIDDLE EAST FZCO—See Canare Electric Co., Ltd.; *Int'l*, pg. 1288
CANARE SINGAPORE PRIVATE LIMITED—See Canare Electric Co., Ltd.; *Int'l*, pg. 1288
CANARGO ENERGY CORPORATION; *Int'l*, pg. 1288
CANARGO GEORGIA LTD—See CanArgo Energy Corporation; *Int'l*, pg. 1288
CANARGO LIMITED—See CanArgo Energy Corporation; *Int'l*, pg. 1288
CANARIABIO INC.; *Int'l*, pg. 1288
CANARIACO COPPER PERU S.A.—See Candente Copper Corp.; *Int'l*, pg. 1289
CAN ART ALUMINUM EXTRUSION L.P.—See TorQuest Partners Inc.; *Int'l*, pg. 7830
CANAR TELECOMMUNICATIONS CO. LTD.—See Bank of Khartoum; *Int'l*, pg. 845
CANARY BLOMSTROM INSURANCE AGENCY, INC.—See GTCR LLC; *U.S. Private*, pg. 1803
CANARY RESOURCES, INC.; *U.S. Private*, pg. 733
CANARYS AUTOMATIONS LIMITED; *Int'l*, pg. 1288
CANARY WHARF GROUP PLC—See Brookfield Corporation; *Int'l*, pg. 1187
CANARY WHARF GROUP PLC—See Qatar Investment Authority; *Int'l*, pg. 6134
CANASIL RESOURCES INC.; *Int'l*, pg. 1288
CAN AS—See CAN (Offshore) Ltd; *Int'l*, pg. 1275
CANATURE HEALTH TECHNOLOGY GROUP CO., LTD.; *Int'l*, pg. 1288
CANBANK COMPUTER SERVICES LIMITED—See Canara Bank; *Int'l*, pg. 1287
CANBANK FACTORS LIMITED—See Canara Bank; *Int'l*, pg. 1287
CANBANK FINANCIAL SERVICES LIMITED—See Canara Bank; *Int'l*, pg. 1287
CANBANK VENTURE CAPITAL FUND LIMITED—See Canara Bank; *Int'l*, pg. 1287
CANBAS CO., LTD.; *Int'l*, pg. 1288
CAN B CORP.; *U.S. Public*, pg. 428
CANBERRA PRIVATE HOSPITAL PTY. LTD.—See Evolution Healthcare Pty. Ltd.; *Int'l*, pg. 2572
CAN-BOW MOTORS LTD.; *Int'l*, pg. 1276
CAN BRIANS 2, S.A.—See ACS, Actividades de Construccion y Servicios, S.A.; *Int'l*, pg. 110
CANBRIDGE PHARMACEUTICALS INC.; *Int'l*, pg. 1288
CANBURG LIMITED; *Int'l*, pg. 1288
CANBY TELECOM; *U.S. Private*, pg. 733
CAN-CAL RESOURCES LTD.; *Int'l*, pg. 1276
CAN CAPITAL, INC.; *U.S. Private*, pg. 732
CAN CAPITAL, INC.—See CAN Capital, Inc.; *U.S. Private*, pg. 732

CAN CAPITAL, INC.

CANCAP PHARMACEUTICAL LTD.—See Sinphar Pharmaceutical Co., Ltd.; *Int'l*, pg. 6956
CANCARB LIMITED—See Tokai Carbon Co., Ltd.; *Int'l*, pg. 7778
CAN-CELL INDUSTRIES INC.; *Int'l*, pg. 1276
CANCER CAPITAL CORP.; *U.S. Public*, pg. 428
THE CANCER CARE CENTER OF NORTH FLORIDA, LLC—See HCA Healthcare, Inc.; *U.S. Public*, pg. 1012
CANCER CARE, INC.; *U.S. Private*, pg. 733
CANCER CARE KENYA LIMITED—See Healthcare Global Enterprises Limited; *Int'l*, pg. 3304
CANCER CENTERS OF SOUTHWEST OKLAHOMA; *U.S. Private*, pg. 733
CANCER CENTRE LONDON LLP—See Tenet Healthcare Corporation; *U.S. Public*, pg. 2001
CANCER CENTRE PTE. LTD.—See Singapore Medical Group Limited; *Int'l*, pg. 6940
CANCER DIAGNOSTICS, INC.; *U.S. Private*, pg. 733
CANCER FUND OF AMERICA, INC.; *U.S. Private*, pg. 733
CANCER GENETICS ITALIA, S.R.L.—See Vyant Bio, Inc.; *U.S. Public*, pg. 2315
CANCER PREVENTION PHARMACEUTICALS, INC.—See Panbela Therapeutics, Inc.; *U.S. Public*, pg. 1635
CANCER TREATMENT CENTERS OF AMERICA—See City of Hope National Medical Center; *U.S. Private*, pg. 906
CANCER TREATMENT HOLDINGS, INC.; *U.S. Public*, pg. 428
CANCER TREATMENT SERVICES INTERNATIONAL, INC.—See Siemens Aktiengesellschaft; *Int'l*, pg. 6894
CANCO GENERAL CONTRACTORS INC.; *U.S. Private*, pg. 733
CANCOM A+D IT SOLUTIONS GMBH—See CANCOM SE; *Int'l*, pg. 1289
CANCOM FINANCIAL SERVICES GMBH—See CANCOM SE; *Int'l*, pg. 1288
CANCOM ICT SERVICE GMBH—See CANCOM SE; *Int'l*, pg. 1288
CANCOM, INC.—See CANCOM SE; *Int'l*, pg. 1289
CANCOM IT SOLUTIONS GMBH—See CANCOM SE; *Int'l*, pg. 1288
CANCOM LTD.—See Telefonica, S.A.; *Int'l*, pg. 7536
CANCOM NSG GIS GMBH—See CANCOM SE; *Int'l*, pg. 1288
CANCOM NSG GMBH—See CANCOM SE; *Int'l*, pg. 1289
CANCOM ON LINE GMBH—See CANCOM SE; *Int'l*, pg. 1289
CANCOM PHYSICAL INFRASTRUCTURE GMBH—See CANCOM SE; *Int'l*, pg. 1289
CANCOM PUBLIC BV—See CANCOM SE; *Int'l*, pg. 1289
CANCOM PUBLIC GMBH—See CANCOM SE; *Int'l*, pg. 1289
CANCOM SE; *Int'l*, pg. 1288
CANCOM SYSDAT GMBH—See CANCOM SE; *Int'l*, pg. 1289
CANCOM UK LIMITED—See Telefonica, S.A.; *Int'l*, pg. 7536
CANCOM VVM GMBH—See CANCOM SE; *Int'l*, pg. 1289
CAN CORPORATION OF AMERICA; *U.S. Private*, pg. 732
CANCOS TILE CORP.; *U.S. Private*, pg. 733
CANDAX ENERGY INC.; *Int'l*, pg. 1289
CANDAX MADAGASCAR LTD.—See Candax Energy Inc.; *Int'l*, pg. 1289
CANDEAL CO., LTD.; *Int'l*, pg. 1289
CANDECO CONFEKTYR AB—See Orkla ASA; *Int'l*, pg. 5638
CANDELA CORPORATION—See Apax Partners LLP; *Int'l*, pg. 506
CANDELA CORPORATION; *U.S. Private*, pg. 733
CANDELA FRANCE SARL—See Apax Partners LLP; *Int'l*, pg. 506
CANDELA INTERNATIONAL CO., LTD.—See Onward Holdings Co., Ltd.; *Int'l*, pg. 5592
CANDELA ITALIA S.R.L.—See Apax Partners LLP; *Int'l*, pg. 506
CANDELA LASER (DEUTSCHLAND) GMBH—See Apax Partners LLP; *Int'l*, pg. 506
CANDELARIA MINING CORP.; *Int'l*, pg. 1289
CANDELA SALES COMPANY INC.; *U.S. Private*, pg. 733
CANDELIS, INC.—See Candle Acquisition Corporation; *U.S. Private*, pg. 733
CANDELIS - INDIA—See Candle Acquisition Corporation; *U.S. Private*, pg. 733
CANDEL THERAPEUTICS, INC.; *U.S. Public*, pg. 428
CANDENTE COPPER CORP.; *Int'l*, pg. 1289
CANDERA GMBH—See CELSYS, Inc.; *Int'l*, pg. 1396
CAN-DER CONSTRUCTION LTD; *Int'l*, pg. 1276
CANDEREL COMMERCIAL SERVICES INC.—See Canderel Management Inc.; *Int'l*, pg. 1289
CANDEREL MANAGEMENT INC.; *Int'l*, pg. 1289
CANDEREL PACIFIC INC.—See Canderel Management Inc.; *Int'l*, pg. 1289
CANDEREL RESIDENTIAL INC.—See Canderel Management Inc.; *Int'l*, pg. 1289
CANDERM GENERAL PARTNERSHIP—See Sanofi; *Int'l*, pg. 6547
CANDESCENT PARTNERS, LLC; *U.S. Private*, pg. 733

CANDESCENT SOFTBASE, LLC—See Brooke Private Equity Associates Management LLC; *U.S. Private*, pg. 663
CANDESCENT SOFTBASE, LLC—See Candescent Partners, LLC; *U.S. Private*, pg. 733
CANDESCENT SOFTBASE, LLC—See Harbert Management Corporation; *U.S. Private*, pg. 1858
CANDIA—See SODIAAL International SAS; *Int'l*, pg. 7047
CANDID COLOR PHOTOGRAPHY, INC.—See Candid Color Systems, Inc.; *U.S. Private*, pg. 733
CANDID COLOR SYSTEMS, INC.; *U.S. Private*, pg. 733
CANDID PARTNERS, LLC—See McKinsey & Company, Inc.; *U.S. Private*, pg. 2639
CANDLE ACQUISITION CORPORATION; *U.S. Private*, pg. 733
CANDLE IT & T RECRUITMENT LIMITED—See Ignite Limited; *Int'l*, pg. 3602
CANDLE IT & T RECRUITMENT PTY LIMITED—See Ignite Limited; *Int'l*, pg. 3602
CANDLE LAMP COMPANY, LLC—See Compass Diversified Holdings; *U.S. Public*, pg. 559
CANDLE-LITE—See Lancaster Colony Corporation; *U.S. Public*, pg. 1291
CANDLE SCIENCE INC.; *U.S. Private*, pg. 733
CANDLE WARMERS ETC. INC.; *U.S. Private*, pg. 733
CANDLEWOOD HOTEL COMPANY, INC.; *U.S. Public*, pg. 428
CAN DO CO., LTD.—See AEON Co., Ltd.; *Int'l*, pg. 177
CAN DON HYDRO POWER JOINT STOCK COMPANY; *Int'l*, pg. 1276
CANDO RAIL SERVICES LTD.—See TorQuest Partners Inc.; *Int'l*, pg. 7830
CANDOUR TECHTEX LTD.; *Int'l*, pg. 1289
CANDOVER INVESTMENTS, PLC; *Int'l*, pg. 1289
CANDOVER SERVICES LIMITED—See Candover Investments plc; *Int'l*, pg. 1289
CANDRAFT DETAILING, INC.; *Int'l*, pg. 1289
CANDRIAM INVESTORS GROUP-BELGIUM—See New York Life Insurance Company; *U.S. Private*, pg. 2911
CANDRIAM INVESTORS GROUP-FRANCE—See New York Life Insurance Company; *U.S. Private*, pg. 2911
CANDRIAM INVESTORS GROUP-GERMANY—See New York Life Insurance Company; *U.S. Private*, pg. 2911
CANDRIAM INVESTORS GROUP-ITALY—See New York Life Insurance Company; *U.S. Private*, pg. 2911
CANDRIAM INVESTORS GROUP—See New York Life Insurance Company; *U.S. Private*, pg. 2911
CANDRIAM INVESTORS GROUP-SPAIN—See New York Life Insurance Company; *U.S. Private*, pg. 2911
CANDRIAM INVESTORS GROUP-SWITZERLAND—See New York Life Insurance Company; *U.S. Private*, pg. 2911
CANDRIAM INVESTORS GROUP-THE NETHERLANDS—See New York Life Insurance Company; *U.S. Private*, pg. 2911
CANDU-ARGENTINA—See AtkinsRealis Group Inc.; *Int'l*, pg. 671
CANDU-CHINA—See AtkinsRealis Group Inc.; *Int'l*, pg. 671
CANDU ENERGY INC.—See AtkinsRealis Group Inc.; *Int'l*, pg. 671
CANDY DOMESTIC APPLIANCES LIMITED—See Haier Smart Home Co., Ltd.; *Int'l*, pg. 3210
CANDY FORD, INC.; *U.S. Private*, pg. 734
CANDY HOOVER AG—See Haier Smart Home Co., Ltd.; *Int'l*, pg. 3209
CANDY HOOVER AUSTRIA GMBH—See Haier Smart Home Co., Ltd.; *Int'l*, pg. 3209
CANDY HOOVER BELGIUM NV—See Haier Smart Home Co., Ltd.; *Int'l*, pg. 3209
CANDY HOOVER CR S.R.O.—See Haier Smart Home Co., Ltd.; *Int'l*, pg. 3209
CANDY HOOVER ELECTRODOMESTICOS SA—See Haier Smart Home Co., Ltd.; *Int'l*, pg. 3210
CANDY HOOVER GMBH—See Haier Smart Home Co., Ltd.; *Int'l*, pg. 3210
CANDY HOOVER GROUP S.R.L. - BRUGHERIO PLANT—See Haier Smart Home Co., Ltd.; *Int'l*, pg. 3210
CANDY HOOVER GROUP S.R.L.—See Haier Smart Home Co., Ltd.; *Int'l*, pg. 3209
CANDY HOOVER HUNGARY KFT.—See Haier Smart Home Co., Ltd.; *Int'l*, pg. 3210
CANDY HOOVER NEDERLAND B.V.—See Haier Smart Home Co., Ltd.; *Int'l*, pg. 3210
CANDY HOOVER POLSKA SP. Z O.O.—See Haier Smart Home Co., Ltd.; *Int'l*, pg. 3210
CANDY HOOVER PORTUGAL, LTDA.—See Haier Smart Home Co., Ltd.; *Int'l*, pg. 3210
CANDY HOOVER ROMANIA S. R. L.—See Haier Smart Home Co., Ltd.; *Int'l*, pg. 3210
CANDYKING DANMARK A/S—See Cloetta AB; *Int'l*, pg. 1660
CANDYKING FINLAND OY—See Cloetta AB; *Int'l*, pg. 1660
CANDYKING HOLDING AB—See Cloetta AB; *Int'l*, pg. 1660
CANDYKING NORGE AS—See Cloetta AB; *Int'l*, pg. 1660

CORPORATE AFFILIATIONS

CANDYKING POLAND SP. Z O.O.—See Cloetta AB; *Int'l*, pg. 1661
CANDYKING SWEDEN AB—See Cloetta AB; *Int'l*, pg. 1661
CANDYKING UK LTD.—See Cloetta AB; *Int'l*, pg. 1661
CANDYM ENTERPRISES LTD.; *Int'l*, pg. 1289
CANDYMIX IRELAND LTD.—See Cloetta AB; *Int'l*, pg. 1661
CANDYRIFIC LLC; *U.S. Private*, pg. 734
CANDYS CAMPERS, INC.—See Redwood Capital Investments, LLC; *U.S. Private*, pg. 3380
CANDY TOY - INDUSTRIA E COMERCIO DE ALIMENTOS E PLASTICOS LTDA; *Int'l*, pg. 1289
CANDYWAREHOUSE.COM; *U.S. Private*, pg. 734
CANEEL BAY—See Chow Tai Fook Enterprises Limited; *Int'l*, pg. 1585
THE CANEEL GROUP, LLC; *U.S. Private*, pg. 4004
CANEFCO LIMITED; *Int'l*, pg. 1289
CANE ISLAND, LLC—See D.R. Horton, Inc.; *U.S. Public*, pg. 619
CANELSON DRILLING (US), INC.—See Ensign Energy Services Inc.; *Int'l*, pg. 2447
CANEM HOLDINGS LTD.—See Bird Construction Inc.; *Int'l*, pg. 1047
CANEO SA; *Int'l*, pg. 1289
CANERDAY BELFSKY & ARROYO ARCHITECTS INC.; *U.S. Private*, pg. 734
CANERECTOR INC.; *Int'l*, pg. 1289
CANEVEL SPUMANTI S.P.A.—See MASI Agricola S.p.A.; *Int'l*, pg. 4721
CANEX METALS INC.; *Int'l*, pg. 1290
CANEY FORK ELECTRIC COOP; *U.S. Private*, pg. 734
CAN-FER UTILITY SERVICES, LLC—See Quanta Services, Inc.; *U.S. Public*, pg. 1750
CANFIELD & JOSEPH, INC.; *U.S. Private*, pg. 734
CANFIELD & TACK INCORPORATED; *U.S. Private*, pg. 734
CANFIELD TECHNOLOGIES, LLC—See Gen Cap America, Inc.; *U.S. Private*, pg. 1659
CAN FIN HOMES LIMITED—See Canara Bank; *Int'l*, pg. 1287
CAN-FITE BIOPHARMA LTD.; *Int'l*, pg. 1276
CANFOR CORPORATION - CAMDEN PLANT—See Canfor Corporation; *Int'l*, pg. 1290
CANFOR CORPORATION - CANAL FLATS SAWMILL FACILITY—See Canfor Corporation; *Int'l*, pg. 1290
CANFOR CORPORATION - CHETWYND SAWMILL FACILITY—See Canfor Corporation; *Int'l*, pg. 1290
CANFOR CORPORATION - FORT ST JOHN SAWMILL FACILITY—See Canfor Corporation; *Int'l*, pg. 1290
CANFOR CORPORATION - GRAHAM PLANT—See Canfor Corporation; *Int'l*, pg. 1290
CANFOR CORPORATION - INTERCONTINENTAL PULP (CPLP) FACILITY—See Canfor Corporation; *Int'l*, pg. 1290
CANFOR CORPORATION - ISLE PIERRE SAWMILL FACILITY—See Canfor Corporation; *Int'l*, pg. 1290
CANFOR CORPORATION - MARION PLANT—See Canfor Corporation; *Int'l*, pg. 1291
CANFOR CORPORATION-POLAR DIVISION—See Canfor Corporation; *Int'l*, pg. 1291
CANFOR CORPORATION - POLAR SAWMILL FACILITY—See Canfor Corporation; *Int'l*, pg. 1291
CANFOR CORPORATION - PRINCE GEORGE PULP & PAPER (CPLP) FACILITY—See Canfor Corporation; *Int'l*, pg. 1291
CANFOR CORPORATION - QUESNEL SAWMILL FACILITY—See Canfor Corporation; *Int'l*, pg. 1291
CANFOR CORPORATION; *Int'l*, pg. 1290
CANFOR EUROPE—See Canfor Corporation; *Int'l*, pg. 1291
CANFOR GEORGIA-PACIFIC JAPAN CORPORATION—See Canfor Corporation; *Int'l*, pg. 1291
CANFOR GEORGIA-PACIFIC JAPAN CORPORATION—See Koch Industries, Inc.; *U.S. Private*, pg. 2327
CANFOR JAPAN CORPORATION—See Canfor Corporation; *Int'l*, pg. 1291
CANFOR PANEL & FIBRE—See Canfor Corporation; *Int'l*, pg. 1290
CANFOR PULP PRODUCTS INC.; *Int'l*, pg. 1291
CANG BAO TIAN XIA INTERNATIONAL ART TRADE CENTER, INC.; *Int'l*, pg. 1291
CANGENE BIOPHARMA, INC.—See Emergent BioSolutions Inc.; *U.S. Public*, pg. 739
CANGEN HOLDINGS, INC.—See Hillenbrand, Inc.; *U.S. Public*, pg. 1037
CAN GEOTECHNICAL LTD—See CAN (Offshore) Ltd; *Int'l*, pg. 1276
CANGGANG RAILWAY LIMITED; *Int'l*, pg. 1291
CANGIANO SONEPAR SPA—See Sonepar S.A.; *Int'l*, pg. 7092
CAN GLOBAL ANGOLA LDA—See CAN (Offshore) Ltd; *Int'l*, pg. 1276
CANGO INC.; *Int'l*, pg. 1291
CANGRO INDUSTRIES INC.—See Applied Industrial Technologies, Inc.; *U.S. Public*, pg. 171

COMPANY NAME INDEX

CANGZHOU DAHUA GROUP CO., LTD.—See China National Chemical Corporation; *Int'l*, pg. 1526
CANGZHOU MINGZHU PLASTIC CO., LTD.—See China National Chemical Corporation; *Int'l*, pg. 1526
CANGZHOU SUNGWOO HITECH AUTOMOBILE PARTS CO., LTD.—See Sungwoo Hitech Co., Ltd.; *Int'l*, pg. 7315
CAN HYGIENE SPA—See Hygianis SpA; *Int'l*, pg. 3549
CANICA AS; *Int'l*, pg. 1291
CANICKEL MINING LIMITED; *Int'l*, pg. 1291
CANIDIUM, LLC; *U.S. Private*, pg. 734
CANINE COMPANIONS FOR INDEPENDENCE, INC.; *U.S. Private*, pg. 734
CANINE FENCE COS., INC.—See Radio Systems Corporation; *U.S. Private*, pg. 3344
CANJET AIRLINES LTD.—See I.M.P. Group International Inc.; *Int'l*, pg. 3566
CANKARJEVA ZALOZBA - ZALOZNISTVO D.O.O.—See Mladinska knjiga Zalozba, d.d.; *Int'l*, pg. 5003
CANLAK COATINGS, INC—See SK Capital Partners, LP; *U.S. Private*, pg. 3679
CANLAN ICE SPORTS CORPORATION; *Int'l*, pg. 1291
CAN LINES INC.; *U.S. Private*, pg. 732
CANLINE SYSTEMS B.V.—See XANO Industri AB; *Int'l*, pg. 8519
CANLINE USA CORPORATION—See XANO Industri AB; *Int'l*, pg. 8519
CANMAX TECHNOLOGIES CO., LTD.; *Int'l*, pg. 1291
CAN MIDDLE EAST L.L.C.—See CAN (Offshore) Ltd; *Int'l*, pg. 1276
CANNA 8 INVESTMENT TRUST; *Int'l*, pg. 1291
CANNABINOID BIOSCIENCES, INC.; *U.S. Private*, pg. 734
CANNABIS BIOSCIENCE INTERNATIONAL HOLDINGS, INC.; *U.S. Public*, pg. 428
THE CANNABIS DEPOT HOLDING CORP.; *U.S. Private*, pg. 4004
CANNABIS POLAND S.A.; *Int'l*, pg. 1291
CANNABIS SATIVA, INC.; *U.S. Public*, pg. 428
CANNABIS SUISSE CORP; *Int'l*, pg. 1292
CANNABIST CO HOLDINGS INC.; *U.S. Public*, pg. 429
CANNABIX TECHNOLOGIES INC.; *Int'l*, pg. 1292
CANNABUSINESS GROUP, INC.; *U.S. Private*, pg. 734
CANNA CABANA INC.—See High Tide, Inc.; *Int'l*, pg. 0000
CANNA CLINICS PTY. LTD.—See Epsilon Healthcare Ltd.; *Int'l*, pg. 2466
CANNA CORP; *U.S. Private*, pg. 734
CANNADOC HEALTH PTY. LTD.—See Vitura Health Limited; *Int'l*, pg. 8264
CANNAE HOLDINGS, INC.; *U.S. Public*, pg. 429
CANNAGISTICS, INC.; *U.S. Public*, pg. 430
CANNA-GLOBAL ACQUISITION CORP.; *U.S. Public*, pg. 428
CANNAGROW HOLDINGS, INC.; *U.S. Public*, pg. 430
CANNAMATRIX, INC.; *U.S. Private*, pg. 734
CANNAMED ENTERPRISES, INC.; *U.S. Private*, pg. 734
CANNAMERICA BRANDS CORP; *Int'l*, pg. 1292
CANN AMERICAN CORP; *U.S. Private*, pg. 734
CANNAMM LIMITED PARTNERSHIP—See Laboratory Corporation of America Holdings; *U.S. Public*, pg. 1285
CANNAPHARMARX, INC; *Int'l*, pg. 1292
CANNAPOWDER, INC.; *U.S. Public*, pg. 430
CANNARA BIOTECH, INC.; *Int'l*, pg. 1292
CANNATA'S CORPORATION; *U.S. Private*, pg. 734
CANNATA'S SUPER MARKET, INC.—See Cannata's Corporation; *U.S. Private*, pg. 734
CANNAWAKE CORPORATION—See American Green, Inc.; *U.S. Public*, pg. 103
CANNAWORLD VENTURES INC.; *Int'l*, pg. 1292
CANNDESCENT LLC; *U.S. Private*, pg. 734
CANNDOC LTD.—See Intercure Ltd.; *Int'l*, pg. 3739
CANNELLA INSURANCE SERVICES INC.—See Achieva Credit Union; *U.S. Private*, pg. 58
CANNERY CASINO RESORTS, LLC; *U.S. Private*, pg. 734
THE CANNERY HOTEL & CASINO, LLC—See Boyd Gaming Corporation; *U.S. Public*, pg. 378
CANNES MARIA AMENAGEMENT SAS—See VINCI S.A.; *Int'l*, pg. 8213
CANN GLOBAL LIMITED; *Int'l*, pg. 1291
CANNGROS APS—See DanCann Pharma A/S; *Int'l*, pg. 1958
CANN GROUP LIMITED; *Int'l*, pg. 1291
CANNIBBLE FOODTECH LTD.; *Int'l*, pg. 1292
CANNIMED LTD.—See Aurora Cannabis Inc.; *Int'l*, pg. 713
CANNINDAH RESOURCES LIMITED; *Int'l*, pg. 1292
CANNINES SUPPLIES DE MEXICO S. DE R.L. DE C.V.—See Spectrum Brands Holdings, Inc.; *U.S. Public*, pg. 1915
CANNING BASIN OIL LIMITED—See Emperor Energy Limited; *Int'l*, pg. 2386
CANNING GUMM LLC—See Element Solutions Inc.; *U.S. Public*, pg. 725
CANNING SHOES, INC.; *U.S. Private*, pg. 734
CANN-IS CAPITAL CORP.; *Int'l*, pg. 1291
CANNIS, INC.; *U.S. Private*, pg. 734
CANNMART INC.—See Simply Solventless Concentrates Ltd.; *Int'l*, pg. 6934

CANNOCK CHASE B.V.—See ARCADIS N.V.; *Int'l*, pg. 541
CANNOCK GATES LTD.—See ARGENT INDUSTRIAL LIMITED; *Int'l*, pg. 560
CANNON ASSET MANAGERS PROPRIETARY LIMITED—See The Bidvest Group Limited; *Int'l*, pg. 7623
CANNONAU CORP.; *U.S. Public*, pg. 430
CANNON AUTOMOTIVE GROUP, INC.; *U.S. Private*, pg. 734
CANNONBALL; *U.S. Private*, pg. 735
CANNON COUNTY KNIT MILLS, INC.; *U.S. Private*, pg. 734
CANNONDALE BICYCLE CORPORATION—See Dorel Industries, Inc.; *Int'l*, pg. 2176
CANNONDALE INVESTMENTS, INC.—See GTCR LLC; *U.S. Private*, pg. 1804
CANNONDALE JAPAN KK—See Dorel Industries, Inc.; *Int'l*, pg. 2176
CANNON DESIGN, INC.; *U.S. Private*, pg. 734
CANNON ENTERPRISES INC.; *U.S. Private*, pg. 735
CANNON EQUIPMENT COMPANY—See IMI plc; *Int'l*, pg. 3624
CANNON FABRICATION, INC.—See Vibration Mountings & Controls, Inc.; *U.S. Private*, pg. 4376
CANNON GROUP ENTERPRISES, LLC—See Charlesbank Capital Partners, LLC; *U.S. Private*, pg. 854
THE CANNON GROUP INC.; *U.S. Private*, pg. 4004
CANNON HYGIENE AUSTRALIA PTY LIMITED—See OCS Group Limited; *Int'l*, pg. 5521
CANNON HYGIENE INTERNATIONAL LIMITED—See Rentokil Initial plc; *Int'l*, pg. 6286
CANNON HYGIENE LTDA—See OCS Group Limited; *Int'l*, pg. 5521
CANNON HYGIENE PORTUGAL LDA—See Rentokil Initial plc; *Int'l*, pg. 6286
CANNON HYGIENE (S.A.) (PTY) LIMITED—See OCS Group Limited; *Int'l*, pg. 5521
CANNON HYGIENE SA—See Rentokil Initial plc; *Int'l*, pg. 6286
CANNON INDUSTRIES LTD.—See Whirlpool Corporation; *U.S. Public*, pg. 2367
CANNON IV INC.—See Oval Partners; *U.S. Private*, pg. 3052
CANNON MUSKEGON CORPORATION—See Berkshire Hathaway Inc.; *U.S. Public*, pg. 314
CANNON PEST CONTROL—See Arrow Exterminators Inc.; *U.S. Private*, pg. 335
CANNON PILING LTD.—See Per Aarsleff Holding A/S; *Int'l*, pg. 5795
CANNON SLINE INC.—See The Halifax Group LLC; *U.S. Private*, pg. 4042
CANNON SLINE INDUSTRIAL, INC. - HOPEWELL DIVISION—See The Halifax Group LLC; *U.S. Private*, pg. 4042
CANNON SLINE INDUSTRIAL, INC. - MID ATLANTIC DIVISION—See The Halifax Group LLC; *U.S. Private*, pg. 4042
CANNON SLINE INDUSTRIAL, INC. - WILMINGTON DIVISION—See The Halifax Group LLC; *U.S. Private*, pg. 4042
CANNON SOLUTIONS—See IMI plc; *Int'l*, pg. 3624
CANNON ST. (H.C.C.) LIMITED—See Co-operative Group Limited; *Int'l*, pg. 1679
CANNON SUPPLY, INC.—See Leonard Green & Partners, L.P.; *U.S. Private*, pg. 2429
CANNON & WENDT ELECTRIC CO.; *U.S. Private*, pg. 734
CANNORDIC A/S—See CS Medica A/S; *Int'l*, pg. 1861
CANNOVUM CANNABIS AG; *Int'l*, pg. 1292
CANNPAL ANIMAL THERAPEUTICS LIMITED—See AusCann Group Holdings Pty Ltd; *Int'l*, pg. 715
CANNTAB THERAPEUTICS LIMITED; *Int'l*, pg. 1292
CANNY ELEVATOR CO., LTD.; *Int'l*, pg. 1292
CANO CONTAINER CORP.; *U.S. Private*, pg. 735
CANOE EIT INCOME FUND—See Canoe Financial LP; *Int'l*, pg. 1292
CANOE FINANCIAL LP; *Int'l*, pg. 1292
CANOE MINING VENTURES CORP.—See Giyani Metals Corp.; *Int'l*, pg. 2982
CANOE VENTURES LLC—See Altice USA, Inc.; *U.S. Public*, pg. 87
CANOE VENTURES LLC—See Charter Communications, Inc.; *U.S. Public*, pg. 483
CANOE VENTURES LLC—See Comcast Corporation; *U.S. Public*, pg. 537
CANOE VENTURES LLC—See Cox Enterprises, Inc.; *U.S. Private*, pg. 1078
CAN (OFFSHORE) LTD; *Int'l*, pg. 1275
CANO HEALTH, INC.; *U.S. Public*, pg. 430
CANO HEALTH, LLC—See Cano Health, Inc.; *U.S. Public*, pg. 430
CANON ADVANCED TECHNOLOGIES TAIWAN, INC.—See Canon Inc.; *Int'l*, pg. 1295
CANON ANELVA CORPORATION—See Canon Inc.; *Int'l*, pg. 1292
CANON ARGENTINA S.A.—See Canon Inc.; *Int'l*, pg. 1297
CANON AUSTRALIA PTY. LTD.—See Canon Inc.; *Int'l*, pg. 1293

CANON INC.

CANON AUSTRIA GMBH—See Canon Inc.; *Int'l*, pg. 1294
CANON BELGIUM N.V./S.A.—See Canon Inc.; *Int'l*, pg. 1294
CANONBIE CONTRACTING LIMITED—See Aecon Group Inc.; *Int'l*, pg. 172
CANON BRETAGNE S.A.—See Canon Inc.; *Int'l*, pg. 1294
CANON BULGARIA EOOD—See Canon Inc.; *Int'l*, pg. 1294
CANON BUSINESS MACHINES (PHILIPPINES), INC.—See Canon Inc.; *Int'l*, pg. 1293
CANON BUSINESS PROCESS SERVICES, INC.—See Canon Inc.; *Int'l*, pg. 1297
CANON BUSINESS SUPPORT INC.—See Canon Inc.; *Int'l*, pg. 1293
CANON CANADA, INC.—See Canon Inc.; *Int'l*, pg. 1297
CANON CEE GMBH—See Canon Inc.; *Int'l*, pg. 1294
CANON CHEMICALS, INC.—See Canon Inc.; *Int'l*, pg. 1293
CANON CHILE S.A.—See Canon Inc.; *Int'l*, pg. 1297
CANON (CHINA) CO., LTD.—See Canon Inc.; *Int'l*, pg. 1292
CANON CITY DAILY RECORD—See Alden Global Capital LLC; *U.S. Private*, pg. 157
CANON COMPONENTS, INC.—See Canon Inc.; *Int'l*, pg. 1293
CANON CUSTOMER SUPPORT INC.—See Canon Inc.; *Int'l*, pg. 1296
CANON CZ SPOL S.R.O.—See Canon Inc.; *Int'l*, pg. 1294
CANON DALIAN BUSINESS MACHINES, INC.—See Canon Inc.; *Int'l*, pg. 1292
CANON DANMARK A/S—See Canon Inc.; *Int'l*, pg. 1294
CANON DEUTSCHLAND GMBH—See Canon Inc.; *Int'l*, pg. 1294
CANON DEVELOPMENT AMERICAS, INC.—See Canon Inc.; *Int'l*, pg. 1297
CANON DO BRASIL INDUSTRIAL E COMERCIO LIMITADA—See Canon Inc.; *Int'l*, pg. 1297
CANON EAST EUROPE VERTRIEBSGESELLSCHAFT MBH—See Canon Inc.; *Int'l*, pg. 1294
CAN-ONE BERHAD; *Int'l*, pg. 1276
CANON ECOLOGY INDUSTRY INC.—See Canon Inc.; *Int'l*, pg. 1293
CANON ELECTRONIC BUSINESS MACHINES (H.K.) CO., LTD.—See Canon Inc.; *Int'l*, pg. 1295
CANON ELECTRONICS BUSINESS SYSTEMS INC.—See Canon Inc.; *Int'l*, pg. 1293
CANON ELECTRONICS, INC.—See Canon Inc.; *Int'l*, pg. 1293
CANON ELECTRONICS VIETNAM CO., LTD.—See Canon Inc.; *Int'l*, pg. 1297
CANON ELECTRON TUBES & DEVICES CO., LTD.—See Canon Inc.; *Int'l*, pg. 1293
CANON EMIRATES LLC—See Canon Inc.; *Int'l*, pg. 1293
CANON ENGINEERING HONG KONG CO., LTD.—See Canon Inc.; *Int'l*, pg. 1295
CANON ESPANA, S.A.—See Canon Inc.; *Int'l*, pg. 1294
CANON EURASIA A.S.—See Canon Inc.; *Int'l*, pg. 1293
CANON EUROPA N.V.—See Canon Inc.; *Int'l*, pg. 1293
CANON EUROPE LTD.—See Canon Inc.; *Int'l*, pg. 1294
CAN-ONE (USA), INC.—See Can-One Berhad; *Int'l*, pg. 1276
CANON FINANCE AUSTRALIA PTY. LTD.—See Canon Inc.; *Int'l*, pg. 1293
CANON FINANCE NEW ZEALAND LTD.—See Canon Inc.; *Int'l*, pg. 1293
CANON FINANCIAL SERVICES, INC.—See Canon Inc.; *Int'l*, pg. 1297
CANON FINETECH INC. - FUKUI PLANT—See Canon Inc.; *Int'l*, pg. 1295
CANON FINETECH INC. - IBARAKI PLANT—See Canon Inc.; *Int'l*, pg. 1295
CANON FINETECH INC.—See Canon Inc.; *Int'l*, pg. 1295
CANON FINETECH NISCA INC.—See Canon Inc.; *Int'l*, pg. 1295
CANON FINETECH NISCA (SHENZHEN) INC.—See Canon Inc.; *Int'l*, pg. 1295
CANON FRANCE S.A.—See Canon Inc.; *Int'l*, pg. 1294
CANON GIESSEN GMBH—See Canon Inc.; *Int'l*, pg. 1294
CANON HI-TECH (THAILAND) LTD.—See Canon Inc.; *Int'l*, pg. 1293
CANON HONGKONG CO., LTD.—See Canon Inc.; *Int'l*, pg. 1295
CANON HUNGARIA KFT.—See Canon Inc.; *Int'l*, pg. 1294
CANONICAL GROUP LIMITED; *Int'l*, pg. 1298
CANONICAL USA INC.—See Canonical Group Limited; *Int'l*, pg. 1298
CANON IMAGING SYSTEMS INC.—See Canon Inc.; *Int'l*, pg. 1295
CANON INC.; *Int'l*, pg. 1292
CANON INC., TAIWAN—See Canon Inc.; *Int'l*, pg. 1295
CANON INDIA PVT. LTD.—See Canon Inc.; *Int'l*, pg. 1295
CANON INFORMATION AND IMAGING SOLUTIONS, INC.—See Canon Inc.; *Int'l*, pg. 1297
CANON INFORMATION TECHNOLOGIES PHILIPPINES, INC.—See Canon Inc.; *Int'l*, pg. 1295
CANON INFORMATION TECHNOLOGY SERVICES INC.—See Canon Inc.; *Int'l*, pg. 1297
CANON IRELAND BUSINESS EQUIPMENT LTD.—See Canon Inc.; *Int'l*, pg. 1293

CANON INC.

CANON (IRL) BUSINESS EQUIPMENT LTD.—See Canon Inc.; *Int'l*, pg. 1294
CANON ITALIA S.P.A.—See Canon Inc.; *Int'l*, pg. 1294
CANON ITS MEDICAL INC.—See Canon Inc.; *Int'l*, pg. 1296
CANON IT SOLUTIONS INC.—See Canon Inc.; *Int'l*, pg. 1296
CANON KOREA CONSUMER IMAGING INC.—See Canon Inc.; *Int'l*, pg. 1295
CANON LATIN AMERICA, INC.—See Canon Inc.; *Int'l*, pg. 1297
CANON LUXEMBOURG S.A.—See Canon Inc.; *Int'l*, pg. 1294
CANON MACHINERY (DALIAN) CO., LTD.—See Canon Inc.; *Int'l*, pg. 1295
CANON MACHINERY INC.—See Canon Inc.; *Int'l*, pg. 1295
CANON MACHINERY (MALAYSIA) SDN BHD.—See Canon Inc.; *Int'l*, pg. 1295
CANON MAILCOM MALAYSIA SDN. BHD.—See Canon Inc.; *Int'l*, pg. 1296
CANON MARKETING JAPAN INC.—See Canon Inc.; *Int'l*, pg. 1295
CANON MARKETING (MALAYSIA) SDN. BHD.—See Canon Inc.; *Int'l*, pg. 1295
CANON MARKETING (PHILIPPINES), INC.—See Canon Inc.; *Int'l*, pg. 1295
CANON MARKETING (TAIWAN) CO., LTD.—See Canon Inc.; *Int'l*, pg. 1295
CANON MARKETING (THAILAND) CO., LTD.—See Canon Inc.; *Int'l*, pg. 1295
CANON MARKETING VIETNAM COMPANY LIMITED—See Canon Inc.; *Int'l*, pg. 1297
CANON MEDICAL FINANCE CO., LTD.—See Canon Inc.; *Int'l*, pg. 1296
CANON MEDICAL SYSTEMS CORPORATION—See Canon Inc.; *Int'l*, pg. 1296
CANON MEDICAL SYSTEMS EUROPE B.V.—See Canon Inc.; *Int'l*, pg. 1296
CANON MEDICAL SYSTEMS USA, INC.—See Canon Inc.; *Int'l*, pg. 1296
CANON MEXICANA, S. DE R.L. DE C.V.—See Canon Inc.; *Int'l*, pg. 1297
CANON MIDDLE EAST, FZ-LLC—See Canon Inc.; *Int'l*, pg. 1294
CANON MJ IT GROUP HOLDINGS INC.—See Canon Inc.; *Int'l*, pg. 1296
CANON MOLD CO., LTD.—See Canon Inc.; *Int'l*, pg. 1296
CANON NEDERLAND N.V. - 'S-HERTOGENBOSCH—See Canon Inc.; *Int'l*, pg. 1294
CANON NEDERLAND N.V.—See Canon Inc.; *Int'l*, pg. 1294
CANON NEW ZEALAND LTD.—See Canon Inc.; *Int'l*, pg. 1293
CANON NORGE A.S.—See Canon Inc.; *Int'l*, pg. 1294
CANON NORTH-EAST OY—See Canon Inc.; *Int'l*, pg. 1294
CANON OPTICAL INDUSTRIAL EQUIPMENT SERVICE (SHANGHAI) INC.—See Canon Inc.; *Int'l*, pg. 1292
CANON OPTICAL INDUSTRIAL EQUIPMENT (SHANGHAI) INC.—See Canon Inc.; *Int'l*, pg. 1292
CANON OPTO (MALAYSIA) SDN. BHD.—See Canon Inc.; *Int'l*, pg. 1296
CANON OPTRON, INC.—See Canon Inc.; *Int'l*, pg. 1296
CANON OY—See Canon Inc.; *Int'l*, pg. 1294
CANON PANAMA, S.A.—See Canon Inc.; *Int'l*, pg. 1297
CANON POLSKA SP. Z O.O.—See Canon Inc.; *Int'l*, pg. 1294
CANON PORTUGAL S.A.—See Canon Inc.; *Int'l*, pg. 1295
CANON PRECISION INC.—See Canon Inc.; *Int'l*, pg. 1296
CANON PRINT SQUARE INC.—See Canon Inc.; *Int'l*, pg. 1296
CANON PRODUCTION PRINTING GERMANY GMBH & CO.KG—See Canon Inc.; *Int'l*, pg. 1296
CANON PRODUCTION PRINTING NETHERLANDS B.V.—See Canon Inc.; *Int'l*, pg. 1296
CANON PROFESSIONAL PRINTING—See Canon Inc.; *Int'l*, pg. 1293
CANON RECRUITING GROUP LLC; *U.S. Private*, pg. 735
CANON RESEARCH CENTRE FRANCE S.A.S.—See Canon Inc.; *Int'l*, pg. 1294
CANON RU LLC—See Canon Inc.; *Int'l*, pg. 1296
CANON SALES CO., INC.—See Canon Inc.; *Int'l*, pg. 1296
CANON (SCHWEIZ) AG - GLATTBRUGG—See Canon Inc.; *Int'l*, pg. 1294
CANON (SCHWEIZ) AG—See Canon Inc.; *Int'l*, pg. 1293
CANON SEMICONDUCTOR ENGINEERING KOREA INC.—See Canon Inc.; *Int'l*, pg. 1296
CANON SEMICONDUCTOR EQUIPMENT INC.—See Canon Inc.; *Int'l*, pg. 1296
CANON SEMICONDUCTOR EQUIPMENT TAIWAN, INC.—See Canon Inc.; *Int'l*, pg. 1296
CANON SINGAPORE PTE. LTD.—See Canon Inc.; *Int'l*, pg. 1296
CANON SLOVAKIA S.R.O.—See Canon Inc.; *Int'l*, pg. 1294
CANON SOFTWARE AMERICA, INC.—See Canon Inc.; *Int'l*, pg. 1296

CANON SOFTWARE, INC.—See Canon Inc.; *Int'l*, pg. 1296
CANON SOFTWARE INFORMATION SYSTEMS INC.—See Canon Inc.; *Int'l*, pg. 1296
CANON SOLUTIONS AMERICA, INC. - BURLINGTON—See Canon Inc.; *Int'l*, pg. 1297
CANON SOLUTIONS AMERICA, INC. - CHICAGO—See Canon Inc.; *Int'l*, pg. 1297
CANON SOLUTIONS AMERICA, INC. - GARDENA—See Canon Inc.; *Int'l*, pg. 1297
CANON SOLUTIONS AMERICA, INC. - SALT LAKE CITY—See Canon Inc.; *Int'l*, pg. 1297
CANON SOLUTIONS AMERICA, INC. - SCHAUMBURG—See Canon Inc.; *Int'l*, pg. 1297
CANON SOLUTIONS AMERICA, INC.—See Canon Inc.; *Int'l*, pg. 1297
CANON SOLUTIONS AMERICA, INC. - TRUMBULL—See Canon Inc.; *Int'l*, pg. 1297
CANON SOUTH AFRICA PTY. LTD.—See Canon Inc.; *Int'l*, pg. 1295
CANON (SUZHOU) INC.—See Canon Inc.; *Int'l*, pg. 1292
CANON SVENSKA AB—See Canon Inc.; *Int'l*, pg. 1295
CANON SYSTEM & SUPPORT—See Canon Inc.; *Int'l*, pg. 1296
CANON TECHNICAL INFORMATION SERVICES INC.—See Canon Inc.; *Int'l*, pg. 1296
CANON TECHNOLOGY EUROPE LTD—See Canon Inc.; *Int'l*, pg. 1294
CANON TOKKI CORPORATION—See Canon Inc.; *Int'l*, pg. 1296
CANON (U.K.) LTD.—See Canon Inc.; *Int'l*, pg. 1293
CANON UK—See Canon Inc.; *Int'l*, pg. 1293
CANON USA, INC.—See Canon Inc.; *Int'l*, pg. 1297
CANON U.S.A., INC.—See Canon Inc.; *Int'l*, pg. 1296
CANON USA, INC.—See Canon Inc.; *Int'l*, pg. 1297
CANON U.S. LIFE SCIENCES, INC.—See Canon Inc.; *Int'l*, pg. 1297
CANON VIETNAM CO., LTD.—See Canon Inc.; *Int'l*, pg. 1297
CANON VIRGINIA, INC.—See Canon Inc.; *Int'l*, pg. 1297
CANON WIND INC.—See Canon Inc.; *Int'l*, pg. 1297
CANON ZHONGSHAN BUSINESS MACHINES CO., LTD.—See Canon Inc.; *Int'l*, pg. 1292
CANON ZHUHAI, INC.—See Canon Inc.; *Int'l*, pg. 1292
CANOOCHEE ELECTRIC MEMBERSHIP CORPORATION; *U.S. Private*, pg. 735
CANOO INC.; *U.S. Public*, pg. 430
CANOPIUS BERMUDA LIMITED—See Centerbridge Partners, L.P.; *U.S. Private*, pg. 813
CANOPIUS GROUP LIMTED—See Centerbridge Partners, L.P.; *U.S. Private*, pg. 813
CANOPIUS MANAGING AGENTS LTD.—See Centerbridge Partners, L.P.; *U.S. Private*, pg. 813
CANOPIUS UNDERWRITING AGENCY INC.—See Centerbridge Partners, L.P.; *U.S. Private*, pg. 813
CANOPTEC INC.—See EssilorLuxottica SA; *Int'l*, pg. 2512
CANOPY FINANCE LIMITED; *Int'l*, pg. 1298
CANOPY FINANCIAL; *U.S. Private*, pg. 735
CANOPY GROWTH CORPORATION; *Int'l*, pg. 1298
CANOPY INC.; *U.S. Private*, pg. 735
CANOVA MANUFACTURING SDN. BHD.—See Engtex Group Berhad; *Int'l*, pg. 2436
CANOX CORPORATION; *Int'l*, pg. 1298
CANPAC SDN BHD—See Yee Lee Corporation Bhd.; *Int'l*, pg. 8575
CANPAC VIETNAM PTE LTD—See Yee Lee Corporation Bhd.; *Int'l*, pg. 8575
CANPAGES INC.—See Yellow Pages Limited; *Int'l*, pg. 8576
CANPANGO, S.A.—See ScanSource, Inc.; *U.S. Public*, pg. 1843
CANPLAS INDUSTRIES LTD.—See Aliaxis S.A./N.V.; *Int'l*, pg. 323
CANPLAS USA INC.—See Aliaxis S.A./N.V.; *Int'l*, pg. 323
CANPOTEX INTERNATIONAL PTE. LIMITED—See Nutrien Ltd.; *Int'l*, pg. 5493
CANPOTEX (JAPAN) LIMITED—See Nutrien Ltd.; *Int'l*, pg. 5493
CANPOTEX LIMITED—See Nutrien Ltd.; *Int'l*, pg. 5493
CANPRINT COMMUNICATIONS PTY LIMITED—See OPUS Group Limited; *Int'l*, pg. 5606
CANPRO CONSTRUCTION LTD.; *Int'l*, pg. 1298
CAN RECYCLING (S.A.) PTY LTD—See COCA-COLA EUROPACIFIC PARTNERS PLC; *Int'l*, pg. 1684
CANRIG DRILLING TECHNOLOGY, LTD.—See Nabors Industries Ltd.; *Int'l*, pg. 5118
CANRON WESTERN CONSTRUCTOR LP—See Supreme Group; *Int'l*, pg. 7340
CANRON WESTERN CONSTRUCTORS INC—See Supreme Group; *Int'l*, pg. 7341
CANROOF CORPORATION INC.—See IKO Enterprises Ltd.; *Int'l*, pg. 3612
CANSA PTY LTD.—See Momar, Inc.; *U.S. Private*, pg. 2767
CANSEL SURVEY EQUIPMENT, LTD.; *Int'l*, pg. 1298
CANSINO BIOLOGICS, INC.; *Int'l*, pg. 1298
CANSO CHEMICALS LIMITED—See Olin Corporation; *U.S. Public*, pg. 1570
CANSO CREDIT INCOME FUND; *Int'l*, pg. 1298

CORPORATE AFFILIATIONS

CANSO ENTERPRISES LTD.; *Int'l*, pg. 1298
CANSO FORD SALES; *Int'l*, pg. 1298
CANSON INC.—See Groupe Hamelin S.A.; *Int'l*, pg. 3104
CANSON SAS—See F.I.L.A. - Fabbrica Italiana Lapis ed Affini S.p.A.; *Int'l*, pg. 2596
CANSORTIUM, INC.; *U.S. Public*, pg. 430
CANSO SELECT OPPORTUNITIES CORP.; *Int'l*, pg. 1299
CANSOURCE, LLC—See Ares Management Corporation; *U.S. Public*, pg. 191
CANSOURCE, LLC—See Ontario Teachers' Pension Plan; *Int'l*, pg. 5590
CANSTAR RESOURCES INC.; *Int'l*, pg. 1299
CAN STRUCTURES LTD—See CAN (Offshore) Ltd; *Int'l*, pg. 1276
CANTABIL RETAIL INDIA LIMITED; *Int'l*, pg. 1299
CANTABRIA - MUNDIVIA S.A—See Atos SE; *Int'l*, pg. 691
CANTALOUPE, INC.; *U.S. Public*, pg. 430
CANTALOUPE SYSTEMS INC.—See Cantaloupe, Inc.; *U.S. Public*, pg. 430
CANTAMAR PROPERTY MANAGEMENT, INC.—See Meruelo Group LLC; *U.S. Private*, pg. 2677
CANTAREY REINOSA, S.A.—See Siemens Energy AG; *Int'l*, pg. 6902
CANTARGIA AB; *Int'l*, pg. 1299
CANTECH HOLDING, INC.; *U.S. Private*, pg. 735
CANTEEN OF CANADA LIMITED—See Compass Group PLC; *Int'l*, pg. 1750
CANTEEN SERVICE CO. OF OWENSBORO, INC.—See Freeman Spogli & Co. Incorporated; *U.S. Private*, pg. 1606
CANTEEN SERVICES INC.; *U.S. Private*, pg. 735
CANTEGA TECHNOLOGIES INC.—See Hubbell Incorporated; *U.S. Public*, pg. 1066
CANTEL (AUSTRALIA) PTY. LTD.—See STERIS plc; *Int'l*, pg. 7209
CANTEL (CANADA) INC.—See STERIS plc; *Int'l*, pg. 7209
CANTEL (FRANCE) SAS—See STERIS plc; *Int'l*, pg. 7209
CANTEL (GERMANY) GMBH—See STERIS plc; *Int'l*, pg. 7209
CANTEL LANKA (PVT.) LTD.—See STERIS plc; *Int'l*, pg. 7209
CANTEL MEDICAL CORP.—See STERIS plc; *Int'l*, pg. 7208
CANTEL MEDICAL DEVICES (CHINA) CO., LTD.—See STERIS plc; *Int'l*, pg. 7209
CANTEL MEDICAL (HONG KONG) LIMITED—See STERIS plc; *Int'l*, pg. 7209
CANTEL MEDICAL (ITALY) S.R.L.—See STERIS plc; *Int'l*, pg. 7209
CANTEL MEDICAL (MALAYSIA) SDN. BHD.—See STERIS plc; *Int'l*, pg. 7209
CANTEL MEDICAL MIDDLE EAST FZ-LLC—See STERIS plc; *Int'l*, pg. 7209
CANTEL MEDICAL (UK) LIMITED—See STERIS plc; *Int'l*, pg. 7209
CANTEL (PRODUCTION) GERMANY GMBH—See STERIS plc; *Int'l*, pg. 7209
CANTEL (UK) LIMITED—See STERIS plc; *Int'l*, pg. 7209
CANTERA CONCRETE COMPANY—See Rooney Holdings, Inc.; *U.S. Private*, pg. 3479
CANTERA DE ARIDOS PUIG BROCA S.A.—See CRH plc; *Int'l*, pg. 1844
CANTERA EL HOYON, S.A.—See Heidelberg Materials AG; *Int'l*, pg. 3309
CANTERAN APPAREL (CAMBODIA) CO., LTD.—See Jerasia Capital Berhad; *Int'l*, pg. 3931
CANTERAN APPAREL SDN. BHD.—See Jerasia Capital Berhad; *Int'l*, pg. 3931
CANTERAS CERRO NEGRO S.A.—See CRH plc; *Int'l*, pg. 1844
CANTERAS LA BELONGA S.A.—See SigmaRoc Plc; *Int'l*, pg. 6909
CANTERAS MECANICAS CARCABA, S.A.U.—See Heidelberg Materials AG; *Int'l*, pg. 3309
CANTERAS PREBETONG S.L.—See Camargo Correa S.A.; *Int'l*, pg. 1267
CANTERBURY APARTMENTS, L.L.C.—See Equity Residential; *U.S. Public*, pg. 791
CANTERBURY CONSULTING GROUP, INC.; *U.S. Private*, pg. 735
CANTERBURY CONSULTING INCORPORATED; *U.S. Private*, pg. 735
CANTERBURY MANAGEMENT GROUP, INC.—See Canterbury Consulting Group, Inc.; *U.S. Private*, pg. 735
CANTERBURY MEDICAL IMAGING LIMITED—See Sonic Healthcare Limited; *Int'l*, pg. 7096
CANTERBURY OF NEW ZEALAND JAPAN INC.—See Goldwin, Inc.; *Int'l*, pg. 3035
CANTERBURY OF SHEPHERDSTOWN LIMITED PARTNERSHIP—See Welltower Inc.; *U.S. Public*, pg. 2348
CANTERBURY-ON-THE-LAKE; *U.S. Private*, pg. 735
CANTERBURY PARK CONCESSIONS, INC.—See Canterbury Park Holding Corporation; *U.S. Public*, pg. 430
CANTERBURY PARK ENTERTAINMENT LLC—See Canterbury Park Holding Corporation; *U.S. Public*, pg. 430
CANTERBURY PARK HOLDING CORPORATION; *U.S. Public*, pg. 430
CANTERBURY RESOURCES LTD.; *Int'l*, pg. 1299

COMPANY NAME INDEX

CANTERBURY TOWERS, INC.; *U.S. Private*, pg. 735
CANTERRA MINERALS CORPORATION; *Int'l*, pg. 1299
CANTEX INC.—See Sumitomo Corporation; *Int'l*, pg. 7273
CANTEX MINE DEVELOPMENT CORP.; *Int'l*, pg. 1299
CAN THO FERTILIZERS AND CHEMICALS JOINT STOCK COMPANY—See Masan Consumer Corp.; *Int'l*, pg. 4719
CAN THO MINERAL & CEMENT JSC; *Int'l*, pg. 1276
CAN THO PESTICIDES JOINT STOCK COMPANY; *Int'l*, pg. 1276
CANTILLANA B.V.—See Cantillana SA/NV; *Int'l*, pg. 1299
CANTILLANA GMBH—See Cantillana SA/NV; *Int'l*, pg. 1299
CANTILLANA SA/NV; *Int'l*, pg. 1299
CANTILLANA SAS—See Cantillana SA/NV; *Int'l*, pg. 1299
CANTIN CHEVROLET, INC.; *U.S. Private*, pg. 735
CANTINE RIUNITE & CIV S.C.AGR.; *Int'l*, pg. 1299
CANTINE TORRESELLA SRL—See Industrie Zignago Santa Margherita SpA; *Int'l*, pg. 3674
CAN'T LIVE WITHOUT IT, LLC—See Lifetime Brands, Inc.; *U.S. Public*, pg. 1313
CANTON AGGREGATE DIVISION—See Central Allied Enterprises; *U.S. Private*, pg. 818
CANTON CROSSING DISTRICT ENERGY LLC—See Constellation Energy Corporation; *U.S. Public*, pg. 571
CANTON CUT STONE CO. INC.—See Sims-Lohman, Inc.; *U.S. Private*, pg. 3669
CANTON DROP FORGE, INC.—See Park-Ohio Holdings Corp.; *U.S. Public*, pg. 1639
CANTON ELEVATOR, INC.—See Nidec Corporation; *Int'l*, pg. 5277
CANTON FOOD COMPANY; *U.S. Private*, pg. 735
CANTONI MOTOR S.A.; *Int'l*, pg. 1299
CANTON MOTOR SALES, INC.; *U.S. Private*, pg. 735
CANTON-POTSDAM HOSPITAL; *U.S. Private*, pg. 735
THE CANTON REPOSITORY—See Gannett Co., Inc.; *U.S. Public*, pg. 904
CANTON SALES & STORAGE CO.—See National Presto Industries, Inc; *U.S. Public*, pg. 1497
CANTONVALLEY MACAU COMPANY LIMITED—See AsianLogic Limited; *Int'l*, pg. 620
CANTOR FITZGERALD & CO.—See Cantor Fitzgerald, L.P.; *U.S. Private*, pg. 736
CANTOR FITZGERALD INCOME TRUST, INC.; *U.S. Private*, pg. 735
CANTOR FITZGERALD INTERNATIONAL—See Cantor Fitzgerald, L.P.; *U.S. Private*, pg. 736
CANTOR FITZGERALD INVESTMENT ADVISORS, L.P.—See Cantor Fitzgerald, L.P.; *U.S. Private*, pg. 736
CANTOR FITZGERALD, L.P.; *U.S. Private*, pg. 736
CANTOR FUTURES EXCHANGE, L.P.—See Cantor Fitzgerald, L.P.; *U.S. Private*, pg. 736
CANTOR GROUP, INC.; *U.S. Private*, pg. 736
CANTOR VENTURES—See Cantor Fitzgerald, L.P.; *U.S. Private*, pg. 736
CANTO SOFTWARE, INC.; *U.S. Private*, pg. 735
CANTOURAGE GROUP SE; *Int'l*, pg. 1299
CANTRELL INTERNATIONAL—See A.C. Horn & Company; *U.S. Private*, pg. 24
CANTRONIC SECURITY SYSTEMS (CHINA) CO., LTD—See Cantronic Systems Inc.; *Int'l*, pg. 1300
CANTRONIC SYSTEMS INC.—See Cantronic Systems Inc.; *Int'l*, pg. 1300
CANTRONIC SYSTEMS INC.; *Int'l*, pg. 1299
CANTU SERVICES INC.; *U.S. Private*, pg. 736
CANTV.NET—See Compania Anonima Nacional Telefonos de Venezuela; *Int'l*, pg. 1748
CANTWELL-CLEARY CO., INC.; *U.S. Private*, pg. 736
THE CANTWELL MACHINERY COMPANY INC.; *U.S. Private*, pg. 4004
CANUCK COMPOUNDERS INC.—See NanoXplore Inc.; *Int'l*, pg. 5145
CANUCKS SPORTS & ENTERTAINMENT—See Aquilini Investment Group; *Int'l*, pg. 528
CANUC RESOURCES CORPORATION; *Int'l*, pg. 1300
CANUELAS MILL S.A.C.I.F.I.A; *Int'l*, pg. 1300
CANUM CAPITAL MANAGEMENT, L.P.; *U.S. Private*, pg. 736
CANUSA AUTOMOTIVE WAREHOUSING INC.; *Int'l*, pg. 1300
CANUSA CORPORATION; *U.S. Private*, pg. 736
CANUSA-CPS—See ShawCor Ltd.; *Int'l*, pg. 6791
CANUSA-CPS—See ShawCor Ltd.; *Int'l*, pg. 6791
CANUSA HERSHMAN RECYCLING, LLC; *U.S. Private*, pg. 736
CAN USA, INC.—See CAN (Offshore) Ltd; *Int'l*, pg. 1276
CAN USA, INC.—See CAN (Offshore) Ltd; *Int'l*, pg. 1276
CANUSA SYSTEMS LIMITED—See ShawCor Ltd.; *Int'l*, pg. 6791
CANUSA WOOD PRODUCTS LIMITED; *Int'l*, pg. 1300
CANVAS HEALTH; *U.S. Private*, pg. 736
CANVAS MAPPLE CO., LTD.—See Shobunsha Holdings Inc.; *Int'l*, pg. 6857
CANVAS SOLUTIONS INC.—See Nemetschek SE; *Int'l*, pg. 5194
CANVAS SYSTEMS B.V.—See Avnet, Inc.; *U.S. Public*, pg. 252
CANVAS SYSTEMS UK LIMITED—See Avnet, Inc.; *U.S. Public*, pg. 252

CANVEDA INC.—See MPX International Corporation; *Int'l*, pg. 5063
CANVEST ENVIRONMENTAL PROTECTION GROUP COMPANY LIMITED; *Int'l*, pg. 1300
CANWEST CRANE & EQUIPMENT LTD.—See Hyduke Energy Services Inc.; *Int'l*, pg. 3548
CANWEST PROPANE LTD.—See Superior Plus Corp.; *Int'l*, pg. 7338
CANXGOLD MINING CORP.; *Int'l*, pg. 1300
CANY CORPORATION—See Mitsui Fudosan Co., Ltd.; *Int'l*, pg. 4986
THE CANYON AT PEACE PARK, LLC—See Universal Health Services, Inc.; *U.S. Public*, pg. 2259
THE CANYON AT SANTA MONICA, LLC—See Universal Health Services, Inc.; *U.S. Public*, pg. 2259
CANYON BAKEHOUSE, LLC—See Flowers Foods, Inc.; *U.S. Public*, pg. 854
CANYON BRIDGE CAPITAL PARTNERS, INC.; *Int'l*, pg. 1300
CANYON CAPITAL ADVISORS LLC; *U.S. Private*, pg. 736
CANYON CONSTRUCTION; *U.S. Private*, pg. 736
CANYON CREEK COUNTRY CLUB—See Apollo Global Management, Inc.; *U.S. Public*, pg. 149
CANYON CREEK FOOD COMPANY LTD.; *Int'l*, pg. 1300
CANYON CREEK TOYOTA INC.; *Int'l*, pg. 1300
CANYON CREST COUNTRY CLUB—See Apollo Global Management, Inc.; *U.S. Public*, pg. 149
CANYON ENGINEERING PRODUCTS, INC.—See ESCO Technologies, Inc.; *U.S. Public*, pg. 793
CANYON FUEL COMPANY, LLC—See Bowie Resources LLC; *U.S. Private*, pg. 625
CANYON GATE COUNTRY CLUB—See Apollo Global Management, Inc.; *U.S. Public*, pg. 149
CANYON MANUFACTURING SERVICES, INC.; *U.S. Private*, pg. 736
CANYON MEDICAL INC.—See Micro-Tech (Nanjing) Co., Ltd.; *Int'l*, pg. 4878
CANYON OFFSHORE, INC.—See Helix Energy Solutions Group, Inc.; *U.S. Public*, pg. 1024
CANYON OFFSHORE LIMITED—See Helix Energy Solutions Group, Inc.; *U.S. Public*, pg. 1024
CANYON PIPELINE CONSTRUCTION INC.—See Southwest Gas Holdings, Inc.; *U.S. Public*, pg. 1913
CANYON PIPE & SUPPLY, INC.—See Nicholas Consolidated Inc.; *U.S. Private*, pg. 2925
CANYON RANCH MANAGEMENT, LLC; *U.S. Private*, pg. 736
CANYON RDG HOSPITAL, INC.—See Universal Health Services, Inc.; *U.S. Public*, pg. 2256
CANYON RESOURCES LTD; *Int'l*, pg. 1300
CANYON RIDGE HOSPITAL, INC.—See Universal Health Services, Inc.; *U.S. Public*, pg. 2256
CANYON ROAD STORAGE, LLC—See National Storage Affiliates Trust; *U.S. Public*, pg. 1498
CANYON SEMICONDUCTOR INC.—See Diodes Incorporated; *U.S. Public*, pg. 667
CANYON SILVER MINES, INC.; *U.S. Public*, pg. 431
CANYON SPRINGS DIALYSIS, LLC—See DaVita Inc.; *U.S. Public*, pg. 636
THE CANYONS RESORT—See Talisker Corporation; *Int'l*, pg. 7447
CANYON STATE AIR CONDITIONING & HEATING, INC.—See Brookfield Corporation; *Int'l*, pg. 1188
CANYON STATE OIL COMPANY INC.—See Southern Counties Oil Co.; *U.S. Private*, pg. 3730
CANYON VISTA MEDICAL CENTER; *U.S. Private*, pg. 737
CANYON VISTA RECOVERY CENTER—See AAC Holdings, Inc.; *U.S. Private*, pg. 30
CAO FASHION COMPANY LIMITED—See Phu Nhuan Jewelry Joint Stock Company; *Int'l*, pg. 5857
CA OIL & GAS (PTY) LTD.—See ADvTECH Limited; *Int'l*, pg. 169
CAP10 PARTNERS LLP; *Int'l*, pg. 1301
CAPABLE B.V.—See TKH Group N.V.; *Int'l*, pg. 7763
CAPACIT'E INFRAPROJECTS LIMITED; *Int'l*, pg. 1301
CAPACITOR TECHNOLOGIES PTY. LTD.—See Washington H. Soul Pattinson & Company Limited; *Int'l*, pg. 8351
CAPACITY BENEFITS GROUP, INC.; *U.S. Private*, pg. 737
CAPACITY COVERAGE CO.—See Insurance Resource Brokerage Group; *U.S. Private*, pg. 2095
CAPACITYGRID UK LTD.—See Bain Capital, LP; *U.S. Private*, pg. 433
CAPACITY LLC; *U.S. Private*, pg. 737
CAPACITY MARINE CORPORATION—See Ambac Financial Group, Inc.; *U.S. Public*, pg. 92
CAPACITY OF TEXAS, INC. - LAYMOR DIVISION—See AIP, LLC; *U.S. Private*, pg. 135
CAPACITY OF TEXAS, INC.—See AIP, LLC; *U.S. Private*, pg. 135
CAPA ECOSYSTEMS, S.L.—See OAT Agrio Co., Ltd.; *Int'l*, pg. 5507
CAPAGRI SAS—See Exel Industries SA; *Int'l*, pg. 2582
CAPALLIANZ HOLDINGS LIMITED; *Int'l*, pg. 1301
CAPARIO, INC.—See McKesson Corporation; *U.S. Public*, pg. 1407

CAPARO ATLAS FASTENINGS LIMITED—See Caparo Group Ltd.; *Int'l*, pg. 1301
CAPARO ENGINEERING INDIA LTD.—See Caparo Group Ltd.; *Int'l*, pg. 1301
CAPARO ENGINEERING LTD. - CLYDESDALE JONES DIVISION—See Caparo Group Ltd.; *Int'l*, pg. 1302
CAPARO ENGINEERING LTD.—See Caparo Group Ltd.; *Int'l*, pg. 1301
CAPARO FASTENERS LIMITED—See Caparo Group Ltd.; *Int'l*, pg. 1301
CAPARO GROUP LTD.; *Int'l*, pg. 1301
CAPARO INDIA PVT. LTD.—See Caparo Group Ltd.; *Int'l*, pg. 1301
CAPARO INDUSTRIES PLC—See Caparo Group Ltd.; *Int'l*, pg. 1301
CAPARO MERCHANT BAR PLC—See Caparo Group Ltd.; *Int'l*, pg. 1302
CAPARO MIDDLE EAST FZ—See Caparo Group Ltd.; *Int'l*, pg. 1301
CAPARO MODULAR SYSTEMS LTD.—See Caparo Group Ltd.; *Int'l*, pg. 1302
CAPARO PLC—See Caparo Group Ltd.; *Int'l*, pg. 1301
CAPARO PRECISION STRIP LIMITED—See Caparo Group Ltd.; *Int'l*, pg. 1302
CAPARO PRECISION STRIP LTD. - DUCTILE STOURBRIDGE COLD MILLS DIVISION—See Caparo Group Ltd.; *Int'l*, pg. 1302
CAPARO PRECISION TUBES LTD. - CAPARO DRAWN PRODUCTS DIVISION—See Caparo Group Ltd.; *Int'l*, pg. 1302
CAPARO PRECISION TUBES LTD.—See Caparo Group Ltd.; *Int'l*, pg. 1302
CAPARO STEEL PRODUCTS LTD. - HUB LE BAS DIVISION—See Caparo Group Ltd.; *Int'l*, pg. 1302
CAPARO TESTING TECHNOLOGIES LTD - MIDDLE EAST FACILITY—See Caparo Group Ltd.; *Int'l*, pg. 1302
CAPARO TESTING TECHNOLOGIES LTD—See Caparo Group Ltd.; *Int'l*, pg. 1302
CAPARO TUBE COMPONENTS LTD.—See Caparo Group Ltd.; *Int'l*, pg. 1302
CAPARO TUBES LIMITED—See Caparo Group Ltd.; *Int'l*, pg. 1301
CAPARO WIRE LIMITED—See Caparo Group Ltd.; *Int'l*, pg. 1302
CAPARROS CORPORATION; *U.S. Private*, pg. 737
CAPASSY B.V.—See TKH Group N.V.; *Int'l*, pg. 7763
C & A PAVING CO.—See Clyde Companies Inc.; *U.S. Private*, pg. 949
CAPAX GLOBAL, LLC—See Hitachi, Ltd.; *Int'l*, pg. 3421
CAPAX MANAGEMENT & INSURANCE SERVICES, INC.—See Hellman & Friedman LLC; *U.S. Private*, pg. 1908
CAP BRAND MARKETING; *U.S. Private*, pg. 737
CAP CANDY, INC.—See Hasbro, Inc.; *U.S. Public*, pg. 987
CAPCARGO AG; *Int'l*, pg. 1302
CAP CARPET, INC.; *U.S. Private*, pg. 737
CAPCELLENCE HOLDING GMBH & CO. KG—See Cerberus Capital Management, L.P.; *U.S. Private*, pg. 838
CAPCELLENCE HOLDING GMBH & CO. KG—See GoldenTree Asset Management LP; *U.S. Private*, pg. 1734
CAPCELLENCE HOLDING GMBH & CO. KG—See J.C. Flowers & Co. LLC; *U.S. Private*, pg. 2159
CAPCELLENCE MITTELSTANDSPARTNER GMBH; *Int'l*, pg. 1302
CAP CINE—See Videlio SA; *Int'l*, pg. 8190
CAP CITY DENTAL LAB, LLC; *U.S. Private*, pg. 737
CAPCO AUSTRIA GMBH—See Wipro Limited; *Int'l*, pg. 8432
CAPCO CONSULTANCY (MALAYSIA) SDN. BHD.—See Wipro Limited; *Int'l*, pg. 8432
CAPCO CONSULTANCY (THAILAND) LTD.—See Wipro Limited; *Int'l*, pg. 8432
CAPCO CONSULTING SERVICES, LLC—See Wipro Limited; *Int'l*, pg. 8432
CAPCO CONSULTING SINGAPORE PTE. LTD.—See Fidelity National Infor; *U.S. Public*, pg. 832
CAPCO CONTRACTORS, INC.; *U.S. Private*, pg. 737
CAPCO COVENT GARDEN LIMITED—See Shaftesbury Capital PLC; *Int'l*, pg. 6748
CAPCO GUANGZHOU, LTD.—See Central Automotive Products Ltd.; *Int'l*, pg. 1404
CAP CO., LTD.—See Sumitomo Osaka Cement Co Ltd; *Int'l*, pg. 7296
CAPCO (MALAYSIA) SDN. BHD.—See Central Automotive Products Ltd.; *Int'l*, pg. 1404
CAPCOM ASIA CO., LTD.—See Capcom Co., Ltd.; *Int'l*, pg. 1302
CAPCOM CO., LTD.; *Int'l*, pg. 1302
CAPCOM CO., LTD. - UENO FACILITY—See Capcom Co., Ltd.; *Int'l*, pg. 1302
CAPCOM ENTERTAINMENT FRANCE, SAS—See Capcom Co., Ltd.; *Int'l*, pg. 1302
CAPCOM ENTERTAINMENT GERMANY GMBH—See Capcom Co., Ltd.; *Int'l*, pg. 1302
CAPCOM ENTERTAINMENT, INC.—See Capcom Co., Ltd.; *Int'l*, pg. 1302
CAPCOM ENTERTAINMENT KOREA CO., LTD.—See Capcom Co., Ltd.; *Int'l*, pg. 1302

CAPCOM CO., LTD.

CAPCO MIDDLE EAST FZCO—See Central Automotive Products Ltd.; *Int'l*, pg. 1404
CAPCOM INC—See Capcom Co., Ltd.; *Int'l*, pg. 1302
CAPCOM INTERACTIVE CANADA, INC—See Capcom Co., Ltd.; *Int'l*, pg. 1302
CAPCOM USA, INC.—See Capcom Co., Ltd.; *Int'l*, pg. 1302
CAPCON ARGEN LIMITED—See Capcon Limited; *Int'l*, pg. 1303
CAP-CON AUTOMOTIVE TECHNOLOGIES, INC.—See The Jordan Company, L.P.; *U.S. Private*, pg. 4060
CAPCON LIMITED; *Int'l*, pg. 1303
CAPCO PLASTICS INC.; *U.S. Private*, pg. 737
CAPCO POLAND SP. Z.O.O.—See Wipro Limited; *Int'l*, pg. 8432
CAPCO PRIVATE LTD.—See Central Automotive Products Ltd.; *Int'l*, pg. 1404
CAPCO RISC CONSULTING, LLC—See Wipro Limited; *Int'l*, pg. 8432
CAPCO U.S.A., INC.—See Central Automotive Products Ltd.; *Int'l*, pg. 1404
CAPE ABILITIES INC.; *U.S. Private*, pg. 737
CAPE ACQUISITION CORP.—See Deutsche Bank Aktiengesellschaft; *Int'l*, pg. 2055
CAPE AIR; *U.S. Private*, pg. 737
CAPE ANN INSURANCE, INC.—See Salem Five Bancorp; *U.S. Private*, pg. 3531
CAPE ANN SAVINGS BANK; *U.S. Private*, pg. 737
CAPE ASSOCIATES, INC.; *U.S. Private*, pg. 737
CAPE BRETON & CENTRAL NOVA SCOTIA RAILWAY LIMITED—See Brookfield Infrastructure Partners L.P.; *Int'l*, pg. 1191
CAPE BRETON & CENTRAL NOVA SCOTIA RAILWAY LIMITED—See GIC Pte. Ltd.; *Int'l*, pg. 2965
CAPE CAVE CORP.—See Rotonda Holdings Inc.; *U.S. Private*, pg. 3487
CAPE CLEAR SOFTWARE, INC.; *U.S. Private*, pg. 737
CAPE CLUB OF BREVARD—See The Goldfield Corporation; *U.S. Public*, pg. 2075
CAPE CODDER—See Gannett Co., Inc.; *U.S. Public*, pg. 902
CAPE COD FIVE CENTS SAVINGS BANK—See Mutual Bancorp; *U.S. Private*, pg. 2819
CAPE COD HAND THERAPY, LIMITED PARTNERSHIP—See U.S. Physical Therapy, Inc.; *U.S. Public*, pg. 2214
CAPE COD LUMBER CO. INC.; *U.S. Private*, pg. 737
CAPE COD MEDICA ENTERPRISES, INC.—See Lundbeckfonden; *Int'l*, pg. 4580
CAPE COD POTATO CHIP COMPANY INC.—See Campbell Soup Company; *U.S. Public*, pg. 427
CAPE COD STONE & MASONRY SUPPLY, INC.—See SiteOne Landscape Supply, Inc.; *U.S. Public*, pg. 1888
CAPE COD TIMES—See Gannett Co., Inc.; *U.S. Public*, pg. 904
CAPE CORAL AMBULATORY SURGERY CENTER, LLC—See Bain Capital, LP; *U.S. Private*, pg. 445
THE CAPE CORAL/FT. MYERS ENDOSCOPY ASC, LLC—See KKR & Co. Inc.; *U.S. Public*, pg. 1247
CAPE CORAL KIDNEY CENTER, LLC—See Nautic Partners, LLC; *U.S. Private*, pg. 2869
CAPE CORAL SURGERY CENTER, INC.—See HCA Healthcare, Inc.; *U.S. Public*, pg. 992
CAPE CORAL SURGERY CENTER, INC.—See HCA Healthcare, Inc.; *U.S. Public*, pg. 992
CAPE CRAFTSMEN, INC.—See Evergreen Enterprises, Inc.; *U.S. Private*, pg. 1439
CAPE CRUSHING & EARTHMOVING CONTRACTORS PTY. LTD.—See CFC Group Pty. Ltd.; *Int'l*, pg. 1429
CAPE EAST LIMITED—See Altrad Investment Authority SAS; *Int'l*, pg. 398
CAPE EAST LLC—See Altrad Investment Authority SAS; *Int'l*, pg. 398
CAPE EAST PHILIPPINES INC—See Altrad Investment Authority SAS; *Int'l*, pg. 398
CAPE EAST PRIVATE LIMITED—See Altrad Investment Authority SAS; *Int'l*, pg. 398
CAPE EAST (THAILAND) LIMITED—See Altrad Investment Authority SAS; *Int'l*, pg. 398
CAPE ELECTRICAL SUPPLY INC.—See Graybar Electric Company, Inc.; *U.S. Private*, pg. 1760
CAPE EMPOWERMENT TRUST LIMITED; *Int'l*, pg. 1303
CAPE FEAR CONSTRUCTION CO. INC.; *U.S. Private*, pg. 737
CAPE FEAR FARM CREDIT, ACA; *U.S. Private*, pg. 737
CAPE FEAR RAILWAYS INC.—See Seaboard Corporation; *U.S. Public*, pg. 1850
CAPE FEAR TRACTOR AND SAW LLC—See Tym Corporation; *Int'l*, pg. 7994
CAPE FEAR TUTORING, INC.; *U.S. Private*, pg. 737
CAPE FEAR VALLEY HOMECARE AND HOSPICE, LLC—See UnitedHealth Group Incorporated; *U.S. Public*, pg. 2244
CAPE FLATTERY SILICA MINES PTY., LTD.—See Mitsubishi Corporation; *Int'l*, pg. 4938
CAPE FOODS (PTY.) LTD.—See Libstar Holdings Ltd.; *Int'l*, pg. 4487
CAPE FOX CORPORATION; *U.S. Private*, pg. 737

CAPE GROUP PTE. LTD.—See Buckthorn Partners LLP; *Int'l*, pg. 1210
CAPE GROUP PTE. LTD.—See OEP Capital Advisors, L.P.; *U.S. Private*, pg. 2997
CAPE HERB & SPICE (PTY) LTD.—See Libstar Holdings Ltd.; *Int'l*, pg. 4487
CAPE INDUSTRIAL SERVICES GROUP LIMITED—See Altrad Investment Authority SAS; *Int'l*, pg. 398
CAPE INDUSTRIAL SERVICES LIMITED—See Altrad Investment Authority SAS; *Int'l*, pg. 398
CAPE INDUSTRIES LTD.; *Int'l*, pg. 1303
CAPE LIME PROPRIETARY LIMITED—See Afrimat Limited; *Int'l*, pg. 192
CAPEL INC.; *U.S. Private*, pg. 738
CAPELLA CAPITAL LEND LEASE PTY LIMITED—See Lendlease Corporation Limited; *Int'l*, pg. 4451
CAPELLA EDUCATION COMPANY—See Strategic Education, Inc.; *U.S. Public*, pg. 1953
CAPELLA MICROSYSTEMS, INC.—See Vishay Intertechnology, Inc.; *U.S. Public*, pg. 2302
CAPELLA MINERALS LIMITED; *Int'l*, pg. 1303
CAPELLA TECHNOLOGIES, INC.—See Levi, Ray & Shoup, Inc.; *U.S. Private*, pg. 2435
CAPELLA TELECOMMUNICATIONS INC.; *Int'l*, pg. 1303
CAPELLA UNIVERSITY, INC.—See Strategic Education, Inc.; *U.S. Public*, pg. 1954
CAPELLI EUROPE GMBH—See GMA Accessories/Capelli of New York; *U.S. Private*, pg. 1721
CAPELLI OF NEW YORK INC.—See GMA Accessories/Capelli of New York; *U.S. Private*, pg. 1721
CAPELLI SA; *Int'l*, pg. 1303
CAPE LTD.—See MBH Corporation Plc; *Int'l*, pg. 4752
CAPE MEDICAL SUPPLY, INC.—See AdaptHealth Corp.; *U.S. Public*, pg. 39
CAPE MENTELLE VINEYARDS LTD.—See LVMH Moet Hennessy Louis Vuitton SE; *Int'l*, pg. 4604
CAPE-NATIXIS S.G.R. S.P.A.—See Cimino & Associati Private Equity S.p.A.; *Int'l*, pg. 1609
CAPE-NATIXIS S.G.R. S.P.A.—See Groupe BPCE; *Int'l*, pg. 3095
CAP ENERGY PLC; *Int'l*, pg. 1300
CAPE PLC—See Altrad Investment Authority SAS; *Int'l*, pg. 398
CAPE POINT HOLDINGS, INC.; *Int'l*, pg. 1303
CAPE PUBLICATIONS, INC.—See TEGNA Inc.; *U.S. Public*, pg. 1990
CAPE QUALITY SEAFOOD LTD.; *U.S. Private*, pg. 738
CAPERA IMMOBILIEN SERVICE GMBH—See COR-ESTATE Capital Holding SA; *Int'l*, pg. 1799
C. A. PERRY & SON INC.; *U.S. Private*, pg. 704
CAPE SOFTWARE, INC.—See John Wood Group PLC; *Int'l*, pg. 3984
CAPESPAN GROUP LIMITED—See Zeder Investments Limited; *Int'l*, pg. 8629
CAPESPAN INTERNATIONAL LIMITED—See Zeder Investments Limited; *Int'l*, pg. 8629
CAPEVIEW CAPITAL LLP—See Affiliated Managers Group, Inc.; *U.S. Public*, pg. 54
CAPEVIN HOLDINGS LIMITED; *Int'l*, pg. 1303
CAPEVIN INVESTMENTS LIMITED; *Int'l*, pg. 1303
CAPEWELL COMPONENTS COMPANY, LLC—See CapitalWorks, LLC; *U.S. Private*, pg. 742
CAPEXO S.A.S.—See Orsero S.p.A.; *Int'l*, pg. 5644
CAPEZIO BALLET MAKERS INC.; *U.S. Private*, pg. 738
THE CAPFINANCIAL GROUP, LLC; *U.S. Private*, pg. 4004
CAPFINANCIAL PARTNERS, LLC—See The CapFinancial Group, LLC; *U.S. Private*, pg. 4004
CAPFIN INDIA LIMITED; *Int'l*, pg. 1303
CAP FOOD SERVICES CO.; *U.S. Private*, pg. 737
CAPFRUIT S.A.—See Hero AG; *Int'l*, pg. 3363
CAPGAS PRIVATE LIMITED—See Attock Refinery Ltd; *Int'l*, pg. 697
CAPGEMINI ARGENTINA S.A.—See Capgemini SE; *Int'l*, pg. 1303
CAPGEMINI ASIA PACIFIC PTE. LTD.—See Capgemini SE; *Int'l*, pg. 1304
CAPGEMINI ASIA PACIFIC—See Capgemini SE; *Int'l*, pg. 1303
CAPGEMINI AUSTRALIA PTY LTD—See Capgemini SE; *Int'l*, pg. 1303
CAPGEMINI BELGIUM N.V/S.A—See Capgemini SE; *Int'l*, pg. 1306
CAPGEMINI BUSINESS SERVICES ASIA LTD.—See Capgemini SE; *Int'l*, pg. 1303
CAPGEMINI BUSINESS SERVICES AUSTRALIA PTY LTD.—See Capgemini SE; *Int'l*, pg. 1304
CAPGEMINI BUSINESS SERVICES BV—See Capgemini SE; *Int'l*, pg. 1306
CAPGEMINI BUSINESS SERVICES CHILE LTDA.—See Capgemini SE; *Int'l*, pg. 1304
CAPGEMINI BUSINESS SERVICES GUATEMALA S.A.—See Capgemini SE; *Int'l*, pg. 1304
CAPGEMINI BUSINESS SERVICES (INDIA) LTD.—See Capgemini SE; *Int'l*, pg. 1304
CAPGEMINI BUSINESS SERVICES USA LLC—See Capgemini SE; *Int'l*, pg. 1304

CORPORATE AFFILIATIONS

CAPGEMINI CANADA INC.—See Capgemini SE; *Int'l*, pg. 1304
CAPGEMINI CHINA—See Capgemini SE; *Int'l*, pg. 1303
CAPGEMINI CONSULTING INDIA PVT. LTD.—See Capgemini SE; *Int'l*, pg. 1304
CAPGEMINI CONSULTING OSTERREICH AG—See Capgemini SE; *Int'l*, pg. 1304
CAPGEMINI CONSULTING S.A.S.—See Capgemini SE; *Int'l*, pg. 1304
CAPGEMINI CONSULTING SLOVAKIA D.O.O.—See Capgemini SE; *Int'l*, pg. 1304
CAPGEMINI CZECH REPUBLIC S.R.O—See Capgemini SE; *Int'l*, pg. 1304
CAPGEMINI DANMARK A/S—See Capgemini SE; *Int'l*, pg. 1304
CAPGEMINI DEUTSCHLAND GMBH - COLOGNE—See Capgemini SE; *Int'l*, pg. 1304
CAPGEMINI DEUTSCHLAND GMBH - HAMBURG—See Capgemini SE; *Int'l*, pg. 1304
CAPGEMINI DEUTSCHLAND GMBH - MUNICH—See Capgemini SE; *Int'l*, pg. 1304
CAPGEMINI DEUTSCHLAND GMBH - OFFENBACH—See Capgemini SE; *Int'l*, pg. 1304
CAPGEMINI DEUTSCHLAND GMBH—See Capgemini SE; *Int'l*, pg. 1304
CAPGEMINI DEUTSCHLAND GMBH - STUTTGART—See Capgemini SE; *Int'l*, pg. 1304
CAPGEMINI DEUTSCHLAND HOLDING GMBH—See Capgemini SE; *Int'l*, pg. 1304
CAPGEMINI DO BRASIL, SERVICOS DE CONSULTORIA E INFORMATICA LTDA.—See Capgemini SE; *Int'l*, pg. 1306
CAPGEMINI EDUCATIONAL SERVICES B.V.—See Capgemini SE; *Int'l*, pg. 1306
CAPGEMINI ENGINEERING—See Capgemini SE; *Int'l*, pg. 1304
CAPGEMINI ESPANA S.L. - BARCELONA—See Capgemini SE; *Int'l*, pg. 1305
CAPGEMINI ESPANA S.L.—See Capgemini SE; *Int'l*, pg. 1305
CAPGEMINI FINANCIAL SERVICES AUSTRALIA PTY LTD.—See Capgemini SE; *Int'l*, pg. 1304
CAPGEMINI FINANCIAL SERVICES INTERNATIONAL INC.—See Capgemini SE; *Int'l*, pg. 1305
CAPGEMINI FINANCIAL SERVICES USA INC.—See Capgemini SE; *Int'l*, pg. 1305
CAPGEMINI FINLAND OY—See Capgemini SE; *Int'l*, pg. 1305
CAPGEMINI FRANCE - GRENOBLE—See Capgemini SE; *Int'l*, pg. 1305
CAPGEMINI FRANCE - RENNES—See Capgemini SE; *Int'l*, pg. 1305
CAPGEMINI FRANCE S.A.S.—See Capgemini SE; *Int'l*, pg. 1305
CAPGEMINI GOUVIEUX S.A.S.—See Capgemini SE; *Int'l*, pg. 1305
CAPGEMINI GOVERNMENT SOLUTIONS LLC—See Capgemini SE; *Int'l*, pg. 1305
CAPGEMINI INDIA PRIVATE LTD.—See Capgemini SE; *Int'l*, pg. 1305
CAPGEMINI ITALIA—See Capgemini SE; *Int'l*, pg. 1305
CAPGEMINI ITALIA—See Capgemini SE; *Int'l*, pg. 1305
CAPGEMINI ITALIA—See Capgemini SE; *Int'l*, pg. 1305
CAPGEMINI ITALIA SPA—See Capgemini SE; *Int'l*, pg. 1305
CAPGEMINI ITALIA SPA—See Capgemini SE; *Int'l*, pg. 1305
CAPGEMINI LTD—See Capgemini SE; *Int'l*, pg. 1305
CAPGEMINI MAGYARORSZAG KFT—See Capgemini SE; *Int'l*, pg. 1305
CAPGEMINI MIDDLE EAST FZ LLC—See Capgemini SE; *Int'l*, pg. 1306
CAPGEMINI NEDERLAND B.V.—See Capgemini SE; *Int'l*, pg. 1306
CAPGEMINI NORGE AS—See Capgemini SE; *Int'l*, pg. 1306
CAPGEMINI NORTH AMERICA INC.—See Capgemini SE; *Int'l*, pg. 1306
CAPGEMINI OUTSOURCING B.V.—See Capgemini SE; *Int'l*, pg. 1306
CAPGEMINI OUTSOURCING SERVICES GMBH—See Capgemini SE; *Int'l*, pg. 1304
CAPGEMINI OUTSOURCING SERVICES S.A.S.—See Capgemini SE; *Int'l*, pg. 1306
CAPGEMINI PHILLIPINES SBOS—See Capgemini SE; *Int'l*, pg. 1306
CAPGEMINI POLSKA SP. Z. O. O—See Capgemini SE; *Int'l*, pg. 1306
CAPGEMINI PORTUGAL, SERVICOS DE CONSULTORIA E INFORMATICA, SA—See Capgemini SE; *Int'l*, pg. 1306
CAPGEMINI RETAIL SOLUTIONS B.V.—See Capgemini SE; *Int'l*, pg. 1306
CAPGEMINI SCHWEIZ AG (BASEL)—See Capgemini SE; *Int'l*, pg. 1306
CAPGEMINI SCHWEIZ AG (GENF)—See Capgemini SE; *Int'l*, pg. 1306
CAPGEMINI SCHWEIZ AG—See Capgemini SE; *Int'l*, pg. 1306

CAPGEMINI SCHWEIZ AG—See Capgemini SE; *Int'l*, pg. 1306
CAPGEMINI SERVICE S.A.S—See Capgemini SE; *Int'l*, pg. 1306
CAPGEMINI SERVICES MALAYSIA SDN BHD—See Capgemini SE; *Int'l*, pg. 1306
CAPGEMINI SERVICES ROMANIA S.R.L.—See Capgemini SE; *Int'l*, pg. 1306
CAPGEMINI SE; *Int'l*, pg. 1303
CAPGEMINI (SHANGHAI)—See Capgemini SE; *Int'l*, pg. 1303
CAPGEMINI SHARED SERVICES BV—See Capgemini SE; *Int'l*, pg. 1306
CAPGEMINI SINGAPORE PTE. LTD.—See Capgemini SE; *Int'l*, pg. 1306
CAPGEMINI SLOVENSKO, S.R.O.—See Capgemini SE; *Int'l*, pg. 1306
CAPGEMINI SOLUTIONS PRIVATE LIMITED—See Capgemini SE; *Int'l*, pg. 1306
CAPGEMINI SUISSE SA—See Capgemini SE; *Int'l*, pg. 1306
CAPGEMINI SVERIGE AB—See Capgemini SE; *Int'l*, pg. 1306
CAPGEMINI TECHNOLOGIES LLC—See Capgemini SE; *Int'l*, pg. 1306
CAPGEMINI TECHNOLOGY SERVICES INDIA LIMITED—See Capgemini SE; *Int'l*, pg. 1306
CAPGEMINI TECHNOLOGY SERVICES MAROC S.A.—See Capgemini SE; *Int'l*, pg. 1306
CAPGEMINI TECHNOLOGY SERVICES S.A.S.—See Capgemini SE; *Int'l*, pg. 1306
CAP GEMINI TELECOM MEDIA & NETWORKS DEUTSCHLAND GMBH—See Capgemini SE; *Int'l*, pg. 1304
CAPGEMINI UK—See Capgemini SE; *Int'l*, pg. 1306
CAPGEMINI UNIVERSITE—See Capgemini SE; *Int'l*, pg. 1306
CAPGEMINI U.S.—See Capgemini SE; *Int'l*, pg. 1306
CAPGEN CAPITAL ADVISERS LLC—See CapGen Financial Group LP; *U.S. Private*, pg. 738
CAPGEN FINANCIAL GROUP LP; *U.S. Private*, pg. 738
CAP HPI LIMITED—See Vista Equity Partners, LLC; *U.S. Private*, pg. 4401
CAPI FRANCE—See Financiere Pinault SCA; *Int'l*, pg. 2668
CAPILANO HONEY LIMITED—See ROC Partners Pty Ltd; *Int'l*, pg. 6372
CAPILANO HONEY LIMITED—See Wattle Hill RHC Funds; *Int'l*, pg. 8359
CAPILLARY SOLUTIONS GMBH—See Geratherm Medical AG; *Int'l*, pg. 2942
CAPILLARY TECHNOLOGIES INTERNATIONAL PTE LTD.; *Int'l*, pg. 1307
CAPILLION INTERNATIONAL PTE. LTD.; *Int'l*, pg. 1308
CAPI-LUX NETHERLANDS B.V.—See B&S Group S.A.; *Int'l*, pg. 784
CAPINFO COMPANY LIMITED; *Int'l*, pg. 1308
CAP INSURANCE COMPANY INC.—See Pacific Marine & Supply Co. Ltd. Inc.; *U.S. Private*, pg. 3068
CAPINTEC INC.—See Mirion Technologies, Inc.; *U.S. Public*, pg. 1450
CAPIO AB—See Apax Partners LLP; *Int'l*, pg. 502
CAPIO PROXIMITY CARE—See Apax Partners LLP; *Int'l*, pg. 502
CAPITA BUSINESS SERVICES LIMITED—See Capita plc; *Int'l*, pg. 1308
CAPITA COMMERCIAL SERVICES LIMITED—See Capita plc; *Int'l*, pg. 1308
CAPITA CUSTOMER SERVICES AG—See Capita plc; *Int'l*, pg. 1308
CAPITA CUSTOMER SERVICES (GERMANY) GMBH—See Capita plc; *Int'l*, pg. 1308
CAPITA FUNDING DE MEXICO, SOCIEDAD ANONIMA DE CAPITAL VARIABLE SOFOM ENR—See First Citizens BancShares, Inc.; *U.S. Public*, pg. 841
CAPITA INSURANCE SERVICES LIMITED—See Capita plc; *Int'l*, pg. 1308
CAPITA INTERNATIONAL DEVELOPMENT—See Capita plc; *Int'l*, pg. 1308
CAPITA INTERNATIONAL FINANCIAL SERVICES LTD.—See Capita plc; *Int'l*, pg. 1308
CAPITAL A BHD; *Int'l*, pg. 1309
CAPITAL ADVANTAGE INSURANCE COMPANY—See Capital BlueCross Inc.; *U.S. Private*, pg. 739
CAPITAL ADVERTISING—See Publicis Groupe S.A.; *Int'l*, pg. 6097
CAPITAL ADVISORS PARTNERS ASIA PTE. LTD.—See TRG Management LP; *U.S. Private*, pg. 4219
CAPITAL ADVISORS PARTNERS ASIA SDN. BHD.—See TRG Management LP; *U.S. Private*, pg. 4219
CAPITAL AG PROPERTY SERVICES INC.; *U.S. Private*, pg. 738
CAPITAL AGRICULTURAL PROPERTY SERVICES, INC.—See Prudential Financial, Inc.; *U.S. Public*, pg. 1734
CAPITAL AIRPORTS HOLDING COMPANY (CAH); *Int'l*, pg. 1309
CAPITAL ALIGNMENT PARTNERS, INC.; *U.S. Private*, pg. 738

CAPITAL ANALYSTS, INC.—See Lincoln Investment Planning Inc.; *U.S. Private*, pg. 2458
CAPITALAND ASCOTT TRUST MANAGEMENT LIMITED; *Int'l*, pg. 1313
CAPITALAND CHINA HOLDINGS PTE LTD—See CapitaLand Investment Limited; *Int'l*, pg. 1313
CAPITALAND (CHINA) INVESTMENT CO., LTD—See CapitaLand Investment Limited; *Int'l*, pg. 1313
CAPITALAND CHINA TRUST; *Int'l*, pg. 1313
CAPITALAND COMMERCIAL LIMITED—See CapitaLand Investment Limited; *Int'l*, pg. 1313
CAPITALAND COMMERCIAL TRUST MANAGEMENT LIMITED—See CapitaLand Investment Limited; *Int'l*, pg. 1313
CAPITALAND COMMERCIAL TRUST—See CapitaLand Investment Limited; *Int'l*, pg. 1313
CAPITALAND FUND MANAGEMENT LIMITED—See CapitaLand Investment Limited; *Int'l*, pg. 1313
CAPITALAND GCC HOLDINGS PTE LTD—See CapitaLand Investment Limited; *Int'l*, pg. 1313
CAPITALAND INDIA TRUST; *Int'l*, pg. 1313
CAPITALAND INTEGRATED COMMERCIAL TRUST—See CapitaLand Investment Limited; *Int'l*, pg. 1313
CAPITALAND INTERNATIONAL PTE. LTD.—See CapitaLand Investment Limited; *Int'l*, pg. 1313
CAPITALAND INVESTMENT LIMITED; *Int'l*, pg. 1313
CAPITALAND (JAPAN) KABUSHIKI KAISHA—See CapitaLand Investment Limited; *Int'l*, pg. 1313
CAPITALAND MALL ASIA LIMITED—See CapitaLand Investment Limited; *Int'l*, pg. 1313
CAPITALAND RESIDENTIAL LIMITED—See CapitaLand Investment Limited; *Int'l*, pg. 1313
CAPITALAND RESIDENTIAL SINGAPORE PTE LTD—See CapitaLand Investment Limited; *Int'l*, pg. 1313
CAPITALAND SINGAPORE LIMITED—See CapitaLand Investment Limited; *Int'l*, pg. 1313
CAPITALAND TREASURY LIMITED—See CapitaLand Investment Limited; *Int'l*, pg. 1313
CAPITALAND UK MANAGEMENT LTD—See CapitaLand Investment Limited; *Int'l*, pg. 1313
CAPITALAND (VIETNAM) HOLDINGS PTE LTD—See CapitaLand Investment Limited; *Int'l*, pg. 1313
CAPITALAND-VISTA JOINT VENTURE CO., LTD.—See CapitaLand Investment Limited; *Int'l*, pg. 1313
CAPITAL APPRECIATION LTD.; *Int'l*, pg. 1309
CAPITAL ARCHITECTURAL SIGNS, INC.—See Facility Solutions Group, Inc.; *U.S. Private*, pg. 1460
CAPITAL AREA COMMUNITY ACTION AGENCY, INC.; *U.S. Private*, pg. 738
CAPITAL AREA COMMUNITY SERVICES, INC.; *U.S. Private*, pg. 738
CAPITAL AREA FOOD BANK; *U.S. Private*, pg. 738
CAPITAL AREA PRIMARY CARE PROVIDERS—See HCA Healthcare, Inc.; *U.S. Public*, pg. 992
CAPITAL AREA PROVIDERS—See HCA Healthcare, Inc.; *U.S. Public*, pg. 992
CAPITAL AREA SERVICE CO. INC.—See CareFirst, Inc.; *U.S. Private*, pg. 753
CAPITAL ART APARTMENTS SP. Z O.O.—See Atlas Estates Limited; *Int'l*, pg. 685
CAPITAL ASSET PLANNING, INC.; *Int'l*, pg. 1309
CAPITAL ASSOCIATED INDUSTRIES, INC.—See Catapult Employers Association, Inc.; *U.S. Private*, pg. 787
CAPITALATWORK FOYER GROUP S.A.—See Foyer S.A.; *Int'l*, pg. 2756
CAPITAL AUTOMOBILE COMPANY; *U.S. Private*, pg. 738
CAPITAL AUTOMOTIVE REAL ESTATE SERVICES, INC.; *U.S. Private*, pg. 738
CAPITAL AUTO RECEIVABLES LLC; *U.S. Private*, pg. 738
CAPITAL AUTO & TRUCK AUCTION; *U.S. Private*, pg. 738
CAPITAL AVIATION PTE LTD—See AT Capital Pte Limited; *Int'l*, pg. 664
CAPITAL AVIONICS, INC.; *U.S. Private*, pg. 738
CAPITAL BANCORP, INC.; *U.S. Public*, pg. 431
CAPITAL BANK - GRAWE GRUPPE AG; *Int'l*, pg. 1310
CAPITAL BANK, INC.—See Mercantil Servicios Financieros Internacional, S.A.; *Int'l*, pg. 4819
CAPITAL BANK KAZAKHSTAN JSC; *Int'l*, pg. 1310
CAPITAL BANK; *Int'l*, pg. 1310
CAPITAL BANK—See Capital Bank - GRAWE Gruppe AG; *Int'l*, pg. 1310
CAPITAL BATTENS PTY LTD—See Brickworks Limited; *Int'l*, pg. 1152
CAPITAL BEVERAGE CORPORATION; *U.S. Private*, pg. 738
CAPITAL BLUECROSS INC.; *U.S. Private*, pg. 738
CAPITAL BONDING CORPORATION; *U.S. Private*, pg. 739
CAPITALBOX AB—See Multitude SE; *Int'l*, pg. 5084
CAPITAL BREWERY CO., INC.; *U.S. Private*, pg. 739
CAPITAL BUICK GMC; *U.S. Private*, pg. 739
CAPITAL BUILDCON PVT. LTD.—See TARC Limited; *Int'l*, pg. 7462
CAPITAL BUSINESS SYSTEMS, INC.—See Xerox Holdings Corporation; *U.S. Public*, pg. 2387
CAPITAL CARGO INTERNATIONAL AIRLINES, INC.—See Air Transport Services Group, Inc.; *U.S. Public*, pg. 67

CAPITAL CDPQ—See Caisse de Depot et Placement du Quebec; *Int'l*, pg. 1254
CAPITAL CHEVROLET, INC.—See Capital Ford Inc.; *U.S. Private*, pg. 740
CAPITAL CITY AUTO AUCTION INC.; *U.S. Private*, pg. 739
CAPITAL CITY BANC INVESTMENTS, INC.—See Capital City Bank Group, Inc.; *U.S. Public*, pg. 431
CAPITAL CITY BANK GROUP, INC.; *U.S. Public*, pg. 431
CAPITAL CITY BANK—See Capital City Bank Group, Inc.; *U.S. Public*, pg. 431
CAPITAL CITY CLUB INC.; *U.S. Private*, pg. 739
CAPITAL CITY COMPANIES INC.; *U.S. Private*, pg. 739
CAPITAL CITY CONSULTING, LLC; *U.S. Private*, pg. 739
CAPITAL CITY CONTROLS—See Harris Companies; *U.S. Private*, pg. 1869
CAPITAL CITY ENERGY GROUP, INC.; *U.S. Private*, pg. 739
CAPITAL CITY GROUP, INC.—See Bay Crane Service, Inc.; *U.S. Private*, pg. 492
CAPITAL CITY HOME LOANS INC.; *U.S. Private*, pg. 739
CAPITAL CITY HOME LOANS, LLC—See Capital City Bank Group, Inc.; *U.S. Public*, pg. 431
CAPITAL CITY INSURANCE CO. INC.; *U.S. Private*, pg. 739
CAPITAL CITY INVESTMENT B.V.—See Enka Insaat ve Sanayi A.S.; *Int'l*, pg. 2440
CAPITAL CITY MOTORS LTD—See The Colonial Motor Company Limited; *Int'l*, pg. 7634
CAPITAL CITY OIL INC.; *U.S. Private*, pg. 739
CAPITAL CITY PETROLEUM, INC.—See Capital City Energy Group, Inc.; *U.S. Private*, pg. 739
CAPITAL CITY PRESS; *U.S. Private*, pg. 739
CAPITAL CITY PROPERTY SDN BHD—See Capital World Limited; *Int'l*, pg. 1313
CAPITAL CITY TRUST COMPANY—See Capital City Bank Group, Inc.; *U.S. Public*, pg. 431
CAPITAL CLEAN ENERGY CARRIERS CORP.; *Int'l*, pg. 1310
CAPITAL COMMUNICATION SERVICES, INC.; *U.S. Private*, pg. 739
CAPITAL COMPUTER ASSOCIATES, INC.—See Constellation Software Inc.; *Int'l*, pg. 1774
CAPITAL CONCEPT LIMITED AD; *Int'l*, pg. 1310
CAPITAL CONCRETE, INC.; *U.S. Private*, pg. 739
CAPITAL CONFIRMATION, INC—See Thomson Reuters Corporation; *Int'l*, pg. 7714
CAPITAL CONSTRUCTION HOLDINGS—See O2 Investment Partners, LLC; *U.S. Private*, pg. 2982
CAPITAL & COUNTIES USA, INC.; *U.S. Private*, pg. 738
CAPITAL C PARTNERS LP—See Stagwell, Inc.; *U.S. Public*, pg. 1926
CAPITAL & CREDIT MERCHANT BANK LIMITED—See JMMB Bank (Jamaica) Limited; *Int'l*, pg. 3975
CAPITAL & CREDIT SECURITIES LIMITED—See JMMB Bank (Jamaica) Limited; *Int'l*, pg. 3975
CAPITAL CREDIT UNION; *U.S. Private*, pg. 739
CAPITALDATA SAS—See HighCo S.A.; *Int'l*, pg. 3386
CAPITAL DEBT RECOVERY PROPRIETARY LIMITED—See Transaction Capital Limited; *Int'l*, pg. 7894
CAPITAL DELIVERY SYSTEM INC.—See NewSpring Capital LLC; *U.S. Private*, pg. 2918
CAPITAL DERMATOLOGY, LTD.—See Harvest Partners L.P.; *U.S. Private*, pg. 1876
CAPITAL DEVELOPMENT COMPANY; *U.S. Private*, pg. 739
CAPITAL DEVELOPMENT CO.; *U.S. Private*, pg. 739
CAPITAL DGMC INC.; *Int'l*, pg. 1310
CAPITAL DIALYSIS PARTNERSHIP—See DaVita Inc.; *U.S. Public*, pg. 636
CAPITAL DIRECTIONS, INC.; *U.S. Public*, pg. 431
CAPITAL DISTRIBUTING, INC.; *U.S. Private*, pg. 739
CAPITAL DISTRICT PHYSICIANS' HEALTH PLAN, INC.; *U.S. Private*, pg. 739
CAPITAL DISTRICT REGIONAL OFF-TRACK BETTING CORPORATION; *U.S. Private*, pg. 739
CAPITAL DRILLING CHILE S.A.—See Capital Limited; *Int'l*, pg. 1311
CAPITAL DRILLING EGYPT (LIMITED LIABILITY COMPANY)—See Capital Limited; *Int'l*, pg. 1311
CAPITAL DRILLING MOZAMBIQUE LIMITADA—See Capital Limited; *Int'l*, pg. 1311
CAPITAL DRILLING (SINGAPORE) PTE. LTD.—See Capital Limited; *Int'l*, pg. 1311
CAPITAL DRILLING ZAMBIA LIMITED—See Capital Limited; *Int'l*, pg. 1311
CAPITAL DYNAMICS AG—See Capital Dynamics Ltd.; *Int'l*, pg. 1310
CAPITAL DYNAMICS ASSET MANAGEMENT SDN. BHD.—See icapital.biz Berhad; *Int'l*, pg. 3578
CAPITAL DYNAMICS, INC.—See Capital Dynamics Ltd.; *Int'l*, pg. 1310
CAPITAL DYNAMICS LTD.; *Int'l*, pg. 1310
CAPITAL EDUCATION LLC—See Stride, Inc.; *U.S. Public*, pg. 1955
CAPITAL ELECTRIC CONSTRUCTION COMPANY INC.; *U.S. Private*, pg. 739

CAPITAL ELECTRIC CONSTRUCTION COMPANY INC. CORPORATE AFFILIATIONS

Company Index

CAPITAL ELECTRIC CONSTRUCTION COMPANY, INC.—See MDU Resources Group, Inc.; *U.S. Public*, pg. 1410
CAPITAL ELECTRIC COOPERATIVE, INC.; *U.S. Private*, pg. 740
CAPITAL ELECTRIC LINE BUILDERS, INC.—See MDU Resources Group, Inc.; *U.S. Public*, pg. 1410
CAPITAL ELEVATOR SERVICE, INC.—See KONE Oyj; *Int'l*, pg. 4249
CAPITAL ENGINEERING NETWORK PUBLIC COMPANY LIMITED; *Int'l*, pg. 1310
CAPITAL ENVIRONMENT HOLDINGS LIMITED; *Int'l*, pg. 1310
CAPITAL EQUIPMENT & HANDLING, INC.—See Mitsubishi Heavy Industries, Ltd.; *Int'l*, pg. 4959
CAPITAL ESTATE LIMITED; *Int'l*, pg. 1310
CAPITAL EXCAVATION COMPANY; *U.S. Private*, pg. 740
CAPITAL EYE INVESTMENTS LIMITED; *Int'l*, pg. 1310
CAPITAL FARM CREDIT, ACA; *U.S. Private*, pg. 740
CAPITAL FINANCE AUSTRALIA LIMITED—See Westpac Banking Corporation; *Int'l*, pg. 8391
CAPITAL FINANCE HOLDINGS LIMITED; *Int'l*, pg. 1311
CAPITAL FINANCE, LLC—See Capital Funding Group, Inc.; *U.S. Private*, pg. 740
CAPITAL FINANCIAL GLOBAL, INC.; *U.S. Public*, pg. 431
CAPITAL FINANCIAL GROUP, INC.—See Arrow Financial Corporation; *U.S. Public*, pg. 200
CAPITAL FINANCIAL HOLDINGS, INC.; *U.S. Public*, pg. 431
CAPITAL FINANCIAL MARKETS LIMITED—See Capital International Group Limited; *Int'l*, pg. 1311
CAPITAL FINANCIAL PRESS LIMITED; *Int'l*, pg. 1311
CAPITAL FINANCIAL SERVICES, INC.—See Capital Financial Holdings, Inc.; *U.S. Public*, pg. 431
CAPITAL FIN S.P.A.—See Banca IFIS S.p.A.; *Int'l*, pg. 815
CAPITAL FIRST LTD.—See IDFC First Bank Limited; *Int'l*, pg. 3592
CAPITAL FIRST REALTY INCORPORATED; *U.S. Private*, pg. 740
CAPITAL FIRST SECURITIES LIMITED—See IDFC First Bank Limited; *Int'l*, pg. 3593
CAPITAL FOR BUSINESS, INC.—See Commerce Bancshares, Inc.; *U.S. Public*, pg. 544
CAPITAL FOR COLLEAGUES PLC; *Int'l*, pg. 1311
CAPITAL FORD INC.; *U.S. Private*, pg. 740
CAPITAL FORD LINCOLN WINNIPEG; *Int'l*, pg. 1311
CAPITAL FOREST PRODUCTS INC.; *U.S. Private*, pg. 740
CAPITAL FUNDING BANCORP, INC.—See Capital Funding Group, Inc.; *U.S. Private*, pg. 740
CAPITAL FUNDING GMBH & CO. KG—See Advent International Corporation; *U.S. Private*, pg. 96
CAPITAL FUNDING GMBH & CO. KG—See Centerbridge Partners, L.P.; *U.S. Private*, pg. 812
CAPITAL FUNDING GROUP, INC.; *U.S. Private*, pg. 740
CAPITAL FUNDING, LLC—See Capital Funding Group, Inc.; *U.S. Private*, pg. 740
CAPITAL GAZETTE COMMUNICATIONS INC.—See Irish Times; *U.S. Private*, pg. 2138
CAPITALG MANAGEMENT COMPANY LLC—See Alphabet Inc.; *U.S. Public*, pg. 82
CAPITAL GRAND EST SAS; *Int'l*, pg. 1311
THE CAPITAL GROUP COMPANIES, INC.; *U.S. Private*, pg. 4004
CAPITAL GROUP HOLDINGS, INC.; *U.S. Public*, pg. 431
CAPITAL GROUP INTERNATIONAL, INC.—See The Capital Group Companies, Inc.; *U.S. Private*, pg. 4004
CAPITALGROUP LIMITED; *Int'l*, pg. 1314
CAPITAL GROWTH MANAGEMENT, L.P.—See Groupe BPCE; *Int'l*, pg. 3096
CAPITAL GUARDIAN LLC; *U.S. Private*, pg. 740
CAPITAL GUARDIAN TRUST COMPANY—See The Capital Group Companies, Inc.; *U.S. Private*, pg. 4004
CAPITAL HAND & PHYSICAL THERAPY, LIMITED PARTNERSHIP—See U.S. Physical Therapy, Inc.; *U.S. Public*, pg. 2214
CAPITAL HEALTH PLAN, INC.—See GuideWell Mutual Holding Corporation; *U.S. Private*, pg. 1813
CAPITAL HEALTH SYSTEMS INC.; *U.S. Private*, pg. 740
CAPITAL HOLDING GROUP, INC.; *U.S. Private*, pg. 740
CAPITAL HOLDING GROUP REIT; *Int'l*, pg. 1311
CAPITAL HOSPICE; *U.S. Private*, pg. 740
CAPITAL HOTELS PLC.; *Int'l*, pg. 1311
CAPITAL HOUSE INVESTMENT MANAGEMENT LIMITED—See NatWest Group plc; *Int'l*, pg. 5170
CAPITA LIFE & PENSIONS LIMITED—See Capita plc; *Int'l*, pg. 1308
CAPITA LIFE & PENSIONS REGULATED SERVICES LIMITED—See Capita plc; *Int'l*, pg. 1308
CAPITA LIFE & PENSIONS SERVICES LIMITED—See Capita plc; *Int'l*, pg. 1308
CAPITAL-IMAGE—See Environics Communications; *U.S. Private*, pg. 1407
CAPITAL IMPACT PARTNERS; *U.S. Private*, pg. 740
CAPITAL INDIA FINANCE LIMITED; *Int'l*, pg. 1311
CAPITAL INDUSTRIAL FINANCIAL SERVICES GROUP LIMITED; *Int'l*, pg. 1311
CAPITAL INDUSTRIES, INC.; *U.S. Private*, pg. 740
CAPITAL INSIGHT PARTNERS, LLC; *U.S. Private*, pg. 740
CAPITAL INSTITUTIONAL SERVICES, INC.; *U.S. Private*, pg. 740
CAPITAL INSURANCE ADVISORY CORP.—See Capital Securities Corporation; *Int'l*, pg. 1312
CAPITAL INSURANCE AGENCY CORP.—See Capital Securities Corporation; *Int'l*, pg. 1312
CAPITAL INSURANCE CORPORATION—See Mitsubishi HC Capital Inc.; *Int'l*, pg. 4950
CAPITAL INTERNATIONAL ASSET MANAGEMENT (CANADA), INC.—See The Capital Group Companies, Inc.; *U.S. Private*, pg. 4004
CAPITAL INTERNATIONAL CDPQ—See Caisse de Depot et Placement du Quebec; *Int'l*, pg. 1254
CAPITAL INTERNATIONAL GROUP LIMITED; *Int'l*, pg. 1311
CAPITAL INTERNATIONAL LIMITED—See Capital International Group Limited; *Int'l*, pg. 1311
CAPITAL INTERNATIONAL PRIVATE EQUITY FUNDS—See The Capital Group Companies, Inc.; *U.S. Private*, pg. 4004
CAPITAL INVESTMENT ADVISORS, INC.; *U.S. Private*, pg. 741
CAPITAL INVESTMENT & BROKERAGE COMPANY LIMITED—See Capital Bank; *Int'l*, pg. 1310
CAPITAL INVESTMENT COMPANY—See Capital Bank; *Int'l*, pg. 1310
CAPITAL INVESTMENT MANAGEMENT CORP.—See Capital Securities Corporation; *Int'l*, pg. 1312
CAPITAL INVESTMENTS & VENTURES CORP.; *U.S. Private*, pg. 741
CAPITAL IQ, INC. - CANADA BRANCH—See S&P Global Inc.; *U.S. Public*, pg. 1831
CAPITAL IQ INFORMATION SYSTEMS (INDIA) PVT. LTD.—See S&P Global Inc.; *U.S. Public*, pg. 1831
CAPITAL IR K.K.—See ad-comm Co., Ltd.; *Int'l*, pg. 123
CAPITAL KYUDEN CORPORATION—See Kyushu Electric Power Co., Inc.; *Int'l*, pg. 4367
CAPITAL LIGHTING, INC.; *U.S. Private*, pg. 741
CAPITAL LIMITED; *Int'l*, pg. 1311
CAPITAL LUMBER COMPANY; *U.S. Private*, pg. 741
CAPITAL MACHINE TECHNOLOGIES, INC.; *U.S. Private*, pg. 741
CAPITAL MANAGEMENT ASSOCIATES INC.—See Central Iowa Power Cooperative; *U.S. Private*, pg. 822
CAPITAL MANOR; *U.S. Private*, pg. 741
THE CAPITAL MARKETS COMPANY GMBH—See Clayton, Dubilier & Rice, LLC; *U.S. Private*, pg. 927
THE CAPITAL MARKETS COMPANY—See Clayton, Dubilier & Rice, LLC; *U.S. Private*, pg. 927
THE CAPITAL MARKETS COMPANY (UK) LIMITED—See Clayton, Dubilier & Rice, LLC; *U.S. Private*, pg. 927
CAPITAL MARKETS COMPLIANCE LLC—See Genstar Capital, LLC; *U.S. Private*, pg. 1677
CAPITAL MARKETS COOPERATIVE, LLC—See Computershare Limited; *Int'l*, pg. 1760
CAPITAL MARKET SERVICES LLC; *U.S. Private*, pg. 741
CAPITAL MEDICAL CENTER—See Apollo Global Management, Inc.; *U.S. Public*, pg. 154
CAPITAL MERCHANT BANKING AND FINANCE LIMITED; *Int'l*, pg. 1311
CAPITAL MERCURY SHIRTMAKERS LLC; *U.S. Private*, pg. 741
CAPITAL METALS PLC; *Int'l*, pg. 1312
CAPITAL MINING LIMITED; *Int'l*, pg. 1312
CAPITAL MOTOR SALES INC.; *U.S. Private*, pg. 741
CAPITAL MS&L—See Publicis Groupe S.A.; *Int'l*, pg. 6103
CAPITAL NOMURA SECURITIES PUBLIC COMPANY LIMITED—See Nomura Holdings, Inc.; *Int'l*, pg. 5409
CAPITAL NOVUS; *U.S. Private*, pg. 741
CAPITAL NURSERY CO.; *U.S. Private*, pg. 741
CAPITAL OFFICE PRODUCTS; *U.S. Private*, pg. 741
CAPITAL OIL INC.; *U.S. Private*, pg. 741
CAPITAL ONE AUTO RECEIVABLES LLC; *U.S. Private*, pg. 741
CAPITAL ONE BANK (USA), NATIONAL ASSOCIATION—See Capital One Financial Corporation; *U.S. Public*, pg. 431
CAPITAL ONE (EUROPE) PLC—See Capital One Financial Corporation; *U.S. Public*, pg. 431
CAPITAL ONE FINANCIAL CORPORATION; *U.S. Public*, pg. 431
CAPITAL ONE HOLDINGS LIMITED—See Capital One Financial Corporation; *U.S. Public*, pg. 431
CAPITAL ONE MULTI-ASSET EXECUTION TRUST; *U.S. Private*, pg. 741
CAPITAL ONE MULTIFAMILY FINANCE—See Capital One Financial Corporation; *U.S. Public*, pg. 431
CAPITAL ONE, N.A.—See Capital One Financial Corporation; *U.S. Public*, pg. 431
CAPITAL ONE SERVICES (CANADA) INC.—See Capital One Financial Corporation; *U.S. Public*, pg. 431
CAPITALONLINE DATA SERVICE CO., LTD.; *Int'l*, pg. 1314
CAPITAL OUTSOURCING GROUP (PTY) LIMITED—See Adcorp Holdings Limited; *Int'l*, pg. 127
CAPITAL PARK S.A.—See Madison International Realty, LLC; *U.S. Private*, pg. 2543
CAPITAL PARTNERS LLC; *U.S. Private*, pg. 741
CAPITAL PARTNERS MORTGAGE, LLC—See Rithm Capital Corp.; *U.S. Public*, pg. 1800
CAPITAL PARTNERS S.A.; *Int'l*, pg. 1312
CAPITALPART PARTICIPACOES S.A.; *Int'l*, pg. 1314
CAPITAL PARTY RENTALS LLC—See Dubin Clark & Company, Inc.; *U.S. Private*, pg. 1283
CAPITAL PATHOLOGY PTY LIMITED—See Sonic Healthcare Limited; *Int'l*, pg. 7096
CAPITAL PEOPLE S.A.; *Int'l*, pg. 1312
CAPITAL PLAZA HOLDING GMBH & CO. SINGAPUR KG—See Munchener Ruckversicherungs AG; *Int'l*, pg. 5085
CAPITAL POINT LTD.; *Int'l*, pg. 1312
CAPITAL POWER CORPORATION; *Int'l*, pg. 1312
CAPITAL PRECAST LIMITED—See Penney Group; *Int'l*, pg. 5787
CAPITAL PRIVATE FINANCE LIMITED—See The Skipton Building Society; *Int'l*, pg. 7686
CAPITAL PROCESSING INT'L INC.; *U.S. Private*, pg. 741
CAPITAL PROFESSIONAL LIMITED; *Int'l*, pg. 1312
CAPITAL PROPERTIES CO., LTD.—See Sotetsu Holdings, Inc.; *Int'l*, pg. 7112
CAPITAL PROPERTIES, INC.; *U.S. Public*, pg. 432
CAPITAL PROPERTIES, LLC—See Sage Partners, LLC; *U.S. Private*, pg. 3526
CAPITAL PROPERTY FUND NOMINEES PROPRIETARY LIMITED—See Barclays PLC; *Int'l*, pg. 862
CAPITAL PUMPING, LP—See Concrete Pumping Holdings, Inc.; *U.S. Public*, pg. 566
CAPITAL RADIOLOGY PTY LTD—See Capitol Health Limited; *Int'l*, pg. 1314
CAPITAL RADIOLOGY WA PTY LTD—See Capitol Health Limited; *Int'l*, pg. 1314
CAPITAL RADIO PRODUCTIONS LTD—See News Corporation; *U.S. Public*, pg. 1520
CAPITAL READY MIX LIMITED—See Penney Group; *Int'l*, pg. 5787
CAPITAL REAL ESTATE PROJECTS B.S.C.—See GFH Financial Group B.S.C.; *Int'l*, pg. 2956
CAPITAL REALM FINANCIAL HOLDINGS GROUP LIMITED; *Int'l*, pg. 1312
CAPITAL RECONSTRUCTION, INC.; *U.S. Private*, pg. 741
THE CAPITAL REFRIGERATION COMPANY—See Comfort Systems USA, Inc.; *U.S. Public*, pg. 544
CAPITAL REGIONAL HEART ASSOCIATES LLC—See HCA Healthcare, Inc.; *U.S. Public*, pg. 992
CAPITAL REGIONAL MEDICAL CENTER—See HCA Healthcare, Inc.; *U.S. Public*, pg. 992
CAPITAL & REGIONAL PLC; *Int'l*, pg. 1309
CAPITAL & REGIONAL PROPERTY MANAGEMENT LIMITED—See Capital & Regional plc; *Int'l*, pg. 1309
CAPITAL REGIONAL PSYCHIATRY ASSOCIATES, LLC—See HCA Healthcare, Inc.; *U.S. Public*, pg. 992
CAPITAL REGION MEDICAL CENTER INC.—See Curators of the University of Missouri; *U.S. Private*, pg. 1124
CAPITAL RELOCATION SERVICES LLC—See JK Moving & Storage Inc.; *U.S. Private*, pg. 2211
THE CAPITAL RESEARCH & MANAGEMENT CO.—See The Capital Group Companies, Inc.; *U.S. Private*, pg. 4004
CAPITAL RESOURCE PARTNERS, L.P.; *U.S. Private*, pg. 741
CAPITAL RESOURCES, INC.—See Alex Lee, Inc.; *U.S. Private*, pg. 163
CAPITAL RESOURCES OF VIRGINIA, INC.—See Alex Lee, Inc.; *U.S. Private*, pg. 163
CAPITAL RESTAURANT CONCEPTS, LTD.; *U.S. Private*, pg. 742
CAPITAL RIVERS COMMERCIAL LLC; *U.S. Private*, pg. 742
CAPITAL SAFETY GROUP EMEA—See 3M Company; *U.S. Public*, pg. 8
CAPITAL SAFETY ROW LTD—See 3M Company; *U.S. Public*, pg. 8
CAPITAL SECURITIES CO., LTD.—See Beijing Capital Group Co., Ltd.; *Int'l*, pg. 947
CAPITAL SECURITIES CORPORATION; *Int'l*, pg. 1312
CAPITAL SECURITIES (HONG KONG) LTD.—See Capital Securities Corporation; *Int'l*, pg. 1312
CAPITAL SENIOR LIVING CORPORATION—See Sonida Senior Living, Inc.; *U.S. Public*, pg. 1903
CAPITAL SENIOR LIVING ILM-B, INC.—See Sonida Senior Living, Inc.; *U.S. Public*, pg. 1903
CAPITAL SERVICES, INC.—See O2 Investment Partners, LLC; *U.S. Private*, pg. 2982
CAPITAL S.M.A.R.T. REPAIRS AUSTRALIA PTY LTD—See AMA Group Limited; *Int'l*, pg. 403
CAPITAL S.M.A.R.T. REPAIRS NEW ZEALAND PTY LTD—See AMA Group Limited; *Int'l*, pg. 403
CAPITALSOURCE—See Banc of California, Inc.; *U.S. Public*, pg. 269
CAPITALSOUTH CORP.; *U.S. Private*, pg. 742
CAPITAL SOUTHWEST CORPORATION; *U.S. Public*, pg. 432
CAPITAL SOUTHWEST VENTURE CORPORATION—See Capital Southwest Corporation; *U.S. Public*, pg. 432

CAPITAL SPORTS GROUP OF COMPANIES; *Int'l*, pg. 1312
CAPITALSPRING LLC; *U.S. Private*, pg. 742
CAPITAL SPRING—See American Securities LLC; *U.S. Private*, pg. 249
CAPITAL SQUARE PARTNERS PTE LTD.; *Int'l*, pg. 1312
CAPITAL SQUARE SDN. BHD.—See Bandar Raya Developments Berhad; *Int'l*, pg. 829
CAPITAL STEEL SERVICE, LLC.—See Hill & Smith PLC; *Int'l*, pg. 3391
CAPITAL STREET DELAWARE LP—See Banco Santander, S.A.; *Int'l*, pg. 827
CAPITAL TECHNOLOGIES, INC—See Hess Industries, Inc.; *U.S. Private*, pg. 1927
CAPITAL TECHSEARCH, INC.; *U.S. Private*, pg. 742
CAPITAL TELECOMMUNICATIONS, INC.; *U.S. Private*, pg. 742
CAPITAL TERMINAL COMPANY—See Capital Properties, Inc.; *U.S. Public*, pg. 432
THE CAPITAL TIMES COMPANY; *U.S. Private*, pg. 4004
THE CAPITAL TIMES—See Lee Enterprises, Incorporated; *U.S. Public*, pg. 1299
THE CAPITAL TIMES—See The Capital Times Company; *U.S. Private*, pg. 4004
CAPITAL TIRE, INC.; *U.S. Private*, pg. 742
CAPITAL TOWER & COMMUNICATIONS INC; *U.S. Private*, pg. 742
CAPITAL TRACTOR INC.; *U.S. Private*, pg. 742
CAPITAL TRADE LINKS LIMITED; *Int'l*, pg. 1312
CAPITAL TRANSMISSION S.A.—See Banque Cantonale de Geneve S.A.; *Int'l*, pg. 852
CAPITAL TRANSPORTATION LOGISTICS, LLC—See Roadrunner Transportation Systems, Inc.; *U.S. Public*, pg. 1802
CAPITAL TRANSPORTATION SOLUTIONS LLC—See Odyssey Logistics & Technology Corp.; *U.S. Private*, pg. 2996
CAPITAL TREASURY SERVICES LIMITED—See Capital International Group Limited; *Int'l*, pg. 1311
CAPITAL TRISTATE CO.—See Sonepar S.A.; *Int'l*, pg. 7093
CAPITAL TRISTATE—See Sonepar S.A.; *Int'l*, pg. 7093
CAPITAL TRUE PARTNER TECHNOLOGY CO., LTD.—See True Partner Capital Holding Limited; *Int'l*, pg 7941
CAPITAL TRUST LIMITED; *Int'l*, pg. 1313
CAPITALVALUE HOMES LIMITED—See CapitaLand Investment Limited; *Int'l*, pg. 1313
CAPITAL VALVES LIMITED—See NOV, Inc.; *U.S. Public*, pg. 1544
CAPITAL VC LIMITED; *Int'l*, pg. 1313
CAPITAL VIDEO CORPORATION; *U.S. Private*, pg. 742
CAPITALVIEW INVESTMENT PARTNERS, LLC; *U.S. Private*, pg. 742
CAPITAL VISION SAS—See Iron Mountain Incorporated; *U.S. Public*, pg. 1172
CAPITAL VOCATIONAL SPECIALISTS—See GIC Pte. Ltd.; *Int'l*, pg. 2964
CAPITAL VOCATIONAL SPECIALISTS—See Leonard Green & Partners, L.P.; *U.S. Private*, pg. 2425
CAPITAL WELDING, INC.; *U.S. Private*, pg. 742
CAPITAL WELDING INC.—See Futuramic Tool & Engineering Company Inc.; *U.S. Private*, pg. 1626
CAPITAL WHOLESALE ELECTRIC CO.; *U.S. Private*, pg. 742
CAPITAL WHOLESALE MEATS INC.; *U.S. Private*, pg. 742
CAPITALWORKS EMERGING MARKETS ACQUISITION CORPORATION; *U.S. Public*, pg. 432
CAPITALWORKS INVESTMENT PARTNERS (PTY) LTD; *Int'l*, pg. 1314
CAPITALWORKS, LLC; *U.S. Private*, pg. 742
CAPITAL WORLD LIMITED; *Int'l*, pg. 1313
CAPITAL Z PARTNERS MANAGEMENT, LLC—See Paine Schwartz Partners, LLC; *U.S. Private*, pg. 3075
CAPITA MORTGAGE SOFTWARE SOLUTIONS LTD.—See Capita plc; *Int'l*, pg. 1308
CAPITAN CORPORATION—See Duke Energy Corporation; *U.S. Public*, pg. 690
CAPITANIA SECURITIES II FII FUND; *Int'l*, pg. 1314
CAPITAN SILVER CORP.; *Int'l*, pg. 1314
CAPITA PLC; *Int'l*, pg. 1308
CAPITA RESOURCING LIMITED—See Capita plc; *Int'l*, pg. 1308
CAPITA SECURE INFORMATION SYSTEMS LIMITED—See Capita plc; *Int'l*, pg. 1308
CAPITA SYMONDS LIMITED—See Capita plc; *Int'l*, pg. 1308
CAPITA TECHNOLOGIES, INC.; *U.S. Private*, pg. 738
CAPITA TRUST COMPANY LIMITED—See Capita plc; *Int'l*, pg. 1308
CAPITA WEST GMBH—See Capita plc; *Int'l*, pg. 1308
CAPITEC BANK HOLDINGS LIMITED; *Int'l*, pg. 1314
CAPITEC BANK LIMITED—See Capitec Bank Holdings Limited; *Int'l*, pg. 1314
CAPITEQ LIMITED—See Bristow Group, Inc.; *U.S. Public*, pg. 387
CAPITOL ADVANTAGE LLC—See The Economist Group Limited; *Int'l*, pg. 7637

CAPITOL, AKCIOVA SPOLOCNOS—See Vienna Insurance Group AG Wiener Versicherung Gruppe; *Int'l*, pg. 8194
CAPITOL AUTO GROUP, INC.; *U.S. Private*, pg. 743
CAPITOL AUTO GROUP; *U.S. Private*, pg. 742
CAPITOL BEARING SERVICE; *U.S. Private*, pg. 743
CAPITOL BEVERAGE SALES L.P.; *U.S. Private*, pg. 743
CAPITOL BODY SHOP INC.; *U.S. Private*, pg. 743
CAPITOL BROADCASTING COMPANY, INC.; *U.S. Private*, pg. 743
CAPITOL BROADCASTING COMPANY, INC. - SUNRISE BROADCASTING DIVISION—See Capitol Broadcasting Company, Inc.; *U.S. Private*, pg. 743
CAPITOL BUILDERS HARDWARE INC.; *U.S. Private*, pg. 743
CAPITOL BUILDING SUPPLY, INC.—See GMS Inc.; *U.S. Public*, pg. 947
CAPITOL BUILDING SUPPLY—See GMS Inc.; *U.S. Public*, pg. 947
CAPITOL BURGER, LLC—See Sonnet BioTherapeutics Holdings, Inc.; *U.S. Public*, pg. 1904
CAPITOL BUSINESS EQUIPMENT, INC.—See Champion Industries, Inc.; *U.S. Public*, pg. 478
CAPITOL BUSINESS INTERIORS—See Champion Industries, Inc.; *U.S. Public*, pg. 478
CAPITOL CHILLED FOODS (AUSTRALIA) PTY. LIMITED—See Bega Cheese Ltd.; *Int'l*, pg. 940
CAPITOL CHRISTIAN MUSIC GROUP—See Universal Music Group N.V.; *Int'l*, pg. 8079
CAPITOL CITY PUBLISHING COMPANY, INC.—See Alden Global Capital LLC; *U.S. Private*, pg. 156
CAPITOL CLEANING CONTRACTORS, INC.; *U.S. Private*, pg. 743
CAPITOL CLUTCH & BRAKE, INC.; *U.S. Private*, pg. 743
CAPITOL CONCIERGE, INC.; *U.S. Private*, pg. 743
CAPITOL CONSULTANTS INC.; *U.S. Private*, pg. 743
CAPITOL CONTRACTORS INC.; *U.S. Private*, pg. 743
CAPITOL COUNTY MUTUAL FIRE INSURANCE CO.—See Kemper Corporation; *U.S. Public*, pg. 1221
CAPITOL CROSSING ADVISORS, LLC—See W.R. Berkley Corporation; *U.S. Public*, pg. 2317
CAPITOL DAIRY SOLUTIONS—See AptarGroup, Inc.; *U.S. Public*, pg. 174
CAPITOL DEVELOPMENT GROUP LLC; *U.S. Private*, pg. 743
CAPITOL DISPOSAL, INC.—See Waste Management, Inc.; *U.S. Public*, pg. 2330
CAPITOL DISTRICT SUPPLY CO, INC.—See Watsco, Inc.; *U.S. Public*, pg. 2336
CAPITOL DOOR SERVICES—See ASSA ABLOY AB; *Int'l*, pg. 639
CAPITOLE FINANCE SAS—See Groupe BPCE; *Int'l*, pg. 3093
CAPITOL ENGINEERING CO.—See Southfield Capital Advisors, LLC; *U.S. Private*, pg. 3736
CAPITOL ENTERTAINMENT MANAGEMENT CO.; *U.S. Private*, pg. 743
CAPITOL ENVIRONMENTAL SERVICES, INC.; *U.S. Private*, pg. 743
CAPITOL EQUIPMENT—See Canerector Inc.; *Int'l*, pg. 1290
CAPITOL FEDERAL FINANCIAL, INC.; *U.S. Public*, pg. 432
CAPITOL FEDERAL SAVINGS BANK—See Capitol Federal Financial, Inc.; *U.S. Public*, pg. 432
CAPITOL FINANCIAL STRATEGIES, LLC; *U.S. Private*, pg. 743
CAPITOL FUNDS INC.; *U.S. Private*, pg. 744
CAPITOL GROUP INC.; *U.S. Private*, pg. 744
CAPITOL HARDWARE COMPANY, INC.; *U.S. Private*, pg. 744
CAPITOL HARDWARE, INC.—See Leggett & Platt, Incorporated; *U.S. Public*, pg. 1301
CAPITOL HEALTH LIMITED; *Int'l*, pg. 1314
CAPITOL HILL HOTEL—See Marriott International, Inc.; *U.S. Public*, pg. 1371
CAPITOL INDEMNITY CORPORATION—See Berkshire Hathaway Inc.; *U.S. Public*, pg. 298
CAPITOL INFORMATION GROUP, INC.; *U.S. Private*, pg. 744
CAPITOL INTERIOR PRODUCTS, INC.—See GMS Inc.; *U.S. Public*, pg. 947
CAPITOL LIFE INSURANCE COMPANY—See National Health Corporation; *U.S. Private*, pg. 2855
CAPITOL LIGHTING; *U.S. Private*, pg. 744
CAPITOL LIGHTING—See Capitol Lighting; *U.S. Private*, pg. 744
CAPITOL MANUFACTURING CO.—See Phoenix Forging Company, Inc.; *U.S. Private*, pg. 3173
CAPITOL MATERIALS COASTAL, INC.—See GMS Inc.; *U.S. Public*, pg. 948
CAPITOL MATERIALS, INCORPORATED—See GMS Inc.; *U.S. Public*, pg. 948
CAPITOL MEDIA SOLUTIONS; *U.S. Private*, pg. 744
CAPITOL MERIDIAN PARTNERS; *U.S. Private*, pg. 744
THE CAPITOL MUSIC GROUP—See Universal Music Group N.V.; *Int'l*, pg. 8079
CAPITOL NATIONAL BANK; *U.S. Private*, pg. 744

CAPITOL NEWS COMPANY, LLC—See Sinclair, Inc.; *U.S. Public*, pg. 1885
CAPITOL OFFICE SOLUTIONS—See Xerox Holdings Corporation; *U.S. Public*, pg. 2389
CAPITOL PAIN INSTITUTE PA—See Iron Path Capital, L.P.; *U.S. Private*, pg. 2139
CAPITOL PARTNERS LLC; *U.S. Private*, pg. 744
CAPITOL PAVING OF D.C., INC.; *U.S. Private*, pg. 744
CAPITOL PEAK PARTNERS, LLC; *U.S. Private*, pg. 744
CAPITOL PIPE & STEEL—See Canerector Inc.; *Int'l*, pg. 1290
CAPITOL PIPE SUPPORTS—See Canerector Inc.; *Int'l*, pg. 1290
CAPITOL PLASTIC PRODUCTS, LLC—See AptarGroup, Inc.; *U.S. Public*, pg. 174
CAPITOL PLYWOOD INC.; *U.S. Private*, pg. 744
CAPITOL PLYWOOD INC.—See Capitol Plywood Inc.; *U.S. Private*, pg. 744
CAPITOL RADIO NETWORK, INC.—See Capitol Broadcasting Company, Inc.; *U.S. Private*, pg. 743
CAPITOL RECORDS, INC.—See Universal Music Group N.V.; *Int'l*, pg. 8079
CAPITOL SCIENTIFIC, INC.; *U.S. Private*, pg. 744
CAPITOL STAMPINGS CORP.—See MiddleGround Management, LP; *U.S. Private*, pg. 2711
CAPITOL STEEL & IRON COMPANY—See Rasmussen Group Inc.; *U.S. Private*, pg. 3356
CAPITOL SUBURU—See Capitol Auto Group, Inc.; *U.S. Private*, pg. 743
CAPITOL SUPPLY, INC.; *U.S. Private*, pg. 744
CAPITOL USA LLC; *U.S. Private*, pg. 744
CAPITOL VENDING & COFFEE—See Sodexo S.A.; *Int'l*, pg. 7047
CAPITOL VIAL, INC.—See Thermo Fisher Scientific Inc.; *U.S. Public*, pg. 2145
CAPITOL VIEW, LLC—See E*TRADE Financial Corporation; *U.S. Private*, pg. 1302
CAPITOL VOLKSWAGEN, INC.; *U.S. Private*, pg. 745
CAPITOL W.B.C. D.O.O.—See Capitol W.B.C. PLC; *Int'l*, pg. 1314
CAPITOL W.B.C. PLC; *Int'l*, pg. 1314
CAPITOL WHOLESALE FENCE COMPANY, INC.—See The Sterling Group, L.P.; *U.S. Private*, pg. 4122
CAPITOL WOOD FLOORS & SUPPLIES INC.; *U.S. Private*, pg. 745
CAPITON AG; *Int'l*, pg. 1314
CAPIZZI INSURANCE AGENCY—See Inszone Insurance Services, LLC; *U.S. Private*, pg. 2096
CAPLAN CORPORATION—See ITOCHU Corporation; *Int'l*, pg. 3835
CAPLAND ASCENDAS REIT; *Int'l*, pg. 1314
CAPLAST KUNSTSTOFFVERARBEITUNGS GMBH—See KAP Beteiligungs-AG; *Int'l*, pg. 4076
CAPLINE PIPELINE COMPANY LLC—See Plains All American Pipeline, L.P.; *U.S. Public*, pg. 1696
CAPLIN POINT LABORATORIES LIMITED - CP-I FACTORY—See Caplin Point Laboratories Limited; *Int'l*, pg. 1315
CAPLIN POINT LABORATORIES LIMITED - CP-II FACTORY—See Caplin Point Laboratories Limited; *Int'l*, pg. 1315
CAPLIN POINT LABORATORIES LIMITED; *Int'l*, pg. 1315
CAPLIN STERILES LIMITED—See Caplin Point Laboratories Limited; *Int'l*, pg. 1315
C.A.P.L. LIMITED—See Patterson Companies, Inc.; *U.S. Public*, pg. 1653
CAP LOGISTICS INC.; *U.S. Private*, pg. 737
CAPLUGS—See Windjammer Capital Investors, LLC; *U.S. Private*, pg. 4538
CA PLUS LIMITED—See Gentrack Group Limited; *Int'l*, pg. 2929
CAPMAN AB—See CapMan PLC; *Int'l*, pg. 1315
CAPMAN CAPITAL MANAGEMENT OY—See CapMan PLC; *Int'l*, pg. 1315
CAPMAN FINANCIALS LIMITED; *Int'l*, pg. 1315
CAPMAN FUND INVESTMENT SICAV-SIF—See CapMan PLC; *Int'l*, pg. 1315
CAPMAN GROWTH EQUITY OY—See CapMan PLC; *Int'l*, pg. 1315
CAPMAN (GUERNSEY) LTD.—See CapMan PLC; *Int'l*, pg. 1315
CAPMAN NORWAY AS—See CapMan PLC; *Int'l*, pg. 1315
CAPMAN PLC; *Int'l*, pg. 1315
CAPMAN PRIVATE EQUITY ADVISORS LIMITED—See CapMan PLC; *Int'l*, pg. 1315
CAPMAN PROCUREMENT SERVICES (CAPS) OY—See CapMan PLC; *Int'l*, pg. 1315
CAPMAN PUBLIC MARKET MANAGER S.A.—See CapMan PLC; *Int'l*, pg. 1315
CAPMAN REAL ESTATE DENMARK, FILIAL AV CAPMAN AB—See CapMan PLC; *Int'l*, pg. 1315
CAPMAN REAL ESTATE OY—See CapMan PLC; *Int'l*, pg. 1315
CAPMAN SWEDEN AB—See CapMan PLC; *Int'l*, pg. 1315
CAPMONT GMBH; *Int'l*, pg. 1315
CAPNIA, INC.—See Soleno Therapeutics, Inc.; *U.S. Public*, pg. 1900
CAP OCEAN S.A.S.—See Nissui Corporation; *Int'l*, pg. 5377

CAPOL GMBH—See Freudenberg SE; *Int'l*, pg. 2782
CAPOL LLC—See Freudenberg SE; *Int'l*, pg. 2782
C&A POLSKA SP.Z.O.O.—See COFRA Holding AG; *Int'l*, pg. 1694
CAPOL (U.K.) LIMITED—See Freudenberg SE; *Int'l*, pg. 2782
CAPONIGRO PUBLIC RELATIONS, INC.; *U.S. Private*, pg. 745
CAPORIN VOYAGES SARL—See Die Schweizerische Post AG; *Int'l*, pg. 2112
CAPPADONNA ELECTRICAL MANAGEMENT CORPORATION; *U.S. Private*, pg. 745
CAP PARTS AG; *Int'l*, pg. 1300
CAPPCO TUBULAR PRODUCTS USA, LLC—See Icahn Enterprises L.P.; *U.S. Public*, pg. 1084
CAPPELEN DAMM AS—See Egmont Fonden; *Int'l*, pg. 2325
CAPPELLE FRERES (UK) LTD.—See Cappelle Pignenes N.V.; *Int'l*, pg. 1315
CAPPELLE INC.—See Cappelle Pignenes N.V.; *Int'l*, pg. 1315
CAPPELLE PIGMENTS NV—See American Securities LLC; *U.S. Private*, pg. 251
CAPPELLE PIGNENES N.V.; *Int'l*, pg. 1315
CAPPELLI MILES (SPRING); *U.S. Private*, pg. 745
CAPPELLI MILES (SPRING)—See Cappelli Miles (Spring); *U.S. Private*, pg. 745
CAPPER'S INSURANCE SERVICE INC.—See The Nutting Company, Inc.; *U.S. Private*, pg. 4086
CAPPEX.COM LLC—See EAB Global, Inc.; *U.S. Private*, pg. 1308
CAPPO MANAGEMENT II, INC.—See Victory Automotive Group, Inc.; *U.S. Private*, pg. 4378
CAPPO MANAGEMENT, INC.—See Victory Automotive Group, Inc.; *U.S. Private*, pg. 4378
CAPPO MANAGEMENT VII, INC.—See Victory Automotive Group, Inc.; *U.S. Private*, pg. 4378
CAPPO MANAGEMENT VI, INC.—See Victory Automotive Group, Inc.; *U.S. Private*, pg. 4378
CAPPO MANAGEMENT XVII, INC.—See Victory Automotive Group, Inc.; *U.S. Private*, pg. 4378
CAPPO MANAGEMENT XXIII, INC.—See Victory Automotive Group, Inc.; *U.S. Private*, pg. 4378
CAPPS INSURANCE AGENCY-MT. PLEASANT LTD.—See Galiot Insurance Services, Inc.; *U.S. Private*, pg. 1638
CAPPS MANUFACTURING, INC.; *U.S. Private*, pg. 745
CAPPS RENT-A-CAR INC.; *U.S. Private*, pg. 745
CAPPTA S.A.—See StoneCo Ltd.; *Int'l*, pg. 7222
CAPPUCCINO'S—See The Copper Cellar Corporation; *U.S. Private*, pg. 4014
CAPP USA, INC.; *U.S. Private*, pg. 745
CAPPY DEVLIN INTERNATIONAL; *U.S. Private*, pg. 745
CAPRAL ALUMINIUM-SHEETS—See Capral Limited; *Int'l*, pg. 1315
CAPRAL LIMITED; *Int'l*, pg. 1315
CAP RECHTSSCHUTZ VERSICHERUNG—See Allianz SE; *Int'l*, pg. 350
CAPREIT INC.; *U.S. Private*, pg. 745
CAPRES A/S—See KLA Corporation; *U.S. Public*, pg. 1267
CAPRI ATLANTIQUE—See Caisse des Depots et Consignations; *Int'l*, pg. 1258
CAPRI CAPITAL PARTNERS, LLC; *U.S. Private*, pg. 745
CAPRICE RESOURCES LIMITED; *Int'l*, pg. 1316
CAPRICORN AMERICAS MEXICO S. DE R.L. DE C.V.—See Capricorn Energy PLC; *Int'l*, pg. 1316
CAPRICORN CHEMICALS LTD.—See Hobart Enterprises Ltd; *Int'l*, pg. 3437
CAPRICORN ENERGY LIMITED—See Capricorn Energy PLC; *Int'l*, pg. 1316
CAPRICORN ENERGY PLC; *Int'l*, pg. 1316
CAPRICORN HOLDINGS, INC.; *U.S. Private*, pg. 745
CAPRICORN INVESTMENT PARTNERS LIMITED; *Int'l*, pg. 1316
CAPRICORN METALS LTD.; *Int'l*, pg. 1316
CAPRICORN SOCIETY LIMITED; *Int'l*, pg. 1317
CAPRICORN SYSTEMS GLOBAL SOLUTIONS LIMITED; *Int'l*, pg. 1317
CAPRICORN SYSTEMS, INC.—See Smart IMS; *U.S. Private*, pg. 3691
CAPRICORNUS EVEN EMPREENDIMENTOS IMOBILIARIOS LTDA.—See Even Construtora e Incorporadora S.A.; *Int'l*, pg. 2561
CAPRICOR THERAPEUTICS, INC.; *U.S. Public*, pg. 432
CAPRI FOODS INC.; *U.S. Private*, pg. 745
CAPRIGHT PROPERTY ADVISORS, LLC; *U.S. Private*, pg. 745
CAPRI GLOBAL CAPITAL LIMITED; *Int'l*, pg. 1315
CAPRI GROUP SRL—See Kering S.A.; *Int'l*, pg. 4134
CAPRIHANS INDIA LIMITED—See Bilcare Limited; *Int'l*, pg. 1023
CAPRI HOLDINGS LIMITED; *Int'l*, pg. 1316
CAPRI LYON MEDITERRANEE—See Caisse des Depots et Consignations; *Int'l*, pg. 1258
CAPRIOLO VENTURINI S.R.L.—See Pozzoni S.p.A.; *Int'l*, pg. 5949
CAPRIOTTI'S SANDWICH SHOP; *U.S. Private*, pg. 745
CAPROCK ENCLOSURES, LLC—See NN, Inc.; *U.S. Public*, pg. 1531

CAPROCK MANUFACTURING, INC.—See NN, Inc.; *U.S. Public*, pg. 1531
CAPROCK MINING CORP.; *Int'l*, pg. 1317
CAPRO CORP.; *Int'l*, pg. 1317
CA PROGRAMAS DE COMPUTADOR PARTICIPACOAS SERVICOS LTDA.—See Broadcom Inc.; *U.S. Public*, pg. 389
CAPROLACTAM CHEMICALS LIMITED; *Int'l*, pg. 1317
CAPRON GMBH—See Thor Industries, Inc.; *U.S. Public*, pg. 2156
CAPSA SOLUTIONS LLC—See Levine Leichtman Capital Partners, LLC; *U.S. Private*, pg. 2435
CAP S.A.; *Int'l*, pg. 1300
CAPSECUR CONSEIL—See Randstad N.V.; *Int'l*, pg. 6201
CAP SECURITE SAS—See VINCI S.A.; *Int'l*, pg. 8213
CAPSENSIXX AG; *Int'l*, pg. 1317
CAP SERVICES, INC.; *U.S. Private*, pg. 737
CAPSICUM RE LATIN AMERICA CORRETORA DE RESSEGUROS LTDA.—See Arthur J. Gallagher & Co.; *U.S. Public*, pg. 204
CAP SOGETI 2005 S.A.S.—See Capgemini SE; *Int'l*, pg. 1303
CAPSONIC GROUP LLC; *U.S. Private*, pg. 745
CAPSOURCE INC.; *U.S. Private*, pg. 745
CAPSPECIALTY, INC.—See Berkshire Hathaway Inc.; *U.S. Public*, pg. 298
CAPSPECIALTY—See Berkshire Hathaway Inc.; *U.S. Public*, pg. 298
CAPSPIRE, INC.; *U.S. Private*, pg. 746
CAPSTAN CALIFORNIA—See Capstan Inc.; *U.S. Private*, pg. 746
CAPSTAN FINANCIAL CONSULTING GROUP LLC; *U.S. Private*, pg. 746
CAPSTAN INC.; *U.S. Private*, pg. 746
CAPSTAR BANK—See Old National Bancorp; *U.S. Public*, pg. 1567
CAPSTAR FINANCIAL HOLDINGS, INC.—See Old National Bancorp; *U.S. Public*, pg. 1566
CAPSTAR SAN FRANCISCO COMPANY, LLC—See Acron AG; *Int'l*, pg. 109
CAPSTEAD, INC.—See Franklin Resources, Inc.; *U.S. Public*, pg. 879
CAPSTEAD MORTGAGE CORPORATION—See Franklin Resources, Inc.; *U.S. Public*, pg. 879
CAPSTONE BROKERAGE, INC.; *U.S. Private*, pg. 746
CAPSTONE COMMODITIES, LLC—See The Andersons Incorporated; *U.S. Public*, pg. 2034
CAPSTONE COMMUNITY ACTION; *U.S. Private*, pg. 746
CAPSTONE COMPANIES, INC.; *U.S. Public*, pg. 432
THE CAPSTONE CONTRACTING COMPANY—See Hourigan Construction Corp.; *U.S. Private*, pg. 1991
CAPSTONE COPPER CORP.; *Int'l*, pg. 1317
CAPSTONE CORPORATION; *U.S. Private*, pg. 746
CAPSTONE EQUIPMENT LEASING LLC—See Wolf Energy Services Inc.; *U.S. Private*, pg. 2376
CAPSTONE FINANCIAL GROUP, INC.; *U.S. Private*, pg. 746
CAPSTONE GREEN ENERGY CORPORATION; *U.S. Private*, pg. 746
CAPSTONE GROUP, INC.; *U.S. Private*, pg. 746
THE CAPSTONE GROUP RECRUITMENT AND CONSULTING (THAILAND) LTD.—See en-japan inc.; *Int'l*, pg. 2395
CAPSTONE HEADWATERS LLC—See Huntington Bancshares Incorporated; *U.S. Public*, pg. 1071
CAPSTONE INDUSTRIES, INC.—See Capstone Companies, Inc.; *U.S. Public*, pg. 432
CAPSTONE INFORMATION TECHNOLOGIES INCORPORATED—See Frontenac Company LLC; *U.S. Private*, pg. 1613
CAPSTONE INFRASTRUCTURE CORPORATION—See iCON Infrastructure LLP; *Int'l*, pg. 3583
CAPSTONE INSURANCE BROKERAGE LIMITED—See Brown & Brown, Inc.; *U.S. Public*, pg. 400
CAPSTONE INTERNATIONAL LTD—See Toyota Tsusho Corporation; *Int'l*, pg. 7875
CAPSTONE LOGISTICS, LLC—See H.I.G. Capital, LLC; *U.S. Private*, pg. 1827
CAPSTONE MECHANICAL, LP.—See Partners Group Holding AG; *Int'l*, pg. 5750
CAPSTONE PARTNERS LLC—See Huntington Bancshares Incorporated; *U.S. Public*, pg. 1071
CAPSTONE PARTNERS LP—See Mizuho Financial Group, Inc.; *Int'l*, pg. 4997
CAPSTONE POLYWEAVE PRIVATE LIMITED—See Clearlake Capital Group, L.P.; *U.S. Private*, pg. 935
CAPSTONE PRECISION GROUP, LLC—See Patria Oyj; *Int'l*, pg. 5757
CAPSTONE PRESS, INC.—See Coughlan Companies, Inc.; *U.S. Public*, pg. 1064
CAPSTONE SYSTEMS, INC.; *Int'l*, pg. 1317
CAPSTONE TECHNOLOGIES GROUP INC.; *Int'l*, pg. 1317
CAPSTONE TECHNOLOGY CORP.—See Spectris Plc; *Int'l*, pg. 7130
CAPSTONE THERAPEUTICS CORP.; *U.S. Public*, pg. 432
CAPSTONE TITLE, LLC; *U.S. Private*, pg. 746

CAPSTONE TURBINE INTERNATIONAL, INC.—See Capstone Green Energy Corporation; *U.S. Private*, pg. 746
CAPSTRAT; *U.S. Private*, pg. 746
THE CAPSTREET GROUP LLC; *U.S. Private*, pg. 4004
CAPSUGEL AUSTRALIA PTY. LTD.—See Lonza Group AG; *Int'l*, pg. 4553
CAPSUGEL BELGIUM NV—See Lonza Group AG; *Int'l*, pg. 4553
CAPSUGEL DE MEXICO, S. DE R.L. DE C.V.—See Pfizer Inc.; *U.S. Public*, pg. 1679
CAPSUGEL FRANCE SAS—See Lonza Group AG; *Int'l*, pg. 4553
CAPSUGEL HEALTHCARE LIMITED—See Pfizer Inc.; *U.S. Public*, pg. 1679
CAPSUGEL, INC. GREENWOOD—See Lonza Group AG; *Int'l*, pg. 4553
CAPSUGEL, INC.—See Lonza Group AG; *Int'l*, pg. 4553
CAPSUGEL JAPAN INC.—See Lonza Group AG; *Int'l*, pg. 4553
CAPSUGEL PLOERMEL—See Lonza Group AG; *Int'l*, pg. 4553
CAPSUGEL (THAILAND) CO., LTD.—See Lonza Group AG; *Int'l*, pg. 4553
CAPSULE TECHNOLOGIES, INC.—See Francisco Partners Management, LP; *U.S. Private*, pg. 1589
CAPSULINE, INC.; *U.S. Private*, pg. 746
CAPSYS CORP.; *U.S. Private*, pg. 746
CAPTAIN CASH HOLDING COMPANY LIMITED—See Chow Steel Industries Public Company Limited; *Int'l*, pg. 1584
CAPTAIN D'S, LLC—See Sentinel Capital Partners, L.L.C.; *U.S. Private*, pg. 3608
CAPTAIN MARDEN'S SEAFOODS, INC.; *U.S. Private*, pg. 746
CAPTAIN PIPES LTD.; *Int'l*, pg. 1317
CAPTAIN POLYPLAST LTD.; *Int'l*, pg. 1317
CAPTAINS CHOICE MARINE, INC.—See OneWater Marine Holdings LLC; *U.S. Private*, pg. 3026
CAPTAIN TECHNOCAST LIMITED; *Int'l*, pg. 1317
CAPTARIS (HONG KONG) LIMITED—See Open Text Corporation; *Int'l*, pg. 5596
CAPTECH VENTURES, INC.; *U.S. Private*, pg. 746
CAPTEK SOFTGEL INTERNATIONAL, INC.—See Swander Pace Capital, LLC; *U.S. Private*, pg. 3890
CAPTERRA, INC.—See Gartner, Inc.; *U.S. Public*, pg. 906
CAPTEX BANCSHARES, INC.; *U.S. Private*, pg. 746
CAPTEX CO., LTD.—See Nagase & Co., Ltd.; *Int'l*, pg. 5126
CAPTII LIMITED; *Int'l*, pg. 1317
CAPTIL AUTOMOTIVE REAL ESTATE SERVICES, INC.; *U.S. Private*, pg. 746
CAPTION COLORADO, L.L.C.—See Verbit Software Limited; *Int'l*, pg. 8165
CAPTION IT, LLC—See Ai-Media Technologies Limited; *Int'l*, pg. 227
CAPTIONMAX, INC.—See Riverside Partners, LLC; *U.S. Private*, pg. 3445
CAPTIRA ANALYTICAL, LLC—See General Catalyst Partners; *U.S. Private*, pg. 1664
CAPTIRA ANALYTICAL, LLC—See iSubscribed Inc.; *U.S. Private*, pg. 2147
CAPTIRA ANALYTICAL, LLC—See WndrCo Holdings, LLC; *U.S. Private*, pg. 4552
CAPTIVA ENERGY SOLUTIONS PRIVATE LIMITED—See Generac Holdings Inc.; *U.S. Public*, pg. 912
CAPTIVA GROUP INC.; *U.S. Private*, pg. 747
CAPTIVA VERDE WELLNESS CORP.; *Int'l*, pg. 1317
CAPTIVE-AIRE SYSTEMS, INC.; *U.S. Private*, pg. 747
CAPTIVE INSURANCE SERVICES, INC.—See Tenet Healthcare Corporation; *U.S. Public*, pg. 2001
CAPTIVE PLASTICS, INC.—See Berry Global Group, Inc; *U.S. Public*, pg. 321
CAPTIVE PLASTICS, INC.—See Berry Global Group, Inc; *U.S. Public*, pg. 321
CAPTIVE POWER PLANT—See National Aluminium Company Limited; *Int'l*, pg. 5150
CAPTIVE RESOURCES, LLC; *U.S. Private*, pg. 747
CAPTIVISION INC.; *Int'l*, pg. 1317
CAPTOR CAPITAL CORP.; *Int'l*, pg. 1317
CAPTOR THERAPEUTICS S.A.; *Int'l*, pg. 1317
CAPTRON CO., LTD.—See Capcom Co., Ltd.; *Int'l*, pg. 1302
CAPTRUST ADVISORS, LLC; *U.S. Private*, pg. 747
CAPTURE 3D, INC.—See Carl-Zeiss-Stiftung; *Int'l*, pg. 1334
CAPTURE ALL LIMITED—See Restore plc; *Int'l*, pg. 6304
CAPTURED LIGHT STUDIO INC.—See Edify Multimedia Group LLC; *U.S. Private*, pg. 1336
CAPTURE; *Int'l*, pg. 1318
CAPTURE TECHNOLOGIES, INC.; *U.S. Private*, pg. 747
CAPTY CO., LTD.—See Tokyo Gas Co., Ltd.; *Int'l*, pg. 7791
CAPULA INVESTMENT JAPAN LIMITED—See Affiliated Managers Group, Inc.; *U.S. Public*, pg. 54
CAPULA INVESTMENT MANAGEMENT LIMITED—See Affiliated Managers Group, Inc.; *U.S. Public*, pg. 54
CAPULA INVESTMENT MANAGEMENT LLP—See Affiliated Managers Group, Inc.; *U.S. Public*, pg. 54

COMPANY NAME INDEX

CAPULA INVESTMENT US LP—See Affiliated Managers Group, Inc.; *U.S. Public*, pg. 54
CAPULA LIMITED; *Int'l*, pg. 1318
CAPULA NUCLEAR—See Capula Limited; *Int'l*, pg. 1318
CAPVEST LIMITED; *Int'l*, pg. 1318
CAPVEST PARTNERS LLP—See CapVest Limited; *Int'l*, pg. 1318
CAPVIS AG; *Int'l*, pg. 1318
CAPXON ELECTRONIC INDUSTRIAL COMPANY LIMITED—See Capxon International Electronic Co Ltd; *Int'l*, pg. 1318
CAPXON ELECTRONIC (SHENZHEN) CO. LTD.—See Capxon International Electronic Co Ltd; *Int'l*, pg. 1318
CAPXON EUROPE GMBH—See Capxon International Electronic Co Ltd; *Int'l*, pg. 1318
CAPXON INTERNATIONAL ELECTRONIC CO LTD; *Int'l*, pg. 1318
CAPX PARTNERS—See Accord Financial Corp.; *Int'l*, pg. 92
CAP-XX LTD.; *Int'l*, pg. 1301
CAQ HOLDINGS LIMITED; *Int'l*, pg. 1319
CAR2GO CANADA LTD.—See Mercedes-Benz Group AG; *Int'l*, pg. 4829
CAR2GO FRANCE SAS—See Mercedes-Benz Group AG; *Int'l*, pg. 4829
CAR2GO GMBH—See Mercedes-Benz Group AG; *Int'l*, pg. 4829
CAR2GO NORTH AMERICA LLC—See Mercedes-Benz Group AG; *Int'l*, pg. 4829
CAR2GO OSTERREICH GMBH—See Mercedes-Benz Group AG; *Int'l*, pg. 4829
CAR360, INC.—See Carvana Co.; *U.S. Public*, pg. 445
CARABAO GROUP PUBLIC COMPANY LIMITED; *Int'l*, pg. 1319
CARABAO TAWANDANG CO., LTD.—See Carabao Group Public Company Limited; *Int'l*, pg. 1319
CARABETTA MANAGEMENT CO., INC.; *U.S. Private*, pg. 748
CARACAL GOLD PLC; *Int'l*, pg. 1319
CARACAS PAPER COMPANY, S.A.; *Int'l*, pg. 1319
CARACOL, S.A.—See Promotora de Informaciones S.A.; *Int'l*, pg. 5995
CARA COMMUNICATIONS LLC—See Clarion Capital Partners, LLC; *U.S. Private*, pg. 911
CARACONSULT GMBH—See Thor Industries, Inc.; *U.S. Public*, pg. 2156
CARADO GMBH—See Thor Industries, Inc.; *U.S. Public*, pg. 2156
CARADONNA DIVE ADVENTURES, INC.—See TUI AG; *Int'l*, pg. 7964
CARAD SA; *Int'l*, pg. 1319
CARAGAS AJL/PARK—See The Interpublic Group of Companies, Inc.; *U.S. Public*, pg. 2092
THE CARA GROUP, INC.; *U.S. Private*, pg. 4005
CARAHSOFT TECHNOLOGY CORP.; *U.S. Private*, pg. 748
CARAIBES QUALITE SERVICE SAS—See VINCI S.A.; *Int'l*, pg. 8213
CARAMAGNO FOODS COMPANY; *U.S. Private*, pg. 748
CARAMBA BREMEN GMBH—See Berner SE; *Int'l*, pg. 988
CARAMBA CHEMIE GMBH & CO. KG—See Berner SE; *Int'l*, pg. 988
CARAMBA HOLDING GMBH—See Berner SE; *Int'l*, pg. 988
CARAMBA NEDERLANDS B.V.—See Berner SE; *Int'l*, pg. 988
CARAMOOR CENTER FOR MUSIC & THE ARTS, INC.; *U.S. Private*, pg. 748
CARANA CORP.; *U.S. Private*, pg. 748
CAR AND DRIVER—See The Hearst Corporation; *U.S. Private*, pg. 4046
CARAN PRECISION ENGINEERING & MANUFACTURING; *U.S. Private*, pg. 748
CARASAP S.A.—See s.a. D'Ieteren n.v.; *Int'l*, pg. 6448
CARASENT ASA; *Int'l*, pg. 1319
CARASENT NORGE AS—See Carasent ASA; *Int'l*, pg. 1319
C.A. RASMUSSEN, INC.; *U.S. Private*, pg. 706
CARASSO MOTORS LTD.; *Int'l*, pg. 1319
CARASSO REAL ESTATE LTD.; *Int'l*, pg. 1319
CARAT ARGENTINA S.A.—See Dentsu Group Inc.; *Int'l*, pg. 2036
CARAT ASIA PACIFIC—See Dentsu Group Inc.; *Int'l*, pg. 2035
CARAT AUSTRIA GMBH—See Dentsu Group Inc.; *Int'l*, pg. 2035
CARAT BEIJING—See Dentsu Group Inc.; *Int'l*, pg. 2035
CARAT BELGIUM—See Dentsu Group Inc.; *Int'l*, pg. 2035
CARAT BUSINESS LTD.—See Dentsu Group Inc.; *Int'l*, pg. 2035
CARAT CANADA—See Dentsu Group Inc.; *Int'l*, pg. 2036
CARAT DUCHATELET S.A.—See Capital People S.A.; *Int'l*, pg. 1312
CARAT - EDINBURGH—See Dentsu Group Inc.; *Int'l*, pg. 2035
CARAT EXPERT - MILAN—See Dentsu Group Inc.; *Int'l*, pg. 2035
CARAT FRANCE—See Dentsu Group Inc.; *Int'l*, pg. 2035
CARAT GUANGZHOU—See Dentsu Group Inc.; *Int'l*, pg. 2035
CARA THERAPEUTICS, INC.; *U.S. Public*, pg. 432
CARAT HONG KONG—See Dentsu Group Inc.; *Int'l*, pg. 2035
CARAT INTERNATIONAL HELLAS—See Dentsu Group Inc.; *Int'l*, pg. 2035
CARAT IRELAND—See Dentsu Group Inc.; *Int'l*, pg. 2035
CARAT ITALIA-FLORENCE—See Dentsu Group Inc.; *Int'l*, pg. 2035
CARAT ITALIA-ROME—See Dentsu Group Inc.; *Int'l*, pg. 2035
CARAT ITALIA-TURIN—See Dentsu Group Inc.; *Int'l*, pg. 2035
CARAT JAPAN CO., LTD.—See Dentsu Group Inc.; *Int'l*, pg. 2034
CARAT KOREA—See Dentsu Group Inc.; *Int'l*, pg. 2035
CARAT MEXICANA—See Dentsu Group Inc.; *Int'l*, pg. 2036
CARAT MUMBAI—See Dentsu Group Inc.; *Int'l*, pg. 2035
CARAT NEW DELHI—See Dentsu Group Inc.; *Int'l*, pg. 2035
CARAT NORDIC AB—See Dentsu Group Inc.; *Int'l*, pg. 2035
CARAT NORGE AS—See Dentsu Group Inc.; *Int'l*, pg. 2035
CARAT SHANGHAI—See Dentsu Group Inc.; *Int'l*, pg. 2035
CARAT SWEDEN AB—See Dentsu Group Inc.; *Int'l*, pg. 2035
CAR AUCTION CO., LTD.; *Int'l*, pg. 1319
CARAUSTAR CONVERTED PRODUCTS GROUP—See Greif Inc.; *U.S. Public*, pg. 966
CARAUSTAR INDUSTRIAL CANADA, INC.—See Greif Inc.; *U.S. Public*, pg. 965
CARAUSTAR INDUSTRIES, INC. - ARLINGTON TUBE PLANT—See Greif Inc.; *U.S. Public*, pg. 965
CARAUSTAR INDUSTRIES, INC. - AUSTELL BOXBOARD MILL—See Greif Inc.; *U.S. Public*, pg. 965
CARAUSTAR INDUSTRIES, INC. - AUSTELL TUBE PLANT—See Greif Inc.; *U.S. Public*, pg. 965
CARAUSTAR INDUSTRIES, INC. - BEARDSTOWN TUBE PLANT—See Greif Inc.; *U.S. Public*, pg. 966
CARAUSTAR INDUSTRIES, INC. - BUCYRUS CONTRACT PACKAGING PLANT—See Greif Inc.; *U.S. Public*, pg. 966
CARAUSTAR INDUSTRIES, INC. - BURLINGTON RIGID BOX PLANT—See Greif Inc.; *U.S. Public*, pg. 966
CARAUSTAR INDUSTRIES, INC. - CANTONMENT TUBE PLANT—See Greif Inc.; *U.S. Public*, pg. 966
CARAUSTAR INDUSTRIES, INC. - CHARLOTTE RECYCLING PLANT—See Greif Inc.; *U.S. Public*, pg. 966
CARAUSTAR INDUSTRIES, INC. - CHATTANOOGA RECYCLING PLANT—See Greif Inc.; *U.S. Public*, pg. 966
CARAUSTAR INDUSTRIES, INC. - CHICAGO CARTON PLANT—See Greif Inc.; *U.S. Public*, pg. 966
CARAUSTAR INDUSTRIES, INC. - CHICAGO PACKAGING PLANT—See Greif Inc.; *U.S. Public*, pg. 966
CARAUSTAR INDUSTRIES, INC. - CLEVELAND RECYCLING PLANT—See Greif Inc.; *U.S. Public*, pg. 966
CARAUSTAR INDUSTRIES, INC. - CORINTH TUBE PLANT—See Greif Inc.; *U.S. Public*, pg. 966
CARAUSTAR INDUSTRIES, INC. - DALTON TUBE PLANT—See Greif Inc.; *U.S. Public*, pg. 966
CARAUSTAR INDUSTRIES, INC. - DENVER CARTON PLANT—See Greif Inc.; *U.S. Public*, pg. 966
CARAUSTAR INDUSTRIES, INC. - FRANKLIN, KY TUBE PLANT—See Greif Inc.; *U.S. Public*, pg. 966
CARAUSTAR INDUSTRIES, INC. - GRAND RAPIDS CARTON PLANT—See Greif Inc.; *U.S. Public*, pg. 966
CARAUSTAR INDUSTRIES, INC. - HARDEEVILLE RECYCLING PLANT—See Greif Inc.; *U.S. Public*, pg. 966
CARAUSTAR INDUSTRIES, INC. - KERNERSVILLE ADHESIVES PLANT—See Greif Inc.; *U.S. Public*, pg. 966
CARAUSTAR INDUSTRIES, INC. - KERNERSVILLE TUBE PLANT—See Greif Inc.; *U.S. Public*, pg. 966
CARAUSTAR INDUSTRIES, INC. - KINGSTON SPRINGS CARTON PLANT—See Greif Inc.; *U.S. Public*, pg. 966
CARAUSTAR INDUSTRIES, INC. - KINGSTON TUBE PLANT—See Greif Inc.; *U.S. Public*, pg. 966
CARAUSTAR INDUSTRIES, INC. - LANCASTER TUBE PLANT—See Greif Inc.; *U.S. Public*, pg. 966
CARAUSTAR INDUSTRIES, INC. - MINERVA TUBE PLANT—See Greif Inc.; *U.S. Public*, pg. 966
CARAUSTAR INDUSTRIES, INC. - PHOENIX TUBE PLANT—See Greif Inc.; *U.S. Public*, pg. 966
CARAUSTAR INDUSTRIES, INC. - ROCK HILL PLANT—See Greif Inc.; *U.S. Public*, pg. 966
CARAUSTAR INDUSTRIES, INC. - SAGINAW TUBE PLANT—See Greif Inc.; *U.S. Public*, pg. 966
CARAUSTAR INDUSTRIES, INC. - SALT LAKE CITY TUBE PLANT—See Greif Inc.; *U.S. Public*, pg. 966
CARAUSTAR INDUSTRIES, INC. - SILSBEE TUBE PLANT—See Greif Inc.; *U.S. Public*, pg. 966
CARAUSTAR INDUSTRIES, INC.—See Greif Inc.; *U.S. Public*, pg. 965
CARAUSTAR INDUSTRIES, INC. - TACOMA TUBE PLANT—See Greif Inc.; *U.S. Public*, pg. 966

CARBOLINEUM WOOD PRESERVING CO.

CARAUSTAR INDUSTRIES, INC. - TAYLORS TUBE PLANT—See Greif Inc.; *U.S. Public*, pg. 966
CARAUSTAR INDUSTRIES, INC. - TEXARKANA RECYCLING PLANT—See Greif Inc.; *U.S. Public*, pg. 966
CARAUSTAR INDUSTRIES, INC. - TEXARKANA TUBE PLANT—See Greif Inc.; *U.S. Public*, pg. 966
CARAUSTAR INDUSTRIES, INC. - TOLEDO TUBE PLANT—See Greif Inc.; *U.S. Public*, pg. 966
CARAUSTAR INDUSTRIES, INC. - TORONTO TUBE PLANT—See Greif Inc.; *U.S. Public*, pg. 966
CARAUSTAR INDUSTRIES, INC. - WEST MONROE TUBE PLANT—See Greif Inc.; *U.S. Public*, pg. 966
CARAUSTAR INDUSTRIES, INC. - WEYERS CAVE TUBE PLANT—See Greif Inc.; *U.S. Public*, pg. 966
CARAUSTAR INDUSTRIES, INC. - WINNIPEG TUBE PLANT—See Greif Inc.; *U.S. Public*, pg. 966
CARAUSTAR INDUSTRIES—See Greif Inc.; *U.S. Public*, pg. 965
CARAUSTAR MILL GROUP, INC.—See Greif Inc.; *U.S. Public*, pg. 966
CARAUSTAR RECOVERED FIBER GROUP, INC.—See Greif Inc.; *U.S. Public*, pg. 966
CARAUSTAR RECYCLING PLANT—See Greif Inc.; *U.S. Public*, pg. 966
CARAVANE 185 INC; *Int'l*, pg. 1320
CARAVAN EAST FABRICS LIMITED; *Int'l*, pg. 1320
CARAVAN ENERGY CORPORATION; *Int'l*, pg. 1320
CARAVAN INGREDIENTS—See Corbion N.V.; *Int'l*, pg. 1795
CARAVAN TOURS, INC.; *U.S. Private*, pg. 748
CARAVEL INFO SYSTEM PRIVATE LIMITED—See Cranes Software International Limited; *Int'l*, pg. 1828
CARAVELLE INTERNATIONAL GROUP; *Int'l*, pg. 1320
CARAVELLE SA; *Int'l*, pg. 1320
CARAVEL MINERALS LIMITED; *Int'l*, pg. 1320
CARAVEL PELLI PREGIATE SPA—See Kering S.A.; *Int'l*, pg. 4134
CARAWINE RESOURCES LIMITED—See QGold Pty. Ltd.; *Int'l*, pg. 6138
CARBACID INVESTMENTS PLC; *Int'l*, pg. 1320
CARBAGAS S.A.—See L'Air Liquide S.A.; *Int'l*, pg. 4375
CARBERY GROUP; *Int'l*, pg. 1320
CARBEX AB—See Addtech AB; *Int'l*, pg. 132
CARBIDE CHEMICAL (THAILAND) LIMITED—See Dow Inc.; *U.S. Public*, pg. 686
CARBIDE INDUSTRIES, LLC.; *U.S. Private*, pg. 748
CARBIDE SWEDEN AB—See Akzo Nobel N.V.; *Int'l*, pg. 273
CARBINE RESOURCES LIMITED; *Int'l*, pg. 1320
CARBIOS SACA; *Int'l*, pg. 1320
CARBIZ AUTOS; *U.S. Private*, pg. 748
CARBO CERAMICS (CHINA) COMPANY LTD.—See CARBO Ceramics Inc.; *U.S. Private*, pg. 748
CARBO CERAMICS INC.; *U.S. Private*, pg. 748
CARBO CERAMICS—See CARBO Ceramics Inc.; *U.S. Private*, pg. 748
CARBO CERAMICS—See CARBO Ceramics Inc.; *U.S. Private*, pg. 748
CARBO CHILE S.A.—See Morgan Advanced Materials plc; *Int'l*, pg. 5041
CARBODERIVADOS S.A.—See China National Chemical Corporation; *Int'l*, pg. 1527
CARBODY S.A.S.—See BAVARIA Industries Group AG; *Int'l*, pg. 899
CARBOEX, S.A.—See Enel S.p.A.; *Int'l*, pg. 2412
CARBOGEN AMCIS AG—See Dishman Carbogen Amcis Limited; *Int'l*, pg. 2135
CARBOGEN AMCIS LTD. (U.K.)—See Dishman Carbogen Amcis Limited; *Int'l*, pg. 2135
CARBOGEN AMCIS REAL ESTATE SAS—See Dishman Carbogen Amcis Limited; *Int'l*, pg. 2135
CARBOIL SRL—See Eni S.p.A.; *Int'l*, pg. 2437
CARBOLIM B.V.—See Air Products & Chemicals, Inc.; *U.S. Public*, pg. 66
CARBOLINE COMPANY—See RPM International Inc.; *U.S. Public*, pg. 1818
CARBOLINE CORP.—See RPM International Inc.; *U.S. Public*, pg. 1818
CARBOLINE (DALIAN) PAINT COMPANY LTD.—See RPM International Inc.; *U.S. Public*, pg. 1816
CARBOLINE DUBAI CORPORATION—See RPM International Inc.; *U.S. Public*, pg. 1818
CARBOLINE FRANCE S.A.S.—See RPM International Inc.; *U.S. Public*, pg. 1818
CARBOLINE GLOBAL, INC.—See RPM International Inc.; *U.S. Public*, pg. 1816
CARBOLINE (INDIA) PRIVATE LIMITED—See RPM International Inc.; *U.S. Public*, pg. 1816
CARBOLINE ITALIA S.P.A.—See RPM International Inc.; *U.S. Public*, pg. 1818
CARBOLINE NORGE AS—See RPM International Inc.; *U.S. Public*, pg. 1818
CARBOLINEUM WOOD PRESERVING CO.; *U.S. Private*, pg. 748
CARBOLITE GERO GMBH & CO. KG—See Verder International B.V.; *Int'l*, pg. 8166
CARBOLITE GMBH—See Verder International B.V.; *Int'l*, pg. 8167

CARBOLITE LIMITED—See Verder International B.V.; *Int'l*, pg. 8167
CARBON60 LIMITED—See HFBG Holding B.V.; *Int'l*, pg. 3374
CARBONAIR ENVIRONMENTAL SYSTEMS; *U.S. Private*, pg. 748
CARBON ASSET MANAGEMENT INTERNATIONAL GMBH—See Invinity Energy Systems plc; *Int'l*, pg. 3789
CARBON ASSET SERVICES SWEDEN AB—See Tricorona AB; *Int'l*, pg. 7920
CARBONBW (THAILAND) LTD.—See EnBW Energie Baden-Wurttemberg AG; *Int'l*, pg. 2398
CARBON BY DESIGN, L.P.—See HEICO Corporation; *U.S. Public*, pg. 1019
CARBON CALIFORNIA OPERATING COMPANY, LLC—See Carbon Energy Corporation; *U.S. Public*, pg. 432
CARBON DELTA AG—See MSCI Inc.; *U.S. Public*, pg. 1483
CARBONE AUTO GROUP; *U.S. Private*, pg. 748
CARBONE AUTOMOTIVE GROUP—See Lithia Motors, Inc.; *U.S. Public*, pg. 1321
CARBON ENERGY CORPORATION; *U.S. Public*, pg. 432
CARBON FIVE INC.—See West Monroe Partners, LLC; *U.S. Private*, pg. 4486
CARBONFOLIO—See Mobius EcoCapital plc; *Int'l*, pg. 5012
CARBON GREEN INC.; *Int'l*, pg. 1320
CARBON INTERNATIONAL LTD—See James Durrans & Sons Limited; *Int'l*, pg. 3875
CARBONITE, INC.—See Open Text Corporation; *Int'l*, pg. 5596
CARBONLITE INDUSTRIES LLC—See HPC Industries LLC; *U.S. Private*, pg. 1996
CARBONMETA RESEARCH LTD.—See CARBONMETA TECHNOLOGIES, INC.; *U.S. Public*, pg. 433
CARBONMETA TECHNOLOGIES, INC.; *U.S. Public*, pg. 432
CARBON MINERALS LIMITED; *Int'l*, pg. 1320
CARBONORTE S.L.—See Mitsubishi Chemical Group Corporation; *Int'l*, pg. 4937
CARBON PARTNERS AS—See Verdo A/S; *Int'l*, pg. 8168
CARBON PARTNERS INC.—See Verdo A/S; *Int'l*, pg. 8168
CARBON PLATE STEEL PRODUCTS, LLC—See Icahn Enterprises L.P.; *U.S. Public*, pg. 1084
CARBON POWER & LIGHT, INC.; *U.S. Private*, pg. 748
CARBON REVOLUTION LIMITED; *Int'l*, pg. 1320
CARBON RX INC.—See Delta CleanTech Inc; *Int'l*, pg. 2016
CARBONXT GROUP LIMITED; *Int'l*, pg. 1320
CARBOPEGO - ABASTECIMENTO DE COMBUSTIVEIS, S.A.—See ENGIE SA; *Int'l*, pg. 2431
CARBOPRESS S.P.A.; *Int'l*, pg. 1321
CARBORUNDUM UNIVERSAL LIMITED—See The Murugappa Group, Ltd.; *Int'l*, pg. 7668
CARBORUNDUM UNIVERSAL LTD. - ELECTRO MINERALS DIVISION—See The Murugappa Group, Ltd.; *Int'l*, pg. 7668
CARBORUNDUM VENTURES INC.—See Compagnie de Saint-Gobain SA; *Int'l*, pg. 1729
CARBO SAN LUIS S.A.—See Morgan Advanced Materials plc; *Int'l*, pg. 5041
CARBOSULF CHEMISCHE WERKE GMBH—See GIC Pte. Ltd.; *Int'l*, pg. 2968
CARBOSULF CHEMISCHE WERKE GMBH—See The Carlyle Group Inc.; *U.S. Public*, pg. 2051
CARBOTECH AC GMBH—See International Chemical Investors S.E.; *Int'l*, pg. 3745
CARBOTECH-POLONIA SP. Z O.O.—See Orica Limited; *Int'l*, pg. 5620
CARBOTRANS SP. Z O.O.—See Jastrzebska Spolka Weglowa S.A.; *Int'l*, pg. 3913
CARBOZULIA, S.A.—See Petroleos de Venezuela S.A.; *Int'l*, pg. 5828
CARB SA—See STRABAG SE; *Int'l*, pg. 7230
CARBUDDY PTY. LTD.—See Primary Opinion Limited; *Int'l*, pg. 5976
CARCADE OOO—See Gazprombank JSC; *Int'l*, pg. 2892
CARCADE SERVICE SP. Z O.O.—See Getin Holding S.A.; *Int'l*, pg. 2947
CARCAFE LTDA C.I.—See ED&F Man Holdings Limited; *Int'l*, pg. 2302
CARCAFE S.A—See ED&F Man Holdings Limited; *Int'l*, pg. 2302
CAR CARE CLINIC, INC.; *U.S. Private*, pg. 747
CARCARE COLLISION CENTERS, INC.; *U.S. Private*, pg. 748
CAR CARE CONSULT VERSICHERUNGSMAKLER GMBH—See Assicurazioni Generali S.p.A.; *Int'l*, pg. 646
CAR CARE PLAN LIMITED—See Stone Point Capital LLC; *U.S. Private*, pg. 3820
CARCERI E INFRAESTRUCTURA, S.A.P.I. DE C.V.—See Empresas ICA S.A.B. de C.V.; *Int'l*, pg. 2390
CARCETTI CAPITAL CORP.; *Int'l*, pg. 1321
CARCHEX; *U.S. Private*, pg. 748
CARCHS CO., LTD.—See Ledax Co., Ltd.; *Int'l*, pg. 4438

CARCHS KYUSHU SALES CO., LTD.—See Ledax Co., Ltd.; *Int'l*, pg. 4438
CAR CITY CHRYSLER; *U.S. Private*, pg. 747
CARCLO DIAGNOSTIC SOLUTIONS LTD—See Carclo plc; *Int'l*, pg. 1321
CARCLO PLC; *Int'l*, pg. 1321
CARCLO PRECISION OPTICS—See Carclo plc; *Int'l*, pg. 1321
CARCLO TECHNICAL PLASTICS (BRNO) S.R.O—See Carclo plc; *Int'l*, pg. 1321
CARCLO TECHNICAL PLASTICS LTD.—See Carclo plc; *Int'l*, pg. 1321
CARCLO TECHNICAL PLASTICS LTD.—See Carclo plc; *Int'l*, pg. 1321
CARCLO TECHNICAL PLASTICS LTD—See Carclo plc; *Int'l*, pg. 1321
CARCLO TECHNICAL PLASTICS MITCHAM LTD.—See Carclo plc; *Int'l*, pg. 1321
CARCLO TECHNICAL PLASTICS SHANGHAI CO. LIMITED—See Carclo plc; *Int'l*, pg. 1321
CARCLO TECHNICAL PLASTICS—See Carclo plc; *Int'l*, pg. 1321
CARCO CAPITAL CORPORATION; *U.S. Private*, pg. 749
CARCO INTERNATIONAL, INC.; *U.S. Private*, pg. 749
CARCO INTERNATIONAL, INC.—See Carco Capital Corporation; *U.S. Private*, pg. 749
CAR CONVENI CLUB CO., LTD.—See Sumitomo Mitsui Financial Group, Inc.; *Int'l*, pg. 7294
CARCO RENTALS, INC.—See Carco Capital Corporation; *U.S. Private*, pg. 749
CARCOUNTRY MOTORS, INC.—See AutoNation, Inc.; *U.S. Public*, pg. 233
CARCOUSTICS AUSTRIA GES.M.B.H.—See Liaoning Dare Industrial Company Ltd.; *Int'l*, pg. 4482
CARCOUSTICS BELGIUM N.V.—See Liaoning Dare Industrial Company Ltd.; *Int'l*, pg. 4482
CARCOUSTICS DEUTSCHLAND GMBH—See Liaoning Dare Industrial Company Ltd.; *Int'l*, pg. 4482
CARCOUSTICS ESPANA SA—See Liaoning Dare Industrial Company Ltd.; *Int'l*, pg. 4482
CARCOUSTICS FRANCE S.A.R.L.—See Liaoning Dare Industrial Company Ltd.; *Int'l*, pg. 4482
CARCOUSTICS HALDENSLEBEN GMBH—See Liaoning Dare Industrial Company Ltd.; *Int'l*, pg. 4482
CARCOUSTICS INDUSTRIAL DE MEXICO S DE RL DE C.V.—See Liaoning Dare Industrial Company Ltd.; *Int'l*, pg. 4482
CARCOUSTICS INTERNATIONAL GMBH—See Liaoning Dare Industrial Company Ltd.; *Int'l*, pg. 4482
CARCOUSTICS TECH CENTER NORTH AMERICA INC.—See Liaoning Dare Industrial Company Ltd.; *Int'l*, pg. 4482
CARCOUSTICS USA, INC.—See Liaoning Dare Industrial Company Ltd.; *Int'l*, pg. 4482
CAR CREDO CO., LTD.—See PROTO CORPORATION; *Int'l*, pg. 6006
CARDADEL SA—See Carrefour SA; *Int'l*, pg. 1344
CARDANO RISK MANAGEMENT LTD—See Marsh & McLennan Companies, Inc.; *U.S. Public*, pg. 1384
CARDATA, INC.; *U.S. Private*, pg. 749
CARDAX, INC.—See Cardax Pharmaceuticals, Inc.; *U.S. Private*, pg. 749
CARDAX PHARMACEUTICALS, INC.; *U.S. Private*, pg. 749
CARDAX PHARMA, INC.—See Cardax Pharmaceuticals, Inc.; *U.S. Private*, pg. 749
CARDAX SALES & SERVICES SDN. BHD.—See AWC Berhad; *Int'l*, pg. 752
CARDBIZ SOLUTIONS SDN. BHD.—See MY E.G. Services Berhad; *Int'l*, pg. 5111
CARDCASH LLC; *U.S. Private*, pg. 749
CARD CENTER LTD.—See Chams Holding Company; *Int'l*, pg. 1440
CARD CENTRE NIGERIA LIMITED—See Chams Holding Company; *Int'l*, pg. 1440
CARD COMPLETE SERVICE BANK AG—See UniCredit S.p.A.; *Int'l*, pg. 8040
CARDCONNECT CORPORATION—See Fiserv, Inc.; *U.S. Public*, pg. 850
CARDCONNECT LLC—See Fiserv, Inc.; *U.S. Public*, pg. 850
CARDEA HEALTH SOLUTONS LIMITED—See Aon plc; *Int'l*, pg. 494
CARDEAN LEARNING GROUP, LLC; *U.S. Private*, pg. 749
CARDELL KITCHEN & BATH CABINETRY; *U.S. Private*, pg. 749
CARDELLO ELECTRIC SUPPLY COMPANY—See Element Partners, LLC; *U.S. Private*, pg. 1357
CAR DEL MAR FERIENAUTOVERMIETUNG GMBH—See Expedia Group, Inc.; *U.S. Public*, pg. 809
CARDEM SAS—See VINCI S.A.; *Int'l*, pg. 8213
CARDENAS MARKETING NETWORK INC.; *U.S. Private*, pg. 749
CARDENAS MARKET, LLC—See KKR & Co. Inc.; *U.S. Public*, pg. 1242
CARDENAS MARKET, LLC—See Victory Park Capital Advisors, LLC; *U.S. Private*, pg. 4379
CARDENAS MOTORS, INC.; *U.S. Private*, pg. 749

CARDENAS PARTNERS, LLC; *U.S. Private*, pg. 749
CARDERO RESOURCE CORP.—See World Copper Ltd.; *Int'l*, pg. 8457
CARD FULFILLMENT SERVICES INC—See Taylor Corporation; *U.S. Private*, pg. 3938
CARDHERO PTY. LTD.—See 8common Limited; *Int'l*, pg. 16
CARDIA BIOPLASTICS (AUSTRALIA) PTY LTD—See SECOS Group Limited; *Int'l*, pg. 6673
CARDI AB—See Sonepar S.A.; *Int'l*, pg. 7090
CARDIACASSIST, INC.—See LivaNova PLC; *Int'l*, pg. 4529
CARDIAC IMAGING SOLUTIONS, LLC; *U.S. Private*, pg. 749
CARDIAC NETWORK, INC.; *U.S. Private*, pg. 749
CARDIAC SCIENCE CORPORATION—See Asahi Kasei Corporation; *Int'l*, pg. 597
CARDIAC SCIENCE HOLDINGS UK LTD.—See Asahi Kasei Corporation; *Int'l*, pg. 597
CARDIAC SCIENCE INTERNATIONAL A/S—See Asahi Kasei Corporation; *Int'l*, pg. 597
CARDIAC SURGICAL ASSOCIATES, LLC—See HCA Healthcare, Inc.; *U.S. Public*, pg. 992
CARDIAQ VALVE TECHNOLOGIES, INC.—See Edwards Lifesciences Corporation; *U.S. Public*, pg. 720
CARDI CORPORATION; *U.S. Private*, pg. 749
CARDIEX LIMITED; *Int'l*, pg. 1321
CARDIF-ASSURANCES RISQUES DIVERS - ITALY—See BNP Paribas SA; *Int'l*, pg. 1083
CARDIF-ASSURANCES RISQUES DIVERS S.A.—See BNP Paribas SA; *Int'l*, pg. 1083
CARDIF BIZTOSITO MAGYARORSZAG ZRT—See BNP Paribas SA; *Int'l*, pg. 1083
CARDIF COLOMBIA SEGUROS GENERALES S.A.—See BNP Paribas SA; *Int'l*, pg. 1083
CARDIF DEL PERU SA COMPANIA DE SEGUROS—See BNP Paribas SA; *Int'l*, pg. 1083
CARDIF EL DJAZAIR, SPA—See BNP Paribas SA; *Int'l*, pg. 1083
CARDIFF CAR CITY PTY LIMITED; *Int'l*, pg. 1321
CARDIFF INTERNATIONAL AIRPORT LTD.; *Int'l*, pg. 1321
CARDIFF LEXINGTON CORPORATION; *U.S. Public*, pg. 433
CARDIFF ONCOLOGY, INC.; *U.S. Public*, pg. 433
THE CARDIFF PROPERTY PLC; *Int'l*, pg. 7630
CARDIF GERMANY—See BNP Paribas SA; *Int'l*, pg. 1083
CARDIF I-SERVICES—See BNP Paribas SA; *Int'l*, pg. 1083
CARDIF LUX VIE SA—See BNP Paribas SA; *Int'l*, pg. 1083
CARDIF MEXICO SEGUROS DE VIDA SA DE CV—See BNP Paribas SA; *Int'l*, pg. 1083
CARDIF POLSKA S.A.—See BNP Paribas SA; *Int'l*, pg. 1083
CARDIF SOCIETE VIE TAIWAN—See BNP Paribas SA; *Int'l*, pg. 1081
CARDIF—See BNP Paribas SA; *Int'l*, pg. 1083
CARDIF—See BNP Paribas SA; *Int'l*, pg. 1083
CARDIF SPAIN—See BNP Paribas SA; *Int'l*, pg. 1083
CARDIF VIE & CARDIF RD—See BNP Paribas SA; *Int'l*, pg. 1083
CARDIF VITA S.P.A.—See BNP Paribas SA; *Int'l*, pg. 1083
CARDINAL ALUMINUM CO.; *U.S. Private*, pg. 749
CARDINAL ASSOCIATES INC.—See Balchem Corporation; *U.S. Public*, pg. 265
CARDINAL BANCORP INC.; *U.S. Private*, pg. 749
CARDINAL BUILDING MATERIALS, INC.; *U.S. Private*, pg. 750
CARDINAL BUSES, INC.—See Riteway Bus Service, Inc.; *U.S. Private*, pg. 3442
CARDINAL CARTRIDGE, INC.; *U.S. Private*, pg. 750
CARDINAL CHEMICALS INC.; *U.S. Private*, pg. 750
CARDINAL CHEVROLET CADILLAC; *U.S. Private*, pg. 750
CARDINAL COGEN, INC.—See General Electric Company; *U.S. Public*, pg. 916
CARDINAL CO., LTD.; *Int'l*, pg. 1321
CARDINALCOMMERCE CORP.—See Visa, Inc.; *U.S. Public*, pg. 2301
CARDINAL COMMUNICATIONS, INC.; *U.S. Private*, pg. 750
CARDINAL COMPONENTS INC.; *U.S. Private*, pg. 750
CARDINAL CONSTRUCTION INC.; *U.S. Private*, pg. 750
CARDINAL CONTRACTORS, INC.—See Primoris Services Corporation; *U.S. Public*, pg. 1718
CARDINAL CREST—See Deli, Inc.; *U.S. Private*, pg. 1196
CARDINAL CUSHING CENTERS, INC.; *U.S. Private*, pg. 750
CARDINALE AUTOMOTIVE GROUP; *U.S. Private*, pg. 751
CARDINAL ENERGY GROUP, INC.; *U.S. Private*, pg. 750
CARDINAL ENERGY LTD.; *Int'l*, pg. 1321
CARDINAL ENGINEERING CORPORATION - OHIO—See Cardinal Engineering Corporation; *U.S. Private*, pg. 750
CARDINAL ENGINEERING CORPORATION; *U.S. Private*, pg. 750
CARDINAL ENGINEERING, INC.—See Enviro Clean Services LLC; *U.S. Private*, pg. 1406

COMPANY NAME INDEX

CARDINAL EQUITY PARTNERS, LLC; *U.S. Private*, pg. 750
CARDINAL ETHANOL, LLC; *U.S. Private*, pg. 750
CARDINAL FINANCE LLC—See Wells Fargo & Company; *U.S. Public*, pg. 2343
CARDINAL FOODS AS—See CapVest Limited; *Int'l*, pg. 1318
CARDINAL FOODS AS—See Lantmannen ek for; *Int'l*, pg. 4413
CARDINAL GAS STORAGE PARTNERS LLC—See Martin Midstream Partners LP; *U.S. Public*, pg. 1389
CARDINAL GLASS COMPANY; *U.S. Private*, pg. 750
CARDINAL HEALTH 102, INC.—See Cardinal Health, Inc.; *U.S. Public*, pg. 433
CARDINAL HEALTH 104 LP—See Cardinal Health, Inc.; *U.S. Public*, pg. 433
CARDINAL HEALTH 107, LLC—See Cardinal Health, Inc.; *U.S. Public*, pg. 433
CARDINAL HEALTH 127, INC.—See Cardinal Health, Inc.; *U.S. Public*, pg. 433
CARDINAL HEALTH 222 (THAILAND) LTD.—See Cardinal Health, Inc.; *U.S. Public*, pg. 433
CARDINAL HEALTH 414, LLC—See Cardinal Health, Inc.; *U.S. Public*, pg. 433
CARDINAL HEALTH 418, INC.—See Cardinal Health, Inc.; *U.S. Public*, pg. 433
CARDINAL HEALTH CANADA 437, INC.—See Cardinal Health, Inc.; *U.S. Public*, pg. 433
CARDINAL HEALTH CANADA, INC.—See Cardinal Health, Inc.; *U.S. Public*, pg. 433
CARDINAL HEALTH CAPITAL CORPORATION—See Cardinal Health, Inc.; *U.S. Public*, pg. 433
CARDINAL HEALTH EQUIPMENT MANAGEMENT SERVICES—See Cardinal Health, Inc.; *U.S. Public*, pg. 433
CARDINAL HEALTH, INC. - CHICAGO—See Cardinal Health, Inc.; *U.S. Public*, pg. 434
CARDINAL HEALTH, INC. - DENVER—See Cardinal Health, Inc.; *U.S. Public*, pg. 434
CARDINAL HEALTH, INC. - GREENSBORO—See Cardinal Health, Inc.; *U.S. Public*, pg. 434
CARDINAL HEALTH, INC. - HOUSTON—See Cardinal Health, Inc.; *U.S. Public*, pg. 434
CARDINAL HEALTH, INC.; *U.S. Public*, pg. 433
CARDINAL HEALTH, INC. - WAYNE—See Cardinal Health, Inc.; *U.S. Public*, pg. 434
CARDINAL HEALTH, INC. - ZANESVILLE—See Cardinal Health, Inc.; *U.S. Public*, pg. 434
CARDINAL HEALTH KOREA LIMITED—See Cardinal Health, Inc.; *U.S. Public*, pg. 433
CARDINAL HEALTH MALAYSIA 211 SDN. BHD.—See Cardinal Health, Inc.; *U.S. Public*, pg. 433
CARDINAL HEALTH MALTA 212 LIMITED—See Cardinal Health, Inc.; *U.S. Public*, pg. 433
CARDINAL HEALTH P.R. 120, INC.—See Cardinal Health, Inc.; *U.S. Public*, pg. 433
CARDINAL HEALTH RADIATION MANAGEMENT SERVICES—See Cardinal Health, Inc.; *U.S. Public*, pg. 433
CARDINAL HEALTH SINGAPORE 225 PTE. LTD.—See Cardinal Health, Inc.; *U.S. Public*, pg. 433
CARDINAL HEALTH SPAIN 219 S.L.—See Cardinal Health, Inc.; *U.S. Public*, pg. 433
CARDINAL HEALTH SPECIALTY PHARMACEUTICAL SERVICES—See Cardinal Health, Inc.; *U.S. Public*, pg. 433
CARDINAL HEALTH SYSTEMS, INC.—See Cardinal Health, Inc.; *U.S. Public*, pg. 434
CARDINAL INDUSTRIAL FINISHES, INC. - POWDER COATING MANUFACTURING—See Cardinal Industrial Finishes, Inc.; *U.S. Public*, pg. 750
CARDINAL INDUSTRIAL FINISHES, INC.; *U.S. Private*, pg. 750
CARDINAL INDUSTRIES, INC.; *U.S. Private*, pg. 750
CARDINAL INDUSTRIES, INC.; *U.S. Private*, pg. 750
CARDINAL INDUSTRIES, INC.—See Spin Master Corp.; *Int'l*, pg. 7136
CARDINAL LABORATORIES, LLC—See Frontenac Company LLC; *U.S. Private*, pg. 1614
CARDINAL LOGISTICS MANAGEMENT CORP—See Ryder System, Inc.; *U.S. Public*, pg. 1828
CARDINAL MACHINERY, INC.; *U.S. Private*, pg. 750
CARDINAL MANUFACTURING COMPANY, INC.; *U.S. Private*, pg. 750
CARDINAL MECHANICAL, INC.—See Primoris Services Corporation; *U.S. Public*, pg. 1718
CARDINAL OFFICE360—See Office Three Sixty, Inc.; *U.S. Private*, pg. 3002
CARDINAL PEAK, LLC—See FPT Corporation; *Int'l*, pg. 2757
CARDINAL PIPELINE CO.—See The Williams Companies, Inc.; *U.S. Public*, pg. 2143
CARDINAL POINT MANAGEMENT, LLC; *U.S. Private*, pg. 750
CARDINAL POWER OF CANADA, L.P.—See iCON Infrastructure LLP; *Int'l*, pg. 3583
CARDINAL PRINTING CO., INC.—See Deluxe Corporation; *U.S. Public*, pg. 653
CARDINAL RESOURCES, INC.; *U.S. Private*, pg. 750

CARDINAL RESOURCES LIMITED—See Shandong Gold Mining Co., Ltd.; *Int'l*, pg. 6753
CARDINAL SCALE MANUFACTURING CO.; *U.S. Private*, pg. 750
CARDINAL SERVICES INC.—See Owner Resource Group, LLC; *U.S. Private*, pg. 3055
CARDINAL SOLUTIONS GROUP, INC.; *U.S. Private*, pg. 751
CARDINAL STATES GATHERING COMPANY—See CNX Resources Corporation; *U.S. Public*, pg. 520
CARDINAL TRANSPORT INC.; *U.S. Private*, pg. 751
CARDINAL UHP LLC—See AMETEK, Inc.; *U.S. Public*, pg. 118
CARDINALUHP LLC—See AMETEK, Inc.; *U.S. Public*, pg. 120
CARDINGTON YUTAKA TECHNOLOGIES INC.—See Honda Motor Co., Ltd.; *Int'l*, pg. 3460
CARDINUS RISK MANAGEMENT LIMITED—See AmWINS Group, Inc.; *U.S. Private*, pg. 270
CARDIOCOMM SOLUTIONS, INC.; *Int'l*, pg. 1321
CARDIO DIAGNOSTICS HOLDINGS, INC.; *U.S. Public*, pg. 434
CARDIO DINAMICA LTDA.—See Halma plc; *Int'l*, pg. 3231
CARDIODX, INC.; *U.S. Private*, pg. 751
CARDIODYNAMICS INTERNATIONAL CORPORATION—See FUJIFILM Holdings Corporation; *Int'l*, pg. 2823
CARDIODYNE, INC.—See Integra LifeSciences Holdings Corporation; *U.S. Public*, pg. 1135
CARDIO FITNESS GMBH & CO. KG—See Dyaco International Inc.; *Int'l*, pg. 2237
CARDIOINSIGHT TECHNOLOGIES INC.—See Medtronic plc; *Int'l*, pg. 4788
CARDIOLABS, INC.—See Alive Cor Inc.; *U.S. Public*, pg. 169
CARDIOLOGY CLINIC OF SAN ANTONIO, PLLC—See HCA Healthcare, Inc.; *U.S. Public*, pg. 992
CARDIOLOGY PHYSICIANS ASSOCIATES, L.L.C.—See Tenet Healthcare Corporation; *U.S. Public*, pg. 2003
CARDIOLOGY PHYSICIANS CORPORATION, L.L.C.—See Tenet Healthcare Corporation; *U.S. Public*, pg. 2003
CARDIOLOGY SPECIALISTS OF NORTH TEXAS, PLLC—See HCA Healthcare, Inc.; *U.S. Public*, pg. 992
CARDIOL THERAPEUTICS, INC.; *Int'l*, pg. 1321
CARDIOMED SUPPLIES INC.—See Nipro Corporation; *Int'l*, pg. 5361
CARDIONET, INC.—See Koninklijke Philips N.V.; *Int'l*, pg. 4267
CARDIONOVUM GMBH—See Grand Pharmaceutical Group Limited; *Int'l*, pg. 3056
CARDIOPAPERS SOLUCOES DIGITAIS LTDA.—See Afya Limited; *Int'l*, pg. 196
CARDIO PARTNERS, INC.—See Investor AB; *Int'l*, pg. 3787
CARDIOSCAN ASIA PTE. LTD.—See Singapore Medical Group Limited; *Int'l*, pg. 6940
CARDIOS SISTEMAS COMERCIAL E INDUSTRIAL LTDA.—See Halma plc; *Int'l*, pg. 3231
CARDIOVASCULAR ASSOCIATES OF AMERICA, LLC—See Webster Equity Partners, LLC; *U.S. Private*, pg. 4467
CARDIOVASCULAR ASSOCIATES OF THE SOUTHEAST, L.L.C.—See Tenet Healthcare Corporation; *U.S. Public*, pg. 2003
CARDIOVASCULAR BIOTHERAPEUTICS, INC.; *U.S. Private*, pg. 751
CARDIOVASCULAR CARE GROUP, INC.; *U.S. Private*, pg. 751
CARDIOVASCULAR RESEARCH FOUNDATION; *U.S. Private*, pg. 751
CARDIO VASCULAR SURGEONS OF NORTH TEXAS, PLLC—See HCA Healthcare, Inc.; *U.S. Public*, pg. 992
CARDIOVASCULAR SYSTEMS, INC.—See Abbott Laboratories; *U.S. Public*, pg. 19
CARDIOVIEW INC.—See CardioComm Solutions, Inc.; *Int'l*, pg. 1321
CARDIOXYL PHARMACEUTICALS, INC.—See Bristol-Myers Squibb Company; *U.S. Public*, pg. 385
CARDIVA MEDICAL, INC.—See Haemonetics Corporation; *U.S. Public*, pg. 979
CARDLINK SYSTEMS LIMITED—See Corpay, Inc.; *U.S. Public*, pg. 579
CARDLYTICS, INC; *U.S. Public*, pg. 434
CARD-MONROE CORP.; *U.S. Private*, pg. 749
CARDNET MERCHANT SERVICES LTD.—See Lloyds Banking Group plc; *Int'l*, pg. 4536
CARDNO ALEXANDER BROWNE PTY. LTD.—See Cardno Limited; *Int'l*, pg. 1322
CARDNO BOWLER PTY. LTD.—See Cardno Limited; *Int'l*, pg. 1322
CARDNO BOWLER—See Cardno Limited; *Int'l*, pg. 1322
CARDNO CHEMRISK, LLC—See Cardno Limited; *Int'l*, pg. 1322
CARDNO CHEMRISK - SAN FRANCISCO—See Cardno Limited; *Int'l*, pg. 1322
CARDNO CHRISTCHURCH—See Cardno Limited; *Int'l*, pg. 1322

CARDS OFF SA

CARDNO ECOLOGY LAB PTY. LTD.—See Cardno Limited; *Int'l*, pg. 1322
CARDNO EMERGING MARKETS (AUSTRALIA) PTY. LTD.—See Cardno Limited; *Int'l*, pg. 1322
CARDNO EMERGING MARKETS BELGIUM S.A.—See Cardno Limited; *Int'l*, pg. 1322
CARDNO EMERGING MARKETS (EAST AFRICA) LIMITED—See Cardno Limited; *Int'l*, pg. 1322
CARDNO EMERGING MARKETS (UK) LIMITED—See Cardno Limited; *Int'l*, pg. 1322
CARDNO EMERGING MARKETS (USA), LTD.—See Cardno Limited; *Int'l*, pg. 1322
CARDNO ENTRIX (COLOMBIA) S.A.S.—See Cardno Limited; *Int'l*, pg. 1322
CARDNO ENTRIX, INC.—See Cardno Limited; *Int'l*, pg. 1322
CARDNO EPPELL OLSEN PTY. LTD.—See Cardno Limited; *Int'l*, pg. 1322
CARDNO ERI, INC.—See Cardno Limited; *Int'l*, pg. 1322
CARDNO HAYNES WHALEY, INC.—See Cardno Limited; *Int'l*, pg. 1322
CARDNO HOLDINGS PTY. LTD.—See Cardno Limited; *Int'l*, pg. 1322
CARDNO ITC PTY. LTD.—See Cardno Limited; *Int'l*, pg. 1322
CARDNO ITC (QLD) PTY. LTD.—See Cardno Limited; *Int'l*, pg. 1322
CARDNO ITC (VIC) PTY. LTD.—See Cardno Limited; *Int'l*, pg. 1322
CARDNO ITC (WA) PTY. LTD.—See Cardno Limited; *Int'l*, pg. 1322
CARDNO LIMITED; *Int'l*, pg. 1321
CARDNO LOW & HOOKE PTY. LTD.—See Cardno Limited; *Int'l*, pg. 1322
CARDNO (NSW/ACT) PTY. LTD.—See Cardno Limited; *Int'l*, pg. 1322
CARDNO (NZ) LIMITED—See Cardno Limited; *Int'l*, pg. 1322
CARDNO (PNG) LTD.—See Cardno Limited; *Int'l*, pg. 1322
CARDNO PTY. LTD.—See Cardno Limited; *Int'l*, pg. 1322
CARDNO (QLD) PTY. LTD.—See Cardno Limited; *Int'l*, pg. 1322
CARDNO SPECTRUM SURVEY PTY. LTD.—See Cardno Limited; *Int'l*, pg. 1322
CARDNO TBE (MICHIGAN), INC.—See Cardno Limited; *Int'l*, pg. 1322
CARDNO TBE—See Cardno Limited; *Int'l*, pg. 1322
CARDNO UK LIMITED—See Cardno Limited; *Int'l*, pg. 1322
CARDNO ULLMAN & NOLAN PTY. LTD.—See Cardno Limited; *Int'l*, pg. 1322
CARDNO UNITED STATES OF AMERICA—See Cardno Limited; *Int'l*, pg. 1322
CARDNO VICTORIA PTY. LTD.—See Cardno Limited; *Int'l*, pg. 1322
CARDNO (WA) PTY. LTD.—See Cardno Limited; *Int'l*, pg. 1322
CARDNO WRG, INC.—See Cardno Limited; *Int'l*, pg. 1322
CARDO AB—See ASSA ABLOY AB; *Int'l*, pg. 634
CARDO DOOR INTERNATIONAL AG—See ASSA ABLOY AB; *Int'l*, pg. 634
CARDO DOOR PRODUCTION AB—See ASSA ABLOY AB; *Int'l*, pg. 634
CARDO DOOR PRODUCTION B.V.—See ASSA ABLOY AB; *Int'l*, pg. 634
CARDO DOOR PRODUCTION GMBH—See ASSA ABLOY AB; *Int'l*, pg. 634
CARDOLITE CORPORATION; *U.S. Private*, pg. 751
CARDONAPLAST, S.A.—See Plastiques du Val de Loire S.A.; *Int'l*, pg. 5892
CARDONE INDUSTRIES, INC.; *U.S. Private*, pg. 751
CARDON GROUP INC.; *Int'l*, pg. 1323
CARDO PRODUCTION LOHMAR GMBH—See Sulzer Ltd.; *Int'l*, pg. 7258
CARDOW JEWELERS; *U.S. Private*, pg. 751
CARDOZ AB—See Forbion Capital Partners Management Holding BV; *Int'l*, pg. 2729
CARD PAYMENT SERVICES INC.—See Global Payments Inc.; *U.S. Public*, pg. 944
CARD PAY SDN. BHD.—See General Atlantic Service Company, L.P.; *U.S. Private*, pg. 1661
CARDPOINT LIMITED—See NCR Voyix Corporation.; *U.S. Public*, pg. 1501
CARD PROCESSING RESELLER, INC.—See Bank of America Corporation; *U.S. Public*, pg. 271
CARDSERVICE INTERNATIONAL, INC.—See Fiserv, Inc.; *U.S. Public*, pg. 850
CARD SERVICES FOR CREDIT UNIONS, INC.; *U.S. Private*, pg. 749
CARDS OFF SA; *Int'l*, pg. 1323
CARDS & SYSTEMS EDV-DIENSTLEISTUNGS GMBH—See UniCredit S.p.A.; *Int'l*, pg. 8040
CARDTREND SYSTEMS SDN. BHD.—See Edenred S.A.; *Int'l*, pg. 2307
CARDTRONICS CANADA ATM PROCESSING PARTNERSHIP—See NCR Voyix Corporation.; *U.S. Public*, pg. 1501
CARDTRONICS CANADA, LTD.—See NCR Voyix Corporation.; *U.S. Public*, pg. 1501

CARDS OFF SA
CORPORATE AFFILIATIONS

CARDTRONICS DE MEXICO S.A. DE C.V.—See NCR Voyix Corporation.; *U.S. Public*, pg. 1502
CARDTRONICS HOLDINGS, LLC—See NCR Voyix Corporation.; *U.S. Public*, pg. 1501
CARDTRONICS, INC.—See NCR Voyix Corporation.; *U.S. Public*, pg. 1501
CARDTRONICS PLC—See NCR Voyix Corporation.; *U.S. Public*, pg. 1501
CARDTRONICS PTY. LTD.—See NCR Voyix Corporation.; *U.S. Public*, pg. 1501
CARDTRONICS UK LIMITED—See NCR Voyix Corporation.; *U.S. Public*, pg. 1501
CARDTRONICS USA, INC.—See NCR Voyix Corporation.; *U.S. Public*, pg. 1502
CARDWELL DISTRIBUTING, INC.—See AIP, LLC; *U.S. Private*, pg. 136
CARDWELL WESTINGHOUSE CO.—See Westinghouse Air Brake Technologies Corporation; *U.S. Public*, pg. 2357
CARDWORKS, INC.; *U.S. Private*, pg. 751
CARDWORKS SERVICING, LLC—See CardWorks, Inc.; *U.S. Private*, pg. 751
CARD X ASSET MANAGEMENT CO., LTD.—See SCB X Public Company Limited; *Int'l*, pg. 6614
CARD X CO., LTD.—See SCB X Public Company Limited; *Int'l*, pg. 6614
CARDXX, INC.; *U.S. Public*, pg. 434
CARE 1ST HEALTH PLAN ARIZONA, INC.—See Centene Corporation; *U.S. Public*, pg. 471
CARE ADVANTAGE, INC.—See Searchlight Capital Partners, L.P.; *U.S. Private*, pg. 3586
CAREAGE INC.; *U.S. Private*, pg. 752
CARE-A-LOT PET SUPPLY; *U.S. Private*, pg. 752
CARE AMBULANCE INC.—See Lundbeckfonden; *Int'l*, pg. 4582
CARE AMBULANCE SERVICE, INC.—See Lundbeckfonden; *Int'l*, pg. 4580
CAREAPT S.R.L.—See Zambon Company S.p.A.; *Int'l*, pg. 8622
CAREATC; *U.S. Private*, pg. 752
CAREBOOK TECHNOLOGIES INC.; *Int'l*, pg. 1323
CARE BOT CORPORATION—See SAINT-CARE HOLDING CORPORATION; *Int'l*, pg. 6484
CARECALL INC.; *U.S. Private*, pg. 752
CARE CANADA; *Int'l*, pg. 1323
CARE CENTER OF ROSSMOOR, L.L.C.—See Apollo Global Management, Inc.; *U.S. Public*, pg. 156
CARECENTRIX, INC.—See Walgreens Boots Alliance, Inc.; *U.S. Public*, pg. 2322
CARECLIX HOLDINGS, INC.; *U.S. Private*, pg. 752
CARECLOUD CORPORATION—See CareCloud, Inc.; *U.S. Public*, pg. 434
CARECLOUD, INC.; *U.S. Public*, pg. 434
CARE.COM EUROPE GMBH—See IAC Inc.; *U.S. Public*, pg. 1082
CARE.COM, INC.—See IAC Inc.; *U.S. Public*, pg. 1082
CARE COMPANY—See WPP plc; *Int'l*, pg. 8484
CARE.COM SWITZERLAND AG—See IAC Inc.; *U.S. Public*, pg. 1082
CARE CONNECTION OF CINCINNATI, LLC—See KKR & Co. Inc.; *U.S. Public*, pg. 1249
CARE CONSULT VERSICHERUNGSMAKLER GMBH—See Assicurazioni Generali S.p.A.; *Int'l*, pg. 645
CARECREDIT LLC—See Synchrony Financial; *U.S. Public*, pg. 1970
CARECREDIT LLC—See Synchrony Financial; *U.S. Public*, pg. 1970
CARECREDIT LLC—See Synchrony Financial; *U.S. Public*, pg. 1970
CARECREDIT LLC—See Synchrony Financial; *U.S. Public*, pg. 1970
CARECYCLE SOLUTIONS, LLC—See Kelso & Company, L.P.; *U.S. Private*, pg. 2278
CARE DIMENSIONS; *U.S. Private*, pg. 751
CARE DIRECT LIMITED—See Rubicor Group Limited; *Int'l*, pg. 6422
CAREDX, INC.; *U.S. Public*, pg. 435
CAREDX INTERNATIONAL AB—See CareDx, Inc.; *U.S. Public*, pg. 435
CAREDX PTY LTD.—See CareDx, Inc.; *U.S. Public*, pg. 435
CAREEN, INC.; *U.S. Private*, pg. 752
CARE ENTREE—See Aon plc; *Int'l*, pg. 489
CAREER AGENT CO., LTD.—See Bain Capital, LP; *U.S. Private*, pg. 433
CAREER BLAZERS LEARNING CENTER OF LOS ANGELES, INC.—See Deutsche Bank Aktiengesellschaft; *Int'l*, pg. 2055
CAREERBUILDER EMPLOYMENT SCREENING, LLC—See Boathouse Capital Management, LLC; *U.S. Private*, pg. 603
CAREERBUILDER GERMANY GMBH—See Ontario Teachers' Pension Plan; *Int'l*, pg. 5588
CAREERBUILDER, LLC—See Ontario Teachers' Pension Plan; *Int'l*, pg. 5588
CAREER CO., LTD.; *Int'l*, pg. 1323
CAREER CONCEPTS STAFFING SERVICES, INC.; *U.S. Private*, pg. 752

CAREER DESIGN ACADEMY (CDA) CO., LTD.—See T-Gaia Corp.; *Int'l*, pg. 7396
CAREER DESIGN CENTER CO., LTD.; *Int'l*, pg. 1323
CAREER ELECTRONIC (KUNSHAN) CO., LTD.—See Career Technology (MFG.) Co., Ltd.; *Int'l*, pg. 1323
CAREERENGINE NETWORK—See Classified Solutions Group, Inc.; *U.S. Private*, pg. 917
CAREER ENGINE SOLUTIONS—See Classified Solutions Group, Inc.; *U.S. Private*, pg. 917
CAREER GROUP INC.; *U.S. Private*, pg. 752
CAREER HARMONY, LTD.—See ManpowerGroup Inc.; *U.S. Public*, pg. 1357
CAREER HORIZONS, INC.; *U.S. Private*, pg. 752
CAREERINDEX, INC.; *Int'l*, pg. 1323
CAREERLINK CO., LTD.; *Int'l*, pg. 1324
CAREERLINK, INC.; *U.S. Private*, pg. 752
CAREERMAG.COM—See Jameson Publishing Inc.; *U.S. Private*, pg. 2185
CAREER MANAGEMENT PARTNERS; *U.S. Private*, pg. 752
CAREER PARTNER GMBH—See Oakley Capital Limited; *Int'l*, pg. 5504
CAREER PATH TRAINING CORP.; *U.S. Private*, pg. 752
CAREER PERSONNEL LIMITED—See HRnetGroup Limited; *Int'l*, pg. 3501
CAREER POINT LTD.; *Int'l*, pg. 1323
CAREER QUEST LEARNING CENTERS, INC.—See Sverica Capital Management LP; *U.S. Private*, pg. 3888
CAREER RESOURCES, INC.—See Adecco Group AG; *Int'l*, pg. 138
CAREERRISE CORPORATION—See Persol Holdings Co., Ltd.; *Int'l*, pg. 5819
CAREERROAD CO., LTD.—See Nippon Express Holdings, Inc.; *Int'l*, pg. 5315
CAREER SERVICES GROUP, INC.—See Talent, Inc.; *U.S. Private*, pg. 3926
CAREERS IN TRANSITION, INC.; *U.S. Private*, pg. 752
CAREERSOURCE BREVARD; *U.S. Private*, pg. 752
CAREERS REGISTER LIMITED—See Bain Capital, LP; *U.S. Private*, pg. 433
CAREERSTAFF UNLIMITED, INC.—See ShiftMed, LLC; *U.S. Private*, pg. 3636
CAREER STEP, LLC—See Revelstoke Capital Partners LLC; *U.S. Private*, pg. 3413
CAREERS TRUST SCOTLAND LIMITED—See Scottish Enterprise; *Int'l*, pg. 6652
CAREER SUPPORT CO., LTD.—See Sumitomo Chemical Company, Limited; *Int'l*, pg. 7264
CAREERSUSA, INC.; *U.S. Private*, pg. 752
CAREER SYSTEMS DEVELOPMENT CORPORATION—See Owl Companies; *U.S. Private*, pg. 3055
CAREER TEACHERS LIMITED—See HFBG Holding B.V.; *Int'l*, pg. 3374
CAREER TECHNOLOGIES USA—See Arsenal Capital Management LP; *U.S. Private*, pg. 338
CAREER TECHNOLOGY (H.K.) LTD.—See Career Technology (MFG.) Co., Ltd.; *Int'l*, pg. 1323
CAREER TECHNOLOGY (MFG.) CO., LTD.; *Int'l*, pg. 1323
CAREER TECHNOLOGY (S) PTE. LTD.—See Career Technology (MFG.) Co., Ltd.; *Int'l*, pg. 1323
CAREER TECHNOLOGY (SUZHOU) CO., LTD.—See Career Technology (MFG.) Co., Ltd.; *Int'l*, pg. 1323
CAREER TIMES ONLINE LIMITED—See Hong Kong Economic Times Holdings Ltd; *Int'l*, pg. 3465
CAREER TRAINING CONCEPTS, INC.; *U.S. Private*, pg. 752
CAREERXCHANGE, INC.; *U.S. Private*, pg. 753
CAREERXCHANGE, INC.—See Careerxchange, Inc.; *U.S. Private*, pg. 753
CAR.E FACILITY MANAGEMENT GMBH—See Clayton, Dubilier & Rice, LLC; *U.S. Private*, pg. 926
CAREFEEL COTTON INDUSTRIES (M) SDN. BHD.—See Hengan International Group Co. Ltd.; *Int'l*, pg. 3345
CARE FINANCIAL OF TEXAS, LLC—See The Allstate Corporation; *U.S. Public*, pg. 2033
CAREFIRST ADMINISTRATORS—See CareFirst, Inc.; *U.S. Private*, pg. 753
CAREFIRST BLUECROSS BLUESHIELD, CLAIMS CENTER—See CareFirst, Inc.; *U.S. Private*, pg. 753
CAREFIRST BLUECROSS BLUESHIELD—See CareFirst, Inc.; *U.S. Private*, pg. 753
CAREFIRST, INC.; *U.S. Private*, pg. 753
CAREFIRST OF MARYLAND, INC.—See CareFirst, Inc.; *U.S. Private*, pg. 753
CAREFLITE; *U.S. Private*, pg. 753
CARE FOCUS, INC.—See Maxim Healthcare Services, Inc.; *U.S. Private*, pg. 2618
CARE FOR BUILDINGS AND CITIES CLEANING CONTRACTING COMPANY - WLL—See Gulf Cable & Electrical Industries Co. K.S.C.; *Int'l*, pg. 3179
CAREFREE INDUSTRIES, INC.; *U.S. Private*, pg. 753
CAREFREE INSURANCE SERVICES, INC.—See CVS Health Corporation; *U.S. Public*, pg. 614
CAREFREE OF COLORADO—See Berkshire Hathaway Inc.; *U.S. Public*, pg. 300
CAREFREE RV RESORTS; *U.S. Private*, pg. 753

CAREFUSION ASIA (HK) LIMITED—See Becton, Dickinson & Company; *U.S. Public*, pg. 291
CAREFUSION CORPORATION—See Becton, Dickinson & Company; *U.S. Public*, pg. 291
CAREFUSION DENMARK 329 A/S—See Becton, Dickinson & Company; *U.S. Public*, pg. 291
CAREFUSION FRANCE 309 S.A.S.—See Becton, Dickinson & Company; *U.S. Public*, pg. 291
CAREFUSION GERMANY 318 GMBH—See Becton, Dickinson & Company; *U.S. Public*, pg. 291
CAREFUSION GERMANY 326 GMBH—See Becton, Dickinson & Company; *U.S. Public*, pg. 291
CAREFUSION HONG KONG LIMITED—See Becton, Dickinson & Company; *U.S. Public*, pg. 291
CAREFUSION ISRAEL 330 LTD.—See Becton, Dickinson & Company; *U.S. Public*, pg. 291
CAREFUSION ITALY 311 S.R.L.—See Becton, Dickinson & Company; *U.S. Public*, pg. 291
CAREFUSION ITALY 327 S.R.L.—See Becton, Dickinson & Company; *U.S. Public*, pg. 291
CAREFUSION MEXICO 215 SA DE CV—See Becton, Dickinson & Company; *U.S. Public*, pg. 291
CAREFUSION NEW ZEALAND 313 LIMITED—See Becton, Dickinson & Company; *U.S. Public*, pg. 291
CAREFUSION NORWAY 315 A/S—See Becton, Dickinson & Company; *U.S. Public*, pg. 291
CAREFUSION S.A. 319 (PROPRIETARY) LIMITED—See Becton, Dickinson & Company; *U.S. Public*, pg. 291
CAREFUSION SOLUTIONS, LLC—See Becton, Dickinson & Company; *U.S. Public*, pg. 291
CAREFUSION U.K. 306 LIMITED—See Becton, Dickinson & Company; *U.S. Public*, pg. 292
CAREGEN CO.,LTD.; *Int'l*, pg. 1324
CAREGIVER, INC.; *U.S. Private*, pg. 753
CAREGLOVE GLOBAL SDN. BHD.—See Careplus Group Berhad; *Int'l*, pg. 1325
CAREGROUP, INC.; *U.S. Private*, pg. 753
CARE HEALTH INSURANCE LIMITED—See Religare Enterprises Limited; *Int'l*, pg. 6264
CARE & HEALTH LIMITED—See Hanison Construction Holdings Limited; *Int'l*, pg. 3252
CAREHERE, LLC; *U.S. Private*, pg. 753
CARE HOTEL MANAGEMENT CO., LTD.—See Biken Techno Corporation Ltd.; *Int'l*, pg. 1023
CARE IMPROVEMENT PLUS GROUP MANAGEMENT, LLC—See UnitedHealth Group Incorporated; *U.S. Public*, pg. 2239
CARE INITIATIVES; *U.S. Private*, pg. 751
CARE KALYPTO RISK TECHNOLOGIES AND ADVISORY SERVICES PVT. LTD.—See CARE Ratings Limited; *Int'l*, pg. 1323
CAREKINESIS, INC.—See Nautic Partners, LLC; *U.S. Private*, pg. 2871
CARELAA B.V.—See Akzo Nobel N.V.; *Int'l*, pg. 273
CARELABS CO., LTD.; *Int'l*, pg. 1324
CAREL ACR SYSTEMS INDIA PVT. LTD.—See Carel Industries S.p.A.; *Int'l*, pg. 1324
CAREL ASIA LTD.—See Carel Industries S.p.A.; *Int'l*, pg. 1324
CAREL AUSTRALIA PTY LTD—See Carel Industries S.p.A.; *Int'l*, pg. 1324
CAREL CONTROLS IBERICA SL—See Carel Industries S.p.A.; *Int'l*, pg. 1324
CAREL CONTROLS SOUTH AFRICA PTY LTD—See Carel Industries S.p.A.; *Int'l*, pg. 1324
CAREL DEUTSCHLAND GMBH—See Carel Industries S.p.A.; *Int'l*, pg. 1324
CAREL ELECTRONIC SUZHOU LTD.—See Carel Industries S.p.A.; *Int'l*, pg. 1324
CAREL FRANCE SAS—See Carel Industries S.p.A.; *Int'l*, pg. 1324
CAREL INDUSTRIES S.P.A.; *Int'l*, pg. 1324
CARE LINE INDUSTRIES INC.; *U.S. Private*, pg. 751
CARELINK COMMUNITY SUPPORT SERVICES; *U.S. Private*, pg. 753
CARELINX INC.—See Altaris Capital Partners, LLC; *U.S. Private*, pg. 206
CAREL JAPAN CO., LTD.—See Carel Industries S.p.A.; *Int'l*, pg. 1324
CAREL MEXICANA S. DE RL. DE CV.—See Carel Industries S.p.A.; *Int'l*, pg. 1324
CAREL MIDDLE EAST DWC-CLC—See Carel Industries S.p.A.; *Int'l*, pg. 1324
CAREL NORDIC AB—See Carel Industries S.p.A.; *Int'l*, pg. 1324
CARELON GLOBAL SOLUTIONS INDIA LLP—See Elevance Health, Inc.; *U.S. Public*, pg. 729
CARELON GLOBAL SOLUTIONS IRELAND LIMITED—See Elevance Health, Inc.; *U.S. Public*, pg. 729
CARELON RESEARCH, INC.—See Elevance Health, Inc.; *U.S. Public*, pg. 729
CARELONRX, INC.—See Elevance Health, Inc.; *U.S. Public*, pg. 729
CAREL RUSSIA LLC—See Carel Industries S.p.A.; *Int'l*, pg. 1324
CAREL SUD AMERICA INSTRUMENTACAO ELETRONICA LTDA—See Carel Industries S.p.A.; *Int'l*, pg. 1324

COMPANY NAME INDEX

CAREL (THAILAND) CO. LTD.—See Carel Industries S.p.A.; *Int'l*, pg. 1324
CAREL UK LTD.—See Carel Industries S.p.A.; *Int'l*, pg. 1324
CAREL UKRAINE LLC—See Carel Industries S.p.A.; *Int'l*, pg. 1324
CAREMALTA FINANCE PLC.—See Vassallo Builders Group Limited; *Int'l*, pg. 8134
CARE MANAGEMENT GROUP, LLC—See Security National Financial Corporation; *U.S. Public*, pg. 1856
CARE MANAGEMENT NETWORK INC.—See Assicurazioni Generali S.p.A.; *Int'l*, pg. 643
CARE MANAGEMENT SYSTEMS LIMITED—See Software Circle plc.; *Int'l*, pg. 7056
CAREMARK, LLC—See CVS Health Corporation; *U.S. Public*, pg. 615
CAREMARKPCS HEALTH LLC—See CVS Health Corporation; *U.S. Public*, pg. 615
CAREMARK RX, LLC—See CVS Health Corporation; *U.S. Public*, pg. 615
CAREMAX, INC.; *U.S. Public*, pg. 435
CARE MEDICAL EQUIPMENT INCORPORATED; *U.S. Private*, pg. 751
CAREMEDIC SYSTEMS, INC.—See UnitedHealth Group Incorporated; *U.S. Public*, pg. 2248
CAREMERIDIAN, LLC—See Centerbridge Partners, L.P.; *U.S. Private*, pg. 813
CAREMETX, LLC—See General Atlantic Service Company, L.P.; *U.S. Private*, pg. 1662
CAREMILE CO., LTD.; *Int'l*, pg. 1324
CAREMOLI DEUTSCHLAND GMBH—See Caremoli SpA; *Int'l*, pg. 1324
CAREMOLI INDIA, PVT. LTD.—See Caremoli SpA; *Int'l*, pg. 1324
CAREMOLI SPA; *Int'l*, pg. 1324
CAREMOLI USA, INC.—See Caremoli SpA; *Int'l*, pg. 1324
CAREMORE HEALTH GROUP, INC.—See Elevance Health, Inc.; *U.S. Public*, pg. 729
CAREMORE HEALTH PLAN—See Elevance Health, Inc.; *U.S. Public*, pg. 729
CAREMORE HEALTH SYSTEM—See Elevance Health, Inc.; *U.S. Public*, pg. 729
CAREMORE HOLDINGS, INC.—See Elevance Health, Inc.; *U.S. Public*, pg. 729
CAREMORE MEDICAL ENTERPRISES—See Elevance Health, Inc.; *U.S. Public*, pg. 729
CAREMORE MEDICAL MANAGEMENT COMPANY—See Elevance Health, Inc.; *U.S. Public*, pg. 729
CARENET INC.; *Int'l*, pg. 1324
CARENET; *U.S. Private*, pg. 753
CARE NETWORK—See Managed Care of America Inc.; *U.S. Private*, pg. 2559
CARE NEW ENGLAND HEALTH SYSTEM, INC.; *U.S. Private*, pg. 751
CARENEX HEALTH SERVICES; *U.S. Private*, pg. 753
CAREO KFT—See Apollo Global Management, Inc.; *U.S. Public*, pg. 159
CAREO LIMITED—See Apollo Global Management, Inc.; *U.S. Public*, pg. 159
CAREOREGON, INC.; *U.S. Private*, pg. 754
CAREO SP. Z O.O.—See Apollo Global Management, Inc.; *U.S. Public*, pg. 159
CAREO S.R.L.—See Apollo Global Management, Inc.; *U.S. Public*, pg. 159
CAREO S.R.O.—See Apollo Global Management, Inc.; *U.S. Public*, pg. 159
CARE PARTNER CO LTD—See Daito Trust Construction Co., Ltd.; *Int'l*, pg. 1943
CAREPATROL FRANCHISE SYSTEMS, LLC—See Riverside Partners, LLC; *U.S. Private*, pg. 3445
CAREPAYMENT TECHNOLOGIES, INC.—See Cedar Spring Capital LLC; *U.S. Private*, pg. 805
CAREPAYMENT TECHNOLOGIES, INC.—See Crestline Investors, Inc.; *U.S. Private*, pg. 1097
CARE PHARMACEUTICALS PTY LIMITED—See Prestige Consumer Healthcare Inc.; *U.S. Public*, pg. 1716
CAREPLUS GROUP BERHAD; *Int'l*, pg. 1325
CAREPLUS HEALTH PLANS, INC.—See Humana, Inc.; *U.S. Public*, pg. 1069
CARE PLUS MEDICINA ASSISTENCIAL LTDA.—See The British United Provident Association Limited; *Int'l*, pg. 7629
CAREPLUS (M) SDN BHD—See Ansell Limited; *Int'l*, pg. 478
CARE PLUS NJ, INC.; *U.S. Private*, pg. 751
CARE POINT MEDICAL CENTRES—See Canadian Back Institute Limited Partnership; *Int'l*, pg. 1282
CAREPOINT PARTNERS; *U.S. Private*, pg. 754
CAREPORT HEALTH, LLC—See Veradigm Inc.; *U.S. Public*, pg. 2280
CARE PROPERTY INVEST NV; *Int'l*, pg. 1323
CARE RATINGS (AFRICA) PRIVATE LIMITED—See CARE Ratings Limited; *Int'l*, pg. 1323
CARE RATINGS LIMITED; *Int'l*, pg. 1323
CARE RATINGS NEPAL LTD.—See CARE Ratings Limited; *Int'l*, pg. 1323
CARERAY DIGITAL MEDICAL TECHNOLOGY CO., LTD.; *Int'l*, pg. 1325

CARE RISK SOLUTIONS PRIVATE LIMITED—See CARE Ratings Limited; *Int'l*, pg. 1323
CARERX CORPORATION; *Int'l*, pg. 1325
CARES - COMPANHIA DE SEGUROS, S.A.—See Fosun International Limited; *Int'l*, pg. 2750
CA RESEARCH, INC.—See Broadcom Inc.; *U.S. Public*, pg. 389
CARE SERVICE CO., LTD.; *Int'l*, pg. 1323
CARES MULTIASSITANCE, S.A.—See Caixa Geral de Depositos S.A.; *Int'l*, pg. 1260
CARESOURCE; *U.S. Private*, pg. 754
CARESPAN HEALTH, INC.; *Int'l*, pg. 1325
CARESPOT OF ORLANDO/HSI URGENT CARE, LLC—See Tenet Healthcare Corporation; *U.S. Public*, pg. 2001
CARESPOT OF OVERLAND PARK (W. 151ST STREET), LLC—See HCA Healthcare, Inc.; *U.S. Public*, pg. 992
CARESPOT—See Tenet Healthcare Corporation; *U.S. Public*, pg. 2013
CARES RH - COMPANHIA DE ASSISTENCIA E REPRESENTACAO DE SEGUROS, S.A.—See Caixa Geral de Depositos S.A.; *Int'l*, pg. 1260
CARESTAFF NURSING SERVICES PTY LTD—See PeopleIn Limited; *Int'l*, pg. 5794
CARESTEPS.COM—See Stone Point Capital LLC; *U.S. Private*, pg. 3825
CARESTREAM DENTAL, LLC—See Clayton, Dubilier & Rice, LLC; *U.S. Private*, pg. 920
CARESTREAM HEALTH, INC.—See ONEX Corporation; *Int'l*, pg. 5578
CARESTREAM HEALTH—See Koninklijke Philips N.V.; *Int'l*, pg. 4267
CARESTREAM MEDICAL LTD.; *Int'l*, pg. 1325
CARESYNTAX, INC.; *U.S. Private*, pg. 754
CARETECH COMMUNITY SERVICES LIMITED—See Sheikh Holdings Group (Investments) Limited; *Int'l*, pg. 6793
CARETECH COMMUNITY SERVICES (NO. 2) LIMITED—See Sheikh Holdings Group (Investments) Limited; *Int'l*, pg. 6793
CARETECH HOLDINGS PLC—See Sheikh Holdings Group (Investments) Limited; *Int'l*, pg. 6793
CARETECH SOLUTIONS INC.; *U.S. Private*, pg. 754
CARETENDERS OF CLEVELAND, INC.—See UnitedHealth Group Incorporated; *U.S. Public*, pg. 2244
CARETENDERS VISITING SERVICES OF GAINESVILLE, LLC—See UnitedHealth Group Incorporated; *U.S. Public*, pg. 2244
CARETENDERS VISITING SERVICES OF KENTUCKIANA, LLC—See UnitedHealth Group Incorporated; *U.S. Public*, pg. 2244
CARETENDERS VISITING SERVICES OF ORLANDO, LLC—See UnitedHealth Group Incorporated; *U.S. Public*, pg. 2244
CARETENDERS VISITING SERVICES OF SOUTHERN ILLINOIS, LLC—See UnitedHealth Group Incorporated; *U.S. Public*, pg. 2244
CARETENDERS VS OF BOSTON, LLC—See UnitedHealth Group Incorporated; *U.S. Public*, pg. 2243
CARETENDERS VS OF LINCOLN TRAIL, LLC—See UnitedHealth Group Incorporated; *U.S. Public*, pg. 2243
CARETENDERS VS OF LOUISVILLE, LLC—See UnitedHealth Group Incorporated; *U.S. Public*, pg. 2243
CARETENDERS VS OF NORTHERN KY, LLC—See UnitedHealth Group Incorporated; *U.S. Public*, pg. 2243
CARETENDERS VS OF OHIO, LLC—See UnitedHealth Group Incorporated; *U.S. Public*, pg. 2243
CARETENDERS VS OF SE OHIO, LLC—See UnitedHealth Group Incorporated; *U.S. Public*, pg. 2243
CARETENDERS VS OF WESTERN KY, LLC—See UnitedHealth Group Incorporated; *U.S. Public*, pg. 2243
CARETEQ LIMITED; *Int'l*, pg. 1325
CARETRACKER, INC.—See Constellation Software Inc.; *Int'l*, pg. 1773
CARETRUST REIT, INC.; *U.S. Public*, pg. 435
CARETTA PARTNERS, LLC; *U.S. Private*, pg. 754
CARETTI, INC.; *U.S. Private*, pg. 754
CARE TWENTYONE CORPORATION; *Int'l*, pg. 1323
CARE UK CLINICAL SERVICES LIMITED—See Bridgepoint Group Plc; *Int'l*, pg. 1154
CARE UK COMMUNITY PARTNERSHIPS GROUP LIMITED—See Bridgepoint Group Plc; *Int'l*, pg. 1154
CARE UK PLC—See Bridgepoint Group Plc; *Int'l*, pg. 1154
CARE UNLIMITED, INC.—See Bain Capital, LP; *U.S. Private*, pg. 439
CARE-USA; *U.S. Private*, pg. 752
CAREVIEW COMMUNICATIONS, INC.; *U.S. Public*, pg. 435
CAREWATCH CARE SERVICES LTD.—See Horizon Capital LLP; *Int'l*, pg. 3479
CAREW CONCRETE & SUPPLY CO. INC.; *U.S. Private*, pg. 754
CARE WISCONSIN FIRST, INC.; *U.S. Private*, pg. 752
CAREXPERT KFZ-SACHVERSTANDIGEN GMBH—See DZ BANK AG Deutsche Zentral-Genossenschaftsbank; *Int'l*, pg. 2245
CAREY COMPANY INC.; *U.S. Private*, pg. 754
CAREY COUNSELING CENTER, INC.; *U.S. Private*, pg. 754

CAREY FINANCIAL, LLC—See W.P. Carey Inc.; *U.S. Public*, pg. 2315
CAREY GROUP PLC; *Int'l*, pg. 1325
CAREY GROUP PLC—See Carey Group PLC; *Int'l*, pg. 1325
CAREY HILLIARDS DRIVE-IN RESTAURANT; *U.S. Private*, pg. 754
CAREY INTERNATIONAL, INC.—See Avis Budget Group, Inc.; *U.S. Public*, pg. 249
CAREY INTERNATIONAL, INC.—See Chartwell Investments; *U.S. Private*, pg. 859
CAREY INTERNATIONAL, INC.—See Ford Motor Company; *U.S. Public*, pg. 864
CAREY JOHNSON OIL COMPANY; *U.S. Private*, pg. 754
CAREY, KRAMER, PETTIT, PANICHELLI & ASSOCIATES, INC.—See M&T Bank Corporation; *U.S. Public*, pg. 1350
CAREY WATERMARK INVESTORS INCORPORATED—See W.P. Carey Inc.; *U.S. Public*, pg. 2316
CARFAIR COMPOSITES INC.—See NFI Group Inc.; *Int'l*, pg. 5252
CAR FINANCE 2U LIMITED—See Time Finance plc; *Int'l*, pg. 7751
CARFINANCE CAPITAL LLC—See Flagship Credit Corporation; *U.S. Private*, pg. 1539
CAR FINANCIAL SERVICES, INC.—See ATLANTICUS HOLDINGS CORPORATION; *U.S. Public*, pg. 223
CARFINCO FINANCIAL GROUP INC.—See Banco Santander, S.A.; *Int'l*, pg. 825
CARFINCO INC.—See Banco Santander, S.A.; *Int'l*, pg. 825
CAR-FRESHENER CORPORATION; *U.S. Private*, pg. 748
CAR-FRESHNER CORPORATION; *U.S. Private*, pg. 748
CARGAS SYSTEMS, INC; *U.S. Private*, pg. 754
CARGEAS ASSICURAZIONI SPA—See BNP Paribas SA; *Int'l*, pg. 1089
CAR & GENERAL (KENYA) LIMITED; *Int'l*, pg. 1319
CAR & GENERAL (TANZANIA) LIMITED—See Car & General (Kenya) Limited; *Int'l*, pg. 1319
CAR & GENERAL (UGANDA) LIMITED—See Car & General (Kenya) Limited; *Int'l*, pg. 1319
CARGIANT LTD.; *Int'l*, pg. 1325
CARGILL AG HORIZONS—See Cargill, Inc.; *U.S. Private*, pg. 755
CARGILL AGHORIZONS—See Cargill, Inc.; *U.S. Private*, pg. 755
CARGILL AG HORIZONS—See Cargill, Inc.; *U.S. Private*, pg. 755
CARGILL AG HORIZONS—See Cargill, Inc.; *U.S. Private*, pg. 757
CARGILL AG HORIZONS—See Cargill, Inc.; *U.S. Private*, pg. 757
CARGILL AG HORIZONS—See Cargill, Inc.; *U.S. Private*, pg. 755
CARGILL AGRICULTURA SRL - CARGILL NUTRITIE ANIMALA FACTROY—See Cargill, Inc.; *U.S. Private*, pg. 755
CARGILL AGRICULTURA SRL—See Cargill, Inc.; *U.S. Private*, pg. 755
CARGILL AGRI PURINA, INC. - CHUNAN PLANT—See Cargill, Inc.; *U.S. Private*, pg. 755
CARGILL AGRI PURINA, INC. - KUNSAN PLANT—See Cargill, Inc.; *U.S. Private*, pg. 755
CARGILL AGRI PURINA, INC. - SONGTAN PLANT—See Cargill, Inc.; *U.S. Private*, pg. 755
CARGILL AGRI PURINA, INC.—See Cargill, Inc.; *U.S. Private*, pg. 755
CARGILL ANIMAL NUTRITION (NANJING) CO., LTD—See Cargill, Inc.; *U.S. Private*, pg. 755
CARGILL ANIMAL NUTRITION—See Cargill, Inc.; *U.S. Private*, pg. 755
CARGILL ANIMAL NUTRITION—See Cargill, Inc.; *U.S. Private*, pg. 757
CARGILL ANIMAL NUTRITION—See Cargill, Inc.; *U.S. Private*, pg. 755
CARGILL ANIMAL NUTRITION—See Cargill, Inc.; *U.S. Private*, pg. 755
CARGILL ANIMAL NUTRITION—See Cargill, Inc.; *U.S. Private*, pg. 755
CARGILL ANIMAL NUTRITION—See Cargill, Inc.; *U.S. Private*, pg. 755
CARGILL ANIMAL NUTRITION—See Cargill, Inc.; *U.S. Private*, pg. 755
CARGILL ANIMAL NUTRITION—See Cargill, Inc.; *U.S. Private*, pg. 755
CARGILL ANIMAL NUTRITION—See Cargill, Inc.; *U.S. Private*, pg. 755
CARGILL ANIMAL NUTRITION—See Cargill, Inc.; *U.S. Private*, pg. 755
CARGILL ANIMAL NUTRITION—See Cargill, Inc.; *U.S. Private*, pg. 755
CARGILL ASIA PACIFIC FOOD SYSTEMS (BEIJING) LTD.—See Cargill, Inc.; *U.S. Private*, pg. 755
CARGILL ASIA PACIFIC HOLDINGS PTE LIMITED—See Cargill, Inc.; *U.S. Private*, pg. 755

CARGIANT LTD.
CORPORATE AFFILIATIONS

CARGILL AT & ENTERPRISE INC—See Cargill, Inc.; *U.S. Private*, pg. 755
CARGILL AUSTRALIA LTD—See Cargill, Inc.; *U.S. Private*, pg. 755
CARGILL AUSTRIA HANDELSGESELLSCHAFT M.B.H.—See Cargill, Inc.; *U.S. Private*, pg. 755
CARGILL BENELUX B.V.—See Cargill, Inc.; *U.S. Private*, pg. 755
CARGILL BULGARIA EOOD—See Cargill, Inc.; *U.S. Private*, pg. 755
CARGILL B.V.—See Cargill, Inc.; *U.S. Private*, pg. 755
CARGILL CARIBE S.A.—See Cargill, Inc.; *U.S. Private*, pg. 755
CARGILL CHOCOLATE BELGIUM SA—See Cargill, Inc.; *U.S. Private*, pg. 756
CARGILL COCOA & CHOCLATE CO., INC. - GEORGETOWN PLANT—See Cargill, Inc.; *U.S. Private*, pg. 755
CARGILL COCOA & CHOCOLATE CO. INC.—See Cargill, Inc.; *U.S. Private*, pg. 755
CARGILL COCOA & CHOCOLATE CO., INC.—See Cargill, Inc.; *U.S. Private*, pg. 755
CARGILL CORN MILLING—See Cargill, Inc.; *U.S. Private*, pg. 756
CARGILL CORN MILLING—See Cargill, Inc.; *U.S. Private*, pg. 756
CARGILL COTTON—See Cargill, Inc.; *U.S. Private*, pg. 756
CARGILL COTTON—See Cargill, Inc.; *U.S. Private*, pg. 756
CARGILL COTTON—See Cargill, Inc.; *U.S. Private*, pg. 756
CARGILL DEICING TECHNOLOGIES—See Cargill, Inc.; *U.S. Private*, pg. 756
CARGILL DEICING TECHNOLOGIES—See Cargill, Inc.; *U.S. Private*, pg. 756
CARGILL DEICING TECHNOLOGIES—See Cargill, Inc.; *U.S. Private*, pg. 756
CARGILL DE MEXICO, S.A. DE C.V.—See Cargill, Inc.; *U.S. Private*, pg. 759
CARGILL DRY CORN INGREDIENTS INC—See Cargill, Inc.; *U.S. Private*, pg. 756
CARGILL EUROPE BVBA—See Cargill, Inc.; *U.S. Private*, pg. 756
CARGILL EUROPE LIMITED—See Cargill, Inc.; *U.S. Private*, pg. 756
CARGILL FEED SDN BHD—See Cargill, Inc.; *U.S. Private*, pg. 756
CARGILL FOOD DISTRIBUTION—See Cargill, Inc.; *U.S. Private*, pg. 758
CARGILL FOOD DISTRIBUTION—See Cargill, Inc.; *U.S. Private*, pg. 758
CARGILL FOOD INGREDIENTS CANADA, INC.—See Cargill, Inc.; *U.S. Private*, pg. 756
CARGILL FOOD INGREDIENTS—See Cargill, Inc.; *U.S. Private*, pg. 756
CARGILL FOODS FRANCE SAS—See Cargill, Inc.; *U.S. Private*, pg. 756
CARGILL FOODS INC.—See Cargill, Inc.; *U.S. Private*, pg. 756
CARGILL FOODS LIMITED—See Cargill, Inc.; *U.S. Private*, pg. 757
CARGILL GHANA LIMITED—See Cargill, Inc.; *U.S. Private*, pg. 756
CARGILL GMBH—See Cargill, Inc.; *U.S. Private*, pg. 756
CARGILL GRAIN & OILSEEDS (NANTONG) CO., LTD.—See Cargill, Inc.; *U.S. Private*, pg. 756
CARGILL HONG KONG LTD.—See Cargill, Inc.; *U.S. Private*, pg. 756
CARGILL, INC. - NUTRENA FEED—See Cargill, Inc.; *U.S. Private*, pg. 759
CARGILL INC.—See Cargill, Inc.; *U.S. Private*, pg. 757
CARGILL INC.—See Cargill, Inc.; *U.S. Private*, pg. 757
CARGILL INC.—See Cargill, Inc.; *U.S. Private*, pg. 756
CARGILL INC.—See Cargill, Inc.; *U.S. Private*, pg. 756
CARGILL INC.—See Cargill, Inc.; *U.S. Private*, pg. 756
CARGILL INC.—See Cargill, Inc.; *U.S. Private*, pg. 756
CARGILL INC.—See Cargill, Inc.; *U.S. Private*, pg. 757
CARGILL INC.—See Cargill, Inc.; *U.S. Private*, pg. 757
CARGILL INC.—See Cargill, Inc.; *U.S. Private*, pg. 757
CARGILL INC.—See Cargill, Inc.; *U.S. Private*, pg. 757
CARGILL INC.—See Cargill, Inc.; *U.S. Private*, pg. 757
CARGILL, INC.; *U.S. Private*, pg. 754
CARGILL INC.—See Cargill, Inc.; *U.S. Private*, pg. 756
CARGILL INC.—See Cargill, Inc.; *U.S. Private*, pg. 756
CARGILL INC.—See Cargill, Inc.; *U.S. Private*, pg. 756
CARGILL INC.—See Cargill, Inc.; *U.S. Private*, pg. 756
CARGILL INC.—See Cargill, Inc.; *U.S. Private*, pg. 756
CARGILL INC.—See Cargill, Inc.; *U.S. Private*, pg. 756
CARGILL INC.—See Cargill, Inc.; *U.S. Private*, pg. 757
CARGILL INC.—See Cargill, Inc.; *U.S. Private*, pg. 757
CARGILL INC.—See Cargill, Inc.; *U.S. Private*, pg. 757
CARGILL INC.—See Cargill, Inc.; *U.S. Private*, pg. 757
CARGILL INC.—See Cargill, Inc.; *U.S. Private*, pg. 757
CARGILL INC.—See Cargill, Inc.; *U.S. Private*, pg. 757
CARGILL INC.—See Cargill, Inc.; *U.S. Private*, pg. 757
CARGILL INC.—See Cargill, Inc.; *U.S. Private*, pg. 757

CARGILL INC.—See Cargill, Inc.; *U.S. Private*, pg. 756
CARGILL INC.—See Cargill, Inc.; *U.S. Private*, pg. 757
CARGILL INC.—See Cargill, Inc.; *U.S. Private*, pg. 757
CARGILL INC.—See Cargill, Inc.; *U.S. Private*, pg. 757
CARGILL INC.—See Cargill, Inc.; *U.S. Private*, pg. 757
CARGILL INC.—See Cargill, Inc.; *U.S. Private*, pg. 756
CARGILL INTERNATIONAL S.A.—See Cargill, Inc.; *U.S. Private*, pg. 757
CARGILL INVESTMENTS (CHINA) LTD.—See Cargill, Inc.; *U.S. Private*, pg. 757
CARGILL JAPAN LIMITED—See Cargill, Inc.; *U.S. Private*, pg. 757
CARGILL KITCHEN SOLUTIONS—See Cargill, Inc.; *U.S. Private*, pg. 757
CARGILL KITCHEN SOLUTIONS—See Cargill, Inc.; *U.S. Private*, pg. 757
CARGILL LIMITED—See Cargill, Inc.; *U.S. Private*, pg. 757
CARGILL LIMITED—See Cargill, Inc.; *U.S. Private*, pg. 757
CARGILL LIMITED—See Cargill, Inc.; *U.S. Private*, pg. 757
CARGILL LIMITED—See Cargill, Inc.; *U.S. Private*, pg. 757
CARGILL LIMITED—See Cargill, Inc.; *U.S. Private*, pg. 757
CARGILL LIMITED—See Cargill, Inc.; *U.S. Private*, pg. 757
CARGILL LIMITED—See Cargill, Inc.; *U.S. Private*, pg. 757
CARGILL LIMITED—See Cargill, Inc.; *U.S. Private*, pg. 757
CARGILL LIMITED—See Cargill, Inc.; *U.S. Private*, pg. 758
CARGILL LIMITED—See Cargill, Inc.; *U.S. Private*, pg. 758
CARGILL LIMITED—See Cargill, Inc.; *U.S. Private*, pg. 758
CARGILL LOGISTICS—See Cargill, Inc.; *U.S. Private*, pg. 758
CARGILL (MALAYSIA) SDN BHD—See Cargill, Inc.; *U.S. Private*, pg. 755
CARGILL MALT—See Axereal Union de Cooperatives Agricoles; *Int'l*, pg. 767
CARGILL MALT—See Axereal Union de Cooperatives Agricoles; *Int'l*, pg. 767
CARGILL MEAT SOLUTIONS, CAPROCK CATTLE FEEDERS—See Cargill, Inc.; *U.S. Private*, pg. 758
CARGILL MEAT SOLUTIONS CORP.—See Cargill, Inc.; *U.S. Private*, pg. 758
CARGILL MEAT SOLUTIONS—See Cargill, Inc.; *U.S. Private*, pg. 758
CARGILL MEAT SOLUTIONS—See Cargill, Inc.; *U.S. Private*, pg. 758
CARGILL MEAT SOLUTIONS—See Cargill, Inc.; *U.S. Private*, pg. 758
CARGILL MEAT SOLUTIONS—See Cargill, Inc.; *U.S. Private*, pg. 758
CARGILL MEAT SOLUTIONS—See Cargill, Inc.; *U.S. Private*, pg. 758
CARGILL MEAT SOLUTIONS—See Cargill, Inc.; *U.S. Private*, pg. 758
CARGILL MEAT SOLUTIONS—See Cargill, Inc.; *U.S. Private*, pg. 758
CARGILL MEAT SOLUTIONS—See Cargill, Inc.; *U.S. Private*, pg. 758
CARGILL MEAT SOLUTIONS—See Cargill, Inc.; *U.S. Private*, pg. 758
CARGILL MEAT SOLUTIONS—See Cargill, Inc.; *U.S. Private*, pg. 758
CARGILL MEAT SOLUTIONS—See Cargill, Inc.; *U.S. Private*, pg. 758
CARGILL MIDDLE EAST DMCC—See Cargill, Inc.; *U.S. Private*, pg. 758
CARGILL NORDIC A/S—See Cargill, Inc.; *U.S. Private*, pg. 758
CARGILL NORDIC OY—See Cargill, Inc.; *U.S. Private*, pg. 758
CARGILL NV—See Cargill, Inc.; *U.S. Private*, pg. 756
CARGILL OIL PACKERS BVBA—See Cargill, Inc.; *U.S. Private*, pg. 756
CARGILL OILS S.A.—See Cargill, Inc.; *U.S. Private*, pg. 755
CARGILL PAKISTAN HOLDINGS (PVT) LTD.—See Cargill, Inc.; *U.S. Private*, pg. 758
CARGILL S.A.C.I.—See Cargill, Inc.; *U.S. Private*, pg. 758
CARGILL SACI SUCURSAL URUGUAY—See Cargill, Inc.; *U.S. Private*, pg. 758
CARGILL SALT, INC.—See Cargill, Inc.; *U.S. Private*, pg. 758
CARGILL SALT—See Cargill, Inc.; *U.S. Private*, pg. 758
CARGILL SALT—See Cargill, Inc.; *U.S. Private*, pg. 758
CARGILL SALT—See Cargill, Inc.; *U.S. Private*, pg. 758
CARGILL SALT—See Cargill, Inc.; *U.S. Private*, pg. 758
CARGILLS BANK LIMITED; *Int'l*, pg. 1325

CARGILLS (CEYLON) PLC; *Int'l*, pg. 1325
CARGILL S.L.U.—See Cargill, Inc.; *U.S. Private*, pg. 758
CARGILL—See Cargill, Inc.; *U.S. Private*, pg. 754
CARGILL—See Cargill, Inc.; *U.S. Private*, pg. 758
CARGILL SOUTH—See Cargill, Inc.; *U.S. Private*, pg. 758
CARGILL SRL—See Cargill, Inc.; *U.S. Private*, pg. 758
CARGILL TAIWAN CORPORATION—See Cargill, Inc.; *U.S. Private*, pg. 758
CARGILL TEXTURIZING SOLUTIONS DEUTSCHLAND GMBH & CO. KG—See Cargill, Inc.; *U.S. Private*, pg. 759
CARGILL TURKEY PRODUCTS FARMS—See Cargill, Inc.; *U.S. Private*, pg. 759
CARGILL TURKEY PRODUCTS FEEDS, INC.—See Cargill, Inc.; *U.S. Private*, pg. 759
CARGILL TURKEY PRODUCTS INC.—See Cargill, Inc.; *U.S. Private*, pg. 759
CARGILL TURKEY PRODUCTS—See Cargill, Inc.; *U.S. Private*, pg. 759
CARGILL TURKEY PRODUCTS—See Cargill, Inc.; *U.S. Private*, pg. 759
CARGILL VALUE ADDED MEATS—See Cargill, Inc.; *U.S. Private*, pg. 758
CARGILL WEST AFRICA S.A.—See Cargill, Inc.; *U.S. Private*, pg. 759
CARGILL YUG, LLC—See Cargill, Inc.; *U.S. Private*, pg. 759
CARGILL ZIMBABWE (PVT) LIMITED—See Cargill, Inc.; *U.S. Private*, pg. 759
CARGLASS YAMATO CO.,LTD.—See AGC Inc.; *Int'l*, pg. 204
CARGO AIRCRAFT MANAGEMENT, INC.—See Air Transport Services Group, Inc.; *U.S. Public*, pg. 67
CARGOBARN INC.—See SheerTrans Solutions, LLC; *U.S. Private*, pg. 3630
CARGO BOAT DEVELOPMENT CO. PLC; *Int'l*, pg. 1325
CARGO CARRIERS LTD.; *Int'l*, pg. 1325
CARGO COMMUNITY NETWORK PTY LTD—See WiseTech Global Limited; *Int'l*, pg. 8436
CARGO COMMUNITY SYSTEMS LTD.—See WiseTech Global Limited; *Int'l*, pg. 8436
CARGO CONSOLIDATION SERVICES—See CT Group; *U.S. Private*, pg. 1118
CARGO EQUIPMENT CORP.—See Prospect Hill Growth Partners, L.P.; *U.S. Private*, pg. 3288
CARGO FUTURE COMMUNICATIONS (CFC) GMBH—See Deutsche Lufthansa AG; *Int'l*, pg. 2069
CARGOGUIDE INTERNATIONAL B.V.—See WiseTech Global Limited; *Int'l*, pg. 8436
CARGO HANDLERS LIMITED—See Massy Holdings Ltd.; *Int'l*, pg. 4723
CARGOIT I SKANDINAVIEN AB—See WiseTech Global Limited; *Int'l*, pg. 8436
CARGOJET HOLDINGS LTD.—See Cargojet Inc.; *Int'l*, pg. 1325
CARGOJET INC.; *Int'l*, pg. 1325
CARGOJET PARTNERSHIP LTD—See Cargojet Inc.; *Int'l*, pg. 1325
CARGO-LINK INTERNATIONAL, INC.—See Gebruder Weiss Gesellschaft m.b.H.; *Int'l*, pg. 2909
CARGO, LLC; *U.S. Private*, pg. 760
CARGO LOGISTICS BY J. CIOFFI INC.; *U.S. Private*, pg. 760
CARGO LOGISTICS GROUP, INC—See Littlejohn & Co., LLC; *U.S. Private*, pg. 2470
CARGOLUTION INC.—See Clasquin S.A.; *Int'l*, pg. 1652
CARGOLUX AIRLINES INTERNATIONAL S.A.; *Int'l*, pg. 1325
CARGO MARINE LTD.—See Albert Ballin KG; *Int'l*, pg. 294
CARGONET SOFTWARE SAS—See VINCI S.A.; *Int'l*, pg. 8213
CARGOPORT LOGISTICS, C.A.; *Int'l*, pg. 1326
CARGOSCAN AS—See Mettler-Toledo International, Inc.; *U.S. Public*, pg. 1432
CARGO SERVICE GMBH—See voestalpine AG; *Int'l*, pg. 8295
CARGO SIGNAL SOLUTIONS, LLC—See Expeditors International of Washington, Inc.; *U.S. Public*, pg. 810
CARGOSOL LOGISTICS LIMITED; *Int'l*, pg. 1326
CARGOSUR, S.A.—See International Consolidated Airlines Group S.A.; *Int'l*, pg. 3746
CARGOTEC ACT B.V.—See Cargotec Corporation; *Int'l*, pg. 1326
CARGOTEC (ARE) GULF WLL—See Cargotec Corporation; *Int'l*, pg. 1326
CARGOTEC ARGENTINA S.R.L.—See Cargotec Corporation; *Int'l*, pg. 1326
CARGOTEC ASIA LIMITED—See Cargotec Corporation; *Int'l*, pg. 1327
CARGOTEC AUSTRALIA PTY. LTD.—See Cargotec Corporation; *Int'l*, pg. 1326
CARGOTEC AUSTRIA GMBH—See Cargotec Corporation; *Int'l*, pg. 1326
CARGOTEC BELGIUM NV—See Cargotec Corporation; *Int'l*, pg. 1326
CARGOTEC BRAZIL INDUSTRIA E COMERCIO DE EQUIPAMENTOS PARA MOVIMENTACAO DE CARGAS LTDA—See Cargotec Corporation; *Int'l*, pg. 1326

COMPANY NAME INDEX

CARGOTEC BRAZIL LTDA—See Cargotec Corporation; *Int'l*, pg. 1326
CARGOTEC CHILE - S.A.—See Cargotec Corporation; *Int'l*, pg. 1326
CARGOTEC CHS ASIA PACIFIC PTE LTD.—See Cargotec Corporation; *Int'l*, pg. 1326
CARGOTEC CORPORATION; *Int'l*, pg. 1326
CARGOTEC CRANE & ELECTRICAL SERVICES INC.—See Cargotec Corporation; *Int'l*, pg. 1326
CARGOTEC CYPRUS LTD.—See Cargotec Corporation; *Int'l*, pg. 1326
CARGOTEC CZECH REPUBLIC S.R.O—See Cargotec Corporation; *Int'l*, pg. 1326
CARGOTEC DE MEXICO, S.A. DE C.V.—See Cargotec Corporation; *Int'l*, pg. 1327
CARGOTEC DENMARK A/S—See Cargotec Corporation; *Int'l*, pg. 1328
CARGOTEC ENGINEERING ITALY S.R.L.—See Cargotec Corporation; *Int'l*, pg. 1326
CARGOTEC FINLAND OY—See Cargotec Corporation; *Int'l*, pg. 1326
CARGOTEC FRANCE S.A.S.—See Cargotec Corporation; *Int'l*, pg. 1326
CARGOTEC GERMANY GMBH—See Cargotec Corporation; *Int'l*, pg. 1327
CARGOTEC HOLDING NETHERLANDS B.V.—See Cargotec Corporation; *Int'l*, pg. 1327
CARGOTEC HOLDING SWEDEN AB—See Cargotec Corporation; *Int'l*, pg. 1327
CARGOTEC IBERIA SA—See Cargotec Corporation; *Int'l*, pg. 1327
CARGOTEC INDIA PRIVATE LIMITED—See Cargotec Corporation; *Int'l*, pg. 1327
CARGOTEC INDUSTRIES (CHINA) CO., LTD—See Cargotec Corporation; *Int'l*, pg. 1327
CARGOTEC ITALIA S.R.L.—See Cargotec Corporation; *Int'l*, pg. 1326
CARGOTEC KOREA LIMITED—See Cargotec Corporation; *Int'l*, pg. 1327
CARGOTEC NETHERLANDS B.V.—See Cargotec Corporation; *Int'l*, pg. 1326
CARGOTEC NETHERLANDS B.V.—See Cargotec Corporation; *Int'l*, pg. 1326
CARGOTEC POLAND SP. Z O.O.—See Cargotec Corporation; *Int'l*, pg. 1326
CARGOTEC RUS LLC—See Cargotec Corporation; *Int'l*, pg. 1326
CARGOTEC (SHANGHAI) TRADING COMPANY LIMITED—See Cargotec Corporation; *Int'l*, pg. 1326
CARGOTEC SOLUTIONS LLC—See Cargotec Corporation; *Int'l*, pg. 1327
CARGOTEC SOLUTIONS OY—See Cargotec Corporation; *Int'l*, pg. 1327
CARGOTEC SWEDEN AB—See Cargotec Corporation; *Int'l*, pg. 1327
CARGOTEC TERMINAL SOLUTIONS (MALAYSIA) SDN BHD—See Cargotec Corporation; *Int'l*, pg. 1327
CARGOTEC UK LTD.—See Cargotec Corporation; *Int'l*, pg. 1327
CARGOTEC UKRAINE, LLC—See Cargotec Corporation; *Int'l*, pg. 1327
CARGOTEC USA INC.—See Cargotec Corporation; *Int'l*, pg. 1326
CARGO THERAPEUTICS, INC.; *U.S. Public*, pg. 435
CARGOTRANS MARITIME LIMITED; *Int'l*, pg. 1329
CARGO TRANSPORTATION SERVICES INC.; *U.S. Private*, pg. 760
CARGO TRANSPORTERS, INC.—See CT Group; *U.S. Private*, pg. 1118
CARGOWORKS PROPRIETARY LIMITED—See Super Group Limited; *Int'l*, pg. 7334
CAR-GRAPH INC.; *U.S. Private*, pg. 748
CARGURUS, INC.; *U.S. Public*, pg. 435
CARGURUS IRELAND LIMITED, AN IRISH PRIVATE COMPANY LIMITED BY SHARES—See CarGurus, Inc.; *U.S. Public*, pg. 435
CARGUS INTERNATIONAL S.R.L.—See Abris Capital Partners Sp. z o.o.; *Int'l*, pg. 69
CARHART LUMBER COMPANY; *U.S. Private*, pg. 760
CARHARTT, INC.; *U.S. Private*, pg. 760
CAR HOUSE HOLDING CO., LTD.; *Int'l*, pg. 1319
CARIAD SE—See Porsche Automobil Holding SE; *Int'l*, pg. 5926
CARI AQUITAINE—See FAYAT SAS; *Int'l*, pg. 2625
CARIATIDE, S.A.—See ACS, Actividades de Construccion y Servicios, S.A.; *Int'l*, pg. 110
CARIBBEAN AIRLINES LIMITED; *Int'l*, pg. 1329
CARIBBEAN AMERICAN LIFE ASSURANCE COMPANY—See Assurant, Inc.; *U.S. Public*, pg. 215
CARIBBEAN AMERICAN PROPERTY INSURANCE COMPANY—See Assurant, Inc.; *U.S. Public*, pg. 215
CARIBBEAN AUTO MART INC.; *U.S. Private*, pg. 760
CARIBBEAN CAPS & CONTAINERS LTD.—See BERICAP GmbH & Co. KG; *Int'l*, pg. 981
CARIBBEAN CEMENT CO., LTD.—See CEMEX, S.A.B. de C.V.; *Int'l*, pg. 1400
CARIBBEAN CINEMAS; *U.S. Private*, pg. 760
CARIBBEAN COFFEE COMPANY, INC.; *U.S. Private*, pg. 760

CARIBBEAN CONSTRUCTION AND DEVELOPMENT LTD.—See Grupo Argos S.A.; *Int'l*, pg. 3121
CARIBBEAN CREAM LTD.; *Int'l*, pg. 1330
CARIBBEAN DEVELOPMENT BANK; *Int'l*, pg. 1330
CARIBBEAN DEVELOPMENT COMPANY LIMITED—See ANSA McAl Limited; *Int'l*, pg. 477
CARIBBEAN DEVELOPMENT COMPANY (ST.KITTS) LIMITED—See ANSA McAl Limited; *Int'l*, pg. 477
CARIBBEAN DIAGNOSTICS LTD.—See HORIBA Ltd; *Int'l*, pg. 3475
CARIBBEAN DISCOVERY, S.A. DE C.V.; *Int'l*, pg. 1330
CARIBBEAN DISPATCH SERVICES LTD.—See Goddard Enterprises Limited; *Int'l*, pg. 3019
CARIBBEAN DIVERSIFIED INVESTMENTS INC.; *Int'l*, pg. 1330
CARIBBEAN FLAVOURS & FRAGRANCES LIMITED—See Derrimon Trading Co., Ltd.; *Int'l*, pg. 2043
CARIBBEAN FOOD DELIGHTS; *U.S. Private*, pg. 760
CARIBBEAN INDUSTRIAL CONSTRUCTION SE; *U.S. Private*, pg. 760
CARIBBEAN INTERNATIONAL FOODS CORPORATION—See TraFon Group; *U.S. Private*, pg. 4203
CARIBBEAN INVESTMENT HOLDINGS LIMITED; *Int'l*, pg. 1330
CARIBBEAN LABEL CRAFTS LTD.—See Goddard Enterprises Limited; *Int'l*, pg. 3018
CARIBBEAN LIFTS LIMITED—See Schindler Holding AG; *Int'l*, pg. 6618
CARIBBEAN MEDICAL BROKERS, INC.; *U.S. Private*, pg. 760
CARIBBEAN MERCANTILE BANK N.V.—See Maduro & Curiel's Bank N.V.; *Int'l*, pg. 4635
CARIBBEAN OUTERWEAR CORP.—See Standard Manufacturing Co., Inc.; *U.S. Private*, pg. 3781
CARIBBEAN PACIFIC MARKETING, INC.; *U.S. Private*, pg. 761
CARIBBEAN PRODUCERS JAMAICA LTD.; *Int'l*, pg. 1330
CARIBBEAN PRODUCTS COMPANY LIMITED—See Seprod Limited; *Int'l*, pg. 6718
CARIBBEAN REFRESCOS INC.—See The Coca-Cola Company; *U.S. Public*, pg. 2063
CARIBBEAN RESOURCES CORPORATION; *Int'l*, pg. 1330
CARIBBEAN ROOF TILE COMPANY LIMITED—See ANSA McAl Limited; *Int'l*, pg. 477
CARIBBEAN ROOF TILE COMPANY LIMITED—See Seven Group Holdings Limited; *Int'l*, pg. 6733
CARIBBEAN SHIPPING SERVICES, INC.—See The Jordan Company, L.P.; *U.S. Private*, pg. 4060
CARIBBEAN TEMPORARY SERVICES INC.; *U.S. Private*, pg. 761
CARIBBEAN UTILITIES COMPANY, LTD.—See Fortis Inc.; *Int'l*, pg. 2739
CARIBBEAN WORLD MAGAZINE—See World Travel Media Ltd.; *Int'l*, pg. 8458
CARIB BREWERY LIMITED—See ANSA McAl Limited; *Int'l*, pg. 477
CARIBCOM, INC.; *U.S. Private*, pg. 761
CARIBE ASISTENCIA, S.A.—See MAPFRE S.A.; *Int'l*, pg. 4684
CARIBEE BOAT SALES & MARINA INC.; *U.S. Private*, pg. 761
CARIBE FOOD CORPORATION; *U.S. Private*, pg. 761
CARIBE FREIGHT—See CaribEx Worldwide Inc.; *U.S. Private*, pg. 761
CARIBE GROLIER INC.—See Scholastic Corporation; *U.S. Public*, pg. 1847
CARIBE MEDIA, INC.; *U.S. Private*, pg. 761
CARIBEX WORLDWIDE INC. - CANCUN FACILITY—See CaribEx Worldwide Inc.; *U.S. Private*, pg. 761
CARIBEX WORLDWIDE INC. - GUATEMALA CITY FACILITY—See CaribEx Worldwide Inc.; *U.S. Private*, pg. 761
CARIBEX WORLDWIDE INC. - MANAGUA FACILITY—See CaribEx Worldwide Inc.; *U.S. Private*, pg. 761
CARIBEX WORLDWIDE INC. - OLOCUILTA FACILITY—See CaribEx Worldwide Inc.; *U.S. Private*, pg. 761
CARIBEX WORLDWIDE INC. - SAN PEDRO SULA FACILITY—See CaribEx Worldwide Inc.; *U.S. Private*, pg. 761
CARIBEX WORLDWIDE INC. - SANTO DOMINGO FACILITY—See CaribEx Worldwide Inc.; *U.S. Private*, pg. 761
CARIBEX WORLDWIDE, INC.—See CaribEx Worldwide Inc.; *U.S. Private*, pg. 761
CARIBEX WORLDWIDE INC.; *U.S. Private*, pg. 761
CARIBEX WORLDWIDE—See CaribEx Worldwide Inc.; *U.S. Private*, pg. 761
CARIB GLASSWORKS LIMITED—See ANSA McAl Limited; *Int'l*, pg. 477
CARIBOO CHEVROLET BUICK GMC; *Int'l*, pg. 1330
CARIBOO ROSE RESOURCES LTD.; *Int'l*, pg. 1330
CARIBOTELS DE MEXICO, S. A. DE C. V.—See Melia Hotels International, S.A.; *Int'l*, pg. 4809

CARIBOU COFFEE COMPANY, INC.—See JAB Holding Company S.a.r.l.; *Int'l*, pg. 3863
CARIBOU CORPORATION; *U.S. Private*, pg. 761
CARIBOU GROUP—See TCS TurControlSysteme AG; *Int'l*, pg. 7485
CARIBOU INSURANCE AGENCY, INC.—See PointeNorth Insurance Group LLC; *U.S. Private*, pg. 3222
CARIB STAR SHIPPING LIMITED—See Israel Corporation Ltd.; *Int'l*, pg. 3823
CARI CAPITAL COMPANY, LLC—See Cari Investment Company; *U.S. Private*, pg. 760
CARICEMENT ANTIGUA LIMITED—See Grupo Argos S.A.; *Int'l*, pg. 3121
CARICO INTERNATIONAL INC.; *U.S. Private*, pg. 761
CARIDEN TECHNOLGOIES LLC—See Cisco Systems, Inc.; *U.S. Public*, pg. 497
CARIDIANBCT TECNOLOGIA MEDICA LTDA.—See Terumo Corporation; *Int'l*, pg. 7569
CARIEL SOFT DRINKS LIMITED—See Nichols Plc; *Int'l*, pg. 5271
CARIGE REOCO SPA—See Banca Carige S.p.A.; *Int'l*, pg. 814
CARI INVESTMENT COMPANY; *U.S. Private*, pg. 760
CARILION HEALTH SYSTEM; *U.S. Private*, pg. 761
CARILLION ALAWI LLC—See Carillion plc; *Int'l*, pg. 1330
CARILLION (AMBS) LTD—See Carillion plc; *Int'l*, pg. 1330
CARILLION (ASPIRE CONSTRUCTION) HOLDINGS NO 2 LTD—See Carillion plc; *Int'l*, pg. 1330
CARILLION CONSTRUCTION CANADA—See Carillion plc; *Int'l*, pg. 1330
CARILLION CONSTRUCTION (CARIBBEAN) LTD.—See Carillion plc; *Int'l*, pg. 1330
CARILLION CONSTRUCTION LTD—See Carillion plc; *Int'l*, pg. 1330
CARILLION DEFENCE—See Carillion plc; *Int'l*, pg. 1330
CARILLION ENERGY SERVICES LIMITED—See Carillion plc; *Int'l*, pg. 1330
CARILLION FACILITIES MANAGEMENT—See Carillion plc; *Int'l*, pg. 1330
CARILLION FLEET MANAGEMENT LTD—See Carillion plc; *Int'l*, pg. 1330
CARILLION PILING—See Carillion plc; *Int'l*, pg. 1330
CARILLION PLANNED MAINTENANCE—See Carillion plc; *Int'l*, pg. 1330
CARILLION PLC; *Int'l*, pg. 1330
CARILLION PRIVATE FINANCE LTD—See Carillion plc; *Int'l*, pg. 1330
CARILLION SERVICES LTD—See Carillion plc; *Int'l*, pg. 1330
CARILLION SPECIALIST SERVICES—See Carillion plc; *Int'l*, pg. 1330
CARILLON FUND DISTRIBUTORS, INC.—See Raymond James Financial, Inc.; *U.S. Public*, pg. 1764
CARILLON TOWER ADVISERS, INC.—See Raymond James Financial, Inc.; *U.S. Public*, pg. 1763
CARILOHA—See Pedersen Worldwide; *U.S. Private*, pg. 3128
CARI LORRAINE—See FAYAT SAS; *Int'l*, pg. 2625
CARIMALO; *Int'l*, pg. 1331
CARI MENUISERIE—See FAYAT SAS; *Int'l*, pg. 2625
CARIMIN PETROLEUM BERHAD; *Int'l*, pg. 1331
CARINA SILICONES SP. Z O.O.—See SELENA FM S.A.; *Int'l*, pg. 6700
CARINA SYSTEM CO., LTD.—See EIZO Corporation; *Int'l*, pg. 2337
CAR INC.—See MBK Partners Ltd.; *Int'l*, pg. 4753
CARINDALE PROPERTY TRUST; *Int'l*, pg. 1331
CARINE GLADES TAVERN (WA) PTY LTD—See Woolworths Group Limited; *Int'l*, pg. 8451
CARING MATTERS HOME CARE; *U.S. Private*, pg. 761
CARINGO, INC.—See DataCore Software Corp.; *U.S. Private*, pg. 1165
CARING PARTNERS INTERNATIONAL; *U.S. Private*, pg. 761
CARING PHARMACY GROUP BHD—See BIG Pharmacy Healthcare Sdn. Bhd; *Int'l*, pg. 1021
CARING SENIOR SERVICE; *U.S. Private*, pg. 761
CARINK, INC.—See Automatic Data Processing, Inc.; *U.S. Public*, pg. 230
CARINOS PROPERTIES, LLC—See IMH Financial Corporation; *U.S. Private*, pg. 2047
CARINTHIA GROUP 1, L.P.—See Vail Resorts, Inc.; *U.S. Public*, pg. 2271
THE CARIOCA COMPANY INC.; *U.S. Private*, pg. 4005
CARI PROVENCE—See FAYAT SAS; *Int'l*, pg. 2625
CARI RHONE LYON—See FAYAT SAS; *Int'l*, pg. 2625
CARISAM-SAMUEL MEISEL (MD), INC.—See MOTCO, Inc.; *U.S. Private*, pg. 2795
CARISBROOKE SHIPPING BV—See Carisbrooke Shipping Limited; *Int'l*, pg. 1331
CARISBROOKE SHIPPING (GERMANY) GMBH—See Carisbrooke Shipping Limited; *Int'l*, pg. 1331
CARISBROOKE SHIPPING GMBH—See Carisbrooke Shipping Limited; *Int'l*, pg. 1331
CARISBROOKE SHIPPING LIMITED; *Int'l*, pg. 1331
CARIS HEALTHCARE L.P.—See National HealthCare Corporation; *U.S. Public*, pg. 1496
CARISK PARTNERS, INC.—See Elements Health Investors, LLC; *U.S. Private*, pg. 1357

CARISK PARTNERS, INC.—See Lee Equity Partners LLC; *U.S. Private*, pg. 2412
CARISK SPECIALTY SERVICES, INC.—See Elements Health Investors, LLC; *U.S. Private*, pg. 1357
CARISK SPECIALTY SERVICES, INC.—See Lee Equity Partners LLC; *U.S. Private*, pg. 2412
CARIS LIFE SCIENCES, LTD.; *U.S. Private*, pg. 761
CARISMA THERAPEUTICS INC.; *U.S. Public*, pg. 435
CARISTRAP EUROPE D.O.O.—See Caristrap International Inc.; *Int'l*, pg. 1331
CARISTRAP INTERNATIONAL INC.; *Int'l*, pg. 1331
CARITA INTERNATIONAL—See L'Oreal S.A.; *Int'l*, pg. 4378
CARITAS CORPORATION; *U.S. Private*, pg. 761
CARITAS REHAB SERVICES, LLC—See Select Medical Holdings Corporation; *U.S. Public*, pg. 1857
CARITHERS WALLACE COURTENAY LLC; *U.S. Private*, pg. 761
CAR KLEEN NEW ZEALAND LTD.; *Int'l*, pg. 1319
CARLA & DAVID CRANE FOUNDATION; *U.S. Private*, pg. 763
CARLAS PASTA INC.—See Tribe 9 Foods LLC; *U.S. Private*, pg. 4227
CARL BARNES FUNERAL HOME, INC.—See Service Corporation International; *U.S. Public*, pg. 1869
CARL BELT INC.; *U.S. Private*, pg. 762
CARL BENNET AB; *Int'l*, pg. 1331
CARL BLACK AUTOMOTIVE GROUP, LLC; *U.S. Private*, pg. 762
CARL BLACK CHEVROLET CO., INC.; *U.S. Private*, pg. 762
CARL BLACK OF ORLANDO, LLC—See Carl Black Automotive Group, LLC; *U.S. Private*, pg. 762
CARL BLOOM ASSOCIATES, INC.; *U.S. Private*, pg. 762
CARL BOLANDER & SONS CO., INC.; *U.S. Private*, pg. 762
CARL BUDDIG & COMPANY; *U.S. Private*, pg. 762
CARL COLTERYAHN DAIRY INC.; *U.S. Private*, pg. 762
CARL DATA SOLUTIONS, INC.; *Int'l*, pg. 1332
CARL EDELMANN GMBH & CO. KG—See Edelmann GmbH; *Int'l*, pg. 2305
CARLE FOUNDATION; *U.S. Private*, pg. 763
CARLE & MONTANARI/C&G S.P.A.—See Sacmi Imola S.C.A.R.L.; *Int'l*, pg. 6463
CARLE & MONTANARI USA INC.—See Sacmi Imola S.C.A.R.L.; *Int'l*, pg. 6463
CARLEN ENTERPRISES INC.; *U.S. Private*, pg. 763
CARLE PLACE RESTAURANT INC.—See Scotto's Holding Corp.; *U.S. Private*, pg. 3578
CARLERBA - PRODUTOS QUIMICOS E FARMACEUTICOS, LDA.—See Pfizer Inc.; *U.S. Public*, pg. 1679
CARL ERIC JOHNSON INC.; *U.S. Private*, pg. 762
CARLETON CONSTRUCTION LTD.; *U.S. Private*, pg. 763
CARLETON EQUIPMENT COMPANY; *U.S. Private*, pg. 763
CARLETON LIFE SUPPORT SYSTEMS INC.—See Eaton Corporation plc; *Int'l*, pg. 2277
CARLETON TECHNOLOGIES INC.—See Eaton Corporation plc; *Int'l*, pg. 2277
CARL E. WOODWARD, LLC; *U.S. Private*, pg. 762
CARLEX GLASS AMERICA, LLC—See Central Glass Co., Ltd.; *Int'l*, pg. 1406
CARLEX GLASS COMPANY, LLC - LIGONIER—See Central Glass Co., Ltd.; *Int'l*, pg. 1406
CARLEX GLASS COMPANY, LLC—See Central Glass Co., Ltd.; *Int'l*, pg. 1406
CARLEX GLASS LUXEMBOURG, S.A.—See Central Glass Co., Ltd.; *Int'l*, pg. 1406
CARLEY FOUNDRY, INC.; *U.S. Private*, pg. 763
CARLEY LAMPS INC.; *U.S. Private*, pg. 763
CARL FISCHER, LLC; *U.S. Private*, pg. 762
CARL FISCHER MUSIC DISTRIBUTORS, INC.—See Carl Fischer, LLC; *U.S. Private*, pg. 762
CARL FROH GMBH; *Int'l*, pg. 1332
CARL F. STATZ & SONS INC.; *U.S. Private*, pg. 762
CARL GREGORY CHRYSLER; *U.S. Private*, pg. 762
CARL HOGAN AUTOMOTIVE, INC.; *U.S. Private*, pg. 762
CARLIE MINING LTD.—See Castle Minerals Limited; *Int'l*, pg. 1357
CARLIER PLASTIQUES; *Int'l*, pg. 1337
CARLIN AUCTION SERVICES (NSW) PTY. LTD.—See Eagers Automotive Limited; *Int'l*, pg. 2264
CARLIN AUCTION SERVICES (QLD) PTY. LTD.—See Eagers Automotive Limited; *Int'l*, pg. 2264
CARLIN CONTRACTING COMPANY, INC.; *U.S. Private*, pg. 763
CARLING CAPITAL PARTNERS PTY LTD.; *Int'l*, pg. 1338
CARLING COMMUNICATIONS—See Lloyds Banking Group plc; *Int'l*, pg. 4537
CARLING MOTORS CO. LIMITED; *Int'l*, pg. 1338
CARLING GOLD CORPORATION; *Int'l*, pg. 1338
CARLING TECHNOLOGIES INC.; *U.S. Private*, pg. 764
CARLIN O'BRIEN INC.; *U.S. Private*, pg. 763
CARLIN SALES CORPORATION; *U.S. Private*, pg. 764
CARLINS AUTOMOTIVE AUCTIONEERS (WA) PTY. LTD.—See Eagers Automotive Limited; *Int'l*, pg. 2264
CARLIN SYSTEMS INC.; *U.S. Private*, pg. 764
CARLINVILLE AREA HOSPITAL; *U.S. Private*, pg. 764

CARLISLE BRAKE & FRICTION, INC.—See Lone Star Funds; *U.S. Private*, pg. 2485
CARLISLE BRAKE PRODUCTS (UK) LIMITED—See Carlisle Companies Incorporated; *U.S. Public*, pg. 436
CARLISLE BRASS LIMITED—See ASSA ABLOY AB; *Int'l*, pg. 638
CARLISLE CANADA—See Carlisle Companies Incorporated; *U.S. Public*, pg. 436
CARLISLE CLEANING SERVICES LTD.—See HFBG Holding B.V.; *Int'l*, pg. 3374
CARLISLE COATINGS & WATERPROOFING INC.—See Carlisle Companies Incorporated; *U.S. Public*, pg. 436
CARLISLE COMPANIES INCORPORATED; *U.S. Public*, pg. 435
CARLISLE CONSTRUCTION MATERIALS BV—See Carlisle Companies Incorporated; *U.S. Public*, pg. 436
CARLISLE CONSTRUCTION MATERIALS GMBH—See Carlisle Companies Incorporated; *U.S. Public*, pg. 436
CARLISLE CONSTRUCTION MATERIALS, LLC—See Carlisle Companies Incorporated; *U.S. Public*, pg. 436
CARLISLE CONSTRUCTION MATERIALS UK—See Carlisle Companies Incorporated; *U.S. Public*, pg. 436
CARLISLE CONTAINER CO.; *U.S. Private*, pg. 764
CARLISLE CORPORATION—See Carlisle Companies Incorporated; *U.S. Public*, pg. 436
CARLISLE ENERGY SERVICES, INC.—See Carlisle Companies Incorporated; *U.S. Public*, pg. 436
CARLISLE EVENTS SERVICES LIMITED—See HFBG Holding B.V.; *Int'l*, pg. 3374
CARLISLE FINISHING, LLC—See Platinum Equity, LLC; *U.S. Private*, pg. 3203
CARLISLE FLUID TECHNOLOGIES, INC.—See Carlisle Companies Incorporated; *U.S. Public*, pg. 436
CARLISLE FOOD INC.; *U.S. Private*, pg. 764
CARLISLE FOODSERVICE PRODUCTS INCORPORATED—See The Jordan Company, L.P.; *U.S. Private*, pg. 4060
CARLISLE HARDCAST EUROPE B.V.—See Carlisle Companies Incorporated; *U.S. Public*, pg. 436
CARLISLE HARDCAST INC.—See Carlisle Companies Incorporated; *U.S. Public*, pg. 436
CARLISLE INDUSTRIAL BRAKE & FRICTION—See Carlisle Companies Incorporated; *U.S. Public*, pg. 436
CARLISLE INTERCONNECT TECHNOLOGIES DE MEXICO—See Amphenol Corporation; *U.S. Public*, pg. 129
CARLISLE INTERCONNECT TECHNOLOGIES, INC.—See Amphenol Corporation; *U.S. Public*, pg. 129
CARLISLE INTERCONNECT TECHNOLOGIES—See Amphenol Corporation; *U.S. Public*, pg. 129
CARLISLE, LLC—See Carlisle Companies Incorporated; *U.S. Public*, pg. 437
CARLISLE MEDICAL TECHNOLOGIES (DONGGUAN) CO., LTD—See Carlisle Companies Incorporated; *U.S. Public*, pg. 436
CARLISLE MEXICO, S.A. DE C.V.—See Carlisle Companies Incorporated; *U.S. Public*, pg. 436
CARLISLE MOTORS, LLC—See AutoNation, Inc.; *U.S. Public*, pg. 233
CARLISLE PRODUCTIONS, INC.; *U.S. Private*, pg. 764
CARLISLE SECURITY SERVICES LTD.—See HFBG Holding B.V.; *Int'l*, pg. 3374
CARLISLE SPECIALTY PRODUCTS GROUP—See Carlisle Companies Incorporated; *U.S. Public*, pg. 436
CARLISLE STAFFING PLC—See HFBG Holding B.V.; *Int'l*, pg. 3374
CARLISLE SYNTEC INC.—See Carlisle Companies Incorporated; *U.S. Public*, pg. 436
CARLISLE WIDE PLANK FLOORS, INC.—See JMH Capital; *U.S. Private*, pg. 2215
CARLIT CO., LTD.; *Int'l*, pg. 1338
CARLIT SANGYO CO., LTD.—See Carlit Co., Ltd.; *Int'l*, pg. 1338
CARLIT SINGAPORE PTE., LTD.—See Carlit Co., Ltd.; *Int'l*, pg. 1338
CARL KARCHER ENTERPRISES, INC.—See Roark Capital Group Inc.; *U.S. Private*, pg. 3454
CARL KING INC.—See Star Group, L.P.; *U.S. Public*, pg. 1937
CARL KLIEM S.A.—See StoneX Group Inc.; *U.S. Public*, pg. 1951
CARL MAHR HOLDING GMBH; *Int'l*, pg. 1332
CARL MARKS & CO., INC.; *U.S. Private*, pg. 762
CARL M. FREEMAN ASSOCIATES, INC.; *U.S. Private*, pg. 762
CARL M. FREEMAN COMMUNITIES, LLC—See Carl M. Freeman Associates, Inc.; *U.S. Private*, pg. 762
CARL M. FREEMAN GOLF, LLC—See Carl M. Freeman Associates, Inc.; *U.S. Private*, pg. 762
CARL M. FREEMAN RETAIL LLC—See Carl M. Freeman Associates, Inc.; *U.S. Private*, pg. 762
CARL M LUNDH AB—See Aderans Co., Ltd.; *Int'l*, pg. 143
CAR LOAN PAL HOLDINGS LLC—See Digital Media Solutions, Inc.; *U.S. Public*, pg. 663
CARLO CAPPELLARI ITALIA S.R.L.—See Fritz Egger GmbH & Co.; *Int'l*, pg. 2793
CARLO ERBA REAGENTI SPA—See UniCredit S.p.A.; *Int'l*, pg. 8034

CARLO GAVAZZI AB—See Carlo Gavazzi Holding AG; *Int'l*, pg. 1338
CARLO GAVAZZI AG—See Carlo Gavazzi Holding AG; *Int'l*, pg. 1338
CARLO GAVAZZI AS—See Carlo Gavazzi Holding AG; *Int'l*, pg. 1338
CARLO GAVAZZI AUTOMACAO LTDA—See Carlo Gavazzi Holding AG; *Int'l*, pg. 1338
CARLO GAVAZZI AUTOMATION (CHINA) CO LTD—See Carlo Gavazzi Holding AG; *Int'l*, pg. 1338
CARLO GAVAZZI AUTOMATION HONG KONG LTD—See Carlo Gavazzi Holding AG; *Int'l*, pg. 1338
CARLO GAVAZZI AUTOMATION (KUNSHAN) CO LTD—See Carlo Gavazzi Holding AG; *Int'l*, pg. 1339
CARLO GAVAZZI AUTOMATION (M) SDN BHD—See Carlo Gavazzi Holding AG; *Int'l*, pg. 1338
CARLO GAVAZZI AUTOMATION SINGAPORE PTE LTD—See Carlo Gavazzi Holding AG; *Int'l*, pg. 1338
CARLO GAVAZZI AUTOMATION SPA—See Carlo Gavazzi Holding AG; *Int'l*, pg. 1338
CARLO GAVAZZI BV—See Carlo Gavazzi Holding AG; *Int'l*, pg. 1339
CARLO GAVAZZI (CANADA) INC.—See Carlo Gavazzi Holding AG; *Int'l*, pg. 1338
CARLO GAVAZZI CONTROLS SPA—See Carlo Gavazzi Holding AG; *Int'l*, pg. 1339
CARLO GAVAZZI GMBH—See Carlo Gavazzi Holding AG; *Int'l*, pg. 1338
CARLO GAVAZZI GMBH—See Carlo Gavazzi Holding AG; *Int'l*, pg. 1339
CARLO GAVAZZI HANDEL A/S—See Carlo Gavazzi Holding AG; *Int'l*, pg. 1339
CARLO GAVAZZI HOLDING AG; *Int'l*, pg. 1338
CARLO GAVAZZI INC.—See Carlo Gavazzi Holding AG; *Int'l*, pg. 1339
CARLO GAVAZZI INDUSTRI A/S—See Carlo Gavazzi Holding AG; *Int'l*, pg. 1339
CARLO GAVAZZI INDUSTRI KAUNAS UAB—See Carlo Gavazzi Holding AG; *Int'l*, pg. 1339
CARLO GAVAZZI LDA—See Carlo Gavazzi Holding AG; *Int'l*, pg. 1339
CARLO GAVAZZI LOGISTICS SPA—See Carlo Gavazzi Holding AG; *Int'l*, pg. 1339
CARLO GAVAZZI LTD—See Carlo Gavazzi Holding AG; *Int'l*, pg. 1339
CARLO GAVAZZI MARKETING AG—See Carlo Gavazzi Holding AG; *Int'l*, pg. 1339
CARLO GAVAZZI MEXICO S.A. DE C.V.—See Carlo Gavazzi Holding AG; *Int'l*, pg. 1339
CARLO GAVAZZI OY AB—See Carlo Gavazzi Holding AG; *Int'l*, pg. 1339
CARLO GAVAZZI PARTICIPATION DANMARK A/S—See Carlo Gavazzi Holding AG; *Int'l*, pg. 1339
CARLO GAVAZZI SARL—See Carlo Gavazzi Holding AG; *Int'l*, pg. 1339
CARLO GAVAZZI SA—See Carlo Gavazzi Holding AG; *Int'l*, pg. 1339
CARLO GAVAZZI SA—See Carlo Gavazzi Holding AG; *Int'l*, pg. 1339
CARLO GAVAZZI SERVICES AG—See Carlo Gavazzi Holding AG; *Int'l*, pg. 1339
CARLO GAVAZZI SPA—See Carlo Gavazzi Holding AG; *Int'l*, pg. 1339
CARLO GAVAZZI UK LTD—See Carlo Gavazzi Holding AG; *Int'l*, pg. 1339
CARLO GAVAZZI UNIPESSOAL LDA—See Carlo Gavazzi Holding AG; *Int'l*, pg. 1339
CARLO LIZZA & SONS PAVING; *U.S. Private*, pg. 764
CARLO MANAGEMENT CORPORATION; *U.S. Private*, pg. 764
CARLO ROSSI VINEYARDS—See E. & J. Gallo Winery; *U.S. Private*, pg. 1303
CARLO'S BAKERY LAS VEGAS LLC—See Las Vegas Sands Corp.; *U.S. Public*, pg. 1293
CARLOS CASADO SA; *Int'l*, pg. 1339
CARLOTA COPPER COMPANY LTD—See KGHM Polska Miedz S.A.; *Int'l*, pg. 4149
CARLOTZ, INC.—See Shift Technologies, Inc.; *U.S. Public*, pg. 1874
CARL OWNBY & CO. INC.; *U.S. Private*, pg. 763
CARL ROSE & SONS INC; *U.S. Private*, pg. 763
CARLSBAD CURRENT-ARGUS—See Gannett Co., Inc.; *U.S. Public*, pg. 899
CARLSBAD DIALYSIS, LLC—See DaVita Inc.; *U.S. Public*, pg. 636
CARLSBAD ISI, INC.—See Kratos Defense & Security Solutions, Inc.; *U.S. Public*, pg. 1276
CARLSBAD MEDICAL CENTER, LLC—See Community Health Systems, Inc.; *U.S. Public*, pg. 552
CARLSBAD TECHNOLOGY INC.—See YungShin Global Holding Corporation; *Int'l*, pg. 8614
CARLSBERG ACCOUNTING SERVICE CENTRE SP. Z.O.O.—See Carlsberg A/S; *Int'l*, pg. 1339
CARLSBERG A/S; *Int'l*, pg. 1339
CARLSBERG BREWERIES A/S—See Carlsberg A/S; *Int'l*, pg. 1339
CARLSBERG BREWERY HONG KONG LIMITED—See Carlsberg A/S; *Int'l*, pg. 1339

COMPANY NAME INDEX

CARLSBERG BREWERY MALAYSIA BERHAD—See Carlsberg A/S; *Int'l*, pg. 1339
CARLSBERG BREWING LIMITED—See Carlsberg A/S; *Int'l*, pg. 1339
CARLSBERG CANADA INC.—See Carlsberg A/S; *Int'l*, pg. 1339
CARLSBERG CHONGQING BREWERIES COMPANY LIMITED—See Carlsberg A/S; *Int'l*, pg. 1339
CARLSBERG CROATIA—See Carlsberg A/S; *Int'l*, pg. 1340
CARLSBERG DANMARK A/S—See Carlsberg A/S; *Int'l*, pg. 1340
CARLSBERG DENMARK A/S FREDERICIA—See Carlsberg A/S; *Int'l*, pg. 1340
CARLSBERG DEUTSCHLAND GMBH—See Carlsberg A/S; *Int'l*, pg. 1340
CARLSBERG EJENDOMME HOLDING A/S—See Carlsberg A/S; *Int'l*, pg. 1340
CARLSBERG FINANS A/S—See Carlsberg A/S; *Int'l*, pg. 1340
CARLSBERG GB LIMITED—See Carlsberg A/S; *Int'l*, pg. 1340
CARLSBERG HUNGARY SALES LIMITED LIABILITY COMPANY—See Carlsberg A/S; *Int'l*, pg. 1340
CARLSBERG IMPORTERS SA—See Carlsberg A/S; *Int'l*, pg. 1340
CARLSBERG INDIA PVT LTD—See Carlsberg A/S; *Int'l*, pg. 1340
CARLSBERG INSURANCE A/S—See Carlsberg A/S; *Int'l*, pg. 1340
CARLSBERG INTERNATIONAL A/S—See Carlsberg A/S; *Int'l*, pg. 1340
CARLSBERG INVEST A/S—See Carlsberg A/S; *Int'l*, pg. 1340
CARLSBERG ITALIA S.P.A.—See Carlsberg A/S; *Int'l*, pg. 1340
CARLSBERG KAZAKHSTAN LTD.—See Carlsberg A/S; *Int'l*, pg. 1340
CARLSBERG MANAGEMENT COMPANY INC.—See CMC Realty Inc.; *U.S. Private*, pg. 950
CARLSBERG MARKETING SDN BHD—See Carlsberg A/S; *Int'l*, pg. 1339
CARLSBERG MARSTON'S BREWING COMPANY LTD.—See Carlsberg A/S; *Int'l*, pg. 1340
CARLSBERG OKOCIM SA—See Carlsberg A/S; *Int'l*, pg. 1340
CARLSBERG POLSKA S. A.—See Carlsberg A/S; *Int'l*, pg. 1340
CARLSBERG (SINGAPORE) PTE. LTD.—See Carlsberg A/S; *Int'l*, pg. 1339
CARLSBERG SVERIGE AB—See Carlsberg A/S; *Int'l*, pg. 1340
CARLSBERG SWEDEN AB—See Carlsberg A/S; *Int'l*, pg. 1340
CARLSBERG UK LTD—See Carlsberg A/S; *Int'l*, pg. 1340
CARL SCHAEFER (AUSTRIA) GMBH—See Carl Schaefer GmbH & Co. KG; *Int'l*, pg. 1333
CARL SCHAEFER (CASTING) GMBH & CO. KG—See Carl Schaefer GmbH & Co. KG; *Int'l*, pg. 1333
CARL SCHAEFER GMBH & CO. KG; *Int'l*, pg. 1333
CARL SCHAEFER GOLD- UND SILBERSCHEIDEANSTALT GMBH—See Blue Cap AG; *Int'l*, pg. 1067
CARL SCHAEFER HUNGARY KFT.—See Carl Schaefer GmbH & Co. KG; *Int'l*, pg. 1333
CARL SCHENCK MACHINES EN INSTALLATIES B.V—See Durr AG; *Int'l*, pg. 2230
CARL SCHOLL GMBH—See RWE AG; *Int'l*, pg. 6433
CARLSEN VERLAG GMBH—See Bonnier AB; *Int'l*, pg. 1108
CARLSEN VOLVO; *U.S. Private*, pg. 764
CARLSHAMN MEJERI AB—See Raisio PLC; *Int'l*, pg. 6190
CARL'S OIL COMPANY; *U.S. Private*, pg. 763
CARLSON CAPITAL, L.P. - NEW YORK OFFICE—See Carlson Capital, L.P.; *U.S. Private*, pg. 764
CARLSON CAPITAL, L.P.; *U.S. Private*, pg. 764
CARLSON & CO LTD.—See Ratos AB; *Int'l*, pg. 6219
CARLSON COMPANIES INC.; *U.S. Private*, pg. 764
CARLSON CRAFT CATALOG—See Taylor Corporation; *U.S. Private*, pg. 3938
CARLSON CRAFT—See Taylor Corporation; *U.S. Private*, pg. 3938
CARLSON HIGHLAND & CO., LLP; *U.S. Private*, pg. 765
CARLSON HOLDINGS, INC.; *U.S. Private*, pg. 765
CARLSON HOTELS MANAGEMENT CORPORATION—See Carlson Companies Inc.; *U.S. Private*, pg. 764
CARLSON JPM STORE FIXTURES—See Stein Industries, Inc.; *U.S. Private*, pg. 3797
CARLSON MARKETING CANADA—See Aimia Inc.; *Int'l*, pg. 233
CARLSON MARKETING GROUP (AUST.) PTY. LIMITED—See Aimia Inc.; *Int'l*, pg. 233
CARLSON MARKETING GROUP HK LTD.—See Aimia Inc.; *Int'l*, pg. 233
CARLSON MARKETING GROUP INTERACT—See Aimia Inc.; *Int'l*, pg. 233
CARLSON MARKETING GROUP LTD.—See Aimia Inc.; *Int'l*, pg. 233

CARLSON MARKETING GROUP NZ LIMITED—See Aimia Inc.; *Int'l*, pg. 233
CARLSON MARKETING GROUP SDN. BHD.—See Aimia Inc.; *Int'l*, pg. 233
CARLSON MARKETING GROUP—See Aimia Inc.; *Int'l*, pg. 233
CARLSON MARKETING GROUP—See Aimia Inc.; *Int'l*, pg. 233
CARLSON MARKETING GROUP—See Aimia Inc.; *Int'l*, pg. 233
CARLSON MARKETING GROUP—See Aimia Inc.; *Int'l*, pg. 233
CARLSON MARKETING GROUP—See Aimia Inc.; *Int'l*, pg. 233
CARLSON MARKETING GROUP—See Aimia Inc.; *Int'l*, pg. 233
CARLSON MARKETING GROUP—See Aimia Inc.; *Int'l*, pg. 233
CARLSON MARKETING GROUP—See Aimia Inc.; *Int'l*, pg. 233
CARLSON MARKETING GROUP (UK) LTD.—See Aimia Inc.; *Int'l*, pg. 233
CARLSON MARKETING—See Aimia Inc.; *Int'l*, pg. 233
CARLSON PAVING PRODUCTS, INC.—See Astec Industries, Inc.; *U.S. Public*, pg. 216
CARLSON REAL ESTATE COMPANY—See Carlson Companies Inc.; *U.S. Private*, pg. 765
CARLSON RESTAURANTS WORLDWIDE INC.—See Carlson Companies Inc.; *U.S. Private*, pg. 765
CARLSON REZIDOR HOTEL GROUP - ASIA PACIFIC—See Carlson Companies Inc.; *U.S. Private*, pg. 764
CARLSON TOOL & MANUFACTURING CORP.; *U.S. Private*, pg. 765
CARLSON TRAVEL/LET'S TALK TRAVEL INC.—See Carlson Companies Inc.; *U.S. Private*, pg. 765
CARLSON WAGONLIT TRAVEL, INC.—See Carlson Companies Inc.; *U.S. Private*, pg. 765
CARL'S PATIO, INC.—See Weinberg Capital Group, Inc.; *U.S. Private*, pg. 4471
CARLSSON & MOLLER AB—See Indutrade AB; *Int'l*, pg. 3677
CARL'S SUPERMARKET INC.; *U.S. Private*, pg. 763
CARLSTAD MACHINE TOOLS AB—See Nicolas Correa S.A.; *Int'l*, pg. 5272
THE CARLSTAR GROUP B.V.—See AIP, LLC; *U.S. Private*, pg. 137
THE CARLSTAR GROUP LLC—See AIP, LLC; *U.S. Private*, pg. 137
CARL TESDORPF GMBH—See Hawesko Holding AG; *Int'l*, pg. 3288
CARL T. MADSEN INC.; *U.S. Private*, pg. 763
CARLTON-BATES COMPANY DE MEXICO S.A. DE C.V.—See WESCO International, Inc.; *U.S. Public*, pg. 2351
CARLTON-BATES COMPANY OF TENNESSEE INC.—See WESCO International, Inc.; *U.S. Public*, pg. 2351
CARLTON-BATES COMPANY - SAINT LOUIS—See WESCO International, Inc.; *U.S. Public*, pg. 2351
CARLTON-BATES COMPANY—See WESCO International, Inc.; *U.S. Public*, pg. 2351
CARLTON CARDS LIMITED—See Clayton, Dubilier & Rice, LLC; *U.S. Private*, pg. 919
CARLTON CARDS RETAIL, INC.—See Clayton, Dubilier & Rice, LLC; *U.S. Private*, pg. 919
CARLTON CREEK IRONWORKS INC.—See Monomoy Capital Partners LLC; *U.S. Private*, pg. 2772
CARLTON CREEK IRONWORKS—See Monomoy Capital Partners LLC; *U.S. Private*, pg. 2772
CARLTON FIELDS JORDEN BURT, P.A. - SIMSBURY—See Carlton Fields Jorden Burt, P.A.; *U.S. Private*, pg. 765
CARLTON FIELDS JORDEN BURT, P.A.; *U.S. Private*, pg. 765
CARLTON FOODS CORP.—See Altamont Capital Partners; *U.S. Private*, pg. 205
CARLTON FORGE WORKS—See Berkshire Hathaway Inc.; *U.S. Public*, pg. 314
CARLTON GROUP, INC.; *U.S. Private*, pg. 765
CARLTON, INC.—See Barry, Bette & Led Duke, Inc.; *U.S. Private*, pg. 481
CARLTON INVESTMENTS LIMITED; *Int'l*, pg. 1341
CARLTON LEBENSMITTEL VERTRIEBS GMBH—See Mondelez International, Inc.; *U.S. Public*, pg. 1462
CARLTON LIFE - RESIDENCIAS E SERVICOS S.A.—See UnitedHealth Group Incorporated; *U.S. Public*, pg. 2239
CARLTON MANUFACTURING, INC.; *U.S. Private*, pg. 765
CARLTON POOLS INC.; *U.S. Private*, pg. 765
CARLTON RESOURCES PLC; *Int'l*, pg. 1341
CARLTON TRAIL RAILWAY COMPANY—See The Broe Companies, Inc.; *U.S. Private*, pg. 4001
CARLTON & UNITED BEVERAGES LIMITED—See Anheuser-Busch InBev SA/NV; *Int'l*, pg. 464
CARLTON & UNITED BREWERIES PTY LTD—See Asahi Group Holdings Ltd.; *Int'l*, pg. 593
CARLUCCIO'S LTD.; *Int'l*, pg. 1341
CARL WARREN & COMPANY; *U.S. Private*, pg. 763

CARLY HOLDINGS LIMITED; *Int'l*, pg. 1341
THE CARLYLE, A ROSEWOOD HOTEL—See Chow Tai Fook Enterprises Limited; *Int'l*, pg. 1585
CARLYLE ASIA INVESTMENT ADVISORS LIMITED—See The Carlyle Group Inc.; *U.S. Public*, pg. 2045
CARLYLE AVIATION GROUP, LLC—See The Carlyle Group Inc.; *U.S. Public*, pg. 2045
CARLYLE AVIATION PARTNERS LLC—See The Carlyle Group Inc.; *U.S. Public*, pg. 2045
CARLYLE AVIATION SECURITIES PARTNERS, LLC—See The Carlyle Group Inc.; *U.S. Public*, pg. 2045
CARLYLE COCOA CO., LLC—See Guan Chong Berhad; *Int'l*, pg. 3152
CARLYLE COMMODITIES CORP.; *Int'l*, pg. 1341
CARLYLE CREDIT SOLUTIONS, INC.; *U.S. Private*, pg. 765
CARLYLE CUSTOM CONVERTIBLES, LTD.; *U.S. Private*, pg. 765
THE CARLYLE GROUP, INC.; *U.S. Private*, pg. 4005
THE CARLYLE GROUP INC.; *U.S. Public*, pg. 2043
THE CARLYLE GROUP (LUXEMBOURG) S.A.R.L.—See The Carlyle Group Inc.; *U.S. Public*, pg. 2055
CARLYLE JAPAN ASSET MANAGEMENT YK—See The Carlyle Group Inc.; *U.S. Public*, pg. 2054
THE CARLYLE JOHNSON MACHINE COMPANY, LLC; *U.S. Private*, pg. 4005
CARLYLE MOTOR PRODUCTS LTD; *Int'l*, pg. 1341
CARLYLE SECURED LENDING, INC.; *U.S. Public*, pg. 437
CARLYLE SINGAPORE INVESTMENT ADVISORS PTE LTD—See The Carlyle Group Inc.; *U.S. Public*, pg. 2045
CARLYLE VAN LINES INC.; *U.S. Private*, pg. 765
CARLYSLE ENGINEERING INC.; *U.S. Private*, pg. 765
CARL ZEISS 3D AUTOMATION GMBH—See Carl-Zeiss-Stiftung; *Int'l*, pg. 1333
CARL ZEISS 3D METROLOGY SERVICES GMBH KOLN—See Carl-Zeiss-Stiftung; *Int'l*, pg. 1333
CARL ZEISS 3D METROLOGY SERVICES GMBH MUNCHEN—See Carl-Zeiss-Stiftung; *Int'l*, pg. 1333
CARL ZEISS 3D METROLOGY SERVICES GMBH PEINE—See Carl-Zeiss-Stiftung; *Int'l*, pg. 1333
CARL ZEISS 3D METROLOGY SERVICES GMBH—See Carl-Zeiss-Stiftung; *Int'l*, pg. 1333
CARL ZEISS AB—See Carl-Zeiss-Stiftung; *Int'l*, pg. 1333
CARL ZEISS AG—See Carl-Zeiss-Stiftung; *Int'l*, pg. 1333
CARL ZEISS ARGENTINA S.A.—See Carl-Zeiss-Stiftung; *Int'l*, pg. 1334
CARL ZEISS ASIA—See Carl-Zeiss-Stiftung; *Int'l*, pg. 1333
CARL ZEISS AS—See Carl-Zeiss-Stiftung; *Int'l*, pg. 1334
CARL ZEISS AUTOMATED INSPECTION GMBH & CO. KG—See Carl-Zeiss-Stiftung; *Int'l*, pg. 1334
CARL ZEISS B.V.—See Carl-Zeiss-Stiftung; *Int'l*, pg. 1334
CARL ZEISS CANADA LTD.—See Carl-Zeiss-Stiftung; *Int'l*, pg. 1333
CARL ZEISS CMP GMBH—See Carl-Zeiss-Stiftung; *Int'l*, pg. 1334
CARL ZEISS CO. LTD.—See Carl-Zeiss-Stiftung; *Int'l*, pg. 1334
CARL ZEISS CO. LTD.—See Carl-Zeiss-Stiftung; *Int'l*, pg. 1334
CARL ZEISS CO., LTD.—See Carl-Zeiss-Stiftung; *Int'l*, pg. 1334
CARL ZEISS CO., LTD.—See Carl-Zeiss-Stiftung; *Int'l*, pg. 1334
CARL ZEISS DE MEXICO, S.A. DE C.V.—See Carl-Zeiss-Stiftung; *Int'l*, pg. 1336
CARL ZEISS DO BRASIL LTDA.—See Carl-Zeiss-Stiftung; *Int'l*, pg. 1336
CARL ZEISS D.O.O.—See Carl-Zeiss-Stiftung; *Int'l*, pg. 1336
CARL ZEISS D.O.O.—See Carl-Zeiss-Stiftung; *Int'l*, pg. 1336
CARL ZEISS FAR EAST COMPANY LIMITED—See Carl-Zeiss-Stiftung; *Int'l*, pg. 1334
CARL ZEISS FIXTURE SYSTEMS GMBH—See Carl-Zeiss-Stiftung; *Int'l*, pg. 1334
CARL ZEISS GMBH—See Carl-Zeiss-Stiftung; *Int'l*, pg. 1334
CARL ZEISS IBERIA, S.L.—See Carl-Zeiss-Stiftung; *Int'l*, pg. 1334
CARL ZEISS IMT CO., LTD.—See Carl-Zeiss-Stiftung; *Int'l*, pg. 1334
CARL ZEISS IMT IBERIA S.L.U.—See Carl-Zeiss-Stiftung; *Int'l*, pg. 1334
CARL ZEISS, INC.—See Carl-Zeiss-Stiftung; *Int'l*, pg. 1334
CARL ZEISS INDIA PTE. LTD.—See Carl-Zeiss-Stiftung; *Int'l*, pg. 1334
CARL ZEISS INDUSTRIAL METROLOGY, LLC—See Carl-Zeiss-Stiftung; *Int'l*, pg. 1334
CARL ZEISS INDUSTRIELLE MESSTECHNIK AUSTRIA GMBH—See Carl-Zeiss-Stiftung; *Int'l*, pg. 1334
CARL ZEISS INNOVATIONSZENTRUM FUR MESSTECHNIK GMBH—See Carl-Zeiss-Stiftung; *Int'l*, pg. 1334
CARL ZEISS INSTRUMENTS S.R.L.—See Carl-Zeiss-Stiftung; *Int'l*, pg. 1334
CARL ZEISS JAPAN GROUP—See Carl-Zeiss-Stiftung; *Int'l*, pg. 1334

CARL ZEISS JENA GMBH—See Carl-Zeiss-Stiftung; *Int'l*, pg. 1334
CARL ZEISS LTD.—See Carl-Zeiss-Stiftung; *Int'l*, pg. 1334
CARL ZEISS MEDITEC AG—See Carl-Zeiss-Stiftung; *Int'l*, pg. 1333
CARL ZEISS MEDITEC CO., LTD.—See Carl-Zeiss-Stiftung; *Int'l*, pg. 1334
CARL ZEISS MEDITEC FRANCE S.A.S.—See Carl-Zeiss-Stiftung; *Int'l*, pg. 1334
CARL ZEISS MEDITEC, INC.—See Carl-Zeiss-Stiftung; *Int'l*, pg. 1334
CARL ZEISS MEDITEC PRODUCTION, LLC—See Carl-Zeiss-Stiftung; *Int'l*, pg. 1334
CARL ZEISS MEDITEC SAS—See Carl-Zeiss-Stiftung; *Int'l*, pg. 1334
CARL ZEISS MEDITEC VERTRIEBSGESELLSCHAFT MBH—See Carl-Zeiss-Stiftung; *Int'l*, pg. 1334
CARL ZEISS MENA FZE—See Carl-Zeiss-Stiftung; *Int'l*, pg. 1334
CARL ZEISS MES SOLUTIONS GMBH—See Carl-Zeiss-Stiftung; *Int'l*, pg. 1334
CARL ZEISS MICROSCOPY CO., LTD.—See Carl-Zeiss-Stiftung; *Int'l*, pg. 1335
CARL ZEISS MICROSCOPY GMBH—See Carl-Zeiss-Stiftung; *Int'l*, pg. 1334
CARL ZEISS MICROSCOPY LIMITED—See Carl-Zeiss-Stiftung; *Int'l*, pg. 1335
CARL ZEISS MICROSCOPY, LLC—See Carl-Zeiss-Stiftung; *Int'l*, pg. 1335
CARL ZEISS N.V-S.A.—See Carl-Zeiss-Stiftung; *Int'l*, pg. 1335
CARL ZEISS (N.Z.) LTD.—See Carl-Zeiss-Stiftung; *Int'l*, pg. 1333
CARL ZEISS OIM GMBH—See Carl-Zeiss-Stiftung; *Int'l*, pg. 1335
CARL ZEISS OPTON KFT.—See Carl-Zeiss-Stiftung; *Int'l*, pg. 1335
CARL ZEISS OY—See Carl-Zeiss-Stiftung; *Int'l*, pg. 1335
CARL ZEISS PTE. LTD.—See Carl-Zeiss-Stiftung; *Int'l*, pg. 1335
CARL ZEISS PTY. LTD.—See Carl-Zeiss-Stiftung; *Int'l*, pg. 1335
CARL ZEISS PTY LTD—See Carl-Zeiss-Stiftung; *Int'l*, pg. 1334
CARL ZEISS QEC GMBH—See Carl-Zeiss-Stiftung; *Int'l*, pg. 1335
CARL ZEISS S.A.S—See Carl-Zeiss-Stiftung; *Int'l*, pg. 1335
CARL ZEISS SBE, LLC—See Carl-Zeiss-Stiftung; *Int'l*, pg. 1335
CARL ZEISS SDN. BHD.—See Carl-Zeiss-Stiftung; *Int'l*, pg. 1335
CARL ZEISS SERVICES S.A.R.L.—See Carl-Zeiss-Stiftung; *Int'l*, pg. 1335
CARL ZEISS SHANGHAI CO., LTD.—See Carl-Zeiss-Stiftung; *Int'l*, pg. 1335
CARL ZEISS SLOVAKIA, S.R.O.—See Carl-Zeiss-Stiftung; *Int'l*, pg. 1335
CARL ZEISS SMT GMBH—See Carl-Zeiss-Stiftung; *Int'l*, pg. 1335
CARL ZEISS S.P.A.—See Carl-Zeiss-Stiftung; *Int'l*, pg. 1335
CARL ZEISS SPECTROSCOPY GMBH—See Carl-Zeiss-Stiftung; *Int'l*, pg. 1335
CARL ZEISS SPOL. S.R.O.—See Carl-Zeiss-Stiftung; *Int'l*, pg. 1336
CARL ZEISS SPOL. S.R.O.—See Carl-Zeiss-Stiftung; *Int'l*, pg. 1336
CARL ZEISS SPORT OPTIKAI HUNGARIA KFT.—See Carl-Zeiss-Stiftung; *Int'l*, pg. 1335
CARL ZEISS SPORTS OPTICS GMBH—See Carl-Zeiss-Stiftung; *Int'l*, pg. 1334
CARL ZEISS SPORTS OPTICS, LLC—See Carl-Zeiss-Stiftung; *Int'l*, pg. 1334
CARL ZEISS SP. Z O. O.—See Carl-Zeiss-Stiftung; *Int'l*, pg. 1335
CARL-ZEISS-STIFTUNG; *Int'l*, pg. 1333
CARL ZEISS SUZHOU CO., LTD.—See Carl-Zeiss-Stiftung; *Int'l*, pg. 1335
CARL ZEISS TECHNIKA KFT.—See Carl-Zeiss-Stiftung; *Int'l*, pg. 1335
CARL ZEISS TEKNOLOJI COZUMLERI TICARET LIMITED SIRKETI—See Carl-Zeiss-Stiftung; *Int'l*, pg. 1335
CARL ZEISS VIETNAM COMPANY LIMITED—See Carl-Zeiss-Stiftung; *Int'l*, pg. 1335
CARL ZEISS VISION AB—See Carl-Zeiss-Stiftung; *Int'l*, pg. 1335
CARL ZEISS VISION ARGENTINA S.A—See Carl-Zeiss-Stiftung; *Int'l*, pg. 1335
CARL ZEISS VISION AUSTRALIA GROUP PTY. LTD.—See Carl-Zeiss-Stiftung; *Int'l*, pg. 1335
CARL ZEISS VISION AUSTRALIA LTD.—See Carl-Zeiss-Stiftung; *Int'l*, pg. 1335
CARL ZEISS VISION AUSTRALIA LTD.—See EQT AB; *Int'l*, pg. 2473
CARL ZEISS VISION BELGIUM NV—See Carl-Zeiss-Stiftung; *Int'l*, pg. 1335
CARL ZEISS VISION BRASIL INDUSTRIA OPTICA LTDA.—See Carl-Zeiss-Stiftung; *Int'l*, pg. 1335

CARL ZEISS VISION BRASIL INDUSTRIA OPTICA LTDA.—See EQT AB; *Int'l*, pg. 2473
CARL ZEISS VISION COLUMBIA LTDA.—See Carl-Zeiss-Stiftung; *Int'l*, pg. 1335
CARL ZEISS VISION DANMARK A/S—See Carl-Zeiss-Stiftung; *Int'l*, pg. 1335
CARL ZEISS VISION ESPANA—See Carl-Zeiss-Stiftung; *Int'l*, pg. 1335
CARL ZEISS VISION FRANCE HOLDING S.A.S.—See Carl-Zeiss-Stiftung; *Int'l*, pg. 1335
CARL ZEISS VISION GMBH—See Carl-Zeiss-Stiftung; *Int'l*, pg. 1335
CARL ZEISS VISION GMBH—See EQT AB; *Int'l*, pg. 2473
CARL ZEISS VISION (GUANGZHOU) LTD.—See Carl-Zeiss-Stiftung; *Int'l*, pg. 1335
CARL ZEISS VISION (GUANGZHOU) LTD.—See EQT AB; *Int'l*, pg. 2473
CARL ZEISS VISION HUNGARY OPTIKAI KFT.—See Carl-Zeiss-Stiftung; *Int'l*, pg. 1335
CARL ZEISS VISION INC.—See Carl-Zeiss-Stiftung; *Int'l*, pg. 1335
CARL ZEISS VISION INC.—See EQT AB; *Int'l*, pg. 2473
CARL ZEISS VISION INTERNATIONAL GMBH—See Carl-Zeiss-Stiftung; *Int'l*, pg. 1335
CARL ZEISS VISION INTERNATIONAL GMBH—See EQT AB; *Int'l*, pg. 2472
CARL ZEISS VISION IRELAND LTD.—See Carl-Zeiss-Stiftung; *Int'l*, pg. 1336
CARL ZEISS VISION IRELAND LTD.—See EQT AB; *Int'l*, pg. 2473
CARL ZEISS VISION ITALIA SPA—See Carl-Zeiss-Stiftung; *Int'l*, pg. 1336
CARL ZEISS VISION ITALIA SPA—See EQT AB; *Int'l*, pg. 2473
CARL ZEISS VISION (MALAYSIA) SDN. BHD.—See Carl-Zeiss-Stiftung; *Int'l*, pg. 1335
CARL ZEISS VISION MANUFACTURA DE MEXICO S. DE R.L. DE C.V.—See Carl-Zeiss-Stiftung; *Int'l*, pg. 1336
CARL ZEISS VISION MEXICO S. DE R.L. DE C.V.—See Carl-Zeiss-Stiftung; *Int'l*, pg. 1336
CARL ZEISS VISION PORTUGAL S.A.—See Carl-Zeiss-Stiftung; *Int'l*, pg. 1336
CARL ZEISS VISION SINGAPORE PTE. LTD.—See Carl-Zeiss-Stiftung; *Int'l*, pg. 1336
CARL ZEISS VISION—See Carl-Zeiss-Stiftung; *Int'l*, pg. 1335
CARL ZEISS VISION—See Carl-Zeiss-Stiftung; *Int'l*, pg. 1335
CARL ZEISS VISION—See EQT AB; *Int'l*, pg. 2472
CARL ZEISS VISION—See EQT AB; *Int'l*, pg. 2473
CARL ZEISS VISION—See EQT AB; *Int'l*, pg. 1335
CARL ZEISS VISION—See EQT AB; *Int'l*, pg. 2473
CARL ZEISS VISION SOUTH AFRICA LTD.—See Carl-Zeiss-Stiftung; *Int'l*, pg. 1336
CARL ZEISS VISION SWISS AG—See Carl-Zeiss-Stiftung; *Int'l*, pg. 1336
CARL ZEISS VISION SWISS AG—See EQT AB; *Int'l*, pg. 2473
CARL ZEISS VISION UK LTD.—See Carl-Zeiss-Stiftung; *Int'l*, pg. 1336
CARL ZEISS VISION UK LTD.—See EQT AB; *Int'l*, pg. 2473
CARL ZEISS VISION VENEZUELA INDUSTRIA OPTICA C.A.—See Carl-Zeiss-Stiftung; *Int'l*, pg. 1336
CARL ZEISS VISION VENEZUELA INDUSTRIA OPTICA C.A.—See EQT AB; *Int'l*, pg. 2473
CARL ZEISS X-RAY MICROSCOPY, INC.—See Carl-Zeiss-Stiftung; *Int'l*, pg. 1336
CARMACK CAR CAPITOL INC.; *U.S. Private*, pg. 766
CARMACKS ENTERPRISES LTD—See VINCI S.A.; *Int'l*, pg. 8219
CARMACKS MAINTENANCE SERVICES LTD.—See VINCI S.A.; *Int'l*, pg. 8213
CARMAGEN ENGINEERING, INC.—See Mistras Group, Inc.; *U.S. Public*, pg. 1451
CARMA HOLDING GMBH—See MEDIQON Group AG; *Int'l*, pg. 4780
CARMA INTERNATIONAL, INC.—See News Group International Holding; *Int'l*, pg. 5238
CARMANAH TECHNOLOGIES CORPORATION; *Int'l*, pg. 1341
CAR MART COMUNICACIONES, S.A. DE C.V.—See CalAmp Corp.; *U.S. Public*, pg. 422
CAR MATE MFG. CO., LTD.; *Int'l*, pg. 1319
CAR MATE USA, INC.—See Car Mate Mfg. Co., Ltd.; *Int'l*, pg. 1319
CARMAT SAS; *Int'l*, pg. 1341
CARMAX AUTO FINANCE—See CarMax, Inc.; *U.S. Public*, pg. 437
CARMAX AUTO SUPERSTORES, INC.—See CarMax, Inc.; *U.S. Public*, pg. 437
CARMAX AUTO SUPERSTORES, INC.—See CarMax, Inc.; *U.S. Public*, pg. 437
CARMAX AUTO SUPERSTORES SERVICES, INC.—See CarMax, Inc.; *U.S. Public*, pg. 437
CARMAX AUTO SUPERSTORES WEST COAST, INC.—See CarMax, Inc.; *U.S. Public*, pg. 437
CARMAX BUSINESS SERVICES, LLC—See CarMax, Inc.; *U.S. Public*, pg. 437

CARMAX CO., LTD.—See Hotai Motor Co., Ltd.; *Int'l*, pg. 3487
CARMAX ENTERPRISE SERVICES, LLC—See CarMax, Inc.; *U.S. Public*, pg. 437
CARMAX, INC.; *U.S. Public*, pg. 437
CARMAX LIMITED—See ANSA McAL Limited; *Int'l*, pg. 477
CARMECO SA; *Int'l*, pg. 1341
CARMECO AB—See W.L. Gore & Associates, Inc.; *U.S. Private*, pg. 4421
CARMEDIALAB CORP.—See init innovation in traffic systems SE; *Int'l*, pg. 3704
CARMEDIALAB GMBH—See init innovation in traffic systems SE; *Int'l*, pg. 3704
CARMEL CITY CENTER COMMUNITY DEVELOPMENT CORPORATION; *U.S. Private*, pg. 766
CARMEL CONTAINER SYSTEMS LTD.—See Veridis Environment Ltd; *Int'l*, pg. 8168
CARMEL COUNTRY CLUB; *U.S. Private*, pg. 766
CARMEL FORGE LTD.—See Bet Shemesh Engines Holdings (1997) Ltd.; *Int'l*, pg. 1001
CARMELINA CAPITAL PARTNERS; *U.S. Private*, pg. 766
CARMELL CORPORATION; *U.S. Public*, pg. 437
CARMEL MOUNTAIN REHABILITATION AND HEALTHCARE CENTER—See The Ensign Group, Inc.; *U.S. Public*, pg. 2070
CARMEL OLEFINS LTD.—See Israel Corporation Ltd.; *Int'l*, pg. 3823
CARMEL OLEFINS LTD.—See Israel Petrochemical Enterprises Ltd.; *Int'l*, pg. 3824
CARMEL SPECIALTY SURGERY CENTER, LLC—See Tenet Healthcare Corporation; *U.S. Public*, pg. 2001
CARMEL STEEL PRODUCTS INC—See Engineered Glass Walls; *U.S. Private*, pg. 1398
CARMEN ANTHONY FISHHOUSE LLC—See Carmen Anthony Restaurant Group, LLC; *U.S. Private*, pg. 766
CARMEN ANTHONY RESTAURANT GROUP, LLC; *U.S. Private*, pg. 766
CARMENITA FORD TRUCK SALES INC.; *U.S. Private*, pg. 766
CARMESIN SA; *Int'l*, pg. 1341
CARMEUSE HOLDING SA; *Int'l*, pg. 1341
CARMEUSE LIME INC.—See Carmeuse Holding SA; *Int'l*, pg. 1341
CARMEUSE LIME & STONE, INC.—See Carmeuse Holding SA; *Int'l*, pg. 1341
CARMEUSE LIME & STONE—See Carmeuse Holding SA; *Int'l*, pg. 1341
CARMEUSE LIME & STONE—See Carmeuse Holding SA; *Int'l*, pg. 1341
CARMEUSE LIME & STONE—See Carmeuse Holding SA; *Int'l*, pg. 1341
CARMEUSE LIME & STONE—See Carmeuse Holding SA; *Int'l*, pg. 1341
CARMEUSE LIME & STONE—See Carmeuse Holding SA; *Int'l*, pg. 1341
CARMEUSE N.A.—See Carmeuse Holding SA; *Int'l*, pg. 1341
CARMEUSE NORTH AMERICA—See Carmeuse Holding SA; *Int'l*, pg. 1341
CARMICHAEL ASSOCIATES, INC.—See Inszone Insurance Services, LLC; *U.S. Private*, pg. 2096
CARMICHAEL ENGINEERING, INC.—See Universal Engineering Sciences, LLC; *U.S. Private*, pg. 4304
CARMICHAEL LEASING CO. INC.; *U.S. Private*, pg. 766
CARMICHAEL LYNCH, INC.—See The Interpublic Group of Companies, Inc.; *U.S. Public*, pg. 2090
CARMICHAEL LYNCH RELATE—See The Interpublic Group of Companies, Inc.; *U.S. Public*, pg. 2090
CARMICHAEL LYNCH SPONG—See The Interpublic Group of Companies, Inc.; *U.S. Public*, pg. 2090
CARMICHAEL LYNCH SPONG—See The Interpublic Group of Companies, Inc.; *U.S. Public*, pg. 2090
CARMICHAEL'S NUTRITIONAL DISTRIBUTOR, INC.—See SunLink Health Systems, Inc.; *U.S. Public*, pg. 1964
CARMIKE CINEMAS, LLC—See Dalian Wanda Group Corporation Ltd.; *Int'l*, pg. 1953
CARMILA SA; *Int'l*, pg. 1342
CARMIT CANDY INDUSTRIES LTD.; *Int'l*, pg. 1342
CARMI & UBERTIS DESIGN S.R.L—See Publicis Groupe S.A.; *Int'l*, pg. 6097
CARMODY TORRANCE SANDAK & HENNESSEY LLP; *U.S. Private*, pg. 766
CAR MONKEYS GROUP; *U.S. Private*, pg. 747
CARNA BIOSCIENCES INC.; *Int'l*, pg. 1342
CARNABIO USA INC.—See Carna Biosciences Inc.; *Int'l*, pg. 1342
CARNABY RESOURCES LIMITED; *Int'l*, pg. 1342
CARNA MEDICAL DATABASE PVT. LTD.—See Konoike Transport Co., Ltd.; *Int'l*, pg. 4274
CARNARVON ENERGY LIMITED; *Int'l*, pg. 1342
CARNATION INDUSTRIES LTD.; *Int'l*, pg. 1342
CARNATION MANUFACTURING CO. (THAILAND) LTD.—See Nestle S.A.; *Int'l*, pg. 5204
CARNAUDMETALBOX ENGINEERING LTD—See Crown Holdings, Inc.; *U.S. Public*, pg. 598

COMPANY NAME INDEX

CARNAUDMETALBOX FINANCE SA—See Crown Holdings, Inc.; *U.S. Public*, pg. 598
CARNAUDMETALBOX FOOD SOUTH AFRICA (PTY) LIMITED—See Crown Holdings, Inc.; *U.S. Public*, pg. 598
CARNAUDMETALBOX ZIMBABWE LTD.—See Nampak Ltd.; *Int'l*, pg. 5136
CARNAVALE RESOURCES LIMITED; *Int'l*, pg. 1342
CARNEGIE CLEAN ENERGY LIMITED; *Int'l*, pg. 1342
CARNEGIE DARTLET LLC; *U.S. Private*, pg. 766
CARNEGIE DEVELOPMENT, INC.; *U.S. Public*, pg. 437
THE CARNEGIE ENDOWMENT FOR INTERNATIONAL PEACE; *U.S. Private*, pg. 4005
CARNEGIE FABRICS, LLC—See Calera Capital Management, Inc.; *U.S. Private*, pg. 717
CARNEGIE FONDER AB—See Altor Equity Partners AB; *Int'l*, pg. 394
CARNEGIE HOTELS, LLC—See Summit Hotel Properties, Inc.; *U.S. Public*, pg. 1959
CARNEGIE INC.—See Altor Equity Partners AB; *Int'l*, pg. 394
CARNEGIE INSTITUTION OF WASHINGTON; *U.S. Private*, pg. 766
CARNEGIE INVESTMENT BANK AB—See Altor Equity Partners AB; *Int'l*, pg. 394
CARNEGIE INVESTMENT COUNSEL; *U.S. Private*, pg. 766
CARNEGIE LEARNING, INC.—See CIP Capital Fund, L.P.; *U.S. Private*, pg. 899
CARNEGIE MORTGAGE PARTNERS, LLC—See Rithm Capital Corp.; *U.S. Public*, pg. 1800
CARNES COMPANY INCORPORATED; *U.S. Private*, pg. 766
CARNES SELECTAS 2000 S.A.—See ALFA, S.A.B. de C.V.; *Int'l*, pg. 314
CARNETT'S MANAGEMENT COMPANY; *U.S. Private*, pg. 766
THE CARNEY GROUP; *U.S. Private*, pg. 4005
CARNEY, INC.; *U.S. Private*, pg. 766
CARNIVAL COMPANY, LTD.—See Sac's Bar Holdings Inc.; *Int'l*, pg. 6463
CARNIVAL CORPORATION HONG KING LIMITED—See Carnival Corporation; *U.S. Public*, pg. 438
CARNIVAL CORPORATION KOREA LTD.—See Carnival Corporation; *U.S. Public*, pg. 438
CARNIVAL CORPORATION; *U.S. Public*, pg. 437
CARNIVAL CRUISE LINES—See Carnival Corporation; *U.S. Public*, pg. 438
CARNIVAL FILM & TELEVISION LIMITED—See Comcast Corporation; *U.S. Public*, pg. 537
CARNIVAL GROUP INTERNATIONAL HOLDINGS LIMITED; *Int'l*, pg. 1342
CARNIVAL INDUSTRIAL CORPORATION; *Int'l*, pg. 1342
CARNIVAL MARITIME GMBH—See Carnival Corporation; *U.S. Public*, pg. 438
CARNIVAL PLC—See Carnival Corporation; *U.S. Public*, pg. 437
CARNIVAL SUPPORT SERVICES INDIA PRIVATE LIMITED—See Carnival Corporation; *U.S. Public*, pg. 438
CARNIVAL (UK) LIMITED—See Carnival Corporation; *U.S. Public*, pg. 437
CARNIVORE MEAT COMPANY, LLC; *U.S. Private*, pg. 766
CAROBEL FOAM LIMITED—See Recticel S.A.; *Int'l*, pg. 6241
CARO COMMUNITY HOSPITAL; *U.S. Private*, pg. 766
CAROFFER, LLC—See CarGurus, Inc.; *U.S. Public*, pg. 435
CARO FOODS, INC.—See Performance Food Group Company; *U.S. Public*, pg. 1674
CARO HOLDINGS, INC.; *Int'l*, pg. 1342
CAROHOME, LLC—See Duke Energy Corporation; *U.S. Public*, pg. 690
CAROLACE EMBROIDERY CO., INC.; *U.S. Private*, pg. 767
CAROLACE INDUSTRIES INC.—See Carolace Embroidery Co., Inc.; *U.S. Private*, pg. 767
CAROLANE PROPANE—See UGI Corporation; *U.S. Public*, pg. 2221
CAROLEE LLC—See Brooks Brothers, Inc.; *U.S. Private*, pg. 664
CAROLE FABRICS CORP.—See 3G Capital Partners L.P.; *U.S. Private*, pg. 13
CAROLE INC.; *U.S. Private*, pg. 767
CAROL ELECTRIC COMPANY INC.; *U.S. Private*, pg. 766
CAROLE WREN, INC.; *U.S. Private*, pg. 767
CAROL H. WILLIAMS ADVERTISING; *U.S. Private*, pg. 766
CAROL H. WILLIAMS ADVERTISING—See Carol H. Williams Advertising; *U.S. Private*, pg. 766
CAROL H. WILLIAMS ADVERTISING—See Carol H. Williams Advertising; *U.S. Private*, pg. 766
CAROLI FOODS GROUP S. R. L.—See ALFA, S.A.B. de C.V.; *Int'l*, pg. 314
CAROLINA ABSORBENT COTTON COMPANY—See Barnhardt Manufacturing Company; *U.S. Private*, pg. 477
CAROLINA AIRCRAFT CORP.; *U.S. Private*, pg. 767

CAROLINA AIRCRAFT INC.; *U.S. Private*, pg. 767
CAROLINA ALLIANCE BANK—See Park National Corporation; *U.S. Public*, pg. 1638
CAROLINA AND NORTHWESTERN RAILWAY COMPANY—See Norfolk Southern Corporation; *U.S. Public*, pg. 1536
CAROLINA BANK AND TRUST CO.; *U.S. Private*, pg. 767
CAROLINA BEER & BEVERAGE, LLC.; *U.S. Private*, pg. 767
CAROLINA BIOLOGICAL SUPPLY COMPANY; *U.S. Private*, pg. 767
CAROLINA BUILDING MATERIALS, INC.—See ThyssenKrupp AG; *Int'l*, pg. 7724
CAROLINA BUSINESS EQUIPMENT, INC.—See Perpetual Capital, LLC; *U.S. Private*, pg. 3153
CAROLINA BUSINESS FURNITURE, LLC; *U.S. Private*, pg. 767
CAROLINA CANNERS INC.; *U.S. Private*, pg. 767
CAROLINA CANNERS MEDIA—See Carolina Canners Inc.; *U.S. Private*, pg. 767
CAROLINA CAPRI INC.; *U.S. Private*, pg. 767
CAROLINA CASUALTY INSURANCE COMPANY—See W.R. Berkley Corporation; *U.S. Public*, pg. 2318
CAROLINA CERAMICS BRICK COMPANY; *U.S. Private*, pg. 767
CAROLINA CHAIN & CABLE CO. INC.—See ALP Industries, Inc.; *U.S. Private*, pg. 196
CAROLINA CHICKEN INC.; *U.S. Private*, pg. 767
CAROLINA CLUB—See Apollo Global Management, Inc.; *U.S. Public*, pg. 149
CAROLINA COACH & MARINE; *U.S. Private*, pg. 767
CAROLINA COLOR CORPORATION OF OHIO—See Arsenal Capital Management LP; *U.S. Private*, pg. 337
CAROLINA COLOR CORPORATION—See Arsenal Capital Management LP; *U.S. Private*, pg. 337
CAROLINA COMPUTERS, INC.; *U.S. Private*, pg. 767
CAROLINA CONTAINER COMPANY—See Schwarz Partners, LP; *U.S. Private*, pg. 3572
CAROLINA CONTAINER COMPANY—See The Kraft Group LLC; *U.S. Private*, pg. 4066
CAROLINA CONVENIENCE CORP.; *U.S. Private*, pg. 767
CAROLINA COUNTRY CLUB; *U.S. Private*, pg. 767
CAROLINA CUT SHEETS, INC.—See Champion Industries, Inc.; *U.S. Public*, pg. 478
CAROLINA DIALYSIS LLC—See Nautic Partners, LLC; *U.S. Private*, pg. 2869
CAROLINA DOOR CONTROLS, INC.; *U.S. Private*, pg. 767
CAROLINA EASTERN AIKEN INC.—See Carolina Eastern Inc.; *U.S. Private*, pg. 767
CAROLINA EASTERN INC.; *U.S. Private*, pg. 767
CAROLINA EASTERN-MOLONY INC.—See Carolina Eastern Inc.; *U.S. Private*, pg. 767
CAROLINA EASTERN-VAIL INC.; *U.S. Private*, pg. 768
CAROLINA EGG COMPANIES, INC.—See Braswell Milling Company; *U.S. Private*, pg. 640
CAROLINA EYE ASSOCIATES, P.A.; *U.S. Private*, pg. 768
CAROLINA FARM CREDIT, ACA; *U.S. Private*, pg. 768
CAROLINA FASHIONS INC.—See Rubie's Costume Company Inc.; *U.S. Private*, pg. 3500
CAROLINA FLUID COMPONENTS, LLC; *U.S. Private*, pg. 768
CAROLINA FOREST IMAGING CENTER, LLC—See HCA Healthcare, Inc.; *U.S. Public*, pg. 992
CAROLINA GLOVE COMPANY - CAROLINA SPECIALTY FABRICS DIVISION—See Carolina Glove Company; *U.S. Private*, pg. 768
CAROLINA GLOVE COMPANY; *U.S. Private*, pg. 768
CAROLINA HANDLING LLC; *U.S. Private*, pg. 768
CAROLINA HEATING SERVICE OF GREENVILLE, INC.—See DLVA, Inc.; *U.S. Private*, pg. 1248
CAROLINA HERRERA LTD—See Puig Brands S.A.; *Int'l*, pg. 6115
CAROLINA HOME CARE, INC.—See Linde plc; *Int'l*, pg. 4508
CAROLINA HOSIERY MILLS INC.; *U.S. Private*, pg. 768
CAROLINA HOUSE OF CHAPEL HILL, LLC—See Brookdale Senior Living Inc.; *U.S. Public*, pg. 394
CAROLINA HOUSE OF DURHAM, LLC—See Brookdale Senior Living Inc.; *U.S. Public*, pg. 394
CAROLINA HOUSE OF FOREST CITY, LLC—See Brookdale Senior Living Inc.; *U.S. Public*, pg. 394
CAROLINA HOUSE OF LEXINGTON, LLC—See Brookdale Senior Living Inc.; *U.S. Public*, pg. 394
CAROLINA HOUSE OF MOREHEAD CITY, LLC—See Brookdale Senior Living Inc.; *U.S. Public*, pg. 394
CAROLINA HOUSE OF SMITHFIELD, LLC—See Brookdale Senior Living Inc.; *U.S. Public*, pg. 394
CAROLINA IMAGING & COMPUTER PRODUCTS, INC.; *U.S. Private*, pg. 768
CAROLINA INNOVATIVE FOOD INGREDIENTS, INC.—See Universal Corporation; *U.S. Public*, pg. 2254
CAROLINA INTERNATIONAL TRUCKS INC.; *U.S. Private*, pg. 768
CAROLINA LANDING CORPORATION—See Equity LifeStyle Properties, Inc.; *U.S. Public*, pg. 790
CAROLINA LEGAL STAFFING LLC; *U.S. Private*, pg. 768

CAROLINA WHOLESALE OFFICE MACHINE COMPANY, INC.

CAROLINA LOGISTICS—See US 1 Industries, Inc.; *U.S. Private*, pg. 4317
CAROLINA LUBES INC.—See Lucor, Inc.; *U.S. Private*, pg. 2512
CAROLINA MACHINE & TOOL INC.; *U.S. Private*, pg. 768
CAROLINA MANAGEMENT, INC.—See Installed Building Products, Inc.; *U.S. Public*, pg. 1132
CAROLINA MEADOWS, INC.; *U.S. Private*, pg. 768
CAROLINA MILLS INC.; *U.S. Private*, pg. 768
CAROLINA MOTOR CLUB, INC.; *U.S. Private*, pg. 768
CAROLINA NATIONAL TRANSPORTATION LLC—See US 1 Industries, Inc.; *U.S. Private*, pg. 4317
CAROLINA NONWOVENS CORPORATION—See National Spinning Company, Inc.; *U.S. Private*, pg. 2863
CAROLINA OFFICE SYSTEMS, INC.—See Xerox Holdings Corporation; *U.S. Public*, pg. 2387
CAROLINA OIL CO. OF CONCORD; *U.S. Private*, pg. 768
CAROLINA ONE MORTGAGE, LLC—See Rithm Capital Corp.; *U.S. Public*, pg. 1800
CAROLINA PAPER TUBES INC.—See Ox Paper Tube & Core, Inc.; *U.S. Private*, pg. 3056
CAROLINA PARENTING, INC.—See Shivers Trading & Operating Company; *U.S. Private*, pg. 3638
CAROLINA PHYSICAL THERAPY & SPORTS MEDICINE, LIMITED PARTNERSHIP—See U.S. Physical Therapy, Inc.; *U.S. Public*, pg. 2214
CAROLINA PIEDMONT RAILROAD—See Brookfield Infrastructure Partners L.P.; *Int'l*, pg. 1191
CAROLINA PIEDMONT RAILROAD—See GIC Pte. Ltd.; *Int'l*, pg. 2965
CAROLINA PRECISION PLASTICS LLC—See BlackBern Partners LLC; *U.S. Private*, pg. 573
CAROLINA PRECISION PLASTICS LLC—See Lee Equity Partners LLC; *U.S. Private*, pg. 2412
CAROLINA PREPRESS—See J.R. Cole Industries Inc.; *U.S. Private*, pg. 2170
CAROLINA PUBLIC RELATIONS/MARKETING ASSOCIATES, INC.—See Chernoff Newman, LLC; *U.S. Private*, pg. 873
CAROLINA PURE WATER SYSTEMS LLC—See BDT Capital Partners, LLC; *U.S. Private*, pg. 502
CAROLINA QUALITY INC.; *U.S. Private*, pg. 768
CAROLINA QUARRIES, INC.—See TorQuest Partners Inc.; *Int'l*, pg. 7830
CAROLINA RESTAURANT GROUP; *U.S. Private*, pg. 768
CAROLINA RIM & WHEEL COMPANY; *U.S. Private*, pg. 768
CAROLINA RUBBER ROLLS—See HBD Industries, Inc.; *U.S. Private*, pg. 1887
CAROLINA SAND - JOHNSONVILLE—See Summit Materials, Inc.; *U.S. Public*, pg. 1959
CAROLINAS CONSTRUCTIONS SOLUTIONS, INC. *U.S. Private*, pg. 769
CAROLINA SEAL, INC.—See Trelleborg AB; *Int'l*, pg. 7912
CAROLINAS HEALTHCARE SYSTEM; *U.S. Private*, pg. 769
CAROLINA SHIPPING CO. INC.—See Biehl International Corporation; *U.S. Private*, pg. 551
CAROLINA'S HOME MEDICAL EQUIPMENT, INC.; *U.S. Private*, pg. 769
CAROLINAS IT, LLC—See The Riverside Company; *U.S. Private*, pg. 4109
CAROLINAS MEDICAL ALLIANCE, INC.—See Medical University Of South Carolina; *U.S. Private*, pg. 2656
CAROLINA SURVEYING SERVICES INC.—See Peak Rock Capital LLC; *U.S. Private*, pg. 3124
CAROLINA TRACTOR & EQUIPMENT CO. - PINNACLE CRANES DIVISION—See Carolina Tractor &; *U.S. Private*, pg. 769
CAROLINA TRACTOR & EQUIPMENT CO.; *U.S. Private*, pg. 768
CAROLINA TRAFFIC DEVICES INC.; *U.S. Private*, pg. 769
CAROLINA TREE CARE; *U.S. Private*, pg. 769
CAROLINA WASTE & RECYCLING LLC—See Waste Connections, Inc.; *Int'l*, pg. 8353
CAROLINA WHOLESALE OFFICE MACHINE COMPANY, INC.; *U.S. Private*, pg. 769
CAROLINE HOLDINGS LLC—See Tiptree Inc.; *U.S. Public*, pg. 2159
CAROLINE LLC—See Primo Water Corporation; *U.S. Public*, pg. 1718
CAR-O-LINER (BEIJING) CO., LTD.—See Snap-on Incorporated; *U.S. Public*, pg. 1897
CAR-O-LINER COMMERCIAL AB—See Snap-on Incorporated; *U.S. Public*, pg. 1897
CAR-O-LINER COMPANY USA—See Snap-on Incorporated; *U.S. Public*, pg. 1897
CAR-O-LINER DEUTSCHLAND GMBH—See Snap-on Incorporated; *U.S. Public*, pg. 1897
CAR-O-LINER GROUP AB—See Snap-on Incorporated; *U.S. Public*, pg. 1897
CAR-O-LINER HOLDING AB—See Snap-on Incorporated; *U.S. Public*, pg. 1897
CAR-O-LINER INDIA PRIVATE LIMITED—See Snap-on Incorporated; *U.S. Public*, pg. 1897
CAR-O-LINER MEA (FZE)—See Snap-on Incorporated; *U.S. Public*, pg. 1897

CAROLINA WHOLESALE OFFICE MACHINE COMPANY, INC.

CAR-O-LINER NORGE AS—See Snap-on Incorporated; *U.S. Public*, pg. 1897
CAR-O-LINER SAS—See Snap-on Incorporated; *U.S. Public*, pg. 1897
CAR-O-LINER S.R.L.—See Snap-on Incorporated; *U.S. Public*, pg. 1897
CAR-O-LINER (THAILAND) CO., LTD.—See Snap-on Incorporated; *U.S. Public*, pg. 1897
CAR-O-LINER (UK) LIMITED—See Snap-on Incorporated; *U.S. Public*, pg. 1897
CAROL INFO SERVICES LTD.; *Int'l*, pg. 1342
CAROLLO ENGINEERS, INC.; *U.S. Private*, pg. 769
CAROL MILGARD BREAST CENTER; *U.S. Private*, pg. 766
CAROLRHODA BOOKS, INC.; *U.S. Private*, pg. 769
CAROL'S LIGHTING AND FAN SHOP; *U.S. Private*, pg. 767
CAROLYN FABRICS INC.; *U.S. Private*, pg. 769
CAROLYN GRISKO & ASSOCIATES INC.; *U.S. Private*, pg. 769
CAROLYN RIVER PROJECTS LTD.; *Int'l*, pg. 1342
CAROMA CONSTRUCTION CO.; *U.S. Private*, pg. 769
CAROMA INDUSTRIES LIMITED—See GWA Group Limited; *Int'l*, pg. 3190
CAROMA INDUSTRIES (NZ) LIMITED—See GWA Group Limited; *Int'l*, pg. 3190
CAROMETEC A/S—See KKR & Co. Inc.; *U.S. Public*, pg. 1241
CAROMETEC S.L.—See KKR & Co. Inc.; *U.S. Public*, pg. 1241
CARONDELET CORPORATION—See MetalTek International; *U.S. Private*, pg. 2682
CARONDELET HEALTH CORPORATION—See Ascension Health Alliance; *U.S. Private*, pg. 347
CARONDELET HEALTH NETWORK—See Ascension Health Alliance; *U.S. Private*, pg. 347
CARONDELET MANAGEMENT COMPANY, INC.—See Ascension Health Alliance; *U.S. Private*, pg. 347
CARONDELET MANOR—See Ascension Health Alliance; *U.S. Private*, pg. 347
CARONDELET PHARMACY AT SAINT JOSEPH HEALTH CENTER INC.—See Ascension Health Alliance; *U.S. Private*, pg. 347
CARONDELET ST. MARY'S-NORTHWEST, L.L.C.—See Tenet Healthcare Corporation; *U.S. Public*, pg. 2001
CARON INTERNATIONAL—See National Spinning Company, Inc.; *U.S. Private*, pg. 2863
CARON TRANSPORTATION SYSTEMS PARTNERSHIP; *Int'l*, pg. 1342
CAROS CO., LTD.; *Int'l*, pg. 1342
CAROTEK INC.—See Ad Bel Ltd.; *U.S. Private*, pg. 71
CAROTRANS INTERNATIONAL, INC.—See Mainfreight Ltd.; *Int'l*, pg. 4650
CAROUSEL CAPITAL PARTNERS; *U.S. Private*, pg. 769
CAROUSEL CHECKS INC.; *U.S. Private*, pg. 770
CAROUSEL DESIGNS LLC—See Crown Crafts, Inc.; *U.S. Public*, pg. 596
CAROUSEL INDUSTRIES OF NORTH AMERICA, INC.—See American Securities LLC; *U.S. Private*, pg. 250
CAROUSEL MOTOR GROUP—See Pohlad Companies; *U.S. Private*, pg. 3220
CAROWINDS—See Six Flags Entertainment Corporation; *U.S. Public*, pg. 1890
CARPARTS.COM, INC.; *U.S. Public*, pg. 438
CARPARTS DISTRIBUTION CENTER; *U.S. Private*, pg. 770
CAR PARTS INDUSTRIES BELGIUM SA—See Aktieselskabet Schouw & Co.; *Int'l*, pg. 265
CAR PARTS WAREHOUSE INC.; *U.S. Private*, pg. 747
CARPATAIR SA; *Int'l*, pg. 1342
CARPAT BETON SERVICII POMPE SRL—See Heidelberg Materials AG; *Int'l*, pg. 3309
CARPAT BETON S.R.L.—See Heidelberg Materials AG; *Int'l*, pg. 3309
CARPATCEMENT HOLDING S.A.—See Heidelberg Materials AG; *Int'l*, pg. 3309
CARPAT CEMTRANS S.R.L.—See Heidelberg Materials AG; *Int'l*, pg. 3309
CARPATERRA CAPITAL PARTNERS SRO; *Int'l*, pg. 1343
CARPATHIA CAPITAL SA; *Int'l*, pg. 1343
CARPEDATUM LLC—See Converge Technology Solutions Corp.; *Int'l*, pg. 1787
CARPENE MALVOLTI S.P.A.; *Int'l*, pg. 1343
CARPENOVA AB—See Peab AB; *Int'l*, pg. 5771
CARPENTARIA GOLD PTY. LTD.—See Resolute Mining Limited; *Int'l*, pg. 6297
CARPENTARIA NEWSPAPERS PTY LTD—See Nine Entertainment Co. Holdings Limited; *Int'l*, pg. 5298
CARPENTER ADDITIVE U.S., LLC—See Carpenter Technology Corporation; *U.S. Public*, pg. 439
CARPENTER BANK PARTNERS, INC.—See CCFW, Inc.; *U.S. Private*, pg. 799
CARPENTER BELGIUM NV—See Carpenter Co.; *U.S. Private*, pg. 770
CARPENTER BROTHERS INC.; *U.S. Private*, pg. 770
CARPENTER CO. - MORNING GLORY PRODUCTS DIV.—See Carpenter Co.; *U.S. Private*, pg. 770
CARPENTER & COMPANY, INC.; *U.S. Private*, pg. 770
CARPENTER COMPANY OF SPOTSYLVANIA INC.—See The Lester Group Inc.; *U.S. Private*, pg. 4069
CARPENTER COMPONENTS OF ILLINOIS—See R&D Thiel Inc.-Carpenter Contractors of America; *U.S. Private*, pg. 3332
CARPENTER CONTRACTORS OF AMERICA—See R&D Thiel Inc.-Carpenter Contractors of America; *U.S. Private*, pg. 3332
CARPENTER CONTRACTORS OF AMERICA—See R&D Thiel Inc.-Carpenter Contractors of America; *U.S. Private*, pg. 3332
CARPENTER CONTRACTORS OF AMERICA—See R&D Thiel Inc.-Carpenter Contractors of America; *U.S. Private*, pg. 3332
CARPENTER CONTRACTORS OF AMERICA—See R&D Thiel Inc.-Carpenter Contractors of America; *U.S. Private*, pg. 3332
CARPENTER CONTRACTORS OF AMERICA—See R&D Thiel Inc.-Carpenter Contractors of America; *U.S. Private*, pg. 3332
CARPENTER CONTRACTORS OF AMERICA—See R&D Thiel Inc.-Carpenter Contractors of America; *U.S. Private*, pg. 3332
CARPENTER CO.; *U.S. Private*, pg. 770
CARPENTER FUND MANAGEMENT COMPANY, LLC—See CCFW, Inc.; *U.S. Private*, pg. 799
THE CARPENTER GROUP; *U.S. Private*, pg. 4005
CARPENTERIE METALLICHE DI COLZATE S.R.L.—See G. Siempelkamp GmbH & Co. KG; *Int'l*, pg. 2864
CARPENTER MOTORS (VANUATU) LTD.—See MBf Holdings Berhad; *Int'l*, pg. 4751
CARPENTER PAPER COMPANY; *U.S. Private*, pg. 770
CARPENTER & PATERSON INC.; *U.S. Private*, pg. 770
CARPENTER POWDER PRODUCTS AB—See Carpenter Technology Corporation; *U.S. Public*, pg. 439
CARPENTER POWDER PRODUCTS GMBH—See Carpenter Technology Corporation; *U.S. Public*, pg. 439
CARPENTER REALTORS; *U.S. Private*, pg. 770
CARPENTER RIGGING—See The Carpenter Group; *U.S. Private*, pg. 4005
CARPENTER'S CAMPERS INC.; *U.S. Private*, pg. 770
CARPENTERS HARDWARE LTD.—See MBf Holdings Berhad; *Int'l*, pg. 4751
CARPENTERS' HEALTH AND WELFARE FUND OF PHILADELPHIA AND VICINITY; *U.S. Private*, pg. 770
CARPENTER SPECIALTY WIRE PRODUCTS—See Carpenter Technology Corporation; *U.S. Public*, pg. 439
CARPENTERS PROPERTIES LTD.—See MBf Holdings Berhad; *Int'l*, pg. 4752
CARPENTERS ROOFING & SHEET METAL, INC.—See Infinity Home Services; *U.S. Private*, pg. 2071
CARPENTER TAN DEVELOPMENT COMPANY LIMITED—See Carpenter Tan Holdings Limited; *Int'l*, pg. 1343
CARPENTER TAN HOLDINGS LIMITED; *Int'l*, pg. 1343
CARPENTER TECHNOLOGY ASIA PACIFIC PTE. LTD.—See Carpenter Technology Corporation; *U.S. Public*, pg. 439
CARPENTER TECHNOLOGY (CANADA) LTD.—See Carpenter Technology Corporation; *U.S. Public*, pg. 439
CARPENTER TECHNOLOGY CORPORATION; *U.S. Public*, pg. 439
CARPENTER TECHNOLOGY (EUROPE) S.A.—See Carpenter Technology Corporation; *U.S. Public*, pg. 439
CARPENTER TECHNOLOGY (UK) LTD.—See Carpenter Technology Corporation; *U.S. Public*, pg. 439
CARPENTER TURNER SA—See Marsh & McLennan Companies, Inc.; *U.S. Public*, pg. 1375
CARPENTRY CONTRACTORS CORP.—See Bain Capital, LP; *U.S. Private*, pg. 450
CARPENTRY & HARDWARE SERVICES—See Harkins Builders, Inc.; *U.S. Private*, pg. 1864
CARPEOPLE DANMARK APS—See MEKO AB; *Int'l*, pg. 4805
CARPET BARN INC.; *U.S. Private*, pg. 770
CARPET CONCEPT OBJEKT-TEPPICHBODEN GMBH—See Egetaepper A/S; *Int'l*, pg. 2324
CARPET CONCEPT TEPPICHFABRIK GMBH & CO. KG—See Egetaepper A/S; *Int'l*, pg. 2324
CARPET CORNER INC.; *U.S. Private*, pg. 770
CARPET CUSHION CO., INC.—See Hickory Springs Manufacturing Company; *U.S. Private*, pg. 1933
CARPET CUSHIONS & SUPPLIES, INC.; *U.S. Private*, pg. 770
CARPET DECORATORS INC.; *U.S. Private*, pg. 770
CARPET FACTORY OUTLET INC.; *U.S. Private*, pg. 770
CARPET FAIR, INC.; *U.S. Private*, pg. 770
CARPETLAND BV—See Carpetright plc; *Int'l*, pg. 1343
CARPETLAND INC—See KW Leasing Inc.; *U.S. Private*, pg. 2359
CARPETLAND NV—See Carpetright plc; *Int'l*, pg. 1343
CARPET LINE DIRECT LIMITED—See Victoria Plc; *Int'l*, pg. 8188
CARPET ONE BY VAN DRIE HOME FURNISHINGS; *U.S. Private*, pg. 770
CARPETRIGHT OF LONDON LIMITED—See Carpetright plc; *Int'l*, pg. 1343
CARPETRIGHT PLC; *Int'l*, pg. 1343
CARPETS INTERNATIONAL THAILAND PUBLIC COMPANY LIMITED—See TCM Corporation Public Company Limited; *Int'l*, pg. 7484

CORPORATE AFFILIATIONS

CARPETS PLUS OF WISCONSIN INC.; *U.S. Private*, pg. 770
CARPET WEAVERS INC.; *U.S. Private*, pg. 770
CARPEVIGO HOLDING AG; *Int'l*, pg. 1343
THE CARPHONE WAREHOUSE LIMITED—See Currys plc; *Int'l*, pg. 1879
CARPI BRASIL LTDA.—See VINCI S.A.; *Int'l*, pg. 8213
CARPIGIANI CENTRO SUDAMERICA, SA—See Ali Holding S.r.l; *Int'l*, pg. 320
CARPIGIANI CENTRO SURAMERICA DO BRASIL LTDA—See Ali Holding S.r.l; *Int'l*, pg. 320
CARPIGIANI DEUTSCHLAND GMBH—See Ali Holding S.r.l; *Int'l*, pg. 320
CARPIGIANI FRANCE S.A.—See Ali Holding S.r.l; *Int'l*, pg. 320
CARPIGIANI GROUP—See Ali Holding S.r.l; *Int'l*, pg. 320
CARPIGIANI JAPAN CO., LTD.—See Ali Holding S.r.l; *Int'l*, pg. 321
CARPIGIANI NEDERLAND—See Ali Holding S.r.l; *Int'l*, pg. 320
CARPIGIANI SHANGHAI—See Ali Holding S.r.l; *Int'l*, pg. 320
CARPIGIANI SOLUTIONS—See Ali Holding S.r.l; *Int'l*, pg. 321
CARPIGIANI UK LTD—See Ali Holding S.r.l; *Int'l*, pg. 321
CARPINIENNE DE PARTICIPATIONS SA—See Finatis SA; *Int'l*, pg. 2670
CARPIN MANUFACTURING INC.; *U.S. Private*, pg. 770
CARPIONATO GROUP LLC; *U.S. Private*, pg. 770
CARPIO SOLUTIONS INC.—See Palladium Equity Partners, LLC; *U.S. Private*, pg. 3077
CARPI TECH BULGARIA O.O.D.—See VINCI S.A.; *Int'l*, pg. 8213
CARPI TECH BV—See VINCI S.A.; *Int'l*, pg. 8213
CARPI TECH CZ A.S—See VINCI S.A.; *Int'l*, pg. 8213
CARPI TECH ITALIA SRL—See VINCI S.A.; *Int'l*, pg. 8213
CARPI TECH SA—See VINCI S.A.; *Int'l*, pg. 8213
CARPI USA INC.—See VINCI S.A.; *Int'l*, pg. 8213
CARPLASTIC S.A. DE C.V.—See Visteon Corporation; *U.S. Public*, pg. 2305
CAR-PLUS AUTO LEASING CORPORATION—See Yulon Finance Corporation; *Int'l*, pg. 8612
CARPOSTAL AGDE SAS—See Die Schweizerische Post AG; *Int'l*, pg. 2112
CARPOSTAL DOLE SAS—See Die Schweizerische Post AG; *Int'l*, pg. 2112
CARPOSTAL MACON SAS—See Die Schweizerische Post AG; *Int'l*, pg. 2112
CARPOSTAL MEDITERRANEE SAS—See Die Schweizerische Post AG; *Int'l*, pg. 2112
CAR PROFESSIONAL FUHRPARKMANAGEMENT UND BERATUNGSGESELLSCHAFT MBH & CO. KG—See Societe Generale S.A.; *Int'l*, pg. 7039
CAR PROS AUTOMOTIVE GROUP, INC.; *U.S. Private*, pg. 747
CAR QUALITY SERVICES GMBH—See OPENLANE, Inc.; *U.S. Public*, pg. 1607
CARQUEST ALBUQUERQUE—See Advance Auto Parts, Inc.; *U.S. Public*, pg. 45
CARQUEST AUTO PARTS INC - CALIFORNIA—See Advance Auto Parts, Inc.; *U.S. Public*, pg. 45
CARQUEST AUTO PARTS OF ANDERSON—See Advance Auto Parts, Inc.; *U.S. Public*, pg. 45
CARQUEST AUTO PARTS OF CARO—See Advance Auto Parts, Inc.; *U.S. Public*, pg. 45
CARQUEST AUTO PARTS OF GRAND FORKS—See Advance Auto Parts, Inc.; *U.S. Public*, pg. 45
CARQUEST AUTO PARTS OF HATTIESBURG—See Advance Auto Parts, Inc.; *U.S. Public*, pg. 45
CARQUEST AUTO PARTS OF MCMINNVILLE—See Advance Auto Parts, Inc.; *U.S. Public*, pg. 45
CARQUEST AUTO PARTS—See Advance Auto Parts, Inc.; *U.S. Public*, pg. 45
CARQUEST CANADA, LTD.—See Advance Auto Parts, Inc.; *U.S. Public*, pg. 45
CARQUEST CORPORATION—See Advance Auto Parts, Inc.; *U.S. Public*, pg. 45
CARQUEST DISTRIBUTION CENTER - ALABAMA—See Advance Auto Parts, Inc.; *U.S. Public*, pg. 45
CARQUEST DISTRIBUTION CENTER - CALIFORNIA—See Advance Auto Parts, Inc.; *U.S. Public*, pg. 45
CARQUEST DISTRIBUTION CENTER - CALIFORNIA—See Advance Auto Parts, Inc.; *U.S. Public*, pg. 45
CARQUEST DISTRIBUTION CENTER - MAINE—See Advance Auto Parts, Inc.; *U.S. Public*, pg. 45
CARQUEST DISTRIBUTION CENTER - MICHIGAN—See Advance Auto Parts, Inc.; *U.S. Public*, pg. 45
CARQUEST DISTRIBUTION CENTER - MICHIGAN—See Advance Auto Parts, Inc.; *U.S. Public*, pg. 45
CARQUEST DISTRIBUTION CENTER - MINNESOTA—See Advance Auto Parts, Inc.; *U.S. Public*, pg. 45
CARQUEST DISTRIBUTION CENTER - MISSOURI—See Advance Auto Parts, Inc.; *U.S. Public*, pg. 45
CARQUEST DISTRIBUTION CENTER - MONTANA—See Advance Auto Parts, Inc.; *U.S. Public*, pg. 45

COMPANY NAME INDEX

CARQUEST DISTRIBUTION CENTER - NEW MEXICO—See Advance Auto Parts, Inc.; *U.S. Public*, pg. 45
CARQUEST DISTRIBUTION CENTER- NEW YORK—See Advance Auto Parts, Inc.; *U.S. Public*, pg. 45
CARQUEST DISTRIBUTION CENTER - NORTH CAROLINA—See Advance Auto Parts, Inc.; *U.S. Public*, pg. 45
CARQUEST DISTRIBUTION CENTER - NORTH CAROLINA—See Advance Auto Parts, Inc.; *U.S. Public*, pg. 45
CARQUEST DISTRIBUTION CENTER - TENNESSEE—See Advance Auto Parts, Inc.; *U.S. Public*, pg. 45
CARQUEST DISTRIBUTION CENTER - TEXAS—See Advance Auto Parts, Inc.; *U.S. Public*, pg. 45
CARQUEST DISTRIBUTION CENTER - TEXAS—See Advance Auto Parts, Inc.; *U.S. Public*, pg. 45
CARQUEST DISTRIBUTION CENTER - WASHINGTON—See Advance Auto Parts, Inc.; *U.S. Public*, pg. 45
CARQUEST DISTRIBUTION CENTER - WISCONSIN—See Advance Auto Parts, Inc.; *U.S. Public*, pg. 45
CARQUEST INC.—See Advance Auto Parts, Inc.; *U.S. Public*, pg. 45
CARQUEST-MEMPHIS—See Advance Auto Parts, Inc.; *U.S. Public*, pg. 45
CARQUEST OF BUTTE—See Advance Auto Parts, Inc.; *U.S. Public*, pg. 45
CARQUEST—See Advance Auto Parts, Inc.; *U.S. Public*, pg. 45
CARQUEST—See Advance Auto Parts, Inc.; *U.S. Public*, pg. 45
CARQUEST—See Advance Auto Parts, Inc.; *U.S. Public*, pg. 45
CARQUEST—See Advance Auto Parts, Inc.; *U.S. Public*, pg. 45
CARQUEST WINCHESTER—See Advance Auto Parts, Inc.; *U.S. Public*, pg. 45
CARR 625 FIRST STREET LLC—See InterContinental Hotels Group PLC; *Int'l*, pg. 3737
CARRABBA'S/COOL SPRINGS, LIMITED PARTNERSHIP—See Bloomin' Brands, Inc.; *U.S. Public*, pg. 363
CARRABBA'S/DEERFIELD TOWNSHIP, LIMITED PARTNERSHIP—See Bloomin' Brands, Inc.; *U.S. Public*, pg. 363
CARRABBA'S/GREEN HILLS, LIMITED PARTNERSHIP—See Bloomin' Brands, Inc.; *U.S. Public*, pg. 363
CARRABBA'S ITALIAN GRILL, LLC—See Bloomin' Brands, Inc.; *U.S. Public*, pg. 363
CARRABBA'S ITALIAN GRILL OF HOWARD COUNTY, INC.—See Bloomin' Brands, Inc.; *U.S. Public*, pg. 363
CARRABBA'S ITALIAN GRILL OF OVERLEA, INC.—See Bloomin' Brands, Inc.; *U.S. Public*, pg. 363
CARRABBA'S/LEXINGTON, LIMITED PARTNERSHIP—See Bloomin' Brands, Inc.; *U.S. Public*, pg. 363
CARRABBA'S/MIAMI BEACH, LIMITED PARTNERSHIP—See Bloomin' Brands, Inc.; *U.S. Public*, pg. 363
CARRABBA'S OF GERMANTOWN, INC.—See Bloomin' Brands, Inc.; *U.S. Public*, pg. 363
CARRABBA'S OF OCEAN CITY, INC.—See Bloomin' Brands, Inc.; *U.S. Public*, pg. 363
CARRABBA'S OF PASADENA, INC.—See Bloomin' Brands, Inc.; *U.S. Public*, pg. 363
CARRABBA'S OF WALDORF, INC.—See Bloomin' Brands, Inc.; *U.S. Public*, pg. 363
CARRAFIELLO-DIEHL & ASSOCIATES, INC.; *U.S. Private*, pg. 771
CARR AND DUFF INC.; *U.S. Private*, pg. 771
CARRARA MARBLE CO. OF AMERICA INC.; *U.S. Private*, pg. 771
CARRARA MID-EAST INDUSTRIAL CO. LLC—See Depa PLC; *Int'l*, pg. 2040
CARRARO ARGENTINA S.A.—See FLY Srl; *Int'l*, pg. 2715
CARRARO CHINA DRIVE SYSTEM CO., LTD.—See FLY Srl; *Int'l*, pg. 2715
CARRARO DRIVE TECH DO BRASIL INC.—See FLY Srl; *Int'l*, pg. 2715
CARRARO INDIA LTD.—See FLY Srl; *Int'l*, pg. 2715
CARRARO NORTH AMERICA INC.—See FLY Srl; *Int'l*, pg. 2715
CARRARO QINGDAO LTD.—See FLY Srl; *Int'l*, pg. 2715
CARRARO S.P.A.—See FLY Srl; *Int'l*, pg. 2715
CARRARO TECHNOLOGIES INDIA PVT. LTD.—See FLY Srl; *Int'l*, pg. 2715
CARR AUTO GROUP; *U.S. Private*, pg. 771
CARR BUSINESS SYSTEMS, INC.—See Xerox Holdings Corporation; *U.S. Public*, pg. 2387
CARR CHEVROLET, INC.; *U.S. Private*, pg. 771
CARR & CO DIVORCE & FAMILY LAWYERS PTY. LTD.—See Shine Justice Ltd.; *Int'l*, pg. 6842
CARR CONCRETE CORP.—See R.W. Sidley, Incorporated; *U.S. Private*, pg. 3340
CARR CONSTRUCTION, INC.; *U.S. Private*, pg. 771

CARREFOUR ADMINISTRATIF FRANCE—See Carrefour SA; *Int'l*, pg. 1344
CARREFOUR ARGENTINA S.A.—See Carrefour SA; *Int'l*, pg. 1344
CARREFOUR ASIA LIMITED—See Carrefour SA; *Int'l*, pg. 1344
CARREFOUR BELGIUM SA—See Carrefour SA; *Int'l*, pg. 1344
CARREFOUR BRASIL—See Carrefour SA; *Int'l*, pg. 1344
CARREFOUR CANARIAS, S.A.—See Carrefour SA; *Int'l*, pg. 1345
CARREFOUR CESKA REPUBLIKA—See Carrefour SA; *Int'l*, pg. 1344
CARREFOUR CHINA HOLDINGS BV—See Carrefour SA; *Int'l*, pg. 1344
CARREFOUR CHINA, INC.—See Suning Holdings Group Co., Ltd.; *Int'l*, pg. 7316
CARREFOUR DRIVE—See Carrefour SA; *Int'l*, pg. 1344
CARREFOUR ESPANA PROPERTIES, S.L.—See Carrefour SA; *Int'l*, pg. 1345
CARREFOUR FINANCE SA—See Carrefour SA; *Int'l*, pg. 1344
CARREFOUR FRANCE—See Carrefour SA; *Int'l*, pg. 1344
CARREFOUR GLOBAL SOURCING ASIA LIMITED—See Carrefour SA; *Int'l*, pg. 1344
CARREFOUR HYPERMARCHES—See Carrefour SA; *Int'l*, pg. 1344
CARREFOUR IMPORT SAS—See Carrefour SA; *Int'l*, pg. 1344
CARREFOUR ITALIA SPA—See Carrefour SA; *Int'l*, pg. 1344
CARREFOUR LATIN AMERICA—See Carrefour SA; *Int'l*, pg. 1344
CARREFOUR MONACO—See Carrefour SA; *Int'l*, pg. 1344
CARREFOUR NAVARRA, S.L.—See Carrefour SA; *Int'l*, pg. 1345
CARREFOUR NEDERLAND B.V.—See Carrefour SA; *Int'l*, pg. 1344
CARREFOUR NORTE, S.L.—See Carrefour SA; *Int'l*, pg. 1345
CARREFOUR POLSKA PROPER SP. Z O.O.—See Carrefour SA; *Int'l*, pg. 1345
CARREFOUR POLSKA SP. Z O.O.—See Carrefour SA; *Int'l*, pg. 1345
CARREFOUR PROCUREMENT INTERNATIONAL AG & CO. KG—See Carrefour SA; *Int'l*, pg. 1345
CARREFOUR PROPERTY B.V.—See Carrefour SA; *Int'l*, pg. 1344
CARREFOUR PROPERTY DEVELOPMENT SA—See Carrefour SA; *Int'l*, pg. 1345
CARREFOUR PROPERTY ESPANA, SLU—See Carrefour SA; *Int'l*, pg. 1345
CARREFOUR PROPERTY FRANCE SAS—See Carrefour SA; *Int'l*, pg. 1345
CARREFOUR PROPERTY GESTION—See Carrefour SA; *Int'l*, pg. 1344
CARREFOUR PROPERTY ITALIA SRL—See Carrefour SA; *Int'l*, pg. 1345
CARREFOUR ROMANIA S.A.—See Carrefour SA; *Int'l*, pg. 1345
CARREFOUR SABANCI TICARET MERKEZI AS CARREFOURSA—See Carrefour SA; *Int'l*, pg. 1345
CARREFOUR SABANCI TICARET MERKEZI AS CARREFOURSA—See Haci Omer Sabanci Holding A.S.; *Int'l*, pg. 3203
CARREFOURSA CARREFOUR SABANCI TICARET MERKEZI A.S.; *Int'l*, pg. 1346
CARREFOUR SA; *Int'l*, pg. 1343
CARREFOURSA TURKIYE GENEL MUDURLUK—See Carrefour SA; *Int'l*, pg. 1345
CARREFOUR SINGAPORE PTE LTD—See Carrefour SA; *Int'l*, pg. 1344
CARREFOUR SLOVENSKO S.R.O.—See Carrefour SA; *Int'l*, pg. 1345
CARREFOUR SOUTH EAST ASIA PTE. LTD.—See Carrefour SA; *Int'l*, pg. 1344
CARREFOUR STATION SERVICE—See Carrefour SA; *Int'l*, pg. 1344
CARREFOUR SYSTEMES D'INFORMATIONS FRANCE—See Carrefour SA; *Int'l*, pg. 1344
CARREFOUR TAIWAN—See Carrefour SA; *Int'l*, pg. 1344
CARREFOUR VOYAGES SAS—See Carrefour SA; *Int'l*, pg. 1345
CARREFOUR WORLD TRADE SA—See Carrefour SA; *Int'l*, pg. 1345
CARREL SA—See Descours & Cabaud; *Int'l*, pg. 2044
CARRE NOIR BARCELONA—See Publicis Groupe S.A.; *Int'l*, pg. 6097
CARRE NOIR LONDON—See Publicis Groupe S.A.; *Int'l*, pg. 6097
CARRE NOIR—See Publicis Groupe S.A.; *Int'l*, pg. 6097
CARRE NOIR TURINO—See Publicis Groupe S.A.; *Int'l*, pg. 6097
CARRE NOIR WARSZAW—See Publicis Groupe S.A.; *Int'l*, pg. 6097
CAR RENTAL 8, LLC; *U.S. Private*, pg. 747
CAR RENTALS INC.; *U.S. Private*, pg. 747
CARR ENTERPRISES INC.; *U.S. Private*, pg. 771

CARRIEREQ, INC.

CARRERA OPTYL D.O.O.—See Safilo Group S.p.A.; *Int'l*, pg. 6472
CARRERA REVELL OF AMERICAS, INC.; *U.S. Private*, pg. 771
CARRERAS LIMITED—See British American Tobacco plc; *Int'l*, pg. 1167
CARRES BLUES—See CNP Assurances SA; *Int'l*, pg. 1678
CAR RESEARCH & DEVELOPMENT CENTER—See Mitsubishi Motors Corporation; *Int'l*, pg. 4966
CARRET ASSET MANAGEMENT, LLC—See SBI Holdings, Inc.; *Int'l*, pg. 6605
CARRFOUR SUPPORTIVE HOUSING, INC.; *U.S. Private*, pg. 771
CARRIAGE CORPORATION; *U.S. Private*, pg. 771
CARRIAGE COVE, LLC—See Sun Communities, Inc.; *U.S. Public*, pg. 1961
CARRIAGE FUNERAL HOLDINGS INC.—See Carriage Services, Inc.; *U.S. Public*, pg. 439
CARRIAGE HOUSE ASSISTED LIVING, INC.—See TPG Capital, L.P.; *U.S. Public*, pg. 2168
CARRIAGE HOUSE EVENT CENTER INC.; *U.S. Public*, pg. 439
CARRIAGE HOUSE INTERIORS SAN DIEGO; *U.S. Private*, pg. 772
CARRIAGE SERVICES, INC.; *U.S. Public*, pg. 439
CARRIANNA (CHIU CHOW) RESTAURANT LIMITED—See Carrianna Group Holdings Company Limited; *Int'l*, pg. 1346
CARRIANNA GROUP HOLDINGS COMPANY LIMITED; *Int'l*, pg. 1346
CARRICK CAPITAL PARTNERS, LLC; *U.S. Private*, pg. 772
CARRICK WILLIAMS HOLDINGS INC.; *U.S. Private*, pg. 772
CARRICO IMPLEMENT CO. INC.; *U.S. Private*, pg. 772
CARRIE ARRAN RESOURCES INC.; *Int'l*, pg. 1346
CARRIER AIRCONDITIONING & REFRIGERATION LIMITED—See Carrier Global Corporation; *U.S. Public*, pg. 440
CARRIER AIR CONDITIONING SALES & SERVICE (SHANGHAI) CO LTD—See Carrier Global Corporation; *U.S. Public*, pg. 440
CARRIER AIRCON LANKA PRIVATE LIMITED—See Carrier Global Corporation; *U.S. Public*, pg. 440
CARRIER AKTIEBOLAG—See Carrier Global Corporation; *U.S. Public*, pg. 440
CARRIER AUSTRALIA PTY LTD—See Carrier Global Corporation; *U.S. Public*, pg. 440
CARRIER BRYANT MIDSOUTH—See Carrier Global Corporation; *U.S. Public*, pg. 440
CARRIER CHLADIACA TECHNIKA SLOVAKIA S.R.O.—See Carrier Global Corporation; *U.S. Public*, pg. 440
CARRIER CHLADICI TECHNIKA SPOL. S.R.O.—See Carrier Global Corporation; *U.S. Public*, pg. 441
CARRIER CHLODNICTWO POLSKA SP. Z O.O.—See Carrier Global Corporation; *U.S. Public*, pg. 441
CARRIER CLINIC—See Hackensack Meridian Health, Inc.; *U.S. Private*, pg. 1838
CARRIER COACH INC.; *U.S. Private*, pg. 772
CARRIER COMMERCIAL REFRIGERATION, INC.—See Haier Smart Home Co., Ltd.; *Int'l*, pg. 3210
CARRIER COMMERCIAL REFRIGERATION (THAILAND) LTD.—See Carrier Global Corporation; *U.S. Public*, pg. 440
CARRIERCOMM INC.—See Moseley Associates, Inc.; *U.S. Private*, pg. 2793
CARRIER CORPORATION—See Carrier Global Corporation; *U.S. Public*, pg. 440
CARRIERE DE LA ROCHE BLAIN—See Eiffage S.A.; *Int'l*, pg. 2330
CARRIERE DE LUCHE—See VINCI S.A.; *Int'l*, pg. 8219
CARRIERE DES CHENES S.A.—See Eiffage S.A.; *Int'l*, pg. 2330
CARRIERE FAMILY FARMS, INC.; *U.S. Private*, pg. 772
CARRIERE INDUSTRIAL SUPPLY LIMITED—See The Weir Group PLC; *Int'l*, pg. 7699
CARRIER ENTERPRISE CANADA, L.P.—See Watsco, Inc.; *U.S. Public*, pg. 2336
CARRIER ENTERPRISE CANADA LTD.—See Carrier Global Corporation; *U.S. Public*, pg. 440
CARRIER ENTERPRISE MEXICO S. DE R.L. DE C.V.—See Watsco, Inc.; *U.S. Public*, pg. 2336
CARRIER ENTERPRISE NORTHEAST, LLC—See Watsco, Inc.; *U.S. Public*, pg. 2336
CARRIEREQ, INC.; *U.S. Private*, pg. 772
CARRIERES DE CHATEAUPANNE SAS—See VINCI S.A.; *Int'l*, pg. 8213
CARRIERES DU HAINAUT SCA—See SigmaRoc Plc; *Int'l*, pg. 6909
CARRIERES KLEBER MOREAU SA—See VINCI S.A.; *Int'l*, pg. 8219
CARRIERES LES PETONS S.P.R.L.—See Solvay S.A.; *Int'l*, pg. 7077
CARRIERES RAUSCHER SAS—See VINCI S.A.; *Int'l*, pg. 8213
CARRIERES UNIES DE PORPHYRE SA—See VINCI S.A.; *Int'l*, pg. 8219

CARRIEREQ, INC.

CARRIER EUROPE SCA—See Carrier Vibrating Equipment, Inc.; *U.S. Private*, pg. 772
CARRIER FIRE & SECURITY AMERICAS CORPORATION—See Carrier Global Corporation; *U.S. Public*, pg. 440
CARRIER FIRE & SECURITY AUSTRALIA PTY LTD—See Carrier Global Corporation; *U.S. Public*, pg. 442
CARRIER FIRE & SECURITY B.V.—See Carrier Global Corporation; *U.S. Public*, pg. 442
CARRIER FIRE & SECURITY DANMARK A/S—See Carrier Global Corporation; *U.S. Public*, pg. 442
CARRIER FIRE & SECURITY DEUTSCHLAND GMBH—See Carrier Global Corporation; *U.S. Public*, pg. 442
CARRIER FIRE & SECURITY EMEA BV—See Carrier Global Corporation; *U.S. Public*, pg. 442
CARRIER FIRE & SECURITY ESPANA SL—See Carrier Global Corporation; *U.S. Public*, pg. 442
CARRIER FIRE & SECURITY FRANCE S.A.S.—See Carrier Global Corporation; *U.S. Public*, pg. 442
CARRIER FIRE & SECURITY IRELAND LIMITED—See Carrier Global Corporation; *U.S. Public*, pg. 442
CARRIER FIRE & SECURITY ITALIA S.R.L.—See Carrier Global Corporation; *U.S. Public*, pg. 442
CARRIER FIRE & SECURITY LTD—See Carrier Global Corporation; *U.S. Public*, pg. 442
CARRIER FIRE & SECURITY NORGE AS—See Carrier Global Corporation; *U.S. Public*, pg. 442
CARRIER FIRE & SECURITY POLSKA SP. Z O.O.—See Carrier Global Corporation; *U.S. Public*, pg. 442
CARRIER FIRE & SECURITY—See Carrier Global Corporation; *U.S. Public*, pg. 440
CARRIER FIRE & SECURITY SOUTH AFRICA PTY LTD—See Carrier Global Corporation; *U.S. Public*, pg. 442
CARRIER FIRE & SECURITY SVERIGE AB—See Carrier Global Corporation; *U.S. Public*, pg. 442
CARRIER FIRE & SECURITY UK LIMITED—See Carrier Global Corporation; *U.S. Public*, pg. 442
CARRIER GLOBAL CORPORATION; *U.S. Public*, pg. 440
CARRIER GUAM, INC.—See Carrier Global Corporation; *U.S. Public*, pg. 442
CARRIER HUTESTECHNIKA FORGALMAZO MAGYARORSZAG KFT—See Carrier Global Corporation; *U.S. Public*, pg. 441
CARRIER INDUSTRIES—See New England Motor Freight, Inc.; *U.S. Private*, pg. 2894
CARRIER INTERAMERICA CORPORATION—See Watsco, Inc.; *U.S. Public*, pg. 2336
CARRIER KALTETECHNIK AUSTRIA GES.M.B.—See Carrier Global Corporation; *U.S. Public*, pg. 441
CARRIER KALTETECHNIK DEUTSCHLAND GMBH—See Carrier Global Corporation; *U.S. Public*, pg. 441
CARRIER KALTETECHNIK SCHWEIZ AG—See Carrier Global Corporation; *U.S. Public*, pg. 441
CARRIER KUWAIT AIRCONDITIONING K.S.C.—See Carrier Global Corporation; *U.S. Public*, pg. 442
CARRIER LTD.—See REWE-Zentral-Aktiengesellschaft; *Int'l*, pg. 6314
CARRIER (MALAYSIA) SDN. BHD.—See Carrier Global Corporation; *U.S. Public*, pg. 440
CARRIER MANAGEMENT SYSTEMS, INC.—See Constellation Software Inc.; *Int'l*, pg. 1774
CARRIER MEXICO S.A. DE C.V.—See Carrier Global Corporation; *U.S. Public*, pg. 442
CARRIER MIDEA INDIA PRIVATE LIMITED—See Carrier Global Corporation; *U.S. Public*, pg. 442
CARRIERNET CORPORATION (SINGAPORE) PTE. LTD.—See Polaris Ltd.; *Int'l*, pg. 5907
CARRIER NORTHEAST—See Carrier Global Corporation; *U.S. Public*, pg. 442
CARRIER OKLAHOMA—See Carrier Global Corporation; *U.S. Public*, pg. 442
CARRIER OY—See Carrier Global Corporation; *U.S. Public*, pg. 443
CARRIER (PUERTO RICO), INC.—See Watsco, Inc.; *U.S. Public*, pg. 2336
CARRIER PUERTO RICO—See Carrier Global Corporation; *U.S. Public*, pg. 442
CARRIER REFRIGERACION IBERICA SA—See Carrier Global Corporation; *U.S. Public*, pg. 441
CARRIER REFRIGERATION BENELUX B.V.—See Haier Smart Home Co., Ltd.; *Int'l*, pg. 3210
CARRIER REFRIGERATION DENMARK A/S—See Carrier Global Corporation; *U.S. Public*, pg. 443
CARRIER REFRIGERATION DISTRIBUTION FRANCE SAS—See Carrier Global Corporation; *U.S. Public*, pg. 443
CARRIER REFRIGERATION IRELAND—See Carrier Global Corporation; *U.S. Public*, pg. 441
CARRIER REFRIGERATION NORWAY AS—See Carrier Global Corporation; *U.S. Public*, pg. 443
CARRIER REFRIGERATION OPERATION ITALY SPA—See Carrier Global Corporation; *U.S. Public*, pg. 441
CARRIER REFRIGERATION OPERATIONS FRANCE SAS—See Carrier Global Corporation; *U.S. Public*, pg. 443

CARRIER REFRIGERATION SWEDEN AB—See Carrier Global Corporation; *U.S. Public*, pg. 443
CARRIER REFRIGERATION UK LTD.—See Carrier Global Corporation; *U.S. Public*, pg. 443
CARRIER RENTAL SYSTEMS ASIA PTE LTD—See Carrier Global Corporation; *U.S. Public*, pg. 443
CARRIER RENTAL SYSTEMS—See Carrier Global Corporation; *U.S. Public*, pg. 442
CARRIER RENTAL SYSTEMS (UK) LIMITED—See Carrier Global Corporation; *U.S. Public*, pg. 443
CARRIER SAUDI SERVICE COMPANY—See Carrier Global Corporation; *U.S. Public*, pg. 443
CARRIER S.C.S.—See Carrier Global Corporation; *U.S. Public*, pg. 443
CARRIER-SERVICES.DE GMBH—See ecotel communication ag; *Int'l*, pg. 2300
CARRIER SINGAPORE (PTE.) LTD.—See Carrier Global Corporation; *U.S. Public*, pg. 442
CARRIERS INSURANCE BROKERS PTY. LTD.—See AUB Group Limited; *Int'l*, pg. 698
CARRIER SRL—See Carrier Global Corporation; *U.S. Public*, pg. 443
CARRIER (THAILAND) LIMITED—See Carrier Global Corporation; *U.S. Public*, pg. 440
CARRIER TRANSICOLD AUSTRIA GMBH—See Carrier Global Corporation; *U.S. Public*, pg. 443
CARRIER TRANSICOLD BELGIUM BVBA—See Carrier Global Corporation; *U.S. Public*, pg. 443
CARRIER TRANSICOLD ESPANA, S.A.—See Carrier Global Corporation; *U.S. Public*, pg. 443
CARRIER TRANSICOLD EUROPE—See Carrier Global Corporation; *U.S. Public*, pg. 442
CARRIER TRANSICOLD FRANCE—See Carrier Global Corporation; *U.S. Public*, pg. 443
CARRIER TRANSICOLD HONG KONG LIMITED—See Carrier Global Corporation; *U.S. Public*, pg. 443
CARRIER TRANSICOLD ITALIA S.R.L.—See Carrier Global Corporation; *U.S. Public*, pg. 443
CARRIER TRANSICOLD NETHERLANDS B.V.—See Carrier Global Corporation; *U.S. Public*, pg. 443
CARRIER TRANSICOLD POLSKA SP. Z O.O.—See Carrier Global Corporation; *U.S. Public*, pg. 443
CARRIER TRANSICOLD SCANDINAVIA A/S—See Carrier Global Corporation; *U.S. Public*, pg. 443
CARRIER TRANSICOLD—See Penn Power Group, LLC; *U.S. Private*, pg. 3134
CARRIER TRANSICOLD SWEDEN AB—See Carrier Global Corporation; *U.S. Public*, pg. 443
CARRIER TRANSICOLD (UK) LIMITED—See Carrier Global Corporation; *U.S. Public*, pg. 443
CARRIER TRUCK SALES, LLC; *U.S. Private*, pg. 772
CARRIER VIBRATING EQUIPMENT (CANADA) LTD.—See Carrier Vibrating Equipment, Inc.; *U.S. Private*, pg. 772
CARRIER VIBRATING EQUIPMENT, INC.; *U.S. Private*, pg. 772
CARRIER VIBRATING EQUIPMENT (SHANGHAI) CO., LTD.—See Carrier Vibrating Equipment, Inc.; *U.S. Private*, pg. 772
CARRIER VIETNAM AIR CONDITIONING COMPANY LIMITED—See Carrier Global Corporation; *U.S. Public*, pg. 443
CARRIERWERKE GMBH—See MEDIQON Group AG; *Int'l*, pg. 4780
CARRIE & SERENA S.L.—See Schibsted ASA; *Int'l*, pg. 6616
CARRIESOFT CO., LTD.; *Int'l*, pg. 1346
CARRIGRES S.A.R.L.—See Texaf SA; *Int'l*, pg. 7582
CARRIKER FORD INC.; *U.S. Private*, pg. 772
CARRILLO BUSINESS TECHNOLOGIES; *U.S. Private*, pg. 772
CARRINGTON COLLEGE, INC.—See Adtalem Global Education Inc.; *U.S. Public*, pg. 43
CARRINGTON FACILITIES PTY LTD—See Toho Zinc Co., Ltd.; *Int'l*, pg. 7776
CARRINGTON HOLDING CO.; *U.S. Private*, pg. 772
CARRIS FINANCIAL CORP.; *U.S. Private*, pg. 772
CARRIS OF CALIFORNIA, INC.—See Carris Financial Corp.; *U.S. Private*, pg. 772
CARRIS OF CONNECTICUT, INC.—See Carris Financial Corp.; *U.S. Private*, pg. 772
CARRIS PLASTICS—See Carris Financial Corp.; *U.S. Private*, pg. 772
CARRIS REELS, INC.-NORTH CAROLINA WOOD DIV—See Carris Financial Corp.; *U.S. Private*, pg. 772
CARRIS REELS, INC.—See Carris Financial Corp.; *U.S. Private*, pg. 772
CARRIX, INC.; *U.S. Private*, pg. 772
CARRIZO OIL & GAS, INC.—See Callon Petroleum Company; *U.S. Public*, pg. 424
CARR LANE MANUFACTURING CO.; *U.S. Private*, pg. 771
CARROLL AIR SYSTEMS INC.—See Daikin Industries, Ltd.; *Int'l*, pg. 1936
CARROLL AREA WIND FARM, LLC—See New Jersey Resources Corporation; *U.S. Public*, pg. 1511
CARROLL CAPITAL LLC; *U.S. Private*, pg. 773
CARROLL & CARROLL INCORPORATED; *U.S. Private*, pg. 773

CORPORATE AFFILIATIONS

CARROLL COMPANIES INC.; *U.S. Private*, pg. 773
CARROLL COMPANY - CLEANWORKS DIVISION—See Montgomery Manufacturing Co.; *U.S. Private*, pg. 2777
CARROLL COMPANY—See Montgomery Manufacturing Co.; *U.S. Private*, pg. 2777
CARROLL COUNTY DIALYSIS FACILITY LIMITED PARTNERSHIP—See DaVita Inc.; *U.S. Public*, pg. 636
CARROLL COUNTY FOODS, INC.—See Performance Food Group Company; *U.S. Public*, pg. 1674
CARROLL COUNTY LIVESTOCK SALES BARN, INC.; *U.S. Private*, pg. 773
CARROLL COUNTY MEMORIAL HOSPITAL; *U.S. Private*, pg. 773
CARROLL COUNTY RADIOLOGY, LLC—See RadNet, Inc.; *U.S. Public*, pg. 1760
CARROLL COUNTY TIMES—See Irish Times; *U.S. Private*, pg. 2138
CARROLL DANIEL CONSTRUCTION COMPANY; *U.S. Private*, pg. 773
CARROLL DISTRIBUTING & CONSTRUCTION SUPPLY; *U.S. Private*, pg. 773
CARROLL ELECTRIC COOPERATIVE CORP.; *U.S. Private*, pg. 773
THE CARROLL ELECTRIC MEMBERSHIP CORPORATION; *U.S. Private*, pg. 4005
CARROLL ENGINEERING CORP.; *U.S. Private*, pg. 773
CARROLL FULMER LOGISTICS CORPORATION; *U.S. Private*, pg. 773
CARROLL HEALTHCARE, INC.—See Invacare Corporation; *U.S. Private*, pg. 2130
CARROLL INDEPENDENT FUEL COMPANY; *U.S. Private*, pg. 773
CARROLL ORGANIZATION, LLC; *U.S. Private*, pg. 773
CARROLL PRODUCTS, INC.; *U.S. Private*, pg. 773
CARROLLPUB, INC.—See TechnoMile LLC; *U.S. Private*, pg. 3956
CARROLL SEATING COMPANY INC.; *U.S. Private*, pg. 773
CARROLL SOUTH SHORE MOTORS INC.; *Int'l*, pg. 1346
CARROLLTON BANK; *U.S. Private*, pg. 774
CARROLLTON ENTERPRISES LP; *U.S. Private*, pg. 774
CARROLLTON FARMERS ELEVATOR CO., INC.—See CHS INC.; *U.S. Public*, pg. 492
CARROLLTON HEIGHTS HEALTHCARE, INC.—See The Ensign Group, Inc.; *U.S. Public*, pg. 2070
CARROLLTON REGIONAL DIALYSIS CENTER, LLC—See Nautic Partners, LLC; *U.S. Private*, pg. 2869
CARROLLTON WOOD PRODUCTS INC—See Magnolia Forest Products Inc.; *U.S. Private*, pg. 2548
CARROLL/WHITE; *U.S. Private*, pg. 774
CARROLS CORPORATION—See Restaurant Brands International Inc.; *Int'l*, pg. 6304
CARROLS RESTAURANT GROUP, INC.—See Restaurant Brands International Inc.; *Int'l*, pg. 6304
CARROM CO.—See The Lightning Group, Inc.; *U.S. Private*, pg. 4070
CARRON NET COMPANY, INC.; *U.S. Private*, pg. 774
CARROT CREATIVE LLC—See Monroe Capital LLC; *U.S. Private*, pg. 2773
CARROT CREATIVE LLC—See SoftBank Group Corp.; *Int'l*, pg. 7054
CARROT CREATIVE LLC—See Soros Fund Management LLC; *U.S. Private*, pg. 3716
CARROT, LLC; *U.S. Private*, pg. 774
CARR PROPERTIES—See JPMorgan Chase & Co.; *U.S. Public*, pg. 1206
CARR, RIGGS & INGRAM, LLC - ATLANTA, GA—See Carr, Riggs & Ingram, LLC; *U.S. Private*, pg. 771
CARR, RIGGS & INGRAM, LLC - CONROE—See Carr, Riggs & Ingram, LLC; *U.S. Private*, pg. 771
CARR, RIGGS & INGRAM, LLC; *U.S. Private*, pg. 771
CARR, RIGGS & INGRAM, LLC - THE WOODLANDS, TX—See Carr, Riggs & Ingram, LLC; *U.S. Private*, pg. 771
CARRS BILLINGTON AGRICULTURE (SALES), ANNAN—See Carr's Group PLC; *Int'l*, pg. 1343
CARRS BILLINGTON AGRICULTURE (SALES) LTD.—See Carr's Group PLC; *Int'l*, pg. 1343
CARRS ENGINEERING LIMITED—See Carr's Group PLC; *Int'l*, pg. 1343
CARR'S FLOUR MILLS LTD.; *Int'l*, pg. 1343
CARR'S GROUP PLC; *Int'l*, pg. 1343
CARRS PROPERTIES LIMITED—See Carr's Group PLC; *Int'l*, pg. 1343
CARR'S TIRE SERVICE OF HARRISONBURG; *U.S. Private*, pg. 771
CARR SUPPLY INC.; *U.S. Private*, pg. 771
CARR TEXTILE CORPORATION; *U.S. Private*, pg. 771
CARRUS TECHNOLOGIES INC.—See KKR & Co. Inc.; *U.S. Public*, pg. 1267
CARRUTH CAPITAL LLC; *U.S. Private*, pg. 774
CARRUTH-DOGGETT INC.—See Doggett Equipment Services, Ltd.; *U.S. Private*, pg. 1253
CARRUTHERS & ROTH, P.A.; *U.S. Private*, pg. 774
CARR VALLEY CHEESE COMPANY, INC.; *U.S. Private*, pg. 771
CARRY-ALL INC.—See Robert's Hawaii Inc.; *U.S. Private*, pg. 3459

COMPANY NAME INDEX

CARRYLIFT GROUP—See CorpAcq Holdings Limited; *Int'l*, pg. 1802
CARRY NET CO., LTD.—See Nissui Corporation; *Int'l*, pg. 5378
CARRY-ON TRAILER, INC.—See Bain Capital, LP; *U.S. Private*, pg. 436
CARRY TRANSPORT INC.—See Heniff Transportation Systems Inc.; *U.S. Private*, pg. 1916
CARRY WEALTH HOLDINGS LIMITED; *Int'l*, pg. 1346
CARRY WEALTH LIMITED—See Carry Wealth Holdings Limited; *Int'l*, pg. 1346
CARSA CONSULTORES, AGENTE DE SEGUROS Y DE FIANZAS, S.A. DE C.V.—See Willis Towers Watson Public Limited Company; *Int'l*, pg. 8414
CARSALES.COM LIMITED; *Int'l*, pg. 1346
CARS COLLISION CENTER, LLC—See Boyd Group Services Inc.; *Int'l*, pg. 1125
CARS.COM INC.; *U.S. Public*, pg. 444
CARS.COM, LLC—See Cars.com Inc.; *U.S. Public*, pg. 444
CARSDIRECT.COM, INC.—See KKR & Co. Inc.; *U.S. Public*, pg. 1253
CARSEN MEDICAL INC.—See Diploma PLC; *Int'l*, pg. 2128
CAR SENSE INC.—See Penske Automotive Group, Inc.; *U.S. Public*, pg. 1664
CARSEY-WERNER LLC; *U.S. Private*, pg. 774
CARS GALORE LTD.; *Int'l*, pg. 1346
CARSGEN THERAPEUTICS HOLDINGS LIMITED; *Int'l*, pg. 1347
CARSHARE AUSTRALIA PTY. LTD.—See Archer Capital Pty. Ltd.; *Int'l*, pg. 547
CAR SHARING JAPAN CO., LTD.—See Mitsui Fudosan Co., Ltd.; *Int'l*, pg. 4987
CARSMARTT; *U.S. Public*, pg. 444
CARSO INFRAESTRUCTURA Y CONSTRUCCION, S.A.B. DE C.V.—See Grupo Carso, S.A.B. de C.V.; *Int'l*, pg. 3123
CARSOME SDN. BHD.; *Int'l*, pg. 1347
CARSON & ASSOCIATES, INC.; *U.S. Private*, pg. 774
CARSON CITY TOYOTA; *U.S. Private*, pg. 774
CARSON COMMUNITY BANK—See Carson Financial Holding Company, Inc.; *U.S. Private*, pg. 774
CARSON CONCRETE CORPORATION; *U.S. Private*, pg. 774
CARSON CUMBERBATCH PLC; *Int'l*, pg. 1347
CARSON-DELLOSA PUBLISHING GROUP, LLC—See IXL Learning, Inc.; *U.S. Private*, pg. 2152
CARSON DISTRIBUTING COMPANY; *U.S. Private*, pg. 774
CARSON DODGE CHRYSLER, INC.; *U.S. Private*, pg. 774
CARSON FINANCIAL HOLDING COMPANY, INC.; *U.S. Private*, pg. 774
CARSON GRAVITY METER & INSTRUMENTATION COMPANY INC.—See Carson Helicopters Inc.; *U.S. Private*, pg. 774
THE CARSON GROUP; *U.S. Private*, pg. 4005
CARSON HELICOPTERS INC.; *U.S. Private*, pg. 774
CARSONITE—See Valmont Industries, Inc.; *U.S. Public*, pg. 2274
CARSON OIL COMPANY; *U.S. Private*, pg. 774
CARSON PIRIE SCOTT & CO.—See The Bon Ton Stores, Inc.; *U.S. Public*, pg. 2041
CARSON PIRIE SCOTT II, INC.—See The Bon Ton Stores, Inc.; *U.S. Public*, pg. 2041
CARSON PRIVATE CAPITAL INCORPORATED; *U.S. Private*, pg. 774
CARSON PROD—See Vivendi SE; *Int'l*, pg. 8275
CARSON RIVER VENTURES CORP.; *Int'l*, pg. 1347
CARSONS INCORPORATED; *U.S. Private*, pg. 774
CARSONS MANAGEMENT SERVICES (PRIVATE) LIMITED—See Carson Cumberbatch PLC; *Int'l*, pg. 1347
CARSON'S NUT-BOLT & TOOL CO.; *U.S. Private*, pg. 774
CARSON TAHOE REGIONAL HEALTHCARE; *U.S. Private*, pg. 774
CARSON TOYOTA—See Fletcher Jones Management Group, Inc.; *U.S. Private*, pg. 1542
CARSON VALLEY CHILDREN'S AID; *U.S. Private*, pg. 774
CARSO PHARM D.O.O.—See Salus Ljubljana d.d.; *Int'l*, pg. 6495
CAR SOUND MAGNAFLOW; *U.S. Private*, pg. 747
CAR SPA INC.; *U.S. Private*, pg. 747
C.A.R.S. PROTECTION PLUS, INC.—See Cornell Capital LLC; *U.S. Private*, pg. 1051
CARSTAR FRANCHISE SYSTEMS, INC.—See Roark Capital Group Inc.; *U.S. Private*, pg. 3454
CAR STATION NIIGATA CO., LTD.—See Nippon Seiki Co., Ltd.; *Int'l*, pg. 5329
CARS TECHNIK UND LOGISTIK GMBH—See Mercedes-Benz Group AG; *Int'l*, pg. 4820
CARSTENS AB—See Holm Travaror AB; *Int'l*, pg. 3452
CARSTENS INC.; *U.S. Private*, pg. 774
CARSTENS I SCHUES POLAND SP. Z O.O.—See Aon plc; *Int'l*, pg. 494
CAR STEREO CITY INC.; *U.S. Private*, pg. 747

CARSTIN BRANDS, INC.—See The Wolf Organization, LLC; *U.S. Private*, pg. 4138
CAR STORE INC.; *U.S. Private*, pg. 747
CARSTORY, LLC—See Vroom, Inc.; *U.S. Public*, pg. 2312
CARST & WALKER AUSTRALIA (PTY) LTD—See Hobart Enterprises Ltd; *Int'l*, pg. 3436
CARST & WALKER (EA) LIMITED—See Hobart Enterprises Ltd; *Int'l*, pg. 3436
CARST & WALKER (PTY) LTD.—See Hobart Enterprises Ltd; *Int'l*, pg. 3436
CARSWELL DISTRIBUTING COMPANY; *U.S. Private*, pg. 775
CAR SYSTEMS B.V.—See LKQ Corporation; *U.S. Public*, pg. 1334
CART ACQUA S.R.L.—See Ascopiave S.p.A.; *Int'l*, pg. 603
THE CARTA GROUP, INC.—See Community Bank System, Inc.; *U.S. Public*, pg. 550
CARTAGZ INC.; *U.S. Private*, pg. 775
CARTA HOLDINGS, INC.—See Polaris Capital Group Co., Ltd.; *Int'l*, pg. 5906
CARTAL RIJSBERGEN AUTOMOTIVE B.V.—See LKQ Corporation; *U.S. Public*, pg. 1334
CARTA MUNDI ASIA PACIFIC PTE. LTD.—See Cartamundi N.V.; *Int'l*, pg. 1347
CARTAMUNDI - DIGITAL NV—See Cartamundi N.V.; *Int'l*, pg. 1348
CARTAMUNDI ESPANA, S.L.—See Cartamundi N.V.; *Int'l*, pg. 1348
CARTA MUNDI HUNGARY KFT.—See Cartamundi N.V.; *Int'l*, pg. 1347
CARTA MUNDI, INC.—See Cartamundi N.V.; *Int'l*, pg. 1348
CARTAMUNDI IRELAND LTD.—See Hasbro, Inc.; *U.S. Public*, pg. 988
CARTAMUNDI ITALY SA—See Cartamundi N.V.; *Int'l*, pg. 1348
CARTAMUNDI NORDIC AB—See Cartamundi N.V.; *Int'l*, pg. 1348
CARTAMUNDI NORTH AMERICA EAST LONGMEADOW LLC—See Cartamundi N.V.; *Int'l*, pg. 1348
CARTAMUNDI N.V.; *Int'l*, pg. 1347
CARTAMUNDI POLSKA SP. Z O.O.—See Cartamundi N.V.; *Int'l*, pg. 1348
CARTA MUNDI UK LTD.—See Cartamundi N.V.; *Int'l*, pg. 1348
CART.COM, INC.; *U.S. Private*, pg. 775
CARTEGRAPH SYSTEMS, LLC—See Pamlico Capital Management, L.P.; *U.S. Private*, pg. 3083
CARTE INTERNATIONAL INC.; *Int'l*, pg. 1348
CARTEL BLUE, INC.; *U.S. Private*, pg. 775
CARTEL ELECTRONICS, INC.—See IGP Industries, LLC; *U.S. Private*, pg. 2039
CAR TELEMATICS SA; *Int'l*, pg. 1319
THE CARTEL GROUP; *U.S. Private*, pg. 4005
CARTEMANI S.R.L.—See Hagleitner Hygiene International GmbH; *Int'l*, pg. 3207
CARTERA COMMERCE, INC.—See Rakuten Group, Inc.; *Int'l*, pg. 6195
CARTER & ASSOCIATES, LLC; *U.S. Private*, pg. 775
CARTERBALDWIN; *U.S. Private*, pg. 776
CARTER BANKSHARES, INC.; *U.S. Public*, pg. 445
CARTER BANK & TRUST—See Carter Bankshares, Inc.; *U.S. Public*, pg. 445
CARTER BLOODCARE; *U.S. Private*, pg. 775
CARTER BROTHERS ARAMARK INTEGRATED FACILITIES MANAGEMENT, LLC—See Aramark; *U.S. Public*, pg. 177
CARTER BROTHERS, LLC; *U.S. Private*, pg. 775
CARTER CHEVROLET CO.; *U.S. Private*, pg. 775
CARTER CHEVROLET, INC.; *U.S. Private*, pg. 775
CARTER DAY INTERNATIONAL, INC.; *U.S. Private*, pg. 775
CARTER DISTRIBUTING COMPANY INC; *U.S. Private*, pg. 775
CARTER DODGE CHRYSLER LTD; *Int'l*, pg. 1348
CARTER DUNCAN CORPORATION; *U.S. Private*, pg. 775
CARTERENERGY CORPORATION—See World Kinect Corporation; *U.S. Public*, pg. 2381
CARTERET-CRAVEN ELECTRIC COOPERATIVE; *U.S. Private*, pg. 776
CARTER FURNITURE—See Tomlinson/Erwin-Lambeth, Inc.; *U.S. Private*, pg. 4184
CARTER-HOFFMANN, LLC—See The Middleby Corporation; *U.S. Public*, pg. 2113
CARTER HOLT BUILDING SUPPLIES—See Rank Group Ltd.; *Int'l*, pg. 6208
CARTER HOLT HARVEY BUILDING PRODUCTS GROUP LIMITED—See Rank Group Ltd.; *Int'l*, pg. 6207
CARTER HOLT HARVEY FORESTS LIMITED—See Rank Group Ltd.; *Int'l*, pg. 6208
CARTER HOLT HARVEY LIMITED—See Rank Group Ltd.; *Int'l*, pg. 6207
CARTER HOLT HARVEY LIMITED—See Rank Group Ltd.; *Int'l*, pg. 6207
CARTER HOLT HARVEY PLASTIC PRODUCTS-BEVERAGE DIVISION—See Rank Group Ltd.; *Int'l*, pg. 6208
CARTER HOLT HARVEY PLASTIC PRODUCTS GROUP LIMITED—See Rank Group Ltd.; *Int'l*, pg. 6207

CARTIERA LUCCHESE S.P.A.

CARTER HOLT HARVEY PLASTIC PRODUCTS—See Rank Group Ltd.; *Int'l*, pg. 6207
CARTER HOLT HARVEY PTY. LIMITED—See Rank Group Ltd.; *Int'l*, pg. 6208
CARTER HOLT HARVEY—See Rank Group Ltd.; *Int'l*, pg. 6208
CARTER HOLT HARVEY—See Rank Group Ltd.; *Int'l*, pg. 6207
CARTER HOLT HARVEY TIMBER LIMITED—See Rank Group Ltd.; *Int'l*, pg. 6208
CARTER HOLT HARVEY WOODPRODUCTS AUSTRALIA PTY LTD—See Rank Group Ltd.; *Int'l*, pg. 6208
CARTER HOLT HARVEY WOOD PRODUCTS LIMITED—See Rank Group Ltd.; *Int'l*, pg. 6208
CARTER INDUSTRIES INC.—See Adrian Steel Company Inc.; *U.S. Private*, pg. 82
THE CARTER-JONES LUMBER COMPANY INC.—See Carter Lumber Co.; *U.S. Private*, pg. 776
CARTER LOGISTICS, LLC—See KKR & Co. Inc.; *U.S. Public*, pg. 1258
CARTER LUMBER CO. - CARTER COMPONENTS PLANT—See Carter Lumber Co.; *U.S. Private*, pg. 775
CARTER LUMBER CO. - CARTER CUSTOM MILLWORK—See Carter Lumber Co.; *U.S. Private*, pg. 775
CARTER LUMBER CO. - GRIGGS LUMBER—See Carter Lumber Co.; *U.S. Private*, pg. 775
CARTER LUMBER CO. INC.—See Carter Lumber Co.; *U.S. Private*, pg. 775
CARTER LUMBER CO. - KEMPSVILLE BUILDING MATERIALS DIVISION—See Carter Lumber Co.; *U.S. Private*, pg. 775
CARTER LUMBER CO. - KIGHT HOME CENTER—See Carter Lumber Co.; *U.S. Private*, pg. 775
CARTER LUMBER CO.; *U.S. Private*, pg. 775
CARTER LUMBER OF THE SOUTH INC.—See Carter Lumber Co.; *U.S. Private*, pg. 775
CARTER LUMBER OF VIRGINIA INC.—See Carter Lumber Co.; *U.S. Private*, pg. 775
CARTER MACHINERY COMPANY, INC.; *U.S. Private*, pg. 776
CARTER MOTOR CARS LTD; *Int'l*, pg. 1348
CARTER MOTOR COMPANY; *U.S. Private*, pg. 776
CARTER MOTORS INC.; *U.S. Private*, pg. 776
CARTER OF MANCHESTER; *U.S. Private*, pg. 776
CARTER PAPER & PACKAGING, INC.; *U.S. Private*, pg. 776
CARTER PRODUCTS (N.Z.) INC.—See Church & Dwight Co., Inc.; *U.S. Public*, pg. 493
CARTER QUEENSTOWN 2015 LTD.—See InterContinental Hotels Group PLC; *Int'l*, pg. 3736
CARTER RESOURCES INC.—See Carter Lumber Co.; *U.S. Private*, pg. 776
CARTER'S INC.; *U.S. Private*, pg. 776
CARTER'S, INC.; *U.S. Public*, pg. 445
CARTER'S SHOOTING CENTER INC.; *U.S. Private*, pg. 776
CARTERS TYRE SERVICE LIMITED—See National Tyre & Wheel Limited; *Int'l*, pg. 5164
CARTERSVILLE CENTER, INC.—See Acadia Healthcare Company, Inc.; *U.S. Public*, pg. 28
CARTERSVILLE MEDICAL CENTER, LLC—See HCA Healthcare, Inc.; *U.S. Public*, pg. 992
CARTERSVILLE OCCUPATIONAL MEDICINE CENTER, LLC—See HCA Healthcare, Inc.; *U.S. Public*, pg. 992
CARTERSVILLE TRANSFER STATION, LLC—See Waste Management, Inc.; *U.S. Public*, pg. 2330
CARTER THERMO KING INC.; *U.S. Private*, pg. 776
CARTER VALIDUS ADVISORS, LLC—See Carter & Associates, LLC; *U.S. Private*, pg. 775
CARTER VALIDUS MISSION CRITICAL REIT, INC.—See Carter & Associates, LLC; *U.S. Private*, pg. 775
CARTER & VERPLANCK, INC.; *U.S. Private*, pg. 775
CARTER-WATERS LLC—See The Sterling Group, L.P.; *U.S. Private*, pg. 4122
CARTESIA GIS AB—See Addnode Group AB; *Int'l*, pg. 130
CARTESIAN CAPITAL GROUP, LLC; *U.S. Private*, pg. 776
CARTESIAN, INC.—See Blackstreet Capital Holdings LLC; *U.S. Private*, pg. 576
CARTESIAN LTD.—See Blackstreet Capital Holdings LLC; *U.S. Private*, pg. 576
CARTESIAN THERAPEUTICS, INC.; *U.S. Public*, pg. 445
CARTHAGE AREA HOSPITAL, INC.; *U.S. Private*, pg. 776
CARTHAGE VETERINARY SERVICE, LTD.; *U.S. Private*, pg. 776
CARTHAGE WATER & ELECTRIC PLANT; *U.S. Private*, pg. 776
CARTHAGO CERAMIC—See Poulina Group Holding S.A.; *Int'l*, pg. 5942
CARTHAGO SRL—See CVC Capital Partners SICAV-FIS S.A.; *Int'l*, pg. 1888
CARTICA ACQUISITION CORP.; *U.S. Public*, pg. 445
CARTIER AGENCY, INC.—See Keystone Agency Investors LLC; *U.S. Private*, pg. 2295
CARTIERA LUCCHESE S.P.A.; *Int'l*, pg. 1348
CARTIERE DEL GARDA SPA—See CVC Capital Partners SICAV-FIS S.A.; *Int'l*, pg. 1888

CARTIERA LUCCHESE S.P.A.

CORPORATE AFFILIATIONS

CARTIERE DI GUARCINO S.P.A.—See Neodecortech S.p.A.; *Int'l*, pg. 5196
CARTIER INTERNATIONAL SA GENEVE—See Compagnie Financiere Richemont S.A.; *Int'l*, pg. 1741
CARTIER RESOURCES INC.; *Int'l*, pg. 1348
CARTIER SAADA; *Int'l*, pg. 1348
CARTIER SA—See Compagnie Financiere Richemont S.A.; *Int'l*, pg. 1741
CARTIER S.A.—See Reinet Investments S.C.A.; *Int'l*, pg. 6257
CARTIER SILVER CORPORATION; *Int'l*, pg. 1348
CARTIKA MEDICAL—See Teleflex Incorporated; *U.S. Public*, pg. 1996
CARTOCOR S.A.—See Arcor Sociedad Anonima, Industrial y Comercial; *Int'l*, pg. 550
CARTOGRAFIA GENERAL, S.A.—See Airtificial Intelligence Structures SA; *Int'l*, pg. 249
CARTOLOGY PTY LIMITED—See Woolworths Group Limited; *Int'l*, pg. 8451
CARTONAJES INTERNATIONAL S.L.—See International Paper Company; *U.S. Public*, pg. 1155
CARTONAJES UNION S.L.—See International Paper Company; *U.S. Public*, pg. 1155
CARTONAJES UNION S.L.—See International Paper Company; *U.S. Public*, pg. 1155
CARTON CRAFT CORPORATION—See Graphic Packaging Holding Company; *U.S. Public*, pg. 958
CARTON DE COLOMBIA, S.A.—See Smurfit Kappa Group plc; *Int'l*, pg. 7017
CARTONERA NACIONAL, S. A.—See Sigma S.A. de C.V.; *Int'l*, pg. 6908
CARTON PLASTICO S.A.—See DS Smith Plc; *Int'l*, pg. 2207
CARTON SERVICE INC.; *U.S. Private*, pg. 776
CARTON Y PAPEL RECICLADO, S.A.—See International Paper Company; *U.S. Public*, pg. 1155
THE CARTOON NETWORK, INC.—See Warner Bros. Discovery, Inc.; *U.S. Public*, pg. 2328
CAR TOYS INC.; *U.S. Private*, pg. 747
CARTRACK ENGINEERING TECHNOLOGIES LIMITED—See Karooooo Ltd.; *Int'l*, pg. 4084
CARTRACK ESPANA, S.L.—See Karooooo Ltd.; *Int'l*, pg. 4084
CARTRACK HOLDINGS LTD.—See Karooooo Ltd.; *Int'l*, pg. 4084
CARTRACK INC.—See Karooooo Ltd.; *Int'l*, pg. 4084
CARTRACK LIMITADA—See Karooooo Ltd.; *Int'l*, pg. 4084
CARTRACK MALAYSIA SDN. BHD.—See Karooooo Ltd.; *Int'l*, pg. 4084
CARTRACK NEW ZEALAND LIMITED—See Karooooo Ltd.; *Int'l*, pg. 4084
CARTRACK POLSKA SP. Z O.O.—See Karooooo Ltd.; *Int'l*, pg. 4084
CARTRACK PORTUGAL S.A.—See Karooooo Ltd.; *Int'l*, pg. 4084
CARTRACK TANZANIA LIMITED—See Karooooo Ltd.; *Int'l*, pg. 4084
CARTRACK TECHNOLOGIES (CHINA) LIMITED—See Karooooo Ltd.; *Int'l*, pg. 4084
CARTRACK TECHNOLOGIES LLC—See Karooooo Ltd.; *Int'l*, pg. 4084
CARTRACK TECHNOLOGIES PHL INC.—See Karooooo Ltd.; *Int'l*, pg. 4084
CARTRACK TECHNOLOGIES PTE. LIMITED—See Karooooo Ltd.; *Int'l*, pg. 4084
CARTRACK TECHNOLOGIES (THAILAND) COMPANY LIMITED—See Karooooo Ltd.; *Int'l*, pg. 4084
THE CAR TRADER PROPRIETARY LIMITED—See Prosus N.V.; *Int'l*, pg. 6003
CARTRADE TECH LTD.; *Int'l*, pg. 1348
CARTRAWLER LTD.—See BC Partners LLP; *Int'l*, pg. 923
CARTRIDGE SAVE LIMITED; *Int'l*, pg. 1348
CARTRIDGE TECHNOLOGIES, LLC—See CenterGate Capital, LP; *U.S. Private*, pg. 816
CARTRIM ZEPCE D.O.O.—See Prevent DEV GmbH; *Int'l*, pg. 5967
CAR & TRUCK RENTALS, INC.; *U.S. Private*, pg. 747
CARTU BANK JSC—See Cartu Group JSC; *Int'l*, pg. 1348
CARTU GROUP JSC; *Int'l*, pg. 1348
CARTUJA INMOBILIARIA, S.A.U.—See Grupo Empresarial San Jose, S.A.; *Int'l*, pg. 3128
CARTUS BRASIL SERVICOS DE RELOCACAO LTDA.—See Anywhere Real Estate Inc.; *U.S. Public*, pg. 142
CARTUS B.V.—See Anywhere Real Estate Inc.; *U.S. Public*, pg. 140
CARTUS CORPORATION PTE. LTD.—See Anywhere Real Estate Inc.; *U.S. Public*, pg. 140
CARTUS CORPORATION—See Anywhere Real Estate Inc.; *U.S. Public*, pg. 140
CARTUS UK PLC—See Anywhere Real Estate Inc.; *U.S. Public*, pg. 140
CARTWRIGHT AERIAL SURVEYS, INC.; *U.S. Private*, pg. 776
CARTWRIGHT DISTRIBUTING, LLC—See ShoreView Industries, LLC; *U.S. Private*, pg. 3642
CARTWRIGHT INTERNATIONAL VAN LINES INC.—See Centre Limited Inc.; *U.S. Private*, pg. 828

CARTWRIGHT VAN LINES INC.—See Centre Limited Inc.; *U.S. Private*, pg. 828
CARUELLE-NICOLAS SAS—See Exel Industries SA; *Int'l*, pg. 2582
CARUS CHEMICAL COMPANY—See Carus Corporation; *U.S. Private*, pg. 776
CARUS CORPORATION; *U.S. Private*, pg. 776
CARUSO AFFILIATED; *U.S. Private*, pg. 776
CARUSO GMBH—See LKQ Corporation; *U.S. Public*, pg. 1334
CARUSO PRODUCE, INC.; *U.S. Private*, pg. 777
CARUS PHOSPHATES, INC.—See Carus Corporation; *U.S. Private*, pg. 776
CARUS PUBLISHING COMPANY—See Cricket Media Group Ltd.; *U.S. Private*, pg. 1100
CARVAJAL EMPAQUES SA; *Int'l*, pg. 1348
CARVAJAL PULPA Y PAPEL S.A.—See Carvajal S.A.; *Int'l*, pg. 1349
CARVAJAL S.A.; *Int'l*, pg. 1348
CARVALOO GMBH—See ThyssenKrupp AG; *Int'l*, pg. 7724
CARVANA CO.; *U.S. Public*, pg. 445
CARVEL CORPORATION—See Roark Capital Group Inc.; *U.S. Private*, pg. 3454
CARVEL PRINT SERIGRAPH, INC.—See Serigraph, Inc.; *U.S. Private*, pg. 3613
CARVEMAGERE MANUTENCAO E ENERGIAS RENOVAVEIS LDA—See Enel S.p.A.; *Int'l*, pg. 2411
CARVER BANCORP INC.; *U.S. Public*, pg. 445
CARVER CONSTRUCTION COMPANY; *U.S. Private*, pg. 777
CARVER FEDERAL SAVINGS BANK—See Carver Bancorp Inc.; *U.S. Public*, pg. 445
CARVER INC.—See Lummus Corporation; *U.S. Private*, pg. 2514
CARVER, INC.—See Harbour Group Industries, Inc.; *U.S. Private*, pg. 1860
CARVER INDUSTRIES, INC.—See Covercraft Direct, LLC; *U.S. Private*, pg. 1072
CARVER TRANSITIONAL CENTER, LLC—See Corecivic, Inc.; *U.S. Public*, pg. 577
CARVE SYSTEMS LLC—See iVision Scale, LLC; *U.S. Private*, pg. 2151
CARVIEW CORPORATION—See SoftBank Group Corp.; *Int'l*, pg. 7052
CARVIN CORP.; *U.S. Private*, pg. 777
CAR WASH EXPRESS—See Car Wash Partners, Inc.; *U.S. Private*, pg. 747
CAR WASH PARTNERS, INC.; *U.S. Private*, pg. 747
CARWELL, LLC—See AutoNation, Inc.; *U.S. Public*, pg. 233
CARWELL, LLC—See AutoNation, Inc.; *U.S. Public*, pg. 234
CARWOOD (BDS) MOTOR UNIT LTD—See Carwood Motor Units Ltd; *Int'l*, pg. 1349
CARWOOD (HK) LIMITED—See Carwood Motor Units Ltd; *Int'l*, pg. 1349
CARWOOD MOTOR UNITS LTD - OLLERTON FACTORY—See Carwood Motor Units Ltd; *Int'l*, pg. 1349
CARWOOD MOTOR UNITS LTD; *Int'l*, pg. 1349
CARWOOD (REWIND) YEOVIL LTD—See Carwood Motor Units Ltd; *Int'l*, pg. 1349
CAR-X ASSOCIATES CORP.—See Tuffy Associates Corporation; *U.S. Private*, pg. 4257
CAR-X AUTO SERVICE, INC.—See Tuffy Associates Corporation; *U.S. Private*, pg. 4257
THE CARY COMPANY; *U.S. Private*, pg. 4005
CARYLON CORPORATION; *U.S. Private*, pg. 777
CARY OIL COMPANY, INC.—See COG Properties, Inc.; *U.S. Private*, pg. 958
CARY RECONSTRUCTION INC.; *U.S. Private*, pg. 777
CARYSIL LIMITED; *Int'l*, pg. 1349
CARY STREET PARTNERS FINANCIAL LLC; *U.S. Private*, pg. 777
CARY STREET PARTNERS INVESTMENT ADVISORY, LLC—See Luxon Financial LLC; *U.S. Private*, pg. 2518
CASA ALBA - INDEPENDENTA SA; *Int'l*, pg. 1349
CASA AUTO GROUP; *U.S. Private*, pg. 777
CASA AUTOMOTIVE GROUP; *U.S. Private*, pg. 777
CASA AUTOPLEX—See Casa Auto Group; *U.S. Private*, pg. 777
CASA BAHIA CONTACT CENTER LTDA—See Companhia Brasileira de Distribuicao; *Int'l*, pg. 1746
CASABLANCA FAN COMPANY—See Griffon Corporation; *U.S. Public*, pg. 969
CASABLANCA GROUP LIMITED; *Int'l*, pg. 1349
CASABLANCA HOME (SHENZHEN) LIMITED—See Casablanca Group Limited; *Int'l*, pg. 1349
CASABLANCA MINING LTD.; *U.S. Private*, pg. 778
CASABLANCA RESORTS, LLC—See Mesquite Gaming, LLC; *U.S. Private*, pg. 2679
CASA BOCOBO HOTEL INC.—See Solid Group, Inc.; *Int'l*, pg. 7072
CASA CENTRAL CORPORATION; *U.S. Private*, pg. 778
CASA CHRYSLER JEEP MITSUBISHI; *U.S. Private*, pg. 778
CASA CIENTIFICA—See Standard Industries Holdings Inc.; *U.S. Private*, pg. 3779

CASA COMMUNICATIONS LIMITED—See Casa Systems, Inc.; *U.S. Private*, pg. 778
CASA COMMUNICATIONS TECHNOLOGY S.L.—See Casa Systems, Inc.; *U.S. Private*, pg. 778
CASA DE BOLSA BBVA MEXICO, S.A. DE C.V.—See Banco Bilbao Vizcaya Argentaria, S.A.; *Int'l*, pg. 817
CASA DE BOLSA CREDIT SUISSE (MEXICO), S.A. DE C.V.—See UBS Group AG; *Int'l*, pg. 8005
CASA DE BOLSA FINAMEX, S.A.B. DE C.V.; *Int'l*, pg. 1349
CASA DE BOLSA SANTANDER SERFIN, S.A. DE C.V.—See Banco Santander, S.A.; *Int'l*, pg. 826
CASA DE CAMBIO BANCOMER—See Banco Bilbao Vizcaya Argentaria, S.A.; *Int'l*, pg. 818
CASA DE CAMBIO DELGADO INC.—See Delgado Travel Agency Corporation; *U.S. Private*, pg. 1196
CASA DELLA SALUTE S.R.L.—See Italmobiliare S.p.A.; *Int'l*, pg. 3829
CASA DEL MAR BEACH RESORT N.V.; *Int'l*, pg. 1349
CASA DE MONTECRISTO INC.—See Imperial Brands PLC; *Int'l*, pg. 3633
CASA DE MONTECRISTO TN LLC—See Imperial Brands PLC; *Int'l*, pg. 3633
CASA DE MONTECRISTO TX LLC—See Imperial Brands PLC; *Int'l*, pg. 3633
CASA DI BERTACCHI—See Rich Holdings, Inc.; *U.S. Private*, pg. 3426
CASA DI CURA PROF. NOBILI S.P.A.—See Garofalo Health Care SpA; *Int'l*, pg. 2886
CASA DI CURA VILLA BERICA S.P.A.—See Garofalo Health Care SpA; *Int'l*, pg. 2886
CASA DI CURA VILLA GARDA S.P.A.—See Garofalo Health Care SpA; *Int'l*, pg. 2886
CASA DOS LIVROS EDITORA LTDA.—See Charlesbank Capital Partners, LLC; *U.S. Private*, pg. 854
CASA FORD INC.; *U.S. Private*, pg. 778
CASA FORMA LIMITED—See PDS Limited; *Int'l*, pg. 5770
CASA GRANDE REGIONAL MEDICAL CENTER; *U.S. Private*, pg. 778
CASA HERRERA INC.; *U.S. Private*, pg. 778
CASA HOLDINGS LTD.; *Int'l*, pg. 1349
CASA, INC.; *Int'l*, pg. 1349
CASALAGO CO., LTD.—See Credit Saison Co., Ltd.; *Int'l*, pg. 1836
CASA LAGOSTINA S.R.L.—See SEB S.A.; *Int'l*, pg. 6667
CA SALES (THAILAND) CO., LTD—See Broadcom Inc.; *U.S. Public*, pg. 389
CASALETTO S.R.L.—See Assicurazioni Generali S.p.A.; *Int'l*, pg. 643
CASA LINDA FURNITURE INC.; *U.S. Private*, pg. 778
CASA MADRONA HOTEL & SPA—See MetWest Realty Advisors LLC; *U.S. Private*, pg. 2691
CASA-MAZOUT S.A.R.L.—See Max Weishaupt GmbH; *Int'l*, pg. 4735
CASAMBA, LLC—See Level Equity Management, LLC; *U.S. Private*, pg. 2434
CASAMBA, LLC—See Silversmith Management, L.P.; *U.S. Private*, pg. 3664
CASAMBA, LLC—See The Carlyle Group Inc.; *U.S. Public*, pg. 2050
CASAMIA IMMOBILIARE SAS—See Emeis SA; *Int'l*, pg. 2376
CASA MINERALS INC.; *Int'l*, pg. 1349
CASA MONICA HOTEL—See The Kessler Enterprise Inc.; *U.S. Private*, pg. 4065
CASAMUNDO GMBH—See HomeToGo SE; *Int'l*, pg. 3456
CASANOVA PENDRILL, LLC—See The Interpublic Group of Companies, Inc.; *U.S. Public*, pg. 2090
CASA PACIFICA CENTERS FOR CHILDREN & FAMILIES; *U.S. Private*, pg. 778
CASA RAMPART LP—See Edison International; *U.S. Public*, pg. 719
CASA REALE CERAMIC INC—See QuattroR SGR S.p.A.; *Int'l*, pg. 6157
CASA REAL HOTEL—See Kingston Financial Group Limited; *Int'l*, pg. 4179
CASAREAL, INC.—See TECHMATRIX CORPORATION; *Int'l*, pg. 7505
CASA REDIMIX CONCRETE CORP.; *U.S. Private*, pg. 778
CASA REHA SENIORENPFLEGEHEIM GMBH—See Clariane SE; *Int'l*, pg. 1642
CASA ROSSIER LTDA.—See THK CO., LTD.; *Int'l*, pg. 7711
CASAS BETA DEL CENTRO, S DE R L DE C V—See Desarrolladora Homex, S.A. de C.V.; *Int'l*, pg. 2044
CASAS BETA DEL NOROESTE, S.A. DE C.V.—See Desarrolladora Homex, S.A. de C.V.; *Int'l*, pg. 2044
CASAS BETA DEL NORTE, S.A. DE C.V.—See Desarrolladora Homex, S.A. de C.V.; *Int'l*, pg. 2044
C.A.S. ASSET CO., LTD.—See Charoen Aksorn Holding Group Co. Ltd.; *Int'l*, pg. 1451
CASA SYSTEMS, INC.; *U.S. Private*, pg. 778
CASA TRUCKING, INC.—See Post Holdings, Inc.; *U.S. Public*, pg. 1703
CASA VISCO; *U.S. Private*, pg. 778
CASBA BOCOBO HOTEL INC.—See Solid Group, Inc.; *Int'l*, pg. 7072
CASBY BROS, INC.; *U.S. Private*, pg. 778
CASCADE ACQUISITION CORP.; *U.S. Public*, pg. 445

CASCADE (AFRICA) PTY. LTD.—See Toyota Industries Corporation; *Int'l*, pg. 7868
CASCADE ASSET MANAGEMENT, LLC.; *U.S. Private*, pg. 778
CASCADE (AUSTRALIA) PTY. LTD.—See Toyota Industries Corporation; *Int'l*, pg. 7868
CASCADE AUTOGLASS INCORPORATED; *U.S. Private*, pg. 778
CASCADE AUTO GROUP, LTD.; *U.S. Private*, pg. 778
CASCADE AUTOMATION SYSTEMS B.V.—See CHINO Corporation; *Int'l*, pg. 1570
CASCADE AUTOVON COMPANY—See Lumen Technologies, Inc.; *U.S. Public*, pg. 1345
CASCADE BEHAVIORAL HOSPITAL, LLC—See Acadia Healthcare Company, Inc.; *U.S. Public*, pg. 28
CASCADE BREWERY COMPANY; *Int'l*, pg. 1349
CASCADE BROADCASTING GROUP LLC; *U.S. Private*, pg. 778
CASCADE (CANADA), INC.-MISSISSAUGA—See Toyota Industries Corporation; *Int'l*, pg. 7868
CASCADE CANADA, INC.—See Toyota Industries Corporation; *Int'l*, pg. 7868
CASCADE CARRIERS L.P.—See Mullen Group Ltd.; *Int'l*, pg. 5080
CASCADE COAL LIMITED—See Galilee Energy Limited; *Int'l*, pg. 2873
CASCADE COFFEE, INC.; *U.S. Private*, pg. 778
CASCADE COLUMBIA DISTRIBUTION COMPANY; *U.S. Private*, pg. 778
CASCADE & COLUMBIA RIVER RAILROAD COMPANY—See Brookfield Infrastructure Partners L.P.; *Int'l*, pg. 1191
CASCADE & COLUMBIA RIVER RAILROAD COMPANY—See GIC Pte. Ltd.; *Int'l*, pg. 2965
CASCADE CONTROLS NORTHWEST; *U.S. Private*, pg. 779
CASCADE CORPORATION—See Toyota Industries Corporation; *Int'l*, pg. 7868
CASCADE CREEK LLC—See Alaska Hydro Corporation; *Int'l*, pg. 291
CASCADE DESIGN PROFESSIONALS, INC.—See Cooper Zietz Engineers, Inc.; *U.S. Private*, pg. 1041
CASCADE DESIGNS, INC. - MSR DIVISION—See Cascade Designs, Inc.; *U.S. Private*, pg. 779
CASCADE DESIGNS, INC.; *U.S. Private*, pg. 779
CASCADE DRILLING, L.P.—See TruArc Partners, L.P.; *U.S. Private*, pg. 4245
CASCADE ENDOSCOPY CENTER, LLC—See KKR & Co. Inc.; *U.S. Public*, pg. 1245
CASCADE ENERGY SERVICES L.P.—See Mullen Group Ltd.; *Int'l*, pg. 5080
CASCADE ENGINEERING EUROPE KFT.—See TI Fluid Systems Plc; *Int'l*, pg. 7736
CASCADE ENGINEERING, INC.; *U.S. Private*, pg. 779
CASCADE ENGINEERING SERVICES INC.; *U.S. Private*, pg. 779
CASCADE EUROPE N.V.—See Toyota Industries Corporation; *Int'l*, pg. 7868
CASCADE EVAPORATOR COMPANY; *U.S. Private*, pg. 779
CASCADE GENERAL INC.—See Stellex Capital Management LP; *U.S. Private*, pg. 3800
CASCADE GENERAL INC.—See The Carlyle Group Inc.; *U.S. Public*, pg. 2056
CASCADE GMBH—See Toyota Industries Corporation; *Int'l*, pg. 7868
CASCADE HARDWOOD LLC; *U.S. Private*, pg. 779
CASCADE HEALTH SERVICES; *U.S. Private*, pg. 779
CASCADE INDIA MATERIAL HANDLING PRIVATE LIMITED—See Toyota Industries Corporation; *Int'l*, pg. 7868
CASCADE INSURANCE CENTER LLC—See Inszone Insurance Services, LLC; *U.S. Private*, pg. 2096
CASCADE INVESTMENT LLC; *U.S. Private*, pg. 779
CASCADE (JAPAN) LTD.—See Toyota Industries Corporation; *Int'l*, pg. 7868
CASCADE KELLY HOLDINGS LLC—See Global Partners LP; *U.S. Public*, pg. 942
CASCADE (KOREA) LTD.—See Toyota Industries Corporation; *Int'l*, pg. 7868
CASCADE LUMBER COMPANY; *U.S. Private*, pg. 781
CASCADE MACHINERY & ELECTRIC; *U.S. Private*, pg. 781
CASCADE MICROTECH CHINA (SHANGHAI) CO., LTD.—See FormFactor, Inc.; *U.S. Public*, pg. 868
CASCADE MICROTECH GMBH—See FormFactor, Inc.; *U.S. Public*, pg. 868
CASCADE MICROTECH, INC.—See FormFactor, Inc.; *U.S. Public*, pg. 868
CASCADE MICROTECH JAPAN, INC.—See FormFactor, Inc.; *U.S. Public*, pg. 868
CASCADE NATURAL GAS CORPORATION—See MDU Resources Group, Inc.; *U.S. Public*, pg. 1409
CASCADE OHIO INC.; *U.S. Private*, pg. 781
CASCADE OPTICAL LTD—See EssilorLuxottica SA; *Int'l*, pg. 2512
CASCADE ORTHOPEDIC SUPPLY INC.; *U.S. Private*, pg. 781

CASCADE RENEWABLE ENERGY—See Cascade Engineering, Inc.; *U.S. Private*, pg. 779
CASCADERO COPPER CORPORATION; *Int'l*, pg. 1349
CASCADERO MINERALS S.A.—See Cascadero Copper Corporation; *Int'l*, pg. 1349
CASCADE SALES—See Nature's Footprint, Inc.; *U.S. Private*, pg. 2867
CASCADES APARTMENTS, LTD—See American Realty Investors, Inc.; *U.S. Public*, pg. 108
CASCADE SAWING & DRILLING, INC.; *U.S. Private*, pg. 781
CASCADES BOXBOARD GROUP INC. - COBOURG—See Cascades Inc.; *Int'l*, pg. 1350
CASCADES BOXBOARD GROUP INC. - EAST ANGUS—See Cascades Inc.; *Int'l*, pg. 1350
CASCADES BOXBOARD GROUP INC. - LACHUTE—See Cascades Inc.; *Int'l*, pg. 1350
CASCADES BOXBOARD GROUP INC.—See Cascades Inc.; *Int'l*, pg. 1350
CASCADES BOXBOARD GROUP INC. - WINNIPEG—See Cascades Inc.; *Int'l*, pg. 1350
CASCADES CANADA ULC—See Cascades Inc.; *Int'l*, pg. 1350
CASCADES CONVERSION, INC.—See Cascades Inc.; *Int'l*, pg. 1350
CASCADES DJUPAFORS A.B.—See Cascades Inc.; *Int'l*, pg. 1350
CASCADES EAST ANGUS, INC.—See Cascades Inc.; *Int'l*, pg. 1350
CASCADES ENVIROPAC HPM LLC—See Cascades Inc.; *Int'l*, pg. 1350
CASCADES ENVIROPAC INC—See Cascades Inc.; *Int'l*, pg. 1350
CASCADES ENVIROPAC ST-CESAIRE—See Cascades Inc.; *Int'l*, pg. 1350
CASCADES FORMA-PAK, INC.—See Cascades Inc.; *Int'l*, pg. 1350
CASCADES GROUPE CARTON PLAT JONQUIERE—See Cascades Inc.; *Int'l*, pg. 1350
CASCADES GROUPE TISSU - AGINCOURT & SCARBOROUGH—See Cascades Inc.; *Int'l*, pg. 1351
CASCADE SIERRA SOLUTIONS; *U.S. Private*, pg. 781
CASCADES IFC—See Cascades Inc.; *Int'l*, pg. 1351
CASCADES INC.; *Int'l*, pg. 1350
CASCADES INOPAK—See Cascades Inc.; *Int'l*, pg. 1350
CASCADES LA ROCHETTE—See Cascades Inc.; *Int'l*, pg. 1350
CASCADES LUPEL, INC.—See Cascades Inc.; *Int'l*, pg. 1350
CASCADES MOULDED PULP, INC.—See Cascades Inc.; *Int'l*, pg. 1350
CASCADES MULTI-PRO, INC.—See Cascades Inc.; *Int'l*, pg. 1350
CASCADE SOTHEBY'S INTERNATIONAL REALTY; *U.S. Private*, pg. 781
CASCADES PAPIER KINGSEY FALLS—See Cascades Inc.; *Int'l*, pg. 1350
CASCADE SPECIALTIES INC.—See Jain Irrigation Systems Limited; *Int'l*, pg. 3872
CASCADE SPINE CENTER, LLC—See Tenet Healthcare Corporation; *U.S. Public*, pg. 2009
CASCADES PLASTICS INC.—See Cascades Inc.; *Int'l*, pg. 1350
CASCADES RECOVERY INC.—See Cascades Inc.; *Int'l*, pg. 1350
CASCADES RECOVERY U.S., INC.—See Cascades Inc.; *Int'l*, pg. 1350
THE CASCADES RETIREMENT RESORT LIMITED—See Arvida Group Limited; *Int'l*, pg. 587
CASCADES S.A.S.—See Cascades Inc.; *Int'l*, pg. 1350
CASCADES SONOCO, INC. - BIRMINGHAM—See Cascades Inc.; *Int'l*, pg. 1350
CASCADES SPECIALTY PRODUCTS GROUP—See Cascades Inc.; *Int'l*, pg. 1350
CASCADES TECHNOLOGIES, INC.; *U.S. Private*, pg. 781
CASCADE STEEL ROLLING MILLS, INC.—See Radius Recycling, Inc.; *U.S. Public*, pg. 1760
CASCADES TENDERCO INC.—See Cascades Inc.; *Int'l*, pg. 1351
CASCADES TISSUE GROUP - KINGSEY FALLS—See Cascades Inc.; *Int'l*, pg. 1351
CASCADES TISSUE GROUP - LACHUTE—See Cascades Inc.; *Int'l*, pg. 1351
CASCADES TISSUE GROUP - LAVAL—See Cascades Inc.; *Int'l*, pg. 1351
CASCADES TISSUE GROUP - NEW YORK INC.—See Cascades Inc.; *Int'l*, pg. 1351
CASCADES TISSUE GROUP - OREGON INC.—See Cascades Inc.; *Int'l*, pg. 1351
CASCADES TISSUE GROUP - PENNSYLVANIA INC. (PITTSTON)—See Cascades Inc.; *Int'l*, pg. 1351
CASCADES TISSUE GROUP - PENNSYLVANIA INC. (RANSOM)—See Cascades Inc.; *Int'l*, pg. 1351
CASCADES TISSUE GROUP - ROCKINGHAM—See Cascades Inc.; *Int'l*, pg. 1351
CASCADES TISSUE GROUP—See Cascades Inc.; *Int'l*, pg. 1351
CASCADES TISSUE GROUP - TENNESSEE INC.—See Cascades Inc.; *Int'l*, pg. 1351

CASCADES TRANSPORT INC.—See Cascades Inc.; *Int'l*, pg. 1351
CASCADES USA INC.—See Cascades Inc.; *Int'l*, pg. 1351
CASCADE TECHNOLOGIES, INC.; *U.S. Private*, pg. 781
CASCADE TECHNOLOGIES LIMITED—See Emerson Electric Co.; *U.S. Public*, pg. 742
CASCADETEQ INC.—See AP Memory Technology Corporation; *Int'l*, pg. 499
CASCADE TRANSPORTATION, INC.—See Radiant Logistics, Inc.; *U.S. Public*, pg. 1759
CASCADE (U.K.) LTD.—See Toyota Industries Corporation; *Int'l*, pg. 7868
CASCADE WHOLESALE HARDWARE INC.—See Parr Lumber Company Inc.; *U.S. Public*, pg. 3099
CASCADE WOOD PRODUCTS, INC.; *U.S. Private*, pg. 781
CASCADE XIAMEN FORKLIFT TRUCK ATTACHMENT CO., LTD.—See Toyota Industries Corporation; *Int'l*, pg. 7868
CASCADIA ACQUISITION CORP.; *U.S. Public*, pg. 445
CASCADIA BLOCKCHAIN GROUP CORP.; *Int'l*, pg. 1351
CASCADIA HEALTHCARE LLC; *U.S. Private*, pg. 781
CASCADIA MOTION, LLC—See BorgWarner Inc.; *U.S. Public*, pg. 371
CASCADIA MOTIVATION INC; *Int'l*, pg. 1351
CASCADIAN THERAPEUTICS, INC.—See Seagen Inc.; *U.S. Public*, pg. 1852
CASCADIA PM, LLC—See Centerline Solutions LLC; *U.S. Private*, pg. 816
CASCADIA VEHICLE TENTS, LLC—See Centre Partners Management LLC; *U.S. Private*, pg. 828
CASCADIA WATER, LLC—See Northwest Natural Holding Company; *U.S. Public*, pg. 1542
CASC CONSTRUCTIONS PTY. LTD.—See SRG Global Limited; *Int'l*, pg. 7148
CAS CENTRAL COMPOUNDING BADEN-WURTTEMBERG GMBH—See Medios AG; *Int'l*, pg. 4778
CASC EU S.A.—See Enovos International S.A.; *Int'l*, pg. 2444
C.A. SCHROEDER COMPANY, INC.; *U.S. Private*, pg. 706
CASCIO MUSIC COMPANY INC.—See Geneva Supply, Inc.; *U.S. Private*, pg. 1670
CASCO ADHESIVES AB—See Akzo Nobel N.V.; *Int'l*, pg. 273
CASCO ADHESIVES (ASIA) PTE LTD—See Akzo Nobel N.V.; *Int'l*, pg. 273
CASCO ADHEZIVI D.O.O.—See Akzo Nobel N.V.; *Int'l*, pg. 273
CASCO AUTOMOTIVE SINGAPORE PTE., LTD.—See Amphenol Corporation; *U.S. Public*, pg. 129
CASCO BAY VENDING ENTERPRISES, LLC; *U.S. Private*, pg. 781
CASCO BAY VENDING, LLC—See Casco Bay Vending Enterprises, LLC; *U.S. Private*, pg. 781
CASCO BYGLIM A/S—See Akzo Nobel N.V.; *Int'l*, pg. 273
CASCO DO BRASIL LTDA—See Amphenol Corporation; *U.S. Public*, pg. 129
CASCO HOLDINGS GMBH—See Amphenol Corporation; *U.S. Public*, pg. 129
CASCO IMOS ITALIA S.P.A.—See Veritas Capital Fund Management, LLC; *U.S. Private*, pg. 4364
CASCO IMOS ITALIA S.R.L.—See Amphenol Corporation; *U.S. Public*, pg. 129
CASCO INDUSTRIES INC.; *U.S. Private*, pg. 781
CASCO LTD.; *Int'l*, pg. 1351
CASCO MANUFACTURING SOLUTIONS, INC.; *U.S. Private*, pg. 781
CAS CONSTRUCTORS, LLC—See Alberici Corporation; *U.S. Private*, pg. 152
CASCO PRODUCTS CORPORATION—See The Jordan Company, L.P.; *U.S. Private*, pg. 4060
CAS CORPORATION - CAS CHEMICAL FACTORY—See CAS Corporation; *Int'l*, pg. 1349
CAS CORPORATION - RUTHERFORD BRANCH—See CAS Corporation; *Int'l*, pg. 1349
CAS CORPORATION; *Int'l*, pg. 1349
C A S CORP.—See Jones Sign Co., Inc.; *U.S. Private*, pg. 2234
CASCO RUSSIA—See CASCO Ltd.; *Int'l*, pg. 1351
CASCO SCHOELLER GMBH—See Amphenol Corporation; *U.S. Public*, pg. 129
CASCO SIGNAL LTD.—See Alstom S.A.; *Int'l*, pg. 381
CASCO SIGNAL LTD.—See China National Railway Signal & Communication Corp.; *Int'l*, pg. 1534
CASCO SINGAPORE—See CASCO Ltd.; *Int'l*, pg. 1351
CASDA BIOMATERIALS CO., LTD.—See Arkema S.A.; *Int'l*, pg. 570
CASDEN BANQUE POPULAIRE—See Groupe BPCE; *Int'l*, pg. 3097
CASDEN PROPERTIES INC.; *U.S. Private*, pg. 781
CASDON LIMITED; *Int'l*, pg. 1351
CASDON TOYS LTD.—See Casdon Limited; *Int'l*, pg. 1351
CASDORPH & CURRY FUNERAL HOME, INC.—See Service Corporation International; *U.S. Public*, pg. 1871
CASD SOLUTIONS SDN. BHD.—See Hong Seng Consolidated Berhad; *Int'l*, pg. 3469
CASE ATLANTIC COMPANY—See Keller Group plc; *Int'l*, pg. 4119

CASE BAUMASCHINEN AG.—See CNH Industrial N.V.; *Int'l*, pg. 1675
CASE CENTRAL; *U.S. Private*, pg. 781
CASE CONSTRUCTION MACHINERY (SHANGHAI) CO., LTD—See CNH Industrial N.V.; *Int'l*, pg. 1675
CASE CONTRACTING COMPANY; *U.S. Private*, pg. 781
CASECO TRUCK BODY; *U.S. Private*, pg. 782
CASE DESIGN/REMODELING, INC.; *U.S. Private*, pg. 781
CASEE (BEIJING) INFORMATION TECHNOLOGY COMPANY LIMITED—See Velti plc; *Int'l*, pg. 8150
CASE FARMS, LLC - GOLDSBORO PROCESSING—See Case Foods, Inc.; *U.S. Private*, pg. 781
CASE FARMS, LLC - MORGANTON PRODUCTION & PROCESSING—See Case Foods, Inc.; *U.S. Private*, pg. 782
CASE FARMS, LLC - OHIO PROCESSING—See Case Foods, Inc.; *U.S. Private*, pg. 782
CASE FARMS, LLC—See Case Foods, Inc.; *U.S. Private*, pg. 781
CASE FOODS, INC.; *U.S. Private*, pg. 781
CASE FORENSICS CORP.—See Gryphon Investors, LLC; *U.S. Private*, pg. 1798
CASE FOUNDATION COMPANY—See Keller Group plc; *Int'l*, pg. 4119
CASE FURNITURE & DESIGN, LLC.; *U.S. Private*, pg. 782
CASE GROUP AB; *Int'l*, pg. 1351
CASEKING GMBH—See Gilde Buy Out Partners B.V.; *Int'l*, pg. 2974
CASELA LIMITED—See Medine Limited; *Int'l*, pg. 4777
CASELEX BV—See RELX plc; *Int'l*, pg. 6267
CASELI GMBH—See voestalpine AG; *Int'l*, pg. 8295
CASELLA ESPANA SA—See IDEAL Industries Inc; *U.S. Private*, pg. 2036
CASELLA ORGANICS—See Casella Waste Systems, Inc.; *U.S. Public*, pg. 446
CASELLA RECYCLING, LLC—See Casella Waste Systems, Inc.; *U.S. Public*, pg. 446
CASELLA TRANSPORTATION, INC.—See Casella Waste Systems, Inc.; *U.S. Public*, pg. 446
CASELLA WASTE MANAGEMENT, INC.—See Casella Waste Systems, Inc.; *U.S. Public*, pg. 446
CASELLA WASTE MANAGEMENT OF N.Y., INC. - DUNKIRK—See Casella Waste Systems, Inc.; *U.S. Public*, pg. 446
CASELLA WASTE MANAGEMENT OF PENNSYLVANIA, INC.—See Casella Waste Systems, Inc.; *U.S. Public*, pg. 446
CASELLA WASTE SYSTEMS, INC.; *U.S. Public*, pg. 445
CASELLA WINES PTY. LTD.; *Int'l*, pg. 1351
CASEMAKER, INC.—See SYSCOM Computer Engineering Company; *Int'l*, pg. 7388
CASEM (ASIA) PTE. LTD.—See Manufacturing Integration Technology Ltd; *Int'l*, pg. 4677
CASE 'N DRUM OIL LP; *Int'l*, pg. 1351
CASENET, LLC—See Zyter, Inc.; *U.S. Private*, pg. 4611
CASEN RECORDATI S.L.—See Recordati S.p.A.; *Int'l*, pg. 6239
CASE PACKING SYSTEMS B.V.—See XANO Industri AB; *Int'l*, pg. 8519
CASE PAPER CO., INC.—See Case Paper Company Inc.; *U.S. Private*, pg. 782
CASE PAPER COMPANY INC.; *U.S. Private*, pg. 782
CASE PAPER CO. OF ILLINOIS, INC—See Case Paper Company Inc.; *U.S. Private*, pg. 782
CASE POMEROY & COMPANY INC.; *U.S. Private*, pg. 782
CA SERVICES, LLC—See Broadcom Inc.; *U.S. Public*, pg. 389
CASES BY SOURCE, INC.; *U.S. Private*, pg. 782
CASESTACK, INC.—See Hub Group, Inc.; *U.S. Public*, pg. 1065
CASE SUPPLY INC.; *U.S. Private*, pg. 782
CASETEK HOLDINGS LIMITED; *Int'l*, pg. 1351
CASETTE S.R.L.—See Encavis AG; *Int'l*, pg. 2401
CASE UNITED KINGDOM LIMITED—See CNH Industrial N.V.; *Int'l*, pg. 1674
CASEWARE INTERNATIONAL, INC.; *Int'l*, pg. 1352
CASEWISE SYSTEMS INC.; *U.S. Private*, pg. 782
CASEY AUTO GROUP, INC.; *U.S. Private*, pg. 782
CASEY CO.; *U.S. Private*, pg. 782
CASEY FIRE SYSTEMS, INC.—See Wind Point Advisors LLC; *U.S. Private*, pg. 4535
CASEY INDUSTRIAL INC.; *U.S. Private*, pg. 782
CASEY POTTERY COMPANY LLP; *U.S. Private*, pg. 782
CASEY QUIRK BY DELOITTE—See Deloitte LLP; *U.S. Private*, pg. 1198
CASEY QUIRK BY DELOITTE—See Deloitte Touche Tohmatsu Limited; *Int'l*, pg. 2014
CASEY RESEARCH, LLC; *U.S. Private*, pg. 782
CASEY & SAYRE; *U.S. Private*, pg. 782
CASEY'S FOODS INC.; *U.S. Private*, pg. 782
CASEY'S GENERAL STORES, INC.; *U.S. Public*, pg. 446
CASEY'S INC.; *U.S. Private*, pg. 782
CASEY'S MARKETING COMPANY—See Casey's General Stores, Inc.; *U.S. Public*, pg. 446
CASEY'S RETAIL COMPANY—See Casey's General Stores, Inc.; *U.S. Public*, pg. 446

CASEY'S SERVICES COMPANY—See Casey's General Stores, Inc.; *U.S. Public*, pg. 446
CASH ACME INC.—See IMI plc; *Int'l*, pg. 3624
CASH AMERICA EAST, INC.—See FirstCash Holdings, Inc.; *U.S. Public*, pg. 849
CASH AMERICA, INC. OF ALASKA—See FirstCash Holdings, Inc.; *U.S. Public*, pg. 849
CASH AMERICA, INC. OF ILLINOIS—See FirstCash Holdings, Inc.; *U.S. Public*, pg. 849
CASH AMERICA, INC. OF NORTH CAROLINA—See FirstCash Holdings, Inc.; *U.S. Public*, pg. 849
CASH AMERICA, INC. OF OKLAHOMA—See FirstCash Holdings, Inc.; *U.S. Public*, pg. 849
CASH AMERICA OF MISSOURI, INC.—See FirstCash Holdings, Inc.; *U.S. Public*, pg. 849
CASH AMERICA PAWN L.P.—See FirstCash Holdings, Inc.; *U.S. Public*, pg. 849
CASH ASSET MANAGEMENT LIMITED—See CASH Financial Services Group Limited; *Int'l*, pg. 1352
CASHBUILD LIMITED; *Int'l*, pg. 1352
CASHCALL, INC.; *U.S. Private*, pg. 783
CASH CANADA GROUP LTD.; *Int'l*, pg. 1352
CASH & CARRY GROCER INC.; *U.S. Private*, pg. 782
CASHCO, INC.—See May River Capital, LLC; *U.S. Private*, pg. 2620
CASH COLORADO, LLC—See CURO Group Holdings Corp.; *U.S. Public*, pg. 611
CASH CONSTRUCTION COMPANY, INC.—See MasTec, Inc.; *U.S. Public*, pg. 1393
CASH CONVERTERS INTERNATIONAL LIMITED; *Int'l*, pg. 1352
CASH CONVERTERS PTY LTD—See Cash Converters International Limited; *Int'l*, pg. 1352
CASH CONVERTERS (STORES) PTY LTD—See Cash Converters International Limited; *Int'l*, pg. 1352
CASH CONVERTERS UK HOLDINGS PLC—See Cash Converters International Limited; *Int'l*, pg. 1352
CASHDASH UK LTD.; *Int'l*, pg. 1352
CASH E-TRADE LIMITED—See CASH Financial Services Group Limited; *Int'l*, pg. 1352
CASH FINANCIAL SERVICES GROUP LIMITED; *Int'l*, pg. 1352
CASHFIRST PTY LTD—See Credit Corp Group Limited; *Int'l*, pg. 1835
CASH FLOW SOLUTIONS INC.; *U.S. Private*, pg. 782
CASH FLOW SPOLKA AKCYJNA; *Int'l*, pg. 1352
CASH FREDERICK TAYLOR LIMITED—See CASH Financial Services Group Limited; *Int'l*, pg. 1352
CASHGATE AG—See Cembra Money Bank AG; *Int'l*, pg. 1396
CASHIDO CORPORATION—See RITEK CORPORATION; *Int'l*, pg. 6351
CASHION'S FOOD MART INC.; *U.S. Private*, pg. 783
CASHLAND FINANCIAL SERVICES, INC.—See FirstCash Holdings, Inc.; *U.S. Public*, pg. 849
CASH.LIFE AG; *Int'l*, pg. 1352
CASHMAN EQUIPMENT COMPANY; *U.S. Private*, pg. 783
CASHMAN & KATZ INTEGRATED COMMUNICATIONS; *U.S. Private*, pg. 783
CASHMERE VALLEY BANK; *U.S. Public*, pg. 446
CASH MONEY CHEQUE CASHING, INC.—See CURO Group Holdings Corp.; *U.S. Public*, pg. 611
CASH-N-PAWN INTERNATIONAL, LTD.—See EZCORP, Inc.; *U.S. Public*, pg. 817
CASH-N-PAWN OF MINNESOTA, LTD.—See EZCORP, Inc.; *U.S. Public*, pg. 817
CASH PAYMASTER SERVICES (KWA-ZULU NATAL) (PTY) LTD—See Lesaka Technologies, Inc.; *Int'l*, pg. 4468
CASH PAYMASTER SERVICES (NORTHERN CAPE) (PTY) LIMITED—See Lesaka Technologies, Inc.; *Int'l*, pg. 4468
CASH PAYMASTER SERVICES (NORTHERN) (PTY) LIMITED—See Lesaka Technologies, Inc.; *Int'l*, pg. 4468
CASH PAYMASTER SERVICES (NORTH WEST) (PTY) LIMITED—See Lesaka Technologies, Inc.; *Int'l*, pg. 4468
CASH PAYMASTER SERVICES (PROPRIETARY) LIMITED—See Lesaka Technologies, Inc.; *Int'l*, pg. 4468
CASH QUANT-FINANCE LAB LIMITED—See Celestial Asia Securities Holdings Limited; *Int'l*, pg. 1392
CASH REGISTER SALES INC.; *U.S. Private*, pg. 782
CASHSTAR, INC.—See P2 Capital Partners, LLC; *U.S. Private*, pg. 3061
CASHSTAR, INC.—See Silver Lake Group, LLC; *U.S. Private*, pg. 3656
CASH TECHNOLOGIES, INC.; *U.S. Private*, pg. 782
CASH VAN MANAGEMENT CO., LTD.—See Thai Beverage Public Company Limited; *Int'l*, pg. 7589
CASH-WA DISTRIBUTING COMPANY; *U.S. Private*, pg. 782
CASH-WA FOOD SERVICE—See Cash-Wa Distributing Company; *U.S. Private*, pg. 783
CASHWAY FINTECH CO., LTD.; *Int'l*, pg. 1352
CASH WEALTH MANAGEMENT LIMITED—See CASH Financial Services Group Limited; *Int'l*, pg. 1352

CASHWELL APPLIANCE PARTS INC.; *U.S. Private*, pg. 783
CASH WISE FLOWER SHOPPE INC.—See Coborn's Incorporated; *U.S. Private*, pg. 958
CASIANO COMMUNICATIONS INC.; *U.S. Private*, pg. 783
CASILOC INC.—See Loto-Quebec; *Int'l*, pg. 4559
CASIL OPTOELECTRONIC PRODUCT DEVELOPMENT LIMITED—See China Aerospace International Holdings Limited; *Int'l*, pg. 1481
CASIL TELECOMMUNICATIONS HOLDINGS LIMITED; *Int'l*, pg. 1352
CAS, INC.—See KBR, Inc.; *U.S. Public*, pg. 1216
CA (SINGAPORE) PTE LTD—See Broadcom Inc.; *U.S. Public*, pg. 388
CASING ASSOCIATES LLC—See Wolfson Casing Corp.; *U.S. Private*, pg. 4554
CASING MACRON TECHNOLOGY CO., LTD.; *Int'l*, pg. 1352
CASINGS INC.; *U.S. Private*, pg. 783
CASINJAC, INC.—See First Reserve Management, L.P.; *U.S. Private*, pg. 1526
CASINO CAFETERIA SAS—See Finatis SA; *Int'l*, pg. 2670
CASINO CANBERRA LIMITED—See Aquis Entertainment Limited; *Int'l*, pg. 528
CASINO GUICHARD-PERRACHON SA—See Finatis SA; *Int'l*, pg. 2670
CASINO JOURNAL PUBLISHING GROUP; *U.S. Private*, pg. 783
CASINO MAGIC NEUQUEN SA—See PENN Entertainment, Inc.; *U.S. Public*, pg. 1662
CASINO MINING CORP.—See Western Copper and Gold Corporation; *Int'l*, pg. 8388
CASINO NOVA SCOTIA—See Great Canadian Gaming Corporation; *Int'l*, pg. 3063
CASINO ONE CORPORATION—See Caesars Entertainment, Inc.; *U.S. Public*, pg. 420
CASINO PROPERTIES, INC.—See Archon Corporation; *U.S. Public*, pg. 185
CASINO QUEEN, INC.; *U.S. Private*, pg. 783
CASINOS AUSTRIA AG; *Int'l*, pg. 1352
CASINOS AUSTRIA INTERNATIONAL GMBH—See Casinos Austria AG; *Int'l*, pg. 1352
CASINOS AUSTRIA INTERNATIONAL HOLDINGS GMBH—See Casinos Austria AG; *Int'l*, pg. 1353
CASINOS DU TOUQUET S.A.S.—See Groupe Partouche S.A.; *Int'l*, pg. 3109
CASINOS POLAND LTD.—See Century Casinos, Inc.; *U.S. Public*, pg. 474
CASINO TAMARINDOS, S.A.—See Melia Hotels International, S.A.; *Int'l*, pg. 4809
CASINO TRAVEL & TOURS, LLC—See Remark Holdings, Inc.; *U.S. Public*, pg. 1782
CASINO VACANCES SNC—See Finatis SA; *Int'l*, pg. 2670
CASIN REAL ESTATE DEVELOPMENT GROUP CO., LTD.; *Int'l*, pg. 1352
CASIO AMERICA, INC.—See Casio Computer Co., Ltd.; *Int'l*, pg. 1353
CASIO BENELUX B.V.—See Casio Computer Co., Ltd.; *Int'l*, pg. 1353
CASIO BRASIL COMERCIO DE PRODUTOS ELETRONICOS LTDA.—See Casio Computer Co., Ltd.; *Int'l*, pg. 1353
CASIO CANADA, LTD.—See Casio Computer Co., Ltd.; *Int'l*, pg. 1353
CASIO (CHINA) CO., LTD.—See Casio Computer Co., Ltd.; *Int'l*, pg. 1353
CASIO COMPUTER CO., LTD.; *Int'l*, pg. 1353
CASIO COMPUTER (HONG KONG) LTD.—See Casio Computer Co., Ltd.; *Int'l*, pg. 1353
CASIO ELECTRONIC MANUFACTURING CO., LTD.—See Casio Computer Co., Ltd.; *Int'l*, pg. 1353
CASIO ELECTRONICS CO., LTD.—See Casio Computer Co., Ltd.; *Int'l*, pg. 1353
CASIO ELECTRONICS (SHAOGUAN) CO., LTD.—See Casio Computer Co., Ltd.; *Int'l*, pg. 1353
CASIO ELECTRONICS (SHENZHEN) CO., LTD.—See Casio Computer Co., Ltd.; *Int'l*, pg. 1353
CASIO ELECTRONIC TECHNOLOGY (ZHONGSHAN) CO., LTD.—See Casio Computer Co., Ltd.; *Int'l*, pg. 1353
CASIO ESPANA, S.L.—See Casio Computer Co., Ltd.; *Int'l*, pg. 1353
CASIO EUROPE GMBH—See Casio Computer Co., Ltd.; *Int'l*, pg. 1353
CASIO FRANCE S.A.—See Casio Computer Co., Ltd.; *Int'l*, pg. 1353
CASIO (GUANGZHOU) CO., LTD.—See Casio Computer Co., Ltd.; *Int'l*, pg. 1353
CASIO, INC.—See Casio Computer Co., Ltd.; *Int'l*, pg. 1353
CASIO INDIA COMPANY PRIVATE LTD—See Casio Computer Co., Ltd.; *Int'l*, pg. 1353
CASIO INFORMATION SYSTEMS CO., LTD.—See Casio Computer Co., Ltd.; *Int'l*, pg. 1353
CASIO ITALIA S.R.L.—See Casio Computer Co., Ltd.; *Int'l*, pg. 1353
CASIO KOREA CO., LTD.—See Casio Computer Co., Ltd.; *Int'l*, pg. 1353

COMPANY NAME INDEX

CASIO LATIN AMERICA S.A.—See Casio Computer Co., Ltd.; *Int'l*, pg. 1353
THE CASIO LEASE COMPANY LIMITED—See Mitsubishi HC Capital Inc.; *Int'l*, pg. 4952
CASIO MALAYSIA, SDN. BHD.—See Casio Computer Co., Ltd.; *Int'l*, pg. 1353
CASIO MARKETING (THAILAND) CO., LTD.—See Casio Computer Co., Ltd.; *Int'l*, pg. 1353
CASIO MEXICO MARKETING, S. DE R. L. DE C.V.—See Casio Computer Co., Ltd.; *Int'l*, pg. 1353
CASIO MICRONICS CO., LTD.—See Casio Computer Co., Ltd.; *Int'l*, pg. 1353
CASIO MIDDLE EAST & AFRICA FZE—See Casio Computer Co., Ltd.; *Int'l*, pg. 1353
CASIO PHILIPPINES CORPORATION—See Casio Computer Co., Ltd.; *Int'l*, pg. 1353
CASIO SCANDINAVIA AS—See Casio Computer Co., Ltd.; *Int'l*, pg. 1353
CASIO SINGAPORE PTE., LTD.—See Casio Computer Co., Ltd.; *Int'l*, pg. 1353
CASIO TAIWAN CO., LTD.—See Casio Computer Co., Ltd.; *Int'l*, pg. 1353
CASIO TECHNO CO., LTD.—See Casio Computer Co., Ltd.; *Int'l*, pg. 1353
CASIO (THAILAND) CO., LTD.—See Casio Computer Co., Ltd.; *Int'l*, pg. 1353
CASIO TIMEPIECE (DONGGUAN) CO., LTD.—See Casio Computer Co., Ltd.; *Int'l*, pg. 1353
CASI PHARMACEUTICALS (CHINA) CO., LTD.—See CASI Pharmaceuticals, Inc.; *Int'l*, pg. 1352
CASI PHARMACEUTICALS, INC.; *Int'l*, pg. 1352
CASITA ENTERPRISES, INC.; *U.S. Private*, pg. 783
CASIX INC.—See H&Q Asia Pacific, Ltd.; *U.S. Private*, pg. 1823
CASKET SHELLS, INC.; *U.S. Private*, pg. 783
CASK, LLC; *U.S. Private*, pg. 783
CASK 'N CLEAVER—See C&C Organization Inc.; *U.S. Private*, pg. 702
CASK 'N CLEAVER—See C&C Organization Inc.; *U.S. Private*, pg. 702
CASK 'N CLEAVER—See C&C Organization Inc.; *U.S. Private*, pg. 702
CAS MEDICAL SYSTEMS, INC.—See Edwards Lifesciences Corporation; *U.S. Public*, pg. 720
CASM, INC.—See CyberAgent, Inc.; *Int'l*, pg. 1002
CASMONT SAS—See HORIBA Ltd; *Int'l*, pg. 3475
CASMYN MINING ZIMBABWE (PRIVATE) LTD—See New Dawn Mining Corp.; *Int'l*, pg. 5222
CASNIK FINANCE, D.O.O.—See Bonnier AB; *Int'l*, pg. 1108
CA SOFTWARE B.V.—See Broadcom Inc.; *U.S. Public*, pg. 389
CA SOFTWARE DE COLOMBIA S.A.—See Broadcom Inc.; *U.S. Public*, pg. 389
CA SOFTWARE DE PERU S.A.—See Broadcom Inc.; *U.S. Public*, pg. 389
CA SOFTWARE FINLAND OY—See Broadcom Inc.; *U.S. Public*, pg. 389
CA SOFTWARE FINLAND OY—See Broadcom Inc.; *U.S. Public*, pg. 389
CA SOFTWARE ISRAEL LTD.—See Broadcom Inc.; *U.S. Public*, pg. 389
CA SOFTWARE NORWAY A/S—See Broadcom Inc.; *U.S. Public*, pg. 389
CA SOFTWARE OSTERREICH GMBH—See Broadcom Inc.; *U.S. Public*, pg. 389
CA SOFTWARE SWEDEN AB—See Broadcom Inc.; *U.S. Public*, pg. 389
CASON NIGHTINGALE CREATIVE COMMUNICATIONS; *U.S. Private*, pg. 783
CA SOUTHERN AFRICA (PTY) LIMITED—See EOH HOLDINGS LIMITED; *Int'l*, pg. 2457
CAS PAPER MILL CO.—See Charoen Aksorn Holding Group Co. Ltd.; *Int'l*, pg. 1451
CASPAR ASSET MANAGEMENT SA; *Int'l*, pg. 1354
CASPARI MCCORMICK—See Aloysius, Butler & Clark Associates, Inc.; *U.S. Private*, pg. 196
CA SPECIALITIES LLC—See Charkit Chemical Company, LLC; *U.S. Private*, pg. 851
C.A. SPENCER INC.; *Int'l*, pg. 1240
CASPER COLOSIMO & SON INC.; *U.S. Private*, pg. 783
CASPERS COMPANY; *U.S. Private*, pg. 783
CASPER'S ICE CREAM, INC.—See MidOcean Partners, LLP; *U.S. Private*, pg. 2716
CASPER SLEEP INC.; *U.S. Public*, pg. 446
CASPIAN BEVERAGE HOLDING JSC; *Int'l*, pg. 1354
CASPIAN CAPITAL B.V.—See Baring Vostok Capital Partners; *Int'l*, pg. 865
CASPIAN CORPORATE SERVICES LIMITED; *Int'l*, pg. 1354
CASPIAN DRILLER PTE. LTD.—See China International Marine Containers (Group) Co., Ltd.; *Int'l*, pg. 1511
CASPIAN DRILLING COMPANY JV—See State Oil Co. of Azerbaijan Republic; *Int'l*, pg. 7184
CASPIAN ENERGY INC.; *Int'l*, pg. 1354
THE CASPIAN INTERNATIONAL RESTAURANTS COMPANY, LLP—See Adeptio LLC; *Int'l*, pg. 143
CASPIAN SERVICES, INC.; *U.S. Public*, pg. 446
CASPIAN SERVICES INC.; *Int'l*, pg. 1354

CASPIAN SHIPYARD COMPANY LIMITED—See Sembcorp Industries Ltd.; *Int'l*, pg. 6703
CASPIAN STAR CAVIAR INC.; *U.S. Private*, pg. 783
CASPIAN SUNRISE PLC; *Int'l*, pg. 1354
CASPIDA, INC.—See Cisco Systems, Inc.; *U.S. Public*, pg. 500
CASPI LIMITED LLP—See Chagala Group Limited; *Int'l*, pg. 1436
CASPIN RESOURCES LIMITED; *Int'l*, pg. 1354
CASPIO, INC.; *U.S. Private*, pg. 783
CASPIY COMMODITY EXCHANGE JSC; *Int'l*, pg. 1354
CAS POLSKA SP. Z O.O.—See CAS Corporation; *Int'l*, pg. 1349
CA SP. Z.O.O.—See Broadcom Inc.; *U.S. Public*, pg. 389
CA S.R.L.—See Broadcom Inc.; *U.S. Public*, pg. 389
CASSA CENTRALE BANCA-CREDITO COOPERATIVO DEL NORD EST SPA; *Int'l*, pg. 1354
CASSADAY & COMPANY, INC.; *U.S. Private*, pg. 783
CASSA DEI RISPARMI DI FORLI E DELLA ROMAGNA S.P.A.—See Intesa Sanpaolo S.p.A.; *Int'l*, pg. 3765
CASSA DEPOSITI E PRESTITI S.P.A.; *Int'l*, pg. 1354
CASSA DI COMPENSAZIONE E GARANZIA S.P.A.—See London Stock Exchange Group plc; *Int'l*, pg. 4547
CASSA DI RISPARMIO DEL FRIULI VENEZIA GIULIA S.P.A.—See Intesa Sanpaolo S.p.A.; *Int'l*, pg. 3765
CASSA DI RISPARMIO DELLA PROVINCIA DELL AQUILA S.P.A.—See BPER BANCA S.p.A; *Int'l*, pg. 1132
CASSA DI RISPARMIO DELLA SPEZIA S.P.A.—See Intesa Sanpaolo S.p.A.; *Int'l*, pg. 3764
CASSA DI RISPARMIO DEL VENETO S.P.A.—See Intesa Sanpaolo S.p.A.; *Int'l*, pg. 3765
CASSA DI RISPARMIO DI ASTI S.P.A.; *Int'l*, pg. 1355
CASSA DI RISPARMIO DI BIELLA E VERCELLI S.P.A.—See Cassa di Risparmio di Asti S.p.A.; *Int'l*, pg. 1355
CASSA DI RISPARMIO DI CITTA DI CASTELLO S.P.A.—See Intesa Sanpaolo S.p.A.; *Int'l*, pg. 3765
CASSA DI RISPARMIO DI FANO S.P.A.—See Credito Valtellinese Societa Cooperativa; *Int'l*, pg. 1837
CASSANDRA TRADING LTD—See N.K. Shacolas (Holdings) Ltd.; *Int'l*, pg. 5116
CASSANO'S INC.; *U.S. Private*, pg. 783
CASSA RURALE ED ARTIGIANA DI BINASCO CREDITO COOPERATIVO; *Int'l*, pg. 1355
CASSAVANT MACHINING, INC.—See Gallant Capital Partners, LLC; *U.S. Private*, pg. 1639
CASSAVA SCIENCES, INC.; *U.S. Public*, pg. 447
CASS-CLAY CREAMERY—See Associated Milk Producers, Inc.; *U.S. Private*, pg. 356
CASS COMMERCIAL BANK—See Cass Information Systems, Inc.; *U.S. Public*, pg. 447
CASS COUNTY BUTANE CO., INC.—See Ferrellgas Partners, L.P.; *U.S. Public*, pg. 829
CASS COUNTY ELECTRIC COOPERATIVE, INC.; *U.S. Private*, pg. 783
CASS COUNTY PUBLISHING COMPANY, INC.—See Chatham Asset Management, LLC; *U.S. Private*, pg. 866
CASSEL & COMPANY—See ADvTECH Limited; *Int'l*, pg. 168
CASSEL SALPETER & CO., LLC; *U.S. Private*, pg. 783
CASSENA CARE LLC; *U.S. Private*, pg. 784
CASSENS TRANSPORT COMPANY; *U.S. Private*, pg. 784
CAS SEVERN INC; *U.S. Private*, pg. 777
CASS HOLDING LLC; *U.S. Private*, pg. 783
CASSIAR GOLD CORP.; *Int'l*, pg. 1355
CASSIDIAN AIR SYSTEMS GMBH.—See Airbus SE; *Int'l*, pg. 242
CASSIDIAN BELGIUM N.V.—See Airbus SE; *Int'l*, pg. 242
CASSIDIAN COMMUNICATIONS GMBH—See Airbus SE; *Int'l*, pg. 242
CASSIDIAN CYBERSECURITY SAS—See Airbus SE; *Int'l*, pg. 242
CASSIDIAN DEFESA E SEGURANCA DO BRASIL LTDA.—See Airbus SE; *Int'l*, pg. 242
CASSIDIAN FINLAND OY—See Airbus SE; *Int'l*, pg. 242
CASSIDIAN HONG KONG LIMITED—See Airbus SE; *Int'l*, pg. 242
CASSIDIAN MEXICO S.A DE C.V.—See Airbus SE; *Int'l*, pg. 242
CASSIDIAN REAL ESTATE MANCHING GMBH & CO. KG—See Airbus SE; *Int'l*, pg. 242
CASSIDIAN REAL ESTATE ULM/UNTERSCHLEISSHEIM GMBH & CO. KG—See Airbus SE; *Int'l*, pg. 242
CASSIDIAN S.A.S.—See Airbus SE; *Int'l*, pg. 242
CASSIDIAN SOLUTIONS S.A.U.—See Airbus SE; *Int'l*, pg. 242
CASSIDY & ASSOCIATES/WEBER SHANDWICK GOVERNMENT RELATIONS—See The Interpublic Group of Companies, Inc.; *U.S. Public*, pg. 2104
CASSIDY & COMPANY, LLC—See Galiot Insurance Services, Inc.; *U.S. Private*, pg. 1638
CASSIDY DAVIS EUROPE BV—See Guardian Holdings Limited; *Int'l*, pg. 3171
CASSIDY GOLD CORP.; *Int'l*, pg. 1355
THE CASSIDY ORGANIZATION, INC.; *U.S. Private*, pg. 4005

CASSIDY TECHNOLOGIES—See Alarmax Distributors Inc.; *U.S. Private*, pg. 150
CASSINA IXC. LTD.—See UNIMAT Life Corporation; *Int'l*, pg. 8048
CASSINA S.P.A.—See Haworth, Inc.; *U.S. Private*, pg. 1883
CASS INFORMATION SYSTEMS, INC.; *U.S. Public*, pg. 447
CASSINI RESOURCES LIMITED—See BHP Group Limited; *Int'l*, pg. 1016
CASS INTERNATIONAL LLC—See Cass Information Systems, Inc.; *U.S. Public*, pg. 447
CASSIOPEA SPA—See Cosmo Pharmaceuticals N.V.; *Int'l*, pg. 1813
CASSITY JONES LP; *U.S. Private*, pg. 784
CASSIUS MINING LIMITED; *Int'l*, pg. 1355
CASSIUS VENTURES LTD.; *Int'l*, pg. 1355
CASSLING DIAGNOSTIC IMAGING INC.; *U.S. Private*, pg. 784
CASSON-MARK CORP.; *U.S. Private*, pg. 784
CASSONS PTY LTD—See MotorCycle Holdings Limited; *Int'l*, pg. 5054
CASS PAK INDUSTRIES LIMITED; *Int'l*, pg. 1354
CASS SCREW MACHINE PRODUCTS LLC—See Heartland Equity Management LLC; *U.S. Private*, pg. 1900
CASTA DIVA GROUP; *Int'l*, pg. 1355
CASTALLOY INC.—See Alcon Industries Inc.; *U.S. Private*, pg. 154
CAST ALUMINUM SOLUTIONS, LLC; *U.S. Private*, pg. 784
CASTANEA PARTNERS, INC.; *U.S. Private*, pg. 784
CAST BENELUX SA—See CAST S.A.; *Int'l*, pg. 1355
CASTCONSULT SDN. BHD.—See Tai Sin Electric Limited; *Int'l*, pg. 7409
CAST-CRETE USA, LLC—See Stonebridge Partners, LLC; *U.S. Private*, pg. 3827
CAST & CREW ENTERTAINMENT SERVICES LLC—See EQT AB; *Int'l*, pg. 2473
CASTEC CO.,LTD.—See Nagano Keiki Co., Ltd.; *Int'l*, pg. 5125
CASTECH INC.; *Int'l*, pg. 1355
CASTEC, INC. & ONA CORPORATION—See CFS Group, Inc.; *Int'l*, pg. 1430
CASTEC KOREA CO., LTD.; *Int'l*, pg. 1355
CASTEEL HEATING AND COOLING, INC.—See New Mountain Capital, LLC; *U.S. Private*, pg. 2902
CASTEL ALU JARNAC—See FAYAT SAS; *Int'l*, pg. 2625
CASTEL ALU—See FAYAT SAS; *Int'l*, pg. 2625
CASTELAN LTD.; *Int'l*, pg. 1356
CASTELBAJAC CO., LTD.; *Int'l*, pg. 1356
CASTEL ET FROMAGET ASIA—See FAYAT SAS; *Int'l*, pg. 2625
CASTEL ET FROMAGET REUNION—See FAYAT SAS; *Int'l*, pg. 2625
CASTEL ET FROMAGET—See FAYAT SAS; *Int'l*, pg. 2625
CASTEL FRERES SA; *Int'l*, pg. 1355
CASTELLA ENTREPRENAD AB—See Sdiptech AB; *Int'l*, pg. 6658
CASTELLA IMPORTS, INC.; *U.S. Private*, pg. 784
CASTELLANA PHYSICIAN SERVICES, LLC—See Elevance Health, Inc.; *U.S. Public*, pg. 309
CASTELLAN SOLUTIONS LLC—See Resurgens Technology Partners, LLC; *U.S. Private*, pg. 3410
CASTELLAR VIDRIO, S.A.—See Vidrala S.A.; *Int'l*, pg. 8192
CASTELL HOWELL FOODS LTD.; *Int'l*, pg. 1356
CASTELLINI COMPANY, INC.; *U.S. Private*, pg. 784
CASTELLI S.P.A.—See Mutares SE & Co. KGaA; *Int'l*, pg. 5104
CASTELLI S.R.L. I.L.—See Mutares SE & Co. KGaA; *Int'l*, pg. 5104
CASTELLI UK LTD—See Groupe Lactalis SA; *Int'l*, pg. 3106
CASTELLO BANFI SRL—See Banfi Product Corp.; *U.S. Private*, pg. 465
CASTELLO SGR S.P.A.—See ANIMA Holding S.p.A.; *Int'l*, pg. 471
CASTELL SAFETY INTERNATIONAL LIMITED—See Halma plc; *Int'l*, pg. 3231
CASTELL SATCOM RADIO LTD—See HAL Trust N.V.; *Int'l*, pg. 3226
CASTELLUM AB; *Int'l*, pg. 1356
CASTELLUM, INC.; *U.S. Public*, pg. 447
CASTELMAC, S.P.A.—See Ali Holding S.r.l; *Int'l*, pg. 321
CASTEL MALAWI LIMITED—See Castel Freres SA; *Int'l*, pg. 1356
CASTELNAU GROUP LIMITED; *Int'l*, pg. 1356
CASTELNOU ENERGIA S.L.—See ENGIE SA; *Int'l*, pg. 2431
CASTEX TECHNOLOGIES LIMITED—See Amtek Auto Limited; *Int'l*, pg. 441
CAST-FAB TECHNOLOGIES, INC.; *U.S. Private*, pg. 784
CASTFAST INDUSTRIAL COMPANY LIMITED—See Huscoke Holdings Limited; *Int'l*, pg. 3538
CASTFAST MAGNETICS MOULDING LIMITED—See Karrie International Holdings Limited; *Int'l*, pg. 4085
CAST FILM JAPAN CO., LTD.—See DIC Corporation; *Int'l*, pg. 2107

CAST-FAB TECHNOLOGIES, INC.

CASTIK CAPITAL PARTNERS GMBH—See Castik Capital S.a.r.l.; *Int'l*, pg. 1356
CASTIK CAPITAL S.A.R.L.; *Int'l*, pg. 1356
CASTLE VENTURES; *U.S. Private*, pg. 784
CASTILLA DESIGN PTE. LTD.—See TT International Limited; *Int'l*, pg. 7960
CASTILLIAN METAIS LTDA.; *Int'l*, pg. 1356
CASTILLO COPPER LIMITED; *Int'l*, pg. 1357
CASTILLO OGILVY & MATHER—See WPP plc; *Int'l*, pg. 8484
CASTING & FORGING CO., LTD.—See Hitachi Zosen Corporation; *Int'l*, pg. 3410
CASTING & SMELTING SUB-CO.—See Taiyuan Heavy Industry Co., Ltd.; *Int'l*, pg. 7427
CASTING SOLUTIONS, LLC—See Burnham Holdings, Inc.; *U.S. Public*, pg. 412
CASTINGS PLC; *Int'l*, pg. 1357
CASTING TECHNOLOGY COMPANY—See Monomoy Capital Partners LLC; *U.S. Private*, pg. 2772
CAST ITALIA S.R.L.—See CAST S.A.; *Int'l*, pg. 1355
CAST LABORATORIES (CAMBODIA) CO. LTD.—See Tai Sin Electric Limited; *Int'l*, pg. 7409
CAST LABORATORIES PTE. LTD.—See Tai Sin Electric Limited; *Int'l*, pg. 7409
CASTLE ADVERTISING; *U.S. Private*, pg. 784
CASTLE (AM) & CO; *U.S. Private*, pg. 784
CASTLE BANK N.A.—See First National of Nebraska, Inc.; *U.S. Private*, pg. 1523
CASTLEBAR CAPITAL CORP.; *Int'l*, pg. 1357
CASTLE BIOSCIENCES, INC.; *U.S. Public*, pg. 447
CASTLE BRANDS INC.—See Pernod Ricard S.A.; *Int'l*, pg. 5809
CASTLE BRANDS SPIRITS COMPANY LIMITED—See Pernod Ricard S.A.; *Int'l*, pg. 5809
CASTLE BRIDGE IMPACT MEDIA INC.; *Int'l*, pg. 1357
CASTLE BUICK PONTIAC GMC INC.; *U.S. Private*, pg. 784
CASTLE BUILDING PRODUCTS LIMITED—See Heidelberg Materials AG; *Int'l*, pg. 3309
CASTLE CAIRN (INSURANCE BROKERS) LIMITED—See Marsh & McLennan Companies, Inc.; *U.S. Public*, pg. 1374
CASTLECAP CAPITAL, INC.; *Int'l*, pg. 1357
CASTLE CEMENT (CHATBURN) LIMITED—See Heidelberg Materials AG; *Int'l*, pg. 3309
CASTLE CEMENT LIMITED—See Heidelberg Materials AG; *Int'l*, pg. 3309
CASTLE CEMENT LTD. - PADESWOOD WORKS—See Heidelberg Materials AG; *Int'l*, pg. 3308
CASTLE CEMENT (RIBBLESDALE) LIMITED—See Heidelberg Materials AG; *Int'l*, pg. 3309
CASTLE CHEVROLET, INC.; *U.S. Private*, pg. 784
CASTLE COLOURS LTD.—See American Securities LLC; *U.S. Private*, pg. 253
CASTLE COMPUTER SERVICES LTD.—See BGF Group PLC; *Int'l*, pg. 1007
CASTLE CONCRETE COMPANY—See Bee Street Holdings LLC; *U.S. Private*, pg. 513
CASTLE CONNOLLY MEDICAL LTD.—See Ziff Davis, Inc.; *U.S. Public*, pg. 2404
CASTLE CONTRACTING, LLC—See McCarthy Holdings, Inc.; *U.S. Private*, pg. 2627
CASTLE & COOKE, INC.—See Murdock Holdings, LLC; *U.S. Private*, pg. 2814
CASTLE & COOKE PROPERTIES, INC.—See Murdock Holdings, LLC; *U.S. Private*, pg. 2814
CASTLE CO-PACKERS LLC; *U.S. Private*, pg. 784
CASTLE CREEK PHARMACEUTICALS HOLDINGS, INC.; *U.S. Public*, pg. 447
CASTLE DENTAL, INC.—See Gryphon Investors, LLC; *U.S. Private*, pg. 1799
CASTLE EXPLORATION INC.—See Veris Gold Corp.; *Int'l*, pg. 8169
CASTLE FUELS INC.; *Int'l*, pg. 1357
THE CASTLE GROUP; *U.S. Private*, pg. 4006
CASTLE HARLAN, INC.; *U.S. Private*, pg. 784
CASTLEHEAD, INC. ESCROWS; *U.S. Private*, pg. 785
CASTLE HILL RSL CLUB LTD.; *Int'l*, pg. 1357
CASTLE HONDA; *U.S. Private*, pg. 785
CASTLE HOSPITALITY GROUP; *U.S. Public*, pg. 447
CASTLE INDUSTRIES—See M.C. Gill Corporation; *U.S. Private*, pg. 2528
CASTLE INSURANCE SERVICES (NORTH EAST) LIMITED—See Brown & Brown, Inc.; *U.S. Public*, pg. 400
CASTLE INVESTMENT SOLUTIONS LIMITED—See Rathbones Group Plc; *Int'l*, pg. 6214
CASTLE ISLAND PARTNERS LLC; *U.S. Private*, pg. 785
CASTLE JEWELRY; *U.S. Private*, pg. 785
CASTLELAKE, L.P.; *U.S. Private*, pg. 785
CASTLELINE HOLDINGS, LLC—See Altisource Portfolio Solutions S.A.; *Int'l*, pg. 393
CASTLEMAINE PERKINS PTY. LTD.—See Kirin Holdings Company, Limited; *Int'l*, pg. 4189
CASTLE METAL-PHOENIX—See A. M. Castle & Co.; *U.S. Public*, pg. 11
CASTLE METALS AEROSPACE—See A. M. Castle & Co.; *U.S. Public*, pg. 11

CASTLE METALS - CLEVELAND—See A. M. Castle & Co.; *U.S. Public*, pg. 11
CASTLE METALS DE MEXICALI, S.A. DE C.V.—See A. M. Castle & Co.; *U.S. Public*, pg. 11
CASTLE METALS FRANCE—See A. M. Castle & Co.; *U.S. Public*, pg. 11
CASTLE METALS FRANCE—See A. M. Castle & Co.; *U.S. Public*, pg. 11
CASTLE METALS - LOS ANGELES—See A. M. Castle & Co.; *U.S. Public*, pg. 11
CASTLE METALS UK LIMITED—See A. M. Castle & Co.; *U.S. Public*, pg. 11
CASTLE MINERALS LIMITED; *Int'l*, pg. 1357
CASTLENET TECHNOLOGY, INC.; *Int'l*, pg. 1357
CASTLE PARCELS - CHRISTCHURCH—See Freightways Group Limited; *Int'l*, pg. 2771
CASTLE PARCELS LIMITED—See Freightways Group Limited; *Int'l*, pg. 2771
CASTLE PARCELS - WELLINGTON—See Freightways Group Limited; *Int'l*, pg. 2771
CASTLE PARK (WEST DURRINGTON) MANAGEMENT COMPANY LIMITED—See Persimmon plc; *Int'l*, pg. 5815
CASTLE PEAK HOLDINGS PUBLIC COMPANY LIMITED; *Int'l*, pg. 1357
CASTLE PEAK MINING LIMITED; *Int'l*, pg. 1357
CASTLE PEAK POWER COMPANY LIMITED—See Exxon Mobil Corporation; *U.S. Public*, pg. 813
CASTLE PEAK REAL ESTATE CO., LTD.—See Castle Peak Holdings Public Company Limited; *Int'l*, pg. 1357
CASTLE PRIVATE EQUITY AG; *Int'l*, pg. 1357
CASTLE RESORTS & HOTELS, INC.—See Castle Hospitality Group; *U.S. Public*, pg. 447
CASTLE ROCK EDINVAR HOUSING ASSOCIATION LIMITED—See Places for People Group Limited; *Int'l*, pg. 5888
CASTLE ROCK ENTERTAINMENT, INC.—See Warner Bros. Discovery, Inc.; *U.S. Public*, pg. 2328
CASTLEROCK INNOVATIONS, LLC—See Bain Capital, LP; *U.S. Private*, pg. 439
CASTLE ROCK SURGERY CENTER, LLC—See Tenet Healthcare Corporation; *U.S. Public*, pg. 2009
CASTLE ROCK SURGICENTER, LLC—See UnitedHealth Group Incorporated; *U.S. Public*, pg. 2239
CASTLES TECHNOLOGY CO., LTD; *Int'l*, pg. 1357
CASTLES TECHNOLOGY EUROPE S.R.L.—See Castles Technology Co., Ltd; *Int'l*, pg. 1357
CASTLES TECHNOLOGY INTERNATIONAL CORP.—See Castles Technology Co., Ltd; *Int'l*, pg. 1357
CASTLES TECHNOLOGY SINGAPORE PTE. LTD.—See Castles Technology Co., Ltd; *Int'l*, pg. 1357
CASTLES TECHNOLOGY SPAIN SL—See Castles Technology Co., Ltd; *Int'l*, pg. 1357
CASTLES TECHNOLOGY UK & IRELAND LTD.—See Castles Technology Co., Ltd; *Int'l*, pg. 1357
CASTLETON COMMODITIES INTERNATIONAL LLC - HOUSTON OFFICE—See Castleton Commodities International LLC; *U.S. Private*, pg. 785
CASTLETON COMMODITIES INTERNATIONAL LLC; *U.S. Private*, pg. 785
CASTLETON TECHNOLOGY PLC—See GI Manager L.P.; *U.S. Private*, pg. 1693
CASTLEVIEW HOSPITAL, LLC—See Apollo Global Management, Inc.; *U.S. Public*, pg. 154
CASTLE VIEW (NETHERTON) MANAGEMENT COMPANY LIMITED—See Persimmon plc; *Int'l*, pg. 5815
CASTLEVIEW PROPERTY FUND LTD.; *Int'l*, pg. 1357
CASTLEWOOD REALTY COMPANY; *U.S. Private*, pg. 785
CASTLEWOOD REINSURANCE COMPANY—See Reinsurance Group of America, Inc.; *U.S. Public*, pg. 1777
CASTLIGHT HEALTH, INC.; *U.S. Public*, pg. 447
CAST METAL SERVICES PTY LIMITED—See Hitachi, Ltd.; *Int'l*, pg. 3415
CASTOLIN AS—See MEC Holding GmbH; *Int'l*, pg. 4764
CASTOLIN EUTECTIC INTERNATIONAL S.A.—See MEC Holding GmbH; *Int'l*, pg. 4764
CASTOLIN EUTECTIC IRELAND LTD.—See MEC Holding GmbH; *Int'l*, pg. 4764
CASTOLIN EUTECTIC LTD.—See MEC Holding GmbH; *Int'l*, pg. 4764
CASTOLIN GMBH—See MEC Holding GmbH; *Int'l*, pg. 4764
CASTOLIN IBERICA, S.A.—See MEC Holding GmbH; *Int'l*, pg. 4764
CASTOLIN KAYNAK SAN. VE TIC. LTD. STI.—See MEC Holding GmbH; *Int'l*, pg. 4764
CASTOLIN KFT.—See MEC Holding GmbH; *Int'l*, pg. 4764
CASTOLIN SCANDINAVIA AB—See MEC Holding GmbH; *Int'l*, pg. 4764
CASTONGIAS INC.; *U.S. Private*, pg. 785
CASTONGUAY BLASTING LIMITED—See Incitec Pivot Limited; *Int'l*, pg. 3647
CASTONGUAY G.P.—See Incitec Pivot Limited; *Int'l*, pg. 3647
CASTORAMA-DUBOIS INVESTISSEMENTS—See Kingfisher plc; *Int'l*, pg. 4173
CASTORAMA FRANCE S.A.S—See Kingfisher plc; *Int'l*, pg. 4173

CORPORATE AFFILIATIONS

CASTORAMA POLSKA SP. Z O.O—See Kingfisher plc; *Int'l*, pg. 4173
CASTORAMA RUS LLC; *Int'l*, pg. 1357
CASTOR DRILLING SOLUTION AS—See Cassa Depositi e Prestiti S.p.A.; *Int'l*, pg. 1355
CASTOR & LADDER PROPRIETARY LIMITED—See ARGENT INDUSTRIAL LIMITED; *Int'l*, pg. 560
CASTOR MARITIME INC.; *Int'l*, pg. 1357
CASTOR & POLLUX PET WORKS; *U.S. Private*, pg. 785
CASTO; *U.S. Private*, pg. 785
CASTO TRAVEL US, LLC—See Flight Centre Travel Group Limited; *Int'l*, pg. 2706
CASTRICO CO., LTD.; *Int'l*, pg. 1358
CAST-RITE INTERNATIONAL INC.—See Perella Weinberg Partners LP; *U.S. Public*, pg. 1674
CASTRO CHEESE COMPANY INC.—See Dairy Farmers of America, Inc.; *U.S. Private*, pg. 1145
CASTROL AUSTRALIA PTY. LTD.—See BP plc; *Int'l*, pg. 1130
CASTROL AUSTRIA GMBH—See BP plc; *Int'l*, pg. 1130
CASTROL BP PETCO CO., LTD.—See BP plc; *Int'l*, pg. 1131
CASTROL BP PETCO CO., LTD.—See Saigon Petroleum Service Company; *Int'l*, pg. 6483
CASTROL BRASIL LIMITADA—See BP plc; *Int'l*, pg. 1130
CASTROL CHILE SA—See BP plc; *Int'l*, pg. 1130
CASTROL COLOMBIA LIMITADA—See BP plc; *Int'l*, pg. 1130
CASTROL CROATIA D.O.O.—See BP plc; *Int'l*, pg. 1130
CASTROL FRANCE SA—See BP plc; *Int'l*, pg. 1130
CASTROL HELLAS S.A.—See BP plc; *Int'l*, pg. 1130
CASTROL HUNGARY LTD—See BP plc; *Int'l*, pg. 1130
CASTROL INDIA LIMITED—See BP plc; *Int'l*, pg. 1130
CASTROL INDUSTRIAL NORTH AMERICA INC.—See BP plc; *Int'l*, pg. 1127
CASTROL INDUSTRIAL NORTH AMERICA—See BP plc; *Int'l*, pg. 1127
CASTROL INDUSTRIA—See BP plc; *Int'l*, pg. 1130
CASTROL INDUSTRIE SCHWITZERLAND—See BP plc; *Int'l*, pg. 1130
CASTROL IRELAND LTD.—See BP plc; *Int'l*, pg. 1130
CASTROL K.K.—See BP plc; *Int'l*, pg. 1130
CASTROL LIMITED—See BP plc; *Int'l*, pg. 1130
CASTROL LUBRICANTS (CR), S.R.O.—See BP plc; *Int'l*, pg. 1130
CASTROL (MALAYSIA) SDN. BHD.—See BP plc; *Int'l*, pg. 1130
CASTROL NEDERLAND B.V.—See BP plc; *Int'l*, pg. 1130
CASTROL NORTH AMERICA AUTO—See BP plc; *Int'l*, pg. 1127
CASTROL NORTH AMERICA INC.—See BP plc; *Int'l*, pg. 1127
CASTROL NZ LTD.—See BP plc; *Int'l*, pg. 1130
CASTROL PAKISTAN PVT. LTD.—See BP plc; *Int'l*, pg. 1130
CASTROL PHILIPPINES, INC.—See BP plc; *Int'l*, pg. 1130
CASTROL (SHENZHEN) CO. LTD.—See BP plc; *Int'l*, pg. 1130
CASTROL SINGAPORE PTE. LTD.—See BP plc; *Int'l*, pg. 1130
CASTROL SLOVENIJA D.O.O.—See BP plc; *Int'l*, pg. 1130
CASTROL SLOVENSKO, S.R.O.—See BP plc; *Int'l*, pg. 1131
CASTROL (SWITZERLAND) AG—See BP plc; *Int'l*, pg. 1130
CASTROL (U.K.) LIMITED—See BP plc; *Int'l*, pg. 1130
CASTROL VIETNAM LTD.—See BP plc; *Int'l*, pg. 1131
CASTROL VIETNAM LTD.—See Saigon Petroleum Service Company; *Int'l*, pg. 6483
CASTRO MODEL LTD.; *Int'l*, pg. 1358
CASTRONICS, INC.—See RNA Inc.; *U.S. Private*, pg. 3452
CAST S.A.; *Int'l*, pg. 1355
CAST SOFTWARE ESPANA SL—See CAST S.A.; *Int'l*, pg. 1355
CAST SOFTWARE INC.—See CAST S.A.; *Int'l*, pg. 1355
CAST SOFTWARE INDIA PRIVATE LIMITED—See CAST S.A.; *Int'l*, pg. 1355
CAST SOFTWARE LTD.—See CAST S.A.; *Int'l*, pg. 1355
CAST TECHNOLOGIES INCORPORATED; *U.S. Private*, pg. 784
CASTTV INC.—See Nexstar Media Group, Inc.; *U.S. Public*, pg. 1524
CASTUP ISRAEL LLC—See Cisco Systems, Inc.; *U.S. Public*, pg. 497
CASTUS A/S—See FMCG Business Partner AB; *Int'l*, pg. 2717
CASUAL DINING GROUP LTD—See Epiris Managers LLP; *Int'l*, pg. 2460
CASUAL ELEGANCE ENTERPRISES, INC.; *U.S. Private*, pg. 786
CASUALFOOD GMBH—See Orior AG; *Int'l*, pg. 5633
CASUAL LAMPS OF CALIFORNIA, INC.; *U.S. Private*, pg. 786
CASUAL LIVING WORLD WIDE—See Littlejohn & Co., LLC; *U.S. Private*, pg. 2470
CASUAL MALE DIRECT, LLC—See Destination XL Group, Inc.; *U.S. Public*, pg. 656

CASUAL MALE RBT, LLC—See Destination XL Group, Inc.; *U.S. Public*, pg. 656
CASUAL MALE RETAIL STORE, LLC—See Destination XL Group, Inc.; *U.S. Public*, pg. 656
CASUAL MALE STORE, LLC—See Destination XL Group, Inc.; *U.S. Public*, pg. 656
CASUARINA MERU SDN. BHD.—See Perak Corporation Berhad; *Int'l*, pg. 5796
CAS WEIGHING INDIA PVT. LTD.—See CAS Corporation; *Int'l*, pg. 1349
CASWELL DIALYSIS, LLC—See DaVita Inc.; *U.S. Public*, pg. 636
CASWELL-MASSEY CO. LTD.—See The Equitium Group, LLC; *U.S. Private*, pg. 4026
CAS (ZHEJIANG) ELECTRONICS CO., LTD.—See CAS Corporation; *Int'l*, pg. 1349
CASZYME, UAB—See Corteva, Inc.; *U.S. Public*, pg. 580
CAT9 GROUP INC.; *Int'l*, pg. 1358
CATA BIOMETRICS GROUP—See Canadian Advanced Technology Alliance; *Int'l*, pg. 1282
CATACAP MANAGEMENT AS; *Int'l*, pg. 1358
CATAI S.R.L.—See Apollo Global Management, Inc.; *U.S. Public*, pg. 160
CATALANA DE SEGURETAT I COMUNICACIONS, S.L.—See Grupo Villar Mir, S.A.U.; *Int'l*, pg. 3138
CATALANA DE TREBALLS PUBLICS, S.A.—See ACS, Actividades de Construccion y Servicios, S.A.; *Int'l*, pg. 110
CATALANO SEAFOOD LIMITED; *Int'l*, pg. 1358
CATALENT ANAGNI S.R.L.—See Catalent, Inc.; *U.S. Public*, pg. 448
CATALENT BRASIL LTDA—See Catalent, Inc.; *U.S. Public*, pg. 448
CATALENT CTS (EDINBURGH) LIMITED—See Catalent, Inc.; *U.S. Public*, pg. 448
CATALENT CTS (SINGAPORE) PVT LTD—See Catalent, Inc.; *U.S. Public*, pg. 448
CATALENT DUSSELDORF GMBH—See Catalent, Inc.; *U.S. Public*, pg. 448
CATALENT GERMANY EBERBACH GMBH—See Catalent, Inc.; *U.S. Public*, pg. 448
CATALENT GERMANY SCHORNDORF GMBH—See Catalent, Inc.; *U.S. Public*, pg. 448
CATALENT HARMANS ROAD, LLC—See Catalent, Inc.; *U.S. Public*, pg. 448
CATALENT HOUSTON, LLC—See Catalent, Inc.; *U.S. Public*, pg. 448
CATALENT, INC.; *U.S. Public*, pg. 448
CATALENT ITALY HOLDING SRL—See Catalent, Inc.; *U.S. Public*, pg. 448
CATALENT JAPAN K.K.—See Catalent, Inc.; *U.S. Public*, pg. 448
CATALENT MICRON TECHNOLOGIES, INC.—See Catalent, Inc.; *U.S. Public*, pg. 448
CATALENT MICRON TECHNOLOGIES LIMITED—See Catalent, Inc.; *U.S. Public*, pg. 448
CATALENT NOTTINGHAM LIMITED—See Catalent, Inc.; *U.S. Public*, pg. 448
CATALENT ONTARIO LIMITED—See Catalent, Inc.; *U.S. Public*, pg. 448
CATALENT OXFORD LIMITED—See Catalent, Inc.; *U.S. Public*, pg. 448
CATALENT PHARMA SOLUTIONS LIMITED—See Catalent, Inc.; *U.S. Public*, pg. 448
CATALENT PHARMA SOLUTIONS, LLC - RALEIGH—See Catalent, Inc.; *U.S. Public*, pg. 448
CATALENT PHARMA SOLUTIONS LTD. - BOLTON—See Catalent, Inc.; *U.S. Public*, pg. 448
CATALENT PRINCETON, LLC—See Catalent, Inc.; *U.S. Public*, pg. 448
CATALENT SAN DIEGO, INC.—See Catalent, Inc.; *U.S. Public*, pg. 448
CATALENT SAN DIEGO INC.—See Catalent, Inc.; *U.S. Public*, pg. 448
CATALENT SHIGA K.K.—See Catalent, Inc.; *U.S. Public*, pg. 448
CATALENT U.K. PACKAGING LIMITED—See Catalent, Inc.; *U.S. Public*, pg. 448
CATALENT URUGUAY S.A.—See Catalent, Inc.; *U.S. Public*, pg. 448
CATALENT USA WOODSTOCK, INC.—See Catalent, Inc.; *U.S. Public*, pg. 448
CATALINA CAFE—See RedEye Coffee Roasting, LLC; *U.S. Private*, pg. 3378
CATALINA CHANNEL EXPRESS INC.; *U.S. Private*, pg. 786
CATALINA CONSULTANTS PTY. LTD.—See Azimut Holding SpA; *Int'l*, pg. 779
CATALINA FINER FOOD CORPORATION—See Promise Holdings, LLC; *U.S. Private*, pg. 3283
CATALINA HOLDINGS (BERMUDA) LTD.—See Apollo Global Management, Inc.; *U.S. Public*, pg. 148
CATALINA HOLDINGS UK LIMITED—See Apollo Global Management, Inc.; *U.S. Public*, pg. 148
CATALINA MARKETING CORPORATION—See Berkshire Partners LLC; *U.S. Private*, pg. 534
CATALINA MARKETING DEUTSCHLAND GMBH—See Berkshire Partners LLC; *U.S. Private*, pg. 534

CATALINA PRODUCTS, LLC—See Coopers Brewery Limited; *Int'l*, pg. 1792
CATALINA RESOURCES LTD; *Int'l*, pg. 1358
CATALINA RESTAURANT GROUP INC.—See Food Management Partners, Inc.; *U.S. Private*, pg. 1561
CATALINA UK LTD.—See Berkshire Partners LLC; *U.S. Private*, pg. 534
CATALINA WORTHING INSURANCE LIMITED—See Apollo Global Management, Inc.; *U.S. Public*, pg. 148
CATALINA YACHTS, INC.; *U.S. Private*, pg. 786
CATALIS LIMITED—See RTC Group Plc; *Int'l*, pg. 6420
CATALIS SE—See NorthEdge Capital LLP; *Int'l*, pg. 5442
CATALOG360 LIMITED—See HCA Healthcare, Inc.; *U.S. Public*, pg. 992
CATALOG HOLDINGS, INC.—See Golden Gate Capital Management II, LLC; *U.S. Private*, pg. 1731
CATALOG MARKETPLACE, INC.—See Capital Resource Partners, L.P.; *U.S. Private*, pg. 742
CATALOGS.COM; *U.S. Private*, pg. 786
CATALONE PIPE & SUPPLY CO.—See Core & Main, Inc.; *U.S. Public*, pg. 576
CATALUNYA BANC, S.A.—See Banco Bilbao Vizcaya Argentaria, S.A.; *Int'l*, pg. 817
CATALYSIS GROUP, INC.; *U.S. Private*, pg. 786
CATALYSIS HOLDING CORPORATION; *U.S. Private*, pg. 786
CATALYSIS LLC—See Catalysis Holding Corporation; *U.S. Private*, pg. 786
CATALYST ACOUSTICS GROUP—See KPS Capital Partners, LP; *U.S. Private*, pg. 2347
CATALYST AWARENESS INC.—See Intertek Group plc; *Int'l*, pg. 3762
CATALYST BANCORP, INC.; *U.S. Public*, pg. 449
CATALYST BIO, INC.—See GNI Group Ltd.; *Int'l*, pg. 3017
CATALYST CANADA INC.—See Catalyst, Inc.; *U.S. Private*, pg. 787
THE CATALYST CAPITAL GROUP INC.; *Int'l*, pg. 7630
CATALYST CHANGERS INC.—See Quanta Services, Inc.; *U.S. Public*, pg. 1750
CATALYST & CHEMICAL CONTAINERS—See First Reserve Management, L.P.; *U.S. Private*, pg. 1526
CATALYST CLINICAL RESEARCH LLC—See NovaQuest Capital Management, LLC; *U.S. Private*, pg. 2967
CATALYST CONSTRUCTION; *U.S. Private*, pg. 786
CATALYST DIRECT INC.; *U.S. Private*, pg. 786
CATALYST EUROPE AG—See Catalyst, Inc.; *U.S. Private*, pg. 787
CATALYST EXPERIENTIAL, LLC; *U.S. Private*, pg. 786
CATALYST HANDLING SERVICE CO., LLC.; *U.S. Private*, pg. 786
CATALYST, INC.; *U.S. Private*, pg. 787
CATALYST, INC.; *U.S. Private*, pg. 787
CATALYST, INC.; *U.S. Private*, pg. 786
CATALYST INDIA WRC—See Catalyst, Inc.; *U.S. Private*, pg. 787
CATALYST INVESTMENT MANAGERS PTY. LIMITED; *Int'l*, pg. 1358
CATALYST INVESTMENTS, L.P.—See Cukierman & Co. Investment House Ltd.; *Int'l*, pg. 1876
CATALYST INVESTORS, LLC; *U.S. Private*, pg. 786
CATALYST MARKETING COMMUNICATIONS INC.; *U.S. Private*, pg. 786
CATALYST MARKETING DESIGN; *U.S. Private*, pg. 786
CATALYST MEDIA GROUP PLC; *Int'l*, pg. 1358
CATALYST METALS LIMITED; *Int'l*, pg. 1358
CATALYST OILFIELD SERVICES—See CES Energy Solutions Corp.; *Int'l*, pg. 1423
CATALYST ONE PTY LTD—See BSA Limited; *Int'l*, pg. 1201
CATALYST PAPER CORPORATION - BIRON—See PT Sinar Mas Group; *Int'l*, pg. 6072
CATALYST PAPER CORPORATION - RUMFORD—See PT Sinar Mas Group; *Int'l*, pg. 6072
CATALYST PAPER CORPORATION—See PT Sinar Mas Group; *Int'l*, pg. 6072
CATALYST PARTNERS ACQUISITION CORP.; *U.S. Private*, pg. 786
CATALYST PHARMACEUTICALS, INC.; *U.S. Public*, pg. 449
CATALYST REFINERS—See Ames Goldsmith Corp.; *U.S. Private*, pg. 262
CATALYST REPOSITORY SYSTEMS, INC.—See Open Text Corporation; *Int'l*, pg. 5596
CATALYSTS FOR PROFITABILITY AND GROWTH LTD—See BTS Group AB; *Int'l*, pg. 1205
CATALYST SOLUTIONS; *U.S. Private*, pg. 786
CATALYST; *U.S. Private*, pg. 786
CATALYST STUDIOS; *U.S. Private*, pg. 786
CATALYST TECHNOLOGY GROUP USA; *U.S. Private*, pg. 786
CATALYSTUX HOLDINGS, INC.—See Trivest Partners, LP; *U.S. Private*, pg. 4241
CATALYTE, INC.; *U.S. Private*, pg. 787
CATALYTIC SOFTWARE, INC.; *U.S. Private*, pg. 787
CATAMARAN CRUISERS LTD./BATEAUX LONDON—See Sodexo S.A.; *Int'l*, pg. 7045
CATAMARAN EXPRESS INC.—See Pacific Marine & Supply Co. Ltd. Inc.; *U.S. Public*, pg. 3068
CATAMARAN SOLUTIONS, LLC; *U.S. Private*, pg. 787

CATAMOUNT CONSTRUCTORS, INC.; *U.S. Private*, pg. 787
CATAMOUNT DAIRY HOLDINGS L.P.; *U.S. Private*, pg. 787
CATANA GROUP SA; *Int'l*, pg. 1358
CATANIA CRUISE TERMINAL SRL—See Global Yatirim Holding A.S.; *Int'l*, pg. 3002
CATAPULT ACQUISITIONS CORP.; *U.S. Private*, pg. 787
CATAPULT CONSULTANTS LLC; *U.S. Private*, pg. 787
CATAPULT DIRECT MARKETING LLC; *U.S. Private*, pg. 787
CATAPULT EMPLOYERS ASSOCIATION, INC.; *U.S. Private*, pg. 787
CATAPULT ENERGY SERVICES GROUP, LLC; *U.S. Private*, pg. 787
CATAPULT GROUP INTERNATIONAL LTD.; *Int'l*, pg. 1358
CATAPULT MARKETING—See Ryan Partnership, LLC; *U.S. Private*, pg. 3510
CATAPULT MARKETING—See Ryan Partnership, LLC; *U.S. Private*, pg. 3510
CATAPULT MARKETING—See Ryan Partnership, LLC; *U.S. Private*, pg. 3510
CATAPULT PR-IR, L.L.C.; *U.S. Private*, pg. 787
CATAPULT SYSTEMS, INC.—See Quisitive Technology Solutions, Inc.; *Int'l*, pg. 6165
CATAPULT TECHNOLOGY, LTD.—See D.C. Capital Partners, LLC; *U.S. Private*, pg. 1141
THE CATARACT SPECIALTY SURGICAL CENTER, LLC—See Bain Capital, LP; *U.S. Private*, pg. 447
CATARACT STEEL INDUSTRIES, INC.; *U.S. Private*, pg. 787
CATARC AUTOMOTIVE PROVING GROUND CO., LTD.; *Int'l*, pg. 1358
CATAUDELLA FUNERAL HOME, INC.—See Carriage Services, Inc.; *U.S. Public*, pg. 439
CATAUMET BOATS, INC.; *U.S. Private*, pg. 788
CATAVOLT, INC.—See Hexagon AB; *Int'l*, pg. 3367
CATAWBA INSURANCE COMPANY—See The Seibels Bruce Group, Inc.; *U.S. Private*, pg. 4116
CATAWBA-PIEDMONT CARDIOTHORACIC SURGERY, L.L.C.—See Tenet Healthcare Corporation; *U.S. Public*, pg. 2008
CATAWBA SOX LLC; *U.S. Private*, pg. 788
CATAWBA TRUCK RENTAL—See CT Group; *U.S. Private*, pg. 1118
CATAWISSA WOOD & COMPONENTS INC.; *U.S. Private*, pg. 788
CATC ALASKA TOURISM CORPORATION—See Viad Corp.; *U.S. Public*, pg. 2291
CATCH66 GMBH—See PCC SE; *Int'l*, pg. 5766
CATCHA DIGITAL BERHAD; *Int'l*, pg. 1359
CATCHA INVESTMENT CORP; *Int'l*, pg. 1359
CATCH.COM.AU PTY LTD—See Wesfarmers Limited; *Int'l*, pg. 8381
CATCHER TECHNOLOGY CO., LTD.; *Int'l*, pg. 1359
CATCHER TECHNOLOGY (SUQIAN) CO., LTD.—See Catcher Technology Co., Ltd.; *Int'l*, pg. 1359
CATCH FISHING SERVICES BV—See Petrolia SE; *Int'l*, pg. 5829
CATCHING FLUIDPOWER INC.—See Littlejohn & Co., LLC; *U.S. Private*, pg. 2470
CATCHMARK TIMBER TRUST, INC.—See PotlatchDeltic Corporation; *U.S. Public*, pg. 1704
CATCH OIL TOOLS PTY LTD—See Petrolia SE; *Int'l*, pg. 5829
CATCH—See Catalyst Investment Managers Pty. Limited; *Int'l*, pg. 1358
CATCH THE MOMENT; *U.S. Private*, pg. 788
CAT COUNTRY 107 FM—See iHeartMedia, Inc.; *U.S. Public*, pg. 1096
CAT DESENVOLUPAMENT DE CONCESSIONS CATALANES, S.L.—See ACS, Actividades de Construccion y Servicios, S.A.; *Int'l*, pg. 110
CATEC B.V.—See Indutrade AB; *Int'l*, pg. 3677
CA TECHNOLOGIES PRIVATE LTD.—See Broadcom Inc.; *U.S. Public*, pg. 389
CA TECHNOLOGIES—See Broadcom Inc.; *U.S. Public*, pg. 389
CA TECHNOLOGIES—See Broadcom Inc.; *U.S. Public*, pg. 389
CA TECHNOLOGIES—See Broadcom Inc.; *U.S. Public*, pg. 389
CATE EQUIPMENT COMPANY INC.; *U.S. Private*, pg. 788
CATEKS D.D.; *Int'l*, pg. 1359
CATELLA AB; *Int'l*, pg. 1359
CATELLA BANK SA—See Catella AB; *Int'l*, pg. 1359
CATELLA CORPORATE FINANCE GOTEBORG HB—See Catella AB; *Int'l*, pg. 1359
CATELLA CORPORATE FINANCE MALMO AB—See Catella AB; *Int'l*, pg. 1359
CATELLA CORPORATE FINANCE SIA—See Catella AB; *Int'l*, pg. 1359
CATELLA CORPORATE FINANCE VILNIUS UAB—See Catella AB; *Int'l*, pg. 1359
CATELLA FRANCE SARL—See Catella AB; *Int'l*, pg. 1359
CATELLA INVESTMENT MANAGEMENT A/S—See Catella AB; *Int'l*, pg. 1359

CATELLA AB

CATELLA PROPERTY BENELUX SA—See Catella AB; *Int'l*, pg. 1359
CATELLA PROPERTY GMBH—See Catella AB; *Int'l*, pg. 1359
CATELLA PROPERTY SPAIN S.A.—See Catella AB; *Int'l*, pg. 1359
CATELLA REAL ESTATE AG—See Catella AB; *Int'l*, pg. 1359
CATELLI BROS INC; *U.S. Private*, pg. 788
CATENA AB; *Int'l*, pg. 1359
CATENAE INNOVATION PLC; *Int'l*, pg. 1359
CATENA MEDIA PLC; *Int'l*, pg. 1359
CATENIC AG—See Serviceware SE; *Int'l*, pg. 6725
CATENO GESTAO DE CONTAS DE PAGTO S.A.—See Cielo S.A.; *Int'l*, pg. 1605
CATENON S.A.; *Int'l*, pg. 1359
CATEQUIP S.A.—See Berkshire Hathaway Inc.; *U.S. Public*, pg. 310
CATERAIR SERVICOS DE BORDO E HOTELARIA S.A.—See Deutsche Lufthansa AG; *Int'l*, pg. 2067
CATER ALLEN LIMITED—See Banco Santander, S.A.; *Int'l*, pg. 827
CATER CHAIN FOODSERVICES (PTY) LTD.—See Famous Brands Limited; *Int'l*, pg. 2612
CATERERS LINEN SUPPLY LIMITED—See Johnson Service Group PLC; *Int'l*, pg. 3993
CATERING AERIEN DEVELOPPEMENT S.A.—See Newrest Group International S.A.S.; *Int'l*, pg. 5236
CATERING BY ROSEMARY, INC.—See The RK Group, LLC; *U.S. Private*, pg. 4110
CATERING ENGROS A/S—See NorgesGruppen ASA; *Int'l*, pg. 5427
CATERING EQUIPMENT INDUSTRY SRL—See The Middleby Corporation; *U.S. Public*, pg. 2113
CATERING INTERNATIONAL & SERVICES S.A.; *Int'l*, pg. 1359
CATERINGPOR - CATERING PORTUGAL, S. A.—See TAP-Transportes Aereos Portugueses, SGPS, S.A.; *Int'l*, pg. 7461
CATERPILLAR AMERICAS MEXICO, S. DE R.L. DE C.V.—See Caterpillar, Inc.; *U.S. Public*, pg. 449
CATERPILLAR ASIA PACIFIC HOLDING, INC.—See Caterpillar, Inc.; *U.S. Public*, pg. 449
CATERPILLAR BELGIUM S.A.—See Caterpillar, Inc.; *U.S. Public*, pg. 451
CATERPILLAR CANADA—See Caterpillar, Inc.; *U.S. Public*, pg. 449
CATERPILLAR CASTINGS KIEL GMBH—See Caterpillar, Inc.; *U.S. Public*, pg. 449
CATERPILLAR CENTRO DE FORMACION, S.L.—See Caterpillar, Inc.; *U.S. Public*, pg. 449
CATERPILLAR CHINA INVESTMENT CO., LTD.—See Caterpillar, Inc.; *U.S. Public*, pg. 451
CATERPILLAR CHINA LIMITED—See Caterpillar, Inc.; *U.S. Public*, pg. 451
CATERPILLAR CLEANAIR SYSTEMS, INC.—See Caterpillar, Inc.; *U.S. Public*, pg. 449
CATERPILLAR COMMERCIAL HOLDING S.A.R.L.—See Caterpillar, Inc.; *U.S. Public*, pg. 449
CATERPILLAR COMMERCIAL S.A.—See Caterpillar, Inc.; *U.S. Public*, pg. 449
CATERPILLAR DISTRIBUTION SERVICES EUROPE B.V.B.A.—See Caterpillar, Inc.; *U.S. Public*, pg. 449
CATERPILLAR EAST JAPAN LTD.—See Caterpillar, Inc.; *U.S. Public*, pg. 449
CATERPILLAR, EAST PEORIA PLANT—See Caterpillar, Inc.; *U.S. Public*, pg. 452
CATERPILLAR ELKADER LLC—See Caterpillar, Inc.; *U.S. Public*, pg. 449
CATERPILLAR ENERGY SOLUTIONS ASIA PACIFIC PTE. LTD.—See Caterpillar, Inc.; *U.S. Public*, pg. 449
CATERPILLAR ENERGY SOLUTIONS GMBH—See Caterpillar, Inc.; *U.S. Public*, pg. 450
CATERPILLAR ENERGY SOLUTIONS INC.—See Caterpillar, Inc.; *U.S. Public*, pg. 450
CATERPILLAR EURASIA LLC—See Caterpillar, Inc.; *U.S. Public*, pg. 450
CATERPILLAR FINANCE CORPORATION—See Caterpillar, Inc.; *U.S. Public*, pg. 450
CATERPILLAR FINANCE FRANCE S.A.—See Caterpillar, Inc.; *U.S. Public*, pg. 450
CATERPILLAR FINANCIAL AUSTRALIA LIMITED—See Caterpillar, Inc.; *U.S. Public*, pg. 450
CATERPILLAR FINANCIAL COMMERCIAL ACCOUNT CORPORATION—See Caterpillar, Inc.; *U.S. Public*, pg. 450
CATERPILLAR FINANCIAL LEASING, S.A.—See Caterpillar, Inc.; *U.S. Public*, pg. 450
CATERPILLAR FINANCIAL NEW ZEALAND LIMITED—See Caterpillar, Inc.; *U.S. Public*, pg. 450
CATERPILLAR FINANCIAL NORDIC SERVICES A.B.—See Caterpillar, Inc.; *U.S. Public*, pg. 450
CATERPILLAR FINANCIAL RECEIVABLES, INC.—See Caterpillar, Inc.; *U.S. Public*, pg. 450
CATERPILLAR FINANCIAL SERVICES ASIA PTE. LTD.—See Caterpillar, Inc.; *U.S. Public*, pg. 450
CATERPILLAR FINANCIAL SERVICES CORPORATION—See Caterpillar, Inc.; *U.S. Public*, pg. 450
CATERPILLAR FINANCIAL SERVICES GMBH—See Caterpillar, Inc.; *U.S. Public*, pg. 450
CATERPILLAR FINANCIAL SERVICES KOREA, LTD.—See Caterpillar, Inc.; *U.S. Public*, pg. 450
CATERPILLAR FINANCIAL SERVICES NETHERLANDS B.V.—See Caterpillar, Inc.; *U.S. Public*, pg. 450
CATERPILLAR FINANCIAL SERVICES NORWAY A/S—See Caterpillar, Inc.; *U.S. Public*, pg. 450
CATERPILLAR FINANCIAL SERVICES N.V.—See Caterpillar, Inc.; *U.S. Public*, pg. 450
CATERPILLAR FINANCIAL SERVICES PHILIPPINES INC.—See Caterpillar, Inc.; *U.S. Public*, pg. 450
CATERPILLAR FINANCIAL SERVICES POLAND SP. Z O.O.—See Caterpillar, Inc.; *U.S. Public*, pg. 450
CATERPILLAR FINANCIAL SERVICES (U.K.) LIMITED—See Caterpillar, Inc.; *U.S. Public*, pg. 450
CATERPILLAR FINANCIAL UKRAINE LLC—See Caterpillar, Inc.; *U.S. Public*, pg. 450
CATERPILLAR FLUID SYSTEMS S.R.L.—See Caterpillar, Inc.; *U.S. Public*, pg. 450
CATERPILLAR FRANCE S A S—See Caterpillar, Inc.; *U.S. Public*, pg. 451
CATERPILLAR GLOBAL MINING COLOMBIA S.A.S.—See Caterpillar, Inc.; *U.S. Public*, pg. 450
CATERPILLAR GLOBAL MINING CZECH REPUBLIC, A.S.—See Caterpillar, Inc.; *U.S. Public*, pg. 450
CATERPILLAR GLOBAL MINING EQUIPAMENTOS DE MINERACAO DO BRASIL LTDA.—See Caterpillar, Inc.; *U.S. Public*, pg. 450
CATERPILLAR GLOBAL MINING EQUIPMENT LLC—See Caterpillar, Inc.; *U.S. Public*, pg. 450
CATERPILLAR GLOBAL MINING EUROPE GMBH—See Caterpillar, Inc.; *U.S. Public*, pg. 450
CATERPILLAR GLOBAL MINING HMS GMBH—See Caterpillar, Inc.; *U.S. Public*, pg. 450
CATERPILLAR GLOBAL MINING, LLC—See Caterpillar, Inc.; *U.S. Public*, pg. 450
CATERPILLAR GLOBAL MINING PTY. LTD.—See Caterpillar, Inc.; *U.S. Public*, pg. 450
CATERPILLAR GLOBAL MINING SARL—See Caterpillar, Inc.; *U.S. Public*, pg. 450
CATERPILLAR HOLDING GERMANY GMBH—See Caterpillar, Inc.; *U.S. Public*, pg. 450
CATERPILLAR HYDRAULICS ITALIA S.R.L.—See Caterpillar, Inc.; *U.S. Public*, pg. 450
CATERPILLAR, INC.; *U.S. Public*, pg. 449
CATERPILLAR INDIA PRIVATE LIMITED—See Caterpillar, Inc.; *U.S. Public*, pg. 451
CATERPILLAR INSURANCE HOLDINGS, INC.—See Caterpillar, Inc.; *U.S. Public*, pg. 451
CATERPILLAR INSURANCE SERVICES CORPORATION—See Caterpillar, Inc.; *U.S. Public*, pg. 451
CATERPILLAR INVESTMENT MANAGEMENT LTD.—See Caterpillar, Inc.; *U.S. Public*, pg. 451
CATERPILLAR JAPAN LTD.—See Caterpillar, Inc.; *U.S. Public*, pg. 451
CATERPILLAR JAPAN LTD.—See Mitsubishi Heavy Industries, Ltd.; *Int'l*, pg. 4953
CATERPILLAR (LANGFANG) MINING EQUIPMENT, CO., LTD.—See Caterpillar, Inc.; *U.S. Public*, pg. 449
CATERPILLAR LATIN AMERICA COMMERCIAL DIVISION—See Caterpillar, Inc.; *U.S. Public*, pg. 451
CATERPILLAR LEASING GMBH (LEIPZIG)—See Caterpillar, Inc.; *U.S. Public*, pg. 450
CATERPILLAR LIFE INSURANCE COMPANY—See Caterpillar, Inc.; *U.S. Public*, pg. 451
CATERPILLAR LOGISTICS SERVICES INDIA PRIVATE LIMITED—See Caterpillar, Inc.; *U.S. Public*, pg. 451
CATERPILLAR (LUXEMBOURG) INVESTMENT CO. S.A.R.L.—See Caterpillar, Inc.; *U.S. Public*, pg. 449
CATERPILLAR LUXEMBOURG LLC—See Caterpillar, Inc.; *U.S. Public*, pg. 451
CATERPILLAR MARINE ASIA PACIFIC PTE. LTD.—See Caterpillar, Inc.; *U.S. Public*, pg. 451
CATERPILLAR MARINE ASSET INTELLIGENCE LLC—See Caterpillar, Inc.; *U.S. Public*, pg. 451
CATERPILLAR MARINE POWER UK LIMITED—See Caterpillar, Inc.; *U.S. Public*, pg. 451
CATERPILLAR MATERIELS ROUTIERS—See Caterpillar, Inc.; *U.S. Public*, pg. 451
CATERPILLAR MEXICO S.A. DE C.V.—See Caterpillar, Inc.; *U.S. Public*, pg. 451
CATERPILLAR MOTOREN GMBH & CO. KG—See Caterpillar, Inc.; *U.S. Public*, pg. 451
CATERPILLAR MOTOREN (GUANGDONG) CO. LTD.—See Caterpillar, Inc.; *U.S. Public*, pg. 451
CATERPILLAR MOTOREN VERWALTUNGS GMBH—See Caterpillar, Inc.; *U.S. Public*, pg. 451
CATERPILLAR (NEWBERRY) LLC—See Caterpillar, Inc.; *U.S. Public*, pg. 449
CATERPILLAR (NI) LIMITED—See Caterpillar, Inc.; *U.S. Public*, pg. 449
CATERPILLAR OEM SOLUTIONS GROUP—See Caterpillar, Inc.; *U.S. Public*, pg. 451
CATERPILLAR OF AUSTRALIA LTD.—See Caterpillar, Inc.; *U.S. Public*, pg. 452
CATERPILLAR OF AUSTRALIA PTY. LTD.—See Caterpillar, Inc.; *U.S. Public*, pg. 452

CORPORATE AFFILIATIONS

CATERPILLAR OF CANADA—See Caterpillar, Inc.; *U.S. Public*, pg. 452
CATERPILLAR OPERATOR TRAINING LTD.—See Caterpillar, Inc.; *U.S. Public*, pg. 451
CATERPILLAR OPERATOR TRAINING LTD.—See Mitsubishi Heavy Industries, Ltd.; *Int'l*, pg. 4953
CATERPILLAR OVERSEAS CREDIT CORPORATION S.A.—See Caterpillar, Inc.; *U.S. Public*, pg. 451
CATERPILLAR OVERSEAS SARL—See Caterpillar, Inc.; *U.S. Public*, pg. 451
CATERPILLAR PARTNERSHIP LTD.—See Caterpillar, Inc.; *U.S. Public*, pg. 451
CATERPILLAR PAVING PRODUCTS, INC.—See Caterpillar, Inc.; *U.S. Public*, pg. 451
CATERPILLAR PRECISION SEALS KOREA—See Caterpillar, Inc.; *U.S. Public*, pg. 451
CATERPILLAR PRODUCT DEVELOPMENT SARL—See Caterpillar, Inc.; *U.S. Public*, pg. 451
CATERPILLAR PROPULSION AB—See Caterpillar, Inc.; *U.S. Public*, pg. 451
CATERPILLAR PROPULSION INTERNATIONAL TRADING (SHANGHAI) CO. LTD.—See Caterpillar, Inc.; *U.S. Public*, pg. 451
CATERPILLAR PROPULSION ISTANBUL MAKINA TICARET LIMITED SIRKETI—See Caterpillar, Inc.; *U.S. Public*, pg. 451
CATERPILLAR PROPULSION ITALY S.R.L.—See Caterpillar, Inc.; *U.S. Public*, pg. 451
CATERPILLAR PROPULSION NAMIBIA (PROPRIETARY) LIMITED—See Caterpillar, Inc.; *U.S. Public*, pg. 451
CATERPILLAR PROPULSION PRODUCTION AB—See Caterpillar, Inc.; *U.S. Public*, pg. 451
CATERPILLAR PROPULSION PRODUCTION PTE. LTD.—See Caterpillar, Inc.; *U.S. Public*, pg. 451
CATERPILLAR PROPULSION PTE. LTD.—See Caterpillar, Inc.; *U.S. Public*, pg. 451
CATERPILLAR PROPULSION SINGAPORE PTE. LTD.—See Caterpillar, Inc.; *U.S. Public*, pg. 451
CATERPILLAR PROPULSION SPAIN, S.L.—See Caterpillar, Inc.; *U.S. Public*, pg. 452
CATERPILLAR PROPULSION SWEDEN AB—See Caterpillar, Inc.; *U.S. Public*, pg. 452
CATERPILLAR RAMOS ARIZPE, S. DE R.L. DE C.V.—See Caterpillar, Inc.; *U.S. Public*, pg. 452
CATERPILLAR REMANUFACTURE FRANKLIN—See Caterpillar, Inc.; *U.S. Public*, pg. 452
CATERPILLAR REMANUFACTURING LIMITED—See Caterpillar, Inc.; *U.S. Public*, pg. 452
CATERPILLAR REMANUFACTURING SERVICES RADOM POLAND—See Caterpillar, Inc.; *U.S. Public*, pg. 452
CATERPILLAR RISK MANAGEMENT SERVICES LTD.—See Caterpillar, Inc.; *U.S. Public*, pg. 452
CATERPILLAR SERVICES GERMANY GMBH—See Caterpillar, Inc.; *U.S. Public*, pg. 452
CATERPILLAR SERVIZI ITALIA SRL—See Caterpillar, Inc.; *U.S. Public*, pg. 452
CATERPILLAR SHANGHAI ENGINE COMPANY, LTD.—See Mitsubishi Heavy Industries, Ltd.; *Int'l*, pg. 4959
CATERPILLAR SOLUTION ENGINEERING LTD.—See Caterpillar, Inc.; *U.S. Public*, pg. 452
CATERPILLAR SOUTHERN AFRICA (PTY) LTD.—See Caterpillar, Inc.; *U.S. Public*, pg. 452
CATERPILLAR SWITCHGEAR AMERICAS LLC—See Caterpillar, Inc.; *U.S. Public*, pg. 452
CATERPILLAR TOHUKU LTD.—See Caterpillar, Inc.; *U.S. Public*, pg. 452
CATERPILLAR TORREON S. DE R.L. DE C.V.—See Caterpillar, Inc.; *U.S. Public*, pg. 452
CATERPILLAR TRANSMISSIONS FRANCE S.A.R.L.—See Caterpillar, Inc.; *U.S. Public*, pg. 452
CATERPILLAR UK HOLDINGS LIMITED—See Caterpillar, Inc.; *U.S. Public*, pg. 452
CATERPILLAR (U.K.) LIMITED—See Caterpillar, Inc.; *U.S. Public*, pg. 451
CATERPILLAR UNDERGROUND MINING PTY. LTD.—See Caterpillar, Inc.; *U.S. Public*, pg. 452
CATERPILLAR USED EQUIPMENT SERVICES INTERNATIONAL SARL—See Caterpillar, Inc.; *U.S. Public*, pg. 452
CATERPILLAR WEST JAPAN LTD.—See Caterpillar, Inc.; *U.S. Public*, pg. 452
CATERPILLAR WORK TOOLS B.V.—See Caterpillar, Inc.; *U.S. Public*, pg. 452
CATERPILLAR WORK TOOLS, INC.—See Caterpillar, Inc.; *U.S. Public*, pg. 452
CATERPILLAR XUZHOU LTD.—See Caterpillar, Inc.; *U.S. Public*, pg. 452
CATERPILLAR (ZHENGZHOU) LTD.—See Caterpillar, Inc.; *U.S. Public*, pg. 449
CATERPLUS (BOTSWANA) (PTY) LIMITED—See The Bidvest Group Limited; *Int'l*, pg. 7623
CATERPLUS NAMIBIA (PTY) LIMITED—See The Bidvest Group Limited; *Int'l*, pg. 7624
CATERSALES (PTY) LIMITED—See The Bidvest Group Limited; *Int'l*, pg. 7624
CATESBY ESTATES PLC—See The Wellcome Trust Ltd; *Int'l*, pg. 7701

COMPANY NAME INDEX

CAT EVEN EMPREENDIMENTOS IMOBILIARIOS LTDA.—See Even Construtora e Incorporadora S.A.; *Int'l*, pg. 2561
CATFISH QUEEN PARTNERSHIP IN COMMENDAM—See Caesars Entertainment, Inc.; *U.S. Public*, pg. 420
CATHAY BANK—See Cathay General Bancorp; *U.S. Public*, pg. 454
CATHAY CENTURY INSURANCE CO., LTD.—See Lin Yuan Investment Co., Ltd.; *Int'l*, pg. 4499
CATHAY CHEMICAL WORKS, INC.; *Int'l*, pg. 1360
CATHAY CINEPLEXES SDN BHD—See Cathay Organisation Holdings Ltd; *Int'l*, pg. 1360
CATHAY COMPOSITES LTD—See Cathay Investments Limited; *Int'l*, pg. 1360
CATHAY FINANCIAL HOLDING CO., LTD.—See Lin Yuan Investment Co., Ltd.; *Int'l*, pg. 4499
CATHAY GENERAL BANCORP; *U.S. Public*, pg. 454
CATHAY GENERAL HOSPITAL—See Lin Yuan Investment Co., Ltd.; *Int'l*, pg. 4499
CATHAY INDUSTRIAL BIOTECH LTD.; *Int'l*, pg. 1360
CATHAY INDUSTRIES EUROPE N.V.; *Int'l*, pg. 1360
CATHAY INTERNATIONAL HOLDINGS LIMITED; *Int'l*, pg. 1360
CATHAY INVESTMENTS LIMITED; *Int'l*, pg. 1360
CATHAY-KERIS FILMS PTE LTD—See Cathay Organisation Holdings Ltd; *Int'l*, pg. 1360
CATHAY LATIN AMERICA LTDA.—See Pabrik Kertas Tjiwi Kimia Tbk; *Int'l*, pg. 5684
CATHAY LEASING CO., LTD.—See Srisawad Finance Public Company Limited; *Int'l*, pg. 7151
CATHAY LIFE INSURANCE CO., LTD.—See Lin Yuan Investment Co., Ltd.; *Int'l*, pg. 4499
CATHAY MEDIA & EDUCATION GROUP, INC.; *Int'l*, pg. 1360
CATHAY NEW ASIA COMMUNITY DEVELOPMENT CORPORATION—See Cathay General Bancorp; *U.S. Public*, pg. 454
CATHAY ORGANISATION HOLDINGS LTD; *Int'l*, pg. 1360
CATHAY PACIFIC AIRWAYS LIMITED; *Int'l*, pg. 1360
CATHAY PACIFIC CATERING SERVICES (H.K.) LTD.—See Cathay Pacific Airways Limited; *Int'l*, pg. 1360
CATHAY PACIFIC SERVICES LIMITED—See Cathay Pacific Airways Limited; *Int'l*, pg. 1360
CATHAY REAL ESTATE DEVELOPMENT COMPANY LTD.—See Lin Yuan Investment Co., Ltd.; *Int'l*, pg. 4500
CATHAY SECURITIES CORPORATION LTD.—See Lin Yuan Investment Co., Ltd.; *Int'l*, pg. 4499
CATHAY SECURITIES INVESTMENT TRUST CO., LTD.—See Lin Yuan Investment Co., Ltd.; *Int'l*, pg. 4499
CATHAY UNITED BANK (CAMBODIA) CORPORATION LIMITED—See Lin Yuan Investment Co., Ltd.; *Int'l*, pg. 4499
CATHAY UNITED BANK CO., LTD.—See Lin Yuan Investment Co., Ltd.; *Int'l*, pg. 4499
CATHAY UNITED BANK—See Lin Yuan Investment Co., Ltd.; *Int'l*, pg. 4499
CATHEDRA BITCOIN INC.; *Int'l*, pg. 1360
CATHEDRAL ARMS INC.; *U.S. Private*, pg. 788
CATHEDRAL CORPORATION; *U.S. Private*, pg. 788
CATHEDRAL ENERGY SERVICES INC.—See Cathedral Energy Services Ltd.; *Int'l*, pg. 1361
CATHEDRAL ENERGY SERVICES LTD.; *Int'l*, pg. 1361
CATHEDRAL VILLAGE; *U.S. Private*, pg. 788
CATHERINES STORES CORPORATION—See Mahwah Bergen Retail Group, Inc.; *U.S. Private*, pg. 2550
CATHERWOOD TOWING LTD.; *Int'l*, pg. 1361
CATHETER PRECISION, INC.; *U.S. Public*, pg. 454
CATHETER RESEARCH, INC.—See ATL Technology, Inc.; *U.S. Private*, pg. 369
CATHETER RESEARCH, INC.—See Wasatch Advantage Group, LLC; *U.S. Private*, pg. 4445
CATH KIDSTON LTD.—See Tanachira Group; *Int'l*, pg. 7454
CATHOLIC CEMETERIES ASSOCIATION; *U.S. Private*, pg. 788
CATHOLIC CHARITIES COMMUNITY SERVICES; *U.S. Private*, pg. 788
CATHOLIC CHARITIES HEALTH & HUMAN SERVICES; *U.S. Private*, pg. 788
CATHOLIC CHARITIES MAINE; *U.S. Private*, pg. 788
CATHOLIC CHARITIES OF FAIRFIELD COUNTY INC.; *U.S. Private*, pg. 788
CATHOLIC CHARITIES OF SOUTHERN NEVADA; *U.S. Private*, pg. 788
CATHOLIC CHURCH INSURANCE LIMITED; *Int'l*, pg. 1361
CATHOLIC COMMUNITY FOUNDATION OF MINNESOTA; *U.S. Private*, pg. 788
CATHOLIC COMMUNITY FOUNDATION; *U.S. Private*, pg. 788
CATHOLIC COMMUNITY SERVICES OF SOUTHERN ARIZONA, INC.; *U.S. Private*, pg. 788
CATHOLIC EDUCATION ARIZONA; *U.S. Private*, pg. 788
CATHOLIC ELDERCARE; *U.S. Private*, pg. 788
CATHOLIC FINANCIAL LIFE; *U.S. Private*, pg. 788

THE CATHOLIC FOUNDATION FOR THE ROMAN CATHOLIC CHURCH IN NORTHERN COLORADO; *U.S. Private*, pg. 4006
CATHOLIC FUNERALS NEWCASTLE PTY LIMITED—See TPG Capital, L.P.; *U.S. Public*, pg. 2174
CATHOLIC HEALTHCARE PARTNERS; *U.S. Private*, pg. 791
CATHOLIC HEALTHCARE SYSTEM; *U.S. Private*, pg. 792
CATHOLIC HEALTH INITIATIVES; *U.S. Private*, pg. 789
CATHOLIC HEALTH SERVICES OF LONG ISLAND; *U.S. Private*, pg. 790
CATHOLIC HEALTH SYSTEM, INC.; *U.S. Private*, pg. 791
CATHOLIC HOLY FAMILY SOCIETY; *U.S. Private*, pg. 792
CATHOLIC HOME CARE—See Catholic Health Services of Long Island; *U.S. Private*, pg. 791
CATHOLIC LIFE INSURANCE; *U.S. Private*, pg. 792
CATHOLIC MEDICAL CENTER; *U.S. Private*, pg. 792
CATHOLIC MEDICAL PARTNERS - ACCOUNTABLE CARE IPA, INC.—See Catholic Health System, Inc.; *U.S. Private*, pg. 791
CATHOLIC MEDICAL PARTNERS - ACCOUNTABLE CARE IPA, INC.—See Mount St. Mary's Hospital of Niagara Falls; *U.S. Private*, pg. 2798
CATHOLIC MUTUAL GROUP; *U.S. Private*, pg. 792
CATHOLIC ORDER OF FORESTERS; *U.S. Private*, pg. 792
CATHOLIC RESIDENTIAL SERVICES, INC.; *U.S. Private*, pg. 792
THE CATHOLIC SCHOOLS FOUNDATION INC; *U.S. Private*, pg. 4006
CATHOLIC SENIOR HOUSING & HEALTHCARE SERVICES, INC.; *U.S. Private*, pg. 792
CATHOLIC SOCIAL SERVICES; *U.S. Private*, pg. 792
CATHOLIC UNITED FINANCIAL; *U.S. Private*, pg. 792
CATHRX LTD; *Int'l*, pg. 1361
CATHY DANIELS LTD.—See Jump Design Group; *U.S. Private*, pg. 2243
CATHY SEAL PTE. LTD.—See Erria A/S; *Int'l*, pg. 2497
CATIE'S CLOSET; *U.S. Private*, pg. 792
CA TINTON FALLS, LLC—See Chelsea Senior Living LLC; *U.S. Private*, pg. 870
CATLETT & COMPANY INC.—See BBG Inc.; *U.S. Private*, pg. 408
CATLIN AUSTRALIA PTY LIMITED—See AXA S.A.; *Int'l*, pg. 760
CATLIN CANADA INC.—See AXA S.A.; *Int'l*, pg. 760
CATLIN EUROPE SE—See AXA S.A.; *Int'l*, pg. 760
CATLIN GUERNSEY—See AXA S.A.; *Int'l*, pg. 760
CATLIN HONG KONG LTD.—See AXA S.A.; *Int'l*, pg. 760
CATLIN, INC.—See AXA S.A.; *Int'l*, pg. 760
CATLIN, INC.—See AXA S.A.; *Int'l*, pg. 760
CATLIN INSURANCE COMPANY LTD.—See AXA S.A.; *Int'l*, pg. 760
CATLIN INSURANCE COMPANY LTD.—See AXA S.A.; *Int'l*, pg. 760
CATLIN (NORTH AMERICAN) HOLDINGS LTD.—See AXA S.A.; *Int'l*, pg. 760
CATLIN RE SCHWEIZ AG—See AXA S.A.; *Int'l*, pg. 760
CATLIN SINGAPORE PTE LTD.—See AXA S.A.; *Int'l*, pg. 760
CATNIC GMBH—See Tata Sons Limited; *Int'l*, pg. 7471
CATOCORP.COM, LLC—See The Cato Corporation; *U.S. Public*, pg. 2058
THE CATO CORPORATION; *U.S. Public*, pg. 2057
CATOCTIN CREEK DISTILLING COMPANY LLC—See Constellation Brands, Inc.; *U.S. Public*, pg. 570
CATO INSTITUTE; *U.S. Private*, pg. 792
CATONI 7 CO.—See Albert Ballin KG; *Int'l*, pg. 294
CATO OF TEXAS L.P.—See The Cato Corporation; *U.S. Public*, pg. 2058
C&A TOOL ENGINEERING, INC.—See Development Bank of Japan, Inc.; *Int'l*, pg. 2087
C&A TOOL ENGINEERING, INC.—See Minebea Mitsumi Inc.; *Int'l*, pg. 4904
CATO RESEARCH, LTD.—See Cato SMS; *Int'l*, pg. 1361
CATO SMS; *Int'l*, pg. 1361
CATO SOFTWARE SOLUTIONS GMBH—See Becton, Dickinson & Company; *U.S. Public*, pg. 292
CATO SOUTHWEST, INC.—See The Cato Corporation; *U.S. Public*, pg. 2058
CATOX CO., LTD.—See Nippon Shokubai Co., Ltd.; *Int'l*, pg. 5332
CAT PUMPS DEUTSCHLAND GMBH—See Diversified Dynamics Corporation; *U.S. Private*, pg. 1242
CAT PUMPS-INTERNATIONAL DIVISION—See Diversified Dynamics Corporation; *U.S. Private*, pg. 1242
CAT PUMPS INTERNATIONAL N.V.—See Diversified Dynamics Corporation; *U.S. Private*, pg. 1242
CAT PUMPS (UK) LTD.—See Diversified Dynamics Corporation; *U.S. Private*, pg. 1242
CA TRAFFIC LTD.—See TagMaster AB; *Int'l*, pg. 7407
THE CAT RENTAL STORE—See Ohio Machinery Co.; *U.S. Private*, pg. 3004
CAT RESOURCE & ASSET HOLDINGS, INC.; *Int'l*, pg. 1358
CATRION CATERING HOLDING COMPANY—See Saudi Arabian Airlines; *Int'l*, pg. 6588

CAUTTRELL ENTERPRISES INC.

CATS ACADEMY BOSTON INC.—See Bright Scholar Education Holdings Limited; *Int'l*, pg. 1161
CAT SCALE COMPANY—See Iowa 80 Group, Inc.; *U.S. Private*, pg. 2134
CATS CANTERBURY LIMITED—See Bright Scholar Education Holdings Limited; *Int'l*, pg. 1161
CATSCLAW AMERICAS, LLC—See PVPII - FNSS Acquisition, Inc.; *U.S. Private*, pg. 3308
CATS COLLEGE LONDON LIMITED—See Bright Scholar Education Holdings Limited; *Int'l*, pg. 1161
CATS COLLEGES HOLDINGS LIMITED—See Bright Scholar Education Holdings Limited; *Int'l*, pg. 1161
CATS CO., LTD.—See Nippon Telegraph & Telephone Corporation; *Int'l*, pg. 5346
CATS CO., LTD - SYSTEM BUSINESS DIVISION—See Nippon Telegraph & Telephone Corporation; *Int'l*, pg. 5346
CATS CO.; *U.S. Private*, pg. 792
CAT SEATTLE, LLC—See Universal Health Services, Inc.; *U.S. Public*, pg. 2256
CATSEYE PEST CONTROL, INC.; *U.S. Private*, pg. 792
CATSKILL HUDSON BANCORP, INC.; *U.S. Public*, pg. 454
CATSKILL HUDSON BANK—See Catskill Hudson Bancorp, Inc.; *U.S. Public*, pg. 454
CATSKILL REGIONAL MEDICAL CENTER; *U.S. Private*, pg. 792
THE CATSKILL REGIONAL OFF-TRACK BETTING CORPORATION; *U.S. Private*, pg. 4006
CATSKILL-VALLEY HOMES, LLC—See Cavco Industries, Inc.; *U.S. Public*, pg. 455
CAT SPEC, LTD.—See Quanta Services, Inc.; *U.S. Public*, pg. 1750
CAT STRATEGIC METALS CORPORATION; *Int'l*, pg. 1358
CATTARAUGUS REHABILITATION CENTER, INC.; *U.S. Private*, pg. 792
CAT TECH ASIA PACIFIC PTE LTD.—See Clean Harbors, Inc.; *U.S. Public*, pg. 509
CAT TECHNOLOGIES LIMITED; *Int'l*, pg. 1358
CAT TECHNOLOGIES LTD—See BATM Advanced Communications Ltd.; *Int'l*, pg. 890
CATTEDOWN WHARVES LIMITED—See James Fisher & Sons Public Limited Company; *Int'l*, pg. 3875
CATTERTON MANAGEMENT COMPANY, LLC; *U.S. Private*, pg. 792
CATTLE BARON RESTAURANTS INC.; *U.S. Private*, pg. 794
CATTLELAND FEEDYARDS LTD.; *Int'l*, pg. 1361
CATTLE LINE TWO PTE. LTD.—See Beng Kuang Marine Limited; *Int'l*, pg. 973
CATTLEMAN'S, INC.; *U.S. Private*, pg. 794
CATTLES INVOICE FINANCE (OXFORD) LIMITED—See Cattles Limited; *Int'l*, pg. 1361
CATTLES LIMITED; *Int'l*, pg. 1361
CATTLEYA SRL—See ITV plc; *Int'l*, pg. 3844
CATT LTD.—See CAT Technologies Limited; *Int'l*, pg. 1358
CATTORINI HNOS. S.A.; *Int'l*, pg. 1361
CATTRELL COMPANIES, INC.; *U.S. Private*, pg. 794
CATTRON HOLDINGS, INC.—See Harbour Group Industries, Inc.; *U.S. Private*, pg. 1860
CATTY CORPORATION; *U.S. Private*, pg. 794
CATVISION LIMITED; *Int'l*, pg. 1361
CATXERE TRANSMISSORA DE ENERGIA, S.A.—See ACS, Actividades de Construccion y Servicios, S.A.; *Int'l*, pg. 110
CATYLIST, INC.—See Moody's Corporation; *U.S. Public*, pg. 1468
CATYLIST REAL ESTATE SOFTWARE, INC.—See Moody's Corporation; *U.S. Public*, pg. 1468
CATZ INTERNATIONAL B.V.—See ACOMO N.V.; *Int'l*, pg. 108
CAUCASIAN PET CO.—See Radici Partecipazioni S.p.A.; *Int'l*, pg. 6175
CAUCASUS MEDICAL CENTER, LLC—See Georgia Capital PLC; *Int'l*, pg. 2939
CAUCASUS PAPER INDUSTRY—See International Sun Group FZCO; *Int'l*, pg. 3753
CAUDAN DEVELOPMENT LIMITED—See Promotion & Development Limited; *Int'l*, pg. 5994
CAUDILL SEED & WAREHOUSE CO.; *U.S. Private*, pg. 794
CAUDLE-HYATT, INC.; *U.S. Private*, pg. 794
CAUGHERTY HAHN COMMUNICATIONS, INC.; *U.S. Private*, pg. 794
CAULDRON ENERGY LIMITED; *Int'l*, pg. 1361
CAUNCE O'HARA & COMPANY LIMITED—See Markel Group Inc.; *U.S. Public*, pg. 1367
CAUSAM ENERGY, INC.; *U.S. Private*, pg. 794
CAUSEWAY AERO GROUP LTD.; *Int'l*, pg. 1361
CAUSEWAY CAPITAL MANAGEMENT LLC; *U.S. Private*, pg. 794
CAUSEWAY LUMBER COMPANY; *U.S. Private*, pg. 794
CAUSEWAY PAINTS LANKA (PRIVATE) LIMITED—See Asian Paints Limited; *Int'l*, pg. 619
CAUSEWAY TECHNOLOGIES LIMITED; *Int'l*, pg. 1361
CAUSTIC JSC—See Central-Asian Power Energy Company JSC; *Int'l*, pg. 1410
CAUTTRELL ENTERPRISES INC.; *U.S. Private*, pg. 794

CAVACHE, INC.—See Ahtna, Inc.; *U.S. Private*, pg. 131
CAVA DELLE CAPANNELLE S.R.L.—See Heidelberg Materials AG; *Int'l*, pg. 3309
CAV AEROSPACE LTD.—See Heritage Group Ltd.; *Int'l*, pg. 3361
CAVAFORM, INC.—See Crestview Partners, L.P.; *U.S. Private*, pg. 1099
CAVAGHAN & GRAY CARLISLE—See Boparan Holdings Limited; *Int'l*, pg. 1111
CAVA GROUP, INC.; *U.S. Public*, pg. 454
CAVALCADE FORD LINCOLN SALES; *Int'l*, pg. 1361
CAVALIER BREMWORTH (AUSTRALIA) LIMITED—See Bremworth Limited; *Int'l*, pg. 1145
CAVALIER BREMWORTH LIMITED—See Bremworth Limited; *Int'l*, pg. 1145
CAVALIER BREMWORTH PTY. LIMITED—See Bremworth Limited; *Int'l*, pg. 1145
CAVALIER FORD INC.; *U.S. Private*, pg. 794
CAVALIER HOME BUILDERS, LLC—See Berkshire Hathaway Inc.; *U.S. Public*, pg. 304
CAVALIER HOMES, INC.—See Berkshire Hathaway Inc.; *U.S. Public*, pg. 304
CAVALIER HOTEL CORP.—See Kyanite Mining Corporation; *U.S. Private*, pg. 2360
CAVALIER LOGISTICS INC; *U.S. Private*, pg. 794
CAVALIER RESOURCES LIMITED; *Int'l*, pg. 1361
CAVALIER SERVICES, INC.; *U.S. Private*, pg. 795
CAVALIERS OPERATING COMPANY, LLC; *U.S. Private*, pg. 795
CAVALIER SPINNERS LIMITED—See Bremworth Limited; *Int'l*, pg. 1145
CAVALIER TELEPHONE, LLC—See Windstream Holdings, Inc.; *U.S. Public*, pg. 2373
THE CAVALRY COMPANY; *U.S. Private*, pg. 4006
CAVALRY CONSTRUCTION COMPANY INC.; *U.S. Private*, pg. 795
CAVALRY LOGISTICS INTERNATIONAL, INC.—See Universal Logistics Holdings, Inc.; *U.S. Public*, pg. 2261
CAVALRY LOGISTICS INTERNATIONAL OF CANADA, INC.—See Universal Logistics Holdings, Inc.; *U.S. Public*, pg. 2261
CAVALRY LOGISTICS, LLC—See Universal Logistics Holdings, Inc.; *U.S. Public*, pg. 2261
CAVANAH ASSOCIATES, INC.—See Caisse de Depot et Placement du Quebec; *Int'l*, pg. 1256
CAVANAH ASSOCIATES, INC.—See KKR & Co. Inc.; *U.S. Public*, pg. 1265
CAVANAUGH & CO., LLP; *U.S. Private*, pg. 795
CAVANAUGH ELECTRICAL CONTRACTING, INC.; *U.S. Private*, pg. 795
CAVATINA HOLDING SA; *Int'l*, pg. 1361
CAVCO INDUSTRIES, INC.; *U.S. Public*, pg. 454
CAVE CITY CHEVROLET/BUICK; *U.S. Private*, pg. 795
CAVEGUIAS—See Compania Anonima Nacional Telefonos de Venezuela; *Int'l*, pg. 1748
CAVE INTERACTIVE CO., LTD.; *Int'l*, pg. 1361
CAVENA IMAGE PRODUCTS AB—See Edgeware AB; *Int'l*, pg. 2309
CAVENDER AUTO GROUP; *U.S. Private*, pg. 795
CAVENDER BROTHERS MANAGEMENT, LTD.; *U.S. Private*, pg. 795
CAVENDER BUICK COMPANY INC.; *U.S. Private*, pg. 795
CAVENDER CADILLAC; *U.S. Private*, pg. 795
CAVENDER'S; *U.S. Private*, pg. 795
CAVENDISH CORPORATE FINANCE LLP—See Cavendish Financial plc; *Int'l*, pg. 1362
CAVENDISH FINANCIAL PLC; *Int'l*, pg. 1362
CAVENDISH KINETICS B.V.—See Qorvo, Inc.; *U.S. Public*, pg. 1743
CAVENDISH KINETICS, INC.—See Qorvo, Inc.; *U.S. Public*, pg. 1743
CAVENDISH MUNRO PROFESSIONAL RISKS LIMITED—See Brown & Brown, Inc.; *U.S. Public*, pg. 400
CAVENDISH SECURITIES PLC—See Cavendish Financial plc; *Int'l*, pg. 1362
CAVENDISH SQUARE HOLDING BV—See WPP plc; *Int'l*, pg. 8462
CAVEO FUND SOLUTIONS PROPRIETARY LIMITED—See Alexander Forbes Group Holdings Limited; *Int'l*, pg. 307
CAVERIN SOLUTIONS S.A.—See Econocom Group SA; *Int'l*, pg. 2297
CAVERION ASIA PTE. LTD.—See Triton Advisers Limited; *Int'l*, pg. 7934
CAVERION CENTRAL EUROPE GMBH—See Triton Advisers Limited; *Int'l*, pg. 7934
CAVERION DANMARK A/S—See Triton Advisers Limited; *Int'l*, pg. 7935
CAVERION DEUTSCHLAND GMBH—See Triton Advisers Limited; *Int'l*, pg. 7935
CAVERION EESTI AS—See Triton Advisers Limited; *Int'l*, pg. 7935
CAVERION INDUSTRIA SVERIGE AB—See Triton Advisers Limited; *Int'l*, pg. 7934
CAVERION LATVIJA SIA—See Triton Advisers Limited; *Int'l*, pg. 7935

CAVERION NORGE AS—See Triton Advisers Limited; *Int'l*, pg. 7935
CAVERION OSTERREICH GMBH—See Triton Advisers Limited; *Int'l*, pg. 7934
CAVERION OYJ—See Triton Advisers Limited; *Int'l*, pg. 7934
CAVERION POLSKA SP.Z.O.O.—See STRABAG SE; *Int'l*, pg. 7232
CAVERION SVERIGE AB—See Triton Advisers Limited; *Int'l*, pg. 7935
CAVERN TECHNOLOGIES INC.—See GI Manager L.P.; *U.S. Private*, pg. 1692
CAVERTON HELICOPTERS LIMITED—See Caverton Offshore Support Group PLC; *Int'l*, pg. 1362
CAVERTON OFFSHORE SUPPORT GROUP PLC; *Int'l*, pg. 1362
CAVERT WIRE COMPANY INCORPORATED; *U.S. Private*, pg. 795
CAVE SAINT-VERNY—See Groupe Limagrain Holding SA; *Int'l*, pg. 3107
CAVE SHEPHERD CARD (BARBADOS) INC.—See Cave Shepherd & Co., Ltd.; *Int'l*, pg. 1362
CAVE SHEPHERD & CO., LTD.; *Int'l*, pg. 1362
CAVE SPRINGS, INC.—See Destination Maternity Corporation; *U.S. Public*, pg. 656
CAVIA INC.—See Marvelous Inc.; *Int'l*, pg. 4717
CAVIAR ANTWERP B.V.—See Liberty Global plc; *Int'l*, pg. 4484
CAVIAR PARIS S.A.S.—See Liberty Global plc; *Int'l*, pg. 4484
CAVIEZEL AG—See Burkhalter Holding AG; *Int'l*, pg. 1224
CAVINKARE PVT. LTD.; *Int'l*, pg. 1362
CAV INTERNATIONAL, INC.; *U.S. Private*, pg. 794
CAVITATION TECHNOLOGIES, INC.; *U.S. Public*, pg. 455
CAVITE UNITED RURAL BANK CORPORATION—See Asia United Bank Corporation; *Int'l*, pg. 616
CAVITY GMBH—See Solvay S.A.; *Int'l*, pg. 7077
CAVIUM LLC—See Marvell Technology Group Ltd.; *Int'l*, pg. 4717
CAVMONT CAPITAL HOLDINGS ZAMBIA PLC.; *Int'l*, pg. 1362
CAVO BROADBAND COMMUNICATIONS, LLC—See Dycom Industries, Inc.; *U.S. Public*, pg. 698
CAVOK—See Marsh & McLennan Companies, Inc.; *U.S. Public*, pg. 1386
CAVOTEC ALFO GMBH—See Cavotec SA; *Int'l*, pg. 1362
CAVOTEC AUSTRALIA—See Cavotec SA; *Int'l*, pg. 1362
CAVOTEC CANADA INC.—See Cavotec SA; *Int'l*, pg. 1362
CAVOTEC CIS LTD.—See Cavotec SA; *Int'l*, pg. 1363
CAVOTEC CONNECTORS AB—See Cavotec SA; *Int'l*, pg. 1362
CAVOTEC DABICO UK LTD.—See Cavotec SA; *Int'l*, pg. 1362
CAVOTEC DABICO US INC.—See Cavotec SA; *Int'l*, pg. 1362
CAVOTEC DANMARK AS—See Cavotec SA; *Int'l*, pg. 1362
CAVOTEC DEUTSCHLAND GMBH—See Cavotec SA; *Int'l*, pg. 1362
CAVOTEC DEUTSCHLAND HOLDINGS GMBH—See Cavotec SA; *Int'l*, pg. 1362
CAVOTEC ENGINEERING SERVICES INDIA PVT. LTD.—See Cavotec SA; *Int'l*, pg. 1363
CAVOTEC FINLAND OY—See Cavotec SA; *Int'l*, pg. 1362
CAVOTEC FLADUNG GMBH—See Cavotec SA; *Int'l*, pg. 1362
CAVOTEC GROUP HOLDINGS NV—See Cavotec SA; *Int'l*, pg. 1362
CAVOTEC HONG KONG LTD.—See Cavotec SA; *Int'l*, pg. 1362
CAVOTEC IBERICA S.L.—See Cavotec SA; *Int'l*, pg. 1362
CAVOTEC INDIA LTD.—See Cavotec SA; *Int'l*, pg. 1362
CAVOTEC INTERNATIONAL LTD—See Cavotec SA; *Int'l*, pg. 1362
CAVOTEC KOREA LTD—See Cavotec SA; *Int'l*, pg. 1363
CAVOTEC LATIN AMERICA S.A.—See Cavotec SA; *Int'l*, pg. 1362
CAVOTEC MICRO-CONTROL AS—See Cavotec SA; *Int'l*, pg. 1362
CAVOTEC MICRO-CONTROL GMBH—See Cavotec SA; *Int'l*, pg. 1362
CAVOTEC MIDDLE EAST FZE—See Cavotec SA; *Int'l*, pg. 1362
CAVOTEC MOORMASTER LTD—See Cavotec SA; *Int'l*, pg. 1362
CAVOTEC MSL HOLDINGS LIMITED - CAVOTEC ITALIA DIVISION—See Cavotec SA; *Int'l*, pg. 1363
CAVOTEC NEDERLAND B.V.—See Cavotec SA; *Int'l*, pg. 1362
CAVOTEC NORGE AS—See Cavotec SA; *Int'l*, pg. 1363
CAVOTEC REALTY ITALIA SRL—See Cavotec SA; *Int'l*, pg. 1363
CAVOTEC REALTY NORWAY AS—See Cavotec SA; *Int'l*, pg. 1363
CAVOTEC RMS SA—See Cavotec SA; *Int'l*, pg. 1363
CAVOTEC SA; *Int'l*, pg. 1362
CAVOTEC SHANGHAI LTD.—See Cavotec SA; *Int'l*, pg. 1363

CAVOTEC SINGAPORE PTE LTD.—See Cavotec SA; *Int'l*, pg. 1363
CAVOTEC SOUTH AFRICA (PTY.) LTD.—See Cavotec SA; *Int'l*, pg. 1363
CAVOTEC SPECIMAS S.P.A.—See Cavotec SA; *Int'l*, pg. 1363
CAVOTEC SVERIGE AB—See Cavotec SA; *Int'l*, pg. 1363
CAVOTEC (SWISS) S.A.—See Cavotec SA; *Int'l*, pg. 1362
CAVOTEC USA INC.—See Cavotec SA; *Int'l*, pg. 1363
CAVOTEC US HOLDINGS INC—See Cavotec SA; *Int'l*, pg. 1363
CAVU CORP PTE. LTD.—See Digilife Technologies Limited; *Int'l*, pg. 2119
CAVU ENERGY METALS CORP.—See Strategic Metals Ltd.; *Int'l*, pg. 7236
CAVU TECHNOLOGY ACQUISITION CORP.; *U.S. Public*, pg. 455
CAWACHI LIMITED; *Int'l*, pg. 1363
CA WASHINGTON, LLC—See Insight Venture Management, LLC; *U.S. Private*, pg. 2087
CAWC, INC—See Uniholdings Inc.; *Int'l*, pg. 8044
CAWOOD AUTO COMPANY; *U.S. Private*, pg. 795
CAWOODS (FISHCURERS) LTD.—See J&J Denholm Ltd.; *Int'l*, pg. 3853
CAWOOD; *U.S. Private*, pg. 795
CAXTON AND CTP PUBLISHERS AND PRINTERS LTD.; *Int'l*, pg. 1363
CAXTON ASSOCIATES LLC; *U.S. Private*, pg. 795
THE CAXTON PRINTERS LTD.; *U.S. Private*, pg. 4006
CAYAN LLC—See Global Payments Inc.; *U.S. Public*, pg. 944
CAYBE 2 SL—See IVS Group S.A.; *Int'l*, pg. 3848
CAYCE COMPANY INC.; *U.S. Private*, pg. 795
CAYCE MILL SUPPLY COMPANY INC.; *U.S. Private*, pg. 795
CAYELI BAKIR ISLETMELERI A.S.—See First Quantum Minerals Ltd.; *Int'l*, pg. 2687
CAYENNE ENTERTAINMENT TECHNOLOGY CO., LTD.; *Int'l*, pg. 1363
CAYENNE GOLD MINES LTD.; *Int'l*, pg. 1363
CAYENNE MEDICAL, INC.—See Zimmer Biomet Holdings, Inc.; *U.S. Public*, pg. 2406
CAYENNE S.A.—See Dentsu Group Inc.; *Int'l*, pg. 2035
CAYENNE/TBWA—See Omnicom Group Inc.; *U.S. Public*, pg. 1594
CAYMAN AIRWAYS LTD.; *Int'l*, pg. 1363
CAYMAN CHEMICAL COMPANY, INC.; *U.S. Private*, pg. 795
CAYMAN ENGLEY INDUSTRIAL CO., LTD.; *Int'l*, pg. 1363
CAYMAN GOLDEN CENTURY WHEEL GROUP LIMITED; *Int'l*, pg. 1364
CAYMAN ISLANDS MONETARY AUTHORITY; *Int'l*, pg. 1364
CAYMAN ISLANDS STOCK EXCHANGE LIMITED; *Int'l*, pg. 1364
CAYMAN NATIONAL BANK & TRUST COMPANY (ISLE OF MAN) LTD.—See Republic Financial Holdings Limited; *Int'l*, pg. 6294
CAYMAN NATIONAL CORPORATION LTD.—See Republic Financial Holdings Limited; *Int'l*, pg. 6294
CAYMAN NATIONAL (DUBAI) LTD.—See Republic Financial Holdings Limited; *Int'l*, pg. 6294
CAYMAN NATIONAL TRUST CO., LTD.—See Republic Financial Holdings Limited; *Int'l*, pg. 6294
CAYMAN TON YI INDUSTRIAL HOLDINGS LTD.—See Uni-President Enterprises Corporation; *Int'l*, pg. 8028
CAYMAN WATER COMPANY LIMITED—See Consolidated Water Co. Ltd.; *Int'l*, pg. 1771
CAYMUS EQUITY PARTNERS LLC; *U.S. Private*, pg. 795
CAYSET FASHIONS LTD.; *U.S. Private*, pg. 795
CAYTHORPE GAS STORAGE LIMITED—See Centrica plc; *Int'l*, pg. 1413
CAYTON MEADOWS (SCARBOROUGH) MANAGEMENT COMPANY LIMITED—See Persimmon plc; *Int'l*, pg. 5815
CAYUGA MEDICAL CENTER AT ITHACA; *U.S. Private*, pg. 795
CAZADOR, LLC—See Nana Regional Corporation, Inc.; *U.S. Private*, pg. 2832
CAZALY RESOURCES LIMITED; *Int'l*, pg. 1364
CAZENOVIA EQUIPMENT CO., INC.; *U.S. Private*, pg. 796
CAZENOVIA RECOVERY SYSTEMS, INC.; *U.S. Private*, pg. 796
CAZLEY INC.; *U.S. Private*, pg. 796
CAZOO GROUP LTD.; *Int'l*, pg. 1364
CAZ (THAILAND) COMPANY LIMITED—See Takuni Group Public Company Limited; *Int'l*, pg. 7443
CAZ (THAILAND) PUBLIC COMPANY LIMITED; *Int'l*, pg. 1364
CBA ASSET MG OR; *Int'l*, pg. 1364
CBA INDUSTRIES INC.; *U.S. Private*, pg. 796
CBAK ENERGY TECHNOLOGY, INC.; *U.S. Public*, pg. 1364
CBAL S.A.—See Erste Abwicklungsanstalt AoR; *Int'l*, pg. 2497
C BANCROFT LTD.—See Frank Key Group Limited; *Int'l*, pg. 2761

COMPANY NAME INDEX

C. BANGE VERLAG GMBH—See Ernst Klett AG; *Int'l*, pg. 2495
CBANK—See Republic Bancorp, Inc.; *U.S. Public*, pg. 1785
C.BANNER INTERNATIONAL HOLDINGS LIMITED; *Int'l*, pg. 1240
CBASE CORPORATION—See en-japan inc.; *Int'l*, pg. 2395
CBA SOURCING S.A.—See Sword Group SE; *Int'l*, pg. 7376
CB AUSTRALIA LIMITED; *Int'l*, pg. 1364
CBB BANCORP, INC.; *U.S. Public*, pg. 455
CBBEAUTY LTD—See MacAndrews & Forbes Incorporated; *U.S. Private*, pg. 2533
CBCA ADMINISTRATORS, INC.—See Simplifi, Inc.; *U.S. Private*, pg. 3667
CBC AMERICA CO., LTD.—See CBC Co., Ltd.; *Int'l*, pg. 1365
CBC AMERICA CO., LTD.—See CBC Co., Ltd.; *Int'l*, pg. 1365
CBC AMERICA CORP. - LOS ANGELES DIVISION—See CBC Co., Ltd.; *Int'l*, pg. 1365
CBC BANCORP; *U.S. Private*, pg. 796
CBC BANQUE S.A.—See KBC Group NV; *Int'l*, pg. 4105
CBC (BEIJING) TRADING CO., LTD.—See CBC Co., Ltd.; *Int'l*, pg. 1365
CBC CO., LTD. - MISHIMA FACTORY—See CBC Co., Ltd.; *Int'l*, pg. 1365
CBC CO., LTD.; *Int'l*, pg. 1365
CBC CO (MILAN) LTD—See CBC Co., Ltd.; *Int'l*, pg. 1365
CBC COMPANIES INC.; *U.S. Private*, pg. 796
CBC COMPANIES INC.—See CBC Companies Inc.; *U.S. Private*, pg. 796
CBC CO. (PARIS) LTD.—See CBC Co., Ltd.; *Int'l*, pg. 1365
CBC CORPORATION (INDIA) PVT. LTD.—See CBC Co., Ltd.; *Int'l*, pg. 1365
CBC (DEUTSCHLAND) GMBH—See CBC Co., Ltd.; *Int'l*, pg. 1365
CB CENTRAL BUILDERS INCORPORATED; *U.S. Private*, pg. 796
CBC (EUROPE) LTD.—See CBC Co., Ltd.; *Int'l*, pg. 1365
CBC EUROPE S.R.L.—See CBC Co., Ltd.; *Int'l*, pg. 1365
CBC FINANCE LIMITED—See Commercial Bank of Ceylon PLC; *Int'l*, pg. 1715
CBC FORMA CO., LTD.—See CBC Co., Ltd.; *Int'l*, pg. 1365
CBC FRAMING INC.; *U.S. Private*, pg. 797
CBC GROUP; *U.S. Private*, pg. 797
CBC (GUANGZHOU) TRADING CO., LTD—See CBC Co., Ltd.; *Int'l*, pg. 1365
CBC (H.K.) CO., LTD. - KWUN TONG BRANCH—See CBC Co., Ltd.; *Int'l*, pg. 1365
CBC (H.K.) CO., LTD.—See CBC Co., Ltd.; *Int'l*, pg. 1365
CBC HOLDING COMPANY; *U.S. Public*, pg. 455
CBC IBERIA S.A.—See CBC Co., Ltd.; *Int'l*, pg. 1365
CBC INDUSTRIAS PESADAS S.A.—See Mitsubishi Heavy Industries, Ltd.; *Int'l*, pg. 4953
CBC INGS AMERICA INC.—See CBC Co., Ltd.; *Int'l*, pg. 1365
CBC INGS (CHANGSHU) CO., LTD.—See CBC Co., Ltd.; *Int'l*, pg. 1365
CBC INGS (DONG GUAN) CO., LTD.—See CBC Co., Ltd.; *Int'l*, pg. 1365
CBC MYANMAR MICROFINANCE COMPANY LIMITED—See Commercial Bank of Ceylon PLC; *Int'l*, pg. 1715
CBC OPTICAL INDUSTRIES BD CO., LTD.—See CBC Co., Ltd.; *Int'l*, pg. 1365
CBC OPTRONICS (BD) CO., LTD.—See CBC Co., Ltd.; *Int'l*, pg. 1365
CBC OPTRONICS (BEIJING) CO., LTD.—See CBC Co., Ltd.; *Int'l*, pg. 1365
CBC (POLAND) SP.ZO.O.—See CBC Co., Ltd.; *Int'l*, pg. 1365
CBC PROPERTIES & COMPUTER CENTER, INC.—See China Banking Corporation; *Int'l*, pg. 1484
CBC SERVICES, INC.; *U.S. Private*, pg. 797
CBC SETTLEMENT FUNDING, LLC—See Asta Funding, Inc.; *U.S. Private*, pg. 360
CBC (SHANGHAI) TRADING CO., LTD.—See CBC Co., Ltd.; *Int'l*, pg. 1365
CBC.S PTE LTD. - DISTRIBUTION DIVISION—See CBC Co., Ltd.; *Int'l*, pg. 1365
CBC.S PTE LTD - TRADE DIVISION—See CBC Co., Ltd.; *Int'l*, pg. 1365
CBCS—See CBC Companies Inc.; *U.S. Private*, pg. 796
CBC STEEL BUILDINGS—See Nucor Corporation; *U.S. Public*, pg. 1553
CBC TECH SOLUTIONS LIMITED—See Commercial Bank of Ceylon PLC; *Int'l*, pg. 1715
CBC (THAILAND) CO., LTD.—See CBC Co., Ltd.; *Int'l*, pg. 1365
C & B DEVELOPMENT, INC.; *U.S. Private*, pg. 701
CB DEVELOPMENT. LLC—See Lions Gate Entertainment Corp.; *Int'l*, pg. 4520
CBD EVISION PTE LTD—See Challenger Technologies Ltd.; *Int'l*, pg. 1438
CBD FINANCIAL SERVICES LLC—See Commercial Bank of Dubai PSC; *Int'l*, pg. 1715
CBD GLOBAL SCIENCES, INC.; *U.S. Public*, pg. 455
CB DIRECT, LLC—See Lions Gate Entertainment Corp.; *Int'l*, pg. 4520
CB DISTRIBUTORS, INC.; *U.S. Private*, pg. 796
C&B DISTRIBUTORS INC.; *U.S. Private*, pg. 702
CBD LIFE SCIENCES, INC.; *U.S. Public*, pg. 455
CBDMD, INC.; *U.S. Public*, pg. 456
CBD OF DENVER, INC.; *U.S. Public*, pg. 456
CBE GROUP; *U.S. Private*, pg. 797
CB ENERGOTRANSBANK JSC; *Int'l*, pg. 1364
CB ENGINEERING LTD; *Int'l*, pg. 1364
C BENNETT BUILDING SUPPLY INC.; *U.S. Private*, pg. 701
CB EUREGIO GMBH—See Commerzbank AG; *Int'l*, pg. 1715
CBFC LIMITED—See Commonwealth Bank of Australia; *Int'l*, pg. 1719
CBF EUROPE GMBH—See INA-Holding Schaeffler GmbH & Co. KG; *Int'l*, pg. 3639
CB FINANCIAL SERVICES, INC.; *U.S. Public*, pg. 455
C.B. FLEET COMPANY, INC.—See Prestige Consumer Healthcare Inc.; *U.S. Public*, pg. 1716
CBG CAPITAL LIMITED—See Clime Capital Limited; *Int'l*, pg. 1659
CBG COMMERZ BETEILIGUNGSGESELLSCHAFT HOLDING MBH—See Commerzbank AG; *Int'l*, pg. 1715
CBG COMMERZ BETEILIGUNGSKAPITAL GMBH & CO. KG—See Commerzbank AG; *Int'l*, pg. 1715
CBG COMMERZ—See Commerzbank AG; *Int'l*, pg. 1715
CB GROUP MANAGEMENT CO., LTD.; *Int'l*, pg. 1364
CBH COMPAGNIE BANCAIRE HELVETIQUE SA; *Int'l*, pg. 1365
CB-HDT HOLDINGS INC.—See Charlesbank Capital Partners, LLC; *U.S. Private*, pg. 855
C&B HOLDINGS, LLC—See Compass Group PLC; *Int'l*, pg. 1750
CBH RESOURCES LIMITED—See Toho Zinc Co., Ltd.; *Int'l*, pg. 7776
CBHSP ARIZONA, INC.—See Centene Corporation; *U.S. Public*, pg. 468
CB&I - ALPHARETTA—See McDermott International, Inc.; *U.S. Public*, pg. 1405
CB&I - CLIVE—See McDermott International, Inc.; *U.S. Public*, pg. 1405
CBI CONSTRUCTORS PTY. LTD. (PERTH)—See McDermott International, Inc.; *U.S. Public*, pg. 1405
CBI CONSTRUCTORS PTY. LTD—See McDermott International, Inc.; *U.S. Public*, pg. 1405
CBI EASTERN ANSTALT—See McDermott International, Inc.; *U.S. Public*, pg. 1405
CBI-ELECTRIC ABERDARE ATC TELECOM CABLES (PTY) LIMITED—See Reunert Limited; *Int'l*, pg. 6311
CBI ELECTRIC-INDUSTRIAL CONTROLS—See Reunert Limited; *Int'l*, pg. 6311
CB&I EUROPE B.V.—See McDermott International, Inc.; *U.S. Public*, pg. 1405
CBI EUROPE B.V.—See Terex Corporation; *U.S. Public*, pg. 2018
CBIG - CANADIAN BENEFITS INVESTMENT & INSURANCE GROUP INC.—See Munchener Ruckversicherungs AG; *Int'l*, pg. 5085
CB&I INC.—See McDermott International, Inc.; *U.S. Public*, pg. 1405
CBI LABORATORIES, INC.—See SunTx Capital Partners, L.P.; *U.S. Private*, pg. 3874
CB&I LONDON—See McDermott International, Inc.; *U.S. Public*, pg. 1405
CB&I LUMMUS B.V.—See McDermott International, Inc.; *U.S. Public*, pg. 1405
CB&I LUMMUS GMBH—See McDermott International, Inc.; *U.S. Public*, pg. 1405
CB&I LUMMUS S.R.O.—See McDermott International, Inc.; *U.S. Public*, pg. 1405
CB INDUSTRIAL PRODUCT HOLDING BERHAD; *Int'l*, pg. 1364
CB&I NEDERLAND B.V.—See McDermott International, Inc.; *U.S. Public*, pg. 1405
CB&I OIL & GAS EUROPE B.V.—See McDermott International, Inc.; *U.S. Public*, pg. 1405
CB&I PADDINGTON LIMITED—See McDermott International, Inc.; *U.S. Public*, pg. 1405
CBI RESEARCH INC.—See Informa plc; *Int'l*, pg. 3691
CB&I SERVICES, INC. (NEW CASTLE)—See McDermott International, Inc.; *U.S. Public*, pg. 1405
CB&I SINGAPORE PTE LTD—See McDermott International, Inc.; *U.S. Public*, pg. 1405
CB&I—See McDermott International, Inc.; *U.S. Public*, pg. 1405
CB&I S.R.O.—See McDermott International, Inc.; *U.S. Public*, pg. 1405
CB&I UK LIMITED—See McDermott International, Inc.; *U.S. Public*, pg. 1405
CBI VENEZOLANA, S.A.—See McDermott International, Inc.; *U.S. Public*, pg. 1405
CBIZ ACCOUNTING, TAX & ADVISORY OF FLORIDA, LLC—See CBIZ, Inc.; *U.S. Public*, pg. 456
CBIZ ACCOUNTING, TAX & ADVISORY OF OHIO, LLC—See CBIZ, Inc.; *U.S. Public*, pg. 456
CBIZ ACCOUNTING, TAX & ADVISORY OF SOUTHWEST FLORIDA, LLC—See CBIZ, Inc.; *U.S. Public*, pg. 456
CBIZ ACCOUNTING, TAX & ADVISORY OF TOPEKA, LLC—See CBIZ, Inc.; *U.S. Public*, pg. 456
CBIZ BEATTY SATCHELL, LLC—See CBIZ, Inc.; *U.S. Public*, pg. 456
CBIZ BENEFITS & INSURANCE SERVICES, INC.—See CBIZ, Inc.; *U.S. Public*, pg. 456
CBIZ CMF, LLC—See CBIZ, Inc.; *U.S. Public*, pg. 456
CBIZ FINANCIAL SOLUTIONS, INC.—See CBIZ, Inc.; *U.S. Public*, pg. 456
CBIZ GIBRALTAR REAL ESTATE SERVICES, LLC—See CBIZ, Inc.; *U.S. Public*, pg. 456
CBIZ, INC.; *U.S. Public*, pg. 456
CBIZ INSURANCE SERVICES, INC.—See CBIZ, Inc.; *U.S. Public*, pg. 456
CBIZ LIFE INSURANCE SOLUTIONS, INC.—See CBIZ, Inc.; *U.S. Public*, pg. 456
CBIZ LIFE INSURANCE SOLUTIONS, INC.—See CBIZ, Inc.; *U.S. Public*, pg. 456
CBIZ MHM, LLC - BAKERSFIELD—See CBIZ, Inc.; *U.S. Public*, pg. 456
CBIZ MHM, LLC - KANSAS CITY—See CBIZ, Inc.; *U.S. Public*, pg. 456
CBIZ MHM, LLC—See CBIZ, Inc.; *U.S. Public*, pg. 456
CBIZ MHM, LLC - TAMPA BAY—See CBIZ, Inc.; *U.S. Public*, pg. 457
CBIZ PRIVATE EQUITY ADVISORY, LLC—See CBIZ, Inc.; *U.S. Public*, pg. 457
CBIZ RISK & ADVISORY SERVICES, LLC—See CBIZ, Inc.; *U.S. Public*, pg. 457
CBIZ SLATON INSURANCE—See CBIZ, Inc.; *U.S. Public*, pg. 457
CBIZ SOUTHERN CALIFORNIA, L.L.C.—See CBIZ, Inc.; *U.S. Public*, pg. 457
CBIZ TECHNOLOGIES, LLC—See CBIZ, Inc.; *U.S. Public*, pg. 457
CBIZ VALUATION GROUP, LLC—See CBIZ, Inc.; *U.S. Public*, pg. 457
CB JENI APPLES CROSSING, LLC—See Green Brick Partners, Inc.; *U.S. Public*, pg. 962
CB JENI IRON HORSE, LLC—See Green Brick Partners, Inc.; *U.S. Public*, pg. 962
CB JENI MAJESTIC GARDENS, LLC—See Green Brick Partners, Inc.; *U.S. Public*, pg. 962
CB JENI MANAGEMENT, LLC—See Green Brick Partners, Inc.; *U.S. Public*, pg. 962
CB JENI MERIDIAN AT SOUTHGATE, LLC—See Green Brick Partners, Inc.; *U.S. Public*, pg. 962
CB JENI PECAN SQUARE, LLC—See Green Brick Partners, Inc.; *U.S. Public*, pg. 962
CB JENI RIDGE VIEW VILLAS, LLC—See Green Brick Partners, Inc.; *U.S. Public*, pg. 962
CB JENI RIVERSET, LLC—See Green Brick Partners, Inc.; *U.S. Public*, pg. 962
CB JENI TERRACES AT LAS COLINAS, LLC—See Green Brick Partners, Inc.; *U.S. Public*, pg. 962
CB JENI TROPHY CLUB, LLC—See Green Brick Partners, Inc.; *U.S. Public*, pg. 962
CB JENI TWIN CREEKS, LLC—See Green Brick Partners, Inc.; *U.S. Public*, pg. 962
CB JENI VISTA DEL LAGO, LLC—See Green Brick Partners, Inc.; *U.S. Public*, pg. 962
CBK GROUP; *U.S. Private*, pg. 797
CB KHLYNOV JSC; *Int'l*, pg. 1364
CBK HOLDINGS LIMITED; *Int'l*, pg. 1365
CBK LTD.—See MVP Group International, Inc.; *U.S. Private*, pg. 2821
CB & K SUPPLY INC.; *U.S. Private*, pg. 796
CB KUBAN CREDIT LIMITED LIABILITY COMPANY; *Int'l*, pg. 1364
C BLADE S.P.A. MANUFACTURING & FORGING—See SIFCO Industries, Inc.; *U.S. Public*, pg. 1877
CBL & ASSOCIATES LIMITED PARTNERSHIP—See CBL & Associates Properties, Inc.; *U.S. Public*, pg. 457
CBL & ASSOCIATES PROPERTIES, INC.; *U.S. Public*, pg. 457
CBL & ASSOCIATES PROPERTIES—See CBL & Associates Properties, Inc.; *U.S. Public*, pg. 457
CBL BROOKFIELD SQUARE OP PROPCO, LLC—See CBL & Associates Properties, Inc.; *U.S. Public*, pg. 457
CBL DAKOTA SQUARE MALL OP PROPCO, LLC—See CBL & Associates Properties, Inc.; *U.S. Public*, pg. 457
CBL FAYETTE HOTEL MEMBER, LLC—See CBL & Associates Properties, Inc.; *U.S. Public*, pg. 458
CBL FAYETTE MALL OP PROPCO, LLC—See CBL & Associates Properties, Inc.; *U.S. Public*, pg. 458
CBL/FOOTHILLS PLAZA PARTNERSHIP—See CBL & Associates Properties, Inc.; *U.S. Public*, pg. 458
CBL-FRIENDLY CENTER, LLC—See CBL & Associates Properties, Inc.; *U.S. Public*, pg. 458
CBL FRONTIER SQUARE PROPCO, LLC—See CBL & Associates Properties, Inc.; *U.S. Public*, pg. 458
CBL HAMILTON PLACE SEARS OP PROPCO, LLC—See CBL & Associates Properties, Inc.; *U.S. Public*, pg. 458
CBL INTERNATIONAL LIMITED; *Int'l*, pg. 1365

CBL INTERNATIONAL LIMITED

CBL JEFFERSON MALL SELF DEV PROPCO, LLC—See CBL & Associates Properties, Inc.; *U.S. Public*, pg. 458
CBL KIRKWOOD MALL OP PROPCO, LLC—See CBL & Associates Properties, Inc.; *U.S. Public*, pg. 458
CBL LANDING AT ARBOR PLACE OP PROPCO, LLC—See CBL & Associates Properties, Inc.; *U.S. Public*, pg. 458
CBL MID RIVERS MALL OP PROPCO, LLC—See CBL & Associates Properties, Inc.; *U.S. Public*, pg. 458
CBL MONEY TRANSFER SDN. BHD.—See The City Bank Limited; *Int'l*, pg. 7633
CBL/MONROEVILLE, L.P.—See CBL & Associates Properties, Inc.; *U.S. Public*, pg. 458
CBL MONROEVILLE MALL OP PROPCO, LLC—See CBL & Associates Properties, Inc.; *U.S. Public*, pg. 458
CBL NORTHPARK MALL OP PROPCO, LLC—See CBL & Associates Properties, Inc.; *U.S. Public*, pg. 458
CB LOCKO-BANK JSC; *Int'l*, pg. 1364
CBL/PARK PLAZA MALL, LLC—See CBL & Associates Properties, Inc.; *U.S. Public*, pg. 458
CBL POST OAK MALL OP PROPCO, LLC—See CBL & Associates Properties, Inc.; *U.S. Public*, pg. 458
CBL SOUTH COUNTY CENTER OP PROPCO, LLC—See CBL & Associates Properties, Inc.; *U.S. Public*, pg. 458
CBL/STROUD, INC.—See CBL & Associates Properties, Inc.; *U.S. Public*, pg. 458
CBLT INC.; *Int'l*, pg. 1366
CBL VALLEY VIEW MALL OP PROPCO, LLC—See CBL & Associates Properties, Inc.; *U.S. Public*, pg. 458
CBL WEST TOWNE CROSSING OP PROPCO, LLC—See CBL & Associates Properties, Inc.; *U.S. Public*, pg. 458
C.B. LYNN COMPANY—See Distribution Solutions Group, Inc.; *U.S. Public*, pg. 668
CBL YORK GALLERIA OP PROPCO, LLC—See CBL & Associates Properties, Inc.; *U.S. Public*, pg. 458
CBL/YORK, INC.—See CBL & Associates Properties, Inc.; *U.S. Public*, pg. 458
CB MANUFACTURING & SALES CO., INC.; *U.S. Private*, pg. 796
CB MART INC.; *U.S. Private*, pg. 796
CBM BANCORP, INC.; *U.S. Public*, pg. 459
CBMI CONSTRUCTION CO., LTD.—See Sinoma International Engineering Co., Ltd.; *Int'l*, pg. 6952
CBM OF AMERICA, INC.; *U.S. Private*, pg. 797
CB NEPTUNE HOLDINGS, LLC—See Charlesbank Capital Partners, LLC; *U.S. Private*, pg. 854
CBN INC.—See Uchida Yoko Co., Ltd.; *Int'l*, pg. 8012
CBN LOTTERY GROUP—See Canadian Bank Note Company Limited; *Int'l*, pg. 1282
C B NORWOOD DISTRIBUTORS LIMITED—See The Zuellig Group Inc.; *Int'l*, pg. 7705
CBOCS DISTRIBUTION, INC.—See Cracker Barrel Old Country Store, Inc.; *U.S. Public*, pg. 589
CBOCS, INC.—See Cracker Barrel Old Country Store, Inc.; *U.S. Public*, pg. 589
CBOCS TEXAS, LLC—See Cracker Barrel Old Country Store, Inc.; *U.S. Public*, pg. 589
CBOCS WEST, INC.—See Cracker Barrel Old Country Store, Inc.; *U.S. Public*, pg. 589
CBOE CLEAR EUROPE N.V.—See Cboe Global Markets, Inc.; *U.S. Public*, pg. 459
CBOE EUROPE LIMITED—See Cboe Global Markets, Inc.; *U.S. Public*, pg. 459
CBOE GLOBAL MARKETS, INC.; *U.S. Public*, pg. 459
CBOL CORP.; *U.S. Private*, pg. 797
C'BON COSMETICS CO., LTD.; *Int'l*, pg. 1239
C'BON COSMETICS CO., LTD. - TOCHIGI FACTORY—See C'BON Cosmetics Co., Ltd.; *Int'l*, pg. 1239
C-BOND SYSTEMS, INC.; *U.S. Public*, pg. 414
C&B OPERATIONS LLC; *U.S. Private*, pg. 702
THE CBORD GROUP INC.—See Roper Technologies, Inc.; *U.S. Public*, pg. 1813
CBO TERRITORIA; *Int'l*, pg. 1366
CBP CARBON INDUSTRIES, INC.; *U.S. Private*, pg. 797
CBPE CAPITAL LLP; *Int'l*, pg. 1366
CBP ENGINEERING CORP.; *U.S. Private*, pg. 797
CBPO ENGENHARIA LTDA.—See Novonor S.A.; *Int'l*, pg. 5470
CB POIDEM JSC—See Sovcombank PJSC; *Int'l*, pg. 7121
CBPO INGENIERIA DE VENEZUELA C.A.—See Novonor S.A.; *Int'l*, pg. 5470
CBP QUILVEST S.A.—See Quilvest S.A.; *Int'l*, pg. 6163
C.B. RAGLAND COMPANY; *U.S. Private*, pg. 706
CBRAIN A/S; *Int'l*, pg. 1366
CBR ASSET MANAGEMENT BELGIUM S.A.—See Heidelberg Materials AG; *Int'l*, pg. 3309
CBR ASSOCIATES INC.—See Clearlake Capital Group, L.P.; *U.S. Private*, pg. 937
CBR ASSOCIATES INC.—See SkyKnight Capital LLC; *U.S. Private*, pg. 3685
CBRE ACQUISITION HOLDINGS, INC.; *U.S. Public*, pg. 459
CBRE CAPITAL MARKETS, INC.—See CBRE Group, Inc.; *U.S. Public*, pg. 460
CBRE CLARION SECURITIES LLC—See CBRE Group, Inc.; *U.S. Public*, pg. 460
CBRE GLOBAL INVESTORS (ASIA) LIMITED—See CBRE Group, Inc.; *U.S. Public*, pg. 460

CBRE GLOBAL INVESTORS (ASIA PACIFIC) LIMITED—See CBRE Group, Inc.; *U.S. Public*, pg. 460
CBRE GLOBAL INVESTORS BELGIUM—See CBRE Group, Inc.; *U.S. Public*, pg. 460
CBRE GLOBAL INVESTORS EUROPE B.V.—See CBRE Group, Inc.; *U.S. Public*, pg. 460
CBRE GLOBAL INVESTORS, LLC - BOSTON—See CBRE Group, Inc.; *U.S. Public*, pg. 460
CBRE GLOBAL INVESTORS (NL) B.V.—See CBRE Group, Inc.; *U.S. Public*, pg. 460
CBRE GLOBAL INVESTORS (UK) LTD.—See CBRE Group, Inc.; *U.S. Public*, pg. 460
CBRE GROUP, INC.; *U.S. Public*, pg. 459
CBRE HEERY, INC.—See CBRE Group, Inc.; *U.S. Public*, pg. 460
CBRE, INC. - HOUSTON—See CBRE Group, Inc.; *U.S. Public*, pg. 460
CBRE INVESTMENT MANAGEMENT, LLC—See CBRE Group, Inc.; *U.S. Public*, pg. 460
CBRE LIMITED; *Int'l*, pg. 1366
CBRE LOAN SERVICES, INC.—See CBRE Group, Inc.; *U.S. Public*, pg. 460
CB RENAISSANCE CREDIT LLC; *Int'l*, pg. 1364
CBRE SERVICEINSIGHT GROUP—See CBRE Group, Inc.; *U.S. Public*, pg. 460
CB RESORT CORPORATION—See Equity LifeStyle Properties, Inc.; *U.S. Public*, pg. 790
CBRE UK—See CBRE Group, Inc.; *U.S. Public*, pg. 460
C. BREWER & CO. LTD.; *U.S. Private*, pg. 704
CB RICHARD ELLIS, INC. - CHICAGO—See CBRE Group, Inc.; *U.S. Public*, pg. 459
CB RICHARD ELLIS, INC. - LOS ANGELES, DOWNTOWN—See CBRE Group, Inc.; *U.S. Public*, pg. 459
CB RICHARD ELLIS, INC. - NEW YORK CITY—See CBRE Group, Inc.; *U.S. Public*, pg. 459
CB RICHARD ELLIS, INC.—See CBRE Group, Inc.; *U.S. Public*, pg. 459
CB RICHARD ELLIS - N.E. PARTNERS, LP—See CBRE Group, Inc.; *U.S. Public*, pg. 459
CB RICHARD ELLIS OF VIRGINIA, INC.—See Colliers International Group Inc.; *Int'l*, pg. 1700
CB RICHARD ELLIS SERVICES, INC.—See CBRE Group, Inc.; *U.S. Public*, pg. 459
C B R INTERNATIONAL CORP.—See TPG Capital, L.P.; *U.S. Public*, pg. 2175
CBR INTERNATIONAL SERVICES S.A.—See Heidelberg Materials AG; *Int'l*, pg. 3309
CBR MANAGEMENT GMBH; *Int'l*, pg. 1366
C. BROWN & SONS (STEEL) LTD; *Int'l*, pg. 1240
C. BROWN & SONS (STEEL) LTD—See C. Brown & Sons (Steel) Ltd; *Int'l*, pg. 1240
CBR PORTLAND B.V.—See Heidelberg Materials AG; *Int'l*, pg. 3309
CBR SYSTEMS, INC.—See GI Manager L.P.; *U.S. Private*, pg. 1691
CB&S ADVERTISING AGENCY INC—See The Kroger Co.; *U.S. Public*, pg. 2107
CB&S BANK, INC.—See CB&S Bank, Inc.; *U.S. Private*, pg. 796
CB&S BANK, INC.; *U.S. Private*, pg. 796
CBS BORING & MACHINE COMPANY, INC.; *U.S. Private*, pg. 797
CBS BROADCASTING INC.—See National Amusements, Inc.; *U.S. Private*, pg. 2839
CBS BUTLER LIMITED—See Staffing 360 Solutions, Inc.; *U.S. Public*, pg. 1925
CBS CANADA CO.—See National Amusements, Inc.; *U.S. Private*, pg. 2840
CB SCIENTIFIC, INC.; *U.S. Public*, pg. 455
CBS COLLEGIATE SPORTS PROPERTIES INC.—See National Amusements, Inc.; *U.S. Private*, pg. 2840
CBS CONSTRUCTION LTD.; *Int'l*, pg. 1366
CBS-CSI INTERNATIONAL B.V.—See National Amusements, Inc.; *U.S. Private*, pg. 2841
CB SENIORENRESIDENZ ARMBRUSTERGASSE GMBH—See Clariane SE; *Int'l*, pg. 1643
CBS ENTERTAINMENT DIVISION—See National Amusements, Inc.; *U.S. Private*, pg. 2839
C&B SERVICES, INC.—See Crochet & Borel, Inc.; *U.S. Private*, pg. 1102
CBSET, INC.; *U.S. Private*, pg. 797
CBS FILMS INC.—See National Amusements, Inc.; *U.S. Private*, pg. 2840
CBS GROUP LTD—See Schneider Electric SE; *Int'l*, pg. 6626
CBSHOME REAL ESTATE—See Berkshire Hathaway Inc.; *U.S. Public*, pg. 306
C B S INSURANCE, L.L.P.—See Arthur J. Gallagher & Co.; *U.S. Public*, pg. 204
CBS INTERACTIVE INC.—See National Amusements, Inc.; *U.S. Private*, pg. 2840
CBS INTERACTIVE INC.—See National Amusements, Inc.; *U.S. Private*, pg. 2840
CBS INTERACTIVE JAPAN K.K.—See National Amusements, Inc.; *U.S. Private*, pg. 2840
CBS INTERACTIVE LIMITED—See National Amusements, Inc.; *U.S. Private*, pg. 2840

CORPORATE AFFILIATIONS

CBS INTERACTIVE PTE. LTD.—See National Amusements, Inc.; *U.S. Private*, pg. 2840
CBS INTERACTIVE PTY. LTD.—See National Amusements, Inc.; *U.S. Private*, pg. 2840
CBS INTERNATIONAL HOLDINGS B.V.—See National Amusements, Inc.; *U.S. Private*, pg. 2840
CBS INTERNATIONAL SALES HOLDINGS B.V.—See National Amusements, Inc.; *U.S. Private*, pg. 2840
CBS INTERNATIONAL TELEVISION AUSTRALIA PTY LIMITED—See National Amusements, Inc.; *U.S. Private*, pg. 2840
CBS INVESTISSEMENTS SAS—See Tata Sons Limited; *Int'l*, pg. 7471
CBSL TRANSPORTATION SERVICES, INC.; *U.S. Private*, pg. 797
CBS MAXPREPS INC.—See National Amusements, Inc.; *U.S. Private*, pg. 2840
CBS NEWS—See National Amusements, Inc.; *U.S. Private*, pg. 2840
CB SOLIDARNOST JSC; *Int'l*, pg. 1364
CBS OUTERNET INC.—See National Amusements, Inc.; *U.S. Private*, pg. 2840
CBS OVERSEAS INC.—See National Amusements, Inc.; *U.S. Private*, pg. 2840
CBS PERSONNEL SERVICES, LLC—See Recruit Holdings Co., Ltd.; *Int'l*, pg. 6241
CB SPIRITS CANADA, INC.—See Constellation Brands, Inc.; *U.S. Public*, pg. 570
CBS SPORTS DIVISION—See National Amusements, Inc.; *U.S. Private*, pg. 2840
CBS SPORTSLINE.COM, INC.—See National Amusements, Inc.; *U.S. Private*, pg. 2840
CBS STUDIOS INC.—See National Amusements, Inc.; *U.S. Private*, pg. 2840
CBS TELEVISION DISTRIBUTION—See National Amusements, Inc.; *U.S. Private*, pg. 2840
CBS TELEVISION STATIONS INC.—See National Amusements, Inc.; *U.S. Private*, pg. 2840
C.B. STRAIN & SON INC.; *U.S. Private*, pg. 706
CB SUPPLIES LTD.—See American Granby, Inc.; *U.S. Private*, pg. 235
CBS WORLDWIDE NETHERLANDS B.V.—See National Amusements, Inc.; *U.S. Private*, pg. 2841
CBT CAMPUS, LLC; *U.S. Private*, pg. 797
CB/TCC GLOBAL HOLDINGS LIMITED—See CBRE Group, Inc.; *U.S. Public*, pg. 460
CBT CO.—See Belting Co. of Cincinnati Inc.; *U.S. Private*, pg. 521
CB&T HOLDING CORPORATION; *U.S. Private*, pg. 796
CBT NUGGETS, LLC; *U.S. Private*, pg. 797
CB TRANSPORTATION; *U.S. Private*, pg. 796
CB TRANSPORT, INC.—See Banco Bilbao Vizcaya Argentaria, S.A.; *Int'l*, pg. 817
CB TRAVEL CORP.; *U.S. Private*, pg. 796
CBT TECHNOLOGY INC.—See AbelConn LLC; *U.S. Private*, pg. 37
C&B WAREHOUSE DISTRIBUTING; *U.S. Private*, pg. 702
CBZ ASSET MANAGEMENT COMPANY (PRIVATE) LIMITED—See CBZ Holdings Limited; *Int'l*, pg. 1366
CBZ BANK LIMITED—See CBZ Holdings Limited; *Int'l*, pg. 1366
CBZ HOLDINGS LIMITED; *Int'l*, pg. 1366
CBZ INSURANCE (PRIVATE) LIMITED—See CBZ Holdings Limited; *Int'l*, pg. 1366
CBZ PROPERTIES (PVT) LIMITED—See CBZ Holdings Limited; *Int'l*, pg. 1366
CC 1 LIMITED PARTNERSHIP; *U.S. Private*, pg. 797
CC1 LIMITED PARTNERSHIP; *U.S. Private*, pg. 799
CC3 ACQUISITION, LLC—See Welltower Inc.; *U.S. Public*, pg. 2348
CCA BAYSWATER PTY LTD—See COCA-COLA EUROPACIFIC PARTNERS PLC; *Int'l*, pg. 1684
CCA ENGINEERING SIMULATION SOFTWARE (SHANGHAI) CO.,LTD—See FUJISOFT INCORPORATED; *Int'l*, pg. 2830
CCA ENGINEERING SIMULATION SOFTWARE (SHANGHAI) CO., LTD.—See FUJISOFT INCORPORATED; *Int'l*, pg. 2830
CCA FOR SOCIAL GOOD—See CCA Global Partners, Inc.; *U.S. Private*, pg. 799
CCA GLOBAL PARTNERS, INC. - BIZUNITE DIVISION—See CCA Global Partners, Inc.; *U.S. Private*, pg. 799
CCA GLOBAL PARTNERS, INC. - MANCHESTER—See CCA Global Partners, Inc.; *U.S. Private*, pg. 799
CCA GLOBAL PARTNERS, INC.; *U.S. Private*, pg. 799
CCA GLOBAL PARTNERS, INC. - THE FLOOR TRADER DIVISION—See CCA Global Partners, Inc.; *U.S. Private*, pg. 799
CCA INC—See Corecivic, Inc.; *U.S. Public*, pg. 577
CCA INDUSTRIES, INC.; *U.S. Public*, pg. 460
CCAIR, INC.—See Mesa Air Group, Inc.; *U.S. Public*, pg. 1425
CC AMERICAN OILFIELD, LLC—See CSE Global Ltd.; *Int'l*, pg. 1863
C-CAM GMBH—See Bechtle AG; *Int'l*, pg. 938
CCA OCCASIONS LTD—See Taylor Corporation; *U.S. Private*, pg. 3938

CCAP AUTO LEASE LTD.—See Banco Santander, S.A.; *Int'l*, pg. 825
C. CARDASSILARIS & SONS - CARDICO S.A.; *Int'l*, pg. 1240
CCA TRS, LLC—See Corecivic, Inc.; *U.S. Public*, pg. 577
CCATT LLC—See Crown Castle Inc.; *U.S. Public*, pg. 596
CCA-WESCO—See WESCO International, Inc.; *U.S. Public*, pg. 2352
CC-BANK AKTIENGESELLSCHAFT—See Banco Santander, S.A.; *Int'l*, pg. 825
CCB FINANCE, S.R.O.—See Banco Santander, S.A.; *Int'l*, pg. 825
CCB FUTURES CO., LTD.—See China Construction Bank Corporation; *Int'l*, pg. 1491
CCB GROUP EAD—See Chimimport AD; *Int'l*, pg. 1479
CCBH PSYCHIATRIC HOSPITALISTS, LLC—See HCA Healthcare, Inc.; *U.S. Public*, pg. 992
CCB INC.; *U.S. Private*, pg. 799
CCB INTERNATIONAL (HOLDINGS) LIMITED—See China Construction Bank Corporation; *Int'l*, pg. 1491
CCB MANAGEMENT SERVICES GMBH—See Coca-Cola HBC AG; *Int'l*, pg. 1685
C.C. BORDEN CONSTRUCTION, INC.; *U.S. Private*, pg. 706
CCB TRUST CO., LTD.—See China Construction Bank Corporation; *Int'l*, pg. 1491
CC CAPITAL PARTNERS, LLC; *U.S. Private*, pg. 797
CC CARPET INC.; *U.S. Private*, pg. 799
CCC ASSOCIATES INC.; *U.S. Private*, pg. 799
CCC CAYMAN, LTD.—See KBR, Inc.; *U.S. Public*, pg. 1215
CCCC DREDGING (GROUP) CO., LTD.—See China Communications Construction Company Limited; *Int'l*, pg. 1490
CCCC FINANCIAL LEASING CO., LTD.—See China Communications Construction Company Limited; *Int'l*, pg. 1490
CCCC FIRST HARBOUR CONSULTANTS CO., LTD.—See China Communications Construction Company Limited; *Int'l*, pg. 1490
CCCC FIRST HARBOUR ENGINEERING CO., LTD.—See China Communications Construction Company Limited; *Int'l*, pg. 1490
CCCC FOURTH HARBOUR ENGINEERING CO., LTD.—See China Communications Construction Company Limited; *Int'l*, pg. 1490
CCCC FOURTH HIGHWAY ENGINEERING CO., LTD.—See China Communications Construction Company Limited; *Int'l*, pg. 1490
CCCC FUND MANAGEMENT CO., LTD.—See China Communications Construction Company Limited; *Int'l*, pg. 1490
CCCC GUANGZHOU DREDGING CO., LTD.—See China Communications Construction Company Limited; *Int'l*, pg. 1490
CCCC HIGHWAY CONSULTANTS CO., LTD.—See China Communications Construction Company Limited; *Int'l*, pg. 1490
CCCC INTERNATIONAL HOLDING LIMITED—See China Communications Construction Company Limited; *Int'l*, pg. 1490
CCCC INVESTMENT CO., LTD.—See China Communications Construction Company Limited; *Int'l*, pg. 1490
CCCC SECOND HARBOUR ENGINEERING CO., LTD.—See China Communications Construction Company Limited; *Int'l*, pg. 1490
CCCC SECOND HIGHWAY CONSULTANTS CO., LTD.—See China Communications Construction Company Limited; *Int'l*, pg. 1490
CCCC SECOND HIGHWAY ENGINEERING CO., LTD.—See China Communications Construction Company Limited; *Int'l*, pg. 1490
CCCC SHANGHAI EQUIPMENT ENGINEERING CO., LTD.—See China Communications Construction Company Limited; *Int'l*, pg. 1490
CCCC THIRD HARBOUR ENGINEERING CO., LTD.—See China Communications Construction Company Limited; *Int'l*, pg. 1490
CCCC XI'AN ROAD CONSTRUCTION MACHINERY CO., LTD.—See China Communications Construction Company Limited; *Int'l*, pg. 1490
CCCG REAL ESTATE CORPORATION LIMITED; *Int'l*, pg. 1366
CCC GROUP INC.; *U.S. Private*, pg. 799
CCC HEAVY DUTY TRUCK PARTS COMPANY—See Platinum Equity, LLC; *U.S. Public*, pg. 3209
CCC INFORMATION SERVICES, INC.—See Advent International Corporation; *U.S. Private*, pg. 98
CCC INTELLIGENT SOLUTIONS HOLDINGS INC.; *U.S. Public*, pg. 461
C.C. CLARK, INC.; *U.S. Private*, pg. 706
CCCL INFRASTRUCTURE LTD.—See Consolidated Construction Consortium Ltd; *Int'l*, pg. 1770
CCCL PEARL CITY FOOD PORT SEZ LIMITED—See Consolidated Construction Consortium Ltd; *Int'l*, pg. 1770
CC & CO AS—See KPP Group Holdings Co., Ltd.; *Int'l*, pg. 4298
CC COMMUNICATIONS; *U.S. Private*, pg. 799

(CC) COMPANY FOR BEVERAGE INDUSTRY/LTD.—See Coca-Cola Icecek A.S.; *Int'l*, pg. 1686
C & C CONSTRUCTIONS LIMITED; *Int'l*, pg. 1237
C.C. CONSULTING CO., LTD.—See JAC Recruitment Co., Ltd.; *Int'l*, pg. 3864
CCC S.A.; *Int'l*, pg. 1366
CCC SHOES & BAGS D.O.O.—See CCC S.A.; *Int'l*, pg. 1366
CCC SHOES & BAGS SP. Z O.O.—See CCC S.A.; *Int'l*, pg. 1366
CCC SHOES BULGARIA EOOD—See CCC S.A.; *Int'l*, pg. 1366
C.C.C. TOURIST ENTERPRISES PUBLIC COMPANY LIMITED—See G.S. Galatariotis & Sons Ltd.; *Int'l*, pg. 2866
C.C.D. COGENT COMMUNICATIONS DEUTSCHLAND GMBH—See Cogent Communications Holdings, Inc.; *U.S. Public*, pg. 522
CC DELIVERY GMBH—See Metro AG; *Int'l*, pg. 4859
CC DILLON CO.; *U.S. Private*, pg. 799
CC DISTRIBUTORS INC; *U.S. Private*, pg. 799
CC DUTCH PROPERTY HOLDING B.V.—See Cintas Corporation; *U.S. Public*, pg. 495
CCECC (BOTSWANA) (PTY) LTD.—See China Railway Construction Corporation Limited; *Int'l*, pg. 1542
CCECC INTERNATIONAL TRADING CO. LTD.—See China Railway Construction Corporation Limited; *Int'l*, pg. 1542
CCECC NIGERIA LTD.—See China Railway Construction Corporation Limited; *Int'l*, pg. 1542
CCEI BANK GE—See Afriland First Bank; *Int'l*, pg. 192
CC ENERGIE SA—See BKW AG; *Int'l*, pg. 1055
CCEP HOLDINGS SVERIGE AB—See COCA-COLA EUROPACIFIC PARTNERS PLC; *Int'l*, pg. 1684
CCF HOLDINGS LLC; *U.S. Public*, pg. 461
CC FILSON CO.; *U.S. Private*, pg. 799
CC FINANCIAL, LLC—See Park Cities Asset Management LLC; *U.S. Private*, pg. 3095
C&C FLORAL INC.; *U.S. Private*, pg. 702
CCF LTD.—See Travis Perkins plc; *Int'l*, pg. 7908
C.C. FORBES, LLC—See Forbes Energy Services Ltd.; *U.S. Public*, pg. 864
C & C FORD SALES, INCORPORATED; *U.S. Private*, pg. 701
CCF REPRESENTACAO E ASSESSORIA S/C LTDA.—See HSBC Holdings plc; *Int'l*, pg. 3505
CCFW, INC.; *U.S. Private*, pg. 799
CCG DE GMBH—See Metro AG; *Int'l*, pg. 4856
CCGI / MALL OF AMERICA, LLC—See Blink Charging Co.; *U.S. Public*, pg. 361
C&C GROUP PLC; *Int'l*, pg. 1238
C-CHANNEL AG—See Constellation Software Inc.; *Int'l*, pg. 1772
C CHANNEL CORPORATION; *Int'l*, pg. 1237
CCH ASIA LIMITED—See Wolters Kluwer n.v.; *Int'l*, pg. 8445
CCH AUSTRALIA LIMITED—See Wolters Kluwer n.v.; *Int'l*, pg. 8445
CCHBC ARMENIA CJSC—See Coca-Cola HBC AG; *Int'l*, pg. 1685
CCHBC BULGARIA AD—See Coca-Cola HBC AG; *Int'l*, pg. 1685
CC-HEFTRUCKS BVBA—See Group Thermote & Vanhalst; *Int'l*, pg. 3089
C-CHEM CO., LTD.—See Nippon Steel Corporation; *Int'l*, pg. 5335
C CHENG HOLDINGS LIMITED; *Int'l*, pg. 1237
CCH HONG KONG LIMITED—See Wolters Kluwer n.v.; *Int'l*, pg. 8445
CCH INC.—See Wolters Kluwer n.v.; *Int'l*, pg. 8445
CCH JAPAN LIMITED—See Wolters Kluwer n.v.; *Int'l*, pg. 8445
CCH-LIS RESEARCH CORPORATION—See Wolters Kluwer n.v.; *Int'l*, pg. 8445
CCH (M) SDN BHD—See Wolters Kluwer n.v.; *Int'l*, pg. 8445
CCH NEW ZEALAND LIMITED—See Wolters Kluwer n.v.; *Int'l*, pg. 8445
CCHN GROUP HOLDINGS, INC.—See Frazier & Company, Inc.; *U.S. Private*, pg. 1599
CCHN GROUP HOLDINGS, INC.—See ModivCare, Inc.; *U.S. Public*, pg. 1455
CC HOGANAS BYGGKERAMIK AB—See QuattroR SGR S.p.A.; *Int'l*, pg. 6157
C&C HOLDING INC.; *U.S. Private*, pg. 702
CCH PROSYSTEMS INDIA PRIVATE LIMITED—See Wolters Kluwer n.v.; *Int'l*, pg. 8444
CCHP WAIKIKI LLC—See Host Hotels & Resorts, Inc.; *U.S. Public*, pg. 1054
C. CHRISTOPHEL MASCHINENHANDEL & VERMITTLUNGEN GMBH; *Int'l*, pg. 1240
CCH SMALL FIRM SERVICES—See Wolters Kluwer n.v.; *Int'l*, pg. 8445
CCH—See Wolters Kluwer n.v.; *Int'l*, pg. 8445
CCH TAX COMPLIANCE—See Wolters Kluwer n.v.; *Int'l*, pg. 8445
CCH WASHINGTON SERVICE BUREAU, INC.—See Wolters Kluwer n.v.; *Int'l*, pg. 8445
C&C HYDRAULICS, INC.; *U.S. Private*, pg. 702

CC HYDROSONICS LTD.—See Crest Group Inc.; *U.S. Private*, pg. 1095
CCI AG—See IMI plc; *Int'l*, pg. 3624
CCI AMERICA, INC. - AUSTIN BRANCH—See Nidec Chaun-Choung Technology Corporation; *Int'l*, pg. 5274
CCI AMERICA, INC.—See Nidec Chaun-Choung Technology Corporation; *Int'l*, pg. 5274
CCIAM FUTURE ENERGY LIMITED; *Int'l*, pg. 1366
CCI CZECH REPUBLIC SRO—See IMI plc; *Int'l*, pg. 3624
CCID CONSULTING COMPANY LIMITED; *Int'l*, pg. 1366
CCI EUROPE A/S; *Int'l*, pg. 1366
CCI GROUP, LLC—See Bristol Bay Native Corporation; *U.S. Private*, pg. 656
CCI INDUSTRIAL SERVICES, LLC—See Bristol Bay Native Corporation; *U.S. Private*, pg. 656
CCI KK—See IMI plc; *Int'l*, pg. 3624
CCI LTD—See IMI plc; *Int'l*, pg. 3625
CCI MANUFACTURING INC.; *U.S. Private*, pg. 799
CC INDUSTRIES, INC.—See Henry Crown & Company; *U.S. Private*, pg. 1917
C&C INTERNATIONAL CO., LTD.; *Int'l*, pg. 1238
C & C INTERNATIONAL LTD—See C&C Group Plc; *Int'l*, pg. 1238
C&CI PARTNERS CO., LTD.—See CoAsia Holdings Co., Ltd.; *Int'l*, pg. 1680
CCIP STERLING, L.P.—See Apartment Investment and Management Company; *U.S. Public*, pg. 144
CCI SOLUTIONS, LLC—See Bristol Bay Native Corporation; *U.S. Private*, pg. 656
CCI SYSTEMS INC.; *U.S. Private*, pg. 799
CCI-TELECOM, INC.—See Fortran Corporation; *U.S. Public*, pg. 872
CCI THERMAL TECHNOLOGIES, INC.—See Thermon Group Holdings, Inc.; *U.S. Public*, pg. 2155
CCI THERMAL TECHNOLOGIES TEXAS, INC.—See Thermon Group Holdings, Inc.; *U.S. Public*, pg. 2155
CCI VALVE TECHNOLOGY AB—See IMI plc; *Int'l*, pg. 3625
CCI VALVE TECHNOLOGY GMBH—See IMI plc; *Int'l*, pg. 3625
CC JAPAN INCOME & GROWTH TRUST PLC; *Int'l*, pg. 1366
C.C. JOHNSON & MALHOTRA, P.C.; *U.S. Private*, pg. 706
CCK CONSOLIDATED HOLDINGS BERHAD; *Int'l*, pg. 1367
CCK FINANCIAL SOLUTIONS (CONSULTING) PTY. LTD.—See CCK Financial Solutions Pty Limited; *Int'l*, pg. 1367
CCK FINANCIAL SOLUTIONS (MALAYSIA) SDN. BHD.—See CCK Financial Solutions Pty Limited; *Int'l*, pg. 1367
CCK FINANCIAL SOLUTIONS PTY LIMITED; *Int'l*, pg. 1367
CC LAND HOLDINGS LIMITED; *Int'l*, pg. 1366
CCL CONTAINER (HERMITAGE), INC.—See CCL Industries, Inc.; *Int'l*, pg. 1367
CCL CONTAINER MEXICO—See CCL Industries Inc.; *Int'l*, pg. 1367
CCL CONTAINER—See CCL Industries Inc.; *Int'l*, pg. 1367
CCL DESIGN GMBH—See CCL Industries Inc.; *Int'l*, pg. 1367
C.C.L.D. TECHNOLOGIES, INC.—See Crestview Partners, L.P.; *U.S. Private*, pg. 1098
CCL INDUSTRIES CORP.—See CCL Industries Inc.; *Int'l*, pg. 1367
CCL INDUSTRIES INC.; *Int'l*, pg. 1367
CCL INSERTCO, LLC—See CCL Industries Inc.; *Int'l*, pg. 1367
CCL INTERNATIONAL LIMITED; *Int'l*, pg. 1369
CCL LABEL AG—See palero capital GmbH; *Int'l*, pg. 5706
CCL LABEL (ASHFORD) LIMITED—See CCL Industries Inc.; *Int'l*, pg. 1368
CCL LABEL A/S—See CCL Industries Inc.; *Int'l*, pg. 1368
CCL LABEL/AUTO-SLEEVE—See CCL Industries Inc.; *Int'l*, pg. 1367
CCL LABEL DE MEXICO S.A. DE C.V.—See CCL Industries Inc.; *Int'l*, pg. 1368
CCL LABEL DO BRASIL S/A—See CCL Industries Inc.; *Int'l*, pg. 1368
CCL LABEL GMBH—See CCL Industries Inc.; *Int'l*, pg. 1368
CCL LABEL (GUANGZHOU) CO., LTD.—See CCL Industries Inc.; *Int'l*, pg. 1368
CCL LABEL (HEFEI) CO., LTD.—See CCL Industries Inc.; *Int'l*, pg. 1368
CCL LABEL, INC.—See CCL Industries Inc.; *Int'l*, pg. 1367
CCL LABEL IRELAND—See CCL Industries Inc.; *Int'l*, pg. 1368
CCL LABEL LIMITED—See CCL Industries Inc.; *Int'l*, pg. 1368
CCL LABEL MEERANE GMBH—See CCL Industries Inc.; *Int'l*, pg. 1368
CCL LABEL PORTLAND, INC—See CCL Industries Inc.; *Int'l*, pg. 1368
CCL LABEL S.A.S—See CCL Industries Inc.; *Int'l*, pg. 1368
CCL LABEL SIOUX FALLS, INC—See CCL Industries Inc.; *Int'l*, pg. 1368
CCL LABEL—See CCL Industries Inc.; *Int'l*, pg. 1367

CCL INTERNATIONAL LIMITED

CCL LABEL—See CCL Industries Inc.; *Int'l*, pg. 1367
CCL LABEL—See CCL Industries Inc.; *Int'l*, pg. 1367
CCL LABEL—See CCL Industries Inc.; *Int'l*, pg. 1367
CCL LABEL—See CCL Industries Inc.; *Int'l*, pg. 1367
CCL LABEL—See CCL Industries Inc.; *Int'l*, pg. 1368
CCL LABEL—See CCL Industries Inc.; *Int'l*, pg. 1368
CCL LABEL SP Z O.O—See CCL Industries Inc.; *Int'l*, pg. 1368
CCL LABEL S.R.L.—See CCL Industries Inc.; *Int'l*, pg. 1368
CCL LABEL (THAI) LTD.—See CCL Industries Inc.; *Int'l*, pg. 1368
CCL LABEL TUBEDEC—See CCL Industries Inc.; *Int'l*, pg. 1367
CCL LABEL (VIC) PTY. LTD.—See CCL Industries Inc.; *Int'l*, pg. 1368
CCL LABEL VIETNAM COMPANY LIMITED—See CCL Industries Inc.; *Int'l*, pg. 1368
CCL LINDAB LTD—See Lindab International AB; *Int'l*, pg. 4504
CCL PACKAGE LABEL S.N.C—See CCL Industries Inc.; *Int'l*, pg. 1368
CCL PRODUCTS (INDIA) LIMITED; *Int'l*, pg. 1369
CCL SECURE PTY LTD—See CCL Industries Inc.; *Int'l*, pg. 1368
CCL SECURITY PRODUCTS—See The Eastern Company; *U.S. Public*, pg. 2069
CCL TUBE, INC.—See CCL Industries Inc.; *Int'l*, pg. 1367
CCL TUBE (WILKES-BARRE), INC—See CCL Industries Inc.; *Int'l*, pg. 1367
CCM ACQUISITION CORP.; *U.S. Private*, pg. 799
C. C. MARINE DISTRIBUTORS INC.; *Int'l*, pg. 1240
C&C MARINE MAINTENANCE COMPANY—See Blue Danube Incorporated; *U.S. Private*, pg. 588
CCMC AFFILIATES, INC.—See Connecticut Children's Medical Center Corporation, Inc.; *U.S. Private*, pg. 1015
CCM CHEMICALS SDN. BHD.—See Batu Kawan Berhad; *Int'l*, pg. 890
CCM COMMUNICATION-CENTER MITTEL-DEUTSCHLAND GMBH—See Bertelsmann SE & Co. KGaA; *Int'l*, pg. 994
CCMC VENTURES, INC.—See Connecticut Children's Medical Center Corporation, Inc.; *U.S. Private*, pg. 1015
C&C MECHANICAL LTD.—See Absolent Air Care Group AB; *Int'l*, pg. 70
C&C METAL PRODUCTS CORP; *U.S. Private*, pg. 702
C&C MILLWRIGHT MAINTENANCE CO.; *U.S. Private*, pg. 702
CCM INNOVATIVE SOLUTIONS SDN BHD—See Batu Kawan Berhad; *Int'l*, pg. 890
CCMI—See United Communications Group; *U.S. Private*, pg. 4289
CCM MARKETING COMMUNICATIONS; *U.S. Private*, pg. 800
CCM MARKETING SDN BHD—See Batu Kawan Berhad; *Int'l*, pg. 890
CCMP CAPITAL ADVISORS, LLC - HOUSTON OFFICE—See CCMP Capital Advisors, LP; *U.S. Private*, pg. 800
CCMP CAPITAL ADVISORS, LP; *U.S. Private*, pg. 800
CCMP CAPITAL ADVISORS (UK), LLP—See CCMP Capital Advisors, LP; *U.S. Private*, pg. 800
CCMP GROWTH ADVISORS, LP—See CCMP Capital Advisors, LP; *U.S. Private*, pg. 800
CCM PHARMACEUTICALS SDN BHD—See Batu Kawan Berhad; *Int'l*, pg. 891
CCM PHARMACEUTICALS (S) PTE LTD—See Batu Kawan Berhad; *Int'l*, pg. 891
CCM POLYMERS SDN. BHD.—See Batu Kawan Berhad; *Int'l*, pg. 890
C.C.M. SAS—See PSB Industries SA; *Int'l*, pg. 6014
CCM SINGAPORE PTE LTD—See Batu Kawan Berhad; *Int'l*, pg. 890
CCM USAHA KIMIA (M) SDN BHD—See Batu Kawan Berhad; *Int'l*, pg. 891
CCM WATERCARE SDN BHD—See Batu Kawan Berhad; *Int'l*, pg. 891
CCM WEST—See CCM Marketing Communications; *U.S. Private*, pg. 800
C.C. MYERS, INC.; *U.S. Private*, pg. 706
CC NAPRED JSC; *Int'l*, pg. 1366
CC NEUBERGER PRINCIPAL HOLDINGS II—See CC Capital Partners, LLC; *U.S. Private*, pg. 797
CC NEUBERGER PRINCIPAL HOLDINGS I—See CC Capital Partners, LLC; *U.S. Private*, pg. 797
CCNG REALTY, INC.; *U.S. Private*, pg. 801
CCN INTERNATIONAL INC.; *U.S. Private*, pg. 801
CCNOW, INC.—See Snorrason Holdings ehf; *Int'l*, pg. 7028
C. COAKLEY RELOCATION SYSTEMS, INC.; *U.S. Private*, pg. 705
CCO CAPITAL, LLC—See CIM Group, LLC; *U.S. Private*, pg. 897
CCO HOLDINGS CAPITAL CORP.—See Charter Communications, Inc.; *U.S. Public*, pg. 483
CCO HOLDINGS, LLC—See Charter Communications, Inc.; *U.S. Public*, pg. 483

CCO INVESTMENT SERVICES CORP.—See Citizens Financial Group, Inc.; *U.S. Public*, pg. 505
CCOM GROUP, INC.—See Daikin Industries, Ltd.; *Int'l*, pg. 1935
C-COM SATELLITE SYSTEMS INC.; *Int'l*, pg. 1239
CCOOP GROUP CO., LTD.; *Int'l*, pg. 1369
CCOP INTERNATIONAL (THAILAND) CO. LTD.—See Lumentum Holdings Inc.; *U.S. Public*, pg. 1348
C-COR ARGENTINA S.R.L.—See CommScope Holding Company, Inc.; *U.S. Public*, pg. 548
C&C ORGANIZATION INC.; *U.S. Private*, pg. 702
C-COR INCORPORATED—See CommScope Holding Company, Inc.; *U.S. Public*, pg. 548
C. COWLES & CO.; *U.S. Private*, pg. 705
C&C PARTNERS SP. Z O.O—See TKH Group N.V.; *Int'l*, pg. 7763
C&C PARTNERS TELECOM SP. Z O.O.—See TKH Group N.V.; *Int'l*, pg. 7763
CCP AUSTRIA ABWICKLUNGSSTELLE FUR BORSENGESCHAFTE GMBH—See CEESEG AG; *Int'l*, pg. 1389
CCP AUSTRIA ABWICKLUNGSSTELLE FUR BORSENGESCHAFTE GMBH—See Oesterreichische Kontrollbank AG; *Int'l*, pg. 5529
CCP CO., LTD.—See BANDAI NAMCO Holdings Inc.; *Int'l*, pg. 829
C C P CONTACT PROBES CO., LTD.; *Int'l*, pg. 1237
CCP FUND III MANAGEMENT LLC; *U.S. Private*, pg. 801
CCP GAMES SHANGHAI—See Pearl Abyss Corp.; *Int'l*, pg. 5774
CCP GAMES UK LTD—See Pearl Abyss Corp.; *Int'l*, pg. 5774
CCP GLOBAL INC.; *U.S. Private*, pg. 801
CCP HF—See Pearl Abyss Corp.; *Int'l*, pg. 5774
CCPI INC.—See Vesuvius plc; *Int'l*, pg. 8178
CCP NORTH AMERICA INC.—See Pearl Abyss Corp.; *Int'l*, pg. 5774
C & C POWER LINE, INC.—See The Goldfield Corporation; *U.S. Public*, pg. 2076
CCP VALENCIA LLC—See The Macerich Company; *U.S. Public*, pg. 2109
CCR ACTIONS S.A.—See UBS Group AG; *Int'l*, pg. 8007
CCR ASSET MANAGEMENT S.A.—See UBS Group AG; *Int'l*, pg. 8007
CCRC - FREEDOM POINTE AT THE VILLAGES, LLC—See Brookdale Senior Living Inc.; *U.S. Public*, pg. 394
CCRC - REGENCY OAKS, LLC—See Brookdale Senior Living Inc.; *U.S. Public*, pg. 394
CC REALITY LLC—See Silver Lake Group, LLC; *U.S. Private*, pg. 3654
CC-RENO, LLC—See Caesars Entertainment, Inc.; *U.S. Public*, pg. 419
CCR ENVIRONMENTAL INC.—See Vanasse Hangen Brustlin, Inc.; *U.S. Private*, pg. 4342
C&C RESEARCH LABORATORIES—See Roche Holding AG; *Int'l*, pg. 6372
CCRES, INC.; *U.S. Private*, pg. 801
C & C RESOURCES INC.—See Callidus Capital Corporation; *Int'l*, pg. 1265
CCR ESPANA - CONCESIONES Y PARTICIPACIONES S.L.—See CCR S.A.; *Int'l*, pg. 1369
CCR GESTION S.A.—See UBS Group AG; *Int'l*, pg. 8007
CCRI, INC.—See DENTSPLY SIRONA Inc.; *U.S. Public*, pg. 654
CCR LOGISTICS SYSTEMS AG—See Monitor Clipper Partners, LLC; *U.S. Private*, pg. 2771
CCR MOTOR CO. LTD.—See VT Holdings Co., Ltd.; *Int'l*, pg. 8315
CCRO, LLC—See Susquehanna International Group, LLLP; *U.S. Private*, pg. 3885
CCR PENNSYLVANIA RACING, INC.—See PENN Entertainment, Inc.; *U.S. Public*, pg. 1662
CCR PLATFORMING CANGREJERA S.A. DE C.V.—See ACS, Actividades de Construccion y Servicios, S.A.; *Int'l*, pg. 110
CC RP LLC—See Sun Communities, Inc.; *U.S. Public*, pg. 1961
CCR S.A.; *Int'l*, pg. 1369
CCR SPECIALTY CHEMICALS LLC—See Palo Duro Capital, LLC; *U.S. Private*, pg. 3082
CCR TECHNOLOGIES LIMITED; *Int'l*, pg. 1369
CCR TECHNOLOGIES LTD.—See CCR Technologies Limited; *Int'l*, pg. 1369
CCS AMERICA INC.—See Optex Group Co., Ltd.; *Int'l*, pg. 5601
CCS ASIA PTE LTD.—See Optex Group Co., Ltd.; *Int'l*, pg. 5601
CCSB FINANCIAL CORP.; *U.S. Public*, pg. 461
CCS CESKA SPOLECNOST PRO PLATEBNI KARTY SRO—See Corpay, Inc.; *U.S. Public*, pg. 579
CCS CHINA INC.—See Optex Group Co., Ltd.; *Int'l*, pg. 5601
CCS ELECTRONICS (UK) LTD.—See Avnet, Inc.; *U.S. Public*, pg. 250
C & C SERVICE, LLC—See Crete Mechanical Group, Inc.; *U.S. Private*, pg. 1099
CC SERVICES, INC.—See COUNTRY Financial; *U.S. Private*, pg. 1066

CORPORATE AFFILIATIONS

CCS EUROPE NV—See Optex Group Co., Ltd.; *Int'l*, pg. 5601
CCS GLOBAL TECH; *U.S. Private*, pg. 801
CCS GROUP INC.; *U.S. Private*, pg. 801
CCS INC.—See Optex Group Co., Ltd.; *Int'l*, pg. 5601
CCS-INC.; *U.S. Private*, pg. 801
CCS INFOTECH LIMITED; *Int'l*, pg. 1369
CCS INFOTECH SINGAPORE PTE LTE—See CCS Infotech Limited; *Int'l*, pg. 1369
CCS JAPAN—See Azenta, Inc.; *U.S. Public*, pg. 258
CCS KOREA INC.—See Optex Group Co., Ltd.; *Int'l*, pg. 5601
CCS/LANSING, INC.—See Universal Health Services, Inc.; *U.S. Public*, pg. 2256
CCS/LANSING, INC.—See Universal Health Services, Inc.; *U.S. Public*, pg. 2256
CCSL LIMITED; *Int'l*, pg. 1369
CCS LOGISTICS—See Oceana Group Limited; *Int'l*, pg. 5517
CCS LOUISIANA—See AEA Investors LP; *U.S. Private*, pg. 116
CCS MEDICAL HOLDINGS, INC.; *U.S. Private*, pg. 801
CCS MEDICAL, INC.—See CCS Medical Holdings, Inc.; *U.S. Private*, pg. 801
CCS MEDICAL, INC.—See CCS Medical Holdings, Inc.; *U.S. Private*, pg. 801
CCS MV (MALAYSIA) SDN. BHD.—See Optex Group Co., Ltd.; *Int'l*, pg. 5601
CCS MV (THAILAND) CO., LTD.—See Optex Group Co., Ltd.; *Int'l*, pg. 5601
C.C. SOUTHERN INC.—See CenTra, Inc.; *U.S. Private*, pg. 818
CCS—See Block Communications, Inc.; *U.S. Private*, pg. 582
CCS SUPPLY CHAIN MANAGEMENT CO., LTD.; *Int'l*, pg. 1369
CC STAFFING, INC.—See Cross Country Healthcare, Inc.; *U.S. Public*, pg. 595
CCTC FRIEND STEVEDORE CO., LTD.—See China Container Terminal Corp.; *Int'l*, pg. 1491
CCT CONSTRUCTORS CORPORATION—See Toyo Construction Co., Ltd.; *Int'l*, pg. 7852
CCTEC ENGINEERING CO., LTD.—See China Rare Earth Resources And Technology Co., Ltd.; *Int'l*, pg. 1545
CCT FORTIS HOLDINGS LIMITED; *Int'l*, pg. 1369
CCT MARKETING LIMITED—See CCT Fortis Holdings Limited; *Int'l*, pg. 1369
C & C TOURS, INC.; *U.S. Private*, pg. 701
C & C TOWERS LTD—See C & C Constructions Limited; *Int'l*, pg. 1237
CCT RAIL SYSTEM CORPORATION; *U.S. Private*, pg. 801
C&C TRUCKS CO., LTD.—See China International Marine Containers (Group) Co., Ltd.; *Int'l*, pg. 1511
CCT—See Marcegaglia S.p.A.; *Int'l*, pg. 4688
CCT TECH (HK) LIMITED—See CCT Fortis Holdings Limited; *Int'l*, pg. 1369
CCT TECH INTERNATIONAL LIMITED—See CCT Fortis Holdings Limited; *Int'l*, pg. 1369
CCT TECHNOLOGIES INC.; *U.S. Private*, pg. 801
CCT TELECOM (HK) LIMITED—See CCT Fortis Holdings Limited; *Int'l*, pg. 1370
CCT TELECOM SECURITIES LIMITED—See CCT Fortis Holdings Limited; *Int'l*, pg. 1370
CCTV CAMERA PROS, LLC; *U.S. Private*, pg. 801
CCU ARGENTINA S.A.—See L'Arche Green N.V.; *Int'l*, pg. 4377
CCU ARGENTINA S.A.—See Quinenco S.A.; *Int'l*, pg. 6164
C-CUBE CORPORATION—See EXEO Group Inc.; *Int'l*, pg. 2583
CCU CHILE LTDA.—See L'Arche Green N.V.; *Int'l*, pg. 4377
CCU CHILE LTDA.—See Quinenco S.A.; *Int'l*, pg. 6164
C-CURE NV—See Liberty Global plc; *Int'l*, pg. 4484
CCUR HOLDINGS INC.; *U.S. Public*, pg. 461
CCV ENGINEERING & MFG., INC.—See Aries Industries Inc.; *U.S. Private*, pg. 322
C&C VINA CO., LTD—See Younghyun Trading co.,Ltd; *Int'l*, pg. 8603
CCV RISK SOLUTIONS LIMITED; *Int'l*, pg. 1370
CCV VIRGINIA, INC.—See EZCORP, Inc.; *U.S. Public*, pg. 817
CCW CATERING SUPPLIES (PTY) LIMITED—See The Bidvest Group Limited; *Int'l*, pg. 7623
CCW PRODUCTS, INC.—See Priority Plastics, Inc.; *U.S. Private*, pg. 3267
CCX CORPORATION; *U.S. Private*, pg. 801
CDA-DS SAS—See Compagnie des Alpes S.A.; *Int'l*, pg. 1737
CDA FINANCEMENT SNC—See Compagnie des Alpes S.A.; *Int'l*, pg. 1737
CDA INCORPORATED; *U.S. Private*, pg. 802
CDA INTERCORP LLC—See TransDigm Group Incorporated; *U.S. Public*, pg. 2182
CDA METALS; *U.S. Private*, pg. 802
CDB AVIATION LEASE FINANCE DESIGNATED ACTIVITY COMPANY—See China Development Bank Financial Leasing Co., Ltd.; *Int'l*, pg. 1497

COMPANY NAME INDEX

CDB LEASING CO., LTD.—See China Development Bank Corporation; *Int'l*, pg. 1497
C&D (CANADA) IMPORT & EXPORT INC.—See Xiamen C&D Inc.; *Int'l*, pg. 8523
CD CAPITAL ASSET MANAGEMENT LTD; *Int'l*, pg. 1370
CDC BALLARAT PTY. LTD.—See ComfortDelGro Corporation Limited; *Int'l*, pg. 1712
CDC CARIBE INC.—See Savino Del Bene S.p.A.; *Int'l*, pg. 6600
CDC CORPORATION—See Owens Corning; *U.S. Public*, pg. 1626
CDC DATA, LLC; *U.S. Private*, pg. 802
CDC FINANCE & LEASING CORP.—See KGI Financial Holding Co., Ltd.; *Int'l*, pg. 4149
CDC FOUNDATION; *U.S. Private*, pg. 802
CDC GEELONG PTY. LTD.—See ComfortDelGro Corporation Limited; *Int'l*, pg. 1712
CDC GROUP PLC; *Int'l*, pg. 1370
CDC OAKLEIGH PTY. LTD.—See ComfortDelGro Corporation Limited; *Int'l*, pg. 1712
CDC PUBLISHING LLC; *U.S. Private*, pg. 802
CDC SAN FRANCISCO LLC—See InterContinental Hotels Group PLC; *Int'l*, pg. 3737
CDC SOFTWARE OY—See TA Associates, Inc.; *U.S. Private*, pg. 3914
CDC SOFTWARE SINGAPORE PTE. LTD.—See TA Associates, Inc.; *U.S. Private*, pg. 3914
CDC S.P.A.—See Savino Del Bene S.p.A.; *Int'l*, pg. 6600
CDC SUNSHINE PTY. LTD.—See ComfortDelGro Corporation Limited; *Int'l*, pg. 1712
CDC TULLAMARINE PTY. LTD.—See ComfortDelGro Corporation Limited; *Int'l*, pg. 1712
CDC VICTORIA PTY. LTD.—See ComfortDelGro Corporation Limited; *Int'l*, pg. 1712
CDC WYNDHAM PTY. LTD.—See ComfortDelGro Corporation Limited; *Int'l*, pg. 1712
CD DEUTSCHE EIGENHEIM AG; *Int'l*, pg. 1370
CD DIAGNOSTICS, INC.—See Zimmer Biomet Holdings, Inc.; *U.S. Public*, pg. 2406
CDD S.P.A.—See Bioera S.p.A.; *Int'l*, pg. 1037
C-D ELECTRIC, INC.—See B&M Industrial, Inc.; *U.S. Private*, pg. 419
C.D. ELECTRONICA DE MEXICO, S.A. DE C.V.—See Knowles Corporation; *U.S. Public*, pg. 1270
CD ENERGY DIRECT CO., LTD.—See Chubu Electric Power Co., Inc.; *Int'l*, pg. 1593
CDE PIPELINE LLC—See Kinder Morgan, Inc.; *U.S. Public*, pg. 1232
CDE SERVICES, INC.—See Milestone Partners Ltd.; *U.S. Private*, pg. 2728
CDEX INC.; *U.S. Private*, pg. 802
CDF COLOMBIA S.A.—See CDF International Cooperatief U.A.; *Int'l*, pg. 1370
CDF CORPORATION; *U.S. Private*, pg. 802
CDF DOMITAB SA—See CDF International Cooperatief U.A.; *Int'l*, pg. 1370
CDF INTERNATIONAL COOPERATIEF U.A.; *Int'l*, pg. 1370
C&D FRUIT & VEGETABLE CO., INC.; *U.S. Private*, pg. 702
CDG CO., LTD.; *Int'l*, pg. 1370
CDG GROUP, LLC—See FTI Consulting, Inc.; *U.S. Public*, pg. 890
CDGGR, P.C.—See Ghafari Associates, L.L.C.; *U.S. Private*, pg. 1690
CDG NAPOLI SRL—See Gambero Rosso S.p.A.; *Int'l*, pg. 2877
CDG PACKAGING HOLDING AG; *Int'l*, pg. 1370
CDG PETCHEM LIMITED; *Int'l*, pg. 1370
CD GROUP, INC.—See TAC Partners, Inc.; *U.S. Private*, pg. 3920
CDG TORINO E PIEMONTE SRL—See Gambero Rosso S.p.A.; *Int'l*, pg. 2877
CD HARTNETT COMPANY; *U.S. Private*, pg. 801
C.D. HAUPT PAPIER-UND PAPPENFABRIK GMBH & CO. KG—See Smurfit Kappa Group plc; *Int'l*, pg. 7018
CDH CHINA MANAGEMENT COMPANY LIMITED; *Int'l*, pg. 1370
CDH-DELNOR HEALTH SYSTEM, INC.—See Northwestern Memorial HealthCare; *U.S. Private*, pg. 2962
CDH INVESTMENTS MANAGEMENT (HONG KONG) LIMITED—See CDH China Management Company Limited; *Int'l*, pg. 1370
CDHM ADVERTISING; *U.S. Private*, pg. 802
C&D HOLSIN ENGINEERING CONSULTING CO., LTD; *Int'l*, pg. 1238
CDIB ASSET MANAGEMENT CO., LTD.—See KGI Financial Holding Co., Ltd.; *Int'l*, pg. 4149
CDIB CAPITAL GROUP—See KGI Financial Holding Co., Ltd.; *Int'l*, pg. 4149
CDIB CAPITAL INNOVATION ADVISORS CORPORATION—See KGI Financial Holding Co., Ltd.; *Int'l*, pg. 4149
CDIB CAPITAL INTERNATIONAL CORPORATION—See KGI Financial Holding Co., Ltd.; *Int'l*, pg. 4149
CDIB CAPITAL INTERNATIONAL (HONG KONG) CORPORATION LIMITED—See KGI Financial Holding Co., Ltd.; *Int'l*, pg. 4149

CDIB CAPITAL INTERNATIONAL (KOREA) CORPORATION LTD.—See KGI Financial Holding Co., Ltd.; *Int'l*, pg. 4149
CDIB PRIVATE EQUITY (CHINA) CORPORATION—See KGI Financial Holding Co., Ltd.; *Int'l*, pg. 4149
CDIB YIDA PRIVATE EQUITY (KUNSHAN) CO., LTD.—See KGI Financial Holding Co., Ltd.; *Int'l*, pg. 4149
CDI CHINA, INC.—See CD International Enterprises, Inc.; *U.S. Public*, pg. 461
CDI COMPUTER DEALERS INC.—See Relational LLC; *U.S. Private*, pg. 3392
CDI CONTRACTORS, LLC—See Dillard's Inc.; *U.S. Public*, pg. 666
CDI CORPORATION—See AE Industrial Partners, LP; *U.S. Private*, pg. 112
CDI ELECTRONICS LLC—See Dometic Group AB; *Int'l*, pg. 2160
CDI ENERGY PRODUCTS, INC.—See Compagnie Generale des Etablissements Michelin SCA; *Int'l*, pg. 1745
CDI ENGINEERING SOLUTIONS, LLC—See AE Industrial Partners, LP; *U.S. Private*, pg. 112
CDI GROUP INC.; *U.S. Private*, pg. 802
CDII MINERALS, INC.—See CD International Enterprises, Inc.; *U.S. Public*, pg. 461
CDI, INC.; *U.S. Private*, pg. 802
CDI-INFRASTRUCTURE, LLC—See Management Recruiters International, Inc.; *U.S. Private*, pg. 2560
CDI INTERNATIONAL INC.; *U.S. Private*, pg. 802
CDI INTERNATIONAL LIMITED; *Int'l*, pg. 1371
CDI MEDIA INC.; *U.S. Private*, pg. 802
C&D INSULATION, INC.; *U.S. Private*, pg. 702
CD INTERNATIONAL ENTERPRISES, INC.; *U.S. Public*, pg. 461
C&D INTERNATIONAL INVESTMENT GROUP LIMITED—See Xiamen C&D Inc.; *Int'l*, pg. 8523
CD INVESTISSEMENTS SARL—See Christian Dior S.A.; *Int'l*, pg. 1586
CDI SAKATA INX CORP.—See Sakata INX Corporation; *Int'l*, pg. 6487
CDI SERVICES INC.; *U.S. Private*, pg. 802
CDI SHANGHAI MANAGEMENT CO., LTD.—See CD International Enterprises, Inc.; *U.S. Public*, pg. 461
CDI - SOCIETE COTONNIERE DE DISTRIBUTION S.A.—See StoneX Group Inc.; *U.S. Public*, pg. 1951
C&D JAPAN CORPORATION—See Xiamen C&D Inc.; *Int'l*, pg. 8523
CDK BUILDERS INC.; *U.S. Private*, pg. 802
CDK GLOBAL (CANADA) LIMITED—See Brookfield Corporation; *Int'l*, pg. 1175
CDK GLOBAL GROUP BV—See Brookfield Corporation; *Int'l*, pg. 1175
CDK GLOBAL, INC.—See Brookfield Corporation; *Int'l*, pg. 1175
CDK GLOBAL (NETHERLAND) BV—See Brookfield Corporation; *Int'l*, pg. 1175
CDK GLOBAL (UK) LIMITED—See Brookfield Corporation; *Int'l*, pg. 1175
CDK KOREA CORPORATION—See CKD Corporation; *Int'l*, pg. 1639
CDK PERFORATING HOLDINGS, INC.—See Nine Energy Service, Inc.; *U.S. Public*, pg. 1529
CD LABORATORIES, INC.—See Zimmer Biomet Holdings, Inc.; *U.S. Public*, pg. 2406
CDL ELECTRIC COMPANY, INC.; *U.S. Private*, pg. 802
CDL HOSPITALITY TRUSTS; *Int'l*, pg. 1371
CDL INVESTMENTS NEW ZEALAND LIMITED; *Int'l*, pg. 1371
CDL LAND NEW ZEALAND LIMITED—See CDL Investments New Zealand Limited; *Int'l*, pg. 1371
CDLX GMBH—See DBAY Advisors Limited; *Int'l*, pg. 1987
CDMA AUSTRALIA PTY. LTD.—See Xiamen C&D Inc.; *Int'l*, pg. 8523
CD&M COMMUNICATIONS; *U.S. Private*, pg. 802
CDM CONSTRUCTORS INC.—See CDM Smith Inc.; *U.S. Private*, pg. 802
CDMDATA, INC.—See Cox Enterprises, Inc.; *U.S. Private*, pg. 1076
C&D METALS KOREA CO.,LTD.—See Xiamen C&D Inc.; *Int'l*, pg. 8523
CDM FEDERAL PROGRAMS CORPORATION—See CDM Smith Inc.; *U.S. Private*, pg. 803
CDM HOLDINGS LLC—See Energy Transfer LP; *U.S. Public*, pg. 762
CDM INVESTMENT GROUP, INC.; *U.S. Private*, pg. 802
CDMM CORP.; *U.S. Private*, pg. 803
CDM RESOURCE MANAGEMENT LLC—See Riverstone Holdings LLC; *U.S. Private*, pg. 3447
CDM RETIREMENT CONSULTANTS, INC.—See Northwest Plan Services, Inc.; *U.S. Private*, pg. 2961
CDM SERVICE GROUP, INC.—See CDM Investment Group, Inc.; *U.S. Private*, pg. 802
CDM SMITH CONSULT GMBH—See CDM Smith Inc.; *U.S. Private*, pg. 803
CDM SMITH INC.; *U.S. Private*, pg. 802
CDM SMITH IRELAND LTD.—See CDM Smith Inc.; *U.S. Private*, pg. 803
CDM SMITH SP. Z O.O.—See CDM Smith Inc.; *U.S. Private*, pg. 803

CDM TOOL & MANUFACTURING CO., INC.—See Jacsten Holdings, LLC; *U.S. Private*, pg. 2180
CDMV INC.; *Int'l*, pg. 1371
CDN COMUNICACAO CORPORATIVA LTDA.—See Omnicom Group Inc.; *U.S. Public*, pg. 1585
CDNETWORKS, INC.—See ChinaNetCenter Co., Ltd.; *Int'l*, pg. 1568
CDN MAVERICK CAPITAL CORP.; *Int'l*, pg. 1371
CDN MSOLAR CORP.; *Int'l*, pg. 1371
CDN-USA, INC.—See Fomento de Construcciones y Contratas, S.A; *Int'l*, pg. 2722
CDOC, INC.—See CNO Financial Group, Inc.; *U.S. Public*, pg. 519
CD OGILVY & MATHER—See WPP plc; *Int'l*, pg. 8484
CDO TECHNOLOGIES INC.; *U.S. Private*, pg. 803
C.D.P.A. - LD3E CO., LTD.—See Mitsubishi Heavy Industries, Ltd.; *Int'l*, pg. 4953
CDP BHARAT FORGE GMBH—See Kalyani Group; *Int'l*, pg. 4059
CDP CAPITAL FINANCING INC.—See Caisse de Depot et Placement du Quebec; *Int'l*, pg. 1253
CDP CAPITAL REAL ESTATE ADVISORY—See Caisse de Depot et Placement du Quebec; *Int'l*, pg. 1253
CDP CAPITAL TECHNOLOGIES—See Caisse de Depot et Placement du Quebec; *Int'l*, pg. 1253
CDP CAPITAL US INC.—See Caisse de Depot et Placement du Quebec; *Int'l*, pg. 1253
CDP EQUITY SPA—See Cassa Depositi e Prestiti S.p.A.; *Int'l*, pg. 1354
CDP FINANCIAL, INC.—See Caisse de Depot et Placement du Quebec; *Int'l*, pg. 1253
CDP HOLDINGS, LTD.; *Int'l*, pg. 1371
CDP IMMOBILIARE SGR S.P.A.—See Cassa Depositi e Prestiti S.p.A.; *Int'l*, pg. 1354
CDP IMMOBILIARE S.R.L.—See Cassa Depositi e Prestiti S.p.A.; *Int'l*, pg. 1354
CDPQ CHINA—See Caisse de Depot et Placement du Quebec; *Int'l*, pg. 1253
CDPQ MORTGAGE CORPORATION—See Caisse de Depot et Placement du Quebec; *Int'l*, pg. 1253
C&D PRODUCTION SPECIALISTS CO., INC.; *U.S. Private*, pg. 702
CD PROJEKT S.A.; *Int'l*, pg. 1370
C & D PROPANE—See UGI Corporation; *U.S. Public*, pg. 2221
C&D PROPERTY MANAGEMENT GROUP CO., LTD.; *Int'l*, pg. 1238
CDP SERVICES LLC; *U.S. Private*, pg. 803
CDP TECHNOLOGIES AS—See Cassa Depositi e Prestiti S.p.A.; *Int'l*, pg. 1354
CDP TECHNOLOGIES—See Caisse de Depot et Placement du Quebec; *Int'l*, pg. 1253
CDP-TRAVISSULLY LTD.; *Int'l*, pg. 1371
CDR ADVANCE CAPITAL S.P.A.; *Int'l*, pg. 1371
CDR DE MEXICO S. DE R.L. DE C.V.—See Hubbell Incorporated; *U.S. Public*, pg. 1066
CDR FUNDRAISING GROUP—See Moore DM Group, LLC; *U.S. Private*, pg. 2780
CD&R LLP—See Clayton, Dubilier & Rice, LLC; *U.S. Private*, pg. 920
CDRL S.A.; *Int'l*, pg. 1371
CDR MAGUIRE INC. - CONNECTICUT OFFICE—See CDR Maguire Inc.; *U.S. Private*, pg. 803
CDR MAGUIRE INC. - PENNSYLVANIA OFFICE—See CDR Maguire Inc.; *U.S. Private*, pg. 803
CDR MAGUIRE INC. - RHODE ISLAND OFFICE—See CDR Maguire Inc.; *U.S. Private*, pg. 803
CDR MAGUIRE INC.; *U.S. Private*, pg. 803
CDR MAGUIRE INC. - VIRGIN ISLANDS OFFICE—See CDR Maguire Inc.; *U.S. Private*, pg. 803
CDR SYSTEMS CORPORATION—See Hubbell Incorporated; *U.S. Public*, pg. 1067
CDS BUSINESS MAPPING, LLC—See Insight Venture Management, LLC; *U.S. Private*, pg. 2088
CDS BUSINESS MAPPING, LLC—See Stone Point Capital LLC; *U.S. Private*, pg. 3822
CDS CO., LTD.; *Int'l*, pg. 1371
CDS CONTAINER DEPOT STUTTGART GMBH—See UNITAINER Trading GmbH; *Int'l*, pg. 8063
C & D SCRAP METAL RECYCLERS CO, INC.—See Merchants Metals Recycling II CD, LLC; *U.S. Private*, pg. 2670
C&D SEMICONDUCTOR SERVICES, INC.; *U.S. Private*, pg. 702
CDS ENSEMBLES, INC.; *U.S. Private*, pg. 803
CD SERVICES INC.—See The Walt Disney Company; *U.S. Public*, pg. 2140
CDS GLOBAL, INC.—See The Hearst Corporation; *U.S. Private*, pg. 4046
CDS GLOBAL LOGISTICS INC.; *U.S. Private*, pg. 803
C&D (SHANGHAI) CO., LTD.—See Xiamen C&D Inc.; *Int'l*, pg. 8523
C&D (SINGAPORE) BUSINESS PTE. LTD.—See Xiamen C&D Inc.; *Int'l*, pg. 8523
CDS, LLC.; *U.S. Private*, pg. 803
C.D. SMITH CONSTRUCTION INC.; *U.S. Private*, pg. 706
CDS MONARCH, INC.; *U.S. Private*, pg. 803
CDS MOVING EQUIPMENT INC.; *U.S. Private*, pg. 803
CDSNET, INC.; *U.S. Private*, pg. 803

C.D.S. OFFICE TECHNOLOGY CORP / **CORPORATE AFFILIATIONS**

C.D.S. OFFICE TECHNOLOGY CORP; *U.S. Private*, pg. 706
CDS OF NEVADA, INC.—See Catholic Health Initiatives; *U.S. Private*, pg. 789
CDS PUBLICATIONS—See Chatham Asset Management, LLC; *U.S. Private*, pg. 862
CDS VISUAL, INC.—See Dover Corporation; *U.S. Public*, pg. 678
C&D TECHNOLOGIES DYNASTY DIVISION—See KPS Capital Partners, LP; *U.S. Private*, pg. 2347
C&D TECHNOLOGIES, INC.—See KPS Capital Partners, LP; *U.S. Private*, pg. 2347
CD-TELEMATIKA A.S.—See Grupo Villar Mir, S.A.U.; *Int'l*, pg. 3139
CDT ENVIRONMENTAL TECHNOLOGY INVESTMENT HOLDINGS LIMITED; *Int'l*, pg. 1371
CDT HOLDINGS LTD.—See Sumitomo Chemical Company, Limited; *Int'l*, pg. 7266
CDTI ADVANCED MATERIALS, INC.; *U.S. Public*, pg. 461
CDTI—See CDTi Advanced Materials, Inc.; *U.S. Public*, pg. 462
CDTI SWEDEN AB—See CDTi Advanced Materials, Inc.; *U.S. Public*, pg. 462
C&D TRADING INC.; *U.S. Private*, pg. 702
C DUGARD LTD; *Int'l*, pg. 1237
CDU PLC; *Int'l*, pg. 1371
C-D UTILITY CONSTRUCTION INC.; *U.S. Private*, pg. 704
C&D VALVE LLC—See JB Industries, Inc.; *U.S. Private*, pg. 2193
CD WAREHOUSE, INC.—See Magnolia Entertainment LLC; *U.S. Private*, pg. 2548
CDW CANADA, INC.—See CDW Corporation; *U.S. Public*, pg. 462
CDW CORPORATION; *U.S. Public*, pg. 462
CDW GOVERNMENT, INC.—See CDW Corporation; *U.S. Public*, pg. 462
CDW HOLDING LTD.; *Int'l*, pg. 1372
CDW LOGISTICS, INC.—See CDW Corporation; *U.S. Public*, pg. 462
CDW MERCHANTS, INC.; *U.S. Private*, pg. 803
CDW TECHNOLOGIES, INC. - APPLETON—See CDW Corporation; *U.S. Public*, pg. 462
CDW TECHNOLOGIES, INC. - CHICAGO—See CDW Corporation; *U.S. Public*, pg. 462
CDW TECHNOLOGIES, INC. - CINCINNATI—See CDW Corporation; *U.S. Public*, pg. 462
CDW TECHNOLOGIES, INC. - CLEVELAND—See CDW Corporation; *U.S. Public*, pg. 462
CDW TECHNOLOGIES, INC. - DETROIT—See CDW Corporation; *U.S. Public*, pg. 462
CDW TECHNOLOGIES, INC. - GRAND RAPIDS—See CDW Corporation; *U.S. Public*, pg. 462
CDW TECHNOLOGIES, INC. - INDIANAPOLIS—See CDW Corporation; *U.S. Public*, pg. 462
CDW TECHNOLOGIES, INC. - MADISON—See CDW Corporation; *U.S. Public*, pg. 462
CDW TECHNOLOGIES, INC. - MILWAUKEE—See CDW Corporation; *U.S. Public*, pg. 462
CDW TECHNOLOGIES, INC. - MINNEAPOLIS—See CDW Corporation; *U.S. Public*, pg. 462
CDW TECHNOLOGIES, INC.—See CDW Corporation; *U.S. Public*, pg. 462
CDW TECHNOLOGIES, INC. - WAUSAU—See CDW Corporation; *U.S. Public*, pg. 462
CDX, INC.—See MyDx, Inc.; *U.S. Private*, pg. 2824
CDYNE CORPORATION; *U.S. Private*, pg. 803
CDZ.T S.R.L.—See Emerson Electric Co.; *U.S. Public*, pg. 742
CE3, INC.—See NovaQuest Capital Management, LLC; *U.S. Private*, pg. 2967
CEACO INC.; *U.S. Private*, pg. 803
CEAG NOTLICHTSYSTEME GMBH—See Eaton Corporation plc; *Int'l*, pg. 2278
CEA INDUSTRIES INC.; *U.S. Public*, pg. 463
CEAPRO INC.—See COSCIENS Biopharma Inc.; *U.S. Public*, pg. 585
CE ASIA HEAVY MACHINERY SDN BHD—See Wong Fong Industries Limited; *Int'l*, pg. 8447
CEAT LTD.; *Int'l*, pg. 1372
C E ATTACHMENTS, INC.—See Manitou BF S.A.; *Int'l*, pg. 4672
CEATUS MEDIA GROUP LLC—See Advice Media LLC; *U.S. Private*, pg. 110
CEAUTAMED WORLDWIDE LLC—See Smart for Life, Inc.; *U.S. Public*, pg. 1895
CEAVCO AUDIO-VISUAL COMPANY; *U.S. Private*, pg. 804
CEBEO—See Sonepar S.A.; *Int'l*, pg. 7091
CEBI DENIZCILIK VE TICARET A.S.—See Kaptan Demir Celik Endustrisi ve Ticaret A.S.; *Int'l*, pg. 4078
CEBI ENERJI ELEKTRIK URETIMI A.S.—See Kaptan Demir Celik Endustrisi ve Ticaret A.S.; *Int'l*, pg. 4078
CEB LLC.—See Gartner, Inc.; *U.S. Public*, pg. 906
CEB MAINTENANCE AFRICA (PROPRIETARY) LIMITED—See Business Connexion Group Limited; *Int'l*, pg. 1228
CEBOS, LTD.—See Thoma Bravo, L.P.; *U.S. Private*, pg. 4151

CEBRACE CRISTAL PLANO LTDA—See Nippon Sheet Glass Co. Ltd.; *Int'l*, pg. 5331
CE BRANDS, INC.; *Int'l*, pg. 1372
CEBU AIR, INC.—See JG Summit Holdings, Inc.; *Int'l*, pg. 3939
CEBU ENTERTAINMENT GALLERY, INC.—See Leisure & Resorts World Corporation; *Int'l*, pg. 4447
CEBU HOLDINGS INC.—See Ayala Corporation; *Int'l*, pg. 774
CEBU LANDMASTERS, INC.; *Int'l*, pg. 1372
CEBU MITSUMI, INC.—See Minebea Mitsumi Inc.; *Int'l*, pg. 4903
CEBU PROPERTY VENTURES AND DEVELOPMENT CORPORATION—See Ayala Corporation; *Int'l*, pg. 774
CECA ITALIANA S.P.A—See Arkema S.A.; *Int'l*, pg. 571
CECA S.A.—See Arkema S.A.; *Int'l*, pg. 571
CECCATO ARIA COMPRESSA S.P.A.—See Atlas Copco AB; *Int'l*, pg. 679
CECCHETTI WINE COMPANY; *U.S. Private*, pg. 804
CECCI—See Sonepar S.A.; *Int'l*, pg. 7090
CEC-COILS SINGAPORE PTE LTD.—See CEC International Holdings Limited; *Int'l*, pg. 1372
CEC COMMERCIAL DEVELOPMENT CORPORATION—See Continental Holdings Corp.; *Int'l*, pg. 1784
CE CAPITAL PARTNER GMBH; *Int'l*, pg. 1372
CECCON FRERES SA; *Int'l*, pg. 1372
CEC CONSTRUCTION ENGINEERING + CONTRACTING GMBH—See Bilfinger SE; *Int'l*, pg. 1028
CEC CONTROLS COMPANY, INC.—See John Wood Group PLC; *Int'l*, pg. 3984
CEC CONTROLS COMPANY S.R.L—See John Wood Group PLC; *Int'l*, pg. 3983
CEC CRANE ENGINEERING & CONSULTING GMBH—See Taiyuan Heavy Industry Co., Ltd.; *Int'l*, pg. 7427
CECE FEINBERG PUBLIC RELATIONS; *U.S. Private*, pg. 804
CEC ENERGIECONSULTING GMBH—See E.ON SE; *Int'l*, pg. 2251
CEC ENTERTAINMENT, INC.—See Apollo Global Management, Inc.; *U.S. Public*, pg. 148
CEC ENVIRONMENTAL PROTECTION CO., LTD.; *Int'l*, pg. 1372
CECEP COSTIN NEW MATERIALS GROUP LIMITED; *Int'l*, pg. 1372
CECEP ENVIRONMENTAL PROTECTION CO., LTD.; *Int'l*, pg. 1372
CECEP GUOZHEN ENVIRONMENTAL PROTECTION TECHNOLOGY CO., LTD.; *Int'l*, pg. 1372
CECEP SOLAR ENERGY CO., LTD.; *Int'l*, pg. 1373
CECEP TECHAND ECOLOGY & ENVIRONMENT CO., LTD.; *Int'l*, pg. 1373
CECEP WIND-POWER CORPORATION CO., LTD.; *Int'l*, pg. 1373
CECE'S VEGGIE CO.; *U.S. Private*, pg. 804
CECG INTERNATIONAL HOLDINGS, INC.—See Constellation Energy Corporation; *U.S. Public*, pg. 571
CE CIDEON ENGINEERING GMBH & CO. KG—See CRCC High-tech Equipment Corporation Limited; *Int'l*, pg. 1830
CE CIDEON ENGINEERING SCHWEIZ AG—See CRCC High-tech Equipment Corporation Limited; *Int'l*, pg. 1830
CECIL BANCORP, INC.; *U.S. Public*, pg. 463
CECIL BANK—See Cecil Bancorp, Inc.; *U.S. Public*, pg. 463
THE CECILIAN BANK—See First Cecilian Bancorp, Inc.; *U.S. Private*, pg. 1515
CECIL I. WALKER MACHINERY CO.; *U.S. Private*, pg. 804
CECIL NURSE (PTY) LIMITED—See The Bidvest Group Limited; *Int'l*, pg. 7624
CECIL VINEGAR WORKS (PTY) LTD.—See Libstar Holdings Ltd.; *Int'l*, pg. 4487
CEC INSURANCE AGENCY, LLC—See Perdoceo Education Corporation; *U.S. Public*, pg. 1673
CEC INTERNATIONAL CORPORATION (INDIA) PRIVATE LIMITED—See Continental Holdings Corp.; *Int'l*, pg. 1784
CEC INTERNATIONAL HOLDINGS LIMITED; *Int'l*, pg. 1372
CEC INTERNATIONAL MALAYSIA SDN. BHD.—See Continental Holdings Corp.; *Int'l*, pg. 1784
CECISA - COMERCIO INTERNACIONAL S.A.—See Camargo Correa S.A.; *Int'l*, pg. 1267
CECITY.COM, INC.—See Premier, Inc.; *U.S. Public*, pg. 1715
CEC MANAGEMENT, INC.—See Perdoceo Education Corporation; *U.S. Public*, pg. 1673
CECO BUILDING SYSTEMS-EASTERN REGION—See Clayton, Dubilier & Rice, LLC; *U.S. Private*, pg. 920
CECO BUILDING SYSTEMS—See Clayton, Dubilier & Rice, LLC; *U.S. Private*, pg. 920
CECO CONCRETE CONSTRUCTION LLC; *U.S. Private*, pg. 804

CECO DOOR PRODUCTS—See ASSA ABLOY AB; *Int'l*, pg. 636
CECO ENVIRONMENTAL CORP.; *U.S. Public*, pg. 463
CECO ENVIRONMENTAL MIDDLE EAST DMCC—See CECO Environmental Corp.; *U.S. Public*, pg. 463
CECO ENVIRONMENTAL NETHERLANDS B.V.—See CECO Environmental Corp.; *U.S. Public*, pg. 463
CECO FILTERS INC.—See CECO Environmental Corp.; *U.S. Public*, pg. 463
CECO (FLOORING) LIMITED—See Headlam Group plc; *Int'l*, pg. 3301
CECO GROUP GLOBAL HOLDINGS LLC—See CECO Environmental Corp.; *U.S. Public*, pg. 463
CECO GROUP, INC.—See CECO Environmental Corp.; *U.S. Public*, pg. 463
CECOL, INC.—See Citizen Watch Co., Ltd.; *Int'l*, pg. 1623
CE COMPETITIVE EDGE LLC; *U.S. Private*, pg. 803
CECONOMY AG; *Int'l*, pg. 1373
CECO PIPELINE SERVICES COMPANY, INC.—See Compressor Engineering Corporation; *U.S. Private*, pg. 1003
CECOR STAFFING INC.—See Essential Personnel, Inc.; *U.S. Private*, pg. 1427
CECOS INTERNATIONAL, INC.—See Republic Services, Inc.; *U.S. Public*, pg. 1786
CECOVILLE SAS—See BNP Paribas SA; *Int'l*, pg. 1089
CECP INVESTMENT ADVISORS FRANCE S.A.R.L.—See The Carlyle Group Inc.; *U.S. Public*, pg. 2045
CEC PUBLISHING INC.—See Quebecor Inc.; *Int'l*, pg. 6158
C.E. CREATE CO., LTD.—See RAITO KOGYO Co., Ltd.; *Int'l*, pg. 6191
CECS INC.—See The Crom Corporation; *U.S. Private*, pg. 4016
CECURITY.COM SA—See ISAGRI S.A.; *Int'l*, pg. 3812
CECYLLS CO., LTD.—See Niterra Co., Ltd.; *Int'l*, pg. 5380
CEDA INTERNATIONAL CORPORATION—See Ontario Municipal Employees Retirement System; *Int'l*, pg. 5583
CEDAN INDUSTRIES INC.—See Richelieu Hardware Ltd.; *Int'l*, pg. 6330
CEDA-PINE VENEER INC—See Idaho Veneer Company; *U.S. Private*, pg. 2035
CEDAR AMERICAN RAIL HOLDINGS, INC.—See Canadian Pacific Kansas City Limited; *Int'l*, pg. 1285
CEDARBRAE VOLKSWAGEN LTD; *Int'l*, pg. 1388
CEDAR BROOK FINANCIAL PARTNERS, LLC; *U.S. Private*, pg. 804
CEDARBROOK SAUNA & STEAM; *U.S. Private*, pg. 805
CEDAR CAPITAL PARTNERS LIMITED; *Int'l*, pg. 1388
CEDARCARE, INC.—See HCA Healthcare, Inc.; *U.S. Public*, pg. 992
CEDARCHEM, LLC—See Platinum Equity, LLC; *U.S. Private*, pg. 3204
CEDAR CLINICAL RESEARCH INC.—See Numinus Wellness Inc.; *Int'l*, pg. 5489
CEDAR COAL CO.—See American Electric Power Company, Inc.; *U.S. Public*, pg. 99
CEDAR CO., LTD.; *Int'l*, pg. 1388
CEDAR CORPORATION—See Steel Partners Holdings L.P.; *U.S. Public*, pg. 1943
CEDAR COUNTRY COOPERATIVE; *U.S. Private*, pg. 804
CEDAR COUNTY COOPERATIVE; *U.S. Private*, pg. 804
CEDAR CREEK - AITKIN—See Cerberus Capital Management, L.P.; *U.S. Private*, pg. 837
CEDAR CREEK ENERGY CORPORATION; *U.S. Private*, pg. 804
CEDAR CREEK INN CORPORATION; *U.S. Private*, pg. 804
CEDAR CREEK LLC—See Cerberus Capital Management, L.P.; *U.S. Private*, pg. 837
CEDAR CREEK MEDICAL GROUP, LLC—See HCA Healthcare, Inc.; *U.S. Public*, pg. 992
CEDAR CREEK PARTNERS LLC; *U.S. Private*, pg. 804
CEDAR CREEK PROPERTIES LLC—See CRH plc; *Int'l*, pg. 1843
CEDAR CREEK REALTY, LLC—See CRH plc; *Int'l*, pg. 1843
CEDAR CREST CLINIC—See Acadia Healthcare Company, Inc.; *U.S. Public*, pg. 29
CEDAR CREST SPECIALTIES INC.; *U.S. Private*, pg. 804
CEDAR CROSSING RETIREMENT COMMUNITY INC.—See Extendicare Inc.; *Int'l*, pg. 2591
CEDAR DEVELOPMENT CO., LTD.; *Int'l*, pg. 1388
CEDAR ENTERPRISES INC.; *U.S. Private*, pg. 804
CEDAR FAIR, L.P.—See Six Flags Entertainment Corporation; *U.S. Public*, pg. 1890
CEDAR FALLS BICKFORD COTTAGE, L.L.C.—See National Health Investors, Inc.; *U.S. Public*, pg. 1495
CEDAR FALLS LUTHERAN HOME; *U.S. Private*, pg. 804
CEDAR FARMS COMPANY, INC.; *U.S. Private*, pg. 804
THE CEDARGLEN GROUP INC; *Int'l*, pg. 7631
CEDAR HEIGHTS CLAY—See Balmoral Funds LLC; *U.S. Private*, pg. 461
CEDAR HILL CEMETERY COMPANY, INC.—See Service Corporation International; *U.S. Public*, pg. 1871
CEDAR HILL FUNERAL HOME, INC.—See Axar Capital Management L.P.; *U.S. Private*, pg. 411

486

COMPANY NAME INDEX

CEDAR HILL PRIMARY CARE, L.L.C.—See Tenet Healthcare Corporation; *U.S. Public*, pg. 2003
CEDAR HOLDINGS GROUP CO., LTD.; *Int'l*, pg. 1388
CEDARINO, S.L.—See Southern Cross Capital Management SA; *Int'l*, pg. 7118
CEDARLAKE ACQUISITION CORP.; *Int'l*, pg. 1388
CEDAR LAKE FOODS - MGM FOODS; *U.S. Private*, pg. 804
CEDAR MARINE TERMINALS, L.P.—See Vertex Energy, Inc.; *U.S. Public*, pg. 2287
CEDAR OF NEW ENGLAND, LTD.—See Cedar Enterprises Inc.; *U.S. Private*, pg. 804
CEDAROME CANADA INC.; *Int'l*, pg. 1388
CEDAR PARK HEALTH SYSTEM, L.P.—See Community Health Systems, Inc.; *U.S. Public*, pg. 552
CEDAR PARK SURGERY CENTER, LLC—See Community Health Systems, Inc.; *U.S. Public*, pg. 552
CEDAR PARK SURGERY CENTER, L.L.P.—See Tenet Healthcare Corporation; *U.S. Public*, pg. 2009
CEDAR PETROCHEMICALS, INC.; *U.S. Private*, pg. 805
CEDAR POINTE CLUB, LLC—See Lennar Corporation; *U.S. Public*, pg. 1306
CEDAR POINT PARK LLC—See Six Flags Entertainment Corporation; *U.S. Public*, pg. 1890
CEDAR POINT—See Six Flags Entertainment Corporation; *U.S. Public*, pg. 1890
CEDAR RAPIDS BANK & TRUST COMPANY—See QCR Holdings, Inc.; *U.S. Public*, pg. 1742
CEDAR REALTY TRUST, INC.—See Wheeler Real Estate Investment Trust, Inc.; *U.S. Public*, pg. 2365
CEDAR RIDGE LANDFILL, INC.—See Waste Management, Inc.; *U.S. Public*, pg. 2330
CEDAR RIVER INTERNATIONAL TRUCKS INC.; *U.S. Private*, pg. 805
CEDAR RUSTIC FENCE CO.; *U.S. Private*, pg. 805
CEDAR SHAKE & SHINGLE BUREAU; *Int'l*, pg. 1388
CEDARS HEALTHCARE GROUP, LTD.—See HCA Healthcare, Inc.; *U.S. Public*, pg. 992
CEDAR SIDING & LUMBER INC.; *U.S. Private*, pg. 805
CEDAR'S MEDITERRANEAN FOODS, INC.; *U.S. Private*, pg. 805
CEDAR—See Omnicom Group Inc.; *U.S. Public*, pg. 1579
CEDAR SPRING CAPITAL LLC; *U.S. Private*, pg. 805
THE CEDARS RETIREMENT COMMUNITY; *U.S. Private*, pg. 4006
CEDARS-SINAI MEDICAL CENTER; *U.S. Private*, pg. 805
CEDARS-SINAI MEDICAL GROUP—See Cedars-Sinai Medical Center; *U.S. Private*, pg. 805
CEDAR VALLEY EXTERIORS, INC.; *U.S. Private*, pg. 805
CEDAR VALLEY SERVICES, INC.; *U.S. Private*, pg. 805
CEDARWOOD ARCHITECTURAL, INC.—See The Cedarwood Companies; *U.S. Private*, pg. 4006
THE CEDARWOOD COMPANIES; *U.S. Private*, pg. 4006
CEDARWOOD DEVELOPMENT, INC.—See The Cedarwood Companies; *U.S. Private*, pg. 4006
CEDAR WOODS PROPERTIES LIMITED; *Int'l*, pg. 1388
CEDARWOOD-YOUNG COMPANY, INC.—See Allan Company; *U.S. Private*, pg. 174
CEDC INTERNATIONAL SP. Z O.O.—See Grupa Maspex Sp. z o.o.; *Int'l*, pg. 3117
CEDCO INC.; *U.S. Private*, pg. 805
CED DIGITAL & SERVIZI SRL—See Caltagirone Editore S.p.A.; *Int'l*, pg. 1265
CE DE CANDY, INC.; *U.S. Private*, pg. 803
CEDEO—See Compagnie de Saint-Gobain SA; *Int'l*, pg. 1722
CEDERVALL ESPANA S.A.—See Wartsila Corporation; *Int'l*, pg. 8346
CEDERVALL ZHANGJIAGANG MARINE PRODUCTS CO. LTD.—See Wartsila Corporation; *Int'l*, pg. 8346
C-E (DEUTSCHLAND) GMBH—See Citizen Watch Co., Ltd.; *Int'l*, pg. 1623
CEDEVITA D.O.O.—See ATLANTIC GRUPA d.d.; *Int'l*, pg. 675
CEDEXIS INC.—See Elliott Management Corporation; *U.S. Private*, pg. 1366
CEDEXIS INC.—See Vista Equity Partners, LLC; *U.S. Private*, pg. 4395
CEDIMA GMBH; *Int'l*, pg. 1388
CEDO FOLIEN UND HAUSHALTSPRODUKTE GMBH—See Rutland Partners LLP; *Int'l*, pg. 6432
CE DONGLI TECHNOLOGY COMPANY LIMITED—See Sino-i Technology Limited; *Int'l*, pg. 6948
CEDREX—See Azenta, Inc.; *U.S. Public*, pg. 258
CEDS INC.—See Apollo Global Management, Inc.; *U.S. Public*, pg. 160
CEDULAS COLON DE CAPITALIZACION COLSEGUROS S.A.—See Allianz SE; *Int'l*, pg. 351
CEDYNA AUTO LEASE CO., LTD.—See Sumitomo Corporation; *Int'l*, pg. 7274
CEDYNA AUTO LEASE CO., LTD.—See Sumitomo Mitsui Financial Group, Inc.; *Int'l*, pg. 7293
CEDYNA SERVICER, INC.—See Sumitomo Mitsui Financial Group, Inc.; *Int'l*, pg. 7293
CEDYNA TOTAL SERVICE CO., LTD.—See Sumitomo Mitsui Financial Group, Inc.; *Int'l*, pg. 7293
CEE ALLIER SAS—See VINCI S.A.; *Int'l*, pg. 8213
CEECO, INC.; *U.S. Private*, pg. 805

CEEDI TAKASAGO ENGINEERING & CONSULTING CO., LTD.—See Takasago Thermal Engineering Co., Ltd.; *Int'l*, pg. 7434
CEEGEX LTD.—See MVM Magyar Villamos Muvek Zrt.; *Int'l*, pg. 5107
CEEG (SHANGHAI) SOLAR SCIENCE TECHNOLOGY CO., LTD.—See China Sunergy Co., Ltd.; *Int'l*, pg. 1556
CEE ITALIANA SRL—See Industrielle De Controle Et D Equipement; *Int'l*, pg. 3675
CEEJAY FINANCE LIMITED; *Int'l*, pg. 1388
CEEKAY DAIKIN LTD. - AURANGABAD PLANT—See Exedy Corporation; *Int'l*, pg. 2581
CEE KAY SUPPLY INC.; *U.S. Private*, pg. 805
CEELOX, INC.; *U.S. Private*, pg. 805
CEENIK EXPORTS (INDIA) LIMITED; *Int'l*, pg. 1388
CEEPOWER CO., LTD.; *Int'l*, pg. 1388
CEE PROPERTIES REIT; *Int'l*, pg. 1388
CEEREF S.A.; *Int'l*, pg. 1389
CEE RELAYS LTD.—See Industrielle De Controle Et D Equipement; *Int'l*, pg. 3675
CEESEG AG; *Int'l*, pg. 1389
CEETA INDUSTRIES LIMITED; *Int'l*, pg. 1389
CEETRUS HUNGARY KFT.—See Auchan Holding S.A.; *Int'l*, pg. 699
CEETRUS ITALY SPA—See Auchan Holding S.A.; *Int'l*, pg. 699
CEETRUS POLSKA SP ZOO—See Auchan Holding S.A.; *Int'l*, pg. 699
CE EUROPE LTD.—See Capcom Co., Ltd.; *Int'l*, pg. 1302
CEFB—See Sonepar S.A.; *Int'l*, pg. 7090
CEFC ANHUI INTERNATIONAL HOLDING CO., LTD.; *Int'l*, pg. 1389
CEFC CHINA ENERGY COMPANY LIMITED; *Int'l*, pg. 1389
CEFC GLOBAL STRATEGIC HOLDINGS, INC.; *Int'l*, pg. 1389
CEFCO CONVENIENCE STORES; *U.S. Private*, pg. 805
CEF ENTERPRISES INC.; *U.S. Private*, pg. 805
CEFETRA B.V.—See BayWa AG; *Int'l*, pg. 917
CEFETRA DAIRY B.V.—See BayWa AG; *Int'l*, pg. 917
CEFETRA DIGITAL SERVICES S.L.—See BayWa AG; *Int'l*, pg. 917
CEFETRA FEED SERVICE B.V.—See BayWa AG; *Int'l*, pg. 917
CEFETRA GROUP B.V.—See BayWa AG; *Int'l*, pg. 917
CEFETRA IBERICA S.L.U.—See BayWa AG; *Int'l*, pg. 917
CEFETRA LIMITED—See BayWa AG; *Int'l*, pg. 917
CEFETRA POLSKA SP. Z O.O.—See BayWa AG; *Int'l*, pg. 917
CEFETRA S.P.A.—See BayWa AG; *Int'l*, pg. 917
CEF INDUSTRIES, LLC—See TransDigm Group Incorporated; *U.S. Public*, pg. 2182
CEFIVAL S.A.—See Montanstahl AG; *Int'l*, pg. 5036
CEFLA ARREDAMENTI GROUP—See Cefla S.C.; *Int'l*, pg. 1389
CEFLA ASIA PTE LTD—See Cefla S.C.; *Int'l*, pg. 1389
CEFLA DENTAL GROUP—See Cefla S.C.; *Int'l*, pg. 1389
CEFLA DEUTSCHLAND GMBH—See Cefla S.C.; *Int'l*, pg. 1389
CEFLA FINISHING EUROPE DEUTSCHLAND—See Cefla S.C.; *Int'l*, pg. 1389
CEFLA FINISHING EUROPE—See Cefla S.C.; *Int'l*, pg. 1389
CEFLA FINISHING GROUP—See Cefla S.C.; *Int'l*, pg. 1389
CEFLA FINISHING INDIA PVT. LTD.—See Cefla S.C.; *Int'l*, pg. 1389
CEFLA FINISHING RUSSIA—See Cefla S.C.; *Int'l*, pg. 1389
CEFLA IMPIANTI GROUP—See Cefla S.C.; *Int'l*, pg. 1389
CEFLA LADENBAU—See Cefla S.C.; *Int'l*, pg. 1389
CEFLA MIDDLE EAST FZE—See Cefla S.C.; *Int'l*, pg. 1389
CEFLA NORTH AMERICA INC.—See Cefla S.C.; *Int'l*, pg. 1389
CEFLA POLSKA SP. Z.O.O.—See Cefla S.C.; *Int'l*, pg. 1389
CEFLA S.C. - DUSPOHL PLANT—See Cefla S.C.; *Int'l*, pg. 1389
CEFLA S.C. - FALCIONI PLANT—See Cefla S.C.; *Int'l*, pg. 1389
CEFLA S.C. - MADRID PLANT—See Cefla S.C.; *Int'l*, pg. 1389
CEFLA S.C. - PARIS PLANT—See Cefla S.C.; *Int'l*, pg. 1389
CEFLA S.C.; *Int'l*, pg. 1389
CEFLA SOC. COOP. A R.L.—See Cefla S.C.; *Int'l*, pg. 1389
CEF NORD SAS—See VINCI S.A.; *Int'l*, pg. 8213
CEF SAFETY SYSTEMS B.V.—See Halma plc; *Int'l*, pg. 3230
C.E.F.S. ECONOMIC OPPORTUNITY CORPORATION; *U.S. Private*, pg. 706
CEF (SOC) LIMITED; *Int'l*, pg. 1389
CEGECOM S.A.—See RWE AG; *Int'l*, pg. 6433
CEGEDEL PARTICIPATIONS S.A.—See Enovos International S.A.; *Int'l*, pg. 2444

CEGEDIM ACTIV SASU—See Cegedim S.A.; *Int'l*, pg. 1390
CEGEDIM CLOUD SASU—See Cegedim S.A.; *Int'l*, pg. 1390
CEGEDIM CUSTOMER INFORMATION SRL—See Cegedim S.A.; *Int'l*, pg. 1390
CEGEDIM LOGICIELS MEDICAUX SAS—See Cegedim S.A.; *Int'l*, pg. 1390
CEGEDIM MAROC SARL—See Cegedim S.A.; *Int'l*, pg. 1390
CEGEDIM MEDIA SARL—See Cegedim S.A.; *Int'l*, pg. 1390
CEGEDIM OUTSOURCING SAS—See Cegedim S.A.; *Int'l*, pg. 1390
CEGEDIM RX LIMITED—See Cegedim S.A.; *Int'l*, pg. 1390
CEGEDIM RX SRL—See Cegedim S.A.; *Int'l*, pg. 1390
CEGEDIM SANTE SASU—See Cegedim S.A.; *Int'l*, pg. 1390
CEGEDIM S.A.; *Int'l*, pg. 1390
CEGEDIM SRH LTD.—See Cegedim S.A.; *Int'l*, pg. 1390
CEGEDIM SRH SA—See Cegedim S.A.; *Int'l*, pg. 1390
CEGEKA DEUTSCHLAND GMBH—See Cegeka Groep NV; *Int'l*, pg. 1390
CEGEKA GROEP NV; *Int'l*, pg. 1390
CEGEKA HEALTH CARE NV—See Cegeka Groep NV; *Int'l*, pg. 1390
CEGEKA NEDERLAND HOLDING B.V.—See Cegeka Groep NV; *Int'l*, pg. 1391
CEGEKA NV—See Cegeka Groep NV; *Int'l*, pg. 1390
CEGELEC ABU DHABI—See VINCI S.A.; *Int'l*, pg. 8215
CEGELEC ANGOLA—See VINCI S.A.; *Int'l*, pg. 8236
CEGELEC ANLAGEN-UND AUTOMATISIERUNGSTECHNIK GMBH & CO. KG—See VINCI S.A.; *Int'l*, pg. 8214
CEGELEC A.S.—See VINCI S.A.; *Int'l*, pg. 8215
CEGELEC AUSTRIA GMBH—See VINCI S.A.; *Int'l*, pg. 8214
CEGELEC BOURGOGNE SAS—See VINCI S.A.; *Int'l*, pg. 8213
CEGELEC BRASIL LTDA—See VINCI S.A.; *Int'l*, pg. 8214
CEGELEC B.U. ENSYSTA—See VINCI S.A.; *Int'l*, pg. 8214
CEGELEC BUILDING SERVICES SA—See VINCI S.A.; *Int'l*, pg. 8213
CEGELEC B.V.—See VINCI S.A.; *Int'l*, pg. 8214
CEGELEC CAMEROUN SA—See VINCI S.A.; *Int'l*, pg. 8213
CEGELEC CEM SAS—See VINCI S.A.; *Int'l*, pg. 8213
CEGELEC CENTRE EST S.A.—See VINCI S.A.; *Int'l*, pg. 8214
CEGELEC CLERMONT-FERRAND—See VINCI S.A.; *Int'l*, pg. 8236
CEGELEC CONTRACTING GMBH—See VINCI S.A.; *Int'l*, pg. 8214
CEGELEC CONTROL SYSTEM & SERVICES SA—See VINCI S.A.; *Int'l*, pg. 8213
CEGELEC DAUPHINE SAS—See VINCI S.A.; *Int'l*, pg. 8213
CEGELEC DEFENSE ET NAVAL SUD-EST SAS—See VINCI S.A.; *Int'l*, pg. 8213
CEGELEC DEFENSE SAS—See VINCI S.A.; *Int'l*, pg. 8213
CEGELEC DEUTSCHLAND GMBH-EAST—See VINCI S.A.; *Int'l*, pg. 8214
CEGELEC DEUTSCHLAND GMBH-NORTH—See VINCI S.A.; *Int'l*, pg. 8214
CEGELEC DEUTSCHLAND GMBH—See VINCI S.A.; *Int'l*, pg. 8214
CEGELEC ELMO SAS—See VINCI S.A.; *Int'l*, pg. 8214
CEGELEC ENTERPRISE S.A.-NON DESTRUCTIVE TESTING DIVISION—See VINCI S.A.; *Int'l*, pg. 8214
CEGELEC ENTERPRISE S.A.—See VINCI S.A.; *Int'l*, pg. 8214
CEGELEC ENTERPRISES S.A.-FRANCE-MID EAST—See VINCI S.A.; *Int'l*, pg. 8214
CEGELEC ENTERPRISES S.A.-FRANCE-NORTH & EAST—See VINCI S.A.; *Int'l*, pg. 8214
CEGELEC ENTERPRISES S.A.-FRANCE-SOUTH EAST—See VINCI S.A.; *Int'l*, pg. 8214
CEGELEC ENTERPRISES S.A.-FRANCE-SOUTH WEST—See VINCI S.A.; *Int'l*, pg. 8214
CEGELEC ENTERPRISES S.A.-FRANCE-WEST—See VINCI S.A.; *Int'l*, pg. 8214
CEGELEC ENTERPRISES S.A.-PARIS—See VINCI S.A.; *Int'l*, pg. 8214
CEGELEC FIRE SOLUTIONS BV—See VINCI S.A.; *Int'l*, pg. 8215
CEGELEC FRANCHE-COMTE SAS—See VINCI S.A.; *Int'l*, pg. 8215
CEGELEC GSS—See VINCI S.A.; *Int'l*, pg. 8215
CEGELEC GUYANE SAS—See VINCI S.A.; *Int'l*, pg. 8215
CEGELEC HAUTE-NORMANDIE SAS—See VINCI S.A.; *Int'l*, pg. 8215
CEGELEC INDUSTRIE SUD-EST SAS—See VINCI S.A.; *Int'l*, pg. 8215
CEGELEC INDUSTRY NV/SA—See VINCI S.A.; *Int'l*, pg. 8215
CEGELEC INFRA BRETAGNE SAS—See VINCI S.A.; *Int'l*, pg. 8215

CEGEKA GROEP NV

CEGELEC INFRASTRUCTURES & MOBILITY—See VINCI S.A.; *Int'l*, pg. 8236
CEGELEC INSTALACOES E SISTEMAS DE AUTOMACAO, LDA.—See VINCI S.A.; *Int'l*, pg. 8214
CEGELEC LOIRE AUVERGNE SAS—See VINCI S.A.; *Int'l*, pg. 8215
CEGELEC LORRAINE ALSACE SAS—See VINCI S.A.; *Int'l*, pg. 8215
CEGELEC MAROC S.A.—See VINCI S.A.; *Int'l*, pg. 8236
CEGELEC MISSENARD SAS—See VINCI S.A.; *Int'l*, pg. 8215
CEGELEC MOBILITY SAS—See VINCI S.A.; *Int'l*, pg. 8215
CEGELEC NETWORK & SECURITY SYSTEMS COMPANY—See VINCI S.A.; *Int'l*, pg. 8215
CEGELEC NON DESTRUCTIVE SYSTEMS—See VINCI S.A.; *Int'l*, pg. 8214
CEGELEC NORD-EST SA—See VINCI S.A.; *Int'l*, pg. 8214
CEGELEC NORD INDUSTRIE SAS—See VINCI S.A.; *Int'l*, pg. 8215
CEGELEC NORD TERTIAIRE SAS—See VINCI S.A.; *Int'l*, pg. 8215
CEGELEC NOUVELLE CALEDONIE S.A.—See VINCI S.A.; *Int'l*, pg. 8214
CEGELEC NUCLEAIRE SUD-EST SAS—See VINCI S.A.; *Int'l*, pg. 8215
CEGELEC PARIS S.A.—See VINCI S.A.; *Int'l*, pg. 8214
CEGELEC PAYS DE SAVOIE SASU—See VINCI S.A.; *Int'l*, pg. 8215
CEGELEC PICARDIE INDUSTRIE SAS—See VINCI S.A.; *Int'l*, pg. 8215
CEGELEC POLYNESIE—See VINCI S.A.; *Int'l*, pg. 8214
CEGELEC PORTES DE BRETAGNE SA—See VINCI S.A.; *Int'l*, pg. 8215
CEGELEC PTE LTD—See VINCI S.A.; *Int'l*, pg. 8214
CEGELEC QATAR W.L.L.—See VINCI S.A.; *Int'l*, pg. 8236
CEGELEC RDC SARL—See VINCI S.A.; *Int'l*, pg. 8215
CEGELEC RESEAUX AUVERGNE DROME ARDECHE SAS—See VINCI S.A.; *Int'l*, pg. 8215
CEGELEC S.A.-CAMEROON—See VINCI S.A.; *Int'l*, pg. 8214
CEGELEC S.A.-CASABLANCA—See VINCI S.A.; *Int'l*, pg. 8214
CEGELEC S.A.-LUXEMBOURG—See VINCI S.A.; *Int'l*, pg. 8214
CEGELEC, S.A.-MADRID—See VINCI S.A.; *Int'l*, pg. 8215
CEGELEC SA/NV—See VINCI S.A.; *Int'l*, pg. 8214
CEGELEC, S.A.—See VINCI S.A.; *Int'l*, pg. 8215
CEGELEC SAS—See VINCI S.A.; *Int'l*, pg. 8215
CEGELEC SDEM SARL—See VINCI S.A.; *Int'l*, pg. 8215
CEGELEC SDN BHD—See VINCI S.A.; *Int'l*, pg. 8214
CEGELEC SPACE SA—See VINCI S.A.; *Int'l*, pg. 8215
CEGELEC SPA—See VINCI S.A.; *Int'l*, pg. 8214
CEGELEC SP. Z O O.—See VINCI S.A.; *Int'l*, pg. 8214
CEGELEC SUD-EST SA—See VINCI S.A.; *Int'l*, pg. 8214
CEGELEC TELECOMS SUD-OUEST—See VINCI S.A.; *Int'l*, pg. 8215
CEGELEC TERTIAIRE IDF SA—See VINCI S.A.; *Int'l*, pg. 8215
CEGELEC TOULOUSE SA—See VINCI S.A.; *Int'l*, pg. 8215
CEGELEC TROYES SA—See VINCI S.A.; *Int'l*, pg. 8215
CEGEMA S.A.—See Swiss Life Holding; *Int'l*, pg. 7368
CEGID CORPORATION—See Silver Lake Group, LLC; *U.S. Private*, pg. 3656
CEGID GROUP SA—See Silver Lake Group, LLC; *U.S. Private*, pg. 3656
CEGID LTD.—See Silver Lake Group, LLC; *U.S. Private*, pg. 3656
CEGID U.S.—See Silver Lake Group, LLC; *U.S. Private*, pg. 3656
CEG INTERACTIVE ENTERTAINMENT GMBH—See Capcom Co., Ltd.; *Int'l*, pg. 1302
CE GLOBAL SOURCING GMBH—See HPI AG; *Int'l*, pg. 3500
CE GLOBAL SOURCING TAIWAN CO LTD.—See HPI AG; *Int'l*, pg. 3500
CEHI ACQUISITION CORPORATION—See Compass Diversified Holdings; *U.S. Public*, pg. 559
CE HOLDINGS CO., LTD.; *Int'l*, pg. 1372
CE HOLDINGS LIMITED—See Nan Hai Corporation Limited; *Int'l*, pg. 5137
C-E (HONG KONG) LTD.—See Citizen Watch Co., Ltd.; *Int'l*, pg. 1623
CEIBA INVESTMENTS LIMITED; *Int'l*, pg. 1391
CEIBA SOLUTIONS, INC.—See Revvity, Inc.; *U.S. Public*, pg. 1793
CEIBA TECHNOLOGIES; *U.S. Private*, pg. 805
CEI BOSTON LLC; *U.S. Private*, pg. 805
CEICA PLASTICOS DE MEXICO—See PSB Industries SA; *Int'l*, pg. 6015
CEI ENTERPRISES, INC.—See Astec Industries, Inc.; *U.S. Public*, pg. 216
CEI EQUIPMENT COMPANY LLC—See Berkshire Hathaway Inc.; *U.S. Public*, pg. 299
THE CEI GROUP INC.—See CSI Holdings Inc.; *U.S. Private*, pg. 1117

CEI INTERNATIONAL INVESTMENTS (VIETNAM) LIMITED—See AEM Holdings Ltd.; *Int'l*, pg. 175
CEI INTERNATIONAL INVESTMENTS (VN) LTD.—See AEM Holdings Ltd.; *Int'l*, pg. 175
CEI LIMITED—See AEM Holdings Ltd.; *Int'l*, pg. 175
CEILINGS & PARTITIONS, INC.; *U.S. Private*, pg. 805
CEILINGS PLUS, INC.—See Gebr. Knauf KG; *Int'l*, pg. 2908
C.E. INFO SYSTEMS LTD.; *Int'l*, pg. 1240
CEINSYS TECH LTD.—See Meghe Group of Institutions; *U.S. Public*, pg. 4795
CEIPAL CORP.; *U.S. Private*, pg. 806
CEI PTE. LTD.—See AEM Holdings Ltd.; *Int'l*, pg. 175
CEI PTY. LTD.—See Platinum Equity, LLC; *U.S. Private*, pg. 3210
CEI ROOFING COLORADO, LLC—See Altas Partners LP; *Int'l*, pg. 386
CEI ROOFING, INC.; *U.S. Private*, pg. 805
CEI ROOFING TEXAS, LLC—See Altas Partners LP; *Int'l*, pg. 386
CEI ROOFING - TEXAS—See Altas Partners LP; *Int'l*, pg. 386
CEJA CORPORATION; *U.S. Private*, pg. 806
CEJKA SEARCH, INC.—See Cross Country Healthcare, Inc.; *U.S. Public*, pg. 595
CEJON ACCESSORIES, INC.—See Steven Madden, Ltd.; *U.S. Public*, pg. 1947
CEKAN/CDT A/S—See Belden, Inc.; *U.S. Public*, pg. 294
CELAD GAME CORPORATION—See Soft-World International Corporation; *Int'l*, pg. 7050
CELADON CANADA INC.—See Celadon Group, Inc.; *U.S. Public*, pg. 464
CELADON E-COMMERCE, INC.—See Celadon Group, Inc.; *U.S. Public*, pg. 464
CELADON GROUP, INC.; *U.S. Public*, pg. 464
CELADON LOGISTICS SERVICES, INC.—See Celadon Group, Inc.; *U.S. Public*, pg. 464
CELADON PHARMACEUTICALS, INC.; *Int'l*, pg. 1391
CELADON SYSTEMS, INC.—See MPI Corporation; *Int'l*, pg. 5062
CELADON TRUCKING SERVICES, INC.—See Celadon Group, Inc.; *U.S. Public*, pg. 464
CELADOR PRODUCTIONS LTD.; *Int'l*, pg. 1391
CELANESE ACETATE, LLC—See Celanese Corporation; *U.S. Public*, pg. 465
CELANESE CHEMICALS, INC.—See Celanese Corporation; *U.S. Public*, pg. 465
CELANESE (CHINA) HOLDING CO., LTD.—See Celanese Corporation; *U.S. Public*, pg. 464
CELANESE CORPORATION; *U.S. Public*, pg. 464
CELANESE EMULSIONS B.V.—See Celanese Corporation; *U.S. Public*, pg. 464
CELANESE EMULSIONS LTD.—See Celanese Corporation; *U.S. Public*, pg. 464
CELANESE EMULSIONS NORDEN AB—See Celanese Corporation; *U.S. Public*, pg. 464
CELANESE EVA PERFORMANCE POLYMERS INC.—See Celanese Corporation; *U.S. Public*, pg. 464
CELANESE FAR EAST LTD.—See Celanese Corporation; *U.S. Public*, pg. 464
CELANESE GMBH—See Celanese Corporation; *U.S. Public*, pg. 465
CELANESE KOREA LTD.—See Celanese Corporation; *U.S. Public*, pg. 465
CELANESE PRODUCTION SWITZERLAND AG—See Celanese Corporation; *U.S. Public*, pg. 465
CELANESE PROPERTY GERMANY GMBH & CO. KG—See Celanese Corporation; *U.S. Public*, pg. 465
CELANESE PTE. LTD.—See Celanese Corporation; *U.S. Public*, pg. 465
CELANESE S.A./N.V.—See Celanese Corporation; *U.S. Public*, pg. 465
CELANESE SERVICES GERMANY GMBH—See Celanese Corporation; *U.S. Public*, pg. 465
CELANESE (SHANGHAI) POLYMERS CO., LTD.—See Celanese Corporation; *U.S. Public*, pg. 464
CELANESE SINGAPORE PTE. LTD.—See Celanese Corporation; *U.S. Public*, pg. 465
CELANESE SWITZERLAND AG—See Celanese Corporation; *U.S. Public*, pg. 465
CELANESE SWITZERLAND AG—See GIC Pte. Ltd.; *Int'l*, pg. 2968
CELANESE SWITZERLAND AG—See The Carlyle Group Inc.; *U.S. Public*, pg. 2051
CELANESE (THAILAND) LIMITED—See Celanese Corporation; *U.S. Public*, pg. 464
CELARTEM TECHNOLOGY INC.; *Int'l*, pg. 1391
CEL AUSTRALIA PTY LTD—See Chip Eng Seng Corporation Ltd.; *Int'l*, pg. 1572
CELBOR CELIK CEKME BORU SANAYI VE TICARET A.S.—See Eregli Demir Ve Celik Fabrikalari T.A.S.; *Int'l*, pg. 2490
CELCITE MANAGEMENT SOLUTIONS, LLC—See Amdocs Limited; *U.S. Public*, pg. 420
CELCOM AXIATA BERHAD—See CelcomDigi Berhad; *Int'l*, pg. 1391
CELCOMDIGI BERHAD; *Int'l*, pg. 1391
CELCOM (MALAYSIA) BERHAD—See Axiata Group Berhad; *Int'l*, pg. 768

CORPORATE AFFILIATIONS

CELCOM TRANSMISSION (M) SDN BHD—See CelcomDigi Berhad; *Int'l*, pg. 1391
CELCOR LTD.—See Illinois Tool Works Inc.; *U.S. Public*, pg. 1102
CELCUITY INC.; *U.S. Public*, pg. 465
CEL DEVELOPMENT PTE. LTD.—See Chip Eng Seng Corporation Ltd.; *Int'l*, pg. 1572
CELEBI BANDIRMA ULUSLARARASI LIMANI ISLETMECILIGI A.S.—See Celebi Holding A.S.; *Int'l*, pg. 1391
CELEBI CARGO GMBH—See Celebi Holding A.S.; *Int'l*, pg. 1391
CELEBIDDY, INC.; *U.S. Private*, pg. 806
CELEBI DELHI CARGO TERMINAL MANAGEMENT INDIA PVT. LTD.—See Celebi Holding A.S.; *Int'l*, pg. 1391
CELEBI GROUND HANDLING HUNGARY KFT.—See Celebi Holding A.S.; *Int'l*, pg. 1391
CELEBI GROUND HANDLING INC.—See Celebi Holding A.S.; *Int'l*, pg. 1391
CELEBI GROUND SERVICES AUSTRIA GMBH—See Celebi Holding A.S.; *Int'l*, pg. 1391
CELEBI HAVA SERVISI AS; *Int'l*, pg. 1391
CELEBI HOLDING A.S.; *Int'l*, pg. 1391
CELEBI IPLIK TIC. VE SAN. A.S.; *Int'l*, pg. 1392
CELEBI NAS AIRPORT SERVICES INDIA PVT. LTD.—See Celebi Hava Servisi AS; *Int'l*, pg. 1391
CELEBRATION CATERING & EVENTS, LLP—See Brigade Enterprises Ltd.; *Int'l*, pg. 1160
CELEBRATIONS.COM, LLC—See 1-800-FLOWERS.COM, Inc.; *U.S. Public*, pg. 1
CELEBRATION WORLD RESORT LTD.; *U.S. Private*, pg. 806
CELEBRITY AUTO GROUP; *U.S. Private*, pg. 806
CELEBRITY FASHIONS LIMITED; *Int'l*, pg. 1392
CELEBRITY FORD OF TOMS RIVER—See Celebrity Motor Car Company; *U.S. Private*, pg. 806
CELEBRITY INTERNATIONAL INC.; *U.S. Private*, pg. 806
CELEBRITY MOTOR CAR COMPANY; *U.S. Private*, pg. 806
CELEBRITY NATIONAL FINANCIAL SERVICE SAOG; *Int'l*, pg. 1392
CELEBROS, INC.; *U.S. Private*, pg. 806
CELEBROS LTD.—See Celebros, Inc.; *U.S. Private*, pg. 806
CELEBROS LTD.—See Celebros, Inc.; *U.S. Private*, pg. 806
CELEBROS LTD.—See Celebros, Inc.; *U.S. Private*, pg. 806
CELEBROS LTD.—See Celebros, Inc.; *U.S. Private*, pg. 806
CEL EDUCATION FUND; *U.S. Private*, pg. 806
CELEKULA A.D.; *Int'l*, pg. 1392
CELEMIAB GROUP AB—See Bure Equity AB; *Int'l*, pg. 1221
CELEMICS, INC.; *Int'l*, pg. 1392
CELEO CONCESIONES E INVERSIONES, S.L.U.—See Elecnor, S.A.; *Int'l*, pg. 2347
CELEO REDES BRASIL, S.A.—See Elecnor, S.A.; *Int'l*, pg. 2347
CELEO REDES CHILE LTDA.—See Elecnor, S.A.; *Int'l*, pg. 2347
CELEO REDES, S.L.U.—See Elecnor, S.A.; *Int'l*, pg. 2347
CELERA CORPORATION—See Quest Diagnostics, Inc.; *U.S. Public*, pg. 1755
CELERANT TECHNOLOGY CORP.; *U.S. Private*, pg. 806
CELERGO; *U.S. Private*, pg. 806
CELERIS D.O.O.—See Cipla Ltd.; *Int'l*, pg. 1616
THE CELERIS GROUP, LLC—See Microwave Transmission Systems, Inc.; *U.S. Private*, pg. 2704
CELERITAS MANAGEMENT, INC.—See Palladium Equity Partners, LLC; *U.S. Private*, pg. 3077
CELERIT CORPORATION; *U.S. Private*, pg. 806
CELERITY CONSULTING GROUP, INC.—See Hastings Equity Partners, LLC; *U.S. Private*, pg. 1879
CELERITY IT, LLC—See Randstad N.V.; *Int'l*, pg. 6201
CELERITY SOLUTIONS, INC.; *U.S. Private*, pg. 806
CELERITY VENTURES LLC; *U.S. Private*, pg. 806
CELERO COMMERCE LLC—See Independence Capital Partners, LLC; *U.S. Private*, pg. 2056
CELESTA INTERNATIONAL ELECTRONICS CO., LTD.—See Jess-Link Products Co., Ltd.; *Int'l*, pg. 3932
CELESTAR CORPORATION; *U.S. Private*, pg. 806
CELESTE INDUSTRIES CORPORATION—See Illinois Tool Works Inc.; *U.S. Public*, pg. 1102
CELESTIAL ASIA SECURITIES HOLDINGS LIMITED; *Int'l*, pg. 1392
CELESTIAL BIOLABS LIMITED; *Int'l*, pg. 1392
CELESTIAL COMMODITIES LIMITED—See CASH Financial Services Group Limited; *Int'l*, pg. 1352
CELESTIAL FILMED ENTERTAINMENT LIMITED—See Astro All Asia Networks plc; *Int'l*, pg. 662
CELESTIAL GREEN VENTURES PLC; *Int'l*, pg. 1392
CELESTIAL MOVIE CHANNEL LIMITED—See Astro All Asia Networks plc; *Int'l*, pg. 662
CELESTIAL PICTURES LIMITED—See Astro All Asia Networks plc; *Int'l*, pg. 662
CELESTIAL SEASONINGS, INC.—See The Hain Celestial Group, Inc.; *U.S. Public*, pg. 2086
CELESTIAL SECURITIES LIMITED—See CASH Financial Services Group Limited; *Int'l*, pg. 1352

COMPANY NAME INDEX

CELESTICA AG—See ONEX Corporation; *Int'l*, pg. 5577
CELESTICA AUTOMATION TECHNOLOGY (WUXI) CO., LTD.—See ONEX Corporation; *Int'l*, pg. 5577
CELESTICA DE MONTERREY S.A. DE C.V.—See ONEX Corporation; *Int'l*, pg. 5578
CELESTICA DO BRAZIL—See ONEX Corporation; *Int'l*, pg. 5578
CELESTICA ELECTRONICS (MALAYSIA) SDN BHD.—See ONEX Corporation; *Int'l*, pg. 5577
CELESTICA ELECTRONICS (S) PTE. LTD. (WOODLANDS)—See ONEX Corporation; *Int'l*, pg. 5577
CELESTICA HOLDINGS PTE LIMITED—See ONEX Corporation; *Int'l*, pg. 5577
CELESTICA HONG KONG LIMITED—See ONEX Corporation; *Int'l*, pg. 5577
CELESTICA INC.-CHINA—See ONEX Corporation; *Int'l*, pg. 5578
CELESTICA INC.-CHINA—See ONEX Corporation; *Int'l*, pg. 5578
CELESTICA, INC.-JAPAN—See ONEX Corporation; *Int'l*, pg. 5578
CELESTICA, INC.—See ONEX Corporation; *Int'l*, pg. 5577
CELESTICA, INC.-THAILAND—See ONEX Corporation; *Int'l*, pg. 5578
CELESTICA, KAWASAKI SRC—See ONEX Corporation; *Int'l*, pg. 5578
CELESTICA MALAYSIA SDN. BHD.—See ONEX Corporation; *Int'l*, pg. 5578
CELESTICA PHILIPPINES—See ONEX Corporation; *Int'l*, pg. 5578
CELESTICA (ROMANIA) S.R.L.—See ONEX Corporation; *Int'l*, pg. 5577
CELESTICA SINGAPORE PTE LTD.—See ONEX Corporation; *Int'l*, pg. 5578
CELESTINE HOTEL CO., LTD.—See Mitsui Fudosan Co., Ltd.; *Int'l*, pg. 4986
CELESTIX NETWORKS, INC.; *U.S. Private*, pg. 806
CELESTIX NETWORKS PTE. LTD.—See Celestix Networks, Inc.; *U.S. Private*, pg. 806
CELEST PAPER KLIPPAN AB; *Int'l*, pg. 1392
CELESTRON, LLC; *U.S. Private*, pg. 806
CELESTYAL CRUISES LTD.—See Louis PLC; *Int'l*, pg. 4502
CELETRONIX USA, INC.—See Jabil Inc.; *U.S. Public*, pg. 1180
CELEXUS, INC.; *U.S. Private*, pg. 806
CELEY'S QUALITY PLUMBING, INC.; *U.S. Private*, pg. 806
CELFA - SOCEDADE INDUSTRIAL DE TRANSFORMACAO DE GESSOS S.A.—See Camargo Correa S.A.; *Int'l*, pg. 1267
CELFINET - CONSULTORIA EM TELECOMUNICACOES, S.A.—See Cyient Limited; *Int'l*, pg. 1895
CELGARD KOREA, LTD.—See Asahi Kasei Corporation; *Int'l*, pg. 596
CELGARD, LLC—See Asahi Kasei Corporation; *Int'l*, pg. 596
CELGENE AB—See Bristol-Myers Squibb Company; *U.S. Public*, pg. 386
CELGENE AB—See Bristol-Myers Squibb Company; *U.S. Public*, pg. 386
CELGENE APS—See Bristol-Myers Squibb Company; *U.S. Public*, pg. 386
CELGENE AVILOMICS RESEARCH, INC.—See Bristol-Myers Squibb Company; *U.S. Public*, pg. 386
CELGENE BVBA—See Bristol-Myers Squibb Company; *U.S. Public*, pg. 386
CELGENE B.V.—See Bristol-Myers Squibb Company; *U.S. Public*, pg. 386
CELGENE CHEMICALS SARL—See Bristol-Myers Squibb Company; *U.S. Public*, pg. 386
CELGENE CORPORATION—See Bristol-Myers Squibb Company; *U.S. Public*, pg. 385
CELGENE CO.—See Bristol-Myers Squibb Company; *U.S. Public*, pg. 386
CELGENE DISTRIBUTION BV—See Bristol-Myers Squibb Company; *U.S. Public*, pg. 386
CELGENE EUROPE, LIMITED—See Bristol-Myers Squibb Company; *U.S. Public*, pg. 386
CELGENE GMBH—See Bristol-Myers Squibb Company; *U.S. Public*, pg. 386
CELGENE GMBH—See Bristol-Myers Squibb Company; *U.S. Public*, pg. 386
CELGENE GMBH—See Bristol-Myers Squibb Company; *U.S. Public*, pg. 386
CELGENE ILAC PAZARLAMA VE TIC. LTD.—See Bristol-Myers Squibb Company; *U.S. Public*, pg. 386
CELGENE INC.—See Bristol-Myers Squibb Company; *U.S. Public*, pg. 386
CELGENE INTERNATIONAL SARL—See Bristol-Myers Squibb Company; *U.S. Public*, pg. 386
CELGENE LIMITED—See Bristol-Myers Squibb Company; *U.S. Public*, pg. 386
CELGENE LIMITED—See Bristol-Myers Squibb Company; *U.S. Public*, pg. 386
CELGENE LIMITED—See Bristol-Myers Squibb Company; *U.S. Public*, pg. 386

CELGENE LLAC PAZARLAMA VE TIC.LTD. STI.—See Bristol-Myers Squibb Company; *U.S. Public*, pg. 386
CELGENE LOGISTICS SARL—See Bristol-Myers Squibb Company; *U.S. Public*, pg. 386
CELGENE NETHERLANDS BV—See Bristol-Myers Squibb Company; *U.S. Public*, pg. 386
CELGENE PHARMACEUTICAL (SHANGHAI) COMPANY LIMITED—See Bristol-Myers Squibb Company; *U.S. Public*, pg. 386
CELGENE PTE LTD—See Bristol-Myers Squibb Company; *U.S. Public*, pg. 386
CELGENE PTY LIMITED—See Bristol-Myers Squibb Company; *U.S. Public*, pg. 386
CELGENE QUANTICEL RESEARCH, INC.—See Bristol-Myers Squibb Company; *U.S. Public*, pg. 386
CELGENE SARL—See Bristol-Myers Squibb Company; *U.S. Public*, pg. 386
CELGENE, S. DE R.L. DE C.V.—See Bristol-Myers Squibb Company; *U.S. Public*, pg. 386
CELGENE, SL—See Bristol-Myers Squibb Company; *U.S. Public*, pg. 386
CELGENE SOCIEDADE UNIPESSOAL LDA—See Bristol-Myers Squibb Company; *U.S. Public*, pg. 386
CELGENE SP. ZOO—See Bristol-Myers Squibb Company; *U.S. Public*, pg. 386
CELGENE SRL—See Bristol-Myers Squibb Company; *U.S. Public*, pg. 386
CELGENE S.R.O—See Bristol-Myers Squibb Company; *U.S. Public*, pg. 386
CELGENE S.R.O.—See Bristol-Myers Squibb Company; *U.S. Public*, pg. 386
CELHART DONARIS SA; *Int'l*, pg. 1392
CELIA CORPORATION; *U.S. Private*, pg. 807
CELIK D.O.O; *Int'l*, pg. 1392
CELIK HALAT VE TEL SANAYII AS—See Adil Bey Holding A.S.; *Int'l*, pg. 148
CELIK HOLDING A.S.—See Parsan Makina Parcalari Sanayii AS; *Int'l*, pg. 5747
CELIK MOTOR TICARET A.S.—See AG Anadolu Grubu Holding A.S.; *Int'l*, pg. 197
CELINA ALUMINUM PRECISION TECHNOLOGY INC.—See Honda Motor Co., Ltd.; *Int'l*, pg. 3461
CELINA INSURANCE GROUP; *U.S. Private*, pg. 807
CELINA LANDFILL, INC—See Republic Services, Inc.; *U.S. Public*, pg. 1786
CELINE BOUTIQUE TAIWAN CO. LTD.—See LVMH Moet Hennessy Louis Vuitton SE; *Int'l*, pg. 4593
CELINE HAWAII INC.—See LVMH Moet Hennessy Louis Vuitton SE; *Int'l*, pg. 4593
CELINE (HONG KONG) LTD—See LVMH Moet Hennessy Louis Vuitton SE; *Int'l*, pg. 4593
CELINE INC.—See LVMH Moet Hennessy Louis Vuitton SE; *Int'l*, pg. 4593
CELINE ITALIA S.R.L.—See LVMH Moet Hennessy Louis Vuitton SE; *Int'l*, pg. 4593
CELINE JAPAN KK—See LVMH Moet Hennessy Louis Vuitton SE; *Int'l*, pg. 4593
CELINE KOREA LTD—See LVMH Moet Hennessy Louis Vuitton SE; *Int'l*, pg. 4591
CELINE MONACO SA—See LVMH Moet Hennessy Louis Vuitton SE; *Int'l*, pg. 4593
CELINE MONTE-CARLO SA—See LVMH Moet Hennessy Louis Vuitton SE; *Int'l*, pg. 4593
CELINE PRODUCTION S.R.L.—See LVMH Moet Hennessy Louis Vuitton SE; *Int'l*, pg. 4593
CELINE S.A.—See LVMH Moet Hennessy Louis Vuitton SE; *Int'l*, pg. 4593
CELINE SUISSE SA—See LVMH Moet Hennessy Louis Vuitton SE; *Int'l*, pg. 4593
CELINE UK LTD.—See LVMH Moet Hennessy Louis Vuitton SE; *Int'l*, pg. 4593
CELITE CORPORATION—See Groupe Bruxelles Lambert SA; *Int'l*, pg. 3100
CELKI INTERNATIONAL LTD—See L'Air Liquide S.A.; *Int'l*, pg. 4375
CELLA ACQUISITION LTD.—See Persephone Capital Partners LLC; *U.S. Private*, pg. 3154
CELLARMASTER WINES PTY LIMITED; *Int'l*, pg. 1392
CELLA SPACE LTD.; *Int'l*, pg. 1392
CELLAVISION AB; *Int'l*, pg. 1392
CELLAVISION CANADA INC.—See CellaVision AB; *Int'l*, pg. 1392
CELLAVISION INC.—See CellaVision AB; *Int'l*, pg. 1392
CELLAVISION JAPAN K.K.—See CellaVision AB; *Int'l*, pg. 1392
CELL BIOTECH CO., LTD.; *Int'l*, pg. 1392
CELL BIOTECH INTERNATIONAL CO., LTD.—See Cell Biotech Co., Ltd.; *Int'l*, pg. 1392
CELL BUSINESS EQUIPMENT; *U.S. Private*, pg. 807
CELL CARE AUSTRALIA PTY. LTD.—See The Cooper Companies, Inc.; *U.S. Public*, pg. 2066
CELLCARTA PRECISION MEDICINE INC—See Arsenal Capital Management LP; *U.S. Private*, pg. 337
CELLCAST MIDDLE EAST—See Vintana plc; *Int'l*, pg. 8242
CELL: CM LTD.—See EQT AB; *Int'l*, pg. 2479
CELL: CM LTD.—See Public Sector Pension Investment Board; *Int'l*, pg. 6096

CELLCOM ISRAEL LTD.—See IDB Development Corporation Ltd.; *Int'l*, pg. 3588
CELLCO PARTNERSHIP—See Verizon Communications Inc.; *U.S. Public*, pg. 2284
CELL-CRETE CORPORATION; *U.S. Private*, pg. 807
CELLCUBE ENERGY STORAGE SYSTEMS INC.; *Int'l*, pg. 1392
CELLCURA ASA—See Dag Dvergsten AS; *Int'l*, pg. 1912
CELLCURA, INC.—See Dag Dvergsten AS; *Int'l*, pg. 1912
CELLCURA SOLUTIONS A/S—See Dag Dvergsten AS; *Int'l*, pg. 1912
CELL CURE NEUROSCIENCES, LTD.—See Lineage Cell Therapeutics, Inc.; *U.S. Public*, pg. 1320
CELLCYTE GENETICS CORPORATION; *U.S. Private*, pg. 807
CELLDEX THERAPEUTICS, INC.; *U.S. Public*, pg. 465
CELLEBRITE APAC PTE LTD—See Sun Corporation; *Int'l*, pg. 7303
CELLEBRITE DI LTD.—See Sun Corporation; *Int'l*, pg. 7303
CELLEBRITE GMBH—See Sun Corporation; *Int'l*, pg. 7303
CELLEBRITE LTDA.—See Sun Corporation; *Int'l*, pg. 7303
CELLEBRITE USA INC.—See Sun Corporation; *Int'l*, pg. 7303
CELLECOR GADGETS LIMITED; *Int'l*, pg. 1392
CELLECTAR BIOSCIENCES, INC.; *U.S. Public*, pg. 465
CELLECT BIOTECHNOLOGY LTD.; *Int'l*, pg. 1392
CELLECTIS S.A.; *Int'l*, pg. 1392
CELLECTIS THERAPEUTICS—See Cellectis S.A.; *Int'l*, pg. 1393
CELLECT LLC; *U.S. Private*, pg. 807
CELLENT MITTELSTANDSBERATUNG GMBH—See Landesbank Baden-Wurttemberg; *Int'l*, pg. 4406
CEL LEP IDIOMAS—See H.I.G. Capital, LLC; *U.S. Private*, pg. 1828
CELLERATION, INC.—See Adynxx, Inc.; *U.S. Public*, pg. 50
CELLER LAW, P.A.—See The Celler Organization; *U.S. Private*, pg. 4006
CELLERO, LLC—See Charles River Laboratories International, Inc.; *U.S. Public*, pg. 479
THE CELLER ORGANIZATION; *U.S. Private*, pg. 4006
CELLERYS AG—See Novartis AG; *Int'l*, pg. 5457
CELLESTIS GMBH—See QIAGEN N.V.; *Int'l*, pg. 6139
CELLESTIS INC.—See QIAGEN N.V.; *Int'l*, pg. 6139
CELLESTIS LTD.—See QIAGEN N.V.; *Int'l*, pg. 6139
CELLE-UELZEN NETZ GMBH—See E.ON SE; *Int'l*, pg. 2251
THE CELL-FACTORY NV—See Esperite N.V.; *Int'l*, pg. 2506
CELLFIE GLOBAL CO.,LTD.; *Int'l*, pg. 1393
CELLFIND (PROPRIETARY) LIMITED—See Blue Label Telecoms Limited; *Int'l*, pg. 1068
CELLFIRE, INC.—See Berkshire Partners LLC; *U.S. Private*, pg. 534
CELLFISH MEDIA, INC.—See Cellfish Media LLC; *U.S. Private*, pg. 807
CELLFISH MEDIA LLC; *U.S. Private*, pg. 807
CELLFORCURE SASU—See Novartis AG; *Int'l*, pg. 5457
CELLGENIX INC—See Sartorius AG; *Int'l*, pg. 6578
CELLGENTEK CO., LTD.; *Int'l*, pg. 1393
CELLHIRE FRANCE SA—See Cellhire Plc; *Int'l*, pg. 1393
CELLHIRE (GERMANY) GMBH—See Cellhire Plc; *Int'l*, pg. 1393
CELLHIRE PLC; *Int'l*, pg. 1393
CELLHIRE USA LLC—See Cellhire Plc; *Int'l*, pg. 1393
CELLID CO., LTD.; *Int'l*, pg. 1393
CELLI ENTERPRISES INC.; *U.S. Private*, pg. 807
CELL IMPACT AB—See Amasten Fastighets AB; *Int'l*, pg. 412
CELLINK BIOPRINTING AB—See BICO Group AB; *Int'l*, pg. 1019
CELLINK KK—See BICO Group AB; *Int'l*, pg. 1019
CELLI S.P.A.—See Ardian SAS; *Int'l*, pg. 555
CELLITE AB—See Addtech AB; *Int'l*, pg. 132
CELLIVERY THERAPEUTICS INC.; *Int'l*, pg. 1393
CELLMARK AB (SHANGHAI)—See CellMark AB; *Int'l*, pg. 1394
CELLMARK AB; *Int'l*, pg. 1393
CELLMARK ASIA PTE LTD—See CellMark AB; *Int'l*, pg. 1393
CELLMARK BELGIUM NV—See CellMark AB; *Int'l*, pg. 1393
CELLMARK CHEMICALS LTD.—See CellMark AB; *Int'l*, pg. 1393
CELLMARK CHEMICALS SINGAPORE PTE LTD.—See CellMark AB; *Int'l*, pg. 1393
CELLMARK CHINA LTD—See CellMark AB; *Int'l*, pg. 1393
CELLMARK DEUTSCHLAND GMBH—See CellMark AB; *Int'l*, pg. 1393
CELLMARK ESPANA SA—See CellMark AB; *Int'l*, pg. 1393
CELLMARK HELLAS SA—See CellMark AB; *Int'l*, pg. 1393
CELLMARK IBERICA SL—See CellMark AB; *Int'l*, pg. 1393
CELLMARK INC.—See CellMark AB; *Int'l*, pg. 1393
CELLMARK INDIA PRIVATE LIMITED—See CellMark AB; *Int'l*, pg. 1393
CELLMARK ITALY S.R.L.—See CellMark AB; *Int'l*, pg. 1393
CELLMARK JAPAN—See CellMark AB; *Int'l*, pg. 1393

CELLMARK AB

CELLMARK KIMYA TIC AS—See CellMark AB; *Int'l*, pg. 1393
CELLMARK LTD—See CellMark AB; *Int'l*, pg. 1393
CELLMARK M.E. LLC—See CellMark AB; *Int'l*, pg. 1393
CELLMARK PAPER CANADA INC—See CellMark AB; *Int'l*, pg. 1393
CELLMARK PAPER SA DE CV—See CellMark AB; *Int'l*, pg. 1393
CELLMARK PAPIER SAS—See CellMark AB; *Int'l*, pg. 1393
CELLMARK PERU S.A.C.—See CellMark AB; *Int'l*, pg. 1393
CELLMARK PULP AND PAPER INC—See CellMark AB; *Int'l*, pg. 1393
CELLMARK RECYCLING BENELUX BV—See CellMark AB; *Int'l*, pg. 1393
CELLMARK SA—See CellMark AB; *Int'l*, pg. 1393
CELLMARK SHANGHAI CO LTD—See CellMark AB; *Int'l*, pg. 1393
CELLMARK TAIWAN CO LTD—See CellMark AB; *Int'l*, pg. 1393
CELLMARK THAILAND CO LTD—See CellMark AB; *Int'l*, pg. 1393
CELLMARK UK LTD—See CellMark AB; *Int'l*, pg. 1393
CELLMARK USA, LLC—See CellMark AB; *Int'l*, pg. 1393
CELL MARQUE CORPORATION—See Merck KGaA; *Int'l*, pg. 4832
CELL MEDX CORP.; *U.S. Public*, pg. 465
CELL MICROSYSTEMS, INC.; *U.S. Private*, pg. 807
CELLNET COMMUNICATIONS INC.; *U.S. Private*, pg. 807
CELLNET GROUP LIMITED—See Wentronic Holding GmbH; *Int'l*, pg. 8377
CELLNETIX PATHOLOGY & LABORATORIES, LLC; *U.S. Private*, pg. 807
CELLNET LIMITED—See Wentronic Holding GmbH; *Int'l*, pg. 8377
CELLNEX AUSTRIA GMBH—See Cellnex Telecom, S.A.; *Int'l*, pg. 1394
CELLNEX CONNECTIVITY SOLUTIONS LIMITED—See Cellnex Telecom, S.A.; *Int'l*, pg. 1394
CELLNEX DENMARK APS—See Cellnex Telecom, S.A.; *Int'l*, pg. 1394
CELLNEX IRELAND LIMITED—See Cellnex Telecom, S.A.; *Int'l*, pg. 1394
CELLNEX ITALIA, S.R.L.—See Cellnex Telecom, S.A.; *Int'l*, pg. 1394
CELLNEX POLAND SP Z O.O.—See Cellnex Telecom, S.A.; *Int'l*, pg. 1394
CELLNEX SWEDEN AB—See Cellnex Telecom, S.A.; *Int'l*, pg. 1394
CELLNEX TELECOM, S.A.; *Int'l*, pg. 1394
CELLNEX UK LIMITED—See Cellnex Telecom, S.A.; *Int'l*, pg. 1394
CELL-NIQUE CORPORATION; *U.S. Private*, pg. 807
CELLNOVO GROUP SA; *Int'l*, pg. 1394
CELLO ELECTRONICS (UK) LTD; *Int'l*, pg. 1394
CELLOFOAM NORTH AMERICA INC.; *U.S. Private*, pg. 807
CELLO-FOIL PRODUCTS, INC.—See Sun Capital Partners, Inc.; *U.S. Private*, pg. 3858
CELLOGLAS LTD.—See Berggruen Holdings, Inc.; *U.S. Private*, pg. 531
CELLO HEALTH PLC—See Arsenal Capital Management LP; *U.S. Private*, pg. 337
CELLO HEALTH—See Arsenal Capital Management LP; *U.S. Private*, pg. 338
CELLO-PACK CORPORATION; *U.S. Private*, pg. 807
CELLO PRODUCTS INC.; *Int'l*, pg. 1394
CELLO PROFESSIONAL PRODUCTS—See Montgomery Manufacturing Co.; *U.S. Private*, pg. 2777
CELLO SIGNAL—See Arsenal Capital Management LP; *U.S. Private*, pg. 338
CELLOTAPE, INC.—See Ares Management Corporation; *U.S. Public*, pg. 190
CELLO WORLD LIMITED; *Int'l*, pg. 1394
CELLO-WRAP PRINTING COMPANY, INC.—See Carroll Products, Inc.; *U.S. Private*, pg. 773
CELL PHARM GESELLSCHAFT FUR PHARMAZEUTISCHE UND DIAGNOSTISCHE PRAPARATE MBH—See Bain Capital, LP; *U.S. Private*, pg. 444
CELL PHARM GESELLSCHAFT FUR PHARMAZEUTISCHE UND DIAGNOSTISCHE PRAPARATE MBH—See Cinven Limited; *Int'l*, pg. 1614
CELLPLUS MOBILE COMMUNICATIONS LTD.—See Mauritius Telecom Ltd.; *Int'l*, pg. 4732
CELLPOINT B.V.—See Galapagos N.V.; *Int'l*, pg. 2870
CELL SCIENCE & TECHNOLOGY INSTITUTE, INC.—See Nipro Corporation; *Int'l*, pg. 5361
CELLSCREEN DIRECT LIMITED; *Int'l*, pg. 1394
CELLSEED INC.; *Int'l*, pg. 1394
CELLSOURCE CO., LTD.; *Int'l*, pg. 1394
CELL SOURCE, INC.; *U.S. Public*, pg. 465
CELLSTAR (ASIA) CORPORATION LIMITED; *Int'l*, pg. 1394
CELLSTAR CHILE, S.A.; *Int'l*, pg. 1394
CELLSTOP SYSTEMS, INC.; *Int'l*, pg. 1394
CELLSURE, L3C—See Predictive Technology Group, Inc.; *U.S. Public*, pg. 1713

CELL SYSTEMS LLC—See Anabios Corporation; *U.S. Private*, pg. 271
CELLTECH ABATEL AB—See Addtech AB; *Int'l*, pg. 132
CELLTECH AS—See Addtech AB; *Int'l*, pg. 132
CELLTECH ENERGY SYSTEMS AB—See Addtech AB; *Int'l*, pg. 132
CELLTECH-HARRING A/S—See Addtech AB; *Int'l*, pg. 132
CELL TECH INTERNATIONAL INCORPORATED; *U.S. Public*, pg. 465
CELLTECH JAPAN LTD—See UCB S.A.; *Int'l*, pg. 8011
CELLTECH LTD—See UCB S.A.; *Int'l*, pg. 8010
CELLTECH OY—See Addtech AB; *Int'l*, pg. 132
CELLTECH R&D LTD—See UCB S.A.; *Int'l*, pg. 8011
CELL TRADE NY INC.; *U.S. Private*, pg. 807
CELLTRION HEALTHCARE CO., LTD.—See Celltrion Pharm. Inc.; *Int'l*, pg. 1394
CELLTRION, INC.; *Int'l*, pg. 1394
CELLTRION PHARM. INC. - JINCHEON FACTORY—See Celltrion Pharm. Inc.; *Int'l*, pg. 1394
CELLTRION PHARM. INC.; *Int'l*, pg. 1394
CELLTRION USA, INC.—See Celltrion, Inc.; *Int'l*, pg. 1395
CELLTRUST ANIMAL THERAPEUTICS CO., LTD.—See FUJIFILM Holdings Corporation; *Int'l*, pg. 2821
CELLTRUST CORPORATION; *U.S. Private*, pg. 807
CELLUCAP MANUFACTURING CO.; *U.S. Private*, pg. 807
CELLUCOR—See Woodbolt Distribution, LLC; *U.S. Private*, pg. 4557
CELLUFUN INC.; *U.S. Private*, pg. 807
CELLULAC LIMITED; *Int'l*, pg. 1395
CELLULAR BIOMEDICINE GROUP, INC.; *U.S. Private*, pg. 807
THE CELLULAR CONNECTION, LLC—See Round Room LLC; *U.S. Private*, pg. 3488
CELLULAR DYNAMICS INTERNATIONAL, INC.—See FUJIFILM Holdings Corporation; *Int'l*, pg. 2822
CELLULAR GMBH; *Int'l*, pg. 1395
CELLULAR GOODS PLC; *Int'l*, pg. 1395
CELLULARLINE SPA; *Int'l*, pg. 1395
CELLULAR ONE OF EAST CENTRAL ILLINOIS; *U.S. Private*, pg. 807
CELLULAR RESEARCH, INC.—See Becton, Dickinson & Company; *U.S. Public*, pg. 292
CELLULAR SALES OF KNOXVILLE, INC; *U.S. Private*, pg. 808
CELLULAR SOUTH INC.—See Telapex Inc.; *U.S. Private*, pg. 3959
CELLULAR SOUTH—See Telapex Inc.; *U.S. Private*, pg. 3959
CELLULAR SPECIALTIES INC.—See Westell Technologies, Inc.; *U.S. Public*, pg. 2354
CELLUMED CO., LTD.; *Int'l*, pg. 1395
CELLVEC PTE. LTD.—See Talkmed Group Limited; *Int'l*, pg. 7447
CELLXION LIGHTWEIGHT DIVISION LLC—See The Jordan Company, L.P.; *U.S. Private*, pg. 4061
CELLXION LLC—See The Jordan Company, L.P.; *U.S. Private*, pg. 4061
CELLY S.P.A.—See Esprinet S.p.A.; *Int'l*, pg. 2506
CELLZOME GMBH—See GSK plc; *Int'l*, pg. 3145
CELMA INDUKTA SA—See Cantoni Motor S.A.; *Int'l*, pg. 1299
CELMA S.A.—See Cantoni Motor S.A.; *Int'l*, pg. 1299
CELMET COMPANY, INC.—See Goldberg Lindsay & Co., LLC; *U.S. Private*, pg. 1729
CELON PHARMA SA; *Int'l*, pg. 1395
CELOXICA HOLDINGS PLC; *Int'l*, pg. 1395
CELOXICA INC.—See Celoxica Holdings plc; *Int'l*, pg. 1395
CELOXICA LTD—See Celoxica Holdings plc; *Int'l*, pg. 1395
CELPAD, INC.; *U.S. Private*, pg. 808
CELRETS PTY LTD.—See Nylex Limited; *Int'l*, pg. 5500
CELSA ARMERINGSSTAL AS—See Celsa Group; *Int'l*, pg. 1395
CELSA ATLANTIC S.A.—See Celsa Group; *Int'l*, pg. 1395
CELSA FRANCE S.A.S.—See Celsa Group; *Int'l*, pg. 1395
CELSA GERMANY—See Celsa Group; *Int'l*, pg. 1395
CELSA GROUP; *Int'l*, pg. 1395
CELSA HUTA OSTROWIEC SP. Z O.O.—See Celsa Group; *Int'l*, pg. 1395
CELSA STEEL SERVICE AB—See Celsa Group; *Int'l*, pg. 1395
CELSA STEEL SERVICE AS—See Celsa Group; *Int'l*, pg. 1395
CELSA STEEL SERVICE A/S—See Celsa Group; *Int'l*, pg. 1395
CELSA STEEL SERVICE OY—See Celsa Group; *Int'l*, pg. 1395
CELSA STEEL (UK) LTD.—See Celsa Group; *Int'l*, pg. 1395
CEL-SCI CORPORATION; *U.S. Public*, pg. 464
CELS ENTERPRISES, INC.; *U.S. Private*, pg. 808
CELSIA SA ESP—See Grupo Argos S.A.; *Int'l*, pg. 3120
CELSIA S.A.—See Grupo Argos S.A.; *Int'l*, pg. 3120
CELSIS INTERNATIONAL BV—See Charles River Laboratories International, Inc.; *U.S. Public*, pg. 479
CELSIUM SERWIS SP. Z O.O.—See E.ON SE; *Int'l*, pg. 2251
CELSIUM SP. Z O.O.—See E.ON SE; *Int'l*, pg. 2251

CORPORATE AFFILIATIONS

CELSIUS HOLDINGS, INC.; *U.S. Public*, pg. 465
CELSIUS INVEST AB—See Saab AB; *Int'l*, pg. 6459
CELSIUS RESOURCES LIMITED; *Int'l*, pg. 1395
CELSTAR GROUP INC.; *U.S. Private*, pg. 808
CELSYS, INC.—See CELSYS, Inc.; *Int'l*, pg. 1396
CELSYS, INC.; *Int'l*, pg. 1396
CELTECH CORP.—See Atec, Inc.; *U.S. Private*, pg. 365
CELTECH SP. Z O.O.—See Grupa Kety S.A.; *Int'l*, pg. 3117
CELTIC CAPITAL CORPORATION—See Banc of California, Inc.; *U.S. Public*, pg. 269
CELTIC COMMUNITY SERVICES OF NE OHIO, INC.—See Graham Holdings Company; *U.S. Public*, pg. 954
CELTIC F.C.—See Celtic plc; *Int'l*, pg. 1396
CELTIC GROUP, INC.—See Centene Corporation; *U.S. Public*, pg. 468
CELTIC HEALTHCARE, INC.—See Graham Holdings Company; *U.S. Public*, pg. 954
CELTIC HEALTHCARE OF CARLISLE, INC.—See Graham Holdings Company; *U.S. Public*, pg. 954
CELTIC HEALTHCARE OF E. MO, LLC—See Graham Holdings Company; *U.S. Public*, pg. 954
CELTIC HEALTHCARE OF NC PA, LLC—See Graham Holdings Company; *U.S. Public*, pg. 954
CELTIC HEALTHCARE OF NE OHIO, INC.—See Graham Holdings Company; *U.S. Public*, pg. 954
CELTIC, INC.—See Zizzo Group, Inc.; *U.S. Private*, pg. 4606
CELTIC INTERNATIONAL, LLC—See TPG Capital, L.P.; *U.S. Public*, pg. 2177
CELTIC ITALY SRL—See CPD S.A.; *Int'l*, pg. 1824
CELTIC LEASING CORP.—See Fifth Third Bancorp; *U.S. Public*, pg. 834
CELTIC LIFE INSURANCE COMPANY INC.—See Centene Corporation; *U.S. Public*, pg. 468
CELTIC MARINE CORPORATION; *U.S. Private*, pg. 808
CELTIC MINERALS LTD.; *Int'l*, pg. 1396
CELTIC PHARMA LIMITED; *Int'l*, pg. 1396
CELTIC PLC; *Int'l*, pg. 1396
CELTIC REHABILITATION, INC.—See Graham Holdings Company; *U.S. Public*, pg. 954
CELTIC SYSTEMS PRIVATE LIMITED—See i3 Verticals, Inc.; *U.S. Public*, pg. 1081
CELTIC TECHNOLOGIES LTD.—See Colliers International Group Inc.; *Int'l*, pg. 1701
CELTYS S.A.S.—See LDC SA; *Int'l*, pg. 4430
CELUCAT SA—See Klabin S.A.; *Int'l*, pg. 4198
CELULARITY INC.; *U.S. Public*, pg. 466
CELULOSA ARAUCO Y CONSTITUCION S.A.—See AntarChile S.A.; *Int'l*, pg. 481
CELULOSA ARGENTINA S.A.; *Int'l*, pg. 1396
CELULOSA DE LEVANTE S.A.—See Miquel y Costas & Miquel, S.A.; *Int'l*, pg. 4915
CELULOSA ENERGIA, S.L.—See ENCE Energia y Celulosa, S.A.; *Int'l*, pg. 2401
CELULOSAS DE ASTURIAS, S.A.—See ENCE Energia y Celulosa, S.A.; *Int'l*, pg. 2401
CELULOSA Y DERIVADOS DE MONTERREY, S.A.—See Cydsa S.A.B. de C.V.; *Int'l*, pg. 1895
CELULOSE BEIRA INDUSTRIAL (CELBI), S.A.—See Altri, SGPS, S.A.; *Int'l*, pg. 398
CELULOSE IRANI S.A. - FOREST FACTORY DIVISION—See Irani Papel e Embalagem S.A.; *Int'l*, pg. 3805
CELULOSE IRANI S.A. - FURNITURE COMMERCIAL AND FACTORY DIVISION—See Irani Papel e Embalagem S.A.; *Int'l*, pg. 3805
CELULOSE IRANI S.A. - PACKAGING COMMERCIAL DIVISION—See Irani Papel e Embalagem S.A.; *Int'l*, pg. 3805
CELULOSE IRANI S.A. - PACKAGING FACTORY DIVISION—See Irani Papel e Embalagem S.A.; *Int'l*, pg. 3805
CELULOSE IRANI S.A. - PAPER COMMERCIAL DIVISION—See Irani Papel e Embalagem S.A.; *Int'l*, pg. 3805
CELULOSE IRANI S.A. - PAPER FACTORY DIVISION—See Irani Papel e Embalagem S.A.; *Int'l*, pg. 3805
CELULOSE IRANI S.A. - RESINS COMMERCIAL DIVISION—See Irani Papel e Embalagem S.A.; *Int'l*, pg. 3805
CELULOSE IRANI S.A. - RESINS FACTORY DIVISION—See Irani Papel e Embalagem S.A.; *Int'l*, pg. 3805
CELULOSE NIPO-BRASILEIRA S.A.—See Oji Holdings Corporation; *Int'l*, pg. 5536
CELUPA - INDUSTRIAL CELULOSE E PAPEL GUAIBA LTDA.—See Melitta Unternehmensgruppe Bentz KG; *Int'l*, pg. 4810
CELVIA—See LDC SA; *Int'l*, pg. 4430
CELVITAE BIOMEDICA S.L.—See VITA 34 AG; *Int'l*, pg. 8257
CELYAD ONCOLOGY SA; *Int'l*, pg. 1396
CEMAC (HONG KONG) LIMITED—See Fletcher Building Limited; *Int'l*, pg. 2699
CEMACON S.A.; *Int'l*, pg. 1396

COMPANY NAME INDEX

CEMMAC AS

C.E. MACPHERSON DIVISION OF CONREX STEEL LTD.—See Canerector Inc.; *Int'l*, pg. 1290
CEMAGID SAS—See Silver Lake Group, LLC; *U.S. Private*, pg. 3656
CEMAI INC.—See Titan Cement Company S.A.; *Int'l*, pg. 7759
C.E.MANAGEMENT INTEGRATED LABORATORY CO.LTD; *Int'l*, pg. 1240
CEMAR - COMPANHIA ENERGETICA DO MARANHAO—See Equatorial Energia SA; *Int'l*, pg. 2484
CEMAS DOKUM SANAYI A.S.—See Isiklar Holding A.S.; *Int'l*, pg. 3818
CEMAT A/S; *Int'l*, pg. 1396
CEMAT REAL ESTATE S.A.—See Cemat A/S; *Int'l*, pg. 1396
CEMATRIX (CALGARY) LTD.—See Cematrix Corporation; *Int'l*, pg. 1396
CEMATRIX (CANADA) INC.—See Cematrix Corporation; *Int'l*, pg. 1396
CEMATRIX CORPORATION; *Int'l*, pg. 1396
CEMATRIX (USA) INC.—See Cematrix Corporation; *Int'l*, pg. 1396
CEMBELL INDUSTRIES INC.; *U.S. Private*, pg. 808
C.E.M. BIOTRONIK S.A.—See Biotronik GmbH & Co.; *Int'l*, pg. 1044
CEMBRA MONEY BANK AG; *Int'l*, pg. 1396
CEMBRE AS—See CEMBRE S.p.A.; *Int'l*, pg. 1396
CEMBRE ESPANA SL—See CEMBRE S.p.A.; *Int'l*, pg. 1396
CEMBRE GMBH—See CEMBRE S.p.A.; *Int'l*, pg. 1396
CEMBRE INC.—See CEMBRE S.p.A.; *Int'l*, pg. 1396
CEMBRE LTD.—See CEMBRE S.p.A.; *Int'l*, pg. 1396
CEMBRE SARL—See CEMBRE S.p.A.; *Int'l*, pg. 1396
CEMBRE S.P.A.; *Int'l*, pg. 1396
CEMBRIT A.S.—See swisspor Management AG; *Int'l*, pg. 7375
CEMBRIT HOLDING A/S—See swisspor Management AG; *Int'l*, pg. 7375
CEMBRIT KFT.—See swisspor Management AG; *Int'l*, pg. 7375
CEMBRIT LTD.—See swisspor Management AG; *Int'l*, pg. 7375
CEMBRIT S.A.—See swisspor Management AG; *Int'l*, pg. 7375
CEMBRIT SAS—See swisspor Management AG; *Int'l*, pg. 7375
CEMCARE, INC.—See Service Corporation International; *U.S. Public*, pg. 1869
CEM CORPORATION; *U.S. Private*, pg. 808
CEM CORPORATION—See SBI Holdings, Inc.; *Int'l*, pg. 6604
CEMEDINE AUTOMOTIVE CO., LTD. - KINUURA PLANT—See Kaneka Corporation; *Int'l*, pg. 4066
CEMEDINE CHEMICAL CO., LTD.—See Kaneka Corporation; *Int'l*, pg. 4066
CEMEDINE CHEMICAL INDUSTRIES CO., LTD.—See Kaneka Corporation; *Int'l*, pg. 4066
CEMEDINE CO., LTD. - MIE PLANT—See Kaneka Corporation; *Int'l*, pg. 4066
CEMEDINE CO., LTD.—See Kaneka Corporation; *Int'l*, pg. 4066
CEMEDINE NORTH AMERICA LLC—See Kaneka Corporation; *Int'l*, pg. 4067
CEMEDINE PHILIPPINES CORP.—See Kaneka Corporation; *Int'l*, pg. 4066
CEMEDINE SALES CO., LTD.—See Kaneka Corporation; *Int'l*, pg. 4066
CEMEDINE SHANGHAI CO., LTD.—See Kaneka Corporation; *Int'l*, pg. 4066
CEMEDINE THAILAND CO., LTD.—See Kaneka Corporation; *Int'l*, pg. 4066
CEMENTA AB (MALMO)—See Heidelberg Materials AG; *Int'l*, pg. 3315
CEMENTA AB (STOCKHOLM)—See Heidelberg Materials AG; *Int'l*, pg. 3315
CEMENTARA KOSJERIC AD—See Titan Cement Company S.A.; *Int'l*, pg. 7759
CEMENTA RESEARCH AB—See Heidelberg Materials AG; *Int'l*, pg. 3315
CEMENTATION CANADA INC.—See Murray & Roberts Holdings Ltd.; *Int'l*, pg. 5100
CEMENTATION FOUNDATIONS SKANSKA LTD.—See Skanska AB; *Int'l*, pg. 6979
CEMENTATION SUDAMERICA SA—See Murray & Roberts Holdings Ltd.; *Int'l*, pg. 5100
CEMENTATION USA INC—See Murray & Roberts Holdings Ltd.; *Int'l*, pg. 5100
CEMENT AUSTRALIA HOLDINGS PTY LTD - BULWER ISLAND PLANT—See Heidelberg Materials AG; *Int'l*, pg. 3311
CEMENT AUSTRALIA HOLDINGS PTY LTD - BULWER ISLAND PLANT—See Holcim Ltd.; *Int'l*, pg. 3446
CEMENT AUSTRALIA HOLDINGS PTY LTD - GLADSTONE PLANT—See Heidelberg Materials AG; *Int'l*, pg. 3311
CEMENT AUSTRALIA HOLDINGS PTY LTD - GLADSTONE PLANT—See Holcim Ltd.; *Int'l*, pg. 3446
CEMENT AUSTRALIA HOLDINGS PTY LTD - RAILTON PLANT—See Heidelberg Materials AG; *Int'l*, pg. 3311
CEMENT AUSTRALIA HOLDINGS PTY LTD - RAILTON PLANT—See Holcim Ltd.; *Int'l*, pg. 3446
CEMENT AUSTRALIA HOLDINGS PTY. LTD.—See Heidelberg Materials AG; *Int'l*, pg. 3311
CEMENT AUSTRALIA HOLDINGS PTY. LTD.—See Holcim Ltd.; *Int'l*, pg. 3446
CEMENTBOUW B.V.—See CRH plc; *Int'l*, pg. 1844
CEMENTECH LIMITED—See Orascom Construction PLC; *Int'l*, pg. 5613
CEM ENTERPRISES INC.; *U.S. Private*, pg. 808
CEMENTHAI HOLDING CO., LTD.—See The Siam Cement Public Company Limited; *Int'l*, pg. 7682
CEMENTHAI HOME SERVICES CO., LTD.—See The Siam Cement Public Company Limited; *Int'l*, pg. 7684
CEMENT HRANICE A.S.—See Buzzi SpA; *Int'l*, pg. 1230
CEMENTI CENTRO SUD SPA—See Vicat S.A.; *Int'l*, pg. 8185
CEMENTI CROTONE S.R.L.—See Titan Cement Company S.A.; *Int'l*, pg. 7759
CEMENT INDUSTRIES, INC.; *U.S. Private*, pg. 808
CEMENTIR DELTA S.P.A.—See Cementir Holding N.V.; *Int'l*, pg. 1397
CEMENTIR HOLDING N.V.; *Int'l*, pg. 1397
CEMENT MANUFACTURING CO. LTD—See Century Plyboards (I) Ltd.; *Int'l*, pg. 1419
CEMENT MARKET D.O.O.—See Nexe Grupa d.d.; *Int'l*, pg. 5243
CEMENTO BAYANO, S.A.—See CEMEX, S.A.B. de C.V.; *Int'l*, pg. 1398
CEMENTO POLPAICO S.A. - MEJILLONES GRINDING PLANT—See Cemento Polpaico S.A.; *Int'l*, pg. 1397
CEMENTO POLPAICO S.A.; *Int'l*, pg. 1397
CEMENTOS ARGOS S.A.—See Grupo Argos S.A.; *Int'l*, pg. 3120
CEMENTOS ARTIGAS S.A.—See Cementos Molins S.A.; *Int'l*, pg. 1397
CEMENTOS AVELLANEDA S.A.—See Cementos Molins S.A.; *Int'l*, pg. 1397
CEMENTOS BIO-BIO S.A.; *Int'l*, pg. 1397
CEMENTOS COSMOS S.A.—See Camargo Correa S.A.; *Int'l*, pg. 1267
CEMENTOS DE ANDALUCIA S.L.—See Camargo Correa C.A.; *Int'l*, pg. 1267
CEMENTOS FORTALEZA, S.A. DE C.V. - EL PALMAR PLANT—See Grupo Empresarial Kaluz S.A. de C.V.; *Int'l*, pg. 3126
CEMENTOS FORTALEZA, S.A. DE C.V. - TULA PLANT—See Grupo Empresarial Kaluz S.A. de C.V.; *Int'l*, pg. 3126
CEMENTOS FORTALEZA, S.A. DE C.V. - VITO PLANT—See Grupo Empresarial Kaluz S.A. de C.V.; *Int'l*, pg. 3126
CEMENTOS HISPANIA S.A.—See Buzzi SpA; *Int'l*, pg. 1230
CEMENTOS LA UNION-SPAIN SA—See Arabian Cement Company; *Int'l*, pg. 533
CEMENTOS MOLINS INDUSTRIAL, S.A.—See Cementos Molins S.A.; *Int'l*, pg. 1397
CEMENTOS MOLINS S.A.; *Int'l*, pg. 1397
CEMENTOS OTORONGO, S.A.C.—See Consorcio Cementero del Sur SA; *Int'l*, pg. 1772
CEMENTOS PACASMAYO S.A.A.; *Int'l*, pg. 1398
CEMENTOS PORTLAND VALDERRIVAS, S.A.—See Fomento de Construcciones y Contratas, S.A.; *Int'l*, pg. 2722
CEMENT OZAROW S.A.—See CRH plc; *Int'l*, pg. 1844
CEMENTRUM I B.V.—See Heidelberg Materials AG; *Int'l*, pg. 3309
CEMENTRUM II B.V.—See Heidelberg Materials AG; *Int'l*, pg. 3309
CEMENT SERVICES COMPANY S.A.E.—See Camargo Correa S.A.; *Int'l*, pg. 1267
CEMENT TRADING ACTIVITIES - COMERCIO INTERNACIONAL S.A.—See Camargo Correa S.A.; *Int'l*, pg. 1267
THE CEMENTWORKS, LLC; *U.S. Private*, pg. 4006
CEMEPE INVESTIMENTOS S.A.; *Int'l*, pg. 1398
CEME S.P.A—See Investindustrial Advisors Ltd.; *Int'l*, pg. 3779
CEMEX AB—See CEMEX, S.A.B. de C.V.; *Int'l*, pg. 1398
CEMEX ASIA HOLDINGS LTD.—See CEMEX, S.A.B. de C.V.; *Int'l*, pg. 1398
CEMEX ASIAN SOUTHEAST CORPORATION—See CEMEX, S.A.B. de C.V.; *Int'l*, pg. 1398
CEMEX AS—See CEMEX, S.A.B. de C.V.; *Int'l*, pg. 1398
CEMEX BRAZIL—See CEMEX, S.A.B. de C.V.; *Int'l*, pg. 1398
CEMEX CANADA—See CEMEX, S.A.B. de C.V.; *Int'l*, pg. 1399
CEMEX COLOMBIA, S.A.—See CEMEX, S.A.B. de C.V.; *Int'l*, pg. 1398
CEMEX CONCRETE PRODUCTS—See CEMEX, S.A.B. de C.V.; *Int'l*, pg. 1399
CEMEX CONSTRUCTION MATERIALS FLORIDA, LLC—See CEMEX, S.A.B. de C.V.; *Int'l*, pg. 1399
CEMEX CORP.—See CEMEX, S.A.B. de C.V.; *Int'l*, pg. 1399
CEMEX COSTA RICA S.A.—See CEMEX, S.A.B. de C.V.; *Int'l*, pg. 1398
CEMEX CZECH REPUBLIC K.S.—See CEMEX, S.A.B. de C.V.; *Int'l*, pg. 1398
CEMEX DE PUERTO RICO INC. - LIME DIVISION—See CEMEX, S.A.B. de C.V.; *Int'l*, pg. 1399
CEMEX DE PUERTO RICO INC.—See CEMEX, S.A.B. de C.V.; *Int'l*, pg. 1399
CEMEX DEUTSCHLAND AG—See CEMEX, S.A.B. de C.V.; *Int'l*, pg. 1398
CEMEX DOMINICANA, S.A.—See CEMEX, S.A.B. de C.V.; *Int'l*, pg. 1398
CEMEX EGYPT—See CEMEX, S.A.B. de C.V.; *Int'l*, pg. 1398
CEMEX EL SALVADOR S.A. DE C.V.—See CEMEX, S.A.B. de C.V.; *Int'l*, pg. 1399
CEMEX ESPANA S.A. - GADOR PLANT—See CEMEX, S.A.B. de C.V.; *Int'l*, pg. 1398
CEMEX ESPANA S.A.—See CEMEX, S.A.B. de C.V.; *Int'l*, pg. 1398
CEMEX FALCON LLC—See CEMEX, S.A.B. de C.V.; *Int'l*, pg. 1400
CEMEX FRANCE GESTION (S.A.S.)—See CEMEX, S.A.B. de C.V.; *Int'l*, pg. 1398
CEMEX FRANCE S.A.—See CEMEX, S.A.B. de C.V.; *Int'l*, pg. 1398
CEMEX GUATEMALA—See CEMEX, S.A.B. de C.V.; *Int'l*, pg. 1398
CEMEX HAITI S.A.—See CEMEX, S.A.B. de C.V.; *Int'l*, pg. 1398
CEMEX HOLDINGS (ISRAEL) LIMITED—See CEMEX, S.A.B. de C.V.; *Int'l*, pg. 1398
CEMEX HOLDINGS PHILIPPINES, INC.—See CEMEX, S.A.B. de C.V.; *Int'l*, pg. 1398
CEMEX HRVATSKA D.D.—See CEMEX, S.A.B. de C.V.; *Int'l*, pg. 1399
CEMEX, INC. - LAKELAND—See CEMEX, S.A.B. de C.V.; *Int'l*, pg. 1399
CEMEX, INC. - MCKELLINGTON CANYON—See CEMEX, S.A.B. de C.V.; *Int'l*, pg. 1399
CEMEX, INC. - MESA—See CEMEX, S.A.B. de C.V.; *Int'l*, pg. 1399
CEMEX, INC. - NAPLES—See CEMEX, S.A.B. de C.V.; *Int'l*, pg. 1399
CEMEX, INC.—See CEMEX, S.A.B. de C.V.; *Int'l*, pg. 1399
CEMEX INNOVATION HOLDING LTD.—See CEMEX, S.A.B. de C.V.; *Int'l*, pg. 1399
CEMEX JAMAICA LIMITED—See CEMEX, S.A.B. de C.V.; *Int'l*, pg. 1398
CEMEX LATAM HOLDINGS SA—See CEMEX, S.A.B. de C.V.; *Int'l*, pg. 1398
CEMEX MATERIALS LLC—See CEMEX, S.A.B. de C.V.; *Int'l*, pg. 1399
CEMEX MEXICO, S.A. DE C.V.—See CEMEX, S.A.B. de C.V.; *Int'l*, pg. 1399
CEMEX NETHERLANDS B.V.—See CEMEX, S.A.B. de C.V.; *Int'l*, pg. 1399
CEMEX NICARAGUA, S.A.—See CEMEX, S.A.B. de C.V.; *Int'l*, pg. 1399
CEMEX OY—See CEMEX, S.A.B. de C.V.; *Int'l*, pg. 1399
CEMEX PAVING SOLUTIONS LIMITED—See CEMEX, S.A.B. de C.V.; *Int'l*, pg. 1399
CEMEX POLSKA SP.Z.O.O.—See CEMEX, S.A.B. de C.V.; *Int'l*, pg. 1399
CEMEX READY MIXED CONCRETE (EAST MIDLANDS) LTD.—See CEMEX, S.A.B. de C.V.; *Int'l*, pg. 1399
CEMEX, S.A.B. DE C.V.; *Int'l*, pg. 1398
CEMEX SIA—See CEMEX, S.A.B. de C.V.; *Int'l*, pg. 1399
CEMEX SPECIALIST PRODUCTS—See CEMEX, S.A.B. de C.V.; *Int'l*, pg. 1399
CEMEX SUPERMIX LLC—See CEMEX, S.A.B. de C.V.; *Int'l*, pg. 1400
CEMEX TOPMIX LLC—See CEMEX, S.A.B. de C.V.; *Int'l*, pg. 1400
CEMEX UK MARINE LTD.—See CEMEX, S.A.B. de C.V.; *Int'l*, pg. 1399
CEMEX UK MATERIALS LIMITED—See CEMEX, S.A.B. de C.V.; *Int'l*, pg. 1399
CEMEX UK—See CEMEX, S.A.B. de C.V.; *Int'l*, pg. 1399
CEM GMBH—See CEM Corporation; *U.S. Private*, pg. 808
CEMIG DISTRIBUICAO S.A.—See Companhia Energetica de Minas Gerais - CEMIG; *Int'l*, pg. 1747
CEMIG GERACAO E TRANSMISSAO S.A.—See Companhia Energetica de Minas Gerais - CEMIG; *Int'l*, pg. 1747
CEMIG TELECOMUNICACOES S.A.—See Companhia Energetica de Minas Gerais - CEMIG; *Int'l*, pg. 1747
CEMIG TRADING S.A.—See Companhia Energetica de Minas Gerais - CEMIG; *Int'l*, pg. 1747
CEM INTERNATIONAL LTD.; *Int'l*, pg. 1396
CEMITALY S.P.A—See Heidelberg Materials AG; *Int'l*, pg. 3309
CEMIT INTERACTIVE MEDIA S.P.A.—See Fininvest S.p.A.; *Int'l*, pg. 2675
CEM JAPAN K.K.—See CEM Corporation; *U.S. Private*, pg. 808
CEMMAC AS; *Int'l*, pg. 1400
CEMM CO., LTD.—See Dowa Holdings Co., Ltd.; *Int'l*, pg. 2182

CEMMAC AS

CEM MICROWAVE TECHNOLOGY (IRELAND) LTD.—See CEM Corporation; *U.S. Private*, pg. 808
CEM MICROWAVE TECHNOLOGY LTD.—See CEM Corporation; *U.S. Private*, pg. 808
CEMM-MEX, S.A. DE C.V.—See Amphenol Corporation; *U.S. Public*, pg. 129
CEM MU WAVES S.A.S.—See CEM Corporation; *U.S. Private*, pg. 808
CEMOI CHOCOLATIER SAS; *Int'l*, pg. 1400
CEM SPECIALTIES INC.—See Kontrol Technologies Corp.; *Int'l*, pg. 4276
CEM S.R.L.—See CEM Corporation; *U.S. Private*, pg. 808
CEMSTONE PRODUCTS COMPANY INC.; *U.S. Private*, pg. 808
CEMSTONE READY MIX, INC.—See Cemstone Products Company Inc.; *U.S. Private*, pg. 808
CEMTAS CELIK MAKINA SANAYI TICARET A.S.—See Bursa Cimento Fabrikasi A.S.; *Int'l*, pg. 1227
CEMTAS CELIK MAKINA SANAYI VE TICARET A.S.; *Int'l*, pg. 1400
CEMTREX, INC.; *U.S. Public*, pg. 466
CENACCHI INT.I S.R.L.—See Dexelance S.p.A.; *Int'l*, pg. 2092
CENADRUCK GMBH—See palero capital GmbH; *Int'l*, pg. 5706
CEN-CAL FIRE SYSTEMS INC.—See The Carlyle Group Inc.; *U.S. Public*, pg. 2053
CENCAR LIMITED (CARREFOUR THAILAND)—See Carrefour SA; *Int'l*, pg. 1344
CEN CHINA EDUCATION NETWORK LTD.—See China Education Resources Inc.; *Int'l*, pg. 1499
CENCORA, INC.; *U.S. Public*, pg. 466
CENCORP AS—See Valoe Oyj; *Int'l*, pg. 8121
CENCOSUD ADMINISTRADORA DE TARJETAS S.A.—See Cencosud S.A.; *Int'l*, pg. 1400
CENCOSUD ADMINISTRADORA DE TARJETAS S.A.—See The Bank of Nova Scotia; *Int'l*, pg. 7618
CENCOSUD PERU S.A.—See Cencosud S.A.; *Int'l*, pg. 1400
CENCOSUD RETAIL S.A.—See Cencosud S.A.; *Int'l*, pg. 1400
CENCOSUD S.A.; *Int'l*, pg. 1400
CENCOSUD S.A.—See Cencosud S.A.; *Int'l*, pg. 1400
CENCOSUD SHOPPING CENTER S.A.—See Cencosud S.A.; *Int'l*, pg. 1400
CENCOSUD VIAJES ARGENTINA S.A.—See Cencosud S.A.; *Int'l*, pg. 1400
CENDANA SUTERA SDN. BHD.—See Dialog Group Berhad; *Int'l*, pg. 2104
CENDEE SDN. BHD.—See Censof Holdings Berhad; *Int'l*, pg. 1401
CENDERAMAN DEVELOPMENT SDN BHD—See Tambun Indah Land Berhad; *Int'l*, pg. 7449
CENDRILL SUPPLY PTY LIMITED—See Downer EDI Limited; *Int'l*, pg. 2185
CENDRIS CUSTOMER CONTACT B.V.—See PostNL N.V.; *Int'l*, pg. 5940
CENDRIS DOCUMENT PRESENTMENT B.V.—See PostNL N.V.; *Int'l*, pg. 5940
CENDROWSKI CORPORATE ADVISORS, LLC—See Unity Partners LP; *U.S. Public*, pg. 2253
CENDUIT GMBH—See IQVIA Holdings Inc.; *U.S. Public*, pg. 1168
CENDUIT (INDIA) SERVICES PRIVATE COMPANY LIMITED—See IQVIA Holdings Inc.; *U.S. Public*, pg. 1168
CENDUIT JAPAN GK—See IQVIA Holdings Inc.; *U.S. Public*, pg. 1168
CENDUIT LLC—See Thermo Fisher Scientific Inc.; *U.S. Public*, pg. 2145
CENDYN CORP.; *U.S. Private*, pg. 808
CENEFOM CORPORATION LIMITED—See BenQ Materials Corp.; *Int'l*, pg. 975
CENEL DEVELOPMENT CORPORATION—See Punch Industry Co., Ltd.; *Int'l*, pg. 6118
CENERGI SEA SDN BHD—See Khazanah Nasional Berhad; *Int'l*, pg. 4152
CENERGIST BV—See Eneraqua Technologies Plc; *Int'l*, pg. 2418
CENERGIST LIMITED—See Eneraqua Technologies Plc; *Int'l*, pg. 2418
CENERGIST SPAIN SL—See Eneraqua Technologies Plc; *Int'l*, pg. 2418
C-ENERGY BOHEMIA SRO—See Carpaterra Capital Partners sro; *Int'l*, pg. 1343
CENERGY COMMUNICATIONS, LLC; *U.S. Private*, pg. 808
CENERGY CORPORATION; *U.S. Private*, pg. 808
CENERGY CORP.; *U.S. Private*, pg. 808
CENERGY HOLDINGS SA; *Int'l*, pg. 1401
CENERGY INTERNATIONAL SERVICES, LLC—See First Tek, Inc.; *U.S. Private*, pg. 1529
CENERGY, LLC; *U.S. Private*, pg. 808
CENERGY PARTNERS LLC; *U.S. Private*, pg. 808
CENERO LLC—See Ricoh Company, Ltd.; *Int'l*, pg. 6336
CENEXEL CLINICAL RESEARCH, INC.; *U.S. Private*, pg. 809
CENEX ZIP TRIP—See CHS INC.; *U.S. Public*, pg. 492

CENGAGE HIGHER EDUCATION—See Apax Partners LLP; *Int'l*, pg. 503
CENGAGE HIGHER EDUCATION—See Apollo Global Management, Inc.; *U.S. Public*, pg. 168
CENGAGE HIGHER EDUCATION—See KKR & Co. Inc.; *U.S. Public*, pg. 1256
CENGAGE HIGHER EDUCATION—See Searchlight Capital Partners, L.P.; *U.S. Private*, pg. 3587
CENGAGE LEARNING ASIA—See Apax Partners LLP; *Int'l*, pg. 503
CENGAGE LEARNING ASIA—See Apollo Global Management, Inc.; *U.S. Public*, pg. 168
CENGAGE LEARNING ASIA—See KKR & Co. Inc.; *U.S. Public*, pg. 1256
CENGAGE LEARNING ASIA—See Searchlight Capital Partners, L.P.; *U.S. Private*, pg. 3587
CENGAGE LEARNING AUSTRALIA PTY. LIMITED—See Apax Partners LLP; *Int'l*, pg. 503
CENGAGE LEARNING AUSTRALIA PTY. LIMITED—See Apollo Global Management, Inc.; *U.S. Public*, pg. 168
CENGAGE LEARNING AUSTRALIA PTY. LIMITED—See KKR & Co. Inc.; *U.S. Public*, pg. 1256
CENGAGE LEARNING AUSTRALIA PTY. LIMITED—See Searchlight Capital Partners, L.P.; *U.S. Private*, pg. 3587
CENGAGE LEARNING HOLDINGS II, INC.—See Apax Partners LLP; *Int'l*, pg. 502
CENGAGE LEARNING HOLDINGS II, INC.—See Apollo Global Management, Inc.; *U.S. Public*, pg. 168
CENGAGE LEARNING HOLDINGS II, INC.—See KKR & Co. Inc.; *U.S. Public*, pg. 1256
CENGAGE LEARNING HOLDINGS II, INC.—See Searchlight Capital Partners, L.P.; *U.S. Private*, pg. 3587
CENGAGE LEARNING, INC.—See Apax Partners LLP; *Int'l*, pg. 502
CENGAGE LEARNING, INC.—See Apollo Global Management, Inc.; *U.S. Public*, pg. 168
CENGAGE LEARNING, INC.—See KKR & Co. Inc.; *U.S. Public*, pg. 1256
CENGAGE LEARNING, INC.—See Searchlight Capital Partners, L.P.; *U.S. Private*, pg. 3587
CENGEA SOLUTIONS INC—See Trimble, Inc.; *U.S. Public*, pg. 2190
CENGILD G.I. MEDICAL CENTRE; *Int'l*, pg. 1401
CENGIZ MAKINA SANAYI VE TICARET ANONIM SIRKETI—See Impro Precision Industries Limited; *Int'l*, pg. 3637
CENIBRA_CELLULOSE NIPO BRASILEIRO S.A.—See Vale S.A.; *Int'l*, pg. 8111
C.E. NIEHOFF & CO.; *U.S. Private*, pg. 706
CENIT AG; *Int'l*, pg. 1401
CENIT CO., LTD.; *Int'l*, pg. 1401
CENIT FRANCE SARL—See CENIT AG; *Int'l*, pg. 1401
CENIT JAPAN K. K.—See CENIT AG; *Int'l*, pg. 1401
CENIT NORTH AMERICA INC.—See CENIT AG; *Int'l*, pg. 1401
CENIT SCHWEIZ AG—See CENIT AG; *Int'l*, pg. 1401
CENIT S.R.L.—See CENIT AG; *Int'l*, pg. 1401
CENIT TRANSPORTE Y LOGISTICA DE HIDROCARBUROS S.A.S.—See Ecopetrol S.A.; *Int'l*, pg. 2298
CENLA BEVERAGE COMPANY, LLC—See Glazer's Family of Companies; *U.S. Private*, pg. 1707
CENLAR CAPITAL CORPORATION; *U.S. Private*, pg. 809
CENLUB INDUSTRIES LTD. - FARIDABAD PLANT -I—See Cenlub Industries Ltd.; *Int'l*, pg. 1401
CENLUB INDUSTRIES LTD.; *Int'l*, pg. 1401
CEN-MED ENTERPRISES, INC.; *U.S. Private*, pg. 808
CENNOX INC.; *U.S. Private*, pg. 809
CENNTRO ELECTRIC GROUP LIMITED; *Int'l*, pg. 1401
CENO MEMBRANE TECHNOLOGY GMBH—See SATTLER AG; *Int'l*, pg. 6587
CENOMI RETAIL; *Int'l*, pg. 1401
CENOTEC CO., LTD.; *Int'l*, pg. 1401
CENOVUS ENERGY INC.; *Int'l*, pg. 1401
CENPA S.A.S.—See Accursia Capital GmbH; *Int'l*, pg. 94
CENPATICO BEHAVIORAL HEALTH LLC—See Centene Corporation; *U.S. Public*, pg. 468
CENPATICO OF ARIZONA INC.—See Centene Corporation; *U.S. Public*, pg. 468
CENPOS, LLC—See U.S. Bancorp; *U.S. Public*, pg. 2212
CENSIS TECHNOLOGIES, INC.—See Fortive Corporation; *U.S. Public*, pg. 870
CENSOF HOLDINGS BERHAD; *Int'l*, pg. 1401
CEN SOLUTIONS CORP.—See CAC Holdings Corporation; *Int'l*, pg. 1247
CENSTAR ENERGY CORP.—See Via Renewables, Inc.; *U.S. Public*, pg. 2290
CENSTAR OPERATING COMPANY, LLC—See Via Renewables, Inc.; *U.S. Public*, pg. 2290
CENTA ANTRIEBE KIRSCHEY GMBH—See Zurn Elkay Water Solutions Corporation; *U.S. Public*, pg. 2413
CENTA CORPORATION—See Zurn Elkay Water Solutions Corporation; *U.S. Public*, pg. 2413
CENTAGE CORPORATION—See Scaleworks, Inc.; *U.S. Private*, pg. 3561
CENTAK CHEMICALS LTD.—See Akzo Nobel N.V.; *Int'l*, pg. 271
CENTAMIN EGYPT LIMITED—See Centamin plc; *Int'l*, pg. 1402

CENTAMIN GROUP SERVICES UK LIMITED—See Centamin plc; *Int'l*, pg. 1402
CENTAMIN PLC; *Int'l*, pg. 1402
CENTANA GROWTH PARTNERS, LLC—See Deutsche Borse AG; *U.S. Public*, pg. 2063
CENTAN INC.—See Macromill Embrain Co., Ltd.; *Int'l*, pg. 4632
CENTA NORDIC AB—See Zurn Elkay Water Solutions Corporation; *U.S. Public*, pg. 2413
CENTARA EHF; *Int'l*, pg. 1402
CENTARA VILLAS PHUKET—See Central Plaza Hotel Public Company Limited; *Int'l*, pg. 1409
CENTAR D.O.O.—See Zagrebacki holding d.o.o.; *Int'l*, pg. 8620
CENTARE GROUP, LTD.; *U.S. Private*, pg. 809
CENTARE HOLDINGS INC.—See Hadley Capital LLC; *U.S. Private*, pg. 1839
CENTAR KAPTOL DOO—See UniCredit S.p.A.; *Int'l*, pg. 8040
CENTAR ZA PUTEVE VOJVODINE A.D.; *Int'l*, pg. 1402
CENTA TRANSM. FAR EAST PTE LTD.—See Zurn Elkay Water Solutions Corporation; *U.S. Public*, pg. 2412
CENTA TRANSMISJONER A.S.—See Zurn Elkay Water Solutions Corporation; *U.S. Public*, pg. 2413
CENTA TRANSMISSIONER A/S—See Zurn Elkay Water Solutions Corporation; *U.S. Public*, pg. 2413
CENTA TRANSMISSIONI S.R.L.—See Zurn Elkay Water Solutions Corporation; *U.S. Public*, pg. 2413
CENTA TRANSMISSIONS FAR EAST PTE LTD.—See Zurn Elkay Water Solutions Corporation; *U.S. Public*, pg. 2413
CENTA TRANSMISSIONS LTD.—See Zurn Elkay Water Solutions Corporation; *U.S. Public*, pg. 2413
CENTA TRANSMISSIONS PTY LTD.—See Zurn Elkay Water Solutions Corporation; *U.S. Public*, pg. 2413
CENTAUR ACQUISITION, LLC—See Caesars Entertainment, Inc.; *U.S. Public*, pg. 420
CENTAUR BUILDING SERVICES, INC.; *U.S. Private*, pg. 809
CENTAUR CORPORATION; *U.S. Private*, pg. 809
CENTAURI HEALTH SOLUTIONS, INC.—See ABRY Partners, LLC; *U.S. Private*, pg. 41
CENTAUR IMPORT MOTORS (1977) LTD.; *Int'l*, pg. 1402
CENTAUR, INC.; *U.S. Private*, pg. 809
CENTAURI SOLUTIONS, LLC.; *U.S. Private*, pg. 809
CENTAURI SPECIALTY INSURANCE HOLDINGS INC.—See Quadrant Management, Inc.; *U.S. Private*, pg. 3316
CENTAURI TECHNOLOGIES, LP—See The Pritzker Group - Chicago, LLC; *U.S. Private*, pg. 4098
CENTAUR MEDIA PLC; *Int'l*, pg. 1402
CENTAUR SERVICES LTD.—See Cencora, Inc.; *U.S. Public*, pg. 467
CENTAUR TECHNOLOGY, INC.—See VIA Technologies, Inc.; *Int'l*, pg. 8183
CENTAURUS DIAMOND TECHNOLOGIES, INC.; *U.S. Public*, pg. 467
CENTAURUS ENERGY INC.; *Int'l*, pg. 1402
CENTAURUS METALS LIMITED; *Int'l*, pg. 1402
CENTBANK FINANCIAL SERVICES LIMITED—See Central Bank of India Limited; *Int'l*, pg. 1404
CENT BANK HOME FINANCE LIMITED—See Central Bank of India Limited; *Int'l*, pg. 1404
CENTECH GROUP INC.; *U.S. Private*, pg. 809
CENTEGRA HEALTH SYSTEM; *U.S. Private*, pg. 809
CENTEK INDUSTRIES INC—See Atlantic Gasket Corp.; *U.S. Private*, pg. 373
CENTELHA EQUIPAMENTOS ELETRICOS LTDA.—See Sonepar S.A.; *Int'l*, pg. 7090
CENTEN AG LLC—See Corteva, Inc.; *U.S. Public*, pg. 581
CENTENARI E ZINELLI SPA; *Int'l*, pg. 1402
CENTENARY INTERNATIONAL CORP.; *Int'l*, pg. 1402
CENTENARY UNITED HOLDINGS LIMITED; *Int'l*, pg. 1402
CENTENE CORPORATION; *U.S. Public*, pg. 467
CENTENE UK LIMITED—See Centene Corporation; *U.S. Public*, pg. 468
CENTENNIAL SURGICAL SUTURE LTD.; *Int'l*, pg. 1402
CENTENNIAL AIRLY PTY LIMITED—See Banpu Public Company Limited; *Int'l*, pg. 852
CENTENNIAL AMERICAN PROPERTIES, LLC; *U.S. Private*, pg. 809
CENTENNIAL ANGUS PLACE PTY LIMITED—See Banpu Public Company Limited; *Int'l*, pg. 852
CENTENNIAL ASC, L.P.—See Tenet Healthcare Corporation; *U.S. Public*, pg. 2002
CENTENNIAL AS—See Groupe Centennial Holding SAH; *Int'l*, pg. 3101
CENTENNIAL AUTOMOTIVE, LLC—See AutoNation, Inc.; *U.S. Public*, pg. 234
CENTENNIAL BANK—See Home BancShares, Inc.; *U.S. Public*, pg. 1045
CENTENNIAL CLARENCE PTY LIMITED—See Banpu Public Company Limited; *Int'l*, pg. 852
CENTENNIAL COAL COMPANY LIMITED—See Banpu Public Company Limited; *Int'l*, pg. 852
CENTENNIAL, COLORADO STORAGE & MOVING—See Johnson Storage & Moving Company; *U.S. Private*, pg. 2229

COMPANY NAME INDEX

CENTENNIAL CONTRACTORS ENTERPRISES, INC.—See Bilfinger SE; *Int'l*, pg. 1028
CENTENNIAL ENERGY HOLDINGS, INC.—See MDU Resources Group, Inc.; *U.S. Public*, pg. 1409
CENTENNIAL FOODSERVICE INC.—See Premium Brands Holdings Corporation; *Int'l*, pg. 5962
CENTENNIAL GAS LIQUIDS, ULC—See NGL Energy Partners LP; *U.S. Public*, pg. 1527
THE CENTENNIAL GROUP LLC; *U.S. Private*, pg. 4006
THE CENTENNIAL GROUP, LLC—See Genstar Capital, LLC; *U.S. Private*, pg. 1675
CENTENNIAL HEART, LLC—See HCA Healthcare, Inc.; *U.S. Public*, pg. 992
CENTENNIAL HOLDING COMPANY, LLC—See Century Communities, Inc.; *U.S. Public*, pg. 475
CENTENNIAL HOMES, INC.; *U.S. Private*, pg. 809
CENTENNIAL LEASING INC.; *U.S. Private*, pg. 809
CENTENNIAL LV, LLC—See DaVita Inc.; *U.S. Public*, pg. 636
CENTENNIAL MANDALONG PTY LIMITED—See Banpu Public Company Limited; *Int'l*, pg. 852
CENTENNIAL MANNERING PTY LIMITED—See Banpu Public Company Limited; *Int'l*, pg. 852
CENTENNIAL MEDICAL CENTER—See HCA Healthcare, Inc.; *U.S. Public*, pg. 992
CENTENNIAL MEDICAL GROUP INC; *U.S. Private*, pg. 809
CENTENNIAL MINING LIMITED; *Int'l*, pg. 1402
CENTENNIAL MUNMORAH PTY LIMITED—See Banpu Public Company Limited; *Int'l*, pg. 852
CENTENNIAL MYUNA PTY LIMITED—See Banpu Public Company Limited; *Int'l*, pg. 852
CENTENNIAL NEUROSCIENCE, LLC—See HCA Healthcare, Inc.; *U.S. Public*, pg. 992
CENTENNIAL NEWSTAN PTY LIMITED—See Banpu Public Company Limited; *Int'l*, pg. 852
CENTENNIAL OPTICAL LTD.; *Int'l*, pg. 1402
CENTENNIAL POWER, INC.—See Beowulf Energy LLC; *U.S. Private*, pg. 529
CENTENNIAL POWER, INC.—See NGP Energy Capital Management, LLC; *U.S. Private*, pg. 2924
CENTENNIAL PRIMARY CARE, LLC—See HCA Healthcare, Inc.; *U.S. Public*, pg. 992
CENTENNIAL PROPERTIES, INC. See Cowles Company; *U.S. Private*, pg. 1073
CENTENNIAL PSYCHIATRIC ASSOCIATES, LLC—See HCA Healthcare, Inc.; *U.S. Public*, pg. 992
CENTENNIAL RESOURCE PRODUCTION, LLC—See Permian Resources Corp; *U.S. Public*, pg. 1677
CENTENNIAL STEEL—See Consolidated Fabricators Corp; *U.S. Private*, pg. 1020
CENTENNIAL SURETY ASSOCIATES, INC.—See GTCR LLC; *U.S. Private*, pg. 1802
CENTENNIAL SURGERY CENTER, L.P.—See HCA Healthcare, Inc.; *U.S. Public*, pg. 992
CENTENNIAL SURGICAL ASSOCIATES, LLC—See HCA Healthcare, Inc.; *U.S. Public*, pg. 992
CENTENNIAL SURGICAL CLINIC, LLC—See HCA Healthcare, Inc.; *U.S. Public*, pg. 992
CENTENNIAL WINDOWS & DOORS; *Int'l*, pg. 1402
CENTERAC TECHNOLOGIES LTD.; *Int'l*, pg. 1403
CENTERA PHOTONICS INC.—See Elite Advanced Laser Corporation; *Int'l*, pg. 2362
THE CENTER AT SLATTEN RANCH, LLC—See Regency Centers Corporation; *U.S. Public*, pg. 1774
CENTERBRIDGE PARTNERS, L.P.; *U.S. Private*, pg. 811
CENTER BROTHERS INCORPORATED; *U.S. Private*, pg. 809
CENTER CAPITAL GENERAL AVIATION DIVISION—See Webster Financial Corporation; *U.S. Public*, pg. 2341
CENTERCHEM, INC.—See LeBaronBrown Industries LLC; *U.S. Private*, pg. 2409
CENTER CLUB, INC.—See BNP Paribas SA; *Int'l*, pg. 1087
CENTER COMMUNICATION SYSTEMS BVBA/SPRL—See STRABAG SE; *Int'l*, pg. 7230
CENTER COMMUNICATION SYSTEMS GMBH—See STRABAG SE; *Int'l*, pg. 7230
CENTER CUT HOSPITALITY, INC.—See Catterton Management Company, LLC; *U.S. Private*, pg. 793
CENTER D'ESSAIS FERROVIAIRES SA—See Alstom S.A.; *Int'l*, pg. 383
CENTERFIELD CAPITAL PARTNERS, LLC; *U.S. Private*, pg. 816
CENTERFIELD MEDIA HOLDINGS, LLC—See Platinum Equity, LLC; *U.S. Private*, pg. 3201
CENTERFIRE REAL ESTATE; *U.S. Private*, pg. 816
CENTER FOR ADULT HEALTHCARE, LLC—See Community Health Systems, Inc.; *U.S. Public*, pg. 552
CENTER FOR ADVANCED DIAGNOSTICS LLC—See HCA Healthcare, Inc.; *U.S. Public*, pg. 992
CENTER FOR AIDS RESEARCH, EDUCATION AND SERVICES; *U.S. Private*, pg. 809
CENTER FOR AMBULATORY SURGERY, LLC—See KKR & Co. Inc.; *U.S. Public*, pg. 1245
THE CENTER FOR AMBULATORY SURGICAL TREATMENT, L.P.—See Tenet Healthcare Corporation; *U.S. Public*, pg. 2013

CENTER FOR AMERICAN PROGRESS; *U.S. Private*, pg. 809
CENTER FOR AUTISM AND RELATED DISORDERS, LLC—See Blackstone Inc.; *U.S. Public*, pg. 352
CENTER FOR COMMUNITY CHANGE; *U.S. Private*, pg. 810
THE CENTER FOR COMPREHENSIVE CARE & DIAGNOSIS OF INHERITED BLOOD DISORDERS; *U.S. Private*, pg. 4006
CENTER FOR COMPUTER RESOURCES, LLC; *U.S. Private*, pg. 810
CENTER FOR CREATIVE LEADERSHIP (CCL) PTE LTD—See Center for Creative Leadership Inc.; *U.S. Private*, pg. 810
CENTER FOR CREATIVE LEADERSHIP INC.; *U.S. Private*, pg. 810
CENTER FOR DIAGNOSTIC IMAGING, INC.—See Wellspring Capital Management LLC; *U.S. Private*, pg. 4477
CENTER FOR DISABILITY SERVICES, INC.; *U.S. Private*, pg. 810
CENTER FOR DISEASE DETECTION, LLC—See Laboratory Corporation of America Holdings; *U.S. Public*, pg. 1285
CENTER FOR EDUCATIONAL INNOVATION - PUBLIC EDUCATION ASSOCIATION; *U.S. Private*, pg. 810
CENTER FOR ELDERS' INDEPENDENCE; *U.S. Private*, pg. 810
CENTER FOR EMERGENCY MEDICINE OF WESTERN PA INC.; *U.S. Private*, pg. 810
CENTER FOR EMPLOYMENT OPPORTUNITIES INC; *U.S. Private*, pg. 810
CENTER FOR EMPLOYMENT TRAINING INC.; *U.S. Private*, pg. 810
THE CENTER FOR EXECUTIVE OPTIONS—See Adecco Group AG; *Int'l*, pg. 139
THE CENTER FOR FAMILY SUPPORT; *U.S. Private*, pg. 4006
CENTER FOR GLOBAL DEVELOPMENT; *U.S. Private*, pg. 810
CENTER FOR HOSPICE CARE; *U.S. Private*, pg. 810
CENTER FOR INDEPENDENCE OF THE DISABLED, NEW YORK; *U.S. Private*, pg. 810
CENTER FOR INDEPENDENT LIVING; *U.S. Private*, pg. 810
THE CENTER FOR INNOVATION, EXCELLENCE & LEADERSHIP; *U.S. Private*, pg. 4006
CENTER FOR INNOVATIVE TECHNOLOGY; *U.S. Private*, pg. 810
CENTER FOR INTERNATIONAL PRIVATE ENTERPRISE; *U.S. Private*, pg. 810
CENTER FOR INVESTIGATIVE REPORTING, INC.; *U.S. Private*, pg. 810
CENTER FOR MAINE CONTEMPORARY ART; *U.S. Private*, pg. 810
CENTER FOR MEDICAL INTEROPERABILITY, INC.—See Community Health Systems, Inc.; *U.S. Public*, pg. 552
CENTER FOR OCCUPATIONAL MEDICINE, LLC—See HCA Healthcare, Inc.; *U.S. Public*, pg. 992
CENTER FOR ORGAN RECOVERY & EDUCATION; *U.S. Private*, pg. 811
CENTER FOR PEOPLE IN NEED, INC.; *U.S. Private*, pg. 811
THE CENTER FOR REPRODUCTIVE RIGHTS, INC.; *U.S. Private*, pg. 4006
CENTER FOR RETINA AND MACULAR DISEASE; *U.S. Private*, pg. 811
CENTER FOR SIGHT, P.L.; *U.S. Private*, pg. 811
CENTER FOR SOCIAL CHANGE; *U.S. Private*, pg. 811
THE CENTER FOR SPECIALIZED SURGERY, LP—See Bain Capital, LP; *U.S. Private*, pg. 447
THE CENTER FOR SPECIAL SURGERY AT TCA—See HCA Healthcare, Inc.; *U.S. Public*, pg. 1008
THE CENTER FOR SPECIAL SURGERY, LLC—See Bain Capital, LP; *U.S. Private*, pg. 447
CENTER FOR SPECIAL SURGERY—See HCA Healthcare, Inc.; *U.S. Public*, pg. 993
THE CENTER FOR STUDYING HEALTH SYSTEM CHANGE INC.—See Mathematica Inc.; *U.S. Private*, pg. 2610
CENTER FOR SUSTAINABLE ENERGY; *U.S. Private*, pg. 811
CENTER FOR TALENT REPORTING, INC—See ROI Institute, Inc.; *U.S. Private*, pg. 3473
CENTER FOR THE ADVANCEMENT OF SCIENCE IN SPACE, INC.; *U.S. Private*, pg. 811
THE CENTER FOR TOXICOLOGY & ENVIRONMENTAL HEALTH, LLC—See Montrose Environmental Group, Inc.; *U.S. Public*, pg. 1466
CENTER FOR TRANSPORTATION SAFETY, LLC—See Onity Group Inc.; *U.S. Public*, pg. 1605
CENTER FOR VEIN RESTORATION—See Cortec Group Management Services, LLC; *U.S. Private*, pg. 1060
CENTERGATE CAPITAL, LP; *U.S. Private*, pg. 816
CENTERGISTIC SOLUTIONS, INC.; *U.S. Private*, pg. 816
CENTER ICE DELMONT, LLC—See Blackstreet Capital Holdings LLC; *U.S. Private*, pg. 576
CENTER INDEPENDENT OIL COMPANY; *U.S. Private*, pg. 811

CENTERSTONE OF AMERICA, INC.

CENTER INTERNATIONAL GROUP CO LTD; *Int'l*, pg. 1402
CENTER-INVEST BANK PJSC; *Int'l*, pg. 1403
CENTER INVEST KFT.—See Immofinanz AG; *Int'l*, pg. 3628
CENTERLIGHT HEALTH SYSTEM; *U.S. Private*, pg. 816
CENTERLINE DRIVERS, LLC—See TrueBlue, Inc.; *U.S. Public*, pg. 2198
CENTER LINE ELECTRIC INC.; *U.S. Public*, pg. 811
CENTERLINE HOMES, INC.; *U.S. Private*, pg. 816
CENTERLINE MACHINE, INC.—See Dielectric Corporation; *U.S. Private*, pg. 1228
CENTERLINE MACHINING & GRINDING, INC.; *U.S. Private*, pg. 816
CENTERLINE SOLUTIONS LLC; *U.S. Private*, pg. 816
CENTER LINE; *U.S. Private*, pg. 811
CENTER LINE WHEELS, INC.; *U.S. Public*, pg. 811
CENTEROAK PARTNERS LLC; *U.S. Private*, pg. 816
CENTER OF INSURANCE—See Houchens Industries, Inc.; *U.S. Private*, pg. 1989
CENTERONE FINANCIAL SERVICES, LLC—See JM Family Enterprises Inc.; *U.S. Private*, pg. 2214
CENTER PARCS EUROPE NV—See Pierre & Vacances SA; *Int'l*, pg. 5864
CENTER PARCS (OPERATING COMPANY) LIMITED—See Brookfield Corporation; *Int'l*, pg. 1187
CENTERPLAN CONSTRUCTION COMPANY; *U.S. Private*, pg. 816
CENTERPLATE, INC.—See Sodexo S.A.; *Int'l*, pg. 7045
CENTERPOINT AMBULATORY SURGERY CENTER—See HCA Healthcare, Inc.; *U.S. Public*, pg. 993
CENTERPOINT CARDIOLOGY SERVICES, LLC—See HCA Healthcare, Inc.; *U.S. Public*, pg. 993
CENTERPOINT CLINIC OF BLUE SPRINGS, LLC—See HCA Healthcare, Inc.; *U.S. Public*, pg. 993
CENTER POINT DEVELOPMENT INC.—See Mitsubishi HC Capital Inc.; *Int'l*, pg. 4950
CENTERPOINTE COMMUNITY BASED SERVICES, LLC—See Acadia Healthcare Company, Inc.; *U.S. Public*, pg. 28
CENTERPOINT ENERGY, INC.; *U.S. Public*, pg. 471
CENTERPOINT ENERGY MISSISSIPPI RIVER TRANSMISSION CORPORATION—See CenterPoint Energy, Inc.; *U.S. Public*, pg. 471
CENTERPOINT ENERGY SERVICES, INC.—See CenterPoint Energy, Inc.; *U.S. Public*, pg. 471
CENTERPOINT ENERGY—See CenterPoint Energy, Inc.; *U.S. Public*, pg. 471
CENTERPOINT ENERGY—See CenterPoint Energy, Inc.; *U.S. Public*, pg. 471
CENTERPOINT HEALTH INC; *U.S. Private*, pg. 817
CENTERPOINT HOSPITAL BASED PHYSICIANS, LLC—See HCA Healthcare, Inc.; *U.S. Public*, pg. 993
CENTERPOINT MEDICAL CENTER OF INDEPENDENCE, LLC—See HCA Healthcare, Inc.; *U.S. Public*, pg. 993
CENTERPOINT ORTHOPEDICS, LLC—See HCA Healthcare, Inc.; *U.S. Public*, pg. 993
CENTERPOINT PHYSICIANS GROUP, LLC—See HCA Healthcare, Inc.; *U.S. Public*, pg. 993
CENTERPOINT PROPERTIES TRUST; *U.S. Private*, pg. 817
C ENTERPRISES, L.P.—See RF Industries, Ltd.; *U.S. Public*, pg. 1796
CENTERPULSE AUSTRALIA PTY LTD; *Int'l*, pg. 1403
CENTERRA GOLD INC.; *Int'l*, pg. 1403
CENTERRA GROUP, LLC—See Apollo Global Management, Inc.; *U.S. Public*, pg. 150
THE CENTER: RESOURCES FOR TEACHING AND LEARNING; *U.S. Private*, pg. 4006
CENTER ROCK CAPITAL PARTNERS, LP; *U.S. Private*, pg. 811
CENTER ROCK, INC.—See Sverica Capital Management LP; *U.S. Private*, pg. 3888
CENTERS FOR DIALYSIS CARE; *U.S. Private*, pg. 817
THE CENTERS FOR FAMILIES AND CHILDREN; *U.S. Private*, pg. 4006
CENTERS FOR YOUTH & FAMILIES, INC.; *U.S. Private*, pg. 817
CENTERSPACE; *U.S. Public*, pg. 472
CENTERSQUARE INVESTMENT MANAGEMENT HOLDINGS, INC.—See Lovell Minnick Partners LLC; *U.S. Private*, pg. 2501
CENTERSQUARE INVESTMENT MANAGEMENT, INC.—See Lovell Minnick Partners LLC; *U.S. Private*, pg. 2501
CENTERSTONE INSURANCE & FINANCIAL SERVICES, INC.—See Truist Financial Corporation; *U.S. Public*, pg. 2199
CENTERSTONE INVESTOR, INC.—See Kuwait Projects Company (Holding) K.S.C.P.; *Int'l*, pg. 4346
CENTERSTONE OF AMERICA, INC.; *U.S. Private*, pg. 817
CENTERSTONE OF FLORIDA, INC.—See Centerstone of America, Inc.; *U.S. Private*, pg. 817
CENTERSTONE OF ILLINOIS, INC.—See Centerstone of America, Inc.; *U.S. Private*, pg. 817
CENTERSTONE OF INDIANA, INC.—See Centerstone of America, Inc.; *U.S. Private*, pg. 817

CENTERSTONE OF AMERICA, INC.

CORPORATE AFFILIATIONS

CENTERSTONE TECHNOLOGIES, INC.—See ONEX Corporation; *Int'l*, pg. 5578
CENTER STREET DP MEDICAL CENTER LLC—See Adeptus Health Inc.; *U.S. Private*, pg. 78
CENTER SUBARU—See GMST, LLC; *U.S. Private*, pg. 1723
CENTER SYSTEMS (DEUTSCHLAND) GMBH—See STRABAG SE; *Int'l*, pg. 7230
CENTER THEATRE GROUP OF LOS ANGELES, INC.; *U.S. Private*, pg. 811
CENTERVIEW CAPITAL, L.P.—See Centerview Partners LLC; *U.S. Private*, pg. 817
CENTERVIEW PARTNERS LLC; *U.S. Private*, pg. 817
CENTERVIEW PARTNERS MANAGEMENT LLC—See Centerview Partners LLC; *U.S. Private*, pg. 817
CENTERWATCH—See Leonard Green & Partners, L.P.; *U.S. Private*, pg. 2429
CENTERWELL SENIOR PRIMARY CARE (FL), INC.—See Humana, Inc.; *U.S. Public*, pg. 1069
CENTE SERVICE CORP.—See Tohokushinsha Film Corporation; *Int'l*, pg. 7777
CENTESSA PHARMACEUTICALS PLC; *Int'l*, pg. 1403
CENTEVO AB—See PROFILE SYSTEMS & SOFTWARE S.R.L.; *Int'l*, pg. 5989
CENTEX HOUSE LEVELING; *U.S. Private*, pg. 817
CENTEX MATERIALS LLC—See Eagle Materials Inc.; *U.S. Public*, pg. 702
CENTIA TECHNOLOGIES SDN BHD—See Digilife Technologies Limited; *Int'l*, pg. 2119
CENTIER BANK INC.—See First Bancshares Inc.; *U.S. Private*, pg. 1513
CENTIGON BRAZIL—See Capital People S.A.; *Int'l*, pg. 1312
CENTIGON COLOMBIA—See Capital People S.A.; *Int'l*, pg. 1312
CENTIGON FRANCE—See Capital People S.A.; *Int'l*, pg. 1312
CENTIGON MEXICO—See Capital People S.A.; *Int'l*, pg. 1312
CENTIGON—See Capital People S.A.; *Int'l*, pg. 1312
CENTIGON VENEZUELA—See Capital People S.A.; *Int'l*, pg. 1312
CENTIMARK CORPORATION - QUESTMARK FLOORING DIVISION—See Centimark Corporation; *U.S. Private*, pg. 817
CENTIMARK CORPORATION; *U.S. Private*, pg. 817
CENTIMARK LTD.—See Centimark Corporation; *U.S. Private*, pg. 817
CENTINEL BANK OF TAOS; *U.S. Private*, pg. 817
CENTIQ LIMITED—See SoftwareONE Holding AG; *Int'l*, pg. 7057
CENTOGENE N.V.; *Int'l*, pg. 1403
CENTON ELECTRONICS, INC.; *U.S. Private*, pg. 818
CENTOR ENERGY, INC.; *U.S. Private*, pg. 818
CENTORK VALVE CONTROL S.L.—See Rotork Plc; *Int'l*, pg. 6405
CENTORR VACUUM INDUSTRIES, INC.; *U.S. Private*, pg. 818
CENTOSTAZIONI S.P.A.—See Altarea SCA; *Int'l*, pg. 385
CENTRA 2000, INC.—See Auto-trol Technology Corporation; *U.S. Private*, pg. 398
CENTRABAIL SA—See Dexia SA; *Int'l*, pg. 2092
CENTRABANC CORPORATION; *U.S. Private*, pg. 818
CENTRACARE HEALTH FOUNDATION; *U.S. Private*, pg. 818
CENTRACOMM COMMUNICATIONS, LTD.; *U.S. Private*, pg. 818
CENTRADE CHEIL ADRIATIC D.O.O.—See Samsung BioLogics Co., Ltd.; *Int'l*, pg. 6510
CENTRADE CHEIL HU KFT.—See Samsung BioLogics Co., Ltd.; *Int'l*, pg. 6510
CENTRADE INTEGRATED S.R.L.—See Samsung BioLogics Co., Ltd.; *Int'l*, pg. 6510
CENTRAFARM B.V.—See Bain Capital, LP; *U.S. Private*, pg. 443
CENTRAFARM B.V.—See Cinven Limited; *Int'l*, pg. 1613
CENTRAFARM NEDERLAND B.V.—See Bain Capital, LP; *U.S. Private*, pg. 443
CENTRAFARM NEDERLAND B.V.—See Cinven Limited; *Int'l*, pg. 1613
CENTRAFARM PHARMACEUTICALS B.V.—See Bain Capital, LP; *U.S. Private*, pg. 443
CENTRAFARM PHARMACEUTICALS B.V.—See Cinven Limited; *Int'l*, pg. 1613
CENTRAFIN PROPRIETARY LIMITED—See Alviva Holdings Limited; *Int'l*, pg. 402
CENTRA, INC.; *U.S. Private*, pg. 818
CENTRA INDUSTRIES INC.—See Berkshire Hathaway Inc.; *U.S. Public*, pg. 314
CENTRAIR ENERGY SUPPLY CO., LTD.—See Chubu Electric Power Co., Inc.; *Int'l*, pg. 1593
CENTRAIS ELETRICAS BRASILEIRAS S.A.; *Int'l*, pg. 1403
CENTRAIS ELETRICAS DA PARAIBA S.A.—See State Grid Corporation of China; *Int'l*, pg. 7182
CENTRAIS ELETRICAS DE SANTA CATARINA S.A. - CELESC; *Int'l*, pg. 1403

CENTRAIS ELETRICAS DO NORTE DO BRASIL SA—See Centrais Eletricas Brasileiras S.A.; *Int'l*, pg. 1403
CENTRAK, INC.—See Halma plc; *Int'l*, pg. 3231
CENTRAL ADMIXTURE PHARMACY SERVICES, INC.—See B. Braun Melsungen AG; *Int'l*, pg. 787
CENTRAL A.D.; *Int'l*, pg. 1403
CENTRAL ALABAMA ELECTRIC COOPERATIVE; *U.S. Private*, pg. 818
CENTRAL ALABAMA TRANSPORT, INC.—See Coral Industries, Inc.; *U.S. Private*, pg. 1046
CENTRAL ALBERTA CO-OP LTD.; *Int'l*, pg. 1404
CENTRAL ALLIED ENTERPRISES - MASSILLON WASHED GRAVEL DIVISION—See Central Allied Enterprises; *U.S. Private*, pg. 818
CENTRAL ALLIED ENTERPRISES; *U.S. Private*, pg. 818
CENTRAL ALUMINIUM MANUFACTORY SDN. BHD.—See CAM Resources Berhad; *Int'l*, pg. 1267
CENTRAL ALUMINUM SUPPLY CORP.—See Installed Building Products, Inc.; *U.S. Public*, pg. 1132
CENTRAL ANALYSIS BUREAU, INC.—See Aurora Capital Group, LLC; *U.S. Private*, pg. 394
CENTRALAND LIMITED; *Int'l*, pg. 1404
CENTRALA PEKAO FACTORING SP. Z O.O.—See Bank Polska Kasa Opieki Spolka Akcyjna; *Int'l*, pg. 849
CENTRAL AREA COUNCIL—See Dairy Farmers of America, Inc.; *U.S. Private*, pg. 1145
CENTRAL AREA ELECTRICAL MECHANICAL JOINT STOCK COMPANY; *Int'l*, pg. 1404
CENTRAL ARKANSAS PETROLEUM INC.; *U.S. Private*, pg. 818
CENTRAL ARKANSAS RADIATION THERAPY INSTITUTE INC; *U.S. Private*, pg. 818
CENTRAL ARKANSAS REHABILITATION ASSOCIATES, L.P.—See Encompass Health Corporation; *U.S. Public*, pg. 754
CENTRAL ASIA CEMENT JSC—See Steppe Cement Ltd.; *Int'l*, pg. 7208
CENTRAL ASIA DEVELOPMENT GROUP, INC.; *Int'l*, pg. 1404
CENTRAL ASIA METALS PLC; *Int'l*, pg. 1404
CENTRAL ASIAN ELECTRIC POWER CORPORATION JSC—See Central-Asian Power Energy Company JSC; *Int'l*, pg. 1410
CENTRAL ASIAN MINERALS & RESOURCES PLC; *Int'l*, pg. 1404
CENTRAL-ASIAN POWER ENERGY COMPANY JSC; *Int'l*, pg. 1410
CENTRAL AUTO BODY REBUILDERS, INC.; *U.S. Private*, pg. 818
CENTRAL AUTOMOTIVE PRODUCTS LTD.; *Int'l*, pg. 1404
CENTRAL AUTO PARTS (SHANGHAI) CO., LTD.—See Motorcar Parts of America, Inc.; *U.S. Public*, pg. 1477
CENTRAL AZUCARERA DE TARLAC, INC.—See CAT Resource & Asset Holdings, Inc.; *Int'l*, pg. 1358
CENTRAL BAG COMPANY; *U.S. Private*, pg. 819
CENTRAL BANCOMPANY, INC.; *U.S. Public*, pg. 472
CENTRAL BANCSHARES, INC.; *U.S. Private*, pg. 819
CENTRAL BANK CORPORATION; *U.S. Private*, pg. 819
CENTRAL BANK & FINANCIAL SERVICES AUTHORITY OF IRELAND; *Int'l*, pg. 1404
CENTRAL BANK OF ARMENIA; *Int'l*, pg. 1404
CENTRAL BANK OF AUDRAIN COUNTY—See Central Bancompany, Inc.; *U.S. Public*, pg. 472
CENTRAL BANK OF BAHRAIN; *Int'l*, pg. 1404
CENTRAL BANK OF BARBADOS; *Int'l*, pg. 1404
CENTRAL BANK OF BELIZE; *Int'l*, pg. 1404
CENTRAL BANK OF EGYPT; *Int'l*, pg. 1404
CENTRAL BANK OF INDIA LIMITED; *Int'l*, pg. 1404
CENTRAL BANK OF IRAQ; *Int'l*, pg. 1404
CENTRAL BANK OF JORDAN; *Int'l*, pg. 1404
CENTRAL BANK OF KENYA; *Int'l*, pg. 1404
CENTRAL BANK OF KUWAIT; *Int'l*, pg. 1404
CENTRAL BANK OF LAKE OF THE OZARKS—See Central Bancompany, Inc.; *U.S. Public*, pg. 472
CENTRAL BANK OF LESOTHO; *Int'l*, pg. 1404
CENTRAL BANK OF LIBYA; *Int'l*, pg. 1404
CENTRAL BANK OF NIGERIA; *Int'l*, pg. 1405
CENTRAL BANK OF OKLAHOMA—See Central Bancompany, Inc.; *U.S. Public*, pg. 472
CENTRAL BANK OF OMAN; *Int'l*, pg. 1405
CENTRAL BANK OF SAMOA; *Int'l*, pg. 1405
CENTRAL BANK OF SEYCHELLES; *Int'l*, pg. 1405
CENTRAL BANK OF SOLOMON ISLANDS; *Int'l*, pg. 1405
CENTRAL BANK OF SRI LANKA; *Int'l*, pg. 1405
CENTRAL BANK OF ST. LOUIS—See Central Bancompany, Inc.; *U.S. Public*, pg. 472
CENTRAL BANK OF SWAZILAND; *Int'l*, pg. 1405
THE CENTRAL BANK OF THE BAHAMAS; *Int'l*, pg. 7631
CENTRAL BANK OF THE MIDWEST—See Central Bancompany, Inc.; *U.S. Public*, pg. 472
CENTRAL BANK OF THE RUSSIAN FEDERATION; *Int'l*, pg. 1405
CENTRAL BANK OF THE UNITED ARAB EMIRATES; *Int'l*, pg. 1405
CENTRAL BANK OF THE UNITED REPUBLIC OF TANZANIA; *Int'l*, pg. 1405

CENTRAL BANK OF TRINIDAD & TOBAGO; *Int'l*, pg. 1405
CENTRAL BANK; *U.S. Private*, pg. 819
CENTRAL BANK—See Central Bank Corporation; *U.S. Private*, pg. 819
CENTRAL BANK—See Central Financial Holdings, Inc.; *U.S. Private*, pg. 820
CENTRAL BANK—See Commercial Financial Corp.; *U.S. Private*, pg. 983
CENTRAL BANK; *U.S. Private*, pg. 819
CENTRAL BANK & TRUST CO.; *U.S. Private*, pg. 819
CENTRAL BAPTIST VILLAGE; *U.S. Private*, pg. 819
CENTRAL BEEF IND., L.L.C.; *U.S. Private*, pg. 819
CENTRAL BERING SEA FISHERMEN'S ASSOCIATION; *U.S. Private*, pg. 819
CENTRAL BLACKTOP CO., INC.; *U.S. Private*, pg. 819
CENTRAL BOATING (PTY) LTD—See Cullinan Holdings Limited; *Int'l*, pg. 1877
CENTRAL BOEKI CALIF., LTD.—See Kamei Corporation; *Int'l*, pg. 4061
CENTRAL BOMBAY CABLE NETWORK LIMITED—See Essel Corporate Resources Pvt. Ltd.; *Int'l*, pg. 2509
CENTRAL BUD SP. Z O. O—See Immofinanz AG; *Int'l*, pg. 3628
CENTRAL BUICK GMC OF NORWOOD; *U.S. Private*, pg. 819
CENTRAL BUILDING LTD.—See Hong Kong Land Holdings Ltd.; *Int'l*, pg. 3466
CENTRAL BUSINESS SYSTEMS INC.—See Advanced Business Methods Inc.; *U.S. Private*, pg. 88
CENTRALBYGGARNA I AKERSBERGA AB—See Sdiptech AB; *Int'l*, pg. 6658
CENTRAL CABLE LIMITED—See Liberty Global plc; *Int'l*, pg. 4486
CENTRAL CABLE LIMITED—See Telefonica, S.A.; *Int'l*, pg. 7536
CENTRAL CADILLAC; *U.S. Private*, pg. 819
CENTRAL CALIFORNIA CHILD DEVELOPMENT SERVICES, INC.; *U.S. Private*, pg. 819
CENTRAL CALIFORNIA TRACTION COMPANY—See Berkshire Hathaway Inc.; *U.S. Public*, pg. 303
CENTRAL CALIFORNIA TRUCK AND TRAILER SALES, LLC—See Rush Enterprises, Inc.; *U.S. Public*, pg. 1826
CENTRAL CAL TRANSPORTATION, LLC—See Universal Logistics Holdings, Inc.; *U.S. Public*, pg. 2261
CENTRAL CARBON CO., LTD.—See Nippon Carbon Co., Ltd.; *Int'l*, pg. 5311
CENTRAL CAROLINA AMBULATORY SURGERY CENTER, LLC—See Apollo Global Management, Inc.; *U.S. Public*, pg. 155
CENTRAL CAROLINA-CIM, L.L.C.—See Apollo Global Management, Inc.; *U.S. Public*, pg. 155
CENTRAL CAROLINA DIALYSIS CENTERS, LLC—See DaVita Inc.; *U.S. Public*, pg. 636
CENTRAL CAROLINA-IMA, L.L.C.—See Apollo Global Management, Inc.; *U.S. Public*, pg. 155
CENTRAL CAROLINA SECURITY—See The Philadelphia Contributionship; *U.S. Private*, pg. 4094
CENTRAL CEILING PARTITION INC.; *U.S. Private*, pg. 819
CENTRAL CHALLENGER (M) SDN. BHD.—See Puncak Niaga Holdings Berhad; *Int'l*, pg. 6118
CENTRAL CHEMICAL CO., LTD.—See Central Glass Co., Ltd.; *Int'l*, pg. 1406
CENTRAL CHEVROLET COMPANY INC.; *U.S. Private*, pg. 819
CENTRAL CHINA EQUITY EXCHANGE CO., LTD.—See Central China Securities Co., Ltd.; *Int'l*, pg. 1405
CENTRAL CHINA INTERNATIONAL LEASING COMPANY LIMITED—See Oversea-Chinese Banking Corporation Limited; *Int'l*, pg. 5671
CENTRAL CHINA LAND MEDIA CO., LTD.; *Int'l*, pg. 1405
CENTRAL CHINA MANAGEMENT COMPANY LIMITED; *Int'l*, pg. 1405
CENTRAL CHINA NEW LIFE LIMITED; *Int'l*, pg. 1405
CENTRAL CHINA REAL ESTATE LIMITED; *Int'l*, pg. 1405
CENTRAL CHINA SECURITIES CO., LTD.; *Int'l*, pg. 1405
CENTRAL CHRYSLER JEEP DODGE; *U.S. Private*, pg. 819
CENTRAL CIRCLE CO.—See HORIBA Ltd; *Int'l*, pg. 3475
CENTRAL CITY COMMUNITY HEALTH CENTER; *U.S. Private*, pg. 819
CENTRAL CITY CONCERN; *U.S. Private*, pg. 819
CENTRAL COAST LEAGUES CLUB LIMITED; *Int'l*, pg. 1405
CENTRAL COAST PROPANE, INC.—See Superior Plus Corp.; *Int'l*, pg. 7338
CENTRAL COAST WINES; *U.S. Private*, pg. 819
CENTRAL COCA-COLA BOTTLING COMPANY, INC.; *U.S. Private*, pg. 819
CENTRAL COLD STORAGE CORPORATION—See The VPS Companies Inc.; *U.S. Private*, pg. 4132
CENTRAL COLUMBIA KIDNEY CENTER, LLC—See Nautic Partners, LLC; *U.S. Private*, pg. 2869
CENTRAL COMPUTER SYSTEMS INC.; *U.S. Private*, pg. 819
CENTRAL CONCRETE CORPORATION; *U.S. Private*, pg. 819

COMPANY NAME INDEX

CENTRAL CONCRETE SUPERMIX INC.—See Titan Cement Company S.A.; *Int'l*, pg. 7760
CENTRAL CONCRETE SUPPLY CO., INC.—See Vulcan Materials Company; *U.S. Public*, pg. 2313
CENTRAL CONTAINER JOINT STOCK COMPANY—See Vietnam Container Shipping Corporation; *Int'l*, pg. 8198
CENTRAL CONTRA COSTA SANITARY DISTRICT; *U.S. Private*, pg. 820
CENTRAL CONTRACTING COMPANY; *U.S. Private*, pg. 820
CENTRAL CONVEYOR CO., LTD.—See IHI Corporation; *Int'l*, pg. 3604
CENTRAL CONVEYOR COMPANY, LLC—See Tsubakimoto Chain Co.; *Int'l*, pg. 7954
CENTRAL COOLING & HEATING INC.—See Morgan Stanley; *U.S. Public*, pg. 1474
CENTRAL COOPERATIVE BANK PLC—See Chimimport AD; *Int'l*, pg. 1479
CENTRAL COOP; *U.S. Private*, pg. 820
CENTRAL CPVC CORPORATION—See Johnson Controls International plc; *Int'l*, pg. 3986
CENTRAL CREDIT AUDIT, INC.—See Creditech, Inc.; *U.S. Private*, pg. 1092
CENTRAL CRUDE INC.; *U.S. Private*, pg. 820
CENTRAL DAIRY COMPANY; *U.S. Private*, pg. 820
CENTRAL DE ABASTECIMIENTO LIMITADA—See Aramark; *U.S. Public*, pg. 177
CENTRAL DE DROGAS S.A. DE C.V.—See Fagron NV; *Int'l*, pg. 2603
CENTRAL DEPOSITORY OF ARMENIA OPEN JOINT STOCK COMPANY—See Nasdaq, Inc.; *U.S. Public*, pg. 1491
THE CENTRAL DEPOSITORY (PTE) LIMITED—See Singapore Exchange Limited; *Int'l*, pg. 6940
CENTRAL DEPOSITORY SERVICES (INDIA) LIMITED—See Bombay Stock Exchange Limited; *Int'l*, pg. 1104
CENTRAL DE RESTAURANTES ARAMARK LIMITADA—See Aramark; *U.S. Public*, pg. 177
CENTRAL DEVELOPMENT HOLDINGS LTD.; *Int'l*, pg. 1405
CENTRAL DISPOSAL LLC—See Superior Waste Industries LLC, *U.S. Private*, pg. 3001
CENTRAL DISPOSAL SYSTEMS, INC.—See Waste Management, Inc.; *U.S. Public*, pg. 2330
CENTRAL DISTRIBUTING CO.; *U.S. Private*, pg. 820
CENTRAL DISTRIBUTORS INC.—See Moon Distributors, Inc.; *U.S. Private*, pg. 2778
CENTRAL DIVISION LOGISTICS, LLC—See Vulcan Materials Company; *U.S. Public*, pg. 2313
CENTRAL DOCK SUD SA—See Enel S.p.A.; *Int'l*, pg. 2411
CENTRAL DUPAGE HOSPITAL ASSOCIATION—See Northwestern Memorial HealthCare; *U.S. Private*, pg. 2962
CENTRAL DYNAMIC INTERNATIONAL LIMITED—See Fulum Group Holdings Limited; *Int'l*, pg. 2844
CENTRALE BANK VAN ARUBA; *Int'l*, pg. 1410
CENTRALE BANK VAN SURINAME; *Int'l*, pg. 1410
CENTRALE DEL LATTE D'ITALIA S.P.A.—See Newlat Food S.p.A.; *Int'l*, pg. 5235
CENTRALE DEL LATTE DI TORINO & C. S.P.A.; *Int'l*, pg. 1410
CENTRALE DEL LATTE DI VICENZA S.P.A.—See Centrale del Latte di Torino & C. S.p.A.; *Int'l*, pg. 1410
CENTRALE EOLIENNE DE FONDS DE FRESNES—See Electricite de France S.A.; *Int'l*, pg. 2350
CENTRALE KREDIETVERLENING NV; *Int'l*, pg. 1410
CENTRALE LATTE RAPALLO S.P.A.—See Centrale del Latte di Torino & C. S.p.A.; *Int'l*, pg. 1410
CENTRAL ELECTRIC COMPANY—See AZZ, Inc.; *U.S. Public*, pg. 259
CENTRAL ELECTRIC COOPERATIVE INC.; *U.S. Private*, pg. 820
CENTRAL ELECTRICITY SUPPLY COMPANY OF ORISSA LIMITED—See The AES Corporation; *U.S. Public*, pg. 2031
CENTRAL ELECTRIC MANUFACTURING COMPANY—See AZZ, Inc.; *U.S. Public*, pg. 259
CENTRAL ELECTRIC POWER ASSOCIATION; *U.S. Private*, pg. 820
CENTRAL ELECTRIC POWER COOPERATIVE INC.; *U.S. Private*, pg. 820
CENTRAL ELECTRIC POWER COOPERATIVE, INC.; *U.S. Private*, pg. 820
CENTRAL ENERGY AUSTRALIA PTY LTD—See Energy World Corporation Ltd; *Int'l*, pg. 2423
CENTRAL ENERGY K.K.—See Idemitsu Kosan Co., Ltd.; *Int'l*, pg. 3590
CENTRAL ENGINEERING CO., LTD.—See Central Glass Co., Ltd.; *Int'l*, pg. 1406
CENTRAL ENVIRONMENTAL INC.; *U.S. Private*, pg. 820
CENTRAL EQUITY LIMITED; *Int'l*, pg. 1406
CENTRALE SUPPORTI OPERATIVI S.P.A.—See Intesa Sanpaolo S.p.A.; *Int'l*, pg. 3765
CENTRALE TECHNIQUE D'APPROVISIONNEMENT INDUSTRIEL; *Int'l*, pg. 1411

CENTRAL EUROPEAN DISTRIBUTION CORPORATION—See CJSC Russian Standard Corporation; *Int'l*, pg. 1634
CENTRAL EUROPEAN GAS HUB AG—See OMV Aktiengesellschaft; *Int'l*, pg. 5568
CENTRAL EUROPEAN MEDIA ENTERPRISES LTD.—See PPF Group N.V.; *Int'l*, pg. 5950
CENTRAL EXTRUSION DIE CO—See Cockburn Enterprises Inc.; *U.S. Private*, pg. 959
CENTRAL FEDERAL SAVINGS & LOAN ASSOCIATION; *U.S. Private*, pg. 820
CENTRAL FIBER LLC; *U.S. Private*, pg. 820
CENTRAL FILES, INC.—See Berkshire Partners LLC; *U.S. Private*, pg. 534
CENTRAL FILM VERLEIH GMBH—See Wild Bunch AG; *Int'l*, pg. 8409
CENTRAL FINANCE COMPANY PLC - CITY OFFICE—See Central Finance Company PLC; *Int'l*, pg. 1406
CENTRAL FINANCE COMPANY PLC; *Int'l*, pg. 1406
CENTRAL FINANCE LIMITED; *Int'l*, pg. 1406
CENTRAL FINANCIAL HOLDINGS, INC.; *U.S. Private*, pg. 820
CENTRAL FINANCIAL MANAGEMENT COMPANY INC.—See Tai Sang Land Development Ltd; *Int'l*, pg. 7408
CENTRAL FLORIDA AUTO AUCTION—See Cox Enterprises, Inc.; *U.S. Private*, pg. 1076
CENTRAL FLORIDA BEHAVIORAL HEALTH NETWORK INC; *U.S. Private*, pg. 820
CENTRAL FLORIDA BOX CORPORATION—See WestRock Company; *U.S. Public*, pg. 2361
CENTRAL FLORIDA CARES HEALTH SYSTEM, INC.; *U.S. Private*, pg. 820
CENTRAL FLORIDA ELECTRIC COOPERATIVE INC.; *U.S. Private*, pg. 820
CENTRAL FLORIDA FAMILY HEALTH CENTER, INC.; *U.S. Private*, pg. 820
CENTRAL FLORIDA INVESTMENTS INC.; *U.S. Private*, pg. 820
CENTRAL FLORIDA PARTNERSHIP, INC.; *U.S. Private*, pg. 820
CENTRAL FLORIDA REGIONAL HOSPITAL, INC.—See HCA Healthcare, Inc.; *U.S. Public*, pg. 993
CENTRAL FLORIDA REGIONAL HOSPITAL—See HCA Healthcare, Inc.; *U.S. Public*, pg. 993
CENTRAL FLORIDA REGIONAL TRANSPORT AUTHORITY; *U.S. Private*, pg. 821
CENTRAL FLYING SERVICE INC.; *U.S. Private*, pg. 821
CENTRAL FOCUS, INC.—See Aloysius, Butler & Clark Associates, Inc.; *U.S. Private*, pg. 196
CENTRAL FOOD RETAIL COMPANY LIMITED—See Central Group Company Limited; *Int'l*, pg. 1407
CENTRAL FOREST PRODUCTS INC.; *U.S. Private*, pg. 821
CENTRAL FREIGHT LINES, INC.; *U.S. Private*, pg. 821
CENTRAL-FUND KOCKAZATI TOKEALAP-KEZELO ZRT—See Central Group; *Int'l*, pg. 1407
CENTRAL FUND OF ISRAEL; *U.S. Private*, pg. 821
CENTRAL GARDEN & PET COMPANY; *U.S. Public*, pg. 473
CENTRAL GENERAL DEVELOPMENT CO., LTD.; *Int'l*, pg. 1406
CENTRAL GEORGIA EMC FOUNDATION, INC.; *U.S. Private*, pg. 821
CENTRAL GEORGIA HEALTH SYSTEM INC.; *U.S. Private*, pg. 821
CENTRAL GEORGIA HEALTH VENTURES, INC.—See Central Georgia Health System Inc.; *U.S. Private*, pg. 821
CENTRAL GERADORA TERMELETRICA FORTALEZA SA—See Enel S.p.A.; *Int'l*, pg. 2412
CENTRAL GLASS CHEMSPEC COMPANY LTD.—See Central Glass Co., Ltd.; *Int'l*, pg. 1406
CENTRAL GLASS CHUBU CO., LTD.—See Central Glass Co., Ltd.; *Int'l*, pg. 1406
CENTRAL GLASS CO., LTD.; *Int'l*, pg. 1406
CENTRAL GLASS CZECH S.R.O.—See Central Glass Co., Ltd.; *Int'l*, pg. 1406
CENTRAL GLASS ENGINEERING CO., LTD.—See Central Glass Co., Ltd.; *Int'l*, pg. 1406
CENTRAL GLASS EUROPE LIMITED—See Central Glass Co., Ltd.; *Int'l*, pg. 1406
CENTRAL GLASS FIBER CO., LTD.—See Central Glass Co., Ltd.; *Int'l*, pg. 1406
CENTRAL GLASS GERMANY GMBH—See Central Glass Co., Ltd.; *Int'l*, pg. 1406
CENTRAL GLASS HOKKAIDO CO., LTD.—See Central Glass Co., Ltd.; *Int'l*, pg. 1406
CENTRAL GLASS INDUSTRIES LTD—See Diageo plc; *Int'l*, pg. 2102
CENTRAL GLASS INTERNATIONAL, INC.—See Central Glass Co., Ltd.; *Int'l*, pg. 1406
CENTRAL GLASS KOREA CO., LTD.—See Central Glass Co., Ltd.; *Int'l*, pg. 1406
CENTRAL GLASS KYUSHU CO., LTD.—See Central Glass Co., Ltd.; *Int'l*, pg. 1406
CENTRAL GLASS MODULE CO., LTD.—See Central Glass Co., Ltd.; *Int'l*, pg. 1406

CENTRAL LAKES COOPERATIVE

CENTRAL GLASS PLANT SERVICES CO., LTD.—See Central Glass Co., Ltd.; *Int'l*, pg. 1406
CENTRAL GLASS SALES CO., LTD.—See Central Glass Co., Ltd.; *Int'l*, pg. 1406
CENTRAL GLASS TOHOKU CO., LTD.—See Central Glass Co., Ltd.; *Int'l*, pg. 1406
CENTRAL GLASS TOKYO CO., LTD.—See Central Glass Co., Ltd.; *Int'l*, pg. 1406
CENTRAL GLASS TRADING (SHANGHAI) CO., LTD.—See Central Glass Co., Ltd.; *Int'l*, pg. 1406
CENTRAL GLASS WOOL CO., LTD.—See Central Glass Co., Ltd.; *Int'l*, pg. 1407
CENTRAL GLOBAL BERHAD; *Int'l*, pg. 1407
CENTRAL GLOBAL CARGO GMBH; *Int'l*, pg. 1407
CENTRAL GROCERS CO-OP; *U.S. Private*, pg. 821
CENTRAL GROUP COMPANY LIMITED; *Int'l*, pg. 1407
CENTRAL GROUP; *Int'l*, pg. 1407
CENTRAL HARDWOODS, INC.; *U.S. Private*, pg. 821
CENTRAL HEALTH PLAN OF CALIFORNIA, INC.—See Molina Healthcare, Inc.; *U.S. Public*, pg. 1458
CENTRAL HOLDING GROUP CO., LTD.; *Int'l*, pg. 1407
CENTRAL HOSPITALITY CO., LTD.—See Home Pottery Public Company Limited; *Int'l*, pg. 3455
CENTRAL HUDSON ENTERPRISES CORPORATION—See Fortis Inc.; *Int'l*, pg. 2739
CENTRAL HUDSON GAS & ELECTRIC CORPORATION—See Fortis Inc.; *Int'l*, pg. 2739
CENTRAL HUIJIN INVESTMENT LTD.—See China Investment Corporation; *Int'l*, pg. 1513
CENTRAL HYDROPOWER JOINT STOCK COMPANY; *Int'l*, pg. 1407
CENTRAL ILLIANA AG INC.; *U.S. Private*, pg. 821
CENTRAL ILLINOIS AG INC.; *U.S. Private*, pg. 821
CENTRAL ILLINOIS STEEL COMPANY; *U.S. Private*, pg. 821
CENTRAL ILLINOIS TRUCKS, INC.; *U.S. Private*, pg. 821
CENTRAL INDIANA COMMUNITY FOUNDATION; *U.S. Private*, pg. 821
CENTRAL INDIANA HARDWARE CO.; *U.S. Private*, pg. 821
CENTRAL INDUSTRIAL SERVICES, INC.—See Well Services Group; *Int'l*, pg. 8373
CENTRAL INDUSTRIES, INC.—See Tyson Foods, Inc.; *U.S. Public*, pg. 2277
CENTRAL INDUSTRIES PLC—See Central Finance Company PLC; *Int'l*, pg. 1406
CENTRAL INFORMATION SYSTEMS CO., LTD.—See JBCC Holdings Inc.; *Int'l*, pg. 3917
CENTRAL INK CORPORATION; *U.S. Private*, pg. 821
CENTRAL INSTITUTE FOR EXPERIMENTAL ANIMALS; *Int'l*, pg. 1408
CENTRAL INSULATION CO., LTD.—See Central Glass Co., Ltd.; *Int'l*, pg. 1407
CENTRAL INSURANCE COMPANY LIMITED; *Int'l*, pg. 1408
CENTRAL INVESTMENT LLC; *U.S. Private*, pg. 821
CENTRALION INDUSTRIAL INC.—See Eaton Corporation plc; *Int'l*, pg. 2277
CENTRAL IOWA ENERGY COOPERATIVE—See Central Iowa Power Cooperative; *U.S. Private*, pg. 822
CENTRAL IOWA POWER COOPERATIVE; *U.S. Private*, pg. 821
CENTRAL IQ, INC.; *U.S. Private*, pg. 822
CENTRAL IRON ORE LIMITED; *Int'l*, pg. 1408
CENTRAL IRRIGATION SUPPLY INC.; *U.S. Private*, pg. 822
CENTRALISED WASTE TREATMENT PLANT SDN. BHD.—See Analabs Resources Berhad; *Int'l*, pg. 446
CENTRALITE SYSTEMS, INC.—See eZLO, Inc.; *U.S. Private*, pg. 1454
CENTRALIZED LEASING CORPORATION—See Golden State Foods Corp.; *U.S. Private*, pg. 1733
CENTRAL JAPAN RAILWAY COMPANY; *Int'l*, pg. 1408
CENTRAL JERSEY SURGERY CENTER, LLC—See Tenet Healthcare Corporation; *U.S. Public*, pg. 2009
CENTRAL JERSEY WASTE & RECYCLING, INC.—See Roark Capital Group Inc.; *U.S. Private*, pg. 3454
CENTRAL KASEI CHEMICAL CO., LTD.—See Central Glass Co., Ltd.; *Int'l*, pg. 1407
CENTRAL KENTUCKY DIALYSIS CENTERS, LLC—See DaVita Inc.; *U.S. Public*, pg. 636
CENTRAL KITTANNING DIALYSIS CENTER LLC—See Nautic Partners, LLC; *U.S. Private*, pg. 2869
CENTRAL KLAIPEDA TERMINAL, UAB—See Koncernas Achemos Grupe; *Int'l*, pg. 4246
CENTRAL KRABI BAY RESORT—See Central Plaza Hotel Public Company Limited; *Int'l*, pg. 1409
CENTRAL LABO EUROPE SAS—See Bio-Rad Laboratories, Inc.; *U.S. Public*, pg. 333
CENTRAL LAKE ARMOR EXPRESS, INC.—See Spanos Barber Jesse & Co.; *U.S. Private*, pg. 3745
CENTRAL LAKES COOPERATIVE; *U.S. Private*, pg. 822
CENTRAL LAW GROUP LIMITED—See Wilmington plc; *Int'l*, pg. 8422
CENTRAL LAW TRAINING LIMITED—See Wilmington plc; *Int'l*, pg. 8422
CENTRAL LAW TRAINING (SCOTLAND) LIMITED—See Wilmington plc; *Int'l*, pg. 8422

CENTRAL LINCOLN PEOPLE'S UTILITY DISTRICT; U.S. Private, pg. 822
CENTRAL LIVESTOCK ASSOCIATION, INC.—See Cooperative Resources International Inc.; U.S. Private, pg. 1043
CENTRAL LOGIC INC.—See Rubicon Technology Partners, LLC; U.S. Private, pg. 3499
CENTRAL LOGISTICS CO., LTD.—See Seino Holdings Co., Ltd.; Int'l, pg. 6690
CENTRAL LOUISIANA REHAB ASSOCIATES, L.P.—See Encompass Health Corporation; U.S. Public, pg. 755
CENTRAL MACHINE & MARINE INC.; Int'l, pg. 1408
CENTRAL MACHINE & TOOL COMPANY—See Parrish Enterprises, Ltd.; U.S. Private, pg. 3100
CENTRAL MAE SOT HILL HOTEL CO LTD—See Central Plaza Hotel Public Company Limited; Int'l, pg. 1409
CENTRAL MAINE MOTORS AUTO GROUP; U.S. Private, pg. 822
CENTRAL MAINE POWER COMPANY—See Iberdrola, S.A.; Int'l, pg. 3570
CENTRAL MAINE POWER COMPANY—See Iberdrola, S.A.; Int'l, pg. 3570
CENTRAL MAINE POWER COMPANY—See Iberdrola, S.A.; Int'l, pg. 3570
CENTRAL MANITOBA RAILWAY INC.—See TorQuest Partners Inc.; Int'l, pg. 7830
CENTRAL-MCGOWAN INC.; U.S. Private, pg. 826
THE CENTRAL MEASUREMENT AND RESEARCH LABORATORY—See Polskie Gornictwo Naftowe i Gazownictwo S.A.; Int'l, pg. 5912
CENTRAL MECHANICAL CONSTRUCTION CO., INC.—See EMCOR Group, Inc.; U.S. Public, pg. 736
CENTRAL MEDIA GROUP PROPRIETARY LIMITED—See African Media Entertainment Limited; Int'l, pg. 192
CENTRAL MEDICAL EQUIPMENT RENTALS; U.S. Private, pg. 822
CENTRAL MEDICAL SOLUTIONS, LLC—See Nobilis Health Corp.; U.S. Private, pg. 2932
CENTRAL MEDICAL SUPPLY, INC.—See Osceola Capital Management, LLC; U.S. Private, pg. 3047
CENTRAL MELAMINEWARE SDN. BHD.—See CAM Resources Berhad; Int'l, pg. 1267
CENTRAL MERCANTILE CORPORATION (S) LTD.—See W T K Holdings Berhad; Int'l, pg. 8320
CENTRAL MICHIGAN PAPER COMPANY; U.S. Private, pg. 822
CENTRAL MICHIGAN UNIVERSITY; U.S. Private, pg. 822
CENTRAL MILLING COMPANY; U.S. Private, pg. 822
CENTRAL MILLS INC.; U.S. Private, pg. 822
CENTRAL MINE EQUIPMENT COMPANY; U.S. Private, pg. 822
CENTRAL MINNESOTA DIAGNOSTIC INC.; U.S. Private, pg. 822
CENTRAL MINNESOTA FABRICATING INC.; U.S. Private, pg. 822
CENTRAL MISSOURI AGRISERVICE LLC; U.S. Private, pg. 822
CENTRAL MOLONEY INC.—See Wind Point Advisors LLC; U.S. Private, pg. 4534
CENTRALMONTAGE I NYKOPING AB—See Sdiptech AB; Int'l, pg. 6658
CENTRAL MONTANA COOPERATIVE—See CHS INC.; U.S. Public, pg. 492
CENTRAL MONTANA MEDICAL CENTER; U.S. Private, pg. 822
CENTRAL MONTANA PROPANE, LLC—See CHS INC.; U.S. Public, pg. 492
CENTRAL MOTEK CO., LTD.; Int'l, pg. 1408
CENTRAL MOTORS & EQUIPMENT LLC—See Al Fahim Group; Int'l, pg. 277
CENTRAL MOTOR WHEEL CO., LTD.—See Toyota Tsusho Corporation; Int'l, pg. 7876
CENTRAL MOTOR WHEEL OF AMERICA; U.S. Private, pg. 822
CENTRAL MOUNTAIN AIR LTD.; Int'l, pg. 1409
CENTRAL MOVING & STORAGE CO.; U.S. Private, pg. 822
CENTRAL MRI CENTRE LIMITED—See The British United Provident Association Limited; Int'l, pg. 7629
CENTRAL MULTISERVICIOS S.R.L.—See Aramark; U.S. Public, pg. 177
CENTRAL MUTUAL INSURANCE CENTRAL REGIONAL OFFICE—See Central Mutual Insurance Company; U.S. Private, pg. 823
CENTRAL MUTUAL INSURANCE COMPANY; U.S. Private, pg. 822
CENTRALNA KOOPERATIVNA BANKA AD—See Chimimport AD; Int'l, pg. 1479
CENTRAL NATIONAL BANK OF ENID; U.S. Private, pg. 823
CENTRAL NATIONAL BANK; U.S. Private, pg. 823
CENTRAL NATIONAL BANK; U.S. Private, pg. 823
CENTRAL NATIONAL BANK—See Centrabanc Corporation; U.S. Private, pg. 818
CENTRAL NATIONAL ESPANOLA S.A.—See Central National Gottesman Inc.; U.S. Private, pg. 823
CENTRAL NATIONAL GOTTESMAN EUROPE GMBH—See Central National Gottesman Inc.; U.S. Private, pg. 823

CENTRAL NATIONAL GOTTESMAN INC. - CENTRAL NATIONAL DIVISION—See Central National Gottesman Inc.; U.S. Private, pg. 823
CENTRAL NATIONAL GOTTESMAN INC.; U.S. Private, pg. 823
CENTRAL NATURAL RESOURCES, INC.; U.S. Public, pg. 473
CENTRAL NEBRASKA PUBLIC POWER & IRRIGATION DISTRICT, INC.; U.S. Private, pg. 823
CENTRALNE LABORATORIUM POMIAROWO-BADAWCZE SP. Z O.O.—See Jastrzebska Spolka Weglowa S.A.; Int'l, pg. 3913
CENTRAL NETWORK RETAIL GROUP, LLC—See Tyndale Advisors, LLC; U.S. Private, pg. 4268
CENTRAL NEW YORK AGENCY, LLC; U.S. Private, pg. 823
CENTRAL NEW YORK OIL & GAS COMPANY, LLC—See Crestwood Equity Partners LP; U.S. Public, pg. 594
CENTRAL NEW YORK REGIONAL TRANSPORTATION AUTHORITY; U.S. Private, pg. 823
CENTRALNIC AUSTRALIA PTY. LTD.—See Team Internet Group plc; Int'l, pg. 7500
CENTRALNIC POLAND SP. Z O.O.—See Team Internet Group plc; Int'l, pg. 7500
CENTRALNIC USA LTD.—See Team Internet Group plc; Int'l, pg. 7500
CENTRAL NUCLEAR DE TRILLO—See Iberdrola, S.A.; Int'l, pg. 3571
CENTRALNY DOM MAKLERSKI PEKAO S.A.—See Bank Polska Kasa Opieki Spolka Akcyjna; Int'l, pg. 849
CENTRAL OF GEORGIA RAILROAD COMPANY—See Norfolk Southern Corporation; U.S. Public, pg. 1536
CENTRAL OHIO DIABETES ASSOCIATION; U.S. Private, pg. 824
CENTRAL OHIO FARMERS COOPERATIVE; U.S. Private, pg. 824
CENTRAL OHIO GAMING VENTURES, LLC—See PENN Entertainment, Inc.; U.S. Public, pg. 1662
CENTRAL OHIO HEALTH CARE CONSORTIUM; U.S. Private, pg. 824
CENTRAL OIL & SUPPLY CORPORATION; U.S. Private, pg. 824
CENTRAL OIL & SUPPLY CORP SHREVEPORT—See Central Oil & Supply Corporation; U.S. Private, pg. 824
CENTRAL OREGON & PACIFIC RAILROAD, INC.—See Brookfield Infrastructure Partners L.P.; Int'l, pg. 1191
CENTRAL OREGON & PACIFIC RAILROAD, INC.—See GIC Pte. Ltd.; Int'l, pg. 2965
CENTRAL OREGON REDI-MIX, LLC—See MDU Resources Group, Inc.; U.S. Public, pg. 1410
CENTRAL OREGON TRUCK COMPANY, INC.—See Daseke, Inc.; U.S. Private, pg. 1161
CENTRAL OXYGEN INC.—See Quipt Home Medical Corp.; U.S. Public, pg. 1757
CENTRAL PACIFIC BANK—See Central Pacific Financial Corporation; U.S. Public, pg. 473
CENTRAL PACIFIC FINANCIAL CORPORATION; U.S. Public, pg. 473
CENTRAL PACIFIC HOMELOANS, INC.—See Central Pacific Financial Corporation; U.S. Public, pg. 473
CENTRAL PACIFIC (THAILAND) CORPORATION LTD.—See Thai Central Chemical Public Company Limited; Int'l, pg. 7592
CENTRAL PANEL, INC.—See Ajax Electric Co.; U.S. Private, pg. 143
CENTRAL PAPER COMPANY INC.; U.S. Private, pg. 824
CENTRAL PAPER PRODUCTS CO., INC.—See Bain Capital, LP; U.S. Private, pg. 440
CENTRAL PARK BUILDING CO., LTD.—See J. Front Retailing Co., Ltd.; Int'l, pg. 3855
CENTRAL PARK ENDOSCOPY CENTER, LLC—See KKR & Co. Inc.; U.S. Public, pg. 1245
CENTRAL PARK GROUP—See Macquarie Group Limited; Int'l, pg. 4624
CENTRAL PARK MEDIA CORP.; U.S. Private, pg. 824
CENTRAL PARK SURGERY CENTER—See HCA Healthcare, Inc.; U.S. Public, pg. 992
CENTRAL PARK WEST DENTISTRY PC; U.S. Private, pg. 824
CENTRAL PATTANA PUBLIC COMPANY LIMITED; Int'l, pg. 1409
CENTRAL PAYMENT; U.S. Private, pg. 824
CENTRAL PENNSYLVANIA MEDICAL FOUNDATION; U.S. Private, pg. 824
CENTRAL PETROLEUM LIMITED; Int'l, pg. 1409
CENTRAL PETROVIETNAM FERTILIZER & CHEMICALS JOINT STOCK COMPANY; Int'l, pg. 1409
CENTRAL PHARMACEUTICALS LIMITED; Int'l, pg. 1409
CENTRAL PLAINS AG SERVICES LLC—See CHS INC.; U.S. Public, pg. 492
CENTRAL PLAINS BANCSHARES, INC.; U.S. Public, pg. 473
CENTRAL PLAINS ENVIRONMENT PROTECTION CO., LTD.; Int'l, pg. 1409
CENTRAL PLAINS STEEL CO.—See Reliance Steel & Aluminum Co.; U.S. Public, pg. 1781
CENTRAL PLASTICS & RUBBER CO., INC.; U.S. Private, pg. 824

CENTRAL PLAZA HOTEL PUBLIC COMPANY LIMITED; Int'l, pg. 1409
CENTRAL POWER DISTRIBUTORS; U.S. Private, pg. 824
CENTRAL POWER SYSTEMS & SERVICES; U.S. Private, pg. 824
CENTRAL PROCESS ENGINEERING, LLC—See Tsubakimoto Chain Co.; Int'l, pg. 7954
CENTRAL PUERTO S.A.; Int'l, pg. 1409
CENTRAL QUEENSLAND RADIOLOGY PTY. LTD.—See Integral Diagnostics Limited; Int'l, pg. 3730
CENTRAL RAILROAD COMPANY OF INDIANAPOLIS—See Brookfield Infrastructure Partners L.P.; Int'l, pg. 1191
CENTRAL RAILROAD COMPANY OF INDIANAPOLIS—See GIC Pte. Ltd.; Int'l, pg. 2965
THE CENTRAL RAILROAD COMPANY OF INDIANA—See Brookfield Infrastructure Partners L.P.; Int'l, pg. 1192
THE CENTRAL RAILROAD COMPANY OF INDIANA—See GIC Pte. Ltd.; Int'l, pg. 2967
CENTRAL RANGES PIPELINE PTY. LTD.—See APA Group; Int'l, pg. 500
CENTRALREACH, LLC; U.S. Private, pg. 824
CENTRAL REFRIGERATION AND AIR CONDITIONING LTD.; Int'l, pg. 1409
CENTRAL REINSURANCE CORPORATION; Int'l, pg. 1409
CENTRAL RESEARCH, INC.; U.S. Private, pg. 824
CENTRAL RESEARCH LABORATORIES—See Stabilus; U.S. Private, pg. 3774
CENTRAL RESEARCH TECHNOLOGY CO.—See Tatung Company; Int'l, pg. 7475
CENTRAL RESERVE BANK OF ATLANTA—See Federal Reserve Bank of Atlanta; U.S. Private, pg. 1490
CENTRAL RESERVE LIFE INSURANCE COMPANY—See American Financial Group, Inc.; U.S. Public, pg. 102
CENTRAL RESTAURANTS GROUP CO., LTD—See Central Plaza Hotel Public Company Limited; Int'l, pg. 1409
CENTRAL RETAIL CORPORATION (CRC) CO. LIMITED—See Central Group Company Limited; Int'l, pg. 1407
CENTRAL RUBBER COMPANY—See Koch Industries, Inc.; U.S. Private, pg. 2335
CENTRAL RURAL ELECTRIC COOPERATIVE; U.S. Private, pg. 824
CENTRAL SAINT-GOBAIN CO., LTD.—See Central Glass Co., Ltd.; Int'l, pg. 1407
CENTRAL SAINT-GOBAIN CO., LTD.—See Compagnie de Saint-Gobain SA; Int'l, pg. 1722
CENTRAL SAMUI BEACH RESORT CO., LTD.—See Central Plaza Hotel Public Company Limited; Int'l, pg. 1409
CENTRAL SAMUI VILLAGE CO., LTD.—See Central Plaza Hotel Public Company Limited; Int'l, pg. 1409
CENTRAL SANITARY LANDFILL, INC.—See Republic Services, Inc.; U.S. Public, pg. 1786
CENTRAL SANITARY SUPPLY COMPANY—See Kelso & Company, L.P.; U.S. Private, pg. 2279
CENTRAL SA—See SIF Banat-Crisana S.A.; Int'l, pg. 6905
CENTRAL SAVINGS BANK; U.S. Private, pg. 824
CENTRALSCHWEIZERISCHE KRAFTWERKE AG—See Axpo Holding AG; Int'l, pg. 771
CENTRAL SCIENTIFIC COMMERCE, INC.—See GSI Creos Corporation; Int'l, pg. 3144
CENTRAL SCOTT TELEPHONE—See LICT Corporation; U.S. Public, pg. 1312
CENTRAL SECURITIES CORPORATION; U.S. Public, pg. 474
CENTRAL SECURITY DISTRIBUTION PTY. LTD.—See WESCO International, Inc.; U.S. Public, pg. 2350
CENTRAL SECURITY GROUP, INC.—See Summit Partners, L.P.; U.S. Private, pg. 3855
CENTRAL SECURITY LIFE INSURANCE CO.—See Maximum Corporation; U.S. Private, pg. 2618
CENTRAL SECURITY PATROLS CO., LTD.; Int'l, pg. 1409
CENTRAL SEMICONDUCTOR CORP; U.S. Private, pg. 824
CENTRAL SERVICE ASSOCIATION; U.S. Private, pg. 824
CENTRAL SERVICE CORP.; U.S. Public, pg. 474
CENTRAL SHARED SERVICES, LLC—See HCA Healthcare, Inc.; U.S. Public, pg. 993
CENTRAL SHIPPEE, INC.; U.S. Private, pg. 824
CENTRAL SOCIETA DI INVESTIMENTO PER AZIONI A CAPITALO FISSO CENTRAL SICAF S.P.A—See Covivio; Int'l, pg. 1821
CENTRAL SOUTH DISTRIBUTION, INC.; U.S. Private, pg. 824
CENTRAL SPECTRUM (M) SDN BHD—See Kumpulan Darul Ehsan Berhad; Int'l, pg. 4331
CENTRAL SPORTS CO., LTD.; Int'l, pg. 1410
CENTRAL SPRINKLER COMPANY—See Johnson Controls International plc; Int'l, pg. 3986
CENTRAL SQUARE AT FRISCO LLC—See UDR, Inc.; U.S. Public, pg. 2218
CENTRALSQUARE TECHNOLOGIES, LLC—See Vista Equity Partners, LLC; U.S. Private, pg. 4395
CENTRAL STATE BANK—See AJJ Bancorp, Inc.; U.S. Private, pg. 144

COMPANY NAME INDEX

CENTRAL STATE BANK—See State Center Financial, Inc.; *U.S. Private*, pg. 3791
CENTRAL STATE CONSTRUCTION, CORPORATION; *U.S. Private*, pg. 825
CENTRAL STATES BUSINESS FORMS—See Adams Investment Company; *U.S. Private*, pg. 74
CENTRAL STATES BUSINESS FORMS - SUWANEE PLANT—See Adams Investment Company; *U.S. Private*, pg. 74
CENTRAL STATES BUS SALES INC. - ARKANSAS FACILITY—See Central States Bus Sales Inc.; *U.S. Private*, pg. 825
CENTRAL STATES BUS SALES INC. - ILLINOIS FACILITY—See Central States Bus Sales Inc.; *U.S. Private*, pg. 825
CENTRAL STATES BUS SALES INC.; *U.S. Private*, pg. 825
CENTRAL STATES BUS SALES INC. - TENNESSEE FACILITY—See Central States Bus Sales Inc.; *U.S. Private*, pg. 825
CENTRAL STATES COCA-COLA BOTTLING COMPANY—See The Coca-Cola Company; *U.S. Public*, pg. 2064
CENTRAL STATES ENTERPRISES, INC.; *U.S. Private*, pg. 825
CENTRAL STATES HEALTH & LIFE CO. OF OMAHA INC.; *U.S. Private*, pg. 825
CENTRAL STATES, INC.; *U.S. Private*, pg. 825
CENTRAL STATES INC.; *U.S. Private*, pg. 825
CENTRAL STATES INDEMNITY CO. OF OMAHA—See Berkshire Hathaway Inc.; *U.S. Public*, pg. 301
CENTRAL STATES INDUSTRIAL SUPPLY, INC.; *U.S. Private*, pg. 825
CENTRAL STATES MANUFACTURING INC.; *U.S. Private*, pg. 825
CENTRAL STATES OF OMAHA COMPANIES, INC.—See Berkshire Hathaway Inc.; *U.S. Public*, pg. 304
CENTRAL STATES TRUCKING CO.—See Forward Air Corporation; *U.S. Public*, pg. 874
CENTRAL STATION MONITORING; *U.S. Private*, pg. 825
CENTRAL STEEL FABRICATORS INC.—See Live Ventures Incorporated; *U.S. Public*, pg. 1332
CENTRAL STEEL & WIRE COMPANY—See Ryerson Holding Corporation; *U.S. Public*, pg. 1829
CENTRAL STONE CO.—See RiverStone Group, Inc.; *U.S. Private*, pg. 3446
CENTRAL SUPPLIES (BRIERLEY HILL) LTD.—See Kitwave Group Plc; *Int'l*, pg. 4196
CENTRAL SUPPLY CO., INC.; *U.S. Private*, pg. 825
CENTRAL SUPPLY COMPANY; *U.S. Private*, pg. 825
CENTRAL TANSHI CO., LTD.; *Int'l*, pg. 1410
CENTRAL TANSHI FX CO., LTD.—See Central Tanshi Co., Ltd.; *Int'l*, pg. 1410
CENTRAL TERMELETRICA DE COGERACAO S.A.—See Companhia Energetica de Minas Gerais - CEMIG; *Int'l*, pg. 1747
CENTRAL TERMICA DE MEJILLONES, S.A.—See ACS, Actividades de Construccion y Servicios, S.A.; *Int'l*, pg. 110
CENTRAL TEXAS COMMUNITY HEALTH CENTERS; *U.S. Private*, pg. 825
CENTRAL TEXAS ENDOSCOPY CENTER, LLC—See KKR & Co. Inc.; *U.S. Public*, pg. 1245
CENTRAL TEXAS IRON WORKS INC.—See The Herrick Corporation; *U.S. Public*, pg. 4052
CENTRAL TEXAS REFUSE, INC.—See Integrated Waste Solutions Group, LLC; *U.S. Private*, pg. 2101
CENTRAL TEXAS TELEPHONE COOPERATIVE, INC.; *U.S. Private*, pg. 825
CENTRAL TIEN PHONG PLASTIC COMPANY LIMITED—See Tien Phong Plastic Joint-Stock company; *Int'l*, pg. 7744
CENTRAL TRANSMISSION UTILITY OF INDIA LIMITED—See Power Grid Corporation of India Limited; *Int'l*, pg. 5945
CENTRAL TRANSPORTATION INTERNATIONAL INC—See CenTra, Inc.; *U.S. Private*, pg. 818
CENTRAL TRANSPORTATION SYSTEMS, INC.; *U.S. Private*, pg. 825
CENTRAL TRANSPORT INTERNATIONAL - GIBSONIA—See CenTra, Inc.; *U.S. Private*, pg. 818
CENTRAL TRANSPORT INTERNATIONAL INC.—See CenTra, Inc.; *U.S. Private*, pg. 818
CENTRAL TRANSPORT INTERNATIONAL—See CenTra, Inc.; *U.S. Private*, pg. 818
CENTRAL TRANSPORT—See CenTra, Inc.; *U.S. Private*, pg. 818
CENTRAL TRUCKING INC.; *U.S. Private*, pg. 825
THE CENTRAL TRUST BANK—See Central Bancompany, Inc.; *U.S. Public*, pg. 473
CENTRAL TRUST & INVESTMENT COMPANY—See Central Bancompany, Inc.; *U.S. Public*, pg. 472
CENTRAL TUBE & BAR, INC.—See Olympic Steel Inc.; *U.S. Public*, pg. 1570
CENTRAL UNI CO., LTD.—See Ship Healthcare Holdings, Inc.; *Int'l*, pg. 6851
CENTRAL UNION MISSION; *U.S. Private*, pg. 825
CENTRAL UTAH TELEPHONE, INC.—See LICT Corporation; *U.S. Public*, pg. 1312

CENTRAL VALLEY AG COOPERATIVE; *U.S. Private*, pg. 825
CENTRAL VALLEY BUILDERS SUPPLY; *U.S. Private*, pg. 825
CENTRAL VALLEY COMMUNITY BANK—See Community West Bancshares; *U.S. Public*, pg. 558
CENTRAL VALLEY CONCRETE INC.; *U.S. Private*, pg. 826
CENTRAL VALLEY MEAT HOLDING COMPANY; *U.S. Private*, pg. 826
CENTRAL VALLEY SWEEPING, INC.—See Warburg Pincus LLC; *U.S. Private*, pg. 4440
CENTRAL VAN & STORAGE, INC.—See Madison Dearborn Partners, LLC; *U.S. Private*, pg. 2542
CENTRAL VAPORS, LLC; *U.S. Private*, pg. 826
CENTRAL VERMONT HOME HEALTH AND HOSPICE; *U.S. Private*, pg. 826
CENTRAL VIETNAM METAL CORPORATION; *Int'l*, pg. 1410
CENTRAL VIRGINIA ELECTRIC COOPERATIVE INC.; *U.S. Private*, pg. 826
CENTRAL VIRGINIA SURGI-CENTER, L.P.—See Tenet Healthcare Corporation; *U.S. Public*, pg. 2009
CENTRAL WAREHOUSE OPERATIONS, INC.—See Peoples Services Inc.; *U.S. Private*, pg. 3142
CENTRAL WASHINGTON CONCRETE; *U.S. Private*, pg. 826
CENTRAL WASHINGTON GRAIN GROWERS, INC.; *U.S. Private*, pg. 826
CENTRAL WASTE SYSTEMS, INC—See Watts Trucking Service, Inc.; *U.S. Private*, pg. 4456
CENTRAL WEALTH GROUP HOLDINGS LIMITED; *Int'l*, pg. 1410
CENTRAL WEALTH SECURITIES INVESTMENT LIMITED—See Central Wealth Group Holdings Limited; *Int'l*, pg. 1410
CENTRAL WELDING SUPPLY CO. INC.; *U.S. Private*, pg. 826
CENTRAL WHOLESALE ELECTRICAL DISTRIBUTORS INC.; *U.S. Private*, pg. 826
CENTRAL WHOLESALERS, INC.; *U.S. Private*, pg. 826
CENTRAL WHOLESALE SUPPLY CORPORATION; *U.S. Private*, pg. 826
CENTRAL WIRE INDUSTRIES LTD; *Int'l*, pg. 1410
CENTRAL WISCONSIN COOPERATIVE; *U.S. Private*, pg. 826
CENTRAL WISCONSIN DEVELOPMENT CORPORATION—See MGE Energy, Inc.; *U.S. Public*, pg. 1434
CENTRAL WOODWORK, INC.; *U.S. Private*, pg. 826
CENTRAL WOODWORK OF NASHVILLE, INC.—See Central Woodwork, Inc.; *U.S. Private*, pg. 826
CENTRAL WORLD HOTEL CO., LTD.—See Central Plaza Hotel Public Company Limited; *Int'l*, pg. 1409
CENTRAL WV AGING SERVICES, INC.; *U.S. Private*, pg. 826
CENTRAL WYOMING COUNSELING CENTER; *U.S. Private*, pg. 826
CENTRA MARKETING & COMMUNICATIONS, LLC; *U.S. Private*, pg. 818
CENTRAMED, INC.—See Analytix On Demand, Inc.; *U.S. Private*, pg. 271
CENTRAPAL S.R.L.—See Aramark; *U.S. Public*, pg. 177
CENTRA SOTA COOPERATIVE; *U.S. Private*, pg. 818
CENTRAS SECURITIES JSC; *Int'l*, pg. 1411
CENTRASTATE HEALTHCARE SYSTEM INC.; *U.S. Private*, pg. 826
CENTRA TECHNOLOGIES S.A.E.—See Telecom Egypt; *Int'l*, pg. 7530
CENTRAUTO SARL—See Stellantis N.V.; *Int'l*, pg. 7201
CENTRA WORLDWIDE, INC.—See The Suddath Companies; *U.S. Private*, pg. 4124
CENTR BRANDS CORP.; *Int'l*, pg. 1403
CENTRE 1 BANCORP, INC.; *U.S. Private*, pg. 827
CENTRE AT LAUREL, LLC—See Kite Realty Group Trust; *U.S. Public*, pg. 1237
CENTRE AUDITIU SANT BOI SL—See Amplifon S.p.A.; *Int'l*, pg. 435
CENTREBET INTERNATIONAL LIMITED—See William Hill Plc; *Int'l*, pg. 8413
CENTREBET PTY LTD—See William Hill Plc; *Int'l*, pg. 8413
CENTRE BRETAGNE MOTOCULTURE; *Int'l*, pg. 1411
CENTRE CARE INC.; *U.S. Private*, pg. 827
CENTRE CDP CAPITAL—See Caisse de Depot et Placement du Quebec; *Int'l*, pg. 1254
CENTRE CLINIC CORP.—See Quorum Health Corporation; *U.S. Private*, pg. 3329
CENTRECORP MANAGEMENT SERVICES LTD.—See North American Development Group; *U.S. Private*, pg. 2940
CENTRE DE FORMATION AERONAUTIQUE ICARE—See Air France-KLM S.A.; *Int'l*, pg. 237
CENTRE DE FORMATION EN HOMEOPATHIE LLC—See Boiron Group; *Int'l*, pg. 1101
CENTRE DE MECANIQUE HENRI-BOURASSA INC.—See TFI International Inc.; *Int'l*, pg. 7585

CENTRE D ENSEIGNEMENT ET DE DEVELOPPEMENT DE L'HOMEOPATHIE LLC—See Boiron Group; *Int'l*, pg. 1101
CENTRE D'ESSAIS FERROVIAIRES SAS—See Alstom S.A.; *Int'l*, pg. 383
CENTRE DE TRAITEMENT DES RETOURS (CTR)—See Vivendi SE; *Int'l*, pg. 8272
CENTRE EST VITRAGE—See Compagnie de Saint-Gobain SA; *Int'l*, pg. 1722
CENTRE FOR EXCELLENCE IN RAIL TRAINING PTY. LTD.—See Engenco Limited; *Int'l*, pg. 2426
THE CENTRE FOR GENOMIC REGULATION (CRG); *Int'l*, pg. 7631
THE CENTRE FOR HEALTH & DISABILITY ASSESSMENTS LTD.—See MAXIMUS, Inc.; *U.S. Public*, pg. 1402
CENTRE GROUP HOLDINGS LIMITED—See Zurich Insurance Group Limited; *Int'l*, pg. 8697
CENTRE GROUP HOLDINGS (U.S.) LIMITED—See Zurich Insurance Group Limited; *Int'l*, pg. 8698
CENTRE HBP SERVICES, LLC—See Quorum Health Corporation; *U.S. Private*, pg. 3329
CENTRE HOSPITAL CORPORATION—See Quorum Health Corporation; *U.S. Private*, pg. 3329
CENTRE INGREDIENT TECHNOLOGY, INC.—See Takasago International Corporation; *Int'l*, pg. 7433
CENTRE INSURANCE INTERNATIONAL COMPANY—See Zurich Insurance Group Limited; *Int'l*, pg. 8697
CENTRE JAUDE CLERMONT SAS—See BNP Paribas SA; *Int'l*, pg. 1089
CENTRE LANE PARTNERS, LLC; *U.S. Private*, pg. 827
CENTRELEC; *Int'l*, pg. 1411
CENTRE LIMITED INC.; *U.S. Private*, pg. 828
CENTRE LINE DIE FORMES—See Visy Industries Holdings Pty. Ltd.; *Int'l*, pg. 8255
CENTRE LIVING HOMES, LLC—See Green Brick Partners, Inc.; *U.S. Public*, pg. 962
CENTREMANOR LTD.; *Int'l*, pg. 1411
CENTRE MARCEL-LA MAS, S. L.—See VITA 34 AG; *Int'l*, pg. 8257
CENTRE MEDICO-CHIRURGICAL DES EAUX-VIVES SA—See AEVIS VICTORIA SA; *Int'l*, pg. 183
CENTRE NORDIQUE D'ALIMENTATION SA—See Royal Unibrew A/S; *Int'l*, pg. 6414
CENTRE PARTNERS MANAGEMENT LLC; *U.S. Private*, pg. 828
CENTREPOINT ALLIANCE LIMITED; *Int'l*, pg. 1412
CENTRE REINSURANCE HOLDINGS LTD.—See Zurich Insurance Group Limited; *Int'l*, pg. 8697
CENTRE REINSURANCE INTERNATIONAL COMPANY—See Zurich Insurance Group Limited; *Int'l*, pg. 8697
CENTRE REINSURANCE LTD.—See Zurich Insurance Group Limited; *Int'l*, pg. 8697
CENTRES DE RECHERCHE ET DEVELOPPEMENT NESTLE S.A.S.—See Nestle S.A.; *Int'l*, pg. 5202
CENTRE STATE INTERNATIONAL TRUCKS; *U.S. Private*, pg. 829
CENTRE SUISSE D'ELECTRONIQUE ET DE MICROTECHNIQUE S.A.—See Sulzer Ltd.; *Int'l*, pg. 7257
CENTRETEK SOLUTIONS, LLC—See Amulet Capital Partners, L.P.; *U.S. Private*, pg. 269
CENTRE TESTING INTERNATIONAL (BEIJING) CO., LTD.—See Centre Testing International Corporation; *Int'l*, pg. 1411
CENTRE TESTING INTERNATIONAL CORPORATION; *Int'l*, pg. 1411
CENTRE TESTING INTERNATIONAL GROUP (SHANDONG) CO., LTD.—See Centre Testing International Corporation; *Int'l*, pg. 1411
CENTRE TESTING INTERNATIONAL (HONG KONG) CO., LTD.—See Centre Testing International Corporation; *Int'l*, pg. 1411
CENTRE VEHICULES INDUSTRIELS; *Int'l*, pg. 1411
CENTREVILLE BANK; *U.S. Private*, pg. 829
CENTRE WEST FOUNDRY SUPPLIES SDN. BHD.—See Huettenes-Albertus Chemische Werke GmbH; *Int'l*, pg. 3522
CENTREWEST LONDON BUSES LIMITED—See FirstGroup plc; *Int'l*, pg. 2688
CENTREX EUROPE ENERGY & GAS AG—See Gazprombank JSC; *Int'l*, pg. 2892
CENTREX HOMES—See Apex Limited Partnership; *Int'l*, pg. 511
CENTREXION THERAPEUTICS CORPORATION; *U.S. Private*, pg. 829
CENTREX LIMITED; *Int'l*, pg. 1412
CENTREX PLASTICS, LLC—See Highview Capital, LLC; *U.S. Private*, pg. 1942
CENTREX PLASTICS, LLC—See Victory Park Capital Advisors, LLC; *U.S. Private*, pg. 4379
CENTREX SA—See L'Oreal S.A.; *Int'l*, pg. 4378
CENTREX TECHNICAL SALES, LLC; *U.S. Private*, pg. 829
CENTRIA ARCHITECTURAL SYSTEMS—See Clayton, Dubilier & Rice, LLC; *U.S. Public*, pg. 920
CENTRIA CAPITAL—See Centria Inc.; *Int'l*, pg. 1412
CENTRIA COMMERCE—See Centria Inc.; *Int'l*, pg. 1412

CENTRIA, INC.—See Clayton, Dubilier & Rice, LLC; *U.S. Private*, pg. 920
CENTRIA INC.; *Int'l*, pg. 1412
CENTRI BUSINESS CONSULTING, LLC; *U.S. Private*, pg. 829
CENTRICA BRIGG LIMITED—See Centrica plc; *Int'l*, pg. 1413
CENTRICA BUSINESS SOLUTIONS BV—See Centrica plc; *Int'l*, pg. 1413
CENTRICA BUSINESS SOLUTIONS ITALIA S.R.L.—See Centrica plc; *Int'l*, pg. 1413
CENTRICA CONNECTED HOME LIMITED—See Centrica plc; *Int'l*, pg. 1413
CENTRICA ENERGY LIMITED—See Centrica plc; *Int'l*, pg. 1413
CENTRICA ENERGY TRADING A/S—See Centrica plc; *Int'l*, pg. 1413
THE CENTRICA GAS PRODUCTION LP—See Centrica plc; *Int'l*, pg. 1413
CENTRICA HIVE CANADA INC.—See Centrica plc; *Int'l*, pg. 1413
CENTRICA HIVE LIMITED—See Centrica plc; *Int'l*, pg. 1413
CENTRICA HIVE US INC.—See Centrica plc; *Int'l*, pg. 1413
CENTRICA PLC; *Int'l*, pg. 1413
CENTRICA RPS LIMITED—See Centrica plc; *Int'l*, pg. 1413
CENTRICA SHB LIMITED—See Centrica plc; *Int'l*, pg. 1413
CENTRICA STORAGE LIMITED—See Centrica plc; *Int'l*, pg. 1413
CENTRICA TELECOMMUNICATIONS LTD.—See Centrica plc; *Int'l*, pg. 1413
CENTRIC BANK—See First Commonwealth Financial Corporation; *U.S. Public*, pg. 842
CENTRIC BELGIUM NV—See Centric Holding B.V.; *Int'l*, pg. 1412
CENTRIC BRANDS INC.; *U.S. Private*, pg. 829
CENTRIC BUSINESS SYSTEMS, INC.; *U.S. Private*, pg. 829
CENTRIC CONSULTING, LLC; *U.S. Private*, pg. 829
CENTRIC DIGITAL LLC; *U.S. Private*, pg. 829
CENTRIC FINANCIAL CORP.—See First Commonwealth Financial Corporation; *U.S. Public*, pg. 842
CENTRIC FINANCIAL PROFESSIONALS B.V.—See Centric Holding B.V.; *Int'l*, pg. 1412
CENTRIC GERMANY GMBH—See Centric Holding B.V.; *Int'l*, pg. 1412
CENTRIC GROUP LLC; *U.S. Private*, pg. 829
CENTRIC HEALTH RESOURCES, INC.—See Dohmen Co.; *U.S. Private*, pg. 1254
CENTRIC HOLDING B.V.; *Int'l*, pg. 1412
CENTRIC HOLDINGS S.A.; *Int'l*, pg. 1413
CENTRIC IT SOLUTIONS ROMANIA—See Centric Holding B.V.; *Int'l*, pg. 1412
CENTRIC IT SOLUTIONS SWITZERLAND AG—See Centric Holding B.V.; *Int'l*, pg. 1412
CENTRIC NETHERLANDS HOLDING B.V.—See Centric Holding B.V.; *Int'l*, pg. 1412
CENTRIC NORWAY—See Centric Holding B.V.; *Int'l*, pg. 1412
CENTRICO—See Myriad Restaurant Group; *U.S. Private*, pg. 2825
CENTRICSIT, LLC; *U.S. Private*, pg. 830
CENTRICS LLC; *U.S. Private*, pg. 830
CENTRIC SOFTWARE, INC.; *U.S. Private*, pg. 830
CENTRIC SOLUTIONS LLC—See Optical Cable Corporation; *U.S. Public*, pg. 1609
CENTRIC SWEDEN AB—See Centric Holding B.V.; *Int'l*, pg. 1412
CENTRIC TELECOM, INC.; *U.S. Private*, pg. 830
CENTRICUS PARTNERS LP; *Int'l*, pg. 1413
CENTRIC WEALTH GROUP—See CHAMP Private Equity Pty. Ltd.; *Int'l*, pg. 1439
CENTRIFUGAL & MECHANICAL INDUSTRIES, INC.—See Elgin Equipment Group, LLC; *U.S. Private*, pg. 1359
CENTRIFUGAL SERVICES, INC.—See Brookfield Corporation; *Int'l*, pg. 1181
CENTRIFUGES UNLIMITED INC.—See GEA Group Aktiengesellschaft; *Int'l*, pg. 2898
CENTRIFUGE SYSTEMS, INC.—See Hale Capital Partners, L.P.; *U.S. Private*, pg. 1842
CENTRIFY CORP.—See TPG Capital, L.P.; *U.S. Public*, pg. 2169
CENTRIFYHEALTH, LLC—See UnitedHealth Group Incorporated; *U.S. Public*, pg. 2239
CENTRI MEDICI UNISALUTE S.R.L.—See Unipol Gruppo S.p.A.; *Int'l*, pg. 8056
CENTRINET CORP; *U.S. Private*, pg. 830
CENTRIPETAL CAPITAL PARTNERS, LLC; *U.S. Private*, pg. 830
CENTRISYS CORPORATION—See Chengdu Techcent Environment Industry Co., Ltd.; *Int'l*, pg. 1469
CENTRIX CONTROL SOLUTIONS LIMITED PARTNERSHIP—See Endress+Hauser (International) Holding AG; *Int'l*, pg. 2405
CENTRIX FINANCIAL LLC; *U.S. Private*, pg. 830

CENTRIX INNOVATIONS (PTY) LTD.—See IQVIA Holdings Inc.; *U.S. Public*, pg. 1168
CENTRIX LIMITED—See Macquarie Group Limited; *Int'l*, pg. 4630
CENTRIX SECURITY SDN. BHD.—See Nexgram Holdings Berhad; *Int'l*, pg. 5244
CENTRLNYI TELEGRAF; *Int'l*, pg. 1413
CENTRO AGRICOLO FRIULANO S.R.L.—See BayWa AG; *Int'l*, pg. 917
CENTRO ALEMAN DE INDUSTRIA Y COMERCIO DE MEXICO S.DE R.L.DE C.V.—See Landesbank Baden-Wurttemberg; *Int'l*, pg. 4404
CENTROAMERICA PORTER NOVELLI-COSTA RICA—See Omnicom Group Inc.; *U.S. Public*, pg. 1590
CENTROAMERICA PORTER NOVELLI-EL SALVADOR—See Omnicom Group Inc.; *U.S. Public*, pg. 1590
CENTROAMERICA PORTER NOVELLI-GUATEMALA—See Omnicom Group Inc.; *U.S. Public*, pg. 1590
CENTROAMERICA PORTER NOVELLI-NICARAGUA—See Omnicom Group Inc.; *U.S. Public*, pg. 1590
CENTRO AUBURN—See Central New York Regional Transportation Authority; *U.S. Private*, pg. 823
CENTRO AUDITIVO TELEX S.A.—See Demant A/S; *Int'l*, pg. 2023
CENTRO AUDITIVO WIDEX BRASITOM LTDA.—See EQT AB; *Int'l*, pg. 2480
CENTROBANCA S.P.A.—See Intesa Sanpaolo S.p.A.; *Int'l*, pg. 3766
CENTROBANCA SVILUPPO IMPRESA SGR S.P.A.—See Intesa Sanpaolo S.p.A.; *Int'l*, pg. 3766
CENTRO CALL-A-BUS INC.—See Central New York Regional Transportation Authority; *U.S. Private*, pg. 823
CENTROCAMIONES INC.; *U.S. Private*, pg. 830
CENTRO CARDIOLOGICO MONZINO S.P.A.; *Int'l*, pg. 1413
CENTROCREDIT BANK; *Int'l*, pg. 1414
CENTRO DE ANALISE E TIPAGEM DE GENOMAS LTDA.—See Eurofins Scientific S.E.; *Int'l*, pg. 2535
CENTRO DE ASISTENCIA TELEFONICA, S.A.—See Promotora de Informacones S.A.; *Int'l*, pg. 5995
CENTRO DE CONSTRUCCION DE CARDIOESTIMULADORES DEL URUGUAY SA—See Integer Holdings Corporation; *U.S. Public*, pg. 1135
CENTRO DE ENSAYOS Y ANALISIS CETEST, S.L.—See Construcciones y Auxiliar de Ferrocarriles S.A.; *Int'l*, pg. 1777
CENTRO DE FOMENTO PARA INCLUSION, S. DE R.L. DE C.V.—See Cummins Inc.; *U.S. Public*, pg. 605
CENTRO DE FORMACAO DE EDUCADORES DA VILA LTDA.—See Bahema Educacao SA; *Int'l*, pg. 800
CENTRO DE IMAGEM DIAGNOSTICOS S.A.; *Int'l*, pg. 1413
CENTRO DE PESQUISAS DE ENERGIA ELETRICA—See Centrais Eletricas Brasileiras S.A.; *Int'l*, pg. 1403
CENTRO DE SALUD DE LARES, INC.; *U.S. Private*, pg. 830
CENTRO DE TECNOLOGIA CANAVIEIRA S.A.—See Cosan S.A.; *Int'l*, pg. 1809
CENTRO DE TRANSFERENCIAS, S.A.—See ACS, Actividades de Construccion y Servicios, S.A.; *Int'l*, pg. 110
CENTRO DIAGNOSTICO ITALIANO S.P.A.—See Bracco S.p.A.; *Int'l*, pg. 1134
CENTRO ESCOLAR UNIVERSITY; *Int'l*, pg. 1414
CENTRO FINANZIAMENTI S.P.A.—See Gruppo MutuiOnline S.p.A; *Int'l*, pg. 3140
CENTROID, INC.—See Hicks Holdings, LLC; *U.S. Private*, pg. 1934
CENTROID, INC.—See The Riverside Company; *U.S. Private*, pg. 4108
CENTROID, INC.—See Weinberg Capital Group, Inc.; *U.S. Private*, pg. 4471
CENTRO INC.; *U.S. Private*, pg. 830
CENTRO INMUNOLOGOCIA DE LA COMUNIDAD VALENCIANA, S.L.—See Centene Corporation; *U.S. Public*, pg. 468
CENTROISTOK A.D.; *Int'l*, pg. 1414
CENTRO LEASING BANCA S.P.A.—See Intesa Sanpaolo S.p.A.; *Int'l*, pg. 3764
CENTROMAN—See Mondragon Corporation; *Int'l*, pg. 5029
CENTRO MART INC.; *U.S. Private*, pg. 830
CENTRO MEDIA, INC.; *U.S. Private*, pg. 830
CENTRO MEDICO DE CHEQUEOS MAPFRE VIDA—See MAPFRE S.A.; *Int'l*, pg. 4684
CENTRO MEDICO SAN BIAGIO S.R.L.—See Garofalo Health Care SpA; *Int'l*, pg. 2886
CENTRO MEDICO SPECIALISTICO SRL—See Clariane SE; *Int'l*, pg. 1642
CENTRO MEDICO UNIVERSITA CASTRENSE S.R.L.—See Garofalo Health Care SpA; *Int'l*, pg. 2886
CENTRO-MEDITERRANEA DE BEBIDAS CARBONICAS PEPSICO, SL—See PepsiCo, Inc.; *U.S. Public*, pg. 1668
CENTROMED QUILPUE S.A.—See UnitedHealth Group Incorporated; *U.S. Public*, pg. 2239

CENTROMOTION—See Lone Star Funds; *U.S. Private*, pg. 2485
CENTRON COMMUNICATION SYSTEM (XIAMEN) CO., LTD—See Centron Telecom International Holding Ltd; *Int'l*, pg. 1414
CENTRONIA; *U.S. Private*, pg. 830
CENTRON—See HealthSTAR Communications, Inc.; *U.S. Private*, pg. 1898
CENTRON TELECOM INTERNATIONAL HOLDING LTD; *Int'l*, pg. 1414
CENTRO OF OSWEGO, INC.—See Central New York Regional Transportation Authority; *U.S. Private*, pg. 824
CENTRO PARKING, INC.—See Central New York Regional Transportation Authority; *U.S. Private*, pg. 823
CENTRO PER GLI STUDI DI TECNICA NAVALE CETENA S.P.A.—See Fincantieri S.p.A.; *Int'l*, pg. 2671
CENTROPLAST ENGINEERING PLASTICS GMBH—See CENTROTEC SE; *Int'l*, pg. 1415
CENTRO PORSCHE PADOVA S.R.L.—See Porsche Automobil Holding SE; *Int'l*, pg. 5927
CENTRO PORSCHE S.R.L.—See Porsche Automobil Holding SE; *Int'l*, pg. 5927
CENTRO PROCESSI ASSICURATIVI S.R.L.—See Gruppo MutuiOnline S.p.A; *Int'l*, pg. 3140
CENTROPROIZVOD A.D.—See Nestle S.A.; *Int'l*, pg. 5202
CENTROPROJEKT-ARCHITECTURE, ENGINEERING & STRUCTURAL SYSTEMS LTD.; *Int'l*, pg. 1414
CENTROPROM A.D.; *Int'l*, pg. 1414
CENTRO PROPERTIES GROUP - NORTHEAST—See Blackstone Inc.; *U.S. Public*, pg. 352
CENTRO REVISIONE AUTO S.C.A.R.L.—See DEKRA e.V.; *Int'l*, pg. 2007
CENTRO RICERCHE FIAT S.C.P.A.—See Stellantis N.V.; *Int'l*, pg. 7198
CENTROS COMERCIALES CARREFOUR, S.A.—See Carrefour SA; *Int'l*, pg. 1345
CENTRO SERVIZI ASSET MANGEMENT S.R.L.—See Gruppo MutuiOnline S.p.A; *Int'l*, pg. 3141
CENTROSLAVIJA A.D.; *Int'l*, pg. 1414
CENTROS LIFE SCIENCE PTE LTD—See Kuala Lumpur Kepong Berhad; *Int'l*, pg. 4318
CENTROSOLAR GLAS GMBH & CO. KG—See Ducatt NV; *Int'l*, pg. 2223
CENTROS SOR ISOLINA FERRE INC; *U.S. Private*, pg. 830
CENTRO STAMPA VENETO SPA—See Caltagirone Editore S.p.A.; *Int'l*, pg. 1265
CENTRO STUDI COMPONENTI PER VEICOLI S.P.A.—See Robert Bosch GmbH; *Int'l*, pg. 6360
CENTRO SUR, S.A. DE C.V.—See Empresas ICA S.A.B. de C.V.; *Int'l*, pg. 2390
CENTRO SVILUPPO MATERIALI S.P.A.—See RINA S.p.A.; *Int'l*, pg. 6342
CENTROTEC BUILDING TECHNOLOGY (JIAXING) CO. LTD.—See CENTROTEC SE; *Int'l*, pg. 1414
CENTROTEC COMPOSITES GMBH—See CENTROTEC SE; *Int'l*, pg. 1414
CENTROTEC J I ASIA PTE. LTD.—See CENTROTEC SE; *Int'l*, pg. 1414
CENTRO TECNICO HERRAMENTAL, S.A. DE C.V.—See Aptiv PLC; *Int'l*, pg. 524
CENTRO TECNICO INDURA LIMITADA—See Air Products & Chemicals, Inc.; *U.S. Public*, pg. 66
CENTROTEC SE; *Int'l*, pg. 1414
CENTROTEXTIL A.D.; *Int'l*, pg. 1415
CENTROTHERM ECO SYSTEMS, LLC—See CENTROTEC SE; *Int'l*, pg. 1414
CENTROTHERM PHOTOVOLTAICS AG; *Int'l*, pg. 1415
CENTROTHERM PHOTOVOLTAICS ITALIA S.R.L.—See centrotherm photovoltaics AG; *Int'l*, pg. 1415
CENTROTHERM PHOTOVOLTAICS TECHNOLOGY GMBH—See centrotherm photovoltaics AG; *Int'l*, pg. 1415
CENTROTHERM PHOTOVOLTAICS TECHNOLOGY SHANGHAI CO. LTD.—See centrotherm photovoltaics AG; *Int'l*, pg. 1415
CENTROTHERM PHOTOVOLTAICS USA INC.—See centrotherm photovoltaics AG; *Int'l*, pg. 1415
CENTROTHERM SITEC GMBH—See centrotherm photovoltaics AG; *Int'l*, pg. 1415
CENTROTHERM SUD EUROPE SAS—See centrotherm photovoltaics AG; *Int'l*, pg. 1415
CENTROTHERM SYSTEMTECHNIK GMBH—See CENTROTEC SE; *Int'l*, pg. 1414
CENTROTRADE CHEMICALS AG—See Raiffeisen Bank International AG; *Int'l*, pg. 6183
CENTROTRADE COMMODITIES MALAYSIA SDN BHD—See Raiffeisen Bank International AG; *Int'l*, pg. 6182
CENTROTRADE DEUTSCHLAND GMBH—See Raiffeisen Bank International AG; *Int'l*, pg. 6183
CENTROTRADE MINERALS & METALS, INC.—See Raiffeisen Bank International AG; *Int'l*, pg. 6183
CENTROTRADE SINGAPORE PTE. LTD.—See Raiffeisen Bank International AG; *Int'l*, pg. 6182
CENTROTRANS A.D.; *Int'l*, pg. 1415
CENTROTRANS-EUROLINES D.D.; *Int'l*, pg. 1415
CENTROTRANS TRANSPORT ROBE D.D. SARAJEVO; *Int'l*, pg. 1415

COMPANY NAME INDEX

CENTROTRANS-TRANZIT D.D.; *Int'l*, pg. 1415
CENTROVIAS SISTEMAS RODOVIARIOS, S.A.—See Brookfield Corporation; *Int'l*, pg. 1175
CENTRUL MEDICAL MATEI BASARAB SRL—See MedLife S.A.; *Int'l*, pg. 4784
CENTRUL MEDICAL MICROMEDICA SRL—See MedLife S.A.; *Int'l*, pg. 4784
CENTRUL MEDICAL PANDURI SA—See MedLife S.A.; *Int'l*, pg. 4785
CENTRUM BADAN JAKOSCI SP. Z O.O.—See KGHM Polska Miedz S.A.; *Int'l*, pg. 4148
CENTRUM CAPITAL LTD.; *Int'l*, pg. 1415
CENTRUM CERNY MOST AS—See Unibail-Rodamco-Westfield SE; *Int'l*, pg. 8029
CENTRUM DIALIZA II SP. Z O.O.—See DaVita Inc.; *U.S. Public*, pg. 636
CENTRUM ELEKTRONICZNYCH USLUG PLATNICZYCH ESERVICE SP. Z O.O.—See Global Payments Inc.; *U.S. Public*, pg. 943
CENTRUM FINANCIAL SERVICES LIMITED—See Centrum Capital Ltd.; *Int'l*, pg. 1415
CENTRUM FINANSOWE PULAWSKA SP. Z O.O.—See PKO Bank Polski SA; *Int'l*, pg. 5887
CENTRUM HAFFNERA SP. Z O.O.—See PKO Bank Polski SA; *Int'l*, pg. 5887
CENTRUM KART S.A.—See Bank Polska Kasa Opieki Spolka Akcyjna; *Int'l*, pg. 849
CENTRUM LE CBY POHYBOVEHO APARATU, S.R.O.—See Fresenius SE & Co. KGaA; *Int'l*, pg. 2777
CENTRUM MEDYCZNE ENEL-MED S.A.; *Int'l*, pg. 1415
CENTRUM MICROCREDIT LIMITED—See Centrum Capital Ltd.; *Int'l*, pg. 1415
CENTRUM NOWOCZESNYCH TECHNOLOGII S.A.; *Int'l*, pg. 1416
CENTRUM PAELE A/S—See Per Aarsleff Holding A/S; *Int'l*, pg. 5795
CENTRUM PALI SP. Z O.O.—See Per Aarsleff Holding A/S; *Int'l*, pg. 5795
CENTRUM PFAHLE GMBH—See Per Aarsleff Holding A/S; *Int'l*, pg. 5795
CENTRUM PILE LIMITED—See Per Aarsleff Holding A/S; *Int'l*, pg. 5795
CENTRUM PRE VEDU A VYSKUM S.R.O.—See Enel 3.p.A., *Int'l*, pg. 2411
CENTRUM SURGERY CENTER, LTD.—See HCA Healthcare, Inc.; *U.S. Public*, pg. 993
CENTRUM SURGICAL CENTER—See HCA Healthcare, Inc.; *U.S. Public*, pg. 993
CENTRUM TMT SP. Z O.O.—See Marie Brizard Wine & Spirits S.A.; *Int'l*, pg. 4693
CENTRUM VYZKUMU REZ S.R.O.—See CEZ, a.s.; *Int'l*, pg. 1429
CENTRUM WEALTH LIMITED—See Centrum Capital Ltd.; *Int'l*, pg. 1415
CENTRUS ENERGY CORP.; *U.S. Public*, pg. 474
CENTRUS INTERNATIONAL, INC.—See Neogen Corporation; *U.S. Public*, pg. 1505
CENTRUS PREMIER HOMECARE, INC.—See Maxim Healthcare Services, Inc.; *U.S. Private*, pg. 2618
CENTUM ADETEL TRANSPORTATION SYSTEM SAS—See Centum Electronics Ltd.; *Int'l*, pg. 1416
CENTUM ELECTRONICS LTD.; *Int'l*, pg. 1416
CENTUM FINANCIAL GROUP INC.—See Charlwood Pacific Group; *Int'l*, pg. 1450
CENTUM IMMOBILIEN GMBH—See Vonovia SE; *Int'l*, pg. 8305
CENTUM INVESTMENT COMPANY LIMITED; *Int'l*, pg. 1416
CENTUM LEARNING LIMITED—See Bharti Enterprises Limited; *Int'l*, pg. 1013
CENTURA COLLEGE; *U.S. Private*, pg. 830
CENTURIA CAPITAL LIMITED; *Int'l*, pg. 1416
CENTURIA CAPITAL NZ NO.1 LTD.—See Centuria Capital Limited; *Int'l*, pg. 1416
CENTURIA CORPORATION; *U.S. Private*, pg. 830
CENTURIA INDUSTRIAL REIT—See Centuria Capital Limited; *Int'l*, pg. 1416
CENTURIA OFFICE REIT—See Centuria Capital Limited; *Int'l*, pg. 1416
CENTURIA PROPERTY FUNDS LIMITED—See Centuria Capital Limited; *Int'l*, pg. 1416
CENTURIA PROPERTY FUNDS NO. 2 LIMITED—See Centuria Capital Limited; *Int'l*, pg. 1416
CENTURIA RIT S.C.A.R.L.—See Hera S.p.A.; *Int'l*, pg. 3356
CENTURI GROUP, INC.—See Southwest Gas Holdings, Inc.; *U.S. Public*, pg. 1913
CENTURION AUTO LOGISTICS; *U.S. Private*, pg. 831
CENTURION AUTO TRANSPORT—See Centurion Auto Logistics; *U.S. Private*, pg. 831
CENTURION CONTAINER LLC—See Greif Inc.; *U.S. Public*, pg. 966
CENTURION CORPORATION LIMITED; *Int'l*, pg. 1416
CENTURION COUNSEL, INC.; *U.S. Private*, pg. 831
CENTURION DORMITORIES PTE LTD.—See Centurion Corporation Limited; *Int'l*, pg. 1417
CENTURION DORMITORIES SDN BHD—See Centurion Corporation Limited; *Int'l*, pg. 1417

CENTURION DORMITORY (WESTLITE) PTE LTD.—See Centurion Corporation Limited; *Int'l*, pg. 1417
CENTURION ELECTRONICS (SHANGHAI) LIMITED—See DuPont de Nemours, Inc.; *U.S. Public*, pg. 693
CENTURION ENERGY INTERNATIONAL INC.—See Dana Gas PJSC; *Int'l*, pg. 1957
CENTURION FINANCE SA; *Int'l*, pg. 1417
CENTURION FUNDING, INC.—See Wells Fargo & Company; *U.S. Public*, pg. 2343
THE CENTURION GROUP, INC.—See Marsh & McLennan Companies, Inc.; *U.S. Public*, pg. 1382
CENTURION GROUP LTD; *Int'l*, pg. 1417
CENTURION INDUSTRIES INC. - A-LERT BUILDING SYSTEMS DIVISION—See Centurion Industries Inc.; *U.S. Private*, pg. 831
CENTURION INDUSTRIES INC.; *U.S. Private*, pg. 831
CENTURION INVESTMENTS INC.; *U.S. Private*, pg. 831
CENTURION LAND TITLE, INC.; *U.S. Private*, pg. 831
CENTURION - LIAN BENG (PAPAN) PTE. LTD.—See Centurion Corporation Limited; *Int'l*, pg. 1417
CENTURION LIFE INSURANCE COMPANY—See Bestow, Inc.; *U.S. Private*, pg. 544
CENTURION LLC—See Centene Corporation; *U.S. Public*, pg. 468
CENTURION MEDICAL PRODUCTS CORPORATION—See Medline Industries, LP; *U.S. Private*, pg. 2657
CENTURION MINERALS LTD.; *Int'l*, pg. 1417
CENTURION OF INDIANA, LLC—See Centene Corporation; *U.S. Public*, pg. 468
CENTURION OF NEW HAMPSHIRE, LLC—See Centene Corporation; *U.S. Public*, pg. 468
CENTURION OF PENNSYLVANIA, LLC—See Centene Corporation; *U.S. Public*, pg. 468
CENTURION PETROLEUM CORPORATION—See Dana Gas PJSC; *Int'l*, pg. 1957
CENTURION PIPELINE LP, INC.—See Occidental Petroleum Corporation; *U.S. Public*, pg. 1561
CENTURION PIPELINE L.P.—See Occidental Petroleum Corporation; *U.S. Public*, pg. 1561
CENTURION PIPELINE—See Occidental Petroleum Corporation; *U.S. Public*, pg. 1561
CENTURION PIPELINE—See Occidental Petroleum Corporation; *U.S. Public*, pg. 1561
CENTURION SAFETY PRODUCTS LIMITED; *Int'l*, pg. 1417
CENTURION SERVICE GROUP, LLC—See Ascension Health Alliance; *U.S. Private*, pg. 346
CENTURION STRATEGIES LLC; *U.S. Private*, pg. 831
CENTURION STUDENT SERVICES PTY. LTD.—See Centurion Corporation Limited; *Int'l*, pg. 1417
CENTURION STUDENT SERVICES (UK) LTD.—See Centurion Corporation Limited; *Int'l*, pg. 1417
CENTURION SYSTEMS, INC.—See Tier 1 Performance Solutions, LLC; *U.S. Private*, pg. 4168
CENTURION TRANSPORT CO. PTY LTD—See CFC Group Pty. Ltd.; *Int'l*, pg. 1429
CENTURION TRUCK RENTAL LTD—See Ballyvesey Holdings Limited; *Int'l*, pg. 809
CENTURY 21 BEGGINS ENTERPRISES, INC.; *U.S. Private*, pg. 831
CENTURY 21 CANADA LIMITED PARTNERSHIP—See Charlwood Pacific Group; *Int'l*, pg. 1450
CENTURY 21 FRANCE SAS—See Citya Immobilier SAS; *Int'l*, pg. 1628
CENTURY 21 HOMETOWN REALTY; *U.S. Private*, pg. 831
CENTURY 21 INC.; *U.S. Private*, pg. 831
CENTURY 21 NACHMAN REALTY, L.L.C.; *U.S. Private*, pg. 831
CENTURY 21 NORTH HOMES REALTY, INC.; *U.S. Private*, pg. 831
CENTURY 21 PINNACLE; *U.S. Private*, pg. 831
CENTURY 21 PROMOTIONS, INC.; *U.S. Private*, pg. 831
CENTURY 21 PROPERTY AGENCY LIMITED—See Huanxi Media Group Limited; *Int'l*, pg. 3513
CENTURY 21 REAL ESTATE LLC—See Anywhere Real Estate Inc.; *U.S. Public*, pg. 140
CENTURY21 REAL ESTATE OF JAPAN LTD.; *Int'l*, pg. 1420
CENTURY 21 RONDEAU; *U.S. Private*, pg. 831
CENTURY AIR CONDITIONING SUPPLY INC.; *U.S. Private*, pg. 831
CENTURY ALUMINUM COMPANY; *U.S. Public*, pg. 474
CENTURY ALUMINUM OF KENTUCKY GENERAL PARTNERSHIP—See Century Aluminum Company; *U.S. Public*, pg. 474
CENTURY ALUMINUM OF KENTUCKY—See Century Aluminum Company; *U.S. Public*, pg. 474
CENTURY ALUMINUM OF SOUTH CAROLINA, INC.—See Century Aluminum Company; *U.S. Public*, pg. 474
CENTURY ALUMINUM OF WEST VIRGINIA, INC.—See Century Aluminum Company; *U.S. Public*, pg. 474
CENTURY ALUMINUM SEBREE, LLC—See Century Aluminum Company; *U.S. Public*, pg. 474
CENTURY AMERICA CORPORATION; *U.S. Private*, pg. 831

CENTURY FENCE COMPANY

CENTURY ARMS, INC.—See Century International Arms Corporation; *U.S. Private*, pg. 833
CENTURY AUSTRALIA INVESTMENTS LIMITED—See WAM Leaders Limited; *Int'l*, pg. 8337
CENTURY BANCORP, INC.—See Eastern Bankshares, Inc.; *U.S. Public*, pg. 703
CENTURY BANCSHARES, INC.; *U.S. Private*, pg. 831
CENTURY BANCSHARES, INC.; *U.S. Private*, pg. 832
CENTURY BANCSHARES OF FLORIDA, INC.; *U.S. Private*, pg. 831
CENTURY BANK FSB—See Century Financial Services Corp.; *U.S. Private*, pg. 833
CENTURY BANK OF FLORIDA—See Century Bancshares of Florida, Inc.; *U.S. Private*, pg. 831
CENTURY BANK OF KENTUCKY, INC.—See Century Bancshares, Inc.; *U.S. Private*, pg. 832
CENTURY BANK OF THE OZARKS; *U.S. Private*, pg. 832
CENTURY BANK; *U.S. Private*, pg. 832
CENTURY BANK & TRUST; *U.S. Private*, pg. 832
CENTURY BATHWORKS, INC.; *U.S. Private*, pg. 832
CENTURY BOND BHD.—See Kumpulan Darul Ehsan Berhad; *Int'l*, pg. 4331
CENTURY BUSINESS SOLUTIONS, INC.; *U.S. Private*, pg. 832
CENTURY BUSINESS TECHNOLOGIES, INC.; *U.S. Private*, pg. 832
CENTURY CAPITAL MANAGEMENT LLC—See Congress Asset Management Co.; *U.S. Private*, pg. 1013
CENTURY CARPET, INC.; *U.S. Private*, pg. 832
CENTURY CASINO BATH, LTD.—See Century Casinos, Inc.; *U.S. Public*, pg. 474
CENTURY CASINO CALGARY INC.—See Century Casinos, Inc.; *U.S. Public*, pg. 474
CENTURY CASINOS AFRICA (PTY) LTD.—See Century Casinos, Inc.; *U.S. Public*, pg. 474
CENTURY CASINOS CALEDON (PTY) LTD.—See Century Casinos, Inc.; *U.S. Public*, pg. 474
CENTURY CASINOS CRIPPLE CREEK, INC.—See Century Casinos, Inc.; *U.S. Public*, pg. 474
CENTURY CASINOS EUROPE GMBH—See Century Casinos, Inc.; *U.S. Public*, pg. 474
CENTURY CASINOS, INC.; *U.S. Public*, pg. 474
CENTURY CASINO ST. ALBERT, INC.—See Century Casinos, Inc.; *U.S. Public*, pg. 474
CENTURY CELLUNET INTERNATIONAL, INC.—See Lumen Technologies, Inc.; *U.S. Public*, pg. 1345
CENTURY CHEMICAL WORKS SDN. BHD.—See Osaka Gas Co., Ltd.; *Int'l*, pg. 5646
CENTURY CITY INTERNATIONAL HOLDINGS LTD; *Int'l*, pg. 1417
CENTURY COBALT CORP.; *U.S. Public*, pg. 474
THE CENTURY CO., LTD.; *Int'l*, pg. 7631
CENTURY COMMUNITIES, INC.; *U.S. Public*, pg. 474
CENTURY COMPANIES, INC.; *U.S. Private*, pg. 832
CENTURY CONSTRUCTION, INC.; *U.S. Private*, pg. 832
CENTURY CONTAINER, LLC; *U.S. Private*, pg. 832
CENTURY CONTRACTORS, INC.; *U.S. Private*, pg. 832
CENTURY CONVEYOR, INC.; *U.S. Private*, pg. 832
CENTURY CORROSION TECHNOLOGIES, INC.—See First Reserve Management, L.P.; *U.S. Private*, pg. 1525
CENTURY CORRUGATED CONTAINER INC.—See Ozark Warehouses, Inc.; *U.S. Private*, pg. 3058
CENTURY DIRECT LLC; *U.S. Private*, pg. 832
CENTURY DISTRIBUTION SYSTEMS (HONG KONG) LIMITED—See Kawasaki Kisen Kaisha, Ltd.; *Int'l*, pg. 4098
CENTURY DISTRIBUTION SYSTEMS, INC.—See Kawasaki Kisen Kaisha, Ltd.; *Int'l*, pg. 4098
CENTURY DISTRIBUTION SYSTEMS (INTERNATIONAL) LIMITED—See Kawasaki Kisen Kaisha, Ltd.; *Int'l*, pg. 4098
CENTURY DISTRIBUTION SYSTEMS (SHIPPING) LIMITED—See Kawasaki Kisen Kaisha, Ltd.; *Int'l*, pg. 4098
CENTURY DISTRIBUTORS, INC.; *U.S. Private*, pg. 832
CENTURY DRAGON INVESTMENT LIMITED—See Smartac International Holdings Limited; *Int'l*, pg. 7001
CENTURY DRILLING & ENERGY SERVICES (NZ) LTD—See MB Holding Company LLC; *Int'l*, pg. 4750
CENTURY ENERGY INTERNATIONAL HOLDINGS LIMITED; *Int'l*, pg. 1418
CENTURY ENERGY LTD. - HOUSTON BRANCH—See Parent Capital Corp.; *Int'l*, pg. 5741
CENTURY ENKA LTD.—See CVC Capital Partners SICAV-FIS S.A.; *Int'l*, pg. 1886
CENTURY ENKA LTD.—See The Aditya Birla Group; *Int'l*, pg. 7610
CENTURY ENTERTAINMENT INTERNATIONAL HOLDINGS LIMITED; *Int'l*, pg. 1418
CENTURY EQUIPMENT INC.; *U.S. Private*, pg. 832
CENTURY EQUIPMENT—See Century Equipment Inc.; *U.S. Private*, pg. 832
CENTURY EQUITY PARTNERS LLC; *U.S. Private*, pg. 832
CENTURY EXTRUSIONS LIMITED; *Int'l*, pg. 1418
CENTURY FASTENERS CORP.; *U.S. Private*, pg. 832
CENTURY FAST FOODS INC.; *U.S. Private*, pg. 832
CENTURY FENCE COMPANY; *U.S. Private*, pg. 833

CENTURY FENCE COMPANY

Company Index

CENTURY FENCE CO.—See Century Fence Company; *U.S. Private*, pg. 833
CENTURY FINANCIAL SERVICES CORP.; *U.S. Private*, pg. 833
CENTURY FIRE PROTECTION, LLC—See FirstService Corporation; *Int'l*, pg. 2691
CENTURY FOOD COMPANY LIMITED—See Century Global Commodities Corporation; *Int'l*, pg. 1418
CENTURY FOODS INTERNATIONAL, LLC—See Hormel Foods Corporation; *U.S. Public*, pg. 1054
CENTURY FURNITURE INDUSTRIES—See CV Industries Inc.; *U.S. Private*, pg. 1132
CENTURY GAMING, INC.—See Accel Entertainment, Inc.; *U.S. Public*, pg. 32
CENTURY GAMING TECHNOLOGIES; *U.S. Private*, pg. 833
CENTURY GINWA RETAIL HOLDINGS LIMITED; *Int'l*, pg. 1418
CENTURY GLOBAL COMMODITIES CORPORATION; *Int'l*, pg. 1418
CENTURY GROUP INC.; *U.S. Private*, pg. 833
CENTURY GROUP INTERNATIONAL HOLDINGS LIMITED; *Int'l*, pg. 1418
CENTURY GROUP LLC—See Century Communities, Inc.; *U.S. Public*, pg. 475
CENTURY HEALTHCARE LLC—See Fringe Benefit Group LP; *U.S. Private*, pg. 1612
CENTURY HOUSING; *U.S. Private*, pg. 833
CENTURY III CHEVY; *U.S. Private*, pg. 833
CENTURY II SERVICES, INC.—See Paychex, Inc.; *U.S. Public*, pg. 1655
CENTURY II—See Paychex, Inc.; *U.S. Public*, pg. 1655
CENTURY II STAFFING, INC.—See Paychex, Inc.; *U.S. Public*, pg. 1655
CENTURY II STAFFING TN, INC.—See Paychex, Inc.; *U.S. Public*, pg. 1655
CENTURY, INC.; *U.S. Private*, pg. 834
CENTURY INDEMNITY COMPANY—See Chubb Limited; *Int'l*, pg. 1590
CENTURY INDUSTRIAL COATINGS INCORPORATED—See Axalta Coating Systems Ltd.; *U.S. Public*, pg. 255
CENTURY INDUSTRIES COMPANY—See Emerson Electric Co.; *U.S. Public*, pg. 751
CENTURY INDUSTRIES INC.; *U.S. Private*, pg. 833
CENTURY INDUSTRIES, LLC; *U.S. Private*, pg. 833
CENTURY INDUSTRIES—See Century Container, LLC; *U.S. Private*, pg. 832
CENTURY INOAC CO., LTD.—See INOAC Corporation; *Int'l*, pg. 3713
CENTURY INSURANCE COMPANY LIMITED—See Lakson Group of Companies; *Int'l*, pg. 4398
CENTURY INSURANCE GROUP—See Fosun International Limited; *Int'l*, pg. 2752
CENTURY INTERNATIONAL ARMS CORPORATION; *U.S. Private*, pg. 833
CENTURY INTERNATIONAL TRADING INC.—See Orleans International, Inc.; *U.S. Private*, pg. 3044
CENTURY INVESTMENT GROUP P.L.C.; *Int'l*, pg. 1418
CENTURY INVESTMENTS INC—See Caruso Affiliated; *U.S. Private*, pg. 777
CENTURY IRON & STEEL INDUSTRIAL CO., LTD.; *Int'l*, pg. 1418
CENTURY IRON & STEEL INDUSTRIAL CO., LTD. - TAOYUAN PLANT—See Century Iron & Steel Industrial Co., Ltd.; *Int'l*, pg. 1418
CENTURY IRRIGATION STATION—See Century Equipment Inc.; *U.S. Private*, pg. 832
CENTURY KENTUCKY, INC.—See Century Aluminum Company; *U.S. Public*, pg. 474
CENTURY LEGEND FINANCE LIMITED—See Century Legend Holdings Ltd; *Int'l*, pg. 1418
CENTURY LEGEND HOLDINGS LTD; *Int'l*, pg. 1418
CENTURY LEGEND MANAGEMENT LIMITED—See Century Legend Holdings Ltd; *Int'l*, pg. 1418
CENTURY LIFE CO., LTD.—See Haseko Corporation; *Int'l*, pg. 3282
CENTURYLINK AUSTRALIA PTY. LTD.—See Lumen Technologies, Inc.; *U.S. Public*, pg. 1345
CENTURYLINK CANADA, INC.—See Lumen Technologies, Inc.; *U.S. Public*, pg. 1345
CENTURYLINK CHILE S.A.—See Lumen Technologies, Inc.; *U.S. Public*, pg. 1345
CENTURYLINK COLOMBIA S.A.—See Lumen Technologies, Inc.; *U.S. Public*, pg. 1345
CENTURYLINK COMMUNICATIONS BELGIUM SA—See Lumen Technologies, Inc.; *U.S. Public*, pg. 1345
CENTURYLINK COMMUNICATIONS (IMPSAT) NEDERLAND B.V.—See Lumen Technologies, Inc.; *U.S. Public*, pg. 1345
CENTURYLINK COMMUNICATIONS ITALIA SRL—See Lumen Technologies, Inc.; *U.S. Public*, pg. 1345
CENTURYLINK COMMUNICATIONS, LLC—See Lumen Technologies, Inc.; *U.S. Public*, pg. 1345
CENTURYLINK COMUNICACOES DO BRASIL LTDA.—See Lumen Technologies, Inc.; *U.S. Public*, pg. 1345
CENTURYLINK CORPORATION JAPAN—See Lumen Technologies, Inc.; *U.S. Public*, pg. 1345

CENTURYLINK COSTA RICA, S.R.L.—See Lumen Technologies, Inc.; *U.S. Public*, pg. 1345
CENTURYLINKECUADOR S.A.—See Lumen Technologies, Inc.; *U.S. Public*, pg. 1346
CENTURYLINK GERMANY GMBH—See Lumen Technologies, Inc.; *U.S. Public*, pg. 1345
CENTURYLINK INVESTMENT MANAGEMENT COMPANY—See Lumen Technologies, Inc.; *U.S. Public*, pg. 1345
CENTURYLINK JAPAN, LTD—See Lumen Technologies, Inc.; *U.S. Public*, pg. 1345
CENTURYLINK LIMITED—See Lumen Technologies, Inc.; *U.S. Public*, pg. 1346
CENTURYLINK OF ADAMSVILLE, INC.—See Lumen Technologies, Inc.; *U.S. Public*, pg. 1346
CENTURYLINK OF MONROE COUNTY, LLC—See Lumen Technologies, Inc.; *U.S. Public*, pg. 1346
CENTURYLINK OF NORTH LOUISIANA, LLC—See Lumen Technologies, Inc.; *U.S. Public*, pg. 1346
CENTURYLINK OF THE SOUTHWEST, INC.—See Lumen Technologies, Inc.; *U.S. Public*, pg. 1346
CENTURYLINK PANAMA—See Lumen Technologies, Inc.; *U.S. Public*, pg. 1346
CENTURYLINK PERU S.A.—See Lumen Technologies, Inc.; *U.S. Public*, pg. 1346
CENTURYLINK PUBLIC COMMUNICATIONS, INC.—See Lumen Technologies, Inc.; *U.S. Public*, pg. 1346
CENTURYLINK SINGAPORE PTE. LTD.—See Lumen Technologies, Inc.; *U.S. Public*, pg. 1346
CENTURYLINK TECHNOLOGIES INDIA PRIVATE LIMITED—See Lumen Technologies, Inc.; *U.S. Public*, pg. 1346
CENTURYLINK TECHNOLOGY AUSTRALIA PTY. LIMITED—See Lumen Technologies, Inc.; *U.S. Public*, pg. 1346
CENTURYLINK TECHNOLOGY HONG KONG LIMITED—See Lumen Technologies, Inc.; *U.S. Public*, pg. 1346
CENTURYLINK TECHNOLOGY SINGAPORE PTE LTD.—See Lumen Technologies, Inc.; *U.S. Public*, pg. 1346
CENTURYLINK TECHNOLOGY UK LIMITED—See Lumen Technologies, Inc.; *U.S. Public*, pg. 1346
CENTURYLINK TELECOMUNICACIONES S.A.—See Lumen Technologies, Inc.; *U.S. Public*, pg. 1346
CENTURY LIVING, LLC—See Century Communities, Inc.; *U.S. Public*, pg. 475
CENTURY LLC; *U.S. Private*, pg. 833
CENTURY LOGISTICS SDN. BHD.—See CJ Century Logistics Holdings Berhad; *Int'l*, pg. 1631
CENTURY MANUFACTURING, INC.; *U.S. Private*, pg. 833
CENTURY MARKETING SOLUTIONS, LLC—See Lumen Technologies, Inc.; *U.S. Public*, pg. 1345
CENTURY MARTIAL ART SUPPLY LLC—See Century LLC; *U.S. Private*, pg. 833
CENTURY MATERIALS INC—See Nesbitt Investment Company; *U.S. Private*, pg. 2886
CENTURY MECHANICAL SOLUTIONS, INC.—See Comfort Systems USA, Inc.; *U.S. Public*, pg. 543
CENTURY MEDICAL, INC.—See ITOCHU Corporation; *Int'l*, pg. 3835
CENTURY MINING CORPORATION—See Mangazeya Mining Ltd.; *Int'l*, pg. 4670
CENTURY MOLD CO., INC.; *U.S. Private*, pg. 833
CENTURY MOVING & STORAGE INC—See Johnson Storage & Moving Company; *U.S. Private*, pg. 2229
CENTURY NATIONAL BANK—See Park National Corporation; *U.S. Public*, pg. 1638
CENTURY-NATIONAL INSURANCE COMPANY—See The Allstate Corporation; *U.S. Public*, pg. 2033
CENTURY NEXT FINANCIAL CORPORATION; *U.S. Public*, pg. 475
CENTURY NOVELTY COMPANY, INC.; *U.S. Private*, pg. 833
CENTURY PACIFIC FOOD, INC. - CANNED MEAT PLANT—See Century Pacific Food, Inc.; *Int'l*, pg. 1418
CENTURY PACIFIC FOOD, INC. - COCONUT PRODUCTS PLANT—See Century Pacific Food, Inc.; *Int'l*, pg. 1419
CENTURY PACIFIC FOOD, INC. - DAIRY & MIXES PLANT—See Century Pacific Food, Inc.; *Int'l*, pg. 1419
CENTURY PACIFIC FOOD, INC. - GENERAL SANTOS CITY PLANT—See Century Pacific Food, Inc.; *Int'l*, pg. 1419
CENTURY PACIFIC FOOD, INC.; *Int'l*, pg. 1418
CENTURY PACIFIC FOOD, INC. - ZAMBOANGA PLANT—See Century Pacific Food, Inc.; *Int'l*, pg. 1419
CENTURY PAPER & BOARD MILLS LIMITED; *Int'l*, pg. 1419
CENTURY PARK CAPITAL PARTNERS, LLC; *U.S. Private*, pg. 833
CENTURY PAYMENTS, INC.—See Advent International Corporation; *U.S. Private*, pg. 108
CENTURY PAYMENTS, INC.—See Bain Capital, LP; *U.S. Private*, pg. 452
CENTURY PEAK HOLDINGS CORP.; *Int'l*, pg. 1419
CENTURY PETROLEUM LTD.; *U.S. Private*, pg. 834
CENTURY PLYBOARDS (I) LTD.; *Int'l*, pg. 1419

CORPORATE AFFILIATIONS

CENTURY PRECAST PRODUCTS, LLC; *U.S. Private*, pg. 834
CENTURY PROPERTIES GROUP, INC.; *Int'l*, pg. 1419
CENTURY READY MIX CORPORATION; *U.S. Private*, pg. 834
CENTURY REPROGRAPHICS—See American CyberSystems, Inc.; *U.S. Private*, pg. 229
CENTURY RESORTS ALBERTA, INC.—See Century Casinos, Inc.; *U.S. Public*, pg. 474
CENTURY RESORTS MANAGEMENT GMBH—See Century Casinos, Inc.; *U.S. Public*, pg. 474
CENTURY RETAIL EUROPE B.V.—See Hangzhou Century Co., Ltd.; *Int'l*, pg. 3246
CENTURY ROLLFORMING, INC.—See Century, Inc.; *U.S. Private*, pg. 834
CENTURY RV, INC.—See Lazydays Holdings, Inc.; *U.S. Public*, pg. 1294
CENTURY SAGE SCIENTIFIC HOLDINGS LIMITED; *Int'l*, pg. 1419
CENTURY SAGE SCIENTIFIC (TAIWAN) LIMITED—See Century Sage Scientific Holdings Limited; *Int'l*, pg. 1419
CENTURY SAVINGS BANK; *U.S. Private*, pg. 834
CENTURY SECURITIES ASSOCIATES, INCORPORATED—See Stifel Financial Corp.; *U.S. Public*, pg. 1949
CENTURY SERVICE AFFILIATES, INC.; *U.S. Private*, pg. 834
CENTURY SNACKS, LLC—See Insignia Capital Group, L.P.; *U.S. Private*, pg. 2091
CENTURY SOFTWARE LIMITED; *U.S. Private*, pg. 834
CENTURY SPECIALTIES—See Century, Inc.; *U.S. Private*, pg. 834
CENTURY SPRING CORP.—See American Securities LLC; *U.S. Private*, pg. 249
CENTURY STEEL—See Esmark Incorporated; *U.S. Private*, pg. 1426
CENTURY STRONG LIMITED—See Asia Resources Holdings Limited; *Int'l*, pg. 615
CENTURY SUNSHINE GROUP HOLDINGS LIMITED; *Int'l*, pg. 1419
CENTURY SUNSHINE PAPER (USA) INC.—See China Sunshine Paper Holdings Company Limited; *Int'l*, pg. 1556
CENTURY SUPPLY CO. INC.; *U.S. Private*, pg. 834
CENTURY TECHNOLOGY GROUP; *U.S. Private*, pg. 834
CENTURYTEL ACQUISITION LLC—See Lumen Technologies, Inc.; *U.S. Public*, pg. 1346
CENTURYTEL ARKANSAS HOLDINGS, INC.—See Lumen Technologies, Inc.; *U.S. Public*, pg. 1346
CENTURYTEL BROADBAND WIRELESS, LLC—See Lumen Technologies, Inc.; *U.S. Public*, pg. 1346
CENTURYTEL.COM, LLC—See Lumen Technologies, Inc.; *U.S. Public*, pg. 1348
CENTURYTEL HOLDINGS MISSOURI, INC.—See Lumen Technologies, Inc.; *U.S. Public*, pg. 1346
CENTURYTEL INTERACTIVE COMPANY—See Lumen Technologies, Inc.; *U.S. Public*, pg. 1346
CENTURYTEL OF CENTRAL ARKANSAS, LLC—See Lumen Technologies, Inc.; *U.S. Public*, pg. 1346
CENTURYTEL OF CENTRAL INDIANA, INC.—See Lumen Technologies, Inc.; *U.S. Public*, pg. 1346
CENTURYTEL OF CLAIBORNE, INC.—See Lumen Technologies, Inc.; *U.S. Public*, pg. 1346
CENTURYTEL OF COLORADO, INC.—See Lumen Technologies, Inc.; *U.S. Public*, pg. 1346
CENTURYTEL OF INTER ISLAND, INC.—See Lumen Technologies, Inc.; *U.S. Public*, pg. 1346
CENTURYTEL OF LAKE DALLAS, INC.—See Lumen Technologies, Inc.; *U.S. Public*, pg. 1346
CENTURYTEL OF NORTHERN WISCONSIN, LLC—See Lumen Technologies, Inc.; *U.S. Public*, pg. 1346
CENTURYTEL OF NORTHWEST LOUISIANA, INC.—See Lumen Technologies, Inc.; *U.S. Public*, pg. 1346
CENTURYTEL OF NORTHWEST WISCONSIN, LLC—See Lumen Technologies, Inc.; *U.S. Public*, pg. 1346
CENTURYTEL OF OHIO, INC.—See Lumen Technologies, Inc.; *U.S. Public*, pg. 1346
CENTURYTEL OF OOLTEWAH-COLLEGEDALE, INC.—See Lumen Technologies, Inc.; *U.S. Public*, pg. 1346
CENTURYTEL OF THE NORTHWEST, INC.—See Lumen Technologies, Inc.; *U.S. Public*, pg. 1346
CENTURYTEL OF WISCONSIN, LLC—See Lumen Technologies, Inc.; *U.S. Public*, pg. 1346
CENTURYTEL OF WYOMING, INC.—See Lumen Technologies, Inc.; *U.S. Public*, pg. 1346
CENTURYTEL SM TELECORP, INC.—See Lumen Technologies, Inc.; *U.S. Public*, pg. 1346
CENTURYTEL TELEVIDEO, INC.—See Lumen Technologies, Inc.; *U.S. Public*, pg. 1346
CENTURYTEL/TELEVIEW OF WISCONSIN, INC.—See Lumen Technologies, Inc.; *U.S. Public*, pg. 1346
CENTURY TEXTILES AND INDUSTRIES LIMITED - BIRLA CENTURY DIVISION—See Century Textiles and Industries Limited; *Int'l*, pg. 1419
CENTURY TEXTILES AND INDUSTRIES LIMITED - CENTURY DENIM DIVISION—See Century Textiles and Industries Limited; *Int'l*, pg. 1419

COMPANY NAME INDEX

CENTURY TEXTILES AND INDUSTRIES LIMITED - CENTURY DENIM WORKS—See Century Textiles and Industries Limited; *Int'l*, pg. 1419
CENTURY TEXTILES AND INDUSTRIES LIMITED - CENTURY PULP AND PAPER DIVISION—See Century Textiles and Industries Limited; *Int'l*, pg. 1419
CENTURY TEXTILES AND INDUSTRIES LIMITED - CENTURY RAYON DIVISION—See Century Textiles and Industries Limited; *Int'l*, pg. 1419
CENTURY TEXTILES AND INDUSTRIES LIMITED - CENTURY RAYON PLANT—See Century Textiles and Industries Limited; *Int'l*, pg. 1419
CENTURY TEXTILES AND INDUSTRIES LIMITED - CENTURY YARN DIVISION—See Century Textiles and Industries Limited; *Int'l*, pg. 1419
CENTURY TEXTILES AND INDUSTRIES LIMITED - CENTURY YARN WORKS—See Century Textiles and Industries Limited; *Int'l*, pg. 1420
CENTURY TEXTILES AND INDUSTRIES LIMITED - COTTONS BY CENTURY DIVISION—See Century Textiles and Industries Limited; *Int'l*, pg. 1420
CENTURY TEXTILES AND INDUSTRIES LIMITED; *Int'l*, pg. 1419
CENTURY THEATRES OF CANADA, ULC—See Cinemark Holdings, Inc.; *U.S. Public*, pg. 495
CENTURY THEATRES SUMMIT SIERRA, L.L.C.—See Cinemark Holdings, Inc.; *U.S. Public*, pg. 495
CENTURY THERAPEUTICS, INC.; *U.S. Public*, pg. 475
CENTURY TOOL & GAGE—See Century Tool & Gage; *U.S. Private*, pg. 834
CENTURY TOOL & GAGE; *U.S. Private*, pg. 834
CENTURYTOUCH LTD, INC.; *Int'l*, pg. 1420
CENTURY TRADING CO., LTD—See ANEST IWATA Corporation; *Int'l*, pg. 458
CENTURY TRADING CO., LTD.—See Isetan Mitsukoshi Holdings Ltd.; *Int'l*, pg. 3814
CENTURY TRAVEL SERVICE INC.; *U.S. Private*, pg. 834
CENTURY WIND POWER CO., LTD.—See Century Iron & Steel Industrial Co., Ltd.; *Int'l*, pg. 1418
CENTURY YUASA BATTERIES (NZ) LTD—See GS Yuasa Corporation; *Int'l*, pg. 3143
CENTURY YUASA BATTERIES PTY LTD—See GS Yuasa Corporation; *Int'l*, pg. 3143
CENUP TIKINTI SERVIS—See Telefon Holding A.S.; *Int'l*, pg. 7526
CENVEO COMMERCIAL PRINTING & PACKAGING - ST. LOUIS—See Cenveo, Inc.; *U.S. Private*, pg. 834
CENVEO CORP. - CUSTOM RESALE GROUP—See Cenveo, Inc.; *U.S. Private*, pg. 834
CENVEO CORPORATION—See Cenveo, Inc.; *U.S. Private*, pg. 834
CENVEO, INC.; *U.S. Private*, pg. 834
CENVEO MCLAREN MORRIS AND TODD COMPANY—See Cenveo, Inc.; *U.S. Private*, pg. 835
CENVEO PUBLISHER SERVICES INDIA LIMITED—See Cenveo, Inc.; *U.S. Private*, pg. 835
CENVEO PUBLISHER SERVICES—See Cenveo, Inc.; *U.S. Private*, pg. 834
CENVEO PUBLISHER SERVICES—See Cenveo, Inc.; *U.S. Private*, pg. 835
CENVIRO SDN BHD—See Khazanah Nasional Berhad; *Int'l*, pg. 4152
CENWOOD KITCHENS—See Central Woodwork, Inc.; *U.S. Private*, pg. 826
CENXI DONGLIN ROSIN CO., LTD.—See Harima Chemicals Group, Inc.; *Int'l*, pg. 3276
CEOBUS—See Regie Autonome des Transports Parisiens; *Int'l*, pg. 6253
CEO CONSTRUCTION JOINT STOCK COMPANY—See C.E.O Group Joint Stock Company; *Int'l*, pg. 1240
CEO EVENT MEDYA AS; *Int'l*, pg. 1420
C.E.O GROUP JOINT STOCK COMPANY; *Int'l*, pg. 1240
CEO IMAGING SYSTEMS, INC.—See Intellinetics, Inc.; *U.S. Public*, pg. 1140
CEO INTERNATIONAL CO., LTD.—See C.E.O Group Joint Stock Company; *Int'l*, pg. 1240
CEOLPAR - CENTRAIS EOLICAS DO PARANA LTDA.—See Companhia Paranaense de Energia; *Int'l*, pg. 1747
CEON CORPORATION—See Concentrix Corporation; *U.S. Public*, pg. 564
CEO SERVICE DEVELOPMENT JOINT STOCK COMPANY—See C.E.O Group Joint Stock Company; *Int'l*, pg. 1240
CEO TOURISM JOINT STOCK COMPANY—See C.E.O Group Joint Stock Company; *Int'l*, pg. 1240
CEOTRONICS AG; *Int'l*, pg. 1420
CEOTRONICS, INC.—See CeoTronics AG; *Int'l*, pg. 1420
CEOTRONICS S.A.R.L.—See CeoTronics AG; *Int'l*, pg. 1420
CEOTRONICS (SCHWEIZ) AG—See CeoTronics AG; *Int'l*, pg. 1420
CEOTRONICS S.L.—See CeoTronics AG; *Int'l*, pg. 1420
CEPAC—See Hayel Saeed Anam Group of Companies; *Int'l*, pg. 3290
CEPATWAWASAN GROUP BERHAD; *Int'l*, pg. 1420
CEPCO TRADING SDN. BHD.—See Omni-Plus System Limited; *Int'l*, pg. 5563

CEPD MANAGEMENT SP. Z O.O.—See CEPD N.V.; *Int'l*, pg. 1420
CEPD N.V.; *Int'l*, pg. 1420
CEPEX FRANCE S.A.S.—See Fluidra SA; *Int'l*, pg. 2714
CEPEX GMBH—See Fluidra SA; *Int'l*, pg. 2714
CEPEX PORTUGAL, LDA—See Fluidra SA; *Int'l*, pg. 2714
CEPEX, S.A.U. (GRANOLLERS)—See Fluidra SA; *Int'l*, pg. 2714
CEPEX, S.A.U. (LA GARRIGA)—See Fluidra SA; *Int'l*, pg. 2714
CEPEX, S.A.U. (SANT JAUME DE LLIERCA)—See Fluidra SA; *Int'l*, pg. 2714
CEPEX S.A.U.—See Fluidra SA; *Int'l*, pg. 2714
CEPEX S.R.L.—See Fluidra SA; *Int'l*, pg. 2714
CEPHAZONE PHARMA LLC—See Aurobindo Pharma Ltd.; *Int'l*, pg. 712
CEPHEID AB—See Danaher Corporation; *U.S. Public*, pg. 625
CEPHEID BENELUX—See Danaher Corporation; *U.S. Public*, pg. 625
CEPHEID EUROPE SAS—See Danaher Corporation; *U.S. Public*, pg. 625
CEPHEID GK—See Danaher Corporation; *U.S. Public*, pg. 625
CEPHEID GMBH—See Danaher Corporation; *U.S. Public*, pg. 625
CEPHEID ITALY SRL—See Danaher Corporation; *U.S. Public*, pg. 625
CEPHEID PROPRIETARY LIMITED—See Danaher Corporation; *U.S. Public*, pg. 625
CEPHEID—See Danaher Corporation; *U.S. Public*, pg. 625
CEPHEID SOUTH AFRICA—See Danaher Corporation; *U.S. Public*, pg. 625
CEPHEID UK—See Danaher Corporation; *U.S. Public*, pg. 625
CEPHEUS EVEN EMPREENDIMENTOS IMOBILIARIOS LTDA.—See Even Construtora e Incorporadora S.A.; *Int'l*, pg. 2561
CEPHEUS INTERNATIONAL CO., LTD.—See Catcher Technology Co., Ltd.; *Int'l*, pg. 1359
CEPIA, LLC; *U.S. Private*, pg. 835
CEPL HOLDING SAS—See ID Logistics SAS; *Int'l*, pg. 3587
CEPL MICHELSTADT GMBH—See ID Logistics SAS; *Int'l*, pg. 3587
CEPLUS CO., LTD.—See Chuo Spring Co., Ltd.; *Int'l*, pg. 1599
CEP MID-CONTINENT LLC—See Evolve Transition Infrastructure LP; *U.S. Public*, pg. 804
CEPO HANDA BIOMASS POWER GENERATION CO., INC.—See Chubu Electric Power Co., Inc.; *Int'l*, pg. 1593
CEPOVETT; *Int'l*, pg. 1420
CE POWER ENGINEERED SERVICES, LLC—See New Mountain Capital, LLC; *U.S. Private*, pg. 2903
CE POWER SOLUTIONS, LLC—See New Mountain Capital, LLC; *U.S. Private*, pg. 2903
C E PRECISION ASSEMBLIES, INC.—See Audax Group, Limited Partnership; *U.S. Private*, pg. 390
CEP RESERVES, INC.—See PPL Corporation; *U.S. Public*, pg. 1711
CEPROCIM S.A.; *Int'l*, pg. 1420
CEPRO INTERNATIONAL BV—See Indutrade AB; *Int'l*, pg. 3677
CEPSA AVIACION, S.A.—See Mubadala Investment Company PJSC; *Int'l*, pg. 5074
CEPSA CARD, S.A.—See Mubadala Investment Company PJSC; *Int'l*, pg. 5074
CEPSA CHEMICAL (SHANGHAI), CO., LTD—See Mubadala Investment Company PJSC; *Int'l*, pg. 5074
CEPSA CHIMIE BECANCOUR, INC.—See Mubadala Investment Company PJSC; *Int'l*, pg. 5074
CEPSA CHIMIE MONTREAL, S.E.C.—See Indorama Ventures Public Company Limited; *Int'l*, pg. 3658
CEPSA COMERCIAL GALICIA SA—See Mubadala Investment Company PJSC; *Int'l*, pg. 5074
CEPSA COMERCIAL NOROESTE, S.L.—See Mubadala Investment Company PJSC; *Int'l*, pg. 5074
CEPSA COMERCIAL NORTE, S.L.—See Mubadala Investment Company PJSC; *Int'l*, pg. 5074
CEPSA EP ESPANA S.L.U.—See Mubadala Investment Company PJSC; *Int'l*, pg. 5074
CEPSA EP S.A.U.—See Mubadala Investment Company PJSC; *Int'l*, pg. 5074
CEPSA ITALIA, S.P.A.—See Mubadala Investment Company PJSC; *Int'l*, pg. 5074
CEPSA MAGHREB, S.A.—See Mubadala Investment Company PJSC; *Int'l*, pg. 5074
CEPSA OLEO E GAS DO BRASIL, LTDA.—See Mubadala Investment Company PJSC; *Int'l*, pg. 5074
CEPSA PANAMA, S.A.—See Minerva Bunkering Pte. Ltd.; *Int'l*, pg. 4908
CEPSA PETRONUBA S.A.U.—See Mubadala Investment Company PJSC; *Int'l*, pg. 5074
CEPSA QUIMICA NETHERLANDS, B.V.—See Mubadala Investment Company PJSC; *Int'l*, pg. 5074
CEPSA QUIMICA, S.A.—See Mubadala Investment Company PJSC; *Int'l*, pg. 5074

CERAMICA LIMA S.A.

CEPSA (RHOURDE EL ROUNI) LIMITED—See Mubadala Investment Company PJSC; *Int'l*, pg. 5074
CEPSA S.A.—See Mubadala Investment Company PJSC; *Int'l*, pg. 5074
CEPS, A.S.; *Int'l*, pg. 1420
CEPSA UK, LTD.—See Mubadala Investment Company PJSC; *Int'l*, pg. 5074
CEP SERVICES COMPANY, INC.—See Evolve Transition Infrastructure LP; *U.S. Public*, pg. 804
CEPS, INC.; *U.S. Private*, pg. 835
CEPS PLC; *Int'l*, pg. 1420
CEPTARIS THERAPEUTICS, INC.—See Johnson & Johnson; *U.S. Public*, pg. 1194
CEPTON, INC.; *U.S. Public*, pg. 475
CEQUEL COMMUNICATIONS HOLDINGS I, LLC—See Altice USA, Inc.; *U.S. Public*, pg. 88
CEQUEL COMMUNICATIONS, LLC—See Altice USA, Inc.; *U.S. Public*, pg. 88
CEQUEL DATA CENTERS, LLC—See Cequel III, LLC; *U.S. Private*, pg. 835
CEQUEL DATA CENTERS, LLC—See Charterhouse Group, Inc.; *U.S. Private*, pg. 859
CEQUEL DATA CENTERS, LLC—See Thompson Street Capital Manager LLC; *U.S. Private*, pg. 4160
CEQUEL III, LLC; *U.S. Private*, pg. 835
CEQUENCE ENERGY LTD.; *Int'l*, pg. 1420
CEQUENT CONSUMER PRODUCTS, INC.—See Crowne Group LLC; *U.S. Private*, pg. 1112
CEQUENT PERFORMANCE PRODUCTS, INC.—See Crowne Group LLC; *U.S. Private*, pg. 1112
CEQUENT PERFORMANCE PRODUCTS - TRAILER DIVISION—See Crowne Group LLC; *U.S. Private*, pg. 1112
CERADEL - SOCOR—See Groupe Bruxelles Lambert SA; *Int'l*, pg. 3100
CER A.D.; *Int'l*, pg. 1420
CERADYNE ESK, LLC—See 3M Company; *U.S. Public*, pg. 8
CERADYNE, INC.—See 3M Company; *U.S. Public*, pg. 8
CERADYNE THERMO MATERIALS—See 3M Company; *U.S. Public*, pg. 8
CERADYNE (TIANJIN) TECHNICAL CERAMICS CO., LTD.—See 3M Company; *U.S. Public*, pg. 8
CERAGON COLOMBIA—See Ceragon Networks Ltd.; *Int'l*, pg. 1421
CERAGON ITALY—See Ceragon Networks Ltd.; *Int'l*, pg. 1421
CERAGON MOSCOW—See Ceragon Networks Ltd.; *Int'l*, pg. 1421
CERAGON NETWORKS APAC (S) PTE LTD—See Ceragon Networks Ltd.; *Int'l*, pg. 1421
CERAGON NETWORKS AS—See Ceragon Networks Ltd.; *Int'l*, pg. 1421
CERAGON NETWORKS AUSTRALIA PTY LTD—See Ceragon Networks Ltd.; *Int'l*, pg. 1421
CERAGON NETWORKS DO BRASIL LTDA—See Ceragon Networks Ltd.; *Int'l*, pg. 1421
CERAGON NETWORKS HELLAS S.A.—See Ceragon Networks Ltd.; *Int'l*, pg. 1421
CERAGON NETWORKS (HK) LTD.—See Ceragon Networks Ltd.; *Int'l*, pg. 1421
CERAGON NETWORKS, INC.—See Ceragon Networks Ltd.; *Int'l*, pg. 1421
CERAGON NETWORKS (INDIA) PRIVATE LIMITED—See Ceragon Networks Ltd.; *Int'l*, pg. 1421
CERAGON NETWORKS LTD.; *Int'l*, pg. 1421
CERAGON NETWORKS (NIGERIA) LIMITED—See Ceragon Networks Ltd.; *Int'l*, pg. 1421
CERAGON NETWORKS PHILIPPINES, INC.—See Ceragon Networks Ltd.; *Int'l*, pg. 1421
CERAGON NETWORKS S.A. DE C.V.—See Ceragon Networks Ltd.; *Int'l*, pg. 1421
CERAGON NETWORKS SARL—See Ceragon Networks Ltd.; *Int'l*, pg. 1421
CERAGON NETWORKS (UK) LIMITED—See Ceragon Networks Ltd.; *Int'l*, pg. 1421
CERAGON POLAND—See Ceragon Networks Ltd.; *Int'l*, pg. 1421
CERAGON THAILAND—See Ceragon Networks Ltd.; *Int'l*, pg. 1421
CERAGON USA—See Ceragon Networks Ltd.; *Int'l*, pg. 1421
CERAH BAKTI SDN BHD—See Berjaya Corporation Berhad; *Int'l*, pg. 983
CERAMATE TECHNICAL (SUZHOU) CO., LTD.—See Brightking Holdings Limited; *Int'l*, pg. 1162
CERAMAX INC.; *Int'l*, pg. 1421
CERA-MET, LLC; *U.S. Private*, pg. 835
CERAMI & ASSOCIATES, INC.—See Keystone Group, L.P.; *U.S. Private*, pg. 2299
CERAMICA AZULEJOS TERRAZZOS; *U.S. Private*, pg. 835
CERAMICA CARABOBO SACA; *Int'l*, pg. 1421
CERAMICA CHIARELLI S.A.; *Int'l*, pg. 1421
CERAMICA E VELAS DE IGNICAO NGK DO BRASIL LTDA.—See Niterra Co., Ltd.; *Int'l*, pg. 5380
CERAMICA INDAH SDN. BHD.—See Kim Hin Industry Berhad; *Int'l*, pg. 4162
CERAMICA LIMA S.A.; *Int'l*, pg. 1421

CERAMICA LIMA S.A.

CERAMICA SAN LORENZO COLOMBIA S.A.—See Etex SA/NV; *Int'l*, pg. 2521
CERAMICA SAN LORENZO DE MEXICO S.A. DE C.V.—See Etex SA/NV; *Int'l*, pg. 2521
CERAMICA SAN LORENZO I.C.S.A.—See Etex SA/NV; *Int'l*, pg. 2521
CERAMICA SAN LORENZO S.A.C.—See Grupo Lamosa S.A. de C.V.; *Int'l*, pg. 3131
CERAMICA SAN LORENZO U.S.A. INC.—See Etex SA/NV; *Int'l*, pg. 2521
CERAMICA SANTA ANITA, S.A. DE C.V.—See Grupo Industrial Saltillo S.A. de C.V.; *Int'l*, pg. 3130
CERAMICAS CORDILLERA S.A.—See Etex SA/NV; *Int'l*, pg. 2521
CERAMIC COLOR & CHEMICAL MFG. CO.; *U.S. Private*, pg. 835
CERAMIC FUEL CELLS (POWDER) LIMITED—See Israel Corporation Ltd.; *Int'l*, pg. 3822
CERAMICHE SERRA S.P.A.—See Victoria Plc; *Int'l*, pg. 8188
CERAMIC INDUSTRIES LIMITED; *Int'l*, pg. 1421
CERAMIC MAGNETICS, INC.—See Thomas & Skinner, Inc.; *U.S. Private*, pg. 4154
CERAMIC & MICROWAVE PRODUCTS—See Dover Corporation; *U.S. Public*, pg. 679
CERAMIC PIPES COMPANY—See Saudi Ceramic Company; *Int'l*, pg. 6592
CERAMIC SENSOR CO., LTD.—See Niterra Co., Ltd.; *Int'l*, pg. 5380
CERAMIDI—See Compagnie de Saint-Gobain SA; *Int'l*, pg. 1722
CERAMIKA GRES SA—See Ceramika Nowa Gala S.A.; *Int'l*, pg. 1421
CERAMIKA NOWA GALA S.A.; *Int'l*, pg. 1421
CERAMIN FZ LLC—See Ras Al Khaimah Ceramics PJSC; *Int'l*, pg. 6211
CERAMI SALES COMPANY, INC.; *U.S. Private*, pg. 835
CERAM LIEGENSCHAFTSVERWALTUNG GMBH—See Ibiden Co., Ltd.; *Int'l*, pg. 3575
CERAMOPTEC GMBH—See biolitec AG; *Int'l*, pg. 1039
CERAMTEC COMMERCIALE ITALIANA—See BC Partners LLP; *Int'l*, pg. 923
CERAMTEC CZECH REPUBLIC S.R.O.—See BC Partners LLP; *Int'l*, pg. 923
CERAMTEC-ETEC GMBH—See BC Partners LLP; *Int'l*, pg. 923
CERAMTEC FRANCE—See BC Partners LLP; *Int'l*, pg. 923
CERAMTEC GMBH—See BC Partners LLP; *Int'l*, pg. 923
CERAMTEC IBERICA, INNOVATIVE CERAMIC ENGINEERING, S.L.—See BC Partners LLP; *Int'l*, pg. 923
CERAMTEC INNOVATIVE CERAMIC ENGINEERING, (M) SDN. BHD.—See BC Partners LLP; *Int'l*, pg. 923
CERAMTEC KOREA LTD., INNOVATIVE CERAMIC ENGINEERING—See BC Partners LLP; *Int'l*, pg. 923
CERAMTEC MEDICAL PRODUCTS DIVISION CHINA—See BC Partners LLP; *Int'l*, pg. 923
CERAMTEC NORTH AMERICA CORP.—See BC Partners LLP; *Int'l*, pg. 923
CERAMTEC SUZHOU LTD.—See BC Partners LLP; *Int'l*, pg. 923
CERAM-TRAZ CORPORATION; *U.S. Private*, pg. 835
CERAN - COMPANHIA ENERGETICA RIO DAS ANTAS—See State Grid Corporation of China; *Int'l*, pg. 7182
CERA SANITARYWARE LTD.; *Int'l*, pg. 1421
CERA SCRL; *Int'l*, pg. 1421
CERASIS, INC.—See Providence Equity Partners L.L.C.; *U.S. Private*, pg. 3292
CERATAZIT S.A.—See PLANSEE Holding AG; *Int'l*, pg. 5889
CERATEC CO., LTD.—See Sumitomo Chemical Company, Limited; *Int'l*, pg. 7264
CERATECHNO CO., LTD.—See Kobe Steel, Ltd.; *Int'l*, pg. 4217
CERATEC, INC.—See Niterra Co., Ltd.; *Int'l*, pg. 5380
CERATERA S A—See Groupe Bruxelles Lambert SA; *Int'l*, pg. 3100
CERATIZIT AMERICA LATINA LTDA.—See PLANSEE Holding AG; *Int'l*, pg. 5889
CERATIZIT DEUTSCHLAND GMBH—See PLANSEE Holding AG; *Int'l*, pg. 5889
CERATIZIT HITZACKER GMBH—See PLANSEE Holding AG; *Int'l*, pg. 5889
CERATIZIT IBERICA S.L.—See PLANSEE Holding AG; *Int'l*, pg. 5889
CERATIZIT INDIA PVT. LTD.—See PLANSEE Holding AG; *Int'l*, pg. 5889
CERATIZIT ITALIA S.P.A.—See PLANSEE Holding AG; *Int'l*, pg. 5889
CERATIZIT JAPAN LTD.—See PLANSEE Holding AG; *Int'l*, pg. 5889
CERATIZIT LOGISTIK GMBH—See PLANSEE Holding AG; *Int'l*, pg. 5889
CERATIZIT MEXICO, S.A. DE C.V.—See PLANSEE Holding AG; *Int'l*, pg. 5889
CERATIZIT NEDERLAND B.V.—See PLANSEE Holding AG; *Int'l*, pg. 5889
CERATIZIT SCHWEIZ AG—See PLANSEE Holding AG; *Int'l*, pg. 5889
CERATIZIT UK LTD.—See PLANSEE Holding AG; *Int'l*, pg. 5890
CERATIZIT USA, INC.—See PLANSEE Holding AG; *Int'l*, pg. 5890
CERATOOL S.A R.L.—See PLANSEE Holding AG; *Int'l*, pg. 5890
CERA TRADING LTD.—See Toto Ltd.; *Int'l*, pg. 7845
CERATUNGSTEN S.A R.L.—See PLANSEE Holding AG; *Int'l*, pg. 5890
CERAVID GMBH—See Geberit AG; *Int'l*, pg. 2904
CERBERUS S.R.O.—See RWE AG; *Int'l*, pg. 6433
CERBERUS BEIJING ADVISORS LTD—See Cerberus Capital Management, L.P.; *U.S. Private*, pg. 837
CERBERUS CALIFORNIA, LLC—See Cerberus Capital Management, L.P.; *U.S. Private*, pg. 837
CERBERUS CAPITAL CHICAGO, LLC—See Cerberus Capital Management, L.P.; *U.S. Private*, pg. 837
CERBERUS CAPITAL MANAGEMENT, L.P.; *U.S. Private*, pg. 835
CERBERUS EUROPEAN CAPITAL ADVISORS, LLP—See Cerberus Capital Management, L.P.; *U.S. Private*, pg. 837
CERBERUS GLOBAL INVESTMENT ADVISORS, LLC—See Cerberus Capital Management, L.P.; *U.S. Private*, pg. 837
CERBERUS JAPAN K.K.—See Cerberus Capital Management, L.P.; *U.S. Private*, pg. 837
CERBERUS MORTGAGE CAPITAL, INC.—See Cerberus Capital Management, L.P.; *U.S. Private*, pg. 837
CERBERUS OPERATIONS AND ADVISORY COMPANY, LLC—See Cerberus Capital Management, L.P.; *U.S. Private*, pg. 837
CERBERUS TELECOM ACQUISITION CORP.—See Cerberus Capital Management, L.P.; *U.S. Private*, pg. 837
CERBEX AG—See Siemens Aktiengesellschaft; *Int'l*, pg. 6888
CERBO FRANCE SARL—See Nolato AB; *Int'l*, pg. 5407
CERBO GROUP AB—See Nolato AB; *Int'l*, pg. 5407
CERCANIAS MOSTOLES NAVALCARNERO, S.A.—See Industry Super Holdings Pty. Ltd.; *Int'l*, pg. 3676
CERCLE ENTREPRISE; *Int'l*, pg. 1421
CERCOL IBERIA S.L.—See Mapei SpA; *Int'l*, pg. 4681
CERCO LLC - CESCO PLANT—See CerCo LLC; *U.S. Private*, pg. 840
CERCO LLC; *U.S. Private*, pg. 840
CER-COLORADO BEND ENERGY PARTNERS LP—See Constellation Energy Corporation; *U.S. Public*, pg. 571
CERCOL S.P.A.—See Mapei SpA; *Int'l*, pg. 4681
CERCONE BROWN CURTIS; *U.S. Private*, pg. 840
CERDANT, INC.; *U.S. Private*, pg. 840
CEREA, A.S.—See Agrofert Holding, a.s.; *Int'l*, pg. 219
C E READY MIX—See Cable Enterprises Inc.; *U.S. Private*, pg. 711
CEREAL BYPRODUCTS COMPANY INC.; *U.S. Private*, pg. 840
CEREALCOM SA; *Int'l*, pg. 1421
CEREAL FOOD PROCESSORS INC. - BILLINGS FACILITY—See Cereal Food Processors Inc.; *U.S. Private*, pg. 840
CEREAL FOOD PROCESSORS INC. - CLEVELAND FACILITY—See Cereal Food Processors Inc.; *U.S. Private*, pg. 840
CEREAL FOOD PROCESSORS INC. - GREAT FALLS FACILITY—See Cereal Food Processors Inc.; *U.S. Private*, pg. 840
CEREAL FOOD PROCESSORS INC. - KANSAS CITY FACILITY—See Cereal Food Processors Inc.; *U.S. Private*, pg. 840
CEREAL FOOD PROCESSORS INC. - LOS ANGELES FACILITY—See Cereal Food Processors Inc.; *U.S. Private*, pg. 840
CEREAL FOOD PROCESSORS INC. - MCPHERSON FACILITY—See Cereal Food Processors Inc.; *U.S. Private*, pg. 840
CEREAL FOOD PROCESSORS INC. - OGDEN FACILITY—See Cereal Food Processors Inc.; *U.S. Private*, pg. 840
CEREAL FOOD PROCESSORS INC. - PORTLAND FACILITY—See Cereal Food Processors Inc.; *U.S. Private*, pg. 840
CEREAL FOOD PROCESSORS INC. - SALT LAKE CITY FACILITY—See Cereal Food Processors Inc.; *U.S. Private*, pg. 840
CEREAL FOOD PROCESSORS INC.; *U.S. Private*, pg. 840
CEREAL FOOD PROCESSORS INC. - WICHITA FACILITY—See Cereal Food Processors Inc.; *U.S. Private*, pg. 840
CEREALIA FOODS & BREAD—See Lantmannen ek for; *Int'l*, pg. 4413
CEREAL INNOVATIONS LIMITED—See Kerry Group plc; *Int'l*, pg. 4138
CEREAL PARTNERS ESPANA AEIE—See Nestle S.A.; *Int'l*, pg. 5205
CEREAL PARTNERS U.K.—See General Mills, Inc.; *U.S. Public*, pg. 921

CORPORATE AFFILIATIONS

CEREAL PARTNERS WORLDWIDE S.A.—See General Mills, Inc.; *U.S. Public*, pg. 921
CEREAL PARTNERS WORLDWIDE S.A.—See Nestle S.A.; *Int'l*, pg. 5202
CEREAL PLANET PLC; *Int'l*, pg. 1421
CEREBAIN BIOTECH CORP.; *U.S. Private*, pg. 840
CEREBOS (AUSTRALIA) LIMITED—See Suntory Holdings Limited; *Int'l*, pg. 7326
CEREBOS PACIFIC LIMITED—See Suntory Holdings Limited; *Int'l*, pg. 7326
CEREBRA INTEGRATED TECHNOLOGIES LTD.; *Int'l*, pg. 1422
CEREBRAL PALSY OF NORTH JERSEY; *U.S. Private*, pg. 840
CEREBRAL PALSY OF WESTCHESTER, INC.; *U.S. Private*, pg. 840
CEREBRA LPO INDIA LIMITED—See Cerebra Integrated Technologies Ltd.; *Int'l*, pg. 1422
CEREBRA MIDDLE EAST FZCO—See Cerebra Integrated Technologies Ltd.; *Int'l*, pg. 1422
CEREBRO Y&R—See WPP plc; *Int'l*, pg. 8491
CEREDEX VALUE ADVISORS LLC—See Virtus Investment Partners, Inc.; *U.S. Public*, pg. 2300
CERENA AGRO SCIENCE—See Rogers & Company Limited; *Int'l*, pg. 6383
CERENA HEALTHCARE—See Rogers & Company Limited; *Int'l*, pg. 6383
CERENA MANAGEMENT LIMITED—See Rogers & Company Limited; *Int'l*, pg. 6383
CERENA TRADE SERVICES—See Rogers & Company Limited; *Int'l*, pg. 6383
CERENCE DEUTSCHLAND GMBH—See Microsoft Corporation; *U.S. Public*, pg. 1442
CERENCE GMBH—See Microsoft Corporation; *U.S. Public*, pg. 1442
CERENCE INC.—See Microsoft Corporation; *U.S. Public*, pg. 1442
CERENCE SWITZERLAND AG—See Microsoft Corporation; *U.S. Public*, pg. 1442
CERENIS THERAPEUTICS INC.—See Abionyx Pharma SA; *Int'l*, pg. 62
CE RENTAL, INC.—See Dubin Clark & Company, Inc.; *U.S. Private*, pg. 1283
CEREP LTD.—See Eurofins Scientific S.E.; *Int'l*, pg. 2542
CERERIA SGARBI S.P.A.; *Int'l*, pg. 1422
CERES CAPITAL MANAGEMENT PTY. LTD.—See Lempriere Pty. Ltd.; *Int'l*, pg. 4450
CERES CLASSIC L.P.; *U.S. Private*, pg. 840
CERESCO MARKETING INC.—See Ceresco; *Int'l*, pg. 1422
CERES COMMODITIES, LLC—See The Redwood Group, LLC; *U.S. Private*, pg. 4103
CERESCO; *Int'l*, pg. 1422
CERES ENVIRONMENTAL SERVICES, INC.; *U.S. Private*, pg. 840
CERES F&D INC.—See Alteogen Inc.; *Int'l*, pg. 391
CERES FRUIT JUICES (PTY) LTD—See PepsiCo, Inc.; *U.S. Public*, pg. 1672
CERES GLOBAL AG CORP.; *U.S. Public*, pg. 475
CERES INC.; *Int'l*, pg. 1422
CERES MANAGED FUTURES LLC—See Morgan Stanley; *U.S. Public*, pg. 1471
CERES MARINE TERMINALS INC.—See Carrix, Inc.; *U.S. Private*, pg. 772
CERES OKINAWA CO., LTD.—See Rohto Pharmaceutical Co. Ltd.; *Int'l*, pg. 6387
CERESPO CO., LTD.; *Int'l*, pg. 1422
CERES POWER HOLDINGS PLC; *Int'l*, pg. 1422
CERES POWER LIMITED—See Ceres Power Holdings plc; *Int'l*, pg. 1422
CERES S.A.—See Etablissements J. Soufflet; *Int'l*, pg. 2519
CERES SOLUTIONS, LLP; *U.S. Private*, pg. 840
CERES SOLUTIONS - TERRE HAUTE—See Ceres Solutions, LLP; *U.S. Private*, pg. 841
CERES S.P.A.—See Royal Unibrew A/S; *Int'l*, pg. 6414
CERESTAR SAS—See Cargill, Inc.; *U.S. Private*, pg. 756
CERES TECHNOLOGIES, INC.—See Atlas Copco AB; *Int'l*, pg. 682
CERES TERMINALS INCORPORATED—See Carrix, Inc.; *U.S. Private*, pg. 772
CERES TERMINALS INC.—See Carrix, Inc.; *U.S. Private*, pg. 773
CERES TRANSPORTATION GROUP, INC.; *U.S. Private*, pg. 841
CERES VENTURES, INC.; *U.S. Public*, pg. 475
CEREVEL THERAPEUTICS HOLDINGS, INC.—See AbbVie Inc.; *U.S. Public*, pg. 24
CEREVEL THERAPEUTICS, INC.—See AbbVie Inc.; *U.S. Public*, pg. 24
CEREVEL THERAPEUTICS, LLC—See AbbVie Inc.; *U.S. Public*, pg. 24
CEREXAGRI BV—See UPL Limited; *Int'l*, pg. 8089
CEREXAGRI S.A.S.—See UPL Limited; *Int'l*, pg. 8090
CEREXAGRI ZIRAAT VE KIMYA SANAYI VE TICARET LIMITED SIRKETI—See UPL Limited; *Int'l*, pg. 8089
C. ERICKSON & SONS INC.; *U.S. Private*, pg. 705
CERIC TECHNOLOGIES; *Int'l*, pg. 1422
CERIDA—See AnswerNet, Inc.; *U.S. Private*, pg. 286

COMPANY NAME INDEX

CERIDIAN BENEFITS SERVICES—See Fidelity National Financial, Inc.; *U.S. Public*, pg. 831
CERIDIAN BENEFITS SERVICES—See Thomas H. Lee Partners, L.P.; *U.S. Private*, pg. 4156
CERIDIAN CARES U.S.—See Dayforce, Inc.; *U.S. Public*, pg. 645
CERIDIAN CORPORATION—See Fidelity National Financial, Inc.; *U.S. Public*, pg. 830
CERIDIAN CORPORATION—See Thomas H. Lee Partners, L.P.; *U.S. Private*, pg. 4156
CERIDIAN DAYFORCE GERMANY GMBH—See Dayforce, Inc.; *U.S. Public*, pg. 645
CERIDIAN EUROPE LIMITED—See Dayforce, Inc.; *U.S. Public*, pg. 645
CERIDIAN (MAURITIUS) LTD.—See Dayforce, Inc.; *U.S. Public*, pg. 645
CERIEL S.A.—See VINCI S.A.; *Int'l*, pg. 8215
CERIFI LLC—See Leeds Equity Partners, LLC; *U.S. Private*, pg. 2414
CERIFONDS (LUXEMBOURG) SA—See Banque Cantonale Vaudoise; *Int'l*, pg. 853
CERILLIANT CORP.—See Merck KGaA; *Int'l*, pg. 4832
CERILLION INC.—See Cerillion plc; *Int'l*, pg. 1422
CERILLION PLC; *Int'l*, pg. 1422
CERILLION TECHNOLOGIES INDIA PRIVATE LIMITED—See Cerillion plc; *Int'l*, pg. 1422
CERILLION TECHNOLOGIES LIMITED—See Cerillion plc; *Int'l*, pg. 1422
CERIMELE, MEYER & WRAY, LLC—See Bodine and Company, LLC; *U.S. Private*, pg. 608
CERINNOV GROUP SA; *Int'l*, pg. 1422
CERINNOV INC.—See Cerinnov Group SA; *Int'l*, pg. 1422
CERINNOV LIMITED—See Cerinnov Group SA; *Int'l*, pg. 1422
CERINNOV SAS—See Cerinnov Group SA; *Int'l*, pg. 1422
CERINNOV, UNIPESSOAL LDA.—See Cerinnov Group SA; *Int'l*, pg. 1422
CERION, LLC—See MW Universal Inc.; *U.S. Private*, pg. 2822
CERITAS ENERGY, LLC—See Energy Spectrum Securities Corporation; *U.S. Private*, pg. 1396
CERITAS ENERGY, LLC—See Quantum Energy Partners, LLC; *U.S. Private*, pg. 3323
CERITECH AG—See Deutsche Rohstoff AG; *Int'l*, pg. 2000
CERITO DIALYSIS PARTNERS, LLC—See DaVita Inc.; *U.S. Public*, pg. 636
CERITY PARTNERS LLC—See Genstar Capital, LLC; *U.S. Private*, pg. 1676
CERIUM HOLDINGS, INC.; *U.S. Private*, pg. 841
CERIUM LABORATORIES, LLC—See Cerium Holdings, Inc.; *U.S. Private*, pg. 841
CERIUM TECHNOLOGY LLC; *U.S. Private*, pg. 841
CERMAK A HRACHOVEC A.S.; *Int'l*, pg. 1422
CERMAQ CANADA LTD.—See Mitsubishi Corporation; *Int'l*, pg. 4938
CERMAQ CHILE S.A.—See Mitsubishi Corporation; *Int'l*, pg. 4938
CERMAQ GROUP AS—See Mitsubishi Corporation; *Int'l*, pg. 4938
CERMAQ NORWAY AS—See Mitsubishi Corporation; *Int'l*, pg. 4938
CERMAS COMPANY LIMITED—See Krung Thai Bank Public Company Limited; *Int'l*, pg. 4308
CERMATE SOFTWARE INC.—See Advantech Co., Ltd.; *Int'l*, pg. 165
CERMATE TECHNOLOGIES INC.—See Advantech Co., Ltd.; *Int'l*, pg. 165
CERMATE TECHNOLOGIES (SHANGHAI) INC.—See Advantech Co., Ltd.; *Int'l*, pg. 165
CERMETEK MICROELECTRONICS, INC.; *U.S. Public*, pg. 476
CERMEX U.K. LTD.—See Tetra Laval International S.A.; *Int'l*, pg. 7576
CERM N.V.—See Heidelberger Druckmaschinen AG; *Int'l*, pg. 3321
CERNA SOLUTIONS, LLC—See Sunstone Partners Management LLC; *U.S. Private*, pg. 3873
CERNAVODA NPP—See S.N. Nuclearelectrica S.A.; *Int'l*, pg. 6456
CERNER CANADA ULC—See Oracle Corporation; *U.S. Public*, pg. 1610
CERNER CORPORATION - CLAIRVIA—See Oracle Corporation; *U.S. Public*, pg. 1610
CERNER CORPORATION PTY LIMITED—See Oracle Corporation; *U.S. Public*, pg. 1610
CERNER CORPORATION—See Oracle Corporation; *U.S. Public*, pg. 1610
CERNER DEUTSCHLAND GMBH—See Oracle Corporation; *U.S. Public*, pg. 1610
CERNER EGYPT L.L.C.—See Oracle Corporation; *U.S. Public*, pg. 1610
CERNER FRANCE SAS—See Oracle Corporation; *U.S. Public*, pg. 1610
CERNER HEALTHCARE SOLUTIONS INDIA PRIVATE LIMITED—See Oracle Corporation; *U.S. Public*, pg. 1610
CERNER HEALTH SERVICES DEUTSCHLAND GMBH—See Oracle Corporation; *U.S. Public*, pg. 1610
CERNER HEALTH SERVICES, INC.—See Oracle Corporation; *U.S. Public*, pg. 1610
CERNER IBERIA, S.L.—See Oracle Corporation; *U.S. Public*, pg. 1610
CERNER IRELAND LIMITED—See Oracle Corporation; *U.S. Public*, pg. 1610
CERNER LIMITED—See Oracle Corporation; *U.S. Public*, pg. 1610
CERNER (MALAYSIA) SDN BHD—See Oracle Corporation; *U.S. Public*, pg. 1610
CERNER MIDDLE EAST FZ-LLC—See Oracle Corporation; *U.S. Public*, pg. 1610
CERNER MULTUM, INC.—See Oracle Corporation; *U.S. Public*, pg. 1610
CERNER NEDERLAND B.V.—See Oracle Corporation; *U.S. Public*, pg. 1610
CERNER OSTERREICH GMBH—See Oracle Corporation; *U.S. Public*, pg. 1610
CERNER PROPERTIES, INC.—See Oracle Corporation; *U.S. Public*, pg. 1610
CERNET-BLACKBOARD INFORMATION TECHNOLOGY (BEIJING) CO. LTD—See Class Technologies Inc.; *U.S. Private*, pg. 915
CERNI MOTOR SALES, INC.; *U.S. Private*, pg. 841
CERNYS FISCH & FEINKOST GMBH—See Raiffeisenlandesbank Oberosterreich Aktiengesellschaft; *Int'l*, pg. 6187
CEROBEAR GMBH—See Minebea Mitsumi Inc.; *Int'l*, pg. 4902
CEROGLASS TECHNOLOGIES INC.—See SWARCO AG; *Int'l*, pg. 7361
CEROS FINANCIAL SERVICES, INC.—See Ceros Holding AG; *Int'l*, pg. 1422
CEROS HOLDING AG; *Int'l*, pg. 1422
CEROS VERMOGENSVERWALTUNG AG—See Ceros Holding AG; *Int'l*, pg. 1422
CERQA COPYRIGHT—See Nationwide Argosy Solutions, LLC; *U.S. Private*, pg. 2865
CER-QUAIL RUN ENERGY PARTNERS LP—See Constellation Energy Corporation; *U.S. Public*, pg. 571
CERQUETI SERVIZI S.R.L.—See KONE Oyj; *Int'l*, pg. 4247
CERRADO GOLD INC.; *Int'l*, pg. 1422
CERRADURAS DE COLOMBIA - CERRACOL S.A.S.—See ASSA ABLOY AB; *Int'l*, pg. 639
CERRELL ASSOCIATES, INC.; *U.S. Private*, pg. 841
CERRINI CONFISERIE GMBH—See EMERAM Capital Partners GmbH; *Int'l*, pg. 2378
CERRITOS BODY WORKS, INC.—See AutoNation, Inc.; *U.S. Public*, pg. 234
CERRITOS DODGE CHRYSLER JEEP—See Dick Browning, Inc.; *U.S. Private*, pg. 1225
CERRITOS FORD, INC.—See The Conant Auto Retail Group; *U.S. Private*, pg. 4013
CERRITOS INFINITI; *U.S. Private*, pg. 841
CERRITOS NISSAN; *U.S. Private*, pg. 841
CERRO DE PASCO RESOURCES INC.; *Int'l*, pg. 1422
CERRO FABRICATED PRODUCTS, INC.—See Berkshire Hathaway Inc.; *U.S. Public*, pg. 310
CERRO FLOW PRODUCTS, INC.—See Berkshire Hathaway Inc.; *U.S. Public*, pg. 310
CERRO FLOW PRODUCTS, INC.—See Berkshire Hathaway Inc.; *U.S. Public*, pg. 310
CERRO GRANDE MINING CORPORATION; *Int'l*, pg. 1423
CERRO GRANDE MINING CORPORATION—See Cerro Grande Mining Corporation; *Int'l*, pg. 1423
CERRO LA MINA S.A.—See Armor Minerals Inc.; *Int'l*, pg. 575
CERRO MINING CORP.; *Int'l*, pg. 1423
CERRO SAN PEDRO PROJECT MINERA SAN XAVIER, S.A. DE C.V.—See New Gold Inc.; *Int'l*, pg. 5223
CERRO VANGUARDIA S.A.—See AngloGold Ashanti plc; *Int'l*, pg. 463
CERRO WIRE LLC—See Berkshire Hathaway Inc.; *U.S. Public*, pg. 309
CERRUTI 1881 SAS—See Trinity Limited; *Int'l*, pg. 7924
CERSANIT ROMANIA SA; *Int'l*, pg. 1423
CERSANIT S.A.; *Int'l*, pg. 1423
CERSOSIMO LUMBER CO. INC.; *U.S. Private*, pg. 841
CERTAIN, INC.; *U.S. Private*, pg. 841
CERTAINTEED CEILINGS—See Compagnie de Saint-Gobain SA; *Int'l*, pg. 1729
CERTAINTEED CORPORATION FOUNDATION—See Compagnie de Saint-Gobain SA; *Int'l*, pg. 1729
CERTAINTEED CORPORATION—See Compagnie de Saint-Gobain SA; *Int'l*, pg. 1729
CERTAINTEED CORPORATION TECHNICAL CENTER—See Compagnie de Saint-Gobain SA; *Int'l*, pg. 1729
CERTAINTEED FOREIGN SALES CORP.—See Compagnie de Saint-Gobain SA; *Int'l*, pg. 1729
CERTAINTEED GYPSUM AND CEILING MANUFACTURING, INC.—See Compagnie de Saint-Gobain SA; *Int'l*, pg. 1729
CERTAINTEED GYPSUM CANADA, INC.—See Compagnie de Saint-Gobain SA; *Int'l*, pg. 1730
CERTAINTEED GYPSUM, INC.—See Compagnie de Saint-Gobain SA; *Int'l*, pg. 1729

CERTIFIED COMPANIES, INC.

CERTAINTEED GYPSUM MANUFACTURING, INC.—See Compagnie de Saint-Gobain SA; *Int'l*, pg. 1729
CERTAINTEED GYPSUM NORTH AMERICAN SERVICES, INC.—See Compagnie de Saint-Gobain SA; *Int'l*, pg. 1729
CERTAINTEED GYPSUM WEST VRGINIA, INC.—See Compagnie de Saint-Gobain SA; *Int'l*, pg. 1729
CERTAINTEED INSULATION—See Compagnie de Saint-Gobain SA; *Int'l*, pg. 1730
CERTAINTEED MACHINE WORKS—See Compagnie de Saint-Gobain SA; *Int'l*, pg. 1729
CERTAINTEED—See Compagnie de Saint-Gobain SA; *Int'l*, pg. 1729
CERTAPRO PAINTERS, LTD.—See FirstService Corporation; *Int'l*, pg. 2691
CERTARA, INC.; *U.S. Public*, pg. 476
CERTARA UK LIMITED—See Certara, Inc.; *U.S. Public*, pg. 476
CERTARA USA, INC. - SAINT LOUIS—See Certara, Inc.; *U.S. Public*, pg. 476
CERTARUS LTD.—See Superior Plus Corp.; *Int'l*, pg. 7338
CERTARUS (USA) LTD.—See Superior Plus Corp.; *Int'l*, pg. 7338
CERTAS AG—See Securitas AB; *Int'l*, pg. 6675
CERTAS AG—See Siemens Aktiengesellschaft; *Int'l*, pg. 6886
CERTAS ENERGY FRANCE SAS—See DCC plc; *Int'l*, pg. 1989
CERTAS ENERGY NORWAY AS—See DCC plc; *Int'l*, pg. 1989
CERTAS ENERGY—See DCC plc; *Int'l*, pg. 1989
CERTASITE GRAND RAPIDS LLC—See The Riverside Company; *U.S. Private*, pg. 4108
CERTECH INC.—See Morgan Advanced Materials plc; *Int'l*, pg. 5041
CERTECH SPA; *Int'l*, pg. 1423
CERTECO LIMITED—See Lonsdale Capital Partners LLP; *Int'l*, pg. 4552
CERTEGO OY—See ASSA ABLOY AB; *Int'l*, pg. 639
CERTEGY CHECK SERVICES, INC.—See Variant Equity Advisors, LLC; *U.S. Private*, pg. 4346
CERTEGY EZI-PAY PTY LTD—See Humm Group Limited; *Int'l*, pg. 3531
CERTEGY FRANCE—See Fidelity National Infor; *U.S. Public*, pg. 832
CERTEGY SNC—See Fidelity National Infor; *U.S. Public*, pg. 832
CERTEUROPE S.A.S.—See Tinexta S.p.A.; *Int'l*, pg. 7753
CERTE WEALTH PROTECTION PTY. LTD.—See Azimut Holding SpA; *Int'l*, pg. 779
CERTEX DANMARK A/S—See Axel Johnson Gruppen AB; *Int'l*, pg. 763
CERTEX EESTI OU—See Axel Johnson Gruppen AB; *Int'l*, pg. 764
CERTEX FINLAND OY—See Axel Johnson Gruppen AB; *Int'l*, pg. 764
CERTEX LATVIJA SIA—See Axel Johnson Gruppen AB; *Int'l*, pg. 764
CERTEX LIETUVA UAB—See Axel Johnson Gruppen AB; *Int'l*, pg. 764
CERTEX LIFTING LTD - OIL & GAS DIVISION—See Axel Johnson Gruppen AB; *Int'l*, pg. 764
CERTEX LIFTING LTD - RENEWABLES DIVISION—See Axel Johnson Gruppen AB; *Int'l*, pg. 764
CERTEX LIFTING LTD—See Axel Johnson Gruppen AB; *Int'l*, pg. 764
CERTEX LIFTING & SERVICE GMBH—See Axel Johnson Gruppen AB; *Int'l*, pg. 764
CERTEX NORGE AS—See Axel Johnson Gruppen AB; *Int'l*, pg. 764
CERTEX OFFSHORE SERVICES AS—See Axel Johnson Gruppen AB; *Int'l*, pg. 764
CERTEX RUS ZAO—See Axel Johnson Gruppen AB; *Int'l*, pg. 764
CERTEX SVENSKA AB—See Axel Johnson Gruppen AB; *Int'l*, pg. 764
CERTICA SOLUTIONS, INC.—See New Harbor Capital Management LLC; *U.S. Private*, pg. 2896
CERTICOM CORP.—See BlackBerry Limited; *Int'l*, pg. 1060
CERTIFICATION ENGINEERS INTERNATIONAL LIMITED—See Engineers India Ltd.; *Int'l*, pg. 2435
CERTIFICATION INTERNATIONAL (UK) LIMITED—See Cobepa S.A.; *Int'l*, pg. 1683
CERTIF-ICE, INC.—See ANSYS, Inc.; *U.S. Public*, pg. 139
CERTIFIED ALLOY PRODUCTS, INC.—See Dubai Holding LLC; *Int'l*, pg. 2218
CERTIFIED APPRAISALS LLC—See C&F Financial Corporation; *U.S. Public*, pg. 414
CERTIFIED AUTOMOTIVE PARTS ASSOCIATION; *U.S. Private*, pg. 841
CERTIFIED AVIATION SERVICES, LLC; *U.S. Private*, pg. 841
CERTIFIED COATINGS COMPANY—See Muehlhan AG; *Int'l*, pg. 5077
CERTIFIED COMPANIES, INC.; *U.S. Private*, pg. 841
CERTIFIED ENVIRONMENTAL PARTICULATE AIR, INC.—See Levine Leichtman Capital Partners, LLC; *U.S. Private*, pg. 2436

CERTIFIED FREIGHT LINES INC.

CERTIFIED FREIGHT LINES INC.; *U.S. Private*, pg. 841
CERTIFIED LABORATORIES, INC.; *U.S. Private*, pg. 841
CERTIFIED LABORATORIES—See NCH Corporation; *U.S. Private*, pg. 2875
CERTIFIED LANGUAGES INTERNATIONAL, INC.; *U.S. Private*, pg. 841
CERTIFIED LUMBER CORPORATION; *U.S. Private*, pg. 841
CERTIFIED MANUFACTURING, INC.; *U.S. Private*, pg. 841
CERTIFIED PARTS CORPORATION; *U.S. Private*, pg. 841
CERTIFIED POWER INC. - DRIVELINE DIVISION—See Brinkmere Capital Partners LLC; *U.S. Private*, pg. 655
CERTIFIED POWER INC.—See Brinkmere Capital Partners LLC; *U.S. Private*, pg. 655
CERTIFIED POWER SOLUTIONS; *U.S. Private*, pg. 841
CERTIFIED RECYCLING, INC.—See Broadview Group Holdings, LLC; *U.S. Private*, pg. 660
CERTIFIED REFRIGERANT SERVICES, INC.—See A-Gas Limited; *Int'l*, pg. 19
CERTIFIED RESTORATION DRYCLEANING NETWORK, LLC; *U.S. Private*, pg. 842
CERTIFIED SLINGS, INC.; *U.S. Private*, pg. 842
CERTIFIED STAINLESS SERVICE INC.; *U.S. Private*, pg. 842
CERTIFIED SUPPLY INC.—See Johnstone Supply Inc.; *U.S. Private*, pg. 2230
CERTIFIED TECHNICAL SERVICES, L.P.—See Forum Energy Technologies, Inc.; *U.S. Public*, pg. 873
CERTIFIED TIRE & SERVICE CENTERS, INC.—See Monro, Inc.; *U.S. Public*, pg. 1465
CERTIFIED TRANSMISSION REBUILDERS INC.; *U.S. Private*, pg. 842
CERTIFIED WHOLESALERS INC.—See Associated Grocers of New England, Inc.; *U.S. Private*, pg. 356
CERTIFIT, INC.; *U.S. Private*, pg. 842
CERTI-FRESH FOODS, INC.; *U.S. Private*, pg. 841
CERTIFY DATA SYSTEMS, INC.—See Humana, Inc.; *U.S. Public*, pg. 1069
CERTIFY, LLC—See K1 Investment Management, LLC; *U.S. Private*, pg. 2252
CERTIGY INC.; *U.S. Private*, pg. 842
CERTIKIN IBERICA S.L.U—See Fluidra SA; *Int'l*, pg. 2714
CERTIKIN INTERNATIONAL LTD.—See Fluidra SA; *Int'l*, pg. 2714
CERTIKIN ITALIA SPA—See Fluidra SA; *Int'l*, pg. 2714
CERTIKIN PORTUGAL SA—See Fluidra SA; *Int'l*, pg. 2714
CERTIKIN SWIMMING POOL PRODUCTS INDIA PVT LTD.—See Fluidra SA; *Int'l*, pg. 2714
CERTINA CONSTRUCTION AG—See Certina Holding AG; *Int'l*, pg. 1423
CERTINA HOLDING AG; *Int'l*, pg. 1423
CERTINA S.A.—See The Swatch Group Ltd.; *Int'l*, pg. 7691
CERTINOMIS SA—See La Poste S.A.; *Int'l*, pg. 4388
CERTIPATH, INC.; *U.S. Private*, pg. 842
CERTIPORT, INC.; *U.S. Private*, pg. 842
CERTIPOST SA/NV—See bpost NV/SA; *Int'l*, pg. 1133
CERTIS BELCHIM B.V.—See Nippon Soda Co., Ltd.; *Int'l*, pg. 5334
CERTIS CISCO SECURITY PTE. LTD.—See Temasek Holdings (Private) Limited; *Int'l*, pg. 7547
CERTIS EUROPE B.V.—See LANXESS AG; *Int'l*, pg. 4415
CERTIS USA LLC—See Mitsui & Co., Ltd.; *Int'l*, pg. 4975
CERTIVE SOLUTIONS INC.; *U.S. Public*, pg. 476
CERTOL INTERNATIONAL, LLC—See MicroCare, LLC; *U.S. Private*, pg. 2703
CERTON SOFTWARE, INC.—See Cyient Limited; *Int'l*, pg. 1895
CERTTECH, L.L.C.; *U.S. Private*, pg. 842
CERTUSBANK, N.A.—See CertusHoldings, Inc.; *U.S. Private*, pg. 842
CERTUSHOLDINGS, INC.; *U.S. Private*, pg. 842
CERTUS LIFE PTY LTD—See PSC Insurance Group Limited; *Int'l*, pg. 6015
CERTUS MANAGEMENT GROUP—See United Claim Solutions, LLC; *U.S. Private*, pg. 4289
CERTUS OIL & GAS INC.—See Pine Cliff Energy Ltd.; *Int'l*, pg. 5868
CERTUSPACT, LLC—See Expeditors International of Washington, Inc.; *U.S. Public*, pg. 810
CERTUS PEST, INC.; *U.S. Private*, pg. 842
CERTUS PORT AUTOMATION B.V.—See Sdiptech AB; *Int'l*, pg. 6658
CERTUSVIEW TECHNOLOGIES, LLC—See Dycom Industries, Inc.; *U.S. Public*, pg. 698
CERTU SYSTEMS INC.—See Thai Beverage Public Company Limited; *Int'l*, pg. 7589
CERULEAN AT THE BLUEBIRD, LLC—See UTG, Inc.; *U.S. Public*, pg. 2267
CERULEAN COMPANIES, INC.—See Elevance Health, Inc.; *U.S. Public*, pg. 729
CERULEAN LTD.—See Coesia S.p.A.; *Int'l*, pg. 1689
CERULEAN SHANGHAI COMPANY LTD.—See Coesia S.p.A.; *Int'l*, pg. 1689
CERUS CORPORATION; *U.S. Public*, pg. 476
CERUS EUROPE B.V.—See Cerus Corporation; *U.S. Public*, pg. 476

CERVANTES CORPORATION LIMITED; *Int'l*, pg. 1423
CERVECERIA ANDINA S.A.—See Anheuser-Busch InBev SA/NV; *Int'l*, pg. 464
CERVECERIA ARGENTINA S.A. ISENBECK—See Anheuser-Busch InBev SA/NV; *Int'l*, pg. 464
CERVECERIA BOLIVIANA NACIONAL S.A.—See Anheuser-Busch InBev SA/NV; *Int'l*, pg. 466
CERVECERIA CUAUHTEMOC MOCTEZUMA S.A. DE C.V.—See Anheuser-Busch InBev SA/NV; *Int'l*, pg. 466
CERVECERIA HONDURENA, S.A DE C.V—See Anheuser-Busch InBev SA/NV; *Int'l*, pg. 464
CERVECERIA NACIONAL (CN) SA—See Anheuser-Busch InBev SA/NV; *Int'l*, pg. 464
CERVECERIA NACIONAL, S.A.—See Anheuser-Busch InBev SA/NV; *Int'l*, pg. 464
CERVECERIA PARAGUAYA S.A.—See Anheuser-Busch InBev SA/NV; *Int'l*, pg. 466
CERVECERIA SAN JUAN S.A.—See Anheuser-Busch InBev SA/NV; *Int'l*, pg. 464
CERVECERIA Y MALTERIA QUILMES SAICA Y G—See Anheuser-Busch InBev SA/NV; *Int'l*, pg. 466
CERVED CREDIT MANAGEMENT GROUP SRL—See GIC Pte. Ltd.; *Int'l*, pg. 2964
CERVED CREDIT MANAGEMENT GROUP SRL—See ION Investment Group Ltd.; *Int'l*, pg. 3793
CERVED CREDIT MANAGEMENT SPA—See GIC Pte. Ltd.; *Int'l*, pg. 2964
CERVED CREDIT MANAGEMENT SPA—See ION Investment Group Ltd.; *Int'l*, pg. 3793
CERVED GROUP S.P.A—See GIC Pte. Ltd.; *Int'l*, pg. 2964
CERVED GROUP S.P.A—See ION Investment Group Ltd.; *Int'l*, pg. 3793
CERVED GROUP SPA—See GIC Pte. Ltd.; *Int'l*, pg. 2964
CERVED GROUP SPA—See ION Investment Group Ltd.; *Int'l*, pg. 3793
CERVED RATING AGENCY S.P.A.—See GIC Pte. Ltd.; *Int'l*, pg. 2964
CERVED RATING AGENCY S.P.A.—See ION Investment Group Ltd.; *Int'l*, pg. 3793
CERVELLO, INC.—See A.T. Kearney, Inc.; *U.S. Private*, pg. 28
CERVELO CYCLES INC.—See Pon Holdings B.V.; *Int'l*, pg. 5918
CERVERA REAL ESTATE, INC.; *U.S. Private*, pg. 842
CERVETTI RICAMBI SPA—See GB Ricambi S.p.A.; *Int'l*, pg. 2893
CERVILLE INVESTMENTS SP. Z O.O.—See Eurocash S.A.; *Int'l*, pg. 2533
CERVO MEDIA GMBH—See Novomatic AG; *Int'l*, pg. 5467
CERVOMED INC.; *U.S. Public*, pg. 476
CERVUS EQUIPMENT CORPORATION—See Brandt Industries Ltd.; *Int'l*, pg. 1140
CERWIN-VEGA, INC.—See Gibson Brands, Inc.; *U.S. Private*, pg. 1696
CESAB CARRELLI ELEVATORI S.P.A.—See Toyota Industries Corporation; *Int'l*, pg. 7867
CESAP VENDITA GAS S.R.L.—See ACEA S.p.A.; *Int'l*, pg. 95
CESAR CASTILLO, INC.; *U.S. Private*, pg. 842
THE CESAR CHAVEZ FOUNDATION; *U.S. Private*, pg. 4007
CESARE FIORUCCI S.P.A—See ALFA, S.A.B. de C.V.; *Int'l*, pg. 313
CESARE PACIOTTI S.P.A.; *Int'l*, pg. 1424
CESAR SA—See Groupe Bruxelles Lambert SA; *Int'l*, pg. 3100
CESAR SA; *Int'l*, pg. 1424
CESBE S.R.L.—See CAD IT S.p.A.; *Int'l*, pg. 1247
CES BUILDING AND CONSTRUCTION PTE LTD—See Chip Eng Seng Corporation Ltd.; *Int'l*, pg. 1572
CE SCHWEIZ AG—See HPI AG; *Int'l*, pg. 3500
CESC LIMITED; *Int'l*, pg. 1424
CESCO AUSTRALIA LTD—See Zicom Group Limited; *Int'l*, pg. 8681
CESC PARK TWO L.L.C.—See Vornado Realty Trust; *U.S. Public*, pg. 2310
CESC PROPERTIES LIMITED—See CESC Limited; *Int'l*, pg. 1424
CES EDUCATION PTE. LTD.—See Chip Eng Seng Corporation Ltd.; *Int'l*, pg. 1572
CES ENERGY SOLUTIONS CORP.; *Int'l*, pg. 1423
CES ENGINEERING & CONSTRUCTION PTE. LTD—See Chip Eng Seng Corporation Ltd.; *Int'l*, pg. 1572
C&E SERVICES INC.; *U.S. Private*, pg. 702
C&E SERVICES, INC. WASHINGTON—See C&E Services Inc.; *U.S. Private*, pg. 703
C.E. SHEPHERD COMPANY LP; *U.S. Private*, pg. 706
CESIMEX S.R.L.—See Grup Simex S.R.L.; *Int'l*, pg. 3115
CES, INC.; *U.S. Private*, pg. 842
C-E (SINGAPORE) PTE. LTD.—See Citizen Watch Co., Ltd.; *Int'l*, pg. 1623
CESIONARIA VALLES OCCIDENTAL, S.A.—See ACS, Actividades de Construccion y Servicios, S.A.; *Int'l*, pg. 110
CESI S.P.A.; *Int'l*, pg. 1424
CESKA DOKA SPOL S R.O.—See Umdasch Group AG; *Int'l*, pg. 8022
CESKA LEKARNA HOLDING, A.S.—See Penta Investments Limited; *Int'l*, pg. 5788

CORPORATE AFFILIATIONS

CESKA PIC S.R.O.—See Genus Plc; *Int'l*, pg. 2931
CESKA PODNIKATELSKA POJISTOVNA, A.S.—See Vienna Insurance Group AG Wiener Versicherung Gruppe; *Int'l*, pg. 8194
CESKA POJISTOVNA A.S.—See PPF Group N.V.; *Int'l*, pg. 5950
CESKA SPORITELNA A.S.—See Erste Group Bank AG; *Int'l*, pg. 2498
CESKA TELEKOMUNIKACNI INFRASTRUKTURA A.S.—See PPF Group N.V.; *Int'l*, pg. 5950
CESKA ZBROJOVKA A.S.—See Colt CZ Group SE; *Int'l*, pg. 1705
CESKE RADIOKOMUNIKACE A.S.—See Macquarie Group Limited; *Int'l*, pg. 4626
CESKOLIPSKE TEPLARENSKA A.S.—See MVV Energie AG; *Int'l*, pg. 5108
CESKOLIPSKE TEPLO A.S.—See Groupe BPCE; *Int'l*, pg. 3094
CESKOMORAVSKY BETON, A.S.—See Heidelberg Materials AG; *Int'l*, pg. 3309
CESKOMORAVSKY CEMENT, A.S.—See Heidelberg Materials AG; *Int'l*, pg. 3309
CESKOMORAVSKY STERK, A.S.—See Heidelberg Materials AG; *Int'l*, pg. 3309
CESKOSLOVENSKA OBCHODNI BANKA A.S.—See KBC Group NV; *Int'l*, pg. 4105
CESKY LODNI A PRUMYSLOVY REGISTR, S.R.O.—See DNV GL Group AS; *Int'l*, pg. 2149
CES LAND PTE. LTD.—See Chip Eng Seng Corporation Ltd.; *Int'l*, pg. 1572
CES LIMITED; *Int'l*, pg. 1423
C E S N W INC—See PACE Engineers, Inc.; *U.S. Private*, pg. 3063
CESPA S.A.—See Schwarz Unternehmenstreuhand KG; *Int'l*, pg. 6645
CESP - COMPANHIA ENERGETICA DE SAO PAULO; *Int'l*, pg. 1424
CESPIA INC.—See JEOL Ltd.; *Int'l*, pg. 3930
CES POWER LLC; *U.S. Private*, pg. 842
CES-PRECAST PTE. LTD.—See Chip Eng Seng Corporation Ltd.; *Int'l*, pg. 1572
CESSATECH A/S; *Int'l*, pg. 1424
CESSFORD CONSTRUCTION COMPANY—See CRH plc; *Int'l*, pg. 1847
CESSNA AIRCRAFT COMPANY—See Textron Inc.; *U.S. Public*, pg. 2028
CESSNA FINANCE CORPORATION—See Textron Inc.; *U.S. Public*, pg. 2029
CESSNA ZURICH CITATION SERVICE CENTER GMBH—See Textron Inc.; *U.S. Public*, pg. 2028
CESSOT DECORATION SARL; *Int'l*, pg. 1424
CES SYNERGIES, INC.; *U.S. Public*, pg. 476
CESTAR D.O.O.—See STRABAG SE; *Int'l*, pg. 7229
CE STAR HOLDINGS, LLC; *U.S. Private*, pg. 803
CES TECHNOLOGY SERVICES PRIVATE LIMITED—See CES Limited; *Int'l*, pg. 1423
CESTNE SATVBY AS; *Int'l*, pg. 1424
CESTNE STAVBY AS; *Int'l*, pg. 1424
C.E. SUNDBERG COMPANY INC.; *U.S. Private*, pg. 706
CESVI FRANCE—See Groupama SA; *Int'l*, pg. 3090
CETAM AUTOMATISMES—See Hiolle Industries S.A.; *Int'l*, pg. 3401
CETAN CORPORATION; *U.S. Private*, pg. 842
C.E. TAYLOR OIL INC.; *U.S. Private*, pg. 706
CETC ACOUSTIC-OPTIC-ELECTRONIC TECHNOLOGY INC.; *Int'l*, pg. 1424
CETC CYBERSPACE SECURITY TECHNOLOGY CO., LTD.; *Int'l*, pg. 1424
CETC DIGITAL TECHNOLOGY CO., LTD; *Int'l*, pg. 1424
CETCO ENERGY SERVICES COMPANY LLC—See Minerals Technologies, Inc.; *U.S. Public*, pg. 1448
CETCO ENERGY SERVICES DE MEXICO, S.A. DE C.V.—See Minerals Technologies, Inc.; *U.S. Public*, pg. 1448
CETCO ENERGY SERVICES LIMITED—See Minerals Technologies, Inc.; *U.S. Public*, pg. 1448
CETCO ENERGY SERVICES (MALAYSIA) SDN. BHD.—See Minerals Technologies, Inc.; *U.S. Public*, pg. 1448
CETCO (EUROPE) LTD.—See Minerals Technologies, Inc.; *U.S. Public*, pg. 1448
CETCO OILFIELD SERVICES COMPANY NIGERIA LIMITED—See Minerals Technologies, Inc.; *U.S. Public*, pg. 1448
CETCOPOLAND, CETCO SP. Z O.O. S.K.A.—See Minerals Technologies, Inc.; *U.S. Public*, pg. 1449
CETCO SP. Z O.O.—See Minerals Technologies, Inc.; *U.S. Public*, pg. 1449
CETEK, LTD.—See J.F. Lehman & Company, Inc.; *U.S. Private*, pg. 2163
CETELEM ALGERIE SPA—See BNP Paribas SA; *Int'l*, pg. 1090
CETELEM BELGIUM—See BNP Paribas SA; *Int'l*, pg. 1089
CETELEM IFN SA—See BNP Paribas SA; *Int'l*, pg. 1090
CETELEM SERVICIOS SA DE CV—See BNP Paribas SA; *Int'l*, pg. 1090
CETELEM SFAC—See BNP Paribas SA; *Int'l*, pg. 1089

COMPANY NAME INDEX

CETELEM SLOVENSKO A.S.—See BNP Paribas SA; *Int'l*, pg. 1090
CETELEM—See BNP Paribas SA; *Int'l*, pg. 1089
CETELEM TAIWAN—See BNP Paribas SA; *Int'l*, pg. 1090
CETERA ADVISOR NETWORKS LLC—See Genstar Capital, LLC; *U.S. Private*, pg. 1676
CETERA ADVISORS LLC—See Genstar Capital, LLC; *U.S. Private*, pg. 1676
CETERA ADVISORS LLC—See TA Associates, Inc.; *U.S. Private*, pg. 3919
CETERA FINANCIAL GROUP, INC.—See Genstar Capital, LLC; *U.S. Private*, pg. 1676
CETERA FINANCIAL HOLDINGS, INC.—See Genstar Capital, LLC; *U.S. Private*, pg. 1676
CETERA INVESTMENT SERVICES LLC—See Genstar Capital, LLC; *U.S. Private*, pg. 1676
CETERO RESEARCH—See Cetero Research; *U.S. Private*, pg. 843
CETERO RESEARCH—See Cetero Research; *U.S. Private*, pg. 843
CETERO RESEARCH; *U.S. Private*, pg. 843
CETERO RESEARCH—See Cetero Research; *U.S. Private*, pg. 843
CETETHERM AB—See NIBE Industrier AB; *Int'l*, pg. 5260
CETETHERM LLC—See NIBE Industrier AB; *Int'l*, pg. 5260
CETETHERM SAS—See NIBE Industrier AB; *Int'l*, pg. 5260
C.E. THURSTON & SONS DISTRIBUTING, LLC—See C.E. Thurston & Sons Incorporated; *U.S. Private*, pg. 706
C.E. THURSTON & SONS INC. - EMPIRE INDUSTRIAL PRODUCTS—See C.E. Thurston & Sons Incorporated; *U.S. Private*, pg. 706
C.E. THURSTON & SONS INCORPORATED; *U.S. Private*, pg. 706
CETISA, S.A.—See Atos SE; *Int'l*, pg. 691
CETIS, D.D.; *Int'l*, pg. 1424
CETIS-ZG D.O.O.,—See CETIS, d.d.; *Int'l*, pg. 1424
CETRA - CENTRO TECNICO DE REPARACAO AUTO-MOVEL, S.A.—See Caixa Geral de Depósitos S.A.; *Int'l*, pg. 1260
CETRA, INC.; *U.S. Private*, pg. 843
CETREL SA—See SIX Group AG; *Int'l*, pg. 6966
CETROM INFORMATION TECHNOLOGY, INC.; *U.S. Private*, pg. 843
CETRON ELECTRONICS MANUFACTURING DIVISION—See Richardson Electronics, Ltd.; *U.S. Public*, pg. 1797
CETRULO LLP; *U.S. Private*, pg. 843
CETTIRE LIMITED; *Int'l*, pg. 1424
CET TOSHIBA (LANGFANG) ARRESTER CO., LTD.—See Japan Industrial Partners, Inc.; *Int'l*, pg. 3892
CE-TUR CELEBI TOURISM TRADE INC.—See Celebi Holding A.S.; *Int'l*, pg. 1391
CETUS CAPITAL ACQUISITION CORP.; *Int'l*, pg. 1424
CE UK LTD.—See HPI AG; *Int'l*, pg. 3500
CEU PARADIGM, LLC—See Constellation Energy Corporation; *U.S. Public*, pg. 571
CEVA AUTOMOTIVE LOGISTICS POLAND—See CMA CGM S.A.; *Int'l*, pg. 1667
CEVA CONTAINER LOGISTICS—See CMA CGM S.A.; *Int'l*, pg. 1667
CEVA D.S.P. LIMITED—See CEVA, Inc.; *U.S. Public*, pg. 476
CEVA FRANCE—See CEVA, Inc.; *U.S. Public*, pg. 476
CEVA FREIGHT MANAGEMENT—See CMA CGM S.A.; *Int'l*, pg. 1667
CEVA GROUP PLC—See CMA CGM S.A.; *Int'l*, pg. 1666
CEVA, INC.; *U.S. Public*, pg. 476
CEVA IRELAND LIMITED—See CEVA, Inc.; *U.S. Public*, pg. 476
CEVA LIMITED—See CEVA, Inc.; *U.S. Public*, pg. 476
CEVA LOGISTICS AG—See CMA CGM S.A.; *Int'l*, pg. 1666
CEVA LOGISTICS ARGENTINA—See CMA CGM S.A.; *Int'l*, pg. 1666
CEVA LOGISTICS AUSTRALIA—See CMA CGM S.A.; *Int'l*, pg. 1666
CEVA LOGISTICS AUSTRIA GMBH—See CMA CGM S.A.; *Int'l*, pg. 1666
CEVA LOGISTICS BELGIUM—See CMA CGM S.A.; *Int'l*, pg. 1666
CEVA LOGISTICS B.V.—See CMA CGM S.A.; *Int'l*, pg. 1666
CEVA LOGISTICS CZECH REPUBLIC—See CMA CGM S.A.; *Int'l*, pg. 1666
CEVA LOGISTICS FRANCE—See CMA CGM S.A.; *Int'l*, pg. 1666
CEVA LOGISTICS GERMANY—See CMA CGM S.A.; *Int'l*, pg. 1666
CEVA LOGISTICS GREECE—See CMA CGM S.A.; *Int'l*, pg. 1666
CEVA LOGISTICS HUNGARY—See CMA CGM S.A.; *Int'l*, pg. 1666
CEVA LOGISTICS INDONESIA—See CMA CGM S.A.; *Int'l*, pg. 1666
CEVA LOGISTICS ITALY—See CMA CGM S.A.; *Int'l*, pg. 1667

CEVA LOGISTICS MALAYSIA—See CMA CGM S.A.; *Int'l*, pg. 1667
CEVA LOGISTICS NORTH AMERICA INC.—See CMA CGM S.A.; *Int'l*, pg. 1667
CEVA LOGISTICS POLAND—See CMA CGM S.A.; *Int'l*, pg. 1667
CEVA LOGISTICS SINGAPORE—See CMA CGM S.A.; *Int'l*, pg. 1667
CEVA LOGISTICS SPAIN—See CMA CGM S.A.; *Int'l*, pg. 1667
CEVA LOGISTICS THAILAND—See CMA CGM S.A.; *Int'l*, pg. 1667
CEVA LOGISTICS TURKEY—See CMA CGM S.A.; *Int'l*, pg. 1667
CEVA LOGISTICS UNITED KINGDOM—See CMA CGM S.A.; *Int'l*, pg. 1667
CEVA SANTE ANIMALE SA; *Int'l*, pg. 1425
CEVIAGRO SPA—See Cevital S.p.A.; *Int'l*, pg. 1425
CEVITAL FOOD PROCESSING INDUSTRY—See Cevital S.p.A.; *Int'l*, pg. 1425
CEVITAL MINERALS, SPA—See Cevital S.p.A.; *Int'l*, pg. 1425
CEVITAL-MTP SPA—See Cevital S.p.A.; *Int'l*, pg. 1425
CEVITAL S.P.A.; *Int'l*, pg. 1425
CEVO MOBILITY CO., LTD.—See CAMMSYS Co., LTD; *Int'l*, pg. 1273
CEVOTEC GMBH; *Int'l*, pg. 1425
CEVOTRANS BV—See Mohawk Industries, Inc.; *U.S. Public*, pg. 1457
CEWAG—See Vicat S.A.; *Int'l*, pg. 8185
CEWE COLOR AG & CO. OHG—See CEWE Stiftung & Co. KGaA; *Int'l*, pg. 1425
CEWE COLOR, A.S.—See CEWE Stiftung & Co. KGaA; *Int'l*, pg. 1425
CEWE COLOR BELGIUM S.A.—See CEWE Stiftung & Co. KGaA; *Int'l*, pg. 1425
CEWE COLOR DANMARK A.S.—See CEWE Stiftung & Co. KGaA; *Int'l*, pg. 1425
CEWE COLOR LIMITED—See CEWE Stiftung & Co. KGaA; *Int'l*, pg. 1425
CEWE COLOR MAGYARORSZAG KFT—See CEWE Stiftung & Co. KGaA; *Int'l*, pg. 1425
CEWE COLOR NEDERLAND B.V.—See CEWE Stiftung & Co. KGaA; *Int'l*, pg. 1425
CEWE COLOR S.A.S—See CEWE Stiftung & Co. KGaA; *Int'l*, pg. 1425
CEWE COLOR SP. Z O. O—See CEWE Stiftung & Co. KGaA; *Int'l*, pg. 1425
CEWE MAGYARORSZAG KFT—See CEWE Stiftung & Co. KGaA; *Int'l*, pg. 1425
CEWE SP. Z O. O.—See CEWE Stiftung & Co. KGaA; *Int'l*, pg. 1425
CEWE STIFTUNG & CO. KGAA; *Int'l*, pg. 1425
THE C.E. WHITE CO.—See Hickory Springs Manufacturing Company; *U.S. Private*, pg. 1933
CEXEC, INC.; *U.S. Private*, pg. 843
CEYBANK HOLIDAY HOMES (PVT) LTD—See Bank of Ceylon; *Int'l*, pg. 840
CEYGEN BIOTECH (PVT) LTD.—See Durdans Hospital; *Int'l*, pg. 2228
CEYLINCO INVESTMENT CORPORATION LTD—See Nation Lanka Finance PLC; *Int'l*, pg. 5149
CEYLON BREWERY LTD.—See Carlsberg A/S; *Int'l*, pg. 1340
CEYLON COLD STORES PLC—See John Keells Holdings PLC; *Int'l*, pg. 3978
CEYLON GRAIN ELEVATORS PLC; *Int'l*, pg. 1426
CEYLON GRAPHITE CORP.; *Int'l*, pg. 1426
CEYLON GUARDIAN INVESTMENT TRUST PLC—See Carson Cumberbatch PLC; *Int'l*, pg. 1347
CEYLON HOLIDAY RESORTS LTD.—See John Keells Holdings PLC; *Int'l*, pg. 3978
CEYLON HOTELS CORPORATION PLC; *Int'l*, pg. 1426
CEYLON INVESTMENT PLC—See Carson Cumberbatch PLC; *Int'l*, pg. 1347
CEYLON LAND & EQUITY PLC; *Int'l*, pg. 1426
CEYLON OXYGEN LIMITED—See Linde plc; *Int'l*, pg. 4505
CEYLON TEA BROKERS PLC; *Int'l*, pg. 1426
CEYLON TOBACCO COMPANY LTD.; *Int'l*, pg. 1426
CEYLON TRADING CO. LTD.—See AAK AB; *Int'l*, pg. 32
CEYONIQ TECHNOLOGY GMBH; *Int'l*, pg. 1426
CEYSAND RESORTS LTD—See Softlogic Holdings PLC; *Int'l*, pg. 7056
CEZANNE S.A.S.—See Thermo Fisher Scientific Inc.; *U.S. Public*, pg. 2145
CEZ, A.S. - DUKOVANY NUCLEAR POWER STATION—See CEZ, a.s.; *Int'l*, pg. 1427
CEZ, A.S. - HODONIN POWER PLANT—See CEZ, a.s.; *Int'l*, pg. 1427
CEZ, A.S. - HYDRO POWER STATIONS—See CEZ, a.s.; *Int'l*, pg. 1427
CEZ, A.S. - LEDVICE POWER STATION—See CEZ, a.s.; *Int'l*, pg. 1427
CEZ, A.S. - MELNIK POWER STATION—See CEZ, a.s.; *Int'l*, pg. 1427
CEZ, A.S. - PORICI POWER STATIONS—See CEZ, a.s.; *Int'l*, pg. 1427

CEZ, A.S. - PRUNEROV POWER STATIONS—See CEZ, a.s.; *Int'l*, pg. 1427
CEZ, A.S.; *Int'l*, pg. 1426
CEZ, A.S. - TEMELIN NUCLEAR POWER STATION—See CEZ, a.s.; *Int'l*, pg. 1427
CEZ, A.S. - TISOVA POWER PLANT—See CEZ, a.s.; *Int'l*, pg. 1427
CEZ, A.S.- TUSIMICE POWER STATIONS—See CEZ, a.s.; *Int'l*, pg. 1427
CEZ BOHUNICE A.S.—See CEZ, a.s.; *Int'l*, pg. 1426
CEZ BULGARIA EAD—See CEZ, a.s.; *Int'l*, pg. 1426
CEZ CHORZOW B.V.—See CEZ, a.s.; *Int'l*, pg. 1426
CEZ CHORZOW S.A.—See CEZ, a.s.; *Int'l*, pg. 1427
CEZDATA, S.R.O.—See CEZ, a.s.; *Int'l*, pg. 1427
CEZ DEUTSCHLAND GMBH—See CEZ, a.s.; *Int'l*, pg. 1426
CEZ DISTRIBUCE, A. S.—See CEZ, a.s.; *Int'l*, pg. 1426
CEZ DISTRIBUCNE SUSTAVY A.S.—See CEZ, a.s.; *Int'l*, pg. 1426
CEZ ELEKTRO BULGARIA AD—See CEZ, a.s.; *Int'l*, pg. 1426
CEZ ENERGETICKE PRODUKTY, S.R.O.—See CEZ, a.s.; *Int'l*, pg. 1426
CEZ ENERGETICKE SLUZBY, S.R.O.—See CEZ, a.s.; *Int'l*, pg. 1426
CEZ ENERGOSERVIS SPOL, S.R.O.—See CEZ, a.s.; *Int'l*, pg. 1426
CEZ ENERGO, S.R.O.—See CEZ, a.s.; *Int'l*, pg. 1426
CEZ ESCO, A.S.—See CEZ, a.s.; *Int'l*, pg. 1426
CEZ ESCO BULGARIA EOOD—See CEZ, a.s.; *Int'l*, pg. 1426
CEZ ESCO POLSKA SP. Z O.O.—See CEZ, a.s.; *Int'l*, pg. 1426
CEZ FINANCE B.V.—See CEZ, a.s.; *Int'l*, pg. 1426
CEZ HUNGARY LTD.—See CEZ, a.s.; *Int'l*, pg. 1426
CEZ ICT SERVICES, A. S.—See CEZ, a.s.; *Int'l*, pg. 1426
CEZ LOGISTIKA, S.R.O.—See CEZ, a.s.; *Int'l*, pg. 1426
CEZ MH B.V.—See CEZ, a.s.; *Int'l*, pg. 1426
CEZNET, A.S.—See CEZ, a.s.; *Int'l*, pg. 1427
CEZ OBNOVITELNE ZDROJE, S.R.O.—See CEZ, a.s.; *Int'l*, pg. 1427
CEZ POLAND DISTRIBUTION B.V.—See CEZ, a.s.; *Int'l*, pg. 1427
CEZ POLSKA SP. Z.O.O.—See CEZ, a.s.; *Int'l*, pg. 1427
CEZ PRODUKTY ENERGETYCZNE POLSKA SP. Z.O.O.—See CEZ, a.s.; *Int'l*, pg. 1427
CEZ RAZPREDELENIE BULGARIA AD—See Eurohold Bulgaria AD; *Int'l*, pg. 2553
CEZ SHPERNDARJE SH.A.—See CEZ, a.s.; *Int'l*, pg. 1427
CEZ SPRAVA MAJETKU, S.R.O.—See CEZ, a.s.; *Int'l*, pg. 1427
CEZ SRBIJA D.O.O.—See CEZ, a.s.; *Int'l*, pg. 1427
CEZTEL, A.S.—See CEZ, a.s.; *Int'l*, pg. 1427
CEZ TRADE ALBANIA SH.P.K.—See CEZ, a.s.; *Int'l*, pg. 1427
CEZ TRADE BULGARIA EAD—See CEZ, a.s.; *Int'l*, pg. 1427
CEZ TRADE POLSKA SP. Z O.O.—See CEZ, a.s.; *Int'l*, pg. 1427
CEZ VANZARE S.A.—See CEZ, a.s.; *Int'l*, pg. 1427
CFA, INC.—See Bowman Consulting Group Ltd.; *U.S. Public*, pg. 376
CFAN INC—See General Electric Company; *U.S. Public*, pg. 918
CFAN INC—See Safran SA; *Int'l*, pg. 6476
CFAN RADIO—See Maritime Broadcasting System Ltd.; *Int'l*, pg. 4695
CFAO (GHANA) LIMITED—See Toyota Tsusho Corporation; *Int'l*, pg. 7875
CFAO MALAWI LIMITED—See Toyota Tsusho Corporation; *Int'l*, pg. 7875
CFAO MOTORS BURKINA S.A.—See Toyota Tsusho Corporation; *Int'l*, pg. 7875
CFAO MOTORS GUINEE BISSAU—See Toyota Tsusho Corporation; *Int'l*, pg. 7875
CFAO MOTORS GUINEE EQUATORIALE—See Toyota Tsusho Corporation; *Int'l*, pg. 7875
CFAO MOTORS MAROC SA—See Toyota Tsusho Corporation; *Int'l*, pg. 7875
CFAO MOTORS RCA—See Toyota Tsusho Corporation; *Int'l*, pg. 7875
CFAO SAS—See Toyota Tsusho Corporation; *Int'l*, pg. 7875
CFAO SENEGAL—See Toyota Tsusho Corporation; *Int'l*, pg. 7875
CFAO TECHNOLOGIES BURKINA S.A.—See Toyota Tsusho Corporation; *Int'l*, pg. 7875
CFAO TECHNOLOGIES GABON S.A.—See Toyota Tsusho Corporation; *Int'l*, pg. 7875
CFAO TECHNOLOGIES MALI SA—See Toyota Tsusho Corporation; *Int'l*, pg. 7875
CFAO TECHNOLOGIES SENEGAL—See Toyota Tsusho Corporation; *Int'l*, pg. 7875
CFAO ZAMBIA LTD.—See Toyota Tsusho Corporation; *Int'l*, pg. 7875
CFBANK, NATIONAL ASSOCIATION—See CF Bankshares Inc.; *U.S. Public*, pg. 476
CF BANKSHARES INC.; *U.S. Public*, pg. 476

CFB COMMERZ FONDS BETEILIGUNGS GMBH—See Commerzbank AG; *Int'l*, pg. 1717
C.F. BEAN, LLC; *U.S. Private*, pg. 706
C.F. BURGER CREAMERY COMPANY; *U.S. Private*, pg. 707
CF CARD FACTORY GMBH—See Die Schweizerische Post AG; *Int'l*, pg. 2112
CFC EUROPE GMBH—See Illinois Tool Works Inc.; *U.S. Public*, pg. 1102
CFC GROUP PTY. LTD.; *Int'l*, pg. 1429
CFC, INC.; *U.S. Private*, pg. 843
CFC, INC.—See Cook Group Incorporated; *U.S. Private*, pg. 1037
CFC INTERNATIONAL, INC.—See Illinois Tool Works Inc.; *U.S. Public*, pg. 1102
CFC INVESTMENT COMPANY—See Cincinnati Financial Corporation; *U.S. Public*, pg. 494
CFC ITALIA SRL—See Solutions 30 SE; *Int'l*, pg. 7077
CF COMUNICACION, S.L.; *Int'l*, pg. 1429
CFCO RADIO AM—See Blackburn Radio Inc; *Int'l*, pg. 1060
CFC PRINT SOLUTIONS; *U.S. Private*, pg. 843
CFC SOLUTIONS LTD.—See Pinewood Technologies Group PLC; *Int'l*, pg. 5868
CFC UNDERWRITING LIMITED; *Int'l*, pg. 1429
CFCY-AM/CHLQ-FM—See Maritime Broadcasting System Ltd.; *Int'l*, pg. 4695
CFCY RADIO—See Maritime Broadcasting System Ltd.; *Int'l*, pg. 4695
C/F DATA SYSTEMS INC.; *U.S. Private*, pg. 709
CFD RESEARCH CORPORATION; *U.S. Private*, pg. 843
CFE BRABANT—See Ackermans & van Haaren NV; *Int'l*, pg. 104
CFE EQUIPMENT; *U.S. Private*, pg. 843
CFE HUNGARY EPITOIPARI KFT.—See Ackermans & van Haaren NV; *Int'l*, pg. 104
CFE IMMO—See Ackermans & van Haaren NV; *Int'l*, pg. 104
CFE INTERNATIONAL—See Ackermans & van Haaren NV; *Int'l*, pg. 104
CF ENERGY CORP.; *Int'l*, pg. 1429
C&F ENTERPRISES, INC.; *U.S. Private*, pg. 703
CFE POLSKA SP. Z O.O.—See Ackermans & van Haaren NV; *Int'l*, pg. 104
CFE TUNISIA—See Ackermans & van Haaren NV; *Int'l*, pg. 105
CFF BELGIUM N.V.—See CFF GmbH & Co. KG; *Int'l*, pg. 1429
CFF FLUID CONTROL LIMITED; *Int'l*, pg. 1429
CFF GMBH & CO. KG; *Int'l*, pg. 1429
CF FINANCE ACQUISITION CORP.—See GCM Grosvenor Inc.; *U.S. Public*, pg. 908
C&F FINANCE COMPANY—See C&F Financial Corporation; *U.S. Public*, pg. 414
C&F FINANCIAL CORPORATION; *U.S. Public*, pg. 414
C&F FOODS INC.; *U.S. Private*, pg. 703
C F FOODS LLC.; *U.S. Private*, pg. 843
CFG COMMUNITY BANK—See Capital Funding Group, Inc.; *U.S. Private*, pg. 740
CFG DEUTSCHLAND GMBH—See ALFA, S.A.B. de C.V.; *Int'l*, pg. 314
CF GEAR HOLDINGS; *U.S. Private*, pg. 843
CFGI, LLC—See The Carlyle Group Inc.; *U.S. Public*, pg. 2045
CF GLOBAL TRADING, LLC—See State Street Corporation; *U.S. Public*, pg. 1940
CFG SERVICES SA—See Bureau de Recherches Geologiques et Miniere; *Int'l*, pg. 1221
C.F. HAGLIN & SONS, INC.; *U.S. Private*, pg. 707
CFH GROUP, LLC; *U.S. Private*, pg. 843
CF HOLDING COMPANY, INC.; *U.S. Private*, pg. 843
CFI-COMPAGNIE FONCIERE INTERNATIONALE; *Int'l*, pg. 1430
CFI HOLDING S.A.; *Int'l*, pg. 1429
CFI HOLDINGS LIMITED; *Int'l*, pg. 1429
CFI HOSPITALITY GROUP, INC.—See Central Florida Investments Inc.; *U.S. Private*, pg. 820
CFI INSULATION, INC.—See Installed Building Products, Inc.; *U.S. Public*, pg. 1132
CF INDUSTRIES HOLDINGS, INC.; *U.S. Public*, pg. 477
CF INDUSTRIES, INC. - DONALDSONVILLE NITROGEN COMPLEX—See CF Industries Holdings, Inc.; *U.S. Public*, pg. 477
CF INDUSTRIES, INC.—See CF Industries Holdings, Inc.; *U.S. Public*, pg. 477
CF INDUSTRIES, INC. - WOODWARD PLANT—See CF Industries Holdings, Inc.; *U.S. Public*, pg. 477
CF INDUSTRIES, INC. - YAZOO CITY PLANT—See CF Industries Holdings, Inc.; *U.S. Public*, pg. 477
CF INDUSTRIES NITROGEN, LLC—See CF Industries Holdings, Inc.; *U.S. Public*, pg. 477
CF INDUSTRIES SALES, LLC—See CF Industries Holdings, Inc.; *U.S. Public*, pg. 477
CFI—See Ali Holding S.r.l; *Int'l*, pg. 320
CF&I STEEL LP—See Evraz plc; *Int'l*, pg. 2573
CF ITALIA SRL; *Int'l*, pg. 1429
CFJ G.K.—See Citigroup Inc.; *U.S. Public*, pg. 501
C.F. JORDAN CONSTRUCTION LLC—See C.F. Jordan L.P.; *U.S. Private*, pg. 707

C.F. JORDAN L.P.; *U.S. Private*, pg. 707
C.F. JORDAN RESIDENTIAL INCORPORATED—See C.F. Jordan L.P.; *U.S. Private*, pg. 707
C.F.K. CNC-FERTIGUNGSTECHNIK KRIFTEL GMBH—See Gesco AG; *Int'l*, pg. 2945
CFL CHEMISCHE FABRIK LEHRTE GMBH & CO. KG—See Schussler Novachem GmbH; *Int'l*, pg. 6644
C-FLEX BEARING CO., INC.; *U.S. Private*, pg. 704
CFL PIZZA, LLC; *U.S. Private*, pg. 843
CF MANAGEMENT SERVICES PTY. LTD.—See Earlypay Ltd.; *Int'l*, pg. 2267
C.F. MARTIN & CO., INC.; *U.S. Private*, pg. 707
CF MCDONALD ELECTRIC INC.; *U.S. Private*, pg. 843
CFM COMPANY; *U.S. Private*, pg. 843
CFM CONSOLIDATED, INC.—See RPM International Inc.; *U.S. Public*, pg. 1816
CFM CORPORATION—See Ontario Teachers' Pension Plan; *Int'l*, pg. 5587
CFM DISTRIBUTORS, INC.; *U.S. Private*, pg. 843
CFM EQUIPMENT DISTRIBUTORS INC.; *U.S. Private*, pg. 843
CFM EUROPE LIMITED—See Ontario Teachers' Pension Plan; *Int'l*, pg. 5588
CFM HOLDINGS LIMITED; *Int'l*, pg. 1430
CFM INDOSUEZ WEALTH SA; *Int'l*, pg. 1430
CFM INFRATRADE PTE. LTD.—See CFM Holdings Limited; *Int'l*, pg. 1430
CFM INTERNATIONAL INC.—See General Electric Company; *U.S. Public*, pg. 918
CFM INTERNATIONAL INC.—See Safran SA; *Int'l*, pg. 6473
CFM LOGISTICS—See Golden State Foods Corp.; *U.S. Private*, pg. 1733
C&F MORTGAGE CORPORATION—See C&F Financial Corporation; *U.S. Public*, pg. 414
CFM PRINTING & STATIONERY SDN. BHD—See Computer Forms (Malaysia) Berhad; *Int'l*, pg. 1759
CFM RELIGION PUBLISHING GROUP, LLC—See The Wicks Group of Companies, LLC; *U.S. Private*, pg. 4135
CFM SLOVAKIA S.R.O.—See CFM Holdings Limited; *Int'l*, pg. 1430
CFM SOGUTMA VE OTOMASYON A.S.—See Carel Industries S.p.A.; *Int'l*, pg. 1324
CFM—See OceanSound Partners, LP; *U.S. Private*, pg. 2990
CFM STRATEGIC COMMUNICATIONS, INC.; *U.S. Private*, pg. 843
CFM STRATEGIC COMMUNICATIONS, INC.—See CFM Strategic Communications, Inc.; *U.S. Private*, pg. 844
CFM TOPPAN FORMS (MALAYSIA) SDN. BHD.—See Computer Forms (Malaysia) Berhad; *Int'l*, pg. 1759
CFM TOPPAN FORMS (MALAYSIA) SDN. BHD.—See TOPPAN Holdings Inc.; *Int'l*, pg. 7818
CFN CORPORATION; *U.S. Public*, pg. 477
CF (NETHERLANDS) HOLDINGS LIMITED B.V.—See Cosmo First Limited; *Int'l*, pg. 1812
CFN PRECISION LTD.; *Int'l*, pg. 1430
CFN SERVICES; *U.S. Private*, pg. 844
CFNY-FM RADIO—See Corus Entertainment Inc.; *Int'l*, pg. 1808
CFOAM LIMITED; *Int'l*, pg. 1430
CFOAM LLC—See CFOAM Limited; *Int'l*, pg. 1430
CFORIA SOFTWARE, LLC—See Highradius Corporation; *U.S. Private*, pg. 1941
CFO SELECTIONS, LLC; *U.S. Private*, pg. 844
CFP BRANDS SUSSWARENHANDELS GMBH & CO. KG—See Perfetti Van Melle Holding B.V.; *Int'l*, pg. 5800
CFPS ENGENHARIA E PROJETOS, S.A.—See Fluor Corporation; *U.S. Public*, pg. 858
CFQ MEDIA, LLC—See Mindfire Entertainment; *U.S. Private*, pg. 2740
CFR, INC.; *U.S. Private*, pg. 844
CFS ASIA LTD.—See GEA Group Aktiengesellschaft; *Int'l*, pg. 2897
CFSB BANCORP, INC.; *U.S. Public*, pg. 477
CFS BRANDS LLC—See The Jordan Company, L.P.; *U.S. Private*, pg. 4060
CFS CHILE COMERCIALIZADORA LIMITADA—See GEA Group Aktiengesellschaft; *Int'l*, pg. 2897
C.F. SCHWARTZ MOTOR COMPANY, INC.; *U.S. Private*, pg. 707
CFS CO., LTD.—See Sintokogio Ltd.; *Int'l*, pg. 6958
CFS COMMERCIAL (BEIJING) LIMITED—See GEA Group Aktiengesellschaft; *Int'l*, pg. 2897
CFS GROUP, INC.; *Int'l*, pg. 1430
CFS GROUP, INC.—See Chemung Financial Corporation; *U.S. Public*, pg. 484
CF SHINYOHOSHO CO., LTD.—See Sumitomo Mitsui Financial Group, Inc.; *Int'l*, pg. 7293
CFS INVESTMENT AND IMPORT EXPORT TRADING JSC; *Int'l*, pg. 1430
CFS ITALY S.P.A.—See GEA Group Aktiengesellschaft; *Int'l*, pg. 2897
CFS KOREA LTD.—See GEA Group Aktiengesellschaft; *Int'l*, pg. 2897
CFS NORDIC A/S—See GEA Group Aktiengesellschaft; *Int'l*, pg. 2897

CFS SERVICE CORPORATION; *U.S. Private*, pg. 844
CFS SWITZERLAND AG—See GEA Group Aktiengesellschaft; *Int'l*, pg. 2897
CF STEEL MOROCCO—See FAYAT SAS; *Int'l*, pg. 2625
C F STINSON, INC.; *U.S. Private*, pg. 701
CFT CONSULTING GMBH—See Easy Software AG; *Int'l*, pg. 2275
CFTC PRECISION (HUIAN) LIMITED—See China Fineblanking Technology Co., Ltd.; *Int'l*, pg. 1503
CFTC PRECISION SDN. BHD.—See China Fineblanking Technology Co., Ltd.; *Int'l*, pg. 1503
CFT DO BRASIL LTD—See ATS Corporation; *Int'l*, pg. 695
CFT GMBH; *Int'l*, pg. 1430
CFT, INC.—See Babcock & Wilcox Enterprises, Inc.; *U.S. Public*, pg. 263
CF TITLE CO.—See U.S. Bancorp; *U.S. Public*, pg. 2212
CFT PACKAGING USA INC.—See ATS Corporation; *Int'l*, pg. 695
CFT S.P.A.—See ATS Corporation; *Int'l*, pg. 695
CFT UKRAINE LTD—See ATS Corporation; *Int'l*, pg. 695
CFT VINA COOPER CO., LTD.—See Toyota Tsusho Corporation; *Int'l*, pg. 7876
CFT VINA COPPER CO., LTD.—See The Furukawa Electric Co., Ltd.; *Int'l*, pg. 7644
CFU COME LIMITED—See C Cheng Holdings Limited; *Int'l*, pg. 1237
CF ULTRA TECH—See Construction Forms, Inc.; *U.S. Private*, pg. 1023
C&F WEALTH MANAGEMENT CORPORATION—See C&F Financial Corporation; *U.S. Public*, pg. 414
C&F WORLDWIDE AGENCY CORP.; *U.S. Private*, pg. 703
CG3N SA—See VINCI S.A.; *Int'l*, pg. 8213
CGA NEWREST CATERING SA—See Newrest Group International S.A.S.; *Int'l*, pg. 5236
CGA STRATEGY LIMITED—See Advent International Corporation; *U.S. Private*, pg. 105
CG AUTOMATION SOLUTIONS USA INC.—See Avantha Group; *Int'l*, pg. 735
CG AUTOMOTIVE GROUP, INC.; *U.S. Private*, pg. 844
CGB DIVERSIFIED SERVICES, INC.—See ITOCHU Corporation; *Int'l*, pg. 3835
CGB DIVERSIFIED SERVICES, INC.—See National Federation of Agricultural Co-Operative Associations; *Int'l*, pg. 5156
C&G BEAULIEU GROUP INC.; *Int'l*, pg. 1238
CGB ENTERPRISES INC.—See ITOCHU Corporation; *Int'l*, pg. 3835
CGB ENTERPRISES INC.—See National Federation of Agricultural Co-Operative Associations; *Int'l*, pg. 5156
THE CG&B GROUP INC.; *Int'l*, pg. 7631
CG&B INVESTMENT SERVICES, INC.—See Arthur J. Gallagher & Co.; *U.S. Public*, pg. 204
C. G. BRETTING MANUFACTURING CO., INC.; *U.S. Private*, pg. 705
CG CAPITAL AND INVESTMENTS LIMITED—See Avantha Group; *Int'l*, pg. 735
C&G CARANDINI—See Leds-C4, S.A.; *Int'l*, pg. 4439
C&G CARANDINI S.A.—See Leds-C4, S.A.; *Int'l*, pg. 4439
CGCA SARL—See CVC Capital Partners SICAV-FIS S.A.; *Int'l*, pg. 1882
CG CO-ISSUER INC.—See Stellantis N.V.; *Int'l*, pg. 7199
CG COMPUTERS SDN. BHD.—See PT Erajaya Swasembada Tbk; *Int'l*, pg. 6038
CGG TECHNOLOGY LIMITED—See Comtech Telecommunications Corp.; *U.S. Public*, pg. 562
C.G. DEVELOPMENT LIMITED—See Universal Electronics, Inc.; *U.S. Public*, pg. 2255
CGD INVESTIMENTOS CVC—See Caixa Geral de Depositos S.A.; *Int'l*, pg. 1260
CGD NORTH AMERICA FINANCE LLC—See Caixa Geral de Depositos S.A.; *Int'l*, pg. 1260
CGEA ISRAEL LTD—See Veolia Environnement S.A.; *Int'l*, pg. 8159
CGE ASSETS, INC.—See Maverick Gold LLC; *U.S. Private*, pg. 2616
CGE CONTINENTAL GLASS ENGINEERING GMBH; *Int'l*, pg. 1430
CGE DISTRIBUCION S.A.—See State Grid Corporation of China; *Int'l*, pg. 7183
CGE DISTRIBUTION - S.A.S.—See Sonepar S.A.; *Int'l*, pg. 7090
CGE ENERGY INC.; *U.S. Public*, pg. 477
CGE GAS NATURAL SA; *Int'l*, pg. 1430
CG ELECTRIC SYSTEMS HUNGARY, ZRT—See Avantha Group; *Int'l*, pg. 735
CGE MAGALLANES S.A.—See State Grid Corporation of China; *Int'l*, pg. 7183
CGE MINAS INDUSTRIA E COMERCIO DE ARTEFATOS PLASTICOS LTDA.; *Int'l*, pg. 1431
C.G. ENTERPRISES INC.; *U.S. Private*, pg. 707
C&G ENVIRONMENTAL PROTECTION HOLDINGS LIMITED; *Int'l*, pg. 1238
CGE SOCIEDADE FABRICADORA DE PECAS PLASTICAS LTDA.—See CGE Minas Industria E Comercio de Artefatos Plasticos Ltda.; *Int'l*, pg. 1431
CG ESTER CORPORATION—See Mitsubishi Gas Chemical Company, Inc.; *Int'l*, pg. 4948

COMPANY NAME INDEX

CGF CAPITAL B.V.—See Heidelberg Materials AG; *Int'l*, pg. 3309
CGF INDUSTRIES, INC.; *U.S. Private*, pg. 844
CGF MARKETING SERVICES LTD.—See The DDC Group; *U.S. Private*, pg. 4019
C&G FOOD BROKERAGE INC.; *U.S. Private*, pg. 703
CGG AIRBORNE SURVEYS (PTY) LTD.—See CGG; *Int'l*, pg. 1431
CGG AMERICAS INC.—See CGG; *Int'l*, pg. 1431
CGG - ARGENTINA—See CGG; *Int'l*, pg. 1431
CGG AVIATION (AUSTRALIA) PTY LTD.—See CGG; *Int'l*, pg. 1431
CGG CANADA GRUNDBESITZ GMBH—See Commerzbank AG; *Int'l*, pg. 1715
CGG CANADA—See CGG; *Int'l*, pg. 1431
CGG DATA SERVICES AG—See CGG; *Int'l*, pg. 1431
CGG DO BRASIL LTDA.—See CGG; *Int'l*, pg. 1431
CGG EXPLO SARL—See CGG; *Int'l*, pg. 1431
CGG GEOPHYSICAL (CANADA) CORPORATION—See CGG; *Int'l*, pg. 1431
CGG GEOPHYSICAL (CHILE) SA—See CGG; *Int'l*, pg. 1431
CGG HOLDING (U.S.) INC.—See CGG; *Int'l*, pg. 1431
CGG I SA—See CGG; *Int'l*, pg. 1431
CGG JAKARTA—See CGG; *Int'l*, pg. 1431
CGG JASON (AUSTRALIA) PTY. LTD.—See CGG; *Int'l*, pg. 1431
CGG JASON (U.S.) INC.—See CGG; *Int'l*, pg. 1431
CGG MARINE (AUSTRALIA) PTY. LTD.—See CGG; *Int'l*, pg. 1431
CGG MARINE (NORWAY) AS—See CGG; *Int'l*, pg. 1431
CGG MARINE RESOURCES NORGE AS—See CGG; *Int'l*, pg. 1431
CGG MARINE USA—See CGG; *Int'l*, pg. 1431
CGG NPA SATELLITE MAPPING LTD.—See CGG; *Int'l*, pg. 1432
CGG - PERU—See CGG; *Int'l*, pg. 1431
CGG SEISMIC IMAGING (AUSTRALIA) PTY. LTD.—See CGG; *Int'l*, pg. 1431
CGG SEISMIC IMAGING (NORWAY) AS—See CGG; *Int'l*, pg. 1431
CGG SEISMIC IMAGING (UK) LIMITED—See CGG; *Int'l*, pg. 1431
CGG SERVICES (AUSTRALIA) PTY. LTD.—See CGG; *Int'l*, pg. 1431
CGG SERVICES (CANADA) INC.—See CGG; *Int'l*, pg. 1431
CGG SERVICES DE MEXICO SA DE CV—See CGG; *Int'l*, pg. 1432
CGG SERVICES HOLDING B.V.—See CGG; *Int'l*, pg. 1432
CGG SERVICES HOLDING (LATIN AMERICA) B.V.—See CGG; *Int'l*, pg. 1432
CGG SERVICES INDIA PRIVATE LTD.—See CGG; *Int'l*, pg. 1432
CGG SERVICES (NORWAY) AS—See CGG; *Int'l*, pg. 1431
CGG SERVICES S.A.—See CGG; *Int'l*, pg. 1431
CGG SERVICES (SINGAPORE) PTE. LTD.—See CGG; *Int'l*, pg. 1431
CGG SERVICES (UK) LTD.—See CGG; *Int'l*, pg. 1432
CGG SERVICES (U.S.) INC.—See CGG; *Int'l*, pg. 1432
CGG; *Int'l*, pg. 1431
CGG TECHNOLOGY SERVICES (BEIJING) CO. LTD.—See CGG; *Int'l*, pg. 1432
C.G. HACKING & SONS LIMITED; *Int'l*, pg. 1240
CGH HOSPITAL, LTD.—See Tenet Healthcare Corporation; *U.S. Public*, pg. 2006
CG HIBBERT LTD—See Siemens Energy AG; *Int'l*, pg. 6902
CGH INDUSTRY SDN BHD—See Jinhua Chunguang Technology Co., Ltd.; *Int'l*, pg. 3968
C&G HI TECH CO., LTD.; *Int'l*, pg. 1238
CGH MEDICAL CENTER; *U.S. Private*, pg. 844
CG HOLDINGS BELGIUM NV—See Avantha Group; *Int'l*, pg. 735
C&G HOLDINGS, INC.—See Flowers Foods, Inc.; *U.S. Public*, pg. 854
CGH TECHNOLOGY (VIETNAM) COMPANY LIMITED—See Jinhua Chunguang Technology Co., Ltd.; *Int'l*, pg. 3968
CGI AB—See CGI Inc.; *Int'l*, pg. 1433
CGI AUSTRALIA PTY LTD.—See CGI Inc.; *Int'l*, pg. 1434
CGI AUTOMATED MANUFACTURING, INC.—See CORE Industrial Partners, LLC; *U.S. Private*, pg. 1048
CGI BELGIUM NV/SA—See CGI Inc.; *Int'l*, pg. 1433
CGI BUSINESS PROCESS OUTSOURCING BV—See CGI Inc.; *Int'l*, pg. 1433
CGI COMMERCIAL, INC.—See Koch Industries, Inc.; *U.S. Private*, pg. 2333
CGI CZECH REPUBLIC SRO—See CGI Inc.; *Int'l*, pg. 1433
CGI DANMARK AS—See CGI Inc.; *Int'l*, pg. 1433
CGI DEUTSCHLAND GMBH & CO. KG—See CGI Inc.; *Int'l*, pg. 1433
CGI-DUBAI—See CGI Inc.; *Int'l*, pg. 1434
CGI FEDERAL, INC.—See CGI Inc.; *Int'l*, pg. 1432
CGI FRANCE S.A.S. - AIX-EN-PROVENCE—See CGI Inc.; *Int'l*, pg. 1433

CGI FRANCE S.A.S. - BORDEAUX—See CGI Inc.; *Int'l*, pg. 1433
CGI FRANCE S.A.S. - BREST—See CGI Inc.; *Int'l*, pg. 1433
CGI FRANCE S.A.S. - LILLE—See CGI Inc.; *Int'l*, pg. 1433
CGI FRANCE S.A.S. - LYON—See CGI Inc.; *Int'l*, pg. 1433
CGI FRANCE S.A.S. - MONTPELLIER—See CGI Inc.; *Int'l*, pg. 1433
CGI FRANCE S.A.S. - NANTES—See CGI Inc.; *Int'l*, pg. 1433
CGI FRANCE S.A.S. - NIORT—See CGI Inc.; *Int'l*, pg. 1433
CGI FRANCE S.A.S. - PAU—See CGI Inc.; *Int'l*, pg. 1433
CGI FRANCE S.A.S. - RENNES—See CGI Inc.; *Int'l*, pg. 1433
CGI FRANCE S.A.S.—See CGI Inc.; *Int'l*, pg. 1433
CGI FRANCE S.A.S. - STRASBOURG—See CGI Inc.; *Int'l*, pg. 1433
CGI FRANCE S.A.S. - TOULOUSE—See CGI Inc.; *Int'l*, pg. 1433
CGIFT AG; *Int'l*, pg. 1434
CGI GLASS LEWIS PTY LIMITED—See Peloton Capital Management, Inc.; *Int'l*, pg. 5784
CGI INC.—See CGI Inc.; *Int'l*, pg. 1433
CGI INC.; *Int'l*, pg. 1432
CGI INFORMATION SYSTEMS AND MANAGEMENT CONSULTANTS (AUSTRALIA) PTY LTD—See CGI Inc.; *Int'l*, pg. 1434
CGI INFORMATION SYSTEMS & MANAGEMENT CONSULTANTS AUSTRALIA PTY LTD—See CGI Inc.; *Int'l*, pg. 1432
CGI INFORMATION SYSTEMS & MANAGEMENT CONSULTANTS DEUTSCHLAND GMBH—See CGI Inc.; *Int'l*, pg. 1432
CGI INFORMATION SYSTEMS & MANAGEMENT CONSULTANTS ESPANA S.A.—See CGI Inc.; *Int'l*, pg. 1432
CGI INFORMATION SYSTEMS & MANAGEMENT CONSULTANTS INC.—See CGI Inc.; *Int'l*, pg. 1433
CGI INFORMATION SYSTEMS & MANAGEMENT CONSULTANTS, INC.—See CGI Inc.; *Int'l*, pg. 1433
CGI INFORMATION SYSTEMS & MANAGEMENT CONSULTANTS NETHERLANDS B.V.—See CGI Inc.; *Int'l*, pg. 1433
CGI INFORMATION SYSTEMS & MANAGEMENT CONSULTANTS POLSKA—See CGI Inc.; *Int'l*, pg. 1433
CGI INFORMATION SYSTEMS & MANAGEMENT CONSULTANTS PORTUGAL—See CGI Inc.; *Int'l*, pg. 1433
CGI INFORMATION SYSTEMS & MANAGEMENT CONSULTANTS SA/NV—See CGI Inc.; *Int'l*, pg. 1433
CGI INFORMATION SYSTEMS & MANAGEMENT CONSULTANTS SWITZERLAND SA—See CGI Inc.; *Int'l*, pg. 1433
CGI INFORMATION SYSTEMS & MANAGEMENT CONSULTANTS UK LTD.—See CGI Inc.; *Int'l*, pg. 1433
CGI INFORMATION SYSTEMS—See CGI Inc.; *Int'l*, pg. 1433
CGI IT UK LIMITED—See CGI Inc.; *Int'l*, pg. 1432
CGI LIMITED—See CGI Inc.; *Int'l*, pg. 1433
CGI LUXEMBOURG S.A.—See CGI Inc.; *Int'l*, pg. 1434
CGI MALAYSIA SDN. BHD.—See CGI Inc.; *Int'l*, pg. 1434
CGI MANAGEMENT, INC.—See Sonida Senior Living, Inc.; *U.S. Public*, pg. 1903
CGI MBH—See Commerzbank AG; *Int'l*, pg. 1715
CGI NEDERLAND B.V. - ARNHEM—See CGI Inc.; *Int'l*, pg. 1434
CGI NEDERLAND B.V. - GRONINGEN—See CGI Inc.; *Int'l*, pg. 1434
CGI NEDERLAND B.V.—See CGI Inc.; *Int'l*, pg. 1434
C+G INFORMATIONSTECHNOLOGIE GMBH; *Int'l*, pg. 1239
CGI NORGE AS—See CGI Inc.; *Int'l*, pg. 1434
CG INTIMATES INC.—See iFabric Corp.; *Int'l*, pg. 3598
CGI—See CGI Inc.; *Int'l*, pg. 1433
CGI SOUTH AMERICA—See CGI Inc.; *Int'l*, pg. 1434
CGI SUOMI OY—See CGI Inc.; *Int'l*, pg. 1434
CGI SVERIGE AB—See CGI Inc.; *Int'l*, pg. 1434
CGI TECHNOLOGIES & SOLUTIONS INC.—See CGI Inc.; *Int'l*, pg. 1434
CGITI PORTUGAL SA—See CGI Inc.; *Int'l*, pg. 1434
CGIT SYSTEMS, INC.—See AZZ, Inc.; *U.S. Public*, pg. 259
CGI UK LTD. - ABERDEEN—See CGI Inc.; *Int'l*, pg. 1434
CGI UK LTD. - BRIDGEND—See CGI Inc.; *Int'l*, pg. 1434
CGI UK LTD. - BRISTOL—See CGI Inc.; *Int'l*, pg. 1434
CGI UK LTD. - CARDIFF—See CGI Inc.; *Int'l*, pg. 1434
CGI UK LTD. - EDINBURGH—See CGI Inc.; *Int'l*, pg. 1434
CGI UK LTD. - LEATHERHEAD—See CGI Inc.; *Int'l*, pg. 1434
CGI UK LTD. - MANCHESTER—See CGI Inc.; *Int'l*, pg. 1434
CGI UK LTD.—See CGI Inc.; *Int'l*, pg. 1434
CGI WINDOWS AND DOORS, INC.—See Koch Industries, Inc.; *U.S. Private*, pg. 2333
CGL CORPORATION; *U.S. Private*, pg. 844
CGL MANAGEMENT GROUP, LLC—See Hunt Companies, Inc.; *U.S. Private*, pg. 2008

CGL PACK ANNECY—See Advent International Corporation; *U.S. Private*, pg. 101
CGL PACK LORIENT—See Advent International Corporation; *U.S. Private*, pg. 101
CGM ACOUSTICS; *U.S. Private*, pg. 844
CGM ARZTSYSTEME OSTERREICH GMBH—See CompuGroup Medical SE & Co. KGaA; *Int'l*, pg. 1755
CGM BILGI SISTEMLERI A.S.—See CompuGroup Medical SE & Co. KGaA; *Int'l*, pg. 1755
CGM CLINICAL DEUTSCHLAND GMBH—See CompuGroup Medical SE & Co. KGaA; *Int'l*, pg. 1756
CGM CLINICAL OSTERREICH GMBH—See CompuGroup Medical SE & Co. KGaA; *Int'l*, pg. 1755
CGM GALLAGHER INSURANCE BROKERS (BARBADOS) LIMITED—See Arthur J. Gallagher & Co.; *U.S. Public*, pg. 204
CGM GALLAGHER INSURANCE BROKERS JAMAICA LTD.—See Arthur J. Gallagher & Co.; *U.S. Public*, pg. 204
CGM GALLAGHER INSURANCE BROKERS ST. KITTS & NEVIS LTD.—See Arthur J. Gallagher & Co.; *U.S. Public*, pg. 204
CGM LAB BELGIUM SA—See CompuGroup Medical SE & Co. KGaA; *Int'l*, pg. 1755
CGM LAB DEUTSCHLAND GMBH—See CompuGroup Medical SE & Co. KGaA; *Int'l*, pg. 1755
CGM LAB FRANCE SAS—See CompuGroup Medical SE & Co. KGaA; *Int'l*, pg. 1755
CGM MARKETING INC.—See Digital Garage, Inc.; *Int'l*, pg. 2121
CGM MEDISTAR SYSTEMHAUS GMBH—See CompuGroup Medical SE & Co. KGaA; *Int'l*, pg. 1756
CGM MOBILE SOFTWARE GMBH—See CompuGroup Medical SE & Co. KGaA; *Int'l*, pg. 1756
CG MOTORS PRIVATE LTD—See Avantha Group; *Int'l*, pg. 735
CGMP CENTRO DE GESTAO DE MEIOS DE PAGAMENTOS LTDA.—See Corpay, Inc.; *U.S. Public*, pg. 579
CGM SOFTWARE RO SRL—See CompuGroup Medical SE & Co. KGaA; *Int'l*, pg. 1756
CGM SOUTH AFRICA (PTY) LTD.—See CompuGroup Medical SE & Co. KGaA; *Int'l*, pg. 1755
CGM (WEST YILGARN) PTY. LTD.—See Chalice Mining Limited; *Int'l*, pg. 1437
CGM XDENT SOFTWARE S.R.L.—See CompuGroup Medical SE & Co. KGaA; *Int'l*, pg. 1756
CGN & ASSOCIATES INC.; *U.S. Private*, pg. 844
CGN MINING CO. LTD.; *Int'l*, pg. 1434
CGN NEW ENERGY HOLDINGS CO., LTD.; *Int'l*, pg. 1435
CGN NUCLEAR TECHNOLOGY DEVELOPMENT CO., LTD.; *Int'l*, pg. 1435
CGNPC URANIUM RESOURCES CO., LTD.—See China Guangdong Nuclear Power Holding Co., Ltd.; *Int'l*, pg. 1506
CGN POWER CO., LTD.; *Int'l*, pg. 1435
CG ONCOLOGY, INC.; *U.S. Public*, pg. 477
C&G PARTNERS, LLC; *U.S. Private*, pg. 703
CGPC AMERICA CORPORATION—See China General Plastics Corporation; *Int'l*, pg. 1504
CG PHARMACEUTICALS, INC.—See CrystalGenomics, Inc.; *Int'l*, pg. 1860
C. G. P., INC.—See Tootsie Roll Industries, Inc.; *U.S. Public*, pg. 2163
CGP-KONECRANES S.A.—See Konecranes Plc; *Int'l*, pg. 4251
CG POWER AND INDUSTRIAL SOLUTIONS LTD.—See Avantha Group; *Int'l*, pg. 735
CG POWER SOLUTIONS USA INC.—See Avantha Group; *Int'l*, pg. 735
CG POWER SYSTEMS BELGIUM NV—See Avantha Group; *Int'l*, pg. 736
CG POWER SYSTEMS CANADA INC.—See Avantha Group; *Int'l*, pg. 736
CG POWER SYSTEMS IRELAND LTD.—See Avantha Group; *Int'l*, pg. 736
CG POWER SYSTEMS USA INC.—See WEG S.A.; *Int'l*, pg. 8368
CG PPI ADHESIVE PRODUCTS LIMITED—See Avantha Group; *Int'l*, pg. 736
CGPR LLC—See Off Madison Ave, LLC; *U.S. Private*, pg. 3000
CG RAILWAY, LLC—See AIP, LLC; *U.S. Private*, pg. 136
CG RAILWAY, LLC—See Brookfield Infrastructure Partners L.P.; *Int'l*, pg. 1191
CG RAILWAY, LLC—See GIC Pte. Ltd.; *Int'l*, pg. 2965
CGR CORNELIO GHINASSI RICAMBI SPA—See GB Ricambi S.p.A.; *Int'l*, pg. 2893
CG REAL ESTATE LUXEMBURG S.A.R.L.—See Commerzbank AG; *Int'l*, pg. 1715
C-GREEN CARBON MANAGEMENT SOLUTIONS INC.—See HTC Purenergy Inc.; *Int'l*, pg. 3508
CGRH, LLC—See Graham Holdings Company; *U.S. Public*, pg. 954
CGRN, INC.—See Anywhere Real Estate Inc.; *U.S. Public*, pg. 140
CGROWTH CAPITAL INC.; *U.S. Public*, pg. 477
CGR PRODUCTS INC.; *U.S. Private*, pg. 844

CGR VALLEY PRODUCTS INCORPORATED / CORPORATE AFFILIATIONS

CGR VALLEY PRODUCTS INCORPORATED; *U.S. Private,* pg. 844
CG SALES NETWORKS FRANCE S.A.—See Avantha Group; *Int'l,* pg. 736
CGS ASIA CO., LTD.—See C&G SYSTEMS INC.; *Int'l,* pg. 1238
C.G. SCHMIDT INC.; *U.S. Private,* pg. 707
CGS-CIMB SECURITIES (SINGAPORE) PTE. LTD—See CIMB Group Holdings Berhad; *Int'l,* pg. 1608
CGS-CIMB SECURITIES (UK) LIMITED—See CIMB Group Holdings Berhad; *Int'l,* pg. 1608
CG SERVICE SYSTEMS CURACAO NV—See Avantha Group; *Int'l,* pg. 736
CGS INDUSTRIES, INC.; *U.S. Private,* pg. 844
CGS INTERNATIONAL, INC.; *Int'l,* pg. 1435
CGS MANAGEMENT AG; *Int'l,* pg. 1435
CGS NORTH AMERICA INC.—See C&G SYSTEMS INC.; *Int'l,* pg. 1238
CGS SERVICES, INC.—See Waste Management, Inc.; *U.S. Public,* pg. 2330
CGS TECHNOLOGIES, INC.—See System Integrators, L.L.C.; *U.S. Private,* pg. 3906
CGS TECHNOLOGY ASSOCIATES, INC.; *U.S. Private,* pg. 844
C&G SYSTEMS INC.; *Int'l,* pg. 1238
CGTECH CO., LTD.—See Sandvik AB; *Int'l,* pg. 6528
CGTECH DEUTSCHLAND GMBH—See Sandvik AB; *Int'l,* pg. 6528
CGTECH INDIA SOFTWARE SOLUTIONS PRIVATE LIMITED—See Sandvik AB; *Int'l,* pg. 6528
CGTECH LIMITED—See Sandvik AB; *Int'l,* pg. 6528
CG TECHNOLOGY, L.P.—See Cantor Fitzgerald, L.P.; *U.S. Private,* pg. 736
CGTECH S.A.R.L.—See Sandvik AB; *Int'l,* pg. 6528
CGTECH—See Sandvik AB; *Int'l,* pg. 6528
CGTECH S.R.L.—See Sandvik AB; *Int'l,* pg. 6528
CG TEC SERVICE GMBH—See Consus Real Estate AG; *Int'l,* pg. 1778
CG TRANSPORTATION, LLC—See Walgreens Boots Alliance, Inc.; *U.S. Public,* pg. 2323
CGT SHANGHAI TRADING CO. LTD.—See Canadian General Tower Limited; *Int'l,* pg. 1283
CGU INSURANCE LIMITED—See Insurance Australia Group Limited; *Int'l,* pg. 3725
CGU UNDERWRITING LIMITED—See Aviva plc; *Int'l,* pg. 746
CG-VAK SOFTWARE & EXPORTS LTD.; *Int'l,* pg. 1430
CG-VAK SOFTWARE USA INC.—See CG-VAK Software & Exports Ltd.; *Int'l,* pg. 1430
C.G. WOOD COMPANY, INC.—See Madison Dearborn Partners, LLC; *U.S. Private,* pg. 2541
CGX ENERGY INC.; *Int'l,* pg. 1435
CGX RESOURCES INC.—See CGX Energy Inc.; *Int'l,* pg. 1435
CGX YAMAGATA JAPAN GK—See Chatham Asset Management, LLC; *U.S. Private,* pg. 862
CH2 CONTORHAUS HANSESTADT HAMBURG AG—See Aves One AG; *Int'l,* pg. 739
CH2 LOGISTICA PORTFOLIOVERWALTUNG, GMBH & CO. KG—See Aves One AG; *Int'l,* pg. 739
CH2M HILL ALASKA, INC.—See Jacobs Engineering Group, Inc.; *U.S. Public,* pg. 1183
CH2M HILL ARGENTINA S.A—See Jacobs Engineering Group, Inc.; *U.S. Public,* pg. 1183
CH2M HILL COMPANIES, LTD.—See Jacobs Engineering Group, Inc.; *U.S. Public,* pg. 1183
CH2M HILL DO BRASIL ENGENHARIA LTDA.—See Jacobs Engineering Group, Inc.; *U.S. Public,* pg. 1184
CH2M HILL ENGINEERS, INC.—See Jacobs Engineering Group, Inc.; *U.S. Public,* pg. 1183
CH2M HILL, INC.—See Jacobs Engineering Group, Inc.; *U.S. Public,* pg. 1183
CH2M HILL SINGAPORE PTE. LTD.—See Jacobs Engineering Group, Inc.; *U.S. Public,* pg. 1184
CH2M HILL UNITED KINGDOM—See Jacobs Engineering Group, Inc.; *U.S. Public,* pg. 1183
CH4 OPERATIONS PTY LTD—See China National Petroleum Corporation; *Int'l,* pg. 1533
CH4 OPERATIONS PTY LTD—See Shell plc; *Int'l,* pg. 6796
CH-9 MEDIA SDN. BHD.—See Media Prima Berhad; *Int'l,* pg. 4771
CHAARAT GOLD HOLDINGS LIMITED; *Int'l,* pg. 1436
CHAARAT OPERATING COMPANY GMBH—See Chaarat Gold Holdings Limited; *Int'l,* pg. 1436
CHAARAT ZAAV CJSC—See Chaarat Gold Holdings Limited; *Int'l,* pg. 1436
CHA ARCHITECTURE, P.C.—See H.I.G. Capital, LLC; *U.S. Private,* pg. 1827
CHA BIOTECH CO., LTD.; *Int'l,* pg. 1435
CHABIOTECH CO., LTD.; *Int'l,* pg. 1436
CHA CANADA—See H.I.G. Capital, LLC; *U.S. Private,* pg. 1827
CHACE BUILDING SUPPLY OF CT, INC.; *U.S. Private,* pg. 845
CHACHA SEARCH, INC.; *U.S. Private,* pg. 845
CHACODAS S.A.—See Corteva, Inc.; *U.S. Public,* pg. 581
CHA CONSULTING, INC.—See H.I.G. Capital, LLC; *U.S. Private,* pg. 1827

CHACOTT CO., LTD.—See Onward Holdings Co., Ltd.; *Int'l,* pg. 5592
CHAD ALLISON CORPORATION—See Noble Jewelry Investment Limited; *Int'l,* pg. 5397
CHADDSFORD WINERY LTD.; *U.S. Private,* pg. 845
CHADHA ORIENTAL FOODS LIMITED—See GraceKennedy Limited; *Int'l,* pg. 3048
CHADHA PAPERS LTD.; *Int'l,* pg. 1436
THE CHADMAR GROUP; *U.S. Private,* pg. 4007
CHADORMALU MINING & INDUSTRIAL COMPANY; *Int'l,* pg. 1436
CHADRON DIALYSIS, LLC—See DaVita Inc.; *U.S. Public,* pg. 636
CHAD T. WILSON LAW FIRM PLLC; *U.S. Private,* pg. 845
CHADWICK-BAROSS, INC.—See Nors S.A.; *Int'l,* pg. 5432
CHADWICK NOTT—See HFBG Holding B.V.; *Int'l,* pg. 3374
CHADWICK ROAD LANDFILL, INC.—See Waste Management, Inc.; *U.S. Public,* pg. 2330
CHAFFEE LYNCHBURG FARMERS ELEVATOR—See Maple River Grain & Agronomy, LLC.; *U.S. Private,* pg. 2568
C. HAFNER GMBH + CO. KG; *Int'l,* pg. 1240
CHAGALA COOPERATIEF U.A.—See Chagala Group Limited; *Int'l,* pg. 1436
CHAGALA GROUP LIMITED; *Int'l,* pg. 1436
CHAGALA INTERNATIONAL HOLDING B.V.—See Chagala Group Limited; *Int'l,* pg. 1436
CHAGALA MANAGEMENT LLP—See Chagala Group Limited; *Int'l,* pg. 1436
C. HAGER & SONS HINGE MANUFACTURING COMPANY INC.; *U.S. Private,* pg. 705
CHAGRIN SAFETY SUPPLY, INC.—See Innovest Global, Inc.; *U.S. Public,* pg. 1127
CHA HOLLYWOOD MEDICAL CENTER, L.P.—See Chabiotech Co., Ltd.; *Int'l,* pg. 1436
CHAHUA MODERN HOUSEWARES CO.LTD; *Int'l,* pg. 1436
CHAI CANNABIS CO. INC.—See Captor Capital Corp.; *Int'l,* pg. 1317
CHAI CHA NA MINING INC.; *Int'l,* pg. 1436
CHAILEASE AUTO RENTAL CO., LTD.—See Chailease Holding Company Limited; *Int'l,* pg. 1436
CHAILEASE BERJAYA CREDIT SDN. BHD.—See Chailease Holding Company Limited; *Int'l,* pg. 1436
CHAILEASE BERJAYA FINANCE CORPORATION—See Chailease Holding Company Limited; *Int'l,* pg. 1436
CHAILEASE CONSUMER FINANCE CO., LTD.—See Chailease Holding Company Limited; *Int'l,* pg. 1436
CHAILEASE ENERGY INTEGRATION CO., LTD.—See Chailease Holding Company Limited; *Int'l,* pg. 1436
CHAILEASE FINANCE CO., LTD.—See Chailease Holding Company Limited; *Int'l,* pg. 1436
CHAILEASE FINANCE INTERNATIONAL CORP.—See Chailease Holding Company Limited; *Int'l,* pg. 1436
CHAILEASE HOLDING COMPANY LIMITED; *Int'l,* pg. 1436
CHAILEASE INSURANCE BROKERS CO., LTD.—See Chailease Holding Company Limited; *Int'l,* pg. 1436
CHAILEASE INTERNATIONAL FINANCE CORPORATION—See Chailease Holding Company Limited; *Int'l,* pg. 1437
CHAILEASE INTERNATIONAL FINANCIAL LEASING CORP.—See Chailease Holding Company Limited; *Int'l,* pg. 1437
CHAILEASE INTERNATIONAL LEASING COMPANY LIMITED—See Chailease Holding Company Limited; *Int'l,* pg. 1436
CHAILEASE INTERNATIONAL TRADING COMPANY LIMITED—See Chailease Holding Company Limited; *Int'l,* pg. 1436
CHAILEASE ROYAL FINANCE PLC—See Chailease Holding Company Limited; *Int'l,* pg. 1437
CHAILEASE ROYAL LEASING PLC—See Chailease Holding Company Limited; *Int'l,* pg. 1437
CHAI LIFELINE; *U.S. Private,* pg. 845
CHAINALYTICS B.V.—See Nippon Telegraph & Telephone Corporation; *Int'l,* pg. 5340
CHAINALYTICS OY—See Nippon Telegraph & Telephone Corporation; *Int'l,* pg. 5340
CHAINALYTICS SERVICES PRIVATE LIMITED—See Nippon Telegraph & Telephone Corporation; *Int'l,* pg. 5340
CHAINALYTICS S.R.L.—See Nippon Telegraph & Telephone Corporation; *Int'l,* pg. 5340
CHAIN CHON INDUSTRIAL CO., LTD.; *Int'l,* pg. 1437
CHAIN CHON STAINLESS STEEL SDN. BHD.—See Chain Chon Industrial Co., Ltd.; *Int'l,* pg. 1437
CHAIN ELECTRIC COMPANY INC.—See VINCI S.A.; *Int'l,* pg. 8215
CHAIN GROWTH CO., LTD.—See Autobacs Seven Co., Ltd.; *Int'l,* pg. 726
CHAIN MANAGEMENT CO., LTD.—See Ship Healthcare Holdings, Inc.; *Int'l,* pg. 6851
CHAINQUI CONSTRUCTION DEVELOPMENT CO., LTD.; *Int'l,* pg. 1437
CHAIN REACTION CYCLES LTD.—See SIGNA Sports United N.V.; *Int'l,* pg. 6910
CHAINTECH TECHNOLOGY CORP.; *Int'l,* pg. 1437

CHAIN YEAR INDUSTRIES CROP.—See Komax Holding AG; *Int'l,* pg. 4240
CHAIONE; *U.S. Private,* pg. 845
CHAIR 10 MARKETING, INC.—See SmartBug Operating LLC; *U.S. Private,* pg. 3691
CHAIR CITY MEATS INC.; *U.S. Private,* pg. 845
CHAIR CITY SUPPLY COMPANY, INC.; *U.S. Private,* pg. 845
THE CHAIR KING, INC.; *U.S. Private,* pg. 4007
CHAIRMAN'S BRANDS CORPORATION; *Int'l,* pg. 1437
CHAI WATANA TANNERY GROUP PUBLIC COMPANY LIMITED; *Int'l,* pg. 1436
CHAKANA COPPER CORP.; *Int'l,* pg. 1437
CHAKRATEC ORD SHS; *Int'l,* pg. 1437
CHAKWAL SPINNING MILLS LTD.; *Int'l,* pg. 1437
CHALCO-TOYO PERMANENT MAGNET MOTOR CO., LTD.—See TOYO DENKI SEIZO K.K.; *Int'l,* pg. 7852
CHALET HOTELS LTD.; *Int'l,* pg. 1437
CHALET LIFESTYLES, INC.; *U.S. Private,* pg. 845
CHALET VILLAGE PROPERTIES, INC.—See Cabins For You, LLC; *U.S. Private,* pg. 711
CHALGREN ENTERPRISES—See The Graham Group, Inc.; *U.S. Private,* pg. 4037
CHALICE MINING LIMITED; *Int'l,* pg. 1437
CHALKER ENERGY PARTNERS III, LLC—See Quantum Energy Partners, LLC; *U.S. Private,* pg. 3323
CHALKIS HEALTH INDUSTRY CO., LTD.; *Int'l,* pg. 1437
CHALKS TRUCK PARTS, INC.; *U.S. Private,* pg. 845
CHALK & VERMILLION FINE ARTS & MARTIN LAWRENCE GALLERIES; *U.S. Private,* pg. 845
CHALLAND PIPELINE LTD; *Int'l,* pg. 1438
CHALLANGE EIGHTEEN SP. Z O.O.—See CPD S.A.; *Int'l,* pg. 1824
CHALLANI CAPITAL LIMITED; *Int'l,* pg. 1438
CHALLENGE DAIRY PRODUCTS INC.; *U.S. Private,* pg. 845
THE CHALLENGE MACHINERY COMPANY; *U.S. Private,* pg. 4007
CHALLENGE MANUFACTURING COMPANY; *U.S. Private,* pg. 845
THE CHALLENGE PRINTING COMPANY; *U.S. Private,* pg. 4007
CHALLENGER ACQUISITIONS LIMITED; *Int'l,* pg. 1438
CHALLENGER BANK LIMITED—See Heartland Group Holdings Limited; *Int'l,* pg. 3304
CHALLENGER DIVERSIFIED PROPERTY GROUP—See Challenger Limited; *Int'l,* pg. 1438
CHALLENGER DOOR, LLC—See LCI Industries; *U.S. Public,* pg. 1295
CHALLENGER ENERGY GROUP PLC; *Int'l,* pg. 1438
CHALLENGER GEOMATICS LTD.; *Int'l,* pg. 1438
CHALLENGER GOLD LIMITED; *Int'l,* pg. 1438
CHALLENGER, GRAY & CHRISTMAS, INC.; *U.S. Private,* pg. 845
CHALLENGER GROUP HOLDINGS LIMITED—See Challenger Limited; *Int'l,* pg. 1438
CHALLENGER GROUP SERVICES PTY LTD—See Challenger Limited; *Int'l,* pg. 1438
CHALLENGER INTERNATIONAL NOMINEES LTD—See Challenger Limited; *Int'l,* pg. 1438
CHALLENGER LIFE HOLDINGS PTY LIMITED—See Challenger Limited; *Int'l,* pg. 1438
CHALLENGER LIFTS, INC.—See Snap-on Incorporated; *U.S. Public,* pg. 1897
CHALLENGER LIMITED; *Int'l,* pg. 1438
CHALLENGER LIMITED—See Challenger Limited; *Int'l,* pg. 1438
CHALLENGER MANAGED INVESTMENTS LTD—See Challenger Limited; *Int'l,* pg. 1438
CHALLENGER MINERALS INC.—See Transocean Ltd.; *Int'l,* pg. 7903
CHALLENGER MOTOR FREIGHT INC.; *Int'l,* pg. 1438
CHALLENGER OVERSEAS LLC—See CAI International, Inc.; *U.S. Public,* pg. 421
CHALLENGER PALLET & SUPPLY INC.; *U.S. Private,* pg. 845
CHALLENGER PIPE & STEEL, LLC; *U.S. Private,* pg. 845
CHALLENGER PORTFOLIO MANAGEMENT LIMITED—See Challenger Limited; *Int'l,* pg. 1438
CHALLENGER PROPERTY ASSET MANAGEMENT PTY LIMITED—See Challenger Limited; *Int'l,* pg. 1438
CHALLENGER SARL—See Carrefour SA; *Int'l,* pg. 1343
CHALLENGER SOS S.A.—See VINCI S.A.; *Int'l,* pg. 8217
CHALLENGER TECHNOLOGIES LTD.; *Int'l,* pg. 1438
CHALLENGER TECHNOLOGIES (M) SDN BHD—See Challenger Technologies Ltd.; *Int'l,* pg. 1438
CHALLENGE TV—See Comcast Corporation; *U.S. Public,* pg. 541
CHALLENGE UNLIMITED, INC.; *U.S. Private,* pg. 845
CHALLENGING FINANCIAL CAREERS INSURANCE MARKETING CORP., LLC—See Allianz SE; *Int'l,* pg. 351
CHALMERS GROUP OF COMPANIES; *Int'l,* pg. 1438
CHALMERS INDUSTRIES (BRISBANE) PTY. LTD—See Qube Holdings Limited; *Int'l,* pg. 6158
CHALMERS INDUSTRIES PTY. LTD—See Qube Holdings Limited; *Int'l,* pg. 6158
CHALMERS & KUBECK, INC.; *U.S. Private,* pg. 845

COMPANY NAME INDEX

CHALMERS LIMITED—See Qube Holdings Limited; *Int'l*, pg. 6158
CHALMERS PROPERTY COMPANY; *U.S. Private*, pg. 845
CHALMETTE REFINING, L.L.C.—See PBF Energy Inc.; *U.S. Public*, pg. 1657
CHALMIT LIGHTING LIMITED—See Hubbell Incorporated; *U.S. Public*, pg. 1066
CHALONE VINEYARD—See Diageo plc; *Int'l*, pg. 2102
CHALWYN LIMITED—See Roper Technologies, Inc.; *U.S. Public*, pg. 1810
CHAMAELEON EVEN EMPREENDIMENTOS IMOBILIARIOS LTDA.—See Even Construtora e Incorporadora S.A.; *Int'l*, pg. 2561
CHAMAK HOLDINGS LTD.; *Int'l*, pg. 1439
CHAMAN LAL SETIA EXPORT LTD.; *Int'l*, pg. 1439
CHAMBAL BREWERIES & DISTILLERIES LIMITED; *Int'l*, pg. 1439
CHAMBAL FERTILISERS & CHEMICALS LTD.—See K.K. Birla Group; *Int'l*, pg. 4044
CHAMBAL INFRASTRUCTURE VENTURES LIMITED—See K.K. Birla Group; *Int'l*, pg. 4044
CHAM BANK; *Int'l*, pg. 1439
CHAMBERLAIN AND ASSOCIATES; *U.S. Private*, pg. 845
THE CHAMBERLAIN GROUP, LLC—See The Duchossois Group, Inc.; *U.S. Private*, pg. 4023
CHAMBERLAIN HEALTHCARE PUBLIC RELATIONS—See Elliott Management Corporation; *U.S. Private*, pg. 1366
CHAMBERLAIN HEALTHCARE PUBLIC RELATIONS—See Patient Square Capital, L.P.; *U.S. Private*, pg. 3108
CHAMBERLAIN HEALTHCARE PUBLIC RELATIONS—See Veritas Capital Fund Management, LLC; *U.S. Private*, pg. 4365
CHAMBERLAIN HOLDINGS LIMITED—See Deere & Company; *U.S. Public*, pg. 646
CHAMBERLAIN HOLDINGS LLC; *U.S. Private*, pg. 845
CHAMBERLAIN MANUFACTURING CORP.—See The Duchossois Group, Inc.; *U.S. Private*, pg. 4023
CHAMBERLAIN OIL CO. INC.; *U.S. Private*, pg. 845
CHAMBERLAIN UNIVERSITY LLC—See Adtalem Global Education Inc.; *U.S. Public*, pg. 43
CHAMBERLAIN WHOLESALE GROCERY CO.; *U.S. Private*, pg. 846
CHAMBERLIN EDMONDS & ASSOCIATES, INC.—See McKesson Corporation; *U.S. Public*, pg. 1407
CHAMBERLIN & HILL CASTINGS LIMITED—See Chamberlin plc; *Int'l*, pg. 1439
CHAMBERLIN NATURAL FOODS INC.—See AMCON Distributing Company; *U.S. Public*, pg. 93
CHAMBERLIN PLC; *Int'l*, pg. 1439
CHAMBERS BANCSHARES INC.; *U.S. Private*, pg. 846
CHAMBERS BANK—See Chambers Bancshares Inc.; *U.S. Private*, pg. 846
CHAMBERS & COOK FREIGHT LTD.; *Int'l*, pg. 1439
CHAMBERS FABRICS INC.; *U.S. Private*, pg. 846
CHAMBERS OF MISSISSIPPI, INC.—See Waste Management, Inc.; *U.S. Public*, pg. 2330
CHAMBERS & OWEN, INC.; *U.S. Private*, pg. 846
CHAMBERS & PARTNERS MEDIA LTD.—See ABRY Partners, LLC; *U.S. Private*, pg. 41
CHAMBLISS LIMITED; *U.S. Private*, pg. 846
CHAMBON SAS—See Haco N.V.; *Int'l*, pg. 3204
CHAMBON SRL—See Haco N.V.; *Int'l*, pg. 3204
CHAMBOURCY ROCHE AUX FEES—See Nestle S.A.; *Int'l*, pg. 5205
CHAMELEO GMBH—See Highlight Event & Entertainment AG; *Int'l*, pg. 3388
CHAMELEON BREWING—See Sprecher Brewing Company, LLC; *U.S. Private*, pg. 3762
CHAMELEON INTEGRATED SERVICES; *U.S. Private*, pg. 846
CHAMELEON TECHNOLOGIES, INC.; *U.S. Private*, pg. 846
CHAM FOODS (ISRAEL) LTD.; *Int'l*, pg. 1439
CHAM GROUP AG; *Int'l*, pg. 1439
CHAM IMMOBILIEN AG—See Cham Group AG; *Int'l*, pg. 1439
CHAMP ACE CO., LTD.—See Saha Pathanapibul Public Company Limited; *Int'l*, pg. 6478
CHAMPADOR; *Int'l*, pg. 1439
CHAMPAGNE ALAIN THIENOT S.A.S.; *Int'l*, pg. 1439
CHAMPAGNE BOIZEL SA—See LANSON-BCC; *Int'l*, pg. 4413
CHAMPAGNE CANARD-DUCHENE S.A.—See Champagne Alain Thienot S.A.S.; *Int'l*, pg. 1439
CHAMPAGNE CHANOINE FRERES SA—See LANSON-BCC; *Int'l*, pg. 4413
CHAMPAGNE DE VENOGE SA—See LANSON-BCC; *Int'l*, pg. 4413
CHAMPAGNE HENRIOT; *Int'l*, pg. 1439
CHAMPAGNE LANSON S.A.S.—See LANSON-BCC; *Int'l*, pg. 4413
CHAMPAGNE LAURENT-PERRIER; *Int'l*, pg. 1439
CHAMPAGNE MERCIER—See LVMH Moet Hennessy Louis Vuitton SE; *Int'l*, pg. 4599

CHAMPAGNE MOBILITES—See Regie Autonome des Transports Parisiens; *Int'l*, pg. 6253
CHAMPAGNE MOET & CHANDON S.A.—See LVMH Moet Hennessy Louis Vuitton SE; *Int'l*, pg. 4599
CHAMPAGNE PERRIER-JOUET—See Pernod Ricard S.A.; *Int'l*, pg. 5809
CHAMPAGNE PHILIPPONNAT SA—See LANSON-BCC; *Int'l*, pg. 4413
CHAMPAGNE POL ROGER; *Int'l*, pg. 1440
CHAMPAGNE RUINART—See LVMH Moet Hennessy Louis Vuitton SE; *Int'l*, pg. 4599
CHAMPAGNE'S ENERGY INC.—See Superior Plus Corp.; *Int'l*, pg. 7338
THE CHAMPAIGN TELEPHONE COMPANY; *U.S. Private*, pg. 4007
CHAMPAIN FINANCIAL SERVICES LIMITED—See Schroders plc; *Int'l*, pg. 6639
CHAM PAPER GROUP SCHWEIZ AG—See Cham Group AG; *Int'l*, pg. 1439
CHAMP CARGOSYSTEMS (GERMANY) GMBH—See SITA Inc. N.V.; *Int'l*, pg. 6964
CHAMP CARGOSYSTEMS PHILIPPINES, INC.—See SITA Inc. N.V.; *Int'l*, pg. 6964
CHAMP CARGOSYSTEMS S.A—See SITA Inc. N.V.; *Int'l*, pg. 6964
CHAMP CARGOSYSTEMS (SWITZERLAND) AG—See SITA Inc. N.V.; *Int'l*, pg. 6964
CHAMP CARGOSYSTEMS (UK) LTD—See SITA Inc. N.V.; *Int'l*, pg. 6964
CHAMP'ENERGIE SA—See Vivescia; *Int'l*, pg. 8279
CHAMPI CANARIAS S.L.—See Dole plc; *Int'l*, pg. 2157
CHAMPION AEROSPACE INC.—See TransDigm Group Incorporated; *U.S. Public*, pg. 2182
CHAMPION ALUMINUM WINDOW CORPORATION; *U.S. Private*, pg. 846
CHAMPION AMERICA; *U.S. Private*, pg. 846
CHAMPION ATHLETICWEAR INC.—See Hanesbrands Inc.; *U.S. Public*, pg. 982
CHAMPION BEAR RESOURCES LTD.; *Int'l*, pg. 1440
CHAMPION BRANDS LLC; *U.S. Private*, pg. 846
CHAMPION BUILDING MATERIALS CO., LTD.; *Int'l*, pg. 1440
CHAMPION BUS, INC.—See AIP, LLC; *U.S. Private*, pg. 135
CHAMPION CHEVROLET INC.; *U.S. Private*, pg. 846
CHAMPION CHEVROLET, LLC—See AutoNation, Inc.; *U.S. Public*, pg. 234
CHAMPION CHEVROLET, PONTIAC, BUICK, INC.—See General Motors Company; *U.S. Public*, pg. 923
CHAMPION CINCO PIPE & SUPPLY LP—See Sumitomo Corporation; *Int'l*, pg. 7273
THE CHAMPION COMPANY INC.; *U.S. Private*, pg. 4007
CHAMPION COMPUTER PRODUCTS INC.; *U.S. Private*, pg. 846
CHAMPION CONSTRUCTION CORPORATION; *U.S. Private*, pg. 846
CHAMPION CONTAINER CORPORATION; *U.S. Private*, pg. 846
CHAMPION CREDIT UNION; *U.S. Private*, pg. 846
CHAMPION DIALYSIS CENTER, LLC—See Nautic Partners, LLC; *U.S. Private*, pg. 2869
CHAMPION DRILLING, LLC.—See Ensign Energy Services Inc.; *Int'l*, pg. 2446
CHAMPION ELECTRIC METALS INC.; *Int'l*, pg. 1440
CHAMPION ELEVATOR CORP.; *U.S. Private*, pg. 846
CHAMPION ENERGY CORPORATION—See Star Group, L.P.; *U.S. Public*, pg. 1937
CHAMPION ENERGY SERVICES, LLC—See Energy Capital Partners Management, LP; *U.S. Private*, pg. 1394
CHAMPION ENTERPRISES HOLDINGS, LLC—See Champion Homes, Inc.; *U.S. Public*, pg. 477
CHAMPION ENVIRONMENTAL TECHNOLOGIES PTY LTD.—See Nylex Limited; *Int'l*, pg. 5500
CHAMPION EUROPE S.R.L—See Hanesbrands Inc.; *U.S. Public*, pg. 982
CHAMPION FERRIES L.T.D.—See Attica Group; *Int'l*, pg. 696
CHAMPION FLOUR MILLING LTD.—See Nisshin Seifun Group, Inc.; *Int'l*, pg. 5372
CHAMPION FOODS, L.L.C.—See Ilitch Holdings, Inc.; *U.S. Private*, pg. 2041
CHAMPION FORD, INC.—See AutoNation, Inc.; *U.S. Public*, pg. 234
CHAMPION GLOBAL SERVICES LIMITED—See Great Eagle Holdings Limited; *Int'l*, pg. 3064
CHAMPION GRAPHIC COMMUNICATIONS—See Champion Industries, Inc.; *U.S. Public*, pg. 478
CHAMPION HOME BUILDERS INC.—See Champion Homes, Inc.; *U.S. Public*, pg. 477
CHAMPION HOMES, INC.; *U.S. Public*, pg. 477
CHAMPION HOMES OF TENNESSEE—See Champion Homes, Inc.; *U.S. Public*, pg. 477
CHAMPION, INC.; *U.S. Private*, pg. 847
CHAMPION INDUSTRIAL CONTRACTORS INC.; *U.S. Private*, pg. 846
CHAMPION INDUSTRIES, INC.; *U.S. Public*, pg. 477
CHAMPION INDUSTRIES, INC.—See Ali Holding S.r.l; *Int'l*, pg. 321

CHAMPION INDUSTRIES, INC.—See Champion Industries, Inc.; *U.S. Public*, pg. 478
CHAMPION INTERNATIONAL MOVING, LTD.—See Atlas World Group, Inc.; *U.S. Private*, pg. 381
CHAMPION IRON LIMITED; *Int'l*, pg. 1440
CHAMPION IRON LIMITED - TORONTO HEAD OFFICE—See Champion Iron Limited; *Int'l*, pg. 1440
CHAMPION LABORATORIES, INC.—See Rank Group Ltd.; *Int'l*, pg. 6208
CHAMPION LUMBER CO.; *U.S. Private*, pg. 846
CHAMPION MACHINE, LLC—See Dulany Industries Inc.; *U.S. Private*, pg. 1286
CHAMPION MANUFACTURING, INC.—See DW Management Services, LLC; *U.S. Private*, pg. 2236
CHAMPION MICROELECTRONIC CORP.; *Int'l*, pg. 1440
CHAMPION MICROELECTRONIC—See Champion Microelectronic Corp.; *Int'l*, pg. 1440
CHAMPION MORTGAGE CO., INC.—See Mr. Cooper Group Inc.; *U.S. Public*, pg. 1480
CHAMPION MOTORSPORT; *U.S. Private*, pg. 846
CHAMPION NUTRITION, INC.; *U.S. Private*, pg. 846
CHAMPION OIL COMPANY INC.—See Star Group, L.P.; *U.S. Public*, pg. 1937
CHAMPION PORSCHE; *U.S. Private*, pg. 846
CHAMPION PUBLISHING, INC.—See Champion Industries, Inc.; *U.S. Public*, pg. 478
CHAMPION RAISIN INTERNATIONAL—See Sunshine Raisin Corporation; *U.S. Private*, pg. 3872
CHAMPION REAL ESTATE INVESTMENT TRUST; *Int'l*, pg. 1440
CHAMPION REALTY INC.—See Berkshire Hathaway Inc.; *U.S. Public*, pg. 306
CHAMPION SCREW MACHINE ENGINEERING, INC.; *U.S. Private*, pg. 846
CHAMPIONS DIALYSIS, LLC—See DaVita Inc.; *U.S. Public*, pg. 636
CHAMPION SEED COMPANY; *U.S. Private*, pg. 847
CHAMPIONS FOR CHILDREN, INC.; *U.S. Private*, pg. 847
CHAMPIONSHIP PRODUCTIONS INC.—See National Amusements, Inc.; *U.S. Public*, pg. 2841
CHAMPIONS LIFE INSURANCE CO.—See Maximum Corporation; *U.S. Private*, pg. 2618
CHAMPIONS MACHINE TOOL SALES, INC.; *U.S. Private*, pg. 847
CHAMPION SOLUTIONS GROUP INC.—See CDW Corporation; *U.S. Public*, pg. 462
CHAMPIONS ONCOLOGY, INC.; *U.S. Public*, pg. 478
CHAMPIONS PIPE & SUPPLY INC.; *U.S. Private*, pg. 847
CHAMPION SPORTS MEDICINE BIRMINGHAM, LLC—See Community Health Systems, Inc.; *U.S. Public*, pg. 552
CHAMPIONS (UK) PLC.; *Int'l*, pg. 1440
CHAMPION SUPERMARCHES FRANCE SAS—See Carrefour SA; *Int'l*, pg. 1345
CHAMPION TECHNOLOGY HOLDINGS LTD; *Int'l*, pg. 1440
CHAMPION TEMPORARIES INC—See Teamsource Inc.; *U.S. Private*, pg. 3951
CHAMPION TRANSPORTATION SERVICES, INC.; *U.S. Private*, pg. 847
CHAMPION WIND FARM, LLC—See E.ON SE; *Int'l*, pg. 2251
CHAMPION WINDOW COMPANY OF OKLAHOMA CITY, LLC—See Champion Windows Manufacturing Inc.; *U.S. Private*, pg. 847
CHAMPION WINDOWS MANUFACTURING INC.; *U.S. Private*, pg. 847
CHAMPION WIRE & CABLE LLC; *U.S. Private*, pg. 847
CHAMPIONX CORPORATION; *U.S. Public*, pg. 478
CHAMPIONX OILFIELD SOLUTIONS NIGERIA LIMITED—See ChampionX Corporation; *U.S. Public*, pg. 478
CHAMP KABIN CO., LTD.—See Saha Pathanapibul Public Company Limited; *Int'l*, pg. 6479
CHAMPLAIN BANK CORPORATION; *U.S. Private*, pg. 847
CHAMPLAIN CABLE CORP.—See American Industrial Acquisition Corporation; *U.S. Private*, pg. 237
CHAMPLAIN CAPITAL MANAGEMENT LLC; *U.S. Private*, pg. 847
CHAMPLAIN FINANCIAL CORPORATION; *Int'l*, pg. 1440
CHAMPLAIN MOTORS LTD.; *Int'l*, pg. 1440
CHAMPLAIN NATIONAL BANK—See Champlain Bank Corporation; *U.S. Private*, pg. 847
CHAMPLAIN OIL CO. INC.; *U.S. Private*, pg. 847
CHAMPLAIN VALLEY OFFICE OF ECONOMIC OPPORTUNITY, INC.; *U.S. Private*, pg. 847
CHAMP LANDFILL COMPANY, LLC—See Waste Connections, Inc.; *Int'l*, pg. 8352
CHAMP, LLC—See Hormel Foods Corporation; *U.S. Public*, pg. 1054
CHAMP PRIVATE EQUITY PTE. LTD.—See CHAMP Private Equity Pty. Ltd.; *Int'l*, pg. 1439
CHAMP PRIVATE EQUITY PTY. LTD.; *Int'l*, pg. 1439
CHAMPS INDUSTRIAL PTE. LTD.—See Zhejiang Xinchai Co., Ltd.; *Int'l*, pg. 8666
CHAMPS MEDIAS—See Publicis Groupe S.A.; *Int'l*, pg. 6097

CHAMP PRIVATE EQUITY PTY. LTD. — CORPORATE AFFILIATIONS

CHAMPS SPORTS—See Foot Locker, Inc.; *U.S. Public*, pg. 863
CHAMS ACCESS LIMITED—See Chams Holding Company; *Int'l*, pg. 1440
CHAMS HOLDING COMPANY; *Int'l*, pg. 1440
CHAMS SWITCH LIMITED—See Chams Holding Company; *Int'l*, pg. 1440
CHAMTOR - LEGAL—See Archer-Daniels-Midland Company; *U.S. Public*, pg. 184
CHAMTOR SA—See Vivescia; *Int'l*, pg. 8279
CHANACHAI LIMITED—See Sansiri pcl; *Int'l*, pg. 6556
CHANCELLOR, INC.; *U.S. Private*, pg. 847
CHANCELLOR OIL TOOLS, INC.—See Team Oil Tools, LLC; *U.S. Private*, pg. 3950
CHANCELLOR & SON INC.; *U.S. Private*, pg. 847
CHANCE RIDES MANUFACTURING, INC.—See Permanent Equity Management, LLC; *U.S. Private*, pg. 3152
CHANCERY PARK (EXNING) RESIDENTS MANAGEMENT COMPANY LIMITED—See Persimmon plc; *Int'l*, pg. 5815
CHANCETON CAPITAL PARTNERS LIMITED—See Unitas Holdings Limited; *Int'l*, pg. 8063
CHANCEY DESIGN PARTNERSHIP, INC.; *U.S. Private*, pg. 847
CHANCEY METALS, LLC—See Indigo South Capital, Inc.; *U.S. Private*, pg. 2063
CHANDAN LTD.—See Indian Restaurants Group Plc; *Int'l*, pg. 3654
CHANDER ELECTRONICS CORP.—See VIA Technologies, Inc.; *Int'l*, pg. 8183
CHANDIS; *Int'l*, pg. 1441
CHANDLER BUILDING SUPPLY COMPANY—See Chandler Concrete Inc.; *U.S. Private*, pg. 848
CHANDLER CHICCO AGENCY - LONDON—See Chandler Chicco Agency; *U.S. Private*, pg. 847
CHANDLER CHICCO AGENCY - LOS ANGELES—See Chandler Chicco Agency; *U.S. Private*, pg. 848
CHANDLER CHICCO AGENCY - PARIS—See Chandler Chicco Agency; *U.S. Private*, pg. 848
CHANDLER CHICCO AGENCY; *U.S. Private*, pg. 847
CHANDLER CHICCO AGENCY - WASHINGTON—See Chandler Chicco Agency; *U.S. Private*, pg. 848
CHANDLER COAL (PTY) LTD—See Salungano Group; *Int'l*, pg. 6495
CHANDLER COLLISION, INC.—See AutoNation, Inc.; *U.S. Public*, pg. 234
CHANDLER CONCRETE COMPANY INC.—See Chandler Concrete Inc.; *U.S. Private*, pg. 848
CHANDLER CONCRETE INC.; *U.S. Private*, pg. 848
CHANDLER CONCRETE OF VIRGINIA, INC.—See Chandler Concrete Inc.; *U.S. Private*, pg. 848
CHANDLER CO-OP; *U.S. Private*, pg. 848
CHANDLER CORPORATION; *Int'l*, pg. 1441
CHANDLER ENDOSCOPY AMBULATORY SURGERY CENTER, LLC—See Tenet Healthcare Corporation; *U.S. Public*, pg. 2009
CHANDLER ENGINEERING COMPANY LLC—See AMETEK, Inc.; *U.S. Public*, pg. 117
CHANDLER ENTERPRISES INC.; *U.S. Private*, pg. 848
CHANDLER GROUP, INC.; *U.S. Private*, pg. 848
CHANDLER HALL HEALTH SERVICES, INC.; *U.S. Private*, pg. 848
CHANDLER HOUSE PRESS—See Tatnuck Booksellers Inc.; *U.S. Private*, pg. 3936
CHANDLER INDUSTRIES -ARROW DIVISION—See Arch Equity Partners, LLC; *U.S. Private*, pg. 310
CHANDLER INDUSTRIES, INC.—See Arch Equity Partners, LLC; *U.S. Private*, pg. 310
CHANDLER INDUSTRIES - LAKE COUNTRY DIVISION—See Arch Equity Partners, LLC; *U.S. Private*, pg. 310
CHANDLER INDUSTRIES - STREMEL DIVISION—See Arch Equity Partners, LLC; *U.S. Private*, pg. 310
CHANDLER MACLEOD - BRISBANE—See Recruit Holdings Co., Ltd.; *Int'l*, pg. 6240
CHANDLER MACLEOD GROUP LIMITED—See Recruit Holdings Co., Ltd.; *Int'l*, pg. 6240
CHANDLER MACLEOD GROUP PTE. LTD.—See Recruit Holdings Co., Ltd.; *Int'l*, pg. 6240
CHANDLER MACLEOD MEDICAL PTY LIMITED—See Recruit Holdings Co., Ltd.; *Int'l*, pg. 6240
CHANDLER MACLEOD PEOPLE INSIGHTS PTY LTD—See Recruit Holdings Co., Ltd.; *Int'l*, pg. 6240
CHANDLER MACLEOD - PERTH—See Recruit Holdings Co., Ltd.; *Int'l*, pg. 6240
CHANDLER MACLEOD SERVICES PTY LIMITED—See Recruit Holdings Co., Ltd.; *Int'l*, pg. 6240
CHANDLER MACLEOD TECHNICAL AND ENGINEERING PTY LTD—See Recruit Holdings Co., Ltd.; *Int'l*, pg. 6240
CHANDLER MHM LIMITED—See Mori Hamada & Matsumoto; *Int'l*, pg. 5045
CHANDLER PRODUCTS—See MW Industries, Inc.; *U.S. Private*, pg. 2822
CHANDLERS GARAGE (BRIGHTON) LIMITED—See Group 1 Automotive, Inc.; *U.S. Public*, pg. 971
CHANDLERS GARAGE WORTHING LIMITED—See Group 1 Automotive, Inc.; *U.S. Public*, pg. 971

CHANDLERS (HAILSHAM) LIMITED—See Group 1 Automotive, Inc.; *U.S. Public*, pg. 971
CHANDLER SIGNS, LP; *U.S. Private*, pg. 848
CHAND, LLC—See Bollinger Shipyards, Inc.; *U.S. Private*, pg. 611
CHANDNI MACHINES LIMITED—See Candour Techtex Ltd.; *Int'l*, pg. 1289
CHANDON DO BRASIL—See LVMH Moet Hennessy Louis Vuitton SE; *Int'l*, pg. 4599
CHANDRA BHAGAT PHARMA LTD.; *Int'l*, pg. 1441
CHANDRA PRABHU INTERNATIONAL LTD.; *Int'l*, pg. 1441
CHANDRA SHOES INDUSTRY CO., LTD.—See Victory New Materials Limited Company; *Int'l*, pg. 8190
CHANDRIMA MERCANTILES LIMITED; *Int'l*, pg. 1441
CHANEL, INC.—See Chanel S.A.; *Int'l*, pg. 1441
CHANEL S.A.; *Int'l*, pg. 1441
CHANEN CONSTRUCTION CO. INC—See Chanen Corporation; *U.S. Private*, pg. 848
CHANEN CORPORATION; *U.S. Private*, pg. 848
CHANEY ENTERPRISES LP; *U.S. Private*, pg. 848
CHANGAN BERJAYA AUTO SDN BHD—See Berjaya Corporation Berhad; *Int'l*, pg. 984
CHANGAN MINSHENG APLL LOGISTICS CO., LTD.; *Int'l*, pg. 1441
CHANG'AN TBK CO., LTD.—See TBK Co. Ltd.; *Int'l*, pg. 7480
CHANGBAI MOUNTAIN TOURISM CO., LTD.; *Int'l*, pg. 1442
CHANGCHAI CO., LTD.; *Int'l*, pg. 1442
CHANG CHENG-TAKENAKA CONSTRUCTION CO., LTD.—See Takenaka Corporation; *Int'l*, pg. 7441
CHANG CHIANG CHEMICAL CO., LTD.—See Adeka Corporation; *Int'l*, pg. 142
CHANG CHIANG CHEMICAL CO., LTD.—See ChangChun Group; *Int'l*, pg. 1442
CHANG CHIANG CHEMICAL (SHANGHAI) CO., LTD.—See ChangChun Group; *Int'l*, pg. 1442
CHANGCHUN BEITE AUTOMOBILE PARTS CO., LTD.—See Shanghai Beite Technology Co., Ltd.; *Int'l*, pg. 6762
CHANGCHUN CECK AUTO. PARTS CO., LTD.—See China Steel Corporation; *Int'l*, pg. 1555
CHANGCHUN CHANGCHUN AUTOMOTIVE INTERIORS CO., LTD.—See Jiangsu Changshu Automotive Trim Group Co., Ltd.; *Int'l*, pg. 3945
CHANGCHUN CHEMETALL CHEMICALS CO., LTD.—See BASF SE; *Int'l*, pg. 873
CHANG CHUN CHEMICAL (JIANGSU) CO., LTD.—See ChangChun Group; *Int'l*, pg. 1442
CHANG CHUN CHEMICAL (ZHANGZHOU) CO., LTD.—See ChangChun Group; *Int'l*, pg. 1442
CHANGCHUN DIHAO FOODSTUFF DEVELOPMENT CO., LTD.—See Global Sweeteners Holdings Limited; *Int'l*, pg. 3001
CHANGCHUN EFTEC CHEMICAL PRODUCTS LTD.—See EMS-Chemie Holding AG; *Int'l*, pg. 2393
CHANGCHUN ELRINGKLINGER LTD.—See ElringKlinger AG; *Int'l*, pg. 2369
CHANGCHUN ENGLEY AUTOMOBILE INDUSTRY CO., LTD.—See Cayman Engley Industrial Co., Ltd.; *Int'l*, pg. 1363
CHANG CHUN EURASIA GROUP CO., LTD; *Int'l*, pg. 1441
CHANGCHUN EXTRAWELL PHARMACEUTICAL CO., LTD.—See Extrawell Pharmaceutical Holdings Ltd.; *Int'l*, pg. 2592
CHANGCHUN FAWAY AUTOMOBILE COMPONENTS CO., LTD.—See China FAW Group Corporation; *Int'l*, pg. 1501
CHANGCHUN FAWER-IHI TURBO CO., LTD.—See IHI Corporation; *Int'l*, pg. 3604
CHANGCHUN FAW MIRACLE TECHNOLOGY EQUIPMENT ENGINEERING CO. LTD.—See Miracle Automation Engineering Co., Ltd.; *Int'l*, pg. 4915
CHANGCHUN FAWSN SWELL AUTOMOTIVE PARTS CO.,LTD.—See Guangdong Hongtu Technology (Holdings) Co., Ltd.; *Int'l*, pg. 3156
CHANGCHUN GAS CO., LTD.; *Int'l*, pg. 1442
CHANGCHUN GBT BIO-CHEMICAL CO., LTD.—See Global Bio-chem Technology Group Company Limited; *Int'l*, pg. 2993
CHANGCHUN GROUP; *Int'l*, pg. 1442
CHANGCHUN HELLA AUTOMOTIVE LIGHTING LTD.—See Hella GmbH & Co. KGaA; *Int'l*, pg. 3331
CHANGCHUN HENKEL SURFACE TECHNOLOGIES CO. LTD.—See Henkel AG & Co. KGaA; *Int'l*, pg. 3348
CHANGCHUN HIGH & NEW TECHNOLOGY INDUSTRY (GROUP) INC.; *Int'l*, pg. 1442
CHANGCHUN HI-LEX AUTO CABLE CO. LTD.—See Hi-Lex Corporation; *Int'l*, pg. 3380
CHANGCHUN HUF AUTOMOTIVE LOCK CO. LTD.—See Huf Hulsbeck & Furst GmbH & Co. KG; *Int'l*, pg. 3523
CHANG CHUN JAPAN CO., LTD.—See ChangChun Group; *Int'l*, pg. 1442
CHANGCHUN JILIN UNIVERSITY ZHENGYUAN INFORMATION TECHNOLOGIES CO., LTD.; *Int'l*, pg. 1442

CHANGCHUN JINGYUETAN SKIING GROUND LTD.—See Huangshan Tourism Development Co., Ltd.; *Int'l*, pg. 3513
CHANGCHUN JIXING PRINTING CO., LTD.—See Shenzhen Jinjia Group Co.; *Int'l*, pg. 6814
CHANGCHUN KUANGDA AUTOMOBILE FABRIC CO., LTD.—See Kuangda Technology Group Co., Ltd.; *Int'l*, pg. 4319
CHANGCHUN MANN+HUMMEL FAWER FILTER CO., LTD.—See Mann+Hummel GmbH; *Int'l*, pg. 4673
CHANGCHUN MEILI SPRING CO., LTD.—See ZheJiang MeiLi High Technology CO., LTD.; *Int'l*, pg. 8660
CHANGCHUN NIKKEI RAILWAY VEHICLE EQUIPMENT CO., LTD.—See Nippon Light Metal Holdings Company, Ltd.; *Int'l*, pg. 5323
CHANGCHUN NOK-FREUDENBERG OILSEAL CO., LTD.—See Freudenberg SE; *Int'l*, pg. 2782
CHANGCHUN PETROCHEMICAL CO., LTD.—See ChangChun Group; *Int'l*, pg. 1442
CHANG CHUN PETROCHEMICAL CO., LTD.—See ChangChun Group; *Int'l*, pg. 1442
CHANGCHUN PILKINGTON SAFETY GLASS CO. LTD.—See Nippon Sheet Glass Co. Ltd.; *Int'l*, pg. 5331
CHANG CHUN PLASTICS CO., LTD.—See ChangChun Group; *Int'l*, pg. 1442
CHANGCHUN RESEARCH INSTITUTE FOR MECHANICAL SCIENCE CO., LTD.—See China National Machinery Industry Corporation; *Int'l*, pg. 1531
CHANGCHUN SB (CHANGSHU) CO., LTD.—See Sumitomo Bakelite Co., Ltd.; *Int'l*, pg. 7262
CHANGCHUN SCHLEMMER AUTOMOTIVE PARTS CO., LTD.—See Ningbo Huaxiang Electronic Co., Ltd.; *Int'l*, pg. 5302
CHANGCHUN SE BORDNETZE CO., LTD.—See Sumitomo Electric Industries, Ltd.; *Int'l*, pg. 7277
CHANG CHUN SPARX AUTO LAMPS CO., LTD.—See TYC Brother Industrial Co., Ltd.; *Int'l*, pg. 7994
CHANG CHUN SUNG MOON ELECTRONICS CO., LTD.—See Sungmoon Electronics Co., Ltd.; *Int'l*, pg. 7315
CHANGCHUN TBK SHILI AUTO PARTS CO., LTD.—See TBK Co. Ltd.; *Int'l*, pg. 7480
CHANGCHUN TERUMO MEDICAL PRODUCTS CO. LTD.—See Terumo Corporation; *Int'l*, pg. 7569
CHANG CHUN TOK (CHANGSHU) CO., LTD.—See Tokyo Ohka Kogyo Co., Ltd.; *Int'l*, pg. 7793
CHANGCHUN TONGMUO FAWER NEW MATERIALS CO., LTD.—See NBTM New Materials Group Co., Ltd.; *Int'l*, pg. 5179
CHANGCHUN UP OPTOTECH CO., LTD.; *Int'l*, pg. 1442
CHANGCHUN VANKE REAL ESTATE DEVELOPMENT COMPANY LIMITED—See China Vanke Co., Ltd.; *Int'l*, pg. 1562
CHANGCHUN VISTEON FAWAY AUTOMOTIVE ELECTRONICS CO., LTD.—See Visteon Corporation; *U.S. Public*, pg. 2305
CHANGCHUN YIDONG CLUTCH CO., LTD.; *Int'l*, pg. 1443
CHANGCHUN ZHIYUAN NEW ENERGY EQUIPMENT CO., LTD.; *Int'l*, pg. 1443
CHANGCHUN ZHONGSHENG STAR AUTOMOBILE SALES & SERVICES CO., LTD.—See Zhongsheng Group Holdings Limited; *Int'l*, pg. 8674
CHANG CORPORATION COMPANY LIMITED—See Thai Beverage Public Company Limited; *Int'l*, pg. 7589
CHANGDA INTERNATIONAL HOLDINGS, INC.; *Int'l*, pg. 1443
CHANGDE XIANGDA CAMEL FEED CO., LTD—See Tangrenshen Group Co., Ltd.; *Int'l*, pg. 7458
CHANGE CAPITAL PARTNERS LLP; *Int'l*, pg. 1443
CHANGE COMMUNICATIONS GMBH—See The Interpublic Group of Companies, Inc.; *U.S. Public*, pg. 2090
CHANGE FINANCIAL LIMITED; *Int'l*, pg. 1443
THE CHANGE GROUP CORPORATION LTD.—See Prosegur Cash SA; *Int'l*, pg. 5999
THE CHANGE GROUP FRANCE, S.A.S.—See Prosegur Cash SA; *Int'l*, pg. 5999
THE CHANGE GROUP HELSINKI OY—See Prosegur Cash SA; *Int'l*, pg. 5999
THE CHANGE GROUP INTERNATIONAL PLC—See Prosegur Cash SA; *Int'l*, pg. 5999
THE CHANGE GROUP LONDON LIMITED—See Prosegur Cash SA; *Int'l*, pg. 5999
THE CHANGE GROUP SPAIN, S.A.—See Prosegur Cash SA; *Int'l*, pg. 5999
CHANGE GROUP SWEDEN AB—See Prosegur Cash SA; *Int'l*, pg. 5999
CHANGE HEALTHCARE CORPORATION—See McKesson Corporation; *U.S. Public*, pg. 1407
CHANGE HEALTHCARE HOLDINGS, INC.—See McKesson Corporation; *U.S. Public*, pg. 1407
CHANGE HEALTHCARE INC.—See UnitedHealth Group Incorporated; *U.S. Public*, pg. 2248
CHANGE HEALTHCARE NEW ZEALAND—See UnitedHealth Group Incorporated; *U.S. Public*, pg. 2248
CHANGE, INC.; *Int'l*, pg. 1443
CHANGE, INC.—See Penn-Mar Organization, Inc.; *U.S. Private*, pg. 3135

COMPANY NAME INDEX

CHANGEMAKER EDUCATIONS AB—See AcadeMedia AB; *Int'l*, pg. 75
CHANGE MANAGEMENT CONSULTING, INC.; *U.S. Private*, pg. 848
THE CHANGE ORGANISATION LTD.; *Int'l*, pg. 7631
CHANGE POINT, INC. - MAIN OFFICE—See Change Point, Inc.; *U.S. Private*, pg. 848
CHANGE POINT, INC.; *U.S. Private*, pg. 848
CHANGE TO WIN; *U.S. Private*, pg. 848
CHANGFENG (GROUP) CO., LTD.; *Int'l*, pg. 1443
CHANG FU STAINLESS STEEL CENTER (SUZHOU) CO., LTD.—See Hanwa Co., Ltd.; *Int'l*, pg. 3261
CHANGGAO ELECTRIC GROUP CO., LTD.; *Int'l*, pg. 1443
CHANGHAE ETHANOL CO., LTD.; *Int'l*, pg. 1443
CHANGHAI BIOLOGICAL COMPANY—See Zhejiang Medicine Co. Ltd.; *Int'l*, pg. 8660
CHANGHA SJM CO., LTD.—See SJM Holdings Co., Ltd.; *Int'l*, pg. 6969
CHANG HEART CORP.—See HKS CO., LTD.; *Int'l*, pg. 3429
CHANGHE INTERNATIONAL TRADING (GZFTZ) CO,. LTD.—See Eternal Materials Co., Ltd.; *Int'l*, pg. 2520
CHANG-HO FIBRE CORPORATION - NANKAN FACTORY—See Chang-Ho Fibre Corporation; *Int'l*, pg. 1442
CHANG-HO FIBRE CORPORATION; *Int'l*, pg. 1441
CHANGHONG ELECTRIC (AUSTRALIA) PTY LTD.—See Sichuan Changhong Electric Co., Ltd.; *Int'l*, pg. 6877
CHANGHONG EUROPE ELECTRIC S.R.O.—See Sichuan Changhong Electric Co., Ltd.; *Int'l*, pg. 6877
CHANGHONG (HONG KONG) TRADING LIMITED—See Sichuan Changhong Electric Co., Ltd.; *Int'l*, pg. 6877
CHANGHONG HUAYI COMPRESSOR CO., LTD.; *Int'l*, pg. 1443
CHANGHONG JIAHUA HOLDINGS LIMITED—See Sichuan Changhong Electric Co., Ltd.; *Int'l*, pg. 6877
CHANGHONG MEILING CO.,LTD.; *Int'l*, pg. 1443
CHANGHUAT CORPORATION BERHAD; *Int'l*, pg. 1443
CHANG HWA BANK (TAICHUNG)—See Chang Hwa Commercial Bank Ltd.; *Int'l*, pg. 1441
CHANG HWA BANK (TAIPEI)—See Chang Hwa Commercial Bank Ltd.; *Int'l*, pg. 1441
CHANG HWA COMMERCIAL BANK LTD.; *Int'l*, pg. 1441
CHANG HWA COMMERCIAL BANK - NEW YORK BRANCH—See Chang Hwa Commercial Bank Ltd.; *Int'l*, pg. 1441
CHANG HWA INTERNATIONAL BANKING—See Chang Hwa Commercial Bank Ltd.; *Int'l*, pg. 1441
CHANGING OUR WORLD—See Omnicom Group Inc.; *U.S. Public*, pg. 1579
CHANG INTERNATIONAL CO., LTD.—See Thai Beverage Public Company Limited; *Int'l*, pg. 7589
CHANG INTERNATIONAL INC.; *U.S. Private*, pg. 848
CHANG JIA M&E ENGINEERING CORP.; *Int'l*, pg. 1441
CHANG JIANG FLOAT GLASS CO., LTD.—See Taiwan Glass Industry Corporation; *Int'l*, pg. 7420
CHANGJIANG PUBLISHING & MEDIA CO., LTD.; *Int'l*, pg. 1443
CHANGJIANG RUNFA MEDICINE CO., LTD.; *Int'l*, pg. 1443
CHANGJIANG SECURITIES COMPANY LIMITED; *Int'l*, pg. 1443
CHANGLAN TECHNOLOGY GROUP CO., LTD; *Int'l*, pg. 1443
CHANGLE JIEYUAN MENTAL SURFACE TREATMENT CO., LTD.—See Shandong Mining Machinery Group Co., Ltd.; *Int'l*, pg. 6756
CHANGLIN COMPANY LIMITED; *Int'l*, pg. 1443
CHANGLI ZHONGYU GAS CO., LTD.—See Zhongyu Energy Holdings Limited; *Int'l*, pg. 8675
CHANG LONG CHEMICAL (SHENZHEN) CO., LTD.—See ChangChun Group; *Int'l*, pg. 1442
CHANGMAO BIOCHEMICAL ENGINEERING COMPANY LIMITED; *Int'l*, pg. 1443
CHANGMING INDUSTRIAL MANAGEMENT GROUP HOLDING; *Int'l*, pg. 1444
CHANGS ASCENDING ENTERPRISE CO., LTD.; *Int'l*, pg. 1444
CHANGSHA BODE METALLURGIC MATERIAL CO., LTD.—See Fujian Longxi Bearing (Group) Corporation Limited; *Int'l*, pg. 2818
CHANGSHA BROAD HOMES INDUSTRIAL GROUP CO., LTD.; *Int'l*, pg. 1444
CHANGSHA CHUANG YUE MOTORS SALES & SERVICES COMPANY LIMITED—See Sime Darby Berhad; *Int'l*, pg. 6928
CHANGSHA DIALINE NEW MATERIAL SCIENCE & TECHNOLOGY CO., LTD.; *Int'l*, pg. 1444
CHANGSHA DIGITAL CHINA COMPANY LIMITED—See Digital China Holdings Limited; *Int'l*, pg. 2121
CHANGSHA FUTABA AUTO PARTS CO., LTD.—See Futaba Industrial Co., Ltd.; *Int'l*, pg. 2851
CHANGSHA HIGH-TECH DEVELOPMENT ZONE KAIQUAN MECHANICAL & ELECTRICAL TECHNOLOGY CO., LTD.—See Endress+Hauser (International) Holding AG; *Int'l*, pg. 2405
CHANGSHA JINGJIA MICROELECTRONICS CO., LTD.; *Int'l*, pg. 1444

CHANGSHA LYRUN NEW MATERIAL CO., LTD.—See Hunan Corun New Energy Co., Ltd.; *Int'l*, pg. 3531
CHANGSHA MEIDONG LEXUS AUTO SALES & SERVICES CO., LTD.—See China MeiDong Auto Holdings Limited; *Int'l*, pg. 1519
CHANGSHAN BIOCHEMICAL PHARMACEUTICAL (JIANGSU) CO., LTD.—See Hebei Changshan Biochemical Pharmaceutical Co. Ltd.; *Int'l*, pg. 3305
CHANGSHAN CONJUCHEM BIOLOGICAL PHARMACEUTICAL R&D CO., LTD.—See Hebei Changshan Biochemical Pharmaceutical Co. Ltd.; *Int'l*, pg. 3305
CHANGSHA PACIFIC HANYA AUTO PARTS CO., LTD.—See PACIFIC INDUSTRIAL CO. LTD.; *Int'l*, pg. 5690
CHANGSHA RISECOMM COMMUNICATION TECHNOLOGY COMPANY LIMITED—See Risecomm Group Holdings Limited; *Int'l*, pg. 6349
CHANGSHA SUNBIRD YACHT LLC—See YaGuang Technology Group Company Limited; *Int'l*, pg. 8545
CHANGSHA TANGRENSHEN XIANGDA CAMEL FEED CO., LTD—See Tangrenshen Group Co., Ltd.; *Int'l*, pg. 7458
CHANGSHA TONGCHENG HOLDINGS CO., LTD.; *Int'l*, pg. 1444
CHANGSHA TON YI INDUSTRIAL CO., LTD.—See Uni-President Enterprises Corporation; *Int'l*, pg. 8028
CHANGSHA ZHONGFU PREFORM CO., LTD.—See Zhuhai Zhongfu Enterprise Co., Ltd.; *Int'l*, pg. 8678
CHANGSHENG CHINA PROPERTY COMPANY LIMITED; *Int'l*, pg. 1444
CHANGSHENG INTERNATIONAL GROUP LIMITED; *U.S. Private*, pg. 848
CHANGSHOUHUA FOOD COMPANY LIMITED—See Shandong Sanxing Group Co., Ltd.; *Int'l*, pg. 6757
CHANGSHU COATEX ADDITIVES CO. LTD—See Arkema S.A.; *Int'l*, pg. 571
CHANGSHU FENGFAN POWER EQUIPMENT CO., LTD.; *Int'l*, pg. 1444
CHANGSHU GUORUI TECHNOLOGY CO., LTD.; *Int'l*, pg. 1444
CHANGSHU HONGLIN CONNECTING-TECHNOLOGY CO., LTD.—See InvesTech Holdings Limited; *Int'l*, pg. 3778
CHANGSHU HONGLIN ELECTRONIC CO., LTD.—See InvesTech Holdings Limited; *Int'l*, pg. 3778
CHANGSHU HONGLIN WIRE & CABLE CO., LTD.—See InvesTech Holdings Limited; *Int'l*, pg. 3778
CHANGSHU HUAYE STEEL STRIP CO.,LTD—See Sutor Technology Group Ltd.; *Int'l*, pg. 7347
CHANGSHU KDAC CO., LTD.—See Aptiv PLC; *Int'l*, pg. 525
CHANGSHU LION ENTERPRISE CO LTD—See Lion Group Management Services Sdn Bhd; *Int'l*, pg. 4518
CHANGSHU MATAI PACKAGING PRODUCTS CO., LTD.—See Rengo Co., Ltd.; *Int'l*, pg. 6280
CHANGSHU MONO HIROSAWA AUTOMOTIVE TRIM CO., LTD.—See Hiroca Holdings Ltd.; *Int'l*, pg. 3404
CHANGSHU NGK SPARK PLUG CO., LTD.—See Niterra Co., Ltd.; *Int'l*, pg. 5380
CHANGSHU NISSIN-NINOTRANS TRANSPORTATION CO., LTD.—See Nissin Corporation; *Int'l*, pg. 5375
CHANGSHU NOF CHEMICAL CO., LTD.—See NOF Corporation; *Int'l*, pg. 5399
CHANGSHU NSK NEEDLE BEARING CO., LTD.—See NSK Ltd.; *Int'l*, pg. 5478
CHANGSHU PACIFIC MILLENNIUM PACKAGING & PAPER INDUSTRIES CO., LTD.—See Pacific Millennium Packaging Group Corporation; *Int'l*, pg. 5691
CHANGSHU PREMIER TECH CHRONOS EQUIPMENT & ENGINEERING CO., LTD.—See Premier Tech Ltd.; *Int'l*, pg. 5962
CHANGSHU SRIXON SPORTS CO., LTD.—See Sumitomo Rubber Industries, Ltd.; *Int'l*, pg. 7298
CHANGSHU SYP SPECIAL GLASS CO., LTD.—See Shanghai Yaohua Pilkington Glass Group Co., Ltd.; *Int'l*, pg. 6781
CHANGSHU TIANYIN ELECTROMECHANICAL CO., LTD.; *Int'l*, pg. 1444
CHANGSHU WALSIN SPECIALTY STEEL CO., LTD.—See Walsin Lihwa Corporation; *Int'l*, pg. 8334
CHANGSHU XINGHUA PORT CO., LTD.—See Xinghua Port Holdings Ltd.; *Int'l*, pg. 8529
CHANGSHU YONGDA LUJIE AUTOMOBILE SALES & SERVICES CO., LTD.—See China Yongda Automobiles Services Holdings Limited; *Int'l*, pg. 1564
CHANGSHU ZHONGLIAN PHOTOELECTRIC NEW MATERIAL CO., LTD.—See Jiangsu Zhongli Group Co., Ltd.; *Int'l*, pg. 3957
CHANGSU SUNREX TECHNOLOGY CORP.—See Sunrex Technology Corporation; *Int'l*, pg. 7321
CHANGTAI GOLDEN APPLE CO., LTD.—See Jinli Group Holdings Limited; *Int'l*, pg. 3969
CHANGTIAN PLASTIC & CHEMICAL LIMITED; *Int'l*, pg. 1444
CHANG TYPE INDUSTRIAL CO., LTD.; *Int'l*, pg. 1441
CHANG WAH ELECTROMATERIALS, INC.; *Int'l*, pg. 1441
CHANG WAH TECHNOLOGY CO., LTD.; *Int'l*, pg. 1441

CHANGXING KIBING ENERGY SAVING GLASS CO., LTD.—See Zhuzhou Kibing Group Co., Ltd.; *Int'l*, pg. 8679
CHANGXING KIBING GLASS CO., LTD.—See Zhuzhou Kibing Group Co., Ltd.; *Int'l*, pg. 8680
CHANGYI ENERSAVE BIOMASS TO ENERGY CO., LTD.—See ecoWise Holdings Limited; *Int'l*, pg. 2300
CHANG YIH CERAMIC JOINT STOCK COMPANY; *Int'l*, pg. 1441
CHANGYOU ALLIANCE GROUP LIMITED; *Int'l*, pg. 1444
CHANGYOU.COM INDIA PRIVATE LIMITED—See SOHU.com Ltd.; *Int'l*, pg. 7060
CHANGYOU.COM LIMITED—See SOHU.com Ltd.; *Int'l*, pg. 7060
CHANGYOU MY SDN. BHD—See SOHU.com Ltd.; *Int'l*, pg. 7060
CHANGYUAN ELECTRONICS (SHENZHEN) CO., LTD.—See ChangYuan Group Ltd.; *Int'l*, pg. 1444
CHANGYUAN GROUP LTD.; *Int'l*, pg. 1444
CHANGZHENG ENGINEERING CO., LTD.; *Int'l*, pg. 1445
CHANGZHI BAOZEN LUFU AUTOMOBILE SALES AND SERVICES CO., LTD.—See China Yongda Automobiles Services Holdings Limited; *Int'l*, pg. 1564
CHANGZHI GAOCE NEW MATERIAL TECHNOLOGY CO., LTD.—See Qingdao GaoCe Technology Co., Ltd.; *Int'l*, pg. 6143
CHANGZHOU 3D TECHNOLOGICAL COMPLETE SET EQUIPMENT CO., LIMITED—See Shanghai Turbo Enterprises Ltd.; *Int'l*, pg. 6780
CHANGZHOU ALMADEN STOCK CO., LTD.; *Int'l*, pg. 1445
CHANGZHOU AMEC GROUP CO., LTD—See John Wood Group PLC; *Int'l*, pg. 3982
CHANGZHOU AMPHENOL FUYANG COMMUNICATION EQUIPMENT COMPANY LIMITED—See Amphenol Corporation; *U.S. Public*, pg. 129
CHANGZHOU AOHONG ELECTRONICS CO., LTD.; *Int'l*, pg. 1445
CHANGZHOU ARCHITECTURAL RESEARCH INSTITUTE GROUP CO., LTD.; *Int'l*, pg. 1445
CHANGZHOU BAOLING HEAVY & INDUSTRIAL MACHINERY CO., LTD.—See Mitsubishi Heavy Industries, Ltd.; *Int'l*, pg. 4953
CHANGZHOU BAOZUN AUTOMOBILE SALES & SERVICES CO., LTD.—See China Yongda Automobiles Services Holdings Limited; *Int'l*, pg. 1564
CHANGZHOU BAYI CABLE CO., LTD.—See Qingdao Hanhe Cable Co., Ltd.; *Int'l*, pg. 6143
CHANGZHOU BIOMET MEDICAL DEVICES CO. LTD.—See Zimmer Biomet Holdings, Inc.; *U.S. Public*, pg. 2406
CHANGZHOU CHANGFA REFRIGERATION TECHNOLOGY CO., LTD. - LIJIA FACTORY—See Jiangsu Leike Defense Technology Co., Ltd.; *Int'l*, pg. 3950
CHANGZHOU CHENGLI ELECTRICAL EQUIPMENT CO., LTD.—See Jiangsu Leili Motor Corporation Limited; *Int'l*, pg. 3950
CHANGZHOU CHINA STEEL PRECISION MATERIALS CO., LTD.—See China Steel Corporation; *Int'l*, pg. 1555
CHANGZHOU EGING PV TECHNOLOGY CO., LTD.—See EGing Photovoltaic Technology Co., Ltd.; *Int'l*, pg. 2324
CHANGZHOU FUJI CHANGCHAI ROBIN GASOLINE ENGINE CO., LTD.—See Subaru Corporation; *Int'l*, pg. 7246
CHANGZHOU FUJI SEIKI CO., LTD.—See Fuji Seiki Co., Ltd.; *Int'l*, pg. 2817
CHANGZHOU GALAXY ELECTRICAL CO., LTD.—See Galaxy Semiconductor Co., Ltd.; *Int'l*, pg. 2871
CHANGZHOU GIKEN PRECISION CO., LTD.—See GSS Energy Ltd.; *Int'l*, pg. 3150
CHANGZHOU GONGLI METAL PRODUCT TECHNOLOGY CO., LTD.—See Jiangsu Leili Motor Corporation Limited; *Int'l*, pg. 3950
CHANGZHOU HAIHONG ELECTRONICS CO., LTD.—See Changzhou Aohong Electronics Co., Ltd.; *Int'l*, pg. 1445
CHANGZHOU HAOJUE SUZUKI MOTORCYCLE CO., LTD.—See Suzuki Motor Corporation; *Int'l*, pg. 7354
CHANGZHOU HENGFENG SPECIAL CONDUCTOR CO., LTD.—See Tongling Jingda Special Magnet Wire Co., Ltd.; *Int'l*, pg. 7808
CHANGZHOU HUARI NEW MATERIAL CO., LTD.—See DIC Corporation; *Int'l*, pg. 2107
CHANGZHOU JINYUAN COPPER CO., LTD.—See Baosheng Science & Technology Innovation Co., Ltd; *Int'l*, pg. 856
CHANGZHOU JINYUAN MACHINERY EQUIPMENT CO., LTD—See WELLE Environmental Group Co., Ltd.; *Int'l*, pg. 8374
CHANGZHOU KAIDI ELECTRICAL, INC.; *Int'l*, pg. 1445
CHANGZHOU KANGDI MEDICAL STAPLER CO., LTD.—See Medtronic plc; *Int'l*, pg. 4786
CHANGZHOU KANGHUI MEDICAL INNOVATION CO., LTD.—See Medtronic plc; *Int'l*, pg. 4788
CHANGZHOU KAWASAKI & KWANG YANG ENGINE CO., LTD.—See Kawasaki Heavy Industries, Ltd.; *Int'l*, pg. 4095

CHANGZHOU KINGSIGNAL FENGSHI COMMUNICATION EQUIPMENT CO., LTD.—See Kingsignal Technology Co., Ltd.; *Int'l*, pg. 4174
CHANGZHOU KINGSIGNAL FIRNIC CO., LTD.—See Kingsignal Technology Co., Ltd.; *Int'l*, pg. 4175
CHANGZHOU KYB LEADRUN VIBRATION REDUCTION TECHNOLOGY CO., LTD.—See KYB Corporation; *Int'l*, pg. 4353
CHANGZHOU LANGBO SEALING TECHNOLOGY CO., LTD.; *Int'l*, pg. 1445
CHANGZHOU LEILI S & T CO., LTD.—See Jiangsu Leili Motor Corporation Limited; *Int'l*, pg. 3950
CHANGZHOU LONGQUAN PIPELINE ENGINEERING CO., LTD.—See Shandong Longquan Pipeline Engineering Co., Ltd.; *Int'l*, pg. 6756
CHANGZHOU MARINE CABLE CO., LTD.—See Jiangsu Zhongli Group Co., Ltd.; *Int'l*, pg. 3957
CHANGZHOU MICRO BATTERY TECHNOLOGY CO., LTD.—See Suzhou Wanxiang Technology Co., Ltd.; *Int'l*, pg. 7353
CHANGZHOU MINGJING IOT SENSING CO., LTD.—See China Security Co., Ltd.; *Int'l*, pg. 1550
CHANGZHOU MINKING ELECTRONICS CO., LTD.—See China Security & Surveillance Technology, Inc.; *Int'l*, pg. 1550
CHANGZHOU NABTESCO PRECISION MACHINERY CO., LTD.—See Nabtesco Corporation; *Int'l*, pg. 5119
CHANGZHOU NRB CORPORATION; *Int'l*, pg. 1445
CHANGZHOU NTN-GUANGYANG CORP.—See NTN Corporation; *Int'l*, pg. 5481
CHANGZHOU PC SPECIALTIES CO., LTD.—See Kingsignal Technology Co., Ltd.; *Int'l*, pg. 4175
CHANGZHOU PHARMACEUTICAL FACTORY CO., LTD.—See Shanghai Pharmaceuticals Holding Co., Ltd.; *Int'l*, pg. 6776
CHANGZHOU POLY GRAND THEATRE MANAGEMENT CORPORATION LIMITED—See Poly Culture Group Corporation Limited; *Int'l*, pg. 5913
CHANGZHOU POWERLONG REAL ESTATE DEVELOPMENT CO., LTD.—See Powerlong Real Estate Holdings Limited; *Int'l*, pg. 5947
CHANGZHOU QIANHONG BIO-PHARMA CO., LTD.; *Int'l*, pg. 1445
CHANGZHOU RANTO METALWORK CO., LTD.; *Int'l*, pg. 1445
CHANGZHOU REGAL-BELOIT SINYA MOTOR CO. LTD.—See Regal Rexnord Corporation; *U.S. Public*, pg. 1773
CHANGZHOU RUIYANG TRANSMISSION TECHNOLOGY CO., LTD.—See TOYO DENKI SEIZO K.K.; *Int'l*, pg. 7852
CHANGZHOU SENIOR NEW ENERGY MATERIAL CO., LTD.—See Shenzhen Senior Technology Mtrl Co Ltd; *Int'l*, pg. 6821
CHANGZHOU SHENLI ELECTRICAL MACHINE INC; *Int'l*, pg. 1445
CHANGZHOU SHIHLIN AUTO PARTS CO., LTD.—See Shihlin Electric & Engineering Co., Inc.; *Int'l*, pg. 6829
CHANGZHOU SHIHLIN MITSUBA ELECTRIC & ENGINEERING CO., LTD.—See MITSUBA Corporation; *Int'l*, pg. 4928
CHANGZHOU SINOCHEM QINFENG PLASTICS CO. LTD.—See Sinochem Corporation; *Int'l*, pg. 6949
CHANG ZHOU SOKEN HEATING BOILER CO., LTD.—See Soken Chemical & Engineering Co., Ltd.; *Int'l*, pg. 7066
CHANGZHOU TAIPING ZHANYUN AUTOMATIC DOOR CO., LTD.—See TOYO DENKI SEIZO K.K.; *Int'l*, pg. 7852
CHANGZHOU TAMOU PRECISION INDUSTRIAL CO., LTD.—See TYC Brother Industrial Co., Ltd.; *Int'l*, pg. 7994
CHANGZHOU TATSUTA CHINA ELECTRIC WIRE & CABLE CO., LTD.—See ENEOS Holdings, Inc.; *Int'l*, pg. 2416
CHANGZHOU TENGLONG AUTO PARTS CO., LTD.; *Int'l*, pg. 1445
CHANGZHOU TENGXING AUTO ACCESSORIES MANUFACTURING CO., LTD.—See Changzhou Tenglong Auto Parts Co., Ltd.; *Int'l*, pg. 1445
CHANGZHOU TEXHONG TEXTILE CO., LTD.—See Texhong Textile Group Limited; *Int'l*, pg. 7583
CHANGZHOU TIANSHENG NEW MATERIALS CO., LTD.; *Int'l*, pg. 1445
CHANGZHOU TOSHIBA TRANSFORMER CO., LTD.—See Japan Industrial Partners, Inc.; *Int'l*, pg. 3889
CHANGZHOU TRINA SOLAR ENERGY CO., LTD.—See Trina Solar Limited; *Int'l*, pg. 7924
CHANGZHOU TRONLY NEW ELECTRONIC MATERIALS CO., LTD.; *Int'l*, pg. 1446
CHANGZHOU XIANGMING INTELLIGENT DRIVE SYSTEM CORPORATION; *Int'l*, pg. 1446
CHANGZHOU XINAO GAS ENGINEERING COMPANY LIMITED—See ENN Energy Holdings Limited; *Int'l*, pg. 2442
CHANGZHOU XINGYU AUTOMOTIVE LIGHTING SYSTEM CO., LTD.; *Int'l*, pg. 1446

CHANGZHOU YANGDIAN ZHANYUN TRANSPORT EQUIPMENT CO., LTD.—See TOYO DENKI SEIZO K.K.; *Int'l*, pg. 7852
CHANGZHOU YINGFU TEXTILE CO., LTD.—See FUJIX Ltd.; *Int'l*, pg. 2838
CHANGZHOU ZHONGYING SCIENCE & TECHNOLOGY CO., LTD.; *Int'l*, pg. 1446
CHANHIGH HOLDINGS LIMITED; *Int'l*, pg. 1446
CHANIC S.A.—See Schindler Holding AG; *Int'l*, pg. 6618
CHANJET INFORMATION TECHNOLOGY COMPANY LIMITED; *Int'l*, pg. 1446
CHAN LIAN CONSTRUCTION PTE LTD—See Downer EDI Limited; *Int'l*, pg. 2185
CHANNEL 40, INC.—See Nexstar Media Group, Inc.; *U.S. Public*, pg. 1524
CHANNEL 5 BROADCASTING LTD.—See National Amusements, Inc.; *U.S. Private*, pg. 849
CHANNELADVISOR ASIA-PACIFIC—See Insight Venture Management, LLC; *U.S. Private*, pg. 2088
CHANNELADVISOR (AU) PTY LIMITED—See Insight Venture Management, LLC; *U.S. Private*, pg. 2088
CHANNELADVISOR BRASIL TECNOLOGIA LTDA.—See Insight Venture Management, LLC; *U.S. Private*, pg. 2088
CHANNELADVISOR CORPORATION—See Insight Venture Management, LLC; *U.S. Private*, pg. 2087
CHANNELADVISOR EMEA—See Insight Venture Management, LLC; *U.S. Private*, pg. 2088
CHANNELADVISOR FRANCE—See Insight Venture Management, LLC; *U.S. Private*, pg. 2088
CHANNELADVISOR GERMANY—See Insight Venture Management, LLC; *U.S. Private*, pg. 2088
CHANNELADVISOR IRELAND LIMITED—See Insight Venture Management, LLC; *U.S. Private*, pg. 2088
CHANNELADVISOR IRELAND—See Insight Venture Management, LLC; *U.S. Private*, pg. 2088
CHANNELADVISOR (SHANGHAI) INFORMATION TECHNOLOGY CO., LIMITED—See Insight Venture Management, LLC; *U.S. Private*, pg. 2088
CHANNELADVISOR SPAIN S.L.—See Insight Venture Management, LLC; *U.S. Private*, pg. 2088
CHANNELADVISOR UK LIMITED—See Insight Venture Management, LLC; *U.S. Private*, pg. 2088
CHANNEL BIO, LLC—See Bayer Aktiengesellschaft; *Int'l*, pg. 908
THE CHANNEL COMPANY LLC—See EagleTree Capital, LP; *U.S. Private*, pg. 1312
CHANNEL DISTRIBUTION CORPORATION—See Wind Point Advisors LLC; *U.S. Private*, pg. 4535
CHANNEL ELECTRIC EQUIPMENT HOLDINGS LTD—See LPA Group plc; *Int'l*, pg. 4567
CHANNEL ELECTRIC EQUIPMENT LTD—See LPA Group plc; *Int'l*, pg. 4567
CHANNELFLIP MEDIA LIMITED—See LOV Group Invest SAS; *Int'l*, pg. 4565
CHANNEL FOUR TELEVISION CORPORATION; *Int'l*, pg. 1446
CHANNEL HOLDINGS INC.; *Int'l*, pg. 1446
CHANNEL INFRASTRUCTURE NZ LIMITED; *Int'l*, pg. 1446
CHANNEL ISLANDS DESIGN; *U.S. Private*, pg. 848
CHANNEL ISLANDS STOCK EXCHANGE; *Int'l*, pg. 1446
CHANNEL ISLANDS SURGICENTER, L.P.—See UnitedHealth Group Incorporated; *U.S. Public*, pg. 2239
CHANNEL J (THAILAND) CO., LTD.—See Piala, Inc.; *Int'l*, pg. 5859
CHANNEL KEY, LLC; *U.S. Private*, pg. 848
CHANNELL CONSULTING COMPANY; *U.S. Private*, pg. 848
CHANNELLOCK, INC.; *U.S. Private*, pg. 848
CHANNEL LUMBER COMPANY INC.; *U.S. Private*, pg. 848
CHANNEL MICRON HOLDINGS COMPANY LIMITED; *Int'l*, pg. 1446
CHANNELNET; *U.S. Private*, pg. 849
CHANNEL NINE ENTERTAINMENT LTD; *Int'l*, pg. 1446
CHANNEL ONE LLC—See Veritas Capital Fund Management, LLC; *U.S. Private*, pg. 4363
CHANNEL PARTNERS LLC; *U.S. Private*, pg. 848
CHANNEL PRIME ALLIANCE INC.—See Ravago Holding S.A.; *Int'l*, pg. 6222
CHANNEL PRODUCTS, INC.—See Weinberg Capital Group, Inc.; *U.S. Private*, pg. 4471
CHANNEL SEVEN ADELAIDE PTY. LIMITED—See Seven West Media Limited; *Int'l*, pg. 6734
CHANNEL SEVEN BRISBANE PTY. LIMITED—See Seven West Media Limited; *Int'l*, pg. 6734
CHANNEL SEVEN MELBOURNE PTY. LIMITED—See Seven West Media Limited; *Int'l*, pg. 6734
CHANNEL SEVEN PERTH PTY. LIMITED—See Seven West Media Limited; *Int'l*, pg. 6734
CHANNEL SEVEN QUEENSLAND PTY. LIMITED—See Seven West Media Limited; *Int'l*, pg. 6734
CHANNEL SEVEN SYDNEY PTY. LIMITED—See Seven West Media Limited; *Int'l*, pg. 6734
CHANNEL TECHNOLOGIES GROUP, INC.—See Blue Wolf Capital Partners LLC; *U.S. Private*, pg. 594
CHANNEL TUNNEL RAIL LINK—See Getlink SE; *Int'l*, pg. 2952

CHANNELVIEW COMPLEX EQUISTAR CHEMICALS, LP—See LyondellBasell Industries N.V.; *Int'l*, pg. 4607
CHANNING BETE CO., INC.; *U.S. Private*, pg. 849
CHANO INTERNATIONAL INC.; *U.S. Private*, pg. 849
CHANSON INTERNATIONAL HOLDING; *Int'l*, pg. 1446
THE CHAN SOON-SHIONG FAMILY FOUNDATION; *U.S. Private*, pg. 4007
CHANTABURI MARINE FARM CO., LTD.—See Surapon Foods Public Company Limited; *Int'l*, pg. 7342
CHANTEST CORPORATION—See Charles River Laboratories International, Inc.; *U.S. Public*, pg. 479
CHANTIER CATANA; *Int'l*, pg. 1446
CHANTIER DAVIE CANADA INC.—See Davie Yards ASA; *Int'l*, pg. 1984
CHANTIER NAVAL DE MARSEILLE SAS—See Carnival Corporation; *U.S. Public*, pg. 438
CHANTIERS AMEL S.A.; *Int'l*, pg. 1446
CHANTIERS DE L'ATLANTIQUE SA; *Int'l*, pg. 1447
CHANTIERS DE L'ATLANTIQUE SERVICES—See Chantiers de l'Atlantique SA; *Int'l*, pg. 1447
CHANTIERS JEANNEAU SA—See Beneteau S.A.; *Int'l*, pg. 972
CHANTIERS MODERNES CONSTRUCTION SAS—See VINCI S.A.; *Int'l*, pg. 8234
CHANTIERS MODERNES SUD-OUEST SAS—See VINCI S.A.; *Int'l*, pg. 8234
THE CHANTLAND COMPANY—See Precision Inc.; *U.S. Private*, pg. 3245
CHANTLAND MHS CO.—See PVS Chemicals, Inc.; *U.S. Private*, pg. 3308
CHANTLER PACKAGES INC.—See Packages Ltd.; *Int'l*, pg. 5693
CHANTLER TRANSPORT; *Int'l*, pg. 1447
CHANTRE & CIE GMBH—See Rotkappchen-Mumm Sektkellereien GmbH; *Int'l*, pg. 6404
CHANT SINCERE CO., LTD.; *Int'l*, pg. 1446
CHANT WEST HOLDINGS LIMITED; *Int'l*, pg. 1446
CHANUTE MANUFACTURING COMPANY—See Babcock & Wilcox Enterprises, Inc.; *U.S. Public*, pg. 263
CHANZY PARDOUX—See VINCI S.A.; *Int'l*, pg. 8230
CHAODA MODERN AGRICULTURE HOLDINGS LIMITED; *Int'l*, pg. 1447
CHAODA VEGETABLE & FRUITS LIMITED—See Chaoda Modern Agriculture Holdings Limited; *Int'l*, pg. 1447
CHAOJU EYE CARE HOLDINGS LIMITED; *Int'l*, pg. 1447
CHAOPRAYA MAHANAKORN PCL; *Int'l*, pg. 1447
CHAOS CONCEPT MANUFACTURING—See McGarrah Jessee; *U.S. Private*, pg. 2634
CHAO SHIN METAL IND. CORP.—See SDI Corporation; *Int'l*, pg. 6657
CHAOS VISUAL PRODUCTIONS LLC—See The Jordan Company, L.P.; *U.S. Private*, pg. 4061
CHAOWEI POWER HOLDINGS LIMITED; *Int'l*, pg. 1447
CHAOWEI POWER (HONG KONG) LIMITED—See Chaowei Power Holdings Limited; *Int'l*, pg. 1447
CHAOZHOU THREE-CIRCLE GROUP CO., LTD.; *Int'l*, pg. 1447
CHAPACINTA S.A. DE C.V.—See Surteco Group SE; *Int'l*, pg. 7344
CHAPADA DO PIAUI II HOLDING S.A.—See ContourGlobal Limited; *Int'l*, pg. 1785
CHAPARRAL BOATS, INC.—See Marine Products Corporation; *U.S. Public*, pg. 1366
CHAPARRAL ENERGY, INC.; *U.S. Private*, pg. 849
CHAPARRAL MATERIALS, INC.—See GMS Inc.; *U.S. Public*, pg. 948
CHAPDELAINE TULLETT PREBON, LLC—See TP ICAP Finance PLC; *Int'l*, pg. 7882
CHAPELCREST INVESTMENTS LIMITED—See Barclays PLC; *Int'l*, pg. 862
CHAPEL DOWN GROUP PLC; *Int'l*, pg. 1447
CHAPEL HILL ASSOCIATES, INC.—See Axar Capital Management L.P.; *U.S. Private*, pg. 411
CHAPEL HILL FUNERAL HOME, INC.—See Axar Capital Management L.P.; *U.S. Private*, pg. 411
CHAPEL HILL PUBLISHING CO.—See Chatham Asset Management, LLC; *U.S. Private*, pg. 866
CHAPEL HILL WINERY PTY. LTD.—See Endeavour Group Limited; *Int'l*, pg. 2402
CHAPEL OF THE VALLEY FUNERAL HOME, INC.—See Service Corporation International; *U.S. Public*, pg. 1871
CHAPEL STEEL CANADA, LTD.—See Reliance Steel & Aluminum Co.; *U.S. Public*, pg. 1779
CHAPEL STEEL COMPANY; *U.S. Private*, pg. 849
CHAPEL STEEL CORP.—See Reliance Steel & Aluminum Co.; *U.S. Public*, pg. 1779
CHAPEL VALLEY HOUSING II LLC—See Kimberly-Clark Corporation; *U.S. Public*, pg. 1229
CHAPEL VALLEY LANDSCAPE COMPANY; *U.S. Private*, pg. 849
CHAPIN HOME FOR THE AGING; *U.S. Private*, pg. 849
CHAPIN INTERNATIONAL, INC.; *U.S. Private*, pg. 849
CHAPIN MEDICAL COMPANY INC.; *U.S. Private*, pg. 849
CHAPLYZHENKY ELEVATOR—See Gruppa Kompaniy Rusagro OOO; *Int'l*, pg. 3140
CHAPMAN AUTOMOTIVE GROUP LLC; *U.S. Private*, pg. 849
CHAPMAN BMW ON CAMELBACK; *U.S. Private*, pg. 849
CHAPMAN CHRYSLER JEEP; *U.S. Private*, pg. 849

COMPANY NAME INDEX

CHARLES B. WANG COMMUNITY HEALTH CENTER, INC.

CHAPMAN & CUTLER LLP; *U.S. Private*, pg. 849
CHAPMAN DODGE CHRYSLER JEEP RAM; *U.S. Private*, pg. 849
CHAPMAN FORD SALES, INC.; *U.S. Private*, pg. 849
CHAPMAN FORD—See Chapman Automotive Group LLC; *U.S. Private*, pg. 849
CHAPMAN FREEBORN AIRCHARTERING BVBA—See Chapman Freeborn Airchartering Ltd.; *Int'l*, pg. 1447
CHAPMAN FREEBORN AIRCHARTERING BV—See Chapman Freeborn Airchartering Ltd.; *Int'l*, pg. 1447
CHAPMAN FREEBORN AIRCHARTERING (CHINA) LTD.—See Chapman Freeborn Airchartering Ltd.; *Int'l*, pg. 1447
CHAPMAN FREEBORN AIRCHARTERING CONSULTING (SHANGHAI) CO., LTD.—See Chapman Freeborn Airchartering Ltd.; *Int'l*, pg. 1447
CHAPMAN FREEBORN AIRCHARTERING FRETAMENTO E LOGISTICA DO BRASIL LTDA.—See Chapman Freeborn Airchartering Ltd.; *Int'l*, pg. 1447
CHAPMAN FREEBORN AIRCHARTERING, INC.—See Chapman Freeborn Airchartering Ltd.; *Int'l*, pg. 1447
CHAPMAN FREEBORN AIRCHARTERING, INC.—See Chapman Freeborn Airchartering Ltd.; *Int'l*, pg. 1448
CHAPMAN FREEBORN AIRCHARTERING (ITALIA) SRL—See Chapman Freeborn Airchartering Ltd.; *Int'l*, pg. 1447
CHAPMAN FREEBORN AIRCHARTERING LIMITED—See Chapman Freeborn Airchartering Ltd.; *Int'l*, pg. 1447
CHAPMAN FREEBORN AIRCHARTERING LTD.; *Int'l*, pg. 1447
CHAPMAN FREEBORN AIRCHARTERING LTD.—See Chapman Freeborn Airchartering Ltd.; *Int'l*, pg. 1447
CHAPMAN FREEBORN AIRCHARTERING PTE LTD.—See Chapman Freeborn Airchartering Ltd.; *Int'l*, pg. 1447
CHAPMAN FREEBORN AIRCHARTERING PVT. LTD.—See Chapman Freeborn Airchartering Ltd.; *Int'l*, pg. 1447
CHAPMAN FREEBORN AIRCHARTERING (SHANGHAI) CO LTD.—See Chapman Freeborn Airchartering Ltd.; *Int'l*, pg. 1447
CHAPMAN FREEBORN AIRCHARTERING S.L—See Chapman Freeborn Airchartering Ltd.; *Int'l*, pg. 1447
CHAPMAN FREEBORN AIRCHARTERING (SOUTH AFRICA) PTY LTD See Chapman Freeborn Airchartering Ltd.; *Int'l*, pg. 1447
CHAPMAN FREEBORN AIRCHARTERING SP Z.O.O—See Chapman Freeborn Airchartering Ltd.; *Int'l*, pg. 1447
CHAPMAN FREEBORN AIRMARKETING GMBH—See Chapman Freeborn Airchartering Ltd.; *Int'l*, pg. 1448
CHAPMAN FREEBORN AIRMARKETING GMBH—See Chapman Freeborn Airchartering Ltd.; *Int'l*, pg. 1448
CHAPMAN FREEBORN AIRMARKETING GMBH—See Chapman Freeborn Airchartering Ltd.; *Int'l*, pg. 1448
CHAPMAN FREEBORN AUSTRALIA—See Chapman Freeborn Airchartering Ltd.; *Int'l*, pg. 1448
CHAPMAN FREEBORN AVIATION SERVICES FZE—See Chapman Freeborn Airchartering Ltd.; *Int'l*, pg. 1448
CHAPMAN FREEBORN C/O COVIO SA—See Chapman Freeborn Airchartering Ltd.; *Int'l*, pg. 1448
CHAPMAN FREEBORN HANDCARRY LTD—See Chapman Freeborn Airchartering Ltd.; *Int'l*, pg. 1448
CHAPMAN FREEBORN HAVACILIK TASIMACILIK TIC. LTD. STI.—See Chapman Freeborn Airchartering Ltd.; *Int'l*, pg. 1448
CHAPMAN FRUIT CO INC.; *U.S. Private*, pg. 849
CHAPMAN & HOGAN INSURANCE GROUP—See Reverence Capital Partners LLC; *U.S. Private*, pg. 3415
CHAPMAN INC.; *U.S. Private*, pg. 849
CHAPMAN INNOVATIONS; *U.S. Private*, pg. 850
CHAPMAN/LEONARD STUDIO EQUIPMENT, INC.; *U.S. Private*, pg. 850
THE CHAPMAN PRINTING COMPANY, INC. - CHARLESTON—See Champion Industries, Inc.; *U.S. Public*, pg. 478
THE CHAPMAN PRINTING COMPANY, INC. - LEXINGTON—See Champion Industries, Inc.; *U.S. Public*, pg. 478
THE CHAPMAN PRINTING COMPANY, INC. - PARKERSBURG—See Champion Industries, Inc.; *U.S. Public*, pg. 478
THE CHAPMAN PRINTING COMPANY, INC.—See Champion Industries, Inc.; *U.S. Public*, pg. 478
CHAPMAN PROPERTIES; *U.S. Private*, pg. 850
CHAPMANS LIMITED; *Int'l*, pg. 1448
CHAPMAN WATERPROOFING CO.; *U.S. Private*, pg. 850
CHAPOMED LTD—See Charilaos Apostolides Public Ltd.; *Int'l*, pg. 1450
CHAPPAL ENERGIES MAURITIUS LIMITED; *Int'l*, pg. 1448
CHAPP & BUSHEY OIL COMPANY; *U.S. Private*, pg. 850
CHAPPELL AGENCY, INC.; *U.S. Private*, pg. 850
CHAPPELL DOOR CO. INC. MAIN OFFICE; *U.S. Private*, pg. 850
CHAPPELLROBERTS INC.; *U.S. Private*, pg. 850
CHAPS HOLDING SAS; *Int'l*, pg. 1448
CHAPSVISION SASU—See CHAPS Holding SAS; *Int'l*, pg. 1448

CHAPTER 4 CORP.—See EssilorLuxottica SA; *Int'l*, pg. 2512
CHAPTER AGENCY LTD.—See The Mission Group Public Limited Company; *Int'l*, pg. 7667
CHAPTERS HEALTH SYSTEM, INC.; *U.S. Private*, pg. 850
CHAPTER TWO HOLDINGS PTY. LTD.—See Credit Intelligence Limited; *Int'l*, pg. 1835
CHARABIA LTD.—See ENL Limited; *Int'l*, pg. 2441
CHARABOT KOREA LTD.—See Robertet S.A.; *Int'l*, pg. 6369
CHARACTER GAMES LIMITED—See The Character Group plc; *Int'l*, pg. 7631
CHARACTER GIFTS LIMITED—See The Character Group plc; *Int'l*, pg. 7631
THE CHARACTER GROUP PLC; *Int'l*, pg. 7631
CHARACTER OPTIONS LIMITED—See The Character Group plc; *Int'l*, pg. 7631
CHARACTER SF, LLC—See Dentsu Group Inc.; *Int'l*, pg. 2035
CHARACTERS UNLIMITED INC.; *U.S. Private*, pg. 850
CHARADE LEASING GESELLSCHAFT M.B.H.—See UniCredit S.p.A.; *Int'l*, pg. 8036
CHARAH, INC.; *U.S. Private*, pg. 850
CHARAH SOLUTIONS, INC.—See SER Capital Partners LLC; *U.S. Private*, pg. 3612
CHARAN INSURANCE PUBLIC COMPANY LIMITED; *Int'l*, pg. 1448
CHARANTELEC SAS—See VINCI S.A.; *Int'l*, pg. 8215
CHARAPP FORD NORTH; *U.S. Private*, pg. 850
CHARBON COAL PTY LIMITED—See Banpu Public Company Limited; *Int'l*, pg. 852
CHARBONE HYDROGEN CORPORATION; *Int'l*, pg. 1448
CHAR-BROIL, LLC—See W.C. Bradley Co.; *U.S. Private*, pg. 4419
CHARCOL LIMITED; *Int'l*, pg. 1448
CHARCON LIMITED—See Holcim Ltd.; *Int'l*, pg. 3446
CHARCUTERIE LA TOUR EIFFEL, INC.—See McCain Foods Limited; *Int'l*, pg. 4756
CHARDAN METROPOL ACQUISITION CORP.; *Int'l*, pg. 1448
CHARDAN NEXTECH ACQUISITION CORP.; *U.S. Public*, pg. 478
CHARD, SNYDER & ASSOCIATES, LLC—See WEX, Inc.; *U.S. Public*, pg. 2364
CHARFEN INSTITUTE; *U.S. Private*, pg. 850
CHARGE ENTERPRISES, INC.; *U.S. Public*, pg. 478
CHARGEMASTER LIMITED—See BP plc; *Int'l*, pg. 1131
CHARGEPANEL AB; *Int'l*, pg. 1448
CHARGEPOINT HOLDINGS, INC.; *U.S. Public*, pg. 479
CHARGEPOINT INC.—See ChargePoint Holdings, Inc.; *U.S. Public*, pg. 479
CHARGEPOINT PTY. LIMITED—See Ventia Services Group Limited; *Int'l*, pg. 8151
CHARGEPOINT TECHNOLOGY LTD.; *Int'l*, pg. 1448
CHARGE & RIDE INC.; *U.S. Private*, pg. 850
CHARGER INVESTMENT PARTNERS LP; *U.S. Private*, pg. 850
CHARGER METALS NL; *Int'l*, pg. 1448
CHARGE SERVICES, LLC—See Charge Enterprises, Inc.; *U.S. Public*, pg. 479
CHARGES MINERALES DU PERIGORD—See Groupe Bruxelles Lambert SA; *Int'l*, pg. 3100
CHARGEURS ENTRETELAS (IBERICA) LTD.—See Chargeurs NV; *Int'l*, pg. 1448
CHARGEURS ENTRETELAS (PORTUGAL) LTD—See Chargeurs SA; *Int'l*, pg. 1448
CHARGEURS FABRICS—See Chargeurs SA; *Int'l*, pg. 1449
CHARGEURS FASHION TECHNOLOGIES—See Chargeurs SA; *Int'l*, pg. 1449
CHARGEURS INTERFODERE ITALIA S.P.A.—See Chargeurs SA; *Int'l*, pg. 1449
CHARGEURS INTERLINING (HK) LIMITED—See Chargeurs SA; *Int'l*, pg. 1449
CHARGEURS INTERLINING—See Chargeurs SA; *Int'l*, pg. 1449
CHARGEURS NV; *Int'l*, pg. 1448
CHARGEURS PROTECTIVE FILMS—See Chargeurs SA; *Int'l*, pg. 1449
CHARGEURS SA; *Int'l*, pg. 1448
CHARGEURS WOOL (ARGENTINA) SA—See Chargeurs SA; *Int'l*, pg. 1449
CHARGEURS WOOL SALES (EUROPE) SRL—See Chargeurs SA; *Int'l*, pg. 1449
CHARGEURS WOOL—See Chargeurs SA; *Int'l*, pg. 1449
CHARGEURS WOOL (SOUTH AFRICA) (PTY) LTD—See Chargeurs SA; *Int'l*, pg. 1449
CHARGEURS WOOL (USA) INC—See Chargeurs SA; *Int'l*, pg. 1449
CHARGIFY LLC; *U.S. Private*, pg. 850
CHAR-GRILLER—See The Middleby Corporation; *U.S. Public*, pg. 2113
THE CHAR GRILL INC.; *U.S. Private*, pg. 4007
CHARIGNON—See FAYAT SAS; *Int'l*, pg. 2625
THE CHARIHO TIMES—See R.I.S.N. Operations Inc.; *U.S. Private*, pg. 3336
CHARILAOS APOSTOLIDES PUBLIC LTD.; *Int'l*, pg. 1450

CHARILOTO CO., LTD.—See mixi, Inc.; *Int'l*, pg. 4996
CHARIOT BRASIL PETROLEO E GAS LTDA.—See Chariot Limited; *Int'l*, pg. 1450
CHARIOT CARRIERS INC.; *Int'l*, pg. 1450
CHARIOT EAGLE, LLC—See Cavco Industries, Inc.; *U.S. Public*, pg. 455
CHARIOT LIMITED; *Int'l*, pg. 1450
CHARIOT LIMITED—See CK Hutchison Holdings Limited; *Int'l*, pg. 1638
CHARIOT LIMITED—See Vodafone Group Plc; *Int'l*, pg. 8285
CHARIOT OIL & GAS STATISTICS LIMITED—See Chariot Limited; *Int'l*, pg. 1450
CHARIOTS ELEVATEURS MANITOU CANADA INC—See Manitou BF S.A.; *Int'l*, pg. 4672
CHARIOT VANS INC.; *U.S. Private*, pg. 850
CHARISMA BRANDS, LLC; *U.S. Private*, pg. 850
CHARISMA! COMMUNICATIONS; *U.S. Private*, pg. 851
CHARISMA ENERGY SERVICES LIMITED; *Int'l*, pg. 1450
CHARISMA MANUFACTURING COMPANY INC.—See Charisma Brands, LLC; *U.S. Private*, pg. 850
CHARISMA MEDIA; *U.S. Private*, pg. 850
CHARITABLE ASSISTANCE TO COMMUNITY'S HOMELESS (CATCH), INC.; *U.S. Private*, pg. 851
CHARITON VALLEY TELEPHONE CORP.; *U.S. Private*, pg. 851
CHARITY DYNAMICS; *U.S. Private*, pg. 851
CHARITY FIRST INSURANCE SERVICES, INC.—See Arthur J. Gallagher & Co.; *U.S. Public*, pg. 202
CHARITY GLOBAL, INC.; *U.S. Private*, pg. 851
CHARITY & TAYLOR (ELECTRONIC SERVICES) LTD—See HAL Trust N.V.; *Int'l*, pg. 3226
CHARITY & WEISS INTERNATIONAL REALTY, LLC; *U.S. Private*, pg. 851
CHARKDELIKATESSER I HALMSTAD AB—See Atria Plc; *Int'l*, pg. 694
CHARKDELIKATESSER PRODUKTION AB—See Atria Plc; *Int'l*, pg. 694
CHARKHESHGAR CO.; *Int'l*, pg. 1450
CHARKIT CHEMICAL COMPANY, LLC; *U.S. Private*, pg. 851
CHARLATTE MANUTENTION—See FAYAT SAS; *Int'l*, pg. 2625
CHARLATTE OF AMERICA—See FAYAT SAS; *Int'l*, pg. 2625
CHARLATTE RESERVOIRS—See FAYAT SAS; *Int'l*, pg. 2625
CHARLATTE (UK) LIMITED—See FAYAT SAS; *Int'l*, pg. 2625
CHARLE CO., LTD.; *Int'l*, pg. 1450
CHARLEE SQM (THAILAND) CO LTD—See Sociedad Quimica y Minera de Chile S.A.; *Int'l*, pg. 7032
CHARLEMAGNE CAPITAL (IOM) LIMITED—See Fiera Capital Corporation; *Int'l*, pg. 2659
CHARLEMAGNE CAPITAL LIMITED—See Fiera Capital Corporation; *Int'l*, pg. 2659
CHARLEROI FEDERAL SAVINGS BANK; *U.S. Private*, pg. 851
CHARLES ADAMS RITCHIE & DUCKWORTH—See Collas Crill; *Int'l*, pg. 1698
CHARLES A. KLEIN AND SONS, INC; *U.S. Private*, pg. 851
CHARLES A LUTHER, C.P.A.; *U.S. Private*, pg. 851
CHARLESANDCOLVARD.COM, LLC—See Charles & Colvard Ltd; *U.S. Public*, pg. 479
CHARLES ATLAS, LTD.; *U.S. Private*, pg. 851
CHARLESBANK CAPITAL PARTNERS, LLC - NEW YORK OFFICE—See Charlesbank Capital Partners, LLC; *U.S. Private*, pg. 855
CHARLESBANK CAPITAL PARTNERS, LLC; *U.S. Private*, pg. 855
CHARLES BERRY & SON PTY. LTD.—See Propel Funeral Partners Limited; *Int'l*, pg. 5997
CHARLES BESELER CO. - SHRINK PACKAGING DIVISION—See Charles Beseler Co.; *U.S. Private*, pg. 851
CHARLES BESELER CO.; *U.S. Private*, pg. 851
CHARLES BLALOCK & SONS INC.; *U.S. Private*, pg. 851
CHARLES BLANCHARD CONSTRUCTION CORPORATION; *U.S. Private*, pg. 851
CHARLES BOWMAN & CO. INC.; *U.S. Private*, pg. 851
CHARLES BROWNLOW RETIREMENT VILLAGE PTY. LTD.—See Ryman Healthcare Ltd.; *Int'l*, pg. 6439
CHARLES B. WANG COMMUNITY HEALTH CENTER, INC.; *U.S. Private*, pg. 851
CHARLES CHURCH DEVELOPMENTS LTD.—See Persimmon plc; *Int'l*, pg. 5816
CHARLES CHURCH ESSEX LIMITED—See Persimmon plc; *Int'l*, pg. 5815
CHARLES CHURCH LONDON LIMITED—See Persimmon plc; *Int'l*, pg. 5815
CHARLES CHURCH (NORTH EAST) LTD—See Persimmon plc; *Int'l*, pg. 5816
CHARLES CHURCH (NORTH LONDON) LTD—See Persimmon plc; *Int'l*, pg. 5816
CHARLES CHURCH (NORTH WEST) LTD—See Persimmon plc; *Int'l*, pg. 5816
CHARLES CHURCH (SOUTH EAST) LTD—See Persimmon plc; *Int'l*, pg. 5816

513

CHARLES CHURCH (SOUTHERN) LTD—See Persimmon plc; Int'l, pg. 5816
CHARLES CHURCH (SPECIAL PROJECTS)—See Persimmon plc; Int'l, pg. 5816
CHARLES CHURCH THAMES VALLEY LIMITED—See Persimmon plc; Int'l, pg. 5815
CHARLES CHURCH (WESTERN) LTD—See Persimmon plc; Int'l, pg. 5816
CHARLES CHURCH (YORKSHIRE) LTD—See Persimmon plc; Int'l, pg. 5816
CHARLES C. LEWIS COMPANY; U.S. Private, pg. 851
CHARLES & COLVARD DIRECT, LLC—See Charles & Colvard Ltd; U.S. Public, pg. 479
CHARLES & COLVARD LTD; U.S. Public, pg. 479
CHARLES DAHER'S COMMONWEALTH MOTORS; U.S. Private, pg. 851
CHARLES DAVID OF CALIFORNIA; U.S. Private, pg. 852
CHARLES DEWEESE CONSTRUCTION, INC.; U.S. Private, pg. 852
CHARLES D. JONES & COMPANY INC.; U.S. Private, pg. 851
CHARLES DONALD PULPWOOD, INC.; U.S. Private, pg. 852
CHARLES D. OWEN MFG. CO.—See Springs Global, Inc.; U.S. Private, pg. 3764
CHARLES DUNN COMPANY, INC.; U.S. Private, pg. 852
CHARLES DUNN REAL ESTATE SERVICES—See Charles Dunn Company, Inc.; U.S. Private, pg. 852
CHARLES E. FORD, LIMITED—See Tate & Lyle PLC; Int'l, pg. 7473
CHARLES E. GILLMAN COMPANY—See ITT Inc.; U.S. Public, pg. 1179
CHARLES E. JARRELL CONTRACTING COMPANY, INC.; U.S. Private, pg. 852
CHARLES EQUIPMENT ENERGY SYSTEMS LLC; U.S. Private, pg. 852
CHARLES E. SINGLETON COMPANY INC; U.S. Private, pg. 852
CHARLES E. SMITH COMMERCIAL REALTY, L.P.—See Vornado Realty Trust; U.S. Public, pg. 2310
CHARLES F. DAY & ASSOCIATES, INC.; U.S. Private, pg. 852
CHARLES F. SHIELS CO. INC.; U.S. Private, pg. 852
CHARLES F. VATTEROTT & CO.; U.S. Private, pg. 852
CHARLES GABUS FORD, INC.; U.S. Private, pg. 852
CHARLES G. ALLEN CO.; U.S. Private, pg. 852
CHARLESGATE REALTY GROUP, LLC; U.S. Private, pg. 856
CHARLES G. HARDY, INC.—See GMS Inc.; U.S. Public, pg. 948
CHARLES G. LAWSON TRUCKING; U.S. Private, pg. 852
CHARLESGLEN LTD.; Int'l, pg. 1450
CHARLES GROUP HOTELS, INC.; U.S. Private, pg. 852
CHARLES HASLER AG—See Beijer Ref AB; Int'l, pg. 944
CHARLES HASWELL AND PARTNERS LIMITED—See Severn Trent Plc; Int'l, pg. 6735
CHARLES H. HODGES & SON, INC.—See On-Point Group, LLC; U.S. Private, pg. 3018
CHARLES HURST DUBLIN LIMITED—See Lookers plc; Int'l, pg. 4555
CHARLES HURST LIMITED—See Lookers plc; Int'l, pg. 4555
CHARLES H. WILSON CONSTRUCTION COMPANY; U.S. Private, pg. 852
CHARLES INDUSTRIES, LTD.—See Amphenol Corporation; U.S. Public, pg. 129
CHARLES JACQUIN ET CIE INC.—See Chatam International Incorporated; U.S. Private, pg. 860
CHARLES KOMAR & SONS, INC.; U.S. Private, pg. 852
CHARLES L. CRANE AGENCY; U.S. Private, pg. 852
CHARLES LEONARD INC.; U.S. Private, pg. 852
CHARLES LEONARD NATIONAL, INC.—See Charles Leonard Inc.; U.S. Private, pg. 852
CHARLES LEONARD (WESTERN), INC.—See Charles Leonard Inc.; U.S. Private, pg. 852
CHARLES MACHINE WORKS, INC.—See The Toro Company; U.S. Public, pg. 2134
CHARLES MCMURRAY COMPANY; U.S. Private, pg. 853
CHARLES NAVASKY & COMPANY; U.S. Private, pg. 853
CHARLES N. WHITE CONSTRUCTION CO. INC.; U.S. Private, pg. 853
CHARLES PANKOW BUILDERS, LTD.; U.S. Private, pg. 853
CHARLES P. BLOUIN, INC.; U.S. Private, pg. 853
CHARLES PENZONE INC.; U.S. Private, pg. 853
CHARLES PERRY PARTNERS, INC.; U.S. Private, pg. 853
CHARLES R. EVANS OIL CO. INC.; U.S. Private, pg. 853
CHARLES RIVER ASSOCIATION FOR RETARDED CITIZENS INC.; U.S. Private, pg. 853
CHARLES RIVER BIOPHARMACEUTICAL SERVICES GMBH—See Charles River Laboratories International, Inc.; U.S. Public, pg. 479
CHARLES RIVER DISCOVERY RESEARCH SERVICES FINLAND—See Charles River Laboratories International, Inc.; U.S. Public, pg. 479
CHARLES RIVER ENDOTOXIN AND MICROBIAL DETECTION SINGAPORE PTE. LTD.—See Charles River Laboratories International, Inc.; U.S. Public, pg. 479

CHARLES RIVER ENDOTOXIN MICROBIAL DETECTION EUROPE SAS—See Charles River Laboratories International, Inc.; U.S. Public, pg. 479
CHARLES RIVER FRANCE S.A.—See Charles River Laboratories International, Inc.; U.S. Public, pg. 479
CHARLES RIVER GERMANY GMBH & CO. KG—See Charles River Laboratories International, Inc.; U.S. Public, pg. 479
CHARLES RIVER GERMANY VERWALTUNGS GMBH—See Charles River Laboratories International, Inc.; U.S. Public, pg. 480
CHARLES RIVER LABORATORIES, INC.—See Charles River Laboratories International, Inc.; U.S. Public, pg. 480
CHARLES RIVER LABORATORIES INDIA PRIVATE LIMITED—See Charles River Laboratories International, Inc.; U.S. Public, pg. 480
CHARLES RIVER LABORATORIES INTERNATIONAL, INC.; U.S. Public, pg. 479
CHARLES RIVER LABORATORIES ITALIA SRL—See Charles River Laboratories International, Inc.; U.S. Public, pg. 480
CHARLES RIVER LABORATORIES JAPAN, INC.—See Charles River Laboratories International, Inc.; U.S. Public, pg. 480
CHARLES RIVER LABORATORIES-MI—See Charles River Laboratories International, Inc.; U.S. Public, pg. 480
CHARLES RIVER LABORATORIES PRECLINICAL SERVICES EDINBURGH LTD.—See Charles River Laboratories International, Inc.; U.S. Public, pg. 480
CHARLES RIVER LABORATORIES PRECLINICAL SERVICES IRELAND LIMITED—See Charles River Laboratories International, Inc.; U.S. Public, pg. 480
CHARLES RIVER LABORATORIES PRECLINICAL SERVICES MONTREAL, ULC—See Charles River Laboratories International, Inc.; U.S. Public, pg. 480
CHARLES RIVER LABORATORIES SAINT-CONSTANT S.A.—See Charles River Laboratories International, Inc.; U.S. Public, pg. 480
CHARLES RIVER LABORATORIES SA NETHERLANDS HOLDINGS BV—See Charles River Laboratories International, Inc.; U.S. Public, pg. 480
CHARLES RIVER LABORATORIES—See Charles River Laboratories International, Inc.; U.S. Public, pg. 480
CHARLES RIVER LABORATORIES—See Charles River Laboratories International, Inc.; U.S. Public, pg. 480
CHARLES RIVER LABORATORIES—See Charles River Laboratories International, Inc.; U.S. Public, pg. 480
CHARLES RIVER SAAB—See Village Automotive Group; U.S. Private, pg. 4383
CHARLES RIVER SPAFAS—See Charles River Laboratories International, Inc.; U.S. Public, pg. 480
CHARLES RIVER SYSTEMS, INC.—See State Street Corporation; U.S. Public, pg. 1940
CHARLES RIVER UK LIMITED—See Charles River Laboratories International, Inc.; U.S. Public, pg. 480
CHARLES RIVER VENTURES; U.S. Private, pg. 853
CHARLES ROSS & SON COMPANY; U.S. Private, pg. 853
CHARLES RUSSELL SPEECHLYS LLP; Int'l, pg. 1450
CHARLES RUTENBERG REALTY, INC.; U.S. Private, pg. 853
CHARLES RUTENBERG REALTY, INC.; U.S. Private, pg. 853
CHARLES R. WOOD OIL CO. INC.; U.S. Private, pg. 853
CHARLES RYAN ASSOCIATES INC.; U.S. Private, pg. 853
CHARLES RYAN ASSOCIATES—See Charles Ryan Associates Inc.; U.S. Private, pg. 853
CHARLES RYAN ASSOCIATES—See Charles Ryan Associates Inc.; U.S. Private, pg. 853
CHARLES SADEK IMPORT COMPANY INC.; U.S. Private, pg. 853
CHARLES SAMELSON, INC.; U.S. Private, pg. 853
CHARLES SARGENT IRRIGATION; U.S. Private, pg. 853
CHARLES SCATURRO & SONS INC.; U.S. Private, pg. 853
CHARLES SCHWAB BANK—See The Charles Schwab Corporation; U.S. Public, pg. 2058
CHARLES SCHWAB & COMPANY, INC.—See The Charles Schwab Corporation; U.S. Public, pg. 2058
THE CHARLES SCHWAB CORPORATION - AUSTIN—See The Charles Schwab Corporation; U.S. Public, pg. 2058
THE CHARLES SCHWAB CORPORATION; U.S. Public, pg. 2058
CHARLES SCHWAB INVESTMENT MANAGEMENT, INC.—See The Charles Schwab Corporation; U.S. Public, pg. 2058
CHARLES SELIGMAN DISTRIBUTING CO.; U.S. Private, pg. 853
CHARLES STANLEY & CO. LTD.—See Raymond James Financial, Inc.; U.S. Public, pg. 1764
CHARLES STANLEY GROUP PLC—See Raymond James Financial, Inc.; U.S. Public, pg. 1764
THE CHARLES STARK DRAPER LABORATORY, INC.; U.S. Private, pg. 4007

CHARLES S. ZEILER & SON, INC.—See Service Corporation International; U.S. Public, pg. 1869
CHARLES TAYLOR ADJUSTING (AUSTRALIA) PTY LTD—See Lovell Minnick Partners LLC; U.S. Private, pg. 2502
CHARLES TAYLOR ADJUSTING LIMITED—See Lovell Minnick Partners LLC; U.S. Private, pg. 2502
CHARLES TAYLOR ADJUSTING SARL—See Lovell Minnick Partners LLC; U.S. Private, pg. 2502
CHARLES TAYLOR ADMINISTRATION SERVICES LIMITED—See Lovell Minnick Partners LLC; U.S. Private, pg. 2502
CHARLES TAYLOR AVIATION (ASSET MANAGEMENT) LIMITED—See Lovell Minnick Partners LLC; U.S. Private, pg. 2502
CHARLES TAYLOR & CO LTD—See Lovell Minnick Partners LLC; U.S. Private, pg. 2502
CHARLES TAYLOR CONSULTING (AUSTRALIA) PTY LTD—See Lovell Minnick Partners LLC; U.S. Private, pg. 2502
CHARLES TAYLOR CONSULTING (CANADA) INC—See Lovell Minnick Partners LLC; U.S. Private, pg. 2502
CHARLES TAYLOR CONSULTING (JAPAN) LIMITED—See Lovell Minnick Partners LLC; U.S. Private, pg. 2502
CHARLES TAYLOR (HAMILTON) LTD—See Lovell Minnick Partners LLC; U.S. Private, pg. 2502
CHARLES TAYLOR INSURANCE SERVICES LIMITED—See Lovell Minnick Partners LLC; U.S. Private, pg. 2502
CHARLES TAYLOR INVESTMENT MANAGEMENT COMPANY LIMITED—See Lovell Minnick Partners LLC; U.S. Private, pg. 2502
CHARLES TAYLOR (JAPAN) LIMITED—See Lovell Minnick Partners LLC; U.S. Private, pg. 2502
CHARLES TAYLOR P&I MANAGEMENT (AMERICAS) INC.—See Lovell Minnick Partners LLC; U.S. Private, pg. 2502
CHARLES TAYLOR PLC—See Lovell Minnick Partners LLC; U.S. Private, pg. 2501
CHARLES TAYLOR RSLAC INC.—See Lovell Minnick Partners LLC; U.S. Private, pg. 2502
CHARLES TOMBRAS ADVERTISING, INC.; U.S. Private, pg. 854
CHARLESTON ANUSA, LLC—See AutoNation, Inc.; U.S. Public, pg. 234
CHARLESTON AREA MEDICAL CENTER FOUNDATION INC.—See Charleston Area Medical Center Inc.; U.S. Private, pg. 856
CHARLESTON AREA MEDICAL CENTER INC.; U.S. Private, pg. 856
CHARLESTON COMMISSIONERS OF PUBLIC WORKS; U.S. Private, pg. 856
CHARLESTON COUNTY AVIATION AUTHORITY; U.S. Private, pg. 856
CHARLESTON DAILY MAIL—See Alden Global Capital LLC; U.S. Private, pg. 156
CHARLESTON GOLD & DIAMOND EXCHANGE, INC.—See Envela Corporation; U.S. Public, pg. 780
CHARLESTON HEATING & AIR, LLC; U.S. Private, pg. 856
CHARLESTON HOLDING HMBH—See Compagnia Finanziaria de Benedetti S.p.A.; Int'l, pg. 1722
CHARLESTON INDUSTRIES INC—See Carlisle Companies Incorporated; U.S. Public, pg. 437
THE CHARLESTON MERCURY—See Evening Post Publishing Co.; U.S. Private, pg. 1436
CHARLESTON METAL PRODUCTS INC.; U.S. Private, pg. 856
CHARLESTON/ORWIG, INC.; U.S. Private, pg. 857
CHARLESTON PLACE HOLDINGS INC.—See LVMH Moet Hennessy Louis Vuitton SE; Int'l, pg. 4591
CHARLESTON SANITARY BOARD; U.S. Private, pg. 857
CHARLESTON STEEL & METAL CO.; U.S. Private, pg. 857
CHARLESTON TEA PLANTATION—See R.C. Bigelow, Inc.; U.S. Private, pg. 3334
CHARLESTON TRANSITIONAL FACILITY; U.S. Private, pg. 857
CHARLESTON TREATMENT CENTER, LLC—See Acadia Healthcare Company, Inc.; U.S. Public, pg. 28
CHARLES TYRWHITT LLP.; Int'l, pg. 1450
CHARLES UPHAM RETIREMENT VILLAGE LIMITED—See Ryman Healthcare Ltd.; Int'l, pg. 6439
CHARLES & VINZANT CONSTRUCTION CO. LLC; U.S. Private, pg. 851
CHARLES WORTHINGTON HAIR AND BEAUTY LTD.—See PZ Cussons Plc; Int'l, pg. 6128
CHARLEVOIX AREA HOSPITAL; U.S. Private, pg. 857
CHARLEYS CONCRETE CO.; U.S. Private, pg. 857
CHARLIE EARHART REALTY; U.S. Private, pg. 857
CHARLIE HILLARD, INC.—See AutoNation, Inc.; U.S. Public, pg. 234
CHARLIE HILLARD, INC.—See AutoNation, Inc.; U.S. Public, pg. 234
CHARLIE'S CONTRACTING, INC.; U.S. Private, pg. 857
CHARLIE'S DODGE, INC.; U.S. Private, pg. 857
CHARLIE'S HOLDINGS, INC.; U.S. Public, pg. 480
CHARLIE'S MOTOR MALL INC.; U.S. Private, pg. 857

CHARLIE'S SPECIALTIES INC.—See Byrnes & Kiefer Company; *U.S. Private*, pg. 701
CHARLIE'S TOBACCO OUTLET; *U.S. Private*, pg. 857
CHARLIE THOMAS CHEVROLET, LTD.—See AutoNation, Inc.; *U.S. Public*, pg. 234
CHARLIE THOMAS COURTESY FORD, LTD.—See AutoNation, Inc.; *U.S. Public*, pg. 234
CHARLIE THOMAS FORD, LTD.—See AutoNation, Inc.; *U.S. Public*, pg. 234
CHARLIE THOMAS FORD, LTD.—See AutoNation, Inc.; *U.S. Public*, pg. 234
CHARLIO'S—See The Riese Organization; *U.S. Private*, pg. 4107
CHARLOMA INC.; *U.S. Private*, pg. 857
CHARLOTTE APPLIANCES INC.; *U.S. Private*, pg. 857
CHARLOTTE BROADCASTING, LLC—See Urban One, Inc.; *U.S. Public*, pg. 2265
CHARLOTTE BUSINESS JOURNAL—See Advance Publications, Inc.; *U.S. Private*, pg. 84
CHARLOTTE CAPITAL CORP.; *U.S. Private*, pg. 857
CHARLOTTE COUNTRY CLUB; *U.S. Private*, pg. 857
CHARLOTTE ENDOSCOPIC SURGERY CENTER, LLC—See Tenet Healthcare Corporation; *U.S. Public*, pg. 2002
CHARLOTTE MOTOR SPEEDWAY, LLC—See Sonic Financial Corporation; *U.S. Private*, pg. 3713
THE CHARLOTTE OBSERVER PUBLISHING CO.—See Chatham Asset Management, LLC; *U.S. Private*, pg. 867
CHARLOTTE OUTLETS, LLC—See Tanger Inc.; *U.S. Public*, pg. 1980
CHARLOTTE PAINT COMPANY INC.; *U.S. Private*, pg. 857
THE CHARLOTTE PALM—See Palm Restaurant Group; *U.S. Private*, pg. 3080
CHARLOTTE PIPE & FOUNDRY COMPANY; *U.S. Private*, pg. 857
CHARLOTTE REGIONAL BUSINESS ALLIANCE; *U.S. Private*, pg. 857
CHARLOTTE REGIONAL PARTNERSHIP, INC.—See Charlotte Regional Business Alliance; *U.S. Private*, pg. 857
CHARLOTTE STATE BANK & TRUST—See Crews Banking Corporation; *U.S. Private*, pg. 1000
CHARLOTTE SUN—See Sun Coast Media Group, Inc.; *U.S. Private*, pg. 3862
CHARLOTTESVILLE AREA COMMUNITY FOUNDATION; *U.S. Private*, pg. 858
CHARLOTTESVILLE FASHION SQUARE, LLC—See Washington Prime Group Inc.; *U.S. Private*, pg. 4448
CHARLOTTESVILLE OIL CO. INC.; *U.S. Private*, pg. 858
CHARLOTTE'S WEB HOLDINGS, INC.; *U.S. Public*, pg. 480
CHARLOTTE TRACTOR COMPANY—See BobCo Inc.; *U.S. Private*, pg. 606
CHARLTON FEEDLOT PTY. LTD.—See Teys Australia Pty Ltd.; *Int'l*, pg. 7585
CHARLWOOD PACIFIC GROUP; *Int'l*, pg. 1450
CHARMACY PHARMACEUTICAL CO., LTD.; *Int'l*, pg. 1451
CHARM CARE CORPORATION K.K.; *Int'l*, pg. 1450
CHARM CO., LTD.—See ASKUL Corporation; *Int'l*, pg. 625
CHARM COMMUNICATIONS INC.; *Int'l*, pg. 1450
CHARM ENGINEERING CO., LTD.; *Int'l*, pg. 1451
CHARMILLES MIKRON—See Georg Fischer AG; *Int'l*, pg. 2934
CHARMILLES TECHNOLOGIES SA—See Georg Fischer AG; *Int'l*, pg. 2934
CHARMING CHARLIE USA CORP.; *U.S. Private*, pg. 858
CHARMING HOLIDAYS LIMITED—See Media Chinese International Limited; *Int'l*, pg. 4770
CHARMING PRINTING LIMITED—See Cirtek Holdings Limited; *Int'l*, pg. 1618
CHARMING SHOPPES, INC.—See Mahwah Bergen Retail Group, Inc.; *U.S. Private*, pg. 2550
CHARM SCIENCES, INC.; *U.S. Private*, pg. 858
CHARMS COMPANY—See Tootsie Roll Industries, Inc.; *U.S. Public*, pg. 2163
CHARMS INDUSTRIES LTD.; *Int'l*, pg. 1451
CHARMS LLC—See Tootsie Roll Industries, Inc.; *U.S. Public*, pg. 2163
CHARMTECH INDUSTRIAL LIMITED—See Win Hanverky Holdings Limited; *Int'l*, pg. 8424
CHARMT, INC.; *Int'l*, pg. 1451
CHARMWELL HOLDINGS LTD.; *Int'l*, pg. 1451
CHARMZONE GLOBAL CO., LTD.; *Int'l*, pg. 1451
CHARNIC CAPITAL TBK PT; *Int'l*, pg. 1451
CHARN ISSARA DEVELOPMENT PUBLIC COMPANY LIMITED; *Int'l*, pg. 1451
CHARN ISSARA VIPHAPOL COMPANY LIMITED—See Charn Issara Development Public Company Limited; *Int'l*, pg. 1451
CHARNWOOD FOREST BRICK LTD.—See Michelmersh Brick Holdings PLC; *Int'l*, pg. 4875
CHAROEN AKSORN HOLDING GROUP CO. LTD.; *Int'l*, pg. 1451
CHAROEN AKSORN TRADING CO., LTD.—See Charoen Aksorn Holding Group Co. Ltd.; *Int'l*, pg. 1451

CHAROEN POKPHAND ENTERPRISE (TAIWAN) CO., LTD.—See Charoen Pokphand Foods Public Company Limited; *Int'l*, pg. 1452
CHAROEN POKPHAND FOODS CANADA INC.—See Charoen Pokphand Foods Public Company Limited; *Int'l*, pg. 1452
CHAROEN POKPHAND FOODS (MALAYSIA) SDN. BHD.—See Charoen Pokphand Foods Public Company Limited; *Int'l*, pg. 1452
CHAROEN POKPHAND FOODS (OVERSEAS) LLC—See Charoen Pokphand Foods Public Company Limited; *Int'l*, pg. 1452
CHAROEN POKPHAND FOODS PHILIPPINES CORPORATION—See Charoen Pokphand Foods Public Company Limited; *Int'l*, pg. 1452
CHAROEN POKPHAND FOODS PUBLIC COMPANY LIMITED; *Int'l*, pg. 1451
CHAROEN POKPHAND GROUP CO., LTD.; *Int'l*, pg. 1453
CHAROEN POKPHAND (INDIA) PRIVATE LIMITED—See Charoen Pokphand Foods Public Company Limited; *Int'l*, pg. 1452
CHAROEN POKPHAND INTERTRADE SINGAPORE (PTE) LTD.—See Charoen Pokphand Group Co., Ltd.; *Int'l*, pg. 1453
CHAROEN POKPHAND NORTHEASTERN PUBLIC COMPANY LIMITED—See Charoen Pokphand Foods Public Company Limited; *Int'l*, pg. 1452
CHAROEN POKPHAND (TAIWAN) CO., LTD.—See Charoen Pokphand Foods Public Company Limited; *Int'l*, pg. 1452
CHAROENRUT KARNTAW CO., LTD.; *Int'l*, pg. 1454
CHARON PLANNING CORPORATION—See Aon plc; *Int'l*, pg. 495
CHAROONG THAI WIRE & CABLE PUBLIC COMPANY LIMITED—See Italian-Thai Development pcl; *Int'l*, pg. 3829
CHAROSA WINERIES LIMITED—See Grover Zampa Vineyards Limited; *Int'l*, pg. 3112
CHAROUNG THAI WIRE & CABLE PUBLIC CO. LTD.—See Asia Pacific Wire & Cable Corporation Limited; *Int'l*, pg. 614
CHARRIER SA; *Int'l*, pg. 1454
CHARTA GLOBAL, INC.—See Pabrik Kertas Tjiwi Kimia Tbk; *Int'l*, pg. 5684
CHART ASIA, INC.—See Chart Industries, Inc.; *U.S. Public*, pg. 481
CHARTA SRL—See Vivaticket; *Int'l*, pg. 8265
CHART AUSTRALIA PTY LTD—See Chart Industries, Inc.; *U.S. Public*, pg. 481
CHARTBEAT INC.—See Cuadrilla Capital LLC; *U.S. Private*, pg. 1119
CHART BIOMEDICAL (CHENGDU) CO., LTD.—See Niterra Co., Ltd.; *Int'l*, pg. 5380
CHART BIOMEDICAL LIMITED—See Niterra Co., Ltd.; *Int'l*, pg. 5380
CHARTCO LTD.—See Equistone Partners Europe Limited; *Int'l*, pg. 2486
CHART COOLER SERVICE COMPANY, INC.—See Chart Industries, Inc.; *U.S. Public*, pg. 481
CHARTCRAFT INC.—See Stockcube Plc; *Int'l*, pg. 7219
CHART CRYOGENIC DISTRIBUTION EQUIPMENT (CHANGZHOU) COMPANY LIMITED—See Chart Industries, Inc.; *U.S. Public*, pg. 481
CHART DISTRIBUTION & STORAGE SYSTEMS INC.—See Chart Industries, Inc.; *U.S. Public*, pg. 481
CHAR TECHNOLOGIES LTD.; *Int'l*, pg. 1448
CHAR TECHNOLOGY (PTY) LIMITED—See Glencore plc; *Int'l*, pg. 2990
CHARTECH SOLUTIONS INC.—See CHAR Technologies Ltd.; *Int'l*, pg. 1448
CHART ENERGY AND CHEMICALS WUXI CO., LTD.—See Chart Industries, Inc.; *U.S. Public*, pg. 481
CHART ENERGY & CHEMICALS INC.—See Chart Industries, Inc.; *U.S. Public*, pg. 481
CHARTER ATLANTIC CORPORATION; *U.S. Private*, pg. 858
CHARTERAUCTION.COM—See AeroShares Charter, LLC; *U.S. Private*, pg. 119
CHARTER AUTOMOTIVE—See Charter Manufacturing Company, Inc.; *U.S. Private*, pg. 858
CHARTER BAKING COMPANY, INC.—See The Hain Celestial Group, Inc.; *U.S. Public*, pg. 2086
CHARTER BANKSHARES, INC.—See Nicolet Bankshares, Inc.; *U.S. Public*, pg. 1528
CHARTER BOARD PARTNERS; *U.S. Private*, pg. 858
CHARTER BROKERAGE LLC—See Berkshire Hathaway Inc.; *U.S. Public*, pg. 304
CHARTER CABLE PARTNERS, L.L.C.—See Charter Communications, Inc.; *U.S. Public*, pg. 483
CHARTER CHEMICAL & COATING CORPORATION—See Chugoku Marine Paints, Ltd.; *Int'l*, pg. 1595
CHARTER COMMUNICATIONS, INC.; *U.S. Public*, pg. 482
CHARTER COURT FINANCIAL SERVICES GROUP PLC—See OneSavings Bank plc; *Int'l*, pg. 5577
CHARTER DIGITAL MEDIA INC.—See Charter Direct Marketing; *U.S. Private*, pg. 858
CHARTER DIRECT MARKETING; *U.S. Private*, pg. 858

CHARTER DURA-BAR—See Charter Manufacturing Company, Inc.; *U.S. Private*, pg. 858
CHARTERED CAPITAL & INVESTMENT LTD.; *Int'l*, pg. 1454
CHARTERED DEVELOPMENT CORP.—See Chartered Homes; *U.S. Private*, pg. 859
CHARTERED HOMES; *U.S. Private*, pg. 858
CHARTERED LOGISTICS LTD.; *Int'l*, pg. 1454
CHARTERED MOTORS PVT LTD—See Chartered Logistics Ltd.; *Int'l*, pg. 1454
CHARTER ENGINEERING, INC.—See HEICO Corporation; *U.S. Public*, pg. 1021
CHARTER FILMS, INC.; *U.S. Private*, pg. 858
CHARTER FINANCIAL PUBLISHING NETWORK; *U.S. Private*, pg. 858
CHARTER GILMAN INSURANCE HOLDINGS LIMITED—See PSC Insurance Group Limited; *Int'l*, pg. 6015
CHARTER HALL LIMITED; *Int'l*, pg. 1454
CHARTER HALL LONG WALE REIT—See Charter Hall Limited; *Int'l*, pg. 1454
CHARTER HALL REAL ESTATE INC.—See Charter Hall Limited; *Int'l*, pg. 1454
CHARTER HALL REAL ESTATE MANAGEMENT SERVICES (NSW) PTY LIMITED—See Charter Hall Limited; *Int'l*, pg. 1454
CHARTER HALL REAL ESTATE MANAGEMENT SERVICES (QLD) PTY LIMITED—See Charter Hall Limited; *Int'l*, pg. 1454
CHARTER HALL REAL ESTATE MANAGEMENT SERVICES (VIC) PTY LIMITED—See Charter Hall Limited; *Int'l*, pg. 1454
CHARTER HALL RETAIL MANAGEMENT PTY LIMITED—See Charter Hall Limited; *Int'l*, pg. 1454
CHARTER HALL RETAIL REIT—See Charter Hall Limited; *Int'l*, pg. 1454
CHARTER HALL SOCIAL INFRASTRUCTURE REIT—See Charter Hall Limited; *Int'l*, pg. 1454
CHARTER HEALTH CARE GROUP LLC—See Pharos Capital Group, LLC; *U.S. Private*, pg. 3166
CHARTERHOUSE CAPITAL PARTNERS LLP; *Int'l*, pg. 1454
CHARTERHOUSE GROUP, INC.; *U.S. Private*, pg. 859
CHARTERHOUSE PRIVATE SCHOOLS (PTY) LTD.—See ADvTECH Limited; *Int'l*, pg. 169
CHARTER INTERNATIONAL PLC—See Enovis Corporation; *U.S. Public*, pg. 770
CHARTER KONTRON LTD—See Mennen Medical Ltd.; *Int'l*, pg. 4816
CHARTER LTD.—See Enovis Corporation; *U.S. Public*, pg. 770
CHARTER MANUFACTURING COMPANY, INC.; *U.S. Private*, pg. 858
CHARTER MEDIA COMPANY—See National Amusements, Inc.; *U.S. Private*, pg. 2841
CHARTER MEDICAL, LTD.—See Compagnie Generale des Etablissements Michelin SCA; *Int'l*, pg. 1744
CHARTER NATIONAL LIFE INSURANCE COMPANY—See The Allstate Corporation; *U.S. Public*, pg. 2033
CHARTER NEX FILMS, INC.—See Keystone Group, L.P.; *U.S. Private*, pg. 2297
CHARTER NEX FILMS, INC.—See Leonard Green & Partners, L.P.; *U.S. Private*, pg. 2425
CHARTER OAK AVIATION, INC.—See Macquarie Group Limited; *Int'l*, pg. 4627
CHARTER OAK EQUITY, L.P.; *U.S. Private*, pg. 858
CHARTER OAK HEALTH CENTER, INC.; *U.S. Private*, pg. 858
CHARTER OAK INTERNATIONAL PARTNERS, LLC—See Charter Oak Equity, L.P.; *U.S. Private*, pg. 858
CHARTER ONE HOTELS & RESORTS, INC.; *U.S. Private*, pg. 858
CHARTER PACIFIC CORPORATION LIMITED; *Int'l*, pg. 1454
CHARTER SCHOOL BUSINESS MANAGEMENT; *U.S. Private*, pg. 858
CHARTER SCHOOLS USA INC.; *U.S. Private*, pg. 858
CHARTER SOFTWARE, INC.—See Constellation Software Inc.; *Int'l*, pg. 1772
CHARTER SOUTH INC.; *U.S. Private*, pg. 858
CHARTER STEEL, INC.—See Charter Manufacturing Company, Inc.; *U.S. Private*, pg. 858
CHARTERS TOWERS GOLD PTY LTD—See Citigold Corporation Limited; *Int'l*, pg. 1622
CHARTER TITLE COMPANY INC.—See Fidelity National Financial, Inc.; *U.S. Public*, pg. 831
CHARTER TRUST COMPANY—See Bar Harbor Bankshares; *U.S. Public*, pg. 275
CHARTERWAY DEVELOPMENTS LIMITED—See Sino-Ocean Group Holdings Limited; *Int'l*, pg. 6949
CHARTER WIRE—See Charter Manufacturing Company, Inc.; *U.S. Private*, pg. 858
CHART FEROX A.S.—See Chart Industries, Inc.; *U.S. Public*, pg. 481
CHART FRANCE SAS—See Chart Industries, Inc.; *U.S. Public*, pg. 481

CHARTER SOUTH INC. — CORPORATE AFFILIATIONS

CHART INDUSTRIES, INC.- DISTRIBUTION & STORAGE - HOUSTON—See Chart Industries, Inc.; *U.S. Public,* pg. 481
CHART INDUSTRIES, INC.; *U.S. Public,* pg. 481
CHARTIO INC.; *U.S. Private,* pg. 859
CHARTIS CLINICAL QUALITY SOLUTIONS—See Audax Group, Limited Partnership; *U.S. Private,* pg. 390
THE CHARTIS GROUP, LLC—See Audax Group, Limited Partnership; *U.S. Private,* pg. 390
CHARTIS INSURANCE COMPANY CHINA LIMITED—See American International Group, Inc.; *U.S. Public,* pg. 105
CHARTIS KAZAKHSTAN INSURANCE COMPANY—See American International Group, Inc.; *U.S. Public,* pg. 106
CHARTIS TAKAFUL-ENAYA B.S.C.—See American International Group, Inc.; *U.S. Public,* pg. 106
CHARTIS VIETNAM INSURANCE COMPANY LIMITED—See American International Group, Inc.; *U.S. Public,* pg. 105
CHART ITALY S.R.L.—See Chart Industries, Inc.; *U.S. Public,* pg. 481
CHART JAPAN CO., LTD.—See Chart Industries, Inc.; *U.S. Public,* pg. 481
CHART LATIN AMERICA S.A.S.—See Chart Industries, Inc.; *U.S. Public,* pg. 481
CHARTLOGIC, INC.—See Medsphere Systems Corp.; *U.S. Private,* pg. 2658
CHARTPAK INC—See GPC International, Inc.; *U.S. Private,* pg. 1748
CHARTRAND FORD; *Int'l,* pg. 1456
CHARTRES POIDS LOURDS (LECHEVALIER-DOURS) S.A.; *Int'l,* pg. 1456
CHARTREUSE & MONT BLANC—See Macquarie Group Limited; *Int'l,* pg. 4625
CHART SEQUAL TECHNOLOGIES, INC.—See Niterra Co., Ltd.; *Int'l,* pg. 5380
CHARTWELL AGENCY; *U.S. Private,* pg. 859
CHARTWELL AGENCY—See Chartwell Agency; *U.S. Private,* pg. 859
CHARTWELL AGENCY—See Chartwell Agency; *U.S. Private,* pg. 859
CHARTWELL DE NUEVO LAREDO, S.A. DE C.V.—See Minor International PCL; *Int'l,* pg. 4911
CHARTWELL ENERGY LIMITED—See Comet Ridge Limited; *Int'l,* pg. 1711
CHARTWELL GROUP LIMITED—See Close Brothers Group plc; *Int'l,* pg. 1661
CHARTWELL INVESTMENT PARTNERS, L.P.—See Raymond James Financial, Inc.; *U.S. Public,* pg. 1765
CHARTWELL INVESTMENTS; *U.S. Private,* pg. 859
THE CHARTWELL LAW OFFICES, LLP - HARRISBURG—See The Chartwell Law Offices, LLP; *U.S. Private,* pg. 4007
THE CHARTWELL LAW OFFICES, LLP - NEW YORK—See The Chartwell Law Offices, LLP; *U.S. Private,* pg. 4007
THE CHARTWELL LAW OFFICES, LLP; *U.S. Private,* pg. 4007
CHARTWELL RETIREMENT RESIDENCES; *Int'l,* pg. 1456
CHARTWELLS HIGHER EDUCATION DINING SERVICES—See Compass Group PLC; *Int'l,* pg. 1750
CHARTWELLS USA—See Compass Group PLC; *Int'l,* pg. 1751
CHARTWELL TRAVEL LTD.—See Global Business Travel Group, Inc.; *U.S. Public,* pg. 940
C.HARTWIG GDYNIA S.A.—See OT Logistics S.A.; *Int'l,* pg. 5656
CHARTWISE MEDICAL SYSTEMS, INC.—See Iodine Software, LLC; *U.S. Private,* pg. 2133
CHARTWORLD AMERICAS MARITIME SERVICES LTD.—See Teledyne Technologies Incorporated; *U.S. Public,* pg. 1992
CHARTWORLD ASIA PACIFIC PTE. LTD.—See Teledyne Technologies Incorporated; *U.S. Public,* pg. 1992
CHARTWORLD GMBH—See Teledyne Technologies Incorporated; *U.S. Public,* pg. 1992
CHARTWORLD INTERNATIONAL LIMITED—See Teledyne Technologies Incorporated; *U.S. Public,* pg. 1992
CHARUN BUSINESS 52 CO., LTD.—See Thai Beverage Public Company Limited; *Int'l,* pg. 7589
THE CHAS. C. HART SEED CO.; *U.S. Private,* pg. 4007
CHASCO CONSTRUCTORS, LTD., LLP; *U.S. Private,* pg. 859
CHASE ASIA PUBLIC COMPANY LIMITED; *Int'l,* pg. 1456
CHASE BRASS & COPPER COMPANY, INC.—See Wieland-Werke AG; *Int'l,* pg. 8403
CHASE BREXTON HEALTH SERVICES, INC.; *U.S. Private,* pg. 859
CHASE BRIGHT STEEL LTD.; *Int'l,* pg. 1456
CHASE CARD SERVICES, INC.—See JPMorgan Chase & Co.; *U.S. Public,* pg. 1206
CHASE CHEVROLET CO., INC.; *U.S. Private,* pg. 859
CHASE, CLARKE, STEWART & FONTANA, INC.; *U.S. Private,* pg. 860
CHASE CORPORATION - PITTSBURGH—See KKR & Co. Inc.; *U.S. Public,* pg. 1242
CHASE CORPORATION—See KKR & Co. Inc.; *U.S. Public,* pg. 1242
THE CHASE CREATIVE CONSULTANTS LIMITED—See Hasgrove plc; *Int'l,* pg. 3283
CHASE DESIGN, LLC—See The Interpublic Group of Companies, Inc.; *U.S. Public,* pg. 2102
CHASE DE VERE FINANCIAL SOLUTIONS LIMITED—See Swiss Life Holding; *Int'l,* pg. 7370
CHASE DE VERE IFA GROUP PLC—See Swiss Life Holding; *Int'l,* pg. 7370
CHASE DE VERE INDEPENDENT FINANCIAL ADVISERS LTD—See Swiss Life Holding; *Int'l,* pg. 7370
CHASE-DURER LTD.; *U.S. Private,* pg. 860
CHASE EDUCATION FINANCE—See JPMorgan Chase & Co.; *U.S. Public,* pg. 1206
CHASE ELASTOMER CORPORATION—See HEXPOL AB; *Int'l,* pg. 3372
CHASE ELASTOMER (UK) LTD.—See HEXPOL AB; *Int'l,* pg. 3372
CHASE ENTERPRISES, INC.; *U.S. Private,* pg. 859
CHASE GENERAL CORPORATION; *U.S. Private,* pg. 860
CHASE G.P. CORPORATION—See Chase Enterprises, Inc.; *U.S. Private,* pg. 859
CHASE HOME FINANCE LLC—See JPMorgan Chase & Co.; *U.S. Public,* pg. 1206
CHASE INDUSTRIES, INC.—See Audax Group, Limited Partnership; *U.S. Private,* pg. 386
CHASE INVESTMENTS LIMITED—See Godfrey Phillips India Ltd.; *Int'l,* pg. 3019
CHASE LUMBER & FUEL COMPANY, INC.—See Bliffert Lumber & Fuel Co. Inc.; *U.S. Private,* pg. 581
CHASE & LUNT INSURANCE AGENCY LLC—See Arthur J. Gallagher & Co.; *U.S. Public,* pg. 204
CHASE MANHATTAN MORTGAGE CORP.—See JPMorgan Chase & Co.; *U.S. Public,* pg. 1206
CHASE MORTGAGE HOLDINGS, INC.—See JPMorgan Chase & Co.; *U.S. Public,* pg. 1206
CHASEN ENGINEERING SDN. BHD.—See Chasen Holdings Limited; *Int'l,* pg. 1457
CHASEN HOLDINGS LIMITED; *Int'l,* pg. 1457
CHASEN LOGISTICS SDN BHD—See Chasen Holdings Limited; *Int'l,* pg. 1457
CHASEN LOGISTICS SERVICES LIMITED—See Chasen Holdings Limited; *Int'l,* pg. 1457
CHASEN (SHANGHAI) HI TECH MACHINERY SERVICES PTE LTD—See Chasen Holdings Limited; *Int'l,* pg. 1457
CHASEN SINO-SIN (BEIJING) HI TECH SERVICES PTE LTD—See Chasen Holdings Limited; *Int'l,* pg. 1457
CHASEN TRANSPORT LOGISTICS CO., LTD.—See Chasen Holdings Limited; *Int'l,* pg. 1457
CHASEN (USA), INC.—See Chasen Holdings Limited; *Int'l,* pg. 1457
CHASE OIL COMPANY INC.; *U.S. Private,* pg. 860
CHASE PACKAGING CORPORATION; *U.S. Public,* pg. 483
CHASE PAYMENTECH EUROPE LIMITED—See JPMorgan Chase & Co.; *U.S. Public,* pg. 1209
CHASE PAYMENTECH SOLUTIONS, LLC—See JPMorgan Chase & Co.; *U.S. Public,* pg. 1206
CHASE PAYMENTECH SOLUTIONS, LLC—See JPMorgan Chase & Co.; *U.S. Public,* pg. 1209
CHASE PAYMENTECH SOLUTIONS—See JPMorgan Chase & Co.; *U.S. Public,* pg. 1206
CHASE PLASTIC SERVICES, INC.; *U.S. Private,* pg. 860
CHASE PRODUCTS CO.—See The Starco Group, Inc.; *U.S. Private,* pg. 4121
CHASE PROTECTIVE COATINGS LIMITED—See KKR & Co. Inc.; *U.S. Public,* pg. 1242
CHASE SCIENCE CO., LTD.; *Int'l,* pg. 1456
CHASE & SONS DIVISION—See KKR & Co. Inc.; *U.S. Public,* pg. 1242
CHASE STUDENT LOANS, INC.—See JPMorgan Chase & Co.; *U.S. Public,* pg. 1206
CHASE TECHNOLOGY CONSULTANTS, LLC; *U.S. Private,* pg. 860
CHASE VENTURES HOLDINGS INC.—See JPMorgan Chase & Co.; *U.S. Public,* pg. 1209
CHASE-WALTON ELASTOMERS INC.; *U.S. Private,* pg. 860
CHAS F. WILLIAMS CO. INC.; *U.S. Private,* pg. 859
CHAS H. BILZ INSURANCE AGENCY, INC.; *U.S. Private,* pg. 859
CHASHMA SUGAR MILLS LIMITED; *Int'l,* pg. 1457
CHASING FIREFLIES, LLC—See DAI Holding, LLC; *U.S. Private,* pg. 1145
CHASM CONSULTING PTY. LTD.—See Envois Corporation; *U.S. Private,* pg. 772
CHAS. PETER NAGEL, LLC—See Service Corporation International; *U.S. Public,* pg. 1869
CHAS P. SMITH & ASSOCIATES, PA, CPA'S; *U.S. Private,* pg. 859
CHAS ROBERTS AIR CONDITIONING, INC.; *U.S. Private,* pg. 859
CHASSAY AUTOMOBILES SAS; *Int'l,* pg. 1457
CHASSIX, INC.—See Platinum Equity, LLC; *U.S. Private,* pg. 3201
CHASTAIN CONSTRUCTION INC.; *U.S. Private,* pg. 860
CHASTAIN-SKILLMAN, INC.—See White Wolf Capital LLC; *U.S. Private,* pg. 4510
CHASTANG ENTERPRISES, INC.; *U.S. Private,* pg. 860
CHASWOOD RESOURCES HOLDINGS LTD.; *Int'l,* pg. 1457
CHASYS CO., LTD; *Int'l,* pg. 1457
CHATAM INTERNATIONAL INCORPORATED; *U.S. Private,* pg. 860
CHATCHING, INC.; *U.S. Private,* pg. 860
CHATEAU BEAUMONT—See Suntory Holdings Limited; *Int'l,* pg. 7326
CHATEAU BEYCHEVELLE—See Suntory Holdings Limited; *Int'l,* pg. 7326
CHATEAU DASSAULT SA—See Groupe Industriel Marcel Dassault S.A.; *Int'l,* pg. 3104
CHATEAUD'EAU SA—See Eden International SA; *Int'l,* pg. 2306
CHATEAU ELAN LTD.—See Fountainhead Development, LLC; *U.S. Private,* pg. 1581
CHATEAU ELAN WINERY & RESORT—See Fountainhead Development, LLC; *U.S. Private,* pg. 1581
CHATEAU GREYSAC—See SAS Domaine Rollan de By; *Int'l,* pg. 6581
CHATEAU HOCHBERG SAS—See Lalique Group S.A.; *Int'l,* pg. 4399
CHATEAU INTERIORS & DESIGN—See The Warmington Group; *U.S. Private,* pg. 4133
CHATEAU INTERNATIONAL DEVELOPMENT CO., LTD.; *Int'l,* pg. 1457
CHATEAU INTERNATIONAL INC.; *U.S. Private,* pg. 860
CHATEAU JULIA HEALTHCARE, INC.—See The Ensign Group, Inc.; *U.S. Public,* pg. 2070
CHATEAU LAFAURIEPEYRAGUEY HOTEL& RESTAURANT LALIQUE S.A.S.—See Lalique Group S.A.; *Int'l,* pg. 4399
CHATEAU LAGRANGE S.A.—See Suntory Holdings Limited; *Int'l,* pg. 7325
CHATEAU LANDSCAPE, INC.—See Landscape Developmental Inc.; *U.S. Private,* pg. 2387
CHATEAU LAROSE TRINTAUDON S.A.—See Allianz SE; *Int'l,* pg. 351
CHATEAU PROPERTIES—See Carpionato Group LLC; *U.S. Private,* pg. 771
CHATEAU RESTAURANT OF WALTHAM INC.; *U.S. Private,* pg. 860
CHATEAU ST. JEAN WINERY—See Treasury Wine Estates Limited; *Int'l,* pg. 7909
CHATEAUX ET DOMAINES WEINHANDELSGESELLSCHAFT MBH—See Hawesko Holding AG; *Int'l,* pg. 3288
CHATEAUX SOFTWARE DEVELOPMENT—See Wells Fargo & Company; *U.S. Public,* pg. 2344
CHA TECHNOLOGIES INC.; *U.S. Private,* pg. 844
CHA TECHNOLOGIES INC.—See CHA Technologies Inc.; *U.S. Private,* pg. 845
CHATEL SA—See VINCI S.A.; *Int'l,* pg. 8215
CHATENET SAS—See VINCI S.A.; *Int'l,* pg. 8215
THE CHATFIELD GROUP, INC.; *U.S. Private,* pg. 4007
CHATHAM ASSET MANAGEMENT, LLC; *U.S. Private,* pg. 860
CHATHAM CORPORATION; *U.S. Private,* pg. 868
CHATHAM CREATED GEMS INC.; *U.S. Private,* pg. 868
THE CHATHAM DAILY NEWS—See Chatham Asset Management, LLC; *U.S. Private,* pg. 861
CHATHAM IMPORTS INC—See Quaker Equities Ltd., Inc.; *U.S. Private,* pg. 3316
CHATHAM INVESTMENT CO. PTY LIMITED—See Washington H. Soul Pattinson & Company Limited; *Int'l,* pg. 8351
CHATHAM LODGING TRUST; *U.S. Public,* pg. 483
CHATHAM MOTOR SALES, INC.; *U.S. Private,* pg. 868
CHATHAM PINES MHP LLC—See Manufactured Housing Properties Inc.; *U.S. Public,* pg. 1362
CHATHAM ROCK PHOSPHATE LIMITED; *Int'l,* pg. 1457
CHATHAM STEEL CORPORATION—See Reliance Steel & Aluminum Co.; *U.S. Public,* pg. 1779
CHATHAM TOWING COMPANY, INC.—See Colonial Group, Inc.; *U.S. Private,* pg. 971
CHAT INC.; *U.S. Private,* pg. 860
CHATMETER; *U.S. Private,* pg. 868
CHATSWOOD CHASE, SYDNEY—See Vicinity Limited; *Int'l,* pg. 8187
CHATSWOOD HILLS TAVERN PTY. LTD—See Woolworths Group Limited; *Int'l,* pg. 8451
CHATSWORTH DATA CORPORATION—See CDC Data, LLC; *U.S. Private,* pg. 802
CHATSWORTH HEATING PRODUCTS LTD—See Zehnder Group AG; *Int'l,* pg. 8630
CHATSWORTH PRODUCTS - CHATSWORTH—See Chatsworth Products Inc.; *U.S. Private,* pg. 868
CHATSWORTH PRODUCTS - GEORGETOWN—See Chatsworth Products Inc.; *U.S. Private,* pg. 868
CHATSWORTH PRODUCTS INC.; *U.S. Private,* pg. 868
CHATSWORTH PRODUCTS INTERNATIONAL, LTD.—See Chatsworth Products Inc.; *U.S. Private,* pg. 868
CHATTAHOOCHEE INDUSTRIAL RAILROAD—See Brookfield Infrastructure Partners L.P.; *U.S. Public,* pg. 1191
CHATTAHOOCHEE INDUSTRIAL RAILROAD—See GIC Pte. Ltd.; *Int'l,* pg. 2965
CHATTANOOGA AREA FOOD BANK; *U.S. Private,* pg. 868

COMPANY NAME INDEX — CHECK POINT SOFTWARE TECHNOLOGIES LTD.

CHATTANOOGA BAKERY INC.; *U.S. Private*, pg. 868
CHATTANOOGA BOILER & TANK CO., INC.—See Williams Enterprises of Georgia, Inc.; *U.S. Private*, pg. 4525
CHATTANOOGA CHOO-CHOO HOLIDAY INN—See Choo Choo Partners L.P.; *U.S. Private*, pg. 888
CHATTANOOGA CHRISTIAN COMMUNITY FOUNDATION; *U.S. Private*, pg. 868
CHATTANOOGA COCA-COLA BOTTLING COMPANY—See Coca-Cola Bottling Co. United, Inc.; *U.S. Private*, pg. 958
CHATTANOOGA DIAGNOSTIC ASSOCIATES, LLC—See HCA Healthcare, Inc.; *U.S. Public*, pg. 993
THE CHATTANOOGA ENDOSCOPY ASC, LLC—See KKR & Co. Inc.; *U.S. Public*, pg. 1247
CHATTANOOGA GAS COMPANY—See The Southern Company; *U.S. Public*, pg. 2131
CHATTANOOGA GROUP—See Enovis Corporation; *U.S. Public*, pg. 772
CHATTANOOGA PAIN MANAGEMENT CENTER, LLC—See Tenet Healthcare Corporation; *U.S. Public*, pg. 2009
CHATTANOOGA PUBLISHING CO. INC.—See Wehco Media, Inc.; *U.S. Private*, pg. 4469
CHATTANOOGA TIMES FREE PRESS COMPANY—See Wehco Media, Inc.; *U.S. Private*, pg. 4469
CHATTARY AJWAN INFOTECH PVT. LTD.—See Caesars Group; *Int'l*, pg. 1249
CHATTEM CHEMICALS, INC.—See Sun Pharmaceutical Industries Ltd.; *Int'l*, pg. 7307
CHATTEM, INC.—See Sanofi; *Int'l*, pg. 6547
CHATTERBOX LIMITED—See CSE Global Ltd.; *Int'l*, pg. 1864
THE CHATTERJEE GROUP; *U.S. Private*, pg. 4007
CHATTERSON JANITORIAL SUPPLIES LTD.—See Sani-Marc inc.; *Int'l*, pg. 6539
CHATTOOGA & CHICKAMAUGA RAILWAY CO.—See Brookfield Infrastructure Partners L.P.; *Int'l*, pg. 1191
CHATTOOGA & CHICKAMAUGA RAILWAY CO.—See GIC Pte. Ltd.; *Int'l*, pg. 2965
CHATUGE REGIONAL HOSPITAL; *U.S. Private*, pg. 868
CHAUCER FOODS HONG KONG LIMITED—See Mitsubishi Corporation; *Int'l*, pg. 4940
CHAUCER FOODS LIMITED—See Mitsubishi Corporation; *Int'l*, pg. 4940
CHAUCER FOODS (QINGDAO) CO. LIMITED—See Mitsubishi Corporation; *Int'l*, pg. 4940
CHAUCER FOODS S.A.S—See Mitsubishi Corporation; *Int'l*, pg. 4940
CHAUCER FOODS UK LIMITED—See Mitsubishi Corporation; *Int'l*, pg. 4940
CHAUCER HOLDINGS LIMITED—See China Reinsurance (Group) Corporation; *Int'l*, pg. 1547
CHAUCER LABUAN LIMITED—See China Reinsurance (Group) Corporation; *Int'l*, pg. 1547
CHAUCER LATIN AMERICA S.A—See China Reinsurance (Group) Corporation; *Int'l*, pg. 1547
CHAUCER MENA LIMITED—See China Reinsurance (Group) Corporation; *Int'l*, pg. 1547
CHAUCER SINGAPORE PTE LIMITED—See China Reinsurance (Group) Corporation; *Int'l*, pg. 1547
CHAUCERS MEADOW (NORTH PETHERTON) MANAGEMENT COMPANY LIMITED—See Persimmon plc; *Int'l*, pg. 5815
CHAUCER SYNDICATE SERVICES LIMITED—See The Hanover Insurance Group, Inc.; *U.S. Public*, pg. 2087
CHAUCER SYNDICATES LIMITED—See China Reinsurance (Group) Corporation; *Int'l*, pg. 1547
CHAUCER UNDERWRITING A/S—See China Reinsurance (Group) Corporation; *Int'l*, pg. 1547
CHAUDRONNERIE DE L'EST; *Int'l*, pg. 1457
CHAUMET HORLOGERIE S.A.—See LVMH Moet Hennessy Louis Vuitton SE; *Int'l*, pg. 4602
CHAUMET INTERNATIONAL SA—See LVMH Moet Hennessy Louis Vuitton SE; *Int'l*, pg. 4602
CHAUMET (LONDON) LTD.—See LVMH Moet Hennessy Louis Vuitton SE; *Int'l*, pg. 4602
CHAUMET UAE—See LVMH Moet Hennessy Louis Vuitton SE; *Int'l*, pg. 4591
THE CHAUNCEY GROUP INTERNATIONAL LTD.—See Educational Testing Service Inc.; *U.S. Private*, pg. 1340
CHAUN CHOUNG TECHNOLOGY CORP. - CHUNG-SHIN PLANT—See Nidec Chaun-Choung Technology Corporation; *Int'l*, pg. 5274
CHAUS ELECTRICAL COMPANY LIMITED—See Solartech International Holdings Limited; *Int'l*, pg. 7070
CHAUTAUQUA AIRLINES INC.—See Republic Airways Holdings Inc.; *U.S. Public*, pg. 3401
CHAUTAUQUA CAPITAL MANAGEMENT LLC—See Baird Financial Group, Inc.; *U.S. Private*, pg. 454
CHAUTAUQUA MALL, LLC—See Washington Prime Group Inc.; *U.S. Private*, pg. 4448
CHAUX ET ENDUITS DE SAINT ASTIER; *Int'l*, pg. 1457
CHA VACCINE INSTITUTE; *Int'l*, pg. 1436
CHAVDA INFRA LIMITED; *Int'l*, pg. 1457
CHAVES BAKERY II, INC.; *U.S. Private*, pg. 868
CHAYAH CONSULTING GROUP LLC; *U.S. Private*, pg. 868

CHAYO GROUP PUBLIC COMPANY LIMITED; *Int'l*, pg. 1458
CHAYSECHEM INC.—See Charkit Chemical Company, LLC; *U.S. Private*, pg. 851
CHAZAK VALUE CORP.; *U.S. Private*, pg. 868
CHBA-IBI INC.—See ARCADIS N.V.; *Int'l*, pg. 541
C.H. BAILEY PLC; *Int'l*, pg. 1240
CHB ELEKTRO UND FERNMELDEBAU GMBH—See VINCI S.A.; *Int'l*, pg. 8215
CHB INSURANCE BROKERAGE COMPANY, LTD.—See Chang Hwa Commercial Bank Ltd.; *Int'l*, pg. 1441
CH BIOTECH R&D CO., LTD.; *Int'l*, pg. 1435
CHB LIFE INSURANCE AGENCY COMPANY, LTD.—See Chang Hwa Commercial Bank Ltd.; *Int'l*, pg. 1441
C.H. BOEHRINGER SOHN AG & CO. KG; *Int'l*, pg. 1240
CHB P H R LIMITED—See Heidelberg Materials AG; *Int'l*, pg. 3309
C.H. BRIGGS COMPANY; *U.S. Private*, pg. 707
C. H. BROWN CO., LLC—See Platte Valley Financial Service Companies Inc.; *U.S. Private*, pg. 3211
C.H. CARPENTER LUMBER COMPANY; *U.S. Private*, pg. 707
CHCA WEST HOUSTON, L.P.—See HCA Healthcare, Inc.; *U.S. Public*, pg. 992
CHC CONSULTING LLC—See Crestview Partners, L.P.; *U.S. Private*, pg. 1098
CHC EUROPE (UK)—See First Reserve Management, L.P.; *U.S. Private*, pg. 1525
CHC GROUP LTD.—See First Reserve Management, L.P.; *U.S. Private*, pg. 1525
CHC (GUANGZHOU) MEDICAL TECHNOLOGY CO., LTD.—See CHC Healthcare Group; *Int'l*, pg. 1458
CH. CHARILAOU GROUP PLC; *Int'l*, pg. 1435
CHC HEALTHCARE GROUP; *Int'l*, pg. 1458
CHC HELICOPTER CORPORATION—See First Reserve Management, L.P.; *U.S. Private*, pg. 1525
CHC HELICOPTERS (AUSTRALIA)—See First Reserve Management, L.P.; *U.S. Private*, pg. 1525
CHC HELICOPTERS, INC.—See First Reserve Management, L.P.; *U.S. Private*, pg. 1525
CHC MECHANICAL CONTRACTORS; *U.S. Private*, pg. 868
CHC NAVIGATION EUROPE KFT.—See Shanghai Huace Navigation Technology Ltd; *Int'l*, pg. 6770
CHC NAVIGATION USA LLC—See Shanghai Huace Navigation Technology Ltd; *Int'l*, pg. 6770
CHC NAVTECH (THAILAND) CO., LTD.—See Shanghai Huace Navigation Technology Ltd; *Int'l*, pg. 6770
C.H. COAKLEY & CO.; *U.S. Private*, pg. 707
C&H COMMUNICATIONS; *Int'l*, pg. 1238
CHC RESOURCES CORPORATION—See China Steel Corporation; *Int'l*, pg. 1555
CHCS SERVICES INC.—See Capgemini SE; *Int'l*, pg. 1303
CHD CHEMICALS LTD.; *Int'l*, pg. 1458
CH&D ENTERPRISES INC.; *U.S. Private*, pg. 844
C&H DISTRIBUTORS, LLC—See Franz Haniel & Cie. GmbH; *Int'l*, pg. 2763
CHEAHA BANK—See Investar Holding Corporation; *U.S. Public*, pg. 1164
CHEAHA FINANCIAL GROUP, INC.—See Investar Holding Corporation; *U.S. Public*, pg. 1164
CHEAHA REGIONAL MENTAL HEALTH CENTER—See Baldwin County Mental Health-Mental Retardation Services, Inc.; *U.S. Private*, pg. 458
CHEAPCARIBBEAN.COM, INC.—See Apple Leisure Group; *U.S. Private*, pg. 296
CHEAP THRILLS CYCLES PTY. LTD.—See Universal Store Holdings Limited; *Int'l*, pg. 8082
CHEBANCA S.P.A.—See Mediobanca-Banca de Credito Finanziario S.p.A.; *Int'l*, pg. 4778
CHEBANSE CROP SERVICE INC.; *U.S. Private*, pg. 868
CHEBELLE CORPORATION; *U.S. Private*, pg. 868
CHEBOYGAN LUMBER COMPANY; *U.S. Private*, pg. 868
CHECK-6, INC.; *U.S. Private*, pg. 869
CHECKAERO BV—See Sogeclair; *Int'l*, pg. 7058
CHECKAERO SARL—See Sogeclair; *Int'l*, pg. 7058
CHECKALT, LLC; *U.S. Private*, pg. 869
CHECK-CAP LTD.; *Int'l*, pg. 1459
THE CHECK CASHING PLACE, INC.; *U.S. Private*, pg. 4007
CHECKERED FLAG MOTOR CAR CO.; *U.S. Private*, pg. 869
CHECKER LEASING INCORPORATED; *U.S. Private*, pg. 869
CHECKER NOTIONS COMPANY INC.; *U.S. Private*, pg. 869
CHECKERS DRIVE-IN RESTAURANTS, INC.—See Keystone Group, L.P.; *U.S. Private*, pg. 2299
CHECKERS INDUSTRIAL PRODUCTS LLC—See Audax Group, Limited Partnership; *U.S. Private*, pg. 386
CHECK INTO CASH INC.; *U.S. Private*, pg. 869
CHECK INTO CASH OF INDIANA LLC—See Check Into Cash Inc.; *U.S. Private*, pg. 869
CHECK INTO CASH OF KENTUCKY LLC—See Check Into Cash Inc.; *U.S. Private*, pg. 869
CHECK INTO CASH OF WISCONSIN LLC—See Check Into Cash Inc.; *U.S. Private*, pg. 869
CHECKIT PLC; *Int'l*, pg. 1459

THE CHECKLEY AGENCY, INC.—See First Mid Bancshares, Inc.; *U.S. Public*, pg. 846
CHECKMARKET BV—See Thoma Bravo, L.P.; *U.S. Private*, pg. 4149
CHECK MART OF LOUISIANA, INC.—See Lone Star Global Acquisitions, LLC; *U.S. Private*, pg. 2487
CHECK MART OF NEW MEXICO, INC.—See Lone Star Global Acquisitions, LLC; *U.S. Private*, pg. 2487
CHECKMATE ADVISORS, LLC; *U.S. Private*, pg. 869
CHECKMATE PHARMACEUTICALS, INC.—See Regeneron Pharmaceuticals, Inc.; *U.S. Public*, pg. 1775
CHECK-N-GO FINANCIAL CORP.; *U.S. Private*, pg. 869
CHECKOUT CHARLIE GMBH—See Bertelsmann SE & Co. KGaA; *Int'l*, pg. 992
CHECKOUTSTORE INC.; *U.S. Private*, pg. 869
CHECKPOINT DISTRIBUTION B.V.—See B&S Group S.A.; *Int'l*, pg. 784
CHECKPOINT DO BRASIL LTDA.—See CCL Industries Inc.; *Int'l*, pg. 1368
CHECK POINT HOLDING AB—See Check Point Software Technologies Ltd.; *Int'l*, pg. 1458
CHECK POINT HOLDING (SINGAPORE) PTE LTD.—See Check Point Software Technologies Ltd.; *Int'l*, pg. 1458
CHECKPOINT MANUFACTURING JAPAN CO., LTD.—See CCL Industries Inc.; *Int'l*, pg. 1368
CHECKPOINT PORTUGAL LDA—See CCL Industries Inc.; *Int'l*, pg. 1367
CHECK POINTS B.V.—See Vimian Group AB; *Int'l*, pg. 8208
CHECK POINTS HEALTH B.V.—See Vimian Group AB; *Int'l*, pg. 8208
CHECK POINT SOFTWARE TECHNOLOGIES AUSTRALIA PTY LTD—See Check Point Software Technologies Ltd.; *Int'l*, pg. 1458
CHECK POINT SOFTWARE TECHNOLOGIES (AUSTRIA) GMBH—See Check Point Software Technologies Ltd.; *Int'l*, pg. 1458
CHECK POINT SOFTWARE TECHNOLOGIES (BELGIUM) S.A.—See Check Point Software Technologies Ltd.; *Int'l*, pg. 1458
CHECK POINT SOFTWARE TECHNOLOGIES (BRAZIL) LTDA—See Check Point Software Technologies Ltd.; *Int'l*, pg. 1458
CHECK POINT SOFTWARE TECHNOLOGIES B.V.—See Check Point Software Technologies Ltd.; *Int'l*, pg. 1458
CHECK POINT SOFTWARE TECHNOLOGIES (CZECH REPUBLIC) S.R.O.—See Check Point Software Technologies Ltd.; *Int'l*, pg. 1458
CHECK POINT SOFTWARE TECHNOLOGIES (DENMARK) APS—See Check Point Software Technologies Ltd.; *Int'l*, pg. 1458
CHECK POINT SOFTWARE TECHNOLOGIES (FINLAND) OY—See Check Point Software Technologies Ltd.; *Int'l*, pg. 1458
CHECK POINT SOFTWARE TECHNOLOGIES GMBH—See Check Point Software Technologies Ltd.; *Int'l*, pg. 1458
CHECK POINT SOFTWARE TECHNOLOGIES (GREECE) SA—See Check Point Software Technologies Ltd.; *Int'l*, pg. 1458
CHECK POINT SOFTWARE TECHNOLOGIES (HONG KONG) LTD.—See Check Point Software Technologies Ltd.; *Int'l*, pg. 1458
CHECK POINT SOFTWARE TECHNOLOGIES (HUNGARY) LTD.—See Check Point Software Technologies Ltd.; *Int'l*, pg. 1458
CHECK POINT SOFTWARE TECHNOLOGIES, INC.—See Check Point Software Technologies Ltd.; *Int'l*, pg. 1458
CHECK POINT SOFTWARE TECHNOLOGIES (INDIA) PRIVATE LIMITED—See Check Point Software Technologies Ltd.; *Int'l*, pg. 1458
CHECK POINT SOFTWARE TECHNOLOGIES (ITALIA) SRL—See Check Point Software Technologies Ltd.; *Int'l*, pg. 1458
CHECK POINT SOFTWARE TECHNOLOGIES (JAPAN) LTD.—See Check Point Software Technologies Ltd.; *Int'l*, pg. 1458
CHECK POINT SOFTWARE TECHNOLOGIES (KOREA) LTD.—See Check Point Software Technologies Ltd.; *Int'l*, pg. 1458
CHECK POINT SOFTWARE TECHNOLOGIES LTD.—See Check Point Software Technologies Ltd.; *Int'l*, pg. 1458
CHECK POINT SOFTWARE TECHNOLOGIES LTD.; *Int'l*, pg. 1458
CHECK POINT SOFTWARE TECHNOLOGIES MEXICO S.A. DE C.V.—See Check Point Software Technologies Ltd.; *Int'l*, pg. 1458
CHECK POINT SOFTWARE TECHNOLOGIES NORWAY A.S.—See Check Point Software Technologies Ltd.; *Int'l*, pg. 1459
CHECK POINT SOFTWARE TECHNOLOGIES (POLAND) SP. Z O. O.—See Check Point Software Technologies Ltd.; *Int'l*, pg. 1458
CHECK POINT SOFTWARE TECHNOLOGIES (RMN) SRL.—See Check Point Software Technologies Ltd.; *Int'l*, pg. 1458
CHECK POINT SOFTWARE TECHNOLOGIES (RUSSIA) OOO—See Check Point Software Technologies Ltd.; *Int'l*, pg. 1458

CHECK POINT SOFTWARE TECHNOLOGIES LTD.

CHECK POINT SOFTWARE TECHNOLOGIES (SINGAPORE) LTD.—See Check Point Software Technologies Ltd.; *Int'l*, pg. 1458
CHECK POINT SOFTWARE TECHNOLOGIES (SWITZERLAND) A.G.—See Check Point Software Technologies Ltd.; *Int'l*, pg. 1458
CHECK POINT SOFTWARE TECHNOLOGIES (UK) LTD.—See Check Point Software Technologies Ltd.; *Int'l*, pg. 1458
CHECKPOINT SOLUTIONS GMBH—See CCL Industries Inc.; *Int'l*, pg. 1367
CHECKPOINT SYSTEMS (AUST/NZ) PTY LTD.—See CCL Industries Inc.; *Int'l*, pg. 1367
CHECKPOINT SYSTEMS BENELUX B.V.—See CCL Industries Inc.; *Int'l*, pg. 1368
CHECKPOINT SYSTEMS CEE SP. Z.O.O.—See CCL Industries Inc.; *Int'l*, pg. 1368
CHECKPOINT SYSTEMS DANMARK A/S—See CCL Industries Inc.; *Int'l*, pg. 1368
CHECKPOINT SYSTEMS ESPANA S.L.U.—See CCL Industries Inc.; *Int'l*, pg. 1368
CHECKPOINT SYSTEMS FRANCE SASU—See CCL Industries Inc.; *Int'l*, pg. 1368
CHECKPOINT SYSTEMS GMBH—See CCL Industries Inc.; *Int'l*, pg. 1368
CHECKPOINT SYSTEMS HONG KONG LIMITED—See CCL Industries Inc.; *Int'l*, pg. 1368
CHECKPOINT SYSTEMS, INC.—See CCL Industries Inc.; *Int'l*, pg. 1367
CHECKPOINT SYSTEMS INDIA PRIVATE LIMITED—See CCL Industries Inc.; *Int'l*, pg. 1368
CHECKPOINT SYSTEMS ITALIA S.P.A.—See CCL Industries Inc.; *Int'l*, pg. 1368
CHECKPOINT SYSTEMS JAPAN CO. LTD.—See CCL Industries Inc.; *Int'l*, pg. 1368
CHECKPOINT SYSTEMS MEXICO—See CCL Industries Inc.; *Int'l*, pg. 1368
CHECKPOINT SYSTEMS (M) SDN. BHD.—See CCL Industries Inc.; *Int'l*, pg. 1368
CHECKPOINT SYSTEMS S.A.—See CCL Industries Inc.; *Int'l*, pg. 1368
CHECKPOINT SYSTEMS SVERIGE AB—See CCL Industries Inc.; *Int'l*, pg. 1368
CHECKPOINT SYSTEMS (UK) LTD.—See CCL Industries Inc.; *Int'l*, pg. 1368
CHECKPOINT TECHNOLOGIES INC.; *U.S. Private*, pg. 869
CHECKPOINT THERAPEUTICS, INC.—See Fortress Biotech, Inc.; *U.S. Public*, pg. 872
CHECKPOINT TRADING B.V.—See B&S Group S.A.; *Int'l*, pg. 784
CHECKPOINT TRENDS LIMITED; *Int'l*, pg. 1459
CHECK SAFETY FIRST LIMITED—See Intertek Group plc; *Int'l*, pg. 3762
CHECKS AND BALANCES INC—See Employment Enterprises Inc.; *U.S. Private*, pg. 1387
CHECKS IN THE MAIL, INC.—See MacAndrews & Forbes Incorporated; *U.S. Private*, pg. 2532
CHECKSMART FINANCIAL COMPANY—See Community Choice Financial Inc.; *U.S. Private*, pg. 991
CHECKSTER, INC.—See Rubicon Technology Partners, LLC; *U.S. Private*, pg. 3499
CHECKVIDEO, LLC—See Kastle Systems International LLC; *U.S. Private*, pg. 2264
CHECON, LLC—See Trent Capital Partners, LLC; *U.S. Private*, pg. 4218
CHEDDAR INC.—See Altice USA, Inc.; *U.S. Public*, pg. 88
CHEDDAR'S SCRATCH KITCHEN—See Darden Restaurants, Inc.; *U.S. Public*, pg. 633
CHEE CORP.; *Int'l*, pg. 1459
CHEEFAT METAL PRODUCTS & PLASTIC PLATING CO., LTD.—See China Aerospace International Holdings Limited; *Int'l*, pg. 1481
CHEEMINMET FINANCE LIMITED—See China Rare Earth Resources And Technology Co., Ltd.; *Int'l*, pg. 1545
CHEERGLORY TRADERS LIMITED—See China Rare Earth Resources And Technology Co., Ltd.; *Int'l*, pg. 1545
CHEER HOLDING, INC.; *Int'l*, pg. 1459
CHEER SECURITIES INC.—See Tokai Tokyo Financial Holdings, Inc.; *Int'l*, pg. 7781
CHEERS HOLDINGS (2004) PTE LTD—See NTUC Fairprice Co-operative Ltd.; *Int'l*, pg. 5485
CHEER TIME ENTERPRISES CO., LTD - KUEI-SHAN PLANT—See Cheer Time Enterprises Co., Ltd.; *Int'l*, pg. 1459
CHEER TIME ENTERPRISES CO., LTD.; *Int'l*, pg. 1459
CHEERWIN GROUP LIMITED; *Int'l*, pg. 1459
CHEERWOOD LIMITED—See IT Ltd; *Int'l*, pg. 3827
CHEESEBURGER IN PARADISE OF ANNE ARUNDEL COUNTY, INC.—See Luby's, Inc.; *U.S. Public*, pg. 1345
CHEESEBURGER OF SOUTHPORT, LLC—See Luby's, Inc.; *U.S. Public*, pg. 1345
THE CHEESECAKE FACTORY BAKERY INCORPORATED—See Cheesecake Factory Incorporated; *U.S. Public*, pg. 483
CHEESECAKE FACTORY INCORPORATED; *U.S. Public*, pg. 483

THE CHEESECAKE FACTORY RESTAURANTS, INC.—See Cheesecake Factory Incorporated; *U.S. Public*, pg. 483
CHEESECAKE FACTORY RESTAURANTS OF KANSAS LLC—See Cheesecake Factory Incorporated; *U.S. Public*, pg. 483
CHEESE MERCHANTS OF AMERICA; *U.S. Private*, pg. 869
THE CHEESE WAREHOUSE LTD—See Ornua Co-operative Limited; *Int'l*, pg. 5642
CHEESMAN LLC; *U.S. Private*, pg. 869
CHEETAH CANYON RESOURCES CORP.; *Int'l*, pg. 1459
CHEETAH DIGITAL, INC.—See Vector Capital Management, L.P.; *U.S. Private*, pg. 4350
CHEETAH DIGITAL—See Vector Capital Management, L.P.; *U.S. Private*, pg. 4350
CHEETAH HOLDING CORPORATION; *U.S. Private*, pg. 869
CHEETAH HOLDINGS BERHAD; *Int'l*, pg. 1459
CHEETAH MEDICAL, INC.—See Baxter International Inc.; *U.S. Public*, pg. 281
CHEETAH MEDICAL (ISRAEL), LTD.—See Baxter International Inc.; *U.S. Public*, pg. 281
CHEETAH MEDICAL (UK) LIMITED—See Baxter International Inc.; *U.S. Public*, pg. 281
CHEETAH MOBILE INC.—See Kingsoft Corporation Limited; *Int'l*, pg. 4176
CHEETAH NET SUPPLY CHAIN SERVICE INC.; *U.S. Public*, pg. 483
CHEETAH OIL & GAS LTD.; *Int'l*, pg. 1459
CHEETAH TELEVISION LTD—See LOV Group Invest SAS; *Int'l*, pg. 4564
CHEETHAM BELL/JWT—See WPP plc; *Int'l*, pg. 8478
CHEETHAM SALT LIMITED—See CK Hutchison Holdings Limited; *Int'l*, pg. 1637
CHEE WAH CORPORATION BERHAD; *Int'l*, pg. 1459
CHEEYUEN ELECTRONICS TECHNOLOGY (HUIZHOU) CO., LTD.—See China Aerospace International Holdings Limited; *Int'l*, pg. 1481
CHEE YUEN PLASTIC PRODUCTS (HUIZHOU) COMPANY LIMITED - BATTERY FACTORY—See China Aerospace International Holdings Limited; *Int'l*, pg. 1481
CHEE YUEN PLASTIC PRODUCTS (HUIZHOU) COMPANY LIMITED—See China Aerospace International Holdings Limited; *Int'l*, pg. 1481
CHEEYUEN SURFACE TREAMENT (HUIZHOU) CO., LTD.—See China Aerospace International Holdings Limited; *Int'l*, pg. 1481
CHEF IN A BOX LIMITED—See Around Noon Foods Limited; *Int'l*, pg. 577
CHEF JON MOLNAR—See Suarez Corporation Industries; *U.S. Private*, pg. 3846
CHEF MAESTRO GALICIA S.L.—See Dole plc; *Int'l*, pg. 2157
CHEF MAESTRO HORECA S.L.—See Dole plc; *Int'l*, pg. 2157
CHEFMASTER—See Byrnes & Kiefer Company; *U.S. Private*, pg. 701
CHEF MIDDLE EAST LLC—See The Chefs' Warehouse, Inc.; *U.S. Public*, pg. 2058
CHEFMOD LLC—See Ark Restaurants Corp.; *U.S. Public*, pg. 193
CHEF'S CATALOGUE, INC.—See JH Partners LLC; *U.S. Private*, pg. 2207
CHEF'S CHOICE PRODUCE CO.—See Sole Source Capital LLC; *U.S. Private*, pg. 3708
CHEF'S HALL, INC.—See Compass Group PLC; *Int'l*, pg. 1750
CHEF'S INTERNATIONAL, INC.; *U.S. Private*, pg. 869
CHEFS PARTNER PTY LTD.—See Australian Agricultural Company Limited; *Int'l*, pg. 720
THE CHEFS' WAREHOUSE, INC.; *U.S. Public*, pg. 2058
THE CHEFS' WAREHOUSE WEST COAST LLC—See The Chefs' Warehouse, Inc.; *U.S. Public*, pg. 2059
CHEGG INC.; *U.S. Public*, pg. 483
CHEGG INDIA PRIVATE LIMITED—See Chegg Inc.; *U.S. Public*, pg. 483
CHEIL AMERICAS—See Samsung Group; *Int'l*, pg. 6511
CHEIL BIO CO., LTD.; *Int'l*, pg. 1459
CHEIL ELECTRIC CO., LTD.; *Int'l*, pg. 1460
CHEIL GRINDING WHEEL IND. CO., LTD.; *Int'l*, pg. 1460
CHEIL INDUSTRY CO. LTD—See ASSA ABLOY AB; *Int'l*, pg. 639
CHEIL TECHNOLOGY CORP.; *Int'l*, pg. 1460
CHEIL USA INC.—See Samsung Group; *Int'l*, pg. 6511
CHEIL WORLDWIDE INC.—See Samsung Group; *Int'l*, pg. 6511
CHE INTERNATIONAL GROUP, LLC; *U.S. Private*, pg. 868
CHELCO GROUP OF COMPANIES INC.; *U.S. Private*, pg. 869
CHELCO REALTY CORP.—See Chelco Group of Companies Inc.; *U.S. Private*, pg. 869
CHELCO SERVICES, INC.—See Choctawhatchee Electric Cooperative Inc.; *U.S. Private*, pg. 888
CHELDA, INC.; *U.S. Private*, pg. 870
CHELEO S.R.L.—See TXT e-Solutions S.p.A.; *Int'l*, pg. 7993

CORPORATE AFFILIATIONS

CHELLARAMS PLC; *Int'l*, pg. 1460
CHELMSFORD LUMBER COMPANY—See Arlington Coal & Lumber Co. Inc.; *U.S. Private*, pg. 329
CHELNYVODOKANAL LLC—See KAMAZ Publicly Traded Company; *Int'l*, pg. 4060
CHELSEA BRIDGE WHARF CAR PARK LIMITED—See The Berkeley Group Holdings plc; *Int'l*, pg. 7620
CHELSEA BUILDING PRODUCTS INC.—See aluplast GmbH; *Int'l*, pg. 401
CHELSEA BUILDING SOCIETY—See Yorkshire Building Society; *Int'l*, pg. 8599
CHELSEA CLOCK CO., INC.; *U.S. Private*, pg. 870
CHELSEA FC PLC—See Clearlake Capital Group, L.P.; *U.S. Public*, pg. 933
CHELSEA FOOTBALL CLUB LIMITED—See Clearlake Capital Group, L.P.; *U.S. Private*, pg. 933
CHELSEA GREEN PUBLISHING COMPANY; *U.S. Private*, pg. 870
CHELSEA GRINDING CO.—See NN, Inc.; *U.S. Public*, pg. 1531
CHELSEA GROTON SAVINGS BANK INC.; *U.S. Private*, pg. 870
CHELSEA GROUP—See Simon Property Group, Inc.; *U.S. Public*, pg. 1881
CHELSEA HEIGHTS HOTEL (BMG) PTY LTD—See Woolworths Group Limited; *Int'l*, pg. 8451
CHELSEA HEIGHTS OPERATIONS PTY LIMITED—See Metcash Limited; *Int'l*, pg. 4852
CHELSEA INTERNATIONAL CO., LTD.—See GEO Holdings Corporation; *Int'l*, pg. 2932
CHELSEA INVESTMENTS CORPORATION; *U.S. Private*, pg. 870
CHELSEA JAPAN CO., LTD.—See Mitsubishi Estate Co., Ltd.; *Int'l*, pg. 4946
CHELSEA JAPAN CO., LTD.—See Simon Property Group, Inc.; *U.S. Public*, pg. 1881
CHELSEA LIGHTING NYC, LLC—See Kinzie Capital Partners LP; *U.S. Private*, pg. 2313
CHELSEA LOGISTICS AND INFRASTRUCTURE HOLDINGS CORP.; *Int'l*, pg. 1460
CHELSEA LUMBER COMPANY; *U.S. Private*, pg. 870
CHELSEA MILLING COMPANY; *U.S. Private*, pg. 870
CHELSEA MORTGAGE SERVICES LIMITED—See Yorkshire Building Society; *Int'l*, pg. 8599
CHELSEA OIL AND GAS LTD.; *Int'l*, pg. 1460
CHELSEA OUTPATIENT CENTRE LLP—See HCA Healthcare, Inc.; *U.S. Public*, pg. 993
CHELSEA PIERS LP; *U.S. Private*, pg. 870
CHELSEA PLACE CARE CENTER, LLC.; *U.S. Private*, pg. 870
CHELSEAROBOT AUTOMATIC (NANTONG) CO., LTD.—See Nantong Guosheng Intelligence Technology Group Co., Ltd.; *Int'l*, pg. 5145
CHELSEA SANDWICH LLC—See Global Partners LP; *U.S. Public*, pg. 942
CHELSEA SAVINGS BANK—See Chebelle Corporation; *U.S. Private*, pg. 868
CHELSEA & SCOTT, LTD.; *U.S. Private*, pg. 870
CHELSEA SENIOR LIVING LLC; *U.S. Private*, pg. 870
CHELSEA SHIPPING CORPORATION—See Chelsea Logistics and Infrastructure Holdings Corp.; *Int'l*, pg. 1460
CHELSEA STATE BANK; *U.S. Private*, pg. 870
CHELSEA TEDDY BEAR COMPANY—See EBSCO Industries, Inc.; *U.S. Private*, pg. 1324
CHELSEY DIRECT, LLC; *U.S. Private*, pg. 870
CHELSFIELD FRANCE LTD—See Chelsfield Partners LLP; *Int'l*, pg. 1460
CHELSFIELD PARTNERS LLP; *Int'l*, pg. 1460
THE CHELTENHAM & GLOUCESTER NUFFIELD HOSPITAL—See Nuffield Health; *Int'l*, pg. 5487
CHELTENHAM & GLOUCESTER PLC—See Lloyds Banking Group plc; *Int'l*, pg. 4536
CHELTON ANTENNAS SA—See Advent International Corporation; *U.S. Public*, pg. 99
CHELTON AVIONICS, INC—See TransDigm Group Incorporated; *U.S. Public*, pg. 2180
CHELTON INC.—See Advent International Corporation; *U.S. Private*, pg. 99
CHELTON LIMITED—See TransDigm Group Incorporated; *U.S. Public*, pg. 2180
CHELVERTON GROWTH TRUST PLC; *Int'l*, pg. 1460
CHELVERTON UK DIVIDEND TRUST PLC; *Int'l*, pg. 1460
CHELYABINSK FORGE & PRESS PLANT PJSC; *Int'l*, pg. 1460
CHELYABINSKIY METALLURGICHESKIY KOMBINAT OAO—See Mechel PAO; *Int'l*, pg. 4765
CHELYABINSK PIPE PLANT PJSC—See PAO TMK; *Int'l*, pg. 5732
CHELYABINSK PLANT OF THE PROFILED STEEL DECKING PJSC; *Int'l*, pg. 1460
CHELYABINSK ZINC PLANT JSC; *Int'l*, pg. 1460
CHELYABINVESTBANK PJSC; *Int'l*, pg. 1460
CHEM32 LLC—See Ecovyst Inc.; *U.S. Public*, pg. 717
CHEMADVISOR, INC.—See Underwriters Laboratories Inc.; *U.S. Private*, pg. 4280
CHEMALLOY COMPANY INC.; *U.S. Private*, pg. 871
CHEMANEX PLC; *Int'l*, pg. 1460
CHEM-AQUA, INC.—See NCH Corporation; *U.S. Private*, pg. 2876

COMPANY NAME INDEX

CHEMARCO, INC.—See JNS-SmithChem, LLC; *U.S. Private*, pg. 2217
CHEM ARROW CORP.—See Motul S.A.; *Int'l*, pg. 5056
CHEMART COMPANY; *U.S. Private*, pg. 871
CHEMAX INTERNATIONAL CORPORATION—See China Petrochemical Development Corp.; *Int'l*, pg. 1540
CHEMBIO DIAGNOSTICS GMBH—See Biosynex SA; *Int'l*, pg. 1042
CHEMBIO DIAGNOSTICS, INC.—See Biosynex SA; *Int'l*, pg. 1042
CHEMBIO DIAGNOSTIC SYSTEMS, INC.—See Biosynex SA; *Int'l*, pg. 1042
CHEMBOND CHEMICALS LTD - BADDI PLANT—See Chembond Chemicals Ltd; *Int'l*, pg. 1461
CHEMBOND CHEMICALS LTD - BALASORE PLANT—See Chembond Chemicals Ltd; *Int'l*, pg. 1461
CHEMBOND CHEMICALS LTD - CHENNAI PLANT—See Chembond Chemicals Ltd; *Int'l*, pg. 1461
CHEMBOND CHEMICALS LTD - CONSTRUCTION CHEMICAL DIVISION—See Chembond Chemicals Ltd; *Int'l*, pg. 1461
CHEMBOND CHEMICALS LTD - DUDHWADA PLANT—See Chembond Chemicals Ltd; *Int'l*, pg. 1461
CHEMBOND CHEMICALS LTD - MANUFACTURING PLANT—See Chembond Chemicals Ltd; *Int'l*, pg. 1461
CHEMBOND CHEMICALS LTD - MANUFACTURING PLANT—See Chembond Chemicals Ltd; *Int'l*, pg. 1461
CHEMBOND CHEMICALS LTD; *Int'l*, pg. 1460
CHEMBOND CHEMICALS LTD - TARAPUR PLANT—See Chembond Chemicals Ltd; *Int'l*, pg. 1461
CHEMBRIDGE CORPORATION; *U.S. Private*, pg. 871
CHEM CAN SERVICES, INC.; *U.S. Private*, pg. 870
CHEMCEL BIO-TECH LIMITED; *Int'l*, pg. 1461
CHEMCHINA GUILIN TIRE CO, LTD—See China National Chemical Corporation; *Int'l*, pg. 1526
CHEMCHINA LOGISTICS CO LTD—See China National Chemical Corporation; *Int'l*, pg. 1526
CHEMCHINA PETROCHEMICAL CO., LTD—See China National Chemical Corporation; *Int'l*, pg. 1526
CHEMCHINA (SINGAPORE) PTE. LTD—See China National Chemical Corporation; *Int'l*, pg. 1526
CHEMCLIN DIAGNOSTICS CO., LTD.; *Int'l*, pg. 1461
CHEMCO ELECTRICAL CONTRACTORS LTD.; *Int'l*, pg. 1461
CHEMCOLOR-BETA D.D.—See DP plc; *Int'l*, pg. 1101
CHEMCO MANUFACTURING COMPANY INC.; *U.S. Private*, pg. 871
CHEMCOM SA—See Floridienne SA; *Int'l*, pg. 2708
CHEMCON SPECIALITY CHEMICALS LIMITED; *Int'l*, pg. 1461
CHEMCONTROL LIMITED—See BASF SE; *Int'l*, pg. 882
CHEMCO PRODUCTS COMPANY; *U.S. Private*, pg. 871
CHEMCOTE, INC.; *U.S. Private*, pg. 871
CHEMCRUX ENTERPRISES LIMITED; *Int'l*, pg. 1461
CHEMDESIGN PRODUCTS, INC.—See Lubar & Co., Inc.; *U.S. Private*, pg. 2510
CHEM-DRY FRANCHISING LIMITED; *Int'l*, pg. 1460
CHEM-DRY UK LIMITED—See Chem-Dry Franchising Limited; *Int'l*, pg. 1460
CHEM-EAST—See Insud Pharma, S.L.; *Int'l*, pg. 3724
CHEMED CORPORATION; *U.S. Public*, pg. 484
CHEMELOT REAL ESTATE B.V.—See Koninklijke DSM N.V.; *Int'l*, pg. 4264
CHEMEMAN AUSTRALIA PTY LTD.—See Chememan Public Company Limited; *Int'l*, pg. 1461
CHEMEMAN PUBLIC COMPANY LIMITED; *Int'l*, pg. 1461
CHEM ENERGY SA (PTY) LTD.—See Chung-Hsin Electric & Machinery Manufacturing Corp.; *Int'l*, pg. 1597
CHEMETALL AB—See BASF SE; *Int'l*, pg. 873
CHEMETALL ASIA PTE. LTD.—See BASF SE; *Int'l*, pg. 873
CHEMETALL (AUSTRALASIA) PTY. LTD.—See BASF SE; *Int'l*, pg. 873
CHEMETALL B.V.—See BASF SE; *Int'l*, pg. 873
CHEMETALL CANADA LIMITED—See BASF SE; *Int'l*, pg. 873
CHEMETALL DANMARK A/S—See BASF SE; *Int'l*, pg. 882
CHEMETALL FINLAND OY—See BASF SE; *Int'l*, pg. 873
CHEMETALL GMBH—See BASF SE; *Int'l*, pg. 873
CHEMETALL HONG KONG LTD.—See BASF SE; *Int'l*, pg. 873
CHEMETALL ITALIA S.R.L.—See BASF SE; *Int'l*, pg. 873
CHEMETALL KFT.—See BASF SE; *Int'l*, pg. 882
CHEMETALL LIMITED—See BASF SE; *Int'l*, pg. 873
CHEMETALL MEXICANA, S.A. DE C.V.—See BASF SE; *Int'l*, pg. 873
CHEMETALL (NEW ZEALAND) LTD.—See BASF SE; *Int'l*, pg. 873
CHEMETALL POLSKA SP.Z O.O.—See BASF SE; *Int'l*, pg. 873
CHEMETALL (PTY) LTD.—See BASF SE; *Int'l*, pg. 873
CHEMETALL SANAYI KIMYASALLARI TICARET VE SANAYI A.S.—See BASF SE; *Int'l*, pg. 873
CHEMETALL S.A.—See BASF SE; *Int'l*, pg. 873
CHEMETALL S.A.S.—See BASF SE; *Int'l*, pg. 873
CHEMETALL S.R.L.—See BASF SE; *Int'l*, pg. 873
CHEMETALL (THAILAND) CO. LTD.—See BASF SE; *Int'l*, pg. 873
CHEMETALL US, INC.—See BASF SE; *Int'l*, pg. 873
CHEMETICS, INC.—See Jacobs Engineering Group, Inc.; *U.S. Public*, pg. 1185
CHEMEX CORPORATION; *U.S. Private*, pg. 871
CHEMEX FOUNDRY SOLUTIONS GMBH—See Huettenes-Albertus Chemische Werke GmbH; *Int'l*, pg. 3522
CHEMFAB ALKALIS LIMITED; *Int'l*, pg. 1461
CHEMFAB INDUSTRIES INC.; *Int'l*, pg. 1461
CHEMFAB JAPAN, LTD.—See Compagnie de Saint-Gobain SA; *Int'l*, pg. 1732
CHEMFIT (PTY) LIMITED—See AECI Limited; *Int'l*, pg. 171
CHEMFLOW PRODUCTS, LLC—See Relevant Industrial LLC; *U.S. Private*, pg. 3393
CHEMFREE CORPORATION—See Berwind Corporation; *U.S. Private*, pg. 541
CHEMGEN CORP.—See Elanco Animal Health Incorporated; *U.S. Public*, pg. 722
CHEM GRO OF HOUGHTON INC.; *U.S. Private*, pg. 870
CHEM-GROW PTE. LTD.—See Heatec JieTong Holdings Ltd; *Int'l*, pg. 3305
CHEMGUARD, INC.—See Johnson Controls International plc; *Int'l*, pg. 3986
CHEMIA.COM S.A.—See Kulczyk Investments S.A.; *Int'l*, pg. 4327
CHEMICAINVEST HOLDING B.V.—See CVC Capital Partners SICAV-FIS S.A.; *Int'l*, pg. 1886
CHEMICAL COATINGS, INC.—See RPM International Inc.; *U.S. Public*, pg. 1819
CHEMICAL COMPANY OF MALAYSIA BERHAD—See Batu Kawan Berhad; *Int'l*, pg. 890
THE CHEMICAL COMPANY; *U.S. Private*, pg. 4007
CHEMICAL CONTROL SRL—See Eurofins Scientific S.E.; *Int'l*, pg. 2535
CHEMICAL DATA, LLC—See RELX plc; *Int'l*, pg. 6266
CHEMICAL ENGINEERING JOINT STOCK CORPORATION—See Masan Consumer Corp.; *Int'l*, pg. 4719
CHEMICAL EQUIPMENT SUB-CO.—See Taiyuan Heavy Industry Co., Ltd.; *Int'l*, pg. 7427
CHEMICAL EXCHANGE INDUSTRIES, INC.; *U.S. Private*, pg. 871
CHEMICAL GROUTING CO., LTD.—See Kajima Corporation; *Int'l*, pg. 4053
CHEMICAL INDUSTRIES (FAR EAST) LTD; *Int'l*, pg. 1461
CHEMICAL INDUSTRIES HOLDING COMPANY; *Int'l*, pg. 1461
CHEMICAL INDUSTRIES (MALAYA) SDN. BHD.—See Hexza Corporation Berhad; *Int'l*, pg. 3373
CHEMICAL INITIATIVES (PTY) LIMITED—See AECI Limited; *Int'l*, pg. 171
CHEMICAL INTERCHANGE CO.; *U.S. Private*, pg. 871
CHEMICAL LIME COMPANY—See Lhoist S.A.; *Int'l*, pg. 4478
CHEMICAL LIME CO.—See Lhoist S.A.; *Int'l*, pg. 4478
CHEMICAL LIME, LTD—See Lhoist S.A.; *Int'l*, pg. 4478
CHEMICAL LOGITEC CO., LTD.—See ITOCHU Corporation; *Int'l*, pg. 3835
CHEMICAL MANUFACTURE AND REFINING LIMITED—See Heidelberg Materials AG; *Int'l*, pg. 3309
CHEMICAL MARKETING CONCEPTS LLC—See Odyssey Logistics & Technology LLC; *U.S. Private*, pg. 2996
CHEMICAL PACKAGING CORPORATION; *U.S. Private*, pg. 871
CHEMICAL PACKAGING CORP.; *U.S. Private*, pg. 871
CHEMICAL SERVICE, CO., LTD.—See Nissan Chemical Corporation; *Int'l*, pg. 5366
THE CHEMICAL SOCIETY ALKIMIA; *Int'l*, pg. 7631
CHEMICAL SOLVENTS INC.; *U.S. Private*, pg. 871
CHEMICAL SPECIALISTS & DEVELOPMENT, INC.—See One Rock Capital Partners, LLC; *U.S. Private*, pg. 3022
CHEMICAL SPECIALTIES, LLC—See Huntsman Corporation; *U.S. Public*, pg. 1073
CHEMICAL SPECIALTIES MANUFACTURING CORP.—See RPM International Inc.; *U.S. Public*, pg. 1819
CHEMICAL TRANSFER COMPANY; *U.S. Private*, pg. 871
CHEMICAL TRANSPORTATION, INC.—See One Rock Capital Partners, LLC; *U.S. Private*, pg. 3022
CHEMICAL WASTE MANAGEMENT, INC.—See Waste Management, Inc.; *U.S. Public*, pg. 2330
CHEMICAL WEEK ASSOCIATES—See Veronis Suhler Stevenson Partners LLC; *U.S. Private*, pg. 4368
CHEMICAL WORKS OF GEDEON RICHTER PLC; *Int'l*, pg. 1462
CHEMICA S.A.S—See Evolem S.A.; *Int'l*, pg. 2572
CHEMIC LABORATORIES, INC.—See Solvias AG; *Int'l*, pg. 7082
CHEMI-CON AMERICAS HOLDING, INC.—See Nippon Chemi-Con Corporation; *Int'l*, pg. 5312
CHEMI-CON ELECTRONICS (KOREA) CO., LTD.—See Nippon Chemi-Con Corporation; *Int'l*, pg. 5312
CHEMI-CON ELECTRONICS (THAILAND) CO., LTD.—See Nippon Chemi-Con Corporation; *Int'l*, pg. 5312
CHEMI-CON FUKUSHIMA CORP.—See Nippon Chemi-Con Corporation; *Int'l*, pg. 5312
CHEMI-CON IWATE CORP.—See Nippon Chemi-Con Corporation; *Int'l*, pg. 5312
CHEMI-CON MACHINERY CORP.—See Nippon Chemi-Con Corporation; *Int'l*, pg. 5312
CHEMI-CON (MALAYSIA) SDN. BHD.—See Nippon Chemi-Con Corporation; *Int'l*, pg. 5312
CHEMI-CON MATERIAL LOGISTICS LTD.—See Nippon Chemi-Con Corporation; *Int'l*, pg. 5312
CHEMI-CON MATERIALS CORP.—See Nippon Chemi-Con Corporation; *Int'l*, pg. 5312
CHEMI-CON MIYAGI CORP.—See Nippon Chemi-Con Corporation; *Int'l*, pg. 5312
CHEMI-CON NAGAOKA CORP.—See Nippon Chemi-Con Corporation; *Int'l*, pg. 5312
CHEMI-CON TECHNICAL CENTER (WUXI) LTD.—See Nippon Chemi-Con Corporation; *Int'l*, pg. 5312
CHEMI-CON TRADING (SHENZHEN) CO., LTD.—See Nippon Chemi-Con Corporation; *Int'l*, pg. 5312
CHEMI-CON (WUXI) CO., LTD.—See Nippon Chemi-Con Corporation; *Int'l*, pg. 5312
CHEMI-CON YAMAGATA CORP.—See Nippon Chemi-Con Corporation; *Int'l*, pg. 5312
CHEMI-CON YONEZAWA CORP.—See Nippon Chemi-Con Corporation; *Int'l*, pg. 5312
CHEMI DAROU INDUSTRIAL COMPANY; *Int'l*, pg. 1461
CHEMIDRO S.P.A.—See Bharti Enterprises Limited; *Int'l*, pg. 1012
CHEMI DYESTUFF INDUSTRIES (PVT) LTD.—See Ittehad Chemicals Limited; *Int'l*, pg. 3844
CHEMIEPARK BITTERFELD-WOLFEN GMBH—See IBU-Tec Advanced Materials AG; *Int'l*, pg. 3577
CHEMIE PENSIONSFONDS AG—See DZ BANK AG Deutsche Zentral-Genossenschaftsbank; *Int'l*, pg. 2243
CHEMIESYNTH (VAPI) LTD.; *Int'l*, pg. 1462
CHEMIE TECHNIK GMBH; *Int'l*, pg. 1462
CHEMIE UETIKON AG—See CPH Chemie + Papier Holding AG; *Int'l*, pg. 1824
CHEMIFORWARD DYRES TRADING CO.—See Sinochem Corporation; *Int'l*, pg. 6949
CHEMILYL S.A.S.—See Tessenderlo Group NV; *Int'l*, pg. 7573
CHEMIMAGE CORP.; *U.S. Private*, pg. 871
CHEM-IMPEX INTERNATIONAL, INC.; *U.S. Private*, pg. 870
CHEMINEER, INC.—See NOV, Inc.; *U.S. Public*, pg. 1544
CHEMINEES SECURITE INTERNATIONAL LTEE—See Lennox International Inc.; *U.S. Public*, pg. 1307
CHEMINOVA AGRO DE ARGENTINA S.A.—See FMC Corporation; *U.S. Public*, pg. 861
CHEMINOVA AGRO DE COLOMBIA SA—See FMC Corporation; *U.S. Public*, pg. 861
CHEMINOVA AGRO FRANCE S.A.S.—See FMC Corporation; *U.S. Public*, pg. 861
CHEMINOVA AGRO ITALIA S.R.L.—See FMC Corporation; *U.S. Public*, pg. 861
CHEMINOVA AGROQUIMICA S.A. DE C.V.—See FMC Corporation; *U.S. Public*, pg. 861
CHEMINOVA AGRO, S.A.—See FMC Corporation; *U.S. Public*, pg. 861
CHEMINOVA A/S—See FMC Corporation; *U.S. Public*, pg. 861
CHEMINOVA AUSTRIA GMBH—See FMC Corporation; *U.S. Public*, pg. 861
CHEMINOVA BULGARIA EOOD—See FMC Corporation; *U.S. Public*, pg. 861
CHEMINOVA DEUTSCHLAND GMBH & CO. KG—See FMC Corporation; *U.S. Public*, pg. 861
CHEMINOVA INDIA LIMITED—See FMC Corporation; *U.S. Public*, pg. 861
CHEMINOVA POLSKA SP. Z O.O.—See FMC Corporation; *U.S. Public*, pg. 861
CHEMINOVA TAIWAN LTD—See FMC Corporation; *U.S. Public*, pg. 861
CHEM-INTER CORPORATION—See Sanyo Trading Co., Ltd.; *Int'l*, pg. 6565
CHEMINVEST AS; *Int'l*, pg. 1462
CHEMIONICS CORPORATION—See Chessco Industries, Inc.; *U.S. Private*, pg. 875
CHEMIPHOS SA (PTY) LIMITED—See AECI Limited; *Int'l*, pg. 171
CHEMI-PLAN S.A.—See PCC SE; *Int'l*, pg. 5766
CHEMIPLASTICA AB—See Chemiplastica S.p.A.; *Int'l*, pg. 1462
CHEMIPLASTICA INC.—See Chemiplastica S.p.A.; *Int'l*, pg. 1462
CHEMIPLASTICA PLS.MEL.TIC.VE SAN. A.S.—See Chemiplastica S.p.A.; *Int'l*, pg. 1462
CHEMIPLASTICA SA DE CV—See Chemiplastica S.p.A.; *Int'l*, pg. 1462
CHEMIPLASTICA S.A.—See Chemiplastica S.p.A.; *Int'l*, pg. 1462
CHEMIPLASTICA S.P.A.; *Int'l*, pg. 1462
CHEMIPLAST INTERNATIONAL—See REHAU Verwaltungszentrale AG; *Int'l*, pg. 6255
CHEMIPRO KASEI KAISHA LTD. - AIOI PLANT—See Chemipro Kasei Kaisha Ltd.; *Int'l*, pg. 1462
CHEMIPRO KASEI KAISHA LTD. - AKASHI PLANT—See Chemipro Kasei Kaisha Ltd.; *Int'l*, pg. 1462

CHEMIPLASTICA S.P.A.

CHEMIPRO KASEI KAISHA LTD. - FUKUSHIMA PLANT—See Chemipro Kasei Kaisha Ltd.; *Int'l*, pg. 1462
CHEMIPRO KASEI KAISHA LTD. - HIMEJI PLANT—See Chemipro Kasei Kaisha Ltd.; *Int'l*, pg. 1462
CHEMIPRO KASEI KAISHA LTD. - OSAKA PLANT—See Chemipro Kasei Kaisha Ltd.; *Int'l*, pg. 1462
CHEMIPRO KASEI KAISHA LTD.; *Int'l*, pg. 1462
CHEMISCHE FABRIK BERG GMBH—See PMC Capital Partners, LLC; *U.S. Private*, pg. 3217
CHEMISCHE FABRIK BUDENHEIM KG—See Dr. August Oetker KG; *Int'l*, pg. 2190
CHEMISCHE FABRIK KALK GMBH—See K+S Aktiengesellschaft; *Int'l*, pg. 4039
CHEMISCHE FABRIK KALK GMBH—See K+S Aktiengesellschaft; *Int'l*, pg. 4039
CHEMISCHE FABRIK KALK GMBH—See K+S Aktiengesellschaft; *Int'l*, pg. 4039
CHEMISCHE FABRIK KALK GMBH—See K+S Aktiengesellschaft; *Int'l*, pg. 4039
CHEMISCH THERMISCHE PROZESSTECHNIK GMBH—See Sintokogio Ltd.; *Int'l*, pg. 6958
CHEMISOL ITALIA S.R.L.; *Int'l*, pg. 1462
CHEMISPHERE CORPORATION; *U.S. Private*, pg. 871
CHEMISTREE TECHNOLOGY, INC.; *Int'l*, pg. 1462
CHEMISTRY COMMUNICATIONS GROUP, PLC—See Publicis Groupe S.A.; *Int'l*, pg. 6097
CHEMISTRY COMMUNICATIONS, INC.; *U.S. Private*, pg. 871
CHEMISTRY.COM—See IAC Inc.; *U.S. Public*, pg. 1082
THE CHEMISTRY RESEARCH SOLUTION LLC—See Welsh, Carson, Anderson & Stowe; *U.S. Private*, pg. 4479
CHEMITALIC DENMARK A/S; *Int'l*, pg. 1462
CHEMITALIC SUZHOU LTD.—See Chemitalic Denmark A/S; *Int'l*, pg. 1462
CHEMITECHNIK PHARMA KFT—See Gedeon Richter Plc.; *Int'l*, pg. 2909
CHEMITHON CONSTRUCTORS LLC—See Chemithon Enterprises, Inc.; *U.S. Private*, pg. 872
THE CHEMITHON CORP.—See Chemithon Enterprises, Inc.; *U.S. Private*, pg. 872
CHEMITHON ENGINEERS PVT. LTD.—See Chemithon Enterprises, Inc.; *U.S. Private*, pg. 872
CHEMITHON ENTERPRISES, INC.; *U.S. Private*, pg. 872
CHEMITHON SURFACE FINISHING INC.—See Chemithon Enterprises, Inc.; *U.S. Private*, pg. 872
CHEMITHON SURFACE FINISHING, INC.—See Chemithon Enterprises, Inc.; *U.S. Private*, pg. 872
CHEMIX INC.—See YungShin Global Holding Corporation; *Int'l*, pg. 8614
CHEMKO TECHNICAL SERVICES, INC.—See Astro Pak Corporation; *U.S. Private*, pg. 362
CHEMLAND INDUSTRIES, INC.—See Lakeland Industries, Inc.; *U.S. Public*, pg. 1288
CHEMLEASE JAPAN K.K.—See Freudenberg SE; *Int'l*, pg. 2782
CHEMLOGICS GROUP, LLC—See Solvay S.A.; *Int'l*, pg. 7079
CHEMLUBE INTERNATIONAL, INC.—See Glencore plc; *Int'l*, pg. 2990
CHEM-MAT TECHNOLOGIES CO., LTD.—See Evermore Chemical Industry Co., Ltd.; *Int'l*, pg. 2568
CHEM-NUCLEAR SYSTEMS, LLC—See The Toronto-Dominion Bank; *Int'l*, pg. 7696
CHEM NUT, INC.; *U.S. Private*, pg. 870
CHEMO ARGENTINA—See Insud Pharma, S.L.; *Int'l*, pg. 3724
CHEMO ASIA—See Insud Pharma, S.L.; *Int'l*, pg. 3724
CHEMO AUSTRIA—See Insud Pharma, S.L.; *Int'l*, pg. 3724
CHEMOCATO LLC—See Becton, Dickinson & Company; *U.S. Public*, pg. 292
CHEMOCENTRYX, INC.—See Amgen Inc.; *U.S. Public*, pg. 123
CHEMO DO BRAZIL—See Insud Pharma, S.L.; *Int'l*, pg. 3725
CHEMO ELECTRIC A/S—See Addtech AB; *Int'l*, pg. 132
CHEMOFAST ANCHORING GMBH—See Henkel AG & Co. KGaA; *Int'l*, pg. 3348
CHEMOFORM AG; *Int'l*, pg. 1462
CHEMOFORM AUSTRIA GMBH—See Chemoform AG; *Int'l*, pg. 1463
CHEMOFORM CZ S.R.O.—See Chemoform AG; *Int'l*, pg. 1463
CHEMOFORM POLSKA SP. Z O.O.—See Chemoform AG; *Int'l*, pg. 1463
CHEMOFORM ROMANIA S.R.L.—See Chemoform AG; *Int'l*, pg. 1463
CHEMO FRANCE—See Insud Pharma, S.L.; *Int'l*, pg. 3725
CHEMOGAS N.V.—See Balchem Corporation; *U.S. Public*, pg. 265
CHEMO IBERICA SA - ALCALA DE HENARES FACILITY—See Insud Pharma, S.L.; *Int'l*, pg. 3725
CHEMO IBERICA SA - AZUQUECA DE HENARES FACILITY—See Insud Pharma, S.L.; *Int'l*, pg. 3725
CHEMO IBERICA SA - BUENOS AIRES FACILITY—See Insud Pharma, S.L.; *Int'l*, pg. 3725

CHEMO IBERICA SA - HYDERABAD FACILITY—See Insud Pharma, S.L.; *Int'l*, pg. 3725
CHEMO IBERICA SA - SARONNO FACILITY—See Insud Pharma, S.L.; *Int'l*, pg. 3725
CHEMO IBERICA SA - SHANGHAI FACILITY—See Insud Pharma, S.L.; *Int'l*, pg. 3725
CHEMOIL CORPORATION—See ITOCHU Corporation; *Int'l*, pg. 3838
CHEMOIL ENERGY LIMITED—See Glencore plc; *Int'l*, pg. 2990
CHEMOIL ENERGY PTE LIMITED—See Glencore plc; *Int'l*, pg. 2990
CHEMOIL LOGISTICS AG—See Schweizerische Bundesbahnen SBB AG; *Int'l*, pg. 6646
CHEMOIL TERMINALS CORPORATION—See ITOCHU Corporation; *Int'l*, pg. 3838
CHEMO INDIA—See EQT AB; *Int'l*, pg. 2469
CHEMOLAK; *Int'l*, pg. 1463
CHEMOL COMPANY, INC.—See The Seydel Companies; *U.S. Private*, pg. 4117
CHEMO LUGANO—See Insud Pharma, S.L.; *Int'l*, pg. 3725
CHEMOLUTIONS CHEMICALS LTD.—See Camlin Fine Sciences Ltd.; *Int'l*, pg. 1273
CHEMOLUX S.A.R.L.—See McBride plc; *Int'l*, pg. 4755
CHEMOMAB THERAPEUTICS INC.—See Chemomab Therapeutics Ltd.; *Int'l*, pg. 1463
CHEMOMAB THERAPEUTICS LTD.; *Int'l*, pg. 1463
CHEMOMETEC A/S; *Int'l*, pg. 1463
CHEMO NEW JERSEY—See Insud Pharma, S.L.; *Int'l*, pg. 3725
CHEMONICS INTERNATIONAL, INC.; *U.S. Private*, pg. 872
CHEMON INC.—See Corestem Inc.; *Int'l*, pg. 1800
CHEMO PHARMA LABORATORIES LTD; *Int'l*, pg. 1462
CHEMOPROJEKT, A.S.; *Int'l*, pg. 1463
CHEMOPROJEKT, A. S.—See Safichem Group AG; *Int'l*, pg. 6471
CHEMOS A.D.; *Int'l*, pg. 1463
THE CHEMOURS CANADA COMPANY—See The Chemours Company; *U.S. Public*, pg. 2059
THE CHEMOURS CHEMICAL (SHANGHAI) COMPANY LIMITED—See The Chemours Company; *U.S. Public*, pg. 2059
THE CHEMOURS CHINA HOLDING CO., LTD.—See The Chemours Company; *U.S. Public*, pg. 2059
THE CHEMOURS COMPANY FC, LLC—See The Chemours Company; *U.S. Public*, pg. 2059
THE CHEMOURS COMPANY SINGAPORE PTE. LTD.—See The Chemours Company; *U.S. Public*, pg. 2059
THE CHEMOURS COMPANY; *U.S. Public*, pg. 2059
CHEMOURS DEUTSCHLAND GMBH—See The Chemours Company; *U.S. Public*, pg. 2059
THE CHEMOURS INDIA PRIVATE LIMITED—See The Chemours Company; *U.S. Public*, pg. 2059
CHEMOURS INTERNATIONAL OPERATIONS SARL—See The Chemours Company; *U.S. Public*, pg. 2059
CHEMOURS KABUSHIKI KAISHA—See The Chemours Company; *U.S. Public*, pg. 2059
CHEMOURS KOREA INC.—See The Chemours Company; *U.S. Public*, pg. 2059
THE CHEMOURS MALAYSIA SDN. BHD.—See The Chemours Company; *U.S. Public*, pg. 2059
CHEMOURS NETHERLANDS BV—See The Chemours Company; *U.S. Public*, pg. 2059
THE CHEMOURS (TAIWAN) COMPANY LIMITED—See The Chemours Company; *U.S. Public*, pg. 2059
THE CHEMOURS (THAILAND) COMPANY LIMITED—See The Chemours Company; *U.S. Public*, pg. 2059
CHEMOVATOR GMBH—See BASF SE; *Int'l*, pg. 882
CHEMOX POUND LIMITED—See Hobart Enterprises Ltd; *Int'l*, pg. 3436
CHEMOXY INTERNATIONAL LIMITED; *Int'l*, pg. 1463
CHEMPACE CORPORATION; *U.S. Private*, pg. 872
CHEMPETITIVE GROUP, LLC; *U.S. Private*, pg. 872
CHEMPLAST INTERNATIONAL CORP.—See McNeel International Corporation; *U.S. Private*, pg. 2643
CHEMPLAST SANMAR LIMITED - CUDDALORE PLANT—See Sanmar Holdings Ltd.; *Int'l*, pg. 6546
CHEMPLAST SANMAR LIMITED - INDUSTRIAL ALCOHOL PLANT II—See Sanmar Holdings Ltd.; *Int'l*, pg. 6546
CHEMPLAST SANMAR LIMITED - KARAIKAL PLANT—See Sanmar Holdings Ltd.; *Int'l*, pg. 6546
CHEMPLAST SANMAR LIMITED - METTUR PLANT I—See Sanmar Holdings Ltd.; *Int'l*, pg. 6546
CHEMPLAST SANMAR LIMITED - METTUR PLANT IV—See Sanmar Holdings Ltd.; *Int'l*, pg. 6546
CHEMPLAST SANMAR LIMITED - VEDARANYAM SALT WORKS—See Sanmar Holdings Ltd.; *Int'l*, pg. 6546
CHEMPLAST SANMAR LTD.—See Sanmar Holdings Ltd.; *Int'l*, pg. 6546
CHEM-PLATE INDUSTRIES INC.; *U.S. Private*, pg. 871
CHEMPLUS LTD.—See Suheung Co., Ltd.; *Int'l*, pg. 7255
CHEMPOINT.COM-EMEA B.V.—See Apollo Global Management, Inc.; *U.S. Public*, pg. 165
CHEMPUMP—See Teikoku Electric Mfg. Co., Ltd.; *Int'l*, pg. 7524

CORPORATE AFFILIATIONS

CHEMQUEST CHEMICALS LLC—See Cotton Creek Capital Management LLC; *U.S. Private*, pg. 1063
CHEMQUEST SDN. BHD.—See Kuok Brothers Sdn. Bhd.; *Int'l*, pg. 4334
CHEM QUIP INC.; *U.S. Private*, pg. 870
CHEMRING AUSTRALIA PTY LTD—See Chemring Group PLC; *Int'l*, pg. 1463
CHEMRING COUNTERMEASURES LTD—See Chemring Group PLC; *Int'l*, pg. 1463
CHEMRING DEFENCE GERMANY GMBH—See Chemring Group PLC; *Int'l*, pg. 1463
CHEMRING DEFENCE SPAIN S.L.—See Chemring Group PLC; *Int'l*, pg. 1463
CHEMRING DEFENCE UK LTD; *Int'l*, pg. 1463
CHEMRING ENERGETIC DEVICES, INC.—See Chemring Group PLC; *Int'l*, pg. 1463
CHEMRING ENERGETICS UK LIMITED—See Chemring Group PLC; *Int'l*, pg. 1463
CHEMRING EOD LIMITED—See Chemring Group PLC; *Int'l*, pg. 1463
CHEMRING GROUP PLC; *Int'l*, pg. 1463
CHEMRING MILITARY PRODUCTS, INC.—See Global Ordnance LLC; *U.S. Private*, pg. 1716
CHEMRING NOBEL AS—See Chemring Group PLC; *Int'l*, pg. 1463
CHEMRING SENSORS & ELECTRONIC SYSTEMS, INC.—See Chemring Group PLC; *Int'l*, pg. 1463
CHEMROCK CORPORATION—See RGP Holding, Inc.; *U.S. Private*, pg. 3420
CHEMSEARCH—See NCH Corporation; *U.S. Private*, pg. 2875
CHEMSERVE PERLITE (PTY) LIMITED—See AECI Limited; *Int'l*, pg. 171
CHEMSERVE SYSTEMS (PTY) LIMITED—See AECI Limited; *Int'l*, pg. 171
CHEMSIL SILICONES, INC.—See Innospec Inc.; *U.S. Public*, pg. 1125
CHEMSOLV INC.; *U.S. Private*, pg. 872
CHEMSON ASIA PTE LTD—See Pidilite Industries Limited; *Int'l*, pg. 5862
CHEMSPEC EUROPE LIMITED—See RPM International Inc.; *U.S. Public*, pg. 1816
CHEMSPEC INTERNATIONAL LIMITED; *Int'l*, pg. 1463
CHEMSPEC LTD.—See Safic-Alcan SAS; *Int'l*, pg. 6471
CHEMSTAFF, INC.—See Ecolab Inc.; *U.S. Public*, pg. 712
CHEMSTAR CORP.—See Ecolab Inc.; *U.S. Public*, pg. 712
CHEMSTAR PRODUCTS COMPANY; *U.S. Private*, pg. 872
CHEMSTATIONS, INC.—See Datacor, Inc.; *U.S. Private*, pg. 1165
CHEMSTER GMBH—See BASF SE; *Int'l*, pg. 882
CHEMSW, INC.—See Dassault Systemes S.A.; *Int'l*, pg. 1974
CHEM-TAINER INDUSTRIES, INC.; *U.S. Private*, pg. 871
CHEM-TAINER OF HAWAII—See Chem-Tainer Industries, Inc.; *U.S. Private*, pg. 871
CHEMTEC CHEMICALS B.V.—See RPM International Inc.; *U.S. Public*, pg. 1816
CHEMTEC ENERGY SERVICES, LLC—See L.B. Foster Company; *U.S. Public*, pg. 1278
CHEMTECH CONSULTING GROUP, INC.—See Morgan Stanley; *U.S. Public*, pg. 1474
CHEM-TECH FINISHERS INC.; *U.S. Private*, pg. 871
CHEMTECH INDUSTRIAL VALVES LIMITED; *Int'l*, pg. 1463
CHEM-TECH, LTD.—See Neogen Corporation; *U.S. Public*, pg. 1505
CHEMTECH SERVICOS DE ENGENHARIA E SOFTWARE LTDA.—See Siemens Aktiengesellschaft; *Int'l*, pg. 6886
CHEMTEC PEST CONTROL CORP.—See EQT AB; *Int'l*, pg. 2468
CHEM - TEC S.R.L.—See Kering S.A.; *Int'l*, pg. 4134
CHEM-TEL INC.—See CVC Capital Partners SICAV-FIS S.A.; *Int'l*, pg. 1885
CHEMTEST LIMITED—See Eurofins Scientific S.E.; *Int'l*, pg. 2535
CHEMTEX INTERNATIONAL, INC.—See Mitsubishi Corporation; *Int'l*, pg. 4941
CHEM-TEX LABORATORIES, INC.—See HeiQ Plc; *Int'l*, pg. 3326
CHEMTEX OVERSEAS, INC.—See Mitsubishi Corporation; *Int'l*, pg. 4941
CHEMTOOL, INC.—See Berkshire Hathaway Inc.; *U.S. Public*, pg. 318
CHEMTOX SAS—See Eurofins Scientific S.E.; *Int'l*, pg. 2542
CHEMTRADE ELECTROCHEM INC.—See Chemtrade Logistics Income Fund; *Int'l*, pg. 1464
CHEMTRADE LOGISTICS INCOME FUND; *Int'l*, pg. 1464
CHEMTRADE LOGISTICS, INC.—See Chemtrade Logistics Income Fund; *Int'l*, pg. 1464
CHEMTRADE LOGISTICS (US), INC.—See Chemtrade Logistics Income Fund; *Int'l*, pg. 1464
CHEMTRADE PERFORMANCE CHEMICALS US, LLC—See Chemtrade Logistics Income Fund; *Int'l*, pg. 1464
CHEMTRADE PHOSPHOROUS SPECIALTIES LLC—See Balmoral Funds LLC; *U.S. Private*, pg. 462

COMPANY NAME INDEX

CHEMTRADE PULP CHEMICALS LIMITED—See Canfor Corporation; *Int'l*, pg. 1291
CHEMTRADE PULP CHEMICALS TRUST—See Chemtrade Logistics Income Fund; *Int'l*, pg. 1464
CHEMTRADE REFINERY SERVICES INC.—See Chemtrade Logistics Income Fund; *Int'l*, pg. 1464
CHEMTRAK, INC.; *U.S. Private*, pg. 872
CHEMTRANS PTY LIMITED—See K&S Corporation Limited; *Int'l*, pg. 4039
CHEMTREAT COMPOSITES INDIA PVT LTD—See Merck KGaA; *Int'l*, pg. 4830
CHEMTREAT, INC.—See Danaher Corporation; *U.S. Public*, pg. 625
CHEMTREAT INTERNATIONAL, INC.—See Danaher Corporation; *U.S. Public*, pg. 625
CHEM-TREND AUSTRALIA PTY LTD—See Freudenberg SE; *Int'l*, pg. 2782
CHEM-TREND CHEMICALS CO. PVT. LTD.—See Freudenberg SE; *Int'l*, pg. 2782
CHEM-TREND COMERCIAL, S.A. DE C.V.—See Freudenberg SE; *Int'l*, pg. 2782
CHEM-TREND (DEUTCHLAND) GMBH—See Freudenberg SE; *Int'l*, pg. 2785
CHEM-TREND (DEUTSCHLAND) GMBH—See Freudenberg SE; *Int'l*, pg. 2782
CHEM-TREND FRANCE S.A.S.U.—See Freudenberg SE; *Int'l*, pg. 2782
CHEM-TREND HOLDING LP—See Freudenberg SE; *Int'l*, pg. 2782
CHEM-TREND INDUSTRIA E COMERCIO DE PRODUTOS QUIMICOS LTDA.—See Freudenberg SE; *Int'l*, pg. 2782
CHEM-TREND ITALY DEL DR. GIAN FRANCO COLORI S.A.S.—See Freudenberg SE; *Int'l*, pg. 2782
CHEM-TREND JAPAN K.K.—See Freudenberg SE; *Int'l*, pg. 2782
CHEM-TREND KOREA LTD.—See Freudenberg SE; *Int'l*, pg. 2782
CHEM-TREND LIMITED PARTNERSHIP—See Freudenberg SE; *Int'l*, pg. 2785
CHEM-TREND POLSKA SP. Z O.O.—See Freudenberg SE; *Int'l*, pg. 2782
CHEM-TREND ROMANIA S.R.L.—See Freudenberg SE; *Int'l*, pg. 2782
CHEM-TREND (SHANGHAI) TRADING CO. LTD.—See Freudenberg SE; *Int'l*, pg. 2782
CHEM-TREND SINGAPORE PTE. LTD.—See Freudenberg SE; *Int'l*, pg. 2782
CHEM-TREND TRADING (THAILAND) CO. LTD.—See Freudenberg SE; *Int'l*, pg. 2782
CHEM-TREND VIETNAM COMPANY LIMITED—See Freudenberg SE; *Int'l*, pg. 2782
CHEMTRONICS CHINA—See Chemtronics Co., Ltd.; *Int'l*, pg. 1464
CHEMTRONICS CO., LTD. - PYEONGTAEK PLANT—See Chemtronics Co., Ltd.; *Int'l*, pg. 1464
CHEMTRONICS CO., LTD. - SEJONG PLANT—See Chemtronics Co., Ltd.; *Int'l*, pg. 1464
CHEMTRONICS CO., LTD.; *Int'l*, pg. 1464
CHEMTRONICS CO., LTD. - YONGIN PLANT—See Chemtronics Co., Ltd.; *Int'l*, pg. 1464
CHEMTRONICS EUROPE S.R.O—See Chemtronics Co., Ltd.; *Int'l*, pg. 1464
CHEMTRONICS USA INC—See Chemtronics Co., Ltd.; *Int'l*, pg. 1464
CHEMTRONIC TECHNOLOGY (THAILAND) CO., LTD.—See KCE Electronics Public Company Limited; *Int'l*, pg. 4109
CHEMTROS CO., LTD.; *Int'l*, pg. 1464
CHEMTROVINA CO. LTD.—See Chemtronics Co., Ltd.; *Int'l*, pg. 1464
CHEMTRUSION, INC.; *U.S. Private*, pg. 872
CHEMTURA CHEMICALS INDIA PRIVATE LIMITED—See Element Solutions Inc.; *U.S. Public*, pg. 725
CHEMTURA COLUMBIA LTDA—See Element Solutions Inc.; *U.S. Public*, pg. 725
CHEMTURA NETHERLANDS B.V.—See Element Solutions Inc.; *U.S. Public*, pg. 725
CHEMTURA PTY LIMITED—See Element Solutions Inc.; *U.S. Public*, pg. 725
CHEMTURA SINGAPORE PTE. LTD.—See LANXESS AG; *Int'l*, pg. 4415
CHEMUNG CANAL TRUST COMPANY—See Chemung Financial Corporation; *U.S. Public*, pg. 484
CHEMUNG FINANCIAL CORPORATION; *U.S. Public*, pg. 484
CHEMUNG SUPPLY CORPORATION; *U.S. Private*, pg. 872
CHEM USA CORP.—See Chung-Hsin Electric & Machinery Manufacturing Corp.; *Int'l*, pg. 1597
CHEMVIN PLASTICS LTD—See Aliaxis S.A./N.V.; *Int'l*, pg. 323
CHEMVIRON CARBON LTD.—See Kuraray Co., Ltd.; *Int'l*, pg. 4336
CHEMVIRON CARBON S.E.—See Kuraray Co., Ltd.; *Int'l*, pg. 4336
CHEMVIRON FRANCE SAS—See Kuraray Co., Ltd.; *Int'l*, pg. 4336

CHEMWARE INC.—See Dohmen Co.; *U.S. Private*, pg. 1254
CHENAB VALLEY POWER PROJECTS PRIVATE LIMITED—See NHPC Ltd.; *Int'l*, pg. 5259
CHENAL COUNTRY CLUB—See PotlatchDeltic Corporation; *U.S. Public*, pg. 1704
CHENAL PROPERTIES, INC.—See PotlatchDeltic Corporation; *U.S. Public*, pg. 1704
CHEN & ASSOCIATES CIVIL & ENVIRONMENTAL ENGINEERS, INC.; *U.S. Private*, pg. 872
CHENAVARI TORO INCOME FUND LIMITED; *Int'l*, pg. 1465
CHENBRO EUROPE B.V.—See Chenbro Micom Co., Ltd.; *Int'l*, pg. 1465
CHENBRO GMBH—See Chenbro Micom Co., Ltd.; *Int'l*, pg. 1465
CHENBRO MICOM CO., LTD.; *Int'l*, pg. 1465
CHENBRO MICOM (SHENZHEN) CO., LTD.—See Chenbro Micom Co., Ltd.; *Int'l*, pg. 1465
CHENBRO MICOM (USA) INC.—See Chenbro Micom Co., Ltd.; *Int'l*, pg. 1465
CHENBRO UK LTD.—See Chenbro Micom Co., Ltd.; *Int'l*, pg. 1465
CHENDU PERFECT TECHNOLOGY CO., LTD.—See Hangzhou Silan Microelectronics Co., Ltd.; *Int'l*, pg. 3250
CHENDU TON YI INDUSTRIAL PACKING CO., LTD.—See Uni-President Enterprises Corporation; *Int'l*, pg. 8028
CHENEGA CORPORATION; *U.S. Private*, pg. 872
CHENEGA INTEGRATED SYSTEMS, LLC—See Chenega Corporation; *U.S. Private*, pg. 872
CH ENERGY GROUP, INC.—See Fortis Inc.; *Int'l*, pg. 2739
CHENEY BROTHERS, INC.; *U.S. Private*, pg. 872
CHENEY LIME & CEMENT CO. INC.; *U.S. Private*, pg. 872
CHEN FULL INTERNATIONAL CO., LTD.; *Int'l*, pg. 1464
CHENG AN ZHONGYU GAS CO., LTD.—See Zhongyu Energy Holdings Limited; *Int'l*, pg. 8675
CHENGBANG ECO-ENVIRONMENT CO., LTD.; *Int'l*, pg. 1466
CHENGDA INTERNATIONAL CO., LTD.—See Liaoning Chengda Co., Ltd.; *Int'l*, pg. 4482
CHENGDA INTERNATIONAL (NEW YORK) CO., LTD.—See Liaoning Chengda Co., Ltd.; *Int'l*, pg. 4482
CHENGDA PHARMACEUTICALS CO., LTD.; *Int'l*, pg. 1467
CHENGDA TECHNOLOGY CO., LTD.; *Int'l*, pg. 1467
CHENGDE MEIBAOHANG AUTO SALES & SERVICES CO., LTD.—See China MeiDong Auto Holdings Limited; *Int'l*, pg. 1519
CHENGDE POWER SUPPLY COMPANY—See State Grid Corporation of China; *Int'l*, pg. 7183
CHENGDE VANADIUM & TITANIUM NEW MATERIALS CO., LTD.—See HBIS Group Co., Ltd.; *Int'l*, pg. 3295
CHENGDOU INOAC POLYMER PRODUCTS CO., LTD.—See INOAC Corporation; *Int'l*, pg. 3713
CHENGDU AIXIN ZHONGHONG BIOLOGICAL TECHNOLOGY CO., LTD.—See AiXin Life International, Inc.; *Int'l*, pg. 254
CHENGDU ALD AVIATION MANUFACTURING CORPORATION; *Int'l*, pg. 1467
CHENGDU ANDISOON MEASURE CO., LTD.—See Houpu Clean Energy Group Co., Ltd; *Int'l*, pg. 3490
CHENGDU ASIARAY ADVERTISING—See Asiaray Media Group Limited; *Int'l*, pg. 620
CHENGDU AUCHAN HYPERMARKETS CO., LTD.—See Alibaba Group Holding Limited; *Int'l*, pg. 326
CHENGDU BOE OPTOELECTRONICS TECHNOLOGY CO., LTD.—See BOE Technology Group Co., Ltd.; *Int'l*, pg. 1099
CHENGDU BOJAY AUTOMATION EQUIPMENT CO., LTD.—See Zhuhai Bojay Electronics Co., Ltd.; *Int'l*, pg. 8677
CHENGDU BOW YUE USED CARS CENTRE CO. LTD.—See Sime Darby Berhad; *Int'l*, pg. 6928
CHENGDU B-RAY MEDIA CO., LTD.; *Int'l*, pg. 1467
CHENGDU BRIGHT EYE HOSPITAL CO., LTD.; *Int'l*, pg. 1467
CHENGDU BUILDING MATERIALS COMPANY—See Dalian Shide Group Co., Ltd.; *Int'l*, pg. 1952
CHENGDU CARBON MATERIAL CO., LTD.—See Fangda Carbon New Material Co., Ltd.; *Int'l*, pg. 2613
CHENGDU CHEMPARTNER CO., LTD.—See TPG Capital, L.P.; *U.S. Public*, pg. 2175
CHENGDU CHENG LOONG PACKING PRODUCTS CO., LTD.—See Cheng Loong Corp.; *Int'l*, pg. 1466
CHENGDU CHIPSCREEN PHARMACEUTICAL CO., LTD.—See Shenzhen Chipscreen Biosciences Co., Ltd.; *Int'l*, pg. 6806
CHENGDU CHUANLU PLASTIC PACKAGING & SERVICE CO. LTD.—See Solvay S.A.; *Int'l*, pg. 7077
CHENGDU COMFORTDELGRO QINGYANG DRIVING SCHOOL CO., LTD.—See ComfortDelGro Corporation Limited; *Int'l*, pg. 1712
CHENGDU COMFORTDELGRO TAXI CO., LTD.—See ComfortDelGro Corporation Limited; *Int'l*, pg. 1712
CHENGDU CORPRO TECHNOLOGY CO., LTD.; *Int'l*, pg. 1467

CHENGDU DAHONGLI MACHINERY CO., LTD.; *Int'l*, pg. 1467
CHENGDU DALI FOODS CO., LTD.—See Dali Foods Group Co. Ltd.; *Int'l*, pg. 1951
CHENGDU DAWN PRECISION M&E SALES CO., LTD.—See Sichuan Dawn Precision Technology Co., Ltd.; *Int'l*, pg. 6878
CHENGDU DESIGN & RESEARCH INSTITUTE OF BUILDING MATERIALS INDUSTRY CO., LTD.—See Sinoma International Engineering Co., Ltd.; *Int'l*, pg. 6952
CHENGDU DIGITAL CHINA LIMITED—See Digital China Holdings Limited; *Int'l*, pg. 2121
CHENGDU DONGJIN SEMICHEM CO., LTD.—See Dongjin Semichem Co., Ltd.; *Int'l*, pg. 2168
CHENGDU EASTON BIOPHARMACEUTICALS CO., LTD.; *Int'l*, pg. 1467
CHENGDU EOPTOLINK TECHNOLOGY INC.; *Int'l*, pg. 1467
CHENGDU EXPRESSWAY CO., LTD.; *Int'l*, pg. 1467
CHENGDU FUSEN NOBLE-HOUSE INDSTRL CO LTD; *Int'l*, pg. 1467
CHENGDU FUYI SWELL AUTO PARTS CO., LTD.—See Guangdong Hongtu Technology (Holdings) Co., Ltd.; *Int'l*, pg. 3156
CHENGDU GALAXY MAGNET CO., LTD.; *Int'l*, pg. 1467
CHENGDU GAS GROUP CO., LTD.; *Int'l*, pg. 1467
CHENGDU GLOBAL INFOTECH INFORMATION TECHNOLOGY CO., LTD.—See Global Infotech Co., Ltd.; *Int'l*, pg. 2997
CHENGDU GOLDEN PHOENIX LIQUID NITROGEN CONTAINER COMPANY LIMITED—See Chart Industries, Inc.; *U.S. Public*, pg. 481
CHENGDU GRANDLAND SOUTH CHINA DECORATION ENGINEERING CO., LTD.—See Shenzhen Grandland Group Co., Ltd.; *Int'l*, pg. 6811
CHENGDU GUIBAO; *Int'l*, pg. 1467
CHENGDU HAONENG TECHNOLOGY CO., LTD.; *Int'l*, pg. 1467
CHENGDU HENKEL ADHESIVE TECHNOLOGIES CO., LTD.—See Henkel AG & Co. KGaA; *Int'l*, pg. 3348
CHENGDU HENKEL ADHESIVE TECHONOLOGIES CO. LTD.—See Henkel AG & Co. KGaA; *Int'l*, pg. 3348
CHENGDU HEXING PACKAGING PRINTING CO., LTD.—See Xiamen Hexing Packaging Printing Co., Ltd.; *Int'l*, pg. 8524
CHENGDU HEZHIHELI PROPERTY MANAGEMENT CO., LTD.—See Country Garden Services Holdings Company Limited; *Int'l*, pg. 1818
CHENGDU HILLSTREET DEVELOPMENT CO., LTD.—See Keppel Corporation Limited; *Int'l*, pg. 4130
CHENGDU HI-TECH CONTROL SYSTEM CO., LTD.—See Shanghai Hi-Tech Control System Co., LTD.; *Int'l*, pg. 6770
CHENGDU HI-TECH DEVELOPMENT CO., LTD.; *Int'l*, pg. 1468
CHENGDU HONGBO INDUSTRIAL CO., LTD.—See Xiamen Tungsten Co., Ltd.; *Int'l*, pg. 8525
CHENGDU HONGQI CHAIN CO., LTD.; *Int'l*, pg. 1468
CHENGDU HOPE TIMES TRADING CO., LTD.—See Shenzhen Prolto Supply Chain Management Co., Ltd.; *Int'l*, pg. 6819
CHENGDU HOP TECHNOLOGY CO., LTD.—See Super Telecom Co., Ltd.; *Int'l*, pg. 7335
CHENGDU HUAMAOKEXIN AUTOMATION CONTROL ENGINEERING CO., LTD.—See Endress+Hauser (International) Holding AG; *Int'l*, pg. 2405
CHENGDU HUASUN TECHNOLOGY GROUP INC., CO., LTD.; *Int'l*, pg. 1468
CHENGDU HUAZE COBALT & NICKEL MATERIAL CO., LTD.; *Int'l*, pg. 1468
CHENGDU INFORMATION TECHNOLOGY OF CHINESE ACADEMY OF SCIENCES CO., LTD.; *Int'l*, pg. 1468
CHENGDU INNOREV INDUSTRIAL CO., LTD.—See Shenzhen Colibri Technologies Co., Ltd.; *Int'l*, pg. 6807
CHENGDU ISETAN DEPARTMENT STORE CO., LTD.—See Isetan Mitsukoshi Holdings Ltd.; *Int'l*, pg. 3814
CHENGDU IXONOS TECHNOLOGY CO., LTD.—See Digitalist Group Oyj; *Int'l*, pg. 2123
CHENGDU JIAFAANTAI EDUCATION TECHNOLOGY CO., LTD.; *Int'l*, pg. 1468
CHENGDU JINGU WHEEL CO. LTD.—See Zhejiang Jingu Co., Ltd.; *Int'l*, pg. 8657
CHENGDU JOUAV AUTOMATION TECHNOLOGY CO., LTD.; *Int'l*, pg. 1468
CHENGDU JUTAL OIL & GAS ENGINEERING CO., LTD.—See Jutal Offshore Oil Services Limited; *Int'l*, pg. 4031
CHENGDU JUYA MEDICAL LETTER TECHNOLOGY CO., LTD.—See Shenzhen DAS Intellitech Co., Ltd.; *Int'l*, pg. 6807
CHENGDU KANGHONG PHARMACEUTICALS GROUP CO., LTD.; *Int'l*, pg. 1468
CHENGDU KANGHUA BIOLOGICAL PRODUCTS CO., LTD.—See Zhejiang Aokang Shoes Co., Ltd.; *Int'l*, pg. 8648
CHENGDU KDT MACHINERY CO., LTD—See Guangzhou KDT Machinery Co.,Ltd; *Int'l*, pg. 3166

CHENGDU KANGHONG PHARMACEUTICALS GROUP CO., LTD. CORPORATE AFFILIATIONS

CHENGDU KEANDA RAIL TRANSIT TECHNOLOGY CO., LTD.—See Shenzhen Keanda Electronic Technology Corp., Ltd.; *Int'l*, pg. 6815
CHENGDU KINGFA SCI & TECH ADVANCED MATERIALS CO., LTD.—See Kingfa Sci &Tech Co., Ltd.; *Int'l*, pg. 4172
CHENGDU KOBELCO CONSTRUCTION MACHINERY FINANCIAL LEASING LTD.—See Kobe Steel, Ltd.; *Int'l*, pg. 4217
CHENGDU LEEJUN INDUSTRIAL CO., LTD.; *Int'l*, pg. 1468
CHENGDU MONOLITHIC POWER SYSTEMS CO., LTD.—See Monolithic Power Systems, Inc.; *U.S. Public*, pg. 1464
CHENGDU M&S ELECTRONICS TECHNOLOGY CO., LTD.; *Int'l*, pg. 1468
CHENGDU NEUSOFT INSTITUTE OF INFORMATION—See Neusoft Corporation; *Int'l*, pg. 5220
CHENGDU NEWTOUCH SOFTWARE CO., LTD.—See Shanghai Newtouch Software Co., Ltd.; *Int'l*, pg. 6776
CHENGDU NEWTOUCH YUANRI SOFTWARE CO., LTD.—See Shanghai Newtouch Software Co., Ltd.; *Int'l*, pg. 6776
CHENGDU NINGJIANG SHOWA AUTOPARTS CO., LTD.—See Hitachi Astemo, Ltd.; *Int'l*, pg. 3409
CHENGDU OLYMVAX BIOPHARMACEUTICALS, INC.; *Int'l*, pg. 1469
CHENGDU O.R.G TECHNOLOGY CO., LTD.—See ORG Technology Co., Ltd.; *Int'l*, pg. 5617
CHENGDU PICO EXHIBITION SERVICES CO., LTD.—See Pico Far East Holdings Limited; *Int'l*, pg. 5860
CHENGDU QIBAO AUTOMOBILE SALES SERVICES CO., LTD.—See China ZhengTong Auto Services Holdings Limited; *Int'l*, pg. 1566
CHENGDU QINCHUAN IOT TECHNOLOGY CO., LTD.; *Int'l*, pg. 1468
CHENGDU Q TECHNOLOGY LIMITED—See Q Technology (Group) Company Limited; *Int'l*, pg. 6129
CHENGDU QUANXING MASION PACIFIC DEPARTMENT STORE CO., LTD.—See The Far Eastern Group; *Int'l*, pg. 7641
CHENGDU QUSHUI SCIENCE & TECHNOLOGY CO., LTD.; *Int'l*, pg. 1468
CHENGDU RAINBOW APPLIANCE (GROUP) SHARES CO., LTD.; *Int'l*, pg. 1468
CHENGDU RENBENXINDONG TECHNOLOGY LTD.—See NSD CO., LTD.; *Int'l*, pg. 5476
CHENGDU RML TECHNOLOGY CO., LTD.; *Int'l*, pg. 1468
CHENGDU ROAD & BRIDGE ENGINEERING CO., LTD.; *Int'l*, pg. 1468
CHENGDU RONGGUANG CARBON CO., LTD.—See Fangda Carbon New Material Co., Ltd.; *Int'l*, pg. 2613
CHENGDU RURAL COMMERCIAL BANK CO., LTD.—See Anbang Insurance Group Co., Ltd.; *Int'l*, pg. 447
CHENGDU SANDIAN CABLES CO., LTD.—See Goldcup Electric Apparatus Co., Ltd.; *Int'l*, pg. 3027
CHENGDU SANFANG ELECTRICAL APPLICATION CO. LTD.—See Suzhou Electrical Apparatus Science Academy Co., Ltd.; *Int'l*, pg. 7349
CHENGDU SEARIVER CLOSURES CO., LTD.—See Shandong Chiway Industry Development Co., Ltd.; *Int'l*, pg. 6752
CHENGDU SE BORDNETZE COMPANY LTD.—See Sumitomo Electric Industries, Ltd.; *Int'l*, pg. 7277
CHENGDU SEI OPTICAL FIBER CO., LTD.—See Sumitomo Electric Industries, Ltd.; *Int'l*, pg. 7277
CHENGDU SHENGBANG SEALS CO., LTD.; *Int'l*, pg. 1469
CHENGDU SHENGNUO BIOPHARMACEUTICAL CO., LTD.; *Int'l*, pg. 1469
CHENGDU SHUODE PHARMACEUTICAL CO., LTD.—See Chengdu Easton Biopharmaceuticals Co., Ltd.; *Int'l*, pg. 1467
CHENGDU SIWI SCIENCE AND TECHNOLOGY COMPANY LIMITED; *Int'l*, pg. 1469
CHENGDU SMITH ADHESIVE NEW MATERIAL CO., LTD.—See Shanghai Smith Adhesive New Material Co., Ltd.; *Int'l*, pg. 6779
CHENGDU SPACEON ELECTRONICS CO., LTD.; *Int'l*, pg. 1469
CHENGDU SUCHUN AUTOMOTIVE PARTS CO., LTD.—See Jiangsu Changshu Automotive Trim Group Co., Ltd.; *Int'l*, pg. 3945
CHENGDU TANGYUAN ELECTRIC CO., LTD.; *Int'l*, pg. 1469
CHENGDU TECHCENT ENVIRONMENT INDUSTRY CO., LTD.; *Int'l*, pg. 1469
CHENGDU TIANJIAN TECHNOLOGY CO., LTD.; *Int'l*, pg. 1469
CHENGDU TIANQI INDUSTRY (GROUP) CO., LTD.; *Int'l*, pg. 1469
CHENGDU TIANQI MACHINERY, METALS & MINERALS IMPORT & EXPORT CO., LTD.—See Chengdu Tianqi Industry (Group) Co., Ltd.; *Int'l*, pg. 1469
CHENGDU TONGTECH CO., LTD.—See Beijing Tongtech Company Limited; *Int'l*, pg. 959

CHENGDU TOYO INK CO., LTD.—See Toyo Ink SC Holdings Co., Ltd.; *Int'l*, pg. 7853
CHENGDU TOYOTA BOSHOKU AUTOMOTIVE PARTS CO., LTD.—See Toyota Boshoku Corporation; *Int'l*, pg. 7863
CHENGDU TOYO TANSO INDUSTRIAL CO., LTD.—See Toyo Tanso Co., Ltd.; *Int'l*, pg. 7858
CHENGDU TSUHAN SCIENCE & TECHNOLOGY CO., LTD.—See Zhongji Innolight Co., Ltd.; *Int'l*, pg. 8673
CHENGDU UBI COMPUTER SOFWARE CO., LTD.—See Ubisoft Entertainment S.A.; *Int'l*, pg. 8003
CHENGDU UNOVEL PHARMACEUTICAL CO., LTD.—See Chengdu Easton Biopharmaceuticals Co., Ltd.; *Int'l*, pg. 1467
CHENGDU VANKE REAL ESTATE COMPANY LIMITED—See China Vanke Co., Ltd.; *Int'l*, pg. 1562
CHENGDU VANTRON TECHNOLOGY INC.—See Eurotech S.p.A.; *Int'l*, pg. 2558
CHENGDU WATER STAR-SOURCE INFORMATION TECHNOLOGY CO.—See Beijing Watertek Information Technology Co., Ltd.; *Int'l*, pg. 960
CHENGDU WATERTEK INFORMATION TECHNOLOGY CO.—See Beijing Watertek Information Technology Co., Ltd.; *Int'l*, pg. 960
CHENGDU WINTRUE HOLDING CO., LTD.; *Int'l*, pg. 1469
CHENGDU XGIMI TECHNOLOGY CO., LTD.; *Int'l*, pg. 1469
CHENGDU XIANGDA CAMEL FEED CO., LTD.—See Tangrenshen Group Co., Ltd.; *Int'l*, pg. 7458
CHENGDU XILING POWER SCIENCE & TECHNOLOGY INCORPORATED COMPANY; *Int'l*, pg. 1469
CHENGDU XINGANG SPONGE CO., LTD.—See Sinomax Group Limited; *Int'l*, pg. 6953
CHENGDU XINGRONG ENVIRONMENT CO., LTD.; *Int'l*, pg. 1469
CHENGDU XINHAI CHUANGXIN TECHNOLOGY CO., LTD.—See Chipsea Technologies (Shenzhen) Corp.; *Int'l*, pg. 1573
CHENGDU XINZHU ROAD & BRIDGE MACHINERY CO., LTD.; *Int'l*, pg. 1469
CHENGDU XUGUANG ELECTRONICS CO., LTD.; *Int'l*, pg. 1469
CHENGDU YONGGUI TOYO ROLLING STOCK EQUIPMENT CO., LTD.—See TOYO DENKI SEIZO K.K.; *Int'l*, pg. 7852
CHENGDU YUNDA TECHNOLOGY CO., LTD.; *Int'l*, pg. 1470
CHENGDU YUSHENG INDUSTRIAL DEVELOPMENT CO—See Carrefour SA; *Int'l*, pg. 1344
CHENGDU ZHENG HENG AUTOMOBILE PARTS CO., LTD.—See Johnson Electric Holdings Limited; *Int'l*, pg. 3990
CHENGDU ZHIMINGDA ELECTRONICS CO., LTD.; *Int'l*, pg. 1470
CHENG EUI PRECISION INDUSTRY CO., LTD.; *Int'l*, pg. 1465
CHENG FONG CHEMICAL CO., LTD.—See Panion & Bf Biotech, Inc.; *Int'l*, pg. 5728
CHENGHE ACQUISITION CO.; *Int'l*, pg. 1470
CHENGHE ACQUISITION I CO.; *U.S. Public*, pg. 484
CHENG LIE NAVIGATION CO., LTD.—See CMA CGM S.A.; *Int'l*, pg. 1668
CHENG LOONG BINH DUONG CONTAINER CO., LTD.—See Cheng Loong Corp.; *Int'l*, pg. 1465
CHENG LOONG BINH DUONG PAPER CO., LTD.—See Cheng Loong Corp.; *Int'l*, pg. 1465
CHENG LOONG CORP. - CHUPEI MILL—See Cheng Loong Corp.; *Int'l*, pg. 1465
CHENG LOONG CORP. - HOULI MILL—See Cheng Loong Corp.; *Int'l*, pg. 1465
CHENG LOONG CORP. - HSINCHU MILL—See Cheng Loong Corp.; *Int'l*, pg. 1465
CHENG LOONG CORP. - LOS ANGELES BRANCH—See Cheng Loong Corp.; *Int'l*, pg. 1465
CHENG LOONG CORP. - MIAOLI PLANT—See Cheng Loong Corp.; *Int'l*, pg. 1465
CHENG LOONG CORP. - NEW JERSEY BRANCH—See Cheng Loong Corp.; *Int'l*, pg. 1465
CHENG LOONG CORP.; *Int'l*, pg. 1465
CHENG LOONG CORP. - TAICHUNG PLANT—See Cheng Loong Corp.; *Int'l*, pg. 1466
CHENG LOONG CORP. - TALIN PLANT—See Cheng Loong Corp.; *Int'l*, pg. 1466
CHENG LOONG CORP. - TAOYUAN MILL—See Cheng Loong Corp.; *Int'l*, pg. 1466
CHENG LOONG CORP. - TAOYUAN PLANT, FORM & PACKAGING MATERIALS—See Cheng Loong Corp.; *Int'l*, pg. 1466
CHENG LOONG CORP. - TAOYUAN PLANT II—See Cheng Loong Corp.; *Int'l*, pg. 1466
CHENG LOONG CORP. - TAOYUAN PLANT—See Cheng Loong Corp.; *Int'l*, pg. 1466
CHENG LOONG CORP. - YENCHAO PLANT—See Cheng Loong Corp.; *Int'l*, pg. 1466
CHENG LOONG (GWANGTUNG) PAPER CO.—See Cheng Loong Corp.; *Int'l*, pg. 1465
CHENG LOONG LONG AN CONTAINER CO., LTD.—See Cheng Loong Corp.; *Int'l*, pg. 1466

CHENG MEI MATERIALS TECHNOLOGY CORPORATION; *Int'l*, pg. 1466
CHENG MING MING'S BEAUTY WORLD LIMITED—See Jinchuan Group International Resources Co., Ltd.; *Int'l*, pg. 3965
CHENG POWER SYSTEMS, INC.—See NRG Energy, Inc.; *U.S. Public*, pg. 1549
CHENG SHIN HOLLAND BV.—See Cheng Shin Rubber (Xiamen) Ind., Ltd.; *Int'l*, pg. 1466
CHENG SHIN RUBBER IND. CO., LTD.—See Cheng Shin Rubber (Xiamen) Ind., Ltd.; *Int'l*, pg. 1466
CHENG SHIN RUBBER USA, INC.—See Cheng Shin Rubber (Xiamen) Ind., Ltd.; *Int'l*, pg. 1466
CHENG SHIN RUBBER (XIAMEN) IND., LTD.; *Int'l*, pg. 1466
CHENG SHIN TIRE (XIAMEN) CO., LTD.—See Cheng Shin Rubber (Xiamen) Ind., Ltd.; *Int'l*, pg. 1466
CHENGTUN MINING GROUP CO., LTD.; *Int'l*, pg. 1470
CHENGUANG BIOTECH GROUP CO., LTD.; *Int'l*, pg. 1470
CHENG UEI PRECISION INDUSTRY CO., LTD.; *Int'l*, pg. 1466
CHENGXIN LITHIUM GROUP CO., LTD.; *Int'l*, pg. 1470
CHENGZHI CO., LTD.; *Int'l*, pg. 1470
CHEN HO & CO., LTD.—See Panasonic Holdings Corporation; *Int'l*, pg. 5723
CHEN HSONG EUROPE B.V.—See Chen Hsong Holdings Ltd.; *Int'l*, pg. 1464
CHEN HSONG GERMANY GMBH—See Chen Hsong Holdings Ltd.; *Int'l*, pg. 1464
CHEN HSONG HOLDINGS LTD.; *Int'l*, pg. 1464
CHEN HSONG MACHINERY CO. LTD.—See Chen Hsong Holdings Ltd.; *Int'l*, pg. 1464
CHEN HSONG MACHINERY TAIWAN CO. LTD.—See Chen Hsong Holdings Ltd.; *Int'l*, pg. 1464
CHEN HSONG (MIDDLE EAST) FZE—See Chen Hsong Holdings Ltd.; *Int'l*, pg. 1464
CHEN HSONG MIDDLE EAST MAKINE TICARET ANONIM SIRKETI—See Chen Hsong Holdings Ltd.; *Int'l*, pg. 1464
CHEN HSONG PRECISION MOULD CO., LTD.—See Chen Hsong Holdings Ltd.; *Int'l*, pg. 1464
CHEN HSONG SOUTH AMERICA IMPORTACAO, EXPORTACAO E COMERCIO DE EQUIPAMENTOS LTDA.—See Chen Hsong Holdings Ltd.; *Int'l*, pg. 1464
CHENIERE CORPUS CHRISTI HOLDINGS, LLC; *U.S. Private*, pg. 872
CHENIERE CORPUS CHRISTI PIPELINE, L.P.—See Cheniere Corpus Christi Holdings, LLC; *U.S. Private*, pg. 872
CHENIERE CREOLE TRAIL PIPELINE, L.P.—See Cheniere Energy, Inc.; *U.S. Public*, pg. 485
CHENIERE ENERGY, INC.; *U.S. Public*, pg. 485
CHENIERE ENERGY PARTNERS LP HOLDINGS, LLC—See Cheniere Energy, Inc.; *U.S. Public*, pg. 485
CHENIERE ENERGY PARTNERS, L.P.—See Cheniere Energy, Inc.; *U.S. Public*, pg. 485
CHENIERE MARKETING, LTD.—See Cheniere Energy, Inc.; *U.S. Public*, pg. 485
CHENILLE INTERNATIONAL PTE. LTD.—See Baneng Holdings Bhd.; *Int'l*, pg. 831
CHEN KE MING FOOD MANUFACTURING CO., LTD; *Int'l*, pg. 1464
CHEN LI EDUCATION CO., LTD.—See Success Prime Corporation; *Int'l*, pg. 7250
CHEN LIN EDUCATION GROUP HOLDINGS LIMITED; *Int'l*, pg. 1465
CHENMING ELECTRONIC (DONGGUAN) CO., LTD.—See Chenming Electronic Tech. Corp.; *Int'l*, pg. 1470
CHENMING ELECTRONIC TECH. CORP; *Int'l*, pg. 1470
CHENMING ELECTRONIC TECHNOLOGY USA, INC.—See Chenming Electronic Tech. Corp.; *Int'l*, pg. 1470
CHENMING GMBH—See Shandong Chenming Paper Holdings Limited; *Int'l*, pg. 6752
CHENMING MOLD IND. CORP. - KEELUNG PLANT—See Chenming Electronic Tech. Corp.; *Int'l*, pg. 1470
CHENMING USA INC.—See Chenming Electronic Tech. Corp.; *Int'l*, pg. 1470
CHENNAI CONTAINER TERMINAL PRIVATE LIMITED—See Dubai World Corporation; *Int'l*, pg. 2220
CHENNAI FERROUS INDUSTRIES LIMITED; *Int'l*, pg. 1470
CHENNAI MEENAKSHI MULTISPECIALITY HOSPITAL LIMITED; *Int'l*, pg. 1470
CHENNAI PETROLEUM CORPORATION LIMITED—See Indian Oil Corporation Limited; *Int'l*, pg. 3654
CHENPOWER INFORMATION TECHNOLOGY (SHANGHAI) CO., LTD.—See Chenbro Micom Co., Ltd.; *Int'l*, pg. 1465
CHEN PR; *U.S. Private*, pg. 872
CHENTEX GARMENT CO., LTD.—See Nien Hsing Textile Co., Ltd.; *Int'l*, pg. 5280
CHENTRONICS CORPORATION—See Koch Industries, Inc.; *U.S. Private*, pg. 2331
CHEN XING DEVELOPMENT HOLDINGS LIMITED; *Int'l*, pg. 1465

CHENYA ENERGY CO., LTD.—See Marubeni Corporation; *Int'l*, pg. 4705
CHENZHOU CITY JINGUI SILVER INDUSTRY CO., LTD.; *Int'l*, pg. 1470
CHENZHOU INTERNATIONAL CONVENTION & EXHIBITION CENTER LIMITED—See Pico Far East Holdings Limited; *Int'l*, pg. 5860
CHENZHOU SHANSHAN NEW MATERIAL CO., LTD.—See Ningbo Shanshan Co., Ltd.; *Int'l*, pg. 5305
CHENZHOU XIANGDA CAMEL FEED CO., LTD—See Tangrenshen Group Co., Ltd.; *Int'l*, pg. 7458
CHENZHOU XIANGNENG SEMICONDUCTOR GAS CO., LTD.—See Guangdong Huate Gas Co., Ltd.; *Int'l*, pg. 3156
CHENZHOU XIPOINT TECHNOLOGY CO., LTD.—See Gospell Digital Technology Co., Ltd.; *Int'l*, pg. 3043
CHEONGBO INDUSTRIAL CO., LTD.; *Int'l*, pg. 1470
CHEONG FATT HOLDINGS PTE. LTD.—See CFM Holdings Limited; *Int'l*, pg. 1430
CHEONG FATT METAL FACTORY PTE LTD—See CFM Holdings Limited; *Int'l*, pg. 1430
CHEONGFULI (HONGKONG) COMPANY LIMITED—See Xiamen C&D Inc.; *Int'l*, pg. 8523
CHEONGFULI (MALAYSIA) SDN. BHD.—See Xiamen C&D Inc.; *Int'l*, pg. 8523
CHEONGHO ICT CO., LTD.; *Int'l*, pg. 1470
CHEONG KWAN JANG TAIWAN CORPORATION—See KT&G Corporation; *Int'l*, pg. 4315
CHEOPS TECHNOLOGY FRANCE SA; *Int'l*, pg. 1471
CHEP AMERICAS—See Brambles Limited; *Int'l*, pg. 1138
CHEP ASIA-PACIFIC—See Brambles Limited; *Int'l*, pg. 1138
CHEP AUSTRALIA LIMITED—See Brambles Limited; *Int'l*, pg. 1138
CHEP BENELUX NEDERLAND BV—See Brambles Limited; *Int'l*, pg. 1138
CHEP BENELUX N.V.—See Brambles Limited; *Int'l*, pg. 1138
CHEP CANADA, INC.—See Brambles Limited; *Int'l*, pg. 1138
CHEP CHILE SA—See Brambles Limited; *Int'l*, pg. 1138
CHEP DENMARK—See Brambles Limited; *Int'l*, pg. 1138
CHEP DEUTSCHLAND GMBH—See Brambles Limited; *Int'l*, pg. 1138
CHEP EMEA—See Brambles Limited; *Int'l*, pg. 1100
CHEP ESPANA SA—See Brambles Limited; *Int'l*, pg. 1138
CHEP EUROPE—See Brambles Limited; *Int'l*, pg. 1138
CHEP FINLAND—See Brambles Limited; *Int'l*, pg. 1138
CHEP FRANCE S.A.—See Brambles Limited; *Int'l*, pg. 1138
CHEP INDIA PVT. LTD.—See Brambles Limited; *Int'l*, pg. 1138
CHEP ITALIA SRL—See Brambles Limited; *Int'l*, pg. 1138
CHEP (MALAYSIA) SDN BHD—See Brambles Limited; *Int'l*, pg. 1138
CHEP MEXICO SA DE CV—See Brambles Limited; *Int'l*, pg. 1138
CHEP NEW ZEALAND—See Brambles Limited; *Int'l*, pg. 1138
CHEP NORWAY—See Brambles Limited; *Int'l*, pg. 1138
CHEP OSTERREICH GMBH—See Brambles Limited; *Int'l*, pg. 1138
CHEP PALLECON SOLUTIONS PTY LTD—See Brambles Limited; *Int'l*, pg. 1138
CHEP PORTUGAL—See Brambles Limited; *Int'l*, pg. 1138
CHEPRI HOLDING B.V.; *Int'l*, pg. 1471
CHEP SCHWEIZ BV—See Brambles Limited; *Int'l*, pg. 1138
CHEP (SHANGHAI) CO., LTD.—See Brambles Limited; *Int'l*, pg. 1138
CHEP SINGAPORE PTE. LTD.—See Brambles Limited; *Int'l*, pg. 1138
CHEP SOUTH AFRICA (PTY) LTD.—See Brambles Limited; *Int'l*, pg. 1139
CHEP SWEDEN—See Brambles Limited; *Int'l*, pg. 1139
CHEP UK LIMITED—See Brambles Limited; *Int'l*, pg. 1139
CHEP USA—See Brambles Limited; *Int'l*, pg. 1138
CHEQUE EXCHANGE LIMITED—See Vanquis Banking Group plc; *Int'l*, pg. 8130
CHEQUEFECTIVO, S.A.; *Int'l*, pg. 1471
CHEQUERS SA; *Int'l*, pg. 1471
CHER A BUMPS & ASSOCIATES, INC.—See The Plexus Groupe, Inc.; *U.S. Private*, pg. 4096
CHERAS MEDICAL CENTRE SDN. BHD—See Khazanah Nasional Berhad; *Int'l*, pg. 4152
CHERAT CEMENT COMPANY LIMITED; *Int'l*, pg. 1471
CHERATING HOLIDAY VILLA BERHAD—See Advance Synergy Berhad; *Int'l*, pg. 156
CHERAT PACKAGING LIMITED; *Int'l*, pg. 1471
CHERAW DIALYSIS, LLC—See DaVita Inc.; *U.S. Public*, pg. 636
CHERBONNIER, MAYER & ASSOCIATES INC.; *U.S. Private*, pg. 873
CHERBOURG MARITIME VOYAGES SARL—See Financiere de L'Odet; *Int'l*, pg. 2667
CHEREPOVETS PLYWOOD & FURNITURE PLANT, JSC; *Int'l*, pg. 1471
CHERGEY INSURANCE—See GCP Capital Partners Holdings LLC; *U.S. Private*, pg. 1654

CHERIE FM AQUITAINE SUD—See NRJ Group SA; *Int'l*, pg. 5474
CHERIE FM SAS—See NRJ Group SA; *Int'l*, pg. 5474
CHERIN TRANSPORTATION, INC.—See Purity Wholesale Grocers, Inc.; *U.S. Private*, pg. 3306
CHERISH SUNSHINE INTERNATIONAL LIMITED; *Int'l*, pg. 1471
CHERKASYOBLENERGO PJSC; *Int'l*, pg. 1471
CHER-MAKE SAUSAGE COMPANY—See Lakeside Foods, Inc.; *U.S. Private*, pg. 2377
CHERMSIDE VETERINARY HOSPITAL PTY LTD.—See TPG Capital, L.P.; *U.S. Public*, pg. 2176
CHERNAN METAL INDUSTRIAL CORP.; *Int'l*, pg. 1471
CHERNE CONTRACTING CORPORATION; *U.S. Private*, pg. 873
CHERNER AUTOMOTIVE GROUP; *U.S. Private*, pg. 873
CHERNG TAY TECHNOLOGY CO., LTD.; *Int'l*, pg. 1471
CHERNG TAY TECHNOLOGY (INDIA) PRIVATE LIMITED—See Cherng Tay Technology Co., Ltd.; *Int'l*, pg. 1471
CHERNIGIVOBLENERGO PJSC; *Int'l*, pg. 1471
CHERNOFF DIAMOND & CO, LLC—See Caisse de Depot et Placement du Quebec; *Int'l*, pg. 1256
CHERNOFF DIAMOND & CO, LLC—See KKR & Co. Inc.; *U.S. Public*, pg. 1265
CHERNOFF NEWMAN, LLC; *U.S. Private*, pg. 873
CHERNOFF SALES INC.; *U.S. Private*, pg. 873
CHERNOMORSKI HOLDING AD; *Int'l*, pg. 1472
CHERNOMORTRANSNEFT, JSC—See OAO AK Transneft; *Int'l*, pg. 5505
CHERNYANSKY SUGAR—See Gruppa Kompaniy Rusagro OOO; *Int'l*, pg. 3140
CHERN YIH ELECTRONICS ENT.CO., LTD.—See Advanced Analog Technology, Inc.; *Int'l*, pg. 157
CHERNYSHEV MOSCOW MACHINE-BUILDING ENTERPRISE, JSC—See Russian Technologies State Corporation; *Int'l*, pg. 6430
CHEROKEE BRICK & TILE COMPANY; *U.S. Private*, pg. 873
CHEROKEE BUILDING MATERIALS INC.—See GMS Inc.; *U.S. Public*, pg. 948
CHEROKEE BUILDING MATERIALS OF OKC, INC.—See GMS Inc.; *U.S. Public*, pg. 948
CHEROKEE CHEMICAL CO. INC.; *U.S. Private*, pg. 873
CHEROKEE COMMUNICATIONS INC.; *U.S. Private*, pg. 873
CHEROKEE COUNTY ELECTRIC COOPERATIVE ASSOCIATION; *U.S. Private*, pg. 873
CHEROKEE COUNTY WATER SEWAGE AUTHORITY; *U.S. Private*, pg. 873
CHEROKEE DATA SOLUTIONS; *U.S. Private*, pg. 873
CHEROKEE DISTRIBUTING COMPANY, INC.; *U.S. Private*, pg. 873
CHEROKEE ENTERPRISES, INC.; *U.S. Private*, pg. 873
CHEROKEE GRILL—See The Copper Cellar Corporation; *U.S. Private*, pg. 4014
CHEROKEE HEALTHCARE, INC.—See The Ensign Group, Inc.; *U.S. Public*, pg. 2071
CHEROKEE INFORMATION SERVICES, INC.; *U.S. Private*, pg. 873
CHEROKEE LANDING CORPORATION—See Equity LifeStyle Properties, Inc.; *U.S. Public*, pg. 790
CHEROKEE MANUFACTURING INC.; *U.S. Private*, pg. 873
CHEROKEE NATIONAL LIFE INSURANCE CO.—See Securian Financial Group, Inc.; *U.S. Private*, pg. 3594
CHEROKEE NATION BUSINESSES; *U.S. Private*, pg. 873
CHEROKEE NATION ENTERTAINMENT—See Cherokee Nation Businesses; *U.S. Private*, pg. 873
CHEROKEE NITROGEN HOLDINGS, INC.—See LSB Industries, Inc.; *U.S. Public*, pg. 1344
CHEROKEE NITROGEN LLC—See LSB Industries, Inc.; *U.S. Public*, pg. 1344
CHEROKEE REGIONAL MEDICAL CENTER; *U.S. Private*, pg. 873
CHERRY AEROSPACE LLC—See Berkshire Hathaway Inc.; *U.S. Public*, pg. 315
CHERRY-AIR INC, CHARTERED AIR CARGO—See Cherry-Air; *U.S. Private*, pg. 874
CHERRY-AIR; *U.S. Private*, pg. 874
CHERRY AMERICAS, LLC—See ZF Friedrichshafen AG; *Int'l*, pg. 8643
CHERRY AUSTRALIA PTY. LTD.—See ZF Friedrichshafen AG; *Int'l*, pg. 8643
CHERRY BEKAERT LLP; *U.S. Private*, pg. 873
CHERRYBRO CO., LTD.; *Int'l*, pg. 1472
CHERRYBROOK PREMIUM PET SUPPLIES; *U.S. Private*, pg. 874
CHERRY CAPITAL CADILLAC SUBARU, LLC.; *U.S. Private*, pg. 874
CHERRY CENTRAL COOPERATIVE, INC.; *U.S. Private*, pg. 874
CHERRY COMPANIES MANAGEMENT, INC.—See Arcosa, Inc.; *U.S. Public*, pg. 186
THE CHERRY COMPANY, LTD.—See Takara Holdings, Inc.; *Int'l*, pg. 7433
CHERRY CREEK BENEFITS—See New Mountain Capital, LLC; *U.S. Private*, pg. 2901

CHERRY CREEK MORTGAGE CO. INC.; *U.S. Private*, pg. 874
CHERRY CREEK MORTGAGE LLC—See McCarthy Group, LLC; *U.S. Private*, pg. 2626
CHERRY ELECTRONICS (HONG KONG) CO., LTD.—See Cherry SE; *Int'l*, pg. 1472
CHERRY ENERGY; *U.S. Private*, pg. 874
CHERRY EUROPE GMBH—See Cherry SE; *Int'l*, pg. 1472
CHERRY GROVE SOUTH CAROLINA, LLC—See Independence Realty Trust, Inc.; *U.S. Public*, pg. 1115
CHERRY GROWERS INC.; *U.S. Private*, pg. 874
CHERRY HILL CONSTRUCTION INC.—See Tutor Perini Corporation; *U.S. Public*, pg. 2205
CHERRY HILL IMPORTS CORP—See HSF Enterprises Inc.; *U.S. Private*, pg. 1999
CHERRY HILL MORTGAGE INVESTMENT CORPORATION; *U.S. Public*, pg. 485
CHERRY HILL PARK, LLC—See Century Communities, Inc.; *U.S. Public*, pg. 475
CHERRY HILL PROGRAMS, INC.—See Keystone Capital, Inc.; *U.S. Private*, pg. 2295
CHERRY HILL TAVERN (BMG) PTY LTD—See Woolworths Group Limited; *Int'l*, pg. 8451
CHERRY HOUSE INC.; *U.S. Private*, pg. 874
CHERRYLAND ELECTRIC COOPERATIVE; *U.S. Private*, pg. 874
CHERRYLANE THEATRE—See A24 Films LLC; *U.S. Private*, pg. 29
CHERRY OPTICAL, INC.—See EssilorLuxottica Inc.; *Int'l*, pg. 2513
CHERRYPICK GAMES SA; *Int'l*, pg. 1472
CHERRYPICKS LIMITED—See NetDragon Websoft Holdings Limited; *Int'l*, pg. 5213
CHERRYROAD TECHNOLOGIES INC.; *U.S. Private*, pg. 874
CHERRY SE; *Int'l*, pg. 1472
CHERRY STIX LTD.; *U.S. Private*, pg. 874
CHERRY STREET CAPITAL; *U.S. Public*, pg. 485
CHERRY TECHNOLOGIES, INC.—See Peterson Farms, Inc.; *U.S. Private*, pg. 3160
CHERRYVALE MALL, LLC—See CBL & Associates Properties, Inc.; *U.S. Public*, pg. 458
CHERRY VALLEY FARMS LTD.—See Beijing Capital Agribusiness Group Co., Ltd.; *Int'l*, pg. 947
CHERRY VALLEY FARMS LTD.—See CITIC Group Corporation; *Int'l*, pg. 1620
THE CHERTOFF GROUP, LLC; *U.S. Private*, pg. 4007
CHERUBIM INTERESTS, INC.; *U.S. Public*, pg. 485
CHERVON HOLDINGS LIMITED; *Int'l*, pg. 1472
CHERY AUTOMOBILE CO., LTD.; *Int'l*, pg. 1472
CHERYL & CO.—See 1-800-FLOWERS.COM, Inc.; *U.S. Public*, pg. 1
CHERYONG ELECTRIC CO., LTD—See Cheryong Industrial Co Ltd; *Int'l*, pg. 1472
CHERYONG INDUSTRIAL CO LTD - DAEJEON FACTORY—See Cheryong Industrial Co Ltd; *Int'l*, pg. 1472
CHERYONG INDUSTRIAL CO LTD; *Int'l*, pg. 1472
CHERY SOUTH AFRICA—See Chery Automobile Co., Ltd.; *Int'l*, pg. 1472
CHESAPEAKE & ALBEMARLE RAILROAD—See Brookfield Infrastructure Partners L.P.; *Int'l*, pg. 1192
CHESAPEAKE & ALBEMARLE RAILROAD—See GIC Pte. Ltd.; *Int'l*, pg. 2966
CHESAPEAKE APPALACHIA, LLC—See Expand Energy Corporation; *U.S. Public*, pg. 808
CHESAPEAKE BANCORP; *U.S. Public*, pg. 485
CHESAPEAKE BANK OF MARYLAND; *U.S. Private*, pg. 874
CHESAPEAKE BANK—See Chesapeake Financial Shares, Inc.; *U.S. Public*, pg. 485
CHESAPEAKE BAY FOUNDATION; *U.S. Private*, pg. 874
CHESAPEAKE BAY SEAFOOD HOUSE ASSOCIATES, LLC; *U.S. Private*, pg. 874
CHESAPEAKE EMPLOYERS' INSURANCE COMPANY; *U.S. Private*, pg. 875
CHESAPEAKE ENERGY MARKETING, LLC—See Expand Energy Corporation; *U.S. Public*, pg. 808
CHESAPEAKE EYE CARE & LASER CENTER, LLC—See Centre Partners Management LLC; *U.S. Private*, pg. 828
CHESAPEAKE FINANCIAL SHARES, INC.; *U.S. Public*, pg. 485
CHESAPEAKE GOLD CORPORATION; *Int'l*, pg. 1472
CHESAPEAKE GRANITE WASH TRUST; *U.S. Public*, pg. 485
CHESAPEAKE-H, LLC—See Lithia Motors, Inc.; *U.S. Public*, pg. 1321
CHESAPEAKE INVESTMENT COMPANY—See Chesapeake Utilities Corporation; *U.S. Public*, pg. 485
THE CHESAPEAKE LIFE INSURANCE CO.—See Blackstone Inc.; *U.S. Public*, pg. 354
CHESAPEAKE LODGING TRUST—See Park Hotels & Resorts Inc.; *U.S. Public*, pg. 1638
CHESAPEAKE LOUSIANA, L.P.—See Expand Energy Corporation; *U.S. Public*, pg. 808
CHESAPEAKE MALL, LLC—See Washington Prime Group Inc.; *U.S. Private*, pg. 4448

CHESAPEAKE GRANITE WASH TRUST — CORPORATE AFFILIATIONS

CHESAPEAKE MEDICAL STAFFING, LLC—See Great Point Partners, LLC; *U.S. Private*, pg. 1767
CHESAPEAKE MID-CONTINENT CORP.—See Expand Energy Corporation; *U.S. Public*, pg. 808
CHESAPEAKE MORTGAGE COMPANY—See Chesapeake Financial Shares, Inc.; *U.S. Public*, pg. 485
CHESAPEAKE NETCRAFTSMEN, LLC—See Source Capital, LLC; *U.S. Private*, pg. 3718
CHESAPEAKE OILFIELD SERVICES, INC.—See Expand Energy Corporation; *U.S. Public*, pg. 808
CHESAPEAKE OPERATING, LLC—See Expand Energy Corporation; *U.S. Public*, pg. 808
CHESAPEAKE PUBLISHING & PRINTING—See American Consolidated Media LP; *U.S. Private*, pg. 228
CHESAPEAKE SERVICE COMPANY—See Chesapeake Utilities Corporation; *U.S. Public*, pg. 485
CHESAPEAKE SPRINKLER COMPANY; *U.S. Private*, pg. 875
CHESAPEAKE'S—See The Copper Cellar Corporation; *U.S. Private*, pg. 4014
CHESAPEAKE TECHNOLOGY INTERNATIONAL CORP.—See Bluestone Investment Partners, LLC; *U.S. Private*, pg. 598
CHESAPEAKE UROLOGY ASSOCIATES PA—See Audax Group, Limited Partnership; *U.S. Private*, pg. 387
CHESAPEAKE UTILITIES CORPORATION; *U.S. Public*, pg. 485
CHESBAY DISTRIBUTING, LLC—See Reyes Holdings, LLC; *U.S. Private*, pg. 3418
CHE SCIENTIFIC COMPANY (H.K.) LIMITED—See CHINO Corporation; *Int'l*, pg. 1570
CHESHAM SPECIALTY INGREDIENTS LTD.—See EQT AB; *Int'l*, pg. 2469
CHESHER EQUIPMENT LTD.; *Int'l*, pg. 1472
THE CHESHIRE & GREATER MANCHESTER COMMUNITY REHABILITATION COMPANY LTD.—See Interserve Plc; *Int'l*, pg. 3760
CHESHIRE LUMBER CO. INC.—See The Lyon & Billard Co., Inc.; *U.S. Private*, pg. 4073
CHESHIRE OIL COMPANY INC.; *U.S. Private*, pg. 875
CHESHIRES OF NOTTINGHAM—See Headlam Group plc; *Int'l*, pg. 3301
CHESKIN ADDED VALUE; *U.S. Private*, pg. 875
CHESLIND TEXTILES LTD.—See RSWM Ltd.; *Int'l*, pg. 6420
CHESNARA PLC; *Int'l*, pg. 1472
CHESROWN CHEVROLET, LLC—See AutoNation, Inc.; *U.S. Public*, pg. 234
CHESROWN COLLISION CENTER, INC.—See AutoNation, Inc.; *U.S. Public*, pg. 234
CHESSCO INDUSTRIES, INC.; *U.S. Private*, pg. 875
CHESS COMMUNICATIONS GROUP; *U.S. Private*, pg. 875
CHESSCO PROCESS RESEARCH PRODUCTS—See Chessco Industries, Inc.; *U.S. Private*, pg. 875
CHESS DYNAMICS LIMITED—See Cohort plc; *Int'l*, pg. 1695
CHESSER ARAMA VE MADENCILIK LIMITED SIRKETI—See Fortuna Mining Corp.; *Int'l*, pg. 2743
CHESSER RESOURCES LIMITED—See Fortuna Mining Corp.; *Int'l*, pg. 2742
CHESSWOOD GP LIMITED—See Chesswood Group Limited; *Int'l*, pg. 1472
CHESSWOOD GROUP LIMITED; *Int'l*, pg. 1472
CHESTER BANCORP, INC.; *U.S. Public*, pg. 486
CHESTER CARTAGE LTD.; *Int'l*, pg. 1473
CHESTER COUNTY COMMUNITY FOUNDATION; *U.S. Private*, pg. 875
CHESTER COUNTY NATURAL GAS AUTHORITY; *U.S. Private*, pg. 875
CHESTER DAIRY COMPANY; *U.S. Private*, pg. 875
CHESTERFIELD AMBULATORY SURGERY CENTER, L.P.—See Tenet Healthcare Corporation; *U.S. Public*, pg. 2009
CHESTERFIELD GENERAL HOSPITAL—See McLeod Health; *U.S. Private*, pg. 2641
CHESTERFIELD IMAGING, LLC—See HCA Healthcare, Inc.; *U.S. Public*, pg. 993
CHESTERFIELD IMAGING, LLC—See HCA Healthcare, Inc.; *U.S. Public*, pg. 993
CHESTERFIELD MACADAM—See CEMEX, S.A.B. de C.V.; *Int'l*, pg. 1399
CHESTERFIELD RESOURCES PLC; *Int'l*, pg. 1473
CHESTERFIELD SPECIAL CYLINDERS LIMITED—See Pressure Technologies Plc; *Int'l*, pg. 5965
CHESTER HMA, INC.—See Medical University Of South Carolina; *U.S. Private*, pg. 2656
CHESTER HOIST—See Columbus McKinnon Corporation; *U.S. Public*, pg. 535
CHESTER INC.; *U.S. Private*, pg. 875
CHESTER LAUNDRY LIMITED—See Johnson Service Group PLC; *Int'l*, pg. 3993
CHESTERMAN CO.; *U.S. Private*, pg. 875
CHESTER MINING CO; *U.S. Public*, pg. 486
CHESTER MUSICE FRANCE—See Music Sales Corporation; *U.S. Private*, pg. 2818
CHESTER MUSIC—See Music Sales Corporation; *U.S. Private*, pg. 2817

CHESTER PROGRESSIVE—See Feather Publishing Co., Inc.; *U.S. Private*, pg. 1486
CHESTER TELEPHONE COMPANY; *U.S. Private*, pg. 875
CHESTERTON CR S.R.O.—See A.W. Chesterton Company; *U.S. Private*, pg. 28
CHESTERTON HUNGARY KFT—See A.W. Chesterton Company; *U.S. Private*, pg. 28
CHESTERTON INTERNATIONAL GMBH—See A.W. Chesterton Company; *U.S. Private*, pg. 28
CHESTERTON MEXICANA S.A. DE C.V.—See A.W. Chesterton Company; *U.S. Private*, pg. 28
CHESTERTON NINGBO SEALING TECHNOLOGY CO. LTD—See A.W. Chesterton Company; *U.S. Private*, pg. 28
CHESTERTON POLSKA SP.Z.O.O—See A.W. Chesterton Company; *U.S. Private*, pg. 28
CHESTERTON ROMA SRL—See A.W. Chesterton Company; *U.S. Private*, pg. 28
CHESTERTON SLOVAKIA S.R.O.—See A.W. Chesterton Company; *U.S. Private*, pg. 28
CHESTERTON SURGERY CENTER, LLC—See Community Health Systems, Inc.; *U.S. Public*, pg. 552
CHESTER WATER AUTHORITY; *U.S. Private*, pg. 875
CHESTER WOODS INC—See LCS Holdings Inc.; *U.S. Private*, pg. 2404
CHESTNUT COMMUNICATIONS, INC.; *U.S. Private*, pg. 875
CHESTNUT FLATS WIND, LLC—See MetLife, Inc.; *U.S. Public*, pg. 1430
CHESTNUT HEALTH SYSTEMS, INC.; *U.S. Private*, pg. 875
CHESTNUT RIDGE COUNSELING SERVICES, INC.; *U.S. Private*, pg. 875
CHESTNUT RIDGE FOAM INC.; *U.S. Private*, pg. 875
CHESTON & GIBBENS INC.; *U.S. Private*, pg. 875
CHET CHEMICALS PTY. LTD.—See Libstar Holdings Ltd.; *Int'l*, pg. 4487
CHET MORRISON CONTRACTORS INC.; *U.S. Private*, pg. 875
CHETTA B INC.; *U.S. Private*, pg. 875
CHETTINAD CEMENTS CORP. LTD. - KARIKKALI PLANT—See Chettinad Group of Companies; *Int'l*, pg. 1473
CHETTINAD CEMENTS CORP. LTD. - PULIYUR PLANT—See Chettinad Group of Companies; *Int'l*, pg. 1473
CHETTINAD CEMENTS CORPORATION LIMITED—See Chettinad Group of Companies; *Int'l*, pg. 1473
CHETTINAD GROUP OF COMPANIES; *Int'l*, pg. 1473
CHETU, INC.; *U.S. Private*, pg. 876
CHEUK NANG (HOLDINGS) LIMITED; *Int'l*, pg. 1473
CHEUK NANG PROPERTY MANAGEMENT COMPANY—See Cheuk Nang (Holdings) Limited; *Int'l*, pg. 1473
CHEUNG HO ELECTRIC CO., LIMITED; *Int'l*, pg. 1473
CHEUNG WOH PRECISION (ZHUHAI) CO., LTD—See Cheung Woh Technologies Ltd.; *Int'l*, pg. 1473
CHEUNG WOH TECHNOLOGIES (JOHOR) SDN. BHD.—See Cheung Woh Technologies Ltd.; *Int'l*, pg. 1473
CHEUNG WOH TECHNOLOGIES LTD.; *Int'l*, pg. 1473
CHEUNG WOH TECHNOLOGIES (MALAYSIA) SDN. BHD.—See Cheung Woh Technologies Ltd.; *Int'l*, pg. 1473
CHEUNG WOH TECHNOLOGIES (ZHUHAI) CO., LTD—See Cheung Woh Technologies Ltd.; *Int'l*, pg. 1473
CHEVAL ELECTRONIC ENCLOSURE CO. LTD.—See Blackstone Inc.; *U.S. Public*, pg. 354
CHEVALIER ADVERTISING, INC.; *U.S. Private*, pg. 876
CHEVALIER (ALUMINIUM ENGINEERING) LIMITED—See Chevalier International Holdings Limited; *Int'l*, pg. 1473
CHEVALIER AUTOMOBILES INC.—See Chevalier International Holdings Limited; *Int'l*, pg. 1473
CHEVALIER (BUILDING SUPPLIES & ENGINEERING) LIMITED—See Chevalier International Holdings Limited; *Int'l*, pg. 1473
CHEVALIER COLD STORAGE & LOGISTICS LIMITED—See Chevalier International Holdings Limited; *Int'l*, pg. 1473
CHEVALIER (CONSTRUCTION) COMPANY LIMITED—See Chevalier International Holdings Limited; *Int'l*, pg. 1473
CHEVALIER (E & M CONTRACTING) LIMITED—See Chevalier International Holdings Limited; *Int'l*, pg. 1473
CHEVALIER (ENVIROTECH) LIMITED—See Chevalier International Holdings Limited; *Int'l*, pg. 1473
CHEVALIER (INSURANCE BROKERS) LIMITED—See Chevalier International Holdings Limited; *Int'l*, pg. 1473
CHEVALIER INSURANCE COMPANY LIMITED—See Chevalier International Holdings Limited; *Int'l*, pg. 1473
CHEVALIER INTERNATIONAL HOLDINGS LIMITED; *Int'l*, pg. 1473
CHEVALIER INTERNATIONAL (USA), INC.—See Chevalier International Holdings Limited; *Int'l*, pg. 1473
CHEVALIER ITECH SERVICES LIMITED—See Chevalier International Holdings Limited; *Int'l*, pg. 1474
CHEVALIER ITECH THAI LIMITED—See Chevalier International Holdings Limited; *Int'l*, pg. 1474

CHEVALIER MACHINERY CO., LTD.—See Falcon Machine Tools Co. Ltd.; *Int'l*, pg. 2611
CHEVALIER MACHINERY, INC.—See Falcon Machine Tools Co. Ltd.; *Int'l*, pg. 2611
CHEVALIER (NETWORK SOLUTIONS) LIMITED—See Chevalier International Holdings Limited; *Int'l*, pg. 1473
CHEVALIER PRODUCTIONS, INC.—See Lions Gate Entertainment Corp.; *Int'l*, pg. 4520
CHEVALIER PROPERTY MANAGEMENT LIMITED—See Chevalier International Holdings Limited; *Int'l*, pg. 1473
CHEVALLIER SUD; *Int'l*, pg. 1473
CHEVAL QUANCARD; *Int'l*, pg. 1473
CHEVAL TECHNOLOGY CO. LTD.—See Blackstone Inc.; *U.S. Public*, pg. 354
C. H. EVENSEN INDUSTRIOVNER AS—See Vow ASA; *Int'l*, pg. 8310
CHEVILLOT S.A.S.—See Merck & Co., Inc.; *U.S. Public*, pg. 1415
CHEVIOT AGRO INDUSTRIES PVT. LTD.—See Cheviot Company Limited; *Int'l*, pg. 1474
CHEVIOT BRIDGE LIMITED; *Int'l*, pg. 1474
CHEVIOT COMPANY LIMITED; *Int'l*, pg. 1474
CHEVIOT INTERNATIONAL LTD.—See Cheviot Company Limited; *Int'l*, pg. 1474
CHEVIOT RECRUITMENT LTD—See MAXIMUS, Inc.; *U.S. Public*, pg. 1402
CHEVITA GMBH; *Int'l*, pg. 1474
CHEVRILLON & ASSOCIES SCA; *Int'l*, pg. 1474
CHEVRILLON PHILIPPE INDUSTRIE; *Int'l*, pg. 1474
CHEVROLET 21, INC.; *U.S. Private*, pg. 876
CHEVROLET AUSTRIA GMBH—See General Motors Company; *U.S. Public*, pg. 927
CHEVROLET-BUICK OF QUINCY; *U.S. Private*, pg. 876
CHEVROLET CENTER INC.; *U.S. Private*, pg. 876
CHEVROLET CENTRAL AND EASTERN EUROPE—See General Motors Company; *U.S. Public*, pg. 926
CHEVROLET DEUTSCHLAND GMBH—See General Motors Company; *U.S. Public*, pg. 926
CHEVROLET ESPANA, S.A.—See General Motors Company; *U.S. Public*, pg. 927
CHEVROLET EURO PARTS CENTER B.V.—See General Motors Company; *U.S. Public*, pg. 927
CHEVROLET EUROPE GMBH—See General Motors Company; *U.S. Public*, pg. 926
CHEVROLET FINLAND OY—See General Motors Company; *U.S. Public*, pg. 927
CHEVROLET ITALIA S.P.A.—See General Motors Company; *U.S. Public*, pg. 926
CHEVROLET OF BOAZ, INC.—See Alexander Automotive; *U.S. Private*, pg. 163
CHEVROLET OF COLUMBUS, INC.—See General Motors Company; *U.S. Public*, pg. 923
CHEVROLET OF MONTEBELLO; *U.S. Private*, pg. 876
CHEVROLET OF NOVATO, INC.—See General Motors Company; *U.S. Public*, pg. 923
CHEVROLET OF WOOSTER; *U.S. Private*, pg. 876
CHEVROLET OTOMOTIV TICARET LIMITED SIRKETI—See General Motors Company; *U.S. Public*, pg. 923
CHEVROLET PORTUGAL, LDA.—See General Motors Company; *U.S. Public*, pg. 927
CHEVROLET SALES INDIA PRIVATE LTD.—See General Motors Company; *U.S. Public*, pg. 923
CHEVROLET SALES (THAILAND) LIMITED—See General Motors Company; *U.S. Public*, pg. 923
CHEVROLET SOCIEDAD ANONIMA DE AHORRO PARA FINES DETERMINADOS—See General Motors Company; *U.S. Public*, pg. 923
CHEVROLET SUISSE S.A.—See General Motors Company; *U.S. Public*, pg. 926
CHEVROLET SVERIGE AB—See General Motors Company; *U.S. Public*, pg. 926
CHEVROLET UK LIMITED LTD—See General Motors Company; *U.S. Public*, pg. 927
CHEVROLET WORLD, INC.—See AutoNation, Inc.; *U.S. Public*, pg. 234
CHEVROLET WORLD, INC.—See AutoNation, Inc.; *U.S. Public*, pg. 234
CHEVRON ARGENTINA S.R.L.—See Chevron Corporation; *U.S. Public*, pg. 486
CHEVRON AUSTRALIA PTY LTD.—See Chevron Corporation; *U.S. Public*, pg. 486
CHEVRON BELGIUM NV/SA—See Chevron Corporation; *U.S. Public*, pg. 486
CHEVRON CANADA FINANCE LTD.—See Chevron Corporation; *U.S. Public*, pg. 486
CHEVRON CANADA LIMITED—See Chevron Corporation; *U.S. Public*, pg. 486
CHEVRON CANADA RESOURCES—See Chevron Corporation; *U.S. Public*, pg. 486
CHEVRON CORPORATION; *U.S. Public*, pg. 486
CHEVRON EXPLORATION & PRODUCTION INC.—See Chevron Corporation; *U.S. Public*, pg. 486
CHEVRON FRANCE SA—See Chevron Corporation; *U.S. Public*, pg. 486
CHEVRON FUNDING CORPORATION—See Chevron Corporation; *U.S. Public*, pg. 486
CHEVRON GLOBAL ENERGY INC.—See Chevron Corporation; *U.S. Public*, pg. 486

COMPANY NAME INDEX

CHEVRON, INC.—See Miller Industries, Inc.; *U.S. Public*, pg. 1446
CHEVRON INFORMATION TECHNOLOGY COMPANY—See Chevron Corporation; *U.S. Public*, pg. 486
CHEVRON INTERNATIONAL PTE. LTD.—See Chevron Corporation; *U.S. Public*, pg. 486
CHEVRON LATIN AMERICA—See Chevron Corporation; *U.S. Public*, pg. 486
CHEVRON LUBRICANTS LANKA PLC; *Int'l*, pg. 1474
CHEVRON MALAMPAYA LLC—See Udenna Corporation; *Int'l*, pg. 8014
CHEVRON NIGERIA LIMITED—See Chevron Corporation; *U.S. Public*, pg. 486
CHEVRON NORTH SEA LIMITED—See Delek Group Ltd.; *Int'l*, pg. 2012
CHEVRON ORONITE COMPANY LLC—See Chevron Corporation; *U.S. Public*, pg. 486
CHEVRON ORONITE PTE. LTD.—See Chevron Corporation; *U.S. Public*, pg. 486
CHEVRON ORONITE S.A.—See Chevron Corporation; *U.S. Public*, pg. 486
CHEVRON OVERSEAS PETROLEUM LIMITED—See Chevron Corporation; *U.S. Public*, pg. 486
CHEVRON PHILIPPINES INC.—See Chevron Corporation; *U.S. Public*, pg. 486
CHEVRON PHILLIPS CHEMICAL COMPANY LLC—See Chevron Corporation; *U.S. Public*, pg. 486
CHEVRON PHILLIPS CHEMICAL COMPANY LLC—See Phillips 66 Company; *U.S. Public*, pg. 1688
CHEVRON PHILLIPS CHEMICALS INTERNATIONAL N.V.—See Chevron Corporation; *U.S. Public*, pg. 486
CHEVRON PHILLIPS CHEMICALS INTERNATIONAL N.V.—See Phillips 66 Company; *U.S. Public*, pg. 1688
CHEVRON PIPE LINE COMPANY—See Chevron Corporation; *U.S. Public*, pg. 486
CHEVRON SHIPPING COMPANY LLC—See Chevron Corporation; *U.S. Public*, pg. 486
CHEVRON THAILAND EXPLORATION & PRODUCTION, LTD.—See Chevron Corporation; *U.S. Public*, pg. 486
CHEVRON (THAILAND) LIMITED—See Chevron Corporation; *U.S. Public*, pg. 486
CHEVRON TRINIDAD, INC.—See Chevron Corporation; *U.S. Public*, pg. 487
CHEVRON UNITED KINGDOM LIMITED—See Chevron Corporation; *U.S. Public*, pg. 487
CHEVRON U.S.A. INC.—See Chevron Corporation; *U.S. Public*, pg. 487
THE CHEVY CHASE ASC, LLC—See KKR & Co. Inc.; *U.S. Public*, pg. 1247
CHEVY CHASE CARS; *U.S. Private*, pg. 876
CHEVYPLAN S.A. SOCIEDAD ADMINISTRADORA DE PLANES DE AUTOFINANCIAMIENTO COMERCIAL—See General Motors Company; *U.S. Public*, pg. 923
CHEWATHAI PLC; *Int'l*, pg. 1474
CHEWDEF GP GMBH—See Barclays PLC; *Int'l*, pg. 862
CHEWNING & WILMER INCORPORATED; *U.S. Private*, pg. 876
CHEW S AGRICULTURE PTE LTD—See OneApex Limited; *Int'l*, pg. 5576
CHEWSE, INC.; *U.S. Private*, pg. 876
CHEWY, INC.—See BC Partners LLP; *Int'l*, pg. 925
CHEWY, INC.—See Caisse de Depot et Placement du Quebec; *Int'l*, pg. 1254
CHEWY, INC.—See StepStone Group LP; *U.S. Private*, pg. 3804
CHEX FINER FOODS; *U.S. Private*, pg. 876
CHEX SYSTEMS INC.—See Fidelity National Infor; *U.S. Public*, pg. 832
CHEX-TV - DURHAM—See Corus Entertainment Inc.; *Int'l*, pg. 1808
CHEX-TV - PETERBOROUGH—See Corus Entertainment Inc.; *Int'l*, pg. 1808
CHEYENNE CAMPING CENTER CO.; *U.S. Private*, pg. 876
CHEYENNE INDUSTRIES, LLC; *U.S. Private*, pg. 876
CHEYENNE LIGHT, FUEL & POWER CO.—See Black Hills Corporation; *U.S. Public*, pg. 341
CHEYENNE LOGISTICS LLC—See HF Sinclair Corporation; *U.S. Public*, pg. 1033
CHEYENNE PLAINS GAS PIPELINE COMPANY, L.L.C.—See Kinder Morgan, Inc.; *U.S. Public*, pg. 1232
CHEYNET ASIA (CO.) LTD—See Cheynet S.A.S.; *Int'l*, pg. 1474
CHEYNET ELASTICS—See Cheynet S.A.S; *Int'l*, pg. 1474
CHEYNET S.A.S; *Int'l*, pg. 1474
CHEYNET TUNISIE—See Cheynet S.A.S.; *Int'l*, pg. 1474
C.H. FENSTERMAKER & ASSOCIATES, INC.; *U.S. Private*, pg. 707
CHF HOME FURNISHINGS; *U.S. Private*, pg. 876
CHF INDUSTRIES, INC.; *U.S. Private*, pg. 876
CHG GROUP, INC.—See Chemring Group PLC; *Int'l*, pg. 1463
CHG HEALTHCARE SERVICES, INC.—See Ares Management Corporation; *U.S. Public*, pg. 188
CHG HEALTHCARE SERVICES, INC.—See Leonard Green & Partners, L.P.; *U.S. Private*, pg. 2425

CHG MANAGEMENT, INC.—See Ares Management Corporation; *U.S. Public*, pg. 188
CHG MANAGEMENT, INC.—See Leonard Green & Partners, L.P.; *U.S. Private*, pg. 2425
CHG MEDICAL STAFFING, INC.—See Ares Management Corporation; *U.S. Public*, pg. 188
CHG MEDICAL STAFFING, INC.—See Leonard Green & Partners, L.P.; *U.S. Private*, pg. 2425
C.H. GUENTHER & SON, INC. - PIONEER FLOUR MILL—See The Pritzker Group - Chicago, LLC; *U.S. Private*, pg. 4098
C.H. GUENTHER & SON, LLC—See The Pritzker Group - Chicago, LLC; *U.S. Private*, pg. 4098
C.H. GUERNSEY & COMPANY, INC.; *U.S. Private*, pg. 707
CHHABRA SPINNERS LIMITED; *Int'l*, pg. 1474
CHHATTISGARH HIGHWAY DEVELOPMENT COMPANY LIMITED—See Infrastructure Leasing & Financial Services Limited; *Int'l*, pg. 3698
CHHAYA PRAKASHANI PRIVATE LIMITED—See S Chand & Company Limited; *Int'l*, pg. 6442
CHHJ FRANCHISING LLC; *U.S. Private*, pg. 876
CHH MICROTECHNIQUE SA—See The Swatch Group Ltd.; *Int'l*, pg. 7691
C.H. HOLDERBY CO.; *U.S. Private*, pg. 707
C.H. HOLDINGS, USA INC.; *U.S. Private*, pg. 707
CH HOLDINGS USA, INC.; *U.S. Private*, pg. 844
CHHS HOSPITAL COMPANY, LLC—See Tower Health; *U.S. Private*, pg. 4193
CHIA CHANG CO., LTD.; *Int'l*, pg. 1475
CHIA CHANG TECHNOLOGY (CHONG QING) CO., LTD.—See Chia Chang Co., Ltd.; *Int'l*, pg. 1475
CHIA CHANG TECHNOLOGY (SUZHOU) CO., LTD.—See Chia Chang Co., Ltd.; *Int'l*, pg. 1475
CHIA HER INDUSTRIAL CO., LTD.; *Int'l*, pg. 1475
CHIA HER INDUSTRIAL CO., LTD. - TAINAN MILL—See Chia Her Industrial Co., Ltd.; *Int'l*, pg. 1475
CHIA HSIN CEMENT CORP.; *Int'l*, pg. 1475
CHIAHUI POWER CORP.—See Asia Cement Corporation; *Int'l*, pg. 611
CHIA LIH PAU CHEMICAL CO., LTD.—See Kao Corporation; *Int'l*, pg. 4074
CHIALIN PRECISION INDUSTRIAL CO., LTD.; *Int'l*, pg. 1475
CHIA LUNG CHEMICAL INDUSTRIAL CORP.—See DIC Corporation; *Int'l*, pg. 2107
CHIANGMAI FROZEN FOODS PUBLIC COMPANY LIMITED - CHIANGMAI FACTORY 1—See Chiangmai Frozen Foods Public Company Limited; *Int'l*, pg. 1476
CHIANGMAI FROZEN FOODS PUBLIC COMPANY LIMITED - CHIANGMAI FACTORY 2—See Chiangmai Frozen Foods Public Company Limited; *Int'l*, pg. 1476
CHIANGMAI FROZEN FOODS PUBLIC COMPANY LIMITED; *Int'l*, pg. 1476
CHIANG MAI RAM MEDICAL BUSINESS PCL; *Int'l*, pg. 1476
CHIANGMAI RIMDOI PCL; *Int'l*, pg. 1476
CHIAN HSING FORGING INDUSTRIAL CO., LTD.; *Int'l*, pg. 1476
CHIAN HSING (HUAI'AN) AUTO PARTS CO., LTD.—See Chian Hsing Forging Industrial Co., Ltd.; *Int'l*, pg. 1476
CHIAN HSING (TAICANG) METAL PRODUCTS CO., LTD.—See Chian Hsing Forging Industrial Co., Ltd.; *Int'l*, pg. 1476
CHIANTI CHEESE COMPANY; *U.S. Private*, pg. 876
CHIAPPE REVELLO ASSOCIATI—See Publicis Groupe S.A.; *Int'l*, pg. 6103
CHIAPPETTI WHOLESALE MEAT CORPORATION; *U.S. Private*, pg. 876
CHIARA ASSICURAZIONI S P A—See Banco Di Desio e Della Brianza S.p.A.; *Int'l*, pg. 822
CHIARO TECHNOLOGIES LLC—See Cognex Corporation; *U.S. Public*, pg. 522
CHIASMA, INC.—See Chiesi Farmaceutici SpA; *Int'l*, pg. 1477
CHIASMA (ISRAEL) LTD.—See Chiesi Farmaceutici SpA; *Int'l*, pg. 1477
CHIASSO LLC; *U.S. Private*, pg. 876
CHIA TAI COMPANY LIMITED—See Charoen Pokphand Group Co., Ltd.; *Int'l*, pg. 1453
CHIA TAI ENTERPRISES INTERNATIONAL LTD.—See Charoen Pokphand Foods Public Company Limited; *Int'l*, pg. 1452
CHIA TAI TIANQING PHARMACEUTICAL GROUP CO., LTD.—See Sino Biopharmaceutical Limited; *Int'l*, pg. 6946
CHIA TAI YONGJI ENTERPRISE CO., LTD.—See Charoen Pokphand Foods Public Company Limited; *Int'l*, pg. 1452
CHIA TA WORLD CO., LTD.; *Int'l*, pg. 1475
CHIA YI STEEL CO., LTD.; *Int'l*, pg. 1475
CHIA YI STEEL (YAN CHENG) CO., LTD.—See Chia Yi Steel Co., Ltd.; *Int'l*, pg. 1475
THE CHIBA BANK, LTD.; *Int'l*, pg. 7631
CHIBA BANK LTD.—See The Chiba Bank, Ltd.; *Int'l*, pg. 7631
THE CHIBA BANK LTD.—See The Chiba Bank, Ltd.; *Int'l*, pg. 7632

THE CHIBA BANK, LTD.-TREASURY DIVISION—See The Chiba Bank, Ltd.; *Int'l*, pg. 7632
THE CHIBA BANK, LTD. - TREASURY OPERATION DIVISION—See The Chiba Bank, Ltd.; *Int'l*, pg. 7632
CHIBA BUTADIENE INDUSTRY COMPANY, LIMITED—See UBE Corporation; *Int'l*, pg. 8000
CHIBA CHUO GYORUI CO., LTD.—See Chuo Gyorui Co., Ltd.; *Int'l*, pg. 1598
CHIBA DATA CENTER CORPORATION—See Toyo Engineering Corporation; *Int'l*, pg. 7853
CHIBA ECO-CREATION CO., LTD.—See Mitsubishi Heavy Industries, Ltd.; *Int'l*, pg. 4953
CHIBA GENERAL LEASE CO., LTD.—See The Chiba Kogyo Bank, Ltd.; *Int'l*, pg. 7632
CHIBA GENERAL SERVICE CO., LTD.—See Sumitomo Chemical Company, Limited; *Int'l*, pg. 7264
CHIBAGIN ACCOUNTING SERVICE CO., LTD.—See The Chiba Bank, Ltd.; *Int'l*, pg. 7631
CHIBAGIN ASSET MANAGEMENT CO., LTD.—See The Chiba Bank, Ltd.; *Int'l*, pg. 7631
CHIBAGIN CAPITAL CO., LTD.—See The Chiba Bank, Ltd.; *Int'l*, pg. 7631
CHIBAGIN CASH BUSINESS CO., LTD.—See The Chiba Bank, Ltd.; *Int'l*, pg. 7631
CHIBAGIN COMPUTER SERVICE CO., LTD.—See The Chiba Bank, Ltd.; *Int'l*, pg. 7631
CHIBAGIN DC CARD CO.,LTD.—See The Chiba Bank, Ltd.; *Int'l*, pg. 7631
CHIBAGIN GUARANTEE COMPANY LTD.—See The Chiba Bank, Ltd.; *Int'l*, pg. 7631
CHIBAGIN HEARTFUL CO.,LTD.—See The Chiba Bank, Ltd.; *Int'l*, pg. 7631
CHIBAGIN JCB CARD CO.,LTD.—See The Chiba Bank, Ltd.; *Int'l*, pg. 7631
CHIBAGIN LEASE CO., LTD.—See The Chiba Bank, Ltd.; *Int'l*, pg. 7631
CHIBAGIN LEASING CO., LTD.—See The Chiba Bank, Ltd.; *Int'l*, pg. 7631
CHIBAGIN RESEARCH INSTITUTE CO.,LTD.—See The Chiba Bank, Ltd.; *Int'l*, pg. 7632
CHIBAGIN SECURITIES CO.,LTD.—See The Chiba Bank, Ltd.; *Int'l*, pg. 7632
CHIBA GRANDY HOUSE CO., LTD.—See Grandy House Corporation; *Int'l*, pg. 3058
CHIBA GYORUI K.K.—See TOHTO SUISAN Co., Ltd.; *Int'l*, pg. 7777
CHIBA HINO MOTOR LTD.—See Toyota Motor Corporation; *Int'l*, pg. 7870
CHIBA KAIUN SANGYO CO., LTD.—See Nippon Yusen Kabushiki Kaisha; *Int'l*, pg. 5357
CHIBA KAKO CO., LTD.—See Dai Nippon Toryo Co., Ltd.; *Int'l*, pg. 1916
CHIBA KOGIN BUSINESS SERVICE CO., LTD.—See The Chiba Kogyo Bank, Ltd.; *Int'l*, pg. 7632
CHIBA KOGIN CARD SERVICE CO., LTD.—See The Chiba Kogyo Bank, Ltd.; *Int'l*, pg. 7632
CHIBA KOGIN COMPUTER SOFT CO., LTD.—See The Chiba Kogyo Bank, Ltd.; *Int'l*, pg. 7632
CHIBA KOGIN FINANCE CO., LTD.—See The Chiba Kogyo Bank, Ltd.; *Int'l*, pg. 7632
CHIBA KOGIN STAFF SERVICES CO., LTD.—See The Chiba Kogyo Bank, Ltd.; *Int'l*, pg. 7632
CHIBA KOGIN UC CARD CO., LTD.—See The Chiba Kogyo Bank, Ltd.; *Int'l*, pg. 7632
CHIBA KOGYO BANK-FINANCIAL MARKET DIV—See The Chiba Kogyo Bank, Ltd.; *Int'l*, pg. 7632
THE CHIBA KOGYO BANK, LTD.; *Int'l*, pg. 7632
CHIBA K TECHNO CO LTD—See Kandenko Co., Ltd.; *Int'l*, pg. 4065
CHIBA KYODO SILO CO., LTD.—See Sumitomo Corporation; *Int'l*, pg. 7268
CHIBA LOTTE MARINES CO., LTD.—See Lotte Co., Ltd.; *Int'l*, pg. 4559
CHIBA PHENOL COMPANY, LIMITED—See Mitsui Chemicals, Inc.; *Int'l*, pg. 4981
CHIBA POLYOL CORPORATION—See Mitsui Chemicals, Inc.; *Int'l*, pg. 4981
CHIBA RIVERMENT AND CEMENT CORPORATION—See UBE Corporation; *Int'l*, pg. 8000
CHIBA SANRITSU KONPO UNYU CO., LTD.—See Nippon Sheet Glass Co. Ltd.; *Int'l*, pg. 5331
CHIBA SENKO TRANSPORT CO., LTD.—See Senko Group Holdings Co., Ltd.; *Int'l*, pg. 6709
CHIBA SERVICER CO., LTD.—See The Chiba Bank, Ltd.; *Int'l*, pg. 7631
CHIBA SHOKUSAN INC.—See Toray Industries, Inc.; *Int'l*, pg. 7822
CHIBA SUBARU INC.—See SUBARU CO., LTD.; *Int'l*, pg. 7246
CHIBA UBE CONCRETE CO., LTD.—See UBE Corporation; *Int'l*, pg. 8000
CHIBA VEGOIL TANK TERMINAL CO., LTD.—See Fuji Oil Holdings Inc.; *Int'l*, pg. 2815
CHIBOUGAMAU DRILLING LTD; *Int'l*, pg. 1476
CHIBOUGAMAU INDEPENDENT MINES INC.; *Int'l*, pg. 1476
CHIBRET PHARMAZEUTISCHE GESELLSCHAFT MIT BESCHRANKTER HAFTUNG—See Merck & Co., Inc.; *U.S. Public*, pg. 1415

CHIBOUGAMAU INDEPENDENT MINES INC.

CHIBULUMA MINES PLC—See Jinchuan Group Limited; *Int'l*, pg. 3965
CHICAGO AEROSOL, LLC; *U.S. Private*, pg. 877
CHICAGO APARTMENT FINDERS INC.; *U.S. Private*, pg. 877
CHICAGO ARCHITECTURE FOUNDATION; *U.S. Private*, pg. 877
CHICAGO ATLANTIC REAL ESTATE FINANCE, INC.; *U.S. Public*, pg. 488
CHICAGO BAR COMPANY LLC—See WK Kellogg Co; *U.S. Public*, pg. 2376
CHICAGO BEARS FOOTBALL CLUB, INC.; *U.S. Private*, pg. 877
CHICAGO BEVERAGE SYSTEMS, LLC—See Reyes Holdings, LLC; *U.S. Private*, pg. 3418
CHICAGO BLACKHAWK HOCKEY TEAM, INC.—See Wirtz Corporation; *U.S. Private*, pg. 4547
CHICAGO BLOWER CORPORATION; *U.S. Private*, pg. 877
CHICAGO BOARD OPTIONS EXCHANGE, INCORPORATED—See Cboe Global Markets, Inc.; *U.S. Public*, pg. 459
CHICAGO BRIDGE & IRON COMPANY B.V.—See McDermott International, Inc.; *U.S. Public*, pg. 1405
CHICAGO BRIDGE & IRON COMPANY N.V.—See McDermott International, Inc.; *U.S. Public*, pg. 1404
CHICAGO BRIDGE & IRON COMPANY—See McDermott International, Inc.; *U.S. Public*, pg. 1405
CHICAGO BRIDGE & IRON COMPANY—See McDermott International, Inc.; *U.S. Public*, pg. 1405
CHICAGO BUS SALES INC.—See Cook-Illinois Corp.; *U.S. Private*, pg. 1038
CHICAGO CEMETERY CORPORATION—See Service Corporation International; *U.S. Public*, pg. 1869
CHICAGO CITY CAPITOL GROUP; *U.S. Private*, pg. 877
CHICAGO CLIMATE EXCHANGE, INC.—See Intercontinental Exchange, Inc.; *U.S. Public*, pg. 1143
CHICAGO COATING SYSTEMS; *U.S. Private*, pg. 877
CHICAGO COMMONS ASSOCIATION; *U.S. Private*, pg. 877
CHICAGO CONVERTING—See Menasha Corporation; *U.S. Private*, pg. 2665
THE CHICAGO COUNCIL ON GLOBAL AFFAIRS; *U.S. Private*, pg. 4008
CHICAGO DEFERRED EXCHANGE COMPANY, LLC—See Wintrust Financial Corporation; *U.S. Public*, pg. 2374
CHICAGO DENTAL SOCIETY; *U.S. Private*, pg. 877
CHICAGO DIVERSIFIED FOODS INC.; *U.S. Private*, pg. 877
CHICAGO EQUITY PARTNERS, LLC—See Affiliated Managers Group, Inc.; *U.S. Public*, pg. 54
CHICAGO EXHIBIT PRODUCTIONS, INC.; *U.S. Private*, pg. 877
CHICAGO EXHIBIT PRODUCTIONS, INC.—See Chicago Exhibit Productions, Inc.; *U.S. Private*, pg. 877
THE CHICAGO FAUCET COMPANY—See Geberit AG; *Int'l*, pg. 2905
CHICAGO FLAG & DECORATING CO.; *U.S. Private*, pg. 877
CHICAGO FOOD CORPORATION; *U.S. Private*, pg. 877
CHICAGO FREIGHT CAR LEASING CO.—See Sasser Family Holdings, Inc.; *U.S. Private*, pg. 3552
CHICAGO GROWTH PARTNERS, LLC; *U.S. Private*, pg. 877
CHICAGO HARDWARE & FIXTURE COMPANY; *U.S. Private*, pg. 877
CHICAGO HARLEY-DAVIDSON INC.; *U.S. Private*, pg. 877
CHICAGO HEIGHTS CONSTRUCTION CO.; *U.S. Private*, pg. 877
CHICAGO HEIGHTS DIALYSIS, LLC—See DaVita Inc.; *U.S. Public*, pg. 636
CHICAGO HEIGHTS STEEL; *U.S. Private*, pg. 878
CHICAGO HILTON LLC—See Park Hotels & Resorts Inc.; *U.S. Public*, pg. 1638
CHICAGO HISTORY MUSEUM; *U.S. Private*, pg. 878
CHICAGO HORTICULTURAL SOCIETY; *U.S. Private*, pg. 878
CHICAGO INSURANCE COMPANY, CORP.—See Allianz SE; *Int'l*, pg. 351
CHICAGO INTERNATIONAL TRUCKS - CHICAGO, LLC—See FreightCar America, Inc.; *U.S. Public*, pg. 885
CHICAGOLAND COACH LINES LLC—See Mobico Group PLC; *Int'l*, pg. 5008
CHICAGOLAND ENTREPRENEURIAL CENTER; *U.S. Private*, pg. 879
CHICAGOLAND PUBLISHING COMPANY—See Tribune Publishing Company; *U.S. Private*, pg. 4227
THE CHICAGO LIGHTHOUSE FOR PEOPLE WHO ARE BLIND OR VISUALLY IMPAIRED; *U.S. Private*, pg. 4008
CHICAGO LUMBER COMPANY OF OMAHA; *U.S. Private*, pg. 878
CHICAGO MACHINERY CO—See Okada Aiyon Corporation; *Int'l*, pg. 5544
CHICAGO MACK SALES & SERVICES INC.; *U.S. Private*, pg. 878
CHICAGO MAGAZINE—See Tribune Publishing Company; *U.S. Private*, pg. 4227
CHICAGO MATERIALS CORPORATION—See K-Five Construction Corporation; *U.S. Private*, pg. 2251
CHICAGO MEAT AUTHORITY, INC.; *U.S. Private*, pg. 878
CHICAGO METAL FABRICATORS, INC.; *U.S. Private*, pg. 878
CHICAGO METALLIC COMPANY LLC—See ROCKWOOL A/S; *Int'l*, pg. 6380
CHICAGO METALLIC - ELKRIDGE—See ROCKWOOL A/S; *Int'l*, pg. 6380
CHICAGO METAL ROLLED PRODUCTS CO.; *U.S. Private*, pg. 878
CHICAGO NATIONAL LEAGUE BALL CLUB, LLC; *U.S. Private*, pg. 878
CHICAGO OAKBROOK FINANCIAL GROUP; *U.S. Private*, pg. 878
CHICAGO OFFICE TECHNOLOGY GROUP—See Xerox Holdings Corporation; *U.S. Public*, pg. 2389
CHICAGO PACIFIC FOUNDERS; *U.S. Private*, pg. 878
CHICAGO PACKAGING CORPORATION; *U.S. Private*, pg. 878
THE CHICAGO PALM—See Palm Restaurant Group; *U.S. Private*, pg. 3080
CHICAGO PETROMARTS INC.; *U.S. Private*, pg. 878
CHICAGO PIZZA & BREWERY, LP—See BJ'S RESTAURANTS, INC.; *U.S. Public*, pg. 340
CHICAGO PIZZA HOSPITALITY HOLDING, INC.—See BJ'S RESTAURANTS, INC.; *U.S. Public*, pg. 340
CHICAGO PNEUMATIC BRASIL LTDA—See Atlas Copco AB; *Int'l*, pg. 681
CHICAGO PNEUMATIC CONSTRUCTION EQUIPMENT AB—See Atlas Copco AB; *Int'l*, pg. 681
CHICAGO PNEUMATIC TOOL COMPANY LLC—See Atlas Copco AB; *Int'l*, pg. 681
CHICAGO PRINTING COMPANY, INC.—See Johns-Byrne Co.; *U.S. Public*, pg. 2226
CHICAGO PROFESSIONAL SPORTS LIMITED PARTNERSHIP; *U.S. Private*, pg. 878
CHICAGO PROTECTIVE APPAREL, INC.—See Gryphon Investors, LLC; *U.S. Private*, pg. 1798
CHICAGO PUBLIC MEDIA, INC.; *U.S. Private*, pg. 879
CHICAGO RADIO, LLC—See Cumulus Media Inc.; *U.S. Public*, pg. 609
CHICAGO RAIL LINK—See The Broe Companies, Inc.; *U.S. Public*, pg. 4001
CHICAGO READER—See Chicago Public Media, Inc.; *U.S. Private*, pg. 879
CHICAGO RIVET & MACHINE COMPANY-ALBIA DIVISION—See Chicago Rivet & Machine Company; *U.S. Public*, pg. 488
CHICAGO RIVET & MACHINE COMPANY-JEFFERSON DIVISION—See Chicago Rivet & Machine Company; *U.S. Public*, pg. 488
CHICAGO RIVET & MACHINE COMPANY; *U.S. Public*, pg. 488
CHICAGO RIVET & MACHINE COMPANY-TYRONE DIVISION—See Chicago Rivet & Machine Company; *U.S. Public*, pg. 488
CHICAGO RIVET & MACHINE CO.—See Chicago Rivet & Machine Company; *U.S. Public*, pg. 488
CHICAGO ROLL CO., INC.—See Roll-Kraft, Inc.; *U.S. Private*, pg. 3474
CHICAGO SCHOOL SUPPLY; *U.S. Private*, pg. 879
CHICAGO-SOFT, LTD.; *U.S. Private*, pg. 879
CHICAGO STEEL & IRON—See Esmark Incorporated; *U.S. Private*, pg. 1426
CHICAGO STEEL LIMITED PARTNERSHIP; *U.S. Private*, pg. 879
CHICAGO SUN-TIMES MEDIA, INC.—See Chicago Public Media, Inc.; *U.S. Private*, pg. 879
CHICAGO SUN-TIMES—See Chicago Public Media, Inc.; *U.S. Private*, pg. 879
CHICAGO SWITCHBOARD CO., INC.—See Greenbriar Equity Group, L.P.; *U.S. Private*, pg. 1776
CHICAGO TITLE AND TRUST COMPANY—See Fidelity National Financial, Inc.; *U.S. Public*, pg. 831
CHICAGO TITLE INSURANCE COMPANY—See Fidelity National Financial, Inc.; *U.S. Public*, pg. 831
CHICAGO TRANSIT AUTHORITY—See Regional Transportation Authority; *U.S. Public*, pg. 3389
CHICAGO TRIBUNE COMPANY, LLC—See Tribune Publishing Company; *U.S. Private*, pg. 4227
CHICAGO TRIBUNE—See Tribune Publishing Company; *U.S. Private*, pg. 4227
THE CHICAGO TRUST COMPANY, N.A.—See Wintrust Financial Corporation; *U.S. Public*, pg. 2375
CHICAGO TUBE & IRON CO.—See Olympic Steel Inc.; *U.S. Public*, pg. 1570
CHICAGO UNION STATION COMPANY—See National Railroad Passenger Corporation; *U.S. Private*, pg. 2861
CHICAGO WHITE METAL CASTING, INC.; *U.S. Private*, pg. 879
CHICAGO WHITE SOX LTD.; *U.S. Private*, pg. 879
CHICAGO-WILCOX MFG. COMPANY, INC.; *U.S. Private*, pg. 879
CHICAGO ZOOLOGICAL SOCIETY, INC.; *U.S. Private*, pg. 879

CORPORATE AFFILIATIONS

THE CHICANO FEDERATION, INC.; *U.S. Private*, pg. 4008
CHICANOS POR LA CAUSA, INC.; *U.S. Private*, pg. 880
CHI CENTERS, INC.; *U.S. Private*, pg. 876
CHI CHENG ENTERPRISE CO., LTD.; *Int'l*, pg. 1474
CHICHESTER METALS PTY LIMITED—See Fortescue Ltd; *Int'l*, pg. 2738
CHICHIBU CONCRETE INDUSTRY CO., LTD.—See Taiheiyo Cement Corporation; *Int'l*, pg. 7411
CHICHIBU FUJI CO., LTD.—See Fuji Electric Co., Ltd.; *Int'l*, pg. 2810
CHICHIBU RAILWAY CO., LTD.; *Int'l*, pg. 1476
CHICHIBU TAIHEIYO CEMENT CORPORATION—See Taiheiyo Cement Corporation; *Int'l*, pg. 7411
CHIC HOLDINGS, INC.—See Hikari Tsushin, Inc.; *Int'l*, pg. 3389
CHICKAMAUGA TELEPHONE COMPANY—See Fail Telecommunications Corp.; *U.S. Private*, pg. 1461
CHICKASAW FINANCE COMPANY—See Chickasaw Holding Company; *U.S. Private*, pg. 880
CHICKASAW FOUNDATION—See The Chickasaw Nation; *U.S. Private*, pg. 4008
CHICKASAW HOLDING COMPANY; *U.S. Private*, pg. 880
CHICKASAW LONG DISTANCE COMPANY—See Chickasaw Holding Company; *U.S. Private*, pg. 880
CHICKASAW NATION INDUSTRIES, INC.—See The Chickasaw Nation; *U.S. Private*, pg. 4008
THE CHICKASAW NATION; *U.S. Private*, pg. 4008
CHICKASAW PERSONAL COMMUNICATIONS, INC.—See Chickasaw Holding Company; *U.S. Private*, pg. 880
CHICKASAW TELECOM, INC.—See Chickasaw Holding Company; *U.S. Private*, pg. 880
CHICKASAW TELECOMMUNICATIONS SERVICES, INC.—See Chickasaw Holding Company; *U.S. Private*, pg. 880
CHICKASAW TELEPHONE COMPANY—See Chickasaw Holding Company; *U.S. Private*, pg. 880
CHICKASHA OF GEORGIA, LLC; *U.S. Private*, pg. 880
CHICKEN HOUSE PUBLISHING LTD.—See Scholastic Corporation; *U.S. Public*, pg. 1848
CHICKEN SOUP FOR THE SOUL ENTERTAINMENT, INC.; *U.S. Public*, pg. 488
CHICK-FIL-A, INC.; *U.S. Private*, pg. 880
CHICK'S SPORTING GOODS INC.—See Dick's Sporting Goods, Inc.; *U.S. Public*, pg. 659
CHICO ENTERPRISES, INC.; *U.S. Private*, pg. 880
CHICO HOT SPRINGS RESORT, INC.—See DiamondRock Hospitality Company; *U.S. Public*, pg. 1280
CHICOLASTIC CHILE, S.A.—See Qntex Group N.V.; *Int'l*, pg. 5591
CHICO NISSAN, INC.; *U.S. Private*, pg. 880
CHICONY AMERICA INC.—See Chicony Electronics Co., Ltd.; *Int'l*, pg. 1476
CHICONY ELECTRONICS CEZ S.R.O—See Chicony Electronics Co., Ltd.; *Int'l*, pg. 1476
CHICONY ELECTRONICS CO., LTD.; *Int'l*, pg. 1476
CHICONY ELECTRONICS (DONGGUAN) CO., LTD.—See Chicony Electronics Co., Ltd.; *Int'l*, pg. 1476
CHICONY ELECTRONICS GMBH—See Chicony Electronics Co., Ltd.; *Int'l*, pg. 1476
CHICONY ELECTRONICS JAPAN CO., LTD.—See Chicony Electronics Co., Ltd.; *Int'l*, pg. 1476
CHICONY ELECTRONICS (MAINLAND CHINA II) CO., LTD.—See Chicony Electronics Co., Ltd.; *Int'l*, pg. 1476
CHICONY ELECTRONICS (SU ZOU, MAINLAND CHINA III) CO., LTD.—See Chicony Electronics Co., Ltd.; *Int'l*, pg. 1476
CHICONY POWER TECHNOLOGY CO., LTD.; *Int'l*, pg. 1476
CHICONY POWER TECHNOLOGY HONG KONG LIMITED—See Chicony Power Technology Co., Ltd.; *Int'l*, pg. 1476
CHICONY POWER TECHNOLOGY (THAILAND) CO., LTD.—See Chicony Electronics Co., Ltd.; *Int'l*, pg. 1476
CHICOPEE EUROPE—See Berry Global Group, Inc; *U.S. Public*, pg. 321
CHICOPEE INC.—See Berry Global Group, Inc; *U.S. Public*, pg. 321
CHICOPEE MANUFACTURING LIMITED—See Magellan Aerospace Corporation; *Int'l*, pg. 4637
CHICO'S DISTRIBUTION SERVICES, LLC—See Sycamore Partners Management, LP; *U.S. Private*, pg. 3895
CHICO'S FAS, INC.—See Sycamore Partners Management, LP; *U.S. Private*, pg. 3895
CHICO'S RETAIL SERVICES, INC.—See Sycamore Partners Management, LP; *U.S. Private*, pg. 3895
CHICO SURGERY CENTER, L.P.—See Tenet Healthcare Corporation; *U.S. Public*, pg. 2009
CHIC PUNTA CANA—See Sunwing Travel Group, Inc.; *Int'l*, pg. 7332
CHIC REPUBLIC PUBLIC COMPANY LIMITED; *Int'l*, pg. 1476
CHIDLOM MARINE SERVICES & SUPPLIES LTD.—See Thoresen Thai Agencies Public Company Limited; *Int'l*, pg. 7718
CHIEF CARRIERS, INC.—See Chief Industries, Inc.; *U.S. Private*, pg. 881

COMPANY NAME INDEX

CHIEF CONSTRUCTION COMPANY—See Chief Industries, Inc.; *U.S. Private*, pg. 881
CHIEF CORPORATION; *U.S. Private*, pg. 880
CHIEF ENERGY, INC.; *U.S. Private*, pg. 880
CHIEF ENVIRONMENTAL PRODUCTS—See Chief Industries, Inc.; *U.S. Private*, pg. 881
CHIEF ETHANOL FUELS, INC.—See Chief Industries, Inc.; *U.S. Private*, pg. 881
CHIEF EXECUTIVES ORGANIZATION; *U.S. Private*, pg. 881
CHIEF INDUSTRIES, INC. - CHIEF AGRI/INDUSTRIAL DIVISION—See Chief Industries, Inc.; *U.S. Private*, pg. 881
CHIEF INDUSTRIES, INC. - CHIEF BUILDINGS DIVISION—See Chief Industries, Inc.; *U.S. Private*, pg. 881
CHIEF INDUSTRIES, INC. - CHIEF CUSTOM PRODUCTS DIVISION—See Chief Industries, Inc.; *U.S. Private*, pg. 881
CHIEF INDUSTRIES, INC. - FABRICATION DIVISION—See Chief Industries, Inc.; *U.S. Private*, pg. 881
CHIEF INDUSTRIES, INC.; *U.S. Private*, pg. 881
CHIEF INDUSTRIES UK LTD—See Chief Industries, Inc.; *U.S. Private*, pg. 881
CHIEF SUPER MARKET, INC.—See Fresh Encounter Inc.; *U.S. Private*, pg. 1609
CHIEFTAIN METALS INC.; *Int'l*, pg. 1476
CHIEFTEK PRECISION CO., LTD.; *Int'l*, pg. 1476
CHIEF TELECOM INC.—See Chunghwa Telecom Co., Ltd.; *Int'l*, pg. 1598
CHIEF TRANSPORTATION PRODUCTS, INC.—See Chief Industries, Inc.; *U.S. Private*, pg. 881
CHIEFTRON INTERNATIONAL INC.—See Av Tech Corporation; *Int'l*, pg. 733
CHIEMGAU RECYCLING GMBH—See Heinzel Holding GmbH; *Int'l*, pg. 3325
CHI ENGINEERING SERVICES, INC.—See NV5 Global, Inc.; *U.S. Public*, pg. 1557
CHIENG YENG ENT. CO., LTD.—See Leggett & Platt, Incorporated; *U.S. Public*, pg. 1301
CHIEN KUO CONSTRUCTION CO., LTD.; *Int'l*, pg. 1476
CHIEN SHING HARBOUR SERVICE CO., LTD.; *Int'l*, pg. 1477
CHIEN SHING STAINLESS STEEL CO., LTD.; *Int'l*, pg. 1477
CHI ENTERPRISES, INC.; *U.S. Private*, pg. 876
CHIEN WEI PRECISE TECHNOLOGY CO., LTD.; *Int'l*, pg. 1477
CHIEN YUEH TECHNOLOGY ENGINEERING CO., LTD.—See TOPCO Scientific Co., Ltd.; *Int'l*, pg. 7814
CHIERU CO., LTD.; *Int'l*, pg. 1477
CHIESI AUSTRALIA PTY LTD—See Chiesi Farmaceutici SpA; *Int'l*, pg. 1477
CHIESI BULGARIA LTD.—See Chiesi Farmaceutici SpA; *Int'l*, pg. 1478
CHIESI CZ S.R.O.—See Chiesi Farmaceutici SpA; *Int'l*, pg. 1478
CHIESI ESPANA S.A.—See Chiesi Farmaceutici SpA; *Int'l*, pg. 1477
CHIESI FARMACEUTICAL ITALIA—See Chiesi Farmaceutici SpA; *Int'l*, pg. 1477
CHIESI FARMACEUTICA LTDA.—See Chiesi Farmaceutici SpA; *Int'l*, pg. 1477
CHIESI FARMACEUTICI SPA; *Int'l*, pg. 1477
CHIESI HELLAS A.E.B.E.—See Chiesi Farmaceutici SpA; *Int'l*, pg. 1477
CHIESI HELLAS S.A.—See Chiesi Farmaceutici SpA; *Int'l*, pg. 1477
CHIESI ILAC TICARET A.S.—See Chiesi Farmaceutici SpA; *Int'l*, pg. 1477
CHIESI ITALIA S.P.A.—See Chiesi Farmaceutici SpA; *Int'l*, pg. 1477
CHIESI LTD.—See Chiesi Farmaceutici SpA; *Int'l*, pg. 1477
CHIESI MEXICO, SA DE CV—See Chiesi Farmaceutici SpA; *Int'l*, pg. 1477
CHIESI PHARMA AB—See Chiesi Farmaceutici SpA; *Int'l*, pg. 1477
CHIESI PHARMACEUTICALS BV—See Chiesi Farmaceutici SpA; *Int'l*, pg. 1478
CHIESI PHARMACEUTICAL (SHANGHAI) CO., LTD—See Chiesi Farmaceutici SpA; *Int'l*, pg. 1477
CHIESI PHARMACEUTICALS INC.—See Chiesi Farmaceutici SpA; *Int'l*, pg. 1478
CHIESI PHARMACEUTICALS LLC—See Chiesi Farmaceutici SpA; *Int'l*, pg. 1478
CHIESI PHARMACEUTICALS (PVT) LIMITED—See Chiesi Farmaceutici SpA; *Int'l*, pg. 1477
CHIESI POLAND SP. Z O.O.—See Chiesi Farmaceutici SpA; *Int'l*, pg. 1478
CHIESI ROMANIA S.R.L.—See Chiesi Farmaceutici SpA; *Int'l*, pg. 1478
CHIESI S.A.—See Chiesi Farmaceutici SpA; *Int'l*, pg. 1478
CHIESI SLOVAKIA S.R.O.—See Chiesi Farmaceutici SpA; *Int'l*, pg. 1478
CHIESI SLOVENIJA, D.O.O—See Chiesi Farmaceutici SpA; *Int'l*, pg. 1478
CHIESI USA INC.—See Chiesi Farmaceutici SpA; *Int'l*, pg. 1478

CHIFENG JILONG GOLD MINING CO., LTD.; *Int'l*, pg. 1478
CHIGA LIGHT INDUSTRIES SDN. BHD.—See HPI Resources Berhad; *Int'l*, pg. 3500
CHIGASAKI RENTAL CO., LTD.—See Aktio Holdings Corporation; *Int'l*, pg. 267
CHIGNOLO D'ISOLA FLAG SPA—See SOPREMA SAS; *Int'l*, pg. 7111
CHIGO HOLDING LIMITED; *Int'l*, pg. 1478
CHI HEALTH CREIGHTON UNIVERSITY MEDICAL CENTER - BERGAN MERCY—See Catholic Health Initiatives; *U.S. Private*, pg. 789
CHI HEMP INDUSTRIES INC.—See Naturally Splendid Enterprises Ltd.; *Int'l*, pg. 5168
CHIH LIEN INDUSTRIAL CO., LTD. - DONG GUAN FACTORY—See Chih Lien Industrial Co., Ltd.; *Int'l*, pg. 1478
CHIH LIEN INDUSTRIAL CO., LTD. - SHIN WU FACTORY—See Chih Lien Industrial Co., Ltd.; *Int'l*, pg. 1478
CHIH LIEN INDUSTRIAL CO., LTD.; *Int'l*, pg. 1478
CHI HO DEVELOPMENT HOLDINGS LIMITED; *Int'l*, pg. 1475
CHIHO ENVIRONMENT GROUP LIMITED—See USUM Investment Group Co., Ltd.; *Int'l*, pg. 8099
CHIHOU SOUSEI INC.—See Pasona Group Inc.; *Int'l*, pg. 5753
CHI HUA FITNESS CO., LTD.; *Int'l*, pg. 1475
CHIHULY INC.; *U.S. Private*, pg. 881
CHIHULY WORKSHOP—See Chihuly Inc.; *U.S. Private*, pg. 881
CHIIKISHINBUNSHA CO., LTD.; *Int'l*, pg. 1478
CHI KAN HOLDINGS LIMITED; *Int'l*, pg. 1475
CHIKARANOMOTO HOLDINGS CO., LTD.; *Int'l*, pg. 1478
CHI-KEN SOGO CONSULTANTS CO., LTD.—See CTI Engineering Co., Ltd.; *Int'l*, pg. 1871
CHIKUMA TSUSHIN INDUSTRY CO., LTD.—See FUJITSU COMPONENT LIMITED; *Int'l*, pg. 2832
CHIKUYO SEIKI KOGYO CO., LTD.—See KYB Corporation; *Int'l*, pg. 4353
CHIKYUJIN.JP CO., LTD.—See Vector Inc.; *Int'l*, pg. 8144
CHILANGA CEMENT PLC—See HUAXIN CEMENT CO., LTD.; *Int'l*, pg. 3515
CHILCO RIVER HOLDINGS, INC.; *U.S. Private*, pg. 881
CHILCOTE COMPANY; *U.S. Private*, pg. 881
CHILD-ADULT RESOURCE SERVICES, INC.; *U.S. Private*, pg. 882
CHILD AND FAMILY CENTER; *U.S. Private*, pg. 881
CHILD AND FAMILY GUIDANCE CENTER; *U.S. Private*, pg. 881
CHILD AND FAMILY SERVICES; *U.S. Private*, pg. 881
CHILD CARE ASSOCIATES; *U.S. Private*, pg. 881
CHILDCAREGROUP; *U.S. Private*, pg. 882
CHILDCARE LEARNING CENTERS, INC.; *U.S. Private*, pg. 882
CHILD CARE LINKS; *U.S. Private*, pg. 881
CHILD CARE RESOURCE CENTER; *U.S. Private*, pg. 882
CHILDCRAFT EDUCATION CORPORATION—See School Specialty, Inc.; *U.S. Public*, pg. 1848
CHILD CRAFT INDUSTRIES, INC.; *U.S. Private*, pg. 882
CHILD DEVELOPMENT INC.; *U.S. Private*, pg. 882
CHILD DEVELOPMENT SCHOOLS, INC.—See Glencoe Capital LLC; *U.S. Private*, pg. 1709
CHILD DIMENSIONS INSURANCE COMPANY; *U.S. Private*, pg. 882
CHILDERS OIL CO.; *U.S. Private*, pg. 882
CHILDERS ROOFING & SHEETMETAL, INC.—See Altas Partners LP; *Int'l*, pg. 386
CHILD & FAMILY SERVICES; *U.S. Private*, pg. 881
CHILD & FAMILY; *U.S. Private*, pg. 881
CHILD FOCUS, INC.; *U.S. Private*, pg. 882
CHILD GUIDANCE & FAMILY SOLUTIONS; *U.S. Private*, pg. 882
CHILD GUIDANCE RESOURCE CENTERS; *U.S. Private*, pg. 882
CHILDHAVEN—See Children'S Home Society Of Washington; *U.S. Private*, pg. 884
CHILDNET; *U.S. Private*, pg. 882
CHILD-PARENT CENTERS, INC.; *U.S. Private*, pg. 882
CHILDREN AND ADULT DISABILITY AND EDUCATIONAL SERVICES; *U.S. Private*, pg. 883
CHILDREN AND FAMILIES FIRST DELAWARE INC; *U.S. Private*, pg. 883
CHILDREN & FAMILIES OF IOWA; *U.S. Private*, pg. 883
CHILDREN & FAMILY SERVICES, CORP.—See KKR & Co. Inc.; *U.S. Public*, pg. 1262
CHILDREN INTERNATIONAL; *U.S. Private*, pg. 883
CHILDRE NISSAN, INC.; *U.S. Private*, pg. 883
CHILDREN'S AID & FAMILY SERVICES, INC.; *U.S. Private*, pg. 883
CHILDREN'S BEHAVIORAL HEALTH, INC.—See ATAR Capital, LLC; *U.S. Private*, pg. 364
CHILDREN'S BEHAVIORAL SOLUTIONS, LLC—See Acadia Healthcare Company, Inc.; *U.S. Public*, pg. 28
CHILDREN'S BETTER HEALTH INSTITUTE—See Saturday Evening Post Society; *U.S. Private*, pg. 3553
CHILDRENS BUREAU, INC.; *U.S. Private*, pg. 885

THE CHILDREN'S PLACE, INC.

CHILDREN'S CANCER RECOVERY FOUNDATION; *U.S. Private*, pg. 883
CHILDREN'S CARE HOSPITAL & SCHOOL; *U.S. Private*, pg. 883
CHILDREN'S CENTER FOR DEVELOPMENTAL ENRICHMENT; *U.S. Private*, pg. 883
CHILDREN'S CENTER FOR TREATMENT AND EDUCATION; *U.S. Private*, pg. 883
THE CHILDREN'S CENTER OF HAMDEN, INC.; *U.S. Private*, pg. 4008
CHILDREN'S CHOICE, INC.; *U.S. Private*, pg. 883
CHILDREN'S CHOICE LEARNING CENTERS, INC.—See Bain Capital, LP; *U.S. Private*, pg. 437
THE CHILDREN'S CLINIC, "SERVING CHILDREN AND THEIR FAMILIES"; *U.S. Private*, pg. 4008
CHILDREN'S COUNCIL SAN FRANCISCO; *U.S. Private*, pg. 883
CHILDREN'S CRISIS TREATMENT CENTER; *U.S. Private*, pg. 883
CHILDREN'S DEFENSE FUND; *U.S. Private*, pg. 883
CHILDREN'S FRIEND; *U.S. Private*, pg. 883
THE CHILDREN'S GUILD INC.; *U.S. Private*, pg. 4008
CHILDREN'S HEALTHCARE OF ATLANTA; *U.S. Private*, pg. 883
CHILDREN'S HEALTH COUNCIL; *U.S. Private*, pg. 883
CHILDREN'S HOME + AID; *U.S. Private*, pg. 883
CHILDREN'S HOME HEALTHCARE—See Children's Hospital & Medical Center; *U.S. Private*, pg. 884
CHILDREN'S HOME OF BRADFORD, PA.; *U.S. Private*, pg. 884
THE CHILDREN'S HOME OF PITTSBURGH & LEMIEUX FAMILY CENTER; *U.S. Private*, pg. 4008
CHILDREN'S HOME OF WYOMING CONFERENCE; *U.S. Private*, pg. 884
CHILDREN'S HOME SOCIETY OF CALIFORNIA; *U.S. Private*, pg. 884
CHILDREN'S HOME SOCIETY OF FLORIDA; *U.S. Private*, pg. 884
THE CHILDREN'S HOME SOCIETY OF NEW JERSEY; *U.S. Private*, pg. 4008
CHILDREN'S HOME SOCIETY OF NORTH CAROLINA, INC.; *U.S. Private*, pg. 884
CHILDREN'S HOME SOCIETY OF SOUTH DAKOTA; *U.S. Private*, pg. 884
CHILDREN'S HOME SOCIETY OF WASHINGTON; *U.S. Private*, pg. 884
CHILDREN'S HOPE ALLIANCE FOUNDATION—See Children's Hope Alliance; *U.S. Private*, pg. 884
CHILDREN'S HOPE ALLIANCE; *U.S. Private*, pg. 884
CHILDREN'S HOSPITAL COLORADO HEALTH SYSTEM; *U.S. Private*, pg. 884
CHILDRENS HOSPITAL FOUNDATION; *Int'l*, pg. 1478
CHILDREN'S HOSPITAL LOS ANGELES; *U.S. Private*, pg. 884
CHILDREN'S HOSPITAL MEDICAL CENTER OF AKRON; *U.S. Private*, pg. 884
CHILDREN'S HOSPITAL & MEDICAL CENTER; *U.S. Private*, pg. 884
CHILDREN'S HOSPITAL MEDICAL PRACTICE CORPORATION; *U.S. Private*, pg. 884
CHILDREN'S HOSPITAL OF NEW JERSEY—See Barnabas Health, Inc.; *U.S. Private*, pg. 476
THE CHILDREN'S HOSPITAL OF PHILADELPHIA FOUNDATION; *U.S. Private*, pg. 4009
THE CHILDREN'S HOSPITAL OF PHILADELPHIA; *U.S. Private*, pg. 4009
CHILDRENS HOSPITAL OF WISCONSIN; *U.S. Private*, pg. 885
CHILDREN'S HOSPITAL PEDIATRIC ASSOCIATES, INC.; *U.S. Private*, pg. 884
CHILDREN'S HOSPITALS AND CLINICS OF MINNESOTA; *U.S. Private*, pg. 885
CHILDREN'S HOSPITAL; *U.S. Private*, pg. 884
CHILDREN'S HOSPITAL TRUST; *U.S. Private*, pg. 1478
CHILDREN'S HUNGER FUND; *U.S. Private*, pg. 885
THE CHILDREN'S INSTITUTE; *U.S. Private*, pg. 4009
CHILDREN'S LAW CENTER OF CALIFORNIA; *U.S. Private*, pg. 885
CHILDREN'S LEUKEMIA RESEARCH ASSOCIATION, INC.; *U.S. Private*, pg. 885
CHILDREN'S LITERACY INITIATIVE; *U.S. Private*, pg. 885
CHILDREN'S MEDICAL CENTER DALLAS; *U.S. Private*, pg. 885
THE CHILDRENS MERCY HOSPITAL; *U.S. Private*, pg. 4009
CHILDREN'S MUSEUM OF HOUSTON; *U.S. Private*, pg. 885
THE CHILDREN'S MUSEUM OF INDIANAPOLIS; *U.S. Private*, pg. 4009
THE CHILDREN'S PLACE (CANADA), LP—See The Children's Place, Inc.; *U.S. Public*, pg. 2059
THE CHILDREN'S PLACE (CANADA), LP—See The Children's Place, Inc.; *U.S. Public*, pg. 2059
THE CHILDREN'S PLACE (HONG KONG) LIMITED—See The Children's Place, Inc.; *U.S. Public*, pg. 2059
THE CHILDREN'S PLACE, INC.; *U.S. Public*, pg. 2059
THE CHILDREN'S PLACE (VIRGINIA), LLC—See The Children's Place, Inc.; *U.S. Public*, pg. 2059

CHILDREN'S POPULATION HEALTH

CHILDREN'S POPULATION HEALTH; *U.S. Private*, pg. 885
CHILDREN'S PROGRESS, INC.; *U.S. Private*, pg. 885
CHILDRENS SERVICE CENTER OF WYOMING VALLEY, INC.; *U.S. Private*, pg. 885
CHILDREN'S SERVICES OF ROXBURY, INC.; *U.S. Private*, pg. 885
CHILDRESS-KLEIN PROPERTIES, INC.; *U.S. Private*, pg. 885
CHILDS MANAGEMENT INC.; *U.S. Private*, pg. 885
CHILD START INC.; *U.S. Private*, pg. 882
CHILD TRENDS, INC.; *U.S. Private*, pg. 882
CHILEAN COBALT CORP.; *U.S. Public*, pg. 488
CHILEAN METALS EXPLORATION LTD.—See Power Nickel Inc.; *Int'l*, pg. 5946
CHILE MINING TECHNOLOGIES INC.; *Int'l*, pg. 1478
CHILENA CONSOLIDADA SEGUROS DE VIDA S.A.—See Zurich Insurance Group Limited; *Int'l*, pg. 8697
CHILENA CONSOLIDADA SEGUROS GENERALES S.A.—See Zurich Insurance Group Limited; *Int'l*, pg. 8697
CHILENA DE MOLDEADOS S.A.—See Empresas CMPC S.A.; *Int'l*, pg. 2390
CHILE SOLDADURA Y CORTE—See Mondragon Corporation; *Int'l*, pg. 5031
CHILHOWEE TRAILER SALES, INC.—See Lazydays Holdings, Inc.; *U.S. Public*, pg. 1294
CHILI ADVERTISING & PROMOTIONS LIMITED—See Transmit Entertainment Limited; *Int'l*, pg. 7901
CHILIME ENGINEERING & SERVICES COMPANY LIMITED—See Chilime Hydropower Company Limited; *Int'l*, pg. 1478
CHILIME HYDROPOWER COMPANY LIMITED; *Int'l*, pg. 1478
C.H.I. LIMITED—See The Coca-Cola Company; *U.S. Public*, pg. 2063
CHILISIN ASIA INVESTMENT LIMITED—See Yageo Corporation; *Int'l*, pg. 8545
CHILI'S, INC.—See Brinker International, Inc.; *U.S. Public*, pg. 384
CHILISIN ELECTRONICS CORP.—See Yageo Corporation; *Int'l*, pg. 8545
CHILISIN ELECTRONICS SINGAPORE PTE. LTD.—See Yageo Corporation; *Int'l*, pg. 8545
CHILISIN INTERNATIONAL LTD.—See Yageo Corporation; *Int'l*, pg. 8545
CHILIS OF KANASA, INC.—See Brinker International, Inc.; *U.S. Public*, pg. 384
CHILI'S OF MARYLAND, INC.—See Brinker International, Inc.; *U.S. Public*, pg. 384
CHILI'S OF SALISBURY, LLC—See Brinker International, Inc.; *U.S. Public*, pg. 384
CHILL BRANDS GROUP PLC; *Int'l*, pg. 1478
CHILLDY CO., LTD—See Nissui Corporation; *Int'l*, pg. 5377
CHILLED & FROZEN LOGISTICS HOLDING CO., LTD.; *Int'l*, pg. 1478
CHILLER SYSTEMS SERVICE, INC.—See The Arcticom Group, LLC; *U.S. Private*, pg. 3987
CHILLER TECHNOLOGY, INC.; *U.S. Private*, pg. 885
CHILL FACTOR GLOBAL PTY LIMITED—See The Character Group plc; *Int'l*, pg. 7631
CHILLFIS BVBA—See Struik Holding N.V.; *Int'l*, pg. 7243
CHILLICOTHE GAZETTE—See Gannett Co., Inc.; *U.S. Public*, pg. 897
CHILLI MANIS CATERING PTE. LTD.—See Neo Group Limited; *Int'l*, pg. 5196
CHILLINGO LIMITED—See Electronic Arts Inc.; *U.S. Public*, pg. 723
CHILL N OUT CRYOTHERAPY, INC.; *U.S. Public*, pg. 489
CHILTERN CAPITAL LLP; *Int'l*, pg. 1479
CHILTERN CLINICAL RESEARCH INDIA PRIVATE LTD.—See Laboratory Corporation of America Holdings; *U.S. Public*, pg. 1285
CHILTERN INTERNATIONAL HOLDINGS LIMITED—See Laboratory Corporation of America Holdings; *U.S. Public*, pg. 1285
CHILTERN INTERNATIONAL INC.—See Laboratory Corporation of America Holdings; *U.S. Public*, pg. 1285
CHILTERN INTERNATIONAL KFT.—See Laboratory Corporation of America Holdings; *U.S. Public*, pg. 1285
CHILTERN INTERNATIONAL LIMITED—See Laboratory Corporation of America Holdings; *U.S. Public*, pg. 1285
CHILTERN INTERNATIONAL PORTUGAL LDA—See Laboratory Corporation of America Holdings; *U.S. Public*, pg. 1285
CHILTERN INTERNATIONAL SRO—See Laboratory Corporation of America Holdings; *U.S. Public*, pg. 1285
THE CHILTERN RAILWAY COMPANY LIMITED—See Deutsche Bahn AG; *Int'l*, pg. 2054
CHILTON ELECTRIC—See The Glen Dimplex Group; *Int'l*, pg. 7649
CHILTON PRODUCTS—See Western Industries, Inc.; *U.S. Private*, pg. 4494
CHILWORTH AMALTHEA S.L.—See DEKRA e.V.; *Int'l*, pg. 2007
CHILWORTH FRANCE S.A.S.—See DEKRA e.V.; *Int'l*, pg. 2007

CHILWORTH PACIFIC FIRE LABORATORIES INC.—See DEKRA e.V.; *Int'l*, pg. 2007
CHILWORTH TECHNOLOGY INC.—See DEKRA e.V.; *Int'l*, pg. 2007
CHILWORTH TECHNOLOGY LTD.—See DEKRA e.V.; *Int'l*, pg. 2007
CHILWORTH TECHNOLOGY (PVT) LTD.—See DEKRA e.V.; *Int'l*, pg. 2008
CHILWORTH VASSALLO, S.R.L.—See DEKRA e.V.; *Int'l*, pg. 2007
CHIMAB S.P.A.—See BRENNTAG SE; *Int'l*, pg. 1149
CHIMAC S.A.—See Element Solutions Inc.; *U.S. Public*, pg. 725
CHIMCOMPLEX S.A. BORZESTI; *Int'l*, pg. 1479
CHIME BALL TECHNOLOGY CO., LTD.; *Int'l*, pg. 1479
CHIME COMMUNICATIONS LIMITED—See Providence Equity Partners L.L.C.; *U.S. Public*, pg. 3291
CHI MEI CORPORATION—See Chi Mei Group; *Int'l*, pg. 1475
CHI MEI CORP - PRP TREE VALLEY PLANT—See Chi Mei Group; *Int'l*, pg. 1475
CHI MEI GROUP; *Int'l*, pg. 1475
CHIME INC.; *U.S. Private*, pg. 885
CHIME INSIGHT & ENGAGEMENT LIMITED—See Providence Equity Partners L.L.C.; *U.S. Public*, pg. 3291
CHIMERA INVESTMENT CORP.; *U.S. Public*, pg. 489
CHIMERA INVESTMENTS LLC; *Int'l*, pg. 1479
CHIMERIC THERAPEUTICS LIMITED; *Int'l*, pg. 1479
CHIMERIX, INC.; *U.S. Public*, pg. 489
CHI MICROINSURANCE LIMITED—See Consolidated Hallmark Insurance Plc.; *Int'l*, pg. 1770
CHIMIELAB CO., LTD.—See YMT Co., Ltd.; *Int'l*, pg. 8590
CHIMIMPORT AD; *Int'l*, pg. 1479
CHIMIN HEALTH MANAGEMENT CO., LTD.; *Int'l*, pg. 1479
CHIMIOTECHNIC—See Orapi S.A.; *Int'l*, pg. 5612
CHIMIREC AVRASYA ENDUSTRIYEL ATIK SAN. VE TIC. LTD.—See Chimirec; *Int'l*, pg. 1479
CHIMIREC POLSKA SP. Z O.O.—See Chimirec; *Int'l*, pg. 1480
CHIMIREC; *Int'l*, pg. 1479
CHIMNEY CO., LTD.—See Yamaya Corporation; *Int'l*, pg. 8556
CHIMNEY ROCK WINERY—See The Terlato Wine Group; *U.S. Private*, pg. 4126
THE CHIMO HOTEL—See Clarke Inc.; *Int'l*, pg. 1650
CHIMPEX S.A.—See Ameropa AG; *Int'l*, pg. 424
CHIMPHARM JSC; *Int'l*, pg. 1480
CHINA 21ST CENTURY EDUCATION GROUP LTD.; *Int'l*, pg. 1480
CHINA 33 MEDIA GROUP LIMITED; *Int'l*, pg. 1481
CHINA 3D DIGITAL DISTRIBUTION LIMITED—See China Creative Digital Entertainment Limited; *Int'l*, pg. 1496
CHINA 9D CONSTRUCTION GROUP, INC.; *Int'l*, pg. 1481
CHINA ACE SHIPPING PTE. LTD.—See Chinese Maritime Transport Ltd.; *Int'l*, pg. 1569
CHINA AEROSPACE INTERNATIONAL HOLDINGS LIMITED; *Int'l*, pg. 1481
CHINA AEROSPACE SCIENCE AND INDUSTRY CORPORATION LIMITED; *Int'l*, pg. 1481
CHINA AEROSPACE SCIENCE AND TECHNOLOGY CORPORATION; *Int'l*, pg. 1481
CHINA AEROSPACE TIMES ELECTRONICS CO., LTD.; *Int'l*, pg. 1481
CHINA AGRI-BUSINESS, INC.; *Int'l*, pg. 1481
CHINA AGRICULTURAL FINANCE CO., LTD.—See Agricultural Bank of China Limited; *Int'l*, pg. 217
CHINA AGRI-INDUSTRIES HOLDINGS LIMITED—See COFCO Limited; *Int'l*, pg. 1692
CHINA AGRI PRODUCTS EXCHANGE LIMITED; *Int'l*, pg. 1481
CHINA AHOKU TECHLAND ELECTRONICS LTD.—See Ahoku Electronic Company; *Int'l*, pg. 225
CHINA AIRCRAFT LEASING GROUP HOLDINGS LIMITED; *Int'l*, pg. 1481
CHINA AIR EXPRESS CO., LIMITED—See China National Aviation Holding Company; *Int'l*, pg. 1525
CHINA AIRLINES LTD.; *Int'l*, pg. 1481
CHINA ALL ACCESS (HOLDINGS) LIMITED; *Int'l*, pg. 1482
CHINA ALUMINUM CANS HOLDINGS LIMITED; *Int'l*, pg. 1482
CHINA ALUMINUM GREAT WALL CONSTRUCTION CO., LTD.—See China Aluminum International Engineering Corporation Limited; *Int'l*, pg. 1482
CHINA ALUMINUM INTERNATIONAL ENGINEERING CORPORATION LIMITED; *Int'l*, pg. 1482
CHINA AMERICAN PETROCHEMICAL CO., LTD.—See BP plc; *Int'l*, pg. 1131
CHINA ANCHU ENERGY STORAGE GROUP LIMITED; *Int'l*, pg. 1482
CHINA ANIMAL HEALTHCARE LTD.; *Int'l*, pg. 1482
CHINA ANIMAL HUSBANDRY INDUSTRY CO., LTD.; *Int'l*, pg. 1482
CHINA ANTIMONY TECHNOLOGY CO., LTD.—See China Rare Earth Resources And Technology Co., Ltd.; *Int'l*, pg. 1545
CHINA AOYUAN GROUP LIMITED; *Int'l*, pg. 1482
CHINA APEX GROUP LIMITED; *Int'l*, pg. 1482

CORPORATE AFFILIATIONS

CHINA ARCHITECTURE DESIGN & RESEARCH GROUP; *Int'l*, pg. 1483
CHINA ART FINANCIAL HOLDINGS LIMITED; *Int'l*, pg. 1483
CHINA-ASEAN CAPITAL ADVISORY COMPANY; *Int'l*, pg. 1567
CHINA ASIA VALLEY GROUP LIMITED; *Int'l*, pg. 1483
CHINA ASSET MANAGEMENT CO., LTD.; *Int'l*, pg. 1483
CHINA ASSET MANAGEMENT (HONG KONG) LIMITED—See China Asset Management Co., Ltd.; *Int'l*, pg. 1483
CHINA ASSETS (HOLDINGS) LIMITED; *Int'l*, pg. 1483
CHINA ASSURANCE FINANCE GROUP LIMITED—See China Assurance Finance Group Limited; *Int'l*, pg. 1483
CHINA ASSURANCE FINANCE GROUP LIMITED—See China Assurance Finance Group Limited; *Int'l*, pg. 1483
CHINA ASSURANCE FINANCE GROUP LIMITED; *Int'l*, pg. 1483
CHINA AUTO ELECTRONICS GROUP LIMITED; *Int'l*, pg. 1483
CHINA AUTOMATION GROUP LIMITED; *Int'l*, pg. 1483
CHINA AUTOMOBILE NEW RETAIL (HOLDINGS) LIMITED; *Int'l*, pg. 1484
CHINA AUTOMOBILE PARTS HOLDINGS LIMITED; *Int'l*, pg. 1484
CHINA AUTOMOBILE TRADING CO., LTD.; *Int'l*, pg. 1484
CHINA AUTOMOTIVE ENGINEERING RESEARCH INSTITUTE CO., LTD.; *Int'l*, pg. 1484
CHINA AUTOMOTIVE INTERIOR DECORATION HOLDINGS LIMITED; *Int'l*, pg. 1484
CHINA AUTOMOTIVE SYSTEMS, INC.; *Int'l*, pg. 1484
CHINA AUTO SYSTEM TECHNOLOGIES LIMITED; *Int'l*, pg. 1483
CHINA AVIATION LITHIUM BATTERY (LUOYANG) CO., LTD.—See Sichuan Chengfei Inte; *Int'l*, pg. 6878
CHINA AVIATION OIL (SINGAPORE) CORPORATION LTD.—See China National Aviation Fuel Group Corporation; *Int'l*, pg. 1525
CHINA BANK CAPITAL CORPORATION—See China Banking Corporation; *Int'l*, pg. 1484
CHINA BANKING CORPORATION; *Int'l*, pg. 1484
CHINABANK INSURANCE BROKERS, INC.—See China Banking Corporation; *Int'l*, pg. 1484
CHINA BANKNOTE SICPA SECURITY INK CO., LTD—See SICPA Holding SA; *Int'l*, pg. 6882
CHINABANK PROPERTIES & COMPUTER CENTER, INC.—See China Banking Corporation; *Int'l*, pg. 1484
CHINABANK SAVINGS, INC.—See China Banking Corporation; *Int'l*, pg. 1484
CHINA BANK SECURITIES CORPORATION—See China Banking Corporation; *Int'l*, pg. 1484
CHINA BAOAN GROUP CO., LTD.; *Int'l*, pg. 1485
CHINA BAOFENG (INTERNATIONAL) LTD.; *Int'l*, pg. 1485
CHINA BAOLI TECHNOLOGIES HOLDINGS LTD.; *Int'l*, pg. 1485
CHINA BAOWU STEEL GROUP CORP., LTD.; *Int'l*, pg. 1485
CHINA BCT PHARMACY GROUP, INC.; *Int'l*, pg. 1486
CHINA BEIDAHUANG INDUSTRY GROUP HOLDINGS LTD.; *Int'l*, pg. 1486
CHINA BESTER GROUP TELECOM CO., LTD.; *Int'l*, pg. 1486
CHINA BEST GROUP HOLDING LIMITED; *Int'l*, pg. 1486
CHINA BESTSTUDY EDUCATION GROUP; *Int'l*, pg. 1486
CHINA BILLS FINANCE CORPORATION; *Int'l*, pg. 1486
CHINA BIOLOGIC PRODUCTS HOLDINGS, INC.; *Int'l*, pg. 1486
CHINA BIOTECH SERVICES HOLDINGS LIMITED; *Int'l*, pg. 1486
CHINA-BIOTICS, INC.; *Int'l*, pg. 1568
CHINA BLUECHEMICAL LTD.; *Int'l*, pg. 1487
CHINA BLUESTAR CHANGSHA CHEMICAL ENGINEERING CO LTD—See Bluestar Adisseo Company Limited; *Int'l*, pg. 1074
CHINA BLUESTAR INTERNATIONAL CHEMICAL CORPORATION—See Bluestar Adisseo Company Limited; *Int'l*, pg. 1074
CHINA BLUESTAR LEHIGH ENGINEERING CORP—See Bluestar Adisseo Company Limited; *Int'l*, pg. 1074
CHINA BOCOM INSURANCE CO., LTD.—See Bank of Communications Co., Ltd.; *Int'l*, pg. 842
CHINA BOHAI BANK CO., LTD.; *Int'l*, pg. 1487
CHINA BOQI ENVIRONMENTAL HOLDING CO., LTD.; *Int'l*, pg. 1487
CHINA BOTON GROUP COMPANY LIMITED; *Int'l*, pg. 1487
CHINA BOZZA DEVELOPMENT HOLDINGS LIMITED; *Int'l*, pg. 1487
CHINA BPIC SURVEYING INSTRUMENTS AG; *Int'l*, pg. 1487
CHINA BRASIL TABACOS EXPORTADORA S.A.—See China Tobacco International (HK) Company Limited; *Int'l*, pg. 1559
CHINA BRIGHT CULTURE GROUP; *Int'l*, pg. 1487
CHINA BRIGHT STONE INVESTMENT MANAGEMENT GROUP; *Int'l*, pg. 1487
CHINA BRILLIANT GLOBAL LIMITED; *Int'l*, pg. 1487

COMPANY NAME INDEX

CHINA BUILDING MATERIAL TEST & CERTIFICATION GROUP CO., LTD; *Int'l*, pg. 1487
CHINA BULL MANAGEMENT INC.; *U.S. Private*, pg. 885
CHINACACHE INTERNATIONAL HOLDINGS LTD.; *Int'l*, pg. 1568
CHINACACHE NETWORKS (HONG KONG) LIMITED—See ChinaCache International Holdings Ltd.; *Int'l*, pg. 1568
CHINA CALXON GROUP CO., LTD.; *Int'l*, pg. 1487
CHINA CAMC ENGINEERING CO., LTD.—See China National Machinery Industry Corporation; *Int'l*, pg. 1531
CHINA CAPITAL MANAGEMENT CO., LTD.—See CSC Financial Co., Ltd; *Int'l*, pg. 1862
CHINA CARBON GRAPHITE GROUP, INC.; *U.S. Public*, pg. 489
CHINA CARBON NEUTRAL DEVELOPMENT GROUP LIMITED; *Int'l*, pg. 1487
CHINACAST EDUCATION CORPORATION; *Int'l*, pg. 1568
CHINA CASTSON 81 FINANCE COMPANY LIMITED"; *Int'l*, pg. 1488
CHINACAST TECHNOLOGY (HK) LIMITED—See ChinaCast Education Corporation; *Int'l*, pg. 1568
CHINA CBM GROUP COMPANY LIMITED; *Int'l*, pg. 1488
CHINA CENTURY CEMENT LTD.—See Heidelberg Materials AG; *Int'l*, pg. 3309
CHINA CENTURY DRAGON MEDIA, INC.; *Int'l*, pg. 1488
CHINA CGAME, INC.; *Int'l*, pg. 1488
CHINACHEM GROUP; *Int'l*, pg. 1568
CHINA CHEMICAL CORP.; *Int'l*, pg. 1488
CHINA CHEMICAL ENGINEERING SECOND CONSTRUCTION CORPORATION—See China National Chemical Engineering Co., Ltd.; *Int'l*, pg. 1530
CHINA CHEMICAL GUILIN ENGINEERING CO., LTD.—See China National Chemical Engineering Co., Ltd.; *Int'l*, pg. 1530
CHINA CHEMICAL & PHARMACEUTICAL CO., LTD. - HSINFONG PLANT—See China Chemical & Pharmaceutical Co., Ltd.; *Int'l*, pg. 1488
CHINA CHEMICAL & PHARMACEUTICAL CO., LTD.; *Int'l*, pg. 1488
CHINA CHEMICAL & PHARMACEUTICAL CO., LTD. - TAICHUNG PLANT—See China Chemical & Pharmaceutical Co., Ltd.; *Int'l*, pg. 1488
CHINA CHENGTONG DEVELOPMENT GROUP LIMITED; *Int'l*, pg. 1488
CHINA CHUNLAI EDUCATION GROUP CO., LTD.; *Int'l*, pg. 1488
CHINA CIFCO INVESTMENT CO., LTD.; *Int'l*, pg. 1488
CHINA CINDA ASSET MANAGEMENT CO., LTD.; *Int'l*, pg. 1488
CHINA CINDA (HK) HOLDINGS CO., LTD.—See China Cinda Asset Management Co., Ltd.; *Int'l*, pg. 1488
CHINA CINDA (MACAU) ASSET MANAGEMENT CO., LTD.—See China Cinda Asset Management Co., Ltd.; *Int'l*, pg. 1488
CHINA CIRCUIT TECHNOLOGY (SHANTOU) CORPORATION—See Guangdong Goworld Co., Ltd.; *Int'l*, pg. 3154
CHINA CITIC BANK CORPORATION LIMITED—See CITIC Group Corporation; *Int'l*, pg. 1620
CHINA CITIC BANK INTERNATIONAL LIMITED—See CITIC Group Corporation; *Int'l*, pg. 1620
CHINA CITIC BANK INTERNATIONAL LTD. - LOS ANGELES BRANCH—See CITIC Group Corporation; *Int'l*, pg. 1620
CHINA CITIC BANK INTERNATIONAL LTD. - NEW YORK BRANCH—See CITIC Group Corporation; *Int'l*, pg. 1620
CHINA CITIC FINANCIAL ASSET MANAGEMENT CO., LTD.; *Int'l*, pg. 1489
CHINA CITY INFRASTRUCTURE GROUP LIMITED; *Int'l*, pg. 1489
CHINA CIVIL ENGINEERING CONSTRUCTION COMPANY(MACAU) LTD..—See China Railway Construction Corporation Limited; *Int'l*, pg. 1543
CHINA CIVIL ENGINEERING CONSTRUCTION CORPORATION—See China Railway Construction Corporation Limited; *Int'l*, pg. 1542
CHINA CLEAN ENERGY INC.; *Int'l*, pg. 1489
CHINA CLEAN ENERGY TECHNOLOGY GROUP LIMITED; *Int'l*, pg. 1489
CHINA CMIIC ENGINEERING & CONSTRUCTION CORP.—See China National Machinery Industry Corporation; *Int'l*, pg. 1531
CHINA COAL ENERGY COMPANY LIMITED; *Int'l*, pg. 1489
CHINA COAL ENERGY SHANDONG CO., LTD.—See China Coal Energy Company Limited; *Int'l*, pg. 1490
CHINA COAL HANDAN DESIGN ENGINEERING CO.,LTD.—See China Coal Energy Company Limited; *Int'l*, pg. 1490
CHINA COAL PINGSHUO INDUSTRY COAL LIMITED LIABILITY CORPORATION—See China Coal Energy Company Limited; *Int'l*, pg. 1490
CHINA COAL XI'AN ENGINEERING DESIGN CO., LTD.—See China Coal Energy Company Limited; *Int'l*, pg. 1490
CHINA COAL XINJI ENERGY CO., LTD.; *Int'l*, pg. 1490

CHINA COME RIDE NEW ENERGY GROUP LIMITED; *Int'l*, pg. 1490
CHINA COMMUNICATIONS CONSTRUCTION COMPANY LIMITED; *Int'l*, pg. 1490
CHINA COMMUNICATIONS IMPORT & EXPORT CORPORATION—See China Merchants Group Limited; *Int'l*, pg. 1521
CHINA COMMUNICATIONS MULTIMEDIA GROUP CO., LTD.; *Int'l*, pg. 1491
CHINA COMMUNICATIONS SERVICES CORPORATION LIMITED—See China Telecommunications Corporation; *Int'l*, pg. 1555
CHINA COMPOSITES GROUP CORPORATION LTD.—See China National Building Material Group Co., Ltd.; *Int'l*, pg. 1525
CHINA CONCENTRIC CAPITAL GROUP, INC.; *U.S. Private*, pg. 885
CHINA CONCH ENVIRONMENT PROTECTION HOLDINGS LIMITED; *Int'l*, pg. 1491
CHINA CONCH VENTURE HOLDINGS LIMITED; *Int'l*, pg. 1491
CHINA CONSTRUCTION AMERICAN CO.—See China State Construction Engineering Corporation Limited; *Int'l*, pg. 1554
CHINA CONSTRUCTION BANK (ASIA) CORPORATION LIMITED—See China Construction Bank Corporation; *Int'l*, pg. 1491
CHINA CONSTRUCTION BANK (BRASIL) BANCO MULTIPLO S/A—See China Construction Bank Corporation; *Int'l*, pg. 1491
CHINA CONSTRUCTION BANK CORPORATION; *Int'l*, pg. 1491
CHINA CONSTRUCTION BANK (EUROPE) S.A.—See China Construction Bank Corporation; *Int'l*, pg. 1491
CHINA CONSTRUCTION BANK (LONDON) LIMITED—See China Construction Bank Corporation; *Int'l*, pg. 1491
CHINA CONSTRUCTION BANK (MALAYSIA) BERHAD—See China Construction Bank Corporation; *Int'l*, pg. 1491
CHINA CONSTRUCTION BANK (NEW ZEALAND) LIMITED—See China Construction Bank Corporation; *Int'l*, pg. 1491
CHINA CONSTRUCTION BANK (RUSSIA) LIMITED; *Int'l*, pg. 1491
CHINA CONSTRUCTION DECORATION ENGINEERING CO.—See China State Construction Engineering Corporation Limited; *Int'l*, pg. 1554
CHINA CONSTRUCTION FIRST BUILDING (GROUP) CORPORATION LTD.—See China State Construction Engineering Corporation Limited; *Int'l*, pg. 1554
CHINA CONSTRUCTION IMPORT & EXPORT CO.—See China State Construction Engineering Corporation Limited; *Int'l*, pg. 1554
CHINA CONSTRUCTION (SOUTH PACIFIC) DEVELOPMENT CO. PTE. LTD.—See China State Construction Engineering Corporation Limited; *Int'l*, pg. 1554
CHINA CONTAINER TERMINAL CORP.; *Int'l*, pg. 1491
CHINA CONTINENT PROPERTY & CASUALTY INSURANCE COMPANY LTD.—See China Reinsurance (Group) Corporation; *Int'l*, pg. 1547
CHINA COSCO SHIPPING CORPORATION LIMITED; *Int'l*, pg. 1491
CHINA CREATIVE DIGITAL ENTERTAINMENT LIMITED; *Int'l*, pg. 1496
CHINA CREATIVE GLOBAL HOLDINGS LIMITED; *Int'l*, pg. 1496
CHINA CRESCENT ENTERPRISES, INC.; *U.S. Private*, pg. 885
CHINA CRYSTAL NEW MATERIAL HOLDINGS CO., LTD; *Int'l*, pg. 1496
CHINA CSSC HOLDINGS LIMITED—See China State Shipbuilding Corporation; *Int'l*, pg. 1554
CHINA CULTURE INDUSTRIAL INVESTMENT FUND MANAGEMENT CO., LTD.; *Int'l*, pg. 1496
CHINA CUSTOMER RELATIONS CENTERS, INC.; *Int'l*, pg. 1496
CHINA CYTS TOURS HOLDING CO., LTD.; *Int'l*, pg. 1496
CHINA DALIAN CFM PRECISION TOOLING CO., LTD.—See CFM Holdings Limited; *Int'l*, pg. 1430
CHINA DATANG CORPORATION RENEWABLE POWER CO., LIMITED—See China Datang Corporation; *Int'l*, pg. 1496
CHINA DATANG CORPORATION; *Int'l*, pg. 1496
CHINA DAYE NON-FERROUS METALS MINING LIMITED; *Int'l*, pg. 1497
CHINA DEMETER FINANCIAL INVESTMENTS LIMITED; *Int'l*, pg. 1497
CHINA DESIGN GROUP CO., LTD.; *Int'l*, pg. 1497
CHINA DEVELOPMENT BANK CAPITAL CO., LTD.—See China Development Bank Corporation; *Int'l*, pg. 1497
CHINA DEVELOPMENT BANK CORPORATION; *Int'l*, pg. 1497
CHINA DEVELOPMENT BANK FINANCIAL LEASING CO., LTD.; *Int'l*, pg. 1497
CHINA DEVELOPMENT BANK INTERNATIONAL INVESTMENT LIMITED—See China Development Bank Corporation; *Int'l*, pg. 1497

CHINA ENVIRONMENTAL ENERGY INVESTMENT LIMITED

CHINA DEVELOPMENT BANK SECURITIES CO., LTD.—See China Development Bank Corporation; *Int'l*, pg. 1497
CHINA DIGITAL CULTURE (GROUP) LIMITED; *Int'l*, pg. 1497
CHINA DIGITAL MEDIA CORPORATION; *Int'l*, pg. 1497
CHINA DIGITAL TV HOLDING CO., LTD.; *Int'l*, pg. 1497
CHINA DIGITAL VIDEO HOLDINGS LIMITED; *Int'l*, pg. 1498
CHINA DILI GROUP MANAGEMENT LIMITED—See China Dili Group; *Int'l*, pg. 1498
CHINA DILI GROUP; *Int'l*, pg. 1498
CHINA DING YI FENG HOLDINGS LIMITED; *Int'l*, pg. 1498
CHINA DISPLAY OPTOELECTRONICS TECHNOLOGY HOLDINGS LIMITED—See TCL Technology Group Corp.; *Int'l*, pg. 7483
CHINA DISPLAY OPTOELECTRONICS TECHNOLOGY (HUIZHOU) CO., LTD.—See TCL Technology Group Corp.; *Int'l*, pg. 7483
CHINA DISTANCE EDUCATION HOLDINGS LIMITED; *Int'l*, pg. 1498
CHINA DISTANCE EDUCATION LIMITED—See China Distance Education Holdings Limited; *Int'l*, pg. 1498
CHINA DIVE COMPANY LIMITED; *Int'l*, pg. 1498
CHINA DONGSHENG INTERNATIONAL, INC.; *Int'l*, pg. 1498
CHINA DONGXIANG (GROUP) COMPANY LIMITED; *Int'l*, pg. 1498
CHINA DREDGING ENVIRONMENTAL PROTECTION HOLDING LIMITED; *Int'l*, pg. 1498
CHINA DREDGING GROUP CO., LTD.—See Pingtan Marine Enterprise Ltd.; *Int'l*, pg. 5870
CHINA DU KANG CO., LTD.; *Int'l*, pg. 1498
CHINA DUTY FREE GROUP CORPORATION—See China Tourism Group Duty Free Corporation Limited; *Int'l*, pg. 1560
CHINA EAST EDUCATION HOLDINGS LIMITED; *Int'l*, pg. 1498
CHINA EASTERN AIRLINES CORPORATION LTD.; *Int'l*, pg. 1498
CHINA-EAST RESOURCES IMPORT & EXPORT CO., LTD.—See China Machinery Engineering Corporation; *Int'l*, pg. 1516
CHINA ECAPITAL CORPORATION; *Int'l*, pg. 1498
CHINA ECO-FARMING LIMITED; *Int'l*, pg. 1498
CHINA ECO-MATERIALS GROUP CO., LIMITED; *Int'l*, pg. 1498
CHINA ECOTEK CORPORATION—See China Steel Corporation; *Int'l*, pg. 1555
CHINA ECOTOURISM GROUP LIMITED; *Int'l*, pg. 1498
CHINA EDUCATION ALLIANCE, INC.; *Int'l*, pg. 1499
CHINA EDUCATION GROUP HOLDINGS LIMITED; *Int'l*, pg. 1499
CHINA EDUCATION, INC.; *Int'l*, pg. 1499
CHINA EDUCATION RESOURCES INC.; *Int'l*, pg. 1499
CHINAEDU CORPORATION—See ChinaEdu Holdings Ltd.; *Int'l*, pg. 1568
CHINAEDU HOLDINGS LTD.; *Int'l*, pg. 1568
CHINA E-INFORMATION TECHNOLOGY GROUP LIMITED; *Int'l*, pg. 1498
CHINA ELECTRIC MFG. CORPORATION; *Int'l*, pg. 1499
CHINA ELECTRIC MOTOR, INC.; *Int'l*, pg. 1499
CHINA ELECTRIC POWER EQUIPMENT AND TECHNOLOGY CO., LTD.—See State Grid Corporation of China; *Int'l*, pg. 7182
CHINA ELECTRONICS CORPORATION; *Int'l*, pg. 1499
CHINA ELECTRONICS HOLDINGS, INC.; *Int'l*, pg. 1499
CHINA ELECTRONICS HUADA TECHNOLOGY COMPANY LIMITED—See China Electronics Corporation; *Int'l*, pg. 1499
CHINA ELECTRONICS TECHNOLOGY CO., LTD.; *Int'l*, pg. 1499
CHINA ELECTRONICS TECHNOLOGY GROUP CORPORATION; *Int'l*, pg. 1499
CHINA ELEVENTH CHEMICAL CONSTRUCTION CO., LTD.—See China National Chemical Engineering Co., Ltd.; *Int'l*, pg. 1530
CHINA ELITE INFORMATION CO., LTD.—See Goldstream Investment Limited; *Int'l*, pg. 3034
CHINA EMEDIA HOLDINGS CORPORATION; *Int'l*, pg. 1499
CHINA ENERGINE INTERNATIONAL (HOLDINGS) LIMITED; *Int'l*, pg. 1500
CHINA ENERGY DEVELOPMENT HOLDINGS LIMITED; *Int'l*, pg. 1500
CHINA ENERGY ENGINEERING CORPORATION LIMITED; *Int'l*, pg. 1500
CHINA ENERGY RECOVERY INC.; *Int'l*, pg. 1500
CHINA ENERGY RESERVE & CHEMICALS GROUP CO., LTD.; *Int'l*, pg. 1500
CHINA ENERGY TECHNOLOGY CORP., LTD.; *Int'l*, pg. 1500
CHINA ENGINE CORPORATION—See China Motor Corporation; *Int'l*, pg. 1525
CHINA ENTERPRISE COMPANY LIMITED; *Int'l*, pg. 1500
CHINA ENTERPRISES LIMITED; *Int'l*, pg. 1500
CHINA ENVIRONMENTAL ENERGY INVESTMENT LIMITED; *Int'l*, pg. 1500

CHINA ENVIRONMENTAL RESOURCES GROUP LIMITED

CORPORATE AFFILIATIONS

CHINA ENVIRONMENTAL RESOURCES GROUP LIMITED; *Int'l*, pg. 1500
CHINA ENVIRONMENTAL TECHNOLOGY & BIOENERGY HOLDINGS LIMITED; *Int'l*, pg. 1500
CHINA ENVIRONMENTAL TECHNOLOGY HOLDINGS LIMITED; *Int'l*, pg. 1500
CHINA ENVIRONMENT LTD.; *Int'l*, pg. 1500
CHINA EQUIPMENT INTERNATIONAL TRADING CO., LTD.—See China Machinery Engineering Corporation; *Int'l*, pg. 1516
CHINA ERZHONG GROUP DEYANG HEAVY INDUSTRIES CO., LTD.; *Int'l*, pg. 1500
CHINAE SAVINGS BANK CO., LTD.—See J Trust Co., Ltd.; *Int'l*, pg. 3852
CHINA ESSENCE GROUP LTD.; *Int'l*, pg. 1500
CHINAETEK SERVICE & TECHNOLOGY CO., LTD.; *Int'l*, pg. 1568
CHINA EVERBEST DEVELOPMENT INTERNATIONAL LIMITED—See China Machinery Engineering Corporation; *Int'l*, pg. 1516
CHINA EVERBRIGHT BANK CO., LTD.—See China Everbright Group Limited; *Int'l*, pg. 1501
CHINA EVERBRIGHT ENVIRONMENT GROUP LIMITED—See China Everbright Group Limited; *Int'l*, pg. 1501
CHINA EVERBRIGHT GREENTECH LTD.—See China Everbright Group Limited; *Int'l*, pg. 1501
CHINA EVERBRIGHT GROUP LIMITED; *Int'l*, pg. 1501
CHINA EVERBRIGHT LIMITED—See China Everbright Group Limited; *Int'l*, pg. 1501
CHINA EVERBRIGHT WATER LIMITED—See China Everbright Group Limited; *Int'l*, pg. 1501
CHINA EVERGRANDE GROUP; *Int'l*, pg. 1501
CHINA EVERGRANDE NEW ENERGY VEHICLE GROUP LIMITED—See China Evergrande Group; *Int'l*, pg. 1501
CHINA EVER GRAND FINANCIAL LEASING GROUP CO., LTD.; *Int'l*, pg. 1500
CHINA EVERGREEN ACQUISITION CORPORATION; *Int'l*, pg. 1501
CHINA E-WALLET PAYMENT GROUP LIMITED; *Int'l*, pg. 1498
CHINA EXECUTIVE EDUCATION CORP.; *Int'l*, pg. 1501
CHINA EXPAND DEVELOPMENT LTD.—See China Rare Earth Resources And Technology Co., Ltd.; *Int'l*, pg. 1545
CHINA EXPRESS AIRLINES CO., LTD.; *Int'l*, pg. 1501
CHINA FANGDA GROUP CO., LTD.; *Int'l*, pg. 1501
CHINA FAW GROUP CORPORATION; *Int'l*, pg. 1501
CHINA FAW GROUP IMPORT & EXPORT CORPORATION—See China FAW Group Corporation; *Int'l*, pg. 1501
CHINA FEIHE LIMITED; *Int'l*, pg. 1502
CHINA FIBER OPTIC NETWORK SYSTEM GROUP LTD.; *Int'l*, pg. 1502
CHINA FIBRETECH LTD.; *Int'l*, pg. 1502
CHINA FILM CO., LTD.; *Int'l*, pg. 1502
CHINA FILMS TECHNOLOGY INC.; *Int'l*, pg. 1502
CHINA FINANCE INVESTMENT HOLDINGS LIMITED; *Int'l*, pg. 1502
CHINA FINANCE ONLINE (BEIJING) CO., LTD.—See China Finance Online Co. Limited; *Int'l*, pg. 1502
CHINA FINANCE ONLINE CO. LIMITED; *Int'l*, pg. 1502
CHINA FINANCE ONLINE—See China Finance Online Co. Limited; *Int'l*, pg. 1502
CHINA FINANCIAL INTERNATIONAL INVESTMENTS LIMITED; *Int'l*, pg. 1502
CHINA FINANCIAL LEASING GROUP LIMITED; *Int'l*, pg. 1502
CHINA FINANCIAL SERVICES HOLDINGS LIMITED; *Int'l*, pg. 1502
CHINA FINEBLANKING TECHNOLOGY CO., LTD.; *Int'l*, pg. 1503
CHINA FIRE & SECURITY GROUP, INC.—See Bain Capital, LP; *U.S. Private*, pg. 437
CHINA FIRST CAPITAL GROUP LIMITED; *Int'l*, pg. 1503
CHINA FIRST HEAVY INDUSTRIES CO., LTD.; *Int'l*, pg. 1503
CHINA FIRST PENCIL CO., LTD.—See Lao Feng Xiang Co., Ltd.; *Int'l*, pg. 4417
CHINA FISHERY GROUP LIMITED—See Pacific Andes International Holdings Limited; *Int'l*, pg. 5685
CHINA FLEXIBLE PACKAGING HOLDINGS LIMITED; *Int'l*, pg. 1503
CHINA FOOD COMPANY PLC; *Int'l*, pg. 1503
CHINA FOOD PACKING INC., LTD.; *Int'l*, pg. 1503
CHINA FOODS HOLDINGS LTD.; *Int'l*, pg. 1503
CHINA FOODS LIMITED—See COFCO Limited; *Int'l*, pg. 1692
CHINA FOREIGN ECONOMY AND TRADE TRUST CO., LTD.—See Sinochem Corporation; *Int'l*, pg. 6949
CHINA FORTUNE GROUP STRATEGIC INVESTMENT COMPANY LIMITED—See GoFintech Innovation Limited; *Int'l*, pg. 3021
CHINA FORTUNE HOLDINGS LIMITED; *Int'l*, pg. 1503
CHINA FORTUNE INVESTMENTS (HOLDING) LIMITED; *Int'l*, pg. 1503
CHINA FORTUNE LAND DEVELOPMENT CO., LTD.; *Int'l*, pg. 1503

CHINA FUND MANAGEMENT CO., LTD.—See CSC Financial Co., Ltd; *Int'l*, pg. 1862
CHINA FUTEX HOLDINGS LIMITED; *Int'l*, pg. 1503
CHINA FUTURES CO., LTD.—See CSC Financial Co., Ltd; *Int'l*, pg. 1862
CHINA GALAXY INTERNATIONAL FINANCIAL HOLDINGS COMPANY LIMITED—See China Galaxy Securities Company Limited; *Int'l*, pg. 1503
CHINA GALAXY SECURITIES COMPANY LIMITED; *Int'l*, pg. 1503
CHINA GAOXIAN FIBRE FABRIC HOLDINGS LTD.; *Int'l*, pg. 1503
CHINA GARMENTS CO., LTD.—See China Hi-Tech Group Corporation; *Int'l*, pg. 1508
CHINA GAS HOLDINGS LIMITED; *Int'l*, pg. 1503
CHINA GAS INDUSTRY INVESTMENT HOLDINGS CO., LTD.; *Int'l*, pg. 1504
CHINAGATE COMPANY LIMITED—See UnitedHealth Group Incorporated; *U.S. Public*, pg. 2239
CHINA GATEWAY PHARMACEUTICAL DEVELOPMENT CO., LTD.—See TPG Capital, L.P.; *U.S. Public*, pg. 2175
CHINA GEM HOLDINGS LIMITED; *Int'l*, pg. 1504
CHINA GENERAL PLASTICS CORPORATION; *Int'l*, pg. 1504
CHINA GENERAL PLASTICS CORPORATION - TOUFEN PLANT—See China General Plastics Corporation; *Int'l*, pg. 1504
CHINA GENERAL TECHNOLOGY (GROUP) HOLDING CO., LTD.; *Int'l*, pg. 1504
CHINA GENERAL TECHNOLOGY (GROUP) PHARMACEUTICAL HOLDING CO., LTD.—See China Meheco Group Co., Ltd.; *Int'l*, pg. 1518
CHINA GENGSHENG MINERALS, INC.; *Int'l*, pg. 1504
CHINA GERUI ADVANCED MATERIALS GROUP LIMITED; *Int'l*, pg. 1504
CHINA GEWANG BIOTECHNOLOGY, INC.; *Int'l*, pg. 1504
CHINA GEZHOUBA GROUP COMPANY LIMITED; *Int'l*, pg. 1504
CHINA GINGKO EDUCATION GROUP COMPANY LIMITED; *Int'l*, pg. 1504
CHINA GINSENG HOLDINGS, INC.; *Int'l*, pg. 1504
CHINA GLASS HOLDINGS LIMITED; *Int'l*, pg. 1504
CHINA GLAZE CO., LTD.; *Int'l*, pg. 1504
CHINAGOHI—See PacificNet Inc.; *Int'l*, pg. 5692
CHINA GOLDEN CLASSIC GROUP LIMITED; *Int'l*, pg. 1505
CHINA GOLD INTERNATIONAL RESOURCES CORP. LTD.; *Int'l*, pg. 1505
CHINA GOLD, PTE. LTD.—See Lippo Limited; *Int'l*, pg. 4522
CHINA GRAND AUTOMOTIVE SERVICES GROUP CO., LTD.—See Xinjiang Guanghui Industry Investment Group Co., Ltd.; *Int'l*, pg. 8531
CHINA GRAPHITE GROUP LIMITED; *Int'l*, pg. 1505
CHINA GREAT LAND HOLDINGS LTD.; *Int'l*, pg. 1505
CHINA GREAT STAR INTERNATIONAL LIMITED; *Int'l*, pg. 1505
CHINA GREAT WALL ASSET MANAGEMENT CORPORATION; *Int'l*, pg. 1505
CHINA GREAT WALL SECURITIES CO., LTD.; *Int'l*, pg. 1505
CHINA GREATWALL TECHNOLOGY GROUP CO., LTD.—See China Electronics Corporation; *Int'l*, pg. 1499
CHINA GREEN AGRICULTURE, INC.; *Int'l*, pg. 1505
CHINA GREEN ELECTRICITY INVESTMENT OF TIANJIN CO., LTD.; *Int'l*, pg. 1505
CHINA GREENFRESH GROUP CO., LTD.; *Int'l*, pg. 1505
CHINA GREEN HOLDINGS LIMITED—See New Energy Exchange Ltd.; *Int'l*, pg. 5223
CHINA GREENLAND BROAD GREENSTATE GROUP CO., LTD.; *Int'l*, pg. 1505
CHINA GREEN MATERIAL TECHNOLOGIES, INC.; *Int'l*, pg. 1505
CHINA GRENTECH CORPORATION LIMITED; *Int'l*, pg. 1505
CHINA GUANGDONG NUCLEAR POWER HOLDING CO., LTD.; *Int'l*, pg. 1506
CHINA GUANGFA BANK CO., LTD.; *Int'l*, pg. 1506
CHINA GUODIAN CORPORATION; *Int'l*, pg. 1506
CHINA HAIDA LTD.; *Int'l*, pg. 1506
CHINA HAINAN RUBBER INDUSTRY GROUP CO., LTD.; *Int'l*, pg. 1506
CHINA HAISHENG JUICE HOLDINGS CO., LTD.; *Int'l*, pg. 1506
CHINA HAISUM ENGINEERING CO., LTD.—See Sinolight Corporation; *Int'l*, pg. 6952
CHINA HANKING HOLDINGS LIMITED; *Int'l*, pg. 1506
CHINA HAOHUA CHEMICAL GROUP CO., LTD.—See China National Chemical Corporation; *Int'l*, pg. 1526
CHINA HAOHUA ENGINEERING CO., LTD.—See China National Chemical Corporation; *Int'l*, pg. 1526
CHINA HAO RAN RECYCLING CO., LTD.; *Int'l*, pg. 1506
CHINA HARBOUR ENGINEERING COMPANY LTD.—See China Communications Construction Company Limited; *Int'l*, pg. 1490
CHINA HARMONY AUTO HOLDING LIMITED; *Int'l*, pg. 1506

CHINA HARZONE INDUSTRY CO., LTD.; *Int'l*, pg. 1507
CHINA HEALTHCARE LIMITED; *Int'l*, pg. 1507
CHINA HEALTH GROUP INC.; *Int'l*, pg. 1507
CHINA HEALTH INDUSTRIES HOLDINGS, INC.; *Int'l*, pg. 1507
CHINA HEALTH MANAGEMENT CORP.; *U.S. Public*, pg. 489
CHINA HEALTH RESOURCE, INC.; *Int'l*, pg. 1507
CHINA HEALTHWISE HOLDINGS LIMITED; *Int'l*, pg. 1507
CHINA HEAVEN CREATION INTERNATIONAL PERFORMING ARTS CO., LTD.—See China Travel International Investment Hong Kong Ltd; *Int'l*, pg. 1560
CHINA HEFENG RESCUE EQUIPMENT, INC.; *Int'l*, pg. 1507
CHINA HENGSHI FOUNDATION CO. LTD.—See Zhenshi Holding Group Co., Ltd.; *Int'l*, pg. 8670
CHINA HIGH PRECISION AUTOMATION GROUP LIMITED; *Int'l*, pg. 1508
CHINA HIGH-SPEED RAILWAY TECHNOLOGY CO., LTD.; *Int'l*, pg. 1508
CHINA HIGH SPEED TRANSMISSION EQUIPMENT GROUP CO., LTD.—See Fullshare Holdings Limited; *Int'l*, pg. 2843
CHINA HI-MENT CORP.—See China Steel Corporation; *Int'l*, pg. 1555
CHINA HI-TECH GROUP CO., LTD.; *Int'l*, pg. 1507
CHINA HI-TECH GROUP CORPORATION; *Int'l*, pg. 1507
CHINA HOLDINGS GROUP, INC.; *U.S. Private*, pg. 886
CHINA HOLDINGS, INC.; *Int'l*, pg. 1508
CHINA HONGBAO HOLDINGS LIMITED; *Int'l*, pg. 1508
CHINA HONGGUANG HOLDINGS LIMITED; *Int'l*, pg. 1508
CHINA-HONG KONG PHOTO PRODUCTS HOLDINGS LIMITED; *Int'l*, pg. 1568
CHINA HONGQIAO GROUP LIMITED; *Int'l*, pg. 1508
CHINA HONGXING SPORTS LIMITED; *Int'l*, pg. 1508
CHINA HOSIDEN CO., LTD.—See Hosiden Corporation; *Int'l*, pg. 3484
CHINA HOUSING & LAND DEVELOPMENT, INC.; *Int'l*, pg. 1508
CHINA HP CO., LTD.—See HP Inc.; *U.S. Public*, pg. 1062
CHINA HUADIAN CORPORATION LTD.; *Int'l*, pg. 1508
CHINA HUAJUN GROUP LIMITED; *Int'l*, pg. 1508
CHINA HUALU PANASONIC AVC NETWORKS CO., LTD.—See Panasonic Holdings Corporation; *Int'l*, pg. 5719
CHINA HUANCHI BEARING GROUP CO., LTD.; *Int'l*, pg. 1509
CHINA HUANENG FINANCE CO., LTD.—See China Huaneng Group Co., Ltd.; *Int'l*, pg. 1509
CHINA HUANENG GROUP CO., LTD.; *Int'l*, pg. 1509
CHINA HUARONG ENERGY CO. LTD.; *Int'l*, pg. 1509
CHINA HUARONG FINANCIAL LEASING CO LTD—See China CITIC Financial Asset Management Co., Ltd.; *Int'l*, pg. 1489
CHINA HUARONG (MACAU) INTERNATIONAL COMPANY LIMITED—See China CITIC Financial Asset Management Co., Ltd.; *Int'l*, pg. 1489
CHINA HUIRONG FINANCIAL HOLDINGS LIMITED; *Int'l*, pg. 1509
CHINA HUISHAN DAIRY HOLDINGS COMPANY LIMITED; *Int'l*, pg. 1509
CHINA HUMAN CAPITAL MANAGEMENT COMPANY LIMITED—See SING TAO NEWS CORPORATION LIMITED; *Int'l*, pg. 6939
CHINA HYDROELECTRIC CORPORATION—See Shenzhen Energy Group Co., Ltd.; *Int'l*, pg. 6808
CHINA INC.; *U.S. Private*, pg. 886
CHINA INDEX HOLDINGS LIMITED; *Int'l*, pg. 1509
CHINA INDUSTRIAL ASSET MANAGEMENT CO., LTD.—See Industrial Bank Co., Ltd.; *Int'l*, pg. 3674
CHINA INDUSTRIAL INTERNATIONAL TRUST LIMITED—See Industrial Bank Co., Ltd.; *Int'l*, pg. 3671
CHINA INDUSTRIAL SECURITIES FINANCIAL GROUP; *Int'l*, pg. 1509
CHINA INDUSTRIAL SECURITIES INTERNATIONAL ASSET MANAGEMENT LIMITED—See China Industrial Securities Financial Group; *Int'l*, pg. 1509
CHINA INDUSTRIAL SECURITIES INTERNATIONAL BROKERAGE LIMITED—See China Industrial Securities Financial Group; *Int'l*, pg. 1509
CHINA INDUSTRIAL SECURITIES INTERNATIONAL CAPITAL LIMITED—See China Industrial Securities Financial Group; *Int'l*, pg. 1509
CHINA INDUSTRIAL SECURITIES INTERNATIONAL FUTURES LIMITED—See China Industrial Securities Financial Group; *Int'l*, pg. 1509
CHINA INDUSTRIAL SECURITIES INTERNATIONAL WEALTH MANAGEMENT LIMITED—See China Industrial Securities Financial Group; *Int'l*, pg. 1510
CHINA INDUSTRIAL STEEL INC.; *U.S. Public*, pg. 489
CHINA INDUSTRIAL WASTE MANAGEMENT, INC.; *Int'l*, pg. 1510
CHINA INFORMATION TECHNOLOGY DEVELOPMENT LIMITED—See Beijing Enterprises Holdings Limited; *Int'l*, pg. 950
CHINA INFRASTRUCTURE CONSTRUCTION CORPORATION; *Int'l*, pg. 1510

COMPANY NAME INDEX

CHINA INFRASTRUCTURE INVESTMENT LIMITED; *Int'l*, pg. 1510
CHINA INFRASTRUCTURE & LOGISTICS GROUP LTD.; *Int'l*, pg. 1510
CHINA INNOVATION INVESTMENT LIMITED; *Int'l*, pg. 1510
CHINA INN RESTAURANTS, INC.—See Cafe de Coral Holdings Limited; *Int'l*, pg. 1250
CHINA INTEGRATED ENERGY, INC.; *Int'l*, pg. 1510
CHINA INTELLIGENCE INFORMATION SYSTEMS, INC.; *Int'l*, pg. 1510
CHINA INTELLIGENT LIGHTING AND ELECTRONICS, INC.; *Int'l*, pg. 1510
CHINA INTERNATIONAL CAPITAL CORPORATION HONG KONG ASSET MANAGEMENT LIMITED—See China International Capital Corporation Limited; *Int'l*, pg. 1510
CHINA INTERNATIONAL CAPITAL CORPORATION (HONG KONG) LIMITED—See China International Capital Corporation Limited; *Int'l*, pg. 1510
CHINA INTERNATIONAL CAPITAL CORPORATION LIMITED; *Int'l*, pg. 1510
CHINA INTERNATIONAL CAPITAL CORPORATION (SINGAPORE) PTE. LIMITED—See China International Capital Corporation Limited; *Int'l*, pg. 1510
CHINA INTERNATIONAL CAPITAL CORPORATION (UK) LIMITED—See China International Capital Corporation Limited; *Int'l*, pg. 1510
CHINA INTERNATIONAL DEVELOPMENT CORPORATION LIMITED; *Int'l*, pg. 1510
CHINA INTERNATIONAL ECONOMIC CONSULTANTS CO., LTD.—See CITIC Group Corporation; *Int'l*, pg. 1621
CHINA INTERNATIONAL ENGINEERING & MATERIALS CORP.—See China Rare Earth Resources And Technology Co., Ltd.; *Int'l*, pg. 1545
CHINA INTERNATIONAL EXHIBITIONS LIMITED—See Informa plc; *Int'l*, pg. 3691
CHINA INTERNATIONAL HOLDINGS LIMITED; *Int'l*, pg. 1510
CHINA INTERNATIONAL MARINE CONTAINERS (GROUP) CO., LTD.; *Int'l*, pg. 1510
CHINA INTERNATIONAL MARINE CONTAINERS (HONG KONG) LIMITED—See China International Marine Containers (Group) Co., Ltd.; *Int'l*, pg. 1511
CHINA INTERNATIONAL TRAVEL SERVICE DALIAN CO., LTD.—See China Tourism Group Duty Free Corporation Limited; *Int'l*, pg. 1560
CHINA INTERNATIONAL TRAVEL SERVICE (QINGDAO) CO., LTD.—See China Tourism Group Duty Free Corporation Limited; *Int'l*, pg. 1560
CHINA INVESTMENT AND FINANCE GROUP LIMITED; *Int'l*, pg. 1513
CHINA INVESTMENT CORPORATION; *Int'l*, pg. 1513
CHINA INVESTMENT INFORMATION SERVICES CO., LTD.—See Hangzhou MDK Opto Electronic Corp., Ltd.; *Int'l*, pg. 3249
CHINA INVESTMENT SECURITIES COMPANY LIMITED—See China International Capital Corporation Limited; *Int'l*, pg. 1510
CHINA INVESTMENTS HOLDINGS LIMITED; *Int'l*, pg. 1513
CHINA ISOTOPE & RADIATION CORPORATION—See China National Nuclear Corporation; *Int'l*, pg. 1532
CHINA ITS (HOLDINGS) CO., LTD.; *Int'l*, pg. 1513
CHINA JIANGSU SUNTORY FOODS CO., LTD.—See Suntory Holdings Limited; *Int'l*, pg. 7326
CHINA JIANYIN INVESTMENT LIMITED—See China Investment Corporation; *Int'l*, pg. 1513
CHINA JICHENG HOLDINGS LIMITED; *Int'l*, pg. 1513
CHINA JIKAN RESEARCH INSTITUTE OF ENGINEERING INVESTIGATIONS & DESIGN CO., LTD.—See China Machinery Engineering Corporation; *Int'l*, pg. 1516
CHINA JINGU INTERNATIONAL TRUST CO., LTD.—See China Cinda Asset Management Co., Ltd.; *Int'l*, pg. 1488
CHINA JINMAO HOLDINGS GROUP LIMITED—See Sinochem Corporation; *Int'l*, pg. 6949
CHINA JINSHAN ASSOCIATED TRADING CORP.—See China Petrochemical Corporation; *Int'l*, pg. 1539
CHINA JISHAN HOLDINGS LIMITED; *Int'l*, pg. 1513
CHINA JO-JO DRUGSTORES, INC.; *Int'l*, pg. 1513
CHINA JUSHI CO., LTD.; *Int'l*, pg. 1513
CHINA KANGDA FOOD COMPANY LIMITED; *Int'l*, pg. 1514
CHINA KELI ELECTRIC COMPANY LTD.; *Int'l*, pg. 1514
CHINA KEPEI EDUCATION GROUP LIMITED; *Int'l*, pg. 1514
CHINA KINGHO ENERGY GROUP CO., LTD.; *Int'l*, pg. 1514
CHINA KING SPIRIT GROUP LTD.; *U.S. Private*, pg. 886
CHINA KINGS RESOURCES GROUP CO., LTD.; *Int'l*, pg. 1514
CHINA KINGSTONE MINING HOLDINGS LIMITED; *Int'l*, pg. 1514
CHINA KUNDA TECHNOLOGY HOLDINGS LIMITED; *Int'l*, pg. 1514
CHINA LEADSHINE TECHNOLOGY CO., LTD.; *Int'l*, pg. 1514

CHINA LEON INSPECTION HOLDING LIMITED; *Int'l*, pg. 1514
CHINA LESSO GROUP HOLDINGS LIMITED; *Int'l*, pg. 1514
CHINA LIAOHUA UNITED FOREIGN TRADE CO. LTD.—See Sinochem Corporation; *Int'l*, pg. 6949
CHINA LIAONING DINGXU ECOLOGICAL AGRICULTURE DEVELOPMENT, INC.; *U.S. Public*, pg. 489
CHINA LIBERAL EDUCATION HOLDINGS LIMITED; *Int'l*, pg. 1514
CHINA LIFE AMP ASSET MANAGEMENT COMPANY—See China Life Insurance Company Limited; *Int'l*, pg. 1515
CHINA LIFE ASSET MANAGEMENT COMPANY LIMITED—See China Life Insurance Company Limited; *Int'l*, pg. 1515
CHINA LIFE INSURANCE ASSET MANAGEMENT COMPANY LIMITED—See China Life Insurance Company Limited; *Int'l*, pg. 1515
CHINA LIFE INSURANCE COMPANY LIMITED; *Int'l*, pg. 1515
CHINA LIFE INSURANCE COMPANY, LTD.—See KGI Financial Holding Co., Ltd.; *Int'l*, pg. 4150
CHINA LIFE PENSION COMPANY LIMITED—See China Life Insurance Company Limited; *Int'l*, pg. 1515
CHINA LIFE REINSURANCE COMPANY LTD.—See China Reinsurance (Group) Corporation; *Int'l*, pg. 1547
CHINA LIFE WEALTH MANAGEMENT COMPANY LIMITED—See China Life Insurance Company Limited; *Int'l*, pg. 1515
CHINA LILANG LIMITED; *Int'l*, pg. 1515
CHINA LINEN TEXTILE INDUSTRY, LTD.; *Int'l*, pg. 1515
CHINALIN SECURITIES CO., LTD.; *Int'l*, pg. 1568
CHINA LITERATURE LTD.; *Int'l*, pg. 1515
CHINA LOGISTICS GROUP, INC.; *Int'l*, pg. 1515
CHINA LOGISTICS PROPERTY HOLDINGS COMPANY LIMITED; *Int'l*, pg. 1515
CHINA LONGEVITY GROUP COMPANY LIMITED; *Int'l*, pg. 1515
CHINA LONGYI GROUP INTERNATIONAL HOLDINGS LIMITED; *Int'l*, pg. 1515
CHINA LONGYUAN POWER GROUP CORP LTD.; *Int'l*, pg. 1515
CHINA LSOTOPE & RADIATION CORPORATION; *Int'l*, pg. 1515
CHINA LUDAO TECHNOLOGY COMPANY LIMITED; *Int'l*, pg. 1515
CHINA MACHINERY ENGINEERING ARGENTINA SA—See China Machinery Engineering Corporation; *Int'l*, pg. 1516
CHINA MACHINERY ENGINEERING CO., HUBEI LTD.—See China Machinery Engineering Corporation; *Int'l*, pg. 1516
CHINA MACHINERY ENGINEERING CORPORATION (PNG) LIMITED—See China Machinery Engineering Corporation; *Int'l*, pg. 1516
CHINA MACHINERY ENGINEERING CORPORATION; *Int'l*, pg. 1515
CHINA MACHINERY ENGINEERING HENAN CO., LTD.—See China Machinery Engineering Corporation; *Int'l*, pg. 1516
CHINA MACHINERY ENGINEERING SUZHOU CO., LTD.—See China Machinery Engineering Corporation; *Int'l*, pg. 1516
CHINA MACHINERY ENGINEERING WUXI CO., LTD.—See China Machinery Engineering Corporation; *Int'l*, pg. 1516
CHINA MACHINERY ENGINEERING YINCHUAN FREE TRADE ZONE CO., LTD.—See China Machinery Engineering Corporation; *Int'l*, pg. 1516
CHINA MACHINERY & EQUIPMENT (HK) CO., LTD.—See China Machinery Engineering Corporation; *Int'l*, pg. 1516
CHINA MACHINERY & EQUIPMENT INTERNATIONAL TENDERING CO., LTD.—See China Machinery Engineering Corporation; *Int'l*, pg. 1516
CHINA MACHINERY INDUSTRIAL PRODUCTS CO., LTD.—See China Machinery Engineering Corporation; *Int'l*, pg. 1516
CHINA MACHINERY INTERNATIONAL ENGINEERING DESIGN & RESEARCH INSTITUTE CO., LTD.—See China Machinery Engineering Corporation; *Int'l*, pg. 1516
CHINA MAGNESIUM CORPORATION LIMITED; *Int'l*, pg. 1516
CHINA MAN-MADE FIBER CORPORATION; *Int'l*, pg. 1516
CHINA MAPLE LEAF EDUCATIONAL SYSTEMS LIMITED; *Int'l*, pg. 1517
CHINA MARINE FOOD GROUP, LTD.; *Int'l*, pg. 1517
CHINA MARINE INFORMATION ELECTRONICS COMPANY LIMITED; *Int'l*, pg. 1517
CHINA MARINE SHIPPING AGENCY COMPANY LIMITED—See China Merchants Group Limited; *Int'l*, pg. 1522
CHINA MARINE SHIPPING AGENCY GUANGDONG CO., LTD.—See China Merchants Group Limited; *Int'l*, pg. 1522

CHINA MARINE SHIPPING AGENCY, JIANGSU COMPANY LIMITED—See China Merchants Group Limited; *Int'l*, pg. 1522
CHINA MARINE SHIPPING AGENCY, NANTONG COMPANY LIMITED—See China Merchants Group Limited; *Int'l*, pg. 1522
CHINA MARINE SHIPPING AGENCY RUGAO CO., LTD.—See China Merchants Group Limited; *Int'l*, pg. 1522
CHINA MARINE SHIPPING AGENCY, TAICANG COMPANY LIMITED—See China Merchants Group Limited; *Int'l*, pg. 1522
CHINA MARINE SHIPPING AGENCY, TAIZHOU COMPANY LIMITED—See China Merchants Group Limited; *Int'l*, pg. 1522
CHINA MARINE SHIPPING AGENCY, ZHANGJIAGANG COMPANY LIMITED—See China Merchants Group Limited; *Int'l*, pg. 1522
CHINA MARINE SHIPPING AGENCY ZHENJIANG CO., LTD.—See China Merchants Group Limited; *Int'l*, pg. 1522
CHINA MASS MEDIA CORP.; *Int'l*, pg. 1517
CHINA MASTER LOGISTICS CO., LTD.; *Int'l*, pg. 1517
CHINAMATE (SHAANXI) NATURAL PRODUCTS CO. LTD.—See CORTICEIRA AMORIM, S.G.P.S., S.A.; *Int'l*, pg. 1807
CHINA MEDIA GROUP; *Int'l*, pg. 1518
CHINA MEDIA INC.; *Int'l*, pg. 1518
CHINA MEDIA (SHANGHAI) MANAGEMENT CONSULTING COMPANY LIMITED—See Ebiquity plc; *Int'l*, pg. 2285
CHINA MEDICAL & HEALTHCARE GROUP LIMITED; *Int'l*, pg. 1518
CHINA MEDICAL (INTERNATIONAL) GROUP LIMITED; *Int'l*, pg. 1518
CHINA MEDICAL SYSTEM HOLDINGS LTD.; *Int'l*, pg. 1518
CHINA MEDICAL TECHNOLOGIES, INC.; *Int'l*, pg. 1518
CHINA MEDICINE CORPORATION; *Int'l*, pg. 1518
CHINA MEHECO BEIJING BAITAI PHARMA CO., LTD.—See China Meheco Group Co., Ltd.; *Int'l*, pg. 1518
CHINA MEHECO BEIJING PHARMA CO., LTD.—See China Meheco Group Co., Ltd.; *Int'l*, pg. 1518
CHINA MEHECO CO., LTD. - TANGGU PROCESSING PLANT—See China Meheco Group Co., Ltd.; *Int'l*, pg. 1518
CHINA MEHECO GREAT WALL PHARMA CO., LTD.—See China Meheco Group Co., Ltd.; *Int'l*, pg. 1518
CHINA MEHECO GROUP CO., LTD.; *Int'l*, pg. 1518
CHINA MEHECO GUANGDONG PHARMA CO., LTD.—See China Meheco Group Co., Ltd.; *Int'l*, pg. 1518
CHINA MEHECO HEILONGJIANG PHARMA CO., LTD.—See China Meheco Group Co., Ltd.; *Int'l*, pg. 1518
CHINA MEHECO HENAN PHARMA CO., LTD.—See China Meheco Group Co., Ltd.; *Int'l*, pg. 1518
CHINA MEHECO HUBEI PHARMA CO., LTD.—See China Meheco Group Co., Ltd.; *Int'l*, pg. 1518
CHINA MEHECO INTERNATIONAL CO., LTD.—See China Meheco Group Co., Ltd.; *Int'l*, pg. 1518
CHINA MEHECO JIANGXI NANHUA PHARMA CO., LTD.—See China Meheco Group Co., Ltd.; *Int'l*, pg. 1518
CHINA MEHECO JIANGXI PHARMA CO., LTD.—See China Meheco Group Co., Ltd.; *Int'l*, pg. 1519
CHINA MEHECO KANGLI PHARMA CO., LTD.—See China Meheco Group Co., Ltd.; *Int'l*, pg. 1519
CHINA MEHECO KEYI PHARMA CO., LTD.—See China Meheco Group Co., Ltd.; *Int'l*, pg. 1519
CHINA MEHECO MED-TECH SERVICE CO., LTD.—See China Meheco Group Co., Ltd.; *Int'l*, pg. 1519
CHINA MEHECO SANYANG PHARMA CO., LTD.—See China Meheco Group Co., Ltd.; *Int'l*, pg. 1519
CHINA MEHECO TOPFOND PHARMA CO., LTD.—See China Meheco Group Co., Ltd.; *Int'l*, pg. 1519
CHINA MEHECO TOPFOND TRADITIONAL CHINESE MEDICINE CO., LTD.—See China Meheco Group Co., Ltd.; *Int'l*, pg. 1519
CHINA MEHECO XINJIANG PHARMA CO., LTD.—See China Meheco Group Co., Ltd.; *Int'l*, pg. 1519
CHINA MEIDONG AUTO HOLDINGS LIMITED; *Int'l*, pg. 1519
CHINA MENGNIU DAIRY COMPANY LIMITED; *Int'l*, pg. 1519
CHINA MERCHANTS BANK CO LTD; *Int'l*, pg. 1520
CHINA MERCHANTS BANK CO., LTD.—See China Merchants Group Limited; *Int'l*, pg. 1520
CHINA MERCHANTS CAPITAL INVESTMENT CO., LTD.—See China Merchants Group Limited; *Int'l*, pg. 1520
CHINA MERCHANTS CHINA DIRECT INVESTMENTS LIMITED—See China Merchants Group Limited; *Int'l*, pg. 1520
CHINA MERCHANTS ENERGY SHIPPING CO., LTD.—See China Merchants Group Limited; *Int'l*, pg. 1520

CHINA MERCHANTS BANK CO LTD

CHINA MERCHANTS EXPRESSWAY NETWORK & TECHNOLOGY HOLDINGS CO., LTD.—See China Merchants Group Limited; *Int'l*, pg. 1520
CHINA MERCHANTS FUND MANAGEMENT CO., LTD.—See China Merchants Group Limited; *Int'l*, pg. 1520
CHINA MERCHANTS GROUP LIMITED; *Int'l*, pg. 1520
CHINA MERCHANTS HOLDINGS (PACIFIC) LIMITED—See China Merchants Group Limited; *Int'l*, pg. 1520
CHINA MERCHANTS HUAJIAN HIGHWAY INVESTMENT CO., LTD.—See China Merchants Group Limited; *Int'l*, pg. 1520
CHINA MERCHANTS INDUSTRY HOLDINGS CO., LTD.—See China Merchants Group Limited; *Int'l*, pg. 1520
CHINA MERCHANTS INSURANCE COMPANY LIMITED—See China Merchants Group Limited; *Int'l*, pg. 1521
CHINA MERCHANTS LAND LIMITED—See China Merchants Group Limited; *Int'l*, pg. 1521
CHINA MERCHANTS LOSCAM (ASIA PACIFIC) CO., LIMITED—See China Merchants Group Limited; *Int'l*, pg. 1521
CHINA MERCHANTS PORT GROUP CO., LTD.—See China Merchants Group Limited; *Int'l*, pg. 1521
CHINA MERCHANTS PORT HOLDINGS COMPANY LIMITED—See China Merchants Group Limited; *Int'l*, pg. 1521
CHINA MERCHANTS PROPERTY DEVELOPMENT CO., LTD.—See China Merchants Group Limited; *Int'l*, pg. 1521
CHINA MERCHANTS PROPERTY OPERATION & SERVICE CO., LTD.—See AVIC International Holdings Limited; *Int'l*, pg. 742
CHINA MERCHANTS SECURITIES CO., LTD.—See China Merchants Group Limited; *Int'l*, pg. 1521
CHINA MERCHANTS SHEKOU INDUSTRIAL ZONE CO., LTD.—See China Merchants Group Limited; *Int'l*, pg. 1521
CHINA MERCHANTS SHEKOU INDUSTRIAL ZONE HOLDINGS CO., LTD.; *Int'l*, pg. 1523
CHINA MERCHANTS TECHNOLOGY HOLDINGS CO., LTD.—See China Merchants Group Limited; *Int'l*, pg. 1521
CHINA MERCHANTS ZHANGZHOU DEVELOPMENT ZONE CO., LTD.—See China Merchants Group Limited; *Int'l*, pg. 1521
CHINA METAL AUTOMOTIVE INTERNATIONAL CO.—See China Metal Products Co., Ltd.; *Int'l*, pg. 1523
CHINA METAL INTERNATIONAL HOLDINGS INC.—See China Metal Products Co., Ltd.; *Int'l*, pg. 1523
CHINA METAL JAPAN CO., LTD.—See China Metal Products Co., Ltd.; *Int'l*, pg. 1523
CHINA METALLURGICAL GROUP CORPORATION—See China Rare Earth Resources And Technology Co., Ltd.; *Int'l*, pg. 1545
CHINA METAL PRODUCTS CO., LTD. - HSINCHU PLANT—See China Metal Products Co., Ltd.; *Int'l*, pg. 1523
CHINA METAL PRODUCTS CO., LTD. - PINGZHEN PLANT—See China Metal Products Co., Ltd.; *Int'l*, pg. 1523
CHINA METAL PRODUCTS CO., LTD. - PLYMOUTH BRANCH—See China Metal Products Co., Ltd.; *Int'l*, pg. 1523
CHINA METAL PRODUCTS CO., LTD.; *Int'l*, pg. 1523
CHINA METAL RECYCLING (HOLDINGS) LIMITED; *Int'l*, pg. 1523
CHINA METAL RESOURCES UTILIZATION LTD.; *Int'l*, pg. 1524
CHINA METRO-RURAL HOLDINGS LIMITED; *Int'l*, pg. 1524
CHINA MING YANG WIND POWER GROUP LIMITED; *Int'l*, pg. 1524
CHINA MINING INTERNATIONAL LIMITED; *Int'l*, pg. 1524
CHINA MINING RESOURCES HOLDINGS LIMITED—See SSC Mandarin Financial Services Limited; *Int'l*, pg. 7155
CHINA MINING UNITED FUND; *Int'l*, pg. 1524
CHINA MINMETALS HAINAN TRADING DEVELOPMENT CORP.—See China Rare Earth Resources And Technology Co., Ltd.; *Int'l*, pg. 1545
CHINA MINMETALS H.K. (HOLDING) LIMITED—See China Rare Earth Resources And Technology Co., Ltd.; *Int'l*, pg. 1545
CHINA MINMETALS NON-FERROUS METALS CO. LTD.—See China Rare Earth Resources And Technology Co., Ltd.; *Int'l*, pg. 1545
CHINA MINMETALS NZ LTD.—See China Rare Earth Resources And Technology Co., Ltd.; *Int'l*, pg. 1545
CHINA MINMETALS SOUTH AMERICA (HOLDING) LTD.—See China Rare Earth Resources And Technology Co., Ltd.; *Int'l*, pg. 1545
CHINA MINMETALS ZHUHAI IMPORT AND EXPORT TRADING CO., LTD.—See China Rare Earth Resources And Technology Co., Ltd.; *Int'l*, pg. 1545

CHINA MINMET INVESTMENT LIMITED—See China Rare Earth Resources And Technology Co., Ltd.; *Int'l*, pg. 1545
CHINA MINSHENG BANKING CORPORATION LTD.; *Int'l*, pg. 1524
CHINA MINSHENG INVESTMENT GROUP CORP., LTD.; *Int'l*, pg. 1524
CHINA MINSHENG JIAYE INVESTMENT CO., LTD.—See China Minsheng Investment Group Corp., Ltd.; *Int'l*, pg. 1524
CHINA MIST BRANDS, INC.—See Farmer Brothers Co.; *U.S. Public*, pg. 821
CHINA MJC (SHANGHAI) CO., LTD.—See MICRONICS JAPAN CO., LTD.; *Int'l*, pg. 4880
CHINA MOBILE COMMUNICATIONS CORPORATION; *Int'l*, pg. 1524
CHINA MOBILE GAMES & ENTERTAINMENT GROUP LIMITED—See Changjiang Securities Company Limited; *Int'l*, pg. 1443
CHINA MOBILE GROUP BEIJING COMPANY LIMITED—See China Mobile Communications Corporation; *Int'l*, pg. 1524
CHINA MOBILE GROUP HEBEI COMPANY LIMITED—See China Mobile Communications Corporation; *Int'l*, pg. 1524
CHINA MOBILE GROUP HEILONGJIANG COMPANY LIMITED—See China Mobile Communications Corporation; *Int'l*, pg. 1524
CHINA MOBILE GROUP NEIMENGGU COMPANY LIMITED—See China Mobile Communications Corporation; *Int'l*, pg. 1524
CHINA MOBILE GROUP NINGXIA COMPANY LIMITED—See China Mobile Communications Corporation; *Int'l*, pg. 1524
CHINA MOBILE GROUP TIANJIN COMPANY LIMITED—See China Mobile Communications Corporation; *Int'l*, pg. 1524
CHINA MOBILE IOT COMPANY LIMITED; *Int'l*, pg. 1524
CHINA MOBILE LIMITED—See China Mobile Communications Corporation; *Int'l*, pg. 1524
CHINA MODERN AGRICULTURAL INFORMATION, INC.; *Int'l*, pg. 1524
CHINA MODERN DAIRY HOLDINGS LTD.—See China Mengniu Dairy Company Limited; *Int'l*, pg. 1520
CHINA MOTION HOLDINGS LIMITED—See Hua Yin International Holdings Ltd.; *Int'l*, pg. 3510
CHINA MOTION TELECOM (HK) LIMITED—See VelaTel Global Communications, Inc.; *U.S. Private*, pg. 4354
CHINA MOTION UNITED TELECOM LIMITED—See Hua Yin International Holdings Ltd.; *Int'l*, pg. 3510
CHINA MOTOR BUS COMPANY LIMITED; *Int'l*, pg. 1524
CHINA MOTOR CORPORATION - HSIN-CHU PLANT—See China Motor Corporation; *Int'l*, pg. 1525
CHINA MOTOR CORPORATION; *Int'l*, pg. 1524
CHINA MOTOR CORPORATION - YANG-MEI PLANT—See China Motor Corporation; *Int'l*, pg. 1525
CHINA MOTOR CORPORATION - YU-SHIH PLANT—See China Motor Corporation; *Int'l*, pg. 1525
CHINA MULANS NANO TECHNOLOGY CORP. LTD.; *U.S. Public*, pg. 489
CHINA NATIONAL ACCORD MEDICINES CORP., LTD.; *Int'l*, pg. 1525
CHINA NATIONAL AERO-TECHNOLOGY GUANGZHOU COMPANY LIMITED—See AVIC International Holdings Limited; *Int'l*, pg. 742
CHINA NATIONAL AUTOMATION CONTROL SYSTEM CORP.—See China National Machinery Industry Corporation; *Int'l*, pg. 1531
CHINA NATIONAL AUTOMOTIVE INDUSTRY INTERNATIONAL CORP.—See China National Machinery Industry Corporation; *Int'l*, pg. 1531
CHINA NATIONAL AVIATION FUEL GROUP CORPORATION; *Int'l*, pg. 1525
CHINA NATIONAL AVIATION HOLDING COMPANY; *Int'l*, pg. 1525
CHINA NATIONAL BLUESTAR (GROUP) CO., LTD.—See China National Chemical Corporation; *Int'l*, pg. 1526
CHINA NATIONAL BUILDING MATERIAL COMPANY LIMITED—See China National Building Material Group Co., Ltd.; *Int'l*, pg. 1525
CHINA NATIONAL BUILDING MATERIAL GROUP CO., LTD.; *Int'l*, pg. 1525
CHINA NATIONAL BUILDING MATERIAL GROUP FZE—See China National Building Material Group Co., Ltd.; *Int'l*, pg. 1525
CHINA NATIONAL CHEMICAL CORPORATION; *Int'l*, pg. 1526
CHINA NATIONAL CHEMICAL ENGINEERING CO., LTD.; *Int'l*, pg. 1530
CHINA NATIONAL CHEMICAL ENGINEERING NO.14 CONSTRUCTION CO., LTD.—See China National Chemical Engineering Co., Ltd.; *Int'l*, pg. 1530
CHINA NATIONAL CHEMICAL ENGINEERING NO.16 CONSTRUCTION COMPANY—See China National Chemical Engineering Co., Ltd.; *Int'l*, pg. 1530
CHINA NATIONAL CHEMICAL ENGINEERING NO.7 CONSTRUCTION COMPANY LTD.—See China National Chemical Engineering Co., Ltd.; *Int'l*, pg. 1530

CORPORATE AFFILIATIONS

CHINA NATIONAL CHEMICAL ENGINEERING SIXTH CONSTRUCTION CO., LTD.—See China National Chemical Engineering Co., Ltd.; *Int'l*, pg. 1530
CHINA NATIONAL CHEMICAL FIBER CORPORATION—See China Hi-Tech Group Corporation; *Int'l*, pg. 1508
CHINA NATIONAL COAL IMPORT & EXPORT (TIANJIN) CO., LTD.—See China Coal Energy Company Limited; *Int'l*, pg. 1490
CHINA NATIONAL COAL INDUSTRY QINHUANGDAO IMP. & EXP. CO., LTD.—See China Coal Energy Company Limited; *Int'l*, pg. 1490
CHINA NATIONAL COAL MINING EQUIPMENT CO., LTD.—See China Coal Energy Company Limited; *Int'l*, pg. 1490
CHINA NATIONAL COMPLETE ENGINEERING CORPORATION—See China Machinery Engineering Corporation; *Int'l*, pg. 1516
CHINA NATIONAL COMPLETE PLANT IMPORT & EXPORT CORPORATION; *Int'l*, pg. 1531
CHINA NATIONAL CULTURE GROUP LTD.; *Int'l*, pg. 1531
CHINA NATIONAL ELECTRIC APPARATUS RESEARCH INSTITUTE CO., LTD.; *Int'l*, pg. 1531
CHINA NATIONAL ELECTRIC ENGINEERING CO., LTD.—See China Machinery Engineering Corporation; *Int'l*, pg. 1516
CHINA NATIONAL ELECTRONIC DEVICES CORP.—See Beijing Shiji Information Technology Co., Ltd.; *Int'l*, pg. 956
CHINA NATIONAL ERZHONG GROUP CO.—See China National Machinery Industry Corporation; *Int'l*, pg. 1531
CHINA NATIONAL GARMENTS GROUP CORPORATION—See China Hi-Tech Group Co., Ltd.; *Int'l*, pg. 1507
CHINA NATIONAL GENERAL MACHINERY ENGINEERING CORP.—See China National Machinery Industry Corporation; *Int'l*, pg. 1531
CHINA NATIONAL GOLD GROUP GOLD JEWELLERY CO., LTD.; *Int'l*, pg. 1531
CHINA NATIONAL GROUP CORPORATION OF TRADITIONAL & HERBAL MEDICINE—See China National Pharmaceutical Group Corporation; *Int'l*, pg. 1533
CHINA NATIONAL HEAVY MACHINERY CORPORATION—See China National Machinery Industry Corporation; *Int'l*, pg. 1531
CHINA NATIONAL MACHINERY & EQUIPMENT I/E CORP.—See China National Machinery Industry Corporation; *Int'l*, pg. 1531
CHINA NATIONAL MACHINERY INDUSTRY CORPORATION; *Int'l*, pg. 1531
CHINA NATIONAL MATERIALS COMPANY LIMITED; *Int'l*, pg. 1531
CHINA NATIONAL MEDICAL EQUIPMENT INDUSTRY CORPORATION—See China National Pharmaceutical Group Corporation; *Int'l*, pg. 1533
CHINA NATIONAL MEDICINES CORPORATION LTD.—See China National Pharmaceutical Group Corporation; *Int'l*, pg. 1533
CHINA NATIONAL METAL PRODUCTS IMP/EXP COMPANY—See China Rare Earth Resources And Technology Co., Ltd.; *Int'l*, pg. 1545
CHINA NATIONAL METALS & MINERALS IMP. & EXP. SHANGHAI PUDONG CORP.—See China Rare Earth Resources And Technology Co., Ltd.; *Int'l*, pg. 1545
CHINA NATIONAL METALS & MINERALS IMP/EXP. SHENZHEN CORP.—See China Rare Earth Resources And Technology Co., Ltd.; *Int'l*, pg. 1545
CHINA NATIONAL METALS & MINERALS IMPORT & EXPORT CORPORATION—See China Rare Earth Resources And Technology Co., Ltd.; *Int'l*, pg. 1545
CHINA NATIONAL MINERALS CO., LTD.—See China Rare Earth Resources And Technology Co., Ltd.; *Int'l*, pg. 1545
CHINA NATIONAL NATIVE PRODUCE & ANIMAL BY-PRODUCTS IMPORT & EXPORT CORPORATION—See COFCO Limited; *Int'l*, pg. 1692
CHINA NATIONAL NUCLEAR CORPORATION; *Int'l*, pg. 1532
CHINA NATIONAL NUCLEAR POWER CO LTD.—See China National Nuclear Corporation; *Int'l*, pg. 1532
CHINA NATIONAL OFFSHORE OIL CORP.; *Int'l*, pg. 1532
CHINA NATIONAL PETROLEUM CORPORATION; *Int'l*, pg. 1533
CHINA NATIONAL PHARMACEUTICAL FOREIGN TRADE CORPORATION—See China National Pharmaceutical Group Corporation; *Int'l*, pg. 1533
CHINA NATIONAL PHARMACEUTICAL GROUP CORPORATION; *Int'l*, pg. 1533
CHINA NATIONAL RAILWAY SIGNAL & COMMUNICATION CORP.; *Int'l*, pg. 1534
CHINA NATIONAL SEED GROUP CO., LTD.—See Sinochem Corporation; *Int'l*, pg. 6949
CHINA NATIONAL SOFTWARE & SERVICE CO., LTD.—See China Electronics Corporation; *Int'l*, pg. 1499
CHINA NATIONAL UNITED EQUIPMENT GROUP CORP.—See China National Building Material Group Co., Ltd.; *Int'l*, pg. 1525

COMPANY NAME INDEX

CHINA NATURAL RESOURCES, INC.; *Int'l*, pg. 1534
CHINA NEPSTAR CHAIN DRUGSTORE LTD.; *Int'l*, pg. 1534
CHINA NERIN ENGINEERING CO. LTD.—See China Nonferrous Metal Mining (Group) Co., Ltd.; *Int'l*, pg. 1535
CHINANETCENTER CO., LTD.; *Int'l*, pg. 1568
CHINA NETCOM GROUP CORPORATION (HONG KONG) LIMITED—See China United Network Communications Group Company Limited; *Int'l*, pg. 1561
CHINA NETCOM TECHNOLOGY HOLDINGS LIMITED; *Int'l*, pg. 1534
CHINA NETCOM (USA) OPERATIONS LIMITED—See China United Network Communications Group Company Limited; *Int'l*, pg. 1561
CHINA NETWORKS INTERNATIONAL HOLDING LTD.; *Int'l*, pg. 1534
CHINA NEW BORUN CORPORATION; *Int'l*, pg. 1534
CHINA NEW CITY COMMERCIAL DEVELOPMENT LIMITED; *Int'l*, pg. 1534
CHINA NEW ECONOMY FUND LIMITED; *Int'l*, pg. 1534
CHINA NEW ENERGY LIMITED; *Int'l*, pg. 1534
CHINA NEW HIGHER EDUCATION GROUP LIMITED; *Int'l*, pg. 1535
CHINA NEW TOWN DEVELOPMENT COMPANY LIMITED - CORPORATE OFFICE—See China New Town Development Company Limited; *Int'l*, pg. 1535
CHINA NEW TOWN DEVELOPMENT COMPANY LIMITED; *Int'l*, pg. 1535
CHINA NEW UNITED IMPORT & EXPORT CORP—See Xinxing Cathay International Group Co., Ltd.; *Int'l*, pg. 8533
CHINA NONFERROUS GOLD LIMITED; *Int'l*, pg. 1535
CHINA NON-FERROUS METAL INDUSTRY'S FOREIGN ENGINEERING & CONSTRUCTION CO., LTD.—See China Nonferrous Metal Mining (Group) Co., Ltd.; *Int'l*, pg. 1535
CHINA NONFERROUS METAL MINING (GROUP) CO., LTD.; *Int'l*, pg. 1535
CHINA NONFERROUS METALS INDUSTRY'S TWELFTH METALLURGICAL CONSTRUCTION CO., LTD.—See China Aluminum International Engineering Corporation Limited; pg. 1482
CHINA NONFERROUS METALS PROCESSING TECHNOLOGY CO., LTD.—See China Aluminum International Engineering Corporation Limited; *Int'l*, pg. 1482
CHINA NONFERROUS MINING CORPORATION LIMITED—See China Nonferrous Metal Mining (Group) Co., Ltd.; *Int'l*, pg. 1535
CHINA NORTHERN RARE-EARTH GROUP HIGHI-TECH COMPANY LIMITED—See Baotou Iron & Steel (Group) Company Limited; *Int'l*, pg. 856
CHINA NORTH INDUSTRIES GROUP CORPORATION; *Int'l*, pg. 1535
CHINA NOVARTIS INSTITUTES FOR BIOMEDICAL RESEARCH CO., LTD.—See Novartis AG; *Int'l*, pg. 5457
CHINA NT PHARMA GROUP COMPANY LIMITED; *Int'l*, pg. 1536
CHINA NUCLEAR ENERGY INDUSTRY CORPORATION—See China National Nuclear Corporation; *Int'l*, pg. 1532
CHINA NUCLEAR ENERGY TECHNOLOGY CORPORATION LIMITED; *Int'l*, pg. 1536
CHINA NUCLEAR ENGINEERING CORPORATION LIMITED; *Int'l*, pg. 1536
CHINA NUCLEAR POWER CO., LTD.; *Int'l*, pg. 1536
CHINA NUCLEAR POWER ENGINEERING CO., LTD.—See CGN Power Co., Ltd.; *Int'l*, pg. 1435
CHINA NUTRIFRUIT GROUP LIMITED; *Int'l*, pg. 1536
CHINA OCEAN AVIATION GROUP INCORPORATION—See China National Machinery Industry Corporation; *Int'l*, pg. 1531
CHINA OCEAN GROUP DEVELOPMENT LIMITED; *Int'l*, pg. 1536
CHINA OCEAN INDUSTRY GROUP LIMITED; *Int'l*, pg. 1536
CHINA OCEANWIDE HOLDINGS GROUP CO., LTD.; *Int'l*, pg. 1536
CHINA OCEANWIDE HOLDINGS LTD.—See China Oceanwide Holdings Group Co., Ltd.; *Int'l*, pg. 1538
CHINA OFFSHORE OIL (SINGAPORE) INTERNATIONAL PTE. LTD.—See China National Offshore Oil Corp.; *Int'l*, pg. 1532
CHINA OILFIELD SERVICES LIMITED—See China National Offshore Oil Corp.; *Int'l*, pg. 1532
CHINA OILFIELD TECHNOLOGY SERVICES GROUP LIMITED; *Int'l*, pg. 1538
CHINA OIL & GAS GROUP LIMITED; *Int'l*, pg. 1538
CHINA OIL HBP SCIENCE & TECHNOLOGY CO., LTD.; *Int'l*, pg. 1538
CHINA ORAL INDUSTRY GROUP HOLDINGS LIMITED; *Int'l*, pg. 1538
CHINA ORIENTAL GROUP COMPANY LIMITED; *Int'l*, pg. 1538
CHINA ORIENTAL SINGAPORE PTE. LTD.—See China Oriental Group Company Limited; *Int'l*, pg. 1538
CHINA ORIENTED INTERNATIONAL HOLDINGS LIMITED; *Int'l*, pg. 1538
CHINA OTSUKA PHARMACEUTICAL CO., LTD.—See Otsuka Holdings Co., Ltd.; *Int'l*, pg. 5659

CHINA OUHUA WINERY HOLDINGS LIMITED; *Int'l*, pg. 1538
CHINA OUTFITTERS HOLDINGS LTD.; *Int'l*, pg. 1538
CHINA OVERSEAS GRAND OCEANS GROUP LTD.—See China State Construction Engineering Corporation Limited; *Int'l*, pg. 1554
CHINA OVERSEAS HOLDING LTD.—See China State Construction Engineering Corporation Limited; *Int'l*, pg. 1554
CHINA OVERSEAS HOLDING LTD.—See China State Construction Engineering Corporation Limited; *Int'l*, pg. 1554
CHINA OVERSEAS LAND & INVESTMENT LIMITED—See China State Construction Engineering Corporation Limited; *Int'l*, pg. 1554
CHINA OVERSEAS NUOXIN INTERNATIONAL HOLDINGS LIMITED; *Int'l*, pg. 1539
CHINA OVERSEAS PROPERTY HOLDINGS LTD.; *Int'l*, pg. 1539
CHINA PA ASSET MANAGEMENT (HONG KONG) COMPANY LIMITED—See Ping An Insurance (Group) Company of China, Ltd.; *Int'l*, pg. 5869
CHINA PACIFIC CATERING SERVICES LTD.—See China Airlines Ltd.; *Int'l*, pg. 1482
CHINA PACIFIC INSURANCE (GROUP) CO., LTD.; *Int'l*, pg. 1539
CHINA PACIFIC PROPERTY INSURANCE CO., LTD.—See China Pacific Insurance (Group) Co., Ltd.; *Int'l*, pg. 1539
THE CHINA PAINT MANUFACTURING COMPANY (1932) LIMITED—See CNT Group Limited; *Int'l*, pg. 1678
THE CHINA PAINT MANUFACTURING (SHENZHEN) CO., LTD.—See CNT Group Limited; *Int'l*, pg. 1678
THE CHINA PAINT MFG. CO., (XINFENG) LTD.—See CNT Group Limited; *Int'l*, pg. 1678
CHINA PALACE INTERNATIONAL TRAVEL SERVICE—See China Rare Earth Resources And Technology Co., Ltd.; *Int'l*, pg. 1545
CHINA PAPER HOLDINGS LIMITED; *Int'l*, pg. 1539
CHINA PARENTING NETWORK HOLDINGS LIMITED; *Int'l*, pg. 1539
CHINA PARTYTIME CULTURE HOLDINGS LIMITED; *Int'l*, pg. 1539
CHINA PA SECURITIES (HONG KONG) COMPANY LIMITED—See Ping An Insurance (Group) Company of China, Ltd.; *Int'l*, pg. 5869
CHINA PENGFEI GROUP LIMITED; *Int'l*, pg. 1539
CHINA PERFECT MACHINERY INDUSTRY CORP., LTD.—See China National Machinery Industry Corporation; *Int'l*, pg. 1531
CHINA PETROCHEMICAL CORPORATION; *Int'l*, pg. 1539
CHINA PETROCHEMICAL DEVELOPMENT CORP. - DASHE PLANT—See China Petrochemical Development Corp.; *Int'l*, pg. 1540
CHINA PETROCHEMICAL DEVELOPMENT CORP. - HSIAOKANG PLANT—See China Petrochemical Development Corp.; *Int'l*, pg. 1540
CHINA PETROCHEMICAL DEVELOPMENT CORP.; *Int'l*, pg. 1540
CHINA PETROCHEMICAL DEVELOPMENT CORP. - TOUFEN PLANT—See China Petrochemical Development Corp.; *Int'l*, pg. 1540
CHINA PETROLEUM & CHEMICAL CORPORATION—See China Petrochemical Corporation; *Int'l*, pg. 1539
CHINA PHARMACEUTICAL ADVERTISING LIMITED COMPANY—See China National Pharmaceutical Group Corporation; *Int'l*, pg. 1533
CHINA PHARMA HOLDINGS, INC.; *Int'l*, pg. 1540
CHINA PING AN INSURANCE (HONG KONG) COMPANY LIMITED—See Ping An Insurance (Group) Company of China, Ltd.; *Int'l*, pg. 5869
CHINA PING AN INSURANCE OVERSEAS (HOLDINGS) LIMITED—See Ping An Insurance (Group) Company of China, Ltd.; *Int'l*, pg. 5869
CHINA PIPE GROUP LIMITED; *Int'l*, pg. 1540
CHINA PNR CO., LTD.—See Huifu Payment Limited; *Int'l*, pg. 3526
CHINA POLY GROUP CORPORATION; *Int'l*, pg. 1540
CHINA POLYPEPTIDE GROUP, INC.; *Int'l*, pg. 1541
CHINA POST GROUP CORPORATION LIMITED; *Int'l*, pg. 1541
CHINA POST LIFE INSURANCE CO., LTD.—See China Post Group Corporation Limited; *Int'l*, pg. 1541
CHINA POWER CLEAN ENERGY DEVELOPMENT COMPANY LIMITED; *Int'l*, pg. 1542
CHINA POWER CONSTRUCTION ENGINEERING CONSULTING CORPORATION—See China Machinery Engineering Corporation; *Int'l*, pg. 1516
CHINA POWER EQUIPMENT, INC.; *Int'l*, pg. 1542
CHINA POWER INTERNATIONAL DEVELOPMENT LIMITED; *Int'l*, pg. 1542
CHINA POWERPLUS LIMITED; *Int'l*, pg. 1542
CHINA PRECISION STEEL, INC.; *Int'l*, pg. 1542
THE CHINA PRESS BERHAD—See Media Chinese International Limited; *Int'l*, pg. 4770
CHINA PRIMARY ENERGY HOLDINGS LIMITED; *Int'l*, pg. 1542
CHINA PROPERTIES GROUP LTD; *Int'l*, pg. 1542

CHINA PROPERTIES INVESTMENT HOLDINGS LIMITED; *Int'l*, pg. 1542
CHINA PROSPERITY DEVELOPMENT CORPORATION—See China Steel Corporation; *Int'l*, pg. 1555
CHINA PROSPEROUS CLEAN ENERGY CORPORATION; *Int'l*, pg. 1542
CHINA PUBLISHING & MEDIA HOLDINGS CO., LTD.; *Int'l*, pg. 1542
CHINA PUTIAN FOOD HOLDING LIMITED; *Int'l*, pg. 1542
CHINA QINBA PHAMACEUTICALS, INC.; *Int'l*, pg. 1542
CHINA QINFA GROUP LIMITED; *Int'l*, pg. 1542
CHINA QUANJUDE (GROUP) CO., LTD.; *Int'l*, pg. 1542
CHINA RAILWAY 11TH BUREAU GROUP CO., LTD.—See China Railway Construction Corporation Limited; *Int'l*, pg. 1543
CHINA RAILWAY 12TH BUREAU GROUP CO., LTD.—See China Railway Construction Corporation Limited; *Int'l*, pg. 1543
CHINA RAILWAY 14TH BUREAU GROUP CO., LTD.—See China Railway Construction Corporation Limited; *Int'l*, pg. 1543
CHINA RAILWAY 16TH BUREAU GROUP CO., LTD.—See China Railway Construction Corporation Limited; *Int'l*, pg. 1543
CHINA RAILWAY 17TH BUREAU GROUP CO., LTD.—See China Railway Construction Corporation Limited; *Int'l*, pg. 1543
CHINA RAILWAY 18TH BUREAU GROUP CO., LTD.—See China Railway Construction Corporation Limited; *Int'l*, pg. 1543
CHINA RAILWAY 19TH BUREAU GROUP CO., LTD.—See China Railway Construction Corporation Limited; *Int'l*, pg. 1543
CHINA RAILWAY 20TH BUREAU GROUP CO., LTD.—See China Railway Construction Corporation Limited; *Int'l*, pg. 1543
CHINA RAILWAY 21ST BUREAU GROUP CO., LTD.—See China Railway Construction Corporation Limited; *Int'l*, pg. 1543
CHINA RAILWAY 22ND BUREAU GROUP CO., LTD.—See China Railway Construction Corporation Limited; *Int'l*, pg. 1543
CHINA RAILWAY 23RD BUREAU GROUP CO., LTD.—See China Railway Construction Corporation Limited; *Int'l*, pg. 1543
CHINA RAILWAY CONSTRUCTION BRIDGE ENGINEERING BUREAU GROUP CO., LTD.—See China Railway Construction Corporation Limited; *Int'l*, pg. 1543
CHINA RAILWAY CONSTRUCTION CORPORATION LIMITED; *Int'l*, pg. 1542
CHINA RAILWAY CONSTRUCTION HEAVY INDUSTRY CORPORATION LIMITED—See China Railway Construction Corporation Limited; *Int'l*, pg. 1543
CHINA RAILWAY CONSTRUCTION (HK) LIMITED—See China Railway Construction Corporation Limited; *Int'l*, pg. 1543
CHINA RAILWAY CONSTRUCTION INVESTMENT GROUP CO., LTD.—See China Railway Construction Corporation Limited; *Int'l*, pg. 1543
CHINA RAILWAY CONSTRUCTION REAL ESTATE GROUP CO., LTD.—See China Railway Construction Corporation Limited; *Int'l*, pg. 1543
CHINA RAILWAY DEVELOPMENT & INVESTMENT CO., LTD.—See China Railway Group Limited; *Int'l*, pg. 1543
CHINA RAILWAY ELECTRIFICATION BUREAU (GROUP) CO., LTD.—See China Railway Construction Corporation Limited; *Int'l*, pg. 1543
CHINA RAILWAY ENGINEERING CONSULTING GROUP CO., LTD.—See China Railway Group Limited; *Int'l*, pg. 1543
CHINA RAILWAY FIFTH SURVEY & DESIGN INSTITUTE GROUP CO., LTD.—See China Railway Construction Corporation Limited; *Int'l*, pg. 1543
CHINA RAILWAY FIRST SURVEY & DESIGN INSTITUTE GROUP CO., LTD.—See China Railway Construction Corporation Limited; *Int'l*, pg. 1543
CHINA RAILWAY FOURTH SURVEY AND DESIGN INSTITUTE GROUP CO., LTD—See China Railway Construction Corporation Limited; *Int'l*, pg. 1543
CHINA RAILWAY GROUP LIMITED; *Int'l*, pg. 1543
CHINA RAILWAY GUANGZHOU ENGINEERING GROUP CO. LTD.—See China Railway Group Limited; *Int'l*, pg. 1543
CHINA RAILWAY HI-TECH INDUSTRY CORPORATION; *Int'l*, pg. 1543
CHINA RAILWAY HUATIE ENGINEERING DESIGNING GROUP CO., LTD.—See China Railway Group Limited; *Int'l*, pg. 1543
CHINA RAILWAY INVESTMENT GROUP CO., LTD.—See China Railway Group Limited; *Int'l*, pg. 1543
CHINA RAILWAY LEASING CO., LTD.—See China Railway Materials Co., Ltd.; *Int'l*, pg. 1544
CHINA RAILWAY LIUYUAN GROUP CO., LTD.—See China Railway Group Limited; *Int'l*, pg. 1543
CHINA RAILWAY MAJOR BRIDGE ENGINEERING GROUP CO., LTD.—See China Railway Group Limited; *Int'l*, pg. 1543

CHINA RAILWAY MAJOR BRIDGE RECONNAISSANCE & DESIGN INSTITUTE CO., LTD.—See China Railway Group Limited; *Int'l*, pg. 1543
CHINA RAILWAY MATERIAL GROUP CO., LTD.—See China Railway Construction Corporation Limited; *Int'l*, pg. 1543
CHINA RAILWAY MATERIALS BEIJING COMPANY—See China Railway Materials Co., Ltd.; *Int'l*, pg. 1544
CHINA RAILWAY MATERIALS CO., LTD. - CRM HARBIN WOOD PRESERVATION FACTORY—See China Railway Materials Co., Ltd.; *Int'l*, pg. 1544
CHINA RAILWAY MATERIALS CO., LTD. - CRM LONGCHANG RAILWAY WORKS EQUIPMENT FACTORY—See China Railway Materials Co., Ltd.; *Int'l*, pg. 1544
CHINA RAILWAY MATERIALS CO., LTD.; *Int'l*, pg. 1544
CHINA RAILWAY MATERIALS COMPANY LIMITED—See China FAW Group Corporation; *Int'l*, pg. 1502
CHINA RAILWAY MATERIALS DEVELOPMENT HOLDING CO., LTD.—See China Railway Materials Co., Ltd.; *Int'l*, pg. 1544
CHINA RAILWAY MATERIALS GUANGZHOU COMPANY—See China Railway Materials Co., Ltd.; *Int'l*, pg. 1544
CHINA RAILWAY MATERIALS HARBIN COMPANY—See China Railway Materials Co., Ltd.; *Int'l*, pg. 1544
CHINA RAILWAY MATERIALS IMPORT & EXPORT CO., LTD.—See China Railway Materials Co., Ltd.; *Int'l*, pg. 1544
CHINA RAILWAY MATERIALS SHANGHAI COMPANY—See China Railway Materials Co., Ltd.; *Int'l*, pg. 1544
CHINA RAILWAY MATERIALS SHENYANG COMPANY—See China Railway Materials Co., Ltd.; *Int'l*, pg. 1544
CHINA RAILWAY MATERIALS TIANJIN COMPANY—See China Railway Materials Co., Ltd.; *Int'l*, pg. 1544
CHINA RAILWAY MATERIALS WUHAN COMPANY—See China Railway Materials Co., Ltd.; *Int'l*, pg. 1544
CHINA RAILWAY MATERIAL TRADING CO., LTD.—See China Railway Materials Co., Ltd.; *Int'l*, pg. 1544
CHINA RAILWAY MODERN LOGISTIC TECHNOLOGY CO., LTD.—See China Railway Materials Co., Ltd.; *Int'l*, pg. 1544
CHINA RAILWAY NO 8 ENGINEERING GROUP CO., LTD.—See China Railway Group Limited; *Int'l*, pg. 1543
CHINA RAILWAY PREFABRICATED CONSTRUCTION CO., LTD.; *Int'l*, pg. 1544
CHINA RAILWAY REAL ESTATE GROUP CO LTD—See China Railway Group Limited; *Int'l*, pg. 1543
CHINA RAILWAY SHANGHAI DESIGN INSTITUTE GROUP CO., LTD.—See China Railway Construction Corporation Limited; *Int'l*, pg. 1543
CHINA RAILWAY SHANHAIGUAN BRIDGE GROUP CO., LTD.—See China Railway Group Limited; *Int'l*, pg. 1543
CHINA RAILWAY SIGNAL & COMMUNICATION CORPORATION LTD.; *Int'l*, pg. 1544
CHINA RAILWAY SOUTHWEST RESEARCH INSTITUTE CO., LTD.—See China Railway Group Limited; *Int'l*, pg. 1543
CHINA RAILWAY SPECIAL CARGO LOGISTICS CO., LTD.; *Int'l*, pg. 1544
CHINA RAILWAY TIELONG CONTAINER LOGISTICS CO., LTD.; *Int'l*, pg. 1544
CHINA RARE EARTH HOLDINGS LIMITED; *Int'l*, pg. 1544
CHINA RARE EARTH RESOURCES AND TECHNOLOGY CO., LTD.; *Int'l*, pg. 1545
CHINA RARE EARTH RESOURCES & TECHNOLOGY CO., LTD.—See China Rare Earth Resources And Technology Co., Ltd.; *Int'l*, pg. 1545
CHINA REDSTONE GROUP, INC.; *Int'l*, pg. 1546
CHINA REFORM CULTURE HOLDINGS CO., LTD.; *Int'l*, pg. 1547
CHINA REFORM HEALTH MANAGEMENT AND SERVICES GROUP CO., LTD.; *Int'l*, pg. 1547
CHINA REGENERATIVE MEDICINE INTERNATIONAL CO., LTD.; *Int'l*, pg. 1547
CHINA REINSURANCE (GROUP) CORPORATION; *Int'l*, pg. 1547
CHINA RENAISSANCE HOLDINGS LTD.; *Int'l*, pg. 1547
CHINA RENAISSANCE SECURITIES (US) INC.—See China Renaissance Holdings Ltd.; *Int'l*, pg. 1547
CHINA RENEWABLE ENERGY INVESTMENT LTD.; *Int'l*, pg. 1547
CHINA RE NEW YORK LIAISON OFFICE INC.—See China Reinsurance (Group) Corporation; *Int'l*, pg. 1547
CHINA RESOURCES AND TRANSPORTATION GROUP LIMITED; *Int'l*, pg. 1548
CHINA RESOURCES BEER (HOLDINGS) COMPANY LIMITED—See China Resources (Holdings) Co., Ltd.; *Int'l*, pg. 1547
CHINA RESOURCES BOYA BIO-PHARMACEUTICAL GROUP CO., LTD.; *Int'l*, pg. 1548
CHINA RESOURCES BUILDING MATERIALS TECHNOLOGY HOLDINGS LIMITED; *Int'l*, pg. 1548

CHINA RESOURCES CEMENT (FENGKAI) LIMITED—See China Resources Building Materials Technology Holdings Limited; *Int'l*, pg. 1548
CHINA RESOURCES CEMENT (SHANGSI) LIMITED—See China Resources Building Materials Technology Holdings Limited; *Int'l*, pg. 1548
CHINA RESOURCES CHEMICALS HOLDINGS LTD.—See China Resources (Holdings) Co., Ltd.; *Int'l*, pg. 1548
CHINA RESOURCES CONCRETE (NANNING) LIMITED—See China Resources Building Materials Technology Holdings Limited; *Int'l*, pg. 1548
CHINA RESOURCES & CONSULTING, INC., *U.S. Private*, pg. 886
CHINA RESOURCES DEVELOPMENT INC.; *Int'l*, pg. 1549
CHINA RESOURCES DOUBLE-CRANE PHARMACEUTICAL CO., LTD.; *Int'l*, pg. 1549
CHINA RESOURCES GAS GROUP LIMITED—See China Resources (Holdings) Co., Ltd.; *Int'l*, pg. 1548
CHINA RESOURCES GAS (HOLDINGS) LTD.—See China Resources (Holdings) Co., Ltd.; *Int'l*, pg. 1548
CHINA RESOURCES (HOLDINGS) CO., LTD.; *Int'l*, pg. 1547
CHINA RESOURCES LAND LIMITED—See China Resources (Holdings) Co., Ltd.; *Int'l*, pg. 1548
CHINA RESOURCES MEDICAL HOLDINGS CO., LTD.; *Int'l*, pg. 1549
CHINA RESOURCES MICROELECTRONICS LTD.—See China Resources (Holdings) Co., Ltd.; *Int'l*, pg. 1548
CHINA RESOURCES MICROELECTRONICS LTD.—See China Resources (Holdings) Co., Ltd.; *Int'l*, pg. 1548
CHINA RESOURCES MIXC LIFESTYLE SERVICES LIMITED; *Int'l*, pg. 1549
CHINA RESOURCES NG FUNG LIMITED—See China Resources (Holdings) Co., Ltd.; *Int'l*, pg. 1548
CHINA RESOURCES PHARMACEUTICAL GROUP LIMITED—See China Resources (Holdings) Co., Ltd.; *Int'l*, pg. 1548
CHINA RESOURCES POWER HOLDINGS CO., LTD.—See China Resources (Holdings) Co., Ltd.; *Int'l*, pg. 1548
CHINA RESOURCES RETAIL (GROUP) CO., LTD.—See China Resources (Holdings) Co., Ltd.; *Int'l*, pg. 1548
CHINA RESOURCES SANJIU MEDICAL & PHARMACEUTICAL CO., LTD.; *Int'l*, pg. 1549
CHINA RESOURCES SNOW BREWERIES LTD.—See China Resources (Holdings) Co., Ltd.; *Int'l*, pg. 1547
CHINA RESOURCES TEXTILES CO., LTD.—See China Resources (Holdings) Co., Ltd.; *Int'l*, pg. 1548
CHINA RESOURCES TEXTILES (HOLDINGS) CO., LTD.—See China Resources (Holdings) Co., Ltd.; *Int'l*, pg. 1548
CHINA RESOURCES VANGUARD CO., LTD.—See China Resources (Holdings) Co., Ltd.; *Int'l*, pg. 1548
CHINA RESOURCES VANGUARD (HONG KONG) CO., LTD.—See China Resources (Holdings) Co., Ltd.; *Int'l*, pg. 1548
CHINA RE UK LIMITED—See China Reinsurance (Group) Corporation; *Int'l*, pg. 1547
CHINA RE UNDERWRITING AGENCY LIMITED—See China Reinsurance (Group) Corporation; *Int'l*, pg. 1547
CHINA RISE SECURITIES ASSET MANAGEMENT COMPANY LIMITED—See Symphony Holdings Limited; *Int'l*, pg. 7379
CHINA RISUN GROUP LTD.; *Int'l*, pg. 1549
CHINA RITAR POWER CORP.; *Int'l*, pg. 1549
CHINA ROAD & BRIDGE CORPORATION—See China Communications Construction Company Limited; *Int'l*, pg. 1490
CHINA RONGZHONG FINANCIAL HOLDINGS CO. LTD.; *Int'l*, pg. 1549
CHINA ROOTS PACKAGING PTE. LTD.—See PCCS Group Berhad; *Int'l*, pg. 5767
CHINA RUIFENG RENEWABLE ENERGY HOLDINGS LIMITED; *Int'l*, pg. 1549
CHINA RUITAI INTERNATIONAL HOLDINGS CO., LTD.; *Int'l*, pg. 1549
CHINA RUNDONG AUTO GROUP LIMITED—See Greenland Holdings Corporation Limited; *Int'l*, pg. 3075
CHINA RUNJI CEMENT, INC.; *Int'l*, pg. 1549
CHINA RUYI HOLDINGS LIMITED; *Int'l*, pg. 1549
CHINA SAFTOWER INTERNATIONAL HOLDING GROUP LIMITED; *Int'l*, pg. 1549
CHINA SAITE GROUP COMPANY LIMITED; *Int'l*, pg. 1549
CHINA SANDI HOLDINGS LIMITED; *Int'l*, pg. 1549
CHINA SANJIANG FINE CHEMICALS COMPANY LIMITED; *Int'l*, pg. 1549
CHINA SATELLITE COMMUNICATIONS CO., LTD.—See China Aerospace Science and Technology Corporation; *Int'l*, pg. 1481
CHINA SCE GROUP HOLDINGS LIMITED; *Int'l*, pg. 1549
CHINA SCIENCE PUBLISHING & MEDIA LTD.; *Int'l*, pg. 1550
CHINA SECURITIES (INTERNATIONAL) FINANCE HOLDING COMPANY LIMITED—See CSC Financial Co., Ltd; *Int'l*, pg. 1862
CHINA SECURITY CO., LTD.; *Int'l*, pg. 1550

CHINA SECURITY & FIRE IOT SENSING (SHENZHEN) CO., LTD.—See China Security Co., Ltd.; *Int'l*, pg. 1550
CHINA SECURITY &FIRE XULONG ELECTRONIC & TECHNOLOGY CO., LTD.—See China Security Co., Ltd.; *Int'l*, pg. 1550
CHINA SECURITY & SURVEILLANCE DISTRIBUTION (PRC), INC—See China Security & Surveillance Technology, Inc.; *Int'l*, pg. 1550
CHINA SECURITY & SURVEILLANCE MANUFACTURING (PRC), INC.—See China Security & Surveillance Technology, Inc.; *Int'l*, pg. 1550
CHINA SECURITY & SURVEILLANCE TECHNOLOGY, INC.; *Int'l*, pg. 1550
CHINA SENIOR LIVING INDUSTRY INTERNATIONAL HOLDING CORPORATION; *Int'l*, pg. 1550
CHINA SEOUL SEMICONDUCTOR—See Seoul Semiconductor Co.; *Int'l*, pg. 6717
CHINA SFECO GROUP—See Shanghai Construction Group Co., Ltd.; *Int'l*, pg. 6764
CHINA SHANSHUI CEMENT GROUP LTD.; *Int'l*, pg. 1550
CHINA SHENGDA PACKAGING GROUP INC.; *Int'l*, pg. 1550
CHINA SHENGHAI GROUP LIMITED; *Int'l*, pg. 1551
CHINA SHENGHUO PHARMACEUTICAL HOLDINGS, INC.; *Int'l*, pg. 1551
CHINA SHENGMU ORGANIC MILK LIMITED; *Int'l*, pg. 1551
CHINA SHENHUA ENERGY COMPANY LIMITED—See Shenhua Group Corporation Limited; *Int'l*, pg. 6802
CHINA SHENSHAN ORCHARD HOLDINGS CO., LTD.; *Int'l*, pg. 1551
CHINA SHESAYS MEDICAL COSMETOLOGY INC.; *Int'l*, pg. 1551
CHINA SHINEWAY PHARMACEUTICAL GROUP LTD.; *Int'l*, pg. 1551
CHINA SHIPBUILDING INDUSTRY COMPANY LIMITED; *Int'l*, pg. 1551
CHINA SHIPBUILDING INDUSTRY GROUP POWER CO., LTD.; *Int'l*, pg. 1551
CHINA SHIPBUILDING MANSION SCIENCE RESEARCH CENTER COMPANY LIMITED—See China Shipbuilding Industry Company Limited; *Int'l*, pg. 1551
CHINA SHIPBUILDING NDRI ENGINEERING CO., LTD—See China State Shipbuilding Corporation; *Int'l*, pg. 1554
CHINA SHIPBUILDING TRADING CO., LTD.—See China State Shipbuilding Corporation; *Int'l*, pg. 1554
CHINA SHIP DESIGN & RESEARCH CENTRE CO., LTD.—See China Shipbuilding Industry Company Limited; *Int'l*, pg. 1551
CHINA SHIPPING AGENCY CO., LTD.—See China COSCO Shipping Corporation Limited; *Int'l*, pg. 1494
CHINA SHIPPING BULK CARRIER CO., LTD.—See China COSCO Shipping Corporation Limited; *Int'l*, pg. 1494
CHINA SHIPPING INVESTMENT CO., LTD—See China COSCO Shipping Corporation Limited; *Int'l*, pg. 1492
CHINA SHOUGUAN INVESTMENT HOLDING GROUP CORPORATION; *Int'l*, pg. 1551
CHINA SHUIFA SINGYES ENERGY HOLDINGS LIMITED; *Int'l*, pg. 1551
CHINA SHUN KE LONG HOLDINGS LTD.—See CCOOP Group Co., Ltd.; *Int'l*, pg. 1369
CHINA SILK INDUSTRIAL CORPORATION—See China Hi-Tech Group Corporation; *Int'l*, pg. 1508
CHINA SILVER GROUP LIMITED; *Int'l*, pg. 1551
CHINA SILVER TECHNOLOGY HOLDINGS LIMITED; *Int'l*, pg. 1551
CHINA-SINGAPORE SUZHOU INDUSTRIAL PARK DEVELOPMENT GROUP CO., LTD.; *Int'l*, pg. 1568
CHINA SINGYES NEW MATERIALS HOLDINGS LIMITED; *Int'l*, pg. 1552
CHINA SINOMACH HEAVY INDUSTRY CORPORATION LTD.—See China National Machinery Industry Corporation; *Int'l*, pg. 1531
CHINA SINOSTAR GROUP COMPANY LIMITED; *Int'l*, pg. 1552
CHINA SKY CHEMICAL FIBRE CO., LTD.; *Int'l*, pg. 1552
CHINA SKY ONE MEDICAL, INC.; *Int'l*, pg. 1552
CHINA SKYRISE DIGITAL SERVICE INC.; *Int'l*, pg. 1552
CHINA SLP FILTRATION TECHNOLOGY, INC.; *Int'l*, pg. 1552
CHINA SMARTER ENERGY GROUP HOLDINGS LTD.; *Int'l*, pg. 1552
CHINA SMARTPAY GROUP HOLDINGS LIMITED; *Int'l*, pg. 1552
CHINA SOAR INFORMATION TECHNOLOGY, INC.; *Int'l*, pg. 1552
CHINASOFT INTERNATIONAL (GUANG ZHOU) INFORMATION TECHNOLOGY LIMITED—See Chinasoft International Ltd.; *Int'l*, pg. 1568
CHINASOFT INTERNATIONAL INC.—See Chinasoft International Ltd.; *Int'l*, pg. 1568
CHINASOFT INTERNATIONAL LTD.; *Int'l*, pg. 1568
CHINASOFT RESOURCE (INTERNATIONAL) LIMITED—See Chinasoft International Ltd.; *Int'l*, pg. 1569
CHINA SOLAR & CLEAN ENERGY SOLUTIONS, INC.; *Int'l*, pg. 1552

COMPANY NAME INDEX

CHINA SOLAR ENERGY HOLDINGS LIMITED; *Int'l*, pg. 1552
CHINA SOUTH CITY HOLDINGS LIMITED; *Int'l*, pg. 1552
CHINA SOUTHERN AIRLINES CO., LTD.; *Int'l*, pg. 1553
CHINA SOUTHERN ASSET MANAGEMENT CO., LTD.—See Huatai Securities Co., Ltd.; *Int'l*, pg. 3514
CHINA SOUTHERN POWER GRID CO., LTD.; *Int'l*, pg. 1553
CHINA SOUTHERN POWER GRID ENERGY EFFICIENCY & CLEAN ENERGY CO., LTD.; *Int'l*, pg. 1553
CHINA SOUTH INDUSTRIES GROUP CORPORATION; *Int'l*, pg. 1552
CHINA SOUTH PUBLISHING & MEDIA GROUP CO., LTD.; *Int'l*, pg. 1552
CHINA SPACESAT CO., LTD.; *Int'l*, pg. 1553
CHINA SPECIAL ARTICLE LOGISTICS CO., LTD.—See CTS International Logistics Corporation Limited; *Int'l*, pg. 1874
CHINA SPORTS INDUSTRY GROUP CO., LTD.; *Int'l*, pg. 1553
CHINA SPORTS INTERNATIONAL CO., LTD.—See China Sports Industry Group Co., Ltd.; *Int'l*, pg. 1553
CHINA SPORTS INTERNATIONAL LIMITED; *Int'l*, pg. 1553
CHINA SPORTS MANAGEMENT GROUP CO., LTD.—See China Sports Industry Group Co., Ltd.; *Int'l*, pg. 1553
CHINA STARCH HOLDINGS LTD.; *Int'l*, pg. 1553
CHINA STAR ENTERTAINMENT HOLDING COMPANY—See China Star Entertainment Limited; *Int'l*, pg. 1553
CHINA STAR ENTERTAINMENT LIMITED; *Int'l*, pg. 1553
CHINA STAR HK DISTRIBUTION LIMITED—See China Star Entertainment Limited; *Int'l*, pg. 1553
CHINA STAR INTERNATIONAL DISTRIBUTION LIMITED—See China Star Entertainment Limited; *Int'l*, pg. 1553
CHINA STAR INTERNATIONAL LIMITED—See Taiwan Paiho Limited; *Int'l*, pg. 7422
CHINA STATE CONSTRUCTION DEVELOPMENT HOLDINGS LIMITED—See China State Construction International Holdings Limited; *Int'l*, pg. 1554
CHINA STATE CONSTRUCTION ENGINEERING CORPORATION LIMITED; *Int'l*, pg. 1554
CHINA STATE CONSTRUCTION INTERNATIONAL CO.—See China State Construction Engineering Corporation Limited; *Int'l*, pg. 1554
CHINA STATE CONSTRUCTION INTERNATIONAL HOLDINGS LIMITED; *Int'l*, pg. 1554
CHINA STATE SHIPBUILDING CORPORATION; *Int'l*, pg. 1554
CHINA STATIONERY LIMITED; *Int'l*, pg. 1554
CHINA STEEL AND NIPPON STEEL VIETNAM JOINT STOCK COMPANY—See China Steel Corporation; *Int'l*, pg. 1555
CHINA STEEL CHEMICAL CO., LTD.—See China Steel Corporation; *Int'l*, pg. 1555
CHINA STEEL CHEMICAL CORP.—See China Steel Corporation; *Int'l*, pg. 1555
CHINA STEEL CORPORATION INDIA PVT. LTD.—See China Steel Corporation; *Int'l*, pg. 1555
CHINA STEEL CORPORATION; *Int'l*, pg. 1555
CHINA STEEL EXPRESS CORPORATION—See China Steel Corporation; *Int'l*, pg. 1555
CHINA STEEL GLOBAL TRADING CORPORATION—See China Steel Corporation; *Int'l*, pg. 1555
CHINA STEEL MACHINERY CORPORATION—See China Steel Corporation; *Int'l*, pg. 1555
CHINASTEEL MANAGEMENT CONSULTING CORPORATION—See China Steel Corporation; *Int'l*, pg. 1555
CHINA STEEL POWER CORPORATION—See China Steel Corporation; *Int'l*, pg. 1555
CHINA STEEL PRECISION METALS KUNSHAN CO., LTD.—See China Steel Corporation; *Int'l*, pg. 1555
CHINA STEEL PRECISION METALS QINGDAO CO., LTD.—See China Steel Corporation; *Int'l*, pg. 1555
CHINA STEEL RESOURCES CORPORATION—See China Steel Corporation; *Int'l*, pg. 1555
CHINA STEEL SECURITY CORPORATION—See China Steel Corporation; *Int'l*, pg. 1555
CHINA STEEL STRUCTURE CO., LTD.; *Int'l*, pg. 1556
CHINA STEEL STRUCTURE CO., LTD.—See China Steel Corporation; *Int'l*, pg. 1555
CHINA STEEL STRUCTURE CO., LTD. - TAINAN GUANTIAN FACTORY—See China Steel Structure Co., Ltd.; *Int'l*, pg. 1556
CHINA STEEL SUMIKIN VIETNAM JOINT STOCK COMPANY—See Nippon Steel Corporation; *Int'l*, pg. 5337
CHINA SUCCESS FINANCE GROUP HOLDINGS LIMITED; *Int'l*, pg. 1556
CHINA SUN BIO-CHEM TECHNOLOGY GROUP COMPANY LTD.; *Int'l*, pg. 1556
CHINA SUNERGY CO., LTD.; *Int'l*, pg. 1556
CHINA SUN GROUP HIGH-TECH CO.; *Int'l*, pg. 1556
CHINA SUNSHINE PAPER HOLDINGS COMPANY LIMITED; *Int'l*, pg. 1556
CHINA SUNSINE CHEMICAL HOLDINGS LTD; *Int'l*, pg. 1556

CHINA SUNTIEN GREEN ENERGY CORPORATION LTD.; *Int'l*, pg. 1556
CHINA SUPPLY CHAIN HOLDINGS LIMITED; *Int'l*, pg. 1556
CHINA SXT PHARMACEUTICALS, INC.; *Int'l*, pg. 1556
CHINA SYNTHETIC RUBBER CORPORATION; *Int'l*, pg. 1557
CHINA TAIFENG BEDDINGS HOLDINGS LIMITED; *Int'l*, pg. 1557
CHINA TAIPING INSURANCE (HK) COMPANY LIMITED—See China Taiping Insurance Holdings Company Limited; *Int'l*, pg. 1557
CHINA TAIPING INSURANCE HOLDINGS COMPANY LIMITED; *Int'l*, pg. 1557
CHINA TAIPING INSURANCE (SINGAPORE) PTE. LTD.—See China Taiping Insurance Holdings Company Limited; *Int'l*, pg. 1557
CHINA TAIPING INSURANCE (UK) COMPANY LIMITED—See China Taiping Insurance Holdings Company Limited; *Int'l*, pg. 1557
CHINA TAISAN TECHNOLOGY GROUP HOLDINGS LIMITED; *Int'l*, pg. 1557
CHINA TANGSHANG HOLDINGS LIMITED; *Int'l*, pg. 1557
CHINA TEA CO., LTD.—See COFCO Limited; *Int'l*, pg. 1692
CHINA TECHFAITH WIRELESS COMMUNICATION TECHNOLOGY LIMITED; *Int'l*, pg. 1557
CHINA TECHNO FOAM CO LTD—See Gurit Holding AG; *Int'l*, pg. 3187
CHINA TECHNOLOGY DEVELOPMENT GROUP CORPORATION; *Int'l*, pg. 1557
CHINA TECHNOLOGY INDUSTRY GROUP LIMITED; *Int'l*, pg. 1557
CHINA TELECOM AMERICAS—See China Telecommunications Corporation; *Int'l*, pg. 1558
CHINA TELECOM (AUSTRALIA) PTY LTD—See China Telecommunications Corporation; *Int'l*, pg. 1557
CHINA TELECOM (CANADA) ULC—See China Telecommunications Corporation; *Int'l*, pg. 1558
CHINA TELECOM CORPORATION LIMITED—See China Telecommunications Corporation; *Int'l*, pg. 1557
CHINA TELECOM (DEUTSCHLAND) GMBH—See China Telecommunications Corporation; *Int'l*, pg. 1558
CHINA TELECOM DO BRASIL LTDA.—See China Telecommunications Corporation; *Int'l*, pg. 1558
CHINA TELECOM (EUROPE) LIMITED—See China Telecommunications Corporation; *Int'l*, pg. 1558
CHINA TELECOM (FRANCE) LTD.—See China Telecommunications Corporation; *Int'l*, pg. 1558
CHINA TELECOM GLOBAL LTD—See China Telecommunications Corporation; *Int'l*, pg. 1558
CHINA TELECOM (INDIA) PRIVATE LIMITED—See China Telecommunications Corporation; *Int'l*, pg. 1558
CHINA TELECOM INFORMATION TECHNOLOGY (VIETNAM) CO., LTD.—See China Telecommunications Corporation; *Int'l*, pg. 1558
CHINA TELECOM (KAZAKHSTAN) LIMITED LIABILITY PARTNERSHIP—See China Telecommunications Corporation; *Int'l*, pg. 1558
CHINA TELECOM KOREA LIMITED—See China Telecommunications Corporation; *Int'l*, pg. 1558
CHINA TELECOM (MALAYSIA) SDN. BHD.—See China Telecommunications Corporation; *Int'l*, pg. 1558
CHINA TELECOM MIDDLE EAST—See China Telecommunications Corporation; *Int'l*, pg. 1558
CHINA TELECOMMUNICATIONS CORPORATION; *Int'l*, pg. 1557
CHINA TELECOM (SINGAPORE) PTE. LTD.—See China Telecommunications Corporation; *Int'l*, pg. 1558
CHINA TELECOM SOUTH AFRICA (PTY) LTD—See China Telecommunications Corporation; *Int'l*, pg. 1558
CHINA TELETECH HOLDING, INC.; *Int'l*, pg. 1558
CHINA TELETECH LIMITED—See China Teletech Holding, Inc.; *Int'l*, pg. 1558
CHINA TELEVISION COMPANY; *Int'l*, pg. 1558
CHINA TELEVISION MEDIA, LTD.; *Int'l*, pg. 1558
CHINATEX CORPORATION LIMITED—See COFCO Limited; *Int'l*, pg. 1692
CHINA TEXMATECH CO., LTD.—See China Hi-Tech Group Corporation; *Int'l*, pg. 1508
CHINA TEXTILE INDUSTRIAL CORPORATION FOR FOREIGN ECONOMIC & TECHNICAL COOPERATION—See China Hi-Tech Group Corporation; *Int'l*, pg. 1508
CHINA TEXTILE SCIENCE & TECHNOLOGY CO., LTD.—See China Hi-Tech Group Co., Ltd.; *Int'l*, pg. 1507
CHINA THREE GORGES BRASIL ENERGIA LTDA.—See China Three Gorges Corporation; *Int'l*, pg. 1558
CHINA THREE GORGES CORPORATION; *Int'l*, pg. 1558
CHINA THREE GORGES RENEWABLES (GROUP) CO., LTD.—See China Three Gorges Corporation; *Int'l*, pg. 1558
CHINA TIANBAO GROUP DEVELOPMENT COMPANY LIMITED; *Int'l*, pg. 1559
CHINA TIANCHEN ENGINEERING CORPORATION—See China National Chemical Engineering Co., Ltd.; *Int'l*, pg. 1531
CHINA TIANFEIHONG WINE, INC.; *Int'l*, pg. 1559

CHINA TIANGONG (HONG KONG) COMPANY LIMITED—See Tiangong International Company Limited; *Int'l*, pg. 7738
CHINA TIANRUI AUTOMOTIVE INTERIORS CO., LTD.; *Int'l*, pg. 1559
CHINA TIANRUI GROUP CEMENT COMPANY LIMITED; *Int'l*, pg. 1559
CHINA TIANYF HOLDINGS GROUP LIMITED; *Int'l*, pg. 1559
CHINA TIANYING INC.; *Int'l*, pg. 1559
CHINA TIAN YUAN HEALTHCARE GROUP LIMITED; *Int'l*, pg. 1559
CHINA TIME SHARE MEDIA CO. LTD.; *Int'l*, pg. 1559
CHINA TING GARMENT MFG (GROUP) LIMITED—See China Ting Group Holdings Limited; *Int'l*, pg. 1559
CHINA TING GROUP HOLDINGS LIMITED; *Int'l*, pg. 1559
CHINA TITANS ENERGY TECHNOLOGY GROUP CO., LTD.; *Int'l*, pg. 1559
CHINA TMK BATTERY SYSTEMS INC.; *Int'l*, pg. 1559
CHINA TOBACCO INTERNATIONAL (HK) COMPANY LIMITED; *Int'l*, pg. 1559
CHINA TOBACCO MAUDUIT (JIANGMEN) PAPER INDUSTRY COMPANY LTD.—See Mativ Holdings, Inc.; *U.S. Public*, pg. 1396
CHINA TONE LIMITED—See Dickson Concepts (International) Limited; *Int'l*, pg. 2112
CHINA TONGHAI ASSET MANAGEMENT LIMITED—See Quam Plus International Financial Limited; *Int'l*, pg. 6152
CHINA TONGHAI CAPITAL LIMITED—See Quam Plus International Financial Limited; *Int'l*, pg. 6152
CHINA TONGHAI COMMUNICATIONS LIMITED—See Quam Plus International Financial Limited; *Int'l*, pg. 6152
CHINA TONTINE WINES GROUP LIMITED; *Int'l*, pg. 1559
CHINA TOPREACH INC.; *Int'l*, pg. 1560
CHINA TOURISM AND CULTURE INVESTMENT GROUP CO., LTD.; *Int'l*, pg. 1560
CHINA TOURISM GROUP DUTY FREE CORPORATION LIMITED; *Int'l*, pg. 1560
CHINA TOWER CORPORATION LIMITED; *Int'l*, pg. 1560
CHINA TRADITIONAL CHINESE MEDICINE HOLDINGS CO. LTD.—See China National Pharmaceutical Group Corporation; *Int'l*, pg. 1534
CHINA TRAVEL HI-TECH COMPUTER HONG KONG LTD.—See China Travel International Investment Hong Kong Ltd; *Int'l*, pg. 1560
CHINA TRAVEL INTERNATIONAL INVESTMENT HONG KONG LTD; *Int'l*, pg. 1560
CHINA TRAVEL SERVICE (AUSTRALIA) PTY. LTD.—See China Travel International Investment Hong Kong Ltd; *Int'l*, pg. 1560
CHINA TRAVEL SERVICE (CANADA) INC.—See China Travel International Investment Hong Kong Ltd; *Int'l*, pg. 1560
CHINA TRAVEL SERVICE (HONG KONG) LTD.—See China Travel International Investment Hong Kong Ltd; *Int'l*, pg. 1560
CHINA TRAVEL SERVICE (KOREA) CO., LTD.—See China Travel International Investment Hong Kong Ltd; *Int'l*, pg. 1560
CHINA TRAVEL SERVICE (N.Z.) LTD.—See China Travel International Investment Hong Kong Ltd; *Int'l*, pg. 1560
CHINA TRAVEL SERVICE (TAIWAN) LIMITED—See The Shanghai Commercial & Savings Bank, Ltd.; *Int'l*, pg. 7681
CHINA TRAVEL SERVICE (U.K.) LTD.—See China Travel International Investment Hong Kong Ltd; *Int'l*, pg. 1560
CHINA TRAVEL SERVICE (U.S.A.), INC.—See China Travel International Investment Hong Kong Ltd; *Int'l*, pg. 1560
CHINA TRAVELSKY INTERNATIONAL LIMITED—See TravelSky Technology Limited; *Int'l*, pg. 7907
CHINA TRAVEL & TRADING (DEUTSCHLAND) GMBH—See China Travel International Investment Hong Kong Ltd; *Int'l*, pg. 1560
CHINA TREASURE MINE TECHNOLOGY HOLDINGS CO., LTD.; *Int'l*, pg. 1560
CHINA TREASURES NEW MATERIALS GROUP LTD.; *Int'l*, pg. 1560
CHINA TRENDS HOLDINGS LIMITED; *Int'l*, pg. 1561
CHINA TRIUMPH INTERNATIONAL ENGINEERING CO., LTD.—See China National Building Material Group Co., Ltd.; *Int'l*, pg. 1525
CHINATRONIC TECHNOLOGY LIMITED—See Avnet, Inc.; *U.S. Public*, pg. 252
CHINA TRUSTFUL GROUP LIMITED; *Int'l*, pg. 1561
CHINATRUST INSURANCE BROKERS CO., LTD.—See CTBC Financial Holding Co., Ltd.; *Int'l*, pg. 1869
CHINATRUST LIFE INSURANCE CO., LTD.—See CTBC Financial Holding Co., Ltd.; *Int'l*, pg. 1869
CHINATRUST (PHILIPPINES) COMMERCIAL BANK CORPORATION—See CTBC Financial Holding Co., Ltd.; *Int'l*, pg. 1869
CHINATRUST SECURITIES CO., INC.—See CTBC Financial Holding Co., Ltd.; *Int'l*, pg. 1869
CHINATRUST SECURITIES CO., LTD.—See CTBC Financial Holding Co., Ltd.; *Int'l*, pg. 1869

CHINA TRUSTFUL GROUP LIMITED

CHINA TUHSU FLAVOURS & FRAGRANCES IMPORT & EXPORT CORPORATION—See COFCO Limited; *Int'l*, pg. 1692
CHINA TUNGSTEN & HIGHTECH MATERIALS CO., LTD.—See Hunan Nonferrous Metals Corporation Ltd.; *Int'l*, pg. 3533
CHINA UNICOM (EUROPE) OPERATIONS LIMITED—See China United Network Communications Group Company Limited; *Int'l*, pg. 1561
CHINA UNICOM (HONG KONG) LIMITED—See China United Network Communications Group Company Limited; *Int'l*, pg. 1561
CHINA UNICOM (JAPAN) OPERATIONS CORPORATION—See China United Network Communications Group Company Limited; *Int'l*, pg. 1561
CHINA UNICOM USA CORPORATION—See China United Network Communications Group Company Limited; *Int'l*, pg. 1561
CHINA UNION HOLDINGS LTD.; *Int'l*, pg. 1561
CHINA UNITED CEMENT CORPORATION—See China National Building Material Group Co., Ltd.; *Int'l*, pg. 1525
CHINA UNITED CEMENT GROUP CORPORATION LIMITED—See China National Building Material Group Co., Ltd.; *Int'l*, pg. 1525
CHINA UNITED INSURANCE SERVICE, INC.; *Int'l*, pg. 1561
CHINA UNITED INTERNATIONAL ADMINISTRATIVE SERVICES LIMITED—See Mason Group Holdings Limited; *Int'l*, pg. 4722
CHINA UNITED NETWORK COMMUNICATIONS GROUP COMPANY LIMITED; *Int'l*, pg. 1561
CHINA UNITED NETWORK COMMUNICATIONS LIMITED—See China United Network Communications Group Company Limited; *Int'l*, pg. 1561
CHINA UNITED PISTON RING CO.,LTD.—See TPR Co., Ltd.; *Int'l*, pg. 7883
CHINA UNITED VENTURE INVESTMENT LIMITED; *Int'l*, pg. 1561
CHINA UPTOWN GROUP COMPANY LIMITED; *Int'l*, pg. 1561
CHINA U-TON FUTURE SPACE INDUSTRIAL GROUP HOLDINGS LTD.; *Int'l*, pg. 1561
CHINA VALVES TECHNOLOGY, INC.; *Int'l*, pg. 1561
CHINA VANADIUM TITANO-MAGNETITE MINING COMPANY LIMITED; *Int'l*, pg. 1561
CHINA VANKE CO., LTD.; *Int'l*, pg. 1561
CHINA VAST INDUSTRIAL URBAN DEVELOPMENT COMPANY LIMITED; *Int'l*, pg. 1562
CHINA VENTURE MANAGEMENT INC.—See KGI Financial Holding Co., Ltd.; *Int'l*, pg. 4149
CHINA VERED FINANCIAL HOLDING CORPORATION LIMITED; *Int'l*, pg. 1562
CHINA VITUP HEALTH CARE HOLDINGS, INC.; *Int'l*, pg. 1562
CHINA VOCATIONAL EDUCATION HOLDINGS LIMITED; *Int'l*, pg. 1562
CHINA VTV LIMITED; *Int'l*, pg. 1562
CHINA WAFER LEVEL CSP CO., LTD.; *Int'l*, pg. 1562
CHINA WAH YAN HEALTHCARE LTD.; *Int'l*, pg. 1562
CHINA WANTIAN HOLDINGS LIMITED; *Int'l*, pg. 1562
CHINA WAN TONG YUAN (HOLDINGS) LTD.; *Int'l*, pg. 1562
CHINA WASTE CORPORATION LIMITED; *Int'l*, pg. 1562
CHINA WATER AFFAIRS GROUP LTD; *Int'l*, pg. 1563
CHINA WATER INDUSTRY GROUP LIMITED; *Int'l*, pg. 1563
CHINA WEAVING MATERIALS HOLDINGS LIMITED; *Int'l*, pg. 1563
CHINA WENXUAN MOVIE & TV CULTURE CO., LTD.—See Xinhua Winshare Publishing and Media Co., Ltd.; *Int'l*, pg. 8530
CHINA WEST CONSTRUCTION CO., LTD.; *Int'l*, pg. 1563
CHINA WESTERN POWER INDUSTRIAL CO., LTD.; *Int'l*, pg. 1563
CHINA WI-MAX COMMUNICATIONS, INC.; *U.S. Private*, pg. 886
CHINA WIND POWER INTERNATIONAL CORP.; *Int'l*, pg. 1563
CHINA WIRE & CABLE CO., LTD.; *Int'l*, pg. 1563
CHINA WOOD, INC.; *Int'l*, pg. 1563
CHINA WOOD OPTIMIZATION (HOLDINGS) LIMITED; *Int'l*, pg. 1563
CHINA WORLD TRADE CENTER CO., LTD.; *Int'l*, pg. 1563
CHINA WUYI CO., LTD.; *Int'l*, pg. 1563
CHINA WU YI MOUNTAIN LTD.; *U.S. Private*, pg. 886
CHINA WUZHOU ENGINEERING CORPORATION LTD.—See China North Industries Group Corporation; *Int'l*, pg. 1535
CHINA XD ELECTRICITY CO., LTD.; *Int'l*, pg. 1563
CHINA XD PLASTICS COMPANY LTD.; *Int'l*, pg. 1563
CHINA XIANGTAI FOOD CO., LTD.; *Int'l*, pg. 1563
CHINA XINHUA EDUCATION GROUP LTD.; *Int'l*, pg. 1563
CHINA XLX FERTILISER LTD; *Int'l*, pg. 1563
CHINA YANGTZE POWER CO., LTD.—See China Three Gorges Corporation; *Int'l*, pg. 1558
CHINA YANGTZE POWER INTERNATIONAL (HONG KONG) CO., LTD.—See China Three Gorges Corporation; *Int'l*, pg. 1558
CHINA YANSHAN UNITED FOREIGN TRADE CO. LTD.—See Sinochem Corporation; *Int'l*, pg. 6949
CHINA YIBAI UNITED GUARANTEE INTERNATIONAL HOLDING, INC.; *Int'l*, pg. 1564
CHINA YIDA HOLDING, CO.; *Int'l*, pg. 1564
CHINA YONGDA AUTOMOBILES SERVICES HOLDINGS LIMITED; *Int'l*, pg. 1564
CHINA YOUNGMAN AUTOMOBILE GROUP CO., LTD.; *Int'l*, pg. 1565
CHINA YOURAN DAIRY GROUP LIMITED; *Int'l*, pg. 1565
CHINA YOUZAN LIMITED; *Int'l*, pg. 1565
CHINA YUANBANG PROPERTY HOLDINGS LIMITED; *Int'l*, pg. 1565
CHINA YUAN HONG FIRE CONTROL GROUP HOLDINGS LTD.; *Int'l*, pg. 1565
CHINA YUCHAI INTERNATIONAL LIMITED—See Hong Leong Investment Holdings Pte. Ltd.; *Int'l*, pg. 3468
CHINA YUHUA EDUCATION CORPORATION LIMITED; *Int'l*, pg. 1565
CHINA YURUN FOOD GROUP LIMITED; *Int'l*, pg. 1566
CHINA YUTIAN HOLDINGS LIMITED; *Int'l*, pg. 1566
CHINA ZENITH CHEMICAL GROUP LIMITED; *Int'l*, pg. 1566
CHINA ZENIX AUTO INTERNATIONAL LIMITED—See Newrace Ltd.; *Int'l*, pg. 5236
CHINA ZHENGTONG AUTO SERVICES HOLDINGS LIMITED; *Int'l*, pg. 1566
CHINA ZHENHUA (GROUP) SCIENCE & TECHNOLOGY CO., LTD.; *Int'l*, pg. 1567
CHINA ZHESHANG BANK CO., LTD.; *Int'l*, pg. 1567
CHINA ZHONGDI DAIRY HOLDINGS COMPANY LIMITED; *Int'l*, pg. 1567
CHINA ZHONGHUA GEOTECHNICAL ENGINEERING CO., LTD.; *Int'l*, pg. 1567
CHINA ZHONG QI HOLDINGS LIMITED; *Int'l*, pg. 1567
CHINA ZHONGWANG HOLDINGS LIMITED; *Int'l*, pg. 1567
CHINA ZHONGYUAN ENGINEERING CORPORATION—See China National Nuclear Corporation; *Int'l*, pg. 1532
CHIN CHIN AGRO-INDUSTRIAL COMPANY; *Int'l*, pg. 1480
CHINDATA GROUP HOLDINGS LIMITED—See Bain Capital, LP; *U.S. Private*, pg. 431
CHINDEX HONG KONG LIMITED—See Shanghai Fosun Pharmaceutical (Group) Co., Ltd.; *Int'l*, pg. 6767
CHINDEX MEDICAL LIMITED—See Shanghai Fosun Pharmaceutical (Group) Co., Ltd.; *Int'l*, pg. 6767
CHINDEX (SHANGHAI) INT'L TRADING CO., LTD.—See Shanghai Fosun Pharmaceutical (Group) Co., Ltd.; *Int'l*, pg. 6767
CHINESE COMMUNITY HEALTH CARE ASSOCIATION; *U.S. Private*, pg. 886
CHINESE ENERGY HOLDINGS LIMITED; *Int'l*, pg. 1569
CHINESE ESTATES (HARCOURT HOUSE) LIMITED—See Chinese Estates Holdings Limited; *Int'l*, pg. 1569
CHINESE ESTATES HOLDINGS LIMITED; *Int'l*, pg. 1569
CHINESE ESTATES LIMITED—See Chinese Estates Holdings Limited; *Int'l*, pg. 1569
CHINESE FOOD & BEVERAGE GROUP LIMITED; *Int'l*, pg. 1569
CHINESE GAMER INTERNATIONAL CORP.; *Int'l*, pg. 1569
CHINESE GLOBAL INVESTORS GROUP LTD.; *Int'l*, pg. 1569
CHINESEINVESTORS.COM, INC.; *U.S. Private*, pg. 886
CHINESE MARITIME TRANSPORT LTD.; *Int'l*, pg. 1569
CHINESE MARITIME TRANSPORT (S) PTE. LTD.—See Chinese Maritime Transport Ltd.; *Int'l*, pg. 1569
CHINESE MEDIA.NET, INC.—See Nan Hai Corporation Limited; *Int'l*, pg. 5137
CHINESE PEOPLE HOLDINGS COMPANY LIMITED; *Int'l*, pg. 1569
CHINESE PETROLEUM ENGINEERING CORPORATION; *Int'l*, pg. 1569
CHINESE STRATEGIC HOLDINGS LIMITED; *Int'l*, pg. 1569
CHINESE UNIVERSE PUBLISHING AND MEDIA GROUP CO., LTD.; *Int'l*, pg. 1569
CHINESEWORLDNET.COM INC.; *Int'l*, pg. 1569
CHINFON CEMENT CORPORATION—See PT Cemindo Gemilang Tbk; *Int'l*, pg. 6033
CHING CHAN OPTICAL TECHNOLOGY CO., LTD.; *Int'l*, pg. 1569
CHING FENG HOME FASHIONS CO., LTD.; *Int'l*, pg. 1570
CHING HING WEAVING DYEING & PRINTING FACTORY LIMITED—See Shenzhou Space Park Group Limited; *Int'l*, pg. 6826
CHINGIS TECHNOLOGY CORPORATION—See MediaTek Inc.; *Int'l*, pg. 4773
CHING LEE HOLDINGS LIMITED; *Int'l*, pg. 1570
CHING-TONG MOTOR CO., LTD.—See Yulon Finance Corporation; *Int'l*, pg. 8613

CORPORATE AFFILIATIONS

CHIN HERR INDUSTRIES (M) SDN. BHD.—See Chin Well Holdings Berhad; *Int'l*, pg. 1480
CHIN HIN CONCRETE (KL) SDN BHD—See Chin Hin Group Berhad; *Int'l*, pg. 1480
CHIN HIN CONCRETE (NORTH) SDN BHD—See Chin Hin Group Berhad; *Int'l*, pg. 1480
CHIN HIN GROUP BERHAD; *Int'l*, pg. 1480
CHIN HIN GROUP PROPERTY BERHAD—See Chin Hin Group Berhad; *Int'l*, pg. 1480
CHIN HSIN ENVIRONMENTAL ENGINEERING CO., LTD.—See Sunny Friend Environmental Technology Co., Ltd.; *Int'l*, pg. 7318
CHIN HUAY PUBLIC COMPANY LIMITED; *Int'l*, pg. 1480
CHINHUNG INTERNATIONAL (INC.); *Int'l*, pg. 1570
CHINLINK FINANCE LEASE COMPANY LIMITED—See ChinLink International Holdings Limited; *Int'l*, pg. 1570
CHINLINK INTERNATIONAL HOLDINGS LIMITED; *Int'l*, pg. 1570
CHINLINK SUPPLY CHAIN SERVICES (SHAANXI) COMPANY LIMITED—See ChinLink International Holdings Limited; *Int'l*, pg. 1570
CHINLINK TIAN HUI COMPANY LIMITED—See ChinLink International Holdings Limited; *Int'l*, pg. 1570
CHINNEY ALLIANCE ENGINEERING LIMITED—See Chinney Alliance Group Limited; *Int'l*, pg. 1570
CHINNEY ALLIANCE GROUP LIMITED; *Int'l*, pg. 1570
CHINNEY CONSTRUCTION COMPANY, LIMITED—See Chinney Alliance Group Limited; *Int'l*, pg. 1570
CHINNEY INVESTMENTS, LIMITED; *Int'l*, pg. 1570
CHINNEY KIN WING HOLDINGS LTD.—See Chinney Alliance Group Limited; *Int'l*, pg. 1570
CHINO COMMERCIAL BANCORP; *U.S. Public*, pg. 489
CHINO COMMERCIAL BANK—See Chino Commercial Bancorp; *U.S. Public*, pg. 489
CHINO CORPORATION INDIA PVT. LTD.—See CHINO Corporation; *Int'l*, pg. 1570
CHINO CORPORATION; *Int'l*, pg. 1570
CHINO CORPORATION (THAILAND) LIMITED—See CHINO Corporation; *Int'l*, pg. 1570
CHINOIN PRIVATE CO. LTD—See Sanofi; *Int'l*, pg. 6547
CHINO INSTRUMENTATION (KUNSHAN) CO., LTD.—See CHINO Corporation; *Int'l*, pg. 1570
CHINOOK DRILLING—See Total Energy Services Inc.; *Int'l*, pg. 7834
CHINOOK ENERGY INC.—See Tourmaline Oil Corp.; *Int'l*, pg. 7848
CHINOOK INDUSTRIAL LTD.; *Int'l*, pg. 1571
CHINOOK LUMBER INC.; *U.S. Private*, pg. 886
CHINOOK THERAPEUTICS, INC.—See Novartis AG; *Int'l*, pg. 5457
CHINO SOFTEX CORPORATION—See CHINO Corporation; *Int'l*, pg. 1570
CHINO VALLEY MEDICAL CENTER—See Prime Healthcare Services, Inc.; *U.S. Private*, pg. 3261
CHINO WATCH CO., LTD.—See Seiko Group Corporation; *Int'l*, pg. 6688
CHINO WORKS AMERICA, INC.—See CHINO Corporation; *Int'l*, pg. 1570
CHINOZ TEXTILE LLC—See National Bank for Foreign Economic Activity of the Republic of Uzbekistan; *Int'l*, pg. 5151
CHIN POON INDUSTRIAL CO., LTD.; *Int'l*, pg. 1480
CHINSAN ELECTRONIC IND. (THAILAND) CO., LTD.—See Taiwan Chinsan Electronic Industrial Co., Ltd.; *Int'l*, pg. 7419
CHIN TECK PLANTATIONS BERHAD; *Int'l*, pg. 1480
CHINT ELECTRICS EUROPE S.R.L—See Chint Group Corporation; *Int'l*, pg. 1571
CHINT ELETRICOS AMERICA DO SUL LTDA—See Chint Group Corporation; *Int'l*, pg. 1571
CHINT ENERGY SLU—See Chint Group Corporation; *Int'l*, pg. 1571
CHINT GROUP CORPORATION; *Int'l*, pg. 1571
CHINT WEST ASIA & AFRICA FZE—See Chint Group Corporation; *Int'l*, pg. 1571
CHINTZ & COMPANY; *Int'l*, pg. 1571
CHINVEST SAS; *Int'l*, pg. 1571
CHIN WELL HOLDINGS BERHAD; *Int'l*, pg. 1480
CHINYANG CHEMICAL CORPORATION; *Int'l*, pg. 1571
CHINYANG HOLDINGS CORPORATION; *Int'l*, pg. 1571
CHIN YANG INDUSTRY CO., LTD.—See Chinyang Holdings Corporation; *Int'l*, pg. 1571
CHINYANG POLY URETHANE CO LTD; *Int'l*, pg. 1572
CHIOME BIOSCIENCE INC.; *Int'l*, pg. 1572
CHI OPERATIONS INC.—See Enel S.p.A.; *Int'l*, pg. 2411
CHIORI APPAREL INC.—See Maran Inc.; *U.S. Private*, pg. 2569
CHIORINO, INC.—See Chiorino S.p.A.; *Int'l*, pg. 1572
CHIORINO S.p.A.; *Int'l*, pg. 1572
C.H.I. OVERHEAD DOORS, INC.—See Nucor Corporation; *U.S. Public*, pg. 1553
CHI & PARTNERS LIMITED; *Int'l*, pg. 1474
CHIPBOND TECHNOLOGY CORPORATION; *Int'l*, pg. 1572
CHIP COMMUNICATIONS GMBH—See Hubert Burda Media Holding Kommanditgesellschaft; *Int'l*, pg. 3520
CHIP ENG SENG CONTRACTORS (1988) PTE LTD.—See Chip Eng Seng Corporation Ltd.; *Int'l*, pg. 1572

CHIP ENG SENG CORPORATION LTD.; *Int'l*, pg. 1572
CHIPETA DIALYSIS, LLC—See DaVita Inc.; *U.S. Public*, pg. 636
CHIP GANASSI RACING TEAMS, INC. - INDYCAR—See Chip Ganassi Racing Teams, Inc.; *U.S. Private*, pg. 886
CHIP GANASSI RACING TEAMS, INC.; *U.S. Private*, pg. 886
CHIP GANASSI RACING WITH FELIX SABATES, LLC—See Chip Ganassi Racing Teams, Inc.; *U.S. Private*, pg. 886
CHIP GOAL ELECTRONICS CORP.—See Fortune Oriental Company Limited; *Int'l*, pg. 2744
CHIP HOLDING GMBH—See Hubert Burda Media Holding Kommanditgesellschaft; *Int'l*, pg. 3520
CHIP HOPE CO., LTD.; *Int'l*, pg. 1572
CHIPICO PICKLES—See Vienna Sausage Mfg. Co.; *U.S. Private*, pg. 4381
CHIPITA AMERICA, INC.—See Chipita S.A.; *Int'l*, pg. 1573
CHIPITA AMERICA, INC. - TULSA—See Chipita S.A.; *Int'l*, pg. 1573
CHIPITA BULGARIA S.A.—See Chipita S.A.; *Int'l*, pg. 1573
CHIPITA CZ S.R.O—See Chipita S.A.; *Int'l*, pg. 1573
CHIPITA GERMANY GMBH—See Chipita S.A.; *Int'l*, pg. 1573
CHIPITA GIDA URETIM A.S.—See Chipita S.A.; *Int'l*, pg. 1573
CHIPITA HUNGARY KFT.—See Chipita S.A.; *Int'l*, pg. 1573
CHIPITA INDIA PVT LTD.—See Chipita S.A.; *Int'l*, pg. 1573
CHIPITA LEFCO LLC—See Chipita S.A.; *Int'l*, pg. 1573
CHIPITA POLAND S.P. Z.O.O.—See Chipita S.A.; *Int'l*, pg. 1573
CHIPITA ROMANIA S.R.L.—See Chipita S.A.; *Int'l*, pg. 1573
CHIPITA SAINT-PETERSBURG LLC—See Chipita S.A.; *Int'l*, pg. 1573
CHIPITA S.A.; *Int'l*, pg. 1573
CHIPITA SLOVAKIA S.R.O.—See Chipita S.A.; *Int'l*, pg. 1573
CHIPITA UKRAINE TRADE LLC—See Chipita S.A.; *Int'l*, pg. 1573
CHIPITA YU A.D.—See Chipita S.A.; *Int'l*, pg. 1573
CHIPKINS BAKERY SUPPLIES (PTY) LIMITED—See The Bidvest Group Limited; *Int'l*, pg. 7624
CHIPKINS CATERING SUPPLIES (PTY) LIMITED—See The Bidvest Group Limited; *Int'l*, pg. 7624
CHIPLUN FINE CHEMICALS LTD.; *Int'l*, pg. 1573
CHIPMAN CORPORATION; *U.S. Private*, pg. 886
CHIPMAN & TAYLOR CHEVROLET; *U.S. Private*, pg. 886
CHIPMOS ASSEMBLY FAB—See ChipMOS Technologies Inc.; *Int'l*, pg. 1573
CHIPMOS GOLD BUMPING FAB—See ChipMOS Technologies Inc.; *Int'l*, pg. 1573
CHIPMOS JAPAN INC.—See ChipMOS Technologies Inc.; *Int'l*, pg. 1573
CHIPMOS TECHNOLOGIES INC.; *Int'l*, pg. 1573
CHIPMOS TESTING FAB—See ChipMOS Technologies Inc.; *Int'l*, pg. 1573
CHIPMOS U.S.A., INC.—See ChipMOS Technologies Inc.; *Int'l*, pg. 1573
CHIP NGAI ENGINEERING WORKS SDN. BHD.—See CN ASIA Corporation Bhd.; *Int'l*, pg. 1672
CHI POLSKA S.A.—See The Coca-Cola Company; *U.S. Public*, pg. 2065
CHIP ONE STOP, INC.—See Arrow Electronics, Inc.; *U.S. Public*, pg. 198
CHIPONE TECHNOLOGY (BEIJING) CO., LTD.; *Int'l*, pg. 1573
CHIPOTLE MEXICAN GRILL CANADA CORP.—See Chipotle Mexican Grill, Inc.; *U.S. Public*, pg. 489
CHIPOTLE MEXICAN GRILL GERMANY GMBH—See Chipotle Mexican Grill, Inc.; *U.S. Public*, pg. 489
CHIPOTLE MEXICAN GRILL, INC.; *U.S. Public*, pg. 489
CHIPOTLE MEXICAN GRILL OF BERWYN HEIGHTS, LLC—See Chipotle Mexican Grill, Inc.; *U.S. Public*, pg. 489
CHIPOTLE MEXICAN GRILL OF COLORADO, LLC—See Chipotle Mexican Grill, Inc.; *U.S. Public*, pg. 489
CHIPOTLE MEXICAN GRILL SERVICE CO., LLC—See Chipotle Mexican Grill, Inc.; *U.S. Public*, pg. 489
CHIPOTLE MEXICAN GRILL U.S. FINANCE CO., LLC—See Chipotle Mexican Grill, Inc.; *U.S. Public*, pg. 489
CHIPPENHAM & JOHNSTON-WILLIS HOSPITALS, INC.—See HCA Healthcare, Inc.; *U.S. Public*, pg. 993
CHIPPENHAM & JOHNSTON-WILLIS SPORTS MEDICINE, LLC—See HCA Healthcare, Inc.; *U.S. Public*, pg. 993
CHIPPENHAM PEDIATRIC SPECIALISTS, LLC—See HCA Healthcare, Inc.; *U.S. Public*, pg. 993
CHIPPENHOOK CORPORATION—See Sigma S.A. de C.V.; *Int'l*, pg. 6908
CHIPPERS, INC.—See The Davey Tree Expert Company; *U.S. Private*, pg. 4018
CHIPPEWA ENTERPRISES INCORPORATED; *U.S. Private*, pg. 886
CHIPPEWA VALLEY AGRAFUELS COOPERATIVE; *U.S. Private*, pg. 886
CHIPPEWA VALLEY BANK; *U.S. Private*, pg. 886

CHIPPEWA VALLEY BEAN COMPANY INC.; *U.S. Private*, pg. 886
CHIPPEWA VALLEY ETHANOL COMPANY, LLC—See Chippewa Valley Agrafuels Cooperative; *U.S. Private*, pg. 886
CHIPPINDALE FOODS LIMITED—See Morrison (Wm) Supermarkets PLC; *Int'l*, pg. 5049
CHIPREWARDS, INC.—See CVC Capital Partners SICAV-FIS S.A.; *Int'l*, pg. 1888
CHIPSEA TECHNOLOGIES (SHENZHEN) CORP.; *Int'l*, pg. 1573
CHIPS MANUFACTURING LLC—See STERIS plc; *Int'l*, pg. 7208
CHIPS&MEDIA, INC.; *Int'l*, pg. 1573
CHIPS TECHNOLOGY GROUP LLC—See IT Solutions Consulting LLC; *U.S. Private*, pg. 2148
CHIP SUPPLY INC.—See Behrman Brothers Management Corp.; *U.S. Private*, pg. 515
CHIPSY FOR FOOD INDUSTRIES SAE (CHIPSY)—See PepsiCo, Inc.; *U.S. Public*, pg. 1668
CHIP-TECH, LTD.; *U.S. Private*, pg. 886
CHIPTOPIA (SHANGHAI) TECHNOLOGY CO., LTD.—See Alchip Technologies, Limited; *Int'l*, pg. 301
CHIQUITA BANANA COMPANY BV—See Banco Safra S.A.; *Int'l*, pg. 824
CHIQUITA BANANA COMPANY BV—See Sucocitrico Cutrale Ltda.; *Int'l*, pg. 7251
CHIQUITA BRANDS INTERNATIONAL, INC.—See Banco Safra S.A.; *Int'l*, pg. 824
CHIQUITA BRANDS INTERNATIONAL, INC.—See Sucocitrico Cutrale Ltda.; *Int'l*, pg. 7251
CHIQUITA BRANDS INTERNATIONAL SARL—See Banco Safra S.A.; *Int'l*, pg. 824
CHIQUITA BRANDS INTERNATIONAL SARL—See Sucocitrico Cutrale Ltda.; *Int'l*, pg. 7251
CHIQUITA BRANDS LLC - BETHLEHEM—See Banco Safra S.A.; *Int'l*, pg. 824
CHIQUITA BRANDS LLC - BETHLEHEM—See Sucocitrico Cutrale Ltda.; *Int'l*, pg. 7251
CHIQUITA BRANDS LLC - FORT LAUDERDALE—See Banco Safra S.A.; *Int'l*, pg. 824
CHIQUITA BRANDS LLC - FORT LAUDERDALE—See Sucocitrico Cutrale Ltda.; *Int'l*, pg. 7251
CHIQUITA BRANDS LLC - FREEPORT—See Banco Safra S.A.; *Int'l*, pg. 824
CHIQUITA BRANDS LLC - FREEPORT—See Sucocitrico Cutrale Ltda.; *Int'l*, pg. 7251
CHIQUITA BRANDS LLC - GULFPORT—See Banco Safra S.A.; *Int'l*, pg. 824
CHIQUITA BRANDS LLC - GULFPORT—See Sucocitrico Cutrale Ltda.; *Int'l*, pg. 7251
CHIQUITA BRANDS LLC—See Banco Safra S.A.; *Int'l*, pg. 824
CHIQUITA BRANDS LLC—See Sucocitrico Cutrale Ltda.; *Int'l*, pg. 7251
CHIQUITA BRANDS LLC - WILMINGTON—See Banco Safra S.A.; *Int'l*, pg. 824
CHIQUITA BRANDS LLC - WILMINGTON—See Sucocitrico Cutrale Ltda.; *Int'l*, pg. 7251
CHIQUITA DEUTSCHLAND GMBH—See Banco Safra S.A.; *Int'l*, pg. 824
CHIQUITA DEUTSCHLAND GMBH—See Sucocitrico Cutrale Ltda.; *Int'l*, pg. 7251
CHIQUITA FRESH NORTH AMERICA LLC—See Banco Safra S.A.; *Int'l*, pg. 824
CHIQUITA FRESH NORTH AMERICA LLC—See Sucocitrico Cutrale Ltda.; *Int'l*, pg. 7251
CHIQUITA FRUIT BAR (GERMANY) GMBH—See Banco Safra S.A.; *Int'l*, pg. 824
CHIQUITA FRUIT BAR (GERMANY) GMBH—See Sucocitrico Cutrale Ltda.; *Int'l*, pg. 7251
CHIQUITA GUATEMALA, S.A.—See Banco Safra S.A.; *Int'l*, pg. 824
CHIQUITA GUATEMALA, S.A.—See Sucocitrico Cutrale Ltda.; *Int'l*, pg. 7251
CHIQUITA LOGISTIC SERVICES EL SALVADOR LTDA.—See Banco Safra S.A.; *Int'l*, pg. 824
CHIQUITA LOGISTIC SERVICES EL SALVADOR LTDA.—See Sucocitrico Cutrale Ltda.; *Int'l*, pg. 7251
CHIQUITO LIMITED—See Apollo Global Management, Inc.; *U.S. Public*, pg. 164
CHIRAG AFRICA LIMITED—See Flame Tree Group Holdings Ltd.; *Int'l*, pg. 2698
CHIRAL QUEST CORP.; *U.S. Private*, pg. 886
CHIRAL QUEST, INC.—See Chiral Quest Corp.; *U.S. Private*, pg. 886
CHIRAL QUEST (JIASHAN) CO., LTD.—See Chiral Quest Corp.; *U.S. Private*, pg. 886
CHIRAL TECHNOLOGIES-EUROPE S.A.R.L.—See Daicel Corporation; *Int'l*, pg. 1918
CHIRAL TECHNOLOGIES INC.—See Daicel Corporation; *Int'l*, pg. 1918
CHIRANA T. INJECTA, A.S.; *Int'l*, pg. 1573
CHIRANO GOLD MINES LTD.—See Kinross Gold Corporation; *Int'l*, pg. 4182
CHIRIPAL INDUSTRIES LTD. - FABRIC DIVISION—See Chiripal Industries Ltd.; *Int'l*, pg. 1573
CHIRIPAL INDUSTRIES LTD. - PETROCHEMICAL DIVISION—See Chiripal Industries Ltd.; *Int'l*, pg. 1573

CHIRIPAL INDUSTRIES LTD.; *Int'l*, pg. 1573
CHIRISA CAPITAL MANAGEMENT LTD.; *Int'l*, pg. 1574
CHIRMARN LIMITED—See Northern Bear Plc; *Int'l*, pg. 5442
CHIRONET LLC; *U.S. Private*, pg. 886
CHIRO ONE WELLNESS CENTERS; *U.S. Private*, pg. 886
CHIROTOUCH; *U.S. Private*, pg. 887
CHIRPIFY, INC.; *U.S. Private*, pg. 887
CHISANO MARKETING GROUP, INC.; *U.S. Private*, pg. 887
CHISESI BROTHERS MEAT PACKING CO.; *U.S. Private*, pg. 887
CHI SHENG PHARMA & BIOTECH CO., LTD.; *Int'l*, pg. 1475
CHISHOLM, BOYD & WHITE CO.—See Venturedyne, Ltd.; *U.S. Private*, pg. 4358
THE CHISHOLM CORPORATION—See INSCO, Inc.; *U.S. Private*, pg. 2085
CHISHOLM ENERGY HOLDINGS, LLC—See Warburg Pincus LLC; *U.S. Private*, pg. 4437
CHISOLM TRAIL RV; *U.S. Private*, pg. 887
CHISON DEUTSCHLAND GMBH—See Chison Medical Technologies Co., Ltd.; *Int'l*, pg. 1574
CHISON MEDICAL TECHNOLOGIES CO., LTD.; *Int'l*, pg. 1574
CHISON USA INC.—See Chison Medical Technologies Co., Ltd.; *Int'l*, pg. 1574
CHISWICK OUTPATIENT CENTRE LLP—See HCA Healthcare, Inc.; *U.S. Public*, pg. 993
CHI SYSTEMS INC.—See OSI Maritime Systems; *Int'l*, pg. 5650
CHITA INC.—See Dassault Systemes S.A.; *Int'l*, pg. 1975
CHITA KOGYO CO., LTD.; *Int'l*, pg. 1574
CHITA KYB MANUFACTURING (ZHENJIANG) CO., LTD.—See KYB Corporation; *Int'l*, pg. 4353
CHITEC TECHNOLOGY CO., LTD.; *Int'l*, pg. 1574
CHITHARANJAN DEVELOPERS LLP—See Mercantile Ventures Limited; *Int'l*, pg. 4819
CHITIKA, INC.; *U.S. Private*, pg. 887
CHITIKA, INC.—See Chitika, Inc.; *U.S. Private*, pg. 887
CHITOGENX INC; *Int'l*, pg. 1574
CHITOSE AIRPORT FUELLING FACILITIES CO., LTD.—See Japan Airlines Co., Ltd.; *Int'l*, pg. 3881
CHITOSE AIRPORT MOTOR SERVICE CO., LTD.—See ANA Holdings Inc.; *Int'l*, pg. 444
CHITOSE SANGYO CO., LTD.—See NSK Ltd.; *Int'l*, pg. 5478
CHITRAKOOT STEEL & POWER PVT. LTD.—See Tulsyan Nec Limited; *Int'l*, pg. 7970
CHITRCHATR COMMUNICATIONS INC.; *Int'l*, pg. 1574
CHITTAGONG CAPITAL LIMITED; *Int'l*, pg. 1574
CHITTAGONG STOCK EXCHANGE LTD.; *Int'l*, pg. 1574
CHITTENDEN & EASTMAN CO.; *U.S. Private*, pg. 887
CHIU HO (CHINA) MEDICAL TECHNOLOGY CO., LTD.—See CHC Healthcare Group; *Int'l*, pg. 1458
CHIULISTA SERVICES, INC.; *U.S. Private*, pg. 887
CHIUO HO AUTOMOTIVE SALES CO.,LTD.—See Universal Cement Corporation; *Int'l*, pg. 8078
CHIU TING INDUSTRIAL (HUIZHOU) CO., LTD.—See Chiu Ting Machinery Co., Ltd.; *Int'l*, pg. 1574
CHIU TING MACHINERY CO., LTD.; *Int'l*, pg. 1574
CHIVAS BROTHERS (HOLDINGS) LTD—See Pernod Ricard S.A.; *Int'l*, pg. 5809
CHIVAS BROTHERS PERNOD RICARD LTD—See Pernod Ricard S.A.; *Int'l*, pg. 5809
CHI WEST INC.—See Enel S.p.A.; *Int'l*, pg. 2411
CHI WO PLASTIC MOULDS FTY. LIMITED—See Sunningdale Tech Ltd; *Int'l*, pg. 7318
CHIYODA ADVANCED SOLUTIONS CORPORATION—See Chiyoda Corporation; *Int'l*, pg. 1574
CHIYODA ALMANA ENGINEERING LLC—See Chiyoda Corporation; *Int'l*, pg. 1574
CHIYODA CO., LTD.; *Int'l*, pg. 1574
CHIYODA CORPORATION (SHANGHAI)—See Chiyoda Corporation; *Int'l*, pg. 1574
CHIYODA CORPORATION; *Int'l*, pg. 1574
CHIYODA DO BRASIL REPRESENTACOES LTDA.—See Chiyoda Corporation; *Int'l*, pg. 1575
CHIYODA ELECTRONICS CO., LTD.—See NF Corporation; *Int'l*, pg. 5252
CHIYODA ENGINEERING CO., LTD.—See Sumitomo Osaka Cement Co Ltd; *Int'l*, pg. 7296
CHIYODA INSPECTION INDUSTRIES CO., LTD—See Konoike Transport Co., Ltd.; *Int'l*, pg. 4274
CHIYODA INTEGRE CO. (JOHOR) SDN. BHD.—See Chiyoda Integre Co., Ltd.; *Int'l*, pg. 1575
CHIYODA INTEGRE CO., LTD.; *Int'l*, pg. 1575
CHIYODA INTEGRE CO. (M) SDN. BHD.—See Chiyoda Integre Co., Ltd.; *Int'l*, pg. 1575
CHIYODA INTEGRE CO. (PENANG) SDN. BHD.—See Chiyoda Integre Co., Ltd.; *Int'l*, pg. 1575
CHIYODA INTEGRE CO. (S) PTE. LTD.—See Chiyoda Integre Co., Ltd.; *Int'l*, pg. 1575
CHIYODA INTEGRE (DALIAN) CO., LTD.—See Chiyoda Integre Co., Ltd.; *Int'l*, pg. 1575
CHIYODA INTEGRE DE BAJA CALIFORNIA, S. A. DE C. V.—See Chiyoda Integre Co., Ltd.; *Int'l*, pg. 1575

CHIYODA INTEGRE CO., LTD.

CHIYODA INTEGRE DE MEXICO, S.A. DE C.V.—See Chiyoda Integre Co., Ltd.; *Int'l*, pg. 1575
CHIYODA INTEGRE (DONG GUAN) CO., LTD.—See Chiyoda Integre Co., Ltd.; *Int'l*, pg. 1575
CHIYODA INTEGRE (GUANGZHOU) CO., LTD.—See Chiyoda Integre Co., Ltd.; *Int'l*, pg. 1575
CHIYODA INTEGRE (HK) LTD.—See Chiyoda Integre Co., Ltd.; *Int'l*, pg. 1575
CHIYODA INTEGRE OF AMERICA (SAN DIEGO), INC.—See Chiyoda Integre Co., Ltd.; *Int'l*, pg. 1575
CHIYODA INTEGRE (PHILIPPINES) CORPORATION—See Chiyoda Integre Co., Ltd.; *Int'l*, pg. 1575
CHIYODA INTEGRE (SHANDONG) CO., LTD.—See Chiyoda Integre Co., Ltd.; *Int'l*, pg. 1575
CHIYODA INTEGRE (SHANGHAI) CO., LTD.—See Chiyoda Integre Co., Ltd.; *Int'l*, pg. 1575
CHIYODA INTEGRE (SHENZHEN) CO., LTD.—See Chiyoda Integre Co., Ltd.; *Int'l*, pg. 1575
CHIYODA INTEGRE SLOVAKIA, S.R.O.—See Chiyoda Integre Co., Ltd.; *Int'l*, pg. 1575
CHIYODA INTEGRE (SUZHOU) CO., LTD.—See Chiyoda Integre Co., Ltd.; *Int'l*, pg. 1575
CHIYODA INTEGRE (THAILAND) CO., LTD.—See Chiyoda Integre Co., Ltd.; *Int'l*, pg. 1575
CHIYODA INTEGRE (TIAN JIN) CO., LTD.—See Chiyoda Integre Co., Ltd.; *Int'l*, pg. 1575
CHIYODA INTEGRE VIETNAM CO., LTD.—See Chiyoda Integre Co., Ltd.; *Int'l*, pg. 1575
CHIYODA INTEGRE (ZHONG SHAN) CO., LTD.—See Chiyoda Integre Co., Ltd.; *Int'l*, pg. 1575
CHIYODA INTERNATIONAL CORPORATION—See Chiyoda Corporation; *Int'l*, pg. 1574
CHIYODA KEISO CO., LTD.—See Chiyoda Corporation; *Int'l*, pg. 1574
CHIYODA KENKOU CO., LTD.—See Toda Corporation; *Int'l*, pg. 7772
CHIYODA KOGYO CO., LTD.—See Suntory Holdings Limited; *Int'l*, pg. 7326
CHIYODA KOSHO CO., LTD.—See Chiyoda Corporation; *Int'l*, pg. 1574
CHIYODA MALAYSIA SDN. BHD.—See Chiyoda Corporation; *Int'l*, pg. 1574
CHIYODA PHILIPPINES CORPORATION—See Chiyoda Corporation; *Int'l*, pg. 1574
CHIYODA & PUBLIC WORKS CO., LTD.—See Chiyoda Corporation; *Int'l*, pg. 1574
CHIYODA SINGAPORE (PTE) LIMITED—See Chiyoda Corporation; *Int'l*, pg. 1574
CHIYODA STAFF SERVICE CO., LTD—See Toda Corporation; *Int'l*, pg. 7772
CHIYODA SYSTEM TECHNOLOGIES CORPORATION—See Chiyoda Corporation; *Int'l*, pg. 1574
CHIYODA TECHNOACE CO., LTD.—See Chiyoda Corporation; *Int'l*, pg. 1575
CHIYODA (THAILAND) LIMITED—See Chiyoda Corporation; *Int'l*, pg. 1574
CHIYODA TOCHI TATEMONO CO., LTD.—See Toda Corporation; *Int'l*, pg. 7772
CHIYODA U-TECH CO., LTD.—See Chiyoda Corporation; *Int'l*, pg. 1575
CHIYODA UTE CO., LTD. - CHIBA PLANT—See Chiyoda Ute Co., Ltd.; *Int'l*, pg. 1575
CHIYODA UTE CO., LTD. - KAIZUKA PLANT—See Chiyoda Ute Co., Ltd.; *Int'l*, pg. 1575
CHIYODA UTE CO., LTD. - MURORAN PLANT—See Chiyoda Ute Co., Ltd.; *Int'l*, pg. 1575
CHIYODA UTE CO., LTD. - OKAYAMA PLANT—See Chiyoda Ute Co., Ltd.; *Int'l*, pg. 1575
CHIYODA UTE CO., LTD. - SHIMONOSEKI PLANT—See Chiyoda Ute Co., Ltd.; *Int'l*, pg. 1575
CHIYODA UTE CO., LTD.; *Int'l*, pg. 1575
CHIYU BANKING CORPORATION LIMITED—See Xiamen International Bank Co., Ltd.; *Int'l*, pg. 8524
CHIZCOMM LTD.—See Kartoon Studios, Inc.; *U.S. Public*, pg. 1214
C.H. JAMES RESTAURANT HOLDINGS, LLC; *U.S. Private*, pg. 707
CH JANKI SP ZOO—See Cromwell Property Group; *Int'l*, pg. 1853
CH JONES LIMITED—See Corpay, Inc.; *U.S. Public*, pg. 579
CH. KARNACHANG-TOKYU CONSTRUCTION CO., LTD.—See Tokyu Construction Co., Ltd.; *Int'l*, pg. 7797
CH. KARNCHANG (LAO) CO., LTD—See CH. Karnchang Public Company Limited; *Int'l*, pg. 1435
CH. KARNCHANG PUBLIC COMPANY LIMITED; *Int'l*, pg. 1435
CH. KARNCHANG REAL ESTATE CO., LTD—See CH. Karnchang Public Company Limited; *Int'l*, pg. 1435
CH. KARNCHANG - TOKYU CONSTRUCTION CO LTD—See CH. Karnchang Public Company Limited; *Int'l*, pg. 1435
CHK OIL LIMITED; *Int'l*, pg. 1575
C H KRUSE PLUMBING, INC.—See Lovett Inc.; *U.S. Private*, pg. 2504
C. H. LANGMAN & SONS INC.; *U.S. Private*, pg. 705
CHL BUSINESS INTERIORS, LLC; *U.S. Private*, pg. 887

CHLITINA HOLDING LIMITED; *Int'l*, pg. 1576
CHL LIMITED; *Int'l*, pg. 1575
CHL MEDICAL PARTNERS; *U.S. Private*, pg. 887
CHLODNICE NISSENS POLSKA SP.ZO.O.—See Standard Motor Products, Inc.; *U.S. Public*, pg. 1929
CHLOE SAS—See Compagnie Financiere Richemont S.A.; *Int'l*, pg. 1741
CHLOPAK, LEONARD, SCHECHTER & ASSOCIATES—See Omnicom Group Inc.; *U.S. Public*, pg. 1587
CHLORELLA SUPPLY CO., LTD—See Daesang Corporation; *Int'l*, pg. 1909
CHLORIDE BATTERIES S E ASIA PTE LIMITED—See EXIDE INDUSTRIES LIMITED; *Int'l*, pg. 2585
CHLORIDE ESPANA, S.A.U.—See Vertiv Holdings Co; *U.S. Public*, pg. 2288
CHLORIDE GROUP LIMITED—See Emerson Electric Co.; *U.S. Public*, pg. 742
CHLORIDE GROUP PLC—See Vertiv Holdings Co; *U.S. Public*, pg. 2288
CHLORIDE ITALIA—See Vertiv Holdings Co; *U.S. Public*, pg. 2288
CHLORIDE KOEXA S.A.—See Emerson Electric Co.; *U.S. Public*, pg. 742
CHLORIDE POWER ELECTRONICS INC.—See Vertiv Holdings Co; *U.S. Public*, pg. 2288
CHLORIDE POWER PROTECTION AUSTRALIA—See Vertiv Holdings Co; *U.S. Public*, pg. 2288
CHLORIDE POWER PROTECTION PTY. LTD.—See Emerson Electric Co.; *U.S. Public*, pg. 742
CHLORIDE POWER PROTECTION—See Vertiv Holdings Co; *U.S. Public*, pg. 2288
CHLORIDE POWER SYSTEMS & SOLUTIONS LIMITED—See EXIDE INDUSTRIES LIMITED; *Int'l*, pg. 2585
CHLORIDE SRL—See Emerson Electric Co.; *U.S. Public*, pg. 742
CHLORIDE ZIMBABWE (PRIVATE) LIMITED—See Amalgamated Regional Trading (ART) Holdings Ltd.; *Int'l*, pg. 409
CHLORKING, LLC—See Hayward Holdings, Inc.; *U.S. Public*, pg. 990
CHL SHIPPING B.V.—See ED&F Man Holdings Limited; *Int'l*, pg. 2302
CHL S.P.A.; *Int'l*, pg. 1576
C.H. MARTIN, INC.; *U.S. Private*, pg. 707
CHMC ANESTHESIA FOUNDATION, INC.; *U.S. Private*, pg. 887
CH MEDIA HOLDING AG; *Int'l*, pg. 1435
C & H MEKONG COMPANY LIMITED—See Dream International Ltd; *Int'l*, pg. 2202
CH MURPHY/CLARK-ULLMAN INC.; *U.S. Private*, pg. 844
CHN ELECTRICAL SERVICES LIMITED—See E.ON SE; *Int'l*, pg. 2256
CHN ENERGY CHANGYUAN ELECTRIC POWER CO., LTD.; *Int'l*, pg. 1576
CHNS/CHFX RADIO—See Maritime Broadcasting System Ltd.; *Int'l*, pg. 4695
CHN SOLUTIONS—See Consolidated Services Group; *U.S. Private*, pg. 1022
CHOA PHARMACEUTICAL CO., LTD.; *Int'l*, pg. 1576
CHO-A PHARM. CO., LTD. - HAMAN FACTORY—See CHO-A Pharm. Co., Ltd.; *Int'l*, pg. 1576
CHO-A PHARM. CO., LTD.; *Int'l*, pg. 1576
CHOATE CONSTRUCTION COMPANY; *U.S. Private*, pg. 887
CHOATE HALL & STEWART LLP; *U.S. Private*, pg. 887
CHOBANI AUSTRALIA PTY LTD—See Chobani, LLC; *U.S. Private*, pg. 887
CHOBANI INC.; *U.S. Private*, pg. 887
CHOBANI, LLC; *U.S. Private*, pg. 887
CHOBI COMPANY LIMITED; *Int'l*, pg. 1576
CHOCOLADEFABRIKEN LINDT & SPRUNGLI AG; *Int'l*, pg. 1576
CHOCOLADEFABRIKEN LINDT & SPRUNGLI GMBH—See Chocoladefabriken Lindt & Sprungli AG; *Int'l*, pg. 1576
CHOCOLADEFABRIKEN LINDT & SPRUNGLI (SCHWEIZ) AG—See Chocoladefabriken Lindt & Sprungli AG; *Int'l*, pg. 1576
CHOCOLATE ACQUISITION SUB, LLC—See Hilton Grand Vacations Inc.; *U.S. Public*, pg. 1039
CHOCOLATE BAYOU WATER COMPANY—See International Paper Company; *U.S. Public*, pg. 1155
CHOCOLATE CANDY CREATIONS INC.; *U.S. Private*, pg. 887
CHOCOLATERIE GUYLIAN NV—See Lotte Co., Ltd.; *Int'l*, pg. 4560
CHOCOLATES A LA CARTE, INC.; *U.S. Private*, pg. 888
CHOCOLATES GAROTO S.A—See Nestle S.A.; *Int'l*, pg. 5202
CHOCOLATE SOUP INC.; *U.S. Private*, pg. 887
CHOCOLATEWORKS NZ LIMITED—See The Warehouse Group Limited; *Int'l*, pg. 7698
CHOCOLAT FREY AG—See The Federation of Migros Cooperatives; *Int'l*, pg. 7642
CHOCOLATS CAMILLE BLOCH S.A.; *Int'l*, pg. 1577

CORPORATE AFFILIATIONS

CHOCOLATS HALBA—See Coop-Gruppe Genossenschaft; *Int'l*, pg. 1790
CHOCOOLATE LIMITED—See IT Ltd; *Int'l*, pg. 3827
CHOCTAW ELECTRIC COOPERATIVE, INC.; *U.S. Private*, pg. 888
CHOCTAW GAS GENERATION LLC—See ENGIE SA; *Int'l*, pg. 2433
CHOCTAWHATCHEE ELECTRIC COOPERATIVE INC.; *U.S. Private*, pg. 888
CHODAI CO., LTD.; *Int'l*, pg. 1577
CHODAI & KISO - JIBAN VIETNAM CO., LTD.—See Chodai Co., Ltd.; *Int'l*, pg. 1577
CHODAI-TEC CO., LTD.—See Chodai Co., Ltd.; *Int'l*, pg. 1577
C. HOFFBERGER COMPANY INC.—See Star Group, L.P.; *U.S. Public*, pg. 1937
CH OFFSHORE LTD—See Baker Technology Limited; *Int'l*, pg. 805
CHOFU DRIVING SCHOOL CORPORATION—See ORIX Corporation; *Int'l*, pg. 5633
CHOFU HOUSING CO., LTD.—See Relo Group, Inc.; *Int'l*, pg. 6265
CHOFU SEISAKUSHO CO., LTD.; *Int'l*, pg. 1577
CHOHEUNG CORPORATION—See Ottogi Corporation; *Int'l*, pg. 5665
CHOHUNG INVESTMENT TRUST AND MANAGEMENT CO., LTD.—See Shinhan Financial Group Co., Ltd.; *Int'l*, pg. 6844
CHOICE CANNING CO., INC.; *U.S. Private*, pg. 888
CHOICE CAPITAL ADVISORS PRIVATE LIMITED—See Choice International Limited; *Int'l*, pg. 1577
CHOICE CONSULTANCY SERVICES PVT. LTD.—See Choice International Limited; *Int'l*, pg. 1577
CHOICE DEVELOPMENT, INC. - LINKOU FACTORY—See Choice Development, Inc.; *Int'l*, pg. 1577
CHOICE DEVELOPMENT, INC.; *Int'l*, pg. 1577
CHOICE DEVELOPMENT, INC. - TAINAN FACTORY—See Choice Development, Inc.; *Int'l*, pg. 1577
CHOICE EQUIPOS Y SERVICIOS S.A.C—See Fluor Corporation; *U.S. Public*, pg. 857
CHOICE EQUITY BROKING PRIVATE LIMITED—See Choice International Limited; *Int'l*, pg. 1577
CHOICE FINANCIAL GROUP—See Northlane Capital Partners, LLC; *U.S. Private*, pg. 2956
CHOICE FINANCIAL HOLDINGS, INC.—See Northlane Capital Partners, LLC; *U.S. Private*, pg. 2956
CHOICE FOOD GROUP, INC.; *U.S. Private*, pg. 888
CHOICE FOOD OF AMERICA, LLC—See Choice Food Group, Inc.; *U.S. Private*, pg. 888
CHOICE FOODSERVICES, INC.; *U.S. Private*, pg. 888
CHOICE FOUNDATION; *U.S. Private*, pg. 888
CHOICE GENETICS ARGENTINA—See Groupe Grimaud La Corbiere SA; *Int'l*, pg. 3103
CHOICE GENETICS BRASIL LTDA—See Groupe Grimaud La Corbiere SA; *Int'l*, pg. 3103
CHOICE GENETICS CANADA INC.—See Groupe Grimaud La Corbiere SA; *Int'l*, pg. 3103
CHOICE GENETICS DEUTSCHLAND GMBH—See Groupe Grimaud La Corbiere SA; *Int'l*, pg. 3103
CHOICE GENETICS POLSKA SP Z O.O.—See Groupe Grimaud La Corbiere SA; *Int'l*, pg. 3103
CHOICE GENETICS SAS—See Groupe Grimaud La Corbiere SA; *Int'l*, pg. 3103
CHOICE GENETICS VIETNAM—See Groupe Grimaud La Corbiere SA; *Int'l*, pg. 3103
THE CHOICE GROUP, LLC; *U.S. Private*, pg. 4009
CHOICE HEALTH AT HOME, LLC—See Coltala Holdings, LLC; *U.S. Private*, pg. 976
CHOICE HOME WARRANTY; *U.S. Private*, pg. 888
CHOICE HOTELS ASIA-PAC PTY. LTD.—See Choice Hotels International, Inc.; *U.S. Public*, pg. 489
CHOICE HOTELS AUSTRALASIA PTY. LTD.—See Choice Hotels International, Inc.; *U.S. Public*, pg. 489
CHOICE HOTELS CANADA, INC.—See Choice Hotels International, Inc.; *U.S. Public*, pg. 489
CHOICE HOTELS FRANCE, S.A.S—See Choice Hotels International, Inc.; *U.S. Public*, pg. 490
CHOICE HOTELS FRANCHISE, GMBH—See Choice Hotels International, Inc.; *U.S. Public*, pg. 490
CHOICE HOTELS INTERNATIONAL, INC.; *U.S. Public*, pg. 489
CHOICE HOTELS INTERNATIONAL SERVICES CORP—See Choice Hotels International, Inc.; *U.S. Public*, pg. 490
CHOICE HOTELS LIMITED—See Choice Hotels International, Inc.; *U.S. Public*, pg. 490
CHOICE INTERNATIONAL LIMITED; *Int'l*, pg. 1577
CHOICE LOGISTICS INC.; *U.S. Private*, pg. 888
CHOICELUNCH; *U.S. Private*, pg. 888
CHOICEMARK INSURANCE SERVICES, INC.—See SelectQuote, Inc.; *U.S. Public*, pg. 1863
CHOICE MINISTRIES INC.; *U.S. Private*, pg. 888
CHOICE N.V.; *Int'l*, pg. 1577
CHOICEONE BANK—See ChoiceOne Financial Services, Inc.; *U.S. Public*, pg. 490
CHOICEONE FINANCIAL SERVICES, INC.; *U.S. Public*, pg. 490

CHOICE PROPERTIES REAL ESTATE INVESTMENT TRUST—See George Weston Limited; *Int'l*, pg. 2938
CHOICE PUBLISHING LTD—See Heinrich Bauer Verlag KG; *Int'l*, pg. 3323
CHOICE RECOVERY, INC.—See Wakefield & Associates, LLC; *U.S. Private*, pg. 4427
CHOICE REEFER SYSTEMS—See Eassons Transport Limited; *Int'l*, pg. 2269
CHOICES GROUP, INC.—See ATAR Capital, LLC; *U.S. Private*, pg. 364
CHOICES MARKETS LTD.; *Int'l*, pg. 1577
CHOICES OF LOUISIANA, INC.—See Webster Equity Partners, LLC; *U.S. Private*, pg. 4466
CHOICE SOLUTIONS, INC.—See Veritas Capital Fund Management, LLC; *U.S. Private*, pg. 4363
CHOICE SOLUTIONS LLC; *U.S. Private*, pg. 888
CHOICE SPINE, LLC—See Altus Capital Partners, Inc.; *U.S. Private*, pg. 211
CHOICE THERAPEUTICS, INC.—See Adynxx, Inc.; *U.S. Public*, pg. 50
CHOICE USA BEVERAGE INC.; *U.S. Private*, pg. 888
CHOICE VACATION RENTALS LLC—See Choice Hotels International, Inc.; *U.S. Public*, pg. 490
CHOI FOOK SEAFOOD RESTAURANT LIMITED—See Net-a-Go Technology Company Limited; *Int'l*, pg. 5212
CHOIL ALUMINUM CO., LTD.; *Int'l*, pg. 1577
CHOKO CO., LTD.—See Nagase & Co., Ltd.; *Int'l*, pg. 5126
CHOKSI ASIA PRIVATE LIMITED; *Int'l*, pg. 1577
CHOKSI IMAGING LTD.; *Int'l*, pg. 1577
CHOKSI LABORATORIES LIMITED; *Int'l*, pg. 1577
CHOKUHAN HAISOU CO., LTD.—See MEGMILK SNOW BRAND Co., Ltd.; *Int'l*, pg. 4796
CHOKWANG JOTUN LTD.—See Jotun A/S; *Int'l*, pg. 4002
CHOKWANG LEATHER CO., LTD.; *Int'l*, pg. 1577
CHOKWANG PAINT CO., LTD.; *Int'l*, pg. 1577
CHOKWANG VINA CO., LTD.—See Chokwang Paint Co., Ltd.; *Int'l*, pg. 1578
CHOLAMANDALAM FINANCIAL HOLDINGS LIMITED; *Int'l*, pg. 1578
CHOLAMANDALAM INVESTMENT & FINANCE COMPANY LTD.—See The Murugappa Group, Ltd.; *Int'l*, pg. 7668
CHOLAMANDALAM MS RISK SERVICES LIMITED—See MS&AD Insurance Group Holdings, Inc.; *Int'l*, pg. 5065
CHOLSIN COMPANY LIMITED—See Tongkah Harbour Public Company Limited; *Int'l*, pg. 7808
CHOMERICS DIVISION-EUROPE—See Parker Hannifin Corporation; *U.S. Public*, pg. 1648
CHOMERICS - MEXICO—See Parker Hannifin Corporation; *U.S. Public*, pg. 1649
THE CHOMTHANA COMPANY LIMITED—See Inner Mongolia Yili Industrial Group Co., Ltd.; *Int'l*, pg. 3708
CHONBANG AUTO CO., LTD.—See Chonbang Co., Ltd.; *Int'l*, pg. 1578
CHONBANG CO., LTD. - GWANGJU FACTORY—See Chonbang Co., Ltd.; *Int'l*, pg. 1578
CHONBANG CO., LTD.; *Int'l*, pg. 1578
CHONBANG CO., LTD. - YOUNGAM FACTORY—See Chonbang Co., Ltd.; *Int'l*, pg. 1578
CHONBURI CONCRETE PRODUCT PUBLIC COMPANY LIMITED; *Int'l*, pg. 1578
CHONBURI KANYONG CO., LTD.—See Chonburi Concrete Product Public Company Limited; *Int'l*, pg. 1578
CHONCHE GROUP NANJING NO.7425 FACTORY—See China National Chemical Corporation; *Int'l*, pg. 1527
CHONGDE LOU HOTEL CO.—See Huangshan Tourism Development Co., Ltd.; *Int'l*, pg. 3513
CHONG FAI JEWELLERY GROUP HOLDINGS COMPANY LIMITED; *Int'l*, pg. 1578
CHONGHERR INVESTMENTS LTD.; *Int'l*, pg. 1578
CHONG HING BANK LIMITED—See Yue Xiu Enterprises (Holdings) Limited; *Int'l*, pg. 8610
CHONG HING COMMODITIES & FUTURES LIMITED—See Yue Xiu Enterprises (Holdings) Limited; *Int'l*, pg. 8610
CHONG HING GOLDSMITH CORP.; *U.S. Private*, pg. 888
CHONG HING INFORMATION TECHNOLOGY LIMITED—See Yue Xiu Enterprises (Holdings) Limited; *Int'l*, pg. 8610
CHONG HING INSURANCE COMPANY LIMITED—See Yue Xiu Enterprises (Holdings) Limited; *Int'l*, pg. 8610
CHONG HING SECURITIES LIMITED—See Yue Xiu Enterprises (Holdings) Limited; *Int'l*, pg. 8610
CHONG HONG CONSTRUCTION CO., LTD.; *Int'l*, pg. 1578
CHONG KIN GROUP HOLDINGS LIMITED; *Int'l*, pg. 1578
CHONG KUN DANG BIO CO., LTD. - ANSAN PLANT—See Chong Kun Dang Holdings Corp.; *Int'l*, pg. 1578
CHONG KUN DANG BIO CO., LTD.—See Chong Kun Dang Holdings Corp.; *Int'l*, pg. 1578
CHONG KUN DANG HEALTHCARE CORP. - DANGJIN-GUN FACTORY—See Chong Kun Dang Holdings Corp.; *Int'l*, pg. 1578
CHONG KUN DANG HEALTHCARE CORP.—See Chong Kun Dang Holdings Corp.; *Int'l*, pg. 1578
CHONG KUN DANG HOLDINGS CORP.; *Int'l*, pg. 1578

CHONG KUNDANG INDUSTRIAL CO., LTD.—See Chong Kun Dang Holdings Corp.; *Int'l*, pg. 1578
CHONG KUN DANG INDUSTRY CO., LTD.—See Kyongbo Pharmaceutical Co., Ltd.; *Int'l*, pg. 4364
CHONG KUN DANG PHARMACEUTICAL CORP. - CHEO-NAN FACTORY—See Chong Kun Dang Holdings Corp.; *Int'l*, pg. 1578
CHONG KUN DANG PHARMACEUTICAL CORP.—See Chong Kun Dang Holdings Corp.; *Int'l*, pg. 1578
CHONG LOONG TRADING CO., LTD.—See USI Corporation; *Int'l*, pg. 8098
CHONGQING AEROSPACE NEW CENTURY SATELLITE APPLICATION TECHNOLOGY CO., LTD.—See Aerosun Corporation; *Int'l*, pg. 182
CHONGQING AIRLINES COMPANY LIMITED—See China Southern Airlines Co., Ltd.; *Int'l*, pg. 1553
CHONGQING AN DAO EDUCATION CONSULTING LIMITED—See NIIT Limited; *Int'l*, pg. 5288
CHONGQING ANJIE ELECTRONICS CO., LTD.—See Suzhou Anjie Technology Co., Ltd.; *Int'l*, pg. 7349
CHONGQING BAIYA SANITARY PRODUCTS CO., LTD.; *Int'l*, pg. 1579
CHONGQING BISHAN ICBC RURAL BANK CO., LTD—See Industrial & Commercial Bank of China Limited; *Int'l*, pg. 3669
CHONGQING BOE OPTOELECTRONICS TECHNOLOGY CO., LTD.—See BOE Technology Group Co., Ltd.; *Int'l*, pg. 1099
CHONGQING BOW CHUANG MOTOR SALES & SERVICES CO. LTD.—See Sime Darby Berhad; *Int'l*, pg. 6928
CHONGQING BREWERY CO., LTD; *Int'l*, pg. 1579
CHONGQING BROADWAY FOAM APPLICATIONS & TOTAL PACKAGING CO., LTD.—See Platinum Equity, LLC; *U.S. Private*, pg. 3201
CHONGQING CAFF AUTOMOTIVE BRAKING & STEERING SYSTEM CO., LTD.—See Chongqing Machinery & Electronics Holding (Group) Co., Ltd.; *Int'l*, pg. 1580
CHONGQING CASIN GROUP CO., LTD.; *Int'l*, pg. 1579
CHONGQING CEC-TECHNOLOGY LIMITED—See CEC International Holdings Limited; *Int'l*, pg. 1372
CHONGQING CHANGAN AUTOMOBILE COMPANY LTD.; *Int'l*, pg. 1579
CHONGQING CHANGAN SUZUKI AUTOMOBILE CO., LTD.—See Chongqing Changan Automobile Company Ltd.; *Int'l*, pg. 1579
CHONGQING CHANGHUA AUTOMOBILE HARNESS CO., LTD.—See The Furukawa Electric Co., Ltd.; *Int'l*, pg. 7644
CHONGQING CHANGJIANG RIVER MOULDING MATERIAL CHANGZHOU CO., LTD.—See Chongqing Changjiang River Moulding Material (Group) Co., Ltd.; *Int'l*, pg. 1579
CHONGQING CHANGJIANG RIVER MOULDING MATERIAL CHENGDU CO., LTD.—See Chongqing Changjiang River Moulding Material (Group) Co., Ltd.; *Int'l*, pg. 1579
CHONGQING CHANGJIANG RIVER MOULDING MATERIAL (GROUP) CO., LTD.; *Int'l*, pg. 1579
CHONGQING CHANGJIANG RIVER MOULDING MATERIAL KUNSHAN CO., LTD.—See Chongqing Changjiang River Moulding Material (Group) Co., Ltd.; *Int'l*, pg. 1579
CHONGQING CHANGJIANG RIVER MOULDING MATERIAL SHIYAN CO., LTD.—See Chongqing Changjiang River Moulding Material (Group) Co., Ltd.; *Int'l*, pg. 1579
CHONGQING CHANGJIANG RIVER MOULDING MATERIAL XIANTAO CO., LTD.—See Chongqing Changjiang River Moulding Material (Group) Co., Ltd.; *Int'l*, pg. 1579
CHONGQING CHANGTAI AUTO PARTS CO., LTD.—See Minth Group Limited; *Int'l*, pg. 4914
CHONGQING CHANGTENG AUTO PARTS MANUFACTURING CO., LTD.—See Changzhou Tenglong Auto Parts Co., Ltd.; *Int'l*, pg. 1445
CHONGQING CHEMETALL CHEMICALS CO., LTD.—See Albemarle Corporation; *U.S. Public*, pg. 73
CHONGQING CHENG LOONG PAPER CO., LTD.—See Cheng Loong Corp.; *Int'l*, pg. 1466
CHONGQING CHINA INTERNATIONAL TRAVEL SERVICE CO., LTD.—See China Tourism Group Duty Free Corporation Limited; *Int'l*, pg. 1560
CHONGQING CHUANYI AUTOMATION CO., LTD.; *Int'l*, pg. 1579
CHONGQING CHUANYI METALLIC FUNCTIONAL MATERIALS CO., LTD.—See Chongqing Chuanyi Automation Co., Ltd.; *Int'l*, pg. 1579
CHONGQING CONSTRUCTION ENGING GRP CO LTD; *Int'l*, pg. 1579
CHONGQING CQPLUS1 TECHNOLOGY CO., LTD.—See Sunplus Technology Co., Ltd.; *Int'l*, pg. 7320
CHONGQING CYUNSIANG HIGH-TECH CO., LTD.—See Nidec Chaun-Choung Technology Corporation; *Int'l*, pg. 5274
CHONGQING DAQO NEW ENERGY CO., LTD.—See Daqo New Energy Corp.; *Int'l*, pg. 1971

CHONGQING DAZU RED BUTTERFLY STRONTIUM INDUSTRY CO., LTD.—See Guizhou Redstar Development Co., Ltd.; *Int'l*, pg. 3175
CHONGQING DAZU RED BUTTERFLY STRONTIUM INDUSTRY CO., LTD. - YONGXI FACTORY—See Guizhou Redstar Development Co., Ltd.; *Int'l*, pg. 3175
CHONGQING DEPARTMENT STORE CO., LTD.; *Int'l*, pg. 1579
CHONGQING DIMA INDUSTRY CO., LTD.; *Int'l*, pg. 1579
CHONGQING ECO-CTIG RUBBER TECHNOLOGY CO., LTD.—See ecoWise Holdings Limited; *Int'l*, pg. 2300
CHONGQING ELECTRONICS LIMITED—See Central Wealth Group Holdings Limited; *Int'l*, pg. 1410
CHONGQING ENDURANCE & SHINMAYWA INDUSTRIES, LTD.—See ShinMaywa Industries, Ltd.; *Int'l*, pg. 6846
CHONGQING ENDURANCE & TOKYO KEISO INSTRUMENT CO., LTD.—See Tokyo Keiso Co., Ltd.; *Int'l*, pg. 7792
CHONGQING FULFIL TECH CO., LTD.—See Syncmold Enterprise Corp.; *Int'l*, pg. 7382
CHONGQING FULING ELECTRIC POWER INDUSTRIAL CO., LTD.; *Int'l*, pg. 1579
CHONGQING FULING ZHACAI GROUP CO., LTD.; *Int'l*, pg. 1579
CHONGQING FUMANDUO FOOD CO., LTD.—See Tingyi (Cayman Islands) Holding Corp.; *Int'l*, pg. 7754
CHONGQING FUTABA AUTO PARTS CO., LTD.—See Futaba Industrial Co., Ltd.; *Int'l*, pg. 2851
CHONGQING GAS COMPRESSOR FACTORY CO., LTD.—See Chongqing Machinery & Electronics Holding (Group) Co., Ltd.; *Int'l*, pg. 1580
CHONGQING GAS GROUP CORPORATION LTD.; *Int'l*, pg. 1579
CHONGQING GENERAL INDUSTRY (GROUP) CO., LTD—See Chongqing Machinery & Electronics Holding (Group) Co., Ltd.; *Int'l*, pg. 1580
CHONGQING GUANGJING PACKAGING MATERIALS CO. LTD—See Teamway International Group Holdings Limited; *Int'l*, pg. 7501
CHONGQING HAONENG XINGFU SYNCHRONIZER CO., LTD.—See Chengdu Haoneng Technology Co., Ltd.; *Int'l*, pg. 1468
CHONGQING HELICOPTER INVESTMENT CO. LTD.; *Int'l*, pg. 1579
CHONGQING HEXIN PACKAGING PRINTING CO., LTD.—See Xiamen Hexing Packaging Printing Co., Ltd.; *Int'l*, pg. 8524
CHONGQING HI-LEX CABLE SYSTEM GROUP CO., LTD.—See Hi-Lex Corporation; *Int'l*, pg. 3380
CHONGQING HI-LEX CONTROL CABLE SYSTEM CO LTD.—See Hi-Lex Corporation; *Int'l*, pg. 3380
CHONGQING HONGJIN PRINTING CO., LTD.—See Shenzhen Jinjia Group Co., Ltd.; *Int'l*, pg. 6814
CHONGQING HONGJIU FRUIT CO., LTD.; *Int'l*, pg. 1579
CHONGQING HONGLIN TECHNOLOGY CO., LTD.—See InvesTech Holdings Limited; *Int'l*, pg. 3777
CHONGQING HUAYU LANDSCAPE & ARCHITECTURE CO., LTD.—See Shandong Chiway Industry Development Co., Ltd.; *Int'l*, pg. 6752
CHONGQING HUA-YU STANLEY ELECTRIC CO., LTD.—See Stanley Electric Co., Ltd.; *Int'l*, pg. 7170
CHONGQING HUF AUTOMOTIVE SYSTEMS CO., LTD.—See Huf Hulsbeck & Furst GmbH & Co. KG; *Int'l*, pg. 3523
CHONGQING IRON & STEEL CO LTD; *Int'l*, pg. 1579
CHONGQING JIAFU CONTAINER CO., LTD.—See Zhuhai Zhongfu Enterprise Co., Ltd.; *Int'l*, pg. 8678
CHONGQING JIANSHE VEHICLE SYSTEM CO., LTD.; *Int'l*, pg. 1580
CHONGQING JING XING PACKAGING CO., LTD.—See Zhejiang Jingxing Paper Joint Stock Co., Ltd.; *Int'l*, pg. 8658
CHONGQING JINTIAN COPPER CO., LTD.—See Ningbo Jintian Copper (Group) Co., Ltd.; *Int'l*, pg. 5302
CHONGQING JIN-ZHU WIRING SYSTEMS CO., LTD.—See Sumitomo Electric Industries, Ltd.; *Int'l*, pg. 7277
CHONGQING KANGLE PHARMACEUTICAL CO., LTD.—See Kontafarma China Holdings Limited; *Int'l*, pg. 4276
CHONGQING KANSAI PAINT CO., LTD.—See Kansai Paint Co., Ltd.; *Int'l*, pg. 4071
CHONGQING LEE & MAN PAPER MANUFACTURING LIMITED—See Lee & Man Paper Manufacturing Limited; *Int'l*, pg. 4440
CHONGQING LIFAN INDUSTRY (GROUP) IMP. & EXP. CO., LTD.; *Int'l*, pg. 1580
CHONGQING L.K. MACHINERY CO., LTD.—See L.K. Technology Holdings Limited; *Int'l*, pg. 4386
CHONGQING LUMMY PHARMACEUTICAL CO., LTD.; *Int'l*, pg. 1580
CHONGQING MACHINERY & ELECTRIC CO., LTD.—See Chongqing Machinery & Electronics Holding (Group) Co., Ltd.; *Int'l*, pg. 1580
CHONGQING MACHINERY & ELECTRONICS HOLDING (GROUP) CO., LTD.; *Int'l*, pg. 1580

CHONGQING MACHINE TOOLS (GROUP) CO., LTD.—See Chongqing Machinery & Electronics Holding (Group) Co., Ltd.; *Int'l*, pg. 1580
CHONGQING MAS GEYI SCIENCE & TECHNOLOGY CO., LTD.—See Chongqing MAS Sci. & Tech. Co., Ltd.; *Int'l*, pg. 1580
CHONGQING MAS SCI. & TECH. CO., LTD.; *Int'l*, pg. 1580
CHONGQING METROPOLITAN PLAZA PACIFIC DEPARTMENT STORE CO. LTD.—See The Far Eastern Group; *Int'l*, pg. 7641
CHONGQING MYS ENVIRONMENTAL PROTECTION & TECHNOLOGY COMPANY LTD.—See MYS Group Co., Ltd.; *Int'l*, pg. 5113
CHONGQING PCI TECHNOLOGY&SERVICE CO., LTD.—See PCI Technology Group Co, Ltd; *Int'l*, pg. 5768
CHONGQING PHARSCIN PHARMACEUTICAL CO., LTD.; *Int'l*, pg. 1580
CHONGQING PIGEON ELECTRIC WIRES & CABLES CO., LTD.—See Chongqing Machinery & Electronics Holding (Group) Co., Ltd.; *Int'l*, pg. 1580
CHONGQING POLY INTERNATIONAL CINEMA—See China Poly Group Corporation; *Int'l*, pg. 1541
CHONGQING POLY THEATRE MANAGEMENT CORPORATION LIMITED—See Poly Culture Group Corporation Limited; *Int'l*, pg. 5913
CHONGQING POLY WANHE CINEMA CHAIN CO., LTD.—See China Poly Group Corporation; *Int'l*, pg. 1541
CHONGQING PORT CO., LTD.; *Int'l*, pg. 1580
CHONGQING PUMP INDUSTRY CO., LTD.—See Chongqing Machinery & Electronics Holding (Group) Co., Ltd.; *Int'l*, pg. 1580
CHONGQING QIN'AN M&E PLC.; *Int'l*, pg. 1580
CHONGQING QINGLING CASTING CO., LTD—See Qingling Motors (Group) Co. Ltd.; *Int'l*, pg. 6145
CHONGQING QINGZHU MACHINERY MANUFACTURING CO., LTD.—See Chengdu Haoneng Technology Co., Ltd.; *Int'l*, pg. 1468
CHONGQING ROAD & BRIDGE CO., LTD.; *Int'l*, pg. 1580
CHONGQING RUIREN ELECTRONIC CO., LTD.—See Shenzhen Deren Electronic Co., Ltd.; *Int'l*, pg. 6807
CHONGQING RURAL COMMERCIAL BANK CO., LTD.; *Int'l*, pg. 1580
CHONGQING SANFENG ENVIRONMENT GROUP CORP., LTD.; *Int'l*, pg. 1581
CHONGQING SANTEN KERUI PHARMACEUTICAL CO., LTD.—See Santen Pharmaceutical Co., Ltd.; *Int'l*, pg. 6557
CHONGQING SANXIA PAINTS CO., LTD.; *Int'l*, pg. 1581
CHONGQING SEJONG AUTO PARTS CO., LTD.—See SJG Sejong Co., Ltd.; *Int'l*, pg. 6969
CHONGQING SHAGANG MODERN LOGISTICS CO., LTD.—See Jiangsu Shagang Group Ltd.; *Int'l*, pg. 3954
CHONGQING SHUNBO ALUMINUM CO., LTD.; *Int'l*, pg. 1581
CHONGQING SIFANG NEW MATERIAL CO., LTD.; *Int'l*, pg. 1581
CHONGQING SKYMAN INDUSTRY (GROUP) CO., LTD.; *Int'l*, pg. 1581
CHONGQING SNR TECHNOLOGY CO., LTD.—See Sinher Technology Inc.; *Int'l*, pg. 6945
CHONGQING STORSACK JIANFENG—See Greif Inc.; *U.S. Public*, pg. 967
CHONGQING SUMISHO YUNXIN LOGISTICS CO., LTD.—See Sumitomo Corporation; *Int'l*, pg. 7268
CHONGQING SUNGWON AUTOMATIVE TECHHNOLOGY CO., LTD.—See Sewon Precision Industry Co., Ltd.; *Int'l*, pg. 6737
CHONGQING SUNGWOO AUTOMOTIVE TECHNOLOGY CO., LTD.—See SEWON CORPORATION Co., Ltd.; *Int'l*, pg. 6736
CHONGQING SUNGWOO HITECH AUTOMOTIVE PARTS CO., LTD.—See Sungwoo Hitech Co., Ltd.; *Int'l*, pg. 7315
CHONGQING SYP ENGINEERING GLASS CO., LTD.—See Shanghai Yaohua Pilkington Glass Group Co., Ltd.; *Int'l*, pg. 6782
CHONGQING TAIJI INDUSTRY (GROUP) CO., LTD.; *Int'l*, pg. 1581
CHONGQING THREE GORGES WATER CONSERVANCY AND ELECTRIC POWER CO., LTD.; *Int'l*, pg. 1581
CHONGQING TIANBANG FOOD CO. LIMITED—See Summi (Group) Holdings Limited; *Int'l*, pg. 7301
CHONGQING TINGJIN FOOD CO., LTD.—See Tingyi (Cayman Islands) Holding Corp.; *Int'l*, pg. 7754
CHONGQING TINGYI FOOD CO., LTD.—See Tingyi (Cayman Islands) Holding Corp.; *Int'l*, pg. 7754
CHONGQING TRANSPORTATION MATERIALS GROUP CO., LTD.—See NICHIREKI CO., Ltd.; *Int'l*, pg. 5270
CHONGQING VDL ELECTRONICS CO., LTD.; *Int'l*, pg. 1581
CHONGQING WANLI NEW ENERGY CO., LTD.; *Int'l*, pg. 1581
CHONGQING WANYOU PARKSON PLAZA CO LTD—See Parkson Holdings Berhad; *Int'l*, pg. 5744
CHONGQING WATER GROUP CO., LTD.; *Int'l*, pg. 1581
CHONGQING WEIFU LIDA AUTOMOBILE COMPONENTS CO., LTD.—See Wuxi Weifu High-technology Co., Ltd.; *Int'l*, pg. 8516
CHONGQING WOTE ZHICHENG ADVANCED MATERIALS TECHNOLOGY CO., LTD.—See Shenzhen Wote Advanced Materials Co., Ltd.; *Int'l*, pg. 6824
CHONGQING XINFU FOOD CO., LTD.—See COFCO Limited; *Int'l*, pg. 1692
CHONGQING XINWEI TELECOM TECHNOLOGY CO., LTD.—See Beijing Xinwei Technology Group Co., Ltd.; *Int'l*, pg. 961
CHONGQING YONGXIN TECHNOLOGY CO., LTD.—See Wuhu Token Sciences Co., Ltd.; *Int'l*, pg. 8502
CHONGQING YOU YOU FOODS SALES CO., LTD.—See YouYou Foods Co., Ltd.; *Int'l*, pg. 8604
CHONGQING YUANLI TECHNOLOGY CO., LTD.—See Yuanli Chemical Group Co., Ltd.; *Int'l*, pg. 8608
CHONGQING YUKAIFA CO., LTD.; *Int'l*, pg. 1581
CHONGQING YUNDA TECHNOLOGY CO., LTD.—See Shenzhen Jasic Technology Co., Ltd.; *Int'l*, pg. 6814
CHONGQING YUXIN PINGRUI ELECTRONIC CO., LTD.; *Int'l*, pg. 1581
CHONGQING YUZHONG XINHAOJUN REAL ESTATE DEVELOPMENT CO., LTD.—See Hong Leong Investment Holdings Pte. Ltd.; *Int'l*, pg. 3468
CHONGQING ZAISHENG TECHNOLOGY CORP., LTD.; *Int'l*, pg. 1581
CHONGQING ZHENGCHUAN PHARMACEUTICAL PACKAGING CO., LTD.; *Int'l*, pg. 1581
CHONGQING ZHENGCHUAN YONGCHENG PHARMACEUTICAL MATERIAL CO., LTD.—See Chongqing Zhengchuan Pharmaceutical Packaging Co., Ltd.; *Int'l*, pg. 1582
CHONGQING ZHIFEI BIOLOGICAL PRODUCTS CO.,LTD; *Int'l*, pg. 1582
CHONGQING ZHONGFU IN-LINE CONTAINER CO. LTD.—See Zhuhai Zhongfu Enterprise Co., Ltd.; *Int'l*, pg. 8679
CHONGQING YIBOHUTONG TECH CO., LTD.—See Beyondsoft Corporation; *Int'l*, pg. 1005
CHONG SHAN SINON AGRICULTURE SERVICE CO., LTD.—See Sinon Corporation; *Int'l*, pg. 6953
CHONG SING HOLDINGS FINTECH GROUP LIMITED; *Int'l*, pg. 1578
CHONG-WAH NTIA SDN. BHD.—See Chong Wah Plastics Sdn Bhd; *Int'l*, pg. 1578
CHONG-WAH NTIA SDN. BHD.—See Northern Technologies International Corporation; *U.S. Public*, pg. 1637
CHONG WAH PLASTICS SDN BHD; *Int'l*, pg. 1578
CHONGYI ZHANGYUAN TUNGSTEN CO., LTD.; *Int'l*, pg. 1582
CHONNAM CITY GAS CO., LTD.—See SK Innovation Co., Ltd.; *Int'l*, pg. 6973
CHOO BEE HARDWARE (SABAH) SDN. BHD.—See Choo Bee Metal Industries Berhad; *Int'l*, pg. 1582
CHOO BEE HARDWARES SDN. BERHAD—See Choo Bee Metal Industries Berhad; *Int'l*, pg. 1582
CHOO BEE METAL INDUSTRIES BERHAD; *Int'l*, pg. 1582
CHOO CHIANG HOLDINGS LTD.; *Int'l*, pg. 1582
CHOO CHOO PARTNERS L.P.; *U.S. Private*, pg. 888
CHOOLET S.A.—See Industria de Diseno Textil, S.A.; *Int'l*, pg. 3665
CHOONGANG VACCINE LABORATORY CO., LTD.; *Int'l*, pg. 1582
CHOOSE NETWORKS, INC.—See Frontenac Company LLC; *U.S. Private*, pg. 1614
CHOO WAN LING WOMEN'S CLINIC PTE. LTD.—See Singapore O&G Ltd.; *Int'l*, pg. 6941
CHOP AIK SENG SDN. BHD.—See Hai-O Enterprise Berhad; *Int'l*, pg. 3209
CHOPARD (ASIA) PTE LTD—See Chopard & Cie S.A.; *Int'l*, pg. 1582
CHOPARD AUTOMOBILES SAS; *Int'l*, pg. 1582
CHOPARD & CIE S.A.; *Int'l*, pg. 1582
CHOPARD DEUTSCHLAND GMBH—See Chopard & Cie S.A.; *Int'l*, pg. 1582
CHOPARD (GREAT BRITAIN) LTD—See Chopard & Cie S.A.; *Int'l*, pg. 1582
CHOPARD HONG KONG LTD—See Chopard & Cie S.A.; *Int'l*, pg. 1582
CHOPARD IBERICA S,L—See Chopard & Cie S.A.; *Int'l*, pg. 1582
CHOPARD ITALIA S.R.L—See Chopard & Cie S.A.; *Int'l*, pg. 1582
CHOPARD JAPAN LTD—See Chopard & Cie S.A.; *Int'l*, pg. 1582
CHOPARD MALAYSIA SDN BHD—See Chopard & Cie S.A.; *Int'l*, pg. 1582
CHOPARD MARKETING SERVICES, INC—See Chopard & Cie S.A.; *Int'l*, pg. 1582
CHOPARD TRADING (SHANGHAI) CO. LTD—See Chopard & Cie S.A.; *Int'l*, pg. 1582
CHOPARD UHRENHANDELS GMBH—See Chopard & Cie S.A.; *Int'l*, pg. 1582
CHOPARD USA LTD.—See Chopard & Cie S.A.; *Int'l*, pg. 1582
CHO-PAT—See Medi-Dyne Healthcare Products Ltd.; *U.S. Private*, pg. 2651
CHO PHARMA, INC.; *Int'l*, pg. 1576
CHOPPER TRADING LLC—See DRW Holdings, LLC; *U.S. Private*, pg. 1280
CHOPPIES ENTERPRISES KENYA LIMITED—See Choppies Enterprises Ltd.; *Int'l*, pg. 1582
CHOPPIES ENTERPRISES LTD.; *Int'l*, pg. 1582
CHOPPIES SUPERMARKET MOZAMBIQUE LIMITADA—See Choppies Enterprises Ltd.; *Int'l*, pg. 1582
CHOPPIES SUPERMARKETS LIMITED—See Choppies Enterprises Ltd.; *Int'l*, pg. 1582
CHOPPIES SUPERMARKETS NAMIBIA (PTY) LTD—See Choppies Enterprises Ltd.; *Int'l*, pg. 1582
CHOPPIES SUPERMARKETS TANZANIA LIMITED—See Choppies Enterprises Ltd.; *Int'l*, pg. 1582
CHOPTANK COMMUNITY HEALTH SYSTEM, INC.; *U.S. Private*, pg. 888
CHOPTANK ELECTRIC COOPERATIVE, INC.; *U.S. Private*, pg. 888
CHOPTANK TRANSPORT INC—See Hub Group, Inc.; *U.S. Public*, pg. 1065
CHOQI CO., LTD.—See EM Systems Co., Ltd.; *Int'l*, pg. 2372
CHORD ENERGY CORPORATION; *U.S. Public*, pg. 490
CHORDIA FOOD PRODUCTS LTD.; *Int'l*, pg. 1582
CHORDOMA FOUNDATION; *U.S. Private*, pg. 888
CHORE-TIME/BROCK INTERNATIONAL—See Berkshire Hathaway Inc.; *U.S. Public*, pg. 303
CHORE-TIME CAGE SYSTEMS—See Berkshire Hathaway Inc.; *U.S. Public*, pg. 303
CHORE-TIME EQUIPMENT—See Berkshire Hathaway Inc.; *U.S. Public*, pg. 303
CHORI AMERICA, INC.—See Chori Co., Ltd.; *Int'l*, pg. 1583
CHORI ANALYSIS & TECHNOLOGY SERVICE (SUZHOU)CO., LTD.—See Chori Co., Ltd.; *Int'l*, pg. 1583
CHORI (CHINA) CO., LTD.—See Chori Co., Ltd.; *Int'l*, pg. 1583
CHORI CO. (HONG KONG) LTD.—See Chori Co., Ltd.; *Int'l*, pg. 1583
CHORI CO., LTD.; *Int'l*, pg. 1583
CHORI COMERCIAL DE MEXICO S.A. DE C.V.—See Chori Co., Ltd.; *Int'l*, pg. 1583
CHORI (DALIAN) COMMERCIAL IMPORT EXPORT CO., LTD.—See Chori Co., Ltd.; *Int'l*, pg. 1583
CHORI (DALIAN) TRADING CO., LTD.—See Chori Co., Ltd.; *Int'l*, pg. 1583
CHORI EUROPE GMBH—See Chori Co., Ltd.; *Int'l*, pg. 1583
CHORI FASHION NETWORK CO., LTD.—See Chori Co., Ltd.; *Int'l*, pg. 1583
CHORI GLEX CO., LTD.—See Chori Co., Ltd.; *Int'l*, pg. 1583
CHORI IMAGING CORPORATION—See Chori Co., Ltd.; *Int'l*, pg. 1583
CHORI KOREA CO., LTD.—See Chori Co., Ltd.; *Int'l*, pg. 1583
CHORI MACHINERY CO., LTD.—See Chori Co., Ltd.; *Int'l*, pg. 1583
CHORI MIDDLE EAST FZE—See Chori Co., Ltd.; *Int'l*, pg. 1583
CHORI MODA CO., LTD.—See Chori Co., Ltd.; *Int'l*, pg. 1583
CHORI SHANGHAI LTD.—See Chori Co., Ltd.; *Int'l*, pg. 1583
CHORI SINGAPORE PTE. LTD.—See Chori Co., Ltd.; *Int'l*, pg. 1583
CHORI (TIANJIN) CO., LTD.—See Chori Co., Ltd.; *Int'l*, pg. 1583
CHORI TRADING INDIA PTE. LTD.—See Chori Co., Ltd.; *Int'l*, pg. 1583
CHORI TRADING MALAYSIA SDN BHD—See Chori Co., Ltd.; *Int'l*, pg. 1583
CHORI URBAN DEVELOPMENT CO., LTD.—See Chori Co., Ltd.; *Int'l*, pg. 1583
CHORI VIETNAM CO., LTD.—See Chori Co., Ltd.; *Int'l*, pg. 1583
CHOROKBAEM COMPANY CO., LTD.; *Int'l*, pg. 1583
CHORUS AVIATION INC.; *Int'l*, pg. 1584
CHORUS CALL AUSTRALIA PTY LTD.—See Chorus Call, Inc.; *U.S. Private*, pg. 889
CHORUS CALL CANADA CORP.—See Chorus Call, Inc.; *U.S. Private*, pg. 889
CHORUS CALL CONFERENCING SERVICES INDIA PRIVATE LTD.—See Chorus Call, Inc.; *U.S. Private*, pg. 889
CHORUS CALL CONFERENCING SERVICES INDIA PRIVATE LTD.—See Chorus Call, Inc.; *U.S. Private*, pg. 889
CHORUS CALL GERMANY GMBH—See Chorus Call, Inc.; *U.S. Private*, pg. 889
CHORUS CALL HELLAS A.E.—See Chorus Call, Inc.; *U.S. Private*, pg. 889
CHORUS CALL, INC.; *U.S. Private*, pg. 888
CHORUS CALL ITALIA S.R.L.—See Chorus Call, Inc.; *U.S. Private*, pg. 889
CHORUS CALL (PTY) LTD.—See Chorus Call, Inc.; *U.S. Private*, pg. 888

COMPANY NAME INDEX

CHORUS CALL SA—See Chorus Call, Inc.; *U.S. Private*, pg. 889
CHORUS COMMUNICATIONS, INC.; *U.S. Private*, pg. 889
CHORUS GIRL INC.; *U.S. Private*, pg. 889
CHORUS LIMITED; *Int'l*, pg. 1584
CHORYO DESIGNING CO., LTD.—See Mitsubishi Heavy Industries, Ltd.; *Int'l*, pg. 4953
CHORYO SENPAKU KOUJI CO., LTD.—See Mitsubishi Heavy Industries, Ltd.; *Int'l*, pg. 4953
CHOR YOUTH AND FAMILY SERVICES, INC.; *U.S. Private*, pg. 888
CHOSA ONCOLOGY AB; *Int'l*, pg. 1584
CHOSEIDO PHARMACEUTICAL CO., LTD.—See Nihon Chouzai Co., Ltd.; *Int'l*, pg. 5283
CHOSEN FOODS LLC—See Butterfly Equity LP; *U.S. Private*, pg. 698
THE CHOSEN, INC.; *U.S. Private*, pg. 4009
CHOSHI TOYO KAISHA, LTD.—See Toyo Suisan Kaisha, Ltd.; *Int'l*, pg. 7858
CHOSUN REFRACTORIES ENG CO., LTD.—See CR Holdings Co., Ltd.; *Int'l*, pg. 1827
CHOSUN WELDING JAPAN CO., LTD.—See CS HOLDINGS CO., LTD.; *Int'l*, pg. 1861
CHOSUN WELDING POHANG CO., LTD.—See CS HOLDINGS CO., LTD.; *Int'l*, pg. 1861
CHOTHANI FOODS LIMITED; *Int'l*, pg. 1584
CHO THAVEE PUBLIC COMPANY LIMITED; *Int'l*, pg. 1576
CHO THAVEE THERMOTECH COMPANY LIMITED—See Cho Thavee Public Company Limited; *Int'l*, pg. 1576
CHOTIWAT MANUFACTURING PUBLIC COMPANY LIMITED; *Int'l*, pg. 1584
CHOU ASSOCIATES MANAGEMENT INC.; *Int'l*, pg. 1584
CHOUBUNSHA PUBLISHING CO., LTD.—See Kadokawa Corporation; *Int'l*, pg. 4047
CHOUGQING FAR EASTERN DEPARTMENT STORE CO., LTD.—See The Far Eastern Group; *Int'l*, pg. 7641
CHOU-KOU MATERIALS CO., LTD.—See Eternal Materials Co., Ltd.; *Int'l*, pg. 2520
CHOUSHIMARU CO., LTD.; *Int'l*, pg. 1584
CHOW ENERGY PUBLIC COMPANY LIMITED; *Int'l*, pg. 1584
CHOWGULE BROTHERS PVT. LTD—See Chowgule & Company Pvt. Ltd.; *Int'l*, pg. 1585
CHOWGULE & COMPANY PVT. LTD.; *Int'l*, pg. 1585
CHOWGULE & COMPANY (SALT) PRIVATE LIMITED—See Chowgule & Company Pvt. Ltd.; *Int'l*, pg. 1585
CHOWGULE CONSTRUCTION TECHNOLOGIES PVT. LTD.—See Chowgule & Company Pvt. Ltd.; *Int'l*, pg. 1585
CHOWGULE INDUSTRIES PVT. LTD.—See Chowgule & Company Pvt. Ltd.; *Int'l*, pg. 1585
CHOWGULE KOSTER (INDIA) CONSTRUCTION CHEMICALS PVT. LTD.—See Chowgule & Company Pvt. Ltd.; *Int'l*, pg. 1585
CHOWGULE KOSTER (INDIA) CONSTRUCTION CHEMICALS PVT. LTD.—See Koster Bauchemie AG; *Int'l*, pg. 4291
CHOWGULE MEDICONSULT PRIVATE LIMITED—See Chowgule & Company Pvt. Ltd.; *Int'l*, pg. 1585
CHOWGULE STEAMSHIPS LIMITED—See Chowgule & Company Pvt. Ltd.; *Int'l*, pg. 1585
CHOW INTERNATIONAL CO., LTD.—See Chow Steel Industries Public Company Limited; *Int'l*, pg. 1584
CHOW SANG SANG HOLDINGS INTERNATIONAL LIMITED; *Int'l*, pg. 1584
CHOW SHINING ENERGY COMPANY LIMITED—See Chow Steel Industries Public Company Limited; *Int'l*, pg. 1584
CHOW STEEL INDUSTRIES PUBLIC COMPANY LIMITED; *Int'l*, pg. 1584
CHOW TAI FOOK ENTERPRISES LIMITED; *Int'l*, pg. 1584
CHOW TAI FOOK JEWELLERY CO., LTD.—See Chow Tai Fook Enterprises Limited; *Int'l*, pg. 1584
CHOW TAI FOOK JEWELLERY GROUP LIMITED—See Chow Tai Fook Enterprises Limited; *Int'l*, pg. 1584
CHOW TAI SENG JEWELLERY COMPANY LIMITED; *Int'l*, pg. 1585
CHOWTAW GENERATION LIMITED PARTNERSHIP—See ENGIE SA; *Int'l*, pg. 2433
CHOYA OPERATING, LLC—See NGL Energy Partners LP; *U.S. Public*, pg. 1527
CHOZ CATERING PTE. LTD.—See Neo Group Limited; *Int'l*, pg. 5196
CHOZEN HOLDINGS LTD.—See Charoen Pokphand Foods Public Company Limited; *Int'l*, pg. 1452
CHP CONSULTING INC—See Alfa Financial Software Holdings PLC; *Int'l*, pg. 308
CHP ENERGIA SP Z O.O.—See Przedsiebiorstwo Przemyslu Spozywczego PEPEES S.A.; *Int'l*, pg. 6014
CHP MERGER CORP.; *U.S. Public*, pg. 490
C.H. POWELL COMPANY; *U.S. Private*, pg. 707
C & H PRECISION LIMITED—See Avingtrans plc; *Int'l*, pg. 743
CHRC LLC—See Pebblebrook Hotel Trust; *U.S. Public*, pg. 1660
CHR CORP.; *U.S. Private*, pg. 889

CH REAL ESTATE II, INC.; *U.S. Private*, pg. 844
CH REYNOLDS, INC.; *U.S. Private*, pg. 844
CHR GROUP LLC; *U.S. Private*, pg. 889
CHR. HANSEN ARGENTINA S.A.I.C.—See Novonesis A/S; *Int'l*, pg. 5468
CHR. HANSEN A/S—See Novonesis A/S; *Int'l*, pg. 5468
CHR. HANSEN CZECH REPUBLIC, S.R.O—See Novonesis A/S; *Int'l*, pg. 5468
CHR. HANSEN DE MEXICO, S.A. DE C.V.—See Novonesis A/S; *Int'l*, pg. 5468
CHR. HANSEN GMBH—See Novonesis A/S; *Int'l*, pg. 5468
CHR. HANSEN GMBH—See Novonesis A/S; *Int'l*, pg. 5468
CHR. HANSEN HOLDING A/S—See Novonesis A/S; *Int'l*, pg. 5468
CHR. HANSEN INDUSTRIA E COMERCIO LTDA.—See Novonesis A/S; *Int'l*, pg. 5468
CHR. HANSEN IRELAND LIMITED—See Novonesis A/S; *Int'l*, pg. 5468
CHR. HANSEN POLAND SP. Z.O.O.—See Novonesis A/S; *Int'l*, pg. 5468
CHR. HANSEN PTY. LTD.—See Novonesis A/S; *Int'l*, pg. 5468
CHRIS ALBRITTON CONSTRUCTION COMPANY, INC.; *U.S. Private*, pg. 889
CHRISAL N.V.—See HeiQ Plc; *Int'l*, pg. 3326
CHRIS ANDERSEN ROOFING & ERECTING., CO.—See Altas Partners LP; *Int'l*, pg. 386
CHRIS AUFFENBERG FORD INC.; *U.S. Private*, pg. 889
CHRIS CAM CORPORATION; *U.S. Private*, pg. 889
CHRIS CANDIES, INC.—See Cemoi Chocolatier SAS; *Int'l*, pg. 1400
CHRIS-CRAFT CORPORATION; *U.S. Private*, pg. 890
THE CHRISKEN RESIDENTIAL TRUST; *U.S. Private*, pg. 4009
CHRIS LEITH CHEVROLET, INC.; *U.S. Private*, pg. 889
CHRIS-MORE INCORPORATED; *U.S. Private*, pg. 890
CHRIS NIKEL'S AUTOHAUS INC.; *U.S. Private*, pg. 889
CHRIS POSEY, INC.; *U.S. Private*, pg. 890
CHRISTA CONSTRUCTION LLC; *U.S. Private*, pg. 890
CHRISTAL RADIO SALES, INC.—See iHeartMedia, Inc.; *U.S. Public*, pg. 1096
CHRISTCHURCH CITY HOLDINGS LTD.; *Int'l*, pg. 1585
CHRISTCHURCH GLASS & GLAZING LIMITED—See Metro Performance Glass Limited; *Int'l*, pg. 4861
CHRISTCHURCH INTERNATIONAL AIRPORT LTD—See Christchurch City Holdings Ltd.; *Int'l*, pg. 1585
THE CHRISTCHURCH PRESS CO. LTD.—See Nine Entertainment Co. Holdings Limited; *Int'l*, pg. 5298
CHRIST COMMUNITY HEALTH SERVICES; *U.S. Private*, pg. 890
CHRISTENSEN BROTHERS INC.; *U.S. Private*, pg. 890
CHRISTENSEN FARMS MIDWEST, LLC; *U.S. Private*, pg. 890
CHRISTENSEN INC.; *U.S. Private*, pg. 890
CHRISTENSEN LUMBER, INC.—See Kodiak Building Partners LLC; *U.S. Private*, pg. 2336
CHRISTENSEN SHIPYARDS LTD.; *U.S. Private*, pg. 890
CHRISTENSEN, BARCLAY & SHAW, INC.; *U.S. Private*, pg. 890
CHRISTENSON ELECTRIC, INC.; *U.S. Private*, pg. 890
THE CHRIST HOSPITAL; *U.S. Private*, pg. 4009
THE CHRIST HOSPITAL SPINE SURGERY CENTER, LLC—See Tenet Healthcare Corporation; *U.S. Public*, pg. 2013
CHRISTIANA CARE CORPORATION; *U.S. Private*, pg. 891
CHRISTIANA CARE HEALTH SYSTEM, INC.; *U.S. Private*, pg. 891
CHRISTIAN AID MINISTRIES; *U.S. Private*, pg. 890
CHRISTIAN AND MISSIONARY ALLIANCE FOUNDATION, INC.; *U.S. Private*, pg. 890
CHRISTIANA TRUST COMPANY OF DELAWARE - LAS VEGAS OFFICE—See WSFS Financial Corporation; *U.S. Public*, pg. 2383
CHRISTIANA TRUST COMPANY OF DELAWARE—See WSFS Financial Corporation; *U.S. Public*, pg. 2383
CHRISTIAN BERNER AS—See Christian Berner Tech Trade AB; *Int'l*, pg. 1586
CHRISTIAN BERNER OY—See Christian Berner Tech Trade AB; *Int'l*, pg. 1586
CHRISTIAN BERNER TECH TRADE AB; *Int'l*, pg. 1586
CHRISTIAN BRANDS—See CBC Group; *U.S. Private*, pg. 797
THE CHRISTIAN BROADCASTING NETWORK INC.; *U.S. Private*, pg. 4009
CHRISTIAN BROTHERS AUTOMOTIVE CORPORATION; *U.S. Private*, pg. 890
CHRISTIAN CARE COMMUNITIES; *U.S. Private*, pg. 890
CHRISTIAN CARE COMPANIES, INC.; *U.S. Private*, pg. 890
CHRISTIAN COMMUNITY CREDIT UNION; *U.S. Private*, pg. 890
CHRISTIAN COMMUNITY DEVELOPMENT CORPORATION; *U.S. Private*, pg. 891
CHRISTIAN COMMUNITY HEALTH CENTER; *U.S. Private*, pg. 891
CHRISTIAN DIERIG GMBH—See Dierig Holding AG; *Int'l*, pg. 2115

CHRISTIAN DIOR COUTURE S.A.—See LVMH Moet Hennessy Louis Vuitton SE; *Int'l*, pg. 4591
CHRISTIAN DIOR KOREA—See LVMH Moet Hennessy Louis Vuitton SE; *Int'l*, pg. 4598
CHRISTIAN DIOR S.A.; *Int'l*, pg. 1586
CHRISTIAN DIOR (THAILAND)—See LVMH Moet Hennessy Louis Vuitton SE; *Int'l*, pg. 4598
CHRISTIAN EMERGENCY RELIEF TEAMS INTERNATIONAL; *U.S. Private*, pg. 891
CHRISTIAN FIDELITY LIFE INSURANCE COMPANY—See U-Haul Holding Company; *U.S. Public*, pg. 2211
CHRISTIAN FOUNDATION FOR CHILDREN AND AGING; *U.S. Private*, pg. 891
CHRISTIAN HANSEN FRANCE S.A.—See Novonesis A/S; *Int'l*, pg. 5468
CHRISTIAN HANSEN ITALY—See Novonesis A/S; *Int'l*, pg. 5468
CHRISTIAN HANSEN S.P.A.—See Novonesis A/S; *Int'l*, pg. 5468
CHRISTIAN HANSEN (UK) LTD.—See Novonesis A/S; *Int'l*, pg. 5468
CHRISTIAN HEALTH CARE CENTER; *U.S. Private*, pg. 891
CHRISTIAN HEALTHCARE MINISTRIES, INC.; *U.S. Private*, pg. 891
CHRISTIAN HORIZONS; *U.S. Private*, pg. 891
CHRISTIAN HOSPITAL FOUNDATION; *U.S. Private*, pg. 891
CHRISTIANIA RORLEGGERBEDRIFT AS—See Instalco AB; *Int'l*, pg. 3721
CHRISTIANIA SPIGERVERK AS—See Simpson Manufacturing Company, Inc.; *U.S. Public*, pg. 1882
CHRISTIANI & NIELSEN (THAI) PUBLIC COMPANY LIMITED; *Int'l*, pg. 1586
CHRISTIANITY TODAY INTERNATIONAL; *U.S. Private*, pg. 891
CHRISTIAN LOUBOUTIN SAS; *Int'l*, pg. 1586
CHRISTIAN MAYR GMBH & CO. KG; *Int'l*, pg. 1586
CHRISTIAN MEDICAL & DENTAL ASSOCIATIONS; *U.S. Private*, pg. 891
CHRISTIAN OPPORTUNITY CENTER; *U.S. Private*, pg. 891
CHRISTIAN POTIER S.A.; *Int'l*, pg. 1586
CHRISTIANSBURG INTERNAL MEDICINE, LLC—See HCA Healthcare, Inc.; *U.S. Public*, pg. 993
CHRISTIANSEN IMPLEMENT COMPANY, INC.; *U.S. Private*, pg. 891
CHRISTIAN SUPPLY CENTERS INC.—See R.B. Pamplin Corporation; *U.S. Private*, pg. 3334
CHRISTIAN WHOLESALE DISTRIBUTORS, INC.; *U.S. Private*, pg. 891
THE CHRISTIE CLINIC LLP—See HCA Healthcare, Inc.; *U.S. Public*, pg. 1012
CHRISTIE & CO AUSTRIA GMBH—See Christie Group plc; *Int'l*, pg. 1586
CHRISTIE + CO GMBH—See Christie Group plc; *Int'l*, pg. 1586
THE CHRISTIE COOKIE COMPANY—See Rich Holdings, Inc.; *U.S. Private*, pg. 3427
CHRISTIE + CO OY—See Christie Group plc; *Int'l*, pg. 1586
CHRISTIE CORROSION CONTROL LTD.—See Corrosion & Abrasion Solutions Ltd.; *Int'l*, pg. 1806
CHRISTIE + CO SARL—See Christie Group plc; *Int'l*, pg. 1587
CHRISTIE & CO S.A.S.—See Christie Group plc; *Int'l*, pg. 1586
CHRISTIE DIGITAL SYSTEMS CANADA INC.—See Ushio, Inc.; *Int'l*, pg. 8097
CHRISTIE DIGITAL SYSTEMS, INC.—See Ushio, Inc.; *Int'l*, pg. 8097
CHRISTIE DIGITAL SYSTEMS (INDIA) PRIVATE LIMITED—See Ushio, Inc.; *Int'l*, pg. 8097
CHRISTIE DIGITAL SYSTEMS (SHANGHAI), CO., LTD.—See Ushio, Inc.; *Int'l*, pg. 8097
CHRISTIE DIGITAL SYSTEMS (SHENZHEN) CO., LTD.—See Ushio, Inc.; *Int'l*, pg. 8097
CHRISTIE DIGITAL SYSTEMS USA, INC.—See Ushio, Inc.; *Int'l*, pg. 8097
CHRISTIE GROUP CENTRAL SERVICES LIMITED—See Christie Group plc; *Int'l*, pg. 1587
CHRISTIE GROUP PLC; *Int'l*, pg. 1586
CHRISTIE INNOMED, INC.; *Int'l*, pg. 1587
CHRISTIE INTRUDER ALARMS LIMITED—See Stanley Black & Decker, Inc.; *U.S. Public*, pg. 1932
CHRISTIE LITES INC.; *Int'l*, pg. 1587
CHRISTIE MANSON & WOODS LIMITED—See Financiere Pinault SCA; *Int'l*, pg. 2668
CHRISTIE MEDICAL HOLDINGS, INC.—See CAREstream Medical Ltd.; *Int'l*, pg. 1325
CHRISTIE, OWEN & DAVIES LTD.—See Christie Group plc; *Int'l*, pg. 1587
CHRISTIE, OWEN & DAVIES SL—See Christie Group plc; *Int'l*, pg. 1587
CHRISTIE'S AMSTERDAM B.V.—See Financiere Pinault SCA; *Int'l*, pg. 2668
CHRISTIE'S AUSTRALIA PTY. LTD.—See Financiere Pinault SCA; *Int'l*, pg. 2668

CHRISTIE LITES INC.

CHRISTIE'S HONG KONG LTD.—See Financiere Pinault SCA; *Int'l*, pg. 2668
CHRISTIE'S INC.—See Financiere Pinault SCA; *Int'l*, pg. 2668
CHRISTIE'S INTERNATIONAL PLC—See Financiere Pinault SCA; *Int'l*, pg. 2668
CHRISTIE'S (INTERNATIONAL) S.A. - FILIALE ITALIANA, ROME—See Financiere Pinault SCA; *Int'l*, pg. 2668
CHRISTIE'S (INTERNATIONAL) S.A.—See Financiere Pinault SCA; *Int'l*, pg. 2668
CHRISTIE'S INTERNATIONAL SINGAPORE PTE. LTD.—See Financiere Pinault SCA; *Int'l*, pg. 2668
CHRISTIE'S (ISRAEL) LTD.—See Financiere Pinault SCA; *Int'l*, pg. 2668
CHRISTIE'S MONACO S.A.M.—See Financiere Pinault SCA; *Int'l*, pg. 2668
CHRISTIE & SON SALES LTD; *Int'l*, pg. 1586
CHRISTIE'S SCOTLAND LIMITED—See Financiere Pinault SCA; *Int'l*, pg. 2668
CHRISTIE'S SOUTH KENSINGTON LTD.—See Financiere Pinault SCA; *Int'l*, pg. 2668
CHRISTIE'S ZURICH S.A.—See Financiere Pinault SCA; *Int'l*, pg. 2668
CHRISTINA LAKE CANNABIS CORP.; *Int'l*, pg. 1587
CHRISTINE INTERNATIONAL HOLDINGS LIMITED; *Int'l*, pg. 1587
CHRISTIS DAIRIES LIMITED—See N.K. Shacolas (Holdings) Ltd.; *Int'l*, pg. 5116
CHRIST JUWELIERE UND UHRMACHER SEIT 1863 GMBH—See 3i Group plc; *Int'l*, pg. 8
THE CHRISTMAN COMPANY INC.; *U.S. Private*, pg. 4009
CHRISTMAN CONSTRUCTORS INC.—See The Christman Company Inc.; *U.S. Private*, pg. 4009
CHRISTMAS BY KREBS CORPORATION; *U.S. Private*, pg. 891
CHRISTMAS CITY PRINTING CO., INC.—See Alcom Printing Group, Inc.; *U.S. Private*, pg. 154
CHRISTMAS GARDEN DEUTSCHLAND GMBH—See DEAG Deutsche Entertainment AG; *Int'l*, pg. 1997
THE CHRISTMAS LIGHT CO.; *U.S. Private*, pg. 4009
CHRISTMAS LIGHTS, ETC.; *U.S. Private*, pg. 891
CHRISTMAS LUMBER COMPANY INC.; *U.S. Private*, pg. 891
CHRISTMAS TREE HILL INC.; *U.S. Private*, pg. 891
CHRIST NISHOTECH WATER SYSTEMS PTE. LTD.—See BWT Aktiengesellschaft; *Int'l*, pg. 1233
CHRISTOF ELECTRICS GMBH & CO KG—See Clayton, Dubilier & Rice, LLC; *U.S. Private*, pg. 926
CHRISTOFFERSON COMMERCIAL BUILDERS; *U.S. Private*, pg. 891
CHRISTOF HOLDING AG; *Int'l*, pg. 1587
CHRISTOPHER & BANKS CORPORATION; *U.S. Public*, pg. 490
CHRISTOPHER B. BURKE ENGINEERING, LLC—See Christopher B. Burke Engineering Ltd.; *U.S. Private*, pg. 892
CHRISTOPHER B. BURKE ENGINEERING LTD.; *U.S. Private*, pg. 891
CHRISTOPHER REEVE FOUNDATION; *U.S. Private*, pg. 892
CHRISTOPHER'S DODGE WORLD; *U.S. Private*, pg. 892
CHRISTOPHER, SMITH, LEONARD, BRISTOW & STANELL, P.A.; *U.S. Private*, pg. 892
CHRISTOPHERSON HOMES INC.; *U.S. Private*, pg. 892
CHRISTOPHER TOOL & MFG CO.; *U.S. Private*, pg. 892
CHRISTOPHER TRIGG LIMITED—See Brown & Brown, Inc.; *U.S. Public*, pg. 400
CHRISTOPH REISEGGER GESELLSCHAFT M.B.H.—See UniCredit S.p.A.; *Int'l*, pg. 8034
CHRISTOVICH & ASSOCIATES, LLC; *U.S. Private*, pg. 892
CHRIST PHARMA & LIFE SCIENCE SHANGHAI LTD.—See BWT Aktiengesellschaft; *Int'l*, pg. 1233
CHRIST'S HOUSEHOLD OF FAITH; *U.S. Private*, pg. 890
CHRISTUS CABRINI SURGERY CENTER, L.L.C.—See Tenet Healthcare Corporation; *U.S. Public*, pg. 2009
CHRISTUS HEALTH; *U.S. Private*, pg. 892
CHRISTUS HOMECARE-ST. MICHAEL, LLC—See UnitedHealth Group Incorporated; *U.S. Public*, pg. 2244
CHRISTUS LAKE AREA HOSPITAL—See CHRISTUS Health; *U.S. Private*, pg. 892
CHRIST & WIRTH HAUSTECHNIK GMBH—See Storskogen Group AB; *Int'l*, pg. 7227
CHRISTWOOD; *U.S. Private*, pg. 892
CHRISTY ENTERPRISES, INC.; *U.S. Private*, pg. 892
CHRISTY-FOLTZ INCORPORATED; *U.S. Private*, pg. 892
CHRISTY GEM CO., LTD.—See Kuwayama Corporation; *Int'l*, pg. 4348
CHRISTY-HALSEY MEENAN—See Star Group, L.P.; *U.S. Public*, pg. 1937
CHRISTY REFRACTORIES COMPANY LLC; *U.S. Private*, pg. 892
CHRISTY SMITH FUNERAL HOMES, INC.—See Birch Hill Equity Partners Management Inc.; *Int'l*, pg. 1046
CHRISTY SMITH FUNERAL HOMES, INC.—See Homesteaders Life Co. Inc.; *U.S. Private*, pg. 1974
CHRISTY SPORTS LLC; *U.S. Private*, pg. 892
CHRISTY WEBBER LANDSCAPES; *U.S. Private*, pg. 892

C.H. ROBINSON AUSTRIA GMBH—See C.H. Robinson Worldwide, Inc.; *U.S. Public*, pg. 414
C.H. ROBINSON COMPANY (CANADA) LTD.—See C.H. Robinson Worldwide, Inc.; *U.S. Public*, pg. 414
C.H. ROBINSON COMPANY—See C.H. Robinson Worldwide, Inc.; *U.S. Public*, pg. 414
C.H. ROBINSON CZECH REPUBLIC S.R.O.—See C.H. Robinson Worldwide, Inc.; *U.S. Public*, pg. 414
C.H. ROBINSON DE MEXICO, S.A. DE C.V.—See C.H. Robinson Worldwide, Inc.; *U.S. Public*, pg. 415
C.H. ROBINSON EUROPE B.V.—See C.H. Robinson Worldwide, Inc.; *U.S. Public*, pg. 414
C.H. ROBINSON FRANCE SAS—See C.H. Robinson Worldwide, Inc.; *U.S. Public*, pg. 415
C.H. ROBINSON FREIGHT SERVICES (CHINA) LTD.—See C.H. Robinson Worldwide, Inc.; *U.S. Public*, pg. 415
C.H. ROBINSON FREIGHT SERVICES, LTD.—See C.H. Robinson Worldwide, Inc.; *U.S. Public*, pg. 414
CH ROBINSON FREIGHT SERVICES (MALAYSIA) SDN. BHD.—See C.H. Robinson Worldwide, Inc.; *U.S. Public*, pg. 415
C.H. ROBINSON FREIGHT SERVICES MIDDLE EAST DMCC—See C.H. Robinson Worldwide, Inc.; *U.S. Public*, pg. 415
C.H. ROBINSON FREIGHT SERVICES (SINGAPORE) PTE. LTD.—See C.H. Robinson Worldwide, Inc.; *U.S. Public*, pg. 415
C.H. ROBINSON FREIGHT SERVICES (TAIWAN) LTD.—See C.H. Robinson Worldwide, Inc.; *U.S. Public*, pg. 415
C.H. ROBINSON FREIGHT SERVICES (THAILAND) LTD.—See C.H. Robinson Worldwide, Inc.; *U.S. Public*, pg. 415
C.H. ROBINSON FREIGHT SERVICES (VIETNAM) COMPANY LIMITED—See C.H. Robinson Worldwide, Inc.; *U.S. Public*, pg. 415
C.H. ROBINSON HUNGARIA KFT.—See C.H. Robinson Worldwide, Inc.; *U.S. Public*, pg. 414
C.H. ROBINSON INTERNATIONAL COLUMBIA SAS—See C.H. Robinson Worldwide, Inc.; *U.S. Public*, pg. 415
C.H. ROBINSON INTERNATIONAL, INC.—See C.H. Robinson Worldwide, Inc.; *U.S. Public*, pg. 415
C.H. ROBINSON INTERNATIONAL (INDIA) PRIVATE LTD.—See C.H. Robinson Worldwide, Inc.; *U.S. Public*, pg. 415
C.H. ROBINSON INTERNATIONAL ITALY, SRL—See C.H. Robinson Worldwide, Inc.; *U.S. Public*, pg. 414
C.H. ROBINSON LUXEMBOURG FINANCE S.A R.L.—See C.H. Robinson Worldwide, Inc.; *U.S. Public*, pg. 415
C.H. ROBINSON POLSKA S.A.—See C.H. Robinson Worldwide, Inc.; *U.S. Public*, pg. 415
C.H. ROBINSON PROJECT LOGISTICS, INC.—See C.H. Robinson Worldwide, Inc.; *U.S. Public*, pg. 415
C.H. ROBINSON PROJECT LOGISTICS LTD.—See C.H. Robinson Worldwide, Inc.; *U.S. Public*, pg. 415
C.H. ROBINSON PROJECT LOGISTICS PTE. LTD.—See C.H. Robinson Worldwide, Inc.; *U.S. Public*, pg. 415
CH ROBINSON PROJECT LOGISTICS SDN. BHD.—See C.H. Robinson Worldwide, Inc.; *U.S. Public*, pg. 415
C.H. ROBINSON SHANGHAI TRADING CO.—See C.H. Robinson Worldwide, Inc.; *U.S. Public*, pg. 415
C.H. ROBINSON-SHANNON INTERNATIONAL—See C.H. Robinson Worldwide, Inc.; *U.S. Public*, pg. 415
C.H. ROBINSON SLOVAKIA, S.R.O.—See C.H. Robinson Worldwide, Inc.; *U.S. Public*, pg. 415
C.H. ROBINSON SWITZERLAND GMBH—See C.H. Robinson Worldwide, Inc.; *U.S. Public*, pg. 415
C.H. ROBINSON TECHNOLOGY LLC—See C.H. Robinson Worldwide, Inc.; *U.S. Public*, pg. 415
C.H. ROBINSON (UK) LTD.—See C.H. Robinson Worldwide, Inc.; *U.S. Public*, pg. 414
C.H. ROBINSON WORLDWIDE ARGENTINA, S.A.—See C.H. Robinson Worldwide, Inc.; *U.S. Public*, pg. 415
C.H. ROBINSON WORLDWIDE (AUSTRALIA) PTY. LTD.—See C.H. Robinson Worldwide, Inc.; *U.S. Public*, pg. 415
C.H. ROBINSON WORLDWIDE FREIGHT INDIA PRIVATE LIMITED—See C.H. Robinson Worldwide, Inc.; *U.S. Public*, pg. 415
C.H. ROBINSON WORLDWIDE FREIGHT LANKA (PRIVATE) LIMITED—See C.H. Robinson Worldwide, Inc.; *U.S. Public*, pg. 415
C.H. ROBINSON WORLDWIDE GMBH—See C.H. Robinson Worldwide, Inc.; *U.S. Public*, pg. 415
C.H. ROBINSON WORLDWIDE, INC.; *U.S. Public*, pg. 414
C.H. ROBINSON WORLDWIDE (IRELAND) LTD.—See C.H. Robinson Worldwide, Inc.; *U.S. Public*, pg. 414
C.H. ROBINSON WORLDWIDE (NZ) LTD.—See C.H. Robinson Worldwide, Inc.; *U.S. Public*, pg. 415
CH ROBINSON WORLDWIDE (SHANGHAI) CO. LTD.—See C.H. Robinson Worldwide, Inc.; *U.S. Public*, pg. 414
C.H. ROBINSON WORLDWIDE SINGAPORE PTE. LTD.—See C.H. Robinson Worldwide, Inc.; *U.S. Public*, pg. 415
C.H. ROBINSON WORLDWIDE (UK) LTD.—See C.H. Robinson Worldwide, Inc.; *U.S. Public*, pg. 414

CORPORATE AFFILIATIONS

CHROMA ATE EUROPE B.V.—See Chroma ATE Inc.; *Int'l*, pg. 1587
CHROMA ATE INC. - LIN-KOU FACTORY—See Chroma ATE Inc.; *Int'l*, pg. 1588
CHROMA ATE INC.; *Int'l*, pg. 1587
CHROMA ATE INC.—See Chroma ATE Inc.; *Int'l*, pg. 1588
CHROMA ATE (SUZHOU) CO., LTD.—See Chroma ATE Inc.; *Int'l*, pg. 1587
CHROMACOL LIMITED—See Thermo Fisher Scientific Inc.; *U.S. Public*, pg. 2145
CHROMA COLOR CORPORATION—See Arsenal Capital Management LP; *U.S. Private*, pg. 337
CHROMADEX ANALYTICS, INC.—See ChromaDex Corporation; *U.S. Public*, pg. 490
CHROMADEX CORPORATION; *U.S. Public*, pg. 490
CHROMADEX, INC.—See ChromaDex Corporation; *U.S. Public*, pg. 490
CHROMA ELECTRONICS (SHANGHAI) CO., LTD.—See Chroma ATE Inc.; *Int'l*, pg. 1588
CHROMA ELECTRONICS (SHENZHEN) CO., LTD.—See Chroma ATE Inc.; *Int'l*, pg. 1588
CHROMA TECHNOLOGIES CHINA MANUFACTURING LTD.—See American Securities LLC; *U.S. Private*, pg. 251
CHROMAFLO TECHNOLOGIES CORPORATION—See American Securities LLC; *U.S. Private*, pg. 250
CHROMAFLO TECHNOLOGIES EUROPE B.V.—See American Securities LLC; *U.S. Private*, pg. 251
CHROMAFLO TECHNOLOGIES FINLAND OY—See American Securities LLC; *U.S. Private*, pg. 251
CHROMAGE PYRENEEN SA.—See Arbonia AG; *Int'l*, pg. 538
CHROMA GERMANY GMBH—See Chroma ATE Inc.; *Int'l*, pg. 1587
CHROMA HOSPITALITY, INC.—See Filinvest Development Corporation; *Int'l*, pg. 2662
CHROMA JAPAN CORP.—See Chroma ATE Inc.; *Int'l*, pg. 1588
CHROMALINE SCREEN PRINT PRODUCTS—See Terawulf, Inc.; *U.S. Public*, pg. 2018
CHROMALLOY CASTINGS TAMPA CORPORATION—See Veritas Capital Fund Management, LLC; *U.S. Private*, pg. 4364
CHROMALLOY GAS TURBINE EUROPA B.V.—See Veritas Capital Fund Management, LLC; *U.S. Private*, pg. 4364
CHROMALLOY GAS TURBINE FRANCE—See Veritas Capital Fund Management, LLC; *U.S. Private*, pg. 4364
CHROMALLOY GAS TURBINE LLC - MIDDLETOWN—See Veritas Capital Fund Management, LLC; *U.S. Private*, pg. 4364
CHROMALLOY GAS TURBINE LLC—See Veritas Capital Fund Management, LLC; *U.S. Private*, pg. 4364
CHROMALLOY GAS TURBINE LLC—See Veritas Capital Fund Management, LLC; *U.S. Private*, pg. 4364
CHROMALLOY HOLLAND B.V.—See Veritas Capital Fund Management, LLC; *U.S. Private*, pg. 4364
CHROMALLOY POWER SERVICES CORP.—See Veritas Capital Fund Management, LLC; *U.S. Private*, pg. 4364
CHROMALLOY S.A. DE C.V.—See Veritas Capital Fund Management, LLC; *U.S. Private*, pg. 4364
CHROMALLOY SAN DIEGO CORPORATION—See Veritas Capital Fund Management, LLC; *U.S. Private*, pg. 4364
CHROMALLOY THAILAND CO, LTD.—See Veritas Capital Fund Management, LLC; *U.S. Private*, pg. 4364
CHROMALLOY UNITED KINGDOM LTD.—See Veritas Capital Fund Management, LLC; *U.S. Private*, pg. 4364
CHROMALOX (ASIA PACIFIC) LTD.—See Spirax-Sarco Engineering plc; *Int'l*, pg. 7137
CHROMALOX ENGENHARIA LTDA.—See Spirax-Sarco Engineering plc; *Int'l*, pg. 7137
CHROMALOX GULF DWC, LLC—See Spirax-Sarco Engineering plc; *Int'l*, pg. 7137
CHROMALOX, INC.—See Spirax-Sarco Engineering plc; *Int'l*, pg. 7137
CHROMALOX (UK) LTD.—See Spirax-Sarco Engineering plc; *Int'l*, pg. 7137
CHROMA NEW MATERIAL CORPORATION—See Chroma ATE Inc.; *Int'l*, pg. 1588
CHROMASCAPE, LLC; *U.S. Private*, pg. 892
CHROMASENS GMBH—See TKH Group N.V.; *Int'l*, pg. 7763
CHROMA SYSTEMS SOLUTIONS, INC.—See Chroma ATE Inc.; *Int'l*, pg. 1588
CHROMA SYSTEMS SOLUTIONS, INC.—See Chroma ATE Inc.; *Int'l*, pg. 1588
CHROMATECH CO., LTD.—See JCR Pharmaceuticals Co., Ltd.; *Int'l*, pg. 3923
CHROMA TECHNOLOGY CORPORATION; *U.S. Private*, pg. 892
CHROMATIC INDIA LIMITED; *Int'l*, pg. 1588
CHROMATIC PRODUCTIONS, INC.—See H.I.G. Capital, LLC; *U.S. Private*, pg. 1834
CHROMATICS, INC.—See Avient Corporation; *U.S. Public*, pg. 247
CHROMATIC TECHNOLOGIES, INC.; *U.S. Private*, pg. 892

CHROMATIN, INC.—See S&W Seed Co.; *U.S. Public*, pg. 1832
CHROMATOGRAPHY RESEARCH SUPPLIES, INC.—See Trajan Group Holdings Limited; *Int'l*, pg. 7891
CHROMCOM INZENIRING VZDRZEVANJE IN MERITVE D.O.O.—See Kansai Paint Co., Ltd.; *Int'l*, pg. 4071
CHROMCRAFT CORPORATION—See Sport Haley Holdings, Inc.; *U.S. Private*, pg. 3760
CHROMCRAFT REVINGTON, INC.—See Sport Haley Holdings, Inc.; *U.S. Private*, pg. 3760
CHROME CAPITAL GROUP LLC—See Jefferies Financial Group Inc.; *U.S. Public*, pg. 1188
CHROME CAPITAL, LLC; *U.S. Private*, pg. 892
CHROME DEPOSIT CORPORATION—See United States Steel Corporation; *U.S. Public*, pg. 2236
CHROME HEARTS JP, GK—See United Arrows Ltd.; *Int'l*, pg. 8064
CHROME RIVER TECHNOLOGIES, INC.—See K1 Investment Management, LLC; *U.S. Private*, pg. 2252
CHROMETCO LIMITED; *Int'l*, pg. 1588
CHROMOCELL THERAPEUTICS CORPORATION; *U.S. Public*, pg. 490
CHROMOGENEX TECHNOLOGIES LTD.; *Int'l*, pg. 1588
CHROMOGENICS AB; *Int'l*, pg. 1588
CHROMOLOGIC LLC; *U.S. Private*, pg. 892
CHROMOS BOJE I LAKOVI D.D.—See Kansai Paint Co., Ltd.; *Int'l*, pg. 4071
CHROMOS GROUP AG—See Basler AG; *Int'l*, pg. 887
CHRONIC DISEASE FUND, INC.; *U.S. Private*, pg. 893
CHRONICLE OF HIGHER EDUCATION; *U.S. Private*, pg. 893
THE CHRONICLE—See Community Media Group; *U.S. Private*, pg. 995
CHRONICLE-TRIBUNE—See Paxton Media Group LLC; *U.S. Private*, pg. 3116
CHRONISTER OIL COMPANY INC.; *U.S. Private*, pg. 893
CHRONOMITE LABORATORIES, INC.—See Acorn Engineering Company, Inc.; *U.S. Private*, pg. 63
CHRONORESTO SA—See Solocal Group; *Int'l*, pg. 7074
CHRONOS RICHARDSON INDIA PVT. LTD.—See Premier Tech Ltd.; *Int'l*, pg. 5962
CHRONOS RICHARDSON LIMITED—See Premier Tech Ltd.; *Int'l*, pg. 5962
CHRONOS RICHARDSON LTD.—See Premier Tech Ltd.; *Int'l*, pg. 5962
CHRONOSWISS ASIA PTE LTD—See Cortina Holdings Limited; *Int'l*, pg. 1808
CHRONOTRACK SYSTEMS CORP.—See Leonard Green & Partners, L.P.; *U.S. Private*, pg. 2426
CHRONOTRACK SYSTEMS CORP.—See TPG Capital, L.P.; *U.S. Public*, pg. 2174
CHRONOTRACK SYSTEMS EUROPE B.V.—See Leonard Green & Partners, L.P.; *U.S. Private*, pg. 2426
CHRONOTRACK SYSTEMS EUROPE B.V.—See TPG Capital, L.P.; *U.S. Public*, pg. 2174
CHR SOLUTIONS INC. - DALLAS—See CHR Solutions, Inc.; *U.S. Private*, pg. 889
CHR SOLUTIONS, INC. - HOUSTON—See CHR Solutions, Inc.; *U.S. Private*, pg. 889
CHR SOLUTIONS, INC. - LUBBOCK—See CHR Solutions, Inc.; *U.S. Private*, pg. 889
CHR SOLUTIONS, INC.; *U.S. Private*, pg. 889
CHRYSALIS GROUP PLC—See Bertelsmann SE & Co. KGaA; *Int'l*, pg. 990
CHRYSALIS INVESTMENTS LIMITED; *Int'l*, pg. 1588
CHRYSALIS SOFTWARE, INC.—See Waterfield Technologies, Inc.; *U.S. Private*, pg. 4453
CHRYSALIS VENTURES; *U.S. Private*, pg. 893
CHRYSAOR E&P LIMITED—See Harbour Energy plc; *Int'l*, pg. 3271
CHRYSAOR HOLDING LIMITED—See Harbour Energy plc; *Int'l*, pg. 3271
CHRYSAOR PRODUCTION (U.K.) LIMITED—See Harbour Energy plc; *Int'l*, pg. 3271
CHRYSCAPITAL INVESTMENT ADVISORS (INDIA) PRIVATE LIMITED; *Int'l*, pg. 1588
CHRYSCAPITAL MANAGEMENT CO.; *Int'l*, pg. 1588
CHRYSLER ASIA PACIFIC INVESTMENT LTD.—See Stellantis N.V.; *Int'l*, pg. 7199
CHRYSLER (ATLANTA) PARTS DISTRIBUTION CENTER—See Stellantis N.V.; *Int'l*, pg. 7199
CHRYSLER AUSTRALIA PTY. LTD.—See Stellantis N.V.; *Int'l*, pg. 7199
CHRYSLER CANADA - BRAMPTON ASSEMBLY PLANT—See Stellantis N.V.; *Int'l*, pg. 7199
CHRYSLER CANADA - ETOBICOKE CASTING PLANT—See Stellantis N.V.; *Int'l*, pg. 7199
CHRYSLER CANADA INC.—See Stellantis N.V.; *Int'l*, pg. 7199
CHRYSLER (CLEVELAND) PARTS DISTRIBUTION CENTER—See Stellantis N.V.; *Int'l*, pg. 7199
CHRYSLER - CONNER STREET ASSEMBLY PLANT—See Stellantis N.V.; *Int'l*, pg. 7199
CHRYSLER CORPORATION—See Stellantis N.V.; *Int'l*, pg. 7199
CHRYSLER CORPORATION—See Stellantis N.V.; *Int'l*, pg. 7199
CHRYSLER CZECH REPUBLIC S.R.O.—See Stellantis N.V.; *Int'l*, pg. 7199

CHRYSLER (DALLAS) PARTS DISTRIBUTION CENTER—See Stellantis N.V.; *Int'l*, pg. 7199
CHRYSLER - DETROIT AXLE PLANT—See Stellantis N.V.; *Int'l*, pg. 7199
CHRYSLER - DETROIT ENGINE PLANT—See Stellantis N.V.; *Int'l*, pg. 7199
CHRYSLER DE VENEZUELA LLC.—See Stellantis N.V.; *Int'l*, pg. 7200
CHRYSLER FRANCE S.A.S.—See Stellantis N.V.; *Int'l*, pg. 7199
CHRYSLER GROUP DO BRASIL COMERCIO DE VEICULOS LTDA.—See Stellantis N.V.; *Int'l*, pg. 7199
CHRYSLER GROUP INTERNATIONAL LLC—See Stellantis N.V.; *Int'l*, pg. 7199
CHRYSLER GROUP INTERNATIONAL SERVICES LLC—See Stellantis N.V.; *Int'l*, pg. 7199
CHRYSLER GROUP REALTY COMPANY LLC—See Stellantis N.V.; *Int'l*, pg. 7199
CHRYSLER GROUP TRANSPORT LLC—See Stellantis N.V.; *Int'l*, pg. 7199
CHRYSLER INVESTMENT HOLDINGS LLC—See Stellantis N.V.; *Int'l*, pg. 7200
CHRYSLER ITALIA S.R.L.—See Stellantis N.V.; *Int'l*, pg. 7200
CHRYSLER JEEP 24; *U.S. Private*, pg. 893
CHRYSLER JEEP-GLEN BURNIE—See Tate Automotive Group; *U.S. Private*, pg. 3935
CHRYSLER JEEP TICARET S.A.—See Stellantis N.V.; *Int'l*, pg. 7200
CHRYSLER & JEEP VERTRIEBSGESELLSCHAFT MBH—See Stellantis N.V.; *Int'l*, pg. 7199
CHRYSLER - KOKOMO CASTING PLANT—See Stellantis N.V.; *Int'l*, pg. 7199
CHRYSLER - KOKOMO TRANSMISSION PLANT—See Stellantis N.V.; *Int'l*, pg. 7200
CHRYSLER KOREA, LTD.—See Stellantis N.V.; *Int'l*, pg. 7200
CHRYSLER MANAGEMENT AUSTRIA GMBH—See Stellantis N.V.; *Int'l*, pg. 7200
CHRYSLER (MEMPHIS) PARTS DISTRIBUTION CENTER—See Stellantis N.V.; *Int'l*, pg. 7199
CHRYSLER MUSEUM OF ART; *U.S. Private*, pg. 893
CHRYSLER - NEWARK ASSEMBLY PLANT—See Stellantis N.V.; *Int'l*, pg. 7199
CHRYSLER - PLYMOUTH ROAD OFFICE COMPLEX (PROC)—See Stellantis N.V.; *Int'l*, pg. 7199
CHRYSLER POLSKA SP. ZO.O.—See Stellantis N.V.; *Int'l*, pg. 7200
CHRYSLER (PORTLAND) PARTS DISTRIBUTION CENTER—See Stellantis N.V.; *Int'l*, pg. 7199
CHRYSLER - PORT OPERATIONS—See Stellantis N.V.; *Int'l*, pg. 7199
CHRYSLER SOUTH AFRICA (PTY) LIMITED—See Stellantis N.V.; *Int'l*, pg. 7200
CHRYSLER - STERLING ASSEMBLY PLANT—See Stellantis N.V.; *Int'l*, pg. 7199
CHRYSLER - STERLING STAMPING PLANT—See Stellantis N.V.; *Int'l*, pg. 7199
CHRYSLER - TOLEDO MACHINING PLANT—See Stellantis N.V.; *Int'l*, pg. 7199
CHRYSLER - TOLEDO NORTH ASSEMBLY PLANT—See Stellantis N.V.; *Int'l*, pg. 7199
CHRYSLER - TRENTON ENGINE PLANT—See Stellantis N.V.; *Int'l*, pg. 7199
CHRYSLER (WARREN) PARTS DISTRIBUTION CENTER—See Stellantis N.V.; *Int'l*, pg. 7199
CHRYSLER - WARREN STAMPING PLANT—See Stellantis N.V.; *Int'l*, pg. 7199
CHRYSLER - WARREN TRUCK ASSEMBLY PLANT—See Stellantis N.V.; *Int'l*, pg. 7199
CHRYSO, INC.—See Compagnie de Saint-Gobain SA; *Int'l*, pg. 1723
CHRYSO SAS—See Compagnie de Saint-Gobain SA; *Int'l*, pg. 1722
CHRYSOS CORPORATION LIMITED; *Int'l*, pg. 1589
CHRYSO UK LTD.—See Compagnie de Saint-Gobain SA; *Int'l*, pg. 1722
CHRYSSAFILIOTISSA PUBLIC LTD—See DIAGNOSTIC AND THERAPEUTIC CENTER OF ATHENS-HYGEIA S.A.; *Int'l*, pg. 2103
CHS AGRITRADE BULGARIA LTD.—See CHS INC.; *U.S. Public*, pg. 491
CHS AGRITRADE D.O.O—See CHS INC.; *U.S. Public*, pg. 491
CHS AGRITRADE HUNGARY LTD.—See CHS INC.; *U.S. Public*, pg. 491
CHS AGROMARKET, LLC—See CHS INC.; *U.S. Public*, pg. 491
CHS BROADBENT PTY. LTD.—See CHS INC.; *U.S. Public*, pg. 491
CHS BULGARIA LTD.—See CHS INC.; *U.S. Public*, pg. 491
CHS CABIN AND HANDLING SERVICE BAYERN GMBH—See Air Berlin PLC & Co. Luftverkehrs KG; *Int'l*, pg. 236
CHS CABIN AND HANDLING SERVICE GMBH—See Air Berlin PLC & Co. Luftverkehrs KG; *Int'l*, pg. 236

CHS CABIN AND HANDLING SERVICE SUD-WEST GMBH—See Air Berlin PLC & Co. Luftverkehrs KG; *Int'l*, pg. 236
CHS CANADA LP—See CHS INC.; *U.S. Public*, pg. 491
CHS CAPITAL, LLC—See CHS INC.; *U.S. Public*, pg. 491
CHS CAPITAL LLC; *U.S. Private*, pg. 893
CHS/COMMUNITY HEALTH SYSTEMS, INC.—See Community Health Systems, Inc.; *U.S. Public*, pg. 551
CHS-CONTAINER A/S—See CHS CONTAINER Handel GmbH; *Int'l*, pg. 1589
CHS CONTAINER BULGARIA LTD.—See CHS CONTAINER Handel GmbH; *Int'l*, pg. 1589
CHS CONTAINER HANDEL B.V.—See CHS CONTAINER Handel GmbH; *Int'l*, pg. 1589
CHS CONTAINER HANDEL GMBH; *Int'l*, pg. 1589
CHS CONTAINER SERVIS LTD STI—See CHS CONTAINER Handel GmbH; *Int'l*, pg. 1589
CHS-CORSICA—See CHS INC.; *U.S. Public*, pg. 492
CHS COUNTRY OPERATIONS CANADA, INC.—See CHS INC.; *U.S. Public*, pg. 491
CHS DATA SYSTEMS GESELLSCHAFT FUR SYSTEMENTWICKLUNG UND BERATUNG GMBH—See Capgemini SE; *Int'l*, pg. 1305
CHS DE PARAGUAY SRL—See CHS INC.; *U.S. Public*, pg. 491
CHS DO BRASIL LTDA.—See CHS INC.; *U.S. Public*, pg. 492
CHS ELBURN—See CHS INC.; *U.S. Public*, pg. 491
CHS-ELKTON—See CHS INC.; *U.S. Public*, pg. 492
CHS ENERGY CANADA, INC.—See CHS INC.; *U.S. Public*, pg. 491
CHS HALLOCK, LLC—See CHS INC.; *U.S. Public*, pg. 491
CHS-HOLDREGE, INC.—See CHS INC.; *U.S. Public*, pg. 492
CHS INC.-FAULKTON—See CHS INC.; *U.S. Public*, pg. 491
CHSINC IBERICA SL—See CHS INC.; *U.S. Public*, pg. 492
CHS INC. - MANKATO OILSEED PROCESSING PLANT—See CHS INC.; *U.S. Public*, pg. 491
CHS INC.; *U.S. Public*, pg. 490
CHS INDUSTRIES LTD.—See CHS INC.; *U.S. Public*, pg. 491
CHS INDUSTRIES LTD—See CHS INC.; *U.S. Public*, pg. 491
CHS ITALY S.R.L.—See CHS INC.; *U.S. Public*, pg. 491
CHS KOREA, LLC—See CHS INC.; *U.S. Public*, pg. 491
CHS-LCC CO-OP—See CHS INC.; *U.S. Public*, pg. 492
CHS MCPHERSON REFINERY INC.—See CHS INC.; *U.S. Public*, pg. 491
CHS-M&M, INC.—See CHS INC.; *U.S. Public*, pg. 492
CHS-M&M, INC. - WIGGINS—See CHS INC.; *U.S. Public*, pg. 492
CHS-NAPOLEON—See CHS INC.; *U.S. Public*, pg. 492
CHS NINGBO PROTEIN FOODS LTD.—See CHS INC.; *U.S. Public*, pg. 491
CHS NORTHWEST—See CHS INC.; *U.S. Public*, pg. 491
C.H. SNYDER COMPANY—See The Snyder Group, Inc.; *U.S. Private*, pg. 4119
CHS OF WALTHAM INC.; *U.S. Private*, pg. 893
CHS-OKLEE—See CHS INC.; *U.S. Public*, pg. 492
CHS-OSTRANDER FARMER COOP ELEVATOR—See CHS INC.; *U.S. Public*, pg. 492
C.H. SPENCER & COMPANY; *U.S. Private*, pg. 707
CHS PRIMELAND - WALLA WALLA—See CHS INC.; *U.S. Public*, pg. 491
CHSPSC, LLC—See Community Health Systems, Inc.; *U.S. Public*, pg. 551
CHS-ROCHESTER—See CHS INC.; *U.S. Public*, pg. 492
CHS SERBIA D.O.O. NOVI SAD—See CHS INC.; *U.S. Public*, pg. 491
CHS (SHANGHAI) TRADING CO., LTD—See CHS INC.; *U.S. Public*, pg. 491
CHS-SHIPMAN, INC.—See CHS INC.; *U.S. Public*, pg. 492
CHS SINGAPORE TRADING COMPANY PTE. LTD.—See CHS INC.; *U.S. Public*, pg. 491
CHS SOUTH SIOUX CITY, INC.—See CHS INC.; *U.S. Public*, pg. 491
CHS SPIRITWOOD FERTILIZER LLC—See CHS INC.; *U.S. Public*, pg. 491
CHS-SUB WHATCOM, INC.—See CHS INC.; *U.S. Public*, pg. 492
CHS SUDCON GMBH—See CHS CONTAINER Handel GmbH; *Int'l*, pg. 1589
CHS (TAIWAN) COMMODITY TRADING CO. LTD—See CHS INC.; *U.S. Public*, pg. 491
CHS TARIM VE GIDA SANAYII LIMITED SIRKETI—See CHS INC.; *U.S. Public*, pg. 491
CHS TRADING COMPANY AUSTRALIA PTY. LTD.—See CHS INC.; *U.S. Public*, pg. 492
C&H SUGAR COMPANY, INC.—See Florida Crystals Corporation; *U.S. Private*, pg. 1548
CHS UKRAINE, LLC—See CHS INC.; *U.S. Public*, pg. 492
CHS URUGUAY SRL—See CHS INC.; *U.S. Public*, pg. 492
CH SWEESTECH DOOR SDN. BHD.—See Chuan Huat Resources Berhad; *Int'l*, pg. 1589

C.H. SPENCER & COMPANY

Company Index

CHS-WINGER—See CHS INC.; *U.S. Public*, pg. 492
C & H TARPS CO., LTD.—See Dream International Ltd; *Int'l*, pg. 2202
CHTC FONG'S INTERNATIONAL COMPANY LIMITED—See China Hi-Tech Group Corporation; *Int'l*, pg. 1507
CHTC HEAVY INDUSTRY CO., LTD.—See China Hi-Tech Group Co., Ltd.; *Int'l*, pg. 1507
CHTC HELON CO., LTD.; *Int'l*, pg. 1589
CHTC HOLDINGS CO., LTD.—See China Hi-Tech Group Co., Ltd.; *Int'l*, pg. 1507
CHTC INVESTMENT MANAGEMENT CO., LTD.—See China Hi-Tech Group Co., Ltd.; *Int'l*, pg. 1507
CHTC KAMA CO., LTD.—See China Hi-Tech Group Co., Ltd.; *Int'l*, pg. 1507
CHTC REAL ESTATE CO., LTD.—See China Hi-Tech Group Co., Ltd.; *Int'l*, pg. 1507
C&H TESTING SERVICE, LLC—See The Aleut Corporation; *U.S. Private*, pg. 3984
C&H TOYS (SUZHOU) CO , LTD—See Dream International Ltd; *Int'l*, pg. 2202
CHT SECURITY CO., LTD.—See Chunghwa Telecom Co., Ltd.; *Int'l*, pg. 1598
CHUANGLIAN HOLDINGS LIMITED; *Int'l*, pg. 1590
CHUANG'S CHINA INVESTMENTS LIMITED; *Int'l*, pg. 1590
CHUANG'S CONSORTIUM INTERNATIONAL LIMITED; *Int'l*, pg. 1590
CHUANG'S PROPERTIES (CENTRAL PLAZA) SDN. BHD.—See Chuang's China Investments Limited; *Int'l*, pg. 1590
CHUAN HOLDINGS LIMITED; *Int'l*, pg. 1589
CHUANHUA AJINOMOTO CO., LTD.—See Ajinomoto Company, Inc.; *Int'l*, pg. 257
CHUAN HUAT RESOURCES BERHAD; *Int'l*, pg. 1589
CHUAN HUP HOLDINGS LIMITED; *Int'l*, pg. 1589
CHUAN SENG LEONG PTE. LTD.; *Int'l*, pg. 1589
CHUAN SIN CACTUS SDN BHD—See Spritzer Bhd.; *Int'l*, pg. 7145
CHUBB AGRIBUSINESS—See Chubb Limited; *Int'l*, pg. 1592
CHUBB ALTERNATIVE RISK LTD.—See Chubb Limited; *Int'l*, pg. 1590
CHUBB ARABIA COOPERATIVE INSURANCE COMPANY—See Chubb Limited; *Int'l*, pg. 1590
CHUBB ASIA PACIFIC SERVICES PTE. LTD.—See Chubb Limited; *Int'l*, pg. 1590
CHUBB ASSET MANAGEMENT INC.—See Chubb Limited; *Int'l*, pg. 1591
CHUBB ASSET MANAGERS, INC.—See Chubb Limited; *Int'l*, pg. 1591
CHUBB ATLANTIC INDEMNITY, LTD.—See Chubb Limited; *Int'l*, pg. 1591
CHUBB BERMUDA INSURANCE LTD.—See Chubb Limited; *Int'l*, pg. 1590
CHUBB COMPUTER SERVICES, INC.—See Chubb Limited; *Int'l*, pg. 1591
CHUBB CUSTOM INSURANCE COMPANY—See Chubb Limited; *Int'l*, pg. 1591
CHUBB CUSTOM MARKET, INC.—See Chubb Limited; *Int'l*, pg. 1591
CHUBB DELTA TELESURVEILLANCE—See Carrier Global Corporation; *U.S. Public*, pg. 443
CHUBB DE MEXICO, COMPANIA AFIANZADORA, S.A. DE C.V.—See Chubb Limited; *Int'l*, pg. 1591
CHUBB DEUTSCHLAND GMBH—See Carrier Global Corporation; *U.S. Public*, pg. 443
CHUBB EUROPEAN GROUP LIMITED—See Chubb Limited; *Int'l*, pg. 1590
CHUBB FINANCIAL SOLUTIONS, INC.—See Chubb Limited; *Int'l*, pg. 1591
CHUBB FIRE & SECURITY B.V.—See Carrier Global Corporation; *U.S. Public*, pg. 443
CHUBB FIRE & SECURITY LIMITED—See Carrier Global Corporation; *U.S. Public*, pg. 440
CHUBB FIRE & SECURITY LIMITED—See Carrier Global Corporation; *U.S. Public*, pg. 441
CHUBB FIRE & SECURITY PTY LTD—See Carrier Global Corporation; *U.S. Public*, pg. 441
CHUBB FRANCE—See Carrier Global Corporation; *U.S. Public*, pg. 441
CHUBB GROUP MANAGEMENT & HOLDINGS LTD.—See Chubb Limited; *Int'l*, pg. 1590
CHUBB GROUP OF INSURANCE COMPANY - OREGON—See Chubb Limited; *Int'l*, pg. 1591
CHUBB GROUP OF INSURANCE COMPANY—See Chubb Limited; *Int'l*, pg. 1591
CHUBB GROUP SECURITY LIMITED—See Carrier Global Corporation; *U.S. Public*, pg. 441
CHUBB HOLDINGS AUSTRALIA PTY LIMITED—See Chubb Limited; *Int'l*, pg. 1592
CHUBB HONG KONG LTD.—See Carrier Global Corporation; *U.S. Public*, pg. 441
CHUBB INA HOLDINGS INC.—See Chubb Limited; *Int'l*, pg. 1590
CHUBB INDEMNITY INSURANCE COMPANY—See Chubb Limited; *Int'l*, pg. 1591
CHUBB INSURANCE AUSTRALIA LIMITED—See Chubb Limited; *Int'l*, pg. 1592

CHUBB INSURANCE COMPANY LIMITED—See Chubb Limited; *Int'l*, pg. 1591
CHUBB INSURANCE COMPANY OF CANADA—See Chubb Limited; *Int'l*, pg. 1591
CHUBB INSURANCE COMPANY OF NEW JERSEY—See Chubb Limited; *Int'l*, pg. 1591
CHUBB INSURANCE COMPANY OF NEW JERSEY—See Chubb Limited; *Int'l*, pg. 1591
CHUBB INSURANCE COMPANY OF PUERTO RICO—See Chubb Limited; *Int'l*, pg. 1592
CHUBB INSURANCE EGYPT S.A.E.—See Chubb Limited; *Int'l*, pg. 1592
CHUBB INSURANCE HONG KONG LIMITED—See Chubb Limited; *Int'l*, pg. 1590
CHUBB INSURANCE JAPAN—See Chubb Limited; *Int'l*, pg. 1592
CHUBB INSURANCE MALAYSIA BERHAD—See Chubb Limited; *Int'l*, pg. 1592
CHUBB INSURANCE NEW ZEALAND LIMITED—See Chubb Limited; *Int'l*, pg. 1592
CHUBB INSURANCE S.A.-N.V.—See Chubb Limited; *Int'l*, pg. 1592
CHUBB INSURANCE SOLUTIONS AGENCY INC.—See Chubb Limited; *Int'l*, pg. 1591
CHUBB INSURANCE SOLUTIONS AGENCY INC.—See Chubb Limited; *Int'l*, pg. 1591
CHUBB INSURANCE SOUTH AFRICA LIMITED—See Chubb Limited; *Int'l*, pg. 1592
CHUBB INSURANCE (SWITZERLAND) LIMITED—See Chubb Limited; *Int'l*, pg. 1592
CHUBB INSURANCE VIETNAM COMPANY LIMITED—See Chubb Limited; *Int'l*, pg. 1592
CHUBB IRELAND LIMITED—See Carrier Global Corporation; *U.S. Public*, pg. 443
CHUBB LIFE ASSURANCE PUBLIC COMPANY LIMITED—See Chubb Limited; *Int'l*, pg. 1592
CHUBB LIFE INSURANCE COMPANY OF CANADA—See Chubb Limited; *Int'l*, pg. 1592
CHUBB LIFE INSURANCE VIETNAM COMPANY LIMITED—See Chubb Limited; *Int'l*, pg. 1592
CHUBB LIMITED; *Int'l*, pg. 1590
CHUBB LLOYDS INSURANCE COMPANY OF TEXAS—See Chubb Limited; *Int'l*, pg. 1591
CHUBB NATIONAL INSURANCE COMPANY—See Chubb Limited; *Int'l*, pg. 1591
CHUBB NEDERLAND B.V.—See Carrier Global Corporation; *U.S. Public*, pg. 441
CHUBB NEW ZEALAND—See Carrier Global Corporation; *U.S. Public*, pg. 443
CHUBB OSTERREICH GMBH—See Carrier Global Corporation; *U.S. Public*, pg. 443
CHUBB PERU S.A. COMPANIA DE SEGUROS Y REASEGUROS—See Chubb Limited; *Int'l*, pg. 1590
CHUBB RE, INC.—See Chubb Limited; *Int'l*, pg. 1591
CHUBB REINSURANCE (SWITZERLAND) LIMITED—See Chubb Limited; *Int'l*, pg. 1592
CHUBB RESSEGURADORA BRASIL S.A.—See Chubb Limited; *Int'l*, pg. 1592
CHUBB SECURITY HOLDINGS AUSTRALIA PTY. LTD—See Carrier Global Corporation; *U.S. Public*, pg. 441
CHUBB SECURITY SYSTEMS B.V.B.A.—See Carrier Global Corporation; *U.S. Public*, pg. 443
CHUBB SEGURADORA MACAU S.A.—See Chubb Limited; *Int'l*, pg. 1592
CHUBB SEGUROS ARGENTINA S.A.—See Chubb Limited; *Int'l*, pg. 1591
CHUBB SEGUROS CHILE SA—See Chubb Limited; *Int'l*, pg. 1592
CHUBB SEGUROS COLOMBIA S.A.—See Chubb Limited; *Int'l*, pg. 1592
CHUBB SEGUROS DE VIDA CHILE S.A.—See Chubb Limited; *Int'l*, pg. 1592
CHUBB SEGUROS ECUADOR S.A.—See Chubb Limited; *Int'l*, pg. 1592
CHUBB SEGUROS MEXICO, S.A.—See Chubb Limited; *Int'l*, pg. 1590
CHUBB SEGUROS PANAMA S.A.—See Chubb Limited; *Int'l*, pg. 1592
CHUBB SEGUROS SA—See PBG S/A; *Int'l*, pg. 5765
CHUBB SERVICES CORPORATION—See Chubb Limited; *Int'l*, pg. 1591
CHUBB SERVICES UK LIMITED—See Chubb Limited; *Int'l*, pg. 1592
CHUBB SINGAPORE PRIVATE LIMITED—See Carrier Global Corporation; *U.S. Public*, pg. 441
CHUBB & SON INC.—See Chubb Limited; *Int'l*, pg. 1591
CHUBB SYSTEMS LIMITED—See Carrier Global Corporation; *U.S. Public*, pg. 441
CHUBB TEMPEST LIFE REINSURANCE LIMITED—See Chubb Limited; *Int'l*, pg. 1592
CHUBB TEMPEST LIFE RE - USA—See Chubb Limited; *Int'l*, pg. 1592
CHUBB TEMPEST RE CANADA, INC.—See Chubb Limited; *Int'l*, pg. 1591
CHUBB TEMPEST RE GROUP—See Chubb Limited; *Int'l*, pg. 1591
CHUBB TEMPEST REINSURANCE LTD.—See Chubb Limited; *Int'l*, pg. 1591

CORPORATE AFFILIATIONS

CHUBB TEMPEST RE USA LLC—See Chubb Limited; *Int'l*, pg. 1590
CHUBB TEMPEST RE USA LLC—See Chubb Limited; *Int'l*, pg. 1592
CHUBB UNDERWRITING (DIFC) LIMITED—See Chubb Limited; *Int'l*, pg. 1590
CHUBB UNDERWRITING (DIFC) LIMITED—See Chubb Limited; *Int'l*, pg. 1590
CHUBB UNION ZIMBABWE (PVT) LTD—See ASSA ABLOY AB; *Int'l*, pg. 639
CHUBB US HOLDINGS INC.—See Chubb Limited; *Int'l*, pg. 1591
CHUBU BUILDING SERVICE CO., LTD.—See Sala Corporation; *Int'l*, pg. 6490
CHUBU CABLE NETWORK COMPANY, INCORPORATED—See Chubu Electric Power Co., Inc.; *Int'l*, pg. 1593
CHUBU ELECTRIC POWER CO., INC.; *Int'l*, pg. 1593
CHUBU ELECTRIC POWER CO., INC. - UK OFFICE—See Chubu Electric Power Co., Inc.; *Int'l*, pg. 1593
CHUBU ELECTRIC POWER COMPANY U.S.A. INC.—See Chubu Electric Power Co., Inc.; *Int'l*, pg. 1593
CHUBU ENERGYS CO., LTD.—See NGK Insulators, Ltd.; *Int'l*, pg. 5254
CHUBU ENGINEERING CORPORATION—See Sala Corporation; *Int'l*, pg. 6490
CHUBU ENGINEERING SERVICE CO., LTD.—See Sala Corporation; *Int'l*, pg. 6490
CHUBU FOODS CO., LTD.—See Valor Holdings Co., Ltd.; *Int'l*, pg. 8122
CHUBU GAS CO., LTD.—See Sala Corporation; *Int'l*, pg. 6490
CHUBU GAS REALTORS CO., LTD.—See Sala Corporation; *Int'l*, pg. 6490
CHUBU HOME SERVICE CO., LTD.—See Sala Corporation; *Int'l*, pg. 6490
CHUBU IBI CO., LTD.—See Yuasa Trading Co., Ltd.; *Int'l*, pg. 8609
CHUBU JUKAN OPERATION CO., LTD.—See Mitsubishi Heavy Industries, Ltd.; *Int'l*, pg. 4953
CHUBU KAIUN KAISHA, LTD.—See Sankyu, Inc.; *Int'l*, pg. 6543
CHUBU LIQUID OXYGEN CO., LTD.—See Chubu Electric Power Co., Inc.; *Int'l*, pg. 1593
CHUBU MEIHAN CO., LTD.—See Meiji Holdings Co., Ltd.; *Int'l*, pg. 4800
CHUBU-NIPPON BROADCASTING CO., LTD.; *Int'l*, pg. 1594
CHUBU NOK SALES CO., LTD.—See NOK Corporation; *Int'l*, pg. 5401
CHUBU PLANT SERVICE CO., LTD.—See Chubu Electric Power Co., Inc.; *Int'l*, pg. 1593
CHUBU PLASTICS MOLDING CO., LTD.—See Okaya & Co., Ltd.; *Int'l*, pg. 5546
CHUBU PROPANE STAND LTD.—See Sala Corporation; *Int'l*, pg. 6490
CHUBU SEIKI CO., LTD.—See Chubu Electric Power Co., Inc.; *Int'l*, pg. 1593
CHUBU SHIRYO CO., LTD.; *Int'l*, pg. 1593
CHUBU STEEL PLATE CO., LTD.; *Int'l*, pg. 1593
CHUBU SUISAN CO., LTD.; *Int'l*, pg. 1594
CHUBU SYOKURYO KAISHA, LTD.—See Toyota Tsusho Corporation; *Int'l*, pg. 7876
CHUBU TELECOMMUNICATIONS CO., INC.—See KDDI Corporation; *Int'l*, pg. 4111
CHUBU TOHUN CO., LTD.—See Tomoku Co., Ltd.; *Int'l*, pg. 7801
CHUCK ANDERSON FORD INC.; *U.S. Private*, pg. 893
CHUCK ATKINSON, INC.—See Crimson Solutions, LLC; *U.S. Private*, pg. 1101
CHUCK CLANCY FORD OF MARIETTA, LLC—See AutoNation, Inc.; *U.S. Public*, pg. 234
CHUCK CLANCY FORD OF MARIETTA, LLC—See AutoNation, Inc.; *U.S. Public*, pg. 234
CHUCK FAIRBANKS CHEVROLET, INC.; *U.S. Private*, pg. 893
CHUCK HUTTON CHEVROLET COMPANY; *U.S. Private*, pg. 893
CHUCK LATHAM ASSOCIATES, INC.; *U.S. Private*, pg. 893
CHUCK PATTERSON AUTO WORLD; *U.S. Private*, pg. 893
CHUCK STEVENS AUTOMOTIVE, INC.; *U.S. Private*, pg. 893
CHUCK VAN HORN DODGE, INC.; *U.S. Private*, pg. 893
CHUCO CO., LTD.; *Int'l*, pg. 1594
CHUDEN AUTO LEASE CO., LTD.—See Chubu Electric Power Co., Inc.; *Int'l*, pg. 1593
CHUDEN CTI CO., LTD.—See Chubu Electric Power Co., Inc.; *Int'l*, pg. 1593
CHUDEN ENGINEERING CONSULTANTS CO., LTD.—See The Chugoku Electric Power Co., Inc.; *Int'l*, pg. 7632
CHUDEN KANKYO TECHNOS CO., LTD.—See The Chugoku Electric Power Co., Inc.; *Int'l*, pg. 7632
CHUDENKO CORPORATION; *Int'l*, pg. 1594
CHUDENKO ELETECH YAMAGUCHI CO., LTD.—See Chudenko Corporation; *Int'l*, pg. 1594

COMPANY NAME INDEX

CHUDEN KOGYO CO., LTD.—See The Chugoku Electric Power Co., Inc.; *Int'l*, pg. 7632
CHUDEN KOSAN CO., LTD.—See Nippon Denko Co., Ltd.; *Int'l*, pg. 5313
CHUDENKO WORLD FARM CO., LTD.—See Chudenko Corporation; *Int'l*, pg. 1594
CHUDEN PLANT CO., LTD.—See The Chugoku Electric Power Co., Inc.; *Int'l*, pg. 7632
CHUDEN REAL ESTATE CO., LTD.—See Chubu Electric Power Co., Inc.; *Int'l*, pg. 1593
CHUDEN SANGYO CO., LTD.—See Nippon Denko Co., Ltd.; *Int'l*, pg. 5314
CHUDEN TRANSPORTATION SERVICE CO., LTD.—See Chubu Electric Power Co., Inc.; *Int'l*, pg. 1593
CHUDEN WING CO., LTD.—See Chubu Electric Power Co., Inc.; *Int'l*, pg. 1593
CHUDY PAPER CO. INC.; *U.S. Private*, pg. 893
CHUEN GAS CO., LTD.—See Shizuokagas Co., Ltd.; *Int'l*, pg. 6856
CHUETSU CO., LTD.—See Oji Holdings Corporation; *Int'l*, pg. 5536
CHUETSU PRECISION WORKS CO., LTD.—See Okaya & Co., Ltd.; *Int'l*, pg. 5546
CHUETSU PULP & PAPER CO., LTD.; *Int'l*, pg. 1594
CHUETSU SUMIDENSO, LTD—See Sumitomo Electric Industries, Ltd.; *Int'l*, pg. 7277
CHUGACH ALASKA CORPORATION; *U.S. Private*, pg. 893
CHUGACH ELECTRIC ASSOCIATION, INC.; *U.S. Private*, pg. 894
CHUGACH GOVERNMENT SOLUTIONS, LLC—See Chugach Alaska Corporation; *U.S. Private*, pg. 893
CHUGACH INDUSTRIES, INC.—See Chugach Alaska Corporation; *U.S. Private*, pg. 894
CHUGACH MANAGEMENT SERVICES INC.—See Chugach Alaska Corporation; *U.S. Private*, pg. 894
CHUGAI AIR SYSTEM CO., LTD.—See Chugai Ro Co., Ltd.; *Int'l*, pg. 1594
CHUGAI BUSINESS SUPPORT CO., LTD.—See Roche Holding AG; *Int'l*, pg. 6372
CHUGAI CLINICAL RESEARCH CENTER CO., LTD.—See Roche Holding AG; *Int'l*, pg. 6372
CHUGAI DISTRIBUTION CO., LTD.—See Roche Holding AG; *Int'l*, pg. 6372
CHUGAI ENGINEERING CO.,LTD.—See Chugai Ro Co., Ltd.; *Int'l*, pg. 1594
CHUGAI MINING CO. LTD. - MOCHIKOSHI PLANT—See Chugai Mining Co. Ltd.; *Int'l*, pg. 1594
CHUGAI MINING CO. LTD.; *Int'l*, pg. 1594
CHUGAI MINING CO. LTD. - TOKYO PLANT—See Chugai Mining Co. Ltd.; *Int'l*, pg. 1594
CHUGAI PHARMABODY RESEARCH PTE. LTD.—See Roche Holding AG; *Int'l*, pg. 6372
CHUGAI PHARMACEUTICAL CO., LTD. - FUJIEDA PLANT—See Roche Holding AG; *Int'l*, pg. 6372
CHUGAI PHARMACEUTICAL CO., LTD.—See Roche Holding AG; *Int'l*, pg. 6372
CHUGAI PHARMACEUTICAL CO., LTD. - UKIMA PLANT—See Roche Holding AG; *Int'l*, pg. 6372
CHUGAI PHARMACEUTICAL CO., LTD. - UTSUNOMIYA PLANT—See Roche Holding AG; *Int'l*, pg. 6372
CHUGAI PHARMA EUROPE LTD.—See Roche Holding AG; *Int'l*, pg. 6372
CHUGAI PHARMA FRANCE S.A.S.—See Roche Holding AG; *Int'l*, pg. 6372
CHUGAI PHARMA MARKETING LTD.—See Roche Holding AG; *Int'l*, pg. 6372
CHUGAI PHARMA SCIENCE (BEIJING) CO.—See Roche Holding AG; *Int'l*, pg. 6372
CHUGAI PHARMA (SHANGHAI) CONSULTING CO., LTD.—See Roche Holding AG; *Int'l*, pg. 6372
CHUGAI PHARMA TAIWAN LTD.—See Roche Holding AG; *Int'l*, pg. 6372
CHUGAI PHARMA U.K. LTD.—See Roche Holding AG; *Int'l*, pg. 6372
CHUGAI PHARMA U.S.A., LLC—See Roche Holding AG; *Int'l*, pg. 6372
CHUGAI PLANT CO., LTD.—See Chugai Ro Co., Ltd.; *Int'l*, pg. 1594
CHUGAI RESEARCH INSTITUTE FOR MEDICAL SCIENCE, INC.—See Roche Holding AG; *Int'l*, pg. 6372
CHUGAI RO ALUMINUM (SHANDONG) CO., LTD.—See Chugai Ro Co., Ltd.; *Int'l*, pg. 1594
CHUGAI RO CO., LTD. - KOKURA FACTORY—See Chugai Ro Co., Ltd.; *Int'l*, pg. 1594
CHUGAI RO CO., LTD. - SAKAI WORKS—See Chugai Ro Co., Ltd.; *Int'l*, pg. 1594
CHUGAI RO CO., LTD.; *Int'l*, pg. 1594
CHUGAI RO SHANGHAI CO., LTD.—See Chugai Ro Co., Ltd.; *Int'l*, pg. 1594
CHUGAI RO (THAILAND) CO., LTD.—See Chugai Ro Co., Ltd.; *Int'l*, pg. 1594
CHUGAI RO THERMAL ENGINEERING (SHANGHAI) CO., LTD.—See Chugai Ro Co., Ltd.; *Int'l*, pg. 1594
CHUGAI SANOFI-AVENTIS S.N.C.—See Roche Holding AG; *Int'l*, pg. 6372
CHUGAI SANOFI-AVENTIS S.N.C.—See Sanofi; *Int'l*, pg. 6550

CHUGAI USA, INC.—See Roche Holding AG; *Int'l*, pg. 6372
CHUGIN ASSET MANAGEMENT COMPANY, LIMITED—See Chugin Financial Group, Inc.; *Int'l*, pg. 1594
THE CHUGIN CREDIT GUARANTEE CO., LIMITED—See Chugin Financial Group, Inc.; *Int'l*, pg. 1595
CHUGIN FINANCIAL GROUP, INC.; *Int'l*, pg. 1594
THE CHUGIN LEASE COMPANY, LIMITED—See Chugin Financial Group, Inc.; *Int'l*, pg. 1595
THE CHUGIN OPERATION CENTER, CO., LIMITED—See Chugin Financial Group, Inc.; *Int'l*, pg. 1595
CHUGIN SECURITIES CO., LTD.—See Chugin Financial Group, Inc.; *Int'l*, pg. 1595
THE CHUGOKU BANK, LIMITED—See Chugin Financial Group, Inc.; *Int'l*, pg. 1594
CHUGOKU BEND CO., LTD.—See The Chugoku Electric Power Co., Inc.; *Int'l*, pg. 7632
CHUGOKU BUSINESS SERVICE CO., LTD.—See Sankyu, Inc.; *Int'l*, pg. 6543
THE CHUGOKU ELECTRIC MANUFACTURING CO., INC—See The Chugoku Electric Power Co., Inc.; *Int'l*, pg. 7632
CHUGOKU ELECTRIC POWER AMERICA, LLC—See The Chugoku Electric Power Co., Inc.; *Int'l*, pg. 7632
THE CHUGOKU ELECTRIC POWER CO., INC.; *Int'l*, pg. 7632
CHUGOKU ELECTRIC WIRE & CABLE CO., LTD.—See ENEOS Holdings, Inc.; *Int'l*, pg. 2416
CHUGOKU FUNAI ELECTRIC CO., LTD.—See Funai Electric Co., Ltd.; *Int'l*, pg. 2844
CHUGOKU JR BUS COMPANY—See West Japan Railway Company; *Int'l*, pg. 8385
CHUGOKU KAKO CO., LTD.—See Nippon Shokubai Co., Ltd.; *Int'l*, pg. 5332
CHUGOKUKOGYO CO., LTD.—See Nomura Holdings, Inc.; *Int'l*, pg. 5409
CHUGOKU MARINE PAINTS (GUANGDONG) LTD—See Chugoku Marine Paints, Ltd.; *Int'l*, pg. 1595
CHUGOKU MARINE PAINTS (HELLAS) S.A.—See Chugoku Marine Paints, Ltd.; *Int'l*, pg. 1595
CHUGOKU MARINE PAINTS (HONGKONG) LTD—See Chugoku Marine Paints, Ltd.; *Int'l*, pg. 1595
CHUGOKU MARINE PAINTS, LTD. - KYUSHU FACTORY—See Chugoku Marine Paints, Ltd.; *Int'l*, pg. 1595
CHUGOKU MARINE PAINTS, LTD. - SHIGA FACTORY—See Chugoku Marine Paints, Ltd.; *Int'l*, pg. 1595
CHUGOKU MARINE PAINTS, LTD.; *Int'l*, pg. 1595
CHUGOKU MARINE PAINTS (NAGASAKI), LTD.—See Chugoku Marine Paints, Ltd.; *Int'l*, pg. 1595
CHUGOKU MARINE PAINTS (SHANGHAI), LTD. - FACTORY & TECHNICAL CENTER—See Chugoku Marine Paints, Ltd.; *Int'l*, pg. 1595
CHUGOKU MARINE PAINTS (SHANGHAI), LTD.—See Chugoku Marine Paints, Ltd.; *Int'l*, pg. 1595
CHUGOKU MARINE PAINTS (SINGAPORE) PTE. LTD.—See Chugoku Marine Paints, Ltd.; *Int'l*, pg. 1595
CHUGOKU MARINE PAINTS (TAIWAN) LTD—See Chugoku Marine Paints, Ltd.; *Int'l*, pg. 1595
CHUGOKU PAINTS BV—See Chugoku Marine Paints, Ltd.; *Int'l*, pg. 1595
CHUGOKU PAINTS (GERMANY) GMBH—See Chugoku Marine Paints, Ltd.; *Int'l*, pg. 1595
CHUGOKU PAINTS (INDIA) PRIVATE LIMITED—See Chugoku Marine Paints, Ltd.; *Int'l*, pg. 1595
CHUGOKU PAINTS (MALAYSIA) SDN. BHD. - JOHOR FACTORY—See Chugoku Marine Paints, Ltd.; *Int'l*, pg. 1595
CHUGOKU PAINTS (MALAYSIA) SDN. BHD.—See Chugoku Marine Paints, Ltd.; *Int'l*, pg. 1595
CHUGOKU PAINTS (UK) LIMITED—See Chugoku Marine Paints, Ltd.; *Int'l*, pg. 1595
CHUGOKU POWER SYSTEMS CO., LTD.—See Yashima Denki Co., Ltd.; *Int'l*, pg. 8568
CHUGOKU READY MIXED CONCRETE CO., LTD.—See Tokuyama Corporation; *Int'l*, pg. 7786
CHUGOKU RECORD MANAGEMENT INC.—See The Chugoku Electric Power Co., Inc.; *Int'l*, pg. 7632
CHUGOKU-SAMHWA PAINTS LTD. - GYEONGNAM FACTORY—See Chugoku Marine Paints, Ltd.; *Int'l*, pg. 1595
CHUGOKU SAMHWA PAINTS LTD.—See Chugoku Marine Paints, Ltd.; *Int'l*, pg. 1595
CHUGOKU SC DEVELOPMENT COMPANY—See West Japan Railway Company; *Int'l*, pg. 8385
CHUGOKUSHIKOKU HAKUHODO INC.—See Hakuhodo DY Holdings Incorporated; *Int'l*, pg. 3220
CHUGOKU SHIPPING AGENCIES LTD.—See Mitsui O.S.K. Lines, Ltd.; *Int'l*, pg. 4989
CHUGOKU SOFT DEVELOPMENT CO. LTD.—See Chugoku Marine Paints, Ltd.; *Int'l*, pg. 1595
CHUHATSU HANBAI CO., LTD.—See Chuo Spring Co., Ltd.; *Int'l*, pg. 1599
CHUHATSU NORTH AMERICA, INC.—See Chuo Spring Co., Ltd.; *Int'l*, pg. 1599
CHUHATSU SEIKOU CO., LTD.—See Chuo Spring Co., Ltd.; *Int'l*, pg. 1599

CHUHATSU-TECHNO CO., LTD.—See Chuo Spring Co., Ltd.; *Int'l*, pg. 1599
CHUHATSU (THAILAND) CO., LTD. - HEMARAJ PLANT—See Chuo Spring Co., Ltd.; *Int'l*, pg. 1599
CHUHATSU (THAILAND) CO., LTD.—See Chuo Spring Co., Ltd.; *Int'l*, pg. 1599
CHUHATSU UNYU CO., LTD.—See Chuo Spring Co., Ltd.; *Int'l*, pg. 1599
CHUHBU PLASTICS MOLDING CO., LTD.—See Okaya & Co., Ltd.; *Int'l*, pg. 5546
CHU KAI PUBLIC COMPANY LIMITED; *Int'l*, pg. 1589
CHUKEN CONSULTANT CO., LTD.—See Sumitomo Osaka Cement Co Ltd; *Int'l*, pg. 7296
CHUKI SEIKI CO., LTD.—See Taiyo Yuden Company Ltd.; *Int'l*, pg. 7426
CHUKONG HOLDINGS LIMITED; *Int'l*, pg. 1595
CHU KONG PETROLEUM AND NATURAL GAS STEEL PIPE HOLDINGS LIMITED; *Int'l*, pg. 1589
CHU KONG SHIPPING ENTERPRISES (GROUP) COMPANY LIMITED—See Chu Kong Shipping Enterprises (Holding) Co. Ltd.; *Int'l*, pg. 1589
CHU KONG SHIPPING ENTERPRISES (HOLDING) CO. LTD.; *Int'l*, pg. 1589
THE CHUKYO BANK, LTD.—See Aichi Financial Group Co., Ltd.; *Int'l*, pg. 229
CHUKYO GENERAL LEASE CO., LTD—See Mitsubishi HC Capital Inc.; *Int'l*, pg. 4950
CHUKYO IYAKUHIN CO., LTD.; *Int'l*, pg. 1595
CHULARAT HOSPITAL PUBLIC COMPANY LIMITED; *Int'l*, pg. 1596
CHULA VISTA CENTER, LP—See Brookfield Corporation; *Int'l*, pg. 1185
CHULA VISTA ELECTRIC CO.; *U.S. Private*, pg. 894
CHULA VISTA MARINA/RV PARK, LTD.—See Sun Communities, Inc.; *U.S. Public*, pg. 1963
CHUMA HOLDINGS INC.; *U.S. Private*, pg. 894
CHUM MINING GROUP INC.; *Int'l*, pg. 1596
CHUMNEY & ASSOCIATES; *U.S. Private*, pg. 894
CHUMPORN PALM OIL INDUSTRY PUBLIC COMPANY LIMITED; *Int'l*, pg. 1596
CHUNBO ADVANCED MATERIALS CO. LTD.—See Chunbo Co., Ltd.; *Int'l*, pg. 1596
CHUNBO CO., LTD.; *Int'l*, pg. 1596
CHUNBO FINE CHEM CO., LTD.—See Chunbo Co., Ltd.; *Int'l*, pg. 1596
CHUN CAN CAPITAL GROUP; *Int'l*, pg. 1596
CHUNGCHEONG ENERGY SERVICE CO., LTD.—See SK Inc.; *Int'l*, pg. 6971
CHUNG CIN ENTERPRISE CO., LTD.—See Test-Rite International Co., Ltd.; *Int'l*, pg. 7575
CHUNGDAHM LEARNING, INC.; *Int'l*, pg. 1597
CHUNGDAHM PHILIPPINES, INC.—See Chungdahm Learning, Inc.; *Int'l*, pg. 1597
CHUNGDAM GLOBAL CO., LTD.; *Int'l*, pg. 1597
CHUNG FU CO., LTD; *Int'l*, pg. 1597
CHUNGHO COMNET CO., LTD. - GIMPO FACTORY—See Cheongho ICT Co., Ltd.; *Int'l*, pg. 1471
CHUNGHONG ELECTRONICS POLAND SP. Z O.O.—See LEAD DATA INC.; *Int'l*, pg. 4432
CHUNGHONG HOLDINGS LIMITED—See LEAD DATA INC.; *Int'l*, pg. 4432
CHUNG-HSIN ELECTRIC & MACHINERY MANUFACTURING CORP.; *Int'l*, pg. 1597
CHUNG - HSIN POWER SYSTEMS (JIANGSU) CORP.—See Chung-Hsin Electric & Machinery Manufacturing Corp.; *Int'l*, pg. 1597
CHUNG HSIN POWER SYSTEMS (SHENYANG) INC.—See Chung-Hsin Electric & Machinery Manufacturing Corp.; *Int'l*, pg. 1597
CHUNG-HSIN PRECISION MACHINERY CO., LTD.—See Chung-Hsin Electric & Machinery Manufacturing Corp.; *Int'l*, pg. 1597
CHUNGHSIN TECHNOLOGY GROUP CO., LTD; *Int'l*, pg. 1597
CHUNG HUNG STEEL CORPORATION—See China Steel Corporation; *Int'l*, pg. 1555
CHUNGHWA BIOMEDICAL TECHNOLOGY CO, LTD.—See Chunghwa Chemical Synthesis & Biotech Co., Ltd.; *Int'l*, pg. 1598
CHUNG HWA CHEMICAL INDUSTRIAL WORKS LTD.; *Int'l*, pg. 1597
CHUNGHWA CHEMICAL SYNTHESIS & BIOTECH CO., LTD.; *Int'l*, pg. 1597
CHUNG HWA FOOD INDUSTRIAL CO., LTD.; *Int'l*, pg. 1597
CHUNGHWA LEADING PHOTONICS TECH CO., LTD.—See Chunghwa Telecom Co., Ltd.; *Int'l*, pg. 1598
CHUNGHWA PICTURE TUBES, LTD.—See Tatung Company; *Int'l*, pg. 7475
CHUNGHWA PICTURE TUBES (MALAYSIA) SDN. BHD.—See Tatung Company; *Int'l*, pg. 7475
CHUNGHWA PICTURE TUBES SDN. BHD.—See Tatung Company; *Int'l*, pg. 7475
CHUNGHWA PRECISION TEST TECH. CO., LTD—See Chunghwa Telecom Co., Ltd.; *Int'l*, pg. 1598
CHUNGHWA PRECISION TEST TECH. USA CORPORATION—See Chunghwa Telecom Co., Ltd.; *Int'l*, pg. 1598

CHUNG HWA FOOD INDUSTRIAL CO., LTD.

CORPORATE AFFILIATIONS

CHUNG HWA PULP CORP. - CHIUTANG MILL—See Chung Hwa Pulp Corp.; *Int'l*, pg. 1597
CHUNG HWA PULP CORP. - HUALIEN MILL—See Chung Hwa Pulp Corp.; *Int'l*, pg. 1597
CHUNG HWA PULP CORP.; *Int'l*, pg. 1597
CHUNG HWA PULP CORP. - TAITUNG MILL—See Chung Hwa Pulp Corp.; *Int'l*, pg. 1597
CHUNGHWA SYSTEM INTEGRATION CO., LTD.—See Chunghwa Telecom Co., Ltd.; *Int'l*, pg. 1598
CHUNGHWA TELECOM CO., LTD.; *Int'l*, pg. 1598
CHUNGHWA TELECOM GLOBAL, INC.—See Chunghwa Telecom Co., Ltd.; *Int'l*, pg. 1598
CHUNGHWA TELECOM JAPAN CO., LTD—See Chunghwa Telecom Co., Ltd.; *Int'l*, pg. 1598
CHUNGHWA TELECOM SINGAPORE PTE LTD—See Chunghwa Telecom Co., Ltd.; *Int'l*, pg. 1598
CHUNGHWA TELECOM (THAILAND) CO., LTD.—See Chunghwa Telecom Co., Ltd.; *Int'l*, pg. 1598
CHUNGHWA TELECOM VIETNAM CO., LTD.—See Chunghwa Telecom Co., Ltd.; *Int'l*, pg. 1598
CHUNGHWA YUMING HEALTHCARE CO., LTD.—See China Chemical & Pharmaceutical Co., Ltd.; *Int'l*, pg. 1488
CHUNG JIH METAL TREATMENT CHEMICALS, INC.—See Nihon Parkerizing Co., Ltd.; *Int'l*, pg. 5286
CHUNG-KANG STEEL STRUCTURE (KUNSHAN) CO., LTD.; *Int'l*, pg. 1597
CHUNG KUO INSURANCE CO., LTD.—See Mega Financial Holding Co., Ltd.; *Int'l*, pg. 4791
CHUNGKWANG CONSTRUCTION CO., LTD.; *Int'l*, pg. 1598
CHUNG LIEN TRANSPORTATION CO., LTD.; *Int'l*, pg. 1597
CHUNG LOONG PAPER HOLDINGS LIMITED—See Cheng Loong Corp.; *Int'l*, pg. 1466
CHUNG-LU CONSTRUCTION CO., LTD.—See Kajima Corporation; *Int'l*, pg. 4055
CHUNG MING CO., LTD.—See Chailease Holding Company Limited; *Int'l*, pg. 1437
CHUNGNAM NATIONAL UNIVERSITY; *Int'l*, pg. 1598
CHUNG'S FOODS INC.; *U.S. Private*, pg. 894
CHUNG TAI TRAVEL AND TOUR CO., LTD.—See ZZLL Information Technology, Inc.; *Int'l*, pg. 8701
CHUNG TAK LIGHTING CONTROL SYSTEMS (GUANGZHOU) LTD.—See Siemens Aktiengesellschaft; *Int'l*, pg. 6886
CHUNG YICK TEXTILE FACTORY LIMITED—See GTI Holdings Limited; *Int'l*, pg. 3151
CHUNG YO MATERIALS CO., LTD.—See Chia Yi Steel Co., Ltd.; *Int'l*, pg. 1475
CHUNG YUAN DAIDO CO., LTD.—See Daido Metal Corporation; *Int'l*, pg. 1921
CHUNG YUAN DAIDO (GUANGZHOU) CO., LTD.—See Daido Metal Corporation; *Int'l*, pg. 1921
CHUNICHI DRAGONS CO., INC.—See Chunichi Shimbun Co., Ltd.; *Int'l*, pg. 1598
CHUNICHI SHIMBUN CO., LTD.; *Int'l*, pg. 1598
CHUNICHI TRANSPORTATION CO., LTD.—See Howa Machinery, Ltd.; *Int'l*, pg. 3493
CHUNIL EXPRESS CO., LTD.; *Int'l*, pg. 1598
CHUN JEE SHIPPING CO., LTD.—See Regional Container Lines Public Company Limited; *Int'l*, pg. 6254
CHUNMO INTERNATIONAL CO., LTD.—See Changzhou Tronly New Electronic Materials Co., Ltd.; *Int'l*, pg. 1446
CHUNTEX ELECTRONIC CO., LTD.; *Int'l*, pg. 1598
CHUN WO BUILDING CONSTRUCTION LIMITED—See Asia Allied Infrastructure Holdings Limited; *Int'l*, pg. 610
CHUN WO (CHINA) LIMITED—See Asia Allied Infrastructure Holdings Limited; *Int'l*, pg. 610
CHUN WO CIVIL ENGINEERING LIMITED—See Asia Allied Infrastructure Holdings Limited; *Int'l*, pg. 610
CHUN WO CONSTRUCTION AND ENGINEERING COMPANY LIMITED—See Asia Allied Infrastructure Holdings Limited; *Int'l*, pg. 610
CHUN WO CONTRACTORS LIMITED—See Asia Allied Infrastructure Holdings Limited; *Int'l*, pg. 610
CHUN WO ELEGANT DECORATION ENGINEERING COMPANY LIMITED—See Asia Allied Infrastructure Holdings Limited; *Int'l*, pg. 610
CHUN WO E & M ENGINEERING LIMITED—See Asia Allied Infrastructure Holdings Limited; *Int'l*, pg. 610
CHUN WO FOUNDATIONS LIMITED—See Asia Allied Infrastructure Holdings Limited; *Int'l*, pg. 610
CHUN YIK (MACAO COMMERCIAL OFFSHORE) LIMITED—See Hop Fung Group Holdings Ltd; *Int'l*, pg. 3473
CHUN YUAN CONSTRUCTION CO., LTD.—See Chun Yuan Steel Industry Co., Ltd.; *Int'l*, pg. 1596
CHUN YUAN STEEL INDUSTRY CO., LTD. - AUTOMATED STORAGE SYSTEM DIVISION—See Chun Yuan Steel Industry Co., Ltd.; *Int'l*, pg. 1596
CHUN YUAN STEEL INDUSTRY CO., LTD. - KAOHSIUNG PLANT—See Chun Yuan Steel Industry Co., Ltd.; *Int'l*, pg. 1596
CHUN YUAN STEEL INDUSTRY CO., LTD. - SHI TSU PLANT—See Chun Yuan Steel Industry Co., Ltd.; *Int'l*, pg. 1596
CHUN YUAN STEEL INDUSTRY CO., LTD.; *Int'l*, pg. 1596

CHUN YUAN STEEL INDUSTRY CO., LTD. - SPECIAL STEEL KAO HSIUNG PLANT—See Chun Yuan Steel Industry Co., Ltd.; *Int'l*, pg. 1596
CHUN YUAN STEEL INDUSTRY CO., LTD. - SPECIAL STEEL STRIP DIVISION—See Chun Yuan Steel Industry Co., Ltd.; *Int'l*, pg. 1596
CHUN YUAN STEEL INDUSTRY CO., LTD. - SPECIAL STEEL TAI CHUNG PLANT—See Chun Yuan Steel Industry Co., Ltd.; *Int'l*, pg. 1596
CHUN YUAN STEEL INDUSTRY CO., LTD. - TAICHUNG PLANT—See Chun Yuan Steel Industry Co., Ltd.; *Int'l*, pg. 1596
CHUN YU BIO-TECH CO., LTD.—See Chun Yu Works & Co., Ltd.; *Int'l*, pg. 1596
CHUN YU (DONGGUAN) METAL PRODUCTS CO., LTD.—See Chun Yu Works & Co., Ltd.; *Int'l*, pg. 1596
CHUN YU METAL PRODUCTS CO., LTD.—See Chun Yu Works & Co., Ltd.; *Int'l*, pg. 1596
CHUN YU WORKS & CO., LTD. - CHIASHING PLANT—See Chun Yu Works & Co., Ltd.; *Int'l*, pg. 1596
CHUN YU WORKS & CO., LTD. - KANGSHAN PLANT—See Chun Yu Works & Co., Ltd.; *Int'l*, pg. 1596
CHUN YU WORKS & CO., LTD.; *Int'l*, pg. 1596
CHUN ZU MACHINERY IND. CO., LTD.—See Chun Yu Works & Co., Ltd.; *Int'l*, pg. 1596
CHUN ZU MACHINERY INDUSTRY CO., LTD.—See Chun Yu Works & Co., Ltd.; *Int'l*, pg. 1596
CHUO BUILD INDUSTRY CO., LTD.—See Asahi Kasei Corporation; *Int'l*, pg. 595
CHUO DENKI CONSTRUCTION CO., LTD.—See TOKAI Holdings Corporation; *Int'l*, pg. 7779
CHUO DENKI KOGYO CO., LTD.—See Nippon Denko Co., Ltd.; *Int'l*, pg. 5313
CHUO DENSETSU CO., LTD.—See Hankyu Hanshin Holdings Inc.; *Int'l*, pg. 3255
CHUO ELECTRONIC MEASUREMENT CO., LTD.—See Otsuka Holdings Co., Ltd.; *Int'l*, pg. 5660
CHUO ELECTRONICS CO., LTD.; *Int'l*, pg. 1598
CHUO FOODS CO., LTD.—See Chuo Gyorui Co., Ltd.; *Int'l*, pg. 1598
CHUO GYORUI CO., LTD.; *Int'l*, pg. 1598
CHUOH CO., LTD.—See Ship Healthcare Holdings, Inc.; *Int'l*, pg. 6852
CHUOH LINEN SUPPLY CO., LTD.—See Central Japan Railway Company; *Int'l*, pg. 1408
CHUOH MEDICAL CO., LTD.—See Toho Holdings Co., Ltd.; *Int'l*, pg. 7776
CHUO KAGAKU CO., LTD.—See Senko Group Holdings Co., Ltd.; *Int'l*, pg. 6709
CHUO KAIHATSU CORPORATION—See Chudenko Corporation; *Int'l*, pg. 1594
CHUOKEIZAI-SHA HOLDINGS, INC.; *Int'l*, pg. 1600
CHUO KOAGE CO., LTD.—See Chuo Gyorui Co., Ltd.; *Int'l*, pg. 1598
CHUOKORON-SHINSHA, INC.—See The Yomiuri Shimbun; *Int'l*, pg. 7705
CHUO LOGISTICS CO., LTD.—See Yamatane Corporation; *Int'l*, pg. 8553
CHUO MALLEABLE IRON CO., LTD.; *Int'l*, pg. 1598
CHUONG DUONG BEVERAGES JOINT STOCK COMPANY; *Int'l*, pg. 1600
CHUONG DUONG CORPORATION; *Int'l*, pg. 1600
CHUO SEISAKUSHO LTD.; *Int'l*, pg. 1599
CHUO SENKO ADVERTISING CO., LTD.; *Int'l*, pg. 1599
CHUO SENKO ADVERTISING CO., LTD.—See Chuo Senko Advertising Co., Ltd.; *Int'l*, pg. 1599
CHUO SENKO ADVERTISING CO., LTD.—See Chuo Senko Advertising Co., Ltd.; *Int'l*, pg. 1599
CHUO SENKO ADVERTISING CO., LTD.—See Chuo Senko Advertising Co., Ltd.; *Int'l*, pg. 1599
CHUO SENKO ADVERTISING CO., LTD.—See Chuo Senko Advertising Co., Ltd.; *Int'l*, pg. 1599
CHUO SENKO ADVERTISING CO., LTD.—See Chuo Senko Advertising Co., Ltd.; *Int'l*, pg. 1599
CHUO SENKO ADVERTISING CO., LTD.—See Chuo Senko Advertising Co., Ltd.; *Int'l*, pg. 1599
CHUO SENKO ADVERTISING CO., LTD.—See Chuo Senko Advertising Co., Ltd.; *Int'l*, pg. 1599
CHUO SENKO ADVERTISING CO., LTD.—See Chuo Senko Advertising Co., Ltd.; *Int'l*, pg. 1599
CHUO SENKO ADVERTISING CO., LTD.—See Chuo Senko Advertising Co., Ltd.; *Int'l*, pg. 1599
CHUO SENKO ADVERTISING (HK) LTD.—See Chuo Senko Advertising Co., Ltd.; *Int'l*, pg. 1599
CHUO SENKO ADVERTISING (S) PTE. LTD.—See Chuo Senko Advertising Co., Ltd.; *Int'l*, pg. 1599
CHUO SENKO ADVERTISING (TAIWAN) CO., LTD.—See Chuo Senko Advertising Co., Ltd.; *Int'l*, pg. 1599
CHUO SENKO (CAMBODIA) HOLDING CO., LTD.—See Chuo Senko Advertising Co., Ltd.; *Int'l*, pg. 1599
CHUO SENKO (THAILAND) PUBLIC CO., LTD.—See Chuo Senko Advertising Co., Ltd.; *Int'l*, pg. 1599
CHUO SENKO VIETNAM REPRESENTATIVE OFFICE—See Chuo Senko Advertising Co., Ltd.; *Int'l*, pg. 1599
CHUO SPRING CO., LTD. - FUJIOKA PLANT—See Chuo Spring Co., Ltd.; *Int'l*, pg. 1599
CHUO SPRING CO., LTD. - HEKINAN PLANT—See Chuo Spring Co., Ltd.; *Int'l*, pg. 1599

CHUO SPRING CO., LTD. - MIYOSHI PLANT—See Chuo Spring Co., Ltd.; *Int'l*, pg. 1599
CHUO SPRING CO., LTD.; *Int'l*, pg. 1599
CHUO SYSTEM CORPORATION—See TIS Inc.; *Int'l*, pg. 7757
CHUOU INTERNATIONAL GROUP CO., LTD.; *Int'l*, pg. 1600
CHUOU SEKKEI ENGINEERING COMPANY LIMITED—See Oriental Consultants Holdings Company Limited; *Int'l*, pg. 5623
CHUO WAREHOUSE CO., LTD.; *Int'l*, pg. 1600
CHUPA CHUPS INDUSTRIAL MEXICANA S. A DE C. V.—See Perfetti Van Melle Holding B.V.; *Int'l*, pg. 5800
CHUPA CHUPS PERFETTI VAN MELLE UK LTD—See Perfetti Van Melle Holding B.V.; *Int'l*, pg. 5800
CHUPA CHUPS PORTUGAL LTD—See Perfetti Van Melle Holding B.V.; *Int'l*, pg. 5800
CHUPA-CHUPS RUS—See Perfetti Van Melle Holding B.V.; *Int'l*, pg. 5800
CHUPA CHUPS S.A.—See Perfetti Van Melle Holding B.V.; *Int'l*, pg. 5800
THE CHURCH AID OF THE PROTESTANT EPISCOPAL CHURCH; *U.S. Private*, pg. 4009
CHURCH & CASUALTY INSURANCE AGENCY INC.; *U.S. Private*, pg. 894
CHURCH CHAIR INDUSTRIES, INC.; *U.S. Private*, pg. 894
CHURCH & CHURCH INC.; *U.S. Private*, pg. 894
CHURCH & CHURCH LUMBER CO.; *U.S. Private*, pg. 894
CHURCH & DWIGHT (AUSTRALIA) PTY. LTD.—See Church & Dwight Co., Inc.; *U.S. Public*, pg. 493
CHURCH & DWIGHT CANADA CORP.—See Church & Dwight Co., Inc.; *U.S. Public*, pg. 493
CHURCH & DWIGHT CANADA CORP.—See Church & Dwight Co., Inc.; *U.S. Public*, pg. 493
CHURCH & DWIGHT CO., INC.; *U.S. Public*, pg. 493
CHURCH & DWIGHT DO BRASIL LTDA—See Church & Dwight Co., Inc.; *U.S. Public*, pg. 493
CHURCH & DWIGHT DOMESTIC CONSUMER PRODUCTS—See Church & Dwight Co., Inc.; *U.S. Public*, pg. 493
CHURCH & DWIGHT INTERNATIONAL CONSUMER PRODUCTS—See Church & Dwight Co., Inc.; *U.S. Public*, pg. 493
CHURCH & DWIGHT SERVICIOS DE R.L. DE C.V.—See Church & Dwight Co., Inc.; *U.S. Public*, pg. 493
CHURCH & DWIGHT SPECIALTY PRODUCTS DIVISION—See Church & Dwight Co., Inc.; *U.S. Public*, pg. 493
CHURCH & DWIGHT (UK) LTD.—See Church & Dwight Co., Inc.; *U.S. Public*, pg. 493
CHURCH HILL CLASSICS; *U.S. Private*, pg. 894
CHURCHILL CAPITAL CORP. VII; *U.S. Public*, pg. 493
CHURCHILL CAPITAL, LLC—See Churohill Equity, Inc.; *U.S. Private*, pg. 894
CHURCHILL CHINA PLC; *Int'l*, pg. 1600
CHURCHILL CORPORATE SERVICES; *U.S. Private*, pg. 894
CHURCHILL DIALYSIS, LLC—See DaVita Inc.; *U.S. Public*, pg. 636
CHURCHILL DOWNS, INC.; *U.S. Public*, pg. 493
CHURCHILL DOWNS MANAGEMENT COMPANY, LLC—See Churchill Downs, Inc.; *U.S. Public*, pg. 493
CHURCHILL DOWNS RACETRACK, LLC—See Churchill Downs, Inc.; *U.S. Public*, pg. 493
CHURCHILL EQUITY, INC.; *U.S. Private*, pg. 894
CHURCHILL FINANCIAL LLC—See The Carlyle Group Inc.; *U.S. Public*, pg. 2045
CHURCHILL FREIGHT SERVICES INC.—See Churchill Transportation Inc.; *U.S. Private*, pg. 895
CHURCHILL INDUSTRIES, INC.—See Churchill Equity, Inc.; *U.S. Private*, pg. 895
CHURCHILL INSURANCE COMPANY LIMITED—See Direct Line Insurance Group plc; *Int'l*, pg. 2129
CHURCHILL LEADERSHIP GROUP, INC.; *U.S. Private*, pg. 895
CHURCHILL LINEN SERVICE INC.—See Alsco Inc.; *U.S. Private*, pg. 202
CHURCHILL NAVIGATION INC.—See Helinet Aviation Services LLC; *U.S. Private*, pg. 1906
CHURCHILL RESOURCES INC.; *Int'l*, pg. 1600
CHURCHILL TRANSPORTATION INC.; *U.S. Private*, pg. 895
CHURCH INSURANCE & FINANCIAL SERVICES, INC.—See GTCR LLC; *U.S. Private*, pg. 1802
CHURCH INTERNATIONAL LTD; *Int'l*, pg. 1600
CHURCH & MAIN ADVERTISING; *U.S. Private*, pg. 894
CHURCH & MURDOCK ELECTRIC, INC.; *U.S. Private*, pg. 894
CHURCH MUTUAL INSURANCE COMPANY; *U.S. Private*, pg. 894
CHURCH OF GOD HOME; *U.S. Private*, pg. 894
CHURCH'S CHICKEN, INC.—See Arcapita Group Holdings Limited; *U.S. Private*, pg. 542
CHURCH & SCHOOL FINANCING—See The Ziegler Companies, Inc.; *U.S. Private*, pg. 4140
CHURCH & STAGG OFFICE SUPPLY INC; *U.S. Private*, pg. 894

COMPANY NAME INDEX

THE CHURCH STREET CORPORATION; *U.S. Private*, pg. 4009
CHURCH STREET ENTERTAINMENT; *U.S. Private*, pg. 894
CHURNY COMPANY INC.—See 3G Capital Inc.; *U.S. Private*, pg. 10
CHURNY COMPANY INC.—See Berkshire Hathaway Inc.; *U.S. Public*, pg. 317
CHURSTON HEARD LTD—See Jones Lang LaSalle Incorporated; *U.S. Public*, pg. 1203
CHURYO ENGINEERING CO., LTD.—See Mitsubishi Heavy Industries, Ltd.; *Int'l*, pg. 4953
CHUSEI GOMU CO., LTD.—See Toyoda Gosei Co., Ltd.; *Int'l*, pg. 7861
CHUSHIKOKU LOGISTICS K.K.—See Senko Group Holdings Co., Ltd.; *Int'l*, pg. 6709
CHU-SHIKOKU MARUWA LOGISTICS CO., LTD.—See AZ-COM MARUWA Holdings Inc.; *Int'l*, pg. 776
CHU-SHIKOKU SEKISUI SHOJI CO., LTD.—See Sekisui Chemical Co., Ltd.; *Int'l*, pg. 6693
CHUSHIKOKU UBE CONCRETE CO., LTD.—See UBE Corporation; *Int'l*, pg. 8000
CHUTES INTERNATIONAL; *U.S. Private*, pg. 895
CHUTIAN DRAGON CO., LTD.; *Int'l*, pg. 1600
CHU UNDERWRITING AGENCIES PTY. LTD.—See Steadfast Group Limited; *Int'l*, pg. 7187
CHUWA BUSSAN CO., LTD.—See China Communications Construction Company Limited; *Int'l*, pg. 1490
CHUYING AGRO-PASTORAL GROUP CO., LTD.; *Int'l*, pg. 1600
CHUY'S HOLDINGS, INC.—See Darden Restaurants, Inc.; *U.S. Public*, pg. 633
CHUZHOU CHUANGCE PACKAGING MATERIALS COMPANY LIMITED—See Teamway International Group Holdings Limited; *Int'l*, pg. 7501
CHUZHOU DUOLI AUTOMOTIVE TECHNOLOGY CO., LTD.; *Int'l*, pg. 1600
CHUZHOU NEW BEST EXTRA CLEAN MATERIALS TECH CO., LTD.—See New Best Wire Industrial Co., Ltd.; *Int'l*, pg. 5221
C & H VINA JOINT STOCK COMPANY—See Dream International Ltd; *Int'l*, pg. 2202
CHW LLC—See The Cato Corporation; *U.S. Public*, pg. 2058
CHW/MERCY HOSPITAL BAKERSFIELD—See Catholic Health Initiatives; *U.S. Private*, pg. 789
C.H. WRIGHT, INC.—See Wright Wisner Distributing Corp.; *U.S. Private*, pg. 4573
CHYANG SHENG DYEING & FINISHING CO., LTD.; *Int'l*, pg. 1600
CH YODOFORM SDN. BHD.—See AYS Ventures Berhad; *Int'l*, pg. 776
CHYRONHEGO AB—See Vector Capital Management, L.P.; *U.S. Private*, pg. 4350
CHYRONHEGO CHILE LIMITADA—See Vector Capital Management, L.P.; *U.S. Private*, pg. 4350
CHYRONHEGO CORPORATION—See Vector Capital Management, L.P.; *U.S. Private*, pg. 4350
CHYRONHEGO CZECH S.R.O.—See Vector Capital Management, L.P.; *U.S. Private*, pg. 4350
CHYRONHEGO DANMARK APS—See Vector Capital Management, L.P.; *U.S. Private*, pg. 4350
CHYRONHEGO FINLAND OY—See Vector Capital Management, L.P.; *U.S. Private*, pg. 4350
CHYRONHEGO GMBH—See Vector Capital Management, L.P.; *U.S. Private*, pg. 4350
CHYRONHEGO NORGE A/S—See Vector Capital Management, L.P.; *U.S. Private*, pg. 4350
CHYRONHEGO SLOVAKIA S.R.O.—See Vector Capital Management, L.P.; *U.S. Private*, pg. 4350
CHYRONHEGO UK LTD.—See Vector Capital Management, L.P.; *U.S. Private*, pg. 4350
CHYY DEVELOPMENT GROUP LIMITED; *Int'l*, pg. 1600
CI2I SERVICES, INC.; *U.S. Private*, pg. 896
CIA. AGRO INDUSTRIAL IGARASSU—See Votorantim S.A.; *Int'l*, pg. 8310
CIAAT CO., LTD.; *Int'l*, pg. 1602
CIA DE GAS DE SAO PAULO - COMGAS ON—See Cosan S.A.; *Int'l*, pg. 1809
CIA DE INVERSIONES LA ESPANOLA SA; *Int'l*, pg. 1601
CIA DE TECIDOS DO NORTE DE MINAS - COTEMINAS; *Int'l*, pg. 1601
CIA DE TIERRAS SUD ARGENTINO S.A.—See Edizione S.r.l.; *Int'l*, pg. 2312
CIA DE TRANSMISSAO DE ENERGIA ELETRICA PAULISTA; *Int'l*, pg. 1601
CIA DISTRIB DE GAS DO RIO DE JANEIRO - CEG; *Int'l*, pg. 1601
CIA ELECTRICA DEL LITORAL SA; *Int'l*, pg. 1602
CIA ENERGETICA DE PERNAMBUCO - CELPE; *Int'l*, pg. 1602
CIA ESTADUAL GER.TRANS.ENER.ELET-CEEE-GT; *Int'l*, pg. 1602
CIA. HERING - AVENIDA BRASIL - ANAPOLIS PLANT—See Grupo de Moda SOMA S.A.; *Int'l*, pg. 3126
CIA. HERING - DAIA - ANAPOLIS PLANT—See Grupo de Moda SOMA S.A.; *Int'l*, pg. 3126

CIA. HERING - GOIANESIA PLANT—See Grupo de Moda SOMA S.A.; *Int'l*, pg. 3126
CIA. HERING - PARAUNA PLANT—See Grupo de Moda SOMA S.A.; *Int'l*, pg. 3126
CIA. HERING - SANTA HELENA PLANT—See Grupo de Moda SOMA S.A.; *Int'l*, pg. 3126
CIA. HERING—See Grupo de Moda SOMA S.A.; *Int'l*, pg. 3126
CIA IGUACU DE CAFE SOLUVEL; *Int'l*, pg. 1602
CIA INDUSTRIAL EL VOLCAN SA—See Compagnie de Saint-Gobain SA; *Int'l*, pg. 1725
CIALDAMIA S.R.L.—See IVS Group S.A.; *Int'l*, pg. 3848
CIA MARITIMA CHILENA SA; *Int'l*, pg. 1602
CIAMPI S.R.L.—See ThyssenKrupp AG; *Int'l*, pg. 7724
CIAN AGRO INDUSTRIES & INFRASTRUCTURE LIMITED; *Int'l*, pg. 1602
CIANBRO CORPORATION - EASTERN MANUFACTURING FACILITY—See Cianbro Corporation; *U.S. Private*, pg. 896
CIANBRO CORPORATION - GEORGETOWN FABRICATION FACILITY—See Cianbro Corporation; *U.S. Private*, pg. 896
CIANBRO CORPORATION - RICKERS WHARF MARINE FACILITY—See Cianbro Corporation; *U.S. Private*, pg. 896
CIANBRO CORPORATION; *U.S. Private*, pg. 896
CIANBRO EQUIPMENT, LLC—See Cianbro Corporation; *U.S. Private*, pg. 896
CIANBRO FABRICATION & COATING CORPORATION—See Cianbro Corporation; *U.S. Private*, pg. 896
CIANFLONE SCIENTIFIC LLC—See Main Line Equity Partners, LLC; *U.S. Private*, pg. 2551
CIAN HEALTHCARE LIMITED; *Int'l*, pg. 1602
CIAN PLC; *Int'l*, pg. 1602
CIAO BELLA GELATO COMPANY—See Encore Associates Inc.; *U.S. Private*, pg. 1390
CIAO BELLA GELATO COMPANY—See Sherbrooke Capital LLC; *U.S. Private*, pg. 3633
CIAO GROUP, INC.; *U.S. Private*, pg. 896
CIA PAULISTA DE FORCA E LUZ LTDA—See Bradespar S.A.; *Int'l*, pg. 1134
CIA PIRATININGA DE FORCA E LUZ LTDA—See Bradespar S.A.; *Int'l*, pg. 1134
C.I.A.P. S.P.A.—See Honda Motor Co., Ltd.; *Int'l*, pg. 3460
CIARGA - ARGAMASSAS SECAS S.A.—See Camargo Correa S.A.; *Int'l*, pg. 1267
CIA SANEAMENTO DO PARANA-SANEPAR; *Int'l*, pg. 1602
CIA SEGUROS ALIANCA DA BAHIA; *Int'l*, pg. 1602
CIA TECIDOS SANTANENSE; *Int'l*, pg. 1602
CIATTO CONSTRUCTION CO.; *U.S. Private*, pg. 896
CI AUSTRALIA PTY LIMITED—See Apollo Global Management, Inc.; *U.S. Public*, pg. 166
C.I.B.A. COMPANIA INTRODUCTORA DE BUENOS AIRES S.A.—See FV S.A.; *Int'l*, pg. 2859
CIBA HOLDING AG—See BASF SE; *Int'l*, pg. 882
CIBANK PLC—See KBC Group NV; *Int'l*, pg. 4105
CIBAR, INC.—See Constellation Software Inc.; *Int'l*, pg. 1775
CIBA SPECIALTY CHEMICALS HOLDING INC.—See BASF SE; *Int'l*, pg. 883
CIBA VISION GMBH—See Novartis AG; *Int'l*, pg. 5455
CIB BANK—See Intesa Sanpaolo S.p.A.; *Int'l*, pg. 3766
CIBC AUSTRALIA LTD.—See Canadian Imperial Bank of Commerce; *Int'l*, pg. 1283
CIBC BANK USA—See Canadian Imperial Bank of Commerce; *Int'l*, pg. 1283
CIBC FIRST CARIBBEAN INTERNATIONAL BANK LIMITED—See Canadian Imperial Bank of Commerce; *Int'l*, pg. 1283
CIBC GLOBAL ASSET MANAGEMENT INC.—See Canadian Imperial Bank of Commerce; *Int'l*, pg. 1283
CIBC INC.—See Canadian Imperial Bank of Commerce; *Int'l*, pg. 1283
CIBC INVESTOR SERVICES INC.—See Canadian Imperial Bank of Commerce; *Int'l*, pg. 1283
CIBC MELLON—See Canadian Imperial Bank of Commerce; *Int'l*, pg. 1283
CIBC MELLON—See The Bank of New York Mellon Corporation; *U.S. Public*, pg. 2037
CIB CORPORATION; *U.S. Private*, pg. 896
CIBC PRIVATE WEALTH GROUP, LLC—See Canadian Imperial Bank of Commerce; *Int'l*, pg. 1283
CIBC REINSURANCE COMPANY LIMITED—See Canadian Imperial Bank of Commerce; *Int'l*, pg. 1283
CIBC SECURITIES, INC.—See Canadian Imperial Bank of Commerce; *Int'l*, pg. 1283
CIBC TRUST CORPORATION—See Canadian Imperial Bank of Commerce; *Int'l*, pg. 1283
CIBC (U.K.) HOLDINGS LIMITED—See Canadian Imperial Bank of Commerce; *Int'l*, pg. 1283
CIBC WM REAL ESTATE LTD.—See Canadian Imperial Bank of Commerce; *Int'l*, pg. 1284
THE CIBC WOOD GUNDY CORPORATION—See Canadian Imperial Bank of Commerce; *Int'l*, pg. 1284
CIBC WOOD GUNDY FINANCIAL SERVICES INC.—See Canadian Imperial Bank of Commerce; *Int'l*, pg. 1284

CIBC WOOD GUNDY—See Canadian Imperial Bank of Commerce; *Int'l*, pg. 1284
CIBC WOOD GUNDY—See Canadian Imperial Bank of Commerce; *Int'l*, pg. 1284
CIBC WORLD MARKETS CORP.—See Canadian Imperial Bank of Commerce; *Int'l*, pg. 1284
CIBC WORLD MARKETS INC.—See Canadian Imperial Bank of Commerce; *Int'l*, pg. 1284
CIBC WORLD MARKETS (JAPAN) INC.—See Canadian Imperial Bank of Commerce; *Int'l*, pg. 1284
CIBC WORLD MARKETS PLC—See Canadian Imperial Bank of Commerce; *Int'l*, pg. 1284
CIB DEVELOPMENT SDN. BHD.—See Asphere Innovations Public Company Limited; *Int'l*, pg. 630
CIBER AG—See HTC Global Services Inc.; *U.S. Private*, pg. 1999
CIBER DANMARK A/S—See HTC Global Services Inc.; *U.S. Private*, pg. 1999
CIBER FRANCE SAS—See HTC Global Services Inc.; *U.S. Private*, pg. 1999
CIBER HOLDING GMBH—See HTC Global Services Inc.; *U.S. Private*, pg. 1999
CIBER LLC—See HTC Global Services Inc.; *U.S. Private*, pg. 1999
CIBER MANAGED SERVICES GMBH—See HTC Global Services Inc.; *U.S. Private*, pg. 1999
CIBER NORGE AS—See ManpowerGroup Inc.; *U.S. Public*, pg. 1360
CIBER PTY LTD.—See HTC Global Services Inc.; *U.S. Private*, pg. 1999
CIBER UK LTD.—See HTC Global Services Inc.; *U.S. Private*, pg. 1999
CIBER UK—See HTC Global Services Inc.; *U.S. Private*, pg. 1999
CIB FUND MANAGEMENT CO., LTD.—See Industrial Bank Co., Ltd.; *Int'l*, pg. 3671
CIBIE ARGENTINA, SA—See Valeo S.A.; *Int'l*, pg. 8112
CIBL, INC.; *U.S. Public*, pg. 494
CIB MARINE BANCSHARES, INC.; *U.S. Public*, pg. 494
CIBM BANK—See CIB Marine Bancshares, Inc.; *U.S. Public*, pg. 494
CIBOLAN GOLD CORPORATION; *U.S. Private*, pg. 896
CIBOODLE LTD.—See Verint Systems Inc.; *U.S. Public*, pg. 2281
CIBOX INTERACTIVE SA; *Int'l*, pg. 1602
CIBRASEC-COMPANHIA BRASILEIRA DE SECURITIZACAO; *Int'l*, pg. 1602
CIBRO MANAGEMENT INC.; *U.S. Private*, pg. 896
CIBT, INC.—See Kohlberg & Company, LLC; *U.S. Private*, pg. 2337
CIBUS CORP.—See Cibus, Inc.; *U.S. Public*, pg. 494
CIBUS, INC.; *U.S. Public*, pg. 494
CIBUS NORDIC REAL ESTATE AB; *Int'l*, pg. 1602
CIC39 CORP.; *Int'l*, pg. 1602
CICA LIFE INSURANCE COMPANY OF AMERICA—See Citizens, Inc.; *U.S. Public*, pg. 506
CI CAPITAL PARTNERS LLC; *U.S. Private*, pg. 895
CICA SA—See Financiere de L'Odet; *Int'l*, pg. 2667
CIC AUSTRALIA LIMITED—See Peet Limited; *Int'l*, pg. 5780
CICA VIETNAM COMPANY LIMITED—See Sime Darby Berhad; *Int'l*, pg. 6928
CICC ALPHA (BEIJING) INVESTMENT FUND MANAGEMENT CO., LTD—See China International Capital Corporation Limited; *Int'l*, pg. 1510
CICC CAPITAL MANAGEMENT CO., LTD.—See Western Mining Co., Ltd.; *Int'l*, pg. 8389
CICC EUROPE—See China International Capital Corporation Limited; *Int'l*, pg. 1510
CICCOLELLA SPA; *Int'l*, pg. 1602
CICC US SECURITIES, INC.—See China International Capital Corporation Limited; *Int'l*, pg. 1510
CICC ZHIDE CAPITAL CORPORATION LIMITED—See China International Capital Corporation Limited; *Int'l*, pg. 1510
CICERO CONSULTING AS—See Itera ASA; *Int'l*, pg. 3832
CICF L.L.C.—See The Carlyle Group Inc.; *U.S. Public*, pg. 2045
CIC GROUP, INC.; *U.S. Private*, pg. 896
CIC HOLDINGS LIMITED; *Int'l*, pg. 1602
CIC IBERBANCO—See Confederation Nationale du Credit Mutuel; *Int'l*, pg. 1767
CICI ENTERPRISES, LP—See Continental Grain Company; *U.S. Private*, pg. 1029
CIC INSURANCE GROUP LIMITED; *Int'l*, pg. 1602
CIC INTERNATIONAL LTD.; *U.S. Private*, pg. 896
CICLAD SA; *Int'l*, pg. 1602
CICLET HOLDINGS INC.; *Int'l*, pg. 1603
CIC MANAGEMENT—See Chelsea Investments Corporation; *U.S. Private*, pg. 870
CIC MARKETING (PTY) LIMITED—See CIC Holdings Limited; *Int'l*, pg. 1602
CIC MARKETING SDN. BHD.—See Central Global Berhad; *Int'l*, pg. 1407
CIC MINING RESOURCES LIMITED; *Int'l*, pg. 1602
CICOA AGING & IN-HOME SOLUTIONS; *U.S. Private*, pg. 896
CI COM SA; *Int'l*, pg. 1600
C.I. CONSTRUCTION, LLC; *U.S. Private*, pg. 707

C.I. CONSTRUCTION, LLC

CICOR AMERICAS INC.—See Cicor Technologies Ltd.; *Int'l*, pg. 1603
CICOR ANAM LTD.—See Cicor Technologies Ltd.; *Int'l*, pg. 1603
CICOR ASIA PTE. LTD.—See Cicor Technologies Ltd.; *Int'l*, pg. 1603
CICOR DEUTSCHLAND GMBH—See Cicor Technologies Ltd.; *Int'l*, pg. 1603
CICOR DIGITAL ELEKTRONIK GMBH—See Cicor Technologies Ltd.; *Int'l*, pg. 1603
CICOR ECOTOOL PTE LTD.—See Cicor Technologies Ltd.; *Int'l*, pg. 1603
CICOR ELECTRONIC SOLUTIONS DIVISION—See Cicor Technologies Ltd.; *Int'l*, pg. 1603
CICOREL SA—See Cicor Technologies Ltd.; *Int'l*, pg. 1603
CICOR MANAGEMENT AG—See Cicor Technologies Ltd.; *Int'l*, pg. 1603
CICOR REINHARDT MICROTECH AG—See Cicor Technologies Ltd.; *Int'l*, pg. 1603
CICOR TECHNOLOGIES LTD.; *Int'l*, pg. 1603
CICOR VIETNAM COMPANY LTD.—See Cicor Technologies Ltd.; *Int'l*, pg. 1603
CI-CO S.A.; *Int'l*, pg. 1601
CIC PARTNERS, L.P.; *U.S. Private*, pg. 896
CICSA INDUSTRIALES DEL CALOR S.L.—See Arbonia AG; *Int'l*, pg. 538
CICS DISTRIBUTORS PTE. LTD.—See Central Global Berhad; *Int'l*, pg. 1407
CIC SERVICES LLC—See CVS Health Corporation; *U.S. Public*, pg. 616
CID ADRIATIC INVESTMENTS GMBH; *Int'l*, pg. 1603
CIDARA THERAPEUTICS, INC.; *U.S. Public*, pg. 494
CIDB INVENTURES SDN BHD—See IJM Corporation Berhad; *Int'l*, pg. 3608
CID CAPITAL II, INC.; *U.S. Private*, pg. 896
CIDEAS S.R.L.—See Dentium Co., Ltd; *Int'l*, pg. 2033
CIDEGAS S.A.—See Vitkovice Holding, A.S.; *Int'l*, pg. 8260
CIDEON HOLDING GMBH & CO. KG—See Friedhelm Loh Stiftung & Co. KG; *Int'l*, pg. 2791
CIDER MILL PRESS BOOK PUBLISHERS LLC—See News Corporation; *U.S. Public*, pg. 1518
CID GROUP; *Int'l*, pg. 1603
CID LINES IBERICA SL—See Ecolab Inc.; *U.S. Public*, pg. 712
CID LINES NV—See Ecolab Inc.; *U.S. Public*, pg. 712
CID LINES SP. Z O. O.—See Ecolab Inc.; *U.S. Public*, pg. 712
CIDP BIOTECH INDIA PRIVATE LIMITED—See Ireland Blyth Limited; *Int'l*, pg. 3806
CIDP BIOTECHNOLOGY SRL—See Ireland Blyth Limited; *Int'l*, pg. 3806
CIDP SINGAPORE LTD.—See Ireland Blyth Limited; *Int'l*, pg. 3806
CIDRA PRECISION SERVICES, LLC—See IDEX Corp; *U.S. Public*, pg. 1090
CID RESOURCES, INC.—See Superior Group Of Companies, Inc.; *U.S. Public*, pg. 1966
CIDRON IT A/S—See Nordic Capital AB; *Int'l*, pg. 5420
CIE AMENAGEMENT COTEAUX DE GASCOGNE; *Int'l*, pg. 1603
CIE AUTOMOTIVE INDIA LIMITED—See Mahindra & Mahindra Limited; *Int'l*, pg. 4645
CIE AUTOMOTIVE MAROC, S.A.R.L. D'AU—See Cie Automotive S.A.; *Int'l*, pg. 1604
CIE AUTOMOTIVE PARTS (SHANGHAI) CO., LTD.—See Cie Automotive S.A.; *Int'l*, pg. 1604
CIE AUTOMOTIVE S.A.; *Int'l*, pg. 1603
CIE AUTOMOTIVE, USA INC.—See Cie Automotive S.A.; *Int'l*, pg. 1604
CIE CELAYA, S.A.P.I. DE C.V.—See Cie Automotive S.A.; *Int'l*, pg. 1604
CIECH NIERUCHOMOSCI S.A.—See Kulczyk Investments S.A.; *Int'l*, pg. 4327
CIECH PIANKI SP. Z O.O.—See Kulczyk Investments S.A.; *Int'l*, pg. 4327
CIECH R&D SP. Z O.O.—See Kulczyk Investments S.A.; *Int'l*, pg. 4327
CIECH SARZYNA S.A.—See Kulczyk Investments S.A.; *Int'l*, pg. 4328
CIECH SERVICE SP. Z.O.O.—See Kulczyk Investments S.A.; *Int'l*, pg. 4328
CIECH SERWIS I REMONTY SP. Z O.O.—See Kulczyk Investments S.A.; *Int'l*, pg. 4328
CIECH SODA POLSKA S.A.—See Kulczyk Investments S.A.; *Int'l*, pg. 4328
CIECH SODA ROMANIA S.A.—See Kulczyk Investments S.A.; *Int'l*, pg. 4327
CIECH TRADING S.A.—See Kulczyk Investments S.A.; *Int'l*, pg. 4328
CIECH VITROSILICON S.A.—See Kulczyk Investments S.A.; *Int'l*, pg. 4327
CIECO ENERGY (US) LIMITED—See ITOCHU Corporation; *Int'l*, pg. 3838
CIECO EXPLORATION AND PRODUCTION (AUSTRALIA) PTY LIMITED—See ITOCHU Corporation; *Int'l*, pg. 3835
CIE COMPIEGNE, S.A.S.—See Cie Automotive S.A.; *Int'l*, pg. 1604

CIECO NORTH SEA LTD.—See ITOCHU Corporation; *Int'l*, pg. 3835
CIE DEUTSCHLAND, GMBH—See Cie Automotive S.A.; *Int'l*, pg. 1604
CIE DUPAQUIER SARL—See ENGIE SA; *Int'l*, pg. 2428
CIE FINANCIERE DE L'OUEST AFRICAIN SA; *Int'l*, pg. 1605
CIE FORJAS MINAS, LTDA.—See Cie Automotive S.A.; *Int'l*, pg. 1604
CIE GALFOR, S.A.U.—See Cie Automotive S.A.; *Int'l*, pg. 1604
CIE IMPORT PRODUITS ALIMENTAIRES; *Int'l*, pg. 1605
CIE INDUSTRIELLE DE MATERIELS DE MANUTENTION—See Manitou BF S.A.; *Int'l*, pg. 4672
CIE INTL ANDRE TRIGANO; *Int'l*, pg. 1605
CIEL LTD.; *Int'l*, pg. 1605
CIELO S.A.; *Int'l*, pg. 1605
CIELO WASTE SOLUTIONS CORP.; *Int'l*, pg. 1605
CIE MECAUTO, S.A.U.—See Cie Automotive S.A.; *Int'l*, pg. 1604
CIE METAL CZ, S.R.O.—See Cie Automotive S.A.; *Int'l*, pg. 1604
CIEMME S.R.L.—See I.M.A. Industria Macchine Automatiche S.p.A.; *Int'l*, pg. 3565
CIEM S.P.A.; *Int'l*, pg. 1605
CIENA CANADA, INC.—See Ciena Corporation; *U.S. Public*, pg. 494
CIENA COMMUNICATIONS, INC.—See Ciena Corporation; *U.S. Public*, pg. 494
CIENA COMMUNICATIONS SINGAPORE PTE. LTD.—See Ciena Corporation; *U.S. Public*, pg. 494
CIENA CORPORATION; *U.S. Public*, pg. 494
CIENA CORPORATION - SPOKANE VALLEY MAIN OFFICE & TRAINING CENTER—See Ciena Corporation; *U.S. Public*, pg. 494
CIENA LIMITED—See Ciena Corporation; *U.S. Public*, pg. 494
C.I. ENERGIA SOLAR S.A.—See Tecnoglass Inc.; *Int'l*, pg. 7516
C & I ENGINEERING, LLC; *U.S. Private*, pg. 701
CIENNA (PROJECT MARKETING) PTY LTD—See Lee Kim Tah Holdings Ltd.; *Int'l*, pg. 4440
CIENTEC INSTRUMENTOS CIENTIFICOS SA—See HORIBA Ltd; *Int'l*, pg. 3475
CIE PLASTICOS MEXICO, S.A. DE C.V.—See Cie Automotive S.A.; *Int'l*, pg. 1604
CIE PLASTY CZ, S.R.O.—See Cie Automotive S.A.; *Int'l*, pg. 1604
CIE PLC.—See Nobia AB; *Int'l*, pg. 5395
CIE PRAGA LOUNY, A.S.—See Cie Automotive S.A.; *Int'l*, pg. 1604
CIESCO INC.—See Novinger Group, Inc.; *U.S. Private*, pg. 2968
CIESSE S.P.A.—See LCI Industries; *U.S. Public*, pg. 1295
CIE STRATIS-TRATAMENTOS, LTDA.—See Cie Automotive S.A.; *Int'l*, pg. 1604
CIE UDALBIDE, S.A.U.—See Cie Automotive S.A.; *Int'l*, pg. 1604
CIE UNITOOLS PRESS CZ, A.S.—See Cie Automotive S.A.; *Int'l*, pg. 1604
C I (EVENTS) LIMITED—See Live Nation Entertainment, Inc.; *U.S. Public*, pg. 1328
CIE ZDANICE, S.R.O.—See Cie Automotive S.A.; *Int'l*, pg. 1604
CIFA S.P.A—See Zoomlion Heavy Industry Science & Technology Co., Ltd.; *Int'l*, pg. 8690
CIFC ASSET MANAGEMENT LLC—See Centricus Partners LP; *Int'l*, pg. 1413
CIFC CORP.—See Centricus Partners LP; *Int'l*, pg. 1413
CIFC LLC—See Centricus Partners LP; *Int'l*, pg. 1413
CIFERAL INDUSTRIA DE ONIBUS LTDA.—See Marcopolo S.A.; *Int'l*, pg. 4690
CIFI EVER SUNSHINE SERVICES GROUP LIMITED; *Int'l*, pg. 1605
CIFI HOLDINGS (GROUP) CO. LTD.; *Int'l*, pg. 1605
CI FINANCIAL CORPORATION; *Int'l*, pg. 1600
CIFIN S.R.L.; *Int'l*, pg. 1605
CIFUNSA DEL BAJIO, S.A. DE C.V.—See Grupo Industrial Saltillo S.A. de C.V.; *Int'l*, pg. 3130
CIFUNSA, S.A. DE C.V.—See Grupo Industrial Saltillo S.A. de C.V.; *Int'l*, pg. 3130
CIFUT CO., LTD.—See Premium Group Co., Ltd.; *Int'l*, pg. 5963
CIGALAH TRADING ESTABLISHMENT; *Int'l*, pg. 1607
CI GAMES S.A.; *Int'l*, pg. 1601
CIGAR CITY BREWING LLC—See Fireman Capital Partners LLC; *Int'l*, pg. 1512
CIGARETTE RACING TEAM, LLC—See Lionheart Capital; *U.S. Private*, pg. 2464
THE CIGARETTE STORE CORP.; *U.S. Private*, pg. 4010
CIGARS INTERNATIONAL, INC.—See Skandinavisk Holding A/S; *Int'l*, pg. 6976
CIGARS ON 6TH—See The Cigarette Store Corp.; *U.S. Private*, pg. 4010
CIGENCO SA PROPRIETARY LIMITED—See Consolidated Infrastructure Group Limited; *Int'l*, pg. 1771
CIGI BEVERAGES OF TEXAS, LLC—See Bloomin' Brands, Inc.; *U.S. Public*, pg. 363

CORPORATE AFFILIATIONS

CIGI DIRECT INSURANCE SERVICES, INC.; *U.S. Private*, pg. 897
CIGLANA A.D.; *Int'l*, pg. 1607
CIGNA BENEFITS FINANCING, INC.—See The Cigna Group; *U.S. Public*, pg. 2060
CIGNA & CMB LIFE INSURANCE COMPANY LIMITED—See The Cigna Group; *U.S. Public*, pg. 2060
CIGNA CORPORATE SERVICES, LLC—See The Cigna Group; *U.S. Public*, pg. 2060
CIGNA DENTAL HEALTH, INC.—See The Cigna Group; *U.S. Public*, pg. 2060
CIGNA DENTAL HEALTH OF KANSAS, INC.—See The Cigna Group; *U.S. Public*, pg. 2060
CIGNA EUROPEAN SERVICES (UK) LIMITED—See The Cigna Group; *U.S. Public*, pg. 2060
CIGNA EUROPE INSURANCE COMPANY S.A.-N.V.—See The Cigna Group; *U.S. Public*, pg. 2060
CIGNA FINANS EMEKLILIK VE HAYAT A.S.—See The Cigna Group; *U.S. Public*, pg. 2060
CIGNA GLOBAL HOLDINGS, INC.—See The Cigna Group; *U.S. Public*, pg. 2060
THE CIGNA GROUP FOUNDATION—See The Cigna Group; *U.S. Public*, pg. 2061
THE CIGNA GROUP; *U.S. Public*, pg. 2059
CIGNA HEALTHCARE OF ARIZONA, INC.—See The Cigna Group; *U.S. Public*, pg. 2060
CIGNA HEALTHCARE OF CALIFORNIA, INC.—See The Cigna Group; *U.S. Public*, pg. 2060
CIGNA HEALTHCARE OF COLORADO, INC.—See The Cigna Group; *U.S. Public*, pg. 2060
CIGNA HEALTHCARE OF CONNECTICUT, INC.—See The Cigna Group; *U.S. Public*, pg. 2060
CIGNA HEALTHCARE OF FLORIDA, INC.—See The Cigna Group; *U.S. Public*, pg. 2060
CIGNA HEALTHCARE OF GEORGIA, INC.—See The Cigna Group; *U.S. Public*, pg. 2060
CIGNA HEALTHCARE OF ILLINOIS, INC.—See The Cigna Group; *U.S. Public*, pg. 2060
CIGNA HEALTHCARE OF INDIANA, INC.—See The Cigna Group; *U.S. Public*, pg. 2060
CIGNA HEALTHCARE OF MASSACHUSETTS, INC.—See The Cigna Group; *U.S. Public*, pg. 2060
CIGNA HEALTHCARE OF NEW HAMPSHIRE, INC.—See The Cigna Group; *U.S. Public*, pg. 2060
CIGNA HEALTHCARE OF NEW JERSEY, INC.—See The Cigna Group; *U.S. Public*, pg. 2060
CIGNA HEALTHCARE OF NORTH CAROLINA, INC.—See The Cigna Group; *U.S. Public*, pg. 2060
CIGNA HEALTHCARE OF OHIO, INC.—See The Cigna Group; *U.S. Public*, pg. 2060
CIGNA HEALTHCARE OF SOUTH CAROLINA, INC.—See The Cigna Group; *U.S. Public*, pg. 2060
CIGNA HEALTHCARE OF ST. LOUIS, INC.—See The Cigna Group; *U.S. Public*, pg. 2060
CIGNA HEALTHCARE OF TENNESSEE, INC.—See The Cigna Group; *U.S. Public*, pg. 2060
CIGNA HEALTHCARE OF TEXAS, INC.—See The Cigna Group; *U.S. Public*, pg. 2060
CIGNA HEALTHCARE OF VIRGINIA, INC.—See The Cigna Group; *U.S. Public*, pg. 2061
CIGNA HEALTH CORPORATION—See The Cigna Group; *U.S. Public*, pg. 2060
CIGNA HOLDING COMPANY—See The Cigna Group; *U.S. Public*, pg. 2060
CIGNA HOLDINGS, INC.—See The Cigna Group; *U.S. Public*, pg. 2060
CIGNA INSURANCE MIDDLE EAST S.A.L.—See The Cigna Group; *U.S. Public*, pg. 2061
CIGNA INSURANCE PUBLIC COMPANY LIMITED—See The Cigna Group; *U.S. Public*, pg. 2060
CIGNA INSURANCE SERVICES (EUROPE) LIMITED—See The Cigna Group; *U.S. Public*, pg. 2061
CIGNA INTEGRATEDCARE, INC.—See The Cigna Group; *U.S. Public*, pg. 2061
CIGNA INTERNATIONAL CORPORATION—See The Cigna Group; *U.S. Public*, pg. 2060
CIGNA INTERNATIONAL HEALTH SERVICES BVBA—See The Cigna Group; *U.S. Public*, pg. 2061
CIGNA INTERNATIONAL SERVICES AUSTRALIA PTY. LTD.—See The Cigna Group; *U.S. Public*, pg. 2061
CIGNA LIFE INSURANCE COMPANY OF CANADA—See The Cigna Group; *U.S. Public*, pg. 2060
CIGNA LIFE INSURANCE COMPANY OF EUROPE S.A.-N.V.—See The Cigna Group; *U.S. Public*, pg. 2060
CIGNA LIFE INSURANCE NEW ZEALAND LIMITED—See The Cigna Group; *U.S. Public*, pg. 2061
CIGNA SAGLIK HAYAT VE EMEKLILIK A.S.—See QNB Finans Varlik Kiralama A.S.; *Int'l*, pg. 6147
CIGNATTK HEALTH INSURANCE COMPANY LIMITED—See The Cigna Group; *U.S. Public*, pg. 2061
CIGNA TTK LIMITED—See TTK Prestige Limited; *Int'l*, pg. 7961
CIGNA WORLDWIDE GENERAL INSURANCE COMPANY LIMITED—See The Cigna Group; *U.S. Public*, pg. 2060
CIGNA WORLDWIDE INSURANCE COMPANY—See The Cigna Group; *U.S. Public*, pg. 2060
CIGNA WORLDWIDE LIFE INSURANCE COMPANY LIMITED—See Chubb Limited; *Int'l*, pg. 1592

COMPANY NAME INDEX

CIGNEX DATAMATICS CORPORATION—See Datamatics Global Services Ltd.; *Int'l*, pg. 1978
CIGNEX DATAMATICS PTE. LIMITED—See Datamatics Global Services Ltd.; *Int'l*, pg. 1978
CIGNEX DATAMATICS TECHNOLOGIES LIMITED—See Datamatics Global Services Ltd.; *Int'l*, pg. 1978
CIGNITI, INC.—See Cigniti Technologies Ltd.; *Int'l*, pg. 1607
CIGNITI TECHNOLOGIES CANADA INC.—See Cigniti Technologies Ltd.; *Int'l*, pg. 1607
CIGNITI TECHNOLOGIES INC.—See Cigniti Technologies Ltd.; *Int'l*, pg. 1607
CIGNITI TECHNOLOGIES LTD.; *Int'l*, pg. 1607
CIGNYS-SAGINAW; *U.S. Private*, pg. 897
CIG PANNONIA ELETBIZTOSITO NYRT—See Opus Global Nyrt; *Int'l*, pg. 5606
CIGPF LTDA EN LIQUIDACION—See Citigroup Inc.; *U.S. Public*, pg. 501
CIG PHOTONICS JAPAN LIMITED—See CIG Shanghai Co., Ltd.; *Int'l*, pg. 1606
C.I. GROUP PUBLIC COMPANY LIMITED - FACTORY 2—See C.I. Group Public Company Limited; *Int'l*, pg. 1243
C.I. GROUP PUBLIC COMPANY LIMITED - FACTORY 3—See C.I. Group Public Company Limited; *Int'l*, pg. 1243
C.I. GROUP PUBLIC COMPANY LIMITED; *Int'l*, pg. 1243
CIG SHANGHAI CO., LTD.; *Int'l*, pg. 1606
CIGTECH JAPAN LIMITED—See CIG Shanghai Co., Ltd.; *Int'l*, pg. 1606
CIGWELD (M) SDN BHD—See Enovis Corporation; *U.S. Public*, pg. 771
CIGWELD PTY LTD.—See Enovis Corporation; *U.S. Public*, pg. 771
C.I. HAYES—See Gasbarre Products Inc.; *U.S. Private*, pg. 1648
CIHELNA KINSKY, SPOL. S R. O.—See Wienerberger AG; *Int'l*, pg. 8405
C.I. HOLDINGS BERHAD; *Int'l*, pg. 1243
C&I HOLDINGS INC.; *U.S. Private*, pg. 703
C I HOST; *U.S. Private*, pg. 701
CII BRIDGES AND ROAD INVESTMENT JOINT STOCK COMPANY; *Int'l*, pg. 1607
CIIEM - TEC SRL—See Kering S.A.; *Int'l*, pg. 4134
CII ENGINEERING & CONSTRUCTION JSC—See Ho Chi Minh City Infrastructure Investment Joint Stock Company; *Int'l*, pg. 3434
CIIG MERGER CORP.; *U.S. Public*, pg. 494
C-III CAPITAL PARTNERS LLC—See Island Capital Group LLC; *U.S. Private*, pg. 2144
CII INFRASTRUCTURE SERVICES CO., LTD.—See Ho Chi Minh City Infrastructure Investment Joint Stock Company; *Int'l*, pg. 3434
CI INVESTMENT SERVICES INC.—See CI Financial Corporation; *Int'l*, pg. 1600
CI INVESTMENTS INC.—See CI Financial Corporation; *Int'l*, pg. 1600
C.I. ITOCHU COLOMBIA S.A.—See ITOCHU Corporation; *Int'l*, pg. 3834
CIJ MANAGE SYSTEM, INC.—See Computer Institute of Japan Ltd.; *Int'l*, pg. 1759
CIJ NEXT CO., LTD.—See Computer Institute of Japan Ltd.; *Int'l*, pg. 1759
CIJ SOLUTIONS, LTD.—See Computer Institute of Japan Ltd.; *Int'l*, pg. 1759
CIJ WAVE LTD.—See Computer Institute of Japan Ltd.; *Int'l*, pg. 1759
CIKER A.D.; *Int'l*, pg. 1607
CIK NANOTEK CORPORATION—See ITOCHU Corporation; *Int'l*, pg. 3835
CIK POWER DISTRIBUTORS, LLC.; *U.S. Private*, pg. 897
CILAG ADVANCED TECHNOLOGIES GMBH—See Johnson & Johnson; *U.S. Public*, pg. 1196
CILAG AG—See Johnson & Johnson; *U.S. Public*, pg. 1196
CILAG HOLDING AG—See Johnson & Johnson; *U.S. Public*, pg. 1196
CILAG PHARMACEUTICALS GMBH—See Johnson & Johnson; *U.S. Public*, pg. 1194
CILAG PRODUCTS GMBH—See Johnson & Johnson; *U.S. Public*, pg. 1194
CILAS SA—See Airbus SE; *Int'l*, pg. 246
C & I LEASING PLC.; *Int'l*, pg. 1237
CIL GROUP SL; *Int'l*, pg. 1607
CIL HOLDINGS LIMITED; *Int'l*, pg. 1607
CIL ISOTOPE SEPARATIONS, LLC—See Otsuka Holdings Co., Ltd.; *Int'l*, pg. 5659
CILIT SA—See BWT Aktiengesellschaft; *Int'l*, pg. 1233
CILLICHEMIE ITALIANA SRL—See BWT Aktiengesellschaft; *Int'l*, pg. 1233
CILMES SUNU BANKA, SIA—See VITA 34 AG; *Int'l*, pg. 8257
CILNET - COMUNICACOES E PROJECTOS ESPECIAIS S.A.—See Datatec Limited; *Int'l*, pg. 1980
CIL NOVA PETROCHEMICALS LIMITED—See Chiripal Industries Ltd.; *Int'l*, pg. 1573
CILSA INVESTMENTS (PTY) LTD.—See Capital International Group Limited; *Int'l*, pg. 1311
CIMAC FZCO—See Schneider Electric SE; *Int'l*, pg. 6626

CIMAC SOFTWARE SYSTEMS PRIVATE LTD—See Schneider Electric SE; *Int'l*, pg. 6626
CIMA DE ACUNA S.A. DE C.V.—See TE Connectivity Ltd.; *Int'l*, pg. 7494
CIMADJUVANTES - COMERCIALIZACAO E PRODUCAO DE ADJUVANTES PARA CIMENTO LDA—See Camargo Correa S.A.; *Int'l*, pg. 1267
CIMA ENERGY, LTD.—See Mitsubishi Corporation; *Int'l*, pg. 4938
CIMA LABS INC.—See Teva Pharmaceutical Industries, Ltd.; *Int'l*, pg. 7580
CIMALUX S.A.—See Buzzi SpA; *Int'l*, pg. 1230
CIMAREX ENERGY CO. OF COLORADO—See Coterra Energy Inc.; *U.S. Public*, pg. 587
CIMAREX ENERGY CO.—See Coterra Energy Inc.; *U.S. Public*, pg. 587
CIMAREX ENERGY, INC.—See Coterra Energy Inc.; *U.S. Public*, pg. 587
CIMAREX RESOLUTE LLC—See Coterra Energy Inc.; *U.S. Public*, pg. 587
CIMARRON DIALYSIS, LLC—See DaVita Inc.; *U.S. Public*, pg. 636
CIMARRON ENERGY, INC.—See Turnbridge Capital, LLC; *U.S. Private*, pg. 4260
CIMARRON EXPRESS INC.; *U.S. Private*, pg. 897
CIMARRON HEALTHCARE CAPITAL LLC; *U.S. Private*, pg. 897
CIMARRON INC. - EXECUTIVE OFFICE—See Cimarron Inc.; *U.S. Private*, pg. 897
CIMARRON INC.; *U.S. Private*, pg. 897
CIMARRON INVESTMENTS LLC—See Morgan Stanley; *U.S. Public*, pg. 1471
CIMARRON TRAILERS, INC.—See Folience, Inc.; *U.S. Private*, pg. 1559
CIMARRON UNDERGROUND SERVICES, LLC; *U.S. Private*, pg. 897
CIMA S.P.A.—See Coesia S.p.A.; *Int'l*, pg. 1689
C. I. MATEX CORPORATION—See ITOCHU Corporation; *Int'l*, pg. 3834
CIMATRON (BEIJING) TECHNOLOGY CO. LTD.—See Battery Ventures, L.P.; *U.S. Private*, pg. 488
CIMATRON GIBBS LLC—See Battery Ventures, L.P.; *U.S. Private*, pg. 488
CIMATRON LTD.—See Battery Ventures, L.P.; *U.S. Private*, pg. 488
CIMATRON TECHNOLOGIES, INC.—See Battery Ventures, L.P.; *U.S. Public*, pg. 488
CIMATRON TECHNOLOGIES INDIA PVT. LTD.—See Battery Ventures, L.P.; *U.S. Private*, pg. 488
CIMBAR PERFORMANCE MINERALS, INC.; *U.S. Private*, pg. 897
CIMB BANK BHD.—See CIMB Group Holdings Berhad; *Int'l*, pg. 1607
CIMB BANK (CAMBODIA) PLC—See CIMB Group Holdings Berhad; *Int'l*, pg. 1607
CIMB BANK (L) LTD.—See CIMB Group Holdings Berhad; *Int'l*, pg. 1607
CIMB BANK (VIETNAM) LIMITED—See CIMB Group Holdings Berhad; *Int'l*, pg. 1607
CIMBENIN S.A.—See Heidelberg Materials AG; *Int'l*, pg. 3315
CIMBETON HAZIRBETON VE PREFABRIK YAPI ELEMANLARI SANAYI VE TICARET A.S.—See Cementir Holding N.V.; *Int'l*, pg. 1397
CIMB GROUP HOLDINGS BERHAD; *Int'l*, pg. 1607
CIMB GROUP SDN. BHD.—See CIMB Group Holdings Berhad; *Int'l*, pg. 1607
CIMB-PRINCIPAL ASSET MANAGEMENT BERHAD—See CIMB Group Holdings Berhad; *Int'l*, pg. 1608
CIMB-PRINCIPAL ASSET MANAGEMENT BERHAD—See Principal Financial Group, Inc.; *U.S. Public*, pg. 1720
CIMB-PRINCIPAL ASSET MANAGEMENT COMPANY LIMITED—See CIMB Group Holdings Berhad; *Int'l*, pg. 1608
CIMB PRINCIPAL ASSET MANAGEMENT COMPANY LIMITED—See CIMB Group Holdings Berhad; *Int'l*, pg. 1608
CIMB-PRINCIPAL ASSET MANAGEMENT COMPANY LIMITED—See Principal Financial Group, Inc.; *U.S. Public*, pg. 1720
CIMB-PRINCIPAL ASSET MANAGEMENT (SINGAPORE) PTE LTD—See CIMB Group Holdings Berhad; *Int'l*, pg. 1608
CIMB-PRINCIPAL ASSET MANAGEMENT (SINGAPORE) PTE LTD—See Principal Financial Group, Inc.; *U.S. Public*, pg. 1720
CIMB PRIVATE EQUITY SDN BHD—See CIMB Group Holdings Berhad; *Int'l*, pg. 1607
CIMBRIA BRATNEY CO.—See K.B.C. Group Inc.; *U.S. Private*, pg. 2251
CIMBRIA HEID ITALIA SRL—See AGCO Corporation; *U.S. Public*, pg. 58
CIMB SECURITIES (HK) LTD—See CIMB Group Holdings Berhad; *Int'l*, pg. 1608
CIMB SECURITIES INTERNATIONAL PTE LTD—See CIMB Group Holdings Berhad; *Int'l*, pg. 1607
CIMB SECURITIES INTERNATIONAL (THAILAND) PUBLIC CO LTD—See LH Financial Group Public Company Limited; *Int'l*, pg. 4477

CIMB THAI BANK PUBLIC COMPANY LIMITED—See CIMB Group Holdings Berhad; *Int'l*, pg. 1608
CIMB WEALTH ADVISORS BERHAD—See CIMB Group Holdings Berhad; *Int'l*, pg. 1608
CIMB WEALTH ADVISORS BERHAD—See Principal Financial Group, Inc.; *U.S. Public*, pg. 1720
CIMC AUSTRALIA PTY LTD.—See China International Marine Containers (Group) Co., Ltd.; *Int'l*, pg. 1511
CIMC BURG B.V.—See China International Marine Containers (Group) Co., Ltd.; *Int'l*, pg. 1511
CIMC ENRIC HOLDINGS LIMITED—See China International Marine Containers (Group) Co., Ltd.; *Int'l*, pg. 1511
CIMC ENRIC TANK & PROCESS B.V.—See China International Marine Containers (Group) Co., Ltd.; *Int'l*, pg. 1511
CIMC FINANCE COMPANY LIMITED—See China International Marine Containers (Group) Co., Ltd.; *Int'l*, pg. 1511
CIMC FINANCING & LEASING CO., LTD.—See China International Marine Containers (Group) Co., Ltd.; *Int'l*, pg. 1511
CIMC HOLDINGS AUSTRALIA PTY LTD—See China International Marine Containers (Group) Co., Ltd.; *Int'l*, pg. 1511
CIMC INTERMODAL EQUIPMENT LLC—See CIMC Vehicle (Group) Co., Ltd.; *Int'l*, pg. 1608
C.I.M.C.I SARL—See Endress+Hauser (International) Holding AG; *Int'l*, pg. 2405
CIMC JIDONG (QINHUANGDAO) VEHICLES MANUFACTURE CO., LTD.—See China International Marine Containers (Group) Co., Ltd.; *Int'l*, pg. 1511
CIMC MODERN LOGISTIC DEVELOPMENT CO., LTD.—See China International Marine Containers (Group) Co., Ltd.; *Int'l*, pg. 1511
CIMC MODERN LOGISTICS DEVELOPMENT CO., LTD.—See China International Marine Containers (Group) Co., Ltd.; *Int'l*, pg. 1511
CIMCO CO., LTD.—See ITOCHU Corporation; *Int'l*, pg. 3835
CIMC OFFSHORE ENGINEERING HOLDINGS CO., LTD.—See China International Marine Containers (Group) Co., Ltd.; *Int'l*, pg. 1511
CIMCO MARINE AB; *Int'l*, pg. 1609
CIMCOOL EUROPE B.V.—See Altas Partners LP; *Int'l*, pg. 386
CIMCOOL INDUSTRIAL PRODUCTS B.V.—See Altas Partners LP; *Int'l*, pg. 386
CIMCOOL INDUSTRIAL PRODUCTS LLC—See Altas Partners LP; *Int'l*, pg. 386
CIMCO REFRIGERATION—See Toromont Industries Ltd.; *Int'l*, pg. 7829
CIMCORP AUTOMATION LTD.—See Murata Machinery, Ltd.; *Int'l*, pg. 5096
CIMCORP OY—See Murata Machinery, Ltd.; *Int'l*, pg. 5096
CIMC RAFFLES OFFSHORE (SINGAPORE) LIMITED—See China International Marine Containers (Group) Co., Ltd.; *Int'l*, pg. 1511
CIMC SECURITY TECHNOLOGY CO., LTD.—See China International Marine Containers (Group) Co., Ltd.; *Int'l*, pg. 1511
CIMC-TIANDA HOLDINGS COMPANY LIMITED; *Int'l*, pg. 1608
CIMC TRAILER POLAND SP. Z O.O.—See CIMC Vehicle (Group) Co., Ltd.; *Int'l*, pg. 1608
CIMC TRANSPACK TECHNOLOGY CO., LTD.—See China International Marine Containers (Group) Co., Ltd.; *Int'l*, pg. 1511
CIMC USA INC.—See China International Marine Containers (Group) Co., Ltd.; *Int'l*, pg. 1511
CIMC VEHICLE AUSTRALIA PTY LTD—See China International Marine Containers (Group) Co., Ltd.; *Int'l*, pg. 1511
CIMC VEHICLE EUROPE GMBH—See CIMC Vehicle (Group) Co., Ltd.; *Int'l*, pg. 1608
CIMC VEHICLE (GROUP) CO., LTD.; *Int'l*, pg. 1608
CIMC VEHICLE (GUANGXI) CO., LTD.—See China International Marine Containers (Group) Co., Ltd.; *Int'l*, pg. 1511
CIMC VEHICLE (LIAONING) CO., LTD.—See China International Marine Containers (Group) Co., Ltd.; *Int'l*, pg. 1511
CIMC VEHICLE (SHANDONG) CO., LTD.—See China International Marine Containers (Group) Co., Ltd.; *Int'l*, pg. 1511
CIMC VEHICLES SOUTH AFRICA (PTY) LTD.—See CIMC Vehicle (Group) Co., Ltd.; *Int'l*, pg. 1608
CI MEDICAL CO., LTD.; *Int'l*, pg. 1601
CIMELIA RESOURCE RECOVERY PTE. LTD.—See Enviro-Hub Holdings Ltd.; *Int'l*, pg. 2454
CIMENTACIONES MEXICANAS S.A. DE C.V.—See VINCI S.A.; *Int'l*, pg. 8230
CIMENTACOR - CIMENTOS DOS ACORES LDA—See Camargo Correa S.A.; *Int'l*, pg. 1267
CIMENTAS IZMIR CIMENTO FABRIKASI TURK A.S.; *Int'l*, pg. 1609
CIMENTERIES CBR S.A.—See Heidelberg Materials AG; *Int'l*, pg. 3309

CIMENTAS IZMIR CIMENTO FABRIKASI TURK A.S.

CIMENTOS DE CABO VERDE S.A.—See OYAK Cement Group; *Int'l*, pg. 5677
CIMENTOS DE MOCAMBIQUE, S.A.—See Camargo Correa S.A.; *Int'l*, pg. 1267
CIMENTOS MADEIRA, LDA.—See SODIM, SGPS, SA; *Int'l*, pg. 7049
CIMENTOS VENCEMOS DO AMAZONAS, LTDA.—See CEMEX, S.A.B. de C.V.; *Int'l*, pg. 1398
CIMENTS CALCIA S.A.S.—See Heidelberg Materials AG; *Int'l*, pg. 3316
CIMENTS DU MAROC SA—See Heidelberg Materials AG; *Int'l*, pg. 3310
CIMENTS DU TOGO, S.A.—See Heidelberg Materials AG; *Int'l*, pg. 3315
CIMENTS ET MATERIAUX DU MALI—See Vicat S.A.; *Int'l*, pg. 8185
CIMENTS FRANCAIS S.A.—See Heidelberg Materials AG; *Int'l*, pg. 3316
CIMENTS LUXEMBOURGEOIS S.A.—See Buzzi SpA; *Int'l*, pg. 1230
CIMENTS RENFORCES INDUSTRIES S.A.S.U.—See Etex SA/NV; *Int'l*, pg. 2521
CIMERWA LIMITADA—See PPC Ltd.; *Int'l*, pg. 5950
CIMETRIX INCORPORATED—See PDF Solutions, Inc.; *U.S. Public*, pg. 1658
CIMETRIX JAPAN KK—See PDF Solutions, Inc.; *U.S. Public*, pg. 1658
CIMETRIX SOFTWARE (SHANGHAI) CO., LTD.—See PDF Solutions, Inc.; *U.S. Public*, pg. 1658
CIMEX CORP.—See Arden Software Ltd.; *Int'l*, pg. 554
C.I. MEXICHEM COMPUESTOS COLOMBIA, S.A.S.—See Grupo Empresarial Kaluz S.A. de C.V.; *Int'l*, pg. 3127
CIMEX-NOR S.A.—See ThyssenKrupp AG; *Int'l*, pg. 7724
CIM FINANCIAL SERVICES LIMITED; *Int'l*, pg. 1607
CIMGABON S.A.—See Heidelberg Materials AG; *Int'l*, pg. 3310
CIM GROUP, LLC; *U.S. Private*, pg. 897
CIMIC GROUP LIMITED—See ACS, Actividades de Construccion y Servicios, S.A.; *Int'l*, pg. 112
CIM INDUSTRIAL SYSTEMS A/S—See XANO Industri AB; *Int'l*, pg. 8519
C.I.M. INDUSTRIES, INC.—See KKR & Co. Inc.; *U.S. Public*, pg. 1242
CIMINELLI DEVELOPMENT COMPANY, INC.; *U.S. Private*, pg. 897
CIMINO & ASSOCIATI PRIVATE EQUITY S.P.A.; *Int'l*, pg. 1609
CIMINPART - INVESTIMENTOS E PARTICIPACOES, SGPS, S.A.—See SODIM, SGPS, SA; *Int'l*, pg. 7049
CIM INTERNATIONAL GROUP, INC; *Int'l*, pg. 1607
CIMLINE INC.—See Hines Corporation; *U.S. Private*, pg. 1949
CIM-NAK TASIMACILIK LIMITED SIRKETI—See Nuh Cimento Sanayi A.S.; *Int'l*, pg. 5488
CIMOS D.D.—See Palladio Holding SpA; *Int'l*, pg. 5708
CIMOS FRANCE, S.A.S.—See Palladio Holding SpA; *Int'l*, pg. 5708
CIMOS TMD AI D.O.O.—See Palladio Holding SpA; *Int'l*, pg. 5708
CIMPA GMBH—See Sopra Steria Group S.A.; *Int'l*, pg. 7109
CIMPA LTD.—See Sopra Steria Group S.A.; *Int'l*, pg. 7109
CIMPA S.A.S.—See Sopra Steria Group S.A.; *Int'l*, pg. 7109
CIMPLAST EMBALAGENS IMPORTACAO, EXPORTACAO E. COMERCIO S.A.—See Greif Inc.; *U.S. Public*, pg. 967
CIMPLEBOX INC.—See NCR Voyix Corporation.; *U.S. Public*, pg. 1502
CIMPL'S, LLC—See Rosens Diversified, Inc.; *U.S. Private*, pg. 3484
CIMPOR BETAO - INDUSTRIA DE BETAO PRONTO S.A.—See Camargo Correa S.A.; *Int'l*, pg. 1267
CIMPOR BETAO MOCAMBIQUE, S.A.—See Camargo Correa S.A.; *Int'l*, pg. 1267
CIMPOR BETAO - SOCIEDADE GESTORA DE PARTICIPACOES SOCIAIS S.A.—See Camargo Correa S.A.; *Int'l*, pg. 1267
CIMPOR BRASIL PARTICIPACOES LTDA—See Camargo Correa S.A.; *Int'l*, pg. 1267
CIMPOR - CIMENTOS DE PORTUGAL, SGPS, S.A.—See Camargo Correa S.A.; *Int'l*, pg. 1267
CIMPOR HORMIGON ESPANA, S.A.—See Camargo Correa S.A.; *Int'l*, pg. 1267
CIMPOR - INDUSTRIA DE CIMENTOS S.A.—See Camargo Correa S.A.; *Int'l*, pg. 1267
CIMPOR INTERNACIONAL SGPS S.A.—See Camargo Correa S.A.; *Int'l*, pg. 1268
CIMPOR INVESTIMENTOS SGPS S.A.—See Camargo Correa S.A.; *Int'l*, pg. 1268
CIMPOR PORTUGAL SGPS S.A.—See Taiwan Cement Corporation; *Int'l*, pg. 7419
CIMPOR - SERVICOS DE APOIO A GESTAO DE EMPRESAS S.A.—See Camargo Correa S.A.; *Int'l*, pg. 1267
CIMPOR TRADING, S.A.—See Camargo Correa S.A.; *Int'l*, pg. 1267
CIM PRECISION MOULDS (HK) LTD.—See Lite-On Technology Corporation; *Int'l*, pg. 4525

CIMPRESS AUSTRALIA PTY LTD—See Cimpress plc; *Int'l*, pg. 1609
CIMPRESS INDIA PRIVATE LIMITED—See Cimpress plc; *Int'l*, pg. 1609
CIMPRESS JAPAN CO., LTD.—See Cimpress plc; *Int'l*, pg. 1609
CIMPRESS PLC; *Int'l*, pg. 1609
CIMPROGETTI S.P.A.—See HANNOVER Finanz GmbH; *Int'l*, pg. 3257
CIMPSHIP - TRANSPORTES MARITIMOS, S.A.—See Camargo Correa S.A.; *Int'l*, pg. 1267
CIMQUEST INC.—See Sandvik AB; *Int'l*, pg. 6528
CIM REAL ESTATE FINANCE TRUST, INC.—See CIM Group, LLC; *U.S. Private*, pg. 897
CIMSA CIMENTO SANAYI VE TICARET A.S.—See Haci Omer Sabanci Holding A.S.; *Int'l*, pg. 3203
CIMSA CINTAS METALICAS, S.A.—See Wieland-Werke AG; *Int'l*, pg. 8402
CIMS LP—See Yellow Point Equity Partners; *Int'l*, pg. 8576
CIMS S.A.; *Int'l*, pg. 1609
CIMTAS BORULAMA SANAYI VE TICARET LTD. STI.—See Enka Insaat ve Sanayi A.S.; *Int'l*, pg. 2440
CIMTAS CELIK IMALAT MONTAJ VE TESISAT A.S.—See Enka Insaat ve Sanayi A.S.; *Int'l*, pg. 2440
CIMTAS GEMI INSA SANAYI VE TICARET A.S.—See Enka Insaat ve Sanayi A.S.; *Int'l*, pg. 2440
CIMTAS (NINGBO) STEEL PROCESSING COMPANY LTD.—See Enka Insaat ve Sanayi A.S.; *Int'l*, pg. 2440
CIMTAS STEEL METAL KONSTRUKSIYA MMC—See Enka Insaat ve Sanayi A.S.; *Int'l*, pg. 2440
CIMTEC GMBH—See Sesa S.p.A.; *Int'l*, pg. 6728
CIMTEK CIMENTO TEKNOLOJISI MUHENDISLIK A.S.—See Nigbas Nigde Beton Sanayi ve Ticaret A.S.; *Int'l*, pg. 5282
CI&M WERBEAGENTUR GMBH—See OBB-Holding AG; *Int'l*, pg. 5509
CINCA COMPANHIA INDUSTRIAL DE CERAMICA S.A.—See QuattroR SGR S.p.A.; *Int'l*, pg. 6157
CINCH CONNECTIVITY SOLUTIONS LTD—See Bel Fuse Inc.; *U.S. Public*, pg. 293
CINCH CONNECTIVITY SOLUTIONS (SHANGHAI) CO., LTD.—See Bel Fuse Inc.; *U.S. Public*, pg. 293
CINCH CONNECTIVITY SOLUTIONS - WASECA—See Bel Fuse Inc.; *U.S. Public*, pg. 293
CINCH CONNECTORS DE MEXICO, S.A. DE C.V.—See Bel Fuse Inc.; *U.S. Public*, pg. 293
CINCH CONNECTORS INC.—See Bel Fuse Inc.; *U.S. Public*, pg. 293
CINCH CONNECTORS LTD.—See Bel Fuse Inc.; *U.S. Public*, pg. 293
CINCINNATI ART MUSEUM; *U.S. Private*, pg. 897
CINCINNATI ARTS ASSOCIATION; *U.S. Private*, pg. 897
CINCINNATI BANCORP, INC.—See LCNB Corp.; *U.S. Public*, pg. 1296
CINCINNATI BELL INC.—See Macquarie Group Limited; *Int'l*, pg. 4628
CINCINNATI BELL TECHNOLOGY SOLUTIONS INC.—See Macquarie Group Limited; *Int'l*, pg. 4628
CINCINNATI BELL TELEPHONE COMPANY LLC—See Macquarie Group Limited; *Int'l*, pg. 4628
CINCINNATI BELL WIRELESS LLC—See Macquarie Group Limited; *Int'l*, pg. 4628
CINCINNATI BENGALS, INC.; *U.S. Private*, pg. 897
CINCINNATI BIOREFINING CORP.—See Marathon Petroleum Corporation; *U.S. Public*, pg. 1364
CINCINNATI BUSINESS COURIER—See Advance Publications, Inc.; *U.S. Private*, pg. 84
THE CINCINNATI CASUALTY COMPANY—See Cincinnati Financial Corporation; *U.S. Public*, pg. 495
CINCINNATI CENTER CITY DEVELOPMENT CORPORATION; *U.S. Private*, pg. 897
CINCINNATI COMMERCIAL CONTRACTING, LLC.; *U.S. Private*, pg. 897
CINCINNATI CONTAINER COMPANY INCORPORATED; *U.S. Private*, pg. 897
THE CINCINNATI ENQUIRER—See Gannett Co., Inc.; *U.S. Public*, pg. 900
CINCINNATI FEDERAL SAVINGS & LOAN ASSOCIATION; *U.S. Private*, pg. 897
CINCINNATI FINANCIAL CORPORATION; *U.S. Public*, pg. 494
CINCINNATI FLOOR COMPANY INC.; *U.S. Private*, pg. 897
CINCINNATI GEARING SYSTEMS INC.; *U.S. Private*, pg. 897
THE CINCINNATI GILBERT MACHINE TOOL COMPANY, LLC; *U.S. Private*, pg. 4010
CINCINNATI GLOBAL UNDERWRITING LIMITED—See Cincinnati Financial Corporation; *U.S. Public*, pg. 495
CINCINNATI HEALTH NETWORK; *U.S. Private*, pg. 898
CINCINNATI INCORPORATED; *U.S. Private*, pg. 898
THE CINCINNATI INDEMNITY COMPANY—See Cincinnati Financial Corporation; *U.S. Public*, pg. 495
CINCINNATI INDUSTRIAL MACHINERY—See The Armor Group, Inc.; *U.S. Private*, pg. 3988
THE CINCINNATI INSURANCE COMPANY—See Cincinnati Financial Corporation; *U.S. Public*, pg. 495
THE CINCINNATI LIFE INSURANCE COMPANY—See Cincinnati Financial Corporation; *U.S. Public*, pg. 495

CORPORATE AFFILIATIONS

CINCINNATI METROPOLITAN HOUSING AUTHORITY; *U.S. Private*, pg. 898
THE CINCINNATI, NEW ORLEANS & TEXAS PACIFIC RAILWAY CO.—See Norfolk Southern Corporation; *U.S. Public*, pg. 1536
CINCINNATI PAPERBOARD—See Greif Inc.; *U.S. Public*, pg. 966
CINCINNATI PARKS FOUNDATION; *U.S. Private*, pg. 898
CINCINNATI PRESERVING COMPANY INC.—See Glencoe Capital LLC; *U.S. Private*, pg. 1709
CINCINNATI SUB-ZERO PRODUCTS, INC. - CSZ TESTING SERVICES LABORATORIES DIVISION—See Schunk GmbH; *Int'l*, pg. 6643
CINCINNATI SUB-ZERO PRODUCTS, LLC—See Schunk GmbH; *Int'l*, pg. 6643
CINCINNATI SYMPHONY ORCHESTRA; *U.S. Private*, pg. 898
CINCINNATI THERMAL SPRAY, INC.; *U.S. Private*, pg. 898
CINCINNATI TIME SYSTEMS, INC.—See Hellman & Friedman LLC; *U.S. Private*, pg. 1910
CINCINNATI TOOL STEEL CO., INC.; *U.S. Private*, pg. 898
CINCINNATI UNITED CONTRACTORS, INC.; *U.S. Private*, pg. 898
CINCO INVESTMENTS PLC; *Int'l*, pg. 1609
CINCO MEDIA COMMUNICATIONS; *U.S. Private*, pg. 898
CINCOM IBERIA, S.A.—See Partner One Capital, Inc.; *Int'l*, pg. 5748
CINCOM ITALIA S.R.L.—See Partner One Capital, Inc.; *Int'l*, pg. 5748
CINCOM MIYANO TAIWAN CO., LTD.—See Citizen Watch Co., Ltd.; *Int'l*, pg. 1623
CINCOM MONACO S.A.M.—See Partner One Capital, Inc.; *Int'l*, pg. 5748
CINCOM NETHERLANDS B.V.—See Partner One Capital, Inc.; *Int'l*, pg. 5748
CINCOM SYSTEMS FRANCE S.A.R.L.—See Partner One Capital, Inc.; *Int'l*, pg. 5748
CINCOM SYSTEMS GMBH & CO. OHG—See Partner One Capital, Inc.; *Int'l*, pg. 5748
CINCOM SYSTEMS, INC.—See Partner One Capital, Inc.; *Int'l*, pg. 5748
CINCOM SYSTEMS OF AUSTRALIA PTY LTD.—See Partner One Capital, Inc.; *Int'l*, pg. 5748
CINCOM SYSTEMS OF CANADA, LTD.—See Partner One Capital, Inc.; *Int'l*, pg. 5748
CINCOM SYSTEMS OF JAPAN LTD.—See Partner One Capital, Inc.; *Int'l*, pg. 5748
CINCOM SYSTEMS (UK) LIMITED—See Partner One Capital, Inc.; *Int'l*, pg. 5748
CINCON ELECTRONICS CO., LTD.; *Int'l*, pg. 1610
CINCO RESOURCES, INC.—See Riley Exploration Group, LLC; *U.S. Private*, pg. 3437
CINCOR PHARMA, INC.—See AstraZeneca PLC; *Int'l*, pg. 661
CINDA CAPITAL MANAGEMENT CO., LTD.—See China Cinda Asset Management Co., Ltd.; *Int'l*, pg. 1488
CINDA - DB NPL SECURITIZATION TRUST 2003-1—See Deutsche Bank Aktiengesellschaft; *Int'l*, pg. 2056
CINDA ENGINEERING & CONSTRUCTION PVT. LTD.—See CTCI Corporation; *Int'l*, pg. 1870
CINDA FINANCIAL LEASING CO., LTD.—See China Cinda Asset Management Co., Ltd.; *Int'l*, pg. 1488
CINDA FUTURES CO., LTD.—See China Cinda Asset Management Co., Ltd.; *Int'l*, pg. 1488
CINDA INNOVATION INVESTMENT CO., LTD.—See China Cinda Asset Management Co., Ltd.; *Int'l*, pg. 1488
CINDA INTERNATIONAL HOLDINGS LIMITED; *Int'l*, pg. 1610
CINDA INVESTMENT CO., LTD.—See China Cinda Asset Management Co., Ltd.; *Int'l*, pg. 1488
CINDA REAL ESTATE CO., LTD.—See China Cinda Asset Management Co., Ltd.; *Int'l*, pg. 1488
CINDA SECURITIES CO., LTD.—See China Cinda Asset Management Co., Ltd.; *Int'l*, pg. 1488
CINDERCRETE PRODUCTS LIMITED—See Heidelberg Materials AG; *Int'l*, pg. 3310
CINDERELLA INC.; *U.S. Private*, pg. 898
CINDERELLA TARGET VALUE ZONES INC.; *U.S. Public*, pg. 495
CINDISUE MINING CORP.; *U.S. Private*, pg. 898
CINDRELLA FINANCIAL SERVICES LIMITED; *Int'l*, pg. 1610
CINDRELLA HOTELS LTD.; *Int'l*, pg. 1610
CINEAD SDN BHD—See Kuok Brothers Sdn. Bhd.; *Int'l*, pg. 4334
CINE-CINEMA CABLE—See Vivendi SE; *Int'l*, pg. 8266
CINEDIGM ENTERTAINMENT CORP.—See Cineverse Corp.; *U.S. Public*, pg. 495
CINEDIGM ENTERTAINMENT HOLDINGS, LLC—See Cineverse Corp.; *U.S. Public*, pg. 495
CINE GROUPE CORPORATION INC.—See Lions Gate Entertainment Corp.; *Int'l*, pg. 4520
CINE LATINO, INC.—See Hemisphere Media Group, Inc.; *U.S. Private*, pg. 1913
CINELEASE, INC.—See Herc Holdings Inc.; *U.S. Public*, pg. 1028

COMPANY NAME INDEX

CINELEASE, LLC—See Herc Holdings Inc.; *U.S. Public*, pg. 1028
CINELINE INDIA LIMITED—See Kanakia Group; *Int'l*, pg. 4064
CINEMA CITY (CHAI WAN) LIMITED—See Transmit Entertainment Limited; *Int'l*, pg. 7901
CINEMA CITY (LANGHAM PLACE) LIMITED—See Transmit Entertainment Limited; *Int'l*, pg. 7901
CINEMA CITY (TW) LIMITED—See Transmit Entertainment Limited; *Int'l*, pg. 7902
CINEMA ENTERTAINMENT CORP.; *U.S. Private*, pg. 898
CINE MAGNETICS, INC.; *U.S. Private*, pg. 898
CINE MAGNETICS VIDEO & DIGITAL LABORATORIES—See Cine Magnetics, Inc.; *U.S. Private*, pg. 898
CINE MAGNETICS VIDEO & DIGITAL LABORATORIES—See Cine Magnetics, Inc.; *U.S. Private*, pg. 898
CINE MAGNETICS VIDEO & DIGITAL LABORATORIES—See Cine Magnetics, Inc.; *U.S. Private*, pg. 898
CINEMARK ARGENTINA, S.R.L.—See Cinemark Holdings, Inc.; *U.S. Public*, pg. 495
CINEMARK DE MEXICO, S.A. DE C.V.—See Entretenimiento GM de Mexico SA de CV; *Int'l*, pg. 2453
CINEMARK HOLDINGS, INC.; *U.S. Public*, pg. 495
CINEMARK, INC.—See Cinemark Holdings, Inc.; *U.S. Public*, pg. 495
CINEMARK INTERNATIONAL, LLC—See Cinemark Holdings, Inc.; *U.S. Public*, pg. 495
CINEMARK MEDIA, INC.—See Cinemark Holdings, Inc.; *U.S. Public*, pg. 495
CINEMARK USA, INC.—See Cinemark Holdings, Inc.; *U.S. Public*, pg. 495
CINEMASSIVE DISPLAYS, LLC—See HaiVision Systems, Inc.; *Int'l*, pg. 3218
CINEMATIC ARTS B.V.—See National Amusements, Inc.; *U.S. Private*, pg. 2842
CINEMA TRUSTS INVESTMENTS IN MOVIES LP; *Int'l*, pg. 1610
CINEMAX INDIA LIMITED—See PVR Limited; *Int'l*, pg. 6125
CINEMEDIA AG; *Int'l*, pg. 1610
CINEMEX HOLDINGS USA, INC.—See Entretenimiento GM de Mexico SA de CV; *Int'l*, pg. 2450
CINEOLIA SAS—See Econocom Group SA; *Int'l*, pg. 2297
CINEOPTIC A.D.; *Int'l*, pg. 1610
CINEPLEX COMPANY LIMITED—See Charoen Pokphand Group Co., Ltd.; *Int'l*, pg. 1453
CINEPLEX DIGITAL MEDIA INC.—See Cineplex Inc.; *Int'l*, pg. 1610
CINEPLEX DIGITAL NETWORKS INC.—See Cineplex Inc.; *Int'l*, pg. 1610
CINEPLEX ENTERTAINMENT LP—See Cineplex Inc.; *Int'l*, pg. 1610
CINEPLEX INC; *Int'l*, pg. 1610
CINEPLEX S.A.; *Int'l*, pg. 1610
CINEQUIPT INC.; *U.S. Private*, pg. 898
CINERAD COMMUNICATIONS LIMITED; *Int'l*, pg. 1610
CINERGETIKA USTI N. L.—See Setuza a.s.; *Int'l*, pg. 6730
CINER GROUP; *Int'l*, pg. 1610
CINERGY ENTERTAINMENT GROUP, INC.; *U.S. Private*, pg. 898
CINERGY TECHNOLOGY, INC.—See Duke Energy Corporation; *U.S. Public*, pg. 690
CINESE INTERNATIONAL GROUP HOLDINGS LIMITED; *Int'l*, pg. 1610
CINESITE (EUROPE) LIMITED—See Endless LLP; *Int'l*, pg. 2403
CINESYSTEM S.A.; *Int'l*, pg. 1610
CINETECH—See Ascent Capital Group, Inc.; *U.S. Private*, pg. 348
CINETIC AUTOMATION—See FIVES, Societe Anonyme; *Int'l*, pg. 2696
CINETIC GIUSTINA S.R.L.—See FIVES, Societe Anonyme; *Int'l*, pg. 2696
CINETIC LABORATORIES ARGENTINA SA—See Perrigo Company plc; *Int'l*, pg. 5812
CINETIC LANDIS LTD.—See FIVES, Societe Anonyme; *Int'l*, pg. 2696
CINETIC SORTING CORP.—See FIVES, Societe Anonyme; *Int'l*, pg. 2696
CINETOPIA, LLC—See Dalian Wanda Group Corporation Ltd.; *Int'l*, pg. 1953
CINETRANSFORMER INTERNATIONAL; *U.S. Private*, pg. 898
CINEVERSE CORP.; *U.S. Public*, pg. 495
CINEVISTA LTD; *Int'l*, pg. 1610
CINEWORLD CINEMA PROPERTIES LIMITED—See Cineworld Group plc; *Int'l*, pg. 1610
CINEWORLD GROUP PLC; *Int'l*, pg. 1610
CINFAB INC.; *U.S. Private*, pg. 898
CINGULATE INC.; *U.S. Public*, pg. 495
CINIONIC BVBA—See Barco N.V.; *Int'l*, pg. 864
CINIONIC INC.—See Barco N.V.; *Int'l*, pg. 864
CINIS FERTILIZER AB; *Int'l*, pg. 1611
CINIUM FINANCIAL SERVICES CORPORATION; *U.S. Private*, pg. 898

CINIX 1 PTY. LTD.—See HeiTech Padu Berhad; *Int'l*, pg. 3326
CINKARNA CELJE D.D.; *Int'l*, pg. 1611
CINKARNA KVARC D. O. O.—See Metalursko Kemicna Industrija Celje, d.d.; *Int'l*, pg. 4850
CINNABON, INC.—See Roark Capital Group Inc.; *U.S. Private*, pg. 3454
CINNAMON HOTELS MANAGEMENT LTD.—See John Keells Holdings PLC; *Int'l*, pg. 3978
CINNAMON INC.—See Vector Inc.; *Int'l*, pg. 8144
CINNOBER FINANCIAL TECHNOLOGY AB—See Nasdaq, Inc.; *U.S. Public*, pg. 1491
CINOXPLAN, S.L.—See The Middleby Corporation; *U.S. Public*, pg. 2113
CINPAK, INC.; *U.S. Private*, pg. 898
CINPRES GAS INJECTION INC—See National Industries Group Holding S.A.K.; *Int'l*, pg. 5159
CINQ MUSIC GROUP, LLC—See GoDigital Media Group, LLC; *U.S. Private*, pg. 1724
CINQ MUSIC PUBLISHING, LLC—See GoDigital Media Group, LLC; *U.S. Private*, pg. 1724
CINSA ENASA PRODUCTOS PARA EL HOGAR, S.A. DE C.V.—See Grupo Industrial Saltillo S.A. de C.V.; *Int'l*, pg. 3130
CINT AB—See Nordic Capital AB; *Int'l*, pg. 5420
CINTAC S.A.—See CAP S.A.; *Int'l*, pg. 1301
CINTAS CANADA LIMITED—See Cintas Corporation; *U.S. Public*, pg. 495
CINTAS CORPORATION NO. 3—See Cintas Corporation; *U.S. Public*, pg. 495
CINTAS CORPORATION; *U.S. Public*, pg. 495
CINTAS DOCUMENT MANAGEMENT INC.—See Cintas Corporation; *U.S. Public*, pg. 495
CINTAS DOCUMENT MANAGEMENT, LLC—See Cintas Corporation; *U.S. Public*, pg. 495
CINTAS (GUANGZHOU) ENTERPRISE SERVICES CO., LTD.—See Cintas Corporation; *U.S. Public*, pg. 495
CINTAS NETHERLANDS HOLDINGS B.V.—See Cintas Corporation; *U.S. Public*, pg. 495
CINTAS - R.U.S., L.P.—See Cintas Corporation; *U.S. Public*, pg. 495
CINT AUSTRALIA PTY. LTD.—See Cint Group AB; *Int'l*, pg. 1611
CINT GROUP AB; *Int'l*, pg. 1611
CINTRA DEVELOPMENTS, LLC—See Ferrovial S A ; *Int'l*, pg. 2644
CINTRA INFRAESTRUCTURAS, S.A.U.—See Ferrovial S.A.; *Int'l*, pg. 2644
CINT UK LTD.—See Cint Group AB; *Int'l*, pg. 1611
CINVEN CAPITAL MANAGEMENT (V) GENERAL PARTNER LIMITED—See Cinven Limited; *Int'l*, pg. 1611
CINVEN GMBH—See Cinven Limited; *Int'l*, pg. 1611
CINVEN HK LIMITED—See Cinven Limited; *Int'l*, pg. 1611
CINVEN LIMITED; *Int'l*, pg. 1611
CINVEN LUXEMBOURG S.A R.L—See Cinven Limited; *Int'l*, pg. 1611
CINVEN PARTNERS LLP—See Cinven Limited; *Int'l*, pg. 1611
CINVEN S.R.L.—See Cinven Limited; *Int'l*, pg. 1611
CIOCIOLA COMMUNICATIONS, INC.; *U.S. Private*, pg. 899
CIO INSIGHT—See Ziff Davis Enterprise, Inc.; *U.S. Private*, pg. 4604
CIOK/CJYC/CFBC RADIO—See Maritime Broadcasting System Ltd.; *Int'l*, pg. 4695
CIONA TECHNOLOGIES LLC—See SRC Holdings Corporation; *U.S. Private*, pg. 3767
CION INVESTMENT CORPORATION; *U.S. Public*, pg. 496
CIO PARTNERS, INC.; *U.S. Private*, pg. 898
CIO SAN TAN II, LIMITED PARTNERSHIP—See City Office REIT, Inc.; *Int'l*, pg. 1627
CIO SOLUTIONS; *U.S. Private*, pg. 899
CIOX HEALTH, LLC - GREEN BAY—See New Mountain Capital, LLC; *U.S. Private*, pg. 2901
CIPA FIERA MILANO PUBLICACOES E EVENTOS LTDA.—See Fiera Milano SpA; *Int'l*, pg. 2660
CIPAG SA—See Ariston Thermo S.p.A.; *Int'l*, pg. 567
CIPA INDUSTRIAL DE PRODUTOS ALIMENTARES LTDA.—See PepsiCo, Inc.; *U.S. Public*, pg. 1668
CIPA LUMBER CO. LTD.—See ITOCHU Corporation; *Int'l*, pg. 3835
CIPA NORDESTE INDUSTRIA DE PRODUTOS ALIMENTARES LTDA.—See PepsiCo, Inc.; *U.S. Public*, pg. 1668
CIPAX AB—See XANO Industri AB; *Int'l*, pg. 8519
CIPAX AS—See XANO Industri AB; *Int'l*, pg. 8519
CIPAX EESTI AS—See XANO Industri AB; *Int'l*, pg. 8519
CIPAX NEDERLAND B.V.—See XANO Industri AB; *Int'l*, pg. 8519
CIPAX NORGE AS—See XANO Industri AB; *Int'l*, pg. 8519
CIPAX OY—See XANO Industri AB; *Int'l*, pg. 8519
CIP CAPITAL FUND, L.P.; *U.S. Private*, pg. 899
CIPE BELGIUM—See Johnson Controls International plc; *Int'l*, pg. 3986
CIPEC CONSTRUCTION INC—See CTCI Corporation; *Int'l*, pg. 1870
CIPHERCLOUD, INC.—See Lookout, Inc.; *U.S. Private*, pg. 2494

CIPHERLAB CO., LTD.; *Int'l*, pg. 1616
CIPHERLAB ELECTRONICS TRADING (SHANGHAI) CO., LTD.—See Cipherlab Co., Ltd.; *Int'l*, pg. 1616
CIPHERLAB USA INC.—See Cipherlab Co., Ltd.; *Int'l*, pg. 1616
CIPHERMAX, INC.; *U.S. Private*, pg. 899
CIPHER MINING INC.; *U.S. Public*, pg. 496
CIPHER PHARMACEUTICALS INC.; *Int'l*, pg. 1616
CIPHER S.A.—See Prosegur Compania de Seguridad S.A.; *Int'l*, pg. 5999
CIPHERTECHS, INC.—See Periscope Equity LLC; *U.S. Private*, pg. 3151
CIPHER TECH SOLUTIONS, INC.; *U.S. Private*, pg. 899
CIPIA VISION LTD.; *Int'l*, pg. 1616
CIPIO PARTNERS GMBH; *Int'l*, pg. 1616
CIPI S.P.A—See Cifin S.r.l.; *Int'l*, pg. 1605
CIPLA AGRIMED (PTY) LTD.—See Cipla Ltd.; *Int'l*, pg. 1617
CIPLA AUSTRALIA PTY LIMITED—See Cipla Ltd.; *Int'l*, pg. 1617
CIPLA (EU) LIMITED—See Cipla Ltd.; *Int'l*, pg. 1616
CIPLA EUROPE NV—See Cipla Ltd.; *Int'l*, pg. 1617
CIPLA HEALTH LIMITED—See Cipla Ltd.; *Int'l*, pg. 1617
CIPLA KENYA LIMITED—See Cipla Ltd.; *Int'l*, pg. 1617
CIPLA LTD.; *Int'l*, pg. 1616
CIPLA MALAYSIA SDN. BHD.—See Cipla Ltd.; *Int'l*, pg. 1617
CIPLA MAROC SA—See Cipla Ltd.; *Int'l*, pg. 1616
CIPLA MAROC SA—See Societe Marocaine De Cooperation Pharmaceutique; *Int'l*, pg. 7043
CIPLA MEDPRO DISTRIBUTION CENTRE (PTY) LIMITED—See Cipla Ltd.; *Int'l*, pg. 1617
CIPLA MEDPRO MANUFACTURING (PTY) LIMITED—See Cipla Ltd.; *Int'l*, pg. 1617
CIPLA MEDPRO (PTY) LIMITED—See Cipla Ltd.; *Int'l*, pg. 1617
CIPLA MEDPRO SOUTH AFRICA LIMITED—See Cipla Ltd.; *Int'l*, pg. 1617
CIPLA QUALITY CHEMICAL INDUSTRIES LIMITED—See Africa Capitalworks Holdings; *Int'l*, pg. 189
CIPLA USA INC.—See Cipla Ltd.; *Int'l*, pg. 1617
CIPLA VET (PTY) LIMITED—See Cipla Ltd.; *Int'l*, pg. 1617
CIPLEX; *U.S. Private*, pg. 899
CIP MERCHANT CAPITAL LIMITED; *Int'l*, pg. 1616
CIPPERMAN COMPLIANCE SERVICES LLC—See Genstar Capital, LLC; *U.S. Private*, pg. 1677
CIPRIANI ACCESSORIES—See Li & Fung Limited; *Int'l*, pg. 4480
CI PRIVATE COUNSEL LP—See CI Financial Corporation; *Int'l*, pg. 1601
CI PRIVATE WEALTH—See CI Financial Corporation; *Int'l*, pg. 1601
C.I. PROPERTY & INVESTMENTS LIMITED—See Financiere Pinault SCA; *Int'l*, pg. 2668
CIPY POLYURETHANES PVT. LTD.—See Pidilite Industries Limited; *Int'l*, pg. 5862
CIRALIGHT GLOBAL, INC.; *U.S. Private*, pg. 899
CIRATA PLC.; *Int'l*, pg. 1617
CIRCA CAPITAL CORPORATION; *U.S. Private*, pg. 899
CIRCA CORPORATION; *U.S. Private*, pg. 899
CIRCADENCE CORPORATION; *U.S. Private*, pg. 899
CIRCA DESTINATION MANAGEMENT COMPANY—See The RK Group, LLC; *U.S. Private*, pg. 4110
CIRCA GROUP AS; *Int'l*, pg. 1617
CIRCA INC.; *U.S. Private*, pg. 899
CIRCA LLC—See Walgreens Boots Alliance, Inc.; *U.S. Public*, pg. 2322
CIRCA METALS INC.—See Equistone Partners Europe Limited; *Int'l*, pg. 2487
CIRCASSIA AB—See Niox Group PLC; *Int'l*, pg. 5309
CIRCASSIA (BEIJING) MEDICAL DEVICE CO. LIMITED—See Niox Group PLC; *Int'l*, pg. 5309
CIRCASSIA LIMITED—See Niox Group PLC; *Int'l*, pg. 5309
CIRCASSIA PHARMA LIMITED—See Niox Group PLC; *Int'l*, pg. 5309
CIRCASSIA (SHANGHAI) MEDICAL DEVICE CO., LIMITED—See Niox Group PLC; *Int'l*, pg. 5309
CIRCA TELECOM USA INC—See Equistone Partners Europe Limited; *Int'l*, pg. 2487
CIRCHEM AB; *Int'l*, pg. 1617
CIRCIO HOLDING ASA; *Int'l*, pg. 1617
CIRCLE 8 LOGISTICS, LLC—See Providence Equity Partners L.L.C.; *U.S. Private*, pg. 3292
CIRCLE A CONSTRUCTION INC.; *U.S. Private*, pg. 899
CIRCLE AUTO GROUP; *U.S. Private*, pg. 899
CIRCLE BOLT & NUT COMPANY INC.; *U.S. Private*, pg. 899
CIRCLE CITY BROADCASTING INC.; *U.S. Private*, pg. 899
CIRCLE CITY HEAT TREATING, INC.—See Incertec Plating Corp.; *U.S. Private*, pg. 2053
CIRCLE COMPUTER RESOURCES, INC.; *U.S. Private*, pg. 899
CIRCLE FOUR LLC—See WH Group Limited; *Int'l*, pg. 8395
CIRCLE FURNITURE INC.; *U.S. Private*, pg. 899
CIRCLE GRAPHICS, INC.—See H.I.G. Capital, LLC; *U.S. Private*, pg. 1827

CIRCLE FURNITURE INC.
CORPORATE AFFILIATIONS

CIRCLE HEALTH 1 LTD.—See Centene Corporation; *U.S. Public*, pg. 468
CIRCLE HEALTH HOLDINGS LIMITED—See Centene Corporation; *U.S. Public*, pg. 468
CIRCLE HEALTH LIMITED—See Centene Corporation; *U.S. Public*, pg. 468
CIRCLE HOME, INC.; *U.S. Private*, pg. 899
CIRCLE IMPORTS; *U.S. Private*, pg. 900
CIRCLE INFINITI; *U.S. Private*, pg. 900
CIRCLE INTERNATIONAL HOLDINGS LIMITED; *Int'l*, pg. 1617
CIRCLE INTERNATIONAL—See Centene Corporation; *U.S. Public*, pg. 468
CIRCLE INTERNET FINANCIAL, LLC; *U.S. Private*, pg. 900
CIRCLE J TRAILERS LIMITED—See Bain Capital, LP; *U.S. Public*, pg. 436
CIRCLE K STORES INC.—See Alimentation Couche-Tard Inc.; *Int'l*, pg. 328
CIRCLE K SVERIGE AB—See FUCHS SE; *Int'l*, pg. 2804
CIRCLE K LUBRICANTS INC.—See AIP, LLC; *U.S. Private*, pg. 136
CIRCLE MACHINE CO.—See Kennametal Inc.; *U.S. Public*, pg. 1222
CIRCLE MEDICAL TECHNOLOGIES, INC.—See WELL Health Technologies Corp.; *Int'l*, pg. 8372
CIRCLE MOBILE COMMUNICATIONS LIMITED—See HKC International Holdings Limited; *Int'l*, pg. 3428
CIRCLE OF CONFUSION TELEVISION STUDIOS LLC—See ITV plc; *Int'l*, pg. 3844
CIRCLE OF LIFE HOSPICE; *U.S. Private*, pg. 900
CIRCLE OIL OMAN LIMITED—See Circle Oil PLC; *Int'l*, pg. 1617
CIRCLE OIL PLC; *Int'l*, pg. 1617
CIRCLE PEAK CAPITAL LLC; *U.S. Private*, pg. 900
CIRCLE PRESSROOM, INC.; *U.S. Private*, pg. 900
CIRCLEPRINTERS HOLDING BV; *Int'l*, pg. 1617
CIRCLE PROPERTY PLC; *Int'l*, pg. 1617
CIRCLE RING NETWORK SDN BHD; *Int'l*, pg. 1617
CIRCLESMARTCARD GMBH—See Rochling SE & Co. KG; *Int'l*, pg. 6376
CIRCLE S.P.A.; *Int'l*, pg. 1617
CIRCLE STAR ENERGY CORP.; *U.S. Private*, pg. 900
CIRCLE TOWERS LLC—See UDR, Inc.; *U.S. Public*, pg. 2218
CIRCLE T WESTERN WEAR INC.; *U.S. Private*, pg. 900
CIRCLEUP NETWORK INC.—See Brightflow.AI, Inc.; *U.S. Private*, pg. 652
CIRCOMP GMBH—See Albany International Corp.; *U.S. Public*, pg. 72
CIRCON HOLDINGS, INC.—See EQT AB; *Int'l*, pg. 2473
CIRCOR AEROSPACE, INC.—See KKR & Co. Inc.; *U.S. Public*, pg. 1242
CIRCOR AEROSPACE—See KKR & Co. Inc.; *U.S. Public*, pg. 1242
CIRCOR DOVIANUS HOLDINGS B.V.—See KKR & Co. Inc.; *U.S. Public*, pg. 1242
CIRCOR ENERGY PRODUCTS (CANADA) ULC—See KKR & Co. Inc.; *U.S. Public*, pg. 1242
CIRCOR ENERGY PRODUCTS, INC—See KKR & Co. Inc.; *U.S. Public*, pg. 1242
CIRCOR, INC.—See KKR & Co. Inc.; *U.S. Public*, pg. 1242
CIRCOR INSTRUMENTATION TECHNOLOGIES, INC.—See KKR & Co. Inc.; *U.S. Public*, pg. 1242
CIRCOR INTERNATIONAL, INC.—See KKR & Co. Inc.; *U.S. Public*, pg. 1242
CIRCOR MAROC SARL A.U.—See KKR & Co. Inc.; *U.S. Public*, pg. 1242
CIRCOR NAVAL SOLUTIONS, LLC—See KKR & Co. Inc.; *U.S. Public*, pg. 1242
CIRCOR NAVAL SOLUTIONS, LLC—See KKR & Co. Inc.; *U.S. Public*, pg. 1242
CIRCOR PUMPING TECHNOLOGIES—See KKR & Co. Inc.; *U.S. Public*, pg. 1242
CIRCUIT AUTOMATION INC—See Parker Hannifin Corporation; *U.S. Public*, pg. 1650
CIRCUIT BREAKER INDUSTRIES INC—See Reunert Limited; *Int'l*, pg. 6311
CIRCUIT BREAKER INDUSTRIES LIMITED—See Reunert Limited; *Int'l*, pg. 6312
CIRCUIT BREAKER INDUSTRIES QWA QWA (PTY) LIMITED—See Reunert Limited; *Int'l*, pg. 6312
CIRCUIT CHECK INC.—See Merit Capital Partners; *U.S. Private*, pg. 2674
CIRCUIT CHEMISTRY EQUIPMENT—See Activar, Inc.; *U.S. Private*, pg. 68
CIRCUIT CONNECT, INC.—See Infinitum Electric, Inc.; *U.S. Private*, pg. 2071
CIRCUIT CONTROLS CORPORATION—See Yazaki Corporation; *Int'l*, pg. 8572
CIRCUIT FABOLOGY MICROELECTRONICS EQUIPMENT CO., LTD.; *Int'l*, pg. 1618
CIRCUIT FOIL LUXEMBOURG S.A.R.L.—See ArcelorMittal S.A.; *Int'l*, pg. 545
CIRCUIT FOIL SERVICE S.A.—See ArcelorMittal S.A.; *Int'l*, pg. 545
CIRCUIT FOIL TAIWAN CORP.—See The Furukawa Electric Co., Ltd.; *Int'l*, pg. 7644

CIRCUIT LOGISTICS INC.—See Deutsche Post AG; *Int'l*, pg. 2072
CIRCUITRONICS, INC; *U.S. Private*, pg. 900
CIRCUIT—See The Interpublic Group of Companies, Inc.; *U.S. Public*, pg. 2092
CIRCUITS PLUS (M) SDN. BHD.—See Shanaya Limited; *Int'l*, pg. 6751
CIRCUITS PLUS PTE. LTD.—See Shanaya Limited; *Int'l*, pg. 6751
CIRCUITS WEST, INC.—See Daniel P. O'Reilly & Company; *U.S. Public*, pg. 1156
CIRCUIT SYSTEMS (INDIA) LIMITED; *Int'l*, pg. 1618
CIRCUIT TREE MEDICAL, INC.—See STAAR Surgical Co.; *U.S. Public*, pg. 1924
CIRCUIT VISION INC.; *U.S. Private*, pg. 900
CIRCUIT WORKS CORPORATION—See IDEX Corp; *U.S. Public*, pg. 1091
CIRCUL-AIRE INC.—See Madison Industries Holdings LLC; *U.S. Private*, pg. 2543
CIRCULAR AGENCY SDN. BHD.—See Batu Kawan Berhad; *Int'l*, pg. 891
CIRCULAR CONNECTORS INC.; *U.S. Private*, pg. 900
CIRCULAR ECONOMY SOLUTIONS GMBH—See Robert Bosch GmbH; *Int'l*, pg. 6360
CIRCULAR KNIT DIVISION—See Fab Industries Corp.; *U.S. Private*, pg. 1458
CIRCULAR PLASTICS AUSTRALIA PTY. LTD.—See Pact Group Holdings Ltd.; *Int'l*, pg. 5693
CIRCULAR WATERS SOLUTIONS S.R.L.; *Int'l*, pg. 1618
CIRCULO CERRADO S.A. DE AHORRO PARA FINES DETERMINADOS—See Mercedes-Benz Group AG; *Int'l*, pg. 4820
CIRCULO DE INVERSIONES S.A.—See Stellantis N.V.; *Int'l*, pg. 7201
CIRCULO DE LECTORES S.A.—See Bertelsmann SE & Co. KGaA; *Int'l*, pg. 992
CIRCULO DE LEITORES—See Porto Editora Lda.; *Int'l*, pg. 5935
CIRCULUS LLC—See Xtglobal Infotech Ltd.; *Int'l*, pg. 8539
THE CIRCUS ARTS CONSERVATORY, INC.; *U.S. Private*, pg. 4010
CIRCUS CIRCUS CASINOS, INC.—See MGM Resorts International; *U.S. Public*, pg. 506
CIRCUS & ELDORADO JOINT VENTURE, LLC—See Caesars Entertainment, Inc.; *U.S. Public*, pg. 420
CIRCUSTRIX LLC; *U.S. Private*, pg. 900
CIRCUTECH INTERNATIONAL HOLDINGS LIMITED; *Int'l*, pg. 1618
CI RESOURCES LIMITED; *Int'l*, pg. 1601
CIRES, S.A.—See Shin-Etsu Chemical Co. Ltd.; *Int'l*, pg. 6839
CIREX BV—See Partners Group Holding AG; *Int'l*, pg. 5749
CIRI LAND DEVELOPMENT COMPANY—See Cook Inlet Region, Inc.; *U.S. Private*, pg. 1038
CIRI SERVICES CORPORATION—See Cook Inlet Region, Inc.; *U.S. Private*, pg. 1038
CIRKEL GMBH & CO.KG; *Int'l*, pg. 1618
THE CIRLOT AGENCY, INC.; *U.S. Private*, pg. 4010
CIRMAC INTERNATIONAL B.V.—See Atlas Copco AB; *Int'l*, pg. 679
CIRMA ENTERPRISE S.A.—See VINCI S.A.; *Int'l*, pg. 8215
CIRMAKER TECHNOLOGY CORPORATION; *Int'l*, pg. 1618
CIRPACK—See Vantiva SA; *Int'l*, pg. 8130
CIRPRO DE DELICIAS S.A. DE C.V.—See Cardinal Health, Inc.; *U.S. Public*, pg. 434
CIRQIT DE COSTA RICA S.A.—See HH Global Group Limited; *Int'l*, pg. 3378
CIRQIT DE HONDURAS S. DE R.L. DE C.V.—See HH Global Group Limited; *Int'l*, pg. 3378
CIRQIT S.A.—See HH Global Group Limited; *Int'l*, pg. 3378
CIRQUE CORPORATION—See Alps Alpine Co., Ltd.; *Int'l*, pg. 376
CIRQUE DU SOLEIL INC.—See TPG Capital, L.P.; *U.S. Public*, pg. 2169
CIRQUE DU SOLEIL ORLANDO INC.—See TPG Capital, L.P.; *U.S. Public*, pg. 2169
CIRQUE ENERGY, INC.; *U.S. Private*, pg. 900
CIRRASCALE CORPORATION—See Craftsman Capital Partners, LLC; *U.S. Private*, pg. 1082
CIRRUS CONCEPT CONSULTING, INC.—See Littlejohn & Co., LLC; *U.S. Private*, pg. 2470
CIRRUS DESIGN CORPORATION—See Aviation Industry Corporation of China; *Int'l*, pg. 741
CIRRUS INTERNATIONAL FZC—See Flame Tree Group Holdings Ltd.; *Int'l*, pg. 2698
CIRRUS LOGIC, INC.; *U.S. Public*, pg. 496
CIRRUS LOGIC INTERNATIONAL LTD.—See Cirrus Logic, Inc.; *U.S. Public*, pg. 496
CIRRUS LOGIC INTERNATIONAL (UK) LTD.—See Cirrus Logic, Inc.; *U.S. Public*, pg. 496
CIRRUS LOGIC K.K.—See Cirrus Logic, Inc.; *U.S. Public*, pg. 496
CIRRUS MEDIA PTY. LIMITED—See Catalyst Investment Managers Pty. Limited; *Int'l*, pg. 1358

CIRRUS MEDICAL STAFFING, INC.—See Webster Equity Partners, LLC; *U.S. Private*, pg. 4467
CIRRUS NETWORKS HOLDINGS LIMITED; *Int'l*, pg. 1618
CIRRUS SERVICES LLC—See Beyond, Inc.; *U.S. Public*, pg. 327
CIRSCO, INC.; *U.S. Private*, pg. 900
CIR S.P.A.—See Compagnia Finanziaria de Benedetti S.p.A.; *Int'l*, pg. 1721
CIRTEC MEDICAL, LLC—See 3i Group plc; *Int'l*, pg. 8
CIRTEK ELECTRONICS CORPORATION—See Cirtek Holdings Philippines Corp.; *Int'l*, pg. 1618
CIRTEK HOLDINGS LIMITED; *Int'l*, pg. 1618
CIRTEK HOLDINGS PHILIPPINES CORP.; *Int'l*, pg. 1618
CIRTRAN CORPORATION; *U.S. Public*, pg. 496
CIRUS CONTROL LLC—See Brinkmere Capital Partners LLC; *U.S. Private*, pg. 655
CISA CERRADURAS S.A.—See Ingersoll Rand Inc.; *U.S. Public*, pg. 1120
CISALFA SPORT S.P.A.; *Int'l*, pg. 1618
CISA S.P.A.—See Ingersoll Rand Inc.; *U.S. Public*, pg. 1120
CIS BAYAD CENTER INC.—See Manila Electric Company; *Int'l*, pg. 4671
CISBIO BIOASSAYS SAS—See Revvity, Inc.; *U.S. Public*, pg. 1794
CIS BRAZIL LTDA—See Catering International & Services S.A.; *Int'l*, pg. 1359
CISCAR; *Int'l*, pg. 1618
CISCO AIR SYSTEMS, INC.—See DXP Enterprises, Inc.; *U.S. Public*, pg. 697
CISCO BROS. CORP.; *U.S. Private*, pg. 900
CISCO (CHINA) INNOVATION TECHNOLOGY CO., LTD.—See Cisco Systems, Inc.; *U.S. Public*, pg. 497
CISCO (CHINA) TECHNOLOGY SERVICES CO., LTD.—See Cisco Systems, Inc.; *U.S. Public*, pg. 497
CISCO DO BRASIL LTDA.—See Cisco Systems, Inc.; *U.S. Public*, pg. 499
CISCO DUTCH HOLDINGS B.V.—See Cisco Systems, Inc.; *U.S. Public*, pg. 497
CISCO-EAGLE INC. - LITTLE ROCK—See Cisco-Eagle Inc.; *U.S. Private*, pg. 900
CISCO-EAGLE INCORPORATED—See Cisco-Eagle Inc.; *U.S. Private*, pg. 900
CISCO-EAGLE INC.; *U.S. Private*, pg. 900
CISCO-EAGLE INC.—See Cisco-Eagle Inc.; *U.S. Private*, pg. 900
CISCO EQUIPMENT - ARTESIA—See Cisco Ford Equipment, Inc.; *U.S. Private*, pg. 900
CISCO EQUIPMENT - LUBBOCK—See Cisco Ford Equipment, Inc.; *U.S. Private*, pg. 900
CISCO EQUIPMENT - SAN ANGELO—See Cisco Ford Equipment, Inc.; *U.S. Private*, pg. 900
CISCO FORD EQUIPMENT, INC.; *U.S. Private*, pg. 900
CISCO HOME, INC.—See Cisco Bros. Corp.; *U.S. Private*, pg. 900
CISCO, INC.—See Morrison Industrial Equipment Company; *U.S. Private*, pg. 2789
CISCO ISH B.V.—See Cisco Systems, Inc.; *U.S. Public*, pg. 497
CIS CO., LTD; *Int'l*, pg. 1618
CISCOM CORP.; *Int'l*, pg. 1618
CIS COMMODITY INSPECTION SERVICES B.V.—See Catering International & Services S.A.; *Int'l*, pg. 1360
CIS COMPANY SECRETARIES (PTY) LTD—See Computershare Limited; *Int'l*, pg. 1760
CISCO NORWAY AS—See Cisco Systems, Inc.; *U.S. Public*, pg. 497
CISCO NORWAY HOLDINGS AS—See Cisco Systems, Inc.; *U.S. Public*, pg. 497
C.I.S. CO. OF ALABAMA—See Central Illinois Steel Company; *U.S. Private*, pg. 821
CISCO OPTICAL GMBH—See Cisco Systems, Inc.; *U.S. Public*, pg. 497
CISCO PHOTONICS ITALY S.R.L.—See Cisco Systems, Inc.; *U.S. Public*, pg. 497
CISCO SYSTEMS (ARGENTINA) S.A.—See Cisco Systems, Inc.; *U.S. Public*, pg. 497
CISCO SYSTEMS AUSTRALIA PTY LIMITED—See Cisco Systems, Inc.; *U.S. Public*, pg. 497
CISCO SYSTEMS AUSTRALIA PTY., LTD.—See Cisco Systems, Inc.; *U.S. Public*, pg. 497
CISCO SYSTEMS AUSTRIA GMBH—See Cisco Systems, Inc.; *U.S. Public*, pg. 497
CISCO SYSTEMS BELGIUM S.P.R.L.—See Cisco Systems, Inc.; *U.S. Public*, pg. 498
CISCO SYSTEMS BULGARIA EOOD—See Cisco Systems, Inc.; *U.S. Public*, pg. 498
CISCO SYSTEMS CANADA CO.—See Cisco Systems, Inc.; *U.S. Public*, pg. 498
CISCO SYSTEMS CAPITAL (AUSTRALIA) PTY. LTD.—See Cisco Systems, Inc.; *U.S. Public*, pg. 498
CISCO SYSTEMS CAPITAL (INDIA) PRIVATE LIMITED—See Cisco Systems, Inc.; *U.S. Public*, pg. 498
CISCO SYSTEMS CAPITAL K.K.—See Cisco Systems, Inc.; *U.S. Public*, pg. 498
CISCO SYSTEMS CAPITAL (KOREA) LIMITED—See Cisco Systems, Inc.; *U.S. Public*, pg. 498

CISCO SYSTEMS CARIBE—See Cisco Systems, Inc.; *U.S. Public*, pg. 498
CISCO SYSTEMS CHILE S.A.—See Cisco Systems, Inc.; *U.S. Public*, pg. 498
CISCO SYSTEMS (CHINA) NETWORKING TECHNOLOGY CO., LTD.—See Cisco Systems, Inc.; *U.S. Public*, pg. 497
CISCO SYSTEMS (COLOMBIA) LIMITADA—See Cisco Systems, Inc.; *U.S. Public*, pg. 498
CISCO SYSTEMS COSTA RICA SA—See Cisco Systems, Inc.; *U.S. Public*, pg. 498
CISCO SYSTEMS CYPRUS LTD.—See Cisco Systems, Inc.; *U.S. Public*, pg. 498
CISCO SYSTEMS (CZECH REPUBLIC) S.R.O—See Cisco Systems, Inc.; *U.S. Public*, pg. 497
CISCO SYSTEMS DANMARK A/S—See Cisco Systems, Inc.; *U.S. Public*, pg. 498
CISCO SYSTEMS DE MEXICO, S.A. DE C.V.—See Cisco Systems, Inc.; *U.S. Public*, pg. 499
CISCO SYSTEMS DO BRASIL LTDA—See Cisco Systems, Inc.; *U.S. Public*, pg. 499
CISCO SYSTEMS EGYPT LTD.—See Cisco Systems, Inc.; *U.S. Public*, pg. 498
CISCO SYSTEMS ESTONIA OU—See Cisco Systems, Inc.; *U.S. Public*, pg. 498
CISCO SYSTEMS FINANCE INTERNATIONAL UNLIMITED COMPANY—See Cisco Systems, Inc.; *U.S. Public*, pg. 498
CISCO SYSTEMS FINLAND OY—See Cisco Systems, Inc.; *U.S. Public*, pg. 498
CISCO SYSTEMS FRANCE SARL—See Cisco Systems, Inc.; *U.S. Public*, pg. 498
CISCO SYSTEMS G.K.—See Cisco Systems, Inc.; *U.S. Public*, pg. 498
CISCO SYSTEMS G.K. TOKYO—See Cisco Systems, Inc.; *U.S. Public*, pg. 498
CISCO SYSTEMS GMBH—See Cisco Systems, Inc.; *U.S. Public*, pg. 498
CISCO SYSTEMS HELLAS S.A.—See Cisco Systems, Inc.; *U.S. Public*, pg. 498
CISCO SYSTEMS (HK), LTD.—See Cisco Systems, Inc.; *U.S. Public*, pg. 497
CISCO SYSTEMS HOLDING GMBH & CO. KG—See Cisco Systems, Inc.; *U.S. Public*, pg. 498
CISCO SYSTEMS, INC.; *U.S. Public*, pg. 400
CISCO SYSTEMS (INDIA) PVT. LTD.—See Cisco Systems, Inc.; *U.S. Public*, pg. 497
CISCO SYSTEMS INTERNETWORKING (IRELAND) LIMITED—See Cisco Systems, Inc.; *U.S. Public*, pg. 498
CISCO SYSTEMS ISRAEL LTD.—See Cisco Systems, Inc.; *U.S. Public*, pg. 498
CISCO SYSTEMS (ITALY) S.R.L.—See Cisco Systems, Inc.; *U.S. Public*, pg. 497
CISCO SYSTEMS (KOREA) LIMITED—See Cisco Systems, Inc.; *U.S. Public*, pg. 497
CISCO SYSTEMS LIMITED—See Cisco Systems, Inc.; *U.S. Public*, pg. 498
CISCO SYSTEMS LLC—See Cisco Systems, Inc.; *U.S. Public*, pg. 498
CISCO SYSTEMS LTD.—See Cisco Systems, Inc.; *U.S. Public*, pg. 498
CISCO SYSTEMS LUXEMBOURG S.A.R.L.—See Cisco Systems, Inc.; *U.S. Public*, pg. 498
CISCO SYSTEMS MACEDONIA DOOEL SKOPJE—See Cisco Systems, Inc.; *U.S. Public*, pg. 498
CISCO SYSTEMS MAGYARORSZG KFT.—See Cisco Systems, Inc.; *U.S. Public*, pg. 498
CISCO SYSTEMS MALAYSIA SDN, BHD—See Cisco Systems, Inc.; *U.S. Public*, pg. 498
CISCO SYSTEMS NETHERLANDS HOLDINGS B.V—See Cisco Systems, Inc.; *U.S. Public*, pg. 498
CISCO SYSTEMS NEW ZEALAND LIMITED—See Cisco Systems, Inc.; *U.S. Public*, pg. 498
CISCO SYSTEMS NORWAY AS—See Cisco Systems, Inc.; *U.S. Public*, pg. 498
CISCO SYSTEMS PERU S.A.—See Cisco Systems, Inc.; *U.S. Public*, pg. 498
CISCO SYSTEMS POLAND SP. Z O.O.—See Cisco Systems, Inc.; *U.S. Public*, pg. 498
CISCO SYSTEMS PORTUGAL SISTEMAS INFORMATICOS SOCIEDADE UNIPESSOAL LTDA.—See Cisco Systems, Inc.; *U.S. Public*, pg. 498
CISCO SYSTEMS ROMANIA S.R.L.—See Cisco Systems, Inc.; *U.S. Public*, pg. 498
CISCO SYSTEMS (SCOTLAND) LIMITED—See Cisco Systems, Inc.; *U.S. Public*, pg. 497
CISCO SYSTEMS SLOVAKIA, SPOL. S R.O.—See Cisco Systems, Inc.; *U.S. Public*, pg. 498
CISCO SYSTEMS—See Cisco Systems, Inc.; *U.S. Public*, pg. 500
CISCO SYSTEMS SOUTH KOREA—See Cisco Systems, Inc.; *U.S. Public*, pg. 499
CISCO SYSTEMS (SPAIN) S.L.—See Cisco Systems, Inc.; *U.S. Public*, pg. 498
CISCO SYSTEMS (SWEDEN) AB—See Cisco Systems, Inc.; *U.S. Public*, pg. 497
CISCO SYSTEMS (SWITZERLAND) GMBH—See Cisco Systems, Inc.; *U.S. Public*, pg. 497

CISCO SYSTEMS TAIWAN LTD.—See Cisco Systems, Inc.; *U.S. Public*, pg. 499
CISCO SYSTEMS (THAILAND) LTD.—See Cisco Systems, Inc.; *U.S. Public*, pg. 497
CISCO SYSTEMS VENEZUELA—See Cisco Systems, Inc.; *U.S. Public*, pg. 499
CISCO SYSTEMS VIETNAM LIMITED—See Cisco Systems, Inc.; *U.S. Public*, pg. 499
CISCO TECHNOLOGIES (BEIJING) CO., LTD.—See Cisco Systems, Inc.; *U.S. Public*, pg. 499
CISCO TECHNOLOGIES (THAILAND) LIMITED—See Cisco Systems, Inc.; *U.S. Public*, pg. 499
CISCO TECHNOLOGY BELGIUM BVBA—See Cisco Systems, Inc.; *U.S. Public*, pg. 499
CISCO TECHNOLOGY DENMARK APS—See Cisco Systems, Inc.; *U.S. Public*, pg. 499
CISCO TECHNOLOGY SERVICES (DALIAN) CO. LTD—See Cisco Systems, Inc.; *U.S. Public*, pg. 499
CISCO THV LLC—See Cisco Systems, Inc.; *U.S. Public*, pg. 499
CISCO TRADING COMPANY—See Al-Kout Industrial Projects Company K.S.C.C.; *Int'l*, pg. 286
CISCO VIDEO TECHNOLOGIES INDIA PRIVATE LIMITED—See Cisco Systems, Inc.; *U.S. Public*, pg. 499
CISCO VIDEO TECHNOLOGIES ISRAEL LTD.—See Cisco Systems, Inc.; *U.S. Public*, pg. 499
CISCO WEBEX LLC—See Cisco Systems, Inc.; *U.S. Public*, pg. 499
CISD (ASIA) CO.,LTD.—See ITOCHU Corporation; *Int'l*, pg. 3835
CISDEG SPA—See Leonardo S.p.A.; *Int'l*, pg. 4460
CISEN PHARMACEUTICAL CO., LTD.; *Int'l*, pg. 1618
CISEN PHARMACEUTICALS INDIA PRIVATE LIMITED—See Cisen Pharmaceutical Co., Ltd.; *Int'l*, pg. 1618
CIS FINANCE LTD—See Co-operative Group Limited; *Int'l*, pg. 1679
CIS FINANCIAL SERVICES, INC.—See ECN Capital Corp.; *Int'l*, pg. 2292
CIS GENERAL INSURANCE LTD—See Markerstudy Insurance Services Limited; *Int'l*, pg. 4696
CI SHOPPING SERVICE CO., LTD.—See ITOCHU Corporation; *Int'l*, pg. 3835
CIS INC.; *U.S. Private*, pg. 900
CISION FINLAND OY—See Platinum Equity, LLC; *U.S. Private*, pg. 3201
CISION GERMANY GMBH—See Platinum Equity, LLC; *U.S. Private*, pg. 3201
CISION GLOBAL SOLUTIONS AB—See Platinum Equity, LLC; *U.S. Private*, pg. 3201
CISION LTD.—See Platinum Equity, LLC; *U.S. Private*, pg. 3201
CISION PORTUGAL S.A.—See Platinum Equity, LLC; *U.S. Private*, pg. 3201
CISION SCANDINAVIA AS—See Platinum Equity, LLC; *U.S. Private*, pg. 3201
CISION SVERIGE AB—See Platinum Equity, LLC; *U.S. Private*, pg. 3201
CISION UK LTD.—See Platinum Equity, LLC; *U.S. Private*, pg. 3201
CISION US INC.—See Platinum Equity, LLC; *U.S. Private*, pg. 3201
CISIVE INC.; *U.S. Private*, pg. 900
THE CISNEROS GROUP OF COMPANIES; *Int'l*, pg. 7632
CISNEROS INTERACTIVE BOLIVIA, S.R.L.—See Entravision Communications Corporation; *U.S. Public*, pg. 779
CISNEROS INTERACTIVE ECUADOR CISTERACTEC, S.A.—See Entravision Communications Corporation; *U.S. Public*, pg. 779
CISNEROS INTERACTIVE GUATEMALA, S.A.—See Entravision Communications Corporation; *U.S. Public*, pg. 779
CISNEROS INTERACTIVE PUERTO RICO, S.A.—See Entravision Communications Corporation; *U.S. Public*, pg. 779
CISNEROS INTERACTIVE, S.A.—See Entravision Communications Corporation; *U.S. Public*, pg. 779
CISO GLOBAL, INC.; *U.S. Public*, pg. 501
CI SOLID CO., LTD.—See SFA Engineering Corp.; *Int'l*, pg. 6738
CIS PROMOTION; *Int'l*, pg. 1618
CISRI DA HUI INVESTMENT CO., LTD.—See Advanced Technology & Materials Co., Ltd.; *Int'l*, pg. 162
CIS SECURE COMPUTING, INC.—See Hammond, Kennedy, Whitney & Company, Inc.; *U.S. Private*, pg. 1850
CIS TCHAD S.A.R.L.—See Catering International & Services S.A.; *Int'l*, pg. 1360
CISTERA NETWORKS, INC.; *U.S. Public*, pg. 501
CISTOCA A.D.; *Int'l*, pg. 1618
CI SYSTEMS (ISRAEL) LTD.; *Int'l*, pg. 1601
CISZEWSKI PUBLIC RELATIONS SP. Z O.O.—See Publicis Groupe S.A.; *Int'l*, pg. 6097
CITADEL CAPITAL S.A.E.; *Int'l*, pg. 1619
CITADEL COMMUNICATIONS LLC; *U.S. Private*, pg. 901
CITADELE LEASING—See UniCredit S.p.A.; *Int'l*, pg. 8036
CITADEL ENTERPRISE AMERICAS LLC; *U.S. Private*, pg. 901
CITADEL EXPLORATION, INC.; *U.S. Public*, pg. 501

CITADEL FEDERAL SOLUTIONS LLC; *U.S. Private*, pg. 901
THE CITADEL GROUP LIMITED—See Pacific Equity Partners Pty. Limited; *Int'l*, pg. 5689
CITADEL HEALTH PTY. LTD.—See Pacific Equity Partners Pty. Limited; *Int'l*, pg. 5689
CITADEL INSURANCE SERVICES, LC; *U.S. Private*, pg. 901
CITADEL PEOPLE PTY. LTD.—See Pacific Equity Partners Pty. Limited; *Int'l*, pg. 5689
CITADEL PLASTICS HOLDINGS, INC.—See LyondellBasell Industries N.V.; *Int'l*, pg. 4607
CITADEL REALTY & DEVELOPERS LTD.; *Int'l*, pg. 1619
CITADEL RESTORATION AND REPAIR, INC.—See RPM International Inc.; *U.S. Public*, pg. 1816
CITADEL TECHNOLOGY SOLUTIONS PTY. LTD.—See Pacific Equity Partners Pty. Limited; *Int'l*, pg. 5689
CITADINES MELBOURNE ON BOURKE PTY LTD—See CapitaLand Investment Limited; *Int'l*, pg. 1314
CIT AEROSPACE ASIA PTE LTD.—See First Citizens BancShares, Inc.; *U.S. Public*, pg. 841
CIT AEROSPACE LLC—See First Citizens BancShares, Inc.; *U.S. Public*, pg. 841
CITAGLOBAL BERHAD; *Int'l*, pg. 1619
CITAGLOBAL CAPITAL SDN. BHD.—See Citaglobal Berhad; *Int'l*, pg. 1619
CITAIR INC.; *Int'l*, pg. 1619
C.I. TAKIRON CORPORATION - ABOSHI PLANT—See ITOCHU Corporation; *Int'l*, pg. 3834
C.I. TAKIRON CORPORATION - HIRATSUKA FACTORY—See ITOCHU Corporation; *Int'l*, pg. 3834
C.I. TAKIRON CORPORATION - IBOGAWA PLANT—See ITOCHU Corporation; *Int'l*, pg. 3834
C.I. TAKIRON CORPORATION - OKAYAMA FACTORY—See ITOCHU Corporation; *Int'l*, pg. 3834
C.I. TAKIRON CORPORATION - SHIGA FACTORY—See ITOCHU Corporation; *Int'l*, pg. 3834
C.I. TAKIRON CORPORATION—See ITOCHU Corporation; *Int'l*, pg. 3834
C.I. TAKIRON CORPORATION - TOCHIGI FACTORY—See ITOCHU Corporation; *Int'l*, pg. 3834
C.I. TAKIRON LOGISTICS CO., LTD.—See ITOCHU Corporation; *Int'l*, pg. 3834
CITALIA HOLIDAYS LIMITED—See TUI AG; *Int'l*, pg. 7968
CITA MINERAL INVESTINDO TBK; *Int'l*, pg. 1618
CITA NEUROPHARMACEUTICALS INC—See Ligand Pharmaceuticals Incorporated; *U.S. Public*, pg. 1314
CITARELLA; *U.S. Private*, pg. 901
CITA TABACOS DE CANARIAS, S.A.—See Imperial Brands PLC; *Int'l*, pg. 3632
CITAT AB—See Bure Equity AB; *Int'l*, pg. 1221
CITATION CRUDE MARKETING, INC.—See Citation Oil & Gas Corp.; *U.S. Private*, pg. 901
CITATION GLOBAL, INC.; *U.S. Private*, pg. 901
CITATION LTD.—See ECI Partners LLP; *Int'l*, pg. 2289
CITATION OIL & GAS CORP.; *U.S. Private*, pg. 901
CITATION PLASTICS CO.—See West Pharmaceutical Services, Inc.; *U.S. Public*, pg. 2352
CITATION RESOURCES LIMITED; *Int'l*, pg. 1619
CITAT OY—See Nordic Morning Plc; *Int'l*, pg. 5422
CITBA FINANCIAL CORP.; *U.S. Public*, pg. 501
CIT BANK, N.A.—See First Citizens BancShares, Inc.; *U.S. Public*, pg. 841
CIT CAPITAL FINANCE (UK) LIMITED—See First Citizens BancShares, Inc.; *U.S. Public*, pg. 841
CIT-CITOXLAB FRANCE SAS—See Charles River Laboratories International, Inc.; *U.S. Public*, pg. 480
CITCO COMMUNITY BANCSHARES, INC.; *U.S. Private*, pg. 901
CITCO CURACAO—See Coeclerici S.p.A.; *Int'l*, pg. 1688
CITCH CO., LTD.; *Int'l*, pg. 1619
CI TECH COMPONENTS AG—See Giesecke & Devrient GmbH; *Int'l*, pg. 2969
CITECH ENERGY RECOVERY SOLUTIONS UK LTD.—See Muhibbah Engineering (M) Bhd.; *Int'l*, pg. 5078
CITECH ENERGY RECOVERY SYSTEM MALAYSIA SDN. BHD.—See Muhibbah Engineering (M) Bhd.; *Int'l*, pg. 5078
CITEC INC.—See GIKEN Ltd.; *Int'l*, pg. 2972
CITEC INFORMATION & ENGINEERING GMBH—See Cyient Limited; *Int'l*, pg. 1895
CITEC NORWAY AS—See Cyient Limited; *Int'l*, pg. 1895
CITEC OY AB—See Cyient Limited; *Int'l*, pg. 1896
CITE DU TEMPS SA—See The Swatch Group Ltd.; *Int'l*, pg. 7691
CITE GOURMANDE—See Holding Le Duff SA; *Int'l*, pg. 3450
CITEL TECHNOLOGIES, INC.—See Tortel Communications Inc.; *Int'l*, pg. 7831
CITELUM SA—See Electricite de France S.A.; *Int'l*, pg. 2350
CITE MARINE S.A.S.—See Nissui Corporation; *Int'l*, pg. 5377
CITEOS SAUMUR SAS—See VINCI S.A.; *Int'l*, pg. 8215
CITEOS—See VINCI S.A.; *Int'l*, pg. 8236
CITEPARK—See FAYAT SAS; *Int'l*, pg. 2625
CI TEXTILE SERVICE CO., LTD.—See ITOCHU Corporation; *Int'l*, pg. 3835

CITECH CO., LTD.
CORPORATE AFFILIATIONS

CIT FINANCE & LEASING CORPORATION—See First Citizens BancShares, Inc.; *U.S. Public*, pg. 841
CIT FINANCE LLC—See First Citizens BancShares, Inc.; *U.S. Public*, pg. 841
CIT (FRANCE) SA—See First Citizens BancShares, Inc.; *U.S. Public*, pg. 841
CITG CAPITAL PARTNERS, LLC; *U.S. Private*, pg. 901
CITGO PETROLEUM CORPORATION—See Petroleos de Venezuela S.A.; *Int'l*, pg. 5828
CITGO PETROLEUM CORPORATION—See Petroleos de Venezuela S.A.; *Int'l*, pg. 5828
CITGO PETROLEUM - LAKE CHARLES REFINERY—See Petroleos de Venezuela S.A.; *Int'l*, pg. 5828
CITGO PIPELINE COMPANY—See Petroleos de Venezuela S.A.; *Int'l*, pg. 5828
THE CIT GROUP/BUSINESS CREDIT, INC.—See First Citizens BancShares, Inc.; *U.S. Public*, pg. 842
THE CIT GROUP/CAPITAL FINANCE, INC.—See First Citizens BancShares, Inc.; *U.S. Public*, pg. 842
THE CIT GROUP/COMMERCIAL SERVICES (ASIA), LIMITED—See First Citizens BancShares, Inc.; *U.S. Public*, pg. 842
THE CIT GROUP/COMMERCIAL SERVICES, INC.—See First Citizens BancShares, Inc.; *U.S. Public*, pg. 842
THE CIT GROUP/COMMERCIAL SERVICES, INC. (VA.)—See First Citizens BancShares, Inc.; *U.S. Public*, pg. 842
THE CIT GROUP/CONSUMER FINANCE, INC.—See First Citizens BancShares, Inc.; *U.S. Public*, pg. 842
THE CIT GROUP/EQUIPMENT FINANCING, INC.—See First Citizens BancShares, Inc.; *U.S. Public*, pg. 842
CIT GROUP (FRANCE) SA—See First Citizens BancShares, Inc.; *U.S. Public*, pg. 841
CIT GROUP (FRANCE) SAS—See First Citizens BancShares, Inc.; *U.S. Public*, pg. 841
CIT GROUP INC.—See First Citizens BancShares, Inc.; *U.S. Public*, pg. 841
THE CIT GROUP/SALES FINANCING, INC.—See First Citizens BancShares, Inc.; *U.S. Public*, pg. 842
CIT HEALTHCARE LLC—See First Citizens BancShares, Inc.; *U.S. Public*, pg. 841
THE C.I. THORNBURG CO., INC.; *U.S. Private*, pg. 4003
CITIBANAMEX SEGUROS, S.A. DE C.V.—See Citigroup Inc.; *U.S. Public*, pg. 502
CITIBANK BERHAD—See Citigroup Inc.; *U.S. Public*, pg. 502
CITIBANK CANADA—See Citigroup Inc.; *U.S. Public*, pg. 502
CITIBANK (CHINA) CO., LTD.—See Citigroup Inc.; *U.S. Public*, pg. 501
CITIBANK-COLOMBIA S.A.—See Citigroup Inc.; *U.S. Public*, pg. 503
CITIBANK (COSTA RICA) S.A.—See Citigroup Inc.; *U.S. Public*, pg. 502
CITIBANK CREDIT CARD ISSUANCE TRUST; *U.S. Private*, pg. 901
CITIBANK DEL PERU S.A.—See Citigroup Inc.; *U.S. Public*, pg. 503
CITIBANK-DISTRIBUIDORA DE TITULOS E VALORES MOBILIARIOS S.A.—See Citigroup Inc.; *U.S. Public*, pg. 501
CITIBANK EUROPE PLC - FINLAND REPRESENTATIVE OFFICE—See Citigroup Inc.; *U.S. Public*, pg. 502
CITIBANK EUROPE PLC - FRANCE REPRESENTATIVE OFFICE—See Citigroup Inc.; *U.S. Public*, pg. 502
CITIBANK EUROPE PLC, ORGANIZACNI SLOZKA—See Citigroup Inc.; *U.S. Public*, pg. 502
CITIBANK EUROPE PLC—See Citigroup Inc.; *U.S. Public*, pg. 502
CITIBANK (HONG KONG) LIMITED—See Citigroup Inc.; *U.S. Public*, pg. 502
CITIBANK INVESTMENTS LIMITED—See Citigroup Inc.; *U.S. Public*, pg. 503
CITIBANK JAPAN LTD.—See Citigroup Inc.; *U.S. Public*, pg. 503
CITIBANK KOREA INC.—See Citigroup Inc.; *U.S. Public*, pg. 503
CITIBANK LEASING S.A.-ARRENDAMENTO MERCANTIL—See Citigroup Inc.; *U.S. Public*, pg. 501
CITIBANK MAGHREB—See Citigroup Inc.; *U.S. Public*, pg. 501
CITIBANK, N.A. PUERTO RICO—See Citigroup Inc.; *U.S. Public*, pg. 502
CITIBANK, N.A.—See Citigroup Inc.; *U.S. Public*, pg. 501
CITIBANK, N.A.—See Citigroup Inc.; *U.S. Public*, pg. 502
CITIBANK, N.A.—See Citigroup Inc.; *U.S. Public*, pg. 502
CITIBANK, N.A.—See Citigroup Inc.; *U.S. Public*, pg. 502
CITIBANK NIGERIA LIMITED—See Citigroup Inc.; *U.S. Public*, pg. 502
CITIBANK OVERSEAS INVESTMENT CORPORATION—See Citigroup Inc.; *U.S. Public*, pg. 502
CITIBANK SINGAPORE LTD.—See Citigroup Inc.; *U.S. Public*, pg. 503
CITIBANK (SOUTH DAKOTA), N.A.—See Citigroup Inc.; *U.S. Public*, pg. 502
CITIBANK (SWITZERLAND) AG—See Citigroup Inc.; *U.S. Public*, pg. 502

CITIBANK TAIWAN LIMITED—See Citigroup Inc.; *U.S. Public*, pg. 503
CITIBANK TANZANIA LIMITED—See Citigroup Inc.; *U.S. Public*, pg. 503
CITIBANK UNITED ARAB EMIRATES—See Citigroup Inc.; *U.S. Public*, pg. 503
CITIBASE HOLDINGS PLC; *Int'l*, pg. 1619
CITI CARDS CANADA INC.—See Citigroup Inc.; *U.S. Public*, pg. 501
CITIC ASSETS MANAGEMENT CORPORATION LTD.—See CITIC Group Corporation; *Int'l*, pg. 1619
CITIC AUSTRALIA PTY. LTD.—See CITIC Group Corporation; *Int'l*, pg. 1620
CITIC AUSTRALIA TRADING LIMITED—See CITIC Group Corporation; *Int'l*, pg. 1620
CITIC AUTOMOBILE CO., LTD.—See CITIC Group Corporation; *Int'l*, pg. 1619
CITIC BOHAI ALUMINIUM INDUSTRIES HOLDING COMPANY LTD.—See CITIC Group Corporation; *Int'l*, pg. 1619
CITIC CAPITAL HOLDINGS LIMITED—See CITIC Group Corporation; *Int'l*, pg. 1619
CITIC CAPITAL PARTNERS LLC—See CITIC Group Corporation; *Int'l*, pg. 1619
CITIC DEVELOPMENT CO., LTD.—See CITIC Group Corporation; *Int'l*, pg. 1620
CITIC ENVIROTECH LTD—See CITIC Group Corporation; *Int'l*, pg. 1620
CITIC GROUP CORPORATION; *Int'l*, pg. 1619
CITIC GSI TOMIDA GROUP CO., LTD.—See CITIC Group Corporation; *Int'l*, pg. 1620
CITIC GSI TOMIDA GROUP CO., LTD.—See GSI Creos Corporation; *Int'l*, pg. 3144
CITIC GUOAN GROUP CO., LTD.—See CITIC Group Corporation; *Int'l*, pg. 1620
CITIC GUOAN INFORMATION INDUSTRY CO., LTD.—See CITIC Group Corporation; *Int'l*, pg. 1620
CITIC GUOAN WINE CO., LTD.; *Int'l*, pg. 1621
CITIC HEAVY INDUSTRIES BRASIL—See CITIC Heavy Industries Co., Ltd.; *Int'l*, pg. 1621
CITIC HEAVY INDUSTRIES CHILE SPA—See CITIC Heavy Industries Co., Ltd.; *Int'l*, pg. 1621
CITIC HEAVY INDUSTRIES CO., LTD.; *Int'l*, pg. 1621
CITIC-HEAVY INDUSTRIES CO., LTD.—See CITIC Heavy Industries Co., Ltd.; *Int'l*, pg. 1621
CITIC HEAVY INDUSTRIES SOUTH AFRICA PTY LTD.—See CITIC Heavy Industries Co., Ltd.; *Int'l*, pg. 1621
CITIC HEAVY MACHINERY CO., LTD.—See CITIC Group Corporation; *Int'l*, pg. 1620
CITIC HIC AUSTRALIA PTY. LTD.—See CITIC Heavy Industries Co., Ltd.; *Int'l*, pg. 1621
CITIC HIC GANDARA CENSA S.A.U.—See CITIC Heavy Industries Co., Ltd.; *Int'l*, pg. 1621
CITIC HIC NORTH AMERICA CO., LTD.—See CITIC Heavy Industries Co., Ltd.; *Int'l*, pg. 1621
CITIC HONG KONG (HOLDINGS) LTD.—See CITIC Group Corporation; *Int'l*, pg. 1620
CITIC INDUSTRIAL INVESTMENT GROUP CORP., LTD.—See CITIC Group Corporation; *Int'l*, pg. 1620
CITIC INSTITUTE OF ARCHITECTURE & DESIGN RESEARCH—See CITIC Group Corporation; *Int'l*, pg. 1620
CITIC INTERNATIONAL CONTRACTING INC.—See CITIC Group Corporation; *Int'l*, pg. 1620
CITIC INTERNATIONAL FINANCIAL HOLDINGS LIMITED—See CITIC Group Corporation; *Int'l*, pg. 1620
CITIC INVESTMENT HOLDINGS LTD.—See CITIC Group Corporation; *Int'l*, pg. 1620
CITIC LTD.—See CITIC Group Corporation; *Int'l*, pg. 1620
CITIC MACHINERY MANUFACTURING CO., LTD.—See CITIC Group Corporation; *Int'l*, pg. 1621
CITIC METAL CO., LTD.—See CITIC Group Corporation; *Int'l*, pg. 1621
CITIC NETWORKS CO., LTD.—See CITIC Group Corporation; *Int'l*, pg. 1621
CITIC NETWORKS MANAGEMENT CO., LTD.—See CITIC Group Corporation; *Int'l*, pg. 1621
CITIC NEW ZEALAND LTD.—See CITIC Group Corporation; *Int'l*, pg. 1620
CITIC NINGBO GROUP—See CITIC Group Corporation; *Int'l*, pg. 1621
CITIC OCEAN HELECOPTER CO., LTD.—See CITIC Group Corporation; *Int'l*, pg. 1621
CITIC OFFSHORE HELICOPTER CO., LTD.; *Int'l*, pg. 1621
CITICOMICS LIMITED—See Culturecom Holdings Ltd; *Int'l*, pg. 1877
CITICON (HONG KONG) LIMITED—See Danaher Corporation; *U.S. Public*, pg. 625
CITI CONSUMER BANKING—See Citigroup Inc.; *U.S. Public*, pg. 501
CITICORE ENERGY REIT CORPORATION; *Int'l*, pg. 1622
CITICORP DATA SYSTEMS INCORPORATED—See Citigroup Inc.; *U.S. Public*, pg. 503
CITICORP FINANCE (INDIA) LIMITED—See Citigroup Inc.; *U.S. Public*, pg. 502

CITICORP INSURANCE AGENCY CO., LTD.—See Citigroup Inc.; *U.S. Public*, pg. 503
CITICORP INTERNATIONAL LIMITED—See Citigroup Inc.; *U.S. Public*, pg. 502
CITICORP SECURITIES INTERNATIONAL, INC.—See Citigroup Inc.; *U.S. Public*, pg. 503
CITICORP TRUST SOUTH DAKOTA; *U.S. Private*, pg. 901
CITIC PACIFIC SPECIAL STEEL GROUP CO., LTD.; *Int'l*, pg. 1621
CITIC PRESS CORPORATION; *Int'l*, pg. 1622
CITIC PRIVATE EQUITY FUNDS MANAGEMENT CO., LTD.—See CITIC Group Corporation; *Int'l*, pg. 1621
CITIC PUBLISHING HOUSE—See CITIC Group Corporation; *Int'l*, pg. 1621
CITIC QINHUANGDAO CO., LTD.—See CITIC Group Corporation; *Int'l*, pg. 1621
CITIC RESOURCES HOLDINGS LIMITED—See CITIC Group Corporation; *Int'l*, pg. 1621
CITIC SECURITIES BROKERAGE (HK) LIMITED—See CITIC Securities Co., Ltd.; *Int'l*, pg. 1622
CITIC SECURITIES CO., LTD.; *Int'l*, pg. 1622
CITIC SECURITIES INTERNATIONAL CO., LTD.—See CITIC Securities Co., Ltd.; *Int'l*, pg. 1622
CITIC SECURITIES INVESTMENT LIMITED—See CITIC Securities Co., Ltd.; *Int'l*, pg. 1622
CITIC SECURITIES SOUTH CHINA COMPANY LIMITED—See CITIC Securities Co., Ltd.; *Int'l*, pg. 1622
CITIC SECURITIES (ZHEJIANG) CO., LTD.—See CITIC Securities Co., Ltd.; *Int'l*, pg. 1622
CITICS FUTURES CO., LTD.—See CITIC Securities Co., Ltd.; *Int'l*, pg. 1622
CITIC SMCC PROCESS TECHNOLOGY PTY LTD.—See CITIC Heavy Industries Co., Ltd.; *Int'l*, pg. 1621
CITIC SOUTH CHINA GROUP CO., LTD.—See CITIC Group Corporation; *Int'l*, pg. 1621
CITIC TELECOM INTERNATIONAL CPC LIMITED—See CITIC Group Corporation; *Int'l*, pg. 1620
CITIC TELECOM INTERNATIONAL HOLDINGS LIMITED—See CITIC Group Corporation; *Int'l*, pg. 1620
CITIC TIANJIN INVESTMENT HOLDING CO., LTD.—See CITIC Group Corporation; *Int'l*, pg. 1621
CITIC TRAVEL CO., LTD.—See CITIC Group Corporation; *Int'l*, pg. 1621
CITIC WANTONG SECURITIES CO., LTD.—See CITIC Securities Co., Ltd.; *Int'l*, pg. 1622
CITIES WEST PUBLISHING; *U.S. Private*, pg. 901
CITIFINANCIAL CANADA EAST CORP.—See Citigroup Inc.; *U.S. Public*, pg. 502
CITIFINANCIAL CREDIT COMPANY—See Citigroup Inc.; *U.S. Public*, pg. 501
CITIFINANCIAL EUROPE PLC—See Citigroup Inc.; *U.S. Public*, pg. 502
CITIFINANCIAL PROMOTORA DE NEGOCIOS E COBRANCA LTDA.—See Itau Unibanco Holding S.A.; *Int'l*, pg. 3830
CITIFLIGHT, INC.—See Citigroup Inc.; *U.S. Public*, pg. 503
CITI FUND SERVICES OHIO, INC.—See Citigroup Inc.; *U.S. Public*, pg. 502
CITIGATE CUNNINGHAM—See Clayton, Dubilier & Rice, LLC; *U.S. Private*, pg. 924
CITIGATE CUNNINGHAM—See Clayton, Dubilier & Rice, LLC; *U.S. Private*, pg. 924
CITIGATE DEWE ROGERSON—See Clayton, Dubilier & Rice, LLC; *U.S. Private*, pg. 924
CITIGATE FIRST FINANCIAL B.V.—See Clayton, Dubilier & Rice, LLC; *U.S. Private*, pg. 924
CITIGATE GUNPOWDER S.R.L.—See Clayton, Dubilier & Rice, LLC; *U.S. Private*, pg. 924
CITIGATE MARCHCOM—See Clayton, Dubilier & Rice, LLC; *U.S. Private*, pg. 924
CITIGATE PUBLIC AFFAIRS—See Clayton, Dubilier & Rice, LLC; *U.S. Private*, pg. 924
CITIGATE SANCHIS—See Clayton, Dubilier & Rice, LLC; *U.S. Private*, pg. 924
CITIGATE SA—See Clayton, Dubilier & Rice, LLC; *U.S. Private*, pg. 924
CITIGEN (LONDON) LIMITED—See E.ON SE; *Int'l*, pg. 2256
CITI GLOBAL CARDS—See Citigroup Inc.; *U.S. Public*, pg. 502
CITI GLOBAL WEALTH MANAGEMENT—See Citigroup Inc.; *U.S. Public*, pg. 502
CITIGOLD CORPORATION LIMITED; *Int'l*, pg. 1622
CITIGROUP ACQUISITION LLC—See Citigroup Inc.; *U.S. Public*, pg. 503
CITIGROUP CAPITAL PARTNERS JAPAN—See Citigroup Inc.; *U.S. Public*, pg. 503
CITIGROUP CAPITAL STRATEGIES INC.—See Citigroup Inc.; *U.S. Public*, pg. 503
CITIGROUP CAPITAL UK LIMITED—See Citigroup Inc.; *U.S. Public*, pg. 504
CITIGROUP CORPORATE AVIATION—See Citigroup Inc.; *U.S. Public*, pg. 503
CITIGROUP CORPORATE & INVESTMENT BANKING—See Citigroup Inc.; *U.S. Public*, pg. 503

COMPANY NAME INDEX

CITIGROUP DERIVATIVES MARKETS INC.—See Citigroup Inc.; *U.S. Public*, pg. 503
CITIGROUP ENERGY INC.—See Citigroup Inc.; *U.S. Public*, pg. 503
CITIGROUP FIRST INVESTMENT MANAGEMENT AMERICAS LLC—See Citigroup Inc.; *U.S. Public*, pg. 503
CITIGROUP GLOBAL MARKETS ASIA LIMITED—See Citigroup Inc.; *U.S. Public*, pg. 503
CITIGROUP GLOBAL MARKETS AUSTRALIA PTY LIMITED—See Citigroup Inc.; *U.S. Public*, pg. 503
CITIGROUP GLOBAL MARKETS DEUTSCHLAND AG—See Citigroup Inc.; *U.S. Public*, pg. 502
CITIGROUP GLOBAL MARKETS EUROPE FINANCE LIMITED—See Citigroup Inc.; *U.S. Public*, pg. 503
CITIGROUP GLOBAL MARKETS EUROPE LIMITED—See Citigroup Inc.; *U.S. Public*, pg. 503
CITIGROUP GLOBAL MARKETS FINANCE CORPORATION & CO. BESCHRANKT HAFTENDE KG—See Citigroup Inc.; *U.S. Public*, pg. 503
CITIGROUP GLOBAL MARKETS HOLDINGS, INC.—See Citigroup Inc.; *U.S. Public*, pg. 503
CITIGROUP GLOBAL MARKETS INC.—See Citigroup Inc.; *U.S. Public*, pg. 503
CITIGROUP GLOBAL MARKETS INDIA PRIVATE LIMITED—See Citigroup Inc.; *U.S. Public*, pg. 503
CITIGROUP GLOBAL MARKETS JAPAN INC.—See Citigroup Inc.; *U.S. Public*, pg. 504
CITIGROUP GLOBAL MARKETS KOREA SECURITIES LIMITED—See Citigroup Inc.; *U.S. Public*, pg. 503
CITIGROUP GLOBAL MARKETS LIMITED—See Citigroup Inc.; *U.S. Public*, pg. 503
CITIGROUP GLOBAL MARKETS MAURITIUS PRIVATE LIMITED—See Citigroup Inc.; *U.S. Public*, pg. 503
CITIGROUP GLOBAL MARKETS (PROPRIETARY) LIMITED—See Citigroup Inc.; *U.S. Public*, pg. 503
CITIGROUP GLOBAL MARKETS SWITZERLAND HOLDING GMBH—See Citigroup Inc.; *U.S. Public*, pg. 503
CITIGROUP GLOBAL MARKETS U.K. EQUITY LIMITED—See Citigroup Inc.; *U.S. Public*, pg. 503
CITIGROUP INC.; *U.S. Public*, pg. 501
CITIGROUP INVESTOR SERVICES, INC.—See Citigroup Inc.; *U.S. Public*, pg. 503
CITIGROUP JAPAN HOLDINGS CORP.—See Citigroup Inc.; *U.S. Public*, pg. 503
CITIGROUP MANAGEMENT CORP.—See Citigroup Inc.; *U.S. Public*, pg. 504
CITIGROUP OVERSEAS HOLDINGS GK—See Citigroup Inc.; *U.S. Public*, pg. 504
CITIGROUP PRIVATE BANK—See Citigroup Inc.; *U.S. Public*, pg. 502
CITIGROUP PTY LIMITED—See Citigroup Inc.; *U.S. Public*, pg. 504
CITI HABITATS—See Anywhere Real Estate Inc.; *U.S. Public*, pg. 141
CITIHOPE INTERNATIONAL, INC.; *U.S. Private*, pg. 901
CITI INSTITUTIONAL CLIENTS GROUP—See Citigroup Inc.; *U.S. Public*, pg. 502
CITI INTERNATIONAL FINANCIAL SERVICES, LLC—See Citigroup Inc.; *U.S. Public*, pg. 502
CITI ISLAMIC INVESTMENT BANK EC—See Citigroup Inc.; *U.S. Public*, pg. 502
CITILABS, INC.—See Bentley Systems, Inc.; *U.S. Public*, pg. 297
CITIMORTGAGE, INC.—See Citigroup Inc.; *U.S. Public*, pg. 501
CITINEA SAS—See VINCI S.A.; *Int'l*, pg. 8235
CITINICKEL MINES AND DEVELOPMENT CORP—See Oriental Peninsula Resources Group, Inc.; *Int'l*, pg. 5626
CITI ORIENT SECURITIES COMPANY LIMITED—See Orient Securities Company Limited; *Int'l*, pg. 5622
CITI OVERSEAS INVESTMENTS BAHAMAS INC.—See Citigroup Inc.; *U.S. Public*, pg. 502
CITI PERFORMING ARTS CENTER, INC.; *U.S. Private*, pg. 901
CITIPORT FINANCIAL SERVICES LIMITED; *Int'l*, pg. 1622
CITIPOST AMP LTD.—See Citipost Group; *Int'l*, pg. 1622
CITIPOST DIRECT DISTRIBUTION LTD.—See Citipost Group; *Int'l*, pg. 1623
CITIPOST DSA LTD.—See Citipost Group; *Int'l*, pg. 1622
CITIPOST GROUP; *Int'l*, pg. 1622
CITIPOST UK LTD—See Citipost Group; *Int'l*, pg. 1623
CITIPOWER—See CK Hutchison Holdings Limited; *Int'l*, pg. 1636
CITIPOWER—See Power Assets Holdings Limited; *Int'l*, pg. 5943
CITI PROPERTIES REIT; *Int'l*, pg. 1619
CITIROOF CORPORATION; *U.S. Private*, pg. 901
CITISCAPE PROPERTY MANAGEMENT GROUP, LLC.—See FirstService Corporation; *Int'l*, pg. 2691
CITISHARE CORPORATION—See Citigroup Inc.; *U.S. Public*, pg. 504
CITITEC ASSOCIATES LIMITED; *Int'l*, pg. 1623
CITITEL HOTEL MANAGEMENT SDN. BHD.—See IGB Berhad; *Int'l*, pg. 3601
CITI TRENDS INC.; *U.S. Public*, pg. 501

CITIUS ONCOLOGY, INC.—See Citius Pharmaceuticals, Inc.; *U.S. Public*, pg. 504
CITIUS PHARMACEUTICALS, INC.; *U.S. Public*, pg. 504
CITIUS RESOURCES PLC; *Int'l*, pg. 1623
CITIUSTECH INC.; *U.S. Private*, pg. 901
CITI VENTURES, INC.—See Citigroup Inc.; *U.S. Public*, pg. 502
CITIWASTE, LLC—See Aurora Capital Group, LLC; *U.S. Private*, pg. 394
CITIZANT INC.; *U.S. Private*, pg. 902
CITIZEN AMERICA CORP.—See Citizen Watch Co., Ltd.; *Int'l*, pg. 1623
CITIZEN BRANDO LIMITED—See Bluefocus Intelligent Communications Group Co., Ltd.; *Int'l*, pg. 1071
CITIZEN BUSINESS EXPERT CO., LTD.—See Citizen Watch Co., Ltd.; *Int'l*, pg. 1623
CITIZEN CHIBA PRECISION CO., LTD.—See Citizen Watch Co., Ltd.; *Int'l*, pg. 1623
CITIZEN (CHINA) PRECISION MACHINERY CO., LTD. - SHANGHAI BRANCH—See Citizen Watch Co., Ltd.; *Int'l*, pg. 1624
CITIZEN (CHINA) PRECISION MACHINERY CO., LTD.—See Citizen Watch Co., Ltd.; *Int'l*, pg. 1623
CITIZEN CUSTOMER SERVICE CO., LTD.—See Citizen Watch Co., Ltd.; *Int'l*, pg. 1623
CITIZEN DE MEXICO, S.A. DE C.V.—See Citizen Watch Co., Ltd.; *Int'l*, pg. 1625
CITIZEN ELECTRONICS (CHINA) CO., LTD.—See Citizen Watch Co., Ltd.; *Int'l*, pg. 1623
CITIZEN ELECTRONICS CO., LTD.—See Citizen Watch Co., Ltd.; *Int'l*, pg. 1623
CITIZEN ELECTRONICS TIMEL CO., LTD.—See Citizen Watch Co., Ltd.; *Int'l*, pg. 1623
CITIZEN ENERGY OPERATING LLC; *U.S. Private*, pg. 902
CITIZEN ENGAGEMENT LABORATORY; *U.S. Private*, pg. 902
CITIZEN FINANCIAL SERVICE CO., LTD.—See Citizen Watch Co., Ltd.; *Int'l*, pg. 1623
CITIZEN FINEDEVICE CO., LTD.—See Citizen Watch Co., Ltd.; *Int'l*, pg. 1623
CITIZEN FINEDEVICE PHILIPPINES CORP.—See Citizen Watch Co., Ltd.; *Int'l*, pg. 1623
CITIZEN FINETECH MIYOTA CO., LTD. - KITAMIMAKI WORKS—See Citizen Watch Co., Ltd.; *Int'l*, pg. 1623
CITIZEN FINETECH MIYOTA CO., LTD.—See Citizen Watch Co., Ltd.; *Int'l*, pg. 1623
CITIZENHAWK, INC.—See Astorg Partners S.A.S.; *Int'l*, pg. 655
CITIZEN, INC.; *U.S. Private*, pg. 902
CITIZEN INFOLINE LIMITED; *Int'l*, pg. 1623
CITIZEN JEWELRY CO., LTD.—See Citizen Watch Co., Ltd.; *Int'l*, pg. 1623
CITIZEN LATINAMERICA CORP.—See Citizen Watch Co., Ltd.; *Int'l*, pg. 1623
CITIZEN LOGISTICS SERVICE CO., LTD.—See Citizen Watch Co., Ltd.; *Int'l*, pg. 1623
CITIZEN MACCHINE ITALIA S.R.L.—See Citizen Watch Co., Ltd.; *Int'l*, pg. 1623
CITIZEN MACHINERY ASIA CO., LTD.—See Citizen Watch Co., Ltd.; *Int'l*, pg. 1624
CITIZEN MACHINERY CO., LTD.—See Citizen Watch Co., Ltd.; *Int'l*, pg. 1624
CITIZEN MACHINERY EUROPE GMBH—See Citizen Watch Co., Ltd.; *Int'l*, pg. 1624
CITIZEN MACHINERY EUROPE GMBH—See Citizen Watch Co., Ltd.; *Int'l*, pg. 1624
CITIZEN MACHINERY MIYANO CO., LTD.—See Citizen Watch Co., Ltd.; *Int'l*, pg. 1624
CITIZEN MACHINERY PHILIPPINES INC.—See Citizen Watch Co., Ltd.; *Int'l*, pg. 1624
CITIZEN MACHINERY SERVICE CO., LTD.—See Citizen Watch Co., Ltd.; *Int'l*, pg. 1624
CITIZEN MACHINERY UNITED KINGDOM, LTD.—See Citizen Watch Co., Ltd.; *Int'l*, pg. 1624
CITIZEN MACHINERY VIETNAM CO., LTD.—See Citizen Watch Co., Ltd.; *Int'l*, pg. 1624
CITIZENM AMSTERDAM-ZUID OPERATIONS B.V.—See KRC Capital B.V.; *Int'l*, pg. 4300
CITIZENM GLASGOW OPERATIONS B.V.—See KRC Capital B.V.; *Int'l*, pg. 4300
CITIZEN MICRO CO., LTD.—See Citizen Watch Co., Ltd.; *Int'l*, pg. 1624
CITIZEN MICRO DEVICES (SUZHOU) CO., LTD.—See Citizen Watch Co., Ltd.; *Int'l*, pg. 1624
CITIZENM SCHIPHOL OPERATIONS B.V.—See KRC Capital B.V.; *Int'l*, pg. 4300
CITIZENNET, INC.—See Advance Publications, Inc.; *U.S. Private*, pg. 85
CITIZEN PLAZA CO., LTD.—See Citizen Watch Co., Ltd.; *Int'l*, pg. 1624
CITIZEN PRECISION GUANGZHOU LTD.—See Citizen Watch Co., Ltd.; *Int'l*, pg. 1623
CITIZEN PRECISION HACHINOHE CO., LTD.—See Citizen Watch Co., Ltd.; *Int'l*, pg. 1623
CITIZEN PUBLISHING COMPANY—See Gannett Co., Inc.; *U.S. Public*, pg. 896

CITIZENS B & T HOLDINGS, INC.

CITIZEN RELATIONS INC. - TORONTO—See Bluefocus Intelligent Communications Group Co., Ltd.; *Int'l*, pg. 1071
CITIZEN RELATIONS INC. - VANCOUVER—See Bluefocus Intelligent Communications Group Co., Ltd.; *Int'l*, pg. 1071
CITIZEN RELATIONS LLC - IRVINE—See Bluefocus Intelligent Communications Group Co., Ltd.; *Int'l*, pg. 1071
CITIZEN RELATIONS LLC - NEW YORK—See Bluefocus Intelligent Communications Group Co., Ltd.; *Int'l*, pg. 1071
CITIZEN RELATIONS LLC—See Bluefocus Intelligent Communications Group Co., Ltd.; *Int'l*, pg. 1071
CITIZEN RETAIL PLANNING., LTD.—See Citizen Watch Co., Ltd.; *Int'l*, pg. 1624
CITIZENS 1ST BANK; *U.S. Private*, pg. 902
CITIZEN SAKAE TRADING CO., LTD.—See Citizen Watch Co., Ltd.; *Int'l*, pg. 1624
CITIZENS ASSET FINANCE, INC.—See Citizens Financial Group, Inc.; *U.S. Public*, pg. 505
CITIZENS BANCORP INVESTMENT, INC.; *U.S. Public*, pg. 504
CITIZENS BANCORP OF VIRGINIA, INC.; *U.S. Public*, pg. 504
CITIZENS BANCORPORATION OF NEW ULM, INC.; *U.S. Private*, pg. 902
CITIZENS BANCSHARES CORPORATION; *U.S. Private*, pg. 902
CITIZENS BANCSHARES CORPORATION; *U.S. Public*, pg. 504
CITIZENS BANCSHARES CO.—See Southern Missouri Bancorp, Inc.; *U.S. Public*, pg. 1911
CITIZENS BANCSHARES, INC.; *U.S. Private*, pg. 902
CITIZENS BANCSHARES, INC.; *U.S. Private*, pg. 903
CITIZENS BANCSHARES OF BATESVILLE, INC.; *U.S. Private*, pg. 902
CITIZENS BANCSHARES OF HUTCHINSON, INC.; *U.S. Private*, pg. 902
CITIZENS BANK AND TRUST CO.; *U.S. Private*, pg. 903
CITIZENS BANK INTERNATIONAL LIMITED; *Int'l*, pg. 1625
CITIZENS BANK MINNESOTA—See Citizens Bancorporation of New Ulm, Inc.; *U.S. Private*, pg. 902
CITIZENS BANK, N.A.—See Citizens Financial Group, Inc.; *U.S. Public*, pg. 505
CITIZENS BANK NEW HAMPSHIRE—See Citizens Financial Group, Inc.; *U.S. Public*, pg. 505
CITIZENS BANK OF CAPE VINCENT, INC.—See Cambray Mutual Holding Company; *U.S. Private*, pg. 726
THE CITIZENS BANK OF COCHRAN—See Putnam-Greene Financial Corporation; *U.S. Private*, pg. 3307
THE CITIZENS BANK OF EDMOND—See Citizens Bancshares, Inc.; *U.S. Private*, pg. 903
CITIZENS BANK OF LAFAYETTE—See Citizens Bancorp Investment, Inc.; *U.S. Public*, pg. 504
CITIZENS BANK OF LOGAN—See The Merchants National Bank; *U.S. Private*, pg. 4078
CITIZENS BANK OF MASSACHUSETTS—See Citizens Financial Group, Inc.; *U.S. Public*, pg. 505
CITIZENS BANK OF PENNSYLVANIA—See Citizens Financial Group, Inc.; *U.S. Public*, pg. 505
THE CITIZENS BANK OF PHILADELPHIA, MISSISSIPPI—See Citizens Holding Company; *U.S. Public*, pg. 506
CITIZENS BANKSHARES INC.; *U.S. Private*, pg. 903
CITIZENS BANK; *U.S. Private*, pg. 903
CITIZENS BANK; *U.S. Private*, pg. 903
CITIZENS BANK; *U.S. Private*, pg. 903
CITIZENS BANK; *U.S. Private*, pg. 903
CITIZENS BANK; *U.S. Public*, pg. 504
CITIZENS BANK—See Citba Financial Corp.; *U.S. Public*, pg. 501
CITIZENS BANK—See Citco Community Bancshares, Inc.; *U.S. Private*, pg. 901
THE CITIZENS BANK—See Citizens Bancshares Corporation; *U.S. Private*, pg. 902
THE CITIZENS BANK—See Citizens Bancshares of Batesville, Inc.; *U.S. Private*, pg. 902
CITIZENS BANK—See Citizens Bankshares Inc.; *U.S. Private*, pg. 903
CITIZENS BANK—See Citizens Corporation; *U.S. Private*, pg. 903
CITIZENS BANK—See East Texas Financial Corporation; *U.S. Private*, pg. 1318
CITIZENS BANK & TRUST COMPANY; *U.S. Private*, pg. 903
CITIZENS BANK & TRUST COMPANY—See Southern Missouri Bancorp, Inc.; *U.S. Public*, pg. 1912
CITIZENS BANK & TRUST CO. OF JACKSON—See John R. Turner Holding Company; *U.S. Private*, pg. 2224
CITIZENS BANK & TRUST CO.—See Citizens Bancshares of Hutchinson, Inc.; *U.S. Private*, pg. 902
CITIZENS BANK & TRUST—See Citizens B & T Holdings, Inc.; *U.S. Private*, pg. 902
CITIZEN'S BANK & TRUST—See Latt Maxcy Corporation; *U.S. Private*, pg. 2397
CITIZENS B & T HOLDINGS, INC.; *U.S. Private*, pg. 902

CITIZENS B & T HOLDINGS, INC.

CITIZENS BUSINESS BANK - BANKCARD SERVICES—See CVB Financial Corp.; *U.S. Public*, pg. 613
CITIZENS BUSINESS BANK - DAIRY & LIVESTOCK INDUSTRIES GROUP—See CVB Financial Corp.; *U.S. Public*, pg. 613
CITIZENS BUSINESS BANK—See CVB Financial Corp.; *U.S. Public*, pg. 613
CITIZENS BUSINESS BANK - WEALTH MANAGEMENT GROUP—See CVB Financial Corp.; *U.S. Public*, pg. 613
CITIZENS BUSINESS CAPITAL—See Citizens Financial Group, Inc.; *U.S. Public*, pg. 505
CITIZENS COMMERCE BANCSHARES, INC.—See City Holding Company; *U.S. Public*, pg. 506
CITIZENS COMMUNITY BANCORP, INC.; *U.S. Public*, pg. 504
CITIZENS COMMUNITY BANK—See Glacier Bancorp, Inc.; *U.S. Public*, pg. 938
CITIZENS COMMUNITY FEDERAL N.A.—See Citizens Community Bancorp, Inc.; *U.S. Public*, pg. 505
CITIZENS CORPORATION; *U.S. Private*, pg. 903
CITIZENS DEPOSIT BANK & TRUST COMPANY—See Premier Financial Bancorp, Inc.; *U.S. Public*, pg. 1715
CITIZENS DISPOSAL, INC.—See Republic Services, Inc.; *U.S. Public*, pg. 1786
CITIZEN SEIMITSU (THAILAND) CO., LTD.—See Citizen Watch Co., Ltd.; *Int'l*, pg. 1624
CITIZENS ELECTRIC CORPORATION; *U.S. Private*, pg. 903
CITIZENS ENERGY GROUP - CITIZENS GAS DIVISION—See Citizens Energy Group; *U.S. Private*, pg. 903
CITIZENS ENERGY GROUP - CITIZENS RESOURCES DIVISION—See Citizens Energy Group; *U.S. Private*, pg. 903
CITIZENS ENERGY GROUP - CITIZENS THERMAL DIVISION—See Citizens Energy Group; *U.S. Private*, pg. 903
CITIZENS ENERGY GROUP - CITIZENS WATER DIVISION—See Citizens Energy Group; *U.S. Private*, pg. 903
CITIZENS ENERGY GROUP; *U.S. Private*, pg. 903
CITIZENS EQUITY FIRST CREDIT UNION; *U.S. Private*, pg. 903
CITIZENS & FARMERS BANK—See C&F Financial Corporation; *U.S. Public*, pg. 414
CITIZENS FINANCE CO.—See Heartland Financial USA, Inc.; *U.S. Public*, pg. 1018
CITIZENS FINANCE OF ILLINOIS CO.—See Heartland Financial USA, Inc.; *U.S. Public*, pg. 1018
CITIZENS FINANCIAL CORPORATION; *U.S. Public*, pg. 505
CITIZENS FINANCIAL CORP.; *U.S. Public*, pg. 505
CITIZENS FINANCIAL GROUP, INC.; *U.S. Public*, pg. 505
CITIZENS FINANCIAL SERVICES CORPORATION—See Citizens Financial Group, Inc.; *U.S. Public*, pg. 505
CITIZENS FINANCIAL SERVICES, INC.; *U.S. Public*, pg. 506
CITIZENS FOR CITIZENS, INC.; *U.S. Private*, pg. 903
CITIZENS GAS FUEL COMPANY—See DTE Energy Company; *U.S. Public*, pg. 689
CITIZENS GAS UTILITY DISTRICT; *U.S. Private*, pg. 903
CITIZEN (SHANGHAI) TRADING CO., LTD.—See Citizen Watch Co., Ltd.; *Int'l*, pg. 1623
CITIZENS HOLDING COMPANY; *U.S. Public*, pg. 506
CITIZENS, INC.; *U.S. Public*, pg. 506
CITIZENS INDEPENDENT BANCORP, INC.—See The Merchants National Bank; *U.S. Public*, pg. 4078
CITIZENS INSURANCE AGENCY OF TEXAS, INC.—See Prosperity Bancshares, Inc.; *U.S. Public*, pg. 1728
CITIZENS INSURANCE COMPANY OF AMERICA—See The Hanover Insurance Group, Inc.; *U.S. Public*, pg. 2087
CITIZENS JMP GROUP, LLC—See Citizens Financial Group, Inc.; *U.S. Public*, pg. 505
CITIZENS JMP SECURITIES, LLC—See Citizens Financial Group, Inc.; *U.S. Public*, pg. 505
CITIZENS LLC; *U.S. Private*, pg. 903
CITIZENS MECHANICAL SERVICES, LLC—See Citizens Energy Group; *U.S. Private*, pg. 903
CITIZENS MORTGAGE CORPORATION—See Citizens Financial Group, Inc.; *U.S. Public*, pg. 505
CITIZENS NATIONAL BANK INC.; *U.S. Private*, pg. 903
THE CITIZENS NATIONAL BANK OF BLUFFTON—See Citizens Bancshares, Inc.; *U.S. Private*, pg. 902
CITIZENS NATIONAL BANK OF CHEBOYGAN—See CNB Corporation; *U.S. Public*, pg. 519
CITIZENS NATIONAL BANK OF GREATER ST LOUIS—See Cardinal Bancorp Inc.; *U.S. Private*, pg. 749
CITIZENS NATIONAL BANK OF MERIDIAN; *U.S. Private*, pg. 904
CITIZENS NATIONAL BANK OF PAINTSVILLE—See Citizens National Corporation; *U.S. Public*, pg. 506
CITIZENS NATIONAL BANK; *U.S. Private*, pg. 903
CITIZENS NATIONAL CORPORATION; *U.S. Public*, pg. 506

CITIZENS NATIONAL LIFE INSURANCE COMPANY—See Citizens, Inc.; *U.S. Public*, pg. 506
CITIZENS & NORTHERN BANK—See Citizens & Northern Corporation; *U.S. Public*, pg. 504
CITIZENS & NORTHERN CORPORATION; *U.S. Public*, pg. 504
CITIZENS OF HUMANITY LLC—See Berkshire Partners LLC; *U.S. Private*, pg. 534
CITIZENS ONE CARD SERVICES—See Citizens Financial Group, Inc.; *U.S. Public*, pg. 505
CITIZENS PROPERTY INSURANCE CORPORATION; *U.S. Private*, pg. 904
CITIZENS RESOURCE DEVELOPMENT CORPORATION, INC.—See Citizens Energy Group; *U.S. Private*, pg. 903
CITIZENS SAVINGS BANK; *U.S. Private*, pg. 904
CITIZENS SECURITY LIFE INSURANCE COMPANY—See Citizens Financial Corporation; *U.S. Public*, pg. 505
CITIZENS STATE BANK; *U.S. Private*, pg. 904
CITIZENS STATE BANK—See C.S.B. BANCSHARES, INC.; *U.S. Private*, pg. 709
CITIZENS STATE BANK—See Herky Hawk Financial Corp.; *U.S. Private*, pg. 1925
CITIZEN STASH CANNABIS CORP.—See The Valens Company Inc.; *Int'l*, pg. 7698
CITIZENS TELECOMMUNICATIONS COMPANY OF MINNESOTA, LLC—See Frontier Communications Parent, Inc.; *U.S. Public*, pg. 887
CITIZENS TELECOMMUNICATIONS COMPANY OF NEBRASKA—See Frontier Communications Parent, Inc.; *U.S. Public*, pg. 887
CITIZENS TELEPHONE COMPANY—See Comporium Group; *U.S. Private*, pg. 1002
CITIZENS TELEPHONE COOPERATIVE; *U.S. Private*, pg. 904
CITIZENS TRUST BANK—See Citizens Bancshares Corporation; *U.S. Public*, pg. 504
CITIZENS UNION BANCORP OF SHELBYVILLE, INC.—See German American Bancorp, Inc.; *U.S. Public*, pg. 934
CITIZENS UNITED; *U.S. Private*, pg. 904
CITIZEN SYSTEMS AMERICA CORPORATION—See Citizen Watch Co., Ltd.; *Int'l*, pg. 1624
CITIZEN SYSTEMS (DONGGUAN) CO., LTD.—See Citizen Watch Co., Ltd.; *Int'l*, pg. 1624
CITIZEN SYSTEMS EUROPE CORPORATION—See Citizen Watch Co., Ltd.; *Int'l*, pg. 1624
CITIZEN SYSTEMS EUROPE GMBH—See Citizen Watch Co., Ltd.; *Int'l*, pg. 1624
CITIZEN SYSTEMS EUROPE GMBH—See Citizen Watch Co., Ltd.; *Int'l*, pg. 1624
CITIZEN SYSTEMS (H.K.) LTD.—See Citizen Watch Co., Ltd.; *Int'l*, pg. 1624
CITIZEN SYSTEMS JAPAN CO., LTD.—See Citizen Watch Co., Ltd.; *Int'l*, pg. 1624
CITIZEN SYSTEMS (JIANGMEN) CO., LTD.—See Citizen Watch Co., Ltd.; *Int'l*, pg. 1624
CITIZEN TECHNO CO., LTD.—See Citizen Watch Co., Ltd.; *Int'l*, pg. 1624
CITIZEN T.I.C. CO., LTD.—See Citizen Watch Co., Ltd.; *Int'l*, pg. 1624
CITIZEN TOKOROZAWA WORKS—See Citizen Watch Co., Ltd.; *Int'l*, pg. 1624
CITIZEN WATCH (CHINA) CO., LTD.—See Citizen Watch Co., Ltd.; *Int'l*, pg. 1624
CITIZEN WATCH CO., LTD.; *Int'l*, pg. 1623
CITIZEN WATCH CO. OF AMERICA, INC.—See Citizen Watch Co., Ltd.; *Int'l*, pg. 1624
CITIZEN WATCH CO. OF CANADA, LTD.—See Citizen Watch Co., Ltd.; *Int'l*, pg. 1624
CITIZEN WATCH DO BRASIL S.A.—See Citizen Watch Co., Ltd.; *Int'l*, pg. 1625
CITIZEN WATCHES AUSTRALIA PTY. LTD.—See Citizen Watch Co., Ltd.; *Int'l*, pg. 1625
CITIZEN WATCHES GULF CO.—See Citizen Watch Co., Ltd.; *Int'l*, pg. 1625
CITIZEN WATCHES (H.K.) LTD.—See Citizen Watch Co., Ltd.; *Int'l*, pg. 1625
CITIZEN WATCHES (INDIA) PVT. LTD.—See Citizen Watch Co., Ltd.; *Int'l*, pg. 1625
CITIZEN WATCHES (MALAYSIA) SDN. BHD.—See Citizen Watch Co., Ltd.; *Int'l*, pg. 1625
CITIZEN WATCHES (N.Z.) LTD.—See Citizen Watch Co., Ltd.; *Int'l*, pg. 1625
CITIZEN WATCH ESPANA S.A.—See Citizen Watch Co., Ltd.; *Int'l*, pg. 1624
CITIZEN WATCH EUROPE GMBH—See Citizen Watch Co., Ltd.; *Int'l*, pg. 1624
CITIZEN WATCH IBERICA S.A.U.—See Citizen Watch Co., Ltd.; *Int'l*, pg. 1624
CITIZEN WATCH ITALY S.P.A.—See Citizen Watch Co., Ltd.; *Int'l*, pg. 1625
CITIZEN WATCH MANUFACTURING CO., LTD—See Citizen Watch Co., Ltd.; *Int'l*, pg. 1625
CITIZEN WATCH MANUFACTURING (THAILAND) CO., LTD.—See Citizen Watch Co., Ltd.; *Int'l*, pg. 1625
CITIZEN WATCH (SWITZERLAND) AG—See Citizen Watch Co., Ltd.; *Int'l*, pg. 1624

CORPORATE AFFILIATIONS

CITIZEN WATCH (U.K.) LTD.—See Citizen Watch Co., Ltd.; *Int'l*, pg. 1624
CITIZEN WATCH UNITED KINGDOM, LTD.—See Citizen Watch Co., Ltd.; *Int'l*, pg. 1625
CITIZEN YARNS LIMITED; *Int'l*, pg. 1625
CITIZEN YUBARII CO., LTD.—See Citizen Watch Co., Ltd.; *Int'l*, pg. 1624
C.I.T. LEASING CORPORATION—See First Citizens BancShares, Inc.; *U.S. Public*, pg. 841
CIT LEASING DE ARGENTINA S.R.L.—See First Citizens BancShares, Inc.; *U.S. Public*, pg. 841
CITOC INC.; *U.S. Private*, pg. 904
CI TOWER INVESTMENTS LIMITED—See CLS Holdings plc; *Int'l*, pg. 1664
CITOXLAB GROUP SAS—See Charles River Laboratories International, Inc.; *U.S. Public*, pg. 480
CITOXLAB HUNGARY LTD.—See Charles River Laboratories International, Inc.; *U.S. Public*, pg. 480
CITOXLAB NORTH AMERICA INC.—See Charles River Laboratories International, Inc.; *U.S. Public*, pg. 480
CITOXLAB SCANTOX A/S—See Charles River Laboratories International, Inc.; *U.S. Public*, pg. 480
CITOYEN RELATIONS INC. - QUEBEC CITY—See Bluefocus Intelligent Communications Group Co., Ltd.; *Int'l*, pg. 1071
CITOYEN RELATIONS INC.—See Bluefocus Intelligent Communications Group Co., Ltd.; *Int'l*, pg. 1071
C.I. TOYOTA TSUSHO DE COLOMBIA S.A.—See Toyota Tsusho Corporation; *Int'l*, pg. 7875
CITP SAS - LYON PLANT—See Carlier Plastiques; *Int'l*, pg. 1338
CITP SAS—See Carlier Plastiques; *Int'l*, pg. 1338
CITRA HEALTH SOLUTIONS, INC.—See Great Point Partners, LLC; *U.S. Private*, pg. 1767
CIT RAIL HOLDINGS (EUROPE) SAS—See Joachim Herz Stiftung; *Int'l*, pg. 3976
CIT RAIL HOLDINGS (EUROPE) SAS—See Morgan Stanley; *U.S. Public*, pg. 1476
CITRA LABS, LLC—See Zimmer Biomet Holdings, Inc.; *U.S. Public*, pg. 2406
CITRA NUSA HOLDINGS BERHAD; *Int'l*, pg. 1626
CITRASHINE (PTY) LTD—See UPL Limited; *Int'l*, pg. 8089
CITRASOURCE HOLDINGS, LLC—See International Flavors & Fragrances Inc.; *U.S. Public*, pg. 1151
CITRIALS, INC.—See CenExel Clinical Research, Inc.; *U.S. Private*, pg. 809
CITRIN COOPERMAN & COMPANY, LLP - MARYLAND—See Citrin Cooperman & Company, LLP; *U.S. Private*, pg. 904
CITRIN COOPERMAN & COMPANY, LLP - MASSACHUSETTS—See Citrin Cooperman & Company, LLP; *U.S. Private*, pg. 904
CITRIN COOPERMAN & COMPANY, LLP - RHODE ISLAND—See Citrin Cooperman & Company, LLP; *U.S. Private*, pg. 904
CITRIN COOPERMAN & COMPANY, LLP; *U.S. Private*, pg. 904
CITRINE GLOBAL CORP.; *Int'l*, pg. 1626
CITRIX ONLINE AUS PTY LTD—See Elliott Management Corporation; *U.S. Private*, pg. 1366
CITRIX ONLINE AUS PTY LTD—See Vista Equity Partners, LLC; *U.S. Private*, pg. 4395
CITRIX ONLINE LLC—See Elliott Management Corporation; *U.S. Private*, pg. 1366
CITRIX ONLINE LLC—See Vista Equity Partners, LLC; *U.S. Private*, pg. 4395
CITRIX R&D INDIA PRIVATE LIMITED—See Elliott Management Corporation; *U.S. Private*, pg. 1366
CITRIX R&D INDIA PRIVATE LIMITED—See Vista Equity Partners, LLC; *U.S. Private*, pg. 4395
CITRIX R&D LIMITED—See Elliott Management Corporation; *U.S. Private*, pg. 1366
CITRIX R&D LIMITED—See Vista Equity Partners, LLC; *U.S. Private*, pg. 4395
CITRIX SISTEMAS DE ARGENTINA, S.R.L.—See Elliott Management Corporation; *U.S. Private*, pg. 1366
CITRIX SISTEMAS DE ARGENTINA, S.R.L.—See Vista Equity Partners, LLC; *U.S. Private*, pg. 4396
CITRIX SISTEMAS DO BRASIL LTDA.—See Elliott Management Corporation; *U.S. Private*, pg. 1366
CITRIX SISTEMAS DO BRASIL LTDA.—See Vista Equity Partners, LLC; *U.S. Private*, pg. 4396
CITRIX SYSTEMS ASIA PACIFIC PTY LTD.—See Elliott Management Corporation; *U.S. Private*, pg. 1366
CITRIX SYSTEMS ASIA PACIFIC PTY LTD.—See Vista Equity Partners, LLC; *U.S. Private*, pg. 4396
CITRIX SYSTEMS BELGIUM S.P.R.L.—See Elliott Management Corporation; *U.S. Private*, pg. 1366
CITRIX SYSTEMS BELGIUM S.P.R.L.—See Vista Equity Partners, LLC; *U.S. Private*, pg. 4396
CITRIX SYSTEMS CANADA, INC.—See Elliott Management Corporation; *U.S. Private*, pg. 1366
CITRIX SYSTEMS CANADA, INC.—See Vista Equity Partners, LLC; *U.S. Private*, pg. 4396
CITRIX SYSTEMS CZECH REPUBLIC SRO—See Elliott Management Corporation; *U.S. Private*, pg. 1366
CITRIX SYSTEMS CZECH REPUBLIC SRO—See Vista Equity Partners, LLC; *U.S. Private*, pg. 4396

COMPANY NAME INDEX

CITRIX SYSTEMS DENMARK APS—See Elliott Management Corporation; *U.S. Private*, pg. 1366
CITRIX SYSTEMS DENMARK APS—See Vista Equity Partners, LLC; *U.S. Private*, pg. 4396
CITRIX SYSTEMS FINLAND OY—See Elliott Management Corporation; *U.S. Private*, pg. 1366
CITRIX SYSTEMS FINLAND OY—See Vista Equity Partners, LLC; *U.S. Private*, pg. 4396
CITRIX SYSTEMS FRANCE SARL—See Elliott Management Corporation; *U.S. Private*, pg. 1367
CITRIX SYSTEMS FRANCE SARL—See Vista Equity Partners, LLC; *U.S. Private*, pg. 4396
CITRIX SYSTEMS GMBH—See Elliott Management Corporation; *U.S. Private*, pg. 1367
CITRIX SYSTEMS GMBH—See Elliott Management Corporation; *U.S. Private*, pg. 1367
CITRIX SYSTEMS GMBH—See Vista Equity Partners, LLC; *U.S. Private*, pg. 4396
CITRIX SYSTEMS GMBH—See Vista Equity Partners, LLC; *U.S. Private*, pg. 4396
CITRIX SYSTEMS, INC.—See Elliott Management Corporation; *U.S. Private*, pg. 1366
CITRIX SYSTEMS, INC.—See Vista Equity Partners, LLC; *U.S. Private*, pg. 4395
CITRIX SYSTEMS INFORMATION TECHNOLOGY (BEIJING) LTD—See Elliott Management Corporation; *U.S. Private*, pg. 1367
CITRIX SYSTEMS INFORMATION TECHNOLOGY (BEIJING) LTD—See Vista Equity Partners, LLC; *U.S. Private*, pg. 4396
CITRIX SYSTEMS INTERNATIONAL GMBH—See Elliott Management Corporation; *U.S. Private*, pg. 1367
CITRIX SYSTEMS INTERNATIONAL GMBH—See Vista Equity Partners, LLC; *U.S. Private*, pg. 4396
CITRIX SYSTEMS NETHERLANDS, B.V.—See Elliott Management Corporation; *U.S. Private*, pg. 1367
CITRIX SYSTEMS NETHERLANDS, B.V.—See Vista Equity Partners, LLC; *U.S. Private*, pg. 4396
CITRIX SYSTEMS NORWAY AS—See Elliott Management Corporation; *U.S. Private*, pg. 1367
CITRIX SYSTEMS NORWAY AS—See Vista Equity Partners, LLC; *U.S. Private*, pg. 4396
CITRIX SYSTEMS POLAND SP. Z O.O—See Elliott Management Corporation; *U.S. Private*, pg. 1367
CITRIX SYSTEMS POLAND SP. Z O.O—See Vista Equity Partners, LLC; *U.S. Private*, pg. 4396
CITRIX SYSTEMS UK LIMITED—See Elliott Management Corporation; *U.S. Private*, pg. 1367
CITRIX SYSTEMS UK LIMITED—See Vista Equity Partners, LLC; *U.S. Private*, pg. 4396
CITROEN BELUX SA NV—See Stellantis N.V.; *Int'l*, pg. 7201
CITROEN DEUTSCHLAND AG—See Stellantis N.V.; *Int'l*, pg. 7201
CITROEN DUNKERQUE S.A.S.—See Stellantis N.V.; *Int'l*, pg. 7201
CITROEN ORLEANS S.A.S.—See Stellantis N.V.; *Int'l*, pg. 7201
CITROEN POLSKA SP. Z.O.O.—See Stellantis N.V.; *Int'l*, pg. 7201
CITROEN SUISSE S.A.—See Stellantis N.V.; *Int'l*, pg. 7201
CITROEN UK LIMITED; *Int'l*, pg. 1626
CITRON EXPORT INC.—See Hero AG; *Int'l*, pg. 3363
CITRON HYGIENE LTD—See Birch Hill Equity Partners Management Inc.; *Int'l*, pg. 1046
CITRONIX INC.—See Brother Industries, Ltd.; *Int'l*, pg. 1197
CITRUS AND ALLIED ESSENCES LTD.; *U.S. Private*, pg. 904
CITRUS CONSULTING SERVICES FZ LLC—See Redington (India) Limited; *Int'l*, pg. 6247
CITRUS COUNTY CHRONICLE—See Irish Times; *U.S. Private*, pg. 2138
CITRUS HEALTH NETWORK, INC.; *U.S. Private*, pg. 904
CITRUS HILL INVESTMENT PROPERTIES; *U.S. Private*, pg. 904
CITRUS HILLS CONSTRUCTION COMPANY LLC; *U.S. Private*, pg. 904
CITRUS HMA, INC.—See Community Health Systems, Inc.; *U.S. Public*, pg. 553
CITRUS HOMEHEALTH, INC.—See HCA Healthcare, Inc.; *U.S. Public*, pg. 993
CITRUS LEISURE PLC; *Int'l*, pg. 1626
CITRUS LLC—See Kinder Morgan, Inc.; *U.S. Public*, pg. 1232
CITRUS MEMORIAL HOSPITAL, INC.—See HCA Healthcare, Inc.; *U.S. Public*, pg. 993
CITRUS MOTORS ONTARIO, INC.; *U.S. Private*, pg. 904
CITRUS PLUS, INC.; *U.S. Private*, pg. 904
CITRUS PRIMARY CARE, INC.—See HCA Healthcare, Inc.; *U.S. Public*, pg. 993
CITRUS PRODUCTS INC.; *U.S. Private*, pg. 904
CITRUS REGIONAL SURGERY CENTER, L.P.—See UnitedHealth Group Incorporated; *U.S. Public*, pg. 2240
CITRUS VALLEY HEALTH PARTNERS; *U.S. Private*, pg. 905
CITRUS WORLD, INC.; *U.S. Private*, pg. 905

CITS GROUP SHANGHAI CO., LTD.—See China Tourism Group Duty Free Corporation Limited; *Int'l*, pg. 1560
CIT STRATEGIC FINANCE, INC.—See First Citizens BancShares, Inc.; *U.S. Public*, pg. 841
CITY24 POLSKA SP. Z.O.O.—See Alma Media Corporation; *Int'l*, pg. 362
CITY ADVERTISING LLC; *U.S. Private*, pg. 905
CITYA IMMOBILIER SAS; *Int'l*, pg. 1628
CITY AIRPORT LTD—See Peel Holdings Ltd.; *Int'l*, pg. 5779
CITY AIR TERMINAL BETRIEBSGESELLSCHAFT M.B.H.—See Flughafen Wien Aktiengesellschaft; *Int'l*, pg. 2712
CITY ANALYSTS LIMITED—See Eurofins Scientific S.E.; *Int'l*, pg. 2535
CITY AND COUNTRY PROPERTIES (BIRMINGHAM) LIMITED—See Centremanor Ltd.; *Int'l*, pg. 1411
CITY AND COUNTRY PROPERTIES (CAMBERLEY) LIMITED—See Centremanor Ltd.; *Int'l*, pg. 1411
CITY AND COUNTRY PROPERTIES (MIDLANDS) LIMITED—See Centremanor Ltd.; *Int'l*, pg. 1411
CITY ANIMATION CO; *U.S. Private*, pg. 905
CITY-ARKADEN WUPPERTAL KG—See Deutsche EuroShop AG; *Int'l*, pg. 2065
CITY AUTOMOTIVE GROUP PTY LTD—See Eagers Automotive Limited; *Int'l*, pg. 2264
CITY AUTO SALES, LLC.; *U.S. Private*, pg. 905
CITY BANK CAPITAL RESOURCES LIMITED—See The City Bank Limited; *Int'l*, pg. 7633
THE CITY BANK LIMITED; *Int'l*, pg. 7633
CITY BANK—See South Plains Financial, Inc.; *U.S. Public*, pg. 1911
CITY BANK & TRUST COMPANY OF MOBERLY—See Central Bancompany, Inc.; *U.S. Public*, pg. 472
CITY BANK & TRUST CO.—See TCM Company; *U.S. Private*, pg. 3942
CITYBASE PROPERTY MANAGEMENT LIMITED—See CK Asset Holdings Limited; *Int'l*, pg. 1635
CITY BEVERAGE COMPANY, INC.; *U.S. Private*, pg. 905
CITY BLUE INC.; *U.S. Private*, pg. 905
CITY BREWING COMPANY, LLC—See Brookfield Corporation; *Int'l*, pg. 1182
CITY BREWING COMPANY, LLC—See Charlesbank Capital Partners, LLC; *U.S. Private*, pg. 855
CITY BROKERAGE LIMITED—See The City Bank Limited; *Int'l*, pg. 7633
CITY BUICK CHEVROLET CADILLAC GMC; *Int'l*, pg. 1626
CITY BUSINESS FINANCE LIMITED—See Rothschild & Co SCA; *Int'l*, pg. 6402
CITYCAB PTE. LTD.—See ComfortDelGro Corporation Limited; *Int'l*, pg. 1712
CITYCAB (SHENYANG) CO., LTD.—See ComfortDelGro Corporation Limited; *Int'l*, pg. 1712
CITY CADILLAC BUICK GMC; *U.S. Private*, pg. 905
CITY CAPITAL ADVISORS, LLC; *U.S. Private*, pg. 905
CITY CAPITAL ANALYSIS LIMITED—See Schroders plc; *Int'l*, pg. 6639
CITY CAPITAL VENTURES, LLC—See City Capital Advisors, LLC; *U.S. Private*, pg. 905
CITY CARE LTD—See Christchurch City Holdings Ltd.; *Int'l*, pg. 1586
CITY CARTING HOLDING COMPANY, INC.—See Macquarie Group Limited; *Int'l*, pg. 4628
CITY CARTON INC.; *U.S. Private*, pg. 905
CITY CEMENT COMPANY; *Int'l*, pg. 1626
CITY CENTER ANNEX TENANT CORPORATION—See Marriott International, Inc.; *U.S. Public*, pg. 1370
CITY CENTER OF MUSIC AND DRAMA INC; *U.S. Private*, pg. 905
CITY CENTER STF, LP—See City Office REIT, Inc.; *Int'l*, pg. 1627
CITY CENTRE RESTAURANTS (UK) LIMITED—See Apollo Global Management, Inc.; *U.S. Public*, pg. 164
CITY CHAIN COMPANY LIMITED—See Stelux Holdings International Limited; *Int'l*, pg. 7204
CITY CHAIN (M) SDN BHD—See Stelux Holdings International Limited; *Int'l*, pg. 7204
CITYCHAMP DARTONG CO., LTD.; *Int'l*, pg. 1628
CITYCHAMP WATCH & JEWELLERY GROUP LIMITED; *Int'l*, pg. 1628
CITY CHIC COLLECTIVE LIMITED; *Int'l*, pg. 1628
CITY CIRCLE UK LTD.—See JTB Corp.; *Int'l*, pg. 4015
CITY CLUB LA—See Apollo Global Management, Inc.; *U.S. Public*, pg. 149
CITYCOMP SERVICE GMBH—See Kontron AG; *Int'l*, pg. 4276
CITYCON AB—See Citycon Oyj; *Int'l*, pg. 1629
CITY CONCRETE, INC.—See Vulcan Materials Company; *U.S. Public*, pg. 2314
CITYCON DEVELOPMENT AB—See Citycon Oyj; *Int'l*, pg. 1629
CITYCON ESTONIA OU—See Citycon Oyj; *Int'l*, pg. 1629
CITYCON FINLAND OY—See Citycon Oyj; *Int'l*, pg. 1629
CITYCON JAKOBSBERGS CENTRUM AB—See Citycon Oyj; *Int'l*, pg. 1629
CITYCON LILJEHOLMSTORGET GALLERIA AB—See Citycon Oyj; *Int'l*, pg. 1629
CITYCON NORWAY AS—See Citycon Oyj; *Int'l*, pg. 1629

CITYCON OYJ; *Int'l*, pg. 1629
CITY COUNTY CREDIT UNION; *U.S. Private*, pg. 905
CITY & COUNTY HEALTHCARE GROUP LIMITED—See Graphite Capital Management LLP; *Int'l*, pg. 3060
CITY CYCLE, INC.—See Qurate Retail, Inc.; *U.S. Public*, pg. 1757
CITY DASH, LLC—See Brixey & Meyer, Inc.; *U.S. Private*, pg. 658
CITY DEVELOPMENT ENVIRONMENT CO., LTD.; *Int'l*, pg. 1626
CITY DEVELOPMENTS LIMITED—See Hong Leong Investment Holdings Pte. Ltd.; *Int'l*, pg. 3468
CITY EAST SPECIALIST DAY HOSPITAL PTY LTD—See Virtus Health Limited; *Int'l*, pg. 8248
CITY ELECTRIC COMPANY INC.; *U.S. Private*, pg. 905
CITY ELECTRIC SARL—See VINCI S.A.; *Int'l*, pg. 8215
CITY ELECTRIC SUPPLY COMPANY; *U.S. Private*, pg. 905
CITY ELEVATOR CO.—See KONE Oyj; *Int'l*, pg. 4249
CITY EMPIRIA A.S.—See Assicurazioni Generali S.p.A.; *Int'l*, pg. 643
CITY EMPLOYEES CLUB OF LOS ANGELES; *U.S. Private*, pg. 905
CITY EXCHANGE L.L.C.—See Mustafa Sultan Enterprises LLC; *Int'l*, pg. 5103
CITY EXPRESS D.O.O.—See Osterreichische Post AG; *Int'l*, pg. 5653
CITY EXPRESS FINANCE COMPANY LIMITED—See Nepal Investment Mega Bank Limited; *Int'l*, pg. 5199
CITY EXPRESS MONTENEGRO D.O.O—See Osterreichische Post AG; *Int'l*, pg. 5653
CITY FEED & LUMBER COMPANY INC.; *U.S. Private*, pg. 905
CITYFEET.COM—See CoStar Group, Inc.; *U.S. Public*, pg. 586
CITY FIBERS INC.; *U.S. Private*, pg. 905
CITYFIBRE INFRASTRUCTURE HOLDINGS LIMITED—See Antin Infrastructure Partners SAS; *Int'l*, pg. 483
CITY FINANCE; *U.S. Private*, pg. 905
CITY FIRE PROTECTION & MAINTENANCE SERVICES LLP—See London Security PLC; *Int'l*, pg. 4547
CITYFLEET NETWORKS LIMITED—See ComfortDelGro Corporation Limited; *Int'l*, pg. 1712
CITY FORD, LLC; *U.S. Private*, pg. 905
CITY FORD SALES LTD.; *Int'l*, pg. 1626
CITY FUEL SERVICES LIMITED—See JLG Group PLC; *Int'l*, pg. 3973
CITY FURNITURE INC.; *U.S. Private*, pg. 906
CITY-GALERIE WOLFSBURG KG—See Deutsche EuroShop AG; *Int'l*, pg. 2065
CITY GATE STUTTGART GMBH—See EPH European Property Holdings PLC; *Int'l*, pg. 2459
CITY GEAR, LLC—See Pentland Group Limited; *Int'l*, pg. 5792
CITY GENERAL INSURANCE COMPANY LIMITED; *Int'l*, pg. 1626
CITY GLASS COMPANY—See Dothan Glass Co. Inc.; *U.S. Private*, pg. 1265
CITY GLATT, INC.; *U.S. Private*, pg. 906
CITY GREAT LIMITED—See Prosper One International Holdings Company Limited; *Int'l*, pg. 6002
CITYGREEN GARTENGESTALTUNGS GMBH—See BayWa AG; *Int'l*, pg. 917
CITY GROUP COMPANY KSCP; *Int'l*, pg. 1626
CITY GROUP PLC—See London Finance & Investment Group P.L.C.; *Int'l*, pg. 4546
CITYGYM INC—See Waterfront Philippines, Incorporated; *Int'l*, pg. 8357
CITY HALL PROPERTIES LLC; *U.S. Private*, pg. 906
CITY-HAUSVERWALTUNG GMBH—See Consus Real Estate AG; *Int'l*, pg. 1778
CITY HOLDING COMPANY; *U.S. Public*, pg. 506
CITY HOLDINGS (AUS) PTY LTD—See City Refrigeration Holdings (UK) Limited; *Int'l*, pg. 1627
CITY ICE CO.—See Centerbridge Partners, L.P.; *U.S. Private*, pg. 815
CITY IMMOBILIEN GMBH & CO. KG—See Wuestenrot & Wuerttembergische AG; *Int'l*, pg. 8499
CITY INDEX (HOLDINGS) LTD.—See StoneX Group Inc.; *U.S. Public*, pg. 1952
CITY INVEST BANK AO; *Int'l*, pg. 1626
CITY ISUZU; *U.S. Private*, pg. 906
CITYJET DAC—See Nefinsa S.A.; *Int'l*, pg. 5191
CITY JET LTD—See Air France-KLM S.A.; *Int'l*, pg. 237
CITY & LAND DEVELOPERS, INC.; *Int'l*, pg. 1626
CITYLAND DEVELOPMENT CORPORATION; *Int'l*, pg. 1629
CITY LASEPARTNER A/S—See ASSA ABLOY AB; *Int'l*, pg. 639
CITY LEASING (DONSIDE) LIMITED—See Deutsche Bank Aktiengesellschaft; *Int'l*, pg. 2056
CITY LEASING LIMITED—See Deutsche Bank Aktiengesellschaft; *Int'l*, pg. 2056
CITY LEASING (WEARSIDE) LIMITED—See Deutsche Bank Aktiengesellschaft; *Int'l*, pg. 2056
CITYLIFE S.P.A.—See Intesa Sanpaolo S.p.A.; *Int'l*, pg. 3764
CITY LIFT PARKING, LLC; *U.S. Private*, pg. 906

CITY LIFT PARKING, LLC

CITYLIFT S.A.—See KONE Oyj; *Int'l*, pg. 4247
CITY LIGHT & POWER, INC.—See Hunt Companies, Inc.; *U.S. Private*, pg. 2008
CITYLIMO LEASING (M) SDN. BHD.—See ComfortDelGro Corporation Limited; *Int'l*, pg. 1712
CITYLINE (NZ) LIMITED—See Infratil Limited; *Int'l*, pg. 3698
CITY LINK EXPRESS, INC.; *U.S. Private*, pg. 906
CITYLINK LIMITED—See Vital Limited; *Int'l*, pg. 8258
CITY LIQUIDATORS INC.; *U.S. Private*, pg. 906
CITY LODGE BRYANSTON (PTY) LIMITED—See City Lodge Hotels Limited; *Int'l*, pg. 1627
CITY LODGE HOLDINGS (SHARE BLOCK) (PTY) LTD—See City Lodge Hotels Limited; *Int'l*, pg. 1627
CITY LODGE HOTELS LIMITED; *Int'l*, pg. 1627
CITY LUMBER INC.; *U.S. Private*, pg. 906
CITY LUMBER & TRUSS COMPANY; *U.S. Private*, pg. 906
CITY MAINTENANCE SUPPLY; *U.S. Private*, pg. 906
CITYMAN LIMITED; *Int'l*, pg. 1629
CITYMARK ANALYS I NORDEN AB—See Byggfakta Group Nordic HoldCo AB; *Int'l*, pg. 1234
CITY MASONRY INC.; *U.S. Private*, pg. 906
CITY MATTRESS INC.; *U.S. Private*, pg. 906
CITYMAX HOSPITALITY INDIA PVT. LTD.—See Landmark Retail Holdings 1 Limited; *Int'l*, pg. 4407
CITYMEALS-ON-WHEELS; *U.S. Private*, pg. 907
CITY MILANO S.P.A.—See RCS MediaGroup S.p.A.; *Int'l*, pg. 6229
CITY MILL COMPANY LTD.; *U.S. Private*, pg. 906
CITY MOTOR COMPANY; *U.S. Private*, pg. 906
CITY MOTORS (1981) PTY LTD—See Eagers Automotive Limited; *Int'l*, pg. 2263
CITY MOV S.A.R.L.—See Enovos International S.A.; *Int'l*, pg. 2444
CITY NATIONAL BANK OF FLORIDA—See Empresas Juan Yarur S.A.C.; *Int'l*, pg. 2391
CITY NATIONAL BANK OF WEST VIRGINIA—See City Holding Company; *U.S. Public*, pg. 506
CITY NATIONAL BANK—See Royal Bank of Canada; *Int'l*, pg. 6409
CITY-NAV SP. Z O.O.—See Axel Springer SE; *Int'l*, pg. 766
CITYNEON DAG INDIA PRIVATE LIMITED—See Cityneon Holdings Limited; *Int'l*, pg. 1630
CITYNEON HOLDINGS LIMITED; *Int'l*, pg. 1629
CITY NORTH GROUP PLC—See Grainger plc; *Int'l*, pg. 3052
CITY OF DREAMS PENANG SDN. BHD.—See Ewein Berhad; *Int'l*, pg. 2576
CITY OFFICE REIT, INC.; *Int'l*, pg. 1627
CITY OF GLENDALE MUNICIPAL PROPERTY CORP.; *U.S. Private*, pg. 906
CITY OF HOPE NATIONAL MEDICAL CENTER; *U.S. Private*, pg. 906
CITY OF LONDON FINANCIAL SERVICES LIMITED—See City of London Group PLC; *Int'l*, pg. 1627
CITY OF LONDON GROUP PLC; *Int'l*, pg. 1627
CITY OF LONDON HELIPORT LIMITED—See Heidelberg Materials AG; *Int'l*, pg. 3310
CITY OF LONDON INVESTMENT GROUP PLC; *Int'l*, pg. 1627
CITY OF LONDON INVESTMENT MANAGEMENT COMPANY LIMITED—See City of London Investment Group PLC; *Int'l*, pg. 1627
CITY OF LONDON INVESTMENT MANAGEMENT (SINGAPORE) PTE. LTD.—See City of London Investment Group PLC; *Int'l*, pg. 1627
THE CITY OF LONDON INVESTMENT TRUST PLC; *Int'l*, pg. 7633
THE CITY OF LONDON REAL PROPERTY COMPANY LIMITED—See Land Securities Group Plc; *Int'l*, pg. 4404
CITY OF LONDON US INVESTMENTS LIMITED—See City of London Investment Group PLC; *Int'l*, pg. 1627
CITY OF OAKLAND PARKING PARTNERS—See Eldridge Industries LLC; *U.S. Private*, pg. 1351
CITY OF OXFORD MOTOR SERVICES LIMITED—See GLOBALVIA Inversiones, S.A.U.; *Int'l*, pg. 3005
CITY OF OXFORD MOTOR SERVICES LIMITED—See Kinetic Group Services Pty Ltd.; *Int'l*, pg. 4167
CITY OF SCOTTSDALE MUNICIPAL PROPERTY CORPORATION; *U.S. Private*, pg. 906
CITY OF WESTMINSTER ASSURANCE COMPANY LIMITED—See Chesnara Plc; *Int'l*, pg. 1472
CITY ONLINE SERVICES LTD.; *Int'l*, pg. 1627
CITYON SYSTEMS (INDIA) LTD.; *Int'l*, pg. 1630
CITY OPTICAL PTY LTD.—See EssilorLuxottica SA; *Int'l*, pg. 2512
CITY PAPER COMPANY; *U.S. Private*, pg. 906
CITY PARK D.D.; *Int'l*, pg. 1627
CITYPARKING INC.; *U.S. Private*, pg. 907
CITY PHARMACY LTD; *Int'l*, pg. 1627
CITY PLUMBING & ELECTRIC SUPPLY COMPANY; *U.S. Private*, pg. 906
CITY PLUMBING SUPPLIES—See Travis Perkins plc; *Int'l*, pg. 7908
CITY POINT PARTNERS LLC—See HDR, Inc.; *U.S. Private*, pg. 1890
CITY POSTAL, INC.; *U.S. Private*, pg. 906

CITY PROFESSIONAL MANAGEMENT LIMITED—See Asia Allied Infrastructure Holdings Limited; *Int'l*, pg. 610
THE CITY PUB GROUP PLC; *Int'l*, pg. 7633
CITY PUB GROUP PLC; *Int'l*, pg. 1627
CITY PUBLIC RELATIONS PTY LIMITED—See Enero Group Limited; *Int'l*, pg. 2423
CITY PULSE MULTIPLEX LIMITED; *Int'l*, pg. 1627
CITY REFRIGERATION HOLDINGS (UK) LIMITED; *Int'l*, pg. 1627
CITY RESPONSE LIMITED—See Guinness Northern Counties Ltd; *Int'l*, pg. 3174
CITY SCHOOLS (PRIVATE) LIMITED—See Pakgen Power Ltd.; *Int'l*, pg. 5703
CITY SEA FOODS, INC.; *U.S. Private*, pg. 906
CITYSEARCH—See IAC Inc.; *U.S. Public*, pg. 1082
CITY SECURITY COMPANY LIMITED—See Asia Allied Infrastructure Holdings Limited; *Int'l*, pg. 610
CITY SELF-STORAGE A/S—See Teachers Insurance Association - College Retirement Fund; *U.S. Private*, pg. 3945
CITY SELF-STORAGE NORGE AS—See Teachers Insurance Association - College Retirement Fund; *U.S. Private*, pg. 3945
CITY SERVICE CO., LTD.—See Seiko Group Corporation; *Int'l*, pg. 6688
CITY SERVICE, INC.; *U.S. Private*, pg. 907
CITY SERVICE POLSKA SP. Z O.O.—See City Service SE; *Int'l*, pg. 1627
CITY SERVICE SE; *Int'l*, pg. 1627
CITYSIDE SUBARU, INC.; *U.S. Private*, pg. 907
CITY SITE ESTATES PLC; *Int'l*, pg. 1628
CITY SITES SPORTSWEAR INC.; *U.S. Private*, pg. 907
CITY SPORTS AND RECREATION PUBLIC COMPANY LIMITED; *Int'l*, pg. 1628
CITY SPORTS—See Highland Capital Partners, LLC; *U.S. Private*, pg. 1938
CITYSPRINT (UK) LIMITED; *Int'l*, pg. 1630
CITYSTATE SAVINGS BANK, INC.; *Int'l*, pg. 1630
CITY STATIONERY INC.; *U.S. Private*, pg. 907
CITY STEEL PRODUCTS COMPANY LIMITED—See City Steel Public Company Limited; *Int'l*, pg. 1628
CITY STEEL PUBLIC COMPANY LIMITED; *Int'l*, pg. 1628
CITY SUNSTONE PROPERTIES LLC; *U.S. Private*, pg. 907
CITYTECH, INC.—See ICF International, Inc.; *U.S. Public*, pg. 1085
CITYTECH S.A.—See Teleperformance SE; *Int'l*, pg. 7540
CITY TELECOM INC.—See Hong Kong Technology Venture Company Limited; *Int'l*, pg. 3467
CITY THEATRICAL, INC.—See Pfingsten Partners, LLC; *U.S. Private*, pg. 3164
CITY TIRE CO. INC.; *U.S. Private*, pg. 907
CITY TOURS INC.; *U.S. Private*, pg. 907
CITY TRANSFER CO. INC.; *U.S. Private*, pg. 907
CITYTWIST; *U.S. Private*, pg. 907
CITY UNION BANK LTD - INTERNATIONAL BANKING DIVISION—See City Union Bank Ltd; *Int'l*, pg. 1628
CITY UNION BANK LTD; *Int'l*, pg. 1628
CITY VENTURES, INC.; *U.S. Private*, pg. 907
CITYVIEW APARTMENTS AND COMMERCIAL CENTRE LIMITED—See Aspial Corporation Limited; *Int'l*, pg. 630
CITYVIEW APARTMENTS AND COMMERCIAL CENTRE LIMITED—See Fragrance Group Limited; *Int'l*, pg. 2758
CITY VIEW GREEN HOLDINGS INC.; *Int'l*, pg. 1628
CITY VIEW—See Essex Property Trust, Inc.; *U.S. Public*, pg. 795
CITY WATER & LIGHT; *U.S. Private*, pg. 907
CITY WHOLESALE INC.—See Imperial Trading Co. Inc.; *U.S. Private*, pg. 2049
CITYWIDE BANKS—See Heartland Financial USA, Inc.; *U.S. Public*, pg. 1018
CITY WIDE BUILDING & TRAINING SERVICES PTY LTD—See Simonds Group Limited; *Int'l*, pg. 6933
CITY WIDE GOURMET FOODS INC.; *U.S. Private*, pg. 907
CITY WIDE INSULATION OF MADISON INC.; *U.S. Private*, pg. 907
CITYWIDE INSULATION; *U.S. Private*, pg. 907
CITYWIDE LOCKSMITHS LTD.—See Avante Corp; *Int'l*, pg. 735
CITY WIDE MAINTENANCE OF COLORADO; *U.S. Private*, pg. 907
CITYWIDE SERVICE SOLUTIONS PTY LTD; *Int'l*, pg. 1630
CITY WINDMILLS LTD.; *Int'l*, pg. 1628
CITY WINDOW & CONSTRUCTION COMPANY; *U.S. Private*, pg. 907
CITYWIRE FINANCIAL PUBLISHERS LTD—See Citywire Holdings Ltd.; *Int'l*, pg. 1630
CITYWIRE HOLDINGS LTD.; *Int'l*, pg. 1630
CITYXPRESS CORPORATION; *Int'l*, pg. 1630
CITY & YOU SAS—See VINCI S.A.; *Int'l*, pg. 8215
CITY ZONE EXPRESS SDN. BHD.—See Kuehne + Nagel International AG; *Int'l*, pg. 4324
CITY ZONE EXPRESS (SHANGHAI) CO., LTD.—See Chasen Holdings Limited; *Int'l*, pg. 1457
CITY ZONE EXPRESS WORLDWIDE CO., LTD.—See Chasen Holdings Limited; *Int'l*, pg. 1457

CORPORATE AFFILIATIONS

CIVARO LANKA (PVT) LIMITED.—See Hayleys PLC; *Int'l*, pg. 3292
CIVCO MEDICAL INSTRUMENTS CO., INC.—See Roper Technologies, Inc.; *U.S. Public*, pg. 1810
CIVCO MEDICAL SOLUTIONS B.V.—See Roper Technologies, Inc.; *U.S. Public*, pg. 1810
CIVCO MEDICAL SOLUTIONS—See Roper Technologies, Inc.; *U.S. Public*, pg. 1810
CIVC PARTNERS LLC; *U.S. Private*, pg. 907
CIVEO CANADA INC.—See Oil States International, Inc.; *U.S. Public*, pg. 1565
CIVEO CORPORATION; *U.S. Public*, pg. 506
CIVEO PREMIUM CAMP SERVICES LTD—See Civeo Corporation; *U.S. Public*, pg. 506
CIVEO PTY LTD—See Civeo Corporation; *U.S. Public*, pg. 506
CIVEO PTY LTD—See Civeo Corporation; *U.S. Public*, pg. 506
CIVEO PTY LTD—See Civeo Corporation; *U.S. Public*, pg. 506
CIVEO PTY LTD—See Civeo Corporation; *U.S. Public*, pg. 506
CIVEO PTY LTD—See Civeo Corporation; *U.S. Public*, pg. 506
CIVEO USA LLC—See Civeo Corporation; *U.S. Public*, pg. 506
CIVES CORPORATION - MID-ATLANTIC DIVISION—See Cives Corporation; *U.S. Private*, pg. 908
CIVES CORPORATION - MID-SOUTH DIVISION—See Cives Corporation; *U.S. Private*, pg. 908
CIVES CORPORATION - MID-WEST DIVISION—See Cives Corporation; *U.S. Private*, pg. 908
CIVES CORPORATION - NEW ENGLAND DIVISION—See Cives Corporation; *U.S. Private*, pg. 908
CIVES CORPORATION - NORTHERN DIVISION—See Cives Corporation; *U.S. Private*, pg. 908
CIVES CORPORATION; *U.S. Private*, pg. 908
CIVES CORPORATION - SOUTHERN DIVISION—See Cives Corporation; *U.S. Private*, pg. 908
CIVES ENGINEERING CORPORATION—See Cives Corporation; *U.S. Private*, pg. 908
CIVICA EDUCATION PTY LIMITED - MELBOURNE—See Blackstone Inc.; *U.S. Public*, pg. 352
CIVICA EDUCATION PTY LIMITED—See Blackstone Inc.; *U.S. Public*, pg. 352
CIVICA GROUP LIMITED—See Blackstone Inc.; *U.S. Public*, pg. 352
CIVICA PTY. LTD.—See Blackstone Inc.; *U.S. Public*, pg. 352
CIVIC AUTOMOTIVE GROUP INC.; *U.S. Private*, pg. 908
CIVIC ENTERTAINMENT GROUP, LLC—See Ryan Seacrest Enterprises, Inc.; *U.S. Private*, pg. 3510
CIVIC FINANCIAL SERVICES, LLC—See Banc of California, Inc.; *U.S. Public*, pg. 268
CIVIC LIGHT OPERA ASSOCIATION OF PITTSBURGH; *U.S. Private*, pg. 908
CIVIC MOTORS HONDA; *Int'l*, pg. 1630
CIVICORE, LLC—See Neon One LLC; *U.S. Private*, pg. 2885
CIVICPLUS, LLC—See Insight Venture Management, LLC; *U.S. Private*, pg. 2087
CIVICSCIENCE, INC.; *U.S. Private*, pg. 908
CIVIC TREES (TREE MOVERS) LIMITED—See Parkwood Holdings Limited; *Int'l*, pg. 5744
CIVIL AND MARINE (HOLDINGS) LIMITED—See Heidelberg Materials AG; *Int'l*, pg. 3310
CIVIL BANK LIMITED; *Int'l*, pg. 1630
CIVIL CONSTRUCTION CONTRACTORS INC.; *U.S. Private*, pg. 908
CIVIL CONSTRUCTORS, INC.—See The Helm Group; *U.S. Private*, pg. 4051
CIVILCORP, LLC—See Strength Capital Partners, LLC; *U.S. Private*, pg. 3839
CIVIL & ENVIRONMENTAL CONSULTANTS, INC.; *U.S. Private*, pg. 908
CIVIL MECHANICAL INC.—See Wolfenson Electric, Inc.; *U.S. Private*, pg. 4554
CIVIL MERCHANT BITTIYA SANSTHA LIMITED; *Int'l*, pg. 1630
CIVIL PENSION FUND INVESTMENT CO.; *Int'l*, pg. 1630
CIVIL SERVICE EMPLOYEES INSURANCE COMPANY—See CSE Insurance Group; *U.S. Private*, pg. 1116
CIVILSOURCE, INC.—See NV5 Global, Inc.; *U.S. Public*, pg. 1557
CIVILTECH ENGINEERING, INC.—See Woolpert Inc.; *U.S. Private*, pg. 4562
CIVIMECH (PVT) LTD—See Daikin Industries, Ltd.; *Int'l*, pg. 1932
CIVIQ SMARTSCAPES LLC—See JMC Capital Partners LLC; *U.S. Private*, pg. 2215
CIVIQ SMARTSCAPES—See JMC Capital Partners LLC; *U.S. Private*, pg. 2215
C.I. VISIONS INC.; *U.S. Private*, pg. 707
CIVIS MANUFACTURING LTD.—See Citizen Watch Co., Ltd.; *Int'l*, pg. 1625
CIVISTA BANCSHARES, INC.; *U.S. Public*, pg. 507
CIVISTA BANK—See Civista Bancshares, Inc.; *U.S. Public*, pg. 507
CIVITANAVI SYSTEMS SPA; *Int'l*, pg. 1630

558

COMPANY NAME INDEX

CIVITANAVI SYSTEMS UK LTD.—See Civitanavi Systems SpA; *Int'l*, pg. 1630
CIVITAS IMMOBILIEN LEASING GESELLSCHAFT M.B.H.—See UniCredit S.p.A.; *Int'l*, pg. 8037
CIVITAS INTERNATIONAL MANAGEMENT CONSULTANTS GMBH; *Int'l*, pg. 1630
CIVITAS LEARNING, INC.—See Warburg Pincus LLC; *U.S. Private*, pg. 4437
CIVITAS MEDIA, LLC—See Independence Capital Partners, LLC; *U.S. Private*, pg. 2057
CIVITAS PUBLIC AFFAIRS GROUP LLC—See O2 Investment Partners, LLC; *U.S. Private*, pg. 2982
CIVITAS RESOURCES, INC.; *U.S. Public*, pg. 507
CIVITAS SOCIAL HOUSING PLC; *Int'l*, pg. 1630
CIVITAS SOLUTIONS, INC.—See Centerbridge Partners, L.P.; *U.S. Private*, pg. 813
CIVITELLA & CIA LTDA—See Klein Tools Inc.; *U.S. Private*, pg. 2319
CIVMEC LIMITED; *Int'l*, pg. 1630
CIWEN MEDIA CO., LTD.; *Int'l*, pg. 1630
CIW ENTERPRISES, INC.; *U.S. Private*, pg. 908
CIXI NEW MEIPEILIN PRECISION BEARING CO., LTD.—See Minebea Mitsumi Inc.; *Int'l*, pg. 4902
CIXI YOUNG-SHIN FOODS CO., LTD.—See Maruha Nichiro Corporation; *Int'l*, pg. 4711
CIXTA ENTERPRISES INC.; *U.S. Private*, pg. 908
CI:Z HOLDINGS CO. LTD.—See Johnson & Johnson; *U.S. Public*, pg. 1194
CI:Z.LABO CO., LTD.—See Kenvue Inc.; *U.S. Public*, pg. 1223
CJ 4DPLEX CO., LTD.—See CJ Corporation; *Int'l*, pg. 1631
CJA & ASSOCIATES, INC.; *U.S. Private*, pg. 909
CJ AFFILIATE-LONDON—See Publicis Groupe S.A.; *Int'l*, pg. 6098
CJ AFFILIATE—See Publicis Groupe S.A.; *Int'l*, pg. 6098
CJ AFFILIATE-WESTBOROUGH—See Publicis Groupe S.A.; *Int'l*, pg. 6098
CJ AMERICA, INC.—See CJ Corporation; *Int'l*, pg. 1631
CJ BAKERY, INC.—See CJ Corporation; *Int'l*, pg. 1631
CJ BEIJING BAKERY CO., LTD.—See CJ Corporation; *Int'l*, pg. 1631
CJ BEIJING FOODS CO., LTD.—See CJ Corporation; *Int'l*, pg. 1631
C.J. BETTERS CORPORATION; *U.S. Private*, pg. 708
CJB INC.—See Laboratory Corporation of America Holdings; *U.S. Public*, pg. 1285
CJ BIO AMERICA INC.—See CJ Corporation; *Int'l*, pg. 1631
CJ BIOSCIENCE, INC.; *Int'l*, pg. 1630
CJB LEASING CO.; *U.S. Private*, pg. 909
CJBS, LLC; *U.S. Private*, pg. 909
CJ CENTURY LOGISTICS HOLDINGS BERHAD; *Int'l*, pg. 1630
CJ CENTURY TECHNOLOGY SDN. BHD.—See CJ Century Logistics Holdings Berhad; *Int'l*, pg. 1631
CJ CGV AMERICA LA LLC—See CJ Corporation; *Int'l*, pg. 1632
CJ CGV CO., LTD.; *Int'l*, pg. 1631
CJ (CHANGCHUN) FEED CO., LTD.—See CJ Corporation; *Int'l*, pg. 1631
CJ CHANGSHA FEED CO., LTD.—See CJ Corporation; *Int'l*, pg. 1631
CJ CHEILJEDANG CORP.—See CJ Corporation; *Int'l*, pg. 1631
CJ (CHENGDU) FEED CO., LTD.—See CJ Corporation; *Int'l*, pg. 1631
CJ CHINA LTD.—See CJ Corporation; *Int'l*, pg. 1632
C&J CLARK CANADA, LTD.—See C&J Clark Limited; *Int'l*, pg. 1238
C&J CLARK LIMITED; *Int'l*, pg. 1238
C.J. COLEMAN & COMPANY LIMITED; *Int'l*, pg. 1243
CJ CORP. (BEIJING)—See CJ Corporation; *Int'l*, pg. 1632
CJ CORP. (MOSCOW)—See CJ Corporation; *Int'l*, pg. 1632
CJ CORPORATION; *Int'l*, pg. 1631
CJ CORP.—See CJ Corporation; *Int'l*, pg. 1632
CJCW RADIO—See Maritime Broadcasting System Ltd.; *Int'l*, pg. 4695
CJ DARCL LOGISTICS LIMITED; *Int'l*, pg. 1634
CJ DCH GUANGDONG FROZEN FOOD CO., LTD.—See CJ Corporation; *Int'l*, pg. 1632
CJ DO BRASIL LTDA—See CJ Corporation; *Int'l*, pg. 1633
CJ EDUCATIONS CORPORATION—See CJ Corporation; *Int'l*, pg. 1632
CJ E&M AMERICA INC.—See CJ Corporation; *Int'l*, pg. 1631
CJ E&M CORPORATION—See CJ Corporation; *Int'l*, pg. 1632
CJ E&M JAPAN INC.—See CJ Corporation; *Int'l*, pg. 1632
CJ ENGINEERING & CONSTRUCTION CORP—See CJ Corporation; *Int'l*, pg. 1632
CJ ENM CO., LTD.—See CJ Corporation; *Int'l*, pg. 1632
CJ ENM JAPAN INC.—See CJ Corporation; *Int'l*, pg. 1632
CJ ENTERTAINMENT AMERICA CORP.—See CJ Corporation; *Int'l*, pg. 1631
C.J. ERICKSON PLUMBING CO.; *U.S. Private*, pg. 708
CJ EUROPE GMBH—See CJ Corporation; *Int'l*, pg. 1632

CJ FALLON LIMITED—See Levine Leichtman Capital Partners, LLC; *U.S. Private*, pg. 2435
C & J FINANCIAL, LLC—See Security National Financial Corporation; *U.S. Public*, pg. 1856
C.J. FOODS, INC.—See J.H. Whitney & Co., LLC; *U.S. Private*, pg. 2166
CJ FOODS, INC.—See CJ Corporation; *Int'l*, pg. 1631
CJ FOODS MANUFACTURING, CORPORATION—See CJ Corporation; *Int'l*, pg. 1632
CJ FOODS MYANMAR CO., LTD.—See CJ Corporation; *Int'l*, pg. 1632
CJ FOODS USA INC.—See CJ Corporation; *Int'l*, pg. 1632
CJ FOODS VIETNAM CO., LTD.—See CJ Corporation; *Int'l*, pg. 1632
CJ FOODVILLE CORP.—See CJ Corporation; *Int'l*, pg. 1632
CJ FOODVILLE USA INC.—See CJ Corporation; *Int'l*, pg. 1632
CJ FRESHWAY AMERICA CORPORATION—See CJ Corporation; *Int'l*, pg. 1632
CJ FRESHWAY CORPORATION; *Int'l*, pg. 1634
CJ FRESHWAY QINGDAO CORPORATION—See CJ Corporation; *Int'l*, pg. 1632
C.J. GELATINE PRODUCTS LIMITED; *Int'l*, pg. 1243
CJ GLS AMERICA, INC.—See CJ Corporation; *Int'l*, pg. 1632
CJ GLS ASIA PTE. LTD.—See CJ Corporation; *Int'l*, pg. 1632
CJ GLS CENTRAL AMERICA, S.A. DE C.V.—See CJ Corporation; *Int'l*, pg. 1633
CJ GLS CORPORATION—See CJ Corporation; *Int'l*, pg. 1632
CJ GLS FORWARDING MALAYSIA SDN. BHD.—See CJ Corporation; *Int'l*, pg. 1633
CJ GLS (HONG KONG) LTD.—See CJ Corporation; *Int'l*, pg. 1633
CJ GLS MALAYSIA SDN. BHD.—See CJ Corporation; *Int'l*, pg. 1633
CJ GLS PHILIPPINES INC.—See CJ Corporation; *Int'l*, pg. 1633
CJ GLS PHILIPPINES VMI WAREHOUSE INC.—See CJ Corporation; *Int'l*, pg. 1633
CJ GLS (S) AIRFREIGHT PTE. LTD.—See CJ Corporation; *Int'l*, pg. 1633
CJ GLS (SHENZHEN) CO., LTD.—See CJ Corporation; *Int'l*, pg. 1633
CJ GLS (S) INFOTECH PTE. LTD.—See CJ Corporation; *Int'l*, pg. 1633
CJ GLS (S) SHIPPING PTE. LTD.—See CJ Corporation; *Int'l*, pg. 1633
CJ GLS (THAILAND) CO., LTD.—See CJ Corporation; *Int'l*, pg. 1633
CJ GRAND, S.A. DE C.V.—See CJ Corporation; *Int'l*, pg. 1632
C & J GULF PIPE COATING EST.—See Bhatia Brothers Group; *Int'l*, pg. 1013
CJ (HAERBIN) FEED CO., LTD.—See CJ Corporation; *Int'l*, pg. 1631
C J HENSCH & ASSOCIATES, INC.—See Miovision Technologies, Inc.; *Int'l*, pg. 4915
C.J. HESSE, INC.—See The Hesse Companies; *U.S. Private*, pg. 4052
CJ HORNER COMPANY INC.; *U.S. Private*, pg. 908
C: J. HUGHES CONSTRUCTION COMPANY, INC.—See Energy Services of America Corporation; *U.S. Public*, pg. 762
CJ ICM AUSTRIA GMBH—See CJ Corporation; *Int'l*, pg. 1632
CJ ICM FZCO—See CJ Corporation; *Int'l*, pg. 1632
CJ ICM ITALIA S.R.L—See CJ Corporation; *Int'l*, pg. 1632
CJ ICM LOGISTICS ESPANA S.L.—See CJ Corporation; *Int'l*, pg. 1632
CJ ICM LOGISTICS GMBH—See CJ Corporation; *Int'l*, pg. 1632
CJ ICM LOGISTICS LLC—See CJ Corporation; *Int'l*, pg. 1632
CJ ICM TASHKENT MCHJ—See CJ Corporation; *Int'l*, pg. 1632
CJ ICM (UK) LTD.—See CJ Corporation; *Int'l*, pg. 1632
CJ INTERNATIONAL TRADING CO., LTD.—See CJ Corporation; *Int'l*, pg. 1632
CJ INTERNET INC.—See CJ Corporation; *Int'l*, pg. 1631
CJ INTERNET JAPAN CORP.—See CJ Corporation; *Int'l*, pg. 1632
CJ JAPAN CORP.—See CJ Corporation; *Int'l*, pg. 1632
CJK CO., LTD.—See Toyota Motor Corporation; *Int'l*, pg. 7870
CJK GROUP, INC.; *U.S. Private*, pg. 909
CJ KOREA EXPRESS BUSAN CONTAINER TERMINAL CORPORATION—See CJ Corporation; *Int'l*, pg. 1633
CJ LIAO CHENG BIOTECH CO., LTD.—See CJ Corporation; *Int'l*, pg. 1632
CJ LION CORPORATION—See Lion Corporation; *Int'l*, pg. 4517
CJ LOGGING EQUIPMENT LLC; *U.S. Private*, pg. 908
CJ LOGISTICS AMERICA, LLC—See CJ Corporation; *Int'l*, pg. 1633
CJ LOGISTICS ASIA PTE. LTD.—See CJ Corporation; *Int'l*, pg. 1632

CJ LOGISTICS CORPORATION—See CJ Corporation; *Int'l*, pg. 1632
CJ LOGISTICS EUROPE GMBH—See CJ Corporation; *Int'l*, pg. 1633
CJ LOGISTICS JAPAN CORPORATION—See CJ Corporation; *Int'l*, pg. 1633
CJ LOGISTICS PH CORP.—See CJ Corporation; *Int'l*, pg. 1633
CJ LOGISTICS USA CORPORATION—See CJ Corporation; *Int'l*, pg. 1633
CJ MABARDY INC.; *U.S. Private*, pg. 908
CJ MAINFROST FOODS GMBH—See CJ Corporation; *Int'l*, pg. 1633
CJ MARKETING PROPRIETARY LIMITED—See Dis-Chem Pharmacies Ltd.; *Int'l*, pg. 2130
C.J. MILLER LLC; *U.S. Private*, pg. 708
CJM SOLUTIONS INC.—See Arthur J. Gallagher & Co.; *U.S. Public*, pg. 204
CJM TRUCKING LTD.—See Petrowest Corp.; *Int'l*, pg. 5833
CJ (NANJING) FEED CO., LTD.—See CJ Corporation; *Int'l*, pg. 1631
CJ N CITY CO., LTD.—See CJ Corporation; *Int'l*, pg. 1633
CJ NUTRACON PTY.—See CJ Corporation; *Int'l*, pg. 1633
CJ OLIVE NETWORKS CO., LTD.—See CJ Freshway Corporation; *Int'l*, pg. 1634
CJ OLIVENETWORKS VINA CO., LTD.—See CJ Corporation; *Int'l*, pg. 1633
CJ OLIVE YOUNG CO., LTD.—See CJ Corporation; *Int'l*, pg. 1632
CJ OLIVE YOUNG (SHANGHAI) CORPORATION—See CJ Corporation; *Int'l*, pg. 1633
CJ OMNI, INC.—See CJ Corporation; *Int'l*, pg. 1631
C J O'SHEA GROUP LTD; *Int'l*, pg. 1238
CJ O'SHEA (PLANT HIRE) LTD—See C J O'Shea Group Ltd; *Int'l*, pg. 1238
C.J.O.-SOCIETE LES CIMENTS DE JBEL OUST—See Camargo Correa S.A.; *Int'l*, pg. 1267
CJ PACIFIC CORPORATION—See CJ Corporation; *Int'l*, pg. 1631
CJ PHARMACEUTICAL ENTERPRISES LIMITED—See Dis-Chem Pharmacies Ltd.; *Int'l*, pg. 2130
CJ PHILIPPINES INC.—See CJ Corporation; *Int'l*, pg. 1633
CJP HOLDINGS INC.—See Citigroup Inc.; *U.S. Public*, pg. 502
CJ PONY PARTS, INC.; *U.S. Private*, pg. 908
CJ POWERCAST INC.—See CJ Corporation; *Int'l*, pg. 1633
CJ QINGDAO FEED CO., LTD.—See CJ Corporation; *Int'l*, pg. 1631
CJ QINGDAO FOODS CO., LTD.—See CJ Corporation; *Int'l*, pg. 1631
CJ RAVIOLLO RUS LLC—See CJ Corporation; *Int'l*, pg. 1633
CJRW NORTHWEST—See Cranford Johnson Robinson Woods, Inc.; *U.S. Private*, pg. 1085
CJSC AGROTON—See Agroton Public Ltd; *Int'l*, pg. 221
CJSC BANK CREDIT SUISSE—See UBS Group AG; *Int'l*, pg. 8005
CJSC BREWERY PIVDENNA—See Turkiye Sise ve Cam Fabrikalari A.S.; *Int'l*, pg. 7977
CJSC CONTAINER TERMINAL SAINT-PETERSBURG—See Universal Cargo Logistics Holding B.V.; *Int'l*, pg. 8077
CJSC DONETSKSTEEL METALLURGICAL PLANT; *Int'l*, pg. 1634
CJSC DOOSAN INTERNATIONAL RUSSIA—See Doosan Corporation; *Int'l*, pg. 2172
CJSC GEDEON RICHTER - RUS—See Gedeon Richter Plc.; *Int'l*, pg. 2909
CJSC GIPROBUM-POYRY—See AFRY AB; *Int'l*, pg. 195
CJSC GLOBALTEL—See PJSC Rostelecom; *Int'l*, pg. 5884
CJSC GLORIA JEANS CORPORATION; *Int'l*, pg. 1634
CJSC GNC ALFA—See PJSC Rostelecom; *Int'l*, pg. 5883
CJSC HALYK LEASING—See Halyk Bank of Kazakhstan JSC; *Int'l*, pg. 3234
CJSC INTEGRATED ENERGY SYSTEMS—See Renova Group; *Int'l*, pg. 6285
CJSC INTERCOS-IV—See OJSC Magnitogorsk Iron & Steel Works; *Int'l*, pg. 5539
CJSC - JTI MARKETING & SALES—See Japan Tobacco Inc.; *Int'l*, pg. 3906
CJSC KAZTELEPORT—See Halyk Bank of Kazakhstan JSC; *Int'l*, pg. 3234
CJSC KONE LIFTS—See KONE Oyj; *Int'l*, pg. 4247
CJSC LIGGETT-DUCAT—See Japan Tobacco Inc.; *Int'l*, pg. 3906
CJSC MAKOMNET—See PJSC Rostelecom; *Int'l*, pg. 5884
CJSC MICEX STOCK EXCHANGE—See OJSC Moscow Exchange MICEX-RTS; *Int'l*, pg. 5540
CJSC NATIONAL CLEARING CENTER—See OJSC Moscow Exchange MICEX-RTS; *Int'l*, pg. 5540
CJSC NEW WAVE GROUP—See New Wave Group AB; *Int'l*, pg. 5229
CJSC NOVGOROD DEITACOM—See PJSC Rostelecom; *Int'l*, pg. 5884

CJSC ORGSYNTES GROUP—See Renova Group; *Int'l*, pg. 6285
CJSC PENZANEFTEPRODUKT—See OJSC Rosneftegaz; *Int'l*, pg. 5541
CJSC PETELINSKAYA—See PJSC Cherkizovo Group; *Int'l*, pg. 5878
CJSC PROFIT—See OJSC Magnitogorsk Iron & Steel Works; *Int'l*, pg. 5539
CJSC "SSMO LENSPETSSMU"—See Etalon Group Plc; *Int'l*, pg. 2520
CJSC ROTEC—See Renova Group; *Int'l*, pg. 6285
CJSC RUSAGRO-AYDAR—See Gruppa Kompaniy Rusagro OOO; *Int'l*, pg. 3140
CJSC RUSSIAN STANDARD CORPORATION; *Int'l*, pg. 1634
CJSC S7 GROUP; *Int'l*, pg. 1634
CJSC SAKHALINMORNEFTEGAZ SHELF—See OJSC Rosneftegaz; *Int'l*, pg. 5541
CJSC SBERBANK CIB; *Int'l*, pg. 1634
CJSC ST.PETERSBURG TRANZIT TELECOM—See PJSC Rostelecom; *Int'l*, pg. 5884
CJSC TAMOZHENNY BROKER—See OJSC Magnitogorsk Iron & Steel Works; *Int'l*, pg. 5539
CJSC TONODA—See PJSC Polyus; *Int'l*, pg. 5883
CJSC ULYANOVSK-GSM—See PJSC Rostelecom; *Int'l*, pg. 5884
CJSC URALMASH - DRILLING EQUIPMENT—See Integra Management LLC; *Int'l*, pg. 3729
CJSC URALMASH-VNIIBT—See Integra Management LLC; *Int'l*, pg. 3729
CJSC VANKORNEFT—See OJSC Rosneftegaz; *Int'l*, pg. 5541
CJ SEAFOOD CORPORATION—See CJ Corporation; *Int'l*, pg. 1631
C.J. SEGERSTROM & SONS, LLC; *U.S. Private*, pg. 708
CJ (SHENYANG) BIOTECH CO., LTD.—See CJ Corporation; *Int'l*, pg. 1631
CJ (SHENYANG) FEED CO., LTD.—See CJ Corporation; *Int'l*, pg. 1631
CJSIC "EUROPEAN TRAVEL INSURANCE"—See Munchener Ruckversicherungs AG; *Int'l*, pg. 5085
CJ SPEEDEX LOGISTICS DEQING CO., LTD.—See CJ Corporation; *Int'l*, pg. 1633
CJS PLV; *Int'l*, pg. 1634
CJ SUPPRESSION, INC.—See Fortis Fire & Safety, Inc.; *U.S. Private*, pg. 1576
CJ SYSTEMS CO., LTD.—See CJ Corporation; *Int'l*, pg. 1633
CJ TELENIX CO., LTD.—See CJ Corporation; *Int'l*, pg. 1632
CJ TIANJIN FEED CO., LTD.—See CJ Corporation; *Int'l*, pg. 1631
CJT KOOLCARB, INC.—See L Squared Capital Management LP; *U.S. Private*, pg. 2361
CJ TUR YEM SANAYI VE TICARET ANONIM SIRKETI—See CJ Corporation; *Int'l*, pg. 1633
CJ. (UK) LIMITED—See Continental Holdings Limited; *Int'l*, pg. 1784
CJ USA LLC—See Continental Holdings Limited; *Int'l*, pg. 1784
CJ VIETNAM COMPANY LIMITED—See CJ Corporation; *Int'l*, pg. 1633
CJ VINA AGRI CO., LTD.—See CJ Corporation; *Int'l*, pg. 1631
C.J. VITNER CO.—See Snak King Corp.; *U.S. Private*, pg. 3699
C&J WELL SERVICES, INC.—See Basic Energy Services Inc.; *U.S. Public*, pg. 279
CJW INFECTIOUS DISEASE, LLC—See HCA Healthcare, Inc.; *U.S. Public*, pg. 992
CJW MEDICAL CENTER—See HCA Healthcare, Inc.; *U.S. Public*, pg. 992
CJ ZHENGZHOU FEED CO., LTD.—See CJ Corporation; *Int'l*, pg. 1631
CJZN-FM—See The Jim Pattison Group; *Int'l*, pg. 7660
CKA RISK SOLUTIONS PTY LIMITED—See Willis Towers Watson Public Limited Company; *Int'l*, pg. 8414
CKA SALES L.L.C.; *U.S. Private*, pg. 909
CK ASSET HOLDINGS LIMITED; *Int'l*, pg. 1634
CK BIRLA GROUP; *Int'l*, pg. 1636
CK CLEAN AD CO., LTD.—See Chubu Steel Plate Co., Ltd.; *Int'l*, pg. 1594
C&K COAL COMPANY—See GRE Ventures, Inc.; *U.S. Private*, pg. 1761
CK COFFEE LTD.—See Tudeley Holdings Limited; *Int'l*, pg. 7963
CK COMMUNICATIONS, INC.; *U.S. Private*, pg. 909
CK COMPANY CO., LTD.; *Int'l*, pg. 1636
C&K COMPONENTS, INC.—See Littelfuse, Inc.; *U.S. Public*, pg. 1326
CKCW-AM/CFQM-FM—See Maritime Broadcasting System Ltd.; *Int'l*, pg. 4695
CKCW/CFQM RADIO—See Maritime Broadcasting System Ltd.; *Int'l*, pg. 4695
CKD BIO CORP.; *Int'l*, pg. 1639
CKD (CHINA) CORPORATION—See CKD Corporation; *Int'l*, pg. 1639
CKD CORPORATION - KASUGAI PLANT—See CKD Corporation; *Int'l*, pg. 1639

CKD CORPORATION; *Int'l*, pg. 1639
CKD CORPORATION—See CKD Corporation; *Int'l*, pg. 1639
CKD CORPORATION—See CKD Corporation; *Int'l*, pg. 1639
CKD CORPORATION—See CKD Corporation; *Int'l*, pg. 1639
CKD CORPORATION - YOKKAICHI PLANT—See CKD Corporation; *Int'l*, pg. 1639
CKD EUROPE B.V.—See CKD Corporation; *Int'l*, pg. 1639
CKD FIELD ENGINEERING CORPORATION—See CKD Corporation; *Int'l*, pg. 1639
CKD GLOBAL SERVICE CORPORATION—See CKD Corporation; *Int'l*, pg. 1639
CKD GLOBAL SERVICES CORPORATION—See CKD Corporation; *Int'l*, pg. 1639
CKDH RADIO-AM—See Maritime Broadcasting System Ltd.; *Int'l*, pg. 4695
CKD INDIA PRIVATE LIMITED—See CKD Corporation; *Int'l*, pg. 1639
CKD KOREA CORPORATION—See CKD Corporation; *Int'l*, pg. 1639
CKD MEXICO, S. DE R.L. DE C.V.—See CKD Corporation; *Int'l*, pg. 1639
CKD NIKKI DENSO CO., LTD.—See CKD Corporation; *Int'l*, pg. 1639
CKD (SHANGHAI) CORPORATION—See CKD Corporation; *Int'l*, pg. 1639
CKD SHIKOKU SEIKO CORPORATION—See CKD Corporation; *Int'l*, pg. 1639
CKD SINGAPORE PTE LTD—See CKD Corporation; *Int'l*, pg. 1639
CKD THAI CORPORATION LTD.—See CKD Corporation; *Int'l*, pg. 1639
CKD USA CORPORATION—See CKD Corporation; *Int'l*, pg. 1639
CKD VENTURE CAPITAL CORP.—See Chong Kun Dang Holdings Corp.; *Int'l*, pg. 1578
CKD VIETNAM ENGINEERING CO., LTD.—See CKD Corporation; *Int'l*, pg. 1639
CKE, INC.—See Roark Capital Group Inc.; *U.S. Private*, pg. 3454
CK ENVIRONMENTAL, INC.; *U.S. Private*, pg. 909
C.K. ENVIRONMENT A/S—See Addtech AB; *Int'l*, pg. 132
CKE RESTAURANTS HOLDINGS, INC.—See Roark Capital Group Inc.; *U.S. Private*, pg. 3454
CKF, INC.; *Int'l*, pg. 1639
CK FIRES LTD.—See NIBE Industrier AB; *Int'l*, pg. 5260
CK FRANCHISING, INC.—See Sodexo S.A.; *Int'l*, pg. 7047
CKG CHEMICALS PTE LTD—See Nylex (Malaysia) Berhad; *Int'l*, pg. 5500
CKGP/PW & ASSOCIATES, INC.—See ATON GmbH; *Int'l*, pg. 689
C.K.H. FOOD TRADING PTE. LTD.—See Hanoi Beer Trading JSC; *Int'l*, pg. 3258
CKH (MT A) PTE. LTD.—See HC Surgical Specialists Limited; *Int'l*, pg. 3297
CK HOBBIE INC.; *U.S. Private*, pg. 909
CK HUTCHISON HOLDINGS LIMITED; *Int'l*, pg. 1636
C.K. INDUSTRIAL ENGINEERS LIMITED—See L3Harris Technologies, Inc.; *U.S. Public*, pg. 1281
CK INFRASTRUCTURE HOLDINGS LIMITED—See CK Hutchison Holdings Limited; *Int'l*, pg. 1636
CK-KS ENGINEERING (GUANGZHOU) TOOLING CENTER CORP.—See Nissan Motor Co., Ltd.; *Int'l*, pg. 5367
CK LIFE SCIENCES INTERNATIONAL, (HOLDINGS) INC.—See CK Hutchison Holdings Limited; *Int'l*, pg. 1637
CK LOGISTICS INC.—See TFI International Inc.; *Int'l*, pg. 7585
CKL SOFTWARE GMBH—See Prodware SA; *Int'l*, pg. 5989
CKM APPLIED MATERIALS CORP.; *Int'l*, pg. 1639
C&K MARKET, INC.; *U.S. Private*, pg. 703
CK METALL AGENTUR GMBH—See Corporacion Nacional del Cobre de Chile; *Int'l*, pg. 1804
CKNB-AM—See Maritime Broadcasting System Ltd.; *Int'l*, pg. 4695
C&K OIL CO. INC.—See Lank Oil Co. Inc.; *U.S. Private*, pg. 2390
CKP (CZ) S.R.O.—See CCL Industries Inc.; *Int'l*, pg. 1367
C&K PETROLEUM PRODUCTS; *U.S. Private*, pg. 703
CKP INSURANCE, LLC—See Brown & Brown, Inc.; *U.S. Public*, pg. 400
CKP LEISURE LIMITED; *Int'l*, pg. 1639
CK POWER PUBLIC COMPANY LIMITED; *Int'l*, pg. 1638
CKP PRODUCTS LIMITED; *Int'l*, pg. 1640
C&K PROPERTIES; *U.S. Private*, pg. 703
CKR INTERACTIVE, INC.—See Gemspring Capital Management, LLC; *U.S. Private*, pg. 1659
CKR INTERACTIVE—See Gemspring Capital Management, LLC; *U.S. Private*, pg. 1659
CK SALES CO., LLC—See Flowers Foods, Inc.; *U.S. Public*, pg. 854
CK SAN-ETSU CO., LTD.; *Int'l*, pg. 1638
CKS MANAGEMENT INC.—See Microwave Transmission Systems, Inc.; *U.S. Private*, pg. 2704
C.K. SMITH & COMPANY INC.; *U.S. Private*, pg. 708

CKS PACKAGING, INC. - NAUGATUCK—See CKS Packaging, Inc.; *U.S. Private*, pg. 909
CKS PACKAGING, INC.; *U.S. Private*, pg. 909
CKS PRECISION MACHINING, INC.—See Gemini Group, Inc.; *U.S. Private*, pg. 1658
CKS PROPERTY CONSULTANTS PTE LTD—See Phillip Capital Pte. Ltd.; *Int'l*, pg. 5846
CKS SYSTEME GMBH—See Johnson Controls International plc; *Int'l*, pg. 3986
CK STORES BELGIUM BVBA—See PVH Corp.; *U.S. Public*, pg. 1739
CK STORES DENMARK APS—See PVH Corp.; *U.S. Public*, pg. 1739
C & K SYSTEMS, INC.; *U.S. Private*, pg. 701
C.K. TANG LIMITED; *Int'l*, pg. 1243
CK TECHNOLOGIES, LLC—See Cascade Engineering, Inc.; *U.S. Private*, pg. 779
CK TRADING CO., LTD.—See CK SAN-ETSU Co., Ltd.; *Int'l*, pg. 1639
CK WATCH & JEWELRY CO., LTD.—See The Swatch Group Ltd.; *Int'l*, pg. 7691
CKW PHARMA-EXTRAKT GMBH & CO. KG—See Danish Crown AmbA; *Int'l*, pg. 1964
CKWS-TV—See Corus Entertainment Inc.; *Int'l*, pg. 1808
CKX LANDS, INC.; *U.S. Public*, pg. 507
CLAAS AGRICOLTURA S.R.L.—See Claas KGaA mbH; *Int'l*, pg. 1640
CLAAS AGRICULTURAL MACHINERY PRIVATE LIMITED—See Claas KGaA mbH; *Int'l*, pg. 1640
CLAAS AGROSYSTEMS KGAA MBH & CO KG—See Claas KGaA mbH; *Int'l*, pg. 1640
CLAAS AMERICA LATINA REPRESENTACAO LTDA.—See Claas KGaA mbH; *Int'l*, pg. 1640
CLAAS ANLAGENMANAGEMENT GMBH—See Claas KGaA mbH; *Int'l*, pg. 1640
CLAAS ARGENTINA S.A.—See Claas KGaA mbH; *Int'l*, pg. 1640
CLAAS BORDESHOLM GMBH—See Claas KGaA mbH; *Int'l*, pg. 1640
CLAAS BRAUNSCHWEIG GMBH—See Claas KGaA mbH; *Int'l*, pg. 1641
CLAAS EASTERN LTD.—See Claas KGaA mbH; *Int'l*, pg. 1640
CLAAS E-SYSTEMS GMBH—See Claas KGaA mbH; *Int'l*, pg. 1640
CLAAS FINANCIAL SERVICES INC.—See BNP Paribas SA; *Int'l*, pg. 1087
CLAAS FRANCE HOLDING S.A.S.—See Claas KGaA mbH; *Int'l*, pg. 1640
CLAAS FRANCE S.A.S.—See Claas KGaA mbH; *Int'l*, pg. 1641
CLAAS HOLDINGS LTD.—See Claas KGaA mbH; *Int'l*, pg. 1641
CLAAS HUNGARIA KFT.—See Claas KGaA mbH; *Int'l*, pg. 1641
CLAAS IBERICA S.A.—See Claas KGaA mbH; *Int'l*, pg. 1641
CLAAS INDIA LTD.—See Claas KGaA mbH; *Int'l*, pg. 1641
CLAAS INDUSTRIETECHNIK GMBH—See Claas KGaA mbH; *Int'l*, pg. 1641
CLAAS ITALIA S.P.A.—See Claas KGaA mbH; *Int'l*, pg. 1640
CLAAS KGAA MBH; *Int'l*, pg. 1640
CLAAS MAIN-DONAU GMBH & CO. KG—See BayWa AG; *Int'l*, pg. 917
CLAAS MANNS LTD.—See Claas KGaA mbH; *Int'l*, pg. 1640
CLAAS MIDDLE EAST - FZE—See Claas KGaA mbH; *Int'l*, pg. 1641
CLAAS NORDOSTBAYERN GMBH & CO. KG—See BayWa AG; *Int'l*, pg. 917
CLAAS NORTH AMERICA HOLDINGS INC.—See Claas KGaA mbH; *Int'l*, pg. 1640
CLAAS OMAHA INC.—See Claas KGaA mbH; *Int'l*, pg. 1641
CLAAS RESEAU AGRICOLE S.A.S.—See Claas KGaA mbH; *Int'l*, pg. 1641
CLAAS SAULGAU GMBH—See Claas KGaA mbH; *Int'l*, pg. 1641
CLAAS SELBSTFAHRENDE ERNTEMASCHINEN GMBH—See Claas KGaA mbH; *Int'l*, pg. 1641
CLAAS SERVICE AND PARTS GMBH—See Claas KGaA mbH; *Int'l*, pg. 1640
CLAAS SUDOSTBAYERN GMBH—See BayWa AG; *Int'l*, pg. 917
CLAAS THURINGEN GMBH—See Claas KGaA mbH; *Int'l*, pg. 1641
CLAAS TRACTOR S.A.S.—See Claas KGaA mbH; *Int'l*, pg. 1640
CLAAS U.K. LTD.—See Claas KGaA mbH; *Int'l*, pg. 1641
CLAAS VERTRIEBSGESELLSCHAFT MBH—See Claas KGaA mbH; *Int'l*, pg. 1641
CLAAS WESER EMS GMBH—See Claas KGaA mbH; *Int'l*, pg. 1641
CLAAS WESTERN LTD.—See Claas KGaA mbH; *Int'l*, pg. 1640
CLAAS WURTTEMBERG GMBH—See BayWa AG; *Int'l*, pg. 917

COMPANY NAME INDEX

CLABBER GIRL CORPORATION—See B&G Foods, Inc.; *U.S. Public*, pg. 260
CLABO S.P.A.; *Int'l*, pg. 1641
C-LABS CORPORATION—See TRUMPF SE + Co. KG; *Int'l*, pg. 7943
CLABUCET ESTIVAL 2002 S.A.; *Int'l*, pg. 1641
CLACKAMAS ULTIMATE AIRSTREAMS, LLC—See Lithia Motors, Inc.; *U.S. Public*, pg. 1321
CLACKAMAS WOODS ASSISTED LIVING, LLC—See Ventas, Inc.; *U.S. Public*, pg. 2278
CLACK CORPORATION; *U.S. Private*, pg. 909
CLACKMANNANSHIRE SCHOOLS EDUCATION PARTNERSHIP (HOLDINGS) LTD.—See Bilfinger SE; *Int'l*, pg. 1028
CLAERH, S.A.—See ACS, Actividades de Construccion y Servicios, S.A.; *Int'l*, pg. 110
C&L AEROSPACE PTY LTD.; *Int'l*, pg. 1239
CLAFFEY POOLS; *U.S. Private*, pg. 909
CLAGGETT & SONS, INC.; *U.S. Private*, pg. 909
CLAIBORNE ELECTRIC CO-OP INC.; *U.S. Private*, pg. 910
CLAIMCOR, LLC—See FedNat Holding Company; *U.S. Public*, pg. 828
CLAIMIFY, LLC; *U.S. Private*, pg. 910
CLAIM MANAGEMENT ADMINISTRATOR, S.L.—See Willis Towers Watson Public Limited Company; *Int'l*, pg. 8416
CLAIM MANAGEMENT SERVICES, INC.—See Elevance Health, Inc.; *U.S. Public*, pg. 729
CLAIMPICKER AG; *Int'l*, pg. 1641
CLAIMS COMPENSATION BUREAU, LLC—See PRA Group, Inc.; *U.S. Public*, pg. 1712
CLAIMSECURE INC.; *Int'l*, pg. 1641
CLAIMS FULFILMENT COMPANY (PTY) LTD.—See Aon plc; *Int'l*, pg. 494
CLAIMS MANAGEMENT OF MISSOURI, LLC—See Brown & Brown, Inc.; *U.S. Public*, pg. 400
CLAIM TECHNOLOGIES INC.—See Brown & Brown, Inc.; *U.S. Public*, pg. 399
CLAIN AUTOMOTIVE TEAM; *U.S. Private*, pg. 910
CLAIR CO., LTD.—See Kuwayama Corporation; *Int'l*, pg. 4348
CLAIRE CO., LTD.—See Santen Pharmaceutical Co., Ltd.; *Int'l*, pg. 6557
CLAIRE DE VIE SPRL—See Clariane SE; *Int'l*, pg. 1642
CLAIREFONTAINE SA—See Carrefour SA; *Int'l*, pg. 1344
THE CLAIRE MANUFACTURING COMPANY—See The Pritzker Group - Chicago, LLC; *U.S. Private*, pg. 4099
CLAIRE'S ACCESSORIES UK LTD.—See Apollo Global Management, Inc.; *U.S. Public*, pg. 148
CLAIRE'S AUSTRIA GMBH—See Apollo Global Management, Inc.; *U.S. Public*, pg. 148
CLAIRE'S BOUTIQUES, INC.—See Apollo Global Management, Inc.; *U.S. Public*, pg. 148
CLAIRE'S CANADA CORP.—See Apollo Global Management, Inc.; *U.S. Public*, pg. 148
CLAIRE'S FRANCE S.A.S.—See Apollo Global Management, Inc.; *U.S. Public*, pg. 148
CLAIRE'S INC.—See Apollo Global Management, Inc.; *U.S. Public*, pg. 148
CLAIRE'S NIPPON CO., LTD.—See Apollo Global Management, Inc.; *U.S. Public*, pg. 148
CLAIRE'S STORES, INC.—See Apollo Global Management, Inc.; *U.S. Public*, pg. 148
CLAIRE'S SWITZERLAND GMBH—See Apollo Global Management, Inc.; *U.S. Public*, pg. 149
CLAIRGUIL; *Int'l*, pg. 1641
CLAIRON METALS CORPORATION; *U.S. Private*, pg. 910
CLAIRSON PLASTICS LLC; *U.S. Private*, pg. 910
CLAIRVEST GROUP INC.; *Int'l*, pg. 1641
CLAIRVOYANT TECHNOSOLUTIONS INC; *U.S. Private*, pg. 910
CLAL BIOTECHNOLOGY INDUSTRIES LTD.—See Access Industries, Inc.; *U.S. Private*, pg. 51
CLAL CREDIT & FINANCING LTD.—See IDB Development Corporation Ltd.; *Int'l*, pg. 3588
CLAL CREDIT INSURANCE LTD.—See IDB Development Corporation Ltd.; *Int'l*, pg. 3588
CLAL ELECTRONIC INDUSTRIES LTD.—See Access Industries, Inc.; *U.S. Private*, pg. 51
CLAL ENERGY—See Access Industries, Inc.; *U.S. Private*, pg. 51
CLAL FACTORING LTD.—See IDB Development Corporation Ltd.; *Int'l*, pg. 3588
CLAL FINANCE LTD.—See IDB Development Corporation Ltd.; *Int'l*, pg. 3588
CLAL FINANCING CONSUMER CREDIT LTD.—See IDB Development Corporation Ltd.; *Int'l*, pg. 3588
CLAL HEALTH INSURANCE COMPANY LTD.—See IDB Development Corporation Ltd.; *Int'l*, pg. 3588
CLAL INDUSTRIES LTD.—See Access Industries, Inc.; *U.S. Private*, pg. 51
CLAL INFORMATION TECHNOLOGY—See Access Industries, Inc.; *U.S. Private*, pg. 51
CLAL INSURANCE COMPANY LTD.—See IDB Development Corporation Ltd.; *Int'l*, pg. 3588

CLAL INSURANCE ENTERPRISES HOLDINGS LTD.—See IDB Development Corporation Ltd.; *Int'l*, pg. 3588
CLALLAM COUNTY PUBLIC UTILITY DISTRICT; *U.S. Private*, pg. 910
CLAL MORTGAGES—See IDB Development Corporation Ltd.; *Int'l*, pg. 3588
CLAMART AUTOMOBILES; *Int'l*, pg. 1641
CLAMPITT PAPER COMPANY; *U.S. Private*, pg. 910
CLANCY CONSULTING LTD; *Int'l*, pg. 1641
CLANCY ENVIRONMENTAL CONSULTANTS, INC.—See Tetra Tech, Inc.; *U.S. Public*, pg. 2022
CLANCY'S FOOD STORES PTY. LTD.—See Metcash Limited; *Int'l*, pg. 4852
CLANCY'S INC.; *U.S. Private*, pg. 910
CLANCY'S TRANSFER & STORAGE, INC.—See Bekins Moving & Storage Co.; *U.S. Public*, pg. 516
CLANCY SYSTEMS INTERNATIONAL, INC.; *U.S. Private*, pg. 910
CLANCY & THEYS CONSTRUCTION COMPANY - NEWPORT NEWS—See Clancy & Theys Construction Company; *U.S. Private*, pg. 910
CLANCY & THEYS CONSTRUCTION COMPANY - ORLANDO—See Clancy & Theys Construction Company; *U.S. Private*, pg. 910
CLANCY & THEYS CONSTRUCTION COMPANY; *U.S. Private*, pg. 910
CLANCY & THEYS CONSTRUCTION COMPANY—See Clancy & Theys Construction Company; *U.S. Private*, pg. 910
CLANOTECH AB—See Rosetta Capital Limited; *Int'l*, pg. 6400
C & L AQUA PROFESSIONALS, INC.—See Hawkins, Inc.; *U.S. Public*, pg. 989
CLARA BARTON HOSPITAL; *U.S. Private*, pg. 910
CLARABRIDGE, INC.—See Canada Pension Plan Investment Board; *Int'l*, pg. 1281
CLARABRIDGE, INC.—See Silver Lake Group, LLC; *U.S. Private*, pg. 3655
CLARA DIAMOND SOLUTIONS LIMITED PARTNERSHIP—See Lucara Diamond Corp.; *Int'l*, pg. 4573
CLARAGE—See Twin City Fan Companies, Ltd.; *U.S. Private*, pg. 4265
CLARA INDUSTRIES LIMITED; *Int'l*, pg. 1642
CLARA MAASS MEDICAL CENTER—See Barnabas Health, Inc.; *U.S. Private*, pg. 476
CLARANET BENELUX BV—See Claranet Limited; *Int'l*, pg. 1642
CLARANET GMBH—See Claranet Limited; *Int'l*, pg. 1642
CLARANET LIMITED; *Int'l*, pg. 1642
CLARANET PORTUGAL—See Claranet Limited; *Int'l*, pg. 1642
CLARANET SAS—See Claranet Limited; *Int'l*, pg. 1642
CLARANET S.A.U.—See Claranet Limited; *Int'l*, pg. 1642
CLARANET SOHO—See Claranet Limited; *Int'l*, pg. 1642
CLARANOVA SA; *Int'l*, pg. 1642
CLARA RESOURCES AUSTRALIA LTD—See DGR Global Limited; *Int'l*, pg. 2097
CLARAVIEW, INC.—See Teradata Corporation; *U.S. Public*, pg. 2017
CLARCOR AIR FILTRATION PRODUCTS INC.—See Parker Hannifin Corporation; *U.S. Public*, pg. 1641
CLARE BEDDING MFG. CO.; *U.S. Private*, pg. 910
CLARE CONTROLS LLC; *U.S. Private*, pg. 910
CLARE INSTRUMENTS US, INC.—See Littelfuse, Inc.; *U.S. Public*, pg. 1327
CLARE ISLAND SEAFARM LTD.—See Mowi ASA; *Int'l*, pg. 5059
CLAREITY CONSULTING LTD.; *U.S. Private*, pg. 910
CLAREMONT BEHAVIORAL SERVICES, INC.—See Integrated Behavioral Health, Inc.; *U.S. Public*, pg. 2099
CLAREMONT COUNTRY CLUB; *U.S. Private*, pg. 910
CLAREMONT FLOCK CORPORATION; *U.S. Private*, pg. 910
CLAREMONT HOSPITAL LLP—See Tenet Healthcare Corporation; *U.S. Public*, pg. 2002
CLAREMONT SAVINGS BANK; *U.S. Private*, pg. 910
CLAREMORE ANESTHESIA, LLC—See Community Health Systems, Inc.; *U.S. Public*, pg. 552
CLAREMORE INTERNAL MEDICINE, LLC—See Community Health Systems, Inc.; *U.S. Public*, pg. 552
CLARENCE COAL PTY LIMITED—See Banpu Public Company Limited; *Int'l*, pg. 852
CLARENCE COLLIERY PTY LIMITED—See Banpu Public Company Limited; *Int'l*, pg. 852
CLARENCE DAVIDS & COMPANY; *U.S. Private*, pg. 910
CLARENCE HOUSE, INC.—See Fabricut Inc.; *U.S. Private*, pg. 1459
CLARENCE L. BOYD COMPANY; *U.S. Private*, pg. 910
CLARENCE W GOSNELL INC; *U.S. Private*, pg. 911
CLARENDON CENTER LLC—See Saul Centers, Inc.; *U.S. Public*, pg. 1842
CLAREN ENERGY CORP.; *Int'l*, pg. 1642
CLAREN ROAD ASSET MANAGEMENT LLC—See The Carlyle Group Inc.; *U.S. Public*, pg. 2045
CLARE ROSE INC.; *U.S. Private*, pg. 910
CLARET MEDICAL, INC.—See Boston Scientific Corporation; *U.S. Public*, pg. 375

CLARIANT AG

CLARFELD FINANCIAL ADVISORS, LLC—See Citizens Financial Group, Inc.; *U.S. Public*, pg. 505
CLARIANA, S.A.—See Miquel y Costas & Miquel, S.A.; *Int'l*, pg. 4915
CLARIANE SE; *Int'l*, pg. 1642
CLARIANT ADVANCED MATERIALS GMBH—See Clariant AG; *Int'l*, pg. 1647
CLARIANT AG; *Int'l*, pg. 1645
CLARIANT (ARGENTINA) S.A.—See Clariant AG; *Int'l*, pg. 1645
CLARIANT (AUSTRALIA) PTY. LTD.—See Clariant AG; *Int'l*, pg. 1645
CLARIANT BENELUX SA/NV—See Clariant AG; *Int'l*, pg. 1646
CLARIANT BENTONITE (JIANGSU) CO., LTD.—See Clariant AG; *Int'l*, pg. 1646
CLARIANT (CANADA), INC.—See Clariant AG; *Int'l*, pg. 1645
CLARIANT CATALYSTS (JAPAN) K.K.—See Clariant AG; *Int'l*, pg. 1646
CLARIANT CHEMICALS (CHINA) LTD.—See Clariant AG; *Int'l*, pg. 1645
CLARIANT CHEMICALS (GUANGZHOU) LTD.—See Clariant AG; *Int'l*, pg. 1645
CLARIANT CHEMICALS (HUIZHOU) LTD.—See Clariant AG; *Int'l*, pg. 1646
CLARIANT CHEMICALS (INDIA) LIMITED—See Clariant AG; *Int'l*, pg. 1646
CLARIANT CHEMICALS (TAIWAN) CO., LTD.—See Clariant AG; *Int'l*, pg. 1646
CLARIANT CHEMICALS TECHNOLOGY (SHANGHAI) LTD.—See Clariant AG; *Int'l*, pg. 1646
CLARIANT CHEMICALS (THAILAND) LTD.—See Clariant AG; *Int'l*, pg. 1646
CLARIANT (CHILE) LTDA.—See Clariant AG; *Int'l*, pg. 1645
CLARIANT (CHINA) LTD.—See Clariant AG; *Int'l*, pg. 1645
CLARIANT (COLOMBIA) S.A.—See Clariant AG; *Int'l*, pg. 1645
CLARIANT COLORQUIMICA (CHILE) LTDA.—See Clariant AG; *Int'l*, pg. 1646
CLARIANT CONSULTING AG—See Clariant AG; *Int'l*, pg. 1646
CLARIANT CORPORATION—See Clariant AG; *Int'l*, pg. 1647
CLARIANT CORPORATION—See Clariant AG; *Int'l*, pg. 1647
CLARIANT CORPORATION—See Clariant AG; *Int'l*, pg. 1647
CLARIANT CORPORATION—See Clariant AG; *Int'l*, pg. 1647
CLARIANT (DENMARK) A/S—See Clariant AG; *Int'l*, pg. 1645
CLARIANT (DEUTSCHLAND) GMBH—See Clariant AG; *Int'l*, pg. 1647
CLARIANT DISTRIBUTION UK LIMITED—See Clariant AG; *Int'l*, pg. 1648
CLARIANT (EGYPT) S.A.E.-EGCODAR—See Clariant AG; *Int'l*, pg. 1646
CLARIANT (EGYPT) S.A.E.—See Clariant AG; *Int'l*, pg. 1646
CLARIANT FINANCE (LUXEMBOURG) S.A.—See Clariant AG; *Int'l*, pg. 1647
CLARIANT (FINLAND) OY—See Clariant AG; *Int'l*, pg. 1646
CLARIANT (FRANCE)—See Clariant AG; *Int'l*, pg. 1646
CLARIANT GMBH—See Clariant AG; *Int'l*, pg. 1647
CLARIANT (GULF) FZE—See Clariant AG; *Int'l*, pg. 1646
CLARIANT (HELLAS) S.A.—See Clariant AG; *Int'l*, pg. 1646
CLARIANT HOLDINGS UK LTD.—See Clariant AG; *Int'l*, pg. 1648
CLARIANT HUAJIN CATALYSTS (PANJIN) LTD.—See Clariant AG; *Int'l*, pg. 1647
CLARIANT HUNINGUE—See Clariant AG; *Int'l*, pg. 1646
CLARIANT IBERICA PRODUCCION S.A.—See Clariant AG; *Int'l*, pg. 1647
CLARIANT IBERICA S.A.—See Clariant AG; *Int'l*, pg. 1647
CLARIANT IBERICA SERVICIOS S.L.—See Clariant AG; *Int'l*, pg. 1647
CLARIANT (INDIA) LTD.—See Clariant AG; *Int'l*, pg. 1646
CLARIANT INDUSTRIES (KOREA) LTD.—See Clariant AG; *Int'l*, pg. 1647
CLARIANT (ITALIA) S.P.A.—See Clariant AG; *Int'l*, pg. 1646
CLARIANT (JAPAN) K.K.—See Clariant AG; *Int'l*, pg. 1646
CLARIANT (KOREA) LTD.—See Clariant AG; *Int'l*, pg. 1646
CLARIANT (MALAYSIA) SDN. BHD.—See Clariant AG; *Int'l*, pg. 1646
CLARIANT (MAROC) S.A.—See Clariant AG; *Int'l*, pg. 1646
CLARIANT MASTERBATCHES (BEIJING) LTD—See Clariant AG; *Int'l*, pg. 1645
CLARIANT MASTERBATCHES BENELUX SA—See Clariant AG; *Int'l*, pg. 1647
CLARIANT MASTERBATCHES (DEUTSCHLAND) GMBH—See Clariant AG; *Int'l*, pg. 1647

CLARIANT AG

CLARIANT-MASTERBATCHES DIVISION—See Clariant AG; *Int'l*, pg. 1647
CLARIANT MASTERBATCHES (FINLAND) OY—See Clariant AG; *Int'l*, pg. 1647
CLARIANT MASTERBATCHES IRELAND LIMITED—See Clariant AG; *Int'l*, pg. 1647
CLARIANT MASTERBATCHES (ITALIA) S.P.A.—See Clariant AG; *Int'l*, pg. 1647
CLARIANT MASTERBATCHES (MALAYSIA) SDN BHD—See Clariant AG; *Int'l*, pg. 1645
CLARIANT MASTERBATCHES NORDEN AB—See Clariant AG; *Int'l*, pg. 1647
CLARIANT MASTERBATCHES (SAUDI ARABIA) LTD—See Clariant AG; *Int'l*, pg. 1645
CLARIANT MASTERBATCHES (SHANGHAI) LTD—See Clariant AG; *Int'l*, pg. 1645
CLARIANT MASTERBATCHES THAILAND LTD—See Clariant AG; *Int'l*, pg. 1645
CLARIANT MASTERBATCH GMBH & CO. OHG—See Clariant AG; *Int'l*, pg. 1647
CLARIANT MASTERBATCH IBERICA—See Clariant AG; *Int'l*, pg. 1647
CLARIANT MATERIAL SCIENCE (GUANGZHOU) LTD.—See Avient Corporation; *U.S. Public*, pg. 247
CLARIANT (MEXICO) S.A. DE C.V.—See Clariant AG; *Int'l*, pg. 1646
CLARIANT (NEW ZEALAND) LTD.—See Clariant AG; *Int'l*, pg. 1646
CLARIANT (NORGE) AS—See Clariant AG; *Int'l*, pg. 1646
CLARIANT OIL SERVICES SCANDINAVIA AS—See Clariant AG; *Int'l*, pg. 1646
CLARIANT OIL SERVICES UK LTD.—See Clariant AG; *Int'l*, pg. 1648
CLARIANT (OSTERREICH) GMBH—See Clariant AG; *Int'l*, pg. 1646
CLARIANT PAKISTAN (PRIVATE) LIMITED—See Clariant AG; *Int'l*, pg. 1647
CLARIANT (PERU) S.A.—See Clariant AG; *Int'l*, pg. 1646
CLARIANT PIGMENTS (TIANJIN) LTD—See Clariant AG; *Int'l*, pg. 1647
CLARIANT PLASTICS AND COATINGS (RUS) LLC—See Avient Corporation; *U.S. Public*, pg. 247
CLARIANT PLASTICS & COATINGS (FRANCE)—See Avient Corporation; *U.S. Public*, pg. 247
CLARIANT PLASTICS & COATINGS (ITALIA) S.P.A.—See Avient Corporation; *U.S. Public*, pg. 247
CLARIANT PLASTICS & COATINGS (JAPAN) K.K.—See Clariant AG; *Int'l*, pg. 1647
CLARIANT PLASTICS & COATINGS MEXICO, S.A. DE C.V.—See Clariant AG; *Int'l*, pg. 1647
CLARIANT PLASTICS & COATINGS (POLSKA) SP. Z O.O.—See Avient Corporation; *U.S. Public*, pg. 247
CLARIANT PLASTICS & COATINGS SOUTHERN AFRICA (PTY) LTD.—See Clariant AG; *Int'l*, pg. 1647
CLARIANT PLASTICS & COATINGS (TAIWAN) CO., LTD.—See Avient Corporation; *U.S. Public*, pg. 247
CLARIANT PLASTICS & COATINGS (THAILAND) LTD.—See Avient Corporation; *U.S. Public*, pg. 247
CLARIANT POLAND SPOLKA Z.O.O.—See Clariant AG; *Int'l*, pg. 1647
CLARIANT POLSKA SP. Z.O.O.—See Clariant AG; *Int'l*, pg. 1647
CLARIANT PRODOTTI (ITALIA) S.P.A.—See Clariant AG; *Int'l*, pg. 1647
CLARIANT PRODUCTOS QUIMICOS S.A. DE C.V.—See Clariant AG; *Int'l*, pg. 1646
CLARIANT PRODUCTS (SCHWEIZ) AG—See Clariant AG; *Int'l*, pg. 1647
CLARIANT PRODUKTE (DEUTSCHLAND) GMBH—See Clariant AG; *Int'l*, pg. 1647
CLARIANT QATAR W.L.L.—See Clariant AG; *Int'l*, pg. 1647
CLARIANT QUIMICOS (PORTUGAL) LTD.—See Clariant AG; *Int'l*, pg. 1647
CLARIANT (RUS) LLC—See Clariant AG; *Int'l*, pg. 1646
CLARIANT SANGHO LTD.—See Clariant AG; *Int'l*, pg. 1648
CLARIANT SASOL CATALYSTS LTD.—See Clariant AG; *Int'l*, pg. 1648
CLARIANT S.A.—See Clariant AG; *Int'l*, pg. 1647
CLARIANT SE - BRANCH MUTTENZ—See Clariant AG; *Int'l*, pg. 1648
CLARIANT SERVICES (FRANCE) SAS—See Clariant AG; *Int'l*, pg. 1648
CLARIANT SERVICES (POLAND) SP. Z O.O.—See Clariant AG; *Int'l*, pg. 1648
CLARIANT SERVICES UK LTD—See Clariant AG; *Int'l*, pg. 1648
CLARIANT (SINGAPORE) PTE. LTD.—See Clariant AG; *Int'l*, pg. 1648
CLARIANT SOUTHERN AFRICA (PTY) LTD.—See Clariant AG; *Int'l*, pg. 1648
CLARIANT SPECIALTY CHEMICALS (ZHENJIANG) CO., LTD.—See Clariant AG; *Int'l*, pg. 1648
CLARIANT (SVERIGE) AB—See Clariant AG; *Int'l*, pg. 1646
CLARIANT (TAIWAN) CO. LTD.—See Clariant AG; *Int'l*, pg. 1646

CLARIANT (THAILAND) LTD.—See Clariant AG; *Int'l*, pg. 1646
CLARIANT (TIANJIN) LTD.—See Clariant AG; *Int'l*, pg. 1645
CLARIANT (TIANJIN) PIGMENTS CO. LTD.—See Clariant AG; *Int'l*, pg. 1645
CLARIANT TUNISIE S.A.—See Clariant AG; *Int'l*, pg. 1648
CLARIANT (TURKIYE) A.S.—See Clariant AG; *Int'l*, pg. 1646
CLARIANT UK LTD.—See Clariant AG; *Int'l*, pg. 1648
CLARIANT UKRAINE LLC—See Clariant AG; *Int'l*, pg. 1648
CLARIANT (URUGUAY) SA—See Clariant AG; *Int'l*, pg. 1646
CLARIANT (VENEZUELA) S.A.—See Clariant AG; *Int'l*, pg. 1646
CLARIANT VERWALTUNGSGESELLSCHAFT MBH—See Clariant AG; *Int'l*, pg. 1647
CLARIDGE HOMES INC.; *Int'l*, pg. 1648
CLARIDGE PUBLIC LIMITED; *Int'l*, pg. 1648
CLARIDGE'S HOTEL LIMITED—See Maybourne Hotels Limited; *Int'l*, pg. 4743
CLARIENCE TECHNOLOGIES, LLC—See Genstar Capital, LLC; *U.S. Private*, pg. 1676
CLARI, INC.; *U.S. Private*, pg. 911
CLARIM ACQUISITION CORP.; *U.S. Public*, pg. 507
CLARINDA CO-OP; *U.S. Private*, pg. 911
CLARIN GLOBAL S.A.—See Grupo Clarin S.A.; *Int'l*, pg. 3125
CLARINS BELGIQUE—See Clarins S.A.; *Int'l*, pg. 1648
CLARINS BV—See Clarins S.A.; *Int'l*, pg. 1648
CLARINS CANADA INC.—See Clarins S.A.; *Int'l*, pg. 1648
CLARINS GMBH—See Clarins S.A.; *Int'l*, pg. 1648
CLARINS K.K.—See Clarins S.A.; *Int'l*, pg. 1648
CLARINS KOREA LTD.—See Clarins S.A.; *Int'l*, pg. 1648
CLARINS LTD.—See Clarins S.A.; *Int'l*, pg. 1648
CLARINS PARIS SA—See Clarins S.A.; *Int'l*, pg. 1648
CLARINS PTE. LTD.—See Clarins S.A.; *Int'l*, pg. 1649
CLARINS S.A.; *Int'l*, pg. 1648
CLARINS SA—See Clarins S.A.; *Int'l*, pg. 1649
CLARINS SDN BHD—See Clarins S.A.; *Int'l*, pg. 1649
CLARINS (U.K.) LTD.—See Clarins S.A.; *Int'l*, pg. 1648
CLARINS USA INC.—See Clarins S.A.; *Int'l*, pg. 1649
CLARION ASIA PTE. LTD.—See FORVIA SE; *Int'l*, pg. 2745
CLARION AUSTRALIA PTY. LTD.—See FORVIA SE; *Int'l*, pg. 2745
CLARION BATHWARE INC.; *U.S. Private*, pg. 911
CLARION CANADA, INC.—See FORVIA SE; *Int'l*, pg. 2745
CLARION CAPITAL PARTNERS, LLC; *U.S. Private*, pg. 911
CLARION CO., LTD.—See FORVIA SE; *Int'l*, pg. 2745
CLARION CONSTRUCTION INC.; *U.S. Private*, pg. 911
CLARION CORPORATION OF AMERICA—See FORVIA SE; *Int'l*, pg. 2745
CLARION CORP.—See FORVIA SE; *Int'l*, pg. 2745
CLARION COUNTY COMMUNITY BANK; *U.S. Public*, pg. 507
CLARION DIALYSIS CENTER, LLC—See Nautic Partners, LLC; *U.S. Private*, pg. 2869
CLARION EUROPA GMBH—See FORVIA SE; *Int'l*, pg. 2745
CLARION EUROPE S.A.S.—See FORVIA SE; *Int'l*, pg. 2745
CLARION EVENTS LTD.—See Blackstone Inc.; *U.S. Public*, pg. 360
CLARION (G.B.) LTD.—See FORVIA SE; *Int'l*, pg. 2745
CLARION GRAMERCY (UK) LIMITED—See Franklin Resources, Inc.; *U.S. Public*, pg. 881
CLARION HEALTHCARE, LLC—See Arsenal Capital Management LP; *U.S. Private*, pg. 338
CLARION HIGHLANDER HOTEL AND CONFERENCE CENTER; *U.S. Private*, pg. 911
CLARION (HK) INDUSTRIES CO., LTD—See FORVIA SE; *Int'l*, pg. 2745
CLARION HOSPITAL; *U.S. Private*, pg. 911
CLARION HUNGARY ELECTRONICS KFT—See FORVIA SE; *Int'l*, pg. 2745
THE CLARION-LEDGER—See Gannett Co., Inc.; *U.S. Public*, pg. 900
CLARION (MALAYSIA) SDN. BHD.—See FORVIA SE; *Int'l*, pg. 2745
CLARION MANUFACTURING CORPORATION OF AMERICA—See FORVIA SE; *Int'l*, pg. 2745
CLARION MEDICAL TECHNOLOGIES INC.—See ALPHAEON Corporation; *U.S. Private*, pg. 200
CLARION PARTNERS (DEUTSCHLAND) EUROPE GMBH—See Franklin Resources, Inc.; *U.S. Public*, pg. 879
CLARION PARTNERS, LLC - BOSTON—See Franklin Resources, Inc.; *U.S. Public*, pg. 881
CLARION PARTNERS, LLC—See Franklin Resources, Inc.; *U.S. Public*, pg. 881
CLARION PARTNERS, LLC - WASHINGTON, DC—See Franklin Resources, Inc.; *U.S. Public*, pg. 881
CLARION S.A. AGROINDUSTRIAL; *Int'l*, pg. 1649
CLARION SAFETY SYSTEMS, LLC; *U.S. Private*, pg. 911

CLARION SALES CORPORATION—See FORVIA SE; *Int'l*, pg. 2745
CLARION (TAIWAN) MANUFACTURING CO., LTD.—See FORVIA SE; *Int'l*, pg. 2745
CLARION TECHNOLOGIES, INC. - AMES—See Clarion Technologies, Inc.; *U.S. Private*, pg. 911
CLARION TECHNOLOGIES, INC. - ANDERSON—See Clarion Technologies, Inc.; *U.S. Private*, pg. 911
CLARION TECHNOLOGIES, INC. - CALEDONIA—See Clarion Technologies, Inc.; *U.S. Private*, pg. 911
CLARION TECHNOLOGIES, INC. - GREENVILLE—See Clarion Technologies, Inc.; *U.S. Private*, pg. 911
CLARION TECHNOLOGIES, INC.; *U.S. Private*, pg. 911
CLARIOS GLOBAL GP LLC—See Brookfield Corporation; *Int'l*, pg. 1175
CLARIOS GLOBAL GP LLC—See Caisse de Depot et Placement du Quebec; *Int'l*, pg. 1254
CLARIOS INTERNATIONAL INC.; *U.S. Public*, pg. 507
CLARIOS VARTA HANNOVER GMBH—See Brookfield Corporation; *Int'l*, pg. 1175
CLARIOS VARTA HANNOVER GMBH—See Caisse de Depot et Placement du Quebec; *Int'l*, pg. 1254
CLARIPHY COMMUNICATIONS, INC.—See Marvell Technology Group Ltd.; *Int'l*, pg. 4717
CLARIS LEASING SPA—See Cassa Centrale Banca-Credito Cooperativo del Nord Est SpA; *Int'l*, pg. 1354
CLARIS LIFESCIENCES LTD.; *Int'l*, pg. 1649
CLARISOFT TECHNOLOGIES, LLC—See Modus Create, LLC; *U.S. Private*, pg. 2764
CLARITAS ADMINISTRACAO DE RECURSOS LTDA.—See Principal Financial Group, Inc.; *U.S. Public*, pg. 1720
CLARITAS, INC.—See Brookfield Corporation; *Int'l*, pg. 1180
CLARITAS, INC.—See Brookfield Corporation; *Int'l*, pg. 1180
CLARITAS, INC.—See Elliott Management Corporation; *U.S. Private*, pg. 1373
CLARITAS, INC.—See Elliott Management Corporation; *U.S. Private*, pg. 1373
CLARITAS LLC—See The Carlyle Group Inc.; *U.S. Public*, pg. 2045
CLARITAS PHARMACEUTICALS, INC.; *U.S. Public*, pg. 507
CLARITY CHILD GUIDANCE CENTER; *U.S. Private*, pg. 911
CLARITY COMMERCE SOLUTIONS, INC.—See Heritage Group Ltd.; *Int'l*, pg. 3361
CLARITY COMMERCE SOLUTIONS LTD.—See Heritage Group Ltd.; *Int'l*, pg. 3361
CLARITY COVERDALE FURY ADVERTISING, INC.; *U.S. Private*, pg. 911
CLARITY GOLD CORP.; *Int'l*, pg. 1649
CLARITY IMAGING TECHNOLOGIES, INC.—See Turbon AG; *Int'l*, pg. 7974
CLARITY IMAGING TECHNOLOGIES, INC.—See Turbon AG; *Int'l*, pg. 7974
CLARITY MEDIA GROUP, INC.—See The Anschutz Corporation; *U.S. Private*, pg. 3987
CLARITY MEDICAL GROUP HOLDING LIMITED; *Int'l*, pg. 1649
CLARITY PARTNERS, L.P.; *U.S. Private*, pg. 911
CLARITY PHARMACEUTICALS LIMITED; *Int'l*, pg. 1649
CLARITY RESOURCE GROUP; *U.S. Private*, pg. 912
CLARITY RETAIL SYSTEMS PLC—See Heritage Group Ltd.; *Int'l*, pg. 3361
CLARITY SERVICES, INC.—See Experian plc; *Int'l*, pg. 2586
CLARITYSOFT LLC; *U.S. Private*, pg. 912
CLARITY SOFTWARE SOLUTIONS, INC.; *U.S. Private*, pg. 912
CLARITY SOLUTION GROUP, LLC—See Accenture plc; *Int'l*, pg. 87
CLARITY—See HP Inc.; *U.S. Public*, pg. 1064
CLARITY TELECOM, LLC—See Keystone Group, L.P.; *U.S. Private*, pg. 2297
CLARITY TELECOM, LLC—See Pamlico Capital Management, L.P.; *U.S. Private*, pg. 3083
CLARIVATE ANALYTICS (COMPUMARK) INC.—See Thomson Reuters Corporation; *Int'l*, pg. 7715
CLARIVATE PLC; *Int'l*, pg. 1649
CLARIVEST ASSET MANAGEMENT, LLC—See Raymond James Financial, Inc.; *U.S. Public*, pg. 1764
CLARIZEN, INC.—See K1 Investment Management, LLC; *U.S. Private*, pg. 2252
CLARK AIRPORT SUPPORT SERVICES CORPORATION—See Transnational Diversified Group of Companies; *Int'l*, pg. 7902
CLARK ASSOCIATES, INC.—See GTCR LLC; *U.S. Private*, pg. 1802
CLARK ASSOCIATES, INC.; *U.S. Private*, pg. 912
CLARK & ASSOCIATES OF NEVADA, INC.—See Peter C. Foy & Associates Insurance Services, Inc.; *U.S. Private*, pg. 3157
CLARK & ASSOCIATES; *U.S. Private*, pg. 912
CLARK & BARLOW HARDWARE CO.—See Logan Square Aluminum Supply, Inc.; *U.S. Private*, pg. 2481
CLARK BEVERAGE GROUP, INC.—See C.C. Clark, Inc.; *U.S. Private*, pg. 706

COMPANY NAME INDEX

CLARK BUILDERS LIMITED—See ACS, Actividades de Construccion y Servicios, S.A.; *Int'l*, pg. 113
CLARK CAPITAL MANAGEMENT GROUP, INC.; *U.S. Private*, pg. 912
CLARK & CLARK INC.; *U.S. Private*, pg. 912
CLARK COMMUNICATIONS LIMITED; *Int'l*, pg. 1650
CLARK CONSTRUCTION GROUP - CALIFORNIA, LP—See Clark Enterprises, Inc.; *U.S. Private*, pg. 912
CLARK CONSTRUCTION GROUP - CHICAGO, LLC—See Clark Enterprises, Inc.; *U.S. Private*, pg. 912
CLARK CONSTRUCTION GROUP, LLC—See Clark Enterprises, Inc.; *U.S. Private*, pg. 912
CLARK CONTAINER INCORPORATED; *U.S. Private*, pg. 912
CLARK CONTRACTS LTD; *Int'l*, pg. 1650
CLARK COTTON—See AFGRI Limited; *Int'l*, pg. 188
CLARK COUNTY BANCORPORATION; *U.S. Public*, pg. 507
CLARKCOUNTY CREDIT UNION; *U.S. Private*, pg. 914
CLARK COUNTY PUBLIC TRANSPORTATION BENEFIT AREA; *U.S. Private*, pg. 912
CLARK COUNTY WATER RECLAMATION DISTRICT; *U.S. Private*, pg. 912
CLARK-CUTLER-MCDERMOTT CO.; *U.S. Private*, pg. 914
CLARK DESIGN; *U.S. Private*, pg. 912
CLARK DISTRIBUTING COMPANY, INC. - PADUCAH—See C.C. Clark, Inc.; *U.S. Private*, pg. 706
CLARK DISTRIBUTING COMPANY, INC.—See C.C. Clark, Inc.; *U.S. Private*, pg. 706
CLARK DISTRIBUTION SYSTEMS, INC.- MECHANICSBURG—See Atlas Holdings, LLC; *U.S. Private*, pg. 377
CLARK DISTRIBUTION SYSTEMS, INC.—See Atlas Holdings, LLC; *U.S. Private*, pg. 376
CLARKE ADVERTISING & PUBLIC RELATIONS, INC.; *U.S. Private*, pg. 914
CLARKE CHAPMAN FACILITIES MANAGEMENT LTD.—See Langley Holdings Plc; *Int'l*, pg. 4410
THE CLARKE CHAPMAN GROUP LIMITED—See Langley Holdings Plc; *Int'l*, pg. 4410
CLARKE CHAPMAN MANUFACTURING LTD—See Langley Holdings Plc; *Int'l*, pg. 4410
CLARKE CHAPMAN SERVICES LTD.—See Langley Holdings Plc; *Int'l*, pg. 4410
CLARKE DISTRIBUTORS INC.; *U.S. Private*, pg. 914
CLARKE ELECTRIC COOPERATIVE, INC.; *U.S. Private*, pg. 914
THE CLARKE GROUP; *Int'l*, pg. 7633
CLARKE HEALTH CARE PRODUCTS; *U.S. Private*, pg. 914
CLARKE INC.; *Int'l*, pg. 1650
CLARK ELECTRIC COOPERATIVE; *U.S. Private*, pg. 912
CLARK ELECTRIC DISTRIBUTION CORPORATION—See Manila Electric Company; *Int'l*, pg. 4671
CLARKE-MOBILE COUNTIES GAS DISTRICT; *U.S. Private*, pg. 914
CLARK ENERGY GROUP LLC—See Clark Enterprises, Inc.; *U.S. Private*, pg. 913
CLARK ENGINEERING & SURVEYING, P.C.—See Ryan Biggs Clark Davis, Engineering & Surveying, P.C.; *U.S. Private*, pg. 3509
CLARK ENTERPRISES, INC.; *U.S. Private*, pg. 912
CLARK ENVIRONMENTAL, INC.—See One Rock Capital Partners, LLC; *U.S. Private*, pg. 3022
CLARKE POWER SERVICES, INC.; *U.S. Private*, pg. 914
CLARK EQUIPMENT CO.—See Doosan Corporation; *Int'l*, pg. 2172
CLARKE REAL ESTATE LTD.; *Int'l*, pg. 1650
CLARKE & SAMPSON, INC.—See ABRY Partners, LLC; *U.S. Private*, pg. 41
CLARKE SECURITY SERVICES INCORPORATED—See Stanley Black & Decker, Inc.; *U.S. Public*, pg. 1932
CLARKE SOLUTIONS, LLC—See Lightview Capital LLC; *U.S. Private*, pg. 2454
CLARKE TELECOM LTD.—See Renew Holdings plc; *Int'l*, pg. 6278
CLARKE TRANSPORT INC.—See TFI International Inc.; *Int'l*, pg. 7585
CLARK FARLEY INSURANCE AGENCY, INC.—See Aquiline Capital Partners LLC; *U.S. Private*, pg. 305
CLARK FILTER, INC.—See Parker Hannifin Corporation; *U.S. Public*, pg. 1641
CLARK FORK AND BLACKFOOT, L.L.C.—See NorthWestern Corporation; *U.S. Public*, pg. 1543
CLARK FOUNDATION COMPANY; *U.S. Private*, pg. 913
CLARK FREIGHT LINES INC.; *U.S. Private*, pg. 913
CLARK GAS & OIL COMPANY INC.; *U.S. Private*, pg. 913
CLARK GRAVE VAULT COMPANY; *U.S. Private*, pg. 913
THE CLARK GROUP, INC.—See Atlas Holdings, LLC; *U.S. Private*, pg. 376
CLARK GUM COMPANY—See Slate Capital Group LLC; *U.S. Private*, pg. 3687
CLARK HILL PLC; *U.S. Private*, pg. 913
CLARK HOLDINGS, INC.—See Atlas Holdings, LLC; *U.S. Private*, pg. 376
CLARK HUNT CONSTRUCTION, INC.; *U.S. Private*, pg. 913

CLARK HUOT LLC—See CHR Group LLC; *U.S. Private*, pg. 889
CLARK, INC.; *U.S. Private*, pg. 914
CLARK KNAPP MOTOR COMPANY, LLC.; *U.S. Private*, pg. 913
CLARK MACHINERY COMPANY; *U.S. Private*, pg. 913
CLARK MATERIAL HANDLING ASIA INC.—See Young An Hat Co., Ltd.; *Int'l*, pg. 8602
CLARK MATERIAL HANDLING BRAZIL S.A.—See Young An Hat Co., Ltd.; *Int'l*, pg. 8602
CLARK MATERIAL HANDLING CHILE S.A.—See Young An Hat Co., Ltd.; *Int'l*, pg. 8602
CLARK MATERIAL HANDLING COMPANY—See Young An Hat Co., Ltd.; *Int'l*, pg. 8602
CLARK MATERIAL HANDLING EUROPE GMBH—See Young An Hat Co., Ltd.; *Int'l*, pg. 8602
CLARK MATERIAL HANDLING INTERNATIONAL INC.—See Young An Hat Co., Ltd.; *Int'l*, pg. 8602
CLARK MECHANICAL SERVICES, INC.—See Clark Associates, Inc.; *U.S. Private*, pg. 912
CLARK METAL WORKS—See Clark Pacific; *U.S. Private*, pg. 913
CLARK MOBILE COUNTIES GAS DISTRICT; *U.S. Private*, pg. 913
CLARK-MORTENSON AGENCY, INC.—See ABRY Partners, LLC; *U.S. Private*, pg. 43
CLARK NEXSEN, INC.; *U.S. Private*, pg. 913
CLARK/NIKDEL/POWELL INC.; *U.S. Private*, pg. 914
CLARK OIL CO. INC.; *U.S. Private*, pg. 913
CLARK ORIENT (BVI) LTD.; *Int'l*, pg. 1650
CLARK PACIFIC - FONTANA PLANT—See Clark Pacific; *U.S. Private*, pg. 913
CLARK PACIFIC - IRWINDALE PLANT—See Clark Pacific; *U.S. Private*, pg. 913
CLARK PACIFIC; *U.S. Private*, pg. 913
CLARK PACIFIC - WOODLAND PLANT—See Clark Pacific; *U.S. Private*, pg. 913
CLARK PEST CONTROL, INC.—See Rollins, Inc.; *U.S. Public*, pg. 1809
CLARK PEST CONTROL OF NEVADA, LLC—See Rollins, Inc.; *U.S. Public*, pg. 1809
CLARK PEST CONTROL OF STOCKTON INC.—See Rollins, Inc.; *U.S. Public*, pg. 1809
CLARK PEST CONTROT OF NEVADA, LLC—See Rollins, Inc.; *U.S. Public*, pg. 1809
CLARK-POWELL ASSOCIATES INC.; *U.S. Private*, pg. 914
CLARK PUBLIC UTILITIES; *U.S. Private*, pg. 913
CLARK PULLEY INDUSTRIES INC.—See AF Holding Company; *U.S. Private*, pg. 121
CLARK REALTY BUILDERS LLC; *U.S. Private*, pg. 913
CLARK REALTY CAPITAL, L.L.C.—See Clark Enterprises, Inc.; *U.S. Private*, pg. 913
CLARK REGIONAL PHYSICIAN PRACTICES, LLC—See Apollo Global Management, Inc.; *U.S. Public*, pg. 155
CLARK & REID COMPANY, INC.—See Wheaton Van Lines, Inc.; *U.S. Private*, pg. 4505
CLARK-RELIANCE CORPORATION; *U.S. Private*, pg. 914
CLARK RETIREMENT COMMUNITY; *U.S. Private*, pg. 913
CLARKSBURG TREATMENT CENTER, LLC—See Acadia Healthcare Company, Inc.; *U.S. Public*, pg. 28
CLARK, SCHAEFER, HACKETT & CO.; *U.S. Private*, pg. 914
CLARKS COMPANIES - IT DIVISION—See C&J Clark Limited; *Int'l*, pg. 1239
CLARKS COMPANIES NORTH AMERICA—See C&J Clark Limited; *Int'l*, pg. 1239
CLARKSDALE HMA, LLC—See Curae Health, Inc.; *U.S. Private*, pg. 1124
CLARK SECURITY PRODUCTS, INC.—See WESCO International, Inc.; *U.S. Public*, pg. 2351
CLARKSON ASIA LTD.—See Clarkson PLC; *Int'l*, pg. 1650
CLARKSON ASIA PTE LTD.—See Clarkson PLC; *Int'l*, pg. 1650
CLARKSON AUSTRALIA HOLDINGS PTY LTD—See Clarkson PLC; *Int'l*, pg. 1650
CLARKSON AUSTRALIA (PTY) LIMITED—See Clarkson PLC; *Int'l*, pg. 1650
CLARKSON CONSTRUCTION COMPANY; *U.S. Private*, pg. 915
CLARKSON (DEUTSCHLAND) GMBH—See Clarkson PLC; *Int'l*, pg. 1650
CLARKSON (HELLAS) LIMITED—See Clarkson PLC; *Int'l*, pg. 1650
CLARKSON INVESTMENT SERVICES (DIFC) LIMITED—See Clarkson PLC; *Int'l*, pg. 1650
CLARKSON ITALIA SRL—See Clarkson PLC; *Int'l*, pg. 1650
CLARKSON MELBOURNE PTY LIMITED—See Clarkson PLC; *Int'l*, pg. 1650
CLARKSON NORWAY AS—See Clarkson PLC; *Int'l*, pg. 1650
CLARKSON OVERSEAS SHIPBROKING LIMITED—See Clarkson PLC; *Int'l*, pg. 1650
CLARKSON PARIS SAS—See Clarkson PLC; *Int'l*, pg. 1651
CLARKSON PLC; *Int'l*, pg. 1650

CLARKSON PORT SERVICES LIMITED—See Clarkson PLC; *Int'l*, pg. 1651
CLARKSON RESEARCH HOLDINGS LIMITED—See Clarkson PLC; *Int'l*, pg. 1651
CLARKSON RESEARCH SERVICES LIMITED—See Clarkson PLC; *Int'l*, pg. 1651
CLARKSONS BRASIL LTDA.—See Clarkson PLC; *Int'l*, pg. 1651
CLARKSONS DENMARK ADS—See Clarkson PLC; *Int'l*, pg. 1651
CLARKSONS DEUTSCHLAND GMBH—See Clarkson PLC; *Int'l*, pg. 1651
CLARKSONS DMCC—See Clarkson PLC; *Int'l*, pg. 1651
CLARKSON SECURITIES LIMITED—See Clarkson PLC; *Int'l*, pg. 1651
CLARKSONS ESG CORE PLUS AS—See Clarkson PLC; *Int'l*, pg. 1651
CLARKSON SHIPBROKING (SHANGHAI) CO. LIMITED—See Clarkson PLC; *Int'l*, pg. 1651
CLARKSON SHIPPING SERVICES INDIA PRIVATE LIMITED—See Clarkson PLC; *Int'l*, pg. 1650
CLARKSON SHIPPING SERVICES USA INC.—See Clarkson PLC; *Int'l*, pg. 1651
CLARKSONS JAPAN K.K.—See Clarkson PLC; *Int'l*, pg. 1651
CLARKSONS KOREA LIMITED—See Clarkson PLC; *Int'l*, pg. 1651
CLARKSONS MARTANKERS, S.L.U.—See Clarkson PLC; *Int'l*, pg. 1651
CLARKSONS NETHERLANDS B.V.—See Clarkson PLC; *Int'l*, pg. 1651
CLARKSONS NORWAY AS—See Clarkson PLC; *Int'l*, pg. 1651
CLARKSONS SOUTH AFRICA (PTY) LIMITED—See Clarkson PLC; *Int'l*, pg. 1651
CLARKSONS PLATOU ASIA LIMITED—See Clarkson PLC; *Int'l*, pg. 1651
CLARKSONS PLATOU ASIA PTE. LIMITED—See Clarkson PLC; *Int'l*, pg. 1651
CLARKSONS PLATOU AS—See Clarkson PLC; *Int'l*, pg. 1650
CLARKSONS PLATOU (AUSTRALIA) PTY LIMITED—See Clarkson PLC; *Int'l*, pg. 1651
CLARKSONS PLATOU (BRASIL) LTDA.—See Clarkson PLC; *Int'l*, pg. 1651
CLARKSONS PLATOU (DENMARK) APS—See Clarkson PLC; *Int'l*, pg. 1651
CLARKSONS PLATOU DMCC—See Clarkson PLC; *Int'l*, pg. 1651
CLARKSONS PLATOU GMBH—See Clarkson PLC; *Int'l*, pg. 1651
CLARKSONS PLATOU JAPAN K.K.—See Clarkson PLC; *Int'l*, pg. 1651
CLARKSONS PLATOU (KOREA) COMPANY LIMITED—See Clarkson PLC; *Int'l*, pg. 1651
CLARKSONS PLATOU (NEDERLAND) B.V.—See Clarkson PLC; *Int'l*, pg. 1651
CLARKSONS PLATOU SECURITIES AS—See Clarkson PLC; *Int'l*, pg. 1650
CLARKSONS PLATOU SHIPBROKING (SWITZERLAND) SA—See Clarkson PLC; *Int'l*, pg. 1651
CLARKSONS PLATOU (SOUTH AFRICA) (PTY) LIMITED—See Clarkson PLC; *Int'l*, pg. 1651
CLARKSONS PLATOU (SWEDEN) AB—See Clarkson PLC; *Int'l*, pg. 1651
CLARKSONS PLATOU (USA) INC.—See Clarkson PLC; *Int'l*, pg. 1651
CLARKSONS SECURITIES CANADA INC.—See Clarkson PLC; *Int'l*, pg. 1651
CLARKSONS SECURITIES INC.—See Clarkson PLC; *Int'l*, pg. 1651
CLARKSONS SINGAPORE PTE. LIMITED—See Clarkson PLC; *Int'l*, pg. 1651
CLARKSONS SOUTH AFRICA (PTY.) LTD.—See Clarkson PLC; *Int'l*, pg. 1651
CLARKSONS SWEDEN AB—See Clarkson PLC; *Int'l*, pg. 1651
CLARKSONS SWITZERLAND S.A.—See Clarkson PLC; *Int'l*, pg. 1651
CLARKSON VALUATIONS LIMITED—See Clarkson PLC; *Int'l*, pg. 1651
CLARKS QUALITY ROOFING INC.; *U.S. Private*, pg. 914
CLARK STEEL FABRICATORS, INC.; *U.S. Private*, pg. 914
CLARK STEEL FRAMING SYSTEMS—See Clark Steel Fabricators, Inc.; *U.S. Private*, pg. 914
CLARKSTON ASC PARTNERS, LLC—See Tenet Healthcare Corporation; *U.S. Public*, pg. 2010
CLARKSTOWN INTERNATIONAL COLLISION, INC.; *U.S. Private*, pg. 915
CLARK'S UK LIMITED—See The Hain Celestial Group, Inc.; *U.S. Public*, pg. 2086
CLARK & SULLIVAN CONSTRUCTION, INC.; *U.S. Private*, pg. 915
CLARK & SULLIVAN CONSTRUCTORS INC.—See C.S. General Inc.; *U.S. Private*, pg. 709
CLARKSVILLE HOME CARE SERVICES, LLC—See Community Health Systems, Inc.; *U.S. Public*, pg. 552

CLARKSVILLE MEDICAL CENTER, G.P.—See Community Health Systems, Inc.; *U.S. Public*, pg. 552
CLARKSVILLE OIL & GAS COMPANY INC.; *U.S. Private*, pg. 915
CLARKSVILLE SURGERY CENTER, LLC—See Tenet Healthcare Corporation; *U.S. Public*, pg. 2010
CLARKSVILLE SURGICENTER, LLC—See HCA Healthcare, Inc.; *U.S. Public*, pg. 993
CLARKSVILLE TREATMENT CENTER, LLC—See Acadia Healthcare Company, Inc.; *U.S. Public*, pg. 28
CLARK THOMSON INSURANCE BROKERS LIMITED—See Marsh & McLennan Companies, Inc.; *U.S. Public*, pg. 1374
CLARK TIRE & AUTO INCORPORATED; *U.S. Private*, pg. 914
CLARK TRANSFER INC.; *U.S. Private*, pg. 914
CLARK TRUCK EQUIPMENT—See Harsh International, Inc.; *Int'l*, pg. 1872
CLARK WATER CORPORATION—See Manila Water Company, Inc.; *Int'l*, pg. 4671
CLARK WAYLAND BUILDERS L.C.; *U.S. Private*, pg. 914
CLARKWESTERN BUILDING SYSTEMS, INC.—See ITOCHU Corporation; *Int'l*, pg. 3840
CLARKWESTERN BUILDING SYSTEMS, INC.—See Marubeni Corporation; *Int'l*, pg. 4709
CLARMIL MANUFACTURING CORPORATION; *U.S. Private*, pg. 915
CLARO CHILE S.A.—See America Movil, S.A.B. de C.V.; *Int'l*, pg. 421
CLAROCITY CORPORATION; *U.S. Public*, pg. 507
CLARO PANAMA, S.A.—See Liberty Global plc; *Int'l*, pg. 4485
CLARO PRODUCTS GMBH; *Int'l*, pg. 1651
CLARO S.A.—See America Movil, S.A.B. de C.V.; *Int'l*, pg. 421
CLARO'S ITALIAN MARKET, INC.; *U.S. Private*, pg. 915
CLARO TELECOM PARTICIPACOES, S.A.—See America Movil, S.A.B. de C.V.; *Int'l*, pg. 421
CLARUS COMMERCE LLC—See Marlin Equity Partners, LLC; *U.S. Private*, pg. 2584
CLARUS CORPORATION; *U.S. Public*, pg. 507
CLARUS THERAPEUTICS HOLDINGS, INC.; *U.S. Public*, pg. 508
CLARUS THERAPEUTICS, INC.—See Clarus Therapeutics Holdings, Inc.; *U.S. Public*, pg. 508
CLARUS VENTURES LLC—See Blackstone Inc.; *U.S. Public*, pg. 352
CLARUS VENTURES LLC—See Blackstone Inc.; *U.S. Public*, pg. 352
CLARVIEW REST HOME INC.; *U.S. Private*, pg. 915
CLARY BUSINESS MACHINES COMPANY; *U.S. Private*, pg. 915
CLARY CORPORATION; *U.S. Private*, pg. 915
CLARY HOOD, INC.; *U.S. Private*, pg. 915
CLARY SOLAR; *U.S. Private*, pg. 915
CLAS OHLSON AB; *Int'l*, pg. 1651
CLAS OHLSON AS—See Clas Ohlson AB; *Int'l*, pg. 1651
CLAS OHLSON LTD.—See Clas Ohlson AB; *Int'l*, pg. 1651
CLAS OHLSON OY—See Clas Ohlson AB; *Int'l*, pg. 1652
CLASON PONTIAC BUICK-GMC INC.; *U.S. Private*, pg. 915
CLASQUIN AUSTRALIA PTY LTD.—See Clasquin S.A.; *Int'l*, pg. 1652
CLASQUIN BURKINA FASO LTD.—See Clasquin S.A.; *Int'l*, pg. 1652
CLASQUIN CHILE SPA—See Clasquin S.A.; *Int'l*, pg. 1652
CLASQUIND INDIA PVT. LTD.—See Clasquin S.A.; *Int'l*, pg. 1652
CLASQUIN ESPANA S.L.—See Clasquin S.A.; *Int'l*, pg. 1652
CLASQUIN (FAR EAST) LTD.—See Clasquin S.A.; *Int'l*, pg. 1652
CLASQUIN FAR EAST LTD.—See Clasquin S.A.; *Int'l*, pg. 1652
CLASQUIN INDIA PVT. LTD.—See Clasquin S.A.; *Int'l*, pg. 1652
CLASQUIN INTERNATIONAL TAIWAN LTD.—See Clasquin S.A.; *Int'l*, pg. 1652
CLASQUIN ITALIA S.R.L.—See Clasquin S.A.; *Int'l*, pg. 1652
CLASQUIN JAPAN CO. LTD.—See Clasquin S.A.; *Int'l*, pg. 1652
CLASQUIN KOREA CO. LTD.—See Clasquin S.A.; *Int'l*, pg. 1652
CLASQUIN MALAYSIA SDN BHD—See Clasquin S.A.; *Int'l*, pg. 1652
CLASQUIN PORTUGAL LDA.—See Clasquin S.A.; *Int'l*, pg. 1652
CLASQUIN S.A.; *Int'l*, pg. 1652
CLASQUIN SHANGHAI LTD.—See Clasquin S.A.; *Int'l*, pg. 1652
CLASQUIN SINGAPORE PTE. LTD.—See Clasquin S.A.; *Int'l*, pg. 1652
CLASQUIN THAILAND (CO.) LTD.—See Clasquin S.A.; *Int'l*, pg. 1652
CLASQUIN USA INC—See Clasquin S.A.; *Int'l*, pg. 1652
CLASQUIN VIETNAM LTD.—See Clasquin S.A.; *Int'l*, pg. 1652

CLASS 1 NICKEL & TECHNOLOGIES LIMITED; *Int'l*, pg. 1652
CLASS 1—See IDEX Corp; *U.S. Public*, pg. 1090
CLASS ACCELERATION CORP.; *U.S. Public*, pg. 508
CLASS A NETWORK CO., LTD.—See Medipal Holdings Corporation; *Int'l*, pg. 4779
CLASSBOOK.COM; *U.S. Private*, pg. 916
CLASS EDITORI S.P.A.; *Int'l*, pg. 1652
CLASS EIGHT TRUCK REPAIR INC.—See The Mennel Milling Company; *U.S. Private*, pg. 4077
CLASSES USA, INC.—See RockBridge Growth Equity, LLC; *U.S. Private*, pg. 3465
CL ASSET HOLDINGS, LIMITED; *Int'l*, pg. 1640
THE CLASS HYOSUNG CO., LTD.; *Int'l*, pg. 7633
CLASSIC ACCESSORIES, LLC—See Z Capital Group, LLC; *U.S. Private*, pg. 4595
CLASSIC ADVANTAGE SDN BHD—See Fu Yu Corporation Limited; *Int'l*, pg. 2801
CLASSIC AIR'S ONE HOUR HEATING & AIR CONDITIONING; *U.S. Private*, pg. 916
CLASSICAL KING FM 98.1; *U.S. Private*, pg. 917
CLASSICAL NUMISMATIC GROUP, INC.; *U.S. Private*, pg. 917
CLASSICAL SOUTH FLORIDA INC—See American Public Media Group; *U.S. Private*, pg. 244
CLASSIC AMERICAN HARDWOODS INC.; *U.S. Private*, pg. 916
CLASSIC AUTO GROUP, INC.—See Penske Automotive Group, Inc.; *U.S. Public*, pg. 1664
CLASSIC AVIATION INC.; *U.S. Private*, pg. 916
CLASSIC BANK; *U.S. Private*, pg. 916
CLASSIC BUILDERS, INC.—See D.R. Horton, Inc.; *U.S. Public*, pg. 619
CLASSIC CADILLAC GMC; *U.S. Private*, pg. 916
CLASSIC CARRIERS, INC.; *U.S. Private*, pg. 916
CLASSIC CHEVROLET INC.; *U.S. Private*, pg. 916
CLASSIC CHEVROLET, INC.; *U.S. Private*, pg. 916
CLASSIC COACHES (CONTINENTAL) LIMITED—See Deutsche Bahn AG; *Int'l*, pg. 2049
CLASSIC COLLECTION HOLIDAYS LIMITED—See On the Beach Group plc; *Int'l*, pg. 5573
CLASSIC COLLISION, INC.; *U.S. Private*, pg. 916
CLASSIC COMMUNICATIONS, INC.—See Altice USA, Inc.; *U.S. Public*, pg. 88
CLASSIC COMPONENTS CORP.; *U.S. Private*, pg. 916
CLASSIC COMPONENTS FRANCE—See Classic Components Corp.; *U.S. Private*, pg. 916
CLASSIC COSMETICS, INC.; *U.S. Private*, pg. 916
CLASSIC DISTRIBUTING & BEVERAGE GROUP, INC.; *U.S. Private*, pg. 916
CLASSIC DREAM PROPERTIES LTD.; *Int'l*, pg. 1652
CLASSIC EGG PRODUCTS INC.—See Moark Productions Inc.; *U.S. Private*, pg. 2756
CLASSIC ELECTRICALS LIMITED; *Int'l*, pg. 1652
CLASSIC EQUINE EQUIPMENT, LLC—See Morton Buildings Inc.; *U.S. Private*, pg. 2792
CLASSIC FILAMENTS LIMITED; *Int'l*, pg. 1652
CLASSIC FINANCE PTY. LTD.—See Earlypay Ltd.; *Int'l*, pg. 2267
CLASSIC FINE FOODS (HONG KONG) LIMITED—See Metro AG; *Int'l*, pg. 4856
CLASSIC FINE FOODS JAPAN HOLDINGS—See Metro AG; *Int'l*, pg. 4856
CLASSIC FINE FOODS (MACAU) LTD.—See Metro AG; *Int'l*, pg. 4856
CLASSIC FINE FOODS PHILIPPINES INC.—See Metro AG; *Int'l*, pg. 4856
CLASSIC FINE FOODS SDN BHD—See Metro AG; *Int'l*, pg. 4857
CLASSIC FINE FOODS (SINGAPORE) PRIVATE LIMITED—See Metro AG; *Int'l*, pg. 4856
CLASSIC FINE FOODSTUFF TRADING LLC—See Metro AG; *Int'l*, pg. 4857
CLASSIC FINE FOODS UK LIMITED—See Metro AG; *Int'l*, pg. 4857
CLASSIC FINE FOODS (VIETNAM) LIMITED—See Metro AG; *Int'l*, pg. 4856
CLASSIC FM—See Global Radio Group Limited; *Int'l*, pg. 3000
CLASSIC FOODS, L.P.; *U.S. Private*, pg. 916
CLASSIC FOODS LTD.; *U.S. Private*, pg. 916
CLASSIC FORWARDING INC.; *U.S. Private*, pg. 916
CLASSIC GLOBAL FINANCE & CAPITAL LTD.; *Int'l*, pg. 1652
CLASSIC GRAPHICS, LLC—See Keystone Group, L.P.; *U.S. Private*, pg. 2298
CLASSIC HONDA—See The AutoPlanet Group Inc.; *Int'l*, pg. 7614
CLASSIC HOSPITALS, LTD.—See Spire Healthcare Group plc; *Int'l*, pg. 7139
CLASSIC HOTELS & RESORTS—See Grossman Company Properties, Inc.; *U.S. Private*, pg. 1792
CLASSIC IMPORTS, INC.—See Penske Automotive Group, Inc.; *U.S. Public*, pg. 1664
CLASSIC INDUSTRIAL SERVICES, INC.—See APi Group Corporation; *U.S. Public*, pg. 513
CLASSIC INDUSTRIES CORP; *U.S. Private*, pg. 916
CLASSIC INSTRUMENTS; *U.S. Private*, pg. 916

CLASSIC INSURANCE SERVICES LIMITED—See White Mountains Insurance Group, Ltd.; *U.S. Public*, pg. 2368
CLASSIC INTERNATIONAL ARMORING—See Classic Limousine Inc.; *U.S. Private*, pg. 916
CLASSIC INTERNATIONAL, INC.; *U.S. Private*, pg. 916
CLASSIC JOURNEYS, LLC—See Lindblad Expeditions Holdings, Inc.; *U.S. Public*, pg. 1319
CLASSIC LEASING & FINANCE LTD.; *Int'l*, pg. 1653
CLASSIC LEATHER, INC.; *U.S. Private*, pg. 916
CLASSIC LIFE INSURANCE—See Assicurazioni Generali S.p.A.; *Int'l*, pg. 646
CLASSIC LIMOUSINE INC.; *U.S. Private*, pg. 916
CLASSIC MINERALS LIMITED; *Int'l*, pg. 1653
CLASSIC MOTORS LTD—See ANSA McAL Limited; *Int'l*, pg. 477
CLASSIC NUMBER TRADING 80 (PTY) LIMITED—See Reunert Limited; *Int'l*, pg. 6312
CLASSIC OAK PRODUCTS (AUS) PTY LTD—See Tonnellerie Francois Freres; *Int'l*, pg. 7810
CLASSIC OAK PRODUCTS (NZ) LTD—See Tonnellerie Francois Freres; *Int'l*, pg. 7810
CLASSIC OPTICAL LABORATORIES, INC.—See EssilorLuxottica SA; *Int'l*, pg. 2513
CLASSIC PARTY RENTALS, INC. - DALLAS—See Apollo Global Management, Inc.; *U.S. Public*, pg. 149
CLASSIC PARTY RENTALS, INC. - EL SEGUNDO—See Apollo Global Management, Inc.; *U.S. Public*, pg. 149
CLASSIC PARTY RENTALS, INC. - PHOENIX—See Apollo Global Management, Inc.; *U.S. Public*, pg. 149
CLASSIC PARTY RENTALS, INC. - SAN DIEGO—See Apollo Global Management, Inc.; *U.S. Public*, pg. 149
CLASSIC PARTY RENTALS, INC.—See Apollo Global Management, Inc.; *U.S. Public*, pg. 149
CLASSIC PRECISION, LLC—See Carlisle Companies Incorporated; *U.S. Public*, pg. 436
CLASSIC PRODUCTS CORP.; *U.S. Private*, pg. 916
CLASSIC RESIDENCE BY HYATT—See Hyatt Hotels Corporation; *U.S. Public*, pg. 1076
CLASSIC SCENIC BERHAD; *Int'l*, pg. 1653
CLASSIC SOFT TRIM INC.; *U.S. Private*, pg. 916
CLASSIC SOLUTIONS, INC.—See Bain Capital, LP; *U.S. Private*, pg. 440
CLASSIC TILE INC.; *U.S. Private*, pg. 916
CLASSIC TRANSPORT, INC.; *U.S. Private*, pg. 917
CLASSIC TURNING, INC.; *U.S. Private*, pg. 917
CLASSIC-TYLER MOTORS INC.—See Southeast Texas Classic Automotive; *U.S. Private*, pg. 3726
CLASSIC VACATIONS, LLC—See Expedia Group, Inc.; *U.S. Public*, pg. 809
CLASSIC WINE IMPORTS, INC.—See Martignetti Companies; *U.S. Private*, pg. 2594
CLASSIFIED ADVERTISING PLUS, LLC; *U.S. Private*, pg. 917
CLASSIFIED GROUP; *Int'l*, pg. 1653
CLASSIFIED SOLUTIONS GROUP, INC.; *U.S. Private*, pg. 917
CLASSIQUE FOOTWEAR INC.; *U.S. Private*, pg. 917
CLASSITA HOLDINGS BERHAD; *Int'l*, pg. 1653
CLASSITA (M) SDN. BHD.—See Classita Holdings Berhad; *Int'l*, pg. 1653
CLASS LEASING, LLC—See Reliant Asset Management LLC; *U.S. Private*, pg. 3395
CLASS LIMITED—See HUB24 Limited; *Int'l*, pg. 3516
CLASS MEASURES INC.—See Tribal Group plc; *Int'l*, pg. 7919
CLASS NORDOSTBAYERN GMBH & CO. KG—See BayWa AG; *Int'l*, pg. 917
CLASSROOM ESSENTIALS ONLINE; *U.S. Private*, pg. 917
CLASSROOM TECHNOLOGY SOLUTIONS, INC.—See Galaxy Next Generation, Inc.; *U.S. Public*, pg. 895
CLASS SUDOSTBAYERN GMBH—See BayWa AG; *Int'l*, pg. 917
CLASS TECHNOLOGIES INC.; *U.S. Private*, pg. 915
CLASS VALUATION, LLC—See Gridiron Capital, LLC; *U.S. Private*, pg. 1786
CLASSYAUTO.COM; *U.S. Private*, pg. 917
CLASSY CLOSETS ETC INC.; *U.S. Private*, pg. 917
CLASSYS INC.; *Int'l*, pg. 1653
CLATSOP COMMUNITY BANK—See Lewis & Clark Bank; *U.S. Public*, pg. 1309
CLAUD BUTLER LIMITED—See Tandem Group PLC; *Int'l*, pg. 7456
CLAUDE GABLE CO. INC.; *U.S. Private*, pg. 917
CLAUDE LAVAL CORPORATION—See Lindsay Corporation; *U.S. Public*, pg. 1319
CLAUDE NEON PTY LTD—See TVG Capital Partners Limited; *Int'l*, pg. 7988
CLAUDE NOLAN CADILLAC INC.; *U.S. Private*, pg. 917
CLAUDE OUTDOOR PTY LTD—See TVG Capital Partners Limited; *Int'l*, pg. 7988
CLAUDIUS PETERS (AMERICAS) INC.—See Langley Holdings Plc; *Int'l*, pg. 4409
CLAUDIUS PETERS (ASIA PACIFIC) PTE LTD.—See Langley Holdings Plc; *Int'l*, pg. 4409
CLAUDIUS PETERS AUTOMATION SRL—See Langley Holdings Plc; *Int'l*, pg. 4409
CLAUDIUS PETERS (CHINA) LTD.—See Langley Holdings Plc; *Int'l*, pg. 4409

COMPANY NAME INDEX

CLAUDIUS PETERS DO BRASIL LTDA.—See Langley Holdings Plc; *Int'l*, pg. 4410
CLAUDIUS PETERS GROUP GMBH—See Langley Holdings Plc; *Int'l*, pg. 4409
CLAUDIUS PETERS (IBERICA) SA—See Langley Holdings Plc; *Int'l*, pg. 4409
CLAUDIUS PETERS (INDIA) PVT. LTD—See Langley Holdings Plc; *Int'l*, pg. 4409
CLAUDIUS PETERS (ITALIANA) S.R.L.—See Langley Holdings Plc; *Int'l*, pg. 4409
CLAUDIUS PETERS MACHINERY SERVICE CO. LTD.—See Langley Holdings Plc; *Int'l*, pg. 4409
CLAUDIUS PETERS ROMANIA S.R.L.—See Langley Holdings Plc; *Int'l*, pg. 4409
CLAUDIUS PETERS TECHNOLOGIES GMBH—See Langley Holdings Plc; *Int'l*, pg. 4409
CLAUDIUS PETERS TECHNOLOGIES S.A.—See Langley Holdings Plc; *Int'l*, pg. 4409
CLAUDIUS PETERS (UK) LTD.—See Langley Holdings Plc; *Int'l*, pg. 4409
CLAUSAL COMPUTING OY; *Int'l*, pg. 1653
CLAUSEN & BOSSE GMBH—See Chevrillon Philippe Industrie; *Int'l*, pg. 1474
CLAUSE S.A.—See Groupe Limagrain Holding SA; *Int'l*, pg. 3108
CLAUSE-TEZIER S.A.—See Groupe Limagrain Holding SA; *Int'l*, pg. 3108
CLAUS ETTENSBERGER CORPORATION; *U.S. Private*, pg. 917
CLAUSING INDUSTRIAL INC—See The 600 Group PLC; *Int'l*, pg. 7609
CLAUS QUECK GMBH—See Hutter & Schrantz PMS Ges.m.b.H; *Int'l*, pg. 3540
CLAUSSEN PICKLE CO.—See 3G Capital Inc.; *U.S. Private*, pg. 10
CLAUSSEN PICKLE CO.—See Berkshire Hathaway Inc.; *U.S. Public*, pg. 317
CLA-VAL AUTOMATIC CONTROL VALVES—See Griswold Industries, Inc.; *U.S. Private*, pg. 1790
CLA-VAL CANADA CORP.—See Griswold Industries, Inc.; *U.S. Private*, pg. 1790
CLA-VAL PACIFIC—See Griswold Industries, Inc.; *U.S. Private*, pg. 1791
CLAVERACK RURAL ELECTRIC COOPERATIVE; *U.S. Private*, pg. 917
CLAVIAG AG—See GIC Pte. Ltd.; *Int'l*, pg. 2968
CLAVIAG AG—See The Carlyle Group Inc.; *U.S. Public*, pg. 2051
C&L AVIATION SERVICES—See C&L Aerospace Pty Ltd.; *Int'l*, pg. 1239
CLAVIS TECHNOLOGIES INTERNATIONAL CO., LTD.; *Int'l*, pg. 1653
CLAVISTER HOLDING AB; *Int'l*, pg. 1653
CLAWSON COMMUNICATIONS INC; *U.S. Private*, pg. 917
CLAXSON INTERACTIVE GROUP, INC.; *Int'l*, pg. 1653
CLAXTON ENGINEERING SERVICES LTD—See Buckthorn Partners LLP; *Int'l*, pg. 1210
CLAXTON ENGINEERING SERVICES LTD—See OEP Capital Advisors, L.P.; *U.S. Private*, pg. 2997
CLAXTON-HEPBURN MEDICAL CENTER; *U.S. Private*, pg. 917
CLAYCO CONSTRUCTION COMPANY INC.; *U.S. Private*, pg. 918
CLAY COUNTY ELECTRIC COOPERATIVE CORPORATION; *U.S. Private*, pg. 917
CLAY COUNTY HOSPITAL HOMECARE, LLC—See UnitedHealth Group Incorporated; *U.S. Public*, pg. 2244
CLAY COUNTY RURAL TELEPHONE COOPERATIVE, INC.; *U.S. Private*, pg. 917
CLAY COUNTY SAVINGS BANK—See CCSB Financial Corp.; *U.S. Public*, pg. 461
CLAYDELLE HEALTHCARE, INC.—See The Ensign Group, Inc.; *U.S. Public*, pg. 2070
CLAY ELECTRIC COOPERATIVE INC.; *U.S. Private*, pg. 917
CLAYENS NP GROUP—See OEP Capital Advisors, L.P.; *U.S. Private*, pg. 2998
CLAY HOME MEDICAL, INC.—See AdaptHealth Corp.; *U.S. Public*, pg. 38
CLAY INGELS COMPANY, LLC; *U.S. Private*, pg. 917
CLAY LACY AVIATION INC.; *U.S. Private*, pg. 917
CLAYMAN ADVERTISING; *U.S. Private*, pg. 917
CLAY MORE INNOVATION LAB CO., LTD.—See AP (Thailand) Public Company Limited; *Int'l*, pg. 499
CLAYMORE SILVER BULLION TRUST; *Int'l*, pg. 1653
CLAYMOUNT ASSEMBLIES PHILIPPINES, INC.—See Varex Imaging Corporation; *U.S. Public*, pg. 2275
CLAYMOUNT HIGH VOLTAGE TECHNOLOGIES (BEIJING) CO. LTD.—See Varex Imaging Corporation; *U.S. Public*, pg. 2275
CLAYMOUNT SWITZERLAND AG—See Varex Imaging Corporation; *U.S. Public*, pg. 2275
CLAY NISSAN; *U.S. Private*, pg. 918
CLAY OIL CORP.; *U.S. Private*, pg. 918
CLAY PAKY S.P.A.—See ams AG; *Int'l*, pg. 438
CLAYS LIMITED—See Pozzoni S.p.A.; *Int'l*, pg. 5949
CLAYS & MINERALS (THAILAND) LTD.—See SCR Sibelco SA; *Int'l*, pg. 6654

CLAY TERRACE PARTNERS, LLC—See Washington Prime Group Inc.; *U.S. Private*, pg. 4448
CLAYTEX SERVICES LTD.—See Addnode Group AB; *Int'l*, pg. 130
CLAYTEX USA INC.—See Addnode Group AB; *Int'l*, pg. 130
CLAYTON BLOCK CO. INC.; *U.S. Private*, pg. 918
CLAYTON CONSTRUCTION CO. LTD.; *Int'l*, pg. 1653
CLAYTON CORPORATION; *U.S. Private*, pg. 918
CLAYTON COUNTY WATER AUTHORITY; *U.S. Private*, pg. 918
CLAYTON-DAVIS & ASSOCIATES, INCORPORATED; *U.S. Private*, pg. 930
CLAYTON DE FRANCE, S.A.R.L.—See Clayton Industries Co.; *U.S. Private*, pg. 918
CLAYTON DE MEXICO, SA DE C.V—See Clayton Industries Co.; *U.S. Private*, pg. 918
CLAYTON DEUTSCHLAND GMBH—See Clayton Industries Co.; *U.S. Private*, pg. 918
CLAYTON, DUBILIER & RICE, LLC; *U.S. Private*, pg. 918
CLAYTON ENGINEERING COMPANY; *U.S. Private*, pg. 918
CLAYTON EURO RISK, LTD.—See Radian Group, Inc.; *U.S. Public*, pg. 1759
CLAYTON FIXED INCOME SERVICES, INC.—See Radian Group, Inc.; *U.S. Public*, pg. 1759
CLAYTON GLASS LTD.; *Int'l*, pg. 1653
CLAYTON GROUP HOLDINGS INC.—See Radian Group, Inc.; *U.S. Public*, pg. 1759
CLAYTON HC, INC.; *U.S. Private*, pg. 918
CLAYTON HOLDINGS, INC.—See Radian Group, Inc.; *U.S. Public*, pg. 1759
CLAYTON HOLDINGS UK, LTD.—See Radian Group, Inc.; *U.S. Public*, pg. 1759
CLAYTON HOMES, INC.—See Berkshire Hathaway Inc.; *U.S. Public*, pg. 304
CLAYTON INDUSTRIES CO.; *U.S. Private*, pg. 918
CLAYTON & LAMBERT MANUFACTURING CO.; *U.S. Public*, pg. 508
CLAYTON-MARCUS COMPANY, INC.—See Sun Capital Partners, Inc.; *U.S. Private*, pg. 3860
CLAYTON METALS, INC.—See Reliance Steel & Aluminum Co.; *U.S. Public*, pg. 1779
CLAYTON NEDERLAND B.V.—See Clayton Industries Co.; *U.S. Private*, pg. 918
CLAYTON OF BELGIUM N.V.—See Clayton Industries Co.; *U.S. Private*, pg. 918
CLAYTON PLASTICS CORP.—See Clayton Corporation; *U.S. Private*, pg. 918
CLAYTON PROPERTIES GROUP, INC.—See Berkshire Hathaway Inc.; *U.S. Public*, pg. 304
CLAYTON SALES & SERVICE LTD.—See Clayton Industries Co.; *U.S. Private*, pg. 918
CLAYTON SCANDINAVIA A/S—See Clayton Industries Co.; *U.S. Private*, pg. 918
CLAYTON SERVICES, LLC—See Covius Holdings, Inc.; *U.S. Private*, pg. 1073
CLAYTON SISTEMAS DE VAPOR, S. L.—See Clayton Industries Co.; *U.S. Private*, pg. 918
CLAYTON THERMAL PRODUCTS, LTD.—See Clayton Industries Co.; *U.S. Private*, pg. 918
CLAYTON WATKINS CONSTRUCTION COMPANY, INC.; *U.S. Private*, pg. 918
C LAZY U RANCH, INC.; *U.S. Private*, pg. 701
C.L. BARNES FURNITURE CO.; *U.S. Private*, pg. 708
CLBL, INC.; *U.S. Private*, pg. 930
CLC CONSTRUCTION GROUP INC.; *U.S. Private*, pg. 930
CLC CONTRACTORS LTD.—See H.I.G. Capital, LLC; *U.S. Private*, pg. 1827
CLC GROUP, INC.—See Corpay, Inc.; *U.S. Public*, pg. 579
CLC GROUP LIMITED—See H.I.G. Capital, LLC; *U.S. Private*, pg. 1827
CLC INDUSTRIES LIMITED; *Int'l*, pg. 1653
CL COATINGS, LLC—See North American Coatings, Inc.; *U.S. Private*, pg. 2940
CL&D GRAPHICS, INC.; *U.S. Private*, pg. 909
C&L DISTRIBUTING; *U.S. Private*, pg. 703
CLD PACIFIC GRAIN LLC—See Cargill, Inc.; *U.S. Private*, pg. 754
CLD PACIFIC GRAIN LLC—See Louis Dreyfus S.A.S.; *Int'l*, pg. 4562
CLEA JAPAN, INC.—See Central Institute for Experimental Animals; *Int'l*, pg. 1408
CLEAN AIR BIKE GMBH—See Masterflex SE; *Int'l*, pg. 4725
CLEAN AIR ENGINEERING INC.; *U.S. Private*, pg. 931
CLEAN AIR GARDENING; *U.S. Private*, pg. 931
CLEAN AIR, INC.—See Ingersoll Rand Inc.; *U.S. Public*, pg. 1120
CLEAN AIR LIMITED—See Perrott Engineering Group Ltd.; *Int'l*, pg. 5814
CLEAN AIR METALS, INC.; *Int'l*, pg. 1654
CLEANAIR SOLUTIONS, INC.; *U.S. Private*, pg. 931
CLEANAWAY COMPANY LIMITED; *Int'l*, pg. 1654
CLEANAWAY DANIELS NSW PTY LTD—See Cleanaway Waste Management Limited; *Int'l*, pg. 1654
CLEANAWAY DANIELS VIC PTY LTD—See Cleanaway Waste Management Limited; *Int'l*, pg. 1654

CLEANGOAL ENERGY, CORP.

CLEANAWAY ENTERPRISE COMPANY LIMITED—See Cleanaway Company Limited; *Int'l*, pg. 1654
CLEANAWAY INDUSTRIES PTY LTD.—See Cleanaway Waste Management Limited; *Int'l*, pg. 1654
CLEANAWAY SUPERIOR PAK PTY LTD—See Cleanaway Waste Management Limited; *Int'l*, pg. 1655
CLEANAWAY WASTE MANAGEMENT LIMITED; *Int'l*, pg. 1654
THE CLEAN BEDROOM; *U.S. Private*, pg. 4010
CLEAN BIOENERGY INC.; *Int'l*, pg. 1654
CLEANBNB SPA; *Int'l*, pg. 1655
CLEAN & CARBON ENERGY S.A.; *Int'l*, pg. 1653
CLEAN CARE A/S—See Bunzl plc; *Int'l*, pg. 1218
CLEAN COAL POWER R&D CO., LTD.; *Int'l*, pg. 1654
CLEAN COAL TECHNOLOGIES, INC.; *U.S. Public*, pg. 508
CLEAN COMMUNICATION LIMITED—See Alphabet Inc.; *U.S. Public*, pg. 84
CLEAN CONTROL CORPORATION; *U.S. Private*, pg. 931
CLEANCOR ENERGY SOLUTIONS LLC—See AIP, LLC; *U.S. Private*, pg. 136
CLEAN CUT LAWNS, LLC—See BrightView Holdings, Inc.; *U.S. Public*, pg. 383
CLEAN DESIGN, INC.; *U.S. Private*, pg. 931
CLEAN DIESEL TECHNOLOGIES LIMITED—See CDTi Advanced Materials, Inc.; *U.S. Public*, pg. 462
CLEAN EARTH DREDGING TECHNOLOGIES, LLC—See Enviri Corporation; *U.S. Public*, pg. 780
CLEAN EARTH HOLDINGS, INC.—See Compass Diversified Holdings; *U.S. Public*, pg. 559
CLEAN EARTH, INC.—See Enviri Corporation; *U.S. Public*, pg. 780
CLEAN EARTH OF ALABAMA, INC.—See Enviri Corporation; *U.S. Public*, pg. 780
CLEAN EARTH OF CARTERET, LLC—See Enviri Corporation; *U.S. Public*, pg. 780
CLEAN EARTH OF CATERET, LLC—See Compass Diversified Holdings; *U.S. Public*, pg. 559
CLEAN EARTH OF GEORGIA, LLC—See Enviri Corporation; *U.S. Public*, pg. 780
CLEAN EARTH OF GREATER WASHINGTON, LLC—See Enviri Corporation; *U.S. Public*, pg. 780
CLEAN EARTH OF MARYLAND, LLC—See Enviri Corporation; *U.S. Public*, pg. 780
CLEAN EARTH OF MICHIGAN, LLC—See Compass Diversified Holdings; *U.S. Public*, pg. 560
CLEAN EARTH OF NEW CASTLE, LLC—See Enviri Corporation; *U.S. Public*, pg. 780
CLEAN EARTH OF NEW YORK, INC.—See Enviri Corporation; *U.S. Public*, pg. 780
CLEAN EARTH OF NORTH JERSEY, INC.—See Enviri Corporation; *U.S. Public*, pg. 780
CLEAN EARTH OF PHILADELPHIA, LLC—See Enviri Corporation; *U.S. Public*, pg. 780
CLEAN EARTH OF SOUTHEAST PENNSYLVANIA, LLC—See Enviri Corporation; *U.S. Public*, pg. 780
CLEAN EARTH OF SOUTHERN FLORIDA, LLC—See Enviri Corporation; *U.S. Public*, pg. 780
CLEAN EARTH OF WEST VIRGINIA, INC.—See Compass Diversified Holdings; *U.S. Public*, pg. 560
CLEAN ENERGY-DALLAS—See Clean Energy Fuels Corp.; *U.S. Public*, pg. 508
CLEAN ENERGY-DENVER—See Clean Energy Fuels Corp.; *U.S. Public*, pg. 508
CLEAN ENERGY DEVELOPMENTS CORP.—See Groundheat Energy Solar Wind Corp.; *Int'l*, pg. 3088
CLEAN ENERGY-EAST COAST—See Clean Energy Fuels Corp.; *U.S. Public*, pg. 508
CLEAN ENERGY FUELS CORP.; *U.S. Public*, pg. 508
CLEAN ENERGY PATHWAYS, INC.; *U.S. Public*, pg. 508
CLEAN ENERGY SOLUTIONS, LLC—See Orion Energy Systems, Inc.; *U.S. Public*, pg. 1618
CLEAN ENERGY SOURCING AG—See BayWa AG; *Int'l*, pg. 917
CLEAN ENERGY SPECIAL SITUATIONS CORP.; *U.S. Public*, pg. 508
CLEAN ENERGY TECHNOLOGIES, INC.; *U.S. Public*, pg. 508
CLEAN ENERGY (THAILAND) CO., LTD.—See Clenergy (Xiamen) Technology Co., Ltd.; *Int'l*, pg. 1658
CLEANERA (MALAYSIA) SDN. BHD.—See Kossan Rubber Industries Bhd; *Int'l*, pg. 4291
CLEANERS CLOSET INC.; *U.S. Private*, pg. 931
CLEANEVENT INTERNATIONAL PTY LTD—See Downer EDI Limited; *Int'l*, pg. 2185
CLEAN FACTOMATION, INC. - ASAN PLANT—See Daifuku Co., Ltd.; *Int'l*, pg. 1924
CLEAN FACTOMATION, INC.—See Daifuku Co., Ltd.; *Int'l*, pg. 1924
CLEAN FARM CO., LTD.—See Prima Meat Packers Ltd.; *Int'l*, pg. 5975
CLEAN FOCUS RENEWABLES INC.—See United Renewable Energy Co., Ltd.; *Int'l*, pg. 8073
CLEAN FUEL CONNECTION INC.; *U.S. Private*, pg. 931
CLEAN GAS FUKUI CO., LTD.—See Mitani Corporation; *Int'l*, pg. 4924
CLEANGOAL ENERGY, CORP.; *U.S. Private*, pg. 931
CLEAN GREEN ENERGY, LLC—See CGE Energy Inc.; *U.S. Public*, pg. 477

CLEAN HARBORS ARIZONA, LLC—See Clean Harbors, Inc.; *U.S. Public*, pg. 509
CLEAN HARBORS BATON ROUGE, LLC—See Clean Harbors, Inc.; *U.S. Public*, pg. 509
CLEAN HARBORS BDT, LLC—See Clean Harbors, Inc.; *U.S. Public*, pg. 509
CLEAN HARBORS BUTTONWILLOW, LLC—See Clean Harbors, Inc.; *U.S. Public*, pg. 509
CLEAN HARBORS CANADA INC—See Clean Harbors, Inc.; *U.S. Public*, pg. 509
CLEAN HARBORS CARIBE, INC.—See Clean Harbors, Inc.; *U.S. Public*, pg. 509
CLEAN HARBORS CATALYST SERVICES, LLC—See Clean Harbors, Inc.; *U.S. Public*, pg. 509
CLEAN HARBORS CATALYST SERVICES TRINIDAD LIMITED—See Clean Harbors, Inc.; *U.S. Public*, pg. 509
CLEAN HARBORS CHATTANOOGA, LLC—See Clean Harbors, Inc.; *U.S. Public*, pg. 509
CLEAN HARBORS COFFEYVILLE, LLC—See Clean Harbors, Inc.; *U.S. Public*, pg. 509
CLEAN HARBORS COLFAX, LLC—See Clean Harbors, Inc.; *U.S. Public*, pg. 509
CLEAN HARBORS DEER PARK, LLC—See Clean Harbors, Inc.; *U.S. Public*, pg. 510
CLEAN HARBORS DEER TRAIL, LLC—See Clean Harbors, Inc.; *U.S. Public*, pg. 509
CLEAN HARBORS EL DORADO, LLC—See Clean Harbors, Inc.; *U.S. Public*, pg. 509
CLEAN HARBORS ENERGY AND INDUSTRIAL SERVICES CORP.—See Clean Harbors, Inc.; *U.S. Public*, pg. 509
CLEAN HARBORS ENERGY AND INDUSTRIAL SERVICES LP—See Clean Harbors, Inc.; *U.S. Public*, pg. 509
CLEAN HARBORS ENERGY & INDUSTRIAL SERVICES CORP.—See Clean Harbors, Inc.; *U.S. Public*, pg. 509
CLEAN HARBORS ENVIRONMENTAL SERVICES, INC.—See Clean Harbors, Inc.; *U.S. Public*, pg. 510
CLEAN HARBORS ENVIRONMENTAL SERVICES, INC.—See Clean Harbors, Inc.; *U.S. Public*, pg. 509
CLEAN HARBORS ENVIRONMENTAL SERVICES, INC.—See Clean Harbors, Inc.; *U.S. Public*, pg. 509
CLEAN HARBORS ENVIRONMENTAL SERVICES, INC.—See Clean Harbors, Inc.; *U.S. Public*, pg. 509
CLEAN HARBORS EXPLORATION SERVICES, INC.—See Clean Harbors, Inc.; *U.S. Public*, pg. 509
CLEAN HARBORS EXPLORATION SERVICES LTD. - SEISMIC SERVICES—See Clean Harbors, Inc.; *U.S. Public*, pg. 509
CLEAN HARBORS EXPLORATION SERVICES LTD.—See Clean Harbors, Inc.; *U.S. Public*, pg. 509
CLEAN HARBORS FLORIDA, LLC—See Clean Harbors, Inc.; *U.S. Public*, pg. 509
CLEAN HARBORS, INC.; *U.S. Public*, pg. 508
CLEAN HARBORS INDUSTRIAL SERVICES CANADA, INC.—See Clean Harbors, Inc.; *U.S. Public*, pg. 509
CLEAN HARBORS INDUSTRIAL SERVICES, INC.—See Clean Harbors, Inc.; *U.S. Public*, pg. 509
CLEAN HARBORS KANSAS, LLC—See Clean Harbors, Inc.; *U.S. Public*, pg. 509
CLEAN HARBORS KIMBALL REALTY, LLC—See Clean Harbors, Inc.; *U.S. Public*, pg. 509
CLEAN HARBORS LODGING SERVICES LTD.—See Clean Harbors, Inc.; *U.S. Public*, pg. 509
CLEAN HARBORS LONE MOUNTAIN, LLC—See Clean Harbors, Inc.; *U.S. Public*, pg. 509
CLEAN HARBORS LOS ANGELES, LLC—See Clean Harbors, Inc.; *U.S. Public*, pg. 509
CLEAN HARBORS MERCIER, INC.—See Clean Harbors, Inc.; *U.S. Public*, pg. 509
CLEAN HARBORS OF BALTIMORE, INC.—See Clean Harbors, Inc.; *U.S. Public*, pg. 510
CLEAN HARBORS OF BRAINTREE, INC.—See Clean Harbors, Inc.; *U.S. Public*, pg. 510
CLEAN HARBORS OF CONNECTICUT, INC.—See Clean Harbors, Inc.; *U.S. Public*, pg. 510
CLEAN HARBORS RECYCLING SERVICES OF CHICAGO, LLC—See Clean Harbors, Inc.; *U.S. Public*, pg. 509
CLEAN HARBORS RECYCLING SERVICES OF OHIO LLC—See Clean Harbors, Inc.; *U.S. Public*, pg. 509
CLEAN HARBORS REIDSVILLE, LLC—See Clean Harbors, Inc.; *U.S. Public*, pg. 509
CLEAN HARBORS SAN LEON, INC.—See Clean Harbors, Inc.; *U.S. Public*, pg. 509
CLEAN HARBORS SERVICES, INC.—See Clean Harbors, Inc.; *U.S. Public*, pg. 509
CLEAN HARBORS SURFACE RENTALS LTD.—See Clean Harbors, Inc.; *U.S. Public*, pg. 509
CLEAN HARBORS SURFACE RENTALS PARTNERSHIP—See Clean Harbors, Inc.; *U.S. Public*, pg. 509
CLEAN HARBORS SURFACE RENTALS USA, INC.—See Clean Harbors, Inc.; *U.S. Public*, pg. 509
CLEAN HARBORS TENNESSEE, LLC—See Clean Harbors, Inc.; *U.S. Public*, pg. 509
CLEAN HARBORS WESTMORLAND, LLC—See Clean Harbors, Inc.; *U.S. Public*, pg. 510

CLEAN HARBORS WHITE CASTLE, LLC—See Clean Harbors, Inc.; *U.S. Public*, pg. 510
CLEAN HARBORS WICHITA, LLC—See Clean Harbors, Inc.; *U.S. Public*, pg. 510
CLEAN HARBORS WILMINGTON, LLC—See Clean Harbors, Inc.; *U.S. Public*, pg. 510
CLEANHILL PARTNERS; *U.S. Private*, pg. 931
THE CLEANING AUTHORITY LLC—See Apax Partners LLP; *Int'l*, pg. 502
CLEANING BUTLERS INTERNATIONAL, INC.; *U.S. Private*, pg. 931
CLEANING SOLUTIONS, INC.; *U.S. Private*, pg. 931
CLEANING TECHNOLOGIES GROUP, LLC—See Alpha Capital Partners, Ltd.; *U.S. Private*, pg. 197
CLEAN KARAOKE CO., LTD.—See GMM Grammy Public Company Limited; *Int'l*, pg. 3012
CLEANLIGHT ENERGY, LLC—See New Jersey Resources Corporation; *U.S. Public*, pg. 1511
CLEAN LINEN SERVICES LIMITED - BANBURY PLANT—See CLEAN Linen Services Limited; *Int'l*, pg. 1654
CLEAN LINEN SERVICES LIMITED - CAMBERLEY PLANT—See CLEAN Linen Services Limited; *Int'l*, pg. 1654
CLEAN LINEN SERVICES LIMITED - READING PLANT—See CLEAN Linen Services Limited; *Int'l*, pg. 1654
CLEAN LINEN SERVICES LIMITED; *Int'l*, pg. 1654
CLEAN METALS CO., LTD.—See Nippon Yakin Kogyo Co., Ltd.; *Int'l*, pg. 5357
CLEAN MODULES LTD—See Atlas Clean Air Ltd.; *Int'l*, pg. 676
CLEAN MOTION AB; *Int'l*, pg. 1654
CLEAN ONES CORPORATION—See Bradshaw International, Inc.; *U.S. Private*, pg. 633
CLEAN PAIR KYUSHU CO., LTD.—See Ship Healthcare Holdings, Inc.; *Int'l*, pg. 6852
CLEAN POWER FINANCE INC.; *U.S. Private*, pg. 931
CLEAN POWER HYDROGEN GROUP LIMITED—See Clean Power Hydrogen Plc; *Int'l*, pg. 1654
CLEAN POWER HYDROGEN PLC; *Int'l*, pg. 1654
CLEANPOWER LLC—See Marsden Holding, L.L.C.; *U.S. Private*, pg. 2591
CLEAN PRODUCTS INTERNATIONAL LTD.—See Saltchuk Resources Inc.; *U.S. Private*, pg. 3534
CLEAN ROOMS WEST, INC.—See Hodess Cleanroom Construction, LLC; *U.S. Private*, pg. 1959
CLEAN R SIA; *Int'l*, pg. 1654
CLEANSCAPES, INC.; *U.S. Private*, pg. 931
CLEAN & SCIENCE CO., LTD. - HANAM FACTORY—See CLEAN & SCIENCE Co., Ltd.; *Int'l*, pg. 1653
CLEAN & SCIENCE CO., LTD. - JEONGEUP FACTORY—See CLEAN & SCIENCE Co., Ltd.; *Int'l*, pg. 1654
CLEAN & SCIENCE CO., LTD.; *Int'l*, pg. 1653
CLEAN SCIENCE & TECHNOLOGY LIMITED; *Int'l*, pg. 1654
CLEAN SEAS SEAFOOD LTD.; *Int'l*, pg. 1654
CLEAN SEED CAPITAL GROUP LTD.; *Int'l*, pg. 1654
CLEANSERVE, INC.—See Mack Operations LLC; *U.S. Private*, pg. 2536
CLEAN SOLUTIONS GROUP, INC.—See Branford Castle, Inc.; *U.S. Private*, pg. 639
CLEANSORB LIMITED—See Newpark Resources, Inc.; *U.S. Public*, pg. 1517
CLEANSPACE HOLDINGS LIMITED; *Int'l*, pg. 1655
CLEANSPACE TECHNOLOGY PTY LIMITED—See Cleanspace Holdings Limited; *Int'l*, pg. 1655
CLEANSPARK, INC.; *U.S. Public*, pg. 510
CLEANSPARK, LLC—See CleanSpark, Inc.; *U.S. Public*, pg. 511
CLEANSTREET INC.—See Warburg Pincus LLC; *U.S. Private*, pg. 4440
CLEANTECH ALPHA CORPORATION; *U.S. Public*, pg. 511
CLEANTECH BIOFUELS, INC.; *U.S. Private*, pg. 931
CLEANTECH ENERGY PTY. LTD.—See Delorean Corporation Limited; *Int'l*, pg. 2015
CLEANTECH GROUP, INC.; *U.S. Private*, pg. 931
CLEANTECH LITHIUM PLC; *Int'l*, pg. 1655
CLEANTECH NRW GMBH—See Bayer Aktiengesellschaft; *Int'l*, pg. 907
CLEANTECH OPEN; *U.S. Private*, pg. 932
CLEANTECH POWER CORP.; *Int'l*, pg. 1655
CLEANTEK INDUSTRIES INC.; *Int'l*, pg. 1655
CLEAN TEQ LIMITED—See Sunrise Energy Metals Limited; *Int'l*, pg. 7321
CLEAN TEQ WATER LIMITED; *Int'l*, pg. 1654
CLEAN TEXTILE SYSTEMS INC.; *U.S. Private*, pg. 931
CLEAN THE WORLD FOUNDATION, INC.; *U.S. Private*, pg. 931
CLEAN TIDE CONTAINER, INC.—See JBC North America Inc.; *U.S. Private*, pg. 2028
CLEAN TRANSPORTATION GROUP, INC.; *Int'l*, pg. 1654
CLEANUP CAREER SERVICE CO., LTD.—See Cleanup Corporation; *Int'l*, pg. 1656
CLEANUP CORPORATION - CRETE FACTORY—See Cleanup Corporation; *Int'l*, pg. 1656

CLEANUP CORPORATION - KASHIMA FACTORY—See Cleanup Corporation; *Int'l*, pg. 1656
CLEANUP CORPORATION - KASHIMA SYSTEM FACTORY—See Cleanup Corporation; *Int'l*, pg. 1656
CLEANUP CORPORATION - PROJECT SALES DIVISION—See Cleanup Corporation; *Int'l*, pg. 1656
CLEANUP CORPORATION; *Int'l*, pg. 1656
CLEANUP CORPORATION - YOTSUKURA FACTORY—See Cleanup Corporation; *Int'l*, pg. 1656
CLEANUP CORPORATION - YUMOTO FACTORY—See Cleanup Corporation; *Int'l*, pg. 1656
CLEANUP HEARTFUL CO., LTD.—See Cleanup Corporation; *Int'l*, pg. 1656
CLEANUP LOGISTICS CO., LTD.—See Cleanup Corporation; *Int'l*, pg. 1656
CLEANUP OKAYAMA INDUSTRIAL CO., LTD.—See Cleanup Corporation; *Int'l*, pg. 1656
CLEANUP OKAYAMA INDUSTRIAL CO., LTD. - TSUYAMA FACTORY—See Cleanup Corporation; *Int'l*, pg. 1656
CLEANUP (SHANGHAI) CO., LTD.—See Cleanup Corporation; *Int'l*, pg. 1656
CLEANUP STEEL PROCESSING CO., LTD. - NODA FACTORY—See Cleanup Corporation; *Int'l*, pg. 1656
CLEANUP STEEL PROCESSING CO., LTD.—See Cleanup Corporation; *Int'l*, pg. 1656
CLEANUP TECHNO SERVICE CO., LTD.—See Cleanup Corporation; *Int'l*, pg. 1656
CLEAN VENTURE INC.; *U.S. Private*, pg. 931
CLEAN VISION CORPORATION; *U.S. Public*, pg. 510
CLEANWATER1, INC.—See Baird Financial Group, Inc.; *U.S. Public*, pg. 453
CLEAN WATER LTD.—See OGM, Ltd.; *U.S. Private*, pg. 3003
CLEAN WATER SERVICES; *U.S. Private*, pg. 931
CLEAN WATER TESTING—See A. O. Smith Corporation; *U.S. Public*, pg. 11
CLEANWAY DISPOSAL SERVICES PTE. LTD.—See Analabs Resources Berhad; *Int'l*, pg. 446
CLEA PR—See Percept Holdings Pvt. Ltd.; *Int'l*, pg. 5796
CLEAR2PAY AMERICAS, INC.—See Fidelity National Infor; *U.S. Public*, pg. 832
CLEAR2PAY APAC PTY LTD.—See Fidelity National Infor; *U.S. Public*, pg. 832
CLEAR2PAY BELGIUM NV—See Fidelity National Infor; *U.S. Public*, pg. 832
CLEAR2PAY SCOTLAND HOLDINGS LIMITED—See Fidelity National Infor; *U.S. Public*, pg. 832
CLEAR2PAY SERVICES NV—See Fidelity National Infor; *U.S. Public*, pg. 832
CLEARABILITY, INC.; *U.S. Private*, pg. 932
THE CLEAR AGENCY—See Highland Productions, LLC; *U.S. Private*, pg. 1939
CLEARAG, INC.—See TBG Treuhand Partner AG; *Int'l*, pg. 7480
CLEARARC CAPITAL, INC.—See Fifth Third Bancorp; *U.S. Public*, pg. 833
CLEARAVENUE, LLC; *U.S. Private*, pg. 932
CLEARBELL CAPITAL LLP; *Int'l*, pg. 1656
CLEAR BLUE FINANCIAL HOLDINGS LLC; *U.S. Private*, pg. 932
CLEAR BLUE INSURANCE SERVICES, INC.—See Clear Blue Financial Holdings LLC; *U.S. Private*, pg. 932
CLEAR BLUE SPECIALTY INSURANCE COMPANY—See Clear Blue Financial Holdings LLC; *U.S. Private*, pg. 932
CLEAR BLUE TECHNOLOGIES INTERNATIONAL, INC.; *Int'l*, pg. 1656
CLEARBRIDGE ASSET MANAGEMENT INC.—See Franklin Resources, Inc.; *U.S. Public*, pg. 881
CLEARBRIDGE ENERGY MIDSTREAM OPPORTUNITY FUND INC—See Franklin Resources, Inc.; *U.S. Public*, pg. 881
CLEARBRIDGE HEALTH LIMITED; *Int'l*, pg. 1656
CLEARBRIDGE INVESTMENTS LIMITED—See Franklin Resources, Inc.; *U.S. Public*, pg. 881
CLEARBRIDGE INVESTMENTS, LLC—See Franklin Resources, Inc.; *U.S. Public*, pg. 881
CLEARBRIDGE LIFESTYLE PTE. LTD.—See Clearbridge Health Limited; *Int'l*, pg. 1656
CLEARBRIDGE, LLC—See Franklin Resources, Inc.; *U.S. Public*, pg. 882
CLEARBRIDGE MEDICAL GROUP PTE. LTD.—See Clearbridge Health Limited; *Int'l*, pg. 1656
CLEARBRIDGE MEDICAL HONG KONG CORPORATION LIMITED—See Clearbridge Health Limited; *Int'l*, pg. 1656
CLEARBRIDGE MEDICAL PHILIPPINES, INC.—See Clearbridge Health Limited; *Int'l*, pg. 1656
CLEARBRIDGE MEDICA SDN BHD—See Clearbridge Health Limited; *Int'l*, pg. 1656
CLEARBRIDGE MLP & MIDSTREAM FUND INC.—See Franklin Resources, Inc.; *U.S. Public*, pg. 881
CLEARBRIDGE TECHNOLOGY GROUP; *U.S. Private*, pg. 932
CLEARBRIDGE WEALTH MANAGEMENT, INC.—See Merit Financial Group, LLC; *U.S. Private*, pg. 2674
CLEAR C2, INC.; *U.S. Private*, pg. 932
CLEARCAPITAL.COM, INC.; *U.S. Private*, pg. 932

COMPANY NAME INDEX

CLEARCASH LIMITED—See ClearDebt Group Plc; *Int'l*, pg. 1656
CLEAR CHANNEL AIDA GMBH—See TX Group AG; *Int'l*, pg. 7992
CLEAR CHANNEL AIRPORTS—See Clear Channel Outdoor Holdings, Inc.; *U.S. Public*, pg. 511
CLEAR CHANNEL AWI AG—See TX Group AG; *Int'l*, pg. 7992
CLEAR CHANNEL BELGIUM SPRL—See iHeartMedia, Inc.; *U.S. Public*, pg. 1095
CLEAR CHANNEL CHILE PUBLICIDAD LTDA—See iHeartMedia, Inc.; *U.S. Public*, pg. 1095
CLEAR CHANNEL DANMARK A/S—See Clear Channel Outdoor Holdings, Inc.; *U.S. Public*, pg. 511
CLEAR CHANNEL FRANCE SA—See Clear Channel Outdoor Holdings, Inc.; *U.S. Public*, pg. 511
CLEAR CHANNEL (GUANGZHOU) LTD.—See Clear Channel Outdoor Holdings, Inc.; *U.S. Public*, pg. 511
CLEAR CHANNEL HILLENAAR BV—See iHeartMedia, Inc.; *U.S. Public*, pg. 1096
CLEAR CHANNEL HOLDINGS LIMITED—See Clear Channel Outdoor Holdings, Inc.; *U.S. Public*, pg. 511
CLEAR CHANNEL INTERNATIONAL LTD.—See iHeartMedia, Inc.; *U.S. Public*, pg. 1096
CLEAR CHANNEL INTERPUBLI AG—See TX Group AG; *Int'l*, pg. 7992
CLEAR CHANNEL ITALY OUTDOOR SRL—See JCDecaux S.A.; *Int'l*, pg. 3920
CLEAR CHANNEL LATVIA—See iHeartMedia, Inc.; *U.S. Public*, pg. 1096
CLEAR CHANNEL MALLS—See Clear Channel Outdoor Holdings, Inc.; *U.S. Public*, pg. 511
CLEAR CHANNEL NEDERLAND BV—See Clear Channel Outdoor Holdings, Inc.; *U.S. Public*, pg. 511
CLEAR CHANNEL NORWAY AS—See iHeartMedia, Inc.; *U.S. Public*, pg. 1096
CLEAR CHANNEL OUTDOOR - AKRON/CANTON—See Clear Channel Outdoor Holdings, Inc.; *U.S. Public*, pg. 511
CLEAR CHANNEL OUTDOOR - ATLANTA—See Clear Channel Outdoor Holdings, Inc.; *U.S. Public*, pg. 511
CLEAR CHANNEL OUTDOOR - BOSTON—See Clear Channel Outdoor Holdings, Inc.; *U.S. Public*, pg. 511
CLEAR CHANNEL OUTDOOR - CHICAGO—See Clear Channel Outdoor Holdings, Inc.; *U.S. Public*, pg. 512
CLEAR CHANNEL OUTDOOR COMPANY CANADA—See Clear Channel Outdoor Holdings, Inc.; *U.S. Public*, pg. 512
CLEAR CHANNEL OUTDOOR - DAYTONA BEACH/MELBOURNE—See Clear Channel Outdoor Holdings, Inc.; *U.S. Public*, pg. 511
CLEAR CHANNEL OUTDOOR - EASTERN REGIONAL OFFICE—See Clear Channel Outdoor Holdings, Inc.; *U.S. Public*, pg. 511
CLEAR CHANNEL OUTDOOR HOLDINGS, INC.; *U.S. Public*, pg. 511
CLEAR CHANNEL OUTDOOR - HOUSTON—See Clear Channel Outdoor Holdings, Inc.; *U.S. Public*, pg. 512
CLEAR CHANNEL OUTDOOR, INC.—See Clear Channel Outdoor Holdings, Inc.; *U.S. Public*, pg. 511
CLEAR CHANNEL OUTDOOR - INDIANAPOLIS—See Clear Channel Outdoor Holdings, Inc.; *U.S. Public*, pg. 511
CLEAR CHANNEL OUTDOOR - JACKSONVILLE—See Clear Channel Outdoor Holdings, Inc.; *U.S. Public*, pg. 511
CLEAR CHANNEL OUTDOOR - LAS VEGAS—See Clear Channel Outdoor Holdings, Inc.; *U.S. Public*, pg. 512
CLEAR CHANNEL OUTDOOR - LOS ANGELES—See Clear Channel Outdoor Holdings, Inc.; *U.S. Public*, pg. 512
CLEAR CHANNEL OUTDOOR MEXICO, OPERACIONES SA DE CV—See iHeartMedia, Inc.; *U.S. Public*, pg. 1096
CLEAR CHANNEL OUTDOOR - MIAMI—See Clear Channel Outdoor Holdings, Inc.; *U.S. Public*, pg. 511
CLEAR CHANNEL OUTDOOR - MILWAUKEE—See Clear Channel Outdoor Holdings, Inc.; *U.S. Public*, pg. 512
CLEAR CHANNEL OUTDOOR - ORLANDO—See Clear Channel Outdoor Holdings, Inc.; *U.S. Public*, pg. 511
CLEAR CHANNEL OUTDOOR - PHILADELPHIA—See Clear Channel Outdoor Holdings, Inc.; *U.S. Public*, pg. 511
CLEAR CHANNEL OUTDOOR - SACRAMENTO—See Clear Channel Outdoor Holdings, Inc.; *U.S. Public*, pg. 512
CLEAR CHANNEL OUTDOOR - SAN ANTONIO—See Clear Channel Outdoor Holdings, Inc.; *U.S. Public*, pg. 512
CLEAR CHANNEL OUTDOOR - SAN DIEGO—See Clear Channel Outdoor Holdings, Inc.; *U.S. Public*, pg. 512
CLEAR CHANNEL OUTDOOR - SAN FRANCISCO—See Clear Channel Outdoor Holdings, Inc.; *U.S. Public*, pg. 512
CLEAR CHANNEL OUTDOOR - WASHINGTON, D.C./BALTIMORE—See Clear Channel Outdoor Holdings, Inc.; *U.S. Public*, pg. 511

CLEAR CHANNEL OUTDOOR - WESTERN REGIONAL OFFICE—See Clear Channel Outdoor Holdings, Inc.; *U.S. Public*, pg. 511
CLEAR CHANNEL OUTDOOR - WICHITA—See Clear Channel Outdoor Holdings, Inc.; *U.S. Public*, pg. 512
CLEAR CHANNEL OUTDOOR - WILMINGTON—See Clear Channel Outdoor Holdings, Inc.; *U.S. Public*, pg. 511
CLEAR CHANNEL PLAKATRON AG—See TX Group AG; *Int'l*, pg. 7992
CLEAR CHANNEL POLAND SP ZO.O.—See iHeartMedia, Inc.; *U.S. Public*, pg. 1096
CLEAR CHANNEL RADIO SALES—See iHeartMedia, Inc.; *U.S. Public*, pg. 1096
CLEAR CHANNEL SPECTACOLOR, LLC—See Clear Channel Outdoor Holdings, Inc.; *U.S. Public*, pg. 512
CLEAR CHANNEL SVERIGE AB—See iHeartMedia, Inc.; *U.S. Public*, pg. 1096
CLEAR CHANNEL UK LIMITED—See Clear Channel Outdoor Holdings, Inc.; *U.S. Public*, pg. 511
CLEAR CHOICE TELEPHONES INC—See Medicus Solutions, LLC; *U.S. Private*, pg. 2656
CLEARCIRCLE ENVIRONMENTAL LIMITED—See Madison Dearborn Partners, LLC; *U.S. Private*, pg. 2541
CLEARCIRCLE ENVIRONMENTAL (NI) LTD—See Madison Dearborn Partners, LLC; *U.S. Private*, pg. 2541
CLEARCIRCLE METALS IRELAND LIMITED—See Madison Dearborn Partners, LLC; *U.S. Private*, pg. 2541
CLEARCIRCLE METALS (LIMERICK) LTD.—See Madison Dearborn Partners, LLC; *U.S. Private*, pg. 2541
CLEAR-COM, LLC—See HM Electronics Incorporated; *U.S. Public*, pg. 1954
CLEARCOMMERCE CORPORATION—See Fidelity National Infor; *U.S. Public*, pg. 832
CLEARCOMM TECHNOLOGIES, LLC—See L3Harris Technologies, Inc.; *U.S. Public*, pg. 1284
CLEARCOMPANY, INC.—See Gemspring Capital Management, LLC; *U.S. Private*, pg. 1658
CLEAR CONSULT GMBH—See Alten S.A.; *Int'l*, pg. 390
CLEARCORRECT, INC.; *U.S. Private*, pg. 932
CLEAR CREEK HOLDINGS, LLC—See Tetra Tech, Inc.; *U.S. Public*, pg. 2022
CLEAR CREEK HUNTING PRESERVE, INC.—See APA Corporation; *U.S. Public*, pg. 143
CLEAR CREEK SURGERY CENTER, LLC—See HCA Healthcare, Inc.; *U.S. Public*, pg. 993
CLEARCUBE TECHNOLOGY, INC.; *U.S. Private*, pg. 932
CLEARDATA (PTY) LTD—See Metrofile Holdings Limited; *Int'l*, pg. 4861
CLEARDAY, INC.; *U.S. Public*, pg. 512
CLEARDEBT GROUP PLC; *Int'l*, pg. 1656
CLEARDEBT LIMITED—See ClearDebt Group Plc; *Int'l*, pg. 1657
CLEAREDGE3D, INC.—See Topcon Corporation; *Int'l*, pg. 7814
CLEAR EDGE FILTRATION (AUSTRALIA) PTY. LTD.—See Gilde Buy Out Partners B.V.; *Int'l*, pg. 2974
CLEAR EDGE FILTRATION (AUSTRALIA) PTY. LTD.—See Parcom Capital Management B.V.; *Int'l*, pg. 5739
CLEAR EDGE FILTRATION CFE GMBH—See Gilde Buy Out Partners B.V.; *Int'l*, pg. 2974
CLEAR EDGE FILTRATION CFE GMBH—See Parcom Capital Management B.V.; *Int'l*, pg. 5739
CLEAR EDGE FILTRATION GMBH—See Gilde Buy Out Partners B.V.; *Int'l*, pg. 2974
CLEAR EDGE FILTRATION GMBH—See Parcom Capital Management B.V.; *Int'l*, pg. 5739
CLEAR EDGE FILTRATION, INC.-SKANEATELES FALLS—See Gilde Buy Out Partners B.V.; *Int'l*, pg. 2974
CLEAR EDGE FILTRATION, INC.-SKANEATELES FALLS—See Parcom Capital Management B.V.; *Int'l*, pg. 5740
CLEAR EDGE FILTRATION, INC.—See Gilde Buy Out Partners B.V.; *Int'l*, pg. 2974
CLEAR EDGE FILTRATION, INC.—See Parcom Capital Management B.V.; *Int'l*, pg. 5739
CLEAR EDGE FILTRATION (NZ) LTD.—See Gilde Buy Out Partners B.V.; *Int'l*, pg. 2974
CLEAR EDGE FILTRATION (NZ) LTD.—See Parcom Capital Management B.V.; *Int'l*, pg. 5739
CLEAR EDGE FILTRATION POLSKA SP. Z O.O.—See Gilde Buy Out Partners B.V.; *Int'l*, pg. 2974
CLEAR EDGE FILTRATION POLSKA SP. Z O.O.—See Parcom Capital Management B.V.; *Int'l*, pg. 5739
CLEAR EDGE FILTRATION SOUTH AFRICA PTY. LTD.—See Gilde Buy Out Partners B.V.; *Int'l*, pg. 2974
CLEAR EDGE FILTRATION SOUTH AFRICA PTY. LTD.—See Parcom Capital Management B.V.; *Int'l*, pg. 5739
CLEAR EDGE FILTRATION SWEDEN AB—See Gilde Buy Out Partners B.V.; *Int'l*, pg. 2974
CLEAR EDGE FILTRATION SWEDEN AB—See Parcom Capital Management B.V.; *Int'l*, pg. 5739
CLEAR EDGE FILTRATION UK LTD.—See Gilde Buy Out Partners B.V.; *Int'l*, pg. 2974
CLEAR EDGE FILTRATION UK LTD.—See Parcom Capital Management B.V.; *Int'l*, pg. 5739

CLEAREDGE IT SOLUTIONS, LLC; *U.S. Private*, pg. 932
CLEAREDGE PARTNERS, INC.—See Accenture plc; *Int'l*, pg. 87
CLEARENT LLC; *U.S. Private*, pg. 932
CLEAR ENVIRONMENTAL SOLUTIONS INC.—See CES Energy Solutions Corp.; *Int'l*, pg. 1423
CLEARESULT CONSULTING, INC.—See TPG Capital, L.P.; *U.S. Private*, pg. 2175
CLEARFIELD BANK & TRUST CO.; *U.S. Private*, pg. 932
CLEARFIELD, INC.; *U.S. Public*, pg. 512
CLEARFLY COMMUNICATIONS; *U.S. Private*, pg. 932
CLEARFORD - KOESTER CANADA, INC.—See Clearford Water Systems Inc.; *Int'l*, pg. 1657
CLEARFORD WATER SYSTEMS INC.; *Int'l*, pg. 1657
CLEARFORK MIDSTREAM LLC; *U.S. Private*, pg. 932
CLEAR GENETICS, INC.—See Invitae Corporation; *U.S. Public*, pg. 1165
CLEAR GOLD RESOURCES, INC.; *Int'l*, pg. 1656
CLEAR HARBOR, LLC; *U.S. Private*, pg. 932
CLEARHAVEN PARTNERS LP; *U.S. Private*, pg. 933
CLEAR IDEAS LTD.—See M&C Saatchi plc; *Int'l*, pg. 4611
THE CLEARING CORPORATION—See Intercontinental Exchange, Inc.; *U.S. Public*, pg. 1143
CLEARINGHOUSE COMMUNITY DEVELOPMENT FINANCIAL INSTITUTION; *U.S. Private*, pg. 933
THE CLEARING, INC.; *U.S. Private*, pg. 4010
CLEAR INTEC SP. Z O.O—See Alten S.A.; *Int'l*, pg. 390
CLEAR INVESTIGATIVE ADVANTAGE, LLC; *U.S. Private*, pg. 932
CLEARLAB SG PTE LTD—See Migwang Contact Lens Co., Ltd.; *Int'l*, pg. 4890
CLEARLAKE CAPITAL GROUP, L.P.; *U.S. Private*, pg. 933
CLEAR LAKE CHEMICALS LLC—See Platte River Ventures, LLC; *U.S. Private*, pg. 3211
CLEAR LAKE FAMILY PHYSICIANS, PLLC—See HCA Healthcare, Inc.; *U.S. Public*, pg. 993
CLEAR LAKE-I, INC.—See Lithia Motors, Inc.; *U.S. Public*, pg. 1321
CLEAR LAKE INFINITI, LP—See John Eagle A Management, LLC; *U.S. Private*, pg. 2221
CLEAR LAKE OBSERVER AMERICAN—See Alden Global Capital LLC; *U.S. Private*, pg. 156
CLEAR LAKE REGIONAL MEDICAL CENTER, INC.—See HCA Healthcare, Inc.; *U.S. Public*, pg. 993
CLEAR LAKE REHABILITATION HOSPITAL, LLC—See Select Rehabilitation, LLC; *U.S. Private*, pg. 3601
CLEAR LAM PACKAGING, INC.—See Sonoco Products Company; *U.S. Public*, pg. 1904
CLEARLEND—See Wells Fargo & Company; *U.S. Public*, pg. 2343
CLEARLEND - WEST COAST—See Wells Fargo & Company; *U.S. Public*, pg. 2343
CLEARLIGHT PARTNERS, LLC—See SECOM Co., Ltd.; *Int'l*, pg. 6670
CLEAR LINK TECHNOLOGIES, LLC—See Creadev SAS; *Int'l*, pg. 1831
CLEARLOGIC FINANCIAL, INC.; *U.S. Private*, pg. 938
CLEARLYBUSINESS.COM LIMITED—See Barclays PLC; *Int'l*, pg. 862
CLEAR M&C SAATCHI—See M&C Saatchi plc; *Int'l*, pg. 4611
CLEAR MEDIA LIMITED; *Int'l*, pg. 1656
CLEARMIND MEDICINE INC.; *Int'l*, pg. 1657
CLEAR MOUNTAIN REFRESHMENT SERVICE, LLC—See Primo Water Corporation; *U.S. Public*, pg. 1717
CLEAR NIGHT GROUP—See Evening Post Publishing Co.; *U.S. Private*, pg. 1436
CLEAROBJECT, INC.—See ABS Capital Partners, L.P.; *U.S. Private*, pg. 44
CLEAROBJECT, INC.—See Egis Capital Partners LLC; *U.S. Private*, pg. 1344
CLEARON CORP.—See Platinum Equity, LLC; *U.S. Private*, pg. 3204
CLEARONE ADVANTAGE, LLC; *U.S. Private*, pg. 938
CLEARONE, INC.; *U.S. Public*, pg. 512
CLEARONE LTD.—See ClearOne, Inc.; *U.S. Public*, pg. 512
CLEAR ONE, S.L.—See Global Payments Inc.; *U.S. Public*, pg. 943
CLEAR PACK COMPANY—See Sonoco Products Company; *U.S. Public*, pg. 1904
CLEARPASS CO., LTD.—See The Kansai Electric Power Co., Inc.; *Int'l*, pg. 7661
CLEARPATH SOLUTIONS GROUP; *U.S. Private*, pg. 938
CLEAR PEAK ENERGY, INC.; *U.S. Public*, pg. 512
CLEARPLAN, LLC—See OPENLANE, Inc.; *U.S. Public*, pg. 1607
CLEAR PLASTICS LIMITED—See Hitech Corporation Ltd.; *Int'l*, pg. 3425
CLEARPOINTE, INC.—See WestView Capital Partners, L.P.; *U.S. Private*, pg. 4501
CLEARPOINT ENTERPRISES, INC.; *U.S. Private*, pg. 938
CLEARPOINT NEURO, INC.; *U.S. Public*, pg. 512
CLEARPOWER SYSTEMS INC.—See Questor Technology Inc.; *Int'l*, pg. 6161
CLEARRIVER COMMUNICATIONS GROUP; *U.S. Private*, pg. 938

CLEARROCK CAPITAL, LLC—See Genstar Capital, LLC; *U.S. Private*, pg. 1677
CLEARROCK CAPITAL, LLC—See Keystone Group, L.P.; *U.S. Private*, pg. 2298
CLEAR SECURE, INC.; *U.S. Public*, pg. 512
CLEARSENSE, LLC; *U.S. Private*, pg. 938
CLEARSHARK LLC—See KKR & Co. Inc.; *U.S. Public*, pg. 1262
CLEARSIDE BIOMEDICAL, INC.; *U.S. Public*, pg. 513
CLEARSIGHT ADVISORS INC.—See Regions Financial Corporation; *U.S. Public*, pg. 1776
CLEARSIGN TECHNOLOGIES CORP.; *U.S. Public*, pg. 513
CLEARSLIDE, INC.—See Bigtincan Holdings Limited; *U.S. Public*, pg. 331
CLEARSOURCE, INC.; *U.S. Private*, pg. 938
CLEARSPEED TECHNOLOGY PLC; *Int'l*, pg. 1657
CLEARSPRING CAPITAL PARTNERS; *Int'l*, pg. 1657
CLEAR SPRINGS FOODS, INC.—See Riverence Holdings LLC; *U.S. Private*, pg. 3444
CLEARSTAR, INC.; *U.S. Private*, pg. 938
CLEARSTAR LOGISTICS, INC.—See ClearStar, Inc.; *U.S. Private*, pg. 938
CLEARSTATE (PTE) LIMITED—See The Economist Group Limited; *Int'l*, pg. 7637
CLEARSTEAD ADVISORS, LLC—See Edwards Capital, LLC; *U.S. Private*, pg. 1341
CLEARSTONE CENTRAL LABORATORIES (CANADA) INC.—See Laboratory Corporation of America Holdings; *U.S. Public*, pg. 1285
CLEARSTONE VENTURE PARTNERS; *U.S. Private*, pg. 938
CLEARSTREAM AUSTRALIA LIMITED—See Deutsche Borse AG; *Int'l*, pg. 2063
CLEARSTREAM BANKING AG—See Deutsche Borse AG; *Int'l*, pg. 2063
CLEARSTREAM BANKING JAPAN, LTD.—See Deutsche Borse AG; *Int'l*, pg. 2063
CLEARSTREAM BANKING S.A.—See Deutsche Borse AG; *Int'l*, pg. 2063
CLEARSTREAM CONTRACTING LP.—See FLINT Corp.; *Int'l*, pg. 2706
CLEARSTREAM FUND CENTRE AG—See Deutsche Borse AG; *Int'l*, pg. 2063
CLEARSTREAM GLOBAL SECURITIES SERVICES LIMITED—See Deutsche Borse AG; *Int'l*, pg. 2063
CLEARSTREAM HOLDING AG—See Deutsche Borse AG; *Int'l*, pg. 2063
CLEARSTREAM INTERNATIONAL S.A.—See Deutsche Borse AG; *Int'l*, pg. 2063
CLEARSTREAM OPERATIONS PRAGUE S.R.O—See Deutsche Borse AG; *Int'l*, pg. 2063
CLEARSTREAM SERVICES S.A.—See Deutsche Borse AG; *Int'l*, pg. 2063
CLEARSTREAM TECHNOLOGIES GROUP LIMITED—See Becton, Dickinson & Company; *U.S. Public*, pg. 291
CLEARSTREAM TECHNOLOGIES LIMITED—See Becton, Dickinson & Company; *U.S. Public*, pg. 291
CLEARSTREAM WEAR TECHNOLOGIES LP—See FLINT Corp.; *Int'l*, pg. 2706
CLEARSTRUCTURE FINANCIAL TECHNOLOGY, LLC—See Broadridge Financial Solutions, Inc.; *U.S. Public*, pg. 391
CLEARSWIFT (ASIA/PACIFIC) PTY LTD—See RUAG Holding AG; *Int'l*, pg. 6421
CLEARSWIFT CORPORATION—See RUAG Holding AG; *Int'l*, pg. 6421
CLEARSWIFT GMBH—See RUAG Holding AG; *Int'l*, pg. 6421
CLEARSWIFT K.K.—See RUAG Holding AG; *Int'l*, pg. 6421
CLEARSWIFT LIMITED—See RUAG Holding AG; *Int'l*, pg. 6421
CLEARTECH BRASIL LTDA—See DXC Technology Company; *U.S. Public*, pg. 695
CLEARTECH INDUSTRIES INC.—See Pic Investment Group Inc.; *Int'l*, pg. 5859
CLEAR TECHNOLOGIES, INC.; *U.S. Private*, pg. 932
CLEAR TOUCH INTERACTIVE, INC.; *U.S. Private*, pg. 932
CLEARTRONIC, INC.; *U.S. Public*, pg. 513
CLEAR VIEW BAG CO. INC.; *U.S. Private*, pg. 932
CLEARVIEW BUSINESS INTELLIGENCE, LLC; *U.S. Private*, pg. 938
CLEARVIEW CAPITAL, LLC; *U.S. Private*, pg. 938
CLEARVIEW ELECTRIC, INC.; *U.S. Private*, pg. 939
CLEARVIEW FINANCIAL ADVICE PTY LIMITED—See ClearView Wealth Limited; *Int'l*, pg. 1657
CLEARVIEW MEDICAL INCORPORATED—See AdaptHealth Corp.; *U.S. Public*, pg. 38
CLEARVIEW WEALTH LIMITED; *Int'l*, pg. 1657
CLEARVISE AG; *Int'l*, pg. 1657
CLEAR VISIONS, INC.—See Chatham Asset Management, LLC; *U.S. Private*, pg. 862
CLEARVUE (ASIA) PTE.LTD.—See ClearVue Technologies Limited; *Int'l*, pg. 1657
CLEARVUE TECHNOLOGIES LIMITED; *Int'l*, pg. 1657

CLEARWATER ANALYTICS HOLDINGS, INC.; *U.S. Public*, pg. 513
CLEARWATER CAPITAL PARTNERS LLC—See Fiera Capital Corporation; *Int'l*, pg. 2659
CLEARWATER COMPLIANCE LLC—See Altaris Capital Partners, LLC; *U.S. Private*, pg. 205
CLEARWATER DEVELOPMENT INC—See EFO Financial Group LLC; *U.S. Private*, pg. 1343
CLEARWATER ENERGY SERVICES LP—See FLINT Corp.; *Int'l*, pg. 2706
CLEARWATER ENVIRO TECHNOLOGIES, INC.; *U.S. Private*, pg. 939
CLEARWATER FIBER, LLC—See Clearwater Paper Corporation; *U.S. Public*, pg. 513
CLEARWATER FINE FOODS EUROPE LIMITED—See Premium Brands Holdings Corporation; *Int'l*, pg. 5963
CLEARWATER FINE FOODS INCORPORATED; *Int'l*, pg. 1657
CLEARWATER INSURANCE COMPANY—See Fairfax Financial Holdings Limited; *Int'l*, pg. 2607
CLEARWATER MARINE AQUARIUM, INC.; *U.S. Private*, pg. 939
CLEARWATER MARINE INC.; *U.S. Private*, pg. 939
CLEARWATER MATTRESS, INC.; *U.S. Private*, pg. 939
CLEARWATER PAIN MANAGEMENT ASSOCIATES DIVISION, LLC—See KKR & Co. Inc.; *U.S. Public*, pg. 1245
CLEARWATER PAPER CORPORATION; *U.S. Public*, pg. 513
CLEARWATER POWER COMPANY; *U.S. Private*, pg. 939
CLEARWATER SEAFOODS INCORPORATED—See Premium Brands Holdings Corporation; *Int'l*, pg. 5962
CLEARWATER SEAFOODS LIMITED PARTNERSHIP—See Premium Brands Holdings Corporation; *Int'l*, pg. 5963
CLEARWATER SELECT INSURANCE COMPANY—See Fairfax Financial Holdings Limited; *Int'l*, pg. 2607
CLEARWATER SYSTEMS INC.; *U.S. Private*, pg. 939
CLEARWATER TECHNOLOGIES LTD—See Clariant AG; *Int'l*, pg. 1648
CLEARWATER TECHNOLOGY LTD.—See Marlowe Plc; *Int'l*, pg. 4698
CLEARWATER THRESHERS—See The Phillies, L.P.; *U.S. Private*, pg. 4095
CLEARWATER UNDERWRITERS, INC.—See AmWINS Group, Inc.; *U.S. Private*, pg. 270
CLEARWAVE TELECOMMUNICATIONS, INC.; *U.S. Public*, pg. 513
CLEARWAY ENERGY, INC.—See BlackRock, Inc.; *U.S. Public*, pg. 345
CLEARWELL QUARRIES LIMITED—See Breedon Group plc; *Int'l*, pg. 1144
CLEARXCHANGE, LLC—See Bank of America Corporation; *U.S. Public*, pg. 272
CLEARXCHANGE, LLC—See Capital One Financial Corporation; *U.S. Public*, pg. 431
CLEARXCHANGE, LLC—See JPMorgan Chase & Co.; *U.S. Public*, pg. 1210
CLEARXCHANGE, LLC—See Wells Fargo & Company; *U.S. Public*, pg. 2343
CLEARY BUILDING CORP.; *U.S. Private*, pg. 939
CLEARY DEVELOPMENTS INC.; *U.S. Private*, pg. 939
CLEARY GOTTLIEB STEEN & HAMILTON LLP; *U.S. Private*, pg. 939
CLEARY GULL HOLDINGS INC.—See Canadian Imperial Bank of Commerce; *Int'l*, pg. 1283
CLEARY GULL INC.—See Canadian Imperial Bank of Commerce; *Int'l*, pg. 1283
CLEAVER-BROOKS INC.—See Harbour Group Industries, Inc.; *U.S. Private*, pg. 1860
CLEAVER-BROOKS SALES AND SERVICE, INC.—See Harbour Group Industries, Inc.; *U.S. Private*, pg. 1860
CLEBURNE DIALYSIS, LLC—See DaVita Inc.; *U.S. Public*, pg. 636
CLE CAPITAL INC.—See Mitsubishi HC Capital Inc.; *Int'l*, pg. 4950
CLECE, S.A.—See ACS, Actividades de Construccion y Servicios, S.A.; *Int'l*, pg. 110
CLECO CORPORATE HOLDINGS LLC; *U.S. Private*, pg. 939
CLEDE SAS—See VINCI S.A.; *Int'l*, pg. 8215
CL EDUCATE LIMITED; *Int'l*, pg. 1640
CLEEN ENERGY AG; *Int'l*, pg. 1657
CLEER VISION TEMPERED GLASS, LLC—See Thor Industries, Inc.; *U.S. Public*, pg. 2156
CLEER VISION WINDOWS, INC.—See Thor Industries, Inc.; *U.S. Public*, pg. 2156
CLEEVE TECHNOLOGY INCORPORATED; *Int'l*, pg. 1657
CLEGG INSURANCE GROUP, INC.; *U.S. Private*, pg. 939
CLEGG'S TERMITE AND PEST CONTROL, INC.; *U.S. Private*, pg. 939
CLEGHORN MINERALS LTD.; *Int'l*, pg. 1657
C&L ELECTRIC CO-OPERATIVE; *U.S. Private*, pg. 703
CLEMCO DANMARK APS—See Clemco Industries Corp.; *U.S. Private*, pg. 939
CLEMCO-ELITE STANDARD SYSTEMS LLC—See Reeve Store Equipment Company; *U.S. Private*, pg. 3384
CLEMCO INDUSTRIES CORP.; *U.S. Private*, pg. 939

CLEMCO INTERNATIONAL GMBH—See Clemco Industries Corp.; *U.S. Private*, pg. 939
CLEMCO INTERNATIONAL, S.A.—See Clemco Industries Corp.; *U.S. Private*, pg. 939
CLEMCO KFT—See Clemco Industries Corp.; *U.S. Private*, pg. 939
CLEMENGER BBDO ADELAIDE—See Omnicom Group Inc.; *U.S. Public*, pg. 1577
CLEMENGER BBDO BRISBANE—See Omnicom Group Inc.; *U.S. Public*, pg. 1577
CLEMENGER BBDO MELBOURNE—See Omnicom Group Inc.; *U.S. Public*, pg. 1577
CLEMENGER BBDO SYDNEY—See Omnicom Group Inc.; *U.S. Public*, pg. 1577
CLEMENGER BBDO WELLINGTON—See Omnicom Group Inc.; *U.S. Public*, pg. 1577
THE CLEMENGER GROUP LTD.—See Omnicom Group Inc.; *U.S. Public*, pg. 1577
CLEMENGER HARVIE EDGE; *Int'l*, pg. 1657
CLEMENS & ASSOCIATES INSURANCE AGENCY INC.; *U.S. Private*, pg. 939
CLEMENS AVIATION LLC; *U.S. Private*, pg. 939
CLEMENS CONSTRUCTION CO. INC.; *U.S. Private*, pg. 940
CLEMENS CONSTRUCTION CO. INC—See Clemens Construction Co. Inc.; *U.S. Private*, pg. 940
CLEMENS FAMILY CORPORATION; *U.S. Private*, pg. 940
CLEMENS GMBH—See Avantor, Inc.; *U.S. Public*, pg. 242
CLEMENT CLARKE INTERNATIONAL LTD.—See Metall Zug AG; *Int'l*, pg. 4846
CLEMENT COMMUNICATIONS INC.—See Brady Corporation; *U.S. Public*, pg. 379
CLEMENT CONTRACTING GROUP INC.; *U.S. Private*, pg. 940
CLEMENT HARDWARE, INC.—See Zeskind's Hardware, Inc.; *U.S. Public*, pg. 4602
CLEMENTIA PHARMACEUTICALS INC.—See Ipsen S.A.; *Int'l*, pg. 3798
CLEMENTINA-CLEMCO HOLDING INC.; *U.S. Private*, pg. 940
CLEMENT MAY LIMITED—See Staffing 360 Solutions, Inc.; *U.S. Public*, pg. 1925
CLEMENT PARK CARE HOME DUNDEE—See Balhousie Holdings Limited; *Int'l*, pg. 808
CLEMENTS AND STREET LTD—See Imperium Crown Limited; *Int'l*, pg. 3635
CLEMENTS CONCRETE CO—See Clyde Companies Inc.; *U.S. Private*, pg. 949
CLEMENTS & CO.—See Arthur J. Gallagher & Co.; *U.S. Public*, pg. 204
CLEMENTS FOODS COMPANY; *U.S. Private*, pg. 940
CLEMENTS NATIONAL COMPANY—See Aptiv PLC; *Int'l*, pg. 526
CLEMENTS NUT CO.—See Clements Foods Company; *U.S. Private*, pg. 940
CLEMESSY EMCS—See Eiffage S.A.; *Int'l*, pg. 2329
CLEMEX TECHNOLOGIES INC.; *Int'l*, pg. 1657
CLEMONDO GROUP AB; *Int'l*, pg. 1657
CLEM SNACKS INC.—See Utz Brands, Inc.; *U.S. Public*, pg. 2267
CLEMSON EYE, P.A.—See Independence Capital Partners, LLC; *U.S. Private*, pg. 2056
CLENDENIN BROTHERS INC.; *U.S. Private*, pg. 940
CLENDENIN LUMBER COMPANY—See Baillie Lumber Co., Inc.; *U.S. Private*, pg. 426
CLENE INC.; *U.S. Public*, pg. 513
CLENERGEN CORPORATION LIMITED—See HNO International, Inc.; *U.S. Public*, pg. 1044
CLENERGEN GHANA LIMITED—See HNO International, Inc.; *U.S. Public*, pg. 1044
CLENERGEN PHILIPPINES CORPORATION—See HNO International, Inc.; *U.S. Public*, pg. 1044
CLENERGY AMERICA INC—See Clenergy (Xiamen) Technology Co., Ltd.; *Int'l*, pg. 1658
CLENERGY EUROPE LIMITED—See Clenergy (Xiamen) Technology Co., Ltd.; *Int'l*, pg. 1658
CLENERGY PTY LTD—See Clenergy (Xiamen) Technology Co., Ltd.; *Int'l*, pg. 1658
CLENERGY (XIAMEN) TECHNOLOGY CO., LTD.; *Int'l*, pg. 1657
CLEO BAY USED CARS; *U.S. Private*, pg. 940
CLEO COMMUNICATIONS, INC.; *U.S. Private*, pg. 940
CLEOPATRA HOLDING B.V.—See Masco Corporation; *U.S. Public*, pg. 1390
CLEOPATRA HOSPITALS; *Int'l*, pg. 1658
CLEOPATRA INTERNATIONAL GROUP, INC.; *Int'l*, pg. 1658
CLEOPATRA'S BARGE FINE JEWELRY; *U.S. Private*, pg. 940
CLERE AG; *Int'l*, pg. 1658
CLERHP ESTRUCTURAS SA; *Int'l*, pg. 1658
CLERICAL MEDICAL INVESTMENT GROUP LTD.—See Lloyds Banking Group plc; *Int'l*, pg. 4537
CLERIO VISION INC.; *U.S. Private*, pg. 940
CLERITY SOLUTIONS, INC.—See Dell Technologies Inc.; *U.S. Public*, pg. 649
CLERMONT DIALYSIS CENTER LLC—See Nautic Partners, LLC; *U.S. Private*, pg. 2869
CLERMONT LEISURE (UK) LIMITED; *Int'l*, pg. 1658

COMPANY NAME INDEX

CLERMONT PARTNERS—See Kohlberg & Company, LLC; *U.S. Private*, pg. 2339
CLERMONT SPECIALTY MANAGERS, LTD.—See W.R. Berkley Corporation; *U.S. Public*, pg. 2317
CLE S.A.—See Ackermans & van Haaren NV; *Int'l*, pg. 105
CLESSIDRA CAPITAL CREDIT SGR S.P.A.—See Italmobiliare S.p.A.; *Int'l*, pg. 3829
CLESSIDRA FACTORING S.P.A.—See Italmobiliare S.p.A.; *Int'l*, pg. 3829
CLESSIDRA HOLDING S.P.A.—See Italmobiliare S.p.A.; *Int'l*, pg. 3829
CLESSIDRA PRIVATE EQUITY SGR S.P.A—See Italmobiliare S.p.A.; *Int'l*, pg. 3829
CLESTRA B.V—See Clestra Hauserman S.A.; *Int'l*, pg. 1658
CLESTRA CLEANROOM SA—See Clestra Hauserman S.A.; *Int'l*, pg. 1658
CLESTRA GMBH—See Clestra Hauserman S.A.; *Int'l*, pg. 1658
CLESTRA HAUSERMAN, INC.—See Clestra Hauserman S.A.; *Int'l*, pg. 1658
CLESTRA HAUSERMAN KOREA—See Clestra Hauserman S.A.; *Int'l*, pg. 1658
CLESTRA HAUSERMAN S.A.; *Int'l*, pg. 1658
CLESTRA HAUSERMAN—See Clestra Hauserman S.A.; *Int'l*, pg. 1658
CLESTRA HAUSERMAN SWITZERLAND—See Clestra Hauserman S.A.; *Int'l*, pg. 1658
CLESTRA K.K.—See Clestra Hauserman S.A.; *Int'l*, pg. 1658
CLESTRA LIMITED—See Clestra Hauserman S.A.; *Int'l*, pg. 1658
CLESTRA LIMITED—See Clestra Hauserman S.A.; *Int'l*, pg. 1658
CLETON INSULATION BV—See Altrad Investment Authority SAS; *Int'l*, pg. 398
CLEVE BATTE CONSTRUCTION INC.; *U.S. Private*, pg. 940
CLEVELAND AIR COMFORT CORP.—See Morgan Stanley; *U.S. Public*, pg. 1474
CLEVELAND BRIDGE & ENGINEERING CO. LTD.—See The Cleveland Group of Companies Limited; *Int'l*, pg. 7633
CLEVELAND BRIDGE & ENGINEERING MIDDLE EAST (PVT) LTD—See The Cleveland Group of Companies Limited; *Int'l*, pg. 7633
CLEVELAND BRIDGE INTERNATIONAL LTD—See The Cleveland Group of Companies Limited; *Int'l*, pg. 7633
CLEVELAND BRIDGE STEEL COMPANY LTD—See The Cleveland Group of Companies Limited; *Int'l*, pg. 7633
CLEVELAND BRIDGE UK LTD.—See The Cleveland Group of Companies Limited; *Int'l*, pg. 7633
CLEVELAND BROTHERS EQUIPMENT CO., INC.; *U.S. Private*, pg. 940
CLEVELAND BROTHERS EQUIPMENT—See Cleveland Brothers Equipment Co., Inc.; *U.S. Private*, pg. 940
CLEVELAND BROWNS FOOTBALL COMPANY LLC; *U.S. Private*, pg. 940
CLEVELAND CAPITAL HOLDINGS, INC.; *U.S. Private*, pg. 940
CLEVELAND CAVALIERS/QUICKEN LOANS ARENA—See Cavaliers Operating Company, LLC; *U.S. Private*, pg. 795
CLEVELAND CEMENT CONTRACTORS INC.; *U.S. Private*, pg. 940
CLEVELAND CHAIR COMPANY—See Jackson Furniture Industries; *U.S. Private*, pg. 2176
CLEVELAND CITY FORGE; *U.S. Private*, pg. 940
CLEVELAND-CLIFFS BURNS HARBOR LLC—See Cleveland-Cliffs, Inc.; *U.S. Public*, pg. 514
CLEVELAND-CLIFFS CLEVELAND WORKS LLC—See Cleveland-Cliffs, Inc.; *U.S. Public*, pg. 514
CLEVELAND-CLIFFS, INC.; *U.S. Public*, pg. 513
CLEVELAND-CLIFFS MINORCA MINE INC.—See Cleveland-Cliffs, Inc.; *U.S. Public*, pg. 514
CLEVELAND-CLIFFS PLATE LLC—See Cleveland-Cliffs, Inc.; *U.S. Public*, pg. 514
CLEVELAND-CLIFFS WEIRTON LLC—See Cleveland-Cliffs, Inc.; *U.S. Public*, pg. 514
THE CLEVELAND CLINIC FOUNDATION; *U.S. Private*, pg. 4010
CLEVELAND CLINIC REHABILITATION HOSPITALS, LLC—See Select Medical Holdings Corporation; *U.S. Public*, pg. 1857
CLEVELAND COIN MACHINE EXCHANGE, INC.; *U.S. Private*, pg. 940
CLEVELAND COMMUNICATIONS; *U.S. Private*, pg. 940
CLEVELAND CONSTRUCTION INC.; *U.S. Private*, pg. 941
CLEVELAND DIE & MANUFACTURING, CO.; *U.S. Private*, pg. 941
CLEVELAND ELECTRIC CO.—See Cleveland Group, Inc.; *U.S. Private*, pg. 941
THE CLEVELAND ELECTRIC ILLUMINATING COMPANY—See FirstEnergy Corp.; *U.S. Public*, pg. 849
CLEVELAND FOUNDATION; *U.S. Private*, pg. 941
CLEVELAND GARDENS PTY. LTD.—See Brookfield Corporation; *Int'l*, pg. 1186

CLEVELAND GOLF ASIA CO., LTD.—See Sumitomo Rubber Industries, Ltd.; *Int'l*, pg. 7300
CLEVELAND GOLF CANADA CORP.—See Sumitomo Rubber Industries, Ltd.; *Int'l*, pg. 7300
CLEVELAND GOLF DEUTSCHLAND GMBH—See Sumitomo Rubber Industries, Ltd.; *Int'l*, pg. 7300
CLEVELAND GROUP, INC.; *U.S. Private*, pg. 941
THE CLEVELAND GROUP OF COMPANIES LIMITED; *Int'l*, pg. 7633
CLEVELAND HARDWARE & FORGING CO.; *U.S. Private*, pg. 941
CLEVELAND HEARTLAB, INC.—See Quest Diagnostics, Inc.; *U.S. Public*, pg. 1755
CLEVELAND HOME CARE SERVICES, LLC—See Community Health Systems, Inc.; *U.S. Public*, pg. 552
CLEVELAND HOSPITAL CORPORATION—See Community Health Systems, Inc.; *U.S. Public*, pg. 552
CLEVELAND HOUSING NETWORK; *U.S. Private*, pg. 941
CLEVELAND INDIANS BASEBALL COMPANY, INC.; *U.S. Private*, pg. 941
CLEVELAND INSTITUTE OF ELECTRONICS; *U.S. Private*, pg. 941
CLEVELAND MACK SALES INC.; *U.S. Private*, pg. 941
CLEVELAND MARBLE MOSAIC COMPANY; *U.S. Private*, pg. 941
CLEVELAND MEDICAL CLINIC, INC.—See Community Health Systems, Inc.; *U.S. Public*, pg. 552
CLEVELAND MEDICAL DEVICES, INC.; *U.S. Private*, pg. 941
CLEVELAND METAL EXCHANGE INC.—See The Mill Steel Co., Inc.; *U.S. Private*, pg. 4079
CLEVELAND MINING COMPANY LIMITED; *Int'l*, pg. 1658
CLEVELAND MUSEUM OF ART; *U.S. Private*, pg. 941
CLEVELAND MUSEUM OF NATURAL HISTORY; *U.S. Private*, pg. 941
CLEVELAND PIGMENT & COLOR INC.—See Lancer Dispersions Inc.; *U.S. Private*, pg. 2382
CLEVELAND PLANT AND FLOWER COMPANY; *U.S. Private*, pg. 941
CLEVELAND PLUMBING SUPPLY CO., INC.; *U.S. Private*, pg. 941
CLEVELAND RANGE LLC—See Ali Holding S.r.l; *Int'l*, pg. 322
CLEVELAND RANGE, LTD.—See Ali Holding S.r.l; *Int'l*, pg. 322
CLEVELAND ROLL FORMING ENVIRONMENTAL DIVISION, INC.—See Fuel Tech, Inc.; *U.S. Public*, pg. 891
CLEVELAND SCENE PUBLISHING LLC—See Great Lakes Publishing Company; *U.S. Private*, pg. 1765
CLEVELAND SHIP REPAIR COMPANY—See Fincantieri S.p.A.; *Int'l*, pg. 2671
CLEVELAND SKIN PATHOLOGY LABORATORY INC.—See Aurora Diagnostics Holdings, LLC; *U.S. Private*, pg. 394
CLEVELAND STEEL CONTAINER CORPORATION; *U.S. Private*, pg. 941
CLEVELAND TENNESSEE HOSPITAL COMPANY, LLC—See Hamilton Health Care System, Inc.; *U.S. Private*, pg. 1848
CLEVELAND TRACK MATERIAL, INC.—See Vossloh AG; *Int'l*, pg. 8308
CLEVELAND TRANSIT LTD.—See Stagecoach Group plc; *Int'l*, pg. 7163
CLEVELAND UTILITIES; *U.S. Private*, pg. 941
CLEVELAND VICON CO. INC.; *U.S. Private*, pg. 941
CLEVELAND WRECKING COMPANY—See AECOM; *U.S. Public*, pg. 51
C-LEVELED LLC—See Direct Online Marketing, LLC; *U.S. Private*, pg. 1235
CLEVERBRIDGE AG—See EMH Partners GmbH; *Int'l*, pg. 2380
CLEVERBRIDGE, INC.—See EMH Partners GmbH; *Int'l*, pg. 2380
CLEVER-CRAWFORD SA—See ASSA ABLOY AB; *Int'l*, pg. 634
CLEVER DEVICES LTD.; *U.S. Private*, pg. 942
CLEVER GLOBAL SA; *Int'l*, pg. 1658
CLEVER INC.—See The Goldman Sachs Group, Inc.; *U.S. Public*, pg. 2082
CLEVER LEAVES HOLDINGS INC.; *U.S. Public*, pg. 514
CLEVERMETHOD, INC.; *U.S. Private*, pg. 942
CLEVER REINFORCEMENT IBERICA-MATERIAIS DE CONSTRUCAO, LDA.—See Simpson Manufacturing Company, Inc.; *U.S. Public*, pg. 1882
CLEVERSAFE, INC.—See International Business Machines Corporation; *U.S. Public*, pg. 1148
CLEVERTECH; *U.S. Private*, pg. 942
CLEVERWORKS; *U.S. Private*, pg. 942
CLEVO COMPANY; *Int'l*, pg. 1658
CLEWISTON DIALYSIS CENTER, LLC—See Nautic Partners, LLC; *U.S. Private*, pg. 2869
CLEWISTON NEWS—See Independent Newspapers, Inc.; *U.S. Private*, pg. 2060
CLEWISTON SUGAR HOUSE—See United States Sugar Corporation; *U.S. Private*, pg. 4300
CLEWS & STRAWBRIDGE; *U.S. Private*, pg. 942
CLEXTRAL INC.—See Groupe Legris Industries; *Int'l*, pg. 3106

CLEXTRAL SAS—See Groupe Legris Industries; *Int'l*, pg. 3106
C L FINANCE LIMITED—See Cattles Limited; *Int'l*, pg. 1361
CL FINANCIAL LIMITED; *Int'l*, pg. 1640
C.L. FRATES AND COMPANY; *U.S. Private*, pg. 708
CLF-SATREM—See Groupe Gorge S.A.; *Int'l*, pg. 3103
CLG HOLDINGS LIMITED—See Serafin Unternehmensgruppe GmbH; *Int'l*, pg. 6720
CL GROUP (HOLDINGS) LIMITED; *Int'l*, pg. 1640
CLH AVIACION, S.A—See Compania Logistica de Hidrocarburos CLH, S.A.; *Int'l*, pg. 1749
CLH INC.; *U.S. Private*, pg. 942
CLH INTERNATIONAL INC.; *U.S. Private*, pg. 942
CL HOLDINGS INC.; *Int'l*, pg. 1640
CLICARS SPAIN SL—See Stellantis N.V.; *Int'l*, pg. 7201
CLICKART, TALLER DE COMUNICACIO, S.L.—See Sanoma Oyj; *Int'l*, pg. 6553
CLICKAWAY CORPORATION; *U.S. Private*, pg. 942
CLICKBOOTH.COM LLC—See Centre Lane Partners, LLC; *U.S. Private*, pg. 827
CLICK CAMERA SHOP INCORPORATED; *U.S. Private*, pg. 942
CLICKCULTURE; *U.S. Private*, pg. 942
CLICKDEALER ASIA PTE LTD.; *Int'l*, pg. 1658
CLICK DISTRIBUTING CO INC.—See Fritz Company; *U.S. Private*, pg. 1612
CLICKER INC.; *U.S. Private*, pg. 942
CLICK HERE, INC.; *U.S. Private*, pg. 942
CLICK HERE—See Click Here, Inc.; *U.S. Private*, pg. 942
CLICK INTERNATIONAL (HK) TRADING CO., LTD.—See Shenzhen Click Technology Co., Ltd.; *Int'l*, pg. 6807
CLICKIT VENTURES, LLC; *U.S. Private*, pg. 942
CLICKMAIL MARKETING, INC.; *U.S. Private*, pg. 942
CLICKON COMMUNICATIONS PROPRIETARY LIMITED—See The Bidvest Group Limited; *Int'l*, pg. 7624
CLICKSAFETY.COM, INC.—See Blackstone Inc.; *U.S. Public*, pg. 348
CLICKSAFETY.COM, INC.—See Canada Pension Plan Investment Board; *Int'l*, pg. 1279
CLICK SALES INC.—See Keynetics, Inc.; *U.S. Private*, pg. 2294
CLICKS DIRECT MEDICINES (PROPRIETARY) LIMITED—See Clicks Group Limited; *Int'l*, pg. 1658
CLICKS GROUP LIMITED; *Int'l*, pg. 1658
CLICKSHOPS INC.; *U.S. Private*, pg. 942
CLICKSOFTWARE AUSTRALIA PTY LIMITED—See Salesforce, Inc.; *U.S. Public*, pg. 1836
CLICKSOFTWARE CENTRAL EUROPE GMBH—See Salesforce, Inc.; *U.S. Public*, pg. 1837
CLICKSOFTWARE EUROPE LIMITED—See Salesforce, Inc.; *U.S. Public*, pg. 1837
CLICKSOFTWARE, INC.—See Salesforce, Inc.; *U.S. Public*, pg. 1837
CLICKSOFTWARE TECHNOLOGIES LTD.—See Salesforce, Inc.; *U.S. Public*, pg. 1836
CLICKSPRING DESIGN; *U.S. Private*, pg. 942
CLICKSQUARED INC.—See Zeta Interactive Corporation; *U.S. Private*, pg. 4602
CLICKSQUARED LTD.—See Zeta Interactive Corporation; *U.S. Private*, pg. 4603
CLICKS RECRUIT (AUSTRALIA) PTY. LTD.—See Bain Capital, LP; *U.S. Private*, pg. 433
CLICKSTOP INC.; *U.S. Private*, pg. 942
CLICKTALE LTD.—See Content Square SAS; *Int'l*, pg. 1779
CLICK TECH INC.—See Shenzhen Click Technology Co., Ltd.; *Int'l*, pg. 6807
CLICKTOOLS LTD.—See SAP SE; *Int'l*, pg. 6567
CLICKTOSHOP, LLC; *U.S. Private*, pg. 942
CLICK TRAVEL LTD.—See TravelPerk SL; *Int'l*, pg. 7907
CLICKTRUE PTE. LTD.—See Singapore Press Holdings Ltd.; *Int'l*, pg. 6942
CLICK WHOLESALE DISTRIBUTING, INC.—See Craig Stein Beverage; *U.S. Private*, pg. 1083
CLICON CO., LTD.—See Sumitomo Osaka Cement Co Ltd; *Int'l*, pg. 7296
CLI CORPORATION; *U.S. Private*, pg. 942
CLICQUOT INC—See LVMH Moet Hennessy Louis Vuitton SE; *Int'l*, pg. 4599
CLICRDV SARL—See Solocal Group; *Int'l*, pg. 7074
CLIC TECHNOLOGY, INC.; *U.S. Private*, pg. 942
CLID SYSTEMES SAS—See Haco N.V.; *Int'l*, pg. 3204
CLIENT 1ST ADVISORS, INC.; *U.S. Private*, pg. 943
CLIENT ATTRACTION LLC; *U.S. Private*, pg. 943
CLIENTELE LIFE ASSURANCE COMPANY LIMITED—See Clientele Limited; *Int'l*, pg. 1659
CLIENTELE LIMITED; *Int'l*, pg. 1658
CLIENT NETWORK SERVICES INC.—See The Carlyle Group Inc.; *U.S. Public*, pg. 2045
CLIENT RESOURCES, INC; *U.S. Private*, pg. 943
CLIENT SERVICE INTERNATIONAL, INC.; *Int'l*, pg. 1658
CLIENT SERVICES INC.; *U.S. Private*, pg. 943
CLIENT SOLUTION ARCHITECTS; *U.S. Private*, pg. 943
CLIENT SOLUTIONS LTD.—See TD Synnex Corp; *U.S. Public*, pg. 1985
CLIENT STRATEGY GROUP, LLC—See Columbus A/S; *Int'l*, pg. 1706

CLIENT SOLUTION ARCHITECTS

CORPORATE AFFILIATIONS

CLIF BAR & COMPANY—See Mondelez International, Inc.; *U.S. Public*, pg. 1461
CLIFF AVE ACCEPTANCE INC.; *U.S. Private*, pg. 943
CLIFF DEVELOPMENT SALES & APPRAISALS, INC.; *U.S. Private*, pg. 943
CLIFF DRYSDALE MANAGEMENT, LLC—See Troon Golf L.L.C.; *U.S. Private*, pg. 4242
CLIFF MODELS AB—See Sdiptech AB; *Int'l*, pg. 6658
CLIFFMONT RESOURCES LTD.; *Int'l*, pg. 1659
CLIFFORD/BRATSKEIR PUBLIC RELATIONS LLC—See Stagwell, Inc.; *U.S. Public*, pg. 1926
CLIFFORD-JACOBS FORGING COMPANY—See Mission Essential Personnel, LLC; *U.S. Private*, pg. 2747
CLIFFORD METAL—See Lapham-Hickey Steel Corp.; *U.S. Private*, pg. 2391
CLIFFORD MODERN LIVING HOLDINGS LIMITED; *Int'l*, pg. 1659
CLIFFORD PAPER INC.; *U.S. Private*, pg. 943
CLIFFORD POWER SYSTEMS INC.; *U.S. Private*, pg. 943
CLIFFORD R. ZINN & SON, INC.—See Genstar Capital, LLC; *U.S. Private*, pg. 1674
CLIFFORD SWAN INVESTMENT COUNSEL LLC—See Royal Bank of Canada; *Int'l*, pg. 6409
CLIFFORD W. PERHAM, INC.—See United Natural Foods, Inc.; *U.S. Public*, pg. 2231
CLIFF ROSS; *U.S. Private*, pg. 943
THE CLIFFS COMMUNITIES, INC.; *U.S. Private*, pg. 4010
CLIFFSIDE CAPITAL LTD.—See Cliffside Ltd.; *Int'l*, pg. 1659
CLIFFSIDE LTD.; *Int'l*, pg. 1659
CLIFFS MINING COMPANY—See Cleveland-Cliffs, Inc.; *U.S. Public*, pg. 514
CLIFFS NETHERLANDS B.V.—See Cleveland-Cliffs, Inc.; *U.S. Public*, pg. 514
CLIFFSNOTES, INC.—See John Wiley & Sons, Inc.; *U.S. Public*, pg. 1193
CLIFFSTAR LLC—See Primo Water Corporation; *U.S. Public*, pg. 1718
CLIFF VIESSMAN INC.; *U.S. Private*, pg. 943
CLIFF WALL AUTOMOTIVE LLC—See Bergstrom Corp.; *U.S. Private*, pg. 531
CLIFFWATER INVESTMENTS, LLC—See Virtus Investment Partners, Inc.; *U.S. Public*, pg. 2300
CLIFROY LIMITED—See Bendigo & Adelaide Bank Ltd.; *Int'l*, pg. 970
CLIFT BUICK GMC; *U.S. Private*, pg. 943
C-LIFT LLC—See AIP, LLC; *U.S. Private*, pg. 136
CLIFTON ASSET MANAGEMENT PLC; *Int'l*, pg. 1659
CLIFTON BRICK MANUFACTURERS PTY LTD.—See Brickworks Limited; *Int'l*, pg. 1152
CLIFTON CONSULTING LTD—See Clifton Asset Management Plc; *Int'l*, pg. 1659
CLIFTON DIALYSIS CENTER, LLC—See Nautic Partners, LLC; *U.S. Private*, pg. 2869
CLIFTON DIALYSIS, LLC—See DaVita Inc.; *U.S. Public*, pg. 636
THE CLIFTON GROUP INVESTMENT MANAGEMENT COMPANY—See Morgan Stanley; *U.S. Public*, pg. 1472
CLIFTONLARSONALLEN LLP; *U.S. Private*, pg. 943
CLIFTON MINING COMPANY; *U.S. Public*, pg. 514
CLIFTON STEEL COMPANY; *U.S. Private*, pg. 943
CLIFTON WEALTH LTD—See Clifton Asset Management Plc; *Int'l*, pg. 1659
CLIKIA CORP.; *U.S. Public*, pg. 514
CLI LAWYERS PTY. LTD.—See Archer Capital Pty. Ltd.; *Int'l*, pg. 547
CLI LAWYERS SA PTY. LTD.—See Archer Capital Pty. Ltd.; *Int'l*, pg. 547
CLIMACOOL CORP.—See NIBE Industrier AB; *Int'l*, pg. 5262
CLIMAESPACO—See ENGIE SA; *Int'l*, pg. 2431
CLIMALEVEL ENERGIESYSTEME GMBH; *Int'l*, pg. 1659
CLIMASOL S.A.—See Bharti Enterprises Limited; *Int'l*, pg. 1012
CLIMA SVERIGE AB—See Beijer Ref AB; *Int'l*, pg. 944
CLIMA TECH AIRCONDITIONERS GMBH—See Zamil Industrial Investment Company; *Int'l*, pg. 8623
CLIMATEC, LLC—See Robert Bosch GmbH; *Int'l*, pg. 6363
THE CLIMATE CONTROL GROUP, INC.—See NIBE Industrier AB; *Int'l*, pg. 5262
CLIMATE CONTROL MECHANICAL SERVICES, INC.; *U.S. Private*, pg. 943
CLIMATE CONTROL PROPERTIES (PTY.) LTD.—See Metair Investments Limited; *Int'l*, pg. 4844
CLIMATE & CONTROLS BENELUX B.V.—See Carrier Global Corporation; *U.S. Public*, pg. 443
THE CLIMATE CORPORATION—See Bayer Aktiengesellschaft; *Int'l*, pg. 909
CLIMATECRAFT, INC.—See NIBE Industrier AB; *Int'l*, pg. 5262
CLIMATE ENGINEERS INC.; *U.S. Private*, pg. 943
CLIMATE EXCHANGE PLC—See Intercontinental Exchange, Inc.; *U.S. Public*, pg. 1143
CLIMATE HUMAN CAPITAL PLC; *Int'l*, pg. 1659
CLIMATE LLC—See Bayer Aktiengesellschaft; *Int'l*, pg. 907
CLIMATEMASTER, INC.—See NIBE Industrier AB; *Int'l*, pg. 5263

CLIMATE PROS, LLC—See Saw Mill Capital LLC; *U.S. Private*, pg. 3557
CLIMA-TEQ CO., LTD.—See Kajima Corporation; *Int'l*, pg. 4053
CLIMATEROCK; *Int'l*, pg. 1659
CLIMATE TECHNOLOGIES PTY. LTD; *Int'l*, pg. 1659
CLIMATIC COMFORT PRODUCTS, LLC—See The Climatic Corporation; *U.S. Private*, pg. 4010
THE CLIMATIC CORPORATION; *U.S. Private*, pg. 4010
THE CLIMATIC DEVELOPMENT CORPORATION.—See The Climatic Corporation; *U.S. Private*, pg. 4010
CLIMATIC HOME PRODUCTS—See The Climatic Corporation; *U.S. Private*, pg. 4010
CLIMATISATION ET CHAUFFAGE URBAINS DE MONTREAL (CCUM)—See Caisse de Depot et Placement du Quebec; *Int'l*, pg. 1256
CLIMAT LOCATION SA—See ANDREWS SYKES GROUP PLC; *Int'l*, pg. 452
CLIMAT LOCATION SAS—See ANDREWS SYKES GROUP PLC; *Int'l*, pg. 452
CLIMATS S.A.S.—See Schunk GmbH; *Int'l*, pg. 6641
CLIMAVENETA DEUTSCHLAND GMBH—See Mitsubishi Electric Corporation; *Int'l*, pg. 4943
CLIMAVENETA FRANCE—See Mitsubishi Electric Corporation; *Int'l*, pg. 4943
CLIMAVENETA POLSKA SP. Z O.O.—See Mitsubishi Electric Corporation; *Int'l*, pg. 4943
CLIMAVENETA S.P.A.—See Mitsubishi Electric Corporation; *Int'l*, pg. 4943
CLIMAX ENGINEERED MATERIALS—See Freeport-McMoRan Inc.; *U.S. Public*, pg. 884
THE CLIMAX ENGINEERING COMPANY LIMITED; *Int'l*, pg. 7633
CLIMAX GMBH—See Gladstone Management Corporation; *U.S. Private*, pg. 1705
CLIMAX MANUFACTURING COMPANY—See DeltaPoint Capital Management, LLC; *U.S. Private*, pg. 1202
CLIMAX METAL PRODUCTS COMPANY—See RBC Bearings Incorporated; *U.S. Public*, pg. 1766
CLIMAX MOLYBDENUM COMPANY—See Freeport-McMoRan Inc.; *U.S. Public*, pg. 884
CLIMAX MOLYBDENUM U.K. LIMITED—See Freeport-McMoRan Inc.; *U.S. Public*, pg. 884
CLIMAX PACKAGING, INC.—See DeltaPoint Capital Management, LLC; *U.S. Private*, pg. 1202
CLIMAX PORTABLE MACHINE TOOLS, INC.—See Gladstone Management Corporation; *U.S. Private*, pg. 1705
CLIMB CHANNEL SOLUTIONS, INC.—See Climb Global Solutions, Inc.; *U.S. Public*, pg. 514
CLIMBER.COM—See Mingle, LLC; *U.S. Private*, pg. 2742
CLIMB GLOBAL SOLUTIONS, INC.; *U.S. Public*, pg. 514
CLIMBTECH; *U.S. Private*, pg. 943
CLIMCO COILS COMPANY; *U.S. Private*, pg. 943
CLIME ASSET MANAGEMENT PTY. LTD.—See Clime Investment Management Limited; *Int'l*, pg. 1659
CLIME CAPITAL LIMITED; *Int'l*, pg. 1659
CLIME INVESTMENT MANAGEMENT LIMITED; *Int'l*, pg. 1659
CLIMEON AB; *Int'l*, pg. 1659
CLIMESPACE—See ENGIE SA; *Int'l*, pg. 2431
CLIMET INSTRUMENTS CO.—See Venturedyne, Ltd.; *U.S. Private*, pg. 4358
CLINAPPS, INC.—See Genstar Capital, LLC; *U.S. Private*, pg. 1675
CLINCHE GAVAZZENI SPA—See Techint S.p.A.; *Int'l*, pg. 7503
CLINCH RIVER CORPORATION—See KBR, Inc.; *U.S. Public*, pg. 1216
CLINCH VALLEY MEDICAL CENTER, INC.—See Apollo Global Management, Inc.; *U.S. Public*, pg. 155
CLINCH VALLEY MEMORIAL CEMETERY, INC.—See Axar Capital Management L.P.; *U.S. Private*, pg. 411
CLINCH VALLEY PHYSICIANS ASSOCIATES, LLC—See Apollo Global Management, Inc.; *U.S. Public*, pg. 155
CLINE ACQUISITION CORP.—See Zurn Elkay Water Solutions Corporation; *U.S. Public*, pg. 2412
CLINECT PTY LTD—See EBOS Group Limited; *Int'l*, pg. 2285
CLINE, DAVIS & MANN, INC. - EUROPE—See Omnicom Group Inc.; *U.S. Public*, pg. 1579
CLINE, DAVIS & MANN, INC. - LOS ANGELES—See Omnicom Group Inc.; *U.S. Public*, pg. 1579
CLINE, DAVIS & MANN, INC. - PRINCETON—See Omnicom Group Inc.; *U.S. Public*, pg. 1579
CLINE, DAVIS & MANN, INC.—See Omnicom Group Inc.; *U.S. Public*, pg. 1579
CLINE ENERGY INC.; *U.S. Private*, pg. 943
CLINE HOSE & HYDRAULICS, LLC—See Bridgestone Corporation; *Int'l*, pg. 1156
C-LINE PRODUCTS, INC.; *U.S. Private*, pg. 704
CLINE RESOURCE & DEVELOPMENT CO.; *U.S. Private*, pg. 943
CLINERION AG—See Informa plc; *Int'l*, pg. 3691
CLINERION TURKEY TEKNOLOJI ARASTIRMA LIMITED SIRKETI—See Informa plc; *Int'l*, pg. 3691
C-LINES FRANCE SAS—See AGCO Corporation; *U.S. Public*, pg. 58
CLINE TOOL & SERVICE COMPANY—See Bertram Capital Management, LLC; *U.S. Private*, pg. 539

CLINE WOOD AGENCY, INC.—See Marsh & McLennan Companies, Inc.; *U.S. Public*, pg. 1380
CLINGAN STEEL INC.; *U.S. Private*, pg. 943
CLINICA BAVIERA S.A.—See Aier Eye Hospital Group Co., Ltd.; *Int'l*, pg. 231
CLINICA BIO BIO S.A.—See UnitedHealth Group Incorporated; *U.S. Public*, pg. 2240
CLINICA CENTRAL DO BONFIM S.A—See DaVita Inc.; *U.S. Public*, pg. 636
CLINICA CIUDAD DEL MAR S.A.—See UnitedHealth Group Incorporated; *U.S. Public*, pg. 2240
CLINICA CUF ALVALADE, S.A.—See Jose de Mello, SGPS, S.A.; *Int'l*, pg. 4001
CLINICA CUF BELEM, S.A.—See Jose de Mello, SGPS, S.A.; *Int'l*, pg. 4001
CLINICA DAVILA Y SERVICIOS MEDICOS S.A.—See UnitedHealth Group Incorporated; *U.S. Public*, pg. 2240
CLINICA DEL COUNTRY S.A.—See UnitedHealth Group Incorporated; *U.S. Public*, pg. 2239
CLINICA DE MARLY SA; *Int'l*, pg. 1659
CLINICA LAS CONDES S.A.; *Int'l*, pg. 1659
CLINICAL COMPUTING, INC.—See Clinical Computing Plc; *Int'l*, pg. 1659
CLINICAL COMPUTING PLC; *Int'l*, pg. 1659
CLINICAL CONSULTANTS INTERNATIONAL LLC—See Novo Integrated Sciences, Inc.; *U.S. Public*, pg. 1549
CLINICAL DESIGN TECHNOLOGIES LTD.; *Int'l*, pg. 1659
CLINICAL DIAGNOSTICS SOLUTIONS INC—See Boule Diagnostics AB; *Int'l*, pg. 1119
CLINICAL ENTERPRISE, INC.—See Eurofins Scientific S.E.; *Int'l*, pg. 2535
CLINICAL GENOMICS PTY. LTD.; *Int'l*, pg. 1659
CLINICAL GRAPHICS BV—See Zimmer Biomet Holdings, Inc.; *U.S. Public*, pg. 2406
CLINICAL INK INC.—See GI Manager L.P.; *U.S. Private*, pg. 1691
CLINICAL INNOVATIONS, LLC—See Investor AB; *Int'l*, pg. 3786
CLINICAL LABORATORIES OF HAWAII, LLP—See Sonic Healthcare Limited; *Int'l*, pg. 7098
CLINICAL LABORATORIES PTY. LTD.—See Crescent Capital Partners Ltd.; *Int'l*, pg. 1839
CLINICAL LABORATORY PARTNERS, LLC—See Hartford HealthCare Corporation; *U.S. Private*, pg. 1873
CLINICAL LASERTHERMIA SYSTEMS AB; *Int'l*, pg. 1659
CLINICAL LASERTHERMIA SYSTEMS AMERICAS INC.—See Clinical Laserthermia Systems AB; *Int'l*, pg. 1660
CLINICALMIND LLC; *U.S. Private*, pg. 944
CLINICAL NETWORK G.K.—See H.U. Group Holdings, Inc.; *Int'l*, pg. 3196
CLINICAL OUTCOMES RESOURCE APPLICATION CORPORATION—See Cencora, Inc.; *U.S. Public*, pg. 467
CLINICAL PATHOLOGY LABORATORIES, INC. - BRYAN—See Sonic Healthcare Limited; *Int'l*, pg. 7098
CLINICAL PATHOLOGY LABORATORIES, INC. - LIMA PATHOLOGY LABORATORIES—See Sonic Healthcare Limited; *Int'l*, pg. 7098
CLINICAL PATHOLOGY LABORATORIES, INC.—See Sonic Healthcare Limited; *Int'l*, pg. 7098
CLINICAL PATHOLOGY LABORATORIES SOUTHEAST, INC.—See Sonic Healthcare Limited; *Int'l*, pg. 7098
CLINICAL PORTER INC.—See Sony Group Corporation; *Int'l*, pg. 7102
CLINICAL RADIOLOGY FOUNDATION; *U.S. Private*, pg. 944
CLINICAL REFERENCE LABORATORY, INC.; *U.S. Private*, pg. 944
CLINICAL RESEARCH ATLANTA—See KKR & Co. Inc.; *U.S. Public*, pg. 1252
CLINICAL RESEARCH MANAGEMENT, INC.—See ICON plc; *Int'l*, pg. 3584
CLINICAL RESOURCE NETWORK, LLC.; *U.S. Private*, pg. 944
CLINICAL RESOURCES LLC; *U.S. Private*, pg. 944
CLINICAL REVENUE MANAGEMENT SERVICES, LLC—See AAC Holdings, Inc.; *U.S. Private*, pg. 31
CLINICAL SERVICES, INC.; *U.S. Private*, pg. 944
CLINICAL SERVICES OF RHODE ISLAND - GREENVILLE—See AAC Holdings, Inc.; *U.S. Private*, pg. 30
CLINICAL SPECIALTIES, INC.; *U.S. Private*, pg. 944
CLINICAL SUPPORT CORPORATION—See Nippon Telegraph & Telephone Corporation; *Int'l*, pg. 5346
CLINICAL SYSTEMS, INC.—See CCL Industries Inc.; *Int'l*, pg. 1369
CLINICAL TRIAL CONSULTANTS AB; *Int'l*, pg. 1660
CLINICAL TRIAL NETWORK; *U.S. Private*, pg. 944
CLINICAL TRIALS INSURANCE SERVICES LIMITED—See Howden Group Holdings Limited; *Int'l*, pg. 3493
CLINICAL TRIALS OF AMERICA, INC.—See IMA Group Management Company, LLC; *U.S. Private*, pg. 2044
CLINICA MEDICA DAVITA LONDRINA SERVICOS DE NEFROLOGIA LTDA.—See DaVita Inc.; *U.S. Public*, pg. 636

COMPANY NAME INDEX

CLINICA MEDICO CIRURGICA DE SANTA TECLA, S.A.—See UnitedHealth Group Incorporated; *U.S. Public*, pg. 2240
CLINICA SABEDOTTI LTDA.—See Centro de Imagem Diagnosticos S.A.; *Int'l*, pg. 1413
CLINICA SAN BORJA—See UnitedHealth Group Incorporated; *U.S. Public*, pg. 2240
CLINICA SANCHEZ FERRER S.A.—See UnitedHealth Group Incorporated; *U.S. Public*, pg. 2240
CLINICA SAN FELIPE S.A.—See UnitedHealth Group Incorporated; *U.S. Public*, pg. 2240
CLINICA SAN FRANCESCO S.R.L.—See Garofalo Health Care SpA; *Int'l*, pg. 2886
CLINICA SANTA MARIA S.A.—See UnitedHealth Group Incorporated; *U.S. Public*, pg. 2240
CLINICA SANTO DOMINGO DE LUGO, S.L.—See Centene Corporation; *U.S. Public*, pg. 468
CLINICAS DEL CAMINO REAL, INC.; *U.S. Private*, pg. 944
CLINICAS DE SALUD DEL PUEBLO, INC.; *U.S. Private*, pg. 944
CLINICA VESPUCIO S.A.—See UnitedHealth Group Incorporated; *U.S. Public*, pg. 2240
CLINICHAIN BV—See ADDvise Group AB; *Int'l*, pg. 136
CLINICHAIN HOLDING B.V.—See ADDvise Group AB; *Int'l*, pg. 136
CLINICIENT, INC.—See Warburg Pincus LLC; *U.S. Private*, pg. 4440
CLINICLANDS AB—See Henry Schein, Inc.; *U.S. Public*, pg. 1025
CLINIC MANAGEMENT SERVICES, INC.—See Blackstone Inc.; *U.S. Public*, pg. 359
CLINIGENCE, LLC—See NUTEX HEALTH INC.; *U.S. Public*, pg. 1555
CLINIGENE INTERNATIONAL LIMITED—See Biocon Ltd.; *Int'l*, pg. 1036
CLINIGEN GROUP PLC—See Triton Advisers Limited; *Int'l*, pg. 7935
CLINILAB LABORATORIO CLINICO HUELVA, S.L.U.—See Eurofins Scientific S.E.; *Int'l*, pg. 2535
CLINILABO B.V.B.A.—See Sonic Healthcare Limited; *Int'l*, pg. 7096
CLINILABS, INC.; *U.S. Private*, pg. 944
CLININTEL LIMITED—See Pamplona Capital Management LLP; *Int'l*, pg. 5712
CLINIPACE, INC.—See dMed Biopharmaceutical Co. Ltd.; *Int'l*, pg. 2143
CLINIPAK LIMITED—See Jourdan plc; *Int'l*, pg. 4003
CLINIPATH (MALAYSIA) SDN BHD—See Malaysian Genomics Resource Centre Berhad; *Int'l*, pg. 4662
CLINIPATH PATHOLOGY PTY LIMITED—See Sonic Healthcare Limited; *Int'l*, pg. 7096
CLINIQA CORPORATION—See Bio-Techne Corporation; *U.S. Public*, pg. 334
CLINIQUE BOIS-CERF S.A.—See Remgro Limited; *Int'l*, pg. 6270
CLINIQUE BON SECOURS SAS—See Eurazeo SE; *Int'l*, pg. 2527
CLINIQUE CECIL SA—See Remgro Limited; *Int'l*, pg. 6270
CLINIQUE DES GRANGETTES SA—See Remgro Limited; *Int'l*, pg. 6269
CLINIQUE DU JURA SAS—See Eurazeo SE; *Int'l*, pg. 2528
CLINIQUE DU PARC LYON SA—See Eurazeo SE; *Int'l*, pg. 2528
CLINIQUE DU RENAISON SAS—See Eurazeo SE; *Int'l*, pg. 2528
CLINIQUE GENERALE-BEAULIEU SA—See AEVIS VICTORIA SA; *Int'l*, pg. 183
CLINIQUE LABORATORIES, INC.—See The Estee Lauder Companies Inc.; *U.S. Public*, pg. 2073
CLINIQUE LA METAIRE—See Apax Partners LLP; *Int'l*, pg. 502
CLINIQUE NOUVELLE DU FOREZ SA—See Eurazeo SE; *Int'l*, pg. 2527
CLINIQUE SAINT MARTIN SA—See Eurazeo SE; *Int'l*, pg. 2527
CLINISYS DEUTSCHLAND GMBH—See Roper Technologies, Inc.; *U.S. Public*, pg. 1810
CLINISYS GROUP LIMITED—See Roper Technologies, Inc.; *U.S. Public*, pg. 1810
CLINISYS N.V.—See Roper Technologies, Inc.; *U.S. Public*, pg. 1810
CLINISYS SCOTLAND LIMITED—See Roper Technologies, Inc.; *U.S. Public*, pg. 1810
CLINITEC PTY LIMITED—See Temenos AG; *Int'l*, pg. 7555
CLINIX MEDICAL INFORMATION SERVICES LLC; *U.S. Private*, pg. 944
C-LINK SQUARED LIMITED; *Int'l*, pg. 1239
CLINLAB, INC.—See Rennova Health, Inc.; *U.S. Public*, pg. 1783
CLINLOGIX, LLC—See ArchiMed SAS; *Int'l*, pg. 549
CLINOMICS INC.; *Int'l*, pg. 1660
CLINOVATIONS, LLC.; *U.S. Private*, pg. 944
CLINPATH LABORATORIES PTY LIMITED—See Sonic Healthcare Limited; *Int'l*, pg. 7096

CLINPSYCH PSYCHOLOGY SERVICES PTY. LTD.—See Madison Dearborn Partners, LLC; *U.S. Private*, pg. 2540
CLINQUE DE LA MUETTE SAS—See Ramsay Health Care Limited; *Int'l*, pg. 6200
CLINTARA, LLC—See Genstar Capital, LLC; *U.S. Private*, pg. 1675
CLINTEC INTERNATIONAL, INC.—See IQVIA Holdings Inc.; *U.S. Public*, pg. 1168
CLINTEC INTERNATIONAL LTD.—See IQVIA Holdings Inc.; *U.S. Public*, pg. 1168
CL INTERNATIONAL CO., LTD.; *Int'l*, pg. 1640
CLINT NEWELL MOTORS INC.; *U.S. Private*, pg. 944
CLINTON BANCSHARES, INC.; *U.S. Private*, pg. 944
CLINTON COUNTY ELECTRIC COOPERATIVE, INC.; *U.S. Private*, pg. 944
CLINTON COUNTY HOSPITAL, INC.; *U.S. Private*, pg. 944
CLINTON COUNTY LANDFILL PARTNERSHIP—See Republic Services, Inc.; *U.S. Public*, pg. 1786
CLINTON DIALYSIS CLINIC, LLC—See Nautic Partners, LLC; *U.S. Private*, pg. 2869
CLINTON ELECTRONICS CORPORATION; *U.S. Private*, pg. 944
CLINTON ENGINEERING CO., INC.—See McCarthy Bush Corporation; *U.S. Private*, pg. 2626
CLINTON FAMILY FORD LINCOLN MERCURY OF ROCK HILL, INC.; *U.S. Private*, pg. 944
CLINTON FORD LINCOLN; *U.S. Private*, pg. 944
CLINTON HEALTH ACCESS INITIATIVE, INC.; *U.S. Private*, pg. 944
CLINTON HMA, LLC—See Community Health Systems, Inc.; *U.S. Public*, pg. 552
CLINTON HOSPITAL CORPORATION—See Quorum Health Corporation; *U.S. Private*, pg. 3329
CLINTON INDUSTRIES, INC.; *U.S. Private*, pg. 945
CLINTON LANDFILL INC.—See Peoria Disposal Company/Area Disposal Service, Inc., *U.S. Private*, pg. 3143
THE CLINTON NATIONAL BANK; *U.S. Private*, pg. 4010
CLINTON NURSERY PRODUCTS INC.; *U.S. Private*, pg. 945
CLINTON SAVINGS BANK; *U.S. Private*, pg. 945
CLINTON TOWNSHIP DIALYSIS, LLC—See DaVita Inc.; *U.S. Public*, pg. 636
CLINTONVILLE LUMBER INC.; *U.S. Private*, pg. 945
CLINTON WIND, LLC—See E.ON SE; *Int'l*, pg. 2251
CLINTRAK PHARMACEUTICAL SERVICES, LLC—See Thermo Fisher Scientific Inc.; *U.S. Public*, pg. 2145
CLINTRAX GLOBAL, INC.—See Leonard Green & Partners, L.P.; *U.S. Private*, pg. 2430
THE CLINT WILLIAMS COMPANY—See Texoma Peanut Company; *U.S. Private*, pg. 3978
CLINUVEL AG—See Clinuvel Pharmaceuticals Limited; *Int'l*, pg. 1660
CLINUVEL PHARMACEUTICALS LIMITED; *Int'l*, pg. 1660
CLINUVEL (UK) LTD.—See Clinuvel Pharmaceuticals Limited; *Int'l*, pg. 1660
CLIO COSMETICS CO LTD; *Int'l*, pg. 1660
CLIO HOLDINGS LLC—See O2 Investment Partners, LLC; *U.S. Private*, pg. 2982
CLIO HOLDINGS LLC—See Oakland Standard Co., LLC; *U.S. Private*, pg. 2984
CLIO INFOTECH LTD.; *Int'l*, pg. 1660
CLIOSOFT, INC.—See Keysight Technologies, Inc.; *U.S. Public*, pg. 1226
CLIO; *Int'l*, pg. 1660
CLIP CORPORATION; *Int'l*, pg. 1660
CLIPPARD EUROPE, S.A.—See Clippard Instrument Laboratory Inc.; *U.S. Private*, pg. 945
CLIPPARD INSTRUMENT LABORATORY INC.; *U.S. Private*, pg. 945
CLIPPER BELT LACER COMPANY—See Flexible Steel Lacing Company; *U.S. Private*, pg. 1544
CLIPPER CARDIOVASCULAR ASSOCIATES, INC.—See HCA Healthcare, Inc.; *U.S. Public*, pg. 993
CLIPPER CARDIOVASCULAR ASSOCIATES, INC.—See HCA Healthcare, Inc.; *U.S. Public*, pg. 993
CLIPPER HARBOR CENTER—See Formation Capital, LLC; *U.S. Private*, pg. 1570
CLIPPER LOGISTICS GROUP LTD.; *Int'l*, pg. 1660
CLIPPER LOGISTICS KG GMBH & CO.—See Clipper Logistics Group Ltd.; *Int'l*, pg. 1660
CLIPPER MAGAZINE, LLC; *U.S. Private*, pg. 945
CLIPPER NAVIGATION, INC.—See FRS GmbH & Co. KG; *Int'l*, pg. 2797
CLIPPER NAVIGATION LTD.—See FRS GmbH & Co. KG; *Int'l*, pg. 2797
CLIPPER PETROLEUM INC.; *U.S. Private*, pg. 945
CLIPPER REALTY INC.; *U.S. Public*, pg. 515
CLIPPER SEAFOODS LTD.—See Bristol Bay Native Corporation; *U.S. Private*, pg. 656
CLIPPER VENTURES PLC; *Int'l*, pg. 1660
CLIPPER WINDPOWER, LLC—See Platinum Equity, LLC; *U.S. Private*, pg. 3202
CLIPPINGER FINANCIAL GROUP, L.L.C.—See Aon plc; *Int'l*, pg. 495
CLIPSAL INTEGRATED SYSTEMS PTY. LIMITED—See Schneider Electric SE; *Int'l*, pg. 6626

CLOFINE DAIRY & FOOD PRODUCTS INC.

CLIPSAL MANUFACTURING (HUIZHOU) LTD—See Schneider Electric SE; *Int'l*, pg. 6626
CLIPSAL MANUFACTURING (M) SDN BHD—See Schneider Electric SE; *Int'l*, pg. 6626
CLIPSAL MIDDLE EAST FZC—See Schneider Electric SE; *Int'l*, pg. 6626
CLIPSOL S.A.—See ENGIE SA; *Int'l*, pg. 2428
CLIQ DIGITAL AG; *Int'l*, pg. 1660
CLIQZ GMBH—See Hubert Burda Media Holding Kommanditgesellschaft; *Int'l*, pg. 3520
CLIRIA - HOSPITAL PRIVADO DE AVEIRO, S.A.—See Fosun International Limited; *Int'l*, pg. 2751
CLISA - CLINICA DE SANTO ANTONIO, S.A.—See UnitedHealth Group Incorporated; *U.S. Public*, pg. 2239
CLIS CO., LTD.—See Prudential Financial, Inc.; *U.S. Public*, pg. 1733
CLISE PROPERTIES, INC.; *U.S. Private*, pg. 945
CLI SINGAPORE PTE. LTD.—See CapitaLand Investment Limited; *Int'l*, pg. 1313
CLIVE ANTHONYS PTY LTD—See JB HI-FI Limited; *Int'l*, pg. 3917
CLIVE CHRISTIAN FURNITURE LIMITED; *Int'l*, pg. 1660
CLIVE CHRISTIAN LIMITED; *Int'l*, pg. 1660
CLIVE CHRISTIAN PERFUME LIMITED—See Clive Christian Limited; *Int'l*, pg. 1660
CLIVE DANIEL HOME - NAPLES, LLC; *U.S. Private*, pg. 945
CLIX MARKETING, LLC; *U.S. Private*, pg. 945
CLJM LLC; *U.S. Private*, pg. 945
CLJM LLC - SPRINGFIELD OFFICE—See CLJM LLC; *U.S. Private*, pg. 945
CLK COLD STORAGE COMPANY LIMITED—See Japan Logistic Systems Corp.; *Int'l*, pg. 3898
CLK HOLDING A.S.; *Int'l*, pg. 1660
CLK, INC.; *U.S. Private*, pg. 945
CLL CHEMNITZER LABORLEISTUNGS GMBH—See Eurofins Scientific S.E.; *Int'l*, pg. 2535
C&L MANAGEMENT INC.; *U.S. Private*, pg. 703
CLM ASSOCIATES LLC; *U.S. Private*, pg. 945
CLM BBDO—See Omnicom Group Inc.; *U.S. Public*, pg. 1575
CLM EQUIPMENT COMPANY, INC.; *U.S. Private*, pg. 945
CLM FLEET MANAGEMENT PLC—See McMillan Shakespeare Limited; *Int'l*, pg. 4760
CLM LLC—See Quad/Graphics, Inc.; *U.S. Public*, pg. 1744
CL MORTGAGES LIMITED—See West Bromwich Building Society; *Int'l*, pg. 8383
CLMO TECHNOLOGY SDN BHD—See Thermo Fisher Scientific Inc.; *U.S. Public*, pg. 2146
CLOAKWARE, INC.—See MultiChoice Group Limited; *Int'l*, pg. 5083
CLOCK RESTAURANT INC.; *U.S. Private*, pg. 945
CLOCKSHARK, LLC; *U.S. Private*, pg. 945
CLOCK SPRING COMPANY, INC.—See Wind Point Advisors LLC; *U.S. Private*, pg. 4534
CLOCK TOWER DENTAL CARE LIMITED—See The British United Provident Association Limited; *Int'l*, pg. 7629
CLOCKWORK B.V.—See Sopra Steria Group S.A.; *Int'l*, pg. 7109
CLOCKWORK, INC.—See Apax Partners LLP; *Int'l*, pg. 502
CLOCKWORK MARKETING SERVICES, INC.; *U.S. Private*, pg. 945
CLOCKWORK SOLUTIONS LLC—See Logistics Management Institute; *U.S. Private*, pg. 2482
CLOETTA AB; *Int'l*, pg. 1660
CLOETTA DANMARK APS—See Cloetta AB; *Int'l*, pg. 1661
CLOETTA DEUTSCHLAND GMBH—See Cloetta AB; *Int'l*, pg. 1661
CLOETTA HOLLAND B.V.—See Cloetta AB; *Int'l*, pg. 1661
CLOETTA ITALIA S.R.L.—See Cloetta AB; *Int'l*, pg. 1661
CLOETTA NORGE AS—See Cloetta AB; *Int'l*, pg. 1661
CLOETTA NUTISAL AB; *Int'l*, pg. 1661
CLOETTA SUOMI OY—See Cloetta AB; *Int'l*, pg. 1661
CLOETTA SVERIGE AB—See Cloetta AB; *Int'l*, pg. 1661
CLOETTA UK LTD.—See Cloetta AB; *Int'l*, pg. 1661
CLOFINE DAIRY & FOOD PRODUCTS INC.; *U.S. Private*, pg. 945
CLOFINE FOOD PRODUCTS INTERNATIONAL INC.—See Clofine Dairy & Food Products Inc.; *U.S. Private*, pg. 945
CLOGRENNANE LIME LIMITED—See SigmaRoc Plc; *Int'l*, pg. 6909
CLO INC.—See Sumitomo Mitsui Financial Group, Inc.; *Int'l*, pg. 7293
CLOISTER HOTEL—See Sea Island Company; *U.S. Private*, pg. 3582
CLONAL PALMS SDN BHD—See Kuok Brothers Sdn. Bhd.; *Int'l*, pg. 4334
CLONDALKIN GROUP HOLDINGS BV—See Egeria Capital Management B.V.; *Int'l*, pg. 2323
CLONDALKIN GROUP HOLDINGS LTD.—See Egeria Capital Management B.V.; *Int'l*, pg. 2323
CLONDALKIN GROUP PLC—See Egeria Capital Management B.V.; *Int'l*, pg. 2323
CLONDALKIN PHARMA & HEALTHCARE (EVV), INC.—See Egeria Capital Management B.V.; *Int'l*, pg. 2323

CLONDALKIN PHARMA & HEALTHCARE INC.—See Egeria Capital Management B.V.; *Int'l*, pg. 2323
CLONDALKIN PHARMA & HEALTHCARE (PORT), INC.—See Egeria Capital Management B.V.; *Int'l*, pg. 2323
CLONE SHIPPER LLC.—See THC Biomed International Ltd.; *Int'l*, pg. 7609
CLONMEL HEALTHCARE LIMITED—See Bain Capital, LP; *U.S. Private*, pg. 443
CLONMEL HEALTHCARE LIMITED—See Cinven Limited; *Int'l*, pg. 1613
CLONTARF ENERGY PLC; *Int'l*, pg. 1661
CLOOPEN GROUP HOLDING LIMITED; *Int'l*, pg. 1661
CLOPAY ASCHERSLEBEN GMBH—See Berry Global Group, Inc; *U.S. Public*, pg. 321
CLOPAY BUILDING PRODUCTS COMPANY, INC.—See Griffon Corporation; *U.S. Public*, pg. 969
CLOPAY CORPORATION—See Griffon Corporation; *U.S. Public*, pg. 969
CLOPAY DO BRASIL LTDA.—See Berry Global Group, Inc; *U.S. Public*, pg. 321
CLOPAY DOMBUHL GMBH—See Griffon Corporation; *U.S. Public*, pg. 969
CLOPAY EUROPE GMBH—See Griffon Corporation; *U.S. Public*, pg. 969
CLOPAY PLASTIC PRODUCTS COMPANY—See Berry Global Group, Inc; *U.S. Public*, pg. 321
CLORACKS CORPORATION; *U.S. Private*, pg. 946
CLORDISYS SOLUTIONS INC.—See Aterian Investment Management, L.P.; *U.S. Private*, pg. 366
CLORE AUTOMOTIVE LLC; *U.S. Private*, pg. 946
CLORE AUTOMOTIVE - SOLAR DIV.—See Clore Automotive LLC; *U.S. Private*, pg. 946
CLORIUS CONTROLS A/S—See Aalberts N.V.; *Int'l*, pg. 33
CLORO DE TEHUANTEPEC, S.A. DE C.V.—See Grupo Empresarial Kaluz de C.V.; *Int'l*, pg. 3127
CLOROX AFRICA HOLDINGS (PROPRIETARY) LTD.—See The Clorox Company; *U.S. Public*, pg. 2063
CLOROX ARGENTINA S.A.—See The Clorox Company; *U.S. Public*, pg. 2062
CLOROX AUSTRALIA PTY. LTD.—See The Clorox Company; *U.S. Public*, pg. 2063
THE CLOROX COMPANY - KENNESAW PLANT—See The Clorox Company; *U.S. Public*, pg. 2062
THE CLOROX COMPANY OF CANADA LTD.—See The Clorox Company; *U.S. Public*, pg. 2063
THE CLOROX COMPANY; *U.S. Public*, pg. 2062
CLOROX DE MEXICO S.A. DE C.V.—See The Clorox Company; *U.S. Public*, pg. 2063
CLOROX DOMINICANA S.R.L.—See The Clorox Company; *U.S. Public*, pg. 2062
THE CLOROX INTERNATIONAL COMPANY - MIAMI OFFICE—See The Clorox Company; *U.S. Public*, pg. 2063
THE CLOROX INTERNATIONAL COMPANY—See The Clorox Company; *U.S. Public*, pg. 2063
CLOROX MANUFACTURING COMPANY OF PUERTO RICO, INC.—See The Clorox Company; *U.S. Public*, pg. 2063
CLOROX MANUFACTURING COMPANY OF PUERTO RICO, INC.—See The Clorox Company; *U.S. Public*, pg. 2063
CLOROX MANUFACTURING COMPANY OF PUERTO RICO, INC.—See The Clorox Company; *U.S. Public*, pg. 2063
CLOROX MEXICANA S. DE R.L. DE C.V.—See The Clorox Company; *U.S. Public*, pg. 2063
CLOROX NEW ZEALAND LIMITED—See The Clorox Company; *U.S. Public*, pg. 2063
CLOROX PRODUCTS MANUFACTURING COMPANY—See The Clorox Company; *U.S. Public*, pg. 2062
CLOROX PROFESSIONAL PRODUCTS COMPANY—See The Clorox Company; *U.S. Public*, pg. 2062
CLOROX SERVICES COMPANY—See The Clorox Company; *U.S. Public*, pg. 2062
CLOSE ASSET MANAGEMENT HOLDINGS LIMITED—See Close Brothers Group plc; *Int'l*, pg. 1661
CLOSE BREWERY RENTALS LIMITED—See Close Brothers Group plc; *Int'l*, pg. 1661
CLOSE BROTHERS ASSET FINANCE GMBH—See Close Brothers Group plc; *Int'l*, pg. 1661
CLOSE BROTHERS GROUP PLC; *Int'l*, pg. 1661
CLOSE BROTHERS LIMITED—See Close Brothers Group plc; *Int'l*, pg. 1661
CLOSE BROTHERS VEHICLE HIRE LIMITED—See Close Brothers Group plc; *Int'l*, pg. 1661
CLOSED JOINED STOCK COMPANY CONSTRUCTION MATERIALS—See Heidelberg Materials AG; *Int'l*, pg. 3310
CLOSED JOINT-STOCK COMPANY DCC—See OJSC Moscow Exchange MICEX-RTS; *Int'l*, pg. 5540
CLOSED LOOP PARTNERS LLC; *U.S. Private*, pg. 946
CLOSE FINANCE (CI) LIMITED—See Close Brothers Group plc; *Int'l*, pg. 1661
CLOSE LUMBER; *U.S. Private*, pg. 946

CLOSEOUT DISTRIBUTION, INC.—See Big Lots, Inc.; *U.S. Public*, pg. 330
CLOSE OUT STORE; *U.S. Private*, pg. 946
CLOSE PREMIUM FINANCE IRELAND—See Close Brothers Group plc; *Int'l*, pg. 1661
CLOSE PREMIUM FINANCE—See Close Brothers Group plc; *Int'l*, pg. 1661
CLOSERLOOK, LLC—See Lloyds Banking Group plc; *Int'l*, pg. 4537
CLOSE THE LOOP LIMITED; *Int'l*, pg. 1661
CLOSETMAID LLC—See Griffon Corporation; *U.S. Public*, pg. 969
CLOSET & STORAGE CONCEPTS; *U.S. Private*, pg. 946
CLOSETS UNLIMITED, INC.; *U.S. Private*, pg. 946
CLOSET WORLD, INC.; *U.S. Private*, pg. 946
CLOSINGCORP, INC.—See Insight Venture Management, LLC; *U.S. Private*, pg. 2088
CLOS LACHANCE WINERY; *U.S. Private*, pg. 946
CLOS SAINT FIACRE SAS—See VINCI S.A.; *Int'l*, pg. 8215
CLOSURELOGIC GMBH—See Guala Closures S.p.A.; *Int'l*, pg. 3152
CLOSURE SYSTEMS INTERNATIONAL, INC.—See Cerberus Capital Management, L.P.; *U.S. Private*, pg. 837
CLOSURE SYSTEMS INTERNATIONAL-KILGORE—See Cerberus Capital Management, L.P.; *U.S. Private*, pg. 837
CLOTHING PLUS ZHEJIANG LTD.—See Jabil Inc.; *U.S. Public*, pg. 1180
CLOUD 8 SIXTEEN, INC.; *U.S. Private*, pg. 946
CLOUD9, INC.—See CROOZ, Inc.; *Int'l*, pg. 1855
CLOUD 9 LIVING, INC.—See Inflexion Private Equity Partners LLP; *Int'l*, pg. 3689
CLOUD AIR CO., LTD.; *Int'l*, pg. 1661
CLOUDARY CORPORATION—See Shanda Interactive Entertainment Limited; *Int'l*, pg. 6751
CLOUDBACKO CORPORATION—See Ahsay Backup Software Development Company Limited; *Int'l*, pg. 226
CLOUD BEAUTY INC.—See Vector Inc.; *Int'l*, pg. 8144
CLOUDBEES EUROPE—See CloudBees, Inc.; *U.S. Private*, pg. 947
CLOUDBEES, INC.; *U.S. Private*, pg. 947
CLOUDBERRY CLEAN ENERGY ASA; *Int'l*, pg. 1662
CLOUD B, INC.—See Vinco Ventures, Inc.; *U.S. Public*, pg. 2298
CLOUDBLUE TECHNOLOGIES, INC.—See Hainan Traffic Administration Holding Co., Ltd.; *Int'l*, pg. 3214
CLOUDBREAK DISCOVERY PLC; *Int'l*, pg. 1662
CLOUDBURST CONSULTING GROUP, INC.; *U.S. Private*, pg. 947
CLOUDBUY INDIA PRIVATE LTD.—See cloudBuy PLC; *Int'l*, pg. 1662
CLOUDBUY PLC; *Int'l*, pg. 1662
CLOUDCALL GROUP LIMITED; *Int'l*, pg. 1662
CLOUDCALL, INC.—See CloudCall Group Limited; *Int'l*, pg. 1662
CLOUDCALL LIMITED—See CloudCall Group Limited; *Int'l*, pg. 1662
CLOUD CAP TECHNOLOGY, INC.—See RTX Corporation; *U.S. Public*, pg. 1821
CLOUDCHECKR LLC—See NetApp, Inc.; *U.S. Public*, pg. 1507
CLOUDCOCO GROUP PLC; *Int'l*, pg. 1662
CLOUDCONNECT, LLC—See Salesforce, Inc.; *U.S. Public*, pg. 1837
CLOUD COUNTY HEALTH CENTER; *U.S. Private*, pg. 946
CLOUD CREEK SYSTEMS, INC.; *U.S. Private*, pg. 946
CLOUD DATA CORPORATION—See Microelectronics Technology Company; *U.S. Private*, pg. 2703
CLOUD DX, INC.; *Int'l*, pg. 1661
CLOUD EQUITY GROUP, LLC; *U.S. Private*, pg. 946
CLOUDERA GMBH—See Clayton, Dubilier & Rice, LLC; *U.S. Private*, pg. 920
CLOUDERA GMBH—See KKR & Co. Inc.; *U.S. Public*, pg. 1243
CLOUDERA HUNGARY KFT.—See Clayton, Dubilier & Rice, LLC; *U.S. Private*, pg. 920
CLOUDERA HUNGARY KFT.—See KKR & Co. Inc.; *U.S. Public*, pg. 1243
CLOUDERA INC.—See Clayton, Dubilier & Rice, LLC; *U.S. Private*, pg. 920
CLOUDERA INC.—See KKR & Co. Inc.; *U.S. Public*, pg. 1243
CLOUDERA, INC.—See Clayton, Dubilier & Rice, LLC; *U.S. Private*, pg. 920
CLOUDERA, INC.—See KKR & Co. Inc.; *U.S. Public*, pg. 1243
CLOUDERA K.K.—See Clayton, Dubilier & Rice, LLC; *U.S. Private*, pg. 920
CLOUDERA K.K.—See KKR & Co. Inc.; *U.S. Public*, pg. 1243
CLOUDERA KOREA, INC.—See Clayton, Dubilier & Rice, LLC; *U.S. Private*, pg. 920
CLOUDERA KOREA, INC.—See KKR & Co. Inc.; *U.S. Public*, pg. 1243
CLOUDERA (SHANGHAI) SOFTWARE CO. LTD.—See Clayton, Dubilier & Rice, LLC; *U.S. Private*, pg. 920

CLOUDERA (SHANGHAI) SOFTWARE CO. LTD.—See KKR & Co. Inc.; *U.S. Public*, pg. 1243
CLOUDERA (UK) LIMITED—See Clayton, Dubilier & Rice, LLC; *U.S. Private*, pg. 920
CLOUDERA (UK) LIMITED—See KKR & Co. Inc.; *U.S. Public*, pg. 1243
CLOUDFLARE, INC.; *U.S. Public*, pg. 515
CLOUDGENIX, INC.—See Palo Alto Networks, Inc.; *U.S. Public*, pg. 1635
CLOUD GLOBAL LTD.; *Int'l*, pg. 1662
CLOUDHEALTH TECHNOLOGIES AUSTRALIA PTY. LTD.—See Dell Technologies Inc.; *U.S. Public*, pg. 649
CLOUDHEALTH TECHNOLOGIES INC.—See Broadcom Inc.; *U.S. Public*, pg. 390
CLOUDICAL DEUTSCHLAND GMBH—See Allgeier SE; *Int'l*, pg. 337
CLOUD INVESTMENT HOLDINGS LIMITED; *Int'l*, pg. 1662
CLOUDIT, LLC; *U.S. Private*, pg. 947
CLOUD JUMPER LLC—See NetApp, Inc.; *U.S. Public*, pg. 1507
CLOUD LENDING, INC.—See Q2 Holdings, Inc.; *U.S. Public*, pg. 1741
CLOUD LIVE TECHNOLOGY GROUP CO., LTD.; *Int'l*, pg. 1662
CLOUDLOCK, INC.—See Cisco Systems, Inc.; *U.S. Public*, pg. 499
CLOUDLOCK, LTD.—See Cisco Systems, Inc.; *U.S. Public*, pg. 499
CLOUDMARK, INC.—See Thoma Bravo, L.P.; *U.S. Private*, pg. 4151
CLOUDMARK LABS SARL—See Thoma Bravo, L.P.; *U.S. Private*, pg. 4151
CLOUDMASTER CO., LTD.—See TOKAI Holdings Corporation; *Int'l*, pg. 7779
CLOUDMATRIX CO., LTD.—See Giga-Byte Technology Co., Ltd.; *Int'l*, pg. 2971
CLOUDMD SOFTWARE & SERVICES, INC.—See CPS Capital; *Int'l*, pg. 1826
CLOUDMED, LLC—See R1 RCM Inc.; *U.S. Public*, pg. 1758
CLOUD MELLOW CONSULTING LTD. CO.; *U.S. Private*, pg. 946
CLOUDMINDS INC.; *Int'l*, pg. 1662
CLOUD MUSIC INC.; *Int'l*, pg. 1662
THE CLOUD NETWORKS GERMANY GMBH—See freenet AG; *Int'l*, pg. 2770
THE CLOUD NETWORKS LIMITED—See Comcast Corporation; *U.S. Public*, pg. 541
CLOUD PACKAGING SOLUTIONS LLC—See Warburg Pincus LLC; *U.S. Private*, pg. 4437
CLOUDPASSAGE INC.—See Fonds de Solidarite des Travailleurs du Quebec; *Int'l*, pg. 2725
CLOUDPAY; *Int'l*, pg. 1662
CLOUD PEAK ENERGY INC.; *U.S. Private*, pg. 946
CLOUD PEAK ENERGY SERVICES COMPANY—See Cloud Peak Energy Inc.; *U.S. Private*, pg. 946
CLOUDPHYSICS, INC.—See Hewlett Packard Enterprise Company; *U.S. Public*, pg. 1030
CLOUDPOINT TECHNOLOGY BERHAD; *Int'l*, pg. 1662
CLOUD PRACTICE INC.—See WELL Health Technologies Corp.; *Int'l*, pg. 8372
CLOUDREPUBLIC AB; *Int'l*, pg. 1662
CLOUDR GROUP LIMITED; *Int'l*, pg. 1662
CLOUDSCALE365, INC.; *U.S. Private*, pg. 947
CLOUD SCOPE TECHNOLOGIES, INC.—See TIS Inc.; *Int'l*, pg. 7757
CLOUD SERVICE PARTNERS, INC.; *U.S. Private*, pg. 946
CLOUD SHERPAS, INC.—See Accenture plc; *Int'l*, pg. 86
CLOUDSQUADS, INC.—See Persistent Systems Ltd.; *Int'l*, pg. 5818
CLOUDTAG INC.; *Int'l*, pg. 1662
CLOUD TECHNOLOGY PARTNERS, INC.—See Hewlett Packard Enterprise Company; *U.S. Public*, pg. 1030
CLOUD TEMPLE SAS—See Neurones S.A.; *Int'l*, pg. 5219
CLOUDTICITY, LLC; *U.S. Private*, pg. 947
CLOUDVEIL LIMITED—See Nanosynth Group PLC; *Int'l*, pg. 5144
CLOUDVISORY LLC—See Alphabet Inc.; *U.S. Public*, pg. 84
CLOUDWEB, INC.; *U.S. Public*, pg. 515
CLOUDWERX DATA SOLUTIONS INC.—See George Weston Limited; *Int'l*, pg. 2939
CLOUDY BAY VINEYARDS LTD—See LVMH Moet Hennessy Louis Vuitton SE; *Int'l*, pg. 4604
CLOUDYN LTD.; *Int'l*, pg. 1662
CLOUGH DIALYSIS, LLC—See DaVita Inc.; *U.S. Public*, pg. 636
CLOUGH ENGINEERING LIMITED—See Salini Costruttori S.p.A.; *Int'l*, pg. 6493
CLOUGHERTY PACKING, LLC—See WH Group Limited; *Int'l*, pg. 8395
CLOUGH GLOBAL DIVIDEND & INCOME FUND; *U.S. Public*, pg. 515
CLOUGH GLOBAL EQUITY FUND; *U.S. Public*, pg. 515
CLOUGH GLOBAL OPPORTUNITIES FUND; *U.S. Public*, pg. 515

COMPANY NAME INDEX

CLOUGH KARACHI—See Salini Costruttori S.p.A.; *Int'l*, pg. 6493
CLOUGH LIMITED—See Salini Costruttori S.p.A.; *Int'l*, pg. 6493
CLOUGH LUCAS—See Salini Costruttori S.p.A.; *Int'l*, pg. 6493
CLOUGH MELBOURNE—See Salini Costruttori S.p.A.; *Int'l*, pg. 6493
CLOUGH NORTH AMERICA HOLDING, INC.—See Salini Costruttori S.p.A.; *Int'l*, pg. 6493
CLOUGH OFFSHORE—See Salini Costruttori S.p.A.; *Int'l*, pg. 6493
CLOUGH TANJUNG BATU—See Salini Costruttori S.p.A.; *Int'l*, pg. 6493
CLOU PANAMA S.A.—See Shenzhen Clou Electronics Co., Ltd.; *Int'l*, pg. 6807
CLOUTEK GMBH—See Shenzhen Clou Electronics Co., Ltd.; *Int'l*, pg. 6807
CLOVELLY CORPORATION; *U.S. Private*, pg. 947
CLOVER BIOPHARMACEUTICALS, LTD.; *Int'l*, pg. 1662
CLOVER CORPORATION LIMITED; *Int'l*, pg. 1663
CLOVER CORPORATION; *U.S. Private*, pg. 947
CLOVER CREEK PARTNERS, LLC; *U.S. Private*, pg. 947
CLOVER DAIRY NAMIBIA (PTY) LTD.—See Clover Industries Limited; *Int'l*, pg. 1663
CLOVERDALE EQUIPMENT CO. OF WEST MICHIGAN—See Cloverdale Equipment Co.; *U.S. Private*, pg. 948
CLOVERDALE EQUIPMENT CO.; *U.S. Private*, pg. 948
CLOVERDALE FOODS COMPANY INC.; *U.S. Private*, pg. 948
CLOVERDALE PAINT INC.; *Int'l*, pg. 1663
CLOVERDALE PARK, INC.—See Carriage Services, Inc.; *U.S. Public*, pg. 439
CLOVER DIALYSIS, LLC—See DaVita Inc.; *U.S. Public*, pg. 636
CLOVER ELECTRONICS INDUSTRIES CO., LTD.—See Unimicron Technology Corporation; *Int'l*, pg. 8050
CLOVER FARMS DAIRY COMPANY; *U.S. Private*, pg. 947
CLOVER FINANCIAL CORPORATION; *U.S. Private*, pg. 947
CLOVER FONTERRA INGREDIENTO (PTY) LTD.—See Clover Industries Limited; *Int'l*, pg. 1663
CLOVER HEALTH INVESTMENTS, CORP.; *U.S. Public*, pg. 515
CLOVER HITECHNOLOGY CO., LTD.; *Int'l*, pg. 1663
CLOVER INDUSTRIES LIMITED; *Int'l*, pg. 1663
CLOVER INTERNACIONAL, C.A.—See Clover Systems Inc.; *U.S. Private*, pg. 947
CLOVER INTERNACIONAL LLC—See Clover Systems Inc.; *U.S. Private*, pg. 947
CLOVER LAKE COUNTY INC.—See Clover Stornetta Farms Inc.; *U.S. Private*, pg. 947
CLOVERLANES, INC.—See Great Lakes Realty Corp.; *U.S. Private*, pg. 1765
CLOVER LEAF CAPITAL CORP.; *U.S. Public*, pg. 515
CLOVERLEAF COLD STORAGE CO. INC. - PLANT 1—See Americold Realty Trust, Inc.; *U.S. Public*, pg. 113
CLOVERLEAF COLD STORAGE CO. INC. - PLANT 6—See Americold Realty Trust, Inc.; *U.S. Public*, pg. 113
CLOVERLEAF COLD STORAGE CO. INC.—See Americold Realty Trust, Inc.; *U.S. Public*, pg. 113
CLOVER LEAF ENVIRONMENTAL SOLUTIONS, INC.; *U.S. Private*, pg. 947
CLOVERLEAF TRANSPORTATION, INC.; *U.S. Private*, pg. 948
CLOVER PAKISTAN LTD.; *Int'l*, pg. 1663
CLOVER S.A. (PTY) LTD—See Danone; *Int'l*, pg. 1965
CLOVER STORNETTA FARMS INC.; *U.S. Private*, pg. 947
CLOVER SWAZILAND (PTY) LTD.—See Clover Industries Limited; *Int'l*, pg. 1663
CLOVER SYSTEMS INC.; *U.S. Private*, pg. 947
CLOVER TECHNOLOGIES GROUP LLC; *U.S. Private*, pg. 947
CLOVER TRADING CO., LTD.—See Yokorei Co.,Ltd.; *Int'l*, pg. 8595
CLOVER WATERS (PTY) LTD.—See Clover Industries Limited; *Int'l*, pg. 1663
CLOVER WIRELESS; *U.S. Private*, pg. 947
CLOVER YARNS INC.; *U.S. Private*, pg. 948
CLOVER YARNS—See Clover Yarns Inc.; *U.S. Private*, pg. 948
CLOVIS MEDIA, INC.; *U.S. Private*, pg. 948
CLOVIS ONCOLOGY, INC.; *U.S. Public*, pg. 515
CLOVIS ONCOLOGY UK LIMITED—See Clovis Oncology, Inc.; *U.S. Public*, pg. 515
CLOW CANADA INC.—See McWane, Inc.; *U.S. Private*, pg. 2645
CLOW STAMPING COMPANY; *U.S. Private*, pg. 948
CLOW VALVE DIVISION—See McWane, Inc.; *U.S. Private*, pg. 2645
CLOW WATER SYSTEMS CO.—See McWane, Inc.; *U.S. Private*, pg. 2645

CLOYES DYNAGEAR MEXICANA S. DE R.L. DE C.V.—See MidOcean Partners, LLP; *U.S. Private*, pg. 2716
CLOYES DYNAGEAR MEXICANA S. DE R.L. DE C.V.—See MidOcean Partners, LLP; *U.S. Private*, pg. 2716
CLOYES DYNAGEAR MEXICANA S. DE R.L. DE C.V.—See MidOcean Partners, LLP; *U.S. Private*, pg. 2716
CLOYES GEAR & PRODUCTS, INC.—See MidOcean Partners, LLP; *U.S. Private*, pg. 2716
CLP BUSINESS MANAGEMENT (BEIJING) COMPANY LIMITED—See CLP Holdings Limited; *Int'l*, pg. 1663
CLP CORPORATION; *U.S. Private*, pg. 948
CLPE HOLDINGS LIMITED—See CLP Holdings Limited; *Int'l*, pg. 1663
CLP ENGINEERING LIMITED—See CLP Holdings Limited; *Int'l*, pg. 1663
CLPG PACKAGING INDUSTRIES SDN. BHD.; *Int'l*, pg. 1663
CLP HOLDINGS CORP—See TrueBlue, Inc.; *U.S. Public*, pg. 2198
CLP HOLDINGS LIMITED; *Int'l*, pg. 1663
CLP HUANYU (SHANDONG) BIOMASS HEAT AND POWER COMPANY LIMITED—See CLP Holdings Limited; *Int'l*, pg. 1663
CLP INDIA PRIVATE LIMITED—See CLP Holdings Limited; *Int'l*, pg. 1663
CLP POWER HONG KONG LIMITED—See CLP Holdings Limited; *Int'l*, pg. 1663
CLP POWER INDIA PVT. LTD.—See CLP Holdings Limited; *Int'l*, pg. 1663
CLP RESEARCH INSTITUTE LIMITED—See CLP Holdings Limited; *Int'l*, pg. 1663
CLP RESOURCES, INC.—See TrueBlue, Inc.; *U.S. Public*, pg. 2198
C.L. PRESSER COMPANY; *U.S. Private*, pg. 708
CLPS INCORPORATION; *Int'l*, pg. 1663
CL RIECKHOFF COMPANY; *U.S. Private*, pg. 909
CLR ROASTERS, LLC—See Youngevity International Corp.; *U.S. Public*, pg. 2399
CLSA AUSTRALIA HOLDINGS PTY .LTD.—See CITIC Securities Co., Ltd.; *Int'l*, pg. 1622
CLS ABERDEEN LIMITED—See CLS Holdings plc; *Int'l*, pg. 1664
CLSA B.V.—See CITIC Securities Co., Ltd.; *Int'l*, pg. 1622
CLSA CAPITAL PARTNERS (HK) LIMITED—See CITIC Securities Co., Ltd.; *Int'l*, pg. 1622
CLSA EUROPE B.V.—See CITIC Securities Co., Ltd.; *Int'l*, pg. 1622
CLSA FUND SERVICES (ASIA) LIMITED—See CITIC Securities Co., Ltd.; *Int'l*, pg. 1622
CLSA LIMITED—See CITIC Securities Co., Ltd.; *Int'l*, pg. 1622
CLS AMERICA, INC.—See Collecte Localisation Satellites; *Int'l*, pg. 1699
CLSA PREMIUM LTD—See CITIC Securities Co., Ltd.; *Int'l*, pg. 1622
CLS AUDIOVISUAIS LD—See WPP plc; *Int'l*, pg. 8472
CLS CATERING SERVICES LTD.—See Deutsche Lufthansa AG; *Int'l*, pg. 2067
CLS CONSTRUCTION LEGAL SERVICES GMBH—See STRABAG SE; *Int'l*, pg. 7229
C & L SERVICES LLC; *U.S. Private*, pg. 701
CLSH MANAGEMENT LIMITED—See CLS Holdings plc; *Int'l*, pg. 1664
CLS HOLDINGS PLC; *Int'l*, pg. 1663
CLS HOLDINGS USA, INC.; *U.S. Public*, pg. 515
CLS INSULATION, LLC—See Installed Building Products, Inc.; *U.S. Public*, pg. 1132
CLS LABS, INC.—See CLS Holdings USA, Inc.; *U.S. Public*, pg. 515
CLS LUXEMBOURG SARL—See CLS Holdings plc; *Int'l*, pg. 1664
C.L. SMITH COMPANY INC.; *U.S. Private*, pg. 708
CL SOLUTION MANAGEMENT CO., LTD—See Mitsubishi HC Capital Inc.; *Int'l*, pg. 4950
CL SOLUTIONS LIMITED—See NCT Alliance Berhad; *Int'l*, pg. 5182
CLS PARTNERS—See Stone Point Capital LLC; *U.S. Private*, pg. 3818
CLS SCOTLAND LIMITED—See CLS Holdings plc; *Int'l*, pg. 1664
CLS SYSTEMS FZCO—See Schneider Electric SE; *Int'l*, pg. 6626
CL STAAL B.V.—See Jacquet Metal Service SA; *Int'l*, pg. 3866
C&L SUPPLY INC.; *U.S. Private*, pg. 703
C.L.T.- COMPANHIA LOGISTICA DE TERM. MARITIMOS, LDA—See Galp Energia SGPS, S.A.; *Int'l*, pg. 2875
CLT ENERGY SERVICES GROUP, L.L.C.—See Constellation Energy Corporation; *U.S. Public*, pg. 571
CLT ENGINEERING SDN. BHD.—See Genetec Technology Berhad; *Int'l*, pg. 2922
C.L. THOMAS, INC.; *U.S. Private*, pg. 708
CLT INTERNATIONAL LIMITED—See Wilmington plc; *Int'l*, pg. 8422
CLUB 24 CONCEPT GYMS, LTD.; *U.S. Private*, pg. 948
CLUB 24 LIMITED—See Capita plc; *Int'l*, pg. 1308

CLUB 7 HOLIDAYS LIMITED—See Centrum Capital Ltd.; *Int'l*, pg. 1415
CLUB ADRIATIC D.O.O.—See Jadran D.D. Crikvenic; *Int'l*, pg. 3869
THE CLUB AT BOCA POINTE; *U.S. Private*, pg. 4010
THE CLUB AT EAGLEBROOKE; *U.S. Private*, pg. 4010
THE CLUB AT FALCON POINT—See Apollo Global Management, Inc.; *U.S. Public*, pg. 150
THE CLUB AT GRAND HAVEN—See Escalante Golf, Inc.; *U.S. Private*, pg. 1424
THE CLUB AT HIDDEN RIVER, LLC—See D.R. Horton, Inc.; *U.S. Public*, pg. 620
THE CLUB AT LAS CAMPANAS, INC.; *U.S. Private*, pg. 4010
THE CLUB AT MEDITERRA INC.; *U.S. Private*, pg. 4010
THE CLUB AT PRADERA, INC.—See D.R. Horton, Inc.; *U.S. Public*, pg. 620
CLUB AT SEABROOK ISLAND INC.; *U.S. Private*, pg. 948
THE CLUB AT TREASURE ISLAND—See Bill Edwards Presents, Inc.; *U.S. Private*, pg. 557
THE CLUB AT YEBISU GARDEN CO., LTD.—See Konami Group Corporation; *Int'l*, pg. 4245
CLUB CAR, LLC—See Platinum Equity, LLC; *U.S. Private*, pg. 3202
CLUB CHEF LLC—See Taylor Fresh Foods Inc.; *U.S. Private*, pg. 3940
CLUBCOM HOLDING COMPANY, INC.—See ANTA Sports Products Limited; *Int'l*, pg. 480
CLUB CONNECT LLC—See Dolphin Entertainment, Inc.; *U.S. Private*, pg. 673
CLUBCORP HOLDINGS, INC.—See Apollo Global Management, Inc.; *U.S. Public*, pg. 149
CLUBCORP USA, INC.—See Apollo Global Management, Inc.; *U.S. Public*, pg. 149
CLUB DE HOCKEY CANADIEN, INC.; *Int'l*, pg. 1664
CLUB DEMONSTRATION SERVICES, INC.; *U.S. Private*, pg. 948
CLUB DE POLO Y EQUITACION SAN CRISTOBAL; *Int'l*, pg. 1664
CLUBESSENTIAL HOLDINGS, LLC; *U.S. Private*, pg. 948
CLUB HIPICO DE SANTIAGO S.A.; *Int'l*, pg. 1664
CLUB HOTEL LOUTRAKI S.A.—See Queenco Leisure International Ltd.; *Int'l*, pg. 6159
CLUBHOTEL MULTIVACANCES SA—See Pierre & Vacances SA; *Int'l*, pg. 5864
CLUBHOUSE MEDIA GROUP, INC.; *U.S. Public*, pg. 515
CLUBHOUSE PROPERTY LIMITED—See Sansiri pcl; *Int'l*, pg. 6556
CLUB INTERNACIONAL DEL LIBRO, MARKETING DIRECTO, S.L.—See CIL Group SL; *Int'l*, pg. 1607
CLUBLINK CORPORATION—See TWC Enterprise Limited; *Int'l*, pg. 7990
CLUB MANAGEMENT (BMG) PTY LTD—See Woolworths Group Limited; *Int'l*, pg. 8451
CLUB MARINE LTD.—See Allianz SE; *Int'l*, pg. 342
CLUB MED AUSTRALIA & NEW ZEALAND—See Fosun International Limited; *Int'l*, pg. 2750
CLUB MED BRASIL SA—See Fosun International Limited; *Int'l*, pg. 2750
CLUB MED FERIAS—See Fosun International Limited; *Int'l*, pg. 2750
CLUB MEDITERRANEE HELLAS S.A.—See Fosun International Limited; *Int'l*, pg. 2750
CLUB MEDITERRANEE HOLLAND BV—See Fosun International Limited; *Int'l*, pg. 2750
CLUB MEDITERRANEE HONG KONG LTD—See Fosun International Limited; *Int'l*, pg. 2750
CLUB MEDITERRANEE ITALIA S.P.A.—See Fosun International Limited; *Int'l*, pg. 2750
CLUB MEDITERRANEE K.K.—See Fosun International Limited; *Int'l*, pg. 2750
CLUB MEDITERRANEE S.A. BELGE—See Fosun International Limited; *Int'l*, pg. 2750
CLUB MEDITERRANEE SAS—See Fosun International Limited; *Int'l*, pg. 2750
CLUB MEDITERRANEE SERVICES INDIA PRIVATE LTD—See Fosun International Limited; *Int'l*, pg. 2750
CLUB MEDITERRANEE SUISSE—See Fosun International Limited; *Int'l*, pg. 2750
CLUB MEDITERRANEE U.K. LTD.—See Fosun International Limited; *Int'l*, pg. 2750
CLUB MED MANAGEMENT SERVICES INC—See Fosun International Limited; *Int'l*, pg. 2750
CLUB MED SALES CANADA INC.—See Fosun International Limited; *Int'l*, pg. 2750
CLUB MED SALES, INC.—See Fosun International Limited; *Int'l*, pg. 2750
CLUB MED—See Fosun International Limited; *Int'l*, pg. 2750
CLUB MED VACANCES (TAIWAN) LTD—See Fosun International Limited; *Int'l*, pg. 2750
CLUB MED VIAGENS UNIPESSOAL, LDA—See Fosun International Limited; *Int'l*, pg. 2750
CLUB MED VILLAS ET CHALETS HOLDING—See Fosun International Limited; *Int'l*, pg. 2750
CLUB MED VILLAS ET CHALETS—See Fosun International Limited; *Int'l*, pg. 2750

CLUBHOUSE MEDIA GROUP, INC.   CORPORATE AFFILIATIONS

CLUB MONACO CORP.—See Ralph Lauren Corporation; *U.S. Public*, pg. 1761
CLUB MONACO INC.—See Ralph Lauren Corporation; *U.S. Public*, pg. 1761
CLUB MONACO U.S., LLC—See Ralph Lauren Corporation; *U.S. Public*, pg. 1761
CLUB MYKONOS LANGEBAAN (PTY) LIMITED—See Trematon Capital Investments Ltd.; *Int'l*, pg. 7915
CLUB NETS CORPORATION—See Crest Investments Co., Ltd.; *Int'l*, pg. 1840
CLUB ONE INC.; *U.S. Private*, pg. 948
CLUB ONYX HOUSTON—See RCI Hospitality Holdings, Inc.; *U.S. Public*, pg. 1767
CLUB PILATES LLC; *U.S. Private*, pg. 948
CLUB RESTAURATION—See Danone; *Int'l*, pg. 1965
CLUB SALES & MERCHANDISING PTY LIMITED—See Navis Capital Partners Limited; *Int'l*, pg. 5176
CLUB STAFFING—See AMN Healthcare Services, Inc.; *U.S. Public*, pg. 125
CLUBSYSTEMS GROUP INC.; *U.S. Private*, pg. 949
CLUB TOURISM INTERNATIONAL INC.—See Kintetsu Group Holdings Co.,Ltd.; *Int'l*, pg. 4183
CLUB TRAVEL SA (PTY) LTD.—See Travelstart Online Travel Operations Pty. Ltd; *Int'l*, pg. 7908
CLUB VIDA AGENCIA DE VIAJES, S.A.—See MAPFRE S.A.; *Int'l*, pg. 4685
CLUETT AMERICAN INVESTMENT CORP.; *U.S. Private*, pg. 949
CLUETT INTERNATIONAL GROUP—See Cluett American Investment Corp.; *U.S. Private*, pg. 949
CLUEY LIMITED; *Int'l*, pg. 1664
CLUJANA S.A.; *Int'l*, pg. 1664
CLUNE CONSTRUCTION CO.; *U.S. Private*, pg. 949
CLUNE TECHNOLOGY GROUP; *Int'l*, pg. 1664
CLUNY CAPITAL CORP.; *Int'l*, pg. 1664
CLUSIAU SALES & RENTAL, INC.; *U.S. Private*, pg. 949
CLUSTER REPLY DYNAMICS GMBH—See Reply S.p.A.; *Int'l*, pg. 6290
CLUSTER REPLY GMBH & CO. KG—See Reply S.p.A.; *Int'l*, pg. 6290
CLUSTER REPLY ROMA S.R.L.—See Reply S.p.A.; *Int'l*, pg. 6290
CLUSTER REPLY S.R.L.—See Reply S.p.A.; *Int'l*, pg. 6290
CLUSTER TECHNOLOGY CO., LTD.; *Int'l*, pg. 1664
CLUSTRIX, INC.—See California Technology Ventures, LLC; *U.S. Private*, pg. 721
CLUTCH AUTO LIMITED; *Int'l*, pg. 1664
CLV DISTRIBUTION—See Carrefour SA; *Int'l*, pg. 1344
C & L WATER SOLUTIONS, INC.—See New Mountain Capital, LLC; *U.S. Private*, pg. 2899
CLW INC.; *U.S. Private*, pg. 949
CLX EUROPE MEDIA SOLUTION GMBH—See eClerx Services Ltd; *Int'l*, pg. 2291
CLX EUROPE S.P.A.—See eClerx Services Ltd; *Int'l*, pg. 2291
CLYDE ARK LLC—See Ark Restaurants Corp.; *U.S. Public*, pg. 193
CLYDE BERGEMANN AFRICA (PTY) LTD—See Clyde Blowers Capital IM LLP; *Int'l*, pg. 1664
CLYDE BERGEMANN BEEKAY INDIA PRIVATE LIMITED—See Clyde Blowers Capital IM LLP; *Int'l*, pg. 1664
CLYDE BERGEMANN CANADA LTD.—See Clyde Blowers Capital IM LLP; *Int'l*, pg. 1665
CLYDE BERGEMANN COLOMBIA S.A.S.—See Clyde Blowers Capital IM LLP; *Int'l*, pg. 1665
CLYDE BERGEMANN CONTROLS PVT. LTD—See Clyde Blowers Capital IM LLP; *Int'l*, pg. 1665
CLYDE BERGEMANN DO BRASIL LTDA.—See Clyde Blowers Capital IM LLP; *Int'l*, pg. 1665
CLYDE BERGEMANN DRYCON GMBH—See Clyde Blowers Capital IM LLP; *Int'l*, pg. 1665
CLYDE BERGEMANN EESTI AS—See Clyde Blowers Capital IM LLP; *Int'l*, pg. 1665
CLYDE BERGEMANN ENERGY & ENVIRONMENTAL TECHNOLOGY (BEIJING) CO., LTD.—See Clyde Blowers Capital IM LLP; *Int'l*, pg. 1665
CLYDE BERGEMANN EP TECH S.R.L—See Clyde Blowers Capital IM LLP; *Int'l*, pg. 1665
CLYDE BERGEMANN FOREST S.A.—See Clyde Blowers Capital IM LLP; *Int'l*, pg. 1665
CLYDE BERGEMANN GMBH—See Clyde Blowers Capital IM LLP; *Int'l*, pg. 1665
CLYDE BERGEMANN HUATONG MATERIALS HANDLING CO., LTD.—See Clyde Blowers Capital IM LLP; *Int'l*, pg. 1665
CLYDE BERGEMANN INC.—See Clyde Blowers Capital IM LLP; *Int'l*, pg. 1665
CLYDE BERGEMANN LIMITED—See Clyde Blowers Capital IM LLP; *Int'l*, pg. 1665
CLYDE BERGEMANN MATERIALS HANDLING LTD—See Clyde Blowers Capital IM LLP; *Int'l*, pg. 1665
CLYDE BERGEMANN POLSKA SP. Z O.O.—See Clyde Blowers Capital IM LLP; *Int'l*, pg. 1665
CLYDE BERGEMANN POWER GROUP AMERICAS INC. - AIR-GAS HANDLING PRODUCT DIVISION—See Clyde Blowers Capital IM LLP; *Int'l*, pg. 1665
CLYDE BERGEMANN POWER GROUP AMERICAS INC. - AIR POLLUTION CONTROL PRODUCT DIVISION—See Clyde Blowers Capital IM LLP; *Int'l*, pg. 1665
CLYDE BERGEMANN POWER GROUP AMERICAS INC. - MATERIAL HANDLING PRODUCT DIVISION—See Clyde Blowers Capital IM LLP; *Int'l*, pg. 1665
CLYDE BERGEMANN POWER GROUP—See Clyde Blowers Capital IM LLP; *Int'l*, pg. 1664
CLYDE BERGEMANN SCANDINAVIA OY—See Clyde Blowers Capital IM LLP; *Int'l*, pg. 1665
CLYDE BERGEMANN TERMOTEC GMBH—See Clyde Blowers Capital IM LLP; *Int'l*, pg. 1665
CLYDE BERGEMANN TR ENERJI SERVIS A. S.—See Clyde Blowers Capital IM LLP; *Int'l*, pg. 1665
CLYDE BLOWERS CAPITAL IM LLP; *Int'l*, pg. 1664
CLYDE BLOWERS LTD.—See Clyde Blowers Capital IM LLP; *Int'l*, pg. 1664
CLYDE & CO LLP; *Int'l*, pg. 1664
CLYDE COMPANIES INC.; *U.S. Private*, pg. 949
CLYDE & CO US LLP—See Clyde & Co LLP; *Int'l*, pg. 1664
CLYDE DUNEIER INC.; *U.S. Private*, pg. 949
CLYDE, INC.; *U.S. Private*, pg. 949
THE CLY-DEL MANUFACTURING COMPANY; *U.S. Private*, pg. 4011
CLYDE NETHERLANDS BV—See BASF SE; *Int'l*, pg. 885
CLYDE PROCESS LTD.—See Blackstone Inc.; *U.S. Public*, pg. 360
CLYDE PUMPS INDIA PVT LIMITED—See Lone Star Funds; *U.S. Private*, pg. 2485
CLYDE REVORD MOTORS; *U.S. Private*, pg. 949
CLYDE'S AT MARK CENTER, LLC—See Graham Holdings Company; *U.S. Public*, pg. 954
CLYDESDALE BANK PLC—See Virgin Money UK PLC; *Int'l*, pg. 8247
CLYDESDALE FORGE—See Caparo Group Ltd.; *Int'l*, pg. 1302
CLYDESDALE RESOURCES, INC.; *Int'l*, pg. 1665
CLYDE'S OF CHEVY CHASE, LLC—See Graham Holdings Company; *U.S. Public*, pg. 954
CLYDESTONE (GHANA) LIMITED; *Int'l*, pg. 1665
CLYDE'S TOWER OAKS LODGE, LLC—See Graham Holdings Company; *U.S. Public*, pg. 954
CLYDE UNION CANADA LIMITED—See Lone Star Funds; *U.S. Private*, pg. 2485
CLYDE UNION DB LIMITED—See Lone Star Funds; *U.S. Private*, pg. 2485
CLYDE UNION (FRANCE) S.A.S.—See Lone Star Funds; *U.S. Private*, pg. 2485
CLYDE UNION INC.—See Lone Star Funds; *U.S. Private*, pg. 2485
CLYDE UNION LTD—See Lone Star Funds; *U.S. Private*, pg. 2485
CLYDE UNION MIDDLE EAST LLC—See Lone Star Funds; *U.S. Private*, pg. 2485
CLYDE UNION PUMPS MIDDLE EAST FZE—See Lone Star Funds; *U.S. Private*, pg. 2485
CLYDE UNION S.A.S.—See Lone Star Funds; *U.S. Private*, pg. 2485
CLYDE UNION SOUTH EAST ASIA PTE. LTD.—See Lone Star Funds; *U.S. Private*, pg. 2485
CLYDE/WEST INC.—See Joshua Green Corporation; *U.S. Private*, pg. 2237
CLYNOL GMBH—See Henkel AG & Co. KGaA; *Int'l*, pg. 3348
CM2.COM, INC.—See Open Text Corporation; *Int'l*, pg. 5598
CM3 BUILDING SOLUTIONS, INC.—See Daikin Industries, Ltd.; *Int'l*, pg. 1936
CM4ALL GMBH—See IONOS Group SE; *Int'l*, pg. 3795
CMA CGM ALGERIA—See CMA CGM S.A.; *Int'l*, pg. 1667
CMA CGM AMERICA LLC—See CMA CGM S.A.; *Int'l*, pg. 1667
CMA CGM AND ANL HONG KONG—See CMA CGM S.A.; *Int'l*, pg. 1667
CMA CGM AND ANL MALAYSIA SDN BHD—See CMA CGM S.A.; *Int'l*, pg. 1667
CMA CGM ANTILLES GUYANE—See CMA CGM S.A.; *Int'l*, pg. 1667
CMA CGM AUSTRALIA—See CMA CGM S.A.; *Int'l*, pg. 1667
CMA CGM BELGIUM NV—See CMA CGM S.A.; *Int'l*, pg. 1667
CMA CGM BOLIVIA—See CMA CGM S.A.; *Int'l*, pg. 1667
CMA CGM CANADA—See CMA CGM S.A.; *Int'l*, pg. 1667
CMA CGM CENTRAL ASIA—See CMA CGM S.A.; *Int'l*, pg. 1667
CMA CGM CHILE SA—See CMA CGM S.A.; *Int'l*, pg. 1667
CMA CGM COLOMBIA S.A.S.—See CMA CGM S.A.; *Int'l*, pg. 1667
CMA CGM COSTA RICA—See CMA CGM S.A.; *Int'l*, pg. 1667
CMA CGM CROATIA—See CMA CGM S.A.; *Int'l*, pg. 1667
CMA CGM DELMAS NIGERIA—See CMA CGM S.A.; *Int'l*, pg. 1667
CMA CGM DENIZ ACENTELIGI A.S.—See CMA CGM S.A.; *Int'l*, pg. 1667
CMA CGM DEUTSCHLAND—See CMA CGM S.A.; *Int'l*, pg. 1667
CMA CGM DO BRASIL AGENCIA MARITIMA LTDA—See CMA CGM S.A.; *Int'l*, pg. 1667
CMA CGM DOMINICANA—See CMA CGM S.A.; *Int'l*, pg. 1667
CMA CGM ECUADOR—See CMA CGM S.A.; *Int'l*, pg. 1667
CMA CGM ESTONIA LTD—See CMA CGM S.A.; *Int'l*, pg. 1667
CMA CGM FINLAND—See CMA CGM S.A.; *Int'l*, pg. 1667
CMA CGM GLOBAL INDIA—See CMA CGM S.A.; *Int'l*, pg. 1667
CMA CGM GREECE—See CMA CGM S.A.; *Int'l*, pg. 1667
CMA CGM HOLLAND BV—See CMA CGM S.A.; *Int'l*, pg. 1667
CMA CGM HUNGARY—See CMA CGM S.A.; *Int'l*, pg. 1667
CMA CGM IBERICA SAU—See CMA CGM S.A.; *Int'l*, pg. 1667
CMA CGM ITALY S.R.L.—See CMA CGM S.A.; *Int'l*, pg. 1667
CMA CGM JAMAICA LTD—See CMA CGM S.A.; *Int'l*, pg. 1667
CMA CGM JAPAN—See CMA CGM S.A.; *Int'l*, pg. 1667
CMA CGM KENYA—See CMA CGM S.A.; *Int'l*, pg. 1667
CMA CGM MADAGASCAR—See CMA CGM S.A.; *Int'l*, pg. 1667
CMA CGM MAROC—See CMA CGM S.A.; *Int'l*, pg. 1667
CMA CGM MEXICO—See CMA CGM S.A.; *Int'l*, pg. 1668
CMA CGM MOZAMBIQUE—See CMA CGM S.A.; *Int'l*, pg. 1668
CMA CGM NOUMEA—See CMA CGM S.A.; *Int'l*, pg. 1668
CMA CGM PAKISTAN (PVT) LTD—See CMA CGM S.A.; *Int'l*, pg. 1668
CMA CGM PANAMA—See CMA CGM S.A.; *Int'l*, pg. 1668
CMA CGM PAPEETE—See CMA CGM S.A.; *Int'l*, pg. 1668
CMA CGM POLSKA LTD—See CMA CGM S.A.; *Int'l*, pg. 1668
CMA CGM PORTUGAL—See CMA CGM S.A.; *Int'l*, pg. 1668
CMA CGM REUNION—See CMA CGM S.A.; *Int'l*, pg. 1668
CMA CGM ROMANIA—See CMA CGM S.A.; *Int'l*, pg. 1668
CMA CGM S.A.; *Int'l*, pg. 1666
CMA CGM SCANDINAVIA AS—See CMA CGM S.A.; *Int'l*, pg. 1668
CMA CGM SERBIA—See CMA CGM S.A.; *Int'l*, pg. 1668
CMA CGM SHIPPING AGENCIES UKRAINE LTD—See CMA CGM S.A.; *Int'l*, pg. 1668
CMA CGM SLOVENIA—See CMA CGM S.A.; *Int'l*, pg. 1668
CMA CGM SOUTH AFRICA (PTY) LTD.—See CMA CGM S.A.; *Int'l*, pg. 1668
CMA CGM ST LUCIA LTD—See CMA CGM S.A.; *Int'l*, pg. 1668
CMA CGM ST MARTEEN—See CMA CGM S.A.; *Int'l*, pg. 1668
CMA CGM SUDAN—See CMA CGM S.A.; *Int'l*, pg. 1668
CMA CGM TRINIDAD LTD—See CMA CGM S.A.; *Int'l*, pg. 1668
CMA CGM TURKEY—See CMA CGM S.A.; *Int'l*, pg. 1668
CMA CGM UK SHIPPING LTD—See CMA CGM S.A.; *Int'l*, pg. 1668
CMA CGM VENEZUELA—See CMA CGM S.A.; *Int'l*, pg. 1668
CMA CONSULTING SERVICES; *U.S. Private*, pg. 949
CMA CONTRACTING PTY LIMITED—See Delta Group Pty Ltd; *Int'l*, pg. 2018
CMA DISHMACHINES—See Ali Holding S.r.l.; *Int'l*, pg. 320
C. MAHENDRA EXPORTS LTD. - DIAMOND FACTORY—See C. Mahendra Exports Ltd.; *Int'l*, pg. 1240
C. MAHENDRA EXPORTS LTD.; *Int'l*, pg. 1240
CMAI INDUSTRIES, INC.—See China Metal Products Co., Ltd.; *Int'l*, pg. 1523
C.M. ALMY & SON, INC.; *U.S. Private*, pg. 708
C-MAP/COMMERCIAL, LTD.—See The Boeing Company; *U.S. Public*, pg. 2041
C-MAP USA, INC.—See Altor Equity Partners AB; *Int'l*, pg. 394
CM&A PVT. LTD.—See WPP plc; *Int'l*, pg. 8484
C-MARK BV—See Eurofins Scientific S.E.; *Int'l*, pg. 2541
C MARKET A.D.; *Int'l*, pg. 1238
C & MARKETING SERVICES INC.—See YG Plus Inc.; *Int'l*, pg. 8579
CMA ROBOTER GMBH—See EFORT Intelligent Equipment Co., Ltd.; *Int'l*, pg. 2321
CMA ROBOTICS S.P.A.—See EFORT Intelligent Equipment Co., Ltd.; *Int'l*, pg. 2321
CM AROMATICS CO LTD—See Cosmo Energy Holdings Co., Ltd.; *Int'l*, pg. 1811
C. MARTIN COMPANY, INC.; *U.S. Private*, pg. 705
CMA SHIPS LANKA (PVT) LTD.—See Hayleys PLC; *Int'l*, pg. 3291
C-MATIC SYSTEMS LTD—See Schneider Electric SE; *Int'l*, pg. 6626
C-MATRIX COMMUNICATIONS AG—See Omnicom Group Inc.; *U.S. Public*, pg. 1586

COMPANY NAME INDEX

C & M AUTO PARTS, INC.—See Blue Point Capital Partners, LLC; *U.S. Private*, pg. 590
CMA VENTURES, INC.—See Central Iowa Power Cooperative; *U.S. Private*, pg. 822
CMA (WUHU) ROBOTICS CO., LTD.—See EFORT Intelligent Equipment Co., Ltd.; *Int'l*, pg. 2321
CMAX CLINICAL RESEARCH PTY LTD—See I'rom Group Co., Ltd.; *Int'l*, pg. 3562
CMAX JAPAN CO., LTD.—See I'rom Group Co., Ltd.; *Int'l*, pg. 3562
CMBC CAPITAL HOLDINGS LIMITED; *Int'l*, pg. 1668
CMB INTERNATIONAL CAPITAL CORPORATION LIMITED—See China Merchants Group Limited; *Int'l*, pg. 1520
CMB JAPAN LIMITED—See Compagnie Maritime Belge S.A.; *Int'l*, pg. 1746
CMB NV—See Compagnie Maritime Belge S.A.; *Int'l*, pg. 1746
CMB SEAFOODS PTY. LTD.—See East 33 Limited; *Int'l*, pg. 2269
CMB SERVICES SA—See Compagnie Maritime Belge S.A.; *Int'l*, pg. 1746
CMB WEALTH MANAGEMENT LTD—See Compagnie Monegasque de Banque; *Int'l*, pg. 1746
CMC ALAMO STEEL—See Commercial Metals Company; *U.S. Public*, pg. 546
CMC ALAMO VICTORIA—See Commercial Metals Company; *U.S. Public*, pg. 546
CMC ASIA PACIFIC CO., LTD.—See CMC Corporation; *Int'l*, pg. 1669
CMC (AUSTRALIA) PTY LIMITED—See Commercial Metals Company; *U.S. Public*, pg. 545
CMC (AUSTRALIA) PTY LIMITED—See Commercial Metals Company; *U.S. Public*, pg. 545
CMC (BEIJING) INTERNATIONAL TRADE COMPANY LTD.—See Commercial Metals Company; *U.S. Public*, pg. 545
CMC CENTROZLOM SP. Z O.O.—See Commercial Metals Company; *U.S. Public*, pg. 545
CMC CONSTRUCTION SERVICES INC—See Commercial Metals Company; *U.S. Public*, pg. 545
CMC CONSTRUCTION SERVICES—See Commercial Metals Company; *U.S. Public*, pg. 545
CMC CONSULTING BOSTON, INC.; *U.S. Private*, pg. 060
CMC CONSUMER MEDICAL CARE GMBH—See PAUL HARTMANN AG; *Int'l*, pg. 5760
CMC CORPORATION; *Int'l*, pg. 1668
CMC ELECTRONICS AURORA LLC—See TransDigm Group Incorporated; *U.S. Public*, pg. 2180
CMC ELECTRONICS INC. - OTTAWA—See TransDigm Group Incorporated; *U.S. Public*, pg. 2180
CMC ELECTRONICS INC.—See TransDigm Group Incorporated; *U.S. Public*, pg. 2180
CMC ELECTRONICS ME INC.—See TransDigm Group Incorporated; *U.S. Public*, pg. 2180
CMC ENERGY SERVICES, INC.; *U.S. Private*, pg. 950
CMC EUROPE AG—See Commercial Metals Company; *U.S. Public*, pg. 545
CMC EUROPE GMBH—See Commercial Metals Company; *U.S. Public*, pg. 545
CMC FAREAST LIMITED—See Commercial Metals Company; *U.S. Public*, pg. 545
CMC FUNDING, INC.—See Computershare Limited; *Int'l*, pg. 1760
CMC GH SISAK D.O.O.—See Commercial Metals Company; *U.S. Public*, pg. 545
CMC GROUP INC.; *U.S. Private*, pg. 950
CM CHAIN DIVISION—See Columbus McKinnon Corporation; *U.S. Public*, pg. 535
CMC HI TEC CONTROLLING SOLUTIONS LTD.—See CMC Technologies Israel Ltd.; *Int'l*, pg. 1669
CMC HOME HEALTH AND HOSPICE, LLC—See UnitedHealth Group Incorporated; *U.S. Public*, pg. 2244
CMC INC.; *U.S. Private*, pg. 950
CMC INDUSTRIAL ELECTRONICS LTD.—See Ag Growth International Inc.; *Int'l*, pg. 198
CMC INDUSTRIAL ELECTRONICS USA, INC.—See Ag Growth International Inc.; *Int'l*, pg. 198
CMC INVESTMENT JOINT STOCK COMPANY; *Int'l*, pg. 1669
CMC JOINT STOCK COMPANY; *Int'l*, pg. 1669
CMC KOREA CO., LTD.—See Entegris, Inc.; *U.S. Public*, pg. 776
CMC MAGNETICS CORPORATION; *Int'l*, pg. 1669
CMC MARINE, INC.—See T-H Marine Supplies Inc.; *U.S. Private*, pg. 3910
CMC MARKETS UK PLC; *Int'l*, pg. 1669
CMC MATERIALS, INC.—See Entegris, Inc.; *U.S. Public*, pg. 776
CMC METAL RECYCLING (AUGUSTA)—See Commercial Metals Company; *U.S. Public*, pg. 546
CMC METAL RECYCLING (CAYCE)—See Commercial Metals Company; *U.S. Public*, pg. 546
CMC METAL RECYCLING (LEXINGTON)—See Commercial Metals Company; *U.S. Public*, pg. 546
CMC METAL RECYCLING (SEGUIN)—See Commercial Metals Company; *U.S. Public*, pg. 546
CMC METALS LTD.; *Int'l*, pg. 1669

CMCM PERNIAGAAN SDN BHD—See YTL Corporation Berhad; *Int'l*, pg. 8606
CMCO MATERIAL HANDLING (PTY), LTD.—See Columbus McKinnon Corporation; *U.S. Public*, pg. 535
CM.COM BELGIUM N.V.—See CM.com N.V.; *Int'l*, pg. 1666
CM.COM DENMARK AS—See CM.com N.V.; *Int'l*, pg. 1666
CM.COM GERMANY GMBH—See CM.com N.V.; *Int'l*, pg. 1666
CM.COM JAPAN KK—See CM.com N.V.; *Int'l*, pg. 1666
CM.COM N.V.; *Int'l*, pg. 1666
CM COMPANY INC.; *U.S. Private*, pg. 949
C&M CONVEYOR INC—See CapitalWorks, LLC; *U.S. Private*, pg. 742
C&M CORPORATION; *U.S. Private*, pg. 703
CMCP - INTERNATIONAL PAPER S.A.S.—See International Paper Company; *U.S. Public*, pg. 1155
CMCP MONTROSE LLC—See Brookdale Senior Living Inc.; *U.S. Public*, pg. 394
CMC POLAND SP. Z O.O.—See Commercial Metals Company; *U.S. Public*, pg. 545
CMC PUTEX SP.Z O.O.—See Commercial Metals Company; *U.S. Public*, pg. 545
CMC REALTY INC.; *U.S. Private*, pg. 950
CMC REBAR CAROLINAS—See Commercial Metals Company; *U.S. Public*, pg. 546
CMC REBAR FLORIDA—See Commercial Metals Company; *U.S. Public*, pg. 546
CMC REBAR GEORGIA—See Commercial Metals Company; *U.S. Public*, pg. 546
CMC REBAR NORTH CAROLINA—See Commercial Metals Company; *U.S. Public*, pg. 546
CMC REBAR—See Commercial Metals Company; *U.S. Public*, pg. 546
CMC REBAR—See Commercial Metals Company; *U.S. Public*, pg. 546
CMC REBAR—See Commercial Metals Company; *U.S. Public*, pg. 546
CMC REBAR—See Commercial Metals Company; *U.S. Public*, pg. 546
CMC REBAR VIRGINIA—See Commercial Metals Company; *U.S. Public*, pg. 546
CMC RECEIVABLES, INC.—See Commercial Metals Company; *U.S. Public*, pg. 545
CMC RECYCLING—See Commercial Metals Company; *U.S. Public*, pg. 545
CMC RECYCLING—See Commercial Metals Company; *U.S. Public*, pg. 545
CMC RECYCLING—See Commercial Metals Company; *U.S. Public*, pg. 545
CMC S.A.R.L.—See Somfy SA; *Int'l*, pg. 7085
CMC SAS—See Exel Industries SA; *Int'l*, pg. 2582
CMC SOLUTIONS INC.—See CMC Corporation; *Int'l*, pg. 1669
CMC STEEL ALABAMA—See Commercial Metals Company; *U.S. Public*, pg. 546
CMC STEEL ARKANSAS—See Commercial Metals Company; *U.S. Public*, pg. 546
CMC STEEL DISTRIBUTION PTY LTD—See Commercial Metals Company; *U.S. Public*, pg. 545
CMC STEEL FABRICATORS, INC.—See Commercial Metals Company; *U.S. Public*, pg. 545
CMC STEEL GROUP—See Commercial Metals Company; *U.S. Public*, pg. 546
CMC STEEL OKLAHOMA, LLC—See Commercial Metals Company; *U.S. Public*, pg. 546
CMC STEEL SOUTH CAROLINA—See Commercial Metals Company; *U.S. Public*, pg. 546
CMC STEEL TEXAS—See Commercial Metals Company; *U.S. Public*, pg. 546
CMC STERLING STEEL—See Commercial Metals Company; *U.S. Public*, pg. 546
CMC SUPPLY INC.; *U.S. Private*, pg. 950
CMC TECHNOLOGIES ISRAEL LTD.; *Int'l*, pg. 1669
CMC TEXAS COLD FINISHED STEEL, INC.—See Commercial Metals Company; *U.S. Public*, pg. 546
CMC UK LTD.—See Commercial Metals Company; *U.S. Public*, pg. 545
CMC XMANICOM CO.—See CMC Corporation; *Int'l*, pg. 1669
CMD AEROPUERTOS CANARIOS SL—See Mubadala Investment Company PJSC; *Int'l*, pg. 5074
CMD CORPORATION; *U.S. Private*, pg. 950
CMD GROUP, LLC—See Roper Technologies, Inc.; *U.S. Public*, pg. 1814
CMD INC.; *U.S. Private*, pg. 950
CMD, LTD.—See Rubicon Partners Limited; *Int'l*, pg. 6422
CMDS; *U.S. Private*, pg. 950
CME AMERICA LLC—See Becton, Dickinson & Company; *U.S. Public*, pg. 291
CME ASSOCIATES, INC.—See H.I.G. Capital, LLC; *U.S. Private*, pg. 1827
CMEC (BEIJING) INTERNATIONAL ECONOMIC & LEGAL ADVISORS INC.—See China Machinery Engineering Corporation; *Int'l*, pg. 1515
CMEC BEIJING PROPERTY DEVELOPMENT CO., LTD.—See China Machinery Engineering Corporation; *Int'l*, pg. 1515

CMG HOLDINGS GROUP, INC.

CMEC COMTRANS INTERNATIONAL CO., LTD.—See China Machinery Engineering Corporation; *Int'l*, pg. 1515
CMEC ENGINEERING C.A.—See China Machinery Engineering Corporation; *Int'l*, pg. 1515
CMEC ENGINEERING MACHINERY IMPORT & EXPORT CO., LTD.—See China Machinery Engineering Corporation; *Int'l*, pg. 1515
CMEC GENERAL MACHINERY IMPORT & EXPORT CO., LTD.—See China Machinery Engineering Corporation; *Int'l*, pg. 1516
CMEC GROUP SHANGHAI INTERNATIONAL FORWARDING CO., LTD.—See China Machinery Engineering Corporation; *Int'l*, pg. 1516
CMEC GUINEA EQUATORIAL, S.L.—See China Machinery Engineering Corporation; *Int'l*, pg. 1516
CME CHILE, SPA—See ACS, Actividades de Construccion y Servicios, S.A.; *Int'l*, pg. 110
CMEC INTERNATIONAL ENGINEERING CO., LTD.—See China Machinery Engineering Corporation; *Int'l*, pg. 1516
CMEC INTERNATIONAL EXHIBITION CO., LTD.—See China Machinery Engineering Corporation; *Int'l*, pg. 1516
CMEC JAPAN COMPANY LTD.—See China Machinery Engineering Corporation; *Int'l*, pg. 1516
CMEC LANKA (PRIVATE) LIMITED—See China Machinery Engineering Corporation; *Int'l*, pg. 1516
CME CLEARING EUROPE LIMITED—See CME Group, Inc.; *U.S. Public*, pg. 516
CMEC MIDDLE EAST FZE—See China Machinery Engineering Corporation; *Int'l*, pg. 1516
CMEC NAMIBIA (PROPRIETARY) LIMITED—See China Machinery Engineering Corporation; *Int'l*, pg. 1516
CMEC NIGERIA DEVELOPMENT LTD.—See China Machinery Engineering Corporation; *Int'l*, pg. 1516
CMEC CORPORATION; *U.S. Private*, pg. 950
CMEC PETROCHEMICAL-GENERAL MACHINERY CO., LTD.—See China Machinery Engineering Corporation; *Int'l*, pg. 1516
CMEC SAUDI FOR CONSTRUCTION LLC—See China Machinery Engineering Corporation; *Int'l*, pg. 1516
CMEC SENEGAL S.A.—See China Machinery Engineering Corporation; *Int'l*, pg. 1516
CMEC ZAMBIA DEVELOPMENT LIMITED—See China Machinery Engineering Corporation; *Int'l*, pg. 1516
C-MEDIA ELECTRONICS INC—See Realtek Semiconductor Corp.; *Int'l*, pg. 6235
CME DIGITAL LIMITED—See CME Group, Inc.; *U.S. Public*, pg. 516
CME EUROPE LIMITED—See CME Group, Inc.; *U.S. Public*, pg. 516
CME GORUP BERHAD; *Int'l*, pg. 1669
CME GROUP ASIA HOLDINGS PTE. LTD—See CME Group, Inc.; *U.S. Public*, pg. 516
CME GROUP AUSTRALIA PTY. LTD.—See CME Group, Inc.; *U.S. Public*, pg. 516
CME GROUP INC.; *U.S. Public*, pg. 515
CME GROUP SINGAPORE OPERATIONS PTE.LTD.—See CME Group, Inc.; *U.S. Public*, pg. 516
CME HOLDCO L.P.—See PPF Group N.V.; *Int'l*, pg. 5950
CME INFORMATION SERVICES (BEIJING) CO., LTD.—See S&P Global Inc.; *U.S. Public*, pg. 1830
CME MEDICAL (UK) LIMITED—See Becton, Dickinson & Company; *U.S. Public*, pg. 291
C. MENDES SAS—See Kering S.A.; *Int'l*, pg. 4134
CM ENERGY TECH CO., LTD.; *Int'l*, pg. 1665
CM EQUITY PARTNERS, L.P.—See Carl Marks & Co., Inc.; *U.S. Private*, pg. 762
C-MER EYE CARE HOLDINGS LTD.; *Int'l*, pg. 1239
CMES, INC.; *U.S. Private*, pg. 950
CMET INC.—See Nabtesco Corporation; *Int'l*, pg. 5119
CMFG LIFE INSURANCE COMPANY; *U.S. Private*, pg. 950
C & M FIRST SERVICES, INC.—See One80 Intermediaries LLC; *U.S. Private*, pg. 3024
C.M. FURUKAWA PHILIPPINES INC.—See The Furukawa Electric Co., Ltd.; *Int'l*, pg. 7644
CMG ELECTRIC MOTORS (ASIA PACIFIC) PTE LTD.—See CMG Pty. Ltd.; *Int'l*, pg. 1669
CMG ELECTRIC MOTORS (MALAYSIA) SDN. BHD.—See Regal Rexnord Corporation; *U.S. Public*, pg. 1773
CMG ELECTRIC MOTORS (NZ) LIMITED—See Regal Rexnord Corporation; *U.S. Public*, pg. 1773
CMG ELECTRIC MOTORS SOUTH AFRICA (PTY) LTD.—See CMG Pty. Ltd.; *Int'l*, pg. 1670
CMG ELECTRIC MOTORS (UK) LTD.—See CMG Pty. Ltd.; *Int'l*, pg. 1670
CMGE TECHNOLOGY GROUP LIMITED; *Int'l*, pg. 1670
CMG (EUROPE) LIMITED—See Computer Modelling Group Ltd.; *Int'l*, pg. 1760
CMG FINANCIAL SERVICES INC.; *U.S. Private*, pg. 950
CMG GESELLSCHAFT FUR BAULOGISTIK GMBH—See Heijmans N.V.; *Int'l*, pg. 3322
CMG GRUNDSTUCKSVERWALTUNGS- UND BETEILIGUNGS - GMBH—See Zuivelcooperatie FrieslandCampina U.A.; *Int'l*, pg. 8693
CMG HOLDINGS GROUP, INC.; *U.S. Public*, pg. 518

CMG HOLDINGS GROUP, INC.

CMG MIDDLE EAST FZ LLC—See Computer Modelling Group Ltd.; *Int'l*, pg. 1760
CMG MORTGAGE, INC.—See CMG Financial Services Inc.; *U.S. Private*, pg. 951
C.M. GOETTSCHE COMPANY, INC.—See Strohmeyer & Arpe Company; *U.S. Private*, pg. 3840
CMG PHARMACEUTICAL CO., LTD.; *Int'l*, pg. 1669
CMG PTY. LTD.; *Int'l*, pg. 1669
THE CM GROUP, LLC; *U.S. Private*, pg. 4011
CMGRP, INC.—See The Interpublic Group of Companies, Inc.; *U.S. Public*, pg. 2090
CMGRP UK LIMITED—See The Interpublic Group of Companies, Inc.; *U.S. Public*, pg. 2090
CM-GRUPPEN AS—See Validus AS; *Int'l*, pg. 8116
CMG WORLDWIDE, INC.; *U.S. Private*, pg. 951
CMH AUTOGAS PRODUCTS (PTY) LTD—See Combined Motor Holdings Limited; *Int'l*, pg. 1709
CMH CAPITAL, INC.—See Berkshire Hathaway Inc.; *U.S. Public*, pg. 303
CMH CAR HIRE (PTY) LTD—See Combined Motor Holdings Limited; *Int'l*, pg. 1709
CMH HOMES, INC.—See Berkshire Hathaway Inc.; *U.S. Public*, pg. 304
CMH INC.; *U.S. Private*, pg. 951
CMH MANUFACTURING, INC.—See Berkshire Hathaway Inc.; *U.S. Public*, pg. 304
CM HOIST DIVISION—See Columbus McKinnon Corporation; *U.S. Public*, pg. 535
C.M. HOLDING CO., INC.—See Mid Oaks Investments LLC; *U.S. Private*, pg. 2706
C.M. HOLTZINGER FRUIT CO. INC.; *U.S. Private*, pg. 708
CM HOSPITALAR SA—See Mafra Hospitalar S/A; *Int'l*, pg. 4636
CMH PARKS, INC.—See Berkshire Hathaway Inc.; *U.S. Public*, pg. 304
CMHR PTY LIMITED—See Recruit Holdings Co., Ltd.; *Int'l*, pg. 6240
CMH SOLUTIONS LLC—See Ardian SAS; *Int'l*, pg. 554
CMH SPACE FLOORING PRODUCTS, INC.—See J.J. Haines & Co. Inc.; *U.S. Private*, pg. 2167
CMH SPACE FLOORING—See J.J. Haines & Co. Inc.; *U.S. Private*, pg. 2167
CMI ARCHITECTURAL PRODUCTS, INC.; *U.S. Private*, pg. 951
CMIC ASHFIELD CO., LTD.—See CMIC Holdings Co., Ltd.; *Int'l*, pg. 1670
CMIC ASIA-PACIFIC (AUSTRALIA) PTY LTD—See CMIC Holdings Co., Ltd.; *Int'l*, pg. 1670
CMIC ASIA-PACIFIC (HONG KONG) LIMITED—See CMIC Holdings Co., Ltd.; *Int'l*, pg. 1670
CMIC ASIA-PACIFIC PTE. LTD.—See CMIC Holdings Co., Ltd.; *Int'l*, pg. 1670
CMIC (BEIJING) CO.LTD.—See CMIC Holdings Co., Ltd.; *Int'l*, pg. 1670
CMIC-BS CO.LTD.—See CMIC Holdings Co., Ltd.; *Int'l*, pg. 1670
CMIC CMO CO., LTD.—See CMIC Holdings Co., Ltd.; *Int'l*, pg. 1670
CMIC CMO KOREA CO., LTD—See CMIC Holdings Co., Ltd.; *Int'l*, pg. 1670
CMIC CMO NISHINE CO., LTD.—See CMIC Holdings Co., Ltd.; *Int'l*, pg. 1670
CMIC CMO USA CORPORATION—See CMIC Holdings Co., Ltd.; *Int'l*, pg. 1670
CMIC-CP CO. LTD.—See CMIC Holdings Co., Ltd.; *Int'l*, pg. 1670
CMIC-CRC CO. LTD.—See CMIC Holdings Co., Ltd.; *Int'l*, pg. 1670
CMIC DATA SCIENCE VIETNAM COMPANY LIMITED—See CMIC Holdings Co., Ltd.; *Int'l*, pg. 1670
CMIC DEVELOPMENT COMPANY LIMITED—See Kiatnakin Bank Public Company Limited; *Int'l*, pg. 4157
CMIC ENMEI CO., LTD.—See China Machinery Engineering Corporation; *Int'l*, pg. 1516
CMIC HEALTHCARE INSTITUTE CO., LTD.—See CMIC Holdings Co., Ltd.; *Int'l*, pg. 1670
CMIC HOLDINGS CO., LTD.; *Int'l*, pg. 1670
CMIC, INC.—See CMIC Holdings Co., Ltd.; *Int'l*, pg. 1670
CMIC INTERNATIONAL EXHIBITION CO., LTD.—See China Machinery Engineering Corporation; *Int'l*, pg. 1516
CMIC KOREA CO.LTD.—See CMIC Holdings Co., Ltd.; *Int'l*, pg. 1670
CMICRO CORPORATION—See Imasen Electric Industrial Co., Ltd.; *Int'l*, pg. 3620
CMIC SHIFTZERO K.K.—See CMIC Holdings Co., Ltd.; *Int'l*, pg. 1670
CMICS MEDICAL ELECTRONIC INSTRUMENT CO., LTD.—See China National Pharmaceutical Group Corporation; *Int'l*, pg. 1533
CMIC SOLUTIONS CO., LTD.—See CMIC Holdings Co., Ltd.; *Int'l*, pg. 1670
CMIC SS CMO CO. LTD.—See CMIC Holdings Co., Ltd.; *Int'l*, pg. 1670
CMI ENTERPRISES INC.; *U.S. Private*, pg. 951
CMI, INC.; *U.S. Private*, pg. 951
CMI, INC.—See MPD, Inc.; *U.S. Private*, pg. 2803
CMI INDUSTRY AMERICAS INC.—See Euremis Holding SA; *Int'l*, pg. 2530

CMI INTERNATIONAL—See Terex Corporation; *U.S. Public*, pg. 2018
CMI LIMITED—See MPD, Inc.; *U.S. Private*, pg. 2803
CMI LLOYDS—See Central Mutual Insurance Company; *U.S. Private*, pg. 822
CMI-MANAGEMENT SERVICES INC.; *U.S. Private*, pg. 951
CMI NESA—See Euremis Holding SA; *Int'l*, pg. 2530
CM INSURANCE COMPANY, INC.—See Columbus McKinnon Corporation; *U.S. Public*, pg. 535
CMI SPRINGS—See Seven Group Holdings Limited; *Int'l*, pg. 6733
CMI STONE GROUP INC.; *U.S. Private*, pg. 951
CMISTONE VIET NAM JOINT STOCK COMPANY; *Int'l*, pg. 1670
CMI TEREX CORPORATION—See Terex Corporation; *U.S. Public*, pg. 2018
CMIT SOLUTIONS LLC—See Hammond, Kennedy, Whitney & Company, Inc.; *U.S. Private*, pg. 1850
C.M. JACKSON ASSOCIATES, INC.—See HPS Investment Partners, LLC; *U.S. Private*, pg. 1997
CMJ CO., LTD.—See China Metal Products Co., Ltd.; *Int'l*, pg. 1523
CMJ ENTERPRISES INC.; *U.S. Private*, pg. 951
CMK AMERICA CORPORATION—See CMK Corporation; *Int'l*, pg. 1670
CMKC (DONG GUAN) LTD.—See CMK Corporation; *Int'l*, pg. 1671
CMKC (HONG KONG) LTD.—See CMK Corporation; *Int'l*, pg. 1671
CMK CORPORATION - G STATION PLANT—See CMK Corporation; *Int'l*, pg. 1670
CMK CORPORATION - KIBAN CENTER PLANT—See CMK Corporation; *Int'l*, pg. 1670
CMK CORPORATION - NIIGATA SATELLITE PLANT—See CMK Corporation; *Int'l*, pg. 1670
CMK CORPORATION; *Int'l*, pg. 1670
CMK CORPORATION - TECHNICAL CENTER PLANT—See CMK Corporation; *Int'l*, pg. 1670
CMK CORPORATION (THAILAND) CO., LTD.—See CMK Corporation; *Int'l*, pg. 1670
CMK ELECTRONICS (WUXI) CO., LTD.—See CMK Corporation; *Int'l*, pg. 1671
CMK ENTERPRISES, INC.—See Electronic Technologies International, Inc.; *U.S. Private*, pg. 1356
CMK EUROPE N.V.—See CMK Corporation; *Int'l*, pg. 1671
CMK FINANCE CORPORATION—See CMK Corporation; *Int'l*, pg. 1671
CMK KANBARA ELECTRONIC CORPORATION—See CMK Corporation; *Int'l*, pg. 1671
CMK MECHANICS CORPORATION—See CMK Corporation; *Int'l*, pg. 1671
CMK MULTI CORPORATION—See CMK Corporation; *Int'l*, pg. 1671
CMK NIIGATA CORPORATION—See CMK Corporation; *Int'l*, pg. 1671
CMK PRODUCTS CORPORATION—See CMK Corporation; *Int'l*, pg. 1671
CMLABS SIMULATIONS INC.—See Spectris Plc; *Int'l*, pg. 7130
CML AIRPORT INTERNATIONAL LOGISTICS CO., LTD.—See China Master Logistics Co., Ltd.; *Int'l*, pg. 1517
CML CHANGXING (TIANJIN) INTERNATIONAL LOGISTICS CO., LTD.—See China Master Logistics Co., Ltd.; *Int'l*, pg. 1517
CML-CHICAGO MARKET LABS, INC.—See Tenet Healthcare Corporation; *U.S. Public*, pg. 2014
CML (DALIAN) LOGISTICS CO., LTD.—See China Master Logistics Co., Ltd.; *Int'l*, pg. 1517
CML GLOBAL CAPITAL LTD.; *Int'l*, pg. 1671
CML GLOBAL LOGISTICS CO., LTD.—See China Master Logistics Co., Ltd.; *Int'l*, pg. 1517
CML GRAND JOURNEY LOGISTICS SHANGHAI CO., LTD.—See China Master Logistics Co., Ltd.; *Int'l*, pg. 1517
CML GRANDRAIL INTERNATIONAL LOGISTICS CO., LTD.—See China Master Logistics Co., Ltd.; *Int'l*, pg. 1517
CML GRANDTRUST LOGISTICS CO., LTD.—See China Master Logistics Co., Ltd.; *Int'l*, pg. 1517
CML GRANDWILL LOGISTICS CO., LTD.—See China Master Logistics Co., Ltd.; *Int'l*, pg. 1517
CML GROUP LTD—See Teledyne Technologies Incorporated; *U.S. Public*, pg. 1994
CML HEALTHCARE INC.—See Ontario Municipal Employees Retirement System; *Int'l*, pg. 5583
C.M. LIFE INSURANCE COMPANY—See Massachusetts Mutual Life Insurance Company; *U.S. Private*, pg. 2605
CML INNOVATIVE TECHNOLOGIES, GMBH & CO. KG—See Grupo Antolin-Irausa, S.A.; *Int'l*, pg. 3119
CML INNOVATIVE TECHNOLOGIES, LTD.—See Grupo Antolin-Irausa, S.A.; *Int'l*, pg. 3119
CML INNOVATIVE TECHNOLOGIES, S.A.S.—See Grupo Antolin-Irausa, S.A.; *Int'l*, pg. 3119
CML INNOVATIVE TECHNOLOGIES—See Havell's India Ltd.; *Int'l*, pg. 3286
CML INNOVATIVE TECHNOLOGIES, S.R.O.—See Grupo Antolin-Irausa, S.A.; *Int'l*, pg. 3119

CORPORATE AFFILIATIONS

CML (LIANYUNGANG) LOGISTICS CO., LTD.—See China Master Logistics Co., Ltd.; *Int'l*, pg. 1517
CML(LONGKOU)LOGISTICS CO., LTD.—See China Master Logistics Co., Ltd.; *Int'l*, pg. 1517
CML MICROCIRCUITS (SINGAPORE) PTE. LTD.—See CML Microsystems Plc; *Int'l*, pg. 1671
CML MICROCIRCUITS (UK) LTD.—See CML Microsystems Plc; *Int'l*, pg. 1671
CML MICROCIRCUITS (USA) INC.—See CML Microsystems Plc; *Int'l*, pg. 1671
CML MICROSYSTEMS PLC; *Int'l*, pg. 1671
CML (NINBO) LOGISTICS CO., LTD.—See China Master Logistics Co., Ltd.; *Int'l*, pg. 1517
CML (NINGBO) LOGISTICS CO., LTD.—See China Master Logistics Co., Ltd.; *Int'l*, pg. 1517
CMLOG TIANCHI SMART COLD CHAIN (QINGDAO) CO., LTD.—See China Master Logistics Co., Ltd.; *Int'l*, pg. 1517
CML (QINGDAO) BONDED LOGISTICS CO., LTD.—See China Master Logistics Co., Ltd.; *Int'l*, pg. 1517
CML-REEFER (QINGDAO) CONTAINER TECHNICAL CO., LTD.—See China Master Logistics Co., Ltd.; *Int'l*, pg. 1517
CML (RIZHAO) LOGISTICS CO., LTD.—See China Master Logistics Co., Ltd.; *Int'l*, pg. 1517
CML (RONGCHENG) LOGISTICS CO., LTD.—See China Master Logistics Co., Ltd.; *Int'l*, pg. 1517
CML (SHAANXI) LOGISTICS CO., LTD.—See China Master Logistics Co., Ltd.; *Int'l*, pg. 1517
CML SUPPLY CHAIN MANAGEMENT CO., LTD.—See China Master Logistics Co., Ltd.; *Int'l*, pg. 1517
CML SUPPLY CHAIN MANAGEMENT (ZHENGZHOU) CO., LTD.—See China Master Logistics Co., Ltd.; *Int'l*, pg. 1517
CML TECHNOLOGIES, GMBH & CO. KG—See Grupo Antolin-Irausa, S.A.; *Int'l*, pg. 3119
CML (TIANJIN) BINHAI LOGISTICS CO., LTD.—See China Master Logistics Co., Ltd.; *Int'l*, pg. 1517
CML (TIANJIN) LOGISTICS CO., LTD.—See China Master Logistics Co., Ltd.; *Int'l*, pg. 1517
CML (TIANJIN) MARITIME CO., LTD.—See China Master Logistics Co., Ltd.; *Int'l*, pg. 1517
CML (WEIHAI) LOGISTICS CO., LTD.—See China Master Logistics Co., Ltd.; *Int'l*, pg. 1517
CML (YANTAI) LOGISTICS CO., LTD.—See China Master Logistics Co., Ltd.; *Int'l*, pg. 1517
CML ZHENGHAI LOGISTICS CO., LTD.—See China Master Logistics Co., Ltd.; *Int'l*, pg. 1517
CMM AUTOMOBILES—See Toyota Tsusho Corporation; *Int'l*, pg. 7875
CM MECHANICAL HANDLING SYSTEMS—See Columbus McKinnon Corporation; *U.S. Public*, pg. 535
CMM INFRAPROJECTS LIMITED; *Int'l*, pg. 1671
C M M MARKETING MANAGEMENT PTE LTD—See Sheng Siong Group Limited; *Int'l*, pg. 6801
CMMP SURGICAL CENTER, L.L.C.—See Bain Capital, LP; *U.S. Private*, pg. 446
CMMS DATA GROUP, INC.; *U.S. Private*, pg. 951
CMN CALGARY INC.—See Colliers International Group Inc.; *Int'l*, pg. 1701
CMNM MINING GROUP SDN. BHD.—See CNMC Goldmine Holdings Limited; *Int'l*, pg. 1677
CMO - CENTRO MEDICO DE OFTALMOLOGIA S/S LTDA.—See UnitedHealth Group Incorporated; *U.S. Public*, pg. 2239
CMOC GROUP LIMITED; *Int'l*, pg. 1671
CMOC MINING SERVICES PTY LTD—See Evolution Mining Limited; *Int'l*, pg. 2572
CMO GROUP PLC; *Int'l*, pg. 1671
CMON LIMITED; *Int'l*, pg. 1671
CMO PUBLIC COMPANY LIMITED; *Int'l*, pg. 1671
CMORE AUTOMOTIVE GMBH—See DXC Technology Company; *U.S. Public*, pg. 694
C MORE ENTERTAINMENT AB—See Telia Company AB; *Int'l*, pg. 7544
C. MORELLO, PTY. LTD.—See Matthews International Corporation; *U.S. Public*, pg. 1399
CMP ADVANCED MECHANICAL SOLUTIONS LTD.; *Int'l*, pg. 1671
THE C. M. PAULA COMPANY; *U.S. Private*, pg. 4003
CMP CAPITAL MANAGEMENT-PARTNERS GMBH; *Int'l*, pg. 1671
CMPC CELULOSA S.A.—See Empresas CMPC S.A.; *Int'l*, pg. 2389
CMPC EUROPE LIMITED—See Empresas CMPC S.A.; *Int'l*, pg. 2389
CMP - CIMENTOS MACEIRA E PATAIAS, S.A.—See SODIM, SGPS, SA; *Int'l*, pg. 7049
CMP - CLASSIC AUTOMOTIVE LTD; *Int'l*, pg. 1671
CMPC MADERAS SPA—See Empresas CMPC S.A.; *Int'l*, pg. 2389
CMP COATINGS INC—See Chugoku Marine Paints, Ltd.; *Int'l*, pg. 1595
CMP COMPONENTES E MODULOS PLASTICOS INDUSTRIA E COMERCIO LTDA.—See Stellantis N.V.; *Int'l*, pg. 7197
CMPC PAPELES S.A.—See Empresas CMPC S.A.; *Int'l*, pg. 2389

COMPANY NAME INDEX

CMPC PRODUCTOS DE PAPEL S.A.—See Empresas CMPC S.A.; *Int'l*, pg. 2389
CMPC TISSUE S.A.—See Empresas CMPC S.A.; *Int'l*, pg. 2389
CMPC USA, INC.—See Empresas CMPC S.A.; *Int'l*, pg. 2390
CMP DUNKERQUE S.A.—See VINCI S.A.; *Int'l*, pg. 8217
CMPEA S.A.R.L—See VINCI S.A.; *Int'l*, pg. 8217
CMPG INC.—See Ontario Teachers' Pension Plan; *Int'l*, pg. 5586
CMP HOLDINGS B.V.—See McDermott International, Inc.; *U.S. Public*, pg. 1405
C&M PLAST AB—See Indutrade AB; *Int'l*, pg. 3677
CMP MINING INC.; *Int'l*, pg. 1672
CM PORTER NOVELLI-SCOTLAND—See Omnicom Group Inc.; *U.S. Public*, pg. 1590
CMP PLANNING LTD.—See Chugoku Marine Paints, Ltd.; *Int'l*, pg. 1595
CMP PRODUCTS LIMITED—See British Engines Ltd.; *Int'l*, pg. 1171
CMR AUTRONIC GMBH—See LBO France S.a.r.l.; *Int'l*, pg. 4429
CMR CONSTRUCTION COLUMBUS—See CMR Construction & Roofing LLC; *U.S. Private*, pg. 951
CMR CONSTRUCTION KANSAS—See CMR Construction & Roofing LLC; *U.S. Private*, pg. 951
CMR CONSTRUCTION LOUISIANA—See CMR Construction & Roofing LLC; *U.S. Private*, pg. 951
CMR CONSTRUCTION MINNESOTA—See CMR Construction & Roofing LLC; *U.S. Private*, pg. 951
CMR CONSTRUCTION MISSOURI - ST LOUIS—See CMR Construction & Roofing LLC; *U.S. Private*, pg. 951
CMR CONSTRUCTION NORTH DAKOTA—See CMR Construction & Roofing LLC; *U.S. Private*, pg. 951
CMR CONSTRUCTION & ROOFING LLC; *U.S. Private*, pg. 951
CMR CONSTRUCTION & ROOFING OF TEXAS—See CMR Construction & Roofing LLC; *U.S. Private*, 951
CMR CONTROL SYSTEMS INDIA PVT LTD—See LBO France S.a.r.l.; *Int'l*, pg. 4429
CMR DIRECT—See Pacific Equity Partners Pty. Limited; *Int'l*, pg. 5689
CM RECYCLING EQUIPMENT SOLUTIONS—See Bengal Machine; *U.S. Private*, pg. 526
CMR (FAR EAST) PTE LTD—See LBO France S.a.r.l.; *Int'l*, pg. 4429
CMR FRANCE SAS—See LBO France S.a.r.l.; *Int'l*, pg. 4429
CMRG APPAREL, LLC—See Destination XL Group, Inc.; *U.S. Public*, pg. 656
CMR GMBH; *Int'l*, pg. 1672
CMR GROUP KOREA LLC—See LBO France S.a.r.l.; *Int'l*, pg. 4429
CMR GROUP LTD.—See Amphenol Corporation; *U.S. Public*, pg. 129
CMR NIKKEI INDIA PREIVATE LTD.—See Nippon Light Metal Holdings Company, Inc.; *Int'l*, pg. 5323
CMR PARTNERS LLP; *U.S. Private*, pg. 951
CMR PHILIPPINES, INC.—See Amphenol Corporation; *U.S. Public*, pg. 129
CMR SUZHOU ELECTRICAL DEVICES CO., LTD.—See LBO France S.a.r.l.; *Int'l*, pg. 4429
C.M.R. U.S.A., INC.—See Amphenol Corporation; *U.S. Public*, pg. 129
CMR USA, LLC—See LBO France S.a.r.l.; *Int'l*, pg. 4429
CMSA ADVERTISING & PUBLIC RELATIONS; *U.S. Private*, pg. 951
CMS CAMERON MCKENNA NABARRO OLSWANG LLP; *Int'l*, pg. 1672
CMS CEMENT INDUSTRIES SDN. BHD.—See Cahya Mata Sarawak Berhad; *Int'l*, pg. 1251
CMS CLINKER SDN. BHD.—See Cahya Mata Sarawak Berhad; *Int'l*, pg. 1251
CMSC, LLC—See Bain Capital, LP; *U.S. Private*, pg. 445
CMS COMMUNICATIONS INC.; *U.S. Private*, pg. 951
CMS COMPUTERS LIMITED—See CMS Computers Ltd.; *Int'l*, pg. 1672
CMS COMPUTERS LTD.; *Int'l*, pg. 1672
CMS CONCRETE PRODUCTS SDN. BHD.—See Cahya Mata Sarawak Berhad; *Int'l*, pg. 1251
CMS EAST, INC.; *U.S. Private*, pg. 951
CM SECURITIES (HONGKONG) COMPANY LIMITED—See China Vered Financial Holding Corporation Limited; *Int'l*, pg. 1562
CMS EDU CO., LTD.—See Chungdahm Learning, Inc.; *Int'l*, pg. 1597
CMS ENERGY CORPORATION; *U.S. Public*, pg. 518
CMS GENERATION SAN NICOLAS COMPANY—See The AES Corporation; *U.S. Public*, pg. 2031
CMS GMBH—See Elekta AB; *Int'l*, pg. 2355
CMSI CONCEPTION ET MOULAGE AU SERVICE DE L'INDUSTRIE SAS—See PSB Industries SA; *Int'l*, pg. 6014
CMS INFO SYSTEMS LIMITED; *Int'l*, pg. 1672
CMS INFRA TRADING SDN. BHD.—See Cahya Mata Sarawak Berhad; *Int'l*, pg. 1251
CMS JAPAN K.K.—See Elekta AB; *Int'l*, pg. 2355

CMS LAB CO., LTD.—See Wonik Corporation; *Int'l*, pg. 8448
CMS LAND COMPANY—See CMS Energy Corporation; *U.S. Public*, pg. 518
CMS LAND SDN. BHD.—See Cahya Mata Sarawak Berhad; *Int'l*, pg. 1251
C.M. SMITH AGENCY, LLC—See Genstar Capital, LLC; *U.S. Private*, pg. 1674
CMS OPERATIONS; *U.S. Private*, pg. 951
CMS PAVEMENT TECH SDN. BHD.—See Cahya Mata Sarawak Berhad; *Int'l*, pg. 1251
CMS PENKUARI SDN. BHD.—See Cahya Mata Sarawak Berhad; *Int'l*, pg. 1251
CMS PREMIX (MIRI) SDN. BHD.—See Cahya Mata Sarawak Berhad; *Int'l*, pg. 1251
CMS PREMIX SDN. BHD.—See Cahya Mata Sarawak Berhad; *Int'l*, pg. 1251
CMS PROCESSING LLC—See Alvarez & Marsal, Inc.; *U.S. Private*, pg. 212
CMS PROPERTY DEVELOPMENT SDN. BHD.—See Cahya Mata Sarawak Berhad; *Int'l*, pg. 1251
CMS QUARRIES SDN. BHD.—See Cahya Mata Sarawak Berhad; *Int'l*, pg. 1251
CMS REHAB OF WF, L.P.—See Encompass Health Corporation; *U.S. Public*, pg. 754
CMS RESEARCH CORPORATION—See Xylem Inc.; *U.S. Public*, pg. 2395
CMS RESOURCES SDN. BHD.—See Cahya Mata Sarawak Berhad; *Int'l*, pg. 1251
CMS ROADS SDN. BHD.—See Cahya Mata Sarawak Berhad; *Int'l*, pg. 1251
C.M.S.R. VENETO MEDICA S.R.L.—See Garofalo Health Care SpA; *Int'l*, pg. 2886
CMST DEVELOPMENT CO., LTD.; *Int'l*, pg. 1672
CMST GUANGZHOU COMPANY—See CMST Development Co., Ltd.; *Int'l*, pg. 1672
CMS TRAFFIC SYSTEMS LIMITED—See CMS Computers Ltd.; *Int'l*, pg. 1672
CMS TRANSPORT SYSTEMS PTY LTD—See WiseTech Global Limited; *Int'l*, pg. 8436
CM SUPPLY APS—See Bunzl plc; *Int'l*, pg. 1218
CMS WIRES SDN. BHD.—See Cahya Mata Sarawak Berhad; *Int'l*, pg. 1251
CMS WORKS SDN. BHD.—See Cahya Mata Sarawak Berhad; *Int'l*, pg. 1251
CMTA INC.; *U.S. Private*, pg. 951
CM TELECOM BV; *Int'l*, pg. 1666
CM TELECOM FRANCE S.A.S.—See CM.com N.V.; *Int'l*, pg. 1666
CM TELECOM SINGAPORE PRIVATE LTD.—See CM.com N.V.; *Int'l*, pg. 1666
CM TELECOM SOUTH AFRICA LTD.—See CM.com N.V.; *Int'l*, pg. 1666
CMT ENGINEERING—See Caparo Group Ltd.; *Int'l*, pg. 1302
CMT HOLDINGS INC.; *U.S. Private*, pg. 951
CMTI, INC.; *U.S. Private*, pg. 951
CMT LOGISTICS CO., LTD.—See Chinese Maritime Transport Ltd.; *Int'l*, pg. 1569
CMTSU LIQUIDATION, INC.—See HTC Global Services Inc.; *U.S. Private*, pg. 1999
CM VISUAL TECHNOLOGY CORP.—See Himax Technologies, Inc.; *Int'l*, pg. 3396
CMV MEDIFORCE S.A.—See BNP Paribas SA; *Int'l*, pg. 1089
C.M.V. S.R.L.—See Certina Holding AG; *Int'l*, pg. 1423
CMW (TIANJIN) INDUSTRY CO., LTD.—See China Metal Products Co., Ltd.; *Int'l*, pg. 1523
CMX GOLD & SILVER CORP.; *Int'l*, pg. 1672
CMXL INC.; *U.S. Private*, pg. 952
CMX MEDICAL IMAGING—See National Healthcare Distribution, Inc.; *U.S. Private*, pg. 2856
CMX TECHNOLOGIES; *U.S. Private*, pg. 951
CN8, THE COMCAST NETWORK—See Comcast Corporation; *U.S. Public*, pg. 537
CNA ENGINEERING PVT LTD—See CNA Group Ltd.; *Int'l*, pg. 1673
CNA FINANCIAL CORPORATION - CHICAGO BRANCH—See Loews Corporation; *U.S. Public*, pg. 1339
CNA FINANCIAL CORPORATION—See Loews Corporation; *U.S. Public*, pg. 1339
CNA GROUP LTD.; *Int'l*, pg. 1673
CNA-HTE VIETNAM CO., LTD.—See CNA Group Ltd.; *Int'l*, pg. 1673
CNA INSURANCE COMPANIES—See Loews Corporation; *U.S. Public*, pg. 1339
CNA INSURANCE COMPANY LIMITED—See Loews Corporation; *U.S. Public*, pg. 1340
CNA INSURANCE - NEW YORK CITY BRANCH—See Loews Corporation; *U.S. Public*, pg. 1339
CNA INSURANCE - OHIO BRANCH—See Loews Corporation; *U.S. Public*, pg. 1339
CNA INSURANCE - READING BRANCH—See Loews Corporation; *U.S. Public*, pg. 1340
CNA INTEGRATED TECHNOLOGIES (LLC)—See CNA Group Ltd.; *Int'l*, pg. 1673
CNA NATIONAL WARRANTY CORPORATION—See Loews Corporation; *U.S. Public*, pg. 1340

CNG VIETNAM JOINT STOCK COMPANY

CN ASIA CORPORATION BHD.; *Int'l*, pg. 1672
CNA SURETY CORPORATION—See Loews Corporation; *U.S. Public*, pg. 1340
CNA SURETY CORPORATION—See Loews Corporation; *U.S. Public*, pg. 1340
CNA TECHNOLOGY INC—See CNA Group Ltd.; *Int'l*, pg. 1673
CNB BANK SHARES, INC.; *U.S. Public*, pg. 519
CNB BANK—See CNB Financial Corporation; *U.S. Public*, pg. 519
CNB BANK & TRUST, N.A.—See CNB Bank Shares, Inc.; *U.S. Public*, pg. 519
CNBC LLC—See Comcast Corporation; *U.S. Public*, pg. 539
CNB COMMUNITY BANCORP, INC.; *U.S. Public*, pg. 519
CNB CORPORATION; *U.S. Public*, pg. 519
CNB CORPORATION; *U.S. Public*, pg. 519
CNB FINANCIAL CORPORATION; *U.S. Public*, pg. 519
CN BIO INNOVATIONS LIMITED—See CN Innovations Holdings Limited; *Int'l*, pg. 1672
CN BIO INNOVATIONS LIMITED—See CN Innovations Holdings Limited; *Int'l*, pg. 1672
CNBM GERMANY GMBH.—See China National Building Material Group Co., Ltd.; *Int'l*, pg. 1525
CNBM INDIA PRIVATE LIMITED—See China National Building Material Group Co., Ltd.; *Int'l*, pg. 1525
CNBM INTERNATIONAL (JORDAN) COMPANY—See China National Building Material Group Co., Ltd.; *Int'l*, pg. 1525
CNBM IN UKRAINE, LLC.—See China National Building Material Group Co., Ltd.; *Int'l*, pg. 1525
CNBMIT CO., LTD—See China National Building Material Group Co., Ltd.; *Int'l*, pg. 1525
CNBM VIETNAM COMPANY LIMITED—See China National Building Material Group Co., Ltd.; *Int'l*, pg. 1525
C.N. BROWN COMPANY INC.; *U.S. Private*, pg. 708
CNB SECURITIES CORPORATION—See CNB Financial Corporation; *U.S. Public*, pg. 519
CNBX PHARMACEUTICALS INC.; *U.S. Public*, pg. 519
CNC AG—See Publicis Groupe S.A.; *Int'l*, pg. 6097
CNC ASSOCIATES NY INC.; *U.S. Private*, pg. 952
C'N'C COSTUME NATIONAL—See IT Holding S.p.A.; *Int'l*, pg. 3826
CNC DIRECT LTD.—See Quaser Machine Tools, Inc.; *Int'l*, pg. 6156
CNC FORCE APS—See Quaser Machine Tools, Inc.; *Int'l*, pg. 6156
C.N. CHEMICALS SDN. BHD.—See Megachem Limited; *Int'l*, pg. 4793
CNC HOLDINGS LIMITED; *Int'l*, pg. 1673
CNC-INAXES S.R.O.—See Quaser Machine Tools, Inc.; *Int'l*, pg. 6156
CNC MACHINE GROUP INC.—See ZYCI LLC; *U.S. Private*, pg. 4611
CNC METAL PRODUCTS; *U.S. Private*, pg. 952
CNC NORDIC APS—See Nicolas Correa S.A.; *Int'l*, pg. 5272
CNC PETROLEUM PTE. LTD.—See YTL Corporation Berhad; *Int'l*, pg. 8606
CNCS FACILITY SOLUTIONS PRIVATE LIMITED.—See A2Z Infra Engineering Limited; *Int'l*, pg. 30
CNC SOFTWARE INC.—See Sandvik AB; *Int'l*, pg. 6528
CNC SPEEDWELL LIMITED—See Castings PLC; *Int'l*, pg. 1357
CNC SYSTEMS INC.; *U.S. Private*, pg. 952
CNC-ZERSPANUNGSTECHNIK BLUG GMBH—See STP SchmiedeTechnik Plettenberg GmbH & Co.; *Int'l*, pg. 7228
CNE DIRECT, INC.; *U.S. Private*, pg. 952
CNE ENERGY SERVICES GROUP, LLC—See Iberdrola, S.A.; *Int'l*, pg. 3570
CNE GAS HOLDINGS, LLC—See Constellation Energy Corporation; *U.S. Public*, pg. 571
CN ENERGY GROUP, INC.; *Int'l*, pg. 1672
CNERGENZ BERHAD; *Int'l*, pg. 1673
CNFA, INC.; *U.S. Private*, pg. 952
CNFC OVERSEAS FISHERY CO., LTD.; *Int'l*, pg. 1673
CNFINANCE HOLDINGS LIMITED; *Int'l*, pg. 1673
C&N FINANCIAL SERVICES CORPORATION—See Citizens & Northern Corporation; *U.S. Public*, pg. 504
CNGC ENERGY CORP.—See MDU Resources Group, Inc.; *U.S. Public*, pg. 1409
CNGC MATRIX INC.—See Matrix Development Group Inc.; *U.S. Private*, pg. 2612
CNGR ADVANCED MATERIAL CO., LTD.; *Int'l*, pg. 1674
C&N GROUP INC.; *U.S. Private*, pg. 703
CNG TRAVEL GROUP PLC; *Int'l*, pg. 1673
CNG VIETNAM JOINT STOCK COMPANY; *Int'l*, pg. 1674
CNH AMERICA - BENSON—See CNH Industrial N.V.; *Int'l*, pg. 1674
CNH AMERICA - FARGO—See CNH Industrial N.V.; *Int'l*, pg. 1674
CNH AMERICA - GOODFIELD—See CNH Industrial N.V.; *Int'l*, pg. 1674
CNH AMERICA LLC—See CNH Industrial N.V.; *Int'l*, pg. 1674
CNH AMERICA - NEW HOLLAND—See CNH Industrial N.V.; *Int'l*, pg. 1674

577

CNH AMERICA - RACINE—See CNH Industrial N.V.; *Int'l*, pg. 1674
CNH AMERICA - WICHITA—See CNH Industrial N.V.; *Int'l*, pg. 1674
CNH BAUMASCHINEN GMBH—See CNH Industrial N.V.; *Int'l*, pg. 1674
CNH BELGIUM N.V.—See CNH Industrial N.V.; *Int'l*, pg. 1674
CNH CANADA, LTD.—See CNH Industrial N.V.; *Int'l*, pg. 1674
CNH CAPITAL EUROPE BV—See BNP Paribas SA; *Int'l*, pg. 1089
CNH CAPITAL EUROPE S.A.S.—See BNP Paribas SA; *Int'l*, pg. 1089
CNH CO., LTD.; *Int'l*, pg. 1674
CNH DEUTSCHLAND GMBH—See CNH Industrial N.V.; *Int'l*, pg. 1674
CNHI-CAN—See The Retirement Systems of Alabama; *U.S. Private*, pg. 4106
CNHI, LLC—See The Retirement Systems of Alabama; *U.S. Private*, pg. 4105
CNH INDUSTRIAL CAPITAL AMERICA LLC—See CNH Industrial N.V.; *Int'l*, pg. 1674
CNH INDUSTRIAL CAPITAL AUSTRALIA PTY LIMITED—See CNH Industrial N.V.; *Int'l*, pg. 1674
CNH INDUSTRIAL CAPITAL CANADA LTD.—See CNH Industrial N.V.; *Int'l*, pg. 1674
CNH INDUSTRIAL CAPITAL (INDIA) PRIVATE LIMITED—See CNH Industrial N.V.; *Int'l*, pg. 1674
CNH INDUSTRIAL CAPITAL LIMITED—See CNH Industrial N.V.; *Int'l*, pg. 1674
CNH INDUSTRIAL CAPITAL LLC—See CNH Industrial N.V.; *Int'l*, pg. 1674
CNH INDUSTRIAL ITALIA S.P.A.—See CNH Industrial N.V.; *Int'l*, pg. 1674
CNH INDUSTRIAL N.V.; *Int'l*, pg. 1674
CNH INTERNATIONAL S.A.—See CNH Industrial N.V.; *Int'l*, pg. 1674
CNH ITALIA S.P.A—See CNH Industrial N.V.; *Int'l*, pg. 1674
CNH LATIN AMERICA LTDA.—See CNH Industrial N.V.; *Int'l*, pg. 1674
C&N HOLDINGS LIMITED; *Int'l*, pg. 1239
CNH PORTUGAL-COMERCIO DE TRACTORES E MAQUINAS AGRICOLAS LTDA—See CNH Industrial N.V.; *Int'l*, pg. 1674
CNH SERVICES S.R.L.—See CNH Industrial N.V.; *Int'l*, pg. 1674
CNH U.K. LIMITED—See CNH Industrial N.V.; *Int'l*, pg. 1675
CNI ENTERPRISE (M) SDN. BHD.—See Citra Nusa Holdings Berhad; *Int'l*, pg. 1626
CNI ENTERPRISES, INC.—See Clearlake Capital Group, L.P.; *U.S. Private*, pg. 934
CNI GLOBAL SOLUTIONS, LLC—See The Chickasaw Nation; *U.S. Private*, pg. 4008
CNIM BABCOCK CENTRAL EUROPE S.R.O.—See CNIM Constructions Industrielles de la Mediterranee SA; *Int'l*, pg. 1677
CNIM BABCOCK POLSKA SP. Z.O.O—See CNIM Constructions Industrielles de la Mediterranee SA; *Int'l*, pg. 1677
CNIM CONSTRUCTIONS INDUSTRIELLES DE LA MEDITERRANEE SA; *Int'l*, pg. 1676
CNIM ECS LTD—See CNIM Constructions Industrielles de la Mediterranee SA; *Int'l*, pg. 1677
CNIM ENVIRONNEMENT SA—See CNIM Constructions Industrielles de la Mediterranee SA; *Int'l*, pg. 1677
CNIM HONG KONG LIMITED—See CNIM Constructions Industrielles de la Mediterranee SA; *Int'l*, pg. 1677
CNIM INSERTION—See CNIM Constructions Industrielles de la Mediterranee SA; *Int'l*, pg. 1677
CNIM OUEST ARMOR—See CNIM Constructions Industrielles de la Mediterranee SA; *Int'l*, pg. 1677
CNIM SINGAPORE PTE LTD—See CNIM Constructions Industrielles de la Mediterranee SA; *Int'l*, pg. 1677
CNIM TRANSPORT EQUIPMENT CO., LTD—See CNIM Constructions Industrielles de la Mediterranee SA; *Int'l*, pg. 1677
CNIM TRANSPORT HOLDING SRL—See CNIM Constructions Industrielles de la Mediterranee SA; *Int'l*, pg. 1677
CNIM UK LTD—See CNIM Constructions Industrielles de la Mediterranee SA; *Int'l*, pg. 1677
CN INNOVATIONS CO., LTD.—See CN Innovations Holdings Limited; *Int'l*, pg. 1672
CN INNOVATIONS HOLDINGS LIMITED; *Int'l*, pg. 1672
CNI RESEARCH LTD; *Int'l*, pg. 1676
CNJ DISTRIBUTING CORPORATION; *U.S. Private*, pg. 952
CNK INC. - NAGASAKI FACTORY—See Nitto Seimo Co., Ltd.; *Int'l*, pg. 5388
CNK INC.—See Nitto Seimo Co., Ltd.; *Int'l*, pg. 5388
CNK INTERNATIONAL CO., LTD.; *Int'l*, pg. 1677
CNL CAPITAL E.K.E.S. AIFM; *Int'l*, pg. 1677
CNL FINANCIAL CORPORATION—See Securian Financial Group, Inc.; *U.S. Private*, pg. 3594
CNL FINANCIAL GROUP, INC.; *U.S. Private*, pg. 952
CNL GROWTH PROPERTIES, INC.—See CNL Financial Group, Inc.; *U.S. Private*, pg. 952

CNL HEALTHCARE PROPERTIES II, INC.—See CNL Financial Group, Inc.; *U.S. Private*, pg. 952
CNL HEALTHCARE PROPERTIES, INC.—See CNL Financial Group, Inc.; *U.S. Private*, pg. 952
CNLIGHT CO., LTD.; *Int'l*, pg. 1677
CNL LIFESTYLE PROPERTIES, INC.—See CNL Financial Group, Inc.; *U.S. Private*, pg. 952
CN LOGISTICS FRANCE S.A.S.—See CN Logistics International Holdings Limited; *Int'l*, pg. 1673
CN LOGISTICS INTERNATIONAL HOLDINGS LIMITED; *Int'l*, pg. 1673
CN LOGISTICS (JAPAN) LIMITED—See CN Logistics International Holdings Limited; *Int'l*, pg. 1673
CN LOGISTICS KOREA CO., LIMITED—See CN Logistics International Holdings Limited; *Int'l*, pg. 1673
CN LOGISTICS SA—See CN Logistics International Holdings Limited; *Int'l*, pg. 1673
CN LOGISTICS S.R.L.—See CN Logistics International Holdings Limited; *Int'l*, pg. 1673
CNL PRIVATE EQUITY CORP.—See CNL Financial Group, Inc.; *U.S. Private*, pg. 952
CNLR HORIZONS LIMITED—See Madison Dearborn Partners, LLC; *U.S. Private*, pg. 2540
CNL SECURITIES CORP.—See CNL Financial Group, Inc.; *U.S. Private*, pg. 952
CNL STRATEGIC CAPITAL, LLC—See CNL Strategic Capital Management LLC; *U.S. Private*, pg. 952
CNL STRATEGIC CAPITAL MANAGEMENT LLC; *U.S. Private*, pg. 952
CNMC ALBETTER ALBRONZE CO., LTD.—See China Nonferrous Metal Mining (Group) Co., Ltd.; *Int'l*, pg. 1535
CNMC COMPANY, INC.—See Best Medical International, Inc.; *U.S. Private*, pg. 543
CNMC GOLDMINE HOLDINGS LIMITED; *Int'l*, pg. 1677
CNMC (GUANGXI) PINGGUI PGMA CO., LTD.—See China Nonferrous Metal Mining (Group) Co., Ltd.; *Int'l*, pg. 1535
CNMC (GUANGXI) PINGGUI PGMA CO., LTD. - TITANIUM DIOXIDE PLANT—See China Nonferrous Metal Mining (Group) Co., Ltd.; *Int'l*, pg. 1535
CNMC (NINGXIA) ORIENT GROUP CO., LTD.—See China Nonferrous Metal Mining (Group) Co., Ltd.; *Int'l*, pg. 1535
CNMC (SHENYANG) MINING INVESTMENT CO., LTD.—See China Nonferrous Metal Mining (Group) Co., Ltd.; *Int'l*, pg. 1535
CNMY TRUCKS SDN BHD—See Chin Hin Group Berhad; *Int'l*, pg. 1480
CNN AMERICA, INC.—See Warner Bros. Discovery, Inc.; *U.S. Public*, pg. 2328
CNNC HUAYUAN TITANIUM DIOXIDE CO., LTD.; *Int'l*, pg. 1677
CNNC INTERNATIONAL LIMITED—See China National Nuclear Corporation; *Int'l*, pg. 1532
CNNC SUFA TECHNOLOGY INDUSTRY CO LTD—See China National Nuclear Corporation; *Int'l*, pg. 1532
CN NEGOCIOS, S.A.; *Int'l*, pg. 1673
CNN HEADLINE NEWS—See Warner Bros. Discovery, Inc.; *U.S. Public*, pg. 2328
CNN MONEY—See Warner Bros. Discovery, Inc.; *U.S. Public*, pg. 2328
CNN NEWSOURCE SALES, INC.—See Warner Bros. Discovery, Inc.; *U.S. Public*, pg. 2328
CNN NEWS SOURCE SALES INC.—See Warner Bros. Discovery, Inc.; *U.S. Public*, pg. 2328
CNN RADIO—See Warner Bros. Discovery, Inc.; *U.S. Public*, pg. 2328
CNO FINANCIAL GROUP, INC.; *U.S. Public*, pg. 519
CNOOC ENERGY TECHNOLOGY & SERVICES LTD.—See China National Offshore Oil Corp.; *Int'l*, pg. 1532
CNOOC LIMITED—See China National Offshore Oil Corp.; *Int'l*, pg. 1532
CNOOC UGANDA LTD—See China National Offshore Oil Corp.; *Int'l*, pg. 1532
CNO SERVICES, LLC—See CNO Financial Group, Inc.; *U.S. Public*, pg. 520
CNOS VILMORIN POLSKA SP ZOO—See Groupe Limagrain Holding SA; *Int'l*, pg. 3107
CNOVA N.V.—See Finatis SA; *Int'l*, pg. 2670
CNP ASFALTISTIKI LTD.—See CNP Assurances SA; *Int'l*, pg. 1677
CNP ASSURANCES COMPANIA DE SEGUROS DE VIDA S.A—See CNP Assurances SA; *Int'l*, pg. 1677
CNP ASSURANCES SA; *Int'l*, pg. 1677
CNPC - AMG JSC—See China National Petroleum Corporation; *Int'l*, pg. 1533
CNPC CAPITAL COMPANY LIMITED—See China National Petroleum Corporation; *Int'l*, pg. 1533
CNP CHINA—See CNP Assurances SA; *Int'l*, pg. 1677
CNP COSMETICS SINGAPORE PTE. LIMITED—See Cornerstone Financial Holdings Limited; *Int'l*, pg. 1801
CNP CYPRUS INSURANCE HOLDINGS LIMITED—See CNP Assurances SA; *Int'l*, pg. 1677
CNP EUROPE LIFE LTD—See CNP Assurances SA; *Int'l*, pg. 1677
CNP IAM—See CNP Assurances SA; *Int'l*, pg. 1677

CNP ITALIA SPA—See CNP Assurances SA; *Int'l*, pg. 1678
CNPLUS CO., LTD.; *Int'l*, pg. 1678
CNP LUXEMBOURG SA—See CNP Assurances SA; *Int'l*, pg. 1678
C-N-P NORTHWEST, LTD.—See EZCORP, Inc.; *U.S. Public*, pg. 817
CNP PROFESSIONAL LIMITED—See The Protein Partners Ltd.; *Int'l*, pg. 7677
CNP PUMPS INDIA PVT. LTD.—See Nanfang Zhongjin Environment Co., Ltd.; *Int'l*, pg. 5139
CN PRECISION CASING LIMITED—See CN Innovations Holdings Limited; *Int'l*, pg. 1673
CN PRECISION CASING (SHENZHEN) CO., LTD-PINGHU—See CN Innovations Holdings Limited; *Int'l*, pg. 1672
CN PRECISION CASING (SHENZHEN) COMPANY LIMITED—See CN Innovations Holdings Limited; *Int'l*, pg. 1673
CNPV DONGYING SOLAR POWER COMPANY LIMITED,—See CNPV Solar Power S.A.; *Int'l*, pg. 1678
CNP VIDA—See CNP Assurances SA; *Int'l*, pg. 1678
CNP VITA ASSICURA S.P.A.—See Aviva plc; *Int'l*, pg. 746
CNPV SOLAR POWER S.A.; *Int'l*, pg. 1678
CNP ZOIS S.A—See CNP Assurances SA; *Int'l*, pg. 1678
CNQC INTERNATIONAL HOLDINGS LTD.; *Int'l*, pg. 1678
CNR DALIAN LOCOMOTIVE RESEARCH INSTITUTE CO., LTD.—See CRRC Corporation Limited; *Int'l*, pg. 1858
CNR (ECHO) RESOURCES INC.—See Canadian Natural Resources Ltd.; *Int'l*, pg. 1284
CN RESOURCES INC.; *Int'l*, pg. 1673
CNR INTERNATIONAL (ANGOLA) LIMITED—See Canadian Natural Resources Ltd.; *Int'l*, pg. 1284
CNR INTERNATIONAL (COTE D'IVOIRE) S A R L—See Canadian Natural Resources Ltd.; *Int'l*, pg. 1284
CNR INTERNATIONAL (GABON) LIMITED—See Canadian Natural Resources Ltd.; *Int'l*, pg. 1284
CNR INTERNATIONAL—See Canadian Natural Resources Ltd.; *Int'l*, pg. 1284
CNR INTERNATIONAL (SOUTH AFRICA) LIMITED—See Canadian Natural Resources Ltd.; *Int'l*, pg. 1284
CNR INTERNATIONAL UK LIMITED—See Canadian Natural Resources Ltd.; *Int'l*, pg. 1284
CNS CORPORATION; *U.S. Private*, pg. 953
CNSHANGQUAN E-COMMERCE CO., LTD.; *Int'l*, pg. 1678
CNSIG INNER MONGOLIA CHEMICAL INDUSTRY CO., LTD.; *Int'l*, pg. 1678
CNS LINK CO., LTD.; *Int'l*, pg. 1678
CNS PHARMACEUTICALS, INC.; *U.S. Public*, pg. 520
CNS PHARMA PTY LTD.—See Lundbeckfonden; *Int'l*, pg. 4580
CNS-SOLUTIONS & SUPPORT GMBH—See Frequentis AG; *Int'l*, pg. 2773
CNS THERAPEUTICS, INC.—See Mallinckrodt Public Limited Company; *Int'l*, pg. 4663
CNSX MARKETS INC.; *Int'l*, pg. 1678
CNT85 INC.; *Int'l*, pg. 1678
CNT BRASIL SERVICOS LTDA.—See Arrow Electronics, Inc.; *U.S. Public*, pg. 198
CNT CATV CO., LTD.—See Taiwan Optical Platform Co., Ltd.; *Int'l*, pg. 7422
CN TEC, INC.—See Sharp Decisions Inc.; *U.S. Private*, pg. 3626
CNTEE TRANSELECTRICA SA; *Int'l*, pg. 1678
CNT GROUP LIMITED; *Int'l*, pg. 1678
CNTUS CO.,LTD; *Int'l*, pg. 1679
CNW GROUP LTD.—See Informa plc; *Int'l*, pg. 3693
CN WOOD CO. INC.; *U.S. Private*, pg. 952
CN WORLDWIDE NORTH AMERICA—See Canadian National Railway Company; *Int'l*, pg. 1284
CNX GAS CORPORATION—See CNX Resources Corporation; *U.S. Public*, pg. 520
CNX MIDSTREAM OPERATING COMPANY LLC—See CNX Resources Corporation; *U.S. Public*, pg. 520
CNX MIDSTREAM PARTNERS LP—See CNX Resources Corporation; *U.S. Public*, pg. 520
CNX RESOURCES CORPORATION; *U.S. Public*, pg. 520
C.N.Y CENTRO INC.—See Central New York Regional Transportation Authority; *U.S. Private*, pg. 823
CO2 CAPSOL AS; *Int'l*, pg. 1680
CO2 GRO INC.; *Int'l*, pg. 1680
CO2 REDUCATION CO., LTD.—See Tokyo Sangyo Co., Ltd.; *Int'l*, pg. 7795
CO2 SOLUTIONS, INC.; *Int'l*, pg. 1680
COA ASC OF FRANKLIN COUNTY, LLC—See KKR & Co. Inc.; *U.S. Public*, pg. 1245
COACH A CO., LTD; *Int'l*, pg. 1680
COACH BUILDERS—See Peter Pan Bus Lines, Inc.; *U.S. Private*, pg. 3159
COACHELLA VALLEY HOUSING COALITION; *U.S. Private*, pg. 953
COACHELLA VALLEY WATER DISTRICT; *U.S. Private*, pg. 953
COACH HONG KONG LIMITED—See Tapestry, Inc.; *U.S. Public*, pg. 1981
COACH HOUSE, INC.; *U.S. Private*, pg. 953

COMPANY NAME INDEX

THE COACHING SPACE LTD—See Pearson plc; *Int'l*, pg. 5778
COACH INTERNATIONAL LIMITED—See Tapestry, Inc.; *U.S. Public*, pg. 1981
COACHMEN RECREATIONAL VEHICLE COMPANY OF GEORGIA—See Berkshire Hathaway Inc.; *U.S. Public*, pg. 305
COACHMEN RECREATIONAL VEHICLE COMPANY—See Berkshire Hathaway Inc.; *U.S. Public*, pg. 305
COACH SERVICES, INC.—See Tapestry, Inc.; *U.S. Public*, pg. 1981
COACH SOLUTIONS APS—See Kongsberg Gruppen ASA; *Int'l*, pg. 4255
COACH STORES BELGIUM—See Tapestry, Inc.; *U.S. Public*, pg. 1981
COACH TECH MANAGEMENT CO.—See SYSCOM Computer Engineering Company; *Int'l*, pg. 7388
COACH U, INC.—See COACH A Co., Ltd; *Int'l*, pg. 1680
COACH USA, INC.—See Variant Equity Advisors, LLC; *U.S. Private*, pg. 4346
COACTION.COM LLC—See Cannae Holdings, Inc.; *U.S. Public*, pg. 430
COACTION.COM LLC—See CC Capital Partners, LLC; *U.S. Private*, pg. 799
COACTION.COM LLC—See Intercontinental Exchange, Inc.; *U.S. Public*, pg. 1142
COAD CHEVROLET-CADILLAC, INC.—See Ancap Management Inc.; *U.S. Private*, pg. 272
COAD CHEVROLET INC—See Ancap Management Inc.; *U.S. Private*, pg. 272
COADNA (HK) LIMITED—See Coherent Corp.; *U.S. Public*, pg. 526
COADNA HOLDINGS, INC.—See Coherent Corp.; *U.S. Public*, pg. 526
COADNA PHOTONICS, INC.—See Coherent Corp.; *U.S. Public*, pg. 526
COADVANTAGE CORPORATION—See Aquiline Capital Partners LLC; *U.S. Private*, pg. 304
CO-ADVANTAGE RESOURCES INC.; *U.S. Private*, pg. 953
COADY DIEMAR PARTNERS, LLC; *U.S. Private*, pg. 953
COAKLEY BROS. COMPANY INC.; *U.S. Private*, pg. 953
COAKLEY & WILLIAMS CONSTRUCTION INC.; *U.S. Private*, pg. 953
COALA-LIFE GROUP AB; *Int'l*, pg. 1680
COAL ASIA HOLDINGS INC.; *Int'l*, pg. 1680
COAL ENERGY RESOURCES INC.; *U.S. Private*, pg. 953
COAL ENERGY S.A.; *Int'l*, pg. 1680
COALESCENCE, LLC—See New Horizons Baking Company; *U.S. Private*, pg. 2897
COALESSE—See Steelcase Inc.; *U.S. Public*, pg. 1944
COALESSE—See Steelcase Inc.; *U.S. Public*, pg. 1944
COALEX PTY LIMITED—See Banpu Public Company Limited; *Int'l*, pg. 852
COALFIELD PIPELINE COMPANY—See CNX Resources Corporation; *U.S. Public*, pg. 520
COALFIRE SYSTEMS, INC.—See Apax Partners LLP; *Int'l*, pg. 503
COAL INDIA LIMITED; *Int'l*, pg. 1680
COALINGA COGENERATION COMPANY—See Chevron Corporation; *U.S. Public*, pg. 487
THE COALINGA RECORD—See Lee Enterprises, Incorporated; *U.S. Public*, pg. 1300
COAL INNOVATIONS, LLC—See Cleveland-Cliffs, Inc.; *U.S. Public*, pg. 514
COALINQ CORPORATION—See Sojitz Corporation; *Int'l*, pg. 7061
COALITION DEVELOPMENT LTD—See S&P Global Inc.; *U.S. Public*, pg. 1830
COALITION DEVELOPMENT SYSTEMS (INDIA) PRIVATE LIMITED—See S&P Global Inc.; *U.S. Public*, pg. 1830
COALITION FOR HISPANIC FAMILY SERVICES; *U.S. Private*, pg. 953
COALITION OF CANCER COOPERATIVE GROUPS; *U.S. Private*, pg. 954
COALITION SINGAPORE PTE. LTD.—See S&P Global Inc.; *U.S. Public*, pg. 1830
COALITION TO SALUTE AMERICA'S HEROES; *U.S. Private*, pg. 954
CO-ALLIANCE LLP; *U.S. Private*, pg. 953
COAL-MAC, INC.—See Arch Resources, Inc.; *U.S. Public*, pg. 180
COALMARCH PRODUCTIONS LLC; *U.S. Private*, pg. 954
COAL NETWORK, INC.; *U.S. Private*, pg. 953
COALSALES, LLC—See Peabody Energy Corporation; *U.S. Public*, pg. 1659
COALSOLV, LLC—See Alpha Natural Resources, Inc.; *U.S. Private*, pg. 198
COALSPUR MINES LIMITED; *Int'l*, pg. 1680
COALSPUR MINES (OPERATIONS) LTD.—See Coalspur Mines Limited; *Int'l*, pg. 1680
COALTRADE INTERNATIONAL, LLC—See Peabody Energy Corporation; *U.S. Public*, pg. 1659
COALTRADE SERVICES INTERNATIONAL PTE LTD—See PT Adaro Energy Indonesia Tbk; *Int'l*, pg. 6019
COASIA CORPORATION—See CoAsia Holdings Co., Ltd.; *Int'l*, pg. 1680

COASIA ELECTRONICS CORP. (SHANGHAI) LIMITED—See CoAsia Microelectronics Corp.; *Int'l*, pg. 1681
COASIA ELECTRONICS CORP. (SHENZHEN) LIMITED—See CoAsia Microelectronics Corp.; *Int'l*, pg. 1681
COASIA ELECTRONICS CORP. (SINGAPORE) PTE. LTD.—See CoAsia Microelectronics Corp.; *Int'l*, pg. 1681
COASIA ELECTRONICS CORP.—See CoAsia Holdings Co., Ltd.; *Int'l*, pg. 1680
COASIA HOLDINGS CO., LTD.; *Int'l*, pg. 1680
COASIA KOREA CO., LTD.—See CoAsia Microelectronics Corp.; *Int'l*, pg. 1681
COASIA MICROELECTRONICS CORP.; *Int'l*, pg. 1681
COASIA NEXELL CO., LTD.—See CoAsia Holdings Co., Ltd.; *Int'l*, pg. 1680
COASIA SEMI KOREA CO., LTD.—See CoAsia Holdings Co., Ltd.; *Int'l*, pg. 1680
COASIN CHILE S.A.—See Datatec Limited; *Int'l*, pg. 1980
COASSETS LIMITED; *Int'l*, pg. 1681
COAST 2 COAST FINANCIAL GROUP, LLC; *U.S. Private*, pg. 954
COAST 2 COAST LENDERS, LLC—See Coast 2 Coast Financial Group, LLC; *U.S. Private*, pg. 954
COASTAL AGROBUSINESS INC. - COLERAIN PLANT—See Coastal AgroBusiness Inc.; *U.S. Private*, pg. 955
COASTAL AGROBUSINESS INC. - DILLON PLANT—See Coastal AgroBusiness Inc.; *U.S. Private*, pg. 955
COASTAL AGROBUSINESS INC. - HAMILTON PLANT—See Coastal AgroBusiness Inc.; *U.S. Private*, pg. 955
COASTAL AGROBUSINESS INC. - HENDERSON PLANT—See Coastal AgroBusiness Inc.; *U.S. Private*, pg. 955
COASTAL AGROBUSINESS INC. - HENDERSONVILLE PLANT—See Coastal AgroBusiness Inc.; *U.S. Private*, pg. 955
COASTAL AGROBUSINESS INC. - KINSTON PLANT—See Coastal AgroBusiness Inc.; *U.S. Private*, pg. 955
COASTAL AGROBUSINESS INC. - MURFREESBORO PLANT—See Coastal AgroBusiness Inc.; *U.S. Private*, pg. 955
COASTAL AGROBUSINESS INC. - PANTEGO PLANT—See Coastal AgroBusiness Inc.; *U.S. Private*, pg. 955
COASTAL AGROBUSINESS INC.; *U.S. Private*, pg. 955
COASTAL AMERICAN INSURANCE COMPANY—See Gulf States Holdings, Inc.; *U.S. Private*, pg. 1817
COASTAL AND INLAND MARINE SERVICES INC.—See HAL Trust N.V.; *Int'l*, pg. 3225
COASTAL BEHAVIORAL HEALTHCARE, INC.; *U.S. Private*, pg. 955
COASTAL BEND COMMUNITY FOUNDATION; *U.S. Private*, pg. 955
COASTAL BRIDGE COMPANY, LLC - CONVENT ASPHALT PLANT—See Coastal Bridge Company, LLC; *U.S. Private*, pg. 955
COASTAL BRIDGE COMPANY, LLC - PORT ALLEN ASPHALT PLANT—See Coastal Bridge Company, LLC; *U.S. Private*, pg. 955
COASTAL BRIDGE COMPANY, LLC; *U.S. Private*, pg. 955
COASTAL CADILLAC, INC.—See AutoNation, Inc.; *U.S. Public*, pg. 234
COASTAL CAGES LTD.—See Hampidjan hf; *Int'l*, pg. 3239
COASTAL CAPITAL ACQUISITION CORP.; *U.S. Private*, pg. 955
COASTAL CAROLINA BANCSHARES, INC.; *U.S. Public*, pg. 520
COASTAL CAROLINA MEDICAL CENTER, INC.—See Tenet Healthcare Corporation; *U.S. Public*, pg. 2008
COASTAL CAROLINA NATIONAL BANK—See Coastal Carolina Bancshares, Inc.; *U.S. Public*, pg. 520
COASTAL CAROLINA PUMPING, INC.—See Concrete Pumping Holdings, Inc.; *U.S. Public*, pg. 566
COASTAL CARRIBEAN OIL & MINERALS LTD.; *Int'l*, pg. 1681
COASTAL CARRIERS, LLC—See AIP, LLC; *U.S. Private*, pg. 136
COASTAL CASUALTY INSURANCE COMPANY—See Strickland Insurance Group Inc.; *U.S. Private*, pg. 3839
COASTAL CEMENT CORPORATION—See Grupo Empresarial Kaluz S.A. de C.V.; *Int'l*, pg. 3127
COASTAL CHEMICAL CO., LLC—See BRENNTAG SE; *Int'l*, pg. 1148
COASTAL CLOUD LLC; *U.S. Private*, pg. 955
COASTAL COCKTAILS INC.; *U.S. Private*, pg. 955
COASTAL COMMUNICATIONS, INC.—See Lumen Technologies, Inc.; *U.S. Public*, pg. 1346
COASTAL COMMUNITY AND TEACHERS CREDIT UNION; *U.S. Private*, pg. 955
COASTAL COMMUNITY BANK; *U.S. Private*, pg. 955
COASTAL COMMUNITY FOUNDATION; *U.S. Private*, pg. 955
THE COASTAL COMPANIES—See Continental Grain Company; *U.S. Private*, pg. 1029

COASTAL CONCRETE INC.; *U.S. Private*, pg. 955
COASTAL CONSERVATION ASSOCIATION; *U.S. Private*, pg. 955
COASTAL CONSTRUCTION GROUP OF SOUTH FLORIDA INC.; *U.S. Private*, pg. 955
COASTAL CONSTRUCTION PRODUCTS, LLC—See Beacon Roofing Supply, Inc.; *U.S. Public*, pg. 285
COASTAL CONTAINERS LTD.—See GrainCorp Limited; *Int'l*, pg. 3052
COASTAL CONTRACTS BHD.; *Int'l*, pg. 1681
COASTAL CORPORATION LIMITED; *Int'l*, pg. 1681
COASTAL CORRUGATED, INC.—See Atlantic Corporation; *U.S. Private*, pg. 372
COASTAL CREDIT, LLC—See PCP Enterprise, L.P.; *U.S. Private*, pg. 3121
COASTAL DENTAL, INC.; *U.S. Private*, pg. 955
COASTAL DEVELOPMENTAL SERVICES FOUNDATION; *U.S. Private*, pg. 956
COASTAL DEVELOPMENT LLC; *U.S. Private*, pg. 956
COASTAL DOOR & WINDOW INC.; *U.S. Private*, pg. 956
COASTAL DUNES (LYTHAM ST ANNES) MANAGEMENT COMPANY LIMITED—See Persimmon plc; *Int'l*, pg. 5815
COASTAL ECONOMIC DEVELOPMENT CORPORATION; *U.S. Private*, pg. 956
COASTAL ENGINEERING CO. INC.—See Tighe & Bond, Inc.; *U.S. Private*, pg. 4170
COASTAL ENTERPRISES, INC.; *U.S. Private*, pg. 956
COASTAL EYE ASSOCIATES PLLC; *U.S. Private*, pg. 956
COASTAL FAMILY HEALTH CENTER; *U.S. Private*, pg. 956
COASTAL FARM & HOME SUPPLY, LLC—See Nolan Capital, Inc.; *U.S. Private*, pg. 2934
COASTAL FEDERAL BANK—See Coastal Financial Corp.; *U.S. Private*, pg. 956
COASTAL FILMS OF FLORIDA—See Alpha Industries, Inc.; *U.S. Private*, pg. 197
COASTAL FINANCIAL CORPORATION; *U.S. Public*, pg. 520
COASTAL FINANCIAL CORP.; *U.S. Private*, pg. 956
COASTAL FORD SALES LTD; *Int'l*, pg. 1681
COASTAL FOREST RESOURCES COMPANY; *U.S. Private*, pg. 956
COASTAL GRAND, LLC—See CBL & Associates Properties, Inc.; *U.S. Public*, pg. 458
COASTAL GREENLAND LIMITED; *Int'l*, pg. 1681
COASTAL GROUP; *U.S. Private*, pg. 956
COASTAL GUNITE CONSTRUCTION CO; *U.S. Private*, pg. 956
COASTAL HARBOR TREATMENT CENTER—See Universal Health Services, Inc.; *U.S. Public*, pg. 2260
COASTAL HEALTHCARE CONSULTING, INC.—See Dynamic Computing Services Corp.; *U.S. Private*, pg. 1297
COASTAL HEALTHCARE SERVICES, INC.—See HCA Healthcare, Inc.; *U.S. Public*, pg. 993
COASTAL HOME MORTGAGE, LLC—See Towne Bank; *U.S. Public*, pg. 2165
COASTAL HOMEOWNERS INSURANCE SPECIALISTS, INC.—See Universal Insurance Holdings, Inc.; *U.S. Public*, pg. 2261
COASTAL INLAND MARINE SERVICES LTD.—See Trico Marine Services, Inc.; *U.S. Private*, pg. 4229
COASTAL INPATIENT PHYSICIANS, LLC—See HCA Healthcare, Inc.; *U.S. Public*, pg. 993
COASTAL INSURANCE UNDERWRITERS, INC.—See Clayton, Dubilier & Rice, LLC; *U.S. Private*, pg. 927
COASTAL INSURANCE UNDERWRITERS, INC.—See Mubadala Investment Company PJSC; *Int'l*, pg. 5076
COASTAL INSURANCE UNDERWRITERS, INC.—See Stone Point Capital LLC; *U.S. Private*, pg. 3826
COASTAL INTEGRATED SERVICES, INC.; *U.S. Private*, pg. 956
COASTAL INTERNATIONAL INC.; *U.S. Private*, pg. 956
COASTAL INTERNATIONAL SECURITY, INC.—See Akal Security, Inc.; *U.S. Private*, pg. 144
THE COASTAL JOURNAL—See MaineToday Media, Inc.; *U.S. Private*, pg. 2553
COASTAL LIFE TECHNOLOGIES, INC.—See Viant Medical, LLC; *U.S. Private*, pg. 4375
COASTAL LOGISTICS GROUP, INC.; *U.S. Private*, pg. 956
COASTAL LUXURY MANAGEMENT; *U.S. Private*, pg. 956
COASTAL MACHINERY COMPANY, INC.; *U.S. Private*, pg. 956
COASTAL MARINA MANAGEMENT LLC; *U.S. Private*, pg. 956
COASTAL MEDICAL ASSOCIATES INC; *U.S. Private*, pg. 956
COASTAL MED TECH, INC.—See Quipt Home Medical Corp.; *U.S. Public*, pg. 1757
COASTAL OCCUPATIONAL MEDICAL GROUP—See Kain Capital, LLC; *U.S. Private*, pg. 2254
COASTAL PACIFIC FOOD DISTRIBUTORS, INC.; *U.S. Private*, pg. 956
COASTAL PACIFIC XPRESS INC.—See Bay Grove Capital LLC; *U.S. Private*, pg. 493

COASTAL PRECAST OF FLORIDA, INC.—See Foley Products Company, LLC; *U.S. Private*, pg. 1558
COASTAL PRIDE CO INC.—See Blue Star Foods Corp.; *U.S. Public*, pg. 365
COASTAL PRINTING, INC.—See Intech Printing & Direct Mail; *U.S. Private*, pg. 2097
COASTAL PROPERTIES GROUP INTERNATIONAL, LLC; *U.S. Private*, pg. 956
COASTAL QSR, LLC—See Prometheus Partners, L.P.; *U.S. Private*, pg. 3283
COASTAL REALTY DEVELOPMENT CO. LIMITED—See Coastal Greenland Limited; *Int'l*, pg. 1681
COASTAL ROADWAYS LIMITED; *Int'l*, pg. 1681
COASTAL SATELLITE, INC.—See Live Media Group, LLC; *U.S. Private*, pg. 2473
COASTAL SECURITIES, INC.—See First Horizon Corporation; *U.S. Public*, pg. 844
COASTAL SHEET METAL, CORP.; *U.S. Private*, pg. 956
COASTAL SOUTH BANCSHARES, INC.; *U.S. Public*, pg. 520
COASTAL STEEL INDUSTRIES LTD.—See Schindler Holding AG; *Int'l*, pg. 6618
COASTAL STRATEGIES, INC.; *U.S. Private*, pg. 957
COASTAL SUNBELT PRODUCE, LLC—See Continental Grain Company; *U.S. Private*, pg. 1029
COASTAL SUPPLY COMPANY INC.—See Beijer Ref AB; *Int'l*, pg. 944
COASTAL TAG & LABEL INC.—See AFE Industries, Inc.; *U.S. Private*, pg. 121
COASTAL TRAINING TECHNOLOGIES CORP.—See DuPont de Nemours, Inc.; *U.S. Public*, pg. 692
COASTAL TRANSPORT CO. INC.; *U.S. Private*, pg. 957
COAST ALUMINUM & ARCHITECTURAL INC.; *U.S. Private*, pg. 954
COASTAL WELDING SUPPLY INC.; *U.S. Private*, pg. 957
COASTAL WINDOWS LTD.—See Atlas Engineered Products Ltd.; *Int'l*, pg. 685
COASTAL WOOD PRODUCTS, INC.—See McConnell Cabinets, Inc.; *U.S. Private*, pg. 2629
COAST AUTO CENTER INC.; *U.S. Private*, pg. 954
COAST BMW NISSAN; *U.S. Private*, pg. 954
COAST CASINOS, INC.—See Boyd Gaming Corporation; *U.S. Public*, pg. 377
COAST CENTRAL CREDIT UNION; *U.S. Private*, pg. 954
COAST CITIES ESCROW INC.—See First Team Real Estate-Orange County Inc.; *U.S. Private*, pg. 1529
COAST CITRUS DISTRIBUTORS INC.; *U.S. Private*, pg. 954
COAST COMPOSITES, INC.—See AIP, LLC; *U.S. Private*, pg. 133
COAST COUNTIES GLASS INC.; *U.S. Private*, pg. 954
COAST COUNTIES TRUCK & EQUIPMENT CO.; *U.S. Private*, pg. 954
COAST & COUNTRY HOUSING LTD.; *Int'l*, pg. 1681
COAST CRANE CO.-BAKERSFIELD—See Apollo Global Management, Inc.; *U.S. Public*, pg. 153
COAST CRANE CO.-CITY OF INDUSTRY—See Apollo Global Management, Inc.; *U.S. Public*, pg. 153
COAST CRANE CO.-PASCO—See Apollo Global Management, Inc.; *U.S. Public*, pg. 153
COAST CRANE CO.-PORTLAND—See Apollo Global Management, Inc.; *U.S. Public*, pg. 153
COAST CRANE CO.-SAN LEANDRO—See Apollo Global Management, Inc.; *U.S. Public*, pg. 153
COAST CRANE CO.—See Apollo Global Management, Inc.; *U.S. Public*, pg. 153
COAST CRANE CO.-TACOMA—See Apollo Global Management, Inc.; *U.S. Public*, pg. 153
COAST CRANE LTD.—See Apollo Global Management, Inc.; *U.S. Public*, pg. 153
COAST CRANE OF UTAH INC.—See Giuffre Bros Cranes, Inc.; *U.S. Private*, pg. 1703
COAST CUTLERY COMPANY; *U.S. Private*, pg. 954
COAST DENTAL SERVICES, INC.; *U.S. Private*, pg. 954
COAST DERMATOLOGY & SKIN CANCER CENTER, P.A.—See Raj Patel, MD LLC; *U.S. Private*, pg. 3349
COAST DIGITAL, LTD.; *Int'l*, pg. 1681
COAST ENTERTAINMENT HOLDINGS LIMITED; *Int'l*, pg. 1681
COAST ENVIRONMENTAL, INC.—See Alliance Environmental Group, Inc.; *U.S. Private*, pg. 182
COASTER OF AMERICA INC.; *U.S. Private*, pg. 957
COAST HEALTHCARE MANAGEMENT, LLC—See Tenet Healthcare Corporation; *U.S. Public*, pg. 2003
COAST HOLDING CORPORATION—See Coast Investment & Development Company K.S.C.C.; *Int'l*, pg. 1681
COAST HOTELS & CASINOS, INC.—See Boyd Gaming Corporation; *U.S. Public*, pg. 377
COAST HOTELS LTD.—See APA Holdings Co., Ltd.; *Int'l*, pg. 500
COAST INTERNATIONAL INN—See Tanadgusix Corp.; *U.S. Private*, pg. 3930
COAST INTERNATIONAL SERVICES, INC.—See Olympus Partners; *U.S. Private*, pg. 3013
COAST INVESTMENT & DEVELOPMENT COMPANY K.S.C.C.; *Int'l*, pg. 1681
COAST LABEL COMPANY—See Ares Management Corporation; *U.S. Public*, pg. 190

COASTLINE ELDERLY SERVICE, INC.; *U.S. Private*, pg. 957
COASTLINE PLASTICS L.L.C.—See Spears Manufacturing Company; *U.S. Private*, pg. 3748
COAST LINE SUPPLY & EQUIPMENT COMPANY; *U.S. Private*, pg. 954
COAST ONE MORTGAGE LLC—See Rithm Capital Corp.; *U.S. Public*, pg. 1800
COAST PACKAGING COMPANY; *U.S. Private*, pg. 954
COAST PACKING COMPANY; *U.S. Private*, pg. 954
COAST PAD & TRIM CORP.; *U.S. Private*, pg. 954
COAST PLATING, INC.; *U.S. Private*, pg. 954
COAST PLAZA DOCTORS HOSPITAL INC.; *U.S. Private*, pg. 954
COAST PRODUCE COMPANY INC.; *U.S. Private*, pg. 954
COAST PROFESSIONAL, INC.; *U.S. Private*, pg. 954
COAST PUMP & SUPPLY CO. INC.; *U.S. Private*, pg. 954
COAST RESOURCES LIMITED—See Astron Corporation Limited; *Int'l*, pg. 662
COAST SEAFOODS COMPANY INC.—See Dulcich, Inc.; *U.S. Private*, pg. 1286
COAST SPAS MANUFACTURING INC; *Int'l*, pg. 1681
COAST SURGERY CENTER, L.P.—See Tenet Healthcare Corporation; *U.S. Public*, pg. 2010
COAST TIRE & AUTO SERVICE, INC.; *Int'l*, pg. 1681
COAST TO COAST ASSISTED LIVING REALTY, LLC—See Ventas, Inc.; *U.S. Public*, pg. 2278
COAST TO COAST CARPORTS, INC.; *U.S. Private*, pg. 954
COAST TO COAST ENTERTAINMENT LLC—See Elaut International N.V.; *Int'l*, pg. 2343
COAST TO COAST TICKETS LLC; *U.S. Private*, pg. 955
COAST UNDERWRITERS LIMITED—See Intact Financial Corporation; *Int'l*, pg. 3727
COAST UNDERWRITERS LIMITED—See Tryg A/S; *Int'l*, pg. 7946
COAST WHOLESALE APPLIANCES INC.; *Int'l*, pg. 1681
COAST WIRE & PLASTIC TECH, LLC—See Belden, Inc.; *U.S. Public*, pg. 293
COATED SAND SOLUTIONS, LLC—See Apollo Global Management, Inc.; *U.S. Public*, pg. 164
COATES BROTHERS (CARIBBEAN) LTD.—See DIC Corporation; *Int'l*, pg. 2109
COATES BROTHERS (SOUTH AFRICA) (PTY). LTD.—See DIC Corporation; *Int'l*, pg. 2107
COATES BROTHERS (ZAMBIA) LTD.—See DIC Corporation; *Int'l*, pg. 2109
COATES ELECTROGRAPHICS INC.—See DIC Corporation; *Int'l*, pg. 2109
COATES FIELD SERVICE, INC.; *U.S. Private*, pg. 957
COATES GROUP HOLDINGS PTY. LIMITED—See Seven Group Holdings Limited; *Int'l*, pg. 6733
COATES HIRE OPERATIONS PTY. LIMITED—See Seven Group Holdings Limited; *Int'l*, pg. 6733
COATES INTERNATIONAL, LTD.; *U.S. Public*, pg. 520
COATES SCREEN INKS GMBH—See DIC Corporation; *Int'l*, pg. 2109
COATESVILLE HOSPITAL CORPORATION—See Tower Health; *U.S. Private*, pg. 4193
COATESVILLE SAVINGS BANK; *U.S. Private*, pg. 957
COATEX ASIA PACIFIC INC.—See Arkema S.A.; *Int'l*, pg. 571
COATEX CENTRAL EASTERN EUROPE S.R.O.—See Arkema S.A.; *Int'l*, pg. 571
COATEX INC.—See Arkema S.A.; *Int'l*, pg. 569
COATEX NETHERLANDS BV—See Arkema S.A.; *Int'l*, pg. 571
COATEX NV—See Sioen Industries NV; *Int'l*, pg. 6959
COATEX SAS—See Arkema S.A.; *Int'l*, pg. 570
COATHAM VALE AND BERRYMEAD GARDENS RESIDENTS MANAGEMENT COMPANY LIMITED—See Persimmon plc; *Int'l*, pg. 5815
COATING & ADHESIVES CORPORATION; *U.S. Private*, pg. 957
COATINGS APPLICATION WATERPROOFING CO., INC.; *U.S. Private*, pg. 957
CQAT-IT INC.—See Diversified Chemical Technologies Inc.; *U.S. Private*, pg. 1241
COATS AUSTRALIAN PTY LTD.—See Coats Group plc; *Int'l*, pg. 1682
COATS BANGLADESH LIMITED—See Coats Group plc; *Int'l*, pg. 1681
COATS BULGARIA EOOD—See Coats Group plc; *Int'l*, pg. 1682
COATS CADENA ANDINA SA—See Coats Group plc; *Int'l*, pg. 1682
COATS CADENA LTDA.—See Coats Group plc; *Int'l*, pg. 1682
COATS CADENA SA ARGENTINA—See Coats Group plc; *Int'l*, pg. 1682
COATS CADENA SA—See Coats Group plc; *Int'l*, pg. 1682
COATS CADENA SA—See Coats Group plc; *Int'l*, pg. 1682
COATS CADENA SA—See Coats Group plc; *Int'l*, pg. 1682
COATS CADENA S.A.—See Coats Group plc; *Int'l*, pg. 1682
COATS CANADA—See Comvest Group Holdings LLC; *U.S. Private*, pg. 1007
COATS & CLARK INC.—See Comvest Group Holdings LLC; *U.S. Private*, pg. 1007

COATS CORRENTE LTDA-FABRICA IPIRANGA—See Coats Group plc; *Int'l*, pg. 1682
COATS CRAFTS UK—See Coats Group plc; *Int'l*, pg. 1682
COATS CUCIRINI S.P.A.—See Coats Group plc; *Int'l*, pg. 1682
COATS DE NICARAGUA SA—See Coats Group plc; *Int'l*, pg. 1682
COATS EESTI AS—See Coats Group plc; *Int'l*, pg. 1682
COATS EGYPT FOR MANUFACTURING & DYEING SEWING THREAD SAE—See Coats Group plc; *Int'l*, pg. 1682
COATS EL SALVADOR, S.A. DE C.V.—See Coats Group plc; *Int'l*, pg. 1682
COATS FABRA SA—See Coats Group plc; *Int'l*, pg. 1682
COATS GMBH—See Coats Group plc; *Int'l*, pg. 1682
COATS GROUP PLC; *Int'l*, pg. 1681
COATS HARLANDER GES.M.B.H.—See Coats Group plc; *Int'l*, pg. 1682
COATS HONDURAS, S.A.—See Coats Group plc; *Int'l*, pg. 1682
COATS INDUSTRIAL SCANDINAVIA AB—See Coats Group plc; *Int'l*, pg. 1682
COATS LLC—See Coats Group plc; *Int'l*, pg. 1682
COATS MANILA BAY, INC.—See Coats Group plc; *Int'l*, pg. 1682
COATS MAROC SA—See Coats Group plc; *Int'l*, pg. 1682
COATS MEXICO S.A. DE C.V.—See Coats Group plc; *Int'l*, pg. 1682
COATS OPTI GERMANY GMBH—See Coats Group plc; *Int'l*, pg. 1682
COATS PATONS (NEW ZEALAND) LTD.—See Coats Group plc; *Int'l*, pg. 1682
COATS PLC—See Coats Group plc; *Int'l*, pg. 1682
COATS POLSKA SP. Z O.O.—See Coats Group plc; *Int'l*, pg. 1682
COATS ROMANIA SRL—See Coats Group plc; *Int'l*, pg. 1682
COATS ROSE, P.C.; *U.S. Private*, pg. 957
COATS SHENZHEN LIMITED—See Coats Group plc; *Int'l*, pg. 1682
COATS SOUTH AFRICA (PTY) LTD.—See Coats Group plc; *Int'l*, pg. 1682
COATS STROPPEL AG—See Coats Group plc; *Int'l*, pg. 1682
COATS THREAD EXPORTS (PRIVATE) LIMITED—See Coats Group plc; *Int'l*, pg. 1682
COATS THREAD GERMANY GMBH—See Coats Group plc; *Int'l*, pg. 1682
COATS THREADS (THAILAND) LTD.—See Coats Group plc; *Int'l*, pg. 1682
COATS (TURKIYE) IPLIK SANAYII AS—See Coats Group plc; *Int'l*, pg. 1681
COATS UKRAINE LTD.—See Coats Group plc; *Int'l*, pg. 1682
COATS-WARNER CORPORATION—See Blower Dempsay Corporation; *U.S. Private*, pg. 584
COAX FIBER SOLUTIONS, LLC—See Orbital Infrastructure Group, Inc.; *U.S. Public*, pg. 1615
COAXIAL COMPONENTS CORP.; *U.S. Private*, pg. 957
COBALT 27 CAPITAL CORP.—See Pala Investments Limited; *Int'l*, pg. 5705
COBALT ASTRA LLC; *U.S. Private*, pg. 957
COBALT BLUE HOLDINGS LIMITED—See New Talisman Gold Mines Limited; *Int'l*, pg. 5228
COBALT BOATS, LLC—See Malibu Boats, Inc.; *U.S. Public*, pg. 1355
COBALT GROUND SOLUTIONS LTD—See Groupe Crit, S.A.; *Int'l*, pg. 3101
COBALT INTERNATIONAL ENERGY, INC.; *U.S. Private*, pg. 957
COBALT INTERNATIONAL ENERGY, L.P.—See Cobalt International Energy, Inc.; *U.S. Private*, pg. 957
COBALT INVESTMENTS LIMITED—See Barclays PLC; *Int'l*, pg. 862
COBALT PROPERTIES LIMITED—See Irving Oil Limited; *Int'l*, pg. 3811
COBALT SERVICE PARTNERS, LLC—See Alpine Investors; *U.S. Private*, pg. 201
COBALT SOFTWARE, LLC—See Centene Corporation; *U.S. Public*, pg. 469
COBALT SPORTSWEAR, LLC—See Malibu Boats, Inc.; *U.S. Public*, pg. 1355
COBALT VENTURES LLC—See Blue Cross & Blue Shield of Kansas City, Inc.; *U.S. Private*, pg. 586
COBANK, ACB; *U.S. Public*, pg. 520
COBAR EUROPE B.V.—See BALVER ZINN Josef Jost GmbH & Co. KG; *Int'l*, pg. 812
COBA / SELECT SIRES INC.—See Select Sires Inc.; *U.S. Private*, pg. 3601
COBB ANA DAMIZLIK TAVUKCULUK SANAYI VE TICARET LIMITED SIRKETI—See Tyson Foods, Inc.; *U.S. Public*, pg. 2209
COBB EUROPE LIMITED—See Tyson Foods, Inc.; *U.S. Public*, pg. 2209
COBB, FENDLEY & ASSOCIATES, INC.; *U.S. Private*, pg. 957
COBB-HALL INSURANCE AGENCIES, INC.; *U.S. Private*, pg. 957

COMPANY NAME INDEX

COBB HONG KONG—See W.R. Cobb Company; *U.S. Private*, pg. 4422
COBBLE - VAN DE WIELE LIMITED—See NV Michel Van de Wiele; *Int'l*, pg. 5497
COBB MECHANICAL CONTRACTORS; *U.S. Private*, pg. 957
COBBOSSEECONTEE TELEPHONE CO.—See Telephone & Data Systems, Inc.; *U.S. Public*, pg. 1998
COBB PEDIATRIC THERAPY SERVICES; *U.S. Private*, pg. 957
COBBS, ALLEN & HALL INC.; *U.S. Private*, pg. 957
COBB TUNING PRODUCTS, LLC—See Promus Holdings, LLC; *U.S. Private*, pg. 3284
COBB-VANTRESS BRASIL LTDA.—See Tyson Foods, Inc.; *U.S. Public*, pg. 2209
COBB-VANTRESS, INC.—See Tyson Foods, Inc.; *U.S. Public*, pg. 2209
COBB WIRE ROPE & SLING COMPANY INC.—See ALP Industries, Inc.; *U.S. Private*, pg. 196
COBE CAPITAL LLC; *U.S. Private*, pg. 957
COBELL LIMITED—See Symrise AG; *Int'l*, pg. 7380
COBELPLAST NV—See BAVARIA Industries Group AG; *Int'l*, pg. 899
COBELSA COSMETICOS, S.A.—See L'Oreal S.A.; *Int'l*, pg. 4378
COBEMA SA—See BNP Paribas SA; *Int'l*, pg. 1090
COBEPA S.A.; *Int'l*, pg. 1682
COBHAM ADVANCED ELECTRONIC SOLUTIONS INC.—See Advent International Corporation; *U.S. Private*, pg. 99
COBHAM ANTENNA SYSTEMS—See Advent International Corporation; *U.S. Private*, pg. 99
COBHAM AVIATION SERVICES PTY LIMITED—See Advent International Corporation; *U.S. Private*, pg. 99
COBHAM DEFENCE COMMUNICATIONS LTD.—See Advent International Corporation; *U.S. Private*, pg. 99
COBHAM ELECTRONIC SYSTEMS, INC. - SAN JOSE—See Advent International Corporation; *U.S. Private*, pg. 99
COBHAM ELECTRONIC SYSTEMS INC.—See Advent International Corporation; *U.S. Private*, pg. 99
COBHAM FLIGHT INSPECTION LIMITED—See Advent International Corporation; *U.S. Private*, pg. 99
COBHAM GAISLER AB—See Advent International Corporation; *U.S. Private*, pg. 99
COBHAM (INDIA) PVT LIMITED—See Advent International Corporation; *U.S. Private*, pg. 99
COBHAM LONG ISLAND INC.—See Advent International Corporation; *U.S. Private*, pg. 99
COBHAM MAL LIMITED—See Advent International Corporation; *U.S. Private*, pg. 99
COBHAM MICROWAVE FILTER COMPONENTS—See Advent International Corporation; *U.S. Private*, pg. 99
COBHAM MISSION SYSTEMS WIMBORNE LIMITED—See Eaton Corporation plc; *Int'l*, pg. 2277
COBHAM MOTION CONTROL—See Advent International Corporation; *U.S. Private*, pg. 99
COBHAM NEW JERSEY INC.—See Advent International Corporation; *U.S. Private*, pg. 99
COBHAM PLC—See Advent International Corporation; *U.S. Private*, pg. 98
COBHAM RAD EUROPE LIMITED—See Advent International Corporation; *U.S. Private*, pg. 99
COBHAM RAD, INC.—See Radiation Test Solutions, Inc.; *U.S. Private*, pg. 3343
COBHAM SEMICONDUCTOR SOLUTIONS—See Advent International Corporation; *U.S. Private*, pg. 99
COBHAM SIGNAL & CONTROL SOLUTIONS—See Advent International Corporation; *U.S. Private*, pg. 99
COBHAM TRACKING AND LOCATING LIMITED—See Advent International Corporation; *U.S. Private*, pg. 99
COBHAN PROPERTIES LTD—See Bank of Cyprus Holdings Public Limited Company; *Int'l*, pg. 842
COBIAN CORP.; *U.S. Private*, pg. 957
C.O. BIGELOW CHEMISTS, INC.; *U.S. Private*, pg. 708
COBIM SARL—See Pierre & Vacances SA; *Int'l*, pg. 5864
COBITO (PTY) LIMITED—See AECI Limited; *Int'l*, pg. 171
COBIUS HEALTHCARE SOLUTIONS, LLC—See PCP Enterprise, L.P.; *U.S. Private*, pg. 3121
COBLANDS NURSERIES LIMITED—See Parkwood Holdings Limited; *Int'l*, pg. 5745
COBLENTZ DISTRIBUTING INC.; *U.S. Private*, pg. 958
COBLESKILL STONE PRODUCTS INC.; *U.S. Private*, pg. 958
COBORNS DELIVERS LLC—See Coborn's Incorporated; *U.S. Private*, pg. 958
COBORN'S INCORPORATED; *U.S. Private*, pg. 958
COBOURG DAILY STAR—See Chatham Asset Management, LLC; *U.S. Private*, pg. 861
COBRA BEC, INC.; *U.S. Private*, pg. 958
COBRA BIOLOGICS HOLDING AB; *Int'l*, pg. 1683
COBRA BIOLOGICS LIMITED—See Cobra Biologics Holding AB; *Int'l*, pg. 1683
COBRA BIOLOGICS LTD - MICROBIAL PRODUCTION & FILL FINISH FACILITY—See Cobra Biologics Holding AB; *Int'l*, pg. 1683
COBRA CHILE, S.A.—See ACS, Actividades de Construccion y Servicios, S.A.; *Int'l*, pg. 110

COBRA CONCESIONES BRASIL, S.L.—See ACS, Actividades de Construccion y Servicios, S.A.; *Int'l*, pg. 110
COBRA CONCESIONES, S.L.—See ACS, Actividades de Construccion y Servicios, S.A.; *Int'l*, pg. 110
COBRA ELECTRONICS CORPORATION—See Monomoy Capital Partners LLC; *U.S. Private*, pg. 2772
COBRA ELECTRONICS EMEA—See Monomoy Capital Partners LLC; *U.S. Private*, pg. 2772
COBRA ELECTRONICS (HK) LIMITED—See Monomoy Capital Partners LLC; *U.S. Private*, pg. 2772
COBRA FINANCIAL SERVICES LIMITED—See Apax Partners LLP; *Int'l*, pg. 505
COBRA GESTION DE INFRAESTRUCTURAS, S.L.U—See ACS, Actividades de Construccion y Servicios, S.A.; *Int'l*, pg. 110
COBRA GMBH—See Comet Umetni brusi in nekovine, d.d.; *Int'l*, pg. 1711
COBRA GOLF INCORPORATED—See Puma SE; *Int'l*, pg. 6117
COBRA HOLDINGS LTD—See Apax Partners LLP; *Int'l*, pg. 505
COBRA INFRAESTRUCTURAS HIDRAULICAS, S.A.—See ACS, Actividades de Construccion y Servicios, S.A.; *Int'l*, pg. 110
COBRA INSTALACIONES Y SERVICIOS INTERNACIONAL, S.L.—See ACS, Actividades de Construccion y Servicios, S.A.; *Int'l*, pg. 110
COBRA LA RIOJA SUR SA—See ACS, Actividades de Construccion y Servicios, S.A.; *Int'l*, pg. 110
COBRAM ESTATE PTY LTD—See Boundary Bend Limited; *Int'l*, pg. 1119
COBRA NATURAL RESOURCES, LLC—See Alpha Natural Resources, Inc.; *U.S. Private*, pg. 199
COBRA NETWORK LIMITED—See Apax Partners LLP; *Int'l*, pg. 505
COBRA PERU, S.A.—See ACS, Actividades de Construccion y Servicios, S.A.; *Int'l*, pg. 110
COBRA PLASTICS, INC.—See Silgan Holdings, Inc.; *U.S. Public*, pg. 1878
COBRA RESOURCES PLC; *Int'l*, pg. 1683
COBRA SERVICIOS AUXILIARES, S.A.—See ACS, Actividades de Construccion y Servicios, S.A.; *Int'l*, pg. 110
COBRA SISTEMAS DE SEGURIDAD, S.A.—See ACS, Actividades de Construccion y Servicios, S.A.; *Int'l*, pg. 110
COBRA SISTEMAS Y REDES, S.A.—See ACS, Actividades de Construccion y Servicios, S.A.; *Int'l*, pg. 110
COBRASMA S.A.; *Int'l*, pg. 1683
COBRA TECHNOLOGIA S.A.—See Banco do Brasil S.A.; *Int'l*, pg. 822
COBRA TERMOSOLAR USA, S.L.—See ACS, Actividades de Construccion y Servicios, S.A.; *Int'l*, pg. 110
COBRA-UDISPORT CONDE DE GUADALHORCE, S.L—See ACS, Actividades de Construccion y Servicios, S.A.; *Int'l*, pg. 110
COBRA UK & IRELAND LIMITED—See Apax Partners LLP; *Int'l*, pg. 505
COBRA UNDERWRITING AGENCIES LIMITED—See Apax Partners LLP; *Int'l*, pg. 505
COBRA VENTURE CORPORATION; *Int'l*, pg. 1683
COBRA WATERTECH (PROPRIETARY) LIMITED—See DISTRIBUTION AND WAREHOUSING NETWORK LIMITED; *Int'l*, pg. 2136
COBRA WIRE & CABLE INC.—See Audax Group, Limited Partnership; *U.S. Private*, pg. 387
COBRE CERRILLOS, S.A.—See Prysmian S.p.A.; *Int'l*, pg. 6011
COBRE DEL MAYO S.A. DE C.V.—See Invecture Group, S.A. de C.V.; *Int'l*, pg. 3772
COBRE LAS CRUCES S.A.—See First Quantum Minerals Ltd.; *Int'l*, pg. 2687
COBRE LIMITED; *Int'l*, pg. 1683
COBRE VALLEY REGIONAL MEDICAL CENTER; *U.S. Private*, pg. 958
COBREW N.V.—See Anheuser-Busch InBev SA/NV; *Int'l*, pg. 466
COBRO ELECTRONICO DE PEAJE S.A. DE C.V.—See Promotora y Operadora de Infraestructura, S.A.B. de C.V.; *Int'l*, pg. 5996
COBS AB—See Lagercrantz Group AB; *Int'l*, pg. 4394
COBURG COFFEE COMPANY LTD.—See Tudeley Holdings Limited; *Int'l*, pg. 7963
COBURG DAIRY—See Capitol Peak Partners, LLC; *U.S. Private*, pg. 744
COBURG DAIRY—See KKR & Co. Inc.; *U.S. Public*, pg. 1241
COBURG GROUP PLC; *Int'l*, pg. 1683
COBURN JAPAN CORPORATION; *Int'l*, pg. 1683
COBURN SUPPLY COMPANY INC; *U.S. Private*, pg. 958
COBURN TECHNOLOGIES, INC.; *U.S. Private*, pg. 958
COBURN TECHNOLOGIES (U.K.), LTD.—See Coburn Technologies, Inc.; *U.S. Private*, pg. 958
COBUS INDUSTRIES GMBH; *Int'l*, pg. 1683
COCA-COLA AFRICA (PROPRIETARY) LIMITED—See The Coca-Cola Company; *U.S. Public*, pg. 2063
COCA-COLA AMATIL (FIJI) LTD—See COCA-COLA EUROPACIFIC PARTNERS PLC; *Int'l*, pg. 1684
COCA-COLA AMATIL LIMITED—See COCA-COLA EUROPACIFIC PARTNERS PLC; *Int'l*, pg. 1684

COCA-COLA BOTTLING CO. UNITED, INC.

COCA-COLA AMATIL (PNG) LTD—See COCA-COLA EUROPACIFIC PARTNERS PLC; *Int'l*, pg. 1684
COCA-COLA AMATIL PTY LTD—See COCA-COLA EUROPACIFIC PARTNERS PLC; *Int'l*, pg. 1684
COCA-COLA-ATLANTA—See The Coca-Cola Company; *U.S. Public*, pg. 2064
COCA-COLA BEVERAGES AUSTRIA GMBH—See Coca-Cola HBC AG; *Int'l*, pg. 1685
COCA-COLA BEVERAGES CESKA REPUBLIKA, S.R.O.—See Coca-Cola HBC AG; *Int'l*, pg. 1685
COCA-COLA BEVERAGES NORTHEAST, INC.—See Kirin Holdings Company, Limited; *Int'l*, pg. 4187
COCA-COLA BEVERAGES PAKISTAN LTD.—See Anadolu Efes Biracilik ve Malt Sanayii A.S.; *Int'l*, pg. 445
COCA-COLA BEVERAGES (SHANGHAI) COMPANY LIMITED—See The Coca-Cola Company; *U.S. Public*, pg. 2063
COCA-COLA BEVERAGES SLOVENIJA D.O.O.—See Coca-Cola HBC AG; *Int'l*, pg. 1685
COCA-COLA BEVERAGES UKRAINE LTD.—See Coca-Cola HBC AG; *Int'l*, pg. 1685
COCA-COLA BEVERAGES VIETNAM LTD.—See John Swire & Sons Limited; *Int'l*, pg. 3980
COCA-COLA BISHKEK BOTTLERS CLOSED JOINT STOCK COMPANY—See Coca-Cola Icecek A.S.; *Int'l*, pg. 1686
COCA-COLA BOTTLERS CHISINAU S.R.L.—See Coca-Cola HBC AG; *Int'l*, pg. 1685
COCA-COLA BOTTLERS JAPAN HOLDINGS INC.; *Int'l*, pg. 1683
COCA-COLA BOTTLERS JAPAN INC.—See Coca-Cola Bottlers Japan Holdings Inc.; *Int'l*, pg. 1684
COCA-COLA BOTTLING CO. CONSOLIDATED - CHARLESTON, WV—See Coca-Cola Consolidated, Inc.; *U.S. Public*, pg. 521
COCA-COLA BOTTLING CO. CONSOLIDATED - COLUMBIA, TN—See Coca-Cola Consolidated, Inc.; *U.S. Public*, pg. 521
COCA-COLA BOTTLING CO. CONSOLIDATED - COLUMBUS, GA—See Coca-Cola Consolidated, Inc.; *U.S. Public*, pg. 521
COCA-COLA BOTTLING CO. CONSOLIDATED - JACKSON, TN—See Coca-Cola Consolidated, Inc.; *U.S. Public*, pg. 521
COCA-COLA BOTTLING CO. CONSOLIDATED - MOBILE, AL—See Coca-Cola Consolidated, Inc.; *U.S. Public*, pg. 521
COCA-COLA BOTTLING CO. CONSOLIDATED - PANAMA CITY, FL—See Coca-Cola Consolidated, Inc.; *U.S. Public*, pg. 521
COCA-COLA BOTTLING CO. CONSOLIDATED - ROANOKE, VA—See Coca-Cola Consolidated, Inc.; *U.S. Public*, pg. 521
COCA-COLA BOTTLING COMPANY HIGH COUNTRY; *U.S. Private*, pg. 959
COCA-COLA BOTTLING COMPANY OF ELIZABETHTOWN—See Coca-Cola Bottling Works of Tullahoma, Inc.; *U.S. Private*, pg. 959
COCA-COLA BOTTLING COMPANY OF INDIANAPOLIS, INC.—See The Coca-Cola Company; *U.S. Public*, pg. 2064
THE COCA-COLA BOTTLING COMPANY OF JORDAN LIMITED—See Coca-Cola Icecek A.S.; *Int'l*, pg. 1686
COCA-COLA BOTTLING COMPANY OF KOKOMO INDIANA; *U.S. Private*, pg. 959
COCA-COLA BOTTLING COMPANY OF NORTHERN NEW ENGLAND, INC.—See Kirin Holdings Company, Limited; *Int'l*, pg. 4187
COCA-COLA BOTTLING COMPANY—See The Coca-Cola Company; *U.S. Public*, pg. 2064
COCA-COLA BOTTLING COMPANY—See The Coca-Cola Company; *U.S. Public*, pg. 2064
COCA-COLA BOTTLING COMPANY—See The Coca-Cola Company; *U.S. Public*, pg. 2064
THE COCA-COLA BOTTLING CO. OF MEMPHIS, TENNESSEE—See The Coca-Cola Company; *U.S. Public*, pg. 2065
COCA-COLA BOTTLING CO. OF NEW ENGLAND—See The Coca-Cola Company; *U.S. Public*, pg. 2064
THE COCA-COLA BOTTLING CO. OF NEW YORK, INC.—See The Coca-Cola Company; *U.S. Public*, pg. 2065
COCA-COLA BOTTLING CO. OF SHREVEPORT—See The Coca-Cola Company; *U.S. Public*, pg. 2064
COCA-COLA BOTTLING CO. OF TEXARKANA—See The Coca-Cola Company; *U.S. Public*, pg. 2064
COCA-COLA BOTTLING CO.—See The Coca-Cola Company; *U.S. Public*, pg. 2064
COCA-COLA BOTTLING CO.—See The Coca-Cola Company; *U.S. Public*, pg. 2064
COCA-COLA BOTTLING CO.—See The Coca-Cola Company; *U.S. Public*, pg. 2064
COCA-COLA BOTTLING CO. UNITED, INC.; *U.S. Private*, pg. 958
COCA-COLA BOTTLING CO. UNITED INC—See The Coca-Cola Company; *U.S. Public*, pg. 2063
COCA-COLA BOTTLING OF LOS ANGELES—See The Coca-Cola Company; *U.S. Public*, pg. 2064

COCA-COLA BOTTLING CO. UNITED, INC.

COCA-COLA BOTTLING OF MEMPHIS—See The Coca-Cola Company; *U.S. Public*, pg. 2064
COCA-COLA BOTTLING OF NORTH TEXAS—See The Coca-Cola Company; *U.S. Public*, pg. 2064
COCA-COLA BOTTLING WORKS OF TULLAHOMA, INC.; *U.S. Private*, pg. 959
COCA-COLA (CHINA) BEVERAGES LTD.—See The Coca-Cola Company; *U.S. Public*, pg. 2063
THE COCA-COLA COMPANY - AVIATION DEPARTMENT—See The Coca-Cola Company; *U.S. Public*, pg. 2065
THE COCA-COLA COMPANY—See The Coca-Cola Company; *U.S. Public*, pg. 2065
THE COCA-COLA COMPANY—See The Coca-Cola Company; *U.S. Public*, pg. 2065
THE COCA-COLA COMPANY; *U.S. Public*, pg. 2063
THE COCA-COLA COMPANY—See The Coca-Cola Company; *U.S. Public*, pg. 2065
THE COCA-COLA COMPANY—See The Coca-Cola Company; *U.S. Public*, pg. 2065
THE COCA-COLA COMPANY—See The Coca-Cola Company; *U.S. Public*, pg. 2065
COCA-COLA CONSOLIDATED, INC.; *U.S. Public*, pg. 521
COCA-COLA DE CHILE, S.A.—See The Coca-Cola Company; *U.S. Public*, pg. 2063
COCA-COLA DE ESPANA—See The Coca-Cola Company; *U.S. Public*, pg. 2065
COCA-COLA EMBONOR S.A.; *Int'l*, pg. 1684
COCA-COLA ENTERPRISE SAS—See COCA-COLA EUROPACIFIC PARTNERS PLC; *Int'l*, pg. 1685
COCA-COLA ENTERPRISES BELGIUM SPRL—See COCA-COLA EUROPACIFIC PARTNERS PLC; *Int'l*, pg. 1685
COCA-COLA ENTERPRISES GREAT BRITAIN LIMITED—See COCA-COLA EUROPACIFIC PARTNERS PLC; *Int'l*, pg. 1685
COCA-COLA ENTERPRISES LIMITED—See COCA-COLA EUROPACIFIC PARTNERS PLC; *Int'l*, pg. 1685
COCA-COLA ENTERPRISES NEDERLAND B.V.—See COCA-COLA EUROPACIFIC PARTNERS PLC; *Int'l*, pg. 1685
COCA-COLA ENTERPRISES NORGE AS—See COCA-COLA EUROPACIFIC PARTNERS PLC; *Int'l*, pg. 1685
COCA-COLA ENTERPRISES SVERIGE AB—See COCA-COLA EUROPACIFIC PARTNERS PLC; *Int'l*, pg. 1685
COCA-COLA ERFRISCHUNGSGETRANKE GMBH—See COCA-COLA EUROPACIFIC PARTNERS PLC; *Int'l*, pg. 1684
COCA-COLA EUROPACIFIC PARTNERS AUSTRALIA PTY. LIMITED—See COCA-COLA EUROPACIFIC PARTNERS PLC; *Int'l*, pg. 1684
COCA-COLA EUROPACIFIC PARTNERS BELGIUM SRL/B.V.—See COCA-COLA EUROPACIFIC PARTNERS PLC; *Int'l*, pg. 1684
COCA-COLA EUROPACIFIC PARTNERS DEUTSCHLAND GMBH—See COCA-COLA EUROPACIFIC PARTNERS PLC; *Int'l*, pg. 1684
COCA-COLA EUROPACIFIC PARTNERS (FIJI) PTE. LIMITED—See COCA-COLA EUROPACIFIC PARTNERS PLC; *Int'l*, pg. 1684
COCA-COLA EUROPACIFIC PARTNERS FRANCE S.A.S.—See COCA-COLA EUROPACIFIC PARTNERS PLC; *Int'l*, pg. 1684
COCA-COLA EUROPACIFIC PARTNERS GREAT BRITAIN LIMITED—See COCA-COLA EUROPACIFIC PARTNERS PLC; *Int'l*, pg. 1684
COCA-COLA EUROPACIFIC PARTNERS IBERIA, S.L.U.—See COCA-COLA EUROPACIFIC PARTNERS PLC; *Int'l*, pg. 1684
COCA-COLA EUROPACIFIC PARTNERS LUXEMBOURG SARL—See COCA-COLA EUROPACIFIC PARTNERS PLC; *Int'l*, pg. 1685
COCA-COLA EUROPACIFIC PARTNERS NEDERLAND B.V.—See COCA-COLA EUROPACIFIC PARTNERS PLC; *Int'l*, pg. 1685
COCA-COLA EUROPACIFIC PARTNERS NEW ZEALAND LIMITED—See COCA-COLA EUROPACIFIC PARTNERS PLC; *Int'l*, pg. 1685
COCA-COLA EUROPACIFIC PARTNERS NORGE AS—See COCA-COLA EUROPACIFIC PARTNERS PLC; *Int'l*, pg. 1685
COCA-COLA EUROPACIFIC PARTNERS PAPUA NEW GUINEA LIMITED—See COCA-COLA EUROPACIFIC PARTNERS PLC; *Int'l*, pg. 1685
COCA-COLA EUROPACIFIC PARTNERS PLC; *Int'l*, pg. 1684
COCA-COLA EUROPACIFIC PARTNERS PORTUGAL UNIPESSOAL LDA—See COCA-COLA EUROPACIFIC PARTNERS PLC; *Int'l*, pg. 1685
COCA-COLA EUROPACIFIC PARTNERS SERVICES BULGARIA EOOD—See COCA-COLA EUROPACIFIC PARTNERS PLC; *Int'l*, pg. 1685
COCA-COLA EUROPACIFIC PARTNERS SVERIGE AB—See COCA-COLA EUROPACIFIC PARTNERS PLC; *Int'l*, pg. 1685
COCA-COLA EUROPEAN PARTNERS FRANCE SAS—See COCA-COLA EUROPACIFIC PARTNERS PLC; *Int'l*, pg. 1685
COCA-COLA EUROPEAN PARTNERS IBERIA, S.L.U.—See COCA-COLA EUROPACIFIC PARTNERS PLC; *Int'l*, pg. 1685
COCA-COLA EUROPEAN PARTNERS ISLAND EHF.—See COCA-COLA EUROPACIFIC PARTNERS PLC; *Int'l*, pg. 1685
COCA-COLA EUROPEAN PARTNERS NEDERLAND B.V.—See COCA-COLA EUROPACIFIC PARTNERS PLC; *Int'l*, pg. 1685
COCA-COLA EUROPEAN PARTNERS NORGE AS—See COCA-COLA EUROPACIFIC PARTNERS PLC; *Int'l*, pg. 1685
COCA-COLA EUROPEAN PARTNERS PORTUGAL UNIPESSOAL, LDA—See COCA-COLA EUROPACIFIC PARTNERS PLC; *Int'l*, pg. 1685
COCA-COLA EUROPEAN PARTNERS US, LLC—See COCA-COLA EUROPACIFIC PARTNERS PLC; *Int'l*, pg. 1685
THE COCA-COLA EXPORT CORPORATION—See The Coca-Cola Company; *U.S. Public*, pg. 2065
COCA-COLA FEMSA, S.A.B. DE C.V.—See Fomento Economico Mexicano, S.A.B. de C.V.; *Int'l*, pg. 2723
COCA-COLA FINANCIAL CORPORATION—See The Coca-Cola Company; *U.S. Public*, pg. 2063
COCA-COLA FOUNTAIN INC.—See The Coca-Cola Company; *U.S. Public*, pg. 2063
COCA-COLA GMBH—See The Coca-Cola Company; *U.S. Public*, pg. 2063
COCA-COLA GREAT BRITAIN—See The Coca-Cola Company; *U.S. Public*, pg. 2063
COCA-COLA HBC AG; *Int'l*, pg. 1685
COCA-COLA HBC AUSTRIA GMBH—See Coca-Cola HBC AG; *Int'l*, pg. 1685
COCA-COLA HBC B-H D.O.O.—See Coca-Cola HBC AG; *Int'l*, pg. 1685
COCA-COLA HBC CESKA A SLOVENSKO, S.R.O.—See Coca-Cola HBC AG; *Int'l*, pg. 1686
COCA-COLA HBC CESKO A SLOVENSKO, S.R.O—See Coca-Cola HBC AG; *Int'l*, pg. 1685
COCA-COLA HBC CYPRUS LTD.—See Coca-Cola HBC AG; *Int'l*, pg. 1685
COCA-COLA HBC HRVATSKA D.O.O.—See Coca-Cola HBC AG; *Int'l*, pg. 1685
COCA-COLA HBC HUNGARY LTD.—See Coca-Cola HBC AG; *Int'l*, pg. 1685
COCA-COLA HBC IRELAND LIMITED—See Coca-Cola HBC AG; *Int'l*, pg. 1685
COCA-COLA HBC ITALIA S.R.L.—See Coca-Cola HBC AG; *Int'l*, pg. 1686
COCA-COLA HBC KOSOVO L.L.C.—See Coca-Cola HBC AG; *Int'l*, pg. 1686
COCA-COLA HBC NORTHERN IRELAND LIMITED—See Coca-Cola HBC AG; *Int'l*, pg. 1686
COCA-COLA HBC POLSKA SP. Z O.O.—See Coca-Cola HBC AG; *Int'l*, pg. 1686
COCA-COLA HBC ROMANIA LTD.—See Coca-Cola HBC AG; *Int'l*, pg. 1686
COCA-COLA HBC SLOVENIJA D.O.O.—See Coca-Cola HBC AG; *Int'l*, pg. 1686
COCA-COLA HBC-SRBIJA D.O.O.—See Coca-Cola HBC AG; *Int'l*, pg. 1686
COCA-COLA HBC SWITZERLAND LTD—See Coca-Cola HBC AG; *Int'l*, pg. 1686
COCA-COLA HELLENIC BOTTLING COMPANY-CRNA GORA D.O.O.—See Coca-Cola HBC AG; *Int'l*, pg. 1686
COCA-COLA HELLENIC PROCUREMENT GMBH—See Coca-Cola HBC AG; *Int'l*, pg. 1686
COCA-COLA HOLDINGS OVERSEAS LTD.—See The Coca-Cola Company; *U.S. Public*, pg. 2064
COCA-COLA HOLDINGS (UNITED KINGDOM) LIMITED—See The Coca-Cola Company; *U.S. Public*, pg. 2063
COCA-COLA IBERIAN PARTNERS, S.A.U.—See COCA-COLA EUROPACIFIC PARTNERS PLC; *Int'l*, pg. 1685
COCA-COLA ICECEK A.S.; *Int'l*, pg. 1686
COCA-COLA INDIA LIMITED—See The Coca-Cola Company; *U.S. Public*, pg. 2064
COCA-COLA INTERAMERICAN CORPORATION—See The Coca-Cola Company; *U.S. Public*, pg. 2064
COCA-COLA INTERAMERICAN CORP.—See The Coca-Cola Company; *U.S. Public*, pg. 2064
COCA-COLA ITALIA SRL—See The Coca-Cola Company; *U.S. Public*, pg. 2064
COCA-COLA (JAPAN) CO., LTD.—See The Coca-Cola Company; *U.S. Public*, pg. 2063
COCA-COLA LATIN AMERICA—See The Coca-Cola Company; *U.S. Public*, pg. 2064
COCA-COLA LTD.—See The Coca-Cola Company; *U.S. Public*, pg. 2064
COCA-COLA LTD.—See The Coca-Cola Company; *U.S. Public*, pg. 2065
COCA-COLA LTD.—See The Coca-Cola Company; *U.S. Public*, pg. 2065
COCA-COLA LTD.—See The Coca-Cola Company; *U.S. Public*, pg. 2065
COCA-COLA NORTH AMERICA—See The Coca-Cola Company; *U.S. Public*, pg. 2064
COCA-COLA NORTH AMERICA—See The Coca-Cola Company; *U.S. Public*, pg. 2064
COCA-COLA NORTH AMERICA—See The Coca-Cola Company; *U.S. Public*, pg. 2064
COCA-COLA OF TUCSON INC.—See The Coca-Cola Company; *U.S. Public*, pg. 2064
COCA-COLA REFRESHMENTS CANADA COMPANY—See The Coca-Cola Company; *U.S. Public*, pg. 2064
COCA-COLA REFRESHMENTS USA, INC. - BELLEVUE—See The Coca-Cola Company; *U.S. Public*, pg. 2064
COCA-COLA REFRESHMENTS USA, INC. - KANSAS—See The Coca-Cola Company; *U.S. Public*, pg. 2064
COCA-COLA REFRESHMENTS USA, INC. - NILES—See The Coca-Cola Company; *U.S. Public*, pg. 2064
COCA-COLA REFRESHMENTS USA, INC.—See The Coca-Cola Company; *U.S. Public*, pg. 2064
COCA-COLA REINSURANCE SERVICES LIMITED—See The Coca-Cola Company; *U.S. Public*, pg. 2065
COCA-COLA SATIS VE DAGITIM A.S.—See Coca-Cola Icecek A.S.; *Int'l*, pg. 1686
COCA-COLA SERVICIOS DE VENEZUELA, C.A.—See The Coca-Cola Company; *U.S. Public*, pg. 2065
COCA-COLA SOUTH ASIA HOLDINGS, INC.—See The Coca-Cola Company; *U.S. Public*, pg. 2065
COCA-COLA SOUTHERN AFRICA (PTY) LTD.—See The Coca-Cola Company; *U.S. Public*, pg. 2065
COCA-COLA SOUTH PACIFIC PTY LIMITED—See The Coca-Cola Company; *U.S. Public*, pg. 2065
COCA-COLA TRADING COMPANY—See The Coca-Cola Company; *U.S. Public*, pg. 2065
COCA-COLA USA ONTARIO SYRUP—See The Coca-Cola Company; *U.S. Public*, pg. 2064
COCA-COLA WEST DAISEN PRODUCTS CO., LTD.—See Coca-Cola Bottlers Japan Holdings Inc.; *Int'l*, pg. 1684
COCA-COLA WEST JAPAN CUSTOMER SERVICE CO LTD—See Coca-Cola Bottlers Japan Holdings Inc.; *Int'l*, pg. 1684
COCA-COLA WEST SERVICE CO., LTD.—See Coca-Cola Bottlers Japan Holdings Inc.; *Int'l*, pg. 1684
COCA-COLA WEST VENDING CO., LTD.—See Coca-Cola Bottlers Japan Holdings Inc.; *Int'l*, pg. 1684
COCALO, INC.—See TG Valentine, LLC; *U.S. Private*, pg. 3979
C.O. CAPITAL AGENCIA DE VALORES, S.A.—See Grupo Catalana Occidente, S.A.; *Int'l*, pg. 3124
COCA SUD-EST—See VINCI S.A.; *Int'l*, pg. 8213
COCCA DEVELOPMENT, LTD.; *U.S. Private*, pg. 959
COCCIA LINCOLN-MERCURY INCORPORATED; *U.S. Private*, pg. 959
COCC, INC.; *U.S. Private*, pg. 959
COCHERY ILE-DE-FRANCE SAS—See VINCI S.A.; *Int'l*, pg. 8216
COCHEZ Y COMPANIA, S.A.; *Int'l*, pg. 1686
THE COCHIN MALABAR ESTATES & INDUSTRIES LIMITED; *Int'l*, pg. 7634
COCHIN MINERALS AND RUTILE LIMITED; *Int'l*, pg. 1686
COCHIN SHIPYARD LIMITED; *Int'l*, pg. 1686
COCHLEAR AG—See Cochlear Limited; *Int'l*, pg. 1686
COCHLEAR AMERICAS INC—See Cochlear Limited; *Int'l*, pg. 1686
COCHLEAR AUSTRIA GMBH—See Cochlear Limited; *Int'l*, pg. 1686
COCHLEAR BENELUX NV—See Cochlear Limited; *Int'l*, pg. 1686
COCHLEAR BONE ANCHORED SOLUTIONS AB—See Cochlear Limited; *Int'l*, pg. 1687
COCHLEAR CANADA INC—See Cochlear Limited; *Int'l*, pg. 1687
COCHLEAR COLOMBIA SAS—See Cochlear Limited; *Int'l*, pg. 1687
COCHLEAR DEUTSCHLAND GMBH & CO. KG—See Cochlear Limited; *Int'l*, pg. 1687
COCHLEAR EUROPE FINANCE GMBH—See Cochlear Limited; *Int'l*, pg. 1687
COCHLEAR EUROPE LIMITED—See Cochlear Limited; *Int'l*, pg. 1687
COCHLEAR FRANCE SAS—See Cochlear Limited; *Int'l*, pg. 1687
COCHLEAR (HK) LIMITED—See Cochlear Limited; *Int'l*, pg. 1686
COCHLEAR ITALIA SRL—See Cochlear Limited; *Int'l*, pg. 1687
COCHLEAR KOREA LIMITED—See Cochlear Limited; *Int'l*, pg. 1687
COCHLEAR LATINOAMERICA S.A.—See Cochlear Limited; *Int'l*, pg. 1687
COCHLEAR LIMITED; *Int'l*, pg. 1686
COCHLEAR MEDICAL DEVICE (BEIJING) CO., LTD.—See Cochlear Limited; *Int'l*, pg. 1687
COCHLEAR MEDICAL DEVICE COMPANY INDIA PRIVATE LIMITED—See Cochlear Limited; *Int'l*, pg. 1687
COCHLEAR MEXICO SA DE CV—See Cochlear Limited; *Int'l*, pg. 1687

COMPANY NAME INDEX

COCHLEAR MIDDLE EAST FZ-LLC—See Cochlear Limited; *Int'l*, pg. 1687
COCHLEAR NORDIC AB—See Cochlear Limited; *Int'l*, pg. 1687
COCHLEAR NORWAY AS—See Cochlear Limited; *Int'l*, pg. 1687
COCHLEAR SWEDEN HOLDINGS AB—See Cochlear Limited; *Int'l*, pg. 1687
COCHLEAR TIBBI CIHAZLAR VE SAGLIK HIZMETLERI LIMITED SIRKETI—See Cochlear Limited; *Int'l*, pg. 1687
COCHLEAR VERWALTUNGS GMBH—See Cochlear Limited; *Int'l*, pg. 1687
COCHRAN BROS COMPANY INCORPORATED; *U.S. Private*, pg. 959
COCHRANE'S CHAPEL OF THE ROSES, INC.—See Carriage Services, Inc.; *U.S. Public*, pg. 439
COCHRANE—See Carriage Services, Inc.; *U.S. Public*, pg. 439
COCHRANE'S TRANSPORT LIMITED—See K&S Corporation Limited; *Int'l*, pg. 4038
COCHRAN EXTERIORS, LLC; *U.S. Private*, pg. 959
COCHRAN INC.; *U.S. Private*, pg. 959
C. O. CHRISTIAN & SONS COMPANY, INC.; *U.S. Private*, pg. 705
COCINA AUTENTICA, LLC—See PepsiCo, Inc.; *U.S. Public*, pg. 1668
COCIO CHOKOLADEMAELK A/S—See Arla Foods amba; *Int'l*, pg. 573
COCKBURN CEMENT—See CRH plc; *Int'l*, pg. 1842
COCKBURN ENTERPRISES INC.; *U.S. Private*, pg. 959
COCKE COUNTY HMA, LLC—See Community Health Systems, Inc.; *U.S. Public*, pg. 552
COCKERILL MAINTENANCE & INGENIERIE SA—See Euremis Holding SA; *Int'l*, pg. 2530
COCKERILL MECANIQUE PRESTATIONS—See ArcelorMittal S.A.; *Int'l*, pg. 545
COCKERILL SAMBRE S.A.—See ArcelorMittal S.A.; *Int'l*, pg. 545
COCKRAM CORPORATION—See Kajima Corporation; *Int'l*, pg. 4054
COCK'S & COWS APS—See NoHo Partners Plc; *Int'l*, pg. 5400
COCLISA S.A. DE C.V.—See Hahn & Company; *Int'l*, pg. 3208
COCOAHOUSE INDUSTRIES SDN. BHD.—See TSH Resources Berhad; *Int'l*, pg. 7950
COCOAHOUSE SDN. BHD.—See TSH Resources Berhad; *Int'l*, pg. 7950
COCOALAND HOLDINGS BERHAD; *Int'l*, pg. 1687
COCOA MARKETING COMPANY (GHANA) LIMITED—See Ghana Cocoa Board; *Int'l*, pg. 2958
COCOA PROCESSING COMPANY LIMITED; *Int'l*, pg. 1687
COCOKARA FINE INC.—See MatsukiyoCocokara & Co.; *Int'l*, pg. 4730
COCOKARAFINE OEC CO., LTD.—See MatsukiyoCocokara & Co.; *Int'l*, pg. 4730
COCOKARA HEALTHCARE INC—See MatsukiyoCocokara & Co.; *Int'l*, pg. 4730
COCOLONET CO., LTD.; *Int'l*, pg. 1687
COCO MART INC.; *U.S. Private*, pg. 959
CO-COMMUNICATIONS, INC.; *U.S. Private*, pg. 953
COCONALA, INC.; *Int'l*, pg. 1687
COCONSTRUCT, LLC—See Buildertrend Solutions Inc.; *U.S. Private*, pg. 682
COCONUT ENTERPRISES INC.—See Unisa Holdings Incorporated; *U.S. Private*, pg. 4286
COCONUT GROVE BANK; *U.S. Private*, pg. 959
COCONUT PRODUCTS LTD.—See Albert Ballin KG; *Int'l*, pg. 294
COCONUTS IN THE GROVE INC.—See Unisa Holdings Incorporated; *U.S. Private*, pg. 4286
COCOON HOLDINGS LIMITED; *Int'l*, pg. 1687
COCO PAZZO OF ILLINOIS LLC; *U.S. Private*, pg. 959
COCO PURE BEVERAGE CORP.—See Herbal Dispatch Inc.; *Int'l*, pg. 3359
COCO-RO PTE LTD—See Meiko Network Japan Co., Ltd.; *Int'l*, pg. 4803
COCORPORT, INC.; *Int'l*, pg. 1687
COCO'S JAPAN CO., LTD.—See Zensho Holdings Co., Ltd.; *Int'l*, pg. 8634
COCO TOURS VERANSTALTUNGS GMBH—See DEAG Deutsche Entertainment AG; *Int'l*, pg. 1998
COC PROPERTIES, INC.; *U.S. Private*, pg. 958
COCRE8 PTE. LTD.—See Hong Fok Corporation Limited; *Int'l*, pg. 3465
COCREATION GRASS CO., LTD.; *Int'l*, pg. 1687
COCREATIV CORP.—See Frontenac Company LLC; *U.S. Private*, pg. 1613
COCREATIV TAMPA BAY LLC; *U.S. Private*, pg. 959
COC RF TECHNOLOGY & INFORMATION PLC—See China GrenTech Corporation Limited; *Int'l*, pg. 1505
COCRYSTAL DISCOVERY, INC.—See Cocrystal Pharma, Inc.; *U.S. Public*, pg. 521
COCRYSTAL PHARMA, INC.; *U.S. Public*, pg. 521
COCUBES TECHNOLOGIES PRIVATE LIMITED—See Aon plc; *Int'l*, pg. 494

C.O. CYPRUS OPPORTUNITY ENERGY PUBLIC LIMITED; *Int'l*, pg. 1243
CODAC BEHAVIORAL HEALTH SERVICES, INC.; *U.S. Private*, pg. 960
CODA GROUP INTERNATIONAL LTD.—See UNIT4 N.V.; *Int'l*, pg. 8062
CODA HOLDINGS, INC.; *U.S. Private*, pg. 959
CODA, INC.; *U.S. Private*, pg. 960
CODALE ELECTRIC SUPPLY, INC.—See Sonepar S.A.; *Int'l*, pg. 7093
CODA MINERALS LTD.; *Int'l*, pg. 1687
CODAN A/S—See Intact Financial Corporation; *Int'l*, pg. 3727
CODAN A/S—See Tryg A/S; *Int'l*, pg. 7946
CODAN FORSIKRING A/S—See Intact Financial Corporation; *Int'l*, pg. 3727
CODAN FORSIKRING A/S—See Tryg A/S; *Int'l*, pg. 7946
CODAN LIMITED; *Int'l*, pg. 1687
CODAN LTD. - NORTH AMERICA - LMR—See Codan Limited; *Int'l*, pg. 1688
CODAN RADIO COMMUNICATIONS ME JLT—See Codan Limited; *Int'l*, pg. 1688
CODAN TECH QINGDAO RUBBER & PLASTIC PARTS CO., LTD.—See Addtech AB; *Int'l*, pg. 132
CODAN (UK) LTD—See Codan Limited; *Int'l*, pg. 1688
CODAN (US) INC—See Codan Limited; *Int'l*, pg. 1688
CODA OCTOPUS COLMEK, INC.—See Coda Octopus Group, Inc.; *U.S. Public*, pg. 521
CODA OCTOPUS GROUP, INC.; *U.S. Public*, pg. 521
CODA OCTOPUS MARTECH LTD—See Coda Octopus Group, Inc.; *U.S. Public*, pg. 521
CODA OCTOPUS PRODUCTS A/S—See Coda Octopus Group, Inc.; *U.S. Public*, pg. 521
CODA OCTOPUS PRODUCTS, INC.—See Coda Octopus Group, Inc.; *U.S. Public*, pg. 521
CODA OCTOPUS PRODUCTS LTD.—See Coda Octopus Group, Inc.; *U.S. Public*, pg. 521
CODA RESOURCES, LTD.; *U.S. Private*, pg. 959
COD CO. INC.; *U.S. Private*, pg. 959
CODDING CONSTRUCTION CO—See Codding Enterprises; *U.S. Private*, pg. 960
CODDING ENTERPRISES; *U.S. Private*, pg. 960
CODDING MAINTENANCE INC—See Codding Enterprises; *U.S. Private*, pg. 960
CODE 3, INC.—See Ecco Safety Group; *U.S. Private*, pg. 1326
CODE 42 SOFTWARE, INC.; *U.S. Private*, pg. 960
CODE AUTHORITY, LLC—See Trinity Hunt Management, L.P.; *U.S. Private*, pg. 4234
CODE COMPUTERLOVE LTD.—See WPP plc; *U.S. Public*, pg. 8463
CODEFIS SOCIETA CONSORTILE PER AZIONI—See Stellantis N.V.; *Int'l*, pg. 7198
CODEFIT SP. Z O.O.—See WIIT SpA; *Int'l*, pg. 8408
CODE GREEN NETWORKS, INC.—See Fairhaven Capital Management, LLC; *U.S. Private*, pg. 1464
CODELCO ANDINA DIVISION—See Corporacion Nacional del Cobre de Chile; *Int'l*, pg. 1804
CODELCO-ASIA—See Corporacion Nacional del Cobre de Chile; *Int'l*, pg. 1804
CODELCO CHUQUICAMATA DIVISION—See Corporacion Nacional del Cobre de Chile; *Int'l*, pg. 1804
CODELCO EL TENIENTE DIVISION—See Corporacion Nacional del Cobre de Chile; *Int'l*, pg. 1804
CODELCO-KUPFERHANDEL GMBH—See Corporacion Nacional del Cobre de Chile; *Int'l*, pg. 1805
CODELCO SALVADOR DIVISION—See Corporacion Nacional del Cobre de Chile; *Int'l*, pg. 1804
CODELCO TALLERES DIVISION—See Corporacion Nacional del Cobre de Chile; *Int'l*, pg. 1804
CODE MASTER INSPECTION SERVICES—See Barry Isett & Associates Inc.; *U.S. Private*, pg. 481
CODEMASTERS GROUP HOLDINGS PLC—See Electronic Arts Inc.; *U.S. Public*, pg. 723
CODEMASTERS LIMITED—See Electronic Arts Inc.; *U.S. Public*, pg. 724
CODEMEDIA SA—See Grupa SMT S.A.; *Int'l*, pg. 3117
CODEMETTLE, LLC—See J.F. Lehman & Company, Inc.; *U.S. Private*, pg. 2163
CODENATURE CO., LTD.; *Int'l*, pg. 1688
CODENOMICON LTD.—See Synopsys, Inc.; *U.S. Public*, pg. 1970
CODENOMICON OY—See Synopsys, Inc.; *U.S. Public*, pg. 1970
CODE ONE ENTERPRISES NJ CORP; *U.S. Private*, pg. 960
CODE.ORG; *U.S. Private*, pg. 960
CODERE ARGENTINA S.A.—See Codere S.A.; *Int'l*, pg. 1688
CODERE COLOMBIA S.A.—See Codere S.A.; *Int'l*, pg. 1688
CODERE DO BRASIL ENTRETENIMENTO LTDA—See Codere S.A.; *Int'l*, pg. 1688
CODERE ITALIA SPA—See Codere S.A.; *Int'l*, pg. 1688
CODERE MEXICO, S.A.—See Codere S.A.; *Int'l*, pg. 1688
CODERE PANAMA, S.A.—See Codere S.A.; *Int'l*, pg. 1688
CODERE S.A.; *Int'l*, pg. 1688
CODERE URUGUAY S.A.—See Codere S.A.; *Int'l*, pg. 1688

CODERYTE, INC.—See 3M Company; *U.S. Public*, pg. 8
CODES COMBINE CO., LTD.; *Int'l*, pg. 1688
CODESI GMBH—See Wurth Verwaltungsgesellschaft mbH; *Int'l*, pg. 8506
CODESMART HOLDINGS, INC.; *U.S. Private*, pg. 960
CODESMITH TOOLS, LLC; *U.S. Private*, pg. 960
CODESPEAR, LLC—See Federal Signal Corporation; *U.S. Public*, pg. 826
CODESQUAD B.V.—See adesso SE; *Int'l*, pg. 144
CODE SYSTEMS INC.—See VOXX International Corporation; *U.S. Public*, pg. 2311
CODETAKT CO.,LTD.—See Nippon Telegraph & Telephone Corporation; *Int'l*, pg. 5340
CODEWORKS, INC.; *U.S. Private*, pg. 960
CODEX ACQUISITIONS PLC; *Int'l*, pg. 1688
CODEX GMBH & CO. KG—See Uzin Utz AG; *Int'l*, pg. 8104
CODEXIS, INC.; *U.S. Public*, pg. 521
CODEXIS LABORATORIES INDIA PVT. LTD.—See Codexis, Inc.; *U.S. Public*, pg. 521
CODEX NEGOCE SARL—See SMC Corporation; *Int'l*, pg. 7003
CODFORD BIOGAS LIMITED—See JLEN Environmental Assets Group Limited; *Int'l*, pg. 3973
CO-DIAGNOSTICS, INC.; *U.S. Public*, pg. 520
CODIAK BIOSCIENCES, INC.; *U.S. Public*, pg. 521
CODIBEL SA/NV; *Int'l*, pg. 1688
CODICES S.R.L.—See Ardian SAS; *Int'l*, pg. 555
CODIFRAIS S.A.S.—See Colruyt Group N.V.; *Int'l*, pg. 1705
CODI-FRANCE S.A.S.—See Colruyt Group N.V.; *Int'l*, pg. 1705
CODIGO LLC—See The Jordan Company, L.P.; *U.S. Private*, pg. 4062
CODI GROUP BV—See Active Capital Company Holding BV; *Int'l*, pg. 120
CODI INTERNATIONAL B.V.—See Active Capital Company Holding BV; *Int'l*, pg. 120
CODIKOAT LTD.—See Greenbank Capital Inc.; *Int'l*, pg. 3073
CODILOG-KNOWLEDGE SAS—See Neurones S.A.; *Int'l*, pg. 5219
CODILOG SA—See Neurones S.A.; *Int'l*, pg. 5219
CODI-M CO., LTD.; *Int'l*, pg. 1688
CODINA CONSTRUCTION CORPORATION—See SoftBank Group Corp.; *Int'l*, pg. 7053
CODIREP SNC—See Groupe Fnac S.A.; *Int'l*, pg. 3103
CODMAN NEUROVASCULAR INC.—See Johnson & Johnson; *U.S. Public*, pg. 1194
CODMAN & SHURTLEFF, INC.—See Johnson & Johnson; *U.S. Public*, pg. 1195
CO.DON AG; *Int'l*, pg. 1680
CODORNIU, S.A.; *Int'l*, pg. 1688
CODORUS VALLEY BANCORP, INC.—See Orrstown Financial Services, Inc.; *U.S. Public*, pg. 1618
CODRAMEX SA DE CV—See HAL Trust N.V.; *Int'l*, pg. 3225
CODY CHEVROLET, INC.; *U.S. Private*, pg. 960
CODY COMPANY INC.; *U.S. Private*, pg. 960
CODY CONSULTING SERVICES, INC.; *U.S. Private*, pg. 960
CODY DIRECT CORP.—See Hanung Toys and Textiles Limited; *Int'l*, pg. 3261
CODY LABORATORIES, INC.—See Lannett Company, Inc.; *U.S. Public*, pg. 1292
COECLERICI BULK TERMINAL TORRES S.P.A.—See Coeclerici S.p.A.; *Int'l*, pg. 1688
COECLERICI COAL & FUELS S.P.A. - RUSSIA BRANCH—See Coeclerici S.p.A.; *Int'l*, pg. 1688
COECLERICI COAL & FUELS SPA—See Coeclerici S.p.A.; *Int'l*, pg. 1688
COECLERICI COAL & FUELS S.P.A—See Coeclerici S.p.A.; *Int'l*, pg. 1688
COECLERICI COAL NETWORK, INC.—See Coeclerici S.p.A.; *Int'l*, pg. 1688
COECLERICI LOGISTICS S.P.A.—See Coeclerici S.p.A.; *Int'l*, pg. 1689
COECLERICI SHIPPING S.P.A.—See Coeclerici S.p.A.; *Int'l*, pg. 1689
COECLERICI S.P.A.; *Int'l*, pg. 1688
COE DISTRIBUTING INC.; *U.S. Private*, pg. 960
COE DRILLING PTY LTD.—See Quanta Services, Inc.; *U.S. Public*, pg. 1750
COE FINANCIAL SERVICES INC.—See Creative Planning, LLC; *U.S. Private*, pg. 1089
COEGIN PHARMA AB; *Int'l*, pg. 1689
COELI AB; *Int'l*, pg. 1689
COEN CO., LTD.—See United Arrows Ltd.; *Int'l*, pg. 8064
COEN COMPANY, INC.—See Koch Industries, Inc.; *U.S. Private*, pg. 2331
COEN DIERENARTS B.V.—See CVS Group Plc; *Int'l*, pg. 1890
COEN OIL COMPANY; *U.S. Private*, pg. 960
COE ORCHARD EQUIPMENT, INC.—See Flory Industries, Inc.; *U.S. Private*, pg. 1551
COE PRESS EQUIPMENT CORP.; *U.S. Private*, pg. 960
COEPTIS THERAPEUTICS HOLDINGS, INC.; *U.S. Public*, pg. 521

COEPTIS THERAPEUTICS HOLDINGS, INC.

COESIA HEALTH & BEAUTY INC.—See Coesia S.p.A.; *Int'l*, pg. 1689
COESIA INDIA PRIVATE LTD.—See Coesia S.p.A.; *Int'l*, pg. 1689
COESIA S.P.A.; *Int'l*, pg. 1689
COESTER VMS; *U.S. Private*, pg. 960
COEUR CAPITAL, INC.—See Coeur Mining, Inc.; *U.S. Public*, pg. 522
COEUR D'ALENE BANCORP, INC.; *U.S. Public*, pg. 521
COEUR D'ALENE BUILDERS SUPPLY; *U.S. Private*, pg. 960
THE COEUR D'ALENE RESORT—See The Hagadone Corporation; *U.S. Private*, pg. 4041
COEUR EXPLORATIONS, INC.—See Coeur Mining, Inc.; *U.S. Public*, pg. 522
COEUR, INC.—See Illinois Tool Works Inc.; *U.S. Public*, pg. 1102
COEUR MEDICAL PRODUCTS, S. DE R.L. DE C.V.—See Illinois Tool Works Inc.; *U.S. Public*, pg. 1102
COEUR MEDICAL PRODUCTS SERVICES, S. DE R.L. DE C.V.—See Illinois Tool Works Inc.; *U.S. Public*, pg. 1102
COEUR MINING, INC.; *U.S. Public*, pg. 522
COEUR MINING, INC.; *U.S. Private*, pg. 960
COEUR ROCHESTER, INC.—See Coeur Mining, Inc.; *U.S. Public*, pg. 522
CO-EX CORP.—See Bayer Aktiengesellschaft; *Int'l*, pg. 902
COEX METALS CORPORATION—See Uranium Energy Corp.; *Int'l*, pg. 8094
COEXPAN BRASIL EMBALAGENS LTDA—See Coexpan S.A.; *Int'l*, pg. 1690
COEXPAN DEUTSCHLAND GMBH—See Coexpan S.A.; *Int'l*, pg. 1690
COEXPAN FRANCE SA—See Coexpan S.A.; *Int'l*, pg. 1690
COEXPAN MEXICO, S.A DE C.V.—See Coexpan S.A.; *Int'l*, pg. 1690
COEXPAN MONTONATE S.R.L.—See Coexpan S.A.; *Int'l*, pg. 1690
COEXPAN S.A.; *Int'l*, pg. 1690
COEX PARTNERS LIMITED—See TP ICAP Finance PLC; *Int'l*, pg. 7881
COFACE ARGENTINA SA—See Groupe BPCE; *Int'l*, pg. 3092
COFACE ASSICURAZIONI S.P.A.—See Coface S.A.; *Int'l*, pg. 1691
COFACE AUSTRALIA PTY LTD.—See Groupe BPCE; *Int'l*, pg. 3092
COFACE AUSTRIA BANK AG—See Coface S.A.; *Int'l*, pg. 1691
COFACE AUSTRIA GMBH—See Groupe BPCE; *Int'l*, pg. 3093
COFACE AUSTRIA HOLDING AG—See Coface S.A.; *Int'l*, pg. 1690
COFACE AUSTRIA KREDITVERSICHERUNG AG—See Coface S.A.; *Int'l*, pg. 1691
COFACE BELGIUM SA—See Groupe BPCE; *Int'l*, pg. 3093
COFACE BULGARIA EOOD—See Groupe BPCE; *Int'l*, pg. 3093
COFACE CANADA INC.—See Groupe BPCE; *Int'l*, pg. 3093
COFACE CENTRAL EUROPE HOLDING AG—See Coface S.A.; *Int'l*, pg. 1691
COFACE CHILE SA—See Groupe BPCE; *Int'l*, pg. 3093
COFACE COLLECTIONS NORTH AMERICA, INC.—See Coface S.A.; *Int'l*, pg. 1691
COFACE CREDIT MANAGEMENT NORTH AMERICA, INC.—See Coface S.A.; *Int'l*, pg. 1691
COFACE CZECH INSURANCE S.R.O—See Groupe BPCE; *Int'l*, pg. 3093
COFACE DANMARK—See Coface S.A.; *Int'l*, pg. 1691
COFACE DEBITOREN GMBH—See Groupe BPCE; *Int'l*, pg. 3093
COFACE DO BRASIL SEGUROS DE CREDITO S.A—See Groupe BPCE; *Int'l*, pg. 3093
COFACE EGYPT—See Coface S.A.; *Int'l*, pg. 1690
COFACE GRECE SA—See Groupe BPCE; *Int'l*, pg. 3093
COFACE HOLDING AG—See Coface S.A.; *Int'l*, pg. 1690
COFACE HUNGARY KFT—See Groupe BPCE; *Int'l*, pg. 3093
COFACE IRELAND LIMITED—See Groupe BPCE; *Int'l*, pg. 3093
COFACE ITALIA S.P.A.—See Coface S.A.; *Int'l*, pg. 1691
COFACE JAPAN CO., LTD.—See Groupe BPCE; *Int'l*, pg. 3093
COFACE KREDITVERSICHERUNG AG—See Coface S.A.; *Int'l*, pg. 1691
COFACE NEDERLAND BV—See Groupe BPCE; *Int'l*, pg. 3093
COFACE NORTH AMERICA HOLDING COMPANY—See Coface S.A.; *Int'l*, pg. 1691
COFACE NORTH AMERICA, INC.—See Coface S.A.; *Int'l*, pg. 1691
COFACE NORTH AMERICA INSURANCE COMPANY, INC.—See Coface S.A.; *Int'l*, pg. 1691
COFACE NORTH AMERICA POLITICAL RISK—See Coface S.A.; *Int'l*, pg. 1691

COFACE PKZ D.D.—See Groupe BPCE; *Int'l*, pg. 3093
COFACE POLAND FACTORING SP. Z O.O.—See Groupe BPCE; *Int'l*, pg. 3093
COFACE PORTUGAL, SA—See Groupe BPCE; *Int'l*, pg. 3093
COFACE RECEIVABLES FINANCE LIMITED—See Coface S.A.; *Int'l*, pg. 1691
COFACE ROMANIA CMS S.R.L.—See Groupe BPCE; *Int'l*, pg. 3093
COFACE ROMANIA INSURANCE SRL—See Groupe BPCE; *Int'l*, pg. 3093
COFACE RUS INSURANCE COMPANY ZAO—See Groupe BPCE; *Int'l*, pg. 3093
COFACE S.A.; *Int'l*, pg. 1690
COFACE SEGURO DE CREDITO MÉXICO S.A. DE C.V.—See Groupe BPCE; *Int'l*, pg. 3093
COFACE SERVICES—See Coface S.A.; *Int'l*, pg. 1691
COFACE SERVICIOS ESPANA S.L.—See Groupe BPCE; *Int'l*, pg. 3093
COFACE SIGORTA TURQUIE A.S—See Groupe BPCE; *Int'l*, pg. 3093
COFACE (SINGAPORE) PTE LTD.—See Groupe BPCE; *Int'l*, pg. 3092
COFACE SLOVAKIA INSURANCE SA—See Groupe BPCE; *Int'l*, pg. 3093
COFACE SOUTH AFRICA PTY LTD.—See Groupe BPCE; *Int'l*, pg. 3093
COFACE SVERIGE AB—See Groupe BPCE; *Int'l*, pg. 3093
COFACE SWITZERLAND SA—See Groupe BPCE; *Int'l*, pg. 3093
COFACE TAIWAN LIMITED—See Groupe BPCE; *Int'l*, pg. 3093
COFACE UK HOLDING LTD.—See Coface S.A.; *Int'l*, pg. 1691
COFACE UK SERVICES LIMITED—See Coface S.A.; *Int'l*, pg. 1691
COFALUX IMMOBILIERE S.A.—See Metro AG; *Int'l*, pg. 4859
COFAM S.R.L.—See KONE Oyj; *Int'l*, pg. 4247
COFC LOGISTICS, LLC; *U.S. Private*, pg. 960
COFCO ARGENTINA S.A.—See COFCO Limited; *Int'l*, pg. 1691
COFCO BIOTECHNOLOGY CO., LTD.; *Int'l*, pg. 1691
COFCO CAPITAL HOLDINGS CO., LTD.; *Int'l*, pg. 1691
COFCO CEREAL WAY FOODS CO., LTD.—See COFCO Limited; *Int'l*, pg. 1691
COFCO COMMERCIAL PROPERTY INVESTMENT CO., LTD.—See COFCO Limited; *Int'l*, pg. 1691
COFCO FOOD MARKETING SERVICES, CO., LTD.—See COFCO Limited; *Int'l*, pg. 1692
COFCO (HAINAN) INVESTMENT & DEVELOPMENT CO., LTD.—See COFCO Limited; *Int'l*, pg. 1691
COFCO (HONG KONG) CO., LTD.—See COFCO Limited; *Int'l*, pg. 1691
COFCO (JAPAN) CO., LTD.—See COFCO Limited; *Int'l*, pg. 1691
COFCO JOYCOME FOODS LIMITED; *Int'l*, pg. 1691
COFCO LE CONTE FOOD (SHENZHEN) CO., LTD.—See COFCO Limited; *Int'l*, pg. 1692
COFCO LECONTE FOODS (SHENZHEN) CO., LTD.—See COFCO Limited; *Int'l*, pg. 1691
COFCO LIMITED; *Int'l*, pg. 1691
COFCO (NEW YORK) CO., LTD.—See COFCO Limited; *Int'l*, pg. 1691
COFCO NUTRITION & HEALTH RESEARCH INSTITUTE CO. LTD.—See COFCO Limited; *Int'l*, pg. 1692
COFCO SHENZHEN CO., LTD.—See COFCO Limited; *Int'l*, pg. 1692
COFCO TECHNOLOGY & INDUSTRY CO., LTD.; *Int'l*, pg. 1692
COFCO TUNHE SUGAR CO., LTD.—See COFCO Limited; *Int'l*, pg. 1692
COFCO WINES & SPIRITS CO. LTD.—See COFCO Limited; *Int'l*, pg. 1692
COFEED FEEDMILL (CHANGCHUN) CO., LTD.—See CJ Corporation; *Int'l*, pg. 1633
COFEL—See Pikolin S.A.; *Int'l*, pg. 5865
COFEL—See Recticel S.A.; *Int'l*, pg. 6241
COFELY AG—See ENGIE SA; *Int'l*, pg. 2429
COFELY AG - WINTERTHUR—See ENGIE SA; *Int'l*, pg. 2429
COFELY AIRPORT & LOGISTICS SERVICES SA—See ENGIE SA; *Int'l*, pg. 2429
COFELY A.S.—See ENGIE SA; *Int'l*, pg. 2431
COFELY A.S.—See ENGIE SA; *Int'l*, pg. 2430
COFELY AXIMA—See ENGIE SA; *Int'l*, pg. 2429
COFELY DELTA CONTROLS BV—See ENGIE SA; *Int'l*, pg. 2430
COFELY DEUTSCHLAND GMBH—See ENGIE SA; *Int'l*, pg. 2429
COFELY DISTRICT ENERGY LTD—See ENGIE SA; *Int'l*, pg. 2429
COFELY ENDEL—See ENGIE SA; *Int'l*, pg. 2429
COFELY ENERGY SOLUTIONS BV—See ENGIE SA; *Int'l*, pg. 2430
COFELY EPULETGEPESZETI KFT.—See ENGIE SA; *Int'l*, pg. 2429

CORPORATE AFFILIATIONS

COFELY ESPANA, S.A.U. - BARCELONA—See ENGIE SA; *Int'l*, pg. 2430
COFELY ESPANA, S.A.U.—See ENGIE SA; *Int'l*, pg. 2430
COFELY FABRICOM S.A.—See ENGIE SA; *Int'l*, pg. 2429
COFELY FMO—See ENGIE SA; *Int'l*, pg. 2430
COFELY FM S.R.O.—See ENGIE SA; *Int'l*, pg. 2430
COFELY GEBAUDETECHNIK GMBH—See ENGIE SA; *Int'l*, pg. 2431
COFELY HELLAS A.E.—See ENGIE SA; *Int'l*, pg. 2430
COFELY INEO - INEO ENGINEERING & SYSTEMS DIVISION—See ENGIE SA; *Int'l*, pg. 2430
COFELY INEO—See ENGIE SA; *Int'l*, pg. 2430
COFELY ITALIA S.P.A.—See ENGIE SA; *Int'l*, pg. 2430
COFELY KALTETECHNIK GMBH—See ENGIE SA; *Int'l*, pg. 2430
COFELY LIMITED—See ENGIE SA; *Int'l*, pg. 2430
COFELY MOROCCO—See ENGIE SA; *Int'l*, pg. 2430
COFELY NEDERLAND N.V.—See ENGIE SA; *Int'l*, pg. 2430
COFELY NOORD BV—See ENGIE SA; *Int'l*, pg. 2430
COFELY PACIFIC—See ENGIE SA; *Int'l*, pg. 2430
COFELY PORTUGAL—See ENGIE SA; *Int'l*, pg. 2430
COFELY REFRIGERATION BV—See ENGIE SA; *Int'l*, pg. 2430
COFELY REFRIGERATION GMBH—See ENGIE SA; *Int'l*, pg. 2430
COFELY SERVICES INC.—See ENGIE SA; *Int'l*, pg. 2430
COFELY SERVICES SA/NV - LIEGE—See ENGIE SA; *Int'l*, pg. 2430
COFELY SERVICES SA/NV - MECHELEN—See ENGIE SA; *Int'l*, pg. 2430
COFELY SERVICES SA/NV—See ENGIE SA; *Int'l*, pg. 2429
COFELY SERVICES S.A.—See ENGIE SA; *Int'l*, pg. 2430
COFELY SERVICES—See ENGIE SA; *Int'l*, pg. 2430
COFELY SERVICES SP. Z O.O.—See ENGIE SA; *Int'l*, pg. 2430
COFELY SOUTH EAST ASIA PTE. LTD.—See ENGIE SA; *Int'l*, pg. 2430
COFELY TERMIKA—See ENGIE SA; *Int'l*, pg. 2430
COFELY (THAILAND) PTE. LTD.—See ENGIE SA; *Int'l*, pg. 2430
COFELY VANUATU—See ENGIE SA; *Int'l*, pg. 2430
COFELY WEST INDUSTRIE BV—See ENGIE SA; *Int'l*, pg. 2430
COFELY WEST NEDERLAND BV—See ENGIE SA; *Int'l*, pg. 2430
COFELY WORKPLACE LIMITED—See ENGIE SA; *Int'l*, pg. 2430
COFELY ZUID NEDERLAND BV—See ENGIE SA; *Int'l*, pg. 2430
COFEX GTM TRAVAUX SPECIAUX SAS—See VINCI S.A.; *Int'l*, pg. 8235
COFEX LITTORAL S.N.C.—See VINCI S.A.; *Int'l*, pg. 8216
COFEX MEDITERRANEE SAS—See VINCI S.A.; *Int'l*, pg. 8235
COFFEE AMERICA (USA) CORPORATION; *U.S. Private*, pg. 961
THE COFFEE BEANERY LTD.; *U.S. Private*, pg. 961
THE COFFEE COMPANY B.V.—See JAB Holding Company S.a.r.l.; *Int'l*, pg. 3862
COFFEECOMPANY HOLDING B.V.—See JAB Holding Company S.a.r.l.; *Int'l*, pg. 3862
COFFEE CONTACT (PROPRIETARY) LIMITED—See Famous Brands Limited; *Int'l*, pg. 2612
COFFEE CUP FUEL STOP, INC.—See Coffee Cup Fuel Stops & Convenience Stores, Inc.; *U.S. Private*, pg. 961
COFFEE CUP FUEL STOPS & CONVENIENCE STORES, INC.; *U.S. Private*, pg. 961
COFFEECUP SOFTWARE INC.; *U.S. Private*, pg. 961
COFFEE DAY ENTERPRISES LIMITED—See Affirma Capital Limited; *Int'l*, pg. 187
COFFEE DAY GLOBAL LIMITED—See Affirma Capital Limited; *Int'l*, pg. 187
COFFEE DAY GLOBAL LTD. - CAFE COFFEE DAY DIVISION—See Affirma Capital Limited; *Int'l*, pg. 187
COFFEE DAY GLOBAL LTD. - EXPORTS DIVISION—See Affirma Capital Limited; *Int'l*, pg. 187
COFFEE DAY GLOBAL LTD. - FRESH & GROUND DIVISION—See Affirma Capital Limited; *Int'l*, pg. 187
COFFEE DAY GLOBAL LTD. - VENDING DIVISION—See Affirma Capital Limited; *Int'l*, pg. 187
COFFEE DIGITAL LLC—See Vivendi SE; *Int'l*, pg. 8271
COFFEE DISTRIBUTING CORP.; *U.S. Private*, pg. 961
COFFEE FOR LESS; *U.S. Private*, pg. 961
COFFEE GMBH—See Bechtle AG; *Int'l*, pg. 937
COFFEE HOLDING COMPANY, INC.; *U.S. Public*, pg. 522
COFFEE INC.; *U.S. Public*, pg. 522
COFFEE KINETICS, L.L.C.—See Coffee Holding Company, Inc.; *U.S. Public*, pg. 522
COFFEE MAME KOUBOU CO., LTD.—See Kobe Bussan Co., Ltd.; *Int'l*, pg. 4217
COFFEE MARK PRODUCTS SDN. BHD.—See Zhulian Corporation Berhad; *Int'l*, pg. 8679
COFFEE NATION LIMITED—See Whitbread PLC; *Int'l*, pg. 8398
COFFEE PARTNERS LP—See Horizon Holdings LLC; *U.S. Private*, pg. 1981

COMPANY NAME INDEX

COFFEE REGIONAL MEDICAL CENTER, INC.; *U.S. Private*, pg. 961
COFFEE REPUBLIC TRADING LTD.; *Int'l*, pg. 1692
COFFEE REPUBLIC (UK) LIMITED—See Coffee Republic Trading Ltd.; *Int'l*, pg. 1692
COFFEE TIME DONUTS INCORPORATED—See Chairman's Brands Corporation; *Int'l*, pg. 1437
THE COFFEE WORKS INC.; *U.S. Private*, pg. 4011
COFFENCO INTERNATIONAL GMBH—See JAB Holding Company S.a.r.l.; *Int'l*, pg. 3862
COFFEY INTERNATIONAL DEVELOPMENT HOLDINGS LIMITED—See Tetra Tech, Inc.; *U.S. Public*, pg. 2022
COFFEY INTERNATIONAL DEVELOPMENT LIMITED—See Tetra Tech, Inc.; *U.S. Public*, pg. 2022
COFFEY INTERNATIONAL DEVELOPMENT PTY. LTD.—See Tetra Tech, Inc.; *U.S. Public*, pg. 2022
COFFEY INTERNATIONAL DEVELOPMENT SP. Z.O.O.—See Tetra Tech, Inc.; *U.S. Public*, pg. 2022
COFFEY INTERNATIONAL LIMITED—See Tetra Tech, Inc.; *U.S. Public*, pg. 2022
COFFEY MINING PTY. LTD.—See Tetra Tech, Inc.; *U.S. Public*, pg. 2022
COFFEY MINING (SOUTH AFRICA) PTY. LTD.—See Tetra Tech, Inc.; *U.S. Public*, pg. 2022
COFFEY PROJECTS (AUSTRALIA) PTY. LTD.—See Tetra Tech, Inc.; *U.S. Public*, pg. 2022
COFFEY PROJECTS (NEW ZEALAND) LIMITED—See Tetra Tech, Inc.; *U.S. Public*, pg. 2022
COFFEYVILLE FINANCE INC.—See Icahn Enterprises L.P.; *U.S. Public*, pg. 1084
COFFEYVILLE NITROGEN FERTILIZERS, INC.—See Icahn Enterprises L.P.; *U.S. Public*, pg. 1084
COFFEYVILLE REGIONAL MEDICAL CENTER; *U.S. Private*, pg. 961
COFFEYVILLE RESOURCES CRUDE TRANSPORTATION, LLC—See Icahn Enterprises L.P.; *U.S. Public*, pg. 1084
COFFEYVILLE RESOURCES NITROGEN FERTILIZERS, LLC—See Icahn Enterprises L.P.; *U.S. Public*, pg. 1084
COFFEYVILLE RESOURCES REFINING & MARKETING, LLC—See Icahn Enterprises L.P.; *U.S. Public*, pg. 1084
COFFEYVILLE RESOURCES TERMINAL, LLC—See Icahn Enterprises L.P.; *U.S. Public*, pg. 1084
COFFIN TURBO PUMP INC.; *U.S. Private*, pg. 961
COFFMAN & COMPANY GROUP—See The SEER Group LLC; *U.S. Private*, pg. 4115
COFFMAN ENGINEERS, INC. - ANCHORAGE OFFICE—See Coffman Engineers, Inc.; *U.S. Private*, pg. 961
COFFMAN ENGINEERS, INC. - HONOLULU OFFICE—See Coffman Engineers, Inc.; *U.S. Private*, pg. 961
COFFMAN ENGINEERS, INC.; *U.S. Private*, pg. 961
COFFMAN ENGINEERS, INC. - SPOKANE OFFICE—See Coffman Engineers, Inc.; *U.S. Private*, pg. 961
COFFMAN EXCAVATION INC.; *U.S. Private*, pg. 961
COFFMAN INTERNATIONAL INC.; *U.S. Private*, pg. 961
COFFMAN TRUCK SALES, INC.; *U.S. Private*, pg. 961
COFFS CENTRAL PTY. LTD.—See Gowing Brothers Limited; *Int'l*, pg. 3044
COFHYLUX SA—See BNP Paribas SA; *Int'l*, pg. 1090
COFI-COM TRADING PTY LIMITED—See ED&F Man Holdings Limited; *Int'l*, pg. 2302
COFIDUR SA; *Int'l*, pg. 1692
COFIELD LIMITED—See Telecom Plus Plc; *Int'l*, pg. 7530
COFILMACCHINE S.R.L.—See Komax Holding AG; *Int'l*, pg. 4240
COFIMCO FAN (CHANGSHU) CO., LTD.—See Chart Industries, Inc.; *U.S. Public*, pg. 481
COFIMCO INTERNATIONAL (SHANGHAI) TRADING CO, INC.—See Chart Industries, Inc.; *U.S. Public*, pg. 481
COFIMCO S.R.L.—See Chart Industries, Inc.; *U.S. Public*, pg. 481
COFINA MEDIA, SGPS, S.A.—See Cofina SGPS, S.A.; *Int'l*, pg. 1692
COFINA SGPS, S.A.; *Int'l*, pg. 1692
COFINIMMO S.A./N.V.; *Int'l*, pg. 1692
COFINITY, INC.—See CVS Health Corporation; *U.S. Public*, pg. 614
COFINLUXE S.A.; *Int'l*, pg. 1692
COFINOGA S.A.—See BNP Paribas SA; *Int'l*, pg. 1091
COFINOGA S.A.—See Galeries Lafayette SA; *Int'l*, pg. 2872
COFINTEX 6 SA—See Groupama SA; *Int'l*, pg. 3090
COFIPARC SNC—See BNP Paribas SA; *Int'l*, pg. 1090
COFIROASTERS S.A.—See Segafredo Zanetti S.p.A.; *Int'l*, pg. 6681
COFIROUTE CORPORATION—See VINCI S.A.; *Int'l*, pg. 8230
COFIROUTE SA—See VINCI S.A.; *Int'l*, pg. 8230
COFIROUTE UK LTD—See VINCI S.A.; *Int'l*, pg. 8230
COFIX GROUP LTD.; *Int'l*, pg. 1692
COFLE DO BRASIL LTDA.—See Cofle SpA; *Int'l*, pg. 1693
COFLE SPA; *Int'l*, pg. 1692
COFLE TK OTOMOTIV AS—See Cofle SpA; *Int'l*, pg. 1693
COFLUSA S.A.; *Int'l*, pg. 1693
COFOE MEDICAL TECHNOLOGY CO., LTD.; *Int'l*, pg. 1693
C&O FOOD SERVICES INC.; *U.S. Private*, pg. 703

COFORGE ADVANTAGEGO LIMITED—See Coforge Ltd.; *Int'l*, pg. 1693
COFORGE AIRLINE TECHNOLOGIES GMBH—See Coforge Ltd.; *Int'l*, pg. 1693
COFORGE BV—See Coforge Ltd.; *Int'l*, pg. 1693
COFORGE DPA IRELAND LIMITED—See Coforge Ltd.; *Int'l*, pg. 1693
COFORGE DPA PRIVATE LTD.—See Coforge Ltd.; *Int'l*, pg. 1693
COFORGE GMBH—See Coforge Ltd.; *Int'l*, pg. 1693
COFORGE INC.—See Coforge Ltd.; *Int'l*, pg. 1693
COFORGE LIMITED—See Coforge Ltd.; *Int'l*, pg. 1693
COFORGE LTD.; *Int'l*, pg. 1693
COFORGE S.A.—See Coforge Ltd.; *Int'l*, pg. 1693
COFORGE SMARTSERVE LTD.—See Coforge Ltd.; *Int'l*, pg. 1693
COFORGE U.K. LIMITED—See Coforge Ltd.; *Int'l*, pg. 1693
COFOR S.A.—See VINCI S.A.; *Int'l*, pg. 8217
COFRA B.V.—See HAL Trust N.V.; *Int'l*, pg. 3225
COFRA DUSSELDORF GMBH—See COFRA Holding AG; *Int'l*, pg. 1694
COFRA HOLDING AG; *Int'l*, pg. 1693
COFRA LIMITED—See HAL Trust N.V.; *Int'l*, pg. 3226
CO-FREE INCORPORATED; *U.S. Private*, pg. 953
COFREN S.A.S.—See Westinghouse Air Brake Technologies Corporation; *U.S. Public*, pg. 2357
COFREN S.R.L.—See Westinghouse Air Brake Technologies Corporation; *U.S. Public*, pg. 2357
COFRESCO FRISCHHALTEPRODUKTE EUROPA—See Melitta Unternehmensgruppe Bentz KG; *Int'l*, pg. 4810
COFRESCO PM S.A.S—See Melitta Unternehmensgruppe Bentz KG; *Int'l*, pg. 4810
COFRESCO POLSKA SP.ZO.O.—See Melitta Unternehmensgruppe Bentz KG; *Int'l*, pg. 4810
COFRETH (M) SDN BHD—See IJM Corporation Berhad; *Int'l*, pg. 3608
COFRISET S.A.S.—See Beijer Ref AB; *Int'l*, pg. 944
COGAS ENERGIE B.V.—See ENGIE SA; *Int'l*, pg. 2431
COGDALL CONSTRUCTION CO.; *U.S. Private*, pg. 962
COGDEV MALAYSIA SDN BHD—See Cognizant Technology Solutions Corporation; *U.S. Public*, pg. 523
COGDILL FARM SUPPLY INC.; *U.S. Private*, pg. 962
COGECO CABLE ONTARIO—See Gestion Audem, Inc.; *Int'l*, pg. 2946
COGECO CABLE QUEBEC—See Gestion Audem, Inc.; *Int'l*, pg. 2946
COGECO COMMUNICATIONS INC.—See Gestion Audem, Inc.; *Int'l*, pg. 2946
COGECO INC.—See Gestion Audem, Inc.; *Int'l*, pg. 2946
COGECO MEDIA INC.—See Gestion Audem, Inc.; *Int'l*, pg. 2946
COGECO PEER 1—See DigitalBridge Group, Inc.; *U.S. Public*, pg. 664
COGEDIM MIDI-PYRENEES—See Altarea SCA; *Int'l*, pg. 385
COGEDIM RESIDENCES SERVICES SNC—See Altarea SCA; *Int'l*, pg. 385
COGEDIM SAS—See Altarea SCA; *Int'l*, pg. 385
COGEDIM SAVOIES-LEMAN SNC—See Altarea SCA; *Int'l*, pg. 385
COGELEC SA; *Int'l*, pg. 1694
COGENCIS INFORMATION SERVICES LTD.—See Samara Capital Management Ltd.; *Int'l*, pg. 6501
COGENCY GLOBAL INC.—See Bertram Capital Management, LLC; *U.S. Private*, pg. 540
COGENCY SOFTWARE, INC.—See Backstop Solutions Group, LLC; *U.S. Private*, pg. 423
COGEN ENERGIA ESPANA S.L—See Arendals Fossekompani ASA; *Int'l*, pg. 558
COGENEX CORPORATION—See Constellation Energy Corporation; *U.S. Public*, pg. 571
COGENIC, LLC; *U.S. Private*, pg. 962
COGENINFRA SPA; *Int'l*, pg. 1694
COGENT B2B LTD.; *Int'l*, pg. 1694
COGENT (BEIJING) TECHNOLOGY COMPANY LIMITED—See Century Sage Scientific Holdings Limited; *Int'l*, pg. 1419
COGENT BIOSCIENCES, INC.; *U.S. Public*, pg. 522
COGENT CANADA, INC.—See Cogent Communications Holdings, Inc.; *U.S. Public*, pg. 522
COGENT COMMUNICATIONS DENMARK APS—See Cogent Communications Holdings, Inc.; *U.S. Public*, pg. 522
COGENT COMMUNICATIONS ESPANA SA—See Cogent Communications Holdings, Inc.; *U.S. Public*, pg. 522
COGENT COMMUNICATIONS FRANCE SAS—See Cogent Communications Holdings, Inc.; *U.S. Public*, pg. 522
COGENT COMMUNICATIONS HOLDINGS, INC.; *U.S. Public*, pg. 522
COGENT COMMUNICATIONS, INC.—See Cogent Communications Holdings, Inc.; *U.S. Public*, pg. 522
COGENT COMMUNICATIONS NETHERLANDS B.V.—See Cogent Communications Holdings, Inc.; *U.S. Public*, pg. 522
COGENT COMMUNICATIONS NORDICS—See Cogent Communications Holdings, Inc.; *U.S. Public*, pg. 522

COGNEX CORPORATION

COGENT COMMUNICATIONS POLAND SP. Z O.O.—See Cogent Communications Holdings, Inc.; *U.S. Public*, pg. 522
COGENT COMMUNICATIONS SWEDEN AB—See Cogent Communications Holdings, Inc.; *U.S. Public*, pg. 522
COGENT COMMUNICATIONS UK LTD.—See Cogent Communications Holdings, Inc.; *U.S. Public*, pg. 522
COGENT DATA SOLUTIONS, LLC; *U.S. Private*, pg. 962
COGENT DEVELOPMENT GROUP LIMITED; *Int'l*, pg. 1694
COGENT ELLIOT; *Int'l*, pg. 1695
COGENT ENERGY PTY LTD—See Origin Energy Ltd.; *Int'l*, pg. 5630
COGENT HEALTHCARE, INC.—See UnitedHealth Group Incorporated; *U.S. Public*, pg. 2240
COGENT HMG, INC.; *U.S. Private*, pg. 962
COGENT HOLDINGS LIMITED—See China COSCO Shipping Corporation Limited; *Int'l*, pg. 1492
COGENT, INC.; *U.S. Private*, pg. 962
COGENT INDUSTRIAL TECHNOLOGIES LTD.—See Kadant Inc.; *U.S. Public*, pg. 1212
COGENTIX MEDICAL, INC.—See Investor AB; *Int'l*, pg. 3786
COGENT LATVIA SIA—See Cogent Communications Holdings, Inc.; *U.S. Public*, pg. 522
COGENT OA LIMITED—See Informa plc; *Int'l*, pg. 3691
COGENT POWER, INC.—See Tata Sons Limited; *Int'l*, pg. 7471
COGENT POWER LTD.—See Tata Sons Limited; *Int'l*, pg. 7471
COGENTRIX ENERGY POWER MANAGEMENT, LLC—See The Carlyle Group Inc.; *U.S. Public*, pg. 2045
COGENT TECHNOLOGIES, INC.—See Engage Technologies Corp.; *U.S. Private*, pg. 1397
COGESA S.P.A.—See ACS, Actividades de Construccion y Servicios, S.A.; *Int'l*, pg. 110
COGES ESPANA MEDIOS DE PAGO, S.L.—See AZKOYEN S.A; *Int'l*, pg. 780
COGES FRANCE, S.A.S.—See AZKOYEN S.A.; *Int'l*, pg. 780
COGES S.P.A.—See AZKOYEN S.A.; *Int'l*, pg. 780
COG FINANCIAL SERVICES LIMITED; *Int'l*, pg. 1694
COGGIN AUTOMOTIVE CORP.—See Asbury Automotive Group, Inc.; *U.S. Public*, pg. 209
COGGIN & FAIRCHILD ENVIRONMENTAL CONSULTANTS, INC.; *U.S. Private*, pg. 962
COGGIN FORD—See Asbury Automotive Group, Inc.; *U.S. Public*, pg. 209
COGHLIN CONSTRUCTION SERVICE; *U.S. Private*, pg. 962
COGIFRANCE SA; *Int'l*, pg. 1695
COGIR LIMITEE—See ENL Limited; *Int'l*, pg. 2441
COGIR MANAGEMENT CORPORATION - ONTARIO DIVISION—See COGIR Management Corporation; *Int'l*, pg. 1695
COGIR MANAGEMENT CORPORATION; *Int'l*, pg. 1695
COGISCAN INC.—See Durr AG; *Int'l*, pg. 2230
COGITO MEDIA GROUP INC.; *Int'l*, pg. 1695
COGIT SA—See VINCI S.A.; *Int'l*, pg. 8216
COG MARKETERS LTD.; *U.S. Private*, pg. 961
COGMED SYSTEMS AB—See Pearson plc; *Int'l*, pg. 5775
COGNAC FERRAND SASU; *Int'l*, pg. 1695
COGNAC GAUTIER SA—See Marie Brizard Wine & Spirits S.A.; *Int'l*, pg. 4693
COGNA EDUCACAO S.A.; *Int'l*, pg. 1695
COGNATE BIOSERVICES, INC.—See Charles River Laboratories International, Inc.; *U.S. Public*, pg. 480
COGNE ACCIAI SPECIALI S.P.A.—See Walsin Lihwa Corporation; *Int'l*, pg. 8334
COGNETIVITY NEUROSCIENCES LTD.; *Int'l*, pg. 1695
COGNETIX, INC.; *U.S. Private*, pg. 962
COGNEX CORPORATION; *U.S. Public*, pg. 522
COGNEX FRANCE—See Cognex Corporation; *U.S. Public*, pg. 523
COGNEX GERMANY, INC.—See Cognex Corporation; *U.S. Public*, pg. 523
COGNEX HUNGARY KFT.—See Cognex Corporation; *U.S. Public*, pg. 523
COGNEX INTERNATIONAL, INC.—See Cognex Corporation; *U.S. Public*, pg. 523
COGNEX K.K.—See Cognex Corporation; *U.S. Public*, pg. 523
COGNEX MALAYSIA SDN. BHD.—See Cognex Corporation; *U.S. Public*, pg. 523
COGNEX POLAND Z.O.O—See Cognex Corporation; *U.S. Public*, pg. 523
COGNEX SINGAPORE MANUFACTURING PTE. LTD.—See Cognex Corporation; *U.S. Public*, pg. 523
COGNEX UK LTD.—See Cognex Corporation; *U.S. Public*, pg. 523
COGNEX VIETNAM COMPANY LTD.—See Cognex Corporation; *U.S. Public*, pg. 523
COGNEX VISION THAILAND LIMITED—See Cognex Corporation; *U.S. Public*, pg. 523
COGNIGEN CORPORATION—See Simulations Plus, Inc.; *U.S. Public*, pg. 1884
COGNIS AUSTRALIA PTY. LTD.—See BASF SE; *Int'l*, pg. 883

COGNIS CHEMICALS (CHINA) CO. LTD.—See BASF SE; *Int'l*, pg. 883
COGNIS FRANCE S.A.S.—See BASF SE; *Int'l*, pg. 883
COGNIS GMBH - ILLERTISSEN—See BASF SE; *Int'l*, pg. 883
COGNIS GMBH—See BASF SE; *Int'l*, pg. 883
COGNIS OLEOCHEMICALS (MALAYSIA) SDN. BHD.—See PTT Global Chemical Public Company Limited; *Int'l*, pg. 6091
COGNIS OLEOCHEMICALS (MALAYSIA) SDN. BHD.—See Sime Darby Berhad; *Int'l*, pg. 6928
COGNIS S.A.—See BASF SE; *Int'l*, pg. 883
COGNIS THAI LTD.—See BASF SE; *Int'l*, pg. 883
COGNITA SCHOOLS LIMITED; *Int'l*, pg. 1695
COGNITAS GMBH—See Etteplan Oyj; *Int'l*, pg. 2524
COGNITEC SYSTEMS GMBH; *Int'l*, pg. 1695
COGNITEC SYSTEMS PTY LTD—See Cognitec Systems GmbH; *Int'l*, pg. 1695
COGNITION FINANCIAL CORPORATION—See Lobster Point Properties Ltd.; *Int'l*, pg. 4539
COGNITION HOLDINGS LIMITED—See Caxton and CTP Publishers and Printers Ltd.; *Int'l*, pg. 1363
COGNITION THERAPEUTICS, INC.; *U.S. Public*, pg. 523
COGNITIVE CONSULTING SDN. BHD.—See Censof Holdings Berhad; *Int'l*, pg. 1401
COGNITIV, INC.; *U.S. Public*, pg. 523
COGNITO SOFTWARE LIMITED—See Onzima Ventures PLC; *Int'l*, pg. 5593
COGNITO THERAPEUTICS, INC.; *U.S. Private*, pg. 962
COGNITRAN INC.—See Snap-on Incorporated; *U.S. Public*, pg. 1897
COGNITRAN LIMITED—See Snap-on Incorporated; *U.S. Public*, pg. 1897
COGNITRAN SP. Z O.O.—See Snap-on Incorporated; *U.S. Public*, pg. 1897
COGNIUS, INC.; *U.S. Private*, pg. 962
COGNIX GROUP LTD.—See Datamatics Consultants Inc.; *U.S. Private*, pg. 1166
COGNIZANT CONSULTING AND SERVICES GMBH—See Cognizant Technology Solutions Corporation; *U.S. Public*, pg. 523
COGNIZANT EL SALVADOR, SOCIEDAD ANONIMA DE CAPITAL VARIABLE—See Cognizant Technology Solutions Corporation; *U.S. Public*, pg. 523
COGNIZANT JAPAN KK—See Cognizant Technology Solutions Corporation; *U.S. Public*, pg. 523
COGNIZANT MOBILITY GMBH—See Cognizant Technology Solutions Corporation; *U.S. Public*, pg. 523
COGNIZANT MORTGAGE SERVICES CORPORATION—See Cognizant Technology Solutions Corporation; *U.S. Public*, pg. 523
COGNIZANT TECHNOLOGY SOLUTIONS A.G.—See Cognizant Technology Solutions Corporation; *U.S. Public*, pg. 524
COGNIZANT TECHNOLOGY SOLUTIONS ASIA PACIFIC PTE LTD.—See Cognizant Technology Solutions Corporation; *U.S. Public*, pg. 524
COGNIZANT TECHNOLOGY SOLUTIONS AUSTRALIA PTY. LTD.—See Cognizant Technology Solutions Corporation; *U.S. Public*, pg. 524
COGNIZANT TECHNOLOGY SOLUTIONS AUSTRALIA PTY. LTD.—See Cognizant Technology Solutions Corporation; *U.S. Public*, pg. 524
COGNIZANT TECHNOLOGY SOLUTIONS BELGIUM S.A.—See Cognizant Technology Solutions Corporation; *U.S. Public*, pg. 524
COGNIZANT TECHNOLOGY SOLUTIONS BENELUX B.V.—See Cognizant Technology Solutions Corporation; *U.S. Public*, pg. 524
COGNIZANT TECHNOLOGY SOLUTIONS CORPORATION; *U.S. Public*, pg. 523
COGNIZANT TECHNOLOGY SOLUTIONS DE ARGENTINA S.R.L.—See Cognizant Technology Solutions Corporation; *U.S. Public*, pg. 524
COGNIZANT TECHNOLOGY SOLUTIONS DENMARK APS—See Cognizant Technology Solutions Corporation; *U.S. Public*, pg. 524
COGNIZANT TECHNOLOGY SOLUTIONS FRANCE S.A.—See Cognizant Technology Solutions Corporation; *U.S. Public*, pg. 524
COGNIZANT TECHNOLOGY SOLUTIONS GMBH—See Cognizant Technology Solutions Corporation; *U.S. Public*, pg. 524
COGNIZANT TECHNOLOGY SOLUTIONS HUNGARY KFT—See Cognizant Technology Solutions Corporation; *U.S. Public*, pg. 524
COGNIZANT TECHNOLOGY SOLUTIONS INDIA PVT. LIMITED—See Cognizant Technology Solutions Corporation; *U.S. Public*, pg. 524
COGNIZANT TECHNOLOGY SOLUTIONS INDIA PVT. LTD.—See Cognizant Technology Solutions Corporation; *U.S. Public*, pg. 524
COGNIZANT TECHNOLOGY SOLUTIONS LITHUANIA, UAB—See Cognizant Technology Solutions Corporation; *U.S. Public*, pg. 524
COGNIZANT TECHNOLOGY SOLUTIONS (NETHERLANDS) B.V.—See Cognizant Technology Solutions Corporation; *U.S. Public*, pg. 523

COGNIZANT TECHNOLOGY SOLUTIONS NEW ZEALAND LIMITED—See Cognizant Technology Solutions Corporation; *U.S. Public*, pg. 524
COGNIZANT TECHNOLOGY SOLUTIONS NORWAY A.S.—See Cognizant Technology Solutions Corporation; *U.S. Public*, pg. 524
COGNIZANT TECHNOLOGY SOLUTIONS PHILIPPINES, INC.—See Cognizant Technology Solutions Corporation; *U.S. Public*, pg. 524
COGNIZANT TECHNOLOGY SOLUTIONS (SHANGHAI) CO., LTD.—See Cognizant Technology Solutions Corporation; *U.S. Public*, pg. 523
COGNIZANT TECHNOLOGY SOLUTIONS—See Cognizant Technology Solutions Corporation; *U.S. Public*, pg. 523
COGNIZANT TECHNOLOGY SOLUTIONS SWEDEN AB—See Cognizant Technology Solutions Corporation; *U.S. Public*, pg. 524
COGNIZANT TECHNOLOGY SOLUTIONS UK LIMITED—See Cognizant Technology Solutions Corporation; *U.S. Public*, pg. 524
COGNIZANT TECHNOLOGY SOLUTIONS U.S. CORPORATION—See Cognizant Technology Solutions Corporation; *U.S. Public*, pg. 524
COGNOR HOLDING S.A.; *Int'l*, pg. 1695
COGNOSANTE LLC—See Accenture plc; *Int'l*, pg. 85
COGNYTE SOFTWARE LTD.; *Int'l*, pg. 1695
COGO'S CO.—See Coen Oil Company; *U.S. Private*, pg. 960
COGRA S.A.; *Int'l*, pg. 1695
COGSDALE CORPORATION—See Constellation Software Inc.; *Int'l*, pg. 1774
COGSDILL-NUNEATON, LTD.—See Cogsdill Tool Products, Inc.; *U.S. Private*, pg. 962
COGSDILL TOOL PRODUCTS, INC.; *U.S. Private*, pg. 962
COGSTATE HEALTHCARE LLC—See CogState Limited; *Int'l*, pg. 1695
COGSTATE LIMITED; *Int'l*, pg. 1695
COGSWELL MOTORS INC.; *U.S. Private*, pg. 962
COGUN INC.; *U.S. Private*, pg. 962
COHASSET MARINER—See Gannett Co., Inc.; *U.S. Public*, pg. 902
COHAS VIETNAM CO., LTD.—See JP Holdings, Inc.; *Int'l*, pg. 4005
COHBAR, INC.; *U.S. Public*, pg. 525
COHEMI GROUP GMBH—See Silver Investment Partners GmbH & Co. KG; *Int'l*, pg. 6923
COHEN BROTHERS, INC.; *U.S. Private*, pg. 962
COHEN & COMPAGNIE, SAS—See Cohen & Company Inc.; *U.S. Public*, pg. 526
COHEN & COMPANY INC.; *U.S. Public*, pg. 525
COHEN & COMPANY; *U.S. Private*, pg. 962
COHEN & COMPANY - ST. CLAIR SHORES—See Cohen & Company; *U.S. Private*, pg. 962
COHEN & COMPANY - YOUNGSTOWN OFFICE—See Cohen & Company; *U.S. Private*, pg. 962
COHEN DEVELOPMENT GAS & OIL LTD—See Delek Group Ltd.; *Int'l*, pg. 2011
COHEN FINANCIAL, LLC—See Truist Financial Corporation; *U.S. Public*, pg. 2199
COHEN FOODS, INC.; *U.S. Private*, pg. 962
COHEN FURNITURE COMPANY; *U.S. Private*, pg. 963
COHEN & GRIGSBY, P.C.—See Dentons Group; *U.S. Private*, pg. 1207
COHEN MEDIA GROUP, LLC; *U.S. Private*, pg. 963
COHEN MEDICAL ASSOCIATES LLC—See Medical Specialists of The Palm Beaches, Inc.; *U.S. Private*, pg. 2656
COHEN PARTNERS CO. LTD.; *Int'l*, pg. 1695
COHEN PARTNERS, LLC—See World Insurance Associates LLC; *U.S. Private*, pg. 4565
COHEN PRIVATE VENTURES, LLC; *U.S. Private*, pg. 963
COHEN-SELTZER, INC.—See Caisse de Depot et Placement du Quebec; *Int'l*, pg. 1256
COHEN-SELTZER, INC.—See KKR & Co. Inc.; *U.S. Public*, pg. 1265
COHEN'S FASHION OPTICAL INC.—See Houchens Industries, Inc.; *U.S. Private*, pg. 1989
COHEN'S HOME FURNISHINGS LTD.; *Int'l*, pg. 1695
COHEN & STEERS ASIA LIMITED—See Cohen & Steers, Inc.; *U.S. Public*, pg. 526
COHEN & STEERS CLOSED-END OPP FD, INC.; *U.S. Public*, pg. 526
COHEN & STEERS EUROPE S.A.—See Cohen & Steers, Inc.; *U.S. Public*, pg. 526
COHEN & STEERS, INC.; *U.S. Public*, pg. 526
COHEN & STEERS JAPAN, LLC—See Cohen & Steers, Inc.; *U.S. Public*, pg. 526
COHEN & STEERS LIMITED DURATION PREFERRED AND INCOME FUND, INC.; *U.S. Public*, pg. 526
COHEN & STEERS MLP INCOME & ENERGY OPP; *U.S. Public*, pg. 526
COHEN & STEERS REIT & PREFERRED INCOME FUND, INC.; *U.S. Public*, pg. 526
COHEN & STEERS SELECT PREFERRED & INCOME FUND, INC.; *U.S. Public*, pg. 526

COHEN & STEERS SINGAPORE PRIVATE LIMITED—See Cohen & Steers, Inc.; *U.S. Public*, pg. 526
COHEN & STEERS TOTAL RETURN REALTY FUND, INC.; *U.S. Public*, pg. 526
COHEN & STEERS UK LIMITED—See Cohen & Steers, Inc.; *U.S. Public*, pg. 526
COHERENT (BEIJING) COMMERCIAL COMPANY LTD.—See Coherent Corp.; *U.S. Public*, pg. 526
COHERENT BV—See Coherent Corp.; *U.S. Public*, pg. 527
COHERENT CORP.; *U.S. Public*, pg. 526
COHERENT CRYSTAL ASSOCIATES—See Coherent Corp.; *U.S. Public*, pg. 527
COHERENT DEOS—See Coherent Corp.; *U.S. Public*, pg. 527
COHERENT (DEUTSCHLAND) GMBH—See Coherent Corp.; *U.S. Public*, pg. 526
COHERENT EUROPE B.V.—See Coherent Corp.; *U.S. Public*, pg. 527
COHERENT FRANCE—See Coherent Corp.; *U.S. Public*, pg. 527
COHERENT GMBH—See Coherent Corp.; *U.S. Public*, pg. 527
COHERENT, INC.—See Coherent Corp.; *U.S. Public*, pg. 526
COHERENT ITALIA—See Coherent Corp.; *U.S. Public*, pg. 527
COHERENT ITALIA S.R.L.—See Coherent Corp.; *U.S. Public*, pg. 527
COHERENT JAPAN, INC.—See Coherent Corp.; *U.S. Public*, pg. 527
COHERENT JAPAN, INC.—See Coherent Corp.; *U.S. Public*, pg. 527
COHERENT KAISERSLAUTERN GMBH—See Coherent Corp.; *U.S. Public*, pg. 527
COHERENT KOREA CO., LTD.—See Coherent Corp.; *U.S. Public*, pg. 527
COHERENT KOREA LTD.—See Coherent Corp.; *U.S. Public*, pg. 527
COHERENT LASER INDIA PVT. LTD.—See Coherent Corp.; *U.S. Public*, pg. 527
COHERENT LASERSYSTEMS GMBH & CO. KG—See Coherent Corp.; *U.S. Public*, pg. 527
COHERENT PATH INC.—See Movable, Inc.; *U.S. Private*, pg. 2801
COHERENT - PORTLAND—See Coherent Corp.; *U.S. Public*, pg. 527
COHERENT SCOTLAND LTD.—See Coherent Corp.; *U.S. Public*, pg. 527
COHERENT SINGAPORE PTE., LTD.—See Coherent Corp.; *U.S. Public*, pg. 527
COHERENT SINGAPORE PTE LTD.—See Coherent Corp.; *U.S. Public*, pg. 527
COHERENT SOLUTIONS, INC.; *U.S. Private*, pg. 963
COHERENT SWITZERLAND AG—See Coherent Corp.; *U.S. Public*, pg. 527
COHERENT (U.K.) LTD.—See Coherent Corp.; *U.S. Public*, pg. 527
COHEREX MEDICAL, INC.—See Johnson & Johnson; *U.S. Public*, pg. 1194
COHERIS INFOCAT LTD.—See Coheris SA; *Int'l*, pg. 1695
COHERIS SA; *Int'l*, pg. 1695
COHERUS BIOSCIENCES, INC.; *U.S. Public*, pg. 529
COHESANT, INC.; *U.S. Private*, pg. 963
COHESION CORPORATION—See System One Holdings, LLC; *U.S. Private*, pg. 3906
COHESIVE CAPITAL PARTNERS; *U.S. Private*, pg. 963
COHESIVE INFORMATION SOLUTIONS, INC.; *U.S. Private*, pg. 963
COHESIVE TECHNOLOGIES INC.—See Thermo Fisher Scientific Inc.; *U.S. Public*, pg. 2145
COHIBA MINERALS LIMITED; *Int'l*, pg. 1695
COHN & GREGORY, INC.; *U.S. Private*, pg. 963
COHNREZNICK LLP - ATLANTA—See CohnReznick LLP; *U.S. Private*, pg. 963
COHNREZNICK LLP - BALTIMORE—See CohnReznick LLP; *U.S. Private*, pg. 963
COHNREZNICK LLP - BETHESDA—See CohnReznick LLP; *U.S. Private*, pg. 963
COHNREZNICK LLP - CHARLOTTE—See CohnReznick LLP; *U.S. Private*, pg. 963
COHNREZNICK LLP - EDISON—See CohnReznick LLP; *U.S. Private*, pg. 964
COHNREZNICK LLP - GLASTONBURY—See CohnReznick LLP; *U.S. Private*, pg. 964
COHNREZNICK LLP - ROSELAND—See CohnReznick LLP; *U.S. Private*, pg. 964
COHNREZNICK LLP - SACRAMENTO—See CohnReznick LLP; *U.S. Private*, pg. 964
COHNREZNICK LLP; *U.S. Private*, pg. 963
COHN ROBBINS HOLDINGS CORP.; *U.S. Public*, pg. 529
COHN WHOLESALE FRUIT & GROCERY; *U.S. Private*, pg. 963
COHN & WOLFE BENELUX—See WPP plc; *Int'l*, pg. 8469
COHN & WOLFE LIMITED—See WPP plc; *Int'l*, pg. 8469
COHN & WOLFE READ-POLAND—See WPP plc; *Int'l*, pg. 8469
COHN & WOLFE—See WPP plc; *Int'l*, pg. 8468

COMPANY NAME INDEX

COHN & WOLFE—See WPP plc; *Int'l*, pg. 8469
COHN & WOLFE—See WPP plc; *Int'l*, pg. 8469
COHN & WOLFE—See WPP plc; *Int'l*, pg. 8469
COHN & WOLFE—See WPP plc; *Int'l*, pg. 8469
COHN & WOLFE—See WPP plc; *Int'l*, pg. 8469
COHN & WOLFE—See WPP plc; *Int'l*, pg. 8469
COHN & WOLFE—See WPP plc; *Int'l*, pg. 8469
COHO DISTRIBUTING LLC; *U.S. Private*, pg. 964
COHORT AUSTRALIA PTY LTD—See Unity4 Holdings Pty Ltd; *Int'l*, pg. 8076
COHORT GLOBAL LIMITED—See Pureprofile Limited; *Int'l*, pg. 6122
COHORT PLC; *Int'l*, pg. 1695
COHUHD—See Cohu, Inc.; *U.S. Public*, pg. 529
COHU, INC.; *U.S. Public*, pg. 529
COHU MALAYSIA SDN. BHD.—See Cohu, Inc.; *U.S. Public*, pg. 529
COHU SEMICONDUCTOR TEST GMBH—See Cohu, Inc.; *U.S. Public*, pg. 529
COI CERAMICS, INC.—See Northrop Grumman Corporation; *U.S. Public*, pg. 1541
COI GMBH—See Certina Holding AG; *Int'l*, pg. 1423
COIG SA—See WASKO S.A.; *Int'l*, pg. 8352
COIL CONSTRUCTION INC.; *U.S. Private*, pg. 964
COIL COUNTS FORD & CHENEY, INC.; *U.S. Private*, pg. 964
COILCRAFT CPS—See Coilcraft, Inc.; *U.S. Private*, pg. 964
COILCRAFT CPS TAIWAN—See Coilcraft, Inc.; *U.S. Private*, pg. 964
COILCRAFT EUROPE LTD—See Coilcraft, Inc.; *U.S. Private*, pg. 964
COILCRAFT HONG KONG LTD.—See Coilcraft, Inc.; *U.S. Private*, pg. 964
COILCRAFT, INC.; *U.S. Private*, pg. 964
COILCRAFT JAPAN, INC.—See Coilcraft, Inc.; *U.S. Private*, pg. 964
COILCRAFT SINGAPORE PTE. LTD.—See Coilcraft, Inc.; *U.S. Private*, pg. 964
COILDNA GMBH—See AMAG Austria Metall AG; *Int'l*, pg. 408
COILHOSE PNEUMATICS INC.; *U.S. Private*, pg. 964
COILLTE LTD.; *Int'l*, pg. 1696
COILLTE NORTH/WESTERN REGION—See Coillte Ltd.; *Int'l*, pg. 1696
COILLTE PANEL PRODUCTS (UK) LIMITED—See Coillte Ltd.; *Int'l*, pg. 1696
COIL PLUS-ILLINOIS INC.—See Mitsubishi Corporation; *Int'l*, pg. 4941
COIL S.A./N.V.; *Int'l*, pg. 1696
COIL SA/NV—See Coil S.A./N.V.; *Int'l*, pg. 1696
COILS ELECTRONIC CO., LIMITED—See CEC International Holdings Limited; *Int'l*, pg. 1372
COILS ELECTRONIC (ZHONGSHAN) CO., LTD.—See CEC International Holdings Limited; *Int'l*, pg. 1372
COIL SERVICES (NORTH SEA) LIMITED—See NOV, Inc.; *U.S. Public*, pg. 1544
COILS INC.; *U.S. Private*, pg. 964
COILS PROPERTY MANAGEMENT LIMITED—See CEC International Holdings Limited; *Int'l*, pg. 1372
COIL STEELS (AUST) PTY LIMITED—See Commercial Metals Company; *U.S. Public*, pg. 546
COIL STEELS GROUP PTY LIMITED—See Commercial Metals Company; *U.S. Public*, pg. 546
COIL STEELS LONG PRODUCTS—See Commercial Metals Company; *U.S. Public*, pg. 546
COIL STEELS PROCESSING—See Commercial Metals Company; *U.S. Public*, pg. 546
COIL STEELS TRADING PTY LTD—See Commercial Metals Company; *U.S. Public*, pg. 546
COILS UNLIMITED—See Standex International; *U.S. Public*, pg. 1930
COIL-TRAN LLC—See discoverIE Group plc; *Int'l*, pg. 2133
COIL TUBING TECHNOLOGY, INC.; *U.S. Private*, pg. 964
COIMA RES SIIQ S.P.A.; *Int'l*, pg. 1696
COIMA RES S.P.A; *Int'l*, pg. 1696
COIMMUNE, INC.—See Genexine Inc.; *Int'l*, pg. 2923
COIMMUNE, INC.—See SCM Lifescience Co., Ltd.; *Int'l*, pg. 6649
COIMPA INDUSTRIAL LTDA.—See Umicore S.A./N.V.; *Int'l*, pg. 8024
COIN ACCEPTORS EUROPE LIMITED—See Coin Acceptors, Inc.; *U.S. Private*, pg. 964
COIN ACCEPTORS GMBH—See Coin Acceptors, Inc.; *U.S. Private*, pg. 964
COIN ACCEPTORS, INC.; *U.S. Private*, pg. 964
COIN ACCEPTORS, INC.—See Coin Acceptors, Inc.; *U.S. Private*, pg. 964
COIN ACCEPTORS PTY LTD—See Coin Acceptors, Inc.; *U.S. Private*, pg. 964
COINALDE POLSKA SP. Z.O.O.—See Mondragon Corporation; *Int'l*, pg. 5028
COINALDE, S. COOP.—See Mondragon Corporation; *Int'l*, pg. 5028
COINBASE ASSET MANAGEMENT, LLC—See Coinbase Global, Inc.; *U.S. Public*, pg. 530
COINBASE GLOBAL, INC.; *U.S. Public*, pg. 530

COIN CITADEL INC.; *U.S. Public*, pg. 530
COINCO INC.; *U.S. Private*, pg. 964
COIN CONSULTECH S.R.L.—See Iren S.p.A.; *Int'l*, pg. 3808
COINEX INC.; *U.S. Private*, pg. 964
COIN FURNITURE LIMITED—See DFS Furniture Ltd.; *Int'l*, pg. 2096
COINING, INC.—See AMETEK, Inc.; *U.S. Public*, pg. 116
COININVEST GMBH—See StoneX Group Inc.; *U.S. Public*, pg. 1951
COINMACH CORPORATION—See Pamplona Capital Management LLP; *Int'l*, pg. 5711
COIN METRICS LIMITED—See Vianet Group plc; *Int'l*, pg. 8183
COIN SERVICE EMPOLI S.P.A.—See IVS Group S.A.; *Int'l*, pg. 3848
COIN SERVICE NORD S.P.A.—See IVS Group S.A.; *Int'l*, pg. 3848
COINS FOR ANYTHING, INC.; *U.S. Private*, pg. 965
COINSHARES CAPITAL, LLC—See CoinShares International Limited; *Int'l*, pg. 1696
COINSHARES INTERNATIONAL LIMITED; *Int'l*, pg. 1696
COINSHARES (UK) LIMITED—See CoinShares International Limited; *Int'l*, pg. 1696
COINSILIUM GROUP LTD.; *Int'l*, pg. 1696
COINS PORTUGAL UNIP LDA—See Cotecna Inspection S.A.; *Int'l*, pg. 1816
COINSTAR LIMITED—See Apollo Global Management, Inc.; *U.S. Public*, pg. 150
COINSTAR, LLC—See Apollo Global Management, Inc.; *U.S. Public*, pg. 150
COIN WRAP INC.; *U.S. Private*, pg. 964
COISSA CORREDURIA INTERNACIONAL DE SEGUROS, S.L.—See Porsche Automobil Holding SE; *Int'l*, pg. 5932
COIT SERVICES, INC.; *U.S. Private*, pg. 965
COIT SERVICES PENNSYLVANIA INC—See Coit Services, Inc.; *U.S. Private*, pg. 965
COIT SERVICES—See Coit Services, Inc.; *U.S. Private*, pg. 965
COJAFEX B.V.—See McDermott International, Inc.; *U.S. Public*, pg. 1405
COJALI FRANCE S.A.R.L.—See Knorr-Bremse AG; *Int'l*, pg. 4210
COJALI ITALIA S.R.L.—See Knorr-Bremse AG; *Int'l*, pg. 4210
COJALI S.L.—See Knorr-Bremse AG; *Int'l*, pg. 4210
COJALI USA INC.—See Knorr-Bremse AG; *Int'l*, pg. 4210
COJAX OIL AND GAS CORPORATION; *U.S. Public*, pg. 530
COJOT OY—See Alaris Holdings Limited; *Int'l*, pg. 291
COKA DUVANSKA INDUSTRIJA A.D.; *Int'l*, pg. 1696
COKAL LIMITED; *Int'l*, pg. 1696
COKEM INTERNATIONAL LTD.; *U.S. Private*, pg. 965
COKE RESOURCES LIMITED; *Int'l*, pg. 1696
COKER GROUP HOLDINGS, LLC—See Trinity Hunt Management, L.P.; *U.S. Private*, pg. 4234
COKER TIRE COMPANY; *U.S. Private*, pg. 965
COKEVA, INC.—See TD Synnex Corp; *U.S. Public*, pg. 1984
COKING EQUIPMENT SUB-CO.—See Taiyuan Heavy Industry Co., Ltd.; *Int'l*, pg. 7427
COKINOS ENERGY CORPORATION; *U.S. Private*, pg. 965
COKINOS NATURAL GAS COMPANY—See Cokinos Energy Corporation; *U.S. Private*, pg. 965
COKOLEND A.D.; *Int'l*, pg. 1696
COKO-WERK GMBH & CO. KG; *Int'l*, pg. 1696
COKO WERK PLASTIK IMALAT SANAYI LIMITED—See Coko-Werk GmbH & Co. KG; *Int'l*, pg. 1696
COKO-WERK POLSKA SP. Z O.O.—See Coko-Werk GmbH & Co. KG; *Int'l*, pg. 1696
COKYVINA JOINT STOCK COMPANY; *Int'l*, pg. 1696
COLAB CLOUD PLATFORMS LIMITED; *Int'l*, pg. 1697
COLABOR GROUP INC.; *Int'l*, pg. 1697
COLABOR LP—See Colabor Group Inc.; *Int'l*, pg. 1697
COLADA CONTINUA CHILENA S.A.—See Prysmian S.p.A.; *Int'l*, pg. 6011
THE COLAD GROUP, INC.—See Bindagraphics Inc.; *U.S. Private*, pg. 560
COLAG E-MOBILITY GMBH—See TVS Motor Company Ltd.; *Int'l*, pg. 7989
COLA, INC.; *U.S. Private*, pg. 965
COLAMCO INC.; *U.S. Private*, pg. 965
COLAND HOLDINGS LIMITED; *Int'l*, pg. 1697
COLANDIS; *Int'l*, pg. 1697
COLAND PHARMACEUTICAL CO., LTD.—See Coland Holdings Limited; *Int'l*, pg. 1697
COLANGELO—See Omnicom Group Inc.; *U.S. Public*, pg. 1578
COLAN TOTTE.CO., LTD.; *Int'l*, pg. 1697
COLA RESOURCES LLC—See Constellation Energy Corporation; *U.S. Public*, pg. 571
COLART AMERICAS INC.—See Lindengruppen AB; *Int'l*, pg. 4510
COLART BENELUX B.V.—See Lindengruppen AB; *Int'l*, pg. 4510
COLART DEUTSCHLAND GMBH—See Lindengruppen AB; *Int'l*, pg. 4510

COLART FINE ART & GRAPHICS LTD—See Lindengruppen AB; *Int'l*, pg. 4510
COLART IBERICA SA—See Lindengruppen AB; *Int'l*, pg. 4510
COLART INTERNATIONAL HOLDINGS LTD.—See Lindengruppen AB; *Int'l*, pg. 4510
COLART INTERNATIONAL SA—See Lindengruppen AB; *Int'l*, pg. 4510
COLART ITALIANA SPA—See Lindengruppen AB; *Int'l*, pg. 4510
COLART SCANDINAVIA AB—See Lindengruppen AB; *Int'l*, pg. 4510
COLART TIANJIN ART MATERIALS CO LTD—See Lindengruppen AB; *Int'l*, pg. 4510
COLASANTI SPECIALTY SERVICES; *U.S. Private*, pg. 965
COLAS BELGIUM SA—See Bouygues S.A.; *Int'l*, pg. 1122
COLAS CANADA INC.—See Bouygues S.A.; *Int'l*, pg. 1122
COLAS CZ, A.S.—See Bouygues S.A.; *Int'l*, pg. 1122
COLAS DANMARK A/S—See Bouygues S.A.; *Int'l*, pg. 1122
COLAS GABON—See Bouygues S.A.; *Int'l*, pg. 1122
COLAS-HUNGARIA ZRT.—See Bouygues S.A.; *Int'l*, pg. 1122
COLAS INC.—See Bouygues S.A.; *Int'l*, pg. 1122
COLASKA INC.; *U.S. Private*, pg. 965
COLAS LTD—See Bouygues S.A.; *Int'l*, pg. 1122
COLAS MARTINIQUE—See Bouygues S.A.; *Int'l*, pg. 1123
COLAS POLSKA SP.Z.O.O—See Bouygues S.A.; *Int'l*, pg. 1123
COLAS RAIL—See Bouygues S.A.; *Int'l*, pg. 1123
COLAS SA—See Bouygues S.A.; *Int'l*, pg. 1122
COLAVITA USA, LLC; *U.S. Private*, pg. 965
COLAW RV SALES; *U.S. Private*, pg. 965
COLBEAR ADVERTISING LIMITED; *Int'l*, pg. 1697
COLBERT PACKAGING CORPORATION; *U.S. Private*, pg. 965
COLBOND BV—See Freudenberg SE; *Int'l*, pg. 2789
COLBOND GEOSYNTHETICS SARL—See Freudenberg SE; *Int'l*, pg. 2789
COLBOND GMBH AND CO. KG—See Freudenberg SE; *Int'l*, pg. 2789
COLBOND HOLDING BV—See Freudenberg SE; *Int'l*, pg. 2789
COLBOND INVESTMENTS BV—See Freudenberg SE; *Int'l*, pg. 2789
COLBOND (NEDERLAND) BVARNHEM—See Freudenberg SE; *Int'l*, pg. 2789
COLBUN S.A.; *Int'l*, pg. 1697
THE COLBURN CORP.—See Caisse de Depot et Placement du Quebec; *Int'l*, pg. 1256
THE COLBURN CORP.—See KKR & Co. Inc.; *U.S. Public*, pg. 1265
COLBYCO D.O.O.—See Yokogawa Electric Corporation; *Int'l*, pg. 8592
COLBY EQUIPMENT COMPANY INC.; *U.S. Private*, pg. 965
COLCAB (PTY) LTD.—See TRG Management LP; *U.S. Private*, pg. 4220
COLCHESTER LATHE COMPANY LTD—See The 600 Group PLC; *Int'l*, pg. 7609
COLCOM FOODS LIMITED—See Innscor Africa Ltd.; *Int'l*, pg. 3713
COLCOM GROUP S.P.A.—See SIMONSWERK GmbH; *Int'l*, pg. 6933
COLCOM HOLDINGS LIMITED—See Innscor Africa Ltd.; *Int'l*, pg. 3713
COLD AIR DISTRIBUTORS WAREHOUSE OF FLORIDA INC.—See TPH Acquisition, LLLP; *U.S. Private*, pg. 4200
COLD BOX INC.—See WillScot Mobile Mini Holdings Corp.; *U.S. Public*, pg. 2372
COLD CANYON LAND FILL, INC.—See Waste Connections, Inc.; *Int'l*, pg. 8353
COLD CHAIN TECHNOLOGIES, INC.—See Aurora Capital Group, LLC; *U.S. Private*, pg. 393
COLD DRAWN PRODUCTS LTD—See NV Bekaert SA; *Int'l*, pg. 5496
COLDER PRODUCTS COMPANY LTD—See Dover Corporation; *U.S. Public*, pg. 679
COLDER PRODUCTS COMPANY—See Dover Corporation; *U.S. Public*, pg. 679
COLDER'S INC.; *U.S. Private*, pg. 966
COLD HEADING CO.; *U.S. Private*, pg. 965
COLDIRON COMPANIES, INC.; *U.S. Private*, pg. 966
COLD JET LLC; *U.S. Private*, pg. 965
COLD LAKE PIPELINE LIMITED PARTNERSHIP—See Brookfield Infrastructure Partners L.P.; *Int'l*, pg. 1193
COLDLIGHT SOLUTIONS, LLC—See PTC Inc.; *U.S. Public*, pg. 1734
COLDQUANTA, INC.; *U.S. Private*, pg. 966
COLD RIVER LAND, LLC—See CBRE Group, Inc.; *U.S. Public*, pg. 460
COLD SPRING BREWING CO.; *U.S. Private*, pg. 965
COLD SPRING CAPITAL LLC.; *U.S. Private*, pg. 965
COLD SPRING GRANITE (CANADA) LTD.—See Cold Spring Granite Company; *U.S. Private*, pg. 965
COLD SPRING GRANITE COMPANY; *U.S. Private*, pg. 965

COLD SPRING GRANITE CO.—See Cold Spring Granite Company; *U.S. Private*, pg. 965
COLD SPRING HARBOR LABORATORY; *U.S. Private*, pg. 966
COLD SPRINGS FARMS LIMITED—See Maple Leaf Foods, Inc.; *Int'l*, pg. 4686
COLD STONE CREAMERY, INC.—See Kahala Corp.; *U.S. Private*, pg. 2254
COLD STONE CREAMERY TAIWAN LTD.—See Uni-President Enterprises Corporation; *Int'l*, pg. 8028
COLD STORAGE SINGAPORE (1983) PTE. LTD.—See Jardine Matheson Holdings Limited; *Int'l*, pg. 3909
COLDSTREAM CAPITAL MANAGEMENT, INC.—See Hersman Serles Almond PLLC; *U.S. Private*, pg. 1927
COLDSTREAM CAPITAL MANAGEMENT, INC.—See Seidman Insurance Consultants LLC; *U.S. Private*, pg. 3599
COLDSTREAM HOLDINGS, INC.; *U.S. Private*, pg. 966
COLDSTREAM LABORATORIES INC.—See Piramal Enterprises Ltd.; *Int'l*, pg. 5874
COLDSTREAM MINERAL VENTURES CORP.—See Giyani Metals Corp.; *Int'l*, pg. 2982
COLDWATER MACHINE COMPANY, LLC—See Lincoln Electric Holdings, Inc.; *U.S. Public*, pg. 1317
COLDWATER SEAFOOD (UK) LIMITED—See Enterprise Investment Fund slhf.; *Int'l*, pg. 2451
COLDWELL BANKER BAIN ASSOCIATES, INC.—See Anywhere Real Estate Inc.; *U.S. Public*, pg. 140
COLDWELL BANKER BURNET RESOURCE CENTER—See Anywhere Real Estate Inc.; *U.S. Public*, pg. 141
COLDWELL BANKER BURNET; *U.S. Private*, pg. 966
COLDWELL BANKER CANADA OPERATIONS ULC—See Anywhere Real Estate Inc.; *U.S. Public*, pg. 140
COLDWELL BANKER COMMERCIAL AFFILIATES—See Anywhere Real Estate Inc.; *U.S. Public*, pg. 141
COLDWELL BANKER COMMERCIAL PACIFIC PROPERTIES LLC—See Anywhere Real Estate Inc.; *U.S. Public*, pg. 141
COLDWELL BANKER LLC—See Anywhere Real Estate Inc.; *U.S. Public*, pg. 140
COLDWELL BANKER MARYL REALTY, INC.—See Maryl Group, Inc.; *U.S. Private*, pg. 2600
COLDWELL BANKER PACIFIC PROPERTIES LLC—See Anywhere Real Estate Inc.; *U.S. Public*, pg. 141
COLDWELL BANKER REAL ESTATE LLC—See Anywhere Real Estate Inc.; *U.S. Public*, pg. 140
COLDWELL BANKER REAL ESTATE SERVICES LLC—See Anywhere Real Estate Inc.; *U.S. Public*, pg. 141
COLDWELL BANKER REAL ESTATE (S) PTE. LTD.—See Morgan Stanley; *U.S. Public*, pg. 1471
COLDWELL BANKER RESIDENTIAL BROKERAGE, INC.—See Anywhere Real Estate Inc.; *U.S. Public*, pg. 141
COLDWELL BANKER RESIDENTIAL BROKERAGE OF UTAH—See Anywhere Real Estate Inc.; *U.S. Public*, pg. 141
COLDWELL BANKER RESIDENTIAL REAL ESTATE INC.—See Anywhere Real Estate Inc.; *U.S. Public*, pg. 141
COLDWELL BANKER RESIDENTIAL REAL ESTATE LLC—See Anywhere Real Estate Inc.; *U.S. Public*, pg. 141
COLDWELL BANKER RESIDENTIAL REAL ESTATE SERVICES INC.—See Anywhere Real Estate Inc.; *U.S. Public*, pg. 141
COLDWELL BANKER SCHMIDT REALTORS; *U.S. Private*, pg. 966
COLDWELL BANKER—See Anywhere Real Estate Inc.; *U.S. Public*, pg. 140
COLDWELL BANKER SUNSTAR-MORRIS REALTY, INC.—See Coldwell Banker Schmidt Realtors; *U.S. Private*, pg. 966
COLDWELL BANKER UNITED, REALTORS—See Anywhere Real Estate Inc.; *U.S. Public*, pg. 141
COLEAMBALLY EAST SOLAR FARM PTY. LTD.—See VH Global Sustainable Energy Opportunities Plc; *Int'l*, pg. 8182
COL-EAST, INC.—See Bluesky International Ltd.; *Int'l*, pg. 1074
COLEBROOK BOSSON SAUNDERS, LTD.—See MillerKnoll, Inc.; *U.S. Public*, pg. 1446
COLEBROOK BOSSON & SAUNDERS (PRODUCTS) LIMITED—See MillerKnoll, Inc.; *U.S. Public*, pg. 1446
COLEBROOK BOSSON SAUNDERS, PTY. LTD.—See MillerKnoll, Inc.; *U.S. Public*, pg. 1447
COLE CAPITAL CORPORATION—See Realty Income Corporation; *U.S. Public*, pg. 1768
COLE CHEMICAL & DISTRIBUTING, INC.; *U.S. Private*, pg. 966
COLE CHEVROLET-GEO INC.; *U.S. Private*, pg. 966
COLE + CO.—See C3G, L.P.; *U.S. Private*, pg. 710
COLEFAX & FOWLER GMBH—See Colefax Group PLC; *Int'l*, pg. 1697
COLEFAX GROUP PLC; *Int'l*, pg. 1697
COLEGIO BRITANICO SAINT MARGARET'S S.A.; *Int'l*, pg. 1697

COLEGIO INGLES CATOLICO DE LA SERENA S.A.; *Int'l*, pg. 1697
COLEGIO LA MAISONNETTE S.A.; *Int'l*, pg. 1698
COLEGRA - EXPLORACAO DE PEDREIRAS, S.A.—See SODIM, SGPS, SA; *Int'l*, pg. 7049
COLE HAAN COMPANY STORE—See Apax Partners LLP; *Int'l*, pg. 503
COLE HAAN, INC.—See Apax Partners LLP; *Int'l*, pg. 503
COLE HAAN JAPAN, INC.—See Apax Partners LLP; *Int'l*, pg. 503
COLE HALL LUMBER CO.—See Lumber Group Inc.; *U.S. Private*, pg. 2513
COLE HERSEE COMPANY—See Littelfuse, Inc.; *U.S. Public*, pg. 1326
COLE INDUSTRIAL, INC.; *U.S. Private*, pg. 966
COLE INFORMATION SERVICES, INC.—See 424 Capital, LLC; *U.S. Private*, pg. 15
COLE INFORMATION SERVICES, INC.—See Eagle Private Capital, LLC; *U.S. Private*, pg. 1310
COLE INFORMATION SERVICES, INC.—See Resolute Administration, Inc.; *U.S. Private*, pg. 3406
COLE LUMBER COMPANY INC.; *U.S. Private*, pg. 966
COLEMAN-ADAMS CONSTRUCTION, INC.; *U.S. Private*, pg. 967
COLEMAN AMERICAN ALLIED—See Coleman American Companies, Inc.; *U.S. Private*, pg. 967
COLEMAN AMERICAN COMPANIES, INC.; *U.S. Private*, pg. 966
COLEMAN AMERICAN MOVING SERVICES INC.—See Coleman American Companies, Inc.; *U.S. Private*, pg. 967
COLEMAN & ASSOCIATES ENTERPRISES, INC.; *U.S. Private*, pg. 966
COLEMAN AUTO GROUP; *U.S. Private*, pg. 967
COLEMAN CABLE, INC. - BREMEN—See Southwire Company, LLC; *U.S. Private*, pg. 3742
COLEMAN CABLE, INC.—See Southwire Company, LLC; *U.S. Private*, pg. 3742
THE COLEMAN COMPANY, INC.—See Newell Brands Inc.; *U.S. Public*, pg. 1515
COLEMAN COMPANY; *U.S. Private*, pg. 967
COLEMAN DISTRIBUTING COMPANY; *U.S. Private*, pg. 967
COLEMAN ENGINEERING, INC.—See Sanderson Bellecci, Inc.; *U.S. Private*, pg. 3543
COLEMAN FLOOR COMPANY—See Littlejohn & Co., LLC; *U.S. Private*, pg. 2470
COLEMAN FLOOR COMPANY—See Platinum Equity, LLC; *U.S. Private*, pg. 3205
COLEMAN FLOOR CO.—See Littlejohn & Co., LLC; *U.S. Private*, pg. 2470
COLEMAN FLOOR CO.—See Platinum Equity, LLC; *U.S. Private*, pg. 3205
COLEMAN FLOOR, LLC—See Littlejohn & Co., LLC; *U.S. Private*, pg. 2470
COLEMAN FLOOR, LLC—See Platinum Equity, LLC; *U.S. Private*, pg. 3205
COLEMAN GUANGZHOU OUTDOOR LEISURE PRODUCTS COMPANY LTD.—See Newell Brands Inc.; *U.S. Public*, pg. 1515
COLEMAN HYDRAULICS LIMITED—See Westinghouse Air Brake Technologies Corporation; *U.S. Public*, pg. 2357
COLEMAN INSIGHTS; *U.S. Private*, pg. 967
COLEMAN INSTRUMENT COMPANY; *U.S. Private*, pg. 967
COLEMAN JAPAN CO., LTD.—See Newell Brands Inc.; *U.S. Public*, pg. 1515
COLEMAN KOREA CO., LTD.—See Newell Brands Inc.; *U.S. Public*, pg. 1513
COLEMAN & LARGE LTD.—See C.J. Coleman & Company Limited; *Int'l*, pg. 1243
COLEMAN MANUFACTURING LIMITED—See Westinghouse Air Brake Technologies Corporation; *U.S. Public*, pg. 2357
COLEMAN NATURAL FOODS, INC.—See Perdue Farms Incorporated; *U.S. Private*, pg. 3147
COLEMAN OIL COMPANY; *U.S. Private*, pg. 967
COLEMAN RESEARCH GROUP, INC. (CRG); *U.S. Private*, pg. 967
COLEMAN RESEARCH GROUP, INC.—See Coleman Research Group, Inc. (CRG); *U.S. Private*, pg. 967
COLEMAN-TAYLOR AUTOMATIC TRANSMISSION COMPANY, INC.; *U.S. Private*, pg. 967
COLEMAN-TOLL LIMITED PARTNERSHIP—See Toll Brothers, Inc.; *U.S. Public*, pg. 2161
COLEMAN UK LIMITED—See Newell Brands Inc.; *U.S. Public*, pg. 1515
COLEMONT FINLAND OY—See Howden Group Holdings Limited; *Int'l*, pg. 3493
COLE MOTORS LTD.—See MITIE Group Plc; *Int'l*, pg. 4926
COLENSO BBDO—See Omnicom Group Inc.; *U.S. Public*, pg. 1575
COLEPAK, INC.—See Greif Inc.; *U.S. Public*, pg. 967
COLE PAPERS INC.; *U.S. Private*, pg. 966
COLE-PARMER CANADA COMPANY—See Thermo Fisher Scientific Inc.; *U.S. Public*, pg. 2148

COLE-PARMER INDIA PVT. LTD.—See GTCR LLC; *U.S. Private*, pg. 1804
COLE-PARMER INSTRUMENT CO. LTD.—See GTCR LLC; *U.S. Private*, pg. 1804
COLE-PARMER INSTRUMENT COMPANY, LLC—See GTCR LLC; *U.S. Private*, pg. 1804
COLERAIN NORTHSIDE, LLC—See Redwood Capital Investments, LLC; *U.S. Private*, pg. 3380
COLERAIN RV AT ALUM CREEK, LLC—See Redwood Capital Investments, LLC; *U.S. Private*, pg. 3380
COLERAIN RV OF DAYTON, LLC—See Redwood Capital Investments, LLC; *U.S. Private*, pg. 3380
COLERAIN TRAILER CENTER, LLC—See Redwood Capital Investments, LLC; *U.S. Private*, pg. 3380
COLERIDGE DESIGN & IMAGING, INC.—See Greystone Graphics, Inc.; *U.S. Private*, pg. 1786
COLES ENERGY INC.; *U.S. Private*, pg. 967
COLES GROUP LIMITED; *Int'l*, pg. 1698
COLES GROUP PROPERTIES HOLDINGS LTD—See Coles Group Limited; *Int'l*, pg. 1698
COLES GROUP PROPERTIES PTY LTD—See Coles Group Limited; *Int'l*, pg. 1698
COLES HARDWARE INC.; *U.S. Private*, pg. 967
COLES MARKETING COMMUNICATIONS, INC.; *U.S. Private*, pg. 967
COLES-MOULTRIE ELECTRIC COOPERATIVE; *U.S. Private*, pg. 967
COLES OF LA JOLLA INCORPORATED; *U.S. Private*, pg. 967
COLES ONLINE PTY LTD—See Coles Group Limited; *Int'l*, pg. 1698
COLE & SON (WALLPAPERS) LTD—See Litorina Capital Management AB; *Int'l*, pg. 4528
COLES PETROLEUM PRODUCTS INC.; *U.S. Private*, pg. 967
COLE SPORT, INC.; *U.S. Private*, pg. 966
COLE'S QUALITY FOODS, INC.; *U.S. Private*, pg. 966
COLES RETAIL GROUP PTY LTD—See Coles Group Limited; *Int'l*, pg. 1698
COLE'S SALON INC; *U.S. Private*, pg. 966
COLES SUPERMARKETS AUSTRALIA PTY. LTD.—See Coles Group Limited; *Int'l*, pg. 1698
COLETO CREEK POWER, LP—See ENGIE SA; *Int'l*, pg. 2433
COLETTE MALOUF INC.; *U.S. Private*, pg. 967
COLETTE; *Int'l*, pg. 1698
COLEUS CROWNS (UGANDA) LTD—See Anheuser-Busch InBev SA/NV; *Int'l*, pg. 464
COLEUS PACKAGING (PTY) LIMITED—See Anheuser-Busch InBev SA/NV; *Int'l*, pg. 464
COLE VALLEY CADILLAC—See Cole Valley Motor Company, Ltd.; *U.S. Private*, pg. 966
COLE VALLEY MOTOR COMPANY, LTD.; *U.S. Private*, pg. 966
COLE & WEBER UNITED—See WPP plc; *Int'l*, pg. 8467
COLE WIRE & CABLE CO. INC.; *U.S. Private*, pg. 966
COLEX ENVIRONMENTAL PTE LTD—See Bonvests Holdings Limited; *Int'l*, pg. 1110
COLEX HOLDINGS LIMITED—See Bonvests Holdings Limited; *Int'l*, pg. 1110
COLEX INTERNATIONAL, LTD.—See NewAge Industries, Inc.; *U.S. Private*, pg. 2913
COLEX SPOLKA Z O.O.—See Clariant AG; *Int'l*, pg. 1647
COLEY PHARMACEUTICAL GROUP, LTD.—See Pfizer Inc.; *U.S. Public*, pg. 1679
COLEY PORTER BELL—See WPP plc; *Int'l*, pg. 8462
COL FINANCIAL GROUP, INC.; *Int'l*, pg. 1697
COLFOR MANUFACTURING, INC.—See American Axle & Manufacturing Holdings, Inc.; *U.S. Public*, pg. 96
COLGATE ORAL PHARMACEUTICAL—See Colgate-Palmolive Company; *U.S. Public*, pg. 531
COLGATE-PALMOLIVE AB—See Colgate-Palmolive Company; *U.S. Public*, pg. 531
COLGATE-PALMOLIVE AG—See Colgate-Palmolive Company; *U.S. Public*, pg. 531
COLGATE PALMOLIVE ARGENTINA S.A.—See Colgate-Palmolive Company; *U.S. Public*, pg. 531
COLGATE-PALMOLIVE (ARKANSAS)—See Colgate-Palmolive Company; *U.S. Public*, pg. 531
COLGATE-PALMOLIVE A/S—See Colgate-Palmolive Company; *U.S. Public*, pg. 531
COLGATE-PALMOLIVE BELGIUM S.A.—See Colgate-Palmolive Company; *U.S. Public*, pg. 531
COLGATE-PALMOLIVE CANADA INC.—See Colgate-Palmolive Company; *U.S. Public*, pg. 531
COLGATE-PALMOLIVE C.A.—See Colgate-Palmolive Company; *U.S. Public*, pg. 531
COLGATE-PALMOLIVE (CENTRAL AMERICA), INC.—See Colgate-Palmolive Company; *U.S. Public*, pg. 531
COLGATE-PALMOLIVE (CENTRAL AMERICA), INC.—See Colgate-Palmolive Company; *U.S. Public*, pg. 531
COLGATE-PALMOLIVE (CENTRAL AMERICA) S.A.—See Colgate-Palmolive Company; *U.S. Public*, pg. 531
COLGATE-PALMOLIVE (CENTRAL AMERICA)—See Colgate-Palmolive Company; *U.S. Public*, pg. 531
COLGATE-PALMOLIVE CESKA REPUBLIKA, S.R.O.—See Colgate-Palmolive Company; *U.S. Public*, pg. 531
COLGATE-PALMOLIVE CHILE S.A.—See Colgate-Palmolive Company; *U.S. Public*, pg. 531

COMPANY NAME INDEX COLLEGIUM HOLDINGS, INC.

Company Index

COLGATE-PALMOLIVE CIA—See Colgate-Palmolive Company; *U.S. Public*, pg. 531
COLGATE-PALMOLIVE CO., INSTITUTIONAL PRODUCTS DIV.—See Colgate-Palmolive Company; *U.S. Public*, pg. 532
COLGATE-PALMOLIVE COMERCIAL LTDA.—See Colgate-Palmolive Company; *U.S. Public*, pg. 532
COLGATE-PALMOLIVE COMPANY; *U.S. Public*, pg. 530
COLGATE-PALMOLIVE DEL ECUADOR, S.A.—See Colgate-Palmolive Company; *U.S. Public*, pg. 532
COLGATE-PALMOLIVE DE PUERTO RICO, INC.—See Colgate-Palmolive Company; *U.S. Public*, pg. 532
COLGATE-PALMOLIVE, (DR), INC.—See Colgate-Palmolive Company; *U.S. Public*, pg. 532
COLGATE-PALMOLIVE (EASTERN) PTE. LTD.—See Colgate-Palmolive Company; *U.S. Public*, pg. 531
COLGATE-PALMOLIVE EESKA REPUBLIKA SPOL. S R.O.—See Colgate-Palmolive Company; *U.S. Public*, pg. 532
COLGATE-PALMOLIVE (FIJI) LTD.—See Colgate-Palmolive Company; *U.S. Public*, pg. 531
COLGATE-PALMOLIVE FRANCE—See Colgate-Palmolive Company; *U.S. Public*, pg. 532
COLGATE-PALMOLIVE GHANA LIMITED—See Colgate-Palmolive Company; *U.S. Public*, pg. 532
COLGATE-PALMOLIVE GMBH—See Colgate-Palmolive Company; *U.S. Public*, pg. 532
COLGATE-PALMOLIVE GMBH—See Colgate-Palmolive Company; *U.S. Public*, pg. 532
COLGATE-PALMOLIVE (GUYANA) LTD.—See Colgate-Palmolive Company; *U.S. Public*, pg. 531
COLGATE-PALMOLIVE (HELLAS) S.A.I.C.—See Colgate-Palmolive Company; *U.S. Public*, pg. 531
COLGATE-PALMOLIVE HOUSEHOLD PRODUCTS DIVISION—See Colgate-Palmolive Company; *U.S. Public*, pg. 532
COLGATE-PALMOLIVE INC. S.A.—See Colgate-Palmolive Company; *U.S. Public*, pg. 532
COLGATE-PALMOLIVE, INC.—See Colgate-Palmolive Company; *U.S. Public*, pg. 532
COLGATE-PALMOLIVE (INDIA) LTD.—See Colgate-Palmolive Company; *U.S. Public*, pg. 531
COLGATE-PALMOLIVE IRELAND—See Colgate-Palmolive Company; *U.S. Public*, pg. 532
COLGATE-PALMOLIVE ITALIA SRL—See Colgate-Palmolive Company; *U.S. Public*, pg. 532
COLGATE-PALMOLIVE LTDA.—See Colgate-Palmolive Company; *U.S. Public*, pg. 532
COLGATE-PALMOLIVE LTD.—See Colgate-Palmolive Company; *U.S. Public*, pg. 532
COLGATE-PALMOLIVE LTD.—See Colgate-Palmolive Company; *U.S. Public*, pg. 532
COLGATE-PALMOLIVE LTD.—See Colgate-Palmolive Company; *U.S. Public*, pg. 532
COLGATE-PALMOLIVE (MALAYSIA) SDN. BHD.—See Colgate-Palmolive Company; *U.S. Public*, pg. 531
COLGATE-PALMOLIVE (MARKETING) SDN BHD—See Colgate-Palmolive Company; *U.S. Public*, pg. 531
COLGATE-PALMOLIVE (MYANMAR) LIMITED—See Colgate-Palmolive Company; *U.S. Public*, pg. 531
COLGATE-PALMOLIVE NEDERLAND B.V.—See Colgate-Palmolive Company; *U.S. Public*, pg. 532
COLGATE-PALMOLIVE (PAKISTAN) LTD; *Int'l*, pg. 1698
COLGATE-PALMOLIVE PERSONAL CARE PRODUCTS DIVISION—See Colgate-Palmolive Company; *U.S. Public*, pg. 532
COLGATE-PALMOLIVE PERU S.A.—See Colgate-Palmolive Company; *U.S. Public*, pg. 532
COLGATE-PALMOLIVE PHILIPPINES INC.—See Colgate-Palmolive Company; *U.S. Public*, pg. 532
COLGATE-PALMOLIVE (POLAND) SP. Z O.O.—See Colgate-Palmolive Company; *U.S. Public*, pg. 531
COLGATE-PALMOLIVE PORTUGUESE LTDA—See Colgate-Palmolive Company; *U.S. Public*, pg. 532
COLGATE-PALMOLIVE PTY. LTD.—See Colgate-Palmolive Company; *U.S. Public*, pg. 532
COLGATE-PALMOLIVE (ROMANIA) SRL—See Colgate-Palmolive Company; *U.S. Public*, pg. 531
COLGATE-PALMOLIVE, S.A. DE C.V.—See Colgate-Palmolive Company; *U.S. Public*, pg. 532
COLGATE-PALMOLIVE SERVICES (BELGIUM) SA/NV—See Colgate-Palmolive Company; *U.S. Public*, pg. 532
COLGATE-PALMOLIVE SERVICES S.A.—See Colgate-Palmolive Company; *U.S. Public*, pg. 532
COLGATE-PALMOLIVE SLOVENSKO, S.R.O.—See Colgate-Palmolive Company; *U.S. Public*, pg. 532
COLGATE-PALMOLIVE S.P.A.—See Colgate-Palmolive Company; *U.S. Public*, pg. 532
COLGATE-PALMOLIVE TEMIZLIK URUNLERI SANAYI VE TICARET ANONIM SIRKETI—See Colgate-Palmolive Company; *U.S. Public*, pg. 532
COLGATE-PALMOLIVE (THAILAND) LIMITED—See Colgate-Palmolive Company; *U.S. Public*, pg. 531
COLGATE U.S.A.—See Colgate-Palmolive Company; *U.S. Public*, pg. 531
COLGIN CELLARS—See LVMH Moet Hennessy Louis Vuitton SE; *Int'l*, pg. 4591
COL GROUP CO., LTD.; *Int'l*, pg. 1697
COLIAENERGIA ESPANA, S.L.—See PNE AG; *Int'l*, pg. 5900
COLIAN HOLDING S.A.; *Int'l*, pg. 1698
COLIBREX GMBH—See LS telcom AG; *Int'l*, pg. 4570
COLIBRI AUTOMATION (SUZHOU) CO., LTD.—See Shenzhen Colibri Technologies Co., Ltd.; *Int'l*, pg. 6807
COLIBRI AUTOMATION (THAILAND) CO., LTD.—See Shenzhen Colibri Technologies Co., Ltd.; *Int'l*, pg. 6807
THE COLIBRI GROUP, INC.—See CITIC Group Corporation; *Int'l*, pg. 1619
THE COLIBRI GROUP, INC.—See Founders Equity, Inc.; *U.S. Private*, pg. 1581
COLIBRI PRECISION HONG KONG COMPANY LIMITED—See Shenzhen Colibri Technologies Co., Ltd.; *Int'l*, pg. 6807
COLIBRI PRECISION PTE. LTD.—See Shenzhen Colibri Technologies Co., Ltd.; *Int'l*, pg. 6807
COLIBRI RESOURCE CORPORATION; *Int'l*, pg. 1698
COLIBRI—See Carrefour SA; *Int'l*, pg. 1344
COLIBRI SPINDLES LTD.—See Fukuda Corporation; *Int'l*, pg. 2839
COLIBRYS SA—See Safran SA; *Int'l*, pg. 6475
COLICITY INC.; *U.S. Public*, pg. 533
COLIMA S R L—See Spirax-Sarco Engineering plc; *Int'l*, pg. 7137
COLINA FINANCIAL ADVISORS LTD.—See Colina Holdings Bahamas Limited; *Int'l*, pg. 1698
COLINA GENERAL INSURANCE AGENCY & BROKERS LIMITED—See Colina Holdings Bahamas Limited; *Int'l*, pg. 1698
COLINA GENERAL INSURANCE AGENTS & BROKERS LIMITED—See Colina Holdings Bahamas Limited; *Int'l*, pg. 1698
COLINA HOLDINGS BAHAMAS LIMITED; *Int'l*, pg. 1698
COLINA INSURANCE LIMITED—See Colina Holdings Bahamas Limited; *Int'l*, pg. 1698
COLINA MORTGAGE CORPORATION LTD.—See Colina Holdings Bahamas Limited; *Int'l*, pg. 1698
COLIN BUCHANAN & PARTNERS LTD.—See Belfius Bank SA/NV; *Int'l*, pg. 963
COLIN CAMPBELL & SONS LTD—See Victoria Plc; *Int'l*, pg. 8188
COLIN MEAR ENGINEERING LTD; *Int'l*, pg. 1698
COLIN'S BELARUS—See Eroglu Holding AS; *Int'l*, pg. 2496
COLIN'S RUSSIA—See Eroglu Holding AS; *Int'l*, pg. 2496
COLIN'S UKRAINE—See Eroglu Holding AS; *Int'l*, pg. 2496
COLINZ LABORATORIES LIMITED; *Int'l*, pg. 1698
COLIPAYS; *Int'l*, pg. 1698
COLISEUM ACQUISITION CORP.; *U.S. Public*, pg. 533
COLISEUM CAPITAL MANAGEMENT LLC; *U.S. Private*, pg. 967
COLISEUM COACHES LIMITED—See Mobico Group PLC.; *Int'l*, pg. 5008
COLISEUM HEALTH GROUP, LLC—See HCA Healthcare, Inc.; *U.S. Public*, pg. 993
COLISEUM HEALTH SYSTEM—See HCA Healthcare, Inc.; *U.S. Public*, pg. 993
COLISEUM LEXUS OF OAKLAND; *U.S. Private*, pg. 967
COLISEUM MEDICAL CENTER, LLC—See HCA Healthcare, Inc.; *U.S. Public*, pg. 993
COLISEUM MOTOR COMPANY; *U.S. Private*, pg. 967
COLISEUM NORTHSIDE HOSPITAL, LLC—See HCA Healthcare, Inc.; *U.S. Public*, pg. 993
COLISEUM—See Andrew Sports Club Inc.; *U.S. Private*, pg. 280
COLLABERA INC.; *U.S. Private*, pg. 968
COLLABNET, INC.—See TPG Capital, L.P.; *U.S. Public*, pg. 2173
COLLABORACTIF PORTAIL SERVICES SARL—See Infotel SA; *Int'l*, pg. 3696
COLLABORATEMD; *U.S. Private*, pg. 968
COLLABORATIVE CARE HOLDINGS, LLC—See UnitedHealth Group Incorporated; *U.S. Public*, pg. 2240
COLLABORATIVE SOLUTIONS EUROPE LIMITED—See Cognizant Technology Solutions Corporation; *U.S. Public*, pg. 524
COLLABORATIVE SOLUTIONS, LLC—See WestView Capital Partners, L.P.; *U.S. Private*, pg. 4501
COLLABOS CORPORATION; *Int'l*, pg. 1698
COLLABRALINK TECHNOLOGIES; *U.S. Private*, pg. 968
COLLABRASPACE, INC.—See Arlington Capital Partners LLC; *U.S. Private*, pg. 327
COLLABRX—See Rennova Health, Inc.; *U.S. Public*, pg. 1783
COLLAB - SOL. I. COM. E COLAB., S.A.—See Novabase SGPS, SA; *Int'l*, pg. 5453
COLLAGEN SOLUTIONS LIMITED—See Montagu Private Equity LLP; *Int'l*, pg. 5036
COLLAGES.NET INC.; *U.S. Private*, pg. 968
COLLARD ROSE—See EssilorLuxottica SA; *Int'l*, pg. 2513
COLLAS CRILL; *Int'l*, pg. 1698
COLLATERAL ANALYTICS, LLC—See Intercontinental Exchange, Inc.; *U.S. Public*, pg. 1141
COLLATERAL FINANCE CORPORATION—See A-Mark Precious Metals, Inc.; *U.S. Public*, pg. 10
COLLATERAL INTELLIGENCE, LLC—See Assurant, Inc.; *U.S. Public*, pg. 215
COLLECT ARTIFICIAL INTELLIGENCE GMBH—See Advent International Corporation; *U.S. Private*, pg. 96
COLLECT ARTIFICIAL INTELLIGENCE GMBH—See Centerbridge Partners, L.P.; *U.S. Private*, pg. 812
COLLECTE LOCALISATION SATELLITES PERU S.A.C.—See Collecte Localisation Satellites; *Int'l*, pg. 1699
COLLECTE LOCALISATION SATELLITES; *Int'l*, pg. 1699
COLLECTIBLES INSURANCE SERVICES, LLC—See Paine Schwartz Partners, LLC; *U.S. Private*, pg. 3075
COLLECTION CENTER, INC.—See StarTek, Inc.; *U.S. Private*, pg. 3788
COLLECTION CONRAD C; *Int'l*, pg. 1699
COLLECTION HOUSE INTERNATIONAL BPO, INC.—See Collection House Limited; *Int'l*, pg. 1699
COLLECTION HOUSE LIMITED; *Int'l*, pg. 1699
THE COLLECTION, INC.; *U.S. Private*, pg. 4011
COLLECTION VENICE SIMPLON-ORIENT-EXPRESS LTD.—See LVMH Moet Hennessy Louis Vuitton SE; *Int'l*, pg. 4591
COLLECTIVE BIAS, INC—See Ontario Municipal Employees Retirement System; *Int'l*, pg. 5584
THE COLLECTIVE GROUP, LLC; *U.S. Private*, pg. 4011
COLLECTIVE GROWTH CORPORATION—See Innoviz Technologies Ltd.; *Int'l*, pg. 3713
COLLECTIVE, INC.—See Zeta Interactive Corporation; *U.S. Private*, pg. 4603
COLLECTIVE LEARNING AND DEVELOPMENT PTY LTD—See Collection House Limited; *Int'l*, pg. 1699
COLLECTIVE LICENSING INTERNATIONAL, LLC—See Payless Holdings LLC; *U.S. Private*, pg. 3117
COLLECTIVE METALS INC.; *Int'l*, pg. 1699
COLLECTIVE MINING LTD.; *Int'l*, pg. 1699
COLLECTIVE POINT OF SALE SOLUTIONS LTD.—See U.S. Bancorp; *U.S. Public*, pg. 2212
COLLECTOR AB; *Int'l*, pg. 1699
COLLECTORS UNIVERSE INC.—See Cohen Private Ventures, LLC; *U.S. Private*, pg. 963
COLLECTORS UNIVERSE INC.—See D1 Capital Partners L.P.; *U.S. Private*, pg. 1143
COLLECT RX INC.—See New Capital Partners; *U.S. Private*, pg. 2892
COLLEGEBOXES, LLC—See U-Haul Holding Company; *U.S. Public*, pg. 2211
COLLEGE CITY HOMES INC.; *U.S. Private*, pg. 968
COLLEGE COMMUNITY SERVICES—See ATAR Capital, LLC; *U.S. Private*, pg. 364
COLLEGE CONCEPTS LLC—See Robinson Manufacturing Company Inc.; *U.S. Private*, pg. 3462
COLLEGE FORD LINCOLN LTD.; *Int'l*, pg. 1699
THE COLLEGE FOR FINANCIAL PLANNING INSTITUTES CORPORATION—See Graham Holdings Company; *U.S. Public*, pg. 956
COLLEGE HILL LIFE SCIENCES—See Lloyds Banking Group plc; *Int'l*, pg. 4537
COLLEGE HILL LIFE SCIENCES—See Lloyds Banking Group plc; *Int'l*, pg. 4537
COLLEGE NETWORK INC.; *U.S. Private*, pg. 968
COLLEGE OF AMERICAN PATHOLOGISTS; *U.S. Private*, pg. 968
THE COLLEGE OF HEALTH CARE PROFESSIONS; *U.S. Private*, pg. 4011
COLLEGE PARK CEMETERY, INC.—See Service Corporation International; *U.S. Public*, pg. 1869
COLLEGE PARK ENDOSCOPY CENTER, LLC—See HCA Healthcare, Inc.; *U.S. Public*, pg. 993
COLLEGE PARK INDUSTRIES, INC.—See Ossur hf; *Int'l*, pg. 5653
COLLEGE PARK MOTOR PRODUCTS LTD; *Int'l*, pg. 1699
COLLEGE POSSIBLE NATIONAL; *U.S. Private*, pg. 968
COLLEGE PROWLER, INC.; *U.S. Private*, pg. 968
COLLEGE RETIREMENT EQUITIES FUND—See Teachers Insurance Association - College Retirement Fund; *U.S. Private*, pg. 3945
COLLEGE STATION HOSPITAL, L.P.—See Community Health Systems, Inc.; *U.S. Public*, pg. 552
COLLEGE STATION PARTNERS, LTD.—See CBL & Associates Properties, Inc.; *U.S. Public*, pg. 458
COLLEGE STATION RHC COMPANY, LLC—See Community Health Systems, Inc.; *U.S. Public*, pg. 552
COLLEGE TRACK; *U.S. Private*, pg. 968
COLLEGE WORKS PAINTING INC.—See National Services Group Inc.; *U.S. Private*, pg. 2863
COLLEGIATE ASSOCIATION RESOURCE OF THE SOUTHWEST; *U.S. Private*, pg. 968
COLLEGIATE ENTREPRENEURS; *U.S. Private*, pg. 968
COLLEGIATE HOUSING SERVICES, INC.; *U.S. Private*, pg. 968
COLLEGIATE MANAGEMENT SERVICES LIMITED—See Stone Point Capital LLC; *U.S. Private*, pg. 3820
COLLEGIATE RETAIL ALLIANCE; *U.S. Private*, pg. 968
COLLEGIATE RISK MANAGEMENT, LLC; *U.S. Private*, pg. 968
COLLEGIS LLC; *U.S. Private*, pg. 968
COLLEGIUM GLASHUTTEN ZENTRUM FUR KOMMUNIKATION GMBH—See Commerzbank AG; *Int'l*, pg. 1715
COLLEGIUM HOLDINGS, INC.; *U.S. Private*, pg. 968

COLLEGIUM PHARMACEUTICAL, INC.

COLLEGIUM PHARMACEUTICAL, INC.; *U.S. Public,* pg. 533
COLLE & MCVOY LLC—See Stagwell, Inc.; *U.S. Public,* pg. 1926
COLLER CAPITAL, INC—See Coller Capital Ltd.; *Int'l,* pg. 1699
COLLER CAPITAL LIMITED—See Coller Capital Ltd.; *Int'l,* pg. 1699
COLLER CAPITAL LTD.; *Int'l,* pg. 1699
COLLETON AMBULATORY SURGERY CENTER—See HCA Healthcare, Inc.; *U.S. Public,* pg. 993
COLLETON DIAGNOSTIC CENTER, LLC—See HCA Healthcare, Inc.; *U.S. Public,* pg. 993
COLLETON MEDICAL CENTER—See HCA Healthcare, Inc.; *U.S. Public,* pg. 993
COLLETTE DINNIGAN PTY. LTD.; *Int'l,* pg. 1699
COLLETTE TRAVEL SERVICES; *U.S. Private,* pg. 968
COLLEX COLLISION EXPERTS, INC.—See Boyd Group Services Inc.; *Int'l,* pg. 1124
COLLICO VERPACKUNGSLOGISTIK UND SERVICE GMBH—See DSV A/S; *Int'l,* pg. 2211
COLLIDER LIMITED; *Int'l,* pg. 1699
COLLIER ARBOR CARE INC.—See The F.A. Bartlett Tree Expert Company; *U.S. Private,* pg. 4027
COLLIER BUILDING SPECIALTIES; *U.S. Private,* pg. 968
THE COLLIER COMPANIES, INC.; *U.S. Private,* pg. 4011
COLLIER DEVELOPMENT CO. INC.; *U.S. Private,* pg. 969
COLLIER DRUG STORES; *U.S. Private,* pg. 969
COLLIER ENTERPRISES, INC.; *U.S. Private,* pg. 969
COLLIER ENTERPRISES MANAGEMENT, INC.—See Collier Enterprises, Inc.; *U.S. Private,* pg. 969
COLLIER HMA NEUROLOGICAL VASCULAR MEDICAL GROUP, LLC—See Community Health Systems, Inc.; *U.S. Public,* pg. 552
COLLIER LAND DEVELOPMENT, INC.—See Collier Enterprises, Inc.; *U.S. Private,* pg. 969
COLLIERS ENGINEERING & DESIGN, INC.—See Colliers International Group Inc.; *Int'l,* pg. 1700
COLLIERS INTERNATIONAL - CANADA, TORONTO DOWNTOWN OFFICE—See Colliers International Group Inc.; *Int'l,* pg. 1701
COLLIERS INTERNATIONAL - CENTRAL CALIFORNIA—See Colliers International Group Inc.; *Int'l,* pg. 1700
COLLIERS INTERNATIONAL - COLUMBUS—See Colliers International Group Inc.; *Int'l,* pg. 1700
COLLIERS INTERNATIONAL CT LLC—See Colliers International Group Inc.; *Int'l,* pg. 1701
COLLIERS INTERNATIONAL GROUP INC.; *Int'l,* pg. 1700
COLLIERS INTERNATIONAL - HAWAII—See Colliers International Group Inc.; *Int'l,* pg. 1700
COLLIERS INTERNATIONAL HOLDINGS (AUSTRALIA) LIMITED—See Colliers International Group Inc.; *Int'l,* pg. 1701
COLLIERS INTERNATIONAL HOLDINGS (USA), INC.—See Colliers International Group Inc.; *Int'l,* pg. 1700
COLLIERS INTERNATIONAL (HONG KONG) LTD.—See Colliers International Group Inc.; *Int'l,* pg. 1700
COLLIERS INTERNATIONAL (ILLINOIS)—See Colliers International Group Inc.; *Int'l,* pg. 1700
COLLIERS INTERNATIONAL KOREA LTD.—See Colliers International Group Inc.; *Int'l,* pg. 1701
COLLIERS INTERNATIONAL LI INC.—See Colliers International Group Inc.; *Int'l,* pg. 1701
COLLIERS INTERNATIONAL MANAGEMENT-ATLANTA, LLC—See Colliers International Group Inc.; *Int'l,* pg. 1701
COLLIERS INTERNATIONAL NEW ENGLAND, LLC—See Colliers International Group Inc.; *Int'l,* pg. 1701
COLLIERS INTERNATIONAL - NEW YORK—See Colliers International Group Inc.; *Int'l,* pg. 1701
COLLIERS INTERNATIONAL NJ LLC—See Colliers International Group Inc.; *Int'l,* pg. 1701
COLLIERS INTERNATIONAL NORTHEAST FLORIDA, INC.—See Colliers International Group Inc.; *Int'l,* pg. 1701
COLLIERS INTERNATIONAL (NSW) PTY. LIMITED—See Colliers International Group Inc.; *Int'l,* pg. 1701
COLLIERS INTERNATIONAL - PHILADELPHIA—See Colliers International Group Inc.; *Int'l,* pg. 1700
COLLIERS INTERNATIONAL REAL ESTATE MANAGEMENT SERVICES (MI), INC.—See Colliers International Group Inc.; *Int'l,* pg. 1701
COLLIERS INTERNATIONAL - RICHMOND—See Colliers International Group Inc.; *Int'l,* pg. 1701
COLLIERS INTERNATIONAL - SAN DIEGO REGION—See Colliers International Group Inc.; *Int'l,* pg. 1700
COLLIERS INTERNATIONAL - SAN FRANCISCO—See Colliers International Group Inc.; *Int'l,* pg. 1701
COLLIERS INTERNATIONAL (SINGAPORE) PTE. LTD.—See Colliers International Group Inc.; *Int'l,* pg. 1700
COLLIERS INTERNATIONAL VALUATION & ADVISORY SERVICES INC.—See Colliers International Group Inc.; *Int'l,* pg. 1701

COLLIERS INTERNATIONAL (VICTORIA) PTY. LIMITED—See Colliers International Group Inc.; *Int'l,* pg. 1701
COLLIERS MACAULAY NICOLLS INC.—See Colliers International Group Inc.; *Int'l,* pg. 1701
COLLIERS MONROE FRIEDLANDER, INC.—See Colliers International Group Inc.; *Int'l,* pg. 1701
COLLIERS OF BIRMINGHAM LIMITED—See Lithia Motors, Inc.; *U.S. Public,* pg. 1323
COLLIERS PARAGON, LLC—See Colliers International Group Inc.; *Int'l,* pg. 1701
COLLIERY TRAINING COLLEGE (PTY) LIMITED—See Anglo American PLC; *Int'l,* pg. 461
COLLIGENT INKASSO AB—See Collector AB; *Int'l,* pg. 1699
COLLIGNON ENG SA - BRUXELLES DIVISION—See Eiffage S.A.; *Int'l,* pg. 2329
COLLIGNON ENG SA - LIEGE DIVISION—See Eiffage S.A.; *Int'l,* pg. 2329
COLLIGNON ENG SA—See Eiffage S.A.; *Int'l,* pg. 2329
COLLIGNON LUXEMBOURG SARL—See Eiffage S.A.; *Int'l,* pg. 2329
COL LIMITED—See Wheelock & Company Limited; *Int'l,* pg. 8397
COLLIN COUNTY DIAGNOSTIC ASSOCIATES, PLLC—See HCA Healthcare, Inc.; *U.S. Public,* pg. 994
COLLIN CREEK MALL, LLC—See Brookfield Corporation; *Int'l,* pg. 1185
COLLINE E OLTRE S.P.A.—See Intesa Sanpaolo S.p.A.; *Int'l,* pg. 3765
COLLINEO ASSET MANAGEMENT GMBH—See Deutsche Bank Aktiengesellschaft; *Int'l,* pg. 2062
COLLIN ESTATES LIMITED—See Great Portland Estates Plc; *Int'l,* pg. 3065
COLLINGWOOD GRAIN INC.—See Archer-Daniels-Midland Company; *U.S. Public,* pg. 181
COLLINGWOOD RESOURCES CORP.; *Int'l,* pg. 1702
COLLINS AEROSPACE – ACTUATION SYSTEMS—See RTX Corporation; *U.S. Public,* pg. 1821
COLLINS AEROSPACE - AEROSTRUCTURES, PRESTWICK SERVICE CENTER—See RTX Corporation; *U.S. Public,* pg. 1821
COLLINS AEROSPACE - AIR MANAGEMENT SYSTEMS—See RTX Corporation; *U.S. Public,* pg. 1821
COLLINS AEROSPACE - CHESHIRE—See RTX Corporation; *U.S. Public,* pg. 1821
COLLINS AEROSPACE - ELECTRIC SYSTEMS—See RTX Corporation; *U.S. Public,* pg. 1821
COLLINS AEROSPACE - ISR SYSTEMS—See RTX Corporation; *U.S. Public,* pg. 1821
COLLINS AEROSPACE - LANDING GEAR—See RTX Corporation; *U.S. Public,* pg. 1821
COLLINS AEROSPACE - RIVERSIDE—See RTX Corporation; *U.S. Public,* pg. 1821
COLLINS AEROSPACE - SAN MARCOS—See RTX Corporation; *U.S. Public,* pg. 1821
COLLINS AEROSPACE—See RTX Corporation; *U.S. Public,* pg. 1821
COLLINS AEROSPACE - WHEELS & BRAKES—See RTX Corporation; *U.S. Public,* pg. 1821
COLLINS AUTO GROUP, LLC; *U.S. Private,* pg. 969
COLLINS AVENUE LLC—See Kew Media Group Inc.; *Int'l,* pg. 4144
COLLINS BENEFITS SOLUTIONS INC.—See Advantage Benefit Solutions; *U.S. Private,* pg. 94
COLLINS BROTHERS CORPORATION; *U.S. Private,* pg. 969
COLLINS BROTHERS MOVING CORP.; *U.S. Private,* pg. 969
COLLINS BUS CORPORATION—See Berkshire Hathaway Inc.; *U.S. Public,* pg. 305
COLLINS COLLEGE—See Perdoceo Education Corporation; *U.S. Public,* pg. 1673
COLLINS CO., LTD.; *Int'l,* pg. 1702
THE COLLINS COMPANIES, INC.; *U.S. Private,* pg. 4011
COLLINS DEBDEN LIMITED—See Nippecraft Limited; *Int'l,* pg. 5309
COLLINS DEBDEN PTY. LTD.—See Nippecraft Limited; *Int'l,* pg. 5309
COLLINS DEBDEN USA, INC.—See Nippecraft Limited; *Int'l,* pg. 5309
COLLINS DISTRIBUTING COMPANY; *U.S. Private,* pg. 969
COLLINS DOOR AND HARDWARE INC.—See DNS Capital, LLC; *U.S. Private,* pg. 1249
COLLINS & DUPONT INTERIORS, INC.; *U.S. Private,* pg. 969
COLLINS ELECTRICAL COMPANY; *U.S. Private,* pg. 969
COLLINS ELECTRIC COMPANY, INC. - BERKSHIRE DIVISION—See Collins Electric Company, Inc.; *U.S. Private,* pg. 969
COLLINS ELECTRIC COMPANY, INC.; *U.S. Private,* pg. 969
COLLINS ENTERTAINMENT INC.; *U.S. Private,* pg. 969
COLLINS FASHION (PVT) LTD.—See Collins Co., Ltd.; *Int'l,* pg. 1702
COLLINS FOODS LIMITED; *Int'l,* pg. 1702

CORPORATE AFFILIATIONS

COLLINS GMBH & CO. KG.—See Eroglu Holding AS; *Int'l,* pg. 2496
COLLINS GMBH & CO. KG—See Otto GmbH & Co. KG; *Int'l,* pg. 5662
COLLINS GROUP—See Tradehold Limited; *Int'l,* pg. 7888
COLLINS & HAYES FURNITURE LTD.—See Airsprung Group PLC; *Int'l,* pg. 248
COLLINS INDUSTRIES, LTD.; *Int'l,* pg. 1702
COLLINS INTERNATIONAL CO., LTD.—See Collins Co., Ltd.; *Int'l,* pg. 1702
COLLINS LEARNING—See News Corporation; *U.S. Public,* pg. 1519
THE COLLINSON GROUP LIMITED; *Int'l,* pg. 7634
COLLINSON INSURANCE GROUP LTD.—See The Collinson Group Limited; *Int'l,* pg. 7634
COLLINSON INSURANCE SERVICES LIMITED—See The Collinson Group Limited; *Int'l,* pg. 7634
COLLINS PIPE & SUPPLY CO., INC.; *U.S. Private,* pg. 969
COLLINS PLACE NO. 2 PTY LTD—See AMP Limited; *Int'l,* pg. 432
COLLINS PLACE PTY LIMITED—See AMP Limited; *Int'l,* pg. 432
COLLINS TECHNOLOGY PARK PARTNERS, LLC—See Digital Realty Trust, Inc.; *U.S. Public,* pg. 663
COLLIN STREET BAKERY; *U.S. Private,* pg. 969
COLLINSWORTH, ALTER, FOWLER DOWLING & FRENCH GROUP INC; *U.S. Private,* pg. 969
COLLIS FOODS INC.; *U.S. Private,* pg. 969
COLLIS INC.—See Trive Capital Inc.; *U.S. Private,* pg. 4240
COLLISIONMAX OF CINNAMINSON—See CSI Holdings Inc.; *U.S. Private,* pg. 1117
COLLISION REVISION 13081 INC.—See Collision Revision, Inc.; *U.S. Private,* pg. 969
COLLISION REVISION, INC.; *U.S. Private,* pg. 969
COLLISION SERVICES INTERNATIONAL INC.—See CSI Holdings Inc.; *U.S. Private,* pg. 1117
COLLISION WORKS, INC.; *U.S. Private,* pg. 969
COLLIS ROOFING, INC.; *U.S. Private,* pg. 969
COLLMAN & KARSKY ARCHITECTS, INC.; *U.S. Private,* pg. 970
COLLOID ENVIRONMENTAL TECHNOLOGIES COMPANY (CETCO)—See Minerals Technologies, Inc.; *U.S. Public,* pg. 1448
COLLOTYPE LABELS CHILE SA—See Platinum Equity, LLC; *U.S. Private,* pg. 3206
COLLOTYPE LABELS INTERNATIONAL PTY, LTD.—See Platinum Equity, LLC; *U.S. Private,* pg. 3206
COLLOTYPE LABELS IRELAND LIMITED—See Platinum Equity, LLC; *U.S. Private,* pg. 3206
COLLOTYPE LABELS USA INC.—See Platinum Equity, LLC; *U.S. Private,* pg. 3206
COLLPLANT BIOTECHNOLOGIES LTD.; *Int'l,* pg. 1702
COLLTEX GARMENT MFY CO. LTD.—See Collins Co., Ltd.; *Int'l,* pg. 1702
COLLUM'S LUMBER MILL, INC.; *U.S. Private,* pg. 970
COLLY COMPANY AB—See Indutrade AB; *Int'l,* pg. 3677
COLLY COMPONENTS AB—See Indutrade AB; *Int'l,* pg. 3677
COLLY COMPONENTS AS—See Indutrade AB; *Int'l,* pg. 3677
COLLY COMPONENTS OY—See Indutrade AB; *Int'l,* pg. 3677
COLLY FILTRERINGSTEKNIK AB—See Indutrade AB; *Int'l,* pg. 3677
COLLY FLOWTECH AB—See Indutrade AB; *Int'l,* pg. 3677
COLLY VERKSTADSTEKNIK AB—See Indutrade AB; *Int'l,* pg. 3677
COLMAC ENERGY, INC.—See Denham Capital Management LP; *U.S. Private,* pg. 1205
COLMAN, BROHAN & DAVIS, INC.; *U.S. Private,* pg. 970
THE COLMAN GROUP INC.—See The Jordan Company, L.P.; *U.S. Private,* pg. 4060
COLMAR BELTING CO., INC.—See Genuine Parts Company; *U.S. Public,* pg. 933
COLMAR BRUNTON—See Bain Capital, LP; *U.S. Private,* pg. 448
COL-MET SPRAY BOOTHS, INC.; *U.S. Private,* pg. 965
COLN GRAVEL COMPANY LIMITED—See Heidelberg Materials AG; *Int'l,* pg. 3310
COLO; *U.S. Private,* pg. 970
COLO ATL, LLC—See American Tower Corporation; *U.S. Public,* pg. 111
COLOGIX, INC.—See Stonepeak Partners L.P.; *U.S. Private,* pg. 3829
COLOGNE BROADCASTING CENTER—See Bertelsmann SE & Co. KGaA; *Int'l,* pg. 994
COLOGNE MH OPERATING COMPANY GMBH—See Marriott International, Inc.; *U.S. Public,* pg. 1370
COLOMA FROZEN FOODS INC.; *U.S. Private,* pg. 970
COLOMBIA MINERALES INDUSTRIALES S.A.—See Gruppo Minerali Maffei S.p.A.; *Int'l,* pg. 3140
COLOMBIA MOVIL S.A E.S.P.—See Empresas Publicas de Medellin ESP; *Int'l,* pg. 2392
COLOMBIANA KIMBERLY COLPAPEL S.A.—See Kimberly-Clark Corporation; *U.S. Public,* pg. 1229
COLOMBIN BEL, S.A. DE C.V. - SANTA CATARINA PLANT—See ALFA, S.A.B. de C.V.; *Int'l,* pg. 313

COMPANY NAME INDEX

COLOMBIN BEL, S.A. DE C.V.—See ALFA, S.A.B. de C.V.; *Int'l*, pg. 313
COLOMBIN BEL, S.A. DE C.V. - TLALNEPANTLA PLANT—See ALFA, S.A.B. de C.V.; *Int'l*, pg. 313
COLOMBINE B.V.B.A.—See United Labels AG; *Int'l*, pg. 8070
COLOMBO CITY HOLDINGS PLC; *Int'l*, pg. 1702
COLOMBO DOCKYARD PLC; *Int'l*, pg. 1702
COLOMBO FORT HOTELS LTD.—See Lankem Ceylon PLC; *Int'l*, pg. 4412
COLOMBO FORT INVESTMENTS PLC; *Int'l*, pg. 1702
THE COLOMBO FORT LAND & BUILDING COMPANY PLC; *Int'l*, pg. 7634
THE COLOMBO ICE COMPANY (PVT.) LTD.—See John Keells Holdings PLC; *Int'l*, pg. 3979
COLOMBO, INC.—See General Mills, Inc.; *U.S. Public*, pg. 921
COLOMBO LAND & DEVELOPMENT CO.; *Int'l*, pg. 1702
COLOMBO POWER (PRIVATE) LIMITED—See Mitsui E&S Holdings Co., Ltd.; *Int'l*, pg. 4984
COLOMBO STOCK EXCHANGE; *Int'l*, pg. 1702
COLOMBUS CONSULTING—See Neurones S.A.; *Int'l*, pg. 5219
COLOMER BEAUTY AND PROFESSIONAL PRODUCTS, S.L.—See MacAndrews & Forbes Incorporated; *U.S. Private*, pg. 2534
COLOMER DENMARK A/S—See MacAndrews & Forbes Incorporated; *U.S. Private*, pg. 2534
COLOMER FRANCE SAS—See MacAndrews & Forbes Incorporated; *U.S. Private*, pg. 2534
COLOMER GERMANY GMBH—See MacAndrews & Forbes Incorporated; *U.S. Private*, pg. 2534
THE COLOMER GROUP—See MacAndrews & Forbes Incorporated; *U.S. Private*, pg. 2533
COLOMER ITALY SPA—See MacAndrews & Forbes Incorporated; *U.S. Private*, pg. 2534
COLOMER NETHERLANDS BV—See MacAndrews & Forbes Incorporated; *U.S. Private*, pg. 2534
COLOMER-PORTUGAL PRODUTOS COSMET. E PROFESIONAIS, LTDA—See MacAndrews & Forbes Incorporated; *U.S. Private*, pg. 2534
COLOMER PROFESSIONAL LTD.- LONDON—See MacAndrews & Forbes Incorporated; *U.S. Private*, pg. 2534
COLOMER PROFESSIONAL LTD.—See MacAndrews & Forbes Incorporated; *U.S. Private*, pg. 2534
COLOMER RUS CJSC—See MacAndrews & Forbes Incorporated; *U.S. Private*, pg. 2534
COLOMER USA, INC.—See MacAndrews & Forbes Incorporated; *U.S. Private*, pg. 2534
COLOMEX INC.; *U.S. Private*, pg. 970
COLON BROTHERS INC.; *U.S. Private*, pg. 970
COLONIAL AMERICAN CASUALTY AND SURETY COMPANY—See Zurich Insurance Group Limited; *Int'l*, pg. 8698
COLONIAL AUTO FINANCE, INC.—See America's Car-Mart, Inc.; *U.S. Public*, pg. 95
COLONIAL AUTOMOTIVE GROUP, INC.; *U.S. Private*, pg. 970
COLONIAL AUTO SUPPLY CO.; *U.S. Private*, pg. 970
COLONIAL BAG COMPANY; *U.S. Private*, pg. 970
COLONIAL BAG CORPORATION—See Ardian SAS; *Int'l*, pg. 554
COLONIAL CARIBBEAN, INC.—See Colonial Group, Inc.; *U.S. Private*, pg. 971
COLONIAL CHEMICAL SOLUTIONS, INC.—See Colonial Group, Inc.; *U.S. Private*, pg. 971
COLONIAL CHEVROLET OF ACTON—See Colonial Automotive Group, Inc.; *U.S. Private*, pg. 970
COLONIAL COAL INTERNATIONAL CORPORATION; *Int'l*, pg. 1702
COLONIAL COMMERCIAL DEVELOPMENT—See Colonial Company; *U.S. Private*, pg. 970
COLONIAL COMMERCIAL REALTY—See Colonial Company; *U.S. Private*, pg. 970
COLONIAL COMPANY; *U.S. Private*, pg. 970
COLONIAL CONCRETE COMPANY—See Vulcan Materials Company; *U.S. Public*, pg. 2314
COLONIAL COUNTRY CLUB; *U.S. Private*, pg. 970
COLONIAL DEALERSHIP GROUP; *U.S. Private*, pg. 970
COLONIAL DIVERSIFIED POLYMER PRODUCTS LLC; *U.S. Private*, pg. 970
COLONIAL DOWNS HOLDINGS, INC.—See Jacobs Entertainment, Inc.; *U.S. Private*, pg. 2180
THE COLONIAL ELECTRIC SUPPLY COMPANY; *U.S. Private*, pg. 4011
COLONIAL ENERGY, INC.—See Colonial Group, Inc.; *U.S. Private*, pg. 971
COLONIAL ENGINEERING INC.; *U.S. Private*, pg. 970
COLONIAL EQUIPMENT COMPANY; *U.S. Private*, pg. 970
COLONIAL FARM CREDIT A.C.A.; *U.S. Private*, pg. 970
COLONIAL FIRST STATE GROUP LIMITED—See Commonwealth Bank of Australia; *Int'l*, pg. 1719
COLONIAL FIRST STATE INVESTMENTS LIMITED—See KKR & Co. Inc.; *U.S. Public*, pg. 1243
COLONIAL FIRST STATE PROPERTY LIMITED—See Commonwealth Bank of Australia; *Int'l*, pg. 1720

COLONIAL FORD TRUCK SALES, INC.; *U.S. Private*, pg. 970
COLONIAL FREIGHT SYSTEMS INC.; *U.S. Private*, pg. 971
COLONIAL GARAGE AND DISTRIBUTORS LIMITED; *Int'l*, pg. 1702
COLONIAL GROUP, INC.; *U.S. Private*, pg. 971
THE COLONIAL GROUP, INC.—See Brown & Brown, Inc.; *U.S. Public*, pg. 401
COLONIAL HARDWARE CORP.; *U.S. Private*, pg. 971
COLONIAL HEIGHTS SURGERY CENTER—See HCA Healthcare, Inc.; *U.S. Public*, pg. 994
COLONIAL HILL CENTER—See Formation Capital, LLC; *U.S. Public*, pg. 1570
COLONIAL HOLDING COMPANY LIMITED—See Commonwealth Bank of Australia; *Int'l*, pg. 1719
COLONIAL HOMES INC.; *U.S. Private*, pg. 971
COLONIAL HYUNDAI OF DOWNINGTOWN; *U.S. Private*, pg. 971
COLONIAL ICE CREAM INC.; *U.S. Private*, pg. 971
COLONIAL IMPORTS CORP.; *U.S. Private*, pg. 971
COLONIAL INC.; *U.S. Private*, pg. 971
COLONIAL INDUSTRIAL PRODUCTS; *U.S. Private*, pg. 971
COLONIAL INSURANCE—See Colonial Company; *U.S. Private*, pg. 970
COLONIAL LIFE & ACCIDENT INSURANCE COMPANY—See Unum Group; *U.S. Public*, pg. 2263
COLONIAL LLC.; *U.S. Private*, pg. 971
COLONIAL MATERIALS INC.—See GMS Inc.; *U.S. Public*, pg. 948
COLONIAL MATERIALS OF FAYETTEVILLE, INC.—See GMS Inc.; *U.S. Public*, pg. 948
COLONIAL METALS CO.; *U.S. Private*, pg. 971
COLONIAL MILLWORKS LTD. INC.—See McDonough Corporation; *U.S. Private*, pg. 2632
THE COLONIAL MOTOR COMPANY LIMITED; *Int'l*, pg. 7634
COLONIAL MOTOR MART; *U.S. Private*, pg. 971
COLONIAL NATIONAL MORTGAGE—See Colonial Savings, F.A.; *U.S. Private*, pg. 972
COLONIAL NISSAN, INC.; *U.S. Private*, pg. 971
COLONIAL OIL INDUSTRIES, INC.—See Colonial Group, Inc.; *U.S. Private*, pg. 971
COLONIAL OUTPATIENT SURGERY CENTER, LLC—See UnitedHealth Group Incorporated; *U.S. Public*, pg. 2240
COLONIAL PANTRY LTD.; *U.S. Private*, pg. 971
COLONIAL PARC APARTMENTS ARKANSAS, LLC—See RAIT Financial Trust; *U.S. Public*, pg. 3348
COLONIAL PARKING, INC.—See Forge Company Inc.; *U.S. Private*, pg. 1568
COLONIAL PARTNERS, INC.; *U.S. Private*, pg. 971
COLONIAL PENN LIFE INSURANCE COMPANY—See CNO Financial Group, Inc.; *U.S. Public*, pg. 520
COLONIAL PIPELINE COMPANY; *U.S. Private*, pg. 971
COLONIAL SAVINGS, F.A.; *U.S. Private*, pg. 971
COLONIAL SPRING COMPANY—See SEI MetalTek; *U.S. Private*, pg. 3599
COLONIAL SQUARE REALTY, INC.; *U.S. Private*, pg. 972
COLONIAL SUBARU, INC.; *U.S. Private*, pg. 972
COLONIAL SUGAR, INC.—See Louis Dreyfus S.A.S.; *Int'l*, pg. 4562
COLONIAL TERMINALS, INC.—See Colonial Group, Inc.; *U.S. Private*, pg. 971
COLONIAL TIRE DISTRIBUTOR INC—See Colonial Ford Truck Sales, Inc.; *U.S. Private*, pg. 971
COLONIAL TOYOTA; *U.S. Private*, pg. 972
COLONIAL TRUCK SALES INC.—See Colonial Ford Truck Sales, Inc.; *U.S. Private*, pg. 971
COLONIAL VOLKSWAGEN; *U.S. Private*, pg. 972
COLONIAL WATER COMPANY—See New England Services Company; *U.S. Public*, pg. 1511
COLONIALWEBB CONTRACTORS COMPANY—See Comfort Systems USA, Inc.; *U.S. Public*, pg. 543
COLONIAL WEST CHEVROLET OF FITCHBURG—See Colonial Automotive Group, Inc.; *U.S. Private*, pg. 970
COLONIA REAL ESTATE AG—See TAG Immobilien AG; *Int'l*, pg. 7406
COLONIE VENTURES, INC.—See Galesi Group; *U.S. Private*, pg. 1637
COLONNA BROS., INC.; *U.S. Private*, pg. 972
COLONNADE INSURANCE S.A.—See Fairfax Financial Holdings Limited; *Int'l*, pg. 2606
COLONNAS SHIPYARD INCORPORATED; *U.S. Private*, pg. 972
COLON OIL AND SERVICES S. A.—See Marquard & Bahls AG; *Int'l*, pg. 4700
COLONY AGENCY SERVICES, INC.—See Brookfield Reinsurance Ltd.; *Int'l*, pg. 1194
COLONY BANKCORP, INC.; *U.S. Public*, pg. 533
COLONY BANK—See Colony Bankcorp, Inc.; *U.S. Public*, pg. 533
COLONY BRANDS, INC.; *U.S. Private*, pg. 972
COLONY DISPLAY LLC—See Kinzie Capital Partners LP; *U.S. Private*, pg. 2313
COLONY FACTORY CRAFTED HOMES—See Cavco Industries, Inc.; *U.S. Public*, pg. 455
COLONY FORD LINCOLN SALES; *Int'l*, pg. 1702

COLOPLAST A/S

COLONY GLOBAL ACQUISITION CORP.—See DigitalBridge Group, Inc.; *U.S. Public*, pg. 664
THE COLONY GROUP, LLC—See Clayton, Dubilier & Rice, LLC; *U.S. Public*, pg. 923
THE COLONY GROUP, LLC—See Stone Point Capital LLC; *U.S. Public*, pg. 3824
COLONY GUMS LLC—See BRENNTAG SE; *Int'l*, pg. 1149
COLONY HARDWARE CORP.—See Audax Group, Limited Partnership; *U.S. Private*, pg. 387
COLONY HARDWARE SUPPLY CO. INC.; *U.S. Private*, pg. 972
COLONY HEATING & AIR CONDITIONING INC.; *U.S. Private*, pg. 972
COLONY HOUSE NURSING AND REHABILITATION CENTER—See Apollo Global Management, Inc.; *U.S. Public*, pg. 156
COLONY INSURANCE COMPANY—See Brookfield Reinsurance Ltd.; *Int'l*, pg. 1194
COLONY INSURANCE GROUP—See Brookfield Reinsurance Ltd.; *Int'l*, pg. 1194
COLONY MANAGEMENT SERVICES—See Brookfield Reinsurance Ltd.; *Int'l*, pg. 1194
COLONY MATERIALS HARDSCAPE & LANDSCAPE SUPPLIES—See Haines & Kibblehouse Inc.; *U.S. Private*, pg. 1840
COLONY MATERIALS, L.L.C.—See Haines & Kibblehouse Inc.; *U.S. Private*, pg. 1841
COLONY PARK FINANCIAL SERVICES LLC—See Sandlapper Securities, LLC; *U.S. Private*, pg. 3544
COLONY REALTY PARTNERS, LLC—See DigitalBridge Group, Inc.; *U.S. Public*, pg. 664
COLONY SPECIALTY INSURANCE COMPANY—See Brookfield Reinsurance Ltd.; *Int'l*, pg. 1194
COLONY SPECIALTY—See Brookfield Reinsurance Ltd.; *Int'l*, pg. 1194
COLONY SQUARE MALL, LLC—See Brookfield Corporation; *Int'l*, pg. 1185
COLONY TEXTILE MILLS LIMITED; *Int'l*, pg. 1702
COLONY TIRE CORPORATION; *U.S. Private*, pg. 972
COLOPLAST AB—See Coloplast A/S; *Int'l*, pg. 1703
COLOPLAST AG—See Coloplast A/S; *Int'l*, pg. 1703
COLOPLAST A/S; *Int'l*, pg. 1702
COLOPLAST BETEILIGUNGS GMBH—See Coloplast A/S; *Int'l*, pg. 1703
COLOPLAST BUSINESS CENTRE SP. Z O.O.—See Coloplast A/S; *Int'l*, pg. 1703
COLOPLAST B.V.—See Coloplast A/S; *Int'l*, pg. 1703
COLOPLAST CANADA CORPORATION—See Coloplast A/S; *Int'l*, pg. 1703
COLOPLAST (CHINA) CO. LTD.—See Coloplast A/S; *Int'l*, pg. 1703
COLOPLAST (CHINA) MEDICAL DEVICES LTD.—See Coloplast A/S; *Int'l*, pg. 1703
COLOPLAST CORP.—See Coloplast A/S; *Int'l*, pg. 1703
COLOPLAST CROATIA—See Coloplast A/S; *Int'l*, pg. 1703
COLOPLAST CZECH REPUBLIC—See Coloplast A/S; *Int'l*, pg. 1703
COLOPLAST DE ARGENTINA S.A.—See Coloplast A/S; *Int'l*, pg. 1704
COLOPLAST DE COSTA RICA S.A.—See Coloplast A/S; *Int'l*, pg. 1704
COLOPLAST DISTRIBUTION CENTER—See Coloplast A/S; *Int'l*, pg. 1703
COLOPLAST DO BRASIL LTDA.—See Coloplast A/S; *Int'l*, pg. 1704
COLOPLAST GMBH—See Coloplast A/S; *Int'l*, pg. 1703
COLOPLAST GMBH—See Coloplast A/S; *Int'l*, pg. 1703
COLOPLAST GREECE—See Coloplast A/S; *Int'l*, pg. 1703
COLOPLAST (HONG KONG) LTD.—See Coloplast A/S; *Int'l*, pg. 1703
COLOPLAST HUNGARY KFT.—See Coloplast A/S; *Int'l*, pg. 1703
COLOPLAST II PORTUGAL, UNIPESSOAL LDA.—See Coloplast A/S; *Int'l*, pg. 1703
COLOPLAST (INDIA) PRIVATE LIMITED—See Coloplast A/S; *Int'l*, pg. 1703
COLOPLAST ISRAEL—See Coloplast A/S; *Int'l*, pg. 1703
COLOPLAST K.K.—See Coloplast A/S; *Int'l*, pg. 1703
COLOPLAST KOREA LIMITED—See Coloplast A/S; *Int'l*, pg. 1703
COLOPLAST MANUFACTURING US, LLC—See Coloplast A/S; *Int'l*, pg. 1703
COLOPLAST NORGE AS—See Coloplast A/S; *Int'l*, pg. 1703
COLOPLAST N.V.—See Coloplast A/S; *Int'l*, pg. 1703
COLOPLAST OOO—See Coloplast A/S; *Int'l*, pg. 1703
COLOPLAST OY—See Coloplast A/S; *Int'l*, pg. 1703
COLOPLAST PORTUGAL LDA.—See Coloplast A/S; *Int'l*, pg. 1703
COLOPLAST PRODUCTOS MEDICOS S.A.—See Coloplast A/S; *Int'l*, pg. 1703
COLOPLAST PTY. LTD.—See Coloplast A/S; *Int'l*, pg. 1703
COLOPLAST SHARED SERVICES SP. Z.O.O—See Coloplast A/S; *Int'l*, pg. 1704
COLOPLAST SLOVAKIA—See Coloplast A/S; *Int'l*, pg. 1704
COLOPLAST SLOVENIA—See Coloplast A/S; *Int'l*, pg. 1704

COLOPLAST A/S

Company Index

COLOPLAST—See Coloplast A/S; *Int'l*, pg. 1703
COLOPLAST SPAIN—See Coloplast A/S; *Int'l*, pg. 1704
COLOPLAST S.P.A.—See Coloplast A/S; *Int'l*, pg. 1704
COLOPLAST SP.Z.O.O.—See Coloplast A/S; *Int'l*, pg. 1704
COLOPLAST TAIWAN CO., LTD.—See Coloplast A/S; *Int'l*, pg. 1704
COLOPLAST TURKIYE MEDIKAL GERECLER SAN. VE TIC. A.S.—See Coloplast A/S; *Int'l*, pg. 1704
COLOPLAST UK LTD.—See Coloplast A/S; *Int'l*, pg. 1704
COLOPLAST UKRAINE A/S—See Coloplast A/S; *Int'l*, pg. 1704
COLOPL INC.; *Int'l*, pg. 1702
COLORADANS FOR RESPONSIBLE ENERGY DEVELOPMENT; *U.S. Private*, pg. 973
COLOR-AD, INC.; *U.S. Private*, pg. 973
COLORADO AUTO AUCTION—See Cox Enterprises, Inc.; *U.S. Private*, pg. 1076
COLORADO AVALANCHE, LLC—See Kroenke Sports & Entertainment, LLC; *U.S. Private*, pg. 2352
COLORADO BAG N' BAGGAGE; *U.S. Private*, pg. 973
COLORADO BANKERS LIFE INSURANCE COMPANY—See Eli Global, LLC; *U.S. Private*, pg. 1360
COLORADO BELLE HOTEL & CASINO—See Marnell Corrao Associates, Inc.; *U.S. Private*, pg. 2586
COLORADO BEST BLOCK, LLC—See The Quikrete Companies, LLC; *U.S. Private*, pg. 4101
COLORADO BOXED BEEF CO. - ATLANTA FACILITY—See Palladium Equity Partners, LLC; *U.S. Private*, pg. 3078
COLORADO BOXED BEEF CO. - CBBC INTERNATIONAL DIVISION—See Palladium Equity Partners, LLC; *U.S. Private*, pg. 3078
COLORADO BOXED BEEF CO.—See Palladium Equity Partners, LLC; *U.S. Private*, pg. 3078
COLORADO BRAKE & SUPPLY INC.—See North American Truck & Trailer, Inc.; *U.S. Private*, pg. 2941
COLORADO BROKERAGE GROUP, LLC—See Leisure, Werden & Terry Agency, Inc.; *U.S. Private*, pg. 2420
COLORADO CATTLEMEN'S AGRICULTURAL LAND TRUST—See Colorado Cattlemen's Association; *U.S. Private*, pg. 973
COLORADO CATTLEMEN'S ASSOCIATION; *U.S. Private*, pg. 973
COLORADO CLEANUP SERVICES, INC.; *U.S. Private*, pg. 973
COLORADO COMMODITY TRADERS; *U.S. Private*, pg. 973
COLORADO COMMUNITY MEDIA—See Macari-Healey Publishing Company, LLC; *U.S. Private*, pg. 2534
COLORADO CRYSTAL CORPORATION—See Taitien Electronics Co., Ltd.; *Int'l*, pg. 7418
COLORADO DAILY—See Alden Global Capital LLC; *U.S. Private*, pg. 157
COLORADO DENTAL SERVICE, INC.; *U.S. Private*, pg. 973
COLORADO DRYWALL SUPPLY LLC; *U.S. Private*, pg. 973
THE COLORADO EDUCATION INITIATIVE; *U.S. Private*, pg. 4011
COLORADO ENERGY MANAGEMENT, LLC—See Beowulf Energy LLC; *U.S. Private*, pg. 529
COLORADO ENERGY MANAGEMENT, LLC—See NGP Energy Capital Management, LLC; *U.S. Private*, pg. 2924
COLORADO ENERGY NATIONS COMPANY, LLLP—See ENGIE SA; *Int'l*, pg. 2433
COLORADO ENGINEERING INC.—See Advent International Corporation; *U.S. Private*, pg. 99
COLORADO FABRICATION LLC—See Kirkwood Holding, Inc.; *U.S. Private*, pg. 2315
COLORADO FARM BUREAU MUTUAL INSURANCE CO.; *U.S. Private*, pg. 973
COLORADO FEDERAL SAVINGS BANK; *U.S. Private*, pg. 973
COLORADO FINANCIAL MANAGEMENT, INC.; *U.S. Private*, pg. 974
COLORADO FIRST CONSTRUCTION CO.; *U.S. Private*, pg. 974
COLORADO FOOD PRODUCTS INC.; *U.S. Private*, pg. 974
COLORADO GOLDFIELDS INC.; *U.S. Private*, pg. 974
COLORADO GRANDE ENTERPRISES, INC.—See Maverick Gold LLC; *U.S. Private*, pg. 2616
COLORADO HEALTH & REHAB, LLC; *U.S. Private*, pg. 974
COLORADO HOMETOWN WEEKLY—See Alden Global Capital LLC; *U.S. Private*, pg. 157
COLORADO INCOME HOLDINGS INC.; *U.S. Private*, pg. 974
COLORADO IN-HOME PARTNER-I, LLC—See UnitedHealth Group Incorporated; *U.S. Public*, pg. 2244
COLORADO INNOVATIVE PHYSICIAN SOLUTIONS, INC.—See DaVita Inc.; *U.S. Public*, pg. 636
COLORADO INSURANCE SALES & SERVICE—See Peter C. Foy & Associates Insurance Services, Inc.; *U.S. Private*, pg. 3157

COLORADO INTERACTIVE, LLC—See Tyler Technologies, Inc.; *U.S. Public*, pg. 2208
COLORADO INTERSTATE GAS COMPANY, L.L.C.—See Kinder Morgan, Inc.; *U.S. Public*, pg. 1232
COLORADO JETCENTER, INC.—See Cordillera Corporation; *U.S. Private*, pg. 1047
COLORADO KENWORTH INC.—See Murphy-Hoffman Company; *U.S. Private*, pg. 2816
COLORADO LEGAL SERVICES; *U.S. Private*, pg. 974
COLORADO LIME COMPANY—See United States Lime & Minerals, Inc.; *U.S. Public*, pg. 2236
COLORADO LINING INTERNATIONAL, INC.—See CNH Industrial N.V.; *Int'l*, pg. 1676
COLORADO LOGOS, INC.—See Lamar Advertising Company; *U.S. Public*, pg. 1290
COLORADO MECHANICAL SERVICES, LLC; *U.S. Private*, pg. 974
THE COLORADO MEDICAL CYCLOTRON, LLC—See Siemens Aktiengesellschaft; *Int'l*, pg. 6891
COLORADO MILLS LP—See Simon Property Group, Inc.; *U.S. Public*, pg. 1882
COLORADO MOUNTAIN EXPRESS LLC—See Vail Resorts, Inc.; *U.S. Public*, pg. 2271
COLORADO MUSEUM OF NATURAL HISTORY; *U.S. Private*, pg. 974
COLORADO NATURAL GAS, INC.—See Summit Utilities Inc.; *U.S. Private*, pg. 3857
COLORADO NONPROFIT DEVELOPMENT CENTER; *U.S. Private*, pg. 974
COLORADO OUTDOOR RETAIL GROUP; *U.S. Private*, pg. 974
COLORADO PAINT COMPANY—See SWARCO AG; *Int'l*, pg. 7361
COLORADO PATHOLOGY CONSULTANTS, P.C.—See Quest Diagnostics, Inc.; *U.S. Public*, pg. 1755
COLORADO PEINTURES; *Int'l*, pg. 1704
COLORADO PETROLEUM PRODUCTS CO.; *U.S. Private*, pg. 974
COLORADO PLAINS PHYSICIAN PRACTICES, LLC—See Apollo Global Management, Inc.; *U.S. Public*, pg. 155
COLORADO PRIME FOODS LLC; *U.S. Private*, pg. 974
COLORADO PRODUCT CONCEPTS, INC.—See Scott's Liquid Gold-Inc.; *U.S. Public*, pg. 1849
COLORADO RETAIL VENTURES SERVICES, LLC—See CHS INC.; *U.S. Public*, pg. 492
COLORADO RIVER CONCRETE, LP—See Holcim Ltd.; *Int'l*, pg. 3446
COLORADO RIVER FORD LINCOLN-MERCURY; *U.S. Private*, pg. 974
COLORADO ROCKIES BASEBALL CLUB, LTD.; *U.S. Private*, pg. 974
COLORADO SATELLITE BROADCASTING, INC.—See L.F.P., Inc.; *U.S. Private*, pg. 2365
COLORADO SCAFFOLDING & EQUIPMENT CO INC.—See C&D Insulation, Inc.; *U.S. Private*, pg. 702
COLORADO SERUM CO.; *U.S. Private*, pg. 974
COLORADO SPRINGS ANUSA, LLC—See AutoNation, Inc.; *U.S. Public*, pg. 234
COLORADO SPRINGS COCA COLA BOTTLING; *U.S. Private*, pg. 974
COLORADO SPRINGS HEALTH PARTNERS, LLC—See DaVita Inc.; *U.S. Public*, pg. 637
COLORADO SPRINGS HOOTERS, INC.—See Restaurants of America, Inc.; *U.S. Private*, pg. 3408
COLORADO SPRINGS UTILITIES, INC.; *U.S. Private*, pg. 974
COLORADO STRUCTURES, INC.; *U.S. Private*, pg. 974
COLORADO SUPERSTORES LLC—See Harco, LLC; *U.S. Private*, pg. 1862
COLORADO SWEET GOLD LLC; *U.S. Private*, pg. 975
COLORADO SYMPHONY ASSOCIATION INC.; *U.S. Private*, pg. 975
COLORADO TECHNICAL UNIVERSITY—See Perdoceo Education Corporation; *U.S. Public*, pg. 1673
COLORADO TRUCK EQUIPMENT & PARTS INC—See North American Truck & Trailer, Inc.; *U.S. Private*, pg. 2941
COLORADO UROLOGIC SURGERY CENTER, LLC—See Tenet Healthcare Corporation; *U.S. Public*, pg. 2002
COLORADO-WEST EQUIPMENT INC.; *U.S. Private*, pg. 975
COLORADO WINDOW SYSTEMS, INC.—See Platform Partners LLC; *U.S. Private*, pg. 3200
COLORADO & WYOMING RAILWAY COMPANY—See Evraz plc; *Int'l*, pg. 2574
COLORANT CHROMATICS AG—See Avient Corporation; *U.S. Public*, pg. 247
COLORANT CHROMATICS EUROPE B.V.—See Avient Corporation; *U.S. Public*, pg. 247
COLORANTS SOLUTIONS (ARGENTINA) S.A.—See Clariant AG; *Int'l*, pg. 1648
COLORANTS SOLUTIONS (BRAZIL) LTDA.—See Clariant AG; *Int'l*, pg. 1648
COLORANTS SOLUTIONS (THAILAND) LTD.—See Clariant AG; *Int'l*, pg. 1648
COLOR ART OFFICE INTERIORS INC.; *U.S. Private*, pg. 974
COLORAY INTERNATIONAL INVESTMENT CO., LTD.; *Int'l*, pg. 1704

CORPORATE AFFILIATIONS

COLOR-BRIDGE PRINTING & PACKAGING COMPANY LIMITED - DONGGUAN COLOR-BRIDGE PRINTING & PAPER PRODUCTS FACTORY—See Evershine Group Holdings Limited; *Int'l*, pg. 2569
COLOR-BRIDGE PRINTING & PACKAGING COMPANY LIMITED—See Evershine Group Holdings Limited; *Int'l*, pg. 2569
COLOR CAULK INC.; *U.S. Private*, pg. 972
COLORCHIPS NEWS MEDIA LTD.; *Int'l*, pg. 1704
COLOR COMMUNICATIONS, INC.; *U.S. Private*, pg. 972
COLORCON, INC. - NORTH AMERICA HEADQUARTERS—See Berwind Corporation; *U.S. Private*, pg. 541
COLORCON, INC.—See Berwind Corporation; *U.S. Private*, pg. 541
COLORCON LTD.—See Berwind Corporation; *U.S. Private*, pg. 541
COLORCRAFT OF VIRGINIA, INC.—See Corporate Press Inc.; *U.S. Private*, pg. 1055
COLOR EDGE LLC - NEW JERSEY PRODUCTION OFFICE—See Saints Capital, LLC; *U.S. Private*, pg. 3530
COLOR EDGE LLC—See Saints Capital, LLC; *U.S. Private*, pg. 3530
COLOREP, INC.; *U.S. Private*, pg. 975
COLORESCIENCE, INC.; *U.S. Private*, pg. 975
COLORFX LLC—See Mittera Group, Inc.; *U.S. Private*, pg. 2751
COLORGRAPHICS, INC. - SAN FRANCISCO—See Cenveo, Inc.; *U.S. Private*, pg. 835
COLORGRAPHICS, INC. - SEATTLE—See Cenveo, Inc.; *U.S. Private*, pg. 835
COLOR IMAGE APPAREL INC.; *U.S. Private*, pg. 972
COLOR IMAGING INC.; *U.S. Private*, pg. 972
COLOR IMPRESSIONS, INC.—See Docuplex, Inc.; *U.S. Private*, pg. 1252
COLOR INC.; *U.S. Private*, pg. 972
COLOR INK, INC.; *U.S. Private*, pg. 972
COLORITE POLYMERS—See Genstar Capital, LLC; *U.S. Private*, pg. 1678
COLORITE SPECIALTY RESINS—See Genstar Capital, LLC; *U.S. Private*, pg. 1678
COLORLAND ANIMATION LTD.; *Int'l*, pg. 1704
COLORLIGHT AB—See Amplex AB; *Int'l*, pg. 434
COLORLIGHT CLOUD B.V.—See Colorlight Cloud Tech Ltd.; *Int'l*, pg. 1704
COLORLIGHT CLOUD TECH LTD.; *Int'l*, pg. 1704
COLORLIGHT US, INC.—See Colorlight Cloud Tech Ltd.; *Int'l*, pg. 1704
COLORLINK JAPAN CO., LTD.—See Arisawa Manufacturing Co., Ltd.; *Int'l*, pg. 566
COLOR MASTER, INC.; *U.S. Private*, pg. 972
COLORMATE CO., LTD.—See NOROO Paint & Coatings Co., Ltd.; *Int'l*, pg. 5431
COLORMATRIX ASIA LIMITED—See Avient Corporation; *U.S. Public*, pg. 247
COLORMATRIX CORPORATION—See Avient Corporation; *U.S. Public*, pg. 247
COLORMATRIX EUROPE BV—See Avient Corporation; *U.S. Public*, pg. 247
COLORMATRIX EUROPE LIMITED—See Avient Corporation; *U.S. Public*, pg. 247
COLORMATRIX GROUP, INC.—See Avient Corporation; *U.S. Public*, pg. 247
COLORMATRIX RUSSIA LLC—See Avient Corporation; *U.S. Public*, pg. 247
COLORMATRIX SOUTH AFRICA (PTY) LTD.—See Avient Corporation; *U.S. Public*, pg. 247
COLORMATRIX UK LIMITED—See Avient Corporation; *U.S. Public*, pg. 247
COLOR ME BEAUTIFUL, INC.; *U.S. Private*, pg. 973
COLOR ME MINE ENTERPRISES, INC.; *U.S. Private*, pg. 973
COLOR ME MINE FRANCHISING, INC.—See Color Me Mine Enterprises, Inc.; *U.S. Private*, pg. 973
COLORMIX INDUSTRIA E COMERCIO DE PIGMENTOS LTDA.—See SKion GmbH; *Int'l*, pg. 6989
COLOR OPTICS INC.—See Atlas Holdings, LLC; *U.S. Private*, pg. 376
COLORPAK INDONESIA TBK; *Int'l*, pg. 1704
COLORPLAY STUDIO; *U.S. Private*, pg. 975
COLORPROOF HAIRCARE LLC—See Cosway Co Inc.; *U.S. Private*, pg. 1063
COLOR RUBBER NUGGETS, INC.—See Allen County Recyclers Inc.; *U.S. Private*, pg. 178
COLORS FOR PLASTICS INC.; *U.S. Private*, pg. 975
COLORSPEC COATINGS INTERNATIONAL; *U.S. Private*, pg. 975
COLOR SPOT NURSERY, INC. - CARSON FACILITY—See Color Spot Nursery, Inc.; *U.S. Private*, pg. 973
COLOR SPOT NURSERY, INC. - CHINO VALLEY FACILITY—See Color Spot Nursery, Inc.; *U.S. Private*, pg. 973
COLOR SPOT NURSERY, INC. - HUNTSVILLE FACILITY—See Color Spot Nursery, Inc.; *U.S. Private*, pg. 973
COLOR SPOT NURSERY, INC. - KATY FACILITY—See Color Spot Nursery, Inc.; *U.S. Private*, pg. 973

COMPANY NAME INDEX

COLOR SPOT NURSERY, INC. - LODI FACILITY—See Color Spot Nursery, Inc.; *U.S. Private*, pg. 973
COLOR SPOT NURSERY, INC. - SALINAS FACILITY—See Color Spot Nursery, Inc.; *U.S. Private*, pg. 973
COLOR SPOT NURSERY, INC. - SAN ANTONIO FACILITY—See Color Spot Nursery, Inc.; *U.S. Private*, pg. 973
COLOR SPOT NURSERY, INC. - SAN JUAN CAPISTRANO FACILITY—See Color Spot Nursery, Inc.; *U.S. Private*, pg. 973
COLOR SPOT NURSERY, INC.; *U.S. Private*, pg. 973
COLOR SPOT NURSERY, INC. - TROUP FACILITY—See Color Spot Nursery, Inc.; *U.S. Private*, pg. 973
COLOR SPOT NURSERY, INC. - WACO FACILITY—See Color Spot Nursery, Inc.; *U.S. Private*, pg. 973
COLOR SPOT NURSERY, INC. - WALNUT SPRINGS FACILITY—See Color Spot Nursery, Inc.; *U.S. Private*, pg. 973
COLORSTARS GROUP; *Int'l*, pg. 1704
COLOR STAR TECHNOLOGY CO., LTD.; *U.S. Public*, pg. 533
COLOR STEELS LIMITED—See Tata Sons Limited; *Int'l*, pg. 7471
COLOR STONE INTERNATIONAL INC.—See Ointon International Inc.; *U.S. Private*, pg. 3006
COLORSUD SA—See Bystronic AG; *Int'l*, pg. 1236
COLORTONE AUDIO VISUAL STAGING & RENTALS, INC.; *U.S. Private*, pg. 975
COLOR TRADING SP. Z O. O.—See ARKRAY, Inc.; *Int'l*, pg. 572
COLORVISION INTERNATIONAL, INC.; *U.S. Private*, pg. 975
COLORWARE INC.; *U.S. Private*, pg. 975
COLOR WHEEL PAINT MANUFACTURING CO. INC.; *U.S. Private*, pg. 973
COLOR WORLD HOUSEPAINTING, INC.—See Apax Partners LLP; *Int'l*, pg. 502
COLOSCEUM MEDIA PRIVATE LIMITED—See Reliance - ADA Group Limited; *Int'l*, pg. 6262
COLOURED TIES CAPITAL INC.; *Int'l*, pg. 1704
COLOUR LIFE SERVICES GROUP CO., LTD.; *Int'l*, pg. 1704
COLOUR LIMITED—See FedEx Corporation; *U.S. Public*, pg. 827
COLOURS INC.; *U.S. Private*, pg. 975
COLOVOS COMPANY; *U.S. Private*, pg. 975
COLOWIDE ASIA CO., LTD.—See Colowide Co., Ltd.; *Int'l*, pg. 1705
COLOWIDE CO., LTD.; *Int'l*, pg. 1704
COLOWIDE MD CO., LTD.—See Colowide Co., Ltd.; *Int'l*, pg. 1705
COLOWIDE VIETNAM., JSC—See Colowide Co., Ltd.; *Int'l*, pg. 1705
COLOWYO COAL COMPANY L.P.—See Tri-State Generation and Transmission Association, Inc.; *U.S. Private*, pg. 4224
COLPHARMA, S.R.L.—See FAES Farma, S.A.; *Int'l*, pg. 2601
COL PUBLIC COMPANY LIMITED; *Int'l*, pg. 1697
COLQUITT ELECTRIC MEMBERSHIP CORPORATION; *U.S. Private*, pg. 975
COLRAIN (ALBURY) PTY LTD—See MaxiPARTS Limited; *Int'l*, pg. 4742
COLRAIN (BALLARAT) PTY LTD—See MaxiPARTS Limited; *Int'l*, pg. 4742
COLRAIN PTY LTD—See MaxiPARTS Limited; *Int'l*, pg. 4742
COLRICH (SAC) LTD—See Guardian Holdings Limited; *Int'l*, pg. 3171
COLRUYT GROUP N.V.; *Int'l*, pg. 1705
COLRUYT IT CONSULTANCY INDIA PRIVATE LIMITED—See Colruyt Group N.V.; *Int'l*, pg. 1705
COLRUYT LUXEMBOURG S.A.—See Colruyt Group N.V.; *Int'l*, pg. 1705
COLRUYT RETAIL FRANCE SAS—See Colruyt Group N.V.; *Int'l*, pg. 1705
COLSA CORPORATION; *U.S. Private*, pg. 975
COLSKY MEDIA; *U.S. Private*, pg. 975
COLSON ASSOCIATES, INC.; *U.S. Private*, pg. 975
COLSON CAPITAL CORP.; *Int'l*, pg. 1705
COLSON & COLSON GENERAL CONTRACTORS; *U.S. Private*, pg. 975
COLSPACE CORPORATION—See Vista Equity Partners, LLC; *U.S. Private*, pg. 4398
COLTALA HOLDINGS, LLC; *U.S. Private*, pg. 976
COLT ATLANTIC SERVICES, INC.; *U.S. Private*, pg. 975
THE COLT CAR COMPANY LTD.—See Mitsubishi Corporation; *Int'l*, pg. 4943
COLT CZ GROUP SE; *Int'l*, pg. 1705
COLT DEFENSE LLC; *U.S. Private*, pg. 975
COLTEC DO BRASIL PRODUCTOS INDUSTRIAIS LTDA.—See Enpro Inc.; *U.S. Public*, pg. 774
COLTEC ENGINEERING, INC.; *U.S. Private*, pg. 976
COLTENE HOLDING AG; *Int'l*, pg. 1705
COLTENE/WHALEDENT AG—See COLTENE Holding AG; *Int'l*, pg. 1705
COLTENE/WHALEDENT GMBH + CO. KG—See COLTENE Holding AG; *Int'l*, pg. 1705

COLTENE/WHALEDENT INC.—See COLTENE Holding AG; *Int'l*, pg. 1706
COLTENE/WHALEDENT LTD—See COLTENE Holding AG; *Int'l*, pg. 1706
COLTENE/WHALEDENT PRIVATE LIMITED—See COLTENE Holding AG; *Int'l*, pg. 1706
COLTENE/WHALEDENT S.A.R.L.—See COLTENE Holding AG; *Int'l*, pg. 1706
COLTER & PETERSON INC.; *U.S. Private*, pg. 976
COLTERRA CAPITAL CORPORATION; *Int'l*, pg. 1706
COLT GROUP S.A.—See FMR LLC; *U.S. Private*, pg. 1554
COLT INSURANCE AGENCY, INC.—See Cross Financial Corporation; *U.S. Private*, pg. 1104
COLT INTERNATIONAL DAS AMERICAS SERVICOS DE AVIACAO LTDA.—See World Kinect Corporation; *U.S. Public*, pg. 2380
COLT INTERNATIONAL EUROPE SARL—See World Kinect Corporation; *U.S. Public*, pg. 2380
COLT INTERNATIONAL HONG KONG LIMITED—See World Kinect Corporation; *U.S. Public*, pg. 2380
COLT INTERNATIONAL, L.L.C.—See World Kinect Corporation; *U.S. Public*, pg. 2380
COLTMAN PRECAST CONCRETE LIMITED—See Ibstock plc; *Int'l*, pg. 3577
COLTON CA MULTI ASC, L.P.—See KKR & Co. Inc.; *U.S. Public*, pg. 1245
COLTON ENTERPRISES, INC.—See Dollar Mutual Bancorp; *U.S. Private*, pg. 1254
COLTON REAL ESTATE GROUP INC.; *U.S. Private*, pg. 976
COLTON'S RESTAURANT GROUP, INC.; *U.S. Private*, pg. 976
COLTON VB, L.P.—See National Storage Affiliates Trust; *U.S. Public*, pg. 1498
COLT PRINT SERVICES, INC.; *U.S. Private*, pg. 975
COLT PRUF UND TEST GMBH—See FACC AG; *Int'l*, pg. 2600
COLT REFINING INC.; *U.S. Private*, pg. 976
COLT RESOURCES INC.; *Int'l*, pg. 1705
COLT'S MANUFACTURING COMPANY, INC.—See Colt Defense LLC; *U.S. Private*, pg. 975
COLT TECHNOLOGY SERVICES GMBH—See FMR LLC; *U.S. Private*, pg. 1554
COLT TECHNOLOGY SERVICES S.P.A.—See FMR LLC; *U.S. Private*, pg. 1554
COLT TELECOM AB—See FMR LLC; *U.S. Private*, pg. 1554
COLT TELECOM AG—See FMR LLC; *U.S. Private*, pg. 1554
COLT TELECOM A/S—See FMR LLC; *U.S. Private*, pg. 1554
COLT TELECOM AUSTRIA GMBH—See FMR LLC; *U.S. Private*, pg. 1554
COLT TELECOM B.V.—See FMR LLC; *U.S. Private*, pg. 1554
COLT TELECOM ESPANA SA—See FMR LLC; *U.S. Private*, pg. 1554
COLT TELECOM IRELAND LIMITED—See FMR LLC; *U.S. Private*, pg. 1554
COLT TELECOMMUNICATIONS FRANCE—See FMR LLC; *U.S. Private*, pg. 1554
COLT TELECOM NV/SA—See FMR LLC; *U.S. Private*, pg. 1554
COLT TELECOM PORTUGAL—See FMR LLC; *U.S. Private*, pg. 1554
COLUMBA EVEN EMPREENDIMENTOS IMOBILIARIOS LTDA.—See Even Construtora e Incorporadora S.A.; *Int'l*, pg. 2561
COLUMBIA/ALLEGHANY REGIONAL HOSPITAL, INCORPORATED—See HCA Healthcare, Inc.; *U.S. Public*, pg. 994
COLUMBIA ARTISTS MANAGEMENT LLC; *U.S. Private*, pg. 976
THE COLUMBIA ASC, LLC—See KKR & Co. Inc.; *U.S. Public*, pg. 1247
THE COLUMBIA ASC NORTHWEST, LLC—See KKR & Co. Inc.; *U.S. Public*, pg. 1247
COLUMBIA ASSOCIATES PSYCHIATRY P.C.—See North-East Health Services, LLC; *U.S. Private*, pg. 2950
COLUMBIA BANKING SYSTEM, INC.; *U.S. Public*, pg. 534
COLUMBIA BANK—See Columbia Financial, Inc.; *U.S. Public*, pg. 534
THE COLUMBIA BANK—See Fulton Financial Corporation; *U.S. Public*, pg. 892
COLUMBIA BASIN PIZZA HUT INC.; *U.S. Private*, pg. 976
COLUMBIA BASIN PUBLISHING CO., INC.—See The Hagadone Corporation; *U.S. Private*, pg. 4041
COLUMBIA BEACHOTEL PISSOURI—See Schoeller Holdings Ltd.; *Int'l*, pg. 6637
COLUMBIA BEACH RESORT PISSOURI—See Schoeller Holdings Ltd.; *Int'l*, pg. 6637
COLUMBIA BRANDS INTERNATIONAL SARL—See Columbia Sportswear Company; *U.S. Public*, pg. 534
COLUMBIA BRANDS USA, LLC—See Columbia Sportswear Company; *U.S. Public*, pg. 534

COLUMBIA BREWING COMPANY—See Anheuser-Busch InBev SA/NV; *Int'l*, pg. 466
COLUMBIA CAPITAL, LLC; *U.S. Private*, pg. 976
COLUMBIA CAPITAL MANAGEMENT; *U.S. Private*, pg. 976
COLUMBIA CARE SERVICE, INC; *U.S. Private*, pg. 976
COLUMBIA CASCADE COMPANY; *U.S. Private*, pg. 976
COLUMBIA CASUALTY COMPANY—See Loews Corporation; *U.S. Public*, pg. 1340
COLUMBIA CHRYSLER DODGE JEEP LTD.—See Go Auto; *Int'l*, pg. 3017
COLUMBIA COMMERCIAL BUILDING PRODUCTS LLC—See Grey Mountain Partners, LLC; *U.S. Private*, pg. 1784
COLUMBIA CORRUGATED BOX CO.; *U.S. Private*, pg. 976
THE COLUMBIA COUNTY NEWS-TIMES—See Shivers Trading & Operating Company; *U.S. Private*, pg. 3638
COLUMBIA & COWLITZ RAILWAY COMPANY, LLC—See Mitsubishi UFJ Financial Group, Inc.; *Int'l*, pg. 4971
COLUMBIA CURB & GUTTER CO.; *U.S. Private*, pg. 976
COLUMBIA DBL (PTY) LIMITED; *Int'l*, pg. 1706
COLUMBIA DENTOFORM CORPORATION—See The DentalEZ Group; *U.S. Private*, pg. 4020
COLUMBIA DEVELOPMENT COMPANIES; *U.S. Private*, pg. 976
COLUMBIA DIE MOLD—See Precision Plastics, Inc.; *U.S. Private*, pg. 3246
COLUMBIA DISTRIBUTING INC.; *U.S. Private*, pg. 976
COLUMBIA ELEKTRONIK AB—See Addtech AB; *Int'l*, pg. 132
COLUMBIA ENERGY GROUP—See TC Energy Corporation; *Int'l*, pg. 7482
COLUMBIA ENGINEERED RUBBER, INC.—See Pema Holding AG; *Int'l*, pg. 5784
COLUMBIA EXECUTIVE ASSOCIATES—See Galesi Group; *U.S. Private*, pg. 1637
COLUMBIA FALLS ALUMINUM COMPANY LLC—See United Company RUSAL Plc; *Int'l*, pg. 8066
COLUMBIA FARMS INC.—See Nash Johnson & Sons Farms Inc.; *U.S. Private*, pg. 2836
COLUMBIA FINANCIAL, INC.; *U.S. Public*, pg. 534
COLUMBIA FOREST PRODUCTS CORPORATION—See Columbia Forest Products Inc.; *U.S. Private*, pg. 976
COLUMBIA FOREST PRODUCTS INC.; *U.S. Private*, pg. 976
COLUMBIA FOREST PRODUCTS—See Columbia Forest Products Inc.; *U.S. Private*, pg. 976
COLUMBIA FREIGHTLINER, LLC—See Mercedes-Benz Group AG; *Int'l*, pg. 4820
COLUMBIA GAS OF KENTUCKY, INC.—See NiSource Inc.; *U.S. Public*, pg. 1530
COLUMBIA GAS OF MARYLAND, INC.—See NiSource Inc.; *U.S. Public*, pg. 1530
COLUMBIA GAS OF OHIO, INC.—See NiSource Inc.; *U.S. Public*, pg. 1530
COLUMBIA GAS OF PENNSYLVANIA, INC.—See NiSource Inc.; *U.S. Public*, pg. 1530
COLUMBIA GAS OF VIRGINIA, INC.—See NiSource Inc.; *U.S. Public*, pg. 1530
COLUMBIA GAS TRANSMISSION, LLC—See TC Energy Corporation; *Int'l*, pg. 7482
COLUMBIA GAS TRANSMISSION, LLC - WEST VIRGINIA OFFICE—See TC Energy Corporation; *Int'l*, pg. 7482
COLUMBIA GLAZING SYSTEMS INC.—See Columbia Manufacturing Co Ltd.; *Int'l*, pg. 1706
COLUMBIA GRAIN INTERNATIONAL—See Marubeni Corporation; *Int'l*, pg. 4706
THE COLUMBIA GROUP, INC.; *U.S. Private*, pg. 4011
COLUMBIA GULF TRANSMISSION, LLC—See TC Energy Corporation; *Int'l*, pg. 7482
COLUMBIA/HCA OF NORTH TEXAS, INC.—See HCA Healthcare, Inc.; *U.S. Public*, pg. 994
COLUMBIA/HCA RETREAT HOSPITAL, INC.—See HCA Healthcare, Inc.; *U.S. Public*, pg. 994
COLUMBIA HEALTHCARE CENTER, LLC—See National HealthCare Corporation; *U.S. Public*, pg. 1495
COLUMBIA HELICOPTERS, INC.—See AE Industrial Partners, LP; *U.S. Private*, pg. 112
COLUMBIA HOSPITAL AT MEDICAL CITY DALLAS SUBSIDIARY, L.P.—See HCA Healthcare, Inc.; *U.S. Public*, pg. 994
COLUMBIA HOSPITAL CORPORATION OF CORPUS CHRISTI—See HCA Healthcare, Inc.; *U.S. Public*, pg. 994
COLUMBIA HOSPITAL CORPORATION OF SOUTH BROWARD—See HCA Healthcare, Inc.; *U.S. Public*, pg. 994
COLUMBIA HOSPITAL (PALM BEACHES) LIMITED PARTNERSHIP—See HCA Healthcare, Inc.; *U.S. Public*, pg. 994
COLUMBIA HOTEL CASINO TRAVEMUENDE—See Schoeller Holdings Ltd.; *Int'l*, pg. 6637
COLUMBIA HOTEL RUESSELSHEIM—See Schoeller Holdings Ltd.; *Int'l*, pg. 6637
COLUMBIA HOUSE CANADA—See Pride Tree Holdings, Inc.; *U.S. Private*, pg. 3260
COLUMBIA HOUSE—See Pride Tree Holdings, Inc.; *U.S. Private*, pg. 3260

THE COLUMBIA GROUP, INC.

COLUMBIA INSURANCE CO.—See Berkshire Hathaway Inc.; *U.S. Public*, pg. 302
COLUMBIA INSURANCE GROUP, INC.; *U.S. Private*, pg. 977
COLUMBIA INSURANCE GROUP INC.—See Columbia Insurance Group, Inc.; *U.S. Private*, pg. 977
COLUMBIA INSURANCE GROUP INC.—See Columbia Insurance Group, Inc.; *U.S. Private*, pg. 977
COLUMBIA MACHINE INC.; *U.S. Private*, pg. 977
COLUMBIA MANAGEMENT GROUP, LLC—See Bank of America Corporation; *U.S. Public*, pg. 271
COLUMBIA MANAGEMENT INVESTMENT ADVISORS, LLC; *U.S. Private*, pg. 977
COLUMBIA MANUFACTURING CO LTD.; *Int'l*, pg. 1706
COLUMBIA-MBF, INC.—See Clayton, Dubilier & Rice, LLC; *U.S. Private*, pg. 919
THE COLUMBIA MD ORTHOPAEDIC ASC, LLC—See KKR & Co. Inc; *U.S. Public*, pg. 1247
COLUMBIA MEDICAL CENTER OF ARLINGTON SUBSIDIARY, L.P.—See HCA Healthcare, Inc.; *U.S. Public*, pg. 994
COLUMBIA MEDICAL CENTER OF DENTON SUBSIDIARY, L.P.—See HCA Healthcare, Inc.; *U.S. Public*, pg. 994
COLUMBIA MEDICAL CENTER OF LAS COLINAS, INC.—See HCA Healthcare, Inc.; *U.S. Public*, pg. 994
COLUMBIA MEDICAL CENTER OF LEWISVILLE SUBSIDIARY, L.P.—See HCA Healthcare, Inc.; *U.S. Public*, pg. 994
COLUMBIA MEDICAL CENTER OF MCKINNEY SUBSIDIARY, L.P.—See HCA Healthcare, Inc.; *U.S. Public*, pg. 994
COLUMBIA MEDICAL CENTER OF PLANO SUBSIDIARY, L.P.—See HCA Healthcare, Inc.; *U.S. Public*, pg. 994
COLUMBIA MEDICAL GROUP - CENTENNIAL, INC.—See HCA Healthcare, Inc.; *U.S. Public*, pg. 994
COLUMBIA MEMORIAL HOSPITAL; *U.S. Private*, pg. 977
COLUMBIA MEMORIAL PARK LLC—See Axar Capital Management L.P.; *U.S. Private*, pg. 411
COLUMBIA NATIONAL GROUP INC; *U.S. Private*, pg. 977
COLUMBIA NATIONAL INSURANCE CO. INC.—See Columbia Insurance Group, Inc.; *U.S. Private*, pg. 977
COLUMBIAN CHEMICALS BRASIL, LTDA.—See The Aditya Birla Group; *Int'l*, pg. 7610
COLUMBIAN CHEMICALS CANADA LTD.—See The Aditya Birla Group; *Int'l*, pg. 7610
COLUMBIAN CHEMICALS EUROPA GMBH—See The Aditya Birla Group; *Int'l*, pg. 7610
COLUMBIAN CHEMICALS KOREA CO., LTD.—See The Aditya Birla Group; *Int'l*, pg. 7610
COLUMBIAN FAMILY LIFE INSURANCE COMPANY—See Columbian Mutual Life Insurance Company; *U.S. Private*, pg. 978
COLUMBIAN FINANCIAL GROUP—See Columbian Mutual Life Insurance Company; *U.S. Private*, pg. 978
COLUMBIAN FOODS INCORPORATED; *U.S. Private*, pg. 978
COLUMBIAN HOME PRODUCTS; *U.S. Private*, pg. 978
COLUMBIA NISSAN INC.—See Dick Smith Automotive Group; *U.S. Private*, pg. 1226
COLUMBIAN LIFE INSURANCE COMPANY—See Columbian Mutual Life Insurance Company; *U.S. Private*, pg. 978
COLUMBIAN MUTUAL LIFE INSURANCE COMPANY—See Columbian Mutual Life Insurance Company; *U.S. Private*, pg. 978
COLUMBIAN MUTUAL LIFE INSURANCE COMPANY; *U.S. Private*, pg. 978
COLUMBIAN MUTUAL LIFE INSURANCE COMPANY - SYRACUSE—See Columbian Mutual Life Insurance Company; *U.S. Private*, pg. 978
COLUMBIA NORTHEAST KIDNEY CENTER, LLC—See Nautic Partners, LLC; *U.S. Private*, pg. 2869
COLUMBIA NORTH HILLS HOSPITAL SUBSIDIARY, L.P.—See HCA Healthcare, Inc.; *U.S. Public*, pg. 994
COLUMBIA NUT & BOLT LLC—See Park-Ohio Holdings Corp.; *U.S. Public*, pg. 1639
COLUMBIA NUTRITIONAL, LLC; *U.S. Private*, pg. 977
COLUMBIA OBJEKT GMBH—See Schoeller Holdings Ltd.; *Int'l*, pg. 6637
COLUMBIA OILFIELD SUPPLY LTD.—See Precision Drilling Corporation; *Int'l*, pg. 5957
COLUMBIA PAINT & COATINGS—See The Sherwin-Williams Company; *U.S. Public*, pg. 2127
COLUMBIA PARCAR CORP.—See Nordic Group of Companies, Ltd.; *U.S. Private*, pg. 2936
COLUMBIA PETRO CHEM PVT. LTD.; *Int'l*, pg. 1706
COLUMBIA PICTURES—See Sony Group Corporation; *Int'l*, pg. 7105
COLUMBIA PIPELINE GROUP, INC.—See TC Energy Corporation; *Int'l*, pg. 7482
COLUMBIA PIPELINE GROUP SERVICES COMPANY—See TC Energy Corporation; *Int'l*, pg. 7482
COLUMBIA PIPELINE PARTNERS LP—See TC Energy Corporation; *Int'l*, pg. 7482
COLUMBIA PIPE & SUPPLY COMPANY; *U.S. Private*, pg. 977

COLUMBIA PLAZA MEDICAL CENTER OF FORT WORTH SUBSIDIARY, L.P.—See HCA Healthcare, Inc.; *U.S. Public*, pg. 994
COLUMBIA PLYWOOD CORPORATION—See Columbia Forest Products Inc.; *U.S. Private*, pg. 976
COLUMBIA POLK GENERAL HOSPITAL, INC.—See HCA Healthcare, Inc.; *U.S. Public*, pg. 994
COLUMBIA POWER & WATER SYSTEMS; *U.S. Private*, pg. 977
COLUMBIA PRIMARY CARE, LLC—See HCA Healthcare, Inc.; *U.S. Public*, pg. 994
COLUMBIA PROJEKTENTWICKLUNG GMBH—See Schoeller Holdings Ltd.; *Int'l*, pg. 6637
COLUMBIA PROPERTIES LAUGHLIN, LLC—See Caesars Entertainment, Inc.; *U.S. Public*, pg. 421
COLUMBIA PROPERTIES TAHOE, LLC—See Caesars Entertainment, Inc.; *U.S. Public*, pg. 421
COLUMBIA PROPERTY MAINTENANCE—See Columbia Sweeping Services Inc.; *U.S. Private*, pg. 978
COLUMBIA PROPERTY TRUST, INC.—See Allianz SE; *Int'l*, pg. 346
COLUMBIA PROPERTY TRUST OPERATING PARTNERSHIP, L.P.—See Allianz SE; *Int'l*, pg. 346
COLUMBIA RECORDS GROUP—See Sony Group Corporation; *Int'l*, pg. 7103
COLUMBIA RESIDENTIAL; *U.S. Private*, pg. 977
COLUMBIA RESTAURANT GROUP; *U.S. Private*, pg. 977
COLUMBIA RETAIL SERVICES—See NiSource Inc.; *U.S. Public*, pg. 1530
COLUMBIA RIDGE CAPITAL MANAGEMENT, INC.—See NBT Bancorp Inc.; *U.S. Public*, pg. 1500
COLUMBIA RIVER CARBONATES; *U.S. Private*, pg. 977
COLUMBIA RIVER DISPOSAL, INC.—See Waste Connections, Inc.; *Int'l*, pg. 8353
COLUMBIA RIVER MEDIA GROUP—See Shivers Trading & Operating Company; *U.S. Private*, pg. 3638
COLUMBIA RIVER MENTAL HEALTH SERVICES; *U.S. Private*, pg. 977
COLUMBIA SELIGMAN PREMIUM TECHNOLOGY GROWTH FUND, INC.; *U.S. Public*, pg. 534
COLUMBIA SERVICES GROUP INC.; *U.S. Private*, pg. 977
COLUMBIA SHELVING & MIRROR CO, INC.—See Installed Building Products, Inc.; *U.S. Public*, pg. 1132
COLUMBIA SHIPMANAGEMENT (DEUTSCHLAND) GMBH—See Schoeller Holdings Ltd.; *Int'l*, pg. 6637
COLUMBIA SHIPMANAGEMENT LTD.—See Schoeller Holdings Ltd.; *Int'l*, pg. 6637
COLUMBIA SHIPMANAGEMENT (NETHERLANDS) B.V.—See Schoeller Holdings Ltd.; *Int'l*, pg. 6637
COLUMBIA SHIPMANAGEMENT RIJEKA D.O.O—See Schoeller Holdings Ltd.; *Int'l*, pg. 6637
COLUMBIA SHIPMANAGEMENT (SINGAPORE) PTE. LTD.—See Schoeller Holdings Ltd.; *Int'l*, pg. 6637
COLUMBIA SHIPMANAGEMENT (ST. PETERSBURG) LTD.—See Schoeller Holdings Ltd.; *Int'l*, pg. 6637
COLUMBIA SHIPMANGEMENT (TCM) SA—See Schoeller Holdings Ltd.; *Int'l*, pg. 6637
COLUMBIA SPECIALTY COMPANY, INC.; *U.S. Private*, pg. 977
COLUMBIA SPORTSWEAR ASIA PACIFIC SARL—See Columbia Sportswear Company; *U.S. Public*, pg. 535
COLUMBIA SPORTSWEAR CANADA LP—See Columbia Sportswear Company; *U.S. Public*, pg. 535
COLUMBIA SPORTSWEAR COMMERCIAL (SHANGHAI) CO., LTD.—See Columbia Sportswear Company; *U.S. Public*, pg. 535
COLUMBIA SPORTSWEAR COMPANY; *U.S. Public*, pg. 534
COLUMBIA SPORTSWEAR DENMARK APS—See Columbia Sportswear Company; *U.S. Public*, pg. 535
COLUMBIA SPORTSWEAR FINLAND OY—See Columbia Sportswear Company; *U.S. Public*, pg. 535
COLUMBIA SPORTSWEAR FRANCE S.A.S.—See Columbia Sportswear Company; *U.S. Public*, pg. 535
COLUMBIA SPORTSWEAR GMBH—See Columbia Sportswear Company; *U.S. Public*, pg. 535
COLUMBIA SPORTSWEAR INTERNATIONAL SARL—See Columbia Sportswear Company; *U.S. Public*, pg. 535
COLUMBIA SPORTSWEAR KOREA—See Columbia Sportswear Company; *U.S. Public*, pg. 535
COLUMBIA SPORTSWEAR USA CORPORATION—See Columbia Sportswear Company; *U.S. Public*, pg. 535
COLUMBIA STEEL CASTING CO., INC.; *U.S. Private*, pg. 977
COLUMBIA ST. MARY'S INC.—See Ascension Health Alliance; *U.S. Public*, pg. 347
COLUMBIA SUSSEX CORPORATION; *U.S. Private*, pg. 978
COLUMBIA SWEEPING SERVICES INC.; *U.S. Private*, pg. 978
COLUMBIA THREADNEEDLE AM (HOLDINGS) PLC—See Bank of Montreal; *Int'l*, pg. 846
COLUMBIA THREADNEEDLE INVESTMENT SERVICES LIMITED—See Bank of Montreal; *Int'l*, pg. 847
COLUMBIA THREADNEEDLE INVESTMENTS (ME) LIMITED—See Ameriprise Financial, Inc.; *U.S. Public*, pg. 114

COLUMBIA TRISTAR FILMS (UK)—See Sony Group Corporation; *Int'l*, pg. 7105
COLUMBIA TRISTAR MOTION PICTURE GROUP—See Sony Group Corporation; *Int'l*, pg. 7105
COLUMBIA TRUST COMPANY—See Columbia Banking System, Inc.; *U.S. Public*, pg. 534
COLUMBIA TRUST COMPANY—See Columbia Banking System, Inc.; *U.S. Public*, pg. 534
COLUMBIA UNIVERSITY PRESS; *U.S. Private*, pg. 978
COLUMBIA VENDING SERVICE INC.; *U.S. Private*, pg. 978
COLUMBIA VENTURES BROADBAND, LLC—See Columbia Ventures Corporation; *U.S. Private*, pg. 978
COLUMBIA VENTURES CORPORATION; *U.S. Private*, pg. 978
COLUMBIA VISTA CORPORATION—See Western Forest Products Inc.; *Int'l*, pg. 8388
COLUMBIA WANGER ASSET MANAGEMENT, LLC—See Ameriprise Financial, Inc.; *U.S. Public*, pg. 114
COLUMBIA WEATHER SYSTEMS, INC.—See Hinds Instruments, Inc.; *U.S. Private*, pg. 1948
COLUMBIA WEST VIRGINIA CORPORATION—See Columbia Forest Products Inc.; *U.S. Private*, pg. 976
COLUMBINE SPECIALTY PRODUCTS, INC.; *U.S. Private*, pg. 978
COLUMBINE VALLEY RESOURCES, INC.; *U.S. Public*, pg. 535
COLUMBITECH INC.—See Sectra AB; *Int'l*, pg. 6673
COLUMBOOLA SOLAR FARM HOLD CO PTY. LTD.—See Korea Electric Power Corporation; *Int'l*, pg. 4283
COLUMBUS AIRPORT AUTHORITY; *U.S. Private*, pg. 978
COLUMBUS ASSOCIATION FOR THE PERFORMING ARTS CORPORATION; *U.S. Private*, pg. 978
COLUMBUS A/S; *Int'l*, pg. 1706
COLUMBUS BLUE JACKETS; *U.S. Private*, pg. 979
COLUMBUS BRICK COMPANY—See Wienerberger AG; *Int'l*, pg. 8405
COLUMBUS BUILDERS SUPPLY INC.; *U.S. Private*, pg. 979
COLUMBUS & CHATTAHOOCHEE RAILROAD, INC.—See Brookfield Infrastructure Partners L.P.; *Int'l*, pg. 1191
COLUMBUS & CHATTAHOOCHEE RAILROAD, INC.—See GIC Pte. Ltd.; *Int'l*, pg. 2965
COLUMBUS CIRCLE FILMS LLC—See National Amusements, Inc.; *U.S. Private*, pg. 2842
COLUMBUS CITIZENS FOUNDATION; *U.S. Private*, pg. 979
COLUMBUS CYBERKNIFE, LLC—See Akumin, Inc.; *U.S. Public*, pg. 70
COLUMBUS DATA SERVICES LLC—See NCR Voyix Corporation.; *U.S. Public*, pg. 1502
COLUMBUS DEUTSCHLAND GMBH—See Columbus A/S; *Int'l*, pg. 1706
COLUMBUS DIRECT LIMITED—See The Collinson Group Limited; *Int'l*, pg. 7634
THE COLUMBUS DISTRIBUTING COMPANY INC.; *U.S. Private*, pg. 4011
COLUMBUS DOWNTOWN DEVELOPMENT CORPORATION; *U.S. Private*, pg. 979
COLUMBUS EESTI AS—See Columbus A/S; *Int'l*, pg. 1706
COLUMBUS ENERGY LIMITED; *Int'l*, pg. 1706
COLUMBUS ENERGY, LLC—See Amplify Energy Corp.; *U.S. Public*, pg. 133
COLUMBUS ENERGY RESOURCES PLC—See Challenger Energy Group PLC; *Int'l*, pg. 1438
COLUMBUS ENERGY SA; *Int'l*, pg. 1706
THE COLUMBUS EQUIPMENT COMPANY INC.; *U.S. Private*, pg. 4011
COLUMBUS FACTORING SOLUTIONS S.A.—See Fast Finance S.A.; *Int'l*, pg. 2621
COLUMBUS FAIR AUTO AUCTION, INC.—See Huron Capital Partners LLC; *U.S. Private*, pg. 2012
COLUMBUS FOODS COMPANY; *U.S. Private*, pg. 979
COLUMBUS GLOBAL (UK) LTD.—See Columbus A/S; *Int'l*, pg. 1706
COLUMBUS GOLD (U.S.) CORPORATION—See Orea Mining Corp.; *Int'l*, pg. 5616
COLUMBUS HOLDINGS—See Banco Bradesco S.A.; *Int'l*, pg. 819
COLUMBUS HOSPICE; *U.S. Private*, pg. 979
COLUMBUS HOSPITAL, LLC—See Universal Health Services, Inc.; *U.S. Public*, pg. 2256
COLUMBUS INDUSTRIES, INC.; *U.S. Private*, pg. 979
COLUMBUS JACK CORPORATION—See Quality Products Inc.; *U.S. Private*, pg. 3320
THE COLUMBUS LEDGER-ENQUIRER—See Chatham Asset Management, LLC; *U.S. Private*, pg. 867
COLUMBUS LIFE AND WATER; *U.S. Private*, pg. 979
COLUMBUS LIFE INSURANCE CO.—See Western & Southern Financial Group, Inc.; *U.S. Private*, pg. 4490
COLUMBUS M3 DANMARK APS—See Columbus A/S; *Int'l*, pg. 1706
COLUMBUS MANUFACTURING, INC.—See Hormel Foods Corporation; *U.S. Public*, pg. 1054
COLUMBUS MCKINNON ASIA PACIFIC LTD.—See Columbus McKinnon Corporation; *U.S. Public*, pg. 535

COMPANY NAME INDEX

COLUMBUS MCKINNON ASIA PACIFIC PTE. LTD.—See Columbus McKinnon Corporation; *U.S. Public*, pg. 535
COLUMBUS MCKINNON AUSTRIA GMBH—See Columbus McKinnon Corporation; *U.S. Public*, pg. 535
COLUMBUS MCKINNON CORPORATION LTD.—See Columbus McKinnon Corporation; *U.S. Public*, pg. 535
COLUMBUS MCKINNON CORPORATION; *U.S. Public*, pg. 535
COLUMBUS MCKINNON DO BRAZIL LTDA.—See Columbus McKinnon Corporation; *U.S. Public*, pg. 536
COLUMBUS MCKINNON ENGINEERED PRODUCTS GMBH—See Columbus McKinnon Corporation; *U.S. Public*, pg. 536
COLUMBUS MCKINNON (HANGZHOU) INDUSTRIAL PRODUCTS CO. LTD.—See Columbus McKinnon Corporation; *U.S. Public*, pg. 535
COLUMBUS MCKINNON (HANGZHOU) INDUSTRIES CO. LTD.—See Columbus McKinnon Corporation; *U.S. Public*, pg. 535
COLUMBUS MCKINNON HUNGARY KFT.—See Columbus McKinnon Corporation; *U.S. Public*, pg. 536
COLUMBUS MCKINNON IBERICA S.L.U.—See Columbus McKinnon Corporation; *U.S. Public*, pg. 536
COLUMBUS MCKINNON INDUSTRIAL PRODUCTS GMBH—See Columbus McKinnon Corporation; *U.S. Public*, pg. 535
COLUMBUS MCKINNON INDUSTRIAL PRODUCTS ME FZE—See Columbus McKinnon Corporation; *U.S. Public*, pg. 536
COLUMBUS MCKINNON IRELAND, LTD.—See Columbus McKinnon Corporation; *U.S. Public*, pg. 536
COLUMBUS MCKINNON ITALIA S.R.L.—See Columbus McKinnon Corporation; *U.S. Public*, pg. 536
COLUMBUS MCKINNON RUSSIA LLC—See Columbus McKinnon Corporation; *U.S. Public*, pg. 536
COLUMBUS MCKINNON (SHANGHAI) INTERNATIONAL TRADING CO. LTD.—See Columbus McKinnon Corporation; *U.S. Public*, pg. 535
COLUMBUS MCKINNON SINGAPORE PTE. LTD.—See Columbus McKinnon Corporation; *U.S. Public*, pg. 535
COLUMBUS MCKINNON SWITZERLAND AG—See Columbus McKinnon Corporation; *U.S. Public*, pg. 536
COLUMBUS MOTOR CAR COMPANY, INC.—See Germain Motor Company; *U.S. Private*, pg. 1686
COLUMBUS NISSAN INC.; *U.S. Private*, pg. 979
COLUMBUS NORWAY AS—See Columbus A/S; *Int'l*, pg. 1706
COLUMBUS NOVA, LLC—See Renova Group; *Int'l*, pg. 6285
COLUMBUS PAPER COMPANY, INC.—See Bain Capital, LP; *U.S. Private*, pg. 440
COLUMBUS PIPE & EQUIPMENT COMPANY; *U.S. Private*, pg. 979
COLUMBUS PRODUCTIONS, INC.—See Global Payments Inc.; *U.S. Public*, pg. 944
COLUMBUS PROPERTIES LP; *U.S. Private*, pg. 979
COLUMBUS RECYCLING PLANT—See Greif Inc.; *U.S. Public*, pg. 966
COLUMBUS-RNA-DAVITA, LLC—See DaVita Inc.; *U.S. Public*, pg. 637
COLUMBUS SOUTHERN POWER COMPANY—See American Electric Power Company, Inc.; *U.S. Public*, pg. 99
COLUMBUS SPECIALTY SURGERY CENTER LLC—See Tenet Healthcare Corporation; *U.S. Public*, pg. 2002
COLUMBUS STAINLESS (PTY) LTD—See Acerinox, S.A.; *Int'l*, pg. 100
COLUMBUS SWEDEN AB—See Columbus A/S; *Int'l*, pg. 1706
COLUMBUS TELEGRAM—See Lee Enterprises, Incorporated; *U.S. Public*, pg. 1299
COLUMBUS TRACTOR, LLC—See SunSouth LLC; *U.S. Private*, pg. 3872
COLUMBUS TRUCK AND EQUIPMENT CO. INC.; *U.S. Private*, pg. 979
COLUMBUS WATER WORKS; *U.S. Private*, pg. 979
COLUMBUS ZOOLOGICAL PARK ASSOCIATION; *U.S. Private*, pg. 979
COLUMN5 CONSULTING; *U.S. Private*, pg. 979
COLUMN FILM NEDERLAND BV—See Television Francaise 1 S.A.; *Int'l*, pg. 7542
COLUMN FINANCIAL, INC.—See UBS Group AG; *Int'l*, pg. 8005
COLUMN TECHNOLOGIES, INC.; *U.S. Private*, pg. 979
COLUSA ELEVATOR COMPANY—See ITOCHU Corporation; *Int'l*, pg. 3835
COLUSA ELEVATOR COMPANY—See ITOCHU Corporation; *Int'l*, pg. 3835
COLUSA ELEVATOR COMPANY—See National Federation of Agricultural Co-Operative Associations; *Int'l*, pg. 5156
COLUSA ELEVATOR COMPANY—See National Federation of Agricultural Co-Operative Associations; *Int'l*, pg. 5156
COLUSSY CHEVROLET INC.; *U.S. Private*, pg. 979
COLVILLE CAPITAL LLC; *U.S. Private*, pg. 979
COLVILLE INC.; *U.S. Private*, pg. 979
COLVILL OFFICE PROPERTIES, LLC—See Ontario Teachers' Pension Plan; *Int'l*, pg. 5588

COLVILL OFFICE PROPERTIES, LLC—See PAG Asia Capital Ltd.; *Int'l*, pg. 5695
COLVILL OFFICE PROPERTIES, LLC—See TPG Capital, L.P.; *U.S. Public*, pg. 2171
COLVIN OIL COMPANY INC.—See Andretti Petroleum, LLC; *U.S. Private*, pg. 279
COLWELL INDUSTRIES, INC.; *U.S. Private*, pg. 979
COLWELL NORTH AMERICA—See Colwell Industries, Inc.; *U.S. Private*, pg. 980
COLWEN MANAGEMENT INC.; *U.S. Private*, pg. 980
COLWILL ENGINEERING, INC.; *U.S. Private*, pg. 980
COLY, INC.; *Int'l*, pg. 1706
COM2000, INC.; *U.S. Private*, pg. 980
COM2M GMBH—See adesso SE; *Int'l*, pg. 144
COM2US CORPORATION; *Int'l*, pg. 1706
COM2US HOLDINGS; *Int'l*, pg. 1706
COM7 PUBLIC COMPANY LIMITED; *Int'l*, pg. 1706
COMACRAFT SDN BHD—See Dynavest Pte. Ltd.; *Int'l*, pg. 2242
CO.MA.DI.S. S.P.A.—See I.M.A. Industria Macchine Automatiche S.p.A.; *Int'l*, pg. 3565
COMADUR S.A.—See The Swatch Group Ltd.; *Int'l*, pg. 7691
COMAG FORWARD—See Advance Publications, Inc.; *U.S. Private*, pg. 85
COMAG FORWARD—See The Hearst Corporation; *U.S. Private*, pg. 4047
COMAG SPECIALIST—See Advance Publications, Inc.; *U.S. Private*, pg. 85
COMAG SPECIALIST—See The Hearst Corporation; *U.S. Private*, pg. 4047
COMAIR REISE UND CHARTER GMBH—See BERGER Holding GmbH; *Int'l*, pg. 979
COMAIR ROTRON SHANGHAI FAN CO., LTD.—See Gentherm Incorporated; *U.S. Public*, pg. 931
COMAIS S.R.L.—See Etex SA/NV; *Int'l*, pg. 2521
COMALEX SA; *Int'l*, pg. 1707
COMALIMENT SA; *Int'l*, pg. 1707
COMAL S.P.A.; *Int'l*, pg. 1707
COMANAV—See CMA CGM S.A.; *Int'l*, pg. 1668
COMANCHE CONSTRUCTION, INC.; *U.S. Private*, pg. 980
COMANCHE COUNTY ELECTRIC COOPERATIVE ASSOCIATION; *U.S. Private*, pg. 980
COMANCHE COUNTY MEDICAL CENTER; *U.S. Private*, pg. 980
COMANCHE COUNTY TELECOM—See First American Communications Enterprise Inc.; *U.S. Private*, pg. 1513
COMANCHE ELECTRIC COOP ASSOCIATION; *U.S. Private*, pg. 980
COMANCHE INTERNATIONAL MALAYSIA SDN. BHD.—See Comanche International PCL; *Int'l*, pg. 1707
COMANCHE INTERNATIONAL PCL; *Int'l*, pg. 1707
COMANCHE INTERNATIONAL VIETNAM CO., LTD.—See Comanche International PCL; *Int'l*, pg. 1707
COMAN S.A.—See A.P. Moller-Maersk A/S; *Int'l*, pg. 26
COMANTEC NV—See VINCI S.A.; *Int'l*, pg. 8216
COMANT INDUSTRIES, INC—See Advent International Corporation; *U.S. Private*, pg. 99
COMANY INC. - MARKET DEVELOPMENT DIVISION—See Comany Inc.; *Int'l*, pg. 1707
COMANY INC.; *Int'l*, pg. 1707
COMAP HELLAS S.A.—See Aalberts N.V.; *Int'l*, pg. 33
COMAP HUNGARIA KERESKEDELMI KFT.—See Aalberts N.V.; *Int'l*, pg. 33
COMAP ITALIA S.R.L.U.—See Aalberts N.V.; *Int'l*, pg. 33
COMAP NORDIC AB—See Aalberts N.V.; *Int'l*, pg. 33
COMAP N.V.—See Aalberts N.V.; *Int'l*, pg. 33
COMAP POLSKA SP. Z.O.O.—See Aalberts N.V.; *Int'l*, pg. 33
COMAP PRAHA S.R.O.—See Aalberts N.V.; *Int'l*, pg. 33
COMAP S.A.—See Aalberts N.V.; *Int'l*, pg. 33
COMAP (UK) LIMITED—See Aalberts N.V.; *Int'l*, pg. 33
COMARA GMBH—See Sandvik AB; *Int'l*, pg. 6528
COMARCH AG—See ComArch S.A.; *Int'l*, pg. 1707
COMARCH CHILE SPA—See ComArch S.A.; *Int'l*, pg. 1707
COMARCH JAPAN KK—See ComArch S.A.; *Int'l*, pg. 1707
COMARCH LLC—See ComArch S.A.; *Int'l*, pg. 1707
COMARCH LUXEMBOURG S.A R.L.—See ComArch S.A.; *Int'l*, pg. 1707
COMARCH MALAYSIA SDN. BHD.—See ComArch S.A.; *Int'l*, pg. 1707
COMARCH MIDDLE EAST FZ-LLC—See ComArch S.A.; *Int'l*, pg. 1707
COMARCH OOO—See ComArch S.A.; *Int'l*, pg. 1707
COMARCH PANAMA INC.—See ComArch S.A.; *Int'l*, pg. 1707
COMARCH R&D S.A.R.L.—See ComArch S.A.; *Int'l*, pg. 1707
COMARCH S.A.; *Int'l*, pg. 1707
COMARCH SCHILLING GMBH—See ComArch S.A.; *Int'l*, pg. 1707
COMARCH SISTEMAS LTDA—See ComArch S.A.; *Int'l*, pg. 1707
COMARCH SOFTWARE S.A.R.L.—See ComArch S.A.; *Int'l*, pg. 1707
COMARCH SOFTWARE UND BERATUNG—See ComArch S.A.; *Int'l*, pg. 1707

COMBE INCORPORATED

COMARCH SOLUTIONS GMBH—See ComArch S.A.; *Int'l*, pg. 1707
COMARCH SOLUTIONS GMBH—See ComArch S.A.; *Int'l*, pg. 1707
COMARCH SWISS AG—See ComArch S.A.; *Int'l*, pg. 1707
COMARCH TECHNOLOGIES OY—See ComArch S.A.; *Int'l*, pg. 1707
COMARCH UK LTD.—See ComArch S.A.; *Int'l*, pg. 1707
COMARCH VIETNAM CO. LTD.—See ComArch S.A.; *Int'l*, pg. 1707
COMARCO, INC.; *U.S. Private*, pg. 980
COMARCO WIRELESS TECHNOLOGIES, INC.—See Comarco, Inc.; *U.S. Private*, pg. 980
COMARI SAS—See VINCI S.A.; *Int'l*, pg. 8216
COMARK COMMUNICATIONS, LLC; *U.S. Private*, pg. 980
COMARK, LLC; *U.S. Private*, pg. 980
CO.MARK TES S.L—See Tinexta S.p.A.; *Int'l*, pg. 7753
COMAR, LLC; *U.S. Private*, pg. 980
COMAR PLANT DESIGN & MANUFACTURING (PTY) LTD.—See Raubex Group Limited; *Int'l*, pg. 6221
COMASEC ITALIA SRL—See Ansell Limited; *Int'l*, pg. 478
COMASEC SAS—See Ansell Limited; *Int'l*, pg. 478
COMA SERVICES AG—See Bechtle AG; *Int'l*, pg. 937
COMAT AUTO SA; *Int'l*, pg. 1707
COMAT CARAS SEVERIN SA; *Int'l*, pg. 1707
COMAT EUROPE—See Comat Technologies (P) Ltd.; *Int'l*, pg. 1708
COMATRAL - C. DE MAROC. DE TRANSF. DU LIEGE, S.A.—See CORTICEIRA AMORIM, S.G.P.S., S.A.; *Int'l*, pg. 1807
COMAT TECHNOLOGIES, INC.—See Comat Technologies (P) Ltd.; *Int'l*, pg. 1708
COMAT TECHNOLOGIES (P) LTD.; *Int'l*, pg. 1708
COMAU ARGENTINA S.A.—See Stellantis N.V.; *Int'l*, pg. 7197
COMAU DEUTSCHLAND GMBH—See Stellantis N.V.; *Int'l*, pg. 7197
COMAU FRANCE S.A.S.—See Stellantis N.V.; *Int'l*, pg. 7197
COMAU INC.—See Stellantis N.V.; *Int'l*, pg. 7197
COMAU INDIA PRIVATE LIMITED—See Stellantis N.V.; *Int'l*, pg. 7197
COMAU (KUNSHAN) AUTOMATION CO. LTD.—See Stellantis N.V.; *Int'l*, pg. 7197
COMAU PICO HOLDINGS CORPORATION—See Stellantis N.V.; *Int'l*, pg. 7197
COMAU PICO LAISA S.DE R.L. DE C.V.—See Stellantis N.V.; *Int'l*, pg. 7197
COMAU PICO MEXICO S.DE R.L. DE C.V.—See Stellantis N.V.; *Int'l*, pg. 7197
COMAU PICO PITEX S.DE R.L. C.V—See Stellantis N.V.; *Int'l*, pg. 7197
COMAU PICO TREBOL S.DE R.L. DE C.V.—See Stellantis N.V.; *Int'l*, pg. 7197
COMAU ROMANIA S.R.L.—See Stellantis N.V.; *Int'l*, pg. 7197
COMAU RUSSIA OOO—See Stellantis N.V.; *Int'l*, pg. 7197
COMAU SERVICE SYSTEMS S.L.—See Stellantis N.V.; *Int'l*, pg. 7197
COMAU (SHANGHAI) INTERNATIONAL TRADING CO. LTD.—See Stellantis N.V.; *Int'l*, pg. 7197
COMAU S.P.A.—See Stellantis N.V.; *Int'l*, pg. 7197
COMAU U.K. LIMITED—See Stellantis N.V.; *Int'l*, pg. 7197
COMBAN TELECOM SYSTEMS AB—See Comba Telecom Systems Holdings Limited; *Int'l*, pg. 1708
COMBAT ADVANCED PROPULSION, LLC—See L3Harris Technologies, Inc.; *U.S. Public*, pg. 1281
COMBAT BRANDS, LLC; *U.S. Private*, pg. 980
COMBAT DRUGS LIMITED; *Int'l*, pg. 1708
COMBA TELECOM CO. LTD.—See Comba Telecom Systems Holdings Limited; *Int'l*, pg. 1708
COMBA TELECOM INC.—See Comba Telecom Systems Holdings Limited; *Int'l*, pg. 1708
COMBA TELECOM INDIA PRIVATE LIMITED—See Comba Telecom Systems Holdings Limited; *Int'l*, pg. 1708
COMBA TELECOM LTDA—See Comba Telecom Systems Holdings Limited; *Int'l*, pg. 1708
COMBA TELECOM SYSTEMS HOLDINGS LIMITED; *Int'l*, pg. 1708
COMBA TELECOM SYSTEMS LIMITED—See Comba Telecom Systems Holdings Limited; *Int'l*, pg. 1708
COMBA TELECOM SYSTEMS (SINGAPORE) PTE. LTD.—See Comba Telecom Systems Holdings Limited; *Int'l*, pg. 1708
COMBA TELECOM TECHNOLOGY (GUANGZHOU) LIMITED—See Comba Telecom Systems Holdings Limited; *Int'l*, pg. 1708
COMBAT HVAC LIMITED—See Madison Industries Holdings LLC; *U.S. Private*, pg. 2543
COMBAT SPORTS—See Fairfax Financial Holdings Limited; *Int'l*, pg. 2605
COMBAT SPORTS—See Power Corporation of Canada; *Int'l*, pg. 5944
COMBEE INSULATION COMPANY, INC.—See Installed Building Products, Inc.; *U.S. Public*, pg. 1132
COMBE INCORPORATED; *U.S. Private*, pg. 980

COMBE INCORPORATED

COMBE INTERNATIONAL LIMITED—See Combe Incorporated; *U.S. Private*, pg. 980
COMBELL NV; *Int'l*, pg. 1708
COMBEST HOLDINGS LIMITED; *Int'l*, pg. 1708
COMBI ASIA LIMITED—See Combi Corporation; *Int'l*, pg. 1708
COMBICARE B.V.—See Advent International Corporation; *U.S. Private*, pg. 104
COMBICARE VASTGOED B.V.—See Advent International Corporation; *U.S. Private*, pg. 104
COMBI CORPORATION; *Int'l*, pg. 1708
COMBIDATA POLAND SP. Z.O.O.—See Asseco Poland S.A.; *Int'l*, pg. 642
COMBIGENE AB; *Int'l*, pg. 1708
COMBI KOREA CO., LTD.—See Combi Corporation; *Int'l*, pg. 1708
COMBILENT A/S—See Indutrade AB; *Int'l*, pg. 3677
COMBI MARITIME CORPORATION.—See Roadrunner Transportation Systems, Inc.; *U.S. Public*, pg. 1802
COMBIMATRIX CORPORATION—See Invitae Corporation; *U.S. Public*, pg. 1165
COMBIMATRIX MOLECULAR DIAGNOSTICS, INC.—See Invitae Corporation; *U.S. Public*, pg. 1165
COMBIMILL OU; *Int'l*, pg. 1708
COMBIMILL REOPALU OU—See Combimill OU; *Int'l*, pg. 1708
COMBINATIE NIJUIS-IPPEL V.O.F.—See Pentair plc; *Int'l*, pg. 5789
THE COMBINATION DOOR CO.—See Paul Argoe Screens, Inc.; *U.S. Private*, pg. 3112
COMBINED BENEFITS ADMINISTRATORS, LLC—See Hellman & Friedman LLC; *U.S. Private*, pg. 1908
COMBINED COMMUNICATIONS CORPORATION OF OKLAHOMA, LLC—See TEGNA Inc.; *U.S. Public*, pg. 1990
COMBINED COMMUNICATIONS NETWORK PTY LTD—See ComfortDelGro Corporation Limited; *Int'l*, pg. 1712
COMBINED EXPRESS INC.; *U.S. Private*, pg. 980
COMBINED GENERAL FOR GENERAL TRADING & CONTRACTING CO. W.L.L.—See Combined Group Contracting Company KSCC; *Int'l*, pg. 1709
COMBINED GROUP CONTRACTING COMPANY KSCC; *Int'l*, pg. 1709
COMBINED GROUP CONTRACTING CO. W.L.L.—See Combined Group Contracting Company KSCC; *Int'l*, pg. 1709
COMBINED GROUP CONTRACTING GLOBAL CO. W.L.L.—See Combined Group Contracting Company KSCC; *Int'l*, pg. 1709
COMBINED GROUP FACTORIES COMPANY W.L.L.—See Combined Group Contracting Company KSCC; *Int'l*, pg. 1709
COMBINED GROUP INSURANCE SERVICES, INC.—See Brown & Brown, Inc.; *U.S. Public*, pg. 400
COMBINED GROUP ROCKS COMPANY- K.S.C.—See Combined Group Contracting Company KSCC; *Int'l*, pg. 1709
COMBINED GROUP TRADING AND CONTRACTING GLOBAL - L.L.C.—See Combined Group Contracting Company KSCC; *Int'l*, pg. 1709
COMBINED GROUP TRADING & CONTRACTING CO. W.L.L.—See Combined Group Contracting Company KSCC; *Int'l*, pg. 1709
COMBINED INSURANCE COMPANY OF AMERICA - CANADA—See Chubb Limited; *Int'l*, pg. 1591
COMBINED INSURANCE COMPANY OF AMERICA - CHICAGO—See Chubb Limited; *Int'l*, pg. 1591
COMBINED INSURANCE COMPANY OF AMERICA—See Chubb Limited; *Int'l*, pg. 1591
COMBINED INTERNATIONAL REAL ESTATE COMPANY-K.S.C.—See Combined Group Contracting Company KSCC; *Int'l*, pg. 1709
COMBINED INVESTIGATORS, INC—See Ethos Risk Services LLC; *U.S. Private*, pg. 1432
COMBINED JEWISH PHILANTHROPIES OF GREATER BOSTON, INC.; *U.S. Private*, pg. 980
COMBINED LIFE INSURANCE COMPANY OF AUSTRALIA, LTD.—See Chubb Limited; *Int'l*, pg. 1591
COMBINED LIFE INSURANCE COMPANY OF NEW YORK—See Chubb Limited; *Int'l*, pg. 1591
COMBINED METALS OF CHICAGO LLC—See Cleveland-Cliffs, Inc.; *U.S. Public*, pg. 514
COMBINED MOTOR HOLDINGS LIMITED; *Int'l*, pg. 1709
COMBINED OIL CO.—See U.S. Venture, Inc.; *U.S. Private*, pg. 4272
COMBINED PRECISION COMPONENTS LIMITED—See Avnet, Inc.; *U.S. Public*, pg. 252
COMBINED RURAL TRADERS PTY LIMITED—See Nutrien Ltd.; *Int'l*, pg. 5492
COMBINED TRANSPORT INC.; *U.S. Private*, pg. 980
COMBINED UNDERWRITERS OF MIAMI—See Kelso & Company, L.P.; *U.S. Private*, pg. 2279
COMBINEDX AB; *Int'l*, pg. 1709
COMBINE INTERNATIONAL INC.; *U.S. Private*, pg. 980
COMBINE WILL INTERNATIONAL HOLDINGS LIMITED; *Int'l*, pg. 1708
COMBI NEXT CORPORATION—See Combi Corporation; *Int'l*, pg. 1708

COMBI PACKAGING SYSTEMS, LLC—See SIAT Societa' Internazionale Applicazioni Tecniche SpA; *Int'l*, pg. 6876
COMBI-PACK SDN BHD—See Thai Plaspac Public Company Limited; *Int'l*, pg. 7594
COMBIS D.O.O.—See Nayax Ltd.; *Int'l*, pg. 5178
COMBI (SHANGHAI) CO., LTD.—See Combi Corporation; *Int'l*, pg. 1708
COMBISPED HANSEATISCHE SPEDITION GMBH—See Hamburger Hafen und Logistik AG; *Int'l*, pg. 3236
COMBI (TAIWAN) CO., LTD.—See Combi Corporation; *Int'l*, pg. 1708
COMBITECH AB—See Saab AB; *Int'l*, pg. 6459
COMBITECH ELECTRONICS—See Kitron ASA; *Int'l*, pg. 4195
COMBITECH OY—See Saab AB; *Int'l*, pg. 6459
COMBI USA, INC.—See Combi Corporation; *Int'l*, pg. 1708
COMBI WEAR PARTS—See The Riverside Company; *U.S. Private*, pg. 4109
COMBI WELLNESS CORPORATION—See Konami Group Corporation; *Int'l*, pg. 4245
COMBIWITH CORPORATION—See Combi Corporation; *Int'l*, pg. 1708
COMBOIOS DE PORTUGAL; *Int'l*, pg. 1709
COMBS & COMPANY; *U.S. Private*, pg. 980
COMBS OIL CO. INC.; *U.S. Private*, pg. 981
COMBS PRODUCE CO., L.P.—See Lipman & Lipman, Inc.; *U.S. Private*, pg. 2465
COMBULEX B.V.—See Van Leeuwen Pipe & Tube Group B.V.; *Int'l*, pg. 8126
COMBUSTIONEER CORP.—See EMCOR Group, Inc.; *U.S. Public*, pg. 737
COMBUSTION PARTS INC.—See Allied Power Group, LLC; *U.S. Private*, pg. 187
COMBUSTION TECHNOLOGIES CORP.—See Environmental Energy Services, Inc.; *U.S. Private*, pg. 1407
COMCAM INTERNATIONAL, INC.; *U.S. Private*, pg. 981
COMCARE MEDICAL B.V.—See Adenia Partners Ltd; *Int'l*, pg. 143
COMCAR INDUSTRIES, INC.; *U.S. Private*, pg. 981
COMCAST CABLE COMMUNICATIONS, LLC—See Comcast Corporation; *U.S. Public*, pg. 537
COMCAST CABLEVISION INVESTMENT CORPORATION—See Comcast Corporation; *U.S. Public*, pg. 537
COMCAST CABLEVISION MD LP; *U.S. Private*, pg. 981
COMCAST CORPORATION; *U.S. Public*, pg. 536
COMCAST CORP.—See Comcast Corporation; *U.S. Public*, pg. 537
COMCAST CORP.—See Comcast Corporation; *U.S. Public*, pg. 537
COMCAST CORP.—See Comcast Corporation; *U.S. Public*, pg. 537
COMCAST CORP.—See Comcast Corporation; *U.S. Public*, pg. 537
COMCAST CORP.—See Comcast Corporation; *U.S. Public*, pg. 537
COMCAST CORP.—See Comcast Corporation; *U.S. Public*, pg. 537
COMCAST ENTERPRISE SERVICES, LLC—See Comcast Corporation; *U.S. Public*, pg. 537
COMCAST INTERACTIVE CAPITAL, L.P.—See Comcast Corporation; *U.S. Public*, pg. 537
COMCAST MO OF DELAWARE, LLC—See Comcast Corporation; *U.S. Public*, pg. 537
COMCAST OF ARIZONA, INC.—See Comcast Corporation; *U.S. Public*, pg. 538
COMCAST OF COLORADO/PENNSYLVANIA/WEST VIRGINIA, LLC—See Comcast Corporation; *U.S. Public*, pg. 538
COMCAST OF DELMARVA, INC.—See Comcast Corporation; *U.S. Public*, pg. 538
COMCAST OF GARDEN STATE, L.P.—See Comcast Corporation; *U.S. Public*, pg. 538
COMCAST OF HARFORD COUNTY, LLC—See Comcast Corporation; *U.S. Public*, pg. 538
COMCAST OF ILLINOIS/INDIANA/OHIO, LLC—See Comcast Corporation; *U.S. Public*, pg. 538
COMCAST OF MAINE/NEW HAMPSHIRE, INC.—See Comcast Corporation; *U.S. Public*, pg. 538
COMCAST OF POTOMAC, LLC—See Comcast Corporation; *U.S. Public*, pg. 538
COMCAST OF SOUTHERN NEW ENGLAND, INC.—See Comcast Corporation; *U.S. Public*, pg. 538
COMCAST PHONE OF COLORADO, LLC—See Comcast Corporation; *U.S. Public*, pg. 537
COMCAST PHONE OF D.C., LLC—See Comcast Corporation; *U.S. Public*, pg. 537
COMCAST-SPECTACOR FOUNDATION—See Comcast Corporation; *U.S. Public*, pg. 537
COMCAST SPECTACOR, L.P.—See Comcast Corporation; *U.S. Public*, pg. 537
COMCAST SPORTS MANAGEMENT SERVICES, LLC—See Comcast Corporation; *U.S. Public*, pg. 539
COMCAST SPORTSNET MID-ATLANTIC, L.P.—See Comcast Corporation; *U.S. Public*, pg. 539
COMCAST SPORTSNET NEW ENGLAND, LLC—See Comcast Corporation; *U.S. Public*, pg. 539

CORPORATE AFFILIATIONS

COMCAST SPORTSNET PHILADELPHIA, L.P.—See Comcast Corporation; *U.S. Public*, pg. 539
COMCAST SPOTLIGHT—See Comcast Corporation; *U.S. Public*, pg. 537
COMCAST VENTURE LLC—See Comcast Corporation; *U.S. Public*, pg. 538
COMCATER PTY. LTD.; *Int'l*, pg. 1709
COMCAVE AG—See Gilde Buy Out Partners B.V.; *Int'l*, pg. 2974
COMCEREAL SA BACAU; *Int'l*, pg. 1709
COMCEREAL SA BOTOSANI; *Int'l*, pg. 1709
COMCEREAL SA BUCURESTI; *Int'l*, pg. 1709
COMCEREAL SA SLOBOZIA; *Int'l*, pg. 1709
COMCEREAL SA TULCEA; *Int'l*, pg. 1709
COMCERTO SRL—See Live Nation Entertainment, Inc.; *U.S. Public*, pg. 1328
COMCM S.A.; *Int'l*, pg. 1709
COMCO MCS S.A.—See RWE AG; *Int'l*, pg. 6433
COMCO PIPE AND SUPPLY COMPANY—See Russel Metals Inc.; *Int'l*, pg. 6430
COMCO PLASTICS INC.; *U.S. Private*, pg. 981
COMCORP FACTORS, INC.—See Kennington Ltd., Inc.; *U.S. Private*, pg. 2286
COMCOUNT INC.; *U.S. Private*, pg. 981
COMDAIN INFRASTRUCTURE PTY. LTD.—See Service Stream Limited; *Int'l*, pg. 6725
COMDATA CORPORATION—See Corpay, Inc.; *U.S. Public*, pg. 579
COMDATA HOLDING SA—See The Carlyle Group Inc.; *U.S. Public*, pg. 2046
COMDATA SPA—See The Carlyle Group Inc.; *U.S. Public*, pg. 2045
COMDAT DATASYSTEMS AG; *Int'l*, pg. 1709
COMDEL, INC.—See XP Power Limited; *Int'l*, pg. 8537
COMDESIGN INC.; *U.S. Private*, pg. 981
COMDESIGN INC.—See Tsuzuki Denki Co., Ltd.; *Int'l*, pg. 7958
COMDIRECT BANK AG—See Commerzbank AG; *Int'l*, pg. 1717
COMDITEL S.A.—See Industria de Diseno Textil, S.A.; *Int'l*, pg. 3665
COMDOC INC.—See Xerox Holdings Corporation; *U.S. Public*, pg. 2389
COME AND STAY S.A.; *Int'l*, pg. 1709
COMEAUS SEA FOODS LIMITED; *Int'l*, pg. 1710
COMEAUX FURNITURE & APPLIANCES INC.; *U.S. Private*, pg. 981
COMECART S.P.A—See Burgo Group S.p.A.; *Int'l*, pg. 1224
COMECER S.P.A.—See ATS Corporation; *Int'l*, pg. 695
COMECO GRAFICO S.L.U.—See Vocento, S.A.; *Int'l*, pg. 8284
COMECO IMPRESION S.L.—See Vocento, S.A.; *Int'l*, pg. 8284
COMECOP—See Grupo Empresarial Kaluz S.A. de C.V.; *Int'l*, pg. 3126
THE COMEDY NETWORK—See BCE Inc.; *Int'l*, pg. 927
COMEDY PARTNERS—See National Amusements, Inc.; *U.S. Private*, pg. 2841
THE COMEDY UNIT—See De Agostini S.p.A.; *Int'l*, pg. 1994
COMEFLY OUTDOOR CO LTD; *Int'l*, pg. 1710
COMEF SP. Z O.O. SP.K.—See HORIBA Ltd; *Int'l*, pg. 3475
COMEGSA—See Empresas Publicas de Medellin ESP; *Int'l*, pg. 2391
COMEGYS INSURANCE AGENCY, INC.; *U.S. Private*, pg. 981
COMELF SA; *Int'l*, pg. 1710
COMENDA ALI SPA.—See Ali Holding S.r.l; *Int'l*, pg. 321
COMENITY CAPITAL BANK—See Bread Financial Holdings Inc.; *U.S. Public*, pg. 381
COMENSURA LTD.—See HFBG Holding B.V.; *Int'l*, pg. 3374
COMENSURA PTY LIMITED—See HFBG Holding B.V.; *Int'l*, pg. 3374
COME ON STRONG INC.; *U.S. Private*, pg. 981
COMERA LIFE SCIENCES HOLDINGS, INC.; *U.S. Public*, pg. 542
COMERCIAL ARGE, S.A.—See Pilot Corporation; *Int'l*, pg. 5866
COMERCIAL ASIANDINA S.A.—See Sigdo Koppers S.A.; *Int'l*, pg. 6907
COMERCIAL CITROEN S.A.—See Stellantis N.V.; *Int'l*, pg. 7201
COMERCIAL DE AUTOPECAS KYB DO BRASIL LTDA.—See KYB Corporation; *Int'l*, pg. 4353
COMERCIAL DEL ACERO S.A.—See Corporacion Aceros Arequipa S.A.; *Int'l*, pg. 1803
COMERCIAL DE LAMINADOS S.A.—See Klockner & Co. SE; *Int'l*, pg. 4202
COMERCIAL DE MATERIALES DE INCENDIOS, S.L.—See Grupo Villar Mir, S.A.U.; *Int'l*, pg. 3138
COMERCIAL DUOMO LIMITADA—See CRH plc; *Int'l*, pg. 1844
COMERCIAL E IMPORTADORA DE PNEUS LTDA—See China National Chemical Corporation; *Int'l*, pg. 1528
COMERCIAL ELECTRICA DW S/A-FILIAL BLUMENAU—See Sonepar S.A.; *Int'l*, pg. 7092

COMPANY NAME INDEX

COMERCIAL ELETRICA DW LTDA—See Sonepar S.A.; *Int'l*, pg. 7093
COMERCIAL GASSO SA; *Int'l*, pg. 1710
COMERCIAL GRUPO ANAYA SA—See Vivendi SE; *Int'l*, pg. 8272
COMERCIAL HISPANOFIL, S.A.—See Sonepar S.A.; *Int'l*, pg. 7092
COMERCIAL HYDRO S.A.—See Sociedad Quimica y Minera de Chile S.A.; *Int'l*, pg. 7032
COMERCIAL INGERSOLL-RAND (CHILE) LIMITADA—See Ingersoll Rand Inc.; *U.S. Public*, pg. 1118
COMERCIALIZADORA DE ELECTRODOS VENEZUELA COMELVEN C.A.—See Enovis Corporation; *U.S. Public*, pg. 772
COMERCIALIZADORA EMERSON NETWORK POWER CHILE LIMITADA—See Emerson Electric Co.; *U.S. Public*, pg. 744
COMERCIALIZADORA LA MODERNA DE TOLUCA, S.A. DE C.V.—See Grupo La Moderna, S.A.B. de C.V.; *Int'l*, pg. 3131
COMERCIALIZADORA NACIONAL SAS LTDA.—See PepsiCo, Inc.; *U.S. Public*, pg. 1668
COMERCIALIZADORA NOVAVERDE S.A.—See Embotelladora Andina S.A.; *Int'l*, pg. 2375
COMERCIALIZADORA REGULADA GAS & POWER, S.A.—See Naturgy Energy Group, S.A.; *Int'l*, pg. 5169
COMERCIALIZADORA SNACKS, S.R.L.—See PepsiCo, Inc.; *U.S. Public*, pg. 1668
COMERCIALIZADORA TIMAC AGRO CHILE LIMITADA—See Compagnie Financiere et de Participations Roullier SA; *Int'l*, pg. 1740
COMERCIAL JANOME LATIN AMERICA LIMITADA—See Janome Sewing Machine Co., Ltd.; *Int'l*, pg. 3880
COMERCIAL KENDALL (CHILE) LIMITADA—See Medtronic plc; *Int'l*, pg. 4786
COMERCIAL MEXICANA DE PINTURAS, S.A. DE C.V.—See PPG Industries, Inc.; *U.S. Public*, pg. 1709
COMERCIAL MULTIMEDIA VOCENTO, S.A.U.—See Vocento, S.A.; *Int'l*, pg. 8284
COMERCIAL NUTRESA S.A.S.—See Grupo Nutresa S.A.; *Int'l*, pg. 3133
COMERCIAL PEUMO LTDA.—See Vina Concha y Toro S.A.; *Int'l*, pg. 0200
COMERCIAL SENSITECH SOUTH AMERICA LIMITADA—See Carrier Global Corporation; *U.S. Public*, pg. 443
COMERCIAL TECNILUZ DE CHILE LTDA.—See A.A.G. STUCCHI s.r.l.; *Int'l*, pg. 22
COMERCIAL UDRA, S.A.U.—See Grupo Empresarial San Jose, S.A.; *Int'l*, pg. 3128
COMERCIALIZADORA PREMIER, S.A. DE C.V.—See Pulsar Internacional S.A. de C.V.; *Int'l*, pg. 6116
COMERCIO DE COMBUSTIVEIS E LUBRIFICANTES S.A.—See BP plc; *Int'l*, pg. 1131
COMERCIO E INDUSTRIA UNIQUIMICA LTDA.—See Meiji Holdings Co., Ltd.; *Int'l*, pg. 4801
COMERGENCE COMPLIANCE MONITORING, LLC—See Constellation Software Inc.; *Int'l*, pg. 1774
COMER GMBH—See Comer Industries S.p.A.; *Int'l*, pg. 1710
COMERICA BANK MEXICO, S.A.—See Comerica Incorporated; *U.S. Public*, pg. 542
COMERICA BANK - MICHIGAN MARKET—See Comerica Incorporated; *U.S. Public*, pg. 542
COMERICA BANK—See Comerica Incorporated; *U.S. Public*, pg. 542
COMERICA BANK & TRUST, NATIONAL ASSOCIATION—See Comerica Incorporated; *U.S. Public*, pg. 542
COMERICA BANK - WESTERN MARKET—See Comerica Incorporated; *U.S. Public*, pg. 542
COMERICA HOLDINGS INCORPORATED—See Comerica Incorporated; *U.S. Public*, pg. 542
COMERICA INCORPORATED; *U.S. Public*, pg. 542
COMERICA INSURANCE GROUP, INC.—See Comerica Incorporated; *U.S. Public*, pg. 542
COMERICA INSURANCE SERVICES, INC.—See Comerica Incorporated; *U.S. Public*, pg. 542
COMERICA LEASING CORPORATION—See Comerica Incorporated; *U.S. Public*, pg. 542
COMERICA SECURITIES, INC.—See Comerica Incorporated; *U.S. Public*, pg. 542
COMERICA WIRE TRANSFER—See Comerica Incorporated; *U.S. Public*, pg. 542
COMERICIALIZADORA KENNAMETAL BOLIVIA S.R.L.—See Kennametal Inc.; *U.S. Public*, pg. 1221
COMER INC.—See Comer Industries S.p.A.; *Int'l*, pg. 1710
COMER INDUSTRIES DO BRASIL LTDA.—See Comer Industries S.p.A.; *Int'l*, pg. 1710
COMER INDUSTRIES GMBH—See Comer Industries S.p.A.; *Int'l*, pg. 1710
COMER INDUSTRIES INC—See Comer Industries S.p.A.; *Int'l*, pg. 1710
COMER INDUSTRIES SARL—See Comer Industries S.p.A.; *Int'l*, pg. 1710
COMER INDUSTRIES (SHAOXING) COMPANY LTD.—See Comer Industries S.p.A.; *Int'l*, pg. 1710

COMER INDUSTRIES S.P.A. - CAVRIAGO UNIT—See Comer Industries S.p.A.; *Int'l*, pg. 1710
COMER INDUSTRIES S.P.A. - MANTOVA UNIT—See Comer Industries S.p.A.; *Int'l*, pg. 1710
COMER INDUSTRIES S.P.A. - MATERA UNIT—See Comer Industries S.p.A.; *Int'l*, pg. 1710
COMER INDUSTRIES S.P.A.; *Int'l*, pg. 1710
COMER INDUSTRIES U.K. LTD—See Comer Industries S.p.A.; *Int'l*, pg. 1710
CO MERI S.P.A—See Salini Costruttori S.p.A.; *Int'l*, pg. 6492
COMER (SHANGHAI) TRADING COMPANY LTD—See Comer Industries S.p.A.; *Int'l*, pg. 1710
COMERTON CORP.; *U.S. Public*, pg. 542
COMESA BUDAPEST KFT.—See Werfen Life Group, S.A.U.; *Int'l*, pg. 8378
COMESA POLSKA SP. Z O. O.—See Werfen Life Group, S.A.U.; *Int'l*, pg. 8378
COMESA SPOL.S.R.O.—See Werfen Life Group, S.A.U.; *Int'l*, pg. 8379
COM-ESCO, LLC; *U.S. Private*, pg. 980
COMESCO, S.A. DE C.V.—See Grupo Industrial Saltillo S.A. de C.V.; *Int'l*, pg. 3130
COME&STAY DKH A/S—See Come and Stay S.A.; *Int'l*, pg. 1710
COME&STAY SPAIN SL.—See Come and Stay S.A.; *Int'l*, pg. 1710
COMESTIBLES LA ROSA S.A.—See Nestle S.A.; *Int'l*, pg. 5210
COME SURE GROUP (HOLDINGS) LIMITED; *Int'l*, pg. 1710
COMET AG—See Comet Holding AG; *Int'l*, pg. 1710
COMETAL ENGINEERING S.P.A.—See Trevisan Cometal SpA; *Int'l*, pg. 7917
COMETALS FAR EAST, INC.—See Commercial Metals Company; *U.S. Public*, pg. 546
THE COMET CLOTHING COMPANY, LLC—See Kynetic LLC; *U.S. Private*, pg. 2360
COMET DISTRIBUCIONES COMMERCIALES S.L.—See Accell Group N.V.; *Int'l*, pg. 80
COMET ELECTRONICS CO. LTD.—See Comet Holding AG; *Int'l*, pg. 1710
COMET ELECTRONICS, LLC—See Comet Industries Inc.; *U.S. Private*, pg. 981
COMETE—See FAYAT SAS; *Int'l*, pg. 2625
COMET FANS S.R.L.—See Knorr-Bremse AG; *Int'l*, pg. 4210
COMET FEUERWERK GMBH—See Li & Fung Limited; *Int'l*, pg. 4479
COMET HOLDING AG; *Int'l*, pg. 1710
COMET INDUSTRIES INC.; *U.S. Private*, pg. 981
COMET INDUSTRIES LTD.; *Int'l*, pg. 1711
COMET MECHANICAL EQUIPMENT (SHANGHAI) CO. LTD—See Comet Holding AG; *Int'l*, pg. 1710
COME TO AGREEMENT LTD.; *Int'l*, pg. 1710
COMET-PRESS NEWSPAPERS, INC.—See Gannett Co., Inc.; *U.S. Public*, pg. 905
COMET RESOURCES LIMITED; *Int'l*, pg. 1711
COMET RIDGE LIMITED; *Int'l*, pg. 1711
COMET RIDGE RESOURCES, LLC—See Comet Ridge Limited; *Int'l*, pg. 1711
COMET RIDGE RESOURCES, LLC—See Pine Brook Partners, LLC; *U.S. Private*, pg. 3182
COMET RIDGE USA, INC.—See Comet Ridge Limited; *Int'l*, pg. 1711
COME TRUE BIOMEDICAL, INC.; *Int'l*, pg. 1710
COMET SA; *Int'l*, pg. 1711
COMET SOLUTIONS, INC.—See Aras Corp; *U.S. Private*, pg. 308
COMET SOLUTIONS TAIWAN LTD.—See Comet Holding AG; *Int'l*, pg. 1710
COMET S.P.A.—See Emak S.p.A.; *Int'l*, pg. 2373
COMET TECHNOLOGIES KOREA CO. LTD.—See Comet Holding AG; *Int'l*, pg. 1710
COMET TECHNOLOGIES USA, INC. - EBEAM TECHNOLOGIES—See Tri-City Electric Co.; *U.S. Private*, pg. 4221
COMET TECHNOLOGIES USA, INC. - PLASMA CONTROL TECHNOLOGIES—See Comet Holding AG; *Int'l*, pg. 1710
COMET TECHNOLOGIES USA, INC.—See Comet Holding AG; *Int'l*, pg. 1710
COMET TECHNOLOGIES USA, INC. - X-RAY SYSTEMS—See Comet Holding AG; *Int'l*, pg. 1710
COMET UMETNI BRUSI IN NEKOVINE, D.D.; *Int'l*, pg. 1711
COMET USA, INC.—See Emak S.p.A.; *Int'l*, pg. 2373
COMETZ SARL—See Bertelsmann SE & Co. KGaA; *Int'l*, pg. 992
COMEX INDUSTRIAL COATINGS, S.A. DE C.V.—See PPG Industries, Inc.; *U.S. Public*, pg. 1707
COMF5 INTERNATIONAL, INC.; *U.S. Public*, pg. 542
COMFOOR BV—See Amplifon S.p.A.; *Int'l*, pg. 435
COMFORCE CORPORATION—See American CyberSystems, Inc.; *U.S. Private*, pg. 229
COMFORCE INFORMATION TECHNOLOGIES, INC.—See American CyberSystems, Inc.; *U.S. Private*, pg. 229

COMFORT SYSTEMS USA, INC.

COMFORCE TECHNICAL SERVICES, INC.—See American CyberSystems, Inc.; *U.S. Private*, pg. 229
COMFORCE TELECOM, INC.—See American CyberSystems, Inc.; *U.S. Private*, pg. 229
COMFORIA RESIDENTIAL REIT, INC.; *Int'l*, pg. 1711
COMFOR STORES A.S.—See AB S.A.; *Int'l*, pg. 41
COMFORTABLE CARE DENTAL GROUP, INC.—See Huron Capital Partners LLC; *U.S. Private*, pg. 2012
COMFORT AIR DISTRIBUTING INC.—See Ridgemont Partners Management LLC; *U.S. Private*, pg. 3433
COMFORTAIRE CORPORATION—See Sleep Number Corporation; *U.S. Public*, pg. 1894
COMFORT-AIR ENGINEERING, INC.; *U.S. Private*, pg. 981
COMFORT AUDIO AB—See Sonova Holding AG; *Int'l*, pg. 7100
COMFORT AUDIO INC.—See Sonova Holding AG; *Int'l*, pg. 7100
COMFORT BILT LLC; *U.S. Private*, pg. 981
COMFORT CARE—See Lew Jan Textile Corp.; *U.S. Private*, pg. 2437
COMFORT COMMOTRADE LIMITED; *Int'l*, pg. 1711
COMFORT CONTROL INC.—See Metals Inc.; *U.S. Private*, pg. 2682
COMFORTDELGRO BUS PTE LTD—See ComfortDelGro Corporation Limited; *Int'l*, pg. 1712
COMFORTDELGRO CABCHARGE PTY. LTD.—See ComfortDelGro Corporation Limited; *Int'l*, pg. 1712
COMFORTDELGRO CORPORATION AUSTRALIA PTY. LTD.—See ComfortDelGro Corporation Limited; *Int'l*, pg. 1712
COMFORTDELGRO CORPORATION LIMITED; *Int'l*, pg. 1711
COMFORTDELGRO DRIVING CENTRE PTE. LTD.—See ComfortDelGro Corporation Limited; *Int'l*, pg. 1713
COMFORTDELGRO ENGINEERING PTE LTD—See ComfortDelGro Corporation Limited; *Int'l*, pg. 1713
COMFORTDELGRO INSURANCE BROKERS PTE. LTD.—See ComfortDelGro Corporation Limited; *Int'l*, pg. 1713
COMFORTDELGRO IRISH CITYLINK LIMITED—See ComfortDelGro Corporation Limited; *Int'l*, pg. 1713
COMFORTDELGRO RENT-A-CAR (CHENGDU) CO., LTD.—See ComfortDelGro Corporation Limited; *Int'l*, pg. 1713
COMFORTDELGRO RENT-A-CAR PTE. LTD.—See ComfortDelGro Corporation Limited; *Int'l*, pg. 1713
COMFORTDELGRO SWAN PTY. LTD.—See ComfortDelGro Corporation Limited; *Int'l*, pg. 1713
COMFORT ENGINEERS, INC.; *U.S. Private*, pg. 981
COMFORTEX CORPORATION—See 3G Capital Partners L.P.; *U.S. Private*, pg. 13
COMFORT EXPERT B.V.—See CENTROTEC SE; *Int'l*, pg. 1414
COMFORT FINCAP LIMITED; *Int'l*, pg. 1711
COMFORT FOODS, INC.—See Coffee Holding Company, Inc.; *U.S. Public*, pg. 522
COMFORT GLOVES BERHAD; *Int'l*, pg. 1711
COMFORTHOST.NET—See Cloud Equity Group, LLC; *U.S. Private*, pg. 946
COMFORT HOTEL AIRPORT NORTH—See Northampton Group Inc.; *Int'l*, pg. 5441
COMFORT HOTEL TORONTO—See Northampton Group Inc.; *Int'l*, pg. 5441
COMFORT INN—See Tramz Hotels Inc.; *U.S. Private*, pg. 4205
COMFORT INSTITUTE, INC.—See Aeroseal, LLC; *U.S. Private*, pg. 119
COMFORT INTECH LIMITED; *Int'l*, pg. 1711
COMFORT MEDICAL, LLC—See Coloplast A/S; *Int'l*, pg. 1704
COMFORT MEDICAL SUPPLY LLC; *U.S. Private*, pg. 981
COMFORT ONE SHOES L-1 CORPORATION; *U.S. Private*, pg. 981
COMFORT PRODUCTS DISTRIBUTING LLC—See Watsco, Inc.; *U.S. Public*, pg. 2336
COMFORT REVOLUTION, LLC—See Tempur Sealy International, Inc.; *U.S. Public*, pg. 1999
COMFORT RUBBER GLOVES INDUSTRIES SDN. BHD.—See Comfort Gloves Berhad; *Int'l*, pg. 1711
COMFORT SECURITIES LIMITED—See Comfort Commotrade Limited; *Int'l*, pg. 1711
COMFORT-SERVICE PJSC; *Int'l*, pg. 1711
COMFORT SERVICES INC.; *U.S. Private*, pg. 981
COMFORT SUPPLY, INC.; *U.S. Private*, pg. 981
COMFORT SUPPLY; *U.S. Private*, pg. 981
COMFORT SYSTEMS USA (ARKANSAS), INC.—See Comfort Systems USA, Inc.; *U.S. Public*, pg. 543
COMFORT SYSTEMS USA (BRISTOL), INC.—See Comfort Systems USA, Inc.; *U.S. Public*, pg. 543
COMFORT SYSTEMS USA (CAROLINAS), LLC—See Comfort Systems USA, Inc.; *U.S. Public*, pg. 543
COMFORT SYSTEMS USA ENERGY SERVICES, INC.—See Comfort Systems USA, Inc.; *U.S. Public*, pg. 543
COMFORT SYSTEMS USA, INC.; *U.S. Public*, pg. 542
COMFORT SYSTEMS USA (INTERMOUNTAIN), INC.—See Comfort Systems USA, Inc.; *U.S. Public*, pg. 543

COMFORT SYSTEMS USA, INC.

COMFORT SYSTEMS USA (KENTUCKY), INC.—See Comfort Systems USA, Inc.; *U.S. Public*, pg. 543
COMFORT SYSTEMS USA (MIDATLANTIC), LLC—See Comfort Systems USA, Inc.; *U.S. Public*, pg. 543
COMFORT SYSTEMS USA (NORTHWEST), INC.—See Comfort Systems USA, Inc.; *U.S. Public*, pg. 543
COMFORT SYSTEMS USA (OHIO), INC.—See Comfort Systems USA, Inc.; *U.S. Public*, pg. 543
COMFORT SYSTEMS USA (SOUTH CENTRAL), INC.—See Comfort Systems USA, Inc.; *U.S. Public*, pg. 543
COMFORT SYSTEMS USA (SOUTHEAST), INC.—See Comfort Systems USA, Inc.; *U.S. Public*, pg. 543
COMFORT SYSTEMS USA (SOUTHWEST), INC.—See Comfort Systems USA, Inc.; *U.S. Public*, pg. 543
COMFORT SYSTEMS USA (SYRACUSE), INC.—See Comfort Systems USA, Inc.; *U.S. Public*, pg. 543
COMFORT TRANSPORTATION PTE LTD—See ComfortDelGro Corporation Limited; *Int'l*, pg. 1712
COMFORT WINDOW CO. INC.; *U.S. Private*, pg. 981
COMFY MEETINGZONE AB—See LoopUp Group plc; *Int'l*, pg. 4556
COMGRAPH CO., LTD.—See FEV GmbH; *Int'l*, pg. 2648
COMGROUP INFORMATION TECHNOLOGY (SHANGHAI) CO., LTD.—See Wurth Verwaltungsgesellschaft mbH; *Int'l*, pg. 8512
COMGROUP (SCHWEIZ) AG—See Wurth Verwaltungsgesellschaft mbH; *Int'l*, pg. 8512
COM-GUARD.COM, INC.; *U.S. Public*, pg. 536
COMHEAR, INC.; *U.S. Private*, pg. 981
COMHLUCHT IASCAIREACHTA FANAD TEORANTA (FANAD FISHERIES)—See Norsk Hydro ASA; *Int'l*, pg. 5432
COMIFAR S.P.A.—See PHOENIX Pharmahandel GmbH & Co. KG; *Int'l*, pg. 5854
COMILOG SA—See Eramet SA; *Int'l*, pg. 2488
COMINAR REAL ESTATE INVESTMENT TRUST—See Canderel Management Inc.; *Int'l*, pg. 1289
COMINCA SA; *Int'l*, pg. 1713
COMINCO S.A.; *Int'l*, pg. 1713
COMINGERSOLL-COMERCIO E INDUSTRIA DE EQUIPAMENTOS S.A.—See Ingersoll Rand Inc.; *U.S. Public*, pg. 1118
COMINIX CO., LTD.; *Int'l*, pg. 1713
COMINIX INDIA PRIVATE LIMITED—See Cominix Co., Ltd.; *Int'l*, pg. 1714
COMINIX MEXICO S.A. DE C.V.—See Cominix Co., Ltd.; *Int'l*, pg. 1714
COMINIX (PHILIPPINES), INC.—See Cominix Co., Ltd.; *Int'l*, pg. 1713
COMINIX TRADING PHILIPPINES, INC.—See Cominix Co., Ltd.; *Int'l*, pg. 1714
COMINIX U.S.A., INC.—See Cominix Co., Ltd.; *Int'l*, pg. 1714
COMINIX VIETNAM CO., LTD.—See Cominix Co., Ltd.; *Int'l*, pg. 1714
COMIN KHMERE CO., LTD.—See Endress+Hauser (International) Holding AG; *Int'l*, pg. 2406
COMINPORT DISTRIBUCION S.L.—See Takara Holdings, Inc.; *Int'l*, pg. 7432
COMINTEL CORPORATION BERHAD; *Int'l*, pg. 1714
COMINTELLI AB; *Int'l*, pg. 1714
COMINVEST ASSET MANAGEMENT GMBH—See Allianz SE; *Int'l*, pg. 347
COMINVEST INVESTMENT LUXEMBOURG S.A.—See Allianz SE; *Int'l*, pg. 347
COMIQ OY—See Alten S.A.; *Int'l*, pg. 390
COMISARIATO DE BAJA CALIFORNIA, S.A. DE C.V.—See Deutsche Lufthansa AG; *Int'l*, pg. 2067
COMISION FEDERAL DE ELECTRICIDAD; *Int'l*, pg. 1714
COMITAL ALLUMINIO VOLPIANO—See Comital S.p.A.; *Int'l*, pg. 1714
COMITAL COFRESCO S.P.A.—See Comital S.p.A.; *Int'l*, pg. 1714
COMITAL SKULTUNA AB—See Comital S.p.A.; *Int'l*, pg. 1714
COMITAL S.P.A.; *Int'l*, pg. 1714
COMITAL URUGUAY S.A.—See Omya (Schweiz) AG; *Int'l*, pg. 5570
COMITEM S.A.S.—See Alan Allman Associates SA; *Int'l*, pg. 290
COMIU-STYLE CORP.—See RIZAP GROUP, Inc.; *Int'l*, pg. 6354
COMJOYFUL INTERNATIONAL COMPANY; *Int'l*, pg. 1714
COMLAND COMMERCIAL LIMITED; *Int'l*, pg. 1714
COMLEAD CO., LTD.—See MIRAIT ONE Corporation; *Int'l*, pg. 4917
COMLINE DOTCOM SDN. BHD.—See Omesti Berhad; *Int'l*, pg. 5562
COMLINE GMBH—See IQVIA Holdings Inc.; *U.S. Public*, pg. 1168
COM-LINE SYSTEMS SDN. BHD.—See Omesti Berhad; *Int'l*, pg. 5562
COMLINK CONTRACTORS INC.; *U.S. Private*, pg. 982
COMLINK FIRE SYSTEMS INC.—See Taiwan Secom Company Ltd.; *Int'l*, pg. 7423
COMLINK MIDWEST INC.—See Comlink Contractors Inc.; *U.S. Private*, pg. 982

COMLINK SOUTHWEST, LLC—See Comlink Contractors Inc.; *U.S. Private*, pg. 982
COMLINX PTY LTD—See Over the Wire Holdings Limited; *Int'l*, pg. 5671
COMM3; *U.S. Private*, pg. 982
COMMAND ALKON CORP—See Thoma Bravo, L.P.; *U.S. Private*, pg. 4146
COMMAND BUILDING SERVICES LIMITED—See Christchurch City Holdings Ltd.; *Int'l*, pg. 1586
COMMAND CONTROL CENTER CORP.—See Znergy, Inc.; *U.S. Private*, pg. 4607
COMMAND DECISIONS SYSTEMS & SOLUTIONS, INCORPORATED; *U.S. Private*, pg. 982
COMMANDER RESOURCES LTD.; *Int'l*, pg. 1714
COMMANDER TERMINALS; *U.S. Private*, pg. 982
COMMAND INFORMATION, INC.—See Bridge Growth Partners, LLC; *U.S. Private*, pg. 649
COMMAND INFORMATION, INC.—See Frontenac Company LLC; *U.S. Private*, pg. 1614
COMMAND LANGUAGES, INC.; *U.S. Private*, pg. 982
COMMAND MANAGEMENT SERVICES, INC.; *U.S. Private*, pg. 982
COMMAND PLASTIC CORPORATION; *U.S. Private*, pg. 982
COMMAND POLYMERS LIMITED; *Int'l*, pg. 1714
COMMAND WEB OFFSET CO.—See Unimac Graphics; *U.S. Private*, pg. 4284
COMMA OIL & CHEMICALS LIMITED—See Cosan S.A.; *Int'l*, pg. 1809
COMMARCO GMBH—See WPP plc; *Int'l*, pg. 8462
.COM MARKETING; *U.S. Private*, pg. 1
COMMAX CO., LTD.; *Int'l*, pg. 1714
COMMBANK EUROPE LIMITED—See Commonwealth Bank of Australia; *Int'l*, pg. 1720
COMMBANK MANAGEMENT CONSULTING (ASIA) CO LIMITED—See Commonwealth Bank of Australia; *Int'l*, pg. 1720
COMMCENTER S.A.; *Int'l*, pg. 1714
COMMCISE SOFTWARE LTD.—See Euronext N.V.; *Int'l*, pg. 2554
COMMDEX CONSULTING, LLC; *U.S. Private*, pg. 982
COMMEMORATIVE BRANDS, INC.—See Fenway Partners, LLC; *U.S. Private*, pg. 1495
COMMENCE CORPORATION; *U.S. Private*, pg. 982
COMMENCEMENT BANK; *U.S. Private*, pg. 982
COMMENDA ADRIA D.O.O.—See Akzo Nobel N.V.; *Int'l*, pg. 273
COMMEND ADRIA D.O.O.—See TKH Group N.V.; *Int'l*, pg. 7763
COMMEND AG—See TKH Group N.V.; *Int'l*, pg. 7763
COMMEND AUSTRALIA INTEGRATED SECURITY AND COMMUNICATION SYSTEMS PTY LTD—See TKH Group N.V.; *Int'l*, pg. 7763
COMMEND BENELUX B.V.—See TKH Group N.V.; *Int'l*, pg. 7763
COMMEND BUSINESS HUB NORDIC—See TKH Group N.V.; *Int'l*, pg. 7763
COMMEND FRANCE S.A.S—See TKH Group N.V.; *Int'l*, pg. 7763
COMMEND (H.K.) LTD.—See Collins Co., Ltd.; *Int'l*, pg. 1702
COMMEND IBERICA S.L.—See TKH Group N.V.; *Int'l*, pg. 7763
COMMEND INC.—See TKH Group N.V.; *Int'l*, pg. 7763
COMMEND ITALIA S.R.L.—See TKH Group N.V.; *Int'l*, pg. 7763
COMMEND OSTERREICH GMBH—See TKH Group N.V.; *Int'l*, pg. 7763
COMMEND SCANDINAVIA AB—See TKH Group N.V.; *Int'l*, pg. 7763
COMMEND SLOVAKIA S.R.O.—See TKH Group N.V.; pg. 7763
COMMEND SOUTH EAST ASIA PTE. LTD.—See TKH Group N.V.; *Int'l*, pg. 7763
COMMEND UK LTD—See TKH Group N.V.; *Int'l*, pg. 7763
COMMERCE ASSET VENTURES SDN BHD—See CIMB Group Holdings Berhad; *Int'l*, pg. 1608
COMMERCE AUSTRALIA PTY LTD—See Nine Entertainment Co. Holdings Limited; *Int'l*, pg. 5298
COMMERCE AUTO GROUP; *U.S. Private*, pg. 982
COMMERCE BANCSHARES, INC.; *U.S. Private*, pg. 982
COMMERCE BANCSHARES, INC.; *U.S. Public*, pg. 544
COMMERCE BANK, N.A.—See Commerce Bancshares, Inc.; *U.S. Public*, pg. 544
THE COMMERCE BANK OF OREGON—See Zions Bancorporation, National Association; *U.S. Public*, pg. 2408
THE COMMERCE BANK OF WASHINGTON—See Zions Bancorporation, National Association; *U.S. Public*, pg. 2408
THE COMMERCE BANK—See Indiana Members Credit Union; *U.S. Private*, pg. 2062
COMMERCE BROKERAGE SERVICES, INC.—See Commerce Bancshares, Inc.; *U.S. Public*, pg. 544
COMMERCEBYUS, INC.; *U.S. Private*, pg. 982
COMMERCE CONTROLS INC.; *U.S. Private*, pg. 982
COMMERCE ENERGY, INC.—See Just Energy Group Inc.; *Int'l*, pg. 4031
COMMERCE ESCROW COMPANY—See Pacific Premier Bancorp, Inc.; *U.S. Public*, pg. 1632

CORPORATE AFFILIATIONS

COMMERCE GROUP CORP.; *U.S. Public*, pg. 545
COMMERCE HOUSE SDN BHD—See IJM Corporation Berhad; *Int'l*, pg. 3608
COMMERCEHUB, INC.—See Insight Venture Management, LLC; *U.S. Private*, pg. 2087
COMMERCE INSURANCE COMPANY—See MAPFRE S.A.; *Int'l*, pg. 4684
COMMERCE INSURANCE SERVICES, INC.—See Commerce Bancshares, Inc.; *U.S. Public*, pg. 545
COMMERCE MEDIA TECH SP. Z O.O.—See Team Internet Group plc; *Int'l*, pg. 7500
COMMERCE MORTGAGE CORP.—See Commerce Bancshares, Inc.; *U.S. Public*, pg. 545
COMMERCE MORTGAGE; *U.S. Public*, pg. 982
COMMERCE ONE HOLDINGS, INC.; *Int'l*, pg. 1714
COMMERCE QUALITY FOODS LLC; *U.S. Private*, pg. 982
COMMERCE RESOURCES CORP.; *Int'l*, pg. 1714
COMMERCE/SANSEB JOINT VENTURE—See Commerce Group Corp.; *U.S. Public*, pg. 545
COMMERCE SUPERVALU WEST REGION—See United Natural Foods, Inc.; *U.S. Public*, pg. 2231
COMMERCE TECHNOLOGIES, LLC—See Insight Venture Management, LLC; *U.S. Private*, pg. 2088
COMMERCE TOWNSHIP DIALYSIS CENTER, LLC—See DaVita Inc.; *U.S. Public*, pg. 637
COMMERCEWEST BANK; *U.S. Public*, pg. 545
COMMERCE WEST INSURANCE COMPANY—See MAPFRE S.A.; *Int'l*, pg. 4684
COMMERCIAL ACCEPTANCES LIMITED—See Close Brothers Group plc; *Int'l*, pg. 1661
COMMERCIAL AIRCRAFT INTERIORS, LLC; *U.S. Private*, pg. 983
COMMERCIAL AIRPLANE COMPANY—See Mitsubishi Heavy Industries, Ltd.; *Int'l*, pg. 4953
THE COMMERCIAL AND SAVINGS BANK OF MILLERSBURG, OHIO—See CSB Bancorp, Inc.; *U.S. Public*, pg. 601
COMMERCIAL ARMATURE WORKS; *U.S. Private*, pg. 983
COMMERCIAL ASSET PARTNERS REALTY; *U.S. Private*, pg. 983
COMMERCIAL BABCOCK INC.—See J.B. Poindexter & Co., Inc.; *U.S. Private*, pg. 2158
COMMERCIAL BAKERIES CORP.—See The Graham Group, Inc.; *U.S. Private*, pg. 4036
COMMERCIAL BANCGROUP, INC.; *U.S. Private*, pg. 983
COMMERCIAL BANK ALLIANZ BULGARIA AD—See Allianz SE; *Int'l*, pg. 344
COMMERCIAL BANK FINANCIAL SERVICES LLC—See The Commercial Bank (P.S.Q.C); *Int'l*, pg. 7635
COMMERCIAL BANK INTERNATIONAL P.S.C.; *Int'l*, pg. 1714
COMMERCIAL BANK MOSKOMMERTSBANK LLC—See Halyk Bank of Kazakhstan JSC; *Int'l*, pg. 3234
COMMERCIAL BANK OF AFRICA LIMITED; *Int'l*, pg. 1714
COMMERCIAL BANK OF CALIFORNIA—See CBC Bancorp; *U.S. Private*, pg. 796
COMMERCIAL BANK OF CEYLON PLC; *Int'l*, pg. 1714
COMMERCIAL BANK OF DUBAI PSC; *Int'l*, pg. 1715
COMMERCIAL BANK OF IRAQ P.S.C.—See Kuwait Finance House K.S.C.; *Int'l*, pg. 4344
COMMERCIAL BANK OF KUWAIT S.A.K.; *Int'l*, pg. 1715
COMMERCIAL BANK OF MALDIVES PRIVATE LIMITED—See Commercial Bank of Ceylon PLC; *Int'l*, pg. 1715
THE COMMERCIAL BANK (P.S.Q.C); *Int'l*, pg. 7635
COMMERCIAL BANK—See Commercial Bancgroup, Inc.; *U.S. Private*, pg. 983
COMMERCIAL BANK & TRUST COMPANY—See Synovus Financial Corp.; *U.S. Public*, pg. 1971
COMMERCIAL BANK & TRUST COMPANY—See Synovus Financial Corp.; *U.S. Public*, pg. 1972
COMMERCIAL BANK & TRUST OF PENNSYLVANIA—See Commercial National Financial Corporation; *U.S. Public*, pg. 547
COMMERCIAL BARGAINS INC.; *U.S. Private*, pg. 983
COMMERCIAL BUILDERS GROUP LLC—See GMS Inc.; *U.S. Public*, pg. 948
COMMERCIAL BUILDING MATERIALS LLC—See National Construction Enterprises Inc.; *U.S. Private*, pg. 2851
COMMERCIAL CARRIERS INSURANCE AGENCY, INC.—See Fosun International Limited; *Int'l*, pg. 2752
COMMERCIAL CLEANING SYSTEMS, INC.—See Silver Oak Services Partners, LLC; *U.S. Private*, pg. 3661
COMMERCIAL COATING SERVICES INTERNATIONAL, LLC—See New Mountain Capital, LLC; *U.S. Private*, pg. 2899
COMMERCIAL & COIN LAUNDRY EQUIPMENT CO.—See BDT Capital Partners, LLC; *U.S. Private*, pg. 502
COMMERCIAL COLD STORAGE (NAMIBIA) (PTY) LIMITED—See Oceana Group Limited; *Int'l*, pg. 5517
COMMERCIAL COLD STORAGE (PORTS) (PTY) LIMITED—See Oceana Group Limited; *Int'l*, pg. 5517
COMMERCIAL COLD STRORAGE GROUP LTD.—See African Infrastructure Investment Managers; *Int'l*, pg. 191

COMPANY NAME INDEX

COMMERCIAL COLD STRORAGE GROUP LTD.—See Old Mutual Life Assurance Company (South Africa) Ltd.; *Int'l*, pg. 5552
COMMERCIAL CONSTRUCTION SERVICES, INC.; *U.S. Private*, pg. 983
COMMERCIAL CONTRACTORS GROUP INC.; *U.S. Private*, pg. 983
COMMERCIAL CONTRACTORS, INC.; *U.S. Private*, pg. 983
COMMERCIAL CONTRACTORS INC.; *U.S. Private*, pg. 983
COMMERCIAL CREAMERY CO.; *U.S. Private*, pg. 983
COMMERCIAL CREDIT GROUP INC.—See BDT Capital Partners, LLC; *U.S. Private*, pg. 502
COMMERCIAL CREDIT, INC.—See BDT Capital Partners, LLC; *U.S. Private*, pg. 502
COMMERCIAL DATA SYSTEMS INC.; *U.S. Private*, pg. 983
COMMERCIAL DESIGN ENGINEERING; *U.S. Private*, pg. 983
COMMERCIAL DESIGN SERVICES, INC.; *U.S. Private*, pg. 983
COMMERCIAL DEVELOPMENT COMPANY LTD.—See Commercial Bank of Ceylon PLC; *Int'l*, pg. 1715
COMMERCIAL DEVELOPMENTS INTERNATIONAL, INC.—See Kajima Corporation; *Int'l*, pg. 4055
COMMERCIAL E INDUSTRIAL ERCO (CHILE) LIMITADA—See Superior Plus Corp.; *Int'l*, pg. 7338
COMMERCIAL ENERGY LLC; *U.S. Private*, pg. 983
COMMERCIAL ENERGY SERVICES PTY LTD—See EnviroSuite Limited; *Int'l*, pg. 2455
COMMERCIAL ENTERPRISES LIMITED; *U.S. Private*, pg. 983
COMMERCIALE SUCRIERE S.A.—See ED&F Man Holdings Limited; *Int'l*, pg. 2302
COMMERCIAL FACILITIES COMPANY S.A.K.C.; *Int'l*, pg. 1715
COMMERCIAL FINANCIAL CORP.; *U.S. Private*, pg. 983
COMMERCIAL FIRE & COMMUNICATIONS, INC.; *U.S. Private*, pg. 983
COMMERCIAL FOODSERVICE REPAIR, INC.—See HCI Equity Management, L.P.; *U.S. Private*, pg. 1889
COMMERCIAL FORGED PRODUCTS—See Wozniak Industries, Inc.; *U.S. Private*, pg. 4571
COMMERCIAL FURNITURE GROUP, INC. - FALCON PRODUCTS DIVISION—See Whippoorwill Associates, Inc.; *U.S. Private*, pg. 4506
COMMERCIAL FURNITURE GROUP, INC.—See Whippoorwill Associates, Inc.; *U.S. Private*, pg. 4506
THE COMMERCIAL GROUP LIFTING PRODUCTS—See The Commercial Group Lifting Products; *U.S. Private*, pg. 4012
THE COMMERCIAL GROUP LIFTING PRODUCTS; *U.S. Private*, pg. 4011
COMMERCIAL GRUPO ANAYA SA—See Vivendi SE; *Int'l*, pg. 8271
COMMERCIAL HEATING SUPPLY—See Torrington Supply Company, Incorporated; *U.S. Private*, pg. 4190
COMMERCIAL & HOME FURNISHINGS, INC.; *U.S. Private*, pg. 982
COMMERCIAL & INDUSTRIAL ACCEPTANCES (PTY.) LTD.—See Talanx AG; *Int'l*, pg. 7443
COMMERCIAL & INDUSTRIAL DESIGN COMPANY INC.; *U.S. Private*, pg. 983
COMMERCIAL INSTALLATION & CONSTRUCTION COMPANY—See Color Art Office Interiors Inc.; *U.S. Private*, pg. 972
COMMERCIAL INSURANCE BROKERS (PVT) LIMITED—See Commercial Bank of Ceylon PLC; *Int'l*, pg. 1715
COMMERCIAL INSURANCE SERVICE CORP; *U.S. Private*, pg. 983
COMMERCIAL INSURANCE SERVICES, INC.—See GTCR LLC; *U.S. Private*, pg. 1802
COMMERCIAL INSURANCE UNDERWRITERS, INC.—See Arthur J. Gallagher & Co.; *U.S. Public*, pg. 204
COMMERCIAL INTERIORS INC.; *U.S. Private*, pg. 983
COMMERCIAL INTERNATIONAL BANK (EGYPT) S.A.E.; *Int'l*, pg. 1715
COMMERCIAL INVESTIGATION INCORPORATED; *U.S. Private*, pg. 984
COMMERCIAL INVESTIGATION & SECURITY—See Security Solutions of America; *U.S. Private*, pg. 3596
COMMERCIAL INVESTMENT CORPORATION (PTY) LIMITED—See CIC Holdings Limited; *Int'l*, pg. 1602
COMMERCIAL KITCHEN PARTS & SERVICE; *U.S. Private*, pg. 984
COMMERCIAL LAUNDRY EQUIPMENT COMPANY, LLC—See EVI Industries, Inc.; *U.S. Public*, pg. 803
COMMERCIAL LAUNDRY PRODUCTS, INC.—See EVI Industries, Inc.; *U.S. Public*, pg. 803
COMMERCIAL LAWN CARE SERVICES INC.; *U.S. Private*, pg. 984
COMMERCIAL LIGHTING PRODUCTS LTD.; *Int'l*, pg. 1715
COMMERCIAL LUMBER & PALLET CO.; *U.S. Private*, pg. 984
COMMERCIAL METALS COMPANY; *U.S. Public*, pg. 545

COMMERCIAL METALS DEUTSCHLAND GMBH—See Commercial Metals Company; *U.S. Public*, pg. 545
COMMERCIAL METALS (INTERNATIONAL) AG—See Commercial Metals Company; *U.S. Public*, pg. 546
COMMERCIAL METALS SF/JV COMPANY—See Commercial Metals Company; *U.S. Public*, pg. 546
COMMERCIAL NATIONAL FINANCIAL CORPORATION; *U.S. Public*, pg. 547
COMMERCIAL NETWORK SERVICES—See Beeks Financial Cloud Group Plc; *Int'l*, pg. 939
COMMERCIAL-NEWS—See The Retirement Systems of Alabama; *U.S. Public*, pg. 4105
COMMERCIAL OFFICE FURNITURE CO.; *U.S. Private*, pg. 984
COMMERCIAL PARTNERS REALTY INC.—See George F. Young, Inc.; *U.S. Private*, pg. 1682
COMMERCIAL PIPE & SUPPLY CORP; *U.S. Private*, pg. 984
COMMERCIAL PLASTERING INC.; *U.S. Private*, pg. 984
COMMERCIAL POOL SPECIALIST, INC.; *U.S. Private*, pg. 984
THE COMMERCIAL PRESS SDN. BHD.—See Pelangi Publishing Group Bhd; *Int'l*, pg. 5782
COMMERCIAL PROGRAMMING SYSTEMS, INC.—See Drishticon Inc.; *U.S. Private*, pg. 1278
COMMERCIAL PROPERTY SOUTHWEST FLORIDA, LLC; *U.S. Private*, pg. 984
COMMERCIAL READY MIX PRODUCTS INC.; *U.S. Private*, pg. 984
THE COMMERCIAL REAL ESTATE COMPANY K.S.C.C.; *Int'l*, pg. 7635
COMMERCIAL REAL ESTATE CONSULTANTS, LLC; *U.S. Private*, pg. 984
COMMERCIAL REALTY & RESOURCES CORP.—See New Jersey Resources Corporation; *U.S. Public*, pg. 1512
COMMERCIAL RECORD CENTER—See Nelson Westerberg, Inc.; *U.S. Private*, pg. 2884
COMMERCIAL RESINS COMPANY, CORROSION COATING AND TECHNOLOGY & SERVICES—See Commercial Resins Company; *U.S. Private*, pg. 984
COMMERCIAL RESINS COMPANY; *U.S. Private*, pg. 984
COMMERCIAL ROOFERS, INC.; *U.S. Private*, pg. 984
COMMERCIAL ROOFING, INC.—See Altas Partners LP; *Int'l*, pg. 386
COMMERCIAL ROOFING SPECIALTIES INC.; *U.S. Private*, pg. 984
COMMERCIAL SERVICES GROUP INCORPORATED; *U.S. Private*, pg. 984
COMMERCIAL SERVICES INC.; *U.S. Private*, pg. 984
COMMERCIAL SIDING AND MAINTENANCE CO; *U.S. Private*, pg. 984
COMMERCIAL SOLUTIONS, INC.—See Paychex, Inc.; *U.S. Public*, pg. 1655
COMMERCIAL SPRING AND TOOL COMPANY LIMITED; *Int'l*, pg. 1715
COMMERCIAL STATE BANK—See Palmer Bancshares, Inc.; *U.S. Private*, pg. 3080
COMMERCIAL STEEL PRODUCTS LLC; *U.S. Private*, pg. 984
COMMERCIAL STEEL TREATING CORP.; *U.S. Private*, pg. 984
COMMERCIAL STOREFRONT SERVICES, INC.; *U.S. Private*, pg. 984
COMMERCIAL SYN BAGS LIMITED; *Int'l*, pg. 1715
COMMERCIAL TEXAS, LLC—See Avison Young (Canada) Inc.; *Int'l*, pg. 745
COMMERCIAL TIRE INC.; *U.S. Private*, pg. 984
COMMERCIAL TRAVELERS MUTUAL INSURANCE COMPANY; *U.S. Private*, pg. 984
COMMERCIAL TREE CARE, INC.—See BrightView Holdings, Inc.; *U.S. Public*, pg. 383
COMMERCIAL TRUCK & VAN EQUIPMENT INC.—See Adrian Steel Company Inc.; *U.S. Private*, pg. 82
COMMERCIAL VEHICLE AUCTIONS LTD—See Ballyvesey Holdings Limited; *Int'l*, pg. 809
COMMERCIAL VEHICLE GROUP, INC.; *U.S. Public*, pg. 547
COMMERCIAL VEHICLE PRODUCTS DIVISION—See Phillips Industries; *U.S. Private*, pg. 3171
COMMERCIAL WAREHOUSE & CARTAGE, INC.; *U.S. Private*, pg. 985
COMMERCIAL WARRANTY SOLUTIONS, LLC; *U.S. Private*, pg. 985
COMMERCIAL WINGS SDN BHD—See IOI Corporation Berhad; *Int'l*, pg. 3791
COMMERCIAL WORKS INC.; *U.S. Private*, pg. 985
COMMERZBANK AG - NEW YORK BRANCH—See Commerzbank AG; *Int'l*, pg. 1717
COMMERZBANK AG; *Int'l*, pg. 1715
COMMERZBANK AUSLANDSBANKEN HOLDING AG—See Commerzbank AG; *Int'l*, pg. 1717
COMMERZBANK AUSLANDSBANKEN HOLDING NOVA GMBH—See Commerzbank AG; *Int'l*, pg. 1717
COMMERZBANK BELGIUM S.A.N.V.—See Commerzbank AG; *Int'l*, pg. 1717
COMMERZBANK BRASIL S.A. - BANCO MULTIPLO—See Commerzbank AG; *Int'l*, pg. 1717

COMMERZBANK AG

COMMERZBANK (BUDAPEST) RT—See Commerzbank AG; *Int'l*, pg. 1717
COMMERZBANK CAPITAL INVESTMENT COMPANY LIMITED—See Commerzbank AG; *Int'l*, pg. 1717
COMMERZBANK CAPITAL MARKETS CORPORATION—See Commerzbank AG; *Int'l*, pg. 1717
COMMERZBANK DUISBURG—See Commerzbank AG; *Int'l*, pg. 1717
COMMERZBANK (EURASIJA) SAO—See Commerzbank AG; *Int'l*, pg. 1717
COMMERZBANK FINANCE BV—See Commerzbank AG; *Int'l*, pg. 1717
COMMERZBANK FINANCE & COVERED BOND S.A.—See Commerzbank AG; *Int'l*, pg. 1717
COMMERZBANK FUTURES LLC—See Commerzbank AG; *Int'l*, pg. 1717
COMMERZBANK HOLDINGS FRANCE SAS—See Commerzbank AG; *Int'l*, pg. 1717
COMMERZBANK HOLDINGS (UK) LIMITED—See Commerzbank AG; *Int'l*, pg. 1717
COMMERZBANK IMMOBILIEN- UND VERMOGENSVERWALTUNGSGESELLSCHAFT MBH—See Commerzbank AG; *Int'l*, pg. 1717
COMMERZBANK INLANDSBANKEN HOLDING GMBH—See Commerzbank AG; *Int'l*, pg. 1717
COMMERZBANK INVESTMENTS (UK) LIMITED—See Commerzbank AG; *Int'l*, pg. 1717
COMMERZBANK LEASING LIMITED—See Commerzbank AG; *Int'l*, pg. 1717
COMMERZBANK (NEDERLAND) N.V.—See Commerzbank AG; *Int'l*, pg. 1717
COMMERZBANK ONLINE VENTURES LIMITED—See Commerzbank AG; *Int'l*, pg. 1717
COMMERZBANK PROPERTY MANAGEMENT & SERVICES LIMITED—See Commerzbank AG; *Int'l*, pg. 1717
COMMERZBANK REPRESENTATIVE OFFICE NIGERIA LIMITED—See Commerzbank AG; *Int'l*, pg. 1717
COMMERZBANK REPRESENTATIVE OFFICE PANAMA, S.A.—See Commerzbank AG; *Int'l*, pg. 1717
COMMERZBANK SAO PAULO SERVICOS LTDA.—See Commerzbank AG; *Int'l*, pg. 1717
COMMERZBANK SECURITIES LTD.—See Commerzbank AG; *Int'l*, pg. 1717
COMMERZBANK SECURITIES NOMINEES LIMITED—See Commerzbank AG; *Int'l*, pg. 1717
COMMERZBANK U.S. FINANCE, INC.—See Commerzbank AG; *Int'l*, pg. 1717
COMMERZBANK ZRT.—See Erste Group Bank AG; *Int'l*, pg. 2498
COMMERZ BUILDING AND MANAGEMENT GMBH—See Commerzbank AG; *Int'l*, pg. 1716
COMMERZ BUSINESS CONSULTING GMBH—See Commerzbank AG; *Int'l*, pg. 1716
COMMERZ (EAST ASIA) LTD.—See Commerzbank AG; *Int'l*, pg. 1716
COMMERZFACTORING GMBH—See Commerzbank AG; *Int'l*, pg. 1716
COMMERZ FINANZ GMBH—See BNP Paribas SA; *Int'l*, pg. 1090
COMMERZ FINANZ-MANAGEMENT GMBH—See Commerzbank AG; *Int'l*, pg. 1716
COMMERZ GLOBAL SERVICE SOLUTIONS SDN. BHD.—See Commerzbank AG; *Int'l*, pg. 1716
COMMERZ GRUNDBESITZ GESTAO DE CENTROS COMMERCIAIS, SOCIEDADE UNIPESSOAL, LDA.—See Commerzbank AG; *Int'l*, pg. 1716
COMMERZ GRUNDBESITZ INVESTMENTGESELLSCHAFT MBH—See Commerzbank AG; *Int'l*, pg. 1716
COMMERZLEASING GMBH—See Commerzbank AG; *Int'l*, pg. 1717
COMMERZLEASING UND IMMOBILIEN GMBH—See Commerzbank AG; *Int'l*, pg. 1717
COMMERZ MARKETS LLC—See Commerzbank AG; *Int'l*, pg. 1716
COMMERZ (NEDERLAND) N.V.—See Commerzbank AG; *Int'l*, pg. 1716
COMMERZ REAL AG—See Commerzbank AG; *Int'l*, pg. 1716
COMMERZ REAL ASSET STRUCTURING GMBH—See Commerzbank AG; *Int'l*, pg. 1716
COMMERZ REAL AUTOSERVICE GMBH I.L.—See Commerzbank AG; *Int'l*, pg. 1716
COMMERZ REAL BAUCONTRACT GMBH—See Commerzbank AG; *Int'l*, pg. 1716
COMMERZ REAL BAUMANAGEMENT GMBH—See Commerzbank AG; *Int'l*, pg. 1716
COMMERZ REAL DIGITALE VERTRIEBS- UND SERVICE GMBH—See Commerzbank AG; *Int'l*, pg. 1716
COMMERZ REAL DIREKT GMBH I.L.—See Commerzbank AG; *Int'l*, pg. 1716
COMMERZ REAL FINANZIERUNGSLEASING GMBH—See Commerzbank AG; *Int'l*, pg. 1716
COMMERZ REAL FONDS BETEILIGUNGS- GESELLSCHAFT MBH—See Commerzbank AG; *Int'l*, pg. 1716
COMMERZ REAL FRANCE & SOUTH EURL—See Commerzbank AG; *Int'l*, pg. 1716

COMMERZ REAL FUND MANAGEMENT S.A.R.L.—See Commerzbank AG; *Int'l*, pg. 1716
COMMERZ REAL INVESTMENTGESELLSCHAFT MBH—See Commerzbank AG; *Int'l*, pg. 1716
COMMERZ REAL IT-LEASING GMBH—See Commerzbank AG; *Int'l*, pg. 1716
COMMERZ REAL KAPITALVERWALTUNGSGESELLSCHAFT MBH—See Commerzbank AG; *Int'l*, pg. 1716
COMMERZ REAL MIETKAUF GMBH—See Commerzbank AG; *Int'l*, pg. 1716
COMMERZ REAL MOBILIENLEASING GMBH—See Commerzbank AG; *Int'l*, pg. 1716
COMMERZ REAL NORTH LTD.—See Commerzbank AG; *Int'l*, pg. 1716
COMMERZ REAL PARTNER SUD GMBH—See Commerzbank AG; *Int'l*, pg. 1716
COMMERZ REAL PROJEKTCONSULT GMBH—See Commerzbank AG; *Int'l*, pg. 1716
COMMERZ REAL VERTRIEB GMBH—See Commerzbank AG; *Int'l*, pg. 1716
COMMERZ REAL VERWALTUNG UND TREUHAND GMBH—See Commerzbank AG; *Int'l*, pg. 1716
COMMERZ REAL WEST BV—See Commerzbank AG; *Int'l*, pg. 1716
COMMERZ REAL WESTERN EUROPE GMBH—See Commerzbank AG; *Int'l*, pg. 1716
COMMERZ SECURITIES HONG KONG LIMITED—See Commerzbank AG; *Int'l*, pg. 1716
COMMERZ SERVICES HOLDING GMBH—See Commerzbank AG; *Int'l*, pg. 1716
COMMERZ SYSTEMS GMBH—See Commerzbank AG; *Int'l*, pg. 1716
COMMERZ TRANSACTION SERVICES MITTE GMBH—See Commerzbank AG; *Int'l*, pg. 1716
COMMERZ TRANSACTION SERVICES NORD GMBH—See Commerzbank AG; *Int'l*, pg. 1716
COMMERZ TRANSACTION SERVICES WEST GMBH—See Commerzbank AG; *Int'l*, pg. 1716
COMMERZTRUST GMBH—See Commerzbank AG; *Int'l*, pg. 1717
COMMET S.A. TECUCI—See UZINEXPORT S.A.; *Int'l*, pg. 8104
COMM EXPRESS SERVICES SA (PROPRIETARY) LIMITED—See Blue Label Telecoms Limited; *Int'l*, pg. 1068
COMMEX TECHNOLOGY LTD.; *Int'l*, pg. 1719
COMMISSIONERS OF PUBLIC WORKS; *U.S. Private*, pg. 985
COMMISSION JUNCTION—See Publicis Groupe S.A.; *Int'l*, pg. 6098
COMMISSION ON ACCREDITATION OF REHABILITATION FACILITIES; *U.S. Private*, pg. 985
COMMISSION ON ECONOMIC OPPORTUNITY; *U.S. Private*, pg. 985
COMMITMENT ENGINEERING SUPPLIES (W.L.L.)—See SMC Corporation; *Int'l*, pg. 7003
COMMITTED CAPITAL ACQUISITION CORPORATION II; *U.S. Private*, pg. 985
COMMITTED CARGO CARE LIMITED; *Int'l*, pg. 1719
COMMITTEE FOR A RESPONSIBLE FEDERAL BUDGET; *U.S. Private*, pg. 985
COMMITTEE FOR ECONOMIC DEVELOPMENT—See The Conference Board, Inc.; *U.S. Private*, pg. 4014
COMMIXT S.A.; *Int'l*, pg. 1719
COMMLINK SYSTEMS—See Innovative, Inc.; *U.S. Private*, pg. 2083
COMMNET BROADBAND, LLC—See ATN International, Inc.; *U.S. Public*, pg. 224
COMMNET FOUR CORNERS, LLC—See ATN International, Inc.; *U.S. Public*, pg. 224
COMM NET INTERNATIONAL INC.; *U.S. Private*, pg. 982
COMMNET WIRELESS, LLC—See ATN International, Inc.; *U.S. Public*, pg. 224
COMMODITIES INTELLIGENCE CENTRE PTE. LTD.—See Zall Smart Commerce Group Ltd.; *Int'l*, pg. 8622
COMMODITIES SOFTWARE (UK) LIMITED—See Brady plc; *Int'l*, pg. 1135
COMMODITY BLENDERS INC.; *U.S. Private*, pg. 985
COMMODITY COMPONENTS INTERNATIONAL; *U.S. Private*, pg. 985
COMMODITY FORWARDERS INC.—See Kuehne + Nagel International AG; *Int'l*, pg. 4324
COMMODITY MARKETING COMPANY; *U.S. Private*, pg. 985
COMMODITY RESOURCE & ENVIRONMENTAL INC; *U.S. Private*, pg. 985
COMMODITY SERVICES INC.; *U.S. Private*, pg. 985
COMMODITY SPECIALISTS COMPANY INC.; *U.S. Private*, pg. 985
COMMODITY TERMINALS INTERNATIONAL NV—See Katoen Natie N.V.; *Int'l*, pg. 4090
COMMODORE BUILDERS; *U.S. Private*, pg. 985
THE COMMODORE CORPORATION—See Cavco Industries, Inc.; *U.S. Public*, pg. 455
COMMODORE FINANCIAL CORP.—See MARCO Global Inc.; *U.S. Public*, pg. 2572
COMMODORE INSURANCE SERVICES; *U.S. Private*, pg. 985

COMMODORE KITCHENS LTD.—See Nobia AB; *Int'l*, pg. 5395
COMMODORE MANUFACTURING CORPORATION; *U.S. Private*, pg. 985
COMMON ANGLE, INC.; *U.S. Private*, pg. 985
COMMON APPLICATION; *U.S. Private*, pg. 985
COMMONBOND COMMUNITIES; *U.S. Private*, pg. 986
COMMON INTEREST MANAGEMENT SERVICES INC.; *U.S. Private*, pg. 986
THE COMMON LINK PTY LTD—See Woolworths Group Limited; *Int'l*, pg. 8452
COMMON SENSE OFFICE FURNITURE; *U.S. Private*, pg. 986
THE COMMON SOURCE; *U.S. Private*, pg. 4012
COMMONSPIRIT HEALTH; *U.S. Private*, pg. 986
COMMONWEALTH AGRI-ENERGY, LLC—See Hopkinsville Elevator Company, Inc.; *U.S. Private*, pg. 1979
COMMONWEALTH-ALTADIS, INC.—See Imperial Brands PLC; *Int'l*, pg. 3633
COMMONWEALTH ALTERNATIVE CARE, INC.—See TILT Holdings Inc.; *U.S. Public*, pg. 2159
COMMONWEALTH ANNUITY & LIFE INSURANCE COMPANY—See KKR & Co. Inc.; *U.S. Public*, pg. 1251
COMMONWEALTH ARCHITECTS, P.C.; *U.S. Private*, pg. 986
COMMONWEALTH BANCORP; *U.S. Private*, pg. 986
COMMONWEALTH BANCSHARES, INC.—See Stock Yards Bancorp, Inc.; *U.S. Public*, pg. 1950
COMMONWEALTH BANK OF AUSTRALIA - BEIJING—See Commonwealth Bank of Australia; *Int'l*, pg. 1720
COMMONWEALTH BANK OF AUSTRALIA - GRAND CAYMAN—See Commonwealth Bank of Australia; *Int'l*, pg. 1720
COMMONWEALTH BANK OF AUSTRALIA - HONG KONG—See Commonwealth Bank of Australia; *Int'l*, pg. 1720
COMMONWEALTH BANK OF AUSTRALIA - JAPAN—See Commonwealth Bank of Australia; *Int'l*, pg. 1720
COMMONWEALTH BANK OF AUSTRALIA - SHANGHAI—See Commonwealth Bank of Australia; *Int'l*, pg. 1720
COMMONWEALTH BANK OF AUSTRALIA; *Int'l*, pg. 1719
COMMONWEALTH BANK OF AUSTRALIA - UK—See Commonwealth Bank of Australia; *Int'l*, pg. 1720
COMMONWEALTH BANK OF AUSTRALIA - U.S.A.—See Commonwealth Bank of Australia; *Int'l*, pg. 1720
COMMONWEALTH BANK & TRUST COMPANY—See Stock Yards Bancorp, Inc.; *U.S. Public*, pg. 1950
COMMONWEALTH BLINDS & SHADES, INC.—See Contexture, Inc; *U.S. Private*, pg. 1028
COMMONWEALTH BRANDS, INC.—See Imperial Brands PLC; *Int'l*, pg. 3633
COMMONWEALTH BUILDING MATERIALS, INC.—See GMS Inc.; *U.S. Public*, pg. 948
COMMONWEALTH BUSINESS BANK—See CBB Bancorp, Inc.; *U.S. Public*, pg. 455
COMMONWEALTH CAPITAL CORP.; *U.S. Private*, pg. 986
COMMONWEALTH CAPITAL SECURITIES CORP.—See Commonwealth Capital Corp.; *U.S. Private*, pg. 986
COMMONWEALTH CARE ALLIANCE, INC.; *U.S. Private*, pg. 986
COMMONWEALTH CENTRAL CREDIT UNION; *U.S. Private*, pg. 986
COMMONWEALTH COMPUTER RESEARCH INC.—See General Atomics; *U.S. Private*, pg. 1663
COMMONWEALTH CREATIVE ASSOCIATES; *U.S. Private*, pg. 986
COMMONWEALTH CREDIT UNION; *U.S. Private*, pg. 986
COMMONWEALTH CRYSTAL HOLDING II, INC.; *U.S. Private*, pg. 986
COMMONWEALTH DESIGNS, INC.; *U.S. Private*, pg. 986
COMMON WEALTH DEVELOPERS LIMITED—See Trent Limited; *Int'l*, pg. 7916
COMMONWEALTH DODGE; *U.S. Private*, pg. 986
COMMONWEALTH DYNAMICS, INC.—See Global Dominion Access SA; *Int'l*, pg. 2995
COMMONWEALTH EDISON COMPANY—See Exelon Corporation; *U.S. Public*, pg. 806
COMMONWEALTH ELECTRICAL TECHNOLOGIES, INC.—See Aterian Investment Management, L.P.; *U.S. Private*, pg. 366
COMMONWEALTH ELECTRIC COMPANY OF THE MIDWEST INC.; *U.S. Private*, pg. 986
COMMONWEALTH EQUITY SERVICES LLP; *U.S. Private*, pg. 986
COMMONWEALTH HEALTH CANCER NETWORK, LLC—See Community Health Systems, Inc.; *U.S. Public*, pg. 552
COMMONWEALTH HOSIERY MILLS; *U.S. Private*, pg. 987
COMMONWEALTH INCOME & GROWTH FUND 8, LP; *U.S. Private*, pg. 987
COMMONWEALTH INFORMATICS, INC.—See Genpact Limited; *Int'l*, pg. 2926
COMMONWEALTH JOURNAL INC.—See The Retirement Systems of Alabama; *U.S. Private*, pg. 4105

COMMONWEALTH LAMINATING & COATING (HONG KONG) LIMITED—See Eastman Chemical Company; *U.S. Public*, pg. 704
COMMONWEALTH LAMINATING & COATING, INC.—See Eastman Chemical Company; *U.S. Public*, pg. 704
COMMONWEALTH LAMINATING & COATING (SHANGHAI) CO., LTD.—See Eastman Chemical Company; *U.S. Public*, pg. 704
COMMONWEALTH LAND TITLE INSURANCE COMPANY—See Fidelity National Financial, Inc.; *U.S. Public*, pg. 831
COMMONWEALTH MANAGED INVESTMENTS LIMITED—See Commonwealth Bank of Australia; *Int'l*, pg. 1720
COMMONWEALTH MATRIX LP—See Matrix Development Group Inc.; *U.S. Private*, pg. 2612
COMMONWEALTH OIL CORPORATION—See Quaker Chemical Corporation; *U.S. Public*, pg. 1745
COMMONWEALTH PACKAGING COMPANY, PACKAGING SERVICE—See Commonwealth Packaging Company; *U.S. Private*, pg. 987
COMMONWEALTH PACKAGING COMPANY; *U.S. Private*, pg. 987
COMMONWEALTH PERINATAL SERVICES, LLC—See HCA Healthcare, Inc.; *U.S. Public*, pg. 994
COMMONWEALTH PHYSICIAN NETWORK, LLC—See Community Health Systems, Inc.; *U.S. Public*, pg. 552
COMMONWEALTH PLYWOOD CO. LTD. - SEASONS FLOORING DIVISION—See Commonwealth Plywood Co. Ltd.; *Int'l*, pg. 1720
COMMONWEALTH PLYWOOD CO. LTD.; *Int'l*, pg. 1720
COMMONWEALTH PREMIUM FINANCE CORPORATION—See Unified Financial Services, Inc.; *U.S. Private*, pg. 4282
COMMONWEALTH PUBLIC BROADCASTING CORP.; *U.S. Private*, pg. 987
COMMONWEALTH REALTY GROUP, LLC—See Berkshire Hathaway Inc.; *U.S. Public*, pg. 304
COMMONWEALTH REALTY PARTNERS, INC.; *U.S. Private*, pg. 987
COMMONWEALTH SECURITIES LIMITED—See Commonwealth Bank of Australia; *Int'l*, pg. 1720
COMMONWEALTH SPECIALISTS OF KENTUCKY, LLC—See HCA Healthcare, Inc.; *U.S. Public*, pg. 994
COMMONWEALTH SPRAGUE CAPACITOR INC.—See Nueva Generacion Manufacturas S.A de C.V.; *Int'l*, pg. 5486
COMMONWEALTH TECHNOLOGY, INC.—See Veritas Capital Fund Management, LLC; *U.S. Private*, pg. 4360
COMMONWEALTH TELEPHONE ENTERPRISES, INC.—See Frontier Communications Parent, Inc.; *U.S. Public*, pg. 887
COMMONWEALTH TITLE OF DALLAS, INC.—See Fidelity National Financial, Inc.; *U.S. Public*, pg. 831
COMMONWEALTH TOY & NOVELTY COMPANY; *U.S. Private*, pg. 987
COMMONWEALTH UNDERWRITERS, LLC—See Hellman & Friedman LLC; *U.S. Private*, pg. 1909
COMMONWEALTH VENTURE FUNDING GROUP; *U.S. Private*, pg. 987
COMMONWEALTH WINE & SPIRITS LLC; *U.S. Private*, pg. 987
COMMONWEALTH WOOD PRESERVERS; *U.S. Private*, pg. 987
COMMONWEALTH WORLDWIDE CHAUFFEURED TRANSPORTATION; *U.S. Private*, pg. 987
COMMONWEALTH ZOOLOGICAL CORPORATION; *U.S. Private*, pg. 987
THE COMMONWELL MUTUAL INSURANCE GROUP; *Int'l*, pg. 7635
COMMOTION PROMOTIONS, LTD.; *U.S. Private*, pg. 987
COMMSCON ITALIA, S.R.L.—See Cellnex Telecom, S.A.; *Int'l*, pg. 1394
COMMSCOPE ASIA (SUZHOU) TECHNOLOGIES CO., LTD.—See CommScope Holding Company, Inc.; *U.S. Public*, pg. 549
COMMSCOPE CABOS DO BRASIL LTDA—See CommScope Holding Company, Inc.; *U.S. Public*, pg. 549
COMMSCOPE HOLDING COMPANY, INC.; *U.S. Public*, pg. 547
COMMSCOPE, INC. OF NORTH CAROLINA—See CommScope Holding Company, Inc.; *U.S. Public*, pg. 549
COMMSCOPE, INC.—See CommScope Holding Company, Inc.; *U.S. Public*, pg. 548
COMMSCOPE, INC. - WESTCHESTER—See CommScope Holding Company, Inc.; *U.S. Public*, pg. 549
COMMSCOPE INTERNATIONAL HOLDINGS, LLC—See CommScope Holding Company, Inc.; *U.S. Public*, pg. 549
COMMSCOPE NEVADA, LLC—See CommScope Holding Company, Inc.; *U.S. Public*, pg. 549
COMMSCOPE OPTICAL TECHNOLOGIES, INC.—See CommScope Holding Company, Inc.; *U.S. Public*, pg. 549
COMMSCOPE SOLUTIONS GERMANY GMBH—See CommScope Holding Company, Inc.; *U.S. Public*, pg. 549

COMMSCOPE SOLUTIONS INTERNATIONAL, INC. - BACHENBULACH—See CommScope Holding Company, Inc.; *U.S. Public*, pg. 549

COMMSCOPE SOLUTIONS IRELAND LTD.—See CommScope Holding Company, Inc.; *U.S. Public*, pg. 549

COMMSCOPE TECHNOLOGIES LLC—See CommScope Holding Company, Inc.; *U.S. Public*, pg. 548

COMMSEED CORP; *Int'l*, pg. 1720

COMMS GROUP LTD; *Int'l*, pg. 1720

COMMS GROUP UK LIMITED—See Macquarie Group Limited; *Int'l*, pg. 4630

COMM-TEC GMBH—See DCC plc; *Int'l*, pg. 1989

COMMTECH ASIA (AUSTRALIA) PTY LTD.—See ISG PLC; *Int'l*, pg. 3816

COMMTECH ASIA (JAPAN) LIMITED—See ISG PLC; *Int'l*, pg. 3816

COMMTECH ASIA LIMITED—See ISG PLC; *Int'l*, pg. 3816

COMMTECH ASIA (SINGAPORE) PTE LIMITED—See ISG PLC; *Int'l*, pg. 3816

COMMTECH COMMISSIONING SERVICES S.A.—See Fagerhult Group AB; *Int'l*, pg. 2601

COMMTONE SOLUTION CO. LTD—See Discretix Technologies Ltd.; *Int'l*, pg. 2134

COMMUNE HOTELS & RESORTS ASIA PTE. LTD.—See Commune Hotels & Resorts, LLC; *U.S. Private*, pg. 987

COMMUNE HOTELS & RESORTS, LLC; *U.S. Private*, pg. 987

COMMUNICA, INC.; *U.S. Private*, pg. 987

COMMUNICA (PTY) LTD.—See P-Duke Technology Co., Ltd.; *Int'l*, pg. 5681

COMMUNICAR CORP.; *U.S. Private*, pg. 987

COMMUNICARE, INC.; *U.S. Private*, pg. 987

COMMUNICATION 2000 SAS—See NRJ Group SA; *Int'l*, pg. 5474

COMMUNICATION AND SYSTEM SOLUTION PUBLIC COMPANY LIMITED; *Int'l*, pg. 1720

COMMUNICATION ARTS, INC.—See Stantec Inc.; *Int'l*, pg. 7171

COMMUNICATION ASSOCIATES—See Belden, Inc.; *U.S. Public*, pg. 294

COMMUNICATION ASSOCIATES; *U.S. Private*, pg. 988

COMMUNICATION BY DESIGN—See Omnicom Group Inc.; *U.S. Public*, pg. 1578

COMMUNICATION CABLES, LLC—See WESCO International, Inc.; *U.S. Public*, pg. 2051

COMMUNICATION COMPANY OF SOUTH BEND, INC.; *U.S. Private*, pg. 988

COMMUNICATION CONCEPT GESELLSCHAFT FUR KOMMUNIKATIONSTECHNIK MBH—See Deutsche Wohnen SE; *Int'l*, pg. 2085

COMMUNICATION CONCEPTS INC.; *U.S. Private*, pg. 988

COMMUNICATION ELECTRONICS INC.—See Pye-Barker Fire & Safety, LLC; *U.S. Private*, pg. 3309

COMMUNICATION GLOBAL CERTIFICATION INC.—See HTC Corporation; *Int'l*, pg. 3508

COMMUNICATION INFRASTRUCTURE CORPORATION; *U.S. Private*, pg. 988

COMMUNICATION NETWORKS, LLC—See ACRE, LLC; *U.S. Private*, pg. 65

COMMUNICATION POWER CORP. (CPC); *U.S. Private*, pg. 988

COMMUNICATIONS BROKERS, INC.—See Keystone Group, L.P.; *U.S. Private*, pg. 2297

COMMUNICATIONS BROKERS, INC.—See Pamlico Capital Management, L.P.; *U.S. Private*, pg. 3083

COMMUNICATION SCIENCE CORPORATION—See Fair Friend Group; *Int'l*, pg. 2604

COMMUNICATIONS CONSTRUCTION GROUP, LLC—See Dycom Industries, Inc.; *U.S. Public*, pg. 698

COMMUNICATIONS CORPORATION OF INDIANA—See Telephone & Data Systems, Inc.; *U.S. Public*, pg. 1997

COMMUNICATIONS DATA GROUP, INC.; *U.S. Private*, pg. 988

COMMUNICATIONS ENGINEERING CO.; *U.S. Private*, pg. 988

COMMUNICATION SERVICE FOR THE DEAF, INC.; *U.S. Private*, pg. 988

COMMUNICATION SERVICES INC.; *U.S. Private*, pg. 988

COMMUNICATION SERVICES; *U.S. Private*, pg. 988

COMMUNICATIONS FIJI LTD.; *Int'l*, pg. 1720

THE COMMUNICATIONS GROUP; *U.S. Private*, pg. 4012

COMMUNICATIONS INFRASTRUCTURE INVESTMENTS, LLC; *U.S. Private*, pg. 988

COMMUNICATIONS INTERNATIONAL INC.; *U.S. Private*, pg. 988

COMMUNICATIONS INTERNATIONAL (NY); *U.S. Private*, pg. 988

COMMUNICATIONS INVESTMENT PARTNERS LIMITED; *Int'l*, pg. 1721

COMMUNICATION SITE MANAGEMENT CORP.—See Chase Enterprises, Inc.; *U.S. Private*, pg. 859

COMMUNICATIONS NETWORK INC—See Kalona Cooperative Telephone Company; *U.S. Private*, pg. 2258

COMMUNICATIONS PAPERS—See Gould Paper Corporation; *U.S. Private*, pg. 1745

COMMUNICATIONS & POWER INDUSTRIES CANADA INC.—See Odyssey Investment Partners, LLC; *U.S. Private*, pg. 2994

COMMUNICATIONS & POWER INDUSTRIES LLC - BEVERLY MICROWAVE DIVISION—See Odyssey Investment Partners, LLC; *U.S. Private*, pg. 2994

COMMUNICATIONS & POWER INDUSTRIES LLC - COMMUNICATIONS & MEDICAL PRODUCTS DIVISION—See Odyssey Investment Partners, LLC; *U.S. Private*, pg. 2994

COMMUNICATIONS & POWER INDUSTRIES LLC - ECONCO DIVISION—See Odyssey Investment Partners, LLC; *U.S. Private*, pg. 2994

COMMUNICATIONS & POWER INDUSTRIES LLC - MICROWAVE POWER PRODUCTS DIVISION—See Odyssey Investment Partners, LLC; *U.S. Private*, pg. 2995

COMMUNICATIONS & POWER INDUSTRIES LLC - SATCOM EAST DIVISION—See Odyssey Investment Partners, LLC; *U.S. Private*, pg. 2995

COMMUNICATIONS & POWER INDUSTRIES LLC - SATCOM WEST DIVISION—See Odyssey Investment Partners, LLC; *U.S. Private*, pg. 2995

COMMUNICATIONS & POWER INDUSTRIES LLC—See Odyssey Investment Partners, LLC; *U.S. Private*, pg. 2994

COMMUNICATIONS PRODUCTS INC.; *U.S. Private*, pg. 988

COMMUNICATIONS PRODUCTS & SERVICES; *U.S. Private*, pg. 988

COMMUNICATIONS RESOURCE, INC.; *U.S. Private*, pg. 988

COMMUNICATIONS SECURITY & COMPLIANCE TECHNOLOGIES INC.—See Japan Communications, Inc.; *Int'l*, pg. 3887

COMMUNICATIONS STRATEGIES, INC.; *U.S. Private*, pg. 988

COMMUNICATIONS SUPPLY CORPORATION—See WESCO International, Inc.; *U.S. Public*, pg. 2351

COMMUNICATIONS TELEVIDEO LTD; *U.S. Private*, pg. 989

COMMUNICATIONS TEST DESIGN INC.; *U.S. Private*, pg. 989

COMMUNICATIONS WORKERS OF AMERICA; *U.S. Private*, pg. 989

COMMUNICATION TECHNOLOGIES, INC.; *U.S. Private*, pg. 988

COMMUNICATION TECHNOLOGIES, INC.—See Consolidated Communications Holdings, Inc.; *U.S. Public*, pg. 569

COMMUNICATION TECHNOLOGY SERVICES; *U.S. Private*, pg. 988

COMMUNICATION WEAVER CO., LTD.; *Int'l*, pg. 1720

COMMUNICORP GROUP LTD.; *Int'l*, pg. 1721

COMMUNICORP, INC.—See Aflac Incorporated; *U.S. Public*, pg. 57

COMMUNICREATIONS; *U.S. Private*, pg. 989

COMMUNIFX PARTNERS LLC—See Stagwell, Inc.; *U.S. Public*, pg. 1926

COMMUNIGROUP OF K.C. INC.—See Telephone Electronics Corporation; *U.S. Private*, pg. 3961

THE COMMUNIQUE GROUP, INC.; *U.S. Private*, pg. 4012

COMMUNIQUE PR—See WPP plc; *Int'l*, pg. 8468

COMMUNIQUE—See Daniel J. Edelman, Inc.; *U.S. Private*, pg. 1154

COMMUNISIS EUROPE LIMITED—See Aquiline Capital Partners LLC; *U.S. Private*, pg. 304

COMMUNISIS PLC—See Aquiline Capital Partners LLC; *U.S. Private*, pg. 304

COMMUNISIS UK LIMITED—See Aquiline Capital Partners LLC; *U.S. Private*, pg. 304

COMMUNITECH; *U.S. Private*, pg. 989

COMMUNITIES FIRST FINANCIAL CORPORATION; *U.S. Public*, pg. 549

COMMUNITIES FOR PEOPLE, INC.; *U.S. Private*, pg. 989

COMMUNITY ACCESS UNLIMITED, INC.; *U.S. Private*, pg. 989

COMMUNITYAMERICA CREDIT UNION; *U.S. Private*, pg. 997

COMMUNITY ANCILLARY SERVICES, INC.; *U.S. Private*, pg. 989

COMMUNITY AND ECONOMIC DEVELOPMENT ASSOCIATION OF COOK COUNTY, INCORPORATED; *U.S. Private*, pg. 989

COMMUNITY ANTI-DRUG COALITIONS OF AMERICA; *U.S. Private*, pg. 989

COMMUNITY ASPHALT CORP.; *U.S. Private*, pg. 989

COMMUNITY ASSOCIATION MANAGEMENT SPECIALIST, INC.; *U.S. Private*, pg. 989

COMMUNITY ASSOCIATIONS INSTITUTE; *U.S. Private*, pg. 989

COMMUNITY ASSOCIATION UNDERWRITERS OF AMERICA; *U.S. Private*, pg. 989

COMMUNITY BANC MORTGAGE CORPORATION—See United Community Bancorp, Inc.; *U.S. Private*, pg. 4289

COMMUNITY BANCORP, INC.; *U.S. Public*, pg. 549

COMMUNITY BANCORP OF LOUISIANA, INC.; *U.S. Private*, pg. 989

COMMUNITY BANCSHARES, INC.; *U.S. Public*, pg. 549

COMMUNITY BANCSHARES OF MISSISSIPPI, INC.; *U.S. Private*, pg. 989

COMMUNITY BANKERS; *U.S. Public*, pg. 550

COMMUNITY BANKERS TRUST CORPORATION—See United Bankshares, Inc.; *U.S. Public*, pg. 2229

COMMUNITY BANK FUNDING COMPANY—See Republic Financial Corporation; *U.S. Private*, pg. 3402

COMMUNITY BANK HOLDINGS OF TEXAS, INC.; *U.S. Private*, pg. 990

COMMUNITY BANK, N.A.—See Community Bank System, Inc.; *U.S. Public*, pg. 549

COMMUNITY BANK NORTH MISSISSIPPI—See Community Bancshares of Mississippi, Inc.; *U.S. Private*, pg. 989

COMMUNITY BANK OF MISSISSIPPI—See Community Bancshares of Mississippi, Inc.; *U.S. Private*, pg. 990

COMMUNITY BANK OF PLEASANT HILL—See Lolyn Financial Corporation; *U.S. Private*, pg. 2483

COMMUNITY BANK OF RAYMORE—See Lolyn Financial Corporation; *U.S. Private*, pg. 2483

COMMUNITY BANK OF SANTA MARIA; *U.S. Public*, pg. 549

COMMUNITYBANK OF TEXAS, N.A.—See Stellar Bancorp, Inc.; *U.S. Public*, pg. 1944

COMMUNITY BANK OF THE BAY; *U.S. Private*, pg. 990

COMMUNITY BANK OF THE CHESAPEAKE—See Shore Bancshares, Inc.; *U.S. Public*, pg. 1875

COMMUNITY BANK OF THE MIDWEST—See Peoples Bank and Trust; *U.S. Private*, pg. 3141

COMMUNITY BANKSHARES, INC.; *U.S. Private*, pg. 990

COMMUNITY BANKS OF COLORADO—See National Bank Holdings Corporation; *U.S. Public*, pg. 1493

THE COMMUNITY BANK—See Campello Bancorp, Inc.; *U.S. Private*, pg. 731

COMMUNITY BANK—See CB Financial Services, Inc.; *U.S. Public*, pg. 455

COMMUNITY BANK—See Nebraska Bankshares, Inc.; *U.S. Private*, pg. 2878

COMMUNITY BANK—See Sooner Southwest Bankshares, Inc.; *U.S. Private*, pg. 3715

COMMUNITY BANK SYSTEM, INC.; *U.S. Public*, pg. 549

COMMUNITY BANK & TRUST - ALABAMA—See Community Bankshares, Inc.; *U.S. Private*, pg. 990

COMMUNITY BANK & TRUST INC.; *U.S. Private*, pg. 990

COMMUNITY BANK & TRUST—See QCR Holdings, Inc.; *U.S. Public*, pg. 1742

COMMUNITY BANK & TRUST - WEST GEORGIA—See Community Bankshares, Inc.; *U.S. Private*, pg. 990

COMMUNITY BASED CARE OF CENTRAL FLORIDA, INC.; *U.S. Private*, pg. 990

COMMUNITY BASED HOUSING ASSOCIATION—See Peabody; *Int'l*, pg. 5773

COMMUNITY BASED SERVICES INC.; *U.S. Private*, pg. 990

COMMUNITY BEHAVIORAL HEALTH; *U.S. Private*, pg. 990

THE COMMUNITY BLOOD CENTER, INC.; *U.S. Private*, pg. 4012

COMMUNITY BLOOD CENTER OF THE CAROLINAS, INC.—See OneBlood, Inc.; *U.S. Private*, pg. 3024

COMMUNITY BLOOD CENTER OF THE OZARKS; *U.S. Private*, pg. 990

COMMUNITY BLOOD CENTER; *U.S. Private*, pg. 990

COMMUNITY BLOOD COUNCIL OF NEW JERSEY, INC.; *U.S. Private*, pg. 990

COMMUNITY BRANDS HOLDCO, LLC—See Insight Venture Management, LLC; *U.S. Private*, pg. 2088

THE COMMUNITY BROADCASTING COMPANY OF SAN DIEGO, INCORPORATED—See Entravision Communications Corporation; *U.S. Public*, pg. 779

COMMUNITY BUILDERS INC.; *U.S. Private*, pg. 990

COMMUNITY CAPITAL BANCSHARES, INC.; *U.S. Public*, pg. 550

COMMUNITY CARE CHANNING WAY, LLC—See Bain Capital, LP; *U.S. Private*, pg. 445

COMMUNITY CARE COMPANIONS INC.; *U.S. Private*, pg. 990

COMMUNITY CARE HEALTH NETWORK, INC.—See Frazier & Company, Inc.; *U.S. Private*, pg. 1599

COMMUNITY CARE HEALTH NETWORK, INC.—See ModivCare, Inc.; *U.S. Public*, pg. 1455

COMMUNITYCARE, INC.; *U.S. Private*, pg. 997

COMMUNITY CARE WEST SIDE, LLC—See Bain Capital, LP; *U.S. Private*, pg. 445

COMMUNITY CENTER OF NORTHERN WESTCHESTER; *U.S. Private*, pg. 990

COMMUNITY CHARITY ADVANCEMENT, INC.; *U.S. Private*, pg. 990

COMMUNITY CHILD CARE COUNCIL OF SANTA CLARA COUNTY, INC.; *U.S. Private*, pg. 990

COMMUNITY CHOICE FINANCIAL INC.; *U.S. Private*, pg. 990

COMMUNITY COFFEE COMPANY LLC; *U.S. Private*, pg. 991

COMMUNITY COMPUTER SERVICE; *U.S. Private*, pg. 991

COMMUNITY CO-OPS OF LAKE PARK; *U.S. Private*, pg. 991

COMMUNITY CORRECTIONAL CENTER OF LINCOLN—See Nebraska Department of Correctional Services; *U.S. Private*, pg. 2878

COMMUNITY COUNCIL OF IDAHO, INC.

CORPORATE AFFILIATIONS

COMMUNITY COUNCIL OF IDAHO, INC.; *U.S. Private*, pg. 991
COMMUNITY COUNSELING CENTERS, INC.; *U.S. Private*, pg. 991
COMMUNITY COUNSELING OF BRISTOL COUNTY, INC.; *U.S. Private*, pg. 991
COMMUNITY COUNSELING SERVICES, INC.; *U.S. Private*, pg. 991
COMMUNITY DATA SOLUTIONS PTY. LTD.—See Vitalhub Corp.; *Int'l*, pg. 8258
COMMUNITY DENTAL CARE; *U.S. Private*, pg. 991
COMMUNITY DEVELOPMENT BANK, FSB—See Midwest Minnesota Community Development Corporation; *U.S. Private*, pg. 2722
COMMUNITY DEVELOPMENT, INC.—See Associations, Inc.; *U.S. Private*, pg. 359
COMMUNITY EMERGENCY MEDICAL SERVICE, INC.—See Beaumont Health; *U.S. Private*, pg. 508
COMMUNITY EMS, INC.—See KKR & Co. Inc.; *U.S. Public*, pg. 1249
COMMUNITY ENERGY AUSTRALIA PTY LTD—See Bendigo & Adelaide Bank Ltd.; *Int'l*, pg. 971
COMMUNITY ENTERPRISES, INC.; *U.S. Private*, pg. 991
COMMUNITY FINANCIAL CORPORATION—See Banner Corporation; *U.S. Public*, pg. 275
THE COMMUNITY FINANCIAL CORPORATION—See Shore Bancshares, Inc.; *U.S. Public*, pg. 1875
COMMUNITY FINANCIAL CORP; *U.S. Private*, pg. 991
COMMUNITY FINANCIAL GROUP, INC.—See Glacier Bancorp, Inc.; *U.S. Public*, pg. 938
COMMUNITY FINANCIAL SERVICES; *U.S. Private*, pg. 991
COMMUNITY FIRST BANCORPORATION; *U.S. Public*, pg. 550
COMMUNITY FIRST BANCSHARES, INC.; *U.S. Private*, pg. 991
COMMUNITY FIRST BANCSHARES, INC.—See Affinity Bancshares, Inc.; *U.S. Public*, pg. 56
COMMUNITY FIRST BANK OF INDIANA; *U.S. Private*, pg. 991
COMMUNITY FIRST BANK—See Community First Bancshares, Inc.; *U.S. Private*, pg. 991
COMMUNITY FIRST BANK—See First Bancshares, Inc.; *U.S. Private*, pg. 1513
COMMUNITY FIRST DATA SERVICES—See The Sturm Financial Group, Inc.; *U.S. Private*, pg. 4124
COMMUNITY FIRST FOUNDATION; *U.S. Private*, pg. 991
COMMUNITY FIRST SOLUTIONS; *U.S. Private*, pg. 991
COMMUNITY FOOD BANK OF EASTERN OKLAHOMA, INC.; *U.S. Private*, pg. 991
COMMUNITY FOUNDATION FOR GREATER ATLANTA INC; *U.S. Private*, pg. 992
COMMUNITY FOUNDATION FOR GREATER BUFFALO; *U.S. Private*, pg. 992
THE COMMUNITY FOUNDATION FOR GREATER NEW HAVEN; *U.S. Private*, pg. 4012
COMMUNITY FOUNDATION FOR MONTEREY COUNTY; *U.S. Private*, pg. 992
COMMUNITY FOUNDATION FOR MUSKEGON COUNTY; *U.S. Private*, pg. 992
THE COMMUNITY FOUNDATION FOR NORTHEAST FLORIDA; *U.S. Private*, pg. 4012
COMMUNITY FOUNDATION FOR PALM BEACH AND MARTIN COUNTIES; *U.S. Private*, pg. 992
COMMUNITY FOUNDATION FOR SOUTHEAST MICHIGAN; *U.S. Private*, pg. 992
COMMUNITY FOUNDATION FOR SOUTHWEST WASHINGTON; *U.S. Private*, pg. 992
COMMUNITY FOUNDATION OF ACADIANA; *U.S. Private*, pg. 992
THE COMMUNITY FOUNDATION OF FREDERICK COUNTY, MD, INC; *U.S. Private*, pg. 4012
COMMUNITY FOUNDATION OF GREATER BIRMINGHAM; *U.S. Private*, pg. 992
COMMUNITY FOUNDATION OF GREATER DES MOINES; *U.S. Private*, pg. 992
COMMUNITY FOUNDATION OF GREATER GREENSBORO; *U.S. Private*, pg. 992
COMMUNITY FOUNDATION OF GREATER MEMPHIS; *U.S. Private*, pg. 992
COMMUNITY FOUNDATION OF KANKAKEE RIVER VALLEY; *U.S. Private*, pg. 992
COMMUNITY FOUNDATION OF LORAIN COUNTY; *U.S. Private*, pg. 992
COMMUNITY FOUNDATION OF MIDDLE TENNESSESE; *U.S. Private*, pg. 992
COMMUNITY FOUNDATION OF NEW JERSEY; *U.S. Private*, pg. 992
COMMUNITY FOUNDATION OF NORTHERN COLORADO; *U.S. Private*, pg. 992
COMMUNITY FOUNDATION OF NORTH LOUISIANA; *U.S. Private*, pg. 992
COMMUNITY FOUNDATION OF NORTH TEXAS; *U.S. Private*, pg. 992
COMMUNITY FOUNDATION OF NORTHWEST CONNECTICUT, INC; *U.S. Private*, pg. 993
COMMUNITY FOUNDATION OF SOUTH GEORGIA; *U.S. Private*, pg. 993

COMMUNITY FOUNDATION OF THE GREAT RIVER BEND; *U.S. Private*, pg. 993
COMMUNITY FOUNDATION OF WESTERN NEVADA; *U.S. Private*, pg. 993
COMMUNITY FOUNDATION OF WESTERN PA & EASTERN OH; *U.S. Private*, pg. 993
COMMUNITY FOUNDATION OF WEST GEORGIA, INC.; *U.S. Private*, pg. 993
COMMUNITY FOUNDATION SANTA CRUZ COUNTY; *U.S. Private*, pg. 993
THE COMMUNITY FOUNDATION SERVING BOULDER COUNTY; *U.S. Private*, pg. 4012
THE COMMUNITY FOUNDATION SERVING RICHMOND & CENTRAL VIRGINIA; *U.S. Private*, pg. 4012
COMMUNITY FOUNDATION SONOMA COUNTY; *U.S. Private*, pg. 993
THE COMMUNITY GROUP; *U.S. Private*, pg. 4012
COMMUNITY HARVEST FOOD BANK OF NORTHEAST INDIANA, INC.; *U.S. Private*, pg. 993
COMMUNITY HEALTH ACCREDITATION PARTNER, INC.; *U.S. Private*, pg. 993
COMMUNITY HEALTH CARE; *U.S. Private*, pg. 993
COMMUNITY HEALTHCARE TRUST INCORPORATED; *U.S. Public*, pg. 557
COMMUNITY HEALTH CENTER, INC.; *U.S. Private*, pg. 993
COMMUNITY HEALTH CENTER OF SOUTHEAST KANSAS; *U.S. Private*, pg. 993
COMMUNITY HEALTH CENTERS OF THE CENTRAL COAST, INC.; *U.S. Private*, pg. 993
COMMUNITY HEALTH CENTERS OF THE RUTLAND REGION; *U.S. Private*, pg. 993
COMMUNITY HEALTH CENTER; *U.S. Private*, pg. 993
COMMUNITY HEALTH CONNECTIONS, INC.; *U.S. Private*, pg. 993
COMMUNITY HEALTH GROUP; *U.S. Private*, pg. 993
COMMUNITY HEALTHLINK INC.; *U.S. Private*, pg. 994
COMMUNITY HEALTH NETWORK FOUNDATION; *U.S. Private*, pg. 993
COMMUNITY HEALTH NETWORK OF CONNECTICUT, INC.; *U.S. Private*, pg. 994
COMMUNITY HEALTH OF SOUTH FLORIDA, INC.; *U.S. Private*, pg. 994
COMMUNITY HEALTH PLAN OF WASHINGTON; *U.S. Private*, pg. 994
COMMUNITY HEALTH PROGRAMS, INC.; *U.S. Private*, pg. 994
COMMUNITY HEALTH RESOURCES; *U.S. Private*, pg. 994
COMMUNITY HEALTH SERVICES, INC.; *U.S. Private*, pg. 994
COMMUNITY HEALTH SERVICES OF GEORGIA; *U.S. Private*, pg. 994
COMMUNITY HEALTH SOLUTIONS OF AMERICA, INC.; *U.S. Private*, pg. 994
COMMUNITYHEALTH; *U.S. Private*, pg. 997
COMMUNITY HEALTH SYSTEMS, INC.; *U.S. Public*, pg. 550
COMMUNITY HERITAGE FINANCIAL, INC.; *U.S. Public*, pg. 558
COMMUNITY HOLDINGS OF KENTUCKY LLC—See The Retirement Systems of Alabama; *U.S. Private*, pg. 4105
COMMUNITY HOME CARE OF VANCE COUNTY, LLC—See Humana, Inc.; *U.S. Public*, pg. 1069
COMMUNITY HOME HEALTH & HOSPICE; *U.S. Private*, pg. 994
COMMUNITY HOME HEALTH SERVICES, INC.; *U.S. Private*, pg. 994
COMMUNITY HOME SUPPLY CO. INC.; *U.S. Private*, pg. 994
COMMUNITY HOSPICE, INC.; *U.S. Private*, pg. 994
THE COMMUNITY HOSPICE, INC.; *U.S. Private*, pg. 4012
COMMUNITY HOSPICE OF TEXAS; *U.S. Private*, pg. 994
COMMUNITY HOSPICE & PALLIATIVE CARE; *U.S. Private*, pg. 994
COMMUNITY HOSPITAL, INC.; *U.S. Private*, pg. 994
COMMUNITY HOSPITAL OF SAN BERNARDINO—See Catholic Health Initiatives; *U.S. Private*, pg. 789
COMMUNITY HOSPITALS AND WELLNESS CENTERS; *U.S. Private*, pg. 994
COMMUNITY HOUSING CONCEPTS, INC.; *U.S. Private*, pg. 994
COMMUNITY HOUSING DEVELOPMENT CORPORATION; *U.S. Private*, pg. 994
COMMUNITY HOUSING INNOVATIONS, INC.; *U.S. Private*, pg. 994
COMMUNITY HOUSING PARTNERS CORPORATION; *U.S. Private*, pg. 995
COMMUNITY INITIATIVES DEVELOPMENT CORPORATION; *U.S. Private*, pg. 995
COMMUNITY INITIATIVES; *U.S. Private*, pg. 995
COMMUNITY INSURANCE COMPANY—See Elevance Health, Inc.; *U.S. Public*, pg. 729
COMMUNITY INTERACTIONS, INC.; *U.S. Private*, pg. 995
COMMUNITY INVESTMENT GROUP, LTD.; *U.S. Private*, pg. 995
COMMUNITY INVESTMENT HOLDINGS (PTY) LTD.; *Int'l*, pg. 1721

COMMUNITY INVESTMENT SERVICES, INC.—See Community Bank System, Inc.; *U.S. Public*, pg. 549
COMMUNITY INVESTORS BANCORP, INC.; *U.S. Public*, pg. 558
COMMUNITY INVESTORS, INC.; *U.S. Private*, pg. 995
COMMUNITY INVOLVEMENT PROGRAMS; *U.S. Private*, pg. 995
COMMUNITY JUSTICE PROJECT; *U.S. Private*, pg. 995
COMMUNITY LEGAL SERVICES OF MID-FLORIDA, INC.; *U.S. Private*, pg. 995
COMMUNITY LIVING ALLIANCE, INC.; *U.S. Private*, pg. 995
COMMUNITY LIVING AND SUPPORT SERVICES; *U.S. Private*, pg. 995
COMMUNITY LIVING OPPORTUNITIES; *U.S. Private*, pg. 995
COMMUNITY LONG DISTANCE, INC.—See Comporium Group; *U.S. Private*, pg. 1002
COMMUNITY MEDIA GROUP; *U.S. Private*, pg. 995
COMMUNITY MEDICAL CENTER, INC.—See Apollo Global Management, Inc.; *U.S. Public*, pg. 154
COMMUNITY MEDICAL CENTERS, INC.; *U.S. Private*, pg. 995
COMMUNITY MEDICAL CENTER—See Barnabas Health, Inc.; *U.S. Private*, pg. 476
COMMUNITY MEMORIAL HEALTHCARE, INC.; *U.S. Private*, pg. 995
COMMUNITY MEMORIAL HEALTHCENTER; *U.S. Private*, pg. 996
COMMUNITY MEMORIAL HEALTH SYSTEM; *U.S. Private*, pg. 995
COMMUNITY MORTGAGE CORPORATION; *U.S. Private*, pg. 996
COMMUNITY MOTOR CO. INC.; *U.S. Private*, pg. 996
COMMUNITY NATIONAL BANK—See Community Bancorp, Inc.; *U.S. Public*, pg. 549
COMMUNITY NATIONAL BANK & TRUST OF TEXAS—See Community Bank Holdings of Texas, Inc.; *U.S. Private*, pg. 990
COMMUNITY NATIONAL BANK & TRUST; *U.S. Private*, pg. 996
COMMUNITY NETWORK CENTER INC.—See Chubu Electric Power Co., Inc.; *Int'l*, pg. 1593
COMMUNITY NEWSPAPERS INC.; *U.S. Private*, pg. 996
COMMUNITY NURSING SERVICE OF DU PAGE COUNTY; *U.S. Private*, pg. 996
COMMUNITY OF CARING; *U.S. Private*, pg. 996
COMMUNITY OF HOPE; *U.S. Private*, pg. 996
COMMUNITY PARTNERSHIP FOR CHILDREN; *U.S. Private*, pg. 996
COMMUNITY PARTNERSHIP OF SOUTHERN ARIZONA; *U.S. Private*, pg. 996
COMMUNITY PARTNERS; *U.S. Private*, pg. 996
COMMUNITY PHARMACY OF RANDOLPH; *U.S. Private*, pg. 996
THE COMMUNITY PHONE BOOK, INC.—See American CyberSystems, Inc.; *U.S. Private*, pg. 230
COMMUNITY PHYSICIANS NETWORK; *U.S. Private*, pg. 996
THE COMMUNITY PRESERVATION CORPORATION; *U.S. Private*, pg. 4012
COMMUNITY PROPERTIES OF OHIO; *U.S. Private*, pg. 996
COMMUNITY REDEVELOPMENT INC.; *U.S. Public*, pg. 558
COMMUNITY REHABILITATION SERVICES, INC.; *U.S. Private*, pg. 996
COMMUNITY RENEWAL TEAM, INC.; *U.S. Private*, pg. 996
COMMUNITY RESOURCE CREDIT UNION; *U.S. Private*, pg. 996
COMMUNITY RESOURCES FOR INDEPENDENCE; *U.S. Private*, pg. 996
COMMUNITY SAVINGS BANCORP, INC.; *U.S. Public*, pg. 558
COMMUNITY SAVINGS BANK—See Community Financial Corp; *U.S. Private*, pg. 991
COMMUNITY SENIOR LIFE INC; *U.S. Private*, pg. 997
COMMUNITY SERVICE ACCEPTANCE COMPANY—See Farm Bureau Mutual Insurance Company of Michigan Inc.; *U.S. Private*, pg. 1474
COMMUNITY SERVICE BUILDING CORPORATION; *U.S. Private*, pg. 997
COMMUNITY SERVICE COUNCIL; *U.S. Private*, pg. 997
COMMUNITY SERVICE, INC.—See BNP Paribas SA; *Int'l*, pg. 1087
COMMUNITY SERVICE NETWORK INC; *U.S. Private*, pg. 997
COMMUNITY SERVICES AND EMPLOYMENT TRAINING, INC.; *U.S. Private*, pg. 997
COMMUNITY SERVICES FOR THE DEVELOPMENTALLY DISABLED, INC.; *U.S. Private*, pg. 997
COMMUNITY SOLUTIONS FOR PRIMARY CARE LTD.—See Morgan Sindall Group Plc; *Int'l*, pg. 5044
COMMUNITY SOLUTIONS LIMITED—See Morgan Sindall Group Plc; *Int'l*, pg. 5044
COMMUNITY SPECIALISTS CORPORATION; *U.S. Private*, pg. 997

COMPANY NAME INDEX

COMMUNITY SPECIALTY PHARMACY, LLC—See Scienture Holdings, Inc.; *U.S. Public*, pg. 1849
COMMUNITY SPIRIT BANK—See Independent Bancshares, Inc.; *U.S. Public*, pg. 2058
COMMUNITY STATE BANK; *U.S. Public*, pg. 997
COMMUNITY STATE BANK—See QCR Holdings, Inc.; *U.S. Public*, pg. 1742
COMMUNITY SUFFOLK INC.; *U.S. Private*, pg. 997
COMMUNITY SUPPORT SERVICES, INC.; *U.S. Private*, pg. 997
COMMUNITY SYSTEMS, INC.; *U.S. Private*, pg. 997
COMMUNITY TECHKNOWLEDGE, INC.—See Social Solutions Global Inc.; *U.S. Private*, pg. 3703
COMMUNITY TELEVISION OF SOUTHERN CALIFORNIA; *U.S. Private*, pg. 997
COMMUNITY TIES OF AMERICA, INC.; *U.S. Private*, pg. 997
COMMUNITY TIRE COMPANY INC.; *U.S. Private*, pg. 997
COMMUNITY TITLE AGENCY, INC.—See Consumers Bancorp, Inc.; *U.S. Public*, pg. 573
COMMUNITY TRUST AND INVESTMENT COMPANY—See Community Trust Bancorp Inc; *U.S. Public*, pg. 558
COMMUNITY TRUST BANCORP INC; *U.S. Public*, pg. 558
COMMUNITY TRUST BANK, INC.—See Community Trust Bancorp Inc; *U.S. Public*, pg. 558
COMMUNITY VENTURES PARTNERSHIPS LIMITED—See Galliford Try Holdings plc; *Int'l*, pg. 2874
COMMUNITY WEST BANCSHARES; *U.S. Public*, pg. 558
COMMUNITY WEST BANCSHARES—See Community West Bancshares; *U.S. Public*, pg. 558
COMMUNITY WEST BANK—See Community West Bancshares; *U.S. Public*, pg. 558
COMMUNITY, WORK & INDEPENDENCE, INC.; *U.S. Private*, pg. 997
COMMURE, INC—See HCA Healthcare, Inc.; *U.S. Public*, pg. 994
COMMUSONIC INDUSTRIES LIMITED—See Alco Holdings Limited; *Int'l*, pg. 301
COMMUTER AIR TECHNOLOGY; *U.S. Private*, pg. 997
COMMUTER HANDLING SERVICES (PTY) LIMITED—See The Didvest Group Limited; *Int'l*, pg. 7624
COMMUTER TRANSPORT ENGINEERING (PTY) LTD.; *Int'l*, pg. 1721
COMMVAULT SYSTEMS AB—See CommVault Systems, Inc.; *U.S. Public*, pg. 559
COMMVAULT SYSTEMS (AUSTRALIA) PTY. LTD.—See CommVault Systems, Inc.; *U.S. Public*, pg. 559
COMMVAULT SYSTEMS BELGIUM BVBA—See CommVault Systems, Inc.; *U.S. Public*, pg. 559
COMMVAULT SYSTEMS (CANADA) INC.—See CommVault Systems, Inc.; *U.S. Public*, pg. 559
COMMVAULT SYSTEMS GMBH—See CommVault Systems, Inc.; *U.S. Public*, pg. 559
COMMVAULT SYSTEMS IBERIA SRL—See CommVault Systems, Inc.; *U.S. Public*, pg. 559
COMMVAULT SYSTEMS, INC.; *U.S. Public*, pg. 558
COMMVAULT SYSTEMS (INDIA) PRIVATE LIMITED—See CommVault Systems, Inc.; *U.S. Public*, pg. 559
COMM VAULT SYSTEMS INTERNATIONAL B.V.—See CommVault Systems, Inc.; *U.S. Public*, pg. 559
COMMVAULT SYSTEMS ITALIA S.R.L.—See CommVault Systems, Inc.; *U.S. Public*, pg. 559
COMMVAULT SYSTEMS LIMITED—See CommVault Systems, Inc.; *U.S. Public*, pg. 559
COMMVAULT SYSTEMS MEXICO S. DE R.L. DE C.V.—See CommVault Systems, Inc.; *U.S. Public*, pg. 559
COMMVAULT SYSTEMS NETHERLANDS B.V.—See CommVault Systems, Inc.; *U.S. Public*, pg. 559
COMMVAULT SYSTEMS (NEW ZEALAND) LIMITED—See CommVault Systems, Inc.; *U.S. Public*, pg. 559
COMMVAULT SYSTEMS SARL—See CommVault Systems, Inc.; *U.S. Public*, pg. 559
COMMVAULT SYSTEMS (SINGAPORE) PRIVATE LIMITED—See CommVault Systems, Inc.; *U.S. Public*, pg. 559
COMMVAULT SYSTEMS (SOUTH AFRICA) (PTY) LTD.—See CommVault Systems, Inc.; *U.S. Public*, pg. 559
COMMVESCO LEVINSON VINER GROUP INC; *Int'l*, pg. 1721
COMM-WORKS, LLC - INDIANAPOLIS—See CommWorks, LLC; *U.S. Private*, pg. 982
COMM-WORKS, LLC; *U.S. Private*, pg. 982
COMM ZED SDN. BHD.—See TFP Solutions Berhad; *Int'l*, pg. 7587
COMNET COMMUNICATIONS LLC; *U.S. Private*, pg. 997
COMNET COMMUNICATIONS LLC—See Comnet Communications LLC; *U.S. Private*, pg. 998
COM-NET SERVICES, LLC—See The Newtron Group Inc.; *U.S. Private*, pg. 4084
COMNET TELECOM SUPPLY, INC.; *U.S. Private*, pg. 998
COMO CO., LTD.; *Int'l*, pg. 1721
COMO DIFFUSION INC.; *Int'l*, pg. 1721

COMODO CO., LTD.—See Sakai Heavy Industries Ltd; *Int'l*, pg. 6487
COMODO GROUP, INC.; *U.S. Private*, pg. 998
CO-MO ELECTRIC COOPERATIVE; *U.S. Private*, pg. 953
COMO ENGINEERS PTY. LTD.; *Int'l*, pg. 1721
COMO GRAIN—See Green Plains Inc.; *U.S. Public*, pg. 963
COMO HOTELS & RESORTS (ASIA) PTE. LTD.; *Int'l*, pg. 1721
COMO HOTELS & RESORTS LTD.—See COMO Hotels & Resorts (Asia) Pte. Ltd.; *Int'l*, pg. 1721
COMO HOTELS & RESORTS USA—See COMO Hotels & Resorts (Asia) Pte. Ltd.; *Int'l*, pg. 1721
COMO LUBE & SUPPLIES, INC.; *U.S. Private*, pg. 998
COMO OIL COMPANY OF FLORIDA—See Palmdale Oil Company, Inc.; *U.S. Private*, pg. 3080
COMO OIL & PROPANE—See Interstate Energy LLC; *U.S. Private*, pg. 2124
COMOX VALLEY DODGE CHRYSLER JEEP RAM LTD.; *Int'l*, pg. 1721
COMP 24 LLC—See Saints Capital, LLC; *U.S. Private*, pg. 3530
COMPAC DEVELOPMENT CORPORATION—See CPI Aerostructures, Inc.; *U.S. Public*, pg. 588
COMPACT DYNAMICS GMBH—See INA-Holding Schaeffler GmbH & Co. KG; *Int'l*, pg. 3640
COMPACT ENERGY SDN. BHD.—See Lion Asiapac Limited; *Int'l*, pg. 4517
COMPACT EQUIPMENT ATTACHMENTS INC—See Manitou BF S.A.; *Int'l*, pg. 4672
COMPACT EXCAVATOR SALES, LLC—See IHI Corporation; *Int'l*, pg. 3604
COMPACT INFORMATION SYSTEMS, INC.; *U.S. Private*, pg. 998
COMPACTION & RECYCLING EQUIPMENT, INC.—See Deep Green Waste & Recycling, Inc.; *U.S. Public*, pg. 645
COMPACT LIGHTING LIMITED—See F.W. Thorpe plc; *Int'l*, pg. 2597
COMPACT METAL INDUSTRIES LTD.; *Int'l*, pg. 1721
COMPACT METAL INDUSTRIES SDN BHD—See Compact Metal Industries Ltd.; *Int'l*, pg. 1721
COMPACT POWER EQUIPMENT, INC.—See The Home Depot, Inc.; *U.S. Public*, pg. 2089
COMPACT POWER SYSTEMS, LLC—See E&S International Enterprises Inc.; *U.S. Private*, pg. 1301
COMPACT SENSATION SDN. BHD.—See 9R Limited; *Int'l*, pg. 17
COMPACT SOLUTIONS LLC—See Canada Pension Plan Investment Board; *Int'l*, pg. 1279
COMPACT SOLUTIONS LLC—See Permira Advisers LLP; *Int'l*, pg. 5805
COMPAGAS - CIA. PARANAENSE DE GAS—See Companhia Paranaense de Energia; *Int'l*, pg. 1747
COMPAGNIA AERONAUTICA EMILIANA S.R.L.—See NRC Group ASA; *Int'l*, pg. 5473
COMPAGNIA ASSICURATRICE LINEAR S.P.A.—See Unipol Gruppo S.p.A.; *Int'l*, pg. 8056
COMPAGNIA DEI CARAIBI S.P.A.; *Int'l*, pg. 1721
COMPAGNIA FINANZIARIA DE BENEDETTI S.P.A.; *Int'l*, pg. 1721
COMPAGNIA IMMOBILIARE AZIONARIA S.P.A.; *Int'l*, pg. 1722
COMPAGNIA ITALIANA FINANZIARIA - CIF S.R.L.—See Intesa Sanpaolo S.p.A.; *Int'l*, pg. 3765
COMPAGNIA ITALPETROLI S.P.A.—See UniCredit S.p.A.; *Int'l*, pg. 8034
COMPAGNIA NAPOLETANA DI ILLUMINAZIONE E SCALDAMENTO COL GAS SPA—See Eni S.p.A.; *Int'l*, pg. 2437
COMPAGNIE AERIENNE DU MALI—See Aga Khan Development Network; *Int'l*, pg. 199
COMPAGNIE AERIENNE INTER REGIONALE EXPRESS SA; *Int'l*, pg. 1722
COMPAGNIE AGRICOLE DE LA CRAU SA; *Int'l*, pg. 1722
COMPAGNIE BELGE DASSURANCES AVIATION NV/SA—See AXIS Capital Holdings Limited; *Int'l*, pg. 770
COMPAGNIE CHAMPENOISE PH-CHPIPER HEIDSIECK SAS; *Int'l*, pg. 1722
COMPAGNIE COLONIALE; *Int'l*, pg. 1722
COMPAGNIE D'AFFRETEMENT ET DE TRANSPORT (C.A.T.) SAS—See Wilh. Wilhelmsen Holding ASA; *Int'l*, pg. 8410
COMPAGNIE D'APPAREILS ELECTRIQUES PEERLESS LIMITEE; *Int'l*, pg. 1722
COMPAGNIE D'ASSURANCE BELAIR, INC.—See Intact Financial Corporation; *Int'l*, pg. 3726
COMPAGNIE D'ASSURANCE DU QUEBEC—See Intact Financial Corporation; *Int'l*, pg. 3727
COMPAGNIE D'ASSURANCE DU QUEBEC—See Tryg A/S; *Int'l*, pg. 7947
COMPAGNIE DE CONSTRUCTION MECANIQUE SULZER S.A.—See Sulzer Ltd.; *Int'l*, pg. 7258
COMPAGNIE DE DISTRIBUTION DES HYDROCARBURES SAS—See LyondellBasell Industries N.V.; *Int'l*, pg. 4607

COMPAGNIE HET ZOUTE NV

COMPAGNIE DE GAZ DE PETROLE PRIMAGAZ S.A.—See SHV Holdings N.V.; *Int'l*, pg. 6872
COMPAGNIE DE GESTION PRIVEE MONEGASQUE SAM—See Azimut Holding SpA; *Int'l*, pg. 779
COMPAGNIE DE L'OCCIDENT POUR LA FINANCE ET L'INDUSTRIE S.A.; *Int'l*, pg. 1722
COMPAGNIE D'ENTERPRISES CFE SA—See Ackermans & van Haaren NV; *Int'l*, pg. 104
COMPAGNIE DE SAINT-GOBAIN SA; *Int'l*, pg. 1722
COMPAGNIE DES ALPES S.A.; *Int'l*, pg. 1737
COMPAGNIE DES ASCENSEURS ET ELEVATEURS S.A.M.—See ThyssenKrupp AG; *Int'l*, pg. 7724
COMPAGNIE DES BAUXITES DE GUINEE SA—See Alcoa Corporation; *U.S. Public*, pg. 74
COMPAGNIE DES CIMENTS BELGES SA—See Cementir Holding N.V.; *Int'l*, pg. 1397
COMPAGNIE DES LEVURES LESAFFRE SA; *Int'l*, pg. 1738
COMPAGNIE DES MONTRES LONGINES, FRANCILLON SA—See The Swatch Group Ltd.; *Int'l*, pg. 7691
COMPAGNIE DES TRAMWAYS DE ROUEN SA; *Int'l*, pg. 1739
COMPAGNIE DES TRANSPORTS DE CHARLEVILLE-MEZIERES—See Regie Autonome des Transports Parisiens; *Int'l*, pg. 6253
COMPAGNIE DE TRANSPORTS DE CEREALES—See SNCF; *Int'l*, pg. 7025
COMPAGNIE DEUTSCH S.A.S.—See TE Connectivity Ltd.; *Int'l*, pg. 7494
COMPAGNIE D'EXPLOITAITION DES SERVICES AUXILIAIRES AERIENS—See Air France-KLM S.A.; *Int'l*, pg. 237
COMPAGNIE D INVESTISSEMENTS DE PARIS C.I.P—See BNP Paribas SA; *Int'l*, pg. 1090
COMPAGNIE DU BOIS SAUVAGE SA; *Int'l*, pg. 1740
COMPAGNIE DU CAMBODGE SA; *Int'l*, pg. 1740
COMPAGNIE DU MONT BLANC - SA; *Int'l*, pg. 1740
COMPAGNIE EIFFAGE DU VIADUC DE MILLAU—See Caisse des Depots et Consignations; *Int'l*, pg. 1257
COMPAGNIE EIFFAGE DU VIADUC DE MILLAU—See Eiffage S.A.; *Int'l*, pg. 2329
COMPAGNIE EQUATORIALE DES BOIS S.A.—See Precious Woods Holding AG; *Int'l*, pg. 5956
COMPAGNIE EUROPEENNE D'ASSURANCES S.A.—See Munchener Ruckversicherungs AG; *Int'l*, pg. 5085
COMPAGNIE EUROPEENNE DE GARANTIES ET DE CAUTIONS SA—See Groupe BPCE; *Int'l*, pg. 3093
COMPAGNIE FERMIERE DE SERVICES PUBLICS SCA—See Veolia Environnement S.A.; *Int'l*, pg. 8153
COMPAGNIE FINANCIERE DE LA COTE D'IVOIRE—See BNP Paribas SA; *Int'l*, pg. 1090
COMPAGNIE FINANCIERE DE NEUFCOUR S.A.; *Int'l*, pg. 1740
COMPAGNIE FINANCIERE DES CIMENTS SA—See Heidelberg Materials AG; *Int'l*, pg. 3316
COMPAGNIE FINANCIERE ET DE PARTICIPATIONS ROULLIER SA; *Int'l*, pg. 1740
COMPAGNIE FINANCIERE LAZARD FRERES SAS—See Lazard Ltd.; *Int'l*, pg. 4427
COMPAGNIE FINANCIERE MICHELIN SCMA—See Compagnie Generale des Etablissements Michelin SCA; *Int'l*, pg. 1742
COMPAGNIE FINANCIERE, MINIERE ET INDUSTRIELLE SA—See Schneider Electric SE; *Int'l*, pg. 6626
COMPAGNIE FINANCIERE OTTOMANE SA—See BNP Paribas SA; *Int'l*, pg. 1090
COMPAGNIE FINANCIERE RICHEMONT S.A.; *Int'l*, pg. 1740
COMPAGNIE FINANCIERE TRADITION S.A.—See Viel & Compagnie SA; *Int'l*, pg. 8192
COMPAGNIE FRANCAISE DE MANUTENTION—See Manitou BF S.A.; *Int'l*, pg. 4672
COMPAGNIE FRANCAISE ECO HUILE S.A.—See Aurea, S.A.; *Int'l*, pg. 707
COMPAGNIE FRANCAISE PHILIPS—See Koninklijke Philips N.V.; *Int'l*, pg. 4267
COMPAGNIE GENERAL BEARING SERVICE, INC.; *Int'l*, pg. 1741
COMPAGNIE GENERALE DE BATIMENT ET DE CONSTRUCTION SAS—See VINCI S.A.; *Int'l*, pg. 8216
COMPAGNIE GENERALE DE CREDIT AUX PARTICULIERS S.A.—See Stellantis N.V.; *Int'l*, pg. 7201
COMPAGNIE GENERALE DE LOCATION D EQUIPEMENTS SA—See Societe Generale S.A.; *Int'l*, pg. 7039
COMPAGNIE GENERALE DES ETABLISSEMENTS MICHELIN SCA; *Int'l*, pg. 1741
COMPAGNIE GENERALE MARITIME—See CMA CGM S.A.; *Int'l*, pg. 1668
COMPAGNIE HET ZOUTE NV; *Int'l*, pg. 1745
COMPAGNIE HOBART S.A.S.—See Illinois Tool Works Inc.; *U.S. Public*, pg. 1102
COMPAGNIE IBM FRANCE, S.A.—See International Business Machines Corporation; *U.S. Public*, pg. 1145
COMPAGNIE IMMOBILIERE DE LOTISSEMENTS (LOTINVEST)—See Immobel SA; *Int'l*, pg. 3627
COMPAGNIE IMMOBILIERE DE PARTICIPATIONS FINANCIERES—See Immobel SA; *Int'l*, pg. 3627
COMPAGNIE IMMOBILIERE DE WALLONIE (CIW)—See Immobel SA; *Int'l*, pg. 3627

COMPAGNIE HET ZOUTE NV

COMPAGNIE IMMOBILIERE D'HARDELOT SAS—See Compagnie Het Zoute NV; *Int'l*, pg. 1745
COMPAGNIE INDUSTRIELLE DES COMPOSANTS BETON—See FAYAT SAS; *Int'l*, pg. 2625
COMPAGNIE INTERNATIONALE ARABE DE RECOUVREMENT—See Banque Internationale Arabe de Tunisie; *Int'l*, pg. 854
COMPAGNIE INTERNATIONALE DES WAGONS LITS ET DU TOURISME S.A.—See Accor S.A.; *Int'l*, pg. 91
COMPAGNIE LAITIERE EUROPEENNE S.A—See Savencia Fromage & Dairy; *Int'l*, pg. 6597
COMPAGNIE LA LUCETTE S.A.—See Caisse des Depots et Consignations; *Int'l*, pg. 1258
COMPAGNIE LEBON SA; *Int'l*, pg. 1745
COMPAGNIE MARITIME BELGE S.A.; *Int'l*, pg. 1745
COMPAGNIE MEDITERRANEENNE D'EXPLOITATION DES SERVICES D'EAU - CMESE—See Veolia Environnement S.A.; *Int'l*, pg. 8153
COMPAGNIE MERCOSUR GRECEMAR SA; *Int'l*, pg. 1746
COMPAGNIE MONEGASQUE DE BANQUE; *Int'l*, pg. 1746
COMPAGNIE NATIONALE A PORTEFEUILLE S.A.—See BNP Paribas SA; *Int'l*, pg. 1090
COMPAGNIE NATIONALE A PORTEFEUILLE S.A.—See Frere-Bourgeois; *Int'l*, pg. 2773
COMPAGNIE NATIONALE DU RHONE—See ENGIE SA; *Int'l*, pg. 2428
COMPAGNIE PARISIENNE DE CHAUFFAGE URBAIN—See ENGIE SA; *Int'l*, pg. 2431
COMPAGNIE PIKOLIN RECTICEL DE LITERIE S.A.S.—See Recticel S.A.; *Int'l*, pg. 6241
COMPAGNIE PLASTIC OMNIUM S.A.—See Burelle S.A.; *Int'l*, pg. 1222
COMPAGNIE POUR LE FINANCEMENT DES LOISIRS - COFI LOISIRS—See BNP Paribas SA; *Int'l*, pg. 1090
COMPAGNIE STEPHANOISE DE SANTE SA—See Bridgepoint Group Plc; *Int'l*, pg. 1154
COMPAIR (AUSTRALASIA) LTD.—See Ingersoll Rand Inc.; *U.S. Public*, pg. 1119
COMPAIR DRUCKLUFTTECHNIK—See Ingersoll Rand Inc.; *U.S. Public*, pg. 1119
COMPAIR GMBH—See Ingersoll Rand Inc.; *U.S. Public*, pg. 1119
COMPAIR KOREA CO., LTD.—See Ingersoll Rand Inc.; *U.S. Public*, pg. 1119
COMPAIR SOUTH AFRICA (PTY) LTD.—See Ingersoll Rand Inc.; *U.S. Public*, pg. 1119
COMPAL BROADBAND NETWORKS, INC.; *Int'l*, pg. 1746
COMPAL ELECTRONICS, INC.; *Int'l*, pg. 1746
COMPAL MEXICO—See Compal Electronics, Inc.; *Int'l*, pg. 1746
COMPANHIA BRASILEIRA DE ALUMINIO—See Votorantim S.A.; *Int'l*, pg. 8310
COMPANHIA BRASILEIRA DE BENTONITA LTDA.—See Clariant AG; *Int'l*, pg. 1648
COMPANHIA BRASILEIRA DE CRISTAL—See Compagnie de Saint-Gobain SA; *Int'l*, pg. 1723
COMPANHIA BRASILEIRA DE DISTRIBUICAO; *Int'l*, pg. 1746
COMPANHIA BRASILEIRA DE SOLUCOES E SERVICOS S.A.—See Banco Bradesco S.A.; *Int'l*, pg. 819
COMPANHIA BRASILIANA DE ENERGIA—See The AES Corporation; *U.S. Public*, pg. 2031
COMPANHIA CACIQUE DE CAFE SOLUVEL; *Int'l*, pg. 1746
COMPANHIA CELG DE PARTICIPACOES - CELGPAR; *Int'l*, pg. 1746
COMPANHIA DA METRO DA BAHIA SA—See CCR S.A.; *Int'l*, pg. 1369
COMPANHIA DE CIMENTOS DO BRASIL LTDA—See Camargo Correa S.A.; *Int'l*, pg. 1268
COMPANHIA DE CONSTRUCAO E ENGENHARIA KIN SUN (MACAU), LIMITADA—See Bilfinger SE; *Int'l*, pg. 1024
COMPANHIA DE ELETRICIDADE DO ESTADO DA BAHIA—See Iberdrola, S.A.; *Int'l*, pg. 3573
COMPANHIA DE FERRO LIGAS DA BAHIA - FERBASA; *Int'l*, pg. 1746
COMPANHIA DE FERRO LIGAS DA BAHIA - FERBASA - THE POJUCA FACTORY—See Companhia de Ferro Ligas da Bahia - Ferbasa; *Int'l*, pg. 1746
COMPANHIA DE FIACAO E TECIDOS CEDRO E CACHOEIRA; *Int'l*, pg. 1747
COMPANHIA DE GAS DE SAO PAULO - COMGAS—See Cosan S.A.; *Int'l*, pg. 1809
COMPANHIA DE GERACAO TERMICA DE ENERGIA ELETRICA—See Centrais Eletricas Brasileiras S.A.; *Int'l*, pg. 1403
COMPANHIA DE LOCACAO DAS AMERICAS—See Localiza Rent A Car S.A.; *Int'l*, pg. 4540
COMPANHIA DE PARTICIPACOES ALIANCA DA BAHIA; *Int'l*, pg. 1747
COMPANHIA DE SANEAMENTO BASICO DO ESTADO DE SAO PAULO - SABESP; *Int'l*, pg. 1747
COMPANHIA DE SANEAMENTO DE MINAS GERAIS COPASA MG; *Int'l*, pg. 1747

COMPANHIA DE SANEAMENTO DO PARANA SANEPAR; *Int'l*, pg. 1747
COMPANHIA DE SEGUROS ALIANCA DA BAHIA; *Int'l*, pg. 1747
COMPANHIA DE SEGUROS ALLIANZ PORTUGAL, S.A.—See Allianz SE; *Int'l*, pg. 351
COMPANHIA DE SEGUROS ASOREANA, SA—See Banco Santander, S.A.; *Int'l*, pg. 825
COMPANHIA DE SEGUROS TRANQUILIDADE, S.A.—See Apollo Global Management, Inc.; *U.S. Public*, pg. 150
COMPANHIA DE TELECOMUNICACOES DE MACAU, S.A.R.L.—See Liberty Global plc; *Int'l*, pg. 4484
COMPANHIA DISTRIBUIDORA DE GAS DO RIO DE JANEIRO, S.A.—See Naturgy Energy Group, S.A.; *Int'l*, pg. 5169
COMPANHIA ENERGETICA DE BRASILIA - CEB; *Int'l*, pg. 1747
COMPANHIA ENERGETICA DE MINAS GERAIS - CEMIG; *Int'l*, pg. 1747
COMPANHIA ENERGETICA DE PERNAMBUCO - CELPE—See Iberdrola, S.A.; *Int'l*, pg. 3573
COMPANHIA ENERGETICA DE RORAIMA—See Centrais Eletricas Brasileiras S.A.; *Int'l*, pg. 1403
COMPANHIA ENERGETICA DO PIAUI SA—See Equatorial Energia SA; *Int'l*, pg. 2484
COMPANHIA ENERGETICA DO RIO GRANDE DO NORTE - COSERN—See Iberdrola, S.A.; *Int'l*, pg. 3573
COMPANHIA ESTADUAL DE DISTRIBUICAO DE ENERGIA ELETRICA—See Equatorial Energia SA; *Int'l*, pg. 2484
COMPANHIA FLUMINENSE DE ADMINISTRACAO E COMERCIO—See Allos SA; *Int'l*, pg. 359
COMPANHIA GERAL DE CREDITO PREDIAL PORTUGUES, S.A.—See Banco Santander, S.A.; *Int'l*, pg. 825
COMPANHIA GOODYEAR DO BRASIL PRODUTOS DE BORRACHA—See The Goodyear Tire & Rubber Company; *U.S. Public*, pg. 2082
COMPANHIA HABITASUL DE PARTICIPACOES; *Int'l*, pg. 1747
COMPANHIA HAMA PORTUGAL, LDA—See Hama GmbH & Co KG; *Int'l*, pg. 3234
COMPANHIA HIDRELETRICA DO SAO FRANCISCO—See Centrais Eletricas Brasileiras S.A.; *Int'l*, pg. 1403
COMPANHIA HIDRO ELETRICA DO SAO FRANCISCO SA—See Centrais Eletricas Brasileiras S.A.; *Int'l*, pg. 1403
COMPANHIA IBM PORTUGUESA, S.A.—See International Business Machines Corporation; *U.S. Public*, pg. 1145
COMPANHIA INDUSTRIAL CATAGUASES; *Int'l*, pg. 1747
COMPANHIA INDUSTRIAL FLUMINENSE MINERACAO S.A.—See AMG Critical Materials N.V.; *Int'l*, pg. 426
COMPANHIA JAGUARI DE ENERGIA—See State Grid Corporation of China; *Int'l*, pg. 7182
COMPANHIA JAGUARI DE GERACAO DE ENERGIA LTDA.—See State Grid Corporation of China; *Int'l*, pg. 7182
COMPANHIA LIBRA DE NAVEGACAO S.A.—See Albert Ballin KG; *Int'l*, pg. 294
COMPANHIA LOCADORA DE EQUIPAMENTOS PETROLIFEROS S.A.—See Petroleo Brasileiro S.A. - PETROBRAS; *Int'l*, pg. 5827
COMPANHIA LOGISTICA DE COMBUSTIVEIS, S.A.—See Galp Energia SGPS, S.A.; *Int'l*, pg. 2875
COMPANHIA MELHORAMENTOS DE SAO PAULO; *Int'l*, pg. 1747
COMPANHIA NIPO-BRASILEIRA DE PELOTIZACAO-NIBRASCO—See JFE Holdings, Inc.; *Int'l*, pg. 3935
COMPANHIA NIPO-BRASILEIRA DE PELOTIZACAO-NIBRASCO—See Vale S.A.; *Int'l*, pg. 8111
COMPANHIA NIQUEL TOCANTINS—See Votorantim S.A.; *Int'l*, pg. 8310
COMPANHIA NORDESTINA DE PAPEL (CONPEL)—See Votorantim S.A.; *Int'l*, pg. 8310
COMPANHIA PARANAENSE DE ENERGIA; *Int'l*, pg. 1747
COMPANHIA PAULISTA DE ENERGIA ELETRICA LTDA.—See State Grid Corporation of China; *Int'l*, pg. 7182
COMPANHIA PORTUGUESA DE RESSEGUROS, S.A.—See Caixa Geral de Depositos S.A.; *Int'l*, pg. 1260
COMPANHIA SIDERURGICA NACIONAL; *Int'l*, pg. 1748
COMPANHIA SUL PAULISTA DE ENERGIA—See State Grid Corporation of China; *Int'l*, pg. 7182
COMPANHIA ULTRAGAZ S.A.—See Ultrapar Participacoes S.A.; *Int'l*, pg. 8019
COMPANHIA UNIAO FABRIL SGPS S.A.—See Jose de Mello, SGPS, S.A.; *Int'l*, pg. 4001
COMPANIA AGROINDUSTRIAL AGROGUEROS S.A.—See Spectrum Brands Holdings, Inc.; *U.S. Public*, pg. 1915
COMPANIA AGROINDUSTRIAL DEL PERU SAC—See Ecom Agroindustrial Corporation Ltd.; *Int'l*, pg. 2296
COMPANIA AGROPECUARIA COPEVAL S.A.; *Int'l*, pg. 1748

CORPORATE AFFILIATIONS

COMPANIA ANONIMA GOODYEAR DE VENEZUELA—See The Goodyear Tire & Rubber Company; *U.S. Public*, pg. 2082
COMPANIA ANONIMA NACIONAL TELEFONOS DE VENEZUELA; *Int'l*, pg. 1748
COMPANIA ARGENTINA DE LEVADURAS S.A.I.C—See The Garfield Weston Foundation; *Int'l*, pg. 7648
COMPANIA AUXILIAR AL CARGO EXPRES, S.A.—See International Consolidated Airlines Group S.A.; *Int'l*, pg. 3745
COMPANIA CENTROAMERICANA DE PRODUCTOS LACTEOS, S.A.—See Nestle S.A.; *Int'l*, pg. 5202
COMPANIA CERVECERA AMBEV DOMINICANA—See Anheuser-Busch InBev SA/NV; *Int'l*, pg. 466
COMPANIA CERVECERA DE CANARIAS SA—See Anheuser-Busch InBev SA/NV; *Int'l*, pg. 464
COMPANIA CERVECERA DE PUERTO RICO; *U.S. Private*, pg. 998
COMPANIA CERVECERIAS UNIDAS S.A.—See L'Arche Green N.V.; *Int'l*, pg. 4377
COMPANIA CERVECERIAS UNIDAS S.A.—See Quinenco S.A.; *Int'l*, pg. 6164
COMPANIA CHILENA DE FOSFOROS S.A.; *Int'l*, pg. 1748
COMPANIA CHILENA DE MEDICION S.A.—See Itron, Inc.; *U.S. Public*, pg. 1175
COMPANIA COLOMBIANA AGROINDUSTRIAL S.A.—See Ecom Agroindustrial Corporation Ltd.; *Int'l*, pg. 2296
COMPANIA COLOMBIANA DE INVERSION COLSEGUROS S.A.—See Allianz SE; *Int'l*, pg. 342
COMPANIA DE DISTRIBUCION INTEGRAL LOGISTA HOLDINGS, S.A.U.—See Imperial Brands PLC; *Int'l*, pg. 3632
COMPANIA DE DISTRIBUCION INTEGRAL LOGISTA, S.A.—See Imperial Brands PLC; *Int'l*, pg. 3632
COMPANIA DE HIDROGENO DEL BIO-BIO S.A.—See Sigdo Koppers S.A.; *Int'l*, pg. 6907
COMPANIA DE INDUSTRIA Y COMERCIO, S.A. DE C.V.—See voestalpine AG; *Int'l*, pg. 8292
COMPANIA DE INVERSIONES DE ENERGIA S.A.—See Grupo EMES S.A.; *Int'l*, pg. 3126
COMPANIA DE LINHA COATS & CLARK, LDA.—See Coats Group plc; *Int'l*, pg. 1682
COMPANIA DE MEDIOS DIGITALES S.A.—See Grupo Clarin S.A.; *Int'l*, pg. 3125
COMPANIA DE MINAS BUENAVENTURA SAA; *Int'l*, pg. 1748
COMPANIA DE MOTORES DOMESTICOS, S.A. DE C.V.—See Nidec Corporation; *Int'l*, pg. 5277
COMPANIA DE NAVIGATIE FLUVIALA ROMANA NAVROM S.A. GALATI; *Int'l*, pg. 1749
COMPANIA DE OPERACIONES DE NITROGENO, S.A. DE C.V.—See Linde plc; *Int'l*, pg. 4504
COMPANIA DE PETROLEOS DE CHILE COPEC S.A.—See AntarChile S.A.; *Int'l*, pg. 481
COMPANIA DE SEGUROS BOLIVAR S.A.—See Grupo Bolivar S.A.; *Int'l*, pg. 3123
COMPANIA DE SEGUROS DE VIDA CAMARA SA; *Int'l*, pg. 1749
COMPANIA DE SEGUROS DE VIDA CRUZ DEL SUR S.A; *Int'l*, pg. 1749
COMPANIA DE TELECOMUNICACIONES DE EL SALVADOR (CTE), S.A. DE C.V.—See America Movil, S.A.B. de C.V.; *Int'l*, pg. 421
COMPANIA DE TRANSPORTE DE ENERGIA ELECTRICA EN ALTA TENSION TRANSENER S.A.—See Grupo EMES S.A.; *Int'l*, pg. 3126
COMPANIA ELECTRICA EL PLATANAL S.A.—See Union Andina de Cementos S.A.A.; *Int'l*, pg. 8050
COMPANIA ELECTRICA TARAPACA SA—See Enel S.p.A.; *Int'l*, pg. 2412
COMPANIA ELECTRO METALURGICA S.A.; *Int'l*, pg. 1749
COMPANIA EOLICA TIERRAS ALTAS SA—See Enel S.p.A.; *Int'l*, pg. 2413
COMPANIA ERICSSON S.A.C.I.—See Telefonaktiebolaget LM Ericsson; *Int'l*, pg. 7531
COMPANIA ERICSSON S.A.—See Telefonaktiebolaget LM Ericsson; *Int'l*, pg. 7530
COMPANIA ERICSSON URUGUAY S.A.—See Telefonaktiebolaget LM Ericsson; *Int'l*, pg. 7531
COMPANIA ESPANOLA DE PETROLEOS ATLANTICO, S.A.—See Mubadala Investment Company PJSC; *Int'l*, pg. 5074
COMPANIA ESPANOLA DE PETROLEOS, S.A.U.—See Mubadala Investment Company PJSC; *Int'l*, pg. 5074
COMPANIA ESPANOLA DE TABACO EN RAMA, S.A.—See Sociedad Estatal de Participaciones Industriales; *Int'l*, pg. 7031
COMPANIA ESPANOLA DE VIVIENDAS EN ALQUILER S.A.; *Int'l*, pg. 1749
COMPANIA FARMACEUTICA UPJOHN, S.A.—See Pfizer Inc.; *U.S. Public*, pg. 1679
COMPANIA GENERAL DE ELECTRICIDAD S.A.—See State Grid Corporation of China; *Int'l*, pg. 7183
COMPANIA GOODYEAR DEL PERU, S.A.—See The Goodyear Tire & Rubber Company; *U.S. Public*, pg. 2082

COMPANY NAME INDEX

COMPANIA GUATEMALTECA DE NIQUEL, S.A.—See Solway Investment Group Limited; *Int'l*, pg. 7083
COMPANIA HIDROELECTRICA LA YESCA, S.A. DE C.V.—See Empresas ICA S.A.B. de C.V.; *Int'l*, pg. 2390
COMPANIA HULERA TACUBA, S.A. DE C.V.—See JK Tyre & Industries Ltd.; *Int'l*, pg. 3972
COMPANIA INDUSTRIAL DE TABACOS MONTE PAZ S.A.; *Int'l*, pg. 1749
COMPANIA INDUSTRIAL EL VOLCAN SA; *Int'l*, pg. 1749
COMPANIA INDUSTRIAL FRONTERA S.A. DE C.V.—See Stellantis N.V.; *Int'l*, pg. 7203
COMPANIA INTEGRADORA MERCANTIL AGRICOLA, S.A. DE C.V.—See Empresas ICA S.A.B. de C.V.; *Int'l*, pg. 2390
COMPANIA INTERNACIONAL DE COMERCIO, S.A.P.I. DE C.V.—See Taisho Pharmaceutical Holdings Co., Ltd; *Int'l*, pg. 7417
COMPANIA INTERNACIONAL DE PRODUCTOS UNIVERSALES ALIMENTICIOS LTDA—See Compagnie des Levures Lesaffre SA; *Int'l*, pg. 1738
COMPANIA LEVANTINA DE EDIFICACION Y OBRAS PUBLICAS SA; *Int'l*, pg. 1749
COMPANIA LOGISTICA DE HIDROCARBUROS CLH, S.A.; *Int'l*, pg. 1749
COMPANIA MEXICANA DE PINTURAS INTERNATIONAL SA DE CV—See Akzo Nobel N.V.; *Int'l*, pg. 273
COMPANIA MINERA ANTAMINA S.A.; *Int'l*, pg. 1749
COMPANIA MINERA ANTAPACCAY S.A.—See Glencore plc; *Int'l*, pg. 2990
COMPANIA MINERA ARES S.A.C.—See Hochschild Mining plc; *Int'l*, pg. 3438
COMPANIA MINERA ARGENTUM S.A.—See Pan American Silver Corp.; *Int'l*, pg. 5713
COMPANIA MINERA ARQUEROS S.A.—See Nittetsu Mining Co., Ltd.; *Int'l*, pg. 5383
COMPANIA MINERA AUTLAN S.A. DE C.V.—See Grupo Ferrominero, S.A. de C.V.; *Int'l*, pg. 3129
COMPANIA MINERA CANADIAN SHIELD PERU S.A.C.—See Silver North Resources Ltd.; *Int'l*, pg. 6924
COMPANIA MINERA CASALE LIMITADA—See Barrick Gold Corporation; *Int'l*, pg. 869
COMPANIA MINERA CERRO COLORADO LIMITADA—See BHP Group Limited; *Int'l*, pg. 1016
COMPANIA MINERA CERROS DEL SUR, S.A. DE C.V.—See Inception Mining, Inc.; *U.S. Public*, pg. 1114
COMPANIA MINERA CUZCATLAN S.A.—See Fortuna Mining Corp.; *Int'l*, pg. 2743
COMPANIA MINERA DEL PACIFICO S.A—See CAP S.A.; *Int'l*, pg. 1300
COMPANIA MINERA DONA INES DE COLLAHUASI SCM—See Anglo American PLC; *Int'l*, pg. 461
COMPANIA MINERA DONA INES DE COLLAHUASI SCM—See Glencore plc; *Int'l*, pg. 2991
COMPANIA MINERA LOS TOLMOS S.A.—See Grupo Mexico, S.A.B. de C.V.; *Int'l*, pg. 3132
COMPANIA MINERA MALKU KHOTA S.A.—See Gold Springs Resource Corp.; *Int'l*, pg. 3026
COMPANIA MINERA MANTOS DE ORO S.A.—See Kinross Gold Corporation; *Int'l*, pg. 4182
COMPANIA MINERA MARICUNGA—See Kinross Gold Corporation; *Int'l*, pg. 4182
COMPANIA MINERA MENA RESOURCES (CHILE) LIMITADA—See Austral Gold Limited; *Int'l*, pg. 719
COMPANIA MINERA MEXICANA DE GRAY ROCK, S.A. DE C.V.—See Silver Wolf Exploration Ltd.; *Int'l*, pg. 6925
COMPANIA MINERA MISKI MAYO S.A.C.—See Vale S.A.; *Int'l*, pg. 8111
COMPANIA MINERA MOLINETES SAC—See eEnergy Group Plc; *Int'l*, pg. 2317
COMPANIA MINERA NEVADA SPA.—See Barrick Gold Corporation; *Int'l*, pg. 869
COMPANIA MINERA PITALLA, S.A. DE C.V.—See Argonaut Gold Inc.; *U.S. Public*, pg. 191
COMPANIA MINERA POLPAICO LTD.—See Cemento Polpaico S.A.; *Int'l*, pg. 1397
COMPANIA MINERA PUNTA DE LOBOS LTDA.—See K+S Aktiengesellschaft; *Int'l*, pg. 4039
COMPANIA MINERA QUEBRADA BLANCA S.A.—See Teck Resources Limited; *Int'l*, pg. 7514
COMPANIA MINERA QUECHUA S.A.—See ENEOS Holdings, Inc.; *Int'l*, pg. 2415
COMPANIA MINERA TECK CARMEN DE ANDACOLLO S.A.—See Teck Resources Limited; *Int'l*, pg. 7514
COMPANIA MINERA VIZCACHITAS HOLDING—See Los Andes Copper Ltd.; *Int'l*, pg. 4558
COMPANIA MINERA ZALDIVAR S.A.—See Antofagasta plc; *Int'l*, pg. 484
COMPANIA MINERA ZALDIVAR S.A.—See Barrick Gold Corporation; *Int'l*, pg. 869
COMPANIA MSA DE ARGENTINA S.A.—See MSA Safety Incorporated; *U.S. Public*, pg. 1481
COMPANIA NACIONAL DE CHOCOLATES DE PERU S.A.—See Grupo Nutresa S.A.; *Int'l*, pg. 3133
COMPANIA NACIONAL DE CHOCOLATES S.A.S.—See Grupo Nutresa S.A.; *Int'l*, pg. 3133
COMPANIA NACIONAL DE TELEFONOS TELEFONICA DEL SUR S.A.; *Int'l*, pg. 1749

COMPANIA NATIONALA POSTA ROMANA S.A.; *Int'l*, pg. 1749
COMPANIA OPERADORA DE GAS DEL AMAZONAS, S.A.C.—See Enagas, S.A.; *Int'l*, pg. 2396
COMPANIA PANAMENA DE AVIACION, S.A.—See Copa Holdings, S.A.; *Int'l*, pg. 1792
COMPANIA PROCTER & GAMBLE MEXICO, S. DE R.L. DE C.V.—See The Procter & Gamble Company; *U.S. Public*, pg. 2120
COMPANIA QUIMICA S.A.—See The Procter & Gamble Company; *U.S. Public*, pg. 2120
COMPANIA SAN FELIPE, S.A. DE C.V.—See Minera Frisco, S.A.B. de C.V.; *Int'l*, pg. 4906
COMPANIAS CIC SA; *Int'l*, pg. 1749
COMPANIA SHERWIN-WILLIAMS, S.A. DE C.V.—See The Sherwin-Williams Company; *U.S. Public*, pg. 2127
COMPANIA SIDERURGICA DE GUADALAJARA S.A. DE C.V.—See Industrias CH, S.A.B. de C.V.; *Int'l*, pg. 3674
COMPANIA SUDAMERICANA DE VAPORES, S.A.; *Int'l*, pg. 1749
COMPANIA SUIZA DE REASEGUROS OFICINA DE REPRESENTACIONE—See Swiss Re Ltd.; *Int'l*, pg. 7371
COMPANIA TRANSPORTADORA DE VALORES PROSEGUR DE COLOMBIA SA—See Prosegur Compania de Seguridad S.A.; *Int'l*, pg. 5999
COMPANIA TRASMEDITERRANEA, S.A.—See Anarafe SL; *Int'l*, pg. 447
COMPANIA UNIVERSAL TEXTIL S.A.—See Grupo Romero; *Int'l*, pg. 3134
COMPANIA URBANIZADORA DEL COTO, S.L.—See Acciona, S.A.; *Int'l*, pg. 90
COMPANIA VINICOLA DEL NORTE DE ESPANA, S.A.; *Int'l*, pg. 1749
COMPANIES (TC) LLC.; *U.S. Private*, pg. 998
COMPANION CARE (CHIPPENHAM) LIMITED—See Pets at Home Group Plc; *Int'l*, pg. 5833
COMPANION CARE (ELY) LIMITED—See Pets at Home Group Plc; *Int'l*, pg. 5833
COMPANION CARE (LLANTRISANT) LIMITED—See Pets at Home Group Plc; *Int'l*, pg. 5833
COMPANION CARE (MAIDSTONE) LIMITED—See Pets at Home Group Plc; *Int'l*, pg. 5833
COMPANION LIFE INSURANCE COMPANY—See Blue Cross & Blue Shield of South Carolina; *U.S. Private*, pg. 587
COMPANION LIFE INSURANCE CO.—See Mutual of Omaha Insurance Company; *U.S. Private*, pg. 2820
COMPANION MANAGEMENT GROUP, LLC—See Webster Equity Partners, LLC; *U.S. Private*, pg. 4467
COMPANION PROFESSIONAL SERVICES LLC; *U.S. Private*, pg. 998
COMPANION PROPERTY & CASUALTY INSURANCE GROUP—See Enstar Group Limited; *Int'l*, pg. 2448
COMPANIONS & HOMEMAKERS INC.; *U.S. Private*, pg. 998
COMPANY 3 LA—See Deluxe Corporation; *U.S. Public*, pg. 652
COMPANY C, INC.; *U.S. Private*, pg. 998
THE COMPANY CORPORATION—See Corporation Service Company; *U.S. Private*, pg. 1058
COMPANY FINANCIERE DE CHAUSEY, S.A.—See Emerson Electric Co.; *U.S. Public*, pg. 742
THE COMPANY FOR COOPERATIVE INSURANCE; *Int'l*, pg. 7635
COMPANY K PARTNERS LIMITED; *Int'l*, pg. 1749
COMPANY MARGIN PURPOSE LTD.; *Int'l*, pg. 1749
THE COMPANY OF OTHERS; *U.S. Private*, pg. 4012
COMPANY SHOP LIMITED—See Biffa Group Limited; *Int'l*, pg. 1020
COMPANY TERA CO., LTD.—See Sunjin Beauty Science Co., Ltd.; *Int'l*, pg. 7316
COMPANY UNIQUE FINANCE PROPRIETARY LIMITED—See Transaction Capital Limited; *Int'l*, pg. 7894
COMPANY WEBCAST B.V.—See Euronext N.V.; *Int'l*, pg. 2554
COMPAPER CONVERTING S.A.—See INFORM P. LYKOS S.A.; *Int'l*, pg. 3691
COMPARE.COM INSURANCE AGENCY LLC—See Admiral Group plc; *Int'l*, pg. 151
COMPARENETWORKS, INC.; *U.S. Private*, pg. 998
COMPAREX AUSTRIA GMBH—See Raiffeisen Bank International AG; *Int'l*, pg. 6183
COMPAREX AUSTRIA GMBH—See Raiffeisen-Holding Niederosterreich-Wien reg. Gen.m.b.H.; *Int'l*, pg. 6185
COMPAREX BELGIUM S.A/N.V.—See Raiffeisen Bank International AG; *Int'l*, pg. 6184
COMPAREX BELGIUM S.A/N.V.—See Raiffeisen-Holding Niederosterreich-Wien reg. Gen.m.b.H.; *Int'l*, pg. 6186
COMPAREX BRASIL SA—See SoftwareONE Holding AG; *Int'l*, pg. 7057
COMPAREX DANMARK A/S—See Raiffeisen Bank International AG; *Int'l*, pg. 6183
COMPAREX DANMARK A/S—See Raiffeisen-Holding Niederosterreich-Wien reg. Gen.m.b.H.; *Int'l*, pg. 6186
COMPAREX DEUTSCHLAND AG—See Raiffeisen Bank International AG; *Int'l*, pg. 6183

COMPASS ADVISERS GROUP LLC

COMPAREX DEUTSCHLAND AG—See Raiffeisen-Holding Niederosterreich-Wien reg. Gen.m.b.H.; *Int'l*, pg. 6185
COMPAREX D.O.O.—See Raiffeisen Bank International AG; *Int'l*, pg. 6183
COMPAREX D.O.O.—See Raiffeisen-Holding Niederosterreich-Wien reg. Gen.m.b.H.; *Int'l*, pg. 6186
COMPAREX ESPANA, S.A.—See Raiffeisen Bank International AG; *Int'l*, pg. 6183
COMPAREX ESPANA, S.A.—See Raiffeisen-Holding Niederosterreich-Wien reg. Gen.m.b.H.; *Int'l*, pg. 6185
COMPAREX FINLAND OY—See Raiffeisen Bank International AG; *Int'l*, pg. 6184
COMPAREX FINLAND OY—See Raiffeisen-Holding Niederosterreich-Wien reg. Gen.m.b.H.; *Int'l*, pg. 6186
COMPAREX FRANCE S.A.S.—See Raiffeisen Bank International AG; *Int'l*, pg. 6184
COMPAREX FRANCE S.A.S.—See Raiffeisen-Holding Niederosterreich-Wien reg. Gen.m.b.H.; *Int'l*, pg. 6186
COMPAREX HRVATSKA DOO—See SoftwareONE Holding AG; *Int'l*, pg. 7057
COMPAREX INDIA PVT. LTD.—See SoftwareONE Holding AG; *Int'l*, pg. 7057
COMPAREX INDONESIA PT—See SoftwareONE Holding AG; *Int'l*, pg. 7057
COMPAREX ITALIA S.R.L.—See Raiffeisen Bank International AG; *Int'l*, pg. 6184
COMPAREX ITALIA S.R.L.—See Raiffeisen-Holding Niederosterreich-Wien reg. Gen.m.b.H.; *Int'l*, pg. 6186
COMPAREX NEDERLAND B.V.—See Raiffeisen Bank International AG; *Int'l*, pg. 6184
COMPAREX NEDERLAND B.V.—See Raiffeisen-Holding Niederosterreich-Wien reg. Gen.m.b.H.; *Int'l*, pg. 6186
COMPAREX NORGE AS—See Raiffeisen Bank International AG; *Int'l*, pg. 6184
COMPAREX NORGE AS—See Raiffeisen-Holding Niederosterreich-Wien reg. Gen.m.b.H.; *Int'l*, pg. 6186
COMPAREX PC-WARE DEUTSCHLAND GMBH—See Raiffeisen Bank International AG; *Int'l*, pg. 6184
COMPAREX PC-WARE DEUTSCHLAND GMBH—See Raiffeisen-Holding Niederosterreich-Wien reg. Gen.m.b.H.; *Int'l*, pg. 6186
COMPAREX POLAND SP. Z O.O.—See Raiffeisen Bank International AG; *Int'l*, pg. 6183
COMPAREX POLAND SP. Z O.O.—See Raiffeisen-Holding Niederosterreich-Wien reg. Gen.m.b.H.; *Int'l*, pg. 6185
COMPAREX SLOVAKIA SPOL. S.R.O.—See Raiffeisen Bank International AG; *Int'l*, pg. 6183
COMPAREX SLOVAKIA SPOL. S.R.O.—See Raiffeisen-Holding Niederosterreich-Wien reg. Gen.m.b.H.; *Int'l*, pg. 6185
COMPAREX SOFTWARE BELGIUM BVBA—See Raiffeisen Bank International AG; *Int'l*, pg. 6184
COMPAREX SOFTWARE BELGIUM BVBA—See Raiffeisen-Holding Niederosterreich-Wien reg. Gen.m.b.H.; *Int'l*, pg. 6186
COMPAREX SOFTWARE LUXEMBURG SARL—See Raiffeisen Bank International AG; *Int'l*, pg. 6184
COMPAREX SOFTWARE LUXEMBURG SARL—See Raiffeisen-Holding Niederosterreich-Wien reg. Gen.m.b.H.; *Int'l*, pg. 6186
COMPAREX SOLUTIONS (SCHWEIZ) AG—See Raiffeisen Bank International AG; *Int'l*, pg. 6184
COMPAREX SOLUTIONS (SCHWEIZ) AG—See Raiffeisen-Holding Niederosterreich-Wien reg. Gen.m.b.H.; *Int'l*, pg. 6186
COMPAREX SWEDEN AB—See Raiffeisen Bank International AG; *Int'l*, pg. 6184
COMPAREX SWEDEN AB—See Raiffeisen-Holding Niederosterreich-Wien reg. Gen.m.b.H.; *Int'l*, pg. 6186
COMPAREX UK LIMITED—See Raiffeisen Bank International AG; *Int'l*, pg. 6184
COMPAREX UK LIMITED—See Raiffeisen-Holding Niederosterreich-Wien reg. Gen.m.b.H.; *Int'l*, pg. 6186
COMPARISON CREATOR LIMITED—See Simplybiz Group plc; *Int'l*, pg. 6934
COMPARTAMOS FINANCIERA; *Int'l*, pg. 1749
COMPART ASIA LIMITED—See Broadway Industrial Group Limited; *Int'l*, pg. 1172
COMPART SAS—See VINCI S.A.; *Int'l*, pg. 8216
COMPA S.A.; *Int'l*, pg. 1721
COMPAS, INC.; *U.S. Private*, pg. 998
COMPASS ABSTRACT, INC.—See Old Republic International Corporation; *U.S. Public*, pg. 1568
COMPASS ADJUSTERS & INVESTIGATORS, INC.; *U.S. Private*, pg. 998
COMPASS ADVISERS GROUP LLC; *U.S. Private*, pg. 998
COMPASS ADVISERS LIMITED—See Compass Advisers Group LLC; *U.S. Private*, pg. 998
COMPASS AMERICA INC.—See Information Services Group, Inc.; *U.S. Public*, pg. 1117
COMPASS ANALYTICS, LLC—See Intercontinental Exchange, Inc.; *U.S. Public*, pg. 1141
COMPASS BANCA S.P.A.—See Mediobanca-Banca de Credito Finanziario S.p.A.; *Int'l*, pg. 4778
COMPASS BANK—See The PNC Financial Services Group, Inc.; *U.S. Public*, pg. 2119
COMPASS CAPITAL MANAGEMENT, LLC—See Aon plc; *Int'l*, pg. 495

COMPASS CATERING SERVICES, IRELAND LIMITED—See Compass Group PLC; *Int'l*, pg. 1750
COMPASS CATERING Y SERVICIOS CHILE LIMITADA—See Compass Group PLC; *Int'l*, pg. 1750
COMPASS CHARTERING CORP.—See TBS INTERNATIONAL PLC; *Int'l*, pg. 7481
COMPASS CHEMICAL INTERNATIONAL LLC—See Bain Capital, LP; *U.S. Private*, pg. 441
COMPASS CONSULTING AB—See Information Services Group, Inc.; *U.S. Public*, pg. 1118
COMPASS CONSULTING GROUP, LLC—See New Mountain Capital, LLC; *U.S. Private*, pg. 2901
COMPASS DATACENTERS, LLC—See RedBird Capital Partners L.P.; *U.S. Private*, pg. 3377
COMPASS DIGITAL ACQUISITION CORP.; *U.S. Public*, pg. 559
COMPASS DIRECTIONAL SERVICES LTD—See Cathedral Energy Services Ltd.; *Int'l*, pg. 1361
COMPASS DISPLAY GROUP, INC.—See Edison Lithographing & Printing Corp.; *U.S. Private*, pg. 1336
COMPASS DIVERSIFIED HOLDINGS; *U.S. Public*, pg. 559
COMPASS ELECTRONICS GROUP—See Compass Group, LLC; *U.S. Private*, pg. 999
COMPASS ENERGY HOLDINGS, INC.; *U.S. Private*, pg. 999
COMPASS EQUITY PARTNERS, LLC; *U.S. Private*, pg. 999
COMPASS EXCHANGE ADVISORS LLC—See Independent Bank Corp.; *U.S. Public*, pg. 1116
COMPASS FINANCIAL PARTNERS, LLC—See Marsh & McLennan Companies, Inc.; *U.S. Public*, pg. 1380
COMPASS FORWARDING CO., INC.; *U.S. Private*, pg. 999
COMPASS FOSTERING—See August Equity LLP; *Int'l*, pg. 703
COMPASS GAS & ENERGIA SA—See Cosan S.A.; *Int'l*, pg. 1809
COMPASS GLASS (PTY) LTD.—See Mazor Group Limited; *Int'l*, pg. 4749
COMPASS GOLD CORPORATION; *Int'l*, pg. 1750
COMPASS GROUP AB—See Compass Group PLC; *Int'l*, pg. 1750
COMPASS GROUP (AUSTRALIA) PTY LTD—See Compass Group PLC; *Int'l*, pg. 1750
COMPASS GROUP BELGILUX S.A.—See Compass Group PLC; *Int'l*, pg. 1750
COMPASS GROUP CANADA LTD.—See Compass Group PLC; *Int'l*, pg. 1750
COMPASS GROUP CZECH REPUBLIC S.R.O.—See Compass Group PLC; *Int'l*, pg. 1750
COMPASS GROUP DANMARK A/S—See Compass Group PLC; *Int'l*, pg. 1750
COMPASS GROUP DEUTSCHLAND GMBH—See Compass Group PLC; *Int'l*, pg. 1750
COMPASS GROUP DIVERSIFIED HOLDINGS LLC—See Compass Diversified Holdings; *U.S. Public*, pg. 560
COMPASS GROUP FRANCE HOLDINGS SAS—See Compass Group PLC; *Int'l*, pg. 1750
COMPASS GROUP FRANCE SAS—See Compass Group PLC; *Int'l*, pg. 1750
COMPASS GROUP FS FINLAND OY—See Compass Group PLC; *Int'l*, pg. 1750
COMPASS GROUP FS NORWAY A/S—See Compass Group PLC; *Int'l*, pg. 1750
COMPASS GROUP HOLDINGS PLC—See Compass Group PLC; *Int'l*, pg. 1750
COMPASS GROUP HONG KONG LTD.—See Compass Group PLC; *Int'l*, pg. 1750
COMPASS GROUP INTERNATIONAL BV—See Compass Group PLC; *Int'l*, pg. 1750
COMPASS GROUP ITALIA S.P.A—See Compass Group PLC; *Int'l*, pg. 1750
COMPASS GROUP, LLC; *U.S. Private*, pg. 999
COMPASS GROUP MANAGEMENT LLC; *U.S. Private*, pg. 999
COMPASS GROUP NEDERLAND BV—See Compass Group PLC; *Int'l*, pg. 1750
COMPASS GROUP NEDERLAND HOLDING BV—See Compass Group PLC; *Int'l*, pg. 1750
COMPASS GROUP NEW ZEALAND LIMITED—See Compass Group PLC; *Int'l*, pg. 1750
COMPASS GROUP NORTH AMERICA—See Compass Group PLC; *Int'l*, pg. 1750
COMPASS GROUP PLC; *Int'l*, pg. 1750
COMPASS GROUP POLAND SP. Z O.O.—See Compass Group PLC; *Int'l*, pg. 1751
COMPASS GROUP PROCUREMENT LTD—See Compass Group PLC; *Int'l*, pg. 1751
COMPASS GROUP RUS OOO—See Compass Group PLC; *Int'l*, pg. 1751
COMPASS GROUP (SCHWEIZ) AG—See Compass Group PLC; *Int'l*, pg. 1750
COMPASS GROUP SERVICES COLOMBIA S.A.—See Compass Group PLC; *Int'l*, pg. 1751
COMPASS GROUP SLOVAKIA S. R. O.—See Compass Group PLC; *Int'l*, pg. 1751
COMPASS GROUP SOUTHERN AFRICA (PTY) LTD—See Compass Group PLC; *Int'l*, pg. 1751

COMPASS GROUP SWEDEN AB—See Compass Group PLC; *Int'l*, pg. 1751
COMPASS GROUP, UK & IRELAND LIMITED—See Compass Group PLC; *Int'l*, pg. 1751
COMPASS GROUP USA, INC. - CANTEEN DIVISION—See Compass Group PLC; *Int'l*, pg. 1751
COMPASS GROUP USA, INC.—See Compass Group PLC; *Int'l*, pg. 1750
COMPASS HEALTH BRANDS CORP.—See Tenex Capital Management, L.P.; *U.S. Private*, pg. 3966
COMPASS HEALTH; *U.S. Private*, pg. 999
COMPASS HOSPICE, INC—See Apollo Global Management, Inc.; *U.S. Public*, pg. 156
COMPASS HOTEL GROUP LTD.—See Woolworths Group Limited; *Int'l*, pg. 8451
COMPASS HOUSING ALLIANCE; *U.S. Private*, pg. 999
COMPASS HRM, INC.—See Asure Software, Inc.; *U.S. Public*, pg. 218
COMPASS IMAGING, LLC—See Community Health Systems, Inc.; *U.S. Public*, pg. 552
COMPASS, INC.; *U.S. Public*, pg. 561
COMPASS INDIA SUPPORT SERVICES PRIVATE LIMITED—See Compass Group PLC; *Int'l*, pg. 1751
COMPASS INSURANCE AGENCY, INC.—See The PNC Financial Services Group, Inc.; *U.S. Public*, pg. 2119
COMPASS INSURANCE COMPANY LTD.—See Talanx AG; *Int'l*, pg. 7444
COMPASS INSURANCE CO. S.A.L.—See Trust International Insurance Company E.C.; *Int'l*, pg. 7944
COMPASSIONATE CARE AT HOME LLC—See Guardian Angels HomeCare, LLC; *U.S. Private*, pg. 1809
COMPASSIONATE CARE HOSPICE OF BRYAN TEXAS, LLC—See Amedisys, Inc.; *U.S. Public*, pg. 93
COMPASSIONATE CARE HOSPICE OF CLIFTON, LLC—See Amedisys, Inc.; *U.S. Public*, pg. 93
COMPASSIONATE CARE HOSPICE OF HOUSTON, LLC—See Amedisys, Inc.; *U.S. Public*, pg. 93
COMPASSIONATE CARE HOSPICE OF ILLINOIS, LLC—See Amedisys, Inc.; *U.S. Public*, pg. 93
COMPASSIONATE CARE HOSPICE OF KANSAS, LLC—See Amedisys, Inc.; *U.S. Public*, pg. 93
COMPASSIONATE CARE HOSPICE OF MICHIGAN, LLC—See Amedisys, Inc.; *U.S. Public*, pg. 93
COMPASSIONATE CARE HOSPICE OF MINNESOTA, LLC—See Amedisys, Inc.; *U.S. Public*, pg. 93
COMPASSIONATE CARE HOSPICE OF PITTSBURG, LLC—See Amedisys, Inc.; *U.S. Public*, pg. 93
COMPASSIONATE CARE HOSPICE OF THE MIDWEST, LLC—See Amedisys, Inc.; *U.S. Public*, pg. 93
COMPASSIONATE CARE HOSPICE OF WISCONSIN, LLC—See Amedisys, Inc.; *U.S. Public*, pg. 93
COMPASSION COALITION, INC.; *U.S. Private*, pg. 999
COMPASS LEXECON - CAMBRIDGE—See FTI Consulting, Inc.; *U.S. Public*, pg. 890
COMPASS LEXECON LLC—See FTI Consulting, Inc.; *U.S. Public*, pg. 890
COMPASS LEXECON SPAIN, S.L.—See FTI Consulting, Inc.; *U.S. Public*, pg. 890
COMPASS MANAGEMENT CONSULTING IBERICA SA—See Information Services Group, Inc.; *U.S. Public*, pg. 1118
COMPASS MANAGEMENT CONSULTING S.A.—See Information Services Group, Inc.; *U.S. Public*, pg. 1118
THE COMPASS MANAGEMENT GROUP, LLC; *U.S. Private*, pg. 4013
COMPASS MINERALS AMERICA INC—See Compass Minerals International, Inc.; *U.S. Public*, pg. 560
COMPASS MINERALS INTERNATIONAL, INC.; *U.S. Public*, pg. 560
COMPASS MINERALS LOUISIANA INC.—See Compass Minerals International, Inc.; *U.S. Public*, pg. 560
COMPASS MINERALS MANITOBA INC.—See Compass Minerals International, Inc.; *U.S. Public*, pg. 560
COMPASS MINERALS OGDEN INC.—See Compass Minerals International, Inc.; *U.S. Public*, pg. 560
COMPASS MINERALS STORAGE & ARCHIVES LIMITED—See Compass Minerals International, Inc.; *U.S. Public*, pg. 560
COMPASS MINERALS UK HOLDINGS LIMITED—See Compass Minerals International, Inc.; *U.S. Public*, pg. 560
COMPASS MINERALS (UK) LIMITED—See Compass Minerals International, Inc.; *U.S. Public*, pg. 560
COMPASS MINERALS USA INC.—See Compass Minerals International, Inc.; *U.S. Public*, pg. 560
COMPASS MINERALS WINNIPEG UNLIMITED LIABILITY COMPANY—See Compass Minerals International, Inc.; *U.S. Public*, pg. 560
COMPASS MINERALS WYNYARD INC.—See Compass Minerals International, Inc.; *U.S. Public*, pg. 560
COMPASSMSP LLC; *U.S. Private*, pg. 999
COMPASS OFFICE SOLUTIONS LLC—See HNI Corporation; *U.S. Public*, pg. 1043
COMPASSO MUNDOCOM—See Publicis Groupe S.A.; *Int'l*, pg. 6097
COMPASS PARTNERS ADVISORS, LLP—See Compass Advisers Group LLC; *U.S. Private*, pg. 998
COMPASS PARTNERS ASSET MANAGEMENT LLC—See Compass Advisers Group LLC; *U.S. Private*, pg. 998

COMPASS PARTNERS CAPITAL LLC—See Compass Advisers Group LLC; *U.S. Private*, pg. 998
COMPASS PARTNERS INTERNATIONAL LLP—See Compass Advisers Group LLC; *U.S. Private*, pg. 998
COMPASS PATHWAYS PLC; *Int'l*, pg. 1752
COMPASS POINT MEDIA; *U.S. Private*, pg. 999
COMPASS POINT RETIREMENT PLANNING, INC.—See Arthur J. Gallagher & Co.; *U.S. Public*, pg. 204
COMPASS PORTER NOVELLI—See Omnicom Group Inc.; *U.S. Public*, pg. 1590
COMPASS PRECISION LLC; *U.S. Private*, pg. 999
COMPASS PRODUCTION PARTNERS, LP—See Spectrum Brands Holdings, Inc.; *U.S. Public*, pg. 1915
COMPASS PROPERTIES, LLC—See F.N.B. Corporation; *U.S. Public*, pg. 818
COMPASS PUBLIC RELATIONS—See WPP plc; *Int'l*, pg. 8468
COMPASS SOLUTIONS, LLC.; *U.S. Private*, pg. 999
COMPASS S.P.A.—See Mediobanca-Banca de Credito Finanziario S.p.A.; *Int'l*, pg. 4778
COMPASS SYSTEMS & SALES, INC.—See Alston Capital Partners LLC; *U.S. Private*, pg. 203
COMPASS TECHNOLOGY SERVICES, INC.—See Jacobs Engineering Group, Inc.; *U.S. Public*, pg. 1184
COMPASS THERAPEUTICS INC.; *U.S. Public*, pg. 561
COMPASS TRANSWORLD LOGISTICS, S.A.—See Siemens Energy AG; *Int'l*, pg. 6902
COMPASS UOL—See Universo Online S.A; *Int'l*, pg. 8083
COMPASS WATER SOLUTIONS, INC—See CECO Environmental Corp.; *U.S. Public*, pg. 463
COMPASS WORKING CAPITAL; *U.S. Private*, pg. 999
COMPATICO, INC.; *U.S. Private*, pg. 999
COMPATRIOT CAPITAL, INC.—See Sammons Enterprises, Inc.; *U.S. Private*, pg. 3537
COMPAX SOFTWARE DEVELOPMENT GMBH; *Int'l*, pg. 1753
COMPBENEFITS CORP.—See Humana, Inc.; *U.S. Public*, pg. 1069
COMPCO HOLDING COMPANY INC.—See S-P Company Inc.; *U.S. Private*, pg. 3514
COMPCO LAND COMPANY INC—See S-P Company Inc.; *U.S. Private*, pg. 3514
COMPCOST INC.—See State Fund Mutual Insurance Co.; *U.S. Private*, pg. 3792
COMPDENT OF GEORGIA, INC.; *U.S. Private*, pg. 1000
COMPEAT, INC.—See DYN365, Inc.; *U.S. Private*, pg. 1296
COMPEER FINANCIAL, ACA; *U.S. Private*, pg. 1000
COMPEL JSC—See SEMIKRON International GmbH; *Int'l*, pg. 6705
COMPELLO BILGI TEKNOLOJISI HIZMETLERI VE TICARET A.S.—See Smartiks Yazilim A.S.; *Int'l*, pg. 7002
COMPELLON, INC.—See Clearsense, LLC; *U.S. Private*, pg. 938
COMPELMA S.A.S.—See Industrielle De Controle Et D Equipement; *Int'l*, pg. 3675
COMPENDIA AS—See Itera ASA; *Int'l*, pg. 3832
COMPENDIA BIOSCIENCE, INC.—See Thermo Fisher Scientific Inc.; *U.S. Public*, pg. 2148
COMPENDIUM CE SP. Z O.O—See Permira Advisers LLP; *Int'l*, pg. 5804
THE COMPENDIUM GROUP LIMITED—See Morgan Sindall Group Plc; *Int'l*, pg. 5045
COMPENDIUM, INC.; *U.S. Private*, pg. 1000
COMPENSA DYSTRYBUCJA SP. Z O. O.—See Vienna Insurance Group AG Wiener Versicherung Gruppe; *Int'l*, pg. 8194
COMPENSA TOWARZYSTWO UBEZPIECZEN S.A.—See Vienna Insurance Group AG Wiener Versicherung Gruppe; *Int'l*, pg. 8194
COMPENSA VIENNA INSURANCE GROUP, ADB—See Vienna Insurance Group AG Wiener Versicherung Gruppe; *Int'l*, pg. 8194
COMPENTEK OY—See Freudenberg SE; *Int'l*, pg. 2783
COMPEQ MANUFACTURING CO., LTD. - LUCHU PLANT—See Compeq Manufacturing Co., Ltd.; *Int'l*, pg. 1753
COMPEQ MANUFACTURING CO., LTD.; *Int'l*, pg. 1753
COMPEQ MANUFACTURING(HUIZHOU) CO., LTD.—See Compeq Manufacturing Co., Ltd.; *Int'l*, pg. 1753
COMPEQ MANUFACTURING(SUZHOU) CO., LTD.—See Compeq Manufacturing Co., Ltd.; *Int'l*, pg. 1753
COMPEQ TECHNOLOGY (HUIZHOU) CO., LTD.—See Compeq Manufacturing Co., Ltd.; *Int'l*, pg. 1753
COMPERA NTIME INTERNET MOVEL S.A.—See Naspers Limited; *Int'l*, pg. 5148
COMPERIA.PL SA; *Int'l*, pg. 1753
COMPERTIS BERATUNGSGESELLSCHAFT FUR BETRIEBLICHES VORSORGEMANAGEMENT MBH—See DZ BANK AG Deutsche Zentral-Genossenschaftsbank; *Int'l*, pg. 2245
COMPETENCES S.R.L.—See ITAB Shop Concept AB; *Int'l*, pg. 3827
COMPETENCY TRAINING PTY LTD—See Verbrec Limited; *Int'l*, pg. 8165
COMPETENT AUTOMOBILES CO. LTD.; *Int'l*, pg. 1753
COMPETENTIA AS—See Reiten & Co AS; *Int'l*, pg. 6259
COMPETENTIA HOLDING AS—See Reiten & Co AS; *Int'l*, pg. 6259

COMPANY NAME INDEX

COMPETENTIA JAPAN CORP.—See Reiten & Co AS; *Int'l*, pg. 6259
COMPETENTIA KOREA LTD.—See Reiten & Co AS; *Int'l*, pg. 6259
COMPETENTIA PTY LTD.—See Reiten & Co AS; *Int'l*, pg. 6259
COMPETENTIA SINGAPORE PTE LTD.—See Reiten & Co AS; *Int'l*, pg. 6259
COMPETENTIA UK LIMITED—See Reiten & Co AS; *Int'l*, pg. 6259
COMPETITION ACCESSORIES; *U.S. Private*, pg. 1000
COMPETITION CAMS INC.; *U.S. Private*, pg. 1000
COMPETITION CHEVROLET LTD.; *Int'l*, pg. 1753
COMPETITION PRODUCTS, INC.; *U.S. Private*, pg. 1000
COMPETITION SPECIALTIES INC.; *U.S. Private*, pg. 1000
COMPETITION SYSTEMS, INCORPORATED—See Z Capital Group, LLC; *U.S. Private*, pg. 4595
COMPETITION TIRE LLC; *U.S. Private*, pg. 1000
COMPETITION TOYOTA LTD.; *Int'l*, pg. 1753
COMPETITIVE COMPUTING, INC.—See Xerox Holdings Corporation; *U.S. Public*, pg. 2386
COMPETITIVE ENGINEERING INC.; *U.S. Private*, pg. 1000
COMPETITIVE FOODS AUSTRALIA PTY. LTD.; *Int'l*, pg. 1753
COMPETITIVE HEALTH, INC.—See WEX, Inc.; *U.S. Public*, pg. 2364
COMPETITIVE INNOVATIONS, LLC; *U.S. Private*, pg. 1000
COMPETITIVE POWER VENTURES HOLDINGS, LLC—See BlackRock, Inc.; *U.S. Public*, pg. 345
COMPETITIVE RANGE SOLUTIONS, LLC; *U.S. Private*, pg. 1000
COMPETITOR GROUP, INC.—See Dalian Wanda Group Corporation Ltd.; *Int'l*, pg. 1953
COMPETROL LUXEMBOURG SARL—See The Olayan Group; *Int'l*, pg. 7672
COMPEX CORPORATION; *U.S. Private*, pg. 1000
COMPEX INC.—See Powermatic Data Systems Limited; *Int'l*, pg. 5947
COMPEX LEGAL SERVICES INC.—See Windjammer Capital Investors, LLC; *U.S. Private*, pg. 4537
COMPEX (GUZI IOU) CO., LTD Soo Powormatic Data Systems Limited; *Int'l*, pg. 5947
COMPEX TECHNOLOGIES SDN. BHD.—See Powermatic Data Systems Limited; *Int'l*, pg. 5947
COMPHANIA ENERGETICA SAO SALVADOR S.A.—See ENGIE SA; *Int'l*, pg. 2433
COMPHEALTH ASSOCIATES, INC.—See Ares Management Corporation; *U.S. Public*, pg. 188
COMPHEALTH ASSOCIATES, INC.—See Leonard Green & Partners, L.P.; *U.S. Private*, pg. 2425
COMPILE, INC.—See Teladoc Health, Inc.; *U.S. Public*, pg. 1992
COM.P.I.S. - COMPAGNIA PETROLIFERA ITALIA SUD SOCIETA A RESPONSABILITA LIMITATA—See UniCredit S.p.A.; *Int'l*, pg. 8034
COMPLEJO INDUSTRIAL TAQSA A.I.E.—See LyondellBasell Industries N.V.; *Int'l*, pg. 4608
COMPLEJO PORTUARIO MEJILLONES S.A.—See Corporacion Nacional del Cobre de Chile; *Int'l*, pg. 1805
COMPLEJO SIDERURGICO DE GUAYANA, C.A.—See Corporacion Venezolana de Guayana; *Int'l*, pg. 1805
COMPLEMAR PARTNERS; *U.S. Private*, pg. 1000
COMPLEO CHARGING SOLUTIONS AG—See Leopold Kostal GmbH & Co. KG; *Int'l*, pg. 4465
COMPLEO CONNECT GMBH—See Leopold Kostal GmbH & Co. KG; *Int'l*, pg. 4465
COMPLERE ENGINEERING GROUP, INC.; *U.S. Private*, pg. 1000
COMPLETE AIR SUPPLY PTY. LTD.—See Beijer Ref AB; *Int'l*, pg. 944
COMPLETE BENEFIT ALLIANCE, LLC—See Arthur J. Gallagher & Co.; *U.S. Public*, pg. 204
COMPLETE BOWLING SERVICE, INC.; *U.S. Private*, pg. 1000
COMPLETE CARE & ENABLEMENT SERVICES LIMITED—See Sheikh Holdings Group (Investments) Limited; *Int'l*, pg. 6793
COMPLETE CARE PHYSICAL THERAPY—See U.S. Physical Therapy, Inc.; *U.S. Public*, pg. 2216
COMPLETE CLAIMS PROCESSING, INC.—See Targeted Medical Pharma, Inc.; *U.S. Public*, pg. 1982
COMPLETE COLLEGE AMERICA INC.; *U.S. Private*, pg. 1000
COMPLETE CRYOGENIC SERVICES, INC.—See ITT Inc.; *U.S. Public*, pg. 1179
COMPLETE DIALYSIS CARE, LLC—See Nautic Partners, LLC; *U.S. Private*, pg. 2869
COMPLETE DISCOVERY SOURCE, INC.; *U.S. Private*, pg. 1000
COMPLETE ENERGY, LLC—See Superior Energy Services, Inc.; *U.S. Private*, pg. 3877
COMPLETE ENERGY SERVICES, INC.—See Superior Energy Services, Inc.; *U.S. Private*, pg. 3877
COMPLETE ENVIRONMENTAL PRODUCTS, INC.; *U.S. Private*, pg. 1000

COMPLETE EQUIPMENT AUSTRALIA PTY. LTD.—See SSH Group Limited; *Int'l*, pg. 7156
COMPLETE FINANCIAL SOLUTIONS, INC.; *U.S. Public*, pg. 561
COMPLETE GENERAL CONSTRUCTION CO. INC.; *U.S. Private*, pg. 1000
COMPLETE GENOMICS, INC.—See BGI-Shenzhen; *Int'l*, pg. 1008
COMPLETE HEALTHCARE INTERNATIONAL PTE LTD—See AsiaMedic Ltd.; *Int'l*, pg. 617
COMPLETE HEALTHCARE RESOURCES INC; *U.S. Private*, pg. 1000
COMPLETE HOME CONCEPTS INC.; *U.S. Private*, pg. 1000
COMPLETE INDUSTRIAL ENTERPRISES; *U.S. Private*, pg. 1001
COMPLETE INNOVATIONS INC.—See PowerFleet, Inc.; *U.S. Public*, pg. 1706
COMPLETELY BARE SPA, INC.; *U.S. Private*, pg. 1001
COMPLETE MECHANICAL SERVICES, LLC; *U.S. Private*, pg. 1001
COMPLETE MEDICAL HOMECARE, INC.—See Advanz Pharma Corp.; *Int'l*, pg. 166
COMPLETE MERCHANT SOLUTIONS (CMS); *U.S. Private*, pg. 1001
COMPLETE MILLWORK SERVICES, INC.; *U.S. Private*, pg. 1001
COMPLETE NUTRITION HOLDINGS INC.; *U.S. Private*, pg. 1001
COMPLETE OFFICE, LLC.—See The ODP Corporation; *U.S. Public*, pg. 2117
COMPLETE OFFICE OF WISCONSIN, INC.—See The ODP Corporation; *U.S. Public*, pg. 2117
COMPLETE PACKAGING, INC.—See Altamont Capital Partners; *U.S. Private*, pg. 205
COMPLETE PETMART INC.; *U.S. Private*, pg. 1001
COMPLETE PROFESSIONAL SERVICES, LLC; *U.S. Private*, pg. 1001
COMPLETE PROPERTY SERVICES, INC.; *U.S. Private*, pg. 1001
COMPLETE PURCHASING SERVICES INC.—See Aramark; *U.S. Public*, pg. 177
COMPLETE RECOVERY CORPORATION; *U.S. Private*, pg. 1001
COMPLETE RECYCLING SOLUTIONS LLC—See TerraCycle Inc.; *U.S. Private*, pg. 3971
COMPLETE RESOURCES COMPANY—See Complete General Construction Co. Inc.; *U.S. Private*, pg. 1000
COMPLETERX, LTD.; *U.S. Private*, pg. 1001
COMPLETE SALES & SERVICE; *U.S. Private*, pg. 1001
COMPLETE SOLARIA, INC.; *U.S. Public*, pg. 561
COMPLETE SUPPLY, INC.—See Beacon Roofing Supply, Inc.; *U.S. Public*, pg. 285
COMPLETE TRANSPORT SYSTEMS, LLC—See Expolanka Holdings PLC; *Int'l*, pg. 2589
COMPLEXA INC.; *U.S. Private*, pg. 1001
COMPLEX AIRCONDITIONING PTY LIMITED—See BSA Limited; *Int'l*, pg. 1201
COMPLEX BIZ INTERNATIONAL CO., LTD.—See RESORT TRUST INC.; *Int'l*, pg. 6301
COMPLEX CHEMICAL COMPANY, INC.; *U.S. Private*, pg. 1001
COMPLEX COMET SA; *Int'l*, pg. 1753
COMPLEXE ENVIRO CONNEXIONS LTEE—See Waste Connections, Inc.; *Int'l*, pg. 8352
COMPLEXE LEBOURGNEUF PHASE II INC.—See BTB Real Estate Investment Trust; *Int'l*, pg. 1204
COMPLEX MAGAZINE—See Complex Media, Inc.; *U.S. Private*, pg. 1001
COMPLEX MEDIA, INC.; *U.S. Private*, pg. 1001
THE COMPLEX SALE, INC.—See Sales Performance International, LLC; *U.S. Private*, pg. 3532
COMPLIA HEALTH, LLC—See Axxess Technology Solutions, Inc; *U.S. Private*, pg. 414
COMPLIANCE CORPORATION; *U.S. Private*, pg. 1001
THE COMPLIANCE DOCTOR, LLC; *U.S. Private*, pg. 4013
THE COMPLIANCE GROUP, INC.—See First Reserve Management, L.P.; *U.S. Private*, pg. 1526
COMPLIANCEQUEST INC.; *U.S. Private*, pg. 1001
COMPLIANCE SCIENCE, INC.; *U.S. Private*, pg. 1001
COMPLIANCESIGNS.COM; *U.S. Private*, pg. 1001
COMPLIANCE SYSTEMS, INC.—See Colonial Group, Inc.; *U.S. Private*, pg. 971
COMPLIANCE WEEK—See Wilmington plc; *Int'l*, pg. 8422
COMPLIANT LOGISTICS AB—See Knightec AB; *Int'l*, pg. 4207
COMPLI, INC.—See Vista Equity Partners, LLC; *U.S. Private*, pg. 4395
COMPLINA GMBH—See DZ BANK AG Deutsche Zentral-Genossenschaftsbank; *Int'l*, pg. 2243
COMPLINET GROUP LIMITED—See Thomson Reuters Corporation; *Int'l*, pg. 7715
COMPLINET GROUP LTD. - DUBAI—See Thomson Reuters Corporation; *Int'l*, pg. 7715
COMPLINET INC.—See Thomson Reuters Corporation; *Int'l*, pg. 7715
COMPLINET UK LIMITED—See Thomson Reuters Corporation; *Int'l*, pg. 7715

COMPONENTE AUTO S.A.

COMPLIOFFICER SLU—See Prosegur Cash SA; *Int'l*, pg. 5999
COMPLIT AS—See Crayon Group Holding ASA; *Int'l*, pg. 1829
COMPLOTT PAPIER UNION, GMBH—See Inapa - Investimentos, Participacoes e Gestao, SA; *Int'l*, pg. 3645
COMPLUS TECHNOLOGIES SE; *Int'l*, pg. 1753
COMPLY365, LLC—See Liberty Hall Capital Partners, L.P.; *U.S. Private*, pg. 2444
COMPNODE SVERIGE AB—See Ratos AB; *Int'l*, pg. 6216
COMPO AUSTRIA GMBH—See K+S Aktiengesellschaft; *Int'l*, pg. 4039
COMPO AUSTRIA GMBH—See Kingenta Ecological Engineering Group Co., Ltd.; *Int'l*, pg. 4172
COMPOBAIE SOLUTIONS SAS—See Platina Partners LLP; *Int'l*, pg. 5893
COMPO BENELUX N.V.—See Kingenta Ecological Engineering Group Co., Ltd.; *Int'l*, pg. 4172
COMPO BENELUX N.V—See K+S Aktiengesellschaft; *Int'l*, pg. 4039
COMPODIUM INTERNATIONAL AB; *Int'l*, pg. 1753
COMPO DO BRASIL S.A.—See Kingenta Ecological Engineering Group Co., Ltd.; *Int'l*, pg. 4172
COMPO EXPERT ARGENTINA SRL—See Grupa Azoty S.A.; *Int'l*, pg. 3115
COMPO EXPERT ASIA PACIFIC SDN. BHD.—See Grupa Azoty S.A.; *Int'l*, pg. 3115
COMPO EXPERT AUSTRIA GMBH—See Grupa Azoty S.A.; *Int'l*, pg. 3115
COMPO EXPERT BENELUX N. V.—See Grupa Azoty S.A.; *Int'l*, pg. 3115
COMPO EXPERT BRASIL FERTILIZANTES LTDA.—See Grupa Azoty S.A.; *Int'l*, pg. 3115
COMPO EXPERT CHILE FERTILIZANTES LTDA.—See Grupa Azoty S.A.; *Int'l*, pg. 3115
COMPO EXPERT FRANCE SAS—See Grupa Azoty S.A.; *Int'l*, pg. 3115
COMPO EXPERT GMBH—See Grupa Azoty S.A.; *Int'l*, pg. 3115
COMPO EXPERT HELLAS S.A.—See Grupa Azoty S.A.; *Int'l*, pg. 3115
COMPO EXPERT INDIA PRIVATE LIMITED—See Grupa Azoty S.A.; *Int'l*, pg. 3115
COMPO EXPERT ITALIA S.R.L.—See Grupa Azoty S.A.; *Int'l*, pg. 3115
COMPO EXPERT MEXICO S. A. DE C. V.—See Grupa Azoty S.A.; *Int'l*, pg. 3115
COMPO EXPERT POLSKA SP. Z O.O.—See Grupa Azoty S.A.; *Int'l*, pg. 3115
COMPO EXPERT PORTUGAL, UNIPESSOAL LDA.—See Grupa Azoty S.A.; *Int'l*, pg. 3115
COMPO EXPERT SOUTH AFRICA (PTY) LTD.—See Grupa Azoty S.A.; *Int'l*, pg. 3115
COMPO EXPERT SPAIN S.L.—See Grupa Azoty S.A.; *Int'l*, pg. 3115
COMPO EXPERT TECHN. (SHENZHEN) CO., LTD.—See Grupa Azoty S.A.; *Int'l*, pg. 3115
COMPO EXPERT TURKIYE TARIM SAN.VE TIC. LTD.—See Grupa Azoty S.A.; *Int'l*, pg. 3115
COMPO EXPERT UK LTD.—See Grupa Azoty S.A.; *Int'l*, pg. 3115
COMPO EXPERT USA & CANADA INC.—See Grupa Azoty S.A.; *Int'l*, pg. 3115
COMPO GMBH—See Kingenta Ecological Engineering Group Co., Ltd.; *Int'l*, pg. 4172
COMPO HELLAS S.A.—See K+S Aktiengesellschaft; *Int'l*, pg. 4039
COMPO IBERIA S.L.—See Kingenta Ecological Engineering Group Co., Ltd.; *Int'l*, pg. 4172
COMPOLUX SPOL. S.R.O.—See A.A.G. STUCCHI s.r.l.; *Int'l*, pg. 22
COMPONENTA ALBIN AB—See Componenta Corporation; *Int'l*, pg. 1753
COMPONENTA A.S.—See Componenta Corporation; *Int'l*, pg. 1753
COMPONENTA CASTINGS OY—See Componenta Corporation; *Int'l*, pg. 1753
COMPONENTA CORPORATION; *Int'l*, pg. 1753
COMPONENTA FINLAND OY—See Componenta Corporation; *Int'l*, pg. 1753
COMPONENTA FRAMMESTAD AB—See Componenta Corporation; *Int'l*, pg. 1753
COMPONENTA FRANCE S.A.S.—See Componenta Corporation; *Int'l*, pg. 1753
COMPONENTA ITALY S.R.L.—See Componenta Corporation; *Int'l*, pg. 1753
COMPONENTA MANUFACTURING OY—See Componenta Corporation; *Int'l*, pg. 1753
COMPONENTA NETHERLANDS B.V.—See Componenta Corporation; *Int'l*, pg. 1753
COMPONENT ASSEMBLY SYSTEMS, INC.; *U.S. Private*, pg. 1001
COMPONENTA UK LTD.—See Parsan Makina Parcalari Sanayii AS; *Int'l*, pg. 5747
COMPONENTA USA, LLC—See Componenta Corporation; *Int'l*, pg. 1753
COMPONENTA WIRSBO AB—See Componenta Corporation; *Int'l*, pg. 1753
COMPONENTE AUTO S.A.; *Int'l*, pg. 1753

607

COMPONENTE AUTO S.A.

COMPONENTES AUTOMOTIVOS TAUBATE, LTDA.—See Cie Automotive S.A.; *Int'l*, pg. 1604
COMPONENTES AVANZADOS DE MEXICO, S.A. DE C.V.—See Emerson Electric Co.; *U.S. Public*, pg. 742
COMPONENTES DE AUTOMOCION RECYTEC, S.L.U.—See Cie Automotive S.A.; *Int'l*, pg. 1604
COMPONENTES DE DIRECCION RECYLAN, S.L.U.—See Cie Automotive S.A.; *Int'l*, pg. 1604
COMPONENTES DELFA, C.A.—See General Motors Company; *U.S. Public*, pg. 923
COMPONENTES DE VEHICULOS DE GALICIA S.A.—See FORVIA SE; *Int'l*, pg. 2745
COMPONENTES INTEL DE COSTA RICA—See Intel Corporation; *U.S. Public*, pg. 1138
COMPONENTES UNIVERSALES DE MATAMOROS, S.A. DE C.V.—See Panasonic Holdings Corporation; *Int'l*, pg. 5717
COMPONENTES VENEZOLANOS DE DIRECCION, S.A.—See Apollo Global Management, Inc.; *U.S. Public*, pg. 160
COMPONENT FOOTWEAR DOMINICANA, S.A.—See V. F. Corporation; *U.S. Public*, pg. 2268
COMPONENT HARDWARE GROUP, INC.; *U.S. Private*, pg. 1002
COMPONENT INTERTECHNOLOGIES, INC.; *U.S. Private*, pg. 1002
COMPONENTONE LLC; *U.S. Private*, pg. 1002
COMPONENT RE-ENGINEERING COMPANY, INC.—See Tinicum Enterprises, Inc.; *U.S. Private*, pg. 4174
COMPONENTS CENTER INC.; *U.S. Private*, pg. 1002
COMPONENTS CORPORATION OF AMERICA, INC.; *U.S. Private*, pg. 1002
COMPONENTS DISTRIBUTORS INC.; *U.S. Private*, pg. 1002
COMPONENTSOURCE HOLDING CORPORATION; *U.S. Private*, pg. 1002
COMPONENT SPECIALTY, INC.—See UCA Group Component Specialty Inc.; *U.S. Private*, pg. 4273
COMPONENT WEST, INC.—See Component Assembly Systems, Inc.; *U.S. Private*, pg. 1002
COMPONEX CORPORATION—See Berwind Corporation; *U.S. Private*, pg. 541
COMPORIUM DATA SERVICES—See Comporium Group; *U.S. Private*, pg. 1002
COMPORIUM GROUP; *U.S. Private*, pg. 1002
COMPORIUM PUBLISHING—See Comporium Group; *U.S. Private*, pg. 1002
COMPORIUM—See Comporium Group; *U.S. Private*, pg. 1002
COMPORIUM TELECOM INC.—See Comporium Group; *U.S. Private*, pg. 1002
COMPOSECURE, INC.; *U.S. Public*, pg. 561
COMPOSIDIE INC.; *U.S. Private*, pg. 1002
COMPOSITE ALLIANCE GROUP INC.; *Int'l*, pg. 1754
COMPOSITE ASSISTANCE LIMITED—See Stone Point Capital LLC; *U.S. Private*, pg. 3820
COMPOSITE ENGINEERING, INC.—See Kratos Defense & Security Solutions, Inc.; *U.S. Public*, pg. 1276
COMPOSITE FABRICS OF AMERICA LLC—See Schneider Mills, Inc.; *U.S. Private*, pg. 3567
COMPOSITE FLOOR DECKS LIMITED—See STEEL & TUBE Holdings Limited; *Int'l*, pg. 7189
COMPOSITE FORGINGS LIMITED PARTNERSHIP—See Swiss Steel Holding AG; *Int'l*, pg. 7372
COMPOSITE LEGAL EXPENSES LIMITED—See Stone Point Capital LLC; *U.S. Private*, pg. 3820
COMPOSITE LEGAL SERVICES LIMITED—See Stone Point Capital LLC; *U.S. Private*, pg. 3820
COMPOSITE LIMITED; *Int'l*, pg. 1754
COMPOSITE MATERIALS (ITALY) S.R.L.—See Toray Industries, Inc.; *Int'l*, pg. 7822
COMPOSITE PRODUCTS LIMITED—See Avingtrans plc; *Int'l*, pg. 743
COMPOSITE RESOURCES, INC.; *U.S. Private*, pg. 1002
COMPOSITES AQUITAINE S.A.—See Airbus SE; *Int'l*, pg. 246
COMPOSITES ATLANTIC LIMITED—See Airbus SE; *Int'l*, pg. 245
COMPOSITES BUSCH S.A.—See Dr. Ing. K. Busch GmbH; *Int'l*, pg. 2193
COMPOSITE SOFTWARE, INC.—See Cisco Systems, Inc.; *U.S. Public*, pg. 499
COMPOSITES ONE LLC—See Avient Corporation; *U.S. Public*, pg. 247
COMPOSITES ONE; *U.S. Private*, pg. 1002
COMPOSITES TECHNOLOGY RESEARCH MALAYSIA SDN. BHD.—See DRB-HICOM Berhad; *Int'l*, pg. 2201
COMPOSITION RESEARCH TECHNOLOGIES, INC.—See Crawford Technologies, Inc.; *Int'l*, pg. 1829
COMPOTECH AB—See Addtech AB; *Int'l*, pg. 132
COMPO TECH PLUS, SPOL. S R.O.—See Fukuda Corporation; *Int'l*, pg. 2839
COMPOTECH PROVIDER AB—See Addtech AB; *Int'l*, pg. 132
COMPOTRON GMBH—See discoverIE Group plc; *Int'l*, pg. 2133
COMPOUNDING & COLOURING SDN. BHD.—See Oriental Holdings Berhad; *Int'l*, pg. 5624

THE COMPOUNDING PHARMACY OF SOUTH AFRICA (PTY) LTD—See Ascendis Health Limited; *Int'l*, pg. 601
THE COMPOUNDING SHOP INC.; *U.S. Private*, pg. 4013
COMPO VERWALTUNGSGESELLSCHAFT MBH—See K+S Aktiengesellschaft; *Int'l*, pg. 4039
COMPPIL SA; *Int'l*, pg. 1754
COMPQSOFT, INC.; *U.S. Private*, pg. 1002
COMP-RAY, INC.—See Christie InnoMed, Inc.; *Int'l*, pg. 1587
COMPRE GROUP HOLDINGS LTD.—See British Columbia Investment Management Corp.; *Int'l*, pg. 1169
COMPRE GROUP HOLDINGS LTD.—See Cinven Limited; *Int'l*, pg. 1611
COMPREHENSIVE BEHAVIORAL HEALTHCARE, INC.; *U.S. Private*, pg. 1002
COMPREHENSIVE BEHAVIORAL HEALTH; *U.S. Private*, pg. 1002
COMPREHENSIVE COMMUNITY ACTION PROGRAM; *U.S. Private*, pg. 1002
COMPREHENSIVE COMPUTER CONSULTING, INC.; *U.S. Private*, pg. 1003
COMPREHENSIVE ENERGY SERVICES, INC.; *U.S. Private*, pg. 1003
COMPREHENSIVE ENVIRONMENTAL ASSESSMENTS, INC.; *U.S. Private*, pg. 1003
COMPREHENSIVE FINANCE, INC.; *U.S. Private*, pg. 1003
COMPREHENSIVE HAND & PHYSICAL THERAPY, LIMITED PARTNERSHIP—See U.S. Physical Therapy, Inc.; *U.S. Public*, pg. 2214
COMPREHENSIVE HEALTHCARE SYSTEMS INC.; *Int'l*, pg. 1754
COMPREHENSIVE HEALTH MANAGEMENT, INC.—See Centene Corporation; *U.S. Public*, pg. 471
COMPREHENSIVE HEALTH SERVICES, INC.; *U.S. Private*, pg. 1003
COMPREHENSIVE HOME CARE—See Nova Leap Health Corp.; *Int'l*, pg. 5451
COMPREHENSIVE LAND DEVELOPMENT & INVESTMENT PLC; *Int'l*, pg. 1754
COMPREHENSIVE LEASING CO.; *Int'l*, pg. 1754
COMPREHENSIVE LOSS MANAGEMENT, INC.—See Waud Capital Partners LLC; *U.S. Private*, pg. 4457
COMPREHENSIVE MANUFACTURING SERVICES, LLC—See Golden Gate Capital Management II, LLC; *U.S. Private*, pg. 1732
COMPREHENSIVE MEDICAL CARE LTD., INC.—See Allina Health System, Inc.; *U.S. Private*, pg. 192
COMPREHENSIVE MEDICAL PRACTICE MANAGEMENT, INC.; *U.S. Private*, pg. 1003
COMPREHENSIVE MULTIPLE PROJECTS COMPANY PLC; *Int'l*, pg. 1754
COMPREHENSIVE OPTIONS FOR DRUG ABUSERS; *U.S. Private*, pg. 1003
COMPREHENSIVE PHARMACY SERVICES, INC.—See PPS, Inc.; *U.S. Private*, pg. 3240
COMPREHENSIVE RADIOLOGY MANAGEMENT SERVICES, LTD.—See HCA Healthcare, Inc.; *U.S. Public*, pg. 994
COMPREHENSIVE SOFTWARE SYSTEMS; *U.S. Private*, pg. 1003
COMPREMED CANADA INC.—See NeuPath Health, Inc.; *Int'l*, pg. 5218
COMPREMUM S.A.; *Int'l*, pg. 1754
COMPRENDIUM STRUCTURED FINANCING GMBH; *Int'l*, pg. 1754
COMPRESSCO CANADA, INC.—See EQT AB; *Int'l*, pg. 2478
COMPRESSCO, INC.—See TETRA Technologies, Inc.; *U.S. Public*, pg. 2024
COMPRESSED AIR INTERNATIONAL INC.—See Xebec Adsorption Inc.; *Int'l*, pg. 8520
COMPRESSED AIR PRODUCTS, INC.—See Atlas Copco AB; *Int'l*, pg. 681
COMPRESSED AIR SYSTEMS, INC.—See Atlas Copco AB; *Int'l*, pg. 681
COMPRESSED AIR TECHNOLOGIES, INC.—See Atlas Copco AB; *Int'l*, pg. 681
COMPRESSEURS MAUGUIERE S.A.S.—See Atlas Copco AB; *Int'l*, pg. 678
COMPRESSEURS WORTHINGTON CREYSSENSAC S.A.S.—See Atlas Copco AB; *Int'l*, pg. 678
COMPRESSION COMPONENTS & SERVICE, LLC—See Operio Group, LLC; *U.S. Private*, pg. 3032
COMPRESSION SERVICES DE MEXICO, S.A. DE C.V.—See Enerflex Ltd.; *Int'l*, pg. 2418
COMPRESSION THERAPY CONCEPTS, INC.—See Zimmer Biomet Holdings, Inc.; *U.S. Public*, pg. 2406
COMPRESSOR CONTROLS (BEIJING) CORPORATION LTD.—See Roper Technologies, Inc.; *U.S. Public*, pg. 1811
COMPRESSOR CONTROLS CORPORATION B.V.—See Roper Technologies, Inc.; *U.S. Public*, pg. 1811
COMPRESSOR CONTROLS CORPORATION—See Roper Technologies, Inc.; *U.S. Public*, pg. 1810
COMPRESSOR CONTROLS CORPORATION S.R.L.—See Roper Technologies, Inc.; *U.S. Public*, pg. 1811

CORPORATE AFFILIATIONS

COMPRESSOR CONTROLS PTY. LTD.—See Roper Technologies, Inc.; *U.S. Public*, pg. 1811
COMPRESSOR CONTROLS SAUDI ARABIA, LLC—See Roper Technologies, Inc.; *U.S. Public*, pg. 1811
COMPRESSOR ENGINEERING CORPORATION; *U.S. Private*, pg. 1003
COMPRESSOR PRODUCTS INTERNATIONAL COLOMBIA S.A.S.—See Enpro Inc.; *U.S. Public*, pg. 774
COMPRESSOR PRODUCTS INTERNATIONAL GMBH—See Enpro Inc.; *U.S. Public*, pg. 774
COMPRESSOR PRODUCTS INTERNATIONAL LTD.—See Enpro Inc.; *U.S. Public*, pg. 774
COMPRESSOR PRODUCTS INTERNATIONAL—See Enpro Inc.; *U.S. Public*, pg. 774
COMPRESSOR PRODUCTS INTERNATIONAL SOUTH KOREA—See Enpro Inc.; *U.S. Public*, pg. 774
COMPRESSOR SAZI TABRIZ CO.; *Int'l*, pg. 1754
COMPRESSOR SYSTEMS INC.—See EQT AB; *Int'l*, pg. 2478
COMPRESSOR WORLD, LLC; *U.S. Private*, pg. 1003
COMPRESSUS, INC.—See ESW Capital, LLC; *U.S. Private*, pg. 1430
COMPRICER AB—See Schibsted ASA; *Int'l*, pg. 6616
COMPRINT MILITARY PUBLICATIONS—See Nash Holdings LLC; *U.S. Private*, pg. 2835
COMPROBASE, INC.; *U.S. Private*, pg. 1003
COMPRODUCTS INC.; *U.S. Private*, pg. 1003
COMPROMISE DOMINO B.V.—See Dustin Group AB; *Int'l*, pg. 2235
COMP S.A.; *Int'l*, pg. 1721
COMPSCRIPT, LLC—See CVS Health Corporation; *U.S. Public*, pg. 616
COMPSEE, INC.—See Control Solutions, Inc.; *U.S. Private*, pg. 1034
COMPSOURCE, INC.; *U.S. Private*, pg. 1003
COMPTA - EQUIPAMENTOS E SERVICOS DE INFORMATICA, S.A.; *Int'l*, pg. 1754
COMPTECH CORPORATION; *U.S. Private*, pg. 1003
COMPTEK KUNSTSTOFFVERARBEITUNG GMBH—See Avient Corporation; *U.S. Public*, pg. 247
COMPTOIR CENTRAL D'ELECTRICITE - DEL—See Sonepar S.A.; *Int'l*, pg. 7090
COMPTOIR COMMERCIAL INTERNATIONAL N.V.—See Aiphone Co., Ltd.; *Int'l*, pg. 235
COMPTOIR DE BRETAGNE SAS—See Bunzl plc; *Int'l*, pg. 1218
COMPTOIR DES BOIS DE BRIVE SAS—See International Paper Company; *U.S. Public*, pg. 1155
COMPTOIR DES COURANTS FAIBLES SA—See Sonepar S.A.; *Int'l*, pg. 7090
COMPTOIR DES FERS ET METAUX SA (CFM)—See Ferguson plc; *Int'l*, pg. 2637
COMPTOIR DU BATIMENT NV—See Etex SA/NV; *Int'l*, pg. 2521
COMPTOIR DU SUD-OUEST SAS—See Sonepar S.A.; *Int'l*, pg. 7090
COMPTOIR ELBEUVIEN D'ELECTRICITE SA—See Sonepar S.A.; *Int'l*, pg. 7090
COMPTOIR GENERAL DES GLACES ET PRODUITS VERRIERS—See Compagnie de Saint-Gobain SA; *Int'l*, pg. 1723
COMPTOIR GROUP PLC; *Int'l*, pg. 1754
COMPTROL INCORPORATED; *U.S. Private*, pg. 1003
COMPUAGE INFOCOM LTD.; *Int'l*, pg. 1754
COMPUAGE INFOCOM (S) PTE. LTD.—See Compuage Infocom Ltd.; *Int'l*, pg. 1754
COMPU B LTD; *Int'l*, pg. 1754
COMPUCASE ENTERPRISE CO., LTD.; *Int'l*, pg. 1754
COMPUCASE EUROPE GMBH—See Compucase Enterprise Co., Ltd.; *Int'l*, pg. 1754
COMPUCASE JAPAN CO., LTD.—See Compucase Enterprise Co., Ltd.; *Int'l*, pg. 1754
COMPUCASE UK LTD.—See Compucase Enterprise Co., Ltd.; *Int'l*, pg. 1754
COMPUCOM CANADA CO.—See Variant Equity Advisors, LLC; *U.S. Private*, pg. 4346
COMPUCOM SOFTWARE LTD; *Int'l*, pg. 1754
COMPUCOM SYSTEMS HOLDINGS LLC—See The ODP Corporation; *U.S. Public*, pg. 2117
COMPUCOM SYSTEMS, INC. - BELLEVUE—See Variant Equity Advisors, LLC; *U.S. Private*, pg. 4346
COMPUCOM SYSTEMS, INC.—See Variant Equity Advisors, LLC; *U.S. Private*, pg. 4346
COMPUCON COMPUTERS LIMITED—See Karin Technology Holdings Limited; *Int'l*, pg. 4081
COMPUCON JAPAN CO. LTD—See COMPUCON S.A.; *Int'l*, pg. 1755
COMPUCON S.A.; *Int'l*, pg. 1754
COMPUCON USA L.L.C.—See COMPUCON S.A.; *Int'l*, pg. 1755
COMPUDATA INC.; *U.S. Private*, pg. 1003
COMPUDENT PRAXISCOMPUTER GMBH & CO. KG—See CompuGroup Medical SE & Co. KGaA; *Int'l*, pg. 1755
COMPUDYNE CORPORATION—See Frontenac Company LLC; *U.S. Private*, pg. 1613
COMPUFIT BVBA—See CompuGroup Medical SE & Co. KGaA; *Int'l*, pg. 1755

COMPANY NAME INDEX

COMPUFIT, INC.—See Anatomy IT, LLC; *U.S. Private,* pg. 272
COMPU-FIX, INC.—See Harvest Partners L.P.; *U.S. Private,* pg. 1877
COMPUFIX LIMITED—See Computacenter plc; *Int'l,* pg. 1758
COMPUGAIN, INC.; *U.S. Private,* pg. 1003
COMPUGATES HOLDINGS BERHAD; *Int'l,* pg. 1755
COMPUGEN FINANCE INC.—See Compugen Inc.; *Int'l,* pg. 1755
COMPUGEN INC.; *Int'l,* pg. 1755
COMPUGEN LTD.; *Int'l,* pg. 1755
COMPUGEN USA, INC.—See Compugen Ltd.; *Int'l,* pg. 1755
COMPUGRAPHICS INTERNATIONAL LTD.—See Element Solutions Inc.; *U.S. Public,* pg. 725
COMPUGRAPHICS JENA GMBH—See Element Solutions Inc.; *U.S. Public,* pg. 725
COMPUGRAPHICS U.S.A. INC. - AUSTIN—See Element Solutions Inc.; *U.S. Public,* pg. 725
COMPUGRAPHICS U.S.A. INC.—See Element Solutions Inc.; *U.S. Public,* pg. 725
COMPUGROUP MEDICAL BELGIUM BVBA—See CompuGroup Medical SE & Co. KGaA; *Int'l,* pg. 1755
COMPUGROUP MEDICAL BILGI SISTEMLERI A.S.—See CompuGroup Medical SE & Co. KGaA; *Int'l,* pg. 1756
COMPUGROUP MEDICAL CEE GMBH—See CompuGroup Medical SE & Co. KGaA; *Int'l,* pg. 1755
COMPUGROUP MEDICAL CEE GMBH—See CompuGroup Medical SE & Co. KGaA; *Int'l,* pg. 1755
COMPUGROUP MEDICAL CESKA REPUBLIKA S.R.O.—See CompuGroup Medical SE & Co. KGaA; *Int'l,* pg. 1755
COMPUGROUP MEDICAL DENMARK A/S—See CompuGroup Medical SE & Co. KGaA; *Int'l,* pg. 1755
COMPUGROUP MEDICAL DENTALSYSTEME GMBH—See CompuGroup Medical SE & Co. KGaA; *Int'l,* pg. 1755
COMPUGROUP MEDICAL DEUTSCHLAND AG GESCHAFTSBEREICH HIS—See CompuGroup Medical SE & Co. KGaA; *Int'l,* pg. 1756
COMPUGROUP MEDICAL DEUTSCHLAND AG—See CompuGroup Medical SE & Co. KGaA; *Int'l,* pg. 1756
COMPUGROUP MEDICAL FRANCE SAS—See CompuGroup Medical SE & Co. KGaA; *Int'l,* pg. 1756
COMPUGROUP MEDICAL HELLAS S.A.—See CompuGroup Medical SE & Co. KGaA; *Int'l,* pg. 1756
COMPUGROUP MEDICAL INC.—See CompuGroup Medical SE & Co. KGaA; *Int'l,* pg. 1756
COMPUGROUP MEDICAL ITALIA HOLDING S.R.L.—See CompuGroup Medical SE & Co. KGaA; *Int'l,* pg. 1756
COMPUGROUP MEDICAL ITALIA S.P.A.—See CompuGroup Medical SE & Co. KGaA; *Int'l,* pg. 1756
COMPUGROUP MEDICAL LAB AB—See CompuGroup Medical SE & Co. KGaA; *Int'l,* pg. 1756
COMPUGROUP MEDICAL MALAYSIA SDN BHD—See CompuGroup Medical SE & Co. KGaA; *Int'l,* pg. 1756
COMPUGROUP MEDICAL MANAGEMENTGESELLSCHAFT MBH—See CompuGroup Medical SE & Co. KGaA; *Int'l,* pg. 1756
COMPUGROUP MEDICAL NEDERLAND B.V.—See PAO Severstal; *Int'l,* pg. 5731
COMPUGROUP MEDICAL NORWAY AS—See CompuGroup Medical SE & Co. KGaA; *Int'l,* pg. 1756
COMPUGROUP MEDICAL POLSKA SP. Z O.O.—See CompuGroup Medical SE & Co. KGaA; *Int'l,* pg. 1756
COMPUGROUP MEDICAL SCHWEIZ AG—See CompuGroup Medical SE & Co. KGaA; *Int'l,* pg. 1756
COMPUGROUP MEDICAL SE & CO. KGAA; *Int'l,* pg. 1755
COMPUGROUP MEDICAL SLOVENSKO S.R.O.—See CompuGroup Medical SE & Co. KGaA; *Int'l,* pg. 1756
COMPUGROUP MEDICAL SOFTWARE GMBH—See CompuGroup Medical SE & Co. KGaA; *Int'l,* pg. 1756
COMPUGROUP MEDICAL SOLUTIONS SAS—See CompuGroup Medical SE & Co. KGaA; *Int'l,* pg. 1756
COMPUGROUP MEDICAL SOUTH AFRICA (PTY) LTD.—See CompuGroup Medical SE & Co. KGaA; *Int'l,* pg. 1756
COMPUGROUP MEDICAL SWEDEN AB—See CompuGroup Medical SE & Co. KGaA; *Int'l,* pg. 1756
COMPUGROUP MEDICAL SWEDEN AB—See CompuGroup Medical SE & Co. KGaA; *Int'l,* pg. 1756
COMPUGROUP MEDICAL SWEDEN AB—See CompuGroup Medical SE & Co. KGaA; *Int'l,* pg. 1756
COMPUGROUP OSTERREICH GMBH—See CompuGroup Medical SE & Co. KGaA; *Int'l,* pg. 1756
COMPUGROUP SERVICES GMBH—See CompuGroup Medical SE & Co. KGaA; *Int'l,* pg. 1756
COMPULAB LTD.; *Int'l,* pg. 1757
COMPULINK BUSINESS SYSTEMS, INC.; *U.S. Private,* pg. 1003
COMPULINK CABLE ASSEMBLIES, INC.; *U.S. Private,* pg. 1004
COMPULINK CABLE ASSEMBLIES OF FLORIDA INC.—See ITT Inc.; *U.S. Public,* pg. 1179
COMPU-LINK CORPORATION; *U.S. Private,* pg. 1003
COMPULIT INC.—See Pitney Bowes Inc.; *U.S. Public,* pg. 1694
COMPUMEDICS EUROPE GMBH—See Compumedics Limited; *Int'l,* pg. 1757
COMPUMEDICS FRANCE SAS—See Compumedics Limited; *Int'l,* pg. 1757
COMPUMEDICS GERMANY GMBH—See Compumedics Limited; *Int'l,* pg. 1757
COMPUMEDICS LIMITED - COMPUMEDICS SLEEP DIVISION—See Compumedics Limited; *Int'l,* pg. 1757
COMPUMEDICS LIMITED - NEUROSCAN DIVISION—See Compumedics Limited; *Int'l,* pg. 1757
COMPUMEDICS LIMITED; *Int'l,* pg. 1757
COMPUMEDICS USA, INC.—See Compumedics Limited; *Int'l,* pg. 1757
COMPUMED, INC.; *U.S. Public,* pg. 561
COMPUNET CLINICAL LABORATORIES, INC.; *U.S. Private,* pg. 1004
COMPUNET CONSULTING GROUP, INC.; *U.S. Private,* pg. 1004
COMPUNNEL SOFTWARE GROUP; *U.S. Private,* pg. 1004
COMPUPOWER CORPORATION—See Arnold Bernhard & Co.; *U.S. Public,* pg. 333
COMPUPROS LTD; *U.S. Private,* pg. 1004
COMPUQUIP TECHNOLOGIES, LLC—See Dosal Capital, LLC; *U.S. Private,* pg. 1264
COMPU-QUOTE INC.; *Int'l,* pg. 1754
COMPUSA INC.—See Insight Enterprises, Inc.; *U.S. Public,* pg. 1130
COMPUSMART LIMITED—See Karin Technology Holdings Limited; *Int'l,* pg. 4081
COMPUSOFT INTEGRATED SOLUTIONS INC.; *U.S. Private,* pg. 1004
COMPUTACENTER AG—See Computacenter plc; *Int'l,* pg. 1758
COMPUTACENTER BV—See Computacenter plc; *Int'l,* pg. 1758
COMPUTACENTER FRANCE S.A.—See Computacenter plc; *Int'l,* pg. 1758
COMPUTACENTER GMBH—See Computacenter plc; *Int'l,* pg. 1758
COMPUTACENTER HOLDING GMBH—See Computacenter plc; *Int'l,* pg. 1758
COMPUTACENTER MEXICO S.A. DE C.V.—See Computacenter plc; *Int'l,* pg. 1758
COMPUTACENTER NV/SA—See Computacenter plc; *Int'l,* pg. 1758
COMPUTACENTER PLC; *Int'l,* pg. 1757
COMPUTACENTER PSF SA—See Computacenter plc; *Int'l,* pg. 1758
COMPUTACENTER SERVICES (IBERIA) SLU—See Computacenter plc; *Int'l,* pg. 1758
COMPUTACENTER SERVICES KFT—See Computacenter plc; *Int'l,* pg. 1758
COMPUTACENTER SERVICES (MALAYSIA) SDN BHD—See Computacenter plc; *Int'l,* pg. 1758
COMPUTACENTER SERVICES & SOLUTIONS (PTY) LIMITED—See Computacenter plc; *Int'l,* pg. 1758
COMPUTACENTER (UK) LTD.—See Computacenter plc; *Int'l,* pg. 1758
COMPUTACENTER (U.S.) INC.—See Computacenter plc; *Int'l,* pg. 1758
COMPUTADORAS, REDES E INGENIERIA SA—See Airbus SE; *Int'l,* pg. 245
COMPUTAPOLE—See Quanta Services, Inc.; *U.S. Public,* pg. 1752
COMPUTARIS INTERNATIONAL LIMITED—See Blackstone Inc.; *U.S. Public,* pg. 357
COMPUTATIONAL DYNAMICS LTD.—See Siemens Aktiengesellschaft; *Int'l,* pg. 6891
COMPUTATIONAL ENGINEERING INTERNATIONAL, INC.—See ANSYS, Inc.; *U.S. Public,* pg. 139
COMPUTATIONAL RESEARCH LABORATORIES LIMITED—See Tata Sons Limited; *Int'l,* pg. 7469
COMPUTATIONAL SYSTEMS, INCORPORATED—See Emerson Electric Co.; *U.S. Public,* pg. 742
COMPUTECH CORPORATION; *U.S. Private,* pg. 1004
COMPUTECH INTERNATIONAL INC.; *U.S. Private,* pg. 1004
COMPUTEC SRL—See Bain Capital, LP; *U.S. Private,* pg. 452
COMPUTER ADD-ONS INC.; *U.S. Private,* pg. 1004
COMPUTER ADVANTAGE, INC.; *U.S. Private,* pg. 1004
COMPUTER AGE ELECTRONICS, INC.; *U.S. Private,* pg. 1004
COMPUTER AGE MANAGEMENT SERVICES LIMITED; *Int'l,* pg. 1758
COMPUTER AIDED PRODUCTS, INC.; *U.S. Private,* pg. 1004
COMPUTER AIDED TECHNOLOGY INC.—See Court Square Capital Partners, L.P.; *U.S. Private,* pg. 1069
COMPUTER AID, INC.; *U.S. Private,* pg. 1004
COMPUTER AND TECHNOLOGIES INTERNATIONAL LIMITED—See Computer & Technologies Holdings Limited; *Int'l,* pg. 1758
COMPUTER ASSISTED TESTING SERVICE, INC.—See Educational Testing Service Inc.; *U.S. Private,* pg. 1340
COMPUTER ASSOCIATES AFRICA (PTY.) LTD.—See Broadcom Inc.; *U.S. Public,* pg. 389
COMPUTER ASSOCIATES AG—See Broadcom Inc.; *U.S. Public,* pg. 389
COMPUTER ASSOCIATES (CAI) DE VENEZUELA, C.A.—See Broadcom Inc.; *U.S. Public,* pg. 389
COMPUTER ASSOCIATES DE ARGENTINA S.A.—See Broadcom Inc.; *U.S. Public,* pg. 389
COMPUTER ASSOCIATES DE CHILE S.A.—See Broadcom Inc.; *U.S. Public,* pg. 390
COMPUTER ASSOCIATES DE COLOMBIA S.A.—See Broadcom Inc.; *U.S. Public,* pg. 390
COMPUTER ASSOCIATES DEL PERU—See Broadcom Inc.; *U.S. Public,* pg. 390
COMPUTER ASSOCIATES DO BRASIL LTDA.—See Broadcom Inc.; *U.S. Public,* pg. 390
COMPUTER ASSOCIATES HUNGARY—See Broadcom Inc.; *U.S. Public,* pg. 389
COMPUTER ASSOCIATES INTERNATIONAL GMBH—See Broadcom Inc.; *U.S. Public,* pg. 389
COMPUTER ASSOCIATES INTERNATIONAL, INC.—See Broadcom Inc.; *U.S. Public,* pg. 389
COMPUTER ASSOCIATES INTERNATIONAL LIMITED—See Broadcom Inc.; *U.S. Public,* pg. 389
COMPUTER ASSOCIATES JAPAN, LTD.—See Broadcom Inc.; *U.S. Public,* pg. 389
COMPUTER ASSOCIATES KOREA LTD.—See Broadcom Inc.; *U.S. Public,* pg. 389
COMPUTER ASSOCIATES MIDDLE EAST—See Broadcom Inc.; *U.S. Public,* pg. 389
COMPUTER ASSOCIATES MIDDLE EAST—See Broadcom Inc.; *U.S. Public,* pg. 389
COMPUTER ASSOCIATES NETHERLANDS—See Broadcom Inc.; *U.S. Public,* pg. 390
COMPUTER ASSOCIATES NORWAY A/S—See Broadcom Inc.; *U.S. Public,* pg. 390
COMPUTER ASSOCIATES PLC—See Broadcom Inc.; *U.S. Public,* pg. 390
COMPUTER ASSOCIATES PTE. LTD.—See Broadcom Inc.; *U.S. Public,* pg. 390
COMPUTER ASSOCIATES PTY. LTD.—See Broadcom Inc.; *U.S. Public,* pg. 390
COMPUTER ASSOCIATES S.A.—See Broadcom Inc.; *U.S. Public,* pg. 390
COMPUTER ASSOCIATES SCANDINAVIA A/S—See Broadcom Inc.; *U.S. Public,* pg. 390
COMPUTER ASSOCIATES S.P.A.—See Broadcom Inc.; *U.S. Public,* pg. 390
COMPUTER ASSOCIATES SWEDEN AB—See Broadcom Inc.; *U.S. Public,* pg. 390
COMPUTER ASSOCIATES TAIWAN LTD.—See Broadcom Inc.; *U.S. Public,* pg. 390
COMPUTER AUTOMATION SYSTEMS, INC.; *U.S. Private,* pg. 1004
COMPUTER BETTING COMPANY GMBH—See Kontron AG; *Int'l,* pg. 4278
COMPUTER BOULEVARD INC.; *Int'l,* pg. 1759
COMPUTER CAB (ABERDEEN) LIMITED—See ComfortDelGro Corporation Limited; *Int'l,* pg. 1712
COMPUTER CABLE CONNECTION INC.; *U.S. Private,* pg. 1004
COMPUTER CAB (LIVERPOOL) LIMITED—See ComfortDelGro Corporation Limited; *Int'l,* pg. 1712
COMPUTER CAB PLC—See ComfortDelGro Corporation Limited; *Int'l,* pg. 1712
COMPUTER CHEQUE—See Paradigm Recovery Solutions, LLC; *U.S. Private,* pg. 3089
COMPUTER & COMMUNICATION TECHNOLOGIES, INC.—See Japan Communications, Inc.; *Int'l,* pg. 3887
THE COMPUTER COMPANY, INC.; *Int'l,* pg. 4013
COMPUTER COMPOSITION OF CANADA LP—See Stagwell, Inc.; *U.S. Public,* pg. 1926
COMPUTER CONCEPTS INC.; *U.S. Private,* pg. 1004
COMPUTER CONCEPTS OF IOWA, INC.—See ICE Technologies, Inc.; *U.S. Private,* pg. 2031
COMPUTER CONFIGURATION SERVICES; *U.S. Private,* pg. 1004
COMPUTER CONSULTANTS OF AMERICA; *U.S. Private,* pg. 1004
COMPUTER DATA SOURCE, INC.—See New State Capital Partners LLC; *U.S. Private,* pg. 2906
COMPUTER DEDUCTIONS, INC.—See Futuris Company; *U.S. Public,* pg. 893
COMPUTER DESIGN & INTEGRATION, LLC—See Berkshire Partners LLC; *U.S. Private,* pg. 534
COMPUTER DIRECT GROUP LTD.; *Int'l,* pg. 1759
COMPUTEREASE SOFTWARE INC.—See Roper Technologies, Inc.; *U.S. Public,* pg. 1811
COMPUTER ENGINEERING & CONSULTING LTD.; *Int'l,* pg. 1759
COMPUTER ENGINEERING & CONSULTING (SHANGHAI), LTD.—See Computer Engineering & Consulting Ltd.; *Int'l,* pg. 1759
COMPUTER ENTERPRISES, INC.—See Computer Enterprises Inc.; *U.S. Private,* pg. 1004
COMPUTER ENTERPRISES INC.; *U.S. Private,* pg. 1004
COMPUTER EXPRESS INC.; *U.S. Private,* pg. 1004
COMPUTER FACTORY (INDIA) PRIVATE LIMITED—See Accel Limited; *Int'l,* pg. 79
COMPUTER FORMS (MALAYSIA) BERHAD; *Int'l,* pg. 1759

COMPUTER FORMS (MALAYSIA) BERHAD ── CORPORATE AFFILIATIONS

COMPUTER FUTURES SOLUTIONS NV—See SThree Plc.; *Int'l*, pg. 7214
COMPUTER GALLERY, INC.—See VC3, Inc.; *U.S. Private*, pg. 4349
COMPUTER GENERATED SOLUTIONS CANADA LTD.—See Computer Generated Solutions Inc.; *U.S. Private*, pg. 1005
COMPUTER GENERATED SOLUTIONS INC.; *U.S. Private*, pg. 1004
COMPUTER GENERATED SOLUTIONS INDIA PVT LTD—See Computer Generated Solutions Inc.; *U.S. Private*, pg. 1005
COMPUTER GENERATED SOLUTIONS ROMANIA—See Computer Generated Solutions Inc.; *U.S. Private*, pg. 1005
COMPUTER GRAPHICS INTERNATIONAL INC.; *Int'l*, pg. 1759
COMPUTER GRAPHICS WORLD—See COP Communications; *U.S. Private*, pg. 1044
COMPUTER GUIDANCE CORPORATION; *U.S. Private*, pg. 1005
COMPUTER INSTITUTE OF JAPAN LTD.; *Int'l*, pg. 1759
COMPUTER INTEGRATED SERVICES COMPANY OF NEW YORK, LLC—See Baymark Partners; *U.S. Private*, pg. 496
COMPUTERIZED ELEVATOR CONTROL CORP.—See Advent International Corporation; *U.S. Private*, pg. 106
COMPUTERIZED ELEVATOR CONTROL CORP.—See Cinven Limited; *Int'l*, pg. 1615
COMPUTERIZED ELEVATOR CONTROL CORP.—See RAG-Stiftung; *Int'l*, pg. 6180
COMPUTERIZED FACILITY INTEGRATION, L.L.C.—See BGC Group, Inc.; *U.S. Public*, pg. 329
COMPUTERIZED MANAGEMENT SERVICES, INC.—See GTCR LLC; *U.S. Private*, pg. 1807
COMPUTERJOBS.COM, INC.—See JobServe Ltd.; *Int'l*, pg. 3976
COMPUTERLAND UK LTD.—See Capita plc; *Int'l*, pg. 1309
COMPUTERLINKS (AUST) PTY LTD.—See Arrow Electronics, Inc.; *U.S. Public*, pg. 198
COMPUTERLINKS DENMARK A/S—See Arrow Electronics, Inc.; *U.S. Public*, pg. 198
COMPUTERLINKS FZCO—See Arrow Electronics, Inc.; *U.S. Public*, pg. 198
COMPUTERLINKS KFT.—See Arrow Electronics, Inc.; *U.S. Public*, pg. 198
COMPUTERLINKS NORTH AMERICA INC.—See Arrow Electronics, Inc.; *U.S. Public*, pg. 198
COMPUTERLINKS SPA—See Arrow Electronics, Inc.; *U.S. Public*, pg. 198
COMPUTERLINKS SWEDEN AB—See Arrow Electronics, Inc.; *U.S. Public*, pg. 198
COMPUTER MAINTENANCE AGENCY, INC.—See WESCO International, Inc.; *U.S. Public*, pg. 2351
COMPUTER MANAGEMENT CO., LTD.; *Int'l*, pg. 1759
THE COMPUTER MERCHANT LTD.; *U.S. Private*, pg. 4013
COMPUTER MIND CO., LTD.; *Int'l*, pg. 1759
COMPUTER MODELLING GROUP INC.—See Computer Modelling Group Ltd.; *Int'l*, pg. 1760
COMPUTER MODELLING GROUP LTD.; *Int'l*, pg. 1759
COMPUTER NETWORK SOLUTIONS LLC; *U.S. Private*, pg. 1005
COMPUTER OPTIONS INC.; *U.S. Private*, pg. 1005
COMPUTER PACKAGES INCORPORATED; *U.S. Private*, pg. 1005
COMPUTER PAPER PRODUCT CO.—See Jeraisy Group; *Int'l*, pg. 3931
COMPUTER PARADISE INC.; *U.S. Private*, pg. 1005
COMPUTER PARTS INTERNATIONAL LTD.—See discoverIE Group plc; *Int'l*, pg. 2133
COMPUTER PERFORMANCE INC.; *U.S. Private*, pg. 1005
THE COMPUTER PLACE, INC.; *U.S. Private*, pg. 4013
COMPUTER PLACEMENT LIMITED—See Bain Capital, LP; *U.S. Private*, pg. 433
COMPUTER POINT LIMITED; *Int'l*, pg. 1760
COMPUTER POWER SYSTEMS INC.—See Incline MGMT Corp.; *U.S. Private*, pg. 2054
COMPUTER PROCESS CONTROLS, INC.—See Emerson Electric Co.; *U.S. Public*, pg. 743
COMPUTER PRODUCTS CORPORATION; *U.S. Private*, pg. 1005
COMPUTER PROFESSIONALS, INC.; *U.S. Private*, pg. 1005
COMPUTER PROTECTION TECHNOLOGY, INC.—See Hyosung Heavy Industries Corp.; *Int'l*, pg. 3552
COMPUTERS4SURE.COM, INC.—See The ODP Corporation; *U.S. Private*, pg. 2117
COMPUTER SCIENCES CORPORATION INDIA PRIVATE LIMITED—See DXC Technology Company; *U.S. Public*, pg. 695
COMPUTER SCIENCES CORPORATION SERVICES (PTY) LIMITED—See DXC Technology Company; *U.S. Public*, pg. 695
COMPUTER SCIENCES CORPORATION—See DXC Technology Company; *U.S. Public*, pg. 695

COMPUTER SCIENCES CORPORATION—See DXC Technology Company; *U.S. Public*, pg. 695
COMPUTER SCIENCES CORPORATION—See DXC Technology Company; *U.S. Public*, pg. 695
COMPUTERS & CONTROLS LTD.; *Int'l*, pg. 1760
COMPUTERS SECURITY SOLUTIONS, LLC—See D.C. Capital Partners, LLC; *U.S. Private*, pg. 1141
COMPUTER SERVICE COMPANY—See Steiny & Company, Inc.; *U.S. Private*, pg. 3799
COMPUTER SERVICES CONSULTANTS (UK) LTD.—See Trimble, Inc.; *U.S. Public*, pg. 2190
COMPUTER SERVICES, INC.; *U.S. Public*, pg. 561
COMPUTER SERVICES, INC—See Computer Services, Inc.; *U.S. Public*, pg. 561
COMPUTERSHARE COMMUNICATION SERVICES GMBH—See Computershare Limited; *Int'l*, pg. 1760
COMPUTERSHARE CORPORATE TRUST—See Computershare Limited; *Int'l*, pg. 1760
COMPUTERSHARE ITALY S.R.L.—See Computershare Limited; *Int'l*, pg. 1760
COMPUTERSHARE LIMITED; *Int'l*, pg. 1760
COMPUTERSHARE NETHERLANDS B.V.—See Computershare Limited; *Int'l*, pg. 1760
COMPUTERSHARE SCHWEIZ AG—See Computershare Limited; *Int'l*, pg. 1760
COMPUTERSHARE SOUTH AFRICA (PTY) LTD—See Computershare Limited; *Int'l*, pg. 1760
COMPUTER SITES INC.; *U.S. Private*, pg. 1005
COMPUTER SOFTWARE INNOVATIONS, INC.—See Constellation Software Inc.; *Int'l*, pg. 1774
COMPUTER SOLUTIONS INTERNATIONAL; *U.S. Private*, pg. 1005
COMPUTER SOLUTIONS & SOFTWARE INTERNATIONAL, INC.; *U.S. Private*, pg. 1005
COMPUTER STATIONERY INDUSTRY S.A.O.G.; *Int'l*, pg. 1760
COMPUTER STOCK FORMS, INC.—See Rotary Forms Press, Inc.; *U.S. Private*, pg. 3486
COMPUTER STORES NORTHWEST INC.; *U.S. Private*, pg. 1005
COMPUTERS UNLIMITED; *U.S. Private*, pg. 1005
COMPUTERS SYSTEMS COMPANY, INC. - HEALTHCARE CONSULTING SERVICES DIVISION—See Thoma Bravo, L.P.; *U.S. Private*, pg. 4148
COMPUTER SYSTEMS COMPANY, INC.—See Thoma Bravo, L.P.; *U.S. Private*, pg. 4148
COMPUTER SYSTEMS INTEGRATION LIMITED—See Blackhawk Capital LLP; *Int'l*, pg. 1061
COMPUTER SYSTEMS PLUS INC.—See Robert J. Young Company, LLC; *U.S. Private*, pg. 3458
COMPUTER TASK GROUP BELGIUM N.V.—See Cegeka Groep NV; *Int'l*, pg. 1391
COMPUTER TASK GROUP (HOLDINGS) LTD.—See Cegeka Groep NV; *Int'l*, pg. 1391
COMPUTER TASK GROUP, INC.—See Cegeka Groep NV; *Int'l*, pg. 1391
COMPUTER TASK GROUP OF CANADA, INC.—See Cegeka Groep NV; *Int'l*, pg. 1391
COMPUTER TASK GROUP OF DELAWARE, INC.—See Cegeka Groep NV; *Int'l*, pg. 1391
COMPUTER TASK GROUP OF LUXEMBOURG PSF—See Cegeka Groep NV; *Int'l*, pg. 1391
COMPUTER & TECHNOLOGIES HOLDINGS LIMITED; *Int'l*, pg. 1758
COMPUTER & TECHNOLOGIES INTEGRATION LIMITED—See Computer & Technologies Holdings Limited; *Int'l*, pg. 1758
COMPUTER & TECHNOLOGIES (SHANGHAI) CO., LTD.—See Computer & Technologies Holdings Limited; *Int'l*, pg. 1758
COMPUTER & TECHNOLOGIES SOLUTIONS LIMITED—See Computer & Technologies Holdings Limited; *Int'l*, pg. 1758
COMPUTER TECHNOLOGY LINK CORP; *U.S. Private*, pg. 1005
COMPUTER TECHNOLOGY RESOURCES, INC.—See Applications Software Technology LLC; *U.S. Private*, pg. 298
COMPUTER TECHNOLOGY SOLUTIONS, INC.—See CGI Inc.; *Int'l*, pg. 1434
COMPUTER TRAINING ASSOCIATES OF CHICAGO, INC.—See Camden Partners Holdings, LLC; *U.S. Private*, pg. 728
COMPUTER TRAINING SOURCE INC.; *U.S. Private*, pg. 1005
COMPUTER TROUBLESHOOTERS W.L.L.—See Gulf Franchising Holding Company K.S.C.C.; *Int'l*, pg. 3180
COMPUTER UNION CO., LTD.—See Saha-Union Public Company Limited; *Int'l*, pg. 6479
COMPUTERUNIVERSE GMBH—See Hubert Burda Media Holding Kommanditgesellschaft; *Int'l*, pg. 3520
COMPUTERWORLD, INC.—See China Oceanwide Holdings Group Co., Ltd.; *Int'l*, pg. 1536
COMPUTERWORLD, INC.—See IDG Capital; *Int'l*, pg. 3593
COMPUTER WORLD, INC.—See VC3, Inc.; *U.S. Private*, pg. 4349
COMPUTER WORLD SERVICES CORP.; *U.S. Private*, pg. 1005

COMPUTER WORLD; *U.S. Private*, pg. 1005
COMPUTICKET (PTY) LTD.—See Shoprite Holdings Limited; *Int'l*, pg. 6859
COMPUTIME GROUP LIMITED; *Int'l*, pg. 1760
COMPUTIME LIMITED—See Computime Group Limited; *Int'l*, pg. 1760
COMPUTING AND PRINTING GLOBAL SERVICES MEXICO, S. DE R.L. DE C.V.—See HP Inc.; *U.S. Public*, pg. 1062
COMPUTING AND PRINTING MEXICO, S. DE R.L. DE C.V.—See HP Inc.; *U.S. Public*, pg. 1062
COMPUTING RESEARCH ASSOCIATION; *U.S. Private*, pg. 1006
COMPUTING SYSTEM INNOCATIONS, LLC—See Tyler Technologies, Inc.; *U.S. Public*, pg. 2208
COMPUTING SYSTEM INNOVATIONS; *U.S. Private*, pg. 1006
COMPUTING TECHNOLOGIES INC.; *U.S. Private*, pg. 1006
COMPUTING TECHNOLOGY INDUSTRY ASSOCIATION; *U.S. Private*, pg. 1006
COMPUTIZE, INC.; *U.S. Private*, pg. 1006
COMPUTRADE TECHNOLOGY MALAYSIA SDN. BHD.—See PT Anabatic Technologies Tbk; *Int'l*, pg. 6021
COMPUTRADE TECHNOLOGY PHILIPPINES INC.—See PT Anabatic Technologies Tbk; *Int'l*, pg. 6021
COMPU'TRAIN BV—See Specialist Computer Holdings Ltd.; *Int'l*, pg. 7128
COMPUTRITION, INC.—See Constellation Software Inc.; *Int'l*, pg. 1773
COMPUTROL, INC.—See Armstrong International, Inc.; *U.S. Private*, pg. 332
COMPUTRONICS HOLDINGS LIMITED; *Int'l*, pg. 1761
COMPUTYPE INC.; *U.S. Private*, pg. 1006
COMPUTYPE LTD.—See RWS Holdings plc; *Int'l*, pg. 6437
COMPUVISION SYSTEMS INC.; *Int'l*, pg. 1761
COMPUWARE CORPORATION—See KKR & Co. Inc.; *U.S. Public*, pg. 1240
COMPUWARE S.A.—See KKR & Co. Inc.; *U.S. Public*, pg. 1240
COMPUWARE SOFTWARE GROUP PTY. LTD.—See KKR & Co. Inc.; *U.S. Public*, pg. 1240
COMPUWAVE INC.; *U.S. Private*, pg. 1006
COMP VIEW INC.; *U.S. Private*, pg. 998
COMPWELL AB—See Peab AB; *Int'l*, pg. 5771
COMPWEST INSURANCE COMPANY; *U.S. Private*, pg. 1006
COMPX FORT—See Contran Corporation; *U.S. Private*, pg. 1033
COMPX INTERNATIONAL INC.—See Contran Corporation; *U.S. Private*, pg. 1033
COMPX NATIONAL, INC.—See Contran Corporation; *U.S. Private*, pg. 1033
COMPX SECURITY PRODUCTS INC.—See Contran Corporation; *U.S. Private*, pg. 1033
COMPX WATERLOO—See Contran Corporation; *U.S. Private*, pg. 1033
COMQI INC.—See AUO Corporation; *Int'l*, pg. 706
COMRADE APPLIANCES LIMITED; *Int'l*, pg. 1761
COMRENT INTERNATIONAL, LLC—See Ashtead Group Plc; *Int'l*, pg. 609
COMREP SA; *Int'l*, pg. 1761
COMRISE TECHNOLOGY, INC.; *U.S. Private*, pg. 1006
COMRIT INVESTMENTS 1 LP; *Int'l*, pg. 1761
COMROD INC.; *U.S. Private*, pg. 1006
COMSA ALTYAPI LTD.STI—See COMSA EMTE S.L.; *Int'l*, pg. 1761
COMSA BRAZIL LTDA.—See COMSA EMTE S.L.; *Int'l*, pg. 1761
COMSA DE ARGENTINA SA—See COMSA EMTE S.L.; *Int'l*, pg. 1761
COMSA EMTE CHINA—See COMSA EMTE S.L.; *Int'l*, pg. 1761
COMSA EMTE-ECUADOR—See COMSA EMTE S.L.; *Int'l*, pg. 1761
COMSA EMTE FRANCE—See COMSA EMTE S.L.; *Int'l*, pg. 1761
COMSA EMTE PERU S.A.C.—See COMSA EMTE S.L.; *Int'l*, pg. 1761
COMSA EMTE, S.A. DE C.V.—See COMSA EMTE S.L.; *Int'l*, pg. 1761
COMSA EMTE SAS—See COMSA EMTE S.L.; *Int'l*, pg. 1761
COMSA EMTE S.L.; *Int'l*, pg. 1761
COMSA EMTE USA, INC.—See COMSA EMTE S.L.; *Int'l*, pg. 1761
COM S.A.—See Indra Sistemas, S.A.; *Int'l*, pg. 3660
COMSA SUISSE SA—See COMSA EMTE S.L.; *Int'l*, pg. 1761
COMSCORE CANADA, INC.—See comScore, Inc.; *U.S. Public*, pg. 561
COMSCORE EUROPE, INC.—See comScore, Inc.; *U.S. Public*, pg. 562
COMSCORE, INC.; *U.S. Public*, pg. 561
COMSCORE MEDIA METRIX, INC.—See comScore, Inc.; *U.S. Public*, pg. 562

COMPANY NAME INDEX

COMSERVE NETWORK NETHERLANDS B.V.—See FIC Global, INC; *Int'l*, pg. 2653
COMS INTERACTIVE, LLC; *U.S. Private*, pg. 1006
COMSIP AL A'ALI W.L.L.—See Ahmed Mansoor Al-A'ali Co.; *Int'l*, pg. 225
COMSIP AL A'ALI W.L.L.—See Ahmed Mansoor Al-A'ali Co.; *Int'l*, pg. 225
COMSIP AL A'ALI W.L.L.—See VINCI S.A.; *Int'l*, pg. 8215
COMSIP AL A'ALI W.L.L.—See VINCI S.A.; *Int'l*, pg. 8215
COMSIP SAS—See VINCI S.A.; *Int'l*, pg. 8216
COMSOFT CORPORATION; *U.S. Private*, pg. 1006
COMSOFT DIRECT AG—See Bechtle AG; *Int'l*, pg. 937
COMSOFT DIRECT B.V—See Bechtle AG; *Int'l*, pg. 938
COMSOFT DIRECT GMBH—See Bechtle AG; *Int'l*, pg. 938
COMSOFT DIRECT NV—See Bechtle AG; *Int'l*, pg. 938
COMSOFT DIRECT S.L.U.—See Bechtle AG; *Int'l*, pg. 938
COMSOFT DIRECT S.R.L—See Bechtle AG; *Int'l*, pg. 938
COMSOFT SOS DEVELOPERS SAS—See Bechtle AG; *Int'l*, pg. 937
COMSONICS, INC. - CALIFORNIA REPAIR FACILITY—See ComSonics, Inc.; *U.S. Private*, pg. 1006
COMSONICS, INC.; *U.S. Private*, pg. 1006
COMSORT, INC.—See Merck & Co., Inc.; *U.S. Public*, pg. 1415
COMSOURCE INC.—See SpeedCast International Limited; *Int'l*, pg. 7132
COMSOURCE, INC.—See Sentinel Capital Partners, L.L.C.; *U.S. Private*, pg. 3609
COMSOVEREIGN HOLDING CORP.; *U.S. Public*, pg. 562
COMSTAR AUTOMOTIVE LLC USA—See Blackstone Inc.; *U.S. Public*, pg. 360
COMSTAR AUTOMOTIVE TECHNOLOGIES PVT LTD—See Blackstone Inc.; *U.S. Public*, pg. 360
COMSTAR UNITED TELESYSTEMS JSC—See MOBILE TELESYSTEMS PUBLIC JOINT STOCK COMPANY; *Int'l*, pg. 5010
COMSTAT/ROWLAND—See Publicis Groupe S.A.; *Int'l*, pg. 6106
COMSTOCK HOLDING COMPANIES, INC.; *U.S. Public*, pg. 562
COMSTOCK IMAGES—See Mecklermedia Corporation; *U.S. Private*, pg. 2649
COMSTOCK INC., *U.S. Public*, pg. 562
COMSTOCK MAXWELL SQUARE, L.C.—See Comstock Holding Companies, Inc.; *U.S. Public*, pg. 562
COMSTOCK METALS LTD.; *Int'l*, pg. 1761
COMSTOCK OIL AND GAS—See Comstock Resources, Inc.; *U.S. Public*, pg. 562
COMSTOCK PARTNERS LC; *U.S. Private*, pg. 1006
COMSTOCK RESOURCES, INC.; *U.S. Public*, pg. 562
COMSTOR CORPORATION—See TD Synnex Corp; *U.S. Public*, pg. 1987
COMSUPPLY CO., LTD.—See Kanamoto Co., Ltd.; *Int'l*, pg. 4064
COMSYS ENGINEERING CO., LTD.—See COMSYS Holdings Corporation; *Int'l*, pg. 1762
COMSYS HOLDINGS CORPORATION; *Int'l*, pg. 1761
COMSYS JOHO SYSTEM CORPORATION—See COMSYS Holdings Corporation; *Int'l*, pg. 1761
COMSYS NET CORPORATION—See COMSYS Holdings Corporation; *Int'l*, pg. 1762
COMSYS SHARED SERVICES CORPORATION—See COMSYS Holdings Corporation; *Int'l*, pg. 1761
COMSYSTO D.O.O.—See Reply S.p.A.; *Int'l*, pg. 6290
COMSYSTO TOHOKU TECHNO CO., LTD.—See COMSYS Holdings Corporation; *Int'l*, pg. 1762
COMSYSTO REPLY GMBH—See Reply S.p.A.; *Int'l*, pg. 6290
COMSYS TSUSAN CO., LTD.—See COMSYS Holdings Corporation; *Int'l*, pg. 1762
COMTECH COMMUNICATION TECHNOLOGY (SHENZHEN) CO., LTD.—See Viewtran Group, Inc.; *Int'l*, pg. 8204
COMTECH EF DATA CORP.—See Comtech Telecommunications Corp.; *U.S. Public*, pg. 562
COMTECH EF DATA CORP. - VIPERSAT NETWORKS GROUP—See Comtech Telecommunications Corp.; *U.S. Public*, pg. 562
COMTECH EF DATA PTE. LTD.—See Comtech Telecommunications Corp.; *U.S. Public*, pg. 562
COMTECH KOREA CO., LTD.—See McWane, Inc.; *U.S. Private*, pg. 2645
COMTECH MARKETING SDN. BHD.—See Pelangi Publishing Group Bhd; *Int'l*, pg. 5782
COMTECH MOBILE DATACOM CORP.—See Comtech Telecommunications Corp.; *U.S. Public*, pg. 562
COMTECH MOBILE DATACOM CORP.—See Comtech Telecommunications Corp.; *U.S. Public*, pg. 563
COMTECH PST CORP.—See Comtech Telecommunications Corp.; *U.S. Public*, pg. 563
COMTECH SATELLITE NETWORK TECHNOLOGIES, INC.—See Comtech Telecommunications Corp.; *U.S. Public*, pg. 563
COMTECH SYSTEMS, INC.—See Comtech Telecommunications Corp.; *U.S. Public*, pg. 563
COMTECH TELECOMMUNICATIONS CORP.; *U.S. Public*, pg. 562

COMTECH XICOM TECHNOLOGY, INC.—See Comtech Telecommunications Corp.; *U.S. Public*, pg. 563
COMTEC INC.; *Int'l*, pg. 1762
COMTEC INFORMATION CO., LTD.—See SsangYong Information & Communications Corp.; *Int'l*, pg. 7155
COMTEC LTD.—See Malam-Team Ltd.; *Int'l*, pg. 4659
COMTEC SOLAR INTERNATIONAL (M) SDN. BHD.—See Comtec Solar Systems Group Limited; *Int'l*, pg. 1762
COMTEC SOLAR (JIANGSU) CO., LIMITED—See Comtec Solar Systems Group Limited; *Int'l*, pg. 1762
COMTEC SOLAR SYSTEMS GROUP LIMITED; *Int'l*, pg. 1762
COMTEC SOLUTIONS; *U.S. Private*, pg. 1006
COMTEC SYSTEMS CO., LTD.; *Int'l*, pg. 1762
COMTEC SYSTEMS, INC.; *U.S. Private*, pg. 1006
COMTEC TRAINING AND MANAGEMENT SERVICES LIMITED—See Safaricom Plc; *Int'l*, pg. 6469
COMTEK ADVANCED STRUCTURES LTD—See Searchlight Capital Partners, L.P.; *U.S. Private*, pg. 3588
COMTEL CORPORATION; *U.S. Private*, pg. 1006
COMTEL FOCUS S.A.—See Warimpex Finanz- und Beteiligungs AG; *Int'l*, pg. 8345
COMTEL HOLDINGS INC.; *U.S. Private*, pg. 1006
COMTEX NEWS NETWORK, INC.; *U.S. Public*, pg. 563
COMTRADE D.O.O.—See ComTrade Group B.V.; *Int'l*, pg. 1762
COMTRADE GMBH—See ComTrade Group B.V.; *Int'l*, pg. 1762
COMTRADE GROUP B.V.; *Int'l*, pg. 1762
COMTRADE INC.—See ComTrade Group B.V.; *Int'l*, pg. 1762
COMTRADE SAS—See DCC plc; *Int'l*, pg. 1989
COMTRADE SOFTWARE SOLUTIONS GMBH—See ComTrade Group B.V.; *Int'l*, pg. 1762
COMTRADE SOFTWARE SOLUTIONS LIMITED—See ComTrade Group B.V.; *Int'l*, pg. 1762
COMTRADE USA WEST, INC.—See ComTrade Group B.V.; *Int'l*, pg. 1762
THE COMTRAN GROUP INC; *U.S. Private*, pg. 4013
COMTRAN INC.—See Mid-South Milling Company, Inc.; *U.S. Private*, pg. 2709
COMTRANS, INC.—See KKR & Co. Inc.; *U.S. Public*, pg. 1251
COMTREX SYSTEMS CORPORATION—See Zonal Hospitality Systems Inc.; *U.S. Private*, pg. 4608
COMTRONIC COMPUTER INC.; *Int'l*, pg. 1762
COMTRON SYSTEMS, INC.—See Pye-Barker Fire & Safety, LLC; *U.S. Private*, pg. 3309
COMTS FINANCE GMBH—See Commerzbank AG; *Int'l*, pg. 1715
COMTS GMBH—See Commerzbank AG; *Int'l*, pg. 1715
COMTS LOGISTICS GMBH—See Commerzbank AG; *Int'l*, pg. 1716
COMTS MITTE GMBH—See Commerzbank AG; *Int'l*, pg. 1716
COMTS NORD GMBH—See Commerzbank AG; *Int'l*, pg. 1716
COMTS OST GMBH—See Commerzbank AG; *Int'l*, pg. 1716
COMTS RHEIN-RUHR GMBH—See Commerzbank AG; *Int'l*, pg. 1716
COMTS WEST GMBH—See Commerzbank AG; *Int'l*, pg. 1716
COMTURE CORPORATION; *Int'l*, pg. 1762
COMTURE NETWORK CORPORATION—See Comture Corporation; *Int'l*, pg. 1763
COMUNIBANC CORP.—See Civista Bancshares, Inc.; *U.S. Public*, pg. 507
COMUNICACION CELULAR S.A.—See America Movil, S.A.B. de C.V.; *Int'l*, pg. 421
COMUNICAD, LLC—See Ruder Finn Group, Inc.; *U.S. Private*, pg. 3501
COMUNICADORA NEXUS—See The Interpublic Group of Companies, Inc.; *U.S. Public*, pg. 2094
COMUNICA—See The Interpublic Group of Companies, Inc.; *U.S. Public*, pg. 2094
COMUS INTERNATIONAL INC.; *U.S. Private*, pg. 1006
COMUTANET (PTY) LTD.—See Primedia Limited; *Int'l*, pg. 5978
COMUTO SA; *Int'l*, pg. 1763
COMVERGE, INC.—See Itron, Inc.; *U.S. Public*, pg. 1175
COMVEST GROUP HOLDINGS LLC - NEW YORK OFFICE—See Comvest Group Holdings LLC; *U.S. Private*, pg. 1007
COMVEST GROUP HOLDINGS LLC; *U.S. Private*, pg. 1006
COMVEX S.A.; *Int'l*, pg. 1763
COMVITA LIMITED; *Int'l*, pg. 1763
COMWARE FINANCIAL SYSTEMS CORPORATION—See Nippon Telegraph & Telephone Corporation; *Int'l*, pg. 5340
COMWAVE NETWORKS, INC.; *Int'l*, pg. 1763
COMWORX INC.—See Advanced Imaging Solutions, Inc.; *U.S. Private*, pg. 90
COMWRAP REPLY GMBH—See Reply S.p.A.; *Int'l*, pg. 6291
COMYMEDIA PROYECTOS Y SERVICIOS SL—See Gamma Communications PLC; *Int'l*, pg. 2878
CONAFI PRESTITO S.P.A.; *Int'l*, pg. 1763

CON-AGG COMPANIES, LLC—See Summit Materials, Inc.; *U.S. Public*, pg. 1959
CON-AGG OF MO, LLC—See Summit Materials, Inc.; *U.S. Public*, pg. 1960
CONAGRA BRANDS CANADA INC.—See Conagra Brands, Inc.; *U.S. Public*, pg. 564
CONAGRA BRANDS, INC.; *U.S. Public*, pg. 563
CONAGRA FOOD INGREDIENTS CO.—See Conagra Brands, Inc.; *U.S. Public*, pg. 563
CONAGRA FOODS CANADA, INC.—See Conagra Brands, Inc.; *U.S. Public*, pg. 563
CONAGRA FOODS - COMPTON—See Conagra Brands, Inc.; *U.S. Public*, pg. 563
CONAGRA FOODS - COUNCIL BLUFFS—See Conagra Brands, Inc.; *U.S. Public*, pg. 563
CONAGRA FOODS FOOD INGREDIENTS COMPANY, INC.—See Conagra Brands, Inc.; *U.S. Public*, pg. 563
CONAGRA FOODS - GILROY—See Conagra Brands, Inc.; *U.S. Public*, pg. 563
CONAGRA FOODS - HAMBURG—See Conagra Brands, Inc.; *U.S. Public*, pg. 563
CONAGRA FOODS - HEBREW NATIONAL KOSHER FOODS—See Conagra Brands, Inc.; *U.S. Public*, pg. 563
CONAGRA FOODS - INDIANAPOLIS—See Conagra Brands, Inc.; *U.S. Public*, pg. 563
CONAGRA FOODS LTD.—See Conagra Brands, Inc.; *U.S. Public*, pg. 563
CONAGRA FOODS - MODESTO—See Conagra Brands, Inc.; *U.S. Public*, pg. 563
CONAGRA FOODS PACKAGED FOODS, LLC—See Conagra Brands, Inc.; *U.S. Public*, pg. 563
CONAGRA FOODS - ROSSVILLE—See Conagra Brands, Inc.; *U.S. Public*, pg. 563
CONAGRA GROCERY PRODUCTS COMPANY, LLC—See Conagra Brands, Inc.; *U.S. Public*, pg. 564
CONAGRA STORE BRANDS—See Conagra Brands, Inc.; *U.S. Public*, pg. 564
CONAIR BRAZIL—See The Conair Group, Inc.; *U.S. Private*, pg. 4013
CONAIR CONSUMER APPLIANCES DIVISION—See American Securities LLC; *U.S. Private*, pg. 247
CONAIR CONSUMER PRODUCTS INC.—See American Securities LLC; *U.S. Private*, pg. 248
CONAIR CORPORATION—See American Securities LLC; *U.S. Private*, pg. 247
CONAIR CORPORATION; *U.S. Public*, pg. 564
CONAIR CORPORATION - WARING DIVISION—See American Securities LLC; *U.S. Private*, pg. 248
CONAIR EAST ASIA—See The Conair Group, Inc.; *U.S. Private*, pg. 4013
CONAIR EUROPE LTD.—See The Conair Group, Inc.; *U.S. Private*, pg. 4013
CONAIR FAR EAST LIMITED—See American Securities LLC; *U.S. Private*, pg. 248
CONAIR GROUP INC.; *Int'l*, pg. 1763
THE CONAIR GROUP, INC.; *U.S. Private*, pg. 4013
CONAIR KAWATA SALES & SERVICE CO.—See KAWATA MFG CO., LTD.; *Int'l*, pg. 4101
CONAIR LIQUIDS DIVISION—See American Securities LLC; *U.S. Private*, pg. 248
CONAIR MEXICANA S.A. DE C.V.—See The Conair Group, Inc.; *U.S. Private*, pg. 4013
CONAIR PACIFIC EQUIPMENT PTE. LTD. - PHILIPPINES—See The Conair Group, Inc.; *U.S. Private*, pg. 4013
CONAIR PACIFIC EQUIPMENT PTE. LTD.—See The Conair Group, Inc.; *U.S. Private*, pg. 4013
CONAIRPRO INC.—See American Securities LLC; *U.S. Private*, pg. 248
CONALVIAS S.A.; *Int'l*, pg. 1763
CONALVIAS SERVICIOS S.A.S.—See Conalvias S.A.; *Int'l*, pg. 1763
CONALVIAS USA, LLC.—See Conalvias S.A.; *Int'l*, pg. 1763
CONAM CONSTRUCTION; *U.S. Private*, pg. 1008
THE CONAM GROUP OF COMPANIES; *U.S. Private*, pg. 4013
CONAM INVESTMENT GROUP—See The ConAm Group of Companies; *U.S. Private*, pg. 4013
CON AM MANAGEMENT CORPORATION; *U.S. Private*, pg. 1008
CONAM MANAGEMENT CORPORATION—See The ConAm Group of Companies; *U.S. Private*, pg. 4013
CONAM MANAGEMENT—See The ConAm Group of Companies; *U.S. Private*, pg. 4013
CONAN ELECTRIC MANUFACTURING LIMITED—See Allan International Holdings Limited; *Int'l*, pg. 332
THE CONANT AUTO RETAIL GROUP; *U.S. Private*, pg. 4013
CONANT OPTICAL INC.—See QITIAN Technology Group Co., Ltd.; *Int'l*, pg. 6146
CONARCO ALAMBRES Y SOLDADURAS S.A—See Enovis Corporation; *U.S. Public*, pg. 772
THE CONARD-PYLE COMPANY—See Ball Horticultural Company; *U.S. Private*, pg. 460
CONA RESOURCES LTD.—See Waterous Energy Fund; *Int'l*, pg. 8357
CONART ENGINEERS LIMITED; *Int'l*, pg. 1763

CONATEL, S.A.

CONATEL, S.A.; *Int'l,* pg. 1763
CONATSER SITE SERVICES TX, L.P.; *U.S. Private,* pg. 1008
CONAX AS—See Kudelski S.A.; *Int'l,* pg. 4323
CONAXESS TRADE AUSTRIA GMBH—See Aurelius Equity Opportunities SE & Co. KGaA; *Int'l,* pg. 708
CONAXESS TRADE SWEDEN AB—See Aurelius Equity Opportunities SE & Co. KGaA; *Int'l,* pg. 708
CONAXESS TRADE SWITZERLAND AG—See Aurelius Equity Opportunities SE & Co. KGaA; *Int'l,* pg. 708
CONAX FLORIDA CORPORATION—See Advent International Corporation; *U.S. Private,* pg. 99
CONAX TECHNOLOGIES LLC; *U.S. Private,* pg. 1008
CONBRACO INDUSTRIES, INC. - PAGELAND—See Aalberts N.V.; *Int'l,* pg. 33
CONBRACO INDUSTRIES, INC.—See Aalberts N.V.; *Int'l,* pg. 33
CONBUZZ CO., LTD.; *Int'l,* pg. 1763
CONCANNON CORPORATION; *U.S. Private,* pg. 1008
CONCANNON LUMBER COMPANY—See Concannon Corporation; *U.S. Private,* pg. 1008
CONCANNON MILLER & CO., P.C.; *U.S. Private,* pg. 1008
CONCARDIS GMBH—See Concardis Payment Group GmbH; *Int'l,* pg. 1763
CONCARDIS PAYMENT GROUP GMBH; *Int'l,* pg. 1763
CONCAS SA; *Int'l,* pg. 1763
CONCAST (INDIA) LTD.—See Mitsubishi Heavy Industries, Ltd.; *Int'l,* pg. 4953
CONCAST METAL PRODUCTS CO. - OHIO PRODUCTION FACILITY—See Concast Metal Products Co.; *U.S. Private,* pg. 1008
CONCAST METAL PRODUCTS CO. - PENNSYLVANIA PRODUCTION FACILITY—See Concast Metal Products Co.; *U.S. Private,* pg. 1008
CONCAST METAL PRODUCTS CO.; *U.S. Private,* pg. 1008
CONCAST TECHNOLOGIES S.R.L—See SMS Holding GmbH; *Int'l,* pg. 7015
CONCAST UK LIMITED—See SMS Holding GmbH; *Int'l,* pg. 7015
CONCAT AG IT. SOLUTIONS—See Meridian Group International, Inc.; *U.S. Private,* pg. 2673
CONCATEL S.L.—See Societe Pour L'Informatique Industrielle; *Int'l,* pg. 7043
CONCEJO AB; *Int'l,* pg. 1763
CONCENTRA AKRON, LLC—See Select Medical Holdings Corporation; *U.S. Public,* pg. 1857
CONCENTRA AKRON, LLC—See Welsh, Carson, Anderson & Stowe; *U.S. Private,* pg. 4479
CONCENTRA BIOSCIENCES, LLC; *U.S. Private,* pg. 1008
CONCENTRA CONSULTING LIMITED; *Int'l,* pg. 1763
CONCENTRADOS INDUSTRIALES, S.A. DE C.V.—See Arca Continental, S.A.B. de C.V.; *Int'l,* pg. 540
CONCENTRA HEALTH SERVICES, INC.—See Select Medical Holdings Corporation; *U.S. Public,* pg. 1857
CONCENTRA HEALTH SERVICES, INC.—See Welsh, Carson, Anderson & Stowe; *U.S. Private,* pg. 4479
CONCENTRA INC.—See Select Medical Holdings Corporation; *U.S. Public,* pg. 1857
CONCENTRA INC.—See Welsh, Carson, Anderson & Stowe; *U.S. Private,* pg. 4479
CONCENTRA MEDICAL CENTER—See Select Medical Holdings Corporation; *U.S. Public,* pg. 1857
CONCENTRA MEDICAL CENTER—See Welsh, Carson, Anderson & Stowe; *U.S. Private,* pg. 4479
CONCENTRA NV; *Int'l,* pg. 1763
CONCENTRA OCCUPATIONAL HEALTH RESEARCH INSTITUTE—See Select Medical Holdings Corporation; *U.S. Public,* pg. 1857
CONCENTRA OCCUPATIONAL HEALTH RESEARCH INSTITUTE—See Welsh, Carson, Anderson & Stowe; *U.S. Private,* pg. 4479
CONCENTRA OPERATING CORPORATION—See Select Medical Holdings Corporation; *U.S. Public,* pg. 1857
CONCENTRA OPERATING CORPORATION—See Welsh, Carson, Anderson & Stowe; *U.S. Private,* pg. 4479
CONCENTRA PRIMARY CARE OF NEW JERSEY PA—See Select Medical Holdings Corporation; *U.S. Public,* pg. 1857
CONCENTRA SOLUTIONS, INC.—See Select Medical Holdings Corporation; *U.S. Public,* pg. 1857
CONCENTRA SOLUTIONS, INC.—See Welsh, Carson, Anderson & Stowe; *U.S. Private,* pg. 4479
CONCENTRATED LEADERS FUND LIMITED; *Int'l,* pg. 1763
THE CONCENTRATE MANUFACTURING COMPANY OF IRELAND—See PepsiCo, Inc.; *U.S. Public,* pg. 1672
THE CONCENTRATE MFR COMPANY OF IRELAND—See PepsiCo, Inc.; *U.S. Public,* pg. 1672
CONCENTRIC AB; *Int'l,* pg. 1763
CONCENTRIC BIRMINGHAM LTD.—See Concentric AB; *Int'l,* pg. 1763
CONCENTRIC COMMUNICATIONS—See Omnicom Group Inc.; *U.S. Public,* pg. 1586
CONCENTRIC EQUITY PARTNERS—See Financial Investments Corporation; *U.S. Private,* pg. 1507

CONCENTRIC HEALTHCARE STAFFING; *U.S. Private,* pg. 1008
CONCENTRIC HEALTH EXPERIENCE LIMITED—See Stagwell, Inc.; *U.S. Public,* pg. 1926
CONCENTRIC HOF GMBH—See Concentric AB; *Int'l,* pg. 1763
CONCENTRIC INNOVATIONS AB—See Concentric AB; *Int'l,* pg. 1763
CONCENTRIC ITASCA INC.—See Concentric AB; *Int'l,* pg. 1763
CONCENTRIC KOREA LLC—See Concentric AB; *Int'l,* pg. 1763
CONCENTRIC, LLC—See Mitsubishi Heavy Industries, Ltd.; *Int'l,* pg. 4953
CONCENTRIC MARKETING; *U.S. Private,* pg. 1008
CONCENTRIC MEDICAL, INC.—See Stryker Corporation; *U.S. Public,* pg. 1955
CONCENTRIC PARTNERS LLC—See Accenture plc; *Int'l,* pg. 87
CONCENTRIC PHARMA ADVERTISING; *U.S. Private,* pg. 1008
CONCENTRIC PIPE & TOOL, INC.—See Superior Energy Services, Inc.; *U.S. Private,* pg. 3877
CONCENTRIC PUMPS PUNE PVT. LTD.—See Concentric AB; *Int'l,* pg. 1764
CONCENTRIC PUMPS (SUZHOU) CO. LTD.—See Concentric AB; *Int'l,* pg. 1764
CONCENTRIC ROCKFORD INC.—See Concentric AB; *Int'l,* pg. 1764
CONCENTRIC SRL—See Concentric AB; *Int'l,* pg. 1764
CONCENTRIX (CANADA) LIMITED—See TD Synnex Corp; *U.S. Public,* pg. 1983
CONCENTRIX CORPORATION; *U.S. Public,* pg. 564
CONCENTRIX CRM SERVICES GERMANY GMBH—See TD Synnex Corp; *U.S. Public,* pg. 1983
CONCENTRIX DUISBURG GMBH—See TD Synnex Corp; *U.S. Public,* pg. 1983
CONCENTRIX DUSSELDORF GMBH—See TD Synnex Corp; *U.S. Public,* pg. 1983
CONCENTRIX EUROPE LIMITED—See TD Synnex Corp; *U.S. Public,* pg. 1984
CONCENTRIX FRANKFURT A. M. GMBH—See TD Synnex Corp; *U.S. Public,* pg. 1984
CONCENTRIX GERA GMBH—See TD Synnex Corp; *U.S. Public,* pg. 1984
CONCENTRIX HALLE GMBH—See TD Synnex Corp; *U.S. Public,* pg. 1984
CONCENTRIX INSURANCE ADMINISTRATION SOLUTIONS CORPORATION—See Concentrix Corporation; *U.S. Public,* pg. 564
CONCENTRIX INTERNATIONAL SERVICES EUROPE B.V.—See Concentrix Corporation; *U.S. Public,* pg. 564
CONCENTRIX LEIPZIG GMBH—See TD Synnex Corp; *U.S. Public,* pg. 1984
CONCENTRIX MANAGEMENT HOLDING GMBH & CO. KG—See TD Synnex Corp; *U.S. Public,* pg. 1984
CONCENTRIX MUNSTER GMBH—See TD Synnex Corp; *U.S. Public,* pg. 1984
CONCENTRIX OSNABRUCK GMBH—See TD Synnex Corp; *U.S. Public,* pg. 1984
CONCENTRIX SCHWERIN GMBH—See TD Synnex Corp; *U.S. Public,* pg. 1984
CONCENTRIX SERVICE HUNGARY KFT.—See TD Synnex Corp; *U.S. Public,* pg. 1984
CONCENTRIX SERVICES (NETHERLANDS) B.V.—See TD Synnex Corp; *U.S. Public,* pg. 1984
CONCENTRIX SERVICES (POLAND) SPOLLKA Z O.O.—See TD Synnex Corp; *U.S. Public,* pg. 1984
CONCENTRIX SERVICES PORTUGAL, SOCIEDADE UNIPESSOAL, LDA—See TD Synnex Corp; *U.S. Public,* pg. 1984
CONCENTRIX SERVICES PTY LTD—See TD Synnex Corp; *U.S. Public,* pg. 1984
CONCENTRIX SREV, INC.—See Concentrix Corporation; *U.S. Public,* pg. 564
CONCENTRIX WISMAR GMBH—See TD Synnex Corp; *U.S. Public,* pg. 1984
CONCENTRIX WUPPERTAL GMBH—See TD Synnex Corp; *U.S. Public,* pg. 1984
CONCEPCION CARRIER AIR CONDITIONING CORPORATION—See Concepcion Industrial Corporation; *Int'l,* pg. 1764
CONCEPCION DURABLES INC.—See Concepcion Industrial Corporation; *Int'l,* pg. 1764
CONCEPCION INDUSTRIAL CORPORATION; *Int'l,* pg. 1764
CONCEP GROUP LIMITED—See Freedom Solutions Group, L.L.C.; *U.S. Private,* pg. 1604
CONCEP INC.—See Freedom Solutions Group, L.L.C.; *U.S. Private,* pg. 1604
CONCEP PTY LTD—See Freedom Solutions Group, L.L.C.; *U.S. Private,* pg. 1604
CONCEPT AG—See Bertrandt AG; *Int'l,* pg. 998
CONCEPTBAIT, INC.; *U.S. Private,* pg. 1009
CONCEPT CHASER CO., INC.; *U.S. Private,* pg. 1008
CONCEPT EFL IMAGING CENTER, LLC—See HCA Healthcare, Inc.; *U.S. Public,* pg. 994
CONCEPT GROUP (SALES) LIMITED—See Xerox Holdings Corporation; *U.S. Public,* pg. 2887

CONCEPT INDUSTRIES INC; *U.S. Private,* pg. 1008
CONCEPT INGENIEURS BV—See VINCI S.A.; *Int'l,* pg. 8216
CONCEPT LASER GMBH—See General Electric Company; *U.S. Public,* pg. 916
CONCEPT LIFE SCIENCES INTEGRATED DISCOVERY & DEVELOPMENT SERVICES LIMITED—See Spectris Plc; *Int'l,* pg. 7130
CONCEPT MACHINE & TOOL INC.—See Industrial Machining Services, Inc.; *U.S. Private,* pg. 2067
CONCEPT MACHINE TOOL SALES, LLC; *U.S. Private,* pg. 1008
CONCEPT ONE ACCESSORIES; *U.S. Private,* pg. 1008
CONCEPTOS E INSTRUMENTOS S.A. DE C.V.—See HORIBA Ltd; *Int'l,* pg. 3475
CONCEPT PETROLEUM, INC.—See Morgan Stanley; *U.S. Public,* pg. 1471
CONCEPT PLASTICS INC.; *U.S. Private,* pg. 1008
CONCEPT REPLY GMBH—See Reply S.p.A.; *Int'l,* pg. 6291
CONCEPT REPLY LLC—See Reply S.p.A.; *Int'l,* pg. 6291
CONCEPT RESTAURANTS INC.; *U.S. Private,* pg. 1009
CONCEPTRONIC—See CVD Equipment Corporation; *U.S. Public,* pg. 613
CONCEPTS FOR TRAVEL LIMITED—See CPPGroup Plc; *Int'l,* pg. 1826
CONCEPTS NREC, INC.; *U.S. Private,* pg. 1009
CONCEPTSOLUTIONS, LLC; *U.S. Private,* pg. 1009
CONCEPTS & STRATEGIES INC; *U.S. Private,* pg. 1009
CONCEPT STAFFING LTD.—See Synergie SA; *Int'l,* pg. 7383
CONCEPT SYSTEMS INC.—See Head B.V.; *Int'l,* pg. 3300
CONCEPT SYSTEMS LTD.—See ION Geophysical Corporation; *U.S. Public,* pg. 1166
CONCEPT TECHNOLOGY INC.; *U.S. Private,* pg. 1009
CONCEPT THREE INC.; *U.S. Private,* pg. 1009
CONCEPTUS, INC.—See Bayer Aktiengesellschaft; *Int'l,* pg. 905
CONCEPTUS MEDICAL LIMITED—See Bayer Aktiengesellschaft; *Int'l,* pg. 905
CONCEPTUS, SAS—See Bayer Aktiengesellschaft; *Int'l,* pg. 905
CONCEPTWARE—See Micropole SA; *Int'l,* pg. 4880
CONCERIA 800 SPA—See Kering S.A.; *Int'l,* pg. 4134
CONCERIA BLU TONIC SPA—See Kering S.A.; *Int'l,* pg. 4134
CONCERN BELNEFTEKHIM; *Int'l,* pg. 1764
CONCERN GALNAFTOGAS PJSC; *Int'l,* pg. 1764
CONCERN GENERAL INVEST LLC; *Int'l,* pg. 1764
CONCERN RADIOELECTRONIC TECHNOLOGIES—See Russian Technologies State Corporation; *Int'l,* pg. 6431
CONCERN SOZVEZDIE OJSC—See Russian Technologies State Corporation; *Int'l,* pg. 6431
CONCERN TSESNA-ASTYK LLP—See Corporation Tsesna JSC; *Int'l,* pg. 1806
CONCERN WORLDWIDE LIMITED—See Concern Worldwide; *Int'l,* pg. 1764
CONCERN WORLDWIDE; *Int'l,* pg. 1764
CONCERT CONCEPT VERANSTALTUNGS GMBH—See DEAG Deutsche Entertainment AG; *Int'l,* pg. 1997
CONCERTED SERVICES, INC.; *U.S. Private,* pg. 1009
CONCERT GOLF PARTNERS, LLC; *U.S. Private,* pg. 1009
CONCERT GROUP LOGISTICS, INC.—See XPO, Inc.; *U.S. Public,* pg. 2392
CONCERTO CLOUD SERVICES, LLC—See DXC Technology Company; *U.S. Public,* pg. 696
CONCERTO DEVELOPMENT SAS—See Kaufman & Broad S.A.; *Int'l,* pg. 4092
CONCERTO INC.—See Credit Saison Co., Ltd.; *Int'l,* pg. 1836
CONCERT PHARMACEUTICALS, INC.—See Sun Pharmaceutical Industries Ltd.; *Int'l,* pg. 7307
CONCERT SRL—See Accenture plc; *Int'l,* pg. 87
CONCERT SUPPLIES SP. Z O.O.—See Live Nation Entertainment, Inc.; *U.S. Public,* pg. 1328
CONCESIONARIA DE EJES TERRESTRES DE COAHUILA, S.A. DE C.V.—See Empresas ICA S.A.B. de C.V.; *Int'l,* pg. 2390
CONCESIONARIA MEXIQUENSE, S.A. DE C.V.—See Industry Super Holdings Pty. Ltd.; *Int'l,* pg. 3675
CONCESIONARIA PANAMERICANA S.A.S.—See Grupo Aval Acciones y Valores S.A.; *Int'l,* pg. 3121
CONCESIONARIA SAN RAFAEL, S.A.—See ACS, Actividades de Construccion y Servicios, S.A.; *Int'l,* pg. 111
CONCESIONARIA VIAL ANDINA S.A.S.—See Grupo Aval Acciones y Valores S.A.; *Int'l,* pg. 3121
CONCESIONARIA VIAL DEL PACIFICO S.A.S.—See Grupo Aval Acciones y Valores S.A.; *Int'l,* pg. 3121
CONCESION CANCHAQUE S.A.C.—See Aenza S.A.A.; *Int'l,* pg. 176
CONCESIONES CCFC S.A.S.—See Grupo Aval Acciones y Valores S.A.; *Int'l,* pg. 3121
CONCESION LA PINTADA S.A.S.—See Grupo Argos S.A.; *Int'l,* pg. 3121
CONCESION VIAL DE LOS LLANOS S.A.S.—See Grupo Argos S.A.; *Int'l,* pg. 3121
CONCESSIONARIA AUTO RAPOSO TAVARES S.A.; *Int'l,* pg. 1764

COMPANY NAME INDEX

CONCESSIONARIA DA RODOVIA DOS LAGOS SA—See CCR S.A.; *Int'l*, pg. 1369
CONCESSIONARIA DA RODOVIA PRESIDENTE DUTRA SA—See CCR S.A.; *Int'l*, pg. 1369
CONCESSIONARIA DE RODOVIAS INTEGRADAS DO OESTE S/A—See CCR S.A.; *Int'l*, pg. 1369
CONCESSIONARIA DO RODOANEL OESTE S.A.—See CCR S.A.; *Int'l*, pg. 1369
CONCESSIONARIA ECOVIAS DOS IMIGRANTES S.A.; *Int'l*, pg. 1764
CONCESSIONARIA RODOVIAS DO TIETE S.A.; *Int'l*, pg. 1764
CONCESSIONARIA ROTA DAS BANDEIRAS S.A.; *Int'l*, pg. 1764
THE CONCESSION GOLF CLUB LLC; *U.S. Private*, pg. 4013
CONCESSIONS INTERNATIONAL INC.; *U.S. Private*, pg. 1009
CONCH ANHUI ENERGY SAVING AND ENVIRONMENT PROTECTION NEW MATERIAL CO LTD; *Int'l*, pg. 1764
CONCHA PLC; *Int'l*, pg. 1764
CONCHA Y TORO FINLAND OY.—See Vina Concha y Toro S.A.; *Int'l*, pg. 8209
CONCHA Y TORO NORWAY AS—See Vina Concha y Toro S.A.; *Int'l*, pg. 8209
CONCHA Y TORO SWEDEN AB—See Vina Concha y Toro S.A.; *Int'l*, pg. 8209
CONCHA Y TORO UK LIMITED—See Vina Concha y Toro S.A.; *Int'l*, pg. 8209
CONCH CONSTRUCTION & ROOFING INC.—See Anhui Conch Cement Company Limited; *Int'l*, pg. 467
CONCHO RESOURCES, INC.—See ConocoPhillips; *U.S. Public*, pg. 568
CONCHO SUPPLY INC.; *U.S. Private*, pg. 1009
CONCH TOUR TRAIN—See Historic Tours of America Inc.; *U.S. Private*, pg. 1952
CONCH VENTURE ENVIRONMENTAL PROTECTION TECHNOLOGY (SHANGHAI) CO., LTD.—See China Conch Venture Holdings Limited; *Int'l*, pg. 1491
CONCIERGE BUILDING SERVICES, LLC; *U.S. Private*, pg. 1009
CONCIERGE SERVICES OF ATLANTA, INC.—See GI Manager L.P.; *U.S. Private*, pg. 1694
CONCILIO DE SALUD INTEGRAL DE LOIZA, INC.; *U.S. Private*, pg. 1009
CONCILIUM TECHNOLOGIES (PTY) LTD.—See Transition Evergreen; *Int'l*, pg. 7901
CONCISE CAPITAL MANAGEMENT LP; *U.S. Private*, pg. 1009
CONCIVIA SA; *Int'l*, pg. 1764
CONCO FOOD SERVICE—See Performance Food Group Company; *U.S. Public*, pg. 1675
CONCOR AIR LTD.—See Container Corporation of India Ltd.; *Int'l*, pg. 1779
CONCORD ACQUISITION CORP.; *U.S. Public*, pg. 565
CONCORDANCE HEALTHCARE SOLUTIONS, LLC; *U.S. Private*, pg. 1010
CONCORD BICYCLE MUSIC—See Massachusetts Mutual Life Insurance Company; *U.S. Private*, pg. 2605
CONCORD BIOSCIENCES LLC—See Hangzhou Tigermed Consulting Co., Ltd.; *Int'l*, pg. 3251
CONCORD BIOTECH LIMITED; *Int'l*, pg. 1764
CONCORD BLUE ENGINEERING GMBH; *Int'l*, pg. 1764
CONCORD BLUE TECHNOLOGY LTD.—See Concord Blue Engineering GmbH; *Int'l*, pg. 1764
CONCORD BLUE USA, INC.—See Concord Blue Engineering GmbH; *Int'l*, pg. 1764
CONCORD COMPANIES INCORPORATED; *U.S. Private*, pg. 1009
CONCORD CONCRETE PUMPS INC.; *Int'l*, pg. 1764
CONCORD CONFECTIONS LTD.—See Tootsie Roll Industries, Inc.; *U.S. Public*, pg. 2163
CONCORD CONTROL SYSTEMS LIMITED; *Int'l*, pg. 1765
CONCORD CORPORATION PTE LTD—See Hollysys Automation Technologies Ltd.; *Int'l*, pg. 3452
CONCORD DISPOSAL SERVICE; *U.S. Private*, pg. 1009
CONCORD DRUGS LIMITED; *Int'l*, pg. 1765
CONCORDE AIR LOGISTICS LTD.—See Deutsche Post AG; *Int'l*, pg. 2072
CONCORDE APPAREL CO. LLC; *U.S. Private*, pg. 1010
CONCORDE AUTOMOBILE LTD—See General Motors Company; *U.S. Public*, pg. 923
CONCORDE BATTERY CORP; *U.S. Private*, pg. 1010
CONCORDE CAREER COLLEGES, INC.—See Universal Technical Institute, Inc.; *U.S. Public*, pg. 2262
THE CONCORDE GROUP, INC.; *U.S. Private*, pg. 4013
CONCORDE HOTEL NEW YORK INC.—See Hotel Properties Limited; *Int'l*, pg. 3488
CONCORD ELECTRONICS INDUSTRIES CO., LTD.—See Sumida Corporation; *Int'l*, pg. 7262
CONCORDE MACHINE TOOL—See Reko International Group Inc.; *Int'l*, pg. 6260
CONCORDE TRAVEL (PTY) LIMITED—See The Bidvest Group Limited; *Int'l*, pg. 7624
CONCORDE TREATMENT CENTER, LLC—See AAC Holdings, Inc.; *U.S. Private*, pg. 30
CONCORD FINANCIAL INTERMEDIARY GMBH—See Concord Investmentbank AG; *Int'l*, pg. 1765

CONCORD GENERAL MUTUAL INSURANCE CO., INC.; *U.S. Private*, pg. 1009
CONCORD HEALTHCARE SINGAPORE PTE. LTD.—See Concord Medical Services Holdings Limited; *Int'l*, pg. 1765
CONCORD HOSPITALITY INC.; *U.S. Private*, pg. 1010
CONCORDIA COFFEE COMPANY, INC.—See The Middleby Corporation; *U.S. Public*, pg. 2113
CONCORDIA ELECTRIC COOPERATIVE, INC.; *U.S. Private*, pg. 1010
CONCORDIA FINANCIAL GROUP, LTD.; *Int'l*, pg. 1765
CONCORDIA HEALTHCARE INC.—See Advanz Pharma Corp.; *Int'l*, pg. 166
CONCORDIA HEALTHCARE (USA) INC.—See Advanz Pharma Corp.; *Int'l*, pg. 166
CONCORDIA HOLDING SARL—See Rothschild & Co SCA; *Int'l*, pg. 6402
CONCORDIA INTERNATIONAL FORWARDING GMBH—See Concordia International Forwarding Inc.; *U.S. Private*, pg. 1010
CONCORDIA INTERNATIONAL FORWARDING INC.; *U.S. Private*, pg. 1010
CONCORDIA INTERNATIONAL FORWARDING LTD.—See Concordia International Forwarding Inc.; *U.S. Private*, pg. 1010
CONCORDIA INTERNATIONAL FORWARDING PTE LTD—See Concordia International Forwarding Inc.; *U.S. Private*, pg. 1010
CONCORDIA INTERNATIONAL FORWARDING PTY. LTD.—See Concordia International Forwarding Inc.; *U.S. Private*, pg. 1010
CONCORDIA INTERNATIONAL RX UK LTD—See Advanz Pharma Corp.; *Int'l*, pg. 166
CONCORDIA MARITIME AB—See STENA AB; *Int'l*, pg. 7207
CONCORDIA PUBLISHING HOUSE; *U.S. Private*, pg. 1010
CONCORD INTERNATIONAL SECURITIES CO., LTD.; *Int'l*, pg. 1765
CONCORD INVESTMENTBANK AG; *Int'l*, pg. 1765
CONCORDIS GROUP, INC.; *U.S. Public*, pg. 565
CONCORD LIMOUSINE, INC.; *U.S. Private*, pg. 1010
CONCORD LITHO GROUP; *U.S. Private*, pg. 1010
CONCORD LUMBER CORP.; *U.S. Private*, pg. 1010
CONCORD MANAGEMENT LTD.; *U.S. Private*, pg. 1010
CONCORD MEDICAL SERVICES HOLDINGS LIMITED; *Int'l*, pg. 1765
CONCORD MILLS LP—See Simon Property Group, Inc.; *U.S. Public*, pg. 1882
CONCORD MUSIC GROUP, INC.—See Massachusetts Mutual Life Insurance Company; *U.S. Private*, pg. 2605
CONCORD NEIGHBORHOOD CORP.—See Concord Hospitality Inc.; *U.S. Private*, pg. 1010
CONCORD NEW ENERGY GROUP LIMITED; *Int'l*, pg. 1765
CONCORD OIL COMPANY INC.—See Energy North Incorporated; *U.S. Private*, pg. 1395
CONCORD OIL OF NEWPORT INC.—See Energy North Incorporated; *U.S. Private*, pg. 1395
CONCORD PACIFIC GROUP—See Adex Securities, Inc.; *Int'l*, pg. 145
CONCORD PAPER CORP.; *U.S. Private*, pg. 1010
CONCORD PREMIUM MEATS LTD.—See Premium Brands Holdings Corporation; *Int'l*, pg. 5963
CONCORD PROJECTS LTD.; *Int'l*, pg. 1765
CONCORD PUBLISHING HOUSE INC.—See Rust Communications; *U.S. Private*, pg. 3507
CONCORD SECURITY CORP.; *Int'l*, pg. 1765
CONCORD SERVICING CORP.; *U.S. Private*, pg. 1010
CONCORD SPECIALTY CORRUGATED—See Buckeye Corrugated Inc.; *U.S. Private*, pg. 677
CONCORD SYSTEM MANAGEMENT CORPORATION—See SYSTEX Corporation; *Int'l*, pg. 7393
CONCORD TRANSPORTATION INC.—See TFI International Inc.; *Int'l*, pg. 7585
CONCORD WATCH COMPANY, S.A.—See Movado Group, Inc.; *U.S. Public*, pg. 1479
CONCORD WEST—See RTM & Associates, Inc.; *U.S. Private*, pg. 3498
CONCOR HOLDINGS (PTY) LIMITED—See Murray & Roberts Holdings Ltd.; *Int'l*, pg. 5100
CONCOR TECHNICRETE (PROPRIETARY) LIMITED—See Murray & Roberts Holdings Ltd.; *Int'l*, pg. 5100
CONCOTE CORPORATION; *U.S. Private*, pg. 1011
CONCOURSE FEDERAL GROUP, LLC; *U.S. Private*, pg. 1011
CONCOURSE FINANCIAL GROUP AGENCY, INC.—See Dai-ichi Life Holdings, Inc.; *Int'l*, pg. 1917
CONCOURS MOTORS INC.; *U.S. Private*, pg. 1011
CONCRAFT HOLDING CO., LTD.; *Int'l*, pg. 1765
CONCRAFT PRECISION ELECTRONIC (BAOYING) CO., LTD.—See Concraft Holding Co., Ltd.; *Int'l*, pg. 1765
CONCRAFT PRECISION INDUSTRIAL CO., LTD.—See Concraft Holding Co., Ltd.; *Int'l*, pg. 1765
CONCREATIVE LLC—See VINCI S.A.; *Int'l*, pg. 8216
CONCREET BETONHERSTEL BV—See VINCI S.A.; *Int'l*, pg. 8216

CONCRETE VALLEY GROUP BV

CONCRETE ACCESSORIES COMPANY, INC.; *U.S. Private*, pg. 1011
CONCRETE AGGREGATES CORPORATION; *Int'l*, pg. 1765
CONCRETE COMPANY SPRINGFIELD; *U.S. Private*, pg. 1011
CONCRETE CUTTING & BREAKING INC.; *U.S. Private*, pg. 1011
THE CONCRETE DOCTOR INC.—See Keller Group plc; *Int'l*, pg. 4121
CONCRETE ENGINEERING PRODUCTS BERHAD - BATANG KALI FACTORY—See Concrete Engineering Products Berhad; *Int'l*, pg. 1765
CONCRETE ENGINEERING PRODUCTS BERHAD - NILAI FACTORY—See Concrete Engineering Products Berhad; *Int'l*, pg. 1765
CONCRETE ENGINEERING PRODUCTS BERHAD - PASIR GUDANG FACTORY—See Concrete Engineering Products Berhad; *Int'l*, pg. 1765
CONCRETE ENGINEERING PRODUCTS BERHAD - RAWANG FACTORY—See Concrete Engineering Products Berhad; *Int'l*, pg. 1765
CONCRETE ENGINEERING PRODUCTS BERHAD; *Int'l*, pg. 1765
CONCRETE ENGINEERING PRODUCTS BERHAD - SUNGAI PETANI FACTORY—See Concrete Engineering Products Berhad; *Int'l*, pg. 1766
CONCRETE EQUIPMENT COMPANY,INC.—See Astec Industries, Inc.; *U.S. Public*, pg. 216
CONCRETE EXPRESS INC.; *U.S. Private*, pg. 1011
CONCRETE GENERAL, INC.; *U.S. Private*, pg. 1011
CONCRETE, INC.—See MDU Resources Group, Inc.; *U.S. Public*, pg. 1410
CONCRETE INDUSTRY DIV—See CEMEX, S.A.B. de C.V.; *Int'l*, pg. 1398
CONCRETE INFRA & MEDIA LIMITED; *Int'l*, pg. 1766
CONCRETE ITALIA S.R.L.—See Heidelberg Materials AG; *Int'l*, pg. 3310
CONCRETE LEVELING SYSTEMS, INC.; *U.S. Public*, pg. 565
CONCRETE MEDIA, INC.—See Quinyx AB; *Int'l*, pg. 6165
CONCRETE MEDIA; *U.S. Private*, pg. 1011
CONCRETE PLUS LIMITED—See Nippon Paint Holdings Co., Ltd.; *Int'l*, pg. 5325
THE CONCRETE PRODUCTS AND AGGREGATE CO., LTD.—See The Siam Cement Public Company Limited; *Int'l*, pg. 7685
CONCRETE PRODUCTS (KIRKCALDY) LIMITED—See J. Smart & Co. (Contractors) PLC; *Int'l*, pg. 3857
CONCRETE PRODUCTS LIMITED—See Penney Group; *Int'l*, pg. 5787
CONCRETE PUMPING HOLDINGS, INC.; *U.S. Public*, pg. 566
CONCRETE RECYCLERS AUSTRALIA PTY. LTD.—See Heidelberg Materials AG; *Int'l*, pg. 3310
CONCRETE SARL—See VINCI S.A.; *Int'l*, pg. 8216
CONCRETE SOLUTIONS, INC.—See Rhino Linings Corporation; *U.S. Private*, pg. 3421
CONCRETE SOLUTIONS LIMITED—See New Mountain Capital, LLC; *U.S. Private*, pg. 2899
CONCRETE SPECIALTIES COMPANY—See CRH plc; *Int'l*, pg. 1844
CONCRETE SUPPLY CO.; *U.S. Private*, pg. 1011
CONCRETE SUPPLY OF TOPEKA, INC.—See Summit Materials, Inc.; *U.S. Public*, pg. 1960
CONCRETE SUPPLY OF TOPEKA, LLC—See Summit Materials, Inc.; *U.S. Public*, pg. 1959
CONCRETE TECHNOLOGIES WORLDWIDE, INC.—See Kohlberg & Company, LLC; *U.S. Private*, pg. 2337
CONCRETE TECHNOLOGY CORP.; *U.S. Private*, pg. 1011
CONCRETE TECHNOLOGY INCORPORATED; *U.S. Private*, pg. 1011
CONCRETE TIE INDUSTRIES INCORPORATED; *U.S. Private*, pg. 1011
CONCRETE VALLEY GROUP BV; *Int'l*, pg. 1766
CONCRETION LIMITED—See ANSA McAL Limited; *Int'l*, pg. 477
CONCRITE PTY LTD—See Seven Group Holdings Limited; *Int'l*, pg. 6733
CONCUR (FRANCE) SAS—See SAP SE; *Int'l*, pg. 6567
CONCURRENT COMPUTER CORP. PTY. LTD—See CCUR Holdings Inc.; *U.S. Public*, pg. 461
CONCURRENT COMPUTER FRANCE S.A.—See CCUR Holdings Inc.; *U.S. Public*, pg. 461
CONCURRENT COMPUTER FRANCE S.A.—See CCUR Holdings Inc.; *U.S. Public*, pg. 461
CONCURRENT COMPUTER HONG KONG LIMITED—See CCUR Holdings Inc.; *U.S. Public*, pg. 461
CONCURRENT DESIGN, INC.—See Voltabox AG; *Int'l*, pg. 8303
CONCURRENT FEDERAL SYSTEMS, INC.—See CCUR Holdings Inc.; *U.S. Public*, pg. 461
CONCURRENT GROUP LLC—See QualTek Services Inc.; *U.S. Public*, pg. 1748
CONCURRENT MANUFACTURING SOLUTIONS LLC—See Balmoral Funds LLC; *U.S. Private*, pg. 461

613

CONCRETE VALLEY GROUP BV

CORPORATE AFFILIATIONS

CONCURRENT NIPPON CORPORATION—See CCUR Holdings Inc.; *U.S. Public*, pg. 461
CONCURRENT REAL-TIME, INC.—See Spectris Plc; *Int'l*, pg. 7130
CONCURRENT TECHNOLOGIES CORPORATION; *U.S. Private*, pg. 1011
CONCURRENT TECHNOLOGIES CORPORATION—See Concurrent Technologies Corporation; *U.S. Private*, pg. 1011
CONCURRENT TECHNOLOGIES INC.—See Concurrent Technologies Plc; *Int'l*, pg. 1766
CONCURRENT TECHNOLOGIES PLC; *Int'l*, pg. 1766
CONCUR TECHNOLOGIES (HONG KONG) LTD.—See SAP SE; *Int'l*, pg. 6567
CONCUR TECHNOLOGIES, INC.—See SAP SE; *Int'l*, pg. 6567
CONCUR TECHNOLOGIES (SINGAPORE) PTE. LTD.—See SAP SE; *Int'l*, pg. 6567
CONCUR TECHNOLOGIES (UK) LTD.—See SAP SE; *Int'l*, pg. 6567
CONCUSSION, LLP; *U.S. Private*, pg. 1011
CONCUT, INC.—See Dixie Diamond Manufacturing, Inc.; *U.S. Private*, pg. 1245
CONDADO PROPERTIES, INC.; *Int'l*, pg. 1766
CONDAIR A/S—See Meier Capital AG; *Int'l*, pg. 4799
CONDAIR LTD.—See Meier Capital AG; *Int'l*, pg. 4799
CONDAIR SASU—See Meier Capital AG; *Int'l*, pg. 4799
CONDAL DISTRIBUTORS INC.; *U.S. Private*, pg. 1011
CONDARIA 87 S.R.L.—See Dometic Group AB; *Int'l*, pg. 2160
CONDAT SAS—See CVC Capital Partners SICAV-FIS S.A.; *Int'l*, pg. 1886
CON-DEA SUPPLY CORP.; *U.S. Private*, pg. 1008
CONDECO LTD.; *Int'l*, pg. 1766
CONDECTA AG—See Paragon Partners GmbH; *Int'l*, pg. 5737
CONDE GROUP, INC.; *U.S. Private*, pg. 1011
CONDE NAST ENTERTAINMENT—See Advance Publications, Inc.; *U.S. Private*, pg. 86
CONDE NAST, INC. - DETROIT—See Advance Publications, Inc.; *U.S. Private*, pg. 86
CONDE NAST, INC. - LOS ANGELES—See Advance Publications, Inc.; *U.S. Private*, pg. 86
CONDE NAST, INC. - SAN FRANCISCO—See Advance Publications, Inc.; *U.S. Private*, pg. 86
CONDE NAST, INC.—See Advance Publications, Inc.; *U.S. Private*, pg. 85
CONDE NAST JOHANSENS LTD.—See Advance Publications, Inc.; *U.S. Private*, pg. 86
CONDE NAST & NATIONAL MAGAZINE DISTRIBUTORS LIMITED—See Advance Publications, Inc.; *U.S. Private*, pg. 85
CONDE NAST & NATIONAL MAGAZINE DISTRIBUTORS LIMITED—See The Hearst Corporation; *U.S. Private*, pg. 4047
CONDE NAST TRAVELER—See Advance Publications, Inc.; *U.S. Private*, pg. 86
CONDENSIL—See Vicat S.A.; *Int'l*, pg. 8185
CONDEPOLS, S.A.; *Int'l*, pg. 1766
CONDER AQUA SOLUTIONS—See Premier Tech Ltd.; *Int'l*, pg. 5962
CONDESA PTY LTD—See Ecom Agroindustrial Corporation Ltd.; *Int'l*, pg. 2296
CONDESSA EMPREENDIMENTOS IMOBILIARIOS LTDA.—See PDG Realty S.A. Empreendimentos e Participacoes; *Int'l*, pg. 5770
CONDIND - CONSERVACAO E DESENVOLVIMENTO INDUSTRIAL, LDA.—See SODIM, SGPS, SA; *Int'l*, pg. 7049
CONDIRE MANAGEMENT LP; *U.S. Private*, pg. 1011
THE CONDIT COMPANY INC.—See Industrial Distribution Resources, LLC; *U.S. Private*, pg. 2065
CONDITE OY—See Orkla ASA; *Int'l*, pg. 5637
CONDITION-AIRE INC.—See Comfort Services Inc.; *U.S. Private*, pg. 981
CONDITIONED AIR COMPANY OF NAPLES LLC—See Gemini Investors LLC; *U.S. Private*, pg. 1658
CONDITIONED AIR CORP. OF NAPLES INC.; *U.S. Private*, pg. 1011
CONDITIONED AIR SOLUTIONS, LLC—See Leap Partners; *U.S. Private*, pg. 2407
CONDMAG S.A.; *Int'l*, pg. 1766
CONDOMINIUM CONCEPTS MANAGEMENT, LLC—See FirstService Corporation; *Int'l*, pg. 2691
CONDOMINIUM MANAGMENT GROUP, INC.; *U.S. Private*, pg. 1012
CONDON-JOHNSON & ASSOCIATES INC.; *U.S. Private*, pg. 1012
CONDON LEASING CO. INC.; *U.S. Private*, pg. 1012
CONDON OIL COMPANY, INC.; *U.S. Private*, pg. 1012
CONDON & ROOT; *U.S. Private*, pg. 1012
CONDOR ALLGEMEINE VERSICHERUNGS-AKTIENGESELLSCHAFT—See DZ BANK AG Deutsche Zentral-Genossenschaftsbank; *Int'l*, pg. 2243
CONDOR CORP.; *U.S. Private*, pg. 1012
CONDOR EXPLORATION PERU S.A.C.—See Condor Resources Inc.; *Int'l*, pg. 1766
CONDOR GOLD PLC; *Int'l*, pg. 1766

CONDOR HOSPITALITY TRUST, INC.; *U.S. Public*, pg. 566
CONDOR LEBENSVERSICHERUNGS-—See DZ BANK AG Deutsche Zentral-Genossenschaftsbank; *Int'l*, pg. 2243
CONDORMINING CORPORATION S.A.—See Lumina Gold Corp.; *Int'l*, pg. 4578
CONDOR PETROLEUM INC.; *Int'l*, pg. 1766
CONDOR RESOURCES INC.; *Int'l*, pg. 1766
CONDOR S.A.—See Condor Gold Plc; *Int'l*, pg. 1766
CONDOR SNACK COMPANY; *U.S. Private*, pg. 1012
CONDOR TCM SA; *Int'l*, pg. 1766
CONDOR TECHNOLOGIES NV; *Int'l*, pg. 1766
CONDORUM SK, S.R.O.; *Int'l*, pg. 1766
CONDOTTE AMERICA INC.—See Ferfina S.p.A.; *Int'l*, pg. 2637
CONDUANT CORPORATION; *U.S. Private*, pg. 1012
CONDUCTIVE INKJET TECHNOLOGY LIMITED—See Carclo plc; *Int'l*, pg. 1321
CONDUCTIX INC.—See CVC Capital Partners SICAV-FIS S.A.; *Int'l*, pg. 1887
CONDUCTIX-WAMPFLER AB—See CVC Capital Partners SICAV-FIS S.A.; *Int'l*, pg. 1886
CONDUCTIX-WAMPFLER AG—See CVC Capital Partners SICAV-FIS S.A.; *Int'l*, pg. 1886
CONDUCTIX-WAMPFLER B.V.—See CVC Capital Partners SICAV-FIS S.A.; *Int'l*, pg. 1886
CONDUCTIX-WAMPFLER LTDA—See CVC Capital Partners SICAV-FIS S.A.; *Int'l*, pg. 1887
CONDUCTIX-WAMPFLER LTD.—See CVC Capital Partners SICAV-FIS S.A.; *Int'l*, pg. 1887
CONDUCTIX-WAMPFLER LTD.—See CVC Capital Partners SICAV-FIS S.A.; *Int'l*, pg. 1887
CONDUCTIX-WAMPFLER O.O.O.—See CVC Capital Partners SICAV-FIS S.A.; *Int'l*, pg. 1887
CONDUCTIX-WAMPFLER PTE LTD—See CVC Capital Partners SICAV-FIS S.A.; *Int'l*, pg. 1887
CONDUCTIX-WAMPFLER PTY LTD—See CVC Capital Partners SICAV-FIS S.A.; *Int'l*, pg. 1887
CONDUCTIX-WAMPFLER PVT LTD—See CVC Capital Partners SICAV-FIS S.A.; *Int'l*, pg. 1887
CONDUCTIX-WAMPFLER S,DE RL DE C.V.—See CVC Capital Partners SICAV-FIS S.A.; *Int'l*, pg. 1887
CONDUCTIX-WAMPFLER SDN BHD—See CVC Capital Partners SICAV-FIS S.A.; *Int'l*, pg. 1887
CONDUCTIX-WAMPFLER SRL—See CVC Capital Partners SICAV-FIS S.A.; *Int'l*, pg. 1887
CONDUCTOR AS—See VINCI S.A.; *Int'l*, pg. 8216
CONDUCTORES TECHNOLOGICOS DE JUAREZ, S.A. DE C.V.—See Sumitomo Electric Industries, Ltd.; *Int'l*, pg. 7277
CONDUCTORES Y CABLES DEL PERU S.A.C.; *Int'l*, pg. 1766
CONDUCTOR, INC.; *U.S. Private*, pg. 1012
CONDUENT CREDIT BALANCE SOLUTIONS, LLC—See Conduent Incorporated; *U.S. Public*, pg. 566
CONDUENT EDUCATION SERVICES, LLC—See Conduent Incorporated; *U.S. Public*, pg. 566
CONDUENT FEDERAL SOLUTIONS, LLC—See Conduent Incorporated; *U.S. Public*, pg. 566
CONDUENT GERMANY HOLDING GMBH—See Conduent Incorporated; *U.S. Public*, pg. 566
CONDUENT HEALTHCARE INFORMATION SERVICES, INC.—See Conduent Incorporated; *U.S. Public*, pg. 566
CONDUENT HEALTHCARE KNOWLEDGE SOLUTIONS, LLC—See Conduent Incorporated; *U.S. Public*, pg. 566
CONDUENT INCORPORATED; *U.S. Public*, pg. 566
CONDUENT MORTGAGE SERVICES, INC.—See Conduent Incorporated; *U.S. Public*, pg. 566
CONDUENT PARKING ENFORCEMENT SOLUTIONS LIMITED—See Conduent Incorporated; *U.S. Public*, pg. 566
CONDUENT PAYMENT INTEGRITY SOLUTIONS, INC,—See Conduent Incorporated; *U.S. Public*, pg. 566
CONDUENT PAYMENT INTEGRITY SOLUTIONS, INC.—See Conduent Incorporated; *U.S. Public*, pg. 566
CONDUENT SECURITIES SERVICES, INC.—See Conduent Incorporated; *U.S. Public*, pg. 566
CONDUENT STATE HEALTHCARE, LLC—See Conduent Incorporated; *U.S. Public*, pg. 566
CONDUENT STATE & LOCAL SOLUTIONS, INC.—See Conduent Incorporated; *U.S. Public*, pg. 566
CONDUENT TRANSPORT SOLUTIONS, INC.—See Conduent Incorporated; *U.S. Public*, pg. 566
CONDUIT CAPITAL LIMITED; *Int'l*, pg. 1766
CONDUIT HOLDINGS LIMITED; *Int'l*, pg. 1766
CONDUIT PHARMACEUTICALS INC.; *U.S. Public*, pg. 566
CONDUITY CAPITAL PLC; *Int'l*, pg. 1766
CONDUMEX INC.—See Grupo Carso, S.A.B. de C.V.; *Int'l*, pg. 3123
CONDURIL, ENGENHARIA S.A.; *Int'l*, pg. 1767
CONDUSIV TECHNOLOGIES CORPORATION; *U.S. Private*, pg. 1012
CONDUSIV TECHNOLOGIES CORPORATION—See Condusiv Technologies Corporation; *U.S. Private*, pg. 1012

CONE AUTOMOBILES; *Int'l*, pg. 1767
CONEC CORPORATION—See Amphenol Corporation; *U.S. Public*, pg. 129
CONEC ELEKTRONISCHE BAUELEMENTE GMBH—See Amphenol Corporation; *U.S. Public*, pg. 129
CONECLI INTERNATIONAL S.A.—See Allcargo Logistics Limited; *Int'l*, pg. 333
CONEC POLSKA SP. Z O.O.—See Amphenol Corporation; *U.S. Public*, pg. 130
CONEC SHANGHAI INTERNATIONAL CO., LTD.—See Amphenol Corporation; *U.S. Public*, pg. 130
CONEC S.R.O.—See Amphenol Corporation; *U.S. Public*, pg. 130
CONECT BUSINESS PARK SA; *Int'l*, pg. 1767
CONECTISYS CORP.; *U.S. Public*, pg. 566
CONECTO AS—See SpareBank 1 Gruppen AS; *Int'l*, pg. 7125
CONECTUM S.A. DE C.V.—See Grupo Posadas S.A.B. de C.V.; *Int'l*, pg. 3134
CONECUH VALLEY RAILWAY, L.L.C.—See Brookfield Infrastructure Partners L.P.; *Int'l*, pg. 1191
CONECUH VALLEY RAILWAY, L.L.C.—See GIC Pte. Ltd.; *Int'l*, pg. 2965
CONE DENIM LLC—See Platinum Equity, LLC; *U.S. Private*, pg. 3203
CON EDISON CLEAN ENERGY BUSINESSES, INC.—See RWE AG; *Int'l*, pg. 6433
CONE DISTRIBUTING INC.; *U.S. Private*, pg. 1012
CONE DRIVE OPERATIONS INC.—See The Timken Company; *U.S. Public*, pg. 2132
CONE ENGINEERING CONTRACTORS; *U.S. Private*, pg. 1012
CONE FINANCIAL GROUP INC.; *U.S. Private*, pg. 1012
CONE & GRAHAM, INC.; *U.S. Private*, pg. 1012
CONELEC OF FLORIDA, LLC—See Main Street Capital Holdings, LLC; *U.S. Private*, pg. 2551
CONEMAUGH STATION;
CONERGY ASIA & ME PTE LTD—See Kawa Capital Management, Inc.; *U.S. Private*, pg. 2266
CONERGY DEUTSCHLAND GMBH—See Kawa Capital Management, Inc.; *U.S. Private*, pg. 2266
CONERGY GLOBAL SOLUTIONS GMBH—See Kawa Capital Management, Inc.; *U.S. Private*, pg. 2266
CONERGY, INC.—See Kawa Capital Management, Inc.; *U.S. Private*, pg. 2266
CONERGY INDIA—See Kawa Capital Management, Inc.; *U.S. Private*, pg. 2266
CONERGY ITALIA SPA—See Kawa Capital Management, Inc.; *U.S. Private*, pg. 2266
CONERGY PTE LTD—See Kawa Capital Management, Inc.; *U.S. Private*, pg. 2266
CONERGY PTY LIMITED—See Kawa Capital Management, Inc.; *U.S. Private*, pg. 2266
CONERGY SAS—See Kawa Capital Management, Inc.; *U.S. Private*, pg. 2266
CONE—See Omnicom Group Inc.; *U.S. Public*, pg. 1579
CONESTOGA AUCTION COMPANY, INC.—See John M. Hess Auction Service, Inc.; *U.S. Private*, pg. 2223
CONESTOGA BUSINESS SOLUTIONS, INC.—See Xerox Holdings Corporation; *U.S. Public*, pg. 2389
CONESTOGA CERAMIC TILE DISTRIBUTORS; *U.S. Private*, pg. 1012
CONESTOGA COLD STORAGE; *Int'l*, pg. 1767
CONESTOGA GOLF CLUB LLC—See PulteGroup, Inc.; *U.S. Public*, pg. 1737
CONESTOGA SUPPLY CORP.; *U.S. Private*, pg. 1012
CONESTOGA WOOD SPECIALTIES CORP.; *U.S. Private*, pg. 1012
CONEST SOFTWARE SYSTEMS—See JDM Technology Group; *Int'l*, pg. 3925
CONESVILLE COAL PREPARATION CO.—See American Electric Power Company, Inc.; *U.S. Public*, pg. 99
CONETEC AUSTRALIA PTY. LTD.—See VINCI S.A.; *Int'l*, pg. 8216
CONETEC INC.—See VINCI S.A.; *Int'l*, pg. 8216
CONETEC INVESTIGATIONS LTD.—See VINCI S.A.; *Int'l*, pg. 8216
CONETEC PERU S.A.C—See VINCI S.A.; *Int'l*, pg. 8216
CONETEC SPA—See VINCI S.A.; *Int'l*, pg. 8216
CONET TAIWAN CO., LTD.—See IDEC Corporation; *Int'l*, pg. 3589
CONEWANGO PRODUCTS CORP—See Skellerup Holdings Limited; *Int'l*, pg. 6980
CONEXA LLC; *U.S. Private*, pg. 1012
CONEXIO CORPORATION—See Nojima Corporation; *Int'l*, pg. 5401
CONEX PRAHOVA SA; *Int'l*, pg. 1767
CO-NEXT INC.—See Mitsui-Soko Holdings Co., Ltd.; *Int'l*, pg. 4992
CONEXUS CATTLE CORP.; *U.S. Private*, pg. 1012
CONEXUS CPA GROUP LLC—See Cherry Bekaert LLP; *U.S. Private*, pg. 874
CONEXUS WORLD GLOBAL LLC—See Creative Realities, Inc.; *U.S. Public*, pg. 593
CONFAB INDUSTRIAL S.A.—See Techint S.p.A.; *Int'l*, pg. 7504
CONFAB LABORATORIES, INC.—See RoundTable Healthcare Management, Inc.; *U.S. Private*, pg. 3489

COMPANY NAME INDEX

CONFAB SERVICOS TUBULARES LTDA.—See Techint S.p.A.; *Int'l*, pg. 7503
CONFECCIONES FIOS, S.A.—See Industria de Diseno Textil, S.A.; *Int'l*, pg. 3665
CONFECCOES PORTO GRANDE, LDA; *Int'l*, pg. 1767
CONFECTA GMBH—See Nexans S.A.; *Int'l*, pg. 5241
CONFECTII VASLUI S.A.; *Int'l*, pg. 1767
CONFECTIONERY & SNACKS (BARBADOS) LTD—See Associated Brands Industries Limited; *Int'l*, pg. 648
CONFECTIONERY & SNACKS (JAMAICA) LTD—See Associated Brands Industries Limited; *Int'l*, pg. 648
CONFECTION TUNISIENNE DE SECURITE SARL - C.T.S. SARL—See Sioen Industries NV; *Int'l*, pg. 6959
CONFEDERATED BUILDERS INC.; *U.S. Private*, pg. 1012
CONFEDERATED TRIBES OF WARM SPRINGS; *U.S. Private*, pg. 1012
CONFEDERATE TECHNOLOGY CO., LTD.—See Linde plc; *Int'l*, pg. 4504
CONFEDERATION NATIONALE DU CREDIT MUTUEL; *Int'l*, pg. 1767
CONFERENCE ASSOCIATES, INC.; *U.S. Private*, pg. 1013
THE CONFERENCE BOARD, INC.; *U.S. Private*, pg. 4013
CONFERENCE CALL DO BRASIL—See Chorus Call, Inc.; *U.S. Private*, pg. 889
CONFERENCECALL SERVICES INDIA PRIVATE LIMITED—See Apollo Global Management, Inc.; *U.S. Public*, pg. 152
CONFERENCE ON JEWISH MATERIAL CLAIMS AGAINST GERMANY, INC.; *U.S. Private*, pg. 1013
CONFERENCE PLUS, INC.—See Nippon Telegraph & Telephone Corporation; *Int'l*, pg. 5344
CONFERENCE TECHNOLOGIES, INC.; *U.S. Private*, pg. 1013
CONFERIZE A/S; *Int'l*, pg. 1767
CONFERO, INC.; *U.S. Private*, pg. 1013
CONFEZIONI MODA ITALIA S.R.L.—See PVH Corp.; *U.S. Public*, pg. 1739
CONFIANCE GROUP; *U.S. Private*, pg. 1013
CONFIANCE GROUP—See Confiance Group; *U.S. Private*, pg. 1013
CONFIDENCE CEMENT PLC; *Int'l*, pg. 1767
CONFIDENCE FINANCE AND TRADING LIMITED; *Int'l*, pg. 1767
CONFIDENCE FUTURISTIC ENERGETECH LIMITED; *Int'l*, pg. 1767
CONFIDENCE INTELLIGENCE HOLDINGS LIMITED; *Int'l*, pg. 1768
CONFIDENCE PETROLEUM INDIA LTD; *Int'l*, pg. 1768
CONFIDENCE PLUS INSURANCE SERVICES; *U.S. Private*, pg. 1013
CONFIDENCE TRADE LIMITED—See Daikin Industries, Ltd.; *Int'l*, pg. 1932
CONFIDENTIAL MATERIALS DESTRUCTION SERVICE LIMITED—See Integrated Waste Solutions Group Holdings Limited; *Int'l*, pg. 3731
CONFIDENTIAL SERVICE CO., LTD.—See Mitani Sangyo Co., Ltd.; *Int'l*, pg. 4924
CONFIDENTIA - TECNOLOGIAS INFORMATICAS APLICADAS, LTDA.—See Eurofins Scientific S.E.; *Int'l*, pg. 2535
CONFIDIO, LLC—See RxBenefits, Inc.; *U.S. Private*, pg. 3509
CONFIE HOLDING II CO.—See Stone Point Capital LLC; *U.S. Private*, pg. 3818
CONFIE SEGUROS INSURANCE SERVICES, INC.—See Stone Point Capital LLC; *U.S. Private*, pg. 3818
CONFIGERO; *U.S. Private*, pg. 1013
CONFIGURA SVERIGE AB; *Int'l*, pg. 1768
CONFIGURATION MANAGEMENT INC.; *U.S. Private*, pg. 1013
CONFIGURE ONE EUROPE LIMITED—See Autodesk, Inc.; *U.S. Public*, pg. 229
CONFIGURE ONE, INC.—See Autodesk, Inc.; *U.S. Public*, pg. 229
CONFINITY GMBH—See TAMBURI INVESTMENT PARTNERS S.p.A; *Int'l*, pg. 7450
CONFINVEST F.L. S.P.A.; *Int'l*, pg. 1768
CONFIPETROL S.A.; *Int'l*, pg. 1768
CONFIRM BIOSCIENCES, INC.—See Clinical Reference Laboratory, Inc.; *U.S. Private*, pg. 944
CONFIRMIT ASA—See EQT AB; *Int'l*, pg. 2475
CONFIRM MONITORING SYSTEMS, INC.—See STERIS plc; *Int'l*, pg. 7209
CONFLANDEY INDUSTRIES SAS—See Saarstahl AG; *Int'l*, pg. 6461
CONFLEX BV—See VINCI S.A.; *Int'l*, pg. 8216
CONFLOW INC.—See Conflow Limited; *Int'l*, pg. 1768
CONFLOW LIMITED; *Int'l*, pg. 1768
CONFLUENCE DISCOVERY TECHNOLOGIES, INC.—See Aclaris Therapeutics, Inc.; *U.S. Public*, pg. 35
CONFLUENCE; *U.S. Private*, pg. 1013
CONFLUENCE TECHNOLOGIES, INC.—See TA Associates, Inc.; *U.S. Private*, pg. 3914
CONFLUENCE WATERSPORTS CO. INC.; *U.S. Private*, pg. 1013
CONFLUENT DEVELOPMENT, LLC; *U.S. Private*, pg. 1013

CONFLUENT HEALTH, LLC; *U.S. Private*, pg. 1013
CONFLUENT, INC.; *U.S. Public*, pg. 567
CONFLUENT MEDICAL TECHNOLOGIES, INC.—See TPG Capital, L.P.; *U.S. Public*, pg. 2169
CONFORCE 1 CONTAINER TERMINALS INC—See Conforce International, Inc.; *Int'l*, pg. 1768
CONFORCE INTERNATIONAL, INC.; *Int'l*, pg. 1768
CONFORMA CLAD, INC.—See Kennametal Inc.; *U.S. Public*, pg. 1221
CONFORMIS, INC.—See restor3d, Inc.; *U.S. Private*, pg. 3409
CON FORMS ASIA SDN BHD—See Construction Forms, Inc.; *U.S. Private*, pg. 1023
CON FORMS—See Construction Forms, Inc.; *U.S. Private*, pg. 1023
CONFY MEETINGZONE AB—See LoopUp Group plc; *Int'l*, pg. 4556
CONGA FOODS PTY. LTD.; *Int'l*, pg. 1768
CONGAREE CONSTRUCTION CO., INC.; *U.S. Private*, pg. 1013
CONGAR INTERNATIONAL CORP.—See Imperial Brands PLC; *Int'l*, pg. 3633
CONGATEC AG; *Int'l*, pg. 1768
CONGATEC ASIA LTD.—See Congatec AG; *Int'l*, pg. 1768
CONGATEC AUSTRALIA PTY LTD.—See Congatec AG; *Int'l*, pg. 1768
CONGATEC CHINA TECHNOLOGY LTD.—See Congatec AG; *Int'l*, pg. 1768
CONGATEC, INC.—See Congatec AG; *Int'l*, pg. 1768
CONGATEC JAPAN K.K.—See Congatec AG; *Int'l*, pg. 1768
CONGATEC SRO—See Congatec AG; *Int'l*, pg. 1768
CONGEBEC CAPITAL LTEE.; *Int'l*, pg. 1768
CONGENITAL HEART SURGERY CENTER, PLLC—See HCA Healthcare, Inc.; *U.S. Public*, pg. 994
CONGLOBAL INDUSTRIES INC.—See AMP Limited; *Int'l*, pg. 432
CONGO IRON S.A.—See Sundance Resources Limited; *Int'l*, pg. 7311
CONGOLEUM CORPORATION—See Congoleum Corporation; *U.S. Private*, pg. 1013
CONGOLEUM CORPORATION; *U.S. Private*, pg. 1013
CONGREGATIONAL HOMES INC; *U.S. Private*, pg. 1013
THE CONGREGATIONAL HOME; *U.S. Private*, pg. 4014
CONGRESS ASSET MANAGEMENT CO.; *U.S. Private*, pg. 1013
CONGRESS CASINO BADEN GMBH—See Casinos Austria AG; *Int'l*, pg. 1353
CONGRESSIONAL BANCSHARES, INC.; *U.S. Private*, pg. 1013
CONGRESSIONAL BANK—See Congressional Bancshares, Inc.; *U.S. Private*, pg. 1014
CONGRESSIONAL COUNTRY CLUB; *U.S. Private*, pg. 1014
CONGRID OY—See SmartCraft ASA; *Int'l*, pg. 7002
CONGRUENT INVESTMENT PARTNERS, LLC; *U.S. Private*, pg. 1014
CONGRUEX LLC—See Crestview Partners, L.P.; *U.S. Private*, pg. 1098
CONGRUITY HR, LLC; *U.S. Private*, pg. 1014
CONGRUITY, LLC.—See EXEO Group Inc.; *Int'l*, pg. 2583
CONGSTER GMBH—See Deutsche Telekom AG; *Int'l*, pg. 2085
CONG TY CO PHAN LOGISTICS VINALINK; *Int'l*, pg. 1768
CONG TY TNHH FILTRAFINE CO., LTD.—See Bright Sheland International Co., Ltd.; *Int'l*, pg. 1162
CONHUI (HUIZHOU) SEMICONDUCTOR COMPANY LIMITED—See China Aerospace International Holdings Limited; *Int'l*, pg. 1481
CONICA AG—See Serafin Unternehmensgruppe GmbH; *Int'l*, pg. 6720
CONICA CORPORATION—See Serafin Unternehmensgruppe GmbH; *Int'l*, pg. 6720
CONICA LTD—See Serafin Unternehmensgruppe GmbH; *Int'l*, pg. 6720
CONICO LIMITED; *Int'l*, pg. 1768
CONIFER CARE CONTINUUM SOLUTIONS, LLC—See Tenet Healthcare Corporation; *U.S. Public*, pg. 2002
CONIFER HEALTH SOLUTIONS, LLC—See Tenet Healthcare Corporation; *U.S. Public*, pg. 2002
CONIFER HOLDINGS, INC.; *U.S. Public*, pg. 567
CONIFER HOLDINGS, INC.—See Tenet Healthcare Corporation; *U.S. Public*, pg. 2002
CONIFER INC—See Omega Healthcare Investors, Inc.; *U.S. Public*, pg. 1571
CONIFER INSURANCE COMPANY—See RedBird Capital Partners L.P.; *U.S. Private*, pg. 3377
CONIFER PHYSICIAN SERVICES, INC.—See Tenet Healthcare Corporation; *U.S. Public*, pg. 2002
CONIFER REALTY, LLC—See Belveron Real Estate Partners, LLC; *U.S. Private*, pg. 522
CONIFER REVENUE CYCLE SOLUTIONS, LLC—See Tenet Healthcare Corporation; *U.S. Public*, pg. 2002
CONIFER VALUE-BASED CARE, LLC—See Tenet Healthcare Corporation; *U.S. Public*, pg. 2002
CONIFEX TIMBER INC.; *Int'l*, pg. 1768
CONIGENT; *U.S. Public*, pg. 1014

CONIHASSET CAPTIAL PARTNERS, INC.; *U.S. Public*, pg. 567
CONILL ADVERTISING, INC.—See Publicis Groupe S.A.; *Int'l*, pg. 6107
CONILL ADVERTISING, INC. - TORRANCE—See Publicis Groupe S.A.; *Int'l*, pg. 6107
CONIMAST INTERNATIONAL SAS—See Hill & Smith PLC; *Int'l*, pg. 3391
CONIMEX CO., LTD.—See The Siam Cement Public Company Limited; *Int'l*, pg. 7682
CONISTER BANK LIMITED—See Manx Financial Group PLC; *Int'l*, pg. 4680
CONISTER FINANCE & LEASING LTD.—See Manx Financial Group PLC; *Int'l*, pg. 4680
CONITEX SONOCO HELLAS S.A.—See Sonoco Products Company; *U.S. Public*, pg. 1904
CONITEX SONOCO INDIA PVT. LTD.—See Sonoco Products Company; *U.S. Public*, pg. 1904
CONITEX-SONOCO—See Sonoco Products Company; *U.S. Public*, pg. 1906
CONITEX SONOCO TAIWAN LTD.—See Sonoco Products Company; *U.S. Public*, pg. 1904
CONITEX SONOCO UK LIMITED—See Sonoco Products Company; *U.S. Public*, pg. 1904
CONITEX SONOCO USA, INC.—See Sonoco Products Company; *U.S. Public*, pg. 1904
CONKLIN COMPANY INC.; *U.S. Private*, pg. 1014
CONKLIN CORPORATION—See Intracom Holdings S.A.; *Int'l*, pg. 3767
CONKLIN FANGMAN INVESTMENT CO.; *U.S. Private*, pg. 1014
CONKLIN METAL INDUSTRIES; *U.S. Private*, pg. 1014
CONKLIN OFFICE SERVICES, INC.; *U.S. Private*, pg. 1014
CONKOR SYSTEMS LTD.—See Amanet Management & Systems Ltd.; *Int'l*, pg. 410
THE CONLAN COMPANY; *U.S. Private*, pg. 4014
CONLEASCO INC.; *U.S. Private*, pg. 1014
CONLEE OIL COMPANY; *U.S. Private*, pg. 1014
CONLEY BUICK GMC SUBARU; *U.S. Private*, pg. 1014
CONLEY FROG/SWITCH & FORGE COMPANY; *U.S. Private*, pg. 1014
CONLEY PUBLISHING GROUP LTD.; *U.S. Private*, pg. 1014
CONLEY SUBARU; *U.S. Private*, pg. 1014
CONLIN'S FURNITURE INC.; *U.S. Private*, pg. 1014
CONLOC S.A.; *Int'l*, pg. 1768
CONLOG (PTY) LTD—See Consolidated Infrastructure Group Limited; *Int'l*, pg. 1771
CONLON CONSTRUCTION CO. INC.; *U.S. Private*, pg. 1014
CONLON & DART LLC—See EP Wealth Advisors, LLC; *U.S. Private*, pg. 1411
CONLUX MATSUMOTO CO. LTD.—See NAGOYA ELECTRIC WORKS CO., LTD.; *Int'l*, pg. 5129
CONMAT—See The Helm Group; *U.S. Private*, pg. 4051
CONMED CORPORATION - DENMARK—See CONMED Corporation; *U.S. Public*, pg. 567
CONMED CORPORATION; *U.S. Public*, pg. 567
CONMED DENMARK APS—See CONMED Corporation; *U.S. Public*, pg. 567
CONMED DEUTSCHLAND GMBH—See CONMED Corporation; *U.S. Public*, pg. 567
CONMED EUROPE BV—See CONMED Corporation; *U.S. Public*, pg. 567
CONMED FRANCE SAS—See CONMED Corporation; *U.S. Public*, pg. 567
CONMED HEALTHCARE MANAGEMENT, INC.—See H.I.G. Capital, LLC; *U.S. Private*, pg. 1829
CONMED IBERIA SL—See CONMED Corporation; *U.S. Public*, pg. 567
CONMED, INC.—See H.I.G. Capital, LLC; *U.S. Private*, pg. 1829
CONMED LINVATEC AUSTRALIA PTY. LTD.—See CONMED Corporation; *U.S. Public*, pg. 567
CONMED LINVATEC BIOMATERIALS OY—See CONMED Corporation; *U.S. Public*, pg. 567
CONMED U.K. LTD.—See CONMED Corporation; *U.S. Public*, pg. 567
CONMETALL GMBH & CO. KG—See Wurth Verwaltungsgesellschaft mbH; *Int'l*, pg. 8504
CONMETALL N.V.—See Wurth Verwaltungsgesellschaft mbH; *Int'l*, pg. 8504
CONMETALL SPOL. S.R.O.—See Wurth Verwaltungsgesellschaft mbH; *Int'l*, pg. 8504
CONMET DE MEXICO—See AMSTED Industries Incorporated; *U.S. Private*, pg. 268
THE CONNABLE OFFICE, INC.—See Cresset Asset Management, LLC; *U.S. Private*, pg. 1095
CONNACHER OIL & GAS LIMITED; *Int'l*, pg. 1768
CONNAUGHT ACCESS FLOORING LTD—See U.K. Spac Plc; *Int'l*, pg. 7998
CONNAUGHT ELECTRONICS LIMITED—See Valeo S.A.; *Int'l*, pg. 8112
CONNAUGHT FREIGHT FORWARDERS LIMITED—See Kawasaki Kisen Kaisha, Ltd.; *Int'l*, pg. 4099
THE CONNAUGHT HOTEL LIMITED—See Maybourne Hotels Limited; *Int'l*, pg. 4743

615

CONNAUGHTON CONSTRUCTION CORP

CONNAUGHTON CONSTRUCTION CORP; *U.S. Private*, pg. 1014
CONNECT2 COMMUNICATIONS; *U.S. Private*, pg. 1015
CONNECT2ONE—See National Association of College Stores, Inc.; *U.S. Private*, pg. 2846
CONNECTA CORPORATION—See LATAM Airlines Group S.A.; *Int'l*, pg. 4422
CONNECTAMERICA.COM, LLC; *U.S. Private*, pg. 1015
CONNECT ASSIST LIMITED—See MAXIMUS, Inc.; *U.S. Public*, pg. 1402
CONNECT BIOPHARMA HOLDINGS LIMITED; *Int'l*, pg. 1768
CONNECT CABLE ACCESSORIES CO., LTD.—See Jiangsu Zhongchao Holding Co., Ltd.; *Int'l*, pg. 3957
CONNECT CO. LTD.—See Daiwa Securities Group Inc.; *Int'l*, pg. 1947
CONNECT CONVEYOR BELTING INC.—See Nitta Corporation; *Int'l*, pg. 5382
CONNECT DIRECT, INC.; *U.S. Private*, pg. 1014
CONNECT DIRECT, INC.—See Connect Direct, Inc.; *U.S. Private*, pg. 1014
CONNECT DISTRIBUTION SERVICES LTD—See Kingfisher plc; *Int'l*, pg. 4173
CONNECTEAST PTY. LIMITED—See CP2 Group Limited; *Int'l*, pg. 1823
CONNECTED APPAREL COMPANY LLC; *U.S. Private*, pg. 1015
CONNECTED DEVELOPMENT; *U.S. Private*, pg. 1015
CONNECTED FREIGHT PTE. LTD.—See Shell plc; *Int'l*, pg. 6794
CONNECTED FREIGHT SOLUTIONS PHILIPPINES, INC.—See Shell plc; *Int'l*, pg. 6794
CONNECTED HEALTHCARE, INC.—See The Ensign Group, Inc.; *U.S. Public*, pg. 2070
CONNECTED LOGISTICS, INC.; *U.S. Private*, pg. 1015
CONNECTED MINERALS LIMITED; *Int'l*, pg. 1769
CONNECTED NATION, INC.; *U.S. Private*, pg. 1015
CONNECTED RISK SOLUTIONS, LLC—See AmWINS Group, Inc.; *U.S. Private*, pg. 269
CONNECTED SERVICES GROUP PTY. LTD.—See FUJIFILM Holdings Corporation; *Int'l*, pg. 2825
CONNECTED SOLUTIONS GROUP, LLC; *U.S. Private*, pg. 1015
CONNECTED WIND SERVICES A/S—See EnBW Energie Baden-Wurttemberg AG; *Int'l*, pg. 2398
CONNECTED WIND SERVICES DANMARK A/S—See EnBW Energie Baden-Wurttemberg AG; *Int'l*, pg. 2398
CONNECTED WIND SERVICES DEUTSCHLAND GMBH—See EnBW Energie Baden-Wurttemberg AG; *Int'l*, pg. 2398
CONNECTED WORLD SERVICES NETHERLANDS BV—See Currys plc; *Int'l*, pg. 1879
CONNECTENS B.V.; *Int'l*, pg. 1769
CONNECTEURS ELECTRIQUES DEUTSCH SAS—See TE Connectivity Ltd.; *Int'l*, pg. 7494
CONNECT FIRST CREDIT UNION LTD.—See Servus Credit Union, Ltd.; *Int'l*, pg. 6726
CONNECT FIRST, INC.—See RingCentral, Inc.; *U.S. Public*, pg. 1799
CONNECT FKM—See The Company of Others; *U.S. Private*, pg. 4013
CONNECT GROUP GMBH—See IPTE Factory Automation n.v.; *Int'l*, pg. 3802
CONNECT GROUP NEDERLAND BV—See IPTE Factory Automation n.v.; *Int'l*, pg. 3802
CONNECT GROUP N.V.—See IPTE Factory Automation n.v.; *Int'l*, pg. 3802
CONNECT HEALTH GROUP LTD.—See Lloyds Banking Group plc; *Int'l*, pg. 4536
CONNECT HEARING HEARING RETAIL GROUP PTY. LTD.—See Sonova Holding AG; *Int'l*, pg. 7100
CONNECT HEARING—See Sonova Holding AG; *Int'l*, pg. 7100
CONNECTICARE, INC.—See EmblemHealth, Inc.; *U.S. Private*, pg. 1378
CONNECTICUT ATTORNEYS TITLE INSURANCE CO.; *U.S. Private*, pg. 1015
CONNECTICUT BAR FOUNDATION, INC; *U.S. Private*, pg. 1015
CONNECTICUT BUSINESS SYSTEMS, LLC—See Xerox Holdings Corporation; *U.S. Public*, pg. 2387
CONNECTICUT CARPENTERS BENEFIT FUNDS; *U.S. Private*, pg. 1015
THE CONNECTICUT CARPENTERS PENSION FUND—See Connecticut Carpenters Benefit Funds; *U.S. Private*, pg. 1015
CONNECTICUT CENTER FOR ADVANCED TECHNOLOGY, INC.; *U.S. Private*, pg. 1015
CONNECTICUT CHILDREN'S MEDICAL CENTER CORPORATION, INC.; *U.S. Private*, pg. 1015
CONNECTICUT CHILDREN'S MEDICAL CENTER FOUNDATION, INC.—See Connecticut Children's Medical Center Corporation, Inc.; *U.S. Private*, pg. 1015
CONNECTICUT CHILDREN'S MEDICAL CENTER—See Connecticut Children's Medical Center Corporation, Inc.; *U.S. Private*, pg. 1015
CONNECTICUT COINING, INC.—See MavenHill Capital; *U.S. Private*, pg. 2615

CONNECTICUT COMMUNITY BANK, N.A.—See Associated Community Bancorp, Inc.; *U.S. Private*, pg. 355
CONNECTICUT COMMUNITY CARE, INC.; *U.S. Private*, pg. 1015
CONNECTICUT CONTAINER CORPORATION; *U.S. Private*, pg. 1015
CONNECTICUT DERMATOLOGY GROUP—See Schweiger Dermatology Group; *U.S. Private*, pg. 3572
CONNECTICUT DISTRIBUTORS, INC.—See Breakthru Beverage Group, LLC; *U.S. Private*, pg. 643
CONNECTICUT ELECTRIC, INC.—See Thompson Street Capital Manager LLC; *U.S. Private*, pg. 4161
CONNECTICUT EYE SURGERY CENTER SOUTH, LLC—See KKR & Co. Inc.; *U.S. Public*, pg. 1249
CONNECTICUT FOOD BANK INC.; *U.S. Private*, pg. 1016
CONNECTICUT HOSPICE INC.; *U.S. Private*, pg. 1016
THE CONNECTICUT LIGHT AND POWER COMPANY—See Eversource Energy; *U.S. Public*, pg. 802
CONNECTICUT MEDICAL INSURANCE COMPANY INC.; *U.S. Private*, pg. 1016
CONNECTICUT MUNICIPAL ELECTRICAL ENERGY COOPERATIVE; *U.S. Private*, pg. 1016
CONNECTICUT NATURAL GAS CORPORATION—See Iberdrola, S.A.; *Int'l*, pg. 3571
CONNECTICUT PEER REVIEW ORGANIZATION, INC.; *U.S. Private*, pg. 1016
CONNECTICUT PLASTICS LLC—See NN, Inc.; *U.S. Public*, pg. 1531
CONNECTICUT PLYWOOD CORP; *U.S. Private*, pg. 1016
CONNECTICUT POST—See The Hearst Corporation; *U.S. Private*, pg. 4047
CONNECTICUT PUBLIC BROADCASTING CORP.; *U.S. Private*, pg. 1016
CONNECTICUT RESOURCES RECOVERY AUTHORITY; *U.S. Private*, pg. 1016
CONNECTICUT SOUTHERN RAILROAD, INC.—See Brookfield Infrastructure Partners L.P.; *Int'l*, pg. 1191
CONNECTICUT SOUTHERN RAILROAD, INC.—See GIC Pte. Ltd.; *Int'l*, pg. 2965
CONNECTICUT SPRING & STAMPING CORPORATION; *U.S. Private*, pg. 1016
CONNECTICUT STATE EMPLOYEES CREDIT UNION, INC.; *U.S. Private*, pg. 1016
CONNECTICUT SURGERY CENTER, LIMITED PARTNERSHIP—See UnitedHealth Group Incorporated; *U.S. Public*, pg. 2240
THE CONNECTICUT WATER COMPANY—See SJW Group; *U.S. Public*, pg. 1891
CONNECTICUT WATER SERVICE, INC.—See SJW Group; *U.S. Public*, pg. 1891
CONNECTIMMO SA—See Proximus PLC; *Int'l*, pg. 6008
THE CONNECTING LINK, INC.—See Dream Center Foundation, a California Nonprofit Corp.; *U.S. Private*, pg. 1272
CONNECTING POINT COMMUNICATIONS—See Clayton, Dubilier & Rice, LLC; *U.S. Private*, pg. 924
CONNECT INTERACTIVE, INC.; *U.S. Private*, pg. 1014
THE CONNECTION, INC.; *U.S. Private*, pg. 4014
CONNECTIONS ACADEMY OF FLORIDA, LLC—See Pearson plc; *Int'l*, pg. 5775
CONNECTIONS ACADEMY OF IOWA, LLC—See Pearson plc; *Int'l*, pg. 5775
CONNECTIONS ACADEMY OF MAINE, LLC—See Pearson plc; *Int'l*, pg. 5775
CONNECTIONS ACADEMY OF MARYLAND, LLC—See Pearson plc; *Int'l*, pg. 5775
CONNECTIONS ACADEMY OF NEVADA, LLC—See Pearson plc; *Int'l*, pg. 5775
CONNECTIONS ACADEMY OF NEW MEXICO, LLC—See Pearson plc; *Int'l*, pg. 5775
CONNECTIONS ACADEMY OF OREGON, LLC—See Pearson plc; *Int'l*, pg. 5775
CONNECTIONS ACADEMY OF TENNESSEE, LLC—See Pearson plc; *Int'l*, pg. 5775
CONNECTIONS ACADEMY OF TEXAS LLC—See Pearson plc; *Int'l*, pg. 5775
CONNECTIONS COMMUNITY SUPPORT PROGRAMS, INC.; *U.S. Private*, pg. 1016
CONNECTIONS EDUCATION LLC—See Pearson plc; *Int'l*, pg. 5775
CONNECTIONS ETC.—See Windstream Holdings, Inc.; *U.S. Public*, pg. 2373
THE CONNECTION; *U.S. Private*, pg. 4014
CONNECTION TECHNOLOGY LTD.—See Superior Energy Services, Inc.; *U.S. Public*, pg. 3877
CONNECTIS ICT SERVICES S.A.—See Aurelius Equity Opportunities SE & Co. KGaA; *Int'l*, pg. 708
CONNECTIS ICT SERVICES S.A.U.—See Aurelius Equity Opportunities SE & Co. KGaA; *Int'l*, pg. 708
CONNECTIVA SYSTEMS, INC.; *U.S. Private*, pg. 1016
CONNECTIVE COMPUTING INC.—See Modern Office Methods Inc.; *U.S. Private*, pg. 2762
CONNECTIVE TECHNOLOGIES, INC.—See Ebix Inc.; *U.S. Public*, pg. 710
CONNECTIVITY MARKETING & MEDIA AGENCY, LLC; *U.S. Private*, pg. 1016
CONNECTIVITY SOLUTIONS—See Bel Fuse Inc.; *U.S. Public*, pg. 293

CORPORATE AFFILIATIONS

CONNECTIVITY TECHNOLOGIES—See Methode Electronics, Inc.; *U.S. Public*, pg. 1428
CONNECTIVITY UNLIMITED RESOURCE ENTERPRISE, INC.—See PLDT Inc.; *Int'l*, pg. 5896
CONNECTIVITY WIRELESS, INC.—See TAO Partners, Inc.; *U.S. Private*, pg. 3920
CONNECT LIFE PTY LTD—See PSC Insurance Group Limited; *Int'l*, pg. 6016
CONNECT LOGISTICS SERVICES INC; *Int'l*, pg. 1769
CONNECT MANAGED SERVICES (UK) LIMITED—See G3 Comms Ltd.; *Int'l*, pg. 2866
CONNECT MARKETING, INC.; *U.S. Private*, pg. 1014
CONNECTM TECHNOLOGY SOLUTIONS, INC.; *U.S. Public*, pg. 567
CONNECT MULTISERVICES KFT—See Veolia Environnement S.A.; *Int'l*, pg. 8159
CONNECT NOW PTY. LTD.—See AGL Energy Limited; *Int'l*, pg. 211
CONNECTO CO., LTD.—See Suntory Holdings Limited; *Int'l*, pg. 7326
CONNECTONE BANCORP, INC.; *U.S. Public*, pg. 567
CONNECTONE BANK—See ConnectOne Bancorp, Inc.; *U.S. Public*, pg. 568
CONNECTONE PREFERRED FUNDING CORP.—See ConnectOne Bancorp, Inc.; *U.S. Public*, pg. 568
CONNECTOR CAPITAL CORPORATION; *U.S. Private*, pg. 1016
CONNECTOR CASTINGS INC.; *U.S. Private*, pg. 1016
CONNECTOR MANUFACTURING COMPANY; *U.S. Private*, pg. 1016
CONNECTOR SPECIALIST INC.; *U.S. Private*, pg. 1016
CONNECTORS VERBINDUNGSTECHNIK AG—See NORMA Group SE; *Int'l*, pg. 5430
CONNECT PACKAGING LTD.—See Corrugated Box Supplies Limited; *Int'l*, pg. 1807
CONNECT PUBLIC RELATIONS; *U.S. Private*, pg. 1015
CONNECT PUBLIC RELATIONS—See Connect Public Relations; *U.S. Private*, pg. 1015
CONNECTRIA LLC—See GI Manager L.P.; *U.S. Private*, pg. 1692
CONNECT ROADS SUNDERLAND LTD—See Balfour Beatty plc; *Int'l*, pg. 807
CONNECTRONICS CORP.—See HEICO Corporation; *U.S. Public*, pg. 1020
CONNECTRONICS S.R.O.—See IPTE Factory Automation n.v.; *Int'l*, pg. 3802
CONNECT SECURITY SOLUTION SDN. BHD.—See Waja Konsortium Berhad; *Int'l*, pg. 8331
CONNECTSHIP, INC.—See United Parcel Service, Inc.; *U.S. Public*, pg. 2233
CONNECTSOLUTIONS, INC.; *U.S. Private*, pg. 1017
CONNECT; *U.S. Private*, pg. 1014
CONNECT TECH INC.—See HEICO Corporation; *U.S. Public*, pg. 1019
CONNECT TECHNOLOGIES CORPORATION—See G Three Holdings Corp.; *Int'l*, pg. 2862
CONNECT THE KNOWLEDGE NETWORK CORP.—See Asseco Poland S.A.; *Int'l*, pg. 642
CONNECTURE, INC.—See Francisco Partners Management, LP; *U.S. Private*, pg. 1589
CONNECTUS GROUP LLC—See Clayton, Dubilier & Rice, LLC; *U.S. Private*, pg. 923
CONNECTUS GROUP LLC—See Stone Point Capital LLC; *U.S. Private*, pg. 3824
CONNECTWAVE CO., LTD—See MBK Partners Ltd.; *Int'l*, pg. 4753
CONNECTWISE, INC.—See Thoma Bravo, L.P.; *U.S. Private*, pg. 4146
CONNECTYOURCARE LLC—See ABS Capital Partners, L.P.; *U.S. Private*, pg. 44
CONNECTYX TECHNOLOGIES HOLDINGS GROUP, INC.; *U.S. Public*, pg. 568
CONNECZONE SDN BHD.—See JAB Holding Company S.a.r.l.; *Int'l*, pg. 3863
CONNELL BROS. CO. LTD.—See Wilbur-Ellis Company; *U.S. Private*, pg. 4517
CONNELL CHEVROLET; *U.S. Private*, pg. 1017
CONNELL COMMUNICATIONS INC.—See China Oceanwide Holdings Group Co., Ltd.; *Int'l*, pg. 1536
CONNELL COMMUNICATIONS INC.—See IDG Capital; *Int'l*, pg. 3593
THE CONNELL COMPANY; *U.S. Private*, pg. 4014
CONNELL EQUIPMENT LEASING—See The Connell Company; *U.S. Private*, pg. 4014
CONNELL FINANCE COMPANY, INC.—See The Connell Company; *U.S. Private*, pg. 4014
CONNELL FINANCIAL SERVICES LIMITED—See The Skipton Building Society; *Int'l*, pg. 7686
CONNELL GRAIN GROWERS INC.; *U.S. Private*, pg. 1017
CONNELL LIMITED PARTNERSHIP; *U.S. Private*, pg. 1017
CONNELL MINING PRODUCTS, LLC.—See The Connell Company; *U.S. Private*, pg. 4014
CONNELL NISSAN; *U.S. Private*, pg. 1017
CONNELL OIL INCORPORATED; *U.S. Private*, pg. 1017
CONNELL REALTY & DEVELOPMENT CO.—See The Connell Company; *U.S. Private*, pg. 4014
CONNELL RESOURCES INC.; *U.S. Private*, pg. 1017

COMPANY NAME INDEX

CONNELL RICE & SUGAR DIV.—See The Connell Company; *U.S. Private*, pg. 4014
CONNELLS LIMITED—See The Skipton Building Society; *Int'l*, pg. 7686
CONNELLS RESIDENTIAL LIMITED—See The Skipton Building Society; *Int'l*, pg. 7686
CONNELLS SURVEY & VALUATION LIMITED—See The Skipton Building Society; *Int'l*, pg. 7686
CONNELLY BILLIARD MANUFACTURING; *U.S. Private*, pg. 1017
CONNELLY PARTNERS, LLC; *U.S. Private*, pg. 1017
CONNELLY PAVING; *U.S. Private*, pg. 1017
CONNELLY SKIS, INC.; *U.S. Private*, pg. 1017
CONNEQT BUSINESS SOLUTIONS LTD.—See Quess Corp Limited; *Int'l*, pg. 6160
CONNER INDUSTRIES, INC. - ALAMO FACILITY—See Conner Industries, Inc.; *U.S. Private*, pg. 1017
CONNER INDUSTRIES, INC. - CONROE FACILITY—See Conner Industries, Inc.; *U.S. Private*, pg. 1017
CONNER INDUSTRIES, INC. - FAYETTEVILLE FACILITY—See Conner Industries, Inc.; *U.S. Private*, pg. 1017
CONNER INDUSTRIES, INC. - HASLET FACILITY—See Conner Industries, Inc.; *U.S. Private*, pg. 1017
CONNER INDUSTRIES, INC. - HOGANSVILLE FACILITY—See Conner Industries, Inc.; *U.S. Private*, pg. 1017
CONNER INDUSTRIES, INC. - HOUSTON FACILITY—See Conner Industries, Inc.; *U.S. Private*, pg. 1017
CONNER INDUSTRIES, INC.; *U.S. Private*, pg. 1017
CONNER INDUSTRIES, INC. - STILWELL FACILITY—See Conner Industries, Inc.; *U.S. Private*, pg. 1017
CONNER INSURANCE AGENCY INC; *U.S. Private*, pg. 1017
CONNER PRAIRIE MUSEUM, INC.; *U.S. Private*, pg. 1017
CONNER STRONG & BUCKELEW; *U.S. Private*, pg. 1017
CONNERSVILLE NEWS EXAMINER—See Paxton Media Group LLC; *U.S. Private*, pg. 3116
CONNER TRANSPORT, INC.—See Conner Industries, Inc.; *U.S. Private*, pg. 1017
CONNESI S.P.A.—See DHH SpA; *Int'l*, pg. 2099
CONNETICS LIMITED—See Christchurch City Holdings Ltd.; *Int'l*, pg. 1586
CONNEXA SPORTS TECHNOLOGIES INC; *U.S. Public*, pg. 568
CONNEXCENTER SA—See Stanley Black & Decker, Inc.; *U.S. Public*, pg. 1932
CONNEX CREDIT UNION; *U.S. Private*, pg. 1018
CONNEX GROUP SA—See Stanley Black & Decker, Inc.; *U.S. Public*, pg. 1932
CONNEX INTERNATIONAL INC.; *U.S. Private*, pg. 1018
CONNEXION MOBILITY LTD; *Int'l*, pg. 1769
CONNEXIONONE CORP.; *U.S. Public*, pg. 568
CONNEXION POINT LLC—See Integrity Marketing Group LLC; *U.S. Private*, pg. 2103
CONNEXION SYSTEMS & ENGINEERING, INC.; *U.S. Private*, pg. 1018
CONNEXION TECHNOLOGIES; *U.S. Private*, pg. 1018
CONNEXIS LLC—See Ygomi LLC; *U.S. Private*, pg. 4589
CONNEXITY, INC.—See Symphony Technology Group, LLC; *U.S. Private*, pg. 3900
CONNEX SVT INC.—See Groupe Bruxelles Lambert SA; *Int'l*, pg. 3099
CONNEX SVT INC.—See Parcom Capital Management B.V.; *Int'l*, pg. 5739
CONNEXTA, LLC—See Arlington Capital Partners LLC; *U.S. Private*, pg. 328
CONNEX TCT LLC—See Caisse des Depots et Consignations; *Int'l*, pg. 1258
CONNEX TELECOMMUNICATIONS INC.; *Int'l*, pg. 1769
CONNEXTION COMPANY LIMITED—See Univentures Public Company Limited; *Int'l*, pg. 8077
CONNEXUS CREDIT UNION; *U.S. Private*, pg. 1018
CONNEXUS ENERGY; *U.S. Private*, pg. 1018
CONNEXXALIFE S.R.L.—See Ardian SAS; *Int'l*, pg. 555
CONNEY SAFETY PRODUCTS, LLC—See WESCO International, Inc.; *U.S. Public*, pg. 2351
CONNING ASSET MANAGEMENT LIMITED—See Lin Yuan Investment Co., Ltd.; *Int'l*, pg. 4499
CONNING & COMPANY—See Lin Yuan Investment Co., Ltd.; *Int'l*, pg. 4499
CONNING, INC.—See Lin Yuan Investment Co., Ltd.; *Int'l*, pg. 4499
CONNOILS LLC; *U.S. Private*, pg. 1018
CONNOISSEUR BELGIUM BVBA—See TUI AG; *Int'l*, pg. 7964
CONNOISSEURS PRODUCTS CORPORATION; *U.S. Private*, pg. 1018
CONNOLLY-PACIFIC CO.—See MDU Resources Group, Inc.; *U.S. Public*, pg. 1410
CONNOLY-PACIFIC COMPANY—See MDU Resources Group, Inc.; *U.S. Public*, pg. 1410
CONNOR, CLARK & LUNN FINANCIAL GROUP; *Int'l*, pg. 1769
CONNOR, CLARK & LUNN INFRASTRUCTURE—See Connor, Clark & Lunn Financial Group; *Int'l*, pg. 1769

CONNOR CO. INC.; *U.S. Private*, pg. 1018
CONNOR CONCEPTS INCORPORATED; *U.S. Private*, pg. 1018
CONNOR CORPORATION; *U.S. Private*, pg. 1018
CONNOR FOREST INDUSTRIES, INC.—See Bridgewater Resources Corporation; *U.S. Private*, pg. 650
CONNOR & GASKINS UNLIMITED LLC; *U.S. Private*, pg. 1018
CONNOR MANUFACTURING SERVICE (ASIA) PTE LTD.—See Amphenol Corporation; *U.S. Public*, pg. 130
CONNOR MANUFACTURING SERVICES (JB) SDN. BHD.—See Amphenol Corporation; *U.S. Public*, pg. 130
CONNOR MANUFACTURING SERVICES (KUSHAN) CO., LTD.—See Amphenol Corporation; *U.S. Public*, pg. 130
CONNOR MANUFACTURING (SUZHOU) CO., LTD.—See Amphenol Corporation; *U.S. Public*, pg. 130
CONNOR METAL STAMPING DE MEXICO S. DE R.L. DE C.V.—See Amphenol Corporation; *U.S. Public*, pg. 130
CONNORS, DAMESHEK, FONG & MANCUSO, INC.; *U.S. Private*, pg. 1018
CONNOR SPORT COURT INTERNATIONAL, INC.—See Cobepa S.A.; *Int'l*, pg. 1683
CONNOR-WINFIELD CORP.; *U.S. Private*, pg. 1018
CONNOTATE, INC.—See Import-io Corporation; *U.S. Private*, pg. 2050
CONN-SELMER, INC.—See Paulson & Co. Inc.; *U.S. Private*, pg. 3114
CONN'S, INC.; *U.S. Public*, pg. 567
CONNTEK INTEGRATED SOLUTIONS INC—See Well Shin Technology Co., Ltd.; *Int'l*, pg. 8373
CONNX SOLUTIONS INC.—See Silver Lake Group, LLC; *U.S. Private*, pg. 3658
CONNXUS, INC.—See Thoma Bravo, L.P.; *U.S. Private*, pg. 4147
CONOCOPHILLIPS ALASKA, INC.—See ConocoPhillips; *U.S. Public*, pg. 568
CONOCOPHILLIPS ASIA VENTURES PTE. LTD.—See ConocoPhillips; *U.S. Public*, pg. 568
CONOCOPHILLIPS AUSTRALIA GAS HOLDINGS PTY LTD—See ConocoPhillips; *U.S. Public*, pg. 568
CONOCOPHILLIPS AUSTRALIA PTY LTD—See ConocoPhillips; *U.S. Public*, pg. 568
CONOCOPHILLIPS AUSTRIA GES, M.B.H.—See ConocoPhillips; *U.S. Public*, pg. 568
CONOCOPHILLIPS (BROWSE BASIN) PTY LTD—See ConocoPhillips; *U.S. Public*, pg. 568
CONOCOPHILLIPS CANADA—See ConocoPhillips; *U.S. Public*, pg. 568
CONOCOPHILLIPS CANADA—See ConocoPhillips; *U.S. Public*, pg. 568
CONOCOPHILLIPS CHINA INC—See ConocoPhillips; *U.S. Public*, pg. 568
CONOCOPHILLIPS CO.—See ConocoPhillips; *U.S. Public*, pg. 568
CONOCO PHILLIPS NORGE—See TotalEnergies SE; *Int'l*, pg. 7841
CONOCOPHILLIPS NORGE—See ConocoPhillips; *U.S. Public*, pg. 568
CONOCOPHILLIPS RUSSIA, INC.—See ConocoPhillips; *U.S. Public*, pg. 568
CONOCOPHILLIPS RUSSIA INC—See ConocoPhillips; *U.S. Public*, pg. 568
CONOCOPHILLIPS SKANDINAVIA AS—See ConocoPhillips; *U.S. Public*, pg. 568
CONOCOPHILLIPS; *U.S. Public*, pg. 568
CONOCOPHILLIPS (U.K.) MARKETING & TRADING LIMITED—See ConocoPhillips; *U.S. Public*, pg. 568
CONOCO SPECIALTY PRODUCTS LTD—See Berkshire Hathaway Inc.; *U.S. Public*, pg. 308
CONOIL PLC.; *Int'l*, pg. 1769
CONOLOG CORPORATION; *U.S. Private*, pg. 1018
CONOPCO, INC.—See Unilever PLC; *Int'l*, pg. 8047
CONOPCO—See Unilever PLC; *Int'l*, pg. 8047
CONOPCO—See Unilever PLC; *Int'l*, pg. 8047
CONOPCO—See Unilever PLC; *Int'l*, pg. 8047
CONOPCO—See Unilever PLC; *Int'l*, pg. 8047
CONOPCO—See Unilever PLC; *Int'l*, pg. 8047
CONOPCO—See Unilever PLC; *Int'l*, pg. 8047
CONOPCO—See Unilever PLC; *Int'l*, pg. 8047
CONOPCO—See Unilever PLC; *Int'l*, pg. 8047
CONOPCO—See Unilever PLC; *Int'l*, pg. 8047
CONOPCO—See Unilever PLC; *Int'l*, pg. 8047
CONOPCO—See Unilever PLC; *Int'l*, pg. 8047
CONOPS INDUSTRIAL LTD.—See Fluor Corporation; *U.S. Public*, pg. 858
CONOVER INSURANCE, INC.—See Hellman & Friedman LLC; *U.S. Private*, pg. 1908
CONOVER TUTTLE PACE; *U.S. Private*, pg. 1018
CONPAC GMBH & CO. KG—See Wurth Verwaltungsgesellschaft mbH; *Int'l*, pg. 8504
CONPAC WAREHOUSING PTE. LTD.—See CJ Corporation; *Int'l*, pg. 1633
CON-PEARL NORTH AMERICA INC.—See Blue Cap AG; *Int'l*, pg. 1067
CONPLAN GMBH—See msg group GmbH; *Int'l*, pg. 5067
CONPOREC INC.; *Int'l*, pg. 1769

CONSEC CORPORATION

CONPOREC S.A.S.—See Conporec Inc.; *Int'l*, pg. 1769
CON-PRO INDUSTRIES CANADA LTD.; *Int'l*, pg. 1763
CONQUEST CARE HOMES (SOHAM) LIMITED—See Acadia Healthcare Company, Inc.; *U.S. Public*, pg. 28
CONQUEST CROP PROTECTION PTY. LTD.—See Property Connect Holdings Limited; *Int'l*, pg. 5998
CONQUEST MANUFACTURING, LLC; *U.S. Private*, pg. 1018
CONQUEST RESOURCES LIMITED; *Int'l*, pg. 1769
CONQUEST SYSTEMS, INC.; *U.S. Private*, pg. 1018
CONQUIMICA S.A.—See BRENNTAG SE; *Int'l*, pg. 1149
CONQUIP ENGINEERING CO. LTD.—See WAMGROUP S.p.A.; *Int'l*, pg. 8337
CONRAC ASIA DISPLAY PRODUCTS PTE LTD.—See Data Modul AG; *Int'l*, pg. 1976
CONRAC GMBH—See Data Modul AG; *Int'l*, pg. 1976
CONRAC, INC.; *U.S. Private*, pg. 1018
CONRAC LTDA.—See Data Modul AG; *Int'l*, pg. 1976
CONRAC MENA FZE—See Data Modul AG; *Int'l*, pg. 1976
CONRAC SOUTH AFRICA (PTY) LTD.—See Data Modul AG; *Int'l*, pg. 1976
CONRAD ALUMINUM, L.L.C.—See Conrad Industries, Inc.; *U.S. Public*, pg. 569
CONRAD ASIA ENERGY LTD.; *Int'l*, pg. 1769
CONRAD & BISCHOFF INC.—See Parkland Corporation; *Int'l*, pg. 5743
CONRAD CHICAGO HOTEL—See DiamondRock Hospitality Company; *U.S. Public*, pg. 659
CONRAD COMPANY INCORPORATED; *U.S. Private*, pg. 1019
CONRAD HOTELS & RESORTS—See Hilton Worldwide Holdings Inc.; *U.S. Public*, pg. 1040
CONRAD IMPORTS INC.; *U.S. Private*, pg. 1019
CONRAD INDUSTRIES, INC.; *U.S. Private*, pg. 1019
CONRAD INDUSTRIES, INC.; *U.S. Public*, pg. 569
CONRAD INTERNATIONAL HOTELS (HK) LIMITED—See Hilton Worldwide Holdings Inc.; *U.S. Public*, pg. 1040
CONRAD J. FREEMAN INC.; *U.S. Private*, pg. 1019
CONRAD O'BRIEN, P.C.—See Clark Hill PLC; *U.S. Private*, pg. 913
THE CONRAD / PEARSON CLINIC, P.C.—See Gauge Capital LLC; *U.S. Private*, pg. 1652
CONRAD SCHMITT STUDIOS, INC.; *U.S. Private*, pg. 1019
CONRAD SECURITY LIMITED—See Allied Group Limited; *Int'l*, pg. 357
CONRAD SHIPYARD, L.L.C.—See Conrad Industries, Inc.; *U.S. Public*, pg. 569
CONRAD'S TIRE SERVICE INC.; *U.S. Private*, pg. 1019
CONRAD YELVINGTON DISTRIBUTORS, INC.—See CRH plc; *Int'l*, pg. 1847
CONRAIL INC.—See CSX Corporation; *U.S. Public*, pg. 602
CONRAIL INC.—See Norfolk Southern Corporation; *U.S. Public*, pg. 1535
CONRAN CONTRACTS LIMITED—See Conran Holdings Limited; *Int'l*, pg. 1769
CONRAN DESIGN GROUP LTD.—See Vivendi SE; *Int'l*, pg. 8268
CONRAN HOLDINGS LIMITED; *Int'l*, pg. 1769
CONRAN OCTOPUS LIMITED—See Vivendi SE; *Int'l*, pg. 8274
CONRAN & PARTNERS LTD.—See Conran Holdings Limited; *Int'l*, pg. 1769
CONRAN SHOP JAPAN LTD.—See UNIMAT Life Corporation; *Int'l*, pg. 8048
THE CONRAN SHOP LTD.—See Conran Holdings Limited; *Int'l*, pg. 1769
CONREN LTD—See VINCI S.A.; *Int'l*, pg. 8236
CONROE REGIONAL MEDICAL CENTER—See HCA Healthcare, Inc.; *U.S. Public*, pg. 994
CONROS CORPORATION; *Int'l*, pg. 1769
CONROY & CONROY CONTRACTORS, INC.; *U.S. Private*, pg. 1019
CONROY GOLD & NATURAL RESOURCES PLC; *Int'l*, pg. 1769
CONROY MEDICAL AB—See Indutrade AB; *Int'l*, pg. 3677
CONROY'S GAP WIND FARM PTY LTD—See Origin Energy Ltd.; *Int'l*, pg. 5629
CONROY'S INC.—See 1-800-FLOWERS.COM, Inc.; *U.S. Public*, pg. 1
CONSARC ENGINEERING LIMITED—See Indel, Inc.; *U.S. Private*, pg. 2055
CONSCIA ENTERPRISE SYSTEMS LIMITED—See McKesson Corporation; *U.S. Public*, pg. 1407
CONSCIOUS CONTENT MEDIA, INC.; *U.S. Private*, pg. 1019
CONS CONSTRUCT SRL—See Bog'Art S.R.L.; *Int'l*, pg. 1100
CONSEC CORPORATION - HIROSHIMA PLANT—See CONSEC CORPORATION; *Int'l*, pg. 1769
CONSEC CORPORATION; *Int'l*, pg. 1769
CONSECO LIFE INSURANCE COMPANY OF TEXAS—See CNO Financial Group, Inc.; *U.S. Public*, pg. 520
CONSECO SENIOR HEALTH INSURANCE COMPANY—See CNO Financial Group, Inc.; *U.S. Public*, pg. 520

CONSECUTIVE INVESTMENT & TRADING COMPANY
LTD.; *Int'l*, pg. 1769
CONSEIL ET ASSISTANCE—See Kering S.A.; *Int'l*, pg. 4134
CONSEILLERS EN GESTION ET INFORMATIQUE CGI INC.—See CGI Inc.; *Int'l*, pg. 1434
CONSEJO DE SALUD DE PUERTO RICO, INC.; *U.S. Private*, pg. 1019
CONSEL CONSORZIO ELIS—See Corpay, Inc.; *U.S. Public*, pg. 579
CONSEL, INC.; *U.S. Private*, pg. 1019
CONSELLGRUPPE; *Int'l*, pg. 1769
CONSELLO CAPITAL LLC—See Consello Management LP; *U.S. Private*, pg. 1019
CONSELLO MANAGEMENT LP; *U.S. Private*, pg. 1019
CONSENEC LTD—See ABB Ltd.; *Int'l*, pg. 54
CONSENS GMBH—See Investment AB Latour; *Int'l*, pg. 3781
CONSENSUS ASSET MANAGEMENT AB; *Int'l*, pg. 1770
CONSENSUS CLOUD SOLUTIONS, INC.; *U.S. Public*, pg. 569
CONSENSYS DIGITAL SECURITIES, LLC—See ConsenSys, Inc.; *U.S. Private*, pg. 1019
CONSENSYS IMAGING SERVICE, INC.—See Galen Partners, L.P.; *U.S. Private*, pg. 1637
CONSENSYS, INC.; *U.S. Private*, pg. 1019
CONSENUR, S.A.—See ACS, Actividades de Construccion y Servicios, S.A.; *Int'l*, pg. 111
CONSERA HEALTHCARE REAL ESTATE LLC—See Ventas, Inc.; *U.S. Public*, pg. 2278
CONSERO GLOBAL SOLUTIONS LLC; *U.S. Private*, pg. 1019
THE CONSERVATION CORPORATION SA LIMITED—See Hollard Insurance Company Ltd; *Int'l*, pg. 3451
CONSERVATION RESOURCES COMPANY, INC.—See Heidelberg Materials AG; *Int'l*, pg. 3310
CONSERVATION SERVICES GROUP, INC.; *U.S. Private*, pg. 1019
CONSERVATION SERVICES, INC.—See Waste Management, Inc.; *U.S. Public*, pg. 2330
CONSERVATION TECHNOLOGY, LTD.—See E&A Industries, Inc.; *U.S. Public*, pg. 1301
CONSERVATIVE BROADCAST MEDIA & JOURNALISM INC.; *U.S. Public*, pg. 569
CONSERVATIVE CONCEPT AG—See Baader Bank AG; *Int'l*, pg. 791
CONSERVATIVE CONCEPT PORTFOLIO MANAGEMENT AG—See Baader Bank AG; *Int'l*, pg. 791
CONSERVATIVE PARTY; *Int'l*, pg. 1770
CONSERVATIVE REFORM NETWORK; *U.S. Private*, pg. 1019
CONSERVED FOODSTUFFS DISTRIBUTING COMPANY W.L.L.—See Mezzan Holding Co KSC; *Int'l*, pg. 4870
CONSERVES ET SALAISONS VANELLI; *Int'l*, pg. 1770
CONSERVE; *U.S. Private*, pg. 1019
CONSERV FS INC.; *U.S. Private*, pg. 1019
CONSERVICE; *U.S. Private*, pg. 1019
CONSEW CONSOLIDATED SEWING MACHINE CORP.—See Consew; *U.S. Private*, pg. 1019
CONSEW; *U.S. Private*, pg. 1019
CONSHOHOCKEN RECYCLING & RAIL TRANSFER LLC—See 3i Group plc; *Int'l*, pg. 9
CONSIGLI CONSTRUCTION CO., INC.; *U.S. Private*, pg. 1019
CONSILIENCE SOFTWARE, INC.—See Conduent Incorporated; *U.S. Public*, pg. 566
CONSILIO HL (UK) LIMITED—See GI Manager L.P.; *U.S. Private*, pg. 1692
CONSILIO, LLC—See GI Manager L.P.; *U.S. Private*, pg. 1692
CONSILIUM FIRE & GAS AB—See Nordic Capital AB; *Int'l*, pg. 5420
CONSILIUM MARINE AB—See Nordic Capital AB; *Int'l*, pg. 5420
CONSILIUM NAVIGATION AB—See Nordic Capital AB; *Int'l*, pg. 5420
CONSILIUM SAFETY GROUP AB—See Nordic Capital AB; *Int'l*, pg. 5420
CONSILIUM SGR P.A.; *Int'l*, pg. 1770
CONSILIUM SGR SPA; *Int'l*, pg. 1770
CONSILIUM TRANSPORT SAFETY AB—See Nordic Capital AB; *Int'l*, pg. 5420
CONSIM INFO USA INC.—See Matrimony.Com Limited; *Int'l*, pg. 4728
CONSISA—See Zurich Insurance Group Limited; *Int'l*, pg. 8697
CONSIS PROIECT SRL—See Indra Sistemas, S.A.; *Int'l*, pg. 3661
CONSISTENT COMPUTER BARGAINS, INC.; *U.S. Private*, pg. 1020
CONSISTENT REACH HOLDINGS SDN. BHD.—See Pappajack Berhad; *Int'l*, pg. 5733
CONSISTENT UNIT TRUST MANAGEMENT CO. LTD.—See London and St. Lawrence Investment Company PLC; *Int'l*, pg. 4546
CONSIST SOFTWARE SOLUTIONS, INC.; *U.S. Private*, pg. 1020
CONSODATA S.P.A.—See VEON Ltd.; *Int'l*, pg. 8164

CONSOFT, S.A.U.—See Glintt - Global Intelligent Technologies, S.A.; *Int'l*, pg. 2992
CONSO INTERNATIONAL CORPORATION; *U.S. Private*, pg. 1020
CONSOL COAL RESOURCES LP—See CONSOL Energy Inc.; *U.S. Public*, pg. 569
CONSOLE AUSTRALIA PTY LTD—See Accel Partners L.P.; *U.S. Public*, pg. 48
CONSOLE AUSTRALIA PTY LTD—See KKR & Co. Inc.; *U.S. Public*, pg. 1238
CONSOLE LABS S.A.; *Int'l*, pg. 1770
CONSOL ENERGY INC.; *U.S. Public*, pg. 569
CONSOLE NEW ZEALAND LIMITED—See Accel Partners L.P.; *U.S. Public*, pg. 48
CONSOLE NEW ZEALAND LIMITED—See KKR & Co. Inc.; *U.S. Public*, pg. 1238
CONSOL FINANCIAL INC.—See CONSOL Energy Inc.; *U.S. Public*, pg. 569
CONSOLIDATED AEROSPACE MANUFACTURING LLC—See Tinicum Enterprises, Inc.; *U.S. Private*, pg. 4174
CONSOLIDATED ALLOYS (NZ) LTD—See Amalgamated Metal Corporation PLC; *Int'l*, pg. 408
CONSOLIDATED ALLOYS PTY LTD—See Amalgamated Metal Corporation PLC; *Int'l*, pg. 408
CONSOLIDATED AMUSEMENT CO. LTD, INC.—See Decurion Corp.; *U.S. Private*, pg. 1188
CONSOLIDATED ANALYTICS, INC.; *U.S. Private*, pg. 1020
CONSOLIDATED ASSET RECOVERY SYSTEMS, INC.—See Kinderhook Industries, LLC; *U.S. Private*, pg. 2307
CONSOLIDATED AVIATION SERVICES LLC—See Temasek Holdings (Private) Limited; *Int'l*, pg. 7550
CONSOLIDATED BAKERIES (JAMAICA) LTD.; *Int'l*, pg. 1770
CONSOLIDATED BEVERAGE CO.—See Coca-Cola Consolidated, Inc.; *U.S. Public*, pg. 521
CONSOLIDATED BOTTLE CORPORATION—See Keystone Group, L.P.; *U.S. Private*, pg. 2297
CONSOLIDATED BRICK & BUILDING SUPPLIES INC.; *U.S. Private*, pg. 1020
CONSOLIDATED CARPET-TRADE WORKROOM; *U.S. Private*, pg. 1020
CONSOLIDATED CARQUEVILLE PRINTING COMPANY—See Chatham Asset Management, LLC; *U.S. Private*, pg. 862
CONSOLIDATED CATFISH COMPANIES, LLC; *U.S. Private*, pg. 1020
CONSOLIDATED CHEMICAL CORPORATION; *U.S. Private*, pg. 1020
CONSOLIDATED COMMUNICATIONS HOLDINGS, INC.; *U.S. Public*, pg. 569
CONSOLIDATED COMMUNICATIONS, INC.—See Consolidated Communications Holdings, Inc.; *U.S. Public*, pg. 570
CONSOLIDATED COMMUNICATIONS OF PENNSYLVANIA, LLC—See Consolidated Communications Holdings, Inc.; *U.S. Public*, pg. 570
CONSOLIDATED COMMUNICATIONS OF TEXAS COMPANY—See Consolidated Communications Holdings, Inc.; *U.S. Public*, pg. 570
CONSOLIDATED CONSTRUCTION CONSORTIUM LTD; *Int'l*, pg. 1770
CONSOLIDATED CONTAINER COMPANY LLC—See Stone Canyon Industries, LLC; *U.S. Private*, pg. 3817
CONSOLIDATED CONTRACTING SERVICE; *U.S. Private*, pg. 1020
CONSOLIDATED CONTRACTORS COMPANY (KUWAIT) W.L.L.—See Consolidated Contractors International Company S.A.L.; *Int'l*, pg. 1770
CONSOLIDATED CONTRACTORS COMPANY LTD.—See Consolidated Contractors International Company S.A.L.; *Int'l*, pg. 1770
CONSOLIDATED CONTRACTORS INTERNATIONAL COMPANY S.A.L.; *Int'l*, pg. 1770
CONSOLIDATED CONTRACTORS INTERNATIONAL (UK) LTD.—See Consolidated Contractors International Company S.A.L.; *Int'l*, pg. 1770
CONSOLIDATED CONVERTING CO.—See Elliott Management Corporation; *U.S. Private*, pg. 1367
CONSOLIDATED CONVERTING CO.—See Veritas Capital Fund Management, LLC; *U.S. Private*, pg. 4361
CONSOLIDATED COTTON CO. INC.; *U.S. Private*, pg. 1020
CONSOLIDATED DIESEL, INC.—See Cummins Inc.; *U.S. Public*, pg. 605
CONSOLIDATED DISPOSAL SYSTEMS—See H.I.G. Capital, LLC; *U.S. Private*, pg. 1833
CONSOLIDATED DISTILLED PRODUCTS—See National Wine & Spirits, Inc.; *U.S. Private*, pg. 2865
CONSOLIDATED DISTRIBUTION CORP LLC—See Bay Grove Capital LLC; *U.S. Private*, pg. 492
CONSOLIDATED EDISON COMPANY OF NEW YORK, INC.—See Consolidated Edison, Inc.; *U.S. Public*, pg. 570
CONSOLIDATED EDISON DEVELOPMENT, INC.—See RWE AG; *Int'l*, pg. 6433
CONSOLIDATED EDISON, INC.; *U.S. Public*, pg. 570

CONSOLIDATED ELECTRICAL DISTRIBUTOR (PTY) LTD—See ARB HOLDINGS LIMITED; *Int'l*, pg. 536
CONSOLIDATED ELECTRICAL DISTRIBUTORS, INC.—See Blackfriars Corp.; *U.S. Private*, pg. 574
CONSOLIDATED ELECTRIC COOPERATIVE; *U.S. Private*, pg. 1020
CONSOLIDATED ENERGY COMPANY—See Hartland Fuel Products, LLC; *U.S. Private*, pg. 1874
CONSOLIDATED ENGINEERING CO; *U.S. Private*, pg. 1020
CONSOLIDATED ENGINEERING LABS; *U.S. Private*, pg. 1020
CONSOLIDATED ENTERTAINMENT, INC.—See Reading International, Inc.; *U.S. Public*, pg. 1768
CONSOLIDATED FABRICATORS CORP., BUILDING PRODUCTS DIVISION—See Consolidated Fabricators Corp.; *U.S. Private*, pg. 1020
CONSOLIDATED FABRICATORS CORP; *U.S. Private*, pg. 1020
CONSOLIDATED FABRICATORS, INC.—See TriWest Capital Management Corp.; *Int'l*, pg. 7937
CONSOLIDATED FASTFRATE INC.; *Int'l*, pg. 1770
CONSOLIDATED FASTFRATE INC.; *Int'l*, pg. 1770
CONSOLIDATED FIBERGLASS PRODUCTS CO.; *U.S. Private*, pg. 1020
CONSOLIDATED FIBERS, INC.; *U.S. Private*, pg. 1020
CONSOLIDATED FINANCE COMPANY LIMITED—See ANSA McAL Limited; *Int'l*, pg. 476
CONSOLIDATED FINANCE GROUP PTY LIMITED—See Consolidated Operations Group Limited; *Int'l*, pg. 1771
CONSOLIDATED FINVEST & HOLDINGS LIMITED; *Int'l*, pg. 1770
CONSOLIDATED FIRE PROTECTION, LLC—See Intermediate Capital Group plc; *Int'l*, pg. 3742
CONSOLIDATED FIRE PROTECTION, LLC—See Kirkbi A/S; *Int'l*, pg. 4190
CONSOLIDATED FIRSTFUND CAPITAL CORPORATION; *Int'l*, pg. 1770
CONSOLIDATED FISHERIES LTD.; *Int'l*, pg. 1770
CONSOLIDATED FUEL OIL COMPANY; *U.S. Private*, pg. 1020
CONSOLIDATED GENERAL MINERALS PLC; *Int'l*, pg. 1770
CONSOLIDATED GLASS HOLDING—See Grey Mountain Partners, LLC; *U.S. Private*, pg. 1784
CONSOLIDATED GRAIN & BARGE CO.—See ITOCHU Corporation; *Int'l*, pg. 3835
CONSOLIDATED GRAIN & BARGE CO.—See National Federation of Agricultural Co-Operative Associations; *Int'l*, pg. 5156
CONSOLIDATED GRAPHIC COMMUNICATIONS—See Champion Industries, Inc.; *U.S. Public*, pg. 478
CONSOLIDATED GRAPHICS GROUP, INC.; *U.S. Private*, pg. 1020
CONSOLIDATED GRAPHICS, INC.—See Chatham Asset Management, LLC; *U.S. Private*, pg. 862
CONSOLIDATED HALLMARK INSURANCE PLC.; *Int'l*, pg. 1770
CONSOLIDATED HCI HOLDINGS CORP.; *Int'l*, pg. 1770
CONSOLIDATED HEALTH SERVICES INC.—See Catholic Health Initiatives; *U.S. Public*, pg. 789
CONSOLIDATED HEALTH SYSTEMS INC; *U.S. Private*, pg. 1021
CONSOLIDATED HYDRO NEW YORK INC—See Enel S.p.A.; *Int'l*, pg. 2411
CONSOLIDATED HYDRO SOUTHEAST INC.—See Enel S.p.A.; *Int'l*, pg. 2411
CONSOLIDATED INDUSTRIES, INC.; *U.S. Private*, pg. 1021
CONSOLIDATED INFORMATION SERVICES SOLUTIONS, LLC—See Lovell Minnick Partners LLC; *U.S. Private*, pg. 2502
CONSOLIDATED INFRASTRUCTURE GROUP LIMITED; *Int'l*, pg. 1770
CONSOLIDATED INSURANCE CENTER, INC.—See JBO Holding Company; *U.S. Private*, pg. 2194
CONSOLIDATED INVESTMENT CORPORATION; *U.S. Private*, pg. 1021
CONSOLIDATED INVESTMENT GROUP, LLC; *U.S. Private*, pg. 1021
CONSOLIDATED LAUNCHER TECHNOLOGY, INC.—See Oceaneering International, Inc.; *U.S. Public*, pg. 1562
CONSOLIDATED LAUNDRY EQUIPMENT, INC.—See EVI Industries, Inc.; *U.S. Public*, pg. 803
CONSOLIDATED LUMBER CO.; *U.S. Private*, pg. 1021
CONSOLIDATED MACHINE & TOOL HOLDINGS, LLC—See White Wolf Capital LLC; *U.S. Private*, pg. 4510
CONSOLIDATED MARKETING SERVICES, INC. OF MA; *U.S. Private*, pg. 1021
CONSOLIDATED MECHANICAL, INC.—See Limbach Holdings, Inc.; *U.S. Public*, pg. 1316
CONSOLIDATED MEDIA HOLDINGS PTY LIMITED—See News Corporation; *U.S. Public*, pg. 1518
CONSOLIDATED MEDICAL & SURGICAL SUPPLY CO, INC.—See Osceola Capital Management, LLC; *U.S. Private*, pg. 3047

COMPANY NAME INDEX

CONSOLIDATED METAL PRODUCTS, INC.-EUROPE—See Consolidated Metal Products, Inc.; *U.S. Private*, pg. 1021
CONSOLIDATED METAL PRODUCTS, INC.-GERMANY—See Consolidated Metal Products, Inc.; *U.S. Private*, pg. 1021
CONSOLIDATED METAL PRODUCTS, INC.-JAPAN—See Consolidated Metal Products, Inc.; *U.S. Private*, pg. 1021
CONSOLIDATED METAL PRODUCTS, INC.; *U.S. Private*, pg. 1021
CONSOLIDATED METAL PRODUCTS, INC.-SOUTH AMERICA—See Consolidated Metal Products, Inc.; *U.S. Private*, pg. 1021
CONSOLIDATED METCO INC.—See AMSTED Industries Incorporated; *U.S. Private*, pg. 268
CONSOLIDATED MIDWEST, INC., *U.S. Private*, pg. 1021
CONSOLIDATED NEURO SUPPLY, INC.; *U.S. Private*, pg. 1021
CONSOLIDATED OPERATIONS GROUP LIMITED; *Int'l*, pg. 1771
CONSOLIDATED PAPER CO.—See VIMPEX Handelsgesellschaft mbH; *Int'l*, pg. 8209
CONSOLIDATED PAPER CO.—See Paper Enterprises, Inc.; *U.S. Private*, pg. 3088
CONSOLIDATED PASTORAL COMPANY PTY. LTD.—See Terra Firma Capital Partners Ltd.; *Int'l*, pg. 7566
CONSOLIDATED PIPE & SUPPLY COMPANY; *U.S. Private*, pg. 1021
CONSOLIDATED PLANNING INC.; *U.S. Private*, pg. 1021
CONSOLIDATED PLASTICS CO. INC.; *U.S. Private*, pg. 1021
CONSOLIDATED PLASTICS CORP.; *U.S. Private*, pg. 1021
CONSOLIDATED POWER MAINTENANCE (PTY) LIMITED—See Consolidated Infrastructure Group Limited; *Int'l*, pg. 1771
CONSOLIDATED POWER PROJECTS AUSTRALIA LTD—See Quanta Services, Inc.; *U.S. Public*, pg. 1750
CONSOLIDATED POWER PROJECTS (PTY) LIMITED—See Consolidated Infrastructure Group Limited; *Int'l*, pg. 1771
CONSOLIDATED PRECISION PRODUCTS CORP. - BLOOMINGTON—See Warburg Pincus LLC; *U.S. Private*, pg. 4437
CONSOLIDATED PRECISION PRODUCTS CORP. - CUDAHY—See Warburg Pincus LLC; *U.S. Private*, pg. 4437
CONSOLIDATED PRECISION PRODUCTS CORP. - POMONA—See Warburg Pincus LLC; *U.S. Private*, pg. 4437
CONSOLIDATED PRECISION PRODUCTS CORP. - RANCHO CUCAMOUNGA—See Warburg Pincus LLC; *U.S. Private*, pg. 4437
CONSOLIDATED PRECISION PRODUCTS CORP—See Warburg Pincus LLC; *U.S. Private*, pg. 4437
CONSOLIDATED PRESS HOLDINGS LIMITED; *Int'l*, pg. 1771
CONSOLIDATED PRESS, INC.; *U.S. Private*, pg. 1021
CONSOLIDATED PRESSURE CONTROL, LLC—See Sara SAE Pvt. Ltd.; *Int'l*, pg. 6575
CONSOLIDATED PRODUCTS SYSTEMS; *U.S. Private*, pg. 1021
CONSOLIDATED RAIL CORPORATION—See CSX Corporation; *U.S. Public*, pg. 602
CONSOLIDATED RAIL CORPORATION—See Norfolk Southern Corporation; *U.S. Public*, pg. 1535
CONSOLIDATED REINFORCEMENTS; *U.S. Private*, pg. 1022
CONSOLIDATED RESOURCE RECOVERY, INC.—See RFE Investment Partners; *U.S. Private*, pg. 3419
CONSOLIDATED RESTAURANT OPERATIONS, INC.—See Cracken, Harkey & Co., LLC; *U.S. Private*, pg. 1081
CONSOLIDATED RESTAURANTS OF CALIFORNIA; *U.S. Private*, pg. 1022
CONSOLIDATED SAFETY SERVICES, INC.; *U.S. Private*, pg. 1022
CONSOLIDATED SCRAP RESOURCES; *U.S. Private*, pg. 1022
CONSOLIDATED SERVICES GROUP; *U.S. Private*, pg. 1022
CONSOLIDATED SHOE COMPANY INC.; *U.S. Private*, pg. 1022
CONSOLIDATED SMART SYSTEMS GROUP; *U.S. Private*, pg. 1022
CONSOLIDATED SNACKS INC.; *U.S. Private*, pg. 1022
CONSOLIDATED STEEL SERVICES, INC.; *U.S. Private*, pg. 1022
CONSOLIDATED STORAGE COMPANIES, INC.; *U.S. Private*, pg. 1022
CONSOLIDATED SUPPLY COMPANY INC; *U.S. Private*, pg. 1022
CONSOLIDATED SUPPLY CO.; *U.S. Private*, pg. 1022
CONSOLIDATED SUPPLY CO.—See Consolidated Supply Co.; *U.S. Private*, pg. 1022
CONSOLIDATED SUPPLY CO.—See Consolidated Supply Co.; *U.S. Private*, pg. 1022
CONSOLIDATED SUPPLY CO. - WATER WORKS DIVISON—See Consolidated Supply Co.; *U.S. Private*, pg. 1022
CONSOLIDATED TECHNOLOGIES, INC.—See Thermo Fisher Scientific Inc.; *U.S. Public*, pg. 2149
CONSOLIDATED TELECOMMUNICATIONS COMPANY; *U.S. Private*, pg. 1022
CONSOLIDATED TIN MINES LIMITED; *Int'l*, pg. 1771
CONSOLIDATED TOOL, INC.—See Gemini Group, Inc.; *U.S. Private*, pg. 1658
CONSOLIDATED TOURS INC.; *U.S. Private*, pg. 1022
CONSOLIDATED TRANSPORTATION WORLD, LLC—See Roadrunner Transportation Systems, Inc.; *U.S. Public*, pg. 1802
CONSOLIDATED TRANSPORT INDUSTRIES PTY LTD—See CTI Logistics Limited; *Int'l*, pg. 1871
CONSOLIDATED TURBINE SPECIALISTS CANADA, LLP—See Kratos Defense & Security Solutions, Inc.; *U.S. Public*, pg. 1276
CONSOLIDATED TURBINE SPECIALISTS, LLC—See Kratos Defense & Security Solutions, Inc.; *U.S. Public*, pg. 1276
CONSOLIDATED URANIUM INC.—See IsoEnergy Ltd.; *Int'l*, pg. 3820
CONSOLIDATED UTILITY DISTRICT; *U.S. Private*, pg. 1022
CONSOLIDATED VENDORS CORP.; *U.S. Private*, pg. 1022
CONSOLIDATED WATER (BAHAMAS) LIMITED—See Consolidated Water Co. Ltd.; *Int'l*, pg. 1771
CONSOLIDATED WATER (BELIZE) LIMITED—See Belize Water Services Limited; *Int'l*, pg. 965
CONSOLIDATED WATER CO. LTD.; *Int'l*, pg. 1771
CONSOLIDATED WATER WORKS DISTRICT 1; *U.S. Private*, pg. 1022
CONSOLIDATED WOODJAM COPPER CORP.—See Vizsla Copper Corp.; *Int'l*, pg. 8280
CONSOLIS OY AB—See Bain Capital, LP; *U.S. Private*, pg. 438
CONSOLIS POLSKA SP. Z O.O.—See Bain Capital, LP; *U.S. Private*, pg. 438
CONSOLIS SAS—See Bain Capital, LP; *U.S. Private*, pg. 438
CONSOL MARINE TERMINALS LLC—See CONSOL Energy Inc.; *U.S. Public*, pg. 569
CONSOL PARTNERS LLC—See Empresaria Group Plc; *Int'l*, pg. 2388
CONSOLVO AS—See AF Gruppen ASA; *Int'l*, pg. 184
CONSONANCE CAPITAL PARTNERS LLC; *U.S. Private*, pg. 1022
CONSORCIO AGUA AZUL S.A.—See ACEA S.p.A.; *Int'l*, pg. 95
CONSORCIO ALFA DE ADMINISTRACAO S.A.; *Int'l*, pg. 1771
CONSORCIO ARA, S.A.B. DE C.V.; *Int'l*, pg. 1771
CONSORCIO ARISTOS, S.A.B. DE C.V.; *Int'l*, pg. 1771
CONSORCIO CEMENTERO DEL SUR SA; *Int'l*, pg. 1771
CONSORCIO COMEX, S.A. DE C.V.—See PPG Industries, Inc.; *U.S. Public*, pg. 1709
CONSORCIO ECUATORIANO DE TELECOMUNICACIONES, S.A.—See America Movil, S.A.B. de C.V.; *Int'l*, pg. 421
CONSORCIO ENERGETICO DE HUANCAVELICA S.A.—See Compania de Minas Buenaventura SAA; *Int'l*, pg. 1748
CONSORCIO HOGAR, S.A.B. DE C.V.; *Int'l*, pg. 1772
CONSORCIO INDUSTRIAL MEXICANO DE AUTOPARTES S. DE R.L. DE C.V.—See Lear Corporation; *U.S. Public*, pg. 1296
CONSORCIO NACIONAL FORD LTDA.—See Ford Motor Company; *U.S. Public*, pg. 864
CONSORCIO NACIONAL VOLKSWAGEN LTDA.—See Porsche Automobil Holding SE; *Int'l*, pg. 5931
CONSORCIO NAVIERO PERUANO S.A.—See Grupo Romero; *Int'l*, pg. 3134
CONSORCIO RIO PALLCA—See Salini Costruttori S.p.A.; *Int'l*, pg. 6492
CONSORCIO TECDRA, S.A.—See ACS, Actividades de Construccion y Servicios, S.A.; *Int'l*, pg. 111
CONSORSIO COMEX, S.A. DE C.V.—See PPG Industries, Inc.; *U.S. Public*, pg. 1707
CONSORTA , INC.; *U.S. Private*, pg. 1023
CONSORTE MEDIA, INC.—See AudienceScience Inc.; *U.S. Private*, pg. 391
CONSORTIUM AMERICA II, LLC—See Wells Fargo & Company; *U.S. Public*, pg. 2343
CONSORTIUM BOOK SALES & DISTRIBUTION, LLC—See Perseus Books, LLC; *U.S. Private*, pg. 3155
CONSORTIUM FOR OCEAN LEADERSHIP, INC.; *U.S. Private*, pg. 1023
CONSORTIUM FOR OLDER ADULT WELLNESS; *U.S. Private*, pg. 1023
CONSORTIUM FOR WORKER EDUCATION INC.; *U.S. Private*, pg. 1023
CONSORTIUM ON REACHING EXCELLENCE IN EDUCATION, INC.—See Korn Ferry; *U.S. Public*, pg. 1273

CONSTELLATION ENERGY CORPORATION

CONSORTIUM STADE DE FRANCE S.A.—See VINCI S.A.; *Int'l*, pg. 8216
CONSORT MEDICAL INC.—See Recipharm AB; *Int'l*, pg. 6236
CONSORT MEDICAL PLC—See Recipharm AB; *Int'l*, pg. 6236
CONSORT NT SA; *Int'l*, pg. 1772
CONSORZIO COCIV—See Salini Costruttori S.p.A.; *Int'l*, pg. 6492
CONSORZIO DEKRA REVISIONI—See DEKRA e.V.; *Int'l*, pg. 2007
CONSORZIO S3LOG S.P.A.—See Leonardo S.p.A.; *Int'l*, pg. 4458
CONSORZIO STABILE CENTO ORIZZONTI SCARL—See GPI S.p.A.; *Int'l*, pg. 3046
CONSOVA CORP.—See Medtech Global Limited; *Int'l*, pg. 4786
CONSPEC INTERNATIONAL (HONG KONG) LTD.—See Construction Specialties, Inc.; *U.S. Private*, pg. 1024
CONSTANCE CAPITAL LIMITED—See Easyknit International Holdings Ltd.; *Int'l*, pg. 2276
CONSTANCE HOTELS SERVICES LIMITED; *Int'l*, pg. 1772
CONSTANCE LA GAIETE CO. LTD.; *Int'l*, pg. 1772
CONSTANT CONTACT, INC.—See Clearlake Capital Group, L.P.; *U.S. Private*, pg. 933
CONSTANT CONTACT, INC.—See Siris Capital Group, LLC; *U.S. Private*, pg. 3672
CONSTANT GAIN INTERNATIONAL LIMITED—See Minth Group Limited; *Int'l*, pg. 4914
CONSTANTIA AFRIPACK LABELS PINETOWN—See One Rock Capital Partners, LLC; *U.S. Private*, pg. 3022
CONSTANTIA AFRIPACK—See One Rock Capital Partners, LLC; *U.S. Private*, pg. 3022
CONSTANTIA FLEXIBLES GROUP GMBH—See One Rock Capital Partners, LLC; *U.S. Private*, pg. 3021
CONSTANTIA INSURANCE COMPANY LIMITED—See CONDUIT CAPITAL LIMITED; *Int'l*, pg. 1766
CONSTANTIA LIFE LIMITED—See CONDUIT CAPITAL LIMITED; *Int'l*, pg. 1766
CONSTANTIA PACKAGING AG—See OEP Capital Advisors, L.P.; *U.S. Private*, pg. 2998
CONSTANTINE ENGINEERING, INC.—See Littlejohn & Co., LLC; *U.S. Private*, pg. 2469
CONSTANTINE METAL RESOURCES LTD.—See American Pacific Mining Corp.; *Int'l*, pg. 422
CONSTANTINE NORTH INC.—See American Pacific Mining Corp.; *Int'l*, pg. 422
CONSTANTIN ENTERTAINMENT GMBH—See Highlight Communications AG; *Int'l*, pg. 3388
CONSTANTINE'S WOOD CENTER OF FLORIDA, INC.; *U.S. Private*, pg. 1023
CONSTANTIN FILM AG—See Highlight Communications AG; *Int'l*, pg. 3388
CONSTANTIN FILM UND ENTERTAINMENT AG—See Highlight Communications AG; *Int'l*, pg. 3388
CONSTANTIN MUSIC GMBH—See Highlight Communications AG; *Int'l*, pg. 3388
CONSTANTINOU BROS DEVELOPERS PLC; *Int'l*, pg. 1772
CONSTANTINOU BROS HOTELS LTD; *Int'l*, pg. 1772
CONSTANTINOU BROS PROPERTIES PLC; *Int'l*, pg. 1772
CONSTANT PRICE MONITOR LIMITED—See Halfords Group plc; *Int'l*, pg. 3229
CONSTAR S.A.—See WH Group Limited; *Int'l*, pg. 8395
CONSTELLAR HOLDINGS PTE. LTD.—See Singapore Press Holdings Ltd.; *Int'l*, pg. 6942
CONSTELLAR HOLDINGS PTE. LTD.—See Temasek Holdings (Private) Limited; *Int'l*, pg. 7547
CONSTELLATION AFFILIATED PARTNERS LLC—See Clayton, Dubilier & Rice, LLC; *U.S. Private*, pg. 927
CONSTELLATION AFFILIATED PARTNERS LLC—See Mubadala Investment Company PJSC; *Int'l*, pg. 5076
CONSTELLATION AFFILIATED PARTNERS LLC—See Stone Point Capital LLC; *U.S. Private*, pg. 3826
CONSTELLATION BEERS LTD.—See Constellation Brands, Inc.; *U.S. Public*, pg. 570
CONSTELLATION BRANDS BEACH HOLDINGS, INC.—See Constellation Brands, Inc.; *U.S. Public*, pg. 570
CONSTELLATION BRANDS EUROPE TRADING S.A R.L.—See Constellation Brands, Inc.; *U.S. Public*, pg. 570
CONSTELLATION BRANDS, INC.; *U.S. Public*, pg. 570
CONSTELLATION BRANDS NEW ZEALAND LIMITED—See Constellation Brands, Inc.; *U.S. Public*, pg. 570
CONSTELLATION BRANDS SCHENLEY, INC.—See Constellation Brands, Inc.; *U.S. Public*, pg. 570
CONSTELLATION ENERGY CONTROL AND DISPATCH, LLC—See Constellation Energy Corporation; *U.S. Public*, pg. 572
CONSTELLATION ENERGY CORPORATION; *U.S. Public*, pg. 571
CONSTELLATION ENERGY GENERATION, LLC—See Constellation Energy Corporation; *U.S. Public*, pg. 571

CONSTELLATION ENERGY CORPORATION

CONSTELLATION ENERGY NUCLEAR GROUP, LLC—See Constellation Energy Corporation; *U.S. Public*, pg. 571
CONSTELLATION ENERGY PARTNERS HOLDINGS, LLC—See Constellation Energy Corporation; *U.S. Public*, pg. 572
CONSTELLATION ENERGY PROJECTS & SERVICES GROUP ADVISORS, LLC—See Constellation Energy Corporation; *U.S. Public*, pg. 572
CONSTELLATION ENERGY RESOURCES, LLC—See Constellation Energy Corporation; *U.S. Public*, pg. 571
CONSTELLATION ENERGY SERVICES, INC.—See Constellation Energy Corporation; *U.S. Public*, pg. 572
CONSTELLATION HEALTHCARE TECHNOLOGIES, INC.; *U.S. Private*, pg. 1023
CONSTELLATION HOMEBUILDER SYSTEMS INC.—See Constellation Software Inc.; *Int'l*, pg. 1772
CONSTELLATION, INC.—See Curi Holdings, Inc.; *U.S. Private*, pg. 1124
CONSTELLATION INSURANCE HOLDINGS INC.—See Caisse de Depot et Placement du Quebec; *Int'l*, pg. 1254
CONSTELLATION INSURANCE HOLDINGS INC.—See Ontario Teachers' Pension Plan; *Int'l*, pg. 5586
CONSTELLATION JUSTICE SYSTEMS INC.—See Constellation Software Inc.; *Int'l*, pg. 1775
CONSTELLATION MYSTIC POWER, LLC—See Constellation Energy Corporation; *U.S. Public*, pg. 572
CONSTELLATION NEWENERGY-GAS DIVISION, LLC—See Constellation Energy Corporation; *U.S. Public*, pg. 572
CONSTELLATION OPERATING SERVICES—See Constellation Energy Corporation; *U.S. Public*, pg. 572
CONSTELLATION PHARMACEUTICALS, INC.—See Novartis AG; *Int'l*, pg. 5457
CONSTELLATION POWERLABS, LLC—See Constellation Energy Corporation; *U.S. Public*, pg. 572
CONSTELLATION REAL ESTATE GROUP, INC.; *U.S. Private*, pg. 1023
CONSTELLATION RESOURCES LIMITED; *Int'l*, pg. 1772
CONSTELLATION SOFTWARE ENGINEERING, CORP.; *U.S. Private*, pg. 1023
CONSTELLATION SOFTWARE INC.; *Int'l*, pg. 1772
CONSTELLATION SOLAR MARYLAND MC, LLC—See Constellation Energy Corporation; *U.S. Public*, pg. 572
CONSTELLATION TECHNOLOGIES LIMITED; *Int'l*, pg. 1776
CONSTELLATION WINES U.S.—See Constellation Brands, Inc.; *U.S. Public*, pg. 570
CONSTELLIS HOLDINGS, INC.—See Apollo Global Management, Inc.; *U.S. Public*, pg. 150
CONSTELLIS, LLC—See Apollo Global Management, Inc.; *U.S. Public*, pg. 150
CONSTELLIUM AUTOMOTIVE USA, LLC—See Constellium SE; *Int'l*, pg. 1776
CONSTELLIUM AVIATUBE SAS—See Constellium SE; *Int'l*, pg. 1776
CONSTELLIUM EXTRUSIONS DECIN S.R.O.—See Constellium SE; *Int'l*, pg. 1776
CONSTELLIUM EXTRUSIONS LANDAU GMBH—See Constellium SE; *Int'l*, pg. 1776
CONSTELLIUM SABART SAS—See Constellium SE; *Int'l*, pg. 1776
CONSTELLIUM SE; *Int'l*, pg. 1776
CONSTELLIUM—See Constellium SE; *Int'l*, pg. 1776
CONSTELLIUM SWITZERLAND AG—See Constellium SE; *Int'l*, pg. 1776
CONSTELLIUM USSEL SAS—See Constellium SE; *Int'l*, pg. 1776
CONSTELLIUM VALAIS SA—See Constellium SE; *Int'l*, pg. 1776
CONSTI OYJ; *Int'l*, pg. 1776
CONSTITUTION LIFE INSURANCE CO.—See Golden Gate Capital Management II, LLC; *U.S. Private*, pg. 1731
CONSTITUTION PIPELINE COMPANY, LLC—See The Williams Companies, Inc.; *U.S. Public*, pg. 2143
CONSTITUTION STATE SERVICE LLC—See The Travelers Companies, Inc.; *U.S. Public*, pg. 2136
CONSTI YHTIOT OY—See Intera Equity Partners Oy; *Int'l*, pg. 3735
CONSTREXIM NO. 8 INVESTMENT & CONSTRUCTION JSC; *Int'l*, pg. 1776
CONSTRONICS INFRA LIMITED; *Int'l*, pg. 1776
CONSTRUCCIONES AERONAUTICAS, S.A.—See Airbus SE; *Int'l*, pg. 246
CONSTRUCCIONES ENRIQUE DE LUIS, S.A.—See Grupo Villar Mir, S.A.U.; *Int'l*, pg. 3139
CONSTRUCCIONES Y AUXILIAR DE FERROCARRILES ARGENTINA, S.A.—See Construcciones y Auxiliar de Ferrocarriles S.A.; *Int'l*, pg. 1777
CONSTRUCCIONES Y AUXILIAR DE FERROCARRILES S.A.; *Int'l*, pg. 1776
CONSTRUCCIONES Y DRENAJES PROFUNDOS S.A. DE C.V.—See Promotora y Operadora de Infraestructura, S.A.B. de C.V.; *Int'l*, pg. 5996
CONSTRUCOES E COMERCIO CAMARGO CORREA SA—See Camargo Correa S.A.; *Int'l*, pg. 1268

CONSTRUCTA-NEFF VERTRIEBS-GMBH—See Robert Bosch GmbH; *Int'l*, pg. 6360
CONSTRUCTIEWERKHUIZEN G. VERBRUGGEN NV—See Nordson Corporation; *U.S. Public*, pg. 1532
CONSTRUCTII BIHOR SA; *Int'l*, pg. 1777
CONSTRUCTII COMPLEXE SA; *Int'l*, pg. 1777
CONSTRUCTII FEROVIARE CRAIOVA SA; *Int'l*, pg. 1777
CONSTRUCTII FEROVIARE SA; *Int'l*, pg. 1777
CONSTRUCTII HIDROTEHNICE SA; *Int'l*, pg. 1777
CONSTRUCTION ALBERT JEAN LTD.; *Int'l*, pg. 1777
CONSTRUCTION AND SERVICE SOLUTIONS CORP.; *U.S. Private*, pg. 1023
CONSTRUCTION ARMBRO BFC INC.—See Aecon Group Inc.; *Int'l*, pg. 172
CONSTRUCTION BOOK EXPRESS—See BNi Publications, Inc.; *U.S. Private*, pg. 602
CONSTRUCTION BUSINESS MEDIA, LLC—See Endeavor Business Media LLC; *U.S. Private*, pg. 1391
CONSTRUCTION-CAD SOLUTIONS, INC.; *U.S. Private*, pg. 1024
CONSTRUCTION CHEMICALS DIVISION IN BASF A/S—See BASF SE; *Int'l*, pg. 883
CONSTRUCTION COMPUTER SOFTWARE (AUSTRALIA) (PTY) LIMITED—See Schneider Electric SE; *Int'l*, pg. 6624
CONSTRUCTION COMPUTER SOFTWARE (GULF) LLC—See Schneider Electric SE; *Int'l*, pg. 6624
CONSTRUCTION COMPUTER SOFTWARE LIMITED—See Schneider Electric SE; *Int'l*, pg. 6624
CONSTRUCTION CONSORTIUM PTE. LTD.—See Koh Brothers Group Limited; *Int'l*, pg. 4228
CONSTRUCTION DISTRIBUTION & SUPPLY COMPANY INC; *Int'l*, pg. 1777
CONSTRUCTION DJL INC.—See VINCI S.A.; *Int'l*, pg. 8219
CONSTRUCTION ELECTRICAL PRODUCTS, LLC—See Southwire Company, LLC; *U.S. Private*, pg. 3742
CONSTRUCTION ELECTRIQUE DU VIVARAIS SAS—See Schneider Electric SE; *Int'l*, pg. 6626
CONSTRUCTION ENGINEERING GROUP CO., LTD.; *Int'l*, pg. 1777
CONSTRUCTION EQUIPMENT COMPANY; *U.S. Private*, pg. 1023
CONSTRUCTION EQUIPMENT PARTS INC.—See Ed Bell Investments Company Inc.; *U.S. Private*, pg. 1331
CONSTRUCTION FORMS, INC.; *U.S. Private*, pg. 1023
CONSTRUCTION JOINT STOCK COMPANY 47; *Int'l*, pg. 1777
CONSTRUCTION JOINT STOCK COMPANY NO 5; *Int'l*, pg. 1777
CONSTRUCTION JOINT STOCK COMPANY NO. 6—See Vietnam Railway Corporation; *Int'l*, pg. 8203
CONSTRUCTION JSC NO 12—See Vietnam Construction Stock Corporation; *Int'l*, pg. 8197
CONSTRUCTION JSC NO 1—See Vietnam Construction Stock Corporation; *Int'l*, pg. 8197
CONSTRUCTION JSC NO. 3—See Vietnam Construction Stock Corporation; *Int'l*, pg. 8198
CONSTRUCTION JSC NO.9—See Vietnam Construction Stock Corporation; *Int'l*, pg. 8198
CONSTRUCTION KIEWIT CIE—See Peter Kiewit Sons', Inc.; *U.S. Private*, pg. 3158
CONSTRUCTION LONGER INC.; *Int'l*, pg. 1778
CONSTRUCTION MACHINERY CO., LTD.—See Taiyuan Heavy Industry Co., Ltd.; *Int'l*, pg. 7427
CONSTRUCTION MANAGEMENT SA/NV—See Ackermans & van Haaren NV; *Int'l*, pg. 105
CONSTRUCTION MANAGEMENT SERVICE; *U.S. Private*, pg. 1023
CONSTRUCTION MARKET DATA GROUP LLC—See Roper Technologies, Inc.; *U.S. Public*, pg. 1811
CONSTRUCTION MARKETING ADVISORS; *U.S. Private*, pg. 1024
CONSTRUCTION & MATERIAL HANDLING COMPANY LTD.—See Ireland Blyth Limited; *Int'l*, pg. 3806
CONSTRUCTION MATERIALS INC.; *U.S. Private*, pg. 1024
CONSTRUCTION MATERIALS INC.; *U.S. Private*, pg. 1024
CONSTRUCTION MATERIALS INDUSTRIES & CONTRACTING CO. SAOG; *Int'l*, pg. 1778
CONSTRUCTION MATERIALS LTD.—See The Sterling Group, L.P.; *U.S. Private*, pg. 4122
CONSTRUCTION MATERIALS SUPPLY, INC.—See Beacon Roofing Supply, Inc.; *U.S. Public*, pg. 285
CONSTRUCTION & MATERIALS TRADING JOINT STOCK COMPANY; *Int'l*, pg. 1777
CONSTRUCTION MATERIAL SUPPLY CO., LTD.—See CH. Karnchang Public Company Limited; *Int'l*, pg. 1435
CONSTRUCTION METALS INC.; *U.S. Private*, pg. 1024
CONSTRUCTION METALS, LLC—See Gibraltar Industries, Inc.; *U.S. Public*, pg. 936
CONSTRUCTION MONITOR LLC—See Byggfakta Group Nordic HoldCo AB; *Int'l*, pg. 1234
CONSTRUCTION NAVALE BORDEAUX SA—See Beneteau S.A; *Int'l*, pg. 972
CONSTRUCTION PARTNERS, INC.; *U.S. Public*, pg. 572
CONSTRUCTION PRODUCTS INC.—See Wilian Holding Co., Inc.; *U.S. Private*, pg. 4520

CORPORATE AFFILIATIONS

CONSTRUCTION PROFESSIONALS PTE LTD—See Downer EDI Limited; *Int'l*, pg. 2185
CONSTRUCTION RESEARCH COMMUNICATIONS LTD.—See Apax Partners LLP; *Int'l*, pg. 507
CONSTRUCTION RESEARCH COMMUNICATIONS LTD.—See The Scott Trust Limited; *Int'l*, pg. 7681
CONSTRUCTION RESEARCH & TECHNOLOGY GMBH—See BASF SE; *Int'l*, pg. 883
CONSTRUCTION RESOURCES LLC—See Guggenheim Partners, LLC; *U.S. Private*, pg. 1811
CONSTRUCTION RISK PARTNERS LLC—See The Baldwin Insurance Group, Inc.; *U.S. Public*, pg. 2036
CONSTRUCTIONS DE LA COTE D'EMERAUDE; *Int'l*, pg. 1778
CONSTRUCTION SEALANTS SUPPLY; *U.S. Private*, pg. 1024
CONSTRUCTIONS ELECTRIQUES DE BEAUCOURT SAS—See Nidec Corporation; *Int'l*, pg. 5277
CONSTRUCTION SERVICES 2000, INC.; *U.S. Private*, pg. 1024
CONSTRUCTION SERVICES BRANFORD LLC; *U.S. Private*, pg. 1024
CONSTRUCTION SITE SERVICES LLC—See Fortiline Waterworks, Inc.; *U.S. Private*, pg. 1576
CONSTRUCTIONS METALLIQUES D'OBERNAI; *Int'l*, pg. 1778
CONSTRUCTION SOCAM LTEE; *Int'l*, pg. 1778
CONSTRUCTION SPECIALITES (UK) LTD.—See Construction Specialties, Inc.; *U.S. Private*, pg. 1024
CONSTRUCTION SPECIALITIES, INC. - DECCOLINK PRODUCTS DIVISION—See Construction Specialties, Inc.; *U.S. Private*, pg. 1024
CONSTRUCTION SPECIALTIES AUSTRALIA PTY. LTD.—See Construction Specialties, Inc.; *U.S. Private*, pg. 1024
CONSTRUCTION SPECIALTIES (GULF) LLC—See Construction Specialties, Inc.; *U.S. Private*, pg. 1024
CONSTRUCTION SPECIALTIES, INC.—See Construction Specialties, Inc.; *U.S. Private*, pg. 1024
CONSTRUCTION SPECIALTIES, INC.; *U.S. Private*, pg. 1024
CONSTRUCTION SPECIALTIES, INC.—See Construction Specialties, Inc.; *U.S. Private*, pg. 1024
CONSTRUCTION SPECIALTIES LTD.—See Construction Specialties, Inc.; *U.S. Private*, pg. 1024
CONSTRUCTION SPECIALTIES (SINGAPORE) PTE. LTD.—See Construction Specialties, Inc.; *U.S. Private*, pg. 1024
CONSTRUCTION STUDY CENTRE LIMITED—See Costain Group PLC; *Int'l*, pg. 1814
CONSTRUCTION SUPPLY GROUP—See The Sterling Group, L.P.; *U.S. Private*, pg. 4122
CONSTRUCTION, SUPPLY & SERVICE PTY LTD—See Domino's Pizza Enterprises Ltd.; *Int'l*, pg. 2162
CONSTRUCTION TECHNOLOGY GROUP; *U.S. Private*, pg. 1024
CONSTRUCTION TECHNOLOGY PTE LTD—See Punj Lloyd Ltd.; *Int'l*, pg. 6119
CONSTRUCTION TOOL SERVICE INC.; *U.S. Private*, pg. 1024
CONSTRUCTION TOOLS GMBH—See Epiroc AB; *Int'l*, pg. 2461
CONSTRUCTION TOOLS GMBH—See Epiroc AB; *Int'l*, pg. 2461
CONSTRUCTIVE MEDIA PTY LTD—See JWH Group Pty Ltd; *Int'l*, pg. 4035
CONSTRUCTIVE TECHNOLOGIES GROUP, INC.—See CI Capital Partners LLC; *U.S. Private*, pg. 895
CONSTRUCTORA ASTALDI FE GRANDE CACHAPOAL LIMITADA—See Salini Costruttori S.p.A.; *Int'l*, pg. 6492
CONSTRUCTORA CABLEMAS, S.A. DE C.V.—See Grupo Televisa, S.A.B.; *Int'l*, pg. 3136
CONSTRUCTORA CONCONCRETO SA; *Int'l*, pg. 1778
CONSTRUCTORA DE PAVIMENTOS ASFALTICOS BITUMIX LIMITADA—See VINCI S.A.; *Int'l*, pg. 8219
CONSTRUCTORA DE PROYECTOS HIDROELECTRICOS, S.A. DE C.V.—See Empresas ICA S.A.B. de C.V.; *Int'l*, pg. 2390
CONSTRUCTORA DE PROYECTOS VIALES DE MEXICO, S.A. DE C.V.—See Industry Super Holdings Pty. Ltd.; *Int'l*, pg. 3675
CONSTRUCTORA DYCVEN, S.A.—See ACS, Actividades de Construccion y Servicios, S.A.; *Int'l*, pg. 111
CONSTRUCTORA EL CAJON, S.A. DE C.V.—See Empresas ICA S.A.B. de C.V.; *Int'l*, pg. 2390
CONSTRUCTORA HIDROELECTRICA LA YESCA, S.A. DE C.V.—See Empresas ICA S.A.B. de C.V.; *Int'l*, pg. 2390
CONSTRUCTORA LOGRO S.A.—See Sigdo Koppers S.A.; *Int'l*, pg. 6907
CONSTRUCTORA MAYALUUM, S.A. DE C.V.—See Industry Super Holdings Pty. Ltd.; *Int'l*, pg. 3675
CONSTRUCTORA NORBERTO ODEBRECHT DE VENEZUELA C.A.—See Novonor S.A.; *Int'l*, pg. 5470
CONSTRUCTORA NORBERTO ODEBRECHT PERU S.A.—See Novonor S.A.; *Int'l*, pg. 5470
CONSTRUCTORA NORBERTO ODEBRECHT S.A.—See Novonor S.A.; *Int'l*, pg. 5470

CONSTRUCTORA NORBERTO ODEBRECHT S.A.—See Novonor S.A.; *Int'l*, pg. 5470
CONSTRUCTORA ODEBRECHT ARGENTINA S.A.—See Novonor S.A.; *Int'l*, pg. 5470
CONSTRUCTORA ODEBRECHT CHILE S.A.—See Novonor S.A.; *Int'l*, pg. 5470
CONSTRUCTORA SAN JOSE ARGENTINA, S.A.—See Grupo Empresarial San Jose, S.A.; *Int'l*, pg. 3128
CONSTRUCTORA SAN JOSE CABO VERDE, S.A.—See Grupo Empresarial San Jose, S.A.; *Int'l*, pg. 3128
CONSTRUCTORA SAN JOSE PORTUGAL S.A.—See Grupo Empresarial San Jose, S.A.; *Int'l*, pg. 3128
CONSTRUCTORAS ICA, S. A. DE C. V.—See Empresas ICA S.A.B. de C.V.; *Int'l*, pg. 2390
CONSTRUCTORA UDRA LIMITADA—See Grupo Empresarial San Jose, S.A.; *Int'l*, pg. 3128
CONSTRUCTOR DANMARK A/S—See Corporacion Gestamp SL; *Int'l*, pg. 1804
CONSTRUCTOR DEXION FRANCE SARL—See Corporacion Gestamp SL; *Int'l*, pg. 1804
CONSTRUCTOR DEXION ITALIA SRL—See Corporacion Gestamp SL; *Int'l*, pg. 1804
CONSTRUCTOR FINLAND OY—See Corporacion Gestamp SL; *Int'l*, pg. 1804
CONSTRUCTOR GROUP AS—See Corporacion Gestamp SL; *Int'l*, pg. 1804
CONSTRUCTOR NORGE AS—See Corporacion Gestamp SL; *Int'l*, pg. 1804
CONSTRUCTORS INC.; *U.S. Private*, pg. 1024
CONSTRUCTOR SVERIGE AB—See Corporacion Gestamp SL; *Int'l*, pg. 1804
CONSTRUCT SOLUTIONS, INC.; *U.S. Private*, pg. 1023
CONSTRUCT TWO GROUP; *U.S. Private*, pg. 1023
CONSTRUEXPORT, S.A. DE C.V.—See Empresas ICA S.A.B. de C.V.; *Int'l*, pg. 2390
CONSTRURAIL, S.A.—See ACS, Actividades de Construccion y Servicios, S.A.; *Int'l*, pg. 111
CONSTRUSOFT GROEP BV—See Trimble, Inc.; *U.S. Public*, pg. 2190
CONSTRUTORA ADOLPHO LINDENBERG S.A.; *Int'l*, pg. 1778
CONSTRUTORA BETER S.A.; *Int'l*, pg. 1778
CONSTRUTORA IMPREGILO Y ASSOCIADOS S.A.-CIGLA S.A.—See Salini Costruttori S.p.A.; *Int'l*, pg. 6493
CONSTRUTORA NORBERTO ODEBRECHT S.A.—See Novonor S.A.; *Int'l*, pg. 5470
CONSTRUTORA NORBERTO ODEBRECHT S.A.—See Novonor S.A.; *Int'l*, pg. 5470
CONSTRUTORA NORBERTO ODEBRECHT S.A.—See Novonor S.A.; *Int'l*, pg. 5470
CONSTRUTORA NORBERTO ODEBRECHT S.A.—See Novonor S.A.; *Int'l*, pg. 5470
CONSTRUTORA NORBERTO ODEBRECHT S.A.—See Novonor S.A.; *Int'l*, pg. 5470
CONSTRUTORA NORBERTO ODEBRECHT S.A.—See Novonor S.A.; *Int'l*, pg. 5470
CONSTRUTORA TEDESCO LTDA. - GRAVATAI UNIT—See Zech Group SE; *Int'l*, pg. 8629
CONSTRUTORA TEDESCO LTDA.—See Zech Group SE; *Int'l*, pg. 8628
CONSTRUTORA TENDA S.A.; *Int'l*, pg. 1778
CONSTRUTORA TODA DO BRASIL S.A.—See Toda Corporation; *Int'l*, pg. 7772
CONSTRUTORA UDRA LTDA.—See Grupo Empresarial San Jose, S.A.; *Int'l*, pg. 3128
CONSULAB MANNHEIM GMBH—See Roche Holding AG; *Int'l*, pg. 6374
CONSULATE HEALTH CARE, LLC; *U.S. Private*, pg. 1025
CONSUL SYSTEM S.P.A.—See A2A S.p.A.; *Int'l*, pg. 29
CONSULTANT CONNECT LIMITED—See Teladoc Health, Inc.; *U.S. Public*, pg. 1992
CONSULTANT & CONSTRUCTION SOLUTIONS SA—See Viohalco SA/NV; *Int'l*, pg. 8243
THE CONSULTANT & INVESTMENT GROUP P.L.C.; *Int'l*, pg. 7635
CONSULTANTS2GO; *U.S. Private*, pg. 1025
CONSULTANTS & BUILDERS, INC.; *U.S. Private*, pg. 1025
CONSULTANTS F.DRAPEAU INC.; *Int'l*, pg. 1778
CONSULTANTS GROUP COMMERCIAL FINANCE—See Blue Owl Capital Inc.; *U.S. Public*, pg. 364
CONSULTANTS IN BUSINESS ENGINEERING AND RESEARCH SWEDEN AB—See Bouvet ASA; *Int'l*, pg. 1121
CONSULTANTS IN PAIN MEDICINE, LLC—See Bain Capital, LP; *U.S. Private*, pg. 445
CONSULTATIO SA; *Int'l*, pg. 1778
CONSULTATIVE INSURANCE GROUP INC.—See Aquiline Capital Partners LLC; *U.S. Private*, pg. 305
CONSULTEC BYGGPROGRAM AB—See Eleco Plc; *Int'l*, pg. 2347
CONSULTEC GROUP AB—See Eleco Plc; *Int'l*, pg. 2347
CONSULTECH—See Omnicom Group Inc.; *U.S. Public*, pg. 1579
CONSULTEC SYSTEM AB—See Eleco Plc; *Int'l*, pg. 2347
CONSULTEDGE, INC.; *U.S. Private*, pg. 1025

CONSULTING & BANKING & ADMINISTRATIVE SERVICES, LTD.—See Brithol Michcoma Mozambique Limited; *Int'l*, pg. 1165
CONSULTING ENGINEERING BUREAU ABDULLAH DABBAGH PARTNERS—See Dabbagh Group Holding Company Ltd.; *Int'l*, pg. 1902
CONSULTING ENGINEERING SERVICES LLC.—See Jacobs Engineering Group, Inc.; *U.S. Public*, pg. 1184
CONSULTING ENGINEERS GROUP, INC.; *U.S. Private*, pg. 1025
CONSULTING ENGINEERS LAHMEYER NIGERIA LTD.—See Lahmeyer Holding GmbH; *Int'l*, pg. 4395
CONSULTING FOR ARCHITECTS INC.; *U.S. Private*, pg. 1025
CONSULTING SERVICES, INC.; *U.S. Private*, pg. 1025
THE CONSULTING SOURCE, INC.1990—See AutoNation, Inc.; *U.S. Public*, pg. 238
CONSULTORA SCHRODERS, S.A. DE C.V.—See Schroders plc; *Int'l*, pg. 6639
CONSULTORES DEL PLATA S.A.—See WPP plc; *Int'l*, pg. 8469
CONSULTORES REGIONALES ASOCIADOS-CRA S.A.S.—See WSP Global, Inc.; *Int'l*, pg. 8495
CONSULTORIA EN GESTION DE RIESGOS IPS SURAMERICANA S.A.—See Grupo de Inversiones Suramericana S.A.; *Int'l*, pg. 3125
CONSULT PARAGON COMPUTER PROFESSIONALS LTD.—See CGI Inc.; *Int'l*, pg. 1434
CONSULTUM FINANCIAL ADVISERS PTY LTD—See Insignia Financial Ltd.; *Int'l*, pg. 3719
CONSULTUS AB—See Softronic AB; *Int'l*, pg. 7056
CONSUMABLE, INC.; *U.S. Private*, pg. 1025
CONSUMER ACQUISITIONS, INC.; *U.S. Private*, pg. 1025
CONSUMER AUTOMOTIVE FINANCE, INC.; *U.S. Public*, pg. 572
CONSUMER BRANDS LIMITED—See GraceKennedy Limited; *Int'l*, pg. 3048
CONSUMER CAPITAL GROUP INC.; *U.S. Private*, pg. 1025
CONSUMER CELLULAR, INC.—See GTCR LLC; *U.S. Private*, pg. 1804
CONSUMER CLUB INC.—See Booking Holdings, Inc.; *U.S. Public*, pg. 368
CONSUMER CREDIT COUNSELING SERVICE OF GREATER ATLANTA, INC.—See Money Management International; *U.S. Private*, pg. 2770
CONSUMER CREDIT COUNSELING SERVICE OF GREATER DALLAS INC.; *U.S. Private*, pg. 1025
CONSUMER CREDIT COUNSELING SERVICE OF SAN FRANCISCO; *U.S. Private*, pg. 1025
CONSUMER CREDIT, LLC—See Encore Capital Group, Inc.; *U.S. Public*, pg. 759
CONSUMER DEPOT LLC; *U.S. Private*, pg. 1025
CONSUMER ENERGY SOLUTIONS, INC.; *U.S. Private*, pg. 1025
CONSUMER FINANCE COMPANY LIMITED—See Bayport Management Limited; *Int'l*, pg. 915
CONSUMER GOODS TECHNOLOGY—See RFE Investment Partners; *U.S. Private*, pg. 3419
CONSUMER GROWTH PARTNERS LLC; *U.S. Private*, pg. 1025
CONSUMER GUILD FOODS, INC.; *U.S. Private*, pg. 1025
CONSUMERINFO.COM, INC.—See Experian plc; *Int'l*, pg. 2587
CONSUMERMETRICS, INC.; *U.S. Private*, pg. 1026
CONSUMER PACKAGES—See Stora Enso Oyj; *Int'l*, pg. 7224
CONSUMER PORTFOLIO SERVICES, INC.; *U.S. Public*, pg. 572
CONSUMER PORTFOLIO SERVICES, INC.—See Consumer Portfolio Services, Inc.; *U.S. Public*, pg. 572
CONSUMER PORTFOLIO SERVICES—See Consumer Portfolio Services, Inc.; *U.S. Public*, pg. 572
CONSUMER POWER INC.; *U.S. Private*, pg. 1025
CONSUMER PRODUCT DISTRIBUTORS, INC.; *U.S. Private*, pg. 1025
CONSUMER PRODUCT END-USE RESEARCH INSTITUTE CO., LTD.—See J. Front Retailing Co., Ltd.; *Int'l*, pg. 3855
CONSUMER RECOVERY ASSOCIATES, LLC; *U.S. Private*, pg. 1025
CONSUMERREVIEW, INC.—See Invenda Corporation; *U.S. Private*, pg. 2131
CONSUMERS 2014 SECURITIZATION FUNDING LLC—See CMS Energy Corporation; *U.S. Public*, pg. 518
CONSUMER SAFETY TECHNOLOGY, LLC—See Welsh, Carson, Anderson & Stowe; *U.S. Private*, pg. 4480
CONSUMERS BANCORP, INC.; *U.S. Public*, pg. 573
CONSUMERS BEVERAGES INC.; *U.S. Private*, pg. 1026
CONSUMERS CHOICE COFFEE, INC.; *U.S. Private*, pg. 1026
CONSUMERS CHOICE HOME IMPROVEMENTS CORP; *Int'l*, pg. 1778
CONSUMERS CONCRETE CORPORATION; *U.S. Private*, pg. 1026
CONSUMERS COOP ASSOCIATION EAU CLAIRE; *U.S. Private*, pg. 1026

CONSUMERS COOP ASSOCIATION LITCHFIELD; *U.S. Private*, pg. 1026
CONSUMERS' CO-OPERATIVE REFINERIES LIMITED—See Federated Co-operatives Limited; *Int'l*, pg. 2630
CONSUMERS COOP RICHLAND COUNTY; *U.S. Private*, pg. 1026
CONSUMERS CREDIT UNION; *U.S. Private*, pg. 1026
CONSUMER SEARCH HONG KONG LIMITED—See Nippon Telegraph & Telephone Corporation; *Int'l*, pg. 5350
CONSUMERSEARCH, INC.—See IAC Inc.; *U.S. Public*, pg. 1081
CONSUMERS ENERGY COMPANY—See CMS Energy Corporation; *U.S. Public*, pg. 518
CONSUMER SERVICES, INC.; *U.S. Private*, pg. 1025
CONSUMERS GASOLINE STATIONS, INC.—See Tri Star Energy, LLC; *U.S. Private*, pg. 4221
CONSUMERS INTERSTATE CORPORATION; *U.S. Private*, pg. 1026
CONSUMERS KITCHENS & BATHS; *U.S. Private*, pg. 1026
CONSUMERS NATIONAL BANK—See Consumers Bancorp, Inc.; *U.S. Public*, pg. 573
CONSUMERSOFT; *U.S. Private*, pg. 1026
CONSUMERS OIL AND SUPPLY CO; *U.S. Private*, pg. 1026
CONSUMER SOURCE INC.—See Redfin Corporation; *U.S. Public*, pg. 1770
CONSUMERS PIPE & SUPPLY CO; *U.S. Private*, pg. 1026
CONSUMERS PRESS—See Gannett Co., Inc.; *U.S. Public*, pg. 897
CONSUMERS SKLO ZORYA—See Compagnie de Saint-Gobain SA; *Int'l*, pg. 1723
CONSUMERS SUPPLY DISTRIBUTING, LLC—See CHS INC.; *U.S. Public*, pg. 492
CONSUMERS WAREHOUSE CENTER INC.—See Consumers Kitchens & Baths; *U.S. Private*, pg. 1026
CONSUMER TESTING LABORATORIES, INC.—See Underwriters Laboratories Inc.; *U.S. Private*, pg. 4280
CONSUMER UNITED; *U.S. Private*, pg. 1025
CONSUN FOOD INDUSTRIES INCORPORATED; *U.S. Private*, pg. 1026
CONSUN PHARMACEUTICAL GROUP LIMITED; *Int'l*, pg. 1778
CONSUPAQ (PTY) LTD—See Berry Global Group, Inc; *U.S. Public*, pg. 324
CONSUS ASSET MANAGEMENT CO., LTD.; *Int'l*, pg. 1778
CONSUS DEUTSCHLAND GMBH—See Consus Real Estate AG; *Int'l*, pg. 1778
CONSUS REAL ESTATE AG; *Int'l*, pg. 1778
CONTACT ADVERTISING—See WPP plc; *Int'l*, pg. 8470
CONTACT ASSOCIATES LIMITED—See Capita plc; *Int'l*, pg. 1309
CONTACT AT ONCE!, LLC—See LivePerson, Inc.; *U.S. Public*, pg. 1332
CONTACT CENTER COMPANY—See StarTek, Inc.; *U.S. Private*, pg. 3788
CONTACT ENERGY LIMITED; *Int'l*, pg. 1778
CONTACT GOLD CORP.—See Orla Mining Ltd.; *Int'l*, pg. 5639
CONTACT IMPACT GMBH—See Axel Springer SE; *Int'l*, pg. 766
CONTACTIM (PTY) LTD.—See Libstar Holdings Ltd.; *Int'l*, pg. 4487
CONTACT INDUSTRIES; *U.S. Private*, pg. 1026
CONTACTLAB; *Int'l*, pg. 1778
CONTACT MOCAMBIQUE—See Randstad N.V.; *Int'l*, pg. 6201
CONTACTO CORREDORES DE SEGUROS S.A.—See Compania de Minas Buenaventura SAA; *Int'l*, pg. 1748
CONTACTUAL, INC.—See 8x8, Inc.; *U.S. Public*, pg. 10
CONTAGIOUS GAMING INC.; *Int'l*, pg. 1778
CONTAINER APPLICATIONS INTERNATIONAL (AUSTRALIA) PTY LTD.—See CAI International, Inc.; *U.S. Public*, pg. 421
CONTAINER APPLICATIONS INTERNATIONAL (U.K.) LIMITED—See CAI International, Inc.; *U.S. Public*, pg. 421
CONTAINERCHAIN AUSTRALIA PTY LTD—See WiseTech Global Limited; *Int'l*, pg. 8437
CONTAINER CHAIN PTY LTD—See WiseTech Global Limited; *Int'l*, pg. 8436
CONTAINERCHAIN (SINGAPORE) PTE LTD—See WiseTech Global Limited; *Int'l*, pg. 8436
CONTAINER COMPANY (ABERDEEN) LTD.—See First Reserve Management, L.P.; *U.S. Private*, pg. 1526
CONTAINER COMPONENTS INC.; *U.S. Private*, pg. 1026
CONTAINER CORPORATION OF INDIA LTD.; *Int'l*, pg. 1779
CONTAINER FABRICATOR (M) SDN BHD—See Mewah International Inc.; *Int'l*, pg. 4868
CONTAINERFREIGHT/EIT LLC; *U.S. Private*, pg. 1027
CONTAINER GRAPHICS CORPORATION—See Container Graphics Corporation; *U.S. Private*, pg. 1026
CONTAINER GRAPHICS CORPORATION; *U.S. Private*, pg. 1026

CONTAINER GRAPHICS CORPORATION

CONTAINER LEASING INTERNATIONAL LLC.—See Ontario Teachers' Pension Plan; *Int'l*, pg. 5590
CONTAINER LIFE CYCLE MANAGEMENT LLC—See Greif Inc.; *U.S. Public*, pg. 967
CONTAINER MARKETING INC.; *U.S. Private*, pg. 1026
CONTAINER OPERATORS S.A.—See A.P. Moller-Maersk A/S; *Int'l*, pg. 26
CONTAINERPOOL—See Stonepeak Partners L.P.; *U.S. Private*, pg. 3829
CONTAINER PORT GROUP—See World Shipping, Inc.; *U.S. Private*, pg. 4567
CONTAINER PRODUCTS CORPORATION; *U.S. Private*, pg. 1026
CONTAINER RAIL ROAD SERVICES PRIVATE LIMITED—See Dubai World Corporation; *Int'l*, pg. 2220
CONTAINER RESEARCH CORPORATION; *U.S. Private*, pg. 1027
CONTAINER RESOURCES INC.—See Kelso & Company, L.P.; *U.S. Private*, pg. 2278
CONTAINER ROYALTY SUPPLEMENTAL CASH BENEFIT PLAN; *U.S. Private*, pg. 1027
CONTAINER SERVICES LLC; *U.S. Private*, pg. 1027
CONTAINERSHIPS-CMA CGM GMBH—See CMA CGM S.A.; *Int'l*, pg. 1668
THE CONTAINER STORE GROUP, INC.—See Leonard Green & Partners, L.P.; *U.S. Private*, pg. 2429
THE CONTAINER STORE INC.—See Leonard Green & Partners, L.P.; *U.S. Private*, pg. 2429
CONTAINER SYSTEMS INC.; *U.S. Private*, pg. 1027
CONTAINER TECHNOLOGY AND SUPPLY INTERNATIONAL INCORPORATED; *U.S. Private*, pg. 1027
CONTAINERWAY INTERNATIONAL LIMITED; *Int'l*, pg. 1779
CONTAINE TECHNOLOGIES LTD.; *Int'l*, pg. 1778
CONTAINMENT SOLUTIONS, INC.—See NOV, Inc.; *U.S. Public*, pg. 1544
CONTAKT WORLD TECHNOLOGIES CORP.; *Int'l*, pg. 1779
CONTAMAC LIMITED—See Shanghai Haohai Biological Technology Co., Ltd.; *Int'l*, pg. 6769
CONTAMINANT CONTROL INC.; *U.S. Private*, pg. 1027
CONTANDA, LLC—See EQT AB; *Int'l*, pg. 2473
CONTANDA STEEL, LLC—See EQT AB; *Int'l*, pg. 2473
CONTANGO FUNDS MANAGEMENT LIMITED—See Associate Global Partners Limited; *Int'l*, pg. 648
CONTANGO GROUP PTY. LTD.; *Int'l*, pg. 1779
CONTANGO HOLDINGS PLC; *Int'l*, pg. 1779
CONTANGO OIL & GAS COMPANY—See KKR & Co. Inc.; *U.S. Public*, pg. 1243
CONTANGO OPERATORS, INC.—See KKR & Co. Inc.; *U.S. Public*, pg. 1243
CONTANGO ORE, INC.; *U.S. Public*, pg. 573
CONTARGO GMBH & CO. KG—See RETHMANN AG & Co. KG; *Int'l*, pg. 6309
CONTARGO WATERWAY LOGISTICS BV—See RETHMANN AG & Co. KG; *Int'l*, pg. 6309
CONTARINI LEOPOLDO S.R.L.—See Interpump Group S.p.A.; *Int'l*, pg. 3755
CONTEC AMERICAS INC.—See Daifuku Co., Ltd.; *Int'l*, pg. 1924
CONTEC CO., LTD.—See Daifuku Co., Ltd.; *Int'l*, pg. 1924
CONTEC DTX INC.—See Daifuku Co., Ltd.; *Int'l*, pg. 1924
CONTEC EMS CO., LTD.—See Daifuku Co., Ltd.; *Int'l*, pg. 1925
CONTEC GMBH—See voestalpine AG; *Int'l*, pg. 8288
CON-TECH COMPANIES; *U.S. Private*, pg. 1008
CONTECH CONSTRUCTION PRODUCTS INC.—See Apax Partners LLP; *Int'l*, pg. 503
CONTECH INC.—See Apax Partners LLP; *Int'l*, pg. 503
CON-TECH LIGHTING—See E&A Industries, Inc.; *U.S. Private*, pg. 1301
CONTECH LLC—See Marathon Asset Management LP; *U.S. Private*, pg. 2570
CONTECH LOGISTICS SOLUTIONS PRIVATE LIMITED—See Allcargo Logistics Limited; *Int'l*, pg. 333
CONTECH MSI CO.—See Kelso-Burnett Company; *U.S. Private*, pg. 2281
CONTEC HOLDINGS, LLC—See Bain Capital, LP; *U.S. Private*, pg. 438
CONTECH PRECAST PTE. LTD.—See Koon Holdings Limited; *Int'l*, pg. 4278
CONTECH RESEARCH, INC.; *U.S. Private*, pg. 1027
CONTECH—See Apax Partners LLP; *Int'l*, pg. 503
CONTEC INC.; *U.S. Private*, pg. 1027
CONTECON GUAYAQUIL, S.A.—See LATAM Airlines Group S.A.; *Int'l*, pg. 4422
CONTECON MANZANILLO S.A.—See International Container Terminal Services, Inc.; *Int'l*, pg. 3746
CONTEC (SHANGHAI) CO., LTD.—See Daifuku Co., Ltd.; *Int'l*, pg. 1924
CONTEC SOLUTION CHINA CORPORATION—See Daifuku Co., Ltd.; *Int'l*, pg. 1925
CONTEC SOLUTION CO., LTD.—See Daifuku Co., Ltd.; *Int'l*, pg. 1925
CONTEGIX, LLC; *U.S. Private*, pg. 1027
CONTEGO PACKAGING B.V.—See Platinum Equity, LLC; *U.S. Private*, pg. 3202
CONTEGO PACKAGING HOLDINGS LIMITED—See Platinum Equity, LLC; *U.S. Private*, pg. 3202

CONTEGO PACKAGING IRELAND LTD.—See Platinum Equity, LLC; *U.S. Private*, pg. 3202
CONTEGO PACKAGING—See Platinum Equity, LLC; *U.S. Private*, pg. 3202
CONTEGO SERVICES GROUP, LLC—See Patriot National, Inc.; *U.S. Private*, pg. 3110
CONTEGO UNDERWRITING LIMITED—See Arthur J. Gallagher & Co.; *U.S. Public*, pg. 202
CONTEGRA CONSTRUCTION COMPANY, L.L.C.; *U.S. Private*, pg. 1027
CONTEL CORPORATION LIMITED; *Int'l*, pg. 1779
CONTEMPERARY FIRE INC.—See Tulikivi Corporation; *Int'l*, pg. 7969
CONTEMPO ADVERTISING + DESIGN; *U.S. Private*, pg. 1027
CONTEMPO CARD CO., INC.; *U.S. Private*, pg. 1027
CONTEMPO CERAMIC TILE CORP.; *U.S. Private*, pg. 1027
CONTEMPORARY AMPEREX TECHNOLOGY CO., LTD.; *Int'l*, pg. 1779
CONTEMPORARY AMPEREX TECHNOLOGY GMBH—See Contemporary Amperex Technology Co., Ltd.; *Int'l*, pg. 1779
CONTEMPORARY AMPEREX TECHNOLOGY JAPAN KK—See Contemporary Amperex Technology Co., Ltd.; *Int'l*, pg. 1779
CONTEMPORARY AMPEREX TECHNOLOGY THURINGIA GMBH—See Contemporary Amperex Technology Co., Ltd.; *Int'l*, pg. 1779
CONTEMPORARY AMPEREX TECHNOLOGY USA INC.—See Contemporary Amperex Technology Co., Ltd.; *Int'l*, pg. 1779
THE CONTEMPORARY ART MUSEUM; *U.S. Private*, pg. 4014
CONTEMPORARY BENEFITS DESIGN, INC.—See Aon plc; *Int'l*, pg. 495
CONTEMPORARY CARS, INC.—See AutoNation, Inc.; *U.S. Public*, pg. 234
CONTEMPORARY COMPUTER SERVICES, INC.; *U.S. Private*, pg. 1027
CONTEMPORARY MOTOR CARS, INC.; *U.S. Private*, pg. 1027
CONTEMPORARY PRODUCTS, LLC—See Bidwell Industrial Group, Inc.; *U.S. Private*, pg. 551
CONTEMPORARY SERVICES CORP.; *U.S. Private*, pg. 1027
CONTEMPORARY SIGNED BOOKS, INC.; *U.S. Private*, pg. 1027
CONTEMPORARY STAFFING SOLUTIONS INC.; *U.S. Private*, pg. 1027
CONTEMPRO FOR HOUSING PROJECTS PLC; *Int'l*, pg. 1779
CONTENT4ALL B.V.—See Bayerische Motoren Werke Aktiengesellschaft; *Int'l*, pg. 912
CONTENTCHECKED HOLDINGS INC.; *U.S. Private*, pg. 1027
CONTENT CONNECT AFRICA (PROPRIETARY) LIMITED—See Blue Label Telecoms Limited; *Int'l*, pg. 1068
CONTENTFILM INTERNATIONAL - LOS ANGELES—See Kew Media Group Inc.; *Int'l*, pg. 4144
CONTENT FLEET GMBH—See Stroer SE & Co. KGaA; *Int'l*, pg. 7242
CONTENTGUARD, INC.—See Pendrell Corporation; *U.S. Public*, pg. 1661
CONTENT MANAGEMENT CONSULTING APS; *Int'l*, pg. 1779
CONTENT MANAGEMENT CORPORATION—See BR Printers, Inc.; *U.S. Private*, pg. 630
CONTENT MARKETING INSTITUTE—See Informa plc; *Int'l*, pg. 3694
CONTENT MEDIA CORPORATION—See Kew Media Group Inc.; *Int'l*, pg. 4144
CONTENT PARTNERS LLC; *U.S. Private*, pg. 1027
CONTENTREEJOONGANG CORP.; *Int'l*, pg. 1779
CONTENT RULES INC.; *U.S. Private*, pg. 1027
CONTENT SQUARE SAS; *Int'l*, pg. 1779
CONTENT VENTURES LIMITED; *Int'l*, pg. 1779
CONTENTWATCH, INC.—See SafeTonet Limited; *Int'l*, pg. 6470
CONTE SASU—See Societe BIC S.A.; *Int'l*, pg. 7037
CONTESSA HEALTH OF TENNESSEE, LLC—See Amedisys, Inc.; *U.S. Public*, pg. 93
CON TESSA IMMOBILIENVERWERTUNG GMBH—See Vonovia SE; *Int'l*, pg. 8305
CONTESSA LIMITED—See AXIS Capital Holdings Limited; *Int'l*, pg. 770
CON-TEST ANALYTICAL LABORATORY—See Leonard Green & Partners, L.P.; *U.S. Private*, pg. 2426
CONTESTA OY—See Sweco AB; *Int'l*, pg. 7363
CONTEX AMERICAS INC.—See Procuritas Partners AB; *Int'l*, pg. 5987
CONTEX A/S—See Procuritas Partners AB; *Int'l*, pg. 5987
CONTEXTA AG; *Int'l*, pg. 1780
CONTEXT CORPORATION—See Medtecs International Corporation Limited; *Int'l*, pg. 4786
CONTEXTMEDIA HEALTH, LLC—See Catterton Management Company, LLC; *U.S. Private*, pg. 793

CORPORATE AFFILIATIONS

CONTEXTMEDIA, INC.—See Catterton Management Company, LLC; *U.S. Private*, pg. 794
CONTEXT THERAPEUTICS INC.; *U.S. Public*, pg. 573
CONTEXT TRAVEL; *U.S. Private*, pg. 1028
CONTEXTURE, INC; *U.S. Private*, pg. 1028
CONTEXTVISION AB; *Int'l*, pg. 1780
CONTGQ PTY. LTD.—See SAP SE; *Int'l*, pg. 6566
CONTIASIA—See Continental Grain Company; *U.S. Private*, pg. 1029
CONTI CAUSEWAY FORD INC.; *U.S. Private*, pg. 1028
CONTICO MANUFACTURING LIMITED—See Robert Scott & Sons Ltd.; *Int'l*, pg. 6368
CONTI ELECTRIC INC.; *U.S. Private*, pg. 1028
CONTIFONTE SA—See Bucher Industries AG; *Int'l*, pg. 1208
CONTIGA AB—See Heidelberg Materials AG; *Int'l*, pg. 3310
CONTIGA AS—See Heidelberg Materials AG; *Int'l*, pg. 3310
CONTIGA TINGLEV A/S—See Heidelberg Materials AG; *Int'l*, pg. 3310
CONTIGEA SA—See Itron, Inc.; *U.S. Public*, pg. 1175
CONTIGO SOFTWARE LIMITED—See Energy One Limited; *Int'l*, pg. 2423
THE CONTI GROUP; *U.S. Private*, pg. 4014
CONTIKI HOLIDAYS (AUSTRALIA) PTY LTD—See Contiki Tours International Limited; *Int'l*, pg. 1780
CONTIKI TOURS INTERNATIONAL LIMITED; *Int'l*, pg. 1780
CONTILATIN—See Continental Grain Company; *U.S. Private*, pg. 1029
CONTIL INDIA LIMITED; *Int'l*, pg. 1780
CONTINAF B.V.—See Amtrada Holding B.V.; *Int'l*, pg. 442
CONTINENT 2001—See Carrefour S.A.; *Int'l*, pg. 1344
CONTINENTAL AEROSPACE TECHNOLOGIES HOLDING LIMITED—See Aviation Industry Corporation of China; *Int'l*, pg. 741
CONTINENTAL AKTIENGESELLSCHAFT; *Int'l*, pg. 1780
CONTINENTAL ALLOYS MIDDLE EAST FZE—See Reliance Steel & Aluminum Co.; *U.S. Public*, pg. 1779
CONTINENTAL ALLOYS & SERVICES (DELAWARE) LLC—See Reliance Steel & Aluminum Co.; *U.S. Public*, pg. 1779
CONTINENTAL ALLOYS & SERVICES INC—See Reliance Steel & Aluminum Co.; *U.S. Public*, pg. 1779
CONTINENTAL ALLOYS & SERVICES INC—See Reliance Steel & Aluminum Co.; *U.S. Public*, pg. 1779
CONTINENTAL ALLOYS & SERVICES LIMITED—See Reliance Steel & Aluminum Co.; *U.S. Public*, pg. 1779
CONTINENTAL ALLOYS & SERVICES (MALAYSIA) SDN. BHD.—See Reliance Steel & Aluminum Co.; *U.S. Public*, pg. 1779
CONTINENTAL ALLOYS & SERVICES PTE. LTD.—See Reliance Steel & Aluminum Co.; *U.S. Public*, pg. 1779
CONTINENTAL ALLOY WHEEL CORPORATION; *U.S. Private*, pg. 1028
CONTINENTAL ALUMINUM COMPANY—See Metal Exchange Corporation; *U.S. Private*, pg. 2680
CONTINENTAL AMERICAN CORPORATION; *U.S. Private*, pg. 1028
CONTINENTAL AMERICAN INSURANCE COMPANY—See Aflac Incorporated; *U.S. Public*, pg. 57
CONTINENTAL ANALYTICAL SERVICES, INC.—See Leonard Green & Partners, L.P.; *U.S. Private*, pg. 2426
CONTINENTAL AUTOMOTIVE AUSTRIA GMBH—See Continental Aktiengesellschaft; *Int'l*, pg. 1781
CONTINENTAL AUTOMOTIVE CANADA, INC.—See Continental Aktiengesellschaft; *Int'l*, pg. 1781
CONTINENTAL AUTOMOTIVE COMPONENTS (INDIA) PRIVATE LTD.—See Continental Aktiengesellschaft; *Int'l*, pg. 1781
CONTINENTAL AUTOMOTIVE COMPONENTS MALAYSIA SDN. BHD.—See Continental Aktiengesellschaft; *Int'l*, pg. 1782
CONTINENTAL AUTOMOTIVE CZECH REPUBLIC S.R.O.—See Continental Aktiengesellschaft; *Int'l*, pg. 1782
CONTINENTAL AUTOMOTIVE ELECTRONICS LLC—See Continental Aktiengesellschaft; *Int'l*, pg. 1781
CONTINENTAL AUTOMOTIVE FRANCE SAS—See Continental Aktiengesellschaft; *Int'l*, pg. 1781
CONTINENTAL AUTOMOTIVE GMBH—See INA-Holding Schaeffler GmbH & Co. KG; *Int'l*, pg. 3641
CONTINENTAL AUTOMOTIVE GMBH—See Continental Aktiengesellschaft; *Int'l*, pg. 1782
CONTINENTAL AUTOMOTIVE GMBH—See Continental Aktiengesellschaft; *Int'l*, pg. 1782
CONTINENTAL AUTOMOTIVE GMBH—See Continental Aktiengesellschaft; *Int'l*, pg. 1782
CONTINENTAL AUTOMOTIVE JAPAN KK—See Continental Aktiengesellschaft; *Int'l*, pg. 1781
CONTINENTAL AUTOMOTIVE PTE. LTD.—See Continental Aktiengesellschaft; *Int'l*, pg. 1782
CONTINENTAL AUTOMOTIVE S.A. DE C.V—See Continental Aktiengesellschaft; *Int'l*, pg. 1781
CONTINENTAL AUTOMOTIVE SPAIN S.A.—See Continental Aktiengesellschaft; *Int'l*, pg. 1781

COMPANY NAME INDEX

CONTINENTAL REAL ESTATE COMPANIES INC.

CONTINENTAL AUTOMOTIVE SPAIN, S.A.—See Continental Aktiengesellschaft; *Int'l*, pg. 1782

CONTINENTAL AUTOMOTIVE SWITZERLAND AG—See Continental Aktiengesellschaft; *Int'l*, pg. 1782

CONTINENTAL AUTOMOTIVE SYSTEMS CZECH REPUBLIC S.R.O.—See Continental Aktiengesellschaft; *Int'l*, pg. 1781

CONTINENTAL AUTOMOTIVE SYSTEMS, INC—See Continental Aktiengesellschaft; *Int'l*, pg. 1782

CONTINENTAL AUTOMOTIVE SYSTEMS MANAGEMENT CO., LTD—See Continental Aktiengesellschaft; *Int'l*, pg. 1781

CONTINENTAL AUTOMOTIVE SYSTEMS (SHANGHAI) CO., LTD—See Continental Aktiengesellschaft; *Int'l*, pg. 1781

CONTINENTAL AUTOMOTIVE SYSTEMS US, INC.—See Continental Aktiengesellschaft; *Int'l*, pg. 1781

CONTINENTAL AUTOMOTIVE SYSTEMS US, INC.—See Continental Aktiengesellschaft; *Int'l*, pg. 1781

CONTINENTAL AUTOMOTIVE SYSTEMS US, INC.—See Continental Aktiengesellschaft; *Int'l*, pg. 1782

CONTINENTAL AUTOMOTIVE SYSTEMS US, INC.—See Continental Aktiengesellschaft; *Int'l*, pg. 1782

CONTINENTAL AUTOMOTIVE (THAILAND) CO. LTD—See Continental Aktiengesellschaft; *Int'l*, pg. 1781

CONTINENTAL AUTOMOTIVE TRADING NEDERLAND B.V.—See Continental Aktiengesellschaft; *Int'l*, pg. 1782

CONTINENTAL AUTOMOTIVE TRADING S.R.L.—See Continental Aktiengesellschaft; *Int'l*, pg. 1782

CONTINENTAL AUTOMOTIVE TRADING UK LTD.—See Continental Aktiengesellschaft; *Int'l*, pg. 1782

CONTINENTAL BAG CO. INC.—See Langston Companies, Inc.; *U.S. Private*, pg. 2390

CONTINENTAL BAKERIES B.V.—See Silverfern Capital Management, LLC; *U.S. Private*, pg. 3663

CONTINENTAL BAKERIES B.V.—See The Goldman Sachs Group, Inc.; *U.S. Public*, pg. 2076

CONTINENTAL BATTERY COMPANY—See H.I.G. Capital, LLC; *U.S. Private*, pg. 1829

CONTINENTAL BENELUX S.A.—See Continental Aktiengesellschaft; *Int'l*, pg. 1782

CONTINENTAL BEVERAGES (PTY) LTD—See PepsiCo, Inc.; *U.S. Public*, pg. 1672

CONTINENTAL BRASIL INDUSTRIA AUTOMOTIVA LTDA.—See Continental Aktiengesellschaft; *Int'l*, pg. 1782

CONTINENTAL BRASIL INDUSTRIA AUTOMOTIVA LTDA.—See Continental Aktiengesellschaft; *Int'l*, pg. 1782

CONTINENTAL BUILDING PRODUCTS, INC.—See Compagnie de Saint-Gobain SA; *Int'l*, pg. 1730

CONTINENTAL BUSINESS CREDIT, INC.—See Republic Business Credit, LLC; *U.S. Private*, pg. 3401

CONTINENTAL CARBON COMPANY—See China Synthetic Rubber Corporation; *Int'l*, pg. 1557

CONTINENTAL CARBONIC PRODUCTS, INC.—See Mitsubishi Chemical Group Corporation; *Int'l*, pg. 4936

CONTINENTAL CARBON INDIA LTD.—See China Synthetic Rubber Corporation; *Int'l*, pg. 1557

CONTINENTAL CAR CLUB, INC.—See Tiptree Inc.; *U.S. Public*, pg. 2159

CONTINENTAL CARS, INC.; *U.S. Private*, pg. 1028

CONTINENTAL CARTAGE INC.—See Landtran Systems Inc.; *Int'l*, pg. 4408

CONTINENTAL CASTING, LLC; *U.S. Private*, pg. 1028

CONTINENTAL CASUALTY COMPANY—See Loews Corporation; *U.S. Public*, pg. 1340

CONTINENTAL CATALINA, INC.—See Bee Street Holdings LLC; *U.S. Private*, pg. 513

CONTINENTAL CEMENT COMPANY, LLC—See Summit Materials, Inc.; *U.S. Public*, pg. 1960

CONTINENTAL CHASSIS & SAFETY DIVISION—See Continental Aktiengesellschaft; *Int'l*, pg. 1782

CONTINENTAL CHEF SUPPLIES LIMITED—See Bunzl plc; *Int'l*, pg. 1218

CONTINENTAL CHEMICALS LIMITED; *Int'l*, pg. 1783

CONTINENTAL CHOCOLATE B.V.—See Sweet Products Logistics NV; *Int'l*, pg. 7366

CONTINENTAL COATINGS—See Continental Plastics Co. Inc.; *U.S. Private*, pg. 1030

CONTINENTAL COMMERCIAL PRODUCTS, LLC—See Highview Capital, LLC; *U.S. Private*, pg. 1942

CONTINENTAL COMMERCIAL PRODUCTS, LLC—See Victory Park Capital Advisors, LLC; *U.S. Private*, pg. 4379

CONTINENTAL COMMERCIAL VEHICLE TIRES DIVISION—See Continental Aktiengesellschaft; *Int'l*, pg. 1782

CONTINENTAL CONAIR, LTD.—See American Securities LLC; *U.S. Private*, pg. 248

CONTINENTAL CONCESSION SUPPLIES, INC.; *U.S. Private*, pg. 1028

CONTINENTAL CONSTRUCTION CO.; *U.S. Private*, pg. 1028

CONTINENTAL CONSULTING LIMITED COMPANY—See Continental Holdings Corp.; *Int'l*, pg. 1784

CONTINENTAL CONTROLS LIMITED; *Int'l*, pg. 1783

CONTINENTAL COPPER, INC.—See Bee Street Holdings LLC; *U.S. Private*, pg. 513

CONTINENTAL CURRENCY SERVICES INC.; *U.S. Private*, pg. 1028

CONTINENTAL CYLINDER INC.—See Corrosion & Abrasion Solutions Ltd.; *Int'l*, pg. 1806

CONTINENTAL DATAGRAPHICS LTD.—See The Boeing Company; *U.S. Public*, pg. 2041

CONTINENTAL DATAGRAPHICS—See The Boeing Company; *U.S. Public*, pg. 2041

CONTINENTAL DATALABEL; *U.S. Private*, pg. 1028

CONTINENTAL DE EQUIPOS ELECTRICOS SA—See Industrielle De Controle Et D Equipement; *Int'l*, pg. 3675

CONTINENTAL DESIGN & ENGINEERING, INC.; *U.S. Private*, pg. 1028

CONTINENTAL DESIGN & MANAGEMENT GROUP INC.—See Stevens Engineers & Constructors; *U.S. Private*, pg. 3809

CONTINENTAL DEVELOPMENT CORP.; *U.S. Private*, pg. 1028

CONTINENTAL DEVICE INDIA PRIVATE LIMITED; *Int'l*, pg. 1783

CONTINENTAL DIALYSIS CENTER OF SPRINGFIELD-FAIRFAX, INC.—See DaVita Inc.; *U.S. Public*, pg. 637

CONTINENTAL DISC CORPORATION—See Tinicum Enterprises, Inc.; *U.S. Private*, pg. 4174

CONTINENTAL DISTRIBUTORS, INC.; *U.S. Private*, pg. 1028

CONTINENTAL DIVIDE ELECTRIC COOPERATIVE INC; *U.S. Private*, pg. 1028

CONTINENTAL DIVIDE INSURANCE COMPANY—See Berkshire Hathaway Inc.; *U.S. Public*, pg. 301

CONTINENTAL DO BRASIL PRODUTOS AUTOMOTIVOS LTDA.—See Continental Aktiengesellschaft; *Int'l*, pg. 1781

CONTINENTALE HOLDING AG; *Int'l*, pg. 1784

CONTINENTAL ELECTRIC CONSTRUCTION COMPANY; *U.S. Private*, pg. 1028

CONTINENTAL ELECTRONICS CORPORATION—See Lone Star Investment Advisors, LLC; *U.S. Private*, pg. 2489

CONTINENTAL ENERGY CORPORATION; *Int'l*, pg. 1783

CONTINENTAL ENGINEERING CORPORATION—See Continental Holdings Corp.; *Int'l*, pg. 1784

CONTINENTAL ENGINES, INC.—See Palmer Johnson Enterprises, Inc.; *U.S. Private*, pg. 3081

CONTINENTAL ESTATES INC.; *U.S. Private*, pg. 1028

CONTINENTAL EXCHANGE SOLUTIONS, INC.—See Euronet Worldwide, Inc.; *U.S. Public*, pg. 797

CONTINENTAL EXPRESS MONEY ORDER COMPANY INC.—See Continental Currency Services Inc.; *U.S. Private*, pg. 1028

CONTINENTAL FARMERS GROUP PLC—See Almarai Company Ltd.; *Int'l*, pg. 363

CONTINENTAL FIELD SYSTEMS INC.; *U.S. Private*, pg. 1028

CONTINENTAL FILM D.O.O.; *Int'l*, pg. 1783

CONTINENTAL FINANCE; *U.S. Private*, pg. 1029

CONTINENTAL FINANCIAL LTD; *U.S. Private*, pg. 1029

CONTINENTAL FLORAL GREENS; *U.S. Private*, pg. 1029

CONTINENTAL FLORIDA MATERIALS, INC.—See Heidelberg Materials AG; *Int'l*, pg. 3313

CONTINENTAL FOODS CO., LTD.—See Hotel Okura Co., Ltd.; *Int'l*, pg. 3488

CONTINENTAL FORGE COMPANY—See Arlington Capital Partners LLC; *U.S. Private*, pg. 327

CONTINENTAL FREIGHT SERVICES (AUST.) PTY. LTD—See Qube Holdings Limited; *Int'l*, pg. 6158

CONTINENTAL GENERAL TIRE INC.—See Continental Aktiengesellschaft; *Int'l*, pg. 1782

CONTINENTAL GLASS SYSTEMS LLC—See The Graham Group, Inc.; *U.S. Private*, pg. 4036

CONTINENTAL GOLD INC.—See Zijin Mining Group Company Limited; *Int'l*, pg. 8683

CONTINENTAL GRAIN COMPANY; *U.S. Private*, pg. 1029

CONTINENTAL HEAT TREATING, INC.; *U.S. Private*, pg. 1029

CONTINENTAL HOLDING COMPANY; *U.S. Private*, pg. 1029

CONTINENTAL HOLDINGS CORP.; *Int'l*, pg. 1783

CONTINENTAL HOLDINGS LIMITED; *Int'l*, pg. 1784

CONTINENTAL HOME CARE, INC.—See Encompass Health Corporation; *U.S. Public*, pg. 755

CONTINENTAL HOMES OF AUSTIN, L.P.—See D.R. Horton, Inc.; *U.S. Public*, pg. 619

CONTINENTAL HOSTS LTD.; *U.S. Private*, pg. 1030

CONTINENTAL INDUSTRIAS DEL CAUCHO S.A.—See Continental Aktiengesellschaft; *Int'l*, pg. 1781

CONTINENTAL INSTRUMENTS, LLC—See Napco Security Technologies, Inc.; *U.S. Public*, pg. 1491

THE CONTINENTAL INSURANCE COMPANY OF NEW JERSEY—See Loews Corporation; *U.S. Public*, pg. 1340

THE CONTINENTAL INSURANCE COMPANY—See Loews Corporation; *U.S. Public*, pg. 1340

CONTINENTAL INSURANCE LANKA LIMITED—See Melstacorp PLC; *Int'l*, pg. 4813

CONTINENTAL INSURANCE LIMITED; *Int'l*, pg. 1784

CONTINENTAL INTERIOR DIVISION—See Continental Aktiengesellschaft; *Int'l*, pg. 1782

CONTINENTAL INTERIORS INC.; *U.S. Private*, pg. 1030

CONTINENTAL ITALIA S.P.A.—See Continental Aktiengesellschaft; *Int'l*, pg. 1782

CONTINENTAL JEWELLERY (JIANGMEN) CO., LTD.—See Continental Holdings Limited; *Int'l*, pg. 1784

CONTINENTAL JEWELLERY (UK) LTD.—See Continental Holdings Limited; *Int'l*, pg. 1784

CONTINENTAL JEWELRY (U.S.A.) INC.—See Continental Holdings Limited; *Int'l*, pg. 1784

CONTINENTAL LABOR RESOURCES INC.; *U.S. Private*, pg. 1030

CONTINENTAL LEASING COMPANY, INC.—See Continental Resources, Inc.; *U.S. Public*, pg. 573

CONTINENTAL LENSA S.A.—See Lone Star Investment Advisors, LLC; *U.S. Private*, pg. 2489

CONTINENTAL LIFE INSURANCE COMPANY OF BRENTWOOD, TENNESSEE—See CVS Health Corporation; *U.S. Public*, pg. 615

CONTINENTAL LINEN SERVICES INC.; *U.S. Private*, pg. 1030

CONTINENTAL MABOR—See Continental Aktiengesellschaft; *Int'l*, pg. 1782

CONTINENTAL MACHINES, INC.—See DoALL Company; *U.S. Private*, pg. 1250

CONTINENTAL MAPPING CONSULTANTS, INC.—See Bluestone Investment Partners, LLC; *U.S. Private*, pg. 598

CONTINENTAL MARITIME OF SAN DIEGO, INC.—See Huntington Ingalls Industries, Inc.; *U.S. Public*, pg. 1072

CONTINENTAL MARKETING; *U.S. Private*, pg. 1030

CONTINENTAL MATADOR S.R.O.—See Continental Aktiengesellschaft; *Int'l*, pg. 1782

CONTINENTAL MECHANICAL COMPONENTS GERMANY GMBH—See Continental Aktiengesellschaft; *Int'l*, pg. 1782

CONTINENTAL MECHATRONIC GERMANY GMBH & CO. KG—See INA-Holding Schaeffler GmbH & Co. KG; *Int'l*, pg. 3641

CONTINENTAL MICROWAVE LIMITED—See Pebble Beach Systems Group PLC; *Int'l*, pg. 5778

CONTINENTAL MICROWAVE & TOOL CO, INC—See Advent International Corporation; *U.S. Private*, pg. 99

CONTINENTAL/MIDLAND, LLC—See A.Agrati S.p.A.; *Int'l*, pg. 23

CONTINENTAL MILLS, INC.; *U.S. Private*, pg. 1030

CONTINENTAL MORTGAGE BANKERS; *U.S. Private*, pg. 1030

CONTINENTAL MOTOR CO. INC.; *U.S. Private*, pg. 1030

CONTINENTAL MOTORS, INC.—See Aviation Industry Corporation of China; *Int'l*, pg. 741

CONTINENTAL MUSHROOM CORP.; *Int'l*, pg. 1784

CONTINENTAL NATIONAL BANK OF MIAMI—See First American Bank Corporation; *U.S. Public*, pg. 1512

CONTINENTAL OFFICE ENVIRONMENTS; *U.S. Private*, pg. 1030

CONTINENTAL PALMS PTE. LTD.—See C.I. Holdings Berhad; *Int'l*, pg. 1243

CONTINENTAL PAPER GRADING CO. INC.; *U.S. Private*, pg. 1030

CONTINENTAL PASSENGER & LIGHT TRUCK TIRES DIVISION—See Continental Aktiengesellschaft; *Int'l*, pg. 1782

CONTINENTAL PETROLEUMS LIMITED; *Int'l*, pg. 1784

CONTINENTAL PHARMACEUTIQUE—See Toyota Tsusho Corporation; *Int'l*, pg. 7875

CONTINENTAL PLASTIC CARD COMPANY; *U.S. Private*, pg. 1030

CONTINENTAL PLASTICS CO. INC.; *U.S. Private*, pg. 1030

CONTINENTAL PRECISION CORP; *U.S. Private*, pg. 1030

CONTINENTAL PREMIUM CORPORATION; *U.S. Private*, pg. 1030

CONTINENTAL PRESS INC.; *U.S. Private*, pg. 1030

CONTINENTAL PRODUCT ENGINEERING LIMITED—See Ferguson plc; *Int'l*, pg. 2637

THE CONTINENTAL PRODUCTS COMPANY, INC.—See Keene Building Products Company, Inc.; *U.S. Private*, pg. 2272

CONTINENTAL PRODUCTS; *U.S. Private*, pg. 1030

CONTINENTAL PROPERTIES MEXICO SA DE CV—See Continental Aktiengesellschaft; *Int'l*, pg. 1783

CONTINENTAL PROPERTY GROUP, INC.; *U.S. Private*, pg. 1030

CONTINENTAL PTY. LTD. - MELBOURNE PLANT—See Continental Aktiengesellschaft; *Int'l*, pg. 1782

CONTINENTAL PTY LTD—See Continental Aktiengesellschaft; *Int'l*, pg. 1782

CONTINENTAL RAIL, S.A.—See ACS, Actividades de Construccion y Servicios, S.A.; *Int'l*, pg. 111

CONTINENTAL REAL ESTATE COMPANIES COMMERCIAL PROPERTIES CORP.—See Colliers International Group Inc.; *Int'l*, pg. 1701

CONTINENTAL REAL ESTATE COMPANIES INC.; *U.S. Private*, pg. 1030

CONTINENTAL REALTY CORPORATION

CORPORATE AFFILIATIONS

CONTINENTAL REALTY CORPORATION; *U.S. Private*, pg. 1030
CONTINENTAL REALTY, LTD.—See Newmark Group, Inc.; *U.S. Public*, pg. 1515
CONTINENTAL REFINING COMPANY; *U.S. Private*, pg. 1031
CONTINENTAL RESEARCH CORPORATION—See C&I Holdings Inc.; *U.S. Private*, pg. 703
CONTINENTAL RESEARCH LTD.—See The BDRC Group; *Int'l*, pg. 7620
CONTINENTAL RESOURCES ILLINOIS, INC.—See Continental Resources, Inc.; *U.S. Private*, pg. 1031
CONTINENTAL RESOURCES, INC.; *U.S. Private*, pg. 1031
CONTINENTAL RESOURCES, INC.; *U.S. Public*, pg. 573
CONTINENTAL RESOURCES SDN. BHD.—See C.I. Holdings Berhad; *Int'l*, pg. 1243
CONTINENTAL RISK INSURANCE SERVICES—See Caisse de Depot et Placement du Quebec; *Int'l*, pg. 1256
CONTINENTAL RISK INSURANCE SERVICES—See KKR & Co. Inc.; *U.S. Public*, pg. 1265
CONTINENTAL SAFETY ENGINEERING INTERNATIONAL GMBH—See Continental Aktiengesellschaft; *Int'l*, pg. 1782
CONTINENTAL SALES COMPANY OF AMERICA, LTD.; *U.S. Private*, pg. 1031
CONTINENTAL S.A. SOCIEDAD ADMINISTRADORA DE FONDOS—See Banco Bilbao Vizcaya Argentaria, S.A.; *Int'l*, pg. 817
CONTINENTAL SECRET SERVICE BUREAU; *U.S. Private*, pg. 1031
CONTINENTAL SECURITIES LIMITED; *Int'l*, pg. 1784
CONTINENTAL SEEDS & CHEMICALS LIMITED; *Int'l*, pg. 1784
CONTINENTAL SERIES SDN BHD—See Jiankun International Berhad; *Int'l*, pg. 3961
CONTINENTAL SERVICES, INC.; *U.S. Private*, pg. 1031
CONTINENTAL SERVICES INC.—See New Heritage Capital LLC; *U.S. Private*, pg. 2896
CONTINENTAL SILVERLINE PRODUCTS INC.—See Restonic Mattress Corporation; *U.S. Private*, pg. 3409
CONTINENTAL SIME TYRE MARKETING SDN. BHD.—See Continental Aktiengesellschaft; *Int'l*, pg. 1783
CONTINENTAL SIME TYRE SDN BHD—See Continental Aktiengesellschaft; *Int'l*, pg. 1783
CONTINENTAL STRUCTURAL PLASTICS, INC. - CAREY PLANT—See Teijin Limited; *Int'l*, pg. 7522
CONTINENTAL STRUCTURAL PLASTICS, INC. - CONNEAUT PLANT—See Teijin Limited; *Int'l*, pg. 7522
CONTINENTAL STRUCTURAL PLASTICS, INC. - NORTH BALTIMORE PLANT—See Teijin Limited; *Int'l*, pg. 7523
CONTINENTAL STRUCTURAL PLASTICS, INC. - POUANCE PLANT—See Teijin Limited; *Int'l*, pg. 7523
CONTINENTAL STRUCTURAL PLASTICS, INC. - SAREPTA PLANT—See Teijin Limited; *Int'l*, pg. 7523
CONTINENTAL STRUCTURAL PLASTICS, INC. - TIJUANA PLANT—See Teijin Limited; *Int'l*, pg. 7523
CONTINENTAL STRUCTURAL PLASTICS, INC. - VAN WERT PLANT—See Teijin Limited; *Int'l*, pg. 7523
CONTINENTAL SUISSE S A—See Continental Aktiengesellschaft; *Int'l*, pg. 1783
CONTINENTAL TELEVISION SALES—See iHeartMedia, Inc.; *U.S. Public*, pg. 1096
CONTINENTAL TEMIC ELECTRONICS PHILIPPINES INC.—See Continental Aktiengesellschaft; *Int'l*, pg. 1783
CONTINENTAL TEVES AG & CO. OHG—See Continental Aktiengesellschaft; *Int'l*, pg. 1783
CONTINENTAL TEVES HUNGARY KFT.—See Continental Aktiengesellschaft; *Int'l*, pg. 1783
CONTINENTAL TEVES INC.—See Continental Aktiengesellschaft; *Int'l*, pg. 1783
CONTINENTAL TEVES PORTUGAL SISTEMAS DE TRAVAGEM LDA—See Continental Aktiengesellschaft; *Int'l*, pg. 1783
CONTINENTAL TEVES UK LTD.—See Continental Aktiengesellschaft; *Int'l*, pg. 1783
CONTINENTAL TICKING CORPORATION AMERICA; *U.S. Private*, pg. 1031
CONTINENTAL TIMBER CO. INC.—See Conner Industries, Inc.; *U.S. Private*, pg. 1017
CONTINENTAL TIRE NORTH AMERICA—See Continental Aktiengesellschaft; *Int'l*, pg. 1783
CONTINENTAL TIRE THE AMERICAS, LLC—See Continental Aktiengesellschaft; *Int'l*, pg. 1783
CONTINENTAL TOBACCO S.A.—See Universal Corporation; *U.S. Public*, pg. 2254
CONTINENTAL TOOL GROUP INCORPORATED—See ShoreView Industries, LLC; *U.S. Private*, pg. 3642
CONTINENTAL TRADING CO. LLC—See GIBCA Limited; *Int'l*, pg. 2962
CONTINENTAL TRADING FRANCE SAS—See Continental Aktiengesellschaft; *Int'l*, pg. 1783
CONTINENTAL TRADING GMBH—See Continental Aktiengesellschaft; *Int'l*, pg. 1782
CONTINENTAL TRADING & HARDWARE INC.; *U.S. Private*, pg. 1031

CONTINENTAL TRADING UK LTD.—See Continental Aktiengesellschaft; *Int'l*, pg. 1783
CONTINENTAL TRUCK BROKERS INC.; *U.S. Private*, pg. 1031
CONTINENTAL TYRE AND RUBBER SINGAPORE PTE. LTD.—See Continental Aktiengesellschaft; *Int'l*, pg. 1781
CONTINENTAL TYRE GROUP LTD.—See Continental Aktiengesellschaft; *Int'l*, pg. 1783
CONTINENTAL UNDERWRITERS LTD.—See Tokio Marine Holdings, Inc.; *Int'l*, pg. 7783
CONTINENTAL VAN LINES INC.; *U.S. Private*, pg. 1031
CONTINENTAL VDO AUTOMOTIVE, S.A.—See Continental Aktiengesellschaft; *Int'l*, pg. 1782
CONTINENTAL VITAMIN CO., INC.; *U.S. Private*, pg. 1031
CONTINENTAL WEB PRESS, INC.; *U.S. Private*, pg. 1031
CONTINENTAL WEB PRESS OF KENTUCKY—See Continental Web Press, Inc.; *U.S. Private*, pg. 1031
CONTINENTAL WESTERN CORPORATION; *U.S. Private*, pg. 1031
CONTINENTAL WESTERN INSURANCE COMPANY - LINCOLN—See W.R. Berkley Corporation; *U.S. Public*, pg. 2318
CONTINENTAL WESTERN INSURANCE COMPANY—See W.R. Berkley Corporation; *U.S. Public*, pg. 2318
CONTINENTAL WESTERN INSURANCE CO—See W.R. Berkley Corporation; *U.S. Public*, pg. 2318
CONTINENTAL WORSTEDS INC.; *U.S. Private*, pg. 1031
CONTINENT S.R.L.—See Societatea de Asigurari-Reasigurari Moldcargo S.A.; *Int'l*, pg. 7034
CONTINUA LIMITED—See Xerox Holdings Corporation; *U.S. Public*, pg. 2387
CONTINUAL LTD.—See RAD Group; *Int'l*, pg. 6172
CONTINUCARE CORPORATION—See Humana, Inc.; *U.S. Public*, pg. 1070
CONTIN-U-CARE HOME HEALTH SERVICES—See Erlanger Health System; *U.S. Private*, pg. 1421
CONTINUCARE MDHC, LLC—See Humana, Inc.; *U.S. Public*, pg. 1069
CONTINUCARE MSO, INC.—See Humana, Inc.; *U.S. Public*, pg. 1070
CONTINUING CARE INC; *U.S. Private*, pg. 1031
CONTINUING EDUCATION NETWORK, INC.—See Moelis Asset Management LP; *U.S. Private*, pg. 2764
CONTINUING MEDICAL EDUCATION LLC—See Informa plc; *Int'l*, pg. 3694
CONTINUOUS COMPUTING INDIA PRIVATE LIMITED—See Reliance - ADA Group Limited; *Int'l*, pg. 6262
CONTINUOUS NETWORK ADVISERS SDN. BHD.—See Omesti Berhad; *Int'l*, pg. 5562
CONTINUOUS TUBING—See Ensign Energy Services Inc.; *Int'l*, pg. 2446
CONTINUUM APPLIED TECHNOLOGY, INC.—See The Hearst Corporation; *U.S. Private*, pg. 4044
CONTINUUM ELECTRO-OPTICS, INC.—See Amplitude Technologies SA; *Int'l*, pg. 436
CONTINUUM GLOBAL SOLUTIONS, LLC—See Skyview Capital, LLC; *U.S. Private*, pg. 3686
CONTINUUM INNOVATION LLC—See EPAM Systems, Inc.; *U.S. Public*, pg. 783
CONTINUUM LLC—See EPAM Systems, Inc.; *U.S. Public*, pg. 783
CONTINUUM MANAGED SERVICES LLC—See Thoma Bravo, L.P.; *U.S. Private*, pg. 4146
CONTINUUM OF CARE, INC.; *U.S. Private*, pg. 1031
CONTINUUM PERFORMANCE SYSTEMS INC.—See MedHOK HealthCare Solutions, LLC; *U.S. Private*, pg. 2651
CONTINUUM SERVICES LLC—See Abbott Laboratories; *U.S. Public*, pg. 19
CONTINUUM SOCS S.A.S.—See DXC Technology Company; *U.S. Public*, pg. 695
CONTINUUM SRL—See EPAM Systems, Inc.; *U.S. Public*, pg. 783
CONTINUUM WORLDWIDE CORPORATION—See CDW Corporation; *U.S. Public*, pg. 462
CONTIPAK NORON SDN. BHD.—See Computer Forms (Malaysia) Berhad; *Int'l*, pg. 1759
CONTIPARK PARKGARAGENGESELLSCHAFT MBH—See Ageas SA/NV; *Int'l*, pg. 204
CONTI SANITARARMATUREN GMBH—See Aalberts N.V.; *Int'l*, pg. 33
CONTITECH AGES S.P.A.—See Continental Aktiengesellschaft; *Int'l*, pg. 1781
CONTITECH AG—See Continental Aktiengesellschaft; *Int'l*, pg. 1780
CONTITECH ANOFLEX S.A.S.—See Continental Aktiengesellschaft; *Int'l*, pg. 1780
CONTITECH ANTRIEBSSYSTEME GMBH—See Continental Aktiengesellschaft; *Int'l*, pg. 1780
CONTITECH BEATTIE CORP.—See Continental Aktiengesellschaft; *Int'l*, pg. 1780
CONTITECH BELGIUM BVBA—See Continental Aktiengesellschaft; *Int'l*, pg. 1780
CONTITECH CONTINENTAL SUISSE S.A.—See Continental Aktiengesellschaft; *Int'l*, pg. 1780

CONTITECH CONVEYOR BELT GROUP—See Continental Aktiengesellschaft; *Int'l*, pg. 1781
CONTITECH DAEWON AIRSPRING SYSTEMS CO. LTD.—See Daewoo Kang Up Co., Ltd.; *Int'l*, pg. 1910
CONTITECH FLUID AUTOMOTIVE HUNGARIA KFT.—See Continental Aktiengesellschaft; *Int'l*, pg. 1780
CONTITECH FLUID AUTOMOTIVE ROMANIA SRL—See Continental Aktiengesellschaft; *Int'l*, pg. 1781
CONTITECH FLUID KOREA LTD.—See Continental Aktiengesellschaft; *Int'l*, pg. 1781
CONTITECH FLUID MONTERREY SERVICIOS, S.A. DE C.V.—See Continental Aktiengesellschaft; *Int'l*, pg. 1780
CONTITECH FLUID SHANGHAI CO., LTD.—See Continental Aktiengesellschaft; *Int'l*, pg. 1781
CONTITECH FRANCE SNC—See Continental Aktiengesellschaft; *Int'l*, pg. 1780
CONTITECH HYCOP AB—See Continental Aktiengesellschaft; *Int'l*, pg. 1781
CONTITECH JAPAN CO. LTD.—See Continental Aktiengesellschaft; *Int'l*, pg. 1780
CONTITECH KAUTSCHUK- UND KUNSTSTOFF-VERTRIEBSGESELLSCHAFT—See Continental Aktiengesellschaft; *Int'l*, pg. 1780
CONTITECH KUHNER GMBH & CIE. KG—See Continental Aktiengesellschaft; *Int'l*, pg. 1781
CONTITECH MGW GMBH—See Continental Aktiengesellschaft; *Int'l*, pg. 1781
CONTITECH NORTH AMERICA, INC.—See Continental Aktiengesellschaft; *Int'l*, pg. 1780
CONTITECH POWER TRANSMISSION SYSTEM (SHANGHAI) CO., LTD.—See Continental Aktiengesellschaft; *Int'l*, pg. 1780
CONTITECH PRINTING BLANKET SHANGHAI LTD.—See Continental Aktiengesellschaft; *Int'l*, pg. 1780
CONTITECH PRINT SERVICE (S) PTE. LTD.—See Continental Aktiengesellschaft; *Int'l*, pg. 1780
CONTITECH ROMANIA S.R.L.—See Continental Aktiengesellschaft; *Int'l*, pg. 1781
CONTITECH ROULUNDS RUBBER A/S—See Continental Aktiengesellschaft; *Int'l*, pg. 1780
CONTITECH RUBBER INDUSTRIAL KFT.—See Continental Aktiengesellschaft; *Int'l*, pg. 1781
CONTITECH SCANDINAVIA AB—See Continental Aktiengesellschaft; *Int'l*, pg. 1780
CONTITECH SCHLAUCH GMBH—See Continental Aktiengesellschaft; *Int'l*, pg. 1781
CONTITECH TECHNO-CHEMIE GMBH—See Continental Aktiengesellschaft; *Int'l*, pg. 1780
CONTITECH THERMOPOL LLC—See Continental Aktiengesellschaft; *Int'l*, pg. 1781
CONTITECH TRANSPORTBANDSYSTEME GMBH—See Continental Aktiengesellschaft; *Int'l*, pg. 1781
CONTITECH TRANSPORTBANDSYSTEME GMBH—See Continental Aktiengesellschaft; *Int'l*, pg. 1781
CONTITECH UNITED KINGDOM LTD.—See Continental Aktiengesellschaft; *Int'l*, pg. 1781
CONTITECH VIBRATION CONTROL GMBH—See Continental Aktiengesellschaft; *Int'l*, pg. 1781
CONTI TEMIC MICROELECTONICS GMBH—See Continental Aktiengesellschaft; *Int'l*, pg. 1782
CONTOUR DATA SOLUTIONS; *U.S. Private*, pg. 1031
CONTOUR ELECTRONICS ASIA LIMITED—See discoverIE Group plc; *Int'l*, pg. 2133
CONTOUR ELECTRONICS LIMITED—See discoverIE Group plc; *Int'l*, pg. 2133
CONTOUR GLOBAL DO BRASIL PARTICIPACOES LTDA—See ContourGlobal Limited; *Int'l*, pg. 1785
CONTOURGLOBAL HYDRO CASCADE CJSC—See ContourGlobal Limited; *Int'l*, pg. 1785
CONTOURGLOBAL LIMITED; *Int'l*, pg. 1785
CONTOUR GLOBAL LLC—See ContourGlobal Limited; *Int'l*, pg. 1785
CONTOUR GLOBAL MANAGEMENT, INC.—See ContourGlobal Limited; *Int'l*, pg. 1785
CONTOURGLOBAL MANAGEMENT SOFIA EOOD—See ContourGlobal Limited; *Int'l*, pg. 1785
CONTOURGLOBAL MARITSA EAST 3 AD—See ContourGlobal Limited; *Int'l*, pg. 1785
CONTOURS EXPRESS, INC.; *U.S. Private*, pg. 1031
CONTOUR SHOWERS LIMITED; *Int'l*, pg. 1785
CONTOUR STEEL INC; *U.S. Private*, pg. 1031
CONTRACK CYPRUS LIMITED—See Orascom Construction PLC; *Int'l*, pg. 5613
CONTRACK INTERNATIONAL INC.; *U.S. Private*, pg. 1032
CONTRACK INTERNATIONAL, INC.—See Orascom Construction PLC; *Int'l*, pg. 5613
CONTRACK WATTS INC.—See Orascom Construction PLC; *Int'l*, pg. 5613
CONTRA COSTA ELECTRIC, INC.—See EMCOR Group, Inc.; *U.S. Public*, pg. 736
CONTRA COSTA NEWSPAPERS, INC.—See Alden Global Capital LLC; *U.S. Private*, pg. 155
CONTRA COSTA TIMES—See Alden Global Capital LLC; *U.S. Private*, pg. 155
CONTRA COSTA WATER DISTRICT INC.; *U.S. Private*, pg. 1031

COMPANY NAME INDEX

CONTRACT ADVERTISING (INDIA) LIMITED—See WPP plc; *Int'l*, pg. 8480
CONTRACT ADVERTISING (INDIA) LIMITED—See WPP plc; *Int'l*, pg. 8480
CONTRACT ADVERTISING (INDIA) LIMITED—See WPP plc; *Int'l*, pg. 8480
CONTRACT ASSOCIATES INC.—See Furniture Marketing Group Inc.; *U.S. Private*, pg. 1624
CONTRACT CHEMICALS LTD.; *Int'l*, pg. 1785
CONTRACT CONVERTING LLC; *U.S. Private*, pg. 1032
CONTRACT DECOR, INC.—See Qurate Retail, Inc.; *U.S. Public*, pg. 1758
CONTRACTED LABOR SERVICES INC.; *U.S. Private*, pg. 1032
CONTRACT EXTERIORS LLC; *U.S. Private*, pg. 1032
CONTRACT FIRE SYSTEMS LTD.—See Stanley Black & Decker, Inc.; *U.S. Public*, pg. 1932
CONTRACT FURNISHERS OF HAWAII; *U.S. Private*, pg. 1032
CONTRACT FURNITURE INC.; *U.S. Private*, pg. 1032
CONTRACT HARDWARE INC.; *U.S. Private*, pg. 1032
CONTRACT INDUSTRIAL TOOLING, INC.; *U.S. Private*, pg. 1032
CONTRACTING ENTERPRISES, LLC—See Cadent Energy Partners, LLC; *U.S. Private*, pg. 713
CONTRACTING & MARINE SERVICES CO. (S.A.K.); *Int'l*, pg. 1785
CONTRACT LAND STAFF LP—See Hammond, Kennedy, Whitney & Company, Inc.; *U.S. Private*, pg. 1850
CONTRACT LOGISTICS—See New Zealand Post Limited; *Int'l*, pg. 5232
CONTRACT LUMBER INC.; *U.S. Private*, pg. 1032
CONTRACT MANUFACTURER, L.L.C.—See Bain Capital, LP; *U.S. Private*, pg. 436
CONTRACT OFFICE GROUP, INC.; *U.S. Private*, pg. 1032
CONTRACT OFFICE PRODUCTS (PTY) LIMITED—See The Bidvest Group Limited; *Int'l*, pg. 7624
CONTRACTOR EQUIPMENT RENTAL & SUPPLY LLC—See Tym Corporation; *Int'l*, pg. 7994
CONTRACTOR MANAGEMENT SERVICES, LLC—See Riverside Partners, LLC; *U.S. Private*, pg. 3445
CONTRACTOR MANAGING GENERAL INSURANCE AGENCY, INC.—See Stone Point Capital LLC; *U.S. Private*, pg. 3820
CONTRACTOR PROPERTY DEVELOPERS CO.—See Scherer Brothers Lumber Company; *U.S. Private*, pg. 3564
CONTRACTORS BONDING AND INSURANCE COMPANY—See RLI Corp.; *U.S. Public*, pg. 1801
CONTRACTORS BUILDING SUPPLY, INC.—See The Building Center, Inc.; *U.S. Private*, pg. 4002
CONTRACTORS CARTAGE INC.—See TFI International Inc.; *Int'l*, pg. 7586
CONTRACTORS CHOICE EQUIPMENT RENTAL INC.—See J&L Building Materials Inc.; *U.S. Private*, pg. 2154
CONTRACTORS COATING SUPPLY INC.—See Walton Industries, Inc.; *U.S. Private*, pg. 4434
CONTRACTORS EQUIPMENT INC.—See Mosser Construction Inc.; *U.S. Private*, pg. 2794
CONTRACTORS EQUIPMENT LP—See Brandt Industries Ltd.; *Int'l*, pg. 1140
CONTRACTORS HEATING-COOLING SUPPLY, LLC; *U.S. Private*, pg. 1032
CONTRACTORS NORTHWEST INC.; *U.S. Private*, pg. 1032
CONTRACTORS PIPE & SUPPLY CORP.; *U.S. Private*, pg. 1032
CONTRACTORS REGISTER INC.—See Symphony Technology Group, LLC; *U.S. Private*, pg. 3900
CONTRACTORS RENTAL CORPORATION; *U.S. Private*, pg. 1033
CONTRACTORS STEEL COMPANY—See UPG Enterprises LLC; *U.S. Private*, pg. 4311
CONTRACTOR'S SUPPLIES, INC. - LONGVIEW PLANT—See Contractor's Supplies, Inc.; *U.S. Private*, pg. 1032
CONTRACTOR'S SUPPLIES, INC. - LUFKIN PLANT—See Contractor's Supplies, Inc.; *U.S. Private*, pg. 1032
CONTRACTOR'S SUPPLIES, INC. - MARSHALL PLANT—See Contractor's Supplies, Inc.; *U.S. Private*, pg. 1032
CONTRACTOR'S SUPPLIES, INC.; *U.S. Private*, pg. 1032
CONTRACTOR'S SUPPLIES, INC. - TYLER PLANT—See Contractor's Supplies, Inc.; *U.S. Private*, pg. 1032
CONTRACTORS TRUSS SYSTEMS, INC.—See Bain Capital, LP; *U.S. Private*, pg. 450
CONTRACT PHARMACAL CORP; *U.S. Private*, pg. 1032
CONTRACT PHARMACEUTICALS LIMITED—See Aterian Investment Management, L.P.; *U.S. Private*, pg. 366
CONTRACT PHARMACY SERVICES; *U.S. Private*, pg. 1032
CONTRACT PLANT RENTAL LTD—See Ballyvesey Holdings Limited; *Int'l*, pg. 809
CONTRACT PLUMBING AND SANITATION (PTY) LIMITED—See Basil Read Holdings Limited; *Int'l*, pg. 887

CONTRACT PROFESSIONALS INC.; *U.S. Private*, pg. 1032
CONTRACT PROFESSIONALS—See Contract Professionals Inc.; *U.S. Private*, pg. 1032
CONTRACT PURCHASING & DESIGN INC.; *U.S. Private*, pg. 1032
CONTRACT RESOURCE GROUP LLC—See HNI Corporation; *U.S. Public*, pg. 1043
CONTRACT STEEL SALES INC.; *U.S. Private*, pg. 1032
CONTRACT SWEEPERS & EQUIPMENT COMPANY—See Warburg Pincus LLC; *U.S. Private*, pg. 4440
CONTRACT TRANSPORT INC.; *U.S. Private*, pg. 1032
CONTRACTUM LIMITED—See Verra Mobility Corporation; *U.S. Public*, pg. 2286
CONTRAFECT CORPORATION; *U.S. Public*, pg. 573
CONTRAF-NICOTEX-TOBACCO GMBH; *Int'l*, pg. 1785
CONTRAIL AVIATION SUPPORT, LLC—See Air T, Inc.; *U.S. Public*, pg. 67
CONTRAN CORPORATION; *U.S. Private*, pg. 1033
CONTRANS CORP—See TFI International Inc.; *Int'l*, pg. 7585
CONTRANS FLATBED GROUP LP—See TFI International Inc.; *Int'l*, pg. 7585
CONTRANS FLATBED GROUP—See TFI International Inc.; *Int'l*, pg. 7585
CONTRANS GROUP INC.—See TFI International Inc.; *Int'l*, pg. 7585
CONTRAPUNTO—See Omnicom Group Inc.; *U.S. Public*, pg. 1575
CONTRAST EQUIPMENT, INC.—See Genstar Capital, LLC; *U.S. Private*, pg. 1678
CONTRAST LIGHTING M.L. INC.; *Int'l*, pg. 1785
CONTRATISTAS IHI E&C MEXICO, S.A.DE C.V.—See IHI Corporation; *Int'l*, pg. 3604
CONTRAVES ADVANCED DEVICES, SDN. BHD.—See Rheinmetall AG; *Int'l*, pg. 6323
CONTRAVEST MANAGEMENT COMPANY; *U.S. Private*, pg. 1034
CONTREL TECHNOLOGY CO., LTD.; *Int'l*, pg. 1785
THE CONTRIBUTIONSHIP COMPANIES; *U.S. Private*, pg. 4014
CONTRIK AG—See Neutrik AG; *Int'l*, pg. 5220
CONTRIMO GMBH—See Orbis SE; *Int'l*, pg. 5614
CONTROL4 APAC PTY. LTD.—See Resideo Technologies, Inc.; *U.S. Public*, pg. 1790
CONTROL4 CORPORATION—See Resideo Technologies, Inc.; *U.S. Public*, pg. 1790
CONTROL4 EMEA LTD—See Resideo Technologies, Inc.; *U.S. Public*, pg. 1790
CONTROL4 EUROPE DOO BELGRADE—See Resideo Technologies, Inc.; *U.S. Public*, pg. 1790
CONTROL4 GERMANY GMBH—See Resideo Technologies, Inc.; *U.S. Public*, pg. 1790
CONTROL 7, S.A—See Infrastructure Leasing & Financial Services Limited; *Int'l*, pg. 3697
CONTROLADORA DE EMPRESAS DE VIVIENDA, S. A. DE C. V.—See Empresas ICA S.A.B. de C.V.; *Int'l*, pg. 2390
CONTROLADORA DE OPERACIONES DE INFRAESTRUCTURA, S. A. DE C. V.—See Empresas ICA S.A.B. de C.V.; *Int'l*, pg. 2390
CONTROLADORA MABE S.A. DE C.V.; *Int'l*, pg. 1785
CONTROLADORA VUELA COMPANIA DE AVIACION, S.A.B. DE C.V.; *Int'l*, pg. 1786
CONTROL AIR CONDITIONING CORPORATION; *U.S. Private*, pg. 1034
CONTROL AND DISPLAY SYSTEMS LIMITED—See voestalpine AG; *Int'l*, pg. 8288
CONTROL & APPLICATIONS GROUP; *Int'l*, pg. 1785
CONTROLAUTO - CONTROLO TECNICO AUTOMOVEL, S.A.—See APG Asset Management NV; *Int'l*, pg. 512
CONTROLAUTO - CONTROLO TECNICO AUTOMOVEL, S.A.—See National Pension Service of Korea; *Int'l*, pg. 5162
CONTROLAUTO - CONTROLO TECNICO AUTOMOVEL, S.A.—See Swiss Life Holding; *Int'l*, pg. 7369
CONTROL BIONICS LIMITED; *Int'l*, pg. 1785
CONTROL BUILDING SERVICES INC.; *U.S. Private*, pg. 1034
CONTROL CABLE INC.; *U.S. Private*, pg. 1034
CONTROL CHIEF CORP.—See Control Chief Holdings, Inc.; *U.S. Private*, pg. 1034
CONTROL CHIEF HOLDINGS, INC.; *U.S. Private*, pg. 1034
CONTROLCIRCLE LTD.; *Int'l*, pg. 1786
CONTROL COMPONENTS, INC.—See IMI plc; *Int'l*, pg. 3624
CONTROL COMPONENTS INDIA PTY LTD—See IMI plc; *Int'l*, pg. 3625
CONTROL CONCEPTS, LLC—See Comfort Systems USA, Inc.; *U.S. Public*, pg. 543
CONTROL CONTRACTORS, INC.; *U.S. Private*, pg. 1034
CONTROL CUTTER AS—See Addtech AB; *Int'l*, pg. 132
CONTROL DEVELOPMENT INC.—See Revvity, Inc.; *U.S. Public*, pg. 1794
CONTROL DEVICES, INC.—See Sensata Technologies Holding plc; *U.S. Public*, pg. 1866

CONTROL SUPPLY CORP.

CONTROL DEVICES, LLC—See HBM Holdings Company; *U.S. Private*, pg. 1887
CONTROLE MESURE REGULATION TUNISIE SARL—See LBO France S.a.r.l.; *Int'l*, pg. 4429
CONTROL ENGINEERING, INC.—See root9B Holdings, Inc.; *U.S. Public*, pg. 1810
CONTROL EQUIPMENT COMPANY—See The Eads Company; *U.S. Private*, pg. 4024
CONTROLES ELECTROMECANICOS S.A. DE C.V.—See Nidec Corporation; *Int'l*, pg. 5277
CONTROLES INDUSTRIELS DE L'ENTANG—See Mistras Group, Inc.; *U.S. Public*, pg. 1451
CONTROLEXPERT COLOMBIA SAS—See Allianz SE; *Int'l*, pg. 351
CONTROLEXPERT GMBH—See Allianz SE; *Int'l*, pg. 351
CONTROLEXPERT HOLDING GMBH—See Allianz SE; *Int'l*, pg. 351
CONTROL FLOW INCORPORATED S. DE R. L. DE C.V.—See Control Flow Inc.; *U.S. Private*, pg. 1034
CONTROL FLOW INC.; *U.S. Private*, pg. 1034
CONTROL GROUP, INC.—See Titan; *U.S. Private*, pg. 4176
CONTROL HOLDINGS CORPORATION; *U.S. Private*, pg. 1034
CONTROL INSTALLATIONS OF IOWA, INC.; *U.S. Private*, pg. 1034
CONTROL LASER CORPORATION—See Han's Laser Technology Industry Group Co., Ltd.; *Int'l*, pg. 3240
CONTROLLED AIR, INC.; *U.S. Private*, pg. 1034
CONTROLLED ELECTRONIC MANAGEMENT SYSTEMS LIMITED—See Johnson Controls International plc; *Int'l*, pg. 3986
CONTROLLED ENVIRONMENT SYSTEMS, LLC; *U.S. Private*, pg. 1034
CONTROLLED POWER COMPANY; *U.S. Private*, pg. 1034
CONTROLLED PRODUCTS, LLC—See Sentinel Capital Partners, L.L.C.; *U.S. Private*, pg. 3609
CONTROLLED PRODUCTS SYSTEMS GROUP, INC. - LOS ANGELES—See The Duchossois Group, Inc.; *U.S. Private*, pg. 4023
CONTROLLED PRODUCTS SYSTEMS GROUP, INC.—See The Duchossois Group, Inc.; *U.S. Private*, pg. 4023
CONTROLLED SYSTEMS OF WISCONSIN, INC.; *U.S. Private*, pg. 1034
CONTROLLED TEMP SUPPLY, LLC—See Gryphon Investors, LLC; *U.S. Private*, pg. 1798
CONTROLLER SERVICE & SALES CO INC; *U.S. Private*, pg. 1034
CONTROLMATIC GESELLSCHAFT FUR AUTOMATION UND ELEKTROTECHNIK MBH—See VINCI S.A.; *Int'l*, pg. 8236
CONTROL MESURE REGULATION (UK) LIMITED—See Amphenol Corporation; *U.S. Public*, pg. 130
CONTROL MICROSYSTEMS BV—See Schneider Electric SE; *Int'l*, pg. 6626
CONTROL MICRO SYSTEMS, INC.—See Laser Photonics Corporation; *U.S. Public*, pg. 1294
CONTROL MODULE, INC.; *U.S. Private*, pg. 1034
CONTROL PRINT LIMITED—See Control Print Ltd.; *Int'l*, pg. 1785
CONTROL PRINT LTD.; *Int'l*, pg. 1785
CONTROL PRODUCTS, INC.—See Emerson Electric Co.; *U.S. Public*, pg. 743
CONTROL PRODUCTS, INC.—See Calculagraph Co.; *U.S. Private*, pg. 716
CONTROL RISKS EAST AFRICA—See Control Risks Group Holdings Ltd.; *Int'l*, pg. 1785
CONTROL RISKS GROUP HOLDINGS LTD.; *Int'l*, pg. 1785
CONTROLSCAN, INC.—See Thompson Street Capital Manager LLC; *U.S. Private*, pg. 4161
CONTROLS & ELECTRIC PTE. LTD.—See Boustead Singapore Limited; *Int'l*, pg. 1120
CONTROLS FOR MOTION AUTOMATION INC.; *U.S. Private*, pg. 1035
CONTROL SOLUTIONS, INC.; *U.S. Private*, pg. 1034
CONTROL SOLUTIONS, INC.—See China National Chemical Corporation; *Int'l*, pg. 1526
CONTROL SOUTHERN INC.; *U.S. Private*, pg. 1034
CONTROLS SOUTHEAST INC.—See AMETEK, Inc.; *U.S. Public*, pg. 118
CONTROL SUPPLY CORP.; *U.S. Private*, pg. 1034
CONTROL SYSTEMS INTERNATIONAL, INC.—See TechnipFMC plc; *Int'l*, pg. 7507
CONTROL TECHNIQUE LIMITED—See Nidec Corporation; *Int'l*, pg. 5275
CONTROL TECHNIQUES AG—See Nidec Corporation; *Int'l*, pg. 5275
CONTROL TECHNIQUES ASIA-PACIFIC PTE.LTD.—See Nidec Corporation; *Int'l*, pg. 5275
CONTROL TECHNIQUES BRNO S.R.O.—See Nidec Corporation; *Int'l*, pg. 5275
CONTROL TECHNIQUES CHINA PTE. LTD.—See Nidec Corporation; *Int'l*, pg. 5275
CONTROL TECHNIQUES DRIVES(MALAYSIA) SDN BHD—See Nidec Corporation; *Int'l*, pg. 5275

CONTROL SUPPLY CORP.

CONTROL TECHNIQUES DYNAMICS LIMITED—See Nidec Corporation; *Int'l*, pg. 5275
CONTROL TECHNIQUES ENDUSTRIYEL KONTROL SISTEMERLI SANAYI VE TICARET AS—See Nidec Corporation; *Int'l*, pg. 5275
CONTROL TECHNIQUES INDIA PRIVATE LIMITED—See Nidec Corporation; *Int'l*, pg. 5275
CONTROL-TEC, LLC—See Aptiv PLC; *Int'l*, pg. 524
CONTROL TECNICO Y REPRESENTACIONES SA DE CV—See HORIBA Ltd; *Int'l*, pg. 3475
CONTROLTEK INC.—See Centre Lane Partners, LLC; *U.S. Private*, pg. 827
CONTROL TOWER TRUCK STOP INC.; *U.S. Private*, pg. 1034
CONTROL TRANSFORMER CORP.—See Park-Ohio Holdings Corp.; *U.S. Public*, pg. 1639
CONTROLVET - SEGURANCA ALIMENTAR, SA—See ALS Limited; *Int'l*, pg. 378
CONTROL Y. MONTAJES INDUSTRIALES CYMI, S.A.—See ACS, Actividades de Construccion y Servicios, S.A.; *Int'l*, pg. 111
CONTSE, S.A.U.—See Air Products & Chemicals, Inc.; *U.S. Public*, pg. 66
CONTSHIP ITALIA S.P.A.—See EUROKAI GmbH & Co. KGaA; *Int'l*, pg. 2553
CONTUBOS S.A.—See NOV, Inc.; *U.S. Public*, pg. 1544
CONTURA COAL SALES, LLC—See Alpha Metallurgical Resources, Inc.; *U.S. Public*, pg. 82
CONTURA STOVES LTD.—See NIBE Industrier AB; *Int'l*, pg. 5260
CONUNDRUM TECHNOLOGIES; *U.S. Private*, pg. 1035
CONVACARE SERVICES INC.—See Linde plc; *Int'l*, pg. 4505
CONVAIR ENGINEERING PTY. LTD.—See Engenco Limited; *Int'l*, pg. 2426
CON VALUE ONE IMMOBILIEN GMBH—See Vonovia SE; *Int'l*, pg. 8305
CONVANO, INC.; *Int'l*, pg. 1786
CONVATEC ARGENTINA SRL—See ConvaTec Group PLC; *Int'l*, pg. 1786
CONVATEC (AUSTRALIA) PTY LIMITED—See ConvaTec Group PLC; *Int'l*, pg. 1786
CONVATEC BELGIUM BVBA—See ConvaTec Group PLC; *Int'l*, pg. 1786
CONVATEC CANADA LIMITED—See ConvaTec Group PLC; *Int'l*, pg. 1786
CONVATEC CESKA REPUBLIKA S.R.O.—See ConvaTec Group PLC; *Int'l*, pg. 1786
CONVATEC CHINA LIMITED—See ConvaTec Group PLC; *Int'l*, pg. 1786
CONVATEC DENMARK A/S—See ConvaTec Group PLC; *Int'l*, pg. 1786
CONVATEC DOMINICAN REPUBLIC INC.—See ConvaTec Group PLC; *Int'l*, pg. 1786
CONVATEC GROUP PLC; *Int'l*, pg. 1786
CONVATEC HELLAS MEDICAL PRODUCTS S.A.—See ConvaTec Group PLC; *Int'l*, pg. 1786
CONVATEC HONG KONG LIMITED—See ConvaTec Group PLC; *Int'l*, pg. 1786
CONVATEC INDIA PRIVATE LIMITED—See ConvaTec Group PLC; *Int'l*, pg. 1786
CONVATEC ITALIA S.R.L.—See ConvaTec Group PLC; *Int'l*, pg. 1786
CONVATEC JAPAN KK—See ConvaTec Group PLC; *Int'l*, pg. 1786
CONVATEC KOREA, LTD.—See ConvaTec Group PLC; *Int'l*, pg. 1786
CONVATEC LIMITED—See ConvaTec Group PLC; *Int'l*, pg. 1786
CONVATEC LTD.—See Avista Capital Partners, L.P.; *U.S. Private*, pg. 408
CONVATEC LTD.—See Nordic Capital AB; *Int'l*, pg. 5420
CONVATEC MALAYSIA SDN BHD—See ConvaTec Group PLC; *Int'l*, pg. 1786
CONVATEC MIDDLE EAST & AFRICA LLC—See ConvaTec Group PLC; *Int'l*, pg. 1786
CONVATEC NEDERLAND B.V.—See ConvaTec Group PLC; *Int'l*, pg. 1786
CONVATEC NORWAY AS—See ConvaTec Group PLC; *Int'l*, pg. 1786
CONVATEC PERU S.A.C.—See ConvaTec Group PLC; *Int'l*, pg. 1786
CONVATEC POLSKA SP. Z O.O.—See ConvaTec Group PLC; *Int'l*, pg. 1786
CONVATEC SAGLIK URUNLERI LIMITED SIRKETI—See ConvaTec Group PLC; *Int'l*, pg. 1786
CONVATEC (SINGAPORE) PTE LIMITED—See ConvaTec Group PLC; *Int'l*, pg. 1786
CONVATEC SOUTH AFRICA (PTY) LIMITED—See ConvaTec Group PLC; *Int'l*, pg. 1786
CONVATEC (SWEDEN) AB—See ConvaTec Group PLC; *Int'l*, pg. 1786
CONVATEC TECHNOLOGIES INC.—See ConvaTec Group PLC; *Int'l*, pg. 1786
CONVATEC (THAILAND) CO. LIMITED—See ConvaTec Group PLC; *Int'l*, pg. 1786
CONVEL S.R.L.—See Antares Vision SpA; *Int'l*, pg. 482
CONVENE, INC.; *U.S. Private*, pg. 1035
CONVENE INDIA PRIVATE LIMITED—See Azeus Systems Holdings Ltd.; *Int'l*, pg. 778
CONVENE PHILADELPHIA—See Sentry Centers Holdings LLC; *U.S. Private*, pg. 3610
CONVENE PTY LTD—See Azeus Systems Holdings Ltd.; *Int'l*, pg. 778
CONVENE SG PTE LTD—See Azeus Systems Holdings Ltd.; *Int'l*, pg. 778
CONVENE UK LIMITED—See Azeus Systems Holdings Ltd.; *Int'l*, pg. 778
CONVENI B.V.; *Int'l*, pg. 1786
CONVENIENCE CONCEPT SL—See REWE-Zentral-Aktiengesellschaft; *Int'l*, pg. 6315
CONVENIENCE FOODS LANKA PLC; *Int'l*, pg. 1786
CONVENIENCE FOOD SYSTEMS S.A. DE C.V.—See GEA Group Aktiengesellschaft; *Int'l*, pg. 2897
CONVENIENCE PRODUCTS, INC.—See Clayton Corporation; *U.S. Private*, pg. 918
CONVENIENCE RETAIL ASIA LIMITED; *Int'l*, pg. 1787
CONVENIENCE SHOPPING (SABAH) SDN. BHD.—See 7-Eleven Malaysia Holdings Berhad; *Int'l*, pg. 14
CONVENIENCE SHOPS, S.A.—See El Corte Ingles, S.A.; *Int'l*, pg. 2340
CONVENIENCE STORE DECISIONS—See Telapex Inc.; *U.S. Private*, pg. 3959
CONVENIENT PAYMENTS, LLC—See The Beekman Group, LLC; *U.S. Private*, pg. 3992
THE CONVENIENT WHOLESALERS OF AMERICA, INC.; *U.S. Private*, pg. 4014
CONVENTION DATA SERVICES; *U.S. Private*, pg. 1035
CONVENTION MODELS & TALENT, INC; *U.S. Private*, pg. 1035
CONVENTIVE TECHNOLOGIES LTD.; *Int'l*, pg. 1787
CONVENUE MARKETING SDN BHD—See Johor Corporation; *Int'l*, pg. 3994
CONVER B.V.—See Alamo Group Inc.; *U.S. Public*, pg. 71
CONVERCENT, INC.—See OneTrust LLC; *U.S. Private*, pg. 3026
CONVERDYN—See General Atomics; *U.S. Private*, pg. 1663
CONVERFLEX S.A.—See Arcor Sociedad Anonima, Industrial y Comercial; *Int'l*, pg. 550
CONVERGA PTY LIMITED—See Canon Inc.; *Int'l*, pg. 1293
CONVERGE CONSULTING INC.—See Ruffalo Noel Levitz, LLC; *U.S. Private*, pg. 3502
CONVERGED COMMUNICATION SYSTEMS, LLC; *U.S. Private*, pg. 1035
CONVERGED SECURITY SOLUTIONS LLC; *U.S. Private*, pg. 1035
CONVERGE MEDIA GROUP, LLC—See Zealot Networks, Inc.; *U.S. Private*, pg. 4599
CONVERGENCE ACCELERATION SOLUTIONS, LLC—See Wipro Limited; *Int'l*, pg. 8432
CONVERGENCE CONSULTING GROUP, INC.; *U.S. Private*, pg. 1035
CONVERGENCE INVESTMENT PARTNERS, LLC—See Mariner Wealth Advisors, LLC; *U.S. Private*, pg. 2575
CONVERGENCE PARTNERS, INC.; *U.S. Private*, pg. 1035
CONVERGENCE PARTNERS (PTY) LIMITED; *Int'l*, pg. 1787
CONVERGENCE PHARMACEUTICALS LTD.—See Biogen Inc.; *U.S. Public*, pg. 337
CONVERGENCE TECHNOLOGY CONSULTING, LLC; *U.S. Private*, pg. 1035
CONVERGE NETHERLANDS BV.—See Arrow Electronics, Inc.; *U.S. Public*, pg. 199
CONVERGENT CAPITAL MANAGEMENT LLC—See Royal Bank of Canada; *Int'l*, pg. 6409
CONVERGENT CAPITAL PARTNERS LLC; *U.S. Private*, pg. 1035
CONVERGENT COMMERCIAL, INC.—See Platinum Equity, LLC; *U.S. Private*, pg. 3209
CONVERGENT FINANCE LLP; *Int'l*, pg. 1787
CONVERGENT HEALTHCARE RECOVERIES, INC.—See Platinum Equity, LLC; *U.S. Private*, pg. 3209
CONVERGENT MEDIA SYSTEMS, LLC—See Woodard Technology & Investments LLC; *U.S. Private*, pg. 4557
CONVERGENT NETWORKS INC.; *U.S. Private*, pg. 1035
CONVERGENT OUTSOURCING, INC.—See Platinum Equity, LLC; *U.S. Private*, pg. 3209
CONVERGENT RESOURCES, INC.—See Platinum Equity, LLC; *U.S. Private*, pg. 3209
CONVERGENT WEALTH ADVISORS—See Royal Bank of Canada; *Int'l*, pg. 6409
CONVERGENZE S.P.A.; *Int'l*, pg. 1787
CONVERGENZ, LLC; *U.S. Private*, pg. 1035
CONVERGEONE ADVANCED SERVICES—See CVC Capital Partners SICAV-FIS S.A.; *Int'l*, pg. 1883
CONVERGEONE HOLDINGS, INC.—See CVC Capital Partners SICAV-FIS S.A.; *Int'l*, pg. 1883
CONVERGEONE, INC.—See CVC Capital Partners SICAV-FIS S.A.; *Int'l*, pg. 1883
CONVERGEONE UNIFIED TECHNOLOGY SOLUTIONS, INC.—See CVC Capital Partners SICAV-FIS S.A.; *Int'l*, pg. 1883
CONVERGE—See Arrow Electronics, Inc.; *U.S. Public*, pg. 199

CORPORATE AFFILIATIONS

CONVERGE TECHNOLOGY SOLUTIONS CORP.; *Int'l*, pg. 1787
CONVERGE TOWERS, LLC—See BGC Group, Inc.; *U.S. Public*, pg. 328
CONVERGINT TECHNOLOGIES, LLC—See Ares Management Corporation; *U.S. Public*, pg. 188
CONVERGYS CORPORATION—See Concentrix Corporation; *U.S. Public*, pg. 564
CONVERGYS CUSTOMER MANAGEMENT GROUP INC.—See Concentrix Corporation; *U.S. Public*, pg. 565
CONVERGYS FRANCE SAS—See Concentrix Corporation; *U.S. Public*, pg. 565
CONVERGYS GLOBAL SERVICES GMBH—See Concentrix Corporation; *U.S. Public*, pg. 565
CONVERGYS GROUP SERVICIOS DE APOYO INFORMATICO, S.L.—See Concentrix Corporation; *U.S. Public*, pg. 565
CONVERGYS HOLDINGS (UK) LTD.—See Concentrix Corporation; *U.S. Public*, pg. 565
CONVERGYS INTERNATIONAL BULGARIA EOOD—See Concentrix Corporation; *U.S. Public*, pg. 565
CONVERGYS INTERNATIONAL NORDIC AB—See Concentrix Corporation; *U.S. Public*, pg. 565
CONVERGYS IRELAND LIMITED—See Concentrix Corporation; *U.S. Public*, pg. 565
CONVERGYS MALAYSIA SDN BHD—See Concentrix Corporation; *U.S. Public*, pg. 565
CONVERGYS NETHERLANDS LLC—See Concentrix Corporation; *U.S. Public*, pg. 565
CONVERGYS PHILIPPINES INC.—See Concentrix Corporation; *U.S. Public*, pg. 565
CONVERGYS PHILIPPINES SERVICES CORPORATION—See Concentrix Corporation; *U.S. Public*, pg. 565
CONVERGYS SERVICES PHILIPPINES, INC.—See Concentrix Corporation; *U.S. Public*, pg. 565
CONVERGYS SERVICES SINGAPORE PTE. LTD.—See Concentrix Corporation; *U.S. Public*, pg. 565
CONVERGYS STREAM PVT. LTD.—See Concentrix Corporation; *U.S. Public*, pg. 565
CONVERMAT CORPORATION; *U.S. Private*, pg. 1035
CONVERSANO ASSOCIATES INC.—See Cobepa S.A.; *Int'l*, pg. 1683
CONVERSANT EUROPE LTD.—See Publicis Groupe S.A.; *Int'l*, pg. 6098
CONVERSANT FRANCE—See IAC Inc.; *U.S. Public*, pg. 1082
CONVERSANT-GERMANY—See Publicis Groupe S.A.; *Int'l*, pg. 6098
CONVERSANT INTELLECTUAL PROPERTY MANAGEMENT INCORPORATED—See Sterling Partners; *U.S. Private*, pg. 3806
CONVERSANT IP JAPAN K.K.—See Sterling Partners; *U.S. Private*, pg. 3806
CONVERSANT, LLC—See Publicis Groupe S.A.; *Int'l*, pg. 6098
CONVERSANT-NEW YORK—See Publicis Groupe S.A.; *Int'l*, pg. 6098
CONVERSANT-SAN FRANCISCO—See Publicis Groupe S.A.; *Int'l*, pg. 6098
CONVERSANT-SANTA BARBARA—See Publicis Groupe S.A.; *Int'l*, pg. 6099
CONVERSA SOLUTIONS, LLC—See Vertex Wireless LLC; *U.S. Private*, pg. 4370
CONVERSE INC.—See NIKE, Inc.; *U.S. Public*, pg. 1528
CONVERSE KOREA LLC—See NIKE, Inc.; *U.S. Public*, pg. 1528
CONVERSE MARKETING; *U.S. Private*, pg. 1035
CONVERSE MEDICAL CENTER LLC—See Adeptus Health Inc.; *U.S. Public*, pg. 78
CONVERSEON, INC.; *U.S. Private*, pg. 1035
CONVERSEON NORDICS—See Converseon, Inc.; *U.S. Private*, pg. 1035
THE CONVERSE PROFESSIONAL GROUP, INC.; *U.S. Private*, pg. 4014
CONVERSIA IT, S.L.U.—See COCA-COLA EUROPACIFIC PARTNERS PLC; *Int'l*, pg. 1685
CONVERSION CAPITAL PARTNERS LTD.; *Int'l*, pg. 1787
CONVERSION INTERACTIVE AGENCY, LLC; *U.S. Private*, pg. 1035
CONVERSIONPOINT HOLDINGS, INC.; *U.S. Public*, pg. 573
CONVERSIONPOINT TECHNOLOGIES, INC.; *U.S. Private*, pg. 1035
CONVERSION RATE EXPERTS LIMITED—See Next 15 Group plc; *Int'l*, pg. 5246
CONVERTEO SAS—See ADLPartner SA; *Int'l*, pg. 151
CONVERTERTECHNOLOGY INC.—See GPS Group Investments Pty. Ltd.; *Int'l*, pg. 1826
CONVERTIBLE CASTLE, INC.; *U.S. Private*, pg. 1035
CONVERTIDORA INDUSTRIAL S.A.B. DE C.V; *Int'l*, pg. 1787
CONVERT ITALIA S.P.A.—See Valmont Industries, Inc.; *U.S. Public*, pg. 2273
CONVERTO AS; *Int'l*, pg. 1787
CONVERTORS DE MEXICO S.A. DE C.V.—See Cardinal Health, Inc.; *U.S. Public*, pg. 434

COMPANY NAME INDEX

CONVEST A.D.—See Nova Ljubljanska banka d.d.; *Int'l*, pg. 5451
CONVEX CAPITAL LIMITED—See RBG Holdings PLC; *Int'l*, pg. 6227
THE CONVEX GROUP, INC.; *U.S. Private*, pg. 4014
CONVEX MOLD, INC.—See Sonoco Products Company; *U.S. Public*, pg. 1906
CONVEX SCHREIBWAREN-HANDELS GMBH—See Pelikan International Corporation Berhad; *Int'l*, pg. 5782
CONVEY-ALL INDUSTRIES INC.—See WGI Westman Group, Inc.; *Int'l*, pg. 8394
CONVEYCO MANUFACTURING COMPANY; *U.S. Private*, pg. 1036
CONVEYCO TECHNOLOGIES INC.; *U.S. Private*, pg. 1036
CONVEY HEALTH SOLUTIONS HOLDINGS, INC.—See TPG Capital, L.P.; *U.S. Public*, pg. 2169
CONVEY HEALTH SOLUTIONS, INC.—See TPG Capital, L.P.; *U.S. Public*, pg. 2170
CONVEYOR AGGREGATE PRODUCTS CORP.—See Purvis Bearing Service Ltd.; *U.S. Private*, pg. 3307
CONVEYOR HANDLING COMPANY, INC.; *U.S. Private*, pg. 1036
CONVEYORS & DRIVES, INC.; *U.S. Private*, pg. 1036
CONVEYORS & MATERIALS HANDLING INC.; *U.S. Private*, pg. 1036
CONVEYOR TECHNOLOGIES INC.; *U.S. Private*, pg. 1036
CONVIBER INC.; *U.S. Private*, pg. 1036
CONVINI SVERIGE AB; *Int'l*, pg. 1787
CONVIVA CARE SOLUTIONS, LLC—See Humana, Inc.; *U.S. Public*, pg. 1069
CONVIVA PHYSICIAN GROUP, LLC—See Humana, Inc.; *U.S. Public*, pg. 1069
CONVIVIALITY PLC; *Int'l*, pg. 1787
CONVIVO GMBH—See REWE-Zentral-Aktiengesellschaft; *Int'l*, pg. 6315
CONVOTHERM ELEKTROGERATE GMBH—See Ali Holding S.r.l; *Int'l*, pg. 323
CONVOY GLOBAL HOLDINGS LIMITED—See National Arts Entertainment & Culture Group Limited; *Int'l*, pg. 5150
CONVOY OF HOPE, INC.; *U.S. Private*, pg. 1036
CONVOY SERVICING COMPANY INC.; *U.S. Private*, pg. 1036
CONVUM KOREA CO., LTD.—See Convum Ltd.; *Int'l*, pg. 1788
CONVUM LTD.; *Int'l*, pg. 1787
CONVUM (THAILAND) CO., LTD.—See Convum Ltd.; *Int'l*, pg. 1787
CONVUM USA, INC.—See Convum Ltd.; *Int'l*, pg. 1787
CONWAY BEAM LEASING INC.—See Beam Mack Sales & Service, Inc.; *U.S. Private*, pg. 506
CONWAY BEHAVIORAL HEALTH, LLC—See Acadia Healthcare Company, Inc.; *U.S. Public*, pg. 28
CONWAY BELGIE N.V.—See REWE-Zentral-Aktiengesellschaft; *Int'l*, pg. 6315
CONWAY CORPORATION; *U.S. Private*, pg. 1036
CONWAY, DIERKING & HILLMAN, INC.; *U.S. Private*, pg. 1036
CONWAY FINANCIAL SERVICES, LLC—See Rithm Capital Corp.; *U.S. Public*, pg. 1800
CONWAY HEATON, INC.; *U.S. Private*, pg. 1036
CONWAY IMPORT CO. INC.; *U.S. Private*, pg. 1036
CONWAY IMPORT CO. INC.—See Conway Import Co. Inc.; *U.S. Private*, pg. 1036
CONWAY MACKENZIE ATLANTA, LLC—See Conway MacKenzie, Inc.; *U.S. Private*, pg. 1036
CONWAY MACKENZIE CHICAGO, LLC—See Conway MacKenzie, Inc.; *U.S. Private*, pg. 1036
CONWAY MACKENZIE HOUSTON, LLC—See Conway MacKenzie, Inc.; *U.S. Private*, pg. 1036
CONWAY MACKENZIE, INC.; *U.S. Private*, pg. 1036
CONWAY MACKENZIE LOS ANGELES, LLC—See Conway MacKenzie, Inc.; *U.S. Private*, pg. 1036
CONWAY MACKENZIE NEW YORK, LLC—See Conway MacKenzie, Inc.; *U.S. Private*, pg. 1036
CONWAY MARSH GARRETT TECHNOLOGIES LIMITED; *Int'l*, pg. 1788
THE CONWAY NATIONAL BANK INC.—See CNB Corporation; *U.S. Public*, pg. 519
CONWAY OFFICE SOLUTIONS, INC.—See Xerox Holdings Corporation; *U.S. Public*, pg. 2387
CONWAY ORGANIZATION; *U.S. Private*, pg. 1036
CONWAY S.A.—See REWE-Zentral-Aktiengesellschaft; *Int'l*, pg. 6315
CONWED PLASTICS LLC—See Mativ Holdings, Inc.; *U.S. Public*, pg. 1396
CONWED PLASTICS N.V.—See Mativ Holdings, Inc.; *U.S. Public*, pg. 1396
CONWELL CORP.—See Frozen Food Express Industries, Inc.; *U.S. Private*, pg. 1617
CONWELL, LLC—See Frozen Food Express Industries, Inc.; *U.S. Private*, pg. 1617
CONWERT ALFHILD INVEST GMBH—See Vonovia SE; *Int'l*, pg. 8305
CONWERT DEUTSCHLAND BETEILIGUNGSHOLDING GMBH—See Vonovia SE; *Int'l*, pg. 8305

CONWERT DEUTSCHLAND GMBH—See Vonovia SE; *Int'l*, pg. 8305
CONWERT DEUTSCHLAND HOLDING GMBH—See Vonovia SE; *Int'l*, pg. 8305
CONWERT GRAZER DAMM DEVELOPMENT GMBH—See Vonovia SE; *Int'l*, pg. 8305
CON WERT HANDELSGES.M.B.H.—See Vonovia SE; *Int'l*, pg. 8305
CONWERT IMMOBILIEN INVEST GMBH—See Vonovia SE; *Int'l*, pg. 8305
CONWERT MANAGEMENT GMBH—See Vonovia SE; *Int'l*, pg. 8305
CONWERT SECURITISATION HOLDING GMBH—See Vonovia SE; *Int'l*, pg. 8305
CONWOOD COMPANY LIMITED—See Siam City Cement Public Company Limited; *Int'l*, pg. 6874
CONXALL CORPORATION—See HEICO Corporation; *U.S. Public*, pg. 1021
CONX CORP.; *U.S. Public*, pg. 573
CONXTECH, INC.; *U.S. Private*, pg. 1037
THE CONYGAR INVESTMENT COMPANY PLC; *Int'l*, pg. 7635
CONZZETA MANAGEMENT AG—See Bystronic AG; *Int'l*, pg. 1236
COOCON CORP.; *Int'l*, pg. 1788
COOEC CANADA COMPANY LTD.—See Offshore Oil Engineering Company Limited; *Int'l*, pg. 5530
COOEC-ENPAL ENGINEERING CO., LTD.—See Offshore Oil Engineering Company Limited; *Int'l*, pg. 5530
COOEC SUBSEA TECHNOLOGY CO., LTD.—See Offshore Oil Engineering Company Limited; *Int'l*, pg. 5530
COOGEE CHEMICALS (MT ISA) PTY LTD—See Coogee Chemicals Pty Ltd.; *Int'l*, pg. 1788
COOGEE CHEMICALS PTY LTD. - METHANOL FACILITY—See Coogee Chemicals Pty Ltd.; *Int'l*, pg. 1788
COOGEE CHEMICALS PTY LTD.; *Int'l*, pg. 1788
COOK ASIA LTD.—See Cook Group Incorporated; *U.S. Private*, pg. 1037
COOK ASSOCIATES, INC.; *U.S. Private*, pg. 1037
COOK AUTOMOTIVE; *U.S. Private*, pg. 1037
COOK AVIATION INC.—See Cook Group Incorporated; *U.S. Private*, pg. 1037
COOK BIOTECH INCORPORATED—See Montagu Private Equity LLP; *Int'l*, pg. 5036
COOKBIZ CO., LTD.; *Int'l*, pg. 1788
THE COOK & BOARDMAN GROUP, LLC—See Platinum Equity, LLC; *U.S. Private*, pg. 3208
COOK & BOARDMAN, LLC - SIMPSONVILLE—See Platinum Equity, LLC; *U.S. Private*, pg. 3208
COOK & BOARDMAN, LLC—See Platinum Equity, LLC; *U.S. Private*, pg. 3208
COOKBOOK PUBLISHERS INC.; *U.S. Private*, pg. 1039
COOK BROS., INC.; *U.S. Private*, pg. 1037
COOK (CANADA) INC.—See Cook Group Incorporated; *U.S. Private*, pg. 1037
COOK (CHINA) MEDICAL TRADING CO., LTD.—See Cook Group Incorporated; *U.S. Private*, pg. 1037
COOK COMMUNICATIONS MINISTRIES; *U.S. Private*, pg. 1037
COOK COMPRESSION LIMITED—See Dover Corporation; *U.S. Public*, pg. 678
COOK COMPRESSION, LLC—See Dover Corporation; *U.S. Public*, pg. 678
COOK COUNTY SCHOOL BUS INC.—See Cook-Illinois Corp.; *U.S. Private*, pg. 1038
COOKE AQUACULTURE INC.—See Cooke, Inc.; *Int'l*, pg. 1788
COOKE & BIELER, LP; *U.S. Private*, pg. 1039
COOKE COMMUNICATIONS FLORIDA, LLC; *U.S. Private*, pg. 1039
COOKE COMMUNICATIONS NORTH CAROLINA, LLC—See Cooke Communications Florida, LLC; *U.S. Private*, pg. 1039
COOKE, INC.; *Int'l*, pg. 1788
COOKE OPTICS LTD.—See Caledonia Investments plc; *Int'l*, pg. 1262
COOKES FOOD STORE INC.; *U.S. Private*, pg. 1039
COOKE TRUCKING COMPANY INC.; *U.S. Private*, pg. 1039
COOKEVILLE COMMUNICATIONS, LLC—See Great Plains Media, Inc.; *U.S. Private*, pg. 1767
COOK FAMILY HEALTH CENTER INC.—See Cook Group Incorporated; *U.S. Private*, pg. 1037
COOK GM SUPERSTORE; *U.S. Private*, pg. 1037
COOK GROUP INCORPORATED; *U.S. Private*, pg. 1037
COOKIE KINGDOM INC.; *U.S. Private*, pg. 1039
COOKIES BY DESIGN, INC.—See Sysco Corporation; *U.S. Public*, pg. 1974
COOKIES-N-MILK, INC.—See Tenex Capital Management, L.P.; *U.S. Private*, pg. 3966
COOKIE TREE BAKERIES; *U.S. Private*, pg. 1039
COOK-ILLINOIS CORP.; *U.S. Private*, pg. 1038
COOK INCORPORATED—See Cook Group Incorporated; *U.S. Private*, pg. 1037
COOKING ENTHUSIAST, LLC; *U.S. Private*, pg. 1039
COOK INLET REGION, INC.; *U.S. Private*, pg. 1038

COOK INLET TRIBAL COUNCIL, INC.; *U.S. Private*, pg. 1038
COOK IRELAND LTD.—See Cook Group Incorporated; *U.S. Private*, pg. 1037
COOK JAPAN INCORPORATED—See Cook Group Incorporated; *U.S. Private*, pg. 1037
COOK JEEP CHRYSLER, INC.; *U.S. Private*, pg. 1038
COOK LABO CO., LTD.—See FP Corporation; *Int'l*, pg. 2756
COOK M&A ADVISORY SERVICES—See Cook Associates, Inc.; *U.S. Private*, pg. 1037
COOK MEDICAL EUROPE LTD.—See Cook Group Incorporated; *U.S. Private*, pg. 1037
COOK MEDICAL INCORPORATED—See Cook Group Incorporated; *U.S. Private*, pg. 1037
COOK MEDICAL (THAILAND) CO., LTD.—See Cook Group Incorporated; *U.S. Private*, pg. 1037
COOK-MFS, INC.—See Dover Corporation; *U.S. Public*, pg. 679
COOK MOVING SYSTEMS, INC. (ILLINOIS CORPORATION)—See Cook Moving Systems, Inc.; *U.S. Private*, pg. 1038
COOK MOVING SYSTEMS, INC.; *U.S. Private*, pg. 1038
COOK MYOSITE INCORPORATED—See Cook Group Incorporated; *U.S. Private*, pg. 1037
COOKPAD INC.; *Int'l*, pg. 1788
COOK PAVING & CONSTRUCTION CO.; *U.S. Private*, pg. 1038
COOK PHARMICA LLC—See Catalent, Inc.; *U.S. Public*, pg. 448
COOK POLYMER TECHNOLOGY—See Cook Group Incorporated; *U.S. Private*, pg. 1037
COOK RESOURCES MINING PTY LTD—See Glencore plc; *Int'l*, pg. 2990
COOKS BODY WORKS PTY LTD—See SIETEL LIMITED; *Int'l*, pg. 6904
COOKS COFFEE COMPANY LIMITED; *Int'l*, pg. 1788
COOK'S COLLISION; *U.S. Private*, pg. 1038
COOKSEY COMMUNICATIONS, INC.; *U.S. Private*, pg. 1039
COOKSEY IRON & METAL CO. INC.—See Reliance Steel & Aluminum Co.; *U.S. Public*, pg. 1779
THE COOKSON COMPANY; *U.S. Private*, pg. 4014
COOKSON DRIJFHOUT B.V.—See L. Possehl & Co. mbH; *Int'l*, pg. 4382
COOKSON ENTHONE CHEMISTRY TRADING (SHANGHAI) CO LTD—See Element Solutions Inc.; *U.S. Public*, pg. 726
COOKSON HILLS ELECTRIC COOP; *U.S. Private*, pg. 1039
COOKSON INDIA PRIVATE LIMITED - ENTHONE INDIA DIVISION—See Element Solutions Inc.; *U.S. Public*, pg. 726
COOKSON METAUX PRECIEUX S.A.—See L. Possehl & Co. mbH; *Int'l*, pg. 4382
COOKSON PRECIOUS METALS LIMITED—See L. Possehl & Co. mbH; *Int'l*, pg. 4383
COOK'S PEST CONTROL, INC.—See Flash Exterminating, Inc.; *U.S. Private*, pg. 1540
COOKSVILLE DODGE CHRYSLER INC.; *Int'l*, pg. 1788
COOK TAIWAN LTD.—See Cook Group Incorporated; *U.S. Private*, pg. 1037
COOKTEK LLC—See The Middleby Corporation; *U.S. Public*, pg. 2113
COOK TRACTOR CO. INC.; *U.S. Private*, pg. 1038
COOK TRAVEL STATION—See Travel Station; *U.S. Private*, pg. 4213
COOK VASCULAR INCORPORATED—See Cook Group Incorporated; *U.S. Private*, pg. 1037
COOK-WHITEHEAD FORD, INC.—See AutoNation, Inc.; *U.S. Public*, pg. 234
COOLABAH METALS LIMITED; *Int'l*, pg. 1789
COOLABI LIMITED—See Edge Group Limited; *Int'l*, pg. 2309
COOLACK SHARGH COMPANY (P.J.S)—See Azarbaijan Investment Development Company; *Int'l*, pg. 776
COOLADATA LTD.—See Thoma Bravo, L.P.; *U.S. Private*, pg. 4149
COOLAIR KLIMASYSTEME GMBH—See Beijer Ref AB; *Int'l*, pg. 944
COOL AIR MECHANICAL, LLC—See Ontario Municipal Employees Retirement System; *Int'l*, pg. 5585
COOLANTS PLUS, INC.; *U.S. Private*, pg. 1039
COOL CAPS INDUSTRIES LIMITED; *Int'l*, pg. 1788
COOL CARRIERS AB—See Baltic Reefers Ltd.; *Int'l*, pg. 812
COOL CARRIERS CHILE S.A.—See Baltic Reefers Ltd.; *Int'l*, pg. 812
COOL CARRIERS NEW ZEALAND LTD—See Baltic Reefers Ltd.; *Int'l*, pg. 812
COOL CARRIERS USA INC.—See Baltic Reefers Ltd.; *Int'l*, pg. 812
COOL CHAIN GROUP PL SP. Z O.O.—See Metro AG; *Int'l*, pg. 4857
COOL CHIPS PLC; *Int'l*, pg. 1789
COOL COMPANY LTD.; *Int'l*, pg. 1789
COOL COOL FROZEN FOOD LIMITED—See Wisdomcome Group Holdings Limited; *Int'l*, pg. 8435

COOL COMPANY LTD.

COOL ENGINEERING AB—See Ettepian Oyj; *Int'l*, pg. 2524
COOLERADO CORP; *U.S. Private*, pg. 1039
COOLER MASTER TECHNOLOGY INC.—See Ban Leong Technologies Limited; *Int'l*, pg. 814
COOLEY GROUP, INC.; *U.S. Private*, pg. 1039
COOLEY GROUP, INC.; *U.S. Private*, pg. 1039
COOLEY INDUSTRIES INC.; *U.S. Private*, pg. 1039
COOLEY LLP - RESTON—See Cooley LLP; *U.S. Private*, pg. 1040
COOLEY LLP; *U.S. Private*, pg. 1039
COOLEY LLP - WASHINGTON, DC—See Cooley LLP; *U.S. Private*, pg. 1040
COOLEY MEDICAL EQUIPMENT, INC.—See Quipt Home Medical Corp.; *U.S. Public*, pg. 1757
COOLEY'S GARDENS INC.; *U.S. Private*, pg. 1040
COOLFIRE MEDIA, LLC; *U.S. Private*, pg. 1040
COOLFIRE MEDIA ORIGINALS, LLC—See Coolfire Media, LLC; *U.S. Private*, pg. 1040
COOLFIRE SOLUTIONS LLC—See Coolfire Media, LLC; *U.S. Private*, pg. 1040
COOLFIRE WEST—See Coolfire Media, LLC; *U.S. Private*, pg. 1040
COOL GEAR INTERNATIONAL LLC—See Dometic Group AB; *Int'l*, pg. 2160
COOLGIANTS AG; *Int'l*, pg. 1789
COOLIBAR, INC.; *U.S. Private*, pg. 1040
COOLIDGE STATION APARTMENTS LLC—See Edison International; *U.S. Public*, pg. 719
COOLING & HEATING SPECIALISTS, INC.—See Southfield Capital Advisors, LLC; *U.S. Private*, pg. 3736
COOLING TECHNOLOGY BY NATURAL GAS CO, (GAS CHILL) S.A.E.—See Egyptian Kuwaiti Holding; *Int'l*, pg. 2327
COOLING TOWER TECHNOLOGIES—See Crown Enterprises Inc.; *U.S. Private*, pg. 1111
COOL INSURING AGENCY, INC.—See Arthur J. Gallagher & Co.; *U.S. Public*, pg. 204
COOLISM CO., LTD.—See RS Public Company Limited; *Int'l*, pg. 6418
COOLLED LIMITED—See Judges Scientific plc; *Int'l*, pg. 4021
COOL LINK (HOLDINGS) LIMITED; *Int'l*, pg. 1789
COOL LINK & MARKETING PTE. LTD.—See Cool Link (Holdings) Limited; *Int'l*, pg. 1789
COOLMARK BV—See Beijer Ref AB; *Int'l*, pg. 944
COOL MAX AUTO PARTS CO., LTD.—See Cryomax Cooling System Corp.; *Int'l*, pg. 1860
COOL OR COSY PERTH—See AWN Holdings Limited; *Int'l*, pg. 753
COOL OR COSY (QLD) PTY. LTD.—See AWN Holdings Limited; *Int'l*, pg. 753
COOLPAD GROUP LIMITED; *Int'l*, pg. 1789
COOLPAD TECHNOLOGIES INC.—See Coolpad Group Limited; *Int'l*, pg. 1789
COOL-PAK, LLC—See Bunzl plc; *Int'l*, pg. 1218
COOL-PAK SOLUTIONS LP—See Americold Realty Trust, Inc.; *U.S. Public*, pg. 113
COOL PLANET ENERGY SYSTEMS, INC.—See Exelon Corporation; *U.S. Public*, pg. 806
COOLPOINT INNONISM HOLDING LIMITED; *Int'l*, pg. 1789
COOLRAY HEATING & AIR CONDITIONING; *U.S. Private*, pg. 1040
COOLREC B.V.—See Renewi plc; *Int'l*, pg. 6278
COOLREC FRANCE S.A.S.—See Renewi plc; *Int'l*, pg. 6278
COOLREC NEDERLAND B.V.—See Renewi plc; *Int'l*, pg. 6278
COOLREC PLASTICS B.V.—See Renewi plc; *Int'l*, pg. 6278
COOL ROOFING SYSTEMS INC.; *U.S. Private*, pg. 1039
COOL SORPTION A/S—See Diamond Key International Pty. Ltd; *Int'l*, pg. 2105
COOLSYS, INC.—See Ares Management Corporation; *U.S. Public*, pg. 189
COOLSYSTEMS, INC.—See Avanos Medical, Inc.; *U.S. Public*, pg. 241
COOLTECH ENERGY WATER TREATMENT LLC—See National Central Cooling Company PJSC; *Int'l*, pg. 5155
COOLTECH ENGINEERING SERVICES (PVT) LTD.—See Daikin Industries, Ltd.; *Int'l*, pg. 1932
COOL TECHNOLOGIES, INC.; *U.S. Public*, pg. 573
COOLTECH POWER INTERNATIONAL PTE LTD—See Shanghai Cooltech Power Co., Ltd.; *Int'l*, pg. 6764
COOLTOUCH, INC.—See Apax Partners LLP; *Int'l*, pg. 506
COOLWEAR INC.; *U.S. Private*, pg. 1040
COOMEVA ENTIDAD PROMOTORA DE SALUD SA; *Int'l*, pg. 1789
COONEN INC.; *U.S. Private*, pg. 1040
COONER WIRE COMPANY; *U.S. Private*, pg. 1040
COONEY BROTHERS COAL CO.; *U.S. Private*, pg. 1040
COONEY BROTHERS INC—See Vergani & Associates, LLC; *U.S. Private*, pg. 4359
COON RAPIDS CHRYSLER, INC.; *U.S. Private*, pg. 1040
COONROD & ASSOCIATES CONSTRUCTION CO., INC.; *U.S. Private*, pg. 1040
COOPACA; *U.S. Private*, pg. 1040

CO-OP ATLANTIC; *Int'l*, pg. 1679
CO-OP CLEAN CO., LTD.—See Adeka Corporation; *Int'l*, pg. 142
CO-OP CONSULTANCY & BANCASSURANCE INTERMEDIARY LTD.—See The Co-operative Bank of Kenya Limited; *Int'l*, pg. 7633
CO-OP COUNTRY FARMERS ELEVATOR; *U.S. Private*, pg. 953
COOP DANMARK A/S—See FDB Group; *Int'l*, pg. 2628
COOPER ALLOY CORPORATION; *U.S. Private*, pg. 1040
COOPERATIE ACTIVISION BLIZZARD INTERNATIONAL U.A—See Microsoft Corporation; *U.S. Public*, pg. 1439
COOPERATIE ACTIVISION BLIZZARD INTERNATIONAL U.A.—See Microsoft Corporation; *U.S. Public*, pg. 1439
COOPERATIEVE CENTRALE RAIFFEISEN-BOERENLEENBANK B.A.; *Int'l*, pg. 1791
COOPERATIVA A.D.; *Int'l*, pg. 1792
COOPERATIVA DE AHORRO Y CEDITO DE BARRANQUITAS; *U.S. Private*, pg. 1042
COOPERATIVA DE AHORRO Y CREDITO AGUADA; *U.S. Private*, pg. 1042
COOPERATIVA DE AHORRO Y CREDITO DE CAMUY; *U.S. Private*, pg. 1042
COOPERATIVA DE AHORRO Y CREDITO DE ISABELA; *U.S. Private*, pg. 1042
COOPERATIVA DE SEGUROS DE VIDA; *U.S. Private*, pg. 1042
COOPERATIVE AGRONOMY SERVICES—See CHS INC.; *U.S. Public*, pg. 492
CO-OPERATIVE ANIMAL HEALTH LIMITED—See Dairygold Co-Operative Society Ltd; *Int'l*, pg. 1940
CO-OPERATIVE ANIMAL HEALTH LIMITED—See Glanbia Co-Operative Society Limited; *Int'l*, pg. 2988
CO-OPERATIVE ASSET MANAGEMENT CORP.—See Taiwan Cooperative Financial Holding Co., Ltd.; *Int'l*, pg. 7419
CO-OPERATIVE ASSETS MANAGEMENT CO., LTD.—See Taiwan Cooperative Financial Holding Co., Ltd.; *Int'l*, pg. 7419
CO-OPERATIVE BANKING GROUP LIMITED—See Co-operative Group Limited; *Int'l*, pg. 1679
THE CO-OPERATIVE BANK OF KENYA LIMITED; *Int'l*, pg. 7633
THE CO-OPERATIVE BANK P.L.C.—See Co-operative Group Limited; *Int'l*, pg. 1679
COOPERATIVE CENTRAL BANK LTD.; *Int'l*, pg. 1792
COOPERATIVE COMMUNICATIONS INC.—See Cooperative Holdings Inc.; *U.S. Private*, pg. 1042
COOPERATIVE DE AHORRO Y CREDITO SAN RAFAEL; *U.S. Private*, pg. 1042
COOPERATIVE ELECTRIC ENERGY UTILITY SUPPLY, INC.; *U.S. Private*, pg. 1042
COOPERATIVE ELEVATOR ASSOCIATION; *U.S. Private*, pg. 1042
COOPERATIVE ELEVATOR CO., INC.; *U.S. Private*, pg. 1042
CO-OPERATIVE ELEVATOR CO. INC.; *U.S. Private*, pg. 953
CO-OPERATIVE ENERGY LIMITED—See Octopus Capital Ltd; *Int'l*, pg. 5523
CO-OPERATIVE FEED DEALERS, INC.; *U.S. Private*, pg. 953
COOPERATIVE FORESTIERE BOURGOGNE LIMOUSIN (CFBL); *Int'l*, pg. 1792
CO-OPERATIVE FUNERALCARE LIMITED—See Co-operative Group Limited; *Int'l*, pg. 1679
COOPERATIVE GAS & OIL CO; *U.S. Private*, pg. 1042
CO-OPERATIVE GROUP FOOD LIMITED—See Co-operative Group Limited; *Int'l*, pg. 1679
CO-OPERATIVE GROUP LIMITED; *Int'l*, pg. 1679
COOPERATIVE HOLDINGS INC.; *U.S. Private*, pg. 1042
COOPERATIVE HOME HEALTH CARE OF ATLANTIC COUNTY INC.; *U.S. Private*, pg. 1042
CO-OPERATIVE HOME STORES—See Co-operative Group Limited; *Int'l*, pg. 1679
CO-OPERATIVE INDUSTRIES DEFENSE, LLC—See ITT Inc.; *U.S. Public*, pg. 1179
COOPERATIVE INSURANCE BROKERS CO., LTD.—See Taiwan Cooperative Financial Holding Co., Ltd.; *Int'l*, pg. 7419
CO-OPERATIVE INSURANCE SOCIETY LIMITED—See The Royal London Mutual Insurance Society Limited; *Int'l*, pg. 7679
CO-OPERATIVE INSURANCE SOCIETY LIMITED; *Int'l*, pg. 1679
CO-OPERATIVE LEGAL SERVICES LIMITED—See Co-operative Group Limited; *Int'l*, pg. 1679
COOPERATIVE LIMAGRAIN—See Groupe Limagrain Holding SA; *Int'l*, pg. 3107
COOPERATIVE OF AMERICAN PHYSICIANS, INC.; *U.S. Private*, pg. 1042
COOPERATIVE OF AMERICAN PHYSICIANS; *U.S. Private*, pg. 1042
COOPERATIVE OPTICAL SERVICES; *U.S. Private*, pg. 1042
COOPERATIVE PRODUCERS, INC.; *U.S. Private*, pg. 1042
COOPERATIVE PRODUCTION, INC.; *U.S. Private*, pg. 1042

CORPORATE AFFILIATIONS

CO-OPERATIVE PURCHASING SERVICES LTD.; *Int'l*, pg. 1679
COOPERATIVE REGIONS OF ORGANIC PRODUCER POOLS; *U.S. Private*, pg. 1043
COOPERATIVE RESOURCES INTERNATIONAL INC.; *U.S. Private*, pg. 1043
CO-OPERATIVES E-STORE LIMITED—See Co-operative Group Limited; *Int'l*, pg. 1679
COOPERATIVE SUPPLY INC.; *U.S. Private*, pg. 1043
COOPERATIVE SYSTEMS, LLC; *U.S. Private*, pg. 1043
COOPER-ATKINS CORPORATION - GAINESVILLE FLORIDA FACILITY—See Emerson Electric Co.; *U.S. Public*, pg. 742
COOPER-ATKINS CORPORATION—See Emerson Electric Co.; *U.S. Public*, pg. 742
CO-OPERATORS FINANCIAL SERVICES LIMITED—See The Co-operators Group Limited; *Int'l*, pg. 7633
CO-OPERATORS GENERAL INSURANCE COMPANY—See The Co-operators Group Limited; *Int'l*, pg. 7633
THE CO-OPERATORS GROUP LIMITED; *Int'l*, pg. 7633
CO-OPERATORS LIFE INSURANCE COMPANY—See The Co-operators Group Limited; *Int'l*, pg. 7633
COOPER BARNETTE & PAGE; *U.S. Private*, pg. 1040
COOPER B-LINE, INC.—See Eaton Corporation plc; *Int'l*, pg. 2277
COOPER BUILDING MATERIALS—See Cooper Communities, Inc.; *U.S. Private*, pg. 1041
COOPER BUSSMANN, LLC—See Eaton Corporation plc; *Int'l*, pg. 2279
COOPER BUSSMANN (U.K.) LIMITED—See Eaton Corporation plc; *Int'l*, pg. 2277
COOPER CAPRI S.A.S.—See Eaton Corporation plc; *Int'l*, pg. 2277
COOPER CARRY, INC; *U.S. Private*, pg. 1041
COOPER (CHINA) CO., LTD.—See Eaton Corporation plc; *Int'l*, pg. 2277
COOPER COATED COIL LTD.—See Cooper Coated Coil Management Limited; *Int'l*, pg. 1791
COOPER COATED COIL MANAGEMENT LIMITED; *Int'l*, pg. 1790
COOPER COMMUNICATIONS; *U.S. Private*, pg. 1041
COOPER COMMUNITIES, INC.; *U.S. Private*, pg. 1041
THE COOPER COMPANIES, INC.; *U.S. Public*, pg. 2065
COOPER & COMPANY INC.; *U.S. Private*, pg. 1040
COOPER CONSOLIDATED—See Cooper/T. Smith Corporation; *U.S. Private*, pg. 1041
COOPER CONTROLS LIMITED—See Eaton Corporation plc; *Int'l*, pg. 2277
COOPER CONTROLS LTD. - NORTH AMERICA—See Eaton Corporation plc; *Int'l*, pg. 2277
COOPER CROUSE-HINDS GMBH—See Eaton Corporation plc; *Int'l*, pg. 2277
COOPER CROUSE-HINDS ICI—See Eaton Corporation plc; *Int'l*, pg. 2277
COOPER CROUSE-HINDS JAPAN KK—See Eaton Corporation plc; *Int'l*, pg. 2278
COOPER CROUSE-HINDS, LLC—See Eaton Corporation plc; *Int'l*, pg. 2277
COOPER CROUSE-HINDS MTL, INC.—See Eaton Corporation plc; *Int'l*, pg. 2278
COOPER CROUSE-HINDS PTE. LTD.—See Eaton Corporation plc; *Int'l*, pg. 2278
COOPER CROUSE-HINDS, S. DE R.L. DE C.V.—See Eaton Corporation plc; *Int'l*, pg. 2278
COOPER CSA SRL—See Eaton Corporation plc; *Int'l*, pg. 2277
COOPER ELECTRICAL AUSTRALIA PTY. LIMITED—See Eaton Corporation plc; *Int'l*, pg. 2277
COOPER ELECTRIC (SHANGHAI) CO. LTD.—See Eaton Corporation plc; *Int'l*, pg. 2278
COOPER ELECTRIC SUPPLY CO.—See Sonepar S.A.; *Int'l*, pg. 7093
COOPER ENERGY LIMITED; *Int'l*, pg. 1791
COOPER ENTERPRISES LLC—See Eaton Corporation plc; *Int'l*, pg. 2277
COOPER ENVIRONMENTAL SERVICES, LLC—See Hebei Sailhero Environmental Protection High-Tech Co., Ltd.; *Int'l*, pg. 3306
COOPER FARMS INC.; *U.S. Private*, pg. 1041
COOPER FINANCE USA, INC.—See Eaton Corporation plc; *Int'l*, pg. 2278
COOPER FULLEON LIMITED—See Eaton Corporation plc; *Int'l*, pg. 2278
COOPER GAY & COMPANY LTD.—See Lightyear Capital LLC; *U.S. Private*, pg. 2454
COOPER GAY RE, LTD.—See Lightyear Capital LLC; *U.S. Private*, pg. 2454
COOPER GAY SWETT & CRAWFORD LIMITED—See Lightyear Capital LLC; *U.S. Private*, pg. 2454
COOPERGENOMICS INC.—See The Cooper Companies, Inc.; *U.S. Public*, pg. 2066
COOPER GLASS COMPANY, LLC—See TopBuild Corp.; *U.S. Public*, pg. 2163
THE COOPER GROUP, LTD.—See Eastport Holdings, Inc.; *U.S. Private*, pg. 1322
COOPER HEALTH SYSTEMS; *U.S. Private*, pg. 1041
COOPERHEAT-MQS INC.—See Team, Inc.; *U.S. Public*, pg. 1987

COMPANY NAME INDEX

COOPERHEAT OF AFRICA PTY. LTD.—See Stanley Black & Decker, Inc.; *U.S. Public*, pg. 1932
COOPER INDUSTRIES HOLDINGS GMBH—See Eaton Corporation plc; *Int'l*, pg. 2277
COOPER INDUSTRIES JAPAN K.K.—See Eaton Corporation plc; *Int'l*, pg. 2277
COOPER INDUSTRIES, LLC—See Eaton Corporation plc; *Int'l*, pg. 2277
COOPER INDUSTRIES RUSSIA LLC—See Eaton Corporation plc; *Int'l*, pg. 2277
COOPER INTERCONNECT, INC. - CAMARILLO—See Eaton Corporation plc; *Int'l*, pg. 2278
COOPER INTERCONNECT, INC. - LA GRANGE—See Eaton Corporation plc; *Int'l*, pg. 2278
COOPER INTERCONNECT, INC. - MOORPARK—See Eaton Corporation plc; *Int'l*, pg. 2278
COOPER INTERCONNECT, INC.—See Eaton Corporation plc; *Int'l*, pg. 2278
COOPER JOHNSON SMITH ARCHITECTS, INC.; *U.S. Private*, pg. 1041
COOPER KOREA LTD.—See Eaton Corporation plc; *Int'l*, pg. 2278
COOPER LAND COMPANY OF NEW JERSEY, INC.—See Bayer Aktiengesellschaft; *Int'l*, pg. 907
COOPER LAND DEVELOPMENT, INC.—See Cooper Communities, Inc.; *U.S. Private*, pg. 1041
COOPERLEASING SPA—See BNP Paribas SA; *Int'l*, pg. 1090
COOPER LIGHTING, LLC - EUFAULA—See Signify N.V.; *Int'l*, pg. 6911
COOPER LIGHTING, LLC—See Signify N.V.; *Int'l*, pg. 6911
COOPER LIGHTING, LLC - VICKSBURG—See Signify N.V.; *Int'l*, pg. 6911
COOPER LIGHTING & SAFETY LTD.—See Eaton Corporation plc; *Int'l*, pg. 2278
COOPER MACHINERY SERVICES—See Arcline Investment Management LP; *U.S. Private*, pg. 313
COOPER MARINE & TIMBERLANDS—See Cooper/T. Smith Corporation; *U.S. Private*, pg. 1041
COOPER METALS LIMITED; *Int'l*, pg. 1791
COOPER (NINGBO) ELECTRIC CO., LTD.—See Eaton Corporation plc; *Int'l*, pg. 2277
COOPER NOTIFICATION, INC.—See Eaton Corporation plc; *Int'l*, pg. 2278
COOPER PERKINS, INC.—See The Carlyle Group Inc.; *U.S. Public*, pg. 2051
COOPER PEST SOLUTION, INC.; *U.S. Private*, pg. 1041
COOPER PETROLEUM INC.; *U.S. Private*, pg. 1041
COOPER POWER SYSTEMS DO BRASIL LTDA.—See Eaton Corporation plc; *Int'l*, pg. 2278
COOPER POWER SYSTEMS, LLC - FAYETTEVILLE PLANT—See Eaton Corporation plc; *Int'l*, pg. 2278
COOPER POWER SYSTEMS, LLC - MINNEAPOLIS PLANT—See Eaton Corporation plc; *Int'l*, pg. 2278
COOPER POWER SYSTEMS, LLC - NACOGDOCHES PLANT—See Eaton Corporation plc; *Int'l*, pg. 2278
COOPER POWER SYSTEMS, LLC - OLEAN PLANT—See Eaton Corporation plc; *Int'l*, pg. 2278
COOPER POWER SYSTEMS, LLC - PEWAUKEE PLANT—See Eaton Corporation plc; *Int'l*, pg. 2278
COOPER POWER SYSTEMS, LLC—See Eaton Corporation plc; *Int'l*, pg. 2278
COOPER POWER SYSTEMS, LLC - SOUTH MILWAUKEE PLANT—See Eaton Corporation plc; *Int'l*, pg. 2278
COOPER POWER SYSTEMS, LLC - TAOYUAN PLANT—See Eaton Corporation plc; *Int'l*, pg. 2278
COOPER POWER SYSTEMS, LLC - WAUKESHA (EAST NORTH STREET) PLANT—See Eaton Corporation plc; *Int'l*, pg. 2278
COOPER POWER SYSTEMS TRANSPORTATION COMPANY—See Eaton Corporation plc; *Int'l*, pg. 2278
COOPER PRETRONICA LDA.—See Eaton Corporation plc; *Int'l*, pg. 2278
COOPER REALTY INVESTMENT INC.—See Cooper Communities, Inc.; *U.S. Private*, pg. 1041
COOPERRIIS HEALING COMMUNITY, INC.; *U.S. Private*, pg. 1043
COOPER RIVER WEST—See Formation Capital, LLC; *U.S. Private*, pg. 1570
COOPER ROLLER BEARINGS COMPANY LIMITED—See SKF AB; *Int'l*, pg. 6985
COOPER SAFETY B.V.—See Eaton Corporation plc; *Int'l*, pg. 2279
COOPER SAFETY LTD.—See Eaton Corporation plc; *Int'l*, pg. 2278
COOPERS BREWERY LIMITED; *Int'l*, pg. 1792
COOPER SECURITE S.A.S.—See Eaton Corporation plc; *Int'l*, pg. 2279
COOPER SHANGHAI POWER CAPACITOR CO., LTD.—See Eaton Corporation plc; *Int'l*, pg. 2279
COOPER'S HAWK WINERY & RESTAURANT, LLC—See Ares Management Corporation; *U.S. Public*, pg. 189
COOPERS PARK CORPORATION; *Int'l*, pg. 1792
COOPERS PARK INVESTMENT HOLDINGS LIMITED—See Coopers Park Corporation; *Int'l*, pg. 1792

THE COOPER SPLIT ROLLER BEARING CORP.—See SKF AB; *Int'l*, pg. 6985
COOPERS STEEL FABRICATORS INC.; *U.S. Private*, pg. 1043
COOPER-STANDARD AUTOMOTIVE BRASIL SEALING LTDA. - CAMACARI PLANT—See Cooper-Standard Holdings Inc.; *U.S. Public*, pg. 574
COOPER-STANDARD AUTOMOTIVE BRASIL SEALING LTDA.—See Cooper-Standard Holdings Inc.; *U.S. Public*, pg. 574
COOPER-STANDARD AUTOMOTIVE CANADA LIMITED—See Cooper-Standard Holdings Inc.; *U.S. Public*, pg. 574
COOPER-STANDARD AUTOMOTIVE CESKA REPUBLIKA S.R.O.—See Cooper-Standard Holdings Inc.; *U.S. Public*, pg. 574
COOPER-STANDARD AUTOMOTIVE (CHANGCHUN) CO., LTD.—See Cooper-Standard Holdings Inc.; *U.S. Public*, pg. 574
COOPER-STANDARD AUTOMOTIVE DE MEXICO S.A. DE C.V.—See Cooper-Standard Holdings Inc.; *U.S. Public*, pg. 574
COOPER-STANDARD AUTOMOTIVE (DEUTSCHLAND) GMBH—See Cooper-Standard Holdings Inc.; *U.S. Public*, pg. 574
COOPER-STANDARD AUTOMOTIVE FLUID SYSTEMS DE MEXICO, S. DE R.L. DE C.V.—See Cooper-Standard Holdings Inc.; *U.S. Public*, pg. 574
COOPER STANDARD AUTOMOTIVE FRANCE S.A.S.—See Cooper-Standard Holdings Inc.; *U.S. Public*, pg. 574
COOPER-STANDARD AUTOMOTIVE FRANCE S.A.S.—See Cooper-Standard Holdings Inc.; *U.S. Public*, pg. 574
COOPER-STANDARD AUTOMOTIVE INC. - BOWLING GREEN PLANT—See Cooper-Standard Holdings Inc.; *U.S. Public*, pg. 574
COOPER-STANDARD AUTOMOTIVE INC.—See Cooper-Standard Holdings Inc.; *U.S. Public*, pg. 574
COOPER-STANDARD AUTOMOTIVE INTERNATIONAL HOLDINGS B.V.—See Cooper-Standard Holdings Inc.; *U.S. Public*, pg. 574
COOPER-STANDARD AUTOMOTIVE ITALY SPA—See Cooper-Standard Holdings Inc.; *U.S. Public*, pg. 574
COOPER-STANDARD AUTOMOTIVE JAPAN K.K.—See Cooper-Standard Holdings Inc.; *U.S. Public*, pg. 574
COOPER-STANDARD AUTOMOTIVE KOREA INC.—See Cooper-Standard Holdings Inc.; *U.S. Public*, pg. 574
COOPER-STANDARD AUTOMOTIVE PIOTRKOW SP ZOO—See Cooper-Standard Holdings Inc.; *U.S. Public*, pg. 574
COOPER STANDARD AUTOMOTIVE POLSKA SP. Z.O.O.—See Cooper-Standard Holdings Inc.; *U.S. Public*, pg. 574
COOPER-STANDARD AUTOMOTIVE SERVICES, S.A. DE C.V.—See Cooper-Standard Holdings Inc.; *U.S. Public*, pg. 574
COOPER-STANDARD AUTOMOTIVE UK LIMITED—See Cooper-Standard Holdings Inc.; *U.S. Public*, pg. 574
COOPER-STANDARD CHONGQING AUTOMOTIVE CO., LTD.—See Cooper-Standard Holdings Inc.; *U.S. Public*, pg. 574
COOPER STANDARD EUROPE GMBH—See Cooper-Standard Holdings Inc.; *U.S. Public*, pg. 573
COOPER STANDARD FRANCE SAS—See Cooper-Standard Holdings Inc.; *U.S. Public*, pg. 573
COOPER-STANDARD HOLDINGS INC.; *U.S. Public*, pg. 573
COOPER-STANDARD ROCKFORD INC.—See Cooper-Standard Holdings Inc.; *U.S. Public*, pg. 574
COOPER STANDARD SEALING (GUANGZOU) CO. LTD.—See Cooper-Standard Holdings Inc.; *U.S. Public*, pg. 573
COOPER-STANDARD SEALING (SHENYANG) CO. LTD.—See Cooper-Standard Holdings Inc.; *U.S. Public*, pg. 574
COOPER STANDARD SRBIJA DOO SREMSKA MITROVICA—See Cooper-Standard Holdings Inc.; *U.S. Public*, pg. 573
COOPER STREET CLINIC PTY LTD—See Healius Limited; *Int'l*, pg. 3302
COOPERSURGICAL, INC.—See The Cooper Companies, Inc.; *U.S. Public*, pg. 2066
COOPER TANK & WELDING CORP; *U.S. Private*, pg. 1041
COOPER TEESSIDE BMW—See Inchcape plc; *Int'l*, pg. 3647
COOPER TIRE & RUBBER COMPANY, CLARKSDALE PLANT—See The Goodyear Tire & Rubber Company; *U.S. Public*, pg. 2083
COOPER TIRE & RUBBER COMPANY DE MEXICO S.A. DE CV—See The Goodyear Tire & Rubber Company; *U.S. Public*, pg. 2083
COOPER TIRE & RUBBER COMPANY DE MEXICO S.A.—See The Goodyear Tire & Rubber Company; *U.S. Public*, pg. 2083
COOPER TIRE & RUBBER COMPANY DEUTSCHLAND GMBH—See The Goodyear Tire & Rubber Company; *U.S. Public*, pg. 2083

COOP-GRUPPE GENOSSENSCHAFT

COOPER TIRE & RUBBER COMPANY ESPANA S.L.—See The Goodyear Tire & Rubber Company; *U.S. Public*, pg. 2083
COOPER TIRE & RUBBER COMPANY EUROPE LTD.—See The Goodyear Tire & Rubber Company; *U.S. Public*, pg. 2082
COOPER TIRE & RUBBER COMPANY—See The Goodyear Tire & Rubber Company; *U.S. Public*, pg. 2082
COOPER TIRE & RUBBER COMPANY, TEXARKANA PLANT—See The Goodyear Tire & Rubber Company; *U.S. Public*, pg. 2083
COOPER TIRE & RUBBER HOLDING NETHERLANDS 1 B.V.—See The Goodyear Tire & Rubber Company; *U.S. Public*, pg. 2083
COOPER TIRE & RUBBER HOLDING NETHERLANDS 2 B.V.—See The Goodyear Tire & Rubber Company; *U.S. Public*, pg. 2083
COOPER TOOLS, LLC—See Bain Capital, LP; *U.S. Private*, pg. 430
COOPER TOOLS, LLC - SUMTER PLANT—See Bain Capital, LP; *U.S. Private*, pg. 430
COOPER TOOLS, LLC - YORK PLANT—See Bain Capital, LP; *U.S. Private*, pg. 430
COOPER TOOLS SAS—See Bain Capital, LP; *U.S. Private*, pg. 430
COOPER TRADING, INC.; *U.S. Private*, pg. 1041
COOPER/T. SMITH CORPORATION; *U.S. Private*, pg. 1041
COOPER/T. SMITH MOORING—See Cooper/T. Smith Corporation; *U.S. Private*, pg. 1041
COOPER/T. SMITH STEVEDORING - CALIFORNIA—See Cooper/T. Smith Corporation; *U.S. Private*, pg. 1042
COOPER/T. SMITH STEVEDORING—See Cooper/T. Smith Corporation; *U.S. Private*, pg. 1041
COOPER/T. SMITH STEVEDORING—See Cooper/T. Smith Corporation; *U.S. Private*, pg. 1041
COOPER/T. SMITH STEVEDORING—See Cooper/T. Smith Corporation; *U.S. Private*, pg. 1041
COOPER/T. SMITH STEVEDORING—See Cooper/T. Smith Corporation; *U.S. Private*, pg. 1041
COOPER/T. SMITH STEVEDORING—See Cooper/T. Smith Corporation; *U.S. Private*, pg. 1042
COOPER/T. SMITH STEVEDORING - TEXAS—See Cooper/T. Smith Corporation; *U.S. Private*, pg. 1042
COOPER TYRE & RUBBER COMPANY UK LIMITED—See The Goodyear Tire & Rubber Company; *U.S. Public*, pg. 2083
COOPER UNIVEL S.A.—See Eaton Corporation plc; *Int'l*, pg. 2279
COOPERVISION CANADA CORP.—See The Cooper Companies, Inc.; *U.S. Public*, pg. 2066
COOPERVISION CL KFT—See The Cooper Companies, Inc.; *U.S. Public*, pg. 2066
COOPERVISION DO BRASIL LTDA—See The Cooper Companies, Inc.; *U.S. Public*, pg. 2066
COOPERVISION GMBH—See The Cooper Companies, Inc.; *U.S. Public*, pg. 2066
COOPERVISION IBERIA SL—See The Cooper Companies, Inc.; *U.S. Public*, pg. 2066
COOPERVISION IBERIA SL—See The Cooper Companies, Inc.; *U.S. Public*, pg. 2066
COOPERVISION, INC.—See The Cooper Companies, Inc.; *U.S. Public*, pg. 2066
COOPERVISION LIMITED—See The Cooper Companies, Inc.; *U.S. Public*, pg. 2066
COOPERVISION NEDERLAND BV—See The Cooper Companies, Inc.; *U.S. Public*, pg. 2066
COOPERVISION NORDIC AB—See The Cooper Companies, Inc.; *U.S. Public*, pg. 2066
COOPERVISION RUS LLC—See The Cooper Companies, Inc.; *U.S. Public*, pg. 2066
COOPERVISION S.A. (PTY) LIMITED—See The Cooper Companies, Inc.; *U.S. Public*, pg. 2066
COOPERVISION S.A. (PTY) LIMITED—See The Cooper Companies, Inc.; *U.S. Public*, pg. 2066
COOPERVISION S.A.S.—See The Cooper Companies, Inc.; *U.S. Public*, pg. 2066
COOPER-WILKINS WELDING & MACHINE CO., INC.—See Cooper/T. Smith Corporation; *U.S. Private*, pg. 1041
COOPER WIRING DEVICES, INC.—See Eaton Corporation plc; *Int'l*, pg. 2278
COOPER XI'AN FUSEGEAR CO., LTD.—See Eaton Corporation plc; *Int'l*, pg. 2279
COOPER YUHUA (CHANGZHOU) ELECTRIC EQUIPMENT MANUFACTURING CO., LTD.—See Eaton Corporation plc; *Int'l*, pg. 2279
COOPER ZIETZ ENGINEERS, INC. - BATTLE GROUND—See Cooper Zietz Engineers, Inc.; *U.S. Private*, pg. 1041
COOPER ZIETZ ENGINEERS, INC.; *U.S. Private*, pg. 1041
COOP-GRUPPE GENOSSENSCHAFT; *Int'l*, pg. 1789
COOP HOSTELLERIE AG—See Coop-Gruppe Genossenschaft; *Int'l*, pg. 1790
COOP IMMOBILIEN AG—See Coop-Gruppe Genossenschaft; *Int'l*, pg. 1790
COOP-ITS-TRAVEL AG—See Coop-Gruppe Genossenschaft; *Int'l*, pg. 1790

COOP-GRUPPE GENOSSENSCHAFT

COOP MINERALOEL AG—See Coop-Gruppe Genossenschaft; *Int'l*, pg. 1790
CO-OP NETWORK—See CU Cooperative Systems, Inc.; *U.S. Private*, pg. 1119
COOP NORGE GRORUD EIENDOM AS—See Coop Norge SA; *Int'l*, pg. 1789
COOP NORGE INDUSTRI AS—See Coop Norge SA; *Int'l*, pg. 1789
COOP NORGE KAFFE AS—See Coop Norge SA; *Int'l*, pg. 1789
COOP NORGE SA; *Int'l*, pg. 1789
COOP PANK AS—See PJSC VTB Bank; *Int'l*, pg. 5886
CO-OP PROMOTIONS; *U.S. Private*, pg. 953
CO-OP PROMOTIONS—See CO-OP PROMOTIONS; *U.S. Private*, pg. 953
COOP SCHWEIZ - CWK-SCS DIVISION—See Coop-Gruppe Genossenschaft; *Int'l*, pg. 1790
COOP SCHWEIZ - INTERDISCOUNT DIVISION—See Coop-Gruppe Genossenschaft; *Int'l*, pg. 1790
COOP SCHWEIZ - SWISSMILL DIVISION—See Coop-Gruppe Genossenschaft; *Int'l*, pg. 1790
CO-OP SERVICE CENTER INC.; *U.S. Private*, pg. 953
COOP SUPERMARKTEN B.V.; *Int'l*, pg. 1789
COOP SVERIGE AB—See Kooperativa Forbundet; *Int'l*, pg. 4279
COOP TRADING A/S—See Coop Norge SA; *Int'l*, pg. 1789
COOP TRADING A/S—See FDB Group; *Int'l*, pg. 2628
COOP TRADING A/S—See Kooperativa Forbundet; *Int'l*, pg. 4279
COOP TRADING A/S—See Suomen Osuuskauppojen Keskuskunta; *Int'l*, pg. 7333
CO-OPTRUST INVESTMENTS SERVICES LTD.—See The Co-operative Bank of Kenya Limited; *Int'l*, pg. 7633
COORD3 S.R.L—See Atlas Copco AB; *Int'l*, pg. 680
COORDINAMOS PORTER NOVELLI—See Omnicom Group Inc.; *U.S. Public*, pg. 1590
COORDINATED BUSINESS SYSTEMS, LTD.; *U.S. Private*, pg. 1043
COORDINATED CARE CORPORATION INDIANA, INC.—See Centene Corporation; *U.S. Public*, pg. 468
COORDINATED CARE CORP.; *U.S. Private*, pg. 1043
COORDINATED RESOURCES, INC. OF SAN FRANCISCO; *U.S. Private*, pg. 1043
COORDINATED SYSTEMS INC.; *U.S. Private*, pg. 1043
COORS BREWING COMPANY—See Molson Coors Beverage Company; *U.S. Public*, pg. 1459
COORS DISTRIBUTING COMPANY—See Molson Coors Beverage Company; *U.S. Public*, pg. 1459
COOR SERVICE MANAGEMENT AS—See Cinven Limited; *Int'l*, pg. 1612
COOR SERVICE MANAGEMENT A/S—See Cinven Limited; *Int'l*, pg. 1612
COOR SERVICE MANAGEMENT HOLDING AB—See Cinven Limited; *Int'l*, pg. 1611
COOR SERVICE MANAGEMENT NV—See Cinven Limited; *Int'l*, pg. 1612
COOR SERVICE MANAGEMENT OY—See Cinven Limited; *Int'l*, pg. 1612
COORSTEK ARMOR SOLUTIONS, INC.—See CoorsTek, Inc.; *U.S. Private*, pg. 1043
COORSTEK ENGINEERED METALS ULC—See CoorsTek, Inc.; *U.S. Private*, pg. 1043
COORSTEK, INC. - COORSTEK LAUF FACILITY—See CoorsTek, Inc.; *U.S. Private*, pg. 1043
COORSTEK, INC. - COORSTEK MONCHENGLADBACH FACILITY—See CoorsTek, Inc.; *U.S. Private*, pg. 1043
COORSTEK, INC. - COORSTEK NEW HAMPSHIRE FACILITY—See CoorsTek, Inc.; *U.S. Private*, pg. 1043
COORSTEK, INC. - COORSTEK NEW MILLS FACILITY—See CoorsTek, Inc.; *U.S. Private*, pg. 1043
COORSTEK, INC. - COORSTEK OREGON OPERATIONS FACILITY—See CoorsTek, Inc.; *U.S. Private*, pg. 1044
COORSTEK, INC. - COORSTEK PARIS FACILITY—See CoorsTek, Inc.; *U.S. Private*, pg. 1044
COORSTEK, INC. - COORSTEK SAN LUIS POTOSI FACILITY—See CoorsTek, Inc.; *U.S. Private*, pg. 1044
COORSTEK, INC. - COORSTEK SWEDEN FACILITY—See CoorsTek, Inc.; *U.S. Private*, pg. 1044
COORSTEK, INC. - COORSTEK TENNESSEE FACILITY—See CoorsTek, Inc.; *U.S. Private*, pg. 1044
COORSTEK, INC. - COORSTEK TULSA FACILITY—See CoorsTek, Inc.; *U.S. Private*, pg. 1043
COORSTEK, INC. - COORSTEK VINHEDO FACILITY—See CoorsTek, Inc.; *U.S. Private*, pg. 1044
COORSTEK, INC. - COORSTEK VISTA FACILITY—See CoorsTek, Inc.; *U.S. Private*, pg. 1044
COORSTEK, INC. - COORSTEK VISTA FACILITY—See CoorsTek, Inc.; *U.S. Private*, pg. 1044
COORSTEK, INC. - COORSTEK WORCESTER FACILITY—See CoorsTek, Inc.; *U.S. Private*, pg. 1044
COORSTEK, INC.; *U.S. Private*, pg. 1043
COORSTEK KK - HADANO FACILITY—See CoorsTek, Inc.; *U.S. Private*, pg. 1043
COORSTEK KK - KARIYA FACILITY—See CoorsTek, Inc.; *U.S. Private*, pg. 1043
COORSTEK KK - OGUNI FACILITY—See CoorsTek, Inc.; *U.S. Private*, pg. 1043
COORSTEK KK—See CoorsTek, Inc.; *U.S. Private*, pg. 1043

COORSTEK MACHINERY CORPORATION—See CoorsTek, Inc.; *U.S. Private*, pg. 1043
COORSTEK NAGASAKI CORPORATION—See CoorsTek, Inc.; *U.S. Private*, pg. 1043
COORSTEK TAIWAN CORP.—See CoorsTek, Inc.; *U.S. Private*, pg. 1043
COORSTEK TOKUYAMA CORPORATION—See CoorsTek, Inc.; *U.S. Private*, pg. 1043
COOSA NURSING ADK, LLC—See Regional Health Properties, Inc.; *U.S. Public*, pg. 1775
COOSA VALLEY HOMECARE, LLC—See UnitedHealth Group Incorporated; *U.S. Public*, pg. 2244
COOS BAY SHIPPING TERMINAL—See Roseburg Forest Products; *U.S. Private*, pg. 3482
COOS BAY TOYOTA INC.—See Teton Auto Group; *U.S. Private*, pg. 3973
COOTEK (CAYMAN) INC.; *Int'l*, pg. 1792
COPACABANA PALACE HOTEL—See LVMH Moet Hennessy Louis Vuitton SE; *Int'l*, pg. 4591
COPAC, INC.; *U.S. Private*, pg. 1044
COPACINO + FUJIKADO, LLC; *U.S. Private*, pg. 1044
COPACK FRANCE S.A.R.L.—See FRoSTA AG; *Int'l*, pg. 2797
COPACK TIEFKUHLKOST-PRODUKTIONS GMBH—See FRoSTA AG; *Int'l*, pg. 2797
COPACQ N.V.—See Molenwijck B.V.; *Int'l*, pg. 5022
COPA CORPORATION, INC.; *Int'l*, pg. 1792
COPA DI VINO; *U.S. Private*, pg. 1044
COPAG-CIA CAPITAL DE ARMAZENS GERAIS S.A.—See ED&F Man Holdings Limited; *Int'l*, pg. 2302
COPAG DA AMAZONIA S.A.—See Cartamundi N.V.; *Int'l*, pg. 1348
COPA HOLDINGS, S.A.; *Int'l*, pg. 1792
COPA HYDROSYSTEM ODD—See Interpump Group S.p.A.; *Int'l*, pg. 3755
COPAIMEX, S.A.—See Iberpapel Gestion SA; *Int'l*, pg. 3574
COPA INC.; *U.S. Private*, pg. 1044
COPAL OPTICAL & ELECTRONIC MACHINERY (SHANGHAI) CO., LTD.—See Nidec Corporation; *Int'l*, pg. 5276
COPAL PARTNERS UK LIMITED—See Moody's Corporation; *U.S. Public*, pg. 1467
COPAL PARTNERS (US) INC.—See Moody's Corporation; *U.S. Public*, pg. 1467
COPAL RESEARCH INDIA PRIVATE LIMITED—See Moody's Corporation; *U.S. Public*, pg. 1467
COPAL RESEARCH LTD. (MAURITIUS)—See Moody's Corporation; *U.S. Public*, pg. 1467
COPAL S.A.S.—See Ball Corporation; *U.S. Public*, pg. 267
COPAL YAMADA CORPORATION—See Nidec Corporation; *Int'l*, pg. 5276
COPAL YAMADA (VIETNAM) CO., LTD.—See Nidec Corporation; *Int'l*, pg. 5276
COPAM-COMPANHIA PORTUGUESA DE AMIDOS SA; *Int'l*, pg. 1792
COPAMEX CORRUGADOS, S.A. DE C.V.—See Corporativo Copamex, S.A. de C.V.; *Int'l*, pg. 1806
COPAMEX EMPAQUE, S.A. DE C.V.—See Corporativo Copamex, S.A. de C.V.; *Int'l*, pg. 1806
COPAMEX NORTH AMERICA—See Corporativo Copamex, S.A. de C.V.; *Int'l*, pg. 1806
COPAM SAS—See Vivescia; *Int'l*, pg. 8279
COPAPAMERICAS LLC—See COPAP Inc.; *Int'l*, pg. 1792
COPAP EUROPE SAS—See COPAP Inc.; *Int'l*, pg. 1792
COPAP INC.; *Int'l*, pg. 1792
COPART CANADA, INC.—See Copart, Inc.; *U.S. Public*, pg. 575
COPART DEUTSCHLAND GMBH—See Copart, Inc.; *U.S. Public*, pg. 575
COPART EXCAVATION, INC.—See Copart, Inc.; *U.S. Public*, pg. 575
COPART, INC.; *U.S. Public*, pg. 574
COPARTNER TECHNOLOGY CORPORATION; *Int'l*, pg. 1792
COPARTNER TECHNOLOGY (SHENZHEN) CO., LTD.—See Copartner Technology Corporation; *Int'l*, pg. 1793
COPARTNER WIRE & CABLE (SHENZHEN) CO LTD—See Copartner Technology Corporation; *Int'l*, pg. 1793
COPART OF ARIZONA, INC.—See Copart, Inc.; *U.S. Public*, pg. 574
COPART OF ARKANSAS, INC.—See Copart, Inc.; *U.S. Public*, pg. 574
COPART OF CONNECTICUT, INC.—See Copart, Inc.; *U.S. Public*, pg. 575
COPART OF HOUSTON, INC.—See Copart, Inc.; *U.S. Public*, pg. 574
COPART OF KANSAS, INC.—See Copart, Inc.; *U.S. Public*, pg. 575
COPART OF LOUISIANA, INC.—See Copart, Inc.; *U.S. Public*, pg. 575
COPART OF OKLAHOMA, INC.—See Copart, Inc.; *U.S. Public*, pg. 575
COPART OF TENNESSEE, INC.—See Copart, Inc.; *U.S. Public*, pg. 574
COPART OF TEXAS, INC.—See Copart, Inc.; *U.S. Public*, pg. 575

CORPORATE AFFILIATIONS

COPART OF WASHINGTON, INC.—See Copart, Inc.; *U.S. Public*, pg. 574
COPART SALVAGE AUTO AUCTIONS, INC.—See Copart, Inc.; *U.S. Public*, pg. 575
COPART UAE AUCTIONS LLC—See Copart, Inc.; *U.S. Public*, pg. 575
COPART UK LIMITED—See Copart, Inc.; *U.S. Public*, pg. 575
COPASAT, LLC; *U.S. Private*, pg. 1044
COPAUR MINERALS INC.; *Int'l*, pg. 1793
COPAZ PACKING CORPORATION; *U.S. Private*, pg. 1044
COPC INC.—See Black Box Limited; *Int'l*, pg. 1058
COP COMMUNICATIONS; *U.S. Private*, pg. 1044
COP CONSTRUCTION CO.; *U.S. Private*, pg. 1044
COPE BESTWAY EXPRESS INC.; *U.S. Private*, pg. 1044
COPEBRAS LIMITADA—See Anglo American PLC; *Int'l*, pg. 461
COPE COMMUNITY SERVICES, INC.; *U.S. Private*, pg. 1044
COPEINCA ASA—See Pacific Andes International Holdings Limited; *Int'l*, pg. 5685
COPELAND CANADA, LTD.—See Emerson Electric Co.; *U.S. Public*, pg. 742
COPELAND CHEVROLET; *U.S. Private*, pg. 1044
COPELAND CORPORATION LLC—See Emerson Electric Co.; *U.S. Public*, pg. 743
COPELAND DE MEXICO, S.A. DE C.V.—See Emerson Electric Co.; *U.S. Public*, pg. 743
COPELAND GMBH—See Emerson Electric Co.; *U.S. Public*, pg. 743
COPELAND ITALIA S.A.R.L.—See Emerson Electric Co.; *U.S. Public*, pg. 744
COPELAND OIL & GAS CO. OF MBL; *U.S. Private*, pg. 1044
COPELANDS OF NEW ORLEANS INC.; *U.S. Private*, pg. 1044
COPEL COMPANHIA ENERGIA S/A—See Companhia Paranaense de Energia; *Int'l*, pg. 1748
COPEL DISTRIBUICAO SA—See Companhia Paranaense de Energia; *Int'l*, pg. 1748
COPEL TELECOMUNICACOES S.A.; *Int'l*, pg. 1793
COPEN ASSOCIATES, INC.; *U.S. Private*, pg. 1044
COPENHAGEN CAPITAL A/S; *Int'l*, pg. 1793
COPENHAGEN IMPORTS INC.; *U.S. Private*, pg. 1044
COPENHAGEN MALMO PORT—See Copenhagen Malmo Port; *Int'l*, pg. 1793
COPENHAGEN MALMO PORT; *Int'l*, pg. 1793
COPE PLASTICS INCORPORATED; *U.S. Private*, pg. 1044
COPE PRIVATE EQUITY SDN. BHD.—See Cahya Mata Sarawak Berhad; *Int'l*, pg. 1251
COPERION AB—See Hillenbrand, Inc.; *U.S. Public*, pg. 1036
COPERION CORPORATION—See Hillenbrand, Inc.; *U.S. Public*, pg. 1036
COPERION CORP.—See Hillenbrand, Inc.; *U.S. Public*, pg. 1036
COPERION GMBH—See Hillenbrand, Inc.; *U.S. Public*, pg. 1036
COPERION GMBH—See Hillenbrand, Inc.; *U.S. Public*, pg. 1035
COPERION IDEAL PVT LTD.—See Hillenbrand, Inc.; *U.S. Public*, pg. 1036
COPERION INTERNATIONAL TRADING (SHANGHAI) CO. LTD.—See Hillenbrand, Inc.; *U.S. Public*, pg. 1036
COPERION K.K.—See Hillenbrand, Inc.; *U.S. Public*, pg. 1036
COPERION K-TRON ASIA PTE. LTD.—See Hillenbrand, Inc.; *U.S. Public*, pg. 1036
COPERION K-TRON DEUTSCHLAND GMBH—See Hillenbrand, Inc.; *U.S. Public*, pg. 1036
COPERION K-TRON FRANCE S.A.R.L.—See Hillenbrand, Inc.; *U.S. Public*, pg. 1036
COPERION K-TRON GREAT BRITAIN LIMITED—See Hillenbrand, Inc.; *U.S. Public*, pg. 1036
COPERION K-TRON PITMAN, INC.—See Hillenbrand, Inc.; *U.S. Public*, pg. 1037
COPERION K-TRON SALINA—See Hillenbrand, Inc.; *U.S. Public*, pg. 1037
COPERION K-TRON (SCHWEIZ) GMBH—See Hillenbrand, Inc.; *U.S. Public*, pg. 1036
COPERION K-TRON (SHANGHAI) CO. LTD.—See Hillenbrand, Inc.; *U.S. Public*, pg. 1036
COPERION LTDA.—See Hillenbrand, Inc.; *U.S. Public*, pg. 1036
COPERION LTD.—See Hillenbrand, Inc.; *U.S. Public*, pg. 1036
COPERION MACHINERY & SYSTEMS (SHANGHAI) CO. LTD.—See Hillenbrand, Inc.; *U.S. Public*, pg. 1036
COPERION MIDDLE EAST CO. LTD.—See Hillenbrand, Inc.; *U.S. Public*, pg. 1036
COPERION (NANJING) MACHINERY CO., LTD.—See Hillenbrand, Inc.; *U.S. Public*, pg. 1036
COPERION N.V.—See Hillenbrand, Inc.; *U.S. Public*, pg. 1036
COPERION PELLETIZING TECHNOLOGY GMBH—See Hillenbrand, Inc.; *U.S. Public*, pg. 1036
COPERION PTE LTD.—See Hillenbrand, Inc.; *U.S. Public*, pg. 1036

COMPANY NAME INDEX

COPERION S.A.R.L.—See Hillenbrand, Inc.; *U.S. Public*, pg. 1036
COPERION S.L.—See Hillenbrand, Inc.; *U.S. Public*, pg. 1036
COPERION S.R.L.—See Hillenbrand, Inc.; *U.S. Public*, pg. 1036
COPERNIC INC.—See Constellation Software Inc.; *Int'l*, pg. 1774
COPERNICO SIM SPA; *Int'l*, pg. 1793
THE COPERNICUS GROUP, INC.—See Arsenal Capital Management LP; *U.S. Private*, pg. 339
COPERSONS CORPORATION—See Nexon Co., Ltd.; *Int'l*, pg. 5245
COPERSUCAR NORTH AMERICA LLC—See Copersucar S.A.; *Int'l*, pg. 1793
COPERSUCAR S.A.; *Int'l*, pg. 1793
COPESAN SERVICES INC.—See Roark Capital Group Inc.; *U.S. Private*, pg. 3456
COPES-VULCAN—See SPX Technologies, Inc.; *U.S. Public*, pg. 1920
COPETRO, S.A.—See Oxbow Corporation; *U.S. Private*, pg. 3056
COPHAR LTD.—See CSL Limited; *Int'l*, pg. 1866
C & O PHARMACEUTICAL TECHNOLOGY (HOLDINGS) LIMITED—See Shionogi & Co., Ltd.; *Int'l*, pg. 6851
CO PHARMA LTD.—See Strides Pharma Science Limited; *Int'l*, pg. 7240
COPIA CREATIVE, INC.—See The Phelps Group; *U.S. Private*, pg. 4094
COPIA SCIENTIFIC, INC.; *U.S. Private*, pg. 1044
COPIC TRUST; *U.S. Private*, pg. 1044
COPIER BUSINESS SOLUTIONS—See Loffler Companies, Inc.; *U.S. Private*, pg. 2480
COPIERSUPPLYSTORE; *U.S. Private*, pg. 1045
COPIJN UTRECHT HOLDING BV—See Hoek Hoveniers B.V.; *Int'l*, pg. 3439
COPILOT CAPITAL LIMITED; *Int'l*, pg. 1793
COPITRAK INC.; *Int'l*, pg. 1793
COPLAND FABRICS, INC.; *U.S. Private*, pg. 1045
COPLAND ROAD CAPITAL CORPORATION; *Int'l*, pg. 1793
COPLEX PETROLEO DO BRASIL LTDA.—See Norse Energy Corp. ASA; *Int'l*, pg. 5432
COPLEY EQUITY PARTNERS, LLC; *U.S. Private*, pg 1045
COPLEY HEALTH CENTER INC—See Communicare, Inc.; *U.S. Private*, pg. 988
COPLEY PROFESSIONAL SERVICES GROUP, INC.; *U.S. Private*, pg. 1045
COPLUS INC.; *Int'l*, pg. 1793
COPOL INTERNATIONAL LTD.; *Int'l*, pg. 1793
COPPA CLUB LIMITED—See Various Eateries Plc; *Int'l*, pg. 8133
COPPELL SPINE & SPORTS REHAB, LIMITED PARTNERSHIP—See U.S. Physical Therapy, Inc.; *U.S. Public*, pg. 2214
COPPER & BRASS SALES, INC.—See ThyssenKrupp AG; *Int'l*, pg. 7729
COPPER CABLE COMPANY LTD.—See TELE-FONIKA Kable Sp. z o.o. S.K.A.; *Int'l*, pg. 7528
THE COPPER CELLAR CORPORATION; *U.S. Private*, pg. 4014
COPPER CLAD MULTILAYER PRODUCTS INC.; *U.S. Private*, pg. 1045
COPPER CORE LTD.; *Int'l*, pg. 1793
COPPERCORP RESOURCES INC.; *Int'l*, pg. 1794
COPPERCRAFT LIMITED—See Kingspan Group PLC; *Int'l*, pg. 4176
COPPER CREST RETIREMENT VILLAGE LIMITED—See Arvida Group Limited; *Int'l*, pg. 587
COPPER CROSSING SOLAR, LLC—See Iberdrola, S.A.; *Int'l*, pg. 3570
COPPER ENVIRONMENTAL CONSULTING, LLC—See The White Oak Group, Inc.; *U.S. Private*, pg. 4135
COPPERFIELD CHIMNEY SUPPLY, INC.—See Olympia Chimney Supply Holdings, LLC; *U.S. Private*, pg. 3012
COPPER FOX METALS INC.; *Int'l*, pg. 1793
COPPER FUNDING, LLC—See White Mountains Insurance Group, Ltd.; *U.S. Public*, pg. 2369
COPPERHEAD RESOURCES INC.; *Int'l*, pg. 1794
COPPERHOUSE GREEN MANAGEMENT COMPANY LIMITED—See Bellway plc; *Int'l*, pg. 968
COPPER & KINGS AMERICAN BRANDY COMPANY—See Constellation Brands, Inc.; *U.S. Public*, pg. 571
COPPER LAKE RESOURCES LTD.; *Int'l*, pg. 1793
COPPERLOGIC, LTD.—See Eaton Corporation plc; *Int'l*, pg. 2279
COPPERMINE CAPITAL, LLC; *U.S. Private*, pg. 1045
COPPER MINES OF TASMANIA PTY LIMITED—See Vedanta Resources Ltd; *Int'l*, pg. 8146
COPPERMOL S.A.—See Corporacion Nacional del Cobre de Chile; *Int'l*, pg. 1805
COPPERMOLY LIMITED; *Int'l*, pg. 1794
COPPER MOUNTAIN, INC.—See Powdr Corp.; *U.S. Private*, pg. 3236
COPPER MOUNTAIN LANDFILL, INC—See Republic Services, Inc.; *U.S. Public*, pg. 1786

COPPER MOUNTAIN MINING CORPORATION—See HudBay Minerals Inc.; *Int'l*, pg. 3521
COPPER NORTH MINING CORP.; *Int'l*, pg. 1793
COPPERPOINT INSURANCE COMPANY—See CopperPoint Mutual Insurance Holding Company; *U.S. Private*, pg. 1045
COPPERPOINT MUTUAL INSURANCE HOLDING COMPANY; *U.S. Private*, pg. 1045
COPPER PROPERTY CTL PASS THROUGH TRUST; *U.S. Public*, pg. 575
COPPER QUEST PNG LTD—See Coppermoly Limited; *Int'l*, pg. 1794
COPPER RESOURCES CORPORATION—See Jinchuan Group Limited; *Int'l*, pg. 3965
COPPER RIVER SEAFOODS, INC.; *U.S. Private*, pg. 1045
COPPER ROCK CAPITAL PARTNERS LLC—See BrightSphere Investment Group Inc.; *U.S. Public*, pg. 383
COPPER SEARCH LIMITED; *Int'l*, pg. 1794
COPPERSMITH CORPORATION; *U.S. Private*, pg. 1045
COPPER STANDARD RESOURCES INC.; *Int'l*, pg. 1794
COPPER STATE BOLT & NUT CO. INC.; *U.S. Private*, pg. 1045
COPPER STATE COMMUNICATIONS, INC.—See BlackPoint IT Services, Inc.; *U.S. Private*, pg. 576
COPPERSTONE RESOURCES AB; *Int'l*, pg. 1794
COPPER STRIKE LIMITED; *Int'l*, pg. 1794
COPPER VALLEY ELECTRIC ASSOCIATION; *U.S. Private*, pg. 1045
COPPER VALLEY TELE COOP INC.; *U.S. Private*, pg. 1045
COPPER VALLEY TELEPHONE COOPERATIVE, INC.; *U.S. Private*, pg. 1045
COPPERWELD BIMETALLICS, LLC—See Fushi Copperweld, Inc.; *Int'l*, pg. 2849
COPPERWELD TUBING EUROPE SPRL—See Fushi Copperweld, Inc.; *Int'l*, pg. 2849
COPPERWIRED PUBLIC COMPANY LIMITED; *Int'l*, pg. 1794
COPPERWOOD MEDICAL CENTER LLC—See Adeptus Health Inc.; *U.S. Private*, pg. 78
COPPES-NAPANEE CO.; *U.S. Private*, pg. 1045
COPPLEY, INC.—See Individualized Apparel Group; *U.S. Private*, pg. 2064
COPRECI - ALTSASUKO S.COOP.—See Mondragon Corporation; *Int'l*, pg. 5028
COPRECI CZ, S.R.O.—See Mondragon Corporation; *Int'l*, pg. 5028
COPRECI DE MEXICO, SA DE CV—See Mondragon Corporation; *Int'l*, pg. 5028
COPRECI DO BRASIL, LTDA.—See Mondragon Corporation; *Int'l*, pg. 5028
COPRECI S.COOP—See Mondragon Corporation; *Int'l*, pg. 5028
COPRECI SYSTEMS, S.R.L.—See Mondragon Corporation; *Int'l*, pg. 5028
COPRECI TR.LTD.STI.—See Mondragon Corporation; *Int'l*, pg. 5028
COPRO HOLDINGS CO., LTD.; *Int'l*, pg. 1794
COPROMED S.A. DE C.V.—See Banco Bilbao Vizcaya Argentaria, S.A.; *Int'l*, pg. 817
CO-PROSPERITY HOLDINGS LIMITED; *Int'l*, pg. 1679
COPRO VIETNAM CO., LTD.—See Copro Holdings Co., Ltd.; *Int'l*, pg. 1794
COPT DC-6, LLC—See COPT Defense Properties; *U.S. Public*, pg. 575
COPT DEFENSE PROPERTIES; *U.S. Public*, pg. 575
COPT NORTHCREEK, LLC—See COPT Defense Properties; *U.S. Public*, pg. 575
COPT PROPERTY MANAGEMENT SERVICES, LLC—See COPT Defense Properties; *U.S. Public*, pg. 575
COPUS KOREA CO., LTD.; *Int'l*, pg. 1794
COPYCO OFFICE SOLUTIONS, INC.—See Xerox Holdings Corporation; *U.S. Public*, pg. 2387
COPY DUPLICATING SYSTEMS—See Dataflow Business Systems, Inc.; *U.S. Private*, pg. 1165
COPY-MOR, INC.—See Chatham Asset Management, LLC; *U.S. Private*, pg. 862
COPYPRO INC.; *U.S. Private*, pg. 1046
COPYRITE BUSINESS SOLUTIONS LIMITED—See Xerox Holdings Corporation; *U.S. Public*, pg. 2386
COPY SOLUTIONS, INC.; *U.S. Private*, pg. 1045
COPYSOURCE INCORPORATED—See Konica Minolta, Inc.; *Int'l*, pg. 4258
COPYTALK, LLC; *U.S. Private*, pg. 1046
COQUET GRANGE (AMBLE) MANAGEMENT COMPANY LIMITED—See Persimmon plc; *Int'l*, pg. 5815
COQUILLE ECONOMIC DEVELOPMENT; *U.S. Private*, pg. 1046
COQUITLAM CHRYSLER DODGE JEEP LTD.; *Int'l*, pg. 1794
COQUITLAM RIDGE CONSTRUCTORS LTD.—See VINCI S.A.; *Int'l*, pg. 8218
COR365 INFORMATION SOLUTIONS; *U.S. Private*, pg. 1046
CORACENT INC.; *U.S. Private*, pg. 1046
CORADIANT (CANADA) INC.—See KKR & Co. Inc.; *U.S. Public*, pg. 1241

CORAD TECHNOLOGY LTD.—See HORIBA Ltd; *Int'l*, pg. 3475
CORAGGIO DESIGN, INC.; *U.S. Private*, pg. 1046
CORAGLASS, INC.—See Coral Industries, Inc.; *U.S. Private*, pg. 1046
CORAL BAY NICKEL CORPORATION—See Mitsui & Co., Ltd.; *Int'l*, pg. 4973
CORAL BAY NICKEL CORPORATION—See Sumitomo Metal Mining Co., Ltd.; *Int'l*, pg. 7291
CORAL BLOOD SERVICES—See Charles River Laboratories International, Inc.; *U.S. Public*, pg. 480
CORAL CADILLAC; *U.S. Private*, pg. 1046
CORAL CHEMICAL COMPANY; *U.S. Private*, pg. 1046
CORAL CO. LTD.—See Husqvarna AB; *Int'l*, pg. 3539
CORAL CONSTRUCTION COMPANY; *U.S. Private*, pg. 1046
CORAL DIALYSIS, LLC—See DaVita Inc.; *U.S. Public*, pg. 637
CORALEC—See Nokia Corporation; *Int'l*, pg. 5404
CORAL ENERGY PRODUCTS (CYPRUS) LTD.—See Motor Oil (Hellas) Corinth Refineries S. A.; *Int'l*, pg. 5053
CORAL GABLES HOSPITAL, INC.—See Tenet Healthcare Corporation; *U.S. Public*, pg. 2006
THE CORAL GABLES TRUST COMPANY; *U.S. Private*, pg. 4014
CORAL GAS CYPRUS LTD.—See Motor Oil (Hellas) Corinth Refineries S. A.; *Int'l*, pg. 5053
CORAL GOLD RESOURCES LTD.—See Sandstorm Gold Ltd.; *Int'l*, pg. 6527
CORAL GRAPHIC SERVICES, INC.; *U.S. Private*, pg. 1046
CORAL HOSPITALITY, LLC; *U.S. Private*, pg. 1046
CORAL INDIA FINANCE & HOUSING LIMITED; *Int'l*, pg. 1794
CORAL INDUSTRIES, INC.; *U.S. Private*, pg. 1046
CORALISLE GROUP LTD.; *Int'l*, pg. 1795
CORAL LABORATORIES LTD.; *Int'l*, pg. 1794
CORALLINE INVESTMENTS (PTY) LTD—See Berry Global Group, Inc; *U.S. Public*, pg. 323
CORAL MINT LTD.—See Daily Mail & General Trust plc; *Int'l*, pg. 1937
CORAL NEWSPRINTS LTD.; *Int'l*, pg. 1794
CORAL PRODUCTS (MOULDINGS) LIMITED—See Coral Products PLC; *Int'l*, pg. 1795
CORAL PRODUCTS PLC; *Int'l*, pg. 1794
CORAL PRODUCTS & TRADING SINGLE MEMBER S.A.—See Motor Oil (Hellas) Corinth Refineries S. A.; *Int'l*, pg. 5053
CORAL RACING LTD.—See ITV plc; *Int'l*, pg. 3844
CORAL RIDGE MINISTRIES MEDIA INC.; *U.S. Private*, pg. 1046
CORAL RIDGE OUTPATIENT CENTER, LLC—See Tenet Healthcare Corporation; *U.S. Public*, pg. 2005
CORAL SEAS - CONSUMER PRODUCTS DIVISION—See Coral Chemical Company; *U.S. Private*, pg. 1046
CORAL SHORES BEHAVIORAL HEALTH, LLC—See Universal Health Services, Inc.; *U.S. Public*, pg. 2256
CORAL SINGLE MEMBER S.A.—See Motor Oil (Hellas) Corinth Refineries S. A.; *Int'l*, pg. 5053
CORAL SPRINGS AMBULATORY SURGERY CENTER, LLC—See KKR & Co. Inc.; *U.S. Public*, pg. 1245
CORAL SPRINGS AUTOMALL; *U.S. Private*, pg. 1046
CORAL SPRINGS SURGI-CENTER, LTD.—See HCA Healthcare, Inc.; *U.S. Public*, pg. 994
CORAL SRB D.O.O.—See Motor Oil (Hellas) Corinth Refineries S. A.; *Int'l*, pg. 5053
CORAL STADIA LIMITED—See Entain PLC; *Int'l*, pg. 2450
CORAL TECHNOLOGIES—See Coral Chemical Company; *U.S. Private*, pg. 1046
CORAMINE S.A.S.—See Compagnie de Saint-Gobain SA; *Int'l*, pg. 1723
CORAM MATERIALS CORP.—See Vulcan Materials Company; *U.S. Public*, pg. 2314
CORAM SPECIALTY INFUSION SERVICES—See Blackstone Inc.; *U.S. Public*, pg. 348
CORA SA—See SIF Banat-Crisana S.A.; *Int'l*, pg. 6905
CORA SERVICES, INC.; *U.S. Private*, pg. 1046
CORASIA CORP.—See Cheng Loong Corp.; *Int'l*, pg. 1466
CORASO SAS—See VINCI S.A.; *Int'l*, pg. 8216
CORASWORKS CORPORATION—See HumanTouch, LLC; *U.S. Private*, pg. 2007
CORA TEXAS MANUFACTURING CO., LLC; *U.S. Private*, pg. 1046
CORA VERLAG GMBH & CO. KG—See Charlesbank Capital Partners, LLC; *U.S. Private*, pg. 854
CORAZA INTEGRATED TECHNOLOGY BERHAD; *Int'l*, pg. 1795
CORAZA SYSTEMS MALAYSIA SDN. BHD.—See Coraza Integrated Technology Berhad; *Int'l*, pg. 1795
CORAZON CAPITAL V838 MONOCEROS CORP.; *U.S. Private*, pg. 1046
CORAZON MINING LIMITED; *Int'l*, pg. 1795
CORBELIS DEVELOPMENT SWFL, LLC—See Corbelis Management, LLC; *U.S. Private*, pg. 1047
CORBELIS MANAGEMENT, LLC; *U.S. Private*, pg. 1047
CORBEL MANAGEMENT LLC; *U.S. Private*, pg. 1047
CORBETT CANYON VINEYARDS—See The Wine Group, Inc.; *U.S. Private*, pg. 4137

CORBIN COMMUNICATIONS LIMITED

CORBIN COMMUNICATIONS LIMITED; *Int'l*, pg. 1795
CORBIN COMMUNICATIONS LIMITED—See Corbin Communications Limited; *Int'l*, pg. 1795
CORBIN GAS PROPANE—See UGI Corporation; *U.S. Public*, pg. 2222
CORBIN-HILL, INC.; *U.S. Private*, pg. 1047
CORBIN-HILLMAN COMMUNICATIONS; *U.S. Private*, pg. 1047
CORBIN PACIFIC INCORPORATED; *U.S. Private*, pg. 1047
CORBIN RUSSWIN, INC.—See ASSA ABLOY AB; *Int'l*, pg. 636
CORBION GROUP NETHERLANDS B.V.—See Corbion N.V.; *Int'l*, pg. 1795
CORBION N.V.; *Int'l*, pg. 1795
CORBION - PURAC DIVISION—See Corbion N.V.; *Int'l*, pg. 1795
CORBI PLASTICS, LLC—See Menasha Corporation; *U.S. Private*, pg. 2665
CORBOX CORPORATION; *Int'l*, pg. 1795
COR BUSINESS DEVELOPMENT COMPANY LLC; *U.S. Private*, pg. 1046
CORBUS PHARMACEUTICALS HOLDINGS, INC.; *U.S. Public*, pg. 575
CORBUS PHARMACEUTICALS, INC.—See Corbus Pharmaceuticals Holdings, Inc.; *U.S. Public*, pg. 575
CORBY INDUSTRIES, INC.; *U.S. Private*, pg. 1047
CORBY SPIRIT AND WINE LIMITED—See Pernod Ricard S.A.; *Int'l*, pg. 5811
CORBY TYRES AND EXHAUSTS LIMITED—See Sumitomo Rubber Industries, Ltd.; *Int'l*, pg. 7298
CORBY VETS4PETS LIMITED—See Pets at Home Group Plc; *Int'l*, pg. 5833
CORCEL PLC; *Int'l*, pg. 1795
CORCENTRIC, INC.; *U.S. Private*, pg. 1047
CORCENTRIC, LLC—See Corcentric, Inc.; *U.S. Private*, pg. 1047
CORCEPT THERAPEUTICS INCORPORATED; *U.S. Public*, pg. 575
COR CLEARING LLC—See Axos Financial, Inc.; *U.S. Public*, pg. 256
CORCORAN GROUP LLC—See Anywhere Real Estate Inc.; *U.S. Public*, pg. 142
THE CORCORAN GROUP—See Anywhere Real Estate Inc.; *U.S. Public*, pg. 141
CORCORAN & HAVLIN INSURANCE GROUP—See Cross Financial Corporation; *U.S. Private*, pg. 1104
CORCORAN & JOHNSTON; *U.S. Private*, pg. 1047
CORCORAN SUNSHINE MARKETING GROUP—See Anywhere Real Estate Inc.; *U.S. Public*, pg. 142
CORCORAN TRUCKING INC.; *U.S. Private*, pg. 1047
CORCOS INDUSTRIALE S.P.A.—See Freudenberg SE; *Int'l*, pg. 2782
CORCYM S.R.L.—See LivaNova PLC; *Int'l*, pg. 4529
CORDANT GROUP PLC; *Int'l*, pg. 1795
CORDAROY'S ORIGINALS, INC.; *U.S. Private*, pg. 1047
CORD CAMERA CENTERS INC.; *U.S. Private*, pg. 1047
CORDEA SAVILLS GMBH—See Savills plc; *Int'l*, pg. 6598
CORDEA SAVILLS INVESTMENT MANAGEMENT LTD.—See Savills plc; *Int'l*, pg. 6598
CORDED STRAP (NZ) LIMITED—See Bunzl plc; *Int'l*, pg. 1218
CORDEL GROUP PLC; *Int'l*, pg. 1796
CORDELL INFORMATION PTY LTD—See Insight Venture Management, LLC; *U.S. Private*, pg. 2088
CORDELL INFORMATION PTY LTD—See Stone Point Capital LLC; *U.S. Private*, pg. 3822
CORDEL NORGE AS—See SmartCraft ASA; *Int'l*, pg. 7002
CORDEN PHARMA BERGAMO S.P.A.—See Astorg Partners S.A.S.; *Int'l*, pg. 656
CORDEN PHARMA BOULDER, INC.—See Astorg Partners S.A.S.; *Int'l*, pg. 656
CORDEN PHARMACHEM IRELAND LTD.—See Astorg Partners S.A.S.; *Int'l*, pg. 656
CORDEN PHARMA COLORADO INC.—See Astorg Partners S.A.S.; *Int'l*, pg. 656
CORDEN PHARMA INTERNATIONAL GMBH—See Astorg Partners S.A.S.; *Int'l*, pg. 655
CORDEN PHARMA LATINA S.P.A.—See Astorg Partners S.A.S.; *Int'l*, pg. 656
CORDEN PHARMA S.P.A.—See Astorg Partners S.A.S.; *Int'l*, pg. 656
CORDEN PHARMA SWITZERLAND LLC—See Astorg Partners S.A.S.; *Int'l*, pg. 656
CORDEN PHARMA SWITZERLAND LLC—See Astorg Partners S.A.S.; *Int'l*, pg. 656
CORDENTAL GROUP MANAGEMENT, LLC—See NMS Capital Services, LLC; *U.S. Private*, pg. 2931
CORDERO & DAVENPORT ADVERTISING; *U.S. Private*, pg. 1047
CORDERY COMPLIANCE LTD.—See RELX plc; *Int'l*, pg. 6266
CORDES & CO. GMBH—See Henkel AG & Co. KGaA; *Int'l*, pg. 3348
CORDET CAPITAL PARTNERS LLP; *Int'l*, pg. 1796
CORDEV INC.; *U.S. Private*, pg. 1047
CORDIA CORP.; *U.S. Public*, pg. 575

CORDIALSA BORICUA EMPAQUE, INC.—See Grupo Nutresa S.A.; *Int'l*, pg. 3133
CORDIALSA USA, INC.—See Grupo Nutresa S.A.; *Int'l*, pg. 3133
CORDIANT DIGITAL INFRASTRUCTURE LIMITED; *Int'l*, pg. 1796
CORDILLERA CORPORATION; *U.S. Private*, pg. 1047
CORDINA CHICKEN FARMS PTY. LTD.; *Int'l*, pg. 1796
CORDIS EUROPA NV—See Johnson & Johnson; *U.S. Public*, pg. 1194
THE CORDISH COMPANIES; *U.S. Private*, pg. 4015
CORDIS HONG KONG LIMITED—See Great Eagle Holdings Limited; *Int'l*, pg. 3064
CORDIS LLC—See Johnson & Johnson; *U.S. Public*, pg. 1194
CORDLIFE GROUP LIMITED; *Int'l*, pg. 1796
CORDLIFE (HONG KONG) LIMITED—See Cordlife Group Limited; *Int'l*, pg. 1796
CORDLIFE MEDICAL PHILS., INC.—See Cordlife Group Limited; *Int'l*, pg. 1796
CORDLIFE SCIENCES (INDIA) PVT. LTD.—See Cordlife Group Limited; *Int'l*, pg. 1796
CORD MEYER DEVELOPMENT LLC; *U.S. Private*, pg. 1047
CORD MOVING & STORAGE CO.; *U.S. Private*, pg. 1047
CORDOBA MINERALS CORP.; *Int'l*, pg. 1796
CORDONSED ARGENTINA S.A.—See Radici Partecipazioni S.p.A.; *Int'l*, pg. 6175
CORDON VERT CO., LTD.—See AEON Co., Ltd.; *Int'l*, pg. 177
CORDOVACANN CORP.; *Int'l*, pg. 1796
CORDOVA CONCRETE INC.; *U.S. Private*, pg. 1048
CORDOVA, SMART & WILLIAMS, LLC—See The Williams Capital Group, L.P.; *U.S. Private*, pg. 4136
CORDS CABLE INDUSTRIES LTD.; *Int'l*, pg. 1796
CORDSEN ENGINEERING GMBH—See Bechtle AG; *Int'l*, pg. 938
CORDSTRAP CANADA—See Cordstrap Netherlands B.V.; *Int'l*, pg. 1796
CORDSTRAP DEUTSCHLAND GMBH—See Cordstrap Netherlands B.V.; *Int'l*, pg. 1796
CORDSTRAP ESPANA S.L.U.—See Cordstrap Netherlands B.V.; *Int'l*, pg. 1796
CORDSTRAP FRANCE SARL—See Cordstrap Netherlands B.V.; *Int'l*, pg. 1796
CORDSTRAP INDIA PRIVATE LIMITED—See Cordstrap Netherlands B.V.; *Int'l*, pg. 1796
CORDSTRAP IRELAND LIMITED—See Cordstrap Netherlands B.V.; *Int'l*, pg. 1796
CORDSTRAP ITALIA S.R.L.—See Cordstrap Netherlands B.V.; *Int'l*, pg. 1796
CORDSTRAP LOAD SECURING SYSTEMS (WUXI) CO., LTD.—See Cordstrap Netherlands B.V.; *Int'l*, pg. 1796
CORDSTRAP MALAYSIA SDN BHD—See Cordstrap Netherlands B.V.; *Int'l*, pg. 1796
CORDSTRAP MEXICO, S.A. DE C.V.—See Cordstrap Netherlands B.V.; *Int'l*, pg. 1797
CORDSTRAP (MIDDLE EAST) LTD.—See Cordstrap Netherlands B.V.; *Int'l*, pg. 1796
CORDSTRAP NETHERLANDS B.V.; *Int'l*, pg. 1796
CORDSTRAP POLSKA SP. Z O.O.—See Cordstrap Netherlands B.V.; *Int'l*, pg. 1797
CORDSTRAP SA (PTY) LTD—See Cordstrap Netherlands B.V.; *Int'l*, pg. 1797
CORDSTRAP, S.R.O.—See Cordstrap Netherlands B.V.; *Int'l*, pg. 1797
CORDSTRAP (THAILAND) CO., LTD.—See Cordstrap Netherlands B.V.; *Int'l*, pg. 1796
CORDSTRAP UK LTD.—See Cordstrap Netherlands B.V.; *Int'l*, pg. 1797
CORDSTRAP USA, INC.—See Cordstrap Netherlands B.V.; *Int'l*, pg. 1797
CORDUSIO SIM - ADVISORY & FAMILY OFFICE SPA—See UniCredit S.p.A.; *Int'l*, pg. 8041
CORDUSIO SOCIETA FIDUCIARIA PER AZIONI—See UniCredit S.p.A.; *Int'l*, pg. 8041
CORDVER S.A.—See ASSA ABLOY AB; *Int'l*, pg. 638
CORD WORLDWIDE LTD.—See Canada Pension Plan Investment Board; *Int'l*, pg. 1280
CORD WORLDWIDE LTD.—See EQT AB; *Int'l*, pg. 2482
CORD WORLDWIDE LTD.—See Temasek Holdings (Private) Limited; *Int'l*, pg. 7548
CORDY ENVIRONMENTAL INC.—See Vertex Resource Group Ltd.; *Int'l*, pg. 8174
CORDY OILFIELD SERVICES INC.—See Vertex Resource Group Ltd.; *Int'l*, pg. 8174
CORE5 INDUSTRIAL PARTNERS LLC—See Kajima Corporation; *Int'l*, pg. 4054
COREA & CO. (1988) LIMITED—See Goddard Enterprises Limited; *Int'l*, pg. 3018
COREALCREDIT BANK AG—See Advent International Corporation; *U.S. Private*, pg. 96
COREALCREDIT BANK AG—See Centerbridge Partners, L.P.; *U.S. Private*, pg. 812
COREAL SA; *Int'l*, pg. 1798
COREANA COSMETICS CO., LTD.; *Int'l*, pg. 1798
COREAS HAZELLS INC.—See Goddard Enterprises Limited; *Int'l*, pg. 3018

CORPORATE AFFILIATIONS

CORE ASIA HUMAN RESOURCES MANAGEMENT CO., LTD.—See BES Engineering Corporation; *Int'l*, pg. 998
CORE ASSETS CORP.; *Int'l*, pg. 1797
CORE ASSOCIATES, LLC—See AvidXchange Holdings, Inc.; *U.S. Private*, pg. 1048
CORE ASSURANCE PARTNERS, INC.; *U.S. Private*, pg. 1048
COREA TITLE COMPANY—See First American Financial Corporation; *U.S. Public*, pg. 835
THE CORE BANKING GROUP LTD.; *Int'l*, pg. 7635
COREBI S.A.—See NowVertical Group Inc.; *Int'l*, pg. 5471
COREBRACE, LLC—See SME Industries Inc.; *U.S. Private*, pg. 3693
COREBRAND, LLC; *U.S. Private*, pg. 1049
COREBRIDGE FINANCIAL, INC.—See American International Group, Inc.; *U.S. Public*, pg. 105
CORE BTS, INC.—See Tailwind Capital Group, LLC; *U.S. Private*, pg. 3924
CORE BTS INC.—See Tailwind Capital Group, LLC; *U.S. Private*, pg. 3924
CORE CABLE CORPORATION—See CableWholesale.Com; *U.S. Private*, pg. 711
CORE CANADIAN DIVIDEND TRUST; *Int'l*, pg. 1797
CORE CAPITAL PARTNERS; *U.S. Private*, pg. 1048
CORECARD CORPORATION; *U.S. Public*, pg. 576
CORECARD SOFTWARE, INC.—See CoreCard Corporation; *U.S. Public*, pg. 577
CORE CAREERS & SKILL DEVELOPMENTS LIMITED—See Core Education and Technologies Ltd.; *Int'l*, pg. 1797
CORECIVIC, INC. - FOX FACILITY—See Corecivic, Inc.; *U.S. Public*, pg. 577
CORECIVIC, INC.; *U.S. Public*, pg. 577
CORE COMMERCIAL GROUP, LLC—See Hilton Grand Vacations Inc.; *U.S. Public*, pg. 1040
CORE COMMUNICATION SERVICES LTD.; *Int'l*, pg. 1797
CORE CONSTRUCTION INC.—See Otto Baum Company, Inc.; *U.S. Private*, pg. 3050
CORE CONSTRUCTION INDIANA, LLC—See Core Construction; *U.S. Private*, pg. 1048
CORE CONSTRUCTION SERVICES, LLC—See Core Construction; *U.S. Private*, pg. 1048
CORE CONSTRUCTION SERVICES OF FLORIDA, LLC—See Core Construction; *U.S. Private*, pg. 1048
CORE CONSTRUCTION SERVICES OF NEVADA, INC.—See Core Construction; *U.S. Private*, pg. 1048
CORE CONSTRUCTION SERVICES OF TEXAS, INC.—See Core Construction; *U.S. Private*, pg. 1048
CORE CONSTRUCTION; *U.S. Private*, pg. 1048
CORE CONSULTING LLC; *U.S. Private*, pg. 1048
CORECON TECHNOLOGIES, INC.—See The Sage Group plc; *Int'l*, pg. 7679
CORE CORPORATION; *Int'l*, pg. 1797
CORE-CREATE INC.; *U.S. Private*, pg. 1049
CORE-CREATE LTD.—See Core-Create Inc.; *U.S. Private*, pg. 1049
COREDIAL, LLC—See Thompson Street Capital Manager LLC; *U.S. Private*, pg. 4160
CORE DIGITAL MEDIA, INC.—See RockBridge Growth Equity, LLC; *U.S. Private*, pg. 3465
COREDIME—See Sonepar S.A.; *Int'l*, pg. 7090
CORE ECONOMY INVESTMENT GROUP LIMITED; *Int'l*, pg. 1797
CORE EDUCATION AND TECHNOLOGIES LTD.; *Int'l*, pg. 1797
CORE EDUCATION & CONSULTING SOLUTIONS FZ-LLC—See Core Education and Technologies Ltd.; *Int'l*, pg. 1797
CORE EDUCATION & CONSULTING SOLUTIONS, INC.—See Core Education and Technologies Ltd.; *Int'l*, pg. 1797
CORE EDUCATION & CONSULTING SOLUTIONS (UK) LTD.—See Core Education and Technologies Ltd.; *Int'l*, pg. 1797
CORE ENERGY RECOVERY SOLUTIONS GMBH—See Zehnder Group AG; *Int'l*, pg. 8630
CORE ENERGY RECOVERY SOLUTIONS INC.—See Zehnder Group AG; *Int'l*, pg. 8630
CORE EQUITY HOLDINGS SA; *Int'l*, pg. 1798
COREFIRST BANK & TRUST; *U.S. Private*, pg. 1049
CORE-FLEX OPTICAL (SUZHOU) CO., LTD.—See Coretronic Corporation; *Int'l*, pg. 1800
CORE FOODSERVICE—See Acosta, Inc.; *U.S. Private*, pg. 64
COREGAS NZ LIMITED—See Wesfarmers Limited; *Int'l*, pg. 8381
COREGAS PTY LTD—See Wesfarmers Limited; *Int'l*, pg. 8382
COREGMEDIA—See Trancos, Inc.; *U.S. Private*, pg. 4205
CORE GOLD INC.—See Titan Minerals Limited; *Int'l*, pg. 7760
CORE HEALTH & FITNESS LLC; *U.S. Private*, pg. 1048
CORE INDUSTRIAL PARTNERS, LLC; *U.S. Private*, pg. 1048
CORE INDUSTRIES CO., LTD—See Core Corporation; *Int'l*, pg. 1797
CORE INFORMATICS, LLC—See Thermo Fisher Scientific Inc.; *U.S. Public*, pg. 2146

COMPANY NAME INDEX

CORE SPECIALTY INSURANCE HOLDINGS, INC.

CORE LAB DE MEXICO S.A. DE C.V.—See Core Laboratories N.V.; *Int'l*, pg. 1798
CORE LABORATORIES AUSTRALIA PTY LTD—See Core Laboratories N.V.; *Int'l*, pg. 1798
CORE LABORATORIES CANADA LTD.—See Core Laboratories N.V.; *Int'l*, pg. 1798
CORE LABORATORIES INTERNATIONAL B.V.—See Core Laboratories N.V.; *Int'l*, pg. 1798
CORE LABORATORIES LP—See Core Laboratories N.V.; *Int'l*, pg. 1798
CORE LABORATORIES MALAYSIA SDN BHD—See Core Laboratories N.V.; *Int'l*, pg. 1798
CORE LABORATORIES N.V.; *Int'l*, pg. 1798
CORE LABORATORIES (U.K.) LIMITED—See Core Laboratories N.V.; *Int'l*, pg. 1798
CORELASE OY—See Coherent Corp.; *U.S. Public*, pg. 527
COREL COMPANY—See KKR & Co. Inc.; *U.S. Public*, pg. 1243
COREL CORPORATION—See KKR & Co. Inc.; *U.S. Public*, pg. 1243
CORELEX DOH-EI CO., LTD.—See Japan Pulp and Paper Company Limited; *Int'l*, pg. 3903
CORELEX SAN-EI CO., LTD.—See Japan Pulp and Paper Company Limited; *Int'l*, pg. 3903
CORELEX SHIN-EI CO., LTD.—See Japan Pulp and Paper Company Limited; *Int'l*, pg. 3903
CORELIS INC.—See Sagewind Capital LLC; *U.S. Private*, pg. 3527
CORE LITHIUM LTD; *Int'l*, pg. 1798
CORELLE BRANDS HOLDINGS INC.—See Cornell Capital Management LLC; *U.S. Private*, pg. 1051
CORELLE BRANDS LLC—See Cornell Capital Management LLC; *U.S. Private*, pg. 1051
CORELLE BRANDS MANUFACTURING (M) SDN. BHD.—See Cornell Capital Management LLC; *U.S. Private*, pg. 1051
CORELOGIC BACKGROUND DATA, LLC—See Insight Venture Management, LLC; *U.S. Private*, pg. 2088
CORELOGIC BACKGROUND DATA, LLC—See Stone Point Capital LLC; *U.S. Private*, pg. 3822
CORELOGIC CREDCO LLC—See Insight Venture Management, LLC; *U.S. Private*, pg. 2088
CORELOGIC CREDCO LLC—See Stone Point Capital LLC; *U.S. Private*, pg. 3822
CORELOGIC FLOOD SERVICES, LLC—See Insight Venture Management, LLC; *U.S. Private*, pg. 2088
CORELOGIC FLOOD SERVICES, LLC—See Stone Point Capital LLC; *U.S. Private*, pg. 3822
CORELOGIC, INC.—See Insight Venture Management, LLC; *U.S. Private*, pg. 2088
CORELOGIC, INC.—See Stone Point Capital LLC; *U.S. Private*, pg. 3822
CORELOGIC NATIONAL BACKGROUND DATA, LLC—See Insight Venture Management, LLC; *U.S. Private*, pg. 2088
CORELOGIC NATIONAL BACKGROUND DATA, LLC—See Stone Point Capital LLC; *U.S. Private*, pg. 3822
CORELOGIC NZ LIMITED—See Insight Venture Management, LLC; *U.S. Private*, pg. 2088
CORELOGIC NZ LIMITED—See Stone Point Capital LLC; *U.S. Private*, pg. 3822
CORELOGIC RENTAL PROPERTY SOLUTIONS, LLC—See Insight Venture Management, LLC; *U.S. Private*, pg. 2088
CORELOGIC RENTAL PROPERTY SOLUTIONS, LLC—See Stone Point Capital LLC; *U.S. Private*, pg. 3822
CORELOGIC REO ASSET MANAGEMENT—See Insight Venture Management, LLC; *U.S. Private*, pg. 2088
CORELOGIC REO ASSET MANAGEMENT—See Stone Point Capital LLC; *U.S. Private*, pg. 3822
CORELOGIC SAFERENT, LLC—See Insight Venture Management, LLC; *U.S. Private*, pg. 2089
CORELOGIC SAFERENT, LLC—See Stone Point Capital LLC; *U.S. Private*, pg. 3822
CORELOGIC SARL—See Insight Venture Management, LLC; *U.S. Private*, pg. 2089
CORELOGIC SARL—See Stone Point Capital LLC; *U.S. Private*, pg. 3822
CORELOGIC SOLUTIONS LIMITED—See Insight Venture Management, LLC; *U.S. Private*, pg. 2089
CORELOGIC SOLUTIONS LIMITED—See Stone Point Capital LLC; *U.S. Private*, pg. 3822
CORELOGIC SOLUTIONS, LLC—See Insight Venture Management, LLC; *U.S. Private*, pg. 2089
CORELOGIC SOLUTIONS, LLC—See Stone Point Capital LLC; *U.S. Private*, pg. 3822
CORELOGIC TAX COLLECTION SERVICES, LLC—See Insight Venture Management, LLC; *U.S. Private*, pg. 2089
CORELOGIC TAX COLLECTION SERVICES, LLC—See Stone Point Capital LLC; *U.S. Private*, pg. 3822
CORELOGIC TRANSPORTATION SERVICES—See Insight Venture Management, LLC; *U.S. Private*, pg. 2089
CORELOGIC TRANSPORTATION SERVICES—See Stone Point Capital LLC; *U.S. Private*, pg. 3822

CORELOGIC UK LIMITED—See Insight Venture Management, LLC; *U.S. Private*, pg. 2089
CORELOGIC UK LIMITED—See Stone Point Capital LLC; *U.S. Private*, pg. 3822
CORELOGIC VALUATION SERVICES, LLC—See Insight Venture Management, LLC; *U.S. Private*, pg. 2089
CORELOGIC VALUATION SERVICES, LLC—See Stone Point Capital LLC; *U.S. Private*, pg. 3822
CORELOGIC VALUATION SOLUTIONS, INC.—See Insight Venture Management, LLC; *U.S. Private*, pg. 2089
CORELOGIC VALUATION SOLUTIONS, INC.—See Stone Point Capital LLC; *U.S. Private*, pg. 3822
COREL UK LIMITED—See KKR & Co. Inc.; *U.S. Public*, pg. 1243
COREL USA—See KKR & Co. Inc.; *U.S. Public*, pg. 1243
CORE & MAIN, INC.; *U.S. Public*, pg. 575
CORE-MARK DISTRIBUTORS, INC.—See Core-Mark Holding Co. Inc.; *U.S. Public*, pg. 576
CORE-MARK DISTRIBUTORS, INC.—See Core-Mark Holding Co. Inc.; *U.S. Public*, pg. 576
CORE-MARK HOLDING CO. INC.; *U.S. Public*, pg. 576
CORE-MARK INTERNATIONAL—See Core-Mark Holding Co. Inc.; *U.S. Public*, pg. 576
CORE-MARK INTERRELATED COMPANIES, INC.—See Core-Mark Holding Co. Inc.; *U.S. Public*, pg. 576
CORE-MARK MIDCONTINENT, INC.—See Core-Mark Holding Co. Inc.; *U.S. Public*, pg. 576
CORE-MARK—See Core-Mark Holding Co. Inc.; *U.S. Public*, pg. 576
COREMAX CORP.; *Int'l*, pg. 1798
COREMAX NINGBO CHEMICAL CO., LTD.—See Coremax Corp.; *Int'l*, pg. 1798
COREMAX (THAILAND) CO., LTD.—See Coremax Corp.; *Int'l*, pg. 1798
COREMAX (ZHANGZHOU) CHEMICAL CO., LTD.—See Coremax Corp.; *Int'l*, pg. 1798
COREMAX ZHUHAI CHEMICAL CO., LTD.—See Coremax Corp.; *Int'l*, pg. 1798
COREMEDIA AG; *Int'l*, pg. 1799
COREMEDIA ASIA PACIFIC PTE. LTD.—See CoreMedia AG; *Int'l*, pg. 1799
COREMEDIA CORPORATION—See CoreMedia AG; *Int'l*, pg. 1799
CORE MEDIA GROUP, INC.—See Apollo Global Management, Inc.; *U.S. Public*, pg. 148
COREMEDIA UK LIMITED—See CoreMedia AG; *Int'l*, pg. 1799
CORE MEDICAL GROUP; *U.S. Private*, pg. 1049
CORE MEDICAL SOLUTIONS PTY LTD—See Veradigm Inc.; *U.S. Public*, pg. 2280
CORE MEDICAL TECHNOLOGY LIMITED—See Minerva Group Holding Limited; *Int'l*, pg. 4908
CORE MISSION SOLUTIONS, LLC—See Citadel Federal Solutions LLC; *U.S. Private*, pg. 901
CORE MOLDING TECHNOLOGIES INC—See Core Molding Technologies, Inc.; *U.S. Public*, pg. 576
CORE MOLDING TECHNOLOGIES, INC.; *U.S. Public*, pg. 576
COREM PROPERTY GROUP AB; *Int'l*, pg. 1798
CORENERGY INFRASTRUCTURE TRUST, INC.; *U.S. Public*, pg. 577
CORENET CO., LTD.—See Samhwa Paints Industrial Co., Ltd.; *Int'l*, pg. 6505
CORENET GLOBAL, INC.; *U.S. Private*, pg. 1049
CORENET INTERNATIONAL CO., LTD.—See Core Corporation; *Int'l*, pg. 1797
CORE NEXT CO., LTD.—See SOLXYZ Co., Ltd.; *Int'l*, pg. 7083
CORE NICKEL CORP.; *Int'l*, pg. 1798
CORENSO EDAM B.V.—See VPK Packaging Group NV; *Int'l*, pg. 8312
CORENSO FRANCE S.A.S.—See VPK Packaging Group NV; *Int'l*, pg. 8312
CORENSO NORTH AMERICA LLC—See Sonoco Products Company; *U.S. Public*, pg. 1904
CORENSO TOLOSANA S.A.—See VPK Packaging Group NV; *Int'l*, pg. 8312
CORENSO (UK) LTD—See VPK Packaging Group NV; *Int'l*, pg. 8312
CORENSO WISCONSIN BOARD, LLC—See Sonoco Products Company; *U.S. Public*, pg. 1904
CORENTEC CO., LTD.; *Int'l*, pg. 1799
CORENTE, INC. - ENGINEERING CENTER—See Oracle Corporation; *U.S. Public*, pg. 1611
CORE ONE LABS INC.; *Int'l*, pg. 1798
COREPA S.N.C.—See Derichebourg S.A.; *Int'l*, pg. 2042
COREPAX (M) SDN. BHD.—See Ohishi Sangyo Co., Ltd.; *Int'l*, pg. 5532
COREP FRANCE SARL—See Corep Lighting group; *Int'l*, pg. 1799
COREPHARMA, LLC; *U.S. Private*, pg. 1049
COREPHOTONICS LTD.—See Samsung BioLogics Co., Ltd.; *Int'l*, pg. 6510
COREP IBERICA, LDA—See Corep Lighting group; *Int'l*, pg. 1799
COREPILE S.A.—See Energizer Holdings, Inc.; *U.S. Public*, pg. 760
CORE PIPE INC.; *U.S. Private*, pg. 1049
COREP LIGHTING GROUP; *Int'l*, pg. 1799

COREP LIGHTING INDIA (P) LTD.—See Corep Lighting group; *Int'l*, pg. 1799
COREPOINTE INSURANCE AGENCY, INC.—See Stone Point Capital LLC; *U.S. Private*, pg. 3820
COREPOINTE INSURANCE COMPANY—See Stone Point Capital LLC; *U.S. Private*, pg. 3820
COREPOINT LODGING INC.—See Cerberus Capital Management, L.P.; *U.S. Private*, pg. 837
COREPOINT LODGING INC.—See Highgate Hotels, L.P.; *U.S. Private*, pg. 1937
COREPOWER YOGA, LLC—See TSG Consumer Partners LLC; *U.S. Private*, pg. 4253
CORE PRODUCTS INTERNATIONAL, INC; *U.S. Private*, pg. 1049
CORE PROJECTS AND TECHNOLOGIES LTD.—See Core Education and Technologies Ltd.; *Int'l*, pg. 1798
CORE PROJECTS & TECHNOLOGIES FZC—See Core Education and Technologies Ltd.; *Int'l*, pg. 1798
CORERD CO. LTD.—See Sobal Corporation; *Int'l*, pg. 7030
CORE RESOURCE MANAGEMENT, INC.; *U.S. Public*, pg. 576
CORERO NETWORK SECURITY, INC.—See Corero Network Security plc; *Int'l*, pg. 1799
CORERO NETWORK SECURITY PLC; *Int'l*, pg. 1799
CORE ROOFING SYSTEMS LLC—See Shoreline Equity Partners, LLC; *U.S. Private*, pg. 3641
CORERX, INC.—See NovaQuest Capital Management, LLC; *U.S. Private*, pg. 2967
CORESA ARGENTINA S.A.—See Coresa S.A.; *Int'l*, pg. 1799
CORESA PERU S.A.—See Coresa S.A.; *Int'l*, pg. 1799
CORESA S.A.; *Int'l*, pg. 1799
CORESCAN PTY. LTD.—See Epiroc AB; *Int'l*, pg. 2461
CORESCAN S.A.C.—See Epiroc AB; *Int'l*, pg. 2461
CORESCAN S.A. DE C.V.—See Epiroc AB; *Int'l*, pg. 2461
CORESCAN SPA—See Epiroc AB; *Int'l*, pg. 2461
CORESCO, INC.; *U.S. Private*, pg. 1049
CORE SECURITY SDI CORPORATION; *U.S. Private*, pg. 1049
CORESENSE INC.—See Constellation Software Inc.; *Int'l*, pg. 1773
CORESHED PTY. LTD.—See Epiroc AB; *Int'l*, pg. 2461
CORESITE DENVER, L.L.C.—See American Tower Corporation; *U.S. Public*, pg. 111
CORESITE, L.P.—See American Tower Corporation; *U.S. Public*, pg. 111
CORESITE REALTY CORPORATION—See American Tower Corporation; *U.S. Public*, pg. 111
CORESLAB INTERNATIONAL, INC.; *Int'l*, pg. 1799
CORESLAB STRUCTURES (ALBUQUERQUE) INC.—See Coreslab International, Inc.; *Int'l*, pg. 1799
CORESLAB STRUCTURES (ARIZ) INC.—See Coreslab International, Inc.; *Int'l*, pg. 1799
CORESLAB STRUCTURES (ARK) INC.—See Coreslab International, Inc.; *Int'l*, pg. 1799
CORESLAB STRUCTURES (ATLANTA) INC.—See Coreslab International, Inc.; *Int'l*, pg. 1799
CORESLAB STRUCTURES (CONN) INC.—See Coreslab International, Inc.; *Int'l*, pg. 1799
CORESLAB STRUCTURES, INC.—See Coreslab International, Inc.; *Int'l*, pg. 1799
CORESLAB STRUCTURES, INC.—See Coreslab International, Inc.; *Int'l*, pg. 1799
CORESLAB STRUCTURES, INC.—See Coreslab International, Inc.; *Int'l*, pg. 1799
CORESLAB STRUCTURES (KANSAS), INC.—See Coreslab International, Inc.; *Int'l*, pg. 1799
CORESLAB STRUCTURES (LA) INC.—See Coreslab International, Inc.; *Int'l*, pg. 1799
CORESLAB STRUCTURES (MIAMI) INC.—See Coreslab International, Inc.; *Int'l*, pg. 1799
CORESLAB STRUCTURES (MISSOURI) INC.—See Coreslab International, Inc.; *Int'l*, pg. 1799
CORESLAB STRUCTURES (ONT) INC.—See Coreslab International, Inc.; *Int'l*, pg. 1799
CORESLAB STRUCTURES (ORLANDO) INC.—See Coreslab International, Inc.; *Int'l*, pg. 1799
CORESLAB STRUCTURES (TAMPA) INC.—See Coreslab International, Inc.; *Int'l*, pg. 1799
CORESLAB STRUCTURES (TEXAS) INC.—See Coreslab International, Inc.; *Int'l*, pg. 1799
CORESLAB STRUCTURES (TULSA) INC.—See Coreslab International, Inc.; *Int'l*, pg. 1799
CORE SOFTWARE CORPORATION; *Int'l*, pg. 1798
CORE SOLAR, LLC—See TotalEnergies SE; *Int'l*, pg. 7835
CORESOLID STORAGE CORPORATION—See TDK Corporation; *Int'l*, pg. 7487
CORESOURCE INC.—See Trustmark Mutual Holding Company; *U.S. Private*, pg. 4251
CORE SPAIN HOLDCO SOCIMI, S.A.U.; *Int'l*, pg. 1798
CORE SPECIALTY INSURANCE HOLDINGS, INC.; *U.S. Private*, pg. 1049
CORESTAFF SERVICES, LP—See HFBG Holding B.V.; *Int'l*, pg. 3374
CORESTAFF SUPPORT SERVICES, INC.—See HFBG Holding B.V.; *Int'l*, pg. 3374
CORESTATE BANK GMBH—See CORESTATE Capital Holding SA; *Int'l*, pg. 1800

CORESTATE CAPITAL ADVISORS GMBH—See CORESTATE Capital Holding SA; *Int'l*, pg. 1800
CORESTATE CAPITAL HOLDING SA; *Int'l*, pg. 1799
CORESTATE CAPITAL PARTNERS GMBH—See CORESTATE Capital Holding SA; *Int'l*, pg. 1800
CORESTATE CAPITAL PARTNERS UK LIMITED—See CORESTATE Capital Holding SA; *Int'l*, pg. 1800
CORESTATES CAPITAL ADVISORS, LLC; *U.S. Private*, pg. 1049
CORESTATES, INC.; *U.S. Private*, pg. 1049
CORESTEM INC.; *Int'l*, pg. 1800
CORE STRATEGY GROUP; *U.S. Private*, pg. 1049
CORESYS CONSULTING; *U.S. Private*, pg. 1050
CORE SYSTEMS LLC; *U.S. Private*, pg. 1049
THE CORETEC GROUP INC.; *U.S. Public*, pg. 2066
CORETECH CONSULTING GROUP LLC—See Asseco Poland S.A.; *Int'l*, pg. 642
CORE TECHNOLOGY CORP.—See Constellation Software Inc.; *Int'l*, pg. 1774
CORETEK SERVICES; *U.S. Private*, pg. 1050
CORETELLIGENT LLC—See Wells Fargo & Company; *U.S. Public*, pg. 2344
CORETEX LIMITED—See EROAD Limited; *Int'l*, pg. 2496
CORETEX USA INC.—See EROAD Limited; *Int'l*, pg. 2496
CORETRAC, INC.—See TA Associates, Inc.; *U.S. Private*, pg. 3914
CORE TRANSPORT TECHNOLOGIES NZ LIMITED—See The Descartes Systems Group Inc.; *Int'l*, pg. 7636
CORETRAX TECHNOLOGY LIMITED—See Buckthorn Partners LLP; *Int'l*, pg. 1210
CORETRONIC CORPORATION; *Int'l*, pg. 1800
CORETRONIC DISPLAY SOLUTION CORPORATION—See Coretronic Corporation; *Int'l*, pg. 1800
CORETRONIC (GUANGZHOU) CO., LTD.—See Coretronic Corporation; *Int'l*, pg. 1800
CORETRONIC MEMS CORPORATION—See Coretronic Corporation; *Int'l*, pg. 1800
CORETRONIC (NANJING) CO., LTD.—See Coretronic Corporation; *Int'l*, pg. 1800
CORETRONIC (NINGBO) CO., LTD.—See Coretronic Corporation; *Int'l*, pg. 1800
CORETRONIC PROJECTION (KUNSHAN) CO., LTD.—See Coretronic Corporation; *Int'l*, pg. 1800
CORETRONIC SYSTEM ENGINEERING CORPORATION—See Coretronic Corporation; *Int'l*, pg. 1800
CORE UTILITY SOLUTIONS LTD—See Iberdrola, S.A.; *Int'l*, pg. 3573
COREVALUE—See Avenga; *Int'l*, pg. 738
COREVEST AMERICAN FINANCE LENDER LLC—See Redwood Trust, Inc.; *U.S. Public*, pg. 1771
COREVITAS, LLC—See Thermo Fisher Scientific Inc.; *U.S. Public*, pg. 2146
CORE WORKS, LLC—See Compass Group PLC; *Int'l*, pg. 1751
COREX CZECH S.R.O—See VPK Packaging Group NV; *Int'l*, pg. 8312
COREX DEUTSCHLAND GMBH—See VPK Packaging Group NV; *Int'l*, pg. 8312
COREX FRANCE SAS—See VPK Packaging Group NV; *Int'l*, pg. 8312
COREX GERMANY GMBH & CO. KG—See VPK Packaging Group NV; *Int'l*, pg. 8312
COREX NEDERLAND BV—See VPK Packaging Group NV; *Int'l*, pg. 8312
COREX POLSKA SP. Z O.O—See VPK Packaging Group NV; *Int'l*, pg. 8312
COREX ROMANIA SRL—See VPK Packaging Group NV; *Int'l*, pg. 8312
COREX—See VPK Packaging Group NV; *Int'l*, pg. 8312
COREX TURKEY AMBALAY SANAYI VE TICARET ANONIM SERKETI—See VPK Packaging Group NV; *Int'l*, pg. 8312
COREX (UK) LTD—See Premier Oilfield Laboratories LLC; *U.S. Private*, pg. 3250
COREX US LLC—See Ox Paper Tube & Core, Inc.; *U.S. Private*, pg. 3056
COREY BROTHERS INC.; *U.S. Private*, pg. 1050
COREY DELTA INC.; *U.S. Private*, pg. 1050
COREY NURSERY CO. INC.; *U.S. Private*, pg. 1050
COREY OIL LTD; *U.S. Public*, pg. 1050
COREZO, LTD.—See Hokkoku Financial Holdings, Inc.; *Int'l*, pg. 3443
CORFACTS, INC.; *U.S. Private*, pg. 1050
CORGENIX MEDICAL CORPORATION—See Caisse de Depot et Placement du Quebec; *Int'l*, pg. 1255
CORGENIX MEDICAL CORPORATION—See CVC Capital Partners SICAV-FIS S.A.; *Int'l*, pg. 1884
CORGENIX MEDICAL CORPORATION—See Tethys Invest SAS; *Int'l*, pg. 7576
CORGI BOOKS LTD.—See Bertelsmann SE & Co. KGaA; *Int'l*, pg. 991
CORHART REFRACTORIES CORP.—See Compagnie de Saint-Gobain SA; *Int'l*, pg. 1730
CORIANCE SAS—See Commonwealth Bank of Australia; *Int'l*, pg. 1720
CORIANT AMERICA, INC.—See Marlin Equity Partners, LLC; *U.S. Private*, pg. 2584

CORIANT AMERICA, INC.—See Marlin Equity Partners, LLC; *U.S. Private*, pg. 2584
CORIANT JAPAN K.K.—See Marlin Equity Partners, LLC; *U.S. Private*, pg. 2584
CORIANT NETWORKS (SHANGHAI) CO., LTD.—See Marlin Equity Partners, LLC; *U.S. Private*, pg. 2584
CORIDIAN TECHNOLOGIES INC.—See Sole Source Capital LLC; *U.S. Private*, pg. 3708
CORIMON, C.A.; *Int'l*, pg. 1800
CORIMON PINTURAS, C.A.—See Corimon, C.A.; *Int'l*, pg. 1801
CORINA SNACKS LIMITED—See PepsiCo, Inc.; *U.S. Public*, pg. 1670
CORIN AUSTRALIA PTY LTD—See Permira Advisers LLP; *Int'l*, pg. 5803
CORINDUS VASCULAR ROBOTICS, INC.—See Siemens Aktiengesellschaft; *Int'l*, pg. 6894
CORINEX COMMUNICATIONS, A.S.—See Corinex Communications Corp.; *Int'l*, pg. 1801
CORINEX COMMUNICATIONS CORP.; *Int'l*, pg. 1801
CORIN GERMANY GMBH—See Permira Advisers LLP; *Int'l*, pg. 5803
CORIN GROUP PLC—See Permira Advisers LLP; *Int'l*, pg. 5803
CORIN JAPAN KK—See Permira Advisers LLP; *Int'l*, pg. 5803
CORINNE MCCORMARK, INC.—See EssilorLuxottica SA; *Int'l*, pg. 2514
CORINPHILA AUKTIONEN AG—See Global Philatelic Network; *Int'l*, pg. 3000
CORINPHILA VEILINGEN BV—See Global Philatelic Network; *Int'l*, pg. 3000
CORINS B.V.—See ASR Nederland N.V.; *Int'l*, pg. 632
CORIN SOUTH AFRICA (PROPRIETARY) LTD—See Permira Advisers LLP; *Int'l*, pg. 5803
CORINTH COCA-COLA BOTTLING WORKS, INC.; *U.S. Private*, pg. 1050
CORINTH HOTELS INTERNATIONAL; *Int'l*, pg. 1801
CORINTHIAN CAPITAL GROUP, LLC; *U.S. Private*, pg. 1050
CORINTHIAN LEASING CORPORATION—See Cannae Holdings, Inc.; *U.S. Public*, pg. 429
CORINTHIAN LEASING CORPORATION—See CC Capital Partners, LLC; *U.S. Private*, pg. 798
CORINTHIAN LEASING CORPORATION—See Intercontinental Exchange, Inc.; *U.S. Public*, pg. 1141
CORINTHIAN MEDIA, INC.; *U.S. Private*, pg. 1050
CORINTHIA PALACE HOTEL COMPANY LIMITED; *Int'l*, pg. 1801
CORINTH PIPEWORKS S.A.—See Viohalco SA/NV; *Int'l*, pg. 8243
CORINTH PIPEWORKS S.A. - THISVI PLANT—See Viohalco SA/NV; *Int'l*, pg. 8243
CORIN USA—See Permira Advisers LLP; *Int'l*, pg. 5803
CORION PTY LIMITED—See Munchener Ruckversicherungs AG; *Int'l*, pg. 5085
CORISTO GMBH—See CENIT AG; *Int'l*, pg. 1401
CORITEL S.A.—See Accenture plc; *Int'l*, pg. 86
CORITY SOFTWARE INC.—See Thoma Bravo, L.P.; *U.S. Private*, pg. 4146
CORIUM INTERNATIONAL, INC.—See Gurnet Point Capital LLC; *U.S. Private*, pg. 1819
CORIX BIOSCIENCE, INC.; *U.S. Private*, pg. 1050
CORIX GROUP—See British Columbia Investment Management Corp.; *Int'l*, pg. 1169
CORIX GROUP—See CAI Private Equity; *Int'l*, pg. 1252
CORIZON HEALTH, INC.—See Flacks Homes LLC; *U.S. Private*, pg. 1538
CORIZON HEALTH, INC.—See Flacks Homes LLC; *U.S. Private*, pg. 1539
CORK BUILDERS PROVIDERS LIMITED—See Grafton Group plc; *Int'l*, pg. 3050
CORK DISTRIBUTORS, LLC; *U.S. Private*, pg. 1050
CORKEN, INC.—See IDEX Corp.; *U.S. Public*, pg. 1091
CORKEN STEEL PRODUCTS COMPANY; *U.S. Private*, pg. 1050
CORKERY GROUP UNLIMITED—See Accenture plc; *Int'l*, pg. 87
CORKILL INSURANCE AGENCY, INC.—See GTCR LLC; *U.S. Private*, pg. 1802
CORK MEDIA ENTERPRISES LIMITED—See News Corporation; *U.S. Public*, pg. 1520
CORK METAL COMPANY LTD.—See Madison Dearborn Partners, LLC; *U.S. Private*, pg. 2541
THE CORKY MCMILLIN COMPANIES; *U.S. Private*, pg. 4015
CORKY'S BAR-B-Q; *U.S. Private*, pg. 1050
CORLAND, CO.; *U.S. Private*, pg. 1050
CORLE BUILDING SYSTEMS; *U.S. Private*, pg. 1050
CORLEY MANUFACTURING CO.; *U.S. Private*, pg. 1050
CORLIANT, INC.—See Accenture plc; *Int'l*, pg. 86
CORLINE BIOMEDICAL AB; *Int'l*, pg. 1801
CORMAN CONSTRUCTION INC.—See C.G. Enterprises Inc.; *U.S. Private*, pg. 707
CORMAN MARINE CONSTRUCTION, INC.—See C.G. Enterprises Inc.; *U.S. Private*, pg. 707
CORMEDIX INC.; *U.S. Public*, pg. 577
CORMELA S.A.—See CRH plc; *Int'l*, pg. 1844
CORMER GROUP INDUSTRIES, INC.; *Int'l*, pg. 1801

CORMETECH, INC.; *U.S. Private*, pg. 1050
CORMIER RICE MILLING COMPANY, INC.; *U.S. Private*, pg. 1050
CORN BELT ENERGY CORPORATION; *U.S. Private*, pg. 1050
CORN BELT POWER COOPERATIVE; *U.S. Private*, pg. 1050
CORNEA HAVACILIK—See Turk Hava Yollari Anonim Ortakligi; *Int'l*, pg. 7974
CORNEC SAS; *Int'l*, pg. 1801
CORNEJO & SONS, LLC—See Summit Materials, Inc.; *U.S. Public*, pg. 1960
CORNELIUS AUSTRALIA PTY. LTD.—See Berkshire Hathaway Inc.; *U.S. Public*, pg. 309
CORNELIUS BEVERAGE TECHNOLOGIES LIMITED—See Berkshire Hathaway Inc.; *U.S. Public*, pg. 309
CORNELIUS DE MEXICO SA DE CV—See Berkshire Hathaway Inc.; *U.S. Public*, pg. 309
CORNELIUS DEUTSCHLAND GMBH—See Berkshire Hathaway Inc.; *U.S. Public*, pg. 309
CORNELIUS ESPANA S.A.—See Berkshire Hathaway Inc.; *U.S. Public*, pg. 309
CORNELIUS EUROPE SA—See Berkshire Hathaway Inc.; *U.S. Public*, pg. 309
CORNELIUS EXPLORATION S. DE R.L. DE C.V.—See QcX Gold Corp.; *Int'l*, pg. 6138
CORNELIUS INC. - GLENDALE HEIGHTS—See Berkshire Hathaway Inc.; *U.S. Public*, pg. 309
CORNELIUS, INC.—See Berkshire Hathaway Inc.; *U.S. Public*, pg. 308
CORNELIUS ITALIA S.R.L.—See Berkshire Hathaway Inc.; *U.S. Public*, pg. 309
CORNELIUS NURSERIES—See Calloway's Nursery, Inc.; *U.S. Private*, pg. 723
CORNELIUS OSTERREICH GES.M.B.H.—See Berkshire Hathaway Inc.; *U.S. Public*, pg. 309
CORNELIUS (PACIFIC) LTD.—See Berkshire Hathaway Inc.; *U.S. Public*, pg. 309
CORNELIUS (SINGAPORE) PTE. LTD.—See Berkshire Hathaway Inc.; *U.S. Public*, pg. 309
CORNELIUS (TIANJIN) CO., LTD.—See Berkshire Hathaway Inc.; *U.S. Public*, pg. 309
CORNELIUS UKRAINE LLC—See Berkshire Hathaway Inc.; *U.S. Public*, pg. 309
CORNELL CAPITAL LLC; *U.S. Private*, pg. 1051
CORNELL CAPITAL MANAGEMENT LLC; *U.S. Private*, pg. 1051
CORNELL & COMPANY, INC.; *U.S. Private*, pg. 1051
CORNELLCOOKSON, INC.—See Griffon Corporation; *U.S. Public*, pg. 969
CORNELL DUBILIER ELECTRONICS, INC.—See Knowles Corporation; *U.S. Public*, pg. 1270
CORNELL DUBILIER MARKETING, INC.—See Knowles Corporation; *U.S. Public*, pg. 1270
CORNELL DUBILIER PROPERTY CORP.—See Knowles Corporation; *U.S. Public*, pg. 1270
CORNELL FORGE COMPANY; *U.S. Private*, pg. 1051
CORNELL INTERVENTIONS, INC.—See The GEO Group, Inc.; *U.S. Public*, pg. 2075
CORNELL PAPER & BOX INC.; *U.S. Private*, pg. 1051
CORNELL PUMP COMPANY—See Roper Technologies, Inc.; *U.S. Public*, pg. 1811
CORNELL SALES & SERVICE SDN. BHD.—See Pensonic Holdings Berhad; *Int'l*, pg. 5788
CORNELL SCOTT-HILL HEALTH CENTER; *U.S. Private*, pg. 1051
CORNELL STOREFRONT SYSTEMS, INC.—See Griffon Corporation; *U.S. Public*, pg. 969
CORNELL UNIVERSITY PRESS; *U.S. Private*, pg. 1051
CORNE PORT-ROYAL CHOCOLATIER S.A.—See Compagnie du Bois Sauvage SA; *Int'l*, pg. 1740
CORNER BANK LTD.—See UBS Group AG; *Int'l*, pg. 8005
CORNER BROOK PULP & PAPER LIMITED—See Kruger Inc.; *Int'l*, pg. 4307
CORNER GROWTH ACQUISITION CORP.; *U.S. Public*, pg. 577
CORNER INVESTMENT COMPANY, LLC—See Caesars Entertainment, Inc.; *U.S. Public*, pg. 420
CORNER OFFICE INC.; *U.S. Private*, pg. 1051
CORNER PANTRY INC.; *U.S. Private*, pg. 1051
CORNERKLOUD ADVISORS GROUP, LLC—See Securekloud Technologies Ltd.; *Int'l*, pg. 6674
CORNERSTONE ADVISORS, INC.; *U.S. Private*, pg. 1051
CORNERSTONE ADVISORS, INC.; *U.S. Private*, pg. 1051
CORNERSTONE ADVISORS, INC.—See Lovell Minnick Partners LLC; *U.S. Private*, pg. 2503
CORNERSTONE AG, LLC—See CHS INC.; *U.S. Public*, pg. 492
CORNERSTONE APPRAISAL SERVICES, INC.—See Compass Equity Partners, LLC; *U.S. Private*, pg. 999
CORNERSTONE BANK—See First York Ban Corp.; *U.S. Private*, pg. 1531
CORNERSTONE BANK—See Princeton Bancorp, Inc.; *U.S. Public*, pg. 1719
CORNERSTONE BIOPHARMA, INC.—See Chiesi Farmaceutici SpA; *Int'l*, pg. 1478
THE CORNERSTONE BRANDS GROUP, INC.—See Qurate Retail, Inc.; *U.S. Public*, pg. 1758

COMPANY NAME INDEX

CORNERSTONE BRANDS, INC.—See Qurate Retail, Inc.; *U.S. Private*, pg. 1758
CORNERSTONE BUILDING BRANDS, INC.—See Clayton, Dubilier & Rice, LLC; *U.S. Private*, pg. 920
CORNERSTONE BUILDING SOLUTIONS, INC.—See Simplex Industries Inc; *U.S. Private*, pg. 3667
CORNERSTONE BUSINESSES INC.; *U.S. Private*, pg. 1051
CORNERSTONE BUSINESS SERVICES, INC.—See Pacific Avenue Capital Partners, LLC; *U.S. Private*, pg. 3065
CORNERSTONE CAPITAL MANAGEMENT HOLDINGS LLC—See New York Life Insurance Company; *U.S. Private*, pg. 2910
CORNERSTONE CAPITAL RESOURCES INC.—See SolGold plc; *Int'l*, pg. 7071
CORNERSTONECAPITAL VERWALTUNGS AG; *Int'l*, pg. 1801
CORNERSTONE CARE, INC.; *U.S. Private*, pg. 1051
CORNERSTONE CHEMICAL COMPANY B.V.—See Littlejohn & Co., LLC; *U.S. Private*, pg. 2470
CORNERSTONE CHEMICAL COMPANY—See Littlejohn & Co., LLC; *U.S. Private*, pg. 2470
CORNERSTONE COMMISSIONING, INC.—See Levine Leichtman Capital Partners, LLC; *U.S. Private*, pg. 2436
CORNERSTONE COMMUNITIES CORPORATION; *U.S. Private*, pg. 1051
CORNERSTONE COMMUNITY BANCORP; *U.S. Public*, pg. 577
CORNERSTONE COMPOSITES INC.—See Wisconsin Thermoset Molding, Inc.; *U.S. Private*, pg. 4549
CORNERSTONE CONSULTING, INC.; *U.S. Private*, pg. 1052
CORNERSTONE CONTROLS INC.; *U.S. Private*, pg. 1052
CORNERSTONE DENTAL LABORATORIES, LLC; *U.S. Private*, pg. 1052
CORNERSTONE DETENTION PRODUCTS, INC.; *U.S. Private*, pg. 1052
CORNERSTONE DEVELOPERS, INC; *U.S. Private*, pg. 1052
CORNERSTONE ECUADOR S.A.—See SolGold plc; *Int'l*, pg. 7071
CORNERSTONE ENVIRONMENTAL GROUP, LLC—See Tetra Tech, Inc.; *U.S. Public*, pg. 2022
CORNERSTONE EQUITY INVESTORS, LLC; *U.S. Private*, pg. 1052
CORNERSTONE EQUITY PARTNERS CO., LTD.—See Korea Investment Holdings Co., Ltd.; *Int'l*, pg. 4285
CORNERSTONE FAMILY SERVICES INC.—See Axar Capital Management L.P.; *U.S. Private*, pg. 411
CORNERSTONE FINANCIAL CORPORATION—See Princeton Bancorp, Inc.; *U.S. Public*, pg. 1719
CORNERSTONE FINANCIAL CREDIT UNION; *U.S. Private*, pg. 1052
CORNERSTONE FINANCIAL HOLDINGS LIMITED; *Int'l*, pg. 1801
CORNERSTONE FIRST FINANCIAL—See Fathom Holdings Inc.; *U.S. Public*, pg. 824
CORNERSTONE FOODSERVICE GROUP, INC.—See ShoreView Industries, LLC; *U.S. Private*, pg. 3642
CORNERSTONE GEOTECHNICAL, INC.—See Robinson Noble, Inc.; *U.S. Private*, pg. 3462
CORNERSTONE GROUP DEVELOPMENT CORPORATION; *U.S. Private*, pg. 1052
CORNERSTONE HEALTHCARE, INC.—See The Pennant Group, Inc.; *U.S. Public*, pg. 2118
CORNERSTONE HEALTHCARE PARTNERS, LLC—See Summit Healthcare REIT, Inc.; *U.S. Private*, pg. 3854
CORNERSTONE HOME MORTGAGE—See Mercedes Homes Inc.; *U.S. Private*, pg. 2668
CORNERSTONE INFORMATION SYSTEM, INC.; *U.S. Private*, pg. 1052
CORNERSTONE INFORMATION TECHNOLOGIES, LLC; *U.S. Private*, pg. 1052
CORNERSTONE INVESTMENT CAPITAL HOLDINGS CO.; *U.S. Private*, pg. 1052
CORNERSTONE LIVING SKILLS, INC.—See Centerbridge Partners, L.P.; *U.S. Private*, pg. 813
CORNERSTONE LOGISTICS LP—See TFI International Inc.; *Int'l*, pg. 7585
CORNERSTONE LOGISTICS USA LP—See TFI International Inc.; *Int'l*, pg. 7585
CORNERSTONE LOGISTICS USA LP—See TFI International Inc.; *Int'l*, pg. 7585
CORNERSTONE MANAGEMENT, INC.; *Int'l*, pg. 1801
CORNERSTONE MANAGEMENT PARTNERS, INC.; *U.S. Private*, pg. 1052
CORNERSTONE MEDIA; *U.S. Private*, pg. 1052
CORNERSTONE MEDICAL SERVICES - AKRON—See Catholic Health Initiatives; *U.S. Private*, pg. 789
CORNERSTONE MEDICAL SERVICES—See Catholic Health Initiatives; *U.S. Private*, pg. 789
CORNERSTONE MORTGAGE CO.; *U.S. Private*, pg. 1052
CORNERSTONE NETWORKS CO., LTD.; *Int'l*, pg. 1801
CORNERSTONE OF NORTH FLORIDA—See Cornerstone Businesses Inc.; *U.S. Private*, pg. 1051
CORNERSTONE ONDEMAND, INC.—See Clearlake Capital Group, L.P.; *U.S. Private*, pg. 933
CORNERSTONE ONDEMAND LIMITED—See Clearlake Capital Group, L.P.; *U.S. Private*, pg. 933
CORNERSTONE PALLIATIVE AND HOSPICE, LLC—See UnitedHealth Group Incorporated; *U.S. Public*, pg. 2244
CORNERSTONE PHARMACY, INC.; *U.S. Private*, pg. 1052
CORNERSTONE PROFESSIONAL LIABILITY CONSULTANTS, INC.; *U.S. Private*, pg. 1052
CORNERSTONE PROMOTION, INC.; *U.S. Private*, pg. 1052
CORNERSTONE RELOCATION GROUP, LLC.—See Atlas World Group, Inc.; *U.S. Private*, pg. 381
CORNERSTONE RESEARCH & DEVELOPMENT, INC.—See Cornell Capital LLC; *U.S. Private*, pg. 1051
CORNERSTONE RESEARCH GROUP, INC.; *U.S. Private*, pg. 1052
CORNERSTONE RETIREMENT GROUP, INC.—See Prime Capital Investment Advisors, LLC; *U.S. Private*, pg. 3261
CORNERSTONE RPO, LLC; *U.S. Private*, pg. 1052
CORNERSTONE SECURITIES LIMITED—See Cornerstone Financial Holdings Limited; *Int'l*, pg. 1801
CORNERSTONE SERVICES GROUP—See Irex Corporation; *U.S. Private*, pg. 2137
CORNERSTONE SOLUTIONS GROUP; *U.S. Private*, pg. 1052
CORNERSTONE STAFFING SOLUTIONS, INC.; *U.S. Private*, pg. 1053
CORNERSTONE STRATEGIC VALUE FUND, INC.; *U.S. Public*, pg. 577
CORNERSTONE SURGERY CENTER, LLC—See UnitedHealth Group Incorporated; *U.S. Public*, pg. 2240
CORNERSTONE SYSTEMS, INC.; *U.S. Private*, pg. 1053
CORNERSTONE TECHNOLOGIES HOLDINGS LIMITED; *Int'l*, pg. 1801
CORNERSTONE TELEPHONE CO. LLC—See NewSpring Capital LLC; *U.S. Private*, pg. 2918
CORNERSTONE THERAPEUTICS, INC.—See Chiesi Farmaceutici SpA; *Int'l*, pg. 1478
CORNERSTONE TITLE COMPANY—See Anywhere Real Estate Inc.; *U.S. Public*, pg. 142
CORNERSTONE TOTAL RETURN FUND, INC.; *U.S. Public*, pg. 577
CORNERSTONE WEALTH MANAGEMENT, LLC—See Vivaldi Capital Management, LLC; *U.S. Private*, pg. 4406
CORNES TECHNOLOGIES LTD.—See Meta Materials Inc.; *Int'l*, pg. 4843
CORNET TECHNOLOGY GMBH—See Cornet Technology Inc.; *U.S. Private*, pg. 1053
CORNET TECHNOLOGY INC.; *U.S. Private*, pg. 1053
CORNET TECHNOLOGY (INDIA) PRIVATE LIMITED—See Cornet Technology Inc.; *U.S. Private*, pg. 1053
CORNETT INTEGRATED MARKETING SOLUTIONS; *U.S. Private*, pg. 1053
CORNEY & BARROW LIMITED—See Drake & Morgan Limited; *Int'l*, pg. 2200
CORNFIELDS, INC.—See Kelso & Company, L.P.; *U.S. Private*, pg. 2278
CORNHUSKER AUTO CENTER INC.; *U.S. Private*, pg. 1053
CORNHUSKER ENERGY LEXINGTON, LLC—See ACI Capital Co. LLC; *U.S. Private*, pg. 59
CORNHUSKER GROWTH CORPORATION; *U.S. Private*, pg. 1053
CORNHUSKER INSULATION, INC.—See Installed Building Products, Inc.; *U.S. Public*, pg. 1132
CORNIANI ACMA GD—See Coesia S.p.A.; *Int'l*, pg. 1690
CORNILLE—See S.V.A. Jean ROZE; *Int'l*, pg. 6457
CORNING BUILDING CO. INC.; *U.S. Private*, pg. 1053
CORNING B.V.—See Corning Incorporated; *U.S. Public*, pg. 578
CORNING CABLE SYSTEMS PTY. LTD.—See Corning Incorporated; *U.S. Public*, pg. 578
CORNING CHINA (SHANGHAI) REGIONAL HEADQUARTER—See Corning Incorporated; *U.S. Public*, pg. 578
CORNING DATA SERVICES INC.; *U.S. Private*, pg. 1053
CORNING DISPLAY TECHNOLOGIES (CHINA) CO., LTD.—See Corning Incorporated; *U.S. Public*, pg. 578
CORNING DISPLAY TECHNOLOGIES (CHONGQING) CO., LTD.—See Corning Incorporated; *U.S. Public*, pg. 578
CORNING DISPLAY TECHNOLOGIES (HEFEI) CO., LTD.—See Corning Incorporated; *U.S. Public*, pg. 578
CORNING FORD, INC.; *U.S. Private*, pg. 1053
CORNING GILBERT INC.—See Corning Incorporated; *U.S. Public*, pg. 578
CORNING GMBH—See Corning Incorporated; *U.S. Public*, pg. 578
CORNING (HAINAN) OPTICAL COMMUNICATIONS CO., LTD.—See Corning Incorporated; *U.S. Public*, pg. 578
CORNING HOLDING GMBH—See Corning Incorporated; *U.S. Public*, pg. 578
CORNING HOLDING JAPAN GK—See Corning Incorporated; *U.S. Public*, pg. 578
CORNING INC. - HARRODSBURG PLANT—See Corning Incorporated; *U.S. Public*, pg. 578
CORNING INCORPORATED; *U.S. Public*, pg. 578
CORNING INDIA—See Corning Incorporated; *U.S. Public*, pg. 578
CORNING INTERNATIONAL CORPORATION—See Corning Incorporated; *U.S. Public*, pg. 578
CORNING JAPAN K.K.—See Corning Incorporated; *U.S. Public*, pg. 578
CORNING LIFE SCIENCES B.V.—See Corning Incorporated; *U.S. Public*, pg. 578
CORNING LIFE SCIENCES (WUJIANG) CO., LTD.—See Corning Incorporated; *U.S. Public*, pg. 578
CORNING MOBILEACCESS, INC.—See Corning Incorporated; *U.S. Public*, pg. 578
CORNING NATURAL GAS CORPORATION—See Argo Infrastructure Partners LLC; *U.S. Private*, pg. 320
CORNING NATURAL GAS HOLDING CORPORATION—See Argo Infrastructure Partners LLC; *U.S. Private*, pg. 320
CORNING NETOPTIX, INC.—See Corning Incorporated; *U.S. Public*, pg. 578
CORNING OPTICAL COMMUNICATIONS GERMANY—See Corning Incorporated; *U.S. Public*, pg. 578
CORNING OPTICAL COMMUNICATIONS LLC—See Corning Incorporated; *U.S. Public*, pg. 578
CORNING OPTICAL COMMUNICATIONS LLC—See Corning Incorporated; *U.S. Public*, pg. 578
CORNING OPTICAL COMMUNICATIONS POLSKA SP. Z O.O.—See Corning Incorporated; *U.S. Public*, pg. 578
CORNING OPTICAL COMMUNICATIONS PTY. LTD.—See Corning Incorporated; *U.S. Public*, pg. 578
CORNING OPTICAL COMMUNICATIONS S. DE R.L. DE C.V.—See Corning Incorporated; *U.S. Public*, pg. 578
CORNING OPTICAL COMMUNICATIONS - UK—See Corning Incorporated; *U.S. Public*, pg. 578
CORNING OPTICAL FIBER CABLE (CHENGDU) CO., LTD.—See Corning Incorporated; *U.S. Public*, pg. 578
CORNING PHARMACEUTICAL GLASS, LLC—See Corning Incorporated; *U.S. Public*, pg. 578
CORNING PHARMACEUTICAL GLASS S.P.A.—See Corning Incorporated; *U.S. Public*, pg. 578
CORNING PRECISION MATERIALS COMPANY LTD.—See Corning Incorporated; *U.S. Public*, pg. 578
CORNING S.A.—See Corning Incorporated; *U.S. Public*, pg. 578
CORNING (SHANGHAI) CO., LTD.—See Corning Incorporated; *U.S. Public*, pg. 578
CORNING SPECIALTY MATERIALS, INC.—See Corning Incorporated; *U.S. Public*, pg. 578
CORNING TECHNOLOGIES INDIA PRIVATE LIMITED—See Corning Incorporated; *U.S. Public*, pg. 578
CORNING TROPEL CORP.—See Corning Incorporated; *U.S. Public*, pg. 578
CORN INVESTMENT LTD.—See Allianz SE; *Int'l*, pg. 352
CORNISH COFFEE CO LTD.—See Miko NV; *Int'l*, pg. 4892
CORNISH COUNTRY LARDER LTD.—See Arla Foods amba; *Int'l*, pg. 573
CORNISH METALS INC.; *Int'l*, pg. 1801
CORNISH ORCHARDS LTD.—See Asahi Group Holdings Ltd.; *Int'l*, pg. 593
CORN PRODUCTS BRASIL INGREDIENTES INDUSTRIAIS LTDA.—See Ingredion Incorporated; *U.S. Public*, pg. 1123
CORN PRODUCTS CHILE-INDUCORN S.A.—See Ingredion Incorporated; *U.S. Public*, pg. 1123
CORN PRODUCTS KENYA LTD.—See Ingredion Incorporated; *U.S. Public*, pg. 1123
CORN PRODUCTS SOUTHERN CONE S.A.—See Ingredion Incorporated; *U.S. Public*, pg. 1123
CORN PRODUCTS (THAILAND) CO. LTD.—See Ingredion Incorporated; *U.S. Public*, pg. 1123
CORN PRODUCTS THAILAND CO., LTD.—See Ingredion Incorporated; *U.S. Public*, pg. 1123
CORN REFINERS ASSOCIATION; *U.S. Private*, pg. 1050
CORNU SAS FONTAIN—See Cornu S.A.; *Int'l*, pg. 1801
CORNU S.A.; *Int'l*, pg. 1801
CORNWALL ELECTRIC INC.—See Fortis Inc.; *Int'l*, pg. 2739
CORNWALL GRAVEL CO. LTD.; *Int'l*, pg. 1801
CORNWALL MANOR; *U.S. Private*, pg. 1053
CORNWALL RESOURCES, INC.; *U.S. Public*, pg. 579
CORNWALL STANDARD-FREEHOLDER—See Chatham Asset Management, LLC; *U.S. Private*, pg. 861
CORNWELL COMMUNICATIONS, INC.—See Matrix Integration LLC; *U.S. Private*, pg. 2612
CORNWELL CORP.; *U.S. Private*, pg. 1053
THE CORNWELL QUALITY TOOLS CO., INC.; *U.S. Private*, pg. 4015
COROB BRASIL—See Graco, Inc.; *U.S. Public*, pg. 953
COROB GMBH—See Graco, Inc.; *U.S. Public*, pg. 953
COROB INDIA PVT. LTD.—See Graco, Inc.; *U.S. Public*, pg. 953

THE CORNWELL QUALITY TOOLS CO., INC.   CORPORATE AFFILIATIONS

COROB NORTH AMERICA, INC.—See Graco, Inc.; *U.S. Public*, pg. 953
COROB OY—See Graco, Inc.; *U.S. Public*, pg. 953
COROB PTE. LTD.—See Graco, Inc.; *U.S. Public*, pg. 953
COROB RUS—See Graco, Inc.; *U.S. Public*, pg. 953
COROB S.A.—See Graco, Inc.; *U.S. Public*, pg. 953
COROB SCANDINAVIA AB—See Graco, Inc.; *U.S. Public*, pg. 953
COROB S.P.A.—See Graco, Inc.; *U.S. Public*, pg. 952
COROB TRADING (SHENZHEN) LIMITED—See Graco, Inc.; *U.S. Public*, pg. 953
COROC/MYRTLE BEACH L.L.C.—See Tanger Inc.; *U.S. Public*, pg. 1980
COROCORD RAUMNETZ GMBH—See KOMPAN A/S; *Int'l*, pg. 4243
COROC/PARK CITY L.L.C.—See Tanger Inc.; *U.S. Public*, pg. 1980
CORO ENERGY PLC; *Int'l*, pg. 1801
CORO GLOBAL INC.; *U.S. Public*, pg. 579
COROI INTERNATIONAL—See Marbour SAS; *Int'l*, pg. 4688
COROI MAURICE—See Marbour SAS; *Int'l*, pg. 4688
COROMAL CARAVANS PTY LTD—See Fleetwood Limited; *Int'l*, pg. 2699
COROMANDEL AGRO PRODUCTS & OILS LTD.; *Int'l*, pg. 1801
COROMANDEL ENGINEERING COMPANY LIMITED; *Int'l*, pg. 1802
COROMANDEL INTERNATIONAL LIMITED—See The Murugappa Group, Ltd.; *Int'l*, pg. 7668
COROMANDEL TRAVELS LIMITED—See The India Cements Limited; *Int'l*, pg. 7654
THE COROMEGA COMPANY, INC.—See PlusPharma, Inc.; *U.S. Private*, pg. 3215
CORONA CLIPPER, INC.—See Ingersoll Tillage Group, Inc.; *Int'l*, pg. 3702
CORONA CONTROL AB—See Indutrade AB; *Int'l*, pg. 3677
CORONA CORPORATION; *Int'l*, pg. 1802
CORONA CURTAIN MANUFACTURING CO. INC.—See Natco Products Corporation; *U.S. Private*, pg. 2838
CORONA DIRECT—See Dexia SA; *Int'l*, pg. 2092
CORONADO CENTER—See Brookfield Corporation; *Int'l*, pg. 1185
CORONADO COAL LLC; *U.S. Private*, pg. 1053
CORONADO CORPORATION—See LTC Properties, Inc.; *U.S. Public*, pg. 1344
CORONADO GLOBAL RESOURCES INC.; *Int'l*, pg. 1802
CORONA ENERGY—See Macquarie Group Limited; *Int'l*, pg. 4625
CORONA LABS INC.; *U.S. Private*, pg. 1053
CORONATION FUND MANAGERS LIMITED; *Int'l*, pg. 1802
CORONATION GLOBAL FUND MANAGERS (IRELAND) LTD—See Coronation Fund Managers Limited; *Int'l*, pg. 1802
CORONATION MINES LIMITED—See Jervois Global Limited; *Int'l*, pg. 3932
CORONET/MTI—See The Phoenix Learning Group, Inc.; *U.S. Private*, pg. 4095
CORONET PAPER PRODUCTS ENTERPRISES OF FLORIDA LLC.; *U.S. Private*, pg. 1053
COROPLAST FRITZ MULLER GMBH UND CO. KG; *Int'l*, pg. 1802
COROPLAST HARNESS TECHNOLOGY (KUNSHAN) CO., LTD.—See Coroplast Fritz Muller GmbH und Co. KG; *Int'l*, pg. 1802
COROPLAST HARNESS TECHNOLOGY (MIANYANG) CO., LTD.—See Coroplast Fritz Muller GmbH und Co. KG; *Int'l*, pg. 1802
COROPLAST HARNESS TECHNOLOGY (TAICANG) CO., LTD.—See Coroplast Fritz Muller GmbH und Co. KG; *Int'l*, pg. 1802
COROPLAST, INC.—See The Jim Pattison Group; *Int'l*, pg. 7660
COROPLAST SPOLKA Z O.O.—See Coroplast Fritz Muller GmbH und Co. KG; *Int'l*, pg. 1802
COROPLAST TAPE CORPORATION—See Coroplast Fritz Muller GmbH und Co. KG; *Int'l*, pg. 1802
COROPLAST TUNISIE SARL—See Coroplast Fritz Muller GmbH und Co. KG; *Int'l*, pg. 1802
CORO REALTY ADVISORS LLC; *U.S. Private*, pg. 1053
COROUS360 SDN. BHD.—See EXEO Group Inc.; *Int'l*, pg. 2583
COROVAN CORPORATION; *U.S. Private*, pg. 1053
COROVAN MOVING & STORAGE CO.—See Corovan Corporation; *U.S. Private*, pg. 1053
CORP2000, INC.—See Apax Partners LLP; *Int'l*, pg. 503
CORPACQ HOLDINGS LIMITED; *Int'l*, pg. 1802
CORPACQ LTD.—See CorpAcq Holdings Limited; *Int'l*, pg. 1802
CORPAC STEEL PRODUCTS CORP.; *U.S. Private*, pg. 1053
CORPAK MEDSYSTEMS, INC.—See Avanos Medical, Inc.; *U.S. Public*, pg. 241
CORPAY, INC.; *U.S. Public*, pg. 579
CORPBANCA ASESORIAS FINANCIERAS S.A.—See Itau Unibanco Holding S.A.; *Int'l*, pg. 3830

CORP. BANK SECURITIES LTD—See Union Bank of India; *Int'l*, pg. 8051
CORPBRASIL COMUNICACAO CORPORATIVA LTDA.—See Grupo MZ; *Int'l*, pg. 3133
CORP. CONSULTANTS PERFORMANCE, INC.—See Automatic Data Processing, Inc.; *U.S. Public*, pg. 230
CORPDIRECT AGENTS, INC.; *U.S. Private*, pg. 1053
CORPERACION GENERAL DE SERVICIOS S.A.—See Grupo Romero; *Int'l*, pg. 3134
CORPESCA S.A.—See AntarChile S.A.; *Int'l*, pg. 482
CORPFIN CAPITAL PRIME RETAIL III SOCIMI SA; *Int'l*, pg. 1802
CORPFIN CAPITAL PRIME RETAIL II SOCIMI SA; *Int'l*, pg. 1802
CORPFIN CAPITAL SA; *Int'l*, pg. 1802
CORPLAST PACKAGING INDUSTRIES SDN. BHD.—See CLPG Packaging Industries Sdn. Bhd.; *Int'l*, pg. 1663
CORPLEX, INC.—See The Carlyle Group Inc.; *U.S. Public*, pg. 2050
CORPOPLAST BEVERAGE EQUIPMENT (SUZHOU) CO., LTD.—See Salzgitter AG; *Int'l*, pg. 6496
CORPORACION ACCIONA ENERGIAS RENOVABLES S.A.; *Int'l*, pg. 1802
CORPORACION ACERINOX PERU, S.A.C.—See Acerinox, S.A.; *Int'l*, pg. 100
CORPORACION ACEROS AREQUIPA S.A.; *Int'l*, pg. 1802
CORPORACION ACTINVER SAB DE CV; *Int'l*, pg. 1803
CORPORACION AMERICA AIRPORTS S.A.; *Int'l*, pg. 1803
CORPORACION AMERICA ITALIA S.P.A.—See Corporacion America Airports S.A.; *Int'l*, pg. 1803
CORPORACION AMERICA S.A.; *Int'l*, pg. 1803
CORPORACION ANDINA DE FOMENTO; *Int'l*, pg. 1803
CORPORACION BONIMA S.A. DE C.V.—See Bayer Aktiengesellschaft; *Int'l*, pg. 907
CORPORACION CERRAJERA ALBA, S.A. DE C.V.—See dormakaba Holding AG; *Int'l*, pg. 2177
CORPORACION CERVESUR S.A.A.; *Int'l*, pg. 1803
CORPORACION CORAL S. DE R.L. DE C.V.—See Illinois Tool Works Inc.; *U.S. Public*, pg. 1102
CORPORACION DE FINANZAS DEL PAIS; *Int'l*, pg. 1803
CORPORACION DE INVERSION Y DESARROLLO BES, S.A.—See BES Engineering Corporation; *Int'l*, pg. 998
CORPORACION DEL COBRE (U.S.A.), INC.—See Corporacion Nacional del Cobre de Chile; *Int'l*, pg. 1805
CORPORACION DE PERSONAL ADMINISTRATIVO S. A. DE C. V.—See Empresas Publicas de Medellin ESP; *Int'l*, pg. 2391
CORPORACION DE RADIO Y TELEVISION ESPANOLA, S.A.—See Sociedad Estatal de Participaciones Industriales; *Int'l*, pg. 7031
CORPORACION DERMOESTETICA, S.A.; *Int'l*, pg. 1803
CORPORACION DISTRIBUIDORA DE ALIMENTOS S.A.—See Grupo Nutresa S.A.; *Int'l*, pg. 3133
CORPORACION EG S.A.; *Int'l*, pg. 1803
CORPORACION EMPRESARIAL DE MATERIALES DE CONSTRUCCION—See Nefinsa S.A.; *Int'l*, pg. 5191
CORPORACION FINANCIERA ALBA S.A.—See Alba Grupo March; *Int'l*, pg. 292
CORPORACION FINANCIERA COLOMBIANA S.A.; *Int'l*, pg. 1803
CORPORACION FINANCIERA DE DESARROLLO SA; *Int'l*, pg. 1803
CORPORACION FINANCIERA DE INVERSIONES SA; *Int'l*, pg. 1803
CORPORACION GESTAMP SL; *Int'l*, pg. 1803
CORPORACION HABANOS, S.A.—See Imperial Brands PLC; *Int'l*, pg. 3632
CORPORACION INMOBILIARIA VESTA, S.A.B. DE C.V.; *Int'l*, pg. 1804
CORPORACION INTERAMERICANA DE ENTRETENIMIENTO, S. A. B. DE C. V.; *Int'l*, pg. 1804
CORPORACION / JWT—See WPP plc; *Int'l*, pg. 8478
CORPORACION LINDLEY S.A.—See Arca Continental, S.A.B. de C.V.; *Int'l*, pg. 540
CORPORACION LOS HERMANOS; *U.S. Private*, pg. 1054
CORPORACION MERCABAN DE COSTA RICA, S.A.—See The Bank of Nova Scotia; *Int'l*, pg. 7618
CORPORACION MEXICANA DE SERVICIO AUTOMOTRIZ, S.A. DE C.V.—See Sumitomo Corporation; *Int'l*, pg. 7274
CORPORACION MICROSOFT DEL ECUADOR S.A.—See Microsoft Corporation; *U.S. Public*, pg. 1440
CORPORACION MITSUBA DE MEXICO, S.A. DE C.V.—See MITSUBA Corporation; *Int'l*, pg. 4928
CORPORACION MOCTEZUMA S.A.B. DE C.V.; *Int'l*, pg. 1804
CORPORACION MULTI INVERSIONES SA; *Int'l*, pg. 1804
CORPORACION NACIONAL DEL COBRE DE CHILE; *Int'l*, pg. 1804
CORPORACION NORDEX ENERGY SPAIN S.L.—See Nordex SE; *Int'l*, pg. 5418
CORPORACION NOROESTE S.A.—See Camargo Correa S.A.; *Int'l*, pg. 1268
CORPORACION PATRICIO ECHEVERRIA, S.A.—See Ingersoll Tillage Group, Inc.; *Int'l*, pg. 3702

CORPORACION PESQUERA INCA S.A.C.—See Pacific Andes International Holdings Limited; *Int'l*, pg. 5685
CORPORACION PROAUTO S.A.—See General Motors Company; *U.S. Public*, pg. 923
CORPORACION TATSUMI DE MEXICO, S.A. DE C.V.—See MITSUBA Corporation; *Int'l*, pg. 4928
CORPORACION TECNOLOGA GLOBAL 21, C.A.—See Abbott Laboratories; *U.S. Public*, pg. 20
CORPORACION UPWARDS 98 S.A.—See Brembo S.p.A.; *Int'l*, pg. 1145
CORPORACION VENEZOLANA DE GUAYANA; *Int'l*, pg. 1805
CORPORATE AIR; *U.S. Private*, pg. 1054
CORPORATE ALLOCATION SERVICES, INC.; *U.S. Private*, pg. 1054
CORPORATE AMERICA FAMILY CREDIT UNION; *U.S. Private*, pg. 1054
CORPORATE ARMOR, INC.—See Tiversa, Inc.; *U.S. Private*, pg. 4177
CORPORATE ASSET BACKED CORPORATION; *U.S. Private*, pg. 1054
CORPORATE ASSET SOLUTIONS LIMITED—See Close Brothers Group plc; *Int'l*, pg. 1661
CORPORATE BANK TRANSIT; *U.S. Private*, pg. 1054
CORPORATE BENEFIT ADVISORS, INC.—See Aon plc; *Int'l*, pg. 495
CORPORATE BENEFIT MARKETING—See GI Manager L.P.; *U.S. Private*, pg. 1693
CORPORATE BENEFIT MARKETING—See Summit Partners, L.P.; *U.S. Private*, pg. 3856
CORPORATE BENEFITS, INC.—See Aon plc; *Int'l*, pg. 495
CORPORATE BILLING, LLC—See SouthState Corporation; *U.S. Public*, pg. 1913
CORPORATE BROKERS LLC; *U.S. Private*, pg. 1054
CORPORATE BUSINESS INTERIORS, INC.; *U.S. Private*, pg. 1054
CORPORATE CAPITAL TRUST, INC.—See Franklin Square Holdings, L.P.; *U.S. Private*, pg. 1598
CORPORATE CAR LTD. INC.—See Communicar Corp.; *U.S. Private*, pg. 987
CORPORATE CENTRAL CREDIT UNION; *U.S. Private*, pg. 1054
CORPORATE CHEFS INC.—See Charterhouse Capital Partners LLP; *Int'l*, pg. 1455
CORPORATE CITIZENSHIP LIMITED—See Charterhouse Capital Partners LLP; *Int'l*, pg. 1455
CORPORATE CLAIMS MANAGEMENT, INC.; *U.S. Private*, pg. 1054
CORPORATE CLAIMS MANAGEMENT, INC.—See Patriot National, Inc.; *U.S. Private*, pg. 3110
CORPORATE COACHES, INC.; *U.S. Private*, pg. 1054
CORPORATE COFFEE SYSTEMS, LLC—See Aramark; *U.S. Public*, pg. 176
CORPORATE COLOR, INC.—See Corporate Press Inc.; *U.S. Private*, pg. 1055
THE CORPORATE COMMISSION OF MILLE LACS BAND OJIBWE INDIANS; *U.S. Private*, pg. 4015
THE CORPORATE COMMUNICATIONS GROUP; *U.S. Private*, pg. 4015
CORPORATE CONCEPTS, INC.—See PARIC Holdings, Inc.; *U.S. Private*, pg. 3094
CORPORATE CONCIERGE SERVICES, INC.—See Jones Lang LaSalle Incorporated; *U.S. Public*, pg. 1201
CORPORATE CONSTRUCTION LTD; *U.S. Private*, pg. 1054
CORPORATE CONSULTING SERVICES—See Marsh & McLennan Companies, Inc.; *U.S. Public*, pg. 1380
CORPORATE CONTRACTORS INC.—See Hendricks Holding Company, Inc.; *U.S. Private*, pg. 1915
CORPORATE CULINARY SERVICE INC.; *U.S. Private*, pg. 1054
CORPORATE DEVELOPMENT BANK LIMITED; *Int'l*, pg. 1805
CORPORATE DEVELOPMENT SERVICES, LLC—See COPT Defense Properties; *U.S. Public*, pg. 575
CORPORATE DIRECT APPAREL LLC; *U.S. Private*, pg. 1054
CORPORATE DIRECT INC.—See Corporate Press Inc.; *U.S. Private*, pg. 1055
CORPORATE DISK COMPANY; *U.S. Private*, pg. 1054
CORPORATE DISPLAY SPECIALTIES, INC.; *U.S. Private*, pg. 1054
CORPORATE DOCUMENT SOLUTIONS, INC.; *U.S. Private*, pg. 1054
THE CORPORATE ENVIRONMENTS GROUP; *U.S. Private*, pg. 4015
CORPORATE ENVIRONMENTS OF GEORGIA INC.; *U.S. Private*, pg. 1054
CORPORATE EQUIPMENT COMPANY, LLC—See DXP Enterprises, Inc.; *U.S. Public*, pg. 697
CORPORATE ESSENTIALS, LLC.; *U.S. Private*, pg. 1054
CORPORATE FACILITIES INC.; *U.S. Private*, pg. 1054
CORPORATE FAMILY NETWORK; *U.S. Private*, pg. 1055
CORPORATE FITNESS WORKS, INC.; *U.S. Private*, pg. 1055
CORPORATE FLIGHT MANAGEMENT INC.; *U.S. Private*, pg. 1055
CORPORATE FLOORS INC.; *U.S. Private*, pg. 1055

COMPANY NAME INDEX

CORPORATE GRAPHICS COMMERCIAL—See Taylor Corporation; *U.S. Private*, pg. 3938
CORPORATE GRAPHICS INTERNATIONAL—See Taylor Corporation; *U.S. Private*, pg. 3938
CORPORATE GRAPHICS INTERNATIONAL—See Taylor Corporation; *U.S. Private*, pg. 3938
CORPORATE HEALTH GROUP, LLC; *U.S. Private*, pg. 1055
CORPORATE HOUSING—See Woodlands Operating Company LP; *U.S. Private*, pg. 4559
CORPORATE IMAGING CONCEPTS, INC—See W.R. Berkley Corporation; *U.S. Public*, pg. 2317
CORPORATE INK PUBLIC RELATIONS, LTD.; *U.S. Private*, pg. 1055
CORPORATE INSTALLATION SERVICES; *U.S. Private*, pg. 1055
CORPORATE INTERIORS INC.; *U.S. Private*, pg. 1055
CORPORATE INTERIORS, INC.; *U.S. Private*, pg. 1055
CORPORATE INTERIOR SYSTEMS; *U.S. Private*, pg. 1055
CORPORATEL, S.A. DE C.V.—See Grupo Televisa, S.A.B.; *Int'l*, pg. 3136
CORPORATE MARKETING, INC.—See Artcraft Promotional Concepts; *U.S. Private*, pg. 340
CORPORATE MERCHANT BANKERS LIMITED; *Int'l*, pg. 1805
CORPORATE MOBILE RECYCLING ESPANA S.L.—See TD Synnex Corp; *U.S. Public*, pg. 1984
CORPORATE MOBILE RECYCLING LTD.—See TD Synnex Corp; *U.S. Public*, pg. 1984
CORPORATE MONTAGE EUROPE GMBH—See MEDIQON Group AG; *Int'l*, pg. 4780
CORPORATE OFFICE PROPERTIES, L.P.—See COPT Defense Properties; *U.S. Public*, pg. 575
CORPORATE PARTNERS LLC; *U.S. Private*, pg. 1055
CORPORATE PRESS INC.; *U.S. Private*, pg. 1055
CORPORATE PROFILES DDB—See Omnicom Group Inc.; *U.S. Public*, pg. 1579
THE CORPORATE PROMOTIONS GROUP; *U.S. Private*, pg. 4015
CORPORATE PROPERTY ASSOCIATES 17 - GLOBAL INCORPORATED—See W.P. Carey Inc.; *U.S. Public*, pg. 2315
CORPORATE PROPERTY ASSOCIATES 18 - GLOBAL INCORPORATED—See W.P. Carey Inc.; *U.S. Public*, pg. 2315
CORPORATE PROPERTY ASSOCIATES 18 GLOBAL INC; *U.S. Private*, pg. 1055
CORPORATE PROTECTIVE SECURITY INC.; *U.S. Private*, pg. 1055
CORPORATE REALTY INCOME FUND 1 LP; *U.S. Private*, pg. 1055
CORPORATE RESEARCH INTERNATIONAL; *U.S. Private*, pg. 1055
CORPORATE & RESOURCE CONSULTANTS PTY LTD; *Int'l*, pg. 1805
CORPORATE RESTAURANT CONCEPTS, INC.; *U.S. Public*, pg. 580
CORPORATE RESULTS INC; *U.S. Private*, pg. 1056
CORPORATE RISK HOLDINGS LLC; *U.S. Private*, pg. 1056
CORPORATE SERVICE CENTER, INC.; *U.S. Private*, pg. 1056
CORPORATE SERVICES INC.; *U.S. Private*, pg. 1056
CORPORATE SERVICE SYSTEMS OAO; *Int'l*, pg. 1805
CORPORATE SPACES, INC.—See Corporate Business Interiors, Inc.; *U.S. Private*, pg. 1054
CORPORATE S.R.L.—See Onward Holdings Co., Ltd.; *Int'l*, pg. 5592
CORPORATE SUITES, LLC; *U.S. Private*, pg. 1056
CORPORATE SYNERGIES GROUP, LLC; *U.S. Private*, pg. 1056
CORPORATE TECHNOLOGIES LLC—See Tonka Bay Equity Partners LLC; *U.S. Private*, pg. 4184
CORPORATE TECHNOLOGY SOLUTIONS LLC—See P.A.G. Capital Partners, LLC; *U.S. Private*, pg. 3060
CORPORATE TRANSLATIONS UK LIMITED—See RWS Holdings plc; *Int'l*, pg. 6436
CORPORATE TRAVEL MANAGEMENT GROUP PTY LTD—See Corporate Travel Management Limited; *Int'l*, pg. 1805
CORPORATE TRAVEL MANAGEMENT GROUP; *U.S. Private*, pg. 1056
CORPORATE TRAVEL MANAGEMENT LIMITED—See Corporate Travel Management Limited; *Int'l*, pg. 1805
CORPORATE TRAVEL MANAGEMENT LIMITED; *Int'l*, pg. 1805
CORPORATE TRAVEL MANAGEMENT NORTH AMERICA INC.—See Corporate Travel Management Limited; *Int'l*, pg. 1805
CORPORATE TRAVEL MANAGEMENT (S) PTE. LIMITED—See Corporate Travel Management Limited; *Int'l*, pg. 1806
CORPORATE TRAVEL MANAGEMENT (S) PTE. LTD.—See Sime Darby Berhad; *Int'l*, pg. 6928
CORPORATE TRAVEL MANAGEMENT (UK) LIMITED—See Corporate Travel Management Limited; *Int'l*, pg. 1805
CORPORATE TRAVEL PLANNERS, INC.—See Corporate Travel Management Limited; *Int'l*, pg. 1805
CORPORATE UNITED, INC.; *U.S. Private*, pg. 1056
CORPORATE UNIVERSE, INC.; *U.S. Public*, pg. 580
CORPORATE VISIONS, INC.—See The Riverside Company; *U.S. Private*, pg. 4108
CORPORATE VOICE-WEBER SHANDWICK—See The Interpublic Group of Companies, Inc.; *U.S. Public*, pg. 2104
CORPORATE VOICE-WEBER SHANDWICK—See The Interpublic Group of Companies, Inc.; *U.S. Public*, pg. 2104
CORPORATE WINGS-CGF, LLC—See Macquarie Group Limited; *Int'l*, pg. 4627
CORPORATE WINGS INC.—See Directional Capital LLC; *U.S. Private*, pg. 1236
CORPORATE WINGS SERVICES CORP.—See Directional Capital LLC; *U.S. Private*, pg. 1236
CORPORATE WINGS—See Directional Capital LLC; *U.S. Private*, pg. 1236
CORPORATION AIC-INVEST LLP; *Int'l*, pg. 1806
CORPORATION BANK—See Union Bank of India; *Int'l*, pg. 8051
CORPORATION FINANCIERE L'EXCELLENCE LTEE (CFE)—See iA Financial Corporation Inc.; *Int'l*, pg. 3567
CORPORATION FOR EDUCATION NETWORK INITIATIVES IN CALIFORNIA; *U.S. Private*, pg. 1056
CORPORATION FOR ENTERPRISE DEVELOPMENT CFED; *U.S. Private*, pg. 1056
CORPORATION FOR PUBLIC BROADCASTING; *U.S. Private*, pg. 1056
CORPORATION FOR REVITALIZING EARTHQUAKE-AFFECTED BUSINESS—See Deposit Insurance Corporation of Japan; *Int'l*, pg. 2041
CORPORATION IP LTD.—See SEMIKRON International GmbH; *Int'l*, pg. 6705
CORPORATION SERVICE COMPANY; *U.S. Private*, pg. 1056
CORPORATION SERVICE COMPANY (UK) LIMITED—See Corporation Service Company; *U.S. Private*, pg. 1057
CORPORATION TO DEVELOP COMMUNITIES OF TAMPA, INC.; *U.S. Private*, pg. 1058
CORPORATION TSESNA JSC; *Int'l*, pg. 1806
CORPORATIVO COPAMEX, S.A. DE C.V.; *Int'l*, pg. 1806
CORPORATIVO DE NEGOCIOS DE COMERCIO EXTERIOR, S.A. DE C.V.—See Accel, S.A.B. de C.V.; *Int'l*, pg. 79
CORPORATIVO FRAGUA, S.A.B. DE C.V.; *Int'l*, pg. 1806
CORPORATIVO MIDAS MEXICO—See Sumitomo Corporation; *Int'l*, pg. 7274
CORPORATIVO TD SPORTS, S.A. DE C.V.—See Grupo Televisa, S.A.B.; *Int'l*, pg. 3136
CORPORATIVO UNILEVER DE MEXICO, S. DE R.L. DE C.V.—See Unilever PLC; *Int'l*, pg. 8044
CORPORATIVO VASCO DE QUIROGA, S.A. DE C.V.—See Grupo Televisa, S.A.B.; *Int'l*, pg. 3136
CORPOREX COMPANIES, INC.; *U.S. Private*, pg. 1058
CORPOREX DEVELOPMENT—See Corporex Companies, Inc.; *U.S. Private*, pg. 1058
CORPRO GROUP LIMITED—See ALS Limited; *Int'l*, pg. 378
CORPTAX, INC.—See Corporation Service Company; *U.S. Private*, pg. 1058
CORPUS CHRISTI ANUSA, LLC—See AutoNation, Inc.; *U.S. Public*, pg. 234
CORPUS CHRISTI BAKING CO., LLC—See Flowers Foods, Inc.; *U.S. Public*, pg. 854
CORPUS CHRISTI BASEBALL CLUB, L.P.—See Ryan Sanders Baseball, L.P.; *U.S. Private*, pg. 3510
CORPUS CHRISTI CALLER-TIMES LLC—See Gannett Co., Inc.; *U.S. Public*, pg. 898
CORPUS CHRISTI COLLISION CENTER, INC.—See AutoNation, Inc.; *U.S. Public*, pg. 234
CORPUS CHRISTI ENDOSCOPY CENTER, L.L.P.—See UnitedHealth Group Incorporated; *U.S. Public*, pg. 2240
CORPUS CHRISTI HEART CLINIC, PLLC—See HCA Healthcare, Inc.; *U.S. Public*, pg. 994
CORPUS CHRISTI LIQUEFACTION, LLC—See Cheniere Corpus Christi Holdings, LLC; *U.S. Private*, pg. 873
CORPUS CHRISTI MEDICAL CENTER—See HCA Healthcare, Inc.; *U.S. Public*, pg. 994
CORPUS CHRISTI PIPELINE GP, LLC—See Cheniere Corpus Christi Holdings, LLC; *U.S. Private*, pg. 873
CORPUS CHRISTI RADIATION ONCOLOGY, PLLC—See HCA Healthcare, Inc.; *U.S. Public*, pg. 994
CORPUS CHRISTI SURGICARE, LTD.—See Tenet Healthcare Corporation; *U.S. Public*, pg. 2010
CORPUS MEDIA LABS, INC.; *U.S. Private*, pg. 1058
CORPUS MEDICAL, LLC—See TPG Capital, L.P.; *U.S. Public*, pg. 2169
CORPUS SIREO PROJEKTENTWICKLUNG WOHNEN GMBH—See Swiss Life Holding; *Int'l*, pg. 7368
CORPUS SIREO REAL ESTATE GMBH—See Swiss Life Holding; *Int'l*, pg. 7368
CORRADAS.P.A.—See EuroGroup Laminations S.p.A.; *Int'l*, pg. 2552

CORROSION SERVICE COMPANY LIMITED

CORRADO'S FAMILY AFFAIR; *U.S. Private*, pg. 1058
CORRA TECHNOLOGY, INC—See Publicis Groupe S.A.; *Int'l*, pg. 6110
CORRCHOICE, INC.—See Greif Inc.; *U.S. Public*, pg. 967
CORREA HOLDING LTD—See ELLAKTOR S.A.; *Int'l*, pg. 2365
CORREA INDIA PVT. LTD.—See Nicolas Correa S.A.; *Int'l*, pg. 5272
CORRECTA INDUSTRIA E COMERCIO LTDO.—See Glencore plc; *Int'l*, pg. 2990
CORRECT CARE SOLUTIONS, LLC—See H.I.G. Capital, LLC; *U.S. Private*, pg. 1829
CORRECT CRAFT, INC.; *U.S. Private*, pg. 1058
CORRECTIONAL ALTERNATIVES, LLC—See Corecivic, Inc.; *U.S. Public*, pg. 577
CORRECTIONAL PROPERTIES, LLC—See The GEO Group, Inc.; *U.S. Public*, pg. 2075
CORRECTION PRODUCTS CO.; *U.S. Private*, pg. 1058
CORREDOR DO DESENVOLVIMENTO DO NORTE S.A.R.L—See Vale S.A.; *Int'l*, pg. 8111
CORREDURIA DE SEGUROS, S.A.—See El Corte Ingles, S.A.; *Int'l*, pg. 2340
CORRE ENERGY B.V.; *Int'l*, pg. 1806
CORRELAGEN DIAGNOSTICS, INC.—See Laboratory Corporation of America Holdings; *U.S. Public*, pg. 1285
CORRELATE ENERGY CORP.; *U.S. Public*, pg. 580
CORRELATE UK SEARCH LTD.—See Pure Recruitment Group Ltd.; *Int'l*, pg. 6122
CORREOS TELECOM, S.A.—See Sociedad Estatal de Participaciones Industriales; *Int'l*, pg. 7031
CORREVIO PHARMA CORP.; *Int'l*, pg. 1806
CORREVIO SAS—See Advanz Pharma Corp.; *Int'l*, pg. 166
CORRIDOR CAPITAL, LLC; *U.S. Private*, pg. 1058
THE CORRIDOR GROUP, INC.—See HealthEdge Investment Partners, LLC; *U.S. Private*, pg. 1896
CORRIENTE RESOURCES, INC.—See China Railway Construction Corporation Limited; *Int'l*, pg. 1543
CORRIENTE RESOURCES, INC.—See Tongling Nonferrous Metals Group Holdings Co., Ltd; *Int'l*, pg. 7808
CORRIERE ADRIATICO SRL—See Caltagirone Editore S.p.A.; *Int'l*, pg. 1265
CORRIGAN BROS., INC.; *U.S. Private*, pg. 1058
CORRIGAN CANADA, LTD.—See OSI Systems, Inc.; *U.S. Public*, pg. 1621
CORRIGAN COMPANY MECHANICAL CONTRACTORS—See Corrigan Bros., Inc.; *U.S. Private*, pg. 1058
CORRIGAN FINANCIAL INC.; *U.S. Private*, pg. 1058
CORRIGAN KRAUSE CPA; *U.S. Private*, pg. 1058
CORRIGAN MOVING SYSTEMS; *U.S. Private*, pg. 1059
CORRIGAN OIL CO.; *U.S. Private*, pg. 1059
CORRIGO INCORPORATED—See Jones Lang LaSalle Incorporated; *U.S. Public*, pg. 1201
CORRISOFT LLC; *U.S. Private*, pg. 1059
CORROHEALTH, INC.; *U.S. Private*, pg. 1059
CORRO-PRO (L) INC.—See Perisai Petroleum Teknologi Bhd.; *Int'l*, pg. 5801
CORROSION & ABRASION SOLUTIONS LTD.; *Int'l*, pg. 1806
CORROSION CONTROL CORPORATION—See Enpro Inc.; *U.S. Public*, pg. 774
CORROSION CONTROL SERVICES LTD.—See VINCI S.A.; *Int'l*, pg. 8232
CORROSION FLUID PRODUCTS CORP.; *U.S. Private*, pg. 1059
CORROSION PRODUCTS & EQUIPMENT, INC. - ALBANY—See Corrosion Products & Equipment, Inc.; *U.S. Private*, pg. 1059
CORROSION PRODUCTS & EQUIPMENT, INC.; *U.S. Private*, pg. 1059
CORROSION RESISTANT PRODUCTS LTD.—See Indutrade AB; *Int'l*, pg. 3677
CORROSION SERVICE COMPANY INC—See Corrosion Service Company Limited; *Int'l*, pg. 1807
CORROSION SERVICE COMPANY LIMITED; *Int'l*, pg. 1806
CORROSION SPECIALTIES, LLC—See Ridgemont Partners Management LLC; *U.S. Private*, pg. 3432
CORROVENTA AVFUKTNING AB—See Volati AB; *Int'l*, pg. 8300
CORROVENTA AVFUKTNING NORGE AS—See Volati AB; *Int'l*, pg. 8300
CORROVENTA DESHUMIDIFICATION S.A.—See Volati AB; *Int'l*, pg. 8300
CORROVENTA ENTFEUCHTNUNG GMBH—See Volati AB; *Int'l*, pg. 8300
CORROVENTA ENTFEUCHTNUNG GMBH—See Volati AB; *Int'l*, pg. 8300
CORROVENTA ENTFEUCHTNUNG GMBH—See Volati AB; *Int'l*, pg. 8300
CORROVENTA ENTFEUCHTNUNG GMBH—See Volati AB; *Int'l*, pg. 8300
CORROVENTA LTD.—See Volati AB; *Int'l*, pg. 8300
CORROVENTA OSUSZANIE SP.Z.O.O.—See Volati AB; *Int'l*, pg. 8300
CORRPRO CANADA INC.—See New Mountain Capital, LLC; *U.S. Private*, pg. 2900

CORROSION SERVICE COMPANY LIMITED

CORPORATE AFFILIATIONS

Company Index

CORRPRO COMPANIES EUROPE LTD.—See New Mountain Capital, LLC; *U.S. Private*, pg. 2900
CORRPRO COMPANIES, INC.—See New Mountain Capital, LLC; *U.S. Private*, pg. 2900
CORR TECH, INC.; *U.S. Private*, pg. 1058
CORRUGATED BOX SUPPLIES LIMITED; *Int'l*, pg. 1807
CORRUGATED CONTAINER CORP; *U.S. Private*, pg. 1059
CORRUGATED METALS, INC.; *U.S. Private*, pg. 1059
CORRUGATED SUPPLIES CORP.; *U.S. Private*, pg. 1059
CORRUVEN, INC.; *Int'l*, pg. 1807
CORR-WILLIAMS COMPANY; *U.S. Private*, pg. 1058
CORR WIRELESS INC.; *U.S. Private*, pg. 1058
CORRY AUTO DEALERS EXCHANGE, INC.—See Huron Capital Partners LLC; *U.S. Private*, pg. 2012
CORRY FORGE COMPANY—See Ellwood Group, Inc.; *U.S. Private*, pg. 1375
CORRY MANUFACTURING COMPANY; *U.S. Private*, pg. 1059
CORRY MEMORIAL HOSPITAL; *U.S. Private*, pg. 1059
CORRY MICRONICS, INC.—See Arcline Investment Management LP; *U.S. Private*, pg. 313
CORSA COAL CORP.—See Quintana Capital Group, L.P.; *U.S. Private*, pg. 3328
CORSAIR CAPITAL, LLC; *U.S. Private*, pg. 1059
CORSAIR CAPITAL LLP—See Corsair Capital, LLC; *U.S. Private*, pg. 1059
CORSAIR COMPONENTS, INC.—See EagleTree Capital, LP; *U.S. Private*, pg. 1311
CORSAIR DISPLAY SYSTEMS, LLC—See The Vollrath Company LLC; *U.S. Private*, pg. 4132
CORSAIR GAMING, INC.; *U.S. Public*, pg. 580
CORSAIR PARTNERING CORPORATION; *U.S. Public*, pg. 580
CORSAIR S.A.—See INTRO-Verwaltungs GmbH; *Int'l*, pg. 3769
CORSA PERFORMANCE EXHAUSTS; *U.S. Private*, pg. 1059
CORS - COMPANHIA DE EXPLORACAO DE ESTACOES DE SERVICO E RETALHO DE SERVICOS AUTO-MOVEL, LDA.—See Galp Energia SGPS, S.A.; *Int'l*, pg. 2875
CORSE COMPOSITES AERONAUTIQUE—See Groupe Industriel Marcel Dassault S.A.; *Int'l*, pg. 3104
CORSE COMPOSITES AERONAUTIQUES—See Safran SA; *Int'l*, pg. 6473
CORSE EXPANSIF JSC—See Societe Anonyme d'Explosifs et de Produits Chimiques; *Int'l*, pg. 7035
CORSETTI STRUCTURAL STEEL INC.; *U.S. Private*, pg. 1059
CORSICA HAUT DEBIT—See Orange S.A.; *Int'l*, pg. 5608
CORSICA IMPLEMENT INC.; *U.S. Private*, pg. 1060
CORSICANA BEDDING, LLC; *U.S. Private*, pg. 1060
CORSICANA MEDIA, INC.—See GTCR LLC; *U.S. Private*, pg. 1805
CORSICAN FURNITURE, INC.; *U.S. Private*, pg. 1060
CORSTONE ASIA CO., LTD.—See Corstone Corporation; *U.S. Private*, pg. 1060
CORSTONE CORPORATION; *U.S. Private*, pg. 1060
CORTAL CONSORS BELGIUM—See BNP Paribas SA; *Int'l*, pg. 1090
CORTAL CONSORS S.A.—See BNP Paribas SA; *Int'l*, pg. 1090
CORTAL CONSORS—See BNP Paribas SA; *Int'l*, pg. 1090
CORT BUSINESS SERVICES CORPORATION—See Berkshire Hathaway Inc.; *U.S. Public*, pg. 303
CORTEC ADVANCED FILMS—See Cortec Corporation; *U.S. Private*, pg. 1060
CORTEC CORPORATION; *U.S. Private*, pg. 1060
CORTEC GROUP MANAGEMENT SERVICES, LLC; *U.S. Private*, pg. 1060
CORTECH ENGINEERING, INC.—See DXP Enterprises, Inc.; *U.S. Public*, pg. 697
CORTECH SOLUTIONS, INC.; *U.S. Private*, pg. 1060
CORTECO CHINA CO. LTD.—See Freudenberg SE; *Int'l*, pg. 2782
CORTECO GMBH—See Freudenberg SE; *Int'l*, pg. 2783
CORTECO LTD.—See Freudenberg SE; *Int'l*, pg. 2783
CORTE CONSTRUCTION CO. INC.; *U.S. Private*, pg. 1060
CORTECO SAS—See Freudenberg SE; *Int'l*, pg. 2783
CORTECO S.R.L.—See Freudenberg SE; *Int'l*, pg. 2783
CORTECO USA—See Freudenberg SE; *Int'l*, pg. 2783
CORTEC PRECISION SHEET METAL, INC.; *U.S. Private*, pg. 1060
CORTECOS D.O.O.—See Cortec Corporation; *U.S. Private*, pg. 1060
CORTECROS D.O.O.—See INA-Industrija Nafte, d.d.; *Int'l*, pg. 3642
CORTEL BUSINESS SOLUTIONS, INC.—See Blueprint Technologies, Inc.; *U.S. Public*, pg. 366
CORTELCO, INC.—See Cortelco Systems Holding Corp.; *U.S. Private*, pg. 1060
CORTELCO SYSTEMS HOLDING CORP.; *U.S. Private*, pg. 1060
CORTELCO SYSTEMS PUERTO RICO, INC.—See Cortelco Systems Holding Corp.; *U.S. Private*, pg. 1060
CORTE MADERA VILLAGE, LLC—See The Macerich Company; *U.S. Public*, pg. 2109

CORTERA, INC.—See Moody's Corporation; *U.S. Public*, pg. 1467
CORTES CAMPERS, LLC—See US Lighting Group, Inc.; *U.S. Public*, pg. 2266
CORTESE DODGE INC.; *U.S. Private*, pg. 1060
CORTESE FORD; *U.S. Private*, pg. 1060
CORTEVA AGRISCIENCE ARGENTINA S.R.L.—See Corteva, Inc.; *U.S. Public*, pg. 581
CORTEVA AGRISCIENCE AUSTRALIA PTY LTD.—See Corteva, Inc.; *U.S. Public*, pg. 581
CORTEVA AGRISCIENCE BOLIVIA S.A.—See Corteva, Inc.; *U.S. Public*, pg. 581
CORTEVA AGRISCIENCE BULGARIA EOOD—See Corteva, Inc.; *U.S. Public*, pg. 581
CORTEVA AGRISCIENCE (CAMBODIA) CO., LTD.—See Corteva, Inc.; *U.S. Public*, pg. 581
CORTEVA AGRISCIENCE CANADA COMPANY—See Corteva, Inc.; *U.S. Public*, pg. 581
CORTEVA AGRISCIENCE CROATIA LLC—See Corteva, Inc.; *U.S. Public*, pg. 581
CORTEVA AGRISCIENCE CZECH S.R.O.—See Corteva, Inc.; *U.S. Public*, pg. 581
CORTEVA AGRISCIENCE CZECH S.R.O.—See Corteva, Inc.; *U.S. Public*, pg. 581
CORTEVA AGRISCIENCE DE COLOMBIA S.A.S.—See Corteva, Inc.; *U.S. Public*, pg. 581
CORTEVA AGRISCIENCE DENMARK A/S—See Corteva, Inc.; *U.S. Public*, pg. 581
CORTEVA AGRISCIENCE EGYPT LLC—See Corteva, Inc.; *U.S. Public*, pg. 581
CORTEVA AGRISCIENCE FRANCE SAS—See Corteva, Inc.; *U.S. Public*, pg. 581
CORTEVA AGRISCIENCE GERMANY GMBH—See Corteva, Inc.; *U.S. Public*, pg. 581
CORTEVA AGRISCIENCE GERMANY GMBH—See Corteva, Inc.; *U.S. Public*, pg. 581
CORTEVA AGRISCIENCE HELLAS S.A.—See Corteva, Inc.; *U.S. Public*, pg. 581
CORTEVA AGRISCIENCE KENYA LIMITED—See Corteva, Inc.; *U.S. Public*, pg. 581
CORTEVA AGRISCIENCE KOREA LTD.—See Corteva, Inc.; *U.S. Public*, pg. 581
CORTEVA AGRISCIENCE LITHUANIA UAB—See Corteva, Inc.; *U.S. Public*, pg. 581
CORTEVA AGRISCIENCE LLC—See Corteva, Inc.; *U.S. Public*, pg. 580
CORTEVA AGRISCIENCE MAROC SARL—See Corteva, Inc.; *U.S. Public*, pg. 581
CORTEVA AGRISCIENCE NETHERLANDS B.V.—See Corteva, Inc.; *U.S. Public*, pg. 581
CORTEVA AGRISCIENCE NEW ZEALAND LTD.—See Corteva, Inc.; *U.S. Public*, pg. 581
CORTEVA AGRISCIENCE PAKISTAN LIMITED—See Corteva, Inc.; *U.S. Public*, pg. 581
CORTEVA AGRISCIENCE PHILIPPINES, INC.—See Corteva, Inc.; *U.S. Public*, pg. 581
CORTEVA AGRISCIENCE POLAND SP. Z O.O.—See Corteva, Inc.; *U.S. Public*, pg. 581
CORTEVA AGRISCIENCE ROMANIA S.R.L.—See Corteva, Inc.; *U.S. Public*, pg. 581
CORTEVA AGRISCIENCE (SINGAPORE) PTE. LTD.—See Corteva, Inc.; *U.S. Public*, pg. 581
CORTEVA AGRISCIENCE SRB D.O.O.—See Corteva, Inc.; *U.S. Public*, pg. 581
CORTEVA AGRISCIENCE (THAILAND) CO., LTD.—See Corteva, Inc.; *U.S. Public*, pg. 581
CORTEVA AGRISCIENCE UK LIMITED—See Corteva, Inc.; *U.S. Public*, pg. 581
CORTEVA AGRISCIENCE URUGUAY S.A.—See Corteva, Inc.; *U.S. Public*, pg. 581
CORTEVA AGRISCIENCE VIETNAM CO., LTD.—See Corteva, Inc.; *U.S. Public*, pg. 581
CORTEVA AGRISCIENCE ZAMBIA LIMITED—See Corteva, Inc.; *U.S. Public*, pg. 581
CORTEVA CROP SOLUTIONS HUN KFT.—See Corteva, Inc.; *U.S. Public*, pg. 581
CORTEVA, INC.; *U.S. Public*, pg. 580
CORTEX BUSINESS SOLUTIONS INC.—See Hellman & Friedman LLC; *U.S. Private*, pg. 1908
CORTEX BUSINESS SOLUTIONS LTD.—See Hellman & Friedman LLC; *U.S. Private*, pg. 1908
CORTEX KORKVERTRIEBS GMBH—See CORTICEIRA AMORIM, S.G.P.S., S.A.; *Int'l*, pg. 1807
CORTEX SOFTWARE GMBH—See Asklepios Kliniken GmbH & Co. KGaA; *Int'l*, pg. 623
CORTEZ GAS COMPANY INC.; *U.S. Private*, pg. 1060
CORTEZ HEATING & AIR CONDITIONING, INC.; *U.S. Private*, pg. 1060
CORT FURNITURE RENTALS & CLEARANCE CENTER—See Berkshire Hathaway Inc.; *U.S. Public*, pg. 303
CORT FURNITURE RENTAL—See Berkshire Hathaway Inc.; *U.S. Public*, pg. 303
CORTICEIRA AMORIM - FRANCE SAS—See CORTICEIRA AMORIM, S.G.P.S., S.A.; *Int'l*, pg. 1807
CORTICEIRA AMORIM, S.G.P.S., S.A.; *Int'l*, pg. 1807
CORTICHAPA S.A.—See Klockner & Co. SE; *Int'l*, pg. 4202

CORTICON TECHNOLOGIES, INC.—See Progress Software Corporation; *U.S. Public*, pg. 1725
CORTINA ACCESS INC.—See Realtek Semiconductor Corp.; *Int'l*, pg. 6235
CORTINA CAPITAL CORP.; *Int'l*, pg. 1808
CORTINA HOLDINGS LIMITED; *Int'l*, pg. 1808
CORTINA INSTITUTE OF LANGUAGES—See Cortina Learning International, Inc.; *U.S. Private*, pg. 1061
CORTINA INTEGRATED WASTE MANAGEMENT INC.—See Earthworks Industries Inc.; *Int'l*, pg. 2269
CORTINA LEARNING INTERNATIONAL, INC.; *U.S. Private*, pg. 1061
CORTINA NETWORK SYSTEMS SHANGHAI CO., LTD.—See Realtek Semiconductor Corp.; *Int'l*, pg. 6235
CORTINA SOLUTIONS, LLC; *U.S. Private*, pg. 1061
CORTINA SYSTEMS TAIWAN LIMITED—See Realtek Semiconductor Corp.; *Int'l*, pg. 6235
CORTINA WATCH CO., LTD.—See Cortina Holdings Limited; *Int'l*, pg. 1808
CORTINA WATCH HK LIMITED—See Cortina Holdings Limited; *Int'l*, pg. 1808
CORTINA WATCH PTE LTD.—See Cortina Holdings Limited; *Int'l*, pg. 1808
CORTINA WATCH SDN BHD—See Cortina Holdings Limited; *Int'l*, pg. 1808
CORTINA WATCH (THAILAND) CO., LTD.—See Cortina Holdings Limited; *Int'l*, pg. 1808
CORTLAND BANCORP, INC.—See Farmers National Banc Corp.; *U.S. Public*, pg. 822
CORTLAND COMPANY, INC.—See Enerpac Tool Group Corp.; *U.S. Public*, pg. 765
CORTLAND FIBRON BX LIMITED—See Enerpac Tool Group Corp.; *U.S. Public*, pg. 765
CORTLAND HARDWOOD PRODUCTS, LLC; *U.S. Private*, pg. 1061
CORTLAND LINE COMPANY, INC.; *U.S. Private*, pg. 1061
CORTLAND PARTNERS, LLC; *U.S. Private*, pg. 1061
CORTLAND PRODUCE COMPANY INC.; *U.S. Private*, pg. 1061
CORTLAND REGIONAL MEDICAL CENTER; *U.S. Private*, pg. 1061
CORTLAND SAVINGS & BANKING CO.—See Farmers National Banc Corp.; *U.S. Public*, pg. 822
CORTLANDT TOWN CENTER LLC—See Acadia Realty Trust; *U.S. Public*, pg. 31
CORTRONIX BIOMEDICAL ADVANCEMENT TECHNOLOGIES INC.; *U.S. Private*, pg. 1061
CORTRUST BANK N.A.—See Hopkins Financial Corporation; *U.S. Private*, pg. 1979
CORTUS ENERGY AB; *Int'l*, pg. 1808
CORTUS METALS, INC.; *Int'l*, pg. 1808
CORTZ, INC.—See Leonard Green & Partners, L.P.; *U.S. Private*, pg. 2426
CORUM DEUTSCHLAND GMBH—See Citychamp Watch & Jewellery Group Limited; *Int'l*, pg. 1628
CORUM ECOMMERCE PTY LTD—See Corum Group Limited; *Int'l*, pg. 1808
CORUM GROUP LIMITED; *Int'l*, pg. 1808
CORUM HEALTH PTY LTD—See Corum Group Limited; *Int'l*, pg. 1808
CORUM ITALIA SRL—See Citychamp Watch & Jewellery Group Limited; *Int'l*, pg. 1628
CORUM USA LLC—See Corum Watches S.A.R.L.; *Int'l*, pg. 1808
CORUM WATCHES S.A.R.L.; *Int'l*, pg. 1808
CORUS BUILDING SYSTEMS BULGARIA AD—See Tata Sons Limited; *Int'l*, pg. 7471
CORUS BUILDING SYSTEMS SAS—See Tata Sons Limited; *Int'l*, pg. 7471
CORUS ENTERTAINMENT INC.; *Int'l*, pg. 1808
CORUS GROUP LIMITED—See Tata Sons Limited; *Int'l*, pg. 7471
THE CORUS GROUP OF LONG & FOSTER—See The Long & Foster Companies, Inc.; *U.S. Private*, pg. 4072
CORUS HOTELS PLC—See Malayan United Industries Berhad; *Int'l*, pg. 4661
CORUS MANUFACTURING LTD.—See Lam Research Corporation; *U.S. Public*, pg. 1289
CORUS PREMIUM TELEVISION LTD.—See Corus Entertainment Inc.; *Int'l*, pg. 1808
CORUS PRIMARY ALUMINIUM B.V.—See Tata Sons Limited; *Int'l*, pg. 7472
CORUS RADIO LTD.—See Corus Entertainment Inc.; *Int'l*, pg. 1808
CORVAL CONSTRUCTORS, INC.; *U.S. Private*, pg. 1061
CORVALLIS GAZETTE-TIMES—See Lee Enterprises, Incorporated; *U.S. Public*, pg. 1299
CORVALLIS NEIGHBORHOOD HOUSING SERVICES, INC.; *U.S. Private*, pg. 1061
CORVEL CORPORATION; *U.S. Public*, pg. 585
CORVEL HEALTHCARE CORPORATION—See CorVel Corporation; *U.S. Public*, pg. 585
CORVEN ENGINEERING, INC.—See Hardesty & Hanover, LLC; *U.S. Private*, pg. 1863
CORVIGLIA-APOTHEKE AG—See CSL Limited; *Int'l*, pg. 1866

COMPANY NAME INDEX

CORVISA SERVICES LLC—See Novation Companies, Inc.; *U.S. Public*, pg. 1548
CORVUS AIRLINES—See J.F. Lehman & Company, Inc.; *U.S. Private*, pg. 2163
CORVUS CAPITAL LTD.; *Int'l*, pg. 1809
CORVUS GOLD INC.—See AngloGold Ashanti plc; *Int'l*, pg. 463
CORVUS PHARMACEUTICALS, INC.; *U.S. Public*, pg. 585
CORWIN BEVERAGE COMPANY; *U.S. Private*, pg. 1061
CORWIN CHRYSLER DODGE JEEP; *U.S. Private*, pg. 1061
CORWIN FORD; *U.S. Private*, pg. 1061
CORWIN HONDA; *U.S. Private*, pg. 1061
CORY BROTHERS SHIPPING AGENCY LIMITED—See Braemar PLC; *Int'l*, pg. 1135
CORY BROTHERS SHIPPING PTE LIMITED—See Braemar PLC; *Int'l*, pg. 1135
CORY BROTHERS—See Braemar PLC; *Int'l*, pg. 1135
CORY BROTHERS (THE NETHERLANDS) B.V.—See Braemar PLC; *Int'l*, pg. 1136
CORYDON STATE BANK—See Dentel Bancorporation; *U.S. Private*, pg. 1206
CORY FAIRBANKS MAZDA INC.; *U.S. Private*, pg. 1061
THE CORY GROUP, INC.; *U.S. Private*, pg. 4015
CORYS BUILDING MATERIALS—See Green Coast Enterprises LLC; *Int'l*, pg. 3070
CORZA MEDICAL INC.—See GTCR LLC; *U.S. Private*, pg. 1804
COSA CERAMICS PRIVATE LIMITED—See Kajaria Ceramics Ltd; *Int'l*, pg. 4053
COSALT BALLYCLARE LIMITED—See Cosalt plc; *Int'l*, pg. 1809
COSALT PLC; *Int'l*, pg. 1809
COSALUD, SA DE SEGUROS—See Grupo Catalana Occidente, S.A.; *Int'l*, pg. 3124
COSAMO (PROPRIETARY) LIMITED—See Mota-Engil SGPS, S.A.; *Int'l*, pg. 5052
COSA NATURPRODUKTE GMBH—See PAI Partners S.A.S.; *Int'l*, pg. 5700
COSAN CAYMAN FINANCE LIMITED—See Cosan S.A.; *Int'l*, pg. 1809
COSAN LIMITED—See Cosan S.A.; *Int'l*, pg. 1809
COSAN S.A.; *Int'l*, pg. 1809
COSA RESOURCES CORP.; *Int'l*, pg. 1809
COSAR PHARMACEUTICAL COMPANY; *Int'l*, pg. 1809
COSBEL S.A. DE C.V.—See L'Oreal S.A.; *Int'l*, pg. 4378
COSBOARD INDUSTRIES LIMITED; *Int'l*, pg. 1809
COS BUSINESS PRODUCTS & INTERIORS, INC.—See The ODP Corporation; *U.S. Public*, pg. 2117
COSBY OIL COMPANY, INC.; *U.S. Private*, pg. 1061
COSCAN WATERWAYS INC.; *U.S. Private*, pg. 1061
COSCIENS BIOPHARMA INC.; *U.S. Public*, pg. 585
COSCO AGENCIES (LOS ANGELES) INC.—See China COSCO Shipping Corporation Limited; *Int'l*, pg. 1493
COSCO ANQING CONTAINER SHIPPING AGENCY CO., LTD.—See China COSCO Shipping Corporation Limited; *Int'l*, pg. 1491
COSCO (BEIJING) ENTERPRISES CO., LTD.—See China COSCO Shipping Corporation Limited; *Int'l*, pg. 1492
COSCO (BEIJING) MARINE ELECTRONIC EQUIPMENT LIMITED—See China COSCO Shipping Corporation Limited; *Int'l*, pg. 1492
COSCO BRASIL S.A.—See China COSCO Shipping Corporation Limited; *Int'l*, pg. 1493
COSCO CAPITAL, INC.; *Int'l*, pg. 1809
COSCO CHILE S.A.—See China COSCO Shipping Corporation Limited; *Int'l*, pg. 1494
COSCO CHONGQING INTERNATIONAL FREIGHT CO., LTD.—See China COSCO Shipping Corporation Limited; *Int'l*, pg. 1491
COSCO CONTAINER INDUSTRIES LIMITED—See COSCO Shipping Holdings Co., Ltd.; *Int'l*, pg. 1810
COSCO CONTAINER LINES NORTH AMERICA INC.—See China COSCO Shipping Corporation Limited; *Int'l*, pg. 1494
COSCO CONTAINER LINES VIETNAM COMPANY LTD.—See China COSCO Shipping Corporation Limited; *Int'l*, pg. 1494
COSCO FINANCE CO., LTD.—See China COSCO Shipping Corporation Limited; *Int'l*, pg. 1491
COSCO FIRE PROTECTION, LLC—See Intermediate Capital Group plc; *Int'l*, pg. 3742
COSCO FIRE PROTECTION, LLC—See Kirkbi A/S; *Int'l*, pg. 4190
COSCO GUANGZHOU MARINE SERVICE CO., LTD.—See China COSCO Shipping Corporation Limited; *Int'l*, pg. 1493
COSCO HEBEI INTERNATIONAL FREIGHT CO., LTD.—See China COSCO Shipping Corporation Limited; *Int'l*, pg. 1491
COSCO (HK) FREIGHT SERVICE HOLDINGS LTD.—See China COSCO Shipping Corporation Limited; *Int'l*, pg. 1492
COSCO (H.K.) SHIPPING CO., LIMITED—See China COSCO Shipping Corporation Limited; *Int'l*, pg. 1491
COSCO HUNAN INTERNATIONAL FREIGHT CO., LTD.—See China COSCO Shipping Corporation Limited; *Int'l*, pg. 1491

COSCO HUZHOU INTERNATIONAL FREIGHT CO., LTD.—See China COSCO Shipping Corporation Limited; *Int'l*, pg. 1491
COSCO (INDIA) LIMITED; *Int'l*, pg. 1809
COSCO INDUSTRIES, INC.—See Taylor Corporation; *U.S. Private*, pg. 3938
COSCO INTERNATIONAL TRAVEL (HK) CO., LTD.—See China COSCO Shipping Corporation Limited; *Int'l*, pg. 1492
COSCO JIANGXI INTERNATIONAL FREIGHT CO., LTD.—See China COSCO Shipping Corporation Limited; *Int'l*, pg. 1491
COSCO JIAXING INTERNATIONAL FREIGHT CO., LTD.—See China COSCO Shipping Corporation Limited; *Int'l*, pg. 1496
COSCO KANSAI PAINT & CHEMICALS (TIANJIN) CO., LTD.—See Kansai Paint Co., Ltd.; *Int'l*, pg. 4071
COSCO KANSAI PAINT & CHEMICALS (ZHUHAI) CO., LTD.—See Kansai Paint Co., Ltd.; *Int'l*, pg. 4071
COSCO KANSAI PAINT (SHANGHAI) CO., LTD.—See Kansai Paint Co., Ltd.; *Int'l*, pg. 4071
COSCOLAB SDN. BHD.—See FCW Holdings Berhad; *Int'l*, pg. 2628
COSCO LANKA (PVT) LTD.—See China COSCO Shipping Corporation Limited; *Int'l*, pg. 1494
COSCO LOGISTICS (DALIAN) CO LTD.—See China COSCO Shipping Corporation Limited; *Int'l*, pg. 1493
COSCO MANNING COOPERATION INC.—See China COSCO Shipping Corporation Limited; *Int'l*, pg. 1491
COSCO MARINE ENGINEERING (SINGAPORE) PTE LTD.—See China COSCO Shipping Corporation Limited; *Int'l*, pg. 1492
COSCO NEIMENGGU INTERNATIONAL FREIGHT CO., LTD.—See China COSCO Shipping Corporation Limited; *Int'l*, pg. 1492
COSCO NINGXIA INTERNATIONAL FREIGHT CO., LTD.—See China COSCO Shipping Corporation Limited; *Int'l*, pg. 1492
COSCO PERU S.A.—See China COSCO Shipping Corporation Limited; *Int'l*, pg. 1494
COSCO QINGDAO INTERNATIONAL FREIGHT CO., LTD.—See China COSCO Shipping Corporation Limited; *Int'l*, pg. 1492
COSCO QINGHAI INTERNATIONAL FREIGHT CO., LTD.—See China COSCO Shipping Corporation Limited; *Int'l*, pg. 1492
COSCO (SHANGHAI) SHIPYARD CO., LTD—See China COSCO Shipping Corporation Limited; *Int'l*, pg. 1492
COSCO SHANXI INTERNATIONAL FREIGHT CO., LTD.—See China COSCO Shipping Corporation Limited; *Int'l*, pg. 1493
COSCO SHAOXING INTERNATIONAL FREIGHT CO., LTD.—See China COSCO Shipping Corporation Limited; *Int'l*, pg. 1493
COSCO SHENZHEN INTERNATIONAL FREIGHT CO., LTD.—See China COSCO Shipping Corporation Limited; *Int'l*, pg. 1493
COSCOSHIP BEIJING COMPANY LIMITED—See China COSCO Shipping Corporation Limited; *Int'l*, pg. 1492
COSCO SHIPPING AGENCY (GREECE) S.A.—See China COSCO Shipping Corporation Limited; *Int'l*, pg. 1494
COSCO SHIPPING ARGENTINA—See China COSCO Shipping Corporation Limited; *Int'l*, pg. 1494
COSCO SHIPPING CONTAINER LINE AGENCIES LIMITED—See COSCO Shipping Holdings Co., Ltd.; *Int'l*, pg. 1810
COSCO SHIPPING DEVELOPMENT CO., LTD.—See China COSCO Shipping Corporation Limited; *Int'l*, pg. 1492
COSCO SHIPPING ENERGY TRANSPORTATION CO., LTD.—See China COSCO Shipping Corporation Limited; *Int'l*, pg. 1492
COSCO SHIPPING FINANCIAL HOLDINGS CO., LIMITED—See China COSCO Shipping Corporation Limited; *Int'l*, pg. 1493
COSCO SHIPPING GUANGXI INTERNATIONAL FREIGHT CO., LTD.—See China COSCO Shipping Corporation Limited; *Int'l*, pg. 1493
COSCO SHIPPING GUANGZHOU INTERNATIONAL FREIGHT CO., LTD.—See China COSCO Shipping Corporation Limited; *Int'l*, pg. 1493
COSCO SHIPPING GUIZHOU INTERNATIONAL FREIGHT CO., LTD.—See China COSCO Shipping Corporation Limited; *Int'l*, pg. 1493
COSCO SHIPPING HEAVY INDUSTRY CO., LTD.—See China COSCO Shipping Corporation Limited; *Int'l*, pg. 1496
COSCO SHIPPING HEAVY TRANSPORT (EUROPE) B.V.—See China COSCO Shipping Corporation Limited; *Int'l*, pg. 1493
COSCO SHIPPING HOLDINGS CO., LTD.; *Int'l*, pg. 1809
COSCO SHIPPING (HONG KONG) CO., LIMITED—See China COSCO Shipping Corporation Limited; *Int'l*, pg. 1492
COSCO SHIPPING (HONG KONG) INSURANCE BROKERS LIMITED—See China COSCO Shipping Corporation Limited; *Int'l*, pg. 1492

COSCO SHIPPING HOLDINGS CO., LTD.

COSCO SHIPPING (HONG KONG) PROPERTY DEVELOPMENT LIMITED—See China COSCO Shipping Corporation Limited; *Int'l*, pg. 1492
COSCO SHIPPING (HONG KONG) SHIP TRADING COMPANY LIMITED—See China COSCO Shipping Corporation Limited; *Int'l*, pg. 1492
COSCO SHIPPING INTERNATIONAL (HONG KONG) CO., LTD.—See China COSCO Shipping Corporation Limited; *Int'l*, pg. 1492
COSCO SHIPPING INTERNATIONAL (SINGAPORE) CO., LTD.—See China COSCO Shipping Corporation Limited; *Int'l*, pg. 1492
COSCO SHIPPING INTERNATIONAL TRADING COMPANY LIMITED—See China COSCO Shipping Corporation Limited; *Int'l*, pg. 1493
COSCO SHIPPING JIANGSU INTERNATIONAL FREIGHT CO., LTD.—See China COSCO Shipping Corporation Limited; *Int'l*, pg. 1493
COSCO SHIPPING JIANGSU INTERNATIONAL FREIGHT CO., LTD.—See China COSCO Shipping Corporation Limited; *Int'l*, pg. 1493
COSCO SHIPPING KOREA CO., LTD.—See China COSCO Shipping Corporation Limited; *Int'l*, pg. 1493
COSCO SHIPPING LINES AMERICAS, INC.—See COSCO Shipping Holdings Co., Ltd.; *Int'l*, pg. 1810
COSCO SHIPPING LINES (BELGIUM) NV—See China COSCO Shipping Corporation Limited; *Int'l*, pg. 1494
COSCO SHIPPING LINES (BRAZIL) S.A.—See COSCO Shipping Holdings Co., Ltd.; *Int'l*, pg. 1810
COSCO SHIPPING LINES (CANADA) INC.—See China COSCO Shipping Corporation Limited; *Int'l*, pg. 1493
COSCO SHIPPING LINES (CENTRAL EUROPE) S.R.O.—See China COSCO Shipping Corporation Limited; *Int'l*, pg. 1494
COSCO SHIPPING LINES CO., LTD.—See China COSCO Shipping Corporation Limited; *Int'l*, pg. 1494
COSCO SHIPPING LINES (DALIAN) CO., LTD.—See COSCO Shipping Holdings Co., Ltd.; *Int'l*, pg. 1810
COSCO SHIPPING LINES EMIRATES LLC—See China COSCO Shipping Corporation Limited; *Int'l*, pg. 1494
COSCO SHIPPING LINES (FRANCE) S.A.S.—See China COSCO Shipping Corporation Limited; *Int'l*, pg. 1493
COSCO SHIPPING LINES (INDIA) PVT. LTD.—See China COSCO Shipping Corporation Limited; *Int'l*, pg. 1494
COSCO SHIPPING LINES (JAPAN) CO., LTD.—See China COSCO Shipping Corporation Limited; *Int'l*, pg. 1494
COSCO SHIPPING LINES (MALAYSIA) SDN. BHD.—See China COSCO Shipping Corporation Limited; *Int'l*, pg. 1494
COSCO SHIPPING LINES (MYANMAR) CO., LTD.—See China COSCO Shipping Corporation Limited; *Int'l*, pg. 1494
COSCO SHIPPING LINES (NEW ZEALAND) LTD—See China COSCO Shipping Corporation Limited; *Int'l*, pg. 1494
COSCO SHIPPING LINES (NORTH AMERICA) INC.—See China COSCO Shipping Corporation Limited; *Int'l*, pg. 1493
COSCO SHIPPING LINES (OCEANIA) PTY. LTD.—See China COSCO Shipping Corporation Limited; *Int'l*, pg. 1493
COSCO SHIPPING LINES PAKISTAN PVT. LTD.—See China COSCO Shipping Corporation Limited; *Int'l*, pg. 1494
COSCO SHIPPING LINES (POLAND) SP. Z OO—See China COSCO Shipping Corporation Limited; *Int'l*, pg. 1494
COSCO SHIPPING LINES (PTY) LTD—See China COSCO Shipping Corporation Limited; *Int'l*, pg. 1494
COSCO SHIPPING LINES (ROMANIA) CO. LTD. SRL—See China COSCO Shipping Corporation Limited; *Int'l*, pg. 1494
COSCO SHIPPING LINES (SPAIN) S.A.—See China COSCO Shipping Corporation Limited; *Int'l*, pg. 1493
COSCO SHIPPING LOGISTICS (BEIJING) CO., LTD.—See China COSCO Shipping Corporation Limited; *Int'l*, pg. 1493
COSCO SHIPPING LOGISTICS CO., LTD.—See China COSCO Shipping Corporation Limited; *Int'l*, pg. 1493
COSCO SHIPPING LOGISTICS (HONG KONG) CO., LTD.—See China COSCO Shipping Corporation Limited; *Int'l*, pg. 1493
COSCO SHIPPING LOGISTICS (NANJING) CO., LTD—See China COSCO Shipping Corporation Limited; *Int'l*, pg. 1493
COSCO SHIPPING LOGISTICS (NINGBO) CO., LTD.—See China COSCO Shipping Corporation Limited; *Int'l*, pg. 1493
COSCO SHIPPING LOGISTICS (QINGDAO) CO., LTD.—See China COSCO Shipping Corporation Limited; *Int'l*, pg. 1493
COSCO SHIPPING LOGISTICS (WEST ASIA) L.L.C.—See China COSCO Shipping Corporation Limited; *Int'l*, pg. 1493
COSCO SHIPPING NETWORK LIMITED—See China COSCO Shipping Corporation Limited; *Int'l*, pg. 1493
COSCO SHIPPING PORTS LIMITED—See COSCO Shipping Holdings Co., Ltd.; *Int'l*, pg. 1810

COSCO SHIPPING HOLDINGS CO., LTD.

CORPORATE AFFILIATIONS

COSCO SHIPPING (SOUTH EAST ASIA) PTE. LTD.—See China COSCO Shipping Corporation Limited; *Int'l*, pg. 1492
COSCO SHIPPING SPECIALIZED CARRIERS CO., LTD.—See China COSCO Shipping Corporation Limited; *Int'l*, pg. 1493
COSCO SHIPPING TECHNOLOGY CO., LTD.—See China COSCO Shipping Corporation Limited; *Int'l*, pg. 1493
COSCO SHIPPING (UK) COMPANY LIMITED—See China COSCO Shipping Corporation Limited; *Int'l*, pg. 1493
COSCO SHIPPING URUGUAY—See China COSCO Shipping Corporation Limited; *Int'l*, pg. 1494
COSCO SHIPPING YUNNAN INTERNATIONAL FREIGHT CO., LTD.—See China COSCO Shipping Corporation Limited; *Int'l*, pg. 1494
COSCO SUZHOU INTERNATIONAL FREIGHT FORWARDING CO., LTD.—See China COSCO Shipping Corporation Limited; *Int'l*, pg. 1494
COSCO TAICANG INTERNATIONAL FREIGHT CO., LTD.—See China COSCO Shipping Corporation Limited; *Int'l*, pg. 1494
COSCO TIANJIN INTERNATIONAL FREIGHT CO., LTD.—See China COSCO Shipping Corporation Limited; *Int'l*, pg. 1494
COSCO WENZHOU INTERNATIONAL FREIGHT CO., LTD.—See China COSCO Shipping Corporation Limited; *Int'l*, pg. 1494
COSCO WUXI INTERNATIONAL FREIGHT CO., LTD.—See China COSCO Shipping Corporation Limited; *Int'l*, pg. 1494
COSCO YANGPU SHIPPING AGENCY LTD.—See China COSCO Shipping Corporation Limited; *Int'l*, pg. 1494
COSCO YANGZHOU INTERNATIONAL FREIGHT CO., LTD.—See China COSCO Shipping Corporation Limited; *Int'l*, pg. 1494
COSCO ZHEJIANG INTERNATIONAL FREIGHT CO., LTD.—See China COSCO Shipping Corporation Limited; *Int'l*, pg. 1494
COSCO ZHENJIANG INTERNATIONAL FREIGHT CO., LTD.—See China COSCO Shipping Corporation Limited; *Int'l*, pg. 1494
COSE BELLE D'ITALIA S.P.A.—See Arrow Global Group PLC; *Int'l*, pg. 579
COSEC COMPANHIA DE SEGURO DE CREDITOS, S.A.—See Allianz SE; *Int'l*, pg. 352
COSEL ASIA LTD.—See COSEL Co., Ltd.; *Int'l*, pg. 1810
COSEL CO., LTD.; *Int'l*, pg. 1810
COSEL EUROPE GMBH—See COSEL Co., Ltd.; *Int'l*, pg. 1810
COSEL (SHANGHAI) ELECTRONICS CO., LTD.—See COSEL Co., Ltd.; *Int'l*, pg. 1810
COSEMI TECHNOLOGIES INC.—See Mobix Labs, Inc.; *U.S. Public*, pg. 1454
COSENTINI ASSOCIATES, INC.—See Tetra Tech, Inc.; *U.S. Public*, pg. 2023
COSENTINO'S FOOD STORES; *U.S. Private*, pg. 1061
COSENTINO USA; *U.S. Private*, pg. 1061
COSERSA CONTRATAS Y SERVICIOS, S.A.—See ACS, Actividades de Construccion y Servicios, S.A.; *Int'l*, pg. 110
COSERV UTILITY HOLDINGS, L.P.; *U.S. Private*, pg. 1062
COSET INC.; *Int'l*, pg. 1810
COSEV@D SAS—See Assicurazioni Generali S.p.A.; *Int'l*, pg. 645
COSGROVE ENTERPRISES INC.—See Bain Capital, LP; *U.S. Private*, pg. 440
COSG—See Carrefour SA; *Int'l*, pg. 1344
COSHIP ELECTRONICS CO., LTD.; *Int'l*, pg. 1810
COSHOCTON COUNTY EMS LLC—See Ohio Medical Transportation; *U.S. Private*, pg. 3004
COSIGO RESOURCES LTD.; *Int'l*, pg. 1810
COSI, INC.; *U.S. Private*, pg. 1062
COSI MEDICAL IT GMBH—See CompuGroup Medical SE & Co. KGaA; *Int'l*, pg. 1755
COSIMO'S MANAGEMENT, INC.; *U.S. Private*, pg. 1062
COSKATA, INC.; *U.S. Private*, pg. 1062
COSKOR SHIPPING CO., LTD.—See China COSCO Shipping Corporation Limited; *Int'l*, pg. 1494
COSL (AUSTRALIA) PTY LTD.—See China National Offshore Oil Corp.; *Int'l*, pg. 1532
COSL CHEMICALS (TIANJIN), LTD.—See China National Offshore Oil Corp.; *Int'l*, pg. 1532
COSL DRILLING PAN-PACIFIC LTD.—See China National Offshore Oil Corp.; *Int'l*, pg. 1532
COSL HOLDING AS—See China National Offshore Oil Corp.; *Int'l*, pg. 1532
COSLIGHT-NEWGEN LTD.—See Coslight Technology International Group Limited; *Int'l*, pg. 1810
COSLIGHT TECHNOLOGY INTERNATIONAL GROUP LIMITED - CHANGDU COSLIGHT LI-MIN PHARMACEUTICAL FACTORY—See Coslight Technology International Group Limited; *Int'l*, pg. 1810
COSLIGHT TECHNOLOGY INTERNATIONAL GROUP LIMITED; *Int'l*, pg. 1810
COSLIGHT USA INC.—See Coslight Technology International Group Limited; *Int'l*, pg. 1810
COSL MEXICO S.A.DE C.V—See China National Offshore Oil Corp.; *Int'l*, pg. 1532

COSL (MIDDLE EAST) FZE—See China National Offshore Oil Corp.; *Int'l*, pg. 1532
COSL NORWEGIAN AS—See China National Offshore Oil Corp.; *Int'l*, pg. 1533
COSMA INTERNATIONAL INC.—See Magna International Inc.; *Int'l*, pg. 4639
COSMA INTERNATIONAL LTD.—See Schwan-STABILO Cosmetics GmbH & Co. KG; *Int'l*, pg. 6644
COSMA INTERNATIONAL OF AMERICA, INC.—See Magna International Inc.; *Int'l*, pg. 4639
COSMAN MEDICAL, LLC—See Boston Scientific Corporation; *U.S. Public*, pg. 374
COSMAX BTI INC.; *Int'l*, pg. 1811
COSMAX INC.; *Int'l*, pg. 1811
COS MAX LIMITED—See Miricor Enterprises Holdings Limited; *Int'l*, pg. 4919
COS MAX MEDICAL CENTRE (CENTRAL) LIMITED—See Miricor Enterprises Holdings Limited; *Int'l*, pg. 4919
COSMAX NBT, INC.; *Int'l*, pg. 1811
COSMAX (THAILAND) CO., LTD.—See Cosmax Inc.; *Int'l*, pg. 1811
COSMECCA FOSHAN, LTD.—See Cosmecca Korea Co., Ltd.; *Int'l*, pg. 1811
COSMECCA KOREA CO.,LTD.; *Int'l*, pg. 1811
COSMECCA SUZHOU CO., LTD.—See Cosmecca Korea Co., Ltd.; *Int'l*, pg. 1811
COSME.COM INC.—See istyle Inc.; *Int'l*, pg. 3825
COS.MEC S.R.L.—See Freund Corporation; *Int'l*, pg. 2791
COSMEDICAL SPA—See Apollo Med Innovations LLC; *U.S. Private*, pg. 295
COSMEDIET - BIOTECHNIE SAS—See Perrigo Company plc; *Int'l*, pg. 5812
COSMED, INC.—See Elah Holdings, Inc.; *U.S. Public*, pg. 722
COSMED PRODUKTIONS GMBH BERLIN—See maxingvest ag; *Int'l*, pg. 4740
COSME LABO CO., LTD.—See KOSE Corporation; *Int'l*, pg. 4290
COSMELOR KK—See L'Oreal S.A.; *Int'l*, pg. 4378
COSMENATURA SA—See Aurelius Equity Opportunities SE & Co. KGaA; *Int'l*, pg. 709
COSME NEXT CO. LTD.—See istyle Inc.; *Int'l*, pg. 3825
COSME SCIENCE CO., LTD.—See Hokkan Holdings Limited; *Int'l*, pg. 3443
COSMETICA NACIONAL S.A.—See Godrej & Boyce Mfg. Co. Ltd.; *Int'l*, pg. 3020
COSMETIC CLINIC LTD.—See Wesfarmers Limited; *Int'l*, pg. 8380
COSMETIC COLORS, S.A. DE C.V.—See Schwan-STABILO Cosmetics GmbH & Co. KG; *Int'l*, pg. 6644
COSMETIC ESSENCE INC.—See ONEX Corporation; *Int'l*, pg. 5578
THE COSMETIC EXECUTIVE WOMEN FOUNDATION LTD.—See Cosmetic Executive Women, Inc.; *U.S. Private*, pg. 1062
COSMETIC EXECUTIVE WOMEN, INC.; *U.S. Private*, pg. 1062
COSMETIC OF FRANCE INC—See LVMH Moet Hennessy Louis Vuitton SE; *Int'l*, pg. 4601
COSMETICOS AVON, S.A.C.I.—See Natura & Co Holding S.A.; *Int'l*, pg. 5167
COSMETICOS AVON S.A.—See Natura & Co Holding S.A.; *Int'l*, pg. 5167
COSMETIC PACKAGING GROUP—See O. Berk Company L.L.C.; *U.S. Private*, pg. 2981
COSMETIC RHEOLOGIES LTD.—See BASF SE; *Int'l*, pg. 883
COSMETICS NORD SIA—See MADARA Cosmetics AS; *Int'l*, pg. 4633
COSMETIC SOLUTIONS, LLC—See Lee Equity Partners LLC; *U.S. Private*, pg. 2412
COSMETIC SPECIALTIES INTERNATIONAL LLC—See Airlite Plastics Company; *U.S. Private*, pg. 141
COSMETIC SUPPLIERS PTY. LTD.—See The Procter & Gamble Company; *U.S. Public*, pg. 2120
COSMETIQUE ACTIVE INTERNATIONAL S.N.C.—See L'Oreal S.A.; *Int'l*, pg. 4378
COSMETIQUE ACTIVE PRODUCTION S.A.S.—See L'Oreal S.A.; *Int'l*, pg. 4378
COSMETIQUE, INC.; *U.S. Private*, pg. 1062
COSMEUROP S.A.—See L'Oreal S.A.; *Int'l*, pg. 4378
COSMIC COMMUNICATION SA—See Altavia S.A.; *Int'l*, pg. 388
COSMIC CRF LIMITED; *Int'l*, pg. 1811
COSMIC GLOBAL LTD—See Tulsyan Nec Limited; *Int'l*, pg. 7970
COSMIC STONE & TILE DISTRIBUTORS, INC.—See Architectural Surfaces Group, LLC; *U.S. Private*, pg. 311
COSM, INC—See Elevate Entertainment, Inc.; *U.S. Private*, pg. 1358
COSMINT S.P.A.—See Intercos S.p.A.; *Int'l*, pg. 3739
COSMO ABU DHABI ENERGY EXPLORATION & PRODUCTION CO., LTD.—See Cosmo Energy Holdings Co., Ltd.; *Int'l*, pg. 1811
COSMO AM & T CO., LTD.; *Int'l*, pg. 1811
COSMO BIO CO., LTD.; *Int'l*, pg. 1811
COSMO BIO USA, INC.—See COSMO BIO Co., Ltd.; *Int'l*, pg. 1811

COSMO BUSINESS ASSOCIATES CO., LTD.—See Cosmo Energy Holdings Co., Ltd.; *Int'l*, pg. 1811
COSMO BUSINESS SUPPORT CO., LTD.—See Cosmo Energy Holdings Co., Ltd.; *Int'l*, pg. 1811
COSMO CHEMICAL CO., LTD. - ONSAN FACTORY—See Cosmo Chemical Co., Ltd.; *Int'l*, pg. 1811
COSMO CHEMICAL CO., LTD.; *Int'l*, pg. 1811
COSMO COMMUNICATIONS CORPORATON; *Int'l*, pg. 1811
COSMO COMMUNICATIONS INC.—See Hakuhodo DY Holdings Incorporated; *Int'l*, pg. 3220
COSMO COMPUTER CENTER CO., LTD.—See Cosmo Energy Holdings Co., Ltd.; *Int'l*, pg. 1811
COSMO CORPORATION; *U.S. Private*, pg. 1062
COSMOCOS CO., LTD.—See KT&G Corporation; *Int'l*, pg. 4315
COSMO DELIVERY SERVICE CO., LTD.—See Cosmo Energy Holdings Co., Ltd.; *Int'l*, pg. 1812
COSMODYNE, LLC—See Nikkiso Co., Ltd.; *Int'l*, pg. 5291
COSMO ECO POWER CO., LTD.—See Cosmo Energy Holdings Co., Ltd.; *Int'l*, pg. 1811
COSMO ELECTRONICS CORPORATION; *Int'l*, pg. 1811
COSMO ELECTRONICS CORP. - YILAN PLANT—See Cosmo Electronics Corporation; *Int'l*, pg. 1811
COSMO ELECTRONICS TECHNOLOGY (KUN SHAN)CO., LTD.—See Cosmo Electronics Corporation; *Int'l*, pg. 1811
COSMO ENERGY EXPLORATION AND DEVELOPMENT LTD.—See Cosmo Energy Holdings Co., Ltd.; *Int'l*, pg. 1812
COSMO ENERGY EXPLORATION & PRODUCTION CO., LTD.—See Cosmo Energy Holdings Co., Ltd.; *Int'l*, pg. 1811
COSMO ENERGY HOLDINGS CO., LTD.; *Int'l*, pg. 1811
COSMO ENERGY SOLUTIONS CO., LTD.—See Cosmo Energy Holdings Co., Ltd.; *Int'l*, pg. 1811
COSMO ENGINEERING CO., LTD.—See Cosmo Energy Holdings Co., Ltd.; *Int'l*, pg. 1812
COSMO ENTERPRISE CO., LTD.—See Japan Airport Terminal Co., Ltd.; *Int'l*, pg. 3885
COSMOFARM LTD.—See COSMOS HEALTH INC.; *U.S. Public*, pg. 585
COSMOFERM B.V.—See RAG-Stiftung; *Int'l*, pg. 6178
COSMO FERRITES LTD.—See Cosmo First Limited; *Int'l*, pg. 1812
COSMO FILMS, INC.—See Cosmo First Limited; *Int'l*, pg. 1812
COSMO FILMS JAPAN, GK—See Cosmo First Limited; *Int'l*, pg. 1812
COSMO FILMS KOREA LIMITED—See Cosmo First Limited; *Int'l*, pg. 1812
COSMO FILMS LTD. - PLANT III—See Cosmo First Limited; *Int'l*, pg. 1812
COSMO FILMS LTD. - PLANT II—See Cosmo First Limited; *Int'l*, pg. 1812
COSMO FILMS LTD. - PLANT I—See Cosmo First Limited; *Int'l*, pg. 1812
COSMO FILMS LTD. - PLANT IV—See Cosmo First Limited; *Int'l*, pg. 1812
COSMO FILMS (NETHERLANDS) COOPERATIEF U.A—See Cosmo First Limited; *Int'l*, pg. 1812
COSMO FILMS (SINGAPORE) PTE LTD—See Cosmo First Limited; *Int'l*, pg. 1812
COSMO FIRST LIMITED; *Int'l*, pg. 1812
COSMOFLEX, INC.—See The Goodyear Tire & Rubber Company; *U.S. Public*, pg. 2083
COSMO FOODS CO., LTD.—See Kirin Holdings Company, Limited; *Int'l*, pg. 4187
COSMO GOLD PTY LTD—See Adelong Gold Limited; *Int'l*, pg. 142
COSMO GRAPHIC CO., LTD.—See Kyodo Printing Co. Ltd.; *Int'l*, pg. 4361
COSMO HOKURIKU HAISO CENTER CO., LTD.—See Seino Holdings Co., Ltd.; *Int'l*, pg. 6690
COSMO KAIUN CO., LTD.—See Cosmo Energy Holdings Co., Ltd.; *Int'l*, pg. 1812
COSMO KASEI KOGYO CO., LTD.—See Shoko Co., Ltd.; *Int'l*, pg. 6858
COSMOLAB DIV.—See Schwan-STABILO Cosmetics GmbH & Co. KG; *Int'l*, pg. 6644
COSMO LADY (CHINA) HOLDINGS COMPANY LIMITED; *Int'l*, pg. 1812
COSMO MATSUYAMA OIL CO., LTD.—See Cosmo Energy Holdings Co., Ltd.; *Int'l*, pg. 1812
COSMO METALS LIMITED; *Int'l*, pg. 1813
COSMO OIL ASHMORE, LTD.—See Cosmo Energy Holdings Co., Ltd.; *Int'l*, pg. 1812
COSMO OIL COMPANY, LIMITED—See Cosmo Energy Holdings Co., Ltd.; *Int'l*, pg. 1811
COSMO OIL INTERNATIONAL PTE LTD—See Cosmo Energy Holdings Co., Ltd.; *Int'l*, pg. 1812
COSMO OIL LUBRICANTS CO., LTD.—See Cosmo Energy Holdings Co., Ltd.; *Int'l*, pg. 1812
COSMO OIL MARKETING CO., LTD.—See Cosmo Energy Holdings Co., Ltd.; *Int'l*, pg. 1812
COSMO OIL OF U.S.A., INC.—See Cosmo Energy Holdings Co., Ltd.; *Int'l*, pg. 1812
COSMO OIL PROPERTY SERVICE CO., LTD.—See Cosmo Energy Holdings Co., Ltd.; *Int'l*, pg. 1812

COMPANY NAME INDEX

COSMO OIL SALES CO., LTD.—See Cosmo Energy Holdings Co., Ltd.; *Int'l*, pg. 1812
COSMO OIL (SHANGHAI) CO., LTD.—See Cosmo Energy Holdings Co., Ltd.; *Int'l*, pg. 1812
COSMO-ONE HELLAS MARKET SITE S.A.—See Hellenic Telecommunications Organization S.A.; *Int'l*, pg. 3333
COSMO PAPER TRADING CO., LTD.—See Japan Pulp and Paper Company Limited; *Int'l*, pg. 3903
COSMO PETROLEUM GAS CO., LTD.—See Cosmo Energy Holdings Co., Ltd.; *Int'l*, pg. 1812
COSMO PETRO SERVICE CO., LTD.—See Cosmo Energy Holdings Co., Ltd.; *Int'l*, pg. 1811
COSMO PHARMACEUTICALS N.V.; *Int'l*, pg. 1813
COSMOPOLITAN CATERING, LLC—See Compass Group PLC; *Int'l*, pg. 1751
COSMOPOLITAN DECORATING CO.; *U.S. Private*, pg. 1062
COSMOPOLITAN HOTEL LIMITED—See Far East Consortium International Limited; *Int'l*, pg. 2615
COSMOPOLITAN INTERNATIONAL HOLDINGS LIMITED—See Century City International Holdings Ltd; *Int'l*, pg. 1417
COSMOPOLITAN—See The Hearst Corporation; *U.S. Private*, pg. 4046
COSMOPOLITAN TRADING CORP.; *U.S. Private*, pg. 1062
COSMOPOLITAN TV IBERIA S.L.—See The Hearst Corporation; *U.S. Private*, pg. 4044
COSMO POLYURETHANE (MALAYSIA) SDN, BHD—See Mitsui Chemicals, Inc.; *Int'l*, pg. 4981
COSMOPOP GMBH—See Live Nation Entertainment, Inc.; *U.S. Public*, pg. 1328
COSMO REFINERY SUPPORT SAKAI CO., LTD.—See Cosmo Energy Holdings Co., Ltd.; *Int'l*, pg. 1812
COSMO RESEARCH & DEVELOPMENT S.R.L.—See Cosmo Pharmaceuticals N.V.; *Int'l*, pg. 1813
COSMOREX A.G.—See TP ICAP Finance PLC; *Int'l*, pg. 7881
COSMOS AUSTRALIA PTY LTD—See Daiwa House Industry Co., Ltd.; *Int'l*, pg. 1945
COSMOS BERRY'S CO., LTD.—See Yamada Holdings Co., Ltd.; *Int'l*, pg. 8548
COSMOS BREWERY (THAILAND) CO., LTD.—See Thai Beverage Public Company Limited; *Int'l*, pg. 7589
COSMOS CLUB; *U.S. Private*, pg. 1062
COSMOS COMMUNICATIONS; *U.S. Private*, pg. 1062
COSMOS CONSULTANTS SA—See Clasquin S.A.; *Int'l*, pg. 1652
COSMOS CORPORATION—See Mitsui Chemicals, Inc.; *Int'l*, pg. 4981
COSMOS EXPLORATION LIMITED; *Int'l*, pg. 1813
COSMOS FEUERLOESCHGERAETEBAU GMBH—See Johnson Controls International plc; *Int'l*, pg. 3986
COSMOS GROUP CO., LTD.; *Int'l*, pg. 1813
COSMOS GROUP HOLDINGS INC.; *Int'l*, pg. 1813
COSMOS HEALTH INC.; *U.S. Public*, pg. 585
COSMOS HOTEL MANAGEMENT CO., LTD.—See Daiwa House Industry Co., Ltd.; *Int'l*, pg. 1945
COSMOS INDUSTRIES LIMITED—See Corporate Merchant Bankers Limited; *Int'l*, pg. 1813
COSMOS INITIA CO., LTD.—See Daiwa House Industry Co., Ltd.; *Int'l*, pg. 1945
COSMOS INSURANCE COMPANY PUBLIC LTD; *Int'l*, pg. 1813
COSMOS INTERNATIONAL, INC.; *U.S. Private*, pg. 1062
COSMOS I-TECH SOLUTIONS LTD.—See Cosmos Machinery Enterprises Limited; *Int'l*, pg. 1813
COSMOS KOGYO CO., LTD.—See Tomoku Co., Ltd.; *Int'l*, pg. 7801
COSMOS MACHINERY ENTERPRISES LIMITED; *Int'l*, pg. 1813
COSMOS MACHINERY INTERNATIONAL LTD.—See Cosmos Machinery Enterprises Limited; *Int'l*, pg. 1813
COSMOS MACHINERY LIMITED—See Cosmos Machinery Enterprises Limited; *Int'l*, pg. 1813
COSMOS MORE CO., LTD.—See Daiwa House Industry Co., Ltd.; *Int'l*, pg. 1945
COSMO SPACE CO., LTD.—See Imagica Group Inc.; *Int'l*, pg. 3618
COSMO SPACE OF AMERICA CO., LTD.—See Imagica Group Inc.; *Int'l*, pg. 3618
COSMO S.P.A.,—See Cosmo Pharmaceuticals N.V.; *Int'l*, pg. 1813
COSMO SPECIALTY FIBERS, INC.—See The Gores Group, LLC; *U.S. Private*, pg. 4034
COSMOS PHARMACEUTICAL CORPORATION; *Int'l*, pg. 1814
COSMOS SERVICES CO., LTD.—See ITOCHU Corporation; *Int'l*, pg. 3835
COSMOS SERVICES (KOREA) CO., LTD.—See ITOCHU Corporation; *Int'l*, pg. 3835
COSMOS SHOJI CO., LTD.—See Sanyo Trading Co., Ltd.; *Int'l*, pg. 6565
COSMOS TECHNOLOGY INTERNATIONAL BERHAD; *Int'l*, pg. 1814
COSMOSTEEL (AUSTRALIA) PTY LTD—See CosmoSteel Holdings Limited; *Int'l*, pg. 1814
COSMOSTEEL HOLDINGS LIMITED; *Int'l*, pg. 1814
COSMOS TRAWL A/S—See Hampidjan hf; *Int'l*, pg. 3239

COSMOS VACUUM TECHNOLOGY CORPORATION—See Topoint Technology Co., Ltd.; *Int'l*, pg. 7816
COSMOS YATIRIM HOLDING A.S.; *Int'l*, pg. 1814
COSMOTEC CORPORATION—See Sony Group Corporation; *Int'l*, pg. 7102
COSMO TECHNO YOKKAICHI CO., LTD.—See Cosmo Energy Holdings Co., Ltd.; *Int'l*, pg. 1812
COSMOTE E-VALUE S.A.—See Hellenic Telecommunications Organization S.A.; *Int'l*, pg. 3333
COSMOTE GLOBAL SOLUTIONS S.A.—See Hellenic Telecommunications Organization S.A.; *Int'l*, pg. 3333
COSMOTE MOBILE TELECOMMUNICATIONS SA—See Hellenic Telecommunications Organization S.A.; *Int'l*, pg. 3333
COSMO TRADE AND SERVICE CO., LTD.—See Cosmo Energy Holdings Co., Ltd.; *Int'l*, pg. 1812
COSMO VENTURES INC.; *U.S. Private*, pg. 1062
COSMUR CONSTRUCTION (LONDON) LTD; *Int'l*, pg. 1814
COSNET, INC.—See Madison Dearborn Partners, LLC; *U.S. Private*, pg. 2541
COSNINE CO., LTD.; *Int'l*, pg. 1814
COSOF CO., LTD.—See Unitika Ltd.; *Int'l*, pg. 8074
COSOL LTD.; *Int'l*, pg. 1814
COSON CO., LTD. - OSAN FACTORY—See Coson Co., Ltd.; *Int'l*, pg. 1814
COSON CO., LTD.; *Int'l*, pg. 1814
COSONIC ACOUSTIC (HK) TECHNOLOGY CO., LIMITED—See Cosonic Intelligent Technologies Co., Ltd.; *Int'l*, pg. 1814
COSONIC ELECTROACOUSTIC TECHNOLOGY CO., LTD.—See Cosonic Intelligent Technologies Co., Ltd.; *Int'l*, pg. 1814
COSONIC INTELLIGENT TECHNOLOGIES CO., LTD.; *Int'l*, pg. 1814
COSO OPERATING COMPANY, LLC—See ArcLight Capital Holdings, LLC; *U.S. Private*, pg. 312
COSPE SRL—See Salini Costruttori S.p.A.; *Int'l*, pg. 6493
COSPOWER ENGINEERING LTD.; *Int'l*, pg. 1814
C.O.S. PRINTERS PTE LIMITED—See Lion Rock Group Ltd; *Int'l*, pg. 4519
COSSETTE COMMUNICATION INC.—See Bluefocus Intelligent Communications Group Co., Ltd.; *Int'l*, pg. 1071
COSSETTE COMMUNICATION INC. - TORONTO—See Bluefocus Intelligent Communications Group Co., Ltd.; *Int'l*, pg. 1071
COSSETTE COMMUNICATION INC. - VANCOUVER—See Bluefocus Intelligent Communications Group Co., Ltd.; *Int'l*, pg. 1071
COSSETTE COMMUNICATION-MARKETING (MONTREAL) INC.—See Bluefocus Intelligent Communications Group Co., Ltd.; *Int'l*, pg. 1071
COSSMA INC.; *U.S. Private*, pg. 1062
COSTA BROTHERS MASONRY; *U.S. Private*, pg. 1062
COSTA CROCIERE S.P.A.—See Carnival Corporation; *U.S. Public*, pg. 438
COSTA CRUCEROS S.A.—See Carnival Corporation; *U.S. Public*, pg. 438
COSTA CRUISE LINES INC.—See Carnival Corporation; *U.S. Public*, pg. 438
COSTA CRUZEIROS AGENCIA MARITIMA E TURISMO LTDA.—See Carnival Corporation; *U.S. Public*, pg. 438
COSTA DEL HAMILO, INC.—See SM Investments Corporation; *Int'l*, pg. 6998
COSTA DEL MAR, INC.—See EssilorLuxottica SA; *Int'l*, pg. 2513
COSTAEXCHANGE LTD—See Costa Group of Companies; *Int'l*, pg. 1814
COSTA FARMS, LLC; *U.S. Private*, pg. 1062
COSTA FRUIT & PRODUCE INC.; *U.S. Private*, pg. 1062
COSTA GROUP HOLDINGS LIMITED—See British Columbia Investment Management Corp.; *Int'l*, pg. 1169
COSTA GROUP HOLDINGS LIMITED—See Driscoll's, Inc; *U.S. Private*, pg. 1278
COSTA GROUP HOLDINGS LIMITED—See Paine Schwartz Partners, LLC; *U.S. Private*, pg. 3075
COSTA GROUP OF COMPANIES; *Int'l*, pg. 1814
COSTAIN ABU DHABI COMPANY—See Costain Group PLC; *Int'l*, pg. 1814
COSTAIN (AFRICA) LIMITED—See Costain Group PLC; *Int'l*, pg. 1814
COSTAIN BUILDING & CIVIL ENGINEERING LTD.—See Costain Group PLC; *Int'l*, pg. 1815
COSTAIN CIVIL ENGINEERING LTD.—See Costain Group PLC; *Int'l*, pg. 1814
COSTAIN CONSTRUCTION LIMITED—See Costain Group PLC; *Int'l*, pg. 1815
COSTA INC.—See EssilorLuxottica SA; *Int'l*, pg. 2513
COSTAIN ENGINEERING & CONSTRUCTION LTD.—See Costain Group PLC; *Int'l*, pg. 1814
COSTAIN GROUP PLC; *Int'l*, pg. 1814
COSTAIN INTERNATIONAL LIMITED—See Costain Group PLC; *Int'l*, pg. 1815
COSTAIN LTD—See Costain Group PLC; *Int'l*, pg. 1815
COSTAIN OIL, GAS & PROCESS LIMITED PIPELINE & OFFSHORE DIVISION—See Costain Group PLC; *Int'l*, pg. 1815

COSTAIN OIL, GAS & PROCESS LTD—See Costain Group PLC; *Int'l*, pg. 1815
COSTA LEAL EL VICTOR ELECTRONICA-PNEUMATICA, LDA.; *Int'l*, pg. 1814
COSTA LTD.—See The Coca-Cola Company; *U.S. Public*, pg. 2065
COSTAMARE INC.; *Int'l*, pg. 1815
COSTAMARE PARTICIPATIONS PLC—See Costamare Inc.; *Int'l*, pg. 1815
COSTAMARE PARTNERS LP—See Costamare Inc.; *Int'l*, pg. 1815
COSTAMAR TRAVEL, CRUISE & TOURS INC.; *U.S. Private*, pg. 1063
COSTA MESA CARS, INC.—See AutoNation, Inc.; *U.S. Public*, pg. 234
COSTAMP GROUP S.P.A.—See Co.Stamp - Srl; *Int'l*, pg. 1680
COSTAMP S.R.L.; *Int'l*, pg. 1815
CO.STAMP - SRL; *Int'l*, pg. 1680
COSTANOA VENTURE CAPITAL MANAGEMENT LLC; *U.S. Private*, pg. 1063
COSTANZO & RIZZETTO S.R.L.—See Kering S.A.; *Int'l*, pg. 4134
COSTA OESTE TRANSMISSORA DE ENERGIA S.A.—See Companhia Paranaense de Energia; *Int'l*, pg. 1748
COSTA ORIENTAL S.A.—See Katoen Natie N.V.; *Int'l*, pg. 4090
COSTAR ESPANA, S.L.—See CoStar Group, Inc.; *U.S. Public*, pg. 585
COS TARGOVISTE S.A.—See Invest Nikarom Srl; *Int'l*, pg. 3775
COSTAR GROUP CO., LTD.; *Int'l*, pg. 1815
COSTAR GROUP, INC.; *U.S. Public*, pg. 585
COSTA RICAN GOLD COFFEE CO.; *U.S. Private*, pg. 1062
COSTAR INTERNATIONAL ENTERPRISES, INC.; *U.S. Private*, pg. 1063
COSTAR LIMITED—See CoStar Group, Inc.; *U.S. Public*, pg. 585
COSTAR PHARMA LABORATORY PTY LTD—See Star Combo Pharma Ltd.; *Int'l*, pg. 7173
COSTAR PORTFOLIO STRATEGY, LLC—See CoStar Group, Inc.; *U.S. Public*, pg. 585
COSTAR REALTY INFORMATION, INC.—See CoStar Group, Inc.; *U.S. Public*, pg. 586
COSTAR TECHNOLOGIES INC.—See IDIS Co., Ltd.; *Int'l*, pg. 3595
COSTAR UK LIMITED—See CoStar Group, Inc.; *U.S. Public*, pg. 585
COSTAR UK LIMITED—See CoStar Group, Inc.; *U.S. Public*, pg. 585
COSTA SECURITY SERVICES, LLC; *U.S. Private*, pg. 1063
COSTAS, INC.; *U.S. Public*, pg. 586
COSTA VERDE AERONAUTICA SA; *Int'l*, pg. 1814
COSTA VICTORIA HEALTHCARE LLC—See The Ensign Group, Inc.; *U.S. Public*, pg. 2070
COSTA VIDA MANAGEMENT, INC.; *U.S. Private*, pg. 1063
COSTCO CANADA HOLDINGS INC.—See Costco Wholesale Corporation; *U.S. Public*, pg. 586
COSTCO DE MEXICO, S.A. DE C.V.—See Costco Wholesale Corporation; *U.S. Public*, pg. 587
COSTCO INSURANCE AGENCY, INC.—See Costco Wholesale Corporation; *U.S. Public*, pg. 586
COST CONTROL ASSOCIATES, INC.—See O2 Investment Partners, LLC; *U.S. Private*, pg. 2982
COSTCO WHOLESALE CANADA LTD.—See Costco Wholesale Corporation; *U.S. Public*, pg. 586
COSTCO WHOLESALE CORPORATION; *U.S. Public*, pg. 586
COSTCO WHOLESALE EMPLOYEE CLUB—See Costco Wholesale Corporation; *U.S. Public*, pg. 586
COSTCO WHOLESALE JAPAN, LTD.—See Costco Wholesale Corporation; *U.S. Public*, pg. 586
COSTCO WHOLESALE KOREA, LTD.—See Costco Wholesale Corporation; *U.S. Public*, pg. 586
COSTCO WHOLESALE MEMBERSHIP, INC.—See Costco Wholesale Corporation; *U.S. Public*, pg. 586
COSTCO WHOLESALE UK LIMITED—See Costco Wholesale Corporation; *U.S. Public*, pg. 587
COSTCUTTER SUPERMARKETS GROUP LIMITED—See Bestway (Holdings) Limited; *Int'l*, pg. 1001
COSTELLO DISMANTLING COMPANY, INC.; *U.S. Private*, pg. 1063
COSTELLO INDUSTRIES INC.; *U.S. Private*, pg. 1063
COST ENTERPRISES INC.—See AC Holding Co.; *U.S. Private*, pg. 45
COST MANAGEMENT SERVICES, INC.; *U.S. Private*, pg. 1062
COST OF WISCONSIN, INC.; *U.S. Private*, pg. 1062
COST PLUS, INC.—See Kingswood Capital Management LLC; *U.S. Private*, pg. 2312
COST PLUS MANAGEMENT SERVICES, INC.—See Kingswood Capital Management LLC; *U.S. Private*, pg. 2312
COST PLUS OF TEXAS, INC.—See Kingswood Capital Management LLC; *U.S. Private*, pg. 2312

COST OF WISCONSIN, INC.

CORPORATE AFFILIATIONS

COSTRACO SDN. BHD.—See Minho (M) Berhad; *Int'l*, pg. 4910
COST RIGHT NASSAU LIMITED—See AML Foods Ltd.; *Int'l*, pg. 428
COSTRONIC S.A.—See Amphenol Corporation; *U.S. Public*, pg. 130
COSTRUZIONI MECCANICHE LEGNANESI SRL—See Rotork Plc; *Int'l*, pg. 6405
COSTUME CRAZE, LLC; *U.S. Private*, pg. 1063
COSUCRA - GROUPE WARCOING; *Int'l*, pg. 1815
COSUMAR SA; *Int'l*, pg. 1815
COSVISION CO., LTD.—See Amorepacific Corp.; *Int'l*, pg. 430
COSWAY (CHINA) CO. LTD—See Berjaya Corporation Berhad; *Int'l*, pg. 984
COSWAY CO INC.; *U.S. Private*, pg. 1063
COSWAY CORPORATION BERHAD—See Berjaya Corporation Berhad; *Int'l*, pg. 984
COSWAY (M) SDN BHD—See Berjaya Corporation Berhad; *Int'l*, pg. 984
COSWORTH RACING INC.—See Ford Motor Company; *U.S. Public*, pg. 864
COSYN LIMITED; *Int'l*, pg. 1815
COSYTEC SA—See Cegedim S.A.; *Int'l*, pg. 1390
COTABIG JOINT STOCK COMPANY—See Cotana Group Joint Stock Company; *Int'l*, pg. 1815
COTAC CORPORATION—See Ansell Limited; *Int'l*, pg. 478
COTA CO., LTD.; *Int'l*, pg. 1815
COTA & COTA INC.; *U.S. Private*, pg. 1063
COTANA CAPITAL HOUSING INVESTMENT & DEVELOPMENT JOINT STOCK COMPANY—See Cotana Group Joint Stock Company; *Int'l*, pg. 1815
COTANA CONSTRUCTION JOINT STOCK COMPANY—See Cotana Group Joint Stock Company; *Int'l*, pg. 1815
COTANA CONSULTANT CONSTRUCTION JOINT STOCK COMPANY—See Cotana Group Joint Stock Company; *Int'l*, pg. 1815
COTANA GREEN LANDSCAPE ARCHITECTURE JOINT STOCK COMPANY—See Cotana Group Joint Stock Company; *Int'l*, pg. 1815
COTANA GROUP JOINT STOCK COMPANY; *Int'l*, pg. 1815
COTANA INFRASTRUCTURE CONSTRUCTION JOINT STOCK COMPANY—See Cotana Group Joint Stock Company; *Int'l*, pg. 1815
COTANA INVESTMENT CONSULTANCY & TRADING JOINT STOCK COMPANY—See Cotana Group Joint Stock Company; *Int'l*, pg. 1815
THE COTEAU PROPERTIES CO.—See NACCO Industries, Inc.; *U.S. Public*, pg. 1490
COTEB ENTREPRISES SAS—See VINCI S.A.; *Int'l*, pg. 8216
COTECCONS CONSTRUCTION JOINT STOCK COMPANY; *Int'l*, pg. 1815
CO-TECH DEVELOPMENT CORP.; *Int'l*, pg. 1680
COTEC HOLDINGS CORP.; *Int'l*, pg. 1815
COTECNA - BEIJING—See Cotecna Inspection S.A.; *Int'l*, pg. 1816
COTECNA CERTIFICADORA SERVICES LTDA.—See Cotecna Inspection S.A.; *Int'l*, pg. 1816
COTECNA DEL ECUADOR SA—See Cotecna Inspection S.A.; *Int'l*, pg. 1816
COTECNA DEL PARAGUAY S.A.—See Cotecna Inspection S.A.; *Int'l*, pg. 1816
COTECNA DESTINATION INSPECTION LTD—See Cotecna Inspection S.A.; *Int'l*, pg. 1816
COTECNA EL SALVADOR—See Cotecna Inspection S.A.; *Int'l*, pg. 1816
COTECNA GOZETIM AS—See Cotecna Inspection S.A.; *Int'l*, pg. 1816
COTECNA, INC.—See Cotecna Inspection S.A.; *Int'l*, pg. 1816
COTECNA INSPECTION ARGENTINA SA—See Cotecna Inspection S.A.; *Int'l*, pg. 1816
COTECNA INSPECTION BANGLADESH LIMITED—See Cotecna Inspection S.A.; *Int'l*, pg. 1816
COTECNA INSPECTION CONGO SARL—See Cotecna Inspection S.A.; *Int'l*, pg. 1816
COTECNA INSPECTION EGYPT, S.A.E.—See Cotecna Inspection S.A.; *Int'l*, pg. 1816
COTECNA INSPECTION FRANCE SARL—See Cotecna Inspection S.A.; *Int'l*, pg. 1816
COTECNA INSPECTION GMBH—See Cotecna Inspection S.A.; *Int'l*, pg. 1816
COTECNA INSPECTION, INC.—See Cotecna Inspection S.A.; *Int'l*, pg. 1816
COTECNA INSPECTION INDIA PVT. LTD.—See Cotecna Inspection S.A.; *Int'l*, pg. 1816
COTECNA INSPECTION JAPAN LIMITED—See Cotecna Inspection S.A.; *Int'l*, pg. 1816
COTECNA INSPECTION KOREA INC.—See Cotecna Inspection S.A.; *Int'l*, pg. 1816
COTECNA INSPECTION LTD.—See Cotecna Inspection S.A.; *Int'l*, pg. 1816
COTECNA INSPECTION PHILIPPINES, INC.—See Cotecna Inspection S.A.; *Int'l*, pg. 1816
COTECNA INSPECTION S.A.; *Int'l*, pg. 1816

COTECNA INSPECTION SA—See Cotecna Inspection S.A.; *Int'l*, pg. 1816
COTECNA INSPECTION SL—See Cotecna Inspection S.A.; *Int'l*, pg. 1816
COTECNA INSPECTION SOUTH AFRICA PTY. LTD.—See Cotecna Inspection S.A.; *Int'l*, pg. 1816
COTECNA INSPECTION THAILAND—See Cotecna Inspection S.A.; *Int'l*, pg. 1816
COTECNA INSPECTION URUGUAY SA—See Cotecna Inspection S.A.; *Int'l*, pg. 1816
COTECNA INSPECTION (VOSTOK) LLC—See Cotecna Inspection S.A.; *Int'l*, pg. 1816
COTECNA INTERNATIONAL TRADE CONSULTING (SHANGHAI) LTD—See Cotecna Inspection S.A.; *Int'l*, pg. 1816
COTECNA IRAQ—See Cotecna Inspection S.A.; *Int'l*, pg. 1816
COTECNA KAZAKHSTAN LLP—See Cotecna Inspection S.A.; *Int'l*, pg. 1816
COTECNA LATIN AMERICA S.A.—See Cotecna Inspection S.A.; *Int'l*, pg. 1816
COTECNA QUALITY SRL—See Cotecna Inspection S.A.; *Int'l*, pg. 1816
COTECNA S.A. - HONG KONG—See Cotecna Inspection S.A.; *Int'l*, pg. 1816
COTECNA SAUDI ARABIA CO., LTD.—See Cotecna Inspection S.A.; *Int'l*, pg. 1816
COTECNA SENEGAL SARL—See Cotecna Inspection S.A.; *Int'l*, pg. 1816
COTECNA SERVICOS ANGOLA LIMITADA—See Cotecna Inspection S.A.; *Int'l*, pg. 1816
COTECNA SERVICOS LTDA.—See Cotecna Inspection S.A.; *Int'l*, pg. 1816
COTECNA SERVICOS LTDA—See Cotecna Inspection S.A.; *Int'l*, pg. 1816
COTECNA SINGAPORE PTE. LTD.—See Cotecna Inspection S.A.; *Int'l*, pg. 1816
COTECNA TRADE SERVICES MALAYSIA SDN BHD—See Cotecna Inspection S.A.; *Int'l*, pg. 1816
COTECNA TRADE SERVICES—See Cotecna Inspection S.A.; *Int'l*, pg. 1816
COTECNA UKRAINE LIMITED—See Cotecna Inspection S.A.; *Int'l*, pg. 1816
COTECNA VIETNAM, CO., LTD.—See Cotecna Inspection S.A.; *Int'l*, pg. 1816
COTEG—See FAYAT SAS; *Int'l*, pg. 2625
COTELLE SA—See Colgate-Palmolive Company; *U.S. Public*, pg. 532
COTEL PRECISION INDUSTRIES SDN BHD—See KVC Industrial Supplies Sdn. Bhd.; *Int'l*, pg. 4349
COTELSA S.A.; *Int'l*, pg. 1817
COTEMINAS ARGENTINA S.A.—See Coteminas Companhia de Tecidos Norte de Minas; *Int'l*, pg. 1817
COTEMINAS COMPANHIA DE TECIDOS NORTE DE MINAS; *Int'l*, pg. 1817
COTERA REED ARCHITECTS INC.—See Dykema Architects Inc.; *U.S. Private*, pg. 1296
COTE RESTAURANTS LTD.—See Partners Group Holding AG; *Int'l*, pg. 5749
COTERRA ENERGY INC.; *U.S. Public*, pg. 587
COTETONIC—See The GAMS Group, Inc.; *U.S. Private*, pg. 4032
COTHERM S.A.S.—See Atlantic Societe Francaise Develop Thermique S.A.; *Int'l*, pg. 675
COTINGA PHARMACEUTICALS INC.; *Int'l*, pg. 1817
COTIVITI CORPORATION—See Veritas Capital Fund Management, LLC; *U.S. Private*, pg. 4366
COTIVITI HOLDINGS, INC.—See Veritas Capital Fund Management, LLC; *U.S. Private*, pg. 4365
COTIVITI, LLC - HEALTHCARE DIVISION—See Veritas Capital Fund Management, LLC; *U.S. Private*, pg. 4366
COTIVITI, LLC—See Veritas Capital Fund Management, LLC; *U.S. Private*, pg. 4366
COTMAN HOUSING ASSOCIATION LIMITED—See Places for People Group Limited; *Int'l*, pg. 5888
COTON COLORS EXPRESS, LLC; *U.S. Private*, pg. 1063
COTONET ENGINEERING CO., LTD.—See MIRAIT ONE Corporation; *Int'l*, pg. 4917
COTO TECHNOLOGY, INC.—See The Dyson-Kissner-Moran Corporation; *U.S. Private*, pg. 4024
COTO TECHNOLOGY, INC.—See The Dyson-Kissner-Moran Corporation; *U.S. Private*, pg. 4024
COTS TECHNOLOGY CO., LTD.; *Int'l*, pg. 1817
COTSWOLD INNS & HOTELS LIMITED—See Fuller, Smith & Turner PLC; *Int'l*, pg. 2842
COTTAGE GROVE PLACE; *U.S. Private*, pg. 1063
COTTAGE GROVE SENTINEL—See News Media Corporation; *U.S. Private*, pg. 2916
COTTAGE HOME OPTIONS, L.L.C.—See Community Health Systems, Inc.; *U.S. Public*, pg. 552
COTTAGE HOSPITAL; *U.S. Private*, pg. 1063
COTTAGES & CASTLES, INC.; *U.S. Private*, pg. 1063
COTTAGE SHEET METAL, LLC; *U.S. Private*, pg. 1063
COTTAGE STREET INVESTMENTS LLC—See Prudential Financial, Inc.; *U.S. Public*, pg. 1731
COTT BEVERAGES CANADA—See KKR & Co. Inc.; *U.S. Public*, pg. 1263
COTTBUSER ENERGIEVERWALTUNGSGESELLSCHAFT MBH—See BayernLB Holding AG; *Int'l*, pg. 913

COTTCO HOLDINGS LIMITED; *Int'l*, pg. 1817
COTTCO INTERNATIONAL (PROPRIETARY) LIMITED—See Cottco Holdings Limited; *Int'l*, pg. 1817
COTT CORPORATION - US CORPORATE HEADQUARTERS—See Primo Water Corporation; *U.S. Public*, pg. 1718
COTTER CONSULTING, INC.; *U.S. Private*, pg. 1063
COTTER CORPORATION—See General Atomics; *U.S. Private*, pg. 1663
COTTERLAZ CONNECTORS SHENZHEN LTD.—See Aalberts N.V.; *Int'l*, pg. 33
COTTERLAZ JEAN S.A.S.—See Aalberts N.V.; *Int'l*, pg. 34
COTTERWEB ENTERPRISES, INC.—See Great Hill Partners, L.P.; *U.S. Private*, pg. 1763
COTTES USINES SAS—See Vandemoortele N.V.; *Int'l*, pg. 8128
COTTI FOODS CORPORATION; *U.S. Private*, pg. 1063
COTT INDEX CO.; *U.S. Private*, pg. 1063
COTT LIMITED—See Primo Water Corporation; *U.S. Public*, pg. 1718
COTTMAN MCCANN ADVERTISING—See The Interpublic Group of Companies, Inc.; *U.S. Public*, pg. 2097
COTTMAN TRANSMISSION SYSTEMS, LLC; *U.S. Private*, pg. 1063
COTT MAQUINARIA Y EQUIPO, S.A. DE C.V.—See Primo Water Corporation; *U.S. Public*, pg. 1718
THE COTTON COMPANY OF ZIMBABWE LIMITED—See Cottco Holdings Limited; *Int'l*, pg. 1817
COTTON & CO.—See Sikich LLP; *U.S. Private*, pg. 3651
COTTON COUNTY RETAIL LIMITED; *Int'l*, pg. 1817
COTTON CREEK CAPITAL MANAGEMENT LLC; *U.S. Private*, pg. 1063
COTTON ELECTRIC COOPERATIVE, INC.; *U.S. Private*, pg. 1064
COTTON ELECTRIC SERVICES, INC.—See Cotton Electric Cooperative, Inc.; *U.S. Private*, pg. 1064
COTTON FIELD ORGANIC CO., LTD.—See Microbio Co., Ltd.; *Int'l*, pg. 4879
COTTON HOLDINGS, INC.; *U.S. Private*, pg. 1064
COTTON INCORPORATED CONSUMER MARKETING HEADQUARTERS—See Cotton Incorporated; *U.S. Private*, pg. 1064
COTTON INCORPORATED; *U.S. Private*, pg. 1064
COTTON PATCH CAFE INC.—See Altamont Capital Partners; *U.S. Private*, pg. 205
COTTONS POINT DESIGN; *U.S. Private*, pg. 1064
COTTONTREE HOSPITALITY GROUP; *U.S. Private*, pg. 1064
COTTONWOOD ACQUISITIONS LLC; *U.S. Private*, pg. 1064
COTTONWOOD COMMUNITIES, INC.; *U.S. Private*, pg. 1064
COTTONWOOD CO-OP OIL COMPANY; *U.S. Private*, pg. 1064
COTTONWOOD FINANCIAL LTD; *U.S. Private*, pg. 1064
COTTONWOOD INCORPORATED; *U.S. Private*, pg. 1064
COTTONWOOD MORTUARY, INC.—See Security National Financial Corporation; *U.S. Public*, pg. 1856
COTTONWOOD REALTY SERVICES LLC; *U.S. Private*, pg. 1064
COTTONWOOD TRADING, INC.—See Home Trends & Design, Inc.; *U.S. Private*, pg. 1972
COTTRELL CONTRACTING CORP; *U.S. Private*, pg. 1064
COTTRELL, INC.—See Markel Group Inc.; *U.S. Public*, pg. 1367
COTT VENDING INC.—See Primo Water Corporation; *U.S. Public*, pg. 1718
COTY ARGENTINA S.A.—See JAB Holding Company S.a.r.l.; *Int'l*, pg. 3860
COTY ASIA PTE. LTD.—See JAB Holding Company S.a.r.l.; *Int'l*, pg. 3860
COTY AUSTRALIA PTY. LIMITED—See JAB Holding Company S.a.r.l.; *Int'l*, pg. 3860
COTY AUSTRIA GMBH, WIEN—See JAB Holding Company S.a.r.l.; *Int'l*, pg. 3860
COTY BENELUX B.V.—See JAB Holding Company S.a.r.l.; *Int'l*, pg. 3860
COTY BENELUX N.V./S.A.—See JAB Holding Company S.a.r.l.; *Int'l*, pg. 3860
COTY BRANDS GROUP LIMITED—See JAB Holding Company S.a.r.l.; *Int'l*, pg. 3860
COTY B.V.—See JAB Holding Company S.a.r.l.; *Int'l*, pg. 3860
COTY CANADA INC.—See JAB Holding Company S.a.r.l.; *Int'l*, pg. 3860
COTY CESKA REPUBLIKA, K.S.—See JAB Holding Company S.a.r.l.; *Int'l*, pg. 3860
COTY COLOMBIA LTDA.—See JAB Holding Company S.a.r.l.; *Int'l*, pg. 3860
COTY COSMETICS CHILE LIMITADA—See JAB Holding Company S.a.r.l.; *Int'l*, pg. 3860
COTY COSMETICS ROMANIA SRL—See JAB Holding Company S.a.r.l.; *Int'l*, pg. 3860
COTY DEUTSCHLAND GMBH—See JAB Holding Company S.a.r.l.; *Int'l*, pg. 3860
COTY FRANCE S.A.S.—See JAB Holding Company S.a.r.l.; *Int'l*, pg. 3860

COMPANY NAME INDEX

COTY GENEVA S.A.—See JAB Holding Company S.a.r.l.; *Int'l*, pg. 3860
COTY GENEVA S.A. VERSOIX—See JAB Holding Company S.a.r.l.; *Int'l*, pg. 3860
COTY GERMANY GMBH—See JAB Holding Company S.a.r.l.; *Int'l*, pg. 3860
COTY HELLAS S.A.—See JAB Holding Company S.a.r.l.; *Int'l*, pg. 3860
COTY HUNGARY KFT.—See JAB Holding Company S.a.r.l.; *Int'l*, pg. 3860
COTY, INC.—See JAB Holding Company S.a.r.l.; *Int'l*, pg. 3860
COTY IRELAND LTD.—See JAB Holding Company S.a.r.l.; *Int'l*, pg. 3860
COTY ITALIA S.P.A.—See JAB Holding Company S.a.r.l.; *Int'l*, pg. 3860
COTY MANUFACTURING UK LTD.—See JAB Holding Company S.a.r.l.; *Int'l*, pg. 3860
COTY MEXICO, S.A. DE C.V.—See JAB Holding Company S.a.r.l.; *Int'l*, pg. 3860
COTY MIDDLE EAST FZCO—See JAB Holding Company S.a.r.l.; *Int'l*, pg. 3860
COTY-OPI INC.—See JAB Holding Company S.a.r.l.; *Int'l*, pg. 3861
COTY POLSKA SP Z.O.O.—See JAB Holding Company S.a.r.l.; *Int'l*, pg. 3860
COTY PRESTIGE AUSTRIA HANDELSGESELLSCHAFT M.B.H.—See JAB Holding Company S.a.r.l.; *Int'l*, pg. 3860
COTY PRESTIGE ESPANA - SURCURSAL EM PORTUGAL—See JAB Holding Company S.a.r.l.; *Int'l*, pg. 3860
COTY PRESTIGE HELLAS S.A.—See JAB Holding Company S.a.r.l.; *Int'l*, pg. 3860
COTY PRESTIGE PORTUGAL—See JAB Holding Company S.a.r.l.; *Int'l*, pg. 3860
COTY PRESTIGE SOUTHEAST ASIA (M) SDN. BHD.—See JAB Holding Company S.a.r.l.; *Int'l*, pg. 3860
COTY PRESTIGE (TAIWAN) LTD.—See JAB Holding Company S.a.r.l.; *Int'l*, pg. 3860
COTY PUERTO RICO INC—See JAB Holding Company S.a.r.l.; *Int'l*, pg. 3860
COTY S.A.S.—See JAB Holding Company S.a.r.l.; *Int'l*, pg. 3800
COTY (SCHWEIZ) AG—See JAB Holding Company S.a.r.l.; *Int'l*, pg. 3860
COTY SERVICES AND LOGISTICS GMBH—See JAB Holding Company S.a.r.l.; *Int'l*, pg. 3861
COTY SERVICES U.K. LTD.—See JAB Holding Company S.a.r.l.; *Int'l*, pg. 3861
COTY SLOVENSKA REPUBLIKA S.R.O.—See JAB Holding Company S.a.r.l.; *Int'l*, pg. 3861
COTY SPAIN S.L.—See JAB Holding Company S.a.r.l.; *Int'l*, pg. 3861
COTY UK LTD.—See JAB Holding Company S.a.r.l.; *Int'l*, pg. 3861
COTY US LLC—See JAB Holding Company S.a.r.l.; *Int'l*, pg. 3861
COUCHBASE, INC.; *U.S. Public*, pg. 587
COUDAL PARTNERS; *U.S. Private*, pg. 1064
COUGAR AUTOMATION LIMITED—See VINCI S.A.; *Int'l*, pg. 8216
COUGAR EXPRESS INC.—See Transportation and Logistics Systems, Inc.; *U.S. Public*, pg. 2184
COUGAR GLOBAL INVESTMENTS LIMITED—See Raymond James Financial, Inc.; *U.S. Public*, pg. 1764
COUGAR INDUSTRIES, INC.—See Martin Engineering; *U.S. Private*, pg. 2595
COUGAR LANDFILL, INC.—See Waste Management, Inc.; *U.S. Public*, pg. 2330
COUGAR LIFE INC.—See Avid Life Media Inc.; *Int'l*, pg. 743
COUGAR LOGISTICS (MALAYSIA) SDN. BHD.—See DRB-HICOM Berhad; *Int'l*, pg. 2201
COUGAR MACHINE LTD.—See Gevelot S.A.; *Int'l*, pg. 2954
COUGAR METALS NL; *Int'l*, pg. 1817
COUGAR OIL INC.; *U.S. Private*, pg. 1064
COUGAR WELLHEAD SERVICES INC.—See Gevelot S.A.; *Int'l*, pg. 2954
COUGH INC.; *U.S. Private*, pg. 1064
COUGHLAN COMPANIES, INC.; *U.S. Private*, pg. 1064
COUGHLIN & ASSOCIATES LTD.—See People Corporation; *Int'l*, pg. 5793
COUGLE COMMISSION COMPANY, INC.; *U.S. Private*, pg. 1065
COULBOURN INSTRUMENTS, LLC—See Harvard Bioscience, Inc.; *U.S. Public*, pg. 987
COULEE TECH, INC.; *U.S. Private*, pg. 1065
COULEURS DE PLANTES SAS—See Plant Advanced Technologies SA; *Int'l*, pg. 5890
COULSON AIRCRANE LTD.—See Coulson Group of Companies; *Int'l*, pg. 1817
COULSON AIRCRANE (U.S.A.), INC.—See Coulson Group of Companies; *Int'l*, pg. 1817
COULSON GROUP OF COMPANIES; *Int'l*, pg. 1817
COULSON MANUFACTURING LTD.—See Coulson Group of Companies; *Int'l*, pg. 1817

COULTER CADILLAC INCORPORATED; *U.S. Private*, pg. 1065
COULTER & JUSTUS, P.C.; *U.S. Private*, pg. 1065
COULTER MOTOR COMPANY LLC.; *U.S. Private*, pg. 1065
COULTER PRESS—See Gannett Co., Inc.; *U.S. Public*, pg. 906
COUNCIL CAPITAL; *U.S. Private*, pg. 1065
COUNCIL FOR CHRISTIAN COLLEGES & UNIVERSITIES; *U.S. Private*, pg. 1065
COUNCIL FOR OPPORTUNITY IN EDUCATION; *U.S. Private*, pg. 1065
COUNCIL OAK PARTNERS, LLC—See BancFirst Corporation; *U.S. Public*, pg. 269
COUNCIL ON AGING OF SOUTHWESTERN OHIO; *U.S. Private*, pg. 1065
COUNCIL ON FOREIGN RELATIONS; *U.S. Private*, pg. 1065
COUNCIL ON FOUNDATIONS; *U.S. Private*, pg. 1065
COUNCIL ON RURAL SERVICES; *U.S. Private*, pg. 1065
COUNSELING ASSOCIATES, INC.; *U.S. Private*, pg. 1065
COUNSELING CENTER & BLANK PSYCHIATRY—See UnityPoint Health; *U.S. Private*, pg. 4303
COUNSELING INTERNATIONAL, INC.; *U.S. Private*, pg. 1066
COUNSELING & RECOVERY SERVICES OF OKLAHOMA; *U.S. Private*, pg. 1065
COUNSELING & RESEARCH ASSOCIATES; *U.S. Private*, pg. 1065
THE COUNSELING SERVICE OF ADDISON COUNTY, INC.; *U.S. Private*, pg. 4015
COUNSELING & SUPPORT SERVICES FOR YOUTH; *U.S. Private*, pg. 1065
COUNSEL ON CALL; *U.S. Private*, pg. 1065
COUNSELOR REALTY INC.; *U.S. Private*, pg. 1066
COUNSEL PRESS, INC—See Align Capital Partners, LLC; *U.S. Private*, pg. 167
COUNSEL WEALTH MANAGEMENT, INC.—See Larson Financial Holdings, LLC; *U.S. Private*, pg. 2394
COUNT + CARE GMBH—See HEAG Sudhessische Energie AG; *Int'l*, pg. 3302
COUNTDOWN MEDIA GMBH—See Bertelsmann SE & Co. KGaA; *Int'l*, pg. 994
COUNTDOWN—See Woolworths Group Limited; *Int'l*, pg. 8452
COUNTERBALANCE CORPORATION—See South Chester Tube Company; *U.S. Private*, pg. 3721
COUNTER BRANDS LLC—See The Carlyle Group Inc.; *U.S. Public*, pg. 2046
COUNTERMAST LIMITED—See Nippon Paint Holdings Co., Ltd.; *Int'l*, pg. 5325
COUNTERPATH CORPORATION—See Alianza Inc.; *U.S. Private*, pg. 167
COUNTERPATH TECHNOLOGIES INC.—See Alianza Inc.; *U.S. Private*, pg. 167
COUNTERPOINT CAPITAL PARTNERS, LLC; *U.S. Private*, pg. 1066
COUNTERPOINT, LLC—See Black Balloon Publishing, LLC; *U.S. Private*, pg. 569
COUNTER PRESS ACQUISITION CORPORATION; *U.S. Public*, pg. 587
COUNTER SERVICE CO., LTD.—See C.P. All Public Company Limited; *Int'l*, pg. 1244
COUNTERTOPS INC.; *U.S. Private*, pg. 1066
COUNTESS MARA, INC.—See Randa Corp.; *U.S. Private*, pg. 3353
COUNT FINANCIAL LIMITED—See Count Limited; *Int'l*, pg. 1817
COUNTIES ENERGY LTD.—See Marsden Maritime Holdings Limited; *Int'l*, pg. 4701
COUNTING HOUSE ASSOCIATES, LLC—See AcuityCFO, LLC; *U.S. Private*, pg. 71
COUNT LIMITED; *Int'l*, pg. 1817
COUNTRY ANNEXE SDN. BHD.—See Malaysian Resources Corporation Berhad; *Int'l*, pg. 4662
COUNTRY BANK FOR SAVINGS; *U.S. Private*, pg. 1066
COUNTRY BANK HOLDING COMPANY, INC.—See OceanFirst Financial Corp.; *U.S. Public*, pg. 1563
COUNTRY BANK SHARES, INC.; *U.S. Private*, pg. 1066
COUNTRY BANK—See OceanFirst Financial Corp.; *U.S. Public*, pg. 1563
COUNTRY BIRD HOLDINGS LIMITED; *Int'l*, pg. 1818
COUNTRY CAPITAL MANAGEMENT COMPANY—See COUNTRY Financial; *U.S. Private*, pg. 1066
COUNTRYCARS.COM.AU PTY LTD—See Nine Entertainment Co. Holdings Limited; *Int'l*, pg. 5298
COUNTRY CHEVROLET, INC.; *U.S. Private*, pg. 1066
COUNTRY CHEVROLET, INC.; *U.S. Private*, pg. 1066
COUNTRY CHRISTMAS SAVINGS CLUB LIMITED—See PayPoint plc; *Int'l*, pg. 5763
THE COUNTRY CLUB AT TAGAYTAY HIGHLANDS, INC.—See Belle Corporation; *Int'l*, pg. 966
THE COUNTRY CLUB AT WOODMORE—See Concert Golf Partners, LLC; *U.S. Private*, pg. 1009
COUNTRY CLUB AUTO GROUP; *U.S. Private*, pg. 1066
COUNTRY CLUB BANK; *U.S. Private*, pg. 1066
COUNTRY CLUB CONDOMINIUM, L.L.C.—See Equity Residential; *U.S. Public*, pg. 791

COUNTRY MALT GROUP

COUNTRY CLUB HOSPITALITY & HOLIDAYS LIMITED; *Int'l*, pg. 1818
THE COUNTRY CLUB JAPAN, INC.—See XYMAX Corporation; *Int'l*, pg. 8542
COUNTRY CLUB OF ASHEVILLE—See McConnell Golf LLC; *U.S. Private*, pg. 2629
COUNTRY CLUB OF BIRMINGHAM; *U.S. Private*, pg. 1066
COUNTRY CLUB OF HILTON HEAD—See Apollo Global Management, Inc.; *U.S. Public*, pg. 149
COUNTRY CLUB OF THE NORTH—See Escalante Golf, Inc.; *U.S. Private*, pg. 1424
THE COUNTRY CLUB OF WINTER HAVEN; *U.S. Private*, pg. 4015
THE COUNTRY CLUB; *U.S. Private*, pg. 4015
COUNTRY CLUB SUPPLY, INC.—See Fore Supply Co.; *U.S. Private*, pg. 1565
COUNTRY COACH CORPORATION; *U.S. Private*, pg. 1066
COUNTRY & COMMERCIAL INSURANCE BROKERS LIMITED—See Brown & Brown, Inc.; *U.S. Public*, pg. 400
COUNTRY CONDOS LTD; *Int'l*, pg. 1818
COUNTRY CORNER INC.—See The Garden City Co-Op Inc.; *U.S. Private*, pg. 4032
COUNTRY CURTAINS RETAIL INC.—See Fitzpatrick Companies Inc.; *U.S. Private*, pg. 1536
COUNTRY DELITE—See Dean Foods Company; *U.S. Private*, pg. 1183
COUNTRY EGGS INC.; *U.S. Private*, pg. 1066
COUNTRY FAIR INC.—See Red Apple Group, Inc.; *U.S. Private*, pg. 3373
COUNTRY FARMS SDN BHD—See Berjaya Corporation Berhad; *Int'l*, pg. 984
COUNTRY FINANCIAL - CENTRAL REGION—See COUNTRY Financial; *U.S. Private*, pg. 1066
COUNTRY FINANCIAL; *U.S. Private*, pg. 1066
COUNTRY FINANCIAL—See COUNTRY Financial; *U.S. Private*, pg. 1066
COUNTRY FLOORS INC.; *U.S. Private*, pg. 1067
COUNTRY FLORAL SUPPLY INC.; *U.S. Private*, pg. 1067
COUNTRY FOODS PTE. LTD.—See Temasek Holdings (Private) Limited; *Int'l*, pg. 7550
COUNTRY FORD TRUCKS INC.; *U.S. Private*, pg. 1067
COUNTRY FRESH BATTER INC.; *U.S. Private*, pg. 1067
COUNTRY FRESH, INC.—See Dean Foods Company; *U.S. Private*, pg. 1183
COUNTRY FRESH, LLC—See Dean Foods Company; *U.S. Private*, pg. 1183
COUNTRY FRESH PACKAGING—See Dominion Holding Corporation; *Int'l*, pg. 2161
COUNTRY GARDEN DANGA BAY SDN. BHD.—See Country Garden Holdings Company Limited; *Int'l*, pg. 1818
COUNTRY GARDEN HOLDINGS COMPANY LIMITED; *Int'l*, pg. 1818
COUNTRY GARDEN PACIFICVIEW SDN. BHD.—See Country Garden Holdings Company Limited; *Int'l*, pg. 1818
COUNTRY GARDEN SERVICES HOLDINGS COMPANY LIMITED; *Int'l*, pg. 1818
COUNTRY GAZETTE—See Gannett Co., Inc.; *U.S. Public*, pg. 902
COUNTRY GROUP DEVELOPMENT PUBLIC COMPANY LIMITED; *Int'l*, pg. 1818
COUNTRY GROUP HOLDINGS PUBLIC COMPANY LIMITED; *Int'l*, pg. 1818
COUNTRY GROUP SECURITIES PUBLIC COMPANY LIMITED; *Int'l*, pg. 1818
COUNTRY HEDGING, INC.—See CHS INC.; *U.S. Public*, pg. 492
COUNTRY HEIGHTS HOLDINGS BERHAD; *Int'l*, pg. 1818
COUNTRY HOME BAKERS, INC.—See J&J Snack Foods Corporation; *U.S. Public*, pg. 1179
COUNTRY HOME MAGAZINE—See Meredith Corporation; *U.S. Private*, pg. 1422
COUNTRY HOME PRODUCTS INC.—See Generac Holdings Inc.; *U.S. Public*, pg. 912
COUNTRY HOUSE PROPERTY MANAGEMENT LIMITED—See Kowloon Development Company Limited; *Int'l*, pg. 4295
COUNTRY HOUSES, LLC; *U.S. Private*, pg. 1067
COUNTRY INNS & SUITES BY CARLSON INC.—See Carlson Companies Inc.; *U.S. Private*, pg. 764
COUNTRY INN & SUITES—See Northampton Group Inc.; *Int'l*, pg. 5442
COUNTRY INVESTORS LIFE ASSURANCE COMPANY—See COUNTRY Financial; *U.S. Private*, pg. 1066
COUNTRY KITCHEN INTERNATIONAL, INC.—See Kitchen Investment Group; *U.S. Private*, pg. 2316
COUNTRY LIFE HOMES INC.; *U.S. Private*, pg. 1067
COUNTRY LIFE INSURANCE COMPANY—See COUNTRY Financial; *U.S. Private*, pg. 1066
COUNTRY LIVING—See The Hearst Corporation; *U.S. Private*, pg. 4046
COUNTRY MAID, INC.; *U.S. Private*, pg. 1067
COUNTRY MALT GROUP; *U.S. Private*, pg. 1067

COUNTRYMARK COOPERATIVE, INC.

COUNTRYMARK COOPERATIVE, INC.; *U.S. Private*, pg. 1067
COUNTRYMARK ENERGY RESOURCES, LLC—See Countrymark Cooperative, Inc.; *U.S. Private*, pg. 1067
COUNTRYMARK REFINING AND LOGISTICS, LLC—See Countrymark Cooperative, Inc.; *U.S. Private*, pg. 1067
COUNTRY MEDICAL PLANS, INC.—See COUNTRY Financial; *U.S. Private*, pg. 1067
COUNTRY MUSIC FOUNDATION, INC.; *U.S. Private*, pg. 1067
COUNTRY MUSIC TELEVISION, INC.—See National Amusements, Inc.; *U.S. Private*, pg. 2841
COUNTRY MUSIC TELEVISION LIMITED—See Corus Entertainment Inc.; *Int'l*, pg. 1808
COUNTRY MUTUAL INSURANCE COMPANY—See COUNTRY Financial; *U.S. Private*, pg. 1067
COUNTRY PARTNERS COOPERATIVE; *U.S. Private*, pg. 1067
COUNTRYPLACE MORTGAGE, LTD.—See Cavco Industries, Inc.; *U.S. Public*, pg. 455
COUNTRY PREFERRED INSURANCE COMPANY—See COUNTRY Financial; *U.S. Private*, pg. 1067
COUNTRY PRIDE CO-OPERATIVE; *U.S. Private*, pg. 1067
COUNTRY PRIDE SERVICES CO-OPERATIVE; *U.S. Private*, pg. 1067
COUNTRY PURE FOODS, INC.—See Blue Point Capital Partners, LLC; *U.S. Private*, pg. 590
COUNTRY RIBBON INC. - COUNTRY RIBBON FEED DIVISION—See Co-op Atlantic; *Int'l*, pg. 1679
COUNTRY RIBBON INC.—See Co-op Atlantic; *Int'l*, pg. 1679
COUNTRY ROAD ASSOCIATES, LTD.; *U.S. Private*, pg. 1067
COUNTRY ROAD AUSTRALIA LIMITED—See Woolworths Holdings Limited; *Int'l*, pg. 8452
COUNTRY ROAD CLOTHING (NZ) LIMITED—See Woolworths Holdings Limited; *Int'l*, pg. 8452
COUNTRY ROAD CLOTHING (PROPRIETARY) LIMITED—See Woolworths Holdings Limited; *Int'l*, pg. 8452
COUNTRY ROAD GROUP PROPRIETARY LIMITED—See Woolworths Holdings Limited; *Int'l*, pg. 8452
COUNTRY SAMPLER, LLC—See Dynamic Resource Group, Inc.; *U.S. Private*, pg. 1299
COUNTRY SELECT CATFISH COMPANY II, LLC—See Consolidated Catfish Companies, LLC; *U.S. Private*, pg. 1020
COUNTRY SERVICES INC.—See National Amusements, Inc.; *U.S. Private*, pg. 2841
COUNTRYSIDE BAKING COMPANY, INC.—See Dawn Food Products, Inc.; *U.S. Private*, pg. 1175
COUNTRYSIDE COOPERATIVE, INC.; *U.S. Private*, pg. 1067
COUNTRYSIDE FOODS, LLC—See Ramex, Inc.; *U.S. Private*, pg. 3351
COUNTRYSIDE LANDFILL INC.—See Waste Management, Inc.; *U.S. Public*, pg. 2330
COUNTRYSIDE MARTS INC.; *U.S. Private*, pg. 1067
COUNTRYSIDE PARTNERSHIPS PLC—See Vistry Group PLC; *Int'l*, pg. 8255
COUNTRYSIDE PROPERTIES (NORTHERN) LIMITED—See Vistry Group PLC; *Int'l*, pg. 8255
COUNTRYSIDE SURGERY CENTER, LTD.—See HCA Healthcare, Inc.; *U.S. Public*, pg. 994
COUNTRYSIDE SURGERY CENTER—See HCA Healthcare, Inc.; *U.S. Public*, pg. 994
COUNTRYSIDE TANK COMPANY—See TerraVest Industries, Inc.; *Int'l*, pg. 7568
COUNTRY SQUIRE FARM PRODUCTS; *U.S. Private*, pg. 1067
COUNTRYSTORE (MAIDENHEAD) LIMITED—See Mid Counties Co-operative; *Int'l*, pg. 4882
COUNTRY STYLE COOKING RESTAURANT CHAIN CO., LTD.; *Int'l*, pg. 1819
COUNTRY STYLE FOODS LIMITED; *Int'l*, pg. 1819
COUNTRY TRUST BANK—See COUNTRY Financial; *U.S. Private*, pg. 1067
COUNTRY VET WHOLESALING PTY. LTD.—See Apiam Animal Health Limited; *Int'l*, pg. 515
COUNTRY VIEW BERHAD; *Int'l*, pg. 1819
COUNTRY VIEW DEVELOPMENT SDN BHD—See Khazanah Nasional Berhad; *Int'l*, pg. 4153
COUNTRY VINTNER OF WV—See The Winebow Group, LLC; *U.S. Private*, pg. 4137
COUNTRY VISIONS COOPERATIVE; *U.S. Private*, pg. 1067
COUNTRY WALKERS, INC.—See TUI AG; *Int'l*, pg. 7964
COUNTRYWIDE ASSURED PLC—See Chesnara Plc; *Int'l*, pg. 1472
COUNTRYWIDE BROADBAND, LLC; *U.S. Private*, pg. 1067
COUNTRYWIDE ESTATE AGENTS (FS) LTD.—See The Skipton Building Society; *Int'l*, pg. 7686
COUNTRYWIDE FINANCIAL CORPORATION—See Bank of America Corporation; *U.S. Public*, pg. 271
COUNTRYWIDE FRANCHISING LIMITED—See The Skipton Building Society; *Int'l*, pg. 7686

COUNTRYWIDE HARDWARE, INC.—See ShoreView Industries, LLC; *U.S. Private*, pg. 3642
COUNTRY-WIDE INSURANCE COMPANY; *U.S. Private*, pg. 1067
COUNTRYWIDE MORTGAGE SERVICES LIMITED—See The Skipton Building Society; *Int'l*, pg. 7686
COUNTRYWIDE PETROLEUM CO.—See Croton Holding Company; *U.S. Private*, pg. 1108
COUNTRYWIDE PLC—See The Skipton Building Society; *Int'l*, pg. 7686
COUNTRYWIDE PRINCIPAL SERVICES LIMITED—See The Skipton Building Society; *Int'l*, pg. 7686
COUNTRYWIDE PROPERTY AUCTIONS LIMITED—See The Skipton Building Society; *Int'l*, pg. 7686
COUNTRYWIDE PROPERTY LAWYERS LTD—See The Skipton Building Society; *Int'l*, pg. 7686
COUNTRYWIDE PROPERTY MANAGEMENT LIMITED—See The Skipton Building Society; *Int'l*, pg. 7686
COUNTRYWIDE TRANSPORTATION, INC.; *U.S. Private*, pg. 1068
COUNTRYWIDE TRUCK INSURANCE AGENCY; *U.S. Private*, pg. 1068
COUNT'S KUSTOMS; *U.S. Private*, pg. 1066
COUNT'S VAMP'D; *U.S. Private*, pg. 1066
COUNTY BANCORP, INC.—See Nicolet Bankshares, Inc.; *U.S. Public*, pg. 1528
COUNTY BANK; *U.S. Private*, pg. 1068
COUNTY CONCRETE CORPORATION; *U.S. Private*, pg. 1068
COUNTY DISTRIBUTING COMPANY; *U.S. Private*, pg. 1068
COUNTY ESTATES LIMITED—See Multiplan Empreendimentos Imobiliarios S.A.; *Int'l*, pg. 5084
COUNTY FAIR FOODS (PTY) LTD—See Astral Foods Limited; *Int'l*, pg. 658
COUNTY FOOTWEAR LIMITED—See Patterson Companies, Inc.; *U.S. Public*, pg. 1653
COUNTY HOME IMPROVEMENT CENTER; *U.S. Private*, pg. 1068
COUNTY HOTELS GROUP PLC—See Malayan United Industries Berhad; *Int'l*, pg. 4661
COUNTY INSURANCE CONSULTANTS LIMITED—See Brown & Brown, Inc.; *U.S. Public*, pg. 400
COUNTY INTERNATIONAL LIMITED; *Int'l*, pg. 1819
THE COUNTY LINE ENTERPRISES, INC.; *U.S. Private*, pg. 4015
COUNTY MATERIALS CORP.; *U.S. Private*, pg. 1068
COUNTY NATIONAL BANK—See CNB Community Bancorp, Inc.; *U.S. Public*, pg. 519
COUNTY SANITATION DISTRICTS OF LOS ANGELES COUNTY; *U.S. Private*, pg. 1068
COUNTY SANITATION DISTRICTS OF ORANGE COUNTY, INC.; *U.S. Private*, pg. 1068
COUNTY SUPER SPUDS, INC.; *U.S. Private*, pg. 1068
COUNTY WASTE AND RECYCLING SERVICE, INC.—See Waste Connections, Inc.; *Int'l*, pg. 8353
COUNTY WASTE SYSTEMS, INC.—See Watts Trucking Service, Inc.; *U.S. Private*, pg. 4456
COUNTY WASTE - ULSTER, LLC—See Waste Connections, Inc.; *Int'l*, pg. 8353
COUNTY WELDING PRODUCTS, INC.—See CI Capital Partners LLC; *U.S. Private*, pg. 895
COUPA DEUTSCHLAND GMBH—See Thoma Bravo, L.P.; *U.S. Private*, pg. 4147
COUPA EMEA—See Thoma Bravo, L.P.; *U.S. Private*, pg. 4147
COUPANG, INC.; *Int'l*, pg. 1819
COUPAR ANGUS CARE HOME—See Balhousie Holdings Limited; *Int'l*, pg. 808
COUPA SOFTWARE INCORPORATED—See Thoma Bravo, L.P.; *U.S. Private*, pg. 4146
COUPA SOFTWARE INDIA PRIVATE LIMITED—See Thoma Bravo, L.P.; *U.S. Private*, pg. 4147
COUPA SOFTWARE SWITZERLAND AG—See Thoma Bravo, L.P.; *U.S. Private*, pg. 4147
COUPLED PRODUCTS, INC.—See Dana Incorporated; *U.S. Public*, pg. 622
COUPON EXPRESS, INC.; *U.S. Private*, pg. 1068
COUPONS.COM LIMITED—See Charlesbank Capital Partners, LLC; *U.S. Private*, pg. 855
COUPONS, INC.—See Charlesbank Capital Partners, LLC; *U.S. Private*, pg. 855
COURAGE INVESTMENT GROUP LIMITED; *Int'l*, pg. 1819
COURAGE MARINE (HK) COMPANY LIMITED—See Courage Investment Group Limited; *Int'l*, pg. 1819
COURAGE - NEW AMEGO SHIPPING AGENCY CO. LTD.—See Courage Investment Group Limited; *Int'l*, pg. 1819
COURAGE - NEW AMEGO SHIPPING CORP.—See Courage Investment Group Limited; *Int'l*, pg. 1819
COURAGE SERVICES, INC.—See Amentum Services, Inc.; *U.S. Private*, pg. 219
COURANT SAS; *Int'l*, pg. 1819
COURBET SA; *Int'l*, pg. 1819
COURBU VITRAGES—See Compagnie de Saint-Gobain SA; *Int'l*, pg. 1723

CORPORATE AFFILIATIONS

COURIER CAPITAL CORPORATION - JAMESTOWN OFFICE—See Financial Institutions, Inc.; *U.S. Public*, pg. 834
COURIER CAPITAL, LLC—See Financial Institutions, Inc.; *U.S. Public*, pg. 834
COURIER GRAPHICS CORP.; *U.S. Private*, pg. 1068
COURIER HOLDINGS LTD.—See Intuit Inc.; *U.S. Public*, pg. 1160
THE COURIER-JOURNAL, INC.—See Gannett Co., Inc.; *U.S. Public*, pg. 900
COURIER NEWSPAPER HOLDINGS PTY LIMITED—See News Corporation; *U.S. Public*, pg. 1519
THE COURIER NEWS—See Chicago Public Media, Inc.; *U.S. Private*, pg. 879
COURIER NEWS—See Gannett Co., Inc.; *U.S. Public*, pg. 897
COURIER PLUS, INC.; *U.S. Private*, pg. 1068
COURIERPOST—See New Zealand Post Limited; *Int'l*, pg. 5232
COURIER-POST—See Gannett Co., Inc.; *U.S. Public*, pg. 897
THE COURIER—See Gannett Co., Inc.; *U.S. Public*, pg. 904
COURIER SYSTEM INC.; *U.S. Private*, pg. 1068
COURIER TECHNOLOGIA EM SERVICOS GRAFICOS LTDA—See Chatham Asset Management, LLC; *U.S. Private*, pg. 863
COURIER TIMES, INC.—See Gannett Co., Inc.; *U.S. Public*, pg. 901
COURIER TIMES NEWSPAPER—See Paxton Media Group LLC; *U.S. Private*, pg. 3116
COURISTAN INC.; *U.S. Private*, pg. 1068
COURSERA, INC.; *U.S. Public*, pg. 587
COURT CAVENDISH LIMITED; *Int'l*, pg. 1819
THE COURT COMPANY; *U.S. Private*, pg. 4015
COURTESY ACURA—See Don Jacobs Automotive Inc.; *U.S. Private*, pg. 1258
COURTESY ASSOCIATES—See SmithBucklin Corporation; *U.S. Private*, pg. 3697
COURTESY AUTOMOTIVE CENTER; *U.S. Private*, pg. 1070
COURTESY BUICK GMC, INC.; *U.S. Private*, pg. 1070
COURTESY CAR CITY; *U.S. Private*, pg. 1070
COURTESY CHEV OLDS LTD.; *Int'l*, pg. 1819
COURTESY CHEVROLET CENTER; *U.S. Private*, pg. 1070
COURTESY CHEVROLET INC.—See AutoNation, Inc.; *U.S. Public*, pg. 234
COURTESY FORD INC.; *U.S. Private*, pg. 1070
COURTESY FORD LINCOLN SALES; *Int'l*, pg. 1819
COURTESY FREIGHT SYSTEMS LTD.—See Mullen Group Ltd.; *Int'l*, pg. 5080
COURTESY GARAGE LIMITED - TROPICAL BATTERY DIVISION—See Goddard Enterprises Limited; *Int'l*, pg. 3018
COURTESY GARAGE LTD.—See Goddard Enterprises Limited; *Int'l*, pg. 3018
COURTESY GLASS INC.; *U.S. Private*, pg. 1070
COURTESY LINCOLN MERCURY INC.; *U.S. Private*, pg. 1070
COURTESY MITSUBISHI; *U.S. Private*, pg. 1070
COURTESY PRODUCTS LLC—See Centric Group LLC; *U.S. Private*, pg. 830
COURTESY QUALITY BRANDON—See Asbury Automotive Group, Inc.; *U.S. Public*, pg. 209
COURTESY SPORTS INC.; *U.S. Private*, pg. 1070
COURTEVILLE BUSINESS SOLUTIONS PLC.; *Int'l*, pg. 1819
COURTEVILLE LOSS ADJUSTERS LTD.—See Courteville Business Solutions Plc.; *Int'l*, pg. 1819
COURTIERS EN DOUANES CARSON LIMITEE; *Int'l*, pg. 1819
COURTLAND HOMES INC.; *U.S. Private*, pg. 1070
COURTLAND PARTNERS LTD.—See StepStone Group LP; *U.S. Private*, pg. 3804
THE COURTNEY GROUP, INCORPORATED; *U.S. Private*, pg. 4015
COURTNEY MARKETING, INC.; *U.S. Private*, pg. 1070
COURTNEY RIDGE LANDFILL, LLC—See Republic Services, Inc.; *U.S. Public*, pg. 1786
COURTOIS SA; *Int'l*, pg. 1819
COURTROOM TELEVISION NETWORK LLC—See Lions Gate Entertainment Corp.; *Int'l*, pg. 4521
COURTROOM TELEVISION NETWORK LLC—See Warner Bros. Discovery, Inc.; *U.S. Public*, pg. 2328
COURTS ASIA LIMITED—See Nojima Corporation; *Int'l*, pg. 5401
COURTS FOR KIDS; *U.S. Private*, pg. 1070
COURTSIDE CELLARS—See E. & J. Gallo Winery; *U.S. Private*, pg. 1303
COURTSIDE CLUB—See KKR & Co. Inc.; *U.S. Public*, pg. 1264
COURTS (JAMAICA) LIMITED; *Int'l*, pg. 1819
COURTSMART DIGITAL SYSTEMS, INC.; *U.S. Private*, pg. 1070
COURT SQUARE CAPITAL PARTNERS, L.P.; *U.S. Private*, pg. 1068
COURT SQUARE GROUP; *U.S. Private*, pg. 1070

COMPANY NAME INDEX

COURTS SINGAPORE LIMITED—See EQT AB; *Int'l*, pg. 2470
COURTS SINGAPORE LIMITED—See The International Investor Company K.S.C.C.; *Int'l*, pg. 7656
COURTVIEW JUSTICE SOLUTIONS INC.—See Constellation Software Inc.; *Int'l*, pg. 1775
COURTYARD ALBUQUERQUE AIRPORT OPERATOR LLC—See W.P. Carey Inc.; *U.S. Public*, pg. 2315
COURTYARD BALTIMORE WASHINGTON AIRPORT OPERATOR LLC—See W.P. Carey Inc.; *U.S. Public*, pg. 2315
COURTYARD BY MARRIOTT - EWING HOPEWELL—See KSL Capital Partners, LLC; *U.S. Private*, pg. 2355
COURTYARD BY MARRIOTT - MIAMI BEACH-SOUTH BEACH—See Robert Finvarb Companies, LLC; *U.S. Private*, pg. 3458
COURTYARD BY MARRIOTT - MIAMI COCONUT GROVE—See Robert Finvarb Companies, LLC; *U.S. Private*, pg. 3458
COURTYARD BY MARRIOTT - SAN DIEGO OLD TOWN—See Westbrook Real Estate Partners, LLC; *U.S. Private*, pg. 4488
COURTYARD CHICAGO OHARE OPERATOR LLC—See W.P. Carey Inc.; *U.S. Public*, pg. 2315
COURTYARD INDIANAPOLIS AIRPORT OPERATOR LLC—See W.P. Carey Inc.; *U.S. Public*, pg. 2315
COURTYARD IRVINE JOHN WAYNE AIRPORT OPERATOR LLC—See W.P. Carey Inc.; *U.S. Public*, pg. 2315
COURTYARD LOUISVILLE EAST OPERATOR LLC—See W.P. Carey Inc.; *U.S. Public*, pg. 2315
COURTYARD MARRIOTT-VACAVILLE INC.—See Marriott International, Inc.; *U.S. Public*, pg. 1370
COURTYARD NEWARK LIBERTY INTERNATIONAL AIRPORT OPERATOR LLC—See W.P. Carey Inc.; *U.S. Public*, pg. 2315
COURTYARD ORLANDO AIRPORT OPERATOR LLC—See W.P. Carey Inc.; *U.S. Public*, pg. 2315
COURTYARD ORLANDO INTERNATIONAL DRIVE CONVENTION CENTER OPERATOR LLC—See W.P. Carey Inc.; *U.S. Public*, pg. 2315
COURTYARDS AT 65TH, L.P.—See Essex Property Trust, Inc.; *U.S. Public*, pg. 796
COURTYARD SPOKANE DOWNTOWN OPERATOR LLC—See W.P. Carey Inc.; *U.S. Public*, pg. 2315
COURY HEALTH SERVICES, LLC—See Genstar Capital, LLC; *U.S. Private*, pg. 1674
COURY MOSS INC.; *U.S. Private*, pg. 1071
COUSIN CORPORATION OF AMERICA; *U.S. Private*, pg. 1071
COUSINEAU FOREST PRODUCTS, INC.—See Cousineau Inc.; *U.S. Private*, pg. 1071
COUSINEAU INC.; *U.S. Private*, pg. 1071
COUSINEAU PROPERTIES—See Cousineau Inc.; *U.S. Private*, pg. 1071
COUSINEAUS HENNIKER—See Cousineau Inc.; *U.S. Private*, pg. 1071
COUSINS FOOD MARKET INC.; *U.S. Private*, pg. 1071
COUSINS HOME LENDING, INC.; *U.S. Private*, pg. 1071
COUSINS PROPERTIES INCORPORATED; *U.S. Public*, pg. 587
COUSINS PROPERTIES LP—See Cousins Properties Incorporated; *U.S. Public*, pg. 587
COUSINS PROPERTIES PALISADES LLC—See Cousins Properties Incorporated; *U.S. Public*, pg. 587
COUSINS PROPERTIES SERVICES LLC—See Cousins Properties Incorporated; *U.S. Public*, pg. 587
COUSINS REALTY SERVICES, LLC—See Cousins Properties Incorporated; *U.S. Public*, pg. 587
COUSINS - SAN JACINTO CENTER LLC—See Cousins Properties Incorporated; *U.S. Public*, pg. 587
COUSINS SUBMARINES, INC.; *U.S. Private*, pg. 1071
COUSINS TERMINUS LLC—See Cousins Properties Incorporated; *U.S. Public*, pg. 587
COUTINHO & FERROSTAAL GMBH & CO. KG—See MPC Munchmeyer Petersen & Co. GmbH; *Int'l*, pg. 5060
COUTINHO & FERROSTAAL INC.—See MPC Munchmeyer Petersen & Co. GmbH; *Int'l*, pg. 5060
COUTTS & CO CHANNEL ISLANDS—See NatWest Group plc; *Int'l*, pg. 5170
COUTTS & CO ISLE OF MAN—See NatWest Group plc; *Int'l*, pg. 5170
COUTTS & COMPANY—See NatWest Group plc; *Int'l*, pg. 5170
COUTURE LAMPS, INC.—See China Baofeng (International) Ltd.; *Int'l*, pg. 1485
COUTURIER—See FAYAT SAS; *Int'l*, pg. 2625
COVAGEN AG—See Johnson & Johnson; *U.S. Public*, pg. 1194
COVALENCE SPECIALTY ADHESIVES LLC—See Berry Global Group, Inc; *U.S. Public*, pg. 321
COVALENT METROLOGY SERVICES, INC.; *U.S. Private*, pg. 1071
THE COVALI GROUP LLC; *Int'l*, pg. 7635
COVALIS CAPITAL (AMERICA) LLC—See Covalis Capital LP; *Int'l*, pg. 1819
COVALIS CAPITAL LLP—See Covalis Capital LP; *Int'l*, pg. 1820
COVALIS CAPITAL LP; *Int'l*, pg. 1819

COVALON TECHNOLOGIES INC.—See Covalon Technologies Ltd.; *Int'l*, pg. 1820
COVALON TECHNOLOGIES LTD.; *Int'l*, pg. 1820
COVAL VACUUM TECHNOLOGY INC.—See Investor AB; *Int'l*, pg. 3787
COVANCE (ASIA) PTE. LTD.—See Laboratory Corporation of America Holdings; *U.S. Public*, pg. 1285
COVANCE BIOANALYTICAL SERVICES LLC—See Laboratory Corporation of America Holdings; *U.S. Public*, pg. 1285
COVANCE CENTRAL LABORATORY SERVICES, INC.—See Laboratory Corporation of America Holdings; *U.S. Public*, pg. 1285
COVANCE CENTRAL LABORATORY SERVICES SA—See Laboratory Corporation of America Holdings; *U.S. Public*, pg. 1285
COVANCE CHILE SERVICES LIMITADA—See Laboratory Corporation of America Holdings; *U.S. Public*, pg. 1285
COVANCE CLASSIC LABORATORY SERVICES INC.—See Laboratory Corporation of America Holdings; *U.S. Public*, pg. 1286
COVANCE CLINICAL AND PERIAPPROVAL SERVICES LIMITED—See Laboratory Corporation of America Holdings; *U.S. Public*, pg. 1286
COVANCE CLINICAL AND PERIAPPROVAL SERVICES SARL—See Laboratory Corporation of America Holdings; *U.S. Public*, pg. 1286
COVANCE CLINICAL & PERIAPPROVAL SERVICES S.A—See Laboratory Corporation of America Holdings; *U.S. Public*, pg. 1286
COVANCE CLINICAL PRODUCT DEVELOPMENTS LTD.—See Laboratory Corporation of America Holdings; *U.S. Public*, pg. 1286
COVANCE CLINICAL RESEARCH UNIT, INC.—See Laboratory Corporation of America Holdings; *U.S. Public*, pg. 1286
COVANCE CLINICAL RESEARCH UNIT LTD.—See Laboratory Corporation of America Holdings; *U.S. Public*, pg. 1286
COVANCE GMBH—See Laboratory Corporation of America Holdings; *U.S. Public*, pg. 1286
COVANCE HEALTH ECONOMICS & OUTCOME SERVICES, INC.—See Laboratory Corporation of America Holdings; *U.S. Public*, pg. 1286
COVANCE HONG KONG SERVICES LIMITED—See Laboratory Corporation of America Holdings; *U.S. Public*, pg. 1286
COVANCE, INC.—See Laboratory Corporation of America Holdings; *U.S. Public*, pg. 1285
COVANCE INDIA PHARMACEUTICAL SERVICES PRIVATE LIMITED—See Laboratory Corporation of America Holdings; *U.S. Public*, pg. 1286
COVANCE JAPAN CO. LTD.—See Laboratory Corporation of America Holdings; *U.S. Public*, pg. 1286
COVANCE KOREA SERVICES LIMITED—See Laboratory Corporation of America Holdings; *U.S. Public*, pg. 1286
COVANCE LABORATORIES GMBH—See Laboratory Corporation of America Holdings; *U.S. Public*, pg. 1286
COVANCE LABORATORIES INC.—See Laboratory Corporation of America Holdings; *U.S. Public*, pg. 1286
COVANCE LABORATORIES KOREA COMPANY LIMITED—See Laboratory Corporation of America Holdings; *U.S. Public*, pg. 1286
COVANCE LABORATORIES LIMITED—See Laboratory Corporation of America Holdings; *U.S. Public*, pg. 1286
COVANCE LIMITED—See Laboratory Corporation of America Holdings; *U.S. Public*, pg. 1286
COVANCE MEXICO SERVICES, S. DE R. L. DE C.V.—See Laboratory Corporation of America Holdings; *U.S. Public*, pg. 1286
COVANCE PERU SERVICES S.A.—See Laboratory Corporation of America Holdings; *U.S. Public*, pg. 1286
COVANCE PRECLINICAL SERVICES GMBH—See Laboratory Corporation of America Holdings; *U.S. Public*, pg. 1286
COVANCE PTY. LTD.—See Laboratory Corporation of America Holdings; *U.S. Public*, pg. 1286
COVANCE RESEARCH PRODUCTS INC.—See Laboratory Corporation of America Holdings; *U.S. Public*, pg. 1286
COVANCE SERVICES (THAILAND) LIMITED—See Laboratory Corporation of America Holdings; *U.S. Public*, pg. 1286
COVANCE TAIWAN SERVICES LIMITED—See Laboratory Corporation of America Holdings; *U.S. Public*, pg. 1286
COVAN INTERNATIONAL INC.—See Coleman American Companies, Inc.; *U.S. Private*, pg. 967
COVANSYS S.L.—See DXC Technology Company; *U.S. Public*, pg. 695
COVANTA ABINGTON TRANSFER SOLUTIONS LLC—See EQT AB; *Int'l*, pg. 2473
COVANTA ALEXANDRIA/ARLINGTON, INC.—See EQT AB; *Int'l*, pg. 2473
COVANTA BABYLON, INC.—See EQT AB; *Int'l*, pg. 2473
COVANTA BRISTOL, INC.—See EQT AB; *Int'l*, pg. 2473
COVANTA BURNABY RENEWABLE ENERGY, INC.—See EQT AB; *Int'l*, pg. 2473
COVANTA COMPANY OF SEMASS, LLC—See EQT AB; *Int'l*, pg. 2473

COVANTA DADE RENEWABLE ENERGY, LLC—See EQT AB; *Int'l*, pg. 2473
COVANTA DELAWARE VALLEY LLC—See EQT AB; *Int'l*, pg. 2473
COVANTA DURHAN YORK RENEWABLE ENERGY LIMITED PARTNERSHIP—See EQT AB; *Int'l*, pg. 2473
COVANTA ENERGY CORPORATION—See EQT AB; *Int'l*, pg. 2473
COVANTA ENVIRONMENTAL SOLUTIONS—See EQT AB; *Int'l*, pg. 2473
COVANTAGE CREDIT UNION; *U.S. Private*, pg. 1071
COVANTA HAVERHILL, INC.—See EQT AB; *Int'l*, pg. 2473
COVANTA HOLDING CORPORATION—See EQT AB; *Int'l*, pg. 2473
COVANTA HUDSON VALLEY RENEWABLE ENERGY LLC—See EQT AB; *Int'l*, pg. 2473
COVANTA HUNTSVILLE, INC.—See EQT AB; *Int'l*, pg. 2473
COVANTA INDIANAPOLIS, INC.—See EQT AB; *Int'l*, pg. 2474
COVANTA KENT, INC.—See EQT AB; *Int'l*, pg. 2474
COVANTA LANCASTER, INC.—See EQT AB; *Int'l*, pg. 2474
COVANTA LONG BEACH RENEWABLE ENERGY CORP.—See EQT AB; *Int'l*, pg. 2474
COVANTA MARION, INC.—See EQT AB; *Int'l*, pg. 2474
COVANTA MENDOTA, L.P.—See EQT AB; *Int'l*, pg. 2474
COVANTA MONTGOMERY, INC.—See EQT AB; *Int'l*, pg. 2474
COVANTA NIAGARA I, LLC—See EQT AB; *Int'l*, pg. 2474
COVANTA NIAGARA, L.P.—See EQT AB; *Int'l*, pg. 2474
COVANTA ONONDAGA LIMITED PARTNERSHIP—See EQT AB; *Int'l*, pg. 2474
COVANTA PITTSFIELD, LLC—See EQT AB; *Int'l*, pg. 2474
COVANTA PLYMOUTH RENEWABLE ENERGY LP—See EQT AB; *Int'l*, pg. 2474
COVANTA PROJECTS OF WALLINGFORD, L.P.—See EQT AB; *Int'l*, pg. 2474
COVANTA RENEWABLE FUELS LLC—See EQT AB; *Int'l*, pg. 2474
COVANTA SOUTHEASTERN FLORIDA RENEWABLE ENERGY LLC—See EQT AB; *Int'l*, pg. 2474
COVANTA STANISLAUS, INC.—See EQT AB; *Int'l*, pg. 2474
COVANTA TULSA RENEWABLE ENERGY LLC—See EQT AB; *Int'l*, pg. 2474
COVANTA UNION, LLC—See EQT AB; *Int'l*, pg. 2474
COVANTA WARREN ENERGY RESOURCE CO., LLC—See EQT AB; *Int'l*, pg. 2474
COVANTA YORK RENEWABLE ENERGY LIMITED PARTNERSHIP—See EQT AB; *Int'l*, pg. 2474
COVANT MANAGEMENT, INC.—See Madison Dearborn Partners, LLC; *U.S. Private*, pg. 2540
COVAN WORLDWIDE MOVING INC.—See Coleman American Companies, Inc.; *U.S. Private*, pg. 967
COVARIO CHINA—See Covario, Inc.; *U.S. Private*, pg. 1071
COVARIO EUROPE—See Covario, Inc.; *U.S. Private*, pg. 1071
COVARIO, INC.; *U.S. Private*, pg. 1071
COVARIO JAPAN—See Covario, Inc.; *U.S. Private*, pg. 1071
COVARIO SINGAPORE—See Covario, Inc.; *U.S. Private*, pg. 1071
COVARIS, INC.—See Revvity, Inc.; *U.S. Public*, pg. 1794
COVEA FINANCE SAS—See Covea Groupe S.A.S.; *Int'l*, pg. 1820
COVEA GROUPE S.A.S.; *Int'l*, pg. 1820
COVEA INSURANCE PLC—See Covea Groupe S.A.S.; *Int'l*, pg. 1820
COVEA RISKS S.A.—See Covea Groupe S.A.S.; *Int'l*, pg. 1820
COVED—See Ardian SAS; *Int'l*, pg. 556
COVED—See Caisse des Depots et Consignations; *Int'l*, pg. 1258
COVE FOUR-SLIDE & STAMPING CORP.; *U.S. Private*, pg. 1071
COVE HAVEN ENTERTAINMENT RESORTS—See Mcsam Hotel Group LLC; *U.S. Private*, pg. 2644
COVE HILL PARTENRS, L.P.; *U.S. Private*, pg. 1071
COVE-ITO ADVERTISING LTD.; *Int'l*, pg. 1820
COVE-ITO INTERACTIVE—See Cove-Ito Advertising Ltd.; *Int'l*, pg. 1820
COVE-ITO INTERNATIONAL LTD.—See Cove-Ito Advertising Ltd.; *Int'l*, pg. 1820
COVE-ITO (THAILAND) LTD.—See Cove-Ito Advertising Ltd.; *Int'l*, pg. 1820
COVELLI ENTERPRISES LLC; *U.S. Private*, pg. 1071
COVENANT BANK; *U.S. Private*, pg. 1071
COVENANT CAPITAL GROUP, LLC; *U.S. Private*, pg. 1071
COVENANT CARE, LLC—See Centre Partners Management LLC; *U.S. Private*, pg. 828
COVENANT EYES, INC.; *U.S. Private*, pg. 1071
COVENANT HEALTH, INC.; *U.S. Private*, pg. 1071
COVENANT HEALTH; *U.S. Private*, pg. 1071
COVENANT LOGISTICS GROUP, INC.; *U.S. Public*, pg. 587

COVENANT MEDICAL CENTER INC; *U.S. Private*, pg. 1071
COVENANT PHYSICIAN PARTNERS, INC.—See KKR & Co. Inc.; *U.S. Public*, pg. 1243
COVENANT PROPERTIES, LLC—See Covenant Logistics Group, Inc.; *U.S. Public*, pg. 588
COVENANT SERVICES WORLDWIDE, LLC; *U.S. Private*, pg. 1072
COVENANT STORAGE INC.—See HI-Boy Group Inc.; *U.S. Private*, pg. 1931
COVENANT TESTING TECHNOLOGIES, LLC—See Kingswood Capital Management LLC; *U.S. Private*, pg. 2312
COVENANT TRANSPORT, INC.—See Covenant Logistics Group, Inc.; *U.S. Public*, pg. 588
COVENTOR, INC.—See Lam Research Corporation; *U.S. Public*, pg. 1289
COVENTOR KOREA LIMITED—See Lam Research Corporation; *U.S. Public*, pg. 1289
COVENTOR SARL—See Lam Research Corporation; *U.S. Public*, pg. 1289
COVENTRY BUILDING SOCIETY; *Int'l*, pg. 1820
COVENTRY COIL-O-MATIC (HARYANA) LIMITED; *Int'l*, pg. 1821
THE COVENTRY COURIER—See R.I.S.N. Operations Inc.; *U.S. Private*, pg. 3336
COVENTRY EDUCATION PARTNERSHIP HOLDINGS LIMITED—See Bilfinger SE; *Int'l*, pg. 1028
COVENTRY ELECTRICAL SUPPLIES LTD.—See City Electric Supply Company; *U.S. Private*, pg. 905
COVENTRY FINANCIAL MANAGEMENT SERVICES, INC.—See CVS Health Corporation; *U.S. Public*, pg. 614
COVENTRY FIRST LLC; *U.S. Private*, pg. 1072
COVENTRY GROUP LIMITED ARTIA DIVISION—See Coventry Group Limited; *Int'l*, pg. 1821
COVENTRY GROUP LIMITED COVENTRY FASTENERS DIVISION—See Coventry Group Limited; *Int'l*, pg. 1821
COVENTRY GROUP LIMITED COVENTRYS DIVISION—See Coventry Group Limited; *Int'l*, pg. 1821
COVENTRY GROUP LIMITED HYLTON PARKER FASTENERS DIVISION—See Coventry Group Limited; *Int'l*, pg. 1821
COVENTRY GROUP LIMITED; *Int'l*, pg. 1821
COVENTRY GROUP (NZ) LIMITED—See Coventry Group Limited; *Int'l*, pg. 1821
COVENTRY HEALTH CARE OF DELAWARE, INC.—See CVS Health Corporation; *U.S. Public*, pg. 614
COVENTRY HEALTH CARE OF GEORGIA, INC.—See CVS Health Corporation; *U.S. Public*, pg. 614
COVENTRY HEALTH CARE OF ILLINOIS, INC.—See CVS Health Corporation; *U.S. Public*, pg. 614
COVENTRY HEALTH CARE OF IOWA, INC.—See CVS Health Corporation; *U.S. Public*, pg. 615
COVENTRY HEALTH CARE OF KANSAS, INC.—See CVS Health Corporation; *U.S. Public*, pg. 615
COVENTRY HEALTH CARE OF MISSOURI, INC.—See CVS Health Corporation; *U.S. Public*, pg. 615
COVENTRY HEALTH CARE OF NEBRASKA, INC.—See CVS Health Corporation; *U.S. Public*, pg. 615
COVENTRY HEALTH CARE OF TEXAS, INC.—See CVS Health Corporation; *U.S. Public*, pg. 615
COVENTRY HEALTH CARE OF THE CAROLINAS, INC.—See CVS Health Corporation; *U.S. Public*, pg. 615
COVENTRY HEALTH CARE OF VIRGINIA, INC.—See CVS Health Corporation; *U.S. Public*, pg. 615
COVENTRY HEALTH CARE OF WEST VIRGINIA, INC.—See CVS Health Corporation; *U.S. Public*, pg. 615
COVENTRY HEALTH PLAN OF FLORIDA, INC.—See CVS Health Corporation; *U.S. Public*, pg. 615
COVENTRY LUMBER INC.; *U.S. Private*, pg. 1072
COVENTRY NEWSPAPERS LTD—See Reach PLC; *Int'l*, pg. 6231
COVENTRY PRESCRIPTION MANAGEMENT SERVICES, INC.—See CVS Health Corporation; *U.S. Public*, pg. 615
COVENTYA AB—See Element Solutions Inc.; *U.S. Public*, pg. 725
COVENTYA ENVIRONMENTAL PLATING TECHNOLOGY (JIANGSU) CO., LTD.—See Element Solutions Inc.; *U.S. Public*, pg. 725
COVENTYA GMBH—See Element Solutions Inc.; *U.S. Public*, pg. 725
COVENTYA HOLDING SAS—See Silverfleet Capital Limited; *Int'l*, pg. 6925
COVENTYA INC.—See Silverfleet Capital Limited; *Int'l*, pg. 6925
COVENTYA INC.—See Silverfleet Capital Limited; *Int'l*, pg. 6925
COVENTYA INDIA PVT. LTD.—See Silverfleet Capital Limited; *Int'l*, pg. 6925
COVENTYA KIMYA SANAYI VE TICARET ANONIM SIRKETI—See Element Solutions Inc.; *U.S. Public*, pg. 725
COVENTYA KOREA CO., LIMITED—See Element Solutions Inc.; *U.S. Public*, pg. 725

COVENTYA LIMITED—See Element Solutions Inc.; *U.S. Public*, pg. 725
COVENTYA MALAYSIA SDN. BHD.—See Element Solutions Inc.; *U.S. Public*, pg. 725
COVENTYA QUIMICA LTDA—See Element Solutions Inc.; *U.S. Public*, pg. 725
COVENTYA SAS—See Silverfleet Capital Limited; *Int'l*, pg. 6925
COVENTYA SOUTH EAST ASIA PTE. LTD.—See Silverfleet Capital Limited; *Int'l*, pg. 6925
COVENTYA SURFACE TREATMENT TECHNOLOGY (SUZHOU) CO. LTD.—See Silverfleet Capital Limited; *Int'l*, pg. 6925
COVENTYA TECHNOLOGIES S.L.—See Element Solutions Inc.; *U.S. Public*, pg. 725
COVE PETROLEUM—See Anchor Gasoline Corporation; *U.S. Private*, pg. 273
COVER 50 S.P.A.; *Int'l*, pg. 1821
C. OVERAA & CO.; *U.S. Private*, pg. 705
COVERALL NORTH AMERICA, INC.; *U.S. Private*, pg. 1072
COVERALL PIPELINE CONSTRUCTION LTD.—See Vertex Resource Group Ltd.; *Int'l*, pg. 8174
COVER CONCEPTS MARKETING SERVICES LLC—See The Walt Disney Company; *U.S. Public*, pg. 2139
COVER CORPORATION; *Int'l*, pg. 1821
COVERCO S.R.L.—See Franklin Electric Co., Inc.; *U.S. Public*, pg. 878
COVERCRAFT DIRECT, LLC; *U.S. Private*, pg. 1072
COVERCRAFT INDUSTRIES INC.—See Audax Group, Limited Partnership; *U.S. Private*, pg. 387
COVERCRESS INC.—See Bayer Aktiengesellschaft; *Int'l*, pg. 907
COVERDELL CANADA CORPORATION—See Arthur J. Gallagher & Co.; *U.S. Public*, pg. 204
COVERDELL & COMPANY, INC.—See Vertrue Inc.; *U.S. Private*, pg. 4370
COVERDELL—See Vertrue Inc.; *U.S. Private*, pg. 4370
COVER GIRL COSMETICS—See The Procter & Gamble Company; *U.S. Public*, pg. 2120
COVERICA, INC.; *U.S. Private*, pg. 1072
COVERIGHT SURFACES USA CO.—See Lone Star Funds; *U.S. Private*, pg. 2484
COVERIS ADVANCED COATINGS HOLDINGS (UK) LTD.—See Sun Capital Partners, Inc.; *U.S. Private*, pg. 3858
COVERIS ADVANCED COATINGS (NORTH WALES) LTD.—See Sun Capital Partners, Inc.; *U.S. Private*, pg. 3858
COVERIS ADVANCED COATINGS US LLC—See Sun Capital Partners, Inc.; *U.S. Private*, pg. 3859
COVERIS FLEXIBLES (THOMASVILLE) US LLC—See Sun Capital Partners, Inc.; *U.S. Private*, pg. 3859
COVERIS FLEXIBLES US LLC - CONSUMER FOOD DIVISION—See Sun Capital Partners, Inc.; *U.S. Private*, pg. 3859
COVERIS FLEXIBLES US LLC - PERFORMANCE FILMS DIVISION—See Sun Capital Partners, Inc.; *U.S. Private*, pg. 3859
COVERIS FLEXIBLES US LLC - PET FOOD DIVISION—See Sun Capital Partners, Inc.; *U.S. Private*, pg. 3859
COVERIS FLEXIBLES US LLC—See Sun Capital Partners, Inc.; *U.S. Private*, pg. 3859
COVERIS HOLDING CORP.—See Sun Capital Partners, Inc.; *U.S. Private*, pg. 3858
COVERIS HOLDINGS S.A.—See Sun Capital Partners, Inc.; *U.S. Private*, pg. 3858
COVERITY, INC.—See Synopsys, Inc.; *U.S. Public*, pg. 1970
COVER-MORE GROUP LIMITED—See Zurich Insurance Group Limited; *Int'l*, pg. 8697
COVERMYMEDS LLC—See McKesson Corporation; *U.S. Public*, pg. 1407
COVEROO, INC.—See Zazzle, Inc.; *U.S. Private*, pg. 4598
COVEROS, INC.; *U.S. Private*, pg. 1072
COVERPOINT CATERING CONSULTANCY LIMITED—See Jones Lang LaSalle Incorporated; *U.S. Public*, pg. 1201
COVERRA INSURANCE SERVICES, INC.—See Keystone Insurers Group, Inc.; *U.S. Public*, pg. 2300
COVER S.R.L.—See Interpump Group S.p.A.; *Int'l*, pg. 3755
COVERT BUICK INC.; *U.S. Private*, pg. 1072
COVER TECHNOLOGIES INC.; *Int'l*, pg. 1821
COVERXSPECIALTY—See Fairfax Financial Holdings Limited; *Int'l*, pg. 2606
COVER YOUR ASSETS, LLC—See RollKall Technologies LLC; *U.S. Private*, pg. 3475
COVERYS; *U.S. Private*, pg. 1072
COVE SHOE COMPANY—See Berkshire Hathaway Inc.; *U.S. Public*, pg. 299
COVE SPORTS & RECONSTRUCTION PTE. LTD.—See Livingstone Health Holdings Limited; *Int'l*, pg. 4532
COVESTIC, INC.—See H.I.G. Capital, LLC; *U.S. Private*, pg. 1831
COVESTOR LIMITED—See Interactive Brokers Group, Inc.; *U.S. Public*, pg. 1140

COVESTRO AG—See Bayer Aktiengesellschaft; *Int'l*, pg. 907
COVESTRO A/S - POLYURETHANES—See Bayer Aktiengesellschaft; *Int'l*, pg. 907
COVESTRO A/S—See Bayer Aktiengesellschaft; *Int'l*, pg. 907
COVESTRO (INDIA) PRIVATE LIMITED—See Bayer Aktiengesellschaft; *Int'l*, pg. 907
COVESTRO JAPAN LTD.—See Bayer Aktiengesellschaft; *Int'l*, pg. 907
COVESTRO LLC - AUTOMOTIVE PRODUCT CENTER—See Bayer Aktiengesellschaft; *Int'l*, pg. 907
COVESTRO LLC—See Bayer Aktiengesellschaft; *Int'l*, pg. 907
COVESTRO LLC - SPECIALTY FILMS BUSINESS—See Bayer Aktiengesellschaft; *Int'l*, pg. 907
COVESTRO N.V.—See Bayer Aktiengesellschaft; *Int'l*, pg. 907
COVESTRO—See Bayer Aktiengesellschaft; *Int'l*, pg. 907
COVESTRO (TIELT) N.V.—See Bayer Aktiengesellschaft; *Int'l*, pg. 907
COVEST WEALTH MANAGERS (PTY) LTD.—See Trustco Group Holdings Limited; *Int'l*, pg. 7945
COVETRUS, INC.—See Clayton, Dubilier & Rice, LLC; *U.S. Private*, pg. 921
COVETRUS, INC.—See TPG Capital, L.P.; *U.S. Public*, pg. 2170
COVEX, S.A.—See Shanghai Pioneer Holding Ltd.; *Int'l*, pg. 6776
COVEY-ODELL ADVERTISING LTD.; *U.S. Private*, pg. 1072
COVIA HOLDINGS CORPORATION; *U.S. Private*, pg. 1072
COVICH & WILLIAMS CO. INC.; *U.S. Private*, pg. 1072
COVIDH TECHNOLOGIES LIMITED; *Int'l*, pg. 1821
COVIDIEN AG—See Medtronic plc; *Int'l*, pg. 4786
COVIDIEN ARGENTINA S.A.—See Medtronic plc; *Int'l*, pg. 4786
COVIDIEN AUSTRALIA PTY LTD—See Medtronic plc; *Int'l*, pg. 4786
COVIDIEN AUSTRIA GMBH—See Medtronic plc; *Int'l*, pg. 4786
COVIDIEN BELGIUM 2 NV—See Medtronic plc; *Int'l*, pg. 4786
COVIDIEN DEUTSCHLAND GMBH—See Medtronic plc; *Int'l*, pg. 4786
COVIDIEN ECE S.R.O.—See Medtronic plc; *Int'l*, pg. 4787
COVIDIEN GI SOLUTIONS—See Medtronic plc; *Int'l*, pg. 4787
COVIDIEN - GREENWOOD—See Medtronic plc; *Int'l*, pg. 4787
COVIDIEN HEALTHCARE INDIA PRIVATE LIMITED—See Medtronic plc; *Int'l*, pg. 4787
COVIDIEN HEALTHCARE INTERNATIONAL TRADING (SHANGHAI) CO., LTD.—See Medtronic plc; *Int'l*, pg. 4787
COVIDIEN HOLDING INC.—See Medtronic plc; *Int'l*, pg. 4787
COVIDIEN HUNGARY KFT.—See Medtronic plc; *Int'l*, pg. 4786
COVIDIEN IRELAND COMMERCIAL LIMITED—See Medtronic plc; *Int'l*, pg. 4787
COVIDIEN (ISRAEL) LTD.—See Medtronic plc; *Int'l*, pg. 4786
COVIDIEN ISRAEL SURGICAL RESEARCH LTD.—See Medtronic plc; *Int'l*, pg. 4787
COVIDIEN LIMITED—See Medtronic plc; *Int'l*, pg. 4786
COVIDIEN LOGISTICS BVBA—See Medtronic plc; *Int'l*, pg. 4789
COVIDIEN MANUFACTURING SOLUTIONS, S.A.—See Medtronic plc; *Int'l*, pg. 4787
COVIDIEN MEDICAL PRODUCTS (SHANGHAI) MANUFACTURING L.L.C.—See Medtronic plc; *Int'l*, pg. 4787
COVIDIEN PHILIPPINES, INC.—See Medtronic plc; *Int'l*, pg. 4787
COVIDIEN PRIVATE LIMITED—See Medtronic plc; *Int'l*, pg. 4787
COVIDIEN PTY LIMITED—See Medtronic plc; *Int'l*, pg. 4787
COVIDIEN SENDIRIAN BERHAD—See Medtronic plc; *Int'l*, pg. 4787
COVIDIEN—See Medtronic plc; *Int'l*, pg. 4786
COVIDIEN SPAIN S.L.—See Medtronic plc; *Int'l*, pg. 4787
COVIDIEN TAIWAN LIMITED—See Medtronic plc; *Int'l*, pg. 4787
COVIDIEN (THAILAND) LIMITED—See Medtronic plc; *Int'l*, pg. 4786
COVIDIEN (UK) COMMERCIAL LIMITED—See Medtronic plc; *Int'l*, pg. 4786
COVINA PRESS-COURIER HIGHLANDER—See Alden Global Capital LLC; *U.S. Private*, pg. 158
COVINGTON & BURLING LLP; *U.S. Private*, pg. 1072
COVINGTON CAPITAL CORPORATION; *Int'l*, pg. 1821
COVINGTON ELECTRIC COOPERATIVE; *U.S. Private*, pg. 1073
COVINGTON FLOORING COMPANY; *U.S. Private*, pg. 1073
COVINGTON GROUP, INC.; *U.S. Private*, pg. 1073

COMPANY NAME INDEX C.P. ALL PUBLIC COMPANY LIMITED
Company Index

COVINGTON HEAVY DUTY PARTS; *U.S. Private*, pg. 1073
COVINGTON MEMORIAL GARDENS, INC.—See Axar Capital Management L.P.; *U.S. Private*, pg. 411
COVINGTON PIKE MOTORS, INC.—See AutoNation, Inc.; *U.S. Public*, pg. 234
COVIPHAMA CO., LTD.—See Socfinasia S.A.; *Int'l*, pg. 7031
COVIPOR-CIA VIDREIRA DO NORTE LTDA.—See Compagnie de Saint-Gobain SA; *Int'l*, pg. 1734
COVISINT CORPORATION—See Open Text Corporation; *Int'l*, pg. 5596
COVISINT GMBH—See Open Text Corporation; *Int'l*, pg. 5597
COVISINT SOFTWARE SERVICES (SHANGHAI) LTD.—See Open Text Corporation; *Int'l*, pg. 5597
COVISION MEDICAL TECHNOLOGIES LIMITED—See Turkiye Is Bankasi A.S.; *Int'l*, pg. 7976
COVIS PHARMACEUTICALS INC.; *U.S. Private*, pg. 1073
COVIT SA—See Vicat S.A.; *Int'l*, pg. 8185
COVIUS DOCUMENT SERVICES, LLC—See Covius Holdings, Inc.; *U.S. Private*, pg. 1073
COVIUS HOLDINGS, INC.; *U.S. Private*, pg. 1073
COVIVIO IMMOBILIEN SE—See Covivio; *Int'l*, pg. 1821
COVIVIO OFFICE AG—See Covivio; *Int'l*, pg. 1821
COVIVIO OFFICE GMBH—See Covivio; *Int'l*, pg. 1821
COVIVIO; *Int'l*, pg. 1821
COVSPOL, A.S.—See Veolia Environnement S.A.; *Int'l*, pg. 8161
COVX RESEARCH LLC—See Pfizer Inc.; *U.S. Public*, pg. 1679
COVX TECHNOLOGIES IRELAND LIMITED—See Pfizer Inc.; *U.S. Public*, pg. 1679
COWABUNGA INC.; *U.S. Private*, pg. 1073
COWAN, BOLDUC, DOHERTY & COMPANY, LLC—See Blum, Shapiro & Company, P.C.; *U.S. Private*, pg. 599
COWAN MANUFACTURING PTY. LIMITED—See James Fisher & Sons Public Limited Company; *Int'l*, pg. 3875
COWAN SYSTEMS INC.; *U.S. Private*, pg. 1073
COWAY CO., LTD.; *Int'l*, pg. 1821
COWAY (M) SDN. BHD.—See Coway Co., Ltd.; *Int'l*, pg. 1821
COWAY USA INC.—See Coway Co., Ltd.; *Int'l*, pg. 1821
COWBOY CHEVROLET BUICK PONTIAC GMC CADILLAC; *U.S. Private*, pg. 1073
COWBOY EXPLORATION LTD.—See Nextraction Energy Corp.; *Int'l*, pg. 5249
COWBOY FOOD COMPANY LIMITED—See Four Seas Mercantile Holdings Limited; *Int'l*, pg. 2755
COWBOY MALONEY APPLIANCE, AUDIO, VIDEO CENTERS, INC.; *U.S. Private*, pg. 1073
COWBOY TOYOTA; *U.S. Private*, pg. 1073
COWELL DIALYSIS, LLC—See DaVita Inc.; *U.S. Public*, pg. 637
COWELL E HOLDINGS INC.; *Int'l*, pg. 1821
COWELL ELECTRONICS COMPANY LIMITED—See Cowell e Holdings Inc.; *Int'l*, pg. 1821
COWELL FASHION CO., LTD.; *Int'l*, pg. 1822
COWELL OPTIC ELECTRONICS LIMITED—See Cowell e Holdings Inc.; *Int'l*, pg. 1821
COWELLS ARROW BINGO—See Arrow International, Inc.; *U.S. Private*, pg. 335
COWEN AND COMPANY (ASIA) LIMITED—See The Toronto-Dominion Bank; *Int'l*, pg. 7695
COWEN AND COMPANY, LLC—See The Toronto-Dominion Bank; *Int'l*, pg. 7695
COWEN ASIA LTD—See The Toronto-Dominion Bank; *Int'l*, pg. 7695
COWEN CONSTRUCTION INC.; *U.S. Private*, pg. 1073
COWEN EXECUTION HOLDCO LLC—See The Toronto-Dominion Bank; *Int'l*, pg. 7695
COWEN EXECUTION SERVICES LIMITED—See The Toronto-Dominion Bank; *Int'l*, pg. 7695
COWEN EXECUTION SERVICES LLC—See The Toronto-Dominion Bank; *Int'l*, pg. 7695
COWEN GERMANY AG—See The Toronto-Dominion Bank; *Int'l*, pg. 7695
COWEN, INC.—See The Toronto-Dominion Bank; *Int'l*, pg. 7695
COWEN PRIME SERVICES LLC—See The Toronto-Dominion Bank; *Int'l*, pg. 7695
COWEN PRIME SERVICES TRADING LLC—See The Toronto-Dominion Bank; *Int'l*, pg. 7695
COWEN STRUCTURED CREDIT GROUP LLC—See The Toronto-Dominion Bank; *Int'l*, pg. 7695
COWEN STRUCTURED HOLDINGS INC.—See The Toronto-Dominion Bank; *Int'l*, pg. 7695
COWERK CO., LTD.—See Toyota Boshoku Corporation; *Int'l*, pg. 7863
COWETA-FAYETTE ELECTRIC MEMBERSHIP CORPORATION; *U.S. Private*, pg. 1073
COWET-FYTTE ELECTRIC MEMBERSHIP CORP.; *U.S. Private*, pg. 1073
COWGIRL CREAMERY—See Emmi AG; *Int'l*, pg. 2384
COWIN & COMPANY, INC.; *U.S. Private*, pg. 1073
COWIN EQUIPMENT COMPANY INC—See C&C Holding Inc.; *U.S. Private*, pg. 702
THE COWLES CENTER; *U.S. Private*, pg. 4015
COWLES COMPANY; *U.S. Private*, pg. 1073
COWLES PUBLISHING COMPANY—See Cowles Company; *U.S. Private*, pg. 1073
COWLEY ASSOCIATES, INC.; *U.S. Private*, pg. 1074
COWLEY DISTRIBUTING INC.; *U.S. Private*, pg. 1074
COWLIN TIMBER FRAME—See Balfour Beatty plc; *Int'l*, pg. 808
COWLITZ CLEAN SWEEP—See Pacific Northern Environmental Corp; *U.S. Private*, pg. 3069
COWLITZ COUNTY PUBLIC UTILITY DISTRICT; *U.S. Private*, pg. 1074
COWON INDONESIA—See Cowon Systems Inc.; *Int'l*, pg. 1822
COWON PLAY CO., LTD.; *Int'l*, pg. 1822
COWON SYSTEMS INC.; *Int'l*, pg. 1822
COWORKRS LLC; *U.S. Private*, pg. 1074
COWORX STAFFING SERVICES LLC; *U.S. Private*, pg. 1074
COWTAN & TOUT, INC.—See Colefax Group PLC; *Int'l*, pg. 1697
COWTOWN BOOT COMPANY; *U.S. Private*, pg. 1074
COWTOWN MATERIALS, INC.—See GMS Inc.; *U.S. Public*, pg. 948
COX AND KINGS GLOBAL SERVICES PRIVATE LIMITED—See Cox & Kings Limited; *Int'l*, pg. 1822
COX AUTOMOTIVE, INC.—See Cox Enterprises, Inc.; *U.S. Private*, pg. 1074
COX AUTOMOTIVE LLC; *U.S. Private*, pg. 1074
COX BUILDING PRODUCTS LIMITED—See H2 Equity Partners B.V.; *Int'l*, pg. 3199
COX CHEVROLET INC.; *U.S. Private*, pg. 1074
COX CO., LTD.; *Int'l*, pg. 1823
COX COMMUNICATIONS CLEVELAND AREA—See Cox Enterprises, Inc.; *U.S. Private*, pg. 1078
COX COMMUNICATIONS GAINESVILLE/OCALA—See Cox Enterprises, Inc.; *U.S. Private*, pg. 1078
COX COMMUNICATIONS GULF COAST, LLC—See Cox Enterprises, Inc.; *U.S. Private*, pg. 1078
COX COMMUNICATIONS, INC.—See Cox Enterprises, Inc.; *U.S. Private*, pg. 1078
COX COMMUNICATIONS KANSAS, LLC—See Cox Enterprises, Inc.; *U.S. Private*, pg. 1078
COX COMMUNICATIONS LAS VEGAS, INC.—See Cox Enterprises, Inc.; *U.S. Private*, pg. 1078
COX COMMUNICATIONS LOUISIANA, LLC—See Cox Enterprises, Inc.; *U.S. Private*, pg. 1078
COX COMMUNICATIONS - MIDDLE GEORGIA—See Cox Enterprises, Inc.; *U.S. Private*, pg. 1078
COX COMMUNICATIONS NORTHERN VIRGINIA—See Cox Enterprises, Inc.; *U.S. Private*, pg. 1078
COX COMMUNICATIONS OMAHA, LLC—See Cox Enterprises, Inc.; *U.S. Private*, pg. 1078
COX COMMUNICATIONS PHOENIX—See Cox Enterprises, Inc.; *U.S. Private*, pg. 1078
COX COMMUNICATIONS ROANOKE—See Cox Enterprises, Inc.; *U.S. Private*, pg. 1078
COX COMMUNICATIONS SANTA BARBARA—See Cox Enterprises, Inc.; *U.S. Private*, pg. 1078
COX & COMPANY, INC.; *U.S. Private*, pg. 1074
COX CROSS MEDIA—See Apollo Global Management, Inc.; *U.S. Public*, pg. 163
COX CUSTOM MEDIA INC.—See Apollo Global Management, Inc.; *U.S. Public*, pg. 163
COX DIGITAL SOLUTIONS, LLC—See Apollo Global Management, Inc.; *U.S. Public*, pg. 163
COX ENGINEERING COMPANY; *U.S. Private*, pg. 1074
COX ENTERPRISES, INC.; *U.S. Private*, pg. 1074
COX FIRE PROTECTION, INC.—See Pye-Barker Fire & Safety, LLC; *U.S. Private*, pg. 3309
COX FLOW MEASUREMENT, INC.—See Badger Meter, Inc.; *U.S. Public*, pg. 263
COX INDUSTRIES, INC.; *U.S. Private*, pg. 1078
COX INTERIOR INC.; *U.S. Private*, pg. 1078
COX & KINGS GLOBAL SERVICES LLC—See Cox & Kings Limited; *Int'l*, pg. 1822
COX & KINGS GLOBAL SERVICES SWEDEN AB—See Cox & Kings Limited; *Int'l*, pg. 1822
COX & KINGS GMBH—See Cox & Kings Limited; *Int'l*, pg. 1822
COX & KINGS JAPAN LIMITED—See Cox & Kings Limited; *Int'l*, pg. 1822
COX & KINGS LIMITED; *Int'l*, pg. 1822
COX & KINGS TOURS LLC—See Cox & Kings Limited; *Int'l*, pg. 1822
COX & KINGS (UK) LIMITED—See Cox & Kings Limited; *Int'l*, pg. 1822
COX MEDIA GROUP, LLC—See Apollo Global Management, Inc.; *U.S. Public*, pg. 163
COX NEWSPAPERS, INC.—See Apollo Global Management, Inc.; *U.S. Public*, pg. 163
COX OIL COMPANY; *U.S. Private*, pg. 1078
COXON INDUSTRIAL LTD. - GUANGDONG PLASTIC & MOULD PLANT—See COXON Precise Industrial Co., Ltd.; *Int'l*, pg. 1823
COXON INDUSTRIAL LTD.—See COXON Precise Industrial Co., Ltd.; *Int'l*, pg. 1823
COXON PRECISE INDUSTRIAL CO., LTD.; *Int'l*, pg. 1823
COX RADIO, INC.—See Apollo Global Management, Inc.; *U.S. Public*, pg. 163
COX RECOVERY SERVICES, LLC—See Koppers Holdings Inc.; *U.S. Public*, pg. 1271
COX REPS—See Apollo Global Management, Inc.; *U.S. Public*, pg. 163
COX & ROBINSON (AGRICULTURAL) LTD—See Mole Valley Farmers Ltd; *Int'l*, pg. 5021
COX'S FOODARAMA INC.; *U.S. Private*, pg. 1078
COX'S WHOLESALE SEAFOOD INC.; *U.S. Private*, pg. 1079
COX TRUCK BROKERAGE INC.; *U.S. Private*, pg. 1078
COYA THERAPEUTICS, INC.; *U.S. Public*, pg. 588
COYNE ADVERTISING & PUBLIC RELATIONS; *U.S. Private*, pg. 1079
COYNE & BLANCHARD, INC.; *U.S. Private*, pg. 1079
COYNE INTERNATIONAL ENTERPRISES CORP.; *U.S. Private*, pg. 1079
COYNE OIL CORPORATION; *U.S. Private*, pg. 1079
COYNE PUBLIC RELATIONS; *U.S. Private*, pg. 1079
COYNE TEXTILE SERVICE INC.—See Coyne International Enterprises Corp.; *U.S. Private*, pg. 1079
COYNI, INC.; *U.S. Public*, pg. 588
COYOTE GRAVEL PRODUCTS, INC.; *U.S. Private*, pg. 1079
COYOTE LOGISTICS, LLC—See RXO Inc.; *U.S. Public*, pg. 1827
COYOTES HOCKEY, LLC—See Renaissance Sports & Entertainment, LLC; *U.S. Private*, pg. 3397
COYOTE SOFTWARE CORPORATION—See Vitalhub Corp.; *Int'l*, pg. 8258
COYOTE SYSTEM SAS; *Int'l*, pg. 1823
COYOTE TECHNOLOGIES INC.—See Gefen International A.I Ltd.; *Int'l*, pg. 2911
COZEN O'CONNOR; *U.S. Private*, pg. 1079
COZI GROUP INC.—See Meredith Corporation; *U.S. Public*, pg. 1422
COZUMEL CORPORATION; *U.S. Private*, pg. 1079
COZUMEL CRUISE TERMINAL S.A. DE C.V.—See Carnival Corporation; *U.S. Public*, pg. 438
COZZINI BROS., INC.—See Birch Hill Equity Partners Management Inc.; *Int'l*, pg. 1046
COZZINI DO BRASIL LTDA—See The Middleby Corporation; *U.S. Public*, pg. 2113
COZZINI, LLC—See The Middleby Corporation; *U.S. Public*, pg. 2113
COZZINI MIDDLEBY DE MEXICO, S. DE R.L.DE C.V.—See The Middleby Corporation; *U.S. Public*, pg. 2113
COZZOLI MACHINE COMPANY; *U.S. Private*, pg. 1079
CP2 GROUP LIMITED; *Int'l*, pg. 1823
CP2 LIMITED—See CP2 Group Limited; *Int'l*, pg. 1823
CP2 (UK) LIMITED—See CP2 Group Limited; *Int'l*, pg. 1823
CPA17 MERGER SUB LLC—See W.P. Carey Inc.; *U.S. Public*, pg. 2315
CPAC AFRICA (PTY.) LTD.—See Buckingham Capital, LLC; *U.S. Private*, pg. 678
CPAC ASIA IMAGING PRODUCTS LIMITED—See Buckingham Capital, LLC; *U.S. Private*, pg. 678
THE CPAC CONCRETE PRODUCTS CO., LTD.—See The Siam Cement Public Company Limited; *Int'l*, pg. 7683
CPAC EQUIPMENT, INC.—See Buckingham Capital, LLC; *U.S. Private*, pg. 678
CPAC EUROPE N.V.—See Buckingham Capital, LLC; *U.S. Private*, pg. 678
CPAC, INC.—See Buckingham Capital, LLC; *U.S. Private*, pg. 678
CPAC ITALIA S.R.L—See Buckingham Capital, LLC; *U.S. Private*, pg. 678
CPAC MONIER VIETNAM CO., LTD.—See The Siam Cement Public Company Limited; *Int'l*, pg. 7684
THE CPAC READY MIXED CONCRETE CO., LTD.—See The Siam Cement Public Company Limited; *Int'l*, pg. 7683
THE CPAC ROOF TILE CO., LTD.—See The Siam Cement Public Company Limited; *Int'l*, pg. 7683
CPA GLOBAL (ASIA) LIMITED—See Clarivate PLC; *Int'l*, pg. 1649
CPA GLOBAL (LANDON IP), INC.—See Clarivate PLC; *Int'l*, pg. 1649
CPA GLOBAL LIMITED—See Clarivate PLC; *Int'l*, pg. 1649
CPA GLOBAL NORTH AMERICA LLC—See Clarivate PLC; *Int'l*, pg. 1649
CPA GLOBAL PATENT RESEARCH LIMITED—See Clarivate PLC; *Int'l*, pg. 1649
CPA GLOBAL PATENT RESEARCH LLC—See Clarivate PLC; *Int'l*, pg. 1649
CPA GLOBAL SOFTWARE SOLUTIONS AUSTRALIA PTY. LTD.—See Clarivate PLC; *Int'l*, pg. 1649
CPA GLOBAL SUPPORT SERVICES INDIA PVT. LIMITED—See Clarivate PLC; *Int'l*, pg. 1649
CPA GMBH—See Artinova AB; *Int'l*, pg. 584
CPA INTERNATIONAL, INC.—See Gryphon Investors, LLC; *U.S. Private*, pg. 1799
CPA LABORATORIES LTD.—See Eurofins Scientific S.E.; *Int'l*, pg. 2535
CPALEAD, LLC; *U.S. Private*, pg. 1080
CP ALL LAOS COMPANY LIMITED—See C.P. All Public Company Limited; *Int'l*, pg. 1243
C.P. ALL PUBLIC COMPANY LIMITED; *Int'l*, pg. 1243

CPAMERICA, INC.

CPAMERICA, INC.; *U.S. Private*, pg. 1080
CPANEL, LLC—See Oakley Capital Limited; *Int'l*, pg. 5504
C.P. AQUACULTURE (BEIHAI) CO., LTD.—See Charoen Pokphand Foods Public Company Limited; *Int'l*, pg. 1451
C.P. AQUACULTURE (DONGFANG) CO., LTD.—See Charoen Pokphand Foods Public Company Limited; *Int'l*, pg. 1451
CPA SITE SOLUTIONS; *U.S. Private*, pg. 1079
CP AXTRA PUBLIC COMPANY LIMITED—See C.P. All Public Company Limited; *Int'l*, pg. 1243
C.P. BAKER & COMPANY, LTD; *U.S. Private*, pg. 708
C.P. BANGLADESH CO., LTD.—See Charoen Pokphand Group Co., Ltd.; *Int'l*, pg. 1453
CP+B BOULDER—See Stagwell, Inc.; *U.S. Public*, pg. 1926
CP+B CANADA—See Stagwell, Inc.; *U.S. Public*, pg. 1926
CPB CONTRACTORS PTY LIMITED—See ACS, Actividades de Construccion y Servicios, S.A.; *Int'l*, pg. 110
CPB PROPERTIES, INC.—See Central Pacific Financial Corporation; *U.S. Public*, pg. 473
CP+B—See Stagwell, Inc.; *U.S. Public*, pg. 1926
CP+B—See Stagwell, Inc.; *U.S. Public*, pg. 1926
C.P. CAMBODIA CO., LTD.—See Charoen Pokphand Foods Public Company Limited; *Int'l*, pg. 1452
CP-CARRILLO, LLC—See Pierer Konzerngesellschaft mbH; *Int'l*, pg. 5863
CPC CONSTRUCTION HONG KONG LIMITED—See Chevalier International Holdings Limited; *Int'l*, pg. 1473
CPC CORPORATION; *Int'l*, pg. 1823
CPC INGENIERIA Y CONSTRUCCIONES SA; *Int'l*, pg. 1824
CPC INTERNATIONAL LTD—See LVMH Moet Hennessy Louis Vuitton SE; *Int'l*, pg. 4591
CPC INTERNATIONAL TRADING PTE LTD—See CPC Corporation; *Int'l*, pg. 1823
CPC LOGISTICS INC.; *U.S. Private*, pg. 1080
CPCM, LLC; *U.S. Private*, pg. 1080
CP COMMUNICATION—See Omnicom Group Inc.; *U.S. Public*, pg. 1575
CP COMPANY—See OEP Capital Advisors, L.P.; *U.S. Private*, pg. 3000
C-P CONVERTERS, INC.—See First Atlantic Capital Ltd.; *U.S. Private*, pg. 1513
CP COSMETICS INC.—See TBS Holdings, Inc.; *Int'l*, pg. 7481
CPC PLC—See Avnet, Inc.; *U.S. Public*, pg. 254
CPC RESOURCES INC.—See The Community Preservation Corporation; *U.S. Private*, pg. 4012
CP-DBS, LLC—See i3 Verticals, Inc.; *U.S. Public*, pg. 1081
C.P.D. CEREAL PARTNERS DEUTSCHLAND GMBH & CO. OHG—See General Mills, Inc.; *U.S. Public*, pg. 921
CPDC GREEN TECHNOLOGY CORP.—See China Petrochemical Development Corp.; *Int'l*, pg. 1540
CP DESIGN CONSULTING CO., LTD.—See Dai Nippon Printing Co., Ltd.; *Int'l*, pg. 1914
CPD S.A.; *Int'l*, pg. 1824
CPEC LLC—See Endo International plc; *Int'l*, pg. 2404
CPE HOLDINGS, INC.—See Sony Group Corporation; *Int'l*, pg. 7105
CP ELECTRONICS LIMITED—See Legrand S.A.; *Int'l*, pg. 4445
CPE LINK—See Wolters Kluwer n.v.; *Int'l*, pg. 8445
CP ENERGY SERVICES, INC.—See Prospect Capital Corporation; *U.S. Public*, pg. 1728
C. PETERS BAUGESELLSCHAFT M.B.H.—See Swietelsky Baugesellschaft m.b.H.; *Int'l*, pg. 7367
CPEX PHARMACEUTICALS, INC.—See Xstelos Holdings, Inc.; *U.S. Private*, pg. 4583
CPF DENMARK A/S—See Charoen Pokphand Foods Public Company Limited; *Int'l*, pg. 1452
CPF DENTAL, LLC; *U.S. Private*, pg. 1080
CPF DISTRIBUTION GMBH—See Charoen Pokphand Foods Public Company Limited; *Int'l*, pg. 1452
CPF EUROPE S.A.—See Charoen Pokphand Foods Public Company Limited; *Int'l*, pg. 1452
CPF FOOD PRODUCTS CO., LTD.—See Charoen Pokphand Foods Public Company Limited; *Int'l*, pg. 1452
CPF HONG KONG CO., LTD.—See Charoen Pokphand Foods Public Company Limited; *Int'l*, pg. 1452
CPFILMS INC.—See Eastman Chemical Company; *U.S. Public*, pg. 705
CP FILMS VERTRIEBS GMBH—See Eastman Chemical Company; *U.S. Public*, pg. 704
CP FINANCE SWITZERLAND AG—See Canadian Pacific Kansas City Limited; *Int'l*, pg. 1285
CPF (INDIA) PRIVATE LTD.—See Charoen Pokphand Foods Public Company Limited; *Int'l*, pg. 1452
CPF IT CENTER CO., LTD.—See Charoen Pokphand Foods Public Company Limited; *Int'l*, pg. 1452
CPF JAPAN CO., LTD.—See Charoen Pokphand Foods Public Company Limited; *Int'l*, pg. 1452
CPFL BIO BURITI S.A.—See State Grid Corporation of China; *Int'l*, pg. 7182
CPFL BIOENERGIA S.A.—See State Grid Corporation of China; *Int'l*, pg. 7182

CPFL BIO PEDRA S.A.—See State Grid Corporation of China; *Int'l*, pg. 7182
CPFL COMERCIALIZACAO CONE SUL S.A.—See State Grid Corporation of China; *Int'l*, pg. 7182
CPFL ENERGIA S.A.—See State Grid Corporation of China; *Int'l*, pg. 7182
CPF LOGISTICS CO., LTD.—See Charoen Pokphand Foods Public Company Limited; *Int'l*, pg. 1452
CPFL SANTA CRUZ—See State Grid Corporation of China; *Int'l*, pg. 7182
CPFL SERVICOS, EQUIPAMENTOS, INDUSTRIA E COMERCIO S.A.—See State Grid Corporation of China; *Int'l*, pg. 7182
C.P. FOOD PRODUCTS CO., LTD.—See Charoen Pokphand Foods Public Company Limited; *Int'l*, pg. 1452
CP FOODS (UK) LIMITED—See Charoen Pokphand Foods Public Company Limited; *Int'l*, pg. 1452
CPF PREMIUM FOODS CO., LTD.—See Charoen Pokphand Foods Public Company Limited; *Int'l*, pg. 1452
CP FRANCHISING, LLC.; *U.S. Private*, pg. 1079
CPF SENIOR LIVING ACQUISITIONS LLC—See Chicago Pacific Founders; *U.S. Private*, pg. 878
CPF TOKYO CO., LTD.—See Charoen Pokphand Foods Public Company Limited; *Int'l*, pg. 1452
CPF TRADING CO., LTD.—See Charoen Pokphand Foods Public Company Limited; *Int'l*, pg. 1452
CPF TRAINING CENTER CO., LTD.—See Charoen Pokphand Foods Public Company Limited; *Int'l*, pg. 1452
CP GABA GMBH—See Colgate-Palmolive Company; *U.S. Public*, pg. 531
CPG ADVISORY (SHANGHAI) CO. LTD.—See China Architecture Design & Research Group; *Int'l*, pg. 1483
CPG CONSULTANTS INDIA PVT LTD—See China Architecture Design & Research Group; *Int'l*, pg. 1483
CPG CONSULTANTS PTE LTD.—See China Architecture Design & Research Group; *Int'l*, pg. 1483
CPG CORPORATION PTE LTD.—See China Architecture Design & Research Group; *Int'l*, pg. 1483
CPG ENVIRONMENTAL ENGINEERING CO. LTD—See Downer EDI Limited; *Int'l*, pg. 2185
CPG FACILITIES MANAGEMENT PTE LTD.—See China Architecture Design & Research Group; *Int'l*, pg. 1483
C.P.G. GARMENT CO., LTD.—See Castle Peak Holdings Public Company Limited; *Int'l*, pg. 1357
CPG INTERNATIONAL GMBH—See CPG International S.p.A.; *Int'l*, pg. 1824
CPG INTERNATIONAL PTY LIMITED—See CPG International S.p.A.; *Int'l*, pg. 1824
CPG INTERNATIONAL S.A.—See CPG International S.p.A.; *Int'l*, pg. 1824
CPG INTERNATIONAL—See CPG International S.p.A.; *Int'l*, pg. 1824
CPG INTERNATIONAL S.P.A.; *Int'l*, pg. 1824
CPG INVESTMENTS PTE LTD.—See China Architecture Design & Research Group; *Int'l*, pg. 1483
CPG NEW ZEALAND—See Downer EDI Limited; *Int'l*, pg. 2185
CPG RESOURCES - MINERAL TECHNOLOGIES (PROPRIETARY) LTD—See Downer EDI Limited; *Int'l*, pg. 2185
CPG RESOURCES - MINERAL TECHNOLOGIES PTY LTD—See Downer EDI Limited; *Int'l*, pg. 2185
CPG RESOURCES - QCC PTY LTD—See Downer EDI Limited; *Int'l*, pg. 2185
CPG SALES & MARKETING INC.; *U.S. Private*, pg. 1080
CPG SIGNATURE PTE. LTD.—See Downer EDI Limited; *Int'l*, pg. 2185
CPG TRAFFIC PTY LTD—See Downer EDI Limited; *Int'l*, pg. 2185
CPG VIETNAM CO LTD—See China Architecture Design & Research Group; *Int'l*, pg. 1483
CPH CAPITAL FONDSMAEGLERSELSKAB A/S—See Equitable Holdings, Inc.; *U.S. Public*, pg. 789
CPH CHEMIE + PAPIER HOLDING AG; *Int'l*, pg. 1824
CPH HOLDING, LLC; *U.S. Private*, pg. 1080
CP HILAI HARBOUR CO., LTD.—See Charoen Pokphand Foods Public Company Limited; *Int'l*, pg. 1452
CP HOLDINGS LTD.; *Int'l*, pg. 1823
CPI AEROSTRUCTURES, INC.; *U.S. Public*, pg. 588
CPI AGROTECH CO., LTD.—See Chumporn Palm Oil Industry Public Company Limited; *Int'l*, pg. 1596
CPI BAUTRAGER UND IMMOBILIENVERWALTUNG GMBH—See CPI Immobilien AG; *Int'l*, pg. 1825
CPI BLACKPRINT IBERICA, S.L.—See Chevrillon Philippe Industrie; *Int'l*, pg. 1474
CPI CARD GROUP-COLCHESTER LIMITED—See Tricor Pacific Capital, Inc.; *Int'l*, pg. 7920
CPI CARD GROUP INC.—See Tricor Pacific Capital, Inc.; *Int'l*, pg. 7920
CPI CARD GROUP-LIVERPOOL LIMITED—See Tricor Pacific Capital, Inc.; *Int'l*, pg. 7920
CPI COLOUR—See Chevrillon Philippe Industrie; *Int'l*, pg. 1474
CPI COMPUTER PERIPHERALS INTERNATIONAL; *Int'l*, pg. 1825
CPI COOPERATIVE; *U.S. Private*, pg. 1080

CORPORATE AFFILIATIONS

CPI EAST, S.R.O.—See CPI Property Group, S.A.; *Int'l*, pg. 1825
CPI ENERGO, A.S.—See CPI Property Group, S.A.; *Int'l*, pg. 1825
CPI ESSCO INC.—See Odyssey Investment Partners, LLC; *U.S. Private*, pg. 2994
CPI FIM S.A.—See CPI Property Group, S.A.; *Int'l*, pg. 1825
CPIF VENTURE, INC.—See Colgate-Palmolive Company; *U.S. Public*, pg. 531
THE CPI GROUP, INC.; *U.S. Private*, pg. 4015
CPI GROUP (UK) LTD—See Chevrillon Philippe Industrie; *Int'l*, pg. 1474
CPI HOLDINGS, LLC—See Cash Technologies, Inc.; *U.S. Private*, pg. 782
CPI HOTELS, A.S.—See CPI Property Group, S.A.; *Int'l*, pg. 1825
CPI HOTELS SLOVAKIA, S.R.O.—See CPI Property Group, S.A.; *Int'l*, pg. 1825
CPI HUNGARY KFT.—See CPI Property Group, S.A.; *Int'l*, pg. 1825
CPI IMMOBILIEN AG; *Int'l*, pg. 1825
CPI IMMO, S.A.R.L.—See CPI Property Group, S.A.; *Int'l*, pg. 1825
CPI INTERNATIONAL, INC.—See Odyssey Investment Partners, LLC; *U.S. Private*, pg. 2994
CPI LIMITED—See Grafton Group plc; *Int'l*, pg. 3050
CPI LOCUS MICROWAVE, INC.—See Odyssey Investment Partners, LLC; *U.S. Private*, pg. 2994
CPI-LOUISIANA INC.—See CPI Wirecloth & Screens, Inc.; *U.S. Private*, pg. 1080
CPI LUBRICATION - CC TECHNOLOGY—See Enpro Inc.; *U.S. Public*, pg. 774
CPI LUBRICATION - PREMIER LUBRICATION SYSTEMS—See Enpro Inc.; *U.S. Public*, pg. 774
CPI MALIBU DIVISION—See Odyssey Investment Partners, LLC; *U.S. Private*, pg. 2994
CPI MARKETING GMBH—See CPI Immobilien AG; *Int'l*, pg. 1825
CPI METEOR CENTRE, S.R.O.—See CPI Property Group, S.A.; *Int'l*, pg. 1825
CPI MORAVIA BOOKS S.R.O.—See Chevrillon Philippe Industrie; *Int'l*, pg. 1474
CPI MORTARS LIMITED—See Grafton Group plc; *Int'l*, pg. 3050
CP INDUSTRIES HOLDINGS, INC—See Everest Kanto Cylinder Limited; *Int'l*, pg. 2564
CPINGREDIENTES, S.A. DE C.V.—See Ingredion Incorporated; *U.S. Public*, pg. 1123
CP INGREDIENTS INDIA PRIVATE LIMITED—See Ingredion Incorporated; *U.S. Public*, pg. 1123
CP INGREDIENTS INDIA PVT. LTD.—See Ingredion Incorporated; *U.S. Public*, pg. 1123
CP INTERTRADE COMPANY LIMITED—See Charoen Pokphand Group Co., Ltd.; *Int'l*, pg. 1453
CPI PACIFIC PTY LIMITED—See Enpro Inc.; *U.S. Public*, pg. 774
CPI POLAND SP. Z O.O.—See CPI Property Group, S.A.; *Int'l*, pg. 1825
CPI PRODUCTS, INC.—See Stabilus; *U.S. Private*, pg. 3774
CPI PROPERTY GROUP, S.A.; *Int'l*, pg. 1825
CPI QUALIFIED PLAN CONSULTANTS INC.—See CMFG Life Insurance Company; *U.S. Private*, pg. 950
CPI RADANT TECHNOLOGIES DIVISION INC.—See Odyssey Investment Partners, LLC; *U.S. Private*, pg. 2994
CPI RETAIL PORTFOLIO I, A.S.—See CPI Property Group, S.A.; *Int'l*, pg. 1825
CPI SALES, INC.—See Central States Industrial Supply, Inc.; *U.S. Private*, pg. 825
CPI SATCOM & ANTENNA TECHNOLOGIES INC.—See Odyssey Investment Partners, LLC; *U.S. Private*, pg. 2994
CPI-THE ALTERNATIVE SUPPLIER; *U.S. Private*, pg. 1080
CPI WACHSTUMS IMMOBILIEN AG—See CPI Immobilien AG; *Int'l*, pg. 1825
CPI WERTPAPIER BERATUNG UND VERMITTLUNG GMBH—See CPI Immobilien AG; *Int'l*, pg. 1825
CPI WIRECLOTH & SCREENS, INC.; *U.S. Private*, pg. 1080
C. P. JAKOBSENS EFTF. APS.—See Groupe SFPI SA; *Int'l*, pg. 3111
CP KELCO APS—See J.M. Huber Corporation; *U.S. Private*, pg. 2168
CP KELCO APS—See J.M. Huber Corporation; *U.S. Private*, pg. 2168
CP KELCO ARGENTINA S.A.—See J.M. Huber Corporation; *U.S. Private*, pg. 2168
CP KELCO BELGIUM B.V.B.A.—See J.M. Huber Corporation; *U.S. Private*, pg. 2168
CP KELCO B.V.—See J.M. Huber Corporation; *U.S. Private*, pg. 2168
CP KELCO GERMANY GMBH—See J.M. Huber Corporation; *U.S. Private*, pg. 2168
CP KELCO JAPAN APS—See J.M. Huber Corporation; *U.S. Private*, pg. 2168
CP KELCO OY—See J.M. Huber Corporation; *U.S. Private*, pg. 2168

COMPANY NAME INDEX

CP KELCO POLAND SP. Z.O.O.—See J.M. Huber Corporation; *U.S. Private*, pg. 2168
CP KELCO SINGAPORE PTE., LTD.—See J.M. Huber Corporation; *U.S. Private*, pg. 2168
CP KELCO—See J.M. Huber Corporation; *U.S. Private*, pg. 2168
CP KELCO—See J.M. Huber Corporation; *U.S. Private*, pg. 2168
CP KELCO UK LIMITED—See J.M. Huber Corporation; *U.S. Private*, pg. 2168
CPK INTERIOR PRODUCTS INC.—See Stellantis N.V.; *Int'l*, pg. 7199
CPK MANUFACTURING LLC—See Hill & Smith PLC; *Int'l*, pg. 3391
C.P. LAND PLC—See Charoen Pokphand Foods Public Company Limited; *Int'l*, pg. 1452
C.P. LAOS CO., LTD.—See Charoen Pokphand Foods Public Company Limited; *Int'l*, pg. 1452
CPL ARCHITECTS, ENGINEERS & LANDSCAPE ARCHITECT D.P.C.; *U.S. Private*, pg. 1080
CP LAUGHLIN REALTY, LLC—See Caesars Entertainment, Inc.; *U.S. Public*, pg. 420
CPL GROUP PUBLIC COMPANY LIMITED; *Int'l*, pg. 1825
CPL JOBS KFT—See Bain Capital, LP; *U.S. Private*, pg. 433
CPL JOBS SP Z.O.O—See Bain Capital, LP; *U.S. Private*, pg. 433
CPL JOBS S.R.O.—See Bain Capital, LP; *U.S. Private*, pg. 433
CPL JOBS S.R.O.—See Bain Capital, LP; *U.S. Private*, pg. 433
CPL JOBS TUNISIE SARL—See Bain Capital, LP; *U.S. Private*, pg. 433
CPL (NORTHERN IRELAND) LIMITED—See Bain Capital, LP; *U.S. Private*, pg. 433
C.P. LOTUS CORPORATION—See Charoen Pokphand Group Co., Ltd.; *Int'l*, pg. 1453
CPL PRODUCTIONS LIMITED—See ProSiebenSat.1 Media SE; *Int'l*, pg. 6000
CPL RESOURCES LIMITED—See Bain Capital, LP; *U.S. Private*, pg. 433
CPL RESOURCES PLC.—See Bain Capital, LP; *U.S. Private*, pg. 433
CPL RESOURCES PLC—See Bain Capital, LP; *U.S. Private*, pg. 433
CPL SOLUTIONS LIMITED—See Bain Capital, LP; *U.S. Private*, pg. 433
CPL SUBACUTE LLC—See Public Sector Pension Investment Board; *Int'l*, pg. 6096
CPL TRAINING LIMITED—See Bain Capital, LP; *U.S. Private*, pg. 433
CPM ANLAGEN VERTRIEB GMBH—See MPC Munchmeyer Petersen & Co. GmbH; *Int'l*, pg. 5061
C-P MANUFACTURING, INC.—See IMS Recycling Service Inc.; *U.S. Private*, pg. 2051
CP MARINE, INC.—See Gold Belt Incorporated; *U.S. Private*, pg. 1727
CPM AUSTRALIA—See Omnicom Group Inc.; *U.S. Public*, pg. 1578
CPM AUSTRALIA—See Omnicom Group Inc.; *U.S. Public*, pg. 1578
CPM AUSTRIA—See Omnicom Group Inc.; *U.S. Public*, pg. 1578
CPM BELGIUM—See Omnicom Group Inc.; *U.S. Public*, pg. 1578
CPM BRAXIS ERP TECNOLOGIA DA INFORMACAO LTDA.—See Capgemini SE; *Int'l*, pg. 1303
CPM BRAXIS OUTSOURCING S.A.—See Capgemini SE; *Int'l*, pg. 1303
CPM BRAXIS USA CORP.—See Capgemini SE; *Int'l*, pg. 1303
CPMC (CHENGDU) COMPANY LIMITED—See CPMC Holdings Limited; *Int'l*, pg. 1825
CPMC HOLDINGS LIMITED; *Int'l*, pg. 1825
CPMC (KUNSHAN) COMPANY LIMITED—See CPMC Holdings Limited; *Int'l*, pg. 1825
C.P.M. CONTRACTPHARMA GMBH & CO. KG—See BC Partners LLP; *Int'l*, pg. 923
CPMC (TIANJIN) COMPANY LIMITED—See CPMC Holdings Limited; *Int'l*, pg. 1825
CPMC (WUHAN) COMPANY LIMITED—See CPMC Holdings Limited; *Int'l*, pg. 1825
CPMC (ZHENJIANG) COMPANY LIMITED—See CPMC Holdings Limited; *Int'l*, pg. 1826
CPM DEVELOPMENT CORPORATION—See CRH plc; *Int'l*, pg. 1843
CPMEDIA & MARKETING SERVICES, INC.; *U.S. Private*, pg. 1080
CP MEDICAL—See Juniper Investment Company, LLC; *U.S. Private*, pg. 2244
CPM EDUCATIONAL PROGRAM; *U.S. Private*, pg. 1080
CPM-MEIJI CO., LTD.—See Meiji Holdings Co., Ltd.; *Int'l*, pg. 4800
C.P. MERCHANDISING CO., LTD.—See Charoen Pokphand Foods Public Company Limited; *Int'l*, pg. 1452
CPM EUROPE B.V.—See Gilbert Global Equity Partners; *U.S. Private*, pg. 1698

CPM EUROPE LTD.—See Gilbert Global Equity Partners; *U.S. Private*, pg. 1698
CPM FRANCE—See Omnicom Group Inc.; *U.S. Public*, pg. 1578
CPM GERMANY GMBH—See Omnicom Group Inc.; *U.S. Public*, pg. 1578
CPM GROUP LIMITED—See CNT Group Limited; *Int'l*, pg. 1678
CPM GROUP LTD.—See Marshalls plc; *Int'l*, pg. 4702
CPM HEALTH CENTRES INC.—See Imperial Capital Group Ltd.; *Int'l*, pg. 3634
CPM HOLDINGS, INC.—See Gilbert Global Equity Partners; *U.S. Private*, pg. 1698
C&P MICROSYSTEMS, LLC—See Colter & Peterson Inc.; *U.S. Private*, pg. 976
CPM INDUSTRIES INC.; *U.S. Private*, pg. 1080
CPM INTERNACIONAL D.O.O.—See Assicurazioni Generali S.p.A.; *Int'l*, pg. 648
CPM IRELAND—See Omnicom Group Inc.; *U.S. Public*, pg. 1578
CPM NETHERLANDS—See Omnicom Group Inc.; *U.S. Public*, pg. 1578
CPM NETHERLANDS—See Omnicom Group Inc.; *U.S. Public*, pg. 1578
CPM—See Omnicom Group Inc.; *U.S. Public*, pg. 1578
CPM SPAIN—See Omnicom Group Inc.; *U.S. Public*, pg. 1578
CPM S.P.A.—See Durr AG; *Int'l*, pg. 2230
CPM SWITZERLAND—See Omnicom Group Inc.; *U.S. Public*, pg. 1578
CPM USA—See Omnicom Group Inc.; *U.S. Public*, pg. 1578
CPM WOLVERINE PROCTOR LLC - LEXINGTON—See Gilbert Global Equity Partners; *U.S. Private*, pg. 1698
CPM WOLVERINE PROCTOR LLC—See Gilbert Global Equity Partners; *U.S. Private*, pg. 1698
CPM WOLVERINE PROCTOR LTD.—See Gilbert Global Equity Partners; *U.S. Private*, pg. 1698
CPN PATTAYA CO., LTD.—See Central Pattana Public Company Limited; *Int'l*, pg. 1409
CPN RETAIL GROWTH LEASEHOLD REIT; *Int'l*, pg. 1826
CPO COMMERCE, INC.—See Sycamore Partners Management, LP; *U.S. Private*, pg. 3896
CP OF BOZEMAN, INC.; *U.S. Private*, pg. 1079
C P & O, LLC—See Cooper/T. Smith Corporation; *U.S. Private*, pg. 1041
CPOWER HOLDINGS, LLC—See Exelon Corporation; *U.S. Public*, pg. 806
C-POWER N.V.—See Ackermans & van Haaren NV; *Int'l*, pg. 105
CP PACKAGING, LLC.—See The Middleby Corporation; *U.S. Public*, pg. 2113
CPPC PUBLIC COMPANY LIMITED—See Charoen Pokphand Group Co., Ltd.; *Int'l*, pg. 1453
CPP CREATING PROFITABLE PARTNERSHIPS GMBH—See CPPGroup Plc; *Int'l*, pg. 1826
CPP GLOBAL ASSISTANCE BANGLADESH LIMITED—See CPPGroup Plc; *Int'l*, pg. 1826
CPPGROUP PLC; *Int'l*, pg. 1826
CP PISTONS LLC—See Pierer Konzerngesellschaft mbH; *Int'l*, pg. 5863
C.P. POKPHAND CO. LTD.—See Charoen Pokphand Foods Public Company Limited; *Int'l*, pg. 1452
CPP PARTICIPACOES S.A.—See Vale S.A.; *Int'l*, pg. 8111
CP PRINTING LIMITED—See Smart Globe Holdings Limited; *Int'l*, pg. 7000
C.P. PRODUCTS, INC.—See Charoen Pokphand Group Co., Ltd.; *Int'l*, pg. 1453
CPRAM CO., LTD.—See C.P. All Public Company Limited; *Int'l*, pg. 1243
C-PRESTO CO., LTD.—See TS Tech Co Ltd; *Int'l*, pg. 7947
CP RETAILINK CO., LTD.—See C.P. All Public Company Limited; *Int'l*, pg. 1243
CPR GOMU INDUSTRIAL PUBLIC COMPANY LIMITED; *Int'l*, pg. 1826
C.P. RICHARDS CONSTRUCTION CO., INC.; *U.S. Private*, pg. 708
CPRIME INC.—See Alten S.A.; *Int'l*, pg. 391
C. PRODUCTIONS SA—See Metropole Television SA; *Int'l*, pg. 4863
C PRODUCTS DEFENSE, INC.; *U.S. Private*, pg. 702
CPR STRONGSVILLE LLC—See Assurant, Inc.; *U.S. Public*, pg. 215
CPR TOOLS, INC.; *U.S. Private*, pg. 1080
CPS CAPITAL; *Int'l*, pg. 1826
CPS CARDS; *U.S. Private*, pg. 1080
CPS CHINA CO., LTD—See CPS GmbH; *Int'l*, pg. 1826
C.P. SCHMIDT VERPACKUNGS-WERK GMBH & CO. KG—See Mayr-Melnhof Karton AG; *Int'l*, pg. 4745
CPS CONVERTIBLE POWER SYSTEMS GMBH—See Enerpac Tool Group Corp.; *U.S. Public*, pg. 765
CPS DISTRIBUTORS, INC.; *U.S. Private*, pg. 1080
CPS DISTRIBUTORS INC.; *U.S. Private*, pg. 1080
CPS ENERGY; *U.S. Public*, pg. 1081
CPS GMBH; *Int'l*, pg. 1826
CPSG PARTNERS LLC—See Marsh & McLennan Companies, Inc.; *U.S. Public*, pg. 1385
CPS GROUP INVESTMENTS PTY. LTD.; *Int'l*, pg. 1826

CP SHADES INC.; *U.S. Private*, pg. 1079
CPS HVAC PARTNERS INC—See CPS Capital; *Int'l*, pg. 1826
CP SOFTWARE GROUP, INC.; *U.S. Private*, pg. 1079
CPS PAYMENT SERVICES, LLC—See Repay Holdings Corporation; *U.S. Public*, pg. 1784
CPS PERFORMANCE MATERIALS CORP.—See Arsenal Capital Management LP; *U.S. Public*, pg. 337
CPS PRODUCTS, INC.—See Harbour Group Industries, Inc.; *U.S. Private*, pg. 1860
CPS PROFESSIONAL SERVICES; *U.S. Private*, pg. 1081
C P S SHAPERS LIMITED; *Int'l*, pg. 1238
C.P. STANDART GIDA SANAYI VE TICARET A.S.—See Charoen Pokphand Foods Public Company Limited; *Int'l*, pg. 1452
CPS TECHNOLOGIES CORPORATION; *U.S. Public*, pg. 588
CPS TECHNOLOGY SOLUTIONS INC.; *U.S. Private*, pg. 1081
CP SURGERY CENTER, LLC—See HCA Healthcare, Inc.; *U.S. Public*, pg. 992
CPT DRIVES & POWER PCL; *Int'l*, pg. 1826
CP TEST A/S—See Per Aarsleff Holding A/S; *Int'l*, pg. 5795
CPT GLOBAL INC—See CPT Global Limited; *Int'l*, pg. 1826
CPT GLOBAL LIMITED; *Int'l*, pg. 1826
CPT NETWORK SOLUTIONS; *U.S. Private*, pg. 1081
CP TOOLS KOREA CO. LTD—See Atlas Copco AB; *Int'l*, pg. 681
CPT SC TITLE HOLDING CORPORATION; *U.S. Private*, pg. 1081
CPT TECHNOLOGY (GROUP) CO., LTD.; *Int'l*, pg. 1826
CPU, LLC—See Life's Time Capsule Services, Inc.; *U.S. Public*, pg. 1312
CPU SOFTWAREHOUSE AG; *Int'l*, pg. 1826
CP VIETNAM CORPORATION—See Charoen Pokphand Group Co., Ltd.; *Int'l*, pg. 1453
CPW AMERICA CO.—See Viohalco SA/NV; *Int'l*, pg. 8243
CP WARD INC.; *U.S. Private*, pg. 1079
CP WELL TESTING LLC—See Prospect Capital Corporation; *U.S. Public*, pg. 1728
CP WHOLESALE INDIA PRIVATE LIMITED—See C.P. All Public Company Limited; *Int'l*, pg. 1243
CPWR-THE CENTER FOR CONSTRUCTION RESEARCH AND TRAINING; *U.S. Private*, pg. 1081
CPX INC.; *U.S. Private*, pg. 1081
CQ ENERGY PTY. LTD.—See Energy One Limited; *Int'l*, pg. 2423
CQENS TECHNOLOGIES INC.; *U.S. Private*, pg. 1081
CQG, INC.; *U.S. Private*, pg. 1081
C.Q. INSULATION, INC.—See Installed Building Products, Inc.; *U.S. Public*, pg. 1132
CQMS RAZER PTY. LTD.—See Epiroc AB; *Int'l*, pg. 2461
C.Q. PHARMACEUTICAL HOLDING CO., LTD.; *Int'l*, pg. 1244
CQRC FINANCIAL LEASING CO., LTD.—See Chongqing Rural Commercial Bank Co., Ltd.; *Int'l*, pg. 1580
CQRC WEALTH MANAGEMENT CO., LTD.—See Shenguan Holdings (Group) Limited; *Int'l*, pg. 6802
CQ ROLL CALL—See The Economist Group Limited; *Int'l*, pg. 7637
CQS NATURAL RESOURCES GROWTH & INCOME PLC; *Int'l*, pg. 1826
C-QUADRAT INVESTMENT AG; *Int'l*, pg. 1239
CQUB INFOSYSTEM PRIVATE LIMITED—See AIRAN Limited; *Int'l*, pg. 241
CQUEST; *U.S. Private*, pg. 1081
CQV CO., LTD.; *Int'l*, pg. 1826
CR2 EMPREENDIMENTOS IMOBILIARIOS S.A.; *Int'l*, pg. 1827
CRABBE BROWN & JAMES, LLP—See Amundsen Davis LLC; *U.S. Private*, pg. 269
CRABTREE BUICK GMC, INC.; *U.S. Private*, pg. 1081
CRABTREE & EVELYN AUSTRALIA PTY LTD—See Nan Hai Corporation Limited; *Int'l*, pg. 5137
CRABTREE & EVELYN AUSTRIA GMBH—See Nan Hai Corporation Limited; *Int'l*, pg. 5137
CRABTREE & EVELYN DEUTSCHLAND GMBH—See Nan Hai Corporation Limited; *Int'l*, pg. 5137
CRABTREE & EVELYN (HK) LTD.—See Nan Hai Corporation Limited; *Int'l*, pg. 5137
CRABTREE & EVELYN, LTD.—See Nan Hai Corporation Limited; *Int'l*, pg. 5137
CRABTREE & EVELYN (MALAYSIA) SDN BHD—See Nan Hai Corporation Limited; *Int'l*, pg. 5137
CRABTREE & EVELYN (OVERSEAS) LTD—See Nan Hai Corporation Limited; *Int'l*, pg. 5137
CRABTREE & EVELYN (SINGAPORE) PTE LTD—See Nan Hai Corporation Limited; *Int'l*, pg. 5137
CRABTREE OF GATESHEAD LTD.; *Int'l*, pg. 1827
CRABTREE SIDING & SUPPLY—See Beacon Roofing Supply, Inc.; *U.S. Public*, pg. 285
CRABTREE SOUTH AFRICA PTY. LIMITED—See Siemens Aktiengesellschaft; *Int'l*, pg. 6886
CRACKEN, HARKEY & CO., LLC; *U.S. Private*, pg. 1081
CRACKER BARREL OLD COUNTRY STORE, INC.; *U.S. Public*, pg. 589

CRACKER BARREL OLD COUNTRY STORE, INC. — CORPORATE AFFILIATIONS

CRACKER BOY BOAT WORKS, INC.—See Jamco Inc.; *U.S. Private*, pg. 2182
CRACKLE—See Sony Group Corporation; *Int'l*, pg. 7103
CRACOW HOLDINGS PTY LTD—See Newmont Corporation; *U.S. Public*, pg. 1517
C-RAD AB; *Int'l*, pg. 1239
C-RAD AUSTRALIA & NEW ZEALAND PTY. LTD.—See C-RAD AB; *Int'l*, pg. 1239
CRADDOCK OIL CO. INC.; *U.S. Private*, pg. 1081
C-RAD INCORPORATED—See C-RAD AB; *Int'l*, pg. 1239
CRADLEPOINT, INC.—See Telefonaktiebolaget LM Ericsson; *Int'l*, pg. 7531
CRADLE RESOURCES LIMITED; *Int'l*, pg. 1827
CRADLE SOLUTION INC.; *U.S. Private*, pg. 1081
CRADLEY SPECIAL BRICK COMPANY LIMITED—See Heidelberg Materials AG; *Int'l*, pg. 3310
CRAFCO, INC.—See Ergon, Inc.; *U.S. Private*, pg. 1418
CRAFT3; *U.S. Private*, pg. 1082
CRAFT BREW ALLIANCE, INC.—See Anheuser-Busch InBev SA/NV; *Int'l*, pg. 465
CRAFT CO., LTD.—See Diamondback Energy, Inc.; *U.S. Public*, pg. 658
THE CRAFT CONSULTING LIMITED—See Next 15 Group plc; *Int'l*, pg. 5247
CRAFTCORPS INC.; *U.S. Private*, pg. 1082
CRAFT EQUIPMENT COMPANY; *U.S. Private*, pg. 1081
CRAFTEX MILLS INC. OF PENNSYLVANIA; *U.S. Private*, pg. 1082
CRAFT MACHINE WORKS INC.; *U.S. Private*, pg. 1081
CRAFTMADE INTERNATIONAL, INC.; *U.S. Private*, pg. 1082
CRAFT MARKETING; *U.S. Private*, pg. 1081
CRAFTMARK HOMES INC.; *U.S. Private*, pg. 1082
CRAFTMASTER FURNITURE CORP.; *U.S. Private*, pg. 1082
CRAFTMASTER MANUFACTURING, INC.—See ONEX Corporation; *Int'l*, pg. 5579
CRAFTMATIC INDUSTRIES, INC.; *U.S. Private*, pg. 1082
CRAFTMATIC ORGANIZATION, INC.—See Craftmatic Industries, Inc.; *U.S. Private*, pg. 1082
CRAFTMETALS PTY. LTD.—See RHEINZINK GmbH & Co. KG; *Int'l*, pg. 6324
CRAFT OF SCANDINAVIA AB—See New Wave Group AB; *Int'l*, pg. 5229
CRAFT PATTERN & MOLD, INC.—See Delos Capital, LLC; *U.S. Private*, pg. 1199
CRAFT PATTERN & MOLD, INC.—See Silverfern Capital Management, LLC; *U.S. Private*, pg. 3663
CRAFTPORT CANNABIS CORP.; *Int'l*, pg. 1827
CRAFTS AMERICANA GROUP INC.—See Blue Point Capital Partners, LLC; *U.S. Private*, pg. 590
CRAFTS, ETC! LTD.—See Hob-Lob Limited Partnership; *U.S. Private*, pg. 1958
CRAFTS INC.; *U.S. Private*, pg. 1082
CRAFTSMAN AUTOMATION LIMITED; *Int'l*, pg. 1827
CRAFTSMAN CAPITAL PARTNERS, LLC; *U.S. Private*, pg. 1082
CRAFTSMAN CUSTOM METALS LLC—See Speyside Equity LLC; *U.S. Private*, pg. 3756
CRAFTSMAN EUROPE B.V.—See Craftsman Automation Limited; *Int'l*, pg. 1827
CRAFTSMEN INDUSTRIES, INC.; *U.S. Private*, pg. 1082
CRAFTSTECH, INC.—See KKR & Co. Inc.; *U.S. Public*, pg. 1252
CRAFTSY INC.; *U.S. Private*, pg. 1082
CRAFTY BEAVER HOME CENTERS; *U.S. Private*, pg. 1082
CRAID INC.—See FreeBit Co., Ltd.; *Int'l*, pg. 2769
CRAIG ASSEMBLY INC.—See NORMA Group SE; *Int'l*, pg. 5430
THE CRAIG BUSINESS GROUP; *U.S. Private*, pg. 4015
CRAIGCOR DISTRIBUTION CO (PTY) LTD—See ARB HOLDINGS LIMITED; *Int'l*, pg. 536
CRAIG DAILY PRESS—See The World Company; *U.S. Private*, pg. 4139
CRAIG & DERRICOTT LTD.—See Addtech AB; *Int'l*, pg. 132
CRAIG DEVELOPMENT PTE LTD—See Guthrie GTS Limited; *Int'l*, pg. 3188
CRAIG ELECTRIC CORPORATION; *U.S. Private*, pg. 1082
CRAIG ELECTRONICS, INC.—See Nova Capital Management Limited; *Int'l*, pg. 5450
CRAIG FRAMES, INC.; *U.S. Private*, pg. 1082
CRAIG HOSPITAL; *U.S. Private*, pg. 1082
CRAIG INDUSTRIES INC.; *U.S. Private*, pg. 1083
CRAIG & LANDRETH LEASING, INC.; *U.S. Private*, pg. 1082
CRAIG MANUFACTURING LTD.; *Int'l*, pg. 1827
CRAIGMICHAELS, INC.; *U.S. Private*, pg. 1083
CRAIG MURRAY PRODUCTIONS LLC; *U.S. Private*, pg. 1083
CRAIG PAVING INC.; *U.S. Private*, pg. 1083
CRAIG SCOTT REALITY INC.; *U.S. Private*, pg. 1083
CRAIG SHEFFIELD & AUSTIN INC.; *U.S. Private*, pg. 1083
CRAIG STEIN BEVERAGE; *U.S. Private*, pg. 1083
CRAIG TAYLOR EQUIPMENT COMPANY; *U.S. Private*, pg. 1083

CRAIG TECHNOLOGIES, INC.; *U.S. Private*, pg. 1083
CRAIG TECHNOLOGIES; *U.S. Private*, pg. 1083
CRAIG TESTING LABORATORIES, INC.—See Colliers International Group Inc.; *Int'l*, pg. 1700
CRAIG TRANSPORTATION CO.; *U.S. Private*, pg. 1083
CRAILAR TECHNOLOGIES INC.; *Int'l*, pg. 1827
CRAIN BROTHERS INC.; *U.S. Private*, pg. 1083
CRAIN COMMUNICATIONS GMBH—See Crain Communications, Inc.; *U.S. Private*, pg. 1083
CRAIN COMMUNICATIONS, INC. - AKRON—See Crain Communications, Inc.; *U.S. Private*, pg. 1084
CRAIN COMMUNICATIONS, INC. - AUTOMOTIVE NEWS CHINA UNIT—See Crain Communications, Inc.; *U.S. Private*, pg. 1083
CRAIN COMMUNICATIONS, INC. - AUTOMOTIVE NEWS EUROPE UNIT—See Crain Communications, Inc.; *U.S. Private*, pg. 1083
CRAIN COMMUNICATIONS, INC. - CHICAGO—See Crain Communications, Inc.; *U.S. Private*, pg. 1084
CRAIN COMMUNICATIONS, INC. - NEW YORK—See Crain Communications, Inc.; *U.S. Private*, pg. 1084
CRAIN COMMUNICATIONS, INC.; *U.S. Private*, pg. 1083
CRAIN COMMUNICATIONS, INC. - STAFFING INDUSTRY ANALYSTS UNIT—See Crain Communications, Inc.; *U.S. Private*, pg. 1084
CRAIN COMMUNICATIONS LTD.—See Crain Communications, Inc.; *U.S. Private*, pg. 1083
CRAIN'S CHICAGO BUSINESS—See Crain Communications, Inc.; *U.S. Private*, pg. 1084
CRAIN'S CLEVELAND BUSINESS—See Crain Communications, Inc.; *U.S. Private*, pg. 1084
CRAIN'S DETROIT BUSINESS—See Crain Communications, Inc.; *U.S. Private*, pg. 1084
CRAIN'S NEW YORK BUSINESS—See Crain Communications, Inc.; *U.S. Private*, pg. 1084
CRA INTERNATIONAL, INC.; *U.S. Public*, pg. 588
CRA INTERNATIONAL LTD.—See CRA International, Inc.; *U.S. Public*, pg. 588
CRA INTERNATIONAL (NETHERLANDS) BV—See CRA International, Inc.; *U.S. Public*, pg. 588
CRA INTERNATIONAL UK LTD.—See CRA International, Inc.; *U.S. Public*, pg. 588
CRAMA CEPTURA SRL—See Purcari Wineries Public Company Limited; *Int'l*, pg. 6121
CRAMCO INC.; *U.S. Private*, pg. 1084
CRAMER ASSET MANAGEMENT SA—See Norinvest Holding SA; *Int'l*, pg. 5428
THE CRAMER-KRASSELT CO. - MILWAUKEE—See The Cramer-Krasselt Co.; *U.S. Private*, pg. 4015
THE CRAMER-KRASSELT CO. - NEW YORK—See The Cramer-Krasselt Co.; *U.S. Private*, pg. 4015
THE CRAMER-KRASSELT CO. - PHOENIX—See The Cramer-Krasselt Co.; *U.S. Private*, pg. 4016
THE CRAMER-KRASSELT CO.; *U.S. Private*, pg. 4015
CRAMER PRODUCTIONS INC.; *U.S. Private*, pg. 1084
CRAMER ROSENTHAL MCGLYNN LLC; *U.S. Private*, pg. 1084
CRAMER'S HOME CENTERS, INC.; *U.S. Private*, pg. 1085
CRAMER SYSTEMS INTERNATIONAL LIMITED—See Amdocs Limited; *Int'l*, pg. 419
CRAMER TOYOTA OF VENICE; *U.S. Private*, pg. 1085
CRAME, S.A.—See Grupo Arbulu S.L.; *Int'l*, pg. 3120
CRAMO AB—See Cramo Plc; *Int'l*, pg. 1827
CRAMO AG—See Cramo Plc; *Int'l*, pg. 1827
CRAMO A/S—See Cramo Plc; *Int'l*, pg. 1827
CRAMO AS—See Cramo Plc; *Int'l*, pg. 1827
CRAMO INSTANT AB—See Cramo Plc; *Int'l*, pg. 1827
CRAMO INSTANT AS—See Cramo Plc; *Int'l*, pg. 1827
CRAMO KALININGRAD OOO—See Cramo Plc; *Int'l*, pg. 1827
CRAMO NEW HOLDING AB—See Cramo Plc; *Int'l*, pg. 1827
CRAMO PLC; *Int'l*, pg. 1827
CRAMO S.R.O.—See Cramo Plc; *Int'l*, pg. 1827
CRAMO SVERIGE AB—See Cramo Plc; *Int'l*, pg. 1827
CRAMP & ASSOCIATES, INC.; *U.S. Private*, pg. 1085
CRAM ROOFING COMPANY INC—See New State Capital Partners LLC; *U.S. Private*, pg. 2907
CRANAB AB - CRANAB 1 FACTORY—See Investindustrial Advisors Ltd.; *Int'l*, pg. 3779
CRANAB AB - CRANAB 2 FACTORY—See Investindustrial Advisors Ltd.; *Int'l*, pg. 3779
CRANAB AB—See Investindustrial Advisors Ltd.; *Int'l*, pg. 3779
CRANACH PHARMA GMBH—See Medios AG; *Int'l*, pg. 4778
CRANAGE FINANCIAL GROUP PTY. LTD.—See Azimut Holding SpA; *Int'l*, pg. 779
CRANBERRY PIPELINE CORPORATION—See Coterra Energy Inc.; *U.S. Public*, pg. 587
CRANBERRY PROPERTIES LLC.—See Verizon Communications Inc.; *U.S. Public*, pg. 2285
CRANBOURNE PANEL BEATERS & SPRAY PAINTERS PROPRIETARY LIMITED—See OneLogix Group Limited; *Int'l*, pg. 5576
CRANBROOK DAILY TOWNSMAN—See Black Press Group Ltd.; *Int'l*, pg. 1059

CRANBROOK UNDERWRITING LIMITED—See H.W. Kaufman Financial Group, Inc.; *U.S. Private*, pg. 1836
CRANBURY INTERNATIONAL LLC—See ProBility Media Corporation; *U.S. Public*, pg. 1723
CRANDALL FORD; *U.S. Private*, pg. 1085
THE CRANDALL-HICKS COMPANY, INC.; *U.S. Private*, pg. 4016
CRANE AEROSPACE & ELECTRONICS, KELTEC OPERATION—See Crane NXT, Co.; *U.S. Public*, pg. 589
CRANE AEROSPACE & ELECTRONICS—See Crane NXT, Co.; *U.S. Public*, pg. 589
CRANE AEROSPACE, INC.—See Crane NXT, Co.; *U.S. Public*, pg. 589
CRANE AEROSPACE STC MICROWAVE SYSTEM OLEKTRON—See Crane NXT, Co.; *U.S. Public*, pg. 589
CRANE (ASIA PACIFIC) PTE. LTD.—See Crane NXT, Co.; *U.S. Public*, pg. 590
CRANE ASSET MANAGEMENT LLC—See Carnegie Investment Counsel; *U.S. Private*, pg. 766
CRANE AUSTRALIA PTY. LTD.—See Crane NXT, Co.; *U.S. Public*, pg. 590
CRANE BUILDING SERVICES & UTILITIES—See Crane NXT, Co.; *U.S. Public*, pg. 590
CRANE CANADA CO.—See Groupe Deschenes Inc.; *Int'l*, pg. 3101
CRANE CARRIER COMPANY—See Platinum Equity, LLC; *U.S. Private*, pg. 3209
CRANE CHEMPHARMA FLOW SOLUTIONS—See Crane NXT, Co.; *U.S. Public*, pg. 590
CRANE & CO., INC.—See Fedrigoni SpA; *Int'l*, pg. 2631
CRANE COMPANY; *U.S. Public*, pg. 589
CRANE COMPOSITES INC.—See Crane NXT, Co.; *U.S. Public*, pg. 590
CRANE COMPOSITES, INC.—See Crane NXT, Co.; *U.S. Public*, pg. 590
CRANE CONSTRUCTION CO.; *U.S. Private*, pg. 1085
CRANE CONTROLS, INC.—See Crane NXT, Co.; *U.S. Public*, pg. 589
CRANE COPPER TUBE—See Fletcher Building Limited; *Int'l*, pg. 2699
CRANE CREDIT UNION; *U.S. Private*, pg. 1085
CRANE CREEK SURGICAL PARTNERS, LLC—See Community Health Systems, Inc.; *U.S. Public*, pg. 552
CRANE CURRENCY MALTA LTD.—See Crane NXT, Co.; *U.S. Public*, pg. 590
CRANE DISTRIBUTION LIMITED—See Blackfriars Corp.; *U.S. Private*, pg. 575
CRANE DISTRIBUTION NZ LIMITED—See Sonepar S.A.; *Int'l*, pg. 7090
CRANE DISTRIBUTION PROPERTIES LIMITED—See Fletcher Building Limited; *Int'l*, pg. 2699
CRANE ELECTRONICS CORPORATION—See Crane NXT, Co.; *U.S. Public*, pg. 589
CRANE ELECTRONICS, INC.—See Crane Group Limited; *Int'l*, pg. 1828
CRANE ELECTRONICS, INC.—See Crane NXT, Co.; *U.S. Public*, pg. 589
CRANE ELECTRONICS LTD.—See Crane Group Limited; *Int'l*, pg. 1828
CRANE ENFIELD METALS PTY LIMITED—See Fletcher Building Limited; *Int'l*, pg. 2699
CRANE ENGINEERED MATERIALS—See Crane NXT, Co.; *U.S. Public*, pg. 590
CRANE ENGINEERING SALES, LLC—See AEA Investors LP; *U.S. Private*, pg. 113
CRANE FLUID HANDLING—See Crane NXT, Co.; *U.S. Public*, pg. 590
CRANE GLOBAL HOLDINGS S.L.—See Crane NXT, Co.; *U.S. Public*, pg. 590
CRANE GROUP CO.; *U.S. Private*, pg. 1085
CRANE GROUP LIMITED—See Fletcher Building Limited; *Int'l*, pg. 2699
CRANE GROUP LIMITED; *Int'l*, pg. 1827
CRANE HOLDINGS (GERMANY) GMBH—See Crane NXT, Co.; *U.S. Public*, pg. 590
CRANE INFRASTRUCTURE LTD.; *Int'l*, pg. 1828
CRANE INSPECTION & CERTIFICATION BUREAU L.L.C.; *U.S. Private*, pg. 1085
CRANE INTERNATIONAL HOLDINGS, INC.—See Crane NXT, Co.; *U.S. Public*, pg. 590
CRANE INVESTMENT CO.—See Crane Group Co.; *U.S. Private*, pg. 1085
CRANE JOHNSON LUMBER COMPANY INC.; *U.S. Private*, pg. 1085
THE CRANE LAEM CHABANG CO., LTD.—See Chu Kai Public Company Limited; *Int'l*, pg. 1589
CRANE LEAR ROMEC CORP.—See Crane NXT, Co.; *U.S. Public*, pg. 589
CRANE LIMITED—See Crane NXT, Co.; *U.S. Public*, pg. 590
CRANEL INCORPORATED; *U.S. Private*, pg. 1085
CRANE MATERIALS INTERNATIONAL (CMI)—See Crane Group Co.; *U.S. Private*, pg. 1085
CRANE MERCHANDISING SYSTEMS, INC.—See Crane NXT, Co.; *U.S. Public*, pg. 591
CRANE MERCHANDISING SYSTEMS LTD.—See Crane NXT, Co.; *U.S. Public*, pg. 590

COMPANY NAME INDEX

THE CRANEMERE GROUP LIMITED; *Int'l*, pg. 7635
CRANE MERGER CO. LLC—See Crane NXT, Co.; *U.S. Public*, pg. 591
CRANE NATIONAL VENDORS CO., LTD.—See Crane NXT, Co.; *U.S. Public*, pg. 591
CRANE NINGJIN VALVE CO.—See Crane NXT, Co.; *U.S. Public*, pg. 590
CRANE NUCLEAR, INC.—See Crane NXT, Co.; *U.S. Public*, pg. 589
CRANE NXT, CO.; *U.S. Public*, pg. 589
CRANE NXT PRIVATE LIMITED—See Crane NXT, Co.; *U.S. Public*, pg. 591
CRANE OVERSEAS LLC—See Crane NXT, Co.; *U.S. Public*, pg. 591
CRANE PAYMENT INNOVATIONS AG—See Crane NXT, Co.; *U.S. Public*, pg. 591
CRANE PAYMENT INNOVATIONS GMBH—See Crane NXT, Co.; *U.S. Public*, pg. 591
CRANE PAYMENT INNOVATIONS, INC.—See Crane NXT, Co.; *U.S. Public*, pg. 591
CRANE PAYMENT INNOVATIONS SRL—See Crane NXT, Co.; *U.S. Public*, pg. 591
CRANE PAYMENT & MERCHANDISING TECHNOLOGIES—See Crane NXT, Co.; *U.S. Public*, pg. 591
CRANE PAYMENTS INNOVATIONS, INC.—See Crane NXT, Co.; *U.S. Public*, pg. 591
CRANE PEST CONTROL, INC.—See Rollins, Inc.; *U.S. Public*, pg. 1809
CRANE PLASTICS HOLDING COMPANY; *U.S. Private*, pg. 1085
CRANE PLUMBING, L.L.C.—See Sun Capital Partners, Inc.; *U.S. Private*, pg. 3858
CRANE PROCESS FLOW TECHNOLOGIES GMBH—See Crane NXT, Co.; *U.S. Public*, pg. 590
CRANE PROCESS FLOW TECHNOLOGIES LTD.—See Crane NXT, Co.; *U.S. Public*, pg. 590
CRANE PROCESS FLOW TECHNOLOGIES S.P.R.L.—See Crane NXT, Co.; *U.S. Public*, pg. 590
CRANE PROCESS FLOW TECHNOLOGIES S.R.L.—See Crane NXT, Co.; *U.S. Public*, pg. 591
CRANE PUMPS AND SYSTEMS CANADA, INC.—See Crane NXT, Co.; *U.S. Public*, pg. 590
CRANE PUMPS & SYSTEMS INC.—See Crane NXT, Co.; *U.S. Public*, pg. 590
THE CRANE RAYONG CO., LTD.—See Chu Kai Public Company Limited; *Int'l*, pg. 1589
CRANE RESISTOFLEX GMBH—See Crane NXT, Co.; *U.S. Public*, pg. 591
CRANE RESISTOFLEX/INDUSTRIAL—See Crane NXT, Co.; *U.S. Public*, pg. 590
THE CRANE SERVICE CO., LTD.—See Chu Kai Public Company Limited; *Int'l*, pg. 1589
CRANES SOFTWARE INTERNATIONAL LIMITED; *Int'l*, pg. 1828
CRANE STOCKHAM VALVE LTD.—See Crane NXT, Co.; *U.S. Public*, pg. 590
CRANE SUB-CO.—See Taiyuan Heavy Industry Co., Ltd.; *Int'l*, pg. 7427
CRANESVILLE BLOCK CO., INC.; *U.S. Private*, pg. 1085
CRANETECH, INC.—See Balance Point Capital Advisors, LLC; *U.S. Private*, pg. 457
CRANE TECH SOLUTIONS, LLC; *U.S. Private*, pg. 1085
CRANE TRANSPORT, INC.—See Titanium Transportation Group Inc.; *Int'l*, pg. 7761
CRANE VALVE SERVICES—See Crane NXT, Co.; *U.S. Public*, pg. 590
CRANEWARE, INC.—See Craneware plc; *Int'l*, pg. 1828
CRANEWARE INSIGHT, INC.—See Craneware plc; *Int'l*, pg. 1828
CRANEWARE PLC; *Int'l*, pg. 1828
CRANEWARE US HOLDINGS, INC.—See Craneware plc; *Int'l*, pg. 1828
CRANE WORLDWIDE LOGISTICS LLC; *U.S. Private*, pg. 1085
CRANEX KONECRANES SP. Z.O.O.—See Konecranes Plc; *Int'l*, pg. 4251
CRANEX LIMITED; *Int'l*, pg. 1828
CRANFIELD AEROSPACE SOLUTIONS LIMITED; *Int'l*, pg. 1828
CRANFORD CONSTRUCTION CO.—See McGeorge Contracting Co., Inc.; *U.S. Private*, pg. 2634
CRANFORD CONTROLS LIMITED—See Halma plc; *Int'l*, pg. 3231
CRANFORD JOHNSON ROBINSON WOODS, INC.; *U.S. Private*, pg. 1085
CRANIAL TECHNOLOGIES, INC.—See Eurazeo SE; *Int'l*, pg. 2528
CRANIUM, INC.—See Hasbro, Inc.; *U.S. Public*, pg. 987
CRANK MEDIA INC.; *Int'l*, pg. 1828
CRANKSHAFT MACHINE COMPANY—See Avis Industrial Corporation; *U.S. Private*, pg. 407
CRANK SOFTWARE ULC—See AMETEK, Inc.; *U.S. Public*, pg. 120
CRANKT PROTEIN INTERNATIONAL PTY. LIMITED—See Noumi Limited; *Int'l*, pg. 5450
CRANKY SIGNS & ADVERTISING; *U.S. Private*, pg. 1085
CRANMORE EUROPE BVBA—See Enstar Group Limited; *Int'l*, pg. 2448

CRANMORE (UK) LIMITED—See Enstar Group Limited; *Int'l*, pg. 2448
CRANMORE (US) INC.—See Enstar Group Limited; *Int'l*, pg. 2448
CRANNEY COMPANIES, INC.—See Koch Industries, Inc.; *U.S. Private*, pg. 2327
CRANNEY COMPANIES, INC.—See The Goldman Sachs Group, Inc.; *U.S. Public*, pg. 2076
CRANSHAW CONSTRUCTION—See National Development; *U.S. Private*, pg. 2852
CRANSTON PRINT WORKS COMPANY; *U.S. Private*, pg. 1086
CRANSWICK CONVENIENCE FOODS—See Cranswick Plc; *Int'l*, pg. 1828
CRANSWICK COUNTRY FOODS (NORFOLK) LIMITED—See Cranswick Plc; *Int'l*, pg. 1828
CRANSWICK COUNTRY FOODS PLC—See Cranswick Plc; *Int'l*, pg. 1828
CRANSWICK GOURMET BACON COMPANY LIMITED—See Cranswick Plc; *Int'l*, pg. 1828
CRANSWICK GOURMET PASTRY COMPANY LIMITED—See Cranswick Plc; *Int'l*, pg. 1828
CRANSWICK GOURMET SAUSAGE COMPANY LIMITED—See Cranswick Plc; *Int'l*, pg. 1828
CRANSWICK PET & AQUATICS LTD.—See Westland Horticulture Ltd.; *Int'l*, pg. 8390
CRANSWICK PLC; *Int'l*, pg. 1828
CRAPIE SAS—See VINCI S.A.; *Int'l*, pg. 8216
CRARY INDUSTRIES—See Yamabiko Corporation; *Int'l*, pg. 8547
CRASH AVOIDANCE METRICS PARTNERSHIPS—See General Motors Company; *U.S. Public*, pg. 923
CRASHED TOYS LLC—See Copart, Inc.; *U.S. Public*, pg. 575
CRA; *U.S. Private*, pg. 1081
CRASSOCIATES, INC.; *U.S. Private*, pg. 1086
CRASTI & COMPANY PTY. LTD.—See Close the Loop Limited; *Int'l*, pg. 1661
CRATE & BARREL HOLDINGS, INC.—See Otto GmbH & Co. KG; *Int'l*, pg. 5662
CRATER GOLD MINING LIMITED; *Int'l*, pg. 1828
CRATE TECH, INC.—See Delos Capital, LLC; *U.S. Private*, pg. 1198
CRATEX MANUFACTURING CO., INC.; *U.S. Private*, pg. 1086
CRAVATEX BRANDS LIMITED—See Paragon Advisor Partners LLP; *Int'l*, pg. 5735
CRAVATEX LTD.; *Int'l*, pg. 1828
CRAVATH, SWAINE & MOORE LLP; *U.S. Private*, pg. 1086
CRAVEN HOUSE CAPITAL PLC; *Int'l*, pg. 1828
CRAVENHURST PROPERTIES LIMITED—See Apollo Global Management, Inc.; *U.S. Public*, pg. 165
CRAVEN POTTERY INC.; *U.S. Private*, pg. 1086
CRAVEROLANIS; *Int'l*, pg. 1828
CRA-WAL—See Buckeye Corrugated Inc.; *U.S. Private*, pg. 677
CRAWFORD ADVERTISING ASSOCIATES, LTD.; *U.S. Private*, pg. 1086
CRAWFORD BROADCASTING CO.; *U.S. Private*, pg. 1086
CRAWFORD COMBURSA S.L.U.—See ASSA ABLOY AB; *Int'l*, pg. 634
CRAWFORD & COMPANY ADJUSTERS LIMITED—See Crawford & Company; *U.S. Public*, pg. 592
CRAWFORD & COMPANY (BERMUDA) LIMITED—See Crawford & Company; *U.S. Public*, pg. 592
CRAWFORD & COMPANY (CANADA), INC.—See Crawford & Company; *U.S. Public*, pg. 592
CRAWFORD & COMPANY (CANADA) INC.—See Crawford & Company; *U.S. Public*, pg. 592
CRAWFORD & COMPANY INTERNATIONAL PTE LTD—See Crawford & Company; *U.S. Public*, pg. 592
CRAWFORD COMPANY; *U.S. Private*, pg. 1086
CRAWFORD & COMPANY; *U.S. Public*, pg. 592
CRAWFORD & COMPANY UK—See Crawford & Company; *U.S. Public*, pg. 592
CRAWFORD & CRAWFORD, INC.—See Adair Feed & Grain Company; *U.S. Private*, pg. 73
CRAWFORD DEUR B.V.—See ASSA ABLOY AB; *Int'l*, pg. 634
CRAWFORD DOOR FORSALJNINGS AB—See ASSA ABLOY AB; *Int'l*, pg. 634
CRAWFORD DOOR (KUNSHAN) CO., LTD.—See ASSA ABLOY AB; *Int'l*, pg. 634
CRAWFORD DOOR M.E. AB—See ASSA ABLOY AB; *Int'l*, pg. 634
CRAWFORD ELECTRIC SUPPLY COMPANY—See Sonepar S.A.; *Int'l*, pg. 7093
CRAWFORD FINANCIAL CONSULTING, LLC—See B. Riley Financial, Inc.; *U.S. Public*, pg. 260
CRAWFORD FURNITURE MANUFACTURING CORPORATION; *U.S. Private*, pg. 1086
THE CRAWFORD GROUP INC.; *U.S. Private*, pg. 4016
THE CRAWFORD GROUP, L.L.C.; *U.S. Private*, pg. 4016
CRAWFORD HAFA AG—See ASSA ABLOY AB; *Int'l*, pg. 635
CRAWFORD HAFA GMBH—See ASSA ABLOY AB; *Int'l*, pg. 635

CRAWFORD HAFA GMBH-WENNINGSEN—See ASSA ABLOY AB; *Int'l*, pg. 635
CRAWFORD-HAFA SRL—See ASSA ABLOY AB; *Int'l*, pg. 635
CRAWFORD HEALTHCARE HOLDINGS LIMITED; *Int'l*, pg. 1828
CRAWFORD HEATING & COOLING CO.; *U.S. Private*, pg. 1086
CRAWFORD INDUSTRIES, LLC—See The Jordan Company, L.P.; *U.S. Private*, pg. 4062
CRAWFORD INTERNATIONAL AB—See ASSA ABLOY AB; *Int'l*, pg. 634
CRAWFORD LABORATORIES, INC.—See Tennant Company; *U.S. Public*, pg. 2016
CRAWFORD NORMSTAHL N.V.—See ASSA ABLOY AB; *Int'l*, pg. 634
CRAWFORD OIL CO. INC.; *U.S. Private*, pg. 1086
CRAWFORD PACKAGING INC.; *Int'l*, pg. 1829
CRAWFORD PHYSICAL THERAPY, LIMITED PARTNERSHIP—See U.S. Physical Therapy, Inc.; *U.S. Public*, pg. 2214
CRAWFORD POLAND SP. ZO.O.—See ASSA ABLOY AB; *Int'l*, pg. 634
CRAWFORD PRODUCTION ROMANIA SRL—See ASSA ABLOY AB; *Int'l*, pg. 635
CRAWFORD RENOVATION; *U.S. Private*, pg. 1086
CRAWFORD SALES COMPANY; *U.S. Private*, pg. 1086
CRAWFORD SERVICES, INC.—See Brookfield Corporation; *Int'l*, pg. 1188
CRAWFORD STREET CORP.—See Radius Recycling, Inc.; *U.S. Public*, pg. 1760
CRAWFORD SUPPLY COMPANY; *U.S. Private*, pg. 1086
CRAWFORD SUPPLY—See Crawford Supply Company; *U.S. Private*, pg. 1086
CRAWFORDSVILLE BICKFORD COTTAGE, L.L.C.—See National Health Investors, Inc.; *U.S. Public*, pg. 1495
CRAWFORDSVILLE ELECTRIC LIGHT & POWER; *U.S. Private*, pg. 1086
CRAWFORD TECHNOLOGIES, INC.; *Int'l*, pg. 1829
CRAWFORD TOR GMBH—See ASSA ABLOY AB; *Int'l*, pg. 635
CRAWFORD TRUCKS & EQUIPMENT, INC.; *U.S. Private*, pg. 1086
CRAWFORD UK LTD.—See ASSA ABLOY AB; *Int'l*, pg. 635
CRAWFORD UNITED CORPORATION; *U.S. Public*, pg. 592
CRAW-KAN TELEPHONE COOPERATIVE; *U.S. Private*, pg. 1086
CRAWLEY & COMPANY INCORPORATED; *U.S. Private*, pg. 1086
CRAY AUSTRALIA PTY. LIMITED—See Hewlett Packard Enterprise Company; *U.S. Public*, pg. 1030
CRAY CANADA ULC—See Hewlett Packard Enterprise Company; *U.S. Public*, pg. 1030
CRAY COMPUTER DEUTSCHLAND GMBH—See Hewlett Packard Enterprise Company; *U.S. Public*, pg. 1030
CRAY COMPUTER GMBH—See Hewlett Packard Enterprise Company; *U.S. Public*, pg. 1030
CRAY COMPUTER SAS—See Hewlett Packard Enterprise Company; *U.S. Public*, pg. 1030
CRAY INC.—See Hewlett Packard Enterprise Company; *U.S. Public*, pg. 1030
CRAY INC.—See Hewlett Packard Enterprise Company; *U.S. Public*, pg. 1030
CRAY JAPAN, INC.—See Hewlett Packard Enterprise Company; *U.S. Public*, pg. 1030
CRAY KOREA, INC.—See Hewlett Packard Enterprise Company; *U.S. Public*, pg. 1030
CRAYNON FIRE PROTECTION, INC.—See The Riverside Company; *U.S. Private*, pg. 4108
CRAYOLA CANADA—See Hallmark Cards, Inc.; *U.S. Private*, pg. 1844
CRAYOLA LLC—See Hallmark Cards, Inc.; *U.S. Private*, pg. 1844
CRAYON AB—See Crayon Group AS; *Int'l*, pg. 1829
CRAYON AFRICA S.A.—See Crayon Group Holding ASA; *Int'l*, pg. 1829
CRAYON A/S—See Crayon Group AS; *Int'l*, pg. 1829
CRAYON AUSTRIA GMBH—See Crayon Group AS; *Int'l*, pg. 1829
CRAYON B.V.—See Crayon Group AS; *Int'l*, pg. 1829
CRAYON, CELOVITE IT RESITVE, D.O.O.—See Crayon Group Holding ASA; *Int'l*, pg. 1829
CRAYON CHANNEL APAC—See Crayon Group AS; *Int'l*, pg. 1829
CRAYON CZECH REPUBLIC AND SLOVAKIA S.R.O.—See Crayon Group Holding ASA; *Int'l*, pg. 1829
CRAYON DEUTSCHLAND GMBH—See Crayon Group Holding ASA; *Int'l*, pg. 1829
CRAYON FRANCE SAS—See Crayon Group AS; *Int'l*, pg. 1829
CRAYON GLOBAL SERVICES GMBH—See Crayon Group AS; *Int'l*, pg. 1829
CRAYON GROUP AS; *Int'l*, pg. 1829
CRAYON GROUP HOLDING ASA; *Int'l*, pg. 1829
CRAYON ICELAND—See Crayon Group AS; *Int'l*, pg. 1829
CRAYON INDIA—See Crayon Group AS; *Int'l*, pg. 1829

CRAYON LTD—See Crayon Group AS; *Int'l*, pg. 1829
CRAYON MAURITIUS LTD.—See Crayon Group Holding ASA; *Int'l*, pg. 1829
CRAYON MIDDLE EAST—See Crayon Group AS; *Int'l*, pg. 1829
CRAYON OY—See Crayon Group AS; *Int'l*, pg. 1829
CRAYON POLAND SP. Z O.O.—See Crayon Group Holding ASA; *Int'l*, pg. 1829
CRAYON PORTUGAL—See Crayon Group AS; *Int'l*, pg. 1829
CRAYON PTE LTD—See Crayon Group AS; *Int'l*, pg. 1829
CRAYON SCHWEIZ AG—See Crayon Group Holding ASA; *Int'l*, pg. 1829
CRAYON SOFTWARE EXPERTS INDIA PVT. LTD.—See Crayon Group Holding ASA; *Int'l*, pg. 1829
CRAYON SOFTWARE EXPERTS MALAYSIA SDN. BHD.—See Crayon Group AS; *Int'l*, pg. 1829
CRAYON SOFTWARE EXPERTS PHILIPPINES INC.—See Crayon Group Holding ASA; *Int'l*, pg. 1829
CRAYON SOFTWARE EXPERTS ROMANIA S.R.L.—See Crayon Group Holding ASA; *Int'l*, pg. 1829
CRAYON SOFTWARE EXPERTS SPAIN S.L.—See Crayon Group Holding ASA; *Int'l*, pg. 1829
CRAYON SOFTWARE LICENSING UNIPESSOAL LDA—See Crayon Group Holding ASA; *Int'l*, pg. 1829
CRAYON; *U.S. Private*, pg. 1086
CRAYON SPAIN—See Crayon Group AS; *Int'l*, pg. 1829
CRAYON UK LTD.—See Crayon Group Holding ASA; pg. 1829
CRAY SUPERCOMPUTERS (INDIA) PRIVATE LIMITED—See Hewlett Packard Enterprise Company; *U.S. Public*, pg. 1031
CRAY TAIWAN, INC.—See Hewlett Packard Enterprise Company; *U.S. Public*, pg. 1031
CRAY U.K. LIMITED—See Hewlett Packard Enterprise Company; *U.S. Public*, pg. 1031
CRAY VALLEY IBERICA SA—See TotalEnergies SE; *Int'l*, pg. 7839
CRAY VALLEY ITALIA SRL—See TotalEnergies SE; *Int'l*, pg. 7839
CRAY VALLEY KOREA—See TotalEnergies SE; *Int'l*, pg. 7839
CRAY VALLEY KUNSTHARZE GMBH—See TotalEnergies SE; *Int'l*, pg. 7839
CRAY VALLEY LTD—See TotalEnergies SE; *Int'l*, pg. 7839
CRAY VALLEY RESINS SOUTH AFRICA PTY. LTD.—See TotalEnergies SE; *Int'l*, pg. 7839
CRAY VALLEY S.A.—See TotalEnergies SE; *Int'l*, pg. 7839
CRAY VALLEY USA, LLC—See TotalEnergies SE; *Int'l*, pg. 7839
CRAY VALLEY USA, LLC—See TotalEnergies SE; *Int'l*, pg. 7839
CRAZY DOG TSHIRTS; *U.S. Private*, pg. 1086
CRAZY DOMAINS FZ-LLC—See Dreamscape Networks Limited; *Int'l*, pg. 2203
CRAZY INFOTECH LTD.; *Int'l*, pg. 1830
CRAZY SPORTS GROUP LIMITED; *Int'l*, pg. 1830
CRAZY WOMAN CREEK BANCORP, INC.; *U.S. Public*, pg. 592
C. R. BARD GMBH—See Becton, Dickinson & Company; *U.S. Public*, pg. 291
C.R. BARD, INC.—See Becton, Dickinson & Company; *U.S. Public*, pg. 290
C.R. BARD, INC.—See Becton, Dickinson & Company; *U.S. Public*, pg. 291
C. R. BARD NETHERLANDS SALES BV—See Becton, Dickinson & Company; *U.S. Public*, pg. 290
CR BASEL; *Int'l*, pg. 1827
CRB BENELUX B.V.—See Intercos S.p.A.; *Int'l*, pg. 3739
CRB INSURANCE AGENCY; *U.S. Private*, pg. 1086
CR BRANDS, INC.—See Resilience Capital Partners, LLC; *U.S. Private*, pg. 3405
CR BRIGGS CORPORATION—See ATNA RESOURCES LTD.; *U.S. Private*, pg. 381
CRB SHARE CUSTODIAN SERVICES LTD.; *Int'l*, pg. 1830
C.R. BUILDING COMPANY—See Klewin Construction Inc.; *U.S. Private*, pg. 2319
C.R. CALDERON CONSTRUCTION, INC.; *U.S. Private*, pg. 708
CR CAPITAL AG—See MPH Health Care AG; *Int'l*, pg. 5061
CR CAPITAL REAL ESTATE AG; *Int'l*, pg. 1827
CRCC FINANCE COMPANY LIMITED—See China Railway Construction Corporation Limited; *Int'l*, pg. 1542
CRCC HARBOUR & CHANNEL ENGINEERING BUREAU GROUP CO., LTD.—See China Railway Construction Corporation Limited; *Int'l*, pg. 1542
CRCC HIGH-TECH EQUIPMENT CORPORATION LIMITED; *Int'l*, pg. 1830
CRCC MEDIA CO., LTD.—See Hisamitsu Pharmaceutical Co., Inc.; *Int'l*, pg. 3406
CRC-EVANS AUTOMATIC WELDING, INC.—See CRC-Evans International, Inc.; *U.S. Private*, pg. 1087
CRC-EVANS B.V.—See CRC-Evans International, Inc.; *U.S. Private*, pg. 1087
CRC-EVANS CANADA LTD.—See CRC-Evans International, Inc.; *U.S. Private*, pg. 1087

CRC-EVANS INTERNATIONAL, INC.; *U.S. Private*, pg. 1087
CRC-EVANS OFFSHORE LIMITED—See Stanley Black & Decker, Inc.; *U.S. Public*, pg. 1932
CRC-EVANS OFFSHORE LTD.—See Stanley Black & Decker, Inc.; *U.S. Public*, pg. 1932
CRC-EVANS PIH SERVIOS DE TUBULAO DO BRASIL LTDA—See Stanley Black & Decker, Inc.; *U.S. Public*, pg. 1932
CRC-EVANS WEIGHTING SYSTEMS, INC.—See Stanley Black & Decker, Inc.; *U.S. Public*, pg. 1932
CRC HEALTH GROUP, INC.—See Acadia Healthcare Company, Inc.; *U.S. Public*, pg. 28
CRC HEALTH, LLC—See Acadia Healthcare Company, Inc.; *U.S. Public*, pg. 28
CRC HEALTH TREATMENT CLINICS, LLC—See Acadia Healthcare Company, Inc.; *U.S. Public*, pg. 28
CR CHIANG MAI (THAILAND) CO., LTD.—See Central Group Company Limited; *Int'l*, pg. 1407
CRC INDUSTRIES, INC.—See Berwind Corporation; *U.S. Private*, pg. 541
CRC INSURANCE SERVICES, INC.—See Truist Financial Corporation; *U.S. Public*, pg. 2200
CRC INTERNATIONAL INC.; *U.S. Private*, pg. 1087
CRC MARKETING SOLUTIONS; *U.S. Private*, pg. 1087
CR CO., LTD.—See Chugai Ro Co., Ltd.; *Int'l*, pg. 1594
CR CONSTRUCTION COMPANY—See Columbia National Group Inc; *U.S. Private*, pg. 977
CRC PROPERTIES INC.—See CSX Corporation; *U.S. Public*, pg. 602
CRC PROPERTIES INC.—See Norfolk Southern Corporation; *U.S. Public*, pg. 1535
CRC PUBLIC RELATIONS; *U.S. Private*, pg. 1087
CRC SERVICES, LLC—See California Resources Corporation; *U.S. Public*, pg. 423
C.R.C. S.R.L.—See Carel Industries S.p.A.; *Int'l*, pg. 1324
CRC SYSTEMS CORP.—See ITOCHU Corporation; *Int'l*, pg. 3840
CRC WISCONSIN RD, LLC—See Acadia Healthcare Company, Inc.; *U.S. Public*, pg. 28
C.R. DANIELS, INC.; *U.S. Private*, pg. 708
CRDB BANK PLC; *Int'l*, pg. 1830
CR DEVELOPPEMENT SAS—See AmRest Holdings SE; *Int'l*, pg. 437
C&R DISTRIBUTING INC.—See Nevada Trio Inc.; *U.S. Private*, pg. 2891
CR DYNAMICS & ASSOCIATES; *U.S. Private*, pg. 1081
CRE8 DIRECT (NINGBO) CO., LTD.; *Int'l*, pg. 1830
CREABETON MATERIAUX SA—See Vicat S.A.; *Int'l*, pg. 8186
CREACION NAZCA SAATCHI & SAATCHI—See Publicis Groupe S.A.; *Int'l*, pg. 6107
CREACTIVES GROUP SPA; *Int'l*, pg. 1830
CREADES AB; *Int'l*, pg. 1830
CREADEV SAS; *Int'l*, pg. 1830
CREADOR ADVISORS INDIA PRIVATE LIMITED—See Creador Sdn. Bhd.; *Int'l*, pg. 1831
CREADOR SDN. BHD.; *Int'l*, pg. 1831
CREAD—See The Interpublic Group of Companies, Inc.; *U.S. Public*, pg. 2092
CREAFORM DEUTSCHLAND GMBH—See AMETEK, Inc.; *U.S. Public*, pg. 119
CREAFORM FRANCE S.A.S.—See AMETEK, Inc.; *U.S. Public*, pg. 120
CREAFORM INC.—See AMETEK, Inc.; *U.S. Public*, pg. 120
CREAFORM JAPAN K.K.—See AMETEK, Inc.; *U.S. Public*, pg. 120
CREAFORM SHANGHAI LTD.—See AMETEK, Inc.; *U.S. Public*, pg. 120
CREAFORM USA, INC.—See AMETEK, Inc.; *U.S. Public*, pg. 120
CREA GERMANY GMBH—See The Carlyle Group Inc.; *U.S. Public*, pg. 2045
CREAGER MERCANTILE; *U.S. Private*, pg. 1087
CREAGH MEDICAL LIMITED—See SurModics, Inc.; *U.S. Public*, pg. 1967
CREAGRI, INC.; *U.S. Private*, pg. 1087
CREA INFORMATICA S.R.L.—See CTS Eventim AG & Co. KGaA; *Int'l*, pg. 1874
CREALIS S.A.S.—See A.S. Creation Tapeten AG; *Int'l*, pg. 28
CRE ALLIANCE, INC.—See CRE, Inc.; *Int'l*, pg. 1830
CREALOGIX AG—See Constellation Software Inc.; *Int'l*, pg. 1772
CREALOGIX BAAS GMBH & CO. KG—See Constellation Software Inc.; *Int'l*, pg. 1772
CREALOGIX (DEUTSCHLAND) AG—See Constellation Software Inc.; *Int'l*, pg. 1772
CREALOGIX HOLDING AG—See Constellation Software Inc.; *Int'l*, pg. 1772
CREALOGIX MBA LTD.—See Constellation Software Inc.; *Int'l*, pg. 1772
CREALOGIX PTE. LTD.—See Constellation Software Inc.; *Int'l*, pg. 1772
CREA MADRID NUEVO NORTE S.A.—See Banco Bilbao Vizcaya Argentaria, S.A.; *Int'l*, pg. 817
CREAM HOLDINGS LIMITED—See Live Nation Entertainment, Inc.; *U.S. Public*, pg. 1328

CREAMISTRY FRANCHISE, INC.; *U.S. Private*, pg. 1087
CREAMLAND DAIRIES, INC.—See Dean Foods Company; *U.S. Private*, pg. 1183
CREAMLAND DAIRIES, INC.—See Dean Foods Company; *U.S. Private*, pg. 1183
CREAM-O-LAND DAIRY INC.; *U.S. Private*, pg. 1087
CREANATE INC.—See Sangetsu Co., Ltd.; *Int'l*, pg. 6537
CREA PUBLICIDAD—See The Interpublic Group of Companies, Inc.; *U.S. Public*, pg. 2092
CREA PUBLICIDAD—See The Interpublic Group of Companies, Inc.; *U.S. Public*, pg. 2092
CREARE PTE LTD—See LVMH Moet Hennessy Louis Vuitton SE; *Int'l*, pg. 4591
CREARE SA—See LVMH Moet Hennessy Louis Vuitton SE; *Int'l*, pg. 4591
CREAREVALORE S.P.A.—See Prismi S.p.A.; *Int'l*, pg. 5982
CREAS F&C CO., LTD.; *Int'l*, pg. 1831
CRE ASIA PTE. LTD.—See CRE, Inc.; *Int'l*, pg. 1830
CREA S.R.L.—See Amada Holdings Co., Ltd.; *Int'l*, pg. 404
CREATA SOFTWARE GMBH—See Mensch und Maschine Software SE; *Int'l*, pg. 4818
CREATD, INC.; *U.S. Public*, pg. 593
CREATECH MEDICAL S.L.U.—See Straumann Holding AG; *Int'l*, pg. 7237
CREATE CORPORATION; *Int'l*, pg. 1831
CREATEC PTY LTD—See Hancock & Gore Ltd.; *Int'l*, pg. 3242
CREATE & CRAFT LTD.—See Aurelius Equity Opportunities SE & Co. KGaA; *Int'l*, pg. 708
CREATE DINING INC.—See create restaurants holdings inc.; *Int'l*, pg. 1832
CREATE FOUNDATION; *U.S. Private*, pg. 1087
CREATE GROUP NYC, LLC—See Clayton, Dubilier & Rice, LLC; *U.S. Private*, pg. 927
CREATE LAB CO., LTD.—See CREO CO., LTD.; *Int'l*, pg. 1838
CREATELIVE, INC.; *U.S. Private*, pg. 1087
CREATE MEDIC CO. LTD.; *Int'l*, pg. 1832
CREATE MEDIC DALIAN INTERNATIONAL TRADING CO., LTD.—See CREATE MEDIC CO. LTD.; *Int'l*, pg. 1832
CREATE OI CO., LTD.—See Oi Electric Co., Ltd.; *Int'l*, pg. 5533
CREATE RESTAURANTS ASIA PTE.LTD.—See create restaurants holdings inc.; *Int'l*, pg. 1832
CREATE RESTAURANTS HOLDINGS INC.; *Int'l*, pg. 1832
CREATE RESTAURANTS HONG KONG LTD.—See create restaurants holdings inc.; *Int'l*, pg. 1832
CREATE RESTAURANTS INC.—See create restaurants holdings inc.; *Int'l*, pg. 1832
CREATE RESTAURANTS TAIWAN CO., LTD.—See create restaurants holdings inc.; *Int'l*, pg. 1832
CREATE S.D. HOLDINGS CO., LTD.; *Int'l*, pg. 1832
CREATE SPORTS & LEISURE INC.—See create restaurants holdings inc.; *Int'l*, pg. 1832
CREATE TECHNOLOGY & SCIENCE CO., LTD.; *Int'l*, pg. 1832
CREATE TECH SOFTWARE SYSTEMS LTD.—See Mobicon Group Limited; *Int'l*, pg. 5009
CREAT GROUP CORPORATION; *Int'l*, pg. 1831
CREATING RESULTS, LLC-STRATEGIC MARKETING; *U.S. Private*, pg. 1087
CREATION CONSUMER FINANCE LTD.—See BNP Paribas SA; *Int'l*, pg. 1090
CREATION EVIDENCE MUSEUM OF TEXAS; *U.S. Private*, pg. 1087
CREATION FINANCIAL SERVICES LTD.—See BNP Paribas SA; *Int'l*, pg. 1090
CREATION GARDENS, INC.; *U.S. Private*, pg. 1087
CREATIONS DE PARIS CAMAFLEX VERTRIEBS GMBH—See Aderans Co., Ltd.; *Int'l*, pg. 143
CREATIONS, INC.; *U.S. Private*, pg. 1087
CREATION TECHNOLOGIES LP—See Goldberg Lindsay & Co., LLC; *U.S. Private*, pg. 1729
CREATIST MEDIA CO., LTD.—See TV Thunder Public Company Limited; *Int'l*, pg. 7987
CREATIVASC MEDICAL, LLC—See Brookhaven Medical, Inc.; *U.S. Private*, pg. 663
CREATIVE ADVANCED TECHNOLOGY CENTER—See Creative Technology Ltd.; *Int'l*, pg. 1833
CREATIVE AGENCY SERVICES TEAM, INC.; *U.S. Private*, pg. 1087
CREATIVE AGE PUBLICATIONS, INC.—See Allured Publishing Corporation; *U.S. Private*, pg. 194
CREATIVE ALIGNMENTS, LLC; *U.S. Private*, pg. 1087
CREATIVE ALTERNATIVES, INC.; *U.S. Private*, pg. 1087
CREATIVE ARTISTS AGENCY, LLC—See TPG Capital, L.P.; *U.S. Public*, pg. 2170
CREATIVE ARTISTS AGENCY, LLC - ST. LOUIS OFFICE—See TPG Capital, L.P.; *U.S. Public*, pg. 2170
CREATIVE ARTISTS AGENCY UK LIMITED—See TPG Capital, L.P.; *U.S. Public*, pg. 2170
CREATIVE ASSOCIATES LTD.—See Dentsu Group Inc.; *Int'l*, pg. 2034
CREATIVEBANK INC.—See SoftBank Group Corp.; *Int'l*, pg. 7052
CREATIVE BATH PRODUCTS INC.; *U.S. Private*, pg. 1087

CREATIVE BOX INC.—See Nissan Motor Co., Ltd.; *Int'l*, pg. 5367
CREATIVE BRANCH; *U.S. Private*, pg. 1087
CREATIVE BREAKTHROUGHS, INC.—See Converge Technology Solutions Corp.; *Int'l*, pg. 1787
CREATIVE BROADCAST CONCEPTS; *U.S. Private*, pg. 1088
CREATIVE BUSINESS INTERIORS, INC.—See Interior Workplace Solutions LLC; *U.S. Private*, pg. 2111
CREATIVE BUSINESS INTERIORS; *U.S. Private*, pg. 1088
CREATIVE BUS SALES INC.; *U.S. Private*, pg. 1088
CREATIVE CARE FOR REACHING INDEPENDENCE; *U.S. Private*, pg. 1088
CREATIVE CASTINGS LTD.; *Int'l*, pg. 1832
CREATIVE CHILD CARE, INC.; *U.S. Private*, pg. 1088
CREATIVE CHINA HOLDINGS LIMITED; *Int'l*, pg. 1832
CREATIVE CIRCLE, LLC—See ASGN Incorporated; *U.S. Public*, pg. 210
CREATIVE CIVILIZATION AN AGUILAR/GIRARD AGENCY; *U.S. Private*, pg. 1088
CREATIVE COLORS S.A.—See Schwan-STABILO Cosmetics GmbH & Co. KG; *Int'l*, pg. 6644
CREATIVE COMMUNICATION ASSOCIATES; *U.S. Private*, pg. 1088
CREATIVE COMMUNICATION LTD.—See Advanced Chemical Industries Limited; *Int'l*, pg. 158
CREATIVE COMMUNICATIONS CONSULTANTS, INC.; *U.S. Private*, pg. 1088
CREATIVE COMMUNICATIONS CONSULTANTS, INC.; *U.S. Private*, pg. 1088
CREATIVE CONNECTIONS, INC.—See Centerbridge Partners, L.P.; *U.S. Private*, pg. 813
CREATIVE CONSERVATION CO., INC.—See TopBuild Corp.; *U.S. Public*, pg. 2163
CREATIVE CONTRACTORS INC.; *U.S. Private*, pg. 1088
CREATIVE CONTRACT PACKAGING CORP.—See Hormel Foods Corporation; *U.S. Public*, pg. 1054
CREATIVE CONVERTING—See Wellspring Capital Management LLC; *U.S. Private*, pg. 4477
THE CREATIVE COUNSEL PTY. LTD.—See Publicis Groupe S.A.; *Int'l*, pg. 6112
CREATIVE CRAFTS GROUP LLC—See Tinicum Enterprises, Inc.; *U.S. Private*, pg. 4174
THE CREATIVE DEPARTMENT; *U.S. Private*, pg. 4016
CREATIVE DESIGN INTERIORS INC.; *U.S. Private*, pg. 1088
CREATIVE DESIGN INTERIORS OF NEVADA, LLC.; *U.S. Private*, pg. 1088
CREATIVE DINING SERVICES, INC.; *U.S. Private*, pg. 1088
CREATIVE DOCUMENT IMAGING, INC.—See Hackworth Reprographics, Inc.; *U.S. Private*, pg. 1838
CREATIVE DOOR SERVICES LTD.—See Sanwa Holdings Corporation; *Int'l*, pg. 6560
CREATIVE EDGE NUTRITION, INC.; *U.S. Public*, pg. 593
CREATIVE ENTERPRISE HOLDINGS LTD.—See China Merchants Group Limited; *Int'l*, pg. 1523
CREATIVE ENTERTAINMENT SERVICES; *U.S. Private*, pg. 1088
CREATIVE EXTRUDED PRODUCTS; *U.S. Private*, pg. 1088
CREATIVE EYE LIMITED; *Int'l*, pg. 1832
CREATIVE FEED; *U.S. Private*, pg. 1088
CREATIVE FINANCIAL STAFFING LLC; *U.S. Private*, pg. 1088
CREATIVE FOAM CORPORATION—See Industrial Opportunity Partners, LLC; *U.S. Public*, pg. 2067
CREATIVE FOOD GROUP LIMITED—See Bakkavor Group plc; *Int'l*, pg. 806
CREATIVE FOODS CORP.; *U.S. Private*, pg. 1088
CREATIVE FOODS—See David Wood Baking Limited; *Int'l*, pg. 1984
CREATIVEFORGE GAMES S.A.; *Int'l*, pg. 1834
CREATIVE GARAGE; *U.S. Private*, pg. 1089
CREATIVE GEMS & JEWELRY PCL—See The Topaz Group, Inc.; *Int'l*, pg. 7694
CREATIVE GENIUS, INC.—See Vera Bradley, Inc.; *U.S. Public*, pg. 2279
CREATIVE GRAPHICS INTERNATIONAL LTD.—See Mobeus Equity Partners LLP; *Int'l*, pg. 5008
CREATIVE GROUP, INC.; *U.S. Private*, pg. 1089
CREATIVE HARDWARE FOR INTEGRATED PRODUCTS SAL—See Aiphone Co., Ltd.; *Int'l*, pg. 235
CREATIVE HEALTHCARE ADVERTISING PARIS—See WPP plc; *Int'l*, pg. 8492
CREATIVE HOLDINGS (HK) LIMITED—See Nam Lee Pressed Metal Industries Limited; *Int'l*, pg. 5134
CREATIVEHUB; *U.S. Private*, pg. 1090
CREATIVE INDUSTRIA E COMERCIO LTDA.—See Sakata INX Corporation; *Int'l*, pg. 6487
CREATIVE INFORMATION SYSTEMS, INC.—See Valsef Group; *Int'l*, pg. 8123
CREATIVE INFORMATION TECHNOLOGY, INC.; *U.S. Private*, pg. 1089
CREATIVE & INNOVATIVE SYSTEM CO., LTD.—See CIS Co., Ltd.; *Int'l*, pg. 1618
CREATIVE INSURANCE MARKETING CO.; *U.S. Private*, pg. 1089

CREATIVE INVESTMENTS PTE LTD—See Amara Holdings Ltd.; *Int'l*, pg. 411
CREATIVE JAPAN CO, LTD.—See Cresco, Ltd.; *Int'l*, pg. 1840
CREATIVE JAR; *Int'l*, pg. 1832
CREATIVE JUICE G1—See Omnicom Group Inc.; *U.S. Public*, pg. 1595
CREATIVE KIDS, INC.—See American Securities LLC; *U.S. Private*, pg. 249
CREATIVE LABEL INC.; *U.S. Private*, pg. 1089
CREATIVE LABS (HK) LIMITED—See Creative Technology Ltd.; *Int'l*, pg. 1833
CREATIVE LABS, INC. - LATIN AMERICA—See Creative Technology Ltd.; *Int'l*, pg. 1833
CREATIVE LABS, INC.—See Creative Technology Ltd.; *Int'l*, pg. 1833
CREATIVE LABS, INC.—See Creative Technology Ltd.; *Int'l*, pg. 1833
CREATIVE LABS IRELAND LTD.—See Creative Technology Ltd.; *Int'l*, pg. 1833
CREATIVE LABS N.V.—See Creative Technology Ltd.; *Int'l*, pg. 1833
CREATIVE LABS—See Creative Technology Ltd.; *Int'l*, pg. 1833
CREATIVE LABS—See Creative Technology Ltd.; *Int'l*, pg. 1833
CREATIVE LABS SRL—See Creative Technology Ltd.; *Int'l*, pg. 1833
CREATIVE LABS (SWEDEN)—See Creative Technology Ltd.; *Int'l*, pg. 1833
CREATIVE LEATHER FURNITURE INC.; *U.S. Private*, pg. 1089
CREATIVE LINK ADVERTISING; *U.S. Private*, pg. 1089
CREATIVE LOAFING ATLANTA, INC.—See SouthComm, Inc.; *U.S. Private*, pg. 3724
CREATIVE LOAFING-CHARLOTTE—See Womack Publishing Company, Inc.; *U.S. Private*, pg. 4555
CREATIVE LOAFING TAMPA, LLC—See SouthComm, Inc.; *U.S. Private*, pg. 3724
CREATIVE LODGING SOLUTIONS, LLC—See Corpay, Inc.; *U.S. Public*, pg. 579
CREATIVE MAILBOX DESIGNS, LLC; *U.S. Private*, pg. 1089
CREATIVE MANUFACTURING INC.; *U.S. Private*, pg. 1089
CREATIVE MARKETING ALLIANCE INC.; *U.S. Private*, pg. 1089
CREATIVE MARKETING RESOURCE, INC.; *U.S. Private*, pg. 1089
CREATIVE MARKETING RESOURCES; *U.S. Private*, pg. 1089
CREATIVE MARKETING SPECIALISTS, INC.; *U.S. Private*, pg. 1089
CREATIVE MARKET LABS, INC.—See Autodesk, Inc.; *U.S. Public*, pg. 229
CREATIVE MASTER BERMUDA LTD.; *Int'l*, pg. 1832
CREATIVE MASTER L&W LIMITED—See Creative Master Bermuda Ltd.; *Int'l*, pg. 1833
CREATIVE MASTER NORTHCORD LIMITED—See Creative Master Bermuda Ltd.; *Int'l*, pg. 1833
CREATIVE MASTER OVERSEAS HOLDINGS LIMITED—See Creative Master Bermuda Ltd.; *Int'l*, pg. 1833
CREATIVE MEDIA & COMMUNITY TRUST CORPORATION; *U.S. Public*, pg. 593
CREATIVE MEDIA K.K.—See Creative Technology Ltd.; *Int'l*, pg. 1833
CREATIVE MEDIA MARKETING INC.; *U.S. Private*, pg. 1089
CREATIVE MEDIA SERVICES GMBH—See The Interpublic Group of Companies, Inc.; *U.S. Public*, pg. 2090
CREATIVE MEDICAL TECHNOLOGIES, INC.—See Creative Medical Technology Holdings, Inc.; *U.S. Public*, pg. 593
CREATIVE MEDICAL TECHNOLOGY HOLDINGS, INC.; *U.S. Public*, pg. 593
CREATIVE NAIL DESIGN, INC.—See MacAndrews & Forbes Incorporated; *U.S. Private*, pg. 2534
CREATIVE NANOSYSTEMS CORPORATION—See Sysmex Corporation; *Int'l*, pg. 7388
CREATIVE NEWTECH LIMITED; *Int'l*, pg. 1833
CREATIVE OCCASIONS INC.—See George Weston Limited; *Int'l*, pg. 2939
CREATIVE OFFICE ENVIRONMENT, LLC; *U.S. Private*, pg. 1089
CREATIVE OFFICE INTERIORS INC.; *U.S. Private*, pg. 1089
CREATIVE OFFICE PAVILION LLC; *U.S. Private*, pg. 1089
CREATIVE PARTNERS GROUP, INC.; *U.S. Private*, pg. 1089
CREATIVE PARTNERS; *U.S. Private*, pg. 1089
CREATIVE PAYMENT SOLUTIONS, INC.—See Truist Financial Corporation; *U.S. Public*, pg. 2200
CREATIVE PLANNING, LLC; *U.S. Private*, pg. 1089
CREATIVE PLAYTHINGS LTD.; *U.S. Private*, pg. 1090
CREATIVEPRO.COM—See PrintingForLess.com, Inc.; *U.S. Private*, pg. 3266
CREATIVE PRODUCTIONS; *U.S. Private*, pg. 1090

CREATIVE PULTRUSIONS INC.—See Hill & Smith PLC; *Int'l*, pg. 3391
CREATIVE REALITIES, INC.; *U.S. Public*, pg. 593
CREATIVE RESOURCE GROUP, LLC; *U.S. Private*, pg. 1090
CREATIVE SALES GROUP, INC.; *U.S. Private*, pg. 1090
CREATIVE SALES INC.; *U.S. Private*, pg. 1090
CREATIVE SALES & MARKETING ASSOCIATES; *U.S. Private*, pg. 1090
CREATIVE SALMON COMPANY LTD.; *Int'l*, pg. 1833
CREATIVE SENSOR INC.; *Int'l*, pg. 1833
CREATIVE SERVICES, INC.; *U.S. Private*, pg. 1090
CREATIVE SIGN DESIGNS; *U.S. Private*, pg. 1090
CREATIVE SNACKS CO., LLC—See KIND LLC; *U.S. Private*, pg. 2306
CREATIVE SOLUTIONS CONSULTING INC; *U.S. Private*, pg. 1090
CREATIVE SOLUTIONS GROUP, INC.; *U.S. Private*, pg. 1090
CREATIVE STAGE LIGHTING CO.; *U.S. Private*, pg. 1090
CREATIVE STUDIO GUAM, INC.—See Kowa Co., Ltd.; *Int'l*, pg. 4294
CREATIVESYSTEMS - SISTEMAS E SERVICOS DE CONSULTORIA, S.A.—See Johnson Controls International plc; *Int'l*, pg. 3985
CREATIVE TEACHING PRESS INC.; *U.S. Private*, pg. 1090
CREATIVE TECHNOLOGIES CORP.; *U.S. Private*, pg. 1090
CREATIVE TECHNOLOGY CENTRE PTE LTD—See Creative Technology Ltd.; *Int'l*, pg. 1833
CREATIVE TECHNOLOGY CHICAGO—See The Carlyle Group Inc.; *U.S. Public*, pg. 2049
CREATIVE TECHNOLOGY (CHINA) CO., LTD.—See Creative Technology Ltd.; *Int'l*, pg. 1833
CREATIVE TECHNOLOGY (CHINA) CO., LTD.—See Creative Technology Ltd.; *Int'l*, pg. 1833
CREATIVE TECHNOLOGY (CHINA) CO., LTD.—See Creative Technology Ltd.; *Int'l*, pg. 1833
CREATIVE TECHNOLOGY GMBH CO. KG—See The Carlyle Group Inc.; *U.S. Public*, pg. 2049
CREATIVE TECHNOLOGY GROUP, INC—See The Carlyle Group Inc.; *U.S. Public*, pg. 2049
CREATIVE TECHNOLOGY LOS ANGELES—See The Carlyle Group Inc.; *U.S. Public*, pg. 2049
CREATIVE TECHNOLOGY LTD.; *Int'l*, pg. 1833
CREATIVE TECHNOLOGY LTD.—See The Carlyle Group Inc.; *U.S. Public*, pg. 2049
CREATIVE TECHNOLOGY SAN FRANCISCO—See The Carlyle Group Inc.; *U.S. Public*, pg. 2049
CREATIVE TECHNO SOLUTION CO., LTD—See Osaka Gas Co., Ltd.; *Int'l*, pg. 5645
CREATIVE TENT INTERNATIONAL, INC.—See XFS Global LLC; *U.S. Private*, pg. 4581
CREATIVE TESTING SOLUTIONS; *U.S. Private*, pg. 1090
CREATIVE TEXTILE TECHNOLOGY COMPANY (GUANGDONG) LIMITED—See Texwinca Holdings Limited; *Int'l*, pg. 7584
CREATIVE TOPS LIMITED—See Lifetime Brands, Inc.; *U.S. Public*, pg. 1313
THE CREATIVE UNDERGROUND; *U.S. Private*, pg. 4016
THE CREATIVE UNIT LIMITED—See Jamaica National Building Society; *Int'l*, pg. 3874
CREATIVE VISION ALLIANCE CORP.; *U.S. Private*, pg. 1090
CREATIVE VISTAS ACQUISITION CORP.—See Creative Vistas Inc.; *Int'l*, pg. 1833
CREATIVE VISTAS INC.; *Int'l*, pg. 1833
CREATIVE WOOD DESIGNS—See Patrick Industries, Inc.; *U.S. Public*, pg. 1652
CREATIVE YOKO CO., LTD.—See Onward Holdings Co., Ltd.; *Int'l*, pg. 5592
CREATIV SOFTWARE AG—See NEXUS AG; *Int'l*, pg. 5250
CREATON AG—See Etex SA/NV; *Int'l*, pg. 2521
CREATON & ETERNIT S.R.L.—See Etex SA/NV; *Int'l*, pg. 2521
CREATON HUNGARY KFT.—See Etex SA/NV; *Int'l*, pg. 2521
CREATON KERA-DACH GMBH & CO. KG—See Etex SA/NV; *Int'l*, pg. 2521
CREATOR CAPITAL LTD.; *Int'l*, pg. 1834
CREAT RESOURCES HOLDINGS LIMITED; *Int'l*, pg. 1831
CRE BUSHKILL GROUP, LLC—See Cerberus Capital Management, L.P.; *U.S. Private*, pg. 837
CRECER SEGUROS; *Int'l*, pg. 1834
CREDATIV GMBH—See NetApp, Inc.; *U.S. Public*, pg. 1507
CREDCO RECEIVABLES CORP.—See American Express Company; *U.S. Public*, pg. 101
CREDEMASSICURAZIONI SPA—See Credito Emiliano S.p.A.; *Int'l*, pg. 1836
CREDEMFACTOR SPA—See Credito Emiliano S.p.A.; *Int'l*, pg. 1836
CREDEM INTERNATIONAL (LUX) S.A.—See Credito Emiliano S.p.A.; *Int'l*, pg. 1836
CREDEMLEASING S.P.A.—See Credito Emiliano S.p.A.; *Int'l*, pg. 1836

CRECER SEGUROS / CORPORATE AFFILIATIONS

CREDEM PRIVATE EQUITY SGR SPA—See Credito Emiliano S.p.A.; *Int'l*, pg. 1836
CREDEMTEL SPA—See Credito Emiliano S.p.A.; *Int'l*, pg. 1836
CREDEMVITA SPA—See Credito Emiliano S.p.A.; *Int'l*, pg. 1836
CREDENCE MANAGEMENT SOLUTIONS; *U.S. Private*, pg. 1090
CREDENCE RESOURCE MANAGEMENT, LLC—See Kriya Capital, LLC; *U.S. Private*, pg. 2352
CREDENCE SOUND & VISION LIMITED; *Int'l*, pg. 1834
CREDENCE SYSTEMS (M) SDN BHD—See Cohu, Inc.; *U.S. Public*, pg. 530
CREDENCE SYSTEMS PTE. LTD.—See Cohu, Inc.; *U.S. Public*, pg. 530
CREDENT CAPITAL CORP.; *Int'l*, pg. 1834
CREDENT GLOBAL FINANCE LIMITED; *Int'l*, pg. 1834
CREDENTIAL LEASING CORP.—See Freeman Spogli & Co. Incorporated; *U.S. Private*, pg. 1606
CREDENTIALS INC.—See SCRIP-SAFE Security Products, Inc.; *U.S. Private*, pg. 3579
CREDENT TECHNOLOGIES LLC.; *U.S. Private*, pg. 1090
CREDENT TECHNOLOGY ASIA PTE. LTD.—See Hexagon AB; *Int'l*, pg. 3368
CREDERA; *U.S. Private*, pg. 1091
CREDEX CORPORATION—See The Cannabis Depot Holding Corp.; *U.S. Private*, pg. 4004
CRED HOLDING CO., LTD.; *Int'l*, pg. 1834
CREDIA CO., LTD.—See J Trust Co., Ltd.; *Int'l*, pg. 3852
CREDIBLE LABS, INC.—See Fox Corporation; *U.S. Public*, pg. 875
CREDICORP BANK; *Int'l*, pg. 1834
CREDICORP CAPITAL PERU S.A.A.; *Int'l*, pg. 1834
CREDICORP CAPITAL USA INC.—See Credicorp Ltd.; *Int'l*, pg. 1834
CREDICORP LTD.; *Int'l*, pg. 1834
CREDICORP SECURITIES INC.—See Credicorp Ltd.; *Int'l*, pg. 1834
CREDIFARMA S.P.A.—See Banca IFIS S.p.A.; *Int'l*, pg. 815
CREDIFY INFORMATIONSDIENSTLEISTUNGEN GMBH—See Bertelsmann SE & Co. KGaA; *Int'l*, pg. 992
CREDIGY LTD.—See National Bank of Canada; *Int'l*, pg. 5152
CREDIINVEST SA—See Credit Andorra, S.A.; *Int'l*, pg. 1834
CREDIMAX B.S.C.—See BBK B.S.C.; *Int'l*, pg. 920
CREDIMO NV; *Int'l*, pg. 1834
CREDIN A/S—See Orkla ASA; *Int'l*, pg. 5637
CREDIN BAGERIPARTNER A/S—See Orkla ASA; *Int'l*, pg. 5637
CREDIN POLSKA SP. Z.O.O.—See Orkla ASA; *Int'l*, pg. 5637
CREDIN PORTUGAL S.A—See Orkla ASA; *Int'l*, pg. 5637
CREDIN PRODUCTOS ALIMENTICIOS S.A.—See Orkla ASA; *Int'l*, pg. 5637
CREDIN RUSSIA LLC—See Orkla ASA; *Int'l*, pg. 5637
CREDIN SVERIGE AB—See Orkla ASA; *Int'l*, pg. 5637
CREDIOP OVERSEAS BANK LTD.—See Dexia SA; *Int'l*, pg. 2092
CREDIPAR SA—See Stellantis N.V.; *Int'l*, pg. 7201
CREDIPASS POLSKA S.A.—See Duna House Holding Public Company Limited; *Int'l*, pg. 2225
CREDIRAMA SPA—See BNP Paribas SA; *Int'l*, pg. 1090
CREDISCOTIA FINANCIERA S.A.—See The Bank of Nova Scotia; *Int'l*, pg. 7618
CREDISSIMO SA—See BNP Paribas SA; *Int'l*, pg. 1090
CREDIST, INC.—See SRA Holdings Inc; *Int'l*, pg. 7147
CREDIT ACCEPTANCE CORPORATION; *U.S. Public*, pg. 593
CREDITACCESS GRAMEEN LIMITED; *Int'l*, pg. 1836
CREDIT AGRICOLE ALPES PROVENCE; *Int'l*, pg. 1834
CREDIT AGRICOLE CIB AO; *Int'l*, pg. 1834
CREDIT AGRICOLE DU MORBIHAN; *Int'l*, pg. 1834
CREDIT AGRICOLE PRIVATE EQUITY S.A.—See Coller Capital Ltd.; *Int'l*, pg. 1699
CREDIT ANDORRA PANAMA SECURITIES SA.—See Credit Andorra, S.A.; *Int'l*, pg. 1834
CREDIT ANDORRA PRIVATE BANKERS—See Credit Andorra, S.A.; *Int'l*, pg. 1834
CREDIT ANDORRA PRIVATE BANKERS—See Mohammed Abdulmohsin Al-Kharafi & Sons WLL; *Int'l*, pg. 5018
CREDIT ANDORRA, S.A.; *Int'l*, pg. 1834
CREDIT ANSWERS, LLC; *U.S. Private*, pg. 1091
CREDIT ASSEGURANCES—See Credit Andorra, S.A.; *Int'l*, pg. 1835
CREDIT ASSOCIATION ORDA CREDIT LLP; *Int'l*, pg. 1835
CREDIT BANK OF IRAQ S.A.—See National Bank of Kuwait S.A.K.; *Int'l*, pg. 5153
CREDIT BANK OF MOSCOW OJSC; *Int'l*, pg. 1835
CREDIT-BASED ASSET SERVICING & SECURITIZATION LLC; *U.S. Private*, pg. 1092
CREDIT BUREAU ASIA LIMITED; *Int'l*, pg. 1835
THE CREDIT BUREAU INC.—See CBC Companies Inc.; *U.S. Private*, pg. 796

THE CREDIT BUREAU OF BATON ROUGE, INC.; *U.S. Private*, pg. 4016
CREDIT BUREAU OF GREATER LANSING INC.—See CBC Companies Inc.; *U.S. Private*, pg. 796
CREDIT BUREAU (SINGAPORE) PTE. LTD.—See Credit Bureau Asia Limited; *Int'l*, pg. 1835
CREDITCARDS.COM, INC.; *U.S. Private*, pg. 1092
CREDITCHECK PARTNERS PRIVATE LIMITED; *Int'l*, pg. 1836
CREDIT CHEX (PRIVATE) LIMITED—See Jahangir Siddiqui & Co. Ltd.; *Int'l*, pg. 3871
CREDIT CLEAR LIMITED; *Int'l*, pg. 1835
CREDIT COLLECTIONS BUREAU COLLECTION AGENCY; *U.S. Private*, pg. 1091
CREDIT CONTROL, LLC; *U.S. Private*, pg. 1091
CREDIT CONTROL RIESGOS, S.L.—See Melia Hotels International, S.A.; *Int'l*, pg. 4809
CREDIT CONTROL SERVICES INC.; *U.S. Private*, pg. 1091
CREDIT COOPERATIF—See Groupe BPCE; *Int'l*, pg. 3097
CREDIT CORP AUSTRALIA PTY LIMITED—See Credit Corp Group Limited; *Int'l*, pg. 1835
CREDIT CORP COLLECTIONS PTY LIMITED—See Credit Corp Group Limited; *Int'l*, pg. 1835
CREDIT CORP. FACILITIES PTY LIMITED—See Credit Corp Group Limited; *Int'l*, pg. 1835
CREDIT CORP GROUP LIMITED; *Int'l*, pg. 1835
CREDITCORP OF TENNESSEE INC.—See Check Into Cash Inc.; *U.S. Private*, pg. 869
CREDIT CORPORATION (PNG) LIMITED; *Int'l*, pg. 1835
CREDIT CORP SERVICES PTY LIMITED—See Credit Corp Group Limited; *Int'l*, pg. 1835
CREDIT CORP SOLUTIONS LLC.—See Credit Corp Group Limited; *Int'l*, pg. 1835
THE CREDIT COUNSELLING AND DEBT MANAGEMENT AGENCY—See Bank Negara Malaysia; *Int'l*, pg. 839
CREDIT DIRECT LIMITED—See FCMB Group Plc; *Int'l*, pg. 2628
CREDIT DU NORD S.A.—See Societe Generale S.A.; *Int'l*, pg. 7039
CREDIT DU NORD—See Societe Generale S.A.; *Int'l*, pg. 7039
CREDITECH, INC.; *U.S. Private*, pg. 1092
CREDITE CONSULTING AB—See TowerBrook Capital Partners, L.P.; *U.S. Private*, pg. 4194
CREDIT EUROPE BANK (DUBAI) LTD.—See Fiba Holding A.S.; *Int'l*, pg. 2651
CREDIT EUROPE BANK LTD.—See Fiba Holding A.S.; *Int'l*, pg. 2651
CREDIT EUROPE BANK N.V.—See Fiba Holding A.S.; *Int'l*, pg. 2651
CREDIT EUROPE BANK (ROMANIA) S.A.—See Fiba Holding A.S.; *Int'l*, pg. 2651
CREDIT EUROPE BANK (SUISSE) S.A—See Fiba Holding A.S.; *Int'l*, pg. 2651
CREDIT EUROPE GROUP N.V.—See Fiba Holding A.S.; *Int'l*, pg. 2651
CREDIT EUROPE LEASING LLC—See Fiba Holding A.S.; *Int'l*, pg. 2651
CREDIT EUROPE LEASING LLC—See Fiba Holding A.S.; *Int'l*, pg. 2651
CREDITEX - ALUGUER DE EQUIPAMENTOS S.A.—See Xerox Holdings Corporation; *U.S. Public*, pg. 2387
CREDITEX GROUP, INC.—See Intercontinental Exchange, Inc.; *U.S. Public*, pg. 1143
CREDIT FIRST NATIONAL ASSOCIATION—See Bridgestone Corporation; *Int'l*, pg. 1157
CREDIT FONCIER DE FRANCE—See Groupe BPCE; *Int'l*, pg. 3094
CREDIT FONCIER IMMOBILIER SA—See Groupe BPCE; *Int'l*, pg. 3093
CREDIT GAIN FINANCE COMPANY LIMITED—See The Bank of East Asia, Limited; *Int'l*, pg. 7615
CREDIT GUARD OF FLORIDA INC.; *U.S. Private*, pg. 1091
CREDIT IMMOBILIER ET HOTELIER SA; *Int'l*, pg. 1835
CREDIT INDEMNITY PROPERTY (PTY) LIMITED—See Peresec South Africa Proprietary Limited; *Int'l*, pg. 5798
CREDIT INDUSTRIEL D'ALSACE ET DE LORRAINE—See Confederation Nationale du Credit Mutuel; *Int'l*, pg. 1767
CREDIT INDUSTRIEL DE NORMANDIE—See Confederation Nationale du Credit Mutuel; *Int'l*, pg. 1767
CREDIT INDUSTRIEL ET COMMERCIAL SA—See Confederation Nationale du Credit Mutuel; *Int'l*, pg. 1767
CREDIT INFONET GROUP, INC.—See Stone Point Capital LLC; *U.S. Private*, pg. 3823
CREDITINFORM AS—See Experian plc; *Int'l*, pg. 2587
CREDIT INFORMATION SYSTEMS COMPANY LIMITED—See TransUnion; *U.S. Public*, pg. 2184
CREDIT INTELLIGENCE LIMITED; *Int'l*, pg. 1835
CREDIT KARMA, INC.—See Intuit Inc.; *U.S. Public*, pg. 1160
CREDIT LENDERS SERVICE AGENCY; *U.S. Private*, pg. 1091
CREDITMAX LLC; *U.S. Private*, pg. 1092
CREDIT MOBILIER DE MONACO S.A.; *Int'l*, pg. 1835

CREDIT MODERNE ANTILLES GUYANE SA—See BNP Paribas SA; *Int'l*, pg. 1090
CREDIT MODERNE OCEAN INDIEN SA—See BNP Paribas SA; *Int'l*, pg. 1090
CREDIT MUTUEL ARKEA S.A.—See Confederation Nationale du Credit Mutuel; *Int'l*, pg. 1767
CREDIT MUTUEL NORD EUROPE BELGIUM NV—See Confederation Nationale du Credit Mutuel; *Int'l*, pg. 1767
CREDITO AFIANZADOR, S.A.—See Grupo BAL; *Int'l*, pg. 3121
CREDITO ARTIGIANO S.P.A.—See Credito Valtellinese Societa Cooperativa; *Int'l*, pg. 1837
CREDITO BERGAMASCO S.P.A.—See Banco BPM S.p.A.; *Int'l*, pg. 819
CREDITO EMILIANO SPA—See Credito Emiliano S.p.A.; *Int'l*, pg. 1836
CREDITO EMILIANO S.P.A.; *Int'l*, pg. 1836
CREDIT ONE BANK N.A.—See Sherman Financial Group LLC; *U.S. Private*, pg. 3634
CREDITO PIEMONTESE S.P.A.—See Credito Valtellinese Societa Cooperativa; *Int'l*, pg. 1837
CREDITO REAL S.A.B. DE C.V.; *Int'l*, pg. 1836
CREDIT ORGANIZATION OF SMALL & MEDIUM-SIZED ENTERPRISES CO., LTD.; *Int'l*, pg. 1836
CREDITOR RESOURCES, INC.—See Aegon N.V.; *Int'l*, pg. 174
CREDITORS INTERCHANGE RECEIVABLES MANAGEMENT LLC; *U.S. Private*, pg. 1092
CREDITOS Y AHORRO CREDIFINANCIERA S.A., COMPANIA DE FINANCIAMIENTO; *Int'l*, pg. 1837
CREDITO VALTELLINESE SOCIETA COOPERATIVA; *Int'l*, pg. 1837
CREDIT PLAN B PTY LIMITED—See Credit Corp Group Limited; *Int'l*, pg. 1835
CREDIT PLUS INC.—See Lovell Minnick Partners LLC; *U.S. Private*, pg. 2503
CREDITPOINT SOFTWARE, INC.—See SIDETRADE S.A.; *Int'l*, pg. 6883
CREDIT POUR HABITATIONS SOCIALES—See BNP Paribas SA; *Int'l*, pg. 1090
CREDITRAS PREVIDENZA SIM S.P.A.—See UniCredit S.p.A.; *Int'l*, pg. 8034
CREDITRAS VITA S.P.A.—See Allianz SE; *Int'l*, pg. 352
CREDIT RATING & COLLECTION COMPANY KSCC; *Int'l*, pg. 1835
CREDIT RECOVERY ASSOCIATES, INC.—See Regional Management Corp.; *U.S. Public*, pg. 1776
CREDITREFORM LATVIJA SIA—See B2Holding AS; *Int'l*, pg. 790
CREDITRISKMONITOR.COM, INC.; *U.S. Public*, pg. 593
CREDITRON CANADA, INC.—See Huntington Bancshares Incorporated; *U.S. Public*, pg. 1071
CREDIT SAISON CO., LTD.; *Int'l*, pg. 1835
CREDIT SERVICE INT'L CORP.; *U.S. Private*, pg. 1091
CREDITSHELF AKTIENGESELLSCHAFT—See Teylor AG; *Int'l*, pg. 7585
CREDITSIGHTS, INC.—See The Hearst Corporation; *U.S. Private*, pg. 4044
CREDIT SOLUTIONS, INC.; *U.S. Private*, pg. 1091
CREDIT SUISSE AG—See UBS Group AG; *Int'l*, pg. 8005
CREDIT SUISSE ASESORIA (PANAMA) S.A.—See UBS Group AG; *Int'l*, pg. 8006
CREDIT SUISSE ASIA INTERNATIONAL (CAYMAN) LIMITED—See UBS Group AG; *Int'l*, pg. 8006
CREDIT SUISSE ASSET MANAGEMENT INTERNATIONAL HOLDING LTD—See UBS Group AG; *Int'l*, pg. 8006
CREDIT SUISSE ASSET MANAGEMENT, LLC—See UBS Group AG; *Int'l*, pg. 8006
CREDIT SUISSE ASSET MANAGEMENT LTD.—See UBS Group AG; *Int'l*, pg. 8005
CREDIT SUISSE ASSET MANAGEMENT—See UBS Group AG; *Int'l*, pg. 8006
CREDIT SUISSE (BAHAMAS) LTD.—See UBS Group AG; *Int'l*, pg. 8005
CREDIT SUISSE BANK—See UBS Group AG; *Int'l*, pg. 8006
CREDIT SUISSE BANK—See UBS Group AG; *Int'l*, pg. 8006
CREDIT SUISSE (BRASIL) DISTRIBUIDORA DE TITULOS E VALORES MOBILIARIOS S.A.—See UBS Group AG; *Int'l*, pg. 8006
CREDIT SUISSE (BRASIL) S.A. CORRETORA DE TITULOS E VALORES MOBILIARIOS—See UBS Group AG; *Int'l*, pg. 8006
CREDIT SUISSE BRASIL S.A.—See UBS Group AG; *Int'l*, pg. 8006
CREDIT SUISSE CONSULTACIONES Y SERVICIOS S.A.—See UBS Group AG; *Int'l*, pg. 8006
CREDIT SUISSE (DEUTSCHLAND) AG—See ABN AMRO Group N.V.; *Int'l*, pg. 65
CREDIT SUISSE ENTREPRENEUR CAPITAL AG—See UBS Group AG; *Int'l*, pg. 8006
CREDIT SUISSE EQUITIES (AUSTRALIA) LIMITED—See UBS Group AG; *Int'l*, pg. 8006
CREDIT SUISSE EQUITY FUND MANAGEMENT COMPANY SA—See UBS Group AG; *Int'l*, pg. 8005

COMPANY NAME INDEX

CREDIT SUISSE FINANCE (GUERNSEY) LIMITED—See UBS Group AG; *Int'l*, pg. 8005
CREDIT SUISSE FIRST BOSTON MORTGAGE CAPITAL LLC—See UBS Group AG; *Int'l*, pg. 8006
CREDIT SUISSE FOUNDER SECURITIES LIMITED—See UBS Group AG; *Int'l*, pg. 8006
CREDIT SUISSE FRANCE—See UBS Group AG; *Int'l*, pg. 8006
CREDIT SUISSE FUND MANAGEMENT S.A.—See UBS Group AG; *Int'l*, pg. 8005
CREDIT SUISSE FUNDS AG—See UBS Group AG; *Int'l*, pg. 8007
CREDIT SUISSE FUND SERVICES (LUXEMBOURG) S.A.—See UBS Group AG; *Int'l*, pg. 8005
CREDIT SUISSE GROUP AG—See UBS Group AG; *Int'l*, pg. 8005
CREDIT SUISSE GROUP FINANCE (GUERNSEY) LIMITED—See UBS Group AG; *Int'l*, pg. 8005
CREDIT SUISSE (GUERNSEY) LTD.—See UBS Group AG; *Int'l*, pg. 8005
CREDIT SUISSE HEDGING-GRIFFO CORRETORA DE VALORES S.A.—See UBS Group AG; *Int'l*, pg. 8006
CREDIT SUISSE HOLDINGS (AUSTRALIA) LIMITED—See UBS Group AG; *Int'l*, pg. 8006
CREDIT SUISSE HOLDINGS (USA), INC.—See UBS Group AG; *Int'l*, pg. 8006
CREDIT SUISSE (HONG KONG) LTD.—See UBS Group AG; *Int'l*, pg. 8005
CREDIT SUISSE (INTERNATIONAL) HOLDING AG—See UBS Group AG; *Int'l*, pg. 8005
CREDIT SUISSE INTERNATIONAL—See UBS Group AG; *Int'l*, pg. 8005
CREDIT SUISSE (INVESTMENT BANKING)—See UBS Group AG; *Int'l*, pg. 8005
CREDIT SUISSE INVESTMENT SERVICES (CAYMAN)—See UBS Group AG; *Int'l*, pg. 8006
CREDIT SUISSE ISTANBUL MENKUL DEGERLER A.S.—See UBS Group AG; *Int'l*, pg. 8006
CREDIT SUISSE (ITALY) S.P.A.—See UBS Group AG; *Int'l*, pg. 8005
CREDIT SUISSE IT SERVICES AG—See UBS Group AG; *Int'l*, pg. 8006
CREDIT SUISSE LEASING AG—See UBS Group AG; *Int'l*, pg. 8006
CREDIT SUISSE (LEBANON) FINANCE S.A.L.—See UBS Group AG; *Int'l*, pg. 8005
CREDIT SUISSE LIFE (BERMUDA) LTD.—See UBS Group AG; *Int'l*, pg. 8006
CREDIT SUISSE LIFE & PENSIONS AG—See UBS Group AG; *Int'l*, pg. 8006
CREDIT SUISSE LIFE & PENSIONS—See UBS Group AG; *Int'l*, pg. 8006
CREDIT SUISSE (LUXEMBOURG) S.A.—See UBS Group AG; *Int'l*, pg. 8005
CREDIT SUISSE MANAGEMENT LLC—See UBS Group AG; *Int'l*, pg. 8006
CREDIT SUISSE PRIVATE EQUITY, LLC—See UBS Group AG; *Int'l*, pg. 8006
CREDIT SUISSE SAUDI ARABIA—See UBS Group AG; *Int'l*, pg. 8006
CREDIT SUISSE SECURITIES (CANADA), INC.—See UBS Group AG; *Int'l*, pg. 8006
CREDIT SUISSE SECURITIES (HONG KONG) LIMITED—See UBS Group AG; *Int'l*, pg. 8007
CREDIT SUISSE SECURITIES (INDIA) PRIVATE LIMITED—See UBS Group AG; *Int'l*, pg. 8007
CREDIT SUISSE SECURITIES (JAPAN) LIMITED—See UBS Group AG; *Int'l*, pg. 8007
CREDIT SUISSE SECURITIES (JOHANNESBURG) (PROPRIETARY) LIMITED—See UBS Group AG; *Int'l*, pg. 8007
CREDIT SUISSE SECURITIES LTD.—See UBS Group AG; *Int'l*, pg. 8005
CREDIT SUISSE SECURITIES (THAILAND) LIMITED—See UBS Group AG; *Int'l*, pg. 8007
CREDIT SUISSE SECURITIES (USA) LLC—See UBS Group AG; *Int'l*, pg. 8006
CREDIT SUISSE SERVICES (INDIA) PRIVATE LIMITED—See UBS Group AG; *Int'l*, pg. 8007
CREDIT SUISSE (SINGAPORE) LIMITED—See UBS Group AG; *Int'l*, pg. 8005
CREDIT SUISSE—See UBS Group AG; *Int'l*, pg. 8006
CREDIT SUISSE TRUST HOLDINGS LTD.—See UBS Group AG; *Int'l*, pg. 8005
CREDIT SUISSE (UK) LIMITED—See UBS Group AG; *Int'l*, pg. 8005
CREDIT SUISSE (USA), INC.—See UBS Group AG; *Int'l*, pg. 8005
CREDIT UNION 1; *U.S. Private*, pg. 1091
CREDIT UNION DISPUTE RESOLUTION CENTRE PTY LIMITED—See Cuscal Ltd.; *Int'l*, pg. 1880
CREDIT UNION EXECUTIVES SOCIETY, INC.; *U.S. Private*, pg. 1091
CREDIT UNION FOUNDATION AUSTRALIA PTY LIMITED—See Cuscal Ltd.; *Int'l*, pg. 1880
CREDIT UNION OF AMERICA; *U.S. Private*, pg. 1091
CREDIT UNION OF DENVER; *U.S. Private*, pg. 1091
CREDIT UNION OF GEORGIA; *U.S. Private*, pg. 1091

CREDIT UNION OF SOUTHERN CALIFORNIA; *U.S. Private*, pg. 1091
CREDIT UNION ONE, INC.; *U.S. Private*, pg. 1091
CREDIT UNION WEST; *U.S. Private*, pg. 1091
CREDIT URAL BANK JSC—See Gazprombank JSC; *Int'l*, pg. 2892
CREDIT VALUE PARTNERS, LP—See New York Life Insurance Company; *U.S. Private*, pg. 2910
CREDITWEST FAKTORING A.S.; *Int'l*, pg. 1837
CREDITWORKS AUSTRALIA PTY LTD—See Equifax Inc.; *U.S. Public*, pg. 785
CREDITWORX (S&V)—See Thebe Investment Corporation; *Int'l*, pg. 7706
CREDIVA LTD.—See RELX plc; *Int'l*, pg. 6266
CREDIVANCE N.V.—See ABN AMRO Group N.V.; *Int'l*, pg. 65
CREDO BRANDS MARKETING LIMITED; *Int'l*, pg. 1837
CREDO INTERACTIVE INC.; *Int'l*, pg. 1837
CREDOMATIC OF FLORIDA INC.—See Banco Bradesco S.A.; *Int'l*, pg. 819
CREDO REFERENCE, INC.; *U.S. Private*, pg. 1092
CREDO TECHNOLOGY GROUP HOLDING LTD.; *U.S. Public*, pg. 593
CREED ASIA (CAMBODIA) CO., LTD.—See CREED Corporation; *Int'l*, pg. 1837
CREED ASIA DEVELOPMENT (M) SDN. BHD.—See CREED Corporation; *Int'l*, pg. 1837
CREED ASIA INVESTMENT CO., LTD.—See CREED Corporation; *Int'l*, pg. 1837
CREED BOUTIQUE BEVERLY HILLS, LLC—See Kering S.A.; *Int'l*, pg. 4134
CREED BOUTIQUE HOUSTON, LLC—See Kering S.A.; *Int'l*, pg. 4134
CREED BOUTIQUE LAS VEGAS CRYSTALS, LLC—See Kering S.A.; *Int'l*, pg. 4134
CREED BOUTIQUE LAS VEGAS, LLC—See Kering S.A.; *Int'l*, pg. 4134
CREED BOUTIQUE LLC—See Kering S.A.; *Int'l*, pg. 4134
CREED BOUTIQUE MIAMI, LLC—See Kering S.A.; pg. 4134
CREED BOUTIQUE NORTHPARK, LLC—See Kering S.A.; *Int'l*, pg. 4134
CREED BOUTIQUE VALLEY FAIR LLC—See Kering S.A.; *Int'l*, pg. 4134
CREED CAPITAL MANAGEMENT AND RESEARCH, INC.—See CREED Corporation; *Int'l*, pg. 1837
CREED CORPORATION; *Int'l*, pg. 1837
CREED HOLDINGS PTE.LTD.—See CREED Corporation; *Int'l*, pg. 1837
CREED HOTEL MANAGEMENT CORPORATION—See CREED Corporation; *Int'l*, pg. 1837
CREED INVESTMENTS PTE. LTD.—See CREED Corporation; *Int'l*, pg. 1837
CREED-MONARCH, INC.; *U.S. Private*, pg. 1092
CREE EUROPE GMBH—See Wolfspeed, Inc.; *U.S. Public*, pg. 2377
CREE FAYETTEVILLE, INC.—See Wolfspeed, Inc.; *U.S. Public*, pg. 2377
CREEHAN & COMPANY CORPORATION—See Inovalon Holdings, Inc.; *U.S. Public*, pg. 1128
CREE HONG KONG LIMITED—See Wolfspeed, Inc.; *U.S. Public*, pg. 2377
CREEK INDIAN ENTERPRISES; *U.S. Private*, pg. 1092
CREEK & RIVER CO., LTD.; *Int'l*, pg. 1837
CREEK & RIVER KOREA CO., LTD.—See CREEK & RIVER Co., Ltd.; *Int'l*, pg. 1837
CREEK & RIVER SHANGHAI CO., LTD.—See CREEK & RIVER Co., Ltd.; *Int'l*, pg. 1837
CREEKSIDE ASSOCIATES LIMITED—See Feit Management Company; *U.S. Private*, pg. 1493
CREEKSIDE CORNERS GEORGIA, LLC—See Independence Realty Trust, Inc.; *U.S. Public*, pg. 1115
CREEKSIDE CUSTOM HOMES LLC—See United Homes Group, Inc; *U.S. Public*, pg. 2231
CREEKSIDE INDUSTRIES; *U.S. Private*, pg. 1092
CREEKSTONE FARMS, INC.—See Triad Foods Group; *U.S. Private*, pg. 4225
CREEKSTONE FARMS PREMIUM BEEF, LLC—See Marubeni Corporation; *Int'l*, pg. 4705
CREEK SYSTEMS, INC.; *U.S. Private*, pg. 1092
CREEKWOOD SURGERY CENTER, L.P.—See Tenet Healthcare Corporation; *U.S. Public*, pg. 2010
CREE LED LIGHTING SOLUTIONS, INC.—See Wolfspeed, Inc.; *U.S. Public*, pg. 2377
CREEL PRINTING, LLC—See Atlas Holdings, LLC; *U.S. Private*, pg. 377
CREEL TRACTOR COMPANY; *U.S. Private*, pg. 1092
CREEMA LTD.; *Int'l*, pg. 1837
CREEMERS COMPRESSORS B.V.—See Atlas Copco AB; *Int'l*, pg. 679
CRE ENERGY LTD—See Iberdrola, S.A.; *Int'l*, pg. 3573
CREEPY JAR S.A.; *Int'l*, pg. 1837
CREESE, SMITH, HUNE & CO., LLC—See Herbein + Company, Inc.; *U.S. Private*, pg. 1920
CREE SWEDEN AB—See Wolfspeed, Inc.; *U.S. Public*, pg. 2377
CREFEEL KOTO CO., LTD.—See Senko Group Holdings Co., Ltd.; *Int'l*, pg. 6709

CREO MEDICAL GROUP PLC

CREGANNA MEDICAL GROUP—See TE Connectivity Ltd.; *Int'l*, pg. 7494
CREGANNA MEDICAL - MINNESOTA—See TE Connectivity Ltd.; *Int'l*, pg. 7494
CREGANNA MEDICAL - OREGON—See TE Connectivity Ltd.; *Int'l*, pg. 7494
CRE GERMAN OFFICE GMBH—See TAG Immobilien AG; *Int'l*, pg. 7407
CREGGER COMPANY INC.; *U.S. Private*, pg. 1092
THE CRE GROUP, INC.—See BGC Group, Inc.; *U.S. Public*, pg. 329
CRE HOLDINGS LLC—See First Citizens BancShares, Inc.; *U.S. Public*, pg. 841
CREIGHTON BROTHERS L.L.C.; *U.S. Private*, pg. 1092
CREIGHTON BROTHERS—See Creighton Brothers L.L.C.; *U.S. Private*, pg. 1092
CREIGHTON MANNING ENGINEERING, LLP.—See Comvest Group Holdings LLC; *U.S. Private*, pg. 1007
CREIGHTONS PLC; *Int'l*, pg. 1837
CRE, INC.; *Int'l*, pg. 1830
THE C. REISS COAL COMPANY—See Koch Industries, Inc.; *U.S. Private*, pg. 2333
CREIST INC.—See MIRAIT ONE Corporation; *Int'l*, pg. 4917
CREIT SOLUTIONS INC.—See Minato Holdings Inc.; *Int'l*, pg. 4899
CRELANCO CVBA; *Int'l*, pg. 1838
CRELAN SA/NV—See CrelanCo CVBA; *Int'l*, pg. 1838
CRELLIN HANDLING EQUIPMENT INC; *U.S. Private*, pg. 1092
CRE LOGISTICS REIT, INC.; *Int'l*, pg. 1830
CRELOGIX ACCEPTANCE CORPORATION—See Travelers Financial Group Limited; *Int'l*, pg. 7907
CREMATION SOCIETY OF PENNSYLVANIA, INC.—See Service Corporation International; *U.S. Public*, pg. 1870
CREMATION SOCIETY OF WINDSOR & ESSEX COUNTY, INC.—See Service Corporation International; *U.S. Public*, pg. 1869
CREME 21 GMBH—See Emami Ltd; *Int'l*, pg. 2374
CREME DE LA CREME, INC.—See Partners Group Holding AG; *Int'l*, pg. 5750
CREME LURE CO., INC.; *U.S. Private*, pg. 1092
CREMER S.A.—See Mafra Hospitalar S/A; *Int'l*, pg. 4636
CREMES UNLIMITED INC.; *U.S. Private*, pg. 1092
CREMINELLI FINE MEATS, LLC—See Entrepreneurial Equity Partners, LLC; *U.S. Private*, pg. 1406
CREM INTERNATIONAL AB—See Ali Holding S.r.l; *Int'l*, pg. 322
CREM INTERNATIONAL GMBH—See Ali Holding S.r.l; *Int'l*, pg. 322
CREM INTERNATIONAL (SHANGHAI) CO., LTD.—See Ali Holding S.r.l; *Int'l*, pg. 322
CREM INTERNATIONAL SPAIN, S.L.—See Ali Holding S.r.l; *Int'l*, pg. 322
CREM INTERNATIONAL UK LTD.—See Ali Holding S.r.l; *Int'l*, pg. 322
CREMONESI WORKSHOP S.R.L.—See Ferrovie dello Stato Italiane S.p.A.; *Int'l*, pg. 2645
CREMONINI CHEF IBERICA S.A.—See Cremonini S.p.A.; *Int'l*, pg. 1838
CREMONINI RAIL IBERICA S.A.—See Cremonini S.p.A.; *Int'l*, pg. 1838
CREMONINI RESTAURATION S.A.S.—See Cremonini S.p.A.; *Int'l*, pg. 1838
CREMONINI—See Air France-KLM S.A.; *Int'l*, pg. 237
CREMONINI S.P.A. - ADMINISTRATIVE HEADQUARTERS—See Cremonini S.p.A.; *Int'l*, pg. 1838
CREMONINI S.P.A.; *Int'l*, pg. 1838
CRENDON INSURANCE BROKERS LIMITED—See Brown & Brown, Inc.; *U.S. Public*, pg. 400
CRENDO; *U.S. Private*, pg. 1092
C.R. ENGLAND, INC.; *U.S. Private*, pg. 708
CRENLO, LLC—See KPS Capital Partners, LP; *U.S. Private*, pg. 2347
CRENNA PLAT AB—See Lindab International AB; *Int'l*, pg. 4503
CRENSHAW COMMUNICATIONS, LLC—See ModOp, LLC; *U.S. Private*, pg. 2763
CRENSHAW CONSULTING GROUP, LLC—See O2 Investment Partners, LLC; *U.S. Private*, pg. 2982
CREO CO., LTD.; *Int'l*, pg. 1838
CREO IL LTD.—See Eastman Kodak Company; *U.S. Public*, pg. 707
CREOKS BEHAVIORAL HEALTH SERVICES; *U.S. Private*, pg. 1092
CREO MARKETING CO., LTD.—See CREO CO., LTD.; *Int'l*, pg. 1838
CREO MEDICAL GROUP PLC; *Int'l*, pg. 1838
CREO MEDICAL LIMITED—See Creo Medical Group PLC; *Int'l*, pg. 1839
CREO NETWORKS CO., LTD.—See CREO CO., LTD.; *Int'l*, pg. 1838
CREONIX, LLC—See Elbit Systems Limited; *Int'l*, pg. 2344
CREO RETAIL MARKETING HOLDINGS LIMITED—See DS Smith Plc; *Int'l*, pg. 2208
CREO RETAIL MARKETING LTD—See DS Smith Plc; *Int'l*, pg. 2208

CREOSALUS, INC.

CREOSALUS, INC.; *U.S. Private*, pg. 1092
CREOS APPAREL CORPORATION—See GSI Creos Corporation; *Int'l*, pg. 3144
CREOS DEUTSCHLAND GMBH—See Envoys International S.A.; *Int'l*, pg. 2444
CREO SOLUTION CO., LTD.—See CREO CO., LTD.; *Int'l*, pg. 1838
CREOTECH INSTRUMENTS S.A.; *Int'l*, pg. 1839
CRE PROPERTIES (HONG KONG) LTD.—See China Resources (Holdings) Co., Ltd.; *Int'l*, pg. 1547
CREPS UNITED PUBLICATIONS; *U.S. Private*, pg. 1093
CRE REIT ADVISERS, INC.—See CRE, Inc.; *Int'l*, pg. 1830
CRE RESOLUTION GMBH—See TAG Immobilien AG; *Int'l*, pg. 7407
CRESAN, S.A.—See Lone Star Funds; *U.S. Private*, pg. 2485
CRESAPARTNERS LLC; *U.S. Private*, pg. 1093
CRESA PARTNERS OF LOS ANGELES, INC.—See Ontario Teachers' Pension Plan; *Int'l*, pg. 5588
CRESA PARTNERS OF LOS ANGELES, INC.—See PAG Asia Capital Ltd.; *Int'l*, pg. 5695
CRESA PARTNERS OF LOS ANGELES, INC.—See TPG Capital, L.P.; *U.S. Public*, pg. 2171
CRESA; *U.S. Private*, pg. 1093
CRESCENDAS PTE. LTD.; *Int'l*, pg. 1839
CRESCENDO BIOSCIENCE, INC.—See Myriad Genetics, Inc.; *U.S. Public*, pg. 1489
CRESCENDO CORPORATION BERHAD; *Int'l*, pg. 1839
CRESCENDO INDUSTRIES; *Int'l*, pg. 1839
CRESCENDO INTERNATIONAL COLLEGE SDN. BHD.—See Crescendo Corporation Berhad; *Int'l*, pg. 1839
CRESCENDO INVESTMENT HOLDINGS LIMITED—See Barclays PLC; *Int'l*, pg. 862
CRESCENDO VENTURE MANAGEMENT, LLC; *U.S. Private*, pg. 1093
CRESCEND TECHNOLOGIES, L.L.C.; *U.S. Private*, pg. 1093
CRESCENT BANK & TRUST—See CB&T Holding Corporation; *U.S. Private*, pg. 796
CRESCENT BOX CORP.; *U.S. Private*, pg. 1093
CRESCENT CAPITAL BDC, INC.; *U.S. Public*, pg. 593
CRESCENT CAPITAL FINANCE GROUP, INC.; *U.S. Private*, pg. 1093
CRESCENT CAPITAL GROUP LP—See Sun Life Financial Inc.; *Int'l*, pg. 7305
CRESCENT CAPITAL PARTNERS LTD.; *Int'l*, pg. 1839
CRESCENT CARDBOARD COMPANY, L.L.C.—See Potomac Corporation; *U.S. Private*, pg. 3235
CRESCENT COMMUNITIES, LLC—See Sumitomo Forestry Co., Ltd.; *Int'l*, pg. 7286
CRESCENT COTTON MILLS LIMITED; *Int'l*, pg. 1839
CRESCENT CREDIT EUROPE LLP—See Sun Life Financial Inc.; *Int'l*, pg. 7305
CRESCENT CREDIT UNION; *U.S. Private*, pg. 1093
CRESCENT CROWN DISTRIBUTING LLC; *U.S. Private*, pg. 1093
CRESCENT CROWN DISTRIBUTING LLC—See Crescent Crown Distributing LLC; *U.S. Private*, pg. 1093
CRESCENT ELECTRIC SUPPLY COMPANY; *U.S. Private*, pg. 1093
CRESCENT ENERGY COMPANY—See KKR & Co. Inc.; *U.S. Public*, pg. 1243
CRESCENT EUROPE GMBH—See Potomac Corporation; *U.S. Private*, pg. 3235
CRESCENT FIBRES LIMITED; *Int'l*, pg. 1839
CRESCENT FOODS INC.; *U.S. Private*, pg. 1093
CRESCENT GOLD LIMITED—See Focus Minerals Limited; *Int'l*, pg. 2719
CRESCENT HEALTHCARE, INC.—See Walgreens Boots Alliance, Inc.; *U.S. Public*, pg. 2323
CRESCENT HEIGHTS OF AMERICA INC.; *U.S. Private*, pg. 1093
CRESCENT HILL CAPITAL CORPORATION; *U.S. Private*, pg. 1093
CRESCENT HOLDING GMBH—See The Olayan Group; *Int'l*, pg. 7672
CRESCENT HOSIERY MILLS INC.; *U.S. Private*, pg. 1093
CRESCENT HOTELS & RESORTS; *U.S. Private*, pg. 1094
CRESCENT JUTE PRODUCTS LIMITED; *Int'l*, pg. 1839
CRESCENT LEASING LTD.; *Int'l*, pg. 1839
CRESCENT MANUFACTURING COMPANY; *U.S. Private*, pg. 1094
CRESCENT MARKETING, INC.; *U.S. Private*, pg. 1094
CRESCENT MOON SNOWSHOES, INC.—See Dunn-Rite Products, Inc.; *U.S. Private*, pg. 1290
CRESCENT MORTGAGE COMPANY—See United Bankshares, Inc.; *U.S. Public*, pg. 2229
CRESCENT N.V.; *Int'l*, pg. 1839
CRESCENT PARTS & EQUIPMENT COMPANY; *U.S. Private*, pg. 1094
CRESCENT PLASTICS, INC.—See Cresline Plastic Pipe Co., Inc.; *U.S. Private*, pg. 1094
CRESCENT PLUMBING SUPPLY CO; *U.S. Private*, pg. 1094
CRESCENT POINT ENERGY U.S. CORP.—See Veren Inc.; *Int'l*, pg. 8168

CRESCENT PRIVATE CREDIT INCOME CORP.; *U.S. Private*, pg. 1094
CRESCENT PROCESSING COMPANY, LP; *U.S. Private*, pg. 1094
CRESCENT REAL ESTATE LLC—See Goff Capital, Inc.; *U.S. Private*, pg. 1726
CRESCENT RESOURCES, LLC; *U.S. Private*, pg. 1094
CRESCENT RIDGE LLC—See Infigen Energy Limited; *Int'l*, pg. 3685
CRESCENT SOLUTIONS; *U.S. Private*, pg. 1094
CRESCENT STAFF CO., LTD.—See PAL GROUP Holdings Co., Ltd.; *Int'l*, pg. 5705
CRESCENT STAR INSURANCE LIMITED; *Int'l*, pg. 1839
CRESCENT STEEL AND ALLIED PRODUCTS LIMITED; *Int'l*, pg. 1839
THE CRESCENT TEXTILE MILLS LIMITED; *Int'l*, pg. 7635
CRESCERA CAPITAL ACQUISITION CORP.; *Int'l*, pg. 1839
CRESCITA THERAPEUTICS, INC.; *Int'l*, pg. 1840
CRESCO BANK & TRUST COMPANY—See Security Agency, Inc.; *U.S. Private*, pg. 3594
CRESCO COMMUNICATIONS INC.—See Cresco, Ltd.; *Int'l*, pg. 1840
CRESCO DIGITAL TECHNOLOGIES LTD.—See Cresco, Ltd.; *Int'l*, pg. 1840
CRESCO E-SOLUTION CO. LTD.—See Cresco, Ltd.; *Int'l*, pg. 1840
CRESCO HOKURIKU LTD.—See Cresco, Ltd.; *Int'l*, pg. 1840
CRESCO ID SYSTEMS INC.—See Cresco, Ltd.; *Int'l*, pg. 1840
CRESCO J CUBE CO., LTD.—See Cresco, Ltd.; *Int'l*, pg. 1840
CRESCO LABS, INC.; *U.S. Public*, pg. 594
CRESCO LINES INC.; *U.S. Private*, pg. 1094
CRESCO, LTD.; *Int'l*, pg. 1840
CRES CO., LTD.—See Sumitomo Corporation; *Int'l*, pg. 7275
CRES CO., LTD.—See Sumitomo Mitsui Financial Group, Inc.; *Int'l*, pg. 7295
CRES-COR; *U.S. Private*, pg. 1093
CRESCO UNION SAVINGS BANK INC.; *U.S. Private*, pg. 1094
CRESCO VIETNAM CO., LTD.—See Cresco, Ltd.; *Int'l*, pg. 1840
CRESCO WIRELESS, INC.—See Cresco, Ltd.; *Int'l*, pg. 1840
CRESEED CORP.—See Terilogy Co., Ltd.; *Int'l*, pg. 7565
CRESENT ENTERPRISES INC.; *U.S. Private*, pg. 1094
CRES INSURANCE SERVICE, LLC—See Arthur J. Gallagher & Co.; *U.S. Public*, pg. 204
CRESLEIGH HOMES ARIZONA INC—See Harbor View Holdings Inc.; *U.S. Private*, pg. 1859
CRESLEIGH MANAGEMENT INC—See Harbor View Holdings Inc.; *U.S. Private*, pg. 1859
CRESLEIGH PROPERTY MANAGEMENT (SHANGHAI) CO., LTD.—See K. Wah International Holdings Limited; *Int'l*, pg. 4043
CRESLINE PLASTIC PIPE CO., INC.; *U.S. Private*, pg. 1094
CRESLINE-WEST, INC.—See Cresline Plastic Pipe Co., Inc.; *U.S. Private*, pg. 1094
CRESSALL RESISTORS LIMITED—See Telema S.p.A; *Int'l*, pg. 7538
CRESSANDA SOLUTIONS LIMITED; *Int'l*, pg. 1840
CRESSET ASSET MANAGEMENT, LLC; *U.S. Private*, pg. 1094
CRESSET LIMITED—See Temasek Holdings (Private) Limited; *Int'l*, pg. 7550
CRESSEY & COMPANY, LP; *U.S. Private*, pg. 1095
CRESS INSURANCE CONSULTANTS, INC.—See Galiot Insurance Services, Inc.; *U.S. Private*, pg. 1638
CRESSWELL BROTHERS GENERAL CONTRACTORS, INC.; *U.S. Private*, pg. 1095
CRESSWELL INDUSTRIES INC.—See Nova Steel Inc.; *Int'l*, pg. 5452
CRESSY & EVERETT COMMERCIAL CORPORATION—See Pokagon Band of Potawatomi Indians; *U.S. Private*, pg. 3223
CRESTA HOSPITALITY HOLDINGS (PVT) LTD.—See Masawara PLC; *Int'l*, pg. 4719
CRESTA HOSPITALITY (PVT) LTD—See Masawara PLC; *Int'l*, pg. 4719
CRESTA HOTELS (PTY) LTD—See Masawara PLC; *Int'l*, pg. 4719
CRESTA INVESTMENT PTE LTD—See Chuan Hup Holdings Limited; *Int'l*, pg. 1589
CRESTA MARAKANELO (PVT) LTD—See Botswana Development Corporation Limited; *Int'l*, pg. 1118
CRESTA MARAKANELO (PVT) LTD—See Masawara PLC; *Int'l*, pg. 4719
CREST AUDIO—See Peavey Electronics Corporation; *U.S. Private*, pg. 3126
CREST AUTO GROUP; *U.S. Private*, pg. 1095
CREST BEVERAGE, LLC—See Reyes Holdings, LLC; *U.S. Private*, pg. 3418
CREST BRICK SLATE & TILE LIMITED—See Brickability Group plc; *Int'l*, pg. 1151

CORPORATE AFFILIATIONS

CREST BUILDER HOLDINGS BERHAD; *Int'l*, pg. 1840
CREST CADILLAC INC.; *U.S. Private*, pg. 1095
CREST CADILLAC OF BIRMINGHAM, INC.; *U.S. Private*, pg. 1095
CREST CELLULOSE PRIVATE LIMITED—See Roquette Freres SA; *Int'l*, pg. 6398
CREST CHEMICALS (PTY) LIMITED—See AECI Limited; *Int'l*, pg. 171
CREST CHEMICALS (PTY) LIMITED—See BRENNTAG SE; *Int'l*, pg. 1149
CRESTCHEM LIMITED; *Int'l*, pg. 1841
CREST CHEVROLET; *U.S. Private*, pg. 1095
CRESTCHIC LIMITED—See Crestchic PLC; *Int'l*, pg. 1841
CRESTCHIC (MIDDLE EAST) FZE—See Crestchic PLC; *Int'l*, pg. 1841
CRESTCHIC PLC; *Int'l*, pg. 1841
CREST DISTRIBUTING INC.; *U.S. Private*, pg. 1095
CRESTEC (ASIA) LIMITED—See Crestec Inc.; *Int'l*, pg. 1841
CRESTEC ELECTRONICS TECHNOLOGY (ZHUHAI) CO., LTD.—See Crestec Inc.; *Int'l*, pg. 1841
CRESTEC EUROPE B.V.—See Crestec Inc.; *Int'l*, pg. 1841
CRESTEC INC.; *Int'l*, pg. 1841
CRESTEC INC. - SURABAYA FACTORY—See Crestec Inc.; *Int'l*, pg. 1841
CRESTEC INFORMATION TECHNOLOGY (SHENZHEN) LIMITED—See Crestec Inc.; *Int'l*, pg. 1841
CRESTEC (MALAYSIA) SDN BHD—See Crestec Inc.; *Int'l*, pg. 1841
CRESTEC PHILIPPINES, INC.—See Crestec Inc.; *Int'l*, pg. 1841
CRESTEC PRINTING (DONGGUAN) LIMITED—See Crestec Inc.; *Int'l*, pg. 1841
CRESTEC (SHANGHAI) CO., LTD.—See Crestec Inc.; *Int'l*, pg. 1841
CRESTEC (THAILAND) CO., LTD.—See Crestec Inc.; *Int'l*, pg. 1841
CRESTEC USA INC.—See Crestec Inc.; *Int'l*, pg. 1841
CRESTEC VIETNAM CO.—See Crestec Inc.; *Int'l*, pg. 1841
CRESTED BUTTE MOUNTAIN RESORT, INC.—See Vail Resorts, Inc.; *U.S. Public*, pg. 2271
CREST FINSERV LIMITED—See Crest Ventures Limited; *Int'l*, pg. 1841
CREST-FOAM CORP.—See Leggett & Platt, Incorporated; *U.S. Public*, pg. 1301
CREST FOAM INDUSTRIES, INC.—See TPG Capital, L.P.; *U.S. Public*, pg. 2175
CREST FOODS CO. INC—See Harwood Capital LLP; *Int'l*, pg. 3282
CREST FORD, INC.; *U.S. Private*, pg. 1095
CREST FURNITURE INC.; *U.S. Private*, pg. 1095
CREST/GOOD MANUFACTURING CO.; *U.S. Private*, pg. 1096
CREST GROUP INC.; *U.S. Private*, pg. 1095
CREST HOMES CORPORATION—See Berkshire Hathaway Inc.; *U.S. Public*, pg. 304
CREST HOMES CORPORATION—See Berkshire Hathaway Inc.; *U.S. Public*, pg. 304
CREST INDUSTRIES, LLC; *U.S. Private*, pg. 1096
CREST INVESTMENTS CO., LTD.; *Int'l*, pg. 1840
CREST LAWN MEMORIAL GARDENS, INC.—See Service Corporation International; *U.S. Public*, pg. 1869
CREST LAWN MEMORIAL PARK, INC.—See Service Corporation International; *U.S. Public*, pg. 1869
CREST LINCOLN MERCURY, INC.; *U.S. Private*, pg. 1096
CRESTLINE COACH LTD.—See Caisse de Depot et Placement du Quebec; *Int'l*, pg. 1254
CRESTLINE COACH LTD.—See Clearspring Capital Partners; *Int'l*, pg. 1657
CRESTLINE FUNDING CORP.; *U.S. Private*, pg. 1096
CRESTLINE HOTELS & RESORTS, LLC—See Barcelo Corporacion Empresarial S.A.; *Int'l*, pg. 859
CRESTLINE INVESTORS, INC.; *U.S. Private*, pg. 1097
CRESTLINER, INC.—See Brunswick Corporation; *U.S. Public*, pg. 407
CREST MARINE, LLC—See MasterCraft Boat Holdings, Inc.; *U.S. Public*, pg. 1395
CRESTMARK—See Pathward Financial, Inc.; *U.S. Public*, pg. 1652
CREST (MEXICO CITY), S.A. DE C.V.—See Grupo Lamosa S.A. de C.V.; *Int'l*, pg. 3131
CRESTMONT CADILLAC CORPORATION; *U.S. Private*, pg. 1097
CRESTMONT FABRICS, LTD.; *U.S. Private*, pg. 1097
CREST NATIONAL FILM LABORATORIES; *U.S. Private*, pg. 1096
CREST NATURAL RESOURCES LLC—See Crest Industries, LLC; *U.S. Private*, pg. 1096
CREST NICHOLSON (CHILTERN) LTD.—See Crest Nicholson PLC; *Int'l*, pg. 1840
CREST NICHOLSON (EASTERN) LTD.—See Crest Nicholson PLC; *Int'l*, pg. 1840
CREST NICHOLSON HOLDINGS PLC; *Int'l*, pg. 1840
CREST NICHOLSON PLC; *Int'l*, pg. 1840
CREST NICHOLSON (SOUTH) LTD.—See Crest Nicholson PLC; *Int'l*, pg. 1840

COMPANY NAME INDEX

CREST NICHOLSON (SOUTH WEST) LTD.—See Crest Nicholson PLC; *Int'l*, pg. 1840
CREST NORTEAMERICA, S. A. DE C. V.—See Grupo Lamosa S.A. de C.V.; *Int'l*, pg. 3131
CRESTON ADVERTISING & MARKETING INC.; *U.S. Private*, pg. 1097
CRESTON BEAN PROCESSING, L.L.C.—See CHS INC.; *U.S. Public*, pg. 492
CRESTONE GROUP BAKING COMPANIES; *U.S. Private*, pg. 1097
CRESTONE SERVICES GROUP LLC; *U.S. Private*, pg. 1097
CRESTONE WEALTH MANAGEMENT LIMITED - MELBOURNE—See Crestone Wealth Management Limited; *Int'l*, pg. 1841
CRESTONE WEALTH MANAGEMENT LIMITED; *Int'l*, pg. 1841
CREST OPERATIONS LLC—See Crest Industries, LLC; *U.S. Private*, pg. 1096
CREST OSTRAVA A.S.—See Tesco PLC; *Int'l*, pg. 7571
CREST PARTNERSHIP HOMES LTD.—See Crest Nicholson PLC; *Int'l*, pg. 1841
CREST PROPERTY SOLUTIONS PRIVATE LIMITED—See Keystone Realtors Limited; *Int'l*, pg. 4147
CREST PUMPING TECHNOLOGIES, LLC—See Nine Energy Service, Inc.; *U.S. Public*, pg. 1529
CREST RADIUS INC.; *Int'l*, pg. 1841
CREST RESOURCES, INC.; *Int'l*, pg. 1841
CRESTRON ELECTRONICS INC.; *U.S. Private*, pg. 1097
CREST, S.A. DE C.V.—See Grupo Lamosa S.A. de C.V.; *Int'l*, pg. 3131
CREST STEEL CORP.—See Reliance Steel & Aluminum Co.; *U.S. Public*, pg. 1779
CRESTTEK LLC—See Alten S.A.; *Int'l*, pg. 390
CREST (TIZAYUCA), S.A. DE C.V.—See Grupo Lamosa S.A. de C.V.; *Int'l*, pg. 3131
CREST ULTRASONICS SHANGHAI LTD.—See Crest Group Inc.; *U.S. Private*, pg. 1095
CREST ULTRASONICS (THAILAND) LTD.—See Crest Group Inc.; *U.S. Private*, pg. 1095
CREST VENTURES LIMITED; *Int'l*, pg. 1841
CRESTVIEW ADVISORS, L.L.C.—See Crestview Partners, L.P.; *U.S. Private*, pg. 1098
CRESTVIEW BUILDERS, INC.; *U.S. Private*, pg. 1097
CRESTVIEW CADILLAC CORPORATION; *U.S. Private*, pg. 1097
CRESTVIEW CENTER—See Formation Capital, LLC; *U.S. Private*, pg. 1570
CRESTVIEW CONVALESCENT HOME, INC.—See Welltower Inc.; *U.S. Public*, pg. 2348
CREST VIEW CORPORATION; *U.S. Private*, pg. 1096
CRESTVIEW COUNTRY CLUB—See Concert Golf Partners, LLC; *U.S. Private*, pg. 1009
CRESTVIEW EXPLORATION, INC.; *Int'l*, pg. 1841
CRESTVIEW NORTH, INC.—See Welltower Inc.; *U.S. Public*, pg. 2348
CRESTVIEW PARTNERS, L.P.; *U.S. Private*, pg. 1097
CRESTWOOD ADVISORS GROUP, LLC—See Clayton, Dubilier & Rice, LLC; *U.S. Private*, pg. 923
CRESTWOOD ADVISORS GROUP, LLC—See Stone Point Capital LLC; *U.S. Private*, pg. 3824
CRESTWOOD ADVISORS LLC—See Clayton, Dubilier & Rice, LLC; *U.S. Private*, pg. 923
CRESTWOOD ADVISORS LLC—See Stone Point Capital LLC; *U.S. Private*, pg. 3824
CRESTWOOD APPALACHIA PIPELINE LLC—See Crestwood Equity Partners LP; *U.S. Public*, pg. 594
CRESTWOOD ARKANSAS PIPELINE LLC—See Crestwood Equity Partners LP; *U.S. Public*, pg. 594
CRESTWOOD ASSOCIATES LLC; *U.S. Private*, pg. 1099
CRESTWOOD CRUDE SERVICES LLC—See Crestwood Equity Partners LP; *U.S. Public*, pg. 594
CRESTWOOD CRUDE TRANSPORTATION LLC—See Crestwood Equity Partners LP; *U.S. Public*, pg. 594
CRESTWOOD DAKOTA PIPELINES LLC—See Crestwood Equity Partners LP; *U.S. Public*, pg. 594
CRESTWOOD EQUITY PARTNERS LP; *U.S. Public*, pg. 594
CRESTWOOD GAS SERVICES OPERATING LLC—See Crestwood Equity Partners LP; *U.S. Public*, pg. 594
CRESTWOOD HOSPITAL, LLC—See Community Health Systems, Inc.; *U.S. Public*, pg. 552
CRESTWOOD INC.; *U.S. Private*, pg. 1099
CRESTWOOD PANHANDLE PIPELINE LLC—See Crestwood Equity Partners LP; *U.S. Public*, pg. 594
CRESTWOOD PARTNERS LLC—See Crestwood Equity Partners LP; *U.S. Public*, pg. 594
CRESTWOOD PHYSICIAN SERVICES, LLC—See Community Health Systems, Inc.; *U.S. Public*, pg. 552
CRESTWOOD PLUMBING, INC.—See User Friendly Home Services, LLC; *U.S. Private*, pg. 4322
CRESTWOOD TECHNOLOGY GROUP; *U.S. Private*, pg. 1099
CRESTWOOD TUBULARS INC.; *U.S. Private*, pg. 1099
CRESUD SOCIEDAD ANONIMA, COMERCIAL, INMOBILIARIA, FINANCIERA Y AGROPECUARIA; *Int'l*, pg. 1842
CRETA FARM S.A.; *Int'l*, pg. 1842

CRETA FARM S.A.—See Creta Farm S.A.; *Int'l*, pg. 1842
CRETAN GROUP PLC; *Int'l*, pg. 1842
CRETCHER HEARTLAND LLC; *U.S. Private*, pg. 1099
CRETE CARRIER CORP.; *U.S. Private*, pg. 1099
CRETE MECHANICAL GROUP, INC.; *U.S. Private*, pg. 1099
THE CRETEX COMPANIES, INC.; *U.S. Private*, pg. 4016
CRETEX CONCRETE PRODUCTS MIDWEST, INC.—See The Cretex Companies, Inc.; *U.S. Private*, pg. 4016
CRETEX CONCRETE PRODUCTS NORTH, INC.—See The Cretex Companies, Inc.; *U.S. Private*, pg. 4016
CRETEX CONCRETE PRODUCTS NORTH, INC.—See The Cretex Companies, Inc.; *U.S. Private*, pg. 4016
CRE (THAILAND) CO., LTD.—See CRE, Inc.; *Int'l*, pg. 1830
CREUERS DEL PORT DE BARCELONA, S.A.—See Global Yatirim Holding A.S.; *Int'l*, pg. 3002
CREUNA AB—See Know IT AB; *Int'l*, pg. 4212
CREUNA A/S—See Know IT AB; *Int'l*, pg. 4212
CREVE COEUR CAMERA INC.; *U.S. Private*, pg. 1099
CREVET PIPELINES PTY LTD—See Fletcher Building Limited; *Int'l*, pg. 2699
CREW2, INC.; *U.S. Private*, pg. 1099
CREW CREATIVE ADVERTISING, LLC.; *U.S. Private*, pg. 1099
CREW CUTS INC.; *U.S. Private*, pg. 1099
CREW ENERGY INC.—See Tourmaline Oil Corp.; *Int'l*, pg. 7848
CREWE OUTPATIENT IMAGING, LLC—See HCA Healthcare, Inc.; *U.S. Public*, pg. 995
CREWE VETS4PETS LIMITED—See Pets at Home Group Plc; *Int'l*, pg. 5833
CRE WOHNEN GMBH—See TAG Immobilien AG; *Int'l*, pg. 7407
CRE WOHNEN SERVICE GMBH—See TAG Immobilien AG; *Int'l*, pg. 7407
CREW RESOURCES INC.—See Tourmaline Oil Corp.; *Int'l*, pg. 7848
CREWS & ASSOCIATES INCORPORATED—See First Security Bancorp; *U.S. Private*, pg. 1527
CREWSAVER—See ONEX Corporation; *Int'l*, pg. 5580
CREWS BANKING CORPORATION; *U.S. Private*, pg. 1099
CREWS ELECTRICAL TESTING, INC.—See Blue Sea Capital Management LLC; *U.S. Private*, pg. 592
CREW TECHNICAL SERVICES; *U.S. Private*, pg. 1099
CREW TRANSPORTATION SPECIALISTS, INC.—See Corpay, Inc.; *U.S. Public*, pg. 579
CREW WINE COMPANY LLC—See Constellation Brands, Inc.; *U.S. Public*, pg. 571
CREXENDO, INC.; *U.S. Public*, pg. 594
C.R. FEDRICK, INC.; *U.S. Private*, pg. 708
CRF INC.; *U.S. Private*, pg. 1099
C.R.F. SOCIETA CONSORTILE PER AZIONI—See Stellantis N.V.; *Int'l*, pg. 7197
CRG HOLDING COMPANY, INC.; *U.S. Private*, pg. 1100
CRG HOLDINGS CO., LTD.; *Int'l*, pg. 1842
CRG HOLDINGS LLC—See Cavco Industries, Inc.; *U.S. Public*, pg. 455
C.R. GIBSON, LLC—See IG Design Group Plc; *Int'l*, pg. 3600
CRG INC.; *U.S. Private*, pg. 1100
CR GROUP NORDIC AB—See Formica Capital Holding AB; *Int'l*, pg. 2734
CR HAD YAI (THAILAND) CO., LTD.—See Central Group Company Limited; *Int'l*, pg. 1407
CRH AGREGATE BETOANE S.A.—See CRH plc; *Int'l*, pg. 1843
CRH BOUWMATEN B.V.—See CRH plc; *Int'l*, pg. 1843
CRH BOUWMATERIALENHANDEL B.V.—See CRH plc; *Int'l*, pg. 1843
CRH CANADA GROUP INC.—See CRH plc; *Int'l*, pg. 1843
CRH CATERING CO., INC.; *U.S. Private*, pg. 1100
CRH CEMENT - JOLIETTE PLANT—See CRH plc; *Int'l*, pg. 1843
CRH CEMENT - MISSISSAUGA PLANT—See CRH plc; *Int'l*, pg. 1843
CRH CIMENT (ROMANIA) S.A.—See CRH plc; *Int'l*, pg. 1843
CRH CONCRETE A/S—See CRH plc; *Int'l*, pg. 1843
CRH EUROPE-MATERIALS—See CRH plc; *Int'l*, pg. 1843
CRH EUROPE - PRODUCTS & DISTRIBUTION—See CRH plc; *Int'l*, pg. 1843
CRH EUROPE—See CRH plc; *Int'l*, pg. 1843
CRH FENCING LIMITED—See CRH plc; *Int'l*, pg. 1843
CRH FRANCE DISTRIBUTION SAS—See CRH plc; *Int'l*, pg. 1843
CRH FRANCE SAS—See CRH plc; *Int'l*, pg. 1843
CRH GETAZ HOLDING AG—See CRH plc; *Int'l*, pg. 1844
CRH ILE DE FRANCE DISTRIBUTION SAS—See CRH plc; *Int'l*, pg. 1843
CRH KLEIWAREN BEHEER B.V.—See CRH plc; *Int'l*, pg. 1844
CRH KLINKIER SP. Z O.O.—See CRH plc; *Int'l*, pg. 1844
CRH MEDICAL CORPORATION—See WELL Health Technologies Corp.; *Int'l*, pg. 8372
CR HOLDINGS CO., LTD.; *Int'l*, pg. 1827
CRH PLC; *Int'l*, pg. 1842
CRH (SRBIJA) D.O.O.—See CRH plc; *Int'l*, pg. 1843

CRH STRUCTURAL CONCRETE B.V.—See CRH plc; *Int'l*, pg. 1844
CRH SUDAMERICANA S.A.—See CRH plc; *Int'l*, pg. 1844
CRH (WIEN) GMBH—See CRH plc; *Int'l*, pg. 1843
CRIADO & ASSOCIATES, INC.—See Dunaway Associates, LLC; *U.S. Private*, pg. 1287
C. RIBAS DE SOUSA LDA—See A.A.G. STUCCHI s.r.l.; *Int'l*, pg. 22
CRIBB TYRE & BATTERY LTD.—See Sumitomo Rubber Industries, Ltd.; *Int'l*, pg. 7298
CRIBIS D&B S.R.L.—See CRIF S.p.A.; *Int'l*, pg. 1849
CRIBIS TELESERVICE S.R.L.—See CRIF S.p.A.; *Int'l*, pg. 1849
CRI CAPITAL CORPORATION—See Sport Haley Holdings, Inc.; *U.S. Private*, pg. 3760
CRICKET AUSTRALIA; *Int'l*, pg. 1849
CRICKET ENERGY HOLDINGS, INC.; *Int'l*, pg. 1849
CRICKET MAGAZINE GROUP—See Cricket Media Group Ltd.; *U.S. Private*, pg. 1100
CRICKET MEDIA GROUP LTD.; *U.S. Private*, pg. 1100
CRICKET MEDIA, INC.—See Cricket Media Group Ltd.; *U.S. Private*, pg. 1100
CRICKET TECHNOLOGIES, LLC; *U.S. Private*, pg. 1100
CRICKET WIRELESS LLC—See AT&T Inc.; *U.S. Public*, pg. 220
CRIC REAL ESTATE DATABASE SERVICES—See E-House (China) Holdings Limited; *Int'l*, pg. 2248
CRICUT, INC.—See North Cove Partners; *U.S. Private*, pg. 2944
CRIDASA - CRISTAL DESTILARIA AUTONOMA DE ALCOOL S/A—See Infinity Bio-Energy Ltd.; *Int'l*, pg. 3687
CRIDER INC.; *U.S. Private*, pg. 1100
CRIE ANABUKI INC.; *Int'l*, pg. 1849
CRIE CO., LTD.—See KOSE Corporation; *Int'l*, pg. 4290
CRIEFF CARE HOME—See Balhousie Holdings Limited; *Int'l*, pg. 808
CRIF AG—See CRIF S.p.A.; *Int'l*, pg. 1849
CRIF ALACAK YONETIM VE DANISMANLIK HIZMETLERI ANONIM SIRKETI—See CRIF S.p.A.; *Int'l*, pg. 1849
CRIF BEIJING LTD.—See CRIF S.p.A.; *Int'l*, pg. 1849
CRIF CORPORATION—See CRIF S.p.A.; *Int'l*, pg. 1849
CRIF CORPORATION—See CRIF S.p.A.; *Int'l*, pg. 1849
CRIF - CZECH CREDIT BUREAU, A. S.—See CRIF S.p.A.; *Int'l*, pg. 1849
CRIF DECISION SOLUTIONS LTD.—See CRIF S.p.A.; *Int'l*, pg. 1849
CRIF GMBH—See CRIF S.p.A.; *Int'l*, pg. 1849
CRIF GULF DWC LLC—See CRIF S.p.A.; *Int'l*, pg. 1849
CRIF HIGH MARK CREDIT INFORMATION SERVICES PVT. LTD.—See CRIF S.p.A.; *Int'l*, pg. 1849
CRIF HONG KONG LIMITED—See CRIF S.p.A.; *Int'l*, pg. 1849
CRIF S.A. DE S.V.—See CRIF S.p.A.; *Int'l*, pg. 1849
CRIF (SHANGHAI) BUSINESS INFORMATION SERVICE CO. LTD—See CRIF S.p.A.; *Int'l*, pg. 1849
CRIF - SLOVAK CREDIT BUREAU, S.R.O.—See CRIF S.p.A.; *Int'l*, pg. 1849
CRIF SOLUTIONS PRIVATE LIMITED—See CRIF S.p.A.; *Int'l*, pg. 1849
CRIF S.P.A.; *Int'l*, pg. 1849
CRIF SP. Z O. O.—See CRIF S.p.A.; *Int'l*, pg. 1849
CRIGLER ENTERPRISES, INC.; *U.S. Private*, pg. 1100
CRI HOLDINGS, LLC—See Waste Connections, Inc.; *Int'l*, pg. 8353
CRI HOTEL INCOME PARTNERS, L.P.; *U.S. Private*, pg. 1100
CRI LIFETREE—See ICON plc; *Int'l*, pg. 3585
CRILLON IMPORTERS LTD.; *U.S. Private*, pg. 1100
CRIME INTERVENTION ALARM CO INC—See Apax Partners LLP; *Int'l*, pg. 501
CRIME PREVENTION INC.; *U.S. Private*, pg. 1100
CRI MIDDLEWARE CO., LTD.; *Int'l*, pg. 1849
THE CRIMINAL JUSTICE INSTITUTE, INC.; *U.S. Private*, pg. 4016
CRIMO ITALIA S.R.L.—See Permira Advisers LLP; *Int'l*, pg. 5808
CRIMSAFE SECURITY SYSTEMS PTY. LTD.—See Oceania Capital Partners Limited; *Int'l*, pg. 5518
CRIMSON BIOENERGY LTD.; *Int'l*, pg. 1849
CRIMSON CONSULTING GROUP, INC.; *U.S. Private*, pg. 1100
CRIMSON FOREST ENTERTAINMENT GROUP INC.; *U.S. Private*, pg. 1100
CRIMSON INSULATIONS CO INC.; *U.S. Private*, pg. 1100
CRIMSON INVESTMENT; *U.S. Private*, pg. 1100
CRIMSONLOGIC BAHRAIN S.P.C—See CRIMSONLOGIC PTE LTD; *Int'l*, pg. 1850
CRIMSONLOGIC CHILE SPA—See CRIMSONLOGIC PTE LTD; *Int'l*, pg. 1850
CRIMSONLOGIC EMIRATES INFORMATION TECHNOLOGY LLC—See CRIMSONLOGIC PTE LTD; *Int'l*, pg. 1850
CRIMSONLOGIC INDIA PRIVATE LIMITED—See CRIMSONLOGIC PTE LTD; *Int'l*, pg. 1850
CRIMSONLOGIC IT SOLUTIONS PRIVATE LIMITED—See CRIMSONLOGIC PTE LTD; *Int'l*, pg. 1850
CRIMSONLOGIC (NORTH AMERICA) INC.—See CRIMSONLOGIC PTE LTD; *Int'l*, pg. 1850

CRIMSON INVESTMENT / CORPORATE AFFILIATIONS

CRIMSONLOGIC PANAMA INC.—See CRIMSONLOGIC PTE LTD; *Int'l*, pg. 1850
CRIMSONLOGIC PTE LTD; *Int'l*, pg. 1850
CRIMSONLOGIC SOFTWARE TECHNOLOGY (SHANGHAI) CO., LTD—See CRIMSONLOGIC PTE LTD; *Int'l*, pg. 1850
CRIMSONLOGIC (TRINIDAD AND TOBAGO) LTD.—See CRIMSONLOGIC PTE LTD; *Int'l*, pg. 1850
CRIMSONLOGIC USA, INC.—See CRIMSONLOGIC PTE LTD; *Int'l*, pg. 1850
CRIMSON METAL ENGINEERING COMPANY LIMITED; *Int'l*, pg. 1849
CRIMSON PHARMACEUTICAL (SHANGHAI) COMPANY LIMITED—See First Shanghai Investments Limited; *Int'l*, pg. 2687
CRIMSON RESOURCE MANAGEMENT; *U.S. Private*, pg. 1101
CRIMSON SOLUTIONS, LLC; *U.S. Private*, pg. 1101
CRIMSON STEEL SUPPLY LLC—See Clayton, Dubilier & Rice, LLC; *U.S. Private*, pg. 930
CRIMSON TIDE (IE) LIMITED—See Crimson Tide plc; *Int'l*, pg. 1850
CRIMSON TIDE MPRO LIMITED—See Crimson Tide plc; *Int'l*, pg. 1850
CRIMSON TIDE PLC; *Int'l*, pg. 1850
CRIMSON TRACE CORPORATION—See Smith & Wesson Brands, Inc.; *U.S. Public*, pg. 1896
CRIMSON WINE GROUP, LTD.; *U.S. Public*, pg. 594
CRINETICS PHARMACEUTICALS, INC.; *U.S. Public*, pg. 594
CRINSURANCE S.A.S.; *Int'l*, pg. 1850
CRIOESTAMINAL-SAUDE E TECNOLOGIA SA—See The Riverside Company; *U.S. Private*, pg. 4108
CRIO INC.; *U.S. Private*, pg. 1101
CRIPPEN AUTO MALL; *U.S. Private*, pg. 1101
CRIPPLE CREEK & VICTOR GOLD MINING COMPANY LLC—See Newmont Corporation; *U.S. Public*, pg. 1516
CRIPPMANN; *U.S. Private*, pg. 1101
CRISAK INC.; *U.S. Private*, pg. 1101
CRISAL - CRISTALARIA AUTOMATICA, S.A.—See Libbey, Inc.; *U.S. Private*, pg. 2442
CRISA LIBBEY MEXICO S. DE R.L. DE C.V.—See Libbey, Inc.; *U.S. Private*, pg. 2442
CRISFIELD TIMES—See Independent Newspapers, Inc.; *U.S. Private*, pg. 2060
CRISIL IREVNA INFORMATION TECHNOLOGY (HANGZHOU) COMPANY LTD.—See S&P Global Inc.; *U.S. Public*, pg. 1830
CRISIL IREVNA POLAND SP. Z.O.O.—See S&P Global Inc.; *U.S. Public*, pg. 1831
CRISIL IREVNA UK LIMITED—See S&P Global Inc.; *U.S. Public*, pg. 1830
CRISIL IREVNA US LLC—See S&P Global Inc.; *U.S. Public*, pg. 1830
CRISIL LTD.—See S&P Global Inc.; *U.S. Public*, pg. 1831
CRISIL RATINGS LIMITED—See S&P Global Inc.; *U.S. Public*, pg. 1830
CRISI MEDICAL SYSTEMS, INC.—See Becton, Dickinson & Company; *U.S. Public*, pg. 291
CRISIS COURIER SOLUTIONS LTD—See CitySprint (UK) Limited; *Int'l*, pg. 1630
CRISIS PREVENTION INSTITUTE, INC.—See Wendel S.A.; *Int'l*, pg. 8376
CRISNOVA VIDRIO, S.A.—See Vidrala S.A.; *Int'l*, pg. 8192
CRISP COUNTY POWER COMMISSION INC.; *U.S. Private*, pg. 1101
CRISPELL-SNYDER, INC.—See Comvest Group Holdings LLC; *U.S. Private*, pg. 1007
CRISPERS, LLC—See Boyne Capital Management, LLC; *U.S. Private*, pg. 629
THE CRISPIN COMPANY; *U.S. Private*, pg. 4016
CRISPIN CORPORATION—See Sony Group Corporation; *Int'l*, pg. 7103
CRISPIN PORTER & BOGUSKY EUROPE AB—See Stagwell, Inc.; *U.S. Public*, pg. 1926
CRISPIN PORTER & BOGUSKY LIMITED—See Stagwell, Inc.; *U.S. Public*, pg. 1926
CRISPIN PORTER & BOGUSKY—See Stagwell, Inc.; *U.S. Public*, pg. 1926
CRISP MARKETING; *U.S. Private*, pg. 1101
CRISP MEDIA INC.—See Charlesbank Capital Partners, LLC; *U.S. Private*, pg. 855
CRISPR THERAPEUTICS AG; *Int'l*, pg. 1850
CRISPR THERAPEUTICS, INC.—See CRISPR Therapeutics AG; *Int'l*, pg. 1850
CRISPWAY LIMITED—See Heidelberg Materials AG; *Int'l*, pg. 3310
CRISSAIR, INC.—See ESCO Technologies, Inc.; *U.S. Public*, pg. 793
CRISS ENTERPRISES, INC.—See Leonard Green & Partners, L.P.; *U.S. Private*, pg. 2430
CRISS FINANCIAL HOLDINGS LIMITED—See Spandana Sphoorty Financial Limited; *Int'l*, pg. 7124
CRISTACOL S.A.—See PPG Industries, Inc.; *U.S. Public*, pg. 1707
CRISTALERIA DEL ECUADOR, S.A.—See O-I Glass, Inc.; *U.S. Public*, pg. 1559
CRISTALERIAS DE CHILE S.A.; *Int'l*, pg. 1850

CRISTALES AUTOMOTRICES, S.A. DE C.V.—See Vitro, S.A.B. de C.V.; *Int'l*, pg. 8262
CRISTAL IMMO SC—See Groupe BPCE; *Int'l*, pg. 3093
CRISTALLERIA ARTISTICA LA PIANA S.P.A.; *Int'l*, pg. 1850
CRISTAL MINING AUSTRALIA LIMITED - AUSTRALIND PLANT—See One Rock Capital Partners, LLC; *U.S. Private*, pg. 3023
CRISTAL PIGMENT UK LTD.—See One Rock Capital Partners, LLC; *U.S. Private*, pg. 3023
CRISTAL US, INC.—See One Rock Capital Partners, LLC; *U.S. Private*, pg. 3023
CRISTEK INTERCONNECTS, INC.—See Windjammer Capital Investors, LLC; *U.S. Private*, pg. 4537
CRIST GROUP INC.—See Bain Capital, LP; *U.S. Private*, pg. 432
CRISTIE DATA LIMITED—See iomart Group plc; *Int'l*, pg. 3792
CRISTIE SOFTWARE LIMITED; *Int'l*, pg. 1850
CRISTIRO S.A.; *Int'l*, pg. 1850
CRISTOFOLI KEELING, INC.; *U.S. Private*, pg. 1101
CRISWELL ACURA; *U.S. Private*, pg. 1101
CRISWELL PERFORMANCE CARS LLC; *U.S. Private*, pg. 1101
CRITCHFIELD MEATS INC.; *U.S. Private*, pg. 1101
CRITCHFIELD MECHANICAL INC.; *U.S. Private*, pg. 1101
CRI-TECH INC.—See Daikin Industries, Ltd.; *Int'l*, pg. 1932
CRITEO ADVERTISING (BEIJING) CO., LTD.—See Criteo S.A.; *Int'l*, pg. 1850
CRITEO B.V.—See Criteo S.A.; *Int'l*, pg. 1850
CRITEO CANADA CORP.—See Criteo S.A.; *Int'l*, pg. 1850
CRITEO DO BRASIL DESENVOLVIMENTO DE SERVICOS DE INTERNET LTDA.—See Criteo S.A.; *Int'l*, pg. 1850
CRITEO ESPANA, S.L.—See Criteo S.A.; *Int'l*, pg. 1850
CRITEO FRANCE S.A.S.—See Criteo S.A.; *Int'l*, pg. 1850
CRITEO GMBH—See Criteo S.A.; *Int'l*, pg. 1850
CRITEO K.K.—See Criteo S.A.; *Int'l*, pg. 1850
CRITEO LLC—See Criteo S.A.; *Int'l*, pg. 1850
CRITEO S.A.; *Int'l*, pg. 1850
CRITEO SINGAPORE PTE. LTD.—See Criteo S.A.; *Int'l*, pg. 1850
CRITEO S.R.L.—See Criteo S.A.; *Int'l*, pg. 1850
CRITERIA CAIXA, S.A.—See Fundacion Bancaria Caixa d'Estalvis i Pensions de Barcelona, la Caixa; *Int'l*, pg. 2845
CRITERIA LABS, INC.—See Dover Corporation; *U.S. Public*, pg. 678
CRITERION ADJUSTERS LIMITED—See Lovell Minnick Partners LLC; *U.S. Private*, pg. 2502
CRITERION BROCK, INC.—See Wedbush Capital Partners; *U.S. Private*, pg. 4468
CRITERION CAPITAL MANAGEMENT LLC; *U.S. Private*, pg. 1101
CRITERION EQUIPMENT (PTY) LTD.—See Invicta Holdings Limited; *Int'l*, pg. 3788
CRITERION EXECUTIVE SEARCH, INC.; *U.S. Private*, pg. 1101
CRITERION GLOBAL; *U.S. Private*, pg. 1101
CRITERION SOFTWARE LTD.—See Electronic Arts Inc.; *U.S. Public*, pg. 724
CRITERION SURVEYORS LIMITED—See Lovell Minnick Partners LLC; *U.S. Private*, pg. 2502
CRITERION SYSTEMS, INC.; *U.S. Private*, pg. 1101
CRITERION TEC LIMITED—See Aviva plc; *Int'l*, pg. 746
CRITES & RIDDELL BASICS; *Int'l*, pg. 1850
CRITICAL ALERT SYSTEMS, LLC—See TigerConnect, Inc.; *U.S. Private*, pg. 4170
CRITICAL CARE SERVICES, INC.; *U.S. Private*, pg. 1101
CRITICAL CARE SYSTEMS OF NEW YORK, INC.—See The Cigna Group; *U.S. Public*, pg. 2062
CRITICAL CARE & VETERINARY SPECIALISTS OF SARASOTA LLC; *U.S. Private*, pg. 1101
CRITICAL CONTROL ENERGY SERVICES CORP.; *Int'l*, pg. 1851
CRITICALCONTROL ENERGY SERVICES—See Critical Control Energy Services Corp.; *Int'l*, pg. 1851
CRITICAL ELEMENTS LITHIUM CORPORATION; *Int'l*, pg. 1851
CRITICAL HOMECARE SOLUTIONS, INC.—See Option Care Health, Inc.; *U.S. Public*, pg. 1609
CRITICAL IMAGING, LLC; *U.S. Private*, pg. 1101
CRITICAL INFORMATION NETWORK, LLC—See Comvest Group Holdings LLC; *U.S. Private*, pg. 1007
CRITICAL INFRASTRUCTURE TECHNOLOGIES LTD.; *Int'l*, pg. 1851
CRITICALITY LLC—See Pyxus International, Inc.; *U.S. Public*, pg. 1740
CRITICAL MASS INC. - CHICAGO—See Omnicom Group Inc.; *U.S. Public*, pg. 1594
CRITICAL MASS INC. - NEW YORK—See Omnicom Group Inc.; *U.S. Public*, pg. 1594
CRITICAL MASS INC.—See Omnicom Group Inc.; *U.S. Public*, pg. 1594
CRITICAL MASS INC.—See Omnicom Group Inc.; *U.S. Public*, pg. 1594
CRITICAL MASS - LONDON—See Omnicom Group Inc.; *U.S. Public*, pg. 1594

CRITICAL MASS MEDIA, INC.—See iHeartMedia, Inc.; *U.S. Public*, pg. 1096
CRITICAL MENTION, INC.; *U.S. Private*, pg. 1101
CRITICAL METALS CORP.—See European Lithium Limited; *Int'l*, pg. 2556
CRITICAL METALS PLC; *Int'l*, pg. 1851
CRITICAL MINERAL RESOURCES PLC; *Int'l*, pg. 1851
CRITICAL MINERALS GROUP LIMITED; *Int'l*, pg. 1851
CRITICAL PARADIGM GESTLAT BPO PVT LIMITED—See Infrastructure Leasing & Financial Services Limited; *Int'l*, pg. 3697
CRITICALPOINT CAPITAL, LLC; *U.S. Private*, pg. 1102
CRITICAL POWER EXCHANGE LLC; *U.S. Private*, pg. 1101
CRITICAL POWER SOLUTIONS PTE. LTD.—See Air Water Inc.; *Int'l*, pg. 240
CRITICAL PROCESS SYSTEMS GROUP, INC.—See Wynnchurch Capital, L.P.; *U.S. Private*, pg. 4577
CRITICAL PROJECT SERVICES, LLC; *U.S. Private*, pg. 1102
CRITICAL PR; *U.S. Private*, pg. 1102
CRITICAL SOLUTIONS INTERNATIONAL, INC.—See Air-Boss of America Corp.; *Int'l*, pg. 241
CRITICAL SYSTEMS SERVICES PTE. LTD.—See Air Water Inc.; *Int'l*, pg. 240
CRITICAL TECHNOLOGIES, INC.—See General Electric Company; *U.S. Public*, pg. 918
CRITICAL TELECOM INC.—See BATM Advanced Communications Ltd.; *Int'l*, pg. 890
CRITICALTOOL INC.; *U.S. Private*, pg. 1102
CRITICARE SYSTEMS, INC.—See Opto Circuits (India) Limited; *Int'l*, pg. 5605
CRITICS' CHOICE VIDEO, INC.—See Infinity Resources, Inc.; *U.S. Private*, pg. 2072
CRITIQUEIT, INC.—See 2U, Inc.; *U.S. Public*, pg. 3
CRIT MAROC—See Groupe Crit, S.A.; *Int'l*, pg. 3101
CRI TOLLING, LLC—See Ascent Industries Co.; *U.S. Public*, pg. 210
CRITTALL WINDOWS LTD.; *Int'l*, pg. 1851
CRITTENDEN BOULEVARD HOUSING COMPANY, INC.; *U.S. Private*, pg. 1102
CRITTENDEN HOSPITAL ASSOCIATION; *U.S. Private*, pg. 1102
CRIT TUNISIE—See Groupe Crit, S.A.; *Int'l*, pg. 3101
CRITZAS INDUSTRIES, INC.; *U.S. Private*, pg. 1102
CRIUS ENERGY, LLC; *U.S. Private*, pg. 1102
CRIVELLI FORD INC.; *U.S. Private*, pg. 1102
CRIVELLI SRL—See UniCredit S.p.A.; *Int'l*, pg. 8034
CRI, ZWEITE BETEILIGUNGSGESELLSCHAFT MBH—See Commerzbank AG; *Int'l*, pg. 1715
C.R. JACKSON INC.; *U.S. Private*, pg. 708
CRJA-IBI GROUP—See ARCADIS N.V.; *Int'l*, pg. 541
CR KENDALL CORPORATION—See ATNA RESOURCES LTD.; *U.S. Private*, pg. 381
C.R. KLEWIN SOUTHEAST—See Klewin Construction Inc.; *U.S. Private*, pg. 2319
CRK, LLC—See Welch Packaging Group, Inc.; *U.S. Private*, pg. 4473
C.R. LAURENCE CO., INC.—See KPS Capital Partners, LP; *U.S. Private*, pg. 2348
C.R. LAURENCE OF AUSTRALIA PTY LTD.—See KPS Capital Partners, LP; *U.S. Private*, pg. 2348
C.R. LAURENCE OF CANADA—See KPS Capital Partners, LP; *U.S. Private*, pg. 2348
C.R. LAURENCE OF EUROPE GMBH—See KPS Capital Partners, LP; *U.S. Private*, pg. 2348
C.R. LAURENCE OF EUROPE LTD.—See KPS Capital Partners, LP; *U.S. Private*, pg. 2348
CRL CAR RAIL LOGISTICS GMBH—See OBB-Holding AG; *Int'l*, pg. 5509
CRL DUTCH HOLDING COMPANY BV—See Charles River Laboratories International, Inc.; *U.S. Public*, pg. 479
C&R LEGAL AGENCY, CO., LTD.—See CREEK & RIVER Co., Ltd.; *Int'l*, pg. 1837
CRL GLASS MACHINERY—See KPS Capital Partners, LP; *U.S. Private*, pg. 2348
C.R. LOUGHEAD; *U.S. Private*, pg. 708
CRL US ALUMINUM - CAROLINA—See KPS Capital Partners, LP; *U.S. Private*, pg. 2348
CRL US ALUMINUM - ILLINOIS—See KPS Capital Partners, LP; *U.S. Private*, pg. 2348
CRL US ALUMINUM OF CANADA - VANCOUVER—See KPS Capital Partners, LP; *U.S. Private*, pg. 2348
CRL US ALUMINUM—See KPS Capital Partners, LP; *U.S. Private*, pg. 2348
CRMA ROAD MACHINERY ALLIANCE (BEIJING) ENGINEERING EQUIPMENT CO., LTD.—See Shaanxi Construction Machinery Co., Ltd.; *Int'l*, pg. 6747
CRMA SARL—See Air France-KLM S.A.; *Int'l*, pg. 237
CRM BEIJING TAIBO REAL ESTATE CO., LTD.—See China Railway Materials Co., Ltd.; *Int'l*, pg. 1544
CRM CHAOHU RAILWAY CEMENT CO., LTD.—See China Railway Materials Co., Ltd.; *Int'l*, pg. 1544
CRM COMPANY GROUP SA; *Int'l*, pg. 1851
CRM DEVELOPMENT COMPANY; *U.S. Private*, pg. 1102
C & R MECHANICAL CO.; *U.S. Private*, pg. 701
CR METAL PRODUCTS INC.; *U.S. Private*, pg. 1081

COMPANY NAME INDEX

C.R. MEYER & SONS COMPANY INC.; *U.S. Private*, pg. 708
CRM (HONG KONG) HOLDINGS LIMITED—See China Railway Materials Co., Ltd.; *Int'l*, pg. 1544
CRM LEARNING LP; *U.S. Private*, pg. 1102
CRM MANAGER, LLC—See Infosys Limited; *Int'l*, pg. 3696
CRM MEDIA, LLC—See Information Today Inc.; *U.S. Private*, pg. 2073
CRM METRIX, INC.; *U.S. Private*, pg. 1102
CRM PROPERTIES—See Caruso Affiliated; *U.S. Private*, pg. 777
CRM SERVICES INDIA PVT. LTD.—See Teleperformance SE; *Int'l*, pg. 7541
CRM STUDENTS LTD.—See CORESTATE Capital Holding SA; *Int'l*, pg. 1799
CRM TAIYUAN RAIL SLEEPERS CO., LTD.—See China Railway Materials Co., Ltd.; *Int'l*, pg. 1544
CRM WUHAN WOOD PRESERVATION CO., LTD.—See China Railway Materials Co., Ltd.; *Int'l*, pg. 1544
CRM YINGTAN WOOD PRESERVATION CO., LTD.—See China Railway Materials Co., Ltd.; *Int'l*, pg. 1544
CRM ZHENLAI WOOD PRESERVATION CO., LTD.—See China Railway Materials Co., Ltd.; *Int'l*, pg. 1544
CR NAKORN SRI THAMMARAT (THAILAND) CO., LTD.—See Central Group Company Limited; *Int'l*, pg. 1407
CRNI MARKO A.D.; *Int'l*, pg. 1851
CRN INTERNATIONAL, INC.; *U.S. Private*, pg. 1102
CRNOGORSKA KOMERCIJALNA BANKA A.D.—See OTP Bank Plc; *Int'l*, pg. 5657
CROAKIES; *U.S. Private*, pg. 1102
CROATIA AIRLINES D.D.; *Int'l*, pg. 1851
CROATIA LLOYD D.D.; *Int'l*, pg. 1851
CROATIA OSIGURANJE D.D.—See Adris Grupa d.d.; *Int'l*, pg. 153
CROATIA POLIKLINIKA—See Adris Grupa d.d.; *Int'l*, pg. 153
CROATIA-TEHNICKI PREGLEDI D.O.O.—See Adris Grupa d.d.; *Int'l*, pg. 153
CROCE DI MALTA SRL—See Clariane SE; *Int'l*, pg. 1642
CROCHET & BOREL, INC.; *U.S. Private*, pg. 1102
CROCKER ART MUSEUM ASSOCIATION; *U.S. Private*, pg. 1102
CROCKER DATA PROCECCING PTY LTD—See Weatherford International plc; *U.S. Public*, pg. 2339
CROCKER PARTNERS LLC; *U.S. Private*, pg. 1102
CROCKER VENTURES LLC; *U.S. Private*, pg. 1102
CROCKER & WINSOR SEAFOODS INC.; *U.S. Private*, pg. 1102
CROCKETT FACILITIES SERVICES, INC.; *U.S. Private*, pg. 1103
CROCKETT HOMES, INC.; *U.S. Private*, pg. 1103
CROCKETT HOSPITAL, LLC—See Apollo Global Management, Inc.; *U.S. Public*, pg. 155
THE CROCKETT HOTEL—See Gal-Tex Hotel Corporation; *U.S. Private*, pg. 1635
CROCKETT TELEPHONE COMPANY, INC.—See Telephone Electronics Corporation; *U.S. Private*, pg. 3961
CROCODILE GARMENTS LIMITED; *Int'l*, pg. 1851
CROCODILE TOOL COMPANY (UGANDA) LTD.—See Alam Group of Companies; *Int'l*, pg. 289
CROCS ASIA PTE. LTD.—See Crocs, Inc.; *U.S. Public*, pg. 595
CROCS AUSTRALIA PTY. LTD.—See Crocs, Inc.; *U.S. Public*, pg. 595
CROCS AUSTRALIA PTY. LTD.—See Crocs, Inc.; *U.S. Public*, pg. 595
CROCS CANADA, INC.—See Crocs, Inc.; *U.S. Public*, pg. 595
CROCS HONG KONG LTD.—See Crocs, Inc.; *U.S. Public*, pg. 595
CROCS, INC.; *U.S. Public*, pg. 594
CROCS INDIA PRIVATE LIMITED—See Crocs, Inc.; *U.S. Public*, pg. 595
CROCS NORDIC OY—See Crocs, Inc.; *U.S. Public*, pg. 595
CROCS NZ LIMITED—See Crocs, Inc.; *U.S. Public*, pg. 595
CROCS ONLINE, INC.—See Crocs, Inc.; *U.S. Public*, pg. 595
CROCS PUERTO RICO, INC.—See Crocs, Inc.; *U.S. Public*, pg. 595
CROCS RETAIL, INC.—See Crocs, Inc.; *U.S. Public*, pg. 595
CROCS SINGAPORE PTE. LTD.—See Crocs, Inc.; *U.S. Public*, pg. 595
CROCS SOUTH AFRICA—See Crocs, Inc.; *U.S. Public*, pg. 595
CROCS STORES IRELAND—See Crocs, Inc.; *U.S. Public*, pg. 595
CROCUS TECHNOLOGY INTERNATIONAL INC.—See Allegro MicroSystems, Inc.; *U.S. Public*, pg. 78
CRODA ARGENTINA SA—See Croda International plc; *Int'l*, pg. 1852
CRODA AUSTRALIA—See Croda International plc; *Int'l*, pg. 1852
CRODA CANADA LTD.—See Croda International plc; *Int'l*, pg. 1851

CRODA CHEMICALS EUROPE LTD—See Croda International plc; *Int'l*, pg. 1851
CRODA CHEMICALS (INDIA) PVT LTD.—See Croda International plc; *Int'l*, pg. 1852
CRODA CHEMICALS INTERNATIONAL LTD.—See Croda International plc; *Int'l*, pg. 1851
CRODA CHEMICALS INTERNATIONAL (MOSCOW) LTD—See Croda International plc; *Int'l*, pg. 1851
CRODA CHEMICALS SA PTY LTD—See Croda International plc; *Int'l*, pg. 1851
CRODA CHILE LTDA.—See Croda International plc; *Int'l*, pg. 1851
CRODA CHINA TRADING COMPANY LTD.—See Croda International plc; *Int'l*, pg. 1851
CRODA CHOCQUES SAS—See Croda International plc; *Int'l*, pg. 1851
CRODA COLOMBIA—See Croda International plc; *Int'l*, pg. 1851
CRODA DO BRASIL LTDA—See Croda International plc; *Int'l*, pg. 1852
CRODA EUROPE LTD.—See Croda International plc; *Int'l*, pg. 1852
CRODA FRANCE SAS—See Croda International plc; *Int'l*, pg. 1852
CRODA GMBH—See Croda International plc; *Int'l*, pg. 1852
CRODA HOLDINGS FRANCE SAS—See Croda International plc; *Int'l*, pg. 1852
CRODA HONG KONG—See Croda International plc; *Int'l*, pg. 1852
CRODA HUNGARY LTD.—See Croda International plc; *Int'l*, pg. 1852
CRODA IBERICA SA—See Croda International plc; *Int'l*, pg. 1852
CRODA INC.—See Croda International plc; *Int'l*, pg. 1852
CRODA INDIA COMPANY PRIVATE LTD.—See Croda International plc; *Int'l*, pg. 1852
CRODA INTERNATIONAL PLC; *Int'l*, pg. 1851
CRODA ITALIANA S.P.A.—See Croda International plc; *Int'l*, pg. 1852
CRODA JAPAN KK—See Croda International plc; *Int'l*, pg. 1852
CRODA KIMYA TICARET LIMITED SIRKET—See Croda International plc; *Int'l*, pg. 1852
CRODA KOREA CHEMICAL INTERNATIONAL LTD.—See Croda International plc; *Int'l*, pg. 1852
CRODA KOREA CO, LTD.—See Croda International plc; *Int'l*, pg. 1852
CRODA MAGYARORSZAG KFT.—See Croda International plc; *Int'l*, pg. 1852
CRODA MEXICO, S.A. DE C.V.—See Croda International plc; *Int'l*, pg. 1852
CRODA MIDDLE EAST—See Croda International plc; *Int'l*, pg. 1852
CRODA NEDERLAND B.V.—See Croda International plc; *Int'l*, pg. 1852
CRODA NORDICA AB—See Croda International plc; *Int'l*, pg. 1852
CRODA OLEOCHEMICALS IBERICA, S.A.—See Croda International plc; *Int'l*, pg. 1852
CRODA OVERSEAS HOLDINGS LTD—See Croda International plc; *Int'l*, pg. 1852
CRODA PARS TRADING CO—See Croda International plc; *Int'l*, pg. 1852
CRODA PERUANA S.A.C—See Croda International plc; *Int'l*, pg. 1852
CRODA POLAND SP. Z O.O.—See Croda International plc; *Int'l*, pg. 1852
CRODAROM SAS—See Croda International plc; *Int'l*, pg. 1852
CRODAROM—See Croda International plc; *Int'l*, pg. 1852
CRODA RUS LLC—See Croda International plc; *Int'l*, pg. 1852
CRODA (SA) (PTY) LTD.—See Croda International plc; *Int'l*, pg. 1851
CRODA SHANGHAI—See Croda International plc; *Int'l*, pg. 1852
CRODA SINGAPORE PTE. LTD.—See Croda International plc; *Int'l*, pg. 1852
CRODA SIPO (SICHUAN) CO., LTD.—See Croda International plc; *Int'l*, pg. 1852
CRODA SPOL. S.R.O—See Croda International plc; *Int'l*, pg. 1852
CRODA (THAILAND) CO., LTD—See Croda International plc; *Int'l*, pg. 1851
CRODA TRADING (SHANGHAI) CO., LTD—See Croda International plc; *Int'l*, pg. 1852
CRODUX DERIVATI DVA D.O.O.—See Petrol, Slovenska energetska druzba, d.d.; *Int'l*, pg. 5827
CRODUX PLIN D.O.O.; *Int'l*, pg. 1853
CROFT DIALYSIS, LLC—See DaVita Inc.; *U.S. Public*, pg. 637
CROFT JEREZ SA—See Diageo plc; *Int'l*, pg. 2102
CROFT LLC; *U.S. Private*, pg. 1103
CROGHAN BANCSHARES, INC.; *U.S. Public*, pg. 595
THE CROGHAN COLONIAL BANK—See Croghan Bancshares, Inc.; *U.S. Public*, pg. 595
CROHN'S & COLITIS FOUNDATION OF AMERICA; *U.S. Private*, pg. 1103

CROISIERES AUSTRALES LTEE—See ENL Limited; *Int'l*, pg. 2441
CROISSANCE LTD.; *Int'l*, pg. 1853
CROIX CONNECT; *U.S. Private*, pg. 1103
CROIX OIL COMPANY; *U.S. Private*, pg. 1103
C. ROKAS INDUSTRIAL COMMERCIAL COMPANY, S.A.—See Iberdrola, S.A.; *Int'l*, pg. 3573
CROMA MEDIC, INC.—See Bain Capital, LP; *U.S. Private*, pg. 443
CROMA MEDIC, INC.—See Cinven Limited; *Int'l*, pg. 1613
CROMAN CORPORATION; *U.S. Private*, pg. 1103
CROMA PHARMACEUTICALS INC.—See Bausch Health Companies Inc.; *Int'l*, pg. 897
CROMA PHARMA SL—See Bausch Health Companies Inc.; *Int'l*, pg. 897
CROMARIS D.D.—See Adris Grupa d.d.; *Int'l*, pg. 153
CROMARIS ITALY S.R.L.—See Adris Grupa d.d.; *Int'l*, pg. 153
CROMA SECURITY SOLUTIONS GROUP PLC; *Int'l*, pg. 1853
CROMBIE LOCKWOOD (NZ) LIMITED—See Arthur J. Gallagher & Co.; *U.S. Public*, pg. 203
CROMBIE REIT—See Empire Company Limited; *Int'l*, pg. 2387
THE CROM CORPORATION; *U.S. Private*, pg. 4016
CROM EQUIPMENT RENTALS INC.—See The Crom Corporation; *U.S. Private*, pg. 4016
CROMEX S/A; *Int'l*, pg. 1853
CROMFORD GROUP PTY. LTD.—See Washington H. Soul Pattinson & Company Limited; *Int'l*, pg. 8351
CROMITAL S.P.A - OSTELLATO PLANT—See Turkiye Sise ve Cam Fabrikalari A.S.; *Int'l*, pg. 7977
CROMITAL S.P.A—See Turkiye Sise ve Cam Fabrikalari A.S.; *Int'l*, pg. 7977
CROMOLOGY SAS—See Wendel S.A.; *Int'l*, pg. 8376
CROMPTON CONTROLS LTD.; *Int'l*, pg. 1853
CROMPTON GREAVES CONSUMER ELECTRICALS LIMITED; *Int'l*, pg. 1853
CROMPTON LIGHTING PTY LIMITED—See Bain Capital, LP; *U.S. Private*, pg. 439
CROMPTON LIGHTING PTY LIMITED—See Investec Limited; *Int'l*, pg. 3777
CROMPTON TECHNOLOGIES—See TE Connectivity Ltd.; *Int'l*, pg. 7498
CROMPTON TECHNOLOGY GROUP LIMITED—See HIX Corporation; *U.S. Public*, pg. 1821
CROMSOURCE INC.—See CROMSOURCE S.r.l.; *Int'l*, pg. 1853
CROMSOURCE LTD.—See CROMSOURCE S.r.l.; *Int'l*, pg. 1853
CROMSOURCE S.R.L.; *Int'l*, pg. 1853
CROMWELL CORPORATE SECRETARIAL LIMITED—See Cromwell Property Group; *Int'l*, pg. 1853
CROMWELL CORPORATION LIMITED—See Cromwell Property Group; *Int'l*, pg. 1853
CROMWELL CZECH REPUBLIC S.R.O.—See W.W. Grainger, Inc.; *U.S. Public*, pg. 2319
CROMWELL DENMARK A/S—See Cromwell Property Group; *Int'l*, pg. 1854
CROMWELL EUROPEAN MANAGEMENT SERVICES LIMITED—See Cromwell Property Group; *Int'l*, pg. 1854
CROMWELL EUROPEAN REAL ESTATE INVESTMENT TRUST; *Int'l*, pg. 1853
CROMWELL FINLAND O/Y—See Cromwell Property Group; *Int'l*, pg. 1854
CROMWELL FRANCE SAS—See W.W. Grainger, Inc.; *U.S. Public*, pg. 2319
CROMWELL GROUP INC.; *U.S. Private*, pg. 1103
CROMWELL GROUP (INTERNATIONAL) LIMITED—See W.W. Grainger, Inc.; *U.S. Public*, pg. 2319
THE CROMWELL (LAS VEGAS) HOTEL & CASINO—See Caesars Entertainment, Inc.; *U.S. Public*, pg. 420
CROMWELL POLAND SP. Z O.O.—See W.W. Grainger, Inc.; *U.S. Public*, pg. 2319
CROMWELL PROPERTY GROUP CZECH REPUBLIC S.R.O.—See Cromwell Property Group; *Int'l*, pg. 1854
CROMWELL PROPERTY GROUP ITALY SRL—See Cromwell Property Group; *Int'l*, pg. 1854
CROMWELL PROPERTY GROUP; *Int'l*, pg. 1853
CROMWELL PROPERTY SECURITIES LIMITED—See Cromwell Property Group; *Int'l*, pg. 1854
CROMWELL PROPERTY SERVICES PTY. LTD.—See Cromwell Property Group; *Int'l*, pg. 1854
CROMWELL PTY LIMITED—See W.W. Grainger, Inc.; *U.S. Public*, pg. 2319
CROMWELL SP Z.O.O—See W.W. Grainger, Inc.; *U.S. Public*, pg. 2319
CROMWELL SWEDEN A/B—See Cromwell Property Group; *Int'l*, pg. 1854
CROMWELL TOOLS LTD.—See W.W. Grainger, Inc.; *U.S. Public*, pg. 2319
CROMWELL TOOLS, PT—See W.W. Grainger, Inc.; *U.S. Public*, pg. 2319
CROMWELL TOOLS SDN. BHD.—See W.W. Grainger, Inc.; *U.S. Public*, pg. 2319
CROMWELL TOOLS (SHANGHAI) CO. LTD.—See W.W. Grainger, Inc.; *U.S. Public*, pg. 2319

CROMWELL PROPERTY GROUP

CROMWELL TOOLS (THAILAND) CO. LTD.—See W.W. Grainger, Inc.; *U.S. Public*, pg. 2319
CROMWELL TRANSPORT COMPANY—See Trojan Holdings Ltd.; *Int'l*, pg. 7938
CRONA CORP.; *Int'l*, pg. 1854
CRONEX CO LTD; *Int'l*, pg. 1854
CRONIC CHRYSLER JEEP DODGE RAM; *U.S. Private*, pg. 1103
CRONIFER U.K. LTD.—See CRONIMET Holding GmbH; *Int'l*, pg. 1854
CRONILEG ROHSTOFFHANDELSGESELLSCHAFT MBH—See CRONIMET Holding GmbH; *Int'l*, pg. 1854
CRONIMET ALFA FERROLEGIERUNGEN HANDELS GMBH—See CRONIMET Holding GmbH; *Int'l*, pg. 1854
CRONIMET BASE METALS GMBH—See CRONIMET Holding GmbH; *Int'l*, pg. 1854
CRONIMET BELGIUM NV—See CRONIMET Holding GmbH; *Int'l*, pg. 1854
CRONIMET BRASIL LTDA.—See CRONIMET Holding GmbH; *Int'l*, pg. 1854
CRONIMET CENTRAL AFRICA AG—See CRONIMET Holding GmbH; *Int'l*, pg. 1854
CRONIMET CHINA—See CRONIMET Holding GmbH; *Int'l*, pg. 1854
CRONIMET CHROME MINING (PTY.) LTD.—See CRONIMET Holding GmbH; *Int'l*, pg. 1854
CRONIMET CORPORATION—See CRONIMET Holding GmbH; *Int'l*, pg. 1854
CRONIMET FAGERSTA AB—See CRONIMET Holding GmbH; *Int'l*, pg. 1854
CRONIMET FERROLEGIERUNGEN HANDELSGES. MBH—See CRONIMET Holding GmbH; *Int'l*, pg. 1854
CRONIMET FRANCE S.A.S.—See CRONIMET Holding GmbH; *Int'l*, pg. 1854
CRONIMET (GREAT BRITAIN) LTD.—See CRONIMET Holding GmbH; *Int'l*, pg. 1854
CRONIMET HISPANIA, S. A.—See CRONIMET Holding GmbH; *Int'l*, pg. 1854
CRONIMET HOLDING GMBH; *Int'l*, pg. 1854
CRONIMET (HOLLAND) B.V.—See CRONIMET Holding GmbH; *Int'l*, pg. 1854
CRONIMET INDIA METALS PVT. LTD.—See CRONIMET Holding GmbH; *Int'l*, pg. 1854
CRONIMET LATVIA SIA—See CRONIMET Holding GmbH; *Int'l*, pg. 1854
CRONIMET LEGIERUNGEN DORTMUND GMBH—See CRONIMET Holding GmbH; *Int'l*, pg. 1854
CRONIMET LONDON LTD.—See CRONIMET Holding GmbH; *Int'l*, pg. 1854
CRONIMET METAL PHILIPPINES, INC.—See CRONIMET Holding GmbH; *Int'l*, pg. 1854
CRONIMET MEXICO—See CRONIMET Holding GmbH; *Int'l*, pg. 1854
CRONIMET MINING AG—See CRONIMET Holding GmbH; *Int'l*, pg. 1854
CRONIMET MINING POWER SOLUTIONS GMBH—See Ohlthaver & List Group of Companies; *Int'l*, pg. 5533
CRONIMET NOBLE ALLOYS HANDELGES. MBH—See CRONIMET Holding GmbH; *Int'l*, pg. 1854
CRONIMET NORDIC OU—See CRONIMET Holding GmbH; *Int'l*, pg. 1854
CRONIMET OSTRAVA, S.R.O—See CRONIMET Holding GmbH; *Int'l*, pg. 1854
CRONIMET PL SP. Z.O.O.—See CRONIMET Holding GmbH; *Int'l*, pg. 1854
CRONIMET RSA (PTY) LTD—See CRONIMET Holding GmbH; *Int'l*, pg. 1854
CRONIMET S.A.—See CRONIMET Holding GmbH; *Int'l*, pg. 1854
CRONIMET SHANGHAI CO., LTD.—See CRONIMET Holding GmbH; *Int'l*, pg. 1854
CRONIMET SINGAPORE PTE. LTD.—See CRONIMET Holding GmbH; *Int'l*, pg. 1855
CRONIN & COMPANY, INC.; *U.S. Private*, pg. 1103
CRONIN CO.; *U.S. Private*, pg. 1103
CRONLAND LUMBER CO. INC.; *U.S. Private*, pg. 1103
CRONOMAR D.O.O—See SIVA SF; *Int'l*, pg. 6965
CRONON AG—See United Internet AG; *Int'l*, pg. 8069
CRONOS GROUP INC.; *Int'l*, pg. 1855
CRONOS HOLDING CO LTD.—See Kelso & Company, L.P.; *U.S. Private*, pg. 2278
CRONOS INC.—See Seiko Group Corporation; *Int'l*, pg. 6688
CRONOS LTD.—See Kelso & Company, L.P.; *U.S. Private*, pg. 2278
CRON - TEK OY—See Quaser Machine Tools, Inc.; *Int'l*, pg. 6156
CRONTO LIMITED—See OneSpan Inc.; *U.S. Public*, pg. 1603
CRON.UP S.R.L.—See KONE Oyj; *Int'l*, pg. 4247
CROOKED TREE GOLF CLUB INC.—See Boyne USA Resorts Inc.; *U.S. Private*, pg. 629
CROOKER CONSTRUCTION, LLC; *U.S. Private*, pg. 1103
CROOKES BROTHERS LIMITED; *Int'l*, pg. 1855
CROOKES PLANTATIONS LTD—See CROOKES BROTHERS LIMITED; *Int'l*, pg. 1855
CROOKHAM COMPANY INC.; *U.S. Private*, pg. 1103
CROOK MOTOR CO. INC.; *U.S. Private*, pg. 1103

CROOK PRODUCTIONS LIMITED—See ITV plc; *Int'l*, pg. 3844
CROOZ, INC.; *Int'l*, pg. 1855
CROP DATA MANAGEMENT SYSTEMS, INC.—See RELX plc; *Int'l*, pg. 6266
CROPDESIGN N.V.—See BASF SE; *Int'l*, pg. 883
CROPENERGIES AG—See Suddeutsche Zuckerruben-Verwertungs-Genossenschaft eG; *Int'l*, pg. 7252
CROPLAND CO-OP, INC.; *U.S. Private*, pg. 1103
CROPLANDS EQUIPMENT PTY LTD—See Nufarm Limited; *Int'l*, pg. 5486
CROPLANDS EQUIPMENT PTY LTD—See Nufarm Limited; *Int'l*, pg. 5486
CROP LIFE SCIENCE LIMITED; *Int'l*, pg. 1855
CROPLIN D.O.O.—See INA-Industrija Nafte, d.d.; *Int'l*, pg. 3642
CROPLOGIC LIMITED; *Int'l*, pg. 1855
CROPPER MOTORS; *Int'l*, pg. 1855
CROPP-METCALFE CO.; *U.S. Private*, pg. 1103
CROPP-METCALFE CO.—See Cropp-Metcalfe Co.; *U.S. Private*, pg. 1103
CROPPMETCALFE, INC.—See Brookfield Corporation; *Int'l*, pg. 1188
CROPPY SOLUTIONS SL—See KARATZIS S.A.; *Int'l*, pg. 4079
CROP QUEST AGRONOMIC SERVICES; *U.S. Private*, pg. 1103
CROP RISK SERVICES, INC.—See American Financial Group, Inc.; *U.S. Public*, pg. 102
CROPS CORPORATION; *Int'l*, pg. 1855
CROPSERVE ZAMBIA LIMITED—See UPL Limited; *Int'l*, pg. 8089
CROPSTER AGRO LIMITED; *Int'l*, pg. 1855
CROSBY & ASSOCIATES, LLC—See National Land Realty, LLC; *U.S. Private*, pg. 2858
THE CROSBY CLUB—See Escalante Golf, Inc.; *U.S. Private*, pg. 1424
CROSBY ELECTRIC COMPANY, INC.; *U.S. Private*, pg. 1103
CROSBY EUROPE N.V.—See KKR & Co. Inc.; *U.S. Public*, pg. 1264
THE CROSBY GROUP LLC—See KKR & Co. Inc.; *U.S. Public*, pg. 1264
CROSBY INSURANCE INC.; *U.S. Private*, pg. 1103
CROSBY MARKETING COMMUNICATIONS; *U.S. Private*, pg. 1103
CROSBY-NATIONAL SWAGE CO.—See KKR & Co. Inc.; *U.S. Public*, pg. 1264
CROSBY-NOONAN CO-OP ELEVATOR COMPANY; *U.S. Private*, pg. 1104
CROSBY & OVERTON, INC.; *U.S. Private*, pg. 1103
CROSBY ROCK LLC; *U.S. Private*, pg. 1104
CROSBY SECURITIES LIMITED—See Quali-Smart Holdings Ltd.; *Int'l*, pg. 6150
CROSBYS MARKETS INC.; *U.S. Private*, pg. 1104
CROSBY VALVE, INC.—See Emerson Electric Co.; *U.S. Public*, pg. 751
CROSBY VOLKSWAGEN INC; *Int'l*, pg. 1855
CROSCILL HOME—See Patriarch Partners, LLC; *U.S. Private*, pg. 3109
CROSCILL, INC.—See Patriarch Partners, LLC; *U.S. Private*, pg. 3109
CROSCO B.V.—See INA-Industrija Nafte, d.d.; *Int'l*, pg. 3642
CROSCO INTEGRATED DRILLING & WELL SERVICES CO., LTD.—See INA-Industrija Nafte, d.d.; *Int'l*, pg. 3642
CROSCO INTERNATIONAL LTD.—See INA-Industrija Nafte, d.d.; *Int'l*, pg. 3642
CROSCO NAFTNI SERVISI D.O.O.—See INA-Industrija Nafte, d.d.; *Int'l*, pg. 3642
THE CROSLAND GROUP INC.; *U.S. Private*, pg. 4016
CROSLAND RETAIL—See The Crosland Group Inc.; *U.S. Private*, pg. 4016
CROSLENE CHEMICAL INDUSTRIES, LTD.—See Lidye Co., Ltd.; *Int'l*, pg. 4488
CROSLENE CHEMICAL INDUSTRIES, LTD.—See Mitsui Chemicals, Inc.; *Int'l*, pg. 4983
CROSLENE CHEMICAL INDUSTRIES, LTD.—See Takeda Pharmaceutical Company Limited; *Int'l*, pg. 7437
CROSMAN CORPORATION—See Bruckmann, Rosser, Sherrill & Co., LLC; *U.S. Private*, pg. 671
CROSMAN SEED CORPORATION; *U.S. Private*, pg. 1104
CROSNO CONSTRUCTION, INC.; *U.S. Private*, pg. 1104
CROS NT SRL—See CMC Consulting Boston, Inc.; *U.S. Private*, pg. 950
CROSPON LIMITED—See Medtronic plc; *Int'l*, pg. 4787
THE CROSS AGENCY; *U.S. Private*, pg. 4016
CROSSALTA GAS STORAGE & SERVICES LTD.—See TC Energy Corporation; *Int'l*, pg. 7482
CROSSAMERICA PARTNERS LP; *U.S. Public*, pg. 596
CROSSBOW GROUP, LLC; *U.S. Private*, pg. 1105
CROSSBOWS OPTICAL LTD—See EssilorLuxottica SA; *Int'l*, pg. 2514
CROSSBOW TECHNOLOGY, INC.—See Moog Inc.; *U.S. Public*, pg. 1469
CROSSBRIDGE CONDOMINIUM SERVICES LTD.—See FirstService Corporation; *Int'l*, pg. 2691

CORPORATE AFFILIATIONS

CROSS BROTHERS IMPLEMENT INC.; *U.S. Private*, pg. 1104
CROSS CAT CO., LTD.; *Int'l*, pg. 1855
CROSSCHECK, INC.—See Startia Holdings, Inc.; *Int'l*, pg. 7179
CROSS CLICK MEDIA INC.; *U.S. Private*, pg. 1104
CROSSCO CO., LTD.—See J-Stream Inc.; *Int'l*, pg. 3854
CROSSCO CO., LTD.—See Transcosmos Inc.; *Int'l*, pg. 7898
CROSSCO INVESTMENT AB—See Enerpac Tool Group Corp.; *U.S. Public*, pg. 765
CROSSCOM NATIONAL INC.; *U.S. Private*, pg. 1106
CROSS COMPANY; *U.S. Private*, pg. 1104
CROSSCONTROL OY—See Enerpac Tool Group Corp.; *U.S. Public*, pg. 765
CROSSCOOP INDIA PVT LTD—See Socialwire Co., Ltd.; *Int'l*, pg. 7031
CROSSCOOP PHILIPPINES INC—See Socialwire Co., Ltd.; *Int'l*, pg. 7031
CROSSCOOP SINGAPORE PTE LTD—See Socialwire Co., Ltd.; *Int'l*, pg. 7031
CROSSCOOP VIETNAM CO LTD—See Socialwire Co., Ltd.; *Int'l*, pg. 7031
CROSSCOUNTRY CONSULTING LLC; *U.S. Private*, pg. 1106
CROSSCOUNTRY COURIER; *U.S. Private*, pg. 1106
CROSSCOUNTRY FREIGHT SOLUTIONS, INC.; *U.S. Private*, pg. 1106
THE CROSS COUNTRY GROUP, LLC; *U.S. Private*, pg. 4016
CROSS COUNTRY HEALTHCARE, INC.; *U.S. Public*, pg. 595
CROSS COUNTRY HOME SERVICES—See The Cross Country Group, LLC; *U.S. Private*, pg. 4017
CROSS COUNTRY INFOTECH, PVT. LTD.—See Cross Country Healthcare, Inc.; *U.S. Public*, pg. 595
CROSS COUNTRY INFRASTRUCTURE SERVICES, INC.—See Odyssey Investment Partners, LLC; *U.S. Private*, pg. 2995
CROSSCOUNTRY MORTGAGE, LLC; *U.S. Private*, pg. 1106
CROSS COUNTRY STAFFING, INC.—See Cross Country Healthcare, Inc.; *U.S. Public*, pg. 595
CROSS COUNTRY TRAVCORPS, INC.—See Cross Country Healthcare, Inc.; *U.S. Public*, pg. 595
CROSS COUNTY BANCSHARES INC.; *U.S. Private*, pg. 1104
CROSS COUNTY FEDERAL SAVINGS BANK; *U.S. Private*, pg. 1104
CROSS CREEK MALL, LLC—See CBL & Associates Properties, Inc.; *U.S. Public*, pg. 458
CROSS CREEK PHYSICAL THERAPY, LIMITED PARTNERSHIP—See U.S. Physical Therapy, Inc.; *U.S. Public*, pg. 2214
CROSS CREEK SALES LLC—See Baillie Lumber Co., Inc.; *U.S. Private*, pg. 426
CROSS CREEK SUBARU, INC.; *U.S. Private*, pg. 1104
CROSS-DILLON TIRE INC.; *U.S. Private*, pg. 1105
CROSS ENTERPRISES INC.; *U.S. Private*, pg. 1104
CROSS ENVIRONMENTAL SERVICES, INC.—See CES Synergies, Inc.; *U.S. Public*, pg. 476
CROSS EQUITY PARTNERS AG; *Int'l*, pg. 1855
CROSSET COMPANY LLC—See Castellini Company, Inc.; *U.S. Private*, pg. 784
CROSSETT INC.; *U.S. Private*, pg. 1106
CROSS, FERNANDEZ & RILEY, LLP; *U.S. Private*, pg. 1105
CROSSFIELD PRODUCTS CORPORATION; *U.S. Private*, pg. 1106
CROSS FINANCIAL CORPORATION; *U.S. Private*, pg. 1104
CROSS FINANZIERUNGS GMBH—See Pierer Konzerngesellschaft mbH; *Int'l*, pg. 5862
CROSS FIRE & SECURITY CO., INC.—See AE Industrial Partners, LP; *U.S. Private*, pg. 112
CROSSFIRE SOUND PRODUCTIONS, LLC; *U.S. Private*, pg. 1106
CROSSFIRST BANKSHARES, INC.; *U.S. Public*, pg. 596
CROSSFIT, INC.—See Berkshire Partners LLC; *U.S. Private*, pg. 534
CROSSFOR CO., LTD.; *Int'l*, pg. 1856
CROSSFOR HK LIMITED—See Crossfor Co., Ltd.; *Int'l*, pg. 1856
CROSSGAR PALLAS LTD—See Sysco Corporation; *U.S. Public*, pg. 1973
CROSSGATE PARTNERS, LLC; *U.S. Private*, pg. 1106
CROSS GATE SERVICES, INC.—See The Budd Group Inc.; *U.S. Private*, pg. 4002
CROSSGATE UK LTD.—See SAP SE; *Int'l*, pg. 6566
CROSSGLOBE DISTRIBUTION SERVICES, INC.—See Blue Wolf Capital Partners LLC; *U.S. Private*, pg. 595
CROSSGLOBE EXPRESS, LLC—See Blue Wolf Capital Partners LLC; *U.S. Private*, pg. 595
CROSSGLOBE TRANSPORT, LTD.—See Blue Wolf Capital Partners LLC; *U.S. Private*, pg. 595
THE CROSS-HARBOUR (HOLDINGS) LIMITED; *Int'l*, pg. 7635
CROSS HARDWARE B.V.—See TKH Group N.V.; *Int'l*, pg. 7763

CROSS HEAD KK—See TECHMATRIX CORPORATION; *Int'l*, pg. 7505
CROSS IMPLEMENT INC.; *U.S. Private*, pg. 1105
CROSSINGBRIDGE ADVISORS LLC—See ENDI Corp.; *U.S. Public*, pg. 760
CROSSING RIVERS HEALTH; *U.S. Private*, pg. 1106
CROSSINGS HEALTHCARE SOLUTIONS, INC.—See Universal Health Services, Inc.; *U.S. Public*, pg. 2256
CROSS INSURANCE INC.—See Cross Financial Corporation; *U.S. Private*, pg. 1104
CROSS INSURANCE TPA, INC.—See Cross Financial Corporation; *U.S. Private*, pg. 1104
CROSS INTERNATIONAL; *U.S. Private*, pg. 1105
CROSSINX GMBH—See Unifiedpost Group SA; *Int'l*, pg. 8043
CROSSIX SOLUTIONS INC.—See Veeva Systems, Inc.; *U.S. Public*, pg. 2277
CROSSJECT SA; *Int'l*, pg. 1856
CROSS J TECH INC.—See Cross Marketing Group Inc.; *Int'l*, pg. 1856
CROSSKEY BANKING SOLUTIONS AB LTD.—See Alandsbanken Abp; *Int'l*, pg. 290
CROSS KEYS ADVERTISING & MARKETING, INC.; *U.S. Private*, pg. 1105
CROSS KEYS BANK—See BSJ Bancshares, Inc.; *U.S. Private*, pg. 675
CROSS KEYS CAPITAL LLC; *U.S. Private*, pg. 1105
CROSSKNOWLEDGE GROUP LIMITED—See John Wiley & Sons, Inc.; *U.S. Public*, pg. 1192
CROSSLAKE SALES INC.; *U.S. Private*, pg. 1106
CROSSLAND ASSOCIATES INC.; *U.S. Private*, pg. 1106
CROSSLAND CONSTRUCTION CO. INC.; *U.S. Private*, pg. 1106
CROSSLANDS CONSTRUCTION CO., INC.; *U.S. Private*, pg. 1106
CROSSLAND STRATEGIC METALS LIMITED; *Int'l*, pg. 1856
CROSSLEY HOLDINGS—See Industrial Development Corporation of South Africa, Ltd.; *Int'l*, pg. 3671
CROSSLIN & ASSOCIATES PC; *U.S. Private*, pg. 1106
CROSSLINK CAPITAL, INC.; *U.S. Private*, pg. 1106
CROSSLOG SA; *Int'l*, pg. 1856
CROSSMAN & COMPANY INC.; *U.S. Private*, pg. 1106
CROSS MANUFACTURING INC.; *U.S. Private*, pg. 1105
CROSSMARK AUSTRALIA PTY. LTD.- MELBOURNE—See Acosta, Inc.; *U.S. Private*, pg. 64
CROSSMARK AUSTRALIA PTY. LTD.—See Acosta, Inc.; *U.S. Private*, pg. 64
CROSS MARKETING ASIA PTE. LTD.—See Cross Marketing Group Inc.; *Int'l*, pg. 1856
CROSS MARKETING GROUP INC.; *Int'l*, pg. 1855
CROSS MARKETING INC.—See Cross Marketing Group Inc.; *Int'l*, pg. 1856
CROSSMARK GRAPHICS INC.; *U.S. Private*, pg. 1107
CROSSMARK, INC.—See Acosta, Inc.; *U.S. Private*, pg. 64
CROSS MATCH TECHNOLOGIES GMBH—See ASSA ABLOY AB; *Int'l*, pg. 637
CROSS MATCH TECHNOLOGIES, INC. - REDWOOD CITY—See ASSA ABLOY AB; *Int'l*, pg. 637
CROSS MATCH TECHNOLOGIES, INC.—See ASSA ABLOY AB; *Int'l*, pg. 637
CROSS MEDIAWORKS, INC.; *U.S. Private*, pg. 1105
CROSSMED S.P.A.—See Penumbra, Inc.; *U.S. Public*, pg. 1667
CROSS-MIDWEST TIRE, INC.; *U.S. Private*, pg. 1105
CROSS MOTORS CORP.; *U.S. Private*, pg. 1105
CROSS OIL COMPANY INC.; *U.S. Private*, pg. 1105
CROSS OIL REFINING & MARKETING COMPANY; *U.S. Private*, pg. 1105
CROSSOVER CREATIVE GROUP; *U.S. Private*, pg. 1107
CROSS PETROLEUM; *U.S. Private*, pg. 1105
CROSSPHARMA LTD.—See Bain Capital, LP; *U.S. Private*, pg. 443
CROSSPHARMA LTD.—See Cinven Limited; *Int'l*, pg. 1613
CROSSPIPE SYSTEMS S.A.—See Golan Plastic Products Ltd.; *Int'l*, pg. 3023
CROSSPLANE CAPITAL MANAGEMENT LP; *U.S. Private*, pg. 1107
CROSS PLUS INC.; *Int'l*, pg. 1856
CROSSPOINT CAPITAL PARTNERS LP; *U.S. Private*, pg. 1107
CROSSPOINT S.A.L—See Transition Evergreen; *Int'l*, pg. 7901
CROSSPOINT VENTURE PARTNERS; *U.S. Private*, pg. 1107
CROSS PROPWORKS INC.—See Cross Marketing Group Inc.; *Int'l*, pg. 1856
CROSS RAPIDS CAPITAL LP; *U.S. Private*, pg. 1105
CROSS RENTAL LIMITED—See Lonsdale Capital Partners LLP; *Int'l*, pg. 4552
CROSS RIVER VENTURES CORP.; *Int'l*, pg. 1856
CROSSROAD CARRIERS LP—See Vertex Energy, Inc.; *U.S. Public*, pg. 2287
CROSSROAD FUEL SERVICE INC.; *U.S. Private*, pg. 1107
CROSSROADS AG LLC; *U.S. Private*, pg. 1108

CROSSROADS AUTOMOTIVE GROUP; *U.S. Private*, pg. 1108
CROSSROADS BANK—See FFW Corporation; *U.S. Public*, pg. 830
CROSSROADS CAPITAL, INC.; *U.S. Private*, pg. 1108
CROSSROADS C&I DISTRIBUTORS, INC.—See TopBuild Corp.; *U.S. Public*, pg. 2163
CROSSROADS COOPERATIVE ASSOCIATION; *U.S. Private*, pg. 1108
CROSSROADS EXTREMITY SYSTEMS, LLC—See Johnson & Johnson; *U.S. Public*, pg. 1194
CROSSROADS EYE CARE ASSOCIATES, LTD.—See Blue Sea Capital Management LLC; *U.S. Private*, pg. 592
CROSSROADS EYE CARE ASSOCIATES, LTD.—See Ophthalmic Consultants of Long Island; *U.S. Private*, pg. 3032
CROSSROADS FILM INC.; *U.S. Private*, pg. 1108
CROSSROADS FORD INC.; *U.S. Private*, pg. 1108
CROSSROADS FORD, INC.—See Crossroads Automotive Group; *U.S. Private*, pg. 1108
CROSSROADS FORD LTD; *U.S. Private*, pg. 1108
CROSSROADS FORD TRUCK SALES INC; *U.S. Private*, pg. 1108
CROSSROADS HOME CARE SERVICES, LLC—See Community Health Systems, Inc.; *U.S. Public*, pg. 552
CROSSROADS HOUSING DEVELOPMENT CORP; *U.S. Private*, pg. 1108
CROSSROADS MALL—See Pennsylvania Real Estate Investment Trust; *U.S. Public*, pg. 1663
CROSSROADS NISSAN OF HICKORY, INC.—See Crossroads Automotive Group; *U.S. Private*, pg. 1108
CROSSROADS OF WESTERN IOWA, INC.; *U.S. Private*, pg. 1108
CROSSROADS PHYSICIAN CORP.—See Quorum Health Corporation; *U.S. Private*, pg. 3329
CROSSROADS PLAZA DEVELOPMENT PARTNERS, LLC—See Alexander & Baldwin, Inc.; *U.S. Public*, pg. 75
CROSSROADS REGIONAL HOSPITAL, LLC—See Acadia Healthcare Company, Inc.; *U.S. Public*, pg. 28
CROSSROADS ROOFING & SUPPLY, INC.—See Beacon Roofing Supply, Inc.; *U.S. Public*, pg. 286
CROSSROADS—See Barkley; *U.S. Private*, pg. 475
CROSSROADS SYSTEMS, INC.; *U.S. Public*, pg. 596
CROSSROADS SYSTEMS (TEXAS), INC.—See Crossroads Systems, Inc.; *U.S. Public*, pg. 596
CROSSROADS TRAILER SALES & SERVICE; *U.S. Private*, pg. 1108
CROSSROADS TRAVEL, INC.—See ABRY Partners, LLC; *U.S. Private*, pg. 41
CROSSROADS YOUTH & FAMILY SERVICES, INC.; *U.S. Private*, pg. 1108
CROSS SOUND CABLE COMPANY, LLC—See Argo Infrastructure Partners LLC; *U.S. Private*, pg. 320
CROSS-SOUND FERRY SERVICES; *U.S. Private*, pg. 1105
CROSS-STRAIT INFORMATION CONSUMPTION INSTITUTE (XIAMEN) CO., LTD.—See Beijing E-Hualu Information Technology Co., Ltd.; *Int'l*, pg. 949
CROSS STREET SERVICE INC.; *U.S. Private*, pg. 1105
CROSS SURETY, INC.—See Cross Financial Corporation; *U.S. Private*, pg. 1105
CROSS SYSTEMS INGENIERIE—See Micropole SA; *Int'l*, pg. 4880
CROSS SYSTEMS SUISSE SA—See Micropole SA; *Int'l*, pg. 4880
CROSSTATES INSURANCE CONSULTANTS; *U.S. Private*, pg. 1108
CROSSTEC GROUP HOLDINGS LIMITED; *Int'l*, pg. 1856
CROSS TECHNOLOGIES PLC—See Checkit plc; *Int'l*, pg. 1459
CROSSTEX INTERNATIONAL INC.—See STERIS plc; *Int'l*, pg. 7209
CROSS TIMBERS ENERGY SERVICES, INC.—See Exxon Mobil Corporation; *U.S. Public*, pg. 813
CROSS TIMBERS ROYALTY TRUST; *U.S. Public*, pg. 595
CROSSUSA, INC.—See American CyberSystems, Inc.; *U.S. Private*, pg. 229
CROSS VETPHARM GROUP LIMITED—See Zoetis, Inc.; *U.S. Public*, pg. 2409
CROSSVIEW, INC.—See GXO Logistics, Inc.; *U.S. Public*, pg. 975
CROSSVILLE, INC.—See Paceline Equity Partners LLC; *U.S. Public*, pg. 3064
CROSSWELL INTERNATIONAL CORP; *U.S. Private*, pg. 1108
CROSSWIND INDUSTRIES, INC.—See Archer-Daniels-Midland Company; *U.S. Public*, pg. 184
CROSSWIND PETFOODS, INC.—See Archer-Daniels-Midland Company; *U.S. Public*, pg. 184
CROSSWINDS FURNITURE COMPANY; *U.S. Private*, pg. 1108
CROSSWIND TRANSMISSION, LLC—See NRG Energy, Inc.; *U.S. Public*, pg. 1549
CROSSWOOD SA; *Int'l*, pg. 1856
CROSSWORD CYBERSECURITY PLC; *Int'l*, pg. 1856
CROSWELL BUS LINES, INC.; *U.S. Private*, pg. 1108

CROTHALL HEALTHCARE INC.—See Compass Group PLC; *Int'l*, pg. 1751
CROTHALL SERVICES GROUP, INC.—See Compass Group PLC; *Int'l*, pg. 1751
CROTON AUTO PARK; *U.S. Private*, pg. 1108
CROTONE CRUISE PORT S.R.L.—See Global Yatirim Holding A.S.; *Int'l*, pg. 3002
CROTON EQUITIES INC.—See Barrier Motor Fuels Inc.; *U.S. Private*, pg. 480
CROTON HOLDING COMPANY; *U.S. Private*, pg. 1108
CROTTY INSURANCE BROKERS LIMITED—See Brown & Brown, Inc.; *U.S. Public*, pg. 400
CROUCH SUPPLY COMPANY, INC.; *U.S. Private*, pg. 1108
CROUNSE CORPORATION; *U.S. Private*, pg. 1108
CROUSE FORD SALES INC.; *U.S. Private*, pg. 1109
CROUSTIFRANCE BENELUX N.V.—See Vandemoortele N.V.; *Int'l*, pg. 8128
CROUSTIFRANCE S.A.—See Vandemoortele N.V.; *Int'l*, pg. 8128
CROUSTIFRANCE S.A.—See Vandemoortele N.V.; *Int'l*, pg. 8128
CROUZET AUTOMATISMES SAS—See LBO France S.a.r.l.; *Int'l*, pg. 4429
CROUZET GMBH—See LBO France S.a.r.l.; *Int'l*, pg. 4429
CROW-BURLINGAME CO. INC.—See Replacement Parts Inc.; *U.S. Private*, pg. 3401
CROW-BURLINGAME CO. INC.—See Replacement Parts Inc.; *U.S. Private*, pg. 3401
CROW-BURLINGAME CO.—See Replacement Parts Inc.; *U.S. Private*, pg. 3401
CROW BURLINGAME OF CONWAY INC.—See Replacement Parts Inc.; *U.S. Private*, pg. 3401
CROWCON DETECTION INSTRUMENTS LIMITED—See Halma plc; *Int'l*, pg. 3231
CROWCON DETECTION INSTRUMENTS LTD.—See Halma plc; *Int'l*, pg. 3231
CROWDCARE B.V.—See Live Nation Entertainment, Inc.; *U.S. Public*, pg. 1328
CROWDCOMPASS, L.L.C.—See Blackstone Inc.; *U.S. Public*, pg. 353
CROWDCUBE LIMITED; *Int'l*, pg. 1857
CROWDER CONSTRUCTION COMPANY; *U.S. Private*, pg. 1109
CROWDICITY LIMITED—See Thoma Bravo, L.P.; *U.S. Private*, pg. 4149
CROWDSPARK LTD; *Int'l*, pg. 1857
CROWDSTAR, INC.—See Electronic Arts Inc.; *U.S. Public*, pg. 724
CROWDSTRIKE HOLDINGS, INC.; *U.S. Public*, pg. 596
CROWDVISION, INC.—See Skyfii Limited; *Int'l*, pg. 6994
CROWDVISION LIMITED—See Skyfii Limited; *Int'l*, pg. 6994
CROWDWORKS INC.; *Int'l*, pg. 1857
CROWE FORD SALES CO—See Morse Operations Inc.; *U.S. Private*, pg. 2790
CROWE GROUP LLP; *U.S. Private*, pg. 1109
CROWE HORWATH AUSTRALASIA LTD.—See Financial Index Australia Pty Ltd.; *Int'l*, pg. 2665
CROWE HORWATH INTERNATIONAL; *U.S. Private*, pg. 1109
CROWE HORWATH LLP; *U.S. Private*, pg. 1109
CROWE HORWATH (NZ) LTD—See Financial Index Australia Pty Ltd.; *Int'l*, pg. 2665
CROWELL ADVERTISING, MARKETING AND PR; *U.S. Private*, pg. 1109
CROWELL & COMPANY INC.; *U.S. Private*, pg. 1109
CROWELL DEVELOPMENT CORP.; *Int'l*, pg. 1857
CROWELL & MORING LLP; *U.S. Private*, pg. 1109
CROWE LLP; *U.S. Private*, pg. 1109
CROWELL, WEEDON & CO.—See D.A. Davidson Companies; *U.S. Private*, pg. 1140
CROW FAMILY HOLDINGS REALTY PARTNERS, L.P.; *U.S. Private*, pg. 1109
CROWLEY CHEMICAL COMPANY, INC.—See Palo Duro Capital, LLC; *U.S. Public*, pg. 3082
CROWLEY FOODS, INC.—See Catamount Dairy Holdings L.P.; *U.S. Private*, pg. 787
CROWLEY FOODS, INC.—See Catamount Dairy Holdings L.P.; *U.S. Private*, pg. 787
THE CROWLEY GROUP INC.; *U.S. Private*, pg. 4017
CROWLEY MARITIME CORPORATION; *U.S. Private*, pg. 1109
CROWLEY MICROGRAPHICS, INC.; *U.S. Private*, pg. 1110
CROWLEY PHYSICAL THERAPY CLINIC, INC.—See Select Medical Holdings Corporation; *U.S. Public*, pg. 1857
CROWLEY STAR—See Alden Global Capital LLC; *U.S. Private*, pg. 156
CROWLEY TAR PRODUCTS CO., INC.—See Palo Duro Capital, LLC; *U.S. Public*, pg. 3082
CROWL, MARKETING & CREATIVE, INC.; *U.S. Private*, pg. 1109
CROWN ACURA/NISSAN, LLC—See Asbury Automotive Group, Inc.; *U.S. Public*, pg. 209
CROWN ADVANCED MATERIAL CO., LTD.; *Int'l*, pg. 1857

CROWN AEROSOLS NEDERLAND BV—See Crown Holdings, Inc.; *U.S. Public*, pg. 597
CROWN AEROSOLS UK LIMITED—See Crown Holdings, Inc.; *U.S. Public*, pg. 597
CROWN AMERICAS LLC—See Crown Holdings, Inc.; *U.S. Public*, pg. 597
CROWN APPRAISAL GROUP—See BBG Inc.; *U.S. Private*, pg. 498
CROWN ARTIST BRUSH LTD—See Lindengruppen AB; *Int'l*, pg. 4510
CROWN ASIA CHEMICALS CORPORATION; *Int'l*, pg. 1857
CROWN ASIA PACIFIC HOLDINGS, LTD.—See Crown Holdings, Inc.; *U.S. Public*, pg. 598
CROWN ASIA PROPERTIES, INC.—See Vista Land & Lifescapes, Inc.; *Int'l*, pg. 8254
CROWN AUDIO, INC.—See Samsung Group; *Int'l*, pg. 6512
CROWN AUTO DEALERSHIPS, INC.; *U.S. Private*, pg. 1110
CROWN AUTO GROUP—See Asbury Automotive Group, Inc.; *U.S. Public*, pg. 209
CROWN AUTOMOBILE COMPANY INC. *U.S. Private*, pg. 1110
CROWN AUTOMOTIVE SALES CO. INC.; *U.S. Private*, pg. 1110
CROWN-BAELE NV/SA; *Int'l*, pg. 1858
CROWN BATTERY MANUFACTURING CO. INC.; *U.S. Private*, pg. 1110
CROWN BAUS CAPITAL CORP.; *U.S. Private*, pg. 1110
CROWN BEERS INDIA LIMITED—See Anheuser-Busch InBev SA/NV; *Int'l*, pg. 466
CROWN BEVCAN ESPANA S.L.—See Crown Holdings, Inc.; *U.S. Public*, pg. 597
CROWN BEVCAN FRANCE SAS—See Crown Holdings, Inc.; *U.S. Public*, pg. 597
CROWN BEVCAN TURKIYE AMBALAJ SANAYI VE TICARET—See Crown Holdings, Inc.; *U.S. Public*, pg. 597
CROWN BEVERAGE CANS BEIJING LIMITED—See Crown Holdings, Inc.; *U.S. Public*, pg. 597
CROWN BEVERAGE CANS (CAMBODIA) LIMITED—See Crown Holdings, Inc.; *U.S. Public*, pg. 597
CROWN BEVERAGE CANS HK LTD.—See Crown Holdings, Inc.; *U.S. Public*, pg. 598
CROWN BEVERAGE CANS MALAYSIA SDN BHD—See Crown Holdings, Inc.; *U.S. Public*, pg. 597
CROWN BEVERAGE CANS SIHANOUKVILLE LIMITED—See Crown Holdings, Inc.; *U.S. Public*, pg. 597
CROWN BEVERAGE CANS SINGAPORE PTE. LTD.—See Crown Holdings, Inc.; *U.S. Public*, pg. 597
CROWN BIOSCIENCE, INC.—See JSR Corp.; *Int'l*, pg. 4013
CROWN BLUE LINE LIMITED—See TUI AG; *Int'l*, pg. 7964
CROWN BUICK GMC; *U.S. Private*, pg. 1110
CROWN BUILDING MAINTENANCE CO.—See ABM Industries, Inc.; *U.S. Public*, pg. 26
CROWN CANADIAN HOLDINGS ULC—See Crown Holdings, Inc.; *U.S. Public*, pg. 598
CROWN CAPITAL INVESTMENTS LLC; *U.S. Private*, pg. 1110
CROWN CAPITAL PARTNERS, INC.; *Int'l*, pg. 1857
CROWN CAPITAL SECURITIES LP—See LPL Financial Holdings Inc.; *U.S. Public*, pg. 1343
CROWN CASTLE INC.; *U.S. Public*, pg. 596
CROWN CASTLE NG WEST LLC—See Crown Castle Inc.; *U.S. Public*, pg. 596
CROWN CASTLE OPERATING COMPANY—See Crown Castle Inc.; *U.S. Public*, pg. 596
CROWN CASTLE USA INC.—See Crown Castle Inc.; *U.S. Public*, pg. 596
CROWN CENTER REDEVELOPMENT CORP—See Hallmark Cards, Inc.; *U.S. Private*, pg. 1844
CROWN CENTRAL HOLDINGS LIMITED—See Chu Kong Petroleum and Natural Gas Steel Pipe Holdings Limited; *Int'l*, pg. 1589
CROWN CENTRAL LLC—See Rosemore Inc.; *U.S. Private*, pg. 3483
CROWN CHICKEN LIMITED—See Cranswick Plc; *Int'l*, pg. 1828
CROWN CHRYSLER JEEP, KIA, & EUROCARS - MERCEDES BENZ; *U.S. Private*, pg. 1110
CROWN CLOSURES SPAIN, S.L.—See Crown Holdings, Inc.; *U.S. Public*, pg. 598
CROWN COAL & COKE CO. INC.; *U.S. Private*, pg. 1110
CROWN COCO INC.; *U.S. Private*, pg. 1110
CROWN COLOMBIANA, S.A.—See Crown Holdings, Inc.; *U.S. Public*, pg. 598
CROWN CO., LTD.—See Adeka Corporation; *Int'l*, pg. 142
CROWN COMERCIAL DE ENVASES, S.L.—See Crown Holdings, Inc.; *U.S. Public*, pg. 598
CROWN COMMERCIAL FRANCE SAS—See Crown Holdings, Inc.; *U.S. Public*, pg. 597
CROWN COMMERCIAL GERMANY GMBH & CO. KG—See Crown Holdings, Inc.; *U.S. Public*, pg. 597
CROWN COMMERCIAL NETHERLANDS B.V.—See Crown Holdings, Inc.; *U.S. Public*, pg. 597

CROWN COMMERCIAL POLSKA SP. Z.O.O.—See Crown Holdings, Inc.; *U.S. Public*, pg. 598
CROWN COMMUNITIES, INC.—See D.R. Horton, Inc.; *U.S. Public*, pg. 619
CROWN COMMUNITIES, LLC; *U.S. Private*, pg. 1110
CROWN CONFECTIONERY CO., LTD.—See Crown Confectionery Co., Ltd.; *Int'l*, pg. 1857
CROWN CONFECTIONERY CO., LTD.; *Int'l*, pg. 1857
CROWN CONSULTING, INC.; *U.S. Private*, pg. 1110
CROWN CORK COMPANY (MOZAMBIQUE) LDA—See Nampak Ltd.; *Int'l*, pg. 5136
CROWN CORK & SEAL AVERY TECHNICAL CENTER—See Crown Holdings, Inc.; *U.S. Public*, pg. 597
CROWN CORK & SEAL CO., INC.—See Crown Holdings, Inc.; *U.S. Public*, pg. 597
CROWN CORK & SEAL CO INC. -SUGAR LAND—See Crown Holdings, Inc.; *U.S. Public*, pg. 597
CROWN CORK & SEAL DE PORTUGAL EMBALAGENS S.A.—See Crown Holdings, Inc.; *U.S. Public*, pg. 598
CROWN CORK & SEAL DEUTSCHLAND HOLDINGS GMBH—See Crown Holdings, Inc.; *U.S. Public*, pg. 598
CROWN CORK & SEAL USA, INC. - MASSILLON—See Crown Holdings, Inc.; *U.S. Public*, pg. 597
CROWN CORK & SEAL USA, INC.—See Crown Holdings, Inc.; *U.S. Public*, pg. 597
CROWN CORR, INC.; *U.S. Private*, pg. 1110
CROWN CRAFTS, INC.; *U.S. Public*, pg. 596
CROWN CRAFTS INFANT PRODUCTS, INC.—See Crown Crafts, Inc.; *U.S. Public*, pg. 596
CROWN C SUPPLY CO., INC.—See Leonard Green & Partners, L.P.; *U.S. Private*, pg. 2429
CROWN DISTRIBUTING INC.; *U.S. Private*, pg. 1110
CROWN DIVERSIFIED INDUSTRIES; *U.S. Private*, pg. 1110
CROWN DODGE OF FAYETTEVILLE; *U.S. Private*, pg. 1111
CROWN DODGE; *U.S. Private*, pg. 1110
CROWN DOOR CORP.—See Owens Corning; *U.S. Public*, pg. 1626
CROWNE GROUP LLC; *U.S. Private*, pg. 1112
CROWN ELECTROKINETICS CORP.; *U.S. Public*, pg. 596
CROWN EMBALAGENS METALICAS DA AMAZONIA S.A.—See Crown Holdings, Inc.; *U.S. Public*, pg. 597
CROWN EMBALAGENS METALICAS DA AMAZONIA S.A.—See Evora S.A.; *Int'l*, pg. 2573
CROWN EMBALLAGE FRANCE SAS—See Crown Holdings, Inc.; *U.S. Public*, pg. 597
CROWN EMIRATES COMPANY LIMITED—See Crown Holdings, Inc.; *U.S. Public*, pg. 597
CROWN ENTERPRISES INC.; *U.S. Private*, pg. 1111
CROWN ENTERPRISES INC.—See CenTra, Inc.; *U.S. Private*, pg. 818
CROWN ENVASES MEXICO, S.A. DE C.V.—See Crown Holdings, Inc.; *U.S. Public*, pg. 598
CROWNE PLAZA BIRMINGHAM CITY CENTRE—See InterContinental Hotels Group PLC; *Int'l*, pg. 3736
CROWNE PLAZA LLC—See InterContinental Hotels Group PLC; *Int'l*, pg. 3737
CROWNE PLAZA OLD TOWN ALEXANDRIA—See InterContinental Hotels Group PLC; *Int'l*, pg. 3737
THE CROWNE PLAZA TIMES SQUARE MANHATTAN; *U.S. Private*, pg. 4017
CROWN EQUIPMENT CORPORATION; *U.S. Private*, pg. 1111
CROWN EQUIPMENT CORPORATION; *U.S. Private*, pg. 1111
CROWN EQUIPMENT PTY LTD—See Crown Equipment Corporation; *U.S. Private*, pg. 1111
CROWN EQUITIES, INC.; *Int'l*, pg. 1857
CROWN EQUITY HOLDINGS INC.; *U.S. Public*, pg. 597
CROWN EQUITY HOLDINGS INC.; *U.S. Public*, pg. 597
CROWN EUROPEAN HOLDINGS SA—See Crown Holdings, Inc.; *U.S. Public*, pg. 598
CROWN FENCE COMPANY; *U.S. Private*, pg. 1111
CROWN FOODCAN GERMANY GMBH—See Crown Holdings, Inc.; *U.S. Public*, pg. 597
CROWN FOOD ESPANA, S.A.U.—See Crown Holdings, Inc.; *U.S. Public*, pg. 599
CROWN FOODS LLC; *U.S. Public*, pg. 1111
CROWN FORD INC.; *U.S. Private*, pg. 1111
CROWN FORD LINCOLN MERCURY, INC.; *U.S. Private*, pg. 1111
CROWN GABELSTAPLER GMBH & CO. KG—See Crown Equipment Corporation; *U.S. Private*, pg. 1111
CROWN GAMING MEXICO S.A. DE C.V.—See Novomatic AG; *Int'l*, pg. 5467
CROWN GARDENEX CO., LTD.—See Beauty Kadan Co., Ltd.; *Int'l*, pg. 935
CROWN GOLD, INC.—See Rosemore Inc.; *U.S. Private*, pg. 3483
CROWN GOLF PROPERTIES, LP—See Henry Crown & Company; *U.S. Private*, pg. 1918
CROWN GRAPHIC NV/SA.—See Nissha Co., Ltd.; *Int'l*, pg. 5372
THE CROWN GROUP CO.—See PPG Industries, Inc.; *U.S. Public*, pg. 1710

THE CROWN GROUP—See Crown Worldwide Holdings Ltd.; *Int'l*, pg. 1858
CROWN HARDWARE, INC.; *U.S. Private*, pg. 1111
CROWN HEALTH CARE LAUNDRY SERVICES—See The Pritzker Organization, LLC; *U.S. Private*, pg. 4100
CROWN HELLAS CAN PACKAGING SA—See Crown Holdings, Inc.; *U.S. Public*, pg. 597
CROWN HELLAS PACKAGING CAN SA—See Crown Holdings, Inc.; *U.S. Public*, pg. 597
CROWN HOLDINGS, INC.; *U.S. Public*, pg. 597
CROWN HOLDINGS ITALIA SRL—See Crown Holdings, Inc.; *U.S. Public*, pg. 598
CROWN HOUSE TECHNOLOGIES LIMITED—See Laing O'Rourke Plc; *Int'l*, pg. 4396
CROWNIA HOLDINGS LTD.; *Int'l*, pg. 1858
CROWN I ENTERPRISES INC.—See Sysco Corporation; *U.S. Public*, pg. 1973
CROWN IMGALLAGGI ITALIA SRL—See Crown Holdings, Inc.; *U.S. Public*, pg. 598
CROWN IMPORTS LLC—See Constellation Brands, Inc.; *U.S. Public*, pg. 571
CROWN INTERNATIONAL CORPORATION LIMITED; *Int'l*, pg. 1857
CROWN INVESTMENTS CORPORATION OF SASKATCHEWAN; *Int'l*, pg. 1857
CROWN INVESTMENTS LTD—See Metro Holdings, Limited; *Int'l*, pg. 4860
CROWN IRON WORKS COMPANY—See Gilbert Global Equity Partners; *U.S. Private*, pg. 1699
CROWN JOY INTERNATIONAL LTD.—See FSP Technology Inc.; *Int'l*, pg. 2800
CROWN KAMIKOGYO CO., LTD.—See Dynapac Co., Ltd.; *Int'l*, pg. 2241
CROWN LABORATORIES, INC.; *U.S. Private*, pg. 1111
CROWN LIFTERS LTD.; *Int'l*, pg. 1857
CROWN LIFTS LIMITED—See KONE Oyj; *Int'l*, pg. 4247
CROWN LIFT TRUCKS—See Crown Equipment Corporation; *U.S. Private*, pg. 1111
CROWN LINEN SERVICE INCORPORATED; *U.S. Private*, pg. 1111
CROWN LIQUORS OF BROWARD INC.; *U.S. Private*, pg. 1111
CROWN MANUFACTURING CORP.—See Mitsubishi Chemical Group Corporation; *Int'l*, pg. 4936
CROWN MARKETING GROUP, INC.; *U.S. Private*, pg. 1111
CROWN MATTING TECHNOLOGIES—See Ludlow Composites Corporation; *U.S. Private*, pg. 2512
CROWN MEDIA HOLDINGS, INC.—See Hallmark Cards, Inc.; *U.S. Private*, pg. 1844
CROWN MEDIA UNITED STATES LLC—See Hallmark Cards, Inc.; *U.S. Private*, pg. 1844
CROWN MELBOURNE LIMITED—See Blackstone Inc.; *U.S. Public*, pg. 352
CROWN METAL PACKAGING CANADA LTEE.—See Crown Holdings, Inc.; *U.S. Public*, pg. 598
CROWN MICRO INC.—See BOLData Technology, Inc.; *U.S. Private*, pg. 610
CROWN MIDDLE EAST CAN CO. LTD.—See Crown Holdings, Inc.; *U.S. Public*, pg. 597
CROWN MILLION INDUSTRIES (INTERNATIONAL) LIMITED—See Value Enhancement Partners B.V.; *Int'l*, pg. 8124
CROWN & MITRE (CARLISLE) LIMITED—See Peel Hotels Plc; *Int'l*, pg. 5779
CROWN MOTORS II LLC—See Crown Motors Ltd.; *U.S. Private*, pg. 1111
CROWN MOTORS LTD.; *U.S. Private*, pg. 1111
CROWN MOTORS LTD—See Inchcape plc; *Int'l*, pg. 3647
CROWN MOTORS OF CLEARWATER, INC.—See Crown Auto Dealerships, Inc.; *U.S. Private*, pg. 1110
CROWN MOTORS OF REDDING; *U.S. Private*, pg. 1111
CROWN MOVING & STORAGE INC.—See Wheaton Van Lines, Inc.; *U.S. Private*, pg. 4505
CROWN NATIONAL (PTY) LIMITED—See The Bidvest Group Limited; *Int'l*, pg. 7624
CROWN OBRIST AG—See Crown Holdings, Inc.; *U.S. Public*, pg. 598
CROWN OF HOLLAND B.V.—See SunOpta Inc.; *Int'l*, pg. 7319
CROWN OPERATIONS INTERNATIONAL, LTD.—See Eastman Chemical Company; *U.S. Public*, pg. 706
CROWN PACKAGING CORP.; *U.S. Private*, pg. 1111
CROWN PACKAGING EUROPEAN DIVISION GMBH—See Crown Holdings, Inc.; *U.S. Public*, pg. 599
CROWN PACKAGING EUROPE GMBH—See Crown Holdings, Inc.; *U.S. Public*, pg. 598
CROWN PACKAGING INTERNATIONAL INC.; *U.S. Private*, pg. 1111
CROWN PACKAGING IRELAND LTD.—See Crown Holdings, Inc.; *U.S. Public*, pg. 598
CROWN PACKAGING LUX I S.A.R.L.—See Crown Holdings, Inc.; *U.S. Public*, pg. 598
CROWN PACKAGING MAROC—See Crown Holdings, Inc.; *U.S. Public*, pg. 598
CROWN PACKAGING POLSKA SP.Z.O.O.—See Crown Holdings, Inc.; *U.S. Public*, pg. 597

CROWN PACKAGING UK PLC—See Crown Holdings, Inc.; *U.S. Public*, pg. 598
CROWN PAINTS KENYA LTD.; *Int'l*, pg. 1858
CROWN PAINTS KENYA PLC; *Int'l*, pg. 1858
CROWN PAINTS LTD.—See Hempel A/S; *Int'l*, pg. 3341
CROWN PARTS AND MACHINE INC.; *U.S. Private*, pg. 1111
CROWNPEAK TECHNOLOGY, INC.; *U.S. Private*, pg. 1112
CROWNPEAK TECHNOLOGY UK—See CrownPeak Technology, Inc.; *U.S. Private*, pg. 1113
CROWN PERTH—See Blackstone Inc.; *U.S. Public*, pg. 352
CROWN PLAZA LTD—See Africa Israel Investments Ltd.; *Int'l*, pg. 190
CROWN POINT ENERGIA S.A.—See Crown Point Energy Inc.; *Int'l*, pg. 1858
CROWN POINT ENERGY INC.; *Int'l*, pg. 1858
CROWN POINT LTD.—See Unaka Company Inc.; *U.S. Private*, pg. 4279
CROWN POINT REGIONAL CENTER, LLC—See Modern Land (China) Co., Ltd.; *Int'l*, pg. 5014
CROWN POINT SURGERY CENTER, LLC—See Tenet Healthcare Corporation; *U.S. Public*, pg. 2010
CROWN POWER & EQUIPMENT CO.; *U.S. Private*, pg. 1112
CROWN PRINCE, INC.; *U.S. Private*, pg. 1112
CROWN PRODUCTS COMPANY INC.; *U.S. Private*, pg. 1112
CROWN PRODUCTS, INC.—See ShoreView Industries, LLC; *U.S. Private*, pg. 3642
CROWN PRODUCTS, LLC—See EBSCO Industries, Inc.; *U.S. Private*, pg. 1324
CROWN PRODUCTS & SERVICES, INC.—See Merit Capital Partners; *U.S. Private*, pg. 2674
THE CROWN PROPERTY BUREAU; *Int'l*, pg. 7636
CROWN PROPTECH ACQUISITIONS; *U.S. Public*, pg. 600
THE CROWN PUBLISHING GROUP—See Bertelsmann SE & Co. KGaA; *Int'l*, pg. 991
CROWN REALTY OF KANSAS INC.; *U.S. Private*, pg. 1112
CROWN RELOCATIONS—See Crown Worldwide Holdings Ltd., *Int'l*, pg. 1858
CROWN RESORTS LIMITED—See Blackstone Inc.; *U.S. Public*, pg. 352
CROWN RESORTS, LTD.; *U.S. Private*, pg. 1112
CROWN ROLL LEAF INC.; *U.S. Private*, pg. 1112
CROWN ROOFING (CENTRES) LIMITED—See Brickability Group plc; *Int'l*, pg. 1151
CROWN SEAL PUBLIC COMPANY LIMITED—See Toyo Seikan Group Holdings, Ltd.; *Int'l*, pg. 7856
CROWN SENEGAL—See Crown Holdings, Inc.; *U.S. Public*, pg. 598
CROWN SERVICES INC.; *U.S. Private*, pg. 1112
CROWN SIEM—See Crown Holdings, Inc.; *U.S. Public*, pg. 597
CROWN SNACK CO., LTD.—See Crown Confectionery Co., Ltd.; *Int'l*, pg. 1857
CROWN SPECIALITY PACKAGING BELGIE NV—See Crown Holdings, Inc.; *U.S. Public*, pg. 598
CROWN SPECIALITY PACKAGING B.V.—See Crown Holdings, Inc.; *U.S. Public*, pg. 598
CROWN SPECIALITY PACKAGING UK PLC—See Crown Holdings, Inc.; *U.S. Public*, pg. 598
CROWN SPECIALTY PACKAGING USA, INC.—See Crown Holdings, Inc.; *U.S. Public*, pg. 597
CROWN STEEL SALES INCORPORATED; *U.S. Private*, pg. 1112
CROWN SYDNEY PTY LTD—See Blackstone Inc.; *U.S. Public*, pg. 352
CROWN TECHNOLOGIES GMBH—See Novomatic AG; *Int'l*, pg. 5467
CROWNTONKA CALIFORNIA, INC.—See Rainey Road Holdings, Inc.; *U.S. Private*, pg. 3348
CROWNTONKA, INC.—See Rainey Road Holdings, Inc.; *U.S. Private*, pg. 3347
CROWN TOURS LIMITED; *Int'l*, pg. 1858
CROWN UK HOLDINGS LTD—See Crown Holdings, Inc.; *U.S. Public*, pg. 598
CROWN VAN UK LIMITED—See Avingtrans plc; *Int'l*, pg. 743
CROWN VAN GELDER B.V.—See Andlinger & Company, Inc.; *U.S. Private*, pg. 278
CROWN VERPAKKING BELGIE NV—See Crown Holdings, Inc.; *U.S. Public*, pg. 598
CROWN VERPAKKING NEDERLAND N.V.—See Crown Holdings, Inc.; *U.S. Public*, pg. 598
CROWN VINALIMEX PACKAGING LTD.—See Crown Holdings, Inc.; *U.S. Public*, pg. 598
CROWN VINALIMEX PACKAGING LTD.—See John Swire & Sons Limited; *Int'l*, pg. 3980
CROWN VOGEL AG—See Crown Holdings, Inc.; *U.S. Public*, pg. 598
CROWN WAREHOUSING & LOGISTICS INC—See Peoples Services Inc.; *U.S. Private*, pg. 3142
CROWN WINE CELLARS LTD—See Crown Worldwide Holdings Ltd.; *Int'l*, pg. 1858
CROWN WORLDWIDE HOLDINGS LTD.; *Int'l*, pg. 1858

CROWN WORLDWIDE MOVING & STORAGE COMPANY; *U.S. Private*, pg. 1112
CROWN WORLDWIDE OY—See Crown Worldwide Holdings Ltd.; *Int'l*, pg. 1858
CROWN WORLDWIDE SRL—See Crown Worldwide Holdings Ltd.; *Int'l*, pg. 1858
CROW TECHNOLOGIES 1977 LTD.; *Int'l*, pg. 1857
CROWTHER ROOFING & SHEET METAL OF FLORIDA, INC.—See FirstService Corporation; *Int'l*, pg. 2691
CROW WING COOPERATIVE POWER & LIGHT COMPANY; *U.S. Private*, pg. 1109
CROXTON PARK HOTEL (BMG) PTY LTD—See Woolworths Group Limited; *Int'l*, pg. 8451
CROYDEX GROUP LTD.—See Norcros plc; *Int'l*, pg. 5415
CROYDON CLOCKTOWER; *Int'l*, pg. 1858
CROZER-KEYSTONE HEALTH SYSTEM INC.; *U.S. Private*, pg. 1113
CROZIER FINE ARTS, INC.—See Iron Mountain Incorporated; *U.S. Public*, pg. 1172
CROZIER FINE ARTS LIMITED—See Iron Mountain Incorporated; *U.S. Public*, pg. 1172
CROZIER SCHWEIZ AG—See Iron Mountain Incorporated; *U.S. Public*, pg. 1172
CRP DE MEXICO S.A. DE C.V.—See CRP Industries Inc.; *U.S. Private*, pg. 1113
CR PHUKET (THAILAND) CO., LTD.—See Central Group Company Limited; *Int'l*, pg. 1407
CRP INDUSTRIES INC.; *U.S. Private*, pg. 1113
CRP INDUSTRIES OF CALIFORNIA INC.—See CRP Industries Inc.; *U.S. Private*, pg. 1113
CRP RISK MANAGEMENT LIMITED; *Int'l*, pg. 1858
C&R RACING INC.—See PWR Holdings Limited; *Int'l*, pg. 6126
CR RATCHABURI (THAILAND) CO., LTD.—See Central Group Company Limited; *Int'l*, pg. 1407
CRRC CHANGCHUN RAILWAY VEHICLE CO., LTD.—See CRRC Corporation Limited; *Int'l*, pg. 1858
CRRC CORPORATION LIMITED; *Int'l*, pg. 1858
CRRC DALIAN R&D CO., LTD.—See CRRC Corporation Limited; *Int'l*, pg. 1858
CRRC DATONG CO., LTD.—See CRRC Corporation Limited; *Int'l*, pg. 1858
CRRC NANJING PUZHEN CO., LTD.—See CRRC Corporation Limited; *Int'l*, pg. 1858
CRRC QINGDAO SIFANG CO., LTD.—See CRRC Corporation Limited; *Int'l*, pg. 1858
CRRC SIFANG CO., LTD.—See CRRC Corporation Limited; *Int'l*, pg. 1858
CRRC TANGSHAN CO., LTD.—See CRRC Corporation Limited; *Int'l*, pg. 1858
CRRC TIMES ELECTRIC USA, LLC—See Zhuzhou CRRC Times Electric Co. Ltd.; *Int'l*, pg. 8679
CRRC YANGTZE GROUP., LTD.—See CRRC Corporation Limited; *Int'l*, pg. 1858
CRRC YONGJI ELECTRIC CO., LTD.—See CRRC Corporation Limited; *Int'l*, pg. 1858
CRRC ZHUZHOU INSTITUTE CO., LTD.—See CRRC Corporation Limited; *Int'l*, pg. 1858
CRRC ZIYANG CO., LTD.—See CRRC Corporation Limited; *Int'l*, pg. 1858
C&R RESEARCH, INC.; *U.S. Private*, pg. 703
CRR INDUSTRIES, INC.—See CSX Corporation; *U.S. Public*, pg. 602
CRR INDUSTRIES, INC.—See Norfolk Southern Corporation; *U.S. Public*, pg. 1535
CRR INVESTMENTS, INC.—See CSX Corporation; *U.S. Public*, pg. 602
CRR INVESTMENTS, INC.—See Norfolk Southern Corporation; *U.S. Public*, pg. 1535
CRSA—See LCS Holdings Inc.; *U.S. Private*, pg. 2404
CRS (BEIJING) CLINICAL RESEARCH CO., LIMITED—See ICON plc; *Int'l*, pg. 3584
CRSC RESEARCH & DESIGN INSTITUTE GROUP CO., LTD.—See China Railway Signal & Communication Corporation Ltd.; *Int'l*, pg. 1544
CRSC WANQUAN SIGNAL EQUIPMENT CO., LTD.—See China Railway Signal & Communication Corporation Ltd.; *Int'l*, pg. 1544
CR SEALS INDIA PVT LTD.—See SKF AB; *Int'l*, pg. 6981
CR SERRATURE SPA—See Groupe SFPI SA; *Int'l*, pg. 3111
CRS HOLDING AG; *Int'l*, pg. 1859
CR SOFTWARE LLC—See Fair Isaac Corporation; *U.S. Public*, pg. 820
CRS ONE SOURCE; *U.S. Private*, pg. 1113
CRS PROPPANTS LLC—See Eagle Materials Inc.; *U.S. Public*, pg. 702
CRS S.P.A.—See Derichebourg S.A.; *Int'l*, pg. 2041
C&R STEAKS INC.; *U.S. Private*, pg. 703
CRS TEMPORARY HOUSING—See GenNx360 Capital Partners, L.P.; *U.S. Private*, pg. 1672
CRST FLATBED INC.—See CRST International, Inc.; *U.S. Private*, pg. 1113
CRST FLATBED, INC.—See CRST International, Inc.; *U.S. Private*, pg. 1113
CRST INTERNATIONAL, INC.; *U.S. Private*, pg. 1113
CRST LOGISTICS INC.—See CRST International, Inc.; *U.S. Private*, pg. 1113

CRST MALONE INC.—See CRST International, Inc.; *U.S. Private*, pg. 1113
C & R SYSTEMS, INC.; *U.S. Private*, pg. 701
CRT CONSTRUCTION INC.; *Int'l*, pg. 1859
CRT CUSTOM PRODUCTS, INC.; *U.S. Private*, pg. 1113
CRT GROUP PTY. LTD.—See Aurizon Holdings Limited; *Int'l*, pg. 711
CRT PARTNERS INC.; *U.S. Private*, pg. 1113
CRT REAL ESTATE PTY LTD—See Nutrien Ltd.; *Int'l*, pg. 5492
CRTS, INC.—See New Mountain Capital, LLC; *U.S. Private*, pg. 2900
CRTS INC.; *U.S. Private*, pg. 1113
CR&T VENTURES AB—See Bure Equity AB; *Int'l*, pg. 1221
CR UBON RATCHATHANI (THAILAND) CO., LTD.—See Central Group Company Limited; *Int'l*, pg. 1407
CRUCELL HOLLAND B.V.—See Johnson & Johnson; *U.S. Public*, pg. 1194
CRUCELL N.V.—See Johnson & Johnson; *U.S. Public*, pg. 1194
CRUCELL SPAIN, S.A.—See Johnson & Johnson; *U.S. Public*, pg. 1194
CRUCELL UK LTD.—See Johnson & Johnson; *U.S. Public*, pg. 1194
CRUCELL VACCINES INC.—See Johnson & Johnson; *U.S. Public*, pg. 1195
CRUCIAL INNOVATIONS, CORP.; *Int'l*, pg. 1859
CRUCIAL INTERACTIVE INC.—See PopReach Corporation; *Int'l*, pg. 5921
CRUCIAL PARADIGM PTY LTD—See Deluxe Corporation; *U.S. Public*, pg. 652
CRUCIALTEC CO., LTD.; *Int'l*, pg. 1859
CRUCIALTEC USA, INC.—See CrucialTec Co., Ltd.; *Int'l*, pg. 1859
CRUCIAL VACUUM; *U.S. Private*, pg. 1113
CRUCIBLE ACQUISITION CORPORATION; *U.S. Public*, pg. 600
CRUCIBLE & CUPEL MANUFACTURING—See Morgan Advanced Materials plc; *Int'l*, pg. 5041
CRUCIBLE INDUSTRIES LLC; *U.S. Private*, pg. 1113
CRU DATA SECURITY GROUP, LLC; *U.S. Private*, pg. 1113
CRUDECORP ASA; *Int'l*, pg. 1859
CRUDELI SA; *Int'l*, pg. 1859
CRUDUP OIL COMPANY INC.; *U.S. Private*, pg. 1113
CRUISE AMERICA, INC.; *U.S. Private*, pg. 1113
CRUISE CANADA, INC.—See Cruise America, Inc.; *U.S. Private*, pg. 1113
CRUISE CAR INC.; *U.S. Private*, pg. 1114
THE CRUISE CLUB TOKYO INC.—See Nippon Yusen Kabushiki Kaisha; *Int'l*, pg. 5359
CRUISE LINE HOLDINGS CO.—See LVMH Moet Hennessy Louis Vuitton SE; *Int'l*, pg. 4601
CRUISE LINES INTERNATIONAL ASSOCIATION; *U.S. Private*, pg. 1114
CRUISE MUNICH GMBH—See General Motors Company; *U.S. Public*, pg. 923
CRUISE NOW INC.—See 3i Group plc; *Int'l*, pg. 8
CRUISEONE AND CRUISES INC.—See World Travel Holdings, Inc.; *U.S. Private*, pg. 4567
CRUISE PLANET CO., LTD.—See H.I.S. Co., Ltd.; *Int'l*, pg. 3195
CRUISER RV, LLC—See Thor Industries, Inc.; *U.S. Public*, pg. 2156
CRUISERS GRILL; *U.S. Private*, pg. 1114
CRUISESHIPCENTERS INTERNATIONAL INC.—See Expedia Group, Inc.; *U.S. Public*, pg. 809
CRUISESHIPCENTERS USA INC.—See Expedia Group, Inc.; *U.S. Public*, pg. 809
CRUISES INTERNATIONAL SA PROPRIETARY LIMITED—See The Bidvest Group Limited; *Int'l*, pg. 7624
CRUISESONLY INC.—See World Travel Holdings, Inc.; *U.S. Private*, pg. 4567
CRUISETOUR AG—See TUI AG; *Int'l*, pg. 7964
CRUMBLEY PAPER CO. INC.; *U.S. Private*, pg. 1114
CRUMBS BAKE SHOP, INC.—See Fisher Enterprises, LLC; *U.S. Private*, pg. 1534
CRUMBS BROADWAY LLC—See Fisher Enterprises, LLC; *U.S. Private*, pg. 1534
CRUMBS COLUMBUS LLC—See Fisher Enterprises, LLC; *U.S. Private*, pg. 1534
CRUMBS FEDERAL STREET, LLC—See Fisher Enterprises, LLC; *U.S. Private*, pg. 1534
CRUMBS GARMENT CENTER LLC—See Fisher Enterprises, LLC; *U.S. Private*, pg. 1534
CRUMBS GRAND CENTRAL LLC—See Fisher Enterprises, LLC; *U.S. Private*, pg. 1534
CRUMBS LEXINGTON LLC—See Fisher Enterprises, LLC; *U.S. Private*, pg. 1534
CRUMBS TIMES SQUARE LLC—See Fisher Enterprises, LLC; *U.S. Private*, pg. 1534
CRUMBS UNION SQUARE LLC—See Fisher Enterprises, LLC; *U.S. Private*, pg. 1534
CRUMBS UNION STATION LLC—See Fisher Enterprises, LLC; *U.S. Private*, pg. 1534
CRUM ELECTRIC SUPPLY CO., INC.; *U.S. Private*, pg. 1114

CRUM & FORSTER HOLDINGS CORP.—See Fairfax Financial Holdings Limited; *Int'l*, pg. 2606
CRUM & FORSTER INSURANCE COMPANY—See Fairfax Financial Holdings Limited; *Int'l*, pg. 2606
CRUM & FORSTER INSURANCE—See Fairfax Financial Holdings Limited; *Int'l*, pg. 2606
CRUM & FORSTER PET INSURANCE GROUP—See Fairfax Financial Holdings Limited; *Int'l*, pg. 2606
CRUM-HALSTED AGENCY, INC.—See New Mountain Capital, LLC; *U.S. Private*, pg. 2901
CRUMP GROUP, INC.—See J.C. Flowers & Co. LLC; *U.S. Private*, pg. 2159
CRUMP INSURANCE SERVICES, INC.—See Truist Financial Corporation; *U.S. Public*, pg. 2200
CRUMP LIFE INSURANCE SERVICES, INC.—See Truist Financial Corporation; *U.S. Public*, pg. 2200
CRUNCHFISH AB; *Int'l*, pg. 1859
CRUNCHIES NATURAL FOOD COMPANY LLC—See Mitsubishi Corporation; *Int'l*, pg. 4940
CRUNCH, LLC—See TPG Capital, L.P.; *U.S. Public*, pg. 2176
CRUNCH NEW MONTGOMERY, LLC—See TPG Capital, L.P.; *U.S. Public*, pg. 2176
CRUNCH PAK; *U.S. Private*, pg. 1114
CRUNCHY LOGISTICS; *U.S. Private*, pg. 1114
CRUSADER ASSISTANCE GROUP HOLDINGS LIMITED—See Watchstone Group plc; *Int'l*, pg. 8356
CRUSADER INSURANCE COMPANY—See Unico American Corporation; *U.S. Public*, pg. 2225
CRUSADER STERLING PENSION LIMITED—See Custodian Investment PLC; *Int'l*, pg. 1880
CRUSADERSTERLING PENSIONS LTD.—See Custodian Investment PLC; *Int'l*, pg. 1880
CRUSHCO (PTY) LIMITED—See Vuwa Investments (Pty) Ltd; *Int'l*, pg. 8318
CRUSHING EQUIPMENT SOLUTIONS, LLC; *U.S. Private*, pg. 1114
CRUSHING SERVICES INTERNATIONAL PTY LTD—See Mineral Resources Limited; *Int'l*, pg. 4906
CRUSOE ENERGY SYSTEMS LLC; *U.S. Private*, pg. 1114
CRUSPI S.A.—See Oettinger IMEX AG; *Int'l*, pg. 5529
CRUSTA FRUIT JUICES PROPRIETARY LIMITED—See COCA-COLA EUROPACIFIC PARTNERS PLC; *Int'l*, pg. 1684
CRUSTBUSTER-SPEED KING, INC.; *U.S. Private*, pg. 1114
CRUST CRAFT INC.; *Int'l*, pg. 1859
CRUSTUM PRODUCTS PVT. LTD.—See Viceroy Hotels Ltd; *Int'l*, pg. 8187
CRUTCHFIELD CORPORATION; *U.S. Private*, pg. 1114
CRUTTENDEN PARTNERS, LLC; *U.S. Private*, pg. 1114
CRUX CAPITAL LTD; *U.S. Private*, pg. 1114
CRUXIN B.V.—See TKH Group N.V.; *Int'l*, pg. 7763
CRUX SUBSURFACE INC.—See Quanta Services, Inc.; *U.S. Public*, pg. 1750
CRUZADOS S.A.D.P.; *Int'l*, pg. 1859
CRUZAN VIRIL LTD.—See Suntory Holdings Limited; *Int'l*, pg. 7325
CRUZ BATTERY METALS CORP.; *Int'l*, pg. 1859
CRUZ CONTRACTORS LLC; *U.S. Private*, pg. 1114
CRUZ DEL SUR INGENIERIA ELECTRA (PERU) S.A. LTD.—See Southern Cross Electrical Engineering Limited; *Int'l*, pg. 7118
CRUZ ENERGY SERVICES LLC—See Cook Inlet Region, Inc.; *U.S. Private*, pg. 1038
CRUZ/KRAVETZ:IDEAS; *U.S. Private*, pg. 1114
CRUZ MANAGEMENT INC.; *U.S. Private*, pg. 1114
CRUZ MARINE LLC—See Cook Inlet Region, Inc.; *U.S. Private*, pg. 1038
CRVENI SIGNAL A.D.; *Int'l*, pg. 1859
CRVENI SIGNAL A.D.; *Int'l*, pg. 1859
CRVENKA FABRIKA SECERA A.D.; *Int'l*, pg. 1859
CRW CORPORATION; *U.S. Private*, pg. 1114
CRW FREIGHT MANAGEMENT SERVICES, INC.—See CRW, Inc.; *U.S. Private*, pg. 1114
CRW, INC.; *U.S. Private*, pg. 1114
CRW PARTS INC.; *U.S. Private*, pg. 1114
CRYDOM, INC.—See Sensata Technologies Holding plc; *U.S. Public*, pg. 1866
CRYDOM SSR LIMITED—See Sensata Technologies Holding plc; *U.S. Public*, pg. 1866
CRYE-LEIKE INC.; *U.S. Private*, pg. 1115
CRYO AKTIEBOLAG—See Linde plc; *Int'l*, pg. 4504
CRYO-CELL INTERNATIONAL, INC.; *U.S. Public*, pg. 600
CRYOCORD HOLDINGS SDN. BHD.; *Int'l*, pg. 1859
CRYOCORD SDN. BHD.—See Cryocord Holdings Sdn. Bhd.; *Int'l*, pg. 1859
CRYO DIFFUSION S.A.S.—See Chart Industries, Inc.; *U.S. Public*, pg. 481
CRYO EXPRESS GMBH—See Cryoport, Inc.; *U.S. Public*, pg. 600
CRYO EXPRESS SP. Z O.O.—See Cryoport, Inc.; *U.S. Public*, pg. 600
CRYOFOCUS MEDTECH (SHANGHAI) CO., LTD.; *Int'l*, pg. 1859
CRYOGAS EXPRESS PROPRIETARY LIMITED—See OneLogix Group Limited; *Int'l*, pg. 5576
CRYOGENIC INDUSTRIAL SOLUTIONS, INC.; *U.S. Private*, pg. 1115

CRYOGENIC INDUSTRIES, INC.—See Nikkiso Co., Ltd.; *Int'l*, pg. 5291
CRYOGENIC INDUSTRIES SERVICE COMPANIES, LLC - HOUSTON—See Nikkiso Co., Ltd.; *Int'l*, pg. 5291
CRYOGENIC TRANSPORTATION, LLC—See Ontario Municipal Employees Retirement System; *Int'l*, pg. 5584
CRYOGENIC VESSEL ALTERNATIVES; *U.S. Private*, pg. 1115
CRYOGENMASH PJSC—See Gazprombank JSC; *Int'l*, pg. 2892
CRYOINFRA S.A. DE C.V.—See Air Products & Chemicals, Inc.; *U.S. Public*, pg. 66
CRYOLAB SRL—See SOL S.p.A.; *Int'l*, pg. 7067
CRYOLIFE ASIA PACIFIC, PTE. LTD.—See Artivion, Inc.; *U.S. Public*, pg. 208
CRYOLIFE EUROPA, LTD.—See Artivion, Inc.; *U.S. Public*, pg. 208
CRYOLOR SA—See L'Air Liquide S.A.; *Int'l*, pg. 4375
CRYOMASS TECHNOLOGIES INC.; *U.S. Public*, pg. 600
CRYOMAX COOLING SYSTEM CORP.; *Int'l*, pg. 1860
CRYOMECH, INC.—See DevCo Partners Oy; *Int'l*, pg. 2086
CRYONIC MEDICAL; *Int'l*, pg. 1860
CRYOPACK VERIFICATION TECHNOLOGIES, INC.—See Integreon Global; *U.S. Private*, pg. 2102
CRYOPAK CANADA - VANCOUVER PLANT—See Integreon Global; *U.S. Private*, pg. 2102
CRYOPAL—See L'Air Liquide S.A.; *Int'l*, pg. 4375
CRYOPORT, INC.; *U.S. Public*, pg. 600
CRYOPORT SYSTEMS, INC.—See Cryoport, Inc.; *U.S. Public*, pg. 600
CRYOPROFIL S.A.—See VITA 34 AG; *Int'l*, pg. 8257
CRYOQUIP, LLC—See Nikkiso Co., Ltd.; *Int'l*, pg. 5291
CRYO-SAVE AG—See Esperite N.V.; *Int'l*, pg. 2506
CRYO-SAVE ESPANA S.A.—See Esperite N.V.; *Int'l*, pg. 2506
CRYO-SAVE GMBH—See Esperite N.V.; *Int'l*, pg. 2506
CRYO-SAVE (INDIA) PVT. LTD.; *Int'l*, pg. 1859
CRYO-SAVE (PTY) LTD.—See Esperite N.V.; *Int'l*, pg. 2506
CRYOSERVICE LIMITED—See Air Products & Chemicals, Inc.; *U.S. Public*, pg. 66
CRYOSITE DISTRIBUTION PTY LIMITED—See Cryosite Limited; *Int'l*, pg. 1860
CRYOSITE LIMITED; *Int'l*, pg. 1860
CRYOS SRL—See SOL S.p.A.; *Int'l*, pg. 7067
CRYOSTAR CRYOGENIC EQUIPMENTS (HANGZHOU) CO. LTD.—See Linde plc; *Int'l*, pg. 4504
CRYOSTAR SAS—See Linde plc; *Int'l*, pg. 4507
CRYOSTAR SINGAPORE PTE LTD—See Linde plc; *Int'l*, pg. 4504
CRYOTHERM GMBH & CO. KG—See L'Air Liquide S.A.; *Int'l*, pg. 4370
CRYOVAC AUSTRALIA PTY. LTD.—See Sealed Air Corporation; *U.S. Public*, pg. 1852
CRYOVAC, INC.—See Sealed Air Corporation; *U.S. Public*, pg. 1852
CRYOVAC INTERNATIONAL HOLDINGS, INC.—See Sealed Air Corporation; *U.S. Public*, pg. 1852
CRYOVAC LONDRINA LTDA.—See Sealed Air Corporation; *U.S. Public*, pg. 1852
CRYPTERA A/S—See Diebold Nixdorf, Inc.; *U.S. Public*, pg. 659
CRYPTIC STUDIOS, INC.—See Perfect World Co., Ltd.; *Int'l*, pg. 5799
CRYPTO BLOCKCHAIN INDUSTRIES S.A.; *Int'l*, pg. 1860
CRYPTOBLOX TECHNOLOGIES INC.; *Int'l*, pg. 1860
THE CRYPTO COMPANY; *U.S. Public*, pg. 2066
CRYPTO FINANCE AG—See Deutsche Borse AG; *Int'l*, pg. 2063
CRYPTO FINANCE (ASSET MANAGEMENT) AG—See Deutsche Borse AG; *Int'l*, pg. 2063
CRYPTO FLOW TECHNOLOGY LIMITED; *Int'l*, pg. 1860
CRYPTOGRAPHY RESEARCH, INC.—See Rambus Inc.; *U.S. Public*, pg. 1762
CRYPTOLOGIC INC.—See Light & Wonder, Inc.; *U.S. Public*, pg. 1314
CRYPTON LLC—See W.R. Berkley Corporation; *U.S. Public*, pg. 2317
CRYPTOSIGN INC.; *U.S. Private*, pg. 1115
CRYPTOSTAR CORP.; *Int'l*, pg. 1860
CRYSBERG A/S—See Indutrade AB; *Int'l*, pg. 3678
CRYSTAL AMBER ASSET MANAGEMENT (GUERNSEY) LLP; *Int'l*, pg. 1860
CRYSTAL AMBER FUND LIMITED—See Crystal Amber Asset Management (Guernsey) LLP; *Int'l*, pg. 1860
CRYSTAL BIOSCIENCE, INC.—See Ligand Pharmaceuticals Incorporated; *U.S. Public*, pg. 1314
CRYSTAL BIOTECH—See Matec Instrument Companies, Inc.; *U.S. Private*, pg. 2609
CRYSTAL CABINET WORKS, INC.; *U.S. Private*, pg. 1115
CRYSTAL CANDY (PRIVATE) LTD.—See Mondelez International, Inc.; *U.S. Public*, pg. 1461
CRYSTAL CATHEDRAL MINISTRIES INC.; *U.S. Private*, pg. 1115
CRYSTAL CERAMIC INDUSTRIES PRIVATE LIMITED—See Asian Granito India Limited; *Int'l*, pg. 617
CRYSTAL CLAIRE COSMETICS INC.; *Int'l*, pg. 1860

CRYSTAL CLEAR CONTRACTOR PTE. LTD.—See Daiki Axis Co., Ltd.; *Int'l*, pg. 1932
CRYSTAL CLEAR DIGITAL MARKETING, LLC; *U.S. Private*, pg. 1115
CRYSTAL CLEAR ELECTRONIC MATERIAL CO., LTD; *Int'l*, pg. 1860
CRYSTAL CLEAR TECHNOLOGIES, INC.; *U.S. Private*, pg. 1115
CRYSTAL COMPUTER CORPORATION—See LTN Global Communications, Inc.; *U.S. Private*, pg. 2509
CRYSTAL CREAM & BUTTER COMPANY—See Atlas Holdings, LLC; *U.S. Private*, pg. 376
CRYSTAL CRUISES, LLC—See Genting Hong Kong Limited; *Int'l*, pg. 2929
CRYSTAL DISTRIBUTION SERVICES; *U.S. Private*, pg. 1115
CRYSTAL ENGINEERING CORPORATION—See AMETEK, Inc.; *U.S. Public*, pg. 117
CRYSTAL FARMS REFRIGERATED DISTRIBUTION COMPANY—See Post Holdings, Inc.; *U.S. Public*, pg. 1703
CRYSTAL FINANCIAL LLC—See SLR Investment Corp.; *U.S. Public*, pg. 1894
CRYSTAL FINISHING SYSTEMS, INC.; *U.S. Private*, pg. 1115
CRYSTAL FLASH ENERGY—See Heritage Group; *U.S. Private*, pg. 1923
CRYSTAL FLASH LP OF MICHIGAN; *U.S. Private*, pg. 1115
CRYSTAL FLASH PETROLEUM CORP.—See Heritage Group; *U.S. Private*, pg. 1923
CRYSTAL FREIGHT SERVICES DISTRIPARK PTE. LTD.—See Vibrant Group Limited; *Int'l*, pg. 8184
CRYSTAL FREIGHT SERVICES PTE. LTD.—See Vibrant Group Limited; *Int'l*, pg. 8184
CRYSTALGENOMICS, INC.; *Int'l*, pg. 1860
CRYSTAL GEYSER ROXANE WATER COMPANY L.L.C.—See Otsuka Holdings Co., Ltd.; *Int'l*, pg. 5660
CRYSTAL GEYSER WATER COMPANY—See Otsuka Holdings Co., Ltd.; *Int'l*, pg. 5660
CRYSTAL GLOBE LIMITED; *Int'l*, pg. 1860
CRYSTAL GMBH—See Silver Investment Partners GmbH & Co. KG; *Int'l*, pg. 6923
CRYSTAL GROUP, INC.—See Dexter Apache Holdings, Inc.; *U.S. Private*, pg. 1220
CRYSTAL HALLMARK SDN. BHD.—See Malaysian Resources Corporation Berhad; *Int'l*, pg. 4662
CRYSTAL, INC. - PMC—See PMC Group, Inc.; *U.S. Private*, pg. 3218
CRYSTAL INTERNATIONAL GROUP LIMITED; *Int'l*, pg. 1860
CRYSTAL IS, INC.—See Asahi Kasei Corporation; *Int'l*, pg. 596
CRYSTAL KOBE LTD. INC.; *U.S. Private*, pg. 1115
CRYSTAL LACE (I) LIMITED—See Pioneer Embroideries Limited; *Int'l*, pg. 5871
CRYSTAL LAKE BANK & TRUST COMPANY, N.A.—See Wintrust Financial Corporation; *U.S. Public*, pg. 2374
CRYSTAL LAKE MINING CORPORATION; *Int'l*, pg. 1860
CRYSTAL MANAGEMENT JSC; *Int'l*, pg. 1860
CRYSTAL MARTIN (VIETNAM) COMPANY LIMITED—See Crystal International Group Limited; *Int'l*, pg. 1860
CRYSTAL MOTOR CAR CO. INC.; *U.S. Private*, pg. 1115
CRYSTAL MOTOR EXPRESS INC.; *U.S. Private*, pg. 1115
CRYSTAL MOUNTAIN, INC.—See KSL Capital Partners, LLC; *U.S. Private*, pg. 2354
CRYSTAL MOUNTAIN PRODUCTS LTD.—See Epsilon Healthcare Ltd.; *Int'l*, pg. 2466
CRYSTAL MOVER SERVICES, INC.—See Mitsubishi Heavy Industries, Ltd.; *Int'l*, pg. 4956
CRYSTAL OAKS; *U.S. Private*, pg. 1115
CRYSTALOX LTD—See PV Crystalox Solar plc; *Int'l*, pg. 6124
CRYSTAL PALMS BEACH RESORT; *U.S. Private*, pg. 1115
CRYSTAL-PIERZ MARINE INC.; *U.S. Private*, pg. 1116
CRYSTAL PROMOTIONS INC.; *U.S. Private*, pg. 1115
THE CRYSTAL RIVER ENDOSCOPY ASC, L.P.—See KKR & Co. Inc.; *U.S. Public*, pg. 1247
CRYSTAL ROSE FUNERAL HOME, INC.—See Security National Financial Corporation; *U.S. Public*, pg. 1856
CRYSTAL RUN VILLAGE, INC.; *U.S. Private*, pg. 1115
CRYSTALSEV COMERCIO E REPRESENTACAO LTDA.—See Raizen S.A.; *Int'l*, pg. 6192
CRYSTAL SODA WATER CO.; *U.S. Private*, pg. 1115
CRYSTAL—See Ligand Pharmaceuticals Incorporated; *U.S. Public*, pg. 1314
CRYSTAL SPRINGS APPAREL LLC; *U.S. Private*, pg. 1115
CRYSTAL SPRINGS RESORT; *U.S. Private*, pg. 1115
CRYSTAL STAIRS, INC.; *U.S. Private*, pg. 1116
CRYSTAL TECHNOLOGY INC.—See TDK Corporation; *Int'l*, pg. 7487
CRYSTAL VALLEY COOPERATIVE; *U.S. Private*, pg. 1116
CRYSTAL VALLEY FINANCIAL CORP.; *U.S. Public*, pg. 600
CRYSTAL VISION MEDIA PRIVATE LIMITED—See DEN Networks Limited; *Int'l*, pg. 2026

COMPANY NAME INDEX

CRYSTALVUE MEDICAL CORPORATION; *Int'l*, pg. 1860
CRYSTAL WINDOW & DOOR SYSTEMS; *U.S. Private*, pg. 1116
CRYSTALWISE TECHNOLOGY, INC.; *Int'l*, pg. 1860
CRYSTEEL MANUFACTURING, INC.—See Federal Signal Corporation; *U.S. Public*, pg. 826
CRYSTEEL TRUCK EQUIPMENT, INC.; *U.S. Private*, pg. 1116
CRY -TECHINC; *U.S. Private*, pg. 1114
CS2 ADVERTISING; *U.S. Private*, pg. 1116
CS3, INC—See Partners Group Holding AG; *Int'l*, pg. 5750
CSA AIR INC.—See Air T, Inc.; *U.S. Public*, pg. 67
CSA AMERICA, INC.—See CSA Group; *Int'l*, pg. 1861
C.S.A. CENTRO SERVIZI AUTOCARRI S.R.L.; *Int'l*, pg. 1244
CSA COMMERZ SOUTH AFRICA (PROPRIETARY) LIMITED—See Commerzbank AG; *Int'l*, pg. 1715
CSA CONSULTING ENGINEERS, LTD.—See Nidec Corporation; *Int'l*, pg. 5275
CSA COSMIC CO., LTD.; *Int'l*, pg. 1861
CSAD AUTOBUSY CESKE BUDEJOVICE A.S.—See OBB-Holding AG; *Int'l*, pg. 5509
CS ADVERTISING SDN. BHD.—See Chuo Senko Advertising Co., Ltd.; *Int'l*, pg. 1599
CSA EQUIPMENT COMPANY LLC—See Cooper/T. Smith Corporation; *U.S. Private*, pg. 1041
CSA FRANCHISING, LLC—See CSA Service Solutions, LLC; *U.S. Private*, pg. 1116
CSA FRATERNAL LIFE; *U.S. Private*, pg. 1116
CSA GROUP EUROPE GMBH—See CSA Group; *Int'l*, pg. 1861
CSA GROUP ITALY S.R.L.—See CSA Group; *Int'l*, pg. 1861
CSA GROUP NETHERLANDS—See CSA Group; *Int'l*, pg. 1861
CSA GROUP; *Int'l*, pg. 1861
CSA GROUP SWITZERLAND GMBH—See CSA Group; *Int'l*, pg. 1861
CSA HOLDINGS INC.; *U.S. Private*, pg. 1116
CSA INTERNATIONAL - ASIA—See CSA Group; *Int'l*, pg. 1861
CSA INTERNATIONAL—See CSA Group; *Int'l*, pg. 1861
C.S. ALUMINIUM CORPORATION—See China Steel Corporation; *Int'l*, pg. 1555
C-SAM AB—See Telia Company AB; *Int'l*, pg. 7543
CSA MATERIALS, INC.—See Reece Albert Inc.; *U.S. Private*, pg. 3381
CSAM CARMENTA TECHNOLOGIES, S.L.—See Omda AS; *Int'l*, pg. 5561
CSAM DENMARK A/S—See Omda AS; *Int'l*, pg. 5561
CSAM HEALTH UK LTD.—See Omda AS; *Int'l*, pg. 5561
CSAM KIBI FINLAND OY—See Virtus Holding ApS; *Int'l*, pg. 8249
CSAM NEW ZEALAND LTD.—See Omda AS; *Int'l*, pg. 5561
CSAM PHILIPPINES INC.—See Omda AS; *Int'l*, pg. 5562
CSAM SWEDEN AB—See Omda AS; *Int'l*, pg. 5562
CSAM UAB MEDSCINET LT—See Omda AS; *Int'l*, pg. 5562
C&S ANTENNAS, INC.—See Amphenol Corporation; *U.S. Public*, pg. 127
CSA SERVICE SOLUTIONS, LLC; *U.S. Private*, pg. 1116
CSA SERVICES—See Cooper/T. Smith Corporation; *U.S. Private*, pg. 1041
CSA SERVIS (M) SDN BHD—See Omesti Berhad; *Int'l*, pg. 5562
C&S ASSET MANAGEMENT CO., LTD.; *Int'l*, pg. 1239
CS (AUSTRALIA) PTY LIMITED—See Illinois Tool Works Inc.; *U.S. Public*, pg. 1102
CS AUTO, LTD.; *U.S. Private*, pg. 1116
CSAV AGENCIAMIENTO MARITIMO SPA—See Albert Ballin KG; *Int'l*, pg. 294
CSAV AGENCY FRANCE S.A.S.—See Albert Ballin KG; *Int'l*, pg. 294
CSAV AGENCY ITALY, S.P.A.—See Albert Ballin KG; *Int'l*, pg. 294
CSAV AGENCY LLC—See Albert Ballin KG; *Int'l*, pg. 294
CSAV AGENCY LTD.—See Albert Ballin KG; *Int'l*, pg. 294
CSAV ARGENTINA S.A.—See Albert Ballin KG; *Int'l*, pg. 294
CSAV DENIZCILIK ACENTASI A.S.—See Albert Ballin KG; *Int'l*, pg. 294
CSAV GROUP AGENCIES (INDIA) PVT LTD—See Albert Ballin KG; *Int'l*, pg. 294
CSAV GROUP AGENCIES (TAIWAN) LTD.—See Albert Ballin KG; *Int'l*, pg. 294
CSAV GROUP AGENCIES URUGUAY S.A.—See Albert Ballin KG; *Int'l*, pg. 294
CSAV GROUP AGENCY COLOMBIA LTDA.—See Albert Ballin KG; *Int'l*, pg. 294
CSAV GROUP (CHINA) SHIPPING CO. LTD.—See Albert Ballin KG; *Int'l*, pg. 294
CSAV GROUP (HONG KONG) LTD.—See Albert Ballin KG; *Int'l*, pg. 294
CSAV INVERSIONES NAVIERAS S.A.—See Compania Sudamericana de Vapores, S.A.; *Int'l*, pg. 1749
CSAV NORTH & CENTRAL EUROPE GMBH—See Albert Ballin KG; *Int'l*, pg. 294

CSAV NORTH & CENTRAL EUROPE N.V.—See Albert Ballin KG; *Int'l*, pg. 294
CSAV UK & IRELAND LIMITED—See Albert Ballin KG; *Int'l*, pg. 294
C.S. BACHLY BUILDERS LTD.; *Int'l*, pg. 1244
CSB AMERICAS INC.—See Zhejiang Changsheng Sliding Bearings Co., Ltd.; *Int'l*, pg. 8649
CSB-AUTOMATION AG—See CSB-System AG; *Int'l*, pg. 1862
CSB BANCORP, INC.; *U.S. Public*, pg. 600
C.S.B. BANCSHARES, INC.; *U.S. Private*, pg. 709
CSB BEARINGS FRANCE SARL—See Zhejiang Changsheng Sliding Bearings Co., Ltd.; *Int'l*, pg. 8649
CSBC COATING SOLUTIONS CO., LTD.—See CSBC Corp. Taiwan; *Int'l*, pg. 1862
CSBC CORP. TAIWAN; *Int'l*, pg. 1862
CS BEARING CO., LTD.; *Int'l*, pg. 1861
CSB GLEITLAGER GMBH—See Zhejiang Changsheng Sliding Bearings Co., Ltd.; *Int'l*, pg. 8649
CSBH LLC; *U.S. Private*, pg. 1116
CSB INVESTMENT SERVICES, LLC—See CSB Bancorp, Inc.; *U.S. Public*, pg. 601
C.S. BITUNOVA S.R.O.—See STRABAG SE; *Int'l*, pg. 7229
CSB MORTGAGE COMPANY, INC.—See Farmers National Banc Corp.; *U.S. Public*, pg. 822
CS BORED PILE SYSTEM PTE. LTD.—See CSC Holdings Limited; *Int'l*, pg. 1862
CSBP LIMITED—See Wesfarmers Limited; *Int'l*, pg. 8381
CSB SERVICES ASIA PACIFIC PVT. LTD—See CSB-System AG; *Int'l*, pg. 1862
CSB SLIDING BEARING (INDIA) PVT. LTD.—See Zhejiang Changsheng Sliding Bearings Co., Ltd.; *Int'l*, pg. 8649
CSB-SYSTEM AG; *Int'l*, pg. 1861
CSB-SYSTEM AUSTRIA GMBH—See CSB-System AG; *Int'l*, pg. 1862
CSB-SYSTEM BENELUX BV—See CSB-System AG; *Int'l*, pg. 1862
CSB-SYSTEM BULGARIA EGMBH—See CSB-System AG; *Int'l*, pg. 1862
CSB-SYSTEM D.O.O.—See CSB-System AG; *Int'l*, pg. 1862
CSB-SYSTEM ESPANA S.L.—See CSB-System AG; *Int'l*, pg. 1862
CSB-SYSTEM HUNGARY KFT.—See CSB-System AG; *Int'l*, pg. 1862
CSB-SYSTEM INTERNATIONAL, INC.—See CSB-System AG; *Int'l*, pg. 1862
CSB-SYSTEM INTERNATIONAL, INC.—See CSB-System AG; *Int'l*, pg. 1862
CSB-SYSTEM POLSKA SP.Z.O.O.—See CSB-System AG; *Int'l*, pg. 1862
CSB-SYSTEM ROMANIA SRL—See CSB-System AG; *Int'l*, pg. 1862
CSB-SYSTEM S.R.L.—See CSB-System AG; *Int'l*, pg. 1862
CSB TRANSTEX CHILE S.A—See Valid Solucoes S.A.; *Int'l*, pg. 8116
CS BUILDING SERVICE CORPORATION—See Nippon Telegraph & Telephone Corporation; *Int'l*, pg. 5340
CS BUSINESS SYSTEMS INC.; *U.S. Private*, pg. 1116
CS CABOT SPOL, S.R.O.—See Cabot Corporation; *U.S. Public*, pg. 416
CSC AGILITY PLATFORM, INC.—See DXC Technology Company; *U.S. Public*, pg. 695
CS CANADA INC.—See Sopra Steria Group S.A.; *Int'l*, pg. 6779
C&S CAPITAL MANAGEMENT; *U.S. Private*, pg. 703
C & S CARPET DISTRIBUTION, INC.—See Best Logistics Group, Inc.; *U.S. Private*, pg. 543
CSC COMMODITIES UK LTD.—See JRJ Ventures LLP; *Int'l*, pg. 4008
CSC COMPUTER SCIENCES BRASIL S/A—See DXC Technology Company; *U.S. Public*, pg. 695
CSC COMPUTER SCIENCES CONSULTING AUSTRIA GMBH—See DXC Technology Company; *U.S. Public*, pg. 695
CSC COMPUTER SCIENCES LIMITED—See DXC Technology Company; *U.S. Public*, pg. 695
CSC COMPUTER SCIENCES S.A.—See DXC Technology Company; *U.S. Public*, pg. 695
CSC COMPUTER SCIENCES (SOUTH AFRICA) (PTY) LIMITED—See DXC Technology Company; *U.S. Public*, pg. 695
CSC DIGITAL BRAND SERVICES LIMITED—See Corporation Service Company; *U.S. Private*, pg. 1057
CSC DIGITAL BRAND SERVICES—See Corporation Service Company; *U.S. Private*, pg. 1057
CSC DISTRIBUTION, INC.—See Big Lots, Inc.; *U.S. Public*, pg. 330
CSC & EC (PTY) LTD.—See China State Construction Engineering Corporation Limited; *Int'l*, pg. 1554
CSCEC SCIMEE SCI & TECH CO., LTD.; *Int'l*, pg. 1863
CSCEC XINJIANG CONSTRUCTION & ENGINEERING (GROUP) CO., LTD.—See China State Construction Engineering Corporation Limited; *Int'l*, pg. 1554
CSC ENTERPRISES L.P.—See DXC Technology Company; *U.S. Public*, pg. 695

CSE GLOBAL LTD.

CS CENTRO STIRLING S. COOP.—See Mondragon Corporation; *Int'l*, pg. 5028
CSC FINANCE LTD.—See Capital Securities Corporation; *Int'l*, pg. 1312
CSC FINANCIAL CO., LTD; *Int'l*, pg. 1862
CSC FINANCIAL SERVICES LIMITED—See Capital Securities Corporation; *Int'l*, pg. 1312
CSC FUTURES (HK) LTD.—See Capital Securities Corporation; *Int'l*, pg. 1312
CSC GENERATION HOLDINGS, INC.; *U.S. Private*, pg. 1116
THE CSC GROUP OF MICHIGAN—See Thoma Bravo, L.P.; *U.S. Private*, pg. 4148
CSC HOLDINGS LIMITED; *Int'l*, pg. 1862
CSC HOLDINGS LIMITED; *Int'l*, pg. 1862
CSC HOLDINGS, LLC—See Altice USA, Inc.; *U.S. Public*, pg. 87
CSC IMPRESA COSTRUZIONI S.A.—See Salini Costruttori S.p.A.; *Int'l*, pg. 6493
CSC INTERNATIONAL HOLDINGS LTD.—See Capital Securities Corporation; *Int'l*, pg. 1312
CSC JAPAN, LTD.—See DXC Technology Company; *U.S. Public*, pg. 695
CSC LABORATORIES, INC.—See EssilorLuxottica SA; *Int'l*, pg. 2513
CSC MACHINING—See Prescott Aerospace, Inc.; *U.S. Private*, pg. 3254
CS CONSTRUCTION & GEOTECHNIC PTE. LTD.—See CSC Holdings Limited; *Int'l*, pg. 1862
C/S CONSTRUCTION SPECIALTIES COMPANY—See Construction Specialties, Inc.; *U.S. Private*, pg. 1024
C/S CONSTRUCTION SPECIALTIES (MALAYSIA) SDN BHD—See Construction Specialties, Inc.; *U.S. Private*, pg. 1024
C/S CONSTRUCTION SPECIALTIES MIDDLE EAST LLC—See Construction Specialties, Inc.; *U.S. Private*, pg. 1024
C.S. CONSULTACIONES Y SERVICIOS S.A—See UBS Group AG; *Int'l*, pg. 8005
CS CONSULTING GMBH—See Capgemini SE; *Int'l*, pg. 1303
C&S CONTRACTORS INC.; *U.S. Private*, pg. 703
CS CORPORATION; *Int'l*, pg. 1861
CSC PHARMACEUTICALS S.A.—See Angelini ACRAF S.p.A.; *Int'l*, pg. 460
C'S CREATE CO., LTD.; *Int'l*, pg. 1239
CSC SECURITIES (HK) LTD.—See Capital Securities Corporation; *Int'l*, pg. 1312
CSC SERVICEWORKS, INC.—See Pamplona Capital Management LLP; *Int'l*, pg. 5711
CSC SOLAR CORPORATION—See China Steel Corporation; *Int'l*, pg. 1555
CSC SONOMA PTY. LTD.—See China Steel Corporation; *Int'l*, pg. 1555
CSC STEEL HOLDINGS BERHAD; *Int'l*, pg. 1863
CSC STEEL SDN. BHD.—See China Steel Corporation; *Int'l*, pg. 1555
CSC TRANSPORTATION LLC—See Commodity Specialists Company Inc.; *U.S. Private*, pg. 985
CSC TRANSPORT INC.—See Altice USA, Inc.; *U.S. Public*, pg. 87
CSC TRAVEL GROUP INC.—See Expedia Group, Inc.; *U.S. Public*, pg. 809
CSD CO., LTD.—See ITFOR Inc.; *Int'l*, pg. 3833
C/S DEUTSCHLAND GMBH—See Construction Specialties, Inc.; *U.S. Private*, pg. 1024
CS DISCO, INC.; *U.S. Public*, pg. 600
CS DISCO INDIA PRIVATE LTD.—See CS Disco, Inc.; *U.S. Public*, pg. 600
C & S DRYWALL INC.—See Paul Johnson Drywall, Inc.; *U.S. Private*, pg. 3113
CSDVRS, LLC—See Kinderhook Industries, LLC; *U.S. Private*, pg. 2306
CSD WATER SERVICE CO., LTD.; *Int'l*, pg. 1863
CS ECO GLASS (M) SDN. BHD.—See Zhuzhou Kibing Group Co., Ltd.; *Int'l*, pg. 8679
CSE COMMUNICATIONS & SECURITY SDN BHD—See CSE Global Ltd.; *Int'l*, pg. 1863
CSE COMSOURCE PTY LTD—See CSE Global Ltd.; *Int'l*, pg. 1863
CSE-CONTROLS S.R.O.—See CSE Global Ltd.; *Int'l*, pg. 1863
CSE CORPORATION; *U.S. Private*, pg. 1116
CSE CROSSCOM PTY LTD—See CSE Global Ltd.; *Int'l*, pg. 1863
CSE-EIS (MALAYSIA) SDN BHD—See CSE Global Ltd.; *Int'l*, pg. 1863
CSE-EIS PTE LTD—See CSE Global Ltd.; *Int'l*, pg. 1863
CSE EQUIPMENT COMPANY (PTY) LTD.—See Invicta Holdings Limited; *Int'l*, pg. 3788
CSE-GLOBAL (AUSTRALIA), LTD.—See CSE Global Ltd.; *Int'l*, pg. 1863
CSE-GLOBAL (AUSTRALIA) PTY LTD—See CSE Global Ltd.; *Int'l*, pg. 1863
CSE GLOBAL LTD.; *Int'l*, pg. 1863
CSE-GLOBAL (UK) LIMITED—See CSE Global Ltd.; *Int'l*, pg. 1863
CSE-HANKIN (CHINA) CO., LTD.—See CSE Global Ltd.; *Int'l*, pg. 1863

CSE GLOBAL LTD.

CSE-HANKIN INC—See CSE Global Ltd.; *Int'l*, pg. 1863
CSE-HANKIN (TAIWAN) LTD.—See CSE Global Ltd.; *Int'l*, pg. 1863
CSE-HEALTHCARE SYSTEMS LIMITED—See CSE Global Ltd.; *Int'l*, pg. 1863
CSE-IAP PTE LTD—See CSE Global Ltd.; *Int'l*, pg. 1863
CSE ICON, INC.—See CSE Global Ltd.; *Int'l*, pg. 1863
CSE INSURANCE GROUP; *U.S. Private*, pg. 1116
CSE-ITS PTE LTD—See CSE Global Ltd.; *Int'l*, pg. 1863
C&S ELECTRIC LIMITED C&S ACB, SWITCHES & MCCB PLANT—See Siemens Aktiengesellschaft; *Int'l*, pg. 6897
C&S ELECTRIC LIMITED C&S BUSDUCT PLANT II—See Siemens Aktiengesellschaft; *Int'l*, pg. 6897
C&S ELECTRIC LIMITED C&S BUSDUCT PLANT- I—See Siemens Aktiengesellschaft; *Int'l*, pg. 6897
C&S ELECTRIC LIMITED C&S BUSTRUNKING PLANT—See Siemens Aktiengesellschaft; *Int'l*, pg. 6897
C&S ELECTRIC LIMITED C&S EXPORT DIVISION PLANT—See Siemens Aktiengesellschaft; *Int'l*, pg. 6897
C&S ELECTRIC LIMITED CSH GENSETS PLANT—See Siemens Aktiengesellschaft; *Int'l*, pg. 6897
C&S ELECTRIC LIMITED C&S LIGHTING & WIRING ACCESSORIES PLANT—See Siemens Aktiengesellschaft; *Int'l*, pg. 6897
C&S ELECTRIC LIMITED C&S MCB PLANT—See Siemens Aktiengesellschaft; *Int'l*, pg. 6897
C&S ELECTRIC LIMITED C&S MV PLANT—See Siemens Aktiengesellschaft; *Int'l*, pg. 6897
C&S ELECTRIC LIMITED C&S SWITCHBOARD PLANT- II—See Siemens Aktiengesellschaft; *Int'l*, pg. 6897
C&S ELECTRIC LIMITED C&S SWITCHBOARD PLANT -I—See Siemens Aktiengesellschaft; *Int'l*, pg. 6897
C&S ELECTRIC LIMITED C&S TC CONTACTOR, OVERLOAD RELAY & MOTOR STARTER PLANT—See Siemens Aktiengesellschaft; *Int'l*, pg. 6897
C&S ELECTRIC LIMITED PROTECTION & MEASUREMENT DEVICES PLANT—See Siemens Aktiengesellschaft; *Int'l*, pg. 6897
C&S ELECTRIC LIMITED—See Siemens Aktiengesellschaft; *Int'l*, pg. 6897
CSENGE ADVISORY GROUP, LLC; *U.S. Private*, pg. 1116
CSENGE ADVISORY GROUP, LLC—See Csenge Advisory Group, LLC; *U.S. Private*, pg. 1116
CSEPEL HOLDING PLC; *Int'l*, pg. 1864
CSE SAFEGUARD INSURANCE COMPANY—See CSE Insurance Group; *U.S. Private*, pg. 1116
CSE SEMAPHORE AUSTRALIA PTY LTD—See CSE Global Ltd.; *Int'l*, pg. 1863
CSE SEMAPHORE BELGIUM SA—See CSE Global Ltd.; *Int'l*, pg. 1863
CSE SEMAPHORE INC—See CSE Global Ltd.; *Int'l*, pg. 1863
CSE-SERVELEC LIMITED—See CSE Global Ltd.; *Int'l*, pg. 1863
CSE-SERVELEC S.R.O.—See CSE Global Ltd.; *Int'l*, pg. 1863
CSE SYSTEMS & ENGINEERING (INDIA) PVT LIMITED—See CSE Global Ltd.; *Int'l*, pg. 1863
CSE SYSTEMS & ENGINEERING (THAILAND) LIMITED—See CSE Global Ltd.; *Int'l*, pg. 1864
C'SET CO., LTD.—See Japan Material Co., Ltd.; *Int'l*, pg. 3899
CSE-TRANSTEL PTY LTD—See CSE Global Ltd.; *Int'l*, pg. 1863
CSE-UNISERVE CORPORATION PTY LTD—See CSE Global Ltd.; *Int'l*, pg. 1863
CSE-UNISERVE PTY LIMITED—See CSE Global Ltd.; *Int'l*, pg. 1863
CSE-W ARTHUR FISHER LIMITED—See CSE Global Ltd.; *Int'l*, pg. 1863
CSE W-INDUSTRIES NIGERIA LTD.—See CSE Global Ltd.; *Int'l*, pg. 1863
CSF GROUP PLC; *Int'l*, pg. 1864
CSF, INC.—See iconectiv, LLC; *U.S. Private*, pg. 2032
CSF POLAND SP. Z O.O.—See Cooper-Standard Holdings Inc.; *U.S. Public*, pg. 573
CSF POLAND Z O.O.—See Cooper-Standard Holdings Inc.; *U.S. Public*, pg. 573
C/S FRANCE—See Construction Specialties, Inc.; *U.S. Private*, pg. 1024
CSG ACTUARIAL, LLC—See Integrity Marketing Group LLC; *U.S. Private*, pg. 2103
CSG COMMUNICATIONS PTY. LTD.—See FUJIFILM Holdings Corporation; *Int'l*, pg. 2825
CSG CONVENIENCE SERVICE GMBH—See REWE-Zentral-Aktiengesellschaft; *Int'l*, pg. 6315
C.S. GENERAL INC.; *U.S. Private*, pg. 709
CS GEOTECHNIC PTE. LTD.—See CSC Holdings Limited; *Int'l*, pg. 1862
CSG FOOD SOLUTIONS PROPRIETARY LIMITED—See CSG Holdings Limited; *Int'l*, pg. 1864
CSG GLOBAL; *U.S. Private*, pg. 1117
CSG GMBH—See Deutsche Post AG; *Int'l*, pg. 2072
CSG GMBH—See EQT AB; *Int'l*, pg. 2469
CSG HOLDING CO., LTD.—See Shenzhen International Holdings Limited; *Int'l*, pg. 6813
CSG HOLDINGS LIMITED; *Int'l*, pg. 1864
CSG INTELLIGENCE TECHNOLOGY (HEFEI) CO., LTD.—See CSG Smart Science & Technology Co., Ltd.; *Int'l*, pg. 1864
CSG INTELLIGENT ELECTRICAL TECHNOLOGY CO., LTD.—See CSG Smart Science & Technology Co., Ltd.; *Int'l*, pg. 1864
CSG INTERACTIVE MESSAGING, INC.—See CSG Systems International, Inc.; *U.S. Public*, pg. 601
CSG INTERNATIONAL COLOMBIA SAS—See CSG Systems International, Inc.; *U.S. Public*, pg. 601
CSG INTERNATIONAL DP, INC.—See CSG Systems International, Inc.; *U.S. Public*, pg. 601
CSG INTERNATIONAL PTY LIMITED—See CSG Systems International, Inc.; *U.S. Public*, pg. 601
CSG LIMITED—See FUJIFILM Holdings Corporation; *Int'l*, pg. 2825
CSG PRINT SERVICES PTY. LTD.—See FUJIFILM Holdings Corporation; *Int'l*, pg. 2825
CSG RESOURCINGS PROPRIETARY LIMITED—See CSG Holdings Limited; *Int'l*, pg. 1864
CS GROUP SA—See Sopra Steria Group S.A.; *Int'l*, pg. 7109
CSG SKILLS INSTITUTE PROPRIETARY LIMITED—See CSG Holdings Limited; *Int'l*, pg. 1864
CSG SMART ELECTRIC TECHNOLOGY CO., LTD.—See CSG Smart Science & Technology Co., Ltd.; *Int'l*, pg. 1864
CSG SMART ROBOT TECHNOLOGY CO., LTD.—See CSG Smart Science & Technology Co., Ltd.; *Int'l*, pg. 1864
CSG SMART SCIENCE & TECHNOLOGY CO., LTD.; *Int'l*, pg. 1864
CSG SYSTEMS, INC.—See CSG Systems International, Inc.; *U.S. Public*, pg. 601
CSG SYSTEMS INTERNATIONAL, INC.; *U.S. Public*, pg. 601
CSG SYSTEMS—See CSG Systems International, Inc.; *U.S. Public*, pg. 601
CSG SYSTEMS—See CSG Systems International, Inc.; *U.S. Public*, pg. 601
CSGT HONG KONG LIMITED—See China Steel Corporation; *Int'l*, pg. 1555
CSGT METALS VIETNAM JOINT STOCK COMPANY—See China Steel Corporation; *Int'l*, pg. 1555
CSGT (SHANGHAI) CO., LTD.—See China Steel Corporation; *Int'l*, pg. 1555
CSGT (SHENZHEN) CO., LTD.—See China Steel Corporation; *Int'l*, pg. 1555
CSGT (SINGAPORE) PTE. LTD.—See China Steel Corporation; *Int'l*, pg. 1555
CSGT TRADING INDIA PRIVATE LIMITED—See China Steel Corporation; *Int'l*, pg. 1555
CSH ALLIANCE BERHAD; *Int'l*, pg. 1865
CS HEALTH STORE SDN BHD—See Apex Healthcare Berhad; *Int'l*, pg. 511
CSH GROUP (PTY) LTD—See Experian plc; *Int'l*, pg. 2586
CSH LAKE ORIENTA LLC—See Brookdale Senior Living Inc.; *U.S. Public*, pg. 394
CSH NORTH RICHLAND HILLS LLC—See Brookdale Senior Living Inc.; *U.S. Public*, pg. 394
CS HOLDINGS CO., LTD.; *Int'l*, pg. 1861
CSH PORT ST. LUCIE LLC—See Brookdale Senior Living Inc.; *U.S. Public*, pg. 394
CSHQA, INC.; *U.S. Private*, pg. 1117
CSH ROUND ROCK LLC—See Brookdale Senior Living Inc.; *U.S. Public*, pg. 394
CSH SAN MARCOS LLC—See Brookdale Senior Living Inc.; *U.S. Public*, pg. 394
CSI ACQUISITION CORP.; *U.S. Private*, pg. 1117
CSI AEROSPACE, INC.—See HEICO Corporation; *U.S. Public*, pg. 1019
THE CSI COMPANIES INC.—See Recruit Holdings Co., Ltd.; *Int'l*, pg. 6241
CSI COMPRESSCO LP—See EQT AB; *Int'l*, pg. 2478
CSIDENTITY CORPORATION—See Experian plc; *Int'l*, pg. 2586
CSI ELECTRICAL CONTRACTORS, INC.—See MYR Group Inc.; *U.S. Public*, pg. 1488
CSI ENTERPRISES, INC.—See Edenred S.A.; *Int'l*, pg. 2307
CSI ENTREPRISES INC.—See Edenred S.A.; *Int'l*, pg. 2307
CSI FINANCIAL SERVICES, LLC—See TPG Capital, L.P.; *U.S. Public*, pg. 2168
CSI FUNERAL SERVICES OF MASSACHUSETTS, INC.—See Carriage Services, Inc.; *U.S. Public*, pg. 439
CSI-GMBH; *Int'l*, pg. 1865
THE CSI GROUP, INC.; *U.S. Private*, pg. 4017
CSI HOLDINGS INC.; *U.S. Private*, pg. 1117
CSI IT, LLC—See White Wolf Capital LLC; *U.S. Private*, pg. 4510
CSI JAPAN LTD.—See Cerberus Capital Management, L.P.; *U.S. Private*, pg. 837
CSI LABORATORIES, INC.—See Fulgent Genetics, Inc.; *U.S. Public*, pg. 892
CSI LATINA ARRENDAMENTO MERCANTIL S/A—See Tokyo Century Corporation; *Int'l*, pg. 7788
CSI LATINA FINANCIAL, INC.—See Tokyo Century Corporation; *Int'l*, pg. 7788
CSI LEASING CANADA LTD.—See Tokyo Century Corporation; *Int'l*, pg. 7788
CSI LEASING CZECH S.R.O.—See Tokyo Century Corporation; *Int'l*, pg. 7788
CSI LEASING DE CENTROAMERICA SRL—See Tokyo Century Corporation; *Int'l*, pg. 7788
CSI LEASING GUATEMALA, S.A.—See Tokyo Century Corporation; *Int'l*, pg. 7788
CSI LEASING, INC.—See Tokyo Century Corporation; *Int'l*, pg. 7788
CSI LEASING MALAYSIA SDN. BHD.—See Tokyo Century Corporation; *Int'l*, pg. 7789
CSI LEASING MEXICO, S. DE R.L. DE C.V.—See Tokyo Century Corporation; *Int'l*, pg. 7788
CSI LEASING POLSKA SP.Z O.O.—See Tokyo Century Corporation; *Int'l*, pg. 7789
CSI LEASING (SHENZHEN) LIMITED—See Tokyo Century Corporation; *Int'l*, pg. 7788
CSI LEASING (SINGAPORE) PTE. LTD.—See Tokyo Century Corporation; *Int'l*, pg. 7788
CSI LEASING SLOVAKIA, S.R.O.—See Tokyo Century Corporation; *Int'l*, pg. 7789
CSI LEASING UK LTD.—See Tokyo Century Corporation; *Int'l*, pg. 7789
CSI LIFECYCLE EUROPE, S.R.O.—See Tokyo Century Corporation; *Int'l*, pg. 7789
CSI LIFECYCLE LEASING GMBH—See Tokyo Century Corporation; *Int'l*, pg. 7789
CSI LIFECYCLE SERVICES ITALIA S.R.L.—See Tokyo Century Corporation; *Int'l*, pg. 7789
CSI LOGISTICS INC.—See Nippon Yusen Kabushiki Kaisha; *Int'l*, pg. 5357
C&S INC.; *U.S. Private*, pg. 703
C&S INC.; *U.S. Private*, pg. 703
C&S INSURANCE AGENCY, INC.; *U.S. Private*, pg. 704
CSI POWERLINE; *U.S. Private*, pg. 1117
CSI PROPERTIES LIMITED; *Int'l*, pg. 1865
CSI RENTING CHILE, S.A.—See Tokyo Century Corporation; *Int'l*, pg. 7788
CSI RENTING COLOMBIA S.A.—See Tokyo Century Corporation; *Int'l*, pg. 7788
CSI RENTING DE TECNOLOGIA SAU—See Tokyo Century Corporation; *Int'l*, pg. 7789
CSI RENTING PERU S.A.C.—See Tokyo Century Corporation; *Int'l*, pg. 7788
CSI SOFTWARE—See GI Manager L.P.; *U.S. Private*, pg. 1692
CSI SOLAR TECHNOLOGIES INC.—See Canadian Solar Inc.; *Int'l*, pg. 1286
CSI SOLARTRONICS (CHANGSHU) CO., LTD.—See Canadian Solar Inc.; *Int'l*, pg. 1286
CSI SPORTS LLC—See Peak Global Holdings, LLC; *U.S. Private*, pg. 3123
CSIT BOTSWANA (PTY) LTD—See Experian plc; *Int'l*, pg. 2586
CSI TECHNOLOGIES—See Superior Energy Services, Inc.; *U.S. Private*, pg. 3877
CSI WORLDWIDE INC.; *U.S. Private*, pg. 1117
CSK ADMINISTRATION SERVICE CORPORATION—See Sumitomo Corporation; *Int'l*, pg. 7270
CSK AGRICOLE CORPORATION—See Sumitomo Corporation; *Int'l*, pg. 7270
CSK INC.—See Atlas Copco AB; *Int'l*, pg. 681
CS KLIMATEKNIK APS—See Triton Advisers Limited; *Int'l*, pg. 7930
CSK NEARSHORE SYSTEMS CORPORATION—See Sumitomo Corporation; *Int'l*, pg. 7270
CSK PRESCENDO CORPORATION—See Sumitomo Corporation; *Int'l*, pg. 7270
CSK SERVICEWARE CORPORATION—See Sumitomo Corporation; *Int'l*, pg. 7270
CSK SP. Z.O.O.—See Commerzbank AG; *Int'l*, pg. 1715
CSK SYSTEM MANAGEMENT CORPORATION—See Sumitomo Corporation; *Int'l*, pg. 7270
CSK SYSTEMS CORPORATION—See Sumitomo Corporation; *Int'l*, pg. 7270
CSK SYSTEMS (SHANGHAI) CO., LTD.—See Sumitomo Corporation; *Int'l*, pg. 7270
CSKTS INC.—See Atlas Copco AB; *Int'l*, pg. 681
CSK WINTECHNOLOGY CORPORATION—See Sumitomo Corporation; *Int'l*, pg. 7270
C&S LAND CO.—See S-P Company Inc.; *U.S. Private*, pg. 3514
CSL ASIA SHIPPING PTE LTD.—See The CSL Group Inc.; *Int'l*, pg. 7636
CS LAUNDRY SYSTEM PHILIPPINES CORP.—See BCM Alliance Berhad; *Int'l*, pg. 928
CS LAUNDRY SYSTEM SDN. BHD.—See BCM Alliance Berhad; *Int'l*, pg. 928
CSL AUSTRALIA LTD.—See The CSL Group Inc.; *Int'l*, pg. 7636
CSL BATESVILLE, LLC—See Sonida Senior Living, Inc.; *U.S. Public*, pg. 1903
CSL BEHRING AB—See CSL Limited; *Int'l*, pg. 1865
CSL BEHRING AG—See CSL Limited; *Int'l*, pg. 1865
CSL BEHRING (AUSTRALIA) PTY LTD.—See CSL Limited; *Int'l*, pg. 1865

COMPANY NAME INDEX

CSL BEHRING B.V.—See CSL Limited; *Int'l*, pg. 1865
CSL BEHRING CANADA INC.—See CSL Limited; *Int'l*, pg. 1865
CSL BEHRING GMBH—See CSL Limited; *Int'l*, pg. 1865
CSL BEHRING K.K.—See CSL Limited; *Int'l*, pg. 1865
CSL BEHRING LDA.—See CSL Limited; *Int'l*, pg. 1865
CSL BEHRING LLC—See CSL Limited; *Int'l*, pg. 1865
CSL BEHRING MEPE—See CSL Limited; *Int'l*, pg. 1865
CSL BEHRING N.V.—See CSL Limited; *Int'l*, pg. 1865
CSL BEHRING S.A.—See CSL Limited; *Int'l*, pg. 1865
CSL BEHRING S.A.—See CSL Limited; *Int'l*, pg. 1865
CSL BEHRING S.P.A.—See CSL Limited; *Int'l*, pg. 1865
CSL BEHRING UK LTD.—See CSL Limited; *Int'l*, pg. 1865
CSL BIOTHERAPIES GMBH.—See CSL Limited; *Int'l*, pg. 1865
CSL BIOTHERAPIES LTD.—See CSL Limited; *Int'l*, pg. 1865
CSL CAPITAL MANAGEMENT, LLC; *U.S. Private*, pg. 1117
CSL CAPITAL (UK) LIMITED—See FCMB Group Plc; *Int'l*, pg. 2628
CSL CE CORPUS, LLC—See Sonida Senior Living, Inc.; *U.S. Public*, pg. 1903
CSL CE STEPHENVILLE, LLC—See Sonida Senior Living, Inc.; *U.S. Public*, pg. 1903
CSL CHARLESTOWN, LLC—See Sonida Senior Living, Inc.; *U.S. Public*, pg. 1903
CSL COLUMBUS, LLC—See Sonida Senior Living, Inc.; *U.S. Public*, pg. 1903
CSL COMMUNICATION (SHENZHEN) CO LTD—See Digilife Technologies Limited; *Int'l*, pg. 2119
CSL EUROPE LIMITED—See The CSL Group Inc.; *Int'l*, pg. 7636
CSL FINANCE PLC—See CSL Limited; *Int'l*, pg. 1865
CSL FITCHBURG MANAGEMENT, LLC—See Sonida Senior Living, Inc.; *U.S. Public*, pg. 1903
CSL GREEN BAY, LLC—See Sonida Senior Living, Inc.; *U.S. Public*, pg. 1903
THE CSL GROUP INC.; *Int'l*, pg. 7636
CSL INTERNATIONAL, INC.—See The CSL Group Inc.; *Int'l*, pg. 7636
CSL KEYSTONE WOODS, LLC—See Sonida Senior Living, Inc.; *U.S. Public*, pg. 1903
CSL LAURELHURST NC, LLC—See Sonida Senior Living, Inc.; *U.S. Public*, pg. 1903
CSL LIMITED; *Int'l*, pg. 1865
CSLM ACQUISITION CORP.; *U.S. Public*, pg. 601
CSL MIRACLE HILLS, LLC—See Sonida Senior Living, Inc.; *U.S. Public*, pg. 1903
CSL MOBILE CARE (M) SDN. BHD.—See Digilife Technologies Limited; *Int'l*, pg. 2119
CSL NORWAY AS—See The CSL Group Inc.; *Int'l*, pg. 7636
CS LOXINFO PUBLIC COMPANY LIMITED—See Advanced Info Service Plc; *Int'l*, pg. 160
CSL PLASMA GMBH—See CSL Limited; *Int'l*, pg. 1865
CSL PLASMA INC.—See CSL Limited; *Int'l*, pg. 1865
CSL RIVERBEND IN, LLC—See Sonida Senior Living, Inc.; *U.S. Public*, pg. 1903
CSL STOCKBROKERS LIMITED—See FCMB Group Plc; *Int'l*, pg. 2628
CSL STUDENT LIVING BENIKEA KP LTD.—See Centurion Corporation Limited; *Int'l*, pg. 1416
CSL STUDENT LIVING (SELEGIE) PTE. LTD.—See Centurion Corporation Limited; *Int'l*, pg. 1416
CSL SUMMIT, LLC—See Sonida Senior Living, Inc.; *U.S. Public*, pg. 1903
CSL TEXAS SYSTEM, LLC—See Windstream Holdings, Inc.; *U.S. Public*, pg. 2373
CSL TOWNE CENTRE, LLC—See Sonida Senior Living, Inc.; *U.S. Public*, pg. 1903
C.S. LUMBER CO., INC.; *Int'l*, pg. 1244
CSL VAN DORN, LLC—See Sonida Senior Living, Inc.; *U.S. Public*, pg. 1903
CSL VIRGINIA BEACH, LLC—See Sonida Senior Living, Inc.; *U.S. Public*, pg. 1903
CSL WHISPERING PINES, LLC—See Sonida Senior Living, Inc.; *U.S. Public*, pg. 1903
CSL WHITCOMB HOUSE, LLC—See Sonida Senior Living, Inc.; *U.S. Public*, pg. 1903
CS MACROLITE—See CS CORPORATION; *Int'l*, pg. 1861
C SMALL GROUP LIMITED—See China Silver Group Limited; *Int'l*, pg. 1551
CS MANUFACTURING, INC.; *U.S. Private*, pg. 1116
C SMART SOLUTION COMPANY LIMITED—See Berli Jucker Public Co. Ltd.; *Int'l*, pg. 985
CSM AUSTRIA GMBH—See Rhone Group, LLC; *U.S. Private*, pg. 3423
CSM BAKERY PRODUCTS - COLTON—See Rhone Group, LLC; *U.S. Private*, pg. 3423
CSM BAKERY PRODUCTS - LANCASTER—See Rhone Group, LLC; *U.S. Private*, pg. 3423
CSM BAKERY PRODUCTS - MINNETONKA—See Rhone Group, LLC; *U.S. Private*, pg. 3423
CSM BAKERY PRODUCTS NORTH AMERICA—See Rhone Group, LLC; *U.S. Private*, pg. 3423
CSM BAKERY SOLUTIONS EUROPE HOLDING B.V.—See Rhone Group, LLC; *U.S. Private*, pg. 3423

CSM BAKERY SUPPLIES GIDA SAN. VE TIC. A.S—See Rhone Group, LLC; *U.S. Private*, pg. 3423
CSM BALTIJA SIA—See Schoeller Holdings Ltd.; *Int'l*, pg. 6637
CSM BENELUX - GOES—See Rhone Group, LLC; *U.S. Private*, pg. 3423
CSM BENELUX NV—See Rhone Group, LLC; *U.S. Private*, pg. 3423
CSM BESSAC—See VINCI S.A.; *Int'l*, pg. 8234
CSM BIOCHEM TRADING SHANGHAI CO., LTD.—See Rhone Group, LLC; *U.S. Private*, pg. 3423
C.S. MCCROSSAN, INC.; *U.S. Private*, pg. 709
C.S. MCKEE LP—See Estancia Capital Management, LLC; *U.S. Private*, pg. 1428
CSM COMPANIES, INC.; *U.S. Private*, pg. 1117
CSM COMPRESSOR INC—See Burckhardt Compression Holding AG; *Int'l*, pg. 1221
CSM CORPORATION; *U.S. Private*, pg. 1117
CSM CRUISE SERVICES GMBH—See Schoeller Holdings Ltd.; *Int'l*, pg. 6637
CSMC TECHNOLOGIES CORPORATION—See China Resources (Holdings) Co., Ltd.; *Int'l*, pg. 1548
CSM DEUTSCHLAND GMBH—See Rhone Group, LLC; *U.S. Private*, pg. 3423
CSM DEUTSCHLAND GMBH—See Rhone Group, LLC; *U.S. Private*, pg. 3423
CS MEDICA A/S; *Int'l*, pg. 1861
C'S MEN CO., LTD.; *Int'l*, pg. 1239
CSM ENGINEERING LTD.—See ARCADIS N.V.; *Int'l*, pg. 541
CS METAL CO., LTD.—See Sumitomo Corporation; *Int'l*, pg. 7268
CSM EVENTS LIMITED—See Wasserman Media Group, LLC; *U.S. Private*, pg. 4450
CSM FRANCE SAS—See Rhone Group, LLC; *U.S. Private*, pg. 3423
CSM HELLAS SA—See Rhone Group, LLC; *U.S. Private*, pg. 3423
CSM IBERIA SA—See Rhone Group, LLC; *U.S. Private*, pg. 3423
CSMI; *U.S. Private*, pg. 1117
CSM ITALIA S.R.L.—See Rhone Group, LLC; *U.S. Private*, pg. 3423
CSM MAGYARORSZAG KFT.—See Rhone Group, LLC; *U.S. Private*, pg. 3423
CSM MOTORSPORTS, INC.—See Providence Equity Partners L.L.C.; *U.S. Private*, pg. 3291
CSM NORDIC A/S—See Rhone Group, LLC; *U.S. Private*, pg. 3423
C&S MOTORS, INC.; *U.S. Private*, pg. 704
CSM POLSKA SP. Z O.O.—See Rhone Group, LLC; *U.S. Private*, pg. 3423
CSM PRODUCTION—See Wasserman Media Group, LLC; *U.S. Private*, pg. 4450
CSM SPORT & ENTERTAINMENT LLP—See Wasserman Media Group, LLC; *U.S. Private*, pg. 4450
CSM SPORT & ENTERTAINMENT NEW ZEALAND LIMITED—See Wasserman Media Group, LLC; *U.S. Private*, pg. 4450
CS MUNDY QUARRIES INC.—See Eagle Corporation; *U.S. Private*, pg. 1309
CSM (UNITED KINGDOM) LTD.—See Rhone Group, LLC; *U.S. Private*, pg. 3423
CS MYERS & SON INC.; *U.S. Private*, pg. 1116
CS CIMENTOS—See Companhia Siderurgica Nacional; *Int'l*, pg. 1748
CS NIPPON CORPORATION—See Nippon Television Holdings Inc.; *Int'l*, pg. 5356
CSNK WORKING CAPITAL FINANCE CORP.—See Heritage Commerce Corp; *U.S. Private*, pg. 1028
CSN PARANA—See Companhia Siderurgica Nacional; *Int'l*, pg. 1748
CSN PORTO REAL—See Companhia Siderurgica Nacional; *Int'l*, pg. 1748
CSOB LEASING A.S.—See KBC Group NV; *Int'l*, pg. 4105
CSOB NADACIA—See KBC Group NV; *Int'l*, pg. 4105
CSOB POJISTOVNA A.S.—See KBC Group NV; *Int'l*, pg. 4106
CSOB STAVEBNA SPORITELNA A.S.—See KBC Group NV; *Int'l*, pg. 4105
CS ONE TEN, LTD.—See TV Asahi Holdings Corporation; *Int'l*, pg. 7986
C&S PACKAGING GROUP INC.; *U.S. Private*, pg. 704
C&S PAPER CO., LTD.; *Int'l*, pg. 1239
C&S PAPER (HUBEI) CO., LTD.—See C&S Paper Co., Ltd.; *Int'l*, pg. 1239
C&S PAPER (SICHUAN) CO., LTD.—See C&S Paper Co., Ltd.; *Int'l*, pg. 1239
C&S PAPER YUNFU CO., LTD.—See C&S Paper Co., Ltd.; *Int'l*, pg. 1239
CSP BUILDING & SERVICE INC.—See Central Security Patrols Co., Ltd.; *Int'l*, pg. 1409
CSPC DERMAY EUROPE GMBH—See CSPC Pharmaceutical Group Limited; *Int'l*, pg. 1867
CSPC DOPHEN CORPORATION—See CSPC Pharmaceutical Group Limited; *Int'l*, pg. 1867
CSPC HEALTHCARE INC.—See CSPC Pharmaceutical Group Limited; *Int'l*, pg. 1867

CSPC HEBEI ZHONGNUO PHARMACEUTICAL (SHIJIAZHUANG) CO., LTD.—See CSPC Pharmaceutical Group Limited; *Int'l*, pg. 1867
CSP CHINA STEEL PLC; *Int'l*, pg. 1867
CSPC PHARMACEUTICAL GROUP LIMITED; *Int'l*, pg. 1867
CSP CREATIVE SERVICE CO., LTD—See Central Security Patrols Co., Ltd.; *Int'l*, pg. 1410
CSPC WEISHENG PHARMACEUTICAL (SHIJIAZHUANG) CO., LTD—See CSPC Pharmaceutical Group Limited; *Int'l*, pg. 1867
C. SPECK MOTORS; *U.S. Private*, pg. 705
CSP INC. SECURITIES CORP.—See CSP Inc.; *U.S. Public*, pg. 601
CSP INC.; *U.S. Public*, pg. 601
CSP INTERNATIONAL FASHION GROUP S.P.A.; *Int'l*, pg. 1867
CSP JAPAN, INC.—See Shimizu Corporation; *Int'l*, pg. 6835
CSP MOBILE PRODUCTIONS, LLC; *U.S. Private*, pg. 1117
C/S POLSKA SP. ZO.O—See Construction Specialties, Inc.; *U.S. Private*, pg. 1024
CSP STEEL CENTER PUBLIC COMPANY LIMITED; *Int'l*, pg. 1867
CSP ZEEBRUGGE TERMINAL NV—See COSCO Shipping Holdings Co., Ltd.; *Int'l*, pg. 1810
CSRA BOLIVIA S.R.L.—See General Dynamics Corporation; *U.S. Public*, pg. 913
CSRA HOLDINGS, LLC—See Quorum Health Corporation; *U.S. Private*, pg. 3329
CSRA PROBATION SERVICES, INC.; *U.S. Private*, pg. 1117
CSR BUILDING PRODUCTS LTD.—See Crescent Capital Partners Ltd.; *Int'l*, pg. 1839
CSR BUILDING PRODUCTS (NZ) LTD.—See CSR Limited; *Int'l*, pg. 1867
CSR COMPANY INC.; *U.S. Private*, pg. 1117
CS REKLAM HIZMETLERI SANAYI VE TICARET A.S.—See WPP plc; *Int'l*, pg. 8491
CSR FEB. 7TH ROLLING STOCK CO., LTD—See CRRC Corporation Limited; *Int'l*, pg. 1858
CSR FRICKER CEILING SYSTEMS QLD—See CSR Limited; *Int'l*, pg. 1867
CSR FRICKER CEILING SYSTEMS—See CSR Limited; *Int'l*, pg. 1867
CSR, INC.—See CVS Health Corporation; *U.S. Public*, pg. 616
CSR INDIA PRIVATE LIMITED—See QUALCOMM Incorporated; *U.S. Public*, pg. 1748
CSR LIMITED; *Int'l*, pg. 1867
CSR MARTINI PTY LIMITED—See CSR Limited; *Int'l*, pg. 1867
CSR MEISHAN ROLLING STOCK CO., LTD—See CRRC Corporation Limited; *Int'l*, pg. 1858
CSR - MONTICELLO CROSSINGS, LLC—See Centerspace; *U.S. Public*, pg. 472
CS ROMANIA SA—See Sopra Steria Group S.A.; *Int'l*, pg. 7109
CSR QISHUYAN LOCOMOTIVE CO., LTD—See CRRC Corporation Limited; *Int'l*, pg. 1858
CSR TECHNOLOGY (INDIA) PRIVATE LIMITED—See QUALCOMM Incorporated; *U.S. Public*, pg. 1748
CSRWARE, INC.—See BC Partners LLP; *Int'l*, pg. 925
CSRWIRE, LLC—See 3BL Media LLC; *U.S. Private*, pg. 8
CSR ZIYANG LOCOMOTIVE CO., LTD—See CRRC Corporation Limited; *Int'l*, pg. 1858
CSSC CUSTOMER SALES SERVICE CENTER GMBH—See Erste Group Bank AG; *Int'l*, pg. 2498
CSSC (HONG KONG) SHIPPING COMPANY LIMITED—See China State Shipbuilding Corporation; *Int'l*, pg. 1554
CSSC OFFSHORE & MARINE ENGINEERING COMPANY LTD.; *Int'l*, pg. 1867
CSS CO., LTD.—See Sumitomo Life Insurance Company; *Int'l*, pg. 7291
CSSC SCIENCE AND TECHNOLOGY CO., LTD—See China State Shipbuilding Corporation; *Int'l*, pg. 1554
CS&S CYBER RESOURCES SOFTWARE TECHNOLOGY (TIANJIN) CO., LTD.—See Chinasoft International Ltd.; *Int'l*, pg. 1568
CSS DISTRIBUTION GROUP, INC.; *U.S. Private*, pg. 1117
CSS FARMS INC.; *U.S. Private*, pg. 1117
CSS HOLDINGS, LTD.; *Int'l*, pg. 1867
CSS HOTELS SERVICES INC.; *U.S. Private*, pg. 1118
CSSI INC.; *U.S. Private*, pg. 1118
CSS INDUSTRIES, INC.—See IG Design Group Plc; *Int'l*, pg. 3600
CSS LABORATORIES INC.; *U.S. Private*, pg. 1118
CSSS.NET; *U.S. Private*, pg. 1118
CS STARS LLC—See Marsh & McLennan Companies, Inc.; *U.S. Public*, pg. 1380
CST/BERGER—See Robert Bosch GmbH; *Int'l*, pg. 6364
CST CANADA COAL LIMITED; *Int'l*, pg. 1868
CST CO., LTD.—See TIS Inc.; *Int'l*, pg. 7757
CS TECHNOLOGY, INC.; *U.S. Private*, pg. 1116
C. STEIN, INC.; *U.S. Private*, pg. 705
CST GMBH—See Minth Group Limited; *Int'l*, pg. 4914
CST GROUP LIMITED; *Int'l*, pg. 1868

CST GROUP LIMITED

Company Index

C'S THREE CO., LTD.—See Nomad Foods Limited; *Int'l*, pg. 5408
CST INDUSTRIES, INC.—See Solace Capital Partners, LLC; *U.S. Private*, pg. 3706
CST INDUSTRIES (MANUFACTURING FACILITY), INC. - UK—See Solace Capital Partners, LLC; *U.S. Private*, pg. 3706
CST LATINO AMERICA COMERCIO E REPRESENTACAO DE PRODUTOS ELECTRICOS E ELESTRONICOS LTDA—See Schneider Electric SE; *Int'l*, pg. 6626
CST LIMITED, LLC—See Duke Energy Corporation; *U.S. Public*, pg. 690
CST MANUFACTURING FACILITY CONROE (CST COVERS)—See Solace Capital Partners, LLC; *U.S. Private*, pg. 3706
CST MINERALS LADY ANNIE PTY LIMITED—See CST Group Limited; *Int'l*, pg. 1868
CSTONE PHARMACEUTICALS; *Int'l*, pg. 1868
C STREET HEALTH ASSOCIATES LLC—See The Ensign Group, Inc.; *U.S. Public*, pg. 2070
CST SENSORS INDIA PRIVATE LIMITED—See Schneider Electric SE; *Int'l*, pg. 6626
CST VALINOX LTD.—See Vallourec SA; *Int'l*, pg. 8118
CSTV NETWORKS, INC.—See National Amusements, Inc.; *U.S. Private*, pg. 2840
CSUBS; *U.S. Private*, pg. 1118
CSU CARDSYSTEM S.A.; *Int'l*, pg. 1868
CSU LLC; *U.S. Private*, pg. 1118
CSUN AUSTRALIA PTY. LTD.—See China Sunergy Co., Ltd.; *Int'l*, pg. 1556
CSUN - CHINA SUNERGY CLEAN TECH INC.—See China Sunergy Co., Ltd.; *Int'l*, pg. 1556
CSUN - CHINA SUNERGY EUROPE GMBH—See China Sunergy Co., Ltd.; *Int'l*, pg. 1556
CSUN - CHINA SUNERGY (SOUTH AFRICA) CO., LTD.—See China Sunergy Co., Ltd.; *Int'l*, pg. 1556
CSUN EURASIA ENERGY SYSTEMS INDUSTRY & TRADE INC.—See China Sunergy Co., Ltd.; *Int'l*, pg. 1556
CSUN JAPAN SOLAR ENERGY CO., LTD.—See China Sunergy Co., Ltd.; *Int'l*, pg. 1556
CSUN MFG. LTD.; *Int'l*, pg. 1868
CSUN RENEWABLE ENERGY (FRANCE) S.A.R.L.—See China Sunergy Co., Ltd.; *Int'l*, pg. 1556
CSUN TECHNOLOGY (GUANGZHOU) CO., LTD.—See CSUN MFG. LTD.; *Int'l*, pg. 1868
C&S WASTE SERVICES INC.—See Peoria Disposal Company/Area Disposal Service, Inc.; *U.S. Private*, pg. 3143
C S & W CONTRACTORS; *U.S. Private*, pg. 702
CS WEALTH SECURITIES LIMITED—See CSC Holdings Limited; *Int'l*, pg. 1862
C&S WHOLESALE GROCERS, INC.; *U.S. Private*, pg. 704
CSW, INC.; *U.S. Private*, pg. 1118
CS WIND CANADA INC.—See CS Wind Corporation; *Int'l*, pg. 1861
CS WIND CHINA CO., LTD.—See CS Wind Corporation; *Int'l*, pg. 1861
CS WIND CORPORATION; *Int'l*, pg. 1861
CS WIND MALAYSIA SDN. BHD.—See CS Wind Corporation; *Int'l*, pg. 1861
CS WIND TAIWAN LTD.—See CS Wind Corporation; *Int'l*, pg. 1861
CS WIND TURKEY IMALATI ENERJI VE CELIK SAN. TIC. A.S.—See CS Wind Corporation; *Int'l*, pg. 1861
CS WIND UK LIMITED—See CS Wind Corporation; *Int'l*, pg. 1861
CSW INDUSTRIALS, INC.; *U.S. Public*, pg. 601
CS WIND VIETNAM CO., LTD.—See CS Wind Corporation; *Int'l*, pg. 1861
C.S. WO & SONS LTD.; *U.S. Private*, pg. 709
CSW SUPERIOR IT SOLUTIONS, INC.—See Summit 7 Systems, LLC; *U.S. Private*, pg. 3853
CSWW INC.; *U.S. Private*, pg. 1118
CSX CORPORATION; *U.S. Public*, pg. 602
CSX INTERMODAL, INC.—See CSX Corporation; *U.S. Public*, pg. 602
CSX REAL PROPERTY INC.—See CSX Corporation; *U.S. Public*, pg. 602
CSX TRANSPORTATION, INC.—See CSX Corporation; *U.S. Public*, pg. 602
CS YAKUHIN CO., LTD.—See Alfresa Holdings Corporation; *Int'l*, pg. 317
CSY S.A.—See PGF Polska Grupa Fotowoltaiczna S.A.; *Int'l*, pg. 5838
C-SYSTEMS INTERNATIONAL CORPORATION; *U.S. Private*, pg. 704
CTA ACOUSTICS, INC. - CORBIN MANUFACTURING FACILITY—See Cerberus Capital Management, L.P.; *U.S. Private*, pg. 837
CTA ACOUSTICS, INC.—See Cerberus Capital Management, L.P.; *U.S. Private*, pg. 837
CTAC BELGIE N.V.—See Ctac N.V.; *Int'l*, pg. 1869
CTAC BELGIUM BVBA—See Ctac N.V.; *Int'l*, pg. 1869
CTAC DEUTSCHLAND GMBH—See Ctac N.V.; *Int'l*, pg. 1869
CTAC FRANCE SAS—See Ctac N.V.; *Int'l*, pg. 1869
CTAC N.V.; *Int'l*, pg. 1869

CT AEROSPACE LLC—See VSE Corporation; *U.S. Public*, pg. 2313
C&T AFFILIATES INC.; *U.S. Private*, pg. 704
CTAG-IDIADA SAFETY TECHNOLOGY, S.L.—See I Squared Capital Advisors (US) LLC; *U.S. Private*, pg. 2022
CTAG-IDIADA SAFETY TECHNOLOGY, S.L.—See TDR Capital LLP; *Int'l*, pg. 7491
CTA HOLDING; *Int'l*, pg. 1869
CTA MANUFACTURING, INC.; *U.S. Private*, pg. 1118
CTAM INC—See Senetas Corporation Limited; *Int'l*, pg. 6708
CTAP LLC—See ITOCHU Corporation; *Int'l*, pg. 3840
CTAP LLC—See Marubeni Corporation; *Int'l*, pg. 4709
CT- ARZNEIMITTEL GMBH—See Teva Pharmaceutical Industries, Ltd.; *Int'l*, pg. 7579
C.T.A. S.A.R.L.—See DEKRA e.V.; *Int'l*, pg. 2007
CTAS CORPORATION—See CTCI Corporation; *Int'l*, pg. 1870
CT ASSIST LLC; *U.S. Private*, pg. 1118
CT AUTOMOTIVE GROUP PLC; *Int'l*, pg. 1868
CT AUTOMOTIVE JAPAN KK—See CT Automotive Group Plc; *Int'l*, pg. 1868
CTB AUSTRALIA LIMITED—See Commonwealth Bank of Australia; *Int'l*, pg. 1719
CTBC ASIA LIMITED—See CTBC Financial Holding Co., Ltd.; *Int'l*, pg. 1869
CTBC ASSET MANAGEMENT CO., LTD.—See CTBC Financial Holding Co., Ltd.; *Int'l*, pg. 1869
CTBC BANK CO., LTD.—See CTBC Financial Holding Co., Ltd.; *Int'l*, pg. 1869
CTBC BANK CORP.—See CTBC Financial Holding Co., Ltd.; *Int'l*, pg. 1869
CTBC BANK CORP. (USA)—See CTBC Financial Holding Co., Ltd.; *Int'l*, pg. 1869
CTBC BANK (PHILIPPINES) CORP.—See CTBC Financial Holding Co., Ltd.; *Int'l*, pg. 1869
CTBC FINANCIAL HOLDING CO., LTD.; *Int'l*, pg. 1869
CTBC INVESTMENTS CO., LTD.—See CTBC Financial Holding Co., Ltd.; *Int'l*, pg. 1869
CTBC LIFE INSURANCE CO., LTD.—See CTBC Financial Holding Co., Ltd.; *Int'l*, pg. 1869
CTBC SECURITY CO., LTD.—See CTBC Financial Holding Co., Ltd.; *Int'l*, pg. 1869
CTBC VENTURE CAPITAL CO., LTD.—See CTBC Financial Holding Co., Ltd.; *Int'l*, pg. 1869
CTB GOLF (HK) LTD.—See Sino Golf Holdings Ltd.; *Int'l*, pg. 6947
CTB, INC.—See Berkshire Hathaway Inc.; *U.S. Public*, pg. 303
CTB INTERNATIONAL CORP.—See Berkshire Hathaway Inc.; *U.S. Public*, pg. 303
CTC AB—See NIBE Industrier AB; *Int'l*, pg. 5260
CTC AVIATION GROUP LIMITED—See L3Harris Technologies, Inc.; *U.S. Public*, pg. 1281
CTC BIO., INC.; *Int'l*, pg. 1869
CTC CONSULTING LLC—See Bank of Montreal; *Int'l*, pg. 846
CTC FERROFIL AS—See NIBE Industrier AB; *Int'l*, pg. 5260
CTC FOOD INTERNATIONAL; *U.S. Private*, pg. 1118
CTC GIERSCH AG—See NIBE Industrier AB; *Int'l*, pg. 5260
CTC GMBH—See Airbus SE; *Int'l*, pg. 242
CTCI ADVANCED SYSTEMS INC.; *Int'l*, pg. 1869
CTCI ADVANCED SYSTEMS SHANGHAI INC.—See CTCI Corporation; *Int'l*, pg. 1870
CTCI AMERICAS, INC.—See CTCI Corporation; *Int'l*, pg. 1870
CTCI ARABIA LTD.—See CTCI Corporation; *Int'l*, pg. 1870
CTCI CHEMICALS CORP.—See CTCI Corporation; *Int'l*, pg. 1870
CTCI CORPORATION; *Int'l*, pg. 1869
CTCI CORPORATION—See CTCI Corporation; *Int'l*, pg. 1870
CTCI ENGINEERING & CONSTRUCTION SDN BHD—See CTCI Corporation; *Int'l*, pg. 1870
CTCI-HDEC (CHUNGLI) CORP.—See CTCI Corporation; *Int'l*, pg. 1870
CTCI MACHINERY CORPORATION—See CTCI Corporation; *Int'l*, pg. 1870
CTC INTERNATIONAL, INC.—See CTC Bio., Inc.; *Int'l*, pg. 1869
CTCI SHANGHAI CO., LTD.—See CTCI Corporation; *Int'l*, pg. 1870
CTCI SINGAPORE PTE. LTD.—See CTCI Corporation; *Int'l*, pg. 1870
CTCI (THAILAND) CO., LTD.—See CTCI Corporation; *Int'l*, pg. 1870
CTCI TRADING SHANGHAI CO., LTD.—See CTCI Corporation; *Int'l*, pg. 1870
CTCI VIETNAM COMPANY LIMITED—See CTCI Corporation; *Int'l*, pg. 1870
CTCI VIETNAM COMPANY LIMITED—See Sincerity Engineering Company Limited; *Int'l*, pg. 6937
CTCI VIETNAM COMPANY LIMITED—See Vietnam Machinery Installation Corporation JSC; *Int'l*, pg. 8200
CTCI VIETNAM COMPANY LIMITED—See CTCI Corporation; *Int'l*, pg. 1870

CORPORATE AFFILIATIONS

CTC LABORATORY SYSTEMS CORPORATION—See Abbott Laboratories; *U.S. Public*, pg. 20
CTC LABORATORY SYSTEMS CORPORATION—See ITOCHU Corporation; *Int'l*, pg. 3840
CTC MEDIA, INC.; *Int'l*, pg. 1869
C&T CONSULTING SERVICES LLP; *U.S. Private*, pg. 704
CT CORPORATION SYSTEM—See Wolters Kluwer n.v.; *Int'l*, pg. 8445
CT CORSEARCH—See Wolters Kluwer n.v.; *Int'l*, pg. 8445
CTC PUBLIC BENEFIT CORPORATION—See Concurrent Technologies Corporation; *U.S. Private*, pg. 1011
CTC SERVICES (MALAYSIA) SDN BHD—See Lovell Minnick Partners LLC; *U.S. Private*, pg. 2502
CTC—See Concurrent Technologies Corporation; *U.S. Private*, pg. 1011
CTCUE B.V.—See IQVIA Holdings Inc.; *U.S. Public*, pg. 1168
CTD CONTAINER-TRANSPORT-DIENST GMBH—See Hamburger Hafen und Logistik AG; *Int'l*, pg. 3236
CTDD BEER IMPORTS LTD.—See Carlsberg A/S; *Int'l*, pg. 1339
CT DEVELOPERS LTD.; *Int'l*, pg. 1868
CTDI - AUSTRALIA PTY LIMITED—See Communications Test Design Inc.; *U.S. Private*, pg. 989
CTDI DO BRAZIL LTDA—See Communications Test Design Inc.; *U.S. Private*, pg. 989
CTDI EUROPE GMBH.—See Communications Test Design Inc.; *U.S. Private*, pg. 989
CTDI HONG KONG LIMITED—See Communications Test Design Inc.; *U.S. Private*, pg. 989
CTDI NETHOUSE SERVICES KFT.—See Communications Test Design Inc.; *U.S. Private*, pg. 989
CTDI NETHOUSE SERVICES LTD—See Communications Test Design Inc.; *U.S. Private*, pg. 989
CTDI S.R.L.—See Communications Test Design Inc.; *U.S. Private*, pg. 989
CTD NETWORKS CO., LTD.—See Central Security Patrols Co., Ltd.; *Int'l*, pg. 1410
C&T DREAM CO., LTD.; *Int'l*, pg. 1239
CTEAM CONSULTING & ANLAGENBAU GMBH; *Int'l*, pg. 1870
CTECH CLOSURES PTY. LTD.—See Pro-Pac Packaging Limited; *Int'l*, pg. 5985
C-TECH INDUSTRIES DE MEXICO, S. DE R.L. DE C.F.—See Alfred Karcher GmbH & Co. KG; *Int'l*, pg. 316
C-TECH INDUSTRIES, LLC—See Group Thermote & Vanhalst; *Int'l*, pg. 3089
C TECHNOLOGIES AB—See Anoto Group AB; *Int'l*, pg. 474
C TECHNOLOGIES, INC.—See Repligen Corporation; *U.S. Public*, pg. 1784
C TECHNOLOGIES—See Anoto Group AB; *Int'l*, pg. 474
CTEEP - COMPANHIA DE TRANSMISSAO DE ENERGIA ELETRICA PAULISTA—See Ecopetrol S.A.; *Int'l*, pg. 2299
CTEK AB; *Int'l*, pg. 1870
CTEK, INC.—See Digi International Inc.; *U.S. Public*, pg. 662
CTEK SECURITY, INC.—See Altaris Capital Partners, LLC; *U.S. Private*, pg. 206
CTE LOGISTICS; *U.S. Private*, pg. 1118
CT ENVIRONMENTAL GROUP LIMITED; *Int'l*, pg. 1868
C.T.E. SYSTEMS, INC.—See Associated Time & Parking Controls, Inc.; *U.S. Private*, pg. 357
CTF GROUP CLOSED JOINT STOCK COMPANY—See Lubawa S.A.; *Int'l*, pg. 4572
CTF HOLDINGS INC.; *U.S. Private*, pg. 1118
CT FORMPOLSTER GMBH—See MBB SE; *Int'l*, pg. 4751
CTF SOLAR GMBH—See China National Building Material Group Co., Ltd.; *Int'l*, pg. 1525
CTF WATCH LIMITED—See Chow Tai Fook Enterprises Limited; *Int'l*, pg. 1584
CTG INTERNATIONAL INC.—See China National Materials; *Int'l*, pg. 1532
CT GLOBAL MANAGED PORTFOLIO TRUST PLC; *Int'l*, pg. 1868
CT GROUP LIMITED—See RTX Corporation; *U.S. Public*, pg. 1821
CT GROUP; *U.S. Private*, pg. 1118
CTG US LLC; *U.S. Private*, pg. 1118
CT HAUP HENG SDN BHD—See Lii Hen Industries Bhd.; *Int'l*, pg. 4497
C.T. HELLMUTH & ASSOCIATES, LLC—See New Mountain Capital, LLC; *U.S. Private*, pg. 2901
CTH GMBH—See Darling Ingredients Inc.; *U.S. Public*, pg. 633
C. THORREZ INDUSTRIES INC.; *U.S. Private*, pg. 705
CTH PORTO - INDUSTRIA ALIMENTAR UNIPESSOAL LDA—See Darling Ingredients Inc.; *U.S. Public*, pg. 633
CTH US INC.—See Darling Ingredients Inc.; *U.S. Public*, pg. 633
CTI ASCEND CO., LTD.—See CTI Engineering Co., Ltd.; *Int'l*, pg. 1870
CTIA-THE WIRELESS ASSOCIATION; *U.S. Private*, pg. 1118
CTI AURA CO., LTD.—See CTI Engineering Co., Ltd.; *Int'l*, pg. 1870

COMPANY NAME INDEX

CTI BALLOONS LTD.—See Yunhong Green CTI Ltd.; *U.S. Public*, pg. 2400
CTI BIOPHARMA CORP.—See Swedish Orphan Biovitrum AB; *Int'l*, pg. 7365
CTI BUSINESS INVESTMENT COMPANY PTY LTD—See CTI Logistics Limited; *Int'l*, pg. 1871
CTI COMPANIA DE TELEFONOS DEL INTERIOR S.A.—See America Movil, S.A.B. de C.V.; *Int'l*, pg. 421
CTI CORP.; *U.S. Private*, pg. 1118
CTI COURIERS PTY LTD—See CTI Logistics Limited; *Int'l*, pg. 1871
CTI EDUCATION GROUP PTY LTD—See Pearson plc; *Int'l*, pg. 5775
CTI ENGINEERING CO., LTD.; *Int'l*, pg. 1870
CTI ENGINEERING INTERNATIONAL CO., LTD.—See CTI Engineering Co., Ltd.; *Int'l*, pg. 1870
CTI FLEET MANAGEMENT PTY LTD—See CTI Logistics Limited; *Int'l*, pg. 1871
CTI FOODS, LLC - CARSON PLANT—See Black Diamond Capital Holdings, LLC; *U.S. Private*, pg. 570
CTI FOODS, LLC - CARSON PLANT—See Massachusetts Mutual Life Insurance Company; *U.S. Private*, pg. 2605
CTI FOODS, LLC—See Black Diamond Capital Holdings, LLC; *U.S. Private*, pg. 570
CTI FOODS, LLC—See Massachusetts Mutual Life Insurance Company; *U.S. Private*, pg. 2605
CTI FREIGHTLINES PTY LTD—See CTI Logistics Limited; *Int'l*, pg. 1871
CTI FREIGHT SYSTEMS PTY LTD—See CTI Logistics Limited; *Int'l*, pg. 1871
CTI GROUND PLANNING CO., LTD.—See CTI Engineering Co., Ltd.; *Int'l*, pg. 1871
CTI GROUP (HOLDINGS) INC.—See Enghouse Systems Limited; *Int'l*, pg. 2427
CTI INDUSTRIES—See Amphenol Corporation; *U.S. Public*, pg. 129
CTI LEASING INC.—See CTI Corp.; *U.S. Private*, pg. 1118
CTI LOGISTICS LIMITED; *Int'l*, pg. 1871
CTI LOGISTICS LTD - FLEET MANAGEMENT DIVISION—See CTI Logistics Limited; *Int'l*, pg. 1871
CTI LOGISTICS LTD - GENERAL & CONTAINER TRANSPORT DIVISION—See CTI Logistics Limited; *Int'l*, pg. 1871
CTI MEDIA; *U.S. Private*, pg. 1118
CTI MYANMAR CO., LTD.—See CTI Engineering Co., Ltd.; *Int'l*, pg. 1871
CT INGENIEROS AAISL; *Int'l*, pg. 1868
CT INTERCONTINENTAL, LTD.—See AutoNation, Inc.; *U.S. Public*, pg. 233
CTI PILIPINAS, INC.—See CTI Engineering Co., Ltd.; *Int'l*, pg. 1871
CTI RECORDS MANAGEMENT PTY LTD—See CTI Logistics Limited; *Int'l*, pg. 1871
CTI RECORDS MANAGEMENT PTY LTD—See CTI Logistics Limited; *Int'l*, pg. 1871
CTI REED CO., LTD.—See CTI Engineering Co., Ltd.; *Int'l*, pg. 1871
CTI RESOURCE MANAGEMENT SERVICES, INC.; *U.S. Private*, pg. 1118
CTI RP, INC.—See Ridgemont Partners Management LLC; *U.S. Private*, pg. 3433
CTI SECURITY SERVICES PTY LTD—See CTI Logistics Limited; *Int'l*, pg. 1871
CTI SECURITY SYSTEMS PTY LTD—See CTI Logistics Limited; *Int'l*, pg. 1871
CTI SUPPLY, INC.—See Yunhong Green CTI Ltd.; *U.S. Public*, pg. 2400
CTI TAXI TRUCKS PTY. LTD.—See CTI Logistics Limited; *Int'l*, pg. 1871
CTI TECNOLOGIA Y GESTION, S.A.—See Informa SA; *Int'l*, pg. 3694
CTI TOWERS, INC.—See Melody Investment Advisors LP; *U.S. Private*, pg. 2663
C.T.I. TRAFFIC INDUSTRIES CO., LTD.; *Int'l*, pg. 1244
CTI TRANSPORT SYSTEMS PTY LTD—See CTI Logistics Limited; *Int'l*, pg. 1871
CTI U.S. INC.—See Centre Testing International Corporation; *Int'l*, pg. 1411
CTI-VIENNA GESELLSCHAFT ZUR PRUFUNG ELEKTROTECHNISCHER INDUSTRIEPRODUKTE GMBH—See Eaton Corporation plc; *Int'l*, pg. 2277
CTI XPRESS SYSTEMS PTY LTD—See CTI Logistics Limited; *Int'l*, pg. 1871
CTKC CORPORATION—See Compagnie de Saint-Gobain SA; *Int'l*, pg. 1729
CTK COSMETICS; *Int'l*, pg. 1871
CTL AEROSPACE INC.; *U.S. Private*, pg. 1118
CTL ENGINEERING, INC.; *U.S. Private*, pg. 1119
CTL LOGISTICS S.A.—See Compass Advisers Group LLC; *U.S. Private*, pg. 998
CTL MANAGEMENT INC.—See The Randall Group Inc.; *U.S. Private*, pg. 4102
CTL MANUFACTURING—See Avnet, Inc.; *U.S. Public*, pg. 250
CTL STEEL CO.—See Clark Grave Vault Company; *U.S. Private*, pg. 913
CTL TRANSPORTATION LLC—See Comcar Industries, Inc.; *U.S. Private*, pg. 981
C&T MATRIX LIMITED—See Synnovia Plc; *Int'l*, pg. 7386

CTM CHILI SA—See VINCI S.A.; *Int'l*, pg. 8216
CTM INDIA LTD—See Samvardhana Motherson International Limited; *Int'l*, pg. 6516
CTM LYNG AS—See Addtech AB; *Int'l*, pg. 132
CTM MEDIA GROUP - CANADIAN DIVISION—See CTM Media Group, Inc.; *U.S. Private*, pg. 1119
CTM MEDIA GROUP, INC.; *U.S. Private*, pg. 1119
CT MOTORS, INC.—See AutoNation, Inc.; *U.S. Public*, pg. 233
CTM OVERSEAS EDUCATION CENTRE LIMITED—See Corporate Travel Management Limited; *Int'l*, pg. 1805
CTM SA; *Int'l*, pg. 1872
CTM SOFTWARE CORP.—See GI Manager L.P.; *U.S. Private*, pg. 1693
CTM SOFTWARE CORP.—See TA Associates, Inc.; *U.S. Private*, pg. 3914
CTNETWORKS CO., LTD.; *Int'l*, pg. 1872
CTO 24/7 (PRIVATE) LIMITED—See Stewart Information Services Corporation; *U.S. Public*, pg. 1947
C.T.O. PUBLIC COMPANY LTD.; *Int'l*, pg. 1244
CTO REALTY GROWTH, INC.; *U.S. Public*, pg. 602
CTOS HOLDING SDN BHD—See Creador Sdn. Bhd.; *Int'l*, pg. 1831
CTP DIGITAL SERVICES PTY LTD—See Caxton and CTP Publishers and Printers Ltd.; *Int'l*, pg. 1363
CTP-DUMAG GMBH—See Sintokogio Ltd.; *Int'l*, pg. 6958
CTP FRANCE—See Sintokogio Ltd.; *Int'l*, pg. 6958
CTP ITALIA S.P.A.—See Information Services Group, Inc.; *U.S. Public*, pg. 1117
CTP N.V.; *Int'l*, pg. 1872
CT PRESOV S.R.O.—See Centene Corporation; *U.S. Public*, pg. 468
CT PRINTING LIMITED—See Litu Holdings Limited; *Int'l*, pg. 4528
CTP PRIVATE EQUITY TRUST PLC; *Int'l*, pg. 1868
CT PROPERTY TRUST LIMITED—See LondonMetric Property Plc; *Int'l*, pg. 4548
CTP SINTO AMERICA INC.—See Sintokogio Ltd.; *Int'l*, pg. 6958
CTP SYSTEM SRL—See Adecco Group AG; *Int'l*, pg. 139
CTQ MEDIA—See Cyger Media; *U.S. Private*, pg. 1134
CTRACK BENELUX BV—See Inseego Corp.; *U.S. Public*, pg. 1129
CTRACK DEUTSCHLAND GMBH—See Inseego Corp.; *U.S. Public*, pg. 1129
CTRACK FINANCE LIMITED—See Inseego Corp.; *U.S. Public*, pg. 1129
CTRACK (PTY) LTD—See Inseego Corp.; *U.S. Public*, pg. 1129
CTRACK (SA) (PTY) LIMITED—See Inseego Corp.; *U.S. Public*, pg. 1129
CTRACK UK LTD—See Inseego Corp.; *U.S. Public*, pg. 1129
CT REAL ESTATE INVESTMENT TRUST; *Int'l*, pg. 1868
C & T REINFORCING STEEL CO (1987) LIMITED; *Int'l*, pg. 1872
CTR HOLDINGS LIMITED; *Int'l*, pg. 1872
CTR INVESTMENTS & CONSULTING, INC.; *U.S. Public*, pg. 602
CTRIP.COM BEIJING—See Trip.com Group Ltd.; *Int'l*, pg. 7926
CTRIP.COM GUANGZHOU—See Trip.com Group Ltd.; *Int'l*, pg. 7926
CTRIP.COM (HONG KONG) LIMITED—See Trip.com Group Ltd.; *Int'l*, pg. 7926
CTRIP COMPUTER TECHNOLOGY (SHANGHAI) CO., LTD.—See Trip.com Group Ltd.; *Int'l*, pg. 7926
CTRIP.COM SHENZHEN—See Trip.com Group Ltd.; *Int'l*, pg. 7926
CTRIP TRAVEL INFORMATION TECHNOLOGY (SHANGHAI) CO., LTD.—See Trip.com Group Ltd.; *Int'l*, pg. 7926
CTRM AERO COMPOSITES SDN. BHD.—See DRB-HICOM Berhad; *Int'l*, pg. 2201
CTRM COMPOSITES ENGINEERING SDN. BHD.—See DRB-HICOM Berhad; *Int'l*, pg. 2201
CTRM TESTING LABORATORY SDN. BHD.—See DRB-HICOM Berhad; *Int'l*, pg. 2201
CTR S.R.L.—See Denso Corporation; *Int'l*, pg. 2028
CTR SYSTEMS INC.; *U.S. Private*, pg. 1119
C T R SYSTEMS INC.; *U.S. Private*, pg. 702
CTS ADVANTAGE LOGISTICS INC.; *U.S. Private*, pg. 1119
CTS AUTOMOTIVE, L.L.C.—See CTS Corporation; *U.S. Public*, pg. 603
CTS AUTOMOTIVE—See CTS Corporation; *U.S. Public*, pg. 603
CTS CO., LTD.; *Int'l*, pg. 1872
CTS CORPORATION - AUTOMOTIVE PRODUCTS—See CTS Corporation; *U.S. Public*, pg. 603
CTS CORPORATION; *U.S. Public*, pg. 602
CTS CORPORATION U.K. LTD.—See CTS Corporation; *U.S. Public*, pg. 603
CTS ELECTRO DE MATAMOROS S.A. DE C.V.—See Benchmark Electronics, Inc.; *U.S. Public*, pg. 295
CTS ELECTRONIC COMPONENTS, INC.—See CTS Corporation; *U.S. Public*, pg. 603
CTS ELECTRONIC COMPONENTS, INC.—See CTS Corporation; *U.S. Public*, pg. 603

CTS ELECTRONIC COMPONENTS—See CTS Corporation; *U.S. Public*, pg. 603
CTS ELECTRONICS MANUFACTURING SOLUTIONS—See Benchmark Electronics, Inc.; *U.S. Public*, pg. 295
CTS ELECTRONICS MANUFACTURING SOLUTIONS—See Benchmark Electronics, Inc.; *U.S. Public*, pg. 296
CTS ELECTRONICS MANUFACTURING SOLUTIONS—See Benchmark Electronics, Inc.; *U.S. Public*, pg. 295
CTS ENGINES, LLC—See J.F. Lehman & Company, Inc.; *U.S. Private*, pg. 2163
CTS EVENTIM AG & CO. KGAA; *Int'l*, pg. 1872
CTS EVENTIM AUSTRIA GMBH—See CTS Eventim AG & Co. KGAA; *Int'l*, pg. 1872
CTS EVENTIM ISRAEL LTD.—See CTS Eventim AG & Co. KGAA; *Int'l*, pg. 1872
CTS EVENTIM NEDERLAND B.V.—See CTS Eventim AG & Co. KGAA; *Int'l*, pg. 1872
CTS EVENTIM RU O.O.O.—See CTS Eventim AG & Co. KGAA; *Int'l*, pg. 1872
CTS EVENTIM SCHWEDEN AB—See CTS Eventim AG & Co. KGAA; *Int'l*, pg. 1872
CTS EVENTIM SOLUTIONS GMBH—See CTS Eventim AG & Co. KGAA; *Int'l*, pg. 1872
CTS EVENTIM SPORTS GMBH—See CTS Eventim AG & Co. KGAA; *Int'l*, pg. 1872
CTS FLOORING; *U.S. Private*, pg. 1119
CTS GLOBAL EQUITY GROUP, INC.; *Int'l*, pg. 1874
CTS GLOBAL LOGISTICS(CANADA) INC.—See CTS International Logistics Corporation Limited; *Int'l*, pg. 1874
CTS GLOBAL LOGISTICS(THAILAND)CO., LTD.—See CTS International Logistics Corporation Limited; *Int'l*, pg. 1874
CTS GLOBAL SUPPLY CHAIN SOLUTIONS—See CTS International Logistics Corporation Limited; *Int'l*, pg. 1874
CTSI, LLC—See Frontier Communications Parent, Inc.; *U.S. Public*, pg. 887
CTSI LOGISTICS, INC.—See Shangtex Holding Co., Ltd.; *Int'l*, pg. 6784
CTSI LOGISTICS (KOREA), INC.—See Shangtex Holding Co., Ltd.; *Int'l*, pg. 6784
CTSI LOGISTICS LIMITED—See Shangtex Holding Co., Ltd.; *Int'l*, pg. 6784
CTS INDIA PRIVATE LIMITED—See CTS Corporation; *U.S. Public*, pg. 603
CTS INTERNATIONAL FREIGHT (SPAIN) S.L.—See CTS International Logistics Corporation Limited; *Int'l*, pg. 1874
CTS INTERNATIONAL LOGISTICS CORPORATION LIMITED; *Int'l*, pg. 1874
CTS INTERNATIONAL LOGISTICS (GERMANY) GMBH—See CTS International Logistics Corporation Limited; *Int'l*, pg. 1874
CTS INTERNATIONAL LOGISTICS (HK) CO., LTD.—See CTS International Logistics Corporation Limited; *Int'l*, pg. 1874
CTS INTERNATIONAL LOGISTICS (JAPAN) CO., LTD.—See CTS International Logistics Corporation Limited; *Int'l*, pg. 1874
CTS INTERNATIONAL LOGISTICS (NETHERLANDS) B.V.—See CTS International Logistics Corporation Limited; *Int'l*, pg. 1874
CTS INTERNATIONAL LOGISTICS (SINGAPORE) PTE LTD.—See CTS International Logistics Corporation Limited; *Int'l*, pg. 1874
CTS INTERNATIONAL LOGISTICS TANZANIA LIMITED—See CTS International Logistics Corporation Limited; *Int'l*, pg. 1874
CTS INTERNATIONAL LOGISTICS (VIET NAM) CO., LTD.—See CTS International Logistics Corporation Limited; *Int'l*, pg. 1874
CTS JAPAN, INC.—See CTS Corporation; *U.S. Public*, pg. 603
CTS NATIONAL CORPORATION—See The Sherwin-Williams Company; *U.S. Public*, pg. 2127
CTS - NORDIC AKTIEBOLAG—See Elliott Management Corporation; *U.S. Private*, pg. 1367
CTS - NORDIC AKTIEBOLAG—See Veritas Capital Fund Management, LLC; *U.S. Private*, pg. 4361
CTS OF CANADA CO.—See CTS Corporation; *U.S. Public*, pg. 603
CTS OF CANADA, LTD.—See CTS Corporation; *U.S. Public*, pg. 603
CTS SINGAPORE PTE., LTD.—See CTS Corporation; *U.S. Public*, pg. 603
CTS SPEDITION GMBH; *Int'l*, pg. 1874
C.T. STAMPS, INC.—See Fred's Inc.; *U.S. Public*, pg. 883
CTS (TIANJIN) ELECTRONICS COMPANY LTD.—See CTS Corporation; *U.S. Public*, pg. 603
CTS VALPEY CORPORATION—See CTS Corporation; *U.S. Public*, pg. 603
CT SYSTEMS—See K-F Management Company, Inc.; *U.S. Private*, pg. 2250
CT&T CO., LTD.; *Int'l*, pg. 1868
CTT CO., LTD.—See Japan Airport Terminal Co., Ltd.; *Int'l*, pg. 3885

CTT - CORREIOS DE PORTUGAL SA

CTT - CORREIOS DE PORTUGAL SA; *Int'l*, pg. 1874
CTTG INC.—See The Goodyear Tire & Rubber Company; *U.S. Public*, pg. 2082
CTT INC.; *U.S. Public*, pg. 1119
CTT PHARMACEUTICAL HOLDINGS INC.; *U.S. Public*, pg. 603
CT TRANSPORTATION LLC—See Comcar Industries, Inc.; *U.S. Private*, pg. 981
CTT SYSTEMS AB; *Int'l*, pg. 1874
CT UK CAPITAL AND INCOME INVESTMENT TRUST PLC; *Int'l*, pg. 1868
CT UK HIGH INCOME TRUST PLC; *Int'l*, pg. 1868
CTV ATLANTIC, HALIFAX—See BCE Inc.; *Int'l*, pg. 927
CTV ATLANTIC, MONCTON—See BCE Inc.; *Int'l*, pg. 927
CTV ATLANTIC, SAINT JOHN—See BCE Inc.; *Int'l*, pg. 927
CTV ATLANTIC, SYDNEY—See BCE Inc.; *Int'l*, pg. 927
CTV CALGARY—See BCE Inc.; *Int'l*, pg. 927
CTV EDMONTON—See BCE Inc.; *Int'l*, pg. 927
CT VEGETABLES & FRUITS PTE LTD—See Neo Group Limited; *Int'l*, pg. 5196
CTV GOLDEN BRIDGE INTERNATIONAL MEDIA (HONG KONG) COMPANY LIMITED—See SinoMedia Holding Limited; *Int'l*, pg. 6953
CT-VIDEO GMBH—See CeoTronics AG; *Int'l*, pg. 1420
CTV INC.—See BCE Inc.; *Int'l*, pg. 927
CT VISION (INTERNATIONAL) HOLDINGS LIMITED—See CT Vision Investment Ltd; *Int'l*, pg. 1868
CT VISION INVESTMENT LTD; *Int'l*, pg. 1868
CTV LETHBRIDGE—See BCE Inc.; *Int'l*, pg. 927
CTV MONTREAL—See BCE Inc.; *Int'l*, pg. 927
CTV NEWSNET—See BCE Inc.; *Int'l*, pg. 927
CTV NORTHERN ONTARIO, NORTH BAY—See BCE Inc.; *Int'l*, pg. 927
CTV NORTHERN ONTARIO, SAULT SAINT MARIE—See BCE Inc.; *Int'l*, pg. 927
CTV NORTHERN ONTARIO, SUDBURY—See BCE Inc.; *Int'l*, pg. 927
CTV NORTHERN ONTARIO, TIMMINS—See BCE Inc.; *Int'l*, pg. 927
CTV OTTAWA—See BCE Inc.; *Int'l*, pg. 927
CTV PRINCE ALBERT—See BCE Inc.; *Int'l*, pg. 927
CTV REGINA—See BCE Inc.; *Int'l*, pg. 927
CTV SASKATOON—See BCE Inc.; *Int'l*, pg. 927
CTV VANCOUVER—See BCE Inc.; *Int'l*, pg. 927
CTV WINNIPEG—See BCE Inc.; *Int'l*, pg. 927
CTV YORKTON—See BCE Inc.; *Int'l*, pg. 927
CT-WEARNES VIETNAM CO LTD—See Wearnes Automotive Pte. Ltd.; *Int'l*, pg. 8363
CTW GROUP INCORPORATED; *U.S. Private*, pg. 1119
CTW GROUP, INC.; *U.S. Private*, pg. 1119
CTW TRANSPORT INC.—See HCI Equity Management, L.P.; *U.S. Private*, pg. 1889
CTX BUSINESS SOLUTIONS, INC.—See Xerox Holdings Corporation; *U.S. Public*, pg. 2387
CTX HOLDINGS JOINT STOCK COMPANY; *Int'l*, pg. 1874
CTX INC.—See Universal Logistics Holdings, Inc.; *U.S. Public*, pg. 2261
CTX VIRTUAL TECHNOLOGIES, INC.; *U.S. Public*, pg. 603
CTY GROUP AS; *Int'l*, pg. 1874
CTZ S.R.O.—See MVV Energie AG; *Int'l*, pg. 5108
CUADRILLA CAPITAL LLC; *U.S. Private*, pg. 1119
CUALICONTROL-ACI S.A.U.—See TUV NORD AG; *Int'l*, pg. 7980
CU*ANSWERS; *U.S. Private*, pg. 1119
CUARTA DIMENSION MEDICA, S.L.—See Substrate Artificial Inteligence SA; *Int'l*, pg. 7249
CUARZO PRODUCCIONES S.L.—See LOV Group Invest SAS; *Int'l*, pg. 4563
CUATTRO, LLC; *U.S. Private*, pg. 1119
CUATTRO MEDICAL, LLC—See Cuattro, LLC; *U.S. Private*, pg. 1119
CUATTRO SOFTWARE, LLC—See Cuattro, LLC; *U.S. Private*, pg. 1119
CUBA BEVERAGE COMPANY; *U.S. Public*, pg. 603
CUBA BUSINESS DEVELOPMENT GROUP, INC.—See Fuego Enterprises, Inc.; *U.S. Public*, pg. 891
CUBA CITY TELEPHONE EXCHANGE CO.—See LICT Corporation; *U.S. Public*, pg. 1312
CUBA MEMORIAL HOSPITAL, INC.; *U.S. Private*, pg. 1119
CUBAN CLUB FOUNDATION, INC.; *U.S. Private*, pg. 1119
CUBBISON COMPANY; *U.S. Private*, pg. 1119
CUBBY'S INC.; *U.S. Public*, pg. 1120
CUBE 3 STUDIO; *U.S. Private*, pg. 1120
CUBE AIRE—See Freeman Spogli & Co. Incorporated; *U.S. Private*, pg. 1606
CUBE BIO-ENERGY PVT LTD.; *Int'l*, pg. 1875
CUBE INFRASTRUCTURE MANAGERS SA—See Groupe BPCE; *Int'l*, pg. 3094
CUBE.ITG SA; *Int'l*, pg. 1875
CUBE LABS S.P.A.; *Int'l*, pg. 1875
CUB ELECPARTS INC. - SHANGHAI FACILITY—See Cub Elecparts Inc.; *Int'l*, pg. 1875
CUB ELECPARTS INC.; *Int'l*, pg. 1875

CUBE MANAGEMENT GMBH—See Allgeier SE; *Int'l*, pg. 337
CUBEN UTBILDNING AB—See Storskogen Group AB; *Int'l*, pg. 7227
CUBE PLANNING CORPORATION—See Crest Investments Co., Ltd.; *Int'l*, pg. 1840
CUBE S CO., LTD.—See No.1 Co., Ltd.; *Int'l*, pg. 5394
CUBESMART ALEXANDRIA, LLC—See CubeSmart; *U.S. Public*, pg. 603
CUBESMART, L.P.—See CubeSmart; *U.S. Public*, pg. 603
CUBESMART; *U.S. Public*, pg. 603
CUBESMART WILTON, LLC—See CubeSmart; *U.S. Public*, pg. 603
CUBE SYSTEM INC.; *Int'l*, pg. 1875
CUBE SYSTEM VIETNAM CO., LTD.—See Cube System Inc.; *Int'l*, pg. 1875
CUBEX TUBINGS LIMITED; *Int'l*, pg. 1875
CUB FOODS, INC.—See United Natural Foods, Inc.; *U.S. Public*, pg. 2232
CUB FOODS OF APPLETON INC.—See United Natural Foods, Inc.; *U.S. Public*, pg. 2232
CUB FOODS OF GREEN BAY INC.—See United Natural Foods, Inc.; *U.S. Public*, pg. 2232
CUBIC ADVANCED LEARNING SOLUTIONS, INC.—See Elliott Management Corporation; *U.S. Private*, pg. 1367
CUBIC ADVANCED LEARNING SOLUTIONS, INC.—See Veritas Capital Fund Management, LLC; *U.S. Private*, pg. 4361
CUBICAL FINANCIAL SERVICES LIMITED; *Int'l*, pg. 1875
CUBIC APPLICATIONS, INC.—See Elliott Management Corporation; *U.S. Private*, pg. 1367
CUBIC APPLICATIONS, INC.—See Veritas Capital Fund Management, LLC; *U.S. Private*, pg. 4361
CUBIC CORPORATION—See Elliott Management Corporation; *U.S. Private*, pg. 1367
CUBIC CORPORATION—See Veritas Capital Fund Management, LLC; *U.S. Private*, pg. 4361
CUBIC CYBER SOLUTIONS, INC.—See Elliott Management Corporation; *U.S. Private*, pg. 1367
CUBIC CYBER SOLUTIONS, INC.—See Veritas Capital Fund Management, LLC; *U.S. Private*, pg. 4361
CUBIC DATA SYSTEMS, INC.—See Elliott Management Corporation; *U.S. Private*, pg. 1367
CUBIC DATA SYSTEMS, INC.—See Veritas Capital Fund Management, LLC; *U.S. Private*, pg. 4361
CUBIC DEFENCE AUSTRALIA PTY. LIMITED—See Elliott Management Corporation; *U.S. Private*, pg. 1367
CUBIC DEFENCE AUSTRALIA PTY. LIMITED—See Veritas Capital Fund Management, LLC; *U.S. Private*, pg. 4361
CUBIC DEFENCE NEW ZEALAND LTD.—See Elliott Management Corporation; *U.S. Private*, pg. 1367
CUBIC DEFENCE NEW ZEALAND LTD.—See Veritas Capital Fund Management, LLC; *U.S. Private*, pg. 4361
CUBIC DEFENCE UK LTD—See Elliott Management Corporation; *U.S. Private*, pg. 1367
CUBIC DEFENCE UK LTD—See Veritas Capital Fund Management, LLC; *U.S. Private*, pg. 4361
CUBIC DEFENSE APPLICATIONS, INC.—See Elliott Management Corporation; *U.S. Private*, pg. 1368
CUBIC DEFENSE APPLICATIONS, INC.—See Veritas Capital Fund Management, LLC; *U.S. Private*, pg. 4361
CUBIC DE MEXICO—See Elliott Management Corporation; *U.S. Private*, pg. 1368
CUBIC DE MEXICO—See Veritas Capital Fund Management, LLC; *U.S. Private*, pg. 4362
CUBIC DESIGNS, INC.—See Berkshire Hathaway Inc.; *U.S. Public*, pg. 312
CUBIC DIGITAL TECHNOLOGY CO., LTD.; *Int'l*, pg. 1875
CUBIC ENERGY, LLC; *U.S. Private*, pg. 1120
CUBICFARM SYSTEMS CORP.; *Int'l*, pg. 1875
CUBIC FOREIGN SALES, INC.—See Elliott Management Corporation; *U.S. Private*, pg. 1368
CUBIC FOREIGN SALES, INC.—See Veritas Capital Fund Management, LLC; *U.S. Private*, pg. 4361
CUBIC GLOBAL TRACKING SOLUTIONS, INC.—See Elliott Management Corporation; *U.S. Private*, pg. 1368
CUBIC GLOBAL TRACKING SOLUTIONS, INC.—See Veritas Capital Fund Management, LLC; *U.S. Private*, pg. 4361
CUBIC KOREA INC. - BUSAN FACTORY—See Cubic Korea INC.; *Int'l*, pg. 1875
CUBIC KOREA INC.; *Int'l*, pg. 1875
CUBIC LAND, INC.—See Elliott Management Corporation; *U.S. Private*, pg. 1368
CUBIC LAND, INC.—See Veritas Capital Fund Management, LLC; *U.S. Private*, pg. 4361
CUBICLE NINJAS LLC; *U.S. Private*, pg. 1120
CUBIC MICROCHIP DEVELOPMENT CORPORATION—See Elliott Management Corporation; *U.S. Private*, pg. 1368
CUBIC MICROCHIP DEVELOPMENT CORPORATION—See Veritas Capital Fund Management, LLC; *U.S. Private*, pg. 4361
CUBIC MODULSYSTEM A/S—See Rockwell Automation, Inc.; *U.S. Public*, pg. 1805
CUBICON INC.—See HyVISION SYSTEM INC.; *Int'l*, pg. 3561

CUBIC SENSOR & INSTRUMENT CO., LTD.; *Int'l*, pg. 1875
CUBIC SIMULATION SYSTEMS, INC.—See Elliott Management Corporation; *U.S. Private*, pg. 1368
CUBIC SIMULATION SYSTEMS, INC.—See Veritas Capital Fund Management, LLC; *U.S. Private*, pg. 4361
CUBIC TECH CORP.—See Koninklijke DSM N.V.; *Int'l*, pg. 4262
CUBIC TECHNOLOGIES PTE. LTD.—See Elliott Management Corporation; *U.S. Private*, pg. 1367
CUBIC TECHNOLOGIES PTE. LTD.—See Veritas Capital Fund Management, LLC; *U.S. Private*, pg. 4361
CUBIC TECHNOLOGIES SINGAPORE PTE. LTD.—See Elliott Management Corporation; *U.S. Private*, pg. 1367
CUBIC TECHNOLOGIES SINGAPORE PTE. LTD.—See Veritas Capital Fund Management, LLC; *U.S. Private*, pg. 4361
CUBIC TRANSPORTATION SYSTEMS (AUSTRALIA) PTY. LIMITED—See Elliott Management Corporation; *U.S. Private*, pg. 1368
CUBIC TRANSPORTATION SYSTEMS (AUSTRALIA) PTY. LIMITED—See Veritas Capital Fund Management, LLC; *U.S. Private*, pg. 4362
CUBIC TRANSPORTATION SYSTEMS CANADA, LTD.—See Elliott Management Corporation; *U.S. Private*, pg. 1368
CUBIC TRANSPORTATION SYSTEMS CANADA, LTD.—See Veritas Capital Fund Management, LLC; *U.S. Private*, pg. 4362
CUBIC TRANSPORTATION SYSTEMS (DEUTSCHLAND) GMBH—See Elliott Management Corporation; *U.S. Private*, pg. 1367
CUBIC TRANSPORTATION SYSTEMS (DEUTSCHLAND) GMBH—See Veritas Capital Fund Management, LLC; *U.S. Private*, pg. 4361
CUBIC TRANSPORTATION SYSTEMS, INC.-EAST—See Elliott Management Corporation; *U.S. Private*, pg. 1368
CUBIC TRANSPORTATION SYSTEMS, INC.-EAST—See Veritas Capital Fund Management, LLC; *U.S. Private*, pg. 4362
CUBIC TRANSPORTATION SYSTEMS, INC.-MANUFACTURING CENTER—See Elliott Management Corporation; *U.S. Private*, pg. 1368
CUBIC TRANSPORTATION SYSTEMS, INC.-MANUFACTURING CENTER—See Veritas Capital Fund Management, LLC; *U.S. Private*, pg. 4362
CUBIC TRANSPORTATION SYSTEMS, INC.—See Elliott Management Corporation; *U.S. Private*, pg. 1368
CUBIC TRANSPORTATION SYSTEMS, INC.—See Veritas Capital Fund Management, LLC; *U.S. Private*, pg. 4362
CUBIC TRANSPORTATION SYSTEMS (INDIA) PVT. LIMITED—See Elliott Management Corporation; *U.S. Private*, pg. 1368
CUBIC TRANSPORTATION SYSTEMS (INDIA) PVT. LIMITED—See Veritas Capital Fund Management, LLC; *U.S. Private*, pg. 4362
CUBIC TRANSPORTATION SYSTEMS (ITMS) LIMITED—See Elliott Management Corporation; *U.S. Private*, pg. 1367
CUBIC TRANSPORTATION SYSTEMS (ITMS) LIMITED—See Veritas Capital Fund Management, LLC; *U.S. Private*, pg. 4361
CUBIC TRANSPORTATION SYSTEMS LIMITED—See Elliott Management Corporation; *U.S. Private*, pg. 1367
CUBIC TRANSPORTATION SYSTEMS LIMITED—See Veritas Capital Fund Management, LLC; *U.S. Private*, pg. 4361
CUBIC (UK) LIMITED—See Elliott Management Corporation; *U.S. Private*, pg. 1367
CUBIC (UK) LIMITED—See Veritas Capital Fund Management, LLC; *U.S. Private*, pg. 4361
CUBIC WORLDWIDE TECHNICAL SERVICES, INC.—See Elliott Management Corporation; *U.S. Private*, pg. 1368
CUBIC WORLDWIDE TECHNICAL SERVICES, INC.—See Veritas Capital Fund Management, LLC; *U.S. Private*, pg. 4362
CUBIX CORPORATION; *U.S. Private*, pg. 1120
CU BLOOD, INC.—See CRYO-CELL International, Inc.; *U.S. Public*, pg. 600
CUBO BRAND COMMUNICATIONS LIMITED—See Cubo Communications Group Plc; *Int'l*, pg. 1875
CUBO COMMUNICATIONS GROUP PLC; *Int'l*, pg. 1875
CUBO DESIGN S.R.L.—See Dexelance S.p.A.; *Int'l*, pg. 2092
CUB OJSC—See Gazprombank JSC; *Int'l*, pg. 2892
CUBOX CO., LTD.; *Int'l*, pg. 1875
CUBRC, INC.; *U.S. Private*, pg. 1120
CUBTEK INC.—See Cub Elecparts Inc.; *Int'l*, pg. 1875
CUBUS AG—See Serviceware SE; *Int'l*, pg. 6726
CUBUS LUX D.O.O—See Cubus Lux Plc; *Int'l*, pg. 1876
CUBUS LUX PLC; *Int'l*, pg. 1876
CUBUS SCHWEIZ GMBH—See Serviceware SE; *Int'l*, pg. 6726
CUCAMONGA VALLEY WATER DISTRICT; *U.S. Private*, pg. 1120
CU CHEMIE UETIKON GMBH—See Eurazeo SE; *Int'l*, pg. 2530
CUCINA ACQUISITION (UK) LIMITED—See Sysco Corporation; *U.S. Public*, pg. 1973

COMPANY NAME INDEX

CUCINA BELLA S.A.; *Int'l*, pg. 1876
CUCINA SANO LTD—See Bakkavor Group plc; *Int'l*, pg. 806
CUCKOO HOLDINGS CO., LTD.; *Int'l*, pg. 1876
CUCKOO HOMESYS CO LTD.; *Int'l*, pg. 1876
CU COOPERATIVE SYSTEMS, INC.; *U.S. Private*, pg. 1119
CUC SOFTWARE INC.—See ServiceTitan, Inc.; *U.S. Private*, pg. 3617
CUDDLE CLONES LLC—See D2C Stores Inc.; *U.S. Private*, pg. 1143
CU DEUTERO + AGRO AG—See CPH Chemie + Papier Holding AG; *Int'l*, pg. 1824
CU DIRECT CORPORATION; *U.S. Private*, pg. 1119
CUE BIOPHARMA, INC.; *U.S. Public*, pg. 604
CUE DEE AB—See Lagercrantz Group AB; *Int'l*, pg. 4394
CUE ENERGY RESOURCES LIMITED—See New Zealand Oil & Gas Limited; *Int'l*, pg. 5231
CUE EXPLORATION PTY. LTD.—See New Zealand Oil & Gas Limited; *Int'l*, pg. 5232
CUE HEALTH INC.; *U.S. Public*, pg. 604
CUEL LTD.—See Salini Costruttori S.p.A.; *Int'l*, pg. 6493
CUENOD S.A.S.—See Ariston Holding N.V.; *Int'l*, pg. 567
CUENTAS INC.; *U.S. Public*, pg. 604
CUESIM LTD—See QinetiQ Group plc; *Int'l*, pg. 6142
CUES, INC.—See SPX Technologies, Inc.; *U.S. Public*, pg. 1921
CUESTA COAL LIMITED; *Int'l*, pg. 1876
CUETER CHRYSLER JEEP DODGE; *U.S. Private*, pg. 1120
CUFE LTD; *Int'l*, pg. 1876
CUFFE AND TAYLOR LIMITED—See Live Nation Entertainment, Inc.; *U.S. Public*, pg. 1328
CUFFLINKS.COM; *U.S. Private*, pg. 1120
CUFFY CO. INCORPORATED; *U.S. Private*, pg. 1120
CUHACI & PETERSON ARCHITECTS LLC; *U.S. Private*, pg. 1120
CUHADAROGLU METAL SANAYI VE PAZARLAMA AS; *Int'l*, pg. 1876
CUI-CANADA, INC.—See Orbital Infrastructure Group, Inc.; *U.S. Public*, pg. 1615
CU IMMOBILIEN LAHR AG—See CPH Chemie + Papier Holding AG; *Int'l*, pg. 1824
CU INC.—See ATCO Ltd., *Int'l*, pg. 007
CUISINART INC.—See American Securities LLC; *U.S. Private*, pg. 248
CUISINE DE FRANCE INC.—See ARYZTA AG; *Int'l*, pg. 588
CUISINE DE FRANCE LIMITED—See ARYZTA AG; pg. 588
CUISINE DE FRANCE (UK) LIMITED—See ARYZTA AG; *Int'l*, pg. 588
CUISINE SOLUTIONS FRANCE—See Cuisine Solutions, Inc.; *U.S. Public*, pg. 604
CUISINE SOLUTIONS, INC.; *U.S. Public*, pg. 604
CUIVRE RIVER ELECTRIC CO-OPERATIVE INC.; *U.S. Private*, pg. 1120
CUIZINA FOOD COMPANY—See Joshua Green Corporation; *U.S. Private*, pg. 2237
CUKIERMAN & CO. INVESTMENT HOUSE LTD.; *Int'l*, pg. 1876
CUKIERMAN & CO. LIFE SCIENCES—See Cukierman & Co. Investment House Ltd.; *Int'l*, pg. 1876
CUKIERMAN & CO. REAL ESTATE LTD.—See Cukierman & Co. Investment House Ltd.; *Int'l*, pg. 1876
CUKIERMAN & CO. S.A.—See Cukierman & Co. Investment House Ltd.; *Int'l*, pg. 1876
CUKURAMBAR LOKANTACILIK GIDA TURIZM A.S—See Dogus Holding AS; *Int'l*, pg. 2154
CUKUROVA HOLDING A.S.; *Int'l*, pg. 1876
CUKUROVA INSAAT MAKINALARI SAN. VE TIC. A.S.—See Cukurova Holding A.S.; *Int'l*, pg. 1876
CUKUROVA KIMYA ENDUSTRISI A.S.—See Cukurova Holding A.S.; *Int'l*, pg. 1876
CUKUROVA ZIRAAT ENDUSTRI VE TIC. A.S.—See Cukurova Holding A.S.; *Int'l*, pg. 1876
CULBERSON CONSTRUCTION, LLC—See Independence Capital Partners, LLC; *U.S. Private*, pg. 2057
CULBERSON STOWERS, INC.; *U.S. Private*, pg. 1120
CULBERT HEALTHCARE SOLUTIONS; *U.S. Private*, pg. 1120
CULEMBORG PHARMACY PROPRIETARY LIMITED—See Dis-Chem Pharmacies Ltd.; *Int'l*, pg. 2130
CULINA GROUP LIMITED—See Unternehmensgruppe Theo Muller S.e.c.s.; *Int'l*, pg. 8085
CULINAIRE DES PAYS DE L'ADOUR SAS—See Compass Group PLC; *Int'l*, pg. 1751
CULINAIRE INTERNATIONAL INC.; *U.S. Private*, pg. 1120
CULINARTE MARKETING GROUP, LLC—See Kainos Capital, LLC; *U.S. Private*, pg. 2255
CULINART GROUP, INC.—See Compass Group PLC; *Int'l*, pg. 1751
CULINART, INC.—See Compass Group PLC; *Int'l*, pg. 1751
CULINARY ADVENTURES, INC.—See Culinary Holdings Inc.; *U.S. Private*, pg. 1120

CULINARY CONCEPTS INC.; *U.S. Private*, pg. 1120
CULINARY DEPOT, INC.; *U.S. Private*, pg. 1120
CULINARY DESTINATIONS LIMITED; *Int'l*, pg. 1876
CULINARY EYE, INC; *U.S. Private*, pg. 1120
CULINARY HOLDINGS INC.; *U.S. Private*, pg. 1120
CULINARY VENTURES VENDING; *U.S. Private*, pg. 1121
CULINEX; *U.S. Private*, pg. 1121
CULINOR NV—See Orior AG; *Int'l*, pg. 5633
CULLEN & DYKMAN LLP; *U.S. Private*, pg. 1121
CULLEN EXPLORATION PTY LTD—See Cullen Resources Limited; *Int'l*, pg. 1877
CULLEN/FROST BANKERS, INC.; *U.S. Public*, pg. 604
CULLEN INVESTMENTS LIMITED; *Int'l*, pg. 1876
CULLEN RESOURCES LIMITED; *Int'l*, pg. 1876
CULLEN & WHIM INC.; *U.S. Private*, pg. 1121
CULLIGAN AUSTRALIA PTY LTD.—See BDT Capital Partners, LLC; *U.S. Private*, pg. 502
CULLIGAN ESPANA S.A.—See BDT Capital Partners, LLC; *U.S. Private*, pg. 502
CULLIGAN FRANCE—See BDT Capital Partners, LLC; *U.S. Private*, pg. 502
CULLIGAN INTERNATIONAL COMPANY—See BDT Capital Partners, LLC; *U.S. Private*, pg. 502
CULLIGAN ITALIANA S.P.A.—See BDT Capital Partners, LLC; *U.S. Private*, pg. 502
CULLIGAN SOFT WATER SERVICE CO.; *U.S. Private*, pg. 1121
CULLIGAN (UK) LTD.—See BWT Aktiengesellschaft; *Int'l*, pg. 1233
CULLIGAN WATER COMPANY OF NEW JERSEY, INC.; *U.S. Private*, pg. 1121
CULLIGAN WATER CONDITIONING SERVICE; *U.S. Private*, pg. 1121
CULLIGAN WATER INDIANA—See BDT Capital Partners, LLC; *U.S. Private*, pg. 502
CULLIGAN WATER—See BDT Capital Partners, LLC; *U.S. Private*, pg. 502
CULLINAN DIAMOND MINE (PTY) LTD—See Petra Diamonds Limited; *Int'l*, pg. 5824
CULLINAN HOLDINGS LIMITED; *Int'l*, pg. 1877
CULLINAN METALS CORP.; *Int'l*, pg. 1877
CULLINAN NAMIBIA (PTY) LTD—See Cullinan Holdings Limited; *Int'l*, pg. 1877
CULLINAN PROPERTIES, LTD.; *U.S. Private*, pg. 1121
CULLINAN THERAPEUTICS; *U.S. Public*, pg. 604
CULLITON BROTHERS LIMITED; *Int'l*, pg. 1877
CULLMAN BANCORP, INC.; *U.S. Public*, pg. 604
CULLMAN COCA-COLA BOTTLING COMPANY—See Coca-Cola Bottling Co. United, Inc.; *U.S. Private*, pg. 958
CULLMAN ELECTRIC CO-OPERATIVE INC.; *U.S. Private*, pg. 1121
CULLMAN JEFFERSON COUNTIES GAS DISTRIBUTION; *U.S. Private*, pg. 1121
CULLMAN REGIONAL MEDICAL CENTER; *U.S. Private*, pg. 1121
CULLMAN SAVINGS BANK—See Cullman Bancorp, Inc.; *U.S. Public*, pg. 604
CULLUM & BROWN INC.; *U.S. Private*, pg. 1121
CULLUM CONSTRUCTION COMPANY; *U.S. Private*, pg. 1121
CULLUM & MAXEY CAMPING CENTER, INC.—See Camping World Holdings, Inc.; *U.S. Public*, pg. 427
CULLUM MECHANICAL CONSTRUCTION, INC.; *U.S. Private*, pg. 1121
CULLUM SEEDS LLC; *U.S. Private*, pg. 1121
CULLY & SULLY LIMITED—See The Hain Celestial Group, Inc.; *U.S. Public*, pg. 2086
CULMEN INTERNATIONAL, LLC—See Hale Capital Partners, L.P.; *U.S. Private*, pg. 1842
CULP CONSTRUCTION CO.; *U.S. Private*, pg. 1121
CULPEO MINERALS LIMITED; *Int'l*, pg. 1877
CULPEPER FARMERS COOPERATIVE INC; *U.S. Private*, pg. 1121
CULPEPER STAR-EXPONENT—See Lee Enterprises, Incorporated; *U.S. Public*, pg. 1298
CULPEPPER & ASSOCIATES SECURITY SERVICES, INC.; *U.S. Private*, pg. 1121
CULP EUROPE—See Culp, Inc.; *U.S. Public*, pg. 604
CULP FABRICS (SHANGHAI) CO., LTD.—See Culp, Inc.; *U.S. Public*, pg. 604
CULP, INC.; *U.S. Public*, pg. 604
CULT360; *U.S. Private*, pg. 1121
CULTEC, INC.—See Advanced Drainage Systems, Inc.; *U.S. Public*, pg. 46
CULT FOOD SCIENCE CORP.; *Int'l*, pg. 1877
CULTI MILANO S.P.A.; *Int'l*, pg. 1877
CULTIVADORA DE SALMONES LINAO S.A.—See Mowi ASA; *Int'l*, pg. 5059
CULTIVA LLC; *U.S. Private*, pg. 1121
CULTIVECS INC.—See Nippon Kayaku Co., Ltd.; *Int'l*, pg. 5320
CULTURAL DATA PROJECT; *U.S. Private*, pg. 1122
CULTURAL EXPERIENCES ABROAD; *U.S. Private*, pg. 1122
CULTURAL INSURANCE SERVICES INTERNATIONAL, INC.—See American Institute for Foreign Study, Inc.; *U.S. Private*, pg. 237

CUMBEY & FAIR, INC.

CULTURAL INVESTMENT HOLDINGS CO., LTD.; *Int'l*, pg. 1877
CULTURA TECHNOLOGIES INC.—See Constellation Software Inc.; *Int'l*, pg. 1775
CULTURECOM CENTRE LIMITED—See Culturecom Holdings Ltd; *Int'l*, pg. 1877
CULTURECOM HOLDINGS LTD; *Int'l*, pg. 1877
CULTURE CONVENIENCE CLUB CO., LTD.; *Int'l*, pg. 1877
CULTURED STONE CORPORATION—See Owens Corning; *U.S. Public*, pg. 1626
CULTURE JAPON S.A.S.—See TOHAN CORPORATION; *Int'l*, pg. 7775
CULTUREMAP LLC—See ViewMarket Inc.; *U.S. Private*, pg. 4381
CULTURE PARTNERS—See Hammond, Kennedy, Whitney & Company, Inc.; *U.S. Private*, pg. 1850
CULTURE PUBLISHERS INC—See Culture Convenience Club Co., Ltd.; *Int'l*, pg. 1877
CULVER CITY MOTOR CARS, INC.; *U.S. Private*, pg. 1122
CULVER FRANCHISING SYSTEM, INC.; *U.S. Private*, pg. 1122
CULVER GLASS COMPANY; *U.S. Private*, pg. 1122
CULVER INSURANCE BROKERS LTD.—See CCV Risk Solutions Limited; *Int'l*, pg. 1370
THE CULVER STUDIOS—See Pacific Coast Capital Partners, LLC; *U.S. Private*, pg. 3066
CULY CONTRACTING, LLC—See New Mountain Capital, LLC; *U.S. Private*, pg. 2899
CUMATIX AB—See Addtech AB; *Int'l*, pg. 132
CUMBERLAND AMERICA DEVELOPMENT COMPANY INC.; *U.S. Private*, pg. 1122
CUMBERLAND ARCHITECTURAL MILLWORK, INC.—See Orion Building Corporation; *U.S. Private*, pg. 3042
CUMBERLAND BUILDING SOCIETY; *Int'l*, pg. 1877
CUMBERLAND CASUALTY & SURETY COMPANY—See Cumberland Technologies, Inc.; *U.S. Private*, pg. 1122
CUMBERLAND CHRYSLER CENTER; *U.S. Private*, pg. 1122
CUMBERLAND CONSULTING GROUP, LLC; *U.S. Private*, pg. 1122
CUMBERLAND CONTURA, LLC—See Alpha Metallurgical Resources, Inc.; *U.S. Public*, pg. 82
CUMBERLAND COUNTY GLASS—See Harvest Partners L.P.; *U.S. Private*, pg. 1877
CUMBERLAND COUNTY GUIDANCE CENTER; *U.S. Private*, pg. 1122
CUMBERLAND COUNTY HOSPITAL ASSOCIATION INC.; *U.S. Private*, pg. 1122
CUMBERLAND DAIRY INCORPORATED; *U.S. Private*, pg. 1122
CUMBERLAND DIVERSIFIED METALS, INC.—See Slate Capital Group LLC; *U.S. Private*, pg. 3687
CUMBERLAND ELECTRIC MEMBERSHIP CORPORATION; *U.S. Private*, pg. 1122
CUMBERLAND ELECTRONICS INC.; *U.S. Private*, pg. 1122
CUMBERLAND ENGINEERING CORPORATION—See Harbour Group Industries, Inc.; *U.S. Private*, pg. 1860
CUMBERLAND EUROPE LTD.—See Harbour Group Industries, Inc.; *U.S. Private*, pg. 1860
CUMBERLAND FARMS, INC.—See TDR Capital LLP; *Int'l*, pg. 7494
THE CUMBERLAND GRILL—See The Copper Cellar Corporation; *U.S. Private*, pg. 4014
CUMBERLAND HOSPITAL, LLC—See Universal Health Services, Inc.; *U.S. Public*, pg. 2256
CUMBERLAND INSURANCE GROUP; *U.S. Private*, pg. 1122
CUMBERLAND INTERNATIONAL TRUCKS, INC.; *U.S. Private*, pg. 1122
CUMBERLAND MALL ASSOCIATES—See Pennsylvania Real Estate Investment Trust; *U.S. Public*, pg. 1663
CUMBERLAND MATERIALS; *U.S. Private*, pg. 1122
CUMBERLAND MEDICAL CENTER, INC.—See HCA Healthcare, Inc.; *U.S. Public*, pg. 995
CUMBERLAND PACKING CORP.; *U.S. Private*, pg. 1122
CUMBERLAND PHARMACEUTICALS, INC.; *U.S. Public*, pg. 605
CUMBERLAND PLACE FINANCIAL MANAGEMENT LIMITED—See abrdn PLC; *Int'l*, pg. 68
CUMBERLAND RECYCLING CORPORATION OF SOUTH JERSEY; *U.S. Private*, pg. 1122
CUMBERLAND TECHNOLOGIES, INC.; *U.S. Private*, pg. 1122
CUMBERLAND TRAIL GOLF COURSE, LLC—See Huntington Bancshares Incorporated; *U.S. Public*, pg. 1071
CUMBERLAND VALLEY FINANCIAL CORPORATION; *U.S. Private*, pg. 1123
CUMBERLAND VALLEY NATIONAL BANK & TRUST COMPANY—See Cumberland Valley Financial Corporation; *U.S. Private*, pg. 1123
CUMBERNAULD HOUSING PARTNERSHIP LIMITED—See Sanctuary Housing Association; *Int'l*, pg. 6523
CUMBEY & FAIR, INC.; *U.S. Private*, pg. 1123
CUMBRA INGENIERIA S.A.—See Aenza S.A.A.; *Int'l*, pg. 176

CUMBEY & FAIR, INC.

CUMBRA PERU S.A.—See Aenza S.A.A.; *Int'l*, pg. 176
CUMBRE NAZCA SAATCHI & SAATCHI—See Publicis Groupe S.A.; *Int'l*, pg. 6107
CU MEDICAL SYSTEMS INC.; *Int'l*, pg. 1875
CUMI AMERICA INC—See The Murugappa Group, Ltd.; *Int'l*, pg. 7668
CUMI AUSTRALIA PTY LTD—See The Murugappa Group, Ltd.; *Int'l*, pg. 7668
CUMICA CORPORATION; *Int'l*, pg. 1878
CUMI MIDDLE EAST FZE—See The Murugappa Group, Ltd.; *Int'l*, pg. 7668
CUMING CORPORATION—See First Reserve Management, L.P.; *U.S. Private*, pg. 1525
CUMING INSULATION CORP.—See First Reserve Management, L.P.; *U.S. Private*, pg. 1525
CUMING MICROWAVE CORPORATION—See PPG Industries, Inc.; *U.S. Public*, pg. 1707
THE CUMIS GROUP LIMITED—See The Co-operators Group Limited; *Int'l*, pg. 7634
CUMIS LIFE INSURANCE COMPANY—See The Co-operators Group Limited; *Int'l*, pg. 7634
CUMMING CONSTRUCTION MANAGEMENT, INC.; *U.S. Private*, pg. 1123
CUMMINGS ACQUISITION, INC.—See Gannett Co., Inc.; *U.S. Public*, pg. 896
CUMMINGS ADVERTISING, INC.; *U.S. Private*, pg. 1123
CUMMINGS-BACCUS INTERESTS; *U.S. Private*, pg. 1123
CUMMINGS GROUP; *U.S. Private*, pg. 1123
THE CUMMINGS GROUP; *U.S. Private*, pg. 4017
CUMMINGS MCGOWAN & WEST INC.; *U.S. Private*, pg. 1123
CUMMINGS-MOORE GRAPHITE CO.—See Great Mill Rock LLC; *U.S. Private*, pg. 1766
CUMMINGS MOVING SYSTEMS L.L.C.—See Cummings Transfer Co.; *U.S. Private*, pg. 1123
CUMMINGS MOVING SYSTEMS—See Cummings Transfer Co.; *U.S. Private*, pg. 1123
CUMMINGS OIL CO. INC.; *U.S. Private*, pg. 1123
CUMMINGS OIL INC.; *U.S. Private*, pg. 1123
CUMMINGS POINT INVESTORS CORP—See Geneve Holdings Corp.; *U.S. Private*, pg. 1670
CUMMINGS RESOURCES LLC—See Prophet Equity L.P.; *U.S. Private*, pg. 3286
CUMMINGS TOOL—See Tap Enterprises Inc.; *U.S. Private*, pg. 3932
CUMMINGS TRANSFER CO.; *U.S. Private*, pg. 1123
CUMMINS AFRICA MIDDLE EAST (PTY.) LTD.—See Cummins Inc.; *U.S. Public*, pg. 605
CUMMINS-ALLISON CORPORATION—See Crane NXT, Co.; *U.S. Public*, pg. 591
CUMMINS-ALLISON GMBH—See Crane NXT, Co.; *U.S. Public*, pg. 591
CUMMINS-ALLISON INC—See Crane NXT, Co.; *U.S. Public*, pg. 591
CUMMINS-ALLISON LTD.—See Crane NXT, Co.; *U.S. Public*, pg. 591
CUMMINS ALLISON PTY LTD—See Crane NXT, Co.; *U.S. Public*, pg. 591
CUMMINS-ALLISON SAS—See Crane NXT, Co.; *U.S. Public*, pg. 591
CUMMINS-ALLISON ULC—See Crane NXT, Co.; *U.S. Public*, pg. 591
CUMMINS AMERICAS, INC.—See Cummins Inc.; *U.S. Public*, pg. 605
CUMMINS ARGENTINA-SERVICIOS MINEROS S.A.—See Cummins Inc.; *U.S. Public*, pg. 605
CUMMINS ATLANTIC LLC—See Cummins Inc.; *U.S. Public*, pg. 605
CUMMINS AUSTRIA GMBH—See Cummins Inc.; *U.S. Public*, pg. 605
CUMMINS BELGIUM N.V.—See Cummins Inc.; *U.S. Public*, pg. 605
CUMMINS BLR LLC—See Cummins Inc.; *U.S. Public*, pg. 605
CUMMINS BRASIL LTDA.—See Cummins Inc.; *U.S. Public*, pg. 605
CUMMINS BRIDGEWAY COLUMBUS, LLC—See Cummins Inc.; *U.S. Public*, pg. 605
CUMMINS BRIDGEWAY GROVE CITY, LLC—See Cummins Inc.; *U.S. Public*, pg. 605
CUMMINS BRIDGEWAY LLC - HILLIARD—See Cummins Inc.; *U.S. Public*, pg. 605
CUMMINS BRIDGEWAY LLC—See Cummins Inc.; *U.S. Public*, pg. 605
CUMMINS BRIDGEWAY TOLEDO, LLC—See Cummins Inc.; *U.S. Public*, pg. 605
CUMMINS CANADA LIMITED—See Cummins Inc.; *U.S. Public*, pg. 605
CUMMINS CENTRAL POWER—See Cummins Inc.; *U.S. Public*, pg. 605
CUMMINS C&G LIMITED—See Car & General (Kenya) Limited; *Int'l*, pg. 1319
CUMMINS CHILD DEVELOPMENT CENTER, INC.—See Cummins Inc.; *U.S. Public*, pg. 605
THE CUMMINS CONSTRUCTION COMPANY INC.—See RLC Holding Co. Inc.; *U.S. Private*, pg. 3450
CUMMINS CORPORATION—See Cummins Inc.; *U.S. Public*, pg. 605

CUMMINS CROSSPOINT—See Cummins Inc.; *U.S. Public*, pg. 605
CUMMINS CZECH REPUBLIC S.R.O.—See Cummins Inc.; *U.S. Public*, pg. 605
CUMMINS DEUTSCHLAND GMBH—See Cummins Inc.; *U.S. Public*, pg. 605
CUMMINS DIESEL SALES CORPORATION—See Cummins Inc.; *U.S. Public*, pg. 605
CUMMINS DISTRIBUTION HOLDCO INC.—See Cummins Inc.; *U.S. Public*, pg. 605
CUMMINS DISTRIBUTOR BELGIUM SA—See Cummins Inc.; *U.S. Public*, pg. 605
CUMMINS EASTERN CANADA LP—See Cummins Inc.; *U.S. Public*, pg. 605
CUMMINS EASTERN MARINE, INC.—See Cummins Inc.; *U.S. Public*, pg. 605
CUMMINS EMISSION SOLUTIONS INC.—See Cummins Inc.; *U.S. Public*, pg. 605
CUMMINS ENERGY SOLUTIONS BUSINESS IBERIA—See Cummins Inc.; *U.S. Public*, pg. 605
CUMMINS ENGINE COMPANY PTY LIMITED—See Cummins Inc.; *U.S. Public*, pg. 605
CUMMINS FILTRATION CO. LTD.—See Cummins Inc.; *U.S. Public*, pg. 605
CUMMINS FILTRATION GMBH—See Cummins Inc.; *U.S. Public*, pg. 606
CUMMINS FILTRATION, INC.—See Cummins Inc.; *U.S. Public*, pg. 606
CUMMINS FILTRATION INTERNATIONAL CORP.—See Cummins Inc.; *U.S. Public*, pg. 605
CUMMINS FILTRATION SARL—See Cummins Inc.; *U.S. Public*, pg. 606
CUMMINS FILTRATION—See Cummins Inc.; *U.S. Public*, pg. 606
CUMMINS FILTRATION—See Cummins Inc.; *U.S. Public*, pg. 606
CUMMINS FUEL SYSTEMS (WUHAN) CO, LTD.—See Cummins Inc.; *U.S. Public*, pg. 606
CUMMINS GENERATOR TECHNOLOGIES CO., LTD.—See Cummins Inc.; *U.S. Public*, pg. 606
CUMMINS GENERATOR TECHNOLOGIES GMBH—See Cummins Inc.; *U.S. Public*, pg. 606
CUMMINS GENERATOR TECHNOLOGIES ITALY SRL—See Cummins Inc.; *U.S. Public*, pg. 606
CUMMINS GENERATOR TECHNOLOGIES MEXICO S DE R.L. DE C.V.—See Cummins Inc.; *U.S. Public*, pg. 606
CUMMINS GENERATOR TECHNOLOGIES NORWAY—See Cummins Inc.; *U.S. Public*, pg. 606
CUMMINS GENERATOR TECHNOLOGIES ROMANIA S.A.—See Cummins Inc.; *U.S. Public*, pg. 606
CUMMINS GENERATOR TECHNOLOGIES SINGAPORE PTE LTD.—See Cummins Inc.; *U.S. Public*, pg. 606
CUMMINS GENERATOR TECHNOLOGIES—See Cummins Inc.; *U.S. Public*, pg. 606
CUMMINS GENERATOR TECHNOLOGIES SPAIN S.A.—See Cummins Inc.; *U.S. Public*, pg. 606
CUMMINS GHANA LIMITED—See Cummins Inc.; *U.S. Public*, pg. 606
CUMMINS HOLLAND B.V.—See Cummins Inc.; *U.S. Public*, pg. 606
CUMMINS HONG KONG LTD.—See Cummins Inc.; *U.S. Public*, pg. 606
CUMMINS INC.—See Cummins Inc.; *U.S. Public*, pg. 606
CUMMINS INC.; *U.S. Public*, pg. 605
CUMMINS INDIA LIMITED—See Cummins Inc.; *U.S. Public*, pg. 606
CUMMINS ITALIA S.P.A.—See Cummins Inc.; *U.S. Public*, pg. 606
CUMMINS JAPAN LTD.—See Cummins Inc.; *U.S. Public*, pg. 606
CUMMINS JUAREZ, S.A. DE C.V.—See Cummins Inc.; *U.S. Public*, pg. 606
CUMMINS KOMATSU ENGINE COMPANY—See Cummins Inc.; *U.S. Public*, pg. 606
CUMMINS KOMATSU ENGINE COMPANY—See Komatsu Ltd.; *Int'l*, pg. 4235
CUMMINS KOREA LTD.—See Cummins Inc.; *U.S. Public*, pg. 606
CUMMINS, LTD.—See Cummins Inc.; *U.S. Public*, pg. 607
CUMMINS MAKINA SANAYI VE TICARET LIMITED SIRKETI—See Cummins Inc.; *U.S. Public*, pg. 606
CUMMINS MERCRUISER DIESEL MARINE LLC—See Cummins Inc.; *U.S. Public*, pg. 606
CUMMINS MIDDLE EAST FZE—See Cummins Inc.; *U.S. Public*, pg. 606
CUMMINS NATURAL GAS ENGINES, INC.—See Cummins Inc.; *U.S. Public*, pg. 606
CUMMINS NIGERIA LTD.—See Cummins Inc.; *U.S. Public*, pg. 606
CUMMINS NORTHEAST INC.—See Cummins Inc.; *U.S. Public*, pg. 606
CUMMINS NORWAY AS—See Cummins Inc.; *U.S. Public*, pg. 606
CUMMINS NPOWER LLC—See Cummins Inc.; *U.S. Public*, pg. 606
CUMMINS N.V.—See Cummins Inc.; *U.S. Public*, pg. 606
CUMMINS POWER GENERATION—See Cummins Inc.; *U.S. Public*, pg. 606

CORPORATE AFFILIATIONS

CUMMINS POWER GENERATION (S) PTE. LTD.—See Cummins Inc.; *U.S. Public*, pg. 606
CUMMINS POWER GENERATION (U.K.) LIMITED—See Cummins Inc.; *U.S. Public*, pg. 606
CUMMINS POWER SYSTEMS INC.—See Cummins Inc.; *U.S. Public*, pg. 606
CUMMINS POWER SYSTEMS—See Cummins Inc.; *U.S. Public*, pg. 606
CUMMINS ROCKY MOUNTAIN LLC—See Cummins Inc.; *U.S. Public*, pg. 607
CUMMINS ROCKY MOUNTAIN—See Cummins Inc.; *U.S. Public*, pg. 607
CUMMINS ROMANIA SRL—See Cummins Inc.; *U.S. Public*, pg. 607
CUMMINS SALES AND SERVICE PHILIPPINES INC.—See Cummins Inc.; *U.S. Public*, pg. 607
CUMMINS SALES AND SERVICE PRIVATE LIMITED—See Cummins Inc.; *U.S. Public*, pg. 607
CUMMINS SALES AND SERVICE (SINGAPORE) PTE. LTD.—See Cummins Inc.; *U.S. Public*, pg. 607
CUMMINS SALES AND SERVICE—See Cummins Inc.; *U.S. Public*, pg. 606
CUMMINS SALES & SERVICE SINGAPORE PTE LTD—See Cummins Inc.; *U.S. Public*, pg. 606
CUMMINS SCOTT & ENGLISH MALAYSIA SDN. BHD.—See Cummins Inc.; *U.S. Public*, pg. 607
CUMMINS SOUTH AFRICA (PTY.) LTD.—See Cummins Inc.; *U.S. Public*, pg. 607
CUMMINS SOUTHEASTERN POWER, INC.—See Cummins Inc.; *U.S. Public*, pg. 607
CUMMINS SOUTHERN PLAINS, LLC—See Cummins Inc.; *U.S. Public*, pg. 607
CUMMINS SOUTH INC.—See Cummins Inc.; *U.S. Public*, pg. 607
CUMMINS SOUTH PACIFIC PTY. LIMITED—See Cummins Inc.; *U.S. Public*, pg. 607
CUMMINS SPAIN, S.L.—See Cummins Inc.; *U.S. Public*, pg. 607
CUMMINS SWEDEN AB—See Cummins Inc.; *U.S. Public*, pg. 607
CUMMINS TECHNOLOGIES INDIA LIMITED—See Cummins Inc.; *U.S. Public*, pg. 607
CUMMINS TURBO TECHNOLOGIES LTD.—See Cummins Inc.; *U.S. Public*, pg. 607
CUMMINS TURBO TECHNOLOGIES—See Cummins Inc.; *U.S. Public*, pg. 607
CUMMINS TURBO TECHNOLOGIES—See Cummins Inc.; *U.S. Public*, pg. 607
CUMMINS U.K. PENSION PLAN TRUSTEE LTD.—See Cummins Inc.; *U.S. Public*, pg. 607
CUMMINS-WAGNER CO., INC.; *U.S. Private*, pg. 1123
CUMMINS WEST AFRICA LIMITED—See Cummins Inc.; *U.S. Public*, pg. 607
CUMMINS WESTERN CANADA LIMITED PARTNERSHIP—See Cummins Inc.; *U.S. Public*, pg. 607
CUMMINS WESTPORT INC.—See Cummins Inc.; *U.S. Public*, pg. 607
CUMMINS WESTPORT INC.—See Westport Fuel Systems Inc.; *Int'l*, pg. 8393
CUMMINS ZAMBIA LTD.—See Cummins Inc.; *U.S. Public*, pg. 607
CUMMINS ZIMBABWE PVT. LTD.—See Cummins Inc.; *U.S. Public*, pg. 607
CUMSA CORP.—See Avis Industrial Corporation; *U.S. Private*, pg. 407
CUMULEX N.V.; *Int'l*, pg. 1878
CUMULUS BROADCASTING INC. - INDIANAPOLIS, IN—See Cumulus Media Inc.; *U.S. Public*, pg. 609
CUMULUS BROADCASTING LLC - ABILENE, TX—See Cumulus Media Inc.; *U.S. Public*, pg. 609
CUMULUS BROADCASTING LLC - ALLENTOWN, PA—See Cumulus Media Inc.; *U.S. Public*, pg. 609
CUMULUS BROADCASTING LLC - ANN ARBOR, MI—See Cumulus Media Inc.; *U.S. Public*, pg. 609
CUMULUS BROADCASTING LLC - BATON ROUGE, LA—See Cumulus Media Inc.; *U.S. Public*, pg. 609
CUMULUS BROADCASTING LLC - BUFFALO, NY—See Cumulus Media Inc.; *U.S. Public*, pg. 609
CUMULUS BROADCASTING LLC - CINCINNATI, OH—See Cumulus Media Inc.; *U.S. Public*, pg. 609
CUMULUS BROADCASTING LLC - COLORADO SPRINGS, CO—See Cumulus Media Inc.; *U.S. Public*, pg. 609
CUMULUS BROADCASTING LLC - COLUMBIA, MO—See Cumulus Media Inc.; *U.S. Public*, pg. 609
CUMULUS BROADCASTING LLC - COLUMBIA, SC—See Cumulus Media Inc.; *U.S. Public*, pg. 609
CUMULUS BROADCASTING LLC - DALLAS, TX—See Cumulus Media Inc.; *U.S. Public*, pg. 609
CUMULUS BROADCASTING LLC - DUBUQUE, IA—See Cumulus Media Inc.; *U.S. Public*, pg. 609
CUMULUS BROADCASTING LLC - FAYETTEVILLE, NC—See Cumulus Media Inc.; *U.S. Public*, pg. 609
CUMULUS BROADCASTING LLC - HARRISBURG, PA—See Cumulus Media Inc.; *U.S. Public*, pg. 610
CUMULUS BROADCASTING LLC - HOUSTON, TX—See Cumulus Media Inc.; *U.S. Public*, pg. 610

COMPANY NAME INDEX

CUMULUS BROADCASTING LLC - JEFFERSON CITY, MO—See Cumulus Media Inc.; *U.S. Public*, pg. 609
CUMULUS BROADCASTING LLC - KANSAS CITY, KS—See Cumulus Media Inc.; *U.S. Public*, pg. 610
CUMULUS BROADCASTING LLC - KOKOMO, IN—See Cumulus Media Inc.; *U.S. Public*, pg. 610
CUMULUS BROADCASTING LLC - LAFAYETTE, LA—See Cumulus Media Inc.; *U.S. Public*, pg. 610
CUMULUS BROADCASTING LLC - LITTLE ROCK, AR—See Cumulus Media Inc.; *U.S. Public*, pg. 610
CUMULUS BROADCASTING LLC - MODESTO/STOCKTON, CA—See Cumulus Media Inc.; *U.S. Public*, pg. 610
CUMULUS BROADCASTING LLC - MUNCIE, IN—See Cumulus Media Inc.; *U.S. Public*, pg. 610
CUMULUS BROADCASTING LLC - NEW ORLEANS, LA—See Cumulus Media Inc.; *U.S. Public*, pg. 610
CUMULUS BROADCASTING LLC - OKLAHOMA CITY, OK—See Cumulus Media Inc.; *U.S. Public*, pg. 610
CUMULUS BROADCASTING LLC - SAGINAW, MI—See Cumulus Media Inc.; *U.S. Public*, pg. 610
CUMULUS BROADCASTING LLC - SALT LAKE CITY, UT—See Cumulus Media Inc.; *U.S. Public*, pg. 610
CUMULUS BROADCASTING LLC—See Cumulus Media Inc.; *U.S. Public*, pg. 609
CUMULUS BROADCASTING LLC - SYRACUSE, NY—See Cumulus Media Inc.; *U.S. Public*, pg. 610
CUMULUS BROADCASTING LLC - WICHITA FALLS, TX—See Cumulus Media Inc.; *U.S. Public*, pg. 610
CUMULUS BROADCASTING LLC - WORCESTER, MA—See Cumulus Media Inc.; *U.S. Public*, pg. 610
CUMULUS BROADCASTING LLC - YORK, PA—See Cumulus Media Inc.; *U.S. Public*, pg. 610
CUMULUS FUNDING, INC.—See Enova International, Inc.; *U.S. Public*, pg. 769
CUMULUS IT AS—See Hafslund ASA; *Int'l*, pg. 3206
CUMULUS MEDIA HOLDINGS, INC.—See Cumulus Media Inc.; *U.S. Public*, pg. 609
CUMULUS MEDIA INC.; *U.S. Public*, pg. 609
CUMULUS NETWORKS, INC.—See NVIDIA Corporation; *U.S. Public*, pg. 1558
CUMULUS SYSTEMS INCORPORATED—See Hitachi, Ltd.; *Int'l*, pg. 3412
CUMULUS SYSTEMS PRIVATE LIMITED—See Hitachi, Ltd.; *Int'l*, pg. 3412
CUNA BROKERAGE SERVICES, INC.—See CMFG Life Insurance Company; *U.S. Private*, pg. 950
CUNA CARIBBEAN INSURANCE SOCIETY LIMITED—See CMFG Life Insurance Company; *U.S. Private*, pg. 950
CUNA MUTUAL INSURANCE AGENCY, INC.—See CMFG Life Insurance Company; *U.S. Private*, pg. 950
CUNA MUTUAL INSURANCE GROUP—See CMFG Life Insurance Company; *U.S. Private*, pg. 950
CUNA MUTUAL MORTGAGE—See Onity Group Inc.; *U.S. Public*, pg. 1604
CUNARD LINE LTD.—See Carnival Corporation; *U.S. Public*, pg. 438
CUNARD LINE LTD. - UK OFFICE—See Carnival Corporation; *U.S. Public*, pg. 438
CUNDARI INTEGRATED ADVERTISING; *Int'l*, pg. 1878
CUNNINGHAM BUTANE GAS COMPANY; *U.S. Private*, pg. 1123
CUNNINGHAM CHILDREN'S HOME; *U.S. Private*, pg. 1123
CUNNINGHAM FARMS INC.; *U.S. Private*, pg. 1123
CUNNINGHAM FIELD & RESEARCH SERVICE; *U.S. Private*, pg. 1123
CUNNINGHAM-LIMP COMPANY; *U.S. Private*, pg. 1123
CUNNINGHAM MOTORS, INC.; *U.S. Private*, pg. 1123
CUNNINGHAM SUPPLY INCORPORATED; *U.S. Private*, pg. 1123
CUNO ENGINEERED PRODUCTS, INC.—See 3M Company; *U.S. Public*, pg. 7
CUNO LATINA LTDA.—See 3M Company; *U.S. Public*, pg. 7
CUONGTHUAN INVESTMENT CORPORATION; *Int'l*, pg. 1878
CUPERTINO ELECTRIC, INC.—See Quanta Services, Inc.; *U.S. Public*, pg. 1750
CUPERTINO ELECTRIC, INC.—See Quanta Services, Inc.; *U.S. Public*, pg. 1751
CUPERTINO ELECTRIC, INC.—See Quanta Services, Inc.; *U.S. Public*, pg. 1751
CUPID CANDIES, INC.—See Brown Sugar Bakery & Cafe, Inc.; *U.S. Private*, pg. 669
CUPID FOUNDATIONS, INC.; *U.S. Private*, pg. 1123
CUPID LTD.—See Columbia Petro Chem Pvt. Ltd.; *Int'l*, pg. 1706
CUP INTERACTIVE SAS; *Int'l*, pg. 1878
CUPONIDAD PERU—See The Cisneros Group of Companies; *Int'l*, pg. 7632
CUPONIDAD VENEZUELA CA—See The Cisneros Group of Companies; *Int'l*, pg. 7632
CUPPLES' J & J COMPANY INCORPORATED; *U.S. Private*, pg. 1123
CUPRAL GROUP LTD.—See PT International Development Corporation Ltd.; *Int'l*, pg. 6047
CUPRIC CANYON CAPITAL LLC; *U.S. Private*, pg. 1124

CUPRIME MATERIAL CO., LTD.—See Ta Ya Electric Wire & Cable Co., Ltd.; *Int'l*, pg. 7400
CUPRINOL LIMITED—See Akzo Nobel N.V.; *Int'l*, pg. 273
CUPRUM S.A. DE C.V.; *Int'l*, pg. 1878
CUPRUM S.A.U.—See Intek Group S.p.A.; *Int'l*, pg. 3732
CURABILL LTD—See Swisscom AG; *Int'l*, pg. 7373
CURACHEM CO., LTD.; *Int'l*, pg. 1878
CURACLE CO., LTD.; *Int'l*, pg. 1878
CURADIGM S.A.S.—See Nanobiotix; *Int'l*, pg. 5143
CURAEGIS TECHNOLOGIES, INC.; *U.S. Private*, pg. 1124
CURAE HEALTH, INC.; *U.S. Private*, pg. 1124
CURAGEN CORPORATION—See Celldex Therapeutics, Inc.; *U.S. Public*, pg. 465
CURA HOSPITALITY INC.—See Eat'n Park Hospitality Group, Inc.; *U.S. Private*, pg. 1323
CURALATE, INC.—See Marlin Equity Partners, LLC; *U.S. Private*, pg. 2584
CURALEAF HOLDINGS, INC.; *U.S. Public*, pg. 610
CURAMED STAFFING, LLC; *U.S. Private*, pg. 1124
CURAMIK ELECTRONICS GMBH—See Rogers Corporation; *U.S. Public*, pg. 1808
CURAMIK ELECTRONICS, INC.—See Rogers Corporation; *U.S. Public*, pg. 1808
CURANUM AG—See Clariane SE; *Int'l*, pg. 1643
CURANUM BAD HERSFELD GMBH—See Clariane SE; *Int'l*, pg. 1643
CURANUM FRANZISKUSHAUS GMBH—See Clariane SE; *Int'l*, pg. 1643
CURANUM SENIORENPFLEGEZENTRUM AM SPESSART—See Clariane SE; *Int'l*, pg. 1643
CURANUM WESTFALEN GMBH—See Clariane SE; *Int'l*, pg. 1643
CURANUS GMBH—See Reclay Holding GmbH; *Int'l*, pg. 6237
CURA PARTNERS, LLC—See Addus HomeCare Corporation; *U.S. Public*, pg. 40
CURAPHAR B.V.—See Fagron NV; *Int'l*, pg. 2603
CURA RISK MANAGEMENT SOFTWARE (PTY) LIMITED—See Cura Technologies Ltd.; *Int'l*, pg. 1878
CURA RISK MANAGEMENT SOFTWARE (PTY) LIMITED—See Cura Technologies Ltd.; *Int'l*, pg. 1878
CURASAN AG; *Int'l*, pg. 1878
CURASCRIPT, INC.—See The Cigna Group; *U.S. Public*, pg. 2061
CURAS, INC.; *U.S. Private*, pg. 1124
CURA SOFTWARE SOLUTIONS UK LIMITED—See Cura Technologies Ltd.; *Int'l*, pg. 1878
CURA TECHNOLOGIES LTD.; *Int'l*, pg. 1878
CURATEK PHARMACEUTICALS LTD.—See Tang Industries Inc.; *U.S. Private*, pg. 3930
CURATEQ BIOLOGICS PRIVATE LIMITED—See Aurobindo Pharma Ltd.; *Int'l*, pg. 713
CURATION FOODS, INC.—See Lifecore Biomedical, Inc.; *U.S. Public*, pg. 1312
CURATIS HOLDING AG; *Int'l*, pg. 1878
CURATIVE BIOSCIENCES, INC.; *U.S. Public*, pg. 610
CURATIVE CARE NETWORK, INC.; *U.S. Private*, pg. 1124
CURATIVE MEDICAL DEVICES GMBH—See ResMed Inc.; *U.S. Public*, pg. 1790
CURATIVE MEDICAL INC.—See ResMed Inc.; *U.S. Public*, pg. 1790
CURATIVE MEDICAL TECHNOLOGY (SUZHOU) LTD—See ResMed Inc.; *U.S. Public*, pg. 1790
CURATORS OF THE UNIVERSITY OF MISSOURI; *U.S. Private*, pg. 1124
CURBELL, INC.; *U.S. Private*, pg. 1124
CURBELL MEDICAL PRODUCTS, INC.—See Curbell, Inc.; *U.S. Private*, pg. 1124
CURBELL PLASTICS, INC.—See Curbell, Inc.; *U.S. Private*, pg. 1124
CURB MEDIA LIMITED—See Wasserman Media Group, LLC; *U.S. Private*, pg. 4450
CURB RECORDS, INC.; *U.S. Private*, pg. 1124
CURBSOFT, LLC—See Sensata Technologies Holding plc; *U.S. Public*, pg. 1865
CURBS PLUS, INC.; *U.S. Private*, pg. 1124
CURCAS OIL N.V.; *Int'l*, pg. 1878
CURE 4 THE KIDS FOUNDATION; *U.S. Private*, pg. 1124
CUREA ELEKTRO AG—See BKW AG; *Int'l*, pg. 1055
CUREATR, INC.—See Vora Ventures LLC; *U.S. Private*, pg. 4412
CURECANTI DIALYSIS, LLC—See DaVita Inc.; *U.S. Public*, pg. 637
CURE CO., LTD.—See 4Cs Holdings Co., Ltd.; *Int'l*, pg. 11
CURE MEDICAL & TECHNICAL SUPPLY LTD—See Eldan Electronic Co. Ltd.; *Int'l*, pg. 2346
CURE STARTS NOW; *U.S. Private*, pg. 1124
CURETIS NV; *Int'l*, pg. 1878
CURETIS USA—See OpGen, Inc.; *U.S. Public*, pg. 1607
CUREVAC NETHERLANDS B.V.—See CureVac N.V.; *Int'l*, pg. 1878
CUREVAC N.V.; *Int'l*, pg. 1878
CUREVAC SE—See CureVac N.V.; *Int'l*, pg. 1878
CUREVAC SWISS AG—See CureVac N.V.; *Int'l*, pg. 1878
CUREVO INC.—See Green Cross WellBeing Corp.; *Int'l*, pg. 3070

CURO GROUP HOLDINGS CORP.

CUREXA HEALTH (PRIVATE) LIMITED—See Highnoon Laboratories Limited; *Int'l*, pg. 3388
CUREXO INC.; *Int'l*, pg. 1878
CURIA FRANCE SAS—See GTCR LLC; *U.S. Private*, pg. 1805
CURIA FRANCE SAS—See The Carlyle Group Inc.; *U.S. Public*, pg. 2046
CURIA GERMANY GMBH—See GTCR LLC; *U.S. Private*, pg. 1805
CURIA GERMANY GMBH—See The Carlyle Group Inc.; *U.S. Public*, pg. 2046
CURIA HOLDINGS (UK) LIMITED—See GTCR LLC; *U.S. Private*, pg. 1805
CURIA HOLDINGS (UK) LIMITED—See The Carlyle Group Inc.; *U.S. Public*, pg. 2046
CURIA, INC.—See GTCR LLC; *U.S. Private*, pg. 1805
CURIA, INC.—See The Carlyle Group Inc.; *U.S. Public*, pg. 2046
CURIA INDIANA, LLC—See GTCR LLC; *U.S. Private*, pg. 1805
CURIA INDIANA, LLC—See The Carlyle Group Inc.; *U.S. Public*, pg. 2046
CURIA INDIA PRIVATE LIMITED—See GTCR LLC; *U.S. Private*, pg. 1805
CURIA INDIA PRIVATE LIMITED—See The Carlyle Group Inc.; *U.S. Public*, pg. 2046
CURIA MASSACHUSETTS, INC.—See GTCR LLC; *U.S. Private*, pg. 1805
CURIA MASSACHUSETTS, INC.—See The Carlyle Group Inc.; *U.S. Public*, pg. 2046
CURIA MISSOURI, INC.—See GTCR LLC; *U.S. Private*, pg. 1805
CURIA MISSOURI, INC.—See The Carlyle Group Inc.; *U.S. Public*, pg. 2046
CURIA NEW MEXICO, LLC—See GTCR LLC; *U.S. Private*, pg. 1805
CURIA NEW MEXICO, LLC—See The Carlyle Group Inc.; *U.S. Public*, pg. 2046
CURIA NEW YORK, INC.—See GTCR LLC; *U.S. Private*, pg. 1805
CURIA NEW YORK, INC.—See The Carlyle Group Inc.; *U.S. Public*, pg. 2046
CURIA (SCOTLAND) LIMITED—See GTCR LLC; *U.S. Private*, pg. 1805
CURIA (SCOTLAND) LIMITED—See The Carlyle Group Inc.; *U.S. Public*, pg. 2046
CURIA SERVICES, INC.—See GTCR LLC; *U.S. Private*, pg. 1805
CURIA SERVICES, INC.—See The Carlyle Group Inc.; *U.S. Public*, pg. 2046
CURIA WASHINGTON, INC.—See GTCR LLC; *U.S. Private*, pg. 1805
CURIA WASHINGTON, INC.—See The Carlyle Group Inc.; *U.S. Public*, pg. 2046
CURI HOLDINGS, INC.; *U.S. Private*, pg. 1124
CURIODYSSEY; *U.S. Private*, pg. 1125
CURIOSITY INC.—See Future Corporation; *Int'l*, pg. 2853
CURIOSITYSTREAM INC.; *U.S. Public*, pg. 610
CURIOSITYVILLE, INC.—See Veritas Capital Fund Management, LLC; *U.S. Private*, pg. 4363
CURIOX BIOSYSTEMS CO., LTD.; *Int'l*, pg. 1878
CURIS, INC.; *U.S. Public*, pg. 610
CURIS SECURITIES CORPORATION—See Curis, Inc.; *U.S. Public*, pg. 610
CURIUM NETHERLANDS HOLDING B.V. - CZECH BRANCH—See Curium SAS; *Int'l*, pg. 1878
CURIUM NETHERLANDS HOLDINGS B.V.—See Curium SAS; *Int'l*, pg. 1878
CURIUM SAS; *Int'l*, pg. 1878
CURIUM SWEDEN AB—See Curium SAS; *Int'l*, pg. 1878
CURIUM US LLC—See Curium SAS; *Int'l*, pg. 1879
CURI WEALTH MANAGEMENT, LLC—See Curi Holdings, Inc.; *U.S. Private*, pg. 1125
CURLEW VALLEY FARMS, LLC—See Compass Minerals International, Inc.; *U.S. Public*, pg. 560
CURLEY ASSOCIATES, INC.—See ABRY Partners, LLC; *U.S. Private*, pg. 42
CURLEYS QUALITY FOODS LIMITED—See Sysco Corporation; *U.S. Public*, pg. 1973
CURLIN, INC.—See Southfield Capital Advisors, LLC; *U.S. Private*, pg. 3736
CURLIN MEDICAL INC.—See Moog Inc.; *U.S. Public*, pg. 1470
THE CURL S.A.C.—See KMD Brands Limited; *Int'l*, pg. 4204
CUR MEDIA INC.; *U.S. Private*, pg. 1124
CURNEAL & HIGNITE INSURANCE, INC.—See Houchens Industries, Inc.; *U.S. Private*, pg. 1990
CURO CARE LIMITED—See Horizon Capital LLP; *Int'l*, pg. 3479
CURO CO., LTD.; *Int'l*, pg. 1879
CURO GROUP HOLDINGS CORP.; *U.S. Public*, pg. 610
CURO HEALTH SERVICES, LLC—See Apollo Global Management, Inc.; *U.S. Public*, pg. 156
CURO TEKNIKA, INC.—See PLDT Inc.; *Int'l*, pg. 5896
THE CUROTTO-CAN, LLC—See Dover Corporation; *U.S. Public*, pg. 683
CURRAGH COAL SALES CO. PTY. LTD.—See Wesfarmers Limited; *Int'l*, pg. 8382

CURO GROUP HOLDINGS CORP.   CORPORATE AFFILIATIONS

CURRAGH QUEENSLAND MINING PTY. LTD.—See Wesfarmers Limited; *Int'l*, pg. 8382
CURRAN & CONNORS, INC.; *U.S. Private*, pg. 1125
CURRAN CONTRACTING COMPANY, INC. - LAKE BLUFF PLANT—See Curran Group, Inc.; *U.S. Private*, pg. 1125
CURRAN CONTRACTING COMPANY, INC. - MCHENRY PLANT—See Curran Group, Inc.; *U.S. Private*, pg. 1125
CURRAN CONTRACTING COMPANY—See Curran Group, Inc.; *U.S. Private*, pg. 1125
CURRAN CONTRACTING INC—See Curran Group, Inc.; *U.S. Private*, pg. 1125
CURRAN GROUP, INC.; *U.S. Private*, pg. 1125
CURRAX HOLDINGS LLC—See JPMorgan Chase & Co.; *U.S. Public*, pg. 1207
CURRAX HOLDINGS USA LLC—See JPMorgan Chase & Co.; *U.S. Public*, pg. 1207
CURRAX PHARMACEUTICALS LLC—See JPMorgan Chase & Co.; *U.S. Public*, pg. 1207
CURRAX PHARMACEUTICALS LLC; *U.S. Private*, pg. 1125
CURRENC GROUP INC; *U.S. Public*, pg. 611
CURRENCY EXCHANGE INTERNATIONAL, CORP.; *U.S. Public*, pg. 611
CURRENCY TECH LTD.—See Giesecke & Devrient GmbH; *Int'l*, pg. 2969
CURRENEX, INC.—See State Street Corporation; *U.S. Public*, pg. 1940
CURRENTA GESCHAFTSFUHRUNGS-GMBH—See Bayer Aktiengesellschaft; *Int'l*, pg. 907
CURRENT ANALYSIS, INC.—See GlobalData Plc; *Int'l*, pg. 3003
CURRENT BUILDERS OF FLORIDA INC; *U.S. Private*, pg. 1125
CURRENT CAPITAL LLC; *U.S. Private*, pg. 1125
CURRENT ENVIRONMENTAL SOLUTIONS LLC—See TruArc Partners, L.P.; *U.S. Private*, pg. 4245
CURRENT, INC.; *U.S. Private*, pg. 1125
CURRENT LIGHTING SOLUTIONS, LLC—See AIP, LLC; *U.S. Private*, pg. 134
CURRENT MEDIA GROUP, LLC—See Regent, L.P.; *U.S. Private*, pg. 3387
CURRENT MOTOR CORPORATION; *Int'l*, pg. 1879
CURRENT POWER SOLUTIONS, INC.—See Patterson-UTI Energy, Inc.; *U.S. Public*, pg. 1654
CURRENT SOLUTIONS, LLC—See River Associates Investments, LLC; *U.S. Private*, pg. 3443
CURRENT TECH CENTER CO., LTD.—See Current Motor Corporation; *Int'l*, pg. 1879
CURRENT TECHNOLOGY CORPORATION; *Int'l*, pg. 1879
CURRENT WATER TECHNOLOGIES INC.; *Int'l*, pg. 1879
CURRIE & BROWN (AUSTRALIA) PTY. LIMITED—See Currie & Brown Holdings Limited; *Int'l*, pg. 1879
CURRIE & BROWN (CI) LIMITED—See Currie & Brown Holdings Limited; *Int'l*, pg. 1879
CURRIE & BROWN HOLDINGS LIMITED; *Int'l*, pg. 1879
CURRIE & BROWN, INC.—See Currie & Brown Holdings Limited; *Int'l*, pg. 1879
CURRIE & BROWN UK LIMITED—See Currie & Brown Holdings Limited; *Int'l*, pg. 1879
CURRIE GIN—See Alabama Farmers Cooperative, Inc.; *U.S. Private*, pg. 148
CURRIER CONSTRUCTION INC.; *U.S. Private*, pg. 1125
CURRIER MCCABE & ASSOCIATES; *U.S. Private*, pg. 1125
CURRIE ROSE RESOURCES INC.; *Int'l*, pg. 1879
CURRO EDUCATION BOTSWANA (PTY) LTD.—See Curro Holdings Ltd.; *Int'l*, pg. 1879
CURRO EDUCATION NAMIBIA (PTY) LTD.—See Curro Holdings Ltd.; *Int'l*, pg. 1879
CURRO HOLDINGS LTD.; *Int'l*, pg. 1879
CURRY ACURA—See Curry Corporation; *U.S. Private*, pg. 1125
CURRY AUTOMOTIVE, LLC.; *U.S. Private*, pg. 1125
CURRY COASTAL PILOT—See Western Communications Inc.; *U.S. Private*, pg. 4491
CURRY CONTROLS COMPANY INC; *U.S. Private*, pg. 1125
CURRY CORPORATION; *U.S. Private*, pg. 1125
CURRY HONDA—See Curry Corporation; *U.S. Private*, pg. 1125
CURRY HONDA—See Curry Corporation; *U.S. Private*, pg. 1126
CURRY HONDA—See Lithia Motors, Inc.; *U.S. Public*, pg. 1321
CURRY INVESTMENT COMPANY; *U.S. Private*, pg. 1126
CURRY'S AUTO SERVICE; *U.S. Private*, pg. 1126
CURRYS PLC; *Int'l*, pg. 1879
CURRY TRANSFER & RECYCLING, INC.—See Waste Connections, Inc.; *Int'l*, pg. 8353
CURRY UP NOW; *U.S. Private*, pg. 1126
CURSOR CONTROLS LIMITED—See discoverIE Group plc; *Int'l*, pg. 2133
CURTAIN WALLS AND WINDOWS INC.—See The Berlin Steel Construction Company; *U.S. Private*, pg. 3994

CURTAINWALLS & WINDOWS, INC. - CW FABRICATION SYSTEMS DIVISION—See The Berlin Steel Construction Company; *U.S. Private*, pg. 3994
CURTAIN WONDERLAND PTY LTD—See Ningbo Xianfeng New Material Co. Ltd; *Int'l*, pg. 5307
CURT BAUER GMBH; *Int'l*, pg. 1879
CURTCO MEDIA LABS LLC; *U.S. Private*, pg. 1126
CURTCO ROBB MEDIA, LLC—See RockBridge Growth Equity, LLC; *U.S. Private*, pg. 3465
CURT GEORGI GMBH & CO. KG; *Int'l*, pg. 1880
CURT G. JOA EUROPE GMBH—See Curt G. Joa, Inc.; *U.S. Private*, pg. 1126
CURT G. JOA, INC.; *U.S. Private*, pg. 1126
CURTIS 1000 FRANCE SARL—See Bong AB; *Int'l*, pg. 1107
CURTIS 1000, INC.—See Taylor Corporation; *U.S. Private*, pg. 3938
CURTIS 1000, INC.—See Taylor Corporation; *U.S. Private*, pg. 3938
CURTIS 1000, INC.—See Taylor Corporation; *U.S. Private*, pg. 3938
CURTIS 1000, INC.—See Taylor Corporation; *U.S. Private*, pg. 3938
CURTIS 1000, INC.—See Taylor Corporation; *U.S. Private*, pg. 3938
CURTIS 1000, INC.—See Taylor Corporation; *U.S. Private*, pg. 3938
CURTIS BANKS GROUP PLC—See Nucleus Financial Platforms Limited; *Int'l*, pg. 5485
CURTIS BAY ENERGY, INC.—See Aurora Capital Group, LLC; *U.S. Private*, pg. 393
CURTIS BUSINESS FORMS INC.—See Ennis, Inc.; *U.S. Public*, pg. 769
CURTIS CANADA INC.—See CNIM Constructions Industrielles de la Mediterranee SA; *Int'l*, pg. 1677
CURTIS C. GUNN, INC.; *U.S. Private*, pg. 1126
CURTIS CIRCULATION COMPANY; *U.S. Private*, pg. 1126
CURTIS CORPORATION; *U.S. Private*, pg. 1126
CURTIS H STOUT INC.; *U.S. Private*, pg. 1126
CURTIS INDUSTRIES INC.—See Powers Holdings, Inc.; *U.S. Private*, pg. 3240
CURTIS INDUSTRIES, LLC—See Nautic Partners, LLC; *U.S. Private*, pg. 2868
CURTIS INSTRUMENTS, INC.; *U.S. Private*, pg. 1126
CURTIS INTERNATIONAL LTD.; *Int'l*, pg. 1880
CURTIS-LAYER CONSTRUCTION CO.; *U.S. Private*, pg. 1127
CURTIS LUMBER COMPANY, INC.; *U.S. Private*, pg. 1126
CURTIS, MALLET-PREVOST, COLT & MOSLE LLP; *U.S. Private*, pg. 1127
CURTIS MEDIA GROUP; *U.S. Private*, pg. 1126
CURTIS METAL FINISHING CO., INC.—See Commercial Steel Treating Corp.; *U.S. Private*, pg. 984
CURTIS OIL CO. INC.; *U.S. Private*, pg. 1126
CURTIS PACKAGING CORPORATION—See Curtis Corporation; *U.S. Private*, pg. 1126
CURTIS PACKING CO., INC.; *U.S. Private*, pg. 1126
CURTIS/PALMER HYDROELECTRIC COMPANY LP—See I Squared Capital Advisors (US) LLC; *U.S. Private*, pg. 2025
CURTIS PARTITION CORP.; *U.S. Private*, pg. 1126
CURTIS PRODUCTS INC.; *U.S. Private*, pg. 1126
THE CURTIS PUBLISHING COMPANY; *U.S. Private*, pg. 4017
CURTIS RESTAURANT EQUIPMENT INC.; *U.S. Private*, pg. 1127
CURTIS SCREW CO., INC.; *U.S. Private*, pg. 1127
CURTIS SCREW COMPANY, LLC—See Curtis Screw Co., Inc.; *U.S. Private*, pg. 1127
CURTISS MOTORCYCLE COMPANY, INC.; *U.S. Public*, pg. 611
CURTIS STEEL COMPANY; *U.S. Private*, pg. 1127
CURTISS-WRIGHT ANTRIEBSTECHNIK GMBH—See Curtiss-Wright Corporation; *U.S. Public*, pg. 611
CURTISS-WRIGHT CONTROLS DEFENSE SOLUTIONS - OTTAWA—See Curtiss-Wright Corporation; *U.S. Public*, pg. 611
CURTISS-WRIGHT CONTROLS EMBEDDED COMPUTING-HIGH WYCOMBE—See Curtiss-Wright Corporation; *U.S. Public*, pg. 611
CURTISS-WRIGHT CONTROLS, INC.—See Curtiss-Wright Corporation; *U.S. Public*, pg. 611
CURTISS-WRIGHT CONTROLS INTEGRATED SENSING—See Curtiss-Wright Corporation; *U.S. Public*, pg. 611
CURTISS-WRIGHT CORPORATION; *U.S. Public*, pg. 611
CURTISS-WRIGHT FLIGHT SYSTEMS, INC.—See Curtiss-Wright Corporation; *U.S. Public*, pg. 611
CURTISS-WRIGHT FLOW CONTROL CORPORATION—See Curtiss-Wright Corporation; *U.S. Public*, pg. 612
CURTISS-WRIGHT FLOW CONTROL SERVICE, LLC—See Curtiss-Wright Corporation; *U.S. Public*, pg. 612
CURTISS-WRIGHT VALVE GROUP-FARRIS—See Curtiss-Wright Corporation; *U.S. Public*, pg. 611
CURTIS-TOLEDO, INC.—See Brookfield Corporation; *Int'l*, pg. 1181
CURTIS TRACTOR CAB, INC.; *U.S. Private*, pg. 1127

CURTIS TRAILERS INC.; *U.S. Private*, pg. 1127
CURTIS V. COOPER PRIMARY HEALTH CARE, INC.; *U.S. Private*, pg. 1127
CURT MANUFACTURING LLC—See LCI Industries; *U.S. Public*, pg. 1295
CURTS GAINES HALL JONES ARCHITECTS, INC.; *U.S. Private*, pg. 1127
CURT WARNER CHEVROLET INC.; *U.S. Private*, pg. 1126
CURVES HOLDINGS CO., LTD.; *Int'l*, pg. 1880
CURVES INTERNATIONAL INC.—See Koshidaka Holdings Co., Ltd.; *Int'l*, pg. 4291
CURVES JAPAN CO., LTD.—See Curves Holdings Co., Ltd.; *Int'l*, pg. 1880
CURWOOD, INC.—See Amcor plc; *Int'l*, pg. 418
CURZON ENERGY PLC; *Int'l*, pg. 1880
CUSCADEN PROPERTIES PTE LTD—See Allgreen Properties Ltd.; *Int'l*, pg. 338
CUSCAL LTD.; *Int'l*, pg. 1880
CUSCAL MANAGEMENT PTY LIMITED—See Cuscal Ltd.; *Int'l*, pg. 1880
CUSCAPI BEIJING CO. LTD.—See Cuscapi Berhad; *Int'l*, pg. 1880
CUSCAPI BERHAD; *Int'l*, pg. 1880
CUSCAPI SINGAPORE PTE. LTD.—See Cuscapi Berhad; *Int'l*, pg. 1880
CUSCAPI SUZHOU CO. LTD.—See Cuscapi Berhad; *Int'l*, pg. 1880
CUSCAPI (THAIL) CO. LTD.—See Cuscapi Berhad; *Int'l*, pg. 1880
CUSCO FABRICATORS, LLC—See H.I.G. Capital, LLC; *U.S. Private*, pg. 1832
CUSH ENTERPRISES INC.; *U.S. Private*, pg. 1127
CUSHING AND COMPANY INC.; *U.S. Private*, pg. 1127
CUSHING ASSET MANAGEMENT, LP—See Swank Capital, LLC; *U.S. Private*, pg. 3890
THE CUSHING ENERGY INCOME FUND—See Swank Capital, LLC; *U.S. Private*, pg. 3890
CUSHING TERRELL; *U.S. Private*, pg. 1127
CUSHING TRANSPORTATION INC.; *U.S. Private*, pg. 1127
CUSHMAN & WAKEFIELD (BAHRAIN) W.L.L—See Ontario Teachers' Pension Plan; *Int'l*, pg. 5588
CUSHMAN & WAKEFIELD (BAHRAIN) W.L.L—See PAG Asia Capital Ltd.; *Int'l*, pg. 5695
CUSHMAN & WAKEFIELD (BAHRAIN) W.L.L—See TPG Capital, L.P.; *U.S. Public*, pg. 2171
CUSHMAN & WAKEFIELD - BRUSSELS—See Ontario Teachers' Pension Plan; *Int'l*, pg. 5588
CUSHMAN & WAKEFIELD - BRUSSELS—See PAG Asia Capital Ltd.; *Int'l*, pg. 5695
CUSHMAN & WAKEFIELD - BRUSSELS—See TPG Capital, L.P.; *U.S. Public*, pg. 2171
CUSHMAN & WAKEFIELD DE MEXICO—See Ontario Teachers' Pension Plan; *Int'l*, pg. 5588
CUSHMAN & WAKEFIELD DE MEXICO—See PAG Asia Capital Ltd.; *Int'l*, pg. 5696
CUSHMAN & WAKEFIELD DE MEXICO—See TPG Capital, L.P.; *U.S. Public*, pg. 2172
CUSHMAN & WAKEFIELD (HK) LIMITED—See Ontario Teachers' Pension Plan; *Int'l*, pg. 5588
CUSHMAN & WAKEFIELD (HK) LIMITED—See PAG Asia Capital Ltd.; *Int'l*, pg. 5695
CUSHMAN & WAKEFIELD (HK) LIMITED—See TPG Capital, L.P.; *U.S. Public*, pg. 2171
CUSHMAN & WAKEFIELD, INC. - INDIANAPOLIS—See Ontario Teachers' Pension Plan; *Int'l*, pg. 5589
CUSHMAN & WAKEFIELD, INC. - INDIANAPOLIS—See PAG Asia Capital Ltd.; *Int'l*, pg. 5696
CUSHMAN & WAKEFIELD, INC. - INDIANAPOLIS—See TPG Capital, L.P.; *U.S. Public*, pg. 2173
CUSHMAN & WAKEFIELD, INC.—See Ontario Teachers' Pension Plan; *Int'l*, pg. 5588
CUSHMAN & WAKEFIELD, INC.—See PAG Asia Capital Ltd.; *Int'l*, pg. 5695
CUSHMAN & WAKEFIELD, INC.—See TPG Capital, L.P.; *U.S. Public*, pg. 2171
CUSHMAN & WAKEFIELD, INC. - TAMPA—See Ontario Teachers' Pension Plan; *Int'l*, pg. 5589
CUSHMAN & WAKEFIELD, INC. - TAMPA—See PAG Asia Capital Ltd.; *Int'l*, pg. 5696
CUSHMAN & WAKEFIELD, INC. - TAMPA—See TPG Capital, L.P.; *U.S. Public*, pg. 2172
CUSHMAN & WAKEFIELD (INDIA) PVT. LTD.—See Ontario Teachers' Pension Plan; *Int'l*, pg. 5588
CUSHMAN & WAKEFIELD (INDIA) PVT. LTD.—See PAG Asia Capital Ltd.; *Int'l*, pg. 5695
CUSHMAN & WAKEFIELD (INDIA) PVT. LTD.—See TPG Capital, L.P.; *U.S. Public*, pg. 2171
CUSHMAN & WAKEFIELD K.K.—See Ontario Teachers' Pension Plan; *Int'l*, pg. 5588
CUSHMAN & WAKEFIELD K.K.—See PAG Asia Capital Ltd.; *Int'l*, pg. 5695
CUSHMAN & WAKEFIELD K.K.—See TPG Capital, L.P.; *U.S. Public*, pg. 2171
CUSHMAN & WAKEFIELD LLP—See Ontario Teachers' Pension Plan; *Int'l*, pg. 5588
CUSHMAN & WAKEFIELD LLP—See PAG Asia Capital Ltd.; *Int'l*, pg. 5695

CUSHMAN & WAKEFIELD LLP—See TPG Capital, L.P.; U.S. Public, pg. 2172
CUSHMAN & WAKEFIELD LTD.—See Ontario Teachers' Pension Plan; Int'l, pg. 5588
CUSHMAN & WAKEFIELD LTD.—See PAG Asia Capital Ltd.; Int'l, pg. 5695
CUSHMAN & WAKEFIELD LTD.—See TPG Capital, L.P.; U.S. Public, pg. 2172
CUSHMAN & WAKEFIELD - MADRID—See Ontario Teachers' Pension Plan; Int'l, pg. 5588
CUSHMAN & WAKEFIELD - MADRID—See PAG Asia Capital Ltd.; Int'l, pg. 5695
CUSHMAN & WAKEFIELD - MADRID—See TPG Capital, L.P.; U.S. Public, pg. 2171
CUSHMAN & WAKEFIELD (NSW) PTY LIMITED—See Ontario Teachers' Pension Plan; Int'l, pg. 5588
CUSHMAN & WAKEFIELD (NSW) PTY LIMITED—See PAG Asia Capital Ltd.; Int'l, pg. 5695
CUSHMAN & WAKEFIELD (NSW) PTY LIMITED—See TPG Capital, L.P.; U.S. Public, pg. 2171
CUSHMAN & WAKEFIELD OF ARIZONA, INC.—See Ontario Teachers' Pension Plan; Int'l, pg. 5588
CUSHMAN & WAKEFIELD OF ARIZONA, INC.—See PAG Asia Capital Ltd.; Int'l, pg. 5696
CUSHMAN & WAKEFIELD OF ARIZONA, INC.—See TPG Capital, L.P.; U.S. Public, pg. 2172
CUSHMAN & WAKEFIELD OF CALIFORNIA, INC.—See Ontario Teachers' Pension Plan; Int'l, pg. 5588
CUSHMAN & WAKEFIELD OF CALIFORNIA, INC.—See PAG Asia Capital Ltd.; Int'l, pg. 5696
CUSHMAN & WAKEFIELD OF CALIFORNIA, INC.—See TPG Capital, L.P.; U.S. Public, pg. 2172
CUSHMAN & WAKEFIELD OF CONNECTICUT, INC.—See Ontario Teachers' Pension Plan; Int'l, pg. 5589
CUSHMAN & WAKEFIELD OF CONNECTICUT, INC.—See PAG Asia Capital Ltd.; Int'l, pg. 5696
CUSHMAN & WAKEFIELD OF CONNECTICUT, INC.—See TPG Capital, L.P.; U.S. Public, pg. 2172
CUSHMAN & WAKEFIELD OF FLORIDA, INC.—See Ontario Teachers' Pension Plan; Int'l, pg. 5589
CUSHMAN & WAKEFIELD OF FLORIDA, INC.—See PAG Asia Capital Ltd.; Int'l, pg. 5696
CUSHMAN & WAKEFIELD OF FLORIDA, INC.—See TPG Capital, L.P.; U.S. Public, pg. 2172
CUSHMAN & WAKEFIELD OF GEORGIA, INC.—See Ontario Teachers' Pension Plan; Int'l, pg. 5589
CUSHMAN & WAKEFIELD OF GEORGIA, INC.—See PAG Asia Capital Ltd.; Int'l, pg. 5696
CUSHMAN & WAKEFIELD OF GEORGIA, INC.—See TPG Capital, L.P.; U.S. Public, pg. 2172
CUSHMAN & WAKEFIELD OF ILLINOIS, INC.—See Ontario Teachers' Pension Plan; Int'l, pg. 5589
CUSHMAN & WAKEFIELD OF ILLINOIS, INC.—See PAG Asia Capital Ltd.; Int'l, pg. 5696
CUSHMAN & WAKEFIELD OF ILLINOIS, INC.—See TPG Capital, L.P.; U.S. Public, pg. 2172
CUSHMAN & WAKEFIELD OF LONG ISLAND, INC.—See Ontario Teachers' Pension Plan; Int'l, pg. 5589
CUSHMAN & WAKEFIELD OF LONG ISLAND, INC.—See PAG Asia Capital Ltd.; Int'l, pg. 5696
CUSHMAN & WAKEFIELD OF LONG ISLAND, INC.—See TPG Capital, L.P.; U.S. Public, pg. 2172
CUSHMAN & WAKEFIELD OF MARYLAND, INC.—See Ontario Teachers' Pension Plan; Int'l, pg. 5589
CUSHMAN & WAKEFIELD OF MARYLAND, INC.—See PAG Asia Capital Ltd.; Int'l, pg. 5696
CUSHMAN & WAKEFIELD OF MARYLAND, INC.—See TPG Capital, L.P.; U.S. Public, pg. 2172
CUSHMAN & WAKEFIELD OF MASSACHUSETTS, INC.—See Ontario Teachers' Pension Plan; Int'l, pg. 5589
CUSHMAN & WAKEFIELD OF MASSACHUSETTS, INC.—See PAG Asia Capital Ltd.; Int'l, pg. 5696
CUSHMAN & WAKEFIELD OF MASSACHUSETTS, INC.—See TPG Capital, L.P.; U.S. Public, pg. 2172
CUSHMAN & WAKEFIELD OF NEW JERSEY, INC.—See Ontario Teachers' Pension Plan; Int'l, pg. 5589
CUSHMAN & WAKEFIELD OF NEW JERSEY, INC.—See PAG Asia Capital Ltd.; Int'l, pg. 5696
CUSHMAN & WAKEFIELD OF NEW JERSEY, INC.—See TPG Capital, L.P.; U.S. Public, pg. 2172
CUSHMAN & WAKEFIELD OF OREGON, INC.—See Ontario Teachers' Pension Plan; Int'l, pg. 5589
CUSHMAN & WAKEFIELD OF OREGON, INC.—See PAG Asia Capital Ltd.; Int'l, pg. 5696
CUSHMAN & WAKEFIELD OF OREGON, INC.—See TPG Capital, L.P.; U.S. Public, pg. 2172
CUSHMAN & WAKEFIELD OF TEXAS, INC. - AUSTIN—See Ontario Teachers' Pension Plan; Int'l, pg. 5589
CUSHMAN & WAKEFIELD OF TEXAS, INC. - AUSTIN—See PAG Asia Capital Ltd.; Int'l, pg. 5696
CUSHMAN & WAKEFIELD OF TEXAS, INC. - AUSTIN—See TPG Capital, L.P.; U.S. Public, pg. 2172
CUSHMAN & WAKEFIELD OF TEXAS, INC.—See Ontario Teachers' Pension Plan; Int'l, pg. 5589
CUSHMAN & WAKEFIELD OF TEXAS, INC.—See PAG Asia Capital Ltd.; Int'l, pg. 5696

CUSHMAN & WAKEFIELD OF TEXAS, INC.—See TPG Capital, L.P.; U.S. Public, pg. 2172
CUSHMAN & WAKEFIELD OF WASHINGTON D.C., INC.—See Ontario Teachers' Pension Plan; Int'l, pg. 5589
CUSHMAN & WAKEFIELD OF WASHINGTON D.C., INC.—See PAG Asia Capital Ltd.; Int'l, pg. 5696
CUSHMAN & WAKEFIELD OF WASHINGTON D.C., INC.—See TPG Capital, L.P.; U.S. Public, pg. 2173
CUSHMAN & WAKEFIELD OF WASHINGTON, INC.—See Ontario Teachers' Pension Plan; Int'l, pg. 5589
CUSHMAN & WAKEFIELD OF WASHINGTON, INC.—See PAG Asia Capital Ltd.; Int'l, pg. 5696
CUSHMAN & WAKEFIELD OF WASHINGTON, INC.—See TPG Capital, L.P.; U.S. Public, pg. 2173
CUSHMAN & WAKEFIELD PLC—See Ontario Teachers' Pension Plan; Int'l, pg. 5588
CUSHMAN & WAKEFIELD PLC—See PAG Asia Capital Ltd.; Int'l, pg. 5695
CUSHMAN & WAKEFIELD PLC—See TPG Capital, L.P.; U.S. Public, pg. 2170
CUSHMAN & WAKEFIELD - SAO PAULO—See Ontario Teachers' Pension Plan; Int'l, pg. 5588
CUSHMAN & WAKEFIELD - SAO PAULO—See PAG Asia Capital Ltd.; Int'l, pg. 5695
CUSHMAN & WAKEFIELD - SAO PAULO—See TPG Capital, L.P.; U.S. Public, pg. 2171
CUSHMAN & WAKEFIELD (SHANGHAI) CO. LTD.—See Ontario Teachers' Pension Plan; Int'l, pg. 5588
CUSHMAN & WAKEFIELD (SHANGHAI) CO. LTD.—See PAG Asia Capital Ltd.; Int'l, pg. 5695
CUSHMAN & WAKEFIELD (SHANGHAI) CO. LTD.—See TPG Capital, L.P.; U.S. Public, pg. 2171
CUSHMAN & WAKEFIELD (S) PTE LTD—See Ontario Teachers' Pension Plan; Int'l, pg. 5588
CUSHMAN & WAKEFIELD (S) PTE LTD—See PAG Asia Capital Ltd.; Int'l, pg. 5695
CUSHMAN & WAKEFIELD (S) PTE LTD—See TPG Capital, L.P.; U.S. Public, pg. 2171
CUSHMAN & WAKEFIELD SWEDEN AB—See Ontario Teachers' Pension Plan; Int'l, pg. 5588
CUSHMAN & WAKEFIELD SWEDEN AB—See PAG Asia Capital Ltd.; Int'l, pg. 5695
CUSHMAN & WAKEFIELD SWEDEN AB—See TPG Capital, L.P.; U.S. Public, pg. 2172
CUSHMAN & WAKEFIELD (U.K.) LTD.—See Ontario Teachers' Pension Plan; Int'l, pg. 5588
CUSHMAN & WAKEFIELD (U.K.) LTD.—See PAG Asia Capital Ltd.; Int'l, pg. 5695
CUSHMAN & WAKEFIELD (U.K.) LTD.—See TPG Capital, L.P.; U.S. Public, pg. 2171
CUSHMAN & WAKEFIELD (VIC) PTY LTD—See Ontario Teachers' Pension Plan; Int'l, pg. 5588
CUSHMAN & WAKEFIELD (VIC) PTY LTD—See PAG Asia Capital Ltd.; Int'l, pg. 5695
CUSHMAN & WAKEFIELD (VIC) PTY LTD—See TPG Capital, L.P.; U.S. Public, pg. 2171
CUSITECH, LLC; U.S. Private, pg. 1127
CUSO FINANCIAL SERVICES, L.P.—See Lee Equity Partners LLC; U.S. Private, pg. 2412
CUSPIDE LIBROS S.A.—See Grupo Clarin S.A.; Int'l, pg. 3124
CUSPIS CAPITAL LTD.; Int'l, pg. 1880
CUST2MATE LTD.—See A2Z Smart Technologies Corp.; Int'l, pg. 30
CUSTANET CO., LTD.—See Computer Institute of Japan Ltd.; Int'l, pg. 1759
CUSTARD INSURANCE ADJUSTERS INC.; U.S. Private, pg. 1127
CUSTER CITY FARMERS COOP EXCHANGE; U.S. Private, pg. 1127
CUSTER OFFICE ENVIRONMENTS INC.; U.S. Private, pg. 1127
CUSTINO ENTERPRISES; U.S. Private, pg. 1127
CUSTODIAL TRUST COMPANY—See JPMorgan Chase & Co.; U.S. Public, pg. 1206
CUSTODIAN CAPITAL LIMITED—See Pollen Street Limited; Int'l, pg. 5910
CUSTODIAN INVESTMENT PLC; Int'l, pg. 1880
CUSTODIAN PROPERTY INCOME REIT PLC—See Pollen Street Limited; Int'l, pg. 5910
CUSTODIAN VENTURES LLC; U.S. Private, pg. 1127
CUST-O-FAB, INC.; U.S. Private, pg. 1127
CUSTOJUSTO UNIPESSOAL, LDA; Int'l, pg. 1880
CUSTOM ACCESSORIES ASIA LTD.—See Custom Accessories Inc.; U.S. Private, pg. 1128
CUSTOM ACCESSORIES EUROPE LTD.—See Custom Accessories Inc.; U.S. Private, pg. 1128
CUSTOM ACCESSORIES INC.; U.S. Private, pg. 1127
CUSTOM ACCESSORIES SCANDINAVIA OY—See Custom Accessories Inc.; U.S. Private, pg. 1128
CUSTOM-ACE LTD.—See Taikisha Ltd.; Int'l, pg. 7413
CUSTOM AIR, INC.; U.S. Private, pg. 1128
CUSTOM ALLOYS CORPORATION—See J.F. Lehman & Company, Inc.; U.S. Private, pg. 2164
CUSTOM ALLOY SCRAP SALES, INC.; U.S. Private, pg. 1128
CUSTOM ALUMINUM PRODUCTS INC.; U.S. Private, pg. 1128

CUSTOM AMERICA, INC.—See Custom SpA; Int'l, pg. 1880
CUSTOMARRAY, INC.—See GenScript Biotech Corporation; Int'l, pg. 2927
CUSTOM BILT METALS; U.S. Private, pg. 1128
CUSTOM BIOGENIC SYSTEMS, INC.—See Standex International; U.S. Public, pg. 1930
CUSTOM BLAST SERVICES, INC.—See AIP, LLC; U.S. Private, pg. 134
CUSTOM BLAST SERVICES, INC.—See AIP, LLC; U.S. Private, pg. 134
CUSTOM BLENDERS, INC.—See Darling Ingredients Inc.; U.S. Public, pg. 633
CUSTOM BLENDS, INC.—See Crest Group Inc.; U.S. Private, pg. 1095
CUSTOM BUILDER SUPPLY COMPANY; U.S. Private, pg. 1128
CUSTOM BUILDING PRODUCTS; U.S. Private, pg. 1128
CUSTOM BUS AUSTRALIA PTY. LTD.—See Allegro Funds Pty. Ltd.; Int'l, pg. 336
CUSTOM BUSINESS SOLUTIONS INC.; U.S. Private, pg. 1128
CUSTOM CABLE INDUSTRIES INC.—See HWI Partners, LLC; U.S. Private, pg. 2015
CUSTOM CABLE SERVICES, INC.; U.S. Private, pg. 1128
CUSTOMCALL DATA SYSTEMS, INC.—See Enghouse Systems Limited; Int'l, pg. 2427
CUSTOMCD, INC.—See Siris Capital Group, LLC; U.S. Private, pg. 3672
CUSTOM CHEMICAL FORMULATORS, INC.; U.S. Private, pg. 1128
CUSTOM CHEMICAL SERVICES INC.—See LeBaron-Brown Industries LLC; U.S. Private, pg. 2409
CUSTOM CHROME INCORPORATED—See Global Motor Sport Group, Inc.; U.S. Private, pg. 1716
CUSTOM COILS INC.—See US Holdings Corporation; U.S. Private, pg. 4319
THE CUSTOM COMPANY, INC.; U.S. Private, pg. 4017
CUSTOM COMPUTER CABLES; U.S. Private, pg. 1128
CUSTOM COMPUTER SPECIALISTS, LLC; U.S. Private, pg. 1128
CUSTOM CONTROLLERS UK LIMITED—See SK Inc.; Int'l, pg. 6971
CUSTOM CONTROL SENSORS, INC.; U.S. Private, pg. 1128
CUSTOM CONTROL SOLUTIONS, INC.; U.S. Private, pg. 1128
CUSTOM CONVEYOR CORP.—See Schwing Bioset, Inc.; U.S. Private, pg. 3573
CUSTOM CORNED BEEF, INC.—See New Water Capital, L.P.; U.S. Private, pg. 2907
CUSTOM CREDIT SYSTEMS LP—See Vista Equity Partners, LLC; U.S. Private, pg. 4397
CUSTOM-CRETE, LLC—See Vulcan Materials Company; U.S. Public, pg. 2314
CUSTOM-CRETE REDI-MIX, LLC—See Vulcan Materials Company; U.S. Public, pg. 2314
CUSTOM CULINARY, INC.—See Griffith Laboratories, Inc.; U.S. Private, pg. 1789
CUSTOM CUTLERY, INC.—See PMC Capital Partners, LLC; U.S. Private, pg. 3217
CUSTOM DECO, LLC—See The Boelter Companies Inc.; U.S. Private, pg. 3995
CUSTOM DECORATORS, INC.; U.S. Private, pg. 1128
CUSTOM DECOR, INC.; U.S. Private, pg. 1128
CUSTOM DESIGN & CONSTRUCTION; U.S. Private, pg. 1128
CUSTOM DESIGNED COMPRESSOR SYSTEMS, INC.; U.S. Public, pg. 612
CUSTOM DRAPERY COMPANY INC.; U.S. Private, pg. 1128
CUSTOM ELECTRIC LTD.; Int'l, pg. 1880
CUSTOM ENERGY SERVICES, LLC—See RWE AG; Int'l, pg. 6434
CUSTOM ENGINEERING AND DESIGNS, INC.—See Marotta Controls, Inc.; U.S. Private, pg. 2586
CUSTOM ENVIRONMENTAL SERVICES, INC.—See Ambipar Participacoes e Empreendimentos SA; Int'l, pg. 414
CUSTOMER 1 ONE INC.; U.S. Private, pg. 1130
CUSTOMER ACQUISITION SPECIALISTS OF AMERICA, INC.—See Energy Professionals, LLC; U.S. Private, pg. 1396
CUSTOMER COMMUNICATIONS GROUP, INC. (CCG); U.S. Private, pg. 1130
CUSTOMER CONNEXX, LLC—See ALT5 Sigma Corporation; U.S. Public, pg. 85
CUSTOMER CONTACT SERVICES CCS; U.S. Private, pg. 1130
CUSTOMER FRONTLINE SOLUTIONS, INC.—See Manila Electric Company; Int'l, pg. 4671
CUSTOMER PORTFOLIOS, LLC—See Stirista, LLC; U.S. Private, pg. 3813
CUSTOMERSAT, INC.—See EQT AB; Int'l, pg. 2475
CUSTOMERS BANCORP, INC.; U.S. Public, pg. 612
CUSTOMERS BANK—See Customers Bancorp, Inc.; U.S. Public, pg. 612
CUSTOMER SERVICE CO., EAST SOLUTION—See Toho Gas Co., Ltd.; Int'l, pg. 7775

CUSTOMERS BANCORP, INC. — CORPORATE AFFILIATIONS

Company Index

CUSTOMER SERVICES CENTRE S.R.L.—See Stellantis N.V.; *Int'l*, pg. 7198
CUSTOMERSTREAM; *U.S. Private*, pg. 1130
CUSTOMER VALUE PARTNERS; *U.S. Private*, pg. 1130
CUSTOMERVILLE, INC.—See EQT AB; *Int'l*, pg. 2477
CUSTOMERWORKS EUROPE SL—See Accenture plc; *Int'l*, pg. 86
CUSTOM FABRICATING & REPAIR INC; *U.S. Private*, pg. 1128
CUSTOM FIBERGLASS MANUFACTURING CO. INC.; *U.S. Private*, pg. 1128
CUSTOM FILTER, LLC—See Audax Group, Limited Partnership; *U.S. Private*, pg. 389
CUSTOM FINANCIAL SOLUTIONS—See Virtual Sourcing, LLC; *U.S. Private*, pg. 4389
CUSTOM FLEET (NZ) LIMITED—See National Australia Bank Limited; *Int'l*, pg. 5151
CUSTOM FLUIDPOWER PTY. LTD.—See Helios Technologies, Inc.; *U.S. Public*, pg. 1023
CUSTOM FLUIDPOWER VIETNAM COMPANY LTD.—See Helios Technologies, Inc.; *U.S. Public*, pg. 1023
CUSTOM FOOD GROUP, L.P.; *U.S. Private*, pg. 1129
CUSTOM GLASS ATLANTA, INC.—See Installed Building Products, Inc.; *U.S. Public*, pg. 1132
CUSTOM GLASS & DOORS, INC.—See Installed Building Products, Inc.; *U.S. Public*, pg. 1132
CUSTOM GLASS SOLUTIONS, LLC—See Stellex Capital Management LP; *U.S. Private*, pg. 3800
CUSTOM HARDWARE ENGINEERING & CONSULTING, INC.—See Charlesbank Capital Partners, LLC; *U.S. Private*, pg. 856
CUSTOM HARDWARE ENGINEERING & CONSULTING, INC.—See GTCR LLC; *U.S. Private*, pg. 1806
CUSTOM HBC, CORP; *U.S. Private*, pg. 1129
CUSTOM HELICOPTERS LTD.—See Exchange Income Corporation; *Int'l*, pg. 2579
CUSTOM HOISTS, INC.—See Standex International; *U.S. Public*, pg. 1930
CUSTOM INDEX INC.; *U.S. Private*, pg. 1129
CUSTOM INDUSTRIES INC.; *U.S. Private*, pg. 1129
CUSTOMINK, LLC; *U.S. Private*, pg. 1130
CUSTOM INTEGRATED TECHNOLOGY INC.—See Canon Inc.; *Int'l*, pg. 1297
CUSTOMISED PACKAGING LIMITED—See Coral Products PLC; *Int'l*, pg. 1795
CUSTOMIZED DISTRIBUTION SERVICES; *U.S. Private*, pg. 1130
CUSTOMIZED ENERGY SOLUTIONS LTD.; *U.S. Private*, pg. 1130
CUSTOMIZED ENGINEERING & DEPOT SUPPORT—See RTX Corporation; *U.S. Public*, pg. 1825
CUSTOMIZED HEALTH SOLUTIONS PTE. LTD.—See Pacific Healthcare Holdings Ltd.; *Int'l*, pg. 5689
CUSTOM LANDTRAN CARRIERS INC.—See Landtran Systems Inc.; *Int'l*, pg. 4408
CUSTOM LEASING OF IOWA INC—See North American Truck & Trailer, Inc.; *U.S. Private*, pg. 2941
CUSTOM LUMBER MFG. CO.—See Lumber Group Inc.; *U.S. Private*, pg. 2513
CUSTOM MADE MEALS LLC—See Stellex Capital Management LP; *U.S. Private*, pg. 3800
CUSTOM MAGNETICS, INC.; *U.S. Private*, pg. 1129
CUSTOM MANUFACTURING & ENGINEERING, INC.; *U.S. Private*, pg. 1129
CUSTOM MARINE INC.—See Contran Corporation; *U.S. Private*, pg. 1033
CUSTOM METAL CRAFTERS, INC.; *U.S. Private*, pg. 1129
CUSTOM METALCRAFT INC.; *U.S. Private*, pg. 1129
CUSTOM-METAL FABRICATORS, INC.; *U.S. Private*, pg. 1130
CUSTOM MICROWAVE, INC.—See Trive Capital Inc.; *U.S. Private*, pg. 4240
CUSTOM MIRRORED WALLS; *U.S. Private*, pg. 1129
CUSTOM MMIC DESIGN SERVICES, INC.—See Qorvo, Inc.; *U.S. Public*, pg. 1743
CUSTOM MOBILITY INC.; *U.S. Private*, pg. 1129
CUSTOM MOLDED PRODUCTS, INC.—See Tenex Capital Management, L.P.; *U.S. Private*, pg. 3966
CUSTOM OPTICAL—See EssilorLuxottica SA; *Int'l*, pg. 2513
CUSTOM PACKAGING INC.; *U.S. Private*, pg. 1129
CUSTOM PACKAGING INC.—See Custom Packaging Inc.; *U.S. Private*, pg. 1129
CUSTOM PACK INC.—See Global Seafood Technologies; *U.S. Private*, pg. 1717
CUSTOM-PAK DE MEXICO S. DE R.L. DE C.V.—See Custom-Pak, Inc.; *U.S. Private*, pg. 1130
CUSTOM-PAK, INC. - DEWITT PLANT—See Custom-Pak, Inc.; *U.S. Private*, pg. 1130
CUSTOM-PAK, INC.; *U.S. Private*, pg. 1130
CUSTOM-PAK, INC. - WALNUT RIDGE PLANT—See Custom-Pak, Inc.; *U.S. Private*, pg. 1130
CUSTOM PHYSICAL THERAPY, LIMITED PARTNERSHIP—See U.S. Physical Therapy, Inc.; *U.S. Public*, pg. 2214
CUSTOM PINE STRAW, INC.; *U.S. Private*, pg. 1129
CUSTOM PIPE COATING, INC.—See AIP, LLC; *U.S. Private*, pg. 134

CUSTOM PIPE & COUPLING CO.—See Shapco, Inc.; *U.S. Private*, pg. 3625
CUSTOM PLASTIC DEVELOPMENTS, INC.; *U.S. Private*, pg. 1129
CUSTOM PLASTICS INTERNATIONAL LTD.; *Int'l*, pg. 1880
CUSTOM PLUS DISTRIBUTING, LLC—See Resideo Technologies, Inc.; *U.S. Public*, pg. 1790
CUSTOM POLYMERS INC. - LATIN & SOUTH AMERICA—See Custom Polymers Inc.; *U.S. Private*, pg. 1129
CUSTOM POLYMERS INC.; *U.S. Private*, pg. 1129
CUSTOM POOL & SPA MECHANICS, INC.—See Astro Aerospace Ltd.; *U.S. Public*, pg. 217
CUSTOM POWER, LLC—See Elan Growth Partners, LLC; *U.S. Private*, pg. 1349
CUSTOM PRINTED PRODUCTS; *U.S. Private*, pg. 1129
CUSTOM PRINTING INC.; *U.S. Private*, pg. 1129
CUSTOM PRINT NOW; *U.S. Private*, pg. 1129
CUSTOM PRODUCE, INC.—See GrubMarket, Inc.; *U.S. Private*, pg. 1797
CUSTOM PRODUCTION GRINDING, INC.—See Blackwell Capital Group LLC; *U.S. Private*, pg. 577
CUSTOM PRO LOGISTICS, LLC; *U.S. Private*, pg. 1129
CUSTOM PROTEIN CORPORATION; *U.S. Private*, pg. 1129
CUSTOM PULTRUSIONS, INC.—See Andersen Corporation; *U.S. Private*, pg. 275
CUSTOM RESINS INC.—See Polymeric Resources Corp.; *U.S. Public*, pg. 1701
CUSTOM RUBBER PRODUCTS, INC.—See Bridgepoint Group Plc; *Int'l*, pg. 1154
CUSTOM SECURITY INDUSTRIES INC.—See Sentry Technology Corporation; *U.S. Public*, pg. 1868
CUSTOM SENSORS & TECHNOLOGIES ASIA (SHANGAI) LTD—See Schneider Electric SE; *Int'l*, pg. 6626
CUSTOM SERVE CORPORATION—See Nippon Fine Chemical Co., Ltd.; *Int'l*, pg. 5318
CUSTOM SERVICE LEASING LIMITED—See National Australia Bank Limited; *Int'l*, pg. 5151
CUSTOM SERVICES INTERNATIONAL LTD.—See Cen-Tra, Inc.; *U.S. Private*, pg. 818
CUSTOM SPA; *Int'l*, pg. 1880
CUSTOM STORAGE, INC.—See Frontier Technology LLC; *U.S. Private*, pg. 1616
CUSTOM STORAGE, INC.—See Frontier Technology LLC; *U.S. Private*, pg. 1616
CUSTOM SYNTHESIS, LLC—See Piedmont Chemical Industries, Inc.; *U.S. Private*, pg. 3177
CUSTOM TAPE CO INC.—See CGR Products Inc.; *U.S. Private*, pg. 844
CUSTOM TOOL AND MANUFACTURING COMPANY; *U.S. Private*, pg. 1129
CUSTOM TOOL SUPPLY, LLC—See Incline MGMT. Corp.; *U.S. Private*, pg. 2053
CUSTOM TRAINING GROUP, INC.—See Universal Technical Institute, Inc.; *U.S. Public*, pg. 2262
CUSTOM TRUCK & EQUIPMENT, LLC—See Custom Truck One Source, Inc.; *U.S. Public*, pg. 612
CUSTOM TRUCK & EQUIPMENT, LLC—See North American Truck & Trailer, Inc.; *U.S. Private*, pg. 2941
CUSTOM TRUCK LEASING, INC.—See North American Truck & Trailer, Inc.; *U.S. Private*, pg. 2941
CUSTOM TRUCK ONE SOURCE, INC.; *U.S. Public*, pg. 612
CUSTOM TRUSS LLC; *U.S. Private*, pg. 1129
CUSTOM UNDERGROUND, INC.; *U.S. Private*, pg. 1129
CUSTOM VAULT CORP; *U.S. Private*, pg. 1130
CUSTOMWEATHER, INC.; *U.S. Private*, pg. 1130
CUSTOM WHOLESALE FLOORS INC.; *U.S. Private*, pg. 1130
CUSTOM WHOLESALE SUPPLY CO. INC.; *U.S. Private*, pg. 1130
CUSTOM WOOD PRODUCTS INC.; *U.S. Private*, pg. 1130
CUSTOMX GMBH—See Mensch und Maschine Software SE; *Int'l*, pg. 4818
CUTANEA LIFE SCIENCES, INC.—See Biofrontera AG; *Int'l*, pg. 1037
CUT BANK GAS COMPANY—See First Reserve Management, L.P.; *U.S. Private*, pg. 1525
CUTBANK TRUCKING LTD.—See Petrowest Corp.; *Int'l*, pg. 5833
CUTCO CORPORATION; *U.S. Private*, pg. 1131
CUTCO CUTLERY CORPORATION—See CUTCO Corporation; *U.S. Private*, pg. 1131
CUTCO INTERNATIONAL INC.—See CUTCO Corporation; *U.S. Private*, pg. 1131
CU-TECH CORPORATION—See Restar Holdings Corporation; *Int'l*, pg. 6303
CUTERA AUSTRALIA PTY LTD—See Cutera, Inc.; *U.S. Public*, pg. 613
CUTERA FRANCE SARL—See Cutera, Inc.; *U.S. Public*, pg. 613
CUTERA, INC.; *U.S. Public*, pg. 612
CUTERA JAPAN KK—See Cutera, Inc.; *U.S. Public*, pg. 613
CUTERA SPAIN SL—See Cutera, Inc.; *U.S. Public*, pg. 613

CUTERA SWITZERLAND GMBH—See Cutera, Inc.; *U.S. Public*, pg. 613
CUTISIN A.S.—See RETHMANN AG & Co. KG; *Int'l*, pg. 6309
CUTIX PLC; *Int'l*, pg. 1881
CUTLER ASSOCIATES INC.; *U.S. Private*, pg. 1131
THE CUTLER CORPORATION; *U.S. Public*, pg. 4017
CUTLER-DICKERSON COMPANY; *U.S. Private*, pg. 1131
CUTLER-DICKERSON & FABRICATION—See Cutler Forest Products Inc.; *Int'l*, pg. 1881
CUTLER FOREST PRODUCTS INC.; *Int'l*, pg. 1881
CUTLER-OWENS INTERNATIONAL INC.—See UM Holdings Limited; *U.S. Private*, pg. 4278
CUTLER REAL ESTATE, INC.; *U.S. Private*, pg. 1131
CUTLITE DO BRASIL LTDA—See El.En. S.p.A.; *Int'l*, pg. 2341
CUTLITE PENTA SRL—See El.En. S.p.A.; *Int'l*, pg. 2341
CUT LOOSE; *U.S. Private*, pg. 1130
CUTRALE CITRUS JUICES USA, INC.—See Sucocitrico Cutrale Ltda.; *Int'l*, pg. 7251
C.U. TRANSPORT INC.; *U.S. Private*, pg. 709
CUTRUBUS MOTORS INC.; *U.S. Private*, pg. 1131
CUTSHAW CHEVROLET, INC.; *U.S. Private*, pg. 1131
CUTTER ASSOCIATES EUROPE LTD.—See Nomura Research Institute, Ltd.; *Int'l*, pg. 5413
CUTTER ASSOCIATES, LLC—See Nomura Research Institute, Ltd.; *Int'l*, pg. 5413
CUTTER AVIATION ALBUQUERQUE, INC.—See Cutter Holding Co.; *U.S. Private*, pg. 1131
CUTTER AVIATION COLORADO SPRINGS, LLC—See Cutter Holding Co.; *U.S. Private*, pg. 1131
CUTTER AVIATION DALLAS-ADDISON, LLC—See Cutter Holding Co.; *U.S. Private*, pg. 1131
CUTTER AVIATION DEER VALLEY, INC.—See Cutter Holding Co.; *U.S. Private*, pg. 1131
CUTTER AVIATION EL PASO LIMITED PARTNERSHIP—See Cutter Holding Co.; *U.S. Private*, pg. 1131
CUTTER AVIATION PHOENIX, INC.—See Cutter Holding Co.; *U.S. Private*, pg. 1131
CUTTER AVIATION SAN ANTONIO, INC.—See Cutter Holding Co.; *U.S. Private*, pg. 1131
CUTTER & BUCK, INC.—See New Wave Group AB; *Int'l*, pg. 5229
CUTTER BUICK GMC—See Cutter of Maui, Inc.; *U.S. Private*, pg. 1131
CUTTER & COMPANY BROKERAGE, INC.; *U.S. Private*, pg. 1131
CUTTER DODGE CHRYSLER JEEP OF PEARL CITY INC.; *U.S. Private*, pg. 1131
CUTTER HOLDING CO. - CUTTER AVIATION - DALLAS-ADDISON FACILITY—See Cutter Holding Co.; *U.S. Private*, pg. 1131
CUTTER HOLDING CO.; *U.S. Private*, pg. 1131
CUTTER INFORMATION, LLC—See Arthur D. Little SAS; *Int'l*, pg. 584
CUTTER MANAGEMENT CO.—See Cutter of Maui, Inc.; *U.S. Private*, pg. 1131
CUTTER MAZDA WAIPAHU—See Cutter of Maui, Inc.; *U.S. Private*, pg. 1131
CUTTER MITSUBISHI - AIEA—See Cutter of Maui, Inc.; *U.S. Private*, pg. 1131
CUTTER OF MAUI, INC.; *U.S. Private*, pg. 1131
CUTTING CORNERS INC.; *U.S. Private*, pg. 1132
CUTTING EDGE PROPERTY MAINTENANCE, INC.—See BrightView Holdings, Inc.; *U.S. Public*, pg. 384
CUTTING EDGE SOLUTIONS LTD.—See Accenture plc; *Int'l*, pg. 87
CUTTING EDGES PTY. LTD.—See Valmont Industries, Inc.; *U.S. Public*, pg. 2273
CUTTING EDGE TEXSTYLES, LLC—See Praesidian Capital Corp.; *U.S. Private*, pg. 3241
CUTTING LOOSE SALON AND SPA; *U.S. Private*, pg. 1132
CUTTING SPECIALISTS, INC.—See Beall Manufacturing, Inc.; *U.S. Private*, pg. 505
CUTTING TOOLS INC.; *U.S. Private*, pg. 1132
CUTWATER ASSET MANAGEMENT CORP.—See The Bank of New York Mellon Corporation; *U.S. Public*, pg. 2037
CUTWATER—See Omnicom Group Inc.; *U.S. Public*, pg. 1598
CUTWATER SPIRITS, LLC—See Anheuser-Busch InBev SA/NV; *Int'l*, pg. 465
CUULONG FISH JOINT STOCK COMPANY; *Int'l*, pg. 1881
CUU LONG PETRO URBAN DEVELOPMENT & INVESTMENT CORPORATION; *Int'l*, pg. 1881
CUU LONG PHARMACEUTICAL JOINT STOCK CORPORATION; *Int'l*, pg. 1881
CUVECO AS—See Royal Unibrew A/S; *Int'l*, pg. 6414
CUVELIER PHILIPPE SA—See SigmaRoc Plc; *Int'l*, pg. 6909
CU VENTURES INC.—See CU Cooperative Systems, Inc.; *U.S. Private*, pg. 1119
CUX, INC.—See Udemy, Inc.; *U.S. Public*, pg. 2217
CUXPORT GMBH—See Hamburger Hafen und Logistik AG; *Int'l*, pg. 3236

COMPANY NAME INDEX

CUYAHOGA LANDFILL, INC.—See Waste Management, Inc.; *U.S. Public*, pg. 2331
CUYAHOGA VENDING CO. INC.; *U.S. Private*, pg. 1132
C.UYEMURA & CO., LTD. - HIRAKATA CHEMICAL PLANT—See C.Uyemura & Co., Ltd.; *Int'l*, pg. 1244
C.UYEMURA & CO., LTD.; *Int'l*, pg. 1244
CVA ADVERTISING & MARKETING, INC.; *U.S. Private*, pg. 1132
CVA EOS S.R.L.—See CVA S.p.A. a s.u.; *Int'l*, pg. 1881
C. VARGAS & ASSOCIATES, LTD.; *U.S. Private*, pg. 705
CVA S.P.A. A S.U.; *Int'l*, pg. 1881
CVB ALBERT CARL GMBH & CO. KG—See BRENNTAG SE; *Int'l*, pg. 1149
CVB FINANCIAL CORP.; *U.S. Public*, pg. 613
CVC ADVISERS LTD.—See CVC Capital Partners SICAV-FIS S.A.; *Int'l*, pg. 1881
CVC ADVISORS (U.S.) INC.—See CVC Capital Partners SICAV-FIS S.A.; *Int'l*, pg. 1884
CVC ASIA PACIFIC (AUSTRALIA) LTD.—See CVC Capital Partners SICAV-FIS S.A.; *Int'l*, pg. 1885
CVC ASIA PACIFIC (BEIJING) LIMITED—See CVC Capital Partners SICAV-FIS S.A.; *Int'l*, pg. 1885
CVC ASIA PACIFIC (JAPAN) KABUSHIKI KAISHA—See CVC Capital Partners SICAV-FIS S.A.; *Int'l*, pg. 1885
CVC ASIA PACIFIC LTD.—See CVC Capital Partners SICAV-FIS S.A.; *Int'l*, pg. 1885
CVC ASIA PACIFIC (SHANGHAI) LIMITED—See CVC Capital Partners SICAV-FIS S.A.; *Int'l*, pg. 1885
CVC ASIA PACIFIC (SINGAPORE) PTE LTD—See CVC Capital Partners SICAV-FIS S.A.; *Int'l*, pg. 1885
CVC BRASIL OPERADORA E AGENCIA DE VIAGENS S.A.; *Int'l*, pg. 1881
CVC CAPITAL PARTNERS ADVISORY (U.S.), INC.—See CVC Capital Partners SICAV-FIS S.A.; *Int'l*, pg. 1885
CVC CAPITAL PARTNERS (BENELUX) SA/NV—See CVC Capital Partners SICAV-FIS S.A.; *Int'l*, pg. 1885
CVC CAPITAL PARTNERS DENMARK A/S—See CVC Capital Partners SICAV-FIS S.A.; *Int'l*, pg. 1888
CVC CAPITAL PARTNERS (DEUTSCHLAND) GMBH—See CVC Capital Partners SICAV-FIS S.A.; *Int'l*, pg. 1886
CVC CAPITAL PARTNERS (ESPANA) SL—See CVC Capital Partners SICAV-FIS S.A.; *Int'l*, pg. 1886
CVC CAPITAL PARTNERS (FRANCE) SA—See CVC Capital Partners SICAV-FIS S.A.; *Int'l*, pg. 1886
CVC CAPITAL PARTNERS JERSEY LIMITED—See CVC Capital Partners SICAV-FIS S.A.; *Int'l*, pg. 1888
CVC CAPITAL PARTNERS NEDERLAND—See CVC Capital Partners SICAV-FIS S.A.; *Int'l*, pg. 1886
CVC CAPITAL PARTNERS SICAV-FIS S.A.; *Int'l*, pg. 1881
CVC CAPITAL PARTNERS SRL—See CVC Capital Partners SICAV-FIS S.A.; *Int'l*, pg. 1888
CVC CAPITAL PARTNERS SVENSKA AB—See CVC Capital Partners SICAV-FIS S.A.; *Int'l*, pg. 1888
CVC CAPITAL PARTNERS SWITZERLAND GMBH—See CVC Capital Partners SICAV-FIS S.A.; *Int'l*, pg. 1888
CVC CREDIT PARTNERS LIMITED—See CVC Capital Partners SICAV-FIS S.A.; *Int'l*, pg. 1888
CVC CREDIT PARTNERS, LLC—See CVC Capital Partners SICAV-FIS S.A.; *Int'l*, pg. 1888
CVC INCOME & GROWTH LIMITED; *Int'l*, pg. 1889
CVC LIMITED; *Int'l*, pg. 1889
CVC MANAGERS PTY. LIMITED—See CVC Limited; *Int'l*, pg. 1889
CVC TECHNOLOGIES, INC.; *Int'l*, pg. 1889
C V C TECHNOLOGIES, INC.—See CVC Technologies, Inc.; *Int'l*, pg. 1889
CVC THERMOSET SPECIALTIES—See Huntsman Corporation; *U.S. Public*, pg. 1072
CVD EQUIPMENT CORPORATION; *U.S. Public*, pg. 613
CVENT EUROPE LTD.—See Blackstone Inc.; *U.S. Public*, pg. 353
CVENT HOLDING CORP.—See Blackstone Inc.; *U.S. Public*, pg. 353
CVENT, INC.—See Blackstone Inc.; *U.S. Public*, pg. 353
CVENT INDIA PRIVATE LIMITED—See Blackstone Inc.; *U.S. Public*, pg. 353
CVF CAPITAL PARTNERS, INC.; *U.S. Private*, pg. 1132
CVF TECHNOLOGIES CORP.; *Int'l*, pg. 1889
CVG - ALABAMA—See Commercial Vehicle Group, Inc.; *U.S. Public*, pg. 547
C.V. GASEXPANSIE IJMOND—See N.V. Nederlandse Gasunie; *Int'l*, pg. 5117
CVG ELECTRICAL SYSTEMS - MONONA—See Commercial Vehicle Group, Inc.; *U.S. Public*, pg. 547
CVG SPRAGUE DEVICES, LLC—See Commercial Vehicle Group, Inc.; *U.S. Public*, pg. 547
CVG SPRAGUE DIVISION—See Commercial Vehicle Group, Inc.; *U.S. Public*, pg. 547
CVG - VONORE—See Commercial Vehicle Group, Inc.; *U.S. Public*, pg. 547
CVH CHEMIE-VERTRIEB GMBH & CO.HANNOVER KG—See BRENNTAG SE; *Int'l*, pg. 1149
CVH CHEMIE-VERTRIEB VERWALTUNGSGESELLSCHAFT MBH—See BRENNTAG SE; *Int'l*, pg. 1149
CV HOLDINGS, LLC.; *U.S. Private*, pg. 1132
CVH SPIRITS LIMITED—See L'Arche Green N.V.; *Int'l*, pg. 4376
CVI DOM MAKLERSKI SP. Z O.O.; *Int'l*, pg. 1889

CVI LASER INTERNATIONAL LLC—See IDEX Corp; *U.S. Public*, pg. 1089
CVI LASER LIMITED—See IDEX Corp; *U.S. Public*, pg. 1089
CVI LASER OPTICS—See IDEX Corp; *U.S. Public*, pg. 1090
CVI LASER SAS—See IDEX Corp; *U.S. Public*, pg. 1090
CVILUX CORPORATION; *Int'l*, pg. 1889
CVILUX ELECTRONICS (DONGGUAN) CO., LTD.—See CviLux Corporation; *Int'l*, pg. 1889
CVILUX KOREA CORPORATION—See CviLux Corporation; *Int'l*, pg. 1889
CVILUX LAO CO., LTD.—See CviLux Corporation; *Int'l*, pg. 1889
CVILUX SDN BHD—See CviLux Corporation; *Int'l*, pg. 1889
CVILUX (SINGAPORE) CORPORATION—See CviLux Corporation; *Int'l*, pg. 1889
CVILUX TECHNOLOGY (CHONGQING) CORPORATION—See CviLux Corporation; *Int'l*, pg. 1889
CVILUX TECHNOLOGY (SHENZHEN) CORPORATION—See CviLux Corporation; *Int'l*, pg. 1889
CVILUX TECHNOLOGY (SUZHOU) CO., LTD.—See CviLux Corporation; *Int'l*, pg. 1889
CVILUX USA CORPORATION—See CviLux Corporation; *Int'l*, pg. 1889
CV INDUSTRIES INC.; *U.S. Private*, pg. 1132
CV INTERNATIONAL, INC.; *U.S. Private*, pg. 1132
CVISION TECHNOLOGIES, INC.—See Foxit Software Inc.; *U.S. Private*, pg. 1585
CVI TECHNICAL OPTICS COMPANY LTD.—See IDEX Corp; *U.S. Public*, pg. 1090
C.V. LANDFILL, INC.—See Casella Waste Systems, Inc.; *U.S. Public*, pg. 445
CVL INTERNATIONAL SAS—See Clasquin S.A.; *Int'l*, pg. 1652
CVM CHEMIE-VERTRIEB MAGDEBURG GMBH & CO. KG—See BRENNTAG SE; *Int'l*, pg. 1149
CVM DIAGNOSTICO VETERINARIO, S.L.—See Mars, Incorporated; *U.S. Private*, pg. 2588
CVM SOLUTIONS, LLC—See Supplier.io, Inc.; *U.S. Private*, pg. 3882
CVO PETROCHEMICAL REFINERY LIMITED; *Int'l*, pg. 1889
CVP CHEMIE-VERTRIEB BERLIN GMBH—See BRENNTAG SE; *Int'l*, pg. 1149
CV PRODUCTS, INC.; *U.S. Private*, pg. 1132
CV PROTEK—See Protek OAO; *Int'l*, pg. 6004
CVR ENERGY, INC.—See Icahn Enterprises L.P.; *U.S. Public*, pg. 1084
CVR MEDICAL CORP.; *Int'l*, pg. 1889
CVR PARTNERS, LP—See Icahn Enterprises L.P.; *U.S. Public*, pg. 1084
CVR REFINING, LP—See Icahn Enterprises L.P.; *U.S. Public*, pg. 1084
CVRX, INC.; *U.S. Public*, pg. 613
C.V. SANCHINARRO, S.L.—See Helvetia Holding AG; *Int'l*, pg. 3339
CVS BAY AREA INC.; *Int'l*, pg. 1889
CV SCIENCES, INC.; *U.S. Public*, pg. 613
CV'S FAMILY FOOD INC.; *U.S. Private*, pg. 1132
CV'S FOODLINER INCORPORATED; *U.S. Private*, pg. 1132
CVS GROUP PLC; *Int'l*, pg. 1889
CVS HEALTH CORPORATION; *U.S. Public*, pg. 613
CVS HOLDINGS, INC.—See Commercial Vehicle Group, Inc.; *U.S. Public*, pg. 547
CV SIMPANA SOFTWARE (PROPRIETARY) LIMITED—See CommVault Systems, Inc.; *U.S. Public*, pg. 558
CVS PHARMACY, INC.—See CVS Health Corporation; *U.S. Public*, pg. 615
CVS SYSTEMS INC.; *U.S. Private*, pg. 1132
C.V. STARR & CO., INC.; *U.S. Private*, pg. 709
CVS TRANSPORTATION, LLC—See CVS Health Corporation; *U.S. Public*, pg. 615
CVS (UK) LIMITED—See CVS Group Plc; *Int'l*, pg. 1890
CVT ARGENTINA—See Societe Pour L'Informatique Industrielle; *Int'l*, pg. 7043
CVTEC CO., LTD.—See AISIN Corporation; *Int'l*, pg. 253
CVTECH-AAB INC.—See Brookfield Corporation; *Int'l*, pg. 1181
CVTECH-IBC INC.; *Int'l*, pg. 1890
CVT ROMANIA—See Societe Pour L'Informatique Industrielle; *Int'l*, pg. 7043
CVW CLEANTECH INC.; *Int'l*, pg. 1890
CWA CONSTRUCTIONS SA—See Doppelmayr Group; *Int'l*, pg. 2174
CWA CONSULTORES & SERVICOS DE PETROLEO LTDA.—See Weatherford International plc; *U.S. Public*, pg. 2339
C&W ACQUISITION CORP.; *U.S. Private*, pg. 704
C&W ADVANCED TECHNOLOGIES PTE. LTD.—See CW Group Holdings Limited; *Int'l*, pg. 1890
C. & W. ASSETS LIMITED—See J. Smart & Co. (Contractors) PLC; *Int'l*, pg. 3857

CW ROEN CONSTRUCTION CO.

C. WATTS AND SONS CONSTRUCTION INC.; *U.S. Private*, pg. 705
CW BAKER INSURANCE AGENCY, INC.—See Stone Point Capital LLC; *U.S. Private*, pg. 3818
CWB AUTOMOTIVE ELECTRONICS CO., LTD.; *Int'l*, pg. 1890
CWB AUTOMOTIVE ELECTRONICS (TAICANG) CO., LTD.—See CWB Automotive Electronics Co., Ltd.; *Int'l*, pg. 1890
CWBJ, PLLC—See CBIZ, Inc.; *U.S. Public*, pg. 457
CWB MCLEAN & PARTNERS WEALTH MANAGEMENT LTD.—See Canadian Western Bank; *Int'l*, pg. 1286
CW BROWER INC.; *U.S. Private*, pg. 1132
C.W. BROWN FOODS, INC.; *U.S. Private*, pg. 709
C.W. BROWN, INC.—See LeChase Construction Services, LLC; *U.S. Private*, pg. 2410
CWCAPITAL ASSET MANAGEMENT LLC—See SoftBank Group Corp.; *Int'l*, pg. 7052
CWC ENERGY SERVICES CORP.—See Brookfield Corporation; *Int'l*, pg. 1175
CWD CHAMPAGNER- UND WEIN-DISTRIBUTIONSGESELLSCHAFT MBH & CO. KG—See Hawesko Holding AG; *Int'l*, pg. 3288
CWDKIDS INC.; *U.S. Private*, pg. 1132
CWD LLC—See Crowne Group LLC; *U.S. Private*, pg. 1112
C. W. DRIVER, INC.; *U.S. Private*, pg. 705
C. WEAVER PHYSICAL THERAPY, INC.—See Athletico Ltd.; *U.S. Private*, pg. 368
CW ENERGY LLP—See The Ince Group Plc; *Int'l*, pg. 7654
CW FACHVERLAG GMBH—See China Oceanwide Holdings Group Co., Ltd.; *Int'l*, pg. 1536
CW FACHVERLAG GMBH—See IDG Capital; *Int'l*, pg. 3593
C&W FACILITY SERVICES, INC.—See Ontario Teachers' Pension Plan; *Int'l*, pg. 5588
C&W FACILITY SERVICES, INC.—See PAG Asia Capital Ltd.; *Int'l*, pg. 5695
C&W FACILITY SERVICES, INC.—See TPG Capital, L.P.; *U.S. Public*, pg. 2171
CW FACILITY SOLUTION INC.—See Kokuyo Co., Ltd.; *Int'l*, pg. 4231
CW FINANCIAL SERVICES LLC—See SoftBank Group Corp.; *Int'l*, pg. 7052
CWG DEVELOPMENT PTY. LTD.—See HHI Holdings Pte. Ltd.; *Int'l*, pg. 6327
CWG HOLDINGS BERHAD; *Int'l*, pg. 1890
CWG INTERNATIONAL LTD.—See RHT Holdings Pte. Ltd.; *Int'l*, pg. 6327
CWG INTERNATIONAL LTD; *Int'l*, pg. 1890
CWG PLC; *Int'l*, pg. 1890
CW GROUP HOLDINGS LIMITED; *Int'l*, pg. 1890
CW GROUP PTE. LTD.—See CW Group Holdings Limited; *Int'l*, pg. 1890
C.W. HAYDEN CO., INC.; *U.S. Private*, pg. 709
CW HAYES CONSTRUCTION COMPANY; *U.S. Private*, pg. 1132
CWI BENEFITS, INC.—See Patriot National, Inc.; *U.S. Private*, pg. 3110
CWI, INC.—See Camping World Holdings, Inc.; *U.S. Public*, pg. 428
CWI INTERNATIONAL CHINA, LTD.—See Waxman Industries, Inc.; *U.S. Private*, pg. 4459
C. WILLIAM HETZER, INC.; *U.S. Private*, pg. 705
CWIND LIMITED—See Inspirit Management Ltd.; *Int'l*, pg. 3720
CWI REAL ESTATE AG; *Int'l*, pg. 1891
CW LUNDBERG AB—See Lagercrantz Group AB; *Int'l*, pg. 4394
C.W. MACKIE PLC; *Int'l*, pg. 1244
C.W. MATTHEWS CONTRACTING COMPANY, INC.; *U.S. Private*, pg. 709
CWM CHEMICAL SERVICES, L.L.C.—See Waste Management, Inc.; *U.S. Public*, pg. 2330
CWM GROUP SDN BHD—See Kuok Brothers Sdn. Bhd.; *Int'l*, pg. 4334
CWM, LLC; *U.S. Private*, pg. 1132
CW PETROLEUM CORP.; *U.S. Public*, pg. 616
CWP GMBH—See Electricite de France S.A.; *Int'l*, pg. 2350
CWPNC INC.—See National Services Group Inc.; *U.S. Private*, pg. 2863
CWPS, INC.; *U.S. Private*, pg. 1132
CWPS ONLINE; *U.S. Private*, pg. 1132
CWR CONSTRUCTION, INC.; *U.S. Private*, pg. 1132
CWR HOLDINGS, LLC—See Waste Connections, Inc.; *Int'l*, pg. 8353
C.W. ROBERTS CONTRACTING, INC.—See Construction Partners, Inc.; *U.S. Public*, pg. 572
C.W. ROD TOOL CO., INC.—See DXP Enterprises, Inc.; *U.S. Public*, pg. 697
CW ROEN CONSTRUCTION CO.; *U.S. Private*, pg. 1132
CWS APARTMENT HOMES LLC—See CWS Capital Partners, LLC; *U.S. Private*, pg. 1132
CWS-BOCO BELUX N.V.—See Franz Haniel & Cie. GmbH; *Int'l*, pg. 2762
CWS-BOCO BULGARIA EOOD—See Franz Haniel & Cie. GmbH; *Int'l*, pg. 2762

CW ROEN CONSTRUCTION CO.

CWS-BOCO CESKA REPUBLIKA S.R.O.—See Franz Haniel & Cie. GmbH; *Int'l*, pg. 2762
CWS-BOCO DEUTSCHLAND GMBH—See Franz Haniel & Cie. GmbH; *Int'l*, pg. 2762
CWS-BOCO D.O.O.—See Franz Haniel & Cie. GmbH; *Int'l*, pg. 2762
CWS-BOCO HIGIENSKI SISTEMI IN VZDRZEVANJE D.O.O.—See Franz Haniel & Cie. GmbH; *Int'l*, pg. 2762
CWS-BOCO HUNGARY KFT.—See Franz Haniel & Cie. GmbH; *Int'l*, pg. 2762
CWS-BOCO INTERNATIONAL GMBH—See Franz Haniel & Cie. GmbH; *Int'l*, pg. 2762
CWS-BOCO IRELAND LIMITED—See Franz Haniel & Cie. GmbH; *Int'l*, pg. 2762
CWS-BOCO ITALIA S.P.A—See Franz Haniel & Cie. GmbH; *Int'l*, pg. 2762
CWS-BOCO OSTERREICH GESELLSCHAFT M.B.H.—See Franz Haniel & Cie. GmbH; *Int'l*, pg. 2762
CWS-BOCO POLSKA SP. Z O.O.—See Franz Haniel & Cie. GmbH; *Int'l*, pg. 2762
CWS-BOCO ROMANIA S.R.L.—See Franz Haniel & Cie. GmbH; *Int'l*, pg. 2762
CWS-BOCO SLOVENSKO, S. R. O.—See Franz Haniel & Cie. GmbH; *Int'l*, pg. 2762
CWS-BOCO SUISSE SA—See Franz Haniel & Cie. GmbH; *Int'l*, pg. 2762
CWS-BOCO SWEDEN AB—See Franz Haniel & Cie. GmbH; *Int'l*, pg. 2762
CWS CAPITAL PARTNERS, LLC; *U.S. Private*, pg. 1133
CWS CORPORATE HOUSING; *U.S. Private*, pg. 1133
C&W SECURE SERVICES INC.—See ACS, Actividades de Construccion y Servicios, S.A.; *Int'l*, pg. 113
CW SERVICE—See Mercer Landmark Inc.; *U.S. Private*, pg. 2669
CWS INDUSTRIES (MFG) CORP.—See KPS Capital Partners, LP; *U.S. Private*, pg. 2347
CWS NEDERLAND B.V.—See Franz Haniel & Cie. GmbH; *Int'l*, pg. 2762
C.W. SUTER SERVICES; *U.S. Private*, pg. 709
CWT ASIA PACIFIC—See Carlson Companies Inc.; *U.S. Private*, pg. 765
CWT CANADA—See Carlson Companies Inc.; *U.S. Private*, pg. 765
CWT DISTRIBUTION LTD.—See PSA Corporation Pte Ltd.; *Int'l*, pg. 6014
CW TECH PTE. LTD.—See CW Group Holdings Limited; *Int'l*, pg. 1890
THE CW TELEVISION NETWORK—See Nexstar Media Group, Inc.; *U.S. Public*, pg. 1524
CWT EUROPE B.V. GROUP—See CWT International Limited; *Int'l*, pg. 1891
CWT FARMS INTERNATIONAL, INC.—See EW GROUP GmbH; *Int'l*, pg. 2575
CWT FRANCE—See Carlson Companies Inc.; *U.S. Private*, pg. 765
CWT GLOBELINK PTE LTD—See CWT International Limited; *Int'l*, pg. 1891
CWT INTERNATIONAL LIMITED; *Int'l*, pg. 1891
CWT LIMITED—See Hainan Traffic Administration Holding Co., Ltd.; *Int'l*, pg. 3213
C&W TRUCKING INC.; *U.S. Private*, pg. 704
CWT WAREHOUSING TRANSPORTATION (SHANGHAI) DEVELOPMENT CO., LTD.—See Yongtaiyun Chemical Logistics Co., Ltd.; *Int'l*, pg. 8597
CWU, INC.; *U.S. Private*, pg. 1133
C-W VALLEY CO-OP; *U.S. Private*, pg. 704
C.W. WRIGHT CONSTRUCTION CO., INC.; *U.S. Private*, pg. 709
CX ADVISORS LLP; *Int'l*, pg. 1891
CXAPP INC.; *U.S. Public*, pg. 616
CX CAPITAL MANAGEMENT LIMITED—See CX Advisors LLP; *Int'l*, pg. 1891
CX COMPANY GMBH—See CM.com N.V.; *Int'l*, pg. 1666
CXD NEXT CO., LTD.—See Casio Computer Co., Ltd.; *Int'l*, pg. 1353
CXG WILLIS CORREDURIA DE SEGUROS S.A.—See Willis Towers Watson Public Limited Company; *Int'l*, pg. 8415
CXI HEALTHCARE TECHNOLOGY GROUP LIMITED; *Int'l*, pg. 1891
CXJ GROUP CO., LIMITED; *Int'l*, pg. 1891
CXLOYALTY GROUP, INC.—See JPMorgan Chase & Co.; *U.S. Public*, pg. 1210
CXLOYALTY, INC.—See JPMorgan Chase & Co.; *U.S. Public*, pg. 1210
CXM INC.; *U.S. Private*, pg. 1133
CXR ANDERSON JACOBSON SAS; *Int'l*, pg. 1891
CX REINSURANCE COMPANY LIMITED—See Financiere Pinault SCA; *Int'l*, pg. 2669
CX TECHNOLOGY CORPORATION; *Int'l*, pg. 1891
CX TECHNOLOGY (SHANGHAI) CORP.—See CX Technology Corporation; *Int'l*, pg. 1891
CXTEC; *U.S. Private*, pg. 1133
CXT, INC.—See L.B. Foster Company; *U.S. Public*, pg. 1278
CY4GATE S.P.A.; *Int'l*, pg. 1891
CYALUME TECHNOLOGIES HOLDINGS, INC.—See Arsenal Capital Management LP; *U.S. Private*, pg. 337

CYALUME TECHNOLOGIES, INC.—See Cadre Holdings, Inc.; *U.S. Public*, pg. 419
CYALUME TECHNOLOGIES S.A.S.—See Cadre Holdings, Inc.; *U.S. Public*, pg. 419
CYAN AG; *Int'l*, pg. 1891
CYANCO COMPANY, LLC—See Cerberus Capital Management, L.P.; *U.S. Private*, pg. 837
CYANCO CORPORATION—See Cerberus Capital Management, L.P.; *U.S. Private*, pg. 837
CYANCO HOLDING CORP.—See Cerberus Capital Management, L.P.; *U.S. Private*, pg. 837
CYANCO INTERNATIONAL, LLC - HOUSTON PLANT—See Cerberus Capital Management, L.P.; *U.S. Private*, pg. 837
CYANCO INTERNATIONAL, LLC—See Cerberus Capital Management, L.P.; *U.S. Private*, pg. 837
CYANCONNODE HOLDINGS PLC; *Int'l*, pg. 1891
CYANOTECH CORPORATION; *U.S. Public*, pg. 616
CYAN PARTNERS, LP; *U.S. Private*, pg. 1133
CYANTEK CORPORATION—See Entegris, Inc.; *U.S. Public*, pg. 776
CYBA-STEVENS MANAGEMENT GROUP; *Int'l*, pg. 1891
CYBELEC NUMERICAL CONTROL TECHNOLOGY (SHANGHAI)—See Perrot Duval Holding S.A.; *Int'l*, pg. 5814
CYBELE CO., LTD.; *Int'l*, pg. 1891
CYBELEC SA—See Perrot Duval Holding S.A.; *Int'l*, pg. 5814
CYBELEC SRL—See Perrot Duval Holding S.A.; *Int'l*, pg. 5814
CYBELE INDUSTRIES LIMITED; *Int'l*, pg. 1891
CYBEM SERVICES PTY LTD.—See Aquirian Limited; *Int'l*, pg. 528
CYBER 360 SOLUTIONS—See Staffing 360 Solutions, Inc.; *U.S. Public*, pg. 1925
THE CYBER ACADEMY PROPRIETARY LIMITED—See Workforce Holdings Ltd.; *Int'l*, pg. 8456
CYBER ADAPT, INC.; *U.S. Private*, pg. 1133
CYBERADVISORS, INC.; *U.S. Private*, pg. 1133
CYBERAGENT, INC.; *Int'l*, pg. 1892
CYBERAGENT VENTURES (BEIJING) CO., LTD—See CyberAgent, Inc.; *Int'l*, pg. 1892
CYBERAGENT VENTURES INC.—See CyberAgent, Inc.; *Int'l*, pg. 1892
CYBERA, INC.—See TA Associates, Inc.; *U.S. Private*, pg. 3917
CYBERARK SOFTWARE, INC.—See CyberArk Software Ltd.; *Int'l*, pg. 1892
CYBERARK SOFTWARE LTD.; *Int'l*, pg. 1892
CYBERARK SOFTWARE (UK) LIMITED—See CyberArk Software Ltd.; *Int'l*, pg. 1892
CYBER BAY CORPORATION; *Int'l*, pg. 1891
CYBERBOND CS S.R.O.—See H.B. Fuller Company; *U.S. Public*, pg. 977
CYBERBOND EUROPE GMBH—See H.B. Fuller Company; *U.S. Public*, pg. 977
CYBERBOND FRANCE S.A.R.L.—See H.B. Fuller Company; *U.S. Public*, pg. 977
CYBERBOND IBERICA S.L.—See H.B. Fuller Company; *U.S. Public*, pg. 977
CYBERBOND, LLC—See H.B. Fuller Company; *U.S. Public*, pg. 977
CYBERBOND UK LTD—See H.B. Fuller Company; *U.S. Public*, pg. 977
CYBER BUZZ, INC.; *Int'l*, pg. 1891
CYBERCATCH HOLDINGS, INC.; *Int'l*, pg. 1892
CYBERCIA SRL—See Redeia Corporation, S.A.; *Int'l*, pg. 6246
CYBER CITY, INC.—See Netsurit (Pty) Ltd; *Int'l*, pg. 5215
CYBER CLOUD TECHNOLOGIES, LLC—See T-Rex Solutions, LLC; *U.S. Private*, pg. 3911
CYBERCODERS INC.—See ASGN Incorporated; *U.S. Public*, pg. 210
CYBER COM CO., LTD.—See FUJISOFT INCORPORATED; *Int'l*, pg. 2830
CYBERCOM FINLAND—See Formica Capital Holding AB; *Int'l*, pg. 2734
CYBERCOM GROUP AB—See Formica Capital Holding AB; *Int'l*, pg. 2734
CYBERCOM INTERNATIONAL CORP.—See Clayton, Dubilier & Rice, LLC; *U.S. Private*, pg. 927
CYBERCOM INTERNATIONAL CORP.—See Mubadala Investment Company PJSC; *Int'l*, pg. 5076
CYBERCOM INTERNATIONAL CORP.—See Stone Point Capital LLC; *U.S. Private*, pg. 3826
CYBER COMMUNICATIONS INC.—See Polaris Capital Group Co., Ltd.; *Int'l*, pg. 5907
CYBERCOM POLAND SP.ZO.O.—See Formica Capital Holding AB; *Int'l*, pg. 2734
CYBERCOM SWEDEN - GOTHENBURG—See Formica Capital Holding AB; *Int'l*, pg. 2734
CYBERCORE TECHNOLOGIES LLC—See Moelis Asset Management LP; *U.S. Private*, pg. 2764
CYBER DIGITAL, INC.; *U.S. Private*, pg. 1133
CYBERDYNE CARE ROBOTICS GMBH—See Cyberdyne Inc.; *Int'l*, pg. 1892
CYBERDYNE INC.; *Int'l*, pg. 1892
CYBER ENERGY CO., LTD.—See CyberPower Systems, Inc.; *Int'l*, pg. 1893

CORPORATE AFFILIATIONS

CYBER ENVIRO-TECH, INC.; *U.S. Public*, pg. 617
CYBER_FOLKS S.A.; *Int'l*, pg. 1892
CYBERFORT SOFTWARE, INC.; *U.S. Public*, pg. 617
CYBERGISTICS, LLC—See Rare Enterprises Ltd.; *Int'l*, pg. 6211
CYBERGRANTS, LLC; *U.S. Private*, pg. 1133
CYBERGUN SA; *Int'l*, pg. 1893
CYBERGY HOLDINGS, INC.; *U.S. Public*, pg. 1133
CYBERGYMNASIET MALMO AB—See AcadeMedia AB; *Int'l*, pg. 75
CYBERHEART, INC.—See Siemens Aktiengesellschaft; *Int'l*, pg. 6894
CYBERHOUND PTY. LTD.—See Superloop Limited; *Int'l*, pg. 7338
CYBERIAN OUTPOST, INC.—See Fry's Electronics, Inc.; *U.S. Private*, pg. 1618
CYBER INTERNET SERVICES (PRIVATE) LIMITED—See COLGATE-PALMOLIVE (PAKISTAN) LTD; *Int'l*, pg. 1698
CYBERJAYA COLLEGE CENTRAL SDN. BHD.—See Cyberjaya Education Group Berhad; *Int'l*, pg. 1893
CYBERJAYA EDUCATION GROUP BERHAD; *Int'l*, pg. 1893
CYBERKNIFE CENTER OF PHILADELPHIA, LLC—See Akumin, Inc.; *U.S. Public*, pg. 70
CYBER LABORATORY INCORPORATION—See Nippon Telegraph & Telephone Corporation; *Int'l*, pg. 5340
CYBERLINK CORP.; *Int'l*, pg. 1893
CYBERLINK EUROPE B.V.—See CyberLink Corp.; *Int'l*, pg. 1893
CYBERLINK INC.—See CyberLink Corp.; *Int'l*, pg. 1893
CYBERLINK PACIFIC TELECOMMUNICATIONS LIMITED; *Int'l*, pg. 1893
CYBERLINKS CO., LTD.; *Int'l*, pg. 1893
CYBERLINK USA—See CyberLink Corp.; *Int'l*, pg. 1893
CYBERLOGISTICS CORPORATION—See TD Synnex Corp; *U.S. Public*, pg. 1984
CYBERLOGITEC GLOBAL PTE. LTD.—See Eusu Holdings Co., Ltd.; *Int'l*, pg. 2559
CYBERLOGITEC SHANGHAI CO., LTD.—See Eusu Holdings Co., Ltd.; *Int'l*, pg. 2559
CYBERLOGITEC SPAIN S.L.U.—See Eusu Holdings Co., Ltd.; *Int'l*, pg. 2559
CYBERLOGITEC VIETNAM CO., LTD.—See Eusu Holdings Co., Ltd.; *Int'l*, pg. 2559
CYBERLOQ TECHNOLOGIES, INC.; *U.S. Public*, pg. 617
CYBERLUX CORPORATION; *U.S. Public*, pg. 617
CYBERMAK INFORMATION SYSTEMS W.L.L.—See Hexagon AB; *Int'l*, pg. 3368
CYBERMAXX, LLC—See Periscope Equity LLC; *U.S. Private*, pg. 3151
CYBER MEDIA INDIA LTD.; *Int'l*, pg. 1892
CYBERMEDIA K.K.—See ad-comm Co., Ltd.; *Int'l*, pg. 123
CYBERMETALS, CORP.—See A-Mark Precious Metals, Inc.; *U.S. Public*, pg. 10
CYBERMETRIX, INC.—See SGS SA; *Int'l*, pg. 6744
CYBERNAUT INTERNATIONAL HOLDINGS COMPANY LIMITED; *Int'l*, pg. 1893
CYBERNET CAE SYSTEMS (SHANGHAI) CO.,LTD—See FUJISOFT INCORPORATED; *Int'l*, pg. 2830
CYBERNETIX S.A.—See TechnipFMC plc; *Int'l*, pg. 7507
CYBERNET MBSE CO., LTD.—See FUJISOFT INCORPORATED; *Int'l*, pg. 2830
CYBERNET SYSTEMS CO., LTD.—See FUJISOFT INCORPORATED; *Int'l*, pg. 2830
CYBERNET SYSTEMS MALAYSIA SDN BHD—See FUJISOFT INCORPORATED; *Int'l*, pg. 2830
CYBERNET SYSTEMS TAIWAN CO., LTD.—See FUJISOFT INCORPORATED; *Int'l*, pg. 2830
CYBERNOOR CORP.—See Lightview Capital LLC; *U.S. Private*, pg. 2453
CYBERNORTH VENTURES INC.; *Int'l*, pg. 1893
CYBERONE CO., LTD.; *Int'l*, pg. 1893
CYBERONICS EUROPE, S.A.—See LivaNova PLC; *Int'l*, pg. 4530
CYBEROO S.P.A.; *Int'l*, pg. 1893
CYBER OPERATIONS, INC.; *U.S. Private*, pg. 1133
CYBEROPTICS CHINA COMPANY LTD.—See Nordson Corporation; *U.S. Public*, pg. 1532
CYBEROPTICS CORPORATION—See Nordson Corporation; *U.S. Public*, pg. 1532
CYBEROPTICS LTD.—See Nordson Corporation; *U.S. Public*, pg. 1532
CYBEROPTICS SEMICONDUCTOR, INC.—See Nordson Corporation; *U.S. Public*, pg. 1532
CYBEROPTICS (SINGAPORE) PTE. LTD.—See Nordson Corporation; *U.S. Public*, pg. 1532
CYBERPLEX INC.-BOSTON—See EQ Inc.; *Int'l*, pg. 2466
CYBERPORT GMBH; *Int'l*, pg. 1893
CYBERPORT SERVICES GMBH—See Hubert Burda Media Holding Kommanditgesellschaft; *Int'l*, pg. 3520
CYBERPORT SOLUTIONS GMBH—See Hubert Burda Media Holding Kommanditgesellschaft; *Int'l*, pg. 3520
CYBERPOWER SYSTEMS B.V.—See CyberPower Systems, Inc.; *Int'l*, pg. 1893
CYBER POWER SYSTEMS FRANCE—See CyberPower Systems, Inc.; *Int'l*, pg. 1893
CYBERPOWER SYSTEMS GMBH—See CyberPower Systems, Inc.; *Int'l*, pg. 1893

COMPANY NAME INDEX

CYBERPOWER SYSTEMS, INC.; *Int'l,* pg. 1893
CYBERPOWER SYSTEMS K.K.—See CyberPower Systems, Inc.; *Int'l,* pg. 1894
CYBER POWER SYSTEMS S.A. DE C.V.—See CyberPower Systems, Inc.; *Int'l,* pg. 1893
CYBERPOWER SYSTEMS (USA), INC.—See CyberPower Systems, Inc.; *Int'l,* pg. 1893
CYBERQUOTE (HK) LTD—See Phillip Capital Pte. Ltd.; *Int'l,* pg. 5846
CYBERQUOTE JAPAN, LTD.—See Phillip Capital Pte. Ltd.; *Int'l,* pg. 5846
CYBERQUOTE PTE LTD—See Phillip Capital Pte. Ltd.; *Int'l,* pg. 5846
CYBERQUOTE (THAILAND) CO., LTD.—See Phillip Capital Pte. Ltd.; *Int'l,* pg. 5846
CYBERRESEARCH INC.; *U.S. Private,* pg. 1133
CYBER RESOURCE GROUP; *U.S. Private,* pg. 1133
CYBERSCAPE MULTIMEDIA LTD.; *Int'l,* pg. 1894
CYBER SCIENCES INC.—See Trystar, LLC; *U.S. Private,* pg. 4252
CYBER SECURITY CLOUD, INC.; *Int'l,* pg. 1892
CYBER SECURITY LAC CO., LTD.—See LAC Co., Ltd.; *Int'l,* pg. 4391
CYBERSECURITY SERVICE LLC—See System1, Inc.; *U.S. Public,* pg. 1977
CYBERSETTLE, INC.; *U.S. Private,* pg. 1133
CYBERSHIELD, INC.; *U.S. Private,* pg. 1133
CYBERSITE SERVICES PTE LIMITED—See Great Wall Terroir Holdings Limited; *Int'l,* pg. 3066
CYBERSOURCE CORPORATION—See Visa, Inc.; *U.S. Public,* pg. 2301
CYBERSOURCE K.K.—See Visa, Inc.; *U.S. Public,* pg. 2301
CYBERSOURCE LTD.—See Visa, Inc.; *U.S. Public,* pg. 2302
CYBERSPACE SOLUTIONS, LLC—See Godspeed Capital Management LP; *U.S. Private,* pg. 1725
CYBERSTEP, INC.; *Int'l,* pg. 1894
CYBERTAN CORPORATION—See CyberTAN Technology, Inc.; *Int'l,* pg. 1894
CYBERTAN TECHNOLOGY, INC.; *Int'l,* pg. 1894
CYBERTECH INFORMATION SERVICES LTD. UK—See CyberTech Systems Inc.; *U.S. Private,* pg. 1133
CYBERTECH SYSTEMS, INC.; *U.S. Private,* pg. 1133
CYBERTECH SYSTEMS & SOFTWARE INC. See CyberTech Systems Inc.; *U.S. Private,* pg. 1133
CYBERTECH SYSTEMS & SOFTWARE LTD.—See CyberTech Systems Inc.; *U.S. Private,* pg. 1133
CYBER-TEST, INC.—See Bain Capital, LP; *U.S. Private,* pg. 444
CYBERTEX INSTITUTE OF TECHNOLOGY; *U.S. Private,* pg. 1134
CYBERTHINK, INC.; *U.S. Private,* pg. 1134
CYBERTREK (MALAYSIA) SDN BHD—See KUB Malaysia Berhad; *Int'l,* pg. 4319
CYBERTROL ENGINEERING, LLC; *U.S. Private,* pg. 1134
CYBERTRUST BELGIUM N.V.—See Verizon Communications Inc.; *U.S. Public,* pg. 2285
CYBERTRUST JAPAN CO., LTD.—See SoftBank Group Corp.; *Int'l,* pg. 7052
CYBERVERSE, INC.—See Evocative, Inc.; *U.S. Private,* pg. 1442
CYBER VILLAGE SDN BHD—See Silverlake Axis Ltd.; *Int'l,* pg. 6926
CYBERVISTA LLC—See Graham Holdings Company; *U.S. Public,* pg. 954
CYBERZ INC.—See CyberAgent, Inc.; *Int'l,* pg. 1892
CYBERZONE PROPERTIES INC.—See Filinvest Development Corporation; *Int'l,* pg. 2663
CYBEX GMBH—See Goodbaby International Holdings Limited; *Int'l,* pg. 3039
CYBEX INTERNATIONAL, INC.—See KPS Capital Partners, LP; *U.S. Private,* pg. 2347
CYBEX RETAIL GMBH—See Goodbaby International Holdings Limited; *Int'l,* pg. 3039
CYBIN INC.; *Int'l,* pg. 1894
CYB INVESTMENTS LTD.—See Virgin Money UK PLC; *Int'l,* pg. 8247
CYBIO NORTHERN EUROPE LTD.—See Endress+Hauser (International) Holding AG; *Int'l,* pg. 2405
CY BIOTECH; *Int'l,* pg. 1891
CYBIRD HOLDINGS CO., LTD.; *Int'l,* pg. 1894
CYBOZU INC.; *Int'l,* pg. 1894
CYBOZU IT SHANGHAI INC.—See Cybozu Inc.; *Int'l,* pg. 1894
CYBOZU MEDIA AND TECHNOLOGY CO.,LTD.—See Cybozu Inc.; *Int'l,* pg. 1894
CYBOZU RESEARCH INSTITUTE, INC.—See Cybozu Inc.; *Int'l,* pg. 1894
CYBOZU VIETNAM CO., LTD.—See Cybozu Inc.; *Int'l,* pg. 1894
CYBRA CORPORATION; *U.S. Public,* pg. 617
CYBRDI, INC.; *U.S. Private,* pg. 1134
CYBRID TECHNOLOGIES, INC.; *Int'l,* pg. 1894
THE CYBRIX GROUP, INC.; *U.S. Private,* pg. 4017
CYBUS CAPITAL MARKETS—See First National of Nebraska, Inc.; *U.S. Private,* pg. 1524
CYC DESIGN CORPORATION—See Aritzia, Inc.; *Int'l,* pg. 567

CYCLACEL LIMITED—See Cyclacel Pharmaceuticals, Inc.; *U.S. Public,* pg. 617
CYCLACEL PHARMACEUTICALS, INC.; *U.S. Public,* pg. 617
CYCLE30, INC.—See Liberty Broadband Corporation; *U.S. Public,* pg. 1310
CYCLE BARN INC.; *U.S. Private,* pg. 1134
CYCLE & CARRIAGE AUTOMOTIVE PTE. LTD.—See Jardine Matheson Holdings Limited; *Int'l,* pg. 3910
CYCLE & CARRIAGE BINTANG BERHAD—See Jardine Matheson Holdings Limited; *Int'l,* pg. 3910
CYCLE & CARRIAGE BINTANG (PERAK) SDN. BHD.—See Jardine Matheson Holdings Limited; *Int'l,* pg. 3910
CYCLE & CARRIAGE FRANCE PTE LTD—See Jardine Matheson Holdings Limited; *Int'l,* pg. 3910
CYCLE & CARRIAGE INDUSTRIES PTE LTD—See Jardine Matheson Holdings Limited; *Int'l,* pg. 3910
CYCLE & CARRIAGE KIA PTE LTD—See Jardine Matheson Holdings Limited; *Int'l,* pg. 3910
CYCLE COUNTRY, INC.; *U.S. Private,* pg. 1134
CYCLE EXPRESS, LLC—See Copart, Inc.; *U.S. Public,* pg. 575
CYCLE GEAR INC.—See Prospect Hill Growth Partners, L.P.; *U.S. Private,* pg. 3288
CYCLE HOLDINGS, LLC—See Penske Automotive Group, Inc.; *U.S. Public,* pg. 1664
CYCLEO SAS—See Semtech Corporation; *U.S. Public,* pg. 1864
CYCLERION THERAPEUTICS, INC.; *U.S. Public,* pg. 617
CYCLE SERVICES NORDIC APS—See Accell Group N.V.; *Int'l,* pg. 80
CYCLES FRANCE-LOIRE S.A.S.—See Accell Group N.V.; *Int'l,* pg. 80
CYCLES LAPIERRE S.A.—See Accell Group N.V.; *Int'l,* pg. 80
CYCLES MERCIER FRANCE-LOIRE S.A.—See Accell Group N.V.; *Int'l,* pg. 80
CYCLE SOLUTIONS, INC.—See WuXi PharmaTech (Cayman) Inc.; *Int'l,* pg. 8515
CYCLEUROPE AB—See Grimaldi Industri AB; *Int'l,* pg. 3086
CYCLEUROPE FINLAND OY—See Grimaldi Industri AB; *Int'l,* pg. 3086
CYCLEUROPE INDUSTRIES SAS—See Grimaldi Industri AB; *Int'l,* pg. 3085
CYCLEUROPE JAPAN CO., LTD.—See Grimaldi Industri AB; *Int'l,* pg. 3086
CYCLEUROPE NORGE AS—See Grimaldi Industri AB; *Int'l,* pg. 3086
CYCLEUROPE SVERIGE AB—See Grimaldi Industri AB; *Int'l,* pg. 3086
CYCLEUROPE UK LTD—See Grimaldi Industri AB; *Int'l,* pg. 3085
CYCLEUROPE USA INC.—See Grimaldi Industri AB; *Int'l,* pg. 3085
CYCLING 74—See Ableton AG; *Int'l,* pg. 63
CYCLING SPORTS GROUP AUSTRALIA PTY LTD—See Dorel Industries, Inc.; *Int'l,* pg. 2176
CYCLING SPORTS GROUP EUROPE B.V—See Dorel Industries, Inc.; *Int'l,* pg. 2176
CYCLING SPORTS GROUP INC.—See Dorel Industries, Inc.; *Int'l,* pg. 2176
CYCLIQ GROUP LIMITED; *Int'l,* pg. 1894
CYCLOCITY INC.—See JCDecaux S.A.; *Int'l,* pg. 3920
CYC LOGISTICS LTD—See CitySprint (UK) Limited; *Int'l,* pg. 1630
CYCLO INDUSTRIES, INC.—See Highlander Partners, LP.; *U.S. Private,* pg. 1939
CYCLOMEDICA AUSTRALIA PTY LTD—See Cyclopharm Limited; *Int'l,* pg. 1894
CYCLOMEDICA CANADA LIMITED—See Cyclopharm Limited; *Int'l,* pg. 1894
CYCLOMEDICA EUROPE LIMITED—See Cyclopharm Limited; *Int'l,* pg. 1894
CYCLOMEDICA GERMANY GMBH—See Cyclopharm Limited; *Int'l,* pg. 1894
CYCLOMEDICA NORDIC AB—See Cyclopharm Limited; *Int'l,* pg. 1894
CYCLONE DRILLING, INC.; *U.S. Private,* pg. 1134
CYCLONE INDUSTRIES PTY LTD—See Illinois Tool Works Inc.; *U.S. Public,* pg. 1104
CYCLONE METALS LIMITED; *Int'l,* pg. 1894
CYCLONE MFG. INC.; *Int'l,* pg. 1894
CYCLONE POWER TECHNOLOGIES, INC.; *U.S. Public,* pg. 617
CYCLONE SPORTS PROPERTIES, LLC—See Atai333 Group, Inc.; *U.S. Private,* pg. 363
CYCLONE SURFACE CLEANING, INC.—See Nilfisk Holding A/S; *U.S. Public,* pg. 5295
CYCLONE URANIUM CORPORATION; *U.S. Private,* pg. 1134
CYCLON HELLAS S.A.—See Motor Oil (Hellas) Corinth Refineries S. A.; *Int'l,* pg. 5054
CYCLOPET PTY LTD—See Cyclopharm Limited; *Int'l,* pg. 1894
CYCLOPHARM LIMITED; *Int'l,* pg. 1894
CYCLOPS TECHNOLOGIES, INC.; *U.S. Private,* pg. 1134
CYCLO THERAPEUTICS, INC.; *U.S. Public,* pg. 617

CYCOS AG; *Int'l,* pg. 1895
CYDCOR, INC.; *U.S. Private,* pg. 1134
CYDEX PHARMACEUTICALS, INC.—See Ligand Pharmaceuticals Incorporated; *U.S. Public,* pg. 1314
THE CYDIO GROUP—See 24 Seven, LLC; *U.S. Private,* pg. 6
CYDSA S.A.B. DE C.V.; *Int'l,* pg. 1895
CYDSA S.A. DE C.V. - ALTAMIRA PLANT—See Cydsa S.A.B. de C.V.; *Int'l,* pg. 1895
CYDSA S.A. DE C.V. - ENVIRONMENTAL SERVICES DIVISION—See Cydsa S.A.B. de C.V.; *Int'l,* pg. 1895
CYDSA S.A. DE C.V. - LA PRESA PLANT—See Cydsa S.A.B. de C.V.; *Int'l,* pg. 1895
CYDSA S.A. DE C.V. - PACKAGING DIVISION—See Cydsa S.A.B. de C.V.; *Int'l,* pg. 1895
CYFADACO SHIP MANAGEMENT LTD.—See Polska Zegluga Morska; *Int'l,* pg. 5911
CY-FAIR MEDICAL CENTER HOSPITAL, LLC—See HCA Healthcare, Inc.; *U.S. Public,* pg. 995
CY-FAIR VOLUNTEER FIRE DEPARTMENT; *U.S. Private,* pg. 1133
CYFIELD DEVELOPMENT CO. LTD.; *Int'l,* pg. 1895
CYFIR, LLC—See eSentire, Inc.; *U.S. Public,* pg. 2503
C.Y. FOOD TRADING (HK) COMPANY LIMITED—See China Wantian Holdings Limited; *Int'l,* pg. 1562
CYFRA+—See Vivendi SE; *Int'l,* pg. 8266
CYFROWY POLSAT S.A.; *Int'l,* pg. 1895
CYFUSE BIOMEDICAL K.K.; *Int'l,* pg. 1895
CYGAM ENERGY INC.; *Int'l,* pg. 1895
CYGATE AB—See Telia Company AB; *Int'l,* pg. 7543
CYGATE OY—See Telia Company AB; *Int'l,* pg. 7543
CYG CONSULTING AND ENGINEERING CO., LTD.—See ChangYuan Group Ltd.; *Int'l,* pg. 1444
CYG CONTRON CO., LTD.—See ChangYuan Group Ltd.; *Int'l,* pg. 1444
CYG ELECTRIC CO., LTD.—See ChangYuan Group Ltd.; *Int'l,* pg. 1444
CYGER MEDIA; *U.S. Private,* pg. 1134
CYG ET CO., LTD.—See ChangYuan Group Ltd.; *Int'l,* pg. 1444
CYG FLYWHEEL CO., LTD.—See ChangYuan Group Ltd.; *Int'l,* pg. 1444
CYGIA CO., LTD.—See ChangYuan Group Ltd.; *Int'l,* pg. 1444
CYG INSULATOR CO., LTD.—See ChangYuan Group Ltd.; *Int'l,* pg. 1444
CYG MEDITECH TECHNOLOGY CO., LTD.—See ChangYuan Group Ltd.; *Int'l,* pg. 1444
CYGNACOM SOLUTIONS, INC.—See DataCard Corporation; *U.S. Private,* pg. 1165
CYGNA ENERGY SERVICES, INC.—See Gryphon Investors, LLC; *U.S. Private,* pg. 1798
CYGNET 2000 LIMITED—See Universal Health Services, Inc.; *U.S. Public,* pg. 2256
CYGNET BEHAVIOURAL HEALTH—See Universal Health Services, Inc.; *U.S. Public,* pg. 2256
CYGNET CARE SERVICES LIMITED—See Universal Health Services, Inc.; *U.S. Public,* pg. 2256
CYGNET CLIFTON LIMITED—See Universal Health Services, Inc.; *U.S. Public,* pg. 2256
CYGNET HEALTH CARE LTD.—See Universal Health Services, Inc.; *U.S. Public,* pg. 2256
CYGNET INDUSTRIES LIMITED—See Kesoram Industries Limited; *Int'l,* pg. 4143
CYGNET SOFTWARE, INC.—See Weatherford International plc; *U.S. Public,* pg. 2339
CYGNET STAMPING & FABRICATING, INC.; *U.S. Private,* pg. 1134
CYGNIFIC B.V.—See Air France-KLM S.A.; *Int'l,* pg. 237
CYGNUS BUSINESS MEDIA INC.—See ABRY Partners, LLC; *U.S. Private,* pg. 41
CYGNUS INTERNATIONAL CO., LTD.—See Catcher Technology Co., Ltd.; *Int'l,* pg. 1359
CYGNUS MANUFACTURING CO.; *U.S. Private,* pg. 1134
CYGNUS METALS LIMITED; *Int'l,* pg. 1895
CYGNUS OIL & GAS CORPORATION; *U.S. Public,* pg. 617
CYGNUS TECHNOLOGIES, INC.—See GTCR LLC; *U.S. Private,* pg. 1805
CYG SUNRI CO., LTD.—See ChangYuan Group Ltd.; *Int'l,* pg. 1444
CYG TIANGONG CO., LTD.—See ChangYuan Group Ltd.; *Int'l,* pg. 1444
CYIENT AUSTRALIA PTY LIMITED—See Cyient Limited; *Int'l,* pg. 1896
CYIENT BENELUX BV—See Cyient Limited; *Int'l,* pg. 1896
CYIENT DLM PRIVATE LIMITED—See Cyient Limited; *Int'l,* pg. 1896
CYIENT EUROPE LIMITED—See Cyient Limited; *Int'l,* pg. 1896
CYIENT GMBH—See Cyient Limited; *Int'l,* pg. 1896
CYIENT KK—See Cyient Limited; *Int'l,* pg. 1896
CYIENT LIMITED; *Int'l,* pg. 1895
CYIENT N.V.—See Cyient Limited; *Int'l,* pg. 1896
CYIENT SCHWEIZ GMBH—See Cyient Limited; *Int'l,* pg. 1896
CYIENT SINGAPORE PTE LIMITED—See Cyient Limited; *Int'l,* pg. 1896
CYIENT SRO—See Cyient Limited; *Int'l,* pg. 1896

CYIOS CORPORATION

CYIOS CORPORATION; *U.S. Public*, pg. 617
CYLANCE, INC.—See BlackBerry Limited; *Int'l*, pg. 1060
CYL CORPORATION BERHAD; *Int'l*, pg. 1896
CYLINGAS COMPANY LLC—See Emirates National Oil Company Limited; *Int'l*, pg. 2381
CYL KNIFE VALVES S.L.—See AVK Holding A/S; *Int'l*, pg. 747
CYLON CONTROLS (BEIJING) LTD—See ABB Ltd.; *Int'l*, pg. 56
CYLON CONTROLS LIMITED—See ABB Ltd.; *Int'l*, pg. 56
CYLON CONTROLS LTD.—See ABB Ltd.; *Int'l*, pg. 56
CYLON CONTROLS (UK) LIMITED—See ABB Ltd.; *Int'l*, pg. 56
CYLON ENERGY INC.—See ABB Ltd.; *Int'l*, pg. 56
CYLON GMBH—See ABB Ltd.; *Int'l*, pg. 56
CYMABAY THERAPEUTICS, INC.—See Gilead Sciences, Inc.; *U.S. Public*, pg. 936
CYMAO PLYWOOD SDN. BHD.—See ANNUM BERHAD; *Int'l*, pg. 474
CYMAT TECHNOLOGIES LTD.; *Int'l*, pg. 1896
CYMBAL DEVELOPMENT; *U.S. Private*, pg. 1134
CYMBRIA CORPORATION; *Int'l*, pg. 1896
CYMECHS INC.; *Int'l*, pg. 1896
CYMER B.V.—See ASML Holding N.V.; *Int'l*, pg. 627
CYMER, INC.—See ASML Holding N.V.; *Int'l*, pg. 627
CYMER JAPAN, INC.—See ASML Holding N.V.; *Int'l*, pg. 627
CYMER KOREA, INC.—See ASML Holding N.V.; *Int'l*, pg. 628
CYMER SEMICONDUCTOR EQUIPMENT (SHANGHAI) CO., LTD.—See ASML Holding N.V.; *Int'l*, pg. 628
CYMER SINGAPORE PTE. LTD.—See ASML Holding N.V.; *Int'l*, pg. 628
CYMER SOUTHEAST ASIA LTD.—See ASML Holding N.V.; *Int'l*, pg. 628
CYMETECH CORPORATION—See Sojitz Corporation; *Int'l*, pg. 7064
CYMETRIX CORPORATION—See Bain Capital, LP; *U.S. Private*, pg. 432
CYMI HOLDING, S.A.—See ACS, Actividades de Construccion y Servicios, S.A.; *Int'l*, pg. 111
CYMIMASA BRASIL, LTDA.—See ACS, Actividades de Construccion y Servicios, S.A.; *Int'l*, pg. 111
CYMI SEGURIDAD, S.A.—See ACS, Actividades de Construccion y Servicios, S.A.; *Int'l*, pg. 111
CYM MATERIALES S.A.—See INDUS Holding AG; *Int'l*, pg. 3664
CYMOT (PTY) LTD.; *Int'l*, pg. 1896
CYNATA THERAPEUTICS LIMITED; *Int'l*, pg. 1896
CYNERGIES CONSULTING, INC.; *U.S. Private*, pg. 1134
CYNERGISTEK, INC.—See Altaris Capital Partners, LLC; *U.S. Private*, pg. 206
CYNERGY3 COMPONENTS LLC—See Sensata Technologies Holding plc; *U.S. Public*, pg. 1865
CYNERGY3 COMPONENTS LTD.—See Sensata Technologies Holding plc; *U.S. Public*, pg. 1865
CYNERGY BANK LTD.—See Cynergy Capital Ltd.; *Int'l*, pg. 1896
CYNERGY CAPITAL LTD.; *Int'l*, pg. 1896
CYNERGY PROFESSIONAL SYSTEMS, LLC; *U.S. Private*, pg. 1134
CYNGN INC.; *U.S. Public*, pg. 617
CYNHYRCHIADAU ALFRESCO PRODUCTIONS CYFYNGEDIG—See Boomerang Plus plc; *Int'l*, pg. 1110
CYNK-MAL S.A.—See Stalprodukt S.A.; *Int'l*, pg. 7164
CYN OIL CORPORATION; *U.S. Private*, pg. 1134
CYNOSURE FRANCE S.A.R.L.—See Clayton, Dubilier & Rice, LLC; *U.S. Private*, pg. 922
CYNOSURE GMBH—See El.En. S.p.A.; *Int'l*, pg. 2341
CYNOSURE GMBH—See Clayton, Dubilier & Rice, LLC; *U.S. Private*, pg. 922
CYNOSURE KK—See El.En. S.p.A.; *Int'l*, pg. 2341
CYNOSURE KOREA LIMITED—See El.En. S.p.A.; *Int'l*, pg. 2341
CYNOSURE, LLC—See Clayton, Dubilier & Rice, LLC; *U.S. Private*, pg. 922
CYNOSURE PORTUGAL, UNIPESSOAL, LIMITADA—See Hologic, Inc.; *U.S. Public*, pg. 1044
CYNOSURE PTY LTD.—See Clayton, Dubilier & Rice, LLC; *U.S. Private*, pg. 922
CYNOSURE SARL—See El.En. S.p.A.; *Int'l*, pg. 2341
CYNOSURE SPAIN S.L.—See El.En. S.p.A.; *Int'l*, pg. 2341
CYNOSURE UK LTD—See El.En. S.p.A.; *Int'l*, pg. 2341
CYNOTECH HOLDINGS LIMITED; *Int'l*, pg. 1896
CYNTEC CO., LTD.—See Delta Electronics, Inc.; *Int'l*, pg. 2016
CYNTECH CANADA INC.—See Keller Group plc; *Int'l*, pg. 4119
CYNTECH CONSTRUCTION LTD.—See Keller Group plc; *Int'l*, pg. 4119
CYNTECH SERVICES INC.—See Keller Group plc; *Int'l*, pg. 4119
CYNTECH U.S. INC.—See Keller Group plc; *Int'l*, pg. 4119
CYNTERGY SERVICES LIMITED—See Heritage Group Ltd.; *Int'l*, pg. 3361
CYNTHIANA PUBLISHING CO.—See Irish Times; *U.S. Private*, pg. 2138

THE CYNTHIA WOODS MITCHELL PAVILION; *U.S. Private*, pg. 4017
CYNUM INDUSTRIE SA—See Perrot Duval Holding S.A.; *Int'l*, pg. 5814
CYOPTICS, INC.—See Broadcom Inc.; *U.S. Public*, pg. 388
CYPARK RESOURCES BERHAD; *Int'l*, pg. 1896
CYPET OILS LTD.—See Petrol, Slovenska energetska druzba, d.d.; *Int'l*, pg. 5827
CYPET-TRADE LTD.—See Petrol, Slovenska energetska druzba, d.d.; *Int'l*, pg. 5827
CYPHER METAVERSE INC.; *Int'l*, pg. 1897
CYPHERPUNK HOLDINGS INC.; *Int'l*, pg. 1897
CYP INTRUST LIMITED—See inTrust Group of Companies; *Int'l*, pg. 3771
CYPRESS CAPITAL MANAGEMENT, LLC—See WSFS Financial Corporation; *U.S. Public*, pg. 2383
CYPRESS CAPITAL MANAGEMENT LTD.—See AGF Management Limited; *Int'l*, pg. 206
CYPRESS CARE, INC.—See UnitedHealth Group Incorporated; *U.S. Public*, pg. 2247
CYPRESS COVE ASSOCIATES—See Edison International; *U.S. Public*, pg. 719
CYPRESS COVE AT HEALTHPARK FLORIDA; *U.S. Private*, pg. 1134
CYPRESS CREEK HEALTHCARE, INC.—See The Ensign Group, Inc.; *U.S. Public*, pg. 2070
CYPRESS CREEK RENEWABLES, LLC; *U.S. Private*, pg. 1134
CYPRESS DESIGN LIMITED—See E. Bon Holdings Ltd; *Int'l*, pg. 2250
CYPRESS DEVELOPMENT CORP.; *Int'l*, pg. 1897
CYPRESS ENERGY PARTNERS, LLC—See Cypress Environmental Partners, L.P.; *U.S. Public*, pg. 618
CYPRESS ENVIRONMENTAL PARTNERS, L.P.; *U.S. Public*, pg. 617
CYPRESS EQUIPMENT FUND A, LLC; *U.S. Private*, pg. 1134
CYPRESS EQUITIES—See Jones Lang LaSalle Incorporated; *U.S. Public*, pg. 1205
CYPRESS FAIRBANKS FUNERAL HOME—See Carriage Services, Inc.; *U.S. Public*, pg. 439
THE CYPRESS GROUP LLC; *U.S. Private*, pg. 4017
CYPRESS GROVE CHEVRE, INC.—See Emmi AG; *Int'l*, pg. 2384
CYPRESS HEALTH CARE MANAGEMENT—See The Schwartzberg Companies; *U.S. Private*, pg. 4115
CYPRESS HILLS RESOURCE CORP.; *Int'l*, pg. 1897
CYPRESS HUMAN CAPITAL MANAGEMENT, LLC.; *U.S. Private*, pg. 1135
CYPRESS INSURANCE COMPANY—See Berkshire Hathaway Inc.; *U.S. Public*, pg. 304
CYPRESS INTERNATIONAL, LLC—See Infineon Technologies AG; *Int'l*, pg. 3685
CYPRESS LAKE COUNTRY CLUB INC.; *U.S. Private*, pg. 1135
CYPRESS LAKES GOLF & COUNTRY CLUB PTY LIMITED—See Lasseters International Holdings Limited; *Int'l*, pg. 4421
CYPRESS MEDIA GROUP; *U.S. Private*, pg. 1135
CYPRESS MEDIA, INC.—See Chatham Asset Management, LLC; *U.S. Private*, pg. 866
CYPRESS MEDIA, LLC—See Chatham Asset Management, LLC; *U.S. Private*, pg. 866
CYPRESS MEDICAL PRODUCTS LTD.; *U.S. Private*, pg. 1135
CYPRESS MEDIC SDN. BHD.—See BCM Alliance Berhad; *Int'l*, pg. 928
CYPRESS PARTNERS, LLC; *U.S. Private*, pg. 1135
CYPRESS POINT REHABILITATION & HEALTH CARE CENTER—See Apollo Global Management, Inc.; *U.S. Public*, pg. 156
CYPRESS PROPERTY & CASUALTY INSURANCE COMPANY; *U.S. Private*, pg. 1135
CYPRESS SEMICONDUCTOR AB—See Infineon Technologies AG; *Int'l*, pg. 3685
CYPRESS SEMICONDUCTOR CORPORATION—See Infineon Technologies AG; *Int'l*, pg. 3685
CYPRESS SEMICONDUCTOR GMBH—See Infineon Technologies AG; *Int'l*, pg. 3685
CYPRESS SEMICONDUCTOR INTERNATIONAL (HONG KONG) LIMITED—See Infineon Technologies AG; *Int'l*, pg. 3685
CYPRESS SEMICONDUCTOR K.K. JAPAN—See Infineon Technologies AG; *Int'l*, pg. 3685
CYPRESS SEMICONDUCTOR KOREA—See Infineon Technologies AG; *Int'l*, pg. 3685
CYPRESS SEMICONDUCTOR LIMITED—See Infineon Technologies AG; *Int'l*, pg. 3685
CYPRESS SEMICONDUCTOR SARL—See Infineon Technologies AG; *Int'l*, pg. 3685
CYPRESS SEMICONDUCTOR (SHANGHAI) TRADING CO., LTD.—See Infineon Technologies AG; *Int'l*, pg. 3685
CYPRESS SEMICONDUCTOR SINGAPORE PTE. LTD.—See Infineon Technologies AG; *Int'l*, pg. 3685
CYPRESS SEMICONDUCTOR TECHNOLOGY INDIA PVT. LTD.—See Infineon Technologies AG; *Int'l*, pg. 3685

CORPORATE AFFILIATIONS

CYPRESS SURGERY CENTER, LLC—See Bain Capital, LP; *U.S. Private*, pg. 446
CYPRESS TECHNOLOGIES CORP.; *U.S. Private*, pg. 1135
CYPRESS TITLE CORPORATION—See Anywhere Real Estate Inc.; *U.S. Public*, pg. 142
CYPRESS TRUCK LEASING COMPANY, INC.—See Cypress Truck Lines, Inc.; *U.S. Private*, pg. 1135
CYPRESS TRUCK LINES, INC.; *U.S. Private*, pg. 1135
CYPRESS WEALTH ADVISORS, LLC—See Cresset Asset Management, LLC; *U.S. Private*, pg. 1095
CYPRIALIFE LTD.—See Bank of Cyprus Holdings Public Limited Company; *Int'l*, pg. 842
CYPRIUM, INC.—See Fortress Biotech, Inc.; *U.S. Public*, pg. 872
CYPRIUM INVESTMENT PARTNERS LLC - NEW YORK—See Cyprium Investment Partners LLC; *U.S. Private*, pg. 1135
CYPRIUM INVESTMENT PARTNERS LLC; *U.S. Private*, pg. 1135
CYPRIUM METALS LIMITED; *Int'l*, pg. 1897
CYPRIUM WIRE TECHNOLOGY SDN. BHD.—See Ta Win Holdings Berhad; *Int'l*, pg. 7400
CYPROTEX DISCOVERY LIMITED—See Evotec SE; *Int'l*, pg. 2573
CYPROTEX LIMITED—See Evotec SE; *Int'l*, pg. 2573
CYPROTEX US—See Evotec SE; *Int'l*, pg. 2573
CYPRUS AIRWAYS (DUTY FREE SHOPS) LTD.—See Cyprus Airways Public Limited; *Int'l*, pg. 1897
CYPRUS AIRWAYS PUBLIC LIMITED; *Int'l*, pg. 1897
CYPRUS AMAX MINERALS COMPANY—See Freeport-McMoRan Inc.; *U.S. Public*, pg. 884
THE CYPRUS CEMENT PUBLIC COMPANY LIMITED—See G.S. Galatariotis & Sons Ltd.; *Int'l*, pg. 2866
CYPRUS FOREST INDUSTRIES PUBLIC LTD; *Int'l*, pg. 1897
THE CYPRUS INVESTMENT AND SECURITIES CORPORATION LTD—See Bank of Cyprus Holdings Public Limited Company; *Int'l*, pg. 842
CYPRUS LEASING ROMANIA IFN SA—See Bank of Cyprus Holdings Public Limited Company; *Int'l*, pg. 842
CYPRUS LIMNI RESORTS & GOLFCOURSES PLC; *Int'l*, pg. 1897
CYPRUS METALS COMPANY—See Freeport-McMoRan Inc.; *U.S. Public*, pg. 884
CYPRUS STOCK EXCHANGE; *Int'l*, pg. 1897
CYPRUS TELECOMMUNICATIONS AUTHORITY; *Int'l*, pg. 1897
CYPRUS THOMPSON CREEK MINING COMPANY—See Centerra Gold Inc.; *Int'l*, pg. 1403
CYPRUS TRADING CORPORATION PLC—See N.K. Shacolas (Holdings) Ltd.; *Int'l*, pg. 5116
CYQUATOR TECHNOLOGIES LIMITED—See Essel Corporate Resources Pvt. Ltd.; *Int'l*, pg. 2509
CYQUENT, INC.; *U.S. Private*, pg. 1135
CYRACOM INTERNATIONAL, INC.; *U.S. Private*, pg. 1135
CYRADAR JOINT STOCK COMPANY LTD.—See FPT Corporation; *Int'l*, pg. 2757
CYRAM INC.—See Namutech Co., Ltd.; *Int'l*, pg. 5137
CYRELA BRAZIL REALTY S.A.; *Int'l*, pg. 1897
CYREN LTD.—See Warburg Pincus LLC; *U.S. Private*, pg. 4437
CYRILLUS SUISSE S.A.—See Kering S.A.; *Int'l*, pg. 4134
THE CYRIL-SCOTT COMPANY—See Chatham Asset Management, LLC; *U.S. Private*, pg. 863
CYRPA INTERNATIONAL SPRL—See C-RAD AB; *Int'l*, pg. 1240
CYRQ ENERGY, INC.; *U.S. Private*, pg. 1135
CYRUS CAPITAL PARTNERS, L.P.; *U.S. Private*, pg. 1135
CYRUS INNOVATION; *U.S. Private*, pg. 1135
CYRUS OLEARYS PIES INC.; *U.S. Private*, pg. 1135
CYRUSONE INC.—See BlackRock, Inc.; *U.S. Public*, pg. 346
CYRUSONE INC.—See KKR & Co.; *U.S. Public*, pg. 1244
CYRUSONE LLC—See BlackRock, Inc.; *U.S. Public*, pg. 346
CYRUSONE LLC—See KKR & Co. Inc.; *U.S. Public*, pg. 1244
CYSORE SA DE CV—See 2G Energy AG; *Int'l*, pg. 5
CYSTECH ELECTRONICS CORP.; *Int'l*, pg. 1897
CYSTIC FIBROSIS FOUNDATION PHARMACY, LLC—See Walgreens Boots Alliance, Inc.; *U.S. Public*, pg. 2323
CYSTIC FIBROSIS FOUNDATION; *U.S. Private*, pg. 1135
CYTACOM SOLUTIONS LIMITED—See Cyprus Telecommunications Authority; *Int'l*, pg. 1897
CYTAGLOBAL HELLAS AE—See Cyprus Telecommunications Authority; *Int'l*, pg. 1897
CYTAGLOBAL—See Cyprus Telecommunications Authority; *Int'l*, pg. 1897
CYTA HELLAS TELECOMMUNICATIONS S.A—See Vodafone Group Plc; *Int'l*, pg. 8286
CYTA (UK) LTD—See Hellenic Television Ltd.; *Int'l*, pg. 3334
CYTEC ASIA PACIFIC HOLDINGS PTY. LTD.—See Solvay S.A.; *Int'l*, pg. 7077

COMPANY NAME INDEX

CYTEC AUSTRALIA HOLDINGS PTY. LTD.—See Solvay S.A.; *Int'l*, pg. 7077
CYTEC CANADA INC.—See Solvay S.A.; *Int'l*, pg. 7077
CYTEC CARBON FIBERS LLC—See Solvay S.A.; *Int'l*, pg. 7077
CYTEC CHILE LIMITADA—See Solvay S.A.; *Int'l*, pg. 7077
CYTEC DE MEXICO S.A. DE C.V.—See Solvay S.A.; *Int'l*, pg. 7078
CYTEC ENGINEERED MATERIALS GMBH—See Solvay S.A.; *Int'l*, pg. 7077
CYTEC ENGINEERED MATERIALS INC.—See Solvay S.A.; *Int'l*, pg. 7078
CYTEC ENGINEERED MATERIALS INC.—See Solvay S.A.; *Int'l*, pg. 7077
CYTEC ENGINEERED MATERIALS INC.—See Solvay S.A.; *Int'l*, pg. 7078
CYTEC ENGINEERED MATERIALS INC.—See Solvay S.A.; *Int'l*, pg. 7078
CYTEC ENGINEERED MATERIALS INC.—See Solvay S.A.; *Int'l*, pg. 7078
CYTEC ENGINEERED MATERIALS INC.—See Solvay S.A.; *Int'l*, pg. 7078
CYTEC ENGINEERED MATERIALS INC.—See Solvay S.A.; *Int'l*, pg. 7078
CYTEC ENGINEERED MATERIALS LTD.—See Solvay S.A.; *Int'l*, pg. 7078
CY-TECH GMBH—See Brunswick Corporation; *U.S. Public*, pg. 407
CYTECH,INC.—See Septeni Holdings Co., Ltd.; *Int'l*, pg. 6718
CYTECH INTERSEARCH PTY LTD.—See Navitas Limited; *Int'l*, pg. 5176
CYTECH PRODUCTS INC.—See Nagase & Co., Ltd.; *Int'l*, pg. 5126
CYTECH TECHNOLOGY LTD.—See Macnica Holdings, Inc.; *Int'l*, pg. 4624
CYTEC INDUSTRIAL MATERIALS (DERBY) LIMITED—See Solvay S.A.; *Int'l*, pg. 7078
CYTEC INDUSTRIAL MATERIALS (OK) INC.—See Solvay S.A.; *Int'l*, pg. 7077
CYTEC INDUSTRIES B.V.—See Solvay S.A.; *Int'l*, pg. 7078
CYTEC INDUSTRIES, INC.—See Solvay S.A.; *Int'l*, pg. 7077
CYTEC INDUSTRIES INC.—See Solvay S.A.; *Int'l*, pg. 7078
CYTEC INDUSTRIES PTE. LTD.—See Solvay S.A.; *Int'l*, pg. 7078
CYTEC INDUSTRIES (SHANGHAI) CO., LTD—See Solvay S.A.; *Int'l*, pg. 7078
CYTEC KOREA INC.—See Solvay S.A.; *Int'l*, pg. 7078
CYTEC - MED-LAB LTD—See Solvay S.A.; *Int'l*, pg. 7078
CYTEC NETHERLANDS HOLDING B.V.—See Solvay S.A.; *Int'l*, pg. 7078
CYTEC PROCESS MATERIALS (CA) INC.—See Solvay S.A.; *Int'l*, pg. 7078
CYTEC PROCESS MATERIALS (KEIGHLEY) LTD.—See Solvay S.A.; *Int'l*, pg. 7078
CYTEC PROCESS MATERIALS SARL—See Solvay S.A.; *Int'l*, pg. 7078
CYTEC PROCESS MATERIALS S.R.L.—See Solvay S.A.; *Int'l*, pg. 7078
CYTEIR THERAPEUTICS, INC.; *U.S. Public*, pg. 618
CYTEK BIOSCIENCES, INC.; *U.S. Public*, pg. 618
CYTEL INC.—See New Mountain Capital, LLC; *U.S. Private*, pg. 2900
CYTEL (SHANGHAI) LTD.—See ASSA ABLOY AB; *Int'l*, pg. 640
CYTENA GMBH—See BICO Group AB; *Int'l*, pg. 1019
CYTERRACE CO., LTD.—See Enviprio Holdings Inc.; *Int'l*, pg. 2454
CYTOCELL LIMITED—See Sysmex Corporation; *Int'l*, pg. 7388
CYTODYN INC.; *U.S. Public*, pg. 618
CYTOGEN CO., LTD; *Int'l*, pg. 1897
CYTOGNOS SPAIN S.L.U.—See Becton, Dickinson & Company; *U.S. Public*, pg. 292
CYTOKINETICS, INC.; *U.S. Public*, pg. 618
CYTOMED THERAPEUTICS LIMITED; *Int'l*, pg. 1897
CYTOMX THERAPEUTICS, INC.; *U.S. Public*, pg. 618
CYTON INDUSTRIES INC.; *U.S. Private*, pg. 1136
CYTOPATH, P.C.—See Aurora Diagnostics Holdings, LLC; *U.S. Private*, pg. 394
CYTOPEIA, INC.—See Becton, Dickinson & Company; *U.S. Public*, pg. 289
CYTOP S.A.—See Motor Oil (Hellas) Corinth Refineries S.A.; *Int'l*, pg. 5054
CYTORI CELL RESEARCH INSTITUTE INC.—See ACA Partners Pte Ltd.; *Int'l*, pg. 74
CYTORI THERAPEUTICS K.K.; *Int'l*, pg. 1897
CYTOSORBENTS CORPORATION; *U.S. Public*, pg. 618
CYTOSORBENTS EUROPE GMBH—See CYTOSORBENTS CORPORATION; *U.S. Public*, pg. 618
CYTOSPORT, INC.—See PepsiCo, Inc.; *U.S. Public*, pg. 1668
CYTOTOOLS AG; *Int'l*, pg. 1898
CYTOVANCE BIOLOGICS, INC.—See Shenzhen Hepalink Pharmaceutical Group Co., Ltd.; *Int'l*, pg. 6811

CYTOZYME LABORATORIES, INC.—See AEA Investors LP; *U.S. Private*, pg. 116
CYTRAD CO., LTD.—See Tajima Industries Ltd.; *Int'l*, pg. 7428
CYTTA CORP.; *U.S. Public*, pg. 618
GYTYC PRENATAL PRODUCTS CORP.—See Hologic, Inc.; *U.S. Public*, pg. 1044
CYTYC SURGICAL PRODUCTS II, LLC—See Hologic, Inc.; *U.S. Public*, pg. 1044
CYVENTURE CAPITAL PUBLIC COMPANY LTD—See SFS Group Public Company Limited; *Int'l*, pg. 6740
CYVIZ AS; *Int'l*, pg. 1898
CYVIZ PTE. LTD.—See Cyviz AS; *Int'l*, pg. 1898
CYWEB HOLDINGS INC.; *U.S. Private*, pg. 1136
CYWORLD CO., LTD.—See SK Telecom Co., Ltd.; *Int'l*, pg. 6976
CYXONE AB; *Int'l*, pg. 1898
CYXPLUS S.A.S.—See Technip Energies N.V.; *Int'l*, pg. 7506
CYXTERA TECHNOLOGIES, INC.—See Cyxtera Technologies, Inc.; *U.S. Public*, pg. 618
CYXTERA TECHNOLOGIES, INC.; *U.S. Public*, pg. 618
CYZE INC.—See TOKAI Holdings Corporation; *Int'l*, pg. 7779
CZAH POMIAR SP. Z O.O.—See Aplisens S.A.; *Int'l*, pg. 515
CZARNOWSKI EXHIBIT SERVICE INC.; *U.S. Private*, pg. 1136
CZ-CARBON PRODCUTS S.R.O.—See Westinghouse Air Brake Technologies Corporation; *U.S. Public*, pg. 2357
CZECH AIRLINES, A.S.; *Int'l*, pg. 1898
CZECH LANA, S.R.O.—See Mondragon Corporation; *Int'l*, pg. 5028
CZECH MEDIA INVEST AS; *Int'l*, pg. 1898
CZECH REPUBLIC ONAMBA S.R.O.—See Onamba Co., Ltd.; *Int'l*, pg. 5573
CZECH SILICAT S.R.O.—See Gruppo Minerali Maffei S.p.A.; *Int'l*, pg. 3140
CZECH TOP VENTURE FUND B.V.—See Erste Group Bank AG; *Int'l*, pg. 2498
CZERWONA TOREBKA SA; *Int'l*, pg. 1898
CZERWONE MAKI PROJECT SP. Z.O.O.—See Africa Israel Investments Ltd.; *Int'l*, pg. 190
C-ZONE S.P.A.—See Bank of America Corporation; *U.S. Public*, pg. 271
CZ PRESS, SPOL. S R.O.—See Vivendi SE; *Int'l*, pg. 8271
CZR RESOURCES LIMITED; *Int'l*, pg. 1898
CZ-USA; *U.S. Private*, pg. 1136

D

D1 CAPITAL PARTNERS L.P.; *U.S. Private*, pg. 1143
D1 OILS INDIA PRIVATE LIMITED—See NEOS Resources plc; *Int'l*, pg. 5198
D1 OILS PLANT SCIENCE BELGIUM N.V.—See NEOS Resources plc; *Int'l*, pg. 5198
D1 SPORTS HOLDINGS, LLC—See Athletes' Performance, Inc.; *U.S. Private*, pg. 368
D2C INC.—See Nippon Telegraph & Telephone Corporation; *Int'l*, pg. 5349
D2C MEDIA INC.—See Cars.com Inc.; *U.S. Public*, pg. 444
D2C SERVICES CO., LTD.—See Thai Beverage Public Company Limited; *Int'l*, pg. 7589
D2C STORES INC.; *U.S. Private*, pg. 1143
D2L GROUP SA; *Int'l*, pg. 1901
D2 LITHIUM CORP.; *Int'l*, pg. 1901
D2M3 LTD.—See Addnode Group AB; *Int'l*, pg. 131
D2 REALTY SERVICES INC.; *U.S. Private*, pg. 1143
D3 INC.—See BANDAI NAMCO Holdings Inc.; *Int'l*, pg. 829
D3 LED, LLC—See Southpaw Sports & Entertainment, Inc.; *U.S. Private*, pg. 3737
D3, LLC—See Ardian SAS; *Int'l*, pg. 555
D3 LOGIC, INC.; *U.S. Private*, pg. 1143
D3PUBLISHER INC.—See BANDAI NAMCO Holdings Inc.; *Int'l*, pg. 829
D3PUBLISHER OF AMERICA, INC.—See Digital Bros SpA; *Int'l*, pg. 2120
D3 TECHNICAL SERVICES, LLC—See Addnode Group AB; *Int'l*, pg. 130
D3T LTD.—See Canada Pension Plan Investment Board; *Int'l*, pg. 1281
D3T LTD.—See EQT AB; *Int'l*, pg. 2483
D3T LTD.—See Temasek Holdings (Private) Limited; *Int'l*, pg. 7548
D4 CREATIVE GROUP; *U.S. Private*, pg. 1143
D4 LLC—See Adecco Group AG; *Int'l*, pg. 141
D4T4 SOLUTIONS INC.—See D4t4 Solutions Plc; *Int'l*, pg. 1901
D4T4 SOLUTIONS PLC; *Int'l*, pg. 1901
D5X S.A.S.—See Schneider Electric SE; *Int'l*, pg. 6626
D7 ENTERPRISES, INC.; *U.S. Public*, pg. 620
D8; *Int'l*, pg. 1901
DA32 LIFE SCIENCE TECH ACQUISITION CORP.; *U.S. Public*, pg. 620
DAA DEUTSCHE AUFTRAGSAGENTUR GMBH—See Robert Bosch GmbH; *Int'l*, pg. 6360

DACHSER GMBH & CO.

DA AN GENE CO., LTD.; *Int'l*, pg. 1901
DAAQUAM LUMBER INC.—See Canfor Corporation; *Int'l*, pg. 1291
DAAR COMMUNICATIONS PLC; *Int'l*, pg. 1902
DAARNHOUWER & CO.—See Amtrada Holding B.V.; *Int'l*, pg. 442
DAAVISION BV—See Archer-Daniels-Midland Company; *U.S. Public*, pg. 184
DABACO GROUP JOINT STOCK COMPANY; *Int'l*, pg. 1902
DABACO HIGH - TECH AGRICULTURE COMPANY LIMITED—See DABACO Group Joint Stock Company; *Int'l*, pg. 1902
DABACO REAL ESTATE—See DABACO Group Joint Stock Company; *Int'l*, pg. 1902
DABACO SUBSTRUCTURE DEVELOPMENT & BUILDING INVESTMENT COMPANY LIMITED—See DABACO Group Joint Stock Company; *Int'l*, pg. 1902
DABAO (DONGGUAN) MOLDING & CUTTING TOOL CO., LTD.—See OSG Corporation; *Int'l*, pg. 5648
D.A. BARANSKI & CO.—See Barancorp, Ltd.; *U.S. Private*, pg. 471
DABBAGH GROUP HOLDING COMPANY LTD.; *Int'l*, pg. 1902
DAB BANK AG—See BNP Paribas SA; *Int'l*, pg. 1090
DABECCA NATURAL FOODS INC.; *U.S. Private*, pg. 1143
DABOMB PROTEIN CORP.; *Int'l*, pg. 1903
DAB PUMPEN DEUTSCHLAND GMBH—See The Poul Due Jensen Foundation; *Int'l*, pg. 7674
DAB PUMPS B.V.—See The Poul Due Jensen Foundation; *Int'l*, pg. 7674
DAB PUMPS IBERICA S.L.—See The Poul Due Jensen Foundation; *Int'l*, pg. 7674
DAB PUMPS LTD.—See The Poul Due Jensen Foundation; *Int'l*, pg. 7674
DAB PUMPS S.P.A.—See The Poul Due Jensen Foundation; *Int'l*, pg. 7674
DABRYAN COACH BUILDERS INC.—See Accubuilt Acquisition Holdings Inc.; *U.S. Private*, pg. 54
DABUR EGYPT LTD—See Dabur India Ltd; *Int'l*, pg. 1903
DABUR INDIA LTD - BADDI - ORAL CARE UNIT—See Dabur India Ltd; *Int'l*, pg. 1903
DABUR INDIA LTD - JAMMU UNIT I., II & III—See Dabur India Ltd; *Int'l*, pg. 1903
DABUR INDIA LTD - NASHIK UNIT—See Dabur India Ltd; *Int'l*, pg. 1903
DABUR INDIA LTD; *Int'l*, pg. 1903
DABUR INTERNATIONAL LIMITED—See Dabur India Ltd; *Int'l*, pg. 1903
DABUR INTERNATIONAL LTD.—See Dabur India Ltd; *Int'l*, pg. 1903
DABURN ELECTRONICS & CABLE CORP.; *U.S. Private*, pg. 1143
DABUR NEPAL PVT. LTD.—See Dabur India Ltd; *Int'l*, pg. 1903
DABUR (UK) LIMITED—See Dabur India Ltd; *Int'l*, pg. 1903
DACARTO BENVIC S.A.; *Int'l*, pg. 1903
THE DACCA DYEING & MANUFACTURING COMPANY LIMITED; *Int'l*, pg. 7636
DACCO DETROIT OF OHIO, INC.—See Blue Point Capital Partners, LLC; *U.S. Private*, pg. 591
DACCO, INC.—See Blue Point Capital Partners, LLC; *U.S. Private*, pg. 591
DAC GROUP/BROOME MARKETING; *U.S. Private*, pg. 1144
DACHAN FOOD (ASIA) LIMITED; *Int'l*, pg. 1903
DACHAN GREAT WALL GROUP; *Int'l*, pg. 1903
DACH AUSTRIA MEDICAL GROUP GMBH—See AddLife AB; *Int'l*, pg. 129
D-A-CH GERMANY MEDICAL GROUP GMBH—See AddLife AB; *Int'l*, pg. 129
DACHSER (BANGLADESH) LTD.—See Dachser GmbH & Co.; *Int'l*, pg. 1903
DACHSER BELGIUM AIR & SEA LOGISTICS NV—See Dachser GmbH & Co.; *Int'l*, pg. 1903
DACHSER BELGIUM N.V.—See Dachser GmbH & Co.; *Int'l*, pg. 1903
DACHSER BRASIL LOGISTICA LTDA.—See Dachser GmbH & Co.; *Int'l*, pg. 1903
DACHSER CHILE S.A.—See Dachser GmbH & Co.; *Int'l*, pg. 1903
DACHSER CZECH REPUBLIC A.S.—See Dachser GmbH & Co.; *Int'l*, pg. 1903
DACHSER DE MEXICO S.A. DE C.V.—See Dachser GmbH & Co.; *Int'l*, pg. 1904
DACHSER DENMARK A/S—See Dachser GmbH & Co.; *Int'l*, pg. 1903
DACHSER FAR EAST LTD—See Dachser GmbH & Co.; *Int'l*, pg. 1903
DACHSER FRANCE S.A.S.—See Dachser GmbH & Co.; *Int'l*, pg. 1903
DACHSER GMBH & CO.; *Int'l*, pg. 1903
DACHSER HONG KONG LTD.—See Dachser GmbH & Co.; *Int'l*, pg. 1904
DACHSER INDIA PRIVATE LIMITED—See Dachser GmbH & Co.; *Int'l*, pg. 1904

DACHSER GMBH & CO.

CORPORATE AFFILIATIONS

DACHSER LTD.—See Dachser GmbH & Co.; *Int'l,* pg. 1904
DACHSER MALAYSIA SDN. BHD.—See Dachser GmbH & Co.; *Int'l,* pg. 1904
DACHSER NETHERLANDS B.V.—See Dachser GmbH & Co.; *Int'l,* pg. 1904
DACHSER NORWAY AS—See Dachser GmbH & Co.; *Int'l,* pg. 1904
DACHSER OOO—See Dachser GmbH & Co.; *Int'l,* pg. 1904
DACHSER ROMANIA SRL—See Dachser GmbH & Co.; *Int'l,* pg. 1904
DACHSER S.A.R.L.—See Dachser GmbH & Co.; *Int'l,* pg. 1904
DACHSER SHENZHEN CO. LTD.—See Dachser GmbH & Co.; *Int'l,* pg. 1904
DACHSER SINGAPORE PTE LTD.—See Dachser GmbH & Co.; *Int'l,* pg. 1904
DACHSER SOUTH AFRICA (PTY.) LTD.—See Dachser GmbH & Co.; *Int'l,* pg. 1904
DACHSER SPEDITION AG—See Dachser GmbH & Co.; *Int'l,* pg. 1904
DACHSER S.R.O.—See Dachser GmbH & Co.; *Int'l,* pg. 1904
DACHSER SWEDEN AB—See Dachser GmbH & Co.; *Int'l,* pg. 1904
DACHSER TAIWAN, INC.—See Dachser GmbH & Co.; *Int'l,* pg. 1904
DACHSER TANGER SARL—See Dachser GmbH & Co.; *Int'l,* pg. 1904
DACHSER (THAILAND) CO., LTD.—See Dachser GmbH & Co.; *Int'l,* pg. 1903
DACHSER TRANSPORT OF AMERICA INC.—See Dachser GmbH & Co.; *Int'l,* pg. 1904
DACHSER VIETNAM CO., LTD.—See Dachser GmbH & Co.; *Int'l,* pg. 1904
DACH SWITZERLAND MEDICAL GROUP GMBH—See AddLife AB; *Int'l,* pg. 129
DACIA ANTENA, S.R.L.—See EQT AB; *Int'l,* pg. 2479
DACIA ANTENA, S.R.L.—See Public Sector Pension Investment Board; *Int'l,* pg. 6096
DACIAN GOLD LIMITED—See Genesis Minerals Limited; *Int'l,* pg. 2921
DA CIN CONSTRUCTION CO., LTD.; *Int'l,* pg. 1901
DACKE INDUSTRI AB—See Nordstjernan AB; *Int'l,* pg. 5424
DACO CORPORATION; *U.S. Private,* pg. 1144
DACODA GMBH—See Nemetschek SE; *Int'l,* pg. 5194
DACO INSTRUMENT COMPANY—See Alinabal Holdings Corporation; *U.S. Private,* pg. 168
THE D.A. COLLINS CONSTRUCTION CO., INC.; *U.S. Private,* pg. 4017
DACOME INTERNATIONAL LTD.; *Int'l,* pg. 1904
DACOM MULTIMEDIA INTERNET CO., LTD.—See STMicroelectronics N.V.; *Int'l,* pg. 7217
DACOMSA, S.A. DE C.V.—See Grupo Kuo, S.A.B. de C.V.; *Int'l,* pg. 3131
DACON CORPORATION—See Quanta Services, Inc.; *U.S. Public,* pg. 1751
D.A. CONSORTIUM, INC.—See Hakuhodo DY Holdings Incorporated; *Int'l,* pg. 3220
DACOR CORPORATION—See Head B.V.; *Int'l,* pg. 3300
DACOR, INC.—See Samsung Group; *Int'l,* pg. 6512
DACOSTA MANNINGS INC.—See Barbados Shipping & Trading Co. Ltd.; *Int'l,* pg. 858
DACOTAH BANKS, INC.; *U.S. Public,* pg. 620
DACOTAH BANK—See Dacotah Banks, Inc.; *U.S. Public,* pg. 620
DACOTAH PAPER CO.; *U.S. Private,* pg. 1144
DACRA DEVELOPMENT CORP.; *U.S. Private,* pg. 1144
DAC REALTY GROUP, INC.; *U.S. Private,* pg. 1144
D.A. CRISWELL SALES INC.—See VanZandt Controls, LLC; *U.S. Private,* pg. 4345
DACRO B.V.—See Illinois Tool Works Inc.; *U.S. Public,* pg. 1102
DACRO INDUSTRIES INC.; *Int'l,* pg. 1904
DACS CO., LTD.—See Nippon Telegraph & Telephone Corporation; *Int'l,* pg. 5346
DACSIS LLC—See Pye-Barker Fire & Safety, LLC; *U.S. Private,* pg. 3309
DAC S.R.L.—See Genextra S.p.A.; *Int'l,* pg. 2923
DACTA AND PITSCO LLC—See Kirkbi A/S; *Int'l,* pg. 4189
DAC TECHNOLOGIES GROUP INTERNATIONAL, INC.; *U.S. Public,* pg. 620
DADA BEHRING S.A.—See Siemens Aktiengesellschaft; *Int'l,* pg. 6893
DADABHAI CONSTRUCTION W.L.L.—See Dadabhai Group; *Int'l,* pg. 1904
DADABHAI GROUP; *Int'l,* pg. 1904
DADABHAI TRAVEL LLC—See Dadabhai Group; *Int'l,* pg. 1904
DADABHOY CEMENT INDUSTRIES LIMITED—See M.H. Dadabhoy Group of Companies; *Int'l,* pg. 4615
DADABHOY CONSTRUCTION TECHNOLOGY LIMITED—See M.H. Dadabhoy Group of Companies; *Int'l,* pg. 4615
DADABHOY SACK LIMITED—See M.H. Dadabhoy Group of Companies; *Int'l,* pg. 4615

DADA ENTERTAINMENT CANADA INC.—See Nippon Telegraph & Telephone Corporation; *Int'l,* pg. 5349
DADA ENTERTAINMENT INC.—See Nippon Telegraph & Telephone Corporation; *Int'l,* pg. 5349
DADAM INVESTMENT CORP.; *Int'l,* pg. 1904
DADAMOBILE S.P.A.—See RCS MediaGroup S.p.A.; *Int'l,* pg. 6229
DADA NEXUS LIMITED; *Int'l,* pg. 1904
DADANT & SONS INC.; *U.S. Private,* pg. 1144
D.A. DAVIDSON & CO. - EQUITY CAPITAL MARKETS—See D.A. Davidson Companies; *U.S. Private,* pg. 1140
D.A. DAVIDSON & CO. - FIXED INCOME CAPITAL MARKETS—See D.A. Davidson Companies; *U.S. Private,* pg. 1140
D.A. DAVIDSON COMPANIES; *U.S. Private,* pg. 1140
D.A. DAVIDSON & CO.—See D.A. Davidson Companies; *U.S. Private,* pg. 1140
DADC LUFT- UND RAUMFAHRT BETEILIGUNGS AG—See Airbus SE; *Int'l,* pg. 242
DADCO ALUMINA & CHEMICALS LTD.; *Int'l,* pg. 1904
DAD CO., LTD.; *Int'l,* pg. 1904
DADCO (SUISSE) S.A.—See Dadco Alumina & Chemicals Ltd.; *Int'l,* pg. 1904
D'ADDA, LORENZINI, VIGORELLI, BBDO—See Omnicom Group Inc.; *U.S. Public,* pg. 1575
D'ADDARIO & COMPANY, INC.; *U.S. Private,* pg. 1138
D'ADDARIO INDUSTRIES INC.; *U.S. Private,* pg. 1138
DADDY RAY'S, INC.—See J&J Snack Foods Corporation; *U.S. Public,* pg. 1179
DADDY RAY—See J&J Snack Foods Corporation; *U.S. Public,* pg. 1179
DADDY'S JUNKY MUSIC STORES; *U.S. Private,* pg. 1144
DADELO S.A.—See OPONEO.PL S.A.; *Int'l,* pg. 5600
DADE MOELLER AND ASSOCIATES, INC.—See NV5 Global, Inc.; *U.S. Public,* pg. 1557
DADE PAPER & BAG, LLC - ATLANTA FACILITY—See Bain Capital, LP; *U.S. Private,* pg. 440
DADE PAPER & BAG, LLC - GREENSBORO FACILITY—See Bain Capital, LP; *U.S. Private,* pg. 440
DADE PAPER & BAG, LLC - GULF STATES FACILITY—See Bain Capital, LP; *U.S. Private,* pg. 440
DADE PAPER & BAG, LLC - JACKSONVILLE FACILITY—See Bain Capital, LP; *U.S. Private,* pg. 440
DADE PAPER & BAG, LLC - MID-ATLANTIC FACILITY—See Bain Capital, LP; *U.S. Private,* pg. 440
DADE PAPER & BAG, LLC - ORLANDO FACILITY—See Bain Capital, LP; *U.S. Private,* pg. 440
DADE PAPER & BAG, LLC - PUERTO RICO FACILITY—See Bain Capital, LP; *U.S. Private,* pg. 440
DADE PAPER & BAG, LLC—See Bain Capital, LP; *U.S. Private,* pg. 440
DADE PAPER & BAG, LLC - TRI-STATE FACILITY—See Bain Capital, LP; *U.S. Private,* pg. 440
DADE PAPER CRUISE LINE—See Bain Capital, LP; *U.S. Private,* pg. 440
DADE PROSTHETICS & ORTHOTICS, INC.—See Select Medical Holdings Corporation; *U.S. Public,* pg. 1857
DADEX ETERNIT LIMITED; *Int'l,* pg. 1904
DADI EARLY-CHILDHOOD EDUCATION GROUP LTD.; *Int'l,* pg. 1904
DADI EDUCATION HOLDINGS LIMITED; *Int'l,* pg. 1905
DADI ENTERTAINMENT LIMITED—See Nan Hai Corporation Limited; *Int'l,* pg. 5137
DADI INTERNATIONAL GROUP LIMITED; *Int'l,* pg. 1905
D.A. DODD, LLC—See Pokagon Band of Potawatomi Indians; *U.S. Private,* pg. 3223
DADO, INC.—See Stanley Black & Decker, Inc.; *U.S. Public,* pg. 1932
DADRA AND NAGAR HAVELI AND DAMAN AND DIU POWER DISTRIBUTION CORPORATION LIMITED—See Torrent Power Limited; *Int'l,* pg. 7831
DAE AIRPORTS—See Dubai Aerospace Enterprise Ltd; *Int'l,* pg. 2218
DAEATI CO., LTD.; *Int'l,* pg. 1905
DAEBO MAGNETIC CO., LTD.; *Int'l,* pg. 1905
DAEBONG LS CO., LTD. - INCHEON FACTORY—See Daebong LS Co., Ltd.; *Int'l,* pg. 1905
DAEBONG LS CO., LTD. - JEJU FACTORY—See Daebong LS Co., Ltd.; *Int'l,* pg. 1905
DAEBONG LS CO., LTD.; *Int'l,* pg. 1905
DAE CAPITAL ADVISORS LLC—See Dubai Aerospace Enterprise Ltd; *Int'l,* pg. 2218
DAE CAPITAL HOLDINGS COOPERATIEF U.A.—See Dubai Aerospace Enterprise Ltd; *Int'l,* pg. 2218
DAECHANG CO., LTD.; *Int'l,* pg. 1906
DAECHANG FORGING CO., LTD.; *Int'l,* pg. 1906
DAECHANG SOLUTION CO., LTD.; *Int'l,* pg. 1906
DAECHANG SOLUTION CO., LTD. - ULJU FACTORY—See Daechang Solution Co., Ltd.; *Int'l,* pg. 1906
DAECHANG STEEL CO., LTD.; *Int'l,* pg. 1906
DAEDALIC ENTERTAINMENT GMBH—See Bastei Lubbe AG; *Int'l,* pg. 888
DAEDALUS BOOKS, INC.; *U.S. Private,* pg. 1144
DAEDONG CORPORATION; *Int'l,* pg. 1906
DAEDONG DOOR INC.—See Hi-Lex Corporation; *Int'l,* pg. 3380

DAEDONG GEAR CO., LTD.; *Int'l,* pg. 1906
DAE DONG HI-LEX INC—See Hi-Lex Corporation; *Int'l,* pg. 3380
DAEDONG HI-LEX OF AMERICA, INC.—See Hi-Lex Corporation; *Int'l,* pg. 3380
DAEDONG KOREA GINSENG CO., LTD.; *Int'l,* pg. 1906
DAEDONG METALS CO., LTD.; *Int'l,* pg. 1906
DAEDONG STEEL CO., LTD. - INCHOEN PLANT—See Daedong Steel Co., Ltd.; *Int'l,* pg. 1906
DAEDONG STEEL CO., LTD. - POHANG PLANT—See Daedong Steel Co., Ltd.; *Int'l,* pg. 1906
DAEDONG STEEL CO., LTD.; *Int'l,* pg. 1906
DAE DONG SYSTEM CO., LTD—See Hi-Lex Corporation; *Int'l,* pg. 3380
DAEDONG USA INC.—See Daedong Corporation; *Int'l,* pg. 1906
DAEDUCK CO., LTD.; *Int'l,* pg. 1906
DAEDUCK ELECTRONICS CO., LTD. - ANSAN PLANT #1—See DAEDUCK Co., Ltd.; *Int'l,* pg. 1906
DAEDUCK ELECTRONICS CO., LTD.—See DAEDUCK Co., Ltd.; *Int'l,* pg. 1906
THE DAEGU BANK, LTD.—See DGB Financial Group Co., Ltd.; *Int'l,* pg. 2096
DAEGU CREDIT INFORMATION CO. LTD.—See DGB Financial Group Co., Ltd.; *Int'l,* pg. 2096
DAEGU DEPARTMENT STORE CO., LTD.; *Int'l,* pg. 1906
DAEHAN FLOUR MILLS CO., LTD; *Int'l,* pg. 1906
DAEHAN LIVESTOCK & FEED CO. LTD. - CHANGWON PLANT—See Daehan Flour Mills co., Ltd; *Int'l,* pg. 1906
DAEHAN LIVESTOCK & FEED CO. LTD. - INCHON PLANT—See Daehan Flour Mills co., Ltd; *Int'l,* pg. 1907
DAEHAN LIVESTOCK & FEED CO. LTD. - JEONJU PLANT—See Daehan Flour Mills co., Ltd; *Int'l,* pg. 1907
DAEHAN NETWORKS CO., LTD—See Daehan Steel Co., Ltd.; *Int'l,* pg. 1907
DAEHAN NEW PHARM CO., LTD.; *Int'l,* pg. 1907
DAE HAN PARKERIZING CO., LTD.—See Nihon Parkerizing Co., Ltd.; *Int'l,* pg. 5286
DAEHAN PRECISION CO., LTD.—See Toray Industries, Inc.; *Int'l,* pg. 7823
DAEHAN SOLVAY SPECIAL CHEMICALS COMPANY, LTD.—See Solvay S.A.; *Int'l,* pg. 7078
DAEHAN STEEL CO., LTD. - NOKSAN PLANT—See Daehan Steel Co., Ltd.; *Int'l,* pg. 1907
DAEHAN STEEL CO., LTD. - PYEONGTAEK PLANT—See Daehan Steel Co., Ltd.; *Int'l,* pg. 1907
DAEHAN STEEL CO., LTD.; *Int'l,* pg. 1907
DAEHAN SYNTHETIC FIBER CO., LTD.—See Taekwang Industrial Co., Ltd.; *Int'l,* pg. 7405
DAEHEUNG INDUSTRIAL CO., LTD.—See YoungWire Co. Ltd.; *Int'l,* pg. 8604
DAEHO AL CO., LTD.; *Int'l,* pg. 1907
DAEHO CO., LTD—See DHSteel; *Int'l,* pg. 2100
DAEHO MACHINERY IND. CO., LTD.—See DAE-IL Corporation; *Int'l,* pg. 1905
DAEHONG COMMUNICATIONS INC.—See Lotte Co., Ltd.; *Int'l,* pg. 4559
DAEHO P&C CO., LTD. - BUSAN FACTORY—See DHSteel; *Int'l,* pg. 2100
DAEHO TECHNOLOGY KOREA CO., LTD.; *Int'l,* pg. 1907
DAE HWA PHARMACEUTICAL CO., LTD.; *Int'l,* pg. 1905
DAE HWA PHARM CO., LTD.; *Int'l,* pg. 1905
DAE HYUN CO., LTD.; *Int'l,* pg. 1905
DAEIL AUTOMOTIVE PARTS CO., LTD.—See DAE-IL Corporation; *Int'l,* pg. 1905
DAE-IL CORPORATION-DUDONG 2 PLANT—See DAE-IL Corporation; *Int'l,* pg. 1905
DAE-IL CORPORATION-HEAVY MACHINERY PLANT—See DAE-IL Corporation; *Int'l,* pg. 1905
DAE-IL CORPORATION; *Int'l,* pg. 1905
DAE-IL CORPORATION-UNYANG PLANT—See DAE-IL Corporation; *Int'l,* pg. 1905
DAEIL INNOTECH CORPORATION—See DAE-IL Corporation; *Int'l,* pg. 1905
DAE-IL USA, INC.—See DAE-IL Corporation; *Int'l,* pg. 1905
D A E INDUSTRIES; *U.S. Private,* pg. 1136
DAEJAN (BRIGHTON) LIMITED—See Centremanor Ltd.; *Int'l,* pg. 1411
DAEJAN (CAMBRIDGE) LIMITED—See Centremanor Ltd.; *Int'l,* pg. 1411
DAEJAN (CARDIFF) LIMITED—See Centremanor Ltd.; *Int'l,* pg. 1411
DAEJAN COMMERCIAL PROPERTIES LIMITED—See Centremanor Ltd.; *Int'l,* pg. 1411
DAEJAN (DARTFORD) LIMITED—See Centremanor Ltd.; *Int'l,* pg. 1411
DAEJAN DEVELOPMENTS LIMITED—See Centremanor Ltd.; *Int'l,* pg. 1411
DAEJAN ENTERPRISES LIMITED—See Centremanor Ltd.; *Int'l,* pg. 1411
DAEJAN ESTATES LIMITED—See Centremanor Ltd.; *Int'l,* pg. 1412
DAEJAN HOLDINGS PLC—See Centremanor Ltd.; *Int'l,* pg. 1411

COMPANY NAME INDEX

DAEJAN INVESTMENTS (GROVE HALL) LIMITED—See Centremanor Ltd.; *Int'l*, pg. 1412
DAEJAN INVESTMENTS (HARROW) LIMITED—See Centremanor Ltd.; *Int'l*, pg. 1412
DAEJAN INVESTMENTS LIMITED—See Centremanor Ltd.; *Int'l*, pg. 1412
DAEJAN (KINGSTON) LIMITED—See Centremanor Ltd.; *Int'l*, pg. 1411
DAEJAN (LAUDERDALE) LIMITED—See Centremanor Ltd.; *Int'l*, pg. 1411
DAEJAN PROPERTIES LIMITED—See Centremanor Ltd.; *Int'l*, pg. 1412
DAEJAN (READING) LIMITED—See Centremanor Ltd.; *Int'l*, pg. 1412
DAEJAN RETAIL PROPERTIES LIMITED—See Centremanor Ltd.; *Int'l*, pg. 1412
DAEJAN (TAUNTON) LIMITED—See Centremanor Ltd.; *Int'l*, pg. 1411
DAEJAN (TRADERS) LIMITED—See Centremanor Ltd.; *Int'l*, pg. 1411
DAEJAN (UK) LIMITED—See Centremanor Ltd.; *Int'l*, pg. 1411
DAEJAN (US) LIMITED—See Centremanor Ltd.; *Int'l*, pg. 1411
DAEJAN (WARWICK) LIMITED—See Centremanor Ltd.; *Int'l*, pg. 1411
DAEJEON RIVERSIDE EXPRESSWAY CO., LTD.—See Groupe Egis S.A.; *Int'l*, pg. 3102
DAE-JIN SEMICONDUCTOR CO., LTD.; *Int'l*, pg. 1905
DAEJOO CO.,LTD; *Int'l*, pg. 1907
DAEJOO ELECTRONIC MATERIALS CO., LTD.; *Int'l*, pg. 1907
DAEJOO ENERGY INNOVATION TECHNOLOGY CO LTD; *Int'l*, pg. 1907
DAEJUNG CHEMICALS & METALS CO., LTD.; *Int'l*, pg. 1907
DAEJUNG EM CO., LTD.—See Daejung Chemicals & Metals Co., Ltd.; *Int'l*, pg. 1907
DAEKYO CO LTD; *Int'l*, pg. 1907
DAEKYO EYE LEVEL SINGAPORE PTE. LTD.—See Daekyo Co Ltd; *Int'l*, pg. 1907
DAEKYO MALAYSIA SND. BHD.—See Daekyo Co Ltd; *Int'l*, pg. 1907
DAEKYO VIETNAM CO., LTD.—See Daekyo Co Ltd; *Int'l*, pg. 1007
D&A ELECTRICAL SYSTEMS SDN. BHD.—See Draexlmaier Gruppe; *Int'l*, pg. 2198
DAELIM B&CO., LTD. - JECHEON PLANT—See DAELIM B&Co., LTD.; *Int'l*, pg. 1907
DAELIM B&CO., LTD.; *Int'l*, pg. 1907
DAELIM CONCRETE PRODUCTS CO., LTD.—See Daelim Industrial Co., Ltd.; *Int'l*, pg. 1908
DAELIM CORPORATION—See Daelim Industrial Co., Ltd.; *Int'l*, pg. 1908
DAELIM C&S CO., LTD. - BU-YEO PLANT—See Samil C&S Co., Ltd.; *Int'l*, pg. 6505
DAELIM C&S CO., LTD. - CHIL-SEO PLANT—See Samil C&S Co., Ltd.; *Int'l*, pg. 6505
DAELIM C&S CO., LTD. - YONG-IN PLANT—See Samil C&S Co., Ltd.; *Int'l*, pg. 6505
DAELIM-DAR CO., LTD.—See Daelim Industrial Co., Ltd.; *Int'l*, pg. 1908
DAELIM INDUSTRIAL CO., LTD.; *Int'l*, pg. 1907
DAELIM I&S CO., LTD.—See Daelim Industrial Co., Ltd.; *Int'l*, pg. 1908
DAELIM (MALAYSIA) SDN. BHD.—See Daelim Industrial Co., Ltd.; *Int'l*, pg. 1908
DAELIM MOTOR CO., LTD.—See Daelim Industrial Co., Ltd.; *Int'l*, pg. 1908
DAELIM (NANJING) CONSTRUCTION PROJECT MANAGEMENT CO., LTD.—See Daelim Industrial Co., Ltd.; *Int'l*, pg. 1908
DAELIM PAPER CO., LTD.; *Int'l*, pg. 1908
DAELIM PHILIPPINES INC.—See Daelim Industrial Co., Ltd.; *Int'l*, pg. 1908
DAELIM SAUDI ARABIA CO., LTD.—See Daelim Industrial Co., Ltd.; *Int'l*, pg. 1908
DAELIM TRADING CO., LTD. - DOBIDOS PLANT—See DAELIM TRADING Co., Ltd.; *Int'l*, pg. 1908
DAELIM TRADING CO., LTD. - FAUCET PLANT—See DAELIM TRADING Co., Ltd.; *Int'l*, pg. 1908
DAELIM TRADING CO., LTD. - JEUNGPYEONG PLANT—See DAELIM TRADING Co., Ltd.; *Int'l*, pg. 1908
DAELIM TRADING CO., LTD.; *Int'l*, pg. 1908
DAEMO ENGINEERING CO.; *Int'l*, pg. 1908
DAEM—See Sonepar S.A.; *Int'l*, pg. 7090
DAEMYONG ENG CO., LTD - GUMI FACTORY—See AVACO CO., Ltd; *Int'l*, pg. 733
DAEMYONG ENG CO., LTD—See AVACO CO., Ltd; *Int'l*, pg. 733
DAE MYONG PRECISION CORPORATION—See Valeo S.A.; *Int'l*, pg. 8112
DAEMYUNG OPTICAL CO.—See Hoya Corporation; *Int'l*, pg. 3495
DAEMYUNG SONOSEASON CO., LTD.; *Int'l*, pg. 1908
DAENEN HENDERSON & CO.—See Hannis T. Bourgeois, LLP; *U.S. Private*, pg. 1855
DAERYUK CAN CO., LTD.; *Int'l*, pg. 1908

DAE RYUK INTERNATIONAL INC—See Daeryuk Can Co., Ltd.; *Int'l*, pg. 1908
DAESAN & CO. LTD—See Sajodongaone Co., Ltd.; *Int'l*, pg. 6485
DAESANG AMERICA, INC.—See Daesang Holdings Co., Ltd.; *Int'l*, pg. 1909
DAESANG (BEIJING) FOODS CO LTD - BEIJING FACTORY—See Daesang Corporation; *Int'l*, pg. 1909
DAESANG (BEIJING) FOODS CO LTD.—See Daesang Corporation; *Int'l*, pg. 1909
DAESANG CORPORATION; *Int'l*, pg. 1909
DAESANG CORPORATION - TAY NINH TAPIOCA STARCH FACTORY—See Daesang Corporation; *Int'l*, pg. 1909
DAESANG EUROPE B.V.—See Daesang Corporation; *Int'l*, pg. 1909
DAESANG FNF CORPORATION—See Daesang Corporation; *Int'l*, pg. 1909
DAESANG (H.K.) LIMITED—See Daesang Corporation; *Int'l*, pg. 1909
DAESANG HOLDINGS CO., LTD.; *Int'l*, pg. 1909
DAESANG INFORMATION TECHNOLOGY CO., LTD.—See Daesang Holdings Co., Ltd.; *Int'l*, pg. 1909
DAESANG JAPAN INC.—See Daesang Corporation; *Int'l*, pg. 1909
DAESANG LIFE SCIENCE CORP.—See Daesang Holdings Co., Ltd.; *Int'l*, pg. 1909
DAESANG RICOR CORPORATION - CAGAYAN DE ORO FACTORY—See Daesang Corporation; *Int'l*, pg. 1909
DAESANG RICOR CORPORATION—See Daesang Corporation; *Int'l*, pg. 1909
DAESUNG CELTIC CO., LTD.—See MBK Partners Ltd.; *Int'l*, pg. 4753
DAESUNG C&S CO., LTD.—See MBK Partners Ltd.; *Int'l*, pg. 4753
DAESUNG ENERGY CO., LTD.—See Daesung Holdings Co., Ltd.; *Int'l*, pg. 1909
DAESUNG FINE TECH. CO., LTD.; *Int'l*, pg. 1909
DAESUNG GROUP PARTNERS CO., LTD.—See MBK Partners Ltd.; *Int'l*, pg. 4753
DAESUNG HOLDINGS CO., LTD.; *Int'l*, pg. 1909
DAESUNG INDUSTRIAL CO., LTD.—See MBK Partners Ltd.; *Int'l*, pg. 4753
DAESUNG MACHINERY—See Mondelez International, Inc.; *U.S. Public*, pg. 1461
DAE SUNG MICROBIOLOGICAL LABS. CO., LTD.; *Int'l*, pg. 1905
DAESUNG NACHI HYDRAULICS CO., LTD.—See Nachi-Fujikoshi Corp.; *Int'l*, pg. 5121
DAESUNG PRIVATE EQUITY, INC.—See Daesung Holdings Co., Ltd.; *Int'l*, pg. 1909
DAESUNG VIETNAM POWER CABLE COMPANY—See Nexans S.A.; *Int'l*, pg. 5241
DAESUNG WOOD IND. CO., LTD.—See DONGWHA HOLDINGS CO., LTD.; *Int'l*, pg. 2170
DAETWYLER CABLES+SYSTEMS (SHANGHAI) CO. LTD—See Pema Holding AG; *Int'l*, pg. 5784
DAETWYLER CABLING SOLUTIONS AG—See Pema Holding AG; *Int'l*, pg. 5784
DAETWYLER GLOBAL TEC HOLDING AG; *Int'l*, pg. 1909
DAETWYLER HOLDING AG—See Pema Holding AG; *Int'l*, pg. 5784
DAETWYLER INTER GMBH—See Pema Holding AG; *Int'l*, pg. 5784
DAETWYLER KABEL+SYSTEME GMBH—See Pema Holding AG; *Int'l*, pg. 5784
DAETWYLER PHARMA PACKAGING DEUTSCHLAND GMBH—See Pema Holding AG; *Int'l*, pg. 5784
DAETWYLER PHARMA PACKAGING ITALY SRL—See Pema Holding AG; *Int'l*, pg. 5784
DAETWYLER PHARMA PACKAGING USA—See Pema Holding AG; *Int'l*, pg. 5784
DAETWYLER (SUZHOU) CABLING SYSTEMS CO. LTD—See Pema Holding AG; *Int'l*, pg. 5784
DAETWYLER TECO HOLDING AG—See Pema Holding AG; *Int'l*, pg. 5784
DAETWYLER (THELMA) CABLES & SYSTEMS PTE LTD—See Pema Holding AG; *Int'l*, pg. 5784
DAETWYLER (UK) LTD—See Pema Holding AG; *Int'l*, pg. 5784
DAEWON AMERICA, INC.—See SAMWONSTEEL Co., Ltd.; *Int'l*, pg. 6519
DAEWON CABLE CO., LTD.; *Int'l*, pg. 1909
DAEWON CHEMICAL CO., LTD. - OSAN FACTORY—See DAEWON Chemical Co., Ltd.; *Int'l*, pg. 1910
DAEWON CHEMICAL CO., LTD.; *Int'l*, pg. 1910
DAEWON CHONG UP CORP.—See SAMWONSTEEL Co., Ltd.; *Int'l*, pg. 6519
DAEWON C.I. INC.—See Daewon Media Co., Ltd.; *Int'l*, pg. 1910
DAEWON CO., LTD.; *Int'l*, pg. 1910
DAEWON EUROPE CO., LTD.—See Daewon Kang Up Co., Ltd.; *Int'l*, pg. 1910
DAEWON INDIA AUTOPARTS PRIVATE LIMITED—See Daewon Kang Up Co., Ltd.; *Int'l*, pg. 1910
DAEWON KANG UP CO., LTD.; *Int'l*, pg. 1910
DAEWON MEDIA CO., LTD.; *Int'l*, pg. 1910

DAEWON MEXICO S. DE R.L. DE C.V.—See Daewon Kang Up Co., Ltd.; *Int'l*, pg. 1910
DAEWON PHARMACEUTICAL CO., LTD. - HYANGNAM FACTORY—See Daewon Pharmaceutical Co., Ltd.; *Int'l*, pg. 1910
DAEWON PHARMACEUTICAL CO., LTD.; *Int'l*, pg. 1910
DAEWON PRECISION INDUSTRIAL CO., LTD.—See SAMWONSTEEL Co., Ltd.; *Int'l*, pg. 6519
DAEWON SANUP CO., LTD.; *Int'l*, pg. 1910
DAEWON SEMICONDUCTOR PACKAGING INDUSTRIAL CORPORATION - IMS DAEWON FACTORY—See Daewon Semiconductor Packaging Industrial Corporation; *Int'l*, pg. 1910
DAEWON SEMICONDUCTOR PACKAGING INDUSTRIAL CORPORATION; *Int'l*, pg. 1910
DAEWON SPRING & SEAT LLC—See Daewon Kang Up Co., Ltd.; *Int'l*, pg. 1910
DAEWOO AMERICA DEVELOPMENT (NEW YORK) INC.—See Korea Development Bank; *Int'l*, pg. 4282
DAEWOO AUTOMOTIVE COMPONENTS, LTD.—See General Motors Company; *U.S. Public*, pg. 924
DAEWOO BUS GLOBAL CORPORATION - DONG-RAE PLANT—See Young An Hat Co., Ltd.; *Int'l*, pg. 8602
DAEWOO BUS GLOBAL CORPORATION - FACTORY NO.1—See Young An Hat Co., Ltd.; *Int'l*, pg. 8602
DAEWOO BUS GLOBAL CORPORATION - FACTORY NO.2—See Young An Hat Co., Ltd.; *Int'l*, pg. 8602
DAEWOO BUS GLOBAL CORPORATION - FACTORY NO.3—See Young An Hat Co., Ltd.; *Int'l*, pg. 8602
DAEWOO BUS GLOBAL CORPORATION - ULSAN PLANT—See Young An Hat Co., Ltd.; *Int'l*, pg. 8602
DAEWOO BUS(SHANGHAI) GLOBAL TRADING CO., LTD.—See Young An Hat Co., Ltd.; *Int'l*, pg. 8602
DAEWOO CORP. AMSTERDAM B.V.—See POSCO Holdings Inc.; *Int'l*, pg. 5937
DAEWOO CORPORATION PHILIPPINES INC.—See Korea Development Bank; *Int'l*, pg. 4282
DAEWOO ELECTRONIC COMPONENTS CO., LTD.; *Int'l*, pg. 1910
DAEWOO ELECTRONIC COMPONENTS SUZHOU A&T TECHNOLOGY CO., LTD.—See DAEWOO ELECTRONIC COMPONENTS Co., Ltd.; *Int'l*, pg. 1910
DAEWOO ELECTRONIC COMPONENTS VIETNAM CORPORATION—See DAEWOO ELECTRONIC COMPONENTS Co., Ltd.; *Int'l*, pg. 1910
DAEWOO ELECTRONIC EQUIPMENT CO., LTD—See DAEWOO ELECTRONIC COMPONENTS Co., Ltd.; *Int'l*, pg. 1910
DAEWOO ELECTRONICS AMERICA, INC.—See Dongbu Group; *Int'l*, pg. 2165
DAEWOO ELECTRONICS CORPORATION—See Dongbu Group; *Int'l*, pg. 2165
DAEWOO ELECTRONICS DEME FZE.—See Dongbu Group; *Int'l*, pg. 2165
DAEWOO ELECTRONICS EUROPE GMBH—See Dongbu Group; *Int'l*, pg. 2165
DAEWOO ELECTRONICS MANUFACTURING POLAND SP. Z O.O.—See Dongbu Group; *Int'l*, pg. 2165
DAEWOO ELECTRONICS MIDDLE EAST FZE LTD.—See Dongbu Group; *Int'l*, pg. 2165
DAEWOO ELECTRONICS (M) SDN. BHD.—See Dongbu Group; *Int'l*, pg. 2165
DAEWOO ELECTRONICS (PANAMA) S.A.—See Dongbu Group; *Int'l*, pg. 2165
DAEWOO ELECTRONICS SALES U.K. LIMITED—See Dongbu Group; *Int'l*, pg. 2165
DAEWOO ELECTRONICS SALES UK LTD.—See Dongbu Group; *Int'l*, pg. 2165
DAEWOO ELECTRONICS S.A.—See Dongbu Group; *Int'l*, pg. 2165
DAEWOO ENGINEERING & CONSTRUCTION CO., LTD.—See Korea Development Bank; *Int'l*, pg. 4282
DAEWOO ENGINEERING & CONSTRUCTION (M) SDN BHD—See Korea Development Bank; *Int'l*, pg. 4282
DAEWOO GLOBAL NIGERIA LTD.—See POSCO Holdings Inc.; *Int'l*, pg. 5937
DAEWOO INTERNATIONAL AMERICA CORP.—See POSCO Holdings Inc.; *Int'l*, pg. 5937
DAEWOO INTERNATIONAL AMERICA CORP.—See POSCO Holdings Inc.; *Int'l*, pg. 5937
DAEWOO INTERNATIONAL (JAPAN) CORP.—See POSCO Holdings Inc.; *Int'l*, pg. 5937
DAEWOO INTERNATIONAL (JAPAN) CORP.—See POSCO Holdings Inc.; *Int'l*, pg. 5937
DAEWOO INTERNATIONAL (SHANGHAI) CO., LTD.—See POSCO Holdings Inc.; *Int'l*, pg. 5937
DAEWOO INTERNATIONAL SINGAPORE PTE. LTD.—See POSCO Holdings Inc.; *Int'l*, pg. 5937
DAEWOO INTL. MEXICO S.A. DE C.V.—See POSCO Holdings Inc.; *Int'l*, pg. 5937
DAEWOO ITALIA S.R.L.—See POSCO Holdings Inc.; *Int'l*, pg. 5937
DAEWOO MOTOR SALES CORPORATION; *Int'l*, pg. 1910
DAE WOONG CO., LTD.; *Int'l*, pg. 1905
DAEWOONG ENGINEERING CO., LTD.—See Punch Industry Co., Ltd.; *Int'l*, pg. 6118
DAEWOONG PHARMACEUTICAL CO., LTD.; *Int'l*, pg. 1911

DAEWOONG PHARMACEUTICAL CO., LTD. CORPORATE AFFILIATIONS

DAEWOONG VIETNAM CO., LTD.—See Daewoong Pharmaceutical Co., Ltd.; *Int'l*, pg. 1911
DAEWOO NIGERIA LIMITED—See POSCO Holdings Inc.; *Int'l*, pg. 5938
DAEWOO PAK MOTORS (PVT.) LTD.—See Young An Hat Co., Ltd.; *Int'l*, pg. 8602
DAEWOO PAPER MANUFACTURING CO. LTD.—See POSCO Holdings Inc.; *Int'l*, pg. 5938
DAEWOO POWER INDIA LTD.—See Korea Development Bank; *Int'l*, pg. 4282
DAEWOO SINGAPORE PTE. LTD.—See POSCO Holdings Inc.; *Int'l*, pg. 5938
DAEWOO SPECIAL PURPOSE ACQUISITION 2 CO., LTD.; *Int'l*, pg. 1910
DAEWOO SPECIAL PURPOSE ACQUISITION 3 CO., LTD.; *Int'l*, pg. 1911
DAEWOO TEXTILE BUKHARA LLC—See POSCO Holdings Inc.; *Int'l*, pg. 5938
DAEYANG ELECTRIC CO., LTD. - ELECTRICAL / ELECTRONIC DIVISION—See Daeyang Electric Co., Ltd.; *Int'l*, pg. 1911
DAEYANG ELECTRIC CO., LTD. - LIGHTING DIVISON—See Daeyang Electric Co., Ltd.; *Int'l*, pg. 1911
DAEYANG ELECTRIC CO., LTD.; *Int'l*, pg. 1911
DAEYANGETS CO., LTD.—See UniTest Inc.; *Int'l*, pg. 8074
DAEYANG INSTRUMENT CO., LTD.—See Daeyang Electric Co., Ltd.; *Int'l*, pg. 1911
DAEYANG PAPER MFG. CO., LTD.; *Int'l*, pg. 1911
DAEYOUNG CABLE CO., LTD.—See Nexans S.A.; *Int'l*, pg. 5241
DAE YOUNG PACKAGING CO., LTD.; *Int'l*, pg. 1905
DAE YU CO., LTD.; *Int'l*, pg. 1905
DAFA PROPERTIES GROUP LTD.; *Int'l*, pg. 1911
DAF CAMINHOES BRASIL INDUSTRIA LTDA.—See PACCAR Inc.; *U.S. Public*, pg. 1630
DAFENG PORT HESHUN TECHNOLOGY COMPANY LIMITED; *Int'l*, pg. 1911
DAFENG TV LTD.; *Int'l*, pg. 1912
DAFFIN'S, INC.; *U.S. Private*, pg. 1144
DAFFODIL COMPUTERS LIMITED; *Int'l*, pg. 1912
DAFINE ENGINEERING OU—See Addtech AB; *Int'l*, pg. 132
DAFORA S.A.; *Int'l*, pg. 1912
DAFTER SANITARY LANDFILL, INC.—See Waste Management, Inc.; *U.S. Public*, pg. 2331
DAF TRUCKS DEUTSCHLAND GMBH—See PACCAR Inc.; *U.S. Public*, pg. 1630
DAF TRUCKS FRANCE, S.A.R.L.—See PACCAR Inc.; *U.S. Public*, pg. 1630
DAF TRUCKS FRANCE, S.A.R.L.—See PACCAR Inc.; *U.S. Public*, pg. 1630
DAF TRUCKS LTD.—See PACCAR Inc.; *U.S. Public*, pg. 1630
DAF TRUCKS N.V.—See PACCAR Inc.; *U.S. Public*, pg. 1630
DAF TRUCKS POLSKA SP.Z.O.O.—See PACCAR Inc.; *U.S. Public*, pg. 1630
DAF TRUCKS VLAANDEREN N.V.—See PACCAR Inc.; *U.S. Public*, pg. 1630
DAF VEHICULOS INDUSTRIALES S.A.—See PACCAR Inc.; *U.S. Public*, pg. 1630
DAF VEICOLI INDUSTRIALI S.P.A.—See PACCAR Inc.; *U.S. Public*, pg. 1630
DAGAB AB—See Axel Johnson Gruppen AB; *Int'l*, pg. 764
DAGANG HOLDING GROUP CO. LTD.; *Int'l*, pg. 1912
DAGANG NET TECHNOLOGIES SDN. BHD.—See Dagang NeXchange Berhad; *Int'l*, pg. 1912
DAGANG NeXCHANGE BERHAD; *Int'l*, pg. 1912
DAGBLADET BORSEN A/S—See Bonnier AB; *Int'l*, pg. 1108
D.A.G. CONSTRUCTION CO., INC.; *U.S. Private*, pg. 1141
DAG DVERGSTEN AS; *Int'l*, pg. 1912
DAGE DEUTSCHLAND GMBH—See Nordson Corporation; *U.S. Public*, pg. 1532
DAGE HOLDINGS LIMITED—See Nordson Corporation; *U.S. Public*, pg. 1532
DAGE JAPAN CO., LTD.—See Nordson Corporation; *U.S. Public*, pg. 1532
DAGE-MTI OF MICHIGAN CITY, INC.; *U.S. Private*, pg. 1144
DAGENS INDUSTRI AB—See Bonnier AB; *Int'l*, pg. 1108
DAGENS MEDIA SVERIGE AB—See Bonnier AB; *Int'l*, pg. 1108
DAGENS MEDICIN A/S—See Bonnier AB; *Int'l*, pg. 1108
DAGENS MEDISIN AS—See Bonnier AB; *Int'l*, pg. 1108
DAGENS NAERINGSLIV AS—See Fred. Olsen & Co.; *Int'l*, pg. 2768
DAGENS NAERINGSLIV-BERGEN—See Fred. Olsen & Co.; *Int'l*, pg. 2768
DAGENS NAERINGSLIV-KRISTIANSAND—See Fred. Olsen & Co.; *Int'l*, pg. 2768
DAGENS NAERINGSLIV-LILLEHAMMER—See Fred. Olsen & Co.; *Int'l*, pg. 2768
DAGENS NAERINGSLIV-STAVANGER—See Fred. Olsen & Co.; *Int'l*, pg. 2768

DAGENS NAERINGSLIV-TELEMARK/VESTFOLD—See Fred. Olsen & Co.; *Int'l*, pg. 2768
DAGENS NAERINGSLIV-TROMSO—See Fred. Olsen & Co.; *Int'l*, pg. 2768
DAGENS NAERINGSLIV-TRONDHEIM—See Fred. Olsen & Co.; *Int'l*, pg. 2768
DAGE PRECISION INDUSTRIES, INC.—See Nordson Corporation; *U.S. Public*, pg. 1532
DAGE PRECISION INDUSTRIES LIMITED—See Nordson Corporation; *U.S. Public*, pg. 1532
DAGE (SEASIA) PTE. LTD.—See Nordson Corporation; *U.S. Public*, pg. 1532
DAGESTAN ENERGOSBYT COMPANY; *Int'l*, pg. 1912
DAGE TEST SYSTEMS (SUZHOU) CO. LTD.—See Nordson Corporation; *U.S. Public*, pg. 1532
DAGGETT VENTURES, LLC; *U.S. Private*, pg. 1144
DAGI GIYIM SANAYI VE TICARET A.S.; *Int'l*, pg. 1912
DAGIT GROUP; *U.S. Private*, pg. 1144
DAGI YATIRIM HOLDING A.S.; *Int'l*, pg. 1912
DAGMAR OY; *Int'l*, pg. 1912
DAGOBA ORGANIC CHOCOLATE—See The Hershey Co.; *U.S. Public*, pg. 2088
D'AGOSTINO SUPERMARKETS INC.; *U.S. Private*, pg. 1138
DA GRASSO SP.Z O.O.—See Orkla ASA; *Int'l*, pg. 5637
DAGRO EISSMANN AUTOMOTIVE GMBH—See Eissmann Automotive Deutschland GmbH; *Int'l*, pg. 2336
DAGROFA A/S—See NorgesGruppen ASA; *Int'l*, pg. 5427
DAGROFA DETAIL A/S—See NorgesGruppen ASA; *Int'l*, pg. 5427
DAGROFA S-ENGROS AS—See NorgesGruppen ASA; *Int'l*, pg. 5427
DA GROUP; *Int'l*, pg. 1901
DAGSBORO MATERIALS—See Haines & Kibblehouse Inc.; *U.S. Private*, pg. 1841
DAG VENTURES, LLC; *U.S. Private*, pg. 1144
DAHANG INTERNATIONAL TRANSPORTATION CO., LTD.—See KKR & Co. Inc.; *U.S. Public*, pg. 1258
DAH BANG PRINTING INK MANUFACTORY LIMITED—See Golik Holdings Limited; *Int'l*, pg. 3036
DAH CHONG HONG HOLDINGS LTD.—See CITIC Group Corporation; *Int'l*, pg. 1620
DAH CHONG HONG INDUSTRIAL MACHINERY CO., LTD.—See Honda Motor Co., Ltd.; *Int'l*, pg. 3460
DAHENG NEW EPOCH TECHNOLOGY, INC.; *Int'l*, pg. 1913
DAHER GROUP; *Int'l*, pg. 1913
DAHER INDUSTRY & DEFENCE—See DAHER Group; *Int'l*, pg. 1913
DAHER SUPPORT MANAGEMENT—See DAHER Group; *Int'l*, pg. 1913
DAHETRA A/S—See New Wave Group AB; *Int'l*, pg. 5229
DAH HSING ELECTRIC CO.,LTD.—See Koa Corporation; *Int'l*, pg. 4215
DAHILL OFFICE TECHNOLOGY CORPORATION—See Xerox Holdings Corporation; *U.S. Public*, pg. 2387
DAHL-BECK ELECTRIC CO.; *U.S. Private*, pg. 1144
DAHLE BUROTECHNIK GMBH—See Erwin Muller Gruppe GmbH; *Int'l*, pg. 2500
DAHLEM COMPANIES, INC.; *U.S. Private*, pg. 1144
DAHLEM ENTERPRISES, INC.—See Dahlem Companies, Inc.; *U.S. Private*, pg. 1144
DAHLEM REALTY COMPANY, INC.—See Dahlem Companies, Inc.; *U.S. Private*, pg. 1144
DAHLE NORTH AMERICA, INC.—See Erwin Muller Gruppe GmbH; *Int'l*, pg. 2500
DAHL FORD-LA CROSSE INC.; *U.S. Private*, pg. 1144
DAHLHEIMER DISTRIBUTING COMPANY, INC.; *U.S. Private*, pg. 1144
DAHLIN JOHANSSON FRANTEXTIL AB—See New Wave Group AB; *Int'l*, pg. 5229
DAHL INTERNATIONAL AB—See Compagnie de Saint-Gobain SA; *Int'l*, pg. 1732
DAHLMEIER INSURANCE AGENCY, INC.—See Aquiline Capital Partners LLC; *U.S. Private*, pg. 305
DAHL'S FOOD MART INC.; *U.S. Private*, pg. 1144
DAHLSTEN TRUCK LINE, INC.—See TFI International Inc.; *Int'l*, pg. 7586
DAHL SVERIGE—See Compagnie de Saint-Gobain SA; *Int'l*, pg. 1733
DAH MEI SILK WEAVING FTY CO., LTD.—See Avery Dennison Corporation; *U.S. Public*, pg. 244
DAHM GASLOG GMBH—See Hoyer GmbH; *Int'l*, pg. 3498
DAHN CORPORATION; *U.S. Public*, pg. 1144
DA HORA ARTIGOS DE EMBALAGEM, LDA.—See Inapa - Investimentos, Participacoes e Gestao, SA; *Int'l*, pg. 3645
DAH SAN ELECTRIC WIRE & CABLE CO., LTD. - SECOND FACTORY—See Dah San Electric Wire & Cable Co., Ltd.; *Int'l*, pg. 1912
DAH SAN ELECTRIC WIRE & CABLE CO., LTD.; *Int'l*, pg. 1912
DAH SHYANG CHEMICAL CO., LTD.—See Sanyo Chemical Industries, Ltd.; *Int'l*, pg. 6563
DAH SING BANKING GROUP LIMITED—See Dah Sing Financial Holdings Limited; *Int'l*, pg. 1913
DAH SING BANK LIMITED—See Dah Sing Financial Holdings Limited; *Int'l*, pg. 1913

DAH SING COMPANY LIMITED—See Dah Sing Financial Holdings Limited; *Int'l*, pg. 1913
DAH SING FINANCE LIMITED—See Dah Sing Financial Holdings Limited; *Int'l*, pg. 1913
DAH SING FINANCIAL HOLDINGS LIMITED; *Int'l*, pg. 1912
DAH SING GENERAL INSURANCE COMPANY LIMITED—See Dah Sing Financial Holdings Limited; *Int'l*, pg. 1913
DAH SING INSURANCE COMPANY (1976) LIMITED—See Dah Sing Financial Holdings Limited; *Int'l*, pg. 1913
DAH SING NOMINEES LTD—See Dah Sing Financial Holdings Limited; *Int'l*, pg. 1913
DAHUA GROUP DALIAN CHEMICAL INDUSTRY CO., LTD.; *Int'l*, pg. 1913
DAHUA GUVENLIK TEKNOLOJILERI SANAYI VE TICARET A.S.—See Zhejiang Dahua Technology Co., Ltd.; *Int'l*, pg. 8650
DAHUA IBERIA S.L.—See Zhejiang Dahua Technology Co., Ltd.; *Int'l*, pg. 8650
DAHUA INC.; *Int'l*, pg. 1913
DAHU AQUACULTURE COMPANY LIMITED; *Int'l*, pg. 1913
DAHUA SECURITY MALAYSIA SDN. BHD.—See Zhejiang Dahua Technology Co., Ltd.; *Int'l*, pg. 8650
DAHUA TECHNOLOGY AUSTRALIA PTY. LTD.—See Zhejiang Dahua Technology Co., Ltd.; *Int'l*, pg. 8650
DAHUA TECHNOLOGY CHILE SPA—See Zhejiang Dahua Technology Co., Ltd.; *Int'l*, pg. 8650
DAHUA TECHNOLOGY COLOMBIA S.A.S.—See Zhejiang Dahua Technology Co., Ltd.; *Int'l*, pg. 8650
DAHUA TECHNOLOGY GMBH—See Zhejiang Dahua Technology Co., Ltd.; *Int'l*, pg. 8650
DAHUA TECHNOLOGY HUNGARY LTD.—See Zhejiang Dahua Technology Co., Ltd.; *Int'l*, pg. 8650
DAHUA TECHNOLOGY INDIA PRIVATE LIMITED—See Zhejiang Dahua Technology Co., Ltd.; *Int'l*, pg. 8650
DAHUA TECHNOLOGY KAZAKHSTAN LLP—See Zhejiang Dahua Technology Co., Ltd.; *Int'l*, pg. 8651
DAHUA TECHNOLOGY KOREA COMPANY LIMITED—See Zhejiang Dahua Technology Co., Ltd.; *Int'l*, pg. 8651
DAHUA TECHNOLOGY MEXICO S.A. DE C.V.—See Zhejiang Dahua Technology Co., Ltd.; *Int'l*, pg. 8651
DAHUA TECHNOLOGY MIDDLE EAST FZE—See Zhejiang Dahua Technology Co., Ltd.; *Int'l*, pg. 8651
DAHUA TECHNOLOGY PERU S.A.C—See Zhejiang Dahua Technology Co., Ltd.; *Int'l*, pg. 8651
DAHUA TECHNOLOGY RUS LLC—See Zhejiang Dahua Technology Co., Ltd.; *Int'l*, pg. 8651
DAHUA TECHNOLOGY SINGAPORE PTE.LTD.—See Zhejiang Dahua Technology Co., Ltd.; *Int'l*, pg. 8651
DAHUA TECHNOLOGY UK LTD.—See Zhejiang Dahua Technology Co., Ltd.; *Int'l*, pg. 8651
DAHUA TECHNOLOGY USA INC.—See Zhejiang Dahua Technology Co., Ltd.; *Int'l*, pg. 8651
DA HUI LIMITED; *Int'l*, pg. 1901
DAI BAI DANG RESTAURANTS INC—See Cafe de Coral Holdings Limited; *Int'l*, pg. 1250
DAIBEA CO., LTD.—See JTEKT Corporation; *Int'l*, pg. 4017
DAIBES BROTHERS INC.; *U.S. Private*, pg. 1145
DAIBIRU CORPORATION—See Mitsui O.S.K. Lines, Ltd.; *Int'l*, pg. 4989
DAIBIRU CSB CO., LTD.—See Mitsui O.S.K. Lines, Ltd.; *Int'l*, pg. 4989
DAIBIRU SAIGON TOWER CO., LTD.—See Mitsui O.S.K. Lines, Ltd.; *Int'l*, pg. 4989
DAIBOCHI AUSTRALIA PTY. LTD.—See Scientex Berhad; *Int'l*, pg. 6648
DAIBOCHI LAND SDN. BHD.—See Scientex Berhad; *Int'l*, pg. 6648
DAICEL ABOSHI SANGYO CO. LTD.—See Daicel Corporation; *Int'l*, pg. 1918
DAICEL-ALLNEX LTD.—See Daicel Corporation; *Int'l*, pg. 1919
DAICEL AMERICA HOLDINGS,INC.—See Daicel Corporation; *Int'l*, pg. 1918
DAICEL ARAI CHEMICAL LTD.—See Daicel Corporation; *Int'l*, pg. 1918
DAICEL (ASIA) PTE. LTD.—See Daicel Corporation; *Int'l*, pg. 1918
DAICEL BEYOND LTD.—See Daicel Corporation; *Int'l*, pg. 1918
DAICEL CHEMICAL (CHINA) INVESTMENT CO., LTD.—See Daicel Corporation; *Int'l*, pg. 1918
DAICEL CHEMICALS CO LTD—See Daicel Corporation; *Int'l*, pg. 1918
DAICEL CHEMTECH, INC.—See Daicel Corporation; *Int'l*, pg. 1918
DAICEL (CHINA) INVESTMENT CO.,LTD.—See Daicel Corporation; *Int'l*, pg. 1918
DAICEL CHIRAL TECHNOLOGIES (CHINA) CO., LTD.—See Daicel Corporation; *Int'l*, pg. 1918
DAICEL CHIRAL TECHNOLOGIES (INDIA) PVT LTD.—See Daicel Corporation; *Int'l*, pg. 1918
DAICEL CORPORATION; *Int'l*, pg. 1918

COMPANY NAME INDEX

DAICEL-CYTEC COMPANY, LTD.—See Daicel Corporation; *Int'l*, pg. 1919
DAICEL EUROPE GMBH—See Daicel Corporation; *Int'l*, pg. 1918
DAICEL-EVONIK LTD.—See Daicel Corporation; *Int'l*, pg. 1919
DAICEL-EVONIK LTD.—See RAG-Stiftung; *Int'l*, pg. 6178
DAICEL FINANCE LTD.—See Daicel Corporation; *Int'l*, pg. 1918
DAICEL LOGISTICS SERVICE CO., LTD.—See Daicel Corporation; *Int'l*, pg. 1919
DAICEL MICRO OPTICS CO. LTD.—See Daicel Corporation; *Int'l*, pg. 1919
DAICEL MIRAIZU LTD.—See Daicel Corporation; *Int'l*, pg. 1919
DAICEL MIRAIZU (THAILAND) CO., LTD.—See Daicel Corporation; *Int'l*, pg. 1919
DAICEL NANNING FOOD INGREDIENTS CO., LTD.—See Daicel Corporation; *Int'l*, pg. 1919
DAICEL NOVAFOAM LTD.—See Daicel Corporation; *Int'l*, pg. 1919
DAICEL OHTAKE SANGYO CO., LTD.—See Daicel Corporation; *Int'l*, pg. 1919
DAICEL PACK SYSTEMS LTD.—See Daicel Corporation; *Int'l*, pg. 1919
DAICEL PACKSYSTEMS LTD.—See Daicel Corporation; *Int'l*, pg. 1919
DAICEL POLYMER (HONG KONG) LIMITED.—See Daicel Corporation; *Int'l*, pg. 1919
DAICEL POLYMER LTD.—See Daicel Corporation; *Int'l*, pg. 1919
DAICEL POLYMER, LTD.—See Daicel Corporation; *Int'l*, pg. 1919
DAICEL PROSPERITY (CHINA) LTD.—See Daicel Corporation; *Int'l*, pg. 1919
DAICEL PYROTECHNICS LTD.—See Sightron Japan Inc.; *Int'l*, pg. 6907
DAICEL SAFETY SYSTEMS AMERICA LLC—See Daicel Corporation; *Int'l*, pg. 1918
DAICEL SAFETY SYSTEMS AMERICAS, INC.—See Daicel Corporation; *Int'l*, pg. 1919
DAICEL SAFETY SYSTEMS EUROPE SP.Z.O.O—See Daicel Corporation; *Int'l*, pg. 1919
DAICEL SAFETY SYSTEMS, INC.—See Daicel Corporation; *Int'l*, pg. 1919
DAICEL SAFETY SYSTEMS INDIA PVT. LTD.—See Daicel Corporation; *Int'l*, pg. 1919
DAICEL SAFETY SYSTEMS (JIANGSU) CO., LTD.—See Daicel Corporation; *Int'l*, pg. 1919
DAICEL SAFETY SYSTEMS KOREA, INC.—See Daicel Corporation; *Int'l*, pg. 1919
DAICEL SAFETY SYSTEMS (THAILAND) CO.,LTD.—See Daicel Corporation; *Int'l*, pg. 1919
DAICEL SAFETY TECHNOLOGIES (THAILAND) CO., LTD.—See Daicel Corporation; *Int'l*, pg. 1919
DAICEL SAKAI JITSUGYO CO. LTD.—See Daicel Corporation; *Int'l*, pg. 1919
DAICEL TRADING (SHANGHAI) LTD.—See Daicel Corporation; *Int'l*, pg. 1919
DAICEL (U.S.A.) INC.—See Daicel Corporation; *Int'l*, pg. 1918
DAICEN MEMBRANE-SYSTEMS LTD.—See Daicel Corporation; *Int'l*, pg. 1919
DAI CHAU JSC; *Int'l*, pg. 1913
DAICHI KASEI CO., LTD.—See TOWA PHARMACEUTICAL CO. LTD.; *Int'l*, pg. 7849
DAICHU CO., LTD.—See Sanoyas Holdings Corporation; *Int'l*, pg. 6554
DAICOLOR DO BRASIL IND. E COM. LTDA.—See Dainichiseika Color & Chemicals Mfg. Co., Ltd.; *Int'l*, pg. 1939
DAICOLOR ITALY S.R.L.—See Dainichiseika Color & Chemicals Mfg. Co., Ltd.; *Int'l*, pg. 1939
DAICOLOR SHANGHAI MFG. CO., LTD.—See Dainichiseika Color & Chemicals Mfg. Co., Ltd.; *Int'l*, pg. 1939
DAICO SUPPLY COMPANY—See Hendricks Holding Company, Inc.; *U.S. Private*, pg. 1915
DAI-DAN CO LTD; *Int'l*, pg. 1917
DAI-DAN CO LTD - TECHNICAL DEVELOPMENT DIVISION—See DAI-DAN Co Ltd; *Int'l*, pg. 1917
DAI-DAN PHILIPPINES, INC.—See DAI-DAN Co Ltd; *Int'l*, pg. 1917
DAI-DAN SERVICE KANTO CO., LTD.—See DAI-DAN Co Ltd; *Int'l*, pg. 1917
DAIDENSHA CO., LTD—See Tachibana Eletech Co., Ltd.; *Int'l*, pg. 7402
DAIDO AMISTAR CO., LTD.—See Daido Steel Co., Ltd.; *Int'l*, pg. 1922
DAIDO AMISTAR (M) SDN. BHD.—See Daido Steel Co., Ltd.; *Int'l*, pg. 1922
DAIDO AMISTAR(S) PTE LTD—See Daido Steel Co., Ltd.; *Int'l*, pg. 1922
DAIDO BUNSEKI RESEARCH INC.—See Daido Steel Co., Ltd.; *Int'l*, pg. 1922
DAIDO CASTINGS CO., LTD.—See Daido Steel Co., Ltd.; *Int'l*, pg. 1922
DAIDO CHAIN (CHANGSHU) CO., LTD.—See Daido Kogyo Co., Ltd.; *Int'l*, pg. 1920
DAIDO CORPORATION OF AMERICA—See Daido Kogyo Co., Ltd.; *Int'l*, pg. 1920
DAIDO DIE & MOLD STEEL SOLUTIONS CO., LTD.—See Daido Steel Co., Ltd.; *Int'l*, pg. 1922
DAIDO D.M.S. INDIA PVT. LTD.—See Daido Steel Co., Ltd.; *Int'l*, pg. 1922
DAIDO DMS MALAYSIA SDN. BHD.—See Daido Steel Co., Ltd.; *Int'l*, pg. 1922
DAIDO DMS MEXICO, S.A. DE C.V.—See Daido Steel Co., Ltd.; *Int'l*, pg. 1922
DAIDO DMS PHILS., INC.—See Daido Steel Co., Ltd.; *Int'l*, pg. 1922
DAIDO DMS SINGAPORE PTE. LTD.—See Daido Steel Co., Ltd.; *Int'l*, pg. 1922
DAIDO DMS (THAILAND) CO., LTD.—See Daido Steel Co., Ltd.; *Int'l*, pg. 1922
DAIDO DMS VIETNAM CO., LTD.—See Daido Steel Co., Ltd.; *Int'l*, pg. 1922
DAIDO ECOMET CO., LTD.—See Daido Steel Co., Ltd.; *Int'l*, pg. 1922
DAIDO ELECTRONICS CO., LTD.—See Daido Steel Co., Ltd.; *Int'l*, pg. 1922
DAIDO ELECTRONICS (GUANGDONG) CO., LTD.—See Daido Steel Co., Ltd.; *Int'l*, pg. 1922
DAIDO ELECTRONICS (SUZHOU) CO., LTD.—See Daido Steel Co., Ltd.; *Int'l*, pg. 1922
DAIDO ELECTRONICS (THAILAND) CO., LTD.—See Daido Steel Co., Ltd.; *Int'l*, pg. 1922
DAIDO ENVIRONMENT ENGINEERING CO.,LTD.,—See Daido Steel Co., Ltd.; *Int'l*, pg. 1922
DAIDO GENERAL SERVICE CO., LTD.—See Daido Kogyo Co., Ltd.; *Int'l*, pg. 1920
DAIDO GROUP LTD; *Int'l*, pg. 1920
DAIDOH LIMITED; *Int'l*, pg. 1923
DAIDO HOME INTERNATIONAL LTD.—See Daido Group Ltd; *Int'l*, pg. 1920
DAIDO INDIA PVT. LTD.—See Daido Kogyo Co., Ltd.; *Int'l*, pg. 1920
DAIDO INDUSTRIA DE CORRENTES DA AMAZONIA LTDA.—See Daido Kogyo Co., Ltd.; *Int'l*, pg. 1920
DAIDO INDUSTRIAL BEARINGS EUROPE LTD.—See Daido Metal Corporation; *Int'l*, pg. 1921
DAIDO INDUSTRIAL BEARINGS JAPAN CO., LTD.—See Daido Metal Corporation; *Int'l*, pg. 1921
DAIDO INDUSTRIAL E COMERCIAL LTDA.—See Daido Kogyo Co., Ltd.; *Int'l*, pg. 1920
DAIDO INDUSTRY CO., LTD.—See Sankyo Kasei Corporation; *Int'l*, pg. 6543
DAIDO IT SOLUTIONS CO., LTD.—See Daido Steel Co., Ltd.; *Int'l*, pg. 1922
DAIDO KENSETSU CO., LTD.—See Daido Kogyo Co., Ltd.; *Int'l*, pg. 1920
DAIDO KOGYO CO., LTD.; *Int'l*, pg. 1920
DAIDO KOGYO INDIA PVT. LTD.—See Daido Steel Co., Ltd.; *Int'l*, pg. 1922
DAIDO KOGYO (THAILAND) CO., LTD.—See Daido Steel Co., Ltd.; *Int'l*, pg. 1922
DAIDO LIFE INSURANCE COMPANY—See T&D Holdings, Inc.; *Int'l*, pg. 7394
DAIDO LIFE SERVICE CO., LTD.—See Daido Steel Co., Ltd.; *Int'l*, pg. 1922
DAIDO LIFE TOTAL MAINTENANCE, INC.—See T&D Holdings, Inc.; *Int'l*, pg. 7394
DAIDO LOGITECH CO., LTD.—See Daido Metal Corporation; *Int'l*, pg. 1921
DAIDO MACHINERY CO., LTD.—See Daido Steel Co., Ltd.; *Int'l*, pg. 1922
DAIDO MANAGEMENT SERVICE CO., LTD.—See T&D Holdings, Inc.; *Int'l*, pg. 7395
DAIDO MATEX CO., LTD.—See Daido Steel Co., Ltd.; *Int'l*, pg. 1923
DAIDO METAL CO., LTD—See Daido Metal Corporation; *Int'l*, pg. 1921
DAIDO METAL CORPORATION - BIMETAL DIVISION—See Daido Metal Corporation; *Int'l*, pg. 1921
DAIDO METAL CORPORATION - GIFU FACTORY—See Daido Metal Corporation; *Int'l*, pg. 1921
DAIDO METAL CORPORATION - INUYAMA FACTORY—See Daido Metal Corporation; *Int'l*, pg. 1921
DAIDO METAL CORPORATION - MAEHARA FACTORY—See Daido Metal Corporation; *Int'l*, pg. 1921
DAIDO METAL CORPORATION; *Int'l*, pg. 1921
DAIDO METAL CZECH S.R.O.—See Daido Metal Corporation; *Int'l*, pg. 1921
DAIDO METAL EUROPE GMBH—See Daido Metal Corporation; *Int'l*, pg. 1921
DAIDO METAL EUROPE LTD—See Daido Metal Corporation; *Int'l*, pg. 1921
DAIDO METAL GERMANY GMBH—See Daido Metal Corporation; *Int'l*, pg. 1921
DAIDO METAL KOTOR AD—See Daido Metal Corporation; *Int'l*, pg. 1921
DAIDO METAL MEXICO, S.A. DE C.V.—See Daido Metal Corporation; *Int'l*, pg. 1921
DAIDO METAL MEXICO SALES, S.A. DE C.V.—See Daido Metal Corporation; *Int'l*, pg. 1921
DAIDO METAL RUSSIA LLC—See Daido Metal Corporation; *Int'l*, pg. 1921
DAIDO METAL SAGA CO., LTD.—See Daido Metal Corporation; *Int'l*, pg. 1921
DAIDO METAL SALES CO., LTD.—See Daido Metal Corporation; *Int'l*, pg. 1921
DAIDO METAL U.S.A. INC—See Daido Metal Corporation; *Int'l*, pg. 1921
DAIDONE ELECTRICAL INC.; *U.S. Private*, pg. 1145
DAIDONG ELECTRONICS CO., LTD.; *Int'l*, pg. 1924
DAIDONG ELECTRONICS (THAILAND) CO., LTD.—See Daidong Electronics Co., Ltd.; *Int'l*, pg. 1924
DAIDONG ENGINEERING MALAYSIA SDN BHD—See Daidong Electronics Co., Ltd.; *Int'l*, pg. 1924
DAIDONG MOLD & PLASTICS (SHANGHAI) CO., LTD.—See Daidong Electronics Co., Ltd.; *Int'l*, pg. 1924
DAI DONG STEEL SDN. BHD.—See Prestar Resources Berhad; *Int'l*, pg. 5965
DAIDO PDM (THAILAND) CO., LTD.—See Daido Steel Co., Ltd.; *Int'l*, pg. 1922
DAIDO PHARMACEUTICAL CORPORATION—See DyDo Group Holdings, Inc.; *Int'l*, pg. 2238
DAIDO PLAIN BEARINGS CO., LTD.—See Daido Metal Corporation; *Int'l*, pg. 1921
DAIDO PLANT INDUSTRIES CO., LTD.—See Daido Steel Co., Ltd.; *Int'l*, pg. 1923
DAIDO PRECISION INDUSTRIES LTD.—See Daido Steel Co., Ltd.; *Int'l*, pg. 1923
DAIDO PRECISION METAL (SUZHOU) CO., LTD.—See Daido Metal Corporation; *Int'l*, pg. 1921
DAIDO REBUILD SERVICES INC.—See Daido Metal Corporation; *Int'l*, pg. 1921
DAIDO SHIZAI SERVICE CO., LTD.—See Daido Steel Co., Ltd.; *Int'l*, pg. 1923
DAIDO SIGNAL CO., LTD.; *Int'l*, pg. 1922
DAIDO SITTIPOL CO., LTD.—See Daido Kogyo Co., Ltd.; *Int'l*, pg. 1920
DAIDO STAINLESS STEEL (DALIAN) CO., LTD.—See Daido Steel Co., Ltd.; *Int'l*, pg. 1923
DAIDO STAR TECHNO CO., LTD.—See Daido Steel Co., Ltd.; *Int'l*, pg. 1923
DAIDO STAR TEKUNO CO., LTD.—See Daido Steel Co., Ltd.; *Int'l*, pg. 1923
DAIDO STEEL (AMERICA) INC—See Daido Steel Co., Ltd.; *Int'l*, pg. 1923
DAIDO STEEL CO., LTD. - CHITA PLANT—See Daido Steel Co., Ltd.; *Int'l*, pg. 1923
DAIDO STEEL CO., LTD. - KAWASAKI PLANT—See Daido Steel Co., Ltd.; *Int'l*, pg. 1923
DAIDO STEEL CO., LTD. - KIMITSU PLANT—See Daido Steel Co., Ltd.; *Int'l*, pg. 1923
DAIDO STEEL CO., LTD. - OJI PLANT—See Daido Steel Co., Ltd.; *Int'l*, pg. 1923
DAIDO STEEL CO., LTD. - SHIBUKAWA PLANT—See Daido Steel Co., Ltd.; *Int'l*, pg. 1923
DAIDO STEEL CO., LTD.; *Int'l*, pg. 1922
DAIDO STEEL GROUP EUROPE GMBH—See Daido Steel Co., Ltd.; *Int'l*, pg. 1922
DAIDO STEEL MATERIALS TECHNOLOGY SHANGHAI CO.,LTD.—See Daido Steel Co., Ltd.; *Int'l*, pg. 1923
DAIDO STEEL (SHANGHAI) CO., LTD.—See Daido Steel Co., Ltd.; *Int'l*, pg. 1923
DAIDO TECHNICA CO., LTD.—See Daido Steel Co., Ltd.; *Int'l*, pg. 1923
DAIDO TIENWEN STEEL CO., LTD.—See Daido Steel Co., Ltd.; *Int'l*, pg. 1923
DAIEI AMET CO., LTD.—See Daiei Kankyo Co., Ltd.; *Int'l*, pg. 1924
DAI-EI AUSTRALIA PTY. LTD.—See Mitsubishi Heavy Industries, Ltd.; *Int'l*, pg. 4957
THE DAIEI, INC.—See AEON Co., Ltd.; *Int'l*, pg. 178
DAIEI KAIHATSU CO., LTD.—See Yamau Holdings Co., Ltd.; *Int'l*, pg. 8555
DAIEI KANKYO CO., LTD.; *Int'l*, pg. 1924
DAIEI KANKYO RESEARCH INSTITUTE CO., LTD.—See Daiei Kankyo Co., Ltd.; *Int'l*, pg. 1924
DAIEI SHIPPING CO., LTD.—See Sankyu, Inc.; *Int'l*, pg. 6543
DAIEI TRADING CO. INC.; *U.S. Private*, pg. 1145
DAIFIT CO., LTD—See Daiken Corporation; *Int'l*, pg. 1931
DAIFU & CO., LTD.—See Dentsu Group Inc.; *Int'l*, pg. 2034
DAIFUKU AMERICA CORPORATION—See Daifuku Co., Ltd.; *Int'l*, pg. 1925
DAIFUKU AUTOMATION (TIANJIN) CO., LTD.—See Daifuku Co., Ltd.; *Int'l*, pg. 1925
DAIFUKU BUSINESS SERVICE CORPORATION—See Daifuku Co., Ltd.; *Int'l*, pg. 1925
DAIFUKU CANADA INC.—See Daifuku Co., Ltd.; *Int'l*, pg. 1925
DAIFUKU CARD CO., LTD.—See SHOEI Printing Co., Ltd.; *Int'l*, pg. 6858
DAIFUKU (CHINA) AUTOMATION CO., LTD.—See Daifuku Co., Ltd.; *Int'l*, pg. 1925
DAIFUKU (CHINA) CO., LTD.—See Daifuku Co., Ltd.; *Int'l*, pg. 1925
DAIFUKU (CHINA) MANUFACTURING CO., LTD.—See Daifuku Co., Ltd.; *Int'l*, pg. 1925

DAIFUKU CLEANROOM AUTOMATION AMERICA CORPORATION—See Daifuku Co., Ltd.; *Int'l*, pg. 1925
DAIFUKU CO., LTD. - SHIGA WORKS—See Daifuku Co., Ltd.; *Int'l*, pg. 1925
DAIFUKU CO., LTD.; *Int'l*, pg. 1924
DAIFUKU DE MEXICO, S.A. DE C.V.—See Daifuku Co., Ltd.; *Int'l*, pg. 1926
DAIFUKU DESIGN & ENGINEERING CO., LTD.—See Daifuku Co., Ltd.; *Int'l*, pg. 1925
DAIFUKU EUROPE LTD.—See Daifuku Co., Ltd.; *Int'l*, pg. 1925
DAIFUKU INDIA PRIVATE LIMITED—See Daifuku Co., Ltd.; *Int'l*, pg. 1925
DAIFUKU INSTITUTE OF TECHNOLOGY & TRAINING CO., LTD.—See Daifuku Co., Ltd.; *Int'l*, pg. 1925
DAIFUKU INTRALOGISTICS VIETNAM CO., LTD.—See Daifuku Co., Ltd.; *Int'l*, pg. 1925
DAIFUKU KOREA CO., LTD. - CARWASH DIVISION—See Daifuku Co., Ltd.; *Int'l*, pg. 1925
DAIFUKU KOREA CO., LTD. - OVERSEAS DIVISION—See Daifuku Co., Ltd.; *Int'l*, pg. 1925
DAIFUKU KOREA CO., LTD.—See Daifuku Co., Ltd.; *Int'l*, pg. 1925
DAIFUKU LOGAN LTD—See Daifuku Co., Ltd.; *Int'l*, pg. 1925
DAIFUKU LOGISTIC TECHNOLOGY CO., LTD.—See Daifuku Co., Ltd.; *Int'l*, pg. 1925
DAIFUKU (MALAYSIA) SDN. BHD.—See Daifuku Co., Ltd.; *Int'l*, pg. 1925
DAIFUKU MANUFACTURING TECHNOLOGY CO., LTD.—See Daifuku Co., Ltd.; *Int'l*, pg. 1925
DAIFUKU MECHATRONICS (SINGAPORE) PTE. LTD.—See Daifuku Co., Ltd.; *Int'l*, pg. 1925
DAIFUKU NORTH AMERICA HOLDING COMPANY—See Daifuku Co., Ltd.; *Int'l*, pg. 1925
DAIFUKU OCEANIA LIMITED—See Daifuku Co., Ltd.; *Int'l*, pg. 1925
DAIFUKU PIONEER CO., LTD.—See Daifuku Co., Ltd.; *Int'l*, pg. 1925
DAIFUKU PLUSMORE CO., LTD.—See Daifuku Co., Ltd.; *Int'l*, pg. 1925
DAIFUKU SOFTWARE DEVELOPMENT CO., LTD.—See Daifuku Co., Ltd.; *Int'l*, pg. 1925
DAIFUKU (SUZHOU) CLEANROOM AUTOMATION CO., LTD.—See Daifuku Co., Ltd.; *Int'l*, pg. 1925
DAIFUKU (THAILAND) LTD.—See Daifuku Co., Ltd.; *Int'l*, pg. 1925
DAIFUKU WEBB HOLDING COMPANY—See Daifuku Co., Ltd.; *Int'l*, pg. 1925
DAI FUNDING CORPORATION—See Daikin Industries, Ltd.; *Int'l*, pg. 1932
DAIG 2. OBJEKTGESELLSCHAFT MBH—See Vonovia SE; *Int'l*, pg. 8305
DAIGLE & HOUGHTON INC.; *U.S. Private*, pg. 1145
DAIGLE OIL COMPANY; *U.S. Private*, pg. 1145
DAI HAN PHARMACEUTICAL CO., LTD.; *Int'l*, pg. 1913
DAIHAN SCIENTIFIC CO., LTD.; *Int'l*, pg. 1926
DAIHATSU AUSTRALIA PTY. LTD.—See Toyota Motor Corporation; *Int'l*, pg. 7870
DAIHATSU BELGIUM S.A.—See Toyota Motor Corporation; *Int'l*, pg. 7870
DAIHATSU BRIGGS & STRATTON CO., LTD.—See Briggs & Stratton Corporation; *U.S. Private*, pg. 651
DAIHATSU BRIGGS & STRATTON CO., LTD.—See Toyota Motor Corporation; *Int'l*, pg. 7870
DAIHATSU CREDIT CO., LTD.—See Toyota Motor Corporation; *Int'l*, pg. 7870
DAIHATSU DE GUATEMALA, S.A.—See Toyota Motor Corporation; *Int'l*, pg. 7870
DAIHATSU DE NICARAGUA, S.A.—See Toyota Motor Corporation; *Int'l*, pg. 7870
DAIHATSU DIESEL (AMERICA) INC.—See Toyota Motor Corporation; *Int'l*, pg. 7870
DAIHATSU DIESEL (EUROPE) LTD.—See Toyota Motor Corporation; *Int'l*, pg. 7870
DAIHATSU DIESEL MFG. CO., LTD.—See Toyota Motor Corporation; *Int'l*, pg. 7870
DAIHATSU FRANCE S.A.S.—See Toyota Motor Corporation; *Int'l*, pg. 7870
DAIHATSU HOLLAND B.V.—See Toyota Motor Corporation; *Int'l*, pg. 7870
DAIHATSU IRELAND LTD.—See Toyota Motor Corporation; *Int'l*, pg. 7870
DAIHATSU ITALIA S.R.L.—See Toyota Tsusho Corporation; *Int'l*, pg. 7870
DAIHATSU (MALAYSIA) SDN. BHD.—See MBM Resources Berhad; *Int'l*, pg. 4754
DAIHATSU METAL CO., LTD.—See Toyota Motor Corporation; *Int'l*, pg. 7870
DAIHATSU MOTOR CO., LTD. - KYOTO PLANT—See Toyota Motor Corporation; *Int'l*, pg. 7870
DAIHATSU MOTOR CO., LTD.—See Toyota Motor Corporation; *Int'l*, pg. 7870
DAIHATSU MOTOR KYUSHU CO., LTD.—See Toyota Motor Corporation; *Int'l*, pg. 7870
DAIHATSU (UK) LTD.—See Toyota Motor Corporation; *Int'l*, pg. 7870
DAIHEN ADVANCED COMPONENT, INC.—See Daihen Corporation; *Int'l*, pg. 1926

DAIHEN ADVANCED MACHINERY (CHANGSHU) CO., LTD.—See Daihen Corporation; *Int'l*, pg. 1926
DAIHEN CORPORATION - CHITOSE PLANT—See Daihen Corporation; *Int'l*, pg. 1926
DAIHEN CORPORATION - KANEHIRA PLANT—See Daihen Corporation; *Int'l*, pg. 1926
DAIHEN CORPORATION - MIE PLANT—See Daihen Corporation; *Int'l*, pg. 1926
DAIHEN CORPORATION - ROKKO PLANT—See Daihen Corporation; *Int'l*, pg. 1926
DAIHEN CORPORATION; *Int'l*, pg. 1926
DAIHEN ELECTRIC CO., LTD.—See Daihen Corporation; *Int'l*, pg. 1926
DAIHEN ENGINEERING CO., LTD.—See Daihen Corporation; *Int'l*, pg. 1926
DAIHEN INC.—See Daihen Corporation; *Int'l*, pg. 1926
DAIHEN INDUSTRIAL MACHINERY CORPORATION—See Daihen Corporation; *Int'l*, pg. 1926
DAIHEN KOREA CO., LTD.—See Daihen Corporation; *Int'l*, pg. 1926
DAIHEN OTC (BEIJING) CO., LTD.—See Daihen Corporation; *Int'l*, pg. 1926
DAIHEN TECHNOS CO., LTD.—See Daihen Corporation; *Int'l*, pg. 1926
DAIHEN VARSTROJ WELDING CUTTING AND ROBOTICS D.D.—See Daihen Corporation; *Int'l*, pg. 1926
DAIHEN WELFARE ENTERPRISE CO., LTD.—See Daihen Corporation; *Int'l*, pg. 1926
DAIHO CORPORATION; *Int'l*, pg. 1927
DAIHOKU INDUSTRY CO., LTD.—See Daihen Corporation; *Int'l*, pg. 1926
DAI HOLDING, LLC; *U.S. Private*, pg. 1145
DAIHO TOSO KOGYO CORP.—See DAIHO CORPORATION; *Int'l*, pg. 1927
DAIHO TRADING CO., LTD.—See Nippi. Inc.; *Int'l*, pg. 5309
DAIICHI ALCOHOL CO., LTD.—See Kirin Holdings Company, Limited; *Int'l*, pg. 4187
DAIICHIBO CO., LTD.—See Sojitz Corporation; *Int'l*, pg. 7061
THE DAI-ICHI BUILDING CO., LTD.—See Dai-ichi Life Holdings, Inc.; *Int'l*, pg. 1918
DAI-ICHI CERAMO CO., LTD.—See DKS Co. Ltd.; *Int'l*, pg. 2139
DAIICHI CHUO KISEN KAISHA; *Int'l*, pg. 1927
DAIICHI CLINICAL LABORATORIES, INC.—See BML, Inc.; *Int'l*, pg. 1076
DAIICHI CO., LTD.; *Int'l*, pg. 1927
DAIICHI CONTAINER CO., LTD.—See Tomoku Co., Ltd.; *Int'l*, pg. 7801
DAI-ICHI CUTTER KOGYO K.K.; *Int'l*, pg. 1917
DAIICHI ENGEI CO., LTD.—See Mitsui Fudosan Co., Ltd.; *Int'l*, pg. 4986
DAIICHI ENGINEERING CO., LTD.—See Daiichi Jitsugyo Co. Ltd.; *Int'l*, pg. 1927
DAIICHI FINE CHEMICAL CO., LTD.—See Kirin Holdings Company, Limited; *Int'l*, pg. 4188
DAIICHI FINE CHEMICAL EUROPE GMBH—See Kirin Holdings Company, Limited; *Int'l*, pg. 4188
THE DAI-ICHI FRONTIER LIFE INSURANCE CO., LTD.—See Dai-ichi Life Holdings, Inc.; *Int'l*, pg. 1918
DAI-ICHI HIGH FREQUENCY CO., LTD.; *Int'l*, pg. 1917
DAIICHI JITSUGYO (AMERICA), INC.—See Daiichi Jitsugyo Co. Ltd.; *Int'l*, pg. 1927
DAIICHI JITSUGYO ASIA PTE LTD—See Daiichi Jitsugyo Co. Ltd.; *Int'l*, pg. 1927
DAIICHI JITSUGYO CO. LTD.; *Int'l*, pg. 1927
DAIICHI JITSUGYO DO BRASIL COMERCIO DE MAQUINAS LTDA.—See Daiichi Jitsugyo Co. Ltd.; *Int'l*, pg. 1927
DAIICHI JITSUGYO (GUANGZHOU), TRADING CO., LTD.—See Daiichi Jitsugyo Co. Ltd.; *Int'l*, pg. 1927
DAIICHI JITSUGYO (HONG KONG), LIMITED—See Daiichi Jitsugyo Co. Ltd.; *Int'l*, pg. 1927
DAIICHI JITSUGYO INDIA PVT. LTD.—See Daiichi Jitsugyo Co. Ltd.; *Int'l*, pg. 1927
DAI-ICHI JITSUGYO (MALAYSIA) SDN. BHD.—See Daiichi Jitsugyo Co. Ltd.; *Int'l*, pg. 1927
DAIICHI JITSUGYO PHILIPPINES, INC.—See Daiichi Jitsugyo Co. Ltd.; *Int'l*, pg. 1927
DAIICHI JITSUGYO PUERTO RICO, INC—See Daiichi Jitsugyo Co. Ltd.; *Int'l*, pg. 1927
DAI-ICHI JITSUGYO (THAILAND) CO., LTD.—See Daiichi Jitsugyo Co. Ltd.; *Int'l*, pg. 1927
DAIICHI JITSUGYO (VIETNAM) CO., LTD.—See Daiichi Jitsugyo Co. Ltd.; *Int'l*, pg. 1927
DAIICHI JITSUGYO VISWILL CO., LTD.—See Daiichi Jitsugyo Co. Ltd.; *Int'l*, pg. 1927
DAI-ICHI KARKARIA LIMITED; *Int'l*, pg. 1917
DAIICHI KASEI CO., LTD.—See Abico Group; *Int'l*, pg. 61
DAI-ICHI KENKOU CO., LTD.—See DKS Co. Ltd.; *Int'l*, pg. 2139
DAIICHI KENSETSU CORPORATION; *Int'l*, pg. 1927
DAIICHI KIGENSO KAGAKU KOGYO CO., LTD.; *Int'l*, pg. 1927
DAIICHIKOUSHO CO., LTD.; *Int'l*, pg. 1930

DAIICHI KOUTSU SANGYO CO., LTD. - FUKUOKA BRANCH—See Daiichi Koutsu Sangyo Co., Ltd.; *Int'l*, pg. 1928
DAIICHI KOUTSU SANGYO CO., LTD. - KAGOSHIMA BRANCH—See Daiichi Koutsu Sangyo Co., Ltd.; *Int'l*, pg. 1928
DAIICHI KOUTSU SANGYO CO., LTD. - KITAKYUSHU HEADQUARTERS TRAFFIC ENTERPRISE DIVISION—See Daiichi Koutsu Sangyo Co., Ltd.; *Int'l*, pg. 1928
DAIICHI KOUTSU SANGYO CO., LTD. - MIYAZAKI BANCH—See Daiichi Koutsu Sangyo Co., Ltd.; *Int'l*, pg. 1928
DAIICHI KOUTSU SANGYO CO., LTD.; *Int'l*, pg. 1928
DAI-ICHI LEASING CO., LTD.—See Mizuho Leasing Company, Limited; *Int'l*, pg. 4999
DAI-ICHI LIFE HOLDINGS, INC.; *Int'l*, pg. 1917
THE DAI-ICHI LIFE INFORMATION SYSTEMS CO., LTD.—See Dai-ichi Life Holdings, Inc.; *Int'l*, pg. 1918
DAI-ICHI LIFE INSURANCE (CAMBODIA) PLC.—See Dai-ichi Life Holdings, Inc.; *Int'l*, pg. 1917
DAI-ICHI LIFE INSURANCE COMPANY OF VIETNAM, LIMITED—See Dai-ichi Life Holdings, Inc.; *Int'l*, pg. 1917
DAI-ICHI LIFE INSURANCE MYANMAR LTD.—See Dai-ichi Life Holdings, Inc.; *Int'l*, pg. 1917
DAI-ICHI LIFE INTERNATIONAL (ASIAPACIFIC) LIMITED—See Dai-ichi Life Holdings, Inc.; *Int'l*, pg. 1917
DAI-ICHI LIFE INTERNATIONAL (EUROPE) LIMITED—See Dai-ichi Life Holdings, Inc.; *Int'l*, pg. 1917
DAI-ICHI LIFE INTERNATIONAL (U.S.A.) INC.—See Dai-ichi Life Holdings, Inc.; *Int'l*, pg. 1917
DAI-ICHI LIFE REALTY ASSET MANAGEMENT CO., LTD.—See Dai-ichi Life Holdings, Inc.; *Int'l*, pg. 1917
DAI-ICHI LIFE RESEARCH INSTITUTE INC.,—See Dai-ichi Life Holdings, Inc.; *Int'l*, pg. 1917
DAIICHI MECHA-TECH CORPORATION—See Daiichi Jitsugyo Co. Ltd.; *Int'l*, pg. 1927
DAI-ICHI PACKAGING CO., LTD.—See Thai President Foods Public Company Limited; *Int'l*, pg. 7594
DAIICHI PROJECT SERVICE CO., LTD.—See Daiichi Jitsugyo Co. Ltd.; *Int'l*, pg. 1927
DAIICHI SANKYO ALTKIRCH SARL—See Daiichi Sankyo Co., Ltd.; *Int'l*, pg. 1929
DAIICHI SANKYO AUSTRIA GMBH—See Daiichi Sankyo Co., Ltd.; *Int'l*, pg. 1929
DAIICHI SANKYO BELGIUM NV/SA—See Daiichi Sankyo Co., Ltd.; *Int'l*, pg. 1929
DAIICHI SANKYO BIOTECH CO., LTD.—See Daiichi Sankyo Co., Ltd.; *Int'l*, pg. 1929
DAIICHI SANKYO BRASIL FARMACEUTICA LTDA.—See Daiichi Sankyo Co., Ltd.; *Int'l*, pg. 1929
DAIICHI SANKYO BUSINESS ASSOCIE CO., LTD.—See Daiichi Sankyo Co., Ltd.; *Int'l*, pg. 1929
DAIICHI SANKYO CHEMICAL PHARMA CO., LTD.—See Daiichi Sankyo Co., Ltd.; *Int'l*, pg. 1929
DAIICHI SANKYO (CHINA) HOLDINGS CO., LTD.—See Daiichi Sankyo Co., Ltd.; *Int'l*, pg. 1929
DAIICHI SANKYO CO., LTD. - AKITA PLANT—See Daiichi Sankyo Co., Ltd.; *Int'l*, pg. 1929
DAIICHI SANKYO CO., LTD. - HIRATSUKA PLANT—See Daiichi Sankyo Co., Ltd.; *Int'l*, pg. 1929
DAIICHI SANKYO CO., LTD. - ODAWARA PLANT—See Daiichi Sankyo Co., Ltd.; *Int'l*, pg. 1929
DAIICHI SANKYO CO., LTD. - ONAHAMA PLANT—See Daiichi Sankyo Co., Ltd.; *Int'l*, pg. 1929
DAIICHI SANKYO CO., LTD.; *Int'l*, pg. 1929
DAIICHI SANKYO CO., LTD. - TAKATSUKI PLANT—See Daiichi Sankyo Co., Ltd.; *Int'l*, pg. 1929
DAIICHI SANKYO DEUTSCHLAND GMBH—See Daiichi Sankyo Co., Ltd.; *Int'l*, pg. 1930
DAIICHI SANKYO DEVELOPMENT LTD.—See Daiichi Sankyo Co., Ltd.; *Int'l*, pg. 1930
DAIICHI SANKYO ESPANA, S.A.—See Daiichi Sankyo Co., Ltd.; *Int'l*, pg. 1930
DAIICHI SANKYO ESPHA CO., LTD.—See Daiichi Sankyo Co., Ltd.; *Int'l*, pg. 1929
DAIICHI SANKYO EUROPE GMBH—See Daiichi Sankyo Co., Ltd.; *Int'l*, pg. 1929
DAIICHI SANKYO FRANCE S.A.S.—See Daiichi Sankyo Co., Ltd.; *Int'l*, pg. 1930
DAIICHI SANKYO HAPPINESS CO., LTD.—See Daiichi Sankyo Co., Ltd.; *Int'l*, pg. 1930
DAIICHI SANKYO HEALTHCARE CO., LTD.—See Daiichi Sankyo Co., Ltd.; *Int'l*, pg. 1930
DAIICHI SANKYO HONG KONG LIMITED—See Daiichi Sankyo Co., Ltd.; *Int'l*, pg. 1930
DAIICHI SANKYO ILAC TICARET LTD, STI.—See Daiichi Sankyo Co., Ltd.; *Int'l*, pg. 1930
DAIICHI SANKYO, INC.—See Daiichi Sankyo Co., Ltd.; *Int'l*, pg. 1930
DAIICHI SANKYO INDIA PVT. LTD.—See Daiichi Sankyo Co., Ltd.; *Int'l*, pg. 1930
DAIICHI SANKYO IRELAND LTD.—See Daiichi Sankyo Co., Ltd.; *Int'l*, pg. 1930
DAIICHI SANKYO ITALIA S.P.A.—See Daiichi Sankyo Co., Ltd.; *Int'l*, pg. 1930

COMPANY NAME INDEX

DAIKIN INDUSTRIES, LTD.

Company Index

DAIICHI SANKYO KOREA CO., LTD.—See Daiichi Sankyo Co., Ltd.; *Int'l*, pg. 1930
DAIICHI SANKYO LOGISTICS CO., LTD.—See Daiichi Sankyo Co., Ltd.; *Int'l*, pg. 1930
DAIICHI SANKYO NEDERLAND B.V.—See Daiichi Sankyo Co., Ltd.; *Int'l*, pg. 1930
DAIICHI SANKYO NORDICS APS—See Daiichi Sankyo Co., Ltd.; *Int'l*, pg. 1930
DAIICHI SANKYO NORTHERN EUROPE GMBH—See Daiichi Sankyo Co., Ltd.; *Int'l*, pg. 1930
DAIICHI SANKYO PHARMACEUTICAL (BEIJING) CO., LTD.—See Daiichi Sankyo Co., Ltd.; *Int'l*, pg. 1930
DAIICHI SANKYO PHARMACEUTICAL (SHANGHAI) CO., LTD.—See Daiichi Sankyo Co., Ltd.; *Int'l*, pg. 1930
DAIICHI SANKYO PORTUGAL, LDA.—See Daiichi Sankyo Co., Ltd.; *Int'l*, pg. 1930
DAIICHI SANKYO PORTUGAL, UNIPESSOAL LDA.—See Daiichi Sankyo Co., Ltd.; *Int'l*, pg. 1930
DAIICHI SANKYO PROPHARMA CO., LTD.—See Daiichi Sankyo Co., Ltd.; *Int'l*, pg. 1930
DAIICHI SANKYO RD NOVARE CO., LTD.—See Daiichi Sankyo Co., Ltd.; *Int'l*, pg. 1930
DAIICHI SANKYO (SCHWEIZ) AG—See Daiichi Sankyo Co., Ltd.; *Int'l*, pg. 1929
DAIICHI SANKYO TAIWAN LTD.—See Daiichi Sankyo Co., Ltd.; *Int'l*, pg. 1930
DAIICHI SANKYO (THAILAND) LTD.—See Daiichi Sankyo Co., Ltd.; *Int'l*, pg. 1929
DAIICHI SANKYO UK LIMITED—See Daiichi Sankyo Co., Ltd.; *Int'l*, pg. 1930
DAIICHI SANKYO VIETNAM CO., LTD.—See Daiichi Sankyo Co., Ltd.; *Int'l*, pg. 1930
DAI-ICHI SEIKO AMERICA, INC.—See I-PEX Inc.; *Int'l*, pg. 3563
DAI-ICHI SEIKO CO., LTD. - JOHOR BAHRU FACTORY—See I-PEX Inc.; *Int'l*, pg. 3563
DAI-ICHI SEIKO CO., LTD. - OGORI PLANT—See I-PEX Inc.; *Int'l*, pg. 3564
DAI-ICHI SEIKO CO., LTD. - ONOJO PLANT—See I-PEX Inc.; *Int'l*, pg. 3564
DAI-ICHI SEIKO CO., LTD. - TACHIARAI PLANT—See I-PEX Inc.; *Int'l*, pg. 3564
DAI-ICHI SEIKO CO., LTD. - YAMANASHI PLANT—See I-PEX Inc.; *Int'l*, pg. 3564
DAI-ICHI SEIKO I-PEX CO., LTD.—See I-PEX Inc.; *Int'l*, pg. 3563
DAIICHI SEIKO (M) SDN. BHD.—See I-PEX Inc.; *Int'l*, pg. 3564
DAIICHI SEIMITSU SANGYO CO., LTD.—See Minebea Mitsumi Inc.; *Int'l*, pg. 4902
DAIICHISEKKEN CO., LTD.—See Toyota Tsusho Corporation; *Int'l*, pg. 7876
DAIICHI SETSUBI ENGINEERING CORPORATION—See Shimizu Corporation; *Int'l*, pg. 6835
DAIICHI SHORIN CO., LTD.—See Pole To Win Holdings, Inc.; *Int'l*, pg. 5908
DAIICHI SOGYO CO. LTD.; *Int'l*, pg. 1930
DAIICHI TANKER CO., LTD.—See Mitsui & Co., Ltd.; *Int'l*, pg. 4973
DAIICHI TOGYO CO., LTD.—See ITOCHU Corporation; *Int'l*, pg. 3835
DAIICHI WAREHOUSE CO., LTD.—See INPEX CORPORATION; *Int'l*, pg. 3716
DAIICHI YAKUHIN KOGYO CO., LTD.—See Carlit Co., Ltd.; *Int'l*, pg. 1338
DAIKAFFIL CHEMICALS INDIA LIMITED.; *Int'l*, pg. 1930
DAIKEI DATA PROCESSING CO., LTD.—See Zenrin Co., Ltd.; *Int'l*, pg. 8634
DAIKEN CO., LTD.; *Int'l*, pg. 1930
DAIKEN CORPORATION - MIE PLANT—See Daiken Corporation; *Int'l*, pg. 1931
DAIKEN CORPORATION - OKAYAMA—See Daiken Corporation; *Int'l*, pg. 1931
DAIKEN CORPORATION; *Int'l*, pg. 1931
DAIKEN CORPORATION - TAKAHAGI PLANT—See Daiken Corporation; *Int'l*, pg. 1931
DAIKEN-DAUER-DANFOSS LTD.—See Danfoss A/S; *Int'l*, pg. 1960
DAIKEN ENGINEERING CORPORATION—See Daiken Corporation; *Int'l*, pg. 1931
DAIKEN INDUSTRIES (NINGBO) CORPORATION—See Daiken Corporation; *Int'l*, pg. 1931
DAIKEN MEDICAL CO., LTD.; *Int'l*, pg. 1931
DAIKEN MIRI SDN. BHD.—See Daiken Corporation; *Int'l*, pg. 1931
DAIKEN NEW ZEALAND LIMITED—See Daiken Corporation; *Int'l*, pg. 1931
DAIKEN NEW ZELAND LIMITED—See Daiken Corporation; *Int'l*, pg. 1931
DAIKEN SARAWAK SDN. BHD.—See Daiken Corporation; *Int'l*, pg. 1931
DAIKEN (SHANGHAI) CORPORATION—See Daiken Corporation; *Int'l*, pg. 1931
DAIKEN SOUTHLAND LIMITED—See Daiken Corporation; *Int'l*, pg. 1931
DAIKI ALUMINIUM INDUSTRY CO., LTD.; *Int'l*, pg. 1931
DAIKI ALUMINIUM INDUSTRY (MALAYSIA) SDN. BHD.—See Daiki Aluminium Industry Co., Ltd.; *Int'l*, pg. 1931
DAIKI ALUMINIUM INDUSTRY THAILAND CO., LTD. - AMATA CITY FACTORY—See Daiki Aluminium Industry Co., Ltd.; *Int'l*, pg. 1931
DAIKI ALUMINIUM INDUSTRY THAILAND CO., LTD.—See Daiki Aluminium Industry Co., Ltd.; *Int'l*, pg. 1931
DAIKI ALUMINIUM VIETNAM CO., LTD.—See Daiki Aluminium Industry Co., Ltd.; *Int'l*, pg. 1931
DAIKI AXIS CO., LTD.; *Int'l*, pg. 1932
DAIKI AXIS INDIA PVT. LTD.—See Daiki Axis Co., Ltd.; *Int'l*, pg. 1932
DAIKI AXIS SINGAPORE PTE. LTD.—See Daiki Axis Co., Ltd.; *Int'l*, pg. 1932
DAIKICHI CORPORATION—See Wanoba Group Inc.; *U.S. Private*, pg. 4436
DAIKI CORPORATION—See Komatsu Ltd.; *Int'l*, pg. 4235
DAIKI ENGINEERING CO., LTD.—See Daiki Aluminium Industry Co., Ltd.; *Int'l*, pg. 1931
DAIKI ENGINEERING (SEA) SDN BHD—See Daiki Aluminium Industry Co., Ltd.; *Int'l*, pg. 1931
DAIKI ENGINEERING THAI CO., LTD.—See Daiki Aluminium Industry Co., Ltd.; *Int'l*, pg. 1931
DAIKI (FOSHAN) TRADING LTD.—See Daiki Aluminium Industry Co., Ltd.; *Int'l*, pg. 1931
DAIKI INTERNATIONAL TRADING CORPORATION—See Daiki Aluminium Industry Co., Ltd.; *Int'l*, pg. 1931
DAIKI MATERIAL CO., LTD.—See Daiki Aluminium Industry Co., Ltd.; *Int'l*, pg. 1931
DAIKIN AC (AMERICAS), INC.—See Daikin Industries, Ltd.; *Int'l*, pg. 1932
DAIKIN ACCOUNTING SOLUTIONS CO., LTD—See Daikin Industries, Ltd.; *Int'l*, pg. 1932
DAIKIN AC SPAIN, S.A.—See Daikin Industries, Ltd.; *Int'l*, pg. 1932
DAIKIN AIR CONDITIONING ARGENTINA S.A.—See Daikin Industries, Ltd.; *Int'l*, pg. 1933
DAIKIN AIRCONDITIONING ARGENTINA—See Daikin Industries, Ltd.; *Int'l*, pg. 1933
DAIKIN AIRCONDITIONING BELGIUM NV—See Daikin Industries, Ltd.; *Int'l*, pg. 1933
DAIKIN AIRCONDITIONING CENTRAL EUROPE GMBH—See Daikin Industries, Ltd.; *Int'l*, pg. 1933
DAIKIN AIRCONDITIONING CHILE S.A.—See Daikin Industries, Ltd.; *Int'l*, pg. 1933
DAIKIN AIRCONDITIONING COLOMBIA S.A.S—See Daikin Industries, Ltd.; *Int'l*, pg. 1933
DAIKIN AIR CONDITIONING EGYPT S.A.E.—See Daikin Industries, Ltd.; *Int'l*, pg. 1933
DAIKIN AIRCONDITIONING FRANCE SAS—See Daikin Industries, Ltd.; *Int'l*, pg. 1933
DAIKIN AIRCONDITIONING GERMANY GMBH—See Daikin Industries, Ltd.; *Int'l*, pg. 1933
DAIKIN AIRCONDITIONING GREECE S. A.—See Daikin Industries, Ltd.; *Int'l*, pg. 1933
DAIKIN AIRCONDITIONING (HONG KONG) LTD.—See Daikin Industries, Ltd.; *Int'l*, pg. 1933
DAIKIN AIRCONDITIONING INDIA PRIVATE LIMITED—See Daikin Industries, Ltd.; *Int'l*, pg. 1933
DAIKIN AIRCONDITIONING INDIA PVT. LTD. - RAJASTHAN FACTORY—See Daikin Industries, Ltd.; *Int'l*, pg. 1933
DAIKIN AIRCONDITIONING ITALY S.P.A.—See Daikin Industries, Ltd.; *Int'l*, pg. 1933
DAIKIN AIRCONDITIONING KOREA CO., LTD.—See Daikin Industries, Ltd.; *Int'l*, pg. 1933
DAIKIN AIRCONDITIONING (MALAYSIA) SDN. BHD.—See Daikin Industries, Ltd.; *Int'l*, pg. 1933
DAIKIN AIRCONDITIONING MEXICO, S. DE R.L. DE C.V.—See Daikin Industries, Ltd.; *Int'l*, pg. 1933
DAIKIN AIR CONDITIONING (M) SDN. BHD.—See Daikin Industries, Ltd.; *Int'l*, pg. 1932
DAIKIN AIRCONDITIONING NETHERLANDS B.V.—See Daikin Industries, Ltd.; *Int'l*, pg. 1933
DAIKIN AIRCONDITIONING PERU S.A.C.—See Daikin Industries, Ltd.; *Int'l*, pg. 1933
DAIKIN AIRCONDITIONING PHILIPPINES, INC.—See Daikin Industries, Ltd.; *Int'l*, pg. 1933
DAIKIN AIRCONDITIONING POLAND SP. Z O.O.—See Daikin Industries, Ltd.; *Int'l*, pg. 1933
DAIKIN AIRCONDITIONING PORTUGAL S.A.—See Daikin Industries, Ltd.; *Int'l*, pg. 1933
DAIKIN AIRCONDITIONING SAUDI ARABIA LLC—See Daikin Industries, Ltd.; *Int'l*, pg. 1933
DAIKIN AIR-CONDITIONING (SHANGHAI) CO., LTD. - HUIZHOU BRANCH—See Daikin Industries, Ltd.; *Int'l*, pg. 1933
DAIKIN AIR-CONDITIONING (SHANGHAI) CO., LTD.—See Daikin Industries, Ltd.; *Int'l*, pg. 1933
DAIKIN AIR CONDITIONING SINGAPORE PTE. LTD.—See Daikin Industries, Ltd.; *Int'l*, pg. 1933
DAIKIN AIRCONDITIONING SOUTH AFRICA PTY. LTD.—See Daikin Industries, Ltd.; *Int'l*, pg. 1933
DAIKIN AIR-CONDITIONING TECHNOLOGY (BEIJING), LTD.—See Daikin Industries, Ltd.; *Int'l*, pg. 1933
DAIKIN AIR-CONDITIONING TECHNOLOGY (SHANGHAI), LTD.—See Daikin Industries, Ltd.; *Int'l*, pg. 1933
DAIKIN AIRCONDITIONING (THAILAND) LTD.—See Daikin Industries, Ltd.; *Int'l*, pg. 1933
DAIKIN AIRCONDITIONING U.K., LTD.—See Daikin Industries, Ltd.; *Int'l*, pg. 1933
DAIKIN AIR CONDITIONING (VIETNAM) JOINT STOCK COMPANY—See Daikin Industries, Ltd.; *Int'l*, pg. 1932
DAIKIN AIRTECHNOLOGY & ENGINEERING CO., LTD.—See Daikin Industries, Ltd.; *Int'l*, pg. 1933
DAIKIN AMERICA, INC.—See Daikin Industries, Ltd.; *Int'l*, pg. 1933
DAIKIN APPLIED AMERICAS INC.—See Daikin Industries, Ltd.; *Int'l*, pg. 1936
DAIKIN APPLIED EUROPE S.P.A.—See Daikin Industries, Ltd.; *Int'l*, pg. 1933
DAIKIN APPLIED GERMANY GMBH—See Daikin Industries, Ltd.; *Int'l*, pg. 1933
DAIKIN APPLIED LATIN AMERICA, L.L.C.—See Daikin Industries, Ltd.; *Int'l*, pg. 1933
DAIKIN APPLIED (MALAYSIA) SDN. BHD.—See Daikin Industries, Ltd.; *Int'l*, pg. 1933
DAIKIN APPLIED SYSTEMS CO., LTD.—See Daikin Industries, Ltd.; *Int'l*, pg. 1933
DAIKIN APPLIED (UK) LTD.—See Daikin Industries, Ltd.; *Int'l*, pg. 1933
DAIKIN AR CONDICIONADO BRASIL LTDA.—See Daikin Industries, Ltd.; *Int'l*, pg. 1934
DAIKIN ARKEMA REFRIGERANTS ASIA LTD.—See Daikin Industries, Ltd.; *Int'l*, pg. 1934
DAIKIN ARKEMA REFRIGERANTS TRADING (SHANGHAI) CO., LTD.—See Daikin Industries, Ltd.; *Int'l*, pg. 1934
DAIKIN ASIA SERVICING PTE., LTD.—See Daikin Industries, Ltd.; *Int'l*, pg. 1934
DAIKIN AUSTRALIA PTY. LTD.—See Daikin Industries, Ltd.; *Int'l*, pg. 1934
DAIKIN CHEMICAL EUROPE GMBH—See Daikin Industries, Ltd.; *Int'l*, pg. 1934
DAIKIN CHEMICAL FRANCE S.A.S.—See Daikin Industries, Ltd.; *Int'l*, pg. 1934
DAIKIN CHEMICAL INTERNATIONAL TRADING (SHANGHAI) CO., LTD—See Daikin Industries, Ltd.; *Int'l*, pg. 1934
DAIKIN CHEMICAL NETHERLANDS B.V.—See Daikin Industries, Ltd.; *Int'l*, pg. 1934
DAIKIN CHEMICAL SOUTHEAST ASIA CO., LTD.—See Daikin Industries, Ltd.; *Int'l*, pg. 1934
DAIKIN (CHINA) INVESTMENT CO., LTD.—See Daikin Industries, Ltd.; *Int'l*, pg. 1932
DAIKIN COMPRESSOR INDUSTRIES, LTD.—See Daikin Industries, Ltd.; *Int'l*, pg. 1934
DAIKIN DEVICE CZECH REPUBLIC S.R.O.—See Daikin Industries, Ltd.; *Int'l*, pg. 1934
DAIKIN ELECTRONIC DEVICES MALAYSIA SDN. BHD.—See Daikin Industries, Ltd.; *Int'l*, pg. 1934
DAIKIN EUROPE COORDINATION CENTER NV—See Daikin Industries, Ltd.; *Int'l*, pg. 1934
DAIKIN EUROPE N.V.—See Daikin Industries, Ltd.; *Int'l*, pg. 1934
DAIKIN FACILITIES CO., LTD.—See Daikin Industries, Ltd.; *Int'l*, pg. 1934
DAIKIN FLUOROCHEMICALS (CHINA) CO., LTD.—See Daikin Industries, Ltd.; *Int'l*, pg. 1934
DAIKIN FLUORO COATINGS (SHANGHAI) CO., LTD.—See Daikin Industries, Ltd.; *Int'l*, pg. 1934
DAIKIN FUKUSHI SERVICE CO., LTD.—See Daikin Industries, Ltd.; *Int'l*, pg. 1934
DAIKIN FUORO COATINGS (SHANGHAI) CO., LTD.—See Daikin Industries, Ltd.; *Int'l*, pg. 1934
DAIKIN HOLDINGS (USA), INC.—See Daikin Industries, Ltd.; *Int'l*, pg. 1934
DAIKIN HVAC SOLUTION HOKKAIDO CO., LTD.—See Daikin Industries, Ltd.; *Int'l*, pg. 1934
DAIKIN HVAC SOLUTION KINKI CO., LTD.—See Daikin Industries, Ltd.; *Int'l*, pg. 1934
DAIKIN HVAC SOLUTION KYUSHU CO., LTD.—See Daikin Industries, Ltd.; *Int'l*, pg. 1934
DAIKIN HVAC SOLUTION NIIGATA CO., LTD.—See Daikin Industries, Ltd.; *Int'l*, pg. 1934
DAIKIN HVAC SOLUTION TOHOKU CO., LTD.—See Daikin Industries, Ltd.; *Int'l*, pg. 1934
DAIKIN HVAC SOLUTION TOKAI CO., LTD.—See Daikin Industries, Ltd.; *Int'l*, pg. 1934
DAIKIN HYDRAULIC ENGINEERING CO., LTD.—See Daikin Industries, Ltd.; *Int'l*, pg. 1934
DAIKIN INDUSTRIES CZECH REPUBLIC S.R.O.—See Daikin Industries, Ltd.; *Int'l*, pg. 1934
DAIKIN INDUSTRIES, LTD. - KANAOKA FACTORY—See Daikin Industries, Ltd.; *Int'l*, pg. 1934
DAIKIN INDUSTRIES, LTD. - KASHIMA PLANT—See Daikin Industries, Ltd.; *Int'l*, pg. 1934
DAIKIN INDUSTRIES, LTD. - RINKAI FACTORY—See Daikin Industries, Ltd.; *Int'l*, pg. 1934
DAIKIN INDUSTRIES, LTD. - SHIGA PLANT—See Daikin Industries, Ltd.; *Int'l*, pg. 1934
DAIKIN INDUSTRIES, LTD.; *Int'l*, pg. 1932
DAIKIN INDUSTRIES, LTD. - YODOGAWA PLANT—See Daikin Industries, Ltd.; *Int'l*, pg. 1934
DAIKIN INDUSTRIES (THAILAND) LTD.—See Daikin Industries, Ltd.; *Int'l*, pg. 1934
DAIKIN INFORMATION SYSTEMS CO., LTD.—See Daikin Industries, Ltd.; *Int'l*, pg. 1934

DAIKIN INDUSTRIES, LTD.

DAIKIN ISITMA VE SOGUTMA SISTEMLERI SANAYI TICARET A.S.—See Daikin Industries, Ltd.; *Int'l*, pg. 1934
DAIKIN KOREA CO., LTD.—See Daikin Industries, Ltd.; *Int'l*, pg. 1934
DAIKIN LUBRICATION PRODUCTS & ENGINEERING CO., LTD.—See Daikin Industries, Ltd.; *Int'l*, pg. 1934
DAIKIN MALAYSIA SALES & SERVICE SDN. BHD.—See Daikin Industries, Ltd.; *Int'l*, pg. 1934
DAIKIN MALAYSIA SDN. BHD.—See Daikin Industries, Ltd.; *Int'l*, pg. 1935
DAIKIN MANUFACTURING GERMANY GMBH—See Daikin Industries, Ltd.; *Int'l*, pg. 1935
DAIKIN MARINE (SHANGHAI) CO., LTD.—See Daikin Industries, Ltd.; *Int'l*, pg. 1935
DAIKIN MCQUAY AR CONDICIONADO BRASIL LTDA.—See Daikin Industries, Ltd.; *Int'l*, pg. 1932
DAIKIN MCQUAY MIDDLE EAST FZE—See Daikin Industries, Ltd.; *Int'l*, pg. 1935
DAIKIN MIDDLE EAST & AFRICA FZE—See Daikin Industries, Ltd.; *Int'l*, pg. 1935
DAIKIN MR ENGINEERING CO., LTD.—See Daikin Industries, Ltd.; *Int'l*, pg. 1934
DAIKIN REFRIGERANTS EUROPE GMBH—See Daikin Industries, Ltd.; *Int'l*, pg. 1935
DAIKIN REFRIGERATION MALAYSIA SDN. BHD.—See Daikin Industries, Ltd.; *Int'l*, pg. 1935
DAIKIN RESEARCH & DEVELOPMENT MALAYSIA SDN. BHD.—See Daikin Industries, Ltd.; *Int'l*, pg. 1935
DAIKIN-SAUER-DANFOSS MANUFACTURING LTD.—See Daikin Industries, Ltd.; *Int'l*, pg. 1935
DAIKIN STEEL MALAYSIA SDN. BHD.—See Daikin Industries, Ltd.; *Int'l*, pg. 1935
DAIKIN SUNRISE SETTSU CO., LTD.—See Daikin Industries, Ltd.; *Int'l*, pg. 1935
DAIKIN SWEDEN A.B.—See Daikin Industries, Ltd.; *Int'l*, pg. 1935
DAIKIN TRADING (THAILAND) LTD.—See Daikin Industries, Ltd.; *Int'l*, pg. 1935
DAIKIN U.S. CORPORATION—See Daikin Industries, Ltd.; *Int'l*, pg. 1935
DAIKI OM ALUMINIUM INDUSTRY (PHILIPPINES), INC.—See Daiki Aluminium Industry Co., Ltd.; *Int'l*, pg. 1931
DAIKI REAL ESTATE INFORMATION CO., LTD.—See DCM Holdings Co., Ltd.; *Int'l*, pg. 1992
DAIKI-SIGMA ENGINEERING (CHINA) INC.—See Daiki Aluminium Industry Co., Ltd.; *Int'l*, pg. 1931
DAIKI-USAFI LTD.—See Daiki Axis Co., Ltd.; *Int'l*, pg. 1932
DAIKO ADVERTISING, INC.—See Hakuhodo DY Holdings Incorporated; *Int'l*, pg. 3220
DAIKO ADVERTISING, INC.—See Hakuhodo DY Holdings Incorporated; *Int'l*, pg. 3220
DAIKO ADVERTISING, INC.—See Hakuhodo DY Holdings Incorporated; *Int'l*, pg. 3220
DAIKO ADVERTISING, INC.—See Hakuhodo DY Holdings Incorporated; *Int'l*, pg. 3220
DAIKO ADVERTISING, INC.—See Hakuhodo DY Holdings Incorporated; *Int'l*, pg. 3220
DAIKO ADVERTISING, INC.—See Hakuhodo DY Holdings Incorporated; *Int'l*, pg. 3220
DAIKO (BEIJING) ADVERTISING CO., LTD.—See Hakuhodo DY Holdings Incorporated; *Int'l*, pg. 3220
DAIKO COMMUNICATIONS ASIA CO., LTD.—See Hakuhodo DY Holdings Incorporated; *Int'l*, pg. 3220
DAIKO DENSHI TSUSHIN, LTD.; *Int'l*, pg. 1937
DAIKO HOKURIKU INC.—See Hakuhodo DY Holdings Incorporated; *Int'l*, pg. 3220
DAIKOH OWANO CO.,LTD.—See Hanwa Co., Ltd.; *Int'l*, pg. 3261
DAIKOH STEEL CO., LTD.—See Hanwa Co., Ltd.; *Int'l*, pg. 3261
DAIKO KANSAI INC.—See Hakuhodo DY Holdings Incorporated; *Int'l*, pg. 3220
DAIKO KOBE INC.—See Hakuhodo DY Holdings Incorporated; *Int'l*, pg. 3220
DAIKOKU DENKI CO., LTD. - KASUGAI DIVISION—See Daikoku Denki Co., Ltd.; *Int'l*, pg. 1937
DAIKOKU DENKI CO., LTD. - KOZOJI DIVISION—See Daikoku Denki Co., Ltd.; *Int'l*, pg. 1937
DAIKOKU DENKI CO., LTD. - SAKASHITA DIVISION—See Daikoku Denki Co., Ltd.; *Int'l*, pg. 1937
DAIKOKU DENKI CO., LTD.; *Int'l*, pg. 1937
DAIKOKU ELECTRIC WIRE CO., LTD. - KUROBANE FACTORY—See Sumitomo Electric Industries, Ltd.; *Int'l*, pg. 7277
DAIKOKU ELECTRIC WIRE CO., LTD. - MUIKAMACHI FACTORY—See Sumitomo Electric Industries, Ltd.; *Int'l*, pg. 7277
DAIKOKU ELECTRIC WIRE CO., LTD. - SENMAYA FACTORY—See Sumitomo Electric Industries, Ltd.; *Int'l*, pg. 7277
DAIKOKU ELECTRIC WIRE CO., LTD.—See Sumitomo Electric Industries, Ltd.; *Int'l*, pg. 7277
DAIKOKU ELECTRONICS (PHILS.), INC.—See Sumitomo Electric Industries, Ltd.; *Int'l*, pg. 7277
DAIKOKU ELECTRONICS (THAILAND), LTD.—See Sumitomo Electric Industries, Ltd.; *Int'l*, pg. 7277

DAIKOKUTENBUSSAN CO., LTD.; *Int'l*, pg. 1937
DAIKOKUYA HOLDINGS CO., LTD.; *Int'l*, pg. 1937
DAIKO KYUSYU ADVERTISING INC.—See Hakuhodo DY Holdings Incorporated; *Int'l*, pg. 3220
DAIKO MEDIAX INC.—See Hakuhodo DY Holdings Incorporated; *Int'l*, pg. 3220
DAIKO MIE INC.—See Hakuhodo DY Holdings Incorporated; *Int'l*, pg. 3220
DAIKO ONES OSAKA INC.—See Hakuhodo DY Holdings Incorporated; *Int'l*, pg. 3220
DAIKO SANGYO CO., LTD.—See Hanwa Co., Ltd.; *Int'l*, pg. 3261
DAIKO TSUSAN CO., LTD.; *Int'l*, pg. 1937
DAIKO WEST INC.—See Hakuhodo DY Holdings Incorporated; *Int'l*, pg. 3220
DAIKYO FERTILIZER CO., LTD.—See euglena Co., Ltd.; *Int'l*, pg. 2526
DAIKYO GYORUI CO., LTD—See Maruha Nichiro Corporation; *Int'l*, pg. 4711
DAIKYO INCORPORATED—See ORIX Corporation; *Int'l*, pg. 5633
DAIKYO L. DESIGN INCORPORATED—See ORIX Corporation; *Int'l*, pg. 5634
DAIKYONISHIKAWA CORPORATION—See Nishikawa Rubber Co., Ltd.; *Int'l*, pg. 5364
DAIKYO REALDO INCORPORATED—See ORIX Corporation; *Int'l*, pg. 5634
DAIKYO SEIKO, LTD.—See West Pharmaceutical Services, Inc.; *U.S. Public*, pg. 2352
DAILEY & ASSOCIATES—See The Interpublic Group of Companies, Inc.; *U.S. Public*, pg. 2090
DAILEY & WELLS COMMUNICATIONS; *U.S. Private*, pg. 1145
DAILITE CO., LTD.—See ITOCHU Corporation; *Int'l*, pg. 3835
DAI LOC FELDSPAR COMPANY LIMITED—See Quang Nam Mineral Industry Corporation; *Int'l*, pg. 6153
THE DAILY ARDMOREITE—See Gannett Co., Inc.; *U.S. Public*, pg. 904
DAILY BAKERY SDN. BHD.—See SDS Group Berhad; *Int'l*, pg. 6659
THE DAILY BEAST COMPANY LLC—See IAC Inc.; *U.S. Public*, pg. 1083
THE DAILY BEAST—See IAC Inc.; *U.S. Public*, pg. 1083
DAILY BREAD MINISTRIES; *U.S. Private*, pg. 1145
THE DAILY BREEZE—See Alden Global Capital LLC; *U.S. Private*, pg. 158
THE DAILY BUZZ, LLC—See Mojo Brands Media, LLC; *U.S. Private*, pg. 2766
DAILY CAMERA—See Alden Global Capital LLC; *U.S. Private*, pg. 157
DAILY CAMERA—See Alden Global Capital LLC; *U.S. Private*, pg. 157
DAILYCANDY, LLC—See Comcast Corporation; *U.S. Public*, pg. 540
DAILYCER BV—See OEP Capital Advisors, L.P.; *U.S. Private*, pg. 2998
DAILYCER NEDERLAND B.V., TILBURG—See OEP Capital Advisors, L.P.; *U.S. Private*, pg. 2998
DAILYCER S.A.—See OEP Capital Advisors, L.P.; *U.S. Private*, pg. 2998
THE DAILY CHRONICLE—See Shaw Suburban Media Group, Inc.; *U.S. Private*, pg. 3628
THE DAILY DEMOCRAT—See Alden Global Capital LLC; *U.S. Private*, pg. 156
THE DAILY DISPATCH—See Paxton Media Group LLC; *U.S. Private*, pg. 3116
DAILY EQUIPMENT COMPANY—See Mitsubishi Heavy Industries, Ltd.; *Int'l*, pg. 4956
DAILY EXPRESS, INC.; *U.S. Private*, pg. 1145
DAILY FISH SUPPLIES—See The Bidvest Group Limited; *Int'l*, pg. 7622
DAILY FREIGHT (1994) LTD—See Mainfreight Ltd.; *Int'l*, pg. 4650
DAILY FREIGHT LTD.—See Mainfreight Ltd.; *Int'l*, pg. 4650
DAILY GAZETTE CO. INC.; *U.S. Private*, pg. 1145
DAILY GROWTH SECURITIES LIMITED—See China Finance Online Co. Limited; *Int'l*, pg. 1502
THE DAILY HERALD COMPANY—See Black Press Group Ltd.; *Int'l*, pg. 1059
THE DAILY HERALD—See Lee Enterprises, Incorporated; *U.S. Public*, pg. 1300
DAILY INCHES, INC.—See Upland Software, Inc.; *U.S. Public*, pg. 2264
THE DAILY INDEPENDENT, INC.—See Gannett Co., Inc.; *U.S. Public*, pg. 906
DAILY INSTRUMENTS INC.; *U.S. Private*, pg. 1145
THE DAILY ITEM; *U.S. Private*, pg. 4017
THE DAILY ITEM—See The Retirement Systems of Alabama; *U.S. Private*, pg. 4105
DAILY JOURNAL CORPORATION; *U.S. Public*, pg. 620
DAILY JOURNAL OF COMMERCE, INC.—See The Dolan Company; *U.S. Private*, pg. 4022
THE DAILY JOURNAL—See Gannett Co., Inc.; *U.S. Public*, pg. 900
DAILY JOURNAL—See Home News Enterprises, LLC; *U.S. Private*, pg. 1971

CORPORATE AFFILIATIONS

THE DAILY JOURNAL—See Lee Enterprises, Incorporated; *U.S. Public*, pg. 1300
THE DAILY LOCAL NEWS—See Alden Global Capital LLC; *U.S. Private*, pg. 158
DAILY MAIL & GENERAL TRUST PLC; *Int'l*, pg. 1937
DAILYMOTION S.A.—See Vivendi SE; *Int'l*, pg. 8266
THE DAILY NEWS - JACKSONVILLE, NC—See Gannett Co., Inc.; *U.S. Public*, pg. 906
DAILY NEWS, L.P.; *U.S. Public*, pg. 1145
THE DAILY NEWS—See Alden Global Capital LLC; *U.S. Private*, pg. 158
THE DAILY NEWS—See The Nutting Company, Inc.; *U.S. Private*, pg. 4086
DAILY NEWS-SUN - SURPRISE TODAY - GLENDALE/PEORIA TODAY—See 10/13 Communications LLC; *U.S. Private*, pg. 2
DAILY NEWS TRIBUNE INC.—See The B. F. Shaw Printing Company; *U.S. Private*, pg. 3990
THE DAILY OAKLAND PRESS—See Alden Global Capital LLC; *U.S. Private*, pg. 158
DAILY POLYMER CO., LTD.; *Int'l*, pg. 1938
THE DAILY PRESS, INC.—See Tribune Publishing Company; *U.S. Public*, pg. 4228
THE DAILY PRESS—See American Consolidated Media LP; *U.S. Private*, pg. 228
DAILY PRESS—See Gannett Co., Inc.; *U.S. Public*, pg. 904
THE DAILY PROGRESS—See Lee Enterprises, Incorporated; *U.S. Public*, pg. 1299
DAILY RACING FORM, INC.—See Arlington Capital Partners LLC; *U.S. Private*, pg. 327
DAILY RACING FORM, LLC—See Z Capital Group, LLC; *U.S. Private*, pg. 4595
THE DAILY RECORD COMPANY, LLC—See The Dolan Company; *U.S. Private*, pg. 4022
DAILY RECORD NEWSPAPER—See Pioneer Newspapers Inc.; *U.S. Private*, pg. 3187
DAILY RECORD—See Gannett Co., Inc.; *U.S. Public*, pg. 897
DAILY REPORTER PUBLISHING COMPANY—See The Dolan Company; *U.S. Private*, pg. 4022
THE DAILY REPORTER—See Gannett Co., Inc.; *U.S. Public*, pg. 904
DAILY REPORTER—See Home News Enterprises, LLC; *U.S. Private*, pg. 1971
DAILY REPUBLICAN REGISTER—See Brehm Communications Inc.; *U.S. Private*, pg. 644
THE DAILY REVIEW—See Alden Global Capital LLC; *U.S. Private*, pg. 155
DAILY SERVICE GMBH—See Raiffeisenlandesbank Oberosterreich Aktiengesellschaft; *Int'l*, pg. 6187
THE DAILY SOUTHERNER—See The Retirement Systems of Alabama; *U.S. Private*, pg. 4105
DAILYS—See Tri Star Energy, LLC; *U.S. Private*, pg. 4221
THE DAILY STAR—See The Retirement Systems of Alabama; *U.S. Private*, pg. 4105
THE DAILY TELEGRAM—See Forum Communications Company; *U.S. Private*, pg. 1577
DAILY TIMES LEADER—See Horizon Publications Inc.; *U.S. Private*, pg. 1982
THE DAILY TIMES—See Gannett Co., Inc.; *U.S. Public*, pg. 900
THE DAILY TIMES—See Gannett Co., Inc.; *U.S. Public*, pg. 900
THE DAILY TRIBUNE—See Alden Global Capital LLC; *U.S. Private*, pg. 158
DAILY TRIBUNE—See Gannett Co., Inc.; *U.S. Public*, pg. 897
DAILY WORLD—See Gannett Co., Inc.; *U.S. Public*, pg. 897
DAIMAN BOWL SDN. BHD.—See Daiman Development Berhad; *Int'l*, pg. 1938
DAIMAN DEVELOPMENT BERHAD; *Int'l*, pg. 1938
DAIMAN GOLF BERHAD—See Daiman Development Berhad; *Int'l*, pg. 1938
DAIMAN JOHOR JAYA SPORTS COMPLEX BERHAD—See Daiman Development Berhad; *Int'l*, pg. 1938
DAIMAN TRADING SDN. BHD.—See Daiman Development Berhad; *Int'l*, pg. 1938
DAIMARU COM DEVELOPMENT INC.—See J. Front Retailing Co., Ltd.; *Int'l*, pg. 3855
DAIMARU ENAWIN CO., LTD.; *Int'l*, pg. 1938
THE DAIMARU HOME SHOPPING, INC.—See J. Front Retailing Co., Ltd.; *Int'l*, pg. 3855
THE DAIMARU, INC.—See J. Front Retailing Co., Ltd.; *Int'l*, pg. 3855
DAIMARU ITAGAMI KAKO CO., LTD.—See Rengo Co., Ltd.; *Int'l*, pg. 6279
DAIMARU KOGYO INTERNATIONAL TRADING (SHANGAI) CO., LTD.—See J. Front Retailing Co., Ltd.; *Int'l*, pg. 3855
DAIMARU KOGYO, LTD.—See J. Front Retailing Co., Ltd.; *Int'l*, pg. 3855
DAIMARU KOGYO (THAILAND) CO., LTD.—See J. Front Retailing Co., Ltd.; *Int'l*, pg. 3855
DAIMARU MATSUZAKAYA DEPARTMENT STORES CO., LTD.—See J. Front Retailing Co., Ltd.; *Int'l*, pg. 3855

COMPANY NAME INDEX

DAIMARU MATSUZAKAYA SALES ASSOCIATES CO. LTD.—See J. Front Retailing Co., Ltd.; *Int'l*, pg. 3855
DAIMARU MATSUZAKAYA TOMONOKAI, CO., LTD.—See J. Front Retailing Co., Ltd.; *Int'l*, pg. 3855
DAIMARU OSAKA SHINSAIBASHI STORE CO., LTD.—See J. Front Retailing Co., Ltd.; *Int'l*, pg. 3855
DAIMEI SLK (PRIVATE) LIMITED—See MIRAIT ONE Corporation; *Int'l*, pg. 4917
DAIMEI TUSAN CO., LTD.—See MIRAIT ONE Corporation; *Int'l*, pg. 4917
DAIMLER AG - MERCEDES-BENZ BERLIN PLANT—See Mercedes-Benz Group AG; *Int'l*, pg. 4820
DAIMLER AG - MERCEDES-BENZ BREMEN PLANT—See Mercedes-Benz Group AG; *Int'l*, pg. 4820
DAIMLER AG - MERCEDES-BENZ GAGGENAU PLANT—See Mercedes-Benz Group AG; *Int'l*, pg. 4820
DAIMLER AG - MERCEDES-BENZ HAMBURG PLANT—See Mercedes-Benz Group AG; *Int'l*, pg. 4820
DAIMLER AG - MERCEDES-BENZ KASSEL PLANT—See Mercedes-Benz Group AG; *Int'l*, pg. 4820
DAIMLER AG - MERCEDES-BENZ MANNHEIM PLANT—See Mercedes-Benz Group AG; *Int'l*, pg. 4820
DAIMLER AG - MERCEDES-BENZ RASTATT PLANT—See Mercedes-Benz Group AG; *Int'l*, pg. 4820
DAIMLER AG - MERCEDES-BENZ SINDELFINGEN PLANT—See Mercedes-Benz Group AG; *Int'l*, pg. 4820
DAIMLER AG - MERCEDES-BENZ WORTH PLANT—See Mercedes-Benz Group AG; *Int'l*, pg. 4820
DAIMLER AUSTRALIA/PACIFIC PTY. LTD.—See Mercedes-Benz Group AG; *Int'l*, pg. 4820
DAIMLER BELGIUM FINANCIAL COMPANY S.A.—See Mercedes-Benz Group AG; *Int'l*, pg. 4820
DAIMLER-BENZ AG & CO. AMICITIA GRUNDSTUCKS-VERMIETUNG POTSDAMER PLATZ OHG—See Mercedes-Benz Group AG; *Int'l*, pg. 4824
DAIMLER-BENZ AG & CO. EFFICIENTIA GRUNDSTUCK-SVERMIETUNG POTSDAMER PLATZ OHG—See Mercedes-Benz Group AG; *Int'l*, pg. 4824
DAIMLER-BENZ AG & CO. LEGITIMA GRUNDSTUCKS-VERMIETUNG POTSDAMER PLATZ OHG—See Mercedes-Benz Group AG; *Int'l*, pg. 4824
DAIMLER-BENZ AG & CO. NEGOTIA GRUNDSTUCKS-VERMIETUNG POTSDAMER PLATZ OHG—See Mercedes-Benz Group AG; *Int'l*, pg. 4824
DAIMLER-BENZ AG & CO. NOBILITAS GRUNDSTUCKS-VERMIETUNG POTSDAMER PLATZ OHG—See Mercedes-Benz Group AG; *Int'l*, pg. 4824
DAIMLER-BENZ AG & CO. PROSPERA GRUNDSTUCKS-VERMIETUNG POTSDAMER PLATZ OHG—See Mercedes-Benz Group AG; *Int'l*, pg. 4824
DAIMLER BUSES GMBH—See Mercedes-Benz Group AG; *Int'l*, pg. 4820
DAIMLER BUSES NORTH CAROLINA LLC—See Mercedes-Benz Group AG; *Int'l*, pg. 4821
DAIMLER CANADA FINANCE INC—See Mercedes-Benz Group AG; *Int'l*, pg. 4821
DAIMLER COLOMBIA S. A.—See Mercedes-Benz Group AG; *Int'l*, pg. 4821
DAIMLER ESPANA GESTION INMOBILIARIA, S.L.—See Mercedes-Benz Group AG; *Int'l*, pg. 4821
DAIMLER EXPORT & TRADE FINANCE GMBH—See Mercedes-Benz Group AG; *Int'l*, pg. 4821
DAIMLER FINANCE NORTH AMERICA LLC—See Mercedes-Benz Group AG; *Int'l*, pg. 4821
DAIMLER FINANCIAL SERVICES JAPAN CO., LTD.—See Mercedes-Benz Group AG; *Int'l*, pg. 4826
DAIMLER FINANCIAL SERVICES MEXICO, S. DE R.L. DE C.V.—See Mercedes-Benz Group AG; *Int'l*, pg. 4821
DAIMLER FLEETBOARD GMBH—See Mercedes-Benz Group AG; *Int'l*, pg. 4821
DAIMLER FLEETBOARD UK LTD.—See Mercedes-Benz Group AG; *Int'l*, pg. 4821
DAIMLER FLEET MANAGEMENT GMBH—See Mercedes-Benz Group AG; *Int'l*, pg. 4821
DAIMLER FLEET SERVICES A.S.—See Mercedes-Benz Group AG; *Int'l*, pg. 4821
DAIMLER GROUP SERVICES MADRID, S.A.—See Mercedes-Benz Group AG; *Int'l*, pg. 4821
DAIMLER INDIA COMMERCIAL VEHICLES PRIVATE LIMITED—See Mercedes-Benz Group AG; *Int'l*, pg. 4821
DAIMLER INSURANCE AGENCY LLC—See Mercedes-Benz Group AG; *Int'l*, pg. 4821
DAIMLER INSURANCE SERVICES GMBH—See Mercedes-Benz Group AG; *Int'l*, pg. 4821
DAIMLER INSURANCE SERVICES UK LIMITED—See Mercedes-Benz Group AG; *Int'l*, pg. 4821
DAIMLER INTERNATIONAL ASSIGNMENT SERVICES USA, LLC—See Mercedes-Benz Group AG; *Int'l*, pg. 4821
DAIMLER INTERNATIONAL FINANCE B.V.—See Mercedes-Benz Group AG; *Int'l*, pg. 4821
DAIMLER IT RETAIL GMBH—See Mercedes-Benz Group AG; *Int'l*, pg. 4821
DAIMLER MANUFACTURA, S.A. DE C.V.—See Mercedes-Benz Group AG; *Int'l*, pg. 4821
DAIMLER MERIDIAN CORPORATION—See Mercedes-Benz Group AG; *Int'l*, pg. 4821
DAIMLER MIDDLE EAST & LEVANT FZE—See Mercedes-Benz Group AG; *Int'l*, pg. 4821
DAIMLER MITARBEITER WOHNFINANZ GMBH—See Mercedes-Benz Group AG; *Int'l*, pg. 4821
DAIMLER MOBILITY AG—See Mercedes-Benz Group AG; *Int'l*, pg. 4821
DAIMLER NORTH AMERICA FINANCE CORPORATION—See Mercedes-Benz Group AG; *Int'l*, pg. 4822
DAIMLER NORTHEAST ASIA PARTS TRADING AND SERVICES CO., LTD.—See Mercedes-Benz Group AG; *Int'l*, pg. 4822
DAIMLER PARTS BRAND GMBH—See Mercedes-Benz Group AG; *Int'l*, pg. 4822
DAIMLER PROTICS GMBH—See Mercedes-Benz Group AG; *Int'l*, pg. 4824
DAIMLER PURCHASING COORDINATION CORP.—See Mercedes-Benz Group AG; *Int'l*, pg. 4822
DAIMLER RE BROKERS GMBH—See Mercedes-Benz Group AG; *Int'l*, pg. 4822
DAIMLER RE INSURANCE S.A. LUXEMBOURG—See Mercedes-Benz Group AG; *Int'l*, pg. 4822
DAIMLER RETAIL RECEIVABLES LLC—See Mercedes-Benz Group AG; *Int'l*, pg. 4822
DAIMLER SERVICIOS CORPORATIVOS MEXICO S. DE R.L. DE C.V—See Mercedes-Benz Group AG; *Int'l*, pg. 4822
DAIMLER SOUTH EAST ASIA PTE. LTD.—See Mercedes-Benz Group AG; *Int'l*, pg. 4822
DAIMLER TRUCK AUSTRALIA PACIFIC PTY. LTD.—See Daimler Truck Holding AG; *Int'l*, pg. 1938
DAIMLER TRUCK FINANCIAL SERVICES BELGIUM N.V.—See Daimler Truck Holding AG; *Int'l*, pg. 1938
DAIMLER TRUCK FINANCIAL SERVICES CANADA CORPORATION—See Daimler Truck Holding AG; *Int'l*, pg. 1938
DAIMLER TRUCK FINANCIAL SERVICES ITALIA S.P.A.—See Daimler Truck Holding AG; *Int'l*, pg. 1938
DAIMLER TRUCK FINANCIAL SERVICES NEDERLAND B.V.—See Daimler Truck Holding AG; *Int'l*, pg. 1938
DAIMLER TRUCK FINANCIAL SERVICES UK LIMITED—See Daimler Truck Holding AG; *Int'l*, pg. 1938
DAIMLER TRUCK HOLDING AG; *Int'l*, pg. 1938
DAIMLER TRUCK NEDERLAND B.V.—See Daimler Truck Holding AG; *Int'l*, pg. 1938
DAIMLER TRUCKS CANADA LTD.—See Mercedes-Benz Group AG; *Int'l*, pg. 4822
DAIMLER TRUCKS KOREA LTD.—See Mercedes-Benz Group AG; *Int'l*, pg. 4822
DAIMLER TRUCKS NORTH AMERICA LLC—See Mercedes-Benz Group AG; *Int'l*, pg. 4822
DAIMLER TRUCKS NORTH AMERICA—See Mercedes-Benz Group AG; *Int'l*, pg. 4822
DAIMLER TRUCK SOUTHERN AFRICA LTD.—See Daimler Truck Holding AG; *Int'l*, pg. 1938
DAIMLER TRUCKS REMARKETING CORPORATION—See Mercedes-Benz Group AG; *Int'l*, pg. 4824
DAIMLER TRUST LEASING LLC—See Mercedes-Benz Group AG; *Int'l*, pg. 4824
DAIMLER TSS GMBH—See Mercedes-Benz Group AG; *Int'l*, pg. 4822
DAIMLER UK SHARE TRUSTEE LTD.—See Mercedes-Benz Group AG; *Int'l*, pg. 4824
DAIMLER UNTERSTUTZUNGSKASSE GMBH—See Mercedes-Benz Group AG; *Int'l*, pg. 4824
DAIMLER VANS MANUFACTURING, LLC—See Mercedes-Benz Group AG; *Int'l*, pg. 4824
DAIMLER VANS USA, LLC—See Mercedes-Benz Group AG; *Int'l*, pg. 4824
DAIMLER VEHICLE INNOVATIONS USA, LLC—See Mercedes-Benz Group AG; *Int'l*, pg. 4824
DAIMLER VEHICULOS COMERCIALES MEXICO S. DE R.L. DE C.V.—See Mercedes-Benz Group AG; *Int'l*, pg. 4824
DAIMLER VORSORGE UND VERSICHERUNGSDIENST GMBH—See Mercedes-Benz Group AG; *Int'l*, pg. 4824
DAIMYO AS; *Int'l*, pg. 1938
DAINAN TECH (S) PTE LTD—See ESPEC Corp.; *Int'l*, pg. 2505
DA INFORMATION CO., LTD.—See Dong-A Socio Holdings, Co., Ltd.; *Int'l*, pg. 2164
DAINGERFIELD HOLDING COMPANY; *U.S. Private*, pg. 1145
DAINICHI BUTSURYU CO., LTD.—See Tradia Corporation; *Int'l*, pg. 7889
DAINICHI CHEMICAL CORP.—See Daicel Corporation; *Int'l*, pg. 1919
DAINICHI COLOR INDIA PRIVATE LTD.—See Dainichiseika Color & Chemicals Mfg. Co., Ltd.; *Int'l*, pg. 1939
DAINICHI COLOR (THAILAND) LTD.—See Dainichiseika Color & Chemicals Mfg. Co., Ltd.; *Int'l*, pg. 1939
DAINICHI COLOR VIETNAM CO., LTD.—See Dainichiseika Color & Chemicals Mfg. Co., Ltd.; *Int'l*, pg. 1939
DAINICHI CO., LTD.; *Int'l*, pg. 1938
DAINICHI PAPER CORPORATION—See Daio Paper Corporation; *Int'l*, pg. 1939
DAINICHISEIKA COLOR & CHEMICALS MFG. CO., LTD.; *Int'l*, pg. 1938
DAINICHISEIKA COLOR & CHEMICALS S.A.—See Dainichiseika Color & Chemicals Mfg. Co., Ltd.; *Int'l*, pg. 1939
DAINICHISEIKA (H.K.) COLOURING CO., LTD.—See Dainichiseika Color & Chemicals Mfg. Co., Ltd.; *Int'l*, pg. 1939
DAINICHISEIKA (H.K.) LTD.—See Dainichiseika Color & Chemicals Mfg. Co., Ltd.; *Int'l*, pg. 1939
DAINICHISEIKA INK (GUANGZHOU) LTD.—See Dainichiseika Color & Chemicals Mfg. Co., Ltd.; *Int'l*, pg. 1939
DAINICHISEIKA (SHANGHAI) TRADING LTD.—See Dainichiseika Color & Chemicals Mfg. Co., Ltd.; *Int'l*, pg. 1939
DAINICHI TSUSHIN CO., LTD.—See COMSYS Holdings Corporation; *Int'l*, pg. 1761
DAINIHON JOCHUGIKU CO., LTD.—See Tecnos Japan Inc.; *Int'l*, pg. 7517
DAI NIPPON CONSTRUCTION—See ENEOS Holdings, Inc.; *Int'l*, pg. 2415
DAINIPPON INK & CHEMICALS, INC.—See DIC Corporation; *Int'l*, pg. 2108
DAINIPPON INK & CHEMICALS (PHILIPPINES), INC.—See DIC Corporation; *Int'l*, pg. 2108
DAINIPPON INK & CHEMICALS (SINGAPORE) PTE., LTD.—See DIC Corporation; *Int'l*, pg. 2108
DAI-NIPPON MEIJI SUGAR CO., LTD.—See Mitsubishi Corporation; *Int'l*, pg. 4938
DAINIPPON PLASTICS CO. LTD.—See ITOCHU Corporation; *Int'l*, pg. 3835
DAI NIPPON PRINTING CO. (AUSTRALIA) PTY. LTD.—See Dai Nippon Printing Co., Ltd.; *Int'l*, pg. 1915
DAI NIPPON PRINTING CO., LTD.; *Int'l*, pg. 1914
DAI NIPPON PRINTING CO. (TAIWAN), LTD.—See Dai Nippon Printing Co., Ltd.; *Int'l*, pg. 1915
DAI NIPPON PRINTING (EUROPA) GMBH—See Dai Nippon Printing Co., Ltd.; *Int'l*, pg. 1915
DAINIPPON SCREEN (AUSTRALIA) PTY. LTD.—See Screen Holdings Co., Ltd.; *Int'l*, pg. 6654
DAINIPPON SCREEN (CHINA) LTD.—See Screen Holdings Co., Ltd.; *Int'l*, pg. 6654
DAINIPPON SCREEN (DEUTSCHLAND) GMBH—See Screen Holdings Co., Ltd.; *Int'l*, pg. 6654
DAINIPPON SCREEN ELECTRONICS FRANCE SARL—See Screen Holdings Co., Ltd.; *Int'l*, pg. 6655
DAINIPPON SCREEN ELECTRONICS (SHANGHAI) CO., LTD—See Screen Holdings Co., Ltd.; *Int'l*, pg. 6655
DAINIPPON SCREEN ELECTRONICS (TAIWAN) CO., LTD—See Screen Holdings Co., Ltd.; *Int'l*, pg. 6655
DAINIPPON SCREEN GRAPHICS (USA), LLC—See Screen Holdings Co., Ltd.; *Int'l*, pg. 6655
DAINIPPON SCREEN (KOREA) CO., LTD. —See Screen Holdings Co., Ltd.; *Int'l*, pg. 6655
DAINIPPON SCREEN MFG. CO., LTD. - HIKONE PLANT—See Screen Holdings Co., Ltd.; *Int'l*, pg. 6655
DAINIPPON SCREEN MFG. CO., LTD. - KUZE PLANT—See Screen Holdings Co., Ltd.; *Int'l*, pg. 6655
DAINIPPON SCREEN MFG. CO., LTD. - RAKUSAI PLANT—See Screen Holdings Co., Ltd.; *Int'l*, pg. 6655
DAINIPPON SCREEN MFG. CO., LTD. - TAGA PLANT—See Screen Holdings Co., Ltd.; *Int'l*, pg. 6655
DAINIPPON SCREEN (NEDERLAND) B.V.—See Screen Holdings Co., Ltd.; *Int'l*, pg. 6655
DAINIPPON SCREEN SINGAPORE PTE. LTD.—See Screen Holdings Co., Ltd.; *Int'l*, pg. 6655
DAINIPPON SCREEN UNTERSTUETZUNGSKASSE GMBH—See Screen Holdings Co., Ltd.; *Int'l*, pg. 6655
DAI NIPPON SHOJI CO., LTD.—See Dai Nippon Printing Co., Ltd.; *Int'l*, pg. 1915
DAINIPPON SUMITOMO PHARMA EUROPE LTD.—See Sumitomo Chemical Company, Limited; *Int'l*, pg. 7267
DAI NIPPON TORYO CO., LTD.; *Int'l*, pg. 1916
DAI NIPPON TORYO HANBAI CO., LTD.—See Dai Nippon Toryo Co., Ltd.; *Int'l*, pg. 1916
DAI NIPPON TORYO HOKKAIDO CO., LTD.—See Dai Nippon Toryo Co., Ltd.; *Int'l*, pg. 1916
DAI NIPPON TORYO MEXICANA S. A. DE C. V.—See Dai Nippon Toryo Co., Ltd.; *Int'l*, pg. 1916
DA INVENT CO., LTD.—See Daiki Axis Co., Ltd.; *Int'l*, pg. 1932
DAIO ENGINEERING CO., LTD.—See Daio Paper Corporation; *Int'l*, pg. 1939
DAIOHS COFFEE COMMERCIAL TRADE (SHANGHAI) CO., LTD.—See Daiohs Corporation; *Int'l*, pg. 1940
DAIOHS CORPORATION; *Int'l*, pg. 1940
DAIOHS HONG KONG LIMITED—See Daiohs Corporation; *Int'l*, pg. 1940
DAIOHS KOREA CO. LTD.—See Daiohs Corporation; *Int'l*, pg. 1940
DAIOHS SINGAPORE PTE. LTD.—See Daiohs Corporation; *Int'l*, pg. 1940
DAIO LOGISTICS CO., LTD.—See Daio Paper Corporation; *Int'l*, pg. 1939
DAIO MILL SUPPORT CO., LTD.—See Daio Paper Corporation; *Int'l*, pg. 1939
DAIO MILL SUPPORT TOKAI CORPORATION—See Daio Paper Corporation; *Int'l*, pg. 1939

DAIOHS CORPORATION

DAIO PACKAGE CORPORATION—See Daio Paper Corporation; *Int'l*, pg. 1939
DAIO PAPER CORPORATION; *Int'l*, pg. 1939
DAIO PAPER PRODUCTS CORPORATION—See Daio Paper Corporation; *Int'l*, pg. 1939
DAIO POSTAL CHEMICAL CORPORATION—See Daio Paper Corporation; *Int'l*, pg. 1939
DAIO PRINTING CORPORATION—See Daio Paper Corporation; *Int'l*, pg. 1939
DAIO PULP & PAPER CO., LTD.—See Daio Paper Corporation; *Int'l*, pg. 1939
DAIOS PLASTICS S.A; *Int'l*, pg. 1940
DAIPLA CORPORATION—See ITOCHU Corporation; *Int'l*, pg. 3835
DAIPLA WINTES CO., LTD.—See ITOCHU Corporation; *Int'l*, pg. 3835
DAIPOLY SYSTEM CORPORATION—See CREATE CORPORATION; *Int'l*, pg. 1832
DAIPRODCO MEXICO S. DE R.L. DE C.V.—See Mercedes-Benz Group AG; *Int'l*, pg. 4824
DAIPUR WIND FARM PTY. LTD.—See BayWa AG; *Int'l*, pg. 917
DAIREI CO., LTD.; *Int'l*, pg. 1940
DAIREN CHEMICAL CORPORATION—See ChangChun Group; *Int'l*, pg. 1442
DAIREN CHEMICAL CORPORATION—See Nan Pao Resins Chemical Co., Ltd.; *Int'l*, pg. 5138
DAIREN CHEMICAL (JIANGSU) CO. LTD.—See ChangChun Group; *Int'l*, pg. 1442
DAIREN CHEMICAL (JIANGSU) CO. LTD.—See Nan Pao Resins Chemical Co., Ltd.; *Int'l*, pg. 5138
DAIREN CHEMICAL (M) SDN. BHD.—See ChangChun Group; *Int'l*, pg. 1442
DAIREN CHEMICAL (M) SDN. BHD.—See Nan Pao Resins Chemical Co., Ltd.; *Int'l*, pg. 5138
DAIRIBORD HOLDINGS LIMITED; *Int'l*, pg. 1940
DAIRIBORD MALAWI LIMITED—See Dairibord Holdings Limited; *Int'l*, pg. 1940
DAIRIBORD ZIMBABWE (PRIVATE) LIMITED—See Dairibord Holdings Limited; *Int'l*, pg. 1940
DAIRICONCEPTS, L.P.—See Dairy Farmers of America, Inc.; *U.S. Private*, pg. 1145
DAIRICONCEPTS, L.P.—See Fonterra Co-Operative Group Ltd.; *Int'l*, pg. 2726
DAIRYAMERICA, INC.; *U.S. Private*, pg. 1146
DAIRY BARN STORES INC.; *U.S. Private*, pg. 1145
DAIRYBORN FOODS LIMITED—See Kerry Group plc; *Int'l*, pg. 4138
DAIRY CONVEYOR CORPORATION; *U.S. Private*, pg. 1145
DAIRY CREST GROUP PLC—See Saputo Inc.; *Int'l*, pg. 6575
DAIRY CREST LIMITED—See Saputo Inc.; *Int'l*, pg. 6575
THE DAIRY FARM CO., LTD. - 7-ELEVEN—See Jardine Matheson Holdings Limited; *Int'l*, pg. 3909
THE DAIRY FARM CO., LTD. - MANNINGS—See Jardine Matheson Holdings Limited; *Int'l*, pg. 3910
THE DAIRY FARM COMPANY, LTD.—See Jardine Matheson Holdings Limited; *Int'l*, pg. 3909
DAIRY FARMERS OF AMERICA, INC.; *U.S. Private*, pg. 1145
DAIRY FARMERS OF AMERICA - READING PLANT—See Dairy Farmers of America, Inc.; *U.S. Private*, pg. 1146
DAIRY FARM INTERNATIONAL HOLDINGS LIMITED—See Jardine Matheson Holdings Limited; *Int'l*, pg. 3909
DAIRY FARM MANAGEMENT LIMITED—See Jardine Matheson Holdings Limited; *Int'l*, pg. 3909
DAIRY FEEDS INC.; *U.S. Private*, pg. 1146
DAIRYFOOD USA INCORPORATED; *U.S. Private*, pg. 1146
DAIRY FRESH FARMS INC.; *U.S. Private*, pg. 1146
DAIRY FRESH FOODS, INC.; *U.S. Private*, pg. 1146
DAIRY FRESH, LLC—See Dean Foods Company; *U.S. Private*, pg. 1183
DAIRY FRUIT A/S—See Dohler GmbH; *Int'l*, pg. 2156
DAIRYGOLD CO-OPERATIVE SOCIETY LTD; *Int'l*, pg. 1940
DAIRYGOLD DEUTSCHLAND HANDLESGESELLSCHAFT MBH—See Dairygold Co-Operative Society Ltd; *Int'l*, pg. 1940
DAIRYGOLD FINANCE LIMITED—See Dairygold Co-Operative Society Ltd; *Int'l*, pg. 1940
DAIRYGOLD FOOD INGREDIENTS (FRANCE) SAS—See Dairygold Co-Operative Society Ltd; *Int'l*, pg. 1940
DAIRYGOLD FOOD INGREDIENTS LIMITED—See Dairygold Co-Operative Society Ltd; *Int'l*, pg. 1940
DAIRYGOLD FOOD INGREDIENTS (UK) LIMITED—See Dairygold Co-Operative Society Ltd; *Int'l*, pg. 1940
DAIRYGOLD TRADING LIMITED—See Dairygold Co-Operative Society Ltd; *Int'l*, pg. 1940
DAIRYLAND COUNTY MUTUAL INSURANCE CO.—See Sentry Insurance Group; *U.S. Private*, pg. 3611
DAIRYLAND INSURANCE CO.—See Sentry Insurance Group; *U.S. Private*, pg. 3611
DAIRYLAND POWER COOPERATIVE; *U.S. Private*, pg. 1146
DAIRYLAND PRODUCE, LLC—See The Chefs' Warehouse, Inc.; *U.S. Public*, pg. 2059

DAIRYLAND SEED CO. INC.; *U.S. Private*, pg. 1146
DAIRYLAND USA CORPORATION—See The Chefs' Warehouse, Inc.; *U.S. Public*, pg. 2059
DAIRY LIVESTOCK SERVICES PTY. LTD.—See Nutrien Ltd.; *Int'l*, pg. 5492
DAIRY, LLC; *U.S. Private*, pg. 1146
DAIRYMAN'S SUPPLY COMPANY INC.; *U.S. Private*, pg. 1146
DAIRYMAN'S SUPPLY COMPANY INC.—See Dairyman's Supply Company Inc.; *U.S. Private*, pg. 1146
DAIRYMANS SUPPLY COMPANY INC.—See Dairyman's Supply Company Inc.; *U.S. Private*, pg. 1146
DAIRY MARKETING SERVICES, LLC—See Dairy Farmers of America, Inc.; *U.S. Private*, pg. 1146
DAIRY-MIX, INC.; *U.S. Private*, pg. 1146
DAIRY ONE COOPERATIVE INC.; *U.S. Private*, pg. 1146
DAIRY QUEEN CANADA, INC.—See Berkshire Hathaway Inc.; *U.S. Public*, pg. 308
DAIRY SERVICE & MANUFACTURING INC.; *U.S. Private*, pg. 1146
DAIRYTOWN PRODUCTS LIMITED—See Agropur Cooperative; *Int'l*, pg. 220
DAIRYU INC.—See Itoham Yonekyu Holdings Inc.; *Int'l*, pg. 3842
THE DAISAN BANK, LTD.—See San ju San Financial Group, Inc.; *Int'l*, pg. 6521
DAISAN CO., LTD.; *Int'l*, pg. 1940
DAISAN SHIKA KOGYO CO., LTD.—See GSI Creos Corporation; *Int'l*, pg. 3144
DAISEI ENGINEERING CO., LTD.—See Bain Capital, LP; *U.S. Private*, pg. 434
DAISEKI CO. LTD. - CHIBA WORKS—See Daiseki Co. Ltd.; *Int'l*, pg. 1941
DAISEKI CO. LTD. - HOKURIKU UNIT—See Daiseki Co. Ltd.; *Int'l*, pg. 1941
DAISEKI CO. LTD. - KANSAI UNIT—See Daiseki Co. Ltd.; *Int'l*, pg. 1941
DAISEKI CO. LTD. - KANTO FIRST PLANT—See Daiseki Co. Ltd.; *Int'l*, pg. 1941
DAISEKI CO. LTD. - KANTO SECOND PLANT—See Daiseki Co. Ltd.; *Int'l*, pg. 1941
DAISEKI CO. LTD. - KANTO THIRD PLANT—See Daiseki Co. Ltd.; *Int'l*, pg. 1941
DAISEKI CO. LTD. - KYUSHU UNIT—See Daiseki Co. Ltd.; *Int'l*, pg. 1941
DAISEKI CO. LTD. - NAGOYA UNIT—See Daiseki Co. Ltd.; *Int'l*, pg. 1941
DAISEKI CO. LTD.; *Int'l*, pg. 1941
DAISEKI ECO. SOLUTION CO., LTD.; *Int'l*, pg. 1941
DAISEKI MCR CO., LTD.—See Daiseki Co. Ltd.; *Int'l*, pg. 1941
DAISEN CO., LTD. - KANTO PLANT—See Watts Co., Ltd.; *Int'l*, pg. 8359
DAISEN CO., LTD. - KYUSHU PLANT—See Watts Co., Ltd.; *Int'l*, pg. 8359
DAISEN CO., LTD.—See Watts Co., Ltd.; *Int'l*, pg. 8359
DAISEN INTERNATIONAL TRADING (SHANGHAI) CO., LTD.—See Watts Co., Ltd.; *Int'l*, pg. 8359
DAISEN KOSAN CO., LTD.—See Unitika Ltd.; *Int'l*, pg. 8074
DAISEN SINGAPORE PTE. LTD.—See Watts Co., Ltd.; *Int'l*, pg. 8359
THE DAISHI BANK, LTD.—See Daishi Hokuetsu Financial Group, Inc.; *Int'l*, pg. 1941
THE DAISHI BUSINESS SERVICE CO., LTD.—See Daishi Hokuetsu Financial Group, Inc.; *Int'l*, pg. 1941
THE DAISHI CASH BUSINESS CO., LTD.—See Daishi Hokuetsu Financial Group, Inc.; *Int'l*, pg. 1941
THE DAISHI COMPUTER SERVICE CO., LTD.—See Daishi Hokuetsu Financial Group, Inc.; *Int'l*, pg. 1941
THE DAISHI DC CARD CO., LTD.—See Daishi Hokuetsu Financial Group, Inc.; *Int'l*, pg. 1941
THE DAISHI GUARANTY CO., LTD.—See Daishi Hokuetsu Financial Group, Inc.; *Int'l*, pg. 1941
THE DAISHI HOKUETSU BANK, LTD.—See Daishi Hokuetsu Financial Group, Inc.; *Int'l*, pg. 1941
DAISHI HOKUETSU CAREER BRIDGE, CO., LTD.—See Daishi Hokuetsu Financial Group, Inc.; *Int'l*, pg. 1941
DAISHI HOKUETSU FINANCIAL GROUP, INC.; *Int'l*, pg. 1941
DAISHI HOKUETSU SECURITIES CO., LTD.—See Daishi Hokuetsu Financial Group, Inc.; *Int'l*, pg. 1941
THE DAISHI JCB CARD CO., LTD.—See Daishi Hokuetsu Financial Group, Inc.; *Int'l*, pg. 1941
THE DAISHI LEASE CO., LTD.—See Daishi Hokuetsu Financial Group, Inc.; *Int'l*, pg. 1941
DAISHIN BALANCE 4TH SPECIAL PURPOSE ACQUISITION CO LTD; *Int'l*, pg. 1941
DAISHIN CHEMICAL CO., LTD.; *Int'l*, pg. 1941
DAISHIN CORPORATION—See Pan Pacific International Holdings Corporation; *Int'l*, pg. 5715
DAISHIN INFORMATION & COMMUNICATIONS CO.,LTD.; *Int'l*, pg. 1941
DAISHINKU (AMERICA) CORP—See Daishinku Corp.; *Int'l*, pg. 1942
DAISHINKU CORP. - KANZAKI PLANT—See Daishinku Corp.; *Int'l*, pg. 1942
DAISHINKU CORP. - NISHIWAKI PLANT—See Daishinku Corp.; *Int'l*, pg. 1942

DAISHINKU CORP.; *Int'l*, pg. 1942
DAISHINKU CORP. - TOKUSHIMA PRODUCTION DIVISION—See Daishinku Corp.; *Int'l*, pg. 1942
DAISHINKU CORP. - TOTTORI PRODUCTION DIVISION—See Daishinku Corp.; *Int'l*, pg. 1942
DAISHINKU (DEUTSCHLAND) GMBH—See Daishinku Corp.; *Int'l*, pg. 1942
DAISHINKU (DEUTSCHLAND) GMBH—See Daishinku Corp.; *Int'l*, pg. 1942
DAISHINKU (HK) LTD—See Daishinku Corp.; *Int'l*, pg. 1942
DAISHINKU (SINGAPORE) PTE. LTD—See Daishinku Corp.; *Int'l*, pg. 1942
DAISHINKU (THAILAND) CO., LTD.—See Daishinku Corp.; *Int'l*, pg. 1942
DAISHIN PLYWOOD CO., LTD.—See ITOCHU Corporation; *Int'l*, pg. 3835
DAISHINSEIKI CO., LTD.—See Denso Corporation; *Int'l*, pg. 2028
THE DAISHI STAFF SERVICE CO., LTD.—See Daishi Hokuetsu Financial Group, Inc.; *Int'l*, pg. 1941
DAISHO CO., LTD. - FUKUOKA FACTORY—See DAISHO Co., Ltd.; *Int'l*, pg. 1942
DAISHO CO., LTD. - FUKUOKA SECOND FACTORY—See DAISHO Co., Ltd.; *Int'l*, pg. 1942
DAISHO CO., LTD. - KANTO FACTORY—See DAISHO Co., Ltd.; *Int'l*, pg. 1942
DAISHO CO., LTD. - KYUSHU FACTORY—See DAISHO Co., Ltd.; *Int'l*, pg. 1942
DAISHO CO., LTD.; *Int'l*, pg. 1942
DAISHO MICROLINE HOLDINGS LIMITED; *Int'l*, pg. 1942
DAISHOWA-MARUBENI INTERNATIONAL LTD.—See Mercer International Inc.; *Int'l*, pg. 4829
DAISHOWA NORTH AMERICA CORPORATION—See Nippon Paper Industries Co., Ltd.; *Int'l*, pg. 5326
DAISHOWA UNIBOARD CO., LTD.—See Nippon Paper Industries Co., Ltd.; *Int'l*, pg. 5326
DAISHOW CO., LTD.—See Yoshimura Food Holdings K.K.; *Int'l*, pg. 8600
DAISIES DAY NURSERIES LIMITED—See Bain Capital, LP; *U.S. Private*, pg. 437
DAISO CHEMICAL CO., LTD.—See Osaka Soda Co., Ltd.; *Int'l*, pg. 5646
DAISO ENGINEERING CO., LTD.—See Osaka Soda Co., Ltd.; *Int'l*, pg. 5646
DAISO FINE CHEM GMBH—See Osaka Soda Co., Ltd.; *Int'l*, pg. 5646
DAISO FINE CHEM USA,INC.—See Osaka Soda Co., Ltd.; *Int'l*, pg. 5646
DAISO SANGYO CO., LTD.; *Int'l*, pg. 1942
DAISUE CONSTRUCTION CO., LTD.; *Int'l*, pg. 1942
DAISUI CO., LTD.; *Int'l*, pg. 1942
DAISUN CO., LTD.—See Hanwa Co., Ltd.; *Int'l*, pg. 3262
DAISY BRAND INC.; *U.S. Private*, pg. 1146
DAISYBROOK LIMITED—See Sheikh Holdings Group (Investments) Limited; *Int'l*, pg. 6793
DAISY COMMUNICATIONS LTD.—See Daisy Group Limited; *Int'l*, pg. 1942
DAISY CORPORATE SERVICES LIMITED—See Daisy Group Limited; *Int'l*, pg. 1942
DAISY CORPORATE SERVICES TRADING LIMITED—See Daisy Group Limited; *Int'l*, pg. 1943
DAISY GROUP LIMITED; *Int'l*, pg. 1942
DAISY MANUFACTURING COMPANY—See Bruckmann, Rosser, Sherrill & Co., LLC; *U.S. Private*, pg. 671
DAISYO CORPORATION; *Int'l*, pg. 1943
DAISY WHOLESALE LIMITED—See Daisy Group Limited; *Int'l*, pg. 1942
DAISY WHOLESALE LIMITED; *Int'l*, pg. 1943
DAISY WORLDWIDE LIMITED—See Daisy Group Limited; *Int'l*, pg. 1942
DAI-TAC CORPORATION—See Daiken Corporation; *Int'l*, pg. 1931
DAITAI KAKO CO., LTD.—See Nippon Molymer Co., Ltd.; *Int'l*, pg. 5325
DAITEC CO., LTD.—See Daiki Axis Co., Ltd.; *Int'l*, pg. 1932
DAI TELECOM LTD.—See DBAY Advisors Limited; *Int'l*, pg. 1987
DAITEX CO., LTD.—See Komatsu Ltd.; *Int'l*, pg. 4235
DAI THIEN LOC CORPORATION; *Int'l*, pg. 1917
DAITIKU LTD.—See AIN Holdings Inc.; *Int'l*, pg. 234
DAITO ASIA DEVELOPMENT (MALAYSIA) SDN. BHD.—See Daito Trust Construction Co., Ltd.; *Int'l*, pg. 1943
THE DAITO BANK LTD.; *Int'l*, pg. 7636
DAITOBO CO., LTD.; *Int'l*, pg. 1944
DAITO BUILDING MANAGEMENT CO LTD—See Daito Trust Construction Co., Ltd.; *Int'l*, pg. 1943
DAITO CACAO CO., LTD.—See The Nisshin OilliO Group, Ltd.; *Int'l*, pg. 7671
DAITO CHEMICAL CO., LTD.—See Air Water Inc.; *Int'l*, pg. 240
DAITO CHEMIX CORPORATION - FUKUI PLANT—See Daito Chemix Corporation; *Int'l*, pg. 1943
DAITO CHEMIX CORPORATION - SHIZUOKA PLANT—See Daito Chemix Corporation; *Int'l*, pg. 1943
DAITO CHEMIX CORPORATION; *Int'l*, pg. 1943

COMPANY NAME INDEX

DAITO CONSTRUCTION CO., LTD.—See Daito Trust Construction Co., Ltd.; *Int'l*, pg. 1943
DAITO CORPORATE SERVICE CO., LTD.—See Daito Trust Construction Co., Ltd.; *Int'l*, pg. 1943
DAITO CORPORATION—See Kawasaki Kisen Kaisha, Ltd.; *Int'l*, pg. 4099
DAITO DENSO CO., LTD.—See Daitron Co., Ltd.; *Int'l*, pg. 1944
DAITO ELECTRON CO., LTD. - EM MACHIDA FACTORY—See Daitron Co., Ltd.; *Int'l*, pg. 1944
DAITO ELECTRON CO., LTD. - MACHIDA FACTORY—See Daitron Co., Ltd.; *Int'l*, pg. 1944
DAITO FINANCE CO., LTD.—See Daito Trust Construction Co., Ltd.; *Int'l*, pg. 1943
DAITO GAS PARTNER CORPORATION—See Daito Trust Construction Co., Ltd.; *Int'l*, pg. 1943
DAITO GYORUI CO., LTD.—See Maruha Nichiro Corporation; *Int'l*, pg. 4711
DAITO KENTAKU PARTNERS CO., LTD.—See Daito Trust Construction Co., Ltd.; *Int'l*, pg. 1943
DAITO KIHAN CO., LTD.—See Sintokogio Ltd., *Int'l*, pg. 6958
DAITO-KISCO CORPORATION—See Kyung-In Synthetic Corporation; *Int'l*, pg. 4367
DAITO KOGYO CO., LTD.—See Sato shoji Corporation; *Int'l*, pg. 6586
DAITO KOUN CO., LTD.; *Int'l*, pg. 1943
DAITOKU K.K.—See Yamazaki Baking Co., Ltd.; *Int'l*, pg. 8556
DAITO ME HOLDINGS CO., LTD.; *Int'l*, pg. 1943
DAITO MIRAI TRUST CO., LTD.—See Daito Trust Construction Co., Ltd.; *Int'l*, pg. 1943
DAITO PHARMACEUTICAL (CHINA) CO., LTD.—See Daito Pharmaceutical Co., Ltd.; *Int'l*, pg. 1943
DAITO PHARMACEUTICAL CO., LTD.; *Int'l*, pg. 1943
DAITO PHARMACEUTICALS AMERICA, INC.—See Daito Pharmaceutical Co., Ltd.; *Int'l*, pg. 1943
DAITO SEIKI CO., LTD.—See THK CO., LTD.; *Int'l*, pg. 7711
DAITO SENKO APOLLO CO., LTD.—See Senko Group Holdings Co., Ltd.; *Int'l*, pg. 6709
DAITO STEEL CO., LTD.—See Daito Trust Construction Co., Ltd.; *Int'l*, pg. 1943
DAITO-TEC CO., LTD.—See Daitron Co., Ltd.; *Int'l*, pg. 1944
DAITO TRUST CONSTRUCTION CO., LTD.; *Int'l*, pg. 1943
DAITRON CO., LTD.; *Int'l*, pg. 1944
DAITRON (H.K.) CO., LTD.—See Daitron Co., Ltd.; *Int'l*, pg. 1944
DAITRON INC.—See Daitron Co., Ltd.; *Int'l*, pg. 1944
DAITRON (KOREA) CO., LTD.—See Daitron Co., Ltd.; *Int'l*, pg. 1944
DAITRON (MALAYSIA) SDN. BHD.—See Daitron Co., Ltd.; *Int'l*, pg. 1944
DAITRON (NETHERLANDS) B.V.—See Daitron Co., Ltd.; *Int'l*, pg. 1944
DAITRON (SHANGHAI) CO., LTD.—See Daitron Co., Ltd.; *Int'l*, pg. 1944
DAITRON (SHENZHEN) CO., LTD.—See Daitron Co., Ltd.; *Int'l*, pg. 1944
DAITRON (TAIWAN) CO., LTD.—See Daitron Co., Ltd.; *Int'l*, pg. 1944
DAITRON TECHNOLOGY CO., LTD.—See Daitron Co., Ltd.; *Int'l*, pg. 1944
DAITRON (THAILAND) CO., LTD.—See Daitron Co., Ltd.; *Int'l*, pg. 1944
DAIUN CO., LTD.; *Int'l*, pg. 1944
DAI VIET ENERGY JOINT STOCK COMPANY—See Phu Nhuan Jewelry Joint Stock Company; *Int'l*, pg. 5857
DAIWA ASSET MANAGEMENT CO. LTD.—See Daiwa Securities Group Inc.; *Int'l*, pg. 1947
DAIWA BANK (CAPITAL MANAGEMENT) LTD.—See Resona Holdings, Inc.; *Int'l*, pg. 6297
DAIWA BAOYE (NANTONG) REAL ESTATE DEVELOPMENT CO., LTD.—See Daiwa House Industry Co., Ltd.; *Int'l*, pg. 1945
DAIWABOADVANCE CO., LTD.—See Daiwabo Holdings Co., Ltd.; *Int'l*, pg. 1949
DAIWABO HOLDINGS CO., LTD.; *Int'l*, pg. 1949
DAIWABO INFORMATION SYSTEM CO., LTD.—See Daiwabo Holdings Co., Ltd.; *Int'l*, pg. 1949
DAIWABO LIFESUPPORT CO., LTD.—See Daiwabo Holdings Co., Ltd.; *Int'l*, pg. 1949
DAIWABO NEU CO., LTD.—See Daiwabo Holdings Co., Ltd.; *Int'l*, pg. 1949
DAIWABO RAYON CO., LTD. - MASUDA MILL—See Daiwabo Holdings Co., Ltd.; *Int'l*, pg. 1949
DAIWABO RAYON CO., LTD.—See Daiwabo Holdings Co., Ltd.; *Int'l*, pg. 1949
DAIWABO SPINTEC CO., LTD.—See Daiwabo Holdings Co., Ltd.; *Int'l*, pg. 1949
DAIWABO TEX INC—See Daiwabo Holdings Co., Ltd.; *Int'l*, pg. 1949
DAIWABOUASOSHIE INC.—See Daiwabo Holdings Co., Ltd.; *Int'l*, pg. 1949
DAIWABOUPORITEKKU INC. - HARIMA PLANT—See Daiwabo Holdings Co., Ltd.; *Int'l*, pg. 1949
DAIWABOUPORITEKKU INC.—See Daiwabo Holdings Co., Ltd.; *Int'l*, pg. 1949
DAIWABOURAIFUSAPOTO INC.—See Daiwabo Holdings Co., Ltd.; *Int'l*, pg. 1949
DAIWA CAN COMPANY; *Int'l*, pg. 1944
DAIWA CAPITAL MARKETS AMERICA HOLDINGS INC.—See Daiwa Securities Group Inc.; *Int'l*, pg. 1948
DAIWA CAPITAL MARKETS AMERICA INC.—See Daiwa Securities Group Inc.; *Int'l*, pg. 1948
DAIWA CAPITAL MARKETS AUSTRALIA LIMITED—See Daiwa Securities Group Inc.; *Int'l*, pg. 1948
DAIWA CAPITAL MARKETS DEUTSCHLAND GMBH—See Daiwa Securities Group Inc.; *Int'l*, pg. 1947
DAIWA CAPITAL MARKETS EUROPE LIMITED—See Daiwa Securities Group Inc.; *Int'l*, pg. 1948
DAIWA CAPITAL MARKETS HONG KONG LIMITED—See Daiwa Securities Group Inc.; *Int'l*, pg. 1948
DAIWA CAPITAL MARKETS INDIA PRIVATE LIMITED—See Daiwa Securities Group Inc.; *Int'l*, pg. 1948
DAIWA CAPITAL MARKETS PHILIPPINES, INC.—See Daiwa Securities Group Inc.; *Int'l*, pg. 1948
DAIWA CAPITAL MARKETS SINGAPORE LIMITED—See Daiwa Securities Group Inc.; *Int'l*, pg. 1948
DAIWA-CATHAY CAPITAL MARKETS CO., LTD.—See Daiwa Securities Group Inc.; *Int'l*, pg. 1948
DAIWA CIRCUIT MODULE CO., LTD.—See Hokuriku Electric Industry Co., Ltd.; *Int'l*, pg. 3444
DAIWA CO., LTD.; *Int'l*, pg. 1944
DAIWA COMPUTER CO., LTD.; *Int'l*, pg. 1944
DAIWA CORE FACTORY CO., LTD.—See Daiwa House REIT Investment Corporation; *Int'l*, pg. 1947
DAIWA CORMORAN SPORTARTIKEL-VERTRIEBS GMBH—See Globeride, Inc.; *Int'l*, pg. 3007
DAIWA CORPORATE ADVISORY GMBH—See Daiwa Securities Group Inc.; *Int'l*, pg. 1948
DAIWA CORPORATE ADVISORY LIMITED—See Daiwa Securities Group Inc.; *Int'l*, pg. 1948
DAIWA CORPORATE ADVISORY SAS—See Daiwa Securities Group Inc.; *Int'l*, pg. 1948
DAIWA CORPORATE ADVISORY SLU—See Daiwa Securities Group Inc.; *Int'l*, pg. 1948
DAIWA CORPORATE ADVISORY S.R.L.—See Daiwa Securities Group Inc.; *Int'l*, pg. 1948
DAIWA CORPORATE INVESTMENT CO., LTD.—See Daiwa Securities Group Inc.; *Int'l*, pg. 1948
DAIWA CORPORATION—See Globeride, Inc.; *Int'l*, pg. 3007
DAIWA COSMOS CONSTRUCTION CO., LTD.—See Daiwa House Industry Co., Ltd.; *Int'l*, pg. 1945
DAIWA CYCLE CO., LTD.; *Int'l*, pg. 1944
DAIWA DENSETSU CORP.—See EXEO Group Inc.; *Int'l*, pg. 2583
DAIWA DISTRIBUTION (B.C.) INC.—See Maxnerva Technology Services Ltd.; *Int'l*, pg. 4742
DAIWA DO BRASIL TEXTIL LTDA.—See Daiwabo Holdings Co., Ltd.; *Int'l*, pg. 1949
DAIWA ENERGY CO., LTD.—See Daiwa House Industry Co., Ltd.; *Int'l*, pg. 1945
DAIWA ENERGY & INFRASTRUCTURE CO. LTD.—See Daiwa Securities Group Inc.; *Int'l*, pg. 1948
DAIWA ESTATE CO., LTD.—See Daiwa House Industry Co., Ltd.; *Int'l*, pg. 1945
DAIWA FACILITIES CO., LTD.—See Daiwa Securities Group Inc.; *Int'l*, pg. 1948
DAIWA FOODS CO., LTD.—See Inabata & Co. Ltd.; *Int'l*, pg. 3643
DAIWA FRANCE S.A.S.—See Globeride, Inc.; *Int'l*, pg. 3007
DAIWA FUND CONSULTING CO. LTD.—See Daiwa Securities Group Inc.; *Int'l*, pg. 1948
DAIWA GUARANTEE CO., LTD.—See Resona Holdings, Inc.; *Int'l*, pg. 6297
DAIWA HEAVY INDUSTRY CO,. LTD.; *Int'l*, pg. 1944
DAIWA (H.K) CO., LTD—See Globeride, Inc.; *Int'l*, pg. 3007
DAIWA HOMES ONLINE CO., LTD.—See Daiwa House REIT Investment Corporation; *Int'l*, pg. 1947
DAIWA HOUSE ASSET MANAGEMENT CO., LTD.—See Daiwa House Industry Co., Ltd.; *Int'l*, pg. 1945
DAIWA HOUSE AUSTRALIA PTY LTD.—See Daiwa House REIT Investment Corporation; *Int'l*, pg. 1947
DAIWA HOUSE CALIFORNIA—See Daiwa House REIT Investment Corporation; *Int'l*, pg. 1947
DAIWA HOUSE (CHANGZHOU) REAL ESTATE DEVELOPMENT CO., LTD.—See Daiwa House Industry Co., Ltd.; *Int'l*, pg. 1945
DAIWA HOUSE CHINTAI REFORM CO., LTD.—See Daiwa House Industry Co., Ltd.; *Int'l*, pg. 1945
DAIWA HOUSE CONSTRUCTION MANAGEMENT INC.—See Daiwa House Industry Co., Ltd.; *Int'l*, pg. 1945
DAIWA HOUSE EUROPE B.V.—See Daiwa House Industry Co., Ltd.; *Int'l*, pg. 1945
DAIWA HOUSE FINANCIAL CO.—See Daiwa House Industry Co., Ltd.; *Int'l*, pg. 1945
DAIWA HOUSE INDUSTRY CO., LTD.; *Int'l*, pg. 1944
DAIWA HOUSE INDUSTRY INDIA PVT. LTD.—See Daiwa House Industry Co., Ltd.; *Int'l*, pg. 1945
DAIWA HOUSE INDUSTRY(THAILAND)CO., LTD.—See Daiwa House Industry Co., Ltd.; *Int'l*, pg. 1945
DAIWA HOUSE INSURANCE CO., LTD.—See Daiwa House Industry Co., Ltd.; *Int'l*, pg. 1945
DAIWA HOUSE LIFE SUPPORT CO., LTD.—See Daiwa House Industry Co., Ltd.; *Int'l*, pg. 1945
DAIWA HOUSE MALAYSIA SDN. BHD.—See Daiwa House Industry Co., Ltd.; *Int'l*, pg. 1945
DAIWA HOUSE MORIMOTO ASSET MANAGEMENT CO., LTD.—See Daiwa House Industry Co., Ltd.; *Int'l*, pg. 1945
DAIWA HOUSE PARKING CO., LTD.—See Daiwa House Industry Co., Ltd.; *Int'l*, pg. 1945
DAIWA HOUSE PROPERTY MANAGEMENT CO., LTD.—See Daiwa House Industry Co., Ltd.; *Int'l*, pg. 1945
DAIWA HOUSE REAL ASSET MANAGEMENT VIETNAM, CO., LTD.—See Daiwa House Industry Co., Ltd.; *Int'l*, pg. 1945
DAIWA HOUSE REAL ESTATE DEVELOPMENT CO., LTD.—See Daiwa House Industry Co., Ltd.; *Int'l*, pg. 1945
DAIWA HOUSE REAL ESTATE INVESTMENT MANAGEMENT CO., LTD.—See Daiwa House Industry Co., Ltd.; *Int'l*, pg. 1945
DAIWA HOUSE REFORM CO., LTD.—See Daiwa House REIT Investment Corporation; *Int'l*, pg. 1947
DAIWA HOUSE REIT INVESTMENT CORPORATION; *Int'l*, pg. 1947
DAIWA HOUSE REIT MANAGEMENT CO., LTD.—See Daiwa House Industry Co., Ltd.; *Int'l*, pg. 1945
DAIWA HOUSE RENEW CO., LTD.—See Daiwa House Industry Co., Ltd.; *Int'l*, pg. 1945
DAIWA HOUSE (SUZHOU) REAL ESTATE DEVELOPMENT CO., LTD.—See Daiwa House Industry Co., Ltd.; *Int'l*, pg. 1945
DAIWA HOUSE TEXAS INC.—See Daiwa House Industry Co., Ltd.; *Int'l*, pg. 1945
DAIWA HOUSE VIETNAM CO., LTD.—See Daiwa House REIT Investment Corporation; *Int'l*, pg. 1947
DAIWA HOUSE (WUXI) REAL ESTATE DEVELOPMENT CO., LTD.—See Daiwa House REIT Investment Corporation; *Int'l*, pg. 1947
DAIWA INDUSTRIES LTD.; *Int'l*, pg. 1947
DAIWA INFORMATION SERVICE CO., LTD.—See Daiwa House Industry Co., Ltd.; *Int'l*, pg. 1945
DAIWA INSTITUTE OF RESEARCH AMERICA INC.—See Daiwa Securities Group Inc.; *Int'l*, pg. 1948
DAIWA INSTITUTE OF RESEARCH BUSINESS INNOVATION LTD.—See Daiwa Securities Group Inc.; *Int'l*, pg. 1948
DAIWA INSTITUTE OF RESEARCH EUROPE LTD.—See Daiwa Securities Group Inc.; *Int'l*, pg. 1948
DAIWA INSTITUTE OF RESEARCH HOLDINGS LTD.—See Daiwa Securities Group Inc.; *Int'l*, pg. 1948
DAIWA INSTITUTE OF RESEARCH HONG KONG LTD.—See Daiwa Securities Group Inc.; *Int'l*, pg. 1948
DAIWA INSTITUTE OF RESEARCH LTD.—See Daiwa Securities Group Inc.; *Int'l*, pg. 1948
DAIWA INTERENATIONAL HOLDINGS LTD.—See Daiwa Securities Group Inc.; *Int'l*, pg. 1948
DAIWA INTERNATIONAL HOLDINGS INC.—See Daiwa Securities Group Inc.; *Int'l*, pg. 1948
DAIWA INVESTMENT MANAGEMENT INC.—See Daiwa Securities Group Inc.; *Int'l*, pg. 1948
DAIWA INVESTOR RELATIONS CO. LTD.—See Daiwa Securities Group Inc.; *Int'l*, pg. 1948
DAIWA KOHTAI CO., LTD.—See JFE Holdings, Inc.; *Int'l*, pg. 3934
DAIWA LANTEC CO., LTD.—See Daiwa House Industry Co., Ltd.; *Int'l*, pg. 1945
DAIWA LEASE CO., LTD.—See Daiwa House Industry Co., Ltd.; *Int'l*, pg. 1945
DAIWA LIFECOSMO CO., LTD.—See Daiwa House Industry Co., Ltd.; *Int'l*, pg. 1945
DAIWA LIFENEXT CO., LTD.—See Daiwa House Industry Co., Ltd.; *Int'l*, pg. 1945
DAIWA LIVING CALIFORNIA INC.—See Daiwa House Industry Co., Ltd.; *Int'l*, pg. 1945
DAIWA LIVING CO., LTD.—See Daiwa House Industry Co., Ltd.; *Int'l*, pg. 1946
DAIWA LIVING NESUTO HOLDINGS PTY LTD—See Daiwa House Industry Co., Ltd.; *Int'l*, pg. 1946
DAIWA LOGISTICS CO., LTD.—See Daiwa House Industry Co., Ltd.; *Int'l*, pg. 1946
DAIWA LOGISTICS VIETNAM CO., LTD.—See Daiwa House Industry Co., Ltd.; *Int'l*, pg. 1946
DAIWA LOGITECH INC.—See Daiwa House Industry Co., Ltd.; *Int'l*, pg. 1946
DAIWA MARUESU INC.—See Daiwabo Holdings Co., Ltd.; *Int'l*, pg. 1949
DAIWA MONTHLY CO., LTD.—See Daiwa House Industry Co., Ltd.; *Int'l*, pg. 1946
DAIWA MOTOR TRANSPORTATION CO., LTD.; *Int'l*, pg. 1947
DAIWA MUSEN DENKI CO., LTD.—See Denkyo Group Holdings Co.,Ltd.; *Int'l*, pg. 2028

DAIWA NEXT BANK, LTD.—See Daiwa Securities Group Inc.; *Int'l*, pg. 1948
DAIWA OFFICE INVESTMENT CORPORATION; *Int'l*, pg. 1947
DAIWA PHARMACEUTICAL CO., LTD.—See Sala Corporation; *Int'l*, pg. 6490
DAIWA PI PARTNERS CO. LTD—See Daiwa Securities Group Inc.; *Int'l*, pg. 1948
DAIWA PROPERTY CO., LTD.—See Daiwa Securities Group Inc.; *Int'l*, pg. 1948
DAIWA REAL ESTATE ASSET MANAGEMENT CO. LTD—See Daiwa Securities Group Inc.; *Int'l*, pg. 1948
DAIWA RESORT CO., LTD.—See Daiwa House Industry Co., Ltd.; *Int'l*, pg. 1946
DAIWA ROYAL CO., LTD.—See Daiwa House Industry Co., Ltd.; *Int'l*, pg. 1946
DAIWA ROYAL GOLF CO., LTD.—See Daiwa House Industry Co., Ltd.; *Int'l*, pg. 1946
DAIWA ROYAL HOTEL CITY CO., LTD.—See Daiwa House Industry Co., Ltd.; *Int'l*, pg. 1946
DAIWA SECURITIES BUSINESS CENTER CO., LTD.—See Daiwa Securities Group Inc.; *Int'l*, pg. 1948
DAIWA SECURITIES CAPITAL MARKETS KOREA CO., LTD.—See Daiwa Securities Group Inc.; *Int'l*, pg. 1948
DAIWA SECURITIES CO., LTD.—See Daiwa Securities Group Inc.; *Int'l*, pg. 1948
DAIWA SECURITIES GROUP INC.; *Int'l*, pg. 1947
DAIWA SECURITIES LIVING INVESTMENT CORPORATION; *Int'l*, pg. 1949
DAIWA SECURITIES REALTY CO. LTD.—See Daiwa Securities Group Inc.; *Int'l*, pg. 1949
DAIWA SECURITIES SMBC PRINCIPAL INVESTMENTS CO. LTD.—See Daiwa Securities Group Inc.; *Int'l*, pg. 1949
DAIWA SECURITIES SMBC PRINCIPAL INVESTMENTS CO. LTD.—See Sumitomo Mitsui Financial Group, Inc.; *Int'l*, pg. 7293
DAIWA SECURITIES TRUST COMPANY—See Daiwa Securities Group Inc.; *Int'l*, pg. 1948
DAIWA SERVICE CO., LTD.—See Daiwa House Industry Co., Ltd.; *Int'l*, pg. 1946
DAIWA (SHANGHAI) CORPORATE STRATEGIC ADVISORY CO. LTD.—See Daiwa Securities Group Inc.; *Int'l*, pg. 1947
DAIWA SHIKO CO., LTD.—See Daio Paper Corporation; *Int'l*, pg. 1940
DAIWA SHOKO CO., LTD—See Subaru Corporation; *Int'l*, pg. 7246
DAIWA SOGYO CO., LTD.—See ShinMaywa Industries, Ltd.; *Int'l*, pg. 6846
DAIWA SPORTS LTD.—See Globeride, Inc.; *Int'l*, pg. 3007
DAIWA STEEL CORP.—See JFE Holdings, Inc.; *Int'l*, pg. 3934
DAIWASYSTEM CO., LTD.; *Int'l*, pg. 1950
DAIWA YOKI CO., LTD.—See Daiwa Can Company; *Int'l*, pg. 1944
DAI-WOOD CORPORATION—See Daiken Corporation; *Int'l*, pg. 1931
DAIYA BUILDING SERVICE CO., LTD.—See Mitsubishi Heavy Industries, Ltd.; *Int'l*, pg. 4953
DAIYA LOGISTICS CO., LTD.—See Mitsubishi Heavy Industries, Ltd.; *Int'l*, pg. 4953
DAIYANG METAL CO., LTD.; *Int'l*, pg. 1950
DAIYA PR CO., LTD.—See Mitsubishi Heavy Industries, Ltd.; *Int'l*, pg. 4953
DAIYA SHOJI CO., LTD.—See Mercedes-Benz Group AG; *Int'l*, pg. 4824
DAIYA TSUSHO CO., LTD.—See Tokai Carbon Co., Ltd.; *Int'l*, pg. 7778
DAIYOSHI TRUST CO., LTD.—See Daiwa House Industry Co., Ltd.; *Int'l*, pg. 1946
DAIYU CO., LTD.—See TS Tech Co Ltd; *Int'l*, pg. 7947
DAIYU EIGHT CO., LTD.—See Alleanza Holdings Co., Ltd.; *Int'l*, pg. 334
DAJIN HEAVY INDUSTRY CORPORATION; *Int'l*, pg. 1950
DAJIN LITHIUM CORP.—See Pluspetrol Resources Corporation BV; *Int'l*, pg. 5899
D AKADEMIE S.R.L.—See DEKRA e.V.; *Int'l*, pg. 2007
DAK AMERICAS LLC—See ALFA, S.A.B. de C.V.; *Int'l*, pg. 313
DAK AMERICAS MISSISSIPPI INC.—See ALFA, S.A.B. de C.V.; *Int'l*, pg. 313
DAKA SERVIS A.D.; *Int'l*, pg. 1950
DAK CO., LTD—See Dongwon Metal Co., Ltd.; *Int'l*, pg. 2171
DAKE CORPORATION—See JSJ Corporation; *U.S. Private*, pg. 2241
DAKE COUPLINGS—See JSJ Corporation; *U.S. Private*, pg. 2241
DAKE OEM FURNITURE—See JSJ Corporation; *U.S. Private*, pg. 2241
DAKERYN INDUSTRIES LTD.; *Int'l*, pg. 1950
DAKILA TRADING CORPORATION—See HORIBA Ltd; *Int'l*, pg. 3475
DAKIN DAIRY FARMS, INC.; *U.S. Private*, pg. 1147
DA KINE HAWAII INC.; *U.S. Private*, pg. 1143
DAKIN ENGINEERING PTE LTD—See CHINO Corporation; *Int'l*, pg. 1570

DAK LAK PHARMACEUTICALS AND MEDICAL EQUIPMENTS JOINT STOCK COMPANY—See Traphaco Joint Stock Company; *Int'l*, pg. 7906
THE DAKMAN VIETNAM COMPANY LIMITED—See ED&F Man Holdings Limited; *Int'l*, pg. 2303
DAKO BELGIUM N.V.—See Agilent Technologies, Inc.; *U.S. Public*, pg. 61
DAKO DENMARK A/S—See Agilent Technologies, Inc.; *U.S. Public*, pg. 61
DAKO DEUTSCHLAND GMBH—See Agilent Technologies, Inc.; *U.S. Public*, pg. 61
DAKO DIAGNOSTICOS S.A.—See Agilent Technologies, Inc.; *U.S. Public*, pg. 61
DAKO FRANCE S.A.S.—See Agilent Technologies, Inc.; *U.S. Public*, pg. 61
DAKO ITALIA S.P.A.—See Agilent Technologies, Inc.; *U.S. Public*, pg. 61
DAKO JAPAN INC.—See Agilent Technologies, Inc.; *U.S. Public*, pg. 61
DAKO NETHERLANDS B.V.—See Agilent Technologies, Inc.; *U.S. Public*, pg. 61
DAKO NORTH AMERICA, INC.—See Agilent Technologies, Inc.; *U.S. Public*, pg. 61
D.A. KOPP & ASSOCIATES, INC.—See Milestone Partners Ltd.; *U.S. Private*, pg. 2728
DAKO SCHWEIZ GMBH—See Agilent Technologies, Inc.; *U.S. Public*, pg. 61
DAKO SWEDEN AB—See Agilent Technologies, Inc.; *U.S. Public*, pg. 61
DAKOTA AGRONOMY PARTNERS, LLC—See CHS INC.; *U.S. Public*, pg. 492
DAKOTA ARMS, LTD—See American Realty Investors, Inc.; *U.S. Public*, pg. 108
DAKOTA BROTHERS INC.; *U.S. Private*, pg. 1147
DAKOTA BULK TERMINAL, INC.—See Kinder Morgan, Inc.; *U.S. Public*, pg. 1233
DAKOTA BULK TERMINAL LLC—See Kinder Morgan, Inc.; *U.S. Public*, pg. 1232
DAKOTA CAPITAL LIFE INSURANCE CORPORATION—See US Alliance Corporation; *U.S. Private*, pg. 4317
DAKOTA CARTAGE COMPANY INC—See Lewis Transportation Systems; *U.S. Private*, pg. 2439
DAKOTA COAL COMPANY—See Basin Electric Power Cooperative; *U.S. Private*, pg. 485
DAKOTA COMMUNITY BANK & TRUST, N.A.—See Dakota Community Banshares, Inc.; *U.S. Private*, pg. 1147
DAKOTA COMMUNITY BANSHARES, INC.; *U.S. Private*, pg. 1147
DAKOTA CORRUGATED BOX COMPANY—See Buckeye Corrugated Inc.; *U.S. Private*, pg. 677
DAKOTA CRAFT INC.; *U.S. Private*, pg. 1147
DAKOTA CREEK INDUSTRIES, INC.; *U.S. Private*, pg. 1147
DAKOTA DRUG, INC.; *U.S. Private*, pg. 1147
DAKOTA DRY BEAN INC.—See Benson Hills, Inc.; *U.S. Public*, pg. 296
DAKOTA ELECTRIC ASSOCIATION; *U.S. Private*, pg. 1147
DAKOTA ENGINEERING, INC.—See Mursix Corporation; *U.S. Private*, pg. 2816
DAKOTA FOUNDRY, INC.—See Anderson Industries LLC; *U.S. Private*, pg. 277
DAKOTA GASIFICATION COMPANY—See Basin Electric Power Cooperative; *U.S. Private*, pg. 485
DAKOTA GOLD CORP.; *U.S. Public*, pg. 620
DAKOTA GRANITE COMPANY; *U.S. Private*, pg. 1147
DAKOTA GROWERS PASTA COMPANY, INC.—See Post Holdings, Inc.; *U.S. Public*, pg. 1703
DAKOTA HOSPITALITY COMPANY—See Jones Lang LaSalle Incorporated; *U.S. Public*, pg. 1204
DAKOTA KING INC.; *U.S. Private*, pg. 1147
DAKOTALAND AUTOGLASS INC.—See West Edge Partners, LLC; *U.S. Private*, pg. 4485
DAKOTA LAYERS, LLP; *U.S. Private*, pg. 1147
DAKOTA LINE, INC.; *U.S. Private*, pg. 1147
DAKOTA MANUFACTURING CO. INC.; *U.S. Private*, pg. 1147
DAKOTA MINERALS LIMITED; *Int'l*, pg. 1950
DAKOTA, MINNESOTA & EASTERN RAILROAD CORPORATION—See Canadian Pacific Kansas City Limited; *Int'l*, pg. 1285
DAKOTA NEWS INC.; *U.S. Private*, pg. 1147
DAKOTA PLAINS AGRICULTURAL CENTER LLC; *U.S. Private*, pg. 1147
DAKOTA PLAINS COOPERATIVE-LISBON—See Dakota Plains Cooperative; *U.S. Private*, pg. 1147
DAKOTA PLAINS COOPERATIVE; *U.S. Private*, pg. 1147
DAKOTA PREMIUM FOODS, LLC—See Rosens Diversified, Inc.; *U.S. Private*, pg. 3484
DAKOTA PREMIUM HARDWOODS LLC—See Wurth Verwaltungsgesellschaft mbH; *Int'l*, pg. 8511
DAKOTA SPECIALTY MILLING COMPANY; *U.S. Private*, pg. 1147
DAKOTA SQUARE MALL CMBS, LLC—See CBL & Associates Properties, Inc.; *U.S. Public*, pg. 458
DAKOTA SUPPLY GROUP INC.; *U.S. Private*, pg. 1147

DAKOTA TRAILER MANUFACTURING, INC.—See Henry Crown & Company; *U.S. Private*, pg. 1918
DAKOTA TUBE INC.; *U.S. Private*, pg. 1147
DAKOTA VALLEY ELECTRIC COORPERATIVE INC.; *U.S. Private*, pg. 1148
DAKOTA WEALTH MANAGEMENT LLC; *U.S. Private*, pg. 1148
DAKOTA WESTMORELAND CORPORATION—See Westmoreland Coal Company; *U.S. Private*, pg. 4499
DAKO UK LTD—See Agilent Technologies, Inc.; *U.S. Public*, pg. 61
DAK RESINAS AMERICAS MEXICO, S.A. DE C.V.—See ALFA, S.A.B. de C.V.; *Int'l*, pg. 313
DAKSHIN BHARAT GATEWAY TERMINAL PRIVATE LIMITED—See Starlog Enterprises Limited; *Int'l*, pg. 7178
DAKS SIMPSON LIMITED—See Sankyo Seiko Co., Ltd.; *Int'l*, pg. 6543
DAK-TANA WIRELINE, LLC—See Nine Energy Service, Inc.; *U.S. Public*, pg. 1529
DAKTRONICS AUSTRALIA PTY LTD.—See Daktronics, Inc.; *U.S. Public*, pg. 620
DAKTRONICS FRANCE SARL—See Daktronics, Inc.; *U.S. Public*, pg. 621
DAKTRONICS FZE—See Daktronics, Inc.; *U.S. Public*, pg. 620
DAKTRONICS, GMBH—See Daktronics, Inc.; *U.S. Public*, pg. 621
DAKTRONICS, INC.; *U.S. Public*, pg. 620
DAKTRONICS IRELAND CO. LTD.—See Daktronics, Inc.; *U.S. Public*, pg. 621
DAKTRONICS JAPAN, INC.—See Daktronics, Inc.; *U.S. Public*, pg. 621
DAKTRONICS SHANGHAI LTD.—See Daktronics, Inc.; *U.S. Public*, pg. 621
DAKTRONICS UK, LTD.—See Daktronics, Inc.; *U.S. Public*, pg. 621
DAKVENSTER.COM B.V.—See VKR Holding A/S; *Int'l*, pg. 8281
DALA BEHEER BV—See KBC Group NV; *Int'l*, pg. 4105
DALAB SVERIGE AB—See Instalco AB; *Int'l*, pg. 3721
DALACO MATERIALS LLC; *U.S. Private*, pg. 1148
DALA ENERGI AB; *Int'l*, pg. 1950
DALAIN HUARUI HEAVY INDUSTRY INDIA COMPANY PRIVIATE LIMITED—See Dalian Huarui Heavy Industry Group Co., Ltd.; *Int'l*, pg. 1952
DALA KYLMECANO AB—See Instalco AB; *Int'l*, pg. 3721
DALAL STREET INVESTMENTS LIMITED; *Int'l*, pg. 1950
DALAND CORPORATION; *U.S. Private*, pg. 1148
DALAROO METAL LIMITED; *Int'l*, pg. 1950
DALATA HOTEL GROUP PLC; *Int'l*, pg. 1950
DALATE CDB VILLAGE BANK CO., LTD.—See China Development Bank Corporation; *Int'l*, pg. 1497
DALAT REAL ESTATE JOINT STOCK COMPANY; *Int'l*, pg. 1950
DALBANI CORPORATION; *U.S. Private*, pg. 1148
DALBA SP. Z O.O.—See Trakcja PRKil S.A.; *Int'l*, pg. 7891
DALB, INC.; *U.S. Private*, pg. 1148
DALBY A.S.—See MOL Magyar Olaj- es Gazipari Nyrt.; *Int'l*, pg. 5020
DAL CHEM, INC.—See AIP, LLC; *U.S. Private*, pg. 136
DALCO INDUSTRIES INC.; *U.S. Private*, pg. 1148
DALCO INDUSTRIES INC.—See Dalco Industries Inc.; *U.S. Private*, pg. 1148
DALCOM ENGINEERING GMBH—See Dalekovod d.d.; *Int'l*, pg. 1951
DALCO METALS, INC.; *U.S. Private*, pg. 1148
DALCO NONWOVENS, LLC—See Snow Peak Capital, LLC; *U.S. Private*, pg. 3701
DALDRUP BOHRTECHNIK AG—See Daldrup & Sohne AG; *Int'l*, pg. 1950
DALDRUP & SOHNE AG; *Int'l*, pg. 1950
DALE ALCOCK HOMES PTY. LTD.; *Int'l*, pg. 1950
DALE BARTON AGENCY—See Hellman & Friedman LLC; *U.S. Private*, pg. 1908
DALE CAPITAL GROUP LIMITED; *Int'l*, pg. 1950
DALE CARNEGIE & ASSOCIATES, INC.; *U.S. Private*, pg. 1148
DALE CARNEGIE DENMARK—See Dale Carnegie & Associates, Inc.; *U.S. Private*, pg. 1148
DALE CARNEGIE INSTITUTE OF LONG ISLAND—See Dale Carnegie & Associates, Inc.; *U.S. Private*, pg. 1148
DALE DOWNIE NISSAN; *Int'l*, pg. 1950
DALE EARNHARDT, INC.; *U.S. Private*, pg. 1148
DALE GROUP INC.; *U.S. Private*, pg. 1148
DALE INCORPORATED; *U.S. Private*, pg. 1148
DALE K. EHRHART, INC.; *U.S. Private*, pg. 1148
DALE KIRK AUTOMOTIVE; *U.S. Private*, pg. 1148
DALEKOVOD AG—See Dalekovod d.d.; *Int'l*, pg. 1951
DALEKOVOD-CINCAONICA D.O.O.—See Dalekovod d.d.; *Int'l*, pg. 1951
DALEKOVOD D.D.; *Int'l*, pg. 1950
DALEKOVOD D.D. - VELIKA GORICA FACTORY—See Dalekovod d.d.; *Int'l*, pg. 1950
DALEKOVOD D.O.O., LJUBLJANA—See Dalekovod d.d.; *Int'l*, pg. 1951
DALEKOVOD EMU D.O.O.—See Dalekovod d.d.; *Int'l*, pg. 1951

COMPANY NAME INDEX

DALEKOVOD KAZAKHSTAN—See Dalekovod d.d.; *Int'l*, pg. 1951
DALEKOVOD PROFESSIO D.O.O—See Dalekovod d.d.; *Int'l*, pg. 1951
DALEKOVOD-PROJEKT D.O.O.—See Dalekovod d.d.; *Int'l*, pg. 1951
DALEKOVOD SKOPJE—See Dalekovod d.d.; *Int'l*, pg. 1951
DALEKOVOD TKS A.D.—See Dalekovod d.d.; *Int'l*, pg. 1951
DALEKOVOD UKRAJINA D.O.O.—See Dalekovod d.d.; *Int'l*, pg. 1951
DALE L PRENTICE CO.; *U.S. Private*, pg. 1148
DALE & MAXEY, INC.; *U.S. Private*, pg. 1148
DALE MEDICAL PRODUCTS INC.; *U.S. Private*, pg. 1149
DALENYS PAYMENT SAS—See Groupe BPCE; *Int'l*, pg. 3093
DALENYS S.A.—See Groupe BPCE; *Int'l*, pg. 3094
DALEPAK FOODS—See Boparan Holdings Limited; *Int'l*, pg. 1111
DALE POWER SYSTEMS PLC—See TT Electronics plc; *Int'l*, pg. 7959
DALE-RIGGS FUNERAL HOME, INC.—See Service Corporation International; *U.S. Public*, pg. 1869
DALE ROGERS TRAINING CENTER, INC.; *U.S. Private*, pg. 1149
DALES AUTO MART INC.; *U.S. Private*, pg. 1149
DALES TIRE & RETREADING INC.; *U.S. Private*, pg. 1149
DALET AUSTRALIA PTY. LTD.—See Long Path Partners, LP; *U.S. Private*, pg. 2491
DALET DIGITAL MEDIA SYSTEMS ME—See Long Path Partners, LP; *U.S. Private*, pg. 2491
DALET DIGITAL MEDIA SYSTEMS MEXICO—See Long Path Partners, LP; *U.S. Private*, pg. 2491
DALET DIGITAL MEDIA SYSTEMS USA, INC.—See Long Path Partners, LP; *U.S. Private*, pg. 2491
DALET GMBH—See Long Path Partners, LP; *U.S. Private*, pg. 2491
DALET HOLDING SAS—See Long Path Partners, LP; *U.S. Private*, pg. 2491
DALETH PARTICIPACOES S.A.; *Int'l*, pg. 1951
DALE TIFFANY INC; *U.S. Private*, pg. 1149
DALE TILE COMPANY, *U.S. Private*, pg. 1149
DALET ITALIA SRL—See Long Path Partners, LP; *U.S. Private*, pg. 2491
DALET LTD.—See Long Path Partners, LP; *U.S. Private*, pg. 2491
DALET S.A.—See Long Path Partners, LP; *U.S. Private*, pg. 2491
DALET SISTEMAS S.A.—See Long Path Partners, LP; *U.S. Private*, pg. 2491
DALET SYSTEMS ASIA PTE LTD.—See Long Path Partners, LP; *U.S. Private*, pg. 2491
DALEVILLE CHRISTIAN CHURCH DAY CARE CENTER; *U.S. Private*, pg. 1149
DALE WILLEY PONTIAC-CADILLAC; *U.S. Private*, pg. 1149
D ALEX MACDONALD FORD LINCOLN; *Int'l*, pg. 1898
DALEY & ASSOCIATES, LLC.; *U.S. Private*, pg. 1149
DALFORT CAPITAL PARTNERS, LLC; *U.S. Private*, pg. 1149
DALGASGROUP A/S—See Det Danske Hedeselskab; *Int'l*, pg. 2047
DAL-GEORG ROST & SOHNE SANITARARMATUREN GMBH—See Development Bank of Japan, Inc.; *Int'l*, pg. 2087
DAL-GEORG ROST & SOHNE SANITARARMATUREN GMBH—See LIXIL Group Corporation; *Int'l*, pg. 4533
DALGETY AGRA POLSKA SP. Z.O.O.—See ARYZTA AG; *Int'l*, pg. 588
DAL GLOBAL SERVICES—See Delta Air Lines, Inc.; *U.S. Public*, pg. 651
THE DALGUISE CENTRE CARE HOME PERTH—See Balhousie Holdings Limited; *Int'l*, pg. 808
DALHART CONSUMERS FUEL ASSOCIATION INC.; *U.S. Private*, pg. 1149
DALIA LTD.; *Int'l*, pg. 1951
DALIAN ACACIA TOWN VILLA CO., LTD.—See Daiwa House Industry Co., Ltd.; *Int'l*, pg. 1946
DALIAN ALPINE ELECTRONICS CO., LTD.—See Alps Alpine Co., Ltd.; *Int'l*, pg. 376
DALIAN ALPS ELECTRONICS CO., LTD.—See Alps Alpine Co., Ltd.; *Int'l*, pg. 376
DALIAN ALPS TEDA LOGISTICS CO., LTD.—See Tianjin Binhai Teda Logistics (Group) Corporation Limited; *Int'l*, pg. 7738
DALIAN ANCHOR BUSINESS SERVICE CO., LTD.—See Chori Co., Ltd.; *Int'l*, pg. 1583
DALIAN AOXIN QUANMIN STOMATOLOGY HOSPITAL CO., LTD.—See Aoxin Q & M Dental Group Limited; *Int'l*, pg. 498
DALIAN APPLE FOODS INGREDIENTS CO., LTD.—See Apple Flavor & Fragrance Group Co., Ltd.; *Int'l*, pg. 520
DALIAN AUTO ITALIA CAR TRADING CO., LTD.—See Auto Italia Holdings Limited; *Int'l*, pg. 725
DALIAN BEST METALS—See Scope Metals Group Ltd.; *Int'l*, pg. 6650

DALIAN BIO-CHEM COMPANY LIMITED - LVSHUN FACTORY—See Dalian Bio-Chem Company Limited; *Int'l*, pg. 1951
DALIAN BIO-CHEM COMPANY LIMITED - SONGMUDAO FACTORY—See Dalian Bio-Chem Company Limited; *Int'l*, pg. 1951
DALIAN BIO-CHEM COMPANY LIMITED; *Int'l*, pg. 1951
DALIAN BUILDING MATERIALS COMPANY—See Dalian Shide Group Co., Ltd.; *Int'l*, pg. 1952
DALIAN CIMC CONTAINER CO., LTD.—See China International Marine Containers (Group) Co., Ltd.; *Int'l*, pg. 1511
DALIAN CIMC LOGISTICS EQUIPMENT CO., LTD.—See China International Marine Containers (Group) Co., Ltd.; *Int'l*, pg. 1511
DALIAN CIMC RAILWAY EQUIPMENT CO., LTD.—See China International Marine Containers (Group) Co., Ltd.; *Int'l*, pg. 1511
DALIAN COSCO KHI SHIP ENGINEERING CO., LTD.—See Kawasaki Heavy Industries, Ltd.; *Int'l*, pg. 4095
DALIAN CREATE MEDICAL PRODUCTS CO., LTD.—See CREATE MEDIC CO. LTD.; *Int'l*, pg. 1832
DALIAN DAFU HOLDINGS CO., LTD.; *Int'l*, pg. 1951
DALIAN DALI STEEL WORKS CO., LTD.—See Hitachi Zosen Corporation; *Int'l*, pg. 3410
DALIAN DASHAN CHRYSTALLIZER CO. LTD.—See Intek Group S.p.A.; *Int'l*, pg. 3732
DALIAN DASHAN HEAVY MACHINERY CO. LTD.—See Intek Group S.p.A.; *Int'l*, pg. 3732
DALIAN DATONG MACHINERY PRODUCTS CO., LTD.—See Hitachi Zosen Corporation; *Int'l*, pg. 3410
DALIAN DAXIAN TAKAGI MOLD CO., LTD.—See Takagi Seiko Corporation; *Int'l*, pg. 7429
DALIAN DYNIC OFFICE PRODUCTS CO., LTD.—See Dynic Corporation; *Int'l*, pg. 2242
DALIAN ELAND INFORMATION TECHNOLOGY CO., LTD.—See Shanghai Newtouch Software Co., Ltd.; *Int'l*, pg. 6776
DALIAN ENERGAS GAS-SYSTEM CO., LTD.; *Int'l*, pg. 1951
DALIAN ES MARINE & OFFSHORE ENGINEERING CO., LTD.—See ES Group (Holdings) Limited; *Int'l*, pg. 2500
DALIAN FREE TRADE ZONE NICHIURA TRADING CO., LTD.—See Azearth Corporation; *Int'l*, pg. 778
DALIAN FRESH FOODS CO., LTD.—See Kobe Bussan Co., Ltd.; *Int'l*, pg. 4217
DALIAN FRIENDSHIP (GROUP) CO., LTD.; *Int'l*, pg. 1951
DALIAN FTZ LUMAX INTERNATIONAL TRADE CO., LTD.—See Lumax International Corp.; *Int'l*, pg. 4577
DALIAN F.T.Z. SIN SOON HUAT INTERNATIONAL TRADE CO. LTD.—See KS Energy Limited; *Int'l*, pg. 4309
DALIAN FUJI BINGSHAN CONTROL SYSTEMS CO., LTD.—See Fuji Electric Co., Ltd.; *Int'l*, pg. 2810
DALIAN FUJI BINGSHAN VENDING MACHINE CO., LTD.—See Fuji Electric Co., Ltd.; *Int'l*, pg. 2810
DALIAN FUJI ELECTRIC MOTOR CO., LTD.—See Fuji Electric Co., Ltd.; *Int'l*, pg. 2810
DALIAN GLOBAL FOOD CORPORATION—See Sojitz Corporation; *Int'l*, pg. 7061
DALIAN GUANGHUA SOFTWARE AND TECHNOLOGY CO., LTD.—See Takeda iP Holdings Co.,Ltd.; *Int'l*, pg. 7437
DALIAN GUNZE FASHION GARMENTS CO., LTD.—See Gunze Limited; *Int'l*, pg. 3185
DALIAN GUOLI PACKAGING CO., LTD.—See Rengo Co., Ltd.; *Int'l*, pg. 6279
DALIAN HAOSEN EQUIPMENT MANUFACTURING CO., LTD.; *Int'l*, pg. 1951
DALIAN HAOSENREAD EQUIPMENT MANUFACTURE CO., LTD.—See Dalian Haosen Equipment Manufacturing Co., Ltd.; *Int'l*, pg. 1951
DALIAN HAOSEN SOFTWARE CO., LTD.—See Dalian Haosen Equipment Manufacturing Co., Ltd.; *Int'l*, pg. 1951
DALIAN HARADA INDUSTRY CO., LTD.—See HARADA INDUSTRY CO., LTD.; *Int'l*, pg. 3269
DALIAN HAYASHI LOST-WAX INDUSTRIES CO., LTD.—See Kawakin Holdings Co., Ltd.; *Int'l*, pg. 4094
DALIAN HITACHI MACHINERY & EQUIPMENT CO. LTD.—See Hitachi, Ltd.; *Int'l*, pg. 3412
DALIAN HONJO CHEMICAL CORPORATION—See Panasonic Holdings Corporation; *Int'l*, pg. 5723
DALIAN HUARUI HEAVY INDUSTRY GROUP CO., LTD.; *Int'l*, pg. 1952
DALIAN IDEMITSU CHINAOIL CO., LTD.—See Idemitsu Kosan Co., Ltd.; *Int'l*, pg. 3590
DALIAN INSULATOR (FUJIAN) CO., LTD.—See Dalian Insulator Group Co., Ltd.; *Int'l*, pg. 1952
DALIAN INSULATOR GROUP CO., LTD.; *Int'l*, pg. 1952
DALIAN INTERNATIONAL CONTAINER SERVICE CO., LTD.—See Nippon Yusen Kabushiki Kaisha; *Int'l*, pg. 5357
DALIAN IWATANI TRADING CO.,LTD.—See Iwatani Corporation; *Int'l*, pg. 3850
DALIAN JINCHUAN ELECTRIC CABLE CO. LTD.—See Fushi Copperweld, Inc.; *Int'l*, pg. 2849

DALIAN SHIDE GROUP CO., LTD.

DALIAN JINGXUE INSULATION TECHNOLOGY CO., LTD.—See Jiangsu Jingxue Insulation Technology Co., Ltd.; *Int'l*, pg. 3949
DALIAN KFC CO., LTD.—See Yum China Holdings, Inc.; *U.S. Public*, pg. 2399
DALIAN KITAMURA VALVE CO. LTD.—See KVK CORPORATION; *Int'l*, pg. 4349
DALIAN KONECRANES COMPANY LTD.—See Konecranes Plc; *Int'l*, pg. 4251
DALIAN KOYO WAZHOU AUTOMOBILE BEARING CO., LTD.—See JTEKT Corporation; *Int'l*, pg. 4017
DALIAN KSB AMRI VALVES CO. LTD.—See KSB SE & Co. KGaA; *Int'l*, pg. 4310
DALIAN LIPP ENVIRONMENTAL ENERGY ENGINEERING & TECHNOLOGY CO., LTD—See China Industrial Waste Management, Inc.; *Int'l*, pg. 1510
DALIAN MARINE DIESEL CO., LTD.—See China Shipbuilding Industry Company Limited; *Int'l*, pg. 1551
DALIAN MARSOL TRADING CO., LTD.—See Rengo Co., Ltd.; *Int'l*, pg. 6279
DALIAN MEDICAL EQUIPMENT HOLDING BV—See Getinge AB; *Int'l*, pg. 2949
DALIAN MORGAN REFRACTORIES LIMITED—See Morgan Advanced Materials plc; *Int'l*, pg. 5042
DALIAN MORNINGSTAR NETWORK TECHNOLOGY CO., LTD.; *Int'l*, pg. 1952
DALIAN MY GYM EDUCATION TECHNOLOGY CO., LTD.; *Int'l*, pg. 1952
DALIAN NEUSOFT INSTITUTE OF INFORMATION—See Neusoft Corporation; *Int'l*, pg. 5220
DALIAN NEW ORIENTAL INTERNATIONAL INSTRUMENT INDUSTRY & TRADE CO., LTD.—See Endress+Hauser (International) Holding AG; *Int'l*, pg. 2406
DALIAN NEWTOUCH SOFTWARE CO., LTD.—See Shanghai Newtouch Software Co., Ltd.; *Int'l*, pg. 6776
DALIAN NEW WORLD HOTEL CO., LTD.—See Chow Tai Fook Enterprises Limited; *Int'l*, pg. 1585
DALIAN OHTA FOODS CO., LTD.—See Maruha Nichiro Corporation; *Int'l*, pg. 4711
DALIAN ONODA CEMENT CO., LTD.—See Taiheiyo Cement Corporation; *Int'l*, pg. 7411
DALIAN ORIENTAL MARINE & HEAVY INDUSTRY CO., LTD—See oriental precision & engineering co., ltd.; *Int'l*, pg. 5626
DALIAN ORO ADVERTISING CO., LTD.—See oRo Co., Ltd.; *Int'l*, pg. 5642
DALIAN PACIFIC MILLENNIUM PACKAGING & PAPER INDUSTRIES CO., LTD.—See Pacific Millennium Packaging Group Corporation; *Int'l*, pg. 5691
DALIAN PACTERA TECHNOLOGY INTERNATIONAL CO., LTD.—See China Electronics Corporation; *Int'l*, pg. 1499
DALIAN PORT BULK LOGISTICS CENTER CO., LTD.—See China Master Logistics Co., Ltd.; *Int'l*, pg. 1517
DALIAN RENGO PACKAGING CO., LTD.—See Rengo Co., Ltd.; *Int'l*, pg. 6279
DALIAN SAMYOUNG DOOSAN METAL PRODUCT CO., LTD.—See Samyoung M-TEK Co., Ltd.; *Int'l*, pg. 6520
DALIAN SANKEN ELECTRIC CO., LTD.—See Sanken Electric Co., Ltd.; *Int'l*, pg. 6540
DALIAN SANKYU INTERNATIONAL LOGISTICS CO., LTD.—See Sankyu, Inc.; *Int'l*, pg. 6543
DALIAN SANYO COLD-CHAIN CO., LTD.—See Panasonic Holdings Corporation; *Int'l*, pg. 5723
DALIAN SANYO COMPRESSOR CO., LTD.—See Panasonic Holdings Corporation; *Int'l*, pg. 5723
DALIAN SANYO REFRIGERATION CO., LTD.—See Panasonic Holdings Corporation; *Int'l*, pg. 5723
DALIAN SCHNELLECKE LOGISTICS CO. LTD.—See Schnellecke Group AG & Co. KG; *Int'l*, pg. 6636
DALIAN SECOM SECURITY CO., LTD.—See SECOM Co., Ltd.; *Int'l*, pg. 6671
DALIAN SEIKO ELECTRIC CONTROL CO., LTD.—See Seiko Electric Co., Ltd.; *Int'l*, pg. 6686
DALIAN SEIKO INSTRUMENTS INC.—See Seiko Group Corporation; *Int'l*, pg. 6688
DALIAN SEKISUI HOUSING TECHNOLOGY CO., LTD.—See Sekisui Chemical Co., Ltd.; *Int'l*, pg. 6693
DALIAN SHIDE GROUP CO., LTD.; *Int'l*, pg. 1952
DALIAN SHIDE PLASTICS INDUSTRY CO., LTD.—See Dalian Shide Group Co., Ltd.; *Int'l*, pg. 1952
DALIAN SHIPBUILDING INDUSTRY CO., LTD.—See China Shipbuilding Industry Company Limited; *Int'l*, pg. 1551
DALIAN SHIZUOKA SEIKI CO., LTD.—See Shizuoka Seiki Co., Ltd.; *Int'l*, pg. 6856
DALIAN SPINDLE ENVIRONMENTAL FACILITIES CO., LTD.—See Sumitomo Heavy Industries, Ltd.; *Int'l*, pg. 7286
DALIAN SUMIKA CHEMPHY CHEMICAL CO., LTD.—See Sumitomo Chemical Company, Limited; *Int'l*, pg. 7264
DALIAN SUMIKA JINGANG CHEMICALS CO., LTD.—See Sumitomo Chemical Company, Limited; *Int'l*, pg. 7264
DALIAN SUMIRIN INFORMATION TECHNOLOGY SERVICE CO., LTD.—See Sumitomo Forestry Co., Ltd.; *Int'l*, pg. 7285

DALIAN SUNAISA TOURISM HOLDINGS CO., LTD.

DALIAN SUNAISA TOURISM HOLDINGS CO., LTD.; *Int'l*, pg. 1952
DALIAN SUNTAK CIRCUIT CO., LTD.—See Suntak Technology Co., Ltd; *Int'l*, pg. 7324
DALIAN SUNYARD SOFTWARE CO., LTD.—See Sunyard Technology Co., Ltd; *Int'l*, pg. 7333
DALIAN SUPERELECTRONICS CO., LTD.—See DTS Corporation; *Int'l*, pg. 2217
DALIAN TAIYO NIPPON SANSO GAS CO., LTD.—See Mitsubishi Chemical Group Corporation; *Int'l*, pg. 4936
DALIAN TEIKOKU CANNED MOTOR PUMP CO.,LTD.—See Teikoku Electric Mfg. Co., Ltd.; *Int'l*, pg. 7524
DALIAN THERMAL POWER CO., LTD.; *Int'l*, pg. 1952
DALIAN THK CO., LTD.—See THK CO., LTD.; *Int'l*, pg. 7711
DALIAN TIAN AN TOWER CO., LTD.—See Tian An China Investments Company Limited; *Int'l*, pg. 7737
DALIAN TIANBAO GREEN FOODS CO., LTD.; *Int'l*, pg. 1952
DALIAN TONGHAI MACHINERY & ELECTRONIC EQUIPMENT CO., LTD.; *Int'l*, pg. 1952
DALIAN TOP-EASTERN GROUP CO., LTD.; *Int'l*, pg. 1952
DALIAN TOSHIBA BROADCASTING SYSTEMS CO., LTD.—See Japan Industrial Partners, Inc.; *Int'l*, pg. 3893
DALIAN TOSHIBA TELEVISION CO., LTD.—See Japan Industrial Partners, Inc.; *Int'l*, pg. 3889
DALIAN TOSHIBA TELEVISON CO., LTD.—See Japan Industrial Partners, Inc.; *Int'l*, pg. 3889
DALIAN TOYO JIDOKI CO., LTD.—See Nabtesco Corporation; *Int'l*, pg. 5121
DALIAN TRI-ENTERPRISE LOGISTICS CO., LTD.—See Senko Group Holdings Co., Ltd.; *Int'l*, pg. 6709
DALIAN UNIVERSITY OF TECHNOLOGY SCIENCE PARK CO., LTD—See Datang Huayin Electric Power Co., Ltd.; *Int'l*, pg. 1979
DALIAN VANKE PROPERTY COMPANY LIMITED—See China Vanke Co., Ltd.; *Int'l*, pg. 1562
DALIAN WACOAL CO., LTD.—See Wacoal Holdings Corp.; *Int'l*, pg. 8325
DALIAN WANDA COMMERCIAL PROPERTIES CO., LTD.—See Dalian Wanda Group Corporation Ltd.; *Int'l*, pg. 1953
DALIAN WANDA GROUP CORPORATION LTD.; *Int'l*, pg. 1953
DALIAN WEST PACIFIC PETROCHEMICAL CO. LTD.—See Sinochem Corporation; *Int'l*, pg. 6949
DALIAN XINHUA INFOTECH CO., LTD—See Chinasoft International Ltd.; *Int'l*, pg. 1569
DALIAN YIHE PROPERTY MANAGEMENT CO., LTD.—See Daiwa House Industry Co., Ltd.; *Int'l*, pg. 1946
DALIAN YKK ZIPPER CO., LTD.—See YKK Corporation; *Int'l*, pg. 8588
DALIAN ZEUS ENTERTAINMENT CO., LTD.; *Int'l*, pg. 1953
DALIAN ZHIYUN AUTOMATION CO., LTD.; *Int'l*, pg. 1953
DALIAN ZHONGJIA FOOD CO., LTD.—See Wellhope Foods Co., Ltd.; *Int'l*, pg. 8374
DALI BEER (GROUP) LIMITED COMPANY—See Carlsberg A/S; *Int'l*, pg. 1340
DA-LI DEVELOPMENT CO., LTD.; *Int'l*, pg. 1902
DA LI DEVELOPMENT LLC—See Da-Li Development Co., Ltd.; *Int'l*, pg. 1902
DA LI DEVELOPMENT USA LLC—See Da-Li Development Co., Ltd.; *Int'l*, pg. 1902
DALI FOODS GROUP CO. LTD.; *Int'l*, pg. 1951
DAL, INC.—See Trivest Partners, LP; *U.S. Private*, pg. 4240
DALIPAL HOLDINGS LIMITED; *Int'l*, pg. 1953
DALI PHARMACEUTICAL CO., LTD.; *Int'l*, pg. 1951
DALIS ELECTRONICS—See Components Center Inc.; *U.S. Private*, pg. 1002
DALIT BAY GOLF & COUNTRY CLUB BERHAD—See Shangri-La Hotels (Malaysia) Berhad; *Int'l*, pg. 6784
DA-LITE—See Legrand S.A.; *Int'l*, pg. 4445
DALKIA AB—See Veolia Environnement S.A.; *Int'l*, pg. 8156
DALKIA ARGENTINA S.A.—See Veolia Environnement S.A.; *Int'l*, pg. 8156
DALKIA ASIA PACIFIC—See Veolia Environnement S.A.; *Int'l*, pg. 8156
DALKIA BRASIL S/A—See Veolia Environnement S.A.; *Int'l*, pg. 8156
DALKIA BREZNO, A.S.—See Veolia Environnement S.A.; *Int'l*, pg. 8156
DALKIA CANADA INC.—See Veolia Environnement S.A.; *Int'l*, pg. 8156
DALKIA CENTRE MEDITERRANEE S.C.A.—See Veolia Environnement S.A.; *Int'l*, pg. 8157
DALKIA CESKA REPUBLIKA, A.S—See Veolia Environnement S.A.; *Int'l*, pg. 8157
DALKIA CHILE S.A.—See Veolia Environnement S.A.; *Int'l*, pg. 8157
DALKIA (CHINA) ENERGY MANAGEMENT CO., LTD.—See Veolia Environnement S.A.; *Int'l*, pg. 8156

DALKIA COMMODITIES CZ, S.R.O.—See Veolia Environnement S.A.; *Int'l*, pg. 8157
DALKIA CROATIA—See Veolia Environnement S.A.; *Int'l*, pg. 8157
DALKIA DO BRASIL LTDA—See Veolia Environnement S.A.; *Int'l*, pg. 8157
DALKIA ENERGIA Y SERVICIOS S.A DE C.V.—See Veolia Environnement S.A.; *Int'l*, pg. 8157
DALKIA ENERGIA Y SERVICIOS SA—See Veolia Environnement S.A.; *Int'l*, pg. 8157
DALKIA ENERGIA ZRT.—See Veolia Environnement S.A.; *Int'l*, pg. 8157
DALKIA ENERGY & SERVICES LTD.—See Veolia Environnement S.A.; *Int'l*, pg. 8156
DALKIA ENERGY & TECHNICAL SERVICES SP. Z O.O.—See Veolia Environnement S.A.; *Int'l*, pg. 8157
DALKIA ENERJI SAN VE TIC A.S.—See Veolia Environnement S.A.; *Int'l*, pg. 8157
DALKIA ESPANA S.L.—See Veolia Environnement S.A.; *Int'l*, pg. 8157
DALKIA EST S.C.A.—See Veolia Environnement S.A.; *Int'l*, pg. 8157
DALKIA FACILITIES MANAGEMENT AB—See Veolia Environnement S.A.; *Int'l*, pg. 8156
DALKIA FRANCE S.C.A.—See Electricite de France S.A.; *Int'l*, pg. 2350
DALKIA GMBH—See Veolia Environnement S.A.; *Int'l*, pg. 8157
DALKIA - HANBUL ENERGY MANAGEMENT CO., LTD.—See Veolia Environnement S.A.; *Int'l*, pg. 8156
DALKIA ILE-DE-FRANCE—See Veolia Environnement S.A.; *Int'l*, pg. 8157
DALKIA INDUSTRIPARTNER AB—See Veolia Environnement S.A.; *Int'l*, pg. 8156
DALKIA INTERNATIONAL S.A.—See Veolia Environnement S.A.; *Int'l*, pg. 8153
DALKIA KOLIN, A.S.—See Veolia Environnement S.A.; *Int'l*, pg. 8157
DALKIA LATVIA, LTD.—See Veolia Environnement S.A.; *Int'l*, pg. 8157
DALKIA LODZ SA—See Veolia Environnement S.A.; *Int'l*, pg. 8157
DALKIA LTD—See Veolia Environnement S.A.; *Int'l*, pg. 8157
DALKIA LUCENEC A.S.—See Veolia Environnement S.A.; *Int'l*, pg. 8157
DALKIA MARIANSKE LAZNE, S.R.O.—See Veolia Environnement S.A.; *Int'l*, pg. 8157
DALKIA MEXICO SA DE CV—See Veolia Environnement S.A.; *Int'l*, pg. 8156
DALKIA NORD S.C.A.—See Veolia Environnement S.A.; *Int'l*, pg. 8157
DALKIA NV-SA—See Electricite de France S.A.; *Int'l*, pg. 2350
DALKIA NV-SA—See Veolia Environnement S.A.; *Int'l*, pg. 8157
DALKIA PLC—See Veolia Environnement S.A.; *Int'l*, pg. 8158
DALKIA PLC—See Veolia Environnement S.A.; *Int'l*, pg. 8157
DALKIA PODUNAJSKE BISKUPICE S.R.O.—See Veolia Environnement S.A.; *Int'l*, pg. 8157
DALKIA POLSKA SA—See Veolia Environnement S.A.; *Int'l*, pg. 8157
DALKIA POPRAD A.S.—See Veolia Environnement S.A.; *Int'l*, pg. 8157
DALKIA PORTUGAL—See Veolia Environnement S.A.; *Int'l*, pg. 8157
DALKIA POWERLINE SP. Z O.O.—See Veolia Environnement S.A.; *Int'l*, pg. 8157
DALKIA - PROMETHEUS RT—See Veolia Environnement S.A.; *Int'l*, pg. 8156
DALKIA - SAINT-ANDRE—See Veolia Environnement S.A.; *Int'l*, pg. 8156
DALKIA SAUDI ARABIA L.L.C.—See Veolia Environnement S.A.; *Int'l*, pg. 8157
DALKIA SENEC A.S.—See Veolia Environnement S.A.; *Int'l*, pg. 8157
DALKIA SERVICES SP. Z O.O.—See Veolia Environnement S.A.; *Int'l*, pg. 8157
DALKIA SGPS SA—See Veolia Environnement S.A.; *Int'l*, pg. 8157
DALKIA—See Veolia Environnement S.A.; *Int'l*, pg. 8156
DALKIA SRL—See Veolia Environnement S.A.; *Int'l*, pg. 8157
DALKIA TERM S.A.—See Veolia Environnement S.A.; *Int'l*, pg. 8158
DALKIA VARNA EAD—See Veolia Environnement S.A.; *Int'l*, pg. 8157
DALKIA VRABLE A.S.—See Veolia Environnement S.A.; *Int'l*, pg. 8157
DALLAH AL BARAKA HOLDING COMPANY E.C.; *Int'l*, pg. 1953
DALLAH ALMUTAQDMAH BUSES & EQUIPMENT CO. LTD.; *Int'l*, pg. 1954
DALLAH HEALTH COMPANY; *Int'l*, pg. 1954
DALLAS 1 CORP.; *U.S. Private*, pg. 1149
DALLAS AEROSPACE OPERATIONS—See RTX Corporation; *U.S. Public*, pg. 1823

CORPORATE AFFILIATIONS

DALLAS AIRMOTIVE, INC. - DALLAS FACILITY—See BlackRock, Inc.; *U.S. Public*, pg. 346
DALLAS AIRMOTIVE, INC. - DALLAS FACILITY—See Blackstone Inc.; *U.S. Public*, pg. 358
DALLAS AIRMOTIVE, INC. - DALLAS FACILITY—See Cascade Investment LLC; *U.S. Private*, pg. 780
DALLAS AIRMOTIVE, INC.—See BlackRock, Inc.; *U.S. Public*, pg. 346
DALLAS AIRMOTIVE, INC.—See Blackstone Inc.; *U.S. Public*, pg. 358
DALLAS AIRMOTIVE, INC.—See Cascade Investment LLC; *U.S. Private*, pg. 780
DALLAS AIRMOTIVE SOUTH AFRICA PTY LIMITED—See BlackRock, Inc.; *U.S. Public*, pg. 346
DALLAS AIRMOTIVE SOUTH AFRICA PTY LIMITED—See Blackstone Inc.; *U.S. Public*, pg. 358
DALLAS AIRMOTIVE SOUTH AFRICA PTY LIMITED—See Cascade Investment LLC; *U.S. Private*, pg. 780
DALLAS AREA RAPID TRANSIT INC.; *U.S. Private*, pg. 1149
DALLAS AUTO AUCTION INC.—See Cox Enterprises, Inc.; *U.S. Private*, pg. 1076
DALLAS BUSINESS JOURNAL—See Advance Publications, Inc.; *U.S. Private*, pg. 84
DALLAS CONTAINER CORPORATION; *U.S. Private*, pg. 1149
DALLAS COPART SALVAGE AUTO AUCTIONS LP—See Copart, Inc.; *U.S. Public*, pg. 575
DALLAS COUNTRY CLUB; *U.S. Private*, pg. 1149
DALLAS COUNTY INDIGENT CARE CORPORATION; *U.S. Private*, pg. 1149
THE DALLAS COUNTY LOCAL WORKFORCE DEVELOPMENT BOARD, INC.; *U.S. Private*, pg. 4017
DALLAS COWBOYS FOOTBALL CLUB, LTD.; *U.S. Private*, pg. 1149
DALLAS FAN FARES, INC.; *U.S. Private*, pg. 1149
DALLAS FASTENER, INC.—See Birmingham Fastener & Supply Inc.; *U.S. Private*, pg. 564
DALLAS FINANCIAL WHOLESALERS—See Thomas H. Lee Partners, L.P.; *U.S. Private*, pg. 4156
DALLAS-FORT WORTH ROOFING SUPPLY, LLC—See Beacon Roofing Supply, Inc.; *U.S. Public*, pg. 286
THE DALLAS FOUNDATION; *U.S. Private*, pg. 4017
DALLAS, GARLAND & NORTHEASTERN RAILROAD, INC.—See Brookfield Infrastructure Partners L.P.; *Int'l*, pg. 1191
DALLAS, GARLAND & NORTHEASTERN RAILROAD, INC.—See GIC Pte. Ltd.; *Int'l*, pg. 2965
THE DALLAS GROUP OF AMERICA, INC.; *U.S. Private*, pg. 4017
DALLAS-H, INC.—See Lithia Motors, Inc.; *U.S. Public*, pg. 1322
DALLAS INDUSTRIES, INC.; *U.S. Private*, pg. 1149
DALLAS JEWISH COMMUNITY FOUNDATION; *U.S. Private*, pg. 1150
DALLAS MANUFACTURING COMPANY INC.—See Brinkmann Corp.; *U.S. Private*, pg. 655
DALLAS MARKET CENTER COMPANY; *U.S. Private*, pg. 1150
DALLAS MAVERICKS; *U.S. Private*, pg. 1150
DALLAS MECHANICAL GROUP, LLC—See EMCOR Group, Inc.; *U.S. Public*, pg. 736
DALLAS MEDICAL SPECIALISTS, PLLC—See HCA Healthcare, Inc.; *U.S. Public*, pg. 995
DALLAS MIDWEST COMPANY—See Franz Haniel & Cie. GmbH; *Int'l*, pg. 2763
THE DALLAS MORNING NEWS, INC.—See DallasNews Corporation; *U.S. Public*, pg. 621
DALLASNEWS CORPORATION; *U.S. Public*, pg. 621
DALLAS OBSERVER, LP—See Village Voice Media Holdings, LLC; *U.S. Private*, pg. 4384
DALLAS PETERBILT, INC.—See Rush Enterprises, Inc.; *U.S. Public*, pg. 1826
DALLAS PLASTICS CORPORATION—See Sole Source Capital LLC; *U.S. Private*, pg. 3708
DALLAS REGIONAL MEDICAL CENTER - WOUND CARE & HYPERBARIC CENTER—See Prime Healthcare Services, Inc.; *U.S. Private*, pg. 3261
DALLAS RETIREMENT VILLAGE; *U.S. Private*, pg. 1150
DALLAS SERVICE CENTER, INC.—See Ryder System, Inc.; *U.S. Public*, pg. 1828
DALLAS SIGHT AND SOUND, INC.—See Echo Group, Inc.; *U.S. Private*, pg. 1327
DALLAS STARS L.P.—See Hicks Holdings, LLC; *U.S. Private*, pg. 1934
DALLAS SURGICAL PARTNERS, L.L.P.—See Tenet Healthcare Corporation; *U.S. Public*, pg. 2014
DALLAS SYMPHONY ASSOCIATION INC.; *U.S. Private*, pg. 1150
DALLAS-T, INC.—See Lithia Motors, Inc.; *U.S. Public*, pg. 1322
DALLAS TOURISM PUBLIC IMPROVEMENT DISTRICT; *U.S. Private*, pg. 1150
DALLAS WHEELS & ACCESSORIES INC.—See Ultra Wheel Company Inc.; *U.S. Private*, pg. 4277
DALLI-DE KLOK B.V.—See DALLI-WERKE GmbH & Co. KG; *Int'l*, pg. 1954
DALLI-WERKE GMBH & CO. KG; *Int'l*, pg. 1954

DALLI-WIN IBERICA SL—See DALLI-WERKE GmbH & Co. KG; *Int'l*, pg. 1954
DALLMAYR AUTOMATEN-SERVICE GMBH—See Alois Dallmayr KG; *Int'l*, pg. 365
DALLMEIER ELECTRONIC ESPANA, S.L.—See Dallmeier electronic GmbH & Co. KG; *Int'l*, pg. 1954
DALLMEIER ELECTRONIC GMBH & CO. KG; *Int'l*, pg. 1954
DALLMEIER ELECTRONIC UK LTD—See Dallmeier electronic GmbH & Co. KG; *Int'l*, pg. 1954
DALLMEIER ELECTRONIC USA INC.—See Dallmeier electronic GmbH & Co. KG; *Int'l*, pg. 1954
DALLMEIER INTERNATIONAL LTD.—See Dallmeier electronic GmbH & Co. KG; *Int'l*, pg. 1954
DALLMEIER INTERNATIONAL LTD.—See Dallmeier electronic GmbH & Co. KG; *Int'l*, pg. 1954
DALLMEIER ITALIA SRL—See Dallmeier electronic GmbH & Co. KG; *Int'l*, pg. 1954
DALLMEIER KOREA CO., LTD—See Dallmeier electronic GmbH & Co. KG; *Int'l*, pg. 1954
DALLMEIER SWITZERLAND DIVINET GMBH—See Dallmeier electronic GmbH & Co. KG; *Int'l*, pg. 1954
DALLMEIER TURKEY NI-TI ELEKTRONIK GUVENLIK SIST SAN.TIC. LTD—See Dallmeier electronic GmbH & Co. KG; *Int'l*, pg. 1954
DALLMER GMBH & CO. KG; *Int'l*, pg. 1954
DALLMER LTD.—See DALLMER GmbH & Co. KG; *Int'l*, pg. 1954
DALLO & CO. INC.; *U.S. Private*, pg. 1150
DALLOZ FORMATION, SAS—See Editions Lefebvre Sarrut SA; *Int'l*, pg. 2311
DALMAC CONSTRUCTION PARTNERS LTD.; *U.S. Private*, pg. 1150
DALMAC DEVELOPMENT CORP.—See DalMac Construction Partners Ltd.; *U.S. Private*, pg. 1150
DALMAR MOTORS LTD.; *Int'l*, pg. 1954
DALMATIAN FIRE INC.; *U.S. Private*, pg. 1150
DALMATIAN PRESS LLC; *U.S. Private*, pg. 1150
DALMIA BHARAT LIMITED; *Int'l*, pg. 1954
DALMIA BHARAT SUGAR AND INDUSTRIES LTD—See Dalmia Bharat Limited; *Int'l*, pg. 1954
DALMIA CEMENT (BHARAT) LIMITED—See Dalmia Bharat Limited; *Int'l*, pg. 1954
DALMIA INDUSTRIAL DEVELOPMENT LIMITED; *Int'l*, pg. 1954
DALMIA REFRACTORIES LIMITED—See Dalmia Bharat Limited; *Int'l*, pg. 1954
DALMINE ENERGIE S.P.A.—See Techint S.p.A.; *Int'l*, pg. 7504
DALMINE S.P.A.—See Techint S.p.A.; *Int'l*, pg. 7504
DALMORE CAPITAL LIMITED; *Int'l*, pg. 1954
DALMOR S.A.—See Polski Holding Nieruchomosci S.A.; *Int'l*, pg. 5912
DALOL OIL SHARE COMPANY; *Int'l*, pg. 1955
DALPEX S.P.A.—See Aliaxis S.A./N.V.; *Int'l*, pg. 323
DALPHI METAL ESPANA, S.A.—See ZF Friedrichshafen AG; *Int'l*, pg. 8641
DALPROMRYBA LLC—See Thai Union Group Public Company Limited; *Int'l*, pg. 7596
DALRADA FINANCIAL CORPORATION; *U.S. Public*, pg. 621
DALRADIAN GOLD LIMITED—See Orion Resource Partners (USA) LP; *U.S. Private*, pg. 3043
DALRADIAN RESOURCES LTD.—See Orion Resource Partners (USA) LP; *U.S. Private*, pg. 3043
DALRYMPLE BAY COAL TERMINAL PTY LTD—See Peabody Energy Corporation; *U.S. Public*, pg. 1659
DALRYMPLE BAY INFRASTRUCTURE LIMITED; *Int'l*, pg. 1955
DALRYMPLE BAY INFRASTRUCTURE MANAGEMENT PTY. LTD.—See Dalrymple Bay Infrastructure Limited; *Int'l*, pg. 1955
DALRYMPLE HOLDING CORP.; *U.S. Private*, pg. 1150
DALSON FOODS INC.; *U.S. Private*, pg. 1150
DAL-TEX CONSULTING, LLC—See Energy Transfer LP; *U.S. Public*, pg. 762
DAL-TILE CORPORATION—See Mohawk Industries, Inc.; *U.S. Public*, pg. 1457
DAL-TILE DISTRIBUTION, INC.—See Mohawk Industries, Inc.; *U.S. Public*, pg. 1457
DAL-TILE GROUP, INC—See Mohawk Industries, Inc.; *U.S. Public*, pg. 1457
DAL-TILE INTERNATIONAL INC.—See Mohawk Industries, Inc.; *U.S. Public*, pg. 1457
DAL-TILE MEXICO S.A. DE C.V.—See Mohawk Industries, Inc.; *U.S. Public*, pg. 1457
DAL-TILE OF CANADA INC—See Mohawk Industries, Inc.; *U.S. Public*, pg. 1457
DAL-TILE SERVICES, INC.—See Mohawk Industries, Inc.; *U.S. Public*, pg. 1457
DALTIX NV—See Colruyt Group N.V.; *Int'l*, pg. 1705
DALTIX UNIPESSOAL LDA.—See Colruyt Group N.V.; *Int'l*, pg. 1705
THE DALTON AGENCY, INC.; *U.S. Private*, pg. 4018
DALTON+ANODE—See The Dalton Agency, Inc.; *U.S. Private*, pg. 4018
DALTON BEARING SERVICE, INC.; *U.S. Private*, pg. 1150

DALTON CARPET ONE FLOOR & HOME; *U.S. Private*, pg. 1150
DALTON CORPORATION—See Speyside Equity LLC; *U.S. Private*, pg. 3756
DALTON CORPORATION—See Itoki Corporation; *Int'l*, pg. 3843
DALTON CORPORATION - STRYKER PLANT—See Speyside Equity LLC; *U.S. Private*, pg. 3756
DALTON, GREINER, HARTMAN & MAHER & CO. LLC—See Boston Private Financial Holdings, Inc.; *U.S. Public*, pg. 372
DALTON INVESTMENTS LLC; *U.S. Private*, pg. 1150
DALTON PETROLEUM INC.; *U.S. Private*, pg. 1150
DALTON'S BEST MAID PRODUCTS INC.; *U.S. Private*, pg. 1150
DALTON TIMMIS INSURANCE GROUP, INC.—See Aon plc; *Int'l*, pg. 495
DALTON TRUCKING INC.; *U.S. Private*, pg. 1150
DALTRADE LTD—See Kulczyk Investments S.A.; *Int'l*, pg. 4328
DALTRON (VANUATU) LTD.—See MBf Holdings Berhad; *Int'l*, pg. 4752
D-A LUBRICANT COMPANY; *U.S. Private*, pg. 1139
DA LUE INTERNATIONAL HOLDING CO., LTD.; *Int'l*, pg. 1901
DALY COMPUTERS INC.; *U.S. Private*, pg. 1150
DALY MERRITT, INC.—See GTCR LLC; *U.S. Private*, pg. 1802
DALYN CORPORATION; *U.S. Private*, pg. 1150
DA-LY REALTY & INSURANCE INC.; *U.S. Private*, pg. 1143
DAL ZEITARBEIT GMBH—See Derichebourg S.A.; *Int'l*, pg. 2041
DAMABOIS, INC.; *Int'l*, pg. 1955
DAMAC AL JAZEIRA CATERING WLL—See DAMAC Group; *Int'l*, pg. 1955
DAMAC GROUP; *Int'l*, pg. 1955
DAMAC INVEST CO. LLC—See DAMAC Group; *Int'l*, pg. 1955
DAMAC PRODUCTS, INC.—See Littlejohn & Co., LLC; *U.S. Private*, pg. 2471
DAMAC PROPERTIES DUBAI CO PJSC—See DAMAC Group; *Int'l*, pg. 1955
DAMAGE CONTROL, INC.; *U.S. Private*, pg. 1150
DAMAGE CONTROL, LLC; *U.S. Private*, pg. 1150
DAMALINI AB—See Indutrade AB; *Int'l*, pg. 3678
DAMAN PRODUCTS COMPANY, INC.—See Helios Technologies, Inc.; *U.S. Public*, pg. 1023
DAMANSARA REALTY BERHAD; *Int'l*, pg. 1955
DAMANSARA REALTY MANAGEMENT SERVICES SDN. BHD.—See Damansara Realty Berhad; *Int'l*, pg. 1955
DAMANSARA ROCK PRODUCTS SDN BHD—See IJM Corporation Berhad; *Int'l*, pg. 3608
DAMANSARA TECHNOLOGY SDN. BHD.—See Damansara Realty Berhad; *Int'l*, pg. 1955
DAMARA GOLD CORP.; *Int'l*, pg. 1955
DAMARIS SA; *Int'l*, pg. 1955
DAMAR PLASTICS MANUFACTURING, INC.—See Evome Medical Technologies Inc.; *U.S. Public*, pg. 805
DAMAR SERVICES, INC.; *U.S. Private*, pg. 1151
DAMARTEX SA; *Int'l*, pg. 1955
DAMARTEX UK LTD—See Damartex SA; *Int'l*, pg. 1956
DAMART SERVIPOSTE S.A.—See Damartex SA; *Int'l*, pg. 1956
DAMART—See Damartex SA; *Int'l*, pg. 1955
DAMART SWISS AG—See Damartex SA; *Int'l*, pg. 1956
DAMASCUS CENTRE, LLC—See First Real Estate Investment Trust New Jersey Co.; *U.S. Public*, pg. 847
DAMASCUS EQUIPMENT, LLC—See Spencer Mac Corporation; *U.S. Private*, pg. 3755
DAMASCUS MINI STORAGE LLC—See National Storage Affiliates Trust; *U.S. Public*, pg. 1498
DAMASCUS MOTOR COMPANY INC.; *U.S. Private*, pg. 1151
DAMAS INTERNATIONAL LIMITED—See Mannai Corporation QPSC; *Int'l*, pg. 4674
DAMAS LLC—See Mannai Corporation QPSC; *Int'l*, pg. 4674
DAMA TRADING PTE. LTD.—See Mitani Corporation; *Int'l*, pg. 4744
DAMAVAND MINING COMPANY; *Int'l*, pg. 1956
DAMBACH CORPORATE DESIGN ELEMENTS GMBH—See SWARCO AG; *Int'l*, pg. 7360
DAMBALLA, INC.—See K1 Investment Management, LLC; *U.S. Private*, pg. 2252
D'AMBROSIO EYE CARE, INC.; *U.S. Private*, pg. 1138
DAMCO A/S—See A.P. Moller-Maersk A/S; *Int'l*, pg. 26
DAMCO AUSTRALIA PTY. LTD.—See A.P. Moller-Maersk A/S; *Int'l*, pg. 26
DAMCO CHINA LIMITED—See A.P. Moller-Maersk A/S; *Int'l*, pg. 26
DAMCO CUSTOMS SERVICES, INC.—See A.P. Moller-Maersk A/S; *Int'l*, pg. 26
DAMCO FRANCE S.A.S.—See A.P. Moller-Maersk A/S; *Int'l*, pg. 26
DAMCO INDIA PRIVATE LIMITED—See A.P. Moller-Maersk A/S; *Int'l*, pg. 26
DAMCO INTERNATIONAL A/S—See A.P. Moller-Maersk A/S; *Int'l*, pg. 26

DAMCO ITALY S.R.L.—See A.P. Moller-Maersk A/S; *Int'l*, pg. 26
DAMCO SWEDEN AB—See A.P. Moller-Maersk A/S; *Int'l*, pg. 26
DAMCO UK LTD.—See A.P. Moller-Maersk A/S; *Int'l*, pg. 26
DAMCO USA INC.—See A.P. Moller-Maersk A/S; *Int'l*, pg. 26
DAMEN DREDGING EQUIPMENT BV—See Damen Shipyards Group; *Int'l*, pg. 1956
DAMEN ENGINEERING GDANSK SP. Z O. O.—See Damen Shipyards Group; *Int'l*, pg. 1956
DAMEN MARINE COMPONENTS BV—See Damen Shipyards Group; *Int'l*, pg. 1956
DAMEN MARINE COMPONENTS GDANSK SP Z O.O.—See Damen Shipyards Group; *Int'l*, pg. 1956
DAMEN MARINE COMPONENTS (SUZHOU) CO., LTD.—See Damen Shipyards Group; *Int'l*, pg. 1956
DAMEN MARINE SERVICES BV—See Damen Shipyards Group; *Int'l*, pg. 1956
DAMEN OSKARSHAMNSVARVET SWEDEN AB—See Damen Shipyards Group; *Int'l*, pg. 1956
DAMEN SCHELDE GEARS BV—See Damen Shipyards Group; *Int'l*, pg. 1956
DAMEN SCHELDE MARINE SERVICES PTE LTD.—See Damen Shipyards Group; *Int'l*, pg. 1956
DAMEN SERVICES BRISBANE PTY LTD.—See Damen Shipyards Group; *Int'l*, pg. 1956
DAMEN SHIPREPAIR BREST S.A.S.—See Damen Shipyards Group; *Int'l*, pg. 1956
DAMEN SHIPREPAIR DUNKERQUE—See Damen Shipyards Group; *Int'l*, pg. 1956
DAMEN SHIPREPAIR—See Damen Shipyards Group; *Int'l*, pg. 1956
DAMEN SHIPREPAIR VLISSINGEN B.V.—See Damen Shipyards Group; *Int'l*, pg. 1956
DAMEN SHIPYARDS BERGUM—See Damen Shipyards Group; *Int'l*, pg. 1956
DAMEN SHIPYARDS CAPE TOWN (PTY) LTD.—See Damen Shipyards Group; *Int'l*, pg. 1956
DAMEN SHIPYARDS DEN HELDER B.V.—See Damen Shipyards Group; *Int'l*, pg. 1956
DAMEN SHIPYARDS GALATI—See Damen Shipyards Group; *Int'l*, pg. 1956
DAMEN SHIPYARDS GDYNIA S.A.—See Damen Shipyards Group; *Int'l*, pg. 1956
DAMEN SHIPYARDS GROUP; *Int'l*, pg. 1956
DAMEN SHIPYARDS HARDINXVELD BV—See Damen Shipyards Group; *Int'l*, pg. 1956
DAMEN SHIPYARDS KOZLE SP Z.O.O.—See Damen Shipyards Group; *Int'l*, pg. 1956
DAMEN SHIPYARDS OOSTENDE NV—See Damen Shipyards Group; *Int'l*, pg. 1956
DAMEN SHIPYARDS SINGAPORE PTE LTD—See Damen Shipyards Group; *Int'l*, pg. 1956
DAMEN SHIPYARDS YICHANG—See Damen Shipyards Group; *Int'l*, pg. 1956
DAMEN TRADING & CHARTERING—See Damen Shipyards Group; *Int'l*, pg. 1956
DAMEN TRADING (SUZHOU) CO., LTD.—See Damen Shipyards Group; *Int'l*, pg. 1956
DAMEN VEROLME ROTTERDAM B.V.—See Damen Shipyards Group; *Int'l*, pg. 1956
DAMEN YICHANG SHIPYARD LTD.—See Damen Shipyards Group; *Int'l*, pg. 1956
DAMERON ALLOY FOUNDRIES; *U.S. Private*, pg. 1151
DAMERON HOSPITAL ASSOCIATION; *U.S. Private*, pg. 1151
DAMES CHEVROLET INC.; *U.S. Private*, pg. 1151
DAMEX SHIPBUILDING & ENGINEERING—See Damen Shipyards Group; *Int'l*, pg. 1956
DAMIA AGRICULTURAL PRODUCTS COMPANY LTD.—See Future Arab Investment Co.; *Int'l*, pg. 2852
DAMIANI INTERNATIONAL B.V.—See Damiani S.p.A.; *Int'l*, pg. 1957
DAMIANI JAPAN K.K.—See Damiani S.p.A.; *Int'l*, pg. 1957
DAMIANI S.P.A.; *Int'l*, pg. 1957
D'AMICO INTERNATIONAL SHIPPING S.A.; *Int'l*, pg. 1899
D'AMICO SISTEMAS S.A.—See Waters Corporation; *U.S. Public*, pg. 2334
D'AMICO & SONS INC.; *U.S. Private*, pg. 1138
D'AMICO TANKERS LTD—See d'Amico International Shipping S.A.; *Int'l*, pg. 1899
D'AMICO TANKERS MONACO SAM—See d'Amico International Shipping S.A.; *Int'l*, pg. 1899
D'AMICO TANKERS UK LTD—See d'Amico International Shipping S.A.; *Int'l*, pg. 1899
DAMI LLC—See Aaron's Company, Inc.; *U.S. Public*, pg. 13
DA MING INTERNATIONAL HOLDINGS LIMITED; *Int'l*, pg. 1901
DAMIXA A/S—See Ostnor AB; *Int'l*, pg. 5655
DAMIXA NEDERLAND BV—See Ostnor AB; *Int'l*, pg. 5655
DAMIXA PTE LTD—See Ostnor AB; *Int'l*, pg. 5655
DAMLORAN RAZAK PHARMACEUTICAL COMPANY; *Int'l*, pg. 1957
DAMMAN FACTORY FOR GLASS BOTTLES—See National Company for Glass Industries; *Int'l*, pg. 5155

DAMM & BIERBAUM AGENTUR FUR MARKETING; *Int'l,* pg. 1957
DAMODAR INDUSTRIES LIMITED; *Int'l,* pg. 1957
DAMON DIALYSIS, LLC—See DaVita Inc.; *U.S. Public,* pg. 638
DAMON G. DOUGLAS COMPANY INC.—See The Greenleaf Company Inc.; *U.S. Private,* pg. 4039
DAMON'S INTERNATIONAL INC.—See Alliance Development Group; *U.S. Private,* pg. 182
DAMON TECHNOLOGY GROUP CORP., LTD.; *Int'l,* pg. 1957
DAMOVO BELGIUM N.V/S.A—See Eli Global, LLC; *U.S. Private,* pg. 1359
DAMOVO DEUTSCHLAND GMBH & CO. KG—See Eli Global, LLC; *U.S. Private,* pg. 1359
DAMOVO POLSKA SP. Z O.O.—See Eli Global, LLC; *U.S. Private,* pg. 1359
DAMOVO SCHWEIZ AG—See Eli Global, LLC; *U.S. Private,* pg. 1359
DAMOVO USA, INC.—See Eli Global, LLC; *U.S. Private,* pg. 1359
DAMO WELLNESS ROMANIA SRL—See Harvia Oyj; *Int'l,* pg. 3281
DAMPA APS—See Metalcolour A/S; *Int'l,* pg. 4846
DAMPER TECHNOLOGY CANADA—See AVK Holding A/S; *Int'l,* pg. 747
DAMPER TECHNOLOGY INDIA PVT. LTD.—See AVK Holding A/S; *Int'l,* pg. 747
DAMPER TECHNOLOGY LTD. - LEICESTER PLANT—See AVK Holding A/S; *Int'l,* pg. 747
DAMPER TECHNOLOGY LTD.—See AVK Holding A/S; *Int'l,* pg. 747
DAM PHU MY PACKAGING JSC; *Int'l,* pg. 1955
DAMPIER SALT LIMITED—See Rio Tinto plc; *Int'l,* pg. 6347
DAMPSKIBSSELSKABET NORDEN A/S; *Int'l,* pg. 1957
DAMP S.R.L.—See Knill Holding GmbH; *Int'l,* pg. 4208
DAM SAFETY INTELLIGENCE LIMITED—See Meridian Energy Limited; *Int'l,* pg. 4835
DAM SEN WATER PARK CORPORATION; *Int'l,* pg. 1955
DAMS FORD LINCOLN SALES LTD.; *Int'l,* pg. 1957
DAMSKY PAPER COMPANY; *U.S. Private,* pg. 1151
DAMSTRA HOLDINGS LTD.; *Int'l,* pg. 1957
DAMSTRA TECHNOLOGY PTY LTD—See Damstra Holdings Ltd.; *Int'l,* pg. 1957
DAMU FUND JSC—See National Managing Holding Baiterek JSC; *Int'l,* pg. 5161
DAMUTH TRANE; *U.S. Private,* pg. 1151
DAMWATCH SERVICES LTD.—See Meridian Energy Limited; *Int'l,* pg. 4835
DAMY CORP.; *U.S. Private,* pg. 1151
DANA AUSTRALIA (HOLDINGS) PTY. LTD.—See Dana Incorporated; *U.S. Public,* pg. 622
DANA AUSTRALIA PTY. LTD.—See Dana Incorporated; *U.S. Public,* pg. 622
DANA AUSTRIA GMBH—See Dana Incorporated; *U.S. Public,* pg. 622
DANA AUTOMOCION, S.A.—See Dana Incorporated; *U.S. Public,* pg. 622
DANA AUTOMOTIVE AFTERMARKET, INC.—See Dana Incorporated; *U.S. Public,* pg. 622
DANA BELGIUM BVBA—See Dana Incorporated; *U.S. Public,* pg. 622
DANA BELGIUM NV—See Dana Incorporated; *U.S. Public,* pg. 622
DANA B. KENYON COMPANY, INC.; *U.S. Private,* pg. 1152
DANA BREVINI POWER - TRANSMISSION S.P.A.—See Dana Incorporated; *U.S. Public,* pg. 622
DANA CANADA CORPORATION—See Dana Incorporated; *U.S. Public,* pg. 622
DANA CANADA CORPORATION—See Dana Incorporated; *U.S. Public,* pg. 622
DANA CELLARS CORPORATION—See Sajodongaone Co., Ltd.; *Int'l,* pg. 6485
DANA CLASSIC FRAGRANCES, INC.—See Dimeling, Schreiber & Park; *U.S. Private,* pg. 1232
DANA CONTAINER INC.—See Dana Transport Inc.; *U.S. Private,* pg. 1152
DANA CORPORATION AUTOMOTIVE SYSTEMS GROUP—See Dana Incorporated; *U.S. Public,* pg. 622
DANA DE MEXICO CORPORACION, S. DE R.L. DE C.V.—See Dana Incorporated; *U.S. Public,* pg. 623
DANA (DEUTSCHLAND) GRUNDSTUCKVERWALTUNGS GMBH—See Dana Incorporated; *U.S. Public,* pg. 622
DANA-FARBER CANCER INSTITUTE; *U.S. Private,* pg. 1152
DANAFILMS CORP.—See Inteplast Group, Ltd.; *U.S. Private,* pg. 2106
DANA FLUID POWER DISTRIBUTION S.R.L.—See Dana Incorporated; *U.S. Public,* pg. 622
DANA GAS PJSC; *Int'l,* pg. 1957
DANAH AL SAFAT FOODSTUFF COMPANY K.S.C.—See Al-Safwa Group Holding Co. K.P.S.C.; *Int'l,* pg. 288
DANA HEAVY VEHICLE TECHNOLOGIES & SYSTEMS—See Dana Incorporated; *U.S. Public,* pg. 622
DANAHER CONTROLS CORP.—See Danaher Corporation; *U.S. Public,* pg. 626

DANAHER CONTROLS—See Danaher Corporation; *U.S. Public,* pg. 625
DANAHER CORPORATION; *U.S. Public,* pg. 623
DANAHER HOLDING B.V.—See Danaher Corporation; *U.S. Public,* pg. 626
DANAHER INDUSTRIAL CONTROLS—See Danaher Corporation; *U.S. Public,* pg. 626
DANAHER MOTION CHINA—See Danaher Corporation; *U.S. Public,* pg. 626
DANAHER MOTION COMPANY—See Danaher Corporation; *U.S. Public,* pg. 626
DANAHER MOTION SARO AB—See Danaher Corporation; *U.S. Public,* pg. 626
DANAHER MOTION—See Danaher Corporation; *U.S. Public,* pg. 626
DANAHER MOTION—See Danaher Corporation; *U.S. Public,* pg. 626
DANAHER MOTION—See Danaher Corporation; *U.S. Public,* pg. 626
DANA HOLDING GMBH—See Dana Incorporated; *U.S. Public,* pg. 622
DAN A. HUGHES COMPANY; *U.S. Private,* pg. 1151
DANA INCORPORATED; *U.S. Public,* pg. 621
DANA INC. - PARIS PLANT—See Dana Incorporated; *U.S. Public,* pg. 622
DANA INDIA TECHNICAL CENTRE PVT. LTD.—See Dana Incorporated; *U.S. Public,* pg. 622
DANA INSURANCE COMPANY; *Int'l,* pg. 1957
DANA ITALIA, SPA—See Dana Incorporated; *U.S. Public,* pg. 622
DANAKALI LIMITED; *Int'l,* pg. 1958
DANA KEPNER COMPANY, LLC—See Core & Main, Inc.; *U.S. Public,* pg. 576
DANAL CO., LTD; *Int'l,* pg. 1958
DANAL, INC.—See Twilio Inc.; *U.S. Public,* pg. 2206
DAN-AM CO.—See SATA GmbH & Co. KG; *Int'l,* pg. 6584
DANAMECO MEDICAL JOINT STOCK CORPORATION; *Int'l,* pg. 1958
DANA MOTION SYSTEMS ITALIA S.R.L.—See Dana Incorporated; *U.S. Public,* pg. 622
DANANG AIRPORT SERVICES COMPANY; *Int'l,* pg. 1958
DANANG BOOKS & SCHOOL EQUIPMENT JOINT STOCK COMPANY; *Int'l,* pg. 1958
DANANG EDUCATION INVESTMENT & DEVELOPMENT JOINT STOCK COMPANY; *Int'l,* pg. 1958
DANANG HOUSING DEVELOPMENT JOINT STOCK COMPANY; *Int'l,* pg. 1958
DANANG HOUSING INVESTMENT AND DEVELOPMENT JOINT STOCK COMPANY; *Int'l,* pg. 1958
DANANG NIPPON SEIKI CO., LTD.—See Nippon Seiki Co., Ltd.; *Int'l,* pg. 5329
DANANG PLASTIC JOINT-STOCK COMPANY; *Int'l,* pg. 1958
DA NANG PORT JSC; *Int'l,* pg. 1901
DA NANG RUBBER JOINT STOCK COMPANY—See Masan Consumer Corp.; *Int'l,* pg. 4719
DANA OFF-HIGHWAY PRODUCTS—See Dana Incorporated; *U.S. Public,* pg. 622
DANA OFF-HIGHWAY PRODUCTS—See Dana Incorporated; *U.S. Public,* pg. 622
DANAOS CORPORATION; *Int'l,* pg. 1958
DANAOS GERMANY—See Danaos Corporation; *Int'l,* pg. 1958
DANAOS MANAGEMENT CONSULTANTS SA—See Danaos Corporation; *Int'l,* pg. 1958
DANAOS NORDIC A.S.—See Danaos Corporation; *Int'l,* pg. 1958
DANAOS PERIPHERALS S.A.—See Danaos Corporation; *Int'l,* pg. 1958
DANAOS SEAROUTES LTD.—See Danaos Corporation; *Int'l,* pg. 1958
DANAOS SHIPPING CO., LTD.—See Danaos Corporation; *Int'l,* pg. 1958
DANAOS SOFTWARE SERVICES PTE LTD.—See Danaos Corporation; *Int'l,* pg. 1958
DANAOS SYSTEMS (CYPRUS) LTD.—See Danaos Corporation; *Int'l,* pg. 1958
DANAPAK FLEXIBLES A/S—See UniCredit S.p.A.; *Int'l,* pg. 8039
DANA PETROLEUM (ALGERIA) LIMITED—See Korea National Oil Corporation; *Int'l,* pg. 4286
DANA PETROLEUM EAST ZEIT LIMITED—See Korea National Oil Corporation; *Int'l,* pg. 4286
DANA PETROLEUM (E&P) LIMITED—See Korea National Oil Corporation; *Int'l,* pg. 4286
DANA PETROLEUM NETHERLANDS B.V.—See Korea National Oil Corporation; *Int'l,* pg. 4286
DANA PETROLEUM (NORTH SEA) LIMITED—See Korea National Oil Corporation; *Int'l,* pg. 4286
DANA PETROLEUM NORWAY AS—See Korea National Oil Corporation; *Int'l,* pg. 4286
DANA PETROLEUM PLC—See Korea National Oil Corporation; *Int'l,* pg. 4286
DANA PETROLEUM (RUSSIA) LIMITED—See Korea National Oil Corporation; *Int'l,* pg. 4286
DANA POWER TRANSMISSION FRANCE—See Dana Incorporated; *U.S. Public,* pg. 622
DANA RAILCARE, INC.—See Dana Transport Inc.; *U.S. Private,* pg. 1152

DANARA INTERNATIONAL, LTD.; *U.S. Private,* pg. 1152
DANA SAC AUSTRALIA PTY. LTD.—See Dana Incorporated; *U.S. Public,* pg. 622
DANA SAC BENELUX B.V.—See Dana Incorporated; *U.S. Public,* pg. 622
DANA SAC CANADA LIMITED—See Dana Incorporated; *U.S. Public,* pg. 622
DANA SAC GERMANY GMBH—See Dana Incorporated; *U.S. Public,* pg. 622
DANA SAC KOREA CO., LTD.—See Dana Incorporated; *U.S. Public,* pg. 622
DANA SAC MEXICO, S.A. DE C.V.—See Dana Incorporated; *U.S. Public,* pg. 622
DANA SAC NEW ZEALAND LIMITED—See Dana Incorporated; *U.S. Public,* pg. 622
DANA SAC NORWAY AS—See Dana Incorporated; *U.S. Public,* pg. 622
DANA SAC S.E. ASIA PTE. LTD.—See Dana Incorporated; *U.S. Public,* pg. 622
DANA SAC SOUTH AFRICA (PTY) LTD.—See Dana Incorporated; *U.S. Public,* pg. 622
DANA SAC TURKEY REDUKTOR SANAYI VE TICARET LIMITED SIRKETI—See Dana Incorporated; *U.S. Public,* pg. 622
DANA SAC UK LIMITED—See Dana Incorporated; *U.S. Public,* pg. 622
DANA SAN LUIS S.A.—See Dana Incorporated; *U.S. Public,* pg. 623
DANA SEALING PRODUCTS—See Dana Incorporated; *U.S. Public,* pg. 623
DANA'S HOUSEKEEPING PERSONNEL SERVICES; *U.S. Private,* pg. 1152
DANA SPICER AXLE SOUTH AFRICA (PTY) LTD.—See Dana Incorporated; *U.S. Public,* pg. 623
DANA STRUCTURAL PRODUCTS, LLC—See Dana Incorporated; *U.S. Public,* pg. 623
DANA TM4 INC.—See Dana Incorporated; *U.S. Public,* pg. 623
DANA TM4 ITALIA S.R.L.—See Dana Incorporated; *U.S. Public,* pg. 623
DANA TM4 UK—See Dana Incorporated; *U.S. Public,* pg. 623
DANA TORQUE TECHNOLOGY—See Dana Incorporated; *U.S. Public,* pg. 623
DANA TRANSPORT INC.; *U.S. Private,* pg. 1152
DANA-Y STEEL JOINT STOCK COMPANY; *Int'l,* pg. 1958
THE DANBERRY, CO.—See Miller Diversified Inc.; *U.S. Private,* pg. 2733
DANBIT A/S—See Nayax Ltd.; *Int'l,* pg. 5178
DANBOLIG A/S—See Nordea Bank Abp; *Int'l,* pg. 5417
DANBOR SERVICE AS—See A.P. Moller-Maersk A/S; *Int'l,* pg. 26
DANBURY AEROSPACE, INC.; *U.S. Private,* pg. 1152
DANBURY KIA; *U.S. Private,* pg. 1153
DANBURY MINT—See MBI, Inc.; *U.S. Private,* pg. 2624
DANBY PRODUCTS LTD.; *Int'l,* pg. 1958
DAN CALLAGHAN ENTERPRISES INC.; *U.S. Private,* pg. 1151
DANCANN PHARMA A/S; *Int'l,* pg. 1958
DANCAP PRIVATE EQUITY INC.; *Int'l,* pg. 1958
DANCARL DIAMONDS (PTY) LTD—See Petra Diamonds Limited; *Int'l,* pg. 5824
DANCE BIOPHARM INC.; *U.S. Private,* pg. 1153
DANCE MAGAZINE—See MacFadden Communications Group, LLC; *U.S. Private,* pg. 2535
DANCENTER A/S—See Axel Springer SE; *Int'l,* pg. 766
DANCHARIA RESEARCH & TRADE EAST AB—See Broadridge Financial Solutions, Inc.; *U.S. Public,* pg. 392
DANCHEM TECHNOLOGIES, INC—See Ascent Industries Co.; *U.S. Public,* pg. 210
DANCIN' DOGG GOLF; *U.S. Private,* pg. 1153
DANCKER, SELLEW & DOUGLAS, INC.; *U.S. Private,* pg. 1153
DANCO INC.; *U.S. Private,* pg. 1153
DANCOMECH HOLDINGS BERHAD; *Int'l,* pg. 1958
DANCO TRANSMISSION; *U.S. Private,* pg. 1153
DAN CUMMINS CHEVROLET-BUICK-PONTIAC, INC.; *U.S. Private,* pg. 1151
DANCUTTER A/S—See Halma plc; *Int'l,* pg. 3231
DAN DAIRIES (UK) LIMITED—See Dairygold Co-Operative Society Ltd; *Int'l,* pg. 1940
DANDARAGAN ESTATE PTY. LTD.—See ORION EQUITIES LIMITED; *Int'l,* pg. 5632
DAN DEERY MOTOR CO. OF WATERLOO, INC.; *U.S. Private,* pg. 1151
DAN DEERY TOYOTA; *U.S. Private,* pg. 1151
DANDELTACO A/S—See DistIT AB; *Int'l,* pg. 2136
DANDENONG VALLEY PRIVATE HOSPITAL PTY LIMITED—See Ramsay Health Care Limited; *Int'l,* pg. 6199
DANDI BIOSCIENCE CO., LTD.—See HLB Global Co Ltd; *Int'l,* pg. 3430
D AND O HOME COLLECTION CO., LTD.; *Int'l,* pg. 1898
DAN DONG ALPINE ELECTRONICS, INC.—See Alps Alpine Co., Ltd.; *Int'l,* pg. 376
DANDONG ALPS ELECTRONICS CO., LTD.—See Alps Alpine Co., Ltd.; *Int'l,* pg. 376

COMPANY NAME INDEX

DANDONG CHINA INTERNATIONAL TRAVEL SERVICE CO., LTD.—See China Tourism Group Duty Free Corporation Limited; *Int'l*, pg. 1560
DANDONG HUANGHAI MOTORS LLC—See Liaoning SG Automotive Group Co., Ltd.; *Int'l*, pg. 4483
DANDONG IWATANI TOYO GAS METER CO., LTD—See Iwatani Corporation; *Int'l*, pg. 3850
DANDONG SG AUTOMOBILE TRADING LLC—See Liaoning SG Automotive Group Co., Ltd.; *Int'l*, pg. 4483
DANDONG SK NETWORKS BUILDING MATERIALS CO., LTD.—See SK Networks Co., Ltd.; *Int'l*, pg. 6974
DANDONG XINTAI ELECTRIC COMPANY LIMITED; *Int'l*, pg. 1959
DANDOT CEMENT CO., LTD.; *Int'l*, pg. 1959
DANDREA PRODUCE, INC.; *U.S. Private*, pg. 1153
DANDRIDGE EQUIPMENT INC.; *U.S. Private*, pg. 1153
DANDY LIONS LIMITED—See International Flavors & Fragrances Inc.; *U.S. Public*, pg. 1151
DANDY MINI MARTS INC.—See Williams Oil Company Inc.; *U.S. Private*, pg. 4526
DANDY OIL CO. INC.; *U.S. Private*, pg. 1153
DANDY PREMIX QUARRIES PTY. LIMITED—See MAAS Group Holdings Limited; *Int'l*, pg. 4618
DANE COLOR UK LIMITED—See RPM International Inc.; *U.S. Public*, pg. 1816
DANE CONSTRUCTION INC.; *U.S. Private*, pg. 1153
DANECRAFT INC.—See American Exchange Group; *U.S. Private*, pg. 232
DAN-ED CORPORATION; *U.S. Private*, pg. 1152
DANEEL MECHATRONICS, S.L.U.—See THK CO., LTD.; *Int'l*, pg. 7711
DANE EQUIPMENT LLC—See Dane Construction Inc.; *U.S. Private*, pg. 1153
DANE EXPLORATION INC.; *U.S. Private*, pg. 1153
DANE GOUGE'S ASTORIA FORD; *U.S. Private*, pg. 1153
DANEL (ADIR YEHOSHUA) LTD.; *Int'l*, pg. 1959
DANELLA ASSOCIATES—See The Danella Companies Inc.; *U.S. Private*, pg. 4018
DANELLA ATLANTIC CORPORATION—See The Danella Companies Inc.; *U.S. Private*, pg. 4018
THE DANELLA COMPANIES INC.; *U.S. Private*, pg. 4018
DANELLA CONSTRUCTION CORP. OF NEW YORK—See The Danella Companies Inc.; *U.S. Private*, pg. 4018
DANELLA CONSTRUCTION CORPORATION OF FLORIDA INC.—See The Danella Companies Inc.; *U.S. Private*, pg. 4018
DANELLA CONSTRUCTION CORPORATION OF NEW JERSEY, INC.—See The Danella Companies Inc.; *U.S. Private*, pg. 4018
DANELLA ENGINEERING AND CONSTRUCTION CORPORATION—See The Danella Companies Inc.; *U.S. Private*, pg. 4018
DANELLA RENTAL SYSTEMS, INC.—See The Danella Companies Inc.; *U.S. Private*, pg. 4018
DANELLA RENTAL SYSTEMS INC.—See The Danella Companies Inc.; *U.S. Private*, pg. 4018
DANELLA UTILITY CONSTRUCTION, INC.—See The Danella Companies Inc.; *U.S. Private*, pg. 4018
DANE MANUFACTURING COMPANY; *U.S. Private*, pg. 1153
DANEN TECHNOLOGY CORPORATION; *Int'l*, pg. 1959
DANERICA ENTERPRISES, INC.; *U.S. Private*, pg. 1153
DANESCO INC.; *Int'l*, pg. 1959
DANE STREET; *U.S. Private*, pg. 1153
DAN-FOAM APS—See Tempur Sealy International, Inc.; *U.S. Public*, pg. 1999
DANFORTH ADVISORS, LLC—See Avesi Partners, LLC; *U.S. Private*, pg. 405
DANFORTH ASSOCIATES, INC.; *U.S. Private*, pg. 1153
DANFORTH SYSTEMS LLC—See The Graham Group, Inc.; *U.S. Private*, pg. 4036
DANFOSS AB—See Danfoss A/S; *Int'l*, pg. 1959
DANFOSS AG—See Danfoss A/S; *Int'l*, pg. 1959
DANFOSS (ANSHAN) CONTROLS CO. LTD.—See Danfoss A/S; *Int'l*, pg. 1959
DANFOSS A/S APPLIANCE CONTROLS DIV.—See Danfoss A/S; *Int'l*, pg. 1959
DANFOSS A/S BUILDING CONTROLS DIV.—See Danfoss A/S; *Int'l*, pg. 1959
DANFOSS A/S - COMFORT CONTROLS DIVISION—See Danfoss A/S; *Int'l*, pg. 1959
DANFOSS A/S FLOW DIV.—See Danfoss A/S; *Int'l*, pg. 1959
DANFOSS A/S INDUSTRIAL CONTROLS DIV.—See Danfoss A/S; *Int'l*, pg. 1959
DANFOSS A/S REFRIGERATION & A/C CONTROLS DIVISION—See Danfoss A/S; *Int'l*, pg. 1959
DANFOSS AS—See Danfoss A/S; *Int'l*, pg. 1959
DANFOSS AS—See Danfoss A/S; *Int'l*, pg. 1959
DANFOSS A/S; *Int'l*, pg. 1959
DANFOSS A/S WATER HYDRAULICS DIVISION—See Danfoss A/S; *Int'l*, pg. 1959
DANFOSS (AUSTRALIA) PTY. LTD.—See Danfoss A/S; *Int'l*, pg. 1959
DANFOSS AUTOMATIC CONTROLS MANAGEMENT (SHANGHAI) CO. LTD.—See Danfoss A/S; *Int'l*, pg. 1959
DANFOSS BAUER GMBH—See Danfoss A/S; *Int'l*, pg. 1959
DANFOSS BURNER COMPONENTS DIVISION—See Danfoss A/S; *Int'l*, pg. 1960
DANFOSS CO. LTD.—See Danfoss A/S; *Int'l*, pg. 1959
DANFOSS COMMERCIAL COMPRESSORS LTD.—See Danfoss A/S; *Int'l*, pg. 1959
DANFOSS COMMERCIAL COMPRESSORS S.A.—See Danfoss A/S; *Int'l*, pg. 1959
DANFOSS DISTRIBUTION SERVICES A/S—See Danfoss A/S; *Int'l*, pg. 1959
DANFOSS DISTRICT HEATING S.R.L.—See Danfoss A/S; *Int'l*, pg. 1959
DANFOSS DO BRASIL INDUSTRIA E COMERCIO LTDA.—See Danfoss A/S; *Int'l*, pg. 1961
DANFOSS D.O.O.—See Danfoss A/S; *Int'l*, pg. 1961
DANFOSS DRIVES A/S—See Danfoss A/S; *Int'l*, pg. 1959
DANFOSS ELECTRONIC DRIVES—See Danfoss A/S; *Int'l*, pg. 1960
DANFOSS EOOD—See Danfoss A/S; *Int'l*, pg. 1960
DANFOSS ESSLINGEN GMBH—See Danfoss A/S; *Int'l*, pg. 1960
DANFOSS FZCO—See Danfoss A/S; *Int'l*, pg. 1960
DANFOSS GESELLSCHAFT M.B.H.—See Danfoss A/S; *Int'l*, pg. 1960
DANFOSS GMBH—See Danfoss A/S; *Int'l*, pg. 1960
DANFOSS GRAHAM—See Danfoss A/S; *Int'l*, pg. 1960
DANFOSS HAGO INC.—See Danfoss A/S; *Int'l*, pg. 1960
DANFOSS HEATING DIVISION—See Danfoss A/S; *Int'l*, pg. 1960
DANFOSS HEAT PUMPS UK LTD.—See Danfoss A/S; *Int'l*, pg. 1960
DANFOSS HF.—See Danfoss A/S; *Int'l*, pg. 1961
DANFOSS INC.—See Danfoss A/S; *Int'l*, pg. 1960
DANFOSS INDUSTRIES LIMITED—See Danfoss A/S; *Int'l*, pg. 1960
DANFOSS INDUSTRIES PTE. LTD.—See Danfoss A/S; *Int'l*, pg. 1960
DANFOSS INDUSTRIES PVT. LIMITED—See Danfoss A/S; *Int'l*, pg. 1960
DANFOSS INDUSTRIES, SA DE CV—See Danfoss A/S; *Int'l*, pg. 1960
DANFOSS INDUSTRIES SDN BHD—See Danfoss A/S; *Int'l*, pg. 1960
DANFOSS IXA A/S—See Danfoss A/S; *Int'l*, pg. 1960
DANFOSS KFT.—See Danfoss A/S; *Int'l*, pg. 1960
DANFOSS LDA—See Danfoss A/S; *Int'l*, pg. 1960
DANFOSS LIMITED—See Danfoss A/S; *Int'l*, pg. 1960
DANFOSS LLC—See Danfoss A/S; *Int'l*, pg. 1960
DANFOSS LLP—See Danfoss A/S; *Int'l*, pg. 1960
DANFOSS LTD.—See Danfoss A/S; *Int'l*, pg. 1960
DANFOSS MICRO CHANNEL HEAT EXCHANGER (JIAXING) CO., LTD.—See Danfoss A/S; *Int'l*, pg. 1960
DANFOSS (NEW ZEALAND) LTD.—See Danfoss A/S; *Int'l*, pg. 1959
DANFOSS OTOMASYON VE URUNLERI TIC LTD.—See Danfoss A/S; *Int'l*, pg. 1960
DANFOSS POLAND SP.Z.O.O.—See Danfoss A/S; *Int'l*, pg. 1960
DANFOSS POWER ELECTRONICS A/S—See Danfoss A/S; *Int'l*, pg. 1960
DANFOSS POWER SOLUTIONS GMBH & CO. OHG—See Danfoss A/S; *Int'l*, pg. 1960
DANFOSS POWER SOLUTIONS, INC.—See Danfoss A/S; *Int'l*, pg. 1960
DANFOSS POWER SOLUTIONS LTDA.—See Danfoss A/S; *Int'l*, pg. 1960
DANFOSS POWER SOLUTIONS OY AB—See Danfoss A/S; *Int'l*, pg. 1960
DANFOSS POWER SOLUTIONS PTE. LTD.—See Danfoss A/S; *Int'l*, pg. 1960
DANFOSS POWER SOLUTIONS PTY. LTD.—See Danfoss A/S; *Int'l*, pg. 1960
DANFOSS POWER SOLUTIONS—See Danfoss A/S; *Int'l*, pg. 1960
DANFOSS POWER SOLUTIONS S.R.L.—See Danfoss A/S; *Int'l*, pg. 1960
DANFOSS (PTY.) LTD.—See Danfoss A/S; *Int'l*, pg. 1959
DANFOSS RANDALL LIMITED—See Danfoss A/S; *Int'l*, pg. 1961
DANFOSS REDAN A/S—See Danfoss A/S; *Int'l*, pg. 1961
DANFOSS S.A. DE C.V.—See Danfoss A/S; *Int'l*, pg. 1961
DANFOSS S.A.R.L.—See Danfoss A/S; *Int'l*, pg. 1961
DANFOSS S.A.—See Danfoss A/S; *Int'l*, pg. 1961
DANFOSS SEMCO A/S—See Danfoss A/S; *Int'l*, pg. 1961
DANFOSS SILICON POWER GMBH—See Danfoss A/S; *Int'l*, pg. 1961
DANFOSS SPOL. S.R.O.—See Danfoss A/S; *Int'l*, pg. 1961
DANFOSS SP. Z.O.O.—See Danfoss A/S; *Int'l*, pg. 1961
DANFOSS S.R.L.—See Danfoss A/S; *Int'l*, pg. 1961
DANFOSS S.R.O.—See Danfoss A/S; *Int'l*, pg. 1961
DANFOSS (THAILAND) CO. LTD.—See Danfoss A/S; *Int'l*, pg. 1959
DANFOSS (TIANJIN) LTD.—See Danfoss A/S; *Int'l*, pg. 1959
DANFOSS T.O.V.—See Danfoss A/S; *Int'l*, pg. 1961
DANFOSS TRATA D.O.O.—See Danfoss A/S; *Int'l*, pg. 1961
DANFOSS TURBOCOR COMPRESSORS INC.—See Danfoss A/S; *Int'l*, pg. 1961
DANFOSS UAB—See Danfoss A/S; *Int'l*, pg. 1961
DANGEE DUMS LTD.; *Int'l*, pg. 1962
DANGER INC.—See Microsoft Corporation; *U.S. Public*, pg. 1440
DANGOTE BAIL LIMITED—See Dangote Group Limited; *Int'l*, pg. 1962
DANGOTE CEMENT PLC—See Dangote Group Limited; *Int'l*, pg. 1962
DANGOTE GLOBAL SERVICES LIMITED—See Dangote Group Limited; *Int'l*, pg. 1962
DANGOTE GROUP LIMITED; *Int'l*, pg. 1962
DANGOTE SUGAR REFINERY PLC—See Dangote Group Limited; *Int'l*, pg. 1962
DAN HEMM AUTO GROUP; *U.S. Private*, pg. 1151
DAN HOTELS LTD.; *Int'l*, pg. 1957
DANHUA CHEMICAL TECHNOLOGY CO., LTD.; *Int'l*, pg. 1962
DA NIANG DUMPLINGS HOLDINGS LIMITED—See CVC Capital Partners SICAV-FIS S.A.; *Int'l*, pg. 1885
DANICA D.O.O.—See Podravka d.d.; *Int'l*, pg. 5902
DANICA LIFE LTD.—See Danske Bank A/S; *Int'l*, pg. 1969
DANICA PENSION—See Danske Bank A/S; *Int'l*, pg. 1969
DANICA PENSJONSFORSIKRING AS—See Storebrand ASA; *Int'l*, pg. 7226
DANICE SERVICES A/S—See Tetra Laval International S.A.; *Int'l*, pg. 7577
DANIEL B. HASTINGS INC.; *U.S. Private*, pg. 1153
DANIEL BOONE AGENCY, LLC—See Shelter Mutual Insurance Company; *U.S. Private*, pg. 3631
DANIEL, BURTON, DEAN ADVERTISING & DESIGN, INC.; *U.S. Private*, pg. 1156
DANIEL CANADA—See Emerson Electric Co.; *U.S. Public*, pg. 746
DANIEL C. BAKER ASSOCIATES, INC.—See Larson Design Group; *U.S. Private*, pg. 2393
DANIEL CORPORATION; *U.S. Private*, pg. 1153
DANIEL DEFENSE; *U.S. Private*, pg. 1153
DANIELE INTERNATIONAL, LLC—See Entrepreneurial Equity Partners, LLC; *U.S. Private*, pg. 1406
DANIEL F. YOUNG, INC.; *U.S. Private*, pg. 1153
THE DANIEL GROUP, LTD.; *U.S. Private*, pg. 4018
DANIEL G. SCHUSTER INC.; *U.S. Private*, pg. 1154
DANIELI AUTOMATION SPA—See Danieli & C. Officine Meccaniche S.p.A.; *Int'l*, pg. 1962
DANIELI CENTRO COMBUSTION SPA—See Danieli & C. Officine Meccaniche S.p.A.; *Int'l*, pg. 1962
DANIELI & C. OFFICINE MECCANICHE S.P.A.; *Int'l*, pg. 1962
DANIELI CO., LTD.—See Danieli & C. Officine Meccaniche S.p.A.; *Int'l*, pg. 1962
DANIELI CONSTR INTERNATIONAL SPA—See Danieli & C. Officine Meccaniche S.p.A.; *Int'l*, pg. 1962
DANIELI CORPORATION—See Danieli & C. Officine Meccaniche S.p.A.; *Int'l*, pg. 1962
DANIELI CORUS, INC.—See Danieli & C. Officine Meccaniche S.p.A.; *Int'l*, pg. 1963
DANIELI CORUS, INC.—See Tata Sons Limited; *Int'l*, pg. 7472
DANIELI CORUS TECHNICAL SERVICES BV—See Danieli & C. Officine Meccaniche S.p.A.; *Int'l*, pg. 1963
DANIELI CORUS TECHNICAL SERVICES BV—See Tata Sons Limited; *Int'l*, pg. 7472
DANIELI DO BRAZIL SA—See Danieli & C. Officine Meccaniche S.p.A.; *Int'l*, pg. 1963
DANIELI ENGINEERING JAPAN LTD.—See Danieli & C. Officine Meccaniche S.p.A.; *Int'l*, pg. 1963
DANIELI ENGINEERING & SERVICE GMBH—See Danieli & C. Officine Meccaniche S.p.A.; *Int'l*, pg. 1963
DANIELI FATA HUNTER, INC.—See Danieli & C. Officine Meccaniche S.p.A.; *Int'l*, pg. 1963
DANIELI FINANCE SOLUTION SA—See Danieli & C. Officine Meccaniche S.p.A.; *Int'l*, pg. 1963
DANIELI GERMANY GMBH—See Danieli & C. Officine Meccaniche S.p.A.; *Int'l*, pg. 1963
DANIELI GERMANY GMBH.—See Danieli & C. Officine Meccaniche S.p.A.; *Int'l*, pg. 1963
DANIELI HENSCHEL SAS—See Danieli & C. Officine Meccaniche S.p.A.; *Int'l*, pg. 1963
DANIELI METALL EQUIPMENT & SERVICE CO., LTD.—See Danieli & C. Officine Meccaniche S.p.A.; *Int'l*, pg. 1963
DANIELI MIDDLE EAST ENG. & SERV.CO.—See Danieli & C. Officine Meccaniche S.p.A.; *Int'l*, pg. 1963
DANIELI MORGARDSHAMMAR SA—See Danieli & C. Officine Meccaniche S.p.A.; *Int'l*, pg. 1963
DANIEL INDUSTRIES CANADA INC.—See Emerson Electric Co.; *U.S. Public*, pg. 746
DANIELI PROCOME IBERICA SA—See Danieli & C. Officine Meccaniche S.p.A.; *Int'l*, pg. 1963
DANIELI SYSTEC DOO—See Danieli & C. Officine Meccaniche S.p.A.; *Int'l*, pg. 1963
DANIELI UK HOLDING LTD.—See Danieli & C. Officine Meccaniche S.p.A.; *Int'l*, pg. 1963
DANIELI VOLGA LLC—See Danieli & C. Officine Meccaniche S.p.A.; *Int'l*, pg. 1963
DANIEL J. EDELMAN HOLDINGS, INC.; *U.S. Private*, pg. 1154
DANIEL J. EDELMAN, INC.; *U.S. Private*, pg. 1154

DANIEL J. KEATING CONSTRUCTION COMPANY, LLC

DANIEL J. KEATING CONSTRUCTION COMPANY, LLC; *U.S. Private*, pg. 1155
DANIEL J QUIRK INC.; *U.S. Private*, pg. 1154
DANIEL K INC.; *U.S. Private*, pg. 1156
DANIEL L. JACOB & CO. INC.; *U.S. Private*, pg. 1156
DANIEL LOISEAU GAMME—See LDC SA; *Int'l*, pg. 4430
DANIEL MEASUREMENT & CONTROL INC.—See Emerson Electric Co.; *U.S. Public*, pg. 746
DANIEL MEASUREMENT CONTROL—See Emerson Electric Co.; *U.S. Public*, pg. 746
DANIEL M. FRIEDMAN & ASSOCIATES, INC.—See Steven Madden, Ltd.; *U.S. Public*, pg. 1947
DANIEL M. POWERS & ASSOCIATES LTD.; *U.S. Private*, pg. 1156
DANIEL O'CONNELL'S SONS INC.—See The O'Connell Companies, Incorporated; *U.S. Private*, pg. 4087
DANIEL P. O'REILLY & COMPANY; *U.S. Private*, pg. 1156
DANIEL REALTY CORPORATION—See Daniel Corporation; *U.S. Private*, pg. 1153
DANIELS BMW; *U.S. Private*, pg. 1156
DANIELS BUILDING & CONSTRUCTION, INC.; *U.S. Private*, pg. 1156
DANIELS CADILLAC, INC.; *U.S. Private*, pg. 1156
DANIELS CHILLED FOODS LTD.—See The Hain Celestial Group, Inc.; *U.S. Public*, pg. 2086
DANIELS CORPORATE ADVISORY COMPANY, INC.; *U.S. Public*, pg. 632
DANIELS ENTERPRISES INC.; *U.S. Private*, pg. 1156
DANIELS FAMILY CUTLERY CORPORATION; *U.S. Private*, pg. 1156
DANIELS GROUP INC.; *U.S. Private*, pg. 1156
DANIELS GROUP LIMITED—See The Hain Celestial Group, Inc.; *U.S. Public*, pg. 2086
DANIELS MANUFACTURING CORPORATION; *U.S. Private*, pg. 1156
DANIEL SMITH, INC.; *U.S. Private*, pg. 1156
DANIELS MOTORS INC.; *U.S. Private*, pg. 1156
DANIEL'S OF ALBION, INC.; *U.S. Private*, pg. 1156
DANIELS-OLSEN BLDG PRODUCTS INC—See Midwest Hardwood Corporation; *U.S. Private*, pg. 2721
DANIELSON DESIGNS, LTD.; *U.S. Private*, pg. 1156
DANIELSON OIL COMPANY OF OKLAHOMA; *U.S. Private*, pg. 1156
DANIELS & ROBERTS, INC.; *U.S. Private*, pg. 1156
DANIELS SENTRY FOODS INC.; *U.S. Private*, pg. 1156
DANIELS TANSEY LLP—See Creative Planning, LLC; *U.S. Private*, pg. 1090
DANIEL STEWART & COMPANY PLC—See Daniel Stewart Securities plc; *Int'l*, pg. 1962
DANIEL STEWART SECURITIES PLC; *Int'l*, pg. 1962
DANIELS TIRE SERVICE INC.; *U.S. Private*, pg. 1156
DANIEL STONE & LANDSCAPING SUPPLIES, INC.—See SiteOne Landscape Supply, Inc.; *U.S. Public*, pg. 1888
DANIEL THWAITES BREWERY—See Daniel Thwaites PLC; *Int'l*, pg. 1962
DANIEL THWAITES PLC; *Int'l*, pg. 1962
DANIEL WEBSTER COLLEGE, INC.—See ITT Educational Services, Inc.; *U.S. Private*, pg. 2150
DANIEL & YEAGER, LLC—See Blackstone Inc.; *U.S. Public*, pg. 359
DANI INSTRUMENTS S.A.—See DANI Instruments SpA; *Int'l*, pg. 1962
DANI INSTRUMENTS SPA; *Int'l*, pg. 1962
DANIMER SCIENTIFIC, INC.; *U.S. Public*, pg. 632
DANINGER + PARTNER ENGINEERING GMBH—See BKW AG; *Int'l*, pg. 1055
DANIR RESOURCES AB; *Int'l*, pg. 1963
DANIS BUILDERS, LLC—See Danis Building Construction Company Inc.; *U.S. Private*, pg. 1156
DANIS BUILDING CONSTRUCTION COMPANY INC.; *U.S. Private*, pg. 1156
DANISCO AUSTRALIA PTY. LTD.—See DuPont de Nemours, Inc.; *U.S. Public*, pg. 692
DANISCO AUSTRIA GMBH—See International Flavors & Fragrances Inc.; *U.S. Public*, pg. 1151
DANISCO BRASIL LTDA.—See DuPont de Nemours, Inc.; *U.S. Public*, pg. 692
DANISCO DEUTSCHLAND GMBH—See DuPont de Nemours, Inc.; *U.S. Public*, pg. 692
DANISCO ITALIA S.P.A.—See International Flavors & Fragrances Inc.; *U.S. Public*, pg. 1151
DANISCO JAPAN LTD.—See DuPont de Nemours, Inc.; *U.S. Public*, pg. 692
DANIS CONSTRUCTION COMPANY LLC—See Danis Building Construction Company Inc.; *U.S. Private*, pg. 1156
DANISCO POLAND SP. Z.O.O—See International Flavors & Fragrances Inc.; *U.S. Public*, pg. 1151
DANISCO (UK) LTD. - BEAMINSTER—See DuPont de Nemours, Inc.; *U.S. Public*, pg. 692
DANISCO (UK) LTD. - REIGATE—See DuPont de Nemours, Inc.; *U.S. Public*, pg. 692
DANISCO (UK) LTD.—See DuPont de Nemours, Inc.; *U.S. Public*, pg. 692
DANISCO USA, INC. - NEW CENTURY—See DuPont de Nemours, Inc.; *U.S. Public*, pg. 692
DANISCO USA, INC.—See DuPont de Nemours, Inc.; *U.S. Public*, pg. 692
DANISH AEROTECH A/S; *Int'l*, pg. 1963

DANISH AGRO AMBA; *Int'l*, pg. 1963
THE DANISH BREWERY GROUP INC.—See Royal Unibrew A/S; *Int'l*, pg. 6414
DANISH CROWN AMBA; *Int'l*, pg. 1964
DANISH CROWN BEEF COMPANY A/S—See Danish Crown AmbA; *Int'l*, pg. 1964
DANISH CROWN - BEEF DIVISION S.A.—See Danish Crown AmbA; *Int'l*, pg. 1964
DANISH CROWN ESPANA S.A.—See Danish Crown AmbA; *Int'l*, pg. 1964
DANISH CROWN FOODS FRANCE S.A.S.—See Danish Crown AmbA; *Int'l*, pg. 1964
DANISH CROWN FOODS GERMANY GMBH—See Danish Crown AmbA; *Int'l*, pg. 1964
DANISH CROWN FOODS HAARLEM B.V.—See Danish Crown AmbA; *Int'l*, pg. 1964
DANISH CROWN FOODS ITALY S.R.L.—See Danish Crown AmbA; *Int'l*, pg. 1964
DANISH CROWN FOODS JONKOPING AB—See Danish Crown AmbA; *Int'l*, pg. 1964
DANISH CROWN FOODS NORWAY AS—See Danish Crown AmbA; *Int'l*, pg. 1964
DANISH CROWN FOODS SWEDEN AB—See Danish Crown AmbA; *Int'l*, pg. 1964
DANISH CROWN FRANCE S.A.S.—See Danish Crown AmbA; *Int'l*, pg. 1964
DANISH CROWN GMBH—See Danish Crown AmbA; *Int'l*, pg. 1964
DANISH CROWN KOREA LLC—See Danish Crown AmbA; *Int'l*, pg. 1964
DANISH CROWN K-PACK AB—See Danish Crown AmbA; *Int'l*, pg. 1964
DANISH CROWN SCHLACHTZENTRUM NORDFRIESLAND GMBH—See Danish Crown AmbA; *Int'l*, pg. 1964
DANISH CROWN SP.Z O.O.—See Danish Crown AmbA; *Int'l*, pg. 1964
DANISH CROWN TETEROWER FLEISCH GMBH—See Danish Crown AmbA; *Int'l*, pg. 1964
DANISH CROWN UK LIMITED—See Danish Crown AmbA; *Int'l*, pg. 1964
DANISH CROWN USA INC.—See Danish Crown AmbA; *Int'l*, pg. 1964
DANISH INSPIRATIONS CORPORATION; *U.S. Private*, pg. 1157
DANISH INSPIRATIONS, SHOWROOM—See Danish Inspirations Corporation; *U.S. Private*, pg. 1157
DANISH MALTING GROUP POLSKA SP. Z.O.O.—See Carlsberg A/S; *Int'l*, pg. 1340
DANISH OFFSHORE GAS SYSTEMS A/S—See Orsted AS; *Int'l*, pg. 5644
DANISH RENEWABLE ENERGY A/S—See Nobao Renewable Energy Holdings Limited; *Int'l*, pg. 5394
DANJAQ LLC; *U.S. Private*, pg. 1157
DAN JORD A/S—See Per Aarsleff Holding A/S; *Int'l*, pg. 5795
DAN KAFFE (MALAYSIA) SDN. BHD—See Takasago International Corporation; *Int'l*, pg. 7433
DAN KANE CHEVROLET CADILLAC; *Int'l*, pg. 1957
DANKER FURNITURE INC.; *U.S. Private*, pg. 1157
DANKER LABORATORIES INC.; *U.S. Private*, pg. 1157
DANKOTUWA PORCELAIN PLC; *Int'l*, pg. 1965
DANKS HOLDINGS LIMITED—See Woolworths Group Limited; *Int'l*, pg. 8452
DAN LACHS GMBH; *Int'l*, pg. 1957
DANLAW, INC.; *U.S. Private*, pg. 1157
DANLAW TECHNOLOGIES, INC.—See Danlaw, Inc.; *U.S. Private*, pg. 1157
DANLAW TECHNOLOGIES INDIA LIMITED—See Danlaw, Inc.; *U.S. Private*, pg. 1157
DANLEY CONSTRUCTION PRODUCTS PTY LTD—See Illinois Tool Works Inc.; *U.S. Public*, pg. 1102
DANLEY LUMBER CO. INC.; *U.S. Private*, pg. 1157
DANLIND A/S—See McBride plc; *Int'l*, pg. 4755
DANLIN INDUSTRIES CORP.—See Arsenal Capital Management LP; *U.S. Public*, pg. 338
DANLY IEM SET DIVISION—See Connell Limited Partnership; *U.S. Private*, pg. 1017
DANMAGI GROUP APS; *Int'l*, pg. 1965
DANMAGI INDIA PVT. LTD—See Danmagi Group ApS; *Int'l*, pg. 1965
DANMAGI SERVICOS DE INFORMATICA LTDA.—See Danmagi Group ApS; *Int'l*, pg. 1965
DANMARE GROUP INC.—See Ag Growth International Inc.; *Int'l*, pg. 198
DANMAR INDUSTRIES, INC.; *U.S. Private*, pg. 1157
DANMARK PROTEIN A/S—See Arla Foods amba; *Int'l*, pg. 573
DANMARKS NATIONALBANK; *Int'l*, pg. 1965
DANMAR LINES AG—See Deutsche Post AG; *Int'l*, pg. 2072
DANMATIC AUTOMATED BAKERY SYSTEMS A/S—See Storskogen Group AB; *Int'l*, pg. 7227
DANMER, INC.; *U.S. Private*, pg. 1157
DANNER, INC.—See ABC-Mart, Inc.; *Int'l*, pg. 57
THE DANNON COMPANY, INC.—See Danone; *Int'l*, pg. 1967
THE DANNON CO.—See Danone; *Int'l*, pg. 1967
THE DANNON CO.—See Danone; *Int'l*, pg. 1967

THE DANNON CO.—See Danone; *Int'l*, pg. 1967
DANNY BECK CHEVROLET, INC.; *U.S. Private*, pg. 1157
DANNY & CLYDE'S FOOD STORE; *U.S. Private*, pg. 1157
DANNY HERMAN TRUCKING INC.; *U.S. Private*, pg. 1157
DANNY NICHOLSON INC.; *U.S. Private*, pg. 1157
DANNY'S CONSTRUCTION CO., INC.; *U.S. Private*, pg. 1157
DANNY'S FAMILY CAROUSEL, INC.—See Danny's Family Companies, LLC; *U.S. Private*, pg. 1157
DANNY'S FAMILY COMPANIES, LLC; *U.S. Private*, pg. 1157
DANNY ZECK FORD LINCOLN MERCURY; *U.S. Private*, pg. 1157
DANOBAT DO BRASIL LTDA—See Mondragon Corporation; *Int'l*, pg. 5028
DANOBAT GROUP MACHINE TOOLS INDIA PVT. LTD.—See Mondragon Corporation; *Int'l*, pg. 5028
DANOBATGROUP S. COOP.—See Mondragon Corporation; *Int'l*, pg. 5028
DANOBAT MACHINE TOOL CO., INC.—See Mondragon Corporation; *Int'l*, pg. 5028
DANOBAT RETTIFICATRICI—See Mondragon Corporation; *Int'l*, pg. 5028
DANONE ARGENTINA SA—See Danone; *Int'l*, pg. 1967
DANONE ASIA-PACIFIC HOLDINGS PTE. LTD.—See Danone; *Int'l*, pg. 1965
DANONE ASIA PTE. LTD.—See Danone; *Int'l*, pg. 1965
DANONE AS—See Danone; *Int'l*, pg. 1965
DANONE BABY & MEDICAL NUTRITION B.V.—See Danone; *Int'l*, pg. 1965
DANONE BEHEER B.V.—See Danone; *Int'l*, pg. 1966
DANONE DE MEXICO SA DE CV—See Danone; *Int'l*, pg. 1967
DANONE DUMEX LTD.—See Danone; *Int'l*, pg. 1965
DANONE DUMEX—See Danone; *Int'l*, pg. 1965
DANONE EAUX FRANCE—See Danone; *Int'l*, pg. 1967
DANONE FINANCIAL CENTER B.V.—See Danone; *Int'l*, pg. 1966
DANONE FINLAND—See Danone; *Int'l*, pg. 1967
DANONE FOODS INC.—See Danone; *Int'l*, pg. 1967
DANONE GMBH—See Danone; *Int'l*, pg. 1968
DANONE INC. - MISSISSAUGA—See Danone; *Int'l*, pg. 1967
DANONE INC.—See Danone; *Int'l*, pg. 1967
DANONE INDIA—See Danone; *Int'l*, pg. 1968
DANONE INDUSTRIA—See Danone; *Int'l*, pg. 1968
DANONE JAPAN—See Danone; *Int'l*, pg. 1968
DANONE KFT.—See Danone; *Int'l*, pg. 1968
DANONE LTD.—See Danone; *Int'l*, pg. 1968
DANONE NEDERLAND B.V. - FOODSERVICE—See Danone; *Int'l*, pg. 1968
DANONE NEDERLAND B.V.—See Danone; *Int'l*, pg. 1968
DANONE OESTERREICH GMBH—See Danone; *Int'l*, pg. 1968
DANONE PORTUGAL, S.A.—See Danone; *Int'l*, pg. 1968
DANONE PRODUITS FRAIS FRANCE—See Danone; *Int'l*, pg. 1968
DANONE RESEARCH B.V.—See Danone; *Int'l*, pg. 1966
DANONE ROMANIA—See Danone; *Int'l*, pg. 1968
DANONE SA ESPANA—See Danone; *Int'l*, pg. 1968
DANONE SA—See Danone; *Int'l*, pg. 1968
DANONE S.A.—See Danone; *Int'l*, pg. 1967
DANONE SERDIKA S.A.—See Danone; *Int'l*, pg. 1968
DANONE; *Int'l*, pg. 1965
DANONE S.P.A.—See Danone; *Int'l*, pg. 1968
DANONE SP. Z O.O.—See Danone; *Int'l*, pg. 1968
DANONE (UK) LIMITED—See Danone; *Int'l*, pg. 1965
DANONE US, INC.—See Danone; *Int'l*, pg. 1967
DANONE WATER BRANDS BENELUX—See Danone; *Int'l*, pg. 1968
DANONE WATERS DEUTSCHLAND GMBH—See Danone; *Int'l*, pg. 1968
DANONE WATERS UK & IRELAND LTD.—See Danone; *Int'l*, pg. 1968
DANOS & CUROLE MARINE CONTRACTORS INC.; *U.S. Private*, pg. 1157
DANOTHERM ELECTRIC A/S—See NIBE Industrier AB; *Int'l*, pg. 5260
DAN PERKINS AUTO GROUP; *U.S. Private*, pg. 1151
DAN PERKINS LEASING INC.—See Dan Perkins Auto Group; *U.S. Private*, pg. 1151
DAN PERKINS SUBARU—See Dan Perkins Auto Group; *U.S. Private*, pg. 1151
DANPIPE A/S—See Per Aarsleff Holding A/S; *Int'l*, pg. 5795
DANPLEJE ONEMED A/S—See Interogo Holding AG; *Int'l*, pg. 3754
DANPO A/S—See Scandi Standard AB; *Int'l*, pg. 6612
DAN PORTER MOTORS INC.; *U.S. Private*, pg. 1151
DAN POST BOOT CO.—See McRae Industries, Inc.; *U.S. Public*, pg. 1409
DANPOWER BIOMASSE PFAFFENHOFEN GMBH—See Stadtwerke Hannover AG; *Int'l*, pg. 7161
DANPOWER EESTI AS—See Stadtwerke Hannover AG; *Int'l*, pg. 7161
DANPOWER ENERGIE SERVICE GMBH—See Stadtwerke Hannover AG; *Int'l*, pg. 7161

COMPANY NAME INDEX

DANPOWER GMBH—See Stadtwerke Hannover AG; *Int'l*, pg. 7161
DANRAD HOLDING APS—See Danaher Corporation; *U.S. Public*, pg. 625
DANRIC HOMES; *U.S. Private*, pg. 1157
DANRIVER TECHNOLOGY (GUANGZHOU) INC.—See FIC Global, INC; *Int'l*, pg. 2653
DAN RYAN BUILDERS, INC.; *U.S. Private*, pg. 1151
DANSAC & HOLLISTER DANMARK—See Hollister Incorporated; *U.S. Private*, pg. 1965
DANSA FOODS LIMITED—See Dangote Group Limited; *Int'l*, pg. 1962
DAN'S CEMENT, INC.; *U.S. Private*, pg. 1152
DAN'S CHOCOLATES; *U.S. Private*, pg. 1152
DANSENSOR ESPANA, S.L.—See AMETEK, Inc.; *U.S. Public*, pg. 120
DANSER, INC.; *U.S. Private*, pg. 1157
DAN'S FAN CITY INC.; *U.S. Private*, pg. 1152
DAN'S FEED & SEED INC.; *U.S. Private*, pg. 1152
DANSFORUM I GOTEBORG AB—See Storskogen Group AB; *Int'l*, pg. 7227
DANSIKRING A/S—See Securitas AB; *Int'l*, pg. 6675
DANSK AFGRATNINGSTEKNIK A/S—See Aktieselskabet Schouw & Co.; *Int'l*, pg. 265
DANSK BEREDSSKABSKOMMUNIKATION A/S—See Motorola Solutions, Inc.; *U.S. Public*, pg. 1477
DANSKE ANDELSKASSERS BANK A/S; *Int'l*, pg. 1969
DANSKE BANK A/S; *Int'l*, pg. 1969
DANSKE BANK INTERNATIONAL S.A.—See Danske Bank A/S; *Int'l*, pg. 1969
DANSKE CAPITAL AS—See Danske Bank A/S; *Int'l*, pg. 1969
DANSKE COMMODITIES DEUTSCHLAND GMBH—See Equinor ASA; *Int'l*, pg. 2484
DANSKE COMMODITIES TURKEY ENERJI TICARET A.S.—See Equinor ASA; *Int'l*, pg. 2484
DANSKE COMMODITIES UK LIMITED—See Equinor ASA; *Int'l*, pg. 2484
DANSKE COMMODITIES US LLC—See Equinor ASA; *Int'l*, pg. 2484
DANSKE INVEST ASSET MANAGEMENT AS—See Danske Bank A/S; *Int'l*, pg. 1969
DANSKE INVEST MANAGEMENT A/S—See Danske Bank A/S; *Int'l*, pg. 1969
DANSKE IT & SUPPORT SERVICES INDIA PRIVATE LIMITED—See Infosys Limited; *Int'l*, pg. 3695
DANSKE LEASING A/S—See Danske Bank A/S; *Int'l*, pg. 1969
DANSKE MARKETS INC.—See Danske Bank A/S; *Int'l*, pg. 1969
DANSKE MORTGAGE BANK PLC—See Danske Bank A/S; *Int'l*, pg. 1969
DANSKE PRIVATE EQUITY—See Danske Bank A/S; *Int'l*, pg. 1969
DANSK GENERATIONSSKIFTE A/S; *Int'l*, pg. 1968
DANSK INDUSTRI INVEST A/S; *Int'l*, pg. 1968
DANSKIN, INC.—See Iconix Acquisition LLC; *U.S. Private*, pg. 2032
DANSKIN—See Iconix Acquisition LLC; *U.S. Private*, pg. 2032
DANSK KABEL TV A/S - ESBJERG—See Arbejdsmarkedets Tillaegspension; *Int'l*, pg. 537
DANSK KABEL TV A/S - ESBJERG—See Macquarie Group Limited; *Int'l*, pg. 4626
DANSK KABEL TV A/S - ESBJERG—See PFA Holding A/S; *Int'l*, pg. 5835
DANSK KABEL TV A/S - ESBJERG—See PKA A/S; *Int'l*, pg. 5887
DANSK NATURSTEN A/S—See Holcim Ltd.; *Int'l*, pg. 3446
DANSKO INC.; *U.S. Private*, pg. 1157
DANSK TANDFORSIKRING A/S—See Gjensidige Forsikring ASA; *Int'l*, pg. 2982
DANSK TRAEEMBALLAGE A/S; *Int'l*, pg. 1969
DANSK VINDUES INDUSTRI A/S—See Ratos AB; *Int'l*, pg. 6219
DANSK VINIMPORT VEJLE APS—See FDB Group; *Int'l*, pg. 2628
DAN'S PRIZE, INC.—See Hormel Foods Corporation; *U.S. Public*, pg. 1054
DAN'S SUPERMARKET INC.; *U.S. Private*, pg. 1152
DAN'S SUPREME SUPER MARKETS INC.; *U.S. Private*, pg. 1152
DANSTAR FERMENT AG—See Lallemand, Inc.; *Int'l*, pg. 4399
DANSTAR LALLEMAND—See Lallemand, Inc.; *Int'l*, pg. 4399
DANSTEEL A/S—See Novolipetski Metallurgicheski Komb OAO; *Int'l*, pg. 5466
DANSTOKER A/S—See Thermax Limited; *Int'l*, pg. 7707
DANSTOKER POLAND SP. Z O.O.—See Thermax Limited; *Int'l*, pg. 7707
DANSUPPORT A/S—See Origo hf.; *Int'l*, pg. 5630
DAN-TAKUMA TECHNOLOGIES INC.—See Takuma Co., Ltd.; *Int'l*, pg. 7442
DANTAX A/S; *Int'l*, pg. 1969
DANTAX RADIO A/S—See Dantax A/S; *Int'l*, pg. 1969
DANT CLAYTON CORPORATION; *U.S. Private*, pg. 1157
DANTHERM AB—See Procuritas Partners AB; *Int'l*, pg. 5988

DANTHERM AIR HANDLING A/S—See Procuritas Partners AB; *Int'l*, pg. 5988
DANTHERM AIR HANDLING LTD.—See Procuritas Partners AB; *Int'l*, pg. 5988
DANTHERM AS—See Procuritas Partners AB; *Int'l*, pg. 5988
DANTHERM COOLING INC.—See Dansk Industri Invest A/S; *Int'l*, pg. 1968
DANTHERM FILTRATION AB—See Nederman Holding AB; *Int'l*, pg. 5189
DANTHERM FILTRATION A/S—See Nederman Holding AB; *Int'l*, pg. 5189
DANTHERM FILTRATION CO LTD—See Nederman Holding AB; *Int'l*, pg. 5189
DANTHERM FILTRATION HOLDING GMBH—See Nederman Holding AB; *Int'l*, pg. 5189
DANTHERM FILTRATION, INC.—See Nederman Holding AB; *Int'l*, pg. 5189
DANTHERM FILTRATION OOO—See Nederman Holding AB; *Int'l*, pg. 5188
DANTHERM FILTRATION (SUZHOU) CO LTD—See Nederman Holding AB; *Int'l*, pg. 5189
DANTHERM HVAC HOLDING A/S—See Procuritas Partners AB; *Int'l*, pg. 5987
DAN T. MOORE CO.; *U.S. Private*, pg. 1151
DAN TOBIN BUICK GMC, INC.; *U.S. Private*, pg. 1151
DANTO HOLDINGS CORPORATION; *Int'l*, pg. 1969
DANTONE INC.; *U.S. Private*, pg. 1158
DANTZLER LUMBER & EXPORT CO., INC.; *U.S. Private*, pg. 1158
DANUBE INDUSTRIES LIMITED; *Int'l*, pg. 1969
DANUBIUS D.O.O. NOVI SAD—See Delta Holding; *Int'l*, pg. 2018
DANUBIUS HOTEL AND SPA NYRT.—See CP Holdings Ltd.; *Int'l*, pg. 1823
DANUCEM MAGYARORSZAG KFT.—See CRH plc; *Int'l*, pg. 1844
DANUFERT HANDELSGESELLSCHAFT MBH—See BayWa AG; *Int'l*, pg. 917
DANUFERT HANDELSGESELLSCHAFT MBH—See Mierka Donauhafen Krems Gesellschaft m.b.H. & Co KG; *Int'l*, pg. 4890
DANUGRAIN LAGEREI GMBH—See BayWa AG; *Int'l*, pg. 917
DANU INVESTMENT PARTNERS LTD.; *Int'l*, pg. 1969
DANUM ENGINEERING PTY. LTD.—See EVZ Limited; *Int'l*, pg. 2574
DANUSER MACHINE COMPANY, INC.; *U.S. Private*, pg. 1158
DANUVIUS EOOD—See Caisse de Depot et Placement du Quebec; *Int'l*, pg. 1255
DANUVIUS EOOD—See Ontario Teachers' Pension Plan; *Int'l*, pg. 5590
DANUVIUS EOOD—See Partners Group Holding AG; *Int'l*, pg. 5750
DAN VADEN CHEVROLET CADILLAC; *U.S. Private*, pg. 1152
DAN VALLEY FOODS INC.; *U.S. Private*, pg. 1152
DANVERS HERALD—See Gannett Co., Inc.; *U.S. Public*, pg. 902
DANVERS MOTOR COMPANY, INC.; *U.S. Private*, pg. 1158
DANVILLE COOPERATIVE ASSOCIATION INC.; *U.S. Private*, pg. 1158
DANVILLE DEVELOPMENT, LLC—See PENN Entertainment, Inc.; *U.S. Public*, pg. 1662
DANVILLE DIAGNOSTIC IMAGING CENTER, LLC—See Apollo Global Management, Inc.; *U.S. Public*, pg. 155
DANVILLE MATERIALS, LLC—See BC Partners LLP; *Int'l*, pg. 925
DANVILLE METAL STAMPING CO. INC.; *U.S. Private*, pg. 1158
DANVILLE PHYSICIAN PRACTICES, LLC—See Apollo Global Management, Inc.; *U.S. Public*, pg. 155
DANVILLE REGIONAL MEDICAL CENTER, LLC—See Apollo Global Management, Inc.; *U.S. Public*, pg. 155
DANVILLE REGIONAL MEDICAL CENTER SCHOOL OF HEALTH PROFESSIONS, LLC—See Apollo Global Management, Inc.; *U.S. Public*, pg. 155
DANVILLE REGISTER & BEE—See Lee Enterprises, Incorporated; *U.S. Public*, pg. 1298
DAN WILLIAMS COMPANY; *U.S. Private*, pg. 1152
DAN WOLF INCORPORATED; *U.S. Private*, pg. 1152
DAN WOLF MOTORS OF NAPERVILLE, INC.—See Dan Wolf Incorporated; *U.S. Private*, pg. 1152
DAN WOLF'S CHEVROLET OF NAPERVILLE, INC.—See Dan Wolf Incorporated; *U.S. Private*, pg. 1152
DANWOOD S.A.—See Enterprise Investors Sp. z o.o.; *Int'l*, pg. 2452
DAN WYLIE'S DREAM ENTERPRISES, INC.; *U.S. Private*, pg. 1152
DANYA CEBUS LTD.—See Africa Israel Investments Ltd.; *Int'l*, pg. 190
DANYA DUTCH BV—See Africa Israel Investments Ltd.; *Int'l*, pg. 190
DANYA FOODS LTD.—See Arla Foods amba; *Int'l*, pg. 573
DANYA INTERNATIONAL, LLC—See DLH Holdings Corp.; *U.S. Public*, pg. 670

DAQING HUAKE COMPANY LIMITED

DANYEL BIOTECH LTD.—See Gamida for Life B.V.; *Int'l*, pg. 2878
DANZANSKY-GOLDBERG MEMORIAL CHAPELS, INC.—See Service Corporation International; *U.S. Public*, pg. 1869
DANZAS ABU DHABI LLC—See Deutsche Post AG; *Int'l*, pg. 2079
DANZAS AEI S.A. DE C.V.—See Deutsche Post AG; *Int'l*, pg. 2073
DANZAS BAHRAIN WLL—See Deutsche Post AG; *Int'l*, pg. 2079
DANZAS DEUTSCHLAND HOLDING GMBH—See Deutsche Post AG; *Int'l*, pg. 2079
DANZAS ECUADOR S.A.—See Deutsche Post AG; *Int'l*, pg. 2073
DANZAS FASHION NV—See Deutsche Post AG; *Int'l*, pg. 2079
DANZAS FASHION SERVICE CENTERS B.V.—See Deutsche Post AG; *Int'l*, pg. 2079
DANZAS GRUNDSTUCKSVERWALTUNG GROSS-GERAU GMBH—See Deutsche Post AG; *Int'l*, pg. 2079
DANZAS HOLDING AG—See Deutsche Post AG; *Int'l*, pg. 2079
DANZAS KIEV LTD.—See Deutsche Post AG; *Int'l*, pg. 2079
DANZAS S.A.—See Deutsche Post AG; *Int'l*, pg. 2073
DANZER AG; *Int'l*, pg. 1969
DANZER BOHEMIA-DYHARNA S.R.O.—See Danzer AG; *Int'l*, pg. 1970
DANZER CORPORATION—See Obsidian Enterprises, Inc.; *U.S. Private*, pg. 2988
DANZER EUROPE VENEER AG—See Danzer AG; *Int'l*, pg. 1969
DANZER FORESTACION S.A.—See Danzer AG; *Int'l*, pg. 1970
DANZER FORESTLAND, INC.—See Danzer AG; *Int'l*, pg. 1970
DANZER INDUSTRIES, INC.—See Obsidian Enterprises, Inc.; *U.S. Private*, pg. 2988
DANZER SERVICES EUROPE GMBH—See Danzer AG; *Int'l*, pg. 1969
DANZER SERVICES, INC.—See Danzer AG; *Int'l*, pg. 1970
DANZER UK LIMITED—See Danzer AG; *Int'l*, pg. 1970
DANZER VENEER AMERICAS, INC.—See Danzer AG; *Int'l*, pg. 1970
DANZHOU HNA INVESTMENT AND DEVELOPMENT CO., LTD.—See Hainan Traffic Administration Holding Co., Ltd.; *Int'l*, pg. 3213
DAODAOQUAN GRAIN AND OIL CO LTD; *Int'l*, pg. 1970
DAOHE GLOBAL GROUP LIMITED; *Int'l*, pg. 1970
DAO HENG SECURITIES LIMITED—See Hong Leong Investment Holdings Pte. Ltd.; *Int'l*, pg. 3468
DAOJIA LIMITED; *Int'l*, pg. 1970
DAOMING OPTICS AND CHEMICAL CO., LTD.; *Int'l*, pg. 1970
DAOU DATA CORP.; *Int'l*, pg. 1970
DAOU JAPAN KK—See Daou Data Corp.; *Int'l*, pg. 1970
DAOU TECHNOLOGY, INC.; *Int'l*, pg. 1970
DAOU VINEYARDS—See Treasury Wine Estates Limited; *Int'l*, pg. 7909
DAPAI INTERNATIONAL HOLDINGS CO. LTD.; *Int'l*, pg. 1970
DAPAN HOLDINGS SDN. BHD.—See Nagacorp Ltd.; *Int'l*, pg. 5124
DAPAT INC.; *U.S. Private*, pg. 1158
DAPAT JAYA BUILDER SDN. BHD.—See MKH Berhad; *Int'l*, pg. 5002
DAPAT VISTA (M) SDN. BHD.—See HeiTech Padu Berhad; *Int'l*, pg. 3326
DAP CANADA CORP.—See RPM International Inc.; *U.S. Public*, pg. 1817
DAP CO., LTD.; *Int'l*, pg. 1970
DAPD MEDIA HOLDING AG; *Int'l*, pg. 1970
DAPD NACHRICHTENAGENTUR GMBH—See dapd Media Holding AG; *Int'l*, pg. 1970
DAPE 74 DISTRIBUTION SASU—See Societe BIC S.A.; *Int'l*, pg. 7037
DAP GLOBAL, INC.—See RPM International Inc.; *U.S. Public*, pg. 1816
DAPHNE INTERNATIONAL HOLDINGS LIMITED; *Int'l*, pg. 1970
DAPHNE UTILITY DEPT; *U.S. Private*, pg. 1158
D'APPOLONIA BELGIUM NV—See RINA S.p.A.; *Int'l*, pg. 6342
D'APPOLONIA S.P.A.—See RINA S.p.A.; *Int'l*, pg. 6342
DAP PRODUCTS, INC.—See RPM International Inc.; *U.S. Public*, pg. 1817
DA-PRO RUBBER INC.; *U.S. Private*, pg. 1143
DAPS ADVERTISING LTD.; *Int'l*, pg. 1970
DAQ ELECTRONICS, INC.; *U.S. Private*, pg. 1158
DAQIAN ECOLOGY & ENVIRONMENT GROUP CO., LTD.; *Int'l*, pg. 1971
DAQI ENVIRONMENTAL PROTECTION ENGINEERING (DALIAN) CO., LTD.—See Daiki Axis Co., Ltd.; *Int'l*, pg. 1932
DAQING BORUN BIOTECHNOLOGY CO., LTD.—See CHINA NEW BORUN CORPORATION; *Int'l*, pg. 1534
DAQING HUAKE COMPANY LIMITED; *Int'l*, pg. 1971

DAQING ZHONGLAN PETROCHEMICAL CO LTD—See China National Chemical Corporation; *Int'l*, pg. 1526
DAQIN RAILWAY CO., LTD.; *Int'l*, pg. 1971
DAQO NEW ENERGY CORP.; *Int'l*, pg. 1971
DARAB CEMENT COMPANY; *Int'l*, pg. 1972
DARAG GROUP LIMITED; *Int'l*, pg. 1972
DAR AL AMAN FOR ISLAMIC FINANCE PLC; *Int'l*, pg. 1971
DAR AL ARKAN REAL ESTATE DEVELOPMENT COMPANY; *Int'l*, pg. 1971
DAR AL DAWA DEVELOPMENT & INVESTMENT CO.; *Int'l*, pg. 1971
DAR AL DHABI HOLDING CO. K.S.C.—See Bayan Investment Holding Company K.S.C.C.; *Int'l*, pg. 901
DAR AL-MAAL AL-ISLAMI TRUST; *Int'l*, pg. 1971
DAR AL SALAM INSURANCE COMPANY—See Fairfax Financial Holdings Limited; *U.S. Public*, pg. 2607
DAR AL-SHIFA'A FOR THE MANUFACTURING OF PHARMACEUTICALS; *Int'l*, pg. 1971
DAR AL TAKAFUL HOUSE PJSC; *Int'l*, pg. 1971
DAR AL THURAYA REAL ESTATE CO KSCP; *Int'l*, pg. 1971
DARAMIC HOLDING S.A.S.—See Asahi Kasei Corporation; *Int'l*, pg. 597
DARAMIC, LLC—See Asahi Kasei Corporation; *Int'l*, pg. 597
DARAMIC S.A.S.—See Asahi Kasei Corporation; *Int'l*, pg. 597
DARAMIC SEPARADORES DE BATERIAS LTDA.—See Asahi Kasei Corporation; *Int'l*, pg. 597
DARAMIC TIANJIN PE SEPARATOR CO., LTD.—See Asahi Kasei Corporation; *Int'l*, pg. 597
DARAMIC XIANGYANG BATTERY SEPARATOR CO., LTD.—See Asahi Kasei Corporation; *Int'l*, pg. 597
DARANT DISTRIBUTING CORP.; *U.S. Private*, pg. 1158
DARAT JORDAN HOLDINGS; *Int'l*, pg. 1972
DARBY ASIA INVESTORS (INDIA) PRIVATE LIMITED—See Franklin Resources, Inc.; *U.S. Public*, pg. 879
DARBY BUICK-GMC, INC.; *U.S. Private*, pg. 1158
DARBY DENTAL SUPPLY, LLC—See Darby Group Companies, Inc.; *U.S. Private*, pg. 1158
DARBY GAS & OIL CO., INC.—See Steinhagen Oil Company, Inc.; *U.S. Private*, pg. 3798
DARBY GLASS LTD.—See Bronsstadet AB; *Int'l*, pg. 1174
DARBY GROUP COMPANIES, INC.; *U.S. Private*, pg. 1158
DARBY OVERSEAS INVESTMENTS, LTD.—See Franklin Resources, Inc.; *U.S. Public*, pg. 879
DARBY TOWNHOUSES PRESERVATION, LP—See Apartment Investment and Management Company; *U.S. Public*, pg. 144
DARCARS AUTOMOTIVE GROUP; *U.S. Private*, pg. 1158
DARCARS FORD—See DARCARS Automotive Group; *U.S. Private*, pg. 1158
DARCARS TOYOTA SCION; *U.S. Private*, pg. 1158
DAR CARS TOYOTA; *U.S. Private*, pg. 1158
DARC CORPORATION; *U.S. Private*, pg. 1158
DARCHEM ENGINEERING LIMITED—See TransDigm Group Incorporated; *U.S. Public*, pg. 2181
DARCO ENGINEERING PTE LTD.—See Darco Water Technologies Limited; *Int'l*, pg. 1972
DARCO ENTERPRISES INC.; *U.S. Private*, pg. 1158
DARCO-ENVIDAN SDN BHD—See Darco Water Technologies Limited; *Int'l*, pg. 1972
DARCO ENVIRONMENTAL (PHILIPPINES) INC.—See Darco Water Technologies Limited; *Int'l*, pg. 1972
DARCO INDUSTRIAL WATER SDN. BHD.—See Darco Water Technologies Limited; *Int'l*, pg. 1972
DARCOR LIMITED; *Int'l*, pg. 1972
DARCO WATER SYSTEMS SDN. BHD.—See Darco Water Technologies Limited; *Int'l*, pg. 1972
DARCO WATER TECHNOLOGIES LIMITED; *Int'l*, pg. 1972
D'ARCY BUICK GMC, INC.; *U.S. Private*, pg. 1138
D'ARCY HYUNDAI; *U.S. Private*, pg. 1138
D'ARCY & PARTNERS, LLC; *U.S. Private*, pg. 1138
DARDANEL ONENTAS GIDA SANAYI AS; *Int'l*, pg. 1972
DARDEN RESTAURANTS, INC.; *U.S. Public*, pg. 632
DARE BIOSCIENCE, INC.; *U.S. Public*, pg. 633
DARE DIGITAL LIMITED—See You & Mr Jones Inc.; *U.S. Private*, pg. 4591
DARE FOODS LIMITED; *Int'l*, pg. 1972
DARELLE MEDIA INC.—See Darelle Online Solutions Inc.; *Int'l*, pg. 1972
DARELLE ONLINE SOLUTIONS INC.; *Int'l*, pg. 1972
DARE POWER DEKOR HOME CO., LTD.; *Int'l*, pg. 1972
DARE PRODUCTS INCORPORATED; *U.S. Private*, pg. 1159
DAR ES SALAM INVESTMENT BANK; *Int'l*, pg. 1972
DA RETAILGROEP B.V.; *Int'l*, pg. 1902
DARET AMMAN FOR HOUSING PROJECTS LLC—See Real Estate Development Co.; *Int'l*, pg. 6233
DARET INC.; *U.S. Private*, pg. 1159
DAREWAY SOFTWARE CO., LTD.; *Int'l*, pg. 1972
DAREX PUERTO RICO, INC.—See Standard Industries Holdings Inc.; *U.S. Public*, pg. 3779
DAREX UK LIMITED—See Standard Industries Holdings Inc.; *U.S. Public*, pg. 3779

DARFON ELECTRONICS CORPORATION—See BenQ Corporation; *Int'l*, pg. 975
DARGUES GOLD MINES PTY. LTD.—See Aurelia Metals Ltd; *Int'l*, pg. 707
DARGUNER BRAUEREI GMBH—See Harboes Bryggeri A/S; *Int'l*, pg. 3271
DAR IBTIKAR AL IRAQ FOR GENERAL SERVICES AND GENERAL TRADE LLC—See Emerson Electric Co.; *U.S. Public*, pg. 742
DARIC CORPORATION; *U.S. Private*, pg. 1159
DARI COUSPATE S.A; *Int'l*, pg. 1972
DARIEN ROWAYTON BANK; *U.S. Public*, pg. 633
DARI-FARMS ICE CREAM CO., INC.—See Diversis Capital, LLC; *U.S. Private*, pg. 1244
DARIGOLD, INC.—See Northwest Dairy Association; *U.S. Private*, pg. 2959
DARI-MART STORES INC.; *U.S. Private*, pg. 1159
DARIN CO., LTD.—See SUN&L Co., Ltd.; *Int'l*, pg. 7309
DARIOHEALTH CORP.; *U.S. Public*, pg. 633
DARJEELING ROPEWAY COMPANY LTD.; *Int'l*, pg. 1972
DARKBLADE SYSTEMS CORPORATION—See Hammond, Kennedy, Whitney & Company, Inc.; *U.S. Private*, pg. 1850
DARKBLUE.COM PTY LIMITED—See Enero Group Limited; *Int'l*, pg. 2423
DARK BLUE SEA LIMITED—See Enero Group Limited; *Int'l*, pg. 2423
DARK GREEN AUSTRALIA PTY LIMITED—See PepsiCo, Inc.; *U.S. Public*, pg. 1668
DARKHAN GURIL TEJEEL JOINT STOCK COMPANY; *Int'l*, pg. 1973
DARK HORSE COMICS, INC.; *U.S. Private*, pg. 1159
DARK HORSE CONSULTING; *U.S. Private*, pg. 1159
DARK HORSE ENTERPRISE, LLC—See Owl Services, Inc.; *U.S. Private*, pg. 3055
DARK HORSE MARKETING; *U.S. Private*, pg. 1159
DARK HORSE TECHNOLOGY GROUP CO., LTD.; *Int'l*, pg. 1973
DAR-KIM, INC.—See Camping World Holdings, Inc.; *U.S. Public*, pg. 427
DARKOM INVESTMENT CO.; *Int'l*, pg. 1973
DARKPULSE, INC.; *U.S. Public*, pg. 633
THE DARK STAR BREWING COMPANY LIMITED—See Asahi Group Holdings Ltd.; *Int'l*, pg. 594
DARK STAR MINERALS, INC.; *Int'l*, pg. 1973
DARKTRACE COLOMBIA S.A.S.—See Thoma Bravo, L.P.; *U.S. Private*, pg. 4147
DARKTRACE GMBH—See Thoma Bravo, L.P.; *U.S. Private*, pg. 4147
DARKTRACE HOLDINGS LIMITED—See Thoma Bravo, L.P.; *U.S. Private*, pg. 4147
DARKTRACE IRELAND LIMITED—See Thoma Bravo, L.P.; *U.S. Private*, pg. 4147
DARKTRACE JAPAN KK—See Thoma Bravo, L.P.; *U.S. Private*, pg. 4147
DARKTRACE MEXICO, S.A. DE C.V.—See Thoma Bravo, L.P.; *U.S. Private*, pg. 4147
DARKTRACE PLC—See Thoma Bravo, L.P.; *U.S. Private*, pg. 4147
DARKTRACE S.A.S.—See Thoma Bravo, L.P.; *U.S. Private*, pg. 4147
DARKTRACE SINGAPORE PTE. LTD.—See Thoma Bravo, L.P.; *U.S. Private*, pg. 4147
DARLAND PROPERTIES; *U.S. Private*, pg. 1159
DARLAVOIX SAS—See VINCI S.A.; *Int'l*, pg. 8216
DARLENE JEWELRY MANUFACTURING COMPANY; *U.S. Private*, pg. 1159
DARLEY BUTLER & CO. LTD.—See E.B. Creasy & Company PLC; *Int'l*, pg. 2251
DARLIND; *U.S. Private*, pg. 1159
DARLING AWS LLC—See Darling Ingredients Inc.; *U.S. Public*, pg. 633
DARLING BOLT CO.; *U.S. Private*, pg. 1159
DARLING DEVELOPMENT INC.—See Chanen Corporation; *U.S. Private*, pg. 848
DARLING HOMES; *U.S. Private*, pg. 1159
DARLING INGREDIENTS INC.; *U.S. Public*, pg. 633
DARLING INGREDIENTS INTERNATIONAL HOLDING B.V.—See Darling Ingredients Inc.; *U.S. Public*, pg. 634
DARLING INGREDIENTS INTERNATIONAL RENDERING AND SPECIALTIES B.V.—See Darling Ingredients Inc.; *U.S. Public*, pg. 634
DARLING INTERESTS, INC.—See Darling Homes; *U.S. Private*, pg. 1159
DARLING INTERNATIONAL NETHERLANDS B.V.—See Darling Ingredients Inc.; *U.S. Public*, pg. 634
DARLING'S INC.; *U.S. Private*, pg. 1159
DARLINGTON BUILDING SOCIETY; *Int'l*, pg. 1973
DARLINGTON FABRICS CORPORATION—See Moore Company; *U.S. Private*, pg. 2779
DARLINGTON RACEWAY OF SOUTH CAROLINA, LLC—See National Association for Stock Car Auto Racing, Inc.; *U.S. Private*, pg. 2845
DARLINGTON VENEER COMPANY; *U.S. Private*, pg. 1159
DAR-MEL INC.; *U.S. Private*, pg. 1158
DARMEX CASINGS SP.Z.O.O—See Icahn Enterprises L.P.; *U.S. Public*, pg. 1084
DARMON IMPRESSIONS; *Int'l*, pg. 1973

DARNU GROUP UAB—See MG Baltic UAB; *Int'l*, pg. 4871
DARNUZER INGENIEURE AG—See BKW AG; *Int'l*, pg. 1055
DAROGA DIALYSIS, LLC—See DaVita Inc.; *U.S. Public*, pg. 638
DARONG AGRICULTURAL & DEVELOPMENT CORPORATION—See Ayala Corporation; *Int'l*, pg. 774
DARON MOTORS LLC—See Lithia Motors, Inc.; *U.S. Public*, pg. 1322
DAROS PISTON RINGS AB—See Apollo Global Management, Inc.; *U.S. Public*, pg. 160
DAROUPAKHSH HOLDING COMPANY; *Int'l*, pg. 1973
DAROU PAKHSH PHARMACEUTICAL MFG CO.; *Int'l*, pg. 1973
DARPRO STORAGE SOLUTIONS LLC—See Darling Ingredients Inc.; *U.S. Public*, pg. 633
DARRAGH COMPANY; *U.S. Private*, pg. 1159
DARRAGH CO; *U.S. Private*, pg. 1159
DAR/RAN FURNITURE INDUSTRIES; *U.S. Private*, pg. 1158
DARRAS ET JOUANIN—See FAYAT SAS; *Int'l*, pg. 2625
DARRELL DINSMORE GRADING INC.; *U.S. Private*, pg. 1159
DARRELL'S SIGN COMPANY; *U.S. Private*, pg. 1159
DARRELL WALTRIP HONDA-VOLVO; *U.S. Private*, pg. 1159
DARR FAMILY FOUNDATION; *U.S. Private*, pg. 1159
D'ARRIGO BROS. COMPANY; *U.S. Private*, pg. 1139
DARROCH LIMITED—See Quotable Value Limited; *Int'l*, pg. 6166
DARRON HOLDINGS LIMITED—See Schoeller-Bleckmann Oilfield Equipment AG; *Int'l*, pg. 6637
DARRON OIL TOOLS LIMITED—See Schoeller-Bleckmann Oilfield Equipment AG; *Int'l*, pg. 6637
DARRON TOOL & ENGINEERING LIMITED—See Schoeller-Bleckmann Oilfield Equipment AG; *Int'l*, pg. 6637
DARSHAN ORNA LIMITED; *Int'l*, pg. 1973
DART AEROSPACE LTD.—See TransDigm Group Incorporated; *U.S. Public*, pg. 2180
DARTAGNAN INC.—See Investcorp Holdings B.S.C.; *Int'l*, pg. 3776
DART APPRAISAL.COM, INC.; *U.S. Private*, pg. 1159
DARTA SAVING LIFE ASSURANCE LTD.—See Allianz SE; *Int'l*, pg. 352
DART BANK; *U.S. Private*, pg. 1159
DARTCO, INC.—See Dart Transit Company; *U.S. Private*, pg. 1160
DART CONTAINER CORPORATION; *U.S. Private*, pg. 1160
DART CUP LTD—See Dart Container Corporation; *U.S. Private*, pg. 1160
DART DO BRASIL INDUSTRIA E COMERCIO LTDA.—See Tupperware Brands Corporation; *U.S. Public*, pg. 2204
DAR-TECH INC.; *U.S. Private*, pg. 1158
DARTEX COATINGS INC.—See Waterlinks Investments Ltd.; *Int'l*, pg. 8357
DARTEX COATINGS LTD.—See Waterlinks Investments Ltd.; *Int'l*, pg. 8357
DART HELICOPTER SERVICES CANADA, INC.—See Bristow Group, Inc.; *U.S. Public*, pg. 387
DART HELICOPTER SERVICES CANADA, INC.—See Eagle Copters Ltd.; *Int'l*, pg. 2264
DART HOLDING COMPANY LTD.—See Bristow Group, Inc.; *U.S. Public*, pg. 387
DART HOLDING COMPANY LTD.—See Eagle Copters Ltd.; *Int'l*, pg. 2264
DART INDUSTRIES (NEW ZEALAND) LIMITED—See Tupperware Brands Corporation; *U.S. Public*, pg. 2204
DART INTERNATIONAL; *U.S. Private*, pg. 1160
DART MINING NL; *Int'l*, pg. 1973
DARTMOUTH BOOKSTORE INC.; *U.S. Private*, pg. 1160
DARTMOUTH BUILDING SUPPLY INC.; *U.S. Private*, pg. 1160
DARTMOUTH CLUB PROPERTIES INC.—See Healthtrax Inc.; *U.S. Private*, pg. 1898
DARTMOUTH PRINTING CO. INC.—See CJK Group, Inc.; *U.S. Private*, pg. 909
DARTNELL ENTERPRISES INC.; *U.S. Private*, pg. 1160
DARTPOINTS LLC—See Astra Capital Management LLC; *U.S. Private*, pg. 361
DART PORTABLE STORAGE, INC.—See Dart Transit Company; *U.S. Private*, pg. 1160
DART PRODUCTS LTD—See Dart Container Corporation; *U.S. Private*, pg. 1160
DART S.A. DE C.V.—See Tupperware Brands Corporation; *U.S. Public*, pg. 2204
DARTSLIVE CO., LTD.—See Sega Sammy Holdings, Inc.; *Int'l*, pg. 6680
DART SUDAMERICANA S.A.—See Dart Container Corporation; *U.S. Private*, pg. 1160
DART TRANSIT COMPANY; *U.S. Private*, pg. 1160
DART WAREHOUSE CORPORATION; *U.S. Private*, pg. 1160
DARU CAR AD—See Eurohold Bulgaria AD; *Int'l*, pg. 2553
DA-RUE OF CALIFORNIA, INC.; *U.S. Public*, pg. 1143
DARULAMAN ASET SDN. BHD.—See Bina Darulaman Berhad; *Int'l*, pg. 1032

COMPANY NAME INDEX

DARULAMAN GOLF RESORT BEHARD—See Bina Darulaman Berhad; *Int'l*, pg. 1032
DARUMA DRUG STORE CO., LTD—See MatsukiyoCocokara & Co.; *Int'l*, pg. 4730
D.A RUS., LLC—See Dong-A Hwasung Co., Ltd.; *Int'l*, pg. 2164
DARVIN FURNITURE; *U.S. Private*, pg. 1160
DARWILL PRESS, INC.; *U.S. Private*, pg. 1160
DARWIN BBDO—See Omnicom Group Inc.; *U.S. Public*, pg. 1575
DARWIN-GREY COMMUNICATIONS LTD.—See Integrated Communications Corp.; *U.S. Private*, pg. 2099
DARWIN-GREY COMMUNICATIONS—See Integrated Communications Corp.; *U.S. Private*, pg. 2099
DARWIN INTERNATIONAL TRADING (SHANGHAI) CO. LTD.—See Hexagon Holdings Berhad; *Int'l*, pg. 3370
DARWIN PRECISIONS CORPORATION; *Int'l*, pg. 1973
DARWIN PRECISIONS (SUZHOU) CORP.—See AUO Corporation; *Int'l*, pg. 706
DARWIN PRECISIONS (XIAMEN) CORP.—See AUO Corporation; *Int'l*, pg. 706
DARWIN PRIVATE EQUITY LLP; *Int'l*, pg. 1973
DARWIN PRIVATE HOSPITAL PTY. LTD.—See Brookfield Corporation; *Int'l*, pg. 1176
DARWIN STRATEGIC LIMITED—See Investec Limited; *Int'l*, pg. 3778
DARWIN TECHNOLOGIES SG PTE. LTD.—See Marsh & McLennan Companies, Inc.; *U.S. Public*, pg. 1374
DARWIN TECHNOLOGIES S.R.L.—See Marsh & McLennan Companies, Inc.; *U.S. Public*, pg. 1374
DARWIN ZONE S.A.—See H.I.G. Capital, LLC; *U.S. Private*, pg. 1830
DARWISH CONSULTING ENGINEERS—See ARCADIS N.V.; *Int'l*, pg. 541
DARWISH CONTRACTING CO. W.L.L.—See Kassem Darwish Fakhro & Sons; *Int'l*, pg. 4088
DARWISH ELEVATORS CO. W.L.L.—See Kassem Darwish Fakhro & Sons; *Int'l*, pg. 4088
DARWISH MECHANICAL & ELECTRICAL CO. W.L.L.—See Kassem Darwish Fakhro & Sons; *Int'l*, pg. 4088
DARWISH TRADING CO. W.L.L.—See Kassem Darwish Fakhro & Sons; *Int'l*, pg. 4088
DARWISH TRAVEL CO. W.L.L.—See Kassem Darwish Fakhro & Sons; *Int'l*, pg. 4088
DARYL FLOOD RELOCATION & LOGISTICS; *U.S. Private*, pg. 1160
DASAA 8010—See Raiffeisen-Landesbank Steiermark AG; *Int'l*, pg. 6186
DASA CNC (WEIHAI) CO., LTD.—See Abpro Bio Co., Ltd.; *Int'l*, pg. 67
DASA CONTROL SYSTEMS AB—See Indutrade AB; *Int'l*, pg. 3678
DAS ACQUISITION COMPANY, LLC; *U.S. Private*, pg. 1160
DASAN INDIA PRIVATE LIMITED—See DZS Inc.; *U.S. Public*, pg. 701
DASAN NETWORKS, INC.; *Int'l*, pg. 1973
DASAN NETWORK SOLUTIONS, INC.—See DZS Inc.; *U.S. Public*, pg. 701
DASAN SOLUETA CO.,LTD.; *Int'l*, pg. 1973
DASAN VIETNAM COMPANY LIMITED—See DZS Inc.; *U.S. Public*, pg. 701
DASAN ZHONE SOLUTIONS, INC. - MIDDLE EAST, AFRICA & PAKISTAN—See DZS Inc.; *U.S. Public*, pg. 701
DASCAN INDUSTRIAL CONTROLS, INC.—See DASCAN Industrial Controls; *Int'l*, pg. 1973
DASCAN INDUSTRIAL CONTROLS; *Int'l*, pg. 1973
DASCO HOME MEDICAL EQUIPMENT; *U.S. Private*, pg. 1161
DASCOM SYSTEMS GROUP LLC—See Strength Capital Partners, LLC; *U.S. Private*, pg. 3839
DAS CONSULTANCY & DETACHERING ROTTERDAM B.V.—See Munchener Ruckversicherungs AG; *Int'l*, pg. 5085
DASCO SYSTEMS, INC.—See Sole Source Capital LLC; *U.S. Private*, pg. 3708
D.A.S. DEFENSA DEL AUTOMOVILISTA Y DE SINIESTROS INTERNACIONAL S.A. DE SEGUROS—See Munchener Ruckversicherungs AG; *Int'l*, pg. 5086
D.A.S. DEUTSCHER AUTOMOBIL SCHUTZ ALLGEMEINE RECHTSSCHUTZ-VERSICHERUNGS-AG—See Munchener Ruckversicherungs AG; *Int'l*, pg. 5086
D.A.S. DIFESA AUTOMOBILISTICA SINISTRI, S.P.A. DI ASSICURAZIONE—See Munchener Ruckversicherungs AG; *Int'l*, pg. 5087
D.A.S. DISTRIBUTORI ARTICOLI SANITARI S.R.L.—See PAUL HARTMANN AG; *Int'l*, pg. 5760
DAS DISTRIBUTORS INC.; *U.S. Private*, pg. 1160
DA SEARCH & LINK INC.—See WPP plc; *Int'l*, pg. 8491
DASEKE COMPANIES, INC.—See Daseke, Inc.; *U.S. Private*, pg. 1161
DASEKE, INC.; *U.S. Private*, pg. 1161
DA SEN HOLDINGS GROUP LIMITED; *Int'l*, pg. 1902
DASER AGRO S.A.—See Corteva, Inc.; *U.S. Public*, pg. 581
DAS GLOBAL CAPITAL CORP.; *U.S. Private*, pg. 1160
DASHAMERICA INC.; *U.S. Private*, pg. 1162

DASHANG GROUP CO., LTD.; *Int'l*, pg. 1973
DASHBOX INC.—See FilmTrack Inc.; *U.S. Private*, pg. 1506
DASH DIVISION—See Sun Capital Partners, Inc.; *U.S. Private*, pg. 1506
DAS HEALTH VENTURES, INC.; *U.S. Private*, pg. 1161
D.A.S. HELLAS ALLGEMEINE RECHTSSCHUTZ-VERSICHERUNGS-AG—See Munchener Ruckversicherungs AG; *Int'l*, pg. 5087
DASH ENGINEERING PHILIPPINES INC.—See Mitsui E&S Holdings Co., Ltd.; *Int'l*, pg. 4984
DASHENG TIMES CULTURAL INVESTMENT CO., LTD.; *Int'l*, pg. 1973
DASHENLIN PHARMACEUTICAL GROUP CO., LTD.; *Int'l*, pg. 1973
DASH ENTERPRISES INC.; *U.S. Private*, pg. 1162
DASHER TECHNOLOGIES INC.; *U.S. Private*, pg. 1162
DASH FINANCIAL SERVICES 2, LLC—See Israel A. Englander & Co., LLC; *U.S. Private*, pg. 2147
DASH FINANCIAL TECHNOLOGIES, LLC—See ION Investment Group Ltd.; *Int'l*, pg. 3793
DASHGO, INC.—See Zealot Networks, Inc.; *U.S. Private*, pg. 4599
DASHIELL CORPORATION—See Quanta Services, Inc.; *U.S. Public*, pg. 1751
DASH IN FOOD STORES, INC.—See The Wills Group, Inc.; *U.S. Private*, pg. 4136
DASHING DIVA INTERNATIONAL CO., LTD.—See Human Holdings Co., Ltd.; *Int'l*, pg. 3529
DASH-IT LTD—See CitySprint (UK) Limited; *Int'l*, pg. 1630
DASH & LOVE, INC.—See Kelso & Company, L.P.; *U.S. Private*, pg. 2279
DAS HOLDING N.V.—See Munchener Ruckversicherungs AG; *Int'l*, pg. 5086
DAS HOLDINGS INC.—See Omnicom Group Inc.; *U.S. Public*, pg. 1579
DASHPAY PROPRIETARY LIMITED—See Capital Appreciation Ltd.; *Int'l*, pg. 1309
DASHTESTAN CEMENT INDUSTRIES COMPANY; *Int'l*, pg. 1974
DASI CORPORATION; *U.S. Private*, pg. 1162
DASIGN SOURCE & CO. INC.; *U.S. Private*, pg. 1162
DAS INCASSO ARNHEM B.V.—See Munchener Ruckversicherungs AG; *Int'l*, pg. 5086
DAS INCASSO ROTTERDAM B.V.—See Munchener Ruckversicherungs AG; *Int'l*, pg. 5086
DAS, INC.; *U.S. Private*, pg. 1161
DASIN RETAIL TRUST MANAGEMENT PTE LTD.; *Int'l*, pg. 1974
D.A.S. INTERNATIONAL, LTD.—See Pentair plc; *Int'l*, pg. 5789
DASI SOLUTIONS, LLC; *U.S. Private*, pg. 1162
DASKOCHREZEPT.DE GMBH—See Hubert Burda Media Holding Kommanditgesellschaft; *Int'l*, pg. 3520
DAS LEGAL EXPENSES CO.—See Munchener Ruckversicherungs AG; *Int'l*, pg. 5087
DAS LEGAL EXPENSES INSURANCE CO., LTD.—See Munchener Ruckversicherungs AG; *Int'l*, pg. 5086
DAS LEGAL EXPENSES INSURANCE COMPANY LIMITED—See ARAG SE; *Int'l*, pg. 534
DAS LEGAL EXPENSES INSURANCE COMPANY LIMITED—See Munchener Ruckversicherungs AG; *Int'l*, pg. 5087
DAS LEGAL FINANCE B.V.—See Munchener Ruckversicherungs AG; *Int'l*, pg. 5086
DAS LEGAL PROTECTION INSURANCE COMPANY LTD.—See ARAG SE; *Int'l*, pg. 534
DAS LEGAL PROTECTION IRELAND LIMITED—See Munchener Ruckversicherungs AG; *Int'l*, pg. 5086
DAS LEGAL SERVICES LIMITED—See Munchener Ruckversicherungs AG; *Int'l*, pg. 5086
D.A.S. LEGAL SERVICES S.R.L.—See Assicurazioni Generali S.p.A.; *Int'l*, pg. 643
D.A.S. LUXEMBURG ALLGEMEINE RECHTSSCHUTZ-VERSICHERUNG SOCIETE ANONYME—See Munchener Ruckversicherungs AG; *Int'l*, pg. 5087
DAS MAGAZIN AG—See TX Group AG; *Int'l*, pg. 7991
D.A.S. OIGUSABIKULUDE KINDLUSTUSE AS—See Munchener Ruckversicherungs AG; *Int'l*, pg. 5085
DAS OSTERREICHISCHE ALLGEMEINE RECHTSSCHUTZ VERSICHERUNG AG—See Munchener Ruckversicherungs AG; *Int'l*, pg. 5087
DASP GROUP LLC; *U.S. Private*, pg. 1162
D.A.S. POISTOVNA PRAVNEJ OCHRANY, A.S.—See Allianz SE; *Int'l*, pg. 352
D.A.S. POJIST'OVNA PRAVNI OCHRANY A.S.—See Munchener Ruckversicherungs AG; *Int'l*, pg. 5087
DAS RECHTSBIJSTAND—See Munchener Ruckversicherungs AG; *Int'l*, pg. 5087
D.A.S. S.A. BELGE D'ASSURANCES DE PROTECTION JURIDIQUE—See Munchener Ruckversicherungs AG; *Int'l*, pg. 5087
DASSAS COMMUNICATION; *Int'l*, pg. 1974
DASSAULT AIRCRAFT SERVICES INDIA PVT. LTD.—See Groupe Industriel Marcel Dassault S.A.; *Int'l*, pg. 3105
DASSAULT ASSURANCES COURTAGE—See Groupe Industriel Marcel Dassault S.A.; *Int'l*, pg. 3104
DASSAULT AVIATION POITIERS—See Groupe Industriel Marcel Dassault S.A.; *Int'l*, pg. 3105

DASSAULT SYSTEMES S.A.

DASSAULT AVIATION SA - ARGONAY FACILITY—See Groupe Industriel Marcel Dassault S.A.; *Int'l*, pg. 3105
DASSAULT AVIATION SAINT-CLOUD—See Groupe Industriel Marcel Dassault S.A.; *Int'l*, pg. 3105
DASSAULT AVIATION—See Groupe Industriel Marcel Dassault S.A.; *Int'l*, pg. 3104
DASSAULT AVIATION—See Groupe Industriel Marcel Dassault S.A.; *Int'l*, pg. 3104
DASSAULT DATA SERVICES—See Dassault Systemes S.A.; *Int'l*, pg. 1974
DASSAULT FALCON BUSINESS SERVICES (BEIJING) CO., LTD.—See Groupe Industriel Marcel Dassault S.A.; *Int'l*, pg. 3105
DASSAULT FALCON JET CORP.—See Groupe Industriel Marcel Dassault S.A.; *Int'l*, pg. 3105
DASSAULT FALCON JET CORP.—See Groupe Industriel Marcel Dassault S.A.; *Int'l*, pg. 3105
DASSAULT FALCON JET DO BRASIL LTDA.—See Groupe Industriel Marcel Dassault S.A.; *Int'l*, pg. 3105
DASSAULT FALCON JET-WILMINGTON CORP.—See Groupe Industriel Marcel Dassault S.A.; *Int'l*, pg. 3105
DASSAULT FALCON MIDDLE EAST—See Groupe Industriel Marcel Dassault S.A.; *Int'l*, pg. 3105
DASSAULT FALCON SERVICE—See Groupe Industriel Marcel Dassault S.A.; *Int'l*, pg. 3105
DASSAULT INTERNATIONAL DO BRASIL LTDA—See Groupe Industriel Marcel Dassault S.A.; *Int'l*, pg. 3105
DASSAULT PROCUREMENT SERVICES—See Groupe Industriel Marcel Dassault S.A.; *Int'l*, pg. 3105
DASSAULT SYSTEMES 3DEXCITE GMBH—See Dassault Systemes S.A.; *Int'l*, pg. 1974
DASSAULT SYSTEMES AB—See Dassault Systemes S.A.; *Int'l*, pg. 1974
DASSAULT SYSTEMES AMERICAS CORP.—See Dassault Systemes S.A.; *Int'l*, pg. 1974
DASSAULT SYSTEMES AMERICAS - WOODLAND HILLS—See Dassault Systemes S.A.; *Int'l*, pg. 1974
DASSAULT SYSTEMES APS—See Dassault Systemes S.A.; *Int'l*, pg. 1974
DASSAULT SYSTEMES AUSTRALIA PTY LTD—See Dassault Systemes S.A.; *Int'l*, pg. 1974
DASSAULT SYSTEMES AUSTRIA GMBH—See Dassault Systemes S.A.; *Int'l*, pg. 1974
DASSAULT SYSTEMES BV—See Dassault Systemes S.A.; *Int'l*, pg. 1974
DASSAULT SYSTEMES CANADA INNOVATION TECHNOLOGIES INC.—See Dassault Systemes S.A.; *Int'l*, pg. 1974
DASSAULT SYSTEMES CHINA—See Dassault Systemes S.A.; *Int'l*, pg. 1974
DASSAULT SYSTEMES CZ S.R.O.—See Dassault Systemes S.A.; *Int'l*, pg. 1974
DASSAULT SYSTEMES DELMIA CORP.—See Dassault Systemes S.A.; *Int'l*, pg. 1974
DASSAULT SYSTEMES DEUTSCHLAND GMBH—See Dassault Systemes S.A.; *Int'l*, pg. 1974
DASSAULT SYSTEMES ENOVIA CORP.—See Dassault Systemes S.A.; *Int'l*, pg. 1974
DASSAULT SYSTEMES INC.—See Dassault Systemes S.A.; *Int'l*, pg. 1974
DASSAULT SYSTEMES INDIA PVT. LTD—See Dassault Systemes S.A.; *Int'l*, pg. 1974
DASSAULT SYSTEMES ISRAEL LTD.—See Dassault Systemes S.A.; *Int'l*, pg. 1975
DASSAULT SYSTEMES ITALIA SRL—See Dassault Systemes S.A.; *Int'l*, pg. 1975
DASSAULT SYSTEMES JAPAN—See Dassault Systemes S.A.; *Int'l*, pg. 1975
DASSAULT SYSTEMES KOREA CORP.—See Dassault Systemes S.A.; *Int'l*, pg. 1975
DASSAULT SYSTEMES MEXICO—See Dassault Systemes S.A.; *Int'l*, pg. 1975
DASSAULT SYSTEMES OY—See Dassault Systemes S.A.; *Int'l*, pg. 1975
DASSAULT SYSTEMES PROVENCE—See Dassault Systemes S.A.; *Int'l*, pg. 1975
DASSAULT SYSTEMES RUSSIA CORP.—See Dassault Systemes S.A.; *Int'l*, pg. 1975
DASSAULT SYSTEMES S.A.; *Int'l*, pg. 1974
DASSAULT SYSTEMES SCHWEIZ AG—See Dassault Systemes S.A.; *Int'l*, pg. 1975
DASSAULT SYSTEMES SIMULIA CORP.—See Dassault Systemes S.A.; *Int'l*, pg. 1975
DASSAULT SYSTEMES SINGAPORE PTE. LTD.—See Dassault Systemes S.A.; *Int'l*, pg. 1975
DASSAULT SYSTEMES SOLIDWORKS CORPORATION—See Dassault Systemes S.A.; *Int'l*, pg. 1975
DASSAULT SYSTEMES SP. Z O.O.—See Dassault Systemes S.A.; *Int'l*, pg. 1975
DASSAULT SYSTEMES (SUISSE) S.A.—See Dassault Systemes S.A.; *Int'l*, pg. 1975
DASSAULT SYSTEMES TAIWAN—See Dassault Systemes S.A.; *Int'l*, pg. 1975
DASSAULT SYSTEMES AUSTRALIA PTY LTD—See Dassault Systemes S.A.; *Int'l*, pg. 1975
DASSELS PETROLEUM INC.—See EDPO, LLC; *U.S. Private*, pg. 1338
DAS SERVICES, INC.—See Convum Ltd.; *Int'l*, pg. 1788

DASSAULT SYSTEMES S.A. CORPORATE AFFILIATIONS

DAS SERVICES LIMITED—See Munchener Ruckversicherungs AG; *Int'l*, pg. 5086
D.A.S. TOWARZYSTWO UBEZPIECZEN OCHRONY PRAWNEJ S.A.—See Munchener Ruckversicherungs AG; *Int'l*, pg. 5085
DA STUART INDIA PRIVATE LIMITED—See Quaker Chemical Corporation; *U.S. Public*, pg. 1745
D.A. STUART S.A.—See Hinduja Group Ltd.; *Int'l*, pg. 3398
DA STUART SHANGHAI CO.—See Quaker Chemical Corporation; *U.S. Public*, pg. 1745
DAS UK HOLDINGS LIMITED—See ARAG SE; *Int'l*, pg. 534
DASVE HOSPITALITY INSTITUTES LIMITED—See Hindustan Construction Co. Ltd; *Int'l*, pg. 3399
DASWANI V. I. INC.; *U.S. Private*, pg. 1162
DASZKAL BOLTON LLP—See CohnReznick LLP; *U.S. Private*, pg. 964
DATA2 CORPORATION; *U.S. Private*, pg. 1164
DATA2 INC.—See Data2 Corporation; *U.S. Private*, pg. 1164
DATA2LOGISTICS EUROPE BV—See Platinum Equity, LLC; *U.S. Private*, pg. 3202
DATA2LOGISTICS, LLC—See Platinum Equity, LLC; *U.S. Private*, pg. 3202
DATA#3 BUSINESS SYSTEMS PTY. LTD.—See Data#3 Limited; *Int'l*, pg. 1977
DATA#3 LIMITED; *Int'l*, pg. 1977
DATA41; *U.S. Private*, pg. 1164
DATA443 RISK MITIGATION, INC.; *U.S. Public*, pg. 635
DATA4VALUE, SRL—See CRIF S.p.A.; *Int'l*, pg. 1849
DATA ADVANTAGE GROUP, INC.—See Toro Data Labs, Inc.; *U.S. Private*, pg. 4189
DATA AGE BUSINESS SYSTEMS, INC.; *U.S. Private*, pg. 1162
DATA AIRE, INC.—See Construction Specialties, Inc.; *U.S. Private*, pg. 1024
DATA ANALYSIS, INC.; *U.S. Private*, pg. 1162
THE DATA APPEAL COMPANY S.P.A.—See Almawave S.p.A.; *Int'l*, pg. 363
DATA APPLICATIONS CO., LTD.; *Int'l*, pg. 1975
DATA ARCHITECTURE & TECHNOLOGY S.L.—See Banco Bilbao Vizcaya Argentaria, S.A.; *Int'l*, pg. 817
DATAART SOLUTIONS, INC.; *U.S. Private*, pg. 1164
DATABANK IMX, LLC—See KYOCERA Corporation; *Int'l*, pg. 4357
DATABANK, LTD.; *U.S. Private*, pg. 1164
DATA BANK SA—See Intracom Holdings S.A.; *Int'l*, pg. 3768
DATABANK TECHNOLOGIES PTY LIMITED—See Freightways Group Limited; *Int'l*, pg. 2771
DATABARRACKS LIMITED; *Int'l*, pg. 1977
THE DATABASE GROUP LTD; *Int'l*, pg. 7636
THE DATABASE MARKETING AGENCY LLC—See The Riverside Company; *U.S. Private*, pg. 4110
DATABASE MARKETING GROUP; *U.S. Private*, pg. 1164
DATABASE PUBLISHING CONSULTANTS, INC.; *U.S. Private*, pg. 1164
DATABAZAAR INDIA PVT. LTD.—See E-Max Group, Inc.; *U.S. Private*, pg. 1302
DATA BEST PRACTICES, LLC—See Incline MGMT Corp.; *U.S. Private*, pg. 2054
DATABIT, INC.; *U.S. Private*, pg. 1164
DATABLE TECHNOLOGY CORP.; *Int'l*, pg. 1977
DATA BLUE LLC—See Court Square Capital Partners, L.P.; *U.S. Private*, pg. 1068
DATA BUSINESS SYSTEMS INC.; *U.S. Private*, pg. 1162
DATA CALL TECHNOLOGIES, INC.; *U.S. Public*, pg. 635
DATA CANOPY COLOCATION LLC—See Intelishift Technologies; *U.S. Private*, pg. 2104
DATA CAPTURE SOLUTIONS INC.; *U.S. Private*, pg. 1162
DATA CAPTURE SYSTEMS—See Mohammed Jalal & Sons WLL; *Int'l*, pg. 5018
DATACARD ASIA PACIFIC LIMITED—See DataCard Corporation; *U.S. Private*, pg. 1164
DATACARD ASIA PACIFIC LIMITED—See DataCard Corporation; *U.S. Private*, pg. 1164
DATACARD CANADA, INC.—See DataCard Corporation; *U.S. Private*, pg. 1164
DATACARD CORPORATION; *U.S. Private*, pg. 1164
DATACARD DEUTSCHLAND GMBH—See DataCard Corporation; *U.S. Private*, pg. 1164
DATACARD EQUIPMENT—See DataCard Corporation; *U.S. Private*, pg. 1164
DATACARD FRANCE S.A.—See DataCard Corporation; *U.S. Private*, pg. 1164
DATACARD IBERICA, S.L.—See DataCard Corporation; *U.S. Private*, pg. 1164
DATACARD JAPAN LTD.—See DataCard Corporation; *U.S. Private*, pg. 1164
DATACARD LTD.—See DataCard Corporation; *U.S. Private*, pg. 1164
DATACARD SERVICE—See DataCard Corporation; *U.S. Private*, pg. 1164
DATACARD (SHANGHAI) TRADING CO., LTD.—See DataCard Corporation; *U.S. Private*, pg. 1164
DATACARD SOUTH PACIFIC (NZ) LTD.—See DataCard Corporation; *U.S. Private*, pg. 1164

DATACARD SOUTH PACIFIC PTY. LTD.—See DataCard Corporation; *U.S. Private*, pg. 1165
DATACEDE LLC; *U.S. Private*, pg. 1165
DATA CENTER DYNAMICS ASIA LIMITED—See Data Center Dynamics Ltd; *Int'l*, pg. 1976
DATA CENTER DYNAMICS INC.—See Data Center Dynamics Ltd; *Int'l*, pg. 1976
DATA CENTER DYNAMICS LTD; *Int'l*, pg. 1976
DATA CENTER DYNAMICS MEA FZ-LLC—See Data Center Dynamics Ltd; *Int'l*, pg. 1976
DATA CENTER DYNAMICS SARL—See Data Center Dynamics Ltd; *Int'l*, pg. 1976
DATA CENTER DYNAMICS SHANGHAI CO. LTD.—See Data Center Dynamics Ltd; *Int'l*, pg. 1976
DATA CENTER INC.; *U.S. Private*, pg. 1162
DATA CENTRE DYNAMICS (HOLLAND) BV—See Data Center Dynamics Ltd; *Int'l*, pg. 1976
DATACENTRE DYNAMICS INDIA PVT. LTD—See Data Center Dynamics Ltd; *Int'l*, pg. 1976
DATA CENTRE DYNAMICS MEXICO S. DE RL DE CV—See Data Center Dynamics Ltd; *Int'l*, pg. 1976
DATA CENTRE DYNAMICS SPAIN S.L.U.—See Data Center Dynamics Ltd; *Int'l*, pg. 1976
DATACENTRIX HOLDINGS LIMITED—See Alviva Holdings Limited; *Int'l*, pg. 402
DATACENTRIX (PROPRIETARY) LIMITED—See Alviva Holdings Limited; *Int'l*, pg. 402
DATACENTRIX SOLUTIONS (PROPRIETARY) LIMITED—See Alviva Holdings Limited; *Int'l*, pg. 402
DATACEP SA—See Capgemini SE; *Int'l*, pg. 1305
DATACHAMBERS LLC—See EQT AB; *Int'l*, pg. 2480
DATA CLEAN CORP.—See Angeles Equity Partners, LLC; *U.S. Private*, pg. 282
DATACO AUSTRALIA PTY LTD.—See Sword Group SE; *Int'l*, pg. 7376
DATACO GLOBAL LTD.—See Sword Group SE; *Int'l*, pg. 7376
DATACOLOR AG; *Int'l*, pg. 1977
DATACOLOR ASIA PACIFIC (HK) LIMITED—See Datacolor AG; *Int'l*, pg. 1977
DATACOLOR BELGIUM BVBA—See Datacolor AG; *Int'l*, pg. 1977
DATACOLOR COLOR TECHNOLOGIES TRADING & SERVICE COMPANY LLC—See Datacolor AG; *Int'l*, pg. 1977
DATACOLOR GMBH—See Datacolor AG; *Int'l*, pg. 1977
DATACOLOR INC.—See Datacolor AG; *Int'l*, pg. 1977
DATACOLOR INTERNATIONAL FRANCE SAS—See Datacolor AG; *Int'l*, pg. 1977
DATACOLOR INTERNATIONAL LTD.—See Datacolor AG; *Int'l*, pg. 1977
DATACOLOR SOLUTIONS PRIVATE LTD.—See Datacolor AG; *Int'l*, pg. 1977
DATACOLOR TRADING (SHANGHAI) CO., LTD.—See Datacolor AG; *Int'l*, pg. 1977
DATACOLOR VIETNAM CO., LTD.—See Datacolor AG; *Int'l*, pg. 1977
DATACOMM NETWORKS, INC.; *U.S. Private*, pg. 1165
DATA COMMUNICATIONS LTD—See Argus Group Holdings Limited; *Int'l*, pg. 563
DATA COMMUNICATIONS MANAGEMENT CORP.; *Int'l*, pg. 1976
DATA COMPUTER CORPORATION OF AMERICA; *U.S. Private*, pg. 1162
DATACOM SYSTEMS INC.; *U.S. Private*, pg. 1165
DATACON HUNGARY TERMELO KFT.—See BE Semiconductor Industries N.V.; *Int'l*, pg. 931
DATA CONNECT CORP.—See Predictive Safety LLC; *U.S. Private*, pg. 3247
DATACON NORTH AMERICA, INC.—See BE Semiconductor Industries N.V.; *Int'l*, pg. 931
DATACONTACT SP. Z O.O.—See Gimv NV; *Int'l*, pg. 2976
DATACORE SOFTWARE CORP.; *U.S. Private*, pg. 1165
DATA CORE SYSTEMS INC.; *U.S. Private*, pg. 1162
DATACORE TECHNOLOGIES PRIVATE LIMITED—See Bain Capital, LP; *U.S. Private*, pg. 433
DATACOR, INC.; *U.S. Private*, pg. 1165
DATA CO & SWORD IT SOLUTIONS LTD.—See Sword Group SE; *Int'l*, pg. 7376
DATACRAFT (MALAYSIA) SDN. BHD.—See Nippon Telegraph & Telephone Corporation; *Int'l*, pg. 5340
DATA DEPOSIT BOX INC.—See HostPapa, Inc.; *Int'l*, pg. 3487
DATA DESIGN S.A.—See AXON Holdings S.A.; *Int'l*, pg. 770
DATA DESIGN SYSTEM AS—See Nemetschek SE; *Int'l*, pg. 5194
DATA DESIGN SYSTEM GMBH—See Nemetschek SE; *Int'l*, pg. 5194
DATA DEVICE CORPORATION—See TransDigm Group Incorporated; *U.S. Public*, pg. 2182
DATA DIMENSIONS CORP.; *U.S. Private*, pg. 1162
DATADIRECT NETWORKS INC.; *U.S. Private*, pg. 1165
DATADIRECT TECHNOLOGIES CORP.—See Progress Software Corporation; *U.S. Public*, pg. 1725
DATADIRECT TECHNOLOGIES, INC.; *U.S. Private*, pg. 1165
DATADIRECT TECHNOLOGIES LTD.—See Progress Software Corporation; *U.S. Public*, pg. 1725

DATADIRECT TECHNOLOGIES NV—See Progress Software Corporation; *U.S. Public*, pg. 1725
DATA DISTRIBUTING, LLC; *U.S. Private*, pg. 1162
DATADOG, INC.; *U.S. Public*, pg. 635
DATADOT TECHNOLOGY LTD; *Int'l*, pg. 1977
DATADOT TECHNOLOGY - TAIWAN—See DataDot Technology Ltd; *Int'l*, pg. 1977
DATADOT TECHNOLOGY (UK) LTD.—See DataDot Technology Ltd; *Int'l*, pg. 1977
THE DATA ENTRY COMPANY; *U.S. Private*, pg. 4018
DATA EXCHANGE CORPORATION; *U.S. Private*, pg. 1162
DATA EXCHANGE EUROPE, LTD.—See Data Exchange Corporation; *U.S. Private*, pg. 1163
DATAFLOR SOFTWARE AG—See Mensch und Maschine Software SE; *Int'l*, pg. 4817
DATAFLOW BUSINESS SYSTEMS, INC.; *U.S. Private*, pg. 1165
DATAFORCE LIMITED—See TwentyCi Holdings Limited; *Int'l*, pg. 7990
DATA FOUNDRY, INC.—See DigitalBridge Group, Inc.; *U.S. Public*, pg. 665
DATA FOUNDRY, INC.—See Industry Super Holdings Pty. Ltd.; *Int'l*, pg. 3676
DATA FUSION TECHNOLOGIES INC.—See Levine Leichtman Capital Partners, LLC; *U.S. Private*, pg. 2435
DATAGARDENS, INC.—See Lumen Technologies, Inc.; *U.S. Public*, pg. 1346
DATAGATE BILGISAYAR MALZEMELERI TICARET A.S.; *Int'l*, pg. 1977
DATA GENOMIX LLC—See Crawford United Corporation; *U.S. Public*, pg. 592
DATAGILITY, INC.—See Industry Data Exchange Association, Inc.; *U.S. Private*, pg. 2069
DATAGRAVITY, INC.—See DataCard Corporation; *U.S. Private*, pg. 1165
DATAGROUP FINANCIAL IT SERVICES GMBH—See DATAGROUP SE; *Int'l*, pg. 1977
DATAGROUP SE; *Int'l*, pg. 1977
DATAGUISE, INC.—See Thompson Street Capital Manager LLC; *U.S. Private*, pg. 4161
DATA HORIZON CORPORATION; *Int'l*, pg. 1976
DATA IMAGING & ASSOCIATES; *U.S. Private*, pg. 1163
DATA-INCRYPT PTY. LTD.—See Kingston Resources Limited; *Int'l*, pg. 4180
DATA INDUSTRIES LTD.; *U.S. Private*, pg. 1163
DATA INFRASTRUCTURE TRUST; *Int'l*, pg. 1976
DATA INTEGRITY INC.; *Int'l*, pg. 1976
DATA INTENSITY, LLC—See EQT AB; *Int'l*, pg. 2474
DATA INTERCONNECT LTD.—See BlackLine, Inc.; *U.S. Public*, pg. 342
DATA I/O CANADA CORPORATION—See Data I/O Corporation; *U.S. Public*, pg. 635
DATA I/O CHINA, LTD.—See Data I/O Corporation; *U.S. Public*, pg. 635
DATA I/O CORPORATION; *U.S. Public*, pg. 635
DATA I/O ELECTRONICS (SHANGHAI) CO., LTD.—See Data I/O Corporation; *U.S. Public*, pg. 635
DATA I/O GMBH—See Data I/O Corporation; *U.S. Public*, pg. 635
DATA I/O INTERNATIONAL, INC.—See Data I/O Corporation; *U.S. Public*, pg. 635
DATAI (SHANGHAI) CHEMICAL TRADING CO., LTD.—See Nagase & Co., Ltd.; *Int'l*, pg. 5126
DATA & JUPITER FREIGHT (BEIJING) CO., LTD.—See Japan Airlines Co., Ltd.; *Int'l*, pg. 3884
DATAKAMP SYSTEM GMBH & CO. KG—See L. Possehl & Co. mbH; *Int'l*, pg. 4385
DATALAB AL SH.P.K.—See Datalab Tehnologije d.d.; *Int'l*, pg. 1977
DATALAB AUTOMOTIVE, D.O.O.—See Datalab Tehnologije d.d.; *Int'l*, pg. 1977
DATALAB BH, D.O.O.—See Datalab Tehnologije d.d.; *Int'l*, pg. 1977
DATALAB BULGARIA, LTD.—See Datalab Tehnologije d.d.; *Int'l*, pg. 1977
DATA LABEL INC.; *U.S. Private*, pg. 1163
DATALAB HR D.O.O.—See Datalab Tehnologije d.d.; *Int'l*, pg. 1977
DATALAB MK, D.O.O.—See Datalab Tehnologije d.d.; *Int'l*, pg. 1977
DATALAB.MN, D.O.O.—See Datalab Tehnologije d.d.; *Int'l*, pg. 1978
DATALAB SI D.O.O.—See Datalab Tehnologije d.d.; *Int'l*, pg. 1978
DATALAB SR, D.O.O.—See Datalab Tehnologije d.d.; *Int'l*, pg. 1978
DATALAB TEHNOLOGIJE D.D.; *Int'l*, pg. 1977
DATALAB TEHNOLOGIJE D.O.O.—See Datalab Tehnologije d.d.; *Int'l*, pg. 1978
DATALAB USA; *U.S. Private*, pg. 1165
DATALAND B.V.—See BNG Bank N.V.; *Int'l*, pg. 1079
DATALEX NETHERLANDS B.V.—See Datalex plc; *Int'l*, pg. 1978
DATALEX PLC; *Int'l*, pg. 1978
DATALEX SOLUTIONS (UK) LIMITED—See Datalex plc; *Int'l*, pg. 1978
DATALEX USA INC.—See Datalex plc; *Int'l*, pg. 1978
DATALINE LLC; *U.S. Private*, pg. 1165

COMPANY NAME INDEX

DATALINER AB; *Int'l*, pg. 1978
DATALINE SYSTEMS, LLC—See CardWorks, Inc.; *U.S. Private*, pg. 751
DATALINK BANKCARD SERVICES, CO.; *U.S. Private*, pg. 1165
DATALINK CORPORATION—See Insight Enterprises, Inc.; *U.S. Public*, pg. 1129
DATALINKS CORPORATION; *Int'l*, pg. 1978
DATA LOCATOR GROUP LIMITED—See DM plc; *Int'l*, pg. 2142
DATALOG DE VENEZUELA SA—See Weatherford International plc; *U.S. Public*, pg. 2339
DATALOGIC ADC S.R.L.—See Datalogic S.p.A.; *Int'l*, pg. 1978
DATALOGIC AUSTRALIA PTY LTD—See Datalogic S.p.A.; *Int'l*, pg. 1978
DATALOGIC AUTOMATION, INC.—See Datalogic S.p.A.; *Int'l*, pg. 1978
DATALOGIC AUTOMATION S.R.L.—See Datalogic S.p.A.; *Int'l*, pg. 1978
DATALOGIC DO BRAZIL COMERCIO DE EQUIPAMENTOS E AUTOMACAO LTDA.—See Datalogic S.p.A.; *Int'l*, pg. 1978
DATALOGIC HOLDINGS, INC.—See Datalogic S.p.A.; *Int'l*, pg. 1978
DATALOGIC HUNGARY KFT—See Datalogic S.p.A.; *Int'l*, pg. 1978
DATALOGIC JAPAN CO., LTD.—See Datalogic S.p.A.; *Int'l*, pg. 1978
DATA LOGIC SERVICES CORP—See Berkshire Partners LLC; *U.S. Private*, pg. 534
DATALOGIC SINGAPORE ASIA PACIFIC PTE LTD—See Datalogic S.p.A.; *Int'l*, pg. 1978
DATALOGIC SLOVAKIA S.R.O.—See Datalogic S.p.A.; *Int'l*, pg. 1978
DATALOGIC S.P.A.; *Int'l*, pg. 1978
DATALOGIC TECHNOLOGIA DE MEXICO S.R.L.—See Datalogic S.p.A.; *Int'l*, pg. 1978
DATALOGIC USA, INC.—See Datalogic S.p.A.; *Int'l*, pg. 1978
DATALOGIC VIETNAM LLC—See Datalogic S.p.A.; *Int'l*, pg. 1978
DATALOG LWT INC.—See Datalog Technology Inc.; *Int'l*, pg. 1978
DATALOG TECHNOLOGY INC.; *Int'l*, pg. 1078
DATALOG TECHNOLOGY INC.—See Datalog Technology Inc.; *Int'l*, pg. 1978
DATALOT INC.—See Platinum Equity, LLC; *U.S. Private*, pg. 3201
DATALUX CORPORATION; *U.S. Private*, pg. 1165
DATALYTICS LTD—See Iris Nation Worldwide Limited; *Int'l*, pg. 3809
DATA-MAIL, INC.—See Incline MGMT Corp.; *U.S. Private*, pg. 2054
DATA MANAGEMENT, INCORPORATED—See CCL Industries Inc.; *Int'l*, pg. 1369
DATAMANUSA, LLC; *U.S. Private*, pg. 1165
DATAMARK INC.; *U.S. Private*, pg. 1166
DATAMARK INC.; *U.S. Private*, pg. 1166
DATAMARK INC.—See Datamark Inc.; *U.S. Private*, pg. 1166
DATAMARS, INC.—See Datamars SA; *Int'l*, pg. 1978
DATAMARS SA; *Int'l*, pg. 1978
DATAMATE DIVISION—See Methode Electronics, Inc.; *U.S. Public*, pg. 1428
DATAMATE PRODUCTS GROUP—See Methode Electronics, Inc.; *U.S. Public*, pg. 1428
DATAMATICS CONSULTANTS INC.; *U.S. Private*, pg. 1166
DATAMATICS GLOBAL SERVICES CORP.—See Datamatics Global Services Ltd.; *Int'l*, pg. 1979
DATAMATICS GLOBAL SERVICES FZ-LLC—See Datamatics Global Services Ltd.; *Int'l*, pg. 1979
DATAMATICS GLOBAL SERVICES LTD.; *Int'l*, pg. 1978
DATAMATICS STAFFING SERVICES LIMITED—See Datamatics Global Services Ltd.; *Int'l*, pg. 1979
DATAMATICS TECHNOLOGIES GMBH—See Datamatics Global Services Ltd.; *Int'l*, pg. 1979
DATAMATICS TECHNOLOGIES U.K. LIMITED—See Datamatics Global Services Ltd.; *Int'l*, pg. 1979
DATAMAXX GROUP, INC.; *U.S. Private*, pg. 1166
DATAMEER INC.; *U.S. Private*, pg. 1166
DATAMENTORS, LLC; *U.S. Private*, pg. 1166
DATAMETREX AI LIMITED; *Int'l*, pg. 1979
DATAMETRIX AS—See Telenor ASA; *Int'l*, pg. 7538
DATAMETRIX INTEGRATION AB—See Tele2 AB; *Int'l*, pg. 7529
DATAMETRIX; *U.S. Private*, pg. 1166
DATAMINR INC.; *U.S. Private*, pg. 1166
DATAMIRROR CORPORATION—See International Business Machines Corporation; *U.S. Public*, pg. 1148
DATAM LIMITED—See New Zealand Post Limited; *Int'l*, pg. 5232
DATA MODUL AG; *Int'l*, pg. 1976
DATA MODUL ELECTRONICS TECHNOLOGY (SHANGHAI) CO. LTD.—See Arrow Electronics, Inc.; *U.S. Public*, pg. 199
DATA MODUL ELECTRONIC TECHNOLOGY (SHANGHAI) CO., LTD.—See Data Modul AG; *Int'l*, pg. 1976

DATA MODUL FRANCE, S.A.R.L—See Data Modul AG; *Int'l*, pg. 1976
DATA MODUL FRANCE S.A R.L—See Arrow Electronics, Inc.; *U.S. Public*, pg. 199
DATA MODUL FRANCE, S.A.R.L.—See Data Modul AG; *Int'l*, pg. 1976
DATA MODUL FZE—See Arrow Electronics, Inc.; *U.S. Public*, pg. 199
DATA MODUL HONG KONG LTD.—See Arrow Electronics, Inc.; *U.S. Public*, pg. 199
DATA MODUL IBERIA S.L.—See Data Modul AG; *Int'l*, pg. 1976
DATA MODUL INC.—See Data Modul AG; *Int'l*, pg. 1976
DATA MODUL ITALIA S.R.L.—See Arrow Electronics, Inc.; *U.S. Public*, pg. 199
DATA MODUL LTD.—See Data Modul AG; *Int'l*, pg. 1976
DATA MODUL POLSKA SP. Z O.O—See Data Modul AG; *Int'l*, pg. 1976
DATA MODUL WEIKERSHEIM GMBH—See Arrow Electronics, Inc.; *U.S. Public*, pg. 199
DATAMONITOR, INC.—See Informa plc; *Int'l*, pg. 3692
DATAMONITOR—See Informa plc; *Int'l*, pg. 3692
DATAMYNE, INC.—See The Descartes Systems Group Inc.; *Int'l*, pg. 7636
DATAMYX LLC—See Deluxe Corporation; *U.S. Public*, pg. 652
DATANATIONAL, INC.—See Yellow Pages Limited; *Int'l*, pg. 8576
DATANET INFRASTRUCTURE GROUP (PTY) LIMITED—See Alviva Holdings Limited; *Int'l*, pg. 402
DATA NETWORK SERVICES INC.—See Cloud Equity Group, LLC; *U.S. Private*, pg. 946
DATA NETWORKS OF AMERICA INC.; *U.S. Private*, pg. 1163
DATANG ENVIRONMENT INDUSTRY GROUP CO., LTD.—See China Datang Corporation; *Int'l*, pg. 1496
DATANG HUAYIN ELECTRIC POWER CO., LTD.; *Int'l*, pg. 1979
DATANG INTERNATIONAL POWER GENERATION CO., LTD.—See China Datang Corporation; *Int'l*, pg. 1497
DATANG NXP SEMICONDUCTORS CO., LTD.—See Datang Telecom Technology Co., Ltd.; *Int'l*, pg. 1979
DATANG TELECOM TECHNOLOGY CO., LTD.; *Int'l*, pg. 1979
DATANOMICS INC.; *U.S. Private*, pg. 1166
DATANYZE, LLC—See ZoomInfo Technologies Inc.; *U.S. Public*, pg. 2411
DATA ONE GMBH—See Orbis SE; *Int'l*, pg. 5614
DATA OUTSOURCING CENTRE DOO—See Iron Mountain Incorporated; *U.S. Public*, pg. 1172
DATA PAPERS INC.; *U.S. Private*, pg. 1163
DATAPATH, INC.—See Gilat Satellite Networks Ltd.; *Int'l*, pg. 2973
DATA PATH; *U.S. Private*, pg. 1163
DATA PATTERNS (INDIA) LTD.; *Int'l*, pg. 1976
DATA PHYSICS (BHARAT/ INDIA) PVT. LTD.—See Battery Ventures, L.P.; *U.S. Private*, pg. 488
DATA PHYSICS CORP.—See Battery Ventures, L.P.; *U.S. Private*, pg. 488
DATA PHYSICS (DEUTSCHLAND/ GERMANY) GMBH—See Battery Ventures, L.P.; *U.S. Private*, pg. 488
DATA PHYSICS (FRANCE) S.A.—See Battery Ventures, L.P.; *U.S. Private*, pg. 488
DATA PHYSICS (UK) LTD.—See Battery Ventures, L.P.; *U.S. Private*, pg. 488
DATAPINE GMBH—See Schneider Electric SE; *Int'l*, pg. 6624
DATAPIPE, INC.—See Apollo Global Management, Inc.; *U.S. Public*, pg. 154
DATAPLOT GMBH; *Int'l*, pg. 1979
DATA PLUS CORPORATION—See Nippon Telegraph & Telephone Corporation; *Int'l*, pg. 5354
DATAPOINT CUSTOMER SOLUTIONS LTD.; *Int'l*, pg. 1979
DATAPOINT FRANCE—See Datapoint Customer Solutions Ltd.; *Int'l*, pg. 1979
DATAPOINT IBERICA S.A.—See Datapoint Customer Solutions Ltd.; *Int'l*, pg. 1979
DATAPOINTLABS; *U.S. Private*, pg. 1166
DATAPOINT NEDERLAND B.V.—See Datapoint Customer Solutions Ltd.; *Int'l*, pg. 1979
DATAPOS (M) SDN. BHD.—See Pos Malaysia Berhad; *Int'l*, pg. 5936
DATAPOST PTE LTD—See Jing King Tech Holdings Pte Ltd.; *Int'l*, pg. 3967
DATAPREP HOLDINGS BERHAD—See Widad Business Group Sdn. Bhd.; *Int'l*, pg. 8401
DATA PRESSE SAS—See Platinum Equity, LLC; *U.S. Private*, pg. 3201
DATAPRISE, INC—See Trinity Hunt Management, L.P.; *U.S. Private*, pg. 4234
DATA PRO ACCOUNTING SOFTWARE, INC.; *U.S. Private*, pg. 1163
DATAPROCES GROUP A/S; *Int'l*, pg. 1979
DATA PROCESSING AIR CORP.; *U.S. Private*, pg. 1163
DATA PROCESSING SCIENCES CORPORATION; *U.S. Private*, pg. 1163
DATA PROCESSING SERVICES; *U.S. Private*, pg. 1163

DATASONIC GROUP BERHAD

DATA PROCESSING SOLUTIONS, INC.; *U.S. Private*, pg. 1163
DATAPRO COMPUTER SYSTEMS CO., LTD.—See Premier Technology Public Company Limited; *Int'l*, pg. 5962
DATAPRO, INC.—See Constellation Software Inc.; *Int'l*, pg. 1775
DATA PRO PROXIMITY—See Omnicom Group Inc.; *U.S. Public*, pg. 1575
DATAPULSE LIMITED—See Enghouse Systems Limited; *Int'l*, pg. 2427
DATAPULSE TECHNOLOGY LTD.; *Int'l*, pg. 1979
DATA QUALITY MANAGEMENT GROUP LIMITED—See Bloom Equity Partners Management, LLC; *U.S. Private*, pg. 583
DATAQUICK INFORMATION SYSTEMS, INC.—See Insight Venture Management, LLC; *U.S. Private*, pg. 2089
DATAQUICK INFORMATION SYSTEMS, INC.—See Stone Point Capital LLC; *U.S. Private*, pg. 3822
DATAQUICK TITLE LLC—See Insight Venture Management, LLC; *U.S. Private*, pg. 2089
DATAQUICK TITLE LLC—See Stone Point Capital LLC; *U.S. Private*, pg. 3822
DATARAN TENAGA (M) SDN. BHD.—See CITIC Group Corporation; *Int'l*, pg. 1620
DATA RECOGNITION CORPORATION; *U.S. Private*, pg. 1163
DATA REPLY S.R.L.—See Reply S.p.A.; *Int'l*, pg. 6291
DATA RESPONS AB—See Adecco Group AG; *Int'l*, pg. 139
DATA RESPONS ASA—See Adecco Group AG; *Int'l*, pg. 139
DATA RESPONS A/S—See Adecco Group AG; *Int'l*, pg. 139
DATA RESPONS GMBH—See Adecco Group AG; *Int'l*, pg. 139
DATA RESPONS NORGE AS—See Adecco Group AG; *Int'l*, pg. 139
DATA RESPONS NORGE AS—See Adecco Group AG; *Int'l*, pg. 140
DATA RESPONS NORGE AS—See Adecco Group AG; *Int'l*, pg. 140
DATA RESPONS SYREN AB—See Adecco Group AG; *Int'l*, pg. 140
DATAROBOT, INC.—See Right Side Capital Management, LLC; *U.S. Private*, pg. 3436
DATARPM LLC—See Progress Software Corporation; *U.S. Public*, pg. 1725
DATASAFE (CAMBODIA) LTD.—See SCGJWD Logistics Public Company Limited; *Int'l*, pg. 6614
DATASAFE CO., LTD.—See SCGJWD Logistics Public Company Limited; *Int'l*, pg. 6614
DATASAFE, INC.; *U.S. Private*, pg. 1166
DATA SALES CO.; *U.S. Private*, pg. 1163
DATASCAN FIELD SERVICES, LLC—See JM Family Enterprises Inc.; *U.S. Private*, pg. 2214
DATASCAN HOLDINGS LLC—See JM Family Enterprises Inc.; *U.S. Private*, pg. 2214
DATA SCANNING A/S—See PostNord AB; *Int'l*, pg. 5940
DATA SCANNING FINLAND AB—See PostNord AB; *Int'l*, pg. 5940
DATASCAN TECHNOLOGIES LLC—See JM Family Enterprises Inc.; *U.S. Private*, pg. 2214
DATA SCIENCE AUTOMATION, INC.—See Blackford Capital LLC; *U.S. Private*, pg. 574
DATA SCIENCES INTERNATIONAL—See Harvard Bioscience, Inc.; *U.S. Public*, pg. 987
DATASCOPE INVESTMENT CORP.—See Getinge AB; *Int'l*, pg. 2951
DATASEA INC.; *Int'l*, pg. 1979
DATA SEARCH NY INC.; *U.S. Private*, pg. 1163
DATASEAT LTD.—See Verve Group SE; *Int'l*, pg. 8176
DATASECTION INC.; *Int'l*, pg. 1979
DATA SECURITY DEVELOPMENT, INC; *U.S. Private*, pg. 1163
DATA SECURITY SOLUTIONS, LLC—See WSFS Financial Corporation; *U.S. Public*, pg. 2384
DATASENSING S.R.L.—See Datalogic S.p.A.; *Int'l*, pg. 1978
DATASENTICS A.S.—See Atos SE; *Int'l*, pg. 692
DATA SERVICE SOLUTIONS, INC.—See The Segerdahl Corporation; *U.S. Private*, pg. 4116
DATASERV, INCORPORATED—See American CyberSystems, Inc.; *U.S. Private*, pg. 229
DATASERV LLC; *U.S. Private*, pg. 1166
DATASHIELD LLC—See Apollo Global Management, Inc.; *U.S. Public*, pg. 146
DATASIFT INC.; *U.S. Private*, pg. 1166
DATASIFT LTD.—See DataSift Inc.; *U.S. Private*, pg. 1166
DATASIGHT CORPORATION; *U.S. Private*, pg. 1166
DATASITE LLC—See CapVest Limited; *Int'l*, pg. 1318
DATASOLUTION, INC.; *Int'l*, pg. 1979
DATASONIC CORPORATION SDN. BHD.—See Sentoria Group Berhad; *Int'l*, pg. 6715
DATASONIC GROUP BERHAD; *Int'l*, pg. 1979
DATASONIC INNOVATION SDN. BHD.—See Datasonic Group Berhad; *Int'l*, pg. 1979

DATASONIC MANUFACTURING SDN. BHD.—See Datasonic Group Berhad; *Int'l*, pg. 1979
DATASONIC SMART SOLUTIONS SDN BHD—See Datasonic Group Berhad; *Int'l*, pg. 1979
DATASONIC TECHNOLOGIES SDN BHD—See Datasonic Group Berhad; *Int'l*, pg. 1979
DATASOURCE CONSULTING, LLC—See ExlService Holdings, Inc.; *U.S. Public*, pg. 807
DATA SOURCE MEDIA INC.; *U.S. Private*, pg. 1163
DATA SPECIALISTS, INC.—See Dairy, LLC; *U.S. Private*, pg. 1146
DATA SPECIALTIES INC.; *U.S. Private*, pg. 1163
DATASPHERE TECHNOLOGIES, INC.—See Sinclair, Inc.; *U.S. Public*, pg. 1885
DATASPRING—See Nippon Telegraph & Telephone Corporation; *Int'l*, pg. 5351
DATA & STAFF SERVICE CO.—See RLI Corp.; *U.S. Public*, pg. 1801
DATASTAX, INC.; *U.S. Private*, pg. 1166
DATA-STITCH INC.; *U.S. Private*, pg. 1164
DATA STORAGE CORPORATION; *U.S. Public*, pg. 635
DATA STORE 365 LIMITED—See Bechtle AG; *Int'l*, pg. 938
DATA STRATEGIES, INC.—See Integrated Solutions Group, Inc.; *U.S. Private*, pg. 2101
DATASTREAM CONTENT SOLUTIONS, LLC—See The Dolan Company; *U.S. Private*, pg. 4022
DATASTREAM MARKET INTELLIGENCE, INC.; *U.S. Private*, pg. 1166
DATA STREAMS CORPORATION; *Int'l*, pg. 1976
DATASTRONG, LLC—See OceanSound Partners, LP; *U.S. Private*, pg. 2992
DATA SYSTEMS ANALYSTS INC. (DSA); *U.S. Private*, pg. 1163
DATA SYSTEMS CONSULTING CO., LTD.; *Int'l*, pg. 1976
DATA SYSTEMS INTERNATIONAL, INC.—See Nextworld, LLC; *U.S. Private*, pg. 2921
DATA SYSTEMS OF TEXAS, INC.; *U.S. Private*, pg. 1163
DATA SYSTEMS TECHNOLOGY SOLUTIONS—See Data Systems of Texas, Inc.; *U.S. Private*, pg. 1163
DATATEC CO., LTD.—See Kanematsu Corporation; *Int'l*, pg. 4068
DATATECHNIC S.A.S.—See Durr AG; *Int'l*, pg. 2233
DATA TECHNOLOGY SOLUTIONS—See ViaSat, Inc.; *U.S. Public*, pg. 2292
DATATEC LIMITED; *Int'l*, pg. 1980
DATATEC MANAGEMENT SERVICES (PTY) LIMITED—See Datatec Limited; *Int'l*, pg. 1980
DATATEL ELEKTRONIK GMBH—See Phoenix Mecano AG; *Int'l*, pg. 5852
DATATEL RESOURCES CORPORATION; *U.S. Private*, pg. 1166
DATATERN, INC.—See Amphion Innovations plc; *Int'l*, pg. 433
DATA TEXTILES LIMITED; *Int'l*, pg. 1976
DATA TRACEID (EUROPE) LIMITED—See DataDot Technology Ltd; *Int'l*, pg. 1977
DATA TRACE INFORMATION SERVICES LLC—See First American Financial Corporation; *U.S. Public*, pg. 835
DATATRAK DEUTSCHLAND, GMBH—See DATATRAK International, Inc.; *U.S. Public*, pg. 635
DATATRAK INTERNATIONAL, INC.; *U.S. Public*, pg. 635
DATA TRANSFER SOLUTIONS, LLC—See AtkinsRealis Group Inc.; *Int'l*, pg. 671
DATA TRANSLATION GMBH—See National Instruments Corporation; *U.S. Private*, pg. 2856
DATA TRANSLATION, INC.—See National Instruments Corporation; *U.S. Private*, pg. 2856
DATATRAX PUBLISHING SYSTEMS, INC.; *U.S. Private*, pg. 1166
DATATREND TECHNOLOGIES, INC.—See Converge Technology Solutions Corp.; *Int'l*, pg. 1787
DATATRON DOCUMENT IMAGE ARCHIVING LIMITED—See HP Inc.; *U.S. Public*, pg. 1062
DATATRONIC DISTRIBUTION, INC.—See Datronix Holdings Limited; *Int'l*, pg. 1982
DATAVAIL CORPORATION—See CIVC Partners LLC; *U.S. Private*, pg. 907
DATAVAN INTERNATIONAL CORP.; *Int'l*, pg. 1981
DATAVANT, INC.—See New Mountain Capital, LLC; *U.S. Private*, pg. 2900
DATA VISION, INC.; *U.S. Private*, pg. 1164
DATAVISION TECHNOLOGIES INC.—See myDigitalOffice Holdings Inc.; *U.S. Private*, pg. 2824
DATAVIZ, INC.; *U.S. Private*, pg. 1166
DATAWALK S.A.; *Int'l*, pg. 1981
DATAWARE, LLC—See Midcontinent Media Inc.; *U.S. Private*, pg. 2711
DATAWATCH AB—See Altair Engineering, Inc.; *U.S. Public*, pg. 86
DATAWATCH ANALYTICS (SINGAPORE) PTE LTD—See Altair Engineering, Inc.; *U.S. Public*, pg. 86
DATAWATCH CORPORATION—See Altair Engineering, Inc.; *U.S. Public*, pg. 86
DATAWATCH INTERNATIONAL LIMITED—See Altair Engineering, Inc.; *U.S. Public*, pg. 86
DATAWING SOFTWARE, LLC—See Great Point Partners, LLC; *U.S. Private*, pg. 1767
DATAWIZ CORPORATION; *U.S. Private*, pg. 1167

DATAWORDS DATASIA SARL; *Int'l*, pg. 1981
DATAX LTD.—See Equifax Inc.; *U.S. Public*, pg. 785
DATAXU, INC.—See Roku, Inc.; *U.S. Public*, pg. 1808
DATBIM SA; *Int'l*, pg. 1981
DATCHAT, INC.; *U.S. Public*, pg. 635
DATCU CREDIT UNION; *U.S. Private*, pg. 1167
DA TECHNOLOGY CO., LTD.; *Int'l*, pg. 1902
D&A TECHNOLOGY (SHANGHAI) CO., LTD.—See Argo Graphics Inc.; *Int'l*, pg. 562
DATECS LTD.; *Int'l*, pg. 1981
DATEC TECHNOLOGIES, LTD.—See Belmont Trading Company; *U.S. Private*, pg. 521
DATEC TECHNOLOGIES, LTD.—See SiPi Metals Corp.; *U.S. Private*, pg. 3671
DATEF S.P.A.—See Sesa S.p.A.; *Int'l*, pg. 6728
DATELINE RESOURCES LTD.; *Int'l*, pg. 1981
DATELINE UK LTD.; *Int'l*, pg. 1981
DATEL SYSTEMS INCORPORATED; *U.S. Private*, pg. 1167
DATENTECHNIK AG; *Int'l*, pg. 1982
DATENTECHNIK D.O.O.—See Datentechnik AG; *Int'l*, pg. 1982
DATES WEISER FURNITURE CORP.—See MillerKnoll, Inc.; *U.S. Public*, pg. 1447
DATEV.AT GMBH—See DATEV eG; *Int'l*, pg. 1982
DATEV.CZ S.R.O.—See DATEV eG; *Int'l*, pg. 1982
DATEV EG; *Int'l*, pg. 1982
DATEV HUNGARY—See DATEV eG; *Int'l*, pg. 1982
DATEV KOINOS S.R.L.—See DATEV eG; *Int'l*, pg. 1982
DATEV.PL SP. Z O.O.—See DATEV eG; *Int'l*, pg. 1982
DATIWARE MARITIME INFRA LTD.; *Int'l*, pg. 1982
DATIX, INC.; *U.S. Private*, pg. 1167
DATONG CDB VILLAGE BANK CO., LTD.—See China Development Bank Corporation; *Int'l*, pg. 1497
DATONG COAL INDUSTRY CO., LTD.; *Int'l*, pg. 1982
DATONG COAL INDUSTRY JINYU KAOLIN CHEMICAL CO., LTD.—See Datong Coal Mine Group Co., Ltd.; *Int'l*, pg. 1982
DATONG COAL MINE GROUP CO., LTD.; *Int'l*, pg. 1982
DATORAMA GMBH—See Salesforce, Inc.; *U.S. Public*, pg. 1837
DATREK PROFESSIONAL BAGS, INC.; *U.S. Private*, pg. 1167
DATRIX S.P.A.; *Int'l*, pg. 1982
DATRON AG; *Int'l*, pg. 1982
DATRON AUSTRIA GMBH—See Datron AG; *Int'l*, pg. 1982
DATRON FRANCE SAS—See Datron AG; *Int'l*, pg. 1982
DATRONIX HOLDINGS LIMITED; *Int'l*, pg. 1982
DATRON TECHNOLOGY CZ S.R.O.—See Datron AG; *Int'l*, pg. 1982
DATRON TECHNOLOGY S.R.O.—See Datron AG; *Int'l*, pg. 1982
DATRON TOOL TECHNOLOGY GMBH—See Datron AG; *Int'l*, pg. 1982
DATRON WORLD COMMUNICATIONS, INC.—See Cyberlux Corporation; *U.S. Public*, pg. 617
DATROSE; *U.S. Private*, pg. 1167
DATS24 N.V.—See Colruyt Group N.V.; *Int'l*, pg. 1705
DAT-SCHAUB AB—See Danish Crown AmbA; *Int'l*, pg. 1964
DAT-SCHAUB A/S—See Danish Crown AmbA; *Int'l*, pg. 1964
DAT-SCHAUB CASINGS (AUSTRALIA) PTY LTD—See Danish Crown AmbA; *Int'l*, pg. 1964
DAT-SCHAUB (DEUTSCHLAND) GMBH—See Danish Crown AmbA; *Int'l*, pg. 1964
DAT-SCHAUB POLSKA SP. Z O.O.—See Danish Crown AmbA; *Int'l*, pg. 1964
DAT-SCHAUB (PORTO) SA—See Danish Crown AmbA; *Int'l*, pg. 1964
DAT SOLUTIONS, LLC—See Roper Technologies, Inc.; *U.S. Public*, pg. 1811
DATSTAT, INC.—See R1 RCM Inc.; *U.S. Public*, pg. 1758
DATS TRUCKING INC.; *U.S. Private*, pg. 1167
DATTO ASIAPAC PTY. LTD.—See Insight Venture Management, LLC; *U.S. Private*, pg. 2090
DATTO CANADA ENTERPRISES, INC.—See Insight Venture Management, LLC; *U.S. Private*, pg. 2090
DATTO EUROPE LTD.—See Vista Equity Partners, LLC; *U.S. Private*, pg. 4396
DATTO GMBH—See Insight Venture Management, LLC; *U.S. Private*, pg. 2090
DATTO HOLDING CORP.—See Insight Venture Management, LLC; *U.S. Private*, pg. 2090
DATTO, INC.—See Vista Equity Partners, LLC; *U.S. Private*, pg. 4396
DATTO NEDERLAND B.V.—See Insight Venture Management, LLC; *U.S. Private*, pg. 2091
DATTO SINGAPORE PTE. LTD.—See Insight Venture Management, LLC; *U.S. Private*, pg. 2091
DATUM CORPORATION; *U.S. Private*, pg. 1167
DATUM ELECTRONICS LTD.—See Indutrade AB; *Int'l*, pg. 3678
DATUM INDUSTRIES, LLC—See Huizenga Manufacturing Group, Inc.; *U.S. Private*, pg. 2004
DATUM PERSONNEL LTD.—See Randstad N.V.; *Int'l*, pg. 6204
DATUM VENTURES INC.; *Int'l*, pg. 1982

DA-TUN CABLE TV CO., LTD.—See Taiwan Optical Platform Co., Ltd.; *Int'l*, pg. 7422
DAT XANH DONG NAM BO SERVICES & INVESTMENT JSC—See Dat Xanh Group Joint Stock Company; *Int'l*, pg. 1975
DAT XANH GROUP JOINT STOCK COMPANY; *Int'l*, pg. 1975
DAT XANH MIEN BAC SERVICES & REAL ESTATE JSC—See Dat Xanh Group Joint Stock Company; *Int'l*, pg. 1975
DAT XANH MIEN NAM INVESTMENT & SERVICES JSC—See Dat Xanh Group Joint Stock Company; *Int'l*, pg. 1975
DAT XANH MIEN TAY SERVICE AND INVESTMENT JOINT STOCK COMPANY—See Dat Xanh Group Joint Stock Company; *Int'l*, pg. 1975
DAT XANH MIEN TRUNG JSC—See Dat Xanh Group Joint Stock Company; *Int'l*, pg. 1975
DATZ; *U.S. Private*, pg. 1167
DAUBERT CHEMICAL COMPANY, INC.—See Daubert Industries, Inc.; *U.S. Private*, pg. 1167
DAUBERT CROMWELL, LLC—See Daubert Industries, Inc.; *U.S. Private*, pg. 1167
DAUBERT INDUSTRIES, INC.; *U.S. Private*, pg. 1167
DAU DRAXLMAIER AUTOMOTIVE UK LTD.—See Draexlmaier Gruppe; *Int'l*, pg. 2198
DAUF SA—See CSL Limited; *Int'l*, pg. 1866
DAUGERON & FILS SAS—See Bunzl plc; *Int'l*, pg. 1218
DAUGHERTY & COMPANY LLC; *U.S. Private*, pg. 1167
DAUGHERTY SYSTEMS INC.; *U.S. Private*, pg. 1167
DAUGHTERS OF CHARITY HEALTH SYSTEM; *U.S. Private*, pg. 1167
DAUGHTERS OF MIRIAM CENTER; *U.S. Private*, pg. 1167
DAUGHTERS OF SARAH SENIOR COMMUNITY; *U.S. Private*, pg. 1167
DAUGHTRIDGE SALES CO., INC.—See Frontenac Company LLC; *U.S. Private*, pg. 1614
DAULAT SECURITIES LIMITED; *Int'l*, pg. 1982
DAUL INSURANCE AGENCY, INC.—See Caisse de Depot et Placement du Quebec; *Int'l*, pg. 1256
DAUL INSURANCE AGENCY, INC.—See KKR & Co. Inc.; *U.S. Public*, pg. 1265
DAUNAT BRETAGNE; *Int'l*, pg. 1982
DAUN & CIE. AG; *Int'l*, pg. 1982
DAUPHINE MAURITIUS INVESTMENT LIMITED—See JPMorgan Chase & Co.; *U.S. Public*, pg. 1206
DAUPHIN ESPANA S.A.—See Dauphin HumanDesign Group GmbH & Co. KG; *Int'l*, pg. 1983
DAUPHIN FRANCE S. A.—See Dauphin HumanDesign Group GmbH & Co. KG; *Int'l*, pg. 1983
DAUPHIN HUMANDESIGN AG—See Dauphin HumanDesign Group GmbH & Co. KG; *Int'l*, pg. 1983
DAUPHIN HUMANDESIGN BELGIUM NV/SA—See Dauphin HumanDesign Group GmbH & Co. KG; *Int'l*, pg. 1983
DAUPHIN HUMANDESIGN B.V.—See Dauphin HumanDesign Group GmbH & Co. KG; *Int'l*, pg. 1983
DAUPHIN HUMANDESIGN GROUP GMBH & CO. KG; *Int'l*, pg. 1982
DAUPHIN HUMANDESIGN UK LIMITED—See Dauphin HumanDesign Group GmbH & Co. KG; *Int'l*, pg. 1983
DAUPHIN INDUSTRY (SCHWEIZ) UNIQ SOLUTION GMBH—See Dauphin HumanDesign Group GmbH & Co. KG; *Int'l*, pg. 1983
DAUPHIN ITALIA—See Dauphin HumanDesign Group GmbH & Co. KG; *Int'l*, pg. 1983
DAUPHIN NORTH AMERICA—See Dauphin HumanDesign Group GmbH & Co. KG; *Int'l*, pg. 1983
DAUPHIN OFFICE SEATING S.A. (PTY) LTD.—See Dauphin HumanDesign Group GmbH & Co. KG; *Int'l*, pg. 1983
DAUPHINOISE DE MATERIAUX ENROBES SAS—See VINCI S.A.; *Int'l*, pg. 8216
DAUPHIN PRECISION TOOL, LLC—See Talbot Holdings Inc.; *U.S. Private*, pg. 3925
DAUPHIN REALTY CORPORATION—See Berkshire Hathaway Inc.; *U.S. Public*, pg. 306
DAUPHIN REALTY OF MOBILE, INC.—See Berkshire Hathaway Inc.; *U.S. Public*, pg. 306
DAUPHIN-RIM POLSKA SP. Z O.O.—See Dauphin HumanDesign Group GmbH & Co. KG; *Int'l*, pg. 1983
DAUPHIN SCANDINAVIA A/S—See Dauphin HumanDesign Group GmbH & Co. KG; *Int'l*, pg. 1983
DAUPHIN (SEA) PTE. LTD.—See Dauphin HumanDesign Group GmbH & Co. KG; *Int'l*, pg. 1982
DAURA CAPITAL CORP.; *Int'l*, pg. 1983
DAUSIN ELECTRIC CO.; *U.S. Private*, pg. 1168
DAUTERIVE HOSPITAL—See HCA Healthcare, Inc.; *U.S. Public*, pg. 995
D-AUTO SUISSE SA—See Dogus Holding AS; *Int'l*, pg. 2154
DAVACO, INC.—See Crane Worldwide Logistics LLC; *U.S. Private*, pg. 1085
DAVALEN, LLC; *U.S. Private*, pg. 1168
DAVALL GEARS LTD.—See Illinois Tool Works Inc.; *U.S. Public*, pg. 1105
DAVALOR MOLD COMPANY, LLC—See Blackford Capital LLC; *U.S. Private*, pg. 574

COMPANY NAME INDEX

DAVANGERE SUGAR COMPANY LIMITED; *Int'l*, pg. 1983
DAVAO CENTRAL CHEMICAL CORPORATION—See Osaka Gas Co., Ltd.; *Int'l*, pg. 5646
DAVAO GULF MARINE SERVICES, INC.—See Chelsea Logistics and Infrastructure Holdings Corp.; *Int'l*, pg. 1460
DAVAO INTEGRATED PORT AND STEVEDORING SERVICES CORPORATION—See International Container Terminal Services, Inc.; *Int'l*, pg. 3746
DAVASO GMBH—See IQVIA Holdings Inc.; *U.S. Public*, pg. 1168
DAVASO HOLDING GMBH—See IQVIA Holdings Inc.; *U.S. Public*, pg. 1168
DAVCO ACQUISITION HOLDING INC.; *U.S. Private*, pg. 1168
DAVCO CONSTRUCTION MATERIALS PTY LIMITED—See Sika AG; *Int'l*, pg. 6915
DAVCO EQUIPMENT, INC.—See Flowserve Corporation; *U.S. Public*, pg. 855
DAVCO RESTAURANTS LLC—See DavCo Acquisition Holding Inc.; *U.S. Private*, pg. 1168
DAVCO TECHNOLOGY, LLC—See Penske Corporation; *U.S. Private*, pg. 3138
DAVE BREWER INC.; *U.S. Private*, pg. 1168
DAVE & BUSTER'S ENTERTAINMENT, INC.—See Keystone Group, L.P.; *U.S. Private*, pg. 2297
DAVE & BUSTER'S, INC.—See Keystone Group, L.P.; *U.S. Private*, pg. 2297
DAVE CANTIN GROUP, LLC; *U.S. Private*, pg. 1168
DAVE CARTER & ASSOCIATES, INC.; *U.S. Private*, pg. 1168
DAVE CUTRIGHT INSURANCE AGENCY—See Seeman Holtz Property & Casualty, LLC; *U.S. Private*, pg. 3598
DAVE DENNIS CHRYSLER JEEP DODGE; *U.S. Private*, pg. 1168
DAVE HAMILTON CHEVROLET-OLDS-JEEP INC.; *U.S. Private*, pg. 1168
DAVE INC.; *U.S. Public*, pg. 635
DAVE JONES, INC.; *U.S. Private*, pg. 1168
DAVE KNAPP FORD LINCOLN INC.; *U.S. Private*, pg. 1168
DAVE KRING CHEVROLET CADILLAC; *U.S. Private*, pg. 1168
DAV-EL LOS ANGELES, INC.—See Marcou Transportation Group LLC; *U.S. Private*, pg. 2572
DAV-EL SERVICES, INC.—See Marcou Transportation Group LLC; *U.S. Private*, pg. 2572
DAV-EL TRANSPORTATION, INC.—See Marcou Transportation Group LLC; *U.S. Private*, pg. 2572
DAVENHAM GROUP HOLDINGS PLC—See Davenham Group Plc; *Int'l*, pg. 1983
DAVENHAM GROUP PLC; *Int'l*, pg. 1983
DAVENHAM TRADE FINANCE LIMITED—See Davenham Group Plc; *Int'l*, pg. 1983
DAVENPORT & COMPANY LLC; *U.S. Private*, pg. 1169
DAVENPORT ENERGY INC.; *U.S. Private*, pg. 1169
DAVENPORT PAPER CO LIMITED—See Franz Haniel & Cie. GmbH; *Int'l*, pg. 2763
DAVENPORT UNION WAREHOUSE COMPANY; *U.S. Private*, pg. 1169
DAVE REISDORF INC.; *U.S. Private*, pg. 1168
DAVE'S CLAREMORE RV INC.—See Lazydays Holdings, Inc.; *U.S. Public*, pg. 1294
DAVE SINCLAIR FORD INC.; *U.S. Private*, pg. 1168
DAVE SINCLAIR LINCOLN MERCURY ST. PETERS INC.; *U.S. Private*, pg. 1168
DAVE—See The Engine Group; *Int'l*, pg. 7640
DAVE'S SPORTS CENTER, INC.; *U.S. Private*, pg. 1168
DAVE'S SUPERMARKET INC.; *U.S. Private*, pg. 1169
DAVE STEEL COMPANY INC.; *U.S. Private*, pg. 1168
DAVE SYVERSON INC.; *U.S. Private*, pg. 1168
DAVE SYVERSON TRUCK CENTER, INC.—See Dave Syverson Inc.; *U.S. Private*, pg. 1168
DAVE WHITE CHEVROLET, INC.; *U.S. Private*, pg. 1168
DAVE WILSON NURSERY, INC.; *U.S. Private*, pg. 1168
DAVEX AUSTRALIA PTY LTD—See Ekuiti Nasional Berhad; *Int'l*, pg. 2340
DAVEX ENGINEERING (M) SDN BHD—See Ekuiti Nasional Berhad; *Int'l*, pg. 2340
DAVEX HOLDINGS BERHAD—See MWE Holdings Berhad; *Int'l*, pg. 5110
DAVEX (MALAYSIA) SDN. BHD.—See Ekuiti Nasional Berhad; *Int'l*, pg. 2340
DAVEX SINGAPORE PTE LTD—See Ekuiti Nasional Berhad; *Int'l*, pg. 2340
DAVEY PRODUCTS NZ LIMITED—See Amotiv Limited; *Int'l*, pg. 431
DAVEY PRODUCTS PTY. LTD.—See Amotiv Limited; *Int'l*, pg. 431
DAVEY RESOURCE GROUP, INC.—See The Davey Tree Expert Company; *U.S. Private*, pg. 4018
DAVEY TREE EXPERT COMPANY OF CANADA, LTD.—See The Davey Tree Expert Company; *U.S. Private*, pg. 4018
THE DAVEY TREE EXPERT COMPANY; *U.S. Private*, pg. 4018
DAVEY TREE SURGERY COMPANY—See The Davey Tree Expert Company; *U.S. Private*, pg. 4018
DAVIAN CONSTRUCTION LTD.; *Int'l*, pg. 1983

DAVICOM SEMICONDUCTOR, INC.; *Int'l*, pg. 1983
DAVICTUS PLC; *Int'l*, pg. 1983
DAVID A. BRAMBLE, INC. - MASSEY FACILITY—See David A. Bramble, Inc.; *U.S. Private*, pg. 1169
DAVID A. BRAMBLE, INC.; *U.S. Private*, pg. 1169
DAVID A. CAMPBELL CORPORATION; *U.S. Private*, pg. 1169
DAVID ALLEN COMPANY INC.; *U.S. Private*, pg. 1169
DAVID A. NOYES & COMPANY; *U.S. Private*, pg. 1169
DAVID A. STRAZ JR. CENTER FOR THE PERFORMING ARTS; *U.S. Private*, pg. 1169
DAVID BARRETT PARTNERS LLC.—See BraddockMatthewsBarrett, LLC; *U.S. Private*, pg. 631
DAVID BIRNBAUM/RARE 1 CORPORATION; *U.S. Private*, pg. 1169
DAVID BOLAND, INC.; *U.S. Private*, pg. 1169
DAVID BROWN GEAR INDUSTRIES AUSTRALIA PTY. LTD.—See Clyde Blowers Capital IM LLP; *Int'l*, pg. 1665
DAVID BROWN GEAR SYSTEMS LIMITED—See Clyde Blowers Capital IM LLP; *Int'l*, pg. 1665
DAVID BRUCE AUTO CENTER INC.; *U.S. Private*, pg. 1169
DAVID C. GREENBAUM CO. INC.; *U.S. Private*, pg. 1169
DAVID CHAPMAN ASSOCIATES LTD.—See The Interpublic Group of Companies, Inc.; *U.S. Public*, pg. 2104
DAVID & CHARLES PLC—See RDA Holding Co.; *U.S. Private*, pg. 3363
DAVID CHEVROLET CORVETTE BUICK GMC LTD.; *Int'l*, pg. 1983
DAVID CLARK COMPANY INCORPORATED; *U.S. Private*, pg. 1169
DAVID CORPORATION—See TA Associates, Inc.; *U.S. Private*, pg. 3918
DAVID C. POOLE COMPANY INC.; *U.S. Private*, pg. 1169
DAVID DOBBS ENTERPRISES INC.; *U.S. Private*, pg. 1169
DAVID DRYE COMPANY LLC; *U.S. Private*, pg. 1169
DAVIDE CAMPARI-MILANO N.V.—See Alicros S.p.A.; *Int'l*, pg. 327
DAVID-EDWARD COMPANY LTD.; *U.S. Private*, pg. 1171
DAVIDE GROPPI S.R.L.—See Dexelance S.p.A.; *Int'l*, pg. 2092
DAVID E. HARVEY BUILDERS INC.; *U.S. Private*, pg. 1170
DAVID ELECTRONICS CO., LTD.—See Chant Sincere Co., Ltd.; *Int'l*, pg. 1446
DAVID ENERGY SYSTEMS, INC.; *U.S. Private*, pg. 1170
DAVID & GOLIATH, INC.; *U.S. Private*, pg. 1169
DAVID & GOLIATH, LLC—See Innocean Worldwide Inc.; *Int'l*, pg. 3709
DAVID GOODING INC.; *U.S. Private*, pg. 1170
DAVID HART AEROSPACE PIPES LIMITED—See Leggett & Platt, Incorporated; *U.S. Public*, pg. 1301
DAVID H. FELL & COMPANY INCORPORATED; *U.S. Private*, pg. 1170
DAVID HOBBS HONDA; *U.S. Private*, pg. 1170
DAVID HOCKER & ASSOCIATES, INC.; *U.S. Private*, pg. 1170
DAVID I. PETERSON INC.; *U.S. Private*, pg. 1170
DAVID JAMES GROUP LTD.; *U.S. Private*, pg. 1170
DAVID J. FRANK LANDSCAPE CONTRACTING, INC.; *U.S. Private*, pg. 1170
THE DAVID J. JOSEPH COMPANY—See Nucor Corporation; *U.S. Public*, pg. 1554
DAVID JOHN GLUCKLE INSURANCE AGENCY LLC; *U.S. Private*, pg. 1170
DAVID JONES (ADELAIDE) PTY LIMITED—See Woolworths Holdings Limited; *Int'l*, pg. 8452
DAVID JONES EMPLOYEE SHARE PLAN PTY LIMITED—See Woolworths Holdings Limited; *Int'l*, pg. 8452
DAVID JONES INSURANCE PTY LIMITED—See Woolworths Holdings Limited; *Int'l*, pg. 8453
DAVID JONES LIMITED—See Woolworths Holdings Limited; *Int'l*, pg. 8452
DAVID JONES PROPERTIES PTY LIMITED—See Woolworths Holdings Limited; *Int'l*, pg. 8453
DAVID J. STANTON AND ASSOCIATES; *U.S. Private*, pg. 1170
DAVID K. BURNAP ADVERTISING AGENCY, INC.; *U.S. Private*, pg. 1170
DAVID KEIGHLEY PRODUCTIONS 70MM INC.—See Imax Corporation; *Int'l*, pg. 3620
DAVID KURLAN & ASSOCIATES, INC.; *U.S. Private*, pg. 1170
DAVID LERNER ASSOCIATES INC.; *U.S. Private*, pg. 1170
DAVID LEWIS ASSOCIATES INC.; *U.S. Private*, pg. 1170
DAVID LEWIS CIVIL ENGINEERING LTD.—See Renew Holdings plc; *Int'l*, pg. 6278
DAVID LLOYD LEISURE LTD.—See TDR Capital LLP; *Int'l*, pg. 7494
DAVID LYNG & ASSOCIATES, INC.; *U.S. Private*, pg. 1170
DAVID MARTIN & ASSOCIATES; *U.S. Private*, pg. 1170
DAVID MCDAVID ACURA OF AUSTIN—See David McDavid Automotive Group; *U.S. Private*, pg. 1170

DAVID MCDAVID ACURA—See David McDavid Automotive Group; *U.S. Private*, pg. 1170
DAVID MCDAVID AUTOMOTIVE GROUP; *U.S. Private*, pg. 1170
DAVID MCDAVID AUTOMOTIVE GROUP—See Asbury Automotive Group, Inc.; *U.S. Public*, pg. 209
DAVID MCDAVID GMC—See David McDavid Automotive Group; *U.S. Private*, pg. 1170
DAVID MCDAVID HONDA—See David McDavid Automotive Group; *U.S. Private*, pg. 1170
DAVID MCDAVID NISSAN—See David McDavid Automotive Group; *U.S. Private*, pg. 1171
DAVID MCDAVID PLANO LINCOLN—See David McDavid Automotive Group; *U.S. Private*, pg. 1171
DAVID MCDERMOTT CHEVROLET—See McDermott Auto Group; *U.S. Private*, pg. 2631
DAVID MCDERMOTT OF NEW HAVEN—See McDermott Auto Group; *U.S. Private*, pg. 2631
DAVID MEISTER—See Sun Capital Partners, Inc.; *U.S. Private*, pg. 3859
DAVID MICHAEL EUROPE S.A.S.—See International Flavors & Fragrances Inc.; *U.S. Public*, pg. 1154
DAVID MILLER FROZEN FOODS LIMITED—See Kitwave Group Plc; *Int'l*, pg. 4196
DAVID MONTOYA CONSTRUCTION, INC.; *U.S. Private*, pg. 1171
DAVID MORRIS FINE CARS LTD.; *Int'l*, pg. 1983
DAVID MORSE & ASSOCIATES; *U.S. Private*, pg. 1171
DAVIDOFF & CIE. SA—See Oettinger IMEX AG; *Int'l*, pg. 5529
DAVIDOFF DISTRIBUTION (UK) LTD.—See Oettinger IMEX AG; *Int'l*, pg. 5529
DAVIDOFF OF GENEVA AUSTRIA GMBH—See Oettinger IMEX AG; *Int'l*, pg. 5529
DAVIDOFF OF GENEVA BENELUX SA/NV—See Oettinger IMEX AG; *Int'l*, pg. 5530
DAVIDOFF OF GENEVA (CC) INC.—See Oettinger IMEX AG; *Int'l*, pg. 5529
DAVIDOFF OF GENEVA FRANCE S.A.R.L.—See Oettinger IMEX AG; *Int'l*, pg. 5530
DAVIDOFF OF GENEVA GERMANY GMBH—See Oettinger IMEX AG; *Int'l*, pg. 5530
DAVIDOFF OF GENEVA HONG KONG LTD.—See Oettinger IMEX AG; *Int'l*, pg. 5530
DAVIDOFF OF GENEVA IBERIA SL—See Oettinger IMEX AG; *Int'l*, pg. 5530
DAVIDOFF OF GENEVA JAPAN K.K.—See Oettinger IMEX AG; *Int'l*, pg. 5530
DAVIDOFF OF GENEVA LUXEMBOURG SARL—See Oettinger IMEX AG; *Int'l*, pg. 5530
DAVIDOFF OF GENEVA MALAYSIA SDN. BHD.—See Oettinger IMEX AG; *Int'l*, pg. 5530
DAVIDOFF OF GENEVA (NY) INC.—See Oettinger IMEX AG; *Int'l*, pg. 5529
DAVIDOFF OF GENEVA RUSSIA LLC—See Oettinger IMEX AG; *Int'l*, pg. 5530
DAVIDOFF OF GENEVA SINGAPORE PTE. LTD.—See Oettinger IMEX AG; *Int'l*, pg. 5530
DAVIDOFF OF GENEVA USA, INC.—See Oettinger IMEX AG; *Int'l*, pg. 5530
DAVID O'KEEFE STUDIOS INC.; *U.S. Private*, pg. 1171
DAVIDON HOMES LTD.; *U.S. Private*, pg. 1171
DAVID OPPENHEIMER & COMPANY I, LLC—See David Oppenheimer & Company; *Int'l*, pg. 1983
DAVID OPPENHEIMER & COMPANY; *Int'l*, pg. 1983
DAVID PAJIC DAKA A.D.; *Int'l*, pg. 1983
DAVID PEARSON ASSOCIATES; *U.S. Private*, pg. 1171
DAVID PEYSER SPORTSWEAR INC.; *U.S. Private*, pg. 1171
DAVID RICE AUTO SALES; *U.S. Private*, pg. 1171
DAVID R. MCGEORGE CAR CO. INC.; *U.S. Private*, pg. 1171
DAVID R. WEBB COMPANY, INC.—See Danzer AG; *Int'l*, pg. 1970
DAVID'S BRIDAL, LLC—See CION Investment Corporation; *U.S. Public*, pg. 496
DAVID S. DE LUZ SR ENTERPRISES; *U.S. Private*, pg. 1171
DAVIDSON CAMERON BOARD & SIMMONS PTY. LTD.—See Nutrien Ltd.; *Int'l*, pg. 5492
DAVIDSON CAMERON CLYDSDALE & CO. PTY. LTD.—See Nutrien Ltd.; *Int'l*, pg. 5492
DAVIDSON CAMERON & CO. NARRABRI PTY. LTD.—See Nutrien Ltd.; *Int'l*, pg. 5492
DAVIDSON CAMERON MCCULLOCH PTY. LTD.—See Nutrien Ltd.; *Int'l*, pg. 5492
DAVIDSON CAMERON PTY. LTD.—See Nutrien Ltd.; *Int'l*, pg. 5492
DAVIDSON CHEVROLET INC.; *U.S. Private*, pg. 1171
DAVIDSON CHEVROLET; *U.S. Private*, pg. 1171
DAVIDSON ENGINEERING, INC.; *U.S. Private*, pg. 1171
DAVIDSON ENMAN LUMBER LTD.; *Int'l*, pg. 1984
DAVIDSON FAMILY MEDICINE, P.A.—See Alo Solutions, LLC; *U.S. Private*, pg. 195
DAVIDSON FIXED INCOME MANAGEMENT, INC.—See D.A. Davidson Companies; *U.S. Private*, pg. 1140
DAVIDSON HEALTH CARE, INC.; *U.S. Private*, pg. 1171
DAVIDSON HOLDING CO.; *U.S. Private*, pg. 1171

DAVIDSON HOLDING CO.

CORPORATE AFFILIATIONS

DAVIDSON HOTEL COMPANY LLC—See Nautic Partners, LLC; *U.S. Private*, pg. 2868
DAVIDSON INSULATION & ACOUSTICS; *U.S. Private*, pg. 1171
DAVIDSON INVESTMENT ADVISORS, INC.—See D.A. Davidson Companies; *U.S. Private*, pg. 1140
DAVIDSON KEMPNER CAPITAL MANAGEMENT LP; *U.S. Private*, pg. 1172
DAVIDSON-KENNEDY CO.; *U.S. Private*, pg. 1172
DAVIDSON OIL COMPANY INC.; *U.S. Private*, pg. 1172
DAVIDSON ORGANICS, LLC; *U.S. Private*, pg. 1172
DAVIDSON PIPE COMPANY INC.—See Ferguson plc; *Int'l*, pg. 2637
DAVIDSON PIPE SUPPLY CO. INC.—See Ferguson plc; *Int'l*, pg. 2637
DAVIDSON PROPERTIES, INC.—See Apartment Investment and Management Company; *U.S. Public*, pg. 144
DAVIDSON REALTY, INC.; *U.S. Private*, pg. 1172
DAVIDSON'S INC.; *U.S. Private*, pg. 1172
DAVIDSON'S OF DUNDEE; *U.S. Private*, pg. 1172
DAVIDSON TECHNOLOGIES, INC.; *U.S. Private*, pg. 1172
DAVIDSON TRUST CO.—See D.A. Davidson Companies; *U.S. Private*, pg. 1140
DAVIDSON WATER INC.; *U.S. Private*, pg. 1172
DAVID S. SMITH AMERICA INC—See Sealed Air Corporation; *U.S. Public*, pg. 1853
DAVIDS SUPERMARKETS INC.; *U.S. Private*, pg. 1171
DAVIDSTEA INC.; *Int'l*, pg. 1984
DAVIDSTEA (USA) INC.—See DAVIDsTEA Inc.; *Int'l*, pg. 1984
DAVID T. CHASE ENTERPRISES INC.—See Chase Enterprises, Inc.; *U.S. Private*, pg. 859
DAVID WEEKLEY HOMES, LP; *U.S. Private*, pg. 1171
DAVID WHITE, LLC—See Robert Bosch GmbH; *Int'l*, pg. 6364
DAVID WILSON AUTOMOTIVE GROUP; *U.S. Private*, pg. 1171
DAVID WILSON HOMES (NORTH MIDLANDS) LIMITED—See Barratt Developments PLC; *Int'l*, pg. 868
DAVID WILSON HOMES (SOUTHERN) LIMITED—See Barratt Developments PLC; *Int'l*, pg. 868
DAVID WILSON HOMES (SOUTH MIDLANDS) LIMITED—See Barratt Developments PLC; *Int'l*, pg. 868
DAVID WILSON HOMES YORKSHIRE LIMITED—See Barratt Developments PLC; *Int'l*, pg. 868
DAVID WOOD BAKING LIMITED; *Int'l*, pg. 1983
DAVID X. MANNERS CO., INC.; *U.S. Private*, pg. 1171
DAVID Z INTERNET, INC.; *U.S. Private*, pg. 1171
DAVIE COUNTY ENTERPRISE-RECORD—See Evening Post Publishing Co.; *U.S. Private*, pg. 1436
DAVIE MEDICAL CENTER, LLC—See HCA Healthcare, Inc.; *U.S. Public*, pg. 995
DAVIES COLLISON CAVE ASIA PTE LTD—See Adamantem Capital Management Pty Limited; *Int'l*, pg. 124
DAVIES CONSULTING INC.—See Accenture plc; *Int'l*, pg. 86
DAVIES GROUP LIMITED—See HGGC, LLC; *U.S. Private*, pg. 1929
DAVIES MOLDING LLC—See The Heico Companies, L.L.C.; *U.S. Private*, pg. 4050
DAVIESMOORE; *U.S. Private*, pg. 1172
DAVIES ODELL LTD.—See Vale Brothers Holdings Limited; *Int'l*, pg. 8111
DAVIES, PACHECO & MURPHY ADVERTISING AGENCY, INC.; *U.S. Private*, pg. 1172
DAVIESS-MARTIN COUNTY RURAL ELECTRIC MEMBERSHIP CORPORATION; *U.S. Private*, pg. 1172
DAVIES; *U.S. Private*, pg. 1172
DAVIE YARDS ASA; *Int'l*, pg. 1984
DAVIGEL BELGILUX S.A.—See Nestle S.A.; *Int'l*, pg. 5202
DAVIGEL BELIGUM S.A.—See Sysco Corporation; *U.S. Public*, pg. 1973
DAVIGEL ESPANA S.A.—See Nestle S.A.; *Int'l*, pg. 5202
DAVIGEL SAS—See Sysco Corporation; *U.S. Public*, pg. 1973
DAVI II FARMACEUTICA S.A.; *Int'l*, pg. 1983
DAVI LUXURY BRAND GROUP, INC.; *U.S. Public*, pg. 635
DAVINCI 3D A/S—See SP Group A/S; *Int'l*, pg. 7122
DA VINCI CAPITAL LLC; *Int'l*, pg. 1902
DAVINCI CONSULTING AS—See Devoteam SA; *Int'l*, pg. 2089
DA VINCI HEALTHCARE, INC.—See The Ensign Group, Inc.; *U.S. Public*, pg. 2070
DAVINCI ROOFSCAPES, LLC—See Westlake Corporation; *U.S. Public*, pg. 2360
DAVINCI SELECTWORK; *U.S. Private*, pg. 1172
DA VINCI STONE CRAFT LTD.—See Parsiena Design, Inc.; *Int'l*, pg. 5748
DAVINCI VIRTUAL, L.L.C.—See Instant Group Limited; *Int'l*, pg. 3723
DAVIS ADVERTISING, INC.; *U.S. Private*, pg. 1173
DAVIS & ASSOCIATES, INC.; *U.S. Private*, pg. 1172
DAVIS AUTOMOTIVE GROUP; *U.S. Private*, pg. 1173
DAVIS BARONE AGENCY; *U.S. Private*, pg. 1173

DAVIS BEWS DESIGN GROUP, INC.; *U.S. Private*, pg. 1173
DAVIS BOAT WORKS INC.; *U.S. Private*, pg. 1173
DAVIS BRODY BOND, LLP.—See Page Southerland Page, Inc.; *U.S. Private*, pg. 3074
DAVIS BUSINESS UNIT—See Douglas Machine, Inc.; *U.S. Private*, pg. 1267
DAVIS CARGO LLC; *U.S. Private*, pg. 1173
DAVIS CARTAGE CO.; *U.S. Private*, pg. 1173
DAVIS & CO. INC.—See Davis & Company; *U.S. Private*, pg. 1172
DAVISCO INTERNATIONAL INC.; *U.S. Private*, pg. 1175
DAVIS COMMODITIES LIMITED; *Int'l*, pg. 1984
DAVISCOMMS (MALAYSIA) SDN. BHD.—See MWE Holdings Berhad; *Int'l*, pg. 5110
DAVISCOMMS (S) PTE. LTD.—See MWE Holdings Berhad; *Int'l*, pg. 5110
THE DAVIS COMPANIES INC.; *U.S. Private*, pg. 4018
THE DAVIS COMPANIES INC.—See The Davis Companies Inc.; *U.S. Private*, pg. 4018
DAVIS COMPANIES—See The Davis Companies Inc.; *U.S. Private*, pg. 4018
DAVIS COMPANIES—See The Davis Companies Inc.; *U.S. Private*, pg. 4018
DAVIS COMPANY INC.; *U.S. Private*, pg. 1173
DAVIS & COMPANY; *U.S. Private*, pg. 1172
DAVIS CONSTRUCTION, INC.; *U.S. Private*, pg. 1173
DAVIS COUNTY CO-OPERATIVE SOCIETY; *U.S. Private*, pg. 1173
DAVISDENNY ADVERTISING & RELATED SERVICES, INC.; *U.S. Private*, pg. 1175
DAVIS DEVELOPMENT, INC.; *U.S. Private*, pg. 1173
DAVIS DIALYSIS, LLC—See DaVita Inc.; *U.S. Public*, pg. 638
DAVIS DISTRIBUTORS, LLC—See Davis Selected Advisors, L.P.; *U.S. Private*, pg. 1174
DAVIS DRYWALL, INC.—See Swanson & Youngdale Inc.; *U.S. Private*, pg. 3890
DAVIS-ELEN ADVERTISING, INC.; *U.S. Private*, pg. 1174
DAVIS-ELEN ADVERTISING, INC.—See Davis-Elen Advertising, Inc.; *U.S. Private*, pg. 1174
DAVIS-ELEN ADVERTISING, INC.—See Davis-Elen Advertising, Inc.; *U.S. Private*, pg. 1174
DAVIS ENERGY GROUP, INC.—See Gas Technology Institute; *U.S. Private*, pg. 1647
DAVIS ENTERPRISES; *U.S. Private*, pg. 1173
DAVIS ERECTION CO. INC.—See Ridgetop Holding Co., Inc.; *U.S. Private*, pg. 3433
DAVIS FIRE PROTECTION CO., INC.—See Joseph Davis, Inc.; *U.S. Private*, pg. 2236
DAVIS & FLOYD, INC.; *U.S. Private*, pg. 1172
DAVIS FOODTOWN INC.; *U.S. Private*, pg. 1173
DAVIS-FROST INC.; *U.S. Private*, pg. 1174
DAVIS FURNITURE, INC.; *U.S. Private*, pg. 1173
DAVIS-GARVIN AGENCY, INC.—See GTCR LLC; *U.S. Private*, pg. 1802
DAVIS GAS PROCESSING, INC.—See J.L. Davis Companies; *U.S. Private*, pg. 2167
THE DAVIS GROUP INC.; *U.S. Private*, pg. 4018
DAVIS HARRISON DION, INC.; *U.S. Private*, pg. 1173
DAVIS H. ELLIOT COMPANY INC.; *U.S. Private*, pg. 1173
DAVIS H. ELLIOT CONSTRUCTION COMPANY, INC.—See Davis H. Elliot Company Inc.; *U.S. Private*, pg. 1173
DAVIS HYUNDAI; *U.S. Private*, pg. 1173
DAVIS INDUSTRIES II, LLC; *U.S. Private*, pg. 1173
DAVIS JEFFERSON ELECTRIC COOP; *U.S. Private*, pg. 1173
DAVIS & KUELTHAU, S.C.—See Amundsen Davis LLC; *U.S. Private*, pg. 269
DAVIS LANDSCAPE, LLC; *U.S. Private*, pg. 1173
DAVIS LANGDON LLP—See AECOM; *U.S. Public*, pg. 51
DAVISLOGIC INC—See Jogan, Inc.; *U.S. Private*, pg. 2219
DAVIS MINING & MANUFACTURING INC.; *U.S. Private*, pg. 1173
DAVIS MOORE AUTO GROUP, INC.; *U.S. Private*, pg. 1174
DAVIS-MOORE AUTOMOTIVE, INC.; *U.S. Private*, pg. 1174
DAVIS-MOORE CHEVROLET, INC.—See Davis-Moore Automotive, Inc.; *U.S. Private*, pg. 1175
DAVISON & ASSOCIATES (NI) LIMITED—See Brown & Brown, Inc.; *U.S. Public*, pg. 400
DAVISON INSURANCE AGENCY, LLC—See Origin Bancorp, Inc.; *U.S. Public*, pg. 1617
DAVISON OIL COMPANY INC.; *U.S. Private*, pg. 1175
DAVISON TRANSPORT INC.; *U.S. Private*, pg. 1175
DAVIS PAINT COMPANY; *U.S. Private*, pg. 1174
DAVIS PIPE & SUPPLY, INC.—See Leonard Green & Partners, L.P.; *U.S. Private*, pg. 2429
DAVIS POLK & WARDWELL LLP; *U.S. Private*, pg. 1174
DAVIS SECURITY SERVICES INC.—See Owen Security Solutions Inc.; *U.S. Private*, pg. 3054
DAVIS SELECTED ADVISERS-NY, INC.—See Davis Selected Advisors, L.P.; *U.S. Private*, pg. 1174
DAVIS SELECTED ADVISORS, L.P.; *U.S. Private*, pg. 1174

DAVIS & SONS CONSTRUCTION CO. LLC; *U.S. Private*, pg. 1172
DAVIS-STANDARD, LLC - EGAN—See ONEX Corporation; *Int'l*, pg. 5578
DAVIS-STANDARD, LLC - FULTON—See ONEX Corporation; *Int'l*, pg. 5578
DAVIS-STANDARD, LLC—See ONEX Corporation; *Int'l*, pg. 5578
DAVIS STRATEGIC INNOVATIONS, INC.; *U.S. Private*, pg. 1174
DAVIS TOOL INC.—See Bertram Capital Management, LLC; *U.S. Private*, pg. 539
DAVIS TRANSFER CO. INC.; *U.S. Private*, pg. 1174
DAVIS TRANSFER LOGISTICS INC.—See Deutsche Bahn AG; *Int'l*, pg. 2054
DAVIS TRANSPORT INC.; *U.S. Private*, pg. 1174
DAVISTRAPP LLC—See FederalConference.com; *U.S. Private*, pg. 1491
DAVIS TRUCKING, LLC; *U.S. Private*, pg. 1174
DAVIS TYPEWRITER COMPANY, INC.—See McNally Operations LLC; *U.S. Private*, pg. 2643
DAVIS-ULMER SPRINKLER CO.—See APi Group Corporation; *Int'l*, pg. 513
DAVIS WHOLESALE ELECTRIC INC.; *U.S. Private*, pg. 1174
DAVIS WHOLESALE SUPPLY INC.; *U.S. Private*, pg. 1174
DAVIS WIRE CORPORATION—See HEICO Corporation; *U.S. Public*, pg. 1019
DAVIS WOOD PRODUCTS, INC.-MISSISSIPPI DIVISION—See Davis Wood Products, Inc.; *U.S. Private*, pg. 1174
DAVIS WOOD PRODUCTS, INC.; *U.S. Private*, pg. 1174
DAVIS WRIGHT TREMAINE LLP; *U.S. Private*, pg. 1174
DAVITA AGUAS CLARAS SERVICOS DE NEFROLOGIA LTDA.—See DaVita Inc.; *U.S. Public*, pg. 637
DAVITA AMERY DIALYSIS, LLC—See DaVita Inc.; *U.S. Public*, pg. 637
DAVITA AMHERST DIALYSIS CENTER—See DaVita Inc.; *U.S. Public*, pg. 637
DAVITA APAC HOLDING B.V.—See DaVita Inc.; *U.S. Public*, pg. 637
DAVITA BAURU SERVICOS DE NEFROLOGIA LTDA.—See DaVita Inc.; *U.S. Public*, pg. 637
DAVITA BEVERLY DIALYSIS—See DaVita Inc.; *U.S. Public*, pg. 637
DAVITA CARE (INDIA) PRIVATE LIMITED—See DaVita Inc.; *U.S. Public*, pg. 637
DAVITA CEILANDIA SERVICOS DE NEFROLOGIA LTDA.—See DaVita Inc.; *U.S. Public*, pg. 637
DAVITA CLINICAL RESEARCH—See DaVita Inc.; *U.S. Public*, pg. 637
DAVITA DAKOTA DIALYSIS CENTER, LLC—See DaVita Inc.; *U.S. Public*, pg. 637
DAVITA DESERT SPRINGS DIALYSIS—See DaVita Inc.; *U.S. Public*, pg. 637
DAVITA DEUTSCHLAND GMBH—See DaVita Inc.; *U.S. Public*, pg. 637
DAVITA DIALYSIS, LLC—See DaVita Inc.; *U.S. Public*, pg. 637
DAVITA EL PASO EAST, L.P.—See DaVita Inc.; *U.S. Public*, pg. 637
DAVITA HEALTHCARE PARTNERS PLAN, INC.—See DaVita Inc.; *U.S. Public*, pg. 637
DAVITA HIGHLAND RANCH DIALYSIS CENTER—See DaVita Inc.; *U.S. Public*, pg. 637
DAVITA INC.; *U.S. Public*, pg. 635
DAVITA KEY WEST DIALYSIS—See DaVita Inc.; *U.S. Public*, pg. 637
DAVITA KIDNEY CARE—See DaVita Inc.; *U.S. Public*, pg. 637
DAVITA MEDICAL ACO CALIFORNIA, LLC—See DaVita Inc.; *U.S. Public*, pg. 637
DAVITA MEDICAL CENTER—See DaVita Inc.; *U.S. Public*, pg. 637
DAVITA MEDICAL GROUP HEALTH INFORMATION MANAGEMENT—See UnitedHealth Group Incorporated; *U.S. Public*, pg. 2243
DAVITA MEDICAL GROUP SOUTH FLORIDA, LLC—See UnitedHealth Group Incorporated; *U.S. Public*, pg. 2243
DAVITA NEPHROLIFE (INDIA) PRIVATE LIMITED—See DaVita Inc.; *U.S. Public*, pg. 637
DAVITA NORTHWEST DIALYSIS CENTER—See DaVita Inc.; *U.S. Public*, pg. 637
DAVITA PASADENA FOOTHILLS DIALYSIS—See DaVita Inc.; *U.S. Public*, pg. 637
DAVITA PDI JOHNSTOWN—See DaVita Inc.; *U.S. Public*, pg. 637
DAVITA PRYOR DIALYSIS—See DaVita Inc.; *U.S. Public*, pg. 637
DAVITA RIDDLE DIALYSIS CENTER—See DaVita Inc.; *U.S. Public*, pg. 637
DAVITA-RIVERSIDE II, LLC—See DaVita Inc.; *U.S. Public*, pg. 638
DAVITA S.A.S.—See DaVita Inc.; *U.S. Public*, pg. 637
DAVITA SERVICOS DE NEFROLOGIA BOA VISTA LTDA.—See DaVita Inc.; *U.S. Public*, pg. 637

COMPANY NAME INDEX

DAVITA SERVICOS DE NEFROLOGIA BOTAFOGO LTDA.—See DaVita Inc.; *U.S. Public*, pg. 637
DAVITA SERVICOS DE NEFROLOGIA CAMPO GRANDE LTDA.—See DaVita Inc.; *U.S. Public*, pg. 638
DAVITA SERVICOS DE NEFROLOGIA CUIABA LTDA.—See DaVita Inc.; *U.S. Public*, pg. 638
DAVITA SERVICOS DE NEFROLOGIA DE ARARAQUARA LTDA.—See DaVita Inc.; *U.S. Public*, pg. 638
DAVITA SERVICOS DE NEFROLOGIA JARDIM DAS IMBUIAS LTDA.—See DaVita Inc.; *U.S. Public*, pg. 638
DAVITA SERVICOS DE NEFROLOGIA JOAO DIAS LTDA.—See DaVita Inc.; *U.S. Public*, pg. 638
DAVITA SERVICOS DE NEFROLOGIA PACINI LTDA.—See DaVita Inc.; *U.S. Public*, pg. 638
DAVITA SERVICOS DE NEFROLOGIA PENHA LTDA.—See DaVita Inc.; *U.S. Public*, pg. 638
DAVITA SERVICOS DE NEFROLOGIA RECIFE LTDA.—See DaVita Inc.; *U.S. Public*, pg. 638
DAVITA SERVICOS DE NEFROLOGIA SANTOS DUMONT LTDA.—See DaVita Inc.; *U.S. Public*, pg. 638
DAVITA SERVICOS DE NEFROLOGIA SANTOS LTDA.—See DaVita Inc.; *U.S. Public*, pg. 638
DAVITA SERVICOS DE NEFROLOGIA SUMARE LTDA.—See DaVita Inc.; *U.S. Public*, pg. 638
DAVITA TIDEWATER-VIRGINIA BEACH, LLC—See DaVita Inc.; *U.S. Public*, pg. 638
DAVITA TOWN & COUNTY WEST AT HOME—See DaVita Inc.; *U.S. Public*, pg. 638
DAVITA VILLAGEHEALTH OF OHIO, INC.—See DaVita Inc.; *U.S. Public*, pg. 638
THE DAVITT & HANSER MUSIC CO.—See Hanser Holdings International; *U.S. Private*, pg. 1856
DAVIZTA, INC.—See Nordic Capital AB; *Int'l*, pg. 5420
DAVLER MEDIA GROUP, LLC; *U.S. Private*, pg. 1175
DAVLEY DARMEX PRECISION LUBRICANTS—See Roto-Precision Inc.; *Int'l*, pg. 6405
DAVLYN INDUSTRIES INC.—See Shiseido Company, Limited; *Int'l*, pg. 6854
DAVMES,S.A.—See Nefinsa S.A.; *Int'l*, pg. 5192
DAVOIL INC.; *U.S. Private*, pg. 1175
DAVOL INC.—See Becton, Dickinson & Company; *U.S. Public*, pg. 291
DAVOLINK INC.; *Int'l*, pg. 1984
DAVOS LIFE SCIENCE MARKETING PTE LTD—See Kuala Lumpur Kepong Berhad; *Int'l*, pg. 4318
DAVOS LIFE SCIENCE PTE LTD—See Kuala Lumpur Kepong Berhad; *Int'l*, pg. 4318
DAV PRODUCTIONS, INC.; *U.S. Private*, pg. 1168
DAV PROFESSIONAL PLACEMENT GROUP (PTY) LIMITED—See Adcorp Holdings Limited; *Int'l*, pg. 127
DAV S.A.—See Valeo S.A.; *Int'l*, pg. 8112
DAV TUNISIE SA—See Valeo S.A.; *Int'l*, pg. 8112
DAVY PROCESS TECHNOLOGY LIMITED—See Johnson Matthey PLC; *Int'l*, pg. 3991
DAVY SECURITIES LTD—See J&E Davy Holdings Limited; *Int'l*, pg. 3853
DAW CONSTRUCTION GROUP, LLC; *U.S. Private*, pg. 1175
DAWES CYCLES LIMITED—See Tandem Group PLC; *Int'l*, pg. 7456
DAWE'S LABORATORIES; *U.S. Private*, pg. 1175
DAWES UNDERWRITING AUSTRALIA PTY. LIMITED—See Steadfast Group Limited; *Int'l*, pg. 7187
D.A. WHITACRE CONSTRUCTION, INC.; *U.S. Private*, pg. 1141
DAWMEC LIMITED—See GEA Group Aktiengesellschaft; *Int'l*, pg. 2897
DAWN ASSOCIATES INC.; *U.S. Private*, pg. 1175
DAWN CORPORATION; *Int'l*, pg. 1984
DAWN ENTERPRISES INCORPORATED; *U.S. Private*, pg. 1175
DAWNEY & CO., LTD.; *Int'l*, pg. 1984
DAWNFIELD PTE. LTD.—See Insas Berhad; *Int'l*, pg. 3718
DAWN FOOD PRODUCTS (CANADA), LTD.—See Dawn Food Products, Inc.; *U.S. Private*, pg. 1175
DAWN FOOD PRODUCTS, INC.; *U.S. Private*, pg. 1175
DAWN FOODS B.V.—See Dawn Food Products, Inc.; *U.S. Private*, pg. 1175
DAWN HODGE ASSOCIATES LIMITED—See Sheikh Holdings Group (Investments) Limited; *Int'l*, pg. 6793
DAWN HOMES LIMITED—See Springfield Properties PLC; *Int'l*, pg. 7144
DAWNING INFORMATION INDUSTRY CO., LTD.; *Int'l*, pg. 1984
DAWNING TECHNOLOGY INC.—See SYSTEX Corporation; *Int'l*, pg. 7393
DAWN KITCHEN FITTINGS (PROPRIETARY) LIMITED—See DISTRIBUTION AND WAREHOUSING NETWORK LIMITED; *Int'l*, pg. 2136
DAWN OF HOPE, INC.; *U.S. Private*, pg. 1175
DAWN PATROL PARTNERS, LLC; *U.S. Private*, pg. 1175
DAWN PROPERTIES LIMITED; *Int'l*, pg. 1984
DAWN PROPERTY CONSULTANCY—See Dawn Properties Limited; *Int'l*, pg. 1984
DAWNRAYS PHARMACEUTICAL (HOLDINGS) LTD; *Int'l*, pg. 1984
DAWONALLOY CO., LTD.—See PJ Metal Co., Ltd.; *Int'l*, pg. 5877
DAWON NEXVIEW CO.,LTD.; *Int'l*, pg. 1984

DAWONSYS CO., LTD. - GIMCHEON FACTORY—See Dawonsys Co., Ltd.; *Int'l*, pg. 1984
DAWONSYS CO., LTD.; *Int'l*, pg. 1984
DAWOOD CORPORATION (PVT.) LTD.; *Int'l*, pg. 1984
DAWOOD EQUITIES LIMITED; *Int'l*, pg. 1984
DAWOOD FAMILY TAKAFUL LIMITED—See B.R.R. Guardian Modaraba; *Int'l*, pg. 790
DAWOOD HERCULES CHEMICALS - SHEIKHUPURA—See Dawood Corporation (Pvt.) Ltd.; *Int'l*, pg. 1984
DAWOOD HERCULES CORPORATION LIMITED—See Dawood Corporation (Pvt.) Ltd.; *Int'l*, pg. 1984
DAWOOD LAWRENCEPUR LIMITED—See Dawood Corporation (Pvt.) Ltd.; *Int'l*, pg. 1984
DAWS MANUFACTURING INC.; *U.S. Private*, pg. 1175
DAWSON & ASSOCIATES, INC.—See HS Holdings, LLC; *U.S. Private*, pg. 1998
DAWSON BOOKS LTD—See Smiths News PLC; *Int'l*, pg. 7013
DAWSON BUILDING CONTRACTORS, INC.; *U.S. Private*, pg. 1175
DAWSON CASHMERE LLC—See Dawson International PLC; *Int'l*, pg. 1984
DAWSON COMPANIES—See GTCR LLC; *U.S. Private*, pg. 1803
DAWSON CONSTRUCTION INC.; *U.S. Private*, pg. 1175
DAWSON COUNTY PUBLIC POWER DISTRICT; *U.S. Private*, pg. 1176
DAWSON DIALYSIS, LLC—See DaVita Inc.; *U.S. Public*, pg. 638
DAWSON FABRICS LTD.—See Dawson International PLC; *Int'l*, pg. 1984
DAWSON FRANCE SAS—See Aurelius Equity Opportunities SE & Co. KGaA; *Int'l*, pg. 708
DAWSON GEOPHYSICAL COMPANY—See Wilks Brothers LLC; *U.S. Private*, pg. 4521
DAWSON HOLDINGS LIMITED—See Smiths News PLC; *Int'l*, pg. 7013
DAWSON INTERNATIONAL PLC; *Int'l*, pg. 1984
DAWSON LOGISTICS; *U.S. Private*, pg. 1176
DAWSON MANUFACTURING COMPANY; *U.S. Private*, pg. 1176
DAWSON MEDIA DIRECT—See Smiths News PLC; *Int'l*, pg. 7013
DAWSON METAL COMPANY INC.; *U.S. Private*, pg. 1176
DAWSON MMP LIMITED—See Ali Holding S.r.l.; *Int'l*, pg. 321
DAWSON OIL CO., INC.; *U.S. Private*, pg. 1176
DAWSON OPERATING COMPANY—See Wilks Brothers LLC; *U.S. Private*, pg. 4521
DAWSON RESOURCES, INC.; *U.S. Private*, pg. 1176
DAWSON SEISMIC SERVICES ULC—See Wilks Brothers LLC; *U.S. Private*, pg. 4521
DAW TECHNOLOGIES, INC.; *U.S. Private*, pg. 1175
DAX-AUTO SA; *Int'l*, pg. 1984
DAXCON ENGINEERING, INC.; *U.S. Private*, pg. 1176
DAX COSMETICS SP. Z O.O.—See Rohto Pharmaceutical Co. Ltd.; *Int'l*, pg. 6387
DAXEN, INC.—See DXN Holdings Bhd.; *Int'l*, pg. 2237
DAXIANG INTERNATIONAL TRADING (SHANGHAI) CO., LTD.—See Sanyo Chemical Industries, Ltd.; *Int'l*, pg. 6563
DAXIN MATERIALS CORPORATION; *Int'l*, pg. 1985
DAXKO, LLC—See GI Manager L.P.; *U.S. Private*, pg. 1692
DAXOR CORPORATION; *U.S. Public*, pg. 644
DAYA BAY NUCLEAR POWER OPERATIONS AND MANAGEMENT CO., LTD.—See CGN Power Co., Ltd.; *Int'l*, pg. 1435
DAYA BUMIMAJU SDN. BHD.; *Int'l*, pg. 1985
DAYA CMT SDN. BHD.; *Int'l*, pg. 1985
DAY AIR CREDIT UNION, INC.; *U.S. Private*, pg. 1176
DAYANG ENTERPRISE HOLDINGS BERHAD; *Int'l*, pg. 1985
DAYANG INTERNATIONAL (SINGAPORE) PTE LTD—See Daheng New Epoch Technology, Inc.; *Int'l*, pg. 1913
DAYANG INTERNATIONAL (THAILAND) CO., LTD—See Daheng New Epoch Technology, Inc.; *Int'l*, pg. 1913
DAYANG TECHNOLOGY DEVELOPMENT INC.—See Daheng New Epoch Technology, Inc.; *Int'l*, pg. 1913
DAYA POLYMER SDN. BHD.—See Propel Global Berhad; *Int'l*, pg. 5997
DAYA PROFFSCORP SDN. BHD.—See Propel Global Berhad; *Int'l*, pg. 5997
DAY ASSOCIATES, INC.—See Thomas Scientific, LLC; *Int'l*, pg. 4157
DAY AUTOMATION SYSTEMS, INC.; *U.S. Private*, pg. 1176
DAYA X-RAY CENTRE SDN. BHD.—See Qualitas Medical Group Limited; *Int'l*, pg. 6151
DAYBREAK FARMS (PTY) LTD.—See Public Investment Corporation (SOC) Limited; *Int'l*, pg. 6094
DAYBREAK FOODS INC.; *U.S. Private*, pg. 1176
DAYBREAK OIL AND GAS, INC.; *U.S. Public*, pg. 644
DAYBREAK SUPERIOR MARKETING (PTY) LTD.—See AFGRI Limited; *Int'l*, pg. 188
DAYBROOK FISHERIES INC.—See Tiger Brands Ltd.; *Int'l*, pg. 7746
DAYBROOK HOLDINGS INC.; *U.S. Private*, pg. 1176

DAYBYDAY STAFF RELIEF, INC.—See Encompass Health Corporation; *U.S. Public*, pg. 755
DAYCARE CLEANING SERVICES, INC.; *U.S. Private*, pg. 1177
DAY-CLICK LIMITED—See Workforce Holdings Ltd.; *Int'l*, pg. 8455
DAYCO CANADA CORP.—See Dayco LLC; *U.S. Private*, pg. 1177
DAYCO EUROPE AUTOMOTIVE—See Dayco LLC; *U.S. Private*, pg. 1177
DAYCO HOLDING CORP.; *U.S. Private*, pg. 1177
DAYCO LLC; *U.S. Private*, pg. 1177
DAYCON PRODUCTS COMPANY, INC.; *U.S. Private*, pg. 1177
DAYCON PRODUCTS COMPANY, INC.—See Daycon Products Company, Inc.; *U.S. Private*, pg. 1177
DAYCON—See Daycon Products Company, Inc.; *U.S. Private*, pg. 1177
DAYCO PRODUCTS LLC—See Dayco LLC; *U.S. Private*, pg. 1177
DAYDREAM ENTERTAINMENT CO., LTD.; *Int'l*, pg. 1985
DAYE CDB VILLAGE BANK CO., LTD.—See China Development Bank Corporation; *Int'l*, pg. 1497
DAYE EUROPE GMBH—See Ningbo Daye Garden Machinery Co., Ltd.; *Int'l*, pg. 5301
DAYEH TAKASHIMAYA DEPARTMENT STORE, INC.—See Takashimaya Company, Limited; *Int'l*, pg. 7435
DAYE JINPENG CAPS MAKING CO., LTD.—See Shandong Chiway Industry Development Co., Ltd.; *Int'l*, pg. 6752
DAY & ENNIS LLC—See Genstar Capital, LLC; *U.S. Private*, pg. 1677
DAY & ENNIS LLC—See Keystone Group, L.P.; *U.S. Private*, pg. 2298
DAY ENTERPRISES INC.; *U.S. Private*, pg. 1176
DAYFORCE, INC.; *U.S. Public*, pg. 645
DAY FORD; *U.S. Private*, pg. 1176
DAY-GLO COLOR CORP.—See RPM International Inc.; *U.S. Public*, pg. 1819
DAYKEN PALLET COMPANY, INC.—See Gerrity Company Incorporated; *U.S. Private*, pg. 1687
DAY KETTERER LTD.; *U.S. Private*, pg. 1176
DAY-LEE FOODS INC.—See NH Foods Ltd.; *Int'l*, pg. 5256
DAY LEWIS PLC.; *Int'l*, pg. 1985
DAYLIGHT DONUT FLOUR COMPANY LLC; *U.S. Private*, pg. 1177
DAYLIGHT SOLUTIONS, INC.—See Leonardo S.p.A.; *Int'l*, pg. 4459
DAYLIGHT TRANSPORT; *U.S. Private*, pg. 1177
DAY MANAGEMENT CORP.; *U.S. Private*, pg. 1176
DAYMARK SOLUTIONS, INC.; *U.S. Private*, pg. 1177
DAYMEN CANADA; *Int'l*, pg. 1985
DAY-MET FINISHING CO. INC.—See Miller Consolidated Industries Inc.; *U.S. Private*, pg. 2733
DAYMON WORLDWIDE INC.—See Bain Capital, LP; *U.S. Private*, pg. 439
DAYMON WORLDWIDE TRADING INC.—See Bain Capital, LP; *U.S. Private*, pg. 439
DAY MOTOR SPORTS LLC—See Gen Cap America, Inc.; *U.S. Private*, pg. 1659
DAYNINE CONSULTING INC.—See Accenture plc; *Int'l*, pg. 86
DAY NITE CO,LTD.—See Nippon Telegraph & Telephone Corporation; *Int'l*, pg. 5340
DAY ONE BIOPHARMACEUTICALS, INC.; *U.S. Public*, pg. 644
DAY ONLINE SOLUTIONS, LLC; *U.S. Private*, pg. 1176
DAYOU PLUS CO., LTD.; *Int'l*, pg. 1985
DAY PITNEY LLP; *U.S. Private*, pg. 1176
DAY PITNEY LLP; *U.S. Private*, pg. 1176
THE DAY PUBLISHER COMPANY; *U.S. Private*, pg. 4019
THE DAY PUBLISHING COMPANY INC.—See The Day Publisher Company; *U.S. Private*, pg. 4019
DAY & ROSS, INC.—See McCain Foods Limited; *Int'l*, pg. 4756
DAYS BEVERAGE INC.; *U.S. Private*, pg. 1177
DAYS HEALTHCARE U.K. LIMITED—See Madison Dearborn Partners, LLC; *U.S. Private*, pg. 2542
DAYS INNS WORLDWIDE, INC.—See Travel & Leisure Co.; *U.S. Public*, pg. 2185
DAYSMART SOFTWARE, INC.—See Independence Capital Partners, LLC; *U.S. Private*, pg. 2056
DAYSMART SOFTWARE, INC.—See PCP Enterprise, L.P.; *U.S. Private*, pg. 3121
DAY'S MOTOR GROUP; *Int'l*, pg. 1985
DAYSPRING CARDS, INC.—See Hallmark Cards, Inc.; *U.S. Private*, pg. 1844
DAY SPRING, INC.; *U.S. Private*, pg. 1176
DAYSPRING INTERNATIONAL; *U.S. Private*, pg. 1177
DAYSPRING RESTORATION, LLC—See Trinity Hunt Management, L.P.; *U.S. Private*, pg. 4234
DAY STAR RESTAURANT HOLDINGS, LLC; *U.S. Private*, pg. 1176
DAY SURGERY CENTER AT DENTON REGIONAL MEDICAL CENTER—See HCA Healthcare, Inc.; *U.S. Public*, pg. 995

DAY STAR RESTAURANT HOLDINGS, LLC   CORPORATE AFFILIATIONS

DAY TECH INDUSTRIES—See Magna International Inc.; *Int'l*, pg. 4639
DAYTHREE DIGITAL BERHAD; *Int'l*, pg. 1985
DAY-TIMERS, INC.—See ACCO Brands Corporation; *U.S. Public*, pg. 33
DAYTNER CONSTRUCTION GROUP; *U.S. Private*, pg. 1177
DAYTONA BEACH NEWS-JOURNAL CORP.—See Gannett Co., Inc.; *U.S. Public*, pg. 905
DAYTONA BR-GD, INC.; *U.S. Private*, pg. 1178
DAYTONA CORPORATION; *Int'l*, pg. 1985
DAYTONA DODGE CHRYSLER JEEP RAM; *U.S. Private*, pg. 1178
DAYTONA HARLEY DAVIDSON; *U.S. Private*, pg. 1178
DAYTONA HEART GROUP HOLDINGS, P.A.—See Webster Equity Partners, LLC; *U.S. Private*, pg. 4467
DAYTONA HOMES; *Int'l*, pg. 1985
DAYTONA INTERNATIONAL SPEEDWAY, LLC—See National Association for Stock Car Auto Racing, Inc.; *U.S. Private*, pg. 2845
DAYTON ANDREWS FIVE STAR CHRYSLER PLYMOUTH JEEP, INC.; *U.S. Private*, pg. 1177
DAYTON APPLIANCE PARTS CO. INC.—See Berkshire Partners LLC; *U.S. Private*, pg. 535
DAYTONA PRODUCTION COMPANY-W.L.L.—See Privatization Holding Company K.S.C.C.; *Int'l*, pg. 5984
DAYTON BAG & BURLAP CO.; *U.S. Private*, pg. 1177
DAYTON BUSINESS JOURNAL—See Advance Publications, Inc.; *U.S. Private*, pg. 84
DAYTON CHILDRENS HOSPITAL; *U.S. Private*, pg. 1177
DAYTON FOODS LIMITED PARTNERSHIP; *U.S. Private*, pg. 1177
DAYTON FORGING & HEAT TREATING COMPANY; *U.S. Private*, pg. 1177
DAYTON FREIGHT LINES INC.; *U.S. Private*, pg. 1177
DAYTON HEART & VASCULAR HOSPITAL—See Catholic Health Initiatives; *U.S. Private*, pg. 790
DAYTON HEIDELBERG DISTRIBUTING CO INC.; *U.S. Private*, pg. 1177
DAYTON INTERNATIONAL AIRPORT; *U.S. Private*, pg. 1177
DAYTON & MICHIGAN RAILROAD CO.—See CSX Corporation; *U.S. Public*, pg. 602
DAYTON NEWSPAPERS, INC.—See Apollo Global Management, Inc.; *U.S. Private*, pg. 163
DAYTON NUT SPECIALTIES INC.; *U.S. Private*, pg. 1177
DAYTON PARTS, LLC—See Dorman Products, Inc.; *U.S. Public*, pg. 677
DAYTON-PHOENIX GROUP INC.; *U.S. Private*, pg. 1178
THE DAYTON POWER AND LIGHT COMPANY—See The AES Corporation; *U.S. Public*, pg. 2031
DAYTON PRECISION PUNCH INC.—See F.C. Industries Inc.; *U.S. Private*, pg. 1456
DAYTON PROGRESS CANADA, LTD.—See MISUMI Group Inc.; *Int'l*, pg. 4921
DAYTON PROGRESS CORPORATION OF JAPAN—See MISUMI Group Inc.; *Int'l*, pg. 4921
DAYTON PROGRESS CORPORATION—See MISUMI Group Inc.; *Int'l*, pg. 4921
DAYTON PROGRESS GMBH—See MISUMI Group Inc.; *Int'l*, pg. 4922
DAYTON PROGRESS LTD.—See MISUMI Group Inc.; *Int'l*, pg. 4922
DAYTON PROGRESS MEXICO, S. DE R.L. DE C.V.—See MISUMI Group Inc.; *Int'l*, pg. 4922
DAYTON PROGRESS PERFURADORES LDA.—See MISUMI Group Inc.; *Int'l*, pg. 4922
DAYTON PROGRESS S.A.S—See MISUMI Group Inc.; *Int'l*, pg. 4922
DAYTON PROGRESS S.R.O.—See MISUMI Group Inc.; *Int'l*, pg. 4922
DAYTON ROGERS MFG. CO.; *U.S. Private*, pg. 1178
DAYTON ROGERS OF CALIFORNIA—See Dayton Rogers Mfg. Co.; *U.S. Private*, pg. 1178
DAYTON ROGERS OF MINNESOTA—See Dayton Rogers Mfg. Co.; *U.S. Private*, pg. 1178
DAYTON ROGERS OF NEW YORK—See Dayton Rogers Mfg. Co.; *U.S. Private*, pg. 1178
DAYTON ROGERS OF OHIO—See Dayton Rogers Mfg. Co.; *U.S. Private*, pg. 1178
DAYTON ROGERS OF TEXAS—See Dayton Rogers Mfg. Co.; *U.S. Private*, pg. 1178
DAYTON SUPERIOR CANADA LTD.—See Dayton Superior Corporation; *U.S. Private*, pg. 1178
DAYTON SUPERIOR CANADA LTD.—See Dayton Superior Corporation; *U.S. Private*, pg. 1178
DAYTON SUPERIOR CORPORATION—See Dayton Superior Corporation; *U.S. Private*, pg. 1178
DAYTON SUPERIOR CORPORATION; *U.S. Private*, pg. 1178
DAYTON SUPERIOR PRODUCTS CO., INC; *U.S. Private*, pg. 1178
DAYTON SUPPLY & TOOL CO.—See Genuine Parts Company; *U.S. Public*, pg. 933
DAYTON T. BROWN INC.; *U.S. Private*, pg. 1178
DAYTRONIC CORPORATION—See METRAWATT International GmbH; *Int'l*, pg. 4856
DA YU FINANCIAL HOLDINGS LTD.; *Int'l*, pg. 1902
DAYU IRRIGATION GROUP CO., LTD.; *Int'l*, pg. 1985

DAY VISION MARKETING; *U.S. Private*, pg. 1176
THE DAY & ZIMMERMANN GROUP, INC.; *U.S. Private*, pg. 4019
DAY & ZIMMERMANN INTERNATIONAL, INC.—See The Day & Zimmermann Group, Inc.; *U.S. Private*, pg. 4019
DAY & ZIMMERMANN - MUNITIONS & GOVERNMENT—See The Day & Zimmermann Group, Inc.; *U.S. Private*, pg. 4019
DAY & ZIMMERMANN NPS, INC.—See The Day & Zimmermann Group, Inc.; *U.S. Private*, pg. 4019
DAY & ZIMMERMANN SECURITY SERVICES—See The Day & Zimmermann Group, Inc.; *U.S. Private*, pg. 4019
DAY & ZIMMERMANN VALIDATION SERVICES—See The Day & Zimmermann Group, Inc.; *U.S. Private*, pg. 4019
DAZADI INC.; *U.S. Private*, pg. 1178
DAZAIFU AMUSEMENT PARK. CO.—See Nishi-Nippon Railroad Co., Ltd.; *Int'l*, pg. 5364
DAZA PRODUCTIONS INC.—See National Amusements, Inc.; *U.S. Private*, pg. 2841
DAZHENG PROPERTY GROUP CO., LTD.; *Int'l*, pg. 1985
DAZHONG TRANSPORTATION (GROUP) CO., LTD.; *Int'l*, pg. 1985
DAZHOU TIANHE WATER SUPPLY AND DRAINAGE CO., LTD.—See Kardan N.V.; *Int'l*, pg. 4079
DAZN GROUP LIMITED—See Vista Equity Partners, LLC; *U.S. Private*, pg. 4401
DAZOR MANUFACTURING CORP.; *U.S. Private*, pg. 1178
DAZ SYSTEMS, INC.—See Accenture plc; *Int'l*, pg. 87
DAZZEL CONFINDIVE LTD.; *Int'l*, pg. 1985
DAZZLE FASHION CO., LTD.; *Int'l*, pg. 1985
DBA BODYWEAR GERMANY GMBH—See Hanesbrands Inc.; *U.S. Public*, pg. 982
D&B ACQUISITION CORP.—See Cannae Holdings, Inc.; *U.S. Public*, pg. 429
D&B ACQUISITION CORP.—See CC Capital Partners, LLC; *U.S. Private*, pg. 798
D&B ACQUISITION CORP.—See Intercontinental Exchange, Inc.; *U.S. Public*, pg. 1141
DBA DEUTSCHLAND GMBH—See Hanesbrands Inc.; *U.S. Public*, pg. 982
DBA DISTRIBUTION SERVICES, INC.—See Radiant Logistics, Inc.; *U.S. Public*, pg. 1759
DB ADVISORS SICAV—See Deutsche Bank Aktiengesellschaft; *Int'l*, pg. 2056
DBA ENGINEERING LTD.—See AtkinsRealis Group Inc.; *Int'l*, pg. 671
DBA GROUP SRL; *Int'l*, pg. 1986
DBAH CAPITAL, LLC—See Deutsche Bank Aktiengesellschaft; *Int'l*, pg. 2057
DB AKELA, S.A.R.L.—See Deutsche Bank Aktiengesellschaft; *Int'l*, pg. 2056
DBA KNOWLEDGE, INC.; *U.S. Private*, pg. 1178
DB ALEX. BROWN HOLDINGS INCORPORATED—See Deutsche Bank Aktiengesellschaft; *Int'l*, pg. 2056
DB ALTERNATIVE STRATEGIES LIMITED—See Deutsche Bank Aktiengesellschaft; *Int'l*, pg. 2056
DB AOTEAROA INVESTMENTS LIMITED—See Deutsche Bank Aktiengesellschaft; *Int'l*, pg. 2056
DBAPPAREL ITALIA SRL—See Hanesbrands Inc.; *U.S. Public*, pg. 982
DBAPPAREL S.A.S.—See Hanesbrands Inc.; *U.S. Public*, pg. 982
DBAPPAREL SOUTH AFRICA (PTY) LIMITED—See Hanesbrands Inc.; *U.S. Public*, pg. 982
DBAPPAREL UK LTD—See Hanesbrands Inc.; *U.S. Public*, pg. 982
DBAPPAREL UK TRADING LTD—See Hanesbrands Inc.; *U.S. Public*, pg. 982
DBAPP SECURITY CO., LTD.; *Int'l*, pg. 1986
DB ARKANSAS HOLDINGS, INC.—See Gannett Co., Inc.; *U.S. Public*, pg. 896
DBA SAS—See Eurazeo SE; *Int'l*, pg. 2528
DBASIX SINGAPORE PTE LTD—See ISDN Holdings Limited; *Int'l*, pg. 3813
DB ASSOCIATES ADVERTISING; *U.S. Private*, pg. 1178
DBA TELECOMMUNICATION (ASIA) HOLDINGS LIMITED; *Int'l*, pg. 1986
D&B AUDIOTECHNIK GMBH—See Ardian SAS; *Int'l*, pg. 556
D&B AUSTRALASIA PTY. LTD.—See Archer Capital Pty. Ltd.; *Int'l*, pg. 547
DBAY ADVISORS LIMITED; *Int'l*, pg. 1986
DB BAGHEERA, S.A.R.L.—See Deutsche Bank Aktiengesellschaft; *Int'l*, pg. 2056
DB BAHN ITALIA S.R.L.—See Deutsche Bahn AG; *Int'l*, pg. 2049
DB BAHNPARK GMBH—See Deutsche Bahn AG; *Int'l*, pg. 2049
DB BARNSDALE AG—See Deutsche Bahn AG; *Int'l*, pg. 2049
DB BEST TECHNOLOGIES, LLC; *U.S. Private*, pg. 1178
DBB JACK-UP SERVICES A/S—See BWB Partners P/S; *Int'l*, pg. 1232
DB BLUEBELL INVESTMENTS (CAYMAN) PARTNERSHIP—See Deutsche Bank Aktiengesellschaft; *Int'l*, pg. 2056
DB BREWERIES LIMITED—See L'Arche Green N.V.; *Int'l*, pg. 4377

DB BROADBAND GMBH—See Deutsche Bahn AG; *Int'l*, pg. 2051
DB BROADCAST LTD.; *Int'l*, pg. 1986
DB BUSVERKEHR HESSEN GMBH—See Deutsche Bahn AG; *Int'l*, pg. 2049
DB CAPITAL MARKETS ASSET MANAGEMENT HOLDING GMBH—See Deutsche Bank Aktiengesellschaft; *Int'l*, pg. 2056
DB CAPITAL MARKETS (DEUTSCHLAND) GMBH—See Deutsche Bank Aktiengesellschaft; *Int'l*, pg. 2056
DB CARGO BELGIUM BV—See Deutsche Bahn AG; *Int'l*, pg. 2050
DB CARGO BULGARIA EOOD—See Deutsche Bahn AG; *Int'l*, pg. 2050
DB CARGO EURASIA GMBH—See Deutsche Bahn AG; *Int'l*, pg. 2050
DB CARGO HUNGARIA KFT.—See Deutsche Bahn AG; *Int'l*, pg. 2050
DB CARGO ITALIA SERVICES S.R.L.—See Deutsche Bahn AG; *Int'l*, pg. 2050
DB CARGO ITALIA S.R.L.—See Deutsche Bahn AG; *Int'l*, pg. 2050
DB CARGO LOGISTICS GMBH—See Deutsche Bahn AG; *Int'l*, pg. 2050
DB CARGO NEDERLAND N.V.—See Deutsche Bahn AG; *Int'l*, pg. 2050
DB CARGO RUSSIJA OOO—See Deutsche Bahn AG; *Int'l*, pg. 2050
DB CARGO SCHWEIZ GMBH—See Deutsche Bahn AG; *Int'l*, pg. 2050
DB CARGO SPEDKOL SP. Z O.O.—See Deutsche Bahn AG; *Int'l*, pg. 2050
DBC CO., LTD.—See Doosan Corporation; *Int'l*, pg. 2172
DBC CONTINUANCE INC.—See Deutsche Bank Aktiengesellschaft; *Int'l*, pg. 2057
DBC DEUTSCHLAND GMBH—See Beter Bed Holding N.V.; *Int'l*, pg. 1002
DB CHESTNUT HOLDINGS LIMITED—See Deutsche Bank Aktiengesellschaft; *Int'l*, pg. 2056
DBC INTERNATIONAL B.V.—See Beter Bed Holding N.V.; *Int'l*, pg. 1002
DBC MARINE SAFETY SYSTEMS LTD.—See ONEX Corporation; *Int'l*, pg. 5580
DB COMMODITIES CANADA LTD.—See Deutsche Bank Aktiengesellschaft; *Int'l*, pg. 2056
THE D&B COMPANIES OF CANADA LTD.—See Cannae Holdings, Inc.; *U.S. Public*, pg. 430
THE D&B COMPANIES OF CANADA LTD.—See CC Capital Partners, LLC; *U.S. Private*, pg. 799
THE D&B COMPANIES OF CANADA LTD.—See Intercontinental Exchange, Inc.; *U.S. Public*, pg. 1142
DB CONCEPTS INC.—See Randstad N.V.; *Int'l*, pg. 6201
DB CONCERTO LIMITED—See Deutsche Bank Aktiengesellschaft; *Int'l*, pg. 2056
DB CONSORZIO S. CONS. A R. L.—See Deutsche Bank Aktiengesellschaft; *Int'l*, pg. 2056
D&B CONSTRUCTION GROUP; *U.S. Private*, pg. 1136
DB CONSULTING GROUP, INC.; *U.S. Private*, pg. 1178
DB CONTROL CORP.—See HEICO Corporation; *U.S. Public*, pg. 1021
DB CORP LIMITED; *Int'l*, pg. 1986
D B CORP LTD.; *Int'l*, pg. 1899
DB CREST LIMITED—See Deutsche Bank Aktiengesellschaft; *Int'l*, pg. 2056
DBDA LIMITED—See Zinc Media Group plc; *Int'l*, pg. 8684
DB DELAWARE HOLDINGS (EUROPE) LIMITED—See Deutsche Bank Aktiengesellschaft; *Int'l*, pg. 2056
DB DEPOSITOR INC.—See Deutsche Bank Aktiengesellschaft; *Int'l*, pg. 2056
DB DESIGN GROUP, INC.—See AEM Holdings Ltd.; *Int'l*, pg. 175
DB DIALOG GMBH—See Deutsche Bahn AG; *Int'l*, pg. 2050
DB DIENSTLEISTUNGEN GMBH—See Deutsche Bahn AG; *Int'l*, pg. 2050
DBD PILGRIM AMERICA CORP.—See Deutsche Bank Aktiengesellschaft; *Int'l*, pg. 2057
DB ELETTRONICA TELECOMUNICAZIONI SPA; *Int'l*, pg. 1986
D. BENEDETTO INC.; *U.S. Private*, pg. 1139
DB ENERGY SA; *Int'l*, pg. 1986
DB ENGINEERING & CONSULTING USA INC.—See Deutsche Bahn AG; *Int'l*, pg. 2050
DB ENGINEERING, INC.—See Blue Sage Capital, L.P.; *U.S. Private*, pg. 592
D.B.E. POULTRY SDN. BHD.—See Lagenda Properties Berhad; *Int'l*, pg. 4393
DB EQUITY S.A R.L.—See Deutsche Bank Aktiengesellschaft; *Int'l*, pg. 2056
D&B EUROPE LIMITED—See Cannae Holdings, Inc.; *U.S. Public*, pg. 429
D&B EUROPE LIMITED—See CC Capital Partners, LLC; *U.S. Private*, pg. 798
D&B EUROPE LIMITED—See Intercontinental Exchange, Inc.; *U.S. Public*, pg. 1141
DB FAHRWEGDIENSTE GMBH—See Deutsche Bahn AG; *Int'l*, pg. 2050
DB FAHRZEUGINSTANDHALTUNG GMBH—See Deutsche Bahn AG; *Int'l*, pg. 2050

COMPANY NAME INDEX

DB FERNVERKEHR AKTIENGESELLSCHAFT—See Deutsche Bahn AG; *Int'l*, pg. 2050
DB FUHRPARKSERVICE GMBH—See Deutsche Bahn AG; *Int'l*, pg. 2050
DB GASTRONOMIE GMBH—See Deutsche Bahn AG; *Int'l*, pg. 2050
DBG BETEILIGUNGSGESELLSCHAFT MBH—See Deutsche Beteiligungs AG; *Int'l*, pg. 2062
DBG CANADA LIMITED; *Int'l*, pg. 1988
DB GLOBAL TECHNOLOGY, INC.—See Deutsche Bank Aktiengesellschaft; *Int'l*, pg. 2056
DB GLOBAL TECHNOLOGY SRL—See Deutsche Bank Aktiengesellschaft; *Int'l*, pg. 2056
DBG NEW FUND MANAGEMENT GMBH & CO. KG—See Deutsche Beteiligungs AG; *Int'l*, pg. 2062
DB GRANT ASSOCIATES INC.—See Madison Dearborn Partners, LLC; *U.S. Private*, pg. 2540
D&B GROUP HOLDINGS (UK)—See Cannae Holdings, Inc.; *U.S. Public*, pg. 429
D&B GROUP HOLDINGS (UK)—See CC Capital Partners, LLC; *U.S. Private*, pg. 798
D&B GROUP HOLDINGS (UK)—See Intercontinental Exchange, Inc.; *U.S. Public*, pg. 1141
DB GROUP SERVICES (UK) LIMITED—See Deutsche Bank Aktiengesellschaft; *Int'l*, pg. 2056
DBG TECHNOLOGY CO., LTD.; *Int'l*, pg. 1988
DBG TECHNOLOGY (INDIA) PRIVATE LIMITED—See DBG Technology Co., Ltd.; *Int'l*, pg. 1988
DBG VERMOGENSVERWALTUNGSGESELLSCHAFT MBH—See Deutsche Bank Aktiengesellschaft; *Int'l*, pg. 2057
DBH FINANCE PLC; *Int'l*, pg. 1988
D&B HOLDINGS AUSTRALIA LIMITED—See Cannae Holdings, Inc.; *U.S. Public*, pg. 429
D&B HOLDINGS AUSTRALIA LIMITED—See CC Capital Partners, LLC; *U.S. Private*, pg. 798
D&B HOLDINGS AUSTRALIA LIMITED—See Intercontinental Exchange, Inc.; *U.S. Public*, pg. 1141
DB HOLDINGS (NEW YORK), INC.—See Deutsche Bank Aktiengesellschaft; *Int'l*, pg. 2056
DB HOME LENDING HOLDINGS LLC—See Deutsche Bank Aktiengesellschaft; *Int'l*, pg. 2062
DB HR SOLUTIONS GMBH—See Deutsche Bank Aktiengesellschaft; *Int'l*, pg. 2056
DBH WORLDWIDE, LLC; *U.S. Private*, pg. 1179
DBI BEVERAGE NAPA; *U.S. Private*, pg. 1179
DBI BUSINESS INTERIORS LLC; *U.S. Private*, pg. 1179
DBI HOLDINGS, INC.—See Mahwah Bergen Retail Group, Inc.; *U.S. Private*, pg. 2550
DBI, INC.—See ERI Solutions, LLC; *U.S. Private*, pg. 1419
DBI INDUSTRIAL SERVICES LIMITED—See Altrad Investment Authority SAS; *Int'l*, pg. 398
DB INDUSTRIAL HOLDINGS BETEILIGUNGS GMBH & CO. KG—See Deutsche Bank Aktiengesellschaft; *Int'l*, pg. 2056
DB INDUSTRIAL HOLDINGS GMBH—See Deutsche Bank Aktiengesellschaft; *Int'l*, pg. 2056
D B INDUSTRIES, LLC—See 3M Company; *U.S. Public*, pg. 5
DB INSURANCE CO., LTD.—See Dongbu Group; *Int'l*, pg. 2165
D&B INTERIORS (PTY) LTD.—See Draexlmaier Gruppe; *Int'l*, pg. 2198
DB INTERMODAL SERVICES GMBH—See Deutsche Bahn AG; *Int'l*, pg. 2050
DB INTERNATIONAL (ASIA) LIMITED—See Deutsche Bank Aktiengesellschaft; *Int'l*, pg. 2056
D.B. INTERNATIONAL DELAWARE, INC.—See Deutsche Bank Aktiengesellschaft; *Int'l*, pg. 2056
DB (INTERNATIONAL) STOCK BROKERS LTD.; *Int'l*, pg. 1985
DB INVESTMENT MANAGEMENT, INC.—See Deutsche Bank Aktiengesellschaft; *Int'l*, pg. 2056
DB INVESTMENT RESOURCES HOLDINGS CORP.—See Deutsche Bank Aktiengesellschaft; *Int'l*, pg. 2056
DB INVESTMENT RESOURCES (US) CORPORATION—See Deutsche Bank Aktiengesellschaft; *Int'l*, pg. 2056
DB INVESTMENT SERVICES GMBH—See Deutsche Bank Aktiengesellschaft; *Int'l*, pg. 2056
DB IO LP—See Deutsche Bank Aktiengesellschaft; *Int'l*, pg. 2056
DB IROC LEASING CORP.—See Deutsche Bank Aktiengesellschaft; *Int'l*, pg. 2056
DBJ AMERICAS INC.—See Development Bank of Japan, Inc.; *Int'l*, pg. 2087
DBJ ASSET MANAGEMENT CO., LTD.—See Development Bank of Japan, Inc.; *Int'l*, pg. 2087
DBJ ENTERPRISES DE COLOMBIA S.A.—See Corteva, Inc.; *U.S. Public*, pg. 584
DBJ EUROPE LIMITED—See Development Bank of Japan, Inc.; *Int'l*, pg. 2087
DBJ INVESTMENT CONSULTING (BEIJING) CO., LTD.—See Development Bank of Japan, Inc.; *Int'l*, pg. 2087
DBJ LIMITED—See Iron Mountain Incorporated; *U.S. Public*, pg. 1172
DBJ SECURITIES CO., LTD.—See Development Bank of Japan, Inc.; *Int'l*, pg. 2087

DBJ SINGAPORE LIMITED—See Development Bank of Japan, Inc.; *Int'l*, pg. 2087
DBK CONCEPTS INC.—See Sole Source Capital LLC; *U.S. Private*, pg. 3708
DBK-LEASING JSC—See National Managing Holding Baiterek JSC; *Int'l*, pg. 5161
DB KOMMUNIKATIONSTECHNIK GMBH—See Deutsche Bahn AG; *Int'l*, pg. 2050
DBK, S.A.—See Informa SA; *Int'l*, pg. 3694
D&B MACHINE, INC.; *U.S. Private*, pg. 1136
DB MAIA LLC—See Deutsche Bank Aktiengesellschaft; *Int'l*, pg. 2056
DBMAKER JAPAN INC.—See SYSCOM Computer Engineering Company; *Int'l*, pg. 7388
DB MANAGEMENT PARTNERS, L.P.—See Deutsche Bank Aktiengesellschaft; *Int'l*, pg. 2056
D&B MANAGEMENT SERVICES CO.—See Cannae Holdings, Inc.; *U.S. Public*, pg. 429
D&B MANAGEMENT SERVICES CO.—See CC Capital Partners, LLC; *U.S. Private*, pg. 798
D&B MANAGEMENT SERVICES CO.—See Intercontinental Exchange, Inc.; *U.S. Public*, pg. 1141
DB MANAGEMENT SUPPORT GMBH—See Deutsche Bank Aktiengesellschaft; *Int'l*, pg. 2056
DBM GLOBAL INC.—See INNOVATE Corp.; *U.S. Public*, pg. 1125
DBM/HATCH INC.—See Dee Brown, Inc.; *U.S. Private*, pg. 1188
DB MOBILITY SERVICES AUSTRIA GMBH—See Deutsche Bahn AG; *Int'l*, pg. 2050
DBMOTION, INC.—See Veradigm Inc.; *U.S. Public*, pg. 2280
DBMOTION, LTD.—See Veradigm Inc.; *U.S. Public*, pg. 2280
DBM REFLEX OF TAIWAN CO., LTD.—See TYC Brother Industrial Co., Ltd.; *Int'l*, pg. 7994
DBM TECHNOLOGIES LLC; *U.S. Private*, pg. 1179
DBM VIRCON SERVICES (CANADA) LTD.—See INNOVATE Corp.; *U.S. Public*, pg. 1126
DBM VIRCON SERVICES (NZ) LTD.—See INNOVATE Corp.; *U.S. Public*, pg. 1126
DBM VIRCON SERVICES (PHILIPPINES) INC.—See INNOVATE Corp.; *U.S. Public*, pg. 1126
DBM VIRCON SERVICES (THAILAND) CO., LTD.—See INNOVATE Corp.; *U.S. Public*, pg. 1126
DB NETZ AG—See Deutsche Bahn AG; *Int'l*, pg. 2050
DBNGP HOLDINGS PTY LIMITED—See CK Hutchison Holdings Limited; *Int'l*, pg. 1636
DBNGP (WA) NOMINEES PTY LIMITED—See CK Hutchison Holdings Limited; *Int'l*, pg. 1636
DBNGP (WA) TRANSMISSION PTY LIMITED—See CK Hutchison Holdings Limited; *Int'l*, pg. 1636
DBOI GLOBAL SERVICES PRIVATE LIMITED—See Deutsche Bank Aktiengesellschaft; *Int'l*, pg. 2057
DBOI GLOBAL SERVICES (UK) LIMITED—See Deutsche Bank Aktiengesellschaft; *Int'l*, pg. 2057
DBO PARTNERS HOLDING LLC—See Piper Sandler Companies; *U.S. Public*, pg. 1693
DB OVERSEAS HOLDINGS LIMITED—See Deutsche Bank Aktiengesellschaft; *Int'l*, pg. 2056
D-BOX TECHNOLOGIES INC.; *Int'l*, pg. 1900
DB PARTNERSHIP MANAGEMENT II, LLC—See Deutsche Bank Aktiengesellschaft; *Int'l*, pg. 2056
DB PARTNERSHIP MANAGEMENT LTD.—See Deutsche Bank Aktiengesellschaft; *Int'l*, pg. 2056
DBP-DAIWA CAPITAL MARKETS PHILIPPINES, INC.—See Daiwa Securities Group Inc.; *Int'l*, pg. 1948
DB PERRY INVESTMENTS LIMITED—See Deutsche Bank Aktiengesellschaft; *Int'l*, pg. 2056
DB PETRI LLC—See Deutsche Bank Aktiengesellschaft; *Int'l*, pg. 2056
DB (PHILIPPINES), INC.—See Batu Kawan Berhad; *Int'l*, pg. 891
DB PLATINUM ADVISORS S.A.—See Deutsche Bank Aktiengesellschaft; *Int'l*, pg. 2056
DB PLUS INC.—See Jerrs Plus Inc.; *U.S. Private*, pg. 2202
DBPORT SZCZECIN SP. Z O.O.—See Deutsche Bahn AG; *Int'l*, pg. 2051
DB PRINT GMBH—See Deutsche Bank Aktiengesellschaft; *Int'l*, pg. 2056
DB PRIVATE CLIENTS CORP.—See Deutsche Bank Aktiengesellschaft; *Int'l*, pg. 2056
DB PRIVATE WEALTH MORTGAGE LTD.—See Deutsche Bank Aktiengesellschaft; *Int'l*, pg. 2056
DB PROFESSIONALS, INC.; *U.S. Private*, pg. 1178
DB PROJEKTBAU GMBH—See Deutsche Bahn AG; *Int'l*, pg. 2050
DBR COMERCIO DE ARTIGOS DO VESTUARIO S.A.—See Otto GmbH & Co. KG; *Int'l*, pg. 5662
DB REAL ESTATE INVESTMENT GMBH—See Deutsche Bank Aktiengesellschaft; *Int'l*, pg. 2058
DB REALTY LIMITED—See Dynamix Balwas Group of Companies; *Int'l*, pg. 2241
DB REGIO BUS MITTE GMBH—See Deutsche Bahn AG; *Int'l*, pg. 2050
D.B. ROBERTS COMPANY—See Heilind Electronics, Inc.; *Int'l*, pg. 1904

DBRS LIMITED—See Morningstar, Inc.; *U.S. Public*, pg. 1476
DBRS RATINGS GMBH—See Morningstar, Inc.; *U.S. Public*, pg. 1476
DBRS RATINGS LIMITED—See Morningstar, Inc.; *U.S. Public*, pg. 1476
DBS ADMINISTRATION PTY LIMITED—See Enero Group Limited; *Int'l*, pg. 2423
D&B SALES & MARKETING SOLUTIONS—See Cannae Holdings, Inc.; *U.S. Public*, pg. 429
D&B SALES & MARKETING SOLUTIONS—See CC Capital Partners, LLC; *U.S. Private*, pg. 798
D&B SALES & MARKETING SOLUTIONS—See Intercontinental Exchange, Inc.; *U.S. Public*, pg. 1141
DBS ASIA CAPITAL LIMITED—See DBS Group Holdings Ltd.; *Int'l*, pg. 1988
DBS ASIA LTD.—See DBS Group Holdings Ltd.; *Int'l*, pg. 1988
DBS ASSET MANAGEMENT (UNITED STATES) PTE LTD—See DBS Group Holdings Ltd.; *Int'l*, pg. 1988
DBS BANK (HONG KONG) LIMITED—See DBS Group Holdings Ltd.; *Int'l*, pg. 1988
DBS BANK INDIA LIMITED—See DBS Group Holdings Ltd.; *Int'l*, pg. 1988
DBS BANK-LONDON BRANCH—See DBS Group Holdings Ltd.; *Int'l*, pg. 1988
DBS BANK LTD.—See DBS Group Holdings Ltd.; *Int'l*, pg. 1988
DBS BANK (TAIWAN) LIMITED—See DBS Group Holdings Ltd.; *Int'l*, pg. 1988
DBS CARD CENTRE PTE. LTD.—See DBS Group Holdings Ltd.; *Int'l*, pg. 1988
DB SCHENKER BTT GMBH—See Deutsche Bahn AG; *Int'l*, pg. 2050
DB SCHENKER (CAMBODIA) LIMITED.—See Deutsche Bahn AG; *Int'l*, pg. 2052
DB SCHENKER FLLC—See Deutsche Bahn AG; *Int'l*, pg. 2052
DB SCHENKER GLOBAL SERVICES EUROPE S.R.L.—See Deutsche Bahn AG; *Int'l*, pg. 2052
DB SCHENKER NIETEN GMBH—See Deutsche Bahn AG; *Int'l*, pg. 2050
DB SCHENKER RAIL AUTOMOTIVE GMBH—See Deutsche Bahn AG; *Int'l*, pg. 2050
DB SCHENKER RAIL BULGARIA EOOD—See Deutsche Bahn AG; *Int'l*, pg. 2050
DB SCHENKER RAIL DANMARK SERVICES A/S—See Deutsche Bahn AG; *Int'l*, pg. 2050
DB SCHENKER RAIL DEUTSCHLAND AG—See Deutsche Bahn AG; *Int'l*, pg. 2050
DB SCHENKER RAIL HUNGARIA KFT.—See Deutsche Bahn AG; *Int'l*, pg. 2050
DB SCHENKER RAIL INFORMATION SERVICES LIMITED—See Deutsche Bahn AG; *Int'l*, pg. 2050
DB SCHENKER RAIL ITALIA S.R.L.—See Deutsche Bahn AG; *Int'l*, pg. 2050
DB SCHENKER RAIL NEDERLAND N. V.—See Deutsche Bahn AG; *Int'l*, pg. 2050
DB SCHENKER RAIL POLSKA S.A.—See Deutsche Bahn AG; *Int'l*, pg. 2050
DB SCHENKER RAIL ROMANIA S.R.L.—See Deutsche Bahn AG; *Int'l*, pg. 2050
DB SCHENKER RAIL SCHWEIZ GMBH—See Deutsche Bahn AG; *Int'l*, pg. 2050
DB SCHENKER RAIL SPEDKOL SP. Z O.O.—See Deutsche Bahn AG; *Int'l*, pg. 2051
DB SCHENKER RAIL (UK) LIMITED—See Deutsche Bahn AG; *Int'l*, pg. 2050
DBS CORPORATION; *U.S. Private*, pg. 1179
DBSD NORTH AMERICA, INC.—See EchoStar Corporation; *U.S. Public*, pg. 711
DB SEIKO CO., LTD.—See Mitsubishi Electric Corporation; *Int'l*, pg. 4943
DB SERVICE CENTRE LIMITED—See Deutsche Bank Aktiengesellschaft; *Int'l*, pg. 2056
DB SERVICES AMERICAS, INC.—See Deutsche Bank Aktiengesellschaft; *Int'l*, pg. 2056
DB SERVICES GMBH—See Deutsche Bahn AG; *Int'l*, pg. 2051
DB SERVICIOS MEXICO, S.A. DE C.V.—See Deutsche Bank Aktiengesellschaft; *Int'l*, pg. 2059
DBS FINANCIAL MANAGEMENT PLC—See Vista Equity Partners, LLC; *U.S. Private*, pg. 4397
DBS GROUP HOLDINGS LTD.; *Int'l*, pg. 1988
DB SICHERHEIT GMBH—See Deutsche Bahn AG; *Int'l*, pg. 2051
DBSI DEVELOPMENT LLC—See DBSI, Inc.; *U.S. Private*, pg. 1179
DBSI HOUSING INC.—See DBSI, Inc.; *U.S. Private*, pg. 1179
DBSI INCORPORATED; *U.S. Private*, pg. 1179
DBSI, INC.; *U.S. Private*, pg. 1179
DBS LEOCH LIMITED—See Leoch International Technology Limited; *Int'l*, pg. 4457
DBS LIFESTYLE INDIA PRIVATE LIMITED—See PDS Limited; *Int'l*, pg. 5770
DBSN SERVICES PTE. LTD.—See DBS Group Holdings Ltd.; *Int'l*, pg. 1988

DBSI, INC.

DBS SECURITIES (JAPAN) CO., LTD.—See DBS Group Holdings Ltd.; *Int'l*, pg. 1988
DB STATION&SERVICE AKTIENGESELLSCHAFT—See Deutsche Bahn AG; *Int'l*, pg. 2051
DB STRATEGIC ADVISORS, INC.—See Deutsche Bank Aktiengesellschaft; *Int'l*, pg. 2056
DBS TRUSTEE LTD.—See DBS Group Holdings Ltd.; *Int'l*, pg. 1988
DB STUDIOS, INC.—See HH Global Group Limited; *Int'l*, pg. 3378
D&B SUPPLY COMPANY INC.; *U.S. Private*, pg. 1136
DBS VICKERS (HONG KONG) LIMITED—See DBS Group Holdings Ltd.; *Int'l*, pg. 1988
DBS VICKERS RESEARCH (SINGAPORE) PTE LTD—See DBS Group Holdings Ltd.; *Int'l*, pg. 1988
DBS VICKERS SECURITIES HOLDINGS PTE LTD—See DBS Group Holdings Ltd.; *Int'l*, pg. 1988
DBS VICKERS SECURITIES (HONG KONG) LIMITED—See DBS Group Holdings Ltd.; *Int'l*, pg. 1988
DBS VICKERS SECURITIES NOMINEES (SINGAPORE) PTE LTD—See DBS Group Holdings Ltd.; *Int'l*, pg. 1988
DBS VICKERS SECURITIES ONLINE HOLDINGS PTE LTD—See DBS Group Holdings Ltd.; *Int'l*, pg. 1988
DBS VICKERS SECURITIES (SINGAPORE) PTE LTD—See DBS Group Holdings Ltd.; *Int'l*, pg. 1988
DBS VICKERS SECURITIES (THAILAND) CO., LTD.—See DBS Group Holdings Ltd.; *Int'l*, pg. 1988
DBS VICKERS SECURITIES (UK) LTD—See DBS Group Holdings Ltd.; *Int'l*, pg. 1988
DB SYSTEL GMBH—See Deutsche Bahn AG; *Int'l*, pg. 2051
DB SYSTEMTECHNIK GMBH—See Deutsche Bahn AG; *Int'l*, pg. 2051
DB TECHNOLOGY, INC.—See Dura Software Series A Qof LLC; *U.S. Private*, pg. 1292
DBTEL; *Int'l*, pg. 1989
DB TEXAS HOLDINGS, INC.—See Gannett Co., Inc.; *U.S. Public*, pg. 896
D&B (THAILAND) CO., LTD.—See Business Online Public Company Limited; *Int'l*, pg. 1229
D&B TILE DISTRIBUTORS; *U.S. Private*, pg. 1136
DB&T INSURANCE, INC.—See Heartland Financial USA, Inc.; *U.S. Public*, pg. 1018
DB TRUST COMPANY LIMITED JAPAN—See Deutsche Bank Aktiengesellschaft; *Int'l*, pg. 2056
DB TRUSTEE SERVICES LIMITED—See Deutsche Bank Aktiengesellschaft; *Int'l*, pg. 2056
DB TRUSTEES (HONG KONG) LIMITED—See Deutsche Bank Aktiengesellschaft; *Int'l*, pg. 2057
DBTS INC.; *U.S. Private*, pg. 1179
DBT; *Int'l*, pg. 1989
DBUB GROUP, INC.; *Int'l*, pg. 1989
DB UK BANK LIMITED—See Deutsche Bank Aktiengesellschaft; *Int'l*, pg. 2057
DBUSBZ2, LLC—See Deutsche Bank Aktiengesellschaft; *Int'l*, pg. 2057
DBV DEUTSCHE BEAMTENVERSICHERUNG AG—See AXA S.A.; *Int'l*, pg. 759
DBV DEUTSCHE BEAMTENVERSICHERUNG LEBENSVERSICHERUNG AG—See AXA S.A.; *Int'l*, pg. 759
DB VERSICHERUNGSMANAGER GMBH—See Deutsche Bank Aktiengesellschaft; *Int'l*, pg. 2057
DB VITA S.A.—See Deutsche Bank Aktiengesellschaft; *Int'l*, pg. 2057
DBV TECHNOLOGIES S.A.; *Int'l*, pg. 1989
DBV-WINTERTHUR HOLDING AG—See AXA S.A.; *Int'l*, pg. 758
DBW ADVANCED FIBER TECHNOLOGIES GMBH—See DMB Dr. Dieter Murmann Beteiligungsgesellschaft mbH; *Int'l*, pg. 2142
DBW AUTOMOTIVE COMPONENTS SHANGHAI CO., LTD.—See Landesbank Baden-Wurttemberg; *Int'l*, pg. 4404
D&B WELLNESS, LLC—See Acreage Holdings, Inc.; *U.S. Public*, pg. 36
DBW FIBER CORPORATION—See Landesbank Baden-Wurttemberg; *Int'l*, pg. 4404
DBW-FIBER-NEUHAUS GMBH—See Landesbank Baden-Wurttemberg; *Int'l*, pg. 4405
DBW HUNGARY KFT—See DMB Dr. Dieter Murmann Beteiligungsgesellschaft mbH; *Int'l*, pg. 2142
DBW IBERICA INDUSTRIA AUTOMOCION, S.A.—See DMB Dr. Dieter Murmann Beteiligungsgesellschaft mbH; *Int'l*, pg. 2142
DBW JAPAN LTD.—See Landesbank Baden-Wurttemberg; *Int'l*, pg. 4404
DBW KALININGRAD O.O.O.—See Landesbank Baden-Wurttemberg; *Int'l*, pg. 4404
DBW METALLVERARBEITUNG GMBH—See DMB Dr. Dieter Murmann Beteiligungsgesellschaft mbH; *Int'l*, pg. 2142
DBW POLSKA SP.Z. O.O.—See Landesbank Baden-Wurttemberg; *Int'l*, pg. 4405
DBX ADVISORS LLC—See Deutsche Bank Aktiengesellschaft; *Int'l*, pg. 2057
DBXB NETHERLANDS B.V.—See Cannae Holdings, Inc.; *U.S. Public*, pg. 429

DBXB NETHERLANDS B.V.—See CC Capital Partners, LLC; *U.S. Private*, pg. 798
DBXB NETHERLANDS B.V.—See Intercontinental Exchange, Inc.; *U.S. Public*, pg. 1141
DBXB S.R.L.—See Cannae Holdings, Inc.; *U.S. Public*, pg. 429
DBXB S.R.L.—See CC Capital Partners, LLC; *U.S. Private*, pg. 798
DBXB S.R.L.—See Intercontinental Exchange, Inc.; *U.S. Public*, pg. 1141
DBX, INC.—See Mahwah Bergen Retail Group, Inc.; *U.S. Private*, pg. 2550
DB ZUGBUS REGIONALVERKEHR ALB-BODENSEE GMBH—See Deutsche Bahn AG; *Int'l*, pg. 2051
DCA/DCPR CHICAGO—See DCA/DCPR; *U.S. Private*, pg. 1179
DCA/DCPR; *U.S. Private*, pg. 1179
DCA/DCPR—See DCA/DCPR; *U.S. Private*, pg. 1179
DC ALABAMA, INC.—See Dow Inc.; *U.S. Public*, pg. 683
DC ALABAMA, INC.—See Dow Inc.; *U.S. Public*, pg. 684
DCA OUTDOOR, INC.; *U.S. Private*, pg. 1179
D. CARR INVESTMENTS INC.; *U.S. Private*, pg. 1139
DCA SERVICES INC.—See Platinum Equity, LLC; *U.S. Private*, pg. 3202
DC AUTO-MOTION (PTY) LTD—See THK CO., LTD.; *Int'l*, pg. 7711
DC AVIATION FLIGHT CREW LTD.—See ATON GmbH; *Int'l*, pg. 688
DC AVIATION GMBH—See ATON GmbH; *Int'l*, pg. 688
DC AVIATION LTD.—See ATON GmbH; *Int'l*, pg. 688
DCB BANK LIMITED; *Int'l*, pg. 1989
DC BERLIN TRAINING GBR—See Dale Carnegie & Associates, Inc.; *U.S. Private*, pg. 1148
DC BRANDS INTERNATIONAL, INC.; *U.S. Private*, pg. 1179
DC BUILDING GROUP LLC; *U.S. Private*, pg. 1179
D.C. CAPITAL PARTNERS, LLC; *U.S. Private*, pg. 1141
DCC ENERGI DANMARK A/S—See DCC plc; *Int'l*, pg. 1989
DCC ENERGY LIMITED—See DCC plc; *Int'l*, pg. 1989
DCC ENERGY—See DCC plc; *Int'l*, pg. 1989
DCC ENVIRONMENTAL—See DCC plc; *Int'l*, pg. 1989
DCC FOOD & BEVERAGE—See DCC plc; *Int'l*, pg. 1989
DCC HEALTH AND BEAUTY SOLUTIONS LIMITED—See DCC plc; *Int'l*, pg. 1989
DCC HEALTHCARE—See DCC plc; *Int'l*, pg. 1990
DCC HONG KONG LTD.—See Adamantem Capital Management Pty Limited; *Int'l*, pg. 123
DCC LPG LTD.—See DCC plc; *Int'l*, pg. 1990
DCCM, LLC—See White Wolf Capital LLC; *U.S. Private*, pg. 4510
DC CO., LTD.—See Taiheiyo Cement Corporation; *Int'l*, pg. 7411
DC COMICS, INC.—See Warner Bros. Discovery, Inc.; *U.S. Public*, pg. 2328
D&C CONSTRUCTION CO. INC.; *U.S. Private*, pg. 1137
DCC PLC; *Int'l*, pg. 1989
DCC PROPANE LLC—See DCC plc; *Int'l*, pg. 1990
DCC RETOUCHING & PHOTOGRAPHY SERVICES; *U.S. Private*, pg. 1179
DCC SERCOM—See DCC plc; *Int'l*, pg. 1990
DCC (SHANGHAI) CO., LTD.—See OCI Holdings Co., Ltd.; *Int'l*, pg. 5519
DCC TECHNOLOGY LIMITED—See DCC plc; *Int'l*, pg. 1990
DCC VITAL LIMITED—See DCC plc; *Int'l*, pg. 1990
DC-DATACENTER-GROUP GMBH—See MVV Energie AG; *Int'l*, pg. 5108
DCD-DORBYL HEAVY ENGINEERING VEREENIGING—See DCD-Dorbyl (Pty) Ltd.; *Int'l*, pg. 1991
DCD-DORBYL (PTY) LTD.; *Int'l*, pg. 1991
DCD-DORBYL ROLLING STOCK DIVISION—See DCD-Dorbyl (Pty) Ltd.; *Int'l*, pg. 1991
DC D.D.; *Int'l*, pg. 1989
DC DENTAL SUPPLIES, LLC; *U.S. Private*, pg. 1179
DC DIAGNOSTICARE, INC.—See Ontario Municipal Employees Retirement System; *Int'l*, pg. 5583
D&C DISTRIBUTORS, LLC—See Advanced Container Technologies, Inc.; *U.S. Public*, pg. 46
DCD MEDIA PLC; *Int'l*, pg. 1991
DCD PUBLISHING LIMITED—See DCD Media plc; *Int'l*, pg. 1991
DCD TRAINING GMBH—See Dale Carnegie & Associates, Inc.; *U.S. Private*, pg. 1148
DC ELEKTRONISCHE ZAHLUNGSSYSTEME GMBH—See UniCredit S.p.A.; *Int'l*, pg. 8035
D-C ELEVATOR CO., INC. - LOUISVILLE—See D-C Elevator Co., Inc.; *U.S. Private*, pg. 1139
D-C ELEVATOR CO., INC.; *U.S. Private*, pg. 1139
DC ENERGY GMBH—See Daiichi Jitsugyo Co. Ltd.; *Int'l*, pg. 1927
DC ENERGY, LLC; *U.S. Private*, pg. 1179
DC FINANCIAL, LLC—See Dollar General Corporation; *U.S. Public*, pg. 672
DCG DEVELOPMENT CO.; *U.S. Private*, pg. 1179
DCG, INC.—See DFNN, Inc.; *Int'l*, pg. 2096
DC GRADACAC D.D.; *Int'l*, pg. 1989
DC GROUP, INC.; *U.S. Private*, pg. 1179

CORPORATE AFFILIATIONS

DC HALSVIK AGGREGATES AS—See Group de Cloedt SA; *Int'l*, pg. 3088
DCH AUTO GROUP (USA) INC.—See Lithia Motors, Inc.; *U.S. Public*, pg. 1322
DCH BLOOMFIELD LLC—See Lithia Motors, Inc.; *U.S. Public*, pg. 1322
DCH CALIFORNIA MOTORS INC.—See Lithia Motors, Inc.; *U.S. Public*, pg. 1322
DCH CA LLC—See Lithia Motors, Inc.; *U.S. Public*, pg. 1322
DCH DELAWARE LLC—See Lithia Motors, Inc.; *U.S. Public*, pg. 1322
DCH DEL NORTE, INC.—See Lithia Motors, Inc.; *U.S. Public*, pg. 1322
DCH DUSSELDORFER CONTAINER-HAFEN GMBH—See Deutsche Bahn AG; *Int'l*, pg. 2051
DC HEALTHCARE HOLDINGS BERHAD; *Int'l*, pg. 1989
DCH FORD OF THOUSAND OAKS—See Lithia Motors, Inc.; *U.S. Public*, pg. 1322
DCH FREEHOLD LLC—See Lithia Motors, Inc.; *U.S. Public*, pg. 1322
DCH HOLDINGS LLC—See Lithia Motors, Inc.; *U.S. Public*, pg. 1322
DCH HONDA OF NANUET—See Lithia Motors, Inc.; *U.S. Public*, pg. 1322
DCH INVESTMENTS INC.—See Lithia Motors, Inc.; *U.S. Public*, pg. 1322
DCH KOREAN IMPORTS LLC—See Lithia Motors, Inc.; *U.S. Public*, pg. 1322
DCH MAMARONECK LLC—See Lithia Motors, Inc.; *U.S. Public*, pg. 1322
DCH MANAGEMENT SERVICES INC.—See Lithia Motors, Inc.; *U.S. Public*, pg. 1322
DCH MISSION VALLEY LLC—See Lithia Motors, Inc.; *U.S. Public*, pg. 1322
DCH MONTCLAIR LLC—See Lithia Motors, Inc.; *U.S. Public*, pg. 1322
DCH MOTORS LLC—See Lithia Motors, Inc.; *U.S. Public*, pg. 1322
D&C HONDA CO. INC.; *U.S. Private*, pg. 1137
DCH OXNARD 1521 IMPORTS INC.—See Lithia Motors, Inc.; *U.S. Public*, pg. 1322
DCH (OXNARD) INC.—See Lithia Motors, Inc.; *U.S. Public*, pg. 1322
DCH PARAMUS HONDA—See Lithia Motors, Inc.; *U.S. Public*, pg. 1322
DCH SIMI VALLEY INC.—See Lithia Motors, Inc.; *U.S. Public*, pg. 1322
DCH TEMECULA IMPORTS LLC—See Lithia Motors, Inc.; *U.S. Public*, pg. 1322
DCH TEMECULA MOTORS LLC—See Lithia Motors, Inc.; *U.S. Public*, pg. 1322
DCH TORRANCE IMPORTS INC.—See Lithia Motors, Inc.; *U.S. Public*, pg. 1322
DCI ADVISORS LIMITED; *Int'l*, pg. 1991
DCI BIOLOGICALS INC.; *U.S. Private*, pg. 1179
DCI-BRAZIL—See Firmenich International SA; *Int'l*, pg. 2681
DCI CONSTRUCTION, LLC; *U.S. Private*, pg. 1180
DCI CONSULTING GROUP, INC.; *U.S. Private*, pg. 1180
DCI DATABASE FOR COMMERCE AND INDUSTRY AG; *Int'l*, pg. 1991
DCI DIGITAL COMMUNICATIONS, INC.—See Kavveri Telecom Products Ltd; *Int'l*, pg. 4093
DCI GROUP; *U.S. Private*, pg. 1180
DCI, INC.; *U.S. Private*, pg. 1180
DCI, INC. - SPRINGFIELD DIVISION—See DCI, Inc.; *U.S. Private*, pg. 1180
DCI INTERNATIONAL, LLC—See Nakanishi Inc.; *Int'l*, pg. 5132
DCI MARKETING INC—See IMI plc; *Int'l*, pg. 3624
DCI MIAMI, INC.—See ANSA McAL Limited; *Int'l*, pg. 477
D&C INC.; *U.S. Private*, pg. 1137
DC INDUSTRIAL N.V.—See Group de Cloedt SA; *Int'l*, pg. 3088
DC INFOTECH & COMMUNICATION LTD.; *Int'l*, pg. 1989
DC INTERNATIONAL; *U.S. Private*, pg. 1179
DCINY; *U.S. Private*, pg. 1180
D-CIRCLE INC.—See Mitani Sangyo Co., Ltd.; *Int'l*, pg. 4924
DCI-WEST—See Development Counsellors International, Ltd.; *U.S. Private*, pg. 1217
DC KATSUYA CO., LTD.—See DIC Corporation; *Int'l*, pg. 2107
DCK CONCESSIONS LTD.; *Int'l*, pg. 1991
DCK INTERNATIONAL, LLC—See Dck Worldwide, LLC; *U.S. Private*, pg. 1180
DCK JEWELLERY SOUTH AFRICA (PTY) LTD—See Lovisa Holdings Limited; *Int'l*, pg. 4566
DCK PACIFIC CONSTRUCTION LLC.; *U.S. Private*, pg. 1180
DCK-TTEC LLC—See Tetra Tech, Inc.; *U.S. Public*, pg. 2023
DCK WORLDWIDE, LLC; *U.S. Private*, pg. 1180
D-CLEAR LLC—See DIFC Investments LLC; *Int'l*, pg. 2118
DCLSA PROPRIETARY LIMITED—See Steinhoff International Holdings N.V.; *Int'l*, pg. 7194
D-CLUE TECHNOLOGIES CO.,LTD.—See Nisshinbo Holdings Inc.; *Int'l*, pg. 5372

COMPANY NAME INDEX

DCL YEAST LIMITED—See Compagnie des Levures Lesaffre SA; *Int'l*, pg. 1738
DC MACHINE VISION LIMITED—See Pebble Beach Systems Group PLC; *Int'l*, pg. 5778
DCM ADVANCED TECHNOLOGIES CO., LTD.—See DCM Holdings Co., Ltd.; *Int'l*, pg. 1992
DC MATERIALS, INC.—See Vulcan Materials Company; *U.S. Public*, pg. 2314
DCM AUSTRIA—See DCM DECOmetal GmbH; *Int'l*, pg. 1992
DCM CORP.; *Int'l*, pg. 1991
DCM DAIKI CO., LTD.—See DCM Holdings Co., Ltd.; *Int'l*, pg. 1992
DCM DATA SYSTEMS LIMITED—See DCM Limited; *Int'l*, pg. 1992
DCM DECOMETAL GMBH; *Int'l*, pg. 1992
DCM DRAEXLMAIER COMPONENTS AUTOMOTIVE DE MEXICO S.A. DE C.V.—See Draexlmaier Gruppe; *Int'l*, pg. 2198
DCM ENGINEERING LIMITED—See DCM Limited; *Int'l*, pg. 1992
DCM FINANCIAL SERVICES LTD.—See DCM Limited; *Int'l*, pg. 1992
DCM HOLDINGS CO., LTD.; *Int'l*, pg. 1992
DCM HOMAC CORP.—See DCM Holdings Co., Ltd.; *Int'l*, pg. 1992
DCM INDUSTRIES, INC.—See Spectris Plc; *Int'l*, pg. 7130
DCM INFOTECH LIMITED—See DCM Limited; *Int'l*, pg. 1992
DCM KAHMA CO., LTD.—See DCM Holdings Co., Ltd.; *Int'l*, pg. 1992
DCM KUROGANEYA CO., LTD.—See DCM Holdings Co., Ltd.; *Int'l*, pg. 1992
DCM LIMITED; *Int'l*, pg. 1992
DCML LIMITED—See Accident Exchange Group Plc; *Int'l*, pg. 90
DCM MANUFACTURING, INC.—See Dreison International, Inc.; *U.S. Private*, pg. 1276
DCM NICOT CO., LTD.—See DCM Holdings Co., Ltd.; *Int'l*, pg. 1992
DC MORTGAGE FINANCE NETHERLAND BV—See Societe Generale S.A.; *Int'l*, pg. 7039
DCM SANWA CO., LTD.—See DCM Holdings Co., Ltd.; *Int'l*, pg. 1992
DCM SHRIRAM INDUSTRIES LIMITED - CHEMICAL & ALCOHOL DIVISION—See DCM Shriram Industries Limited; *Int'l*, pg. 1992
DCM SHRIRAM INDUSTRIES LIMITED - RAYONS DIVISION—See DCM Shriram Industries Limited; *Int'l*, pg. 1992
DCM SHRIRAM INDUSTRIES LIMITED - SHRIRAM RAYONS WORKS—See DCM Shriram Industries Limited; *Int'l*, pg. 1992
DCM SHRIRAM INDUSTRIES LIMITED; *Int'l*, pg. 1992
DCM SHRIRAM INDUSTRIES LIMITED - SUGAR DIVISION—See DCM Shriram Industries Limited; *Int'l*, pg. 1992
DCM SHRIRAM LIMITED; *Int'l*, pg. 1992
DCM TEXTILES LIMITED—See DCM Limited; *Int'l*, pg. 1992
DCM TOOLS NV—See LKQ Corporation; *U.S. Public*, pg. 1334
DCN, LLC; *U.S. Private*, pg. 1180
DCODR DIGITAL AGENCY; *Int'l*, pg. 1992
DC OIL CO INC.—See The Kent Companies; *U.S. Private*, pg. 4065
DCOM CO. LTD.—See Bain Capital, LP; *U.S. Private*, pg. 434
DCON PRODUCTS PUBLIC COMPANY LIMITED - LOPBURI FACTORY 1—See DCON Products Public Company Limited; *Int'l*, pg. 1993
DCON PRODUCTS PUBLIC COMPANY LIMITED - LOPBURI FACTORY 2—See DCON Products Public Company Limited; *Int'l*, pg. 1993
DCON PRODUCTS PUBLIC COMPANY LIMITED; *Int'l*, pg. 1992
DCON PRODUCTS PUBLIC COMPANY LIMITED - SURAT THANI FACTORY—See DCON Products Public Company Limited; *Int'l*, pg. 1993
D. CONSTRUCTION; *U.S. Private*, pg. 1139
DCP HOLDING COMPANY—See Sun Life Financial Inc.; *Int'l*, pg. 7305
DCP, INC.—See Arthur J. Gallagher & Co.; *U.S. Public*, pg. 204
D.C. PLASTICS INC.; *U.S. Private*, pg. 1141
DCP MICHIGAN PIPELINE & PROCESSING, LLC—See Phillips 66 Company; *U.S. Public*, pg. 1688
DCP MIDSTREAM, LLC—See Phillips 66 Company; *U.S. Public*, pg. 1688
DCP MIDSTREAM, LP—See Phillips 66 Company; *U.S. Public*, pg. 1688
DC RADIO ASSETS, LLC—See Cumulus Media Inc.; *U.S. Public*, pg. 610
D-CREATE INC.—See Hakuhodo DY Holdings Incorporated; *Int'l*, pg. 3220
DCRE CO., LTD.—See OCI Holdings Co., Ltd.; *Int'l*, pg. 5519
DCR (FI) LIMITED—See Howden Group Holdings Limited; *Int'l*, pg. 3493

D.C.R. SERVICES; *U.S. Private*, pg. 1141
DCS ADVISORY LLC—See Daiwa Securities Group Inc.; *Int'l*, pg. 1947
DC SAFETY SALES, INC.—See Dubilier & Company, Inc.; *U.S. Private*, pg. 1283
DC SCIENTIFIC PEST CONTROL, INC.—See Arrow Exterminators Inc.; *U.S. Private*, pg. 335
DCS CO., LTD.—See Sika AG; *Int'l*, pg. 6917
DCS CONSULTING, INC.—See Bluestone Investment Partners, LLC; *U.S. Private*, pg. 598
DCS CORPORATION; *U.S. Private*, pg. 1180
D C SECURITY INC; *Int'l*, pg. 1899
DCS GROUP PLC—See The Reynolds & Reynolds Company; *U.S. Private*, pg. 4106
DC SHOES, INC.—See Leonard Green & Partners, L.P.; *U.S. Private*, pg. 2424
DCS INTERNATIONAL PTY. LTD.—See Pental Limited; *Int'l*, pg. 5791
DC SIX LESSEE, L.L.C.—See Pebblebrook Hotel Trust; *U.S. Public*, pg. 1660
DC-SOFTWARE DOSTER & CHRISTMANN GMBH—See Nemetschek SE; *Int'l*, pg. 5194
DCS PHARMA AG—See IMCD N.V.; *Int'l*, pg. 3621
DCS SANITATION MANAGEMENT; *U.S. Private*, pg. 1180
DCS TOWER SUB, LLC—See American Tower Corporation; *U.S. Public*, pg. 111
DC SYSTEM SP. Z O.O.—See Impel S.A.; *Int'l*, pg. 3631
D.C. TAYLOR CO.; *U.S. Private*, pg. 1141
DCT CHAMBERS TRUCKING LTD.; *Int'l*, pg. 1993
D.C. THOMSON & CO. LTD.; *Int'l*, pg. 1900
DC THOMSON VENTURES—See D.C. Thomson & Co. Ltd.; *Int'l*, pg. 1900
DCT INDUSTRIAL TRUST INC.—See Prologis, Inc.; *U.S. Public*, pg. 1726
DCT MEXICO REIT LLC—See Prologis, Inc.; *U.S. Public*, pg. 1726
DCT PAN AMERICAN LLC—See Prologis, Inc.; *U.S. Public*, pg. 1726
DC TRADING CO., LTD—See Danish Crown AmbA; *Int'l*, pg. 1964
D CUBED GROUP LLC; *U.S. Private*, pg. 1136
DC VALUE ADDED SERVICE TECHNOLOGY; *U.S. Private*, pg. 1179
D.C. VIENT INC.; *U.S. Private*, pg. 1141
DCV INC.; *U.S. Private*, pg. 1180
DCW CASING LLC—See Danish Crown AmbA; *Int'l*, pg. 1964
DCW LIMITED - SAHUPURAM UNIT—See DCW Limited; *Int'l*, pg. 1993
DCW LIMITED; *Int'l*, pg. 1993
DCX-CHOL ENTERPRISES, INC. - NEWVAC / DCX DIVISION—See DCX-CHOL Enterprises, Inc.; *U.S. Private*, pg. 1180
DCX-CHOL ENTERPRISES, INC. - SMI DIVISION—See DCX-CHOL Enterprises, Inc.; *U.S. Private*, pg. 1180
DCX-CHOL ENTERPRISES, INC.; *U.S. Private*, pg. 1180
DCX-CHOL, INC.—See DCX-CHOL Enterprises, Inc.; *U.S. Private*, pg. 1180
DCX SYSTEMS LIMITED; *Int'l*, pg. 1993
DD3 ACQUISITION CORP.; *Int'l*, pg. 1993
D. DAHLE MAZDA OF MURRAY; *U.S. Private*, pg. 1139
DDB ADVIS—See Omnicom Group Inc.; *U.S. Public*, pg. 1579
DDB AMSTERDAM—See Omnicom Group Inc.; *U.S. Public*, pg. 1579
DDB ARGENTINA—See Omnicom Group Inc.; *U.S. Public*, pg. 1580
DDB BARCELONA S.A.—See Omnicom Group Inc.; *U.S. Public*, pg. 1580
DDB BERLIN—See Omnicom Group Inc.; *U.S. Public*, pg. 1580
DDB BRAINSTORM—See Omnicom Group Inc.; *U.S. Public*, pg. 1580
DDB BRATISLAVA—See Omnicom Group Inc.; *U.S. Public*, pg. 1580
DDB BRAZIL—See Omnicom Group Inc.; *U.S. Public*, pg. 1580
DDB BUCHAREST—See Omnicom Group Inc.; *U.S. Public*, pg. 1580
DDB BUDAPEST—See Omnicom Group Inc.; *U.S. Public*, pg. 1580
DDB CANADA - EDMONTON—See Omnicom Group Inc.; *U.S. Public*, pg. 1580
DDB CANADA - TORONTO—See Omnicom Group Inc.; *U.S. Public*, pg. 1580
DDB CANADA - VANCOUVER—See Omnicom Group Inc.; *U.S. Public*, pg. 1580
DDB CASERS—See Omnicom Group Inc.; *U.S. Public*, pg. 1580
DDB CHICAGO—See Omnicom Group Inc.; *U.S. Public*, pg. 1580
DDB CHILE—See Omnicom Group Inc.; *U.S. Public*, pg. 1580
DDB CHINA - SHANGHAI—See Omnicom Group Inc.; *U.S. Public*, pg. 1580
DDB COMMUNICATION FRANCE—See Omnicom Group Inc.; *U.S. Public*, pg. 1580
DDB COSTA RICA—See Omnicom Group Inc.; *U.S. Public*, pg. 1580

DDB DENMARK—See Omnicom Group Inc.; *U.S. Public*, pg. 1580
DDB DUSSELDORF—See Omnicom Group Inc.; *U.S. Public*, pg. 1580
D.D. BEAN & SONS CO.; *U.S. Private*, pg. 1141
DDB EGYPT—See Omnicom Group Inc.; *U.S. Public*, pg. 1580
DDB ESTONIA LTD.—See Omnicom Group Inc.; *U.S. Public*, pg. 1580
DDB EUROPE—See Omnicom Group Inc.; *U.S. Public*, pg. 1580
DDB GROUP BELGIUM—See Omnicom Group Inc.; *U.S. Public*, pg. 1580
DDB GROUP GERMANY—See Omnicom Group Inc.; *U.S. Public*, pg. 1580
DDB GROUP KOREA—See Omnicom Group Inc.; *U.S. Public*, pg. 1579
DDB GUOAN COMMUNICATIONS BEIJING CO., LTD.—See Omnicom Group Inc.; *U.S. Public*, pg. 1580
DDB GUOAN - GUANGZHOU—See Omnicom Group Inc.; *U.S. Public*, pg. 1580
DDB HAMBURG GMBH—See Omnicom Group Inc.; *U.S. Public*, pg. 1580
DDB HASH THREE—See Omnicom Group Inc.; *U.S. Public*, pg. 1580
DDB HELSINKI—See Omnicom Group Inc.; *U.S. Public*, pg. 1580
DDB HONDURAS—See Omnicom Group Inc.; *U.S. Public*, pg. 1580
DDB INDONESIA—See Omnicom Group Inc.; *U.S. Public*, pg. 1580
DD BIOLAB S.L.—See Dominique Dutscher SAS; *Int'l*, pg. 2161
DDB JAPAN—See Omnicom Group Inc.; *U.S. Public*, pg. 1580
DDB LATIN AMERICA—See Omnicom Group Inc.; *U.S. Public*, pg. 1580
DDB LISBOA—See Omnicom Group Inc.; *U.S. Public*, pg. 1580
DDB LOS ANGELES—See Omnicom Group Inc.; *U.S. Public*, pg. 1580
DDB MADRID, S.A.—See Omnicom Group Inc.; *U.S. Public*, pg. 1580
DDB MELBOURNE PTY. LTD.—See Omnicom Group Inc.; *U.S. Public*, pg. 1581
DDB MEXICO—See Omnicom Group Inc.; *U.S. Public*, pg. 1581
DDB MIAMI—See Omnicom Group Inc.; *U.S. Public*, pg. 1581
DDB MOZAMBIQUE—See Omnicom Group Inc.; *U.S. Public*, pg. 1581
DDB NEW YORK—See Omnicom Group Inc.; *U.S. Public*, pg. 1581
DDB NEW ZEALAND LTD.—See Omnicom Group Inc.; *U.S. Public*, pg. 1581
DDB OSLO A.S.—See Omnicom Group Inc.; *U.S. Public*, pg. 1581
DDB PARIS—See Omnicom Group Inc.; *U.S. Public*, pg. 1581
DDB PHILIPPINES INC.—See Omnicom Group Inc.; *U.S. Public*, pg. 1581
DDB PRAGUE—See Omnicom Group Inc.; *U.S. Public*, pg. 1581
DDB REMEDY—See Omnicom Group Inc.; *U.S. Public*, pg. 1579
DDB RUSSIA—See Omnicom Group Inc.; *U.S. Public*, pg. 1581
DDB SAN FRANCISCO—See Omnicom Group Inc.; *U.S. Public*, pg. 1581
DDB SOFIA—See Omnicom Group Inc.; *U.S. Public*, pg. 1581
DDB—See Omnicom Group Inc.; *U.S. Public*, pg. 1579
DDB SOUTH AFRICA—See Omnicom Group Inc.; *U.S. Public*, pg. 1581
DDB S.R.L. ADVERTISING—See Omnicom Group Inc.; *U.S. Public*, pg. 1581
DDB SRL ADVERTISING—See Omnicom Group Inc.; *U.S. Public*, pg. 1581
DDB STOCKHOLM—See Omnicom Group Inc.; *U.S. Public*, pg. 1581
DDB SYDNEY PTY. LTD.—See Omnicom Group Inc.; *U.S. Public*, pg. 1581
DDB TRIBAL VIENNA—See Omnicom Group Inc.; *U.S. Public*, pg. 1581
D & D BUILDING, INC.; *U.S. Private*, pg. 1136
DDB UNLIMITED, INC.; *U.S. Private*, pg. 1180
DDB VIETNAM ADVERTISING—See Omnicom Group Inc.; *U.S. Public*, pg. 1581
DDB WIEN GMBH—See Omnicom Group Inc.; *U.S. Public*, pg. 1581
DDB WORLDWIDE COLOMBIA S.A.—See Omnicom Group Inc.; *U.S. Public*, pg. 1581
DDB WORLDWIDE COLOMBIA S.A.—See Omnicom Group Inc.; *U.S. Public*, pg. 1581
DDB WORLDWIDE COLOMBIA, S.A.—See Omnicom Group Inc.; *U.S. Public*, pg. 1581
DDB WORLDWIDE COMMUNICATIONS GROUP INC.—See Omnicom Group Inc.; *U.S. Public*, pg. 1579

DDB UNLIMITED, INC.

DDB WORLDWIDE INC.—See Omnicom Group Inc.; *U.S. Public*, pg. 1581
DDB WORLDWIDE LTD.—See Omnicom Group Inc.; *U.S. Public*, pg. 1581
DDB WORLDWIDE PTY. LTD.—See Omnicom Group Inc.; *U.S. Public*, pg. 1582
DDB WORLDWIDE—See Omnicom Group Inc.; *U.S. Public*, pg. 1581
DDC ELECTRONICS K.K.—See TransDigm Group Incorporated; *U.S. Public*, pg. 2182
DDC ELECTRONICS LTD.—See TransDigm Group Incorporated; *U.S. Public*, pg. 2182
DDC ELECTRONIQUE, S.A.R.L.—See TransDigm Group Incorporated; *U.S. Public*, pg. 2182
DDC ELEKTRONIK, GMBH—See TransDigm Group Incorporated; *U.S. Public*, pg. 2182
DDC ENTERPRISE LIMITED; *Int'l*, pg. 1993
DDC FREIGHT PROCESS OUTSOURCING LLC—See The DDC Group; *U.S. Private*, pg. 4019
THE DDC GROUP; *U.S. Private*, pg. 4019
D&D COMMODITIES LTD.; *U.S. Private*, pg. 1137
DD DIAMOND CORPORATION—See Semtek Co., Ltd.; *Int'l*, pg. 6706
D&D DISTRIBUTION SERVICES; *U.S. Private*, pg. 1137
DDD LTD.; *Int'l*, pg. 1993
DD DOBOJPUTEVI; *Int'l*, pg. 1993
D-DESIGN NORDIC AB—See Symphony Technology Group, LLC; *U.S. Private*, pg. 3901
DDEV PLASTIKS INDUSTRIES LIMITED; *Int'l*, pg. 1993
DDFH&B ADVERTISING LTD.—See WPP plc; *Int'l*, pg. 8479
DDFOODSOLUTIONS; *U.S. Private*, pg. 1181
DDG INC.; *U.S. Private*, pg. 1181
DDH1 LIMITED—See Perenti Global Limited; *Int'l*, pg. 5798
DD HAPPYHOMES RESIDENTIAL CENTERS INC.—See DoubleDragon Corporation; *Int'l*, pg. 2181
DDH INVESTMENTS OF SOUTH TEXAS; *U.S. Private*, pg. 1181
DDH&M ADVERTISING PTY. LTD.—See WPP plc; *Int'l*, pg. 8479
DD HOLDINGS CO., LTD.; *Int'l*, pg. 1993
DDI CUSTOMER SERVICE, INC.; *U.S. Private*, pg. 1181
DDI HOLDING AS—See Aban Offshore Limited; *Int'l*, pg. 48
DDINNOVATION CO., LTD.—See Daiwa House Industry Co., Ltd.; *Int'l*, pg. 1945
D&D INTERACTIVE; *U.S. Private*, pg. 1137
DDI TRANSPORTATION, INC.—See Ridgemont Partners Management LLC; *U.S. Private*, pg. 3433
DDJ CAPITAL MANAGEMENT, LLC—See Polen Capital Management, Inc.; *U.S. Private*, pg. 3224
DDK LTD. - MOKA PLANT—See Fujikura Ltd.; *Int'l*, pg. 2827
DDK LTD.—See Fujikura Ltd.; *Int'l*, pg. 2827
DDK (SHANGHAI) LTD.—See Fujikura Ltd.; *Int'l*, pg. 2827
DDK (THAILAND) LTD.—See Fujikura Ltd.; *Int'l*, pg. 2827
DDK (VIETNAM) LTD.—See Fujikura Ltd.; *Int'l*, pg. 2827
DDL, INC.—See Integreon Global; *U.S. Private*, pg. 2102
D. D. LITVATRANS BANOVICI; *Int'l*, pg. 1900
D&D LONDON LTD.—See Lloyds Banking Group plc; *Int'l*, pg. 4536
DDLS AUSTRALIA PTY LTD—See AWN Holdings Limited; *Int'l*, pg. 753
D&D MANAGEMENT INC.; *U.S. Private*, pg. 1137
DD MAPEX MAGLAJ; *Int'l*, pg. 1993
DDM-DIGITAL IMAGING, DATA PROCESSING AND MAILING SERVICES, L.C.—See Chatham Asset Management, LLC; *U.S. Private*, pg. 863
DDM HOLDING AG; *Int'l*, pg. 1993
DDM INVEST VII D.O.O.—See DDM Holding AG; *Int'l*, pg. 1993
DDMP REIT, INC.; *Int'l*, pg. 1993
DDN—See Dohmen Co.; *U.S. Private*, pg. 1254
D&D OF LEE COUNTY INC.; *U.S. Private*, pg. 1137
D&D OIL CO. INC.; *U.S. Private*, pg. 1137
DDOR GARANT A.D.—See Prva Group plc; *Int'l*, pg. 6010
DDOR NOVI SAD A.D.O.; *Int'l*, pg. 1993
DDP DIRECT GMBH—See Fred. Olsen & Co.; *Int'l*, pg. 2768
DD PERFORMANCE RESEARCH LLC—See HKS CO., LTD.; *Int'l*, pg. 3429
D&D PLATFORM REIT CO., LTD.; *Int'l*, pg. 1899
DD POWER HOLDINGS (PTY) LIMITED—See Hudaco Industries Limited; *Int'l*, pg. 3521
D & D POWER INC.—See Bernhard Capital Partners Management, LP; *U.S. Private*, pg. 537
DD POWER (PTY) LIMITED—See Hudaco Industries Limited; *Int'l*, pg. 3521
D.D. PROMOTERM S.R.L.—See BDR Thermea Group B.V.; *Int'l*, pg. 930
DDP ROOFING SERVICES, INC.; *U.S. Private*, pg. 1181
DDR AMERICAS INC.—See BDR Thermea Group B.V.; *Int'l*, pg. 930
DDR BUILDERS, LLC; *U.S. Private*, pg. 1181
DDR HOLDINGS LTD.; *U.S. Private*, pg. 1181
DD-ROADMAP UNTERNEHMENSBERATUNG GMBH—See BAWAG Group AG; *Int'l*, pg. 900

DDR PUERTO RICO—See SITE Centers Corp.; *U.S. Public*, pg. 1888
DDR REALTY, LLC—See DDR Builders, LLC; *U.S. Private*, pg. 1181
D&D SALADS—See Hy-Vee, Inc.; *U.S. Private*, pg. 2016
DDSB (M) SDN. BHD.—See EA Holdings Berhad; *Int'l*, pg. 2261
DDS BUILDING INNOVATION AS—See Nemetschek SE; *Int'l*, pg. 5194
THE DDS COMPANIES—See Feeney Brothers Excavation LLC; *U.S. Private*, pg. 1493
DDS CONTRACTS & INTERIOR SOLUTIONS PTE LTD—See Design Studio Group Ltd.; *Int'l*, pg. 2045
DDS CONTRACTS & INTERIOR SOLUTIONS SDN BHD—See Design Studio Group Ltd.; *Int'l*, pg. 2045
DDS CONTRACTS & INTERIOR SOLUTIONS (THAILAND) CO., LTD.—See Design Studio Group Ltd.; *Int'l*, pg. 2045
DD'S DELUXE ROD HOLDER, INC.; *Int'l*, pg. 1993
DDS DIGITAL DATA SERVICES GMBH—See Porsche Automobil Holding SE; *Int'l*, pg. 5926
DDS EFLEET SERVICES INC—See DDS Wireless International Inc.; *Int'l*, pg. 1994
D&D SERVICES (AUSTRALIA) PTY LTD.—See AVADA Group Limited; *Int'l*, pg. 734
D&D SEXTON INC.—See TFI International Inc.; *Int'l*, pg. 7586
DD & SF INVESTMENTS, INC.; *U.S. Private*, pg. 1180
DDS, INC.; *Int'l*, pg. 1994
DDS KOREA, INC.—See DDS, Inc.; *Int'l*, pg. 1994
DDS LAB, LLC—See RoundTable Healthcare Management, Inc.; *U.S. Private*, pg. 3489
D&D SPRINGS POLAND CO., LTD—See SAMWON-STEEL Co., Ltd.; *Int'l*, pg. 6519
DDS S.P.A.—See IVS Group S.A.; *Int'l*, pg. 3848
DDS WIRELESS INTERNATIONAL INC.; *Int'l*, pg. 1993
DD TECHNICHE SDN. BHD.—See AWC Berhad; *Int'l*, pg. 752
D&D TEXAS OUTFITTERS INC.; *U.S. Private*, pg. 1137
D&D TOOLING MANUFACTURING, INC.; *U.S. Private*, pg. 1137
DD TRADERS, INC.; *U.S. Private*, pg. 1180
D&D TRAFFIC MANAGEMENT PTY LTD.—See AVADA Group Limited; *Int'l*, pg. 734
D&D TRANSPORTATION SERVICES; *U.S. Private*, pg. 1137
DDW COLOURS SDN. BHD.—See Givaudan S.A.; *Int'l*, pg. 2979
D.D. WILLIAMSON & CO., INC.; *U.S. Private*, pg. 1141
DDW, INC.; *U.S. Private*, pg. 1181
DDW OFFSHORE AS—See Akastor ASA; *Int'l*, pg. 260
DDW-PAXOCEAN ASIA - GRAHA—See Kuok (Singapore) Limited; *Int'l*, pg. 4334
DDW-PAXOCEAN ASIA - NANINDAH—See Kuok (Singapore) Limited; *Int'l*, pg. 4334
DDW-PAXOCEAN ASIA PTE. LTD.—See Kuok (Singapore) Limited; *Int'l*, pg. 4334
DE 100 WILSHIRE, LLC—See Douglas Emmett, Inc.; *U.S. Public*, pg. 678
DE 8484 WILSHIRE, LLC—See Douglas Emmett, Inc.; *U.S. Public*, pg. 678
DEA CAPITAL SPA—See De Agostini S.p.A.; *Int'l*, pg. 1994
DEA COMMUNICATIONS SA—See De Agostini S.p.A.; *Int'l*, pg. 1995
DEACONESS ABUNDANT LIFE COMMUNITIES; *U.S. Private*, pg. 1182
DEACONESS HOLDINGS, LLC—See Community Health Systems, Inc.; *U.S. Public*, pg. 552
DEACONESS HOMECARE, LLC—See UnitedHealth Group Incorporated; *U.S. Public*, pg. 2244
DEACONESS PHYSICIAN SERVICES, LLC—See Community Health Systems, Inc.; *U.S. Public*, pg. 552
DEACON INDUSTRIAL SUPPLY COMPANY INC.—See The Macomb Group, Inc.; *U.S. Private*, pg. 4073
DEACON JONES AUTO GROUP; *U.S. Private*, pg. 1181
DEACON JONES AUTO PARK; *U.S. Private*, pg. 1181
DEACON'S LODGE GOLF COURSE—See Whitebirch Enterprises, Inc.; *U.S. Private*, pg. 4511
DEACON TRANSPORTATION INC.—See Historic Tours of America Inc.; *U.S. Private*, pg. 1952
DEA DEUTSCHE ERDOEL AG—See BASF SE; *Int'l*, pg. 885
DEADLINE BUSINESS MEDIA, LLC—See Penske Media Corporation; *U.S. Private*, pg. 3139
DEAD RIVER COMPANY - COUNTRY OIL—See Dead River Company; *U.S. Private*, pg. 1182
DEAD RIVER COMPANY - FLEMING OIL DIVISION—See Dead River Company; *U.S. Private*, pg. 1182
DEAD RIVER COMPANY; *U.S. Private*, pg. 1182
DEAD RIVER COMPANY - WEBBER ENERGY FUELS DIVISION—See Dead River Company; *U.S. Private*, pg. 1182
DEAD RIVER PETROLEUM CO.—See Dead River Company; *U.S. Private*, pg. 1182
DEAD RIVER PROPERTIES—See Dead River Company; *U.S. Private*, pg. 1182
DEAD RIVER TRANSPORT—See Dead River Company; *U.S. Private*, pg. 1182

DEAD SEA BROMINE COMPANY LTD.—See Israel Corporation Ltd.; *Int'l*, pg. 3823
DEAG CLASSICS AG—See DEAG Deutsche Entertainment AG; *Int'l*, pg. 1997
DEAG CONCERTS GMBH—See DEAG Deutsche Entertainment AG; *Int'l*, pg. 1997
DEAG DEUTSCHE ENTERTAINMENT AG; *Int'l*, pg. 1997
DEA GENERAL AVIATION HOLDING CO., LTD.; *Int'l*, pg. 1997
DEAG MUSIC GMBH—See DEAG Deutsche Entertainment AG; *Int'l*, pg. 1998
DE AGOSTINI COMMUNICATIONS S.P.A—See De Agostini S.p.A.; *Int'l*, pg. 1994
DE AGOSTINI EDITORE S.P.A.—See De Agostini S.p.A.; *Int'l*, pg. 1994
DE AGOSTINI LIBRI S.P.A.—See De Agostini S.p.A.; *Int'l*, pg. 1994
DE AGOSTINI PUBLISHING ITALIA S.P.A.—See De Agostini S.p.A.; *Int'l*, pg. 1994
DE AGOSTINI S.P.A.; *Int'l*, pg. 1994
D&E AIR CONDITIONING PTY. LIMITED; *Int'l*, pg. 1899
DEALCYBER LIMITED—See GSK plc; *Int'l*, pg. 3145
DEA LEASING IFN S.A.—See Banca Transilvania S.A.; *Int'l*, pg. 816
DEALER ASSOCIATES, INC.—See Brown & Brown, Inc.; *U.S. Public*, pg. 399
DEALER.COM, INC.; *U.S. Private*, pg. 1182
DEALER DOT COM, INC.—See Cox Enterprises, Inc.; *U.S. Private*, pg. 1074
DEALER FUSION, INC.—See Flick Fusion LLC; *U.S. Private*, pg. 1544
DEALER-FX GROUP—See Snap-on Incorporated; *U.S. Public*, pg. 1897
DEALER-FX NORTH AMERICA GROUP INC.—See Snap-on Incorporated; *U.S. Public*, pg. 1897
DEALER IGNITION, LLC; *U.S. Private*, pg. 1182
DEALER IMPORTS INC.; *U.S. Private*, pg. 1182
DEALER INFO SYSTEMS CORP.; *U.S. Private*, pg. 1182
DEALER INSPIRE INC.—See Cars.com Inc.; *U.S. Public*, pg. 444
DEALERON, INC.; *U.S. Private*, pg. 1182
DEALER PRODUCT SERVICES, INC.—See Affinitiv, Inc.; *U.S. Private*, pg. 122
DEALERRATER; *U.S. Private*, pg. 1182
DEALERS ALLIANCE CORPORATION; *U.S. Private*, pg. 1182
DEALERS ASSURANCE COMPANY—See iA Financial Corporation Inc.; *Int'l*, pg. 3567
DEALER'S AUTO AUCTION GROUP; *U.S. Private*, pg. 1182
DEALERSCIENCE, LLC—See TrueCar, Inc.; *U.S. Public*, pg. 2199
DEALERS ELECTRICAL SUPPLY CO.; *U.S. Private*, pg. 1182
DEALERS' FINANCIAL SERVICES, LLC—See Lone Star Global Acquisitions, LLC; *U.S. Private*, pg. 2487
DEALERSHIP LIQUIDATIONS, INC.—See General Motors Company; *U.S. Public*, pg. 924
DEALERSOCKET, INC.—See Vista Equity Partners, LLC; *U.S. Private*, pg. 4400
DEALERS SUPPLY COMPANY INC.; *U.S. Private*, pg. 1182
DEALERS SUPPLY COMPANY; *U.S. Private*, pg. 1182
DEALERS TRUCK EQUIPMENT CO. INC.; *U.S. Private*, pg. 1182
DEALERS TRUCK EQUIPMENT, INC.—See Manning Enterprises Inc.; *U.S. Private*, pg. 2565
DEALERS UNITED LLC; *U.S. Private*, pg. 1182
DEALERTRACK DIGITAL SERVICES, INC.—See Cox Enterprises, Inc.; *U.S. Private*, pg. 1074
DEALERTRACK, INC.—See Cox Enterprises, Inc.; *U.S. Private*, pg. 1074
DEALERTRACK REGISTRATION AND TITLING SOLUTIONS, INC.—See Cox Enterprises, Inc.; *U.S. Private*, pg. 1074
DEALERTRACK REGISTRATION & TITLING SERVICES-LOUISIANA, LLC—See Cox Enterprises, Inc.; *U.S. Private*, pg. 1074
DEALERTRACK SYSTEMS, INC.—See Cox Enterprises, Inc.; *U.S. Private*, pg. 1074
DEALERWEB INC.—See Tradeweb Markets Inc.; *U.S. Public*, pg. 2178
DEALER WORLD LLC; *U.S. Private*, pg. 1182
DEALIX CORPORATION—See One Planet Group LLC; *U.S. Private*, pg. 3020
THE DEAL, LLC—See Astorg Partners S.A.S.; *Int'l*, pg. 656
THE DEAL, LLC—See Epiris Managers LLP; *Int'l*, pg. 2461
DEALMED MEDICAL SUPPLIES LLC; *U.S. Private*, pg. 1182
DEALMONEY DISTRIBUTION & E-MARKETING PRIVATE LIMITED—See Onelife Capital Advisors Limited; *Int'l*, pg. 5576
DEALMONEY REAL ESTATE PRIVATE LIMITED—See Onelife Capital Advisors Limited; *Int'l*, pg. 5576
DEALNET CAPITAL CORP.—See Simply Group; *Int'l*, pg. 6934
DEALOGIC LIMITED—See Ion Equity Limited; *Int'l*, pg. 3793

COMPANY NAME INDEX

DEALOGIC LIMITED—See Ion Equity Limited; *Int'l*, pg. 3793
DEALOGIC LLC—See Ion Equity Limited; *Int'l*, pg. 3793
DEALON, LLC—See Gannett Co., Inc.; *U.S. Public*, pg. 899
DEAL TAG S.A.—See TXCOM S.A.; *Int'l*, pg. 7993
DEALT LIMITED; *Int'l*, pg. 1998
DE AMERSFOORTSE VERZEKERINGEN N.V.—See ASR Nederland N.V.; *Int'l*, pg. 632
DE AMERTEK CORPORATION INC.; *U.S. Private*, pg. 1181
DEAN ARBOUR CHEVROLET CADILLAC; *U.S. Private*, pg. 1183
DEANCO AUCTION & REAL ESTATE CO, INC.; *U.S. Private*, pg. 1185
DEAN & COMPANY; *U.S. Private*, pg. 1183
DEAN COOLEY GM; *Int'l*, pg. 1998
DEAN DAIRY HOLDINGS, LLC—See Dean Foods Company; *U.S. Private*, pg. 1183
DEAN DAIRY PRODUCTS COMPANY, LLC—See Dean Foods Company; *U.S. Private*, pg. 1183
DEAN & DELUCA—See Pace Development Corporation Public Co., Ltd.; *Int'l*, pg. 5685
DEAN DORTON ALLEN FORD, PLLC; *U.S. Private*, pg. 1183
DEAN & DRAPER INSURANCE AGENCY, LP; *U.S. Private*, pg. 1183
DEAN EVANS & ASSOCIATES, INC.; *U.S. Private*, pg. 1183
DEAN FENCE & GATE, INC.; *U.S. Private*, pg. 1183
DEAN FOODS COMPANY OF INDIANA, LLC—See Dean Foods Company; *U.S. Private*, pg. 1183
DEAN FOODS COMPANY—See Dean Foods Company; *U.S. Private*, pg. 1184
DEAN FOODS COMPANY—See Dean Foods Company; *U.S. Private*, pg. 1184
DEAN FOODS COMPANY; *U.S. Private*, pg. 1183
DEAN FOODS NORTH CENTRAL, LLC—See Dean Foods Company; *U.S. Private*, pg. 1184
DEANGELIS DIAMOND CONSTRUCTION, INC.; *U.S. Private*, pg. 1185
DEANGELO BROTHERS INC.—See Sterling Partners; *U.S. Private*, pg. 3806
DEAN HEALTH SYSTEMS, INC.—See SSM Health Care Corporation; *U.S. Private*, pg. 3789
DEANHOUSTON, INC.; *U.S. Private*, pg. 1185
DEAN JOHNSTON INC.; *U.S. Private*, pg. 1184
DEAN KURTZ CONSTRUCTION; *U.S. Private*, pg. 1184
DEAN LUMBER & SUPPLY CO.; *U.S. Private*, pg. 1184
DEAN MARKLEY STRINGS, INC.; *U.S. Private*, pg. 1184
DEAN MILK COMPANY, LLC—See Dean Foods Company; *U.S. Private*, pg. 1183
DEAN MORGAN K.K.—See Link & Motivation Inc.; *Int'l*, pg. 4513
DEANNA ENTERPRISES INC.; *U.S. Private*, pg. 1185
DEANNES OFFICE & COMPUTER SUPPLIES; *U.S. Private*, pg. 1185
DEAN ONE B.V.—See Gamma Communications PLC; *Int'l*, pg. 2878
DEAN OPERATIONS, INC.; *U.S. Private*, pg. 1184
DEA NORGE AS—See BASF SE; *Int'l*, pg. 885
DEA NORGE AS—See LetterOne Holdings S.A.; *Int'l*, pg. 4470
DEAN PUMP—See CECO Environmental Corp.; *U.S. Public*, pg. 464
DEAN REALTY CO—See Dean Operations, Inc.; *U.S. Private*, pg. 1184
DEAN ROOFING CO. INC.; *U.S. Private*, pg. 1184
DEAN SAUSAGE COMPANY INC.; *U.S. Private*, pg. 1184
DEAN SELLERS FORD INC.; *U.S. Private*, pg. 1184
DEAN'S ICE CREAM—See Dean Foods Company; *U.S. Private*, pg. 1184
DEANS KNIGHT CAPITAL MANAGEMENT LTD.—See Affiliated Managers Group, Inc.; *U.S. Public*, pg. 54
DEAN SNYDER CONSTRUCTION COMPANY; *U.S. Private*, pg. 1184
DEANS OIL COMPANY INC.; *U.S. Private*, pg. 1185
DEAN'S PROFESSIONAL SERVICES, INC.; *U.S. Private*, pg. 1184
DEANS RV SUPERSTORE INC.; *U.S. Private*, pg. 1185
DEAN STEEL BUILDINGS INC.; *U.S. Private*, pg. 1184
DEAN & WOOD LTD.—See Beijer Ref AB; *Int'l*, pg. 944
DEAN WORD COMPANY LTD.; *U.S. Private*, pg. 1184
DEAP CAPITAL MANAGEMENT & TRUST PLC; *Int'l*, pg. 1998
DEARBORN COUNTY HOSPITAL; *U.S. Private*, pg. 1185
DEARBORN CRANE & ENGINEERING CO.; *U.S. Private*, pg. 1185
DEARBORN FEDERAL SAVINGS BANK; *U.S. Private*, pg. 1185
DEARBORN INDUSTRIAL GENERATION, L.L.C.—See CMS Energy Corporation; *U.S. Public*, pg. 518
DEARBORN KIDNEY CENTER, LLC—See Nautic Partners, LLC; *U.S. Private*, pg. 2869
DEARBORN MIDWEST CONVEYOR CO.—See ONEX Corporation; *Int'l*, pg. 5578
DEARBORN MOTORS; *Int'l*, pg. 1998
DEARBORN MOVING & STORAGE INC.; *U.S. Private*, pg. 1185

DEARBORN NATIONAL LIFE INSURANCE COMPANY—See Health Care Service Corporation; *U.S. Private*, pg. 1892
DEARBORN RESOURCES, INC.; *U.S. Private*, pg. 1185
DEARBORN SAVINGS BANK—See DSA Financial Corp.; *U.S. Public*, pg. 689
DEARBORN WHOLESALE GROCERS LP; *U.S. Private*, pg. 1185
DEARCO DISTRIBUTING INC.—See Eponk Group Ltd.; *U.S. Private*, pg. 1414
DEARDEN'S; *U.S. Private*, pg. 1185
DEARDORFF-JACKSON COMPANY; *U.S. Private*, pg. 1185
DEAR GARDEN ASSOCIATES, INC.; *U.S. Private*, pg. 1185
DEARING & DEARING; *U.S. Private*, pg. 1185
DEAR LIFE CO., LTD.; *Int'l*, pg. 1998
DEARONE, INC.—See Nippon Telegraph & Telephone Corporation; *Int'l*, pg. 5340
DEARYBURY OIL & GAS INC.; *U.S. Private*, pg. 1185
DEAS A/S—See Montagu Private Equity LLP; *Int'l*, pg. 5036
DEAS HOLDING A/S—See Montagu Private Equity LLP; *Int'l*, pg. 5036
DEATH VALLEY CONSERVANCY; *U.S. Private*, pg. 1185
DEATLEY CRUSHING COMPANY; *U.S. Private*, pg. 1185
DEAUVILLE DIAMOND PROPERTIES SA; *Int'l*, pg. 1998
DEAUVILLE HOTEL MANAGEMENT, LLC; *U.S. Private*, pg. 1185
DEBARTOLO CORPORATION; *U.S. Private*, pg. 1186
DEBARTOLO DEVELOPMENT, LLC—See DeBartolo Holdings, LLC; *U.S. Private*, pg. 1186
DEBARTOLO FAMILY FOUNDATION—See DeBartolo Holdings, LLC; *U.S. Private*, pg. 1186
DEBARTOLO HOLDINGS, LLC; *U.S. Private*, pg. 1186
DEBARY GOLF & COUNTRY CLUB—See Apollo Global Management, Inc.; *U.S. Public*, pg. 149
DEBATIN UK LTD—See Anton Debatin GmbH; *Int'l*, pg. 484
DEB AUSTRALIA PTY LIMITED—See S.C. Johnson & Son, Inc.; *U.S. Private*, pg. 3515
DEBBIE'S STAFFING SERVICES; *U.S. Private*, pg. 1186
DEB CANADA—See S.C. Johnson & Son, Inc.; *U.S. Private*, pg. 3515
DEB CONSTRUCTION; *U.S. Private*, pg. 1186
D&E BEARINGS AB; *Int'l*, pg. 1899
D&E BEARINGS OY; *Int'l*, pg. 1899
DE BEERS AUCTION SALES BELGIUM N.V.—See Anglo American PLC; *Int'l*, pg. 462
DE BEERS AUCTION SALES HONG KONG LIMITED—See Anglo American PLC; *Int'l*, pg. 462
DE BEERS AUCTION SALES ISRAEL LTD—See Anglo American PLC; *Int'l*, pg. 462
DE BEERS AUCTION SALES SINGAPORE PTE LTD—See Anglo American PLC; *Int'l*, pg. 462
DE BEERS CANADA—See Anglo American PLC; *Int'l*, pg. 462
DE BEERS CONSOLIDATED MINES LIMITED—See Anglo American PLC; *Int'l*, pg. 462
DE BEERS DIAMOND JEWELLERS US, INC.—See Anglo American PLC; *Int'l*, pg. 462
DE BEERS GROUP OF COMPANIES—See Anglo American PLC; *Int'l*, pg. 462
DE BEERS INDIA PVT. LTD—See Anglo American PLC; *Int'l*, pg. 462
DE BEERS JEWELLERS JAPAN K.K.—See Anglo American PLC; *Int'l*, pg. 462
DE BEERS NAMIBIA HOLDINGS (PTY) LTD.—See Anglo American PLC; *Int'l*, pg. 462
DE BEERS PLC.—See Anglo American PLC; *Int'l*, pg. 462
DE BEERS SOCIETE ANONYME—See Anglo American PLC; *Int'l*, pg. 462
DE BEERS UK LIMITED—See Anglo American PLC; *Int'l*, pg. 462
DEBEKO IMMOBILIEN GMBH & CO GRUNDBESITZ OHG—See Deutsche Bank Aktiengesellschaft; *Int'l*, pg. 2057
DEBEL ROOFING SUPPLY, INC.—See Leonard Green & Partners, L.P.; *U.S. Private*, pg. 2429
DEBENHAMS PLC; *Int'l*, pg. 1998
DEBENHAMS PROPERTIES LIMITED—See Debenhams plc; *Int'l*, pg. 1998
DEBEN UK LIMITED—See Judges Scientific plc; *Int'l*, pg. 4021
DEBEVOISE & PLIMPTON LLP; *U.S. Private*, pg. 1186
DEBFLEX INC.; *U.S. Private*, pg. 1998
DEB FRANCE SAS—See S.C. Johnson & Son, Inc.; *U.S. Private*, pg. 3515
DEB GROUP LIMITED—See S.C. Johnson & Son, Inc.; *U.S. Private*, pg. 3515
DEB GROUP MALAYSIA SDN BHD—See S.C. Johnson & Son, Inc.; *U.S. Private*, pg. 3515
DEB IBERIA S.L.—See S.C. Johnson & Son, Inc.; *U.S. Private*, pg. 3515
DE BIJENKORF—See KKR & Co. Inc.; *U.S. Public*, pg. 1261
DEBITEK, INC.—See Global Payments Inc.; *U.S. Public*, pg. 944
DEBITEL AG—See freenet AG; *Int'l*, pg. 2770

DEBITEL KONZERNFINANZIERUNGS GMBH—See freenet AG; *Int'l*, pg. 2770
DEBITOR-INKASSO GMBH—See IK Investment Partners Limited; *Int'l*, pg. 3609
DEBITUM INVEST REIT; *Int'l*, pg. 1998
DEBMAR-MERCURY, LLC—See Lions Gate Entertainment Corp.; *Int'l*, pg. 4520
DEB NEW ZEALAND—See S.C. Johnson & Son, Inc.; *U.S. Private*, pg. 3515
DEBOCK SALES & MARKETING LTD.; *Int'l*, pg. 1998
DE BOERTIEN GROEP B.V.; *Int'l*, pg. 1995
DEBOER TRANSPORTATION, INC.—See Schneider National, Inc.; *U.S. Public*, pg. 1847
DEBOFFE; *Int'l*, pg. 1998
DEBOLES NUTRITIONAL FOODS, INC.—See The Hain Celestial Group, Inc.; *U.S. Public*, pg. 2086
DEBONAIRS PIZZA (PTY) LTD.—See Famous Brands Limited; *Int'l*, pg. 2612
DEBORAH SERVICES LIMITED—See Siteserv Investments Limited; *Int'l*, pg. 6964
DE BOSMAN BEDRIJVEN B.V.—See VINCI S.A.; *Int'l*, pg. 8216
DEBRA-KUEMPEL—See EMCOR Group, Inc.; *U.S. Public*, pg. 736
DEBRAND INC.; *U.S. Private*, pg. 1186
DEBRECENI KOMBINALT CIKLUSU EROMU KFT.—See E.ON SE; *Int'l*, pg. 2251
DEBRINO CAULKING ASSOCIATES; *U.S. Private*, pg. 1186
DEBRO CHEMICALS LTD; *Int'l*, pg. 1998
DEBRO STEEL LTD.—See Amalgamated Metal Corporation PLC; *Int'l*, pg. 408
DEBRUNNER ACIFER AG—See Klockner & Co. SE; *Int'l*, pg. 4202
DEBRUNNER ACIFER AG WALLIS—See Klockner & Co. SE; *Int'l*, pg. 4202
DEBRUNNER ACIFER BEWEHRUNGEN AG—See Klockner & Co. SE; *Int'l*, pg. 4202
DEBRUNNER ACIFER S.A. GIUBIASCO—See Klockner & Co. SE; *Int'l*, pg. 4202
DEBRUNNER ACIFER S.A. ROMANDIE—See Klockner & Co. SE; *Int'l*, pg. 4202
DEBRUNNER KOENIG HOLDING AG—See Klockner & Co. SE; *Int'l*, pg. 4202
DEBRUNNER KOENIG MANAGEMENT AG—See Klockner & Co. SE; *Int'l*, pg. 4202
DEBRUNNER KOENIG—See Klockner & Co. SE; *Int'l*, pg. 4202
DE BRUYN PROFESSIONAL COATINGS NV—See LKQ Corporation; *U.S. Public*, pg. 1334
DEB SHOPS, INC.—See Lee Equity Partners LLC; *U.S. Private*, pg. 2412
DEB SINGAPORE PTE. LTD.—See S.C. Johnson & Son, Inc.; *U.S. Private*, pg. 3515
DEB-STOKO EUROPE GMBH—See S.C. Johnson & Son, Inc.; *U.S. Private*, pg. 3516
DEB-STOKO EUROPE GMBH—See S.C. Johnson & Son, Inc.; *U.S. Private*, pg. 3516
DEB SVERIGE AB—See S.C. Johnson & Son, Inc.; *U.S. Private*, pg. 3515
DEBSWANA DIAMOND COMPANY (PTY) LTD—See Anglo American PLC; *Int'l*, pg. 462
DEB SWARFEGA A/S—See S.C. Johnson & Son, Inc.; *U.S. Private*, pg. 3515
DEB SWARFEGA NORGE AS—See S.C. Johnson & Son, Inc.; *U.S. Private*, pg. 3515
THE DEBT ADVICE PORTAL LIMITED—See ClearDebt Group Plc; *Int'l*, pg. 1657
DEBT FREE ASSOCIATES; *U.S. Private*, pg. 1186
DEBTMERICA, LLC; *U.S. Private*, pg. 1186
DEBT RESOLVE, INC.; *U.S. Public*, pg. 645
DEBTSCAPE, INC.; *U.S. Private*, pg. 1186
DEBTVISION GMBH—See Landesbank Baden-Wurttemberg; *Int'l*, pg. 4405
DEB USA, INC.—See S.C. Johnson & Son, Inc.; *U.S. Private*, pg. 3516
DEBUSCHERE SA; *Int'l*, pg. 1999
DEBUT BROADCASTING CORPORATION, INC.; *U.S. Private*, pg. 1186
DEBUT DIAMONDS INC.; *Int'l*, pg. 1999
DEB WHOLESALE, INC.; *U.S. Private*, pg. 1186
DECA CABLES INC.; *Int'l*, pg. 1999
DECADE RESOURCES LTD.; *Int'l*, pg. 1999
DECADIA GMBH—See RWE AG; *Int'l*, pg. 6434
DECAHEDRON LTD.—See COSMOS HEALTH INC.; *U.S. Public*, pg. 585
DECA INVESTMENTS AIFM; *Int'l*, pg. 1999
DECALU NV—See Deceuninck NV; *Int'l*, pg. 1999
DECALU SOLUTIONS SP. Z O.O.—See Deceuninck NV; *Int'l*, pg. 1999
DECAMA CAPITAL LTD.; *Int'l*, pg. 1999
DECA PIAZZA—See Itausa - Investimentos Itau S.A.; *Int'l*, pg. 3831
DE CAPUA ENTERPRISES INC.; *U.S. Private*, pg. 1181
DECARE DENTAL INSURANCE IRELAND, LTD.—See Elevance Health, Inc.; *U.S. Public*, pg. 729
DECARE DENTAL; *U.S. Private*, pg. 1186
DECARE OPERATIONS IRELAND, LIMITED—See Elevance Health, Inc.; *U.S. Public*, pg. 729

DECARE DENTAL

DECARE SYSTEMS IRELAND, LIMITED—See Elevance Health, Inc.; *U.S. Public*, pg. 729
DECAROLIS DESIGN & MARKETING, INC.; *U.S. Private*, pg. 1186
DECAROLIS TRUCK RENTAL INC.—See Mitsui & Co., Ltd.; *Int'l*, pg. 4979
DECAROLIS TRUCK RENTAL INC.—See Penske Automotive Group, Inc.; *U.S. Public*, pg. 1665
DECAROLIS TRUCK RENTAL INC.—See Penske Corporation; *U.S. Private*, pg. 3139
DECA—See Itausa - Investimentos Itau S.A.; *Int'l*, pg. 3831
DECA SYSTEM INC.; *Int'l*, pg. 1999
DECA TECHNOLOGIES INC.—See Infineon Technologies AG; *Int'l*, pg. 3685
DECATHLON CLUB—See KKR & Co. Inc.; *U.S. Public*, pg. 1264
DECATHLON SA; *Int'l*, pg. 1999
DECATHLON USA—See Decathlon SA; *Int'l*, pg. 1999
DECATUR COOPERATIVE ASSOCIATION; *U.S. Private*, pg. 1186
DECATUR HAND AND PHYSICAL THERAPY SPECIALISTS, LIMITED PARTNERSHIP—See U.S. Physical Therapy, Inc.; *U.S. Public*, pg. 2214
DECATUR INDUSTRIAL ELECTRIC; *U.S. Private*, pg. 1186
DECATUR MORGAN HOMECARE—See UnitedHealth Group Incorporated; *U.S. Public*, pg. 2244
DECATUR TRUCK & TRACTOR INC.; *U.S. Private*, pg. 1186
DECAVO LLC—See HEICO Corporation; *U.S. Public*, pg. 1019
DECAWAVE LIMITED—See Qorvo, Inc.; *U.S. Public*, pg. 1743
DECAWAVE (SHENZHEN) LIMITED—See Qorvo, Inc.; *U.S. Public*, pg. 1743
DECCA DESIGN & DEVELOPMENT INC.; *U.S. Private*, pg. 1187
DECCA MUSIC GROUP LTD.—See Universal Music Group N.V.; *Int'l*, pg. 8079
DECCAN ALLOY METAL INDUSTRIES PVT. LTD.—See Chowgule & Company Pvt. Ltd.; *Int'l*, pg. 1585
DECCAN BEARINGS LIMITED; *Int'l*, pg. 1999
DECCAN CEMENTS LIMITED; *Int'l*, pg. 1999
DECCAN CHRONICLE HOLDINGS LTD.; *Int'l*, pg. 1999
DECCAN FINE CHEMICALS (INDIA) PVT. LTD.—See Mitsubishi Corporation; *Int'l*, pg. 4938
DECCAN GOLD MINES LTD.; *Int'l*, pg. 1999
DECCAN HEALTH CARE LTD.; *Int'l*, pg. 1999
DECCAN POLYPACKS LIMITED; *Int'l*, pg. 1999
DECCO IBERICA POST COSECHA, S.A.—See UPL Limited; *Int'l*, pg. 8089
DECCO IBERICA POST COSECHA S.A.U.—See UPL Limited; *Int'l*, pg. 8089
DECCO INC.—See Comfort Systems USA, Inc.; *U.S. Public*, pg. 543
DECCO ITALIA SRL—See UPL Limited; *Int'l*, pg. 8089
DECCO US POST-HARVEST, INC.—See UPL Limited; *Int'l*, pg. 8089
DE CECCO DEUTSCHLAND GMBH—See Fratelli De Cecco Di Filippo Fara San Martino S.p.A.; *Int'l*, pg. 2767
DE CECCO FRANCE SARL—See Fratelli De Cecco Di Filippo Fara San Martino S.p.A.; *Int'l*, pg. 2767
DE CECCO U.K. LTD—See Fratelli De Cecco Di Filippo Fara San Martino S.p.A.; *Int'l*, pg. 2767
DECENCIA INC.—See Pola Orbis Holdings Inc.; *Int'l*, pg. 5905
DECENTRAL LIFE, INC.; *U.S. Public*, pg. 645
DE CENTRUM DEVELOPMENT SDN BHD—See Protasco Berhad; *Int'l*, pg. 6003
DECERNIS LLC—See Berkshire Partners LLC; *U.S. Private*, pg. 534
DECERNO AB—See Addnode Group AB; *Int'l*, pg. 130
DECERNO VAST AB—See Addnode Group AB; *Int'l*, pg. 130
DECEUNINCK BALTIC UAB—See Deceuninck NV; *Int'l*, pg. 1999
DECEUNINCK BEHEER BV—See Deceuninck NV; *Int'l*, pg. 1999
DECEUNINCK BULGARIA EOOD—See Deceuninck NV; *Int'l*, pg. 2000
DECEUNINCK DE MEXICO S.A. DE C.V.—See Deceuninck NV; *Int'l*, pg. 2000
DECEUNINCK DO BRAZIL LTDA.—See Deceuninck NV; *Int'l*, pg. 2000
DECEUNINCK D.O.O.—See Deceuninck NV; *Int'l*, pg. 2000
DECEUNINCK D.O.O.—See Deceuninck NV; *Int'l*, pg. 2000
DECEUNINCK D.O.O.—See Deceuninck NV; *Int'l*, pg. 2000
DECEUNINCK GERMANY GMBH—See Deceuninck NV; *Int'l*, pg. 2000
DECEUNINCK GERMANY PRODUKTIONS GMBH & CO. KG—See Deceuninck NV; *Int'l*, pg. 2000
DECEUNINCK HOLDING GERMANY GMBH—See Deceuninck NV; *Int'l*, pg. 1999

DECEUNINCK HOLDINGS UK LTD—See Deceuninck NV; *Int'l*, pg. 2000
DECEUNINCK IMPORTADORA LIMITADA—See Deceuninck NV; *Int'l*, pg. 2000
DECEUNINCK ITALIA SRL—See Deceuninck NV; *Int'l*, pg. 1999
DECEUNINCK KUNSTSTOF B.V.—See Deceuninck NV; *Int'l*, pg. 2000
DECEUNINCK LTD.—See Deceuninck NV; *Int'l*, pg. 2000
DECEUNINCK NORTH AMERICA INC.—See Deceuninck NV; *Int'l*, pg. 2000
DECEUNINCK NORTH AMERICA LLC—See Deceuninck NV; *Int'l*, pg. 2000
DECEUNINCK NV; *Int'l*, pg. 1999
DECEUNINCK NV SUCURSAL EM PORTUGAL—See Deceuninck NV; *Int'l*, pg. 2000
DECEUNINCK NV SUCURSAL EN ESPANA—See Deceuninck NV; *Int'l*, pg. 2000
DECEUNINCK POLAND SP. Z O.O.—See Deceuninck NV; *Int'l*, pg. 2000
DECEUNINCK PROFILES INDIA PRIVATE LIMITED—See Deceuninck NV; *Int'l*, pg. 2000
DECEUNINCK PTY. LTD.—See Deceuninck NV; *Int'l*, pg. 2000
DECEUNINCK ROMANIA SRL—See Deceuninck NV; *Int'l*, pg. 2000
DECEUNINCK RUS OOO—See Deceuninck NV; *Int'l*, pg. 2000
DECEUNINCK SA—See Deceuninck NV; *Int'l*, pg. 2000
DECEUNINCK S.A.S.—See Deceuninck NV; *Int'l*, pg. 2000
DECEUNINCK SP. Z O.O.—See Deceuninck NV; *Int'l*, pg. 2000
DECEUNINCK (THAILAND) CO., LTD.—See Deceuninck NV; *Int'l*, pg. 1999
DE CEUYNCK & CO NV—See EssilorLuxottica SA; *Int'l*, pg. 2512
DECHAN II, INC.; *U.S. Private*, pg. 1187
DECHANOZ SAS—See VINCI S.A.; *Int'l*, pg. 8216
DECHELETTE MALLEVAL SA; *Int'l*, pg. 2000
DECHENG TECHNOLOGY AG—See Rostra Holdings Pte. Ltd.; *Int'l*, pg. 6401
DECHERT LLP; *U.S. Private*, pg. 1187
DECHOW DIENSTLEISTUNGS GMBH—See VINCI S.A.; *Int'l*, pg. 8236
DECHRA LABORATORY SERVICES—See Patterson Companies, Inc.; *U.S. Public*, pg. 1654
DECHRA LTD.—See EQT AB; *Int'l*, pg. 2474
DECHRA PHARMACEUTICALS MANUFACTURING - UK—See EQT AB; *Int'l*, pg. 2474
DECHRA PHARMACEUTICALS PLC—See EQT AB; *Int'l*, pg. 2474
DECHRA PRODUCTOS VETERINARIOS, S.A. DE C.V.—See EQT AB; *Int'l*, pg. 2474
DECHRA VETERINARY PRODUCTS AB—See EQT AB; *Int'l*, pg. 2474
DECHRA VETERINARY PRODUCTS AS—See EQT AB; *Int'l*, pg. 2474
DECHRA VETERINARY PRODUCTS (AUSTRALIA) PTY LIMITED—See EQT AB; *Int'l*, pg. 2474
DECHRA VETERINARY PRODUCTS BV—See EQT AB; *Int'l*, pg. 2474
DECHRA VETERINARY PRODUCTS, INC.—See EQT AB; *Int'l*, pg. 2474
DECHRA VETERINARY PRODUCTS LIMITED—See EQT AB; *Int'l*, pg. 2474
DECHRA VETERINARY PRODUCTS, LLC—See EQT AB; *Int'l*, pg. 2474
DECHRA VETERINARY PRODUCTS OY—See EQT AB; *Int'l*, pg. 2474
DECHRA VETERINARY PRODUCTS SAS—See EQT AB; *Int'l*, pg. 2474
DECHRA VETERINARY PRODUCTS SLU—See EQT AB; *Int'l*, pg. 2474
DECHRA VETERINARY PRODUCTS SP. Z O.O.—See EQT AB; *Int'l*, pg. 2474
DECIBEL CANNABIS COMPANY, INC.; *Int'l*, pg. 2000
DECIBEL RESEARCH, INC.; *U.S. Private*, pg. 1187
DECIBEL THERAPEUTICS, INC.—See Regeneron Pharmaceuticals, Inc.; *U.S. Public*, pg. 1775
DECIDEBLOOM LTD.; *Int'l*, pg. 2000
DECILLION FINANCE LTD.; *Int'l*, pg. 2000
.DECIMAL, INC; *U.S. Private*, pg. 1
DECIMAL SOFTWARE LIMITED—See Sargon Capital Pty Ltd.; *Int'l*, pg. 6577
DECIMAL TECHNOLOGIES INC.; *Int'l*, pg. 2001
DECIPHERA PHARMACEUTICALS, INC.—See Ono Pharmaceutical Co., Ltd.; *Int'l*, pg. 5582
DECIPHER INC.—See EQT AB; *Int'l*, pg. 2475
DECIPHER, INC.; *U.S. Private*, pg. 1187
DECIPHER, INC.—See decipher, inc.; *U.S. Private*, pg. 1187
DECISION BIOMARKERS, INC.; *U.S. Private*, pg. 1187
DECISION DIAGNOSTICS CORP.; *U.S. Private*, pg. 1187
DECISION DISTRIBUTION; *U.S. Private*, pg. 1187
DECISION DYNAMICS, LLC—See RB Global, Inc.; *Int'l*, pg. 6226
DECISION ECONOMICS, INC.; *U.S. Private*, pg. 1187
DECISIONHEALTH LLC—See United Communications Group; *U.S. Private*, pg. 4289

CORPORATE AFFILIATIONS

DECISION INSIGHT, INC.—See TELUS CORPORATION; *Int'l*, pg. 7546
DECISION INSIGHT INFORMATION GROUP (EUROPE) LIMITED—See Daily Mail & General Trust plc; *Int'l*, pg. 1937
DECISION INSIGHT INFORMATION GROUP, INC.—See TPG Capital, L.P.; *U.S. Public*, pg. 2173
DECISION INTELLECT PTY. LTD.—See Archer Capital Pty. Ltd.; *Int'l*, pg. 547
DECISIONMETRICS LTD.—See GTCR LLC; *U.S. Private*, pg. 1804
DECISIONPATH CONSULTING; *U.S. Private*, pg. 1187
DECISIONPOINT INTERNATIONAL; *U.S. Private*, pg. 1187
DECISIONPOINT SYSTEMS CA, INC.—See The Graham Group, Inc.; *U.S. Private*, pg. 4036
DECISIONPOINT SYSTEMS CT, INC.—See The Graham Group, Inc.; *U.S. Private*, pg. 4036
DECISIONPOINT SYSTEMS, INC.—See The Graham Group, Inc.; *U.S. Private*, pg. 4036
DECISIONQUEST, INC.—See U.S. Legal Support, Inc.; *U.S. Private*, pg. 4271
DECISION RESEARCH CORP.—See Thoma Bravo, L.P.; *U.S. Private*, pg. 4149
DECISION RESOURCES, LLC—See Clarivate PLC; *Int'l*, pg. 1649
DECISION TECHNOLOGIES, INC.; *U.S. Private*, pg. 1187
DECISION TECHNOLOGIES LIMITED—See Moneysupermarket.com Group PLC; *Int'l*, pg. 5033
DECISIVE ANALYTICS CORPORATION—See Serco Group plc; *Int'l*, pg. 6721
DECISIVE DIVIDEND CORPORATION; *Int'l*, pg. 2001
DECK BUILDING RESEARCH INSTITUTE INC.—See NIPPON CARBIDE INDUSTRIES CO., INC.; *Int'l*, pg. 5311
DECKEL MAHO GILDEMEISTER (SHANGHAI) MACHINE TOOLS CO., LTD.—See DMG MORI Co., Ltd.; *Int'l*, pg. 2144
DECKEL MAHO PFRONTEN GMBH—See DMG MORI Co., Ltd.; *Int'l*, pg. 2144
DECKEL MAHO SEEBACH GMBH—See DMG MORI Co., Ltd.; *Int'l*, pg. 2144
DECKER COAL COMPANY; *U.S. Private*, pg. 1187
THE DECKER COMPANIES INC.; *U.S. Private*, pg. 4019
DECKER CREATIVE MARKETING; *U.S. Private*, pg. 1187
DECKER LAKE FOREST PRODUCTS LTD.—See West Fraser Timber Co., Ltd.; *Int'l*, pg. 8383
DECKER MANUFACTURING CORP.; *U.S. Public*, pg. 645
DECKER ROSS INTERIORS, INC.; *U.S. Private*, pg. 1187
DECKERS ASIA PACIFIC LIMITED—See Deckers Outdoor Corporation; *U.S. Public*, pg. 645
DECKERS ASIA PACIFIC RETAIL LIMITED—See Deckers Outdoor Corporation; *U.S. Public*, pg. 645
DECKERS BENELUX BV—See Deckers Outdoor Corporation; *U.S. Public*, pg. 645
DECKERS CONSUMER DIRECT CORPORATION—See Deckers Outdoor Corporation; *U.S. Public*, pg. 645
DECKERS EUROPE LTD.—See Deckers Outdoor Corporation; *U.S. Public*, pg. 645
DECKERS FOOTWEAR (SHANGHAI) CO., LTD.—See Deckers Outdoor Corporation; *U.S. Public*, pg. 645
DECKERS FRANCE 2 SAS—See Deckers Outdoor Corporation; *U.S. Public*, pg. 645
DECKERS FRANCE SAS—See Deckers Outdoor Corporation; *U.S. Public*, pg. 645
DECKERS JAPAN GK—See Deckers Outdoor Corporation; *U.S. Public*, pg. 645
DECKERS OUTDOOR CORPORATION; *U.S. Public*, pg. 645
DECKERS OUTDOOR INTERNATIONAL LIMITED—See Deckers Outdoor Corporation; *U.S. Public*, pg. 645
DECKERS RETAIL, LLC—See Deckers Outdoor Corporation; *U.S. Public*, pg. 645
DECKERS UK, LTD—See Deckers Outdoor Corporation; *U.S. Public*, pg. 645
DECKER TRUCK LINE INC.—See The Decker Companies Inc.; *U.S. Private*, pg. 4019
DECKERWRIGHT CORPORATION—See Beringer Associates, Inc.; *U.S. Private*, pg. 532
DECKLAR RESOURCES INC.; *Int'l*, pg. 2001
DECKMA HAMBURG GMBH; *Int'l*, pg. 2001
DECKORATORS, INC.—See UFP Industries, Inc.; *U.S. Public*, pg. 2579
DECKS & DOCKS LUMBER COMPANY INC.—See CCMP Capital Advisors, LP; *U.S. Private*, pg. 800
DECK'S HARDSCAPE & LANDSCAPE SUPPLIES—See Haines & Kibblehouse Inc.; *U.S. Private*, pg. 1841
DECKSIDE POOL SERVICE; *U.S. Private*, pg. 1187
DECK THE WALLS—See Franchise Concepts, Inc.; *U.S. Private*, pg. 1587
DECLAN DISTILLERS, LLC—See Constellation Brands, Inc.; *U.S. Public*, pg. 571
DECLAN RESOURCES INC.; *Int'l*, pg. 2001
DE CLERCQ OFFICE GROUP, LTD.—See Creative Office Pavilion LLC; *U.S. Private*, pg. 1089
DECLOET GREENHOUSE MANUFACTURING LTD.; *Int'l*, pg. 2001
DECLOUT LIMITED—See EXEO Group Inc.; *Int'l*, pg. 2583

DECMIL AUSTRALIA PTY. LTD.—See Macmahon Holdings Limited; *Int'l*, pg. 4623
DECMIL GROUP LIMITED—See Macmahon Holdings Limited; *Int'l*, pg. 4623
DECOART INC—See MPE Partners, LLC; *U.S. Private*, pg. 2803
DECODE GENETICS, INC.—See Amgen Inc.; *U.S. Public*, pg. 123
DECODE GENETICS, INC.—See Amgen Inc.; *U.S. Public*, pg. 124
DECO&E CO., LTD.; *Int'l*, pg. 2001
DECO EMIRATES COMPANY LLC—See Depa PLC; *Int'l*, pg. 2040
DECO INC.—See IDS International Government Services LLC; *U.S. Private*, pg. 2038
DECOLAV, INC.; *U.S. Private*, pg. 1187
DECOLIGHT TRADING CO. LLC—See Depa PLC; *Int'l*, pg. 2040
DE COLLEGIALE BEREIDING BV—See Fagron NV; *Int'l*, pg. 2603
DECO LOGISTICS, INC.—See Universal Logistics Holdings, Inc.; *U.S. Public*, pg. 2261
DECO-MICA LIMITED - RAJPUR FACTORY—See DECO-MICA LIMITED; *Int'l*, pg. 2001
DECO-MICA LIMITED; *Int'l*, pg. 2001
DE CONSTRUCTII NAPOCA S.A.; *Int'l*, pg. 1995
DECOPAC, INC.—See Kohlberg & Company, LLC; *U.S. Private*, pg. 2337
DECO PRODUCTS CO.; *U.S. Private*, pg. 1187
DECORA BALT UAB—See Decora S.A.; *Int'l*, pg. 2001
DECORAH BANK & TRUST COMPANY—See Security Agency, Inc.; *U.S. Private*, pg. 3594
DECORA HUNGARIA KFT—See Decora S.A.; *Int'l*, pg. 2001
DECORA NOVA S.R.O.—See Decora S.A.; *Int'l*, pg. 2001
DECORA RU OOO—See Decora S.A.; *Int'l*, pg. 2001
DECORA S.A.; *Int'l*, pg. 2001
DECORATIVE CASTINGS INC.; *U.S. Private*, pg. 1187
DECORATIVE CRAFTS, INC.; *U.S. Private*, pg. 1188
DECORATIVE OUEST S.A.S.—See Akzo Nobel N.V.; *Int'l*, pg. 273
DECORATIVE SPECIALTIES; *U.S. Private*, pg. 1188
DECORATOR'S OFFICE FURNITURE INC.; *U.S. Private*, pg. 1188
THE DECORATORS UNLIMITED INC.; *U.S. Private*, pg. 4019
DECORA UKRAINA TOB—See Decora S.A.; *Int'l*, pg. 2001
DECOR CABINETS LTD.; *Int'l*, pg. 2001
DECOR HOLDINGS, INC.; *U.S. Private*, pg. 1187
DECOR INC.; *U.S. Private*, pg. 1187
DECORINT SA; *Int'l*, pg. 2001
DE CORMIER MOTOR SALES, INC.; *U.S. Private*, pg. 1181
DECOROUS INVESTMENT & TRADING CO. LTD.; *Int'l*, pg. 2001
DECORPLANET.COM; *U.S. Private*, pg. 1188
DECOR PRODUCTS INTERNATIONAL, INC.; *Int'l*, pg. 2001
DECOR-REST FURNITURE LTD.; *Int'l*, pg. 2001
DECORUS REALTY LLC—See One Sotheby's International Realty, Inc.; *U.S. Private*, pg. 3023
DECOTEC PRINTING, S.A.—See TOPPAN Holdings Inc.; *Int'l*, pg. 7816
DECOTEX JSC; *Int'l*, pg. 2001
DECO TOOL SUPPLY COMPANY—See MSC Industrial Direct Co., Inc.; *U.S. Public*, pg. 1483
DECOTRADE GMBH—See JAB Holding Company S.a.r.l.; *Int'l*, pg. 3862
DECOY COFFEE COMPANY; *U.S. Private*, pg. 1188
DECOUFLE S.A.R.L.—See Korber AG; *Int'l*, pg. 4280
DECOUPAGE ET MECANIQUE DE L'OUEST—See Compagnie de Saint-Gobain SA; *Int'l*, pg. 1723
DECOUSTICS LIMITED—See Compagnie de Saint-Gobain SA; *Int'l*, pg. 1729
DECRA ROOFING SYSTEMS INC.—See Fletcher Building Limited; *Int'l*, pg. 2699
DECRESCENTE DISTRIBUTING CO., INC.; *U.S. Private*, pg. 1188
DEC-TAM CORPORATION—See The White Oak Group, Inc.; *U.S. Private*, pg. 4135
DEC TECHNOLOGIES, INC.—See HEICO Corporation; *U.S. Public*, pg. 1019
DECURION CORP.; *U.S. Private*, pg. 1188
DEDAGROUP SPA—See Lillo SpA; *Int'l*, pg. 4498
DEDALE S.A.—See Apollo Global Management, Inc.; *U.S. Public*, pg. 147
DEDALO GRUPO GRAFICO, S.L.; *Int'l*, pg. 2001
DEDALO HELIOCOLOR—See Dedalo Grupo Grafico, S.L.; *Int'l*, pg. 2002
DEDALUS S.P.A.—See Ardian SAS; *Int'l*, pg. 555
DEDA S.A.—See Italgas S.p.A.; *Int'l*, pg. 3828
DEDC, INC.; *Int'l*, pg. 2002
DEDERT CORPORATION; *U.S. Private*, pg. 1188
DEDERT (SHANGHAI) DRYING AND EVAPORATING TECHNOLOGY CO., LTD—See Dedert Corporation; *U.S. Private*, pg. 1188
DEDHAM INSTITUTION FOR SAVINGS INC.; *U.S. Private*, pg. 1188
DEDHAM NISSAN, INC.; *U.S. Private*, pg. 1188

DEDICARE AB; *Int'l*, pg. 2002
DEDICARE AS—See Dedicare AB; *Int'l*, pg. 2002
DEDICATED COMPUTING, LLC—See McNally Capital, LLC; *U.S. Private*, pg. 2643
DEDICATED FLEET SYSTEMS, INC.—See The Osterkamp Group; *U.S. Private*, pg. 4089
DEDICATED LOGISTICS INC.; *U.S. Private*, pg. 1188
DEDICATED TRANSPORT LLC; *U.S. Private*, pg. 1188
DEDIENNE MULTIPLASTURGY GROUP SAS; *Int'l*, pg. 2002
DE DIETRICH DO BRASIL LTDA—See De Dietrich Process Systems S.A.; *Int'l*, pg. 1995
DE DIETRICH EQUIPOS QUIMICOS SL—See De Dietrich Process Systems S.A.; *Int'l*, pg. 1995
DE DIETRICH PROCESS SYSTEMS AG—See De Dietrich Process Systems S.A.; *Int'l*, pg. 1995
DE DIETRICH PROCESS SYSTEMS GMBH—See De Dietrich Process Systems S.A.; *Int'l*, pg. 1995
DE DIETRICH PROCESS SYSTEMS, INC.—See De Dietrich Process Systems S.A.; *Int'l*, pg. 1995
DE DIETRICH PROCESS SYSTEMS INDIA PRIVATE LIMITED—See De Dietrich Process Systems S.A.; *Int'l*, pg. 1995
DE DIETRICH PROCESS SYSTEMS IRELAND LTD.—See De Dietrich Process Systems S.A.; *Int'l*, pg. 1995
DE DIETRICH PROCESS SYSTEMS N.V.—See De Dietrich Process Systems S.A.; *Int'l*, pg. 1995
DE DIETRICH PROCESS SYSTEMS-ROSENMUND DIVISION—See De Dietrich Process Systems S.A.; *Int'l*, pg. 1995
DE DIETRICH PROCESS SYSTEMS - COURCOURONNES SITE—See De Dietrich Process Systems S.A.; *Int'l*, pg. 1995
DE DIETRICH PROCESS SYSTEMS S.A. - GLASS-LINING PLANT—See De Dietrich Process Systems S.A.; *Int'l*, pg. 1995
DE DIETRICH PROCESS SYSTEMS S.A.; *Int'l*, pg. 1995
DE DIETRICH PROCESS SYSTEMS SEMUR SAS—See De Dietrich Process Systems S.A.; *Int'l*, pg. 1995
DE DIETRICH PROCESS SYSTEMS—See De Dietrich Process Systems S.A.; *Int'l*, pg. 1995
DE DIETRICH PROCESS SYSTEMS SRL.—See De Dietrich Process Systems S.A.; *Int'l*, pg. 1995
DE DIETRICH PROCESS SYSTEMS (WUXI) CO, LTD.—See De Dietrich Process Systems S.A.; *Int'l*, pg. 1995
DE DIETRICH REMEHA GMBH—See BDR Thermea Group B.V.; *Int'l*, pg. 930
DE DIETRICH SINGAPORE (PTE) LTD.—See De Dietrich Process Systems S.A.; *Int'l*, pg. 1995
DE DIETRICH SOUTH AFRICA (PTY) LTD.—See De Dietrich Process Systems S.A.; *Int'l*, pg. 1995
DE DIETRICH TECHNIKA GRZEWCZA SP. Z O.O—See BDR Thermea Group B.V.; *Int'l*, pg. 931
DE DIETRICH THERMIQUE IBERIA S.L.U—See BDR Thermea Group B.V.; *Int'l*, pg. 931
DE DIETRICH THERMIQUE, S.A.S.—See BDR Thermea Group B.V.; *Int'l*, pg. 931
DEDINJE A.D.; *Int'l*, pg. 2002
DEDOES INDUSTRIES INC.; *U.S. Private*, pg. 1188
DEDOLA GLOBAL LOGISTICS; *U.S. Private*, pg. 1188
DEDOT TRADING (SHANGHAI) CO., LTD.—See Matex International Limited; *Int'l*, pg. 4727
DEDRAX AD—See Billboard JSC; *Int'l*, pg. 1030
DEEB CONSTRUCTION & DEVELOPMENT CO.; *U.S. Private*, pg. 1189
DEE BLAA OMNIBUSSER A/S—See Nobina AB; *Int'l*, pg. 5396
DEE BROWN, INC.; *U.S. Private*, pg. 1188
DEECO METALS CORPORATION; *U.S. Private*, pg. 1189
DEECORP LIMITED—See SoftBank Group Corp.; *Int'l*, pg. 7051
DEE CRAMER INC.; *U.S. Private*, pg. 1188
DEE & DEE OIL CO.; *U.S. Private*, pg. 1188
DEE DRAXLMAIER ELEKTRIK-UND ELEKTRONIKSYS-TEME GMBH—See Draexlmaier Gruppe; *Int'l*, pg. 2198
DEE ENGINEERING INC.; *U.S. Private*, pg. 1189
DEEGIT INC.; *U.S. Private*, pg. 1189
DEEL, INC.; *U.S. Private*, pg. 1189
DEEL VOLVO; *U.S. Private*, pg. 1189
DEEM STEEL; *U.S. Private*, pg. 1189
DE EN ENK GROEN & GOLF B.V.; *Int'l*, pg. 1995
DEEN MEAT CO.; *U.S. Private*, pg. 1189
DEEPAK FASTENERS (AUSTRALIA) PTY LTD.—See Deepak Fasteners Limited; *Int'l*, pg. 2002
DEEPAK FASTENERS LIMITED; *Int'l*, pg. 2002
DEEPAK FASTENERS (SHANNON) LTD.—See Deepak Fasteners Limited; *Int'l*, pg. 2002
DEEPAK FASTENERS (U.K.) LTD.—See Deepak Fasteners Limited; *Int'l*, pg. 2002
DEEPAK FERTILISERS & PETROCHEMICALS CORPORATION LIMITED; *Int'l*, pg. 2003
DEEPAK NITRITE LIMITED; *Int'l*, pg. 2003
DEEPAK SPINNERS LIMITED; *Int'l*, pg. 2003
DEE PAPER COMPANY; *U.S. Private*, pg. 1189
DEEP BLUE COMMUNICATIONS, LLC—See Comcast Corporation; *U.S. Public*, pg. 538
DEEP BLUE MARINE, INC.; *U.S. Public*, pg. 645

DEEPBLUE NETWORKS AG—See WPP plc; *Int'l*, pg. 8463
DEEP DIAMOND INDIA LIMITED; *Int'l*, pg. 2002
DEEP EAST TEXAS ELECTRIC COOPERATIVE, INC.; *U.S. Private*, pg. 1189
DEE PEE ELECTRIC MEMBERSHIP; *U.S. Private*, pg. 1189
DEEP ENERGY LLC—See Deep Energy Resources Ltd.; *Int'l*, pg. 2002
DEEP ENERGY RESOURCES LTD.; *Int'l*, pg. 2002
DEEPEYE CO., LTD.—See ESTsoft Corp; *Int'l*, pg. 2519
DEEP FOCUS HONG KONG—See The Engine Group; *Int'l*, pg. 7640
DEEP FOCUS SHANGHAI—See The Engine Group; *Int'l*, pg. 7640
DEEP FOCUS—See The Engine Group; *Int'l*, pg. 7640
DEEP FOODS, INC.; *U.S. Private*, pg. 1189
DEEP GREEN WASTE & RECYCLING, INC.; *U.S. Public*, pg. 645
DEEPIDEAS GMBH—See Metro AG; *Int'l*, pg. 4857
DEEP IMAGING TECHNOLOGIES, INC.; *U.S. Private*, pg. 1189
DEEPINTENT TECHNOLOGIES, INC.—See Propel Media, Inc.; *U.S. Public*, pg. 1727
DEEP LAKE CAPITAL ACQUISITION CORP.; *U.S. Public*, pg. 645
DEEP LIQUIDITY, INC.; *U.S. Private*, pg. 1189
DEEPLOCAL, INC.—See WPP plc; *Int'l*, pg. 8469
DEEPMALA INFRASTRUCTURE PRIVATE LIMITED—See Gammon India Limited; *Int'l*, pg. 2879
DEEPMARKIT CORP.; *Int'l*, pg. 2003
DEEPMATTER GROUP PLC; *Int'l*, pg. 2003
DEEP MEDICINE ACQUISITION CORP.; *U.S. Public*, pg. 645
DEEPMIND PLATFORM CO., LTD.; *Int'l*, pg. 2003
DEEP NATURAL RESOURCES LIMITED—See Deep Energy Resources Ltd.; *Int'l*, pg. 2002
DEEP NINES INC.—See Netsweeper Inc.; *Int'l*, pg. 5215
DEEPNOID INC.; *Int'l*, pg. 2003
DEEPOCEAN AS—See Triton Advisers Limited; *Int'l*, pg. 7930
DEEPOCEAN B.V.—See Triton Advisers Limited; *Int'l*, pg. 7930
DEEPOCEAN DE MEXICO S. DE R.L. DE C.V—See Triton Advisers Limited; *Int'l*, pg. 7930
DEEP OCEAN ENGINEERING INC.—See Vortex Marine Construction; *U.S. Private*, pg. 4413
DEEPOCEAN GHANA LIMITED—See Triton Advisers Limited; *Int'l*, pg. 7930
DEEPOCEAN GROUP HOLDING AS—See Triton Advisers Limited; *Int'l*, pg. 7930
DEEPOCEAN GROUP HOLDING BV.—See Triton Advisers Limited; *Int'l*, pg. 7930
DEEPOCEAN UK LTD.—See Triton Advisers Limited; *Int'l*, pg. 7930
DEEP POLYMERS LTD.; *Int'l*, pg. 2002
DEEP RIVER PLASTICS, LLC—See Smith & Wesson Brands, Inc.; *U.S. Public*, pg. 1896
DEEPROCK MINERALS, INC.; *Int'l*, pg. 2003
DEEP SEA ELECTRONICS INDIA PRIVATE LIMITED—See Generac Holdings Inc.; *U.S. Public*, pg. 912
DEEP SEA ELECTRONICS INDIA PTE. LTD.—See Caledonia Investments plc; *Int'l*, pg. 1262
DEEP SEA ELECTRONICS LIMITED—See Generac Holdings Inc.; *U.S. Public*, pg. 912
DEEP SEA MANAGEMENT FZE LTD.—See Odfjell Drilling Ltd.; *Int'l*, pg. 5525
DEEP SEA MOORING AS—See Delmar Systems, Inc.; *U.S. Private*, pg. 1197
DEEP SILVER AUSTRIA—See Koch Media GmbH; *Int'l*, pg. 4225
DEEP SILVER GERMANY—See Koch Media GmbH; *Int'l*, pg. 4225
DEEP SILVER INC.—See Koch Media GmbH; *Int'l*, pg. 4225
DEEP SILVER VOLITION, LLC—See Koch Media GmbH; *Int'l*, pg. 4225
DEEP—See The Marlin Network, Inc.; *U.S. Private*, pg. 4075
DEEP SOUTH EQUIPMENT COMPANY; *U.S. Private*, pg. 1189
DEEP SOUTH INDUSTRIAL SERVICES, INC.—See Carylon Corporation; *U.S. Private*, pg. 777
DEEP SOUTH INSURANCE; *U.S. Private*, pg. 1189
DEEP-SOUTH RESOURCES INC.; *U.S. Private*, pg. 2002
DEEP SPACE MEDIA GROUP AG; *Int'l*, pg. 2002
DEEP SPACE SYSTEMS, INC.—See Redwire Corporation; *U.S. Public*, pg. 1771
DEEPSPATIAL INC.; *Int'l*, pg. 2003
DEEP SURPLUS; *U.S. Private*, pg. 1189
DEEP VALUE DRILLER AS; *Int'l*, pg. 2002
DEEPVERGE IRELAND LIMITED—See Deepverge PLC; *Int'l*, pg. 2003
DEEPVERGE PLC; *Int'l*, pg. 2003
DEEPWATER CHEMICALS, INC.—See Toyota Tsusho Corporation; *Int'l*, pg. 7879
DEEPWATER CORROSION SERVICES, INC.; *U.S. Private*, pg. 1190

DEEPWATER CORROSION SERVICES, INC.   CORPORATE AFFILIATIONS

DEEPWATER EU LIMITED—See Deepwater Corrosion Services, Inc.; *U.S. Private*, pg. 1190
DEEP WATER POINT LLC; *U.S. Private*, pg. 1189
DEEPWATER SPECIALISTS INC—See John Wood Group PLC; *Int'l*, pg. 3984
DEEPWATER TECHNOLOGY GROUP PTE LTD—See Keppel Corporation Limited; *Int'l*, pg. 4130
DEEPWATER WIND, LLC—See Orsted AS; *Int'l*, pg. 5644
DEEPWATER WIND RHODE ISLAND, LLC—See Orsted AS; *Int'l*, pg. 5644
DEEP WEB TECHNOLOGIES—See AMPLYFI Ltd; *Int'l*, pg. 436
DEEP WELL OIL & GAS, INC.; *Int'l*, pg. 2002
DEEP YELLOW LIMITED; *Int'l*, pg. 2002
DEERA INVESTMENT & REAL ESTATE DEVELOPMENT CO.; *Int'l*, pg. 2003
DEER BRIDGE PLUMBING & HEATING LTD.; *Int'l*, pg. 2003
DEERBROOK INSURANCE COMPANY—See The Allstate Corporation; *U.S. Public*, pg. 2033
DEER CONSUMER PRODUCTS, INC.; *Int'l*, pg. 2003
DEERCREEK COUNTRY CLUB—See Apollo Global Management, Inc.; *U.S. Public*, pg. 149
DEER CROSSING, INC.; *U.S. Private*, pg. 1190
DEERE & AULT CONSULTANTS INC.—See Schnabel Engineering, Inc.; *U.S. Private*, pg. 3566
DEERE & COMPANY; *U.S. Public*, pg. 646
DEERE-HITACHI CONSTRUCTION MACHINERY CORPORATION—See Deere & Company; *U.S. Public*, pg. 647
DEERE-HITACHI CONSTRUCTION MACHINERY CORPORATION—See Hitachi, Ltd.; *Int'l*, pg. 3415
DEER ELECTRONICS (DONG GUAN) CO., LTD.—See Solytech Enterprise Corporation; *Int'l*, pg. 7083
DEERFIELD BUILDERS SUPPLY CO.; *U.S. Private*, pg. 1190
DEERFIELD COMMUNICATIONS INC.; *U.S. Private*, pg. 1190
DEERFIELD CONSTRUCTION CO., INC.; *U.S. Private*, pg. 1190
DEERFIELD CONSTRUCTION GROUP INC.; *U.S. Private*, pg. 1190
DEERFIELD DISTRIBUTING INC.; *U.S. Private*, pg. 1190
DEERFIELD EPISCOPAL RETIREMENT COMMUNITY, INC.; *U.S. Private*, pg. 1190
DEERFIELD INSURANCE COMPANY—See Markel Group Inc.; *U.S. Public*, pg. 1368
DEERFIELD MANAGEMENT COMPANY L.P.; *U.S. Private*, pg. 1190
DEERFIELD MANUFACTURING, INC.—See Ice Industries Inc.; *U.S. Private*, pg. 2030
DEERFOOT INN & CASINO INC.—See Gamehost Inc.; *Int'l*, pg. 2877
DEER IMPROVEMENT—See Livestock Improvement Corporation Limited; *Int'l*, pg. 4531
DEERING LUMBER INC.—See Bain Capital, LP; *U.S. Private*, pg. 450
DEERLAND FARM EQUIPMENT (1985) LTD.; *Int'l*, pg. 2003
DEERNS ITALIA SPA—See Deerns Raadgevende Ingenieurs B.V; *Int'l*, pg. 2003
DEERNS RAADGEVENDE INGENIEURS B.V; *Int'l*, pg. 2003
DEER PARK ROOFING, LLC; *U.S. Private*, pg. 1190
DEERPATH CORPORATION; *U.S. Private*, pg. 1190
DEER STAGS CONCEPTS, INC.; *U.S. Private*, pg. 1190
DEER TRACK PARK LANDFILL, INC.—See Waste Management, Inc.; *U.S. Public*, pg. 2331
DEER VALLEY CORPORATION—See LCV Capital Management, LLC; *U.S. Private*, pg. 2404
DEER VALLEY HOMEBUILDERS, INC.—See LCV Capital Management, LLC; *U.S. Private*, pg. 2404
DEER VALLEY RESORT COMPANY, LLC—See KSL Capital Partners, LLC; *U.S. Private*, pg. 2354
DEERWOOD BANCSHARES, INC.; *U.S. Private*, pg. 1190
DEERWOOD BANK—See Deerwood Bancshares, Inc.; *U.S. Private*, pg. 1190
DEERWOOD FASTENERS INTERNATIONAL—See Berkshire Hathaway Inc.; *U.S. Public*, pg. 310
DEERY BROTHERS CHEVROLET, INC.; *U.S. Private*, pg. 1190
DEESIDE POWER (UK) LIMITED—See ENGIE SA; *Int'l*, pg. 2432
DEESIDE POWER (UK) LIMITED—See Mitsui & Co., Ltd.; *Int'l*, pg. 4973
DEE SIGN COMPANY - ANAHEIM FACILITY—See Dee Sign Company; *U.S. Private*, pg. 1189
DEE SIGN COMPANY - LOS ANGELES FACILITY—See Dee Sign Company; *U.S. Private*, pg. 1189
DEE SIGN COMPANY - OAKLAND FACILITY—See Dee Sign Company; *U.S. Private*, pg. 1189
DEE SIGN COMPANY - SAN DIEGO FACILITY—See Dee Sign Company; *U.S. Private*, pg. 1189
DEE SIGN COMPANY; *U.S. Private*, pg. 1189
DEESON GROUP LIMITED—See TPXimpact Holdings PLC; *Int'l*, pg. 7885
DEESSE AG—See Oriflame Cosmetics S.A.; *Int'l*, pg. 5627
DEE TECH SA; *Int'l*, pg. 2002

DEE VALLEY GROUP LIMITED—See Severn Trent Plc; *Int'l*, pg. 6735
DEE VALLEY PLC—See Severn Trent Plc; *Int'l*, pg. 6735
DEE VALLEY WATER (HOLDINGS) LIMITED—See Severn Trent Plc; *Int'l*, pg. 6735
DEE VALLEY WATER PLC—See Severn Trent Plc; *Int'l*, pg. 6735
DEEWIN TIANXIA CO., LTD.; *Int'l*, pg. 2003
DEE ZEE, INC.; *U.S. Private*, pg. 1189
DE FACTO COMMUNICATIONS LTD.—See Providence Equity Partners L.L.C.; *U.S. Private*, pg. 3291
DEFACTO OZON GIYIM SANAYI VE TICARET A.S.; *Int'l*, pg. 2004
DEFACTOSTANDARD, LTD.—See BEENOS Inc.; *Int'l*, pg. 939
DEFAM B.V.—See ABN AMRO Group N.V.; *Int'l*, pg. 65
DEFAQTO LTD.—See Simplybiz Group plc; *Int'l*, pg. 6934
DEFAQTO NORDIC AS—See Simplybiz Group plc; *Int'l*, pg. 6934
DEFENCE TECH HOLDING S.P.A. SB; *Int'l*, pg. 2004
DEFENCE THERAPEUTICS INC.; *Int'l*, pg. 2004
DEFENDER SECURITY COMPANY; *U.S. Private*, pg. 1190
DEFENDER SERVICES, INC.; *U.S. Private*, pg. 1190
DEFENDERS OF WILDLIFE; *U.S. Private*, pg. 1190
DEFENSE ACADEMICS—See Excelsior Defense, Inc.; *U.S. Private*, pg. 1446
DEFENSE CONTRACT SERVICES, INC.; *U.S. Private*, pg. 1191
DEFENSE INDUSTRIES INTERNATIONAL, INC.; *Int'l*, pg. 2004
DEFENSE MARITIME SOLUTIONS, INC.—See Wartsila Corporation; *Int'l*, pg. 8346
DEFENSE METALS CORP.; *Int'l*, pg. 2004
DEFENSE SYSTEMS, INC.—See Kratos Defense & Security Solutions, Inc.; *U.S. Public*, pg. 1276
DEFENSE TECHNOLOGIES INTERNATIONAL CORP.; *U.S. Public*, pg. 648
DEFENSE VENTURE GROUP LTD.—See J.F. Lehman & Company, Inc.; *U.S. Private*, pg. 2163
DEFENSEWEB TECHNOLOGIES, INC.—See Humana, Inc.; *U.S. Public*, pg. 1069
DEFENTECT GROUP, INC.; *U.S. Public*, pg. 648
DEFENX PLC; *Int'l*, pg. 2004
DEFEX, S.A.—See Sociedad Estatal de Participaciones Industriales; *Int'l*, pg. 7031
DEFFENBAUGH INDUSTRIES, INC.—See Waste Management, Inc.; *U.S. Public*, pg. 2331
DEFIANCE METAL PRODUCTS CO. INC. - CHINA PLANT—See Mayville Engineering Company, Inc.; *U.S. Public*, pg. 1403
DEFIANCE METAL PRODUCTS CO. INC. - DEFIANCE NORTH PLANT—See Mayville Engineering Company, Inc.; *U.S. Public*, pg. 1403
DEFIANCE METAL PRODUCTS CO. INC. - OSHKOSH PLANT—See Mayville Engineering Company, Inc.; *U.S. Public*, pg. 1403
DEFIANCE METAL PRODUCTS CO.—See Mayville Engineering Company, Inc.; *U.S. Public*, pg. 1403
DEFIANCE METAL PRODUCTS, INC.—See Mayville Engineering Company, Inc.; *U.S. Public*, pg. 1403
DEFIANCE METAL PRODUCTS OF ARKANSAS INC.—See Mayville Engineering Company, Inc.; *U.S. Public*, pg. 1403
DEFIANCE PUBLISHING COMPANY, LLC—See Adams Publishing Group, LLC; *U.S. Private*, pg. 75
DEFIANCE SILVER CORP.; *Int'l*, pg. 2004
DEFIANCE VENTURES LLC; *U.S. Private*, pg. 1191
DEFIANT REQUIEM FOUNDATION; *U.S. Private*, pg. 1191
DEFIBTECH, LLC—See Nihon Kohden Corporation; *Int'l*, pg. 5285
DEFI COMMUNICATION MARKETING INC.; *Int'l*, pg. 2004
DEFI DEUTSCHLAND GMBH—See DEFI Group SAS; *Int'l*, pg. 2004
DEFI FRANCE SAS—See DEFI Group SAS; *Int'l*, pg. 2004
DEFI GROUP ASIA LTD.—See DEFI Group SAS; *Int'l*, pg. 2004
DEFI GROUP SAS; *Int'l*, pg. 2004
DEFI HUNGARY KFT—See DEFI Group SAS; *Int'l*, pg. 2004
DEFI ITALIA S.P.A.—See DEFI Group SAS; *Int'l*, pg. 2004
DEFILIPPO BROS MOTORCARS AUTO SALES INC; *U.S. Private*, pg. 1191
DEFINED CONTRIBUTION PLAN CONSULTING OF JAPAN CO., LTD.—See Mitsubishi UFJ Financial Group, Inc.; *Int'l*, pg. 4969
DEFINED FINANCIAL PLANNING, LLC; *U.S. Private*, pg. 1191
DEFINED HEALTH, INC.—See Arsenal Capital Management LP; *U.S. Private*, pg. 338
DEFI NEOLUX—See DEFI Group SAS; *Int'l*, pg. 2004
DEFINITION 6, LLC—See Kelso & Company, L.P.; *U.S. Private*, pg. 2277
DEFINITIVEDATA, INC.—See L.I.S.T. Inc.; *U.S. Private*, pg. 2366
DEFINITIVE HEALTHCARE CORP.; *U.S. Public*, pg. 648

DEFINITIVE HEALTHCARE LLC—See Definitive Healthcare Corp.; *U.S. Public*, pg. 648
DEFINITIVE LOGIC CORPORATION—See The Carlyle Group Inc.; *U.S. Public*, pg. 2048
DEFINITIVE MEDIA CORP.—See JLL Partners, LLC; *U.S. Private*, pg. 2212
DEFINITIVE MEDIA CORP.—See Water Street Healthcare Partners, LLC; *U.S. Private*, pg. 4452
DEFINITIVE REST MATTRESS COMPANY; *U.S. Private*, pg. 1191
DEFINITIVE RESULTS, LLC; *U.S. Private*, pg. 1191
DEFINITIVE TECHNOLOGY, INC.—See Charlesbank Capital Partners, LLC; *U.S. Private*, pg. 855
DEFINITY FINANCIAL CORP.; *Int'l*, pg. 2004
DEFINOX (BEIJING) STAINLESS STEEL EQUIPMENT LTD—See Alfa Laval AB; *Int'l*, pg. 309
DEFINOX INC.—See Alfa Laval AB; *Int'l*, pg. 309
DEFINOX SAS—See Alfa Laval AB; *Int'l*, pg. 309
DEFI POLAND SP. Z O.O.—See DEFI Group SAS; *Int'l*, pg. 2004
DEFI SOLUTIONS, INC.; *U.S. Private*, pg. 1191
DEFLECTO CANADA LIMITED—See Jordan Industries, Inc.; *U.S. Private*, pg. 2235
DEFLECT-O CORP.—See Jordan Industries, Inc.; *U.S. Private*, pg. 2235
DEF MEDIA GMBH—See The Social Chain AG; *Int'l*, pg. 7687
DEFONTAINE IBERICA S.A.—See ThyssenKrupp AG; *Int'l*, pg. 7724
DEFONTAINE OF AMERICA INC.—See ThyssenKrupp AG; *Int'l*, pg. 7731
DEFONTAINE S.A.—See ThyssenKrupp AG; *Int'l*, pg. 7731
DEFONTAINE TUNISIE S.A.—See ThyssenKrupp AG; *Int'l*, pg. 7724
DEFONTAINE UK LTD.—See ThyssenKrupp AG; *Int'l*, pg. 7731
DEFORD LUMBER COMPANY INC.—See Builders First-Source, Inc.; *U.S. Public*, pg. 410
DEFOREST CREATIVE GROUP; *U.S. Private*, pg. 1191
DEFRAN SYSTEMS, INC.; *U.S. Private*, pg. 1191
DEFRAQ VENTURES AG; *Int'l*, pg. 2004
DEFTECH SYSTEMS INTEGRATION SDN. BHD.—See DRB-HICOM Berhad; *Int'l*, pg. 2201
DEFTECH UNMANNED SYSTEMS SDN. BHD.—See DRB-HICOM Berhad; *Int'l*, pg. 2201
DEFT, INC. OF OHIO—See PPG Industries, Inc.; *U.S. Public*, pg. 1707
DEFT, INC.—See PPG Industries, Inc.; *U.S. Public*, pg. 1707
DEFT RESEARCH, LLC—See Integrity Marketing Group LLC; *U.S. Private*, pg. 2103
DE FURSAC SA—See SMCP S.A.; *Int'l*, pg. 7006
DEFY APPLIANCES (PROPRIETARY) LIMITED—See Koc Holding A.S.; *Int'l*, pg. 4223
DEFY MEDIA, LLC - LOS ANGELES—See ZelnickMedia Corp.; *U.S. Private*, pg. 4600
DEFY MEDIA, LLC—See ZelnickMedia Corp.; *U.S. Private*, pg. 4600
DEFYSUPPLY; *U.S. Private*, pg. 1191
DEFY VENTURES INC.; *U.S. Private*, pg. 1191
DEGAMA SOFTWARE SOLUTIONS, INC.; *Int'l*, pg. 2004
DEGELMAN INDUSTRIES LTD.; *Int'l*, pg. 2004
DEGELS GMBH—See Tata Sons Limited; *Int'l*, pg. 7471
DEGEM BERHAD; *Int'l*, pg. 2004
DEGENKOLB ENGINEERS; *U.S. Private*, pg. 1191
DEGER VARLIK KIRALAMA A.S.—See Albaraka Turk Katilim Bankasi A.S.; *Int'l*, pg. 293
DEGETEL BENELUX—See Degetel; *Int'l*, pg. 2004
DEGETEL PORTUGAL - SOCIEDADE UNIPESSOAL LDA—See Degetel; *Int'l*, pg. 2004
DEGETEL; *Int'l*, pg. 2004
DEGGINGER, MCINTOSH & ASSOCIATES, INC.—See Stone Point Capital LLC; *U.S. Private*, pg. 3819
DEGG'S IMMOBILIENPROJEKTENTWICKLUNG GMBH & CO. EINKAUFSPASSAGE KG—See BayernLB Holding AG; *Int'l*, pg. 913
DEGIDESIGN ITALY S.R.L—See Symphony Technology Group, LLC; *U.S. Private*, pg. 3901
DEGIL SAFETY PRODUCTS, INC.—See Delta Plus Group; *Int'l*, pg. 2019
DEG, LLC—See Douglas Emmett, Inc.; *U.S. Public*, pg. 678
DEGLMANN ENERGIE GMBH & CO. KG—See Marquard & Bahls AG; *Int'l*, pg. 4699
DEGOL AVIATION, INC.—See The DeGol Organization; *U.S. Private*, pg. 4019
DEGOL BROTHERS CARPET—See The DeGol Organization; *U.S. Private*, pg. 4019
THE DEGOL ORGANIZATION; *U.S. Private*, pg. 4019
DE GOUDSE N.V.; *Int'l*, pg. 1995
DE GRAEVE ENTREPRISES GENERALES SA—See Eiffage S.A.; *Int'l*, pg. 2329
DEGREANE HORIZON SAS—See VINCI S.A.; *Int'l*, pg. 8216
DEGREE OF HONOR PROTECTIVE ASSOCIATION—See Catholic Financial Life; *U.S. Private*, pg. 789
DEGREMONT SA—See Veolia Environnement S.A.; *Int'l*, pg. 8154

COMPANY NAME INDEX

DEGREMONT S.A.—See Veolia Environnement S.A.; *Int'l*, pg. 8154
DEGREMONT—See Veolia Environnement S.A.; *Int'l*, pg. 8154
DEGREMONT SPA—See Veolia Environnement S.A.; *Int'l*, pg. 8154
DEGREMONT TECHNOLOGIES AG—See Veolia Environnement S.A.; *Int'l*, pg. 8154
DE GREY MINING LIMITED; *Int'l*, pg. 1995
DE GRISOGONO SA—See DAMAC Group; *Int'l*, pg. 1955
DEGROOD OIL INC.; *U.S. Private*, pg. 1191
DEGROOF BANQUE PRIVEE S.A.—See ODDO BHF SCA; *Int'l*, pg. 5524
DEGROOF PETERCAM CORPORATE FINANCE SA/NV—See Banque Degroof S.A.; *Int'l*, pg. 853
DEG; *U.S. Private*, pg. 1191
DEGUSSA BANK AG—See Apollo Global Management, Inc.; *U.S. Public*, pg. 148
DEGUSSA BANK AG—See Grovepoint Capital LLP; *Int'l*, pg. 3112
DEGUSSA BANK AG—See Teacher Retirement System of Texas; *U.S. Private*, pg. 3944
DEGW FRANCE SAS—See VINCI S.A.; *Int'l*, pg. 8216
DEHCO, INC.—See Patrick Industries, Inc.; *U.S. Public*, pg. 1652
DEHESA BARON DE LEY S.A.—See Baron de Ley, S.A.; *Int'l*, pg. 867
DEHOFF ENTERPRISES INC.; *U.S. Private*, pg. 1191
DEHOPLAST POLSKA SP. Z O.O.—See Simona AG; *Int'l*, pg. 6932
DEHUA TB NEW DECORATION MATERIAL CO., LTD.; *Int'l*, pg. 2004
DEIBAR - MAQUINAS FERRAMENTA, LDA.—See Nicolas Correa S.A.; *Int'l*, pg. 5272
DEICHMANN OBUV S.R.O.—See Deichmann SE; *Int'l*, pg. 2005
DEICHMANN-OBUWIE SP.Z. O.O.—See Deichmann SE; *Int'l*, pg. 2005
DEICHMANN-SCHUHVERTRIEBSGESELLSCHAFT M.B.H.—See Deichmann SE; *Int'l*, pg. 2005
DEICHMANN SE; *Int'l*, pg. 2005
DEICHMANN-SHOES UK LTD.—See Deichmann SE; *Int'l*, pg. 2005
DEICHMANN SKO APS—See Deichmann SE; *Int'l*, pg. 2005
DEIG BROS. LUMBER & CONSTRUCTION CO. INC.; *U.S. Private*, pg. 1191
DEI HOLDINGS, INC. - DIRECTED DIVISION—See Charlesbank Capital Partners, LLC; *U.S. Private*, pg. 855
DEI HOLDINGS, INC.—See Charlesbank Capital Partners, LLC; *U.S. Private*, pg. 855
DEI HOLDINGS, INC. - SOUND UNITED DIVISION—See Charlesbank Capital Partners, LLC; *U.S. Private*, pg. 855
DEILMANN-HANIEL INTERNATIONAL MINING & TUNNELING GMBH—See ATON GmbH; *Int'l*, pg. 688
DEILMANN-HANIEL MINING SYSTEMS GMBH—See ATON GmbH; *Int'l*, pg. 688
DEILMANN-HANIEL SHAFT SINKING GMBH—See ATON GmbH; *Int'l*, pg. 688
DEI LOGISTICS (USA) CORP.—See Delta Electronics, Inc.; *Int'l*, pg. 2016
DEIMOS IMAGING S.L.U.—See UrtheCast Corp.; *Int'l*, pg. 8095
DEIMOS SPACE, S.L.U.—See Elecnor, S.A.; *Int'l*, pg. 2347
DEINDESIGN GMBH—See CEWE Stiftung & Co. KGaA; *Int'l*, pg. 1425
DEINOVE SA; *Int'l*, pg. 2005
DE INTERNATIONAL DE MEXICO S. A. DE C. V.—See Messe Munchen GmbH; *Int'l*, pg. 4841
DEINTERNATIONAL DOOEL SKOPJE—See Messe Munchen GmbH; *Int'l*, pg. 4841
DE INTERNATIONAL LTDA. FILIAL DE LA CAMARA DE IND. Y COM COLOMBO-ALEMANA—See Messe Munchen GmbH; *Int'l*, pg. 4841
DEIORIO FOODS, INC.—See LSCG Management, Inc.; *U.S. Private*, pg. 2508
DEI SERVICES CORPORATION—See Kratos Defense & Security Solutions, Inc.; *U.S. Public*, pg. 1276
DEISTER MACHINE CO. INC.; *U.S. Private*, pg. 1191
DEIST INDUSTRIES, INC.—See Federal Signal Corporation; *U.S. Public*, pg. 826
DEITER BROTHERS; *U.S. Private*, pg. 1192
DEITSCH PLASTICS COMPANY; *U.S. Private*, pg. 1192
DEI WORLDWIDE, INC.; *U.S. Private*, pg. 1191
DE JAGER CONSTRUCTION, INC.; *U.S. Private*, pg. 1181
DEJANA TRUCK & UTILITY EQUIPMENT CO., INC.—See Douglas Dynamics, Inc.; *U.S. Public*, pg. 677
DEJEAN CONSTRUCTION COMPANY, INC.; *U.S. Private*, pg. 1192
DEJEAN-SERVIERES—See FAYAT SAS; *Int'l*, pg. 2625
DEJI ELECTRONIC CO., LTD.—See Tak Shun Technology Group Limited; *Int'l*, pg. 7428
DEJIMA OPTICAL FILMS B.V.—See Nippon Kayaku Co., Ltd.; *Int'l*, pg. 5321
DEJIN RESOURCES GROUP COMPANY LIMITED; *Int'l*, pg. 2005

DEJMARK GROUP S.R.O.; *Int'l*, pg. 2005
DEJMARK KFT.—See Dejmark Group s.r.o.; *Int'l*, pg. 2005
DEJMARK PARTNERS SRL—See Dejmark Group s.r.o.; *Int'l*, pg. 2005
DEJMARK SPOL. S R.O.—See Dejmark Group s.r.o.; *Int'l*, pg. 2005
DEJOUR ENERGY (ALBERTA) LTD.—See Tobinsnet Oil & Gas Ltd.; *Int'l*, pg. 7771
DEJOUR ENERGY USA, INC.—See DXI Capital Corp.; *Int'l*, pg. 2237
DEKABANK DEUTSCHE GIROZENTRALE LUXEMBOURG S.A.—See DekaBank; *Int'l*, pg. 2005
DEKABANK; *Int'l*, pg. 2005
DEKA BETEILIGUNGS GMBH—See DekaBank; *Int'l*, pg. 2005
DE-KA ELEKTROTEKNIK SANAYI VE TICARET ANONIM SIRKETI—See Volex plc; *Int'l*, pg. 8301
DEKA GRUNDSTUCKSVERWALTUNGSGESELLSCHAFT I (GBR)—See DekaBank; *Int'l*, pg. 2005
DEKA IMMOBILIEN GMBH—See DekaBank; *Int'l*, pg. 2005
DEKA IMMOBILIEN INVESTMENT GMBH—See DekaBank; *Int'l*, pg. 2005
DEKA INTERNATIONAL (IRELAND) LTD.—See DekaBank; *Int'l*, pg. 2005
DEKA INTERNATIONAL S.A.—See DekaBank; *Int'l*, pg. 2005
DEKA INVESTMENT GMBH—See DekaBank; *Int'l*, pg. 2005
DEKA JAPAN CO. LTD—See El.En. S.p.A.; *Int'l*, pg. 2342
DEKA LASERTECHNOLOGIE GMBH—See El.En. S.p.A.; *Int'l*, pg. 2342
DEKA LASER TECHNOLOGIES LLC—See El.En. S.p.A.; *Int'l*, pg. 2342
DEKALB AREA RETIREMENT CENTER; *U.S. Private*, pg. 1192
DEKALB CHEROKEE COUNTIES GAS DISTRIBUTORS; *U.S. Private*, pg. 1192
DEKALB COMPREHENSIVE PHYSICAL THERAPY, LIMITED PARTNERSHIP—See U.S. Physical Therapy, Inc.; *U.S. Public*, pg. 2214
DEKALB FEEDS INC.; *U.S. Private*, pg. 1192
DEKALB MANUFACTURING FACILITY (CST STORAGE)—See Solace Capital Partners, LLC; *U.S. Private*, pg. 3706
DEKALB MECHANICAL, INC.; *U.S. Private*, pg. 1192
DEKALB MEDICAL DOWNTOWN DECATUR—See Dekalb Regional Healthcare System, Inc.; *U.S. Private*, pg. 1192
DEKALB MOLDED PLASTICS INC.; *U.S. Private*, pg. 1192
DEKALB REGIONAL HEALTHCARE SYSTEM, INC.; *U.S. Private*, pg. 1192
DEKALB STEEL & COWART IRON; *U.S. Private*, pg. 1192
DEKALB TELEPHONE COOPERATIVE; *U.S. Private*, pg. 1192
DEKA MEDICAL INC—See El.En. S.p.A.; *Int'l*, pg. 2342
DEKA M.E.L.A. SRL—See El.En. S.p.A.; *Int'l*, pg. 2342
DEKAPRINT S.A.; *Int'l*, pg. 2005
DEK ASIA PACIFIC PRIVATE LIMITED—See Dover Corporation; *U.S. Public*, pg. 680
DEKA TECHNOLOGIES LASER SARL—See El.En. S.p.A.; *Int'l*, pg. 2342
DEKA VERMOGENSVERWALTUNGS GMBH—See DekaBank; *Int'l*, pg. 2005
DEKEL AGRI-VISION PLC; *Int'l*, pg. 2005
DEKKER VACUUM TECHNOLOGIES, INC.—See Atlas Copco AB; *Int'l*, pg. 681
DEKKO TECHNICAL CENTER—See Graham Holdings Company; *U.S. Public*, pg. 955
DE KLEEF B.V.—See Vattenfall AB; *Int'l*, pg. 8136
DE KLOK DRANKEN B.V.—See Asahi Group Holdings Ltd.; *Int'l*, pg. 593
DEKO-LIGHT ELEKTRONIK-VERTRIEBS GMBH—See Wurth Verwaltungsgesellschaft mbH; *Int'l*, pg. 8504
DEKOMTE BENELUX BVBA.—See DEKOMTE de Temple Kompensator-Technik GmbH; *Int'l*, pg. 2006
DEKOMTE BOHEMIA, S.R.O.—See DEKOMTE de Temple Kompensator-Technik GmbH; *Int'l*, pg. 2006
DEKOMTE DE TEMPLE IBERIA S.L.—See DEKOMTE de Temple Kompensator-Technik GmbH; *Int'l*, pg. 2006
DEKOMTE DE TEMPLE KOMPENSATOR-TECHNIK GMBH; *Int'l*, pg. 2006
DEKOMTE DE TEMPLE KOMPENSATOR-TECHNIK LLC—See DEKOMTE de Temple Kompensator-Technik GmbH; *Int'l*, pg. 2006
DEKOMTE DE TEMPLE KOMPENSATOR-TECHNIK OOO—See DEKOMTE de Temple Kompensator-Technik GmbH; *Int'l*, pg. 2006
DEKOMTE DE TEMPLE KOMPENSATOR-TECHNIK SAUDI ARABIA—See DEKOMTE de Temple Kompensator-Technik GmbH; *Int'l*, pg. 2006
DEKOMTE DE TEMPLE KOMPENSATOR-TECHNIK (S) PTE. LTD.—See DEKOMTE de Temple Kompensator-Technik GmbH; *Int'l*, pg. 2006
DEKOMTE DE TEMPLE KOMPENSATOR-TECHNIK (UK) LTD.—See DEKOMTE de Temple Kompensator-Technik GmbH; *Int'l*, pg. 2006

DEKPOL S.A.

DEKOMTE DE TEMPLE LLC—See DEKOMTE de Temple Kompensator-Technik GmbH; *Int'l*, pg. 2006
DEKOMTE FRANCE SARL.—See DEKOMTE de Temple Kompensator-Technik GmbH; *Int'l*, pg. 2006
DEKOMTE POLSKA SP. Z O.O.—See DEKOMTE de Temple Kompensator-Technik GmbH; *Int'l*, pg. 2006
DEKORON UNITHERM, INC.—See Berkshire Hathaway Inc.; *U.S. Public*, pg. 309
DEKORON WIRE & CABLE ASIA PTE LTD—See Berkshire Hathaway Inc.; *U.S. Public*, pg. 310
DEKORON WIRE & CABLE, INC.—See Berkshire Hathaway Inc.; *U.S. Public*, pg. 309
DEKO SOLUTIONS BV—See Wienerberger AG; *Int'l*, pg. 8406
DEKO STEENZAGERIJ BV—See Wienerberger AG; *Int'l*, pg. 8406
DEKPOL S.A.; *Int'l*, pg. 2006
DEKPOL STEEL SP. Z O.O.—See Dekpol S.A.; *Int'l*, pg. 2006
DEK PRINTING MACHINES GMBH—See Dover Corporation; *U.S. Public*, pg. 680
DEK PRINTING MACHINES LIMITED—See Dover Corporation; *U.S. Public*, pg. 680
DEKRA AGENCIJA D.O.O.—See DEKRA e.V.; *Int'l*, pg. 2010
DEKRA AKADEMIE GMBH—See DEKRA e.V.; *Int'l*, pg. 2008
DEKRA AKADEMIE KFT.—See DEKRA e.V.; *Int'l*, pg. 2008
DEKRA AMBIO S.A.U.—See DEKRA e.V.; *Int'l*, pg. 2007
DEKRA AMERICA, INC.—See DEKRA e.V.; *Int'l*, pg. 2008
DEKRA ARBEIT AG—See DEKRA e.V.; *Int'l*, pg. 2006
DEKRA ARBEIT AUSTRIA GMBH—See DEKRA e.V.; *Int'l*, pg. 2006
DEKRA ARBEIT BULGARIA EOOD—See DEKRA e.V.; *Int'l*, pg. 2006
DEKRA ARBEIT GMBH—See DEKRA e.V.; *Int'l*, pg. 2008
DEKRA ARBEIT ISGUCU SECME VE YERLESTIRME HIZMETLERI LTD.—See DEKRA e.V.; *Int'l*, pg. 2007
DEKRA ARBEIT MAGYAROSZAG SZOLGALTATO KFT.—See DEKRA e.V.; *Int'l*, pg. 2008
DEKRA ARBEIT (SCHWEIZ) HOLDING AG—See DEKRA e.V.; *Int'l*, pg. 2006
DEKRA ARBEIT (SCHWEIZ) VERWALTUNGS AG—See DEKRA e.V.; *Int'l*, pg. 2006
DEKRA AUSTRIA AUTOMOTIVE GMBH—See DEKRA e.V.; *Int'l*, pg. 2007
DEKRA AUTOMOBIL GMBH—See DEKRA e.V.; *Int'l*, pg. 2008
DEKRA AUTOMOTIVE AB—See DEKRA e.V.; *Int'l*, pg. 2007
DEKRA AUTOMOTIVE LTD.—See DEKRA e.V.; *Int'l*, pg. 2006
DEKRA AUTOMOTIVE MAROC S.A.—See DEKRA e.V.; *Int'l*, pg. 2007
DEKRA AUTOMOTIVE OOD—See DEKRA e.V.; *Int'l*, pg. 2007
DEKRA AUTOMOTIVE PTY. LTD.—See DEKRA e.V.; *Int'l*, pg. 2006
DEKRA AUTOMOTIVE S.A R.L.—See DEKRA e.V.; *Int'l*, pg. 2006
DEKRA AUTOMOTIVE S.A.—See DEKRA e.V.; *Int'l*, pg. 2007
DEKRA AUTOMOTIVE SOLUTIONS BELGIUM NV—See DEKRA e.V.; *Int'l*, pg. 2009
DEKRA AUTOMOTIVE SOLUTIONS GERMANY GMBH—See DEKRA e.V.; *Int'l*, pg. 2007
DEKRA AUTOMOTIVE SOLUTIONS ITALY S.R.L.—See DEKRA e.V.; *Int'l*, pg. 2007
DEKRA AUTOMOTIVE SOLUTIONS PORTUGAL LDA.—See DEKRA e.V.; *Int'l*, pg. 2007
DEKRA AUTOMOTIVE SOLUTIONS S.A.S.U.—See DEKRA e.V.; *Int'l*, pg. 2007
DEKRA AUTOMOTIVE SOLUTIONS SPAIN S.L.—See DEKRA e.V.; *Int'l*, pg. 2007
DEKRA BELGIUM N.V.—See DEKRA e.V.; *Int'l*, pg. 2006
DEKRA CANADA INC.—See DEKRA e.V.; *Int'l*, pg. 2007
DEKRA CARIBBEAN B.V.—See DEKRA e.V.; *Int'l*, pg. 2007
DEKRA CERTIFICATION B.V.—See DEKRA e.V.; *Int'l*, pg. 2007
DEKRA CERTIFICATION HONG KONG LTD.—See DEKRA e.V.; *Int'l*, pg. 2007
DEKRA CERTIFICATION INC.—See DEKRA e.V.; *Int'l*, pg. 2007
DEKRA CERTIFICATION K.K.—See DEKRA e.V.; *Int'l*, pg. 2007
DEKRA CERTIFICATION LTD.—See DEKRA e.V.; *Int'l*, pg. 2007
DEKRA CERTIFICATION (PROPRIETARY) LTD.—See DEKRA e.V.; *Int'l*, pg. 2007
DEKRA CERTIFICATION S.A.S.—See DEKRA e.V.; *Int'l*, pg. 2008
DEKRA CERTIFICATION, S.L.U.—See DEKRA e.V.; *Int'l*, pg. 2008
DEKRA CERTIFICATION—See DEKRA e.V.; *Int'l*, pg. 2007
DEKRA CERTIFICATION SP. Z O.O.—See DEKRA e.V.; *Int'l*, pg. 2008
DEKRA CERTIFICATION S.R.L.—See DEKRA e.V.; *Int'l*, pg. 2008

DEKPOL S.A.

DEKRA CLAIMS & EXPERT SERVICES (SWITZERLAND) SA—See DEKRA e.V.; *Int'l*, pg. 2009
DEKRA CLAIMS SERVICES AUSTRIA GMBH—See DEKRA e.V.; *Int'l*, pg. 2008
DEKRA CLAIMS SERVICES CZ S.R.O.—See DEKRA e.V.; *Int'l*, pg. 2008
DEKRA CLAIMS SERVICES FINLAND—See DEKRA e.V.; *Int'l*, pg. 2008
DEKRA CLAIMS SERVICES HUNGARY SERVICE LTD.—See DEKRA e.V.; *Int'l*, pg. 2008
DEKRA CLAIMS SERVICES INTERNATIONAL BVBA—See DEKRA e.V.; *Int'l*, pg. 2008
DEKRA CLAIMS SERVICES LUXEMBOURG S.A.—See DEKRA e.V.; *Int'l*, pg. 2008
DEKRA CLAIMS SERVICES MAROC S.A.R.L.—See DEKRA e.V.; *Int'l*, pg. 2006
DEKRA CLAIMS SERVICES PORTUGAL S.A.—See DEKRA e.V.; *Int'l*, pg. 2008
DEKRA CLAIMS SERVICES SPAIN, S.A.—See DEKRA e.V.; *Int'l*, pg. 2008
DEKRA CLAIMS SERVICES TURKEY LTD.—See DEKRA e.V.; *Int'l*, pg. 2008
DEKRA CLAIMS SERVICES UK LTD.—See DEKRA e.V.; *Int'l*, pg. 2008
DEKRA CLAIMS SERVICES UKRAINE—See DEKRA e.V.; *Int'l*, pg. 2008
DEKRA CTI TESTING AND CERTIFICATION LTD.—See DEKRA e.V.; *Int'l*, pg. 2007
DEKRA CZ A.S.—See DEKRA e.V.; *Int'l*, pg. 2006
DEKRA EKSPERT D.O.O.—See DEKRA e.V.; *Int'l*, pg. 2008
DEKRA EMPLEO ETT S.L.—See DEKRA e.V.; *Int'l*, pg. 2008
DEKRA EMPLOYMENT LTD.—See DEKRA e.V.; *Int'l*, pg. 2008
DEKRA ENDUSTRI YATIRIMLARI A.S.—See DEKRA e.V.; *Int'l*, pg. 2008
DEKRA EVENT & LOGISTIC SERVICES GMBH—See DEKRA e.V.; *Int'l*, pg. 2008
DEKRA E.V.; *Int'l*, pg. 2006
DEKRA EXAM GMBH—See DEKRA e.V.; *Int'l*, pg. 2008
DEKRA EXPERTISE S.A.S.—See DEKRA e.V.; *Int'l*, pg. 2008
DEKRA EXPERTISES LTDA.—See DEKRA e.V.; *Int'l*, pg. 2008
DEKRA EXPERTISE SPAIN S.L.U.—See DEKRA e.V.; *Int'l*, pg. 2008
DEKRA EXPERT LTD—See DEKRA e.V.; *Int'l*, pg. 2009
DEKRA EXPERT MUSZAKI SZAKERTOI KFT.—See UNIQA Insurance Group AG; *Int'l*, pg. 8057
DEKRA EXPERTS B.V.—See DEKRA e.V.; *Int'l*, pg. 2008
DEKRA EXPERTS NV—See DEKRA e.V.; *Int'l*, pg. 2008
DEKRA-FORMARE PROFESIONALA SRL—See DEKRA e.V.; *Int'l*, pg. 2009
DEKRA FRANCE S.A.S.—See DEKRA e.V.; *Int'l*, pg. 2008
DEKRA FYN APS—See DEKRA e.V.; *Int'l*, pg. 2006
DEKRA HASAR SERVISI LTD. STI.—See DEKRA e.V.; *Int'l*, pg. 2006
DEKRA HOVEDSTADEN A/S—See DEKRA e.V.; *Int'l*, pg. 2006
DEKRA INCOS GMBH—See DEKRA e.V.; *Int'l*, pg. 2008
DEKRA (INDIA) PVT. LTD.—See DEKRA e.V.; *Int'l*, pg. 2006
DEKRA INDUSTRIAL AB—See DEKRA e.V.; *Int'l*, pg. 2008
DEKRA INDUSTRIAL GMBH—See DEKRA e.V.; *Int'l*, pg. 2008
DEKRA INDUSTRIAL (GUANGZHOU) CO., LTD.—See DEKRA e.V.; *Int'l*, pg. 2006
DEKRA INDUSTRIAL OY—See DEKRA e.V.; *Int'l*, pg. 2008
DEKRA INDUSTRIAL (PTY) LTD.—See DEKRA e.V.; *Int'l*, pg. 2008
DEKRA INDUSTRIAL RSA—See DEKRA e.V.; *Int'l*, pg. 2009
DEKRA INDUSTRIAL S.R.O.—See DEKRA e.V.; *Int'l*, pg. 2009
DEKRA INSIGHT AB—See DEKRA e.V.; *Int'l*, pg. 2009
DEKRA INSPECOES PORTUGAL - UNIPESSOAL LDA—See DEKRA e.V.; *Int'l*, pg. 2006
DEKRA INSPECTION S.A.—See DEKRA e.V.; *Int'l*, pg. 2009
DEKRA INTERNATIONAL GMBH—See DEKRA e.V.; *Int'l*, pg. 2008
DEKRA IST RELIABILITY SERVICES INC.—See DEKRA e.V.; *Int'l*, pg. 2010
DEKRA IST RELIABILITY SERVICES LIMITED—See DEKRA e.V.; *Int'l*, pg. 2010
DEKRA JOB APS—See DEKRA e.V.; *Int'l*, pg. 2006
DEKRA KVALIFIKACIA A PORADENSTVO S.R.O.—See DEKRA e.V.; *Int'l*, pg. 2006
DEKRA MEDIA GMBH—See DEKRA e.V.; *Int'l*, pg. 2009
DEKRA MIDDLE EAST FZE—See DEKRA e.V.; *Int'l*, pg. 2006
DEKRA MIDTJYLLAND APS—See DEKRA e.V.; *Int'l*, pg. 2006
DEKRA NORDJYLLAND A/S—See DEKRA e.V.; *Int'l*, pg. 2006
DEKRA ORGANISATIONAL RELIABILITY LTD.—See DEKRA e.V.; *Int'l*, pg. 2006
DEKRA PEOPLE B.V.—See DEKRA e.V.; *Int'l*, pg. 2009
DEKRA PERSONALDIENSTE GMBH—See DEKRA e.V.; *Int'l*, pg. 2008
DEKRA POLSKA SP. Z O.O.—See DEKRA e.V.; *Int'l*, pg. 2009
DEKRA PORTUGAL EXPERTISES-PERITAGEM AUTOMOVEL S.A.—See DEKRA e.V.; *Int'l*, pg. 2009
DEKRA PRACA SP. Z O.O.—See DEKRA e.V.; *Int'l*, pg. 2009
DEKRA QUALITY MANAGEMENT AB—See DEKRA e.V.; *Int'l*, pg. 2006
DEKRA RAIL B.V.—See DEKRA e.V.; *Int'l*, pg. 2006
DEKRA RUSS O.O.O.—See DEKRA e.V.; *Int'l*, pg. 2009
DEKRA SAVJETOVANJE DOO—See DEKRA e.V.; *Int'l*, pg. 2009
DEKRA SERTIFIKASYON A.S.—See DEKRA e.V.; *Int'l*, pg. 2009
DEKRA SERVICIOS RECURSOS HUMANO S.L.—See DEKRA e.V.; *Int'l*, pg. 2009
DEKRA SE—See DEKRA e.V.; *Int'l*, pg. 2007
DEKRA (SHANGHAI) CO., LTD.—See DEKRA e.V.; *Int'l*, pg. 2007
DEKRA SJAELLAND A/S—See DEKRA e.V.; *Int'l*, pg. 2010
DEKRA SLOVENSKO S.R.O.—See DEKRA e.V.; *Int'l*, pg. 2010
DEKRA SOLUTIONS B.V.—See DEKRA e.V.; *Int'l*, pg. 2009
DEKRA SOLUTIONS SP. Z O.O.—See DEKRA e.V.; *Int'l*, pg. 2009
DEKRA SYDJYLLAND A/S—See DEKRA e.V.; *Int'l*, pg. 2010
DEKRA TEST CENTER S.A.—See DEKRA e.V.; *Int'l*, pg. 2009
DEKRA TESTING AND CERTIFICATION CHINA LTD.—See DEKRA e.V.; *Int'l*, pg. 2009
DEKRA TESTING AND CERTIFICATION GMBH—See DEKRA e.V.; *Int'l*, pg. 2009
DEKRA TESTING & CERTIFICATION CO., LTD.—See DEKRA e.V.; *Int'l*, pg. 2010
DEKRA TESTING & CERTIFICATION LTDA.—See DEKRA e.V.; *Int'l*, pg. 2010
DEKRA TESTING & CERTIFICATION, S.A.U—See DEKRA e.V.; *Int'l*, pg. 2010
DEKRA TESTING & CERTIFICATION (SHANGHAI) LTD.—See DEKRA e.V.; *Int'l*, pg. 2010
DEKRA TESTING & CERTIFICATION SPOL S R.O.—See DEKRA e.V.; *Int'l*, pg. 2009
DEKRA TESTING & CERTIFICATION (SUZHOU) CO., LTD.—See DEKRA e.V.; *Int'l*, pg. 2010
DEKRA TESTING SERVICES (ZHEJIANG) LTD.—See DEKRA e.V.; *Int'l*, pg. 2009
DEKRA UK LTD.—See DEKRA e.V.; *Int'l*, pg. 2010
DEKRA VISATEC GMBH—See DEKRA e.V.; *Int'l*, pg. 2010
DEKRA VRABOTUVANJE DOOEL—See DEKRA e.V.; *Int'l*, pg. 2009
DEKRA WIT (HANGZHOU) CERTIFICATION CO., LTD.—See DEKRA e.V.; *Int'l*, pg. 2009
DEKRA ZAPOSLITEV D.O.O.—See DEKRA e.V.; *Int'l*, pg. 2009
DEKRA ZAPOSLJAVANJE D.O.O.—See DEKRA e.V.; *Int'l*, pg. 2009
DEKRA ZAPOSLJAVANJE D.O.O.—See DEKRA e.V.; *Int'l*, pg. 2009
DEKRA ZAPOSLJAVANJE D.O.O.—See DEKRA e.V.; *Int'l*, pg. 2010
DEKRA ZA PRIVREMENO ZAPOSLJAVANJE D.O.O.—See DEKRA e.V.; *Int'l*, pg. 2009
DEKRON GMBH—See Krones AG; *Int'l*, pg. 4305
DEKRO PAINTS (PTY) LTD; *Int'l*, pg. 2010
DEKSIA LLC; *U.S. Private*, pg. 1192
DEKS INDUSTRIES PTY LIMITED—See Skellerup Holdings Limited; *Int'l*, pg. 6980
DEKSON CASTINGS LIMITED; *Int'l*, pg. 2010
DE LA CALLE, MADRAZO, MANCERA, S.C.—See WPP plc; *Int'l*, pg. 8483
DELACHAUX METAL INC.—See CVC Capital Partners SICAV-FIS S.A.; *Int'l*, pg. 1887
DELACHAUX SA—See CVC Capital Partners SICAV-FIS S.A.; *Int'l*, pg. 1886
DELACO KASLE LLC—See Delaco Steel Corp.; *U.S. Private*, pg. 1193
DELACO KASLE LLC—See Mitsui & Co., Ltd.; *Int'l*, pg. 4975
DELACO STEEL CORP.; *U.S. Private*, pg. 1193
DELACOUR ASIA PACIFIC PTE. LTD.—See Eurosports Global Limited; *Int'l*, pg. 2558
DE LA CRUZ GROUP—See WPP plc; *Int'l*, pg. 8488
DELACY FORD INC.; *U.S. Private*, pg. 1193
DE LADDERSPECIALIST BV—See Manitou BF S.A.; *Int'l*, pg. 4672
DELAFIELD CORPORATION; *U.S. Private*, pg. 1193
DELAGAR DIVISION—See Belcam Inc.; *U.S. Private*, pg. 516
DE LA GARZA PUBLIC RELATIONS, INC.; *U.S. Private*, pg. 1181
DE LAGE LANDEN CHILE S.A.—See Cooperatieve Centrale Raiffeisen-Boerenleenbank B.A.; *Int'l*, pg. 1791
DE LAGE LANDEN CO., LTD.—See Cooperatieve Centrale Raiffeisen-Boerenleenbank B.A.; *Int'l*, pg. 1791

CORPORATE AFFILIATIONS

DE LAGE LANDEN FAKTORING A.S.—See Cooperatieve Centrale Raiffeisen-Boerenleenbank B.A.; *Int'l*, pg. 1791
DE LAGE LANDEN FINANCIAL SERVICES CANADA INC.—See Cooperatieve Centrale Raiffeisen-Boerenleenbank B.A.; *Int'l*, pg. 1791
DE LAGE LANDEN INTERNATIONAL BV—See Cooperatieve Centrale Raiffeisen-Boerenleenbank B.A.; *Int'l*, pg. 1791
DE LAGE LANDEN K.K.—See Cooperatieve Centrale Raiffeisen-Boerenleenbank B.A.; *Int'l*, pg. 1791
DE LAGE LANDEN LEASING GMBH—See Cooperatieve Centrale Raiffeisen-Boerenleenbank B.A.; *Int'l*, pg. 1791
DE LAGE LANDEN LEASING LTD.—See Cooperatieve Centrale Raiffeisen-Boerenleenbank B.A.; *Int'l*, pg. 1791
DE LAGE LANDEN LEASING LTD.—See Cooperatieve Centrale Raiffeisen-Boerenleenbank B.A.; *Int'l*, pg. 1791
DE LAGE LANDEN LEASING N.V.—See Cooperatieve Centrale Raiffeisen-Boerenleenbank B.A.; *Int'l*, pg. 1791
DE LAGE LANDEN LEASING S.P.A.—See Cooperatieve Centrale Raiffeisen-Boerenleenbank B.A.; *Int'l*, pg. 1791
DE LAGE LANDEN PTE. LIMITED—See Cooperatieve Centrale Raiffeisen-Boerenleenbank B.A.; *Int'l*, pg. 1791
DELAGRAVE SA; *Int'l*, pg. 2010
DELAHAYE INDUSTRIES S.A.S.—See Empteezy Ltd; *Int'l*, pg. 2392
DELAIR CFD—See VINCI S.A.; *Int'l*, pg. 8216
DELAIRE-SDEL SAS—See VINCI S.A.; *Int'l*, pg. 8216
DELAIR GROUP, LLC—See H.I.G. Capital, LLC; *U.S. Private*, pg. 1831
DEL-AIR HEATING, AIR CONDITIONING & REFRIGERATION CORP.; *U.S. Private*, pg. 1193
DELAMAC DE MEXICO, S.A. DE C.V.—See Rodamientos y Accesorios SA de CV; *Int'l*, pg. 6382
DE LA MA/MCCANN ERICKSON—See The Interpublic Group of Companies, Inc.; *U.S. Public*, pg. 2097
DELAMINE B.V.—See GIC Pte. Ltd.; *Int'l*, pg. 2967
DELAMINE B.V.—See The Carlyle Group Inc; *U.S. Public*, pg. 2050
DELAMINE B.V.—See Tosoh Corporation; *Int'l*, pg. 7832
DELAMIN NITRIDING SALTS U.S. INC.—See Nihon Parkerizing Co., Ltd.; *Int'l*, pg. 5286
DEL AMO HOSPITAL—See Universal Health Services, Inc.; *U.S. Public*, pg. 2260
DELAN ASSOCIATES, INC.; *U.S. Private*, pg. 1193
DELANCE LIMITED; *Int'l*, pg. 2010
DELANCEY REAL ESTATE ASSET MANAGEMENT LTD.; *Int'l*, pg. 2010
DELANDE SUPPLY CO. INC.; *U.S. Private*, pg. 1193
THE DELANEY, CO.—See HCI Equity Management, L.P.; *U.S. Private*, pg. 1889
DELANEY CRUSHED STONE PRODUCTS, INC.—See Tetra Tech, Inc.; *U.S. Public*, pg. 2023
DELANO KIDNEY CENTER, LLC—See Nautic Partners, LLC; *U.S. Private*, pg. 2869
DELANO OIL COMPANY; *U.S. Private*, pg. 1193
DELANT CONSTRUCTION CO.; *U.S. Private*, pg. 1193
DELANY CAPITAL MANAGEMENT CORP.; *U.S. Private*, pg. 1193
DE LA RUE AUTHENTICATION SOLUTIONS INC.—See De La Rue plc; *Int'l*, pg. 1996
DE LA RUE BV—See De La Rue plc; *Int'l*, pg. 1996
DE LA RUE CIS—See De La Rue plc; *Int'l*, pg. 1996
DE LA RUE CURRENCY AND SECURITY PRINT LIMITED—See De La Rue plc; *Int'l*, pg. 1996
DE LA RUE CURRENCY AND SECURITY PRINT—See De La Rue plc; *Int'l*, pg. 1996
DE LA RUE CURRENCY AND SECURITY PRINT—See De La Rue plc; *Int'l*, pg. 1996
DE LA RUE CURRENCY (DIVISIONAL ENGINEERING UNIT)—See De La Rue plc; *Int'l*, pg. 1996
DE LA RUE HOLDINGS PLC—See De La Rue plc; *Int'l*, pg. 1996
DE LA RUE INTERNATIONAL LIMITED—See De La Rue plc; *Int'l*, pg. 1996
DE LA RUE LTD.—See De La Rue plc; *Int'l*, pg. 1996
DE LA RUE MALAYSIA SDN. BHD.—See De La Rue plc; *Int'l*, pg. 1996
DE LA RUE (MALAYSIA) SDN. BHD.—See De La Rue plc; *Int'l*, pg. 1996
DE LA RUE MEXICO, S.A. DE C.V.—See De La Rue plc; *Int'l*, pg. 1996
DE LA RUE NORTH AMERICA INC.—See De La Rue plc; *Int'l*, pg. 1996
DE LA RUE PLC; *Int'l*, pg. 1996
DE LA RUE SECURITY PAPERS—See De La Rue plc; *Int'l*, pg. 1996
DE LA RUE SECURITY PRINT INC.—See De La Rue plc; *Int'l*, pg. 1996
DE LA RUE SECURITY PRODUCTS—See De La Rue plc; *Int'l*, pg. 1996
DE LA RUE SECURITY PRODUCTS—See De La Rue plc; *Int'l*, pg. 1996

COMPANY NAME INDEX

DE LA RUE SECURITY PRODUCTS—See De La Rue plc; *Int'l*, pg. 1996
DE LA RUE SMURFIT LIMITED—See De La Rue plc; *Int'l*, pg. 1996
DE LA RUE SYSTEMS LIMITED—See De La Rue plc; *Int'l*, pg. 1996
DE LA RUE (THAILAND) LIMITED—See De La Rue plc; *Int'l*, pg. 1996
DELATTRE BEZONS NIGERIA LIMITED—See VINCI S.A.; *Int'l*, pg. 8217
DELATTRE LEVIVIER MAROC; *Int'l*, pg. 2010
DELAVACO RESIDENTIAL PROPERTIES CORP.; *Int'l*, pg. 2010
DELAVAL INC.—See Tetra Laval International S.A.; *Int'l*, pg. 7576
DELAVAL INTERNATIONAL AB—See Tetra Laval International S.A.; *Int'l*, pg. 7576
DELAVAL MANUFACTURING INC.—See Tetra Laval International S.A.; *Int'l*, pg. 7576
DELAVAL S.A.—See Alfa Laval AB; *Int'l*, pg. 311
DELAVAL SIA—See Alfa Laval AB; *Int'l*, pg. 311
DELAVAN LIMITED—See R.W. Beckett Corporation; *U.S. Private*, pg. 3340
DELAVAN SPRAY, LLC—See R.W. Beckett Corporation; *U.S. Private*, pg. 3340
DELAWARE AMERICAN LIFE INSURANCE COMPANY—See American International Group, Inc.; *U.S. Public*, pg. 106
DELAWARE BASIN MIDSTREAM, LLC—See Occidental Petroleum Corporation; *U.S. Public*, pg. 1561
DELAWARE BOOK INC.; *U.S. Private*, pg. 1194
DELAWARE CHARTER GUARANTEE & TRUST CO.—See Principal Financial Group, Inc.; *U.S. Public*, pg. 1720
DELAWARE CHEMICALS CORPORATION—See Arkema S.A.; *Int'l*, pg. 569
DELAWARE CITY REFINING COMPANY LLC—See PBF Energy Inc.; *U.S. Public*, pg. 1657
DELAWARE COCA-COLA BOTTLING COMPANY, INC.—See The Coca-Cola Company; *U.S. Public*, pg. 2064
DELAWARE CORPORATE SERVICES INC.—See The Law Debenture Corporation p.l.c.; *Int'l*, pg. 7664
DELAWARE COUNTY REAL ESTATE; *U.S. Private*, pg. 1194
DELAWARE COUNTY REGIONAL WATER QUALITY CONTROL AUTHORITY; *U.S. Private*, pg. 1194
DELAWARE ELECTRIC COOPERATIVE; *U.S. Private*, pg. 1194
DELAWARE ELECTRO INDUSTRIES INC.; *U.S. Private*, pg. 1194
DELAWARE ENHANCED GLOBAL DIVIDEND & INCOME FUND; *U.S. Public*, pg. 648
DELAWARE HOSPICE, INC.; *U.S. Private*, pg. 1194
DELAWARE & HUDSON RAILWAY COMPANY, INC.—See Canadian Pacific Kansas City Limited; *Int'l*, pg. 1285
DELAWARE INTERACTIVE, LLC—See Tyler Technologies, Inc.; *U.S. Public*, pg. 2208
DELAWARE INVESTMENTS COLORADO INSURED MUNICIPAL INCOME FUND; *U.S. Public*, pg. 648
DELAWARE INVESTMENTS DIV & INCOME FUND; *U.S. Public*, pg. 648
DELAWARE INVESTMENTS MINNESOTA MUNICIPAL INCOME FUND II, INC.; *U.S. Public*, pg. 648
DELAWARE LOGOS, L.L.C.—See Lamar Advertising Company; *U.S. Public*, pg. 1290
DELAWARE MANAGEMENT HOLDINGS INC.—See Macquarie Group Limited; *Int'l*, pg. 4629
DELAWARE MOTOR SALES INC.; *U.S. Private*, pg. 1194
DELAWARE MUSEUM OF NATURAL HISTORY; *U.S. Private*, pg. 1194
DELAWARE.NET, INC.; *U.S. Private*, pg. 1196
DELAWARE NORTH COMPANIES (AUSTRALIA) PTY. LTD.—See Delaware North Companies, Inc.; *U.S. Private*, pg. 1194
DELAWARE NORTH COMPANIES GAMING & ENTERTAINMENT—See Delaware North Companies, Inc.; *U.S. Private*, pg. 1194
DELAWARE NORTH COMPANIES, INC.; *U.S. Private*, pg. 1194
DELAWARE NORTH COMPANIES INTERNATIONAL LTD—See Delaware North Companies, Inc.; *U.S. Private*, pg. 1194
DELAWARE NORTH COMPANIES INTERNATIONAL, LTD.—See Delaware North Companies, Inc.; *U.S. Private*, pg. 1194
DELAWARE NORTH COMPANIES PARKS & RESORTS—See Delaware North Companies, Inc.; *U.S. Private*, pg. 1194
DELAWARE NORTH COMPANIES SPORTSERVICE—See Delaware North Companies, Inc.; *U.S. Private*, pg. 1194
DELAWARE NORTH COMPANIES TRAVEL HOSPITALITY SERVICES—See Delaware North Companies, Inc.; *U.S. Private*, pg. 1194
DELAWARE OTSEGO CORP.; *U.S. Private*, pg. 1195
DELAWARE OUTPATIENT CENTER FOR SURGERY, LLC—See Bain Capital, LP; *U.S. Private*, pg. 446

DELAWARE PIPELINE COMPANY LLC—See PBF Energy Inc.; *U.S. Public*, pg. 1657
DELAWARE PLACE BANK—See Security Chicago Corporation; *U.S. Private*, pg. 3595
DELAWARE PRINTING COMPANY—See Independent Newspapers, Inc.; *U.S. Private*, pg. 2060
DELAWARE RACING ASSOCIATION; *U.S. Private*, pg. 1195
DELAWARE RECYCLABLE PRODUCTS, INC.—See Waste Management, Inc.; *U.S. Public*, pg. 2331
DELAWARE RIVER & BAY AUTHORITY; *U.S. Private*, pg. 1195
DELAWARE RIVER JOINT TOLL BRIDGE COMMISSION; *U.S. Private*, pg. 1195
DELAWARE RIVER PORT AUTHORITY OF PENNSYLVANIA & NEW JERSEY; *U.S. Private*, pg. 1195
DELAWARE RIVER STEVEDORES INC.; *U.S. Private*, pg. 1195
DELAWARE RIVER WATERFRONT CORPORATION; *U.S. Private*, pg. 1195
DELAWARE STATE NEWS—See Independent Newspapers, Inc.; *U.S. Private*, pg. 2060
DELAWARE STATE UNIVERSITY; *U.S. Private*, pg. 1195
DELAWARE STEEL CO.—See MNP Corporation; *U.S. Private*, pg. 2756
DELAWARE SUPERMARKETS INC.; *U.S. Private*, pg. 1195
DELAWARE THIRTEEN LTD.; *Int'l*, pg. 2010
DELAWARE USS CORPORATION—See United States Steel Corporation; *U.S. Public*, pg. 2236
DELAWARE VALLEY COMMUNITY HEALTH, INC.; *U.S. Private*, pg. 1196
DELAWARE VALLEY CONCRETE CO.; *U.S. Private*, pg. 1196
DELAWARE VALLEY MANAGEMENT HOLDINGS, INC.—See Sun Capital Partners, Inc.; *U.S. Private*, pg. 3859
DELAWARE VALLEY RECYCLING, INC.—See Haines & Kibblehouse Inc.; *U.S. Private*, pg. 1841
DELAWARE VALLEY STEEL CO.; *U.S. Private*, pg. 1196
DELAWARE VALLEY WHOLESALE FLORIST INC.; *U.S. Private*, pg. 1196
DELAWARE WATER MANAGEMENT COMPANY, LLC—See Matador Resources Company; *U.S. Public*, pg. 1395
DELBAG GMBH—See Hengst SE & Co. KG; *Int'l*, pg. 3347
DELBAG S.A.S.—See Hengst SE & Co. KG; *Int'l*, pg. 3347
DELBAG S.R.O.—See Hengst SE & Co. KG; *Int'l*, pg. 3347
DELBAR PRODUCTS INCORPORATED; *U.S. Private*, pg. 1196
DELBERT CRAIG FOOD BROKERS; *U.S. Private*, pg. 1196
DELCA DISTRIBUTORS INC.—See BMT Commodity Corporation; *U.S. Private*, pg. 601
DELCAM FRANCE—See Autodesk, Inc.; *U.S. Public*, pg. 229
DELCAM HOLDINGS, LLC; *U.S. Private*, pg. 1196
DELCAM INDONESIA—See Autodesk, Inc.; *U.S. Public*, pg. 229
DELCAM ITALIA S.R.L.—See Autodesk, Inc.; *U.S. Public*, pg. 229
DELCAM JAPAN KABUSHIKI KAISYA—See Autodesk, Inc.; *U.S. Public*, pg. 229
DELCAM PARTMAKER LIMITED—See Autodesk, Inc.; *U.S. Public*, pg. 229
DEL CAMPO NAZCA SAATCHI & SAATCHI—See Publicis Groupe S.A.; *Int'l*, pg. 6107
DELCAN TECHNOLOGIES, INC.—See Parsons Corporation; *U.S. Public*, pg. 1651
DEL CARPIO ANALISIS Y ASESORIAS LTDA.—See HORIBA Ltd; *Int'l*, pg. 3475
DELCATH SYSTEMS, INC.; *U.S. Public*, pg. 648
DELCLIMA S.P.A.—See Mitsubishi Electric Corporation; *Int'l*, pg. 4943
DELCO BUILDERS & DEVELOPERS, INC.; *U.S. Private*, pg. 1196
DELCO INTERNATIONAL, LTD.—See EveryWare Global, Inc.; *U.S. Private*, pg. 1441
DELCOM OILFIELD SERVICES SDN. BHD.—See Deleum Berhad; *Int'l*, pg. 2012
DEL.COM S.R.L.—See Tod's S.p.A.; *Int'l*, pg. 7772
DEL CORPORATION; *U.S. Private*, pg. 1192
DEL-CO. WATER CO.; *U.S. Private*, pg. 1193
DELCO WIRE AND CABLE LIMITED—See Industrial Electric Wire & Cable Inc.; *U.S. Private*, pg. 2066
DELEC—See Sonepar S.A.; *Int'l*, pg. 7090
DELECTA S.A.—See Innova Capital Sp. z o.o.; *Int'l*, pg. 3711
DELECTO FOODS PRIVATE LIMITED—See Vintage Coffee & Beverages Ltd.; *Int'l*, pg. 8242
DELEFORTRIE SARL—See QuattroR SGR S.p.A.; *Int'l*, pg. 6157
DELEGACION ANDALUCIA—See Mondragon Corporation; *Int'l*, pg. 5029
DELEGACION CANARIAS—See Mondragon Corporation; *Int'l*, pg. 5029

DELEGACION CATALUNA—See Mondragon Corporation; *Int'l*, pg. 5029
DELEGACION CENTRO S.L.—See Mondragon Corporation; *Int'l*, pg. 5029
DELEGACION ESTE S.L.—See Mondragon Corporation; *Int'l*, pg. 5029
DELEGACION LEVANTE S.L.—See Mondragon Corporation; *Int'l*, pg. 5029
DELEGACION OESTE—See Mondragon Corporation; *Int'l*, pg. 5029
DELEGACION SUR S.L.—See Mondragon Corporation; *Int'l*, pg. 5029
DELEGARD TOOL COMPANY INC; *U.S. Private*, pg. 1196
DELEGAT LIMITED—See Delegat's Group Limited; *Int'l*, pg. 2011
DELEGAT LIMITED—See Delegat's Group Limited; *Int'l*, pg. 2011
DELEGAT'S GROUP LIMITED; *Int'l*, pg. 2010
DELEGAT—See Delegat's Group Limited; *Int'l*, pg. 2010
DELEGO SOFTWARE ULC—See Global Payments Inc.; *U.S. Public*, pg. 943
DELEHANTY FORD INC.—See LaFontaine Automotive Group, LLC; *U.S. Private*, pg. 2373
DELEK AUTOMOTIVE SYSTEMS, LTD.—See Delek Group Ltd.; *Int'l*, pg. 2011
DELEK BENELUX BV—See Delek Group Ltd.; *Int'l*, pg. 2011
DELEK CAPITAL LTD.—See Delek Group Ltd.; *Int'l*, pg. 2011
DELEK CRUDE LOGISTICS, LLC—See Delek Group Ltd.; *Int'l*, pg. 2011
DELEK EUROPE HOLDINGS LTD.—See Delek Group Ltd.; *Int'l*, pg. 2011
DELEK FINANCE, INC.—See Delek Group Ltd.; *Int'l*, pg. 2011
DELEK FRANCE BV—See Delek Group Ltd.; *Int'l*, pg. 2011
DELEK GROUP LTD.; *Int'l*, pg. 2011
DELEK INFRASTRUCTURES LTD.—See Delek Group Ltd.; *Int'l*, pg. 2011
DELEK INVESTMENTS & PROPERTIES LTD.—See Delek Group Ltd.; *Int'l*, pg. 2011
DELEK LOGISTICS PARTNERS, LP—See Delek Group Ltd.; *Int'l*, pg. 2011
DELEK MARKETING-BIG SANDY, LLC—See Delek Group Ltd.; *Int'l*, pg. 2011
DELEK MARKETING & SUPPLY, INC.—See Delek Group Ltd.; *Int'l*, pg. 2011
DELEK MARKETING & SUPPLY, LP—See Delek Group Ltd.; *Int'l*, pg. 2011
DELEK MOTORS LTD.—See Delek Group Ltd.; *Int'l*, pg. 2011
DELEK PETROLEUM LTD.—See Delek Group Ltd.; *Int'l*, pg. 2011
DELEK PI GLILOT - LIMITED PARTNERSHIP—See Delek Group Ltd.; *Int'l*, pg. 2012
DELEK REFINING, INC.—See Delek Group Ltd.; *Int'l*, pg. 2011
DELEK REFINING, LTD.—See Delek Group Ltd.; *Int'l*, pg. 2012
DELEK RENEWABLES, LLC—See Delek Group Ltd.; *Int'l*, pg. 2012
DELEK THE ISRAEL FUEL CORPORATION LTD.—See Delek Group Ltd.; *Int'l*, pg. 2011
DELEK TRANSPORTATION LTD.—See Delek Group Ltd.; *Int'l*, pg. 2012
DELEK US HOLDINGS, INC.—See Delek Group Ltd.; *Int'l*, pg. 2011
DELEN PRIVATE BANK NV—See Ackermans & van Haaren NV; *Int'l*, pg. 105
DELEON GROUP, LLC; *U.S. Private*, pg. 1196
DEL EQUIPMENT (UK) LTD.—See Cargotec Corporation; *Int'l*, pg. 1327
DELESLINE CONSTRUCTION, INC.; *U.S. Private*, pg. 1196
DELETE SWEDEN AB—See Axcel Management A/S; *Int'l*, pg. 762
DELEUM BERHAD; *Int'l*, pg. 2012
DELEUM PRIMERA SDN. BHD.—See Deleum Berhad; *Int'l*, pg. 2012
DELEUM ROTARY SERVICES SDN. BHD.—See Deleum Berhad; *Int'l*, pg. 2012
DELEUM TECHNOLOGY SOLUTIONS SDN. BHD.—See Deleum Berhad; *Int'l*, pg. 2012
DELFI AS—See AS Ekspress Grupp; *Int'l*, pg. 589
DELFI DISTOMON A.M.E.—See Metlen Energy & Metals S.A.; *Int'l*, pg. 4854
DELFIELD COMPANY—See Ali Holding S.r.l; *Int'l*, pg. 322
DELFI LIMITED; *Int'l*, pg. 2012
DELFI MARKETING SDN. BHD.—See Delfi Limited; *Int'l*, pg. 2012
DELFINGEN AUTOMOTIVE PARTS (WUHAN) CO., LTD.—See Delfingen Industry, S.A.; *Int'l*, pg. 2012
DELFINGEN BR-SAO PAULO LTDA—See Delfingen Industry, S.A.; *Int'l*, pg. 2012
DELFINGEN HN-CORTES—See Delfingen Industry, S.A.; *Int'l*, pg. 2012
DELFINGEN INDIA PRIVATE LIMITED—See Delfingen Industry, S.A.; *Int'l*, pg. 2012

DELFINGEN INDUSTRY, S.A.

DELFINGEN INDUSTRY, S.A.; *Int'l*, pg. 2012
DELFINGEN MA-CASABLANCA SARL—See Delfingen Industry, S.A.; *Int'l*, pg. 2012
DELFINGEN MA-TANGER SARL—See Delfingen Industry, S.A.; *Int'l*, pg. 2012
DELFINGEN MX-COAHUILA SRL—See Delfingen Industry, S.A.; *Int'l*, pg. 2012
DELFINGEN PH-FILIPINAS, INC—See Delfingen Industry, S.A.; *Int'l*, pg. 2012
DELFINGEN PT-PORTO S.A.—See Delfingen Industry, S.A.; *Int'l*, pg. 2012
DELFINGEN RO-TRANSILVANIA S.R.L—See Delfingen Industry, S.A.; *Int'l*, pg. 2012
DELFINGEN RO-VALAHIA S.R.L—See Delfingen Industry, S.A.; *Int'l*, pg. 2012
DELFINGEN SK-NITRA S.R.O.—See Delfingen Industry, S.A.; *Int'l*, pg. 2012
DELFINGEN TN-TUNIS—See Delfingen Industry, S.A.; *Int'l*, pg. 2012
DELFINGEN TR-MARMARA PLASTIK SAN. VE DIS TIC. LTD. STI.—See Delfingen Industry, S.A.; *Int'l*, pg. 2012
DELFINGEN US, INC—See Delfingen Industry, S.A.; *Int'l*, pg. 2012
DELFINGEN US-NEW YORK, INC.—See Delfingen Industry, S.A.; *Int'l*, pg. 2012
DELFINGEN US-TEXAS LP—See Delfingen Industry, S.A.; *Int'l*, pg. 2012
DELFINO MARKETING COMMUNICATIONS, INC.; *U.S. Private*, pg. 1196
DELFISOUND INC.—See Marvelous Inc.; *Int'l*, pg. 4717
DELFI UAB—See AS Ekspress Grupp; *Int'l*, pg. 590
DELFONT MACKINTOSH THEATRES LIMITED; *Int'l*, pg. 2013
DELFORTGROUP AG; *Int'l*, pg. 2013
DEL FRAILE FRUTAS Y VERDURAS S.L.—See Dole plc; *Int'l*, pg. 2157
DEL FRISCO'S - DALLAS, L.P.—See Catterton Management Company, LLC; *U.S. Private*, pg. 793
DEL FRISCO'S DOUBLE EAGLE STEAK HOUSE—See Fertitta Entertainment, Inc.; *U.S. Private*, pg. 1499
DEL FRISCO'S - FORT WORTH, L.P.—See Catterton Management Company, LLC; *U.S. Private*, pg. 793
DEL FRISCO'S GRILLE OF ATLANTA, LLC—See Catterton Management Company, LLC; *U.S. Private*, pg. 793
DEL FRISCO'S GRILLE OF NEW YORK, LLC—See Catterton Management Company, LLC; *U.S. Private*, pg. 793
DEL FRISCO'S GRILLE OF PHOENIX, LLC—See Catterton Management Company, LLC; *U.S. Private*, pg. 793
DEL FRISCO'S GRILLE OF WASHINGTON DC, LLC—See Catterton Management Company, LLC; *U.S. Private*, pg. 793
DEL FRISCO'S OF BOSTON, LLC—See Catterton Management Company, LLC; *U.S. Private*, pg. 793
DEL FRISCO'S OF CHICAGO, LLC—See Catterton Management Company, LLC; *U.S. Private*, pg. 793
DEL FRISCO'S OF COLORADO, INC.—See Catterton Management Company, LLC; *U.S. Private*, pg. 793
DEL FRISCO'S OF NEVADA, INC.—See Catterton Management Company, LLC; *U.S. Private*, pg. 793
DEL FRISCO'S OF NEW YORK, LLC—See Catterton Management Company, LLC; *U.S. Private*, pg. 793
DEL FRISCO'S OF NORTH CAROLINA, INC.—See Catterton Management Company, LLC; *U.S. Private*, pg. 793
DEL FRISCO'S OF PHILADELPHIA, INC.—See Catterton Management Company, LLC; *U.S. Private*, pg. 793
DEL FRISCO'S RESTAURANT GROUP, INC.—See Catterton Management Company, LLC; *U.S. Private*, pg. 793
DELF SAND (PTY) LIMITED—See Afrimat Limited; *Int'l*, pg. 192
DELF SILICA COASTAL—See Afrimat Limited; *Int'l*, pg. 193
DELF (UK) LIMITED—See Neogen Corporation; *U.S. Public*, pg. 1505
DELGADO COMMUNICATIONS INC.—See Delgado Travel Agency Corporation; *U.S. Private*, pg. 1196
DELGADO COURIER INC.—See Delgado Travel Agency Corporation; *U.S. Private*, pg. 1196
DELGADO TRAVEL AGENCY CORPORATION; *U.S. Private*, pg. 1196
DELGASCO, LLC—See Essential Utilities Inc.; *U.S. Public*, pg. 795
DEL GAUDIO; *Int'l*, pg. 2010
DELGAZ GRID S.A.—See E.ON SE; *Int'l*, pg. 2252
DELHAIZE AMERICA, LLC—See Koninklijke Ahold Delhaize N.V.; *Int'l*, pg. 4260
DELHAIZE LUXEMBOURG S.A.—See Koninklijke Ahold Delhaize N.V.; *Int'l*, pg. 4260
DELHAIZE "THE LION" NEDERLAND B.V.—See Koninklijke Ahold Delhaize N.V.; *Int'l*, pg. 4260
DELHI BANK CORP.; *U.S. Public*, pg. 648
DELHI HILLS FLOWER & GARDEN CENTER; *U.S. Private*, pg. 1196
DELHIVERY PRIVATE LIMITED; *Int'l*, pg. 2013
DELIA ASSOCIATES; *U.S. Private*, pg. 1196
DELIA INC.; *U.S. Private*, pg. 1197
DELIAN TRADING (HK) CO., LTD.—See Guangdong Delian Group Co., Ltd.; *Int'l*, pg. 3153
DELI ART CO., LTD.—See Fullcast Holdings Co., Ltd.; *Int'l*, pg. 2842
DELIAS CLEANERS INC.—See Delphi Management Group, Inc.; *U.S. Private*, pg. 1199
DELIA'S, INC.; *U.S. Private*, pg. 1197
DELI-BOY INC.; *U.S. Private*, pg. 1196
DELICA ACE CO., LTD.—See Ajinomoto Company, Inc.; *Int'l*, pg. 257
DELICA CHEF CORPORATION—See House Foods Group Inc.; *Int'l*, pg. 3490
DE LICACY INDUSTRIAL CO., LTD.; *Int'l*, pg. 1996
DELICA FOODS CO., LTD.—See Delica Foods Holdings Co., Ltd.; *Int'l*, pg. 2013
DELICA FOODS HOKKAIDO CO., LTD.—See Delica Foods Holdings Co., Ltd.; *Int'l*, pg. 2013
DELICA FOODS HOLDINGS CO., LTD.; *Int'l*, pg. 2013
DELICA FOODS NAGASAKI CO., LTD.—See Delica Foods Holdings Co., Ltd.; *Int'l*, pg. 2013
DELICARD AB—See Edenred S.A.; *Int'l*, pg. 2307
DELICARD GROUP AB—See Edenred S.A.; *Int'l*, pg. 2307
DELICATO VINEYARDS; *U.S. Private*, pg. 1197
DELICE DE FRANCE LIMITED; *Int'l*, pg. 2013
DELICIA SDN. BHD.—See QAF Limited; *Int'l*, pg. 6131
DELICO HANDELS GMBH—See Unilever PLC; *Int'l*, pg. 8044
DELICO LIMITED—See Cranswick Plc; *Int'l*, pg. 1828
DELIFRANCE ASIA LTD—See Lippo Limited; *Int'l*, pg. 4522
DELIFRANCE (HK) LIMITED—See Lippo Limited; *Int'l*, pg. 4522
DELIFRANCE S.A.—See Vivescia; *Int'l*, pg. 8279
DELIFRANCE SINGAPORE PTE LTD—See Lippo Limited; *Int'l*, pg. 4522
DELIGHTFUL.COM, LLC—See IAC Inc.; *U.S. Public*, pg. 1082
DELIGHT SOURCE LIMITED—See Neway Group Holdings Limited; *Int'l*, pg. 5232
DELIGNIT AG; *Int'l*, pg. 2013
DELI-HTL TABAK MAATSCHAPPIJ B. V.—See Universal Corporation; *U.S. Public*, pg. 2254
DELI HUB CATERING PTE. LTD.—See Neo Group Limited; *Int'l*, pg. 5196
DELI, INC.; *U.S. Private*, pg. 1196
DELIKATESA D.D. LJUBLJANA—See Terme Catez, d.d.; *Int'l*, pg. 7565
DELIKATESSKUNGEN AB—See Storskogen Group AB; *Int'l*, pg. 7227
DELIKATESS SKINKOR AB—See Atria Plc; *Int'l*, pg. 694
DELILLE OXYGEN CO.; *U.S. Private*, pg. 1197
DE LILLO CHEVROLET; *U.S. Private*, pg. 1181
DELIMA MARSH S.A. - LOS CORREDORES DE SEGUROS S.A.—See Marsh & McLennan Companies, Inc.; *U.S. Public*, pg. 1378
DELI MANAGEMENT INC.; *U.S. Private*, pg. 1196
DELIMA OIL PRODUCTS SDN. BHD.—See FGV Holdings Bhd; *Int'l*, pg. 2649
DELIMEX DE MEXICO S.A. DE C.V.—See 3G Capital Inc.; *U.S. Private*, pg. 9
DELIMEX DE MEXICO S.A. DE C.V.—See Berkshire Hathaway Inc.; *U.S. Public*, pg. 317
DELIMOBIL HOLDING S.A.; *Int'l*, pg. 2013
DELINIAN LIMITED—See Astorg Partners S.A.S.; *Int'l*, pg. 656
DELINIAN LIMITED—See Epiris Managers LLP; *Int'l*, pg. 2460
DELIVER MEDIA; *U.S. Private*, pg. 1197
DELIVER NET LIMITED—See Bunzl plc; *Int'l*, pg. 1218
DELIVEROO PLC; *Int'l*, pg. 2013
DELIVERY ACE CO., LTD.—See Senko Group Holdings Co., Ltd.; *Int'l*, pg. 6709
DELIVERY AGENT, INC.; *U.S. Private*, pg. 1197
DELIVERY HERO SE; *Int'l*, pg. 2013
DELIVRA CORP.—See Hygrovest Limited; *Int'l*, pg. 3549
DELIVRA HEALTH BRANDS INC.—See Hygrovest Limited; *Int'l*, pg. 3549
DELIVRA, INC.—See Redbrick Technologies Inc.; *Int'l*, pg. 6245
DELIXI ELECTRIC ALGERIE SARL—See Schneider Electric SE; *Int'l*, pg. 6626
DELIXI ELECTRIC SEE EOOD—See Schneider Electric SE; *Int'l*, pg. 6626
DELIXI ELECTRIC SOUTH AFRICA (PTY) LTD—See Schneider Electric SE; *Int'l*, pg. 6626
DELIXI XINJIANG TRANSPORTATION GROUP CO., LTD; *Int'l*, pg. 2013
DELI XL BELGIE NV—See The Bidvest Group Limited; *Int'l*, pg. 7624
DELIZZA, INC.; *U.S. Private*, pg. 1197
DELKA SA—See Floridienne SA; *Int'l*, pg. 2708
DELKOR CORP. LTD.—See Brookfield Corporation; *Int'l*, pg. 1175
DELKOR CORP. LTD.—See Caisse de Depot et Placement du Quebec; *Int'l*, pg. 1254
DELKOR SYSTEMS INC.; *U.S. Private*, pg. 1197
DELKO S.A.; *Int'l*, pg. 2013
DELL AB—See Dell Technologies Inc.; *U.S. Public*, pg. 649
DELLA LAMB COMMUNITY SERVICES; *U.S. Private*, pg. 1197
DELLA PONTIAC; *U.S. Private*, pg. 1197
DELLARIA SALONS; *U.S. Private*, pg. 1197
DELLAS FOR NATURAL PRODUCTS LTD.—See The Jordanian Pharmaceutical Manufacturing Co., P.L.C.; *Int'l*, pg. 7660
DELL ASIA PACIFIC SDN.—See Dell Technologies Inc.; *U.S. Public*, pg. 649
DELL A/S—See Dell Technologies Inc.; *U.S. Public*, pg. 649
DELL A.S.—See Dell Technologies Inc.; *U.S. Public*, pg. 649
DELL AUSTRALIA PTY. LIMITED—See Dell Technologies Inc.; *U.S. Public*, pg. 649
DELL B.V.—See Dell Technologies Inc.; *U.S. Public*, pg. 649
DELL CANADA INC.—See Dell Technologies Inc.; *U.S. Public*, pg. 649
DELL CAPITAL PARTNERS, L.P.; *U.S. Private*, pg. 1197
DELL (CHINA) COMPANY LIMITED—See Dell Technologies Inc.; *U.S. Public*, pg. 649
DELL (CHINA) COMPANY LIMTED—See Dell Technologies Inc.; *U.S. Public*, pg. 649
DELL-COMM INC.; *U.S. Private*, pg. 1197
DELL COMPUTADORES DO BRASIL LTDA.—See Dell Technologies Inc.; *U.S. Public*, pg. 649
DELL COMPUTER DE CHILE LTDA—See Dell Technologies Inc.; *U.S. Public*, pg. 649
DELL COMPUTER INDIA PRIVATE LIMITED—See Dell Technologies Inc.; *U.S. Public*, pg. 649
DELL COMPUTER (PROPRIETARY) S.A.—See Dell Technologies Inc.; *U.S. Public*, pg. 649
DELL COMPUTER S.A.—See Dell Technologies Inc.; *U.S. Public*, pg. 649
DELL COMPUTER SPOL. S R.O.—See Dell Technologies Inc.; *U.S. Public*, pg. 649
DELL CORPORATION LIMITED—See Dell Technologies Inc.; *U.S. Public*, pg. 649
DELL CORPORATION (THAILAND) CO., LTD.—See Dell Technologies Inc.; *U.S. Public*, pg. 649
DELLEN AUTOMOTIVE INC.; *U.S. Private*, pg. 1197
DELLENBACH MOTORS; *U.S. Private*, pg. 1197
DELLE VEDOVE S.P.A.—See Cefla S.C.; *Int'l*, pg. 1390
DELLE VEDOVE USA, INC.—See Cefla S.C.; *Int'l*, pg. 1389
DELL FASTENER CORPORATION—See Bertram Capital Management, LLC; *U.S. Private*, pg. 540
DELL FUNDING L.L.C.—See Dell Technologies Inc.; *U.S. Public*, pg. 649
DELL GESM.B.H.—See Dell Technologies Inc.; *U.S. Public*, pg. 649
DELL GMBH—See Dell Technologies Inc.; *U.S. Public*, pg. 649
DELL GMBH—See Dell Technologies Inc.; *U.S. Public*, pg. 649
DELL HALLE GMBH—See Dell Technologies Inc.; *U.S. Public*, pg. 649
DELL INC. - FREMONT—See Dell Technologies Inc.; *U.S. Public*, pg. 649
DELL INC. - NASHUA—See Dell Technologies Inc.; *U.S. Public*, pg. 649
DELL INC. - NASHVILLE—See Dell Technologies Inc.; *U.S. Public*, pg. 649
DELL INC.—See Dell Technologies Inc.; *U.S. Public*, pg. 649
DELL INDIA PRIVATE LTD.—See Dell Technologies Inc.; *U.S. Public*, pg. 649
DELLING ENTERPRISES; *U.S. Private*, pg. 1197
DELL INTERNATIONAL SERVICES INDIA PRIVATE LIMITED—See Dell Technologies Inc.; *U.S. Public*, pg. 650
DELL INTERNATIONAL SERVICES PHILIPPINES INC.—See Dell Technologies Inc.; *U.S. Public*, pg. 650
DELL JAPAN INC.—See Dell Technologies Inc.; *U.S. Public*, pg. 650
DELL MARKING SYSTEMS INC.—See Gage Corporation; *U.S. Private*, pg. 1634
DELL MESSAGEONE—See Dell Technologies Inc.; *U.S. Public*, pg. 650
DELLNER BRAKES AB; *Int'l*, pg. 2013
DELL NEW ZEALAND LIMITED—See Dell Technologies Inc.; *U.S. Public*, pg. 650
DELL N.V.—See Dell Technologies Inc.; *U.S. Public*, pg. 650
DELLOYD INDUSTRIES (M) SDN BHD—See Delloyd Ventures Sdn Bhd; *Int'l*, pg. 2014
DELLOYD PLANTATION SDN. BHD.—See Delloyd Ventures Sdn Bhd; *Int'l*, pg. 2014
DELLOYD VENTURES SDN BHD; *Int'l*, pg. 2014
DELL PUBLISHING—See Bertelsmann SE & Co. KGaA; *Int'l*, pg. 990
DELL S.A.—See Dell Technologies Inc.; *U.S. Public*, pg. 650
DELL SA—See Dell Technologies Inc.; *U.S. Public*, pg. 650
DELL S.A.—See Dell Technologies Inc.; *U.S. Public*, pg. 650
DELL SINGAPORE PTE. LTD.—See Dell Technologies Inc.; *U.S. Public*, pg. 650
DELL SP.Z.O.O—See Dell Technologies Inc.; *U.S. Public*, pg. 650

COMPANY NAME INDEX

DELL S.R.O.—See Dell Technologies Inc.; *U.S. Public*, pg. 650
DELL TECHNOLOGIES INC.; *U.S. Public*, pg. 649
DELLTRON CO. INC.; *U.S. Private*, pg. 1197
DELL WILL CUSTOMS BROKERS (U.S.A.) INC.—See ATL Partners, LLC; *Int'l*, pg. 369
DEL MAR AVIONICS; *U.S. Private*, pg. 1192
DELMAR CENGAGE LEARNING—See Apax Partners LLP; *Int'l*, pg. 503
DELMAR CENGAGE LEARNING—See Apollo Global Management, Inc.; *U.S. Public*, pg. 168
DELMAR CENGAGE LEARNING—See KKR & Co. Inc.; *U.S. Public*, pg. 1256
DELMAR CENGAGE LEARNING—See Searchlight Capital Partners, L.P.; *U.S. Private*, pg. 3587
DELMAR COMMODITIES LTD. - BEAUSEJOUR FACILITY—See Ceres Global Ag Corp.; *U.S. Public*, pg. 475
DELMAR COMMODITIES LTD. - GLADSTONE ELEVATOR FACILITY—See Ceres Global Ag Corp.; *U.S. Public*, pg. 475
DELMAR COMMODITIES LTD. - NEWDALE ELEVATOR FACILITY—See Ceres Global Ag Corp.; *U.S. Public*, pg. 475
DELMAR COMMODITIES LTD. - SOMERSET ELEVATOR FACILITY—See Ceres Global Ag Corp.; *U.S. Public*, pg. 475
DELMAR COMMODITIES LTD.—See Ceres Global Ag Corp.; *U.S. Public*, pg. 475
DELMAR COMMODITIES LTD. - WESTROC ELEVATOR FACILITY—See Ceres Global Ag Corp.; *U.S. Public*, pg. 475
DEL MAR DESIGNS, INC.; *U.S. Private*, pg. 1192
DELMAR DISPOSAL—See TAS Environmental Services, L.P.; *U.S. Private*, pg. 3934
DELMAR FINANCIAL COMPANY; *U.S. Private*, pg. 1197
DEL MAR FOOD PRODUCTS CORP.; *U.S. Private*, pg. 1192
DELMAR HALL, LLC—See Live Nation Entertainment, Inc.; *U.S. Public*, pg. 1328
DEL MAR INDUSTRIES INC.; *U.S. Private*, pg. 1192
DELMAR INTERNATIONAL, INC.; *Int'l*, pg. 2014
DEL MAR SEAFOODS INC.; *U.S. Private*, pg. 1192
DELMAR SYSTEMS, INC.; *U.S. Private*, pg. 1197
DELMARVA BANCSHARES, INC.; *U.S. Private*, pg. 1197
DELMARVA COMMUNITY SERVICES, INC.; *U.S. Private*, pg. 1197
DELMARVA POWER & LIGHT COMPANY—See Exelon Corporation; *U.S. Public*, pg. 807
DELMARVA REAL ESTATE—See Independent Newspapers, Inc.; *U.S. Private*, pg. 2060
DELMARVA RV CENTER IN SEAFORD; *U.S. Private*, pg. 1197
DELMARVA SURETY ASSOCIATES, INC.—See Kelso & Company, L.P.; *U.S. Private*, pg. 2279
DELMAS—See CMA CGM S.A.; *Int'l*, pg. 1668
DELMAS (UK) LIMITED—See CMA CGM S.A.; *Int'l*, pg. 1668
DELMEGE FORSYTH & CO.(SHIPPING) LTD.—See Regional Container Lines Public Company Limited; *Int'l*, pg. 6254
DELMET PROD SRL—See Pelikan International Corporation Berhad; *Int'l*, pg. 5782
DELMIA GMBH—See Dassault Systemes S.A.; *Int'l*, pg. 1975
DEL MONACO FOODS, INC.—See Kainos Capital, LLC; *U.S. Private*, pg. 2255
DEL-MONDE INC.; *U.S. Private*, pg. 1193
DELMON POULTRY CO. B.S.C.; *Int'l*, pg. 2014
DELMON PRECAST COMPANY WLL—See Abdulla Ahmed Nass Group WLL; *Int'l*, pg. 58
DELMON READY MIXED CONCRETE & PRODUCTS CO. WLL—See Abdulla Ahmed Nass Group WLL; *Int'l*, pg. 58
DEL MONTE ASIA PTE LTD.—See Kikkoman Corporation; *Int'l*, pg. 4160
DEL MONTE B.V.—See Fresh Del Monte Produce Inc.; *U.S. Public*, pg. 885
DEL MONTE CAPITAL MEAT CO. INC.; *U.S. Private*, pg. 1192
DEL MONTE ELECTRIC CO. INC.; *U.S. Private*, pg. 1192
DEL MONTE FOODS, INC.—See Nutri-Asia Inc.; *Int'l*, pg. 5491
DEL MONTE FOODS (XIAMEN) CO., LTD—See Kikkoman Corporation; *Int'l*, pg. 4160
DEL MONTELL MOTORS LIMITED; *U.S. Private*, pg. 1192
DEL MONTE PACIFIC LIMITED—See Nutri-Asia Inc.; *Int'l*, pg. 5491
DEL MONTE (UK) LTD.—See Fresh Del Monte Produce Inc.; *U.S. Public*, pg. 885
DELMO SA—See Beijer Ref AB; *Int'l*, pg. 944
DELNEMO A/S—See REWE-Zentral-Aktiengesellschaft; *Int'l*, pg. 6314
DELNOR-COMMUNITY HOSPITAL—See Northwestern Memorial HealthCare; *U.S. Private*, pg. 2962
DELNOR CONSTRUCTION 2012 LTD.—See Delnor Construction Ltd.; *Int'l*, pg. 2014
DELNOR CONSTRUCTION LTD.; *Int'l*, pg. 2014

DEL NORTE CREDIT UNION; *U.S. Private*, pg. 1193
THE DEL NORTE TRIPLICATE—See Western Communications Inc.; *U.S. Private*, pg. 4492
DELOACH VINEYARDS—See Boisset, La Famille des Grands Vins; *Int'l*, pg. 1101
DELO-CENTER LLC—See Delo Group; *Int'l*, pg. 2014
DE LOGE SCHOONMAAKDIENSTEN B.V.—See EQT AB; *Int'l*, pg. 2476
DE LOGE SCHOONMAAKDIENSTEN B.V.—See The Goldman Sachs Group, Inc.; *U.S. Public*, pg. 2078
DELO GROUP; *Int'l*, pg. 2014
DELOITTE AUDIT OOD—See Deloitte Bulgaria EOOD; *Int'l*, pg. 2014
DELOITTE BULGARIA EOOD; *Int'l*, pg. 2014
DELOITTE CHILE; *Int'l*, pg. 2014
DELOITTE CONSULTING LLP—See Deloitte LLP; *U.S. Private*, pg. 1198
DELOITTE CONSULTING LLP—See Deloitte Touche Tohmatsu Limited; *Int'l*, pg. 2014
DELOITTE DEVELOPMENT LLC—See Deloitte LLP; *U.S. Private*, pg. 1198
DELOITTE DEVELOPMENT LLC—See Deloitte Touche Tohmatsu Limited; *Int'l*, pg. 2014
DELOITTE HOLDING B.V.; *Int'l*, pg. 2014
DELOITTE LEGAL BV—See Deloitte Holding B.V.; *Int'l*, pg. 2014
DELOITTE LLP; *Int'l*, pg. 2014
DELOITTE LLP; *U.S. Private*, pg. 1197
DELOITTE TAX LLP—See Deloitte LLP; *U.S. Private*, pg. 1198
DELOITTE & TOUCHE LLP—See Deloitte LLP; *U.S. Private*, pg. 1198
DELOITTE TOUCHE TOHMATSU LIMITED; *Int'l*, pg. 2014
THE DE LONG CO. INC.; *U.S. Private*, pg. 4019
THE DE LONG COMPANY, INC.—See The De Long Co. Inc.; *U.S. Private*, pg. 4019
DELONG COMPOSITE ENERGY GROUP CO., LTD.; *Int'l*, pg. 2015
DE'LONGHI AMERICA INC.—See De'Longhi S.p.A.; *Int'l*, pg. 1997
DE'LONGHI S.P.A.; *Int'l*, pg. 1997
DE'LONGHI SWITZERLAND AG—See De'Longhi S.p.A.; *Int'l*, pg. 1997
DELONG HOLDINGS LIMITED; *Int'l*, pg. 2015
DELONG SPORTSWEAR, INC.; *U.S. Private*, pg. 1198
DELON HAMPTON & ASSOCIATES, CHARTERED; *U.S. Private*, pg. 1198
DELO PRODAJA, D.D.; *Int'l*, pg. 2014
DELOREAN CORPORATION LIMITED; *Int'l*, pg. 2015
DELORME PUBLISHING COMPANY, INC.—See Garmin Ltd.; *Int'l*, pg. 2884
DELORO STELLITE, L.P.—See Kennametal Inc.; *U.S. Public*, pg. 1221
DELORO STELLITE UK LIMITED—See Kennametal Inc.; *U.S. Public*, pg. 1221
DELOS CAPITAL, LLC; *U.S. Private*, pg. 1198
DELOS MARINAS S.A.—See Technical Olympic SA; *Int'l*, pg. 7506
DELOTA CORP.; *Int'l*, pg. 2015
DELOTT & ASSOCIATES, INC.—See Aon plc; *Int'l*, pg. 495
DELO WELDING & INDUSTRIAL SUPPLY, INC.—See Jackson Welding Supply Co., Inc.; *U.S. Private*, pg. 2178
DEL PAPA DISTRIBUTING CO.; *U.S. Private*, pg. 1193
DELPHA CONSTRUCTION CO., LTD.; *Int'l*, pg. 2015
DELPHARM EVREUX SAS—See Delpharm S.A.S.; *Int'l*, pg. 2015
DELPHARM S.A.S. - BRETIGNY PLANT—See Delpharm S.A.S.; *Int'l*, pg. 2015
DELPHARM S.A.S. - DIJON PLANT—See Delpharm S.A.S.; *Int'l*, pg. 2015
DELPHARM S.A.S. - DROGENBOS PLANT—See Delpharm S.A.S.; *Int'l*, pg. 2015
DELPHARM S.A.S. - GAILLARD PLANT—See Delpharm S.A.S.; *Int'l*, pg. 2015
DELPHARM S.A.S. - HUNINGUE PLANT—See Delpharm S.A.S.; *Int'l*, pg. 2015
DELPHARM S.A.S. - LILLE PLANT—See Delpharm S.A.S.; *Int'l*, pg. 2015
DELPHARM S.A.S. - LYON BIOTECH PLANT—See Delpharm S.A.S.; *Int'l*, pg. 2015
DELPHARM S.A.S. - REIMS PLANT—See Delpharm S.A.S.; *Int'l*, pg. 2015
DELPHARM S.A.S.; *Int'l*, pg. 2015
DELPHARM TOURS SAS—See Delpharm S.A.S.; *Int'l*, pg. 2015
DELPHAX TECHNOLOGIES INC.; *U.S. Public*, pg. 651
DELPHAX TECHNOLOGIES LTD.—See Delphax Technologies Inc.; *U.S. Public*, pg. 651
DELPHI AFTERMARKET AMERICA DO SUL—See Aptiv PLC; *Int'l*, pg. 524
DELPHI ALAMBRADOS AUTOMOTRICES, S.A. DE C.V.—See Aptiv PLC; *Int'l*, pg. 524
DELPHIAN CORPORATION—See American Gas & Chemical Co., Ltd.; *U.S. Private*, pg. 235
DELPHI AUTOMOTIVE CUSTOMER TECHNOLOGY CENTER—See Aptiv PLC; *Int'l*, pg. 524
DELPHI AUTOMOTIVE LLP—See Aptiv PLC; *Int'l*, pg. 524

DELPHI MANAGEMENT GROUP, INC.

DELPHI AUTOMOTIVE SYSTEMS DO BRASIL LTDA.—See Aptiv PLC; *Int'l*, pg. 524
DELPHI AUTOMOTIVE SYSTEMS LIMITED SIRKETI—See Aptiv PLC; *Int'l*, pg. 524
DELPHI AUTOMOTIVE SYSTEMS - PORTUGAL S.A.—See Aptiv PLC; *Int'l*, pg. 524
DELPHI AUTOMOTIVE SYSTEMS SWEDEN AB—See Aptiv PLC; *Int'l*, pg. 524
DELPHI AUTOMOTIVE SYSTEMS (THAILAND) LTD.—See Aptiv PLC; *Int'l*, pg. 524
DELPHI AUTOMOTIVE SYSTEMS UK LIMITED—See Aptiv PLC; *Int'l*, pg. 524
DELPHI CABLEADOS, S.A. DE C.V.—See Aptiv PLC; *Int'l*, pg. 525
DELPHI CAPITAL MANAGEMENT, INC.—See Tokio Marine Holdings, Inc.; *Int'l*, pg. 7782
DELPHI CHASSIS NSK DO BRASIL LTDA.—See NSK Ltd.; *Int'l*, pg. 5478
DELPHI CHINA LLC—See Aptiv PLC; *Int'l*, pg. 524
DELPHI CONNECTION SYSTEMS BELGIUM NV—See Aptiv PLC; *Int'l*, pg. 525
DELPHI CONNECTION SYSTEMS JAPAN LTD.—See Aptiv PLC; *Int'l*, pg. 525
DELPHI CONNECTION SYSTEMS MEXICO S. DE R.L. DE C.V.—See Aptiv PLC; *Int'l*, pg. 525
DELPHI CONNECTION SYSTEMS NANTONG LTD.—See Aptiv PLC; *Int'l*, pg. 525
DELPHI DELCO ELECTRONICS DE MEXICO S.A. DE C.V.—See Aptiv PLC; *Int'l*, pg. 524
DELPHI DELCO ELECTRONICS OPERATIONS DEL-NOSA, S.A. DE C.V.—See Aptiv PLC; *Int'l*, pg. 524
DELPHI DEUTSCHLAND GMBH—See Aptiv PLC; *Int'l*, pg. 525
DELPHI DISPLAY SYSTEMS INC.—See Toast, Inc.; *U.S. Public*, pg. 2161
DELPHI ELECTRICAL CENTERS (SHANGHAI) CO., LTD.—See Aptiv PLC; *Int'l*, pg. 524
DELPHI ELECTRONICS & SAFETY—See Aptiv PLC; *Int'l*, pg. 524
DELPHI ELECTRONICS (SUZHOU) CO. LTD.—See Aptiv PLC; *Int'l*, pg. 524
DELPHI ENERGY CHASSIS SYSTEMS, ASIA HEADQUARTERS—See Aptiv PLC; *Int'l*, pg. 524
DELPHI ENERGY CHASSIS SYSTEMS, EUROPEAN REGIONAL HEADQUARTERS—See Aptiv PLC; *Int'l*, pg. 524
DELPHI ENERGY CHASSIS SYSTEMS—See Aptiv PLC; *Int'l*, pg. 524
DELPHI ENERGY CHASSIS SYSTEMS, SOUTH AMERICAN REGIONAL HEADQUARTERS—See Aptiv PLC; *Int'l*, pg. 524
DELPHI ENERGY & ENGINE MANAGEMENT SYSTEMS—See Aptiv PLC; *Int'l*, pg. 525
DELPHI FINANCIAL GROUP, INC.—See Tokio Marine Holdings, Inc.; *Int'l*, pg. 7782
DELPHI GROWTH CAPITAL CORP.; *U.S. Private*, pg. 1199
DELPHI HOLDING GMBH—See Aptiv PLC; *Int'l*, pg. 525
DELPHI HOLDINGS LUXEMBOURG S.A.R.L.—See Aptiv PLC; *Int'l*, pg. 525
DELPHI INSURANCE LIMITED—See Aptiv PLC; *Int'l*, pg. 525
DELPHI ITALIA AUTOMOTIVE SYSTEMS S.R.L.—See Aptiv PLC; *Int'l*, pg. 525
DELPHI MANAGEMENT GROUP, INC.; *U.S. Private*, pg. 1199
DELPHI MEDICAL SYSTEMS CORPORATION—See Aptiv PLC; *Int'l*, pg. 524
DELPHI PACKARD AUSTRIA GES.M.B.H.—See Aptiv PLC; *Int'l*, pg. 525
DELPHI PACKARD ELECTRIC SYSTEMS—See Aptiv PLC; *Int'l*, pg. 525
DELPHI PACKARD ESPANA, SL—See Aptiv PLC; *Int'l*, pg. 525
DELPHI PACKARD TANGER SA—See Aptiv PLC; *Int'l*, pg. 524
DELPHI POLAND S.A.—See Aptiv PLC; *Int'l*, pg. 525
DELPHI PRIVATE ADVISORS—See Lourd Capital LLC; *U.S. Private*, pg. 2500
DELPHI PRODUCT & SERVICE SOLUTIONS—See Aptiv PLC; *Int'l*, pg. 524
DELPHI RIMIR S.A. DE CV—See Aptiv PLC; *Int'l*, pg. 525
DELPHI SAGINAW NSK CO., LTD.—See NSK Ltd.; *Int'l*, pg. 5478
DELPHI SISTEMAS DE ENERGIA, S.A. DE C.V.—See Aptiv PLC; *Int'l*, pg. 525
DELPHI SLOVENSKO S.R.O.—See Aptiv PLC; *Int'l*, pg. 525
DELPHI—See Aptiv PLC; *Int'l*, pg. 524
DELPHI—See Aptiv PLC; *Int'l*, pg. 524
DELPHI TECHNICAL CENTRE LUXEMBOURG—See Aptiv PLC; *Int'l*, pg. 525
DELPHI TECHNOLOGY INC.—See Sapiens International Corporation N.V.; *Int'l*, pg. 6571
DELPHI THERMAL HUNGARY KFT—See Aptiv PLC; *Int'l*, pg. 525
DELPHIX CORP.—See Clearlake Capital Group, L.P.; *U.S. Private*, pg. 936

DELPHIX CORP.—See Francisco Partners Management, LP; *U.S. Private*, pg. 1591
DELPHON INDUSTRIES, LLC; *U.S. Private*, pg. 1199
DELPHOS COOPERATIVE ASSOCIATION; *U.S. Private*, pg. 1199
DELPHOS HERALD INC.; *U.S. Private*, pg. 1199
DELPHOS INTERNATIONAL, LTD.—See APQ Global Limited; *Int'l*, pg. 522
DELPHX CAPITAL MARKETS, INC.; *Int'l*, pg. 2015
DELPHX CORPORATION—See Delphx Capital Markets, Inc.; *Int'l*, pg. 2015
DELPHYS INC.—See Toyota Motor Corporation; *Int'l*, pg. 7870
DELPORTE SAS—See VINCI S.A.; *Int'l*, pg. 8216
DELRAY BEACH ASC, LLC—See Tenet Healthcare Corporation; *U.S. Public*, pg. 2002
DELRAY BEACH DIALYSIS CENTER LLC—See Nautic Partners, LLC; *U.S. Private*, pg. 2869
DELRAY CONNECTING RAILROAD COMPANY—See United States Steel Corporation; *U.S. Public*, pg. 2236
DELRAY IMPORTS INC.; *U.S. Private*, pg. 1199
DELRAY MEDICAL CENTER, INC.—See Tenet Healthcare Corporation; *U.S. Public*, pg. 2003
DELRAY MOTORS; *U.S. Private*, pg. 1199
DELRAY TIRE & RETREADING INC.; *U.S. Private*, pg. 1199
DEL REAL FOODS; *U.S. Private*, pg. 1193
DEL REY JUICE CO.; *U.S. Private*, pg. 1193
DELSBO CANDLE AB; *Int'l*, pg. 2015
DELSCO NORTHWEST, INC.—See Savage Services Corporation; *U.S. Private*, pg. 3555
DELSEA DRIVE SUPERMARKET LLC; *U.S. Private*, pg. 1199
DEL'S FARM SUPPLY LLC—See Tractor Supply Company; *U.S. Public*, pg. 2178
DELSOLAR (WUJIANG) LTD.—See Delta Electronics, Inc.; *Int'l*, pg. 2016
DELSOL CO., LTD.—See Nippon Telegraph & Telephone Corporation; *Int'l*, pg. 5354
DELSOLE CORPORATION; *Int'l*, pg. 2015
DEL SOL FOOD COMPANY, INC.; *U.S. Private*, pg. 1193
DELSOL KYUSHU CO., LTD.—See Nippon Telegraph & Telephone Corporation; *Int'l*, pg. 5354
DEL SOL LLC—See Pedersen Worldwide; *U.S. Private*, pg. 3128
DEL SOL MEDICAL CENTER—See HCA Healthcare, Inc.; *U.S. Public*, pg. 995
DELSOL TOKAI CO., LTD.—See Nippon Telegraph & Telephone Corporation; *Int'l*, pg. 5355
DELSON LUMBER, LLC; *U.S. Private*, pg. 1199
DELSTAR COMPANIES INC.—See Vivendi SE; *Int'l*, pg. 8272
DELSTAR INTERNATIONAL, LIMITED—See Mativ Holdings, Inc.; *U.S. Public*, pg. 1396
DELSTAR TECHNOLOGIES, INC.—See Mativ Holdings, Inc.; *U.S. Public*, pg. 1396
DELTA 9 CANNABIS, INC.; *Int'l*, pg. 2015
DELTA 9 LIFESTYLE CANNABIS CLINIC INC.—See Delta 9 Cannabis, Inc.; *Int'l*, pg. 2015
DELTA ADVERTISING GMBH—See Bertelsmann SE & Co. KGaA; *Int'l*, pg. 994
DELTA AGRAR D.O.O.—See Delta Holding; *Int'l*, pg. 2018
DELTA AIR LINES FRANCE—See Delta Air Lines, Inc.; *U.S. Public*, pg. 651
DELTA AIR LINES FRANKFURT—See Delta Air Lines, Inc.; *U.S. Public*, pg. 651
DELTA AIR LINES, INC.; *U.S. Public*, pg. 651
DELTA AIR LINES UK—See Delta Air Lines, Inc.; *U.S. Public*, pg. 651
DELTA AMERICA LTD.—See Delta Electronics, Inc.; *Int'l*, pg. 2016
DELTA APPAREL, INC.; *U.S. Public*, pg. 652
DELTA AREA ECONOMIC OPPORTUNITY CORPORATION; *U.S. Private*, pg. 1199
DELTA AUTO SALES SERVICE, INC.; *U.S. Private*, pg. 1199
DELTA BANCSHARES COMPANY—See First Mid Bancshares, Inc.; *U.S. Public*, pg. 846
DELTA BANK JSC; *Int'l*, pg. 2015
DELTA BEVERAGES (PVT) LIMITED—See Delta Corporation Limited; *Int'l*, pg. 2016
DELTA BIOLOGICALS S.R.L.—See Transasia Bio-Medicals Ltd.; *Int'l*, pg. 7896
DELTA BRIDGE, INC.—See Amentum Services, Inc.; *U.S. Private*, pg. 219
DELTA BUSINESS SYSTEMS, INC.—See LKCM Headwater Investments; *U.S. Private*, pg. 2475
DELTA CEDAR PRODUCTS LTD; *Int'l*, pg. 2015
DELTA CHEMICAL CORP.—See Nolan Capital, Inc.; *U.S. Private*, pg. 2934
DELTA CLEANTECH INC.; *Int'l*, pg. 2015
DEL TACO LLC—See Jack in the Box Inc.; *U.S. Public*, pg. 1183
DELTA COMMUNICATIONS, LLC—See Cable One, Inc.; *U.S. Public*, pg. 416
DELTA COMPANIES GROUP—See Greif Inc.; *U.S. Public*, pg. 967
THE DELTA COMPANIES; *U.S. Private*, pg. 4019

DELTA CONCEPT S.A.R.L.—See Stroer SE & Co. KGaA; *Int'l*, pg. 7242
DELTA CONSOLIDATED INDUSTRIES, INC.—See Bain Capital, LP; *U.S. Private*, pg. 430
DELTA CONSTRUCTION PARTNERS, INC.; *U.S. Private*, pg. 1199
DELTA CONSULTING GROUP, INC.; *U.S. Private*, pg. 1199
DELTA CONTAINER CORPORATION—See Republic Services, Inc.; *U.S. Public*, pg. 1786
DELTA CONTAINERS INC.—See Landaal Packaging Systems; *U.S. Private*, pg. 2384
DELTA CONTRACTING, INC.—See SurfaceCycle, Inc.; *U.S. Private*, pg. 3884
DEL TACO RESTAURANTS, INC.—See Jack in the Box Inc.; *U.S. Public*, pg. 1183
DELTA CORP HOLDINGS LIMITED; *Int'l*, pg. 2016
DELTA CORP LTD.; *Int'l*, pg. 2016
DELTA CORPORATE SERVICES INC.; *U.S. Private*, pg. 1199
DELTA CORPORATION LIMITED; *Int'l*, pg. 2016
DELTA CORPORATION LIMITED—See Schaffer Corporation Limited; *Int'l*, pg. 6615
DELTA COUNTY TELE-COMM INC.—See Telephone & Data Systems, Inc.; *U.S. Public*, pg. 1998
DELTACRAFT PAPER & CONVERTING COMPANY—See The Millcraft Paper Company Inc.; *U.S. Private*, pg. 4079
DELTA CREDIT SPV; *Int'l*, pg. 2016
DELTA DATA SOFTWARE, INC.—See Terminus Capital Partners, LLC; *U.S. Private*, pg. 3969
DELTA DEFENSE, LLC; *U.S. Private*, pg. 1199
DELTA DENTAL OF SOUTH DAKOTA; *U.S. Private*, pg. 1199
DELTA DENTAL PLAN OF NEW HAMPSHIRE, INC.; *U.S. Private*, pg. 1199
DELTA DENTAL PLAN OF VIRGINIA INC.; *U.S. Private*, pg. 1200
DELTA DENTAL PLAN OF WYOMING; *U.S. Private*, pg. 1200
DELTA DENTAL PLANS ASSOCIATION; *U.S. Private*, pg. 1200
DELTA DESIGN, INC.—See Cohu, Inc.; *U.S. Public*, pg. 529
DELTA DESIGN SINGAPORE PTE. LTD.—See Cohu, Inc.; *U.S. Public*, pg. 529
DELTA DESIGNS LTD.—See Gilde Equity Management (GEM) Benelux Partners B.V.; *Int'l*, pg. 2975
DELTA DIGITAL LTD.—See Inter-Gamma Investment Company Ltd.; *Int'l*, pg. 3735
DELTA DISASTER SERVICES LLC—See Baird Financial Group, Inc.; *U.S. Private*, pg. 453
DELTA DIVERSIFIED ENTERPRISES INC.; *U.S. Private*, pg. 1200
DELTA DJAKARTA TBK; *Int'l*, pg. 2016
DELTADNA LIMITED—See Unity Software Inc.; *U.S. Public*, pg. 2254
DELTA DOOR & HARDWARE, LLC—See Platinum Equity, LLC; *U.S. Private*, pg. 3208
DELTA DRONE SA; *Int'l*, pg. 2016
DELTA EDUCATION, LLC—See School Specialty, Inc.; *U.S. Public*, pg. 1848
DELTA EGG FARM, LLC—See Cal-Maine Foods, Inc.; *U.S. Public*, pg. 421
DELTA ELECTRIC POWER ASSOCIATION; *U.S. Private*, pg. 1200
DELTA ELECTRONICS (ARGENTINA) S.R.L.—See Delta Electronics, Inc.; *Int'l*, pg. 2016
DELTA ELECTRONICS (AUTOMOTIVE) AMERICAS INC.—See Delta Electronics, Inc.; *Int'l*, pg. 2016
DELTA ELECTRONICS (CHENZHOU) CO., LTD.—See Delta Electronics, Inc.; *Int'l*, pg. 2016
DELTA ELECTRONICS (COLOMBIA) S.A.S—See Delta Electronics, Inc.; *Int'l*, pg. 2016
DELTA ELECTRONICS COMPONENTS (DONGGUAN) CO., LTD.—See Delta Electronics, Inc.; *Int'l*, pg. 2017
DELTA ELECTRONICS (DONGGUAN) CO., LTD.—See Delta Electronics, Inc.; *Int'l*, pg. 2016
DELTA ELECTRONICS EUROPE LTD.—See Delta Electronics, Inc.; *Int'l*, pg. 2018
DELTA ELECTRONICS (FRANCE) S.A.S.—See Delta Electronics, Inc.; *Int'l*, pg. 2016
DELTA ELECTRONICS (GERMANY) GMBH—See Delta Electronics, Inc.; *Int'l*, pg. 2016
DELTA ELECTRONICS (HONG KONG) LTD.—See Delta Electronics, Inc.; *Int'l*, pg. 2016
DELTA ELECTRONICS, INC.; *Int'l*, pg. 2016
DELTA ELECTRONICS INTERNATIONAL LTD.—See Delta Electronics, Inc.; *Int'l*, pg. 2018
DELTA ELECTRONICS INTERNATIONAL (SINGAPORE) PTE LTD—See Delta Electronics, Inc.; *Int'l*, pg. 2018
DELTA ELECTRONICS INT'L (SINGAPORE) PTE LTD—See Delta Electronics, Inc.; *Int'l*, pg. 2018
DELTA ELECTRONICS (ITALY) S.R.L.—See Delta Electronics, Inc.; *Int'l*, pg. 2017
DELTA ELECTRONICS (JAPAN) INC.—See Delta Electronics, Inc.; *Int'l*, pg. 2017
DELTA ELECTRONICS (JIANGSU) LTD.—See Delta Electronics, Inc.; *Int'l*, pg. 2017

DELTA ELECTRONICS (KOREA), INC.—See Delta Electronics, Inc.; *Int'l*, pg. 2017
DELTA ELECTRONICS MEXICO S.A. DE C.V.—See Delta Electronics, Inc.; *Int'l*, pg. 2018
DELTA ELECTRONICS (NETHERLANDS) B.V.—See Delta Electronics, Inc.; *Int'l*, pg. 2017
DELTA ELECTRONICS (PERU) INC. S.R.L.—See Delta Electronics, Inc.; *Int'l*, pg. 2017
DELTA ELECTRONICS (POLAND) SP. Z.O.O.—See Delta Electronics, Inc.; *Int'l*, pg. 2016
DELTA ELECTRONICS POWER (DONGGUAN) CO., LTD.—See Delta Electronics, Inc.; *Int'l*, pg. 2017
DELTA ELECTRONICS (SHANGHAI) CO., LTD.—See Delta Electronics, Inc.; *Int'l*, pg. 2016
DELTA ELECTRONICS (SLOVAKIA) S.R.O.—See Delta Electronics, Inc.; *Int'l*, pg. 2018
DELTA ELECTRONICS SOLUTIONS (SPAIN) SLU—See Delta Electronics, Inc.; *Int'l*, pg. 2016
DELTA ELECTRONICS (SWEDEN) AB—See Delta Electronics, Inc.; *Int'l*, pg. 2018
DELTA ELECTRONICS (SWITZERLAND) AG—See Delta Electronics, Inc.; *Int'l*, pg. 2018
DELTA ELECTRONICS (THAILAND) PUBLIC COMPANY LIMITED—See Delta Electronics, Inc.; *Int'l*, pg. 2018
DELTA ELECTRONICS (UK) LTD.—See Delta Electronics, Inc.; *Int'l*, pg. 2018
DELTA ELECTRONICS (WUHU) CO., LTD.—See Delta Electronics, Inc.; *Int'l*, pg. 2018
DELTA ELEVATOR SERVICE CORP.—See Otis Worldwide Corporation; *U.S. Public*, pg. 1623
DELTA END AUSTRALIA PTY. LTD.—See BHP Group Limited; *Int'l*, pg. 1016
DELTA ENERGY B.V.—See Delta N.V.; *Int'l*, pg. 2019
DELTA ENERGY SYSTEMS (CZECH REPUBLIC) SPOL. S.R.O.—See Delta Electronics, Inc.; *Int'l*, pg. 2016
DELTA ENERGY SYSTEMS (FRANCE) S.A.—See Delta Electronics, Inc.; *Int'l*, pg. 2018
DELTA ENERGY SYSTEMS (GERMANY) GMBH—See Delta Electronics, Inc.; *Int'l*, pg. 2018
DELTA ENERGY SYSTEMS (INDIA) PRIVATE LTD.—See Delta Electronics, Inc.; *Int'l*, pg. 2017
DELTA ENERGY SYSTEMS (ITALY) S.R.L.—See Delta Electronics, Inc.; *Int'l*, pg. 2017
DELTA ENERGY SYSTEMS (SINGAPORE) PTE. LTD.—See Delta Electronics, Inc.; *Int'l*, pg. 2018
DELTA ENERGY SYSTEMS (SWEDEN) AB—See Delta Electronics, Inc.; *Int'l*, pg. 2017
DELTA ENERGY SYSTEMS (UK) LIMITED—See Delta Electronics, Inc.; *Int'l*, pg. 2018
DEL-TA ENGINEERING EQUIPMENT LTD—See Inter-Gamma Investment Company Ltd.; *Int'l*, pg. 3735
DELTA ENTERPRISE CORPORATION; *U.S. Private*, pg. 1200
DELTA EQUIPMENT S.A.—See Convum Ltd.; *Int'l*, pg. 1788
DELTA EURONET GMBH—See Euronet Worldwide, Inc.; *U.S. Public*, pg. 797
DELTA FABRICATION & MACHINE, INC.; *U.S. Private*, pg. 1200
DELTA FARM PRESS, INC.—See Informa plc; *Int'l*, pg. 3692
DELTA FAUCET COMPANY INDIA PRIVATE LIMITED—See Masco Corporation; *U.S. Public*, pg. 1390
DELTA FAUCET COMPANY MEXICO, S. DE R.L. DE C.V.—See Masco Corporation; *U.S. Public*, pg. 1390
DELTA FAUCET COMPANY—See Masco Corporation; *U.S. Public*, pg. 1391
DELTA FAUCET COMPANY—See Masco Corporation; *U.S. Public*, pg. 1391
DELTA FAUCET COMPANY—See Masco Corporation; *U.S. Public*, pg. 1391
DELTA FAUCET COMPANY—See Masco Corporation; *U.S. Public*, pg. 1391
DELTA FAUCET OF OKLAHOMA, INC.—See Masco Corporation; *U.S. Public*, pg. 1391
DELTA FIRE SYSTEMS INC.—See APi Group Corporation; *Int'l*, pg. 514
DELTA FLEISCH HANDELS GMBH; *Int'l*, pg. 2018
DELTA FLORAL DISTRIBUTORS INC.; *U.S. Private*, pg. 1200
DELTA-FLY PHARMA, INC.; *Int'l*, pg. 2020
DELTAFORCE PERSONNEL SERVICES, INC.—See The Supporting Cast, Inc.; *U.S. Private*, pg. 4125
DELTA FOR CONSTRUCTION & REBUILDING; *Int'l*, pg. 2018
DELTA FOREMOST CHEMICAL CORP.; *U.S. Private*, pg. 1200
DELTAFORM LTD—See Apollo Global Management, Inc.; *U.S. Public*, pg. 154
DELTA FOUNDATION—See Delta Holding; *Int'l*, pg. 2018
DELTA FUNDING CORPORATION; *U.S. Private*, pg. 1200
DELTA GALIL GERMANY GMBH—See GMM Capital LLC; *U.S. Private*, pg. 1722
DELTA GALIL INDUSTRIES LTD.—See GMM Capital LLC; *U.S. Private*, pg. 1722
DELTA GALIL USA INC.—See GMM Capital LLC; *U.S. Private*, pg. 1722

DELTA GAS TRANSPORTATION LIMITED—See PTT Public Company Limited; *Int'l*, pg. 6092
DELTA GEAR CO. INC.; *U.S. Private*, pg. 1200
DELTA GENERALI HOLDING D.O.O.—See Assicurazioni Generali S.p.A.; *Int'l*, pg. 646
DELTA GENERALI OSIGURANJE AD—See Assicurazioni Generali S.p.A.; *Int'l*, pg. 646
DELTA GENERALI RE A.D.—See Assicurazioni Generali S.p.A.; *Int'l*, pg. 646
DELTAGEN, INC.; *U.S. Public*, pg. 652
DELTA GLASS B.V.—See LCI Industries; *U.S. Public*, pg. 1295
DELTA GRANITE AND MARBLE INC.; *U.S. Private*, pg. 1200
DELTA GREEK FOODS USA INC.—See Marfin Investment Group Holdings S.A.; *Int'l*, pg. 4691
DELTA GREENTECH (BRASIL) S.A.—See Delta Electronics, Inc.; *Int'l*, pg. 2017
DELTA GREENTECH (CHINA) CO., LTD.—See Delta Electronics, Inc.; *Int'l*, pg. 2018
DELTA GREEN TIANJIN INDUSTRIES CO., LTD.—See Delta Electronics, Inc.; *Int'l*, pg. 2018
DELTA GROUP ELECTRONIC INC.; *U.S. Private*, pg. 1200
DELTA GROUP PTY LTD - CONCRETE RECYCLING DIVISION—See Delta Group Pty Ltd; *Int'l*, pg. 2018
DELTA GROUP PTY LTD - METAL RECYCLING DIVISION—See Delta Group Pty Ltd; *Int'l*, pg. 2018
DELTA GROUP PTY LTD; *Int'l*, pg. 2018
DELTA GROWERS ASSOCIATION; *U.S. Private*, pg. 1200
DELTA GYPSUM, LLC—See Hendricks Holding Company, Inc.; *U.S. Private*, pg. 1915
DELTA HEALTH ALLIANCE; *U.S. Private*, pg. 1200
DELTA HEALTH TECHNOLOGIES, LLC—See Alaya Care Inc.; *Int'l*, pg. 292
DELTA HOLDINGS, INC.; *U.S. Private*, pg. 1200
DELTA HOLDING; *Int'l*, pg. 2018
DELTA HOUSING INVESTMENT INC.; *U.S. Private*, pg. 1200
DELTA IMPLEMENT COMPANY—See Ayres-Delta Implement, Inc.; *U.S. Private*, pg. 414
DELTA IMPLEMENT CO. OF ROLLING FORK—See Ayres-Delta Implement, Inc.; *U.S. Private*, pg. 414
DELTA INDUCTRIAL RESOURCES LIMITED; *Int'l*, pg. 2019
DELTA INDUSTRIAL SERVICES, INC.; *U.S. Private*, pg. 1200
DELTA INDUSTRIES INC.; *U.S. Private*, pg. 1200
DELTA INDUSTRIES—See Zuckerman-Honickman Inc.; *U.S. Private*, pg. 4609
DELTA INFORMATION SYSTEMS INC.; *U.S. Private*, pg. 1201
DELTA INFRA B.V.—See Delta N.V.; *Int'l*, pg. 2019
DELTA INN INC.; *U.S. Private*, pg. 1201
DELTA INSTRUMENTS B.V.—See Revvity, Inc.; *U.S. Public*, pg. 1795
DELTA INSURANCE COMPANY LTD.; *Int'l*, pg. 2019
DELTA INSURANCE—See Egypt Kuwait Holding Co. S.A.E; *Int'l*, pg. 2327
DELTA INVESTERINGS MAATSCHAPPIJ B.V.—See Delta N.V.; *Int'l*, pg. 2019
DELTA INVESTORS—See Omega Healthcare Investors, Inc.; *U.S. Public*, pg. 1571
DELTA-KN OY—See Rejlers AB; *Int'l*, pg. 6259
DELTA LABORATORIES INC.; *U.S. Private*, pg. 1201
DELTA LEASING & FINANCE LIMITED; *Int'l*, pg. 2019
DELTA LIFE INSURANCE COMPANY LIMITED; *Int'l*, pg. 2019
DELTA LIFE INSURANCE CO.; *U.S. Private*, pg. 1201
DELTA LIQUID ENERGY; *U.S. Private*, pg. 1201
DELTAMAC (TAIWAN) CO., LTD.; *Int'l*, pg. 2020
DELTA MANUFACTURING LTD; *Int'l*, pg. 2019
DELTAMARIN (CHINA) CO., LTD.—See China Merchants Group Limited; *Int'l*, pg. 1520
DELTA MARINE INDUSTRIES, INC.; *U.S. Private*, pg. 1201
DELTAMARIN LTD.—See China Merchants Group Limited; *Int'l*, pg. 1520
DELTAMARIN SP.Z O.O.—See China Merchants Group Limited; *Int'l*, pg. 1520
DELTA MARKETING INC.; *U.S. Private*, pg. 1201
DELTA MATERIAL SERVICES, LLC—See Delta Air Lines, Inc.; *U.S. Public*, pg. 651
DELTA MATERIALS HANDLING INC.; *U.S. Private*, pg. 1201
DELTA MAX; *U.S. Private*, pg. 1201
DELTAMEDIA SA/NV—See bpost NV/SA; *Int'l*, pg. 1133
DELTA MEDICAL SYSTEMS INC.; *U.S. Private*, pg. 1201
DELTAMED S.A.—See ArchiMed SAS; *Int'l*, pg. 548
DELTA METAL RECYCLING (HOLDINGS) LTD.—See Daiki Aluminium Industry Co., Ltd.; *Int'l*, pg. 1931
DELTA METALS COMPANY INC.; *U.S. Private*, pg. 1201
DELTAMETAL (THAILAND) LIMITED—See KS Energy Limited; *Int'l*, pg. 4310
DELTA MILIEU GROENCOMPOST B.V.—See Delta N.V.; *Int'l*, pg. 2019
DELTA MILIEU RECYCLING B.V.—See Delta N.V.; *Int'l*, pg. 2019

DELTA-MONTROSE ELECTRIC ASSOCIATION; *U.S. Private*, pg. 1202
DELTA MOTORS—See Delta Holding; *Int'l*, pg. 2018
DELTA NATURAL GAS COMPANY, INC.—See Essential Utilities Inc.; *U.S. Public*, pg. 795
DELTA NETWERKBEDRIJF B.V.—See Delta N.V.; *Int'l*, pg. 2019
DELTA NETWORKS (DONGGUAN) CO., LTD.—See Delta Electronics, Inc.; *Int'l*, pg. 2018
DELTA NETWORKS, INC.—See Delta Electronics, Inc.; *Int'l*, pg. 2018
DELTA NETWORKS (SHANGHAI) LTD.—See Delta Electronics, Inc.; *Int'l*, pg. 2018
DELTA NEU BENELUX N.V.—See Groupe SFPI SA; *Int'l*, pg. 3111
DELTA NEU LIMITED—See Groupe SFPI SA; *Int'l*, pg. 3111
DELTA NEU MAROC S.A.—See Groupe SFPI SA; *Int'l*, pg. 3111
DELTA NEU NEDERLAND BV—See Groupe SFPI SA; *Int'l*, pg. 3111
DELTA NEU S.A.S.—See Groupe SFPI SA; *Int'l*, pg. 3111
DELTA N.V.; *Int'l*, pg. 2019
DELTA OHM S.R.L.—See GHM Messtechnik GmbH; *Int'l*, pg. 2959
DELTA OIL & GAS, INC.; *Int'l*, pg. 2019
DELTA OIL MILL; *U.S. Private*, pg. 1201
DELTAONE CAPITAL PARTNERS CORP.—See iA Financial Corporation Inc.; *Int'l*, pg. 3567
DELTA PACIFIC PRODUCTS, INC.—See BlackBern Partners LLC; *U.S. Private*, pg. 573
DELTA PACIFIC PRODUCTS, INC.—See Lee Equity Partners LLC; *U.S. Private*, pg. 2412
DELTA PACKAGING SERVICES GMBH—See DS Smith Plc; *Int'l*, pg. 2209
DELTA PACKAGING & SUPPLY, LLC—See Kelso & Company, L.P.; *U.S. Private*, pg. 2279
DELTA PACKAGING & SUPPLY, LLC—See Warburg Pincus LLC; *U.S. Private*, pg. 4436
DELTA PETROLEUM COMPANY INC.—See Aurora Capital Group, LLC; *U.S. Private*, pg. 394
DELTA PETROLEUM COMPANY INC.—See The Jordan Company, L.P.; *U.S. Private*, pg. 4061
DELTA PHARMA—See Randstad N.V.; *Int'l*, pg. 6203
DELTA PILOTS MUTUAL AID; *U.S. Private*, pg. 1201
DELTA PLUS BENELUX N.V.—See Delta Plus Group; *Int'l*, pg. 2019
DELTA PLUS CENTROAMERICA S.A.—See Delta Plus Group; *Int'l*, pg. 2019
DELTA PLUS CESKA REPUBLIKA S.R.O.—See Delta Plus Group; *Int'l*, pg. 2019
DELTA PLUS CHINA CO., LTD.—See Delta Plus Group; *Int'l*, pg. 2019
DELTA PLUS CROATIA D.O.O.—See Delta Plus Group; *Int'l*, pg. 2020
DELTA PLUS-E SA—See Delta Plus Group; *Int'l*, pg. 2020
DELTA PLUS GROUP; *Int'l*, pg. 2019
DELTA PLUS HELLAS SRL—See Delta Plus Group; *Int'l*, pg. 2020
DELTA PLUS IBERIA S.A.U.—See Delta Plus Group; *Int'l*, pg. 2020
DELTA PLUS INDIA PVT. LTD.—See Delta Plus Group; *Int'l*, pg. 2019
DELTA PLUS MAGYARORSZAG KFT—See Delta Plus Group; *Int'l*, pg. 2020
DELTA PLUS MIDDLE EAST FZE—See Delta Plus Group; *Int'l*, pg. 2020
DELTA PLUS PERSONEL GIYIM VE IS GUVENLIGI EKIPMANLARI SANAYI VE TICARET LIMITED SIRKET—See Delta Plus Group; *Int'l*, pg. 2020
DELTA PLUS PERU SAC—See Delta Plus Group; *Int'l*, pg. 2020
DELTA PLUS PHILIPPINES, INC.—See Delta Plus Group; *Int'l*, pg. 2020
DELTA PLUS POLSKA SP ZO.O—See Delta Plus Group; *Int'l*, pg. 2020
DELTA PLUS ROMANIA SRL—See Delta Plus Group; *Int'l*, pg. 2020
DELTA PLUS RUSSIE OOO—See Delta Plus Group; *Int'l*, pg. 2020
DELTA PLUS SAS—See Delta Plus Group; *Int'l*, pg. 2020
DELTA PLUS SICUREX SRL—See Delta Plus Group; *Int'l*, pg. 2020
DELTA PLUS SLOVENSKO SRO—See Delta Plus Group; *Int'l*, pg. 2020
DELTA PLUS (U.K.) LTD—See Delta Plus Group; *Int'l*, pg. 2019
DELTA PLUS UKRAINA SARL—See Delta Plus Group; *Int'l*, pg. 2019
DELTAPOINT CAPITAL MANAGEMENT, LLC; *U.S. Private*, pg. 1202
DELTA POMPAGE SARL—See Vicat S.A.; *Int'l*, pg. 8185
DELTA PORTER-CABLE—See Stanley Black & Decker, Inc.; *U.S. Public*, pg. 1932
DELTA POWER CO.; *U.S. Private*, pg. 1201
DELTA POWER SERVICES, LLC—See Babcock & Wilcox Enterprises, Inc.; *U.S. Public*, pg. 262
DELTA-PREG S.P.A.—See Toray Industries, Inc.; *Int'l*, pg. 7823

DELTA PRIVATE JETS, INC.—See Wheels Up Experience Inc.; *U.S. Public*, pg. 2366
DELTA PROCESS EQUIPMENT INC.—See DXP Enterprises, Inc.; *U.S. Public*, pg. 697
DELTA PRODUCE MARKETING INC.; *U.S. Private*, pg. 1201
DELTA PROJECT MANAGEMENT, INC.—See Lightview Capital LLC; *U.S. Private*, pg. 2454
DELTA PROJECTS GMBH—See Azerion Group N.V.; *Int'l*, pg. 778
DELTA PROJECTS, INC.; *U.S. Private*, pg. 1201
DELTA PROPERTY FUND LIMITED; *Int'l*, pg. 2020
DELTA-P TECHNOLOGIES LTD.—See Hydac International GmbH; *Int'l*, pg. 3544
DELTA PUBLICIDAD - GUAYAQUIL—See Delta Publicidad; *Int'l*, pg. 2020
DELTA PUBLICIDAD; *Int'l*, pg. 2020
DELTA PURE FILTRATION CORPORATION; *U.S. Private*, pg. 1201
DELTARAIL GROUP LIMITED—See Vision Capital, LLP; *Int'l*, pg. 8251
DELTARAIL GROUP LIMITED—See Vision Capital, LLP; *Int'l*, pg. 8251
DELTA RAILROAD CONSTRUCTION; *U.S. Private*, pg. 1201
DELTA RASSIS KSA—See Mansour Group; *Int'l*, pg. 4676
DELTA REAL ESTATE D.O.O.—See Delta Holding; *Int'l*, pg. 2018
DELTA REGIONAL MEDICAL CENTER; *U.S. Private*, pg. 1201
DELTA RESOURCES, INC.—See Alvarez & Marsal, Inc.; *U.S. Private*, pg. 213
DELTA RESOURCES LIMITED; *Int'l*, pg. 2020
DELTA RESOURCES, LLC—See Essential Utilities Inc.; *U.S. Public*, pg. 795
DELTA SAND & GRAVEL, INC.; *U.S. Private*, pg. 1201
DELTA SANITATION, LLC—See Waste Pro USA, Inc.; *U.S. Private*, pg. 4450
DELTA SCIENTIFIC CORP.; *U.S. Private*, pg. 1201
DELTASELECT GMBH—See aligna AG; *Int'l*, pg. 327
DELTA SIGMA THETA SORORITY, INC.; *U.S. Private*, pg. 1201
DELTA SOLUTIONS (FINLAND) OY—See Delta Electronics, Inc.; *Int'l*, pg. 2018
DELTA SOLUTIONS & STRATEGIES, LLC—See Hammond, Kennedy, Whitney & Company, Inc.; *U.S. Private*, pg. 1850
DELTA SONIC CAR WASH SYSTEMS INC.; *U.S. Private*, pg. 1201
DELTA SOUTHERN RAILROAD, INC.—See Mitsubishi UFJ Financial Group, Inc.; *Int'l*, pg. 4971
DELTA SPINNERS LIMITED; *Int'l*, pg. 2020
DELTA-STAHL GMBH—See Knauf Interfer SE; *Int'l*, pg. 4205
DELTA STAR CORPORATION—See Collins Brothers Corporation; *U.S. Private*, pg. 969
DELTA STAR INC.; *U.S. Private*, pg. 1202
DELTA STAR WEST—See Delta Star Inc.; *U.S. Private*, pg. 1202
DELTA STEEL, L.P.—See Reliance Steel & Aluminum Co.; *U.S. Public*, pg. 1779
DELTA SUGAR COMPANY; *Int'l*, pg. 2020
DELTA SYSTEMS & AUTOMATION INC.—See ILAPAK S.A.; *Int'l*, pg. 3613
DELTA TAU DATA SYSTEMS INC.—See OMRON Corporation; *Int'l*, pg. 5564
DELTA T CONSTRUCTION COMPANY; *U.S. Private*, pg. 1202
DELTA-T CORP.—See Madison Industries Holdings LLC; *U.S. Private*, pg. 2543
DELTATECH CONTROLS GMBH—See Sensata Technologies Holding plc; *U.S. Public*, pg. 1865
DELTATECH CONTROLS USA, LLC—See Sensata Technologies Holding plc; *U.S. Public*, pg. 1866
DELTATECH GAMING LIMITED—See Delta Corp Ltd.; *Int'l*, pg. 2016
DELTA TECHNOLOGIES PLC; *Int'l*, pg. 2020
DELTA TECHNOLOGY INC.—See Delta Air Lines, Inc.; *U.S. Public*, pg. 651
DELTA-TECH S.P.A.—See Toray Industries, Inc.; *Int'l*, pg. 7823
DELTA TELEPHONE CO. INC.—See Telapex Inc.; *U.S. Private*, pg. 3959
DELTA T EQUIPMENT; *U.S. Private*, pg. 1202
DELTA TEXTILES NEW YORK LTD.—See GMM Capital LLC; *U.S. Private*, pg. 1722
DELTA-THERM CORPORATION—See Groupe Ouellet Canada Inc.; *Int'l*, pg. 3109
DELTATHREE, INC.; *U.S. Private*, pg. 1202
DELTATHREE, LTD.—See deltathree, Inc.; *U.S. Private*, pg. 1202
DELTA TOOLING CO. INC.; *U.S. Private*, pg. 1202
DELTA TOUR & TRAVEL SERVICES (CANADA), INC.—See Media Chinese International Limited; *Int'l*, pg. 4770
DELTA TOUR & TRAVEL SERVICES, INC.—See Media Chinese International Limited; *Int'l*, pg. 4770
DELTA TRANSFORMERS INC.—See Hammond Power Solutions Inc.; *Int'l*, pg. 3239

DELTA TOOLING CO. INC.

DELTA TRANSPORT (PVT.) LTD.—See Albert Ballin KG; *Int'l*, pg. 294
DELTA TREATMENT SYSTEMS, LLC—See Advanced Drainage Systems, Inc.; *U.S. Private*, pg. 46
DELTATRE SPA—See Bruins Sports Capital, LLC; *U.S. Private*, pg. 671
DELTA TUCKER HOLDINGS, INC.—See Cerberus Capital Management, L.P.; *U.S. Private*, pg. 837
DELTAVALVE, LLC—See SCF Partners Ltd.; *U.S. Private*, pg. 3562
DELTA (VANCOUVER), B.C.—See Daechang Forging Co., Ltd.; *Int'l*, pg. 1906
DELTA-V CAPITAL, LLC; *U.S. Private*, pg. 1202
DELTA VIDEO DISPLAY SYSTEM (WUJIANG) LTD.—See Delta Electronics, Inc.; *Int'l*, pg. 2017
DELTA WASTE SYSTEMS, INC.—See Watts Trucking Service, Inc.; *U.S. Private*, pg. 3679
DELTA WESTERN INC.—See Saltchuk Resources Inc.; *U.S. Private*, pg. 3534
DELTA WHOLESALE LIQUORS, INC.—See Berkshire Hathaway Inc.; *U.S. Public*, pg. 304
DELTA WIRE & MFG.; *Int'l*, pg. 2020
DELTEC BATTERIES—See Sebata Holdings; *Int'l*, pg. 6669
DELTECH LLC—See SK Capital Partners, LP; *U.S. Private*, pg. 3679
DELTECH POLYMERS CORPORATION—See SK Capital Partners, LP; *U.S. Private*, pg. 3679
DELTECH RESIN CO.—See SK Capital Partners, LP; *U.S. Private*, pg. 3679
DELTECO S.A.—See Nicolas Correa S.A.; *Int'l*, pg. 5272
DELTEC SHUNTS, LLC—See Riedon, Inc.; *U.S. Private*, pg. 3434
DELTEK DANMARK A/S—See Roper Technologies, Inc.; *U.S. Public*, pg. 1811
DELTEK GB LIMITED—See Roper Technologies, Inc.; *U.S. Public*, pg. 1811
DELTEK, INC.—See Roper Technologies, Inc.; *U.S. Public*, pg. 1811
DELTEK NEDERLAND B.V.—See Roper Technologies, Inc.; *U.S. Public*, pg. 1811
DELTEK NETHERLANDS B.V.—See Roper Technologies, Inc.; *U.S. Public*, pg. 1811
DELTEK NORGE AS—See Roper Technologies, Inc.; *U.S. Public*, pg. 1811
DELTEK PHILIPPINES LLC—See Roper Technologies, Inc.; *U.S. Public*, pg. 1811
DELTEK SVERIGE AB—See Roper Technologies, Inc.; *U.S. Public*, pg. 1811
DELTEK SYSTEMS (PHILIPPINES) LTD.—See Roper Technologies, Inc.; *U.S. Public*, pg. 1811
DELTEQ PTE. LTD.—See Digilife Technologies Limited; *Int'l*, pg. 2119
DELTEQ SYSTEMS (M) SDN BHD—See Digilife Technologies Limited; *Int'l*, pg. 2119
DELTEX MEDICAL ESPANA—See Deltex Medical Group plc; *Int'l*, pg. 2020
DELTEX MEDICAL GROUP PLC; *Int'l*, pg. 2020
DELTEX MEDICAL LIMITED—See Deltex Medical Group plc; *Int'l*, pg. 2020
DELTEX MEDICAL SC INC.—See Deltex Medical Group plc; *Int'l*, pg. 2021
DEL-THO INDUSTRIES INC.; *U.S. Private*, pg. 1193
DELTIC ENERGY PLC; *Int'l*, pg. 2021
DELTICOM AG; *Int'l*, pg. 2021
DELTICOM O.E. S.R.L.—See Delticom AG; *Int'l*, pg. 2021
DELTILOG LTD.—See Delticom AG; *Int'l*, pg. 2021
DEL-TIN FIBER L.L.C.—See Roseburg Forest Products; *U.S. Private*, pg. 3482
DELTIUS B.V.—See Delta N.V.; *Int'l*, pg. 2019
THE DELTONA CORPORATION; *U.S. Private*, pg. 4020
DELTONA CORP. REALTY CO.—See The Deltona Corporation; *U.S. Private*, pg. 4020
DELTON AG; *Int'l*, pg. 2021
DELTONA LAND & INVESTMENT CORP.—See The Deltona Corporation; *U.S. Private*, pg. 4020
DELTONA MARKETING CORP.—See The Deltona Corporation; *U.S. Private*, pg. 4020
DELTON CABLES LIMITED - DHARUHERA WORKS—See Delton Cables Limited; *Int'l*, pg. 2022
DELTON CABLES LIMITED - FARIDABAD WORKS—See Delton Cables Limited; *Int'l*, pg. 2022
DELTON CABLES LIMITED - NEW DELHI WORKS—See Delton Cables Limited; *Int'l*, pg. 2022
DELTON CABLES LIMITED; *Int'l*, pg. 2022
DELTON HEALTH AG—See Delton AG; *Int'l*, pg. 2021
DELTON LOGISTICS SARL—See Delton AG; *Int'l*, pg. 2021
DELTON RESTAURANTS INC.; *U.S. Private*, pg. 1202
DELTON TECHNOLOGY (GUANGZHOU) INC.—See FIC Global, INC; *Int'l*, pg. 2653
DELTON TECHNOLOGY SE—See Delton AG; *Int'l*, pg. 2021
DEL TORO LOAN SERVICING, INC.; *U.S. Private*, pg. 1193
DELTRECS, INC.—See Vail Resorts, Inc.; *U.S. Public*, pg. 2271
DELTROL CORP.; *U.S. Private*, pg. 1202
DELTRON LTD.; *Int'l*, pg. 2022

DEL-TRON PRECISION, INC.; *U.S. Private*, pg. 1193
DE LUCA BANANA MARKETING PTY LTD—See Maui Capital Ltd.; *Int'l*, pg. 4731
DE LUCA ENTERPRISES INC.; *U.S. Private*, pg. 1181
DELUCA FRIGOLETTO ADVERTISING, INC.; *U.S. Private*, pg. 1202
DELUCA TOYOTA SCION; *U.S. Private*, pg. 1202
DELUCCHI +; *U.S. Private*, pg. 1202
DELUVIA INC.; *U.S. Private*, pg. 1202
DELUXE BUILDING SYSTEMS, INC.; *U.S. Private*, pg. 1202
DELUXE CORPORATION OMNIBUS PLAN VEBA TRUST; *U.S. Private*, pg. 1202
DELUXE CORPORATION; *U.S. Public*, pg. 652
DELUXE FAMILY CO., LTD.; *Int'l*, pg. 2022
DELUXE FEEDS INC.; *U.S. Private*, pg. 1202
DELUXE FINANCIAL SERVICES, INC.—See Augeo Affinity Marketing, Inc.; *U.S. Private*, pg. 391
DE-LUXE FOOD SERVICES SDN. BHD.—See Envictus International Holdings Limited; *Int'l*, pg. 2453
DE LUXE GROUP INC.—See Apollo Global Management, Inc.; *U.S. Public*, pg. 153
DELUXE LABORATORIES, INC.—See MacAndrews & Forbes Incorporated; *U.S. Private*, pg. 2532
DELUXE LABORATORIES, LTD.—See MacAndrews & Forbes Incorporated; *U.S. Private*, pg. 2532
DELUXE MARKETING, INC. (DMI); *U.S. Private*, pg. 1202
DELUXE PACKAGES—See Amcor plc; *Int'l*, pg. 417
DELUXE SHEET METAL, INC.—See Alpine 4 Holdings, Inc.; *U.S. Public*, pg. 85
DELUXE SMALL BUSINESS SALES, INC.—See Deluxe Corporation; *U.S. Public*, pg. 652
DELUXE SMALL BUSINESS SERVICES—See Deluxe Corporation; *U.S. Public*, pg. 652
DELUXE STRATEGIC SOURCING, INC.—See Deluxe Corporation; *U.S. Public*, pg. 652
DELUX S.R.O.—See Descours & Cabaud SA; *Int'l*, pg. 2044
DELVAG LUFTFAHRTVERSICHERUNGS-AG—See Deutsche Lufthansa AG; *Int'l*, pg. 2068
DELVAG VERSICHERUNGS-AG—See Deutsche Lufthansa AG; *Int'l*, pg. 2066
DELVA TOOL & MACHINE CORP.—See White Wolf Capital LLC; *U.S. Private*, pg. 4510
DELVIS GMBH—See Uno Minda Limited; *Int'l*, pg. 8084
DELVITA A.S.—See REWE-Zentral-Aktiengesellschaft; *Int'l*, pg. 6314
DEL WEBB COMMUNITIES OF VIRGINIA, INC.—See PulteGroup, Inc.; *U.S. Public*, pg. 1737
DEL WEBB CORPORATION—See PulteGroup, Inc.; *U.S. Public*, pg. 1737
DEL WEBB TEXAS LIMITED PARTNERSHIP—See PulteGroup, Inc.; *U.S. Public*, pg. 1737
DEL WEST ENGINEERING INC.; *U.S. Private*, pg. 1193
DELWOOD SUPPLY COMPANY—See Progressive Plumbing Supply, Co.; *U.S. Private*, pg. 3279
DELYSE, INC.; *U.S. Private*, pg. 1202
DELZER LITHOGRAPH COMPANY; *U.S. Private*, pg. 1202
DEMAAGD ENTERPRISES, LLC; *U.S. Private*, pg. 1203
DEMAAGD GMC-NISSAN, INC.—See Demaagd Enterprises, LLC; *U.S. Private*, pg. 1203
DEMAE-CAN CO., LTD.; *Int'l*, pg. 2022
DEMA ENGINEERING CO.; *U.S. Private*, pg. 1203
DE MAESSCHALCK H N.V.—See LKQ Corporation; *U.S. Public*, pg. 1334
DEMA EUROPE LLC—See Dema Engineering Co.; *U.S. Private*, pg. 1203
DEMAG CRANES & COMPONENTS CORP. - HOUSTON REGION—See Konecranes Plc; *Int'l*, pg. 4253
DEMAG CRANES & COMPONENTS CORP.—See Konecranes Plc; *Int'l*, pg. 4253
DEMAG CRANES & COMPONENTS GESMBH—See Konecranes Plc; *Int'l*, pg. 4253
DEMAG CRANES & COMPONENTS GMBH—See Konecranes Plc; *Int'l*, pg. 4253
DEMAG CRANES & COMPONENTS PTY. LTD.—See Konecranes Plc; *Int'l*, pg. 4253
DEMAG CRANES & COMPONENTS S.A.S.—See Konecranes Plc; *Int'l*, pg. 4253
DEMAG CRANES & COMPONENTS S.A.U—See Konecranes Plc; *Int'l*, pg. 4253
DEMAG CRANES & COMPONENTS SRL—See Konecranes Plc; *Int'l*, pg. 4253
DEMAG CRANES & COMPONENTS TRADING (SHANGHAI) CO. LTD.—See Konecranes Plc; *Int'l*, pg. 4253
DEMAG DELAVAL DESOIL SERVICES (SHERKATE SAHAMI KHASS)—See Siemens Aktiengesellschaft; *Int'l*, pg. 6886
DEMAG DELAVAL TURBOMACHINERY CORP.—See Siemens Aktiengesellschaft; *Int'l*, pg. 6889
DEMAG PLASTICS MACHINERY (NINGBO) CO., LTD.—See Sumitomo Heavy Industries, Ltd.; *Int'l*, pg. 7286
DEMAKES ENTERPRISES INC.; *U.S. Private*, pg. 1203
DEMANDBASE, INC.; *U.S. Private*, pg. 1203
DEMAND BRANDS, INC.; *U.S. Public*, pg. 653
DEMANDBRIDGE LLC—See Valsef Group; *Int'l*, pg. 8123
DEMANDDRIVE, LLC; *U.S. Private*, pg. 1203

CORPORATE AFFILIATIONS

DEMAND ENERGY NETWORKS, INC.—See Enel S.p.A.; *Int'l*, pg. 2413
DEMANDFORCE, INC.—See KKR & Co. Inc.; *U.S. Public*, pg. 1253
DEMANDGEN AG—See BDO USA, LLP; *U.S. Private*, pg. 501
DEMANDGEN AUSTRALIA PTY LTD.—See BDO USA, LLP; *U.S. Private*, pg. 501
DEMANDGEN INTERNATIONAL, INC.—See BDO USA, LLP; *U.S. Private*, pg. 501
DEMANDGEN INTERNATIONAL—See BDO USA, LLP; *U.S. Private*, pg. 501
DEMANDGEN UK—See BDO USA, LLP; *U.S. Private*, pg. 501
DEMANDG, LLC; *U.S. Private*, pg. 1203
DEMAND MANAGEMENT, INC.—See American Software, Inc.; *U.S. Public*, pg. 109
DEMAND POOLING, INC.; *U.S. Private*, pg. 1203
DEMAND SCIENCE GROUP, LLC; *U.S. Private*, pg. 1203
DEMANDWARE GMBH—See Salesforce, Inc.; *U.S. Public*, pg. 1837
DEMANT A/S; *Int'l*, pg. 2022
DEMANT SCHWEIZ AG—See Demant A/S; *Int'l*, pg. 2023
DEMANT TECHNOLOGY CENTRE SP. Z.O. O.—See Demant A/S; *Int'l*, pg. 2023
DEMARAIS INDUSTRIES; *Int'l*, pg. 2025
DEMARAIS SAS—See VINCI S.A.; *Int'l*, pg. 8216
DEMARCO PTE. LTD.—See Travelite Holdings Ltd.; *Int'l*, pg. 7907
DEMARIA BUILDING COMPANY INC.; *U.S. Private*, pg. 1203
DEMAR LTD.—See Burrow Global, LLC; *U.S. Private*, pg. 692
DE MARTIN & GASPARINI CONCRETE PLACERS PTY LTD—See Seven Group Holdings Limited; *Int'l*, pg. 6732
DE MARTIN & GASPARINI CONTRACTORS PTY LTD—See Seven Group Holdings Limited; *Int'l*, pg. 6732
DE MARTIN & GASPARINI PTY LTD—See Seven Group Holdings Limited; *Int'l*, pg. 6732
DE MARTIN & GASPARINI PUMPING PTY LTD—See Seven Group Holdings Limited; *Int'l*, pg. 6732
DE MARURI PUBLICIDAD DMP—See Publicis Groupe S.A.; *Int'l*, pg. 6103
DEMA SERVICE S.P.A.—See C.H. Robinson Worldwide, Inc.; *U.S. Public*, pg. 415
D.E. MASTER BLENDERS 1753 - SPAIN—See JAB Holding Company S.a.r.t.; *Int'l*, pg. 3862
DEMASZ PRIMAVILL HALOZATSZERELO IPARI KFT—See Electricite de France S.A.; *Int'l*, pg. 2350
DEMATIC CORP.—See KKR & Co. Inc.; *U.S. Public*, pg. 1254
DEMATIC CORP.—See The Goldman Sachs Group, Inc.; *U.S. Public*, pg. 2078
DEMATIC GMBH—See KKR & Co. Inc.; *U.S. Public*, pg. 1254
DEMATIC GMBH—See KKR & Co. Inc.; *U.S. Public*, pg. 1254
DEMATIC GMBH—See The Goldman Sachs Group, Inc.; *U.S. Public*, pg. 2078
DEMATIC GMBH—See The Goldman Sachs Group, Inc.; *U.S. Public*, pg. 2078
DEMATIC GMBH—See KKR & Co. Inc.; *U.S. Public*, pg. 1254
DEMATIC GMBH—See The Goldman Sachs Group, Inc.; *U.S. Public*, pg. 2078
DEMATIC-HOLDINGS PTY. LTD.—See KKR & Co. Inc.; *U.S. Public*, pg. 1254
DEMATIC HOLDINGS PTY. LTD.—See The Goldman Sachs Group, Inc.; *U.S. Public*, pg. 2079
DEMATIC LOGISTICS GMBH—See KKR & Co. Inc.; *U.S. Public*, pg. 1254
DEMATIC LOGISTICS GMBH—See KKR & Co. Inc.; *U.S. Public*, pg. 1254
DEMATIC LOGISTICS GMBH—See The Goldman Sachs Group, Inc.; *U.S. Public*, pg. 2078
DEMATIC LOGISTICS GMBH—See The Goldman Sachs Group, Inc.; *U.S. Public*, pg. 2078
DEMATIC LTD.—See KKR & Co. Inc.; *U.S. Public*, pg. 1254
DEMATIC LTD.—See The Goldman Sachs Group, Inc.; *U.S. Public*, pg. 2078
DEMATIC PTY. LTD.—See KKR & Co. Inc.; *U.S. Public*, pg. 1254
DEMATIC PTY. LTD.—See The Goldman Sachs Group, Inc.; *U.S. Public*, pg. 2079
DEMATIC REDDWERKS—See KKR & Co. Inc.; *U.S. Public*, pg. 1254
DEMATIC REDDWERKS—See The Goldman Sachs Group, Inc.; *U.S. Public*, pg. 2079
DEMATIC RETROTECH—See Egemin Automation Inc.; *U.S. Private*, pg. 1344
DEMATTIA GROUP; *U.S. Private*, pg. 1203
DE MATTOS & SULLIVAN LIMITED—See BASF SE; *Int'l*, pg. 883
DEMBO JONES, P.C.; *U.S. Private*, pg. 1203
DEMCO EUROPE LIMITED—See Wall Family Enterprise, Inc.; *U.S. Private*, pg. 4430

COMPANY NAME INDEX

DEMCO INC.; *U.S. Private*, pg. 1203
DEMCO, INC.—See Wall Family Enterprise, Inc.; *U.S. Private*, pg. 4430
DEMCO POWER CO., LTD.—See Demco Public Company Limited; *Int'l*, pg. 2025
DEMCO PUBLIC COMPANY LIMITED; *Int'l*, pg. 2025
DEMD PRODUCTIONS S.A.S—See Vivendi SE; *Int'l*, pg. 8275
DEME BLUE ENERGY N.V.—See Ackermans & van Haaren NV; *Int'l*, pg. 105
DEME BUILDING MATERIALS N.V.—See Ackermans & van Haaren NV; *Int'l*, pg. 105
DEMEDCO INC.—See DeRoyal Industries Inc.; *U.S. Private*, pg. 1210
DEME ENVIRONMENTAL NV—See Ackermans & van Haaren NV; *Int'l*, pg. 105
DEME INFRA MARINE CONTRACTORS B.V.—See Ackermans & van Haaren NV; *Int'l*, pg. 105
DE.MEM LIMITED; *Int'l*, pg. 1997
DE MENSEN NV—See Television Francaise 1 S.A.; *Int'l*, pg. 7542
DEMENT CONSTRUCTION COMPANY INC.; *U.S. Private*, pg. 1203
DEME NV—See Ackermans & van Haaren NV; *Int'l*, pg. 105
DEME OFFSHORE BE NV—See Ackermans & van Haaren NV; *Int'l*, pg. 105
DEMERARA DISTILLERS EUROPE BV—See Demerara Distillers Ltd.; *Int'l*, pg. 2025
DEMERARA DISTILLERS LTD.; *Int'l*, pg. 2025
DEMERARA DISTILLERS (USA) INC.—See Demerara Distillers Ltd.; *Int'l*, pg. 2025
DEMERARA OXYGEN COMPANY LIMITED—See Massy Holdings Ltd.; *Int'l*, pg. 4723
DEMERARA TOBACCO CO. LTD.—See British American Tobacco plc; *Int'l*, pg. 1167
DEMERS, MANUFACTURIER D'AMBULANCES INC.—See Caisse de Depot et Placement du Quebec; *Int'l*, pg. 1254
DEMERS, MANUFACTURIER D'AMBULANCES INC.—See Clearspring Capital Partners; *Int'l*, pg. 1657
DEMERY RESOURCES COMPANY, LLC—See NACCO Industries, Inc.; *U.S. Public*, pg. 1489
DEMESNE ELECTRICAL SALES LIMITED; *Int'l*, pg. 2025
DEMESNE ELECTRICAL SALES UK LIMITED—See Demesne Electrical Sales Limited; *Int'l*, pg. 2025
DEMESNE RESOURCES LTD.; *Int'l*, pg. 2025
DEMETER-CHEMUNG/ HARVARD DIVISION—See Demeter LP; *U.S. Private*, pg. 1203
DEMETER CORPORATION PUBLIC COMPANY LIMITED; *Int'l*, pg. 2025
DEMETER LP; *U.S. Private*, pg. 1203
DEMETER-RIDGEFIELD DIVISION—See Demeter LP; *U.S. Private*, pg. 1203
DEMETER-SOUTH BELOIT DIVISION—See Demeter LP; *U.S. Private*, pg. 1203
DEMETRA HOLDINGS PLC; *Int'l*, pg. 2025
DEMET'S CANDY COMPANY—See Yildiz Holding AS; *Int'l*, pg. 8583
DEMI BEIJING INTERNATIONAL TRADING CO., LTD.—See Nicca Chemical Co., Ltd.; *Int'l*, pg. 5263
DEMIBOOKS INC.—See Educational Develop; *U.S. Public*, pg. 720
DEMICA LIMITED—See JRJ Ventures LLP; *Int'l*, pg. 4008
DEMI KOREA CO., LTD.—See Nicca Chemical Co., Ltd.; *Int'l*, pg. 5263
DEMILEC INC.—See Huntsman Corporation; *U.S. Public*, pg. 1072
DEMILEC (USA) INC.—See Huntsman Corporation; *U.S. Public*, pg. 1072
THE DEMING HEADLIGHT—See Gannett Co., Inc.; *U.S. Public*, pg. 900
DEMING HOSPITAL CORPORATION—See Quorum Health Corporation; *U.S. Private*, pg. 3329
DEMIRE DEUTSCHE MITTELSTAND REAL ESTATE AG; *Int'l*, pg. 2025
DEMIRE LEIPZIG AM ALTEN FLUGHAFEN 1 GMBH—See DEMIRE Deutsche Mittelstand Real Estate AG; *Int'l*, pg. 2025
DEMIRER KABLO TESISLERI SAN. VE TIC. A.S—See Jiangsu Zhongtian Technology Co., Ltd.; *Int'l*, pg. 3958
DEMIR EXPORT A.S.—See Koc Holding A.S.; *Int'l*, pg. 4223
DEMISAS DOKUM EMAYE MAMULLERI SANAYI AS; *Int'l*, pg. 2025
D & E MITSUBISHI; *U.S. Private*, pg. 1136
DEMIURGE STUDIOS, LLC—See Embracer Group AB; *Int'l*, pg. 2375
DEMIX AGREGATS - LAVAL—See CRH plc; *Int'l*, pg. 1843
DEMIX BETON - QUEBEC—See CRH plc; *Int'l*, pg. 1843
DEMIX CONSTRUCTION - LAVAL—See CRH plc; *Int'l*, pg. 1843
DEM MANUFACTURING—See Avnet, Inc.; *U.S. Public*, pg. 250
DEMMEL AG; *Int'l*, pg. 2025
DEMMER ENGINEERING & MACHINE CO.; *U.S. Private*, pg. 1203
DEMNER, MERLICEK & BERGMANN WERBEGESELLSCHAFT MBH; *Int'l*, pg. 2025

DEMOCRACY CLOTHING—See Sun Capital Partners, Inc.; *U.S. Private*, pg. 3859
DEMOCRACY NOW!; *U.S. Private*, pg. 1203
DEMOCRACY WORKS INC.; *U.S. Private*, pg. 1204
DEMOCRASOFT HOLDINGS, INC.; *U.S. Public*, pg. 653
DEMOCRAT & CHRONICLE—See Gannett Co., Inc.; *U.S. Public*, pg. 897
THE DEMOCRAT CO.—See Brehm Communications Inc.; *U.S. Private*, pg. 644
DEMOCRAT NEWS—See Lee Enterprises, Incorporated; *U.S. Public*, pg. 1299
DEMOCRAT PRINTING & LITHOGRAPH COMPANY; *U.S. Private*, pg. 1204
DEMO MAKINA ELEKTRIK ELEKTRONIK TAAH.SAN.VE TIC.LTD.—See Zhejiang Xinchai Co., Ltd.; *Int'l*, pg. 8666
DEMOMATIC S.A.—See IVS Group S.A.; *Int'l*, pg. 3848
DEMONTROND AUTO COUNTRY, INC.; *U.S. Private*, pg. 1204
DEMONTROND AUTOMOTIVE GROUP; *U.S. Private*, pg. 1204
DEMON TRUCKING INC.—See Phoenix Beverages, Inc.; *U.S. Private*, pg. 3172
DEMOS (BEIJING) MANAGEMENT & TECHNICAL TRAINING CO., LTD.—See Demos S.A.; *Int'l*, pg. 2025
DEMOS BENELUX—See Demos S.A.; *Int'l*, pg. 2025
DEMOS GMBH—See Demos S.A.; *Int'l*, pg. 2025
DEMOS-INTERNET—See Demos LLC; *Int'l*, pg. 2025
DEMOS LLC; *Int'l*, pg. 2025
DEMOS MEDICAL PUBLISHING, LLC—See Mannheim, LLC; *U.S. Private*, pg. 2565
DEMOS MIDDLE EAST FZ—See Demos S.A.; *Int'l*, pg. 2025
DEMOS POLSKA SP. Z O.O.—See Demos S.A.; *Int'l*, pg. 2026
DEMOS S.A.; *Int'l*, pg. 2025
DEMOSS CAPITAL INC.—See Blue Creek Investment Partners; *U.S. Private*, pg. 586
THE DEMOSS COMPANY; *U.S. Private*, pg. 4020
DEMOTELLER SYSTEMS, INC.—See ASSA ABLOY AB; *Int'l*, pg. 637
DEMOULAS SUPER MARKETS, INC.; *U.S. Private*, pg. 1204
DE MOULIN BROTHERS & COMPANY; *U.S. Private*, pg. 1181
DE MOYA GROUP INC.; *U.S. Private*, pg. 1181
DEMPEWOLF FORD LINCOLN; *U.S. Private*, pg. 1204
DEMPO SHIPBUILDING & ENGINEERING PVT. LTD.—See Goa Carbon Ltd.; *Int'l*, pg. 3018
DEMPO SPORTS CLUB PVT. LTD.—See Goa Carbon Ltd.; *Int'l*, pg. 3018
DEM PRODUCTION AB—See Beijer Ref AB; *Int'l*, pg. 944
DEMPSEY CONSTRUCTION, INC.; *U.S. Private*, pg. 1204
DEMPSEY GROUP, INC.—See CI Capital Partners LLC; *U.S. Private*, pg. 895
DEMPSEY INDUSTRIES, INC.—See TruArc Partners, L.P.; *U.S. Private*, pg. 4245
DEMPSEY & SIDERS INSURANCE AGENCY—See American Financial Group, Inc.; *U.S. Public*, pg. 102
DEMPSEY UNIFORM & LINEN SUPPLY, INC.; *U.S. Private*, pg. 1204
DEMPTOS ESPANA—See Tonnellerie Francois Freres; *Int'l*, pg. 7810
DEMPTOS GLASS COMPANY—See Atlas Holdings, LLC; *U.S. Private*, pg. 378
DEMPTOS NAPA COOPERAGE, INC—See Tonnellerie Francois Freres; *Int'l*, pg. 7810
DEMPTOS SA (PTY) LTD—See Tonnellerie Francois Freres; *Int'l*, pg. 7810
DEMSTAR RENTALS 2005 LTD.—See AUTOHELLAS S.A.; *Int'l*, pg. 727
DEM. TH. BERTZELETOS & BROS. SA; *Int'l*, pg. 2022
DEMUTH AG—See Poenina Holding AG; *Int'l*, pg. 5903
DENA CO., LTD.; *Int'l*, pg. 2026
DEN ADN NETWORK PRIVATE LIMITED—See DEN Networks Limited; *Int'l*, pg. 2026
DENA GLOBAL, INC.—See DeNA Co., Ltd.; *Int'l*, pg. 2026
DENAIR ENERGY SAVING TECHNOLOGY (SHANGHAI) CO., LTD.—See Shanghai Hanbell Precise Machinery Co., Ltd.; *Int'l*, pg. 6769
DENALI ADVANCED INTEGRATION, INC.; *U.S. Private*, pg. 1204
DENALI BANCORP INC.; *U.S. Public*, pg. 653
DENALI CAPITAL ACQUISITION CORP.; *U.S. Public*, pg. 653
DENALI FAMILY SERVICES; *U.S. Private*, pg. 1204
DENALI FLAVORS, INC.; *U.S. Private*, pg. 1204
DENALI GROUP, INC.—See WNS (Holdings) Limited; *Int'l*, pg. 8441
DENALI INCORPORATED—See NOV, Inc.; *U.S. Public*, pg. 1544
DENALI INGREDIENTS, LLC—See Orkla ASA; *Int'l*, pg. 5638
DENALI MEDIA ANCHORAGE, CORP.—See Liberty Broadband Corporation; *U.S. Public*, pg. 1310
DENALI MEDIA HOLDINGS, CORP.—See Liberty Broadband Corporation; *U.S. Public*, pg. 1310
DENALI MEDIA JUNEAU, CORP.—See Liberty Broadband Corporation; *U.S. Public*, pg. 1310

DENALI MEDIA SOUTHEAST, CORP.—See Liberty Broadband Corporation; *U.S. Public*, pg. 1310
DENALI PHYSICAL THERAPY, LIMITED PARTNERSHIP—See U.S. Physical Therapy, Inc.; *U.S. Public*, pg. 2214
DENALI STATE BANK—See Denali Bancorp Inc.; *U.S. Public*, pg. 653
DENALI THERAPEUTICS INC.; *U.S. Public*, pg. 653
DENALI WATER SOLUTIONS LLC; *U.S. Private*, pg. 1204
DEN AMBEY CABLE NETWORKS PRIVATE LIMITED—See DEN Networks Limited; *Int'l*, pg. 2026
DENAPLES AUTO PARTS INC.; *U.S. Private*, pg. 1204
DENARK CONSTRUCTION, INC.; *U.S. Private*, pg. 1204
DENAT 2007, S.L.U.—See Cie Automotive S.A.; *Int'l*, pg. 1604
DENAULTS HARDWARE-HOME CENTERS; *U.S. Private*, pg. 1204
DENAVE INDIA PRIVATE LIMITED—See Updater Services Limited; *Int'l*, pg. 8087
DENAVE (M) SDN. BHD.—See Updater Services Limited; *Int'l*, pg. 8087
DENAVE SG PTE. LTD.—See Updater Services Limited; *Int'l*, pg. 8087
DEN BLA AVIS A/S—See eBay Inc.; *U.S. Public*, pg. 709
DEN BRAVEN FRANCE S.A.R.L.—See Arkema S.A.; *Int'l*, pg. 571
DEN BRAVEN SA (PROPRIETARY) LTD.—See Arkema S.A.; *Int'l*, pg. 571
DEN BRAVEN SEALANTS GMBH—See Arkema S.A.; *Int'l*, pg. 571
DEN BROADBAND PRIVATE LIMITED—See DEN Networks Limited; *Int'l*, pg. 2026
DENBURY GREEN PIPELINE - TEXAS, LLC—See Exxon Mobil Corporation; *U.S. Public*, pg. 813
DENBURY INC.—See Exxon Mobil Corporation; *U.S. Public*, pg. 813
DENBURY OPERATING COMPANY—See Exxon Mobil Corporation; *U.S. Public*, pg. 814
DENCAP DENTAL PLANS, INC.; *U.S. Private*, pg. 1204
DENCHELS INCORPORATED; *U.S. Private*, pg. 1204
DENCO DIVISION—See Belcam Inc.; *U.S. Private*, pg. 516
DENCOHAPPEL AUSTRIA GMBH—See Triton Advisers Limited; *Int'l*, pg. 7930
DENCOHAPPEL BALTICS UAB—See Triton Advisers Limited; *Int'l*, pg. 7930
DENCOHAPPEL BELGIUM N.V.—See Triton Advisers Limited; *Int'l*, pg. 7930
DENCOHAPPEL KLIMA SANAYI A.S.—See Triton Advisers Limited; *Int'l*, pg. 7930
DENCOHAPPEL NEDERLAND B.V.—See Triton Advisers Limited; *Int'l*, pg. 7930
DENCOHAPPEL S.A.S.—See Triton Advisers Limited; *Int'l*, pg. 7930
DENCOHAPPEL UK LIMITED—See Triton Advisers Limited; *Int'l*, pg. 7930
DEN COL SUPPLY CO.; *U.S. Private*, pg. 1204
DENCO SALES CO.; *U.S. Private*, pg. 1204
DENCRAFT (LEICESTER) LTD.—See The British United Provident Association Limited; *Int'l*, pg. 7629
DENDEN KOUKOKU CO., LTD.—See Nippon Telegraph & Telephone Corporation; *Int'l*, pg. 5355
DENDREON PHARMACEUTICALS LLC—See Bausch Health Companies Inc.; *Int'l*, pg. 897
DENDRIO SOLUTIONS SRL—See Bittnet Systems SA Bucuresti; *Int'l*, pg. 1050
DENDRIT HAUSTECHNIK-SOFTWARE GMBH—See Gebr. Kemper GmbH & Co. KG; *Int'l*, pg. 2906
DENDRON GMBH—See Medtronic plc; *Int'l*, pg. 4787
DENDRON LTD.—See DDD Ltd.; *Int'l*, pg. 1993
DENEB INVESTMENTS LIMITED—See E Media Holdings Limited; *Int'l*, pg. 2246
DE NEDERLANDSCHE BANK N.V.; *Int'l*, pg. 1996
DE NEEF CONSTRUCTION CHEMICALS NV—See Standard Industries Holdings Inc.; *U.S. Private*, pg. 3779
DE NEEF CONSTRUCTION CHEMICALS (US) INC.—See Standard Industries Holdings Inc.; *U.S. Private*, pg. 3779
DE NEEF DEUTSCHLAND GMBH—See Standard Industries Holdings Inc.; *U.S. Private*, pg. 3779
DE NEEFE PTY LTD—See Traffic Technologies Ltd.; *Int'l*, pg. 7889
DE NEEF FRANCE S.A.R.L.—See Standard Industries Holdings Inc.; *U.S. Private*, pg. 3779
DE NEEF SCANDANAVIA AB—See Standard Industries Holdings Inc.; *U.S. Private*, pg. 3779
DE NEEF SCANDINAVIA AB—See Standard Industries Holdings Inc.; *U.S. Private*, pg. 3779
DE NEEF TECHNOLOGIES S.L.—See Standard Industries Holdings Inc.; *U.S. Private*, pg. 3779
DE NEERS TOOLS LIMITED; *Int'l*, pg. 1996
DENEL AERONAUTICS—See Denel SOC Ltd.; *Int'l*, pg. 2026
DENEL SOC LTD.; *Int'l*, pg. 2026
DEN ENJOY CABLE NETWORKS PRIVATE LIMITED—See DEN Networks Limited; *Int'l*, pg. 2026
DENESOLINE WESTERN EXPLOSIVES INC.—See Incitec Pivot Limited; *Int'l*, pg. 3647
DENGE VARLIK YONETIM A.S.; *Int'l*, pg. 2026

**DENHAM CAPITAL MANAGEMENT LP; ** U.S. Private, pg. 1204
DENHAM FORD SALES LTD.; Int'l, pg. 2026
DENHAM INVESTMENTS LIMITED—See Barclays PLC; Int'l, pg. 862
DENHAM SUSTAINABLE PERFORMANCE ACQUISITION CORP.; U.S. Public, pg. 653
DEN HARTOGH ASIA PACIFIC PTE LTD.—See Den Hartogh Holding BV; Int'l, pg. 2026
DEN HARTOGH DRY BULK LOGISTICS LIMITED—See Den Hartogh Holding BV; Int'l, pg. 2026
DEN HARTOGH HOLDING BV; Int'l, pg. 2026
DEN HARTOGH LOGISTICS AB—See Den Hartogh Holding BV; Int'l, pg. 2026
DEN HARTOGH LOGISTICS LATIN AMERICA LTDA.—See Den Hartogh Holding BV; Int'l, pg. 2026
DEN HOLLANDER FOOD B.V—See Zuivelcooperatie FrieslandCampina U.A.; Int'l, pg. 8693
DENHOLM BARWIL LTD.—See J&J Denholm Ltd.; Int'l, pg. 3853
DENHOLM BARWIL LTD.—See Wilh. Wilhelmsen Holding ASA; Int'l, pg. 8410
DENHOLM FISHSELLING LTD.—See J&J Denholm Ltd.; Int'l, pg. 3853
DENHOLM FORWARDING—See J&J Denholm Ltd.; Int'l, pg. 3853
DENHOLM HANDLING LTD—See J&J Denholm Ltd.; Int'l, pg. 3853
DENHOLM INDUSTRIAL SERVICES LTD.—See J&J Denholm Ltd.; Int'l, pg. 3853
DENHOLM LOGISTICS LTD.—See J&J Denholm Ltd.; Int'l, pg. 3853
DENHOLM MACNAMEE LIMITED—See J&J Denholm Ltd.; Int'l, pg. 3853
DENHOLM SEAFOODS LTD.—See J&J Denholm Ltd.; Int'l, pg. 3853
DENHOLM SHIPPING COMPANY—See J&J Denholm Ltd.; Int'l, pg. 3853
DENHOLM TRANSPORT LTD.—See J&J Denholm Ltd.; Int'l, pg. 3853
DENHOLM YAM—See J&J Denholm Ltd.; Int'l, pg. 8853
DENHOLM ZHOLDAS LLP—See J&J Denholm Ltd.; Int'l, pg. 3853
DENHOLTZ MANAGEMENT CORP.; U.S. Private, pg. 1205
DENICAR S.R.L.—See General Motors Company; U.S. Public, pg. 926
DENIER ELECTRIC CO. INC.; U.S. Private, pg. 1205
DENIHAN HOSPITALITY GROUP, LLC; U.S. Private, pg. 1205
DENIMATRIX S.A.—See Monomoy Capital Partners LLC; U.S. Private, pg. 2772
DENIM GROUP, LTD.—See Apax Partners LLP; Int'l, pg. 503
DENIS CHEM LAB LIMITED; Int'l, pg. 2026
DENIS CIMAF INC.—See Alamo Group Inc.; U.S. Public, pg. 71
DENISON-CANNON CO.; U.S. Private, pg. 1205
DENISON INC.; U.S. Private, pg. 1205
DENISON MAYES GROUP LTD.—See Amphenol Corporation; U.S. Public, pg. 130
DENISON MINES CORP.; Int'l, pg. 2026
DENISON MINES CORP. - VANCOUVER OFFICE—See Denison Mines Corp.; Int'l, pg. 2026
DENISON PARKING INC.—See Denison Inc.; U.S. Private, pg. 1205
DENISON PROPERTIES INC.—See Denison Inc.; U.S. Private, pg. 1205
DENISON YACHTING, LLC—See OneWater Marine Inc.; U.S. Public, pg. 1604
DENITECH CORPORATION—See Xerox Holdings Corporation; U.S. Public, pg. 2387
DENIZBANK AG—See Emirates NBD PJSC; Int'l, pg. 2381
DENIZBANK A.S.—See Emirates NBD PJSC; Int'l, pg. 2381
DENIZBANK MOSCOW JSC; Int'l, pg. 2027
DENIZ FINANSAL KIRALAMA A.S.; Int'l, pg. 2027
DENIZ GAYRIMENKUL YATIRIM ORTAKLIGI AS; Int'l, pg. 2027
DENIZLI CAM SANAYII VE TICARET A.S.; Int'l, pg. 2027
DENIZ YATIRIM MENKUL KIYMETLER A.S.; Int'l, pg. 2027
DEN JYSKE SPAREKASSE AS—See Arbejdernes Landsbank A/S; Int'l, pg. 537
DENKA ADVANCED MATERIALS (SUZHOU) CO. LTD.—See Denki Company Limited; Int'l, pg. 2027
DENKA ADVANCED MATERIALS VIETNAM CO., LTD.—See Denki Company Limited; Int'l, pg. 2027
DENKA ADVANTECH PRIVATE LIMITED—See Denki Company Limited; Int'l, pg. 2027
DENKA CHEMICALS DEVELOPMENT SUZHOU CO., LTD.—See Denki Company Limited; Int'l, pg. 2027
DENKA CHEMICALS GMBH—See Denki Company Limited; Int'l, pg. 2027
DENKA CHEMICALS HOLDINGS ASIA PACIFIC PTE. LTD.—See Denki Company Limited; Int'l, pg. 2027
DENKA CHEMICALS HONG KONG LTD.—See Denki Company Limited; Int'l, pg. 2027
DENKA CHEMICALS SHANGHAI CO., LTD.—See Denki Company Limited; Int'l, pg. 2027
DENKA CONSTRUCTION SOLUTIONS MALAYSIA SDN. BHD.—See Denki Company Limited; Int'l, pg. 2027
DENKA CONSULTANT & ENGINEERING CO., LTD.—See Denki Company Limited; Int'l, pg. 2027
DENKA CORPORATION—See Denki Company Limited; Int'l, pg. 2027
DENKA ELASTLUTION CO., LTD.—See Denki Company Limited; Int'l, pg. 2027
DENKA ELECTRONICS MATERIALS DALIAN CO., LTD.—See Denki Company Limited; Int'l, pg. 2027
DENKA INFRASTRUCTURE TECHNOLOGIES SHANGHAI CO., LTD.—See Denki Company Limited; Int'l, pg. 2027
DENKA INORGANIC MATERIALS (TIANJIN) CO., LTD.—See Denki Company Limited; Int'l, pg. 2027
DENKA KOREA CO., LTD.—See Denki Company Limited; Int'l, pg. 2027
DENKA LIFE INNOVATION RESEARCH PTE. LTD.—See Denki Company Limited; Int'l, pg. 2027
DENKA PERFORMANCE ELASTOMER LLC—See Denki Company Limited; Int'l, pg. 2027
DENKA SEIKEN CO., LTD.—See Denki Company Limited; Int'l, pg. 2027
DENKA SEIKEN (SHANGHAI) CO., LTD.—See Denki Company Limited; Int'l, pg. 2027
DENKA SEIKEN UK LIMITED—See Denki Company Limited; Int'l, pg. 2027
DENKA SEIKEN USA INCORPORATED—See Denki Company Limited; Int'l, pg. 2027
DENKA SINGAPORE PRIVATE LIMITED—See Denki Company Limited; Int'l, pg. 2027
DENKA TAIWAN CORPORATION—See Denki Company Limited; Int'l, pg. 2027
DENKEI MEASUREMENT AND CONTROL TECHNOLOGY (XIAMEN) CO., LTD.—See NIHON DENKEI CO., LTD.; Int'l, pg. 5283
DENKEI SCIENCE & TECHNOLOGY DEVELOPMENT (SHANGHAI) CO., LTD.—See NIHON DENKEI CO., LTD.; Int'l, pg. 5283
DENKEI TECHNOLOGY R&D(SUZHOU)CO., LTD.—See NIHON DENKEI CO., LTD.; Int'l, pg. 5283
DENKEI TRADING (SHANGHAI) CO., LTD—See NIHON DENKEI CO., LTD.; Int'l, pg. 5284
DENKEN-HIGHDENTAL CO., LTD.—See Air Water Inc.; Int'l, pg. 240
DENKI BLDG. CO., LTD.—See Kyushu Electric Power Co., Inc.; Int'l, pg. 4367
DENKI COMPANY LIMITED; Int'l, pg. 2027
DENKI KOGYO (CHANGZHOU) HEAT TREATMENT EQUIPMENT CO., LTD.—See DKK Co., Ltd.; Int'l, pg. 2139
DENKI KOGYO CO., LTD. - ATSUGI PLANT—See DKK Co., Ltd.; Int'l, pg. 2139
DENKI KOGYO CO., LTD. - KANUMA PLANT—See DKK Co., Ltd.; Int'l, pg. 2139
DENKI KOGYO CO., LTD. - KAWAGOE PLANT—See DKK Co., Ltd.; Int'l, pg. 2139
DENKI KOGYO CO., LTD. - SUZUKA PLANT—See DKK Co., Ltd.; Int'l, pg. 2139
DENKIRO SERVICE CO., LTD.; Int'l, pg. 2027
DENKI TAIWAN CO., LTD.—See TERASAKI ELECTRIC CO.,LTD; Int'l, pg. 7564
DENKO CO., LTD.—See DKK Co., Ltd.; Int'l, pg. 2139
DENKO ISI KONTROL TEKNIGI VE SERVIS A.S.—See Max Weishaupt GmbH; Int'l, pg. 4735
DENKO SEISAKUSHO CO., LTD.—See DKK Co., Ltd.; Int'l, pg. 2139
DENKO TECHNO HEAT CO., LTD. - HAMAMATSU PLANT—See DKK Co., Ltd.; Int'l, pg. 2139
DENKO TECHNO HEAT CO., LTD.—See DKK Co., Ltd.; Int'l, pg. 2139
DENKYO GROUP HOLDINGS CO.,LTD.; Int'l, pg. 2028
DENLLO S.A.—See Industria de Diseno Textil, S.A.; Int'l, pg. 3665
DENMANS ELECTRICAL WHOLESALERS LTD—See Rexel, S.A.; Int'l, pg. 6317
DENMAR ASSOCIATES LLC; U.S. Private, pg. 1205
DENMARK BANCSHARES, INC.—See Bank First Corporation; U.S. Public, pg. 270
DENMARK SENIOR LIVING, INC.—See The Ensign Group, Inc.; U.S. Public, pg. 2070
DENMAR SPECIALIST PSYCHIATRIC HOSPITAL (PTY.) LTD.—See Remgro Limited; Int'l, pg. 6269
DENMAS SDN BHD—See Tambun Indah Land Berhad; Int'l, pg. 7449
DEN-MAT HOLDINGS, LLC—See Centre Partners Management LLC; U.S. Private, pg. 828
DEN-MAT HOLDINGS, LLC—See Mill Street Partners LLC; U.S. Private, pg. 2730
DENNECREPE CORPORATION—See Seaman Paper Company of Massachusetts Inc.; U.S. Private, pg. 3585
DENNEMEYER SA; Int'l, pg. 2028
DEN NETWORKS LIMITED; Int'l, pg. 2026
DENNEY ELECTRIC SUPPLY; U.S. Private, pg. 1205
DENNIS CORPORATION—See Bowman Consulting Group Ltd.; U.S. Public, pg. 376
DENNIS DILLON AUTO PARK TRUCK CENTER; U.S. Private, pg. 1205
DENNIS, GARTLAND & NIERGARTH, CPA; U.S. Private, pg. 1205
DENNIS K. BURKE INC.; U.S. Private, pg. 1205
DENNIS M. MCCOY & SONS; U.S. Private, pg. 1205
DENNISON CORPORATION; U.S. Private, pg. 1205
DENNISON LUBRICANTS; U.S. Private, pg. 1205
DENNIS PAPER COMPANY; U.S. Private, pg. 1205
DENNIS PR GROUP; U.S. Private, pg. 1205
DENNIS PUBLISHING LTD.—See Future plc; Int'l, pg. 2857
DENNIS SALES CO. INC.; U.S. Private, pg. 1205
DENNIS SUPPLY COMPANY; U.S. Private, pg. 1205
DENNY ANDREWS FORD SALES INC.; Int'l, pg. 2028
DENNY MENHOLT FRONTIER CHEVROLET; U.S. Private, pg. 1205
DENNY MOUNTAIN MEDIA, LLC—See RedCloud Consulting Inc.; U.S. Private, pg. 3377
DENNY MUSHROOMS (PTY) LIMITED—See FirstRand Limited; Int'l, pg. 2690
DENNY'S CORPORATION; U.S. Public, pg. 653
DENNY'S, INC.—See Denny's Corporation; U.S. Public, pg. 654
DENNY'S MARINA INC.—See Reeder-Trausch Marine; U.S. Private, pg. 3383
DENON CORPORATION—See Bain Capital, LP; U.S. Private, pg. 438
DENON ELECTRONICS USA LLC—See Bain Capital, LP; U.S. Private, pg. 438
DE NOOTELAER PLC—See Clariane SE; Int'l, pg. 1642
DENOOYER CHEVROLET INC.; U.S. Private, pg. 1205
DE NORA DEUTSCHLAND GMBH—See Industrie De Nora S.p.A; Int'l, pg. 3674
DE NORA DO BRASIL LTDA—See Industrie De Nora S.p.A; Int'l, pg. 3674
DE NORA ELETTRODI (SUZHOU) CO. LTD—See Industrie De Nora S.p.A; Int'l, pg. 3674
DE NORA INDIA LIMITED—See Industrie De Nora S.p.A; Int'l, pg. 3674
DE NORA PERMELEC TECHNO SERVICE LTD.—See Industrie De Nora S.p.A; Int'l, pg. 3674
DE NORA TECH, INC.—See Industrie De Nora S.p.A; Int'l, pg. 3674
DE NORA WATER TECHNOLOGIES, INC.—See Industrie De Nora S.p.A; Int'l, pg. 3674
DE NORA WATER TECHNOLOGIES TEXAS, LLC—See Industrie De Nora S.p.A; Int'l, pg. 3674
DE NORA WATER TECHNOLOGIES UK SERVICES LTD—See Industrie De Nora S.p.A; Int'l, pg. 3674
DE NORSKE BOKKLUBBENE AS—See H. Aschehoug & Co. W. Nygaard AS; Int'l, pg. 3194
DE NORSKE BOKKLUBBENE AS—See Pax Forlag AS; Int'l, pg. 5763
DENOVO VENTURES LLC—See TAC Partners, Inc.; U.S. Private, pg. 3920
DENOVUS L.L.C.—See Orscheln Group; U.S. Private, pg. 3045
DENOX ENVIRONMENTAL & TECHNOLOGY HOLDINGS LIMITED; Int'l, pg. 2028
DENOX MANAGEMENT LIMITED—See Wang On Group Ltd; Int'l, pg. 8341
DENPLAN LIMITED—See Simplyhealth Group Limited; Int'l, pg. 6935
DENRON PLUMBING & HVAC, LLC.; U.S. Private, pg. 1205
DENRYOKU SUPPORT CHUGOKU CO., INC.—See The Chugoku Electric Power Co., Inc.; Int'l, pg. 7632
DENSAM INDUSTRIAL CO. LTD.—See voestalpine AG; Int'l, pg. 8289
DENSAN CO., LTD.; Int'l, pg. 2028
DENSAN SYSTEM CO., LTD.; Int'l, pg. 2028
DENSIMIX-E&B INC.—See American Securities LLC; U.S. Private, pg. 253
DENSIQ AB—See Investment AB Latour; Int'l, pg. 3782
DENSIQ AB—See Investment AB Latour; Int'l, pg. 3782
DENSIQ AS—See Investment AB Latour; Int'l, pg. 3782
DENSIQ OY—See Investment AB Latour; Int'l, pg. 3782
DENSIT APS—See Illinois Tool Works Inc.; U.S. Public, pg. 1102
DENSIT ASIA PACIFIC SDN BHD—See Illinois Tool Works Inc.; U.S. Public, pg. 1102
DENSITRON CORPORATION OF JAPAN—See Quixant PLC; Int'l, pg. 6165
DENSITRON CORPORATION—See Quixant PLC; Int'l, pg. 6165
DENSITRON DEUTSCHLAND GMBH—See Quixant PLC; Int'l, pg. 6165
DENSITRON DISPLAY TAIWAN LIMITED—See Quixant PLC; Int'l, pg. 6165
DENSITRON EUROPE LIMITED—See Quixant PLC; Int'l, pg. 6165
DENSITRON FRANCE—See Quixant PLC; Int'l, pg. 6165
DENSITRON NORDIC OY—See Quixant PLC; Int'l, pg. 6165
DENSITRON TECHNOLOGIES LIMITED—See Quixant PLC; Int'l, pg. 6165
DENSO ABASHIRI TEST CENTER CORPORATION—See Denso Corporation; Int'l, pg. 2029

COMPANY NAME INDEX

DENSO ACE CORPORATION—See Denso Corporation; *Int'l*, pg. 2029
DENSO AGRITECH SOLUTIONS, INC.—See Denso Corporation; *Int'l*, pg. 2029
DENSO AIRCOOL CORPORATION—See Denso Corporation; *Int'l*, pg. 2031
DENSO AIR SYSTEMS CORPORATION—See Denso Corporation; *Int'l*, pg. 2029
DENSO AIR SYSTEMS CZECH S.R.O—See Denso Corporation; *Int'l*, pg. 2031
DENSO AIR SYSTEMS MICHIGAN, INC.—See Denso Corporation; *Int'l*, pg. 2029
DENSO AIR SYSTEMS TOYOSHINA CORPORATION—See Denso Corporation; *Int'l*, pg. 2029
DENSO AIR SYSTEMS YASAKA CORPORATION—See Denso Corporation; *Int'l*, pg. 2029
DENSO AUSTRALIAN AUTOMOTIVE AIR PTY. LTD.—See Denso Corporation; *Int'l*, pg. 2032
DENSO AUTOMOTIVE DEUTSCHLAND GMBH—See Denso Corporation; *Int'l*, pg. 2031
DENSO AUTOMOTIVE SYSTEMS AUSTRALIA PTY. LTD.—See Denso Corporation; *Int'l*, pg. 2029
DENSO BARCELONA S.A.—See Denso Corporation; *Int'l*, pg. 2031
DENSO BLOSSOM CO., LTD.—See Denso Corporation; *Int'l*, pg. 2031
DENSO (CHANGZHOU) FUEL INJECTION SYSTEM CO., LTD.—See Denso Corporation; *Int'l*, pg. 2028
DENSO (CHINA) INVESTMENT CO., LTD.—See Denso Corporation; *Int'l*, pg. 2028
DENSO CHUGOKU CORPORATION—See Denso Corporation; *Int'l*, pg. 2029
DENSO COMMUNICATIONS CORPORATION—See Denso Corporation; *Int'l*, pg. 2029
DENSO CORPORATION; *Int'l*, pg. 2028
DENSO CREATE INC..—See Denso Corporation; *Int'l*, pg. 2031
DENSO DO BRASIL LTDA.—See Denso Corporation; *Int'l*, pg. 2029
DENSO ELECTRONICS CORPORATION—See Denso Corporation; *Int'l*, pg. 2029
DENSO EMC ENGINEERING SERVICE CORPORATION—See Denso Corporation; *Int'l*, pg. 2029
DENSO E & TS TRAINING CENTER CORPORATION—See Denso Corporation; *Int'l*, pg. 2029
DENSO EUROPE B.V.—See Denso Corporation; *Int'l*, pg. 2031
DENSO FACILITIES CORPORATION—See Denso Corporation; *Int'l*, pg. 2029
DENSO FINANCE & ACCOUNTING CENTER CO., LTD.—See Denso Corporation; *Int'l*, pg. 2029
DENSO FINANCE HOLLAND B.V.—See Denso Corporation; *Int'l*, pg. 2029
DENSO FUKUSHIMA CORPORATION—See Denso Corporation; *Int'l*, pg. 2031
DENSO (GUANGZHOU NANSHA) CO., LTD—See Denso Corporation; *Int'l*, pg. 2028
DENSO HARYANA PVT. LTD.—See Denso Corporation; *Int'l*, pg. 2029
DENSO HOKKAIDO CORPORATION—See Denso Corporation; *Int'l*, pg. 2029
DENSO INDUSTRIAL DA AMAZONIA LTDA.—See Denso Corporation; *Int'l*, pg. 2031
DENSO INTERNATIONAL AMERICA—See Denso Corporation; *Int'l*, pg. 2031
DENSO INTERNATIONAL ASIA PTE. LTD.—See Denso Corporation; *Int'l*, pg. 2031
DENSO INTERNATIONAL AUSTRALIA PTY. LTD.—See Denso Corporation; *Int'l*, pg. 2031
DENSO INTERNATIONAL EUROPE B.V.—See Denso Corporation; *Int'l*, pg. 2031
DENSO INTERNATIONAL INDIA PVT. LTD.—See Denso Corporation; *Int'l*, pg. 2029
DENSO INTERNATIONAL UK LTD.—See Denso Corporation; *Int'l*, pg. 2029
DENSO IT LABORATORY, INC.—See Denso Corporation; *Int'l*, pg. 2031
DENSO IT SOLUTIONS, INC.—See Denso Corporation; *Int'l*, pg. 2029
DENSO IWATE CORPORATION—See Denso Corporation; *Int'l*, pg. 2032
DENSO KANSAI CORPORATION—See Denso Corporation; *Int'l*, pg. 2029
DENSO KATSUYAMA CO., LTD.—See Denso Corporation; *Int'l*, pg. 2029
DENSO KIKO CO., LTD.—See Denso Corporation; *Int'l*, pg. 2029
DENSO KOTEI AUTOMOTIVE ELECTRONICS (WUHAN) CO., LTD.—See Wuhan Kotei Informatics Co., Ltd.; *Int'l*, pg. 8501
DENSO KYUSHU CORPORATION—See Denso Corporation; *Int'l*, pg. 2029
DENSO LOGITEM CORPORATION—See Denso Corporation; *Int'l*, pg. 2029
DENSO MANUFACTURING ARGENTINA S.A.—See Denso Corporation; *Int'l*, pg. 2029

DENSO MANUFACTURING ARKANSAS, INC.—See Denso Corporation; *Int'l*, pg. 2031
DENSO MANUFACTURING ATHENS TENNESSEE, INC.—See Denso Corporation; *Int'l*, pg. 2029
DENSO MANUFACTURING CANADA, INC—See Denso Corporation; *Int'l*, pg. 2029
DENSO MANUFACTURING CZECH S.R.O.—See Denso Corporation; *Int'l*, pg. 2031
DENSO MANUFACTURING HUNGARY LTD.—See Denso Corporation; *Int'l*, pg. 2031
DENSO MANUFACTURING ITALIA SPA—See Denso Corporation; *Int'l*, pg. 2031
DENSO MANUFACTURING KITAKYUSHU CO.,LTD.—See Denso Corporation; *Int'l*, pg. 2029
DENSO MANUFACTURING MICHIGAN, INC.—See Denso Corporation; *Int'l*, pg. 2031
DENSO MANUFACTURING MIDLANDS LTD.—See Denso Corporation; *Int'l*, pg. 2031
DENSO MANUFACTURING TENNESSEE, INC.—See Denso Corporation; *Int'l*, pg. 2029
DENSO MANUFACTURING UK LTD.—See Denso Corporation; *Int'l*, pg. 2031
DENSO MAQUINAS ROTANTES DO BRASIL LTDA.—See Denso Corporation; *Int'l*, pg. 2029
DENSO MARSTON LTD.—See Denso Corporation; *Int'l*, pg. 2031
DENSO MEXICO S.A. DE C.V—See Denso Corporation; *Int'l*, pg. 2030
DENSO MIYAZAKI, INC.—See Denso Corporation; *Int'l*, pg. 2032
DENSO MTEC CORPORATION—See Denso Corporation; *Int'l*, pg. 2032
DENSON OIL COMPANY, INC.; *U.S. Private*, pg. 1206
DENSO OTOMOTIV PARCALARI SANAYI ANONIM SIRKET—See Denso Corporation; *Int'l*, pg. 2030
DENSO OTOMOTIV PARCALARI SANAYI A.S.—See Denso Corporation; *Int'l*, pg. 2030
DENSO POWERTRAIN TECHNOLOGIES CORPORATION—See Denso Corporation; *Int'l*, pg. 2032
DENSO PREAS CO., LTD.—See Denso Corporation; *Int'l*, pg. 2030
DENSO PRESS TECH CO., LTD.—See Denso Corporation; *Int'l*, pg. 2032
DENSO PS CORPORATION - HONGSEONG FACTORY—See Denso Corporation; *Int'l*, pg. 2030
DENSO PS CORPORATION—See Denso Corporation; *Int'l*, pg. 2030
DENSO REMANI CORPORATION—See Denso Corporation; *Int'l*, pg. 2030
DENSO SALES BELGIUM N.V.—See Denso Corporation; *Int'l*, pg. 2031
DENSO SALES CALIFORNIA, INC.—See Denso Corporation; *Int'l*, pg. 2032
DENSO SALES CANADA, INC.—See Denso Corporation; *Int'l*, pg. 2030
DENSO SALES FRANCE S.A.R.L.—See Denso Corporation; *Int'l*, pg. 2030
DENSO SALES ITALIA SRL—See Denso Corporation; *Int'l*, pg. 2031
DENSO SALES RUS L.L.C.—See Denso Corporation; *Int'l*, pg. 2030
DENSO SALES SOUTH AFRICA (PTY.) LTD.—See Metair Investments Limited; *Int'l*, pg. 4844
DENSO SALES SWEDEN AB—See Denso Corporation; *Int'l*, pg. 2031
DENSO SALES UK LTD.—See Denso Corporation; *Int'l*, pg. 2031
DENSO SEIBI CO., LTD.—See Denso Corporation; *Int'l*, pg. 2030
DENSO SERVICE NISHISAITAMA CO., LTD.—See Denso Corporation; *Int'l*, pg. 2030
DENSO SERVICE OKINAWA CO., LTD.—See Denso Corporation; *Int'l*, pg. 2030
DENSO SI CORPORATION—See Denso Corporation; *Int'l*, pg. 2030
DENSO SISTEMAS TERMICOS ESPANA S.A.—See Denso Corporation; *Int'l*, pg. 2030
DENSO SOFTWARE SHANGHAI CO., LTD.—See Denso Corporation; *Int'l*, pg. 2030
DENSO SOLUTION JAPAN CORPORATION—See Denso Corporation; *Int'l*, pg. 2032
DENSO TAIWAN CORP.—See Denso Corporation; *Int'l*, pg. 2030
DENSO TAIYO CO., LTD.—See Denso Corporation; *Int'l*, pg. 2030
DENSO TECHNO CO., LTD.—See Denso Corporation; *Int'l*, pg. 2030
DENSO TECHNO PHILIPPINES, INC.—See Denso Corporation; *Int'l*, pg. 2030
DENSO TEN AMERICA LIMITED - LOS ANGELES—See Denso Corporation; *Int'l*, pg. 2030
DENSO TEN AMERICA LIMITED—See Denso Corporation; *Int'l*, pg. 2030
DENSO TEN (CHINA) LIMITED—See Denso Corporation; *Int'l*, pg. 2030
DENSO TEN (CHINA) LIMITED—See Denso Corporation; *Int'l*, pg. 2030

DENSO TEN DE MEXICO, S.A. DE C.V.—See Denso Corporation; *Int'l*, pg. 2030
DENSO TEN ELECTRONICS (WUXI) LIMITED—See Denso Corporation; *Int'l*, pg. 2030
DENSO TEN ESPANA, S.A.—See Denso Corporation; *Int'l*, pg. 2030
DENSO TEN LIMITED - NAKATSUGAWA PLANT—See Denso Corporation; *Int'l*, pg. 2030
DENSO TEN LIMITED—See Denso Corporation; *Int'l*, pg. 2030
DENSO TEN MINDA INDIA PRIVATE LIMITED—See Denso Corporation; *Int'l*, pg. 2030
DENSO TEN PHILIPPINES CORPORATION—See Denso Corporation; *Int'l*, pg. 2030
DENSO TEN RESEARCH AND DEVELOPMENT (TIANJIN) LIMITED—See Denso Corporation; *Int'l*, pg. 2030
DENSO TEN SINGAPORE PRIVATE LIMITED—See Denso Corporation; *Int'l*, pg. 2030
DENSO TEN STAFF LIMITED—See Denso Corporation; *Int'l*, pg. 2030
DENSO TEN STAFF LIMITED—See Denso Corporation; *Int'l*, pg. 2030
DENSO TEN TECHNOLOGY LIMITED—See Denso Corporation; *Int'l*, pg. 2030
DENSO TEN TECHNOSEPTA LIMITED—See Denso Corporation; *Int'l*, pg. 2030
DENSO TEN TECHNOSEPTA LIMITED—See Denso Corporation; *Int'l*, pg. 2030
DENSO TEN (THAILAND) LIMITED—See Denso Corporation; *Int'l*, pg. 2030
DENSO TEN (THAILAND) LIMITED—See Denso Corporation; *Int'l*, pg. 2030
DENSO (THAILAND) CO., LTD - WELLGROW PLANT—See Denso Corporation; *Int'l*, pg. 2028
DENSO THERMAL SYSTEMS POLSKA SP.Z.O.O.—See Denso Corporation; *Int'l*, pg. 2031
DENSO THERMAL SYSTEMS PUNE PVT. LTD.—See Denso Corporation; *Int'l*, pg. 2030
DENSO THERMAL SYSTEMS SPA—See Denso Corporation; *Int'l*, pg. 2031
DENSO (TIANJIN) THERMAL PRODUCTS CO., LTD.—See Denso Corporation; *Int'l*, pg. 2028
DENSO TOHOKU CORPORATION—See Denso Corporation; *Int'l*, pg. 2031
DENSO TOKYO CORPORATION—See Denso Corporation; *Int'l*, pg. 2031
DENSO TOOL AND DIE (THAILAND) CO., LTD.—See Denso Corporation; *Int'l*, pg. 2032
DENSOTRIM CO., LTD.—See Denso Corporation; *Int'l*, pg. 2031
DENSO UNITY SERVICE CORPORATION—See Denso Corporation; *Int'l*, pg. 2031
DENSO WAVE INC.—See Denso Corporation; *Int'l*, pg. 2032
DENSO WELL CORPORATION—See Denso Corporation; *Int'l*, pg. 2031
DENSO WIPER SYSTEMS, INC.—See Denso Corporation; *Int'l*, pg. 2032
DENSO WIRELESS SYSTEMS AMERICA, INC.—See Denso Corporation; *Int'l*, pg. 2031
DENSO WISETECH CORPORATION—See Denso Corporation; *Int'l*, pg. 2032
DENSO YAMAGATA CO., LTD.—See Denso Corporation; *Int'l*, pg. 2032
DENSO YUSEN TRAVEL CORPORATION—See Denso Corporation; *Int'l*, pg. 2031
DENS PARTNERS, INC.; *U.S. Private*, pg. 1206
DEN STOLTE HANE AS—See Scandi Standard AB; *Int'l*, pg. 6612
DENTAL BENEFIT PROVIDERS, INC.—See UnitedHealth Group Incorporated; *U.S. Public*, pg. 2240
DENTAL BURS USA; *U.S. Private*, pg. 1206
DENTAL CARE ALLIANCE, LLC—See Mubadala Investment Company PJSC; *Int'l*, pg. 5074
DENTALCARE PARTNERS INC.; *U.S. Private*, pg. 1206
THE DENTAL CARE PLUS GROUP; *U.S. Private*, pg. 4020
DENTAL COMPLEX—See Danaher Corporation; *U.S. Public*, pg. 626
DENTAL CORPORATION PUBLIC COMPANY LIMITED; *Int'l*, pg. 2033
DENTAL DIAMOND CO.—See GC Corporation; *Int'l*, pg. 2894
DENTAL EQUIPMENT LIQUIDATORS, INC.; *U.S. Private*, pg. 1206
DENTAL EQUIPMENT, LLC—See Danaher Corporation; *U.S. Public*, pg. 626
THE DENTALEZ GROUP; *U.S. Private*, pg. 4020
DENTAL FOCUS (BENDEMEER) PTE. LTD.—See Clearbridge Health Limited; *Int'l*, pg. 1656
DENTAL FOCUS (PEOPLE'S PARK) PTE. LTD.—See Clearbridge Health Limited; *Int'l*, pg. 1656
DENTAL FOCUS (PIONEER) PTE. LTD.—See Clearbridge Health Limited; *Int'l*, pg. 1656
DENTAL HEALTH ALLIANCE, L.L.C.—See Assurant, Inc.; *U.S. Public*, pg. 216
DENTAL HEALTH MANAGEMENT SOLUTIONS (DHMS); *U.S. Private*, pg. 1206

DENTAL HEALTH PRODUCTS INC.

DENTAL HEALTH PRODUCTS INC.; *U.S. Private,* pg. 1206
DENTALHOLDING SP. Z.O.O.—See Dentium Co., Ltd; *Int'l,* pg. 2033
THE DENTAL HUB@SG PTE. LTD.—See New Silkroutes Group Limited; *Int'l,* pg. 5227
DENTALIA KFT—See COLTENE Holding AG; *Int'l,* pg. 1706
DENTAL IMAGING TECHNOLOGIES CORPORATION—See Danaher Corporation; *U.S. Public,* pg. 626
DENTAL IMPLANT TRAINING CENTER CORP.—See DENTSPLY SIRONA Inc.; *U.S. Public,* pg. 654
DENTAL INTELLIGENCE, INC.; *U.S. Private,* pg. 1206
DENTAL NETWORK OF AMERICA INC.; *U.S. Private,* pg. 1206
DENTAL PARTNERS PTY LIMITED—See BGH Capital Pty Ltd; *Int'l,* pg. 1008
DENTAL PARTNERS PTY LIMITED—See Ontario Teachers' Pension Plan; *Int'l,* pg. 5585
DENTAL PATIENT CARE AMERICA, INC.; *U.S. Public,* pg. 654
DENTALPLANS.COM, INC.—See KKR & Co. Inc.; *U.S. Public,* pg. 1253
DENTAL POST, INC.—See 424 Capital, LLC; *U.S. Private,* pg. 15
DENTAL POST, INC.—See HealthEdge Investment Partners, LLC; *U.S. Private,* pg. 1896
DENTAL SALON; *U.S. Private,* pg. 1206
DENTAL SELECT; *U.S. Private,* pg. 1206
DENTAL SORRIA LTDA.—See Bunzl plc; *Int'l,* pg. 1218
THE DENTAL STUDIO PTE. LTD.—See Singapore Medical Group Limited; *Int'l,* pg. 6941
DENTAL WINGS GMBH—See Straumann Holding AG; *Int'l,* pg. 7237
DENTAL WINGS INC.—See Straumann Holding AG; *Int'l,* pg. 7237
DENTAL X S.P.A—See Nakanishi Inc.; *Int'l,* pg. 5132
DENT-A-MED INC.—See Harbert Management Corporation; *U.S. Private,* pg. 1858
DENTAPLY PROSTHETICS AUSTRIA GMBH—See DENTSPLY SIRONA Inc.; *U.S. Public,* pg. 654
DENTAQUEST, LLC—See Sun Life Financial Inc.; *Int'l,* pg. 7305
DENTAS CO., LTD.; *Int'l,* pg. 2033
DENTATUS AB; *Int'l,* pg. 2033
DENTATUS USA, LTD.—See Dentatus AB; *Int'l,* pg. 2033
DENTCA, INC.—See Mitsui Chemicals, Inc.; *Int'l,* pg. 4981
DENTCARE DELIVERY SYSTEMS, INC.; *U.S. Private,* pg. 1206
DENTECO 2000 SA—See Fagron NV; *Int'l,* pg. 2603
DENTEL BANCORPORATION; *U.S. Private,* pg. 1206
DENTELLE SOPHIE HALLETTE; *Int'l,* pg. 2033
DENTEMAX, LLC—See Health Care Service Corporation; *U.S. Private,* pg. 1892
DENT ENTERPRISES INC.; *U.S. Private,* pg. 1206
DENT ESTET CLINIC SA—See MedLife S.A.; *Int'l,* pg. 4785
DENTINO MARKETING; *U.S. Private,* pg. 1206
DENTISAN LTD.—See Getinge AB; *Int'l,* pg. 2949
DENTIS CO., LTD.; *Int'l,* pg. 2033
DENTISTAT, INC.—See The Beekman Group, LLC; *U.S. Private,* pg. 3993
DENTIUM BALTIC, SIA—See Dentium Co., Ltd; *Int'l,* pg. 2033
DENTIUM CHINA CO., LTD.—See Dentium Co., Ltd; *Int'l,* pg. 2033
DENTIUM CO., LTD; *Int'l,* pg. 2033
DENTIUM-COM S.R.L—See Dentium Co., Ltd; *Int'l,* pg. 2033
DENTIUM IBERIA SL—See Dentium Co., Ltd; *Int'l,* pg. 2033
DENTIUM KFT.—See Dentium Co., Ltd; *Int'l,* pg. 2033
DENTIUM SHANGHAI CO., LTD.—See Dentium Co., Ltd; *Int'l,* pg. 2033
DENTIUM SINGAPORE PTE LTD.—See Dentium Co., Ltd; *Int'l,* pg. 2033
DENTIUM USA INC.—See Dentium Co., Ltd; *Int'l,* pg. 2033
DENTON CONCRETE SERVICES INC.—See Denton Enterprises Inc.; *U.S. Private,* pg. 1206
DENTON COUNTY ELECTRIC COOPERATIVE, INC.—See CoServ Utility Holdings, L.P.; *U.S. Private,* pg. 1062
DENTON COUNTY TERMITE & HOUSE LEVELING, INC.; *U.S. Private,* pg. 1206
DENTON ENTERPRISES INC.; *U.S. Private,* pg. 1206
DENTON HINES PROPERTIES, INC.; *U.S. Private,* pg. 1206
DENTON-RENFROE, INC.; *U.S. Private,* pg. 1206
DENTONS BOEKEL N.V.—See Dentons Group; *U.S. Private,* pg. 1207
DENTONS CANADA LLP—See Dentons Group; *U.S. Private,* pg. 1207
DENTONS EUROPE LLP—See Dentons Group; *U.S. Private,* pg. 1207
DENTONS GROUP; *U.S. Private,* pg. 1206
DENTONS UKMEA LLP—See Dentons Group; *U.S. Private,* pg. 1207

DENTON SURGICARE PARTNERS, LTD.—See Tenet Healthcare Corporation; *U.S. Public,* pg. 2010
DENTONS US LLP—See Dentons Group; *U.S. Private,* pg. 1207
DENTON VACUUM INC.; *U.S. Private,* pg. 1206
DENTRIX DENTAL SYSTEMS, INC.-PMT—See Henry Schein, Inc.; *U.S. Public,* pg. 1025
DENTSABLE, INC.; *U.S. Private,* pg. 1207
DENTSPLY ARGENTINA—See DENTSPLY SIRONA Inc.; *U.S. Public,* pg. 654
DENTSPLY DETREY GMBH—See DENTSPLY SIRONA Inc.; *U.S. Public,* pg. 654
DENTSPLY GAC EUROPE SAS—See DENTSPLY SIRONA Inc.; *U.S. Public,* pg. 654
DENTSPLY GERMANY INVESTMENTS GMBH—See DENTSPLY SIRONA Inc.; *U.S. Public,* pg. 654
DENTSPLY IH AB—See DENTSPLY SIRONA Inc.; *U.S. Public,* pg. 654
DENTSPLY IH AB—See DENTSPLY SIRONA Inc.; *U.S. Public,* pg. 654
DENTSPLY IH AB—See DENTSPLY SIRONA Inc.; *U.S. Public,* pg. 654
DENTSPLY IH AB—See DENTSPLY SIRONA Inc.; *U.S. Public,* pg. 654
DENTSPLY IH A/S—See DENTSPLY SIRONA Inc.; *U.S. Public,* pg. 654
DENTSPLY IH GMBH—See DENTSPLY SIRONA Inc.; *U.S. Public,* pg. 654
DENTSPLY IH GMBH—See DENTSPLY SIRONA Inc.; *U.S. Public,* pg. 654
DENTSPLY IH INC—See DENTSPLY SIRONA Inc.; *U.S. Public,* pg. 654
DENTSPLY IH LTD—See DENTSPLY SIRONA Inc.; *U.S. Public,* pg. 654
DENTSPLY IH OY—See DENTSPLY SIRONA Inc.; *U.S. Public,* pg. 654
DENTSPLY IH S.A.—See DENTSPLY SIRONA Inc.; *U.S. Public,* pg. 655
DENTSPLY IMPLANTS MANUFACTURING GMBH—See DENTSPLY SIRONA Inc.; *U.S. Public,* pg. 654
DENTSPLY IMPLANTS TAIWAN CO, LTD.—See DENTSPLY SIRONA Inc.; *U.S. Public,* pg. 654
DENTSPLY IMPLANTS TURKEY A.S.—See DENTSPLY SIRONA Inc.; *U.S. Public,* pg. 654
DENTSPLY INDIA PVT. LTD.—See DENTSPLY SIRONA Inc.; *U.S. Public,* pg. 654
DENTSPLY ITALIA S.R.L.—See DENTSPLY SIRONA Inc.; *U.S. Public,* pg. 654
DENTSPLY LIMITED—See DENTSPLY SIRONA Inc.; *U.S. Public,* pg. 654
DENTSPLY MEXICO, S.A. DE C.V.—See DENTSPLY SIRONA Inc.; *U.S. Public,* pg. 654
DENTSPLY (SINGAPORE) PTE. LTD.—See DENTSPLY SIRONA Inc.; *U.S. Public,* pg. 654
DENTSPLY SIRONA BENELUX B.V.—See DENTSPLY SIRONA Inc.; *U.S. Public,* pg. 654
DENTSPLY SIRONA CANADA—See DENTSPLY SIRONA Inc.; *U.S. Public,* pg. 655
DENTSPLY SIRONA ENDODONTICS—See DENTSPLY SIRONA Inc.; *U.S. Public,* pg. 655
DENTSPLY SIRONA EUROPE GMBH—See DENTSPLY SIRONA Inc.; *U.S. Public,* pg. 655
DENTSPLY SIRONA FRANCE S.A.S.—See DENTSPLY SIRONA Inc.; *U.S. Public,* pg. 655
DENTSPLY SIRONA IMPLANTS NORWAY—See DENTSPLY SIRONA Inc.; *U.S. Public,* pg. 655
DENTSPLY SIRONA INC. - PREVENTIVE DIVISION—See DENTSPLY SIRONA Inc.; *U.S. Public,* pg. 654
DENTSPLY SIRONA INC. - RESTORATIVE—See DENTSPLY SIRONA Inc.; *U.S. Public,* pg. 654
DENTSPLY SIRONA INC.; *U.S. Public,* pg. 654
DENTSPLY SIRONA K.K.—See DENTSPLY SIRONA Inc.; *U.S. Public,* pg. 654
DENTSPLY SIRONA KOREA—See DENTSPLY SIRONA Inc.; *U.S. Public,* pg. 655
DENTSPLY SIRONA - NORWAY—See DENTSPLY SIRONA Inc.; *U.S. Public,* pg. 654
DENTSPLY SIRONA (PHILS.), INC.—See DENTSPLY SIRONA Inc.; *U.S. Public,* pg. 654
DENTSPLY SIRONA PTY. LTD.—See DENTSPLY SIRONA Inc.; *U.S. Public,* pg. 655
DENTSPLY SIRONA PTY. LTD.—See DENTSPLY SIRONA Inc.; *U.S. Public,* pg. 655
DENTSPLY SIRONA SWITZERLAND SARL—See DENTSPLY SIRONA Inc.; *U.S. Public,* pg. 655
DENTSPLY (THAILAND) LTD.—See DENTSPLY SIRONA Inc.; *U.S. Public,* pg. 654
DENT STEEL SERVICES LTD; *Int'l,* pg. 2033
DENTSU 24/7 SEARCH HOLDINGS B.V.—See Dentsu Group Inc.; *Int'l,* pg. 2036
DENTSU AD-GEAR INC.—See Dentsu Group Inc.; *Int'l,* pg. 2034
DENTSU AEGIS JAPAN INC.—See Dentsu Group Inc.; *Int'l,* pg. 2034
DENTSU AEGIS NETWORK AMERICAS—See Dentsu Group Inc.; *Int'l,* pg. 2036
DENTSU AEGIS NETWORK ASIA PACIFIC—See Dentsu Group Inc.; *Int'l,* pg. 2036

CORPORATE AFFILIATIONS

DENTSU AEGIS NETWORK AUSTRALIA—See Dentsu Group Inc.; *Int'l,* pg. 2036
DENTSU AEGIS NETWORK (DEUTSCHLAND) GMBH—See Dentsu Group Inc.; *Int'l,* pg. 2036
DENTSU AEGIS NETWORK IBERIA S.L—See Dentsu Group Inc.; *Int'l,* pg. 2036
DENTSU AEGIS NETWORK INDIA—See Dentsu Group Inc.; *Int'l,* pg. 2036
DENTSU AEGIS NETWORK ITALIA SRL—See Dentsu Group Inc.; *Int'l,* pg. 2036
DENTSU AEGIS NETWORK NETHERLANDS B.V.—See Dentsu Group Inc.; *Int'l,* pg. 2036
DENTSU AEGIS NETWORK—See Dentsu Group Inc.; *Int'l,* pg. 2036
DENTSU AMERICA LLC—See Dentsu Group Inc.; *Int'l,* pg. 2036
DENTSU ARGENTINA S.A.—See Dentsu Group Inc.; *Int'l,* pg. 2036
DENTSU ASIA PTE. LTD.—See Dentsu Group Inc.; *Int'l,* pg. 2036
DENTSU AUSTRALIA PTY LTD—See Dentsu Group Inc.; *Int'l,* pg. 2036
DENTSUBOS - ANTIBODY HEALTHCARE COMMUNICATIONS DIVISION—See Dentsu Group Inc.; *Int'l,* pg. 2036
DENTSUBOS—See Dentsu Group Inc.; *Int'l,* pg. 2036
DENTSU BRUSSELS GROUP—See Dentsu Group Inc.; *Int'l,* pg. 2036
DENTSU CASTING AND ENTERTAINMENT INC.—See Dentsu Group Inc.; *Int'l,* pg. 2034
DENTSU CHINA LIMITED—See Dentsu Group Inc.; *Int'l,* pg. 2036
DENTSU COMMUNICATION INSTITUTE INC.—See Dentsu Group Inc.; *Int'l,* pg. 2034
DENTSU CONSULTING INC.—See Dentsu Group Inc.; *Int'l,* pg. 2034
DENTSU CORPORATE ONE INC.—See Dentsu Group Inc.; *Int'l,* pg. 2034
DENTSU CREATIVE FORCE INC.—See Dentsu Group Inc.; *Int'l,* pg. 2034
DENTSU CREATIVE GMBH—See Dentsu Group Inc.; *Int'l,* pg. 2037
DENTSU CREATIVE IMPACT PVT. LTD.—See Dentsu Group Inc.; *Int'l,* pg. 2037
DENTSU CREATIVE X INC.—See Dentsu Group Inc.; *Int'l,* pg. 2034
DENTSU CUSTOMER ACCESS CENTER INC—See Dentsu Group Inc.; *Int'l,* pg. 2034
DENTSU DIGITAL CO., LTD.—See Dentsu Group Inc.; *Int'l,* pg. 2034
DENTSU DIGITAL DRIVE INC.—See Dentsu Group Inc.; *Int'l,* pg. 2034
DENTSU DIGITAL HOLDINGS INC.—See Dentsu Group Inc.; *Int'l,* pg. 2034
DENTSU DIGITAL INC—See Dentsu Group Inc.; *Int'l,* pg. 2034
DENTSU DIGITAL NETWORKS INC.—See Dentsu Group Inc.; *Int'l,* pg. 2034
DENTSU DIRECT INC.—See Septeni Holdings Co., Ltd.; *Int'l,* pg. 6718
DENTSU EAST JAPAN INC.—See Dentsu Group Inc.; *Int'l,* pg. 2034
DENTSU EVENT OPERATIONS INC.—See Dentsu Group Inc.; *Int'l,* pg. 2034
DENTSU FACILITY MANAGEMENT INC.—See Dentsu Group Inc.; *Int'l,* pg. 2034
DENTSU GROUP INC.; *Int'l,* pg. 2034
DENTSU HOKKAIDO INC.—See Dentsu Group Inc.; *Int'l,* pg. 2034
DENTSU HOLDINGS PHILIPPINES INC.—See Dentsu Group Inc.; *Int'l,* pg. 2036
DENTSU HOLDINGS (THAILAND) LTD.—See Dentsu Group Inc.; *Int'l,* pg. 2036
DENTSU HONG KONG LTD.—See Dentsu Group Inc.; *Int'l,* pg. 2037
DENTSU INNOVATION PARTNERS INC.—See Dentsu Group Inc.; *Int'l,* pg. 2035
DENTSU INTERNATIONAL LIMITED—See Dentsu Group Inc.; *Int'l,* pg. 2035
DENTSU ISOBAR, INC.—See Dentsu Group Inc.; *Int'l,* pg. 2034
DENTSU KOREA INC—See Dentsu Group Inc.; *Int'l,* pg. 2037
DENTSU KUOHUA—See Dentsu Group Inc.; *Int'l,* pg. 2037
DENTSU KYUSHU INC.—See Dentsu Group Inc.; *Int'l,* pg. 2038
DENTSU LATIN AMERICA PROPAGANDA LTDA.—See Dentsu Group Inc.; *Int'l,* pg. 2036
DENTSU MACROMILL INSIGHT, INC.—See Dentsu Group Inc.; *Int'l,* pg. 2038
DENTSU (MALAYSIA) SDN. BHD.—See Dentsu Group Inc.; *Int'l,* pg. 2035
DENTSU MANAGEMENT SERVICES INC.—See Dentsu Group Inc.; *Int'l,* pg. 2038
DENTSU MARCOM PVT. LTD.—See Dentsu Group Inc.; *Int'l,* pg. 2037
DENTSU MARKETING EAST ASIA INC.—See Dentsu Group Inc.; *Int'l,* pg. 2038

COMPANY NAME INDEX

DENTSU MEDIA HONG KONG LTD.—See Dentsu Group Inc.; *Int'l*, pg. 2037
DENTSU MEDIA KOREA INC.—See Dentsu Group Inc.; *Int'l*, pg. 2037
DENTSU MEDIA (THAILAND) LTD.—See Dentsu Group Inc.; *Int'l*, pg. 2035
DENTSU MEDIA VIETNAM LTD—See Dentsu Group Inc.; *Int'l*, pg. 2037
DENTSU MEDICAL COMMUNICATIONS, INC.—See Dentsu Group Inc.; *Int'l*, pg. 2038
DENTSU MEITETSU COMMUNICATIONS INC.—See Dentsu Group Inc.; *Int'l*, pg. 2038
DENTSU MUSIC AND ENTERTAINMENT INC.—See Dentsu Group Inc.; *Int'l*, pg. 2038
DENTSU NEW IDEAS LLC—See Dentsu Group Inc.; *Int'l*, pg. 2038
DENTSU OKINAWA INC.—See Dentsu Group Inc.; *Int'l*, pg. 2038
DENTSU ON-DEMAND GRAPHICS INC.—See Dentsu Group Inc.; *Int'l*, pg. 2038
DENTSU OPERATION PARTNERS INC.—See Dentsu Group Inc.; *Int'l*, pg. 2038
DENTSU OPERATIONS DEVELOPMENT INC.—See Dentsu Group Inc.; *Int'l*, pg. 2038
DENTSU PLUS CO., LTD—See Dentsu Group Inc.; *Int'l*, pg. 2037
DENTSU PROMOTION PLUS INC.—See Dentsu Group Inc.; *Int'l*, pg. 2038
DENTSU RESEARCH INC.—See Dentsu Group Inc.; *Int'l*, pg. 2038
DENTSU RETAIL MARKETING INC.—See Dentsu Group Inc.; *Int'l*, pg. 2038
DENTSU RUNWAY INC.—See Dentsu Group Inc.; *Int'l*, pg. 2038
DENTSU SCIENCEJAM INC.—See Dentsu Group Inc.; *Int'l*, pg. 2038
DENTSU SINGAPORE PVT. LTD.—See Dentsu Group Inc.; *Int'l*, pg. 2037
DENTSU-SMART LLC—See Dentsu Group Inc.; *Int'l*, pg. 2037
DENTSU SOKEN INC—See Dentsu Group Inc.; *Int'l*, pg. 2038
DENTSU SOLARI INC.—See Dentsu Group Inc.; *Int'l*, pg. 2038
DENTSU SPORTS ASIA, PTE. LTD.—See Dentsu Group Inc.; *Int'l*, pg. 2037
DENTSU SPORTS EUROPE, LTD.—See Dentsu Group Inc.; *Int'l*, pg. 2037
DENTSU SPORTS PARTNERS INC.—See Dentsu Group Inc.; *Int'l*, pg. 2038
DENTSU, SUDLER & HENNESSEY INC.—See Dentsu Group Inc.; *Int'l*, pg. 2039
DENTSU, SUDLER & HENNESSEY INC.—See WPP plc; *Int'l*, pg. 8492
DENTSU TABLE MEDIA COMMUNICATIONS INC—See Dentsu Group Inc.; *Int'l*, pg. 2038
DENTSU (TAIWAN) INC.—See Dentsu Group Inc.; *Int'l*, pg. 2035
DENTSU TEC INC.—See Dentsu Group Inc.; *Int'l*, pg. 2034
DENTSU (THAILAND) LTD.—See Dentsu Group Inc.; *Int'l*, pg. 2035
DENTSU TOP CO., LTD.—See Dentsu Group Inc.; *Int'l*, pg. 2037
DENTSU UTAMA SDN. BHD.—See Dentsu Group Inc.; *Int'l*, pg. 2037
DENTSU VIETNAM LTD.—See Dentsu Group Inc.; *Int'l*, pg. 2037
DENTSU WEST JAPAN INC.—See Dentsu Group Inc.; *Int'l*, pg. 2038
DENTSU WORKS INC.—See Dentsu Group Inc.; *Int'l*, pg. 2038
DENTSVILLE KIDNEY CENTER, LLC—See Nautic Partners, LLC; *U.S. Private*, pg. 2869
DENTUSBOS MONTREAL—See Dentsu Group Inc.; *Int'l*, pg. 2036
DENT WIZARD GMBH—See Gridiron Capital, LLC; *U.S. Private*, pg. 1786
DENT WIZARD INTERNATIONAL CORP.—See Gridiron Capital, LLC; *U.S. Private*, pg. 1786
DENT WIZARD S.A.S.—See Gridiron Capital, LLC; *U.S. Private*, pg. 1786
DENT WIZARD VENTURES LIMITED—See Stone Point Capital LLC; *U.S. Private*, pg. 3821
DENT-X CORPORATION—See SMK Imaging, LLC; *U.S. Private*, pg. 3698
DENUO—See Publicis Groupe S.A.; *Int'l*, pg. 6097
DENUO—See Publicis Groupe S.A.; *Int'l*, pg. 6097
DENVER 104 ANUSA, LLC—See AutoNation, Inc.; *U.S. Public*, pg. 234
DENVER AGENCY COMPANY—See Arthur J. Gallagher & Co.; *U.S. Public*, pg. 204
DENVER ART MUSEUM; *U.S. Private*, pg. 1207
DENVER AUTO AUCTION—See Cox Enterprises, Inc.; *U.S. Private*, pg. 1076
DENVER BANKSHARES, INC.; *U.S. Public*, pg. 656
DENVER BOTANIC GARDENS; *U.S. Private*, pg. 1207
DENVER BRONCOS FOOTBALL CLUB—See Bowlen Sports, Inc.; *U.S. Private*, pg. 626

DENVER BUSINESS JOURNAL—See Advance Publications, Inc.; *U.S. Private*, pg. 84
DENVER CENTER FOR THE PERFORMING ARTS INC.; *U.S. Private*, pg. 1207
DENVER DRYWALL CO. INC.; *U.S. Private*, pg. 1207
DENVER EQUIPMENT PTY., LTD.—See Metso Oyj; *Int'l*, pg. 4865
DENVER FOUNDATION; *U.S. Private*, pg. 1207
DENVER GLASS INTERIORS, INC.—See Baymark Partners; *U.S. Private*, pg. 496
THE DENVER HOSPICE AND OPTIO HEALTH SERVICES; *U.S. Private*, pg. 4020
DENVER JETCENTER, INC.—See Cordillera Corporation; *U.S. Private*, pg. 1048
DENVER MATTRESS COMPANY—See Funiture Row LLC; *U.S. Private*, pg. 1623
DENVER MERCHANDISE MART, INC.—See American Realty Investors, Inc.; *U.S. Public*, pg. 108
DENVER MID-TOWN SURGERY CENTER, LTD.—See HCA Healthcare, Inc.; *U.S. Public*, pg. 995
DENVER MINING FINANCE COMPANY, INC.—See Royal Gold, Inc.; *U.S. Public*, pg. 1815
THE DENVER NUGGETS LIMITED PARTNERSHIP—See Kroenke Sports & Entertainment, LLC; *U.S. Private*, pg. 2352
THE DENVER PALM—See Palm Restaurant Group; *U.S. Private*, pg. 3080
DENVER PARENT CORPORATION; *U.S. Private*, pg. 1207
THE DENVER POST CORPORATION—See Alden Global Capital LLC; *U.S. Private*, pg. 158
DENVER QUARRIES (PTY) LIMITED—See Afrimat Limited; *Int'l*, pg. 192
DENVER REEL & PALLET CO.—See Conner Industries, Inc.; *U.S. Private*, pg. 1017
DENVER REGIONAL LANDFILL, INC.—See Waste Connections, Inc.; *Int'l*, pg. 8353
DENVER RESCUE MISSION; *U.S. Private*, pg. 1207
DENVER SIGN SUPPLY CO., INC.; *U.S. Private*, pg. 1208
DENVER SURGICENTER, LLC—See HCA Healthcare, Inc.; *U.S. Public*, pg. 995
DENVER TECHNOLOGICAL CENTER—See Dubai World Corporation; *Int'l*, pg. 2220
DENVER TRANSIT PARTNERS, LLC—See Fluor Corporation; *U.S. Public*, pg. 858
DENVER WEST LEASING—See Stevinson Automotive Inc.; *U.S. Private*, pg. 3810
DENVER WESTWORD, LLC—See Village Voice Media Holdings, LLC; *U.S. Private*, pg. 4384
DENVER WHOLESALE FLORISTS COMPANY; *U.S. Private*, pg. 1208
DENVER WHOLESALE FLORISTS OF ALBUQUERQUE—See Denver Wholesale Florists Company; *U.S. Private*, pg. 1208
DENVER ZOOLOGICAL FOUNDATION; *U.S. Private*, pg. 1208
DENVIEW LIMITED MOSCOW—See Remy Cointreau S.A.; *Int'l*, pg. 6272
DENVILLE SCIENTIFIC, INC.—See Harvard Bioscience, Inc.; *U.S. Public*, pg. 987
DENVILLE SURGERY CENTER, LLC—See Tenet Healthcare Corporation; *U.S. Public*, pg. 2010
DENVISIO BIOMED LIMITED—See Prevest DenPro Limited; *Int'l*, pg. 5968
DENWAY MOTORS LTD—See Guangzhou Automobile Industry Group Co., Ltd.; *Int'l*, pg. 3164
DENY FONTAINE—See Groupe SFPI SA; *Int'l*, pg. 3111
DENYO AMERICA CORPORATION—See Denyo Co., Ltd.; *Int'l*, pg. 2040
DENYO CO., LTD.; *Int'l*, pg. 2040
DENYO EUROPE B.V.—See Denyo Co., Ltd.; *Int'l*, pg. 2040
DENYO KOSAN CO., LTD.—See Denyo Co., Ltd.; *Int'l*, pg. 2040
DENYO MANUFACTURING CORPORATION—See Denyo Co., Ltd.; *Int'l*, pg. 2040
DENYO TRADING CO LTD—See Denyo Co., Ltd.; *Int'l*, pg. 2040
DENYO UNITED MACHINERY PTE LTD.—See Denyo Co., Ltd.; *Int'l*, pg. 2040
DENYO VIETNAM CO., LTD.—See Denyo Co., Ltd.; *Int'l*, pg. 2040
DENZ OFFICE AG—See Lienhard Office Group AG; *Int'l*, pg. 4492
DEODATO GALLERY S.P.A.; *Int'l*, pg. 2040
DEODIS SA—See Neurones S.A.; *Int'l*, pg. 5219
DEOGYUSAN RESORT CO., LTD.; *Int'l*, pg. 2040
DEOLEO, S.A.—See CVC Capital Partners SICAV-FIS S.A.; *Int'l*, pg. 1883
DEOLIX S.A.—See Allcargo Logistics Limited; *Int'l*, pg. 333
DEPA AL BARAKAH L.L.C.—See Depa PLC; *Int'l*, pg. 2040
DEPAC ANSTALT GMBH—See Investment AB Latour; *Int'l*, pg. 3781
DEPA EGYPT—See Depa PLC; *Int'l*, pg. 2040
DEPA INDIA PVT. LTD.—See Depa PLC; *Int'l*, pg. 2040
DEPA INTERIORS L.L.C.—See Depa PLC; *Int'l*, pg. 2040
DEPA JORDAN—See Depa PLC; *Int'l*, pg. 2040
DEPANNAGE 2000 NV—See KBC Group NV; *Int'l*, pg. 4106

DEPPON LOGISTICS CO., LTD.

DEPA PLC; *Int'l*, pg. 2040
DEPA QATAR CO. W.L.L.—See Depa PLC; *Int'l*, pg. 2040
DE PARK AVENUE 10880, LLC—See Douglas Emmett, Inc.; *U.S. Public*, pg. 678
DE PARK AVENUE 10960, LLC—See Douglas Emmett, Inc.; *U.S. Public*, pg. 678
THE DEPARTMENT OF DOING; *Int'l*, pg. 7636
DEPARTMENTS & STORES NORWAY AS—See Coala-Life Group AB; *Int'l*, pg. 1680
DEPARTURES MAGAZINE—See Meredith Corporation; *U.S. Public*, pg. 1422
DEPARTURE; *U.S. Private*, pg. 1208
DEPA SAUDI ARABIA—See Depa PLC; *Int'l*, pg. 2040
DEPATCO, INC.—See Clyde Companies Inc.; *U.S. Private*, pg. 949
DEPA UK LIMITED—See Depa PLC; *Int'l*, pg. 2040
DEPAULA CHEVROLET - HUMMER; *U.S. Private*, pg. 1208
DEPAUL COMMUNITY SERVICES, INC.; *U.S. Private*, pg. 1208
DEPAUL; *U.S. Private*, pg. 1208
DEPCOM POWER, INC.; *U.S. Private*, pg. 1208
DEP DISTRIBUTION EXCLUSIVE LTEE; *Int'l*, pg. 2040
DEPECHE MODE COMPANY; *U.S. Private*, pg. 1208
DEPENDABLE AUTO SHIPPERS, INC.; *U.S. Private*, pg. 1208
DEPENDABLE CLEANERS INC.; *U.S. Private*, pg. 1208
DEPENDABLE COMPONENT SUPPLY CORP.; *U.S. Private*, pg. 1208
DEPENDABLE DISTRIBUTION CENTERS—See Dependable Highway Express Inc.; *U.S. Private*, pg. 1209
DEPENDABLE GLOBAL EXPRESS—See Dependable Highway Express Inc.; *U.S. Private*, pg. 1209
DEPENDABLE HAWAIIAN EXPRESS—See Dependable Highway Express Inc.; *U.S. Private*, pg. 1209
DEPENDABLE HEALTH SERVICES, INC.; *U.S. Private*, pg. 1209
DEPENDABLE HIGHWAY EXPRESS INC.; *U.S. Private*, pg. 1209
DEPENDABLE HOMETECH—See Creative Vistas Inc.; *Int'l*, pg. 1834
DEPENDABLE LOGISTICS SOLUTIONS—See Dependable Highway Express Inc.; *U.S. Private*, pg. 1209
DEPENDABLE MAIL SERVICES INC.; *U.S. Private*, pg. 1209
DEP ENGINEERING CO., LTD.—See Sonepar S.A.; *Int'l*, pg. 7090
DE PERE CABINET, INC.—See HCI Equity Management, L.P.; *U.S. Private*, pg. 1889
DE PERSGROEP PRINTING B.V.—See DPG Media Group NV; *Int'l*, pg. 2188
DE PERSGROEP PUBLISHING NV—See DPG Media Group NV; *Int'l*, pg. 2188
DEPFA ACS BANK PLC—See FMS Wertmanagement Aor; *Int'l*, pg. 2717
DEPFA BANK PLC—See FMS Wertmanagement Aor; *Int'l*, pg. 2717
DEPFA FINANCE N.V.—See FMS Wertmanagement Aor; *Int'l*, pg. 2717
DEPLOYABLE SPACE SYSTEMS, INC.—See Redwire Corporation; *U.S. Public*, pg. 1771
D&E PLUMBING & HEATING INC.; *U.S. Private*, pg. 1137
DE POAN PNEUMATIC CORP.; *Int'l*, pg. 1996
DEPO AUTO PARTS IND. CO., LTD.; *Int'l*, pg. 2041
DEPO HOLDINGS, LLC—See Trinity Hunt Management, L.P.; *U.S. Private*, pg. 4234
DEPOMURES SA—See ENGIE SA; *Int'l*, pg. 2434
DEPOR INDUSTRIES INC.—See Magni Group Inc.; *U.S. Private*, pg. 2547
DEPORTES CLUB GOLF SANTIAGO SA; *Int'l*, pg. 2041
DEPOSIT INSURANCE AND CREDIT GUARANTEE CORPORATION—See Reserve Bank of India; *Int'l*, pg. 6295
DEPOSIT INSURANCE CORPORATION OF JAPAN; *Int'l*, pg. 2041
DEPOSITION SCIENCES, INC.—See Lockheed Martin Corporation; *U.S. Public*, pg. 1337
DEPOSITION SOLUTIONS, LLC - RECORDS RETRIEVAL DIVISION—See Apax Partners LLP; *Int'l*, pg. 503
DEPOSITION SOLUTIONS, LLC—See Apax Partners LLP; *Int'l*, pg. 503
DEPOSITORS INSURANCE FUND; *U.S. Private*, pg. 1209
THE DEPOSITORY TRUST & CLEARING CORPORATION; *U.S. Private*, pg. 4020
THE DEPOSITORY TRUST COMPANY—See The Depository Trust & Clearing Corporation; *U.S. Private*, pg. 4020
DEPOSIT PROTECTION CORPORATION—See Soneri Bank Limited; *Int'l*, pg. 7094
DEPOSIT TELEPHONE CO. INC.—See Telephone & Data Systems, Inc.; *U.S. Public*, pg. 1998
DEPOT INTERNATIONAL; *U.S. Private*, pg. 1209
DEPOTS PETROLIERS DE FOS; *Int'l*, pg. 2041
DEPOT STARVILLAS SARL—See Cox & Kings Limited; *Int'l*, pg. 1822
DEPPON LOGISTICS CO., LTD.; *Int'l*, pg. 2041
DEPRO CO., LTD.—See Seiren Co., Ltd.; *Int'l*, pg. 6691
DEPSA, SA DE SEGUROS Y REASEGUROS—See Grupo Catalana Occidente, S.A.; *Int'l*, pg. 3124

DEPUY FRANCE S.A.—See Johnson & Johnson; *U.S. Public*, pg. 1195
DEPUY INTERNATIONAL (HOLDINGS) LTD.—See Johnson & Johnson; *U.S. Public*, pg. 1195
DEPUY INTERNATIONAL LIMITED—See Johnson & Johnson; *U.S. Public*, pg. 1195
DEPUY (IRELAND) LIMITED—See Johnson & Johnson; *U.S. Public*, pg. 1195
DEPUY MITEK, INC.—See Johnson & Johnson; *U.S. Public*, pg. 1195
DEPUY ORTHOPAEDICS, INC.—See Johnson & Johnson; *U.S. Public*, pg. 1195
DEPUY ORTHOPEDIE S.A.—See Johnson & Johnson; *U.S. Public*, pg. 1195
DEPUY PRODUCTS, INC.—See Johnson & Johnson; *U.S. Public*, pg. 1195
DEPUY SPINE, INC.—See Johnson & Johnson; *U.S. Public*, pg. 1195
DEPUY SPINE SARL—See Johnson & Johnson; *U.S. Public*, pg. 1195
DEPUY SYNTHES A/S—See Johnson & Johnson; *U.S. Public*, pg. 1195
DEPUY SYNTHES, INC.—See Johnson & Johnson; *U.S. Public*, pg. 1195
DEPUY SYNTHES PRODUCTS, INC.—See Johnson & Johnson; *U.S. Public*, pg. 1195
DEQING CESCO MACHINERY CO.,LTD—See Zicom Group Limited; *Int'l*, pg. 8681
DEQING CESCO MACHINERY CO., LTD.—See Zicom Group Limited; *Int'l*, pg. 8681
DEQING DIC SYNTHETIC RESINS, LTD.—See DIC Corporation; *Int'l*, pg. 2109
DEQUEEN & EASTERN RAILROAD COMPANY, LLC—See Mitsubishi UFJ Financial Group, Inc.; *Int'l*, pg. 4971
DEQUE SYSTEMS, INC.; *U.S. Private*, pg. 1209
DERA FOOD TECHNOLOGY CZ SRO—See Kerry Group plc; *Int'l*, pg. 4138
DE RAJ GROUP AG; *Int'l*, pg. 1996
DERA LIMITED—See Kerry Group plc; *Int'l*, pg. 4138
DERA, ROSLAN & CAMPION PUBLIC RELATIONS; *U.S. Private*, pg. 1209
DERBIGUM AMERICAS, INC.; *U.S. Private*, pg. 1209
DERBY CITY GAMING, LLC—See Churchill Downs, Inc.; *U.S. Public*, pg. 493
THE DERBY CONFERENCE CENTRE LIMITED—See RTC Group Plc; *Int'l*, pg. 6420
DERBY CYCLE AG—See Pon Holdings B.V.; *Int'l*, pg. 5918
DERBY FABRICATING SOLUTIONS, LLC—See Prophet Equity L.P.; *U.S. Private*, pg. 3286
DERBY INDUSTRIES, LLC; *U.S. Private*, pg. 1209
DERBYSHIRE BUILDING SOCIETY—See Nationwide Building Society; *Int'l*, pg. 5165
THE DERBYSHIRE LEICESTERSHIRE NOTTINGHAMSHIRE & RUTLAND COMMUNITY REHABILITATION COMPANY LIMITED—See ModivCare, Inc.; *U.S. Public*, pg. 1456
DER CLUB GMBH—See Bertelsmann SE & Co. KGaA; *Int'l*, pg. 992
DERDAP TURIST A.D.; *Int'l*, pg. 2041
DERECKTOR GUNNELL INC.; *U.S. Private*, pg. 1209
DE REGT GERMANY GMBH—See CGG; *Int'l*, pg. 1432
DE REGT MARINE CABLES BV—See CGG; *Int'l*, pg. 1432
DEREK AND CONSTANCE LEE CORP.; *U.S. Private*, pg. 1209
DEREK LAM INTERNATIONAL, LLC—See Public Clothing Company Inc.; *U.S. Private*, pg. 3298
DEREK LANE & CO LIMITED—See Flowtech Fluidpower plc; *Int'l*, pg. 2709
DEREK POBJOY INVESTMENTS LTD.; *Int'l*, pg. 2041
DEREK RESOURCES (USA) INC.—See Newcastle Energy Corp.; *Int'l*, pg. 5234
DEREN AUTO PARTS (CHONGQING) CO., LTD.—See Shenzhen Deren Electronic Co., Ltd.; *Int'l*, pg. 6807
DEREN ELECTRONIC (HONG KONG) CO., LIMITED—See Shenzhen Deren Electronic Co., Ltd.; *Int'l*, pg. 6808
DEREN ELECTRONIC (VIETNAM) COMPANY LIMITED—See Shenzhen Deren Electronic Co., Ltd.; *Int'l*, pg. 6808
DEREN ILAC SANAYI VE DIS TICARET ANONIM SIRKETI—See Ecolab Inc.; *U.S. Public*, pg. 712
DERFLAN INC; *U.S. Private*, pg. 1209
DER GRUNE PUNKT - DUALES SYSTEM DEUTSCHLAND GMBH—See H.I.G. Capital, LLC; *U.S. Private*, pg. 1828
DERIA FOODS CO., LTD.—See Kewpie Corporation; *Int'l*, pg. 4144
D.E. RICE CONSTRUCTION CO., INC.; *U.S. Private*, pg. 1141
DERICHEBOURG AERONAUTICS SERVICES GERMANY GMBH—See Derichebourg S.A.; *Int'l*, pg. 2041
DERICHEBOURG AQUA SAS—See Derichebourg S.A.; *Int'l*, pg. 2041
DERICHEBOURG ATIS AERONAUTIQUE SAS—See Derichebourg S.A.; *Int'l*, pg. 2042

DERICHEBOURG ATIS GMBH—See Derichebourg S.A.; *Int'l*, pg. 2042
DERICHEBOURG AVIATION & ENERGY RESOURCES LTD.—See Derichebourg S.A.; *Int'l*, pg. 2042
DERICHEBOURG BELGIUM NV—See Derichebourg S.A.; *Int'l*, pg. 2041
DERICHEBOURG CANADA ENVIRONNEMENT INC.—See Derichebourg S.A.; *Int'l*, pg. 2041
DERICHEBOURG ENERGIE SA—See Derichebourg S.A.; *Int'l*, pg. 2042
DERICHEBOURG ENTREPRISES-VALERCO - ECOVAL—See Derichebourg S.A.; *Int'l*, pg. 2042
DERICHEBOURG ENVIRONNEMENT—See Derichebourg S.A.; *Int'l*, pg. 2041
DERICHEBOURG ESPACES VERTS SAS—See Derichebourg S.A.; *Int'l*, pg. 2042
DERICHEBOURG EVOLUTION FORMATION EURL—See Derichebourg S.A.; *Int'l*, pg. 2042
DERICHEBOURG INTERIM AERONAUTIQUE SAS—See Derichebourg S.A.; *Int'l*, pg. 2042
DERICHEBOURG INTERIM SAS—See Derichebourg S.A.; *Int'l*, pg. 2042
DERICHEBOURG MEDIO AMBIENTE SA—See Derichebourg S.A.; *Int'l*, pg. 2042
DERICHEBOURG MULTISERVICES SAS—See Derichebourg S.A.; *Int'l*, pg. 2042
DERICHEBOURG PROPRETE SAS—See Derichebourg S.A.; *Int'l*, pg. 2042
DERICHEBOURG RECYCLING MEXICO SA—See Derichebourg S.A.; *Int'l*, pg. 2042
DERICHEBOURG RECYCLING USA, INC.—See Derichebourg S.A.; *Int'l*, pg. 2042
DERICHEBOURG S.A.; *Int'l*, pg. 2041
DERICHEBOURG SNG SAS—See Derichebourg S.A.; *Int'l*, pg. 2042
DERICHEBOURG SOURCING AERO & ENERGY SAS—See Derichebourg S.A.; *Int'l*, pg. 2042
DERICHEBOURG TECHNOLOGIES SAS—See Derichebourg S.A.; *Int'l*, pg. 2042
DERICHEBOURG UMWELT GMBH—See Derichebourg S.A.; *Int'l*, pg. 2042
DERICHEM (M) SDN BHD—See IQI Corporation Berhad; *Int'l*, pg. 3791
DE RIDDER B.V—See Bunzl plc; *Int'l*, pg. 1218
DE RIGO D.A.CH. GMBH—See De Rigo S.p.A.; *Int'l*, pg. 1996
DE RIGO FRANCE SAS—See De Rigo S.p.A.; *Int'l*, pg. 1996
DE RIGO HELLAS S.A.—See De Rigo S.p.A.; *Int'l*, pg. 1996
DE RIGO HONG KONG LTD.—See De Rigo S.p.A.; *Int'l*, pg. 1997
DE RIGO JAPAN CO., LTD.—See De Rigo S.p.A.; *Int'l*, pg. 1997
DERIGO OY—See De Rigo S.p.A.; *Int'l*, pg. 1997
DE RIGO PORTUGAL, LDA.—See De Rigo S.p.A.; *Int'l*, pg. 1997
DE RIGO REM INC.—See De Rigo S.p.A.; *Int'l*, pg. 1997
DERIGO SALES INC.; *U.S. Private*, pg. 1209
DE RIGO S.P.A.; *Int'l*, pg. 1996
DE RIGO UK LTD—See De Rigo S.p.A.; *Int'l*, pg. 1997
DE RIGO VE SESA GRUP GOZLUK SAN VE TIC AS—See De Rigo S.p.A.; *Int'l*, pg. 1997
DE RIGO VISION AUSTRALIA PTY LTD—See De Rigo S.p.A.; *Int'l*, pg. 1997
DE RIGO VISION ESPANA SA—See De Rigo S.p.A.; *Int'l*, pg. 1997
DE RIGO VISION MIDDLE EAST FZCO—See De Rigo S.p.A.; *Int'l*, pg. 1997
DE RIGO VISION S.P.A.—See De Rigo S.p.A.; *Int'l*, pg. 1997
DE RIGO VISION TRADING CO., LTD.—See De Rigo S.p.A.; *Int'l*, pg. 1997
DERIMOD KONFEKSIYON AYAKKABI DERI SANAYI VE TICARET A.S.; *Int'l*, pg. 2042
DERING ELLIOTT & ASSOCIATES; *U.S. Private*, pg. 1209
DERINGER-NEY INC; *U.S. Private*, pg. 1209
DERIVADOS ACRILICOS S.A. DE C.V. - AGUASCALIENTES PLANT—See Cydsa S.A.B. de C.V.; *Int'l*, pg. 1895
DERIVADOS DE MAIZ ALIMENTICIO, S.A.—See Gruma, S.A.B. de C.V.; *Int'l*, pg. 3114
DERIVADOS DE MAIZ DE EL SALVADOR, S.A.—See Gruma, S.A.B. de C.V.; *Int'l*, pg. 3114
THE DERIVATIVES CONSULTING GROUP LIMITED—See Publicis Groupe S.A.; *Int'l*, pg. 6111
DERIVE TECHNOLOGIES; *U.S. Private*, pg. 1209
DERKWOO ELECTRONICS CO., LTD.; *Int'l*, pg. 2042
DERLE FARMS INC.; *U.S. Private*, pg. 1209
DERLITE CO LTD.—See Active Energy Group plc; *Int'l*, pg. 120
DERLUKS YATIRIM HOLDING A.S; *Int'l*, pg. 2042
DERMADOCTOR, LLC; *U.S. Private*, pg. 1209
DERMA GLISTEN, INC.; *U.S. Private*, pg. 1209
DERMA HEALTH; *U.S. Private*, pg. 1209
DERMALAB S.A.—See Standard Foods Corporation; *Int'l*, pg. 7168
DERMALOGICA GMBH—See Unilever PLC; *Int'l*, pg. 8044

DERMALOGICA, INC.—See Unilever PLC; *Int'l*, pg. 8047
DERMAPHARM AG—See Dermapharm Holding SE; *Int'l*, pg. 2043
DERMAPHARM AG—See Dermapharm Holding SE; *Int'l*, pg. 2043
DERMAPHARM HOLDING SE; *Int'l*, pg. 2042
DERMA SCIENCES, INC.—See Integra LifeSciences Holdings Corporation; *U.S. Public*, pg. 1135
DERMATA THERAPEUTICS, INC.; *U.S. Public*, pg. 656
DERMATOLOGY ASSOCIATES OF CENTRAL TEXAS—See ABRY Partners, LLC; *U.S. Private*, pg. 42
DERMATOLOGY & LASER CENTER OF FORT WORTH—See ABRY Partners, LLC; *U.S. Private*, pg. 42
DERMATOLOGY & LASER-DEL MAR INC.—See West Dermatology Med Management, Inc.; *U.S. Private*, pg. 4485
DERMATOLOGY OF NORTHERN COLORADO, P.C.—See Harvest Partners L.P.; *U.S. Private*, pg. 1876
DERMATOLOGY PROFESSIONALS, INC.—See Adult & Pediatric Dermatology, PC; *U.S. Private*, pg. 83
DERMATOLOGY & SKIN SURGERY CENTER; *U.S. Private*, pg. 1209
DERMATOLOGY & SURGERY CLINIC (ORCHARD) PTE. LTD.—See RMH Holdings Limited; *Int'l*, pg. 6357
DERMATOLOGY & SURGERY CLINIC (SHENTON) PTE. LTD.—See RMH Holdings Limited; *Int'l*, pg. 6357
DERMA TRONNIER INSTITUT FUR EXPERIMENTELLE DERMATOLOGIE GMBH & CO. KG—See Eurofins Scientific S.E.; *Int'l*, pg. 2536
DERMAVANT SCIENCES GMBH—See Roivant Sciences Ltd.; *Int'l*, pg. 6388
DERMAVANT SCIENCES LTD.—See Organon & Co.; *U.S. Public*, pg. 1616
DERMAVEST, INC.—See Bausch Health Companies Inc.; *Int'l*, pg. 898
DERMAZONE SOLUTIONS, INC.; *U.S. Private*, pg. 1210
DERMICUS AB—See Barco N.V.; *Int'l*, pg. 864
DERMIRA, INC.—See Eli Lilly & Company; *U.S. Public*, pg. 731
DERMISONICS, INC.; *U.S. Public*, pg. 656
DERMODY PROPERTIES INC; *U.S. Private*, pg. 1210
DERMOGROUP SRL—See Viatris Inc.; *U.S. Public*, pg. 2293
DERMPATH DIAGNOSTICS—See Quest Diagnostics, Inc.; *U.S. Public*, pg. 1755
DERMSCAN POLAND SP. Z.O.O.—See Eurofins Scientific S.E.; *Int'l*, pg. 2536
DERMTECH, INC.—See DermTech, LLC; *U.S. Private*, pg. 1210
DERMTECH, LLC; *U.S. Private*, pg. 1210
DERMTECH OPERATIONS, INC.—See DermTech, LLC; *U.S. Private*, pg. 1210
DERNE TEMIZ ENERJI URETIM A.S.—See Parsan Makina Parcalari Sanayii AS; *Int'l*, pg. 5747
DE RONDE CASING INTERNATIONAL INC.; *U.S. Private*, pg. 1181
DE RONDE TIRE SUPPLY, INC.; *U.S. Private*, pg. 1181
DEROSA CORPORATION; *U.S. Private*, pg. 1210
DEROSA MEDICAL PC—See Nobilis Health Corp.; *U.S. Private*, pg. 2932
DEROVIS GMBH—See init innovation in traffic systems SE; *Int'l*, pg. 3704
DEROYAL INDUSTRIES INC.; *U.S. Private*, pg. 1210
DERR FLOORING CO. INC.; *U.S. Private*, pg. 1210
DERRICK CORPORATION; *U.S. Private*, pg. 1210
DERRICK PUBLISHING CO.; *U.S. Private*, pg. 1210
DERRIMON TRADING CO., LTD.; *Int'l*, pg. 2043
DERRYARKIN SAND AND GRAVEL LIMITED—See Bord na Mona Plc; *Int'l*, pg. 1113
DERRY ENTERPRISES INC.; *U.S. Private*, pg. 1210
DERRY PUBLISHING CO. INC.—See The Retirement Systems of Alabama; *U.S. Private*, pg. 4105
DERRY SURGICAL CENTER, LLC—See UnitedHealth Group Incorporated; *U.S. Public*, pg. 2240
DERSCH ENERGIES INCORPORATED; *U.S. Private*, pg. 1210
DERSE INC.; *U.S. Private*, pg. 1210
DERSIMO BV—See Headlam Group plc; *Int'l*, pg. 3301
DERST BAKING COMPANY, LLC—See Flowers Foods, Inc.; *U.S. Public*, pg. 854
DERTICKETSERVICE DE GMBH & CO. KG—See CTS Eventim AG & Co. KGAA; *Int'l*, pg. 1872
DER TOURISTIK DENMARK—See REWE-Zentral-Aktiengesellschaft; *Int'l*, pg. 6314
DER TOURISTIK DEUTSCHLAND GMBH—See REWE-Zentral-Aktiengesellschaft; *Int'l*, pg. 6314
DER TOURISTIK NORDIC AB—See REWE-Zentral-Aktiengesellschaft; *Int'l*, pg. 6314
DER TOURISTIK NORWAY—See REWE-Zentral-Aktiengesellschaft; *Int'l*, pg. 6314
DER TOURISTIK SUISSE AG—See REWE-Zentral-Aktiengesellschaft; *Int'l*, pg. 6314
DER TOURISTIK SUISSE AG, ZWEIGNIEDERLASSUNG KONTIKI REISEN—See REWE-Zentral-Aktiengesellschaft; *Int'l*, pg. 6314

COMPANY NAME INDEX

DER TOURISTIK SUISSE AG, ZWEIGNIEDERLASSUNG KUONI REISEN, KUSNACHT—See REWE-Zentral-Aktiengesellschaft; *Int'l*, pg. 6314
DER TOURISTIK SUISSE AG, ZWEIGNIEDERLASSUNG PRIVATE SAFARIS, ZURICH—See REWE-Zentral-Aktiengesellschaft; *Int'l*, pg. 6314
DER TOURISTIK UK LTD—See REWE-Zentral-Aktiengesellschaft; *Int'l*, pg. 6314
DE RUCCI HEALTHY SLEEP CO., LTD.; *Int'l*, pg. 1997
DE RUITER STAALKABEL BV—See Usha Martin Limited; *Int'l*, pg. 8096
DERUNGS AG—See Burkhalter Holding AG; *Int'l*, pg. 1224
DERWENT FACILITIES MANAGEMENT LIMITED—See Places for People Group Limited; *Int'l*, pg. 5888
DERWENT LONDON PLC; *Int'l*, pg. 2043
DERYPOL SA—See Ecolab Inc.; *U.S. Private*, pg. 712
DERZHAVA PJSCB; *Int'l*, pg. 2043
DESAB S.A.—See Corteva, Inc.; *U.S. Public*, pg. 581
DESA CARGILL SDN BHD—See Cargill, Inc.; *U.S. Private*, pg. 759
DESA DERI SANAYI VE TICARET A.S.; *Int'l*, pg. 2043
D.E.S AGENCIES (PTY) LTD.—See Sherpa Capital SL; *Int'l*, pg. 6826
DESAI CAPITAL MANAGEMENT INCORPORATED; *U.S. Private*, pg. 1210
DESAILLY SA; *Int'l*, pg. 2043
DESA ILMU SDN. BHD.—See Naim Holdings Berhad; *Int'l*, pg. 5131
DESAI SYSTEMS INC.; *U.S. Private*, pg. 1210
DESALARI LTDA.—See GS Holdings Corp.; *Int'l*, pg. 3142
DESALCO (BARBADOS) LTD—See Consolidated Water Co. Ltd.; *Int'l*, pg. 1771
DESALCO LIMITED—See Consolidated Water Co. Ltd.; *Int'l*, pg. 1771
DESA LLC—See H.I.G. Capital, LLC; *U.S. Private*, pg. 1829
DESANCTIS INSURANCE AGENCY, INC.; *U.S. Private*, pg. 1211
DESANE GROUP HOLDINGS LTD; *Int'l*, pg. 2043
DESANE PROPERTIES PTY. LTD.—See Desane Group Holdings Ltd; *Int'l*, pg. 2043
DESANTIS BREINDEL; *U.S. Private*, pg. 1211
DESARROLLADORA DE CASAS DEL NOROESTE, S.A. DE C.V.—See Desarrolladora Homex, S.A. de C.V.; *Int'l*, pg. 2044
DESARROLLADORA HOMEX, S.A. DE C.V.; *Int'l*, pg. 2043
DESARROLLO DE CONCESIONARIAS VIARIAS DOS, S.L.—See ACS, Actividades de Construccion y Servicios, S.A.; *Int'l*, pg. 111
DESARROLLO DE CONCESIONARIAS VIARIAS UNO, S.L.—See ACS, Actividades de Construccion y Servicios, S.A.; *Int'l*, pg. 111
DESARROLLO DE CONCESIONES FERROVIARIAS, S.L.—See ACS, Actividades de Construccion y Servicios, S.A.; *Int'l*, pg. 111
DESARROLLO INFORMATICO, S.A.—See ACS, Actividades de Construccion y Servicios, S.A.; *Int'l*, pg. 111
DESARROLLOS EOLICOS PROMOCION, S.A.—See EDP - Energias de Portugal, S.A.; *Int'l*, pg. 2314
DESARROLLOS EOLICOS, S.A.—See EDP - Energias de Portugal, S.A.; *Int'l*, pg. 2314
DESARROLLOS ESPECIALES DE SISTEMAS DE ANCLAJE, S.A.; *Int'l*, pg. 2044
DESARROLLOS METROPOLITANOS, LLC.; *U.S. Private*, pg. 1211
DESARROLLOS MULTIPLES INSULARES, INC.—See CEMEX, S.A.B. de C.V.; *Int'l*, pg. 1399
DESARROLLOS URBANOS CI., S.A.—See MAPFRE S.A.; *Int'l*, pg. 4685
DESA TALISAI SDN BHD—See IJM Corporation Berhad; *Int'l*, pg. 3608
DESA TEA SDN BHD—See Yee Lee Corporation Bhd.; *Int'l*, pg. 8575
DESAUTEL HEGE COMMUNICATIONS; *U.S. Private*, pg. 1211
DESBROW THOMPSON CHAFFE; *Int'l*, pg. 2044
DESBUILD INCORPORATED; *U.S. Private*, pg. 1211
DESCAIR INC.—See Groupe Deschenes Inc.; *Int'l*, pg. 3101
DESCAMPS LTD.—See Vincenzo Zucchi S.p.A.; *Int'l*, pg. 8211
DESCAMPS S.A.S.—See Vincenzo Zucchi S.p.A.; *Int'l*, pg. 8211
DESCAR NV—See KBC Group NV; *Int'l*, pg. 4104
DESCARTES STEPCOM AG—See The Descartes Systems Group Inc.; *Int'l*, pg. 7636
THE DESCARTES SYSTEMS GROUP INC.; *Int'l*, pg. 7636
DESCARTES SYSTEMS (USA) LLC—See The Descartes Systems Group Inc.; *Int'l*, pg. 7636
DESCARTES VISUAL COMPLIANCE (USA) LLC—See The Descartes Systems Group Inc.; *Int'l*, pg. 7636
DES-CASE CORPORATION—See The Timken Company; *U.S. Public*, pg. 2132
DESCCO DESIGN & CONSTRUCTION; *U.S. Private*, pg. 1211
DESCENTE APPAREL LTD.—See ITOCHU Corporation; *Int'l*, pg. 3836

DESCENTE KOREA, LTD.—See ITOCHU Corporation; *Int'l*, pg. 3836
DESCENTE LTD.—See ITOCHU Corporation; *Int'l*, pg. 3835
DESCENTE NORTH AMERICA, INC.—See ITOCHU Corporation; *Int'l*, pg. 3836
DESCENTE NORTH AMERICA, INC.—See ITOCHU Corporation; *Int'l*, pg. 3836
DESCHENES & FILS LTEE—See Groupe Deschenes Inc.; *Int'l*, pg. 3102
DESCHENES & FILS LTEE—See Groupe Deschenes Inc.; *Int'l*, pg. 3101
DESCHENES & FILS LTEE—See Groupe Deschenes Inc.; *Int'l*, pg. 3102
DESCHUTES BREWERY INC.; *U.S. Private*, pg. 1211
DESCHUTES PINE SALES, INC.—See Ochoco Lumber Company; *U.S. Private*, pg. 2992
DESCO ACQUISITION LLC—See Desco Corporation; *U.S. Private*, pg. 1211
DESCO CAPITAL—See Desco Corporation; *U.S. Private*, pg. 1211
DESCO CORPORATION; *U.S. Private*, pg. 1211
DESCO EQUIPMENT CORP.—See Apex Machine Co.; *U.S. Private*, pg. 293
DESCO INC.; *U.S. Private*, pg. 1211
DESCO, INC.—See Globeride, Inc.; *Int'l*, pg. 3007
DESCO INDUSTRIES INC.; *U.S. Private*, pg. 1211
DESCO, LLC; *U.S. Private*, pg. 1211
DES COMPANIES; *U.S. Private*, pg. 1210
DESCON CHEMICALS (PVT) LIMITED—See Nimir Resins Limited; *Int'l*, pg. 5297
DESCON ENGINEERING ABU DHABI—See Nimir Resins Limited; *Int'l*, pg. 5297
DESCON ENGINEERING LIMITED—See Nimir Resins Limited; *Int'l*, pg. 5297
DESCON INTEGRATED PROJECTS (PRIVATE) LIMITED—See Nimir Resins Limited; *Int'l*, pg. 5297
DESCON OXYCHEM LIMITED—See Nimir Resins Limited; *Int'l*, pg. 5297
DESCO PLUMBING & HEATING SUPPLY INC.—See Groupe Deschenes Inc.; *Int'l*, pg. 3102
DESCOURS & CABAUD ILE-DE-F—See Descours & Cabaud SA; *Int'l*, pg. 2044
DESCOURS & CABAUD NORMANDIE—See Descours & Cabaud SA; *Int'l*, pg. 2044
DESCOURS & CABAUD PACA—See Descours & Cabaud SA; *Int'l*, pg. 2044
DESCOURS & CABAUD RHONE ALPES AUVERGNE—See Descours & Cabaud SA; *Int'l*, pg. 2044
DESCOURS & CABAUD SA; *Int'l*, pg. 2044
DESCOURS & CABAUD SAVOIE—See Descours & Cabaud SA; *Int'l*, pg. 2044
DESCRIPTIVE VIDEO WORKS INC.—See Canada Pension Plan Investment Board; *Int'l*, pg. 1280
DESCRIPTIVE VIDEO WORKS INC.—See EQT AB; *Int'l*, pg. 2482
DESCRIPTIVE VIDEO WORKS INC.—See Temasek Holdings (Private) Limited; *Int'l*, pg. 7548
DESEA SDN BHD—See Schneider Electric SE; *Int'l*, pg. 6626
DES EAUX DE DOUAI SA; *Int'l*, pg. 2043
DESENIO GROUP AB; *Int'l*, pg. 2044
DESENVOLVIMENTO TURISTICO E HOTELEIRO, SA—See Estoril Sol, SGPS, S.A.; *Int'l*, pg. 2518
DESE RESEARCH INC.; *U.S. Private*, pg. 1211
DESERET BIOLOGICALS; *U.S. Private*, pg. 1211
DESERET BOOK CO.—See Deseret Management Corporation; *U.S. Private*, pg. 1212
DESERET DIGITAL MEDIA—See Deseret Management Corporation; *U.S. Private*, pg. 1212
DESERET FIRST CREDIT UNION INC.; *U.S. Private*, pg. 1212
DESERET GENERATION & TRANSMISSION COOPERATIVE, INC.; *U.S. Private*, pg. 1212
DESERET LABORATORIES, INC.; *U.S. Private*, pg. 1212
DESERET MANAGEMENT CORPORATION; *U.S. Private*, pg. 1212
DESERET MEMORIAL, INC.—See Security National Financial Corporation; *U.S. Public*, pg. 1856
DESERET MORNING NEWS—See Deseret Management Corporation; *U.S. Private*, pg. 1212
DESERET RANCHES OF FLORIDA; *U.S. Private*, pg. 1212
DESERT ADVENTURES TOURISM LLC—See Fairfax Financial Holdings Limited; *Int'l*, pg. 2608
DESERT AIRE CORP.—See Multistack, LLC; *U.S. Private*, pg. 2813
DESERT BUICK-GMC TRUCKS, L.L.C.—See AutoNation, Inc.; *U.S. Public*, pg. 234
DESERT COASTAL TRANSPORT INCORPORATION; *U.S. Private*, pg. 1212
DESERT COMMUNICATIONS, INC.; *U.S. Private*, pg. 1212
DESERT COMMUNITY BANK—See New York Community Bancorp, Inc.; *U.S. Public*, pg. 1512
DESERT CONTROL AS; *Int'l*, pg. 2044

THE DESIGN AGENCY INC.

DESERT CORNERSTONE INSURANCE SERVICE, INC.—See Inszone Insurance Services, LLC; *U.S. Private*, pg. 2096
DESERT DIAMOND FISHING (PTY) LIMITED—See Oceana Group Limited; *Int'l*, pg. 5517
DESERT DISPATCH—See Gannett Co., Inc.; *U.S. Public*, pg. 904
DESERT ELECTRIC SUPPLY; *U.S. Private*, pg. 1212
DESERT ENERGY EQUIPMENT, INC.; *U.S. Private*, pg. 1212
DESERT EUROPEAN MOTORCARS, LTD.; *U.S. Private*, pg. 1212
DESERT FIRE HOLDINGS, INC.—See MDU Resources Group, Inc.; *U.S. Public*, pg. 1410
DESERT FIRE PROTECTION, INC.—See MDU Resources Group, Inc.; *U.S. Public*, pg. 1410
DESERT FIRE PROTECTION LP; *U.S. Private*, pg. 1212
DESERT FLEET-SERV, INC.—See OEP Capital Advisors, L.P.; *U.S. Private*, pg. 3000
DESERT FRESH, INC.; *U.S. Private*, pg. 1212
DESERT GMC, L.L.C.—See AutoNation, Inc.; *U.S. Public*, pg. 234
DESERT GOLD VENTURES INC.; *Int'l*, pg. 2044
DESERT HAWK GOLD CORP.; *U.S. Private*, pg. 1212
DESERT JET; *U.S. Private*, pg. 1212
DESERT LUMBER, INC.—See Bain Capital, LP; *U.S. Private*, pg. 450
DESERT MECHANICAL INC.—See Tutor Perini Corporation; *U.S. Public*, pg. 2205
DESERT METALS LIMITED; *Int'l*, pg. 2044
DESERT MOUNTAIN CLUB, INC.; *U.S. Private*, pg. 1213
DESERT MOUNTAIN ENERGY CORP.; *Int'l*, pg. 2045
DESERT MOUNTAIN PROPERTIES LIMITED PARTNERSHIP; *U.S. Private*, pg. 1213
DESERT NDT, LLC—See ShawCor Ltd.; *Int'l*, pg. 6791
DESERTOAK LTD; *Int'l*, pg. 2045
DESERT PAVING, INC.; *U.S. Private*, pg. 1213
DESERT PEAK MINERALS INC.; *U.S. Private*, pg. 1213
DESERT PERSONNEL SERVICES—See AtWorkGroup LLC; *U.S. Private*, pg. 384
DESERT PET, LLC—See Cardinal Health, Inc.; *U.S. Public*, pg. 434
DESERT PUBLICATIONS INC.; *U.S. Private*, pg. 1213
DESERT REGIONAL MEDICAL CENTER, INC.—See Tenet Healthcare Corporation; *U.S. Public*, pg. 2003
DESERT RIDGE OUTPATIENT SURGERY, LLC—See Tenet Healthcare Corporation; *U.S. Public*, pg. 2010
DESERT SKY MALL LLC—See The Macerich Company; *U.S. Public*, pg. 2109
DESERT SPRINGS POOLS & SPAS; *U.S. Private*, pg. 1213
DESERT STATES ELECTRICAL SALES—See McGee Co.; *U.S. Private*, pg. 2634
DESERT SUN MOTORS; *U.S. Private*, pg. 1213
THE DESERT SUN PUBLISHING COMPANY—See Gannett Co., Inc.; *U.S. Public*, pg. 900
THE DESERT SUN—See Gannett Co., Inc.; *U.S. Public*, pg. 900
DESERT WHALE JOJOBA COMPANY, INC.—See H.I.G. Capital, LLC; *U.S. Private*, pg. 1832
DESERT WIND APARTMENTS ARIZONA, LLC—See RAIT Financial Trust; *U.S. Private*, pg. 3348
DESGRANGES OUTILS COUPANTS S.A.—See OSG Corporation; *Int'l*, pg. 5649
DESHANO CONSTRUCTION COMPANY; *U.S. Private*, pg. 1213
D. E. SHAW & CO. (ASIA PACIFIC) LIMITED—See D. E. Shaw & Co., L.P.; *U.S. Private*, pg. 1139
D. E. SHAW & CO. (BERMUDA), LTD.—See D. E. Shaw & Co., L.P.; *U.S. Private*, pg. 1139
D. E. SHAW & CO. (LONDON), LLP—See D. E. Shaw & Co., L.P.; *U.S. Private*, pg. 1139
D. E. SHAW & CO., L.P.; *U.S. Private*, pg. 1139
D. E. SHAW INDIA SECURITIES PRIVATE LIMITED—See D. E. Shaw & Co., L.P.; *U.S. Private*, pg. 1139
D. E. SHAW INDIA SOFTWARE PRIVATE LIMITED—See D. E. Shaw & Co., L.P.; *U.S. Private*, pg. 1139
D. E. SHAW PRIVATE EQUITY INVESTMENT MANAGEMENT (SHANGHAI) CO., LIMITED—See D. E. Shaw & Co., L.P.; *U.S. Private*, pg. 1139
D. E. SHAW RESEARCH, LLC—See D. E. Shaw & Co., L.P.; *U.S. Private*, pg. 1139
DESHAZO SERVICE COMPANY, LLC; *U.S. Private*, pg. 1213
DESHBANDHU POLYMER LIMITED; *Int'l*, pg. 2045
DESH GARMENTS LIMITED; *Int'l*, pg. 2045
DESHLER FARMERS ELEVATOR CO.; *U.S. Private*, pg. 1213
DESH RAKSHAK AUSHDHALAYA LIMITED; *Int'l*, pg. 2045
DESICCARE, INC.; *U.S. Private*, pg. 1213
DESIGNAFFAIRS BUSINESS CONSULTING (SHANGHAI) CO. LTD.—See Accenture plc; *Int'l*, pg. 87
DESIGNAFFAIRS GMBH—See Accenture plc; *Int'l*, pg. 87
THE DESIGN AGENCY INC.; *U.S. Private*, pg. 4020
DESIGN AIR, LTD.—See EMCOR Group, Inc.; *U.S. Public*, pg. 736
DESIGN AIR—See U.S. Venture, Inc.; *U.S. Private*, pg. 4272

DESIGN ANALYSIS ASSOCIATES, INC.—See Xylem Inc.; U.S. Public, pg. 2395
DESIGNARC CO., LTD.—See Daiwa House Industry Co., Ltd.; Int'l, pg. 1946
DESIGNATRONICS, INC. - ADVANCED ANTIVIBRATION COMPONENTS DIVISION—See Designatronics, Inc.; U.S. Private, pg. 1214
DESIGNATRONICS, INC. - ALL METRIC SMALL PARTS DIVISION—See Designatronics, Inc.; U.S. Private, pg. 1214
DESIGNATRONICS, INC. - QUALITY BEARINGS & COMPONENTS DIVISION—See Designatronics, Inc.; U.S. Private, pg. 1214
DESIGNATRONICS, INC. - QUALITY TRANSMISSION COMPONENTS DIVISION—See Designatronics, Inc.; U.S. Private, pg. 1214
DESIGNATRONICS, INC.; U.S. Private, pg. 1214
DESIGN BENEFIT PLANS, INC.—See CNO Financial Group, Inc.; U.S. Public, pg. 520
DESIGN BENEFITS INC.—See Principal Financial Group, Inc.; U.S. Public, pg. 1721
DESIGN+BUILD GROUP; U.S. Private, pg. 1214
DESIGN-BUILD SOLUTIONS, INC.—See Garland Industries Inc.; U.S. Private, pg. 1644
DESIGN BUREAU OF EXPERIMENTAL WORKS OJSC—See Russian Technologies State Corporation; Int'l, pg. 6431
DESIGN CAPITAL LIMITED; Int'l, pg. 2045
DESIGNCAPITAL PLC; Int'l, pg. 2045
DESIGN CENTER EUROPE, S.L.—See Porsche Automobil Holding SE; Int'l, pg. 5926
DESIGN CENTER INC.; U.S. Private, pg. 1213
DESIGN CENTER—See Omnicom Group Inc.; U.S. Public, pg. 1594
THE DESIGN CENTRE—See Reid-World Wide Corporation; Int'l, pg. 6256
DESIGN CONCEPTS; U.S. Private, pg. 1213
DESIGN & CONSTRUCTION GIFFELS QUEBEC INC.—See The Ingenium Group Inc.; Int'l, pg. 7655
DESIGN CONTEMPO INC.; U.S. Private, pg. 1213
DESIGN COST DATA—See BNi Publications, Inc.; U.S. Private, pg. 602
DESIGN DATA CORP.—See Nemetschek SE; Int'l, pg. 5194
DESIGN DISPLAY GROUP INC.; U.S. Private, pg. 1213
DESIGN DISTRIBUTING INC.—See William M. Bird & Company, Inc.; U.S. Private, pg. 4523
DESIGNED ALLOYS INC.; U.S. Private, pg. 1214
DESIGNED METAL CONNECTIONS, INC.—See Berkshire Hathaway Inc.; U.S. Public, pg. 314
DESIGNED MOBILE SYSTEMS INDUSTRIES, INC.; U.S. Private, pg. 1214
DESIGNED STAIRS INC.; U.S. Private, pg. 1214
DESIGN ELECTRIC INC.; U.S. Private, pg. 1213
DESIGN ENVIROMENTS, INC.—See Blackford Capital LLC; U.S. Private, pg. 574
DESIGNER APPLIANCES; U.S. Private, pg. 1214
DESIGNER BRANDS, INC.—See Schottenstein Stores Corporation; U.S. Private, pg. 3569
DESIGNER DOORS, INC.; U.S. Private, pg. 1214
DESIGNER FOODS CO., LTD.—See Delica Foods Holdings Co., Ltd.; Int'l, pg. 2013
DESIGNER GREETINGS; U.S. Private, pg. 1214
DESIGNER IMPORTS INTERNATIONAL; U.S. Private, pg. 1214
DESIGNER OUTLET ATHENS S.M. LLC—See Lamda Development SA; Int'l, pg. 4401
DESIGNER SASH & DOOR SYSTEMS, INC.; U.S. Private, pg. 1215
DESIGNERS FOUNTAIN; U.S. Private, pg. 1215
DESIGNERS REMIX A/S—See Friheden Invest A/S; Int'l, pg. 2792
DESIGN EXTENSIONS, LLC; U.S. Private, pg. 1213
DESIGN EYE PUBLISHING LTD—See The Quarto Group, Inc.; Int'l, pg. 7677
DESIGN FACTORY CO., LTD.—See Oriental Land Co., Ltd.; Int'l, pg. 5625
DESIGN FORCE AB—See Stora Enso Oyj; Int'l, pg. 7223
DESIGN FORCE CORPORATION—See Valiant Products Corp.; U.S. Private, pg. 4332
DESIGNGEN, COMUNICACAO VISUAL, UNIPESSOAL LDA.—See CSG Systems International, Inc.; U.S. Public, pg. 601
DESIGN GROUP ITALIA CORP.—See Alkemy SpA; Int'l, pg. 331
DESIGN GROUP ITALIA I.D. S.R.L.—See Alkemy SpA; Int'l, pg. 331
DESIGN HOMES INC.; U.S. Private, pg. 1213
DESIGN HOTELS AG—See Marriott International, Inc.; U.S. Public, pg. 1371
DESIGNING HEALTH, INC.; U.S. Private, pg. 1215
DESIGNING SUCCESS, INC.—See MPACT Strategic Consulting LLC; U.S. Private, pg. 2803
DESIGN & INSTALLATION DIVISION—See KVL Audio Visual Services; U.S. Private, pg. 2359
DESIGN INTEGRATED TECHNOLOGY, INC.—See SPARC Holding Company; U.S. Private, pg. 3745
DESIGN INTERACTIVE, INC.; U.S. Private, pg. 1213

DESIGN IS DEAD BVBA—See Emakina Group S.A.; Int'l, pg. 2373
DESIGNIT DENMARK A/S—See Wipro Limited; Int'l, pg. 8432
DESIGNIT GERMANY GMBH—See Wipro Limited; Int'l, pg. 8432
DESIGNIT OSLO A/S—See Wipro Limited; Int'l, pg. 8432
DESIGNIT SPAIN DIGITAL, S.L.—See Wipro Limited; Int'l, pg. 8432
DESIGNIT SWEDEN AB—See Wipro Limited; Int'l, pg. 8432
DESIGNIT TLV LTD.—See Wipro Limited; Int'l, pg. 8432
DESIGNIT TOKYO LTD.—See Wipro Limited; Int'l, pg. 8432
DESIGNKITCHEN—See WPP plc; Int'l, pg. 8479
DESIGNKUPP AS—See Brodrene A & O Johansen A/S; Int'l, pg. 1173
DESIGN LABORATORY, INC.; U.S. Private, pg. 1213
DESIGN LINES, INC.—See TRIO, Inc.; U.S. Private, pg. 4236
DESIGN MACHINING UNLIMITED INC.—See Appulse Corporation; Int'l, pg. 522
DESIGN MARKETING GROUP, INC.; U.S. Private, pg. 1213
DESIGN MATERIALS INCORPORATED; U.S. Private, pg. 1213
DESIGN MECHANICAL INCORPORATED—See Comfort Systems USA, Inc.; U.S. Public, pg. 543
DESIGN MILK CO. LIMITED; Int'l, pg. 2045
DESIGN MOLDED PLASTICS INC.—See Big Shoulders Capital LLC; U.S. Private, pg. 554
DESIGNONE JAPAN, INC.; Int'l, pg. 2045
DESIGN ON STAGE HAIR, INC.; U.S. Private, pg. 1213
DESIGN OPTIONS; U.S. Private, pg. 1214
THE DESIGNORY—See Omnicom Group Inc.; U.S. Public, pg. 1599
DESIGN PACKAGING COMPANY INC.; U.S. Private, pg. 1214
DESIGN PACKAGING, INC.—See Clayton, Dubilier & Rice, LLC; U.S. Private, pg. 930
THE DESIGN PEOPLE, INC.; U.S. Private, pg. 4020
DESIGN PICKLE, LLC; U.S. Private, pg. 1214
DESIGNPLAN LIGHTING LTD—See Fagerhult Group AB; Int'l, pg. 2602
DESIGN PLASTICS, INC.—See Coda Resources, Ltd.; U.S. Private, pg. 959
DESIGN REACTOR, INC.—See XTI Aerospace, Inc.; U.S. Public, pg. 2393
DESIGN RESOURCES GROUP ARCHITECTS, A.I.A., INC.; U.S. Private, pg. 1214
DESIGN SCIENCE, INC.—See Maths for More SL; Int'l, pg. 4727
DESIGN SECURITY INC.—See Detex Corporation; U.S. Private, pg. 1216
DESIGNS FOR HEALTH, INC.; U.S. Private, pg. 1215
DESIGN SOUTH PROFESSIONALS, INC.—See Littlejohn & Co., LLC; U.S. Private, pg. 2469
DESIGN SPACE MODULAR BUILDINGS PNW, LP—See McGrath RentCorp.; U.S. Public, pg. 1407
DESIGN SPECIALTIES, INC.—See Blackthorne Partners Ltd.; U.S. Private, pg. 577
DESIGN SPECIALTIES, INC.—See Precision Walls, Inc.; U.S. Private, pg. 3247
DESIGN STRATEGY CORPORATION; U.S. Private, pg. 1214
DESIGN STUDIO GROUP LTD.; Int'l, pg. 2045
DESIGN STUDIO (HUIZHOU) HOME FURNISHING CO., LTD.—See Design Studio Group Ltd.; Int'l, pg. 2045
DESIGN STUDIO LONDON—See Yamaha Corporation; Int'l, pg. 8549
DESIGN STYLES INC.; U.S. Private, pg. 1214
DESIGN & SUPPLY CO., INC.—See Delta Holdings, Inc.; U.S. Private, pg. 1200
DESIGN/SYSTEMS GROUP, INC.—See GTCR LLC; U.S. Private, pg. 1802
DESIGN SYSTEMS INC.; U.S. Private, pg. 1214
DESIGN TANKS LLC—See Aldine Capital Partners, Inc.; U.S. Private, pg. 159
DESIGN TANKS LLC—See Verdane Capital Advisors AS; Int'l, pg. 8165
DESIGN & TECHNICAL SERBICES UK LTD.—See Nicolas Correa S.A.; Int'l, pg. 5272
DESIGNTEX GROUP INC.—See Steelcase Inc.; U.S. Public, pg. 1944
DESIGNTEX - PORTLAND—See Steelcase Inc.; U.S. Public, pg. 1944
DESIGN THERAPEUTICS, INC.; U.S. Public, pg. 656
DESIGN TOSCANO, INC.; U.S. Private, pg. 1214
DESIGN TRENDS, LLC—See Craftmade International, Inc.; U.S. Private, pg. 1082
DESIGN WITHIN REACH—See MillerKnoll, Inc.; U.S. Public, pg. 1447
DESIGNWORKS ADVERTISING INC.; U.S. Private, pg. 1215
DESIGNWORKS CLOTHING COMPANY PTY. LTD.—See Queens Lane Capital Pty Ltd; Int'l, pg. 6159
DESIGNWORKS (NZ) LIMITED—See WPP plc; Int'l, pg. 8463

DESIGNWORKS USA—See Bayerische Motoren Werke Aktiengesellschaft; Int'l, pg. 912
DESIGN YOUR HOME HOLDING AB; Int'l, pg. 2045
DE SIKKENS GROSSIER B.V.—See Akzo Nobel N.V.; Int'l, pg. 273
DESILVA GATES CONSTRUCTION; U.S. Private, pg. 1215
DESILVA+PHILLIPS LLC; U.S. Private, pg. 1215
DESIMO-DESENVOLVIMENTO E GESTAO IMOBILIARIA, LDA.—See Jeronimo Martins SGPS SA; Int'l, pg. 3931
DESIMPEL BRICK LIMITED—See Heidelberg Materials AG; Int'l, pg. 3310
DES INC.; U.S. Private, pg. 1210
DESIREPATH MISSISSIPPI LLC—See The Thymes, LLC; U.S. Public, pg. 4127
DESJARDINS FINANCIAL CORPORATION INC.—See Mouvement des caisses Desjardins; Int'l, pg. 5058
DESJARDINS FINANCIAL SECURITY INVESTMENTS INC.—See Mouvement des caisses Desjardins; Int'l, pg. 5058
DESJARDINS FINANCIAL SEGURITY LIFE ASSURANCE COMPANY—See Mouvement des caisses Desjardins; Int'l, pg. 5058
DESJARDINS GENERAL INSURANCE GROUP—See Mouvement des caisses Desjardins; Int'l, pg. 5058
DESJARDINS SECURITIES INC.—See Mouvement des caisses Desjardins; Int'l, pg. 5058
DESJOYAUX DEUTSCHLAND GMBH.—See Piscines Desjoyaux SA; Int'l, pg. 5876
DESJOYAUX IBERICA DISA—See Piscines Desjoyaux SA; Int'l, pg. 5876
DESJOYAUX PISCINAS LISBOA, LDA—See Piscines Desjoyaux SA; Int'l, pg. 5876
DESJOYAUX PISCINES 06 SARL—See Piscines Desjoyaux SA; Int'l, pg. 5875
DESJOYAUX PISCINES 24 SARL—See Piscines Desjoyaux SA; Int'l, pg. 5875
DESJOYAUX PISCINES 77 SARL—See Piscines Desjoyaux SA; Int'l, pg. 5875
DESJOYAUX PISCINES 78 SARL—See Piscines Desjoyaux SA; Int'l, pg. 5875
DESJOYAUX PISCINES CAEN SARL—See Piscines Desjoyaux SA; Int'l, pg. 5876
DESJOYAUX PISCINES FRANCE SARL—See Piscines Desjoyaux SA; Int'l, pg. 5875
DESJOYAUX PISCINES ST ETIENNE SARL—See Piscines Desjoyaux SA; Int'l, pg. 5876
DESKS INC.; U.S. Private, pg. 1215
DESK TOP GRAPHICS INC.; U.S. Private, pg. 1215
DESK TOP IDEAS LTD—See New Wave Group AB; Int'l, pg. 5229
DESKTOP METAL, INC.; U.S. Public, pg. 656
DESLAURIER CUSTOM CABINETS INC.; Int'l, pg. 2045
DESMA (GUANGZHOU) MACHINERY & ENGINEERING CO., LTD.—See Salzgitter AG; Int'l, pg. 6497
DESMA-KDE SALES & SERVICE, INC.—See Salzgitter AG; Int'l, pg. 6497
DESMA RUBBER INJECTION MACHINERY (WUXI) CO. LTD.—See Salzgitter AG; Int'l, pg. 6496
DESMA SCHUHMASCHINEN GMBH—See Salzgitter AG; Int'l, pg. 6496
DESMA SLOVAKIA S.R.O.—See Salzgitter AG; Int'l, pg. 6497
DESMA USA, INC.—See Salzgitter AG; Int'l, pg. 6496
DESMAZIERES SA; Int'l, pg. 2045
DESMED, LLC—See Universal Health Realty Income Trust; U.S. Public, pg. 2255
DE SMET ENGINEERS & CONTRACTORS SA—See Moret Industries Group SAS; Int'l, pg. 5040
DESMET ROSEDOWNS LTD.—See Alfa Laval AB; Int'l, pg. 312
DES MOINES ASPHALT & PAVING CO.—See CRH plc; Int'l, pg. 1847
DES MOINES FLYING SERVICE, INC.—See Muncie Aviation Co.; U.S. Private, pg. 2813
DES MOINES REGISTER AND TRIBUNE COMPANY—See Gannett Co., Inc.; U.S. Public, pg. 897
DES MOINES SYMPHONY ASSOCIATION; U.S. Private, pg. 1210
DES MOINES TRUCK BROKERS, INC.—See Allen Lund Company, LLC; U.S. Private, pg. 179
DES MOINES WATER WORKS; U.S. Private, pg. 1210
THE DESMOND ALBANY HOTEL & CONFERENCE CENTER—See Delta Holdings, Inc.; U.S. Private, pg. 1200
THE DESMOND GREAT VALLEY HOTEL & CONFERENCE CENTER—See Delta Holdings, Inc.; U.S. Private, pg. 1200
DESMON S.P.A.—See The Middleby Corporation; U.S. Public, pg. 2113
DESON DEVELOPMENT INTERNATIONAL HOLDINGS LTD; Int'l, pg. 2045
DESON INNOVATIVE LIMITED—See Deson Development International Holdings Ltd; Int'l, pg. 2045
DESON JAPAN CO., LTD.—See Huisheng International Holdings Limited; Int'l, pg. 3527
DESOTO AUTOMOTIVE ENTERPRISES INC; U.S. Private, pg. 1215

COMPANY NAME INDEX

DESOTO DIALYSIS, LLC—See DaVita Inc.; *U.S. Public*, pg. 638
DE SOTO FUELS INC.; *U.S. Private*, pg. 1181
DESOTO HOSPITAL ASSOCIATION; *U.S. Private*, pg. 1215
DESOTO MILLS, INC.—See Berkshire Hathaway Inc.; *U.S. Public*, pg. 305
DESOTO REGIONAL DIALYSIS CENTER LLC—See Nautic Partners, LLC; *U.S. Public*, pg. 2869
DESOTO RESOURCES LIMITED; *Int'l*, pg. 2045
DESOTO SALES INC.; *U.S. Private*, pg. 1215
DESOTO SUN—See Sun Coast Media Group, Inc.; *U.S. Private*, pg. 3862
DESOTO SURGICARE PARTNERS, LTD.—See Tenet Healthcare Corporation; *U.S. Public*, pg. 2010
DESOUTTER GMBH—See Atlas Copco AB; *Int'l*, pg. 682
DESOUTTER ITALIANA S.R.L.—See Atlas Copco AB; *Int'l*, pg. 682
DESOUTTER S.A.—See Atlas Copco AB; *Int'l*, pg. 682
DESPACHO DE ABOGADOS MIEMBRO DE HOGAN LOVELLS—See Hogan Lovells International LLP; *Int'l*, pg. 3441
DE SPARRENHORST, B.V.—See Minor International PCL; *Int'l*, pg. 4911
DESPATCH INDUSTRIES GMBH EMEA OPERATION—See Illinois Tool Works Inc.; *U.S. Public*, pg. 1102
DESPATCH INDUSTRIES INC.—See Illinois Tool Works Inc.; *U.S. Public*, pg. 1102
DESPATCH INDUSTRIES, INC.—See Illinois Tool Works Inc.; *U.S. Public*, pg. 1102
DESPATCH INDUSTRIES LIMITED PARTNERSHIP—See Illinois Tool Works Inc.; *U.S. Public*, pg. 1102
DESPATCH INDUSTRIES (SHANGHAI) TRADING CO., LTD.—See Illinois Tool Works Inc.; *U.S. Public*, pg. 1102
DESPATCH INDUSTRIES TAIWAN LTD.—See Illinois Tool Works Inc.; *U.S. Public*, pg. 1102
DESPEC AFRICA EPZ LTD—See Despec Group B.V.; *Int'l*, pg. 2046
DESPEC BILGISAYAR PAZARLAMA VE TICARET A.S.; *Int'l*, pg. 2046
DESPEC DENMARK A/S—See Despec Group B.V.; *Int'l*, pg. 2046
DESPEC DOO—See Despec Group B.V.; *Int'l*, pg. 2046
DESPEC EUROPE B.V.—See Despec Group B.V.; *Int'l*, pg. 2046
DESPEC GROUP B.V.; *Int'l*, pg. 2046
DESPEC IBERIA SL.—See Despec Group B.V.; *Int'l*, pg. 2046
DESPEC JORDAN FZE—See Despec Group B.V.; *Int'l*, pg. 2046
DESPEC KENYA LTD—See Despec Group B.V.; *Int'l*, pg. 2046
DESPEC LEBANON SAL—See Despec Group B.V.; *Int'l*, pg. 2046
DESPEC MERA LTD.—See Despec Group B.V.; *Int'l*, pg. 2046
DESPEC SUPPLIES BVBA—See Despec Group B.V.; *Int'l*, pg. 2046
DESPEC SUPPLIES UTIBU A ISLANDI AS—See Despec Group B.V.; *Int'l*, pg. 2046
DESPEC SWEDEN AB—See Despec Group B.V.; *Int'l*, pg. 2046
DESPEC TANZANIA LTD—See Despec Group B.V.; *Int'l*, pg. 2046
DESPEC TURKEY A.S.—See Despec Group B.V.; *Int'l*, pg. 2046
DESPEC UGANDA LTD—See Despec Group B.V.; *Int'l*, pg. 2046
DESPEGAR.COM, CORP.; *Int'l*, pg. 2046
DESPEGAR.COM USA, INC.—See Despegar.com, Corp.; *Int'l*, pg. 2046
DESPRED PLC; *Int'l*, pg. 2046
DESQUESNES SNC—See Eiffage S.A.; *Int'l*, pg. 2330
DESRI INC.; *U.S. Private*, pg. 1215
DESSANGE INTERNATIONAL SA—See Eurazeo SE; *Int'l*, pg. 2528
DESSER TIRE & RUBBER CO., LLC—See VSE Corporation; *U.S. Public*, pg. 2313
DESSERT PRODUCTS INTERNATIONAL—See McCormick & Company, Incorporated; *U.S. Public*, pg. 1404
DESSIN/FOURNIR, INC.; *U.S. Private*, pg. 1215
DESSO CZECH REPUBLIC S.R.O.—See Tarkett S.A.; *Int'l*, pg. 7462
DESSO GROUP B.V.—See Tarkett S.A.; *Int'l*, pg. 7462
DESSO USA INC.—See Tarkett S.A.; *Int'l*, pg. 7462
DE-STA-CO (ASIA) COMPANY, LIMITED—See Stabilus; *U.S. Private*, pg. 3774
DE-STA-CO BENELUX B.V.—See Stabilus; *U.S. Private*, pg. 3774
DE-STA-CO EUROPE GMBH—See Stabilus; *U.S. Private*, pg. 3774
DE-STA-CO SHANGHAI CO., LTD.—See Stabilus; *U.S. Private*, pg. 3774
DESTACO—See Stabilus; *U.S. Private*, pg. 3774
DESTACO UK LIMITED—See Dover Corporation; *U.S. Public*, pg. 678
DESTAMPES EMBALLAGES; *Int'l*, pg. 2046

DESTEK FAKTORING A.S.; *Int'l*, pg. 2046
DESTICON TRANSPORTATION SERVICES INC; *Int'l*, pg. 2046
DESTILACIJA A.D.; *Int'l*, pg. 2046
DESTIN ANESTHESIA, LLC—See WELL Health Technologies Corp.; *Int'l*, pg. 8372
DESTINAS AG—See Die Schweizerische Post AG; *Int'l*, pg. 2112
DESTINATION ASIA DESTINATION MANAGEMENT SDN BHD—See The Emirates Group; *Int'l*, pg. 7639
DESTINATION ASIA JAPAN LIMITED—See The Emirates Group; *Int'l*, pg. 7639
DESTINATION ASIA (SINGAPORE) PTE LIMITED—See The Emirates Group; *Int'l*, pg. 7639
DESTINATION ASIA (THAILAND) LIMITED—See The Emirates Group; *Int'l*, pg. 7639
DESTINATION AUTO VENTURES INC; *Int'l*, pg. 2046
DESTINATION CINEMA INC.; *U.S. Private*, pg. 1215
DESTINATION CMS LTD.—See The Mission Group Public Limited Company; *Int'l*, pg. 7667
DESTINATION CONCEPTS, INC.; *U.S. Private*, pg. 1215
DESTINATION HARLEY DAVIDSON LLC; *U.S. Private*, pg. 1215
DESTINATION HOTELS AND RESORTS, INC.—See Commune Hotels & Resorts, LLC; *U.S. Private*, pg. 987
DESTINATION ITALIA SPA; *Int'l*, pg. 2046
DESTINATION KOSTA AB—See New Wave Group AB; *Int'l*, pg. 5229
DESTINATION MARKETING; *U.S. Private*, pg. 1215
DESTINATION MATERNITY CORPORATION; *U.S. Public*, pg. 656
DESTINATION MAZDA VANCOUVER; *Int'l*, pg. 2046
DESTINATION MEDIA GROUP—See WPP plc; *Int'l*, pg. 8474
DESTINATION MEDIA, INC.—See RockBridge Growth Equity, LLC; *U.S. Private*, pg. 3465
DESTINATION PACKWOOD ASSOCIATION; *U.S. Private*, pg. 1215
DESTINATION RESIDENCES HAWAII LLC—See Hyatt Hotels Corporation; *U.S. Public*, pg. 1077
DESTINATION RESIDENCES—See Hyatt Hotels Corporation; *U.S. Public*, pg. 1077
DESTINATION S.A.S.—See PAI Partners S.A.S.; *Int'l*, pg. 5700
DESTINATION SERVICES GREECE TRAVEL & TOURISM SA—See TUI AG; *Int'l*, pg. 7964
DESTINATION SERVICES MOROCCO SA—See TUI AG; *Int'l*, pg. 7964
DESTINATION SERVICES SINGAPORE PTE LIMITED—See TUI AG; *Int'l*, pg. 7964
DESTINATIONS NETWORK TOURISM MARKETING & PR COMPANY LIMITED—See Shun Tak Holdings Limited; *Int'l*, pg. 6870
DESTINATIONS UNLIMITED, INC.; *U.S. Private*, pg. 1215
DESTINATION XL GROUP, INC.; *U.S. Public*, pg. 656
DESTINI BERHAD; *Int'l*, pg. 2046
DESTINI MARINE SAFETY SOLUTIONS LTD.—See Destini Berhad; *Int'l*, pg. 2046
DESTINI PRIMA SDN. BHD.—See Destini Berhad; *Int'l*, pg. 2046
DESTINI SHIPBUILDING & ENGINEERING SDN. BHD.—See Destini Berhad; *Int'l*, pg. 2046
DESTIN JET—See The Sterling Group, L.P.; *U.S. Private*, pg. 4122
THE DESTIN LOG—See Gannett Co., Inc.; *U.S. Public*, pg. 906
DESTINOLOGY LIMITED—See Saga plc; *Int'l*, pg. 6477
DESTIN SURGERY CENTER, LLC—See Tenet Healthcare Corporation; *U.S. Public*, pg. 2010
DESTINY CORPORATE ENTERPRISES, INC.; *U.S. Private*, pg. 1216
DESTINY LOGISTICS & INFRA LIMITED; *Int'l*, pg. 2047
DESTINY MEDIA TECHNOLOGIES, INC.; *Int'l*, pg. 2047
DESTINY ORGANICS, LLC.; *U.S. Private*, pg. 1216
DESTINY PACKAGING, LLC—See Bunzl plc; *Int'l*, pg. 1218
DESTINY PHARMA PLC; *Int'l*, pg. 2047
DESTINY SOLUTIONS, INC.; *Int'l*, pg. 2047
DESTRA U.S. LIQUIDITY ALPHA AND INCOME FUND; *U.S. Private*, pg. 1216
DESTRON FEARING CORPORATION—See Merck & Co., Inc.; *U.S. Public*, pg. 1415
DESTYLERNIA POLMOS KRAKOWIE SA—See Marie Brizard Wine & Spirits S.A.; *Int'l*, pg. 4693
DESUN REAL ESTATE INVESTMENT SERVICES GROUP CO., LTD.; *Int'l*, pg. 2047
DE SURINAAMSCHE BANK N.V.—See Assuria N.V.; *Int'l*, pg. 650
DESWELL INDUSTRIES, INC.; *Int'l*, pg. 2047
DESWIK CANADA INC.—See Sandvik AB; *Int'l*, pg. 6529
DESWIK COLOMBIA S.A.S.—See Sandvik AB; *Int'l*, pg. 6529
DESWIK GROUP PTY. LTD.—See Sandvik AB; *Int'l*, pg. 6529
DESWIK KAZAKHSTAN LLP—See Sandvik AB; *Int'l*, pg. 6529
DESWIK MINING CONSULTANTS (PTY.) LTD.—See Sandvik AB; *Int'l*, pg. 6529
DESWIK PERU S.A.C.—See Sandvik AB; *Int'l*, pg. 6529

DESWIK USA INC.—See Sandvik AB; *Int'l*, pg. 6529
DETACH AB; *Int'l*, pg. 2047
DETAIL INOX SAS—See Jacquet Metal Service SA; *Int'l*, pg. 3866
DETAILS MAGAZINE—See Advance Publications, Inc.; *U.S. Private*, pg. 86
DETAI NEW ENERGY GROUP LIMITED; *Int'l*, pg. 2047
DETALJHANDELSHUSET I HYLLINGE AB—See BNP Paribas SA; *Int'l*, pg. 1090
DETAL KONCEPT SP. Z O.O.—See Emperia Holding S.A; *Int'l*, pg. 2385
DETAR HOSPITAL, LLC—See Community Health Systems, Inc.; *U.S. Public*, pg. 552
DET BESTE A/S—See RDA Holding Co.; *U.S. Private*, pg. 3363
DE&T CO., LTD.; *Int'l*, pg. 1997
DETCON, INC.—See Battery Ventures, L.P.; *U.S. Private*, pg. 488
DET DANSKE FILMINSTITUT; *Int'l*, pg. 2047
DET DANSKE HEDESELSKAB; *Int'l*, pg. 2047
DET DISTRIBUTING COMPANY INC.; *U.S. Private*, pg. 1216
DETEC DECISION TECHNOLOGY SOFTWARE GMBH.—See SPARTA AG; *Int'l*, pg. 7127
DETECT CANADA—See DeTect, Inc.; *U.S. Private*, pg. 1216
DETECT EU LTD.—See DeTect, Inc.; *U.S. Private*, pg. 1216
DETECT, INC. - AVIATION & SECURITY SYSTEMS GROUP—See DeTect, Inc.; *U.S. Private*, pg. 1216
DETECT, INC. - INTERNATIONAL DIVISION—See DeTect, Inc.; *U.S. Private*, pg. 1216
DETECT, INC. - METEOROLOGICAL RADAR GROUP—See DeTect, Inc.; *U.S. Private*, pg. 1216
DETECT, INC.; *U.S. Private*, pg. 1216
DETECTION TECHNOLOGY, INC.—See Detection Technology Oyj; *Int'l*, pg. 2048
DETECTION TECHNOLOGY OYJ; *Int'l*, pg. 2047
DETECTION TECHNOLOGY S.A.S.—See Detection Technology Oyj; *Int'l*, pg. 2048
DETECTOR ELECTRONICS CORPORATION—See Carrier Global Corporation; *U.S. Public*, pg. 440
DETECTOR TECHNOLOGY LIMITED—See Newell Brands Inc.; *U.S. Public*, pg. 1514
DETECTO SCALE COMPANY—See Cardinal Scale Manufacturing Co.; *U.S. Private*, pg. 751
DETEMEDIEN, DEUTSCHE TELEKOM MEDIEN GMBH—See Deutsche Telekom AG; *Int'l*, pg. 2083
DETEN QUIMICA, S.A.—See Mubadala Investment Company PJSC; *Int'l*, pg. 5074
DETERING COMPANY OF HOUSTON LP; *U.S. Private*, pg. 1216
DETERLING COMPANY, INC.; *U.S. Private*, pg. 1216
DETERMINA INC.; *U.S. Private*, pg. 1216
DETERMINE, INC.—See Corcentric, Inc.; *U.S. Private*, pg. 1047
DETERMINE SAS—See Corcentric, Inc.; *U.S. Private*, pg. 1047
DETER MOTOR CO.; *U.S. Private*, pg. 1216
DETERRA ROYALTIES LIMITED; *Int'l*, pg. 2048
DETERRENT TECHNOLOGIES INC.; *U.S. Private*, pg. 1216
DETEWE COMMUNICATIONS GMBH—See Searchlight Capital Partners, L.P.; *U.S. Private*, pg. 3589
DETEX CORPORATION; *U.S. Private*, pg. 1216
DETHLEFFS FRANCE S.A.R.L.—See Thor Industries, Inc.; *U.S. Public*, pg. 2156
DETHLEFFS GMBH & CO. KG—See Thor Industries, Inc.; *U.S. Public*, pg. 2156
DETHMERS MANUFACTURING COMPANY; *U.S. Private*, pg. 1216
DETICA CONSULTING LLC—See BAE Systems plc; *Int'l*, pg. 798
DETICA GROUP LIMITED—See BAE Systems plc; *Int'l*, pg. 798
DETICA LIMITED—See BAE Systems plc; *Int'l*, pg. 798
DETICA SOLUTIONS, INC.—See BAE Systems plc; *Int'l*, pg. 798
DETICA-STREAMSHIELD—See BAE Systems plc; *Int'l*, pg. 798
DETICA SYSTEM INTEGRATION LIMITED—See BAE Systems plc; *Int'l*, pg. 798
DETI CO., LTD.—See Applicad Public Company Limited; *Int'l*, pg. 521
DET LOGISTICS (USA) CORPORATION—See Delta Electronics, Inc.; *Int'l*, pg. 2018
DETNET SOUTH AFRICA (PTY) LTD.—See AECI Limited; *Int'l*, pg. 171
DETNET SOUTH AFRICA (PTY) LTD.—See Incitec Pivot Limited; *Int'l*, pg. 3647
DET NORSKE VERITAS CERTIFICATION INC.—See DNV GL Group AS; *Int'l*, pg. 2151
DET NORSKE VERITAS CERTIFICATION—See DNV GL Group AS; *Int'l*, pg. 2151
DET NORSKE VERITAS EIENDOM AS - HARSTAD—See DNV GL Group AS; *Int'l*, pg. 2151
DET NORSKE VERITAS EIENDOM AS—See DNV GL Group AS; *Int'l*, pg. 2151

DETHMERS MANUFACTURING COMPANY

DET NORSKE VERITAS EIENDOM AS - TRONDHEIM—See DNV GL Group AS; *Int'l*, pg. 2151
DET NORSKE VERITAS HOLDING USA INC.—See DNV GL Group AS; *Int'l*, pg. 2151
DET NORSKE VERITAS-NORTH & CENTRAL AMERICA—See DNV GL Group AS; *Int'l*, pg. 2151
DET NORSKE VERITAS PUERTO RICO—See DNV GL Group AS; *Int'l*, pg. 2151
DET NORSKE VERITAS TECHNOLOGY SERVICES—See DNV GL Group AS; *Int'l*, pg. 2151
DET NORSKE VERITAS USA INC.—See DNV GL Group AS; *Int'l*, pg. 2151
DE TOEKOMST VZW—See Ackermans & van Haaren NV; *Int'l*, pg. 105
DETON, INC.—See VINCI S.A.; *Int'l*, pg. 8216
D&E TRANSPORT INC.—See Roadrunner Transportation Systems, Inc.; *U.S. Public*, pg. 1802
DETROIT BEHAVIORAL INSTITUTE, INC.—See Acadia Healthcare Company, Inc.; *U.S. Public*, pg. 28
DETROIT CHAIN PRODUCTS INC.—See The Commercial Group Lifting Products; *U.S. Private*, pg. 4011
DETROIT CHILE S.A.; *Int'l*, pg. 2048
DETROIT DIESEL CORPORATION—See Mercedes-Benz Group AG; *Int'l*, pg. 4822
DETROIT DIESEL-ALLISON CANADA EAST—See Wajax Corporation; *Int'l*, pg. 8331
DETROIT DIESEL-ALLISON DE MEXICO, S.A. DE C.V.—See Mercedes-Benz Group AG; *Int'l*, pg. 4824
DETROIT DIESEL CORP. - CANTON—See Mercedes-Benz Group AG; *Int'l*, pg. 4822
DETROIT DIESEL CORP. - IRVINE—See Mercedes-Benz Group AG; *Int'l*, pg. 4822
DETROIT DIESEL CORP. - LAREDO—See Mercedes-Benz Group AG; *Int'l*, pg. 4822
DETROIT DIESEL CORPORATION—See Mercedes-Benz Group AG; *Int'l*, pg. 4822
DETROIT DIESEL OF CANADA LTD.—See Mercedes-Benz Group AG; *Int'l*, pg. 4823
DETROIT DIESEL OVERSEAS CORPORATION—See Mercedes-Benz Group AG; *Int'l*, pg. 4824
DETROIT DIESEL OVERSEAS DISTRIBUTION CORP.—See Mercedes-Benz Group AG; *Int'l*, pg. 4822
DETROIT DIESEL REALTY, INC.—See Mercedes-Benz Group AG; *Int'l*, pg. 4824
DETROIT DIESEL REMANUFACTURING-CENTRAL—See Mercedes-Benz Group AG; *Int'l*, pg. 4822
DETROIT DIESEL REMANUFACTURING-EAST—See Mercedes-Benz Group AG; *Int'l*, pg. 4822
DETROIT DIESEL REMANUFACTURING MEXICANA, S DE R.L. DE C.V.—See Mercedes-Benz Group AG; *Int'l*, pg. 4824
DETROIT DIESEL REMANUFACTURING-WEST—See Mercedes-Benz Group AG; *Int'l*, pg. 4823
DETROIT EDGE TOOL COMPANY; *U.S. Private*, pg. 1216
DETROIT ELECTRIC CO., LTD.—See Far East Smarter Energy Co., Ltd.; *Int'l*, pg. 2617
DETROIT ELECTRO-COATINGS CO. LLC; *U.S. Private*, pg. 1216
DETROIT ELEVATOR COMPANY—See KONE Oyj; *Int'l*, pg. 4247
DETROIT ENTERTAINMENT, LLC—See Ilitch Holdings, Inc.; *U.S. Private*, pg. 2041
DETROIT EXCAVATION, INC.—See Motor City Electric Co., Inc.; *U.S. Private*, pg. 2796
DETROIT FREE PRESS, INC.—See Gannett Co., Inc.; *U.S. Public*, pg. 897
DETROIT INTERNATIONAL BRIDGE CO. INC.—See Cen-Tra, Inc.; *U.S. Private*, pg. 818
DETROIT LEGAL NEWS COMPANY; *U.S. Public*, pg. 657
DETROIT LEGAL NEWS PUBLISHING LLC—See Detroit Legal News Company; *U.S. Public*, pg. 657
THE DETROIT LIONS, INC.; *U.S. Private*, pg. 4020
DETROIT MEDICAL CENTER—See Tenet Healthcare Corporation; *U.S. Public*, pg. 2015
THE DETROIT NEWS, INC.—See Alden Global Capital LLC; *U.S. Private*, pg. 158
DETROIT NEWSPAPER PARTNERSHIP, L.P.—See Gannett Co., Inc.; *U.S. Public*, pg. 897
THE DETROIT NEWS - STERLING HEIGHTS PRINTING FACILITY—See Alden Global Capital LLC; *U.S. Private*, pg. 158
DETROIT PISTONS BASKETBALL COMPANY—See Platinum Equity, LLC; *U.S. Private*, pg. 3206
DETROIT RADIO, LLC—See Cumulus Media Inc.; *U.S. Public*, pg. 610
DETROIT RED WINGS, INC.—See Ilitch Holdings, Inc.; *U.S. Private*, pg. 2041
DETROIT RESCUE MISSION MINISTRIES; *U.S. Private*, pg. 1216
THE DETROIT SALT COMPANY—See Stone Canyon Industries, LLC; *U.S. Private*, pg. 3818
DETROIT SHOREWAY COMMUNITY DEVELOPMENT ORGANIZATION; *U.S. Private*, pg. 1216
DETROIT SONAVOX INC.—See Suzhou Sonavox Electronics Co., Ltd.; *Int'l*, pg. 7352
DETROIT STOKER CO.; *U.S. Private*, pg. 1216
DETROIT SYMPHONY ORCHESTRA, INC.; *U.S. Private*, pg. 1216

DETROIT TELEVISION STATION WKBD INC.—See National Amusements, Inc.; *U.S. Private*, pg. 2841
DETROIT TIGERS BASEBALL CLUB, INC.—See Ilitch Holdings, Inc.; *U.S. Private*, pg. 2041
DETROIT TOOL & ENGINEERING COMPANY—See Thompson Street Capital Manager LLC; *U.S. Private*, pg. 4161
DETROIT TRADING COMPANY; *U.S. Private*, pg. 1216
DETROIT TRUCK MANUFACTURING, LLC—See AIP, LLC; *U.S. Private*, pg. 135
DETRON ICT SOLUTIONS BV; *Int'l*, pg. 2048
DETROW & UNDERWOOD; *U.S. Private*, pg. 1216
DETSKY MIR GROUP; *Int'l*, pg. 2048
DETWILER FENTON GROUP, INC.; *U.S. Public*, pg. 657
DETYENS SHIPYARDS INC.; *U.S. Private*, pg. 1217
DEUBLIN ASIA PACIFIC PTE LTD—See Hoerbiger Holding AG; *Int'l*, pg. 3439
DEUBLIN AUSTRIA GMBH—See Hoerbiger Holding AG; *Int'l*, pg. 3439
DEUBLIN COMPANY—See Hoerbiger Holding AG; *Int'l*, pg. 3439
DEUBLIN DE MEXICO—See Hoerbiger Holding AG; *Int'l*, pg. 3439
DEUBLIN GMBH—See Hoerbiger Holding AG; *Int'l*, pg. 3439
DEUBLIN IBERICA, S.L.—See Hoerbiger Holding AG; *Int'l*, pg. 3439
DEUBLIN ITALIANA—See Hoerbiger Holding AG; *Int'l*, pg. 3439
DEUBLIN ITALIANA S.R.L.—See Hoerbiger Holding AG; *Int'l*, pg. 3439
DEUBLIN JAPAN LTD.—See Hoerbiger Holding AG; *Int'l*, pg. 3439
DEUBLIN KOREA CO. LTD.—See Hoerbiger Holding AG; *Int'l*, pg. 3439
DEUBLIN LTD.—See Hoerbiger Holding AG; *Int'l*, pg. 3439
DEUBLIN POLSKA SP. Z O.O.—See Hoerbiger Holding AG; *Int'l*, pg. 3439
DEUBLIN S.A.R.L.—See Hoerbiger Holding AG; *Int'l*, pg. 3440
DEUCE ENTERTAINMENT, LLC; *U.S. Private*, pg. 1217
DEUFOL AUSTRIA SUPPLY CHAIN SOLUTIONS GMBH—See Deufol SE; *Int'l*, pg. 2048
DEUFOL BELGIE N.V.—See Deufol SE; *Int'l*, pg. 2048
DEUFOL BERLIN GMBH—See Deufol SE; *Int'l*, pg. 2048
DEUFOL BOCHUM GMBH—See Deufol SE; *Int'l*, pg. 2048
DEUFOL CESKA REPUBLIKA A.S.—See Deufol SE; *Int'l*, pg. 2048
DEUFOL CZ PRODUCTION S. R. O.—See Deufol SE; *Int'l*, pg. 2048
DEUFOL FRANKFURT GMBH—See Deufol SE; *Int'l*, pg. 2048
DEUFOL HAMBURG GMBH—See Deufol SE; *Int'l*, pg. 2048
DEUFOL ITALIA S.P.A.—See Deufol SE; *Int'l*, pg. 2048
DEUFOL LIER NV—See Deufol SE; *Int'l*, pg. 2048
DEUFOL MUNCHEN GMBH—See Deufol SE; *Int'l*, pg. 2048
DEUFOL NORD GMBH—See Deufol SE; *Int'l*, pg. 2048
DEUFOL NURNBERG GMBH—See Deufol SE; *Int'l*, pg. 2048
DEUFOL PACKAGING TIENEN N.V.—See Deufol SE; *Int'l*, pg. 2048
DEUFOL PORT OF ANTWERP NV—See Deufol SE; *Int'l*, pg. 2048
DEUFOL REMSCHEID GMBH—See Deufol SE; *Int'l*, pg. 2048
DEUFOL SE; *Int'l*, pg. 2048
DEUFOL SLOVENSKO S.R.O.—See Deufol SE; *Int'l*, pg. 2048
DEUFOL SUD GMBH—See Deufol SE; *Int'l*, pg. 2048
DEUFOL SUNMAN INC.—See Deufol SE; *Int'l*, pg. 2048
DEUFOL (SUZHOU) PACKAGING CO., LTD.—See Deufol SE; *Int'l*, pg. 2048
DEUFOL TAILLEUR GMBH—See Deufol SE; *Int'l*, pg. 2048
DEUFOL TECHNICS NV—See Deufol SE; *Int'l*, pg. 2049
DEUFOL WAREMME S.A.—See Deufol SE; *Int'l*, pg. 2048
DEUFOL WEST GMBH—See Deufol SE; *Int'l*, pg. 2048
DEUKONA VERSICHERUNGS-VERMITTLUNGS-GMBH—See Deutsche Bank Aktiengesellschaft; *Int'l*, pg. 2057
DEUM DEUTSCHE ERZ UND METALL UNION GMBH—See Salzgitter AG; *Int'l*, pg. 6496
DEUNA ZEMENT GMBH—See Buzzi SpA; *Int'l*, pg. 1230
DEURAG DEUTSCHE RECHTSSCHUTZ-VERSICHERUNG AG—See SIGNAL IDUNA Gruppe; *Int'l*, pg. 6910
DEUTA AMERICA CORP.—See DEUTA-WERKE GmbH; *Int'l*, pg. 2049
DEUTA-WERKE GMBH; *Int'l*, pg. 2049
DEUTER SPORT GMBH & CO. KG—See Schwan-STABILO Cosmetics GmbH & Co. KG; *Int'l*, pg. 6644
DEUTRUCK GMBH; *Int'l*, pg. 2049
DEUTSCH-BALTISCHE HANDELSKAMMER—See Messe Munchen GmbH; *Int'l*, pg. 4841
DEUTSCH-BULGARISCHE INDUSTRIE- UND HANDELSKAMMER—See Messe Munchen GmbH; *Int'l*, pg. 4841

CORPORATE AFFILIATIONS

DEUTSCHE ACCESS INVESTMENTS LIMITED—See Deutsche Bank Aktiengesellschaft; *Int'l*, pg. 2057
DEUTSCHE ACCUMOTIVE VERWALTUNGS-GMBH—See Mercedes-Benz Group AG; *Int'l*, pg. 4824
DEUTSCHE APOTHEKER- UND ARZTEBANK EG; *Int'l*, pg. 2049
DEUTSCHE APPARATE VERTRIEBSORGANISATION DAVO GMBH & CO. POLYREMA KG—See Reifenhauser GmbH & Co. KG Maschinenfabrik; *Int'l*, pg. 6257
DEUTSCHE ASIA PACIFIC HOLDINGS PTE LTD.—See Deutsche Bank Aktiengesellschaft; *Int'l*, pg. 2057
DEUTSCHE ASPHALT GMBH—See STRABAG SE; *Int'l*, pg. 7230
DEUTSCHE ASSET MANAGEMENT (ASIA) LIMITED—See Deutsche Bank Aktiengesellschaft; *Int'l*, pg. 2057
DEUTSCHE ASSET MANAGEMENT CANADA LIMITED—See Deutsche Bank Aktiengesellschaft; *Int'l*, pg. 2058
DEUTSCHE ASSET MANAGEMENT GMBH—See Deutsche Bank Aktiengesellschaft; *Int'l*, pg. 2058
DEUTSCHE ASSET MANAGEMENT ITALY S.P.A.—See Deutsche Bank Aktiengesellschaft; *Int'l*, pg. 2059
DEUTSCHE ASSET MANAGEMENT (JAPAN) LIMITED—See Deutsche Bank Aktiengesellschaft; *Int'l*, pg. 2058
DEUTSCHE ASSET MANAGEMENT (KOREA) COMPANY LIMITED—See Deutsche Bank Aktiengesellschaft; *Int'l*, pg. 2058
DEUTSCHE ASSET MANAGEMENT SCHWEIZ—See Deutsche Bank Aktiengesellschaft; *Int'l*, pg. 2058
DEUTSCHE ASSET MANAGEMENT SWITZERLAND—See Deutsche Bank Aktiengesellschaft; *Int'l*, pg. 2058
DEUTSCHE ASSET MANAGEMENT (UK) LTD.—See Deutsche Bank Aktiengesellschaft; *Int'l*, pg. 2059
DEUTSCHE ASSET & WEALTH MANAGEMENT—See Deutsche Bank Aktiengesellschaft; *Int'l*, pg. 2057
DEUTSCHE AUSTRALIA LIMITED—See Deutsche Bank Aktiengesellschaft; *Int'l*, pg. 2058
DEUTSCHE BABCOCK AL JABER W.L.L.—See Al Jaber Group; *Int'l*, pg. 280
DEUTSCHE BABCOCK MIDDLE EAST FZE—See Bilfinger SE; *Int'l*, pg. 1028
DEUTSCHE BAHN AG; *Int'l*, pg. 2049
DEUTSCHE BAHN CARGO ROMANIA S.R.L.—See Deutsche Bahn AG; *Int'l*, pg. 2051
DEUTSCHE BAHN CONNECT GMBH—See Deutsche Bahn AG; *Int'l*, pg. 2051
DEUTSCHE BAHN ENGINEERING&CONSULTING INDIA PRIVATE LIMITED—See Deutsche Bahn AG; *Int'l*, pg. 2051
DEUTSCHE BAHN FINANCE B. V.—See Deutsche Bahn AG; *Int'l*, pg. 2051
DEUTSCHE BAHN FRANCE VOYAGES&TOURISME SAS—See Deutsche Bahn AG; *Int'l*, pg. 2051
DEUTSCHE BAHN IBERICA HOLDING, S.L.—See Deutsche Bahn AG; *Int'l*, pg. 2051
DEUTSCHE BAHN INTERNATIONAL OPERATIONS GMBH—See Deutsche Bahn AG; *Int'l*, pg. 2051
DEUTSCHE BAHN STIFTUNG GGMBH—See Deutsche Bahn AG; *Int'l*, pg. 2051
DEUTSCHE BALATON AG; *Int'l*, pg. 2055
DEUTSCHE BANK AG-AMSTERDAM—See Deutsche Bank Aktiengesellschaft; *Int'l*, pg. 2058
DEUTSCHE BANK AG-BANGKOK—See Deutsche Bank Aktiengesellschaft; *Int'l*, pg. 2058
DEUTSCHE BANK AG-BERLIN—See Deutsche Bank Aktiengesellschaft; *Int'l*, pg. 2059
DEUTSCHE BANK AG (BOMBAY)—See Deutsche Bank Aktiengesellschaft; *Int'l*, pg. 2058
DEUTSCHE BANK AG-CAIRO—See Deutsche Bank Aktiengesellschaft; *Int'l*, pg. 2059
DEUTSCHE BANK AG CANADA—See Deutsche Bank Aktiengesellschaft; *Int'l*, pg. 2058
DEUTSCHE BANK AG-COLOMBO—See Deutsche Bank Aktiengesellschaft; *Int'l*, pg. 2059
DEUTSCHE BANK AG (ISTANBUL)—See Deutsche Bank Aktiengesellschaft; *Int'l*, pg. 2059
DEUTSCHE BANK AG-JAKARTA—See Deutsche Bank Aktiengesellschaft; *Int'l*, pg. 2059
DEUTSCHE BANK AG JOHANNESBURG—See Deutsche Bank Aktiengesellschaft; *Int'l*, pg. 2058
DEUTSCHE BANK AG-KARACHI—See Deutsche Bank Aktiengesellschaft; *Int'l*, pg. 2059
DEUTSCHE BANK AG-LAHORE—See Deutsche Bank Aktiengesellschaft; *Int'l*, pg. 2059
DEUTSCHE BANK AG-LONDON—See Deutsche Bank Aktiengesellschaft; *Int'l*, pg. 2059
DEUTSCHE BANK AG (MACAU)—See Deutsche Bank Aktiengesellschaft; *Int'l*, pg. 2058
DEUTSCHE BANK AG-MANAMA—See Deutsche Bank Aktiengesellschaft; *Int'l*, pg. 2059
DEUTSCHE BANK AG (MANILA)—See Deutsche Bank Aktiengesellschaft; *Int'l*, pg. 2058
DEUTSCHE BANK AG-MELBOURNE—See Deutsche Bank Aktiengesellschaft; *Int'l*, pg. 2059

COMPANY NAME INDEX

DEUTSCHE BANK AG (NEW DELHI)—See Deutsche Bank Aktiengesellschaft; *Int'l*, pg. 2058
DEUTSCHE BANK AG (NEW YORK)—See Deutsche Bank Aktiengesellschaft; *Int'l*, pg. 2058
DEUTSCHE BANK AG-PARIS—See Deutsche Bank Aktiengesellschaft; *Int'l*, pg. 2059
DEUTSCHE BANK AG (PRAGUE)—See Deutsche Bank Aktiengesellschaft; *Int'l*, pg. 2058
DEUTSCHE BANK AG (SEOUL)—See Deutsche Bank Aktiengesellschaft; *Int'l*, pg. 2058
DEUTSCHE BANK AG-SINGAPORE—See Deutsche Bank Aktiengesellschaft; *Int'l*, pg. 2057
DEUTSCHE BANK AG—See Deutsche Bank Aktiengesellschaft; *Int'l*, pg. 2058
DEUTSCHE BANK AG—See Deutsche Bank Aktiengesellschaft; *Int'l*, pg. 2058
DEUTSCHE BANK AG-SURABAYA—See Deutsche Bank Aktiengesellschaft; *Int'l*, pg. 2059
DEUTSCHE BANK AG (TAIPEI)—See Deutsche Bank Aktiengesellschaft; *Int'l*, pg. 2058
DEUTSCHE BANK AG (TEHRAN)—See Deutsche Bank Aktiengesellschaft; *Int'l*, pg. 2058
DEUTSCHE BANK AG (TOKYO)—See Deutsche Bank Aktiengesellschaft; *Int'l*, pg. 2058
DEUTSCHE BANK AG - UK REPRESENTATIVE OFFICE—See Deutsche Bank Aktiengesellschaft; *Int'l*, pg. 2058
DEUTSCHE BANK AG-VIENNA—See Deutsche Bank Aktiengesellschaft; *Int'l*, pg. 2059
DEUTSCHE BANK AKTIENGESELLSCHAFT; *Int'l*, pg. 2055
DEUTSCHE BANK ALEX. BROWN INCORPORATED—See Deutsche Bank Aktiengesellschaft; *Int'l*, pg. 2060
DEUTSCHE BANK AMERICAS FINANCE LLC—See Deutsche Bank Aktiengesellschaft; *Int'l*, pg. 2059
DEUTSCHE BANK A.S.—See Deutsche Bank Aktiengesellschaft; *Int'l*, pg. 2057
DEUTSCHE BANK AUSTRALIA—See Deutsche Bank Aktiengesellschaft; *Int'l*, pg. 2059
DEUTSCHE BANK CAPITAL CORPORATION—See Deutsche Bank Aktiengesellschaft; *Int'l*, pg. 2059
DEUTSCHE BANK CAPITAL MARKETS S.R.L.—See Deutsche Bank Aktiengesellschaft; *Int'l*, pg. 2059
DEUTSCHE BANK (CHILE) S.A.—See Deutsche Bank Aktiengesellschaft; *Int'l*, pg. 2058
DEUTSCHE BANK (CHINA) CO., LTD.—See Deutsche Bank Aktiengesellschaft; *Int'l*, pg. 2058
DEUTSCHE BANK CORRETORA DE VALORES S.A.—See Deutsche Bank Aktiengesellschaft; *Int'l*, pg. 2059
DEUTSCHE BANK EUROPE GMBH—See Deutsche Bank Aktiengesellschaft; *Int'l*, pg. 2059
DEUTSCHE BANK FACTORING S.P.A.—See Deutsche Bank Aktiengesellschaft; *Int'l*, pg. 2059
DEUTSCHE BANK FINANCE N.V.—See Deutsche Bank Aktiengesellschaft; *Int'l*, pg. 2059
DEUTSCHE BANK GOVERNMENT SECURITIES, INC.—See Deutsche Bank Aktiengesellschaft; *Int'l*, pg. 2059
DEUTSCHE BANK GROUP SERVICES LTD.—See Deutsche Bank Aktiengesellschaft; *Int'l*, pg. 2059
DEUTSCHE BANK HOLDINGS, INC.—See Deutsche Bank Aktiengesellschaft; *Int'l*, pg. 2059
DEUTSCHE BANK INSURANCE AGENCY OF DELAWARE, INC.—See Deutsche Bank Aktiengesellschaft; *Int'l*, pg. 2059
DEUTSCHE BANK INTERNATIONAL LIMITED—See Deutsche Bank Aktiengesellschaft; *Int'l*, pg. 2059
DEUTSCHE BANK INTERNATIONAL—See Deutsche Bank Aktiengesellschaft; *Int'l*, pg. 2059
DEUTSCHE BANK INTERNATIONAL TRUST CO. (CAYMAN) LIMITED—See Deutsche Bank Aktiengesellschaft; *Int'l*, pg. 2059
DEUTSCHE BANK INTERNATIONAL TRUST CO. (JERSEY) LIMITED—See Deutsche Bank Aktiengesellschaft; *Int'l*, pg. 2059
DEUTSCHE BANK INTERNATIONAL TRUST CO. LIMITED—See Deutsche Bank Aktiengesellschaft; *Int'l*, pg. 2059
DEUTSCHE BANK INVESTMENTS (GUERNSEY) LIMITED—See Deutsche Bank Aktiengesellschaft; *Int'l*, pg. 2059
DEUTSCHE BANK LTD.—See Deutsche Bank Aktiengesellschaft; *Int'l*, pg. 2059
DEUTSCHE BANK LUXEMBOURG S.A.—See Deutsche Bank Aktiengesellschaft; *Int'l*, pg. 2059
DEUTSCHE BANK (MALAYSIA) BERHAD—See Deutsche Bank Aktiengesellschaft; *Int'l*, pg. 2058
DEUTSCHE BANK (MALTA) LTD—See Deutsche Bank Aktiengesellschaft; *Int'l*, pg. 2058
DEUTSCHE BANK (MAURITIUS) LIMITED—See Deutsche Bank Aktiengesellschaft; *Int'l*, pg. 2058
DEUTSCHE BANK MEXICO S.A. DE C.V.—See Deutsche Bank Aktiengesellschaft; *Int'l*, pg. 2059
DEUTSCHE BANK MUTUI S.P.A.—See Deutsche Bank Aktiengesellschaft; *Int'l*, pg. 2059
DEUTSCHE BANK NEDERLAND N.V.—See Deutsche Bank Aktiengesellschaft; *Int'l*, pg. 2059

DEUTSCHE BANK NOMINEES (JERSEY) LIMITED—See Deutsche Bank Aktiengesellschaft; *Int'l*, pg. 2059
DEUTSCHE BANK OSTERREICH AG—See Deutsche Bank Aktiengesellschaft; *Int'l*, pg. 2062
DEUTSCHE BANK (PERU) S.A.—See Deutsche Bank Aktiengesellschaft; *Int'l*, pg. 2058
DEUTSCHE BANK POLSKA S.A.—See Deutsche Bank Aktiengesellschaft; *Int'l*, pg. 2059
DEUTSCHE BANK (PORTUGAL) SA—See ABANCA CORPORACION BANCARIA, SA; *Int'l*, pg. 48
DEUTSCHE BANK PRIVATE WEALTH MANAGEMENT—See Deutsche Bank Aktiengesellschaft; *Int'l*, pg. 2060
DEUTSCHE BANK PRIVAT UND GESCHAFTSKUNDEN AG—See Deutsche Bank Aktiengesellschaft; *Int'l*, pg. 2060
DEUTSCHE BANK REAL ESTATE (JAPAN) Y.K.—See Deutsche Bank Aktiengesellschaft; *Int'l*, pg. 2060
DEUTSCHE BANK REALTY ADVISORS, INC.—See Deutsche Bank Aktiengesellschaft; *Int'l*, pg. 2060
DEUTSCHE BANK REPRESENTATIVE OFFICE NIGERIA LIMITED—See Deutsche Bank Aktiengesellschaft; *Int'l*, pg. 2060
DEUTSCHE BANK RT—See Deutsche Bank Aktiengesellschaft; *Int'l*, pg. 2060
DEUTSCHE BANK SAAR AG—See Deutsche Bank Aktiengesellschaft; *Int'l*, pg. 2060
DEUTSCHE BANK S.A.-BANCO ALEMAO—See Deutsche Bank Aktiengesellschaft; *Int'l*, pg. 2060
DEUTSCHE BANK S.A.E.—See Deutsche Bank Aktiengesellschaft; *Int'l*, pg. 2060
DEUTSCHE BANK S.A.E.—See Deutsche Bank Aktiengesellschaft; *Int'l*, pg. 2060
DEUTSCHE BANK SAO PAULO—See Deutsche Bank Aktiengesellschaft; *Int'l*, pg. 2060
DEUTSCHE BANK (SCHWEIZ) AG—See Deutsche Bank Aktiengesellschaft; *Int'l*, pg. 2058
DEUTSCHE BANK SECURITIES INC.—See Deutsche Bank Aktiengesellschaft; *Int'l*, pg. 2060
DEUTSCHE BANK SECURITIES LIMITED—See Deutsche Bank Aktiengesellschaft; *Int'l*, pg. 2060
DEUTSCHE BANK SERVICES (JERSEY) LIMITED—See Deutsche Bank Aktiengesellschaft; *Int'l*, pg. 2060
DEUTSCHE BANK—See Deutsche Bank Aktiengesellschaft; *Int'l*, pg. 2058
DEUTSCHE BANK S.P.A.—See Deutsche Bank Aktiengesellschaft; *Int'l*, pg. 2060
DEUTSCHE BANK (SUISSE) S.A.—See Deutsche Bank Aktiengesellschaft; *Int'l*, pg. 2058
DEUTSCHE BANK (SVIZZERA) S.A.—See Deutsche Bank Aktiengesellschaft; *Int'l*, pg. 2058
DEUTSCHE BANK TRUST COMPANY DELAWARE—See Deutsche Bank Aktiengesellschaft; *Int'l*, pg. 2060
DEUTSCHE BANK TRUST COMPANY, NATIONAL ASSOCIATION—See Deutsche Bank Aktiengesellschaft; *Int'l*, pg. 2060
DEUTSCHE BANK TRUST COMPANY NEW JERSEY LTD.—See Deutsche Bank Aktiengesellschaft; *Int'l*, pg. 2060
DEUTSCHE BANK TRUST CORPORATION—See Deutsche Bank Aktiengesellschaft; *Int'l*, pg. 2060
DEUTSCHE BANK TRUSTEE SERVICES (GUERNSEY) LIMITED—See Deutsche Bank Aktiengesellschaft; *Int'l*, pg. 2060
DEUTSCHE BANK (URUGUAY) S.A.I.F.E.—See Deutsche Bank Aktiengesellschaft; *Int'l*, pg. 2058
DEUTSCHE BARYT-INDUSTRIE DR. RUDOLF ALBERTI GMBH UND CO. KG—See Sachtleben Minerals GmbH & Co. KG; *Int'l*, pg. 6463
DEUTSCHE BETEILIGUNGS AG; *Int'l*, pg. 2062
DEUTSCHE BETEILIGUNGSGESELLSCHAFT MBH—See Deutsche Beteiligungs AG; *Int'l*, pg. 2062
DEUTSCHE BINNENREEDEREI AG—See OT Logistics S.A.; *Int'l*, pg. 5656
DEUTSCHE BIOTECH INNOVATIV AG; *Int'l*, pg. 2063
DEUTSCHE BOERSE MARKET DATA + SERVICES SINGAPORE PTE. LTD.—See Deutsche Borse AG; *Int'l*, pg. 2063
DEUTSCHE BOERSE SYSTEMS INC.—See Deutsche Borse AG; *Int'l*, pg. 2063
DEUTSCHE BORSE AG; *Int'l*, pg. 2063
DEUTSCHE BORSE IT-HOLDING GMBH—See Deutsche Borse AG; *Int'l*, pg. 2063
DEUTSCHE BORSE PHOTOGRAPHY FOUNDATION GGMBH—See Deutsche Borse AG; *Int'l*, pg. 2063
DEUTSCHE BORSE SERVICES S.R.O—See Deutsche Borse AG; *Int'l*, pg. 2063
DEUTSCHE BP AG—See BP plc; *Int'l*, pg. 1131
DEUTSCHE BUNDESBANK HAUPTVERWALTUNG BERLIN—See Deutsche Bundesbank; *Int'l*, pg. 2065
DEUTSCHE BUNDESBANK HAUPTVERWALTUNG DUSSELDORF—See Deutsche Bundesbank; *Int'l*, pg. 2065
DEUTSCHE BUNDESBANK HAUPTVERWALTUNG FRANKFURT—See Deutsche Bundesbank; *Int'l*, pg. 2065
DEUTSCHE BUNDESBANK HAUPTVERWALTUNG HAMBURG—See Deutsche Bundesbank; *Int'l*, pg. 2065

DEUTSCHE INDUSTRIE REIT-AG

DEUTSCHE BUNDESBANK HAUPTVERWALTUNG HANNOVER—See Deutsche Bundesbank; *Int'l*, pg. 2065
DEUTSCHE BUNDESBANK HAUPTVERWALTUNG LEIPZIG—See Deutsche Bundesbank; *Int'l*, pg. 2065
DEUTSCHE BUNDESBANK HAUPTVERWALTUNG MAINZ—See Deutsche Bundesbank; *Int'l*, pg. 2065
DEUTSCHE BUNDESBANK; *Int'l*, pg. 2065
DEUTSCHE CALPAM GMBH—See Financiere de L'Odet; *Int'l*, pg. 2667
DEUTSCHE-CAP GMBH—See VKR Holding A/S; *Int'l*, pg. 8281
DEUTSCHE CAPITAL MARKETS AUSTRALIA LIMITED—See Deutsche Bank Aktiengesellschaft; *Int'l*, pg. 2060
DEUTSCHE CASTROL VERTRIEBSGESELLSCHAFT MBH—See BP plc; *Int'l*, pg. 1131
DEUTSCHE CLIMATE CHANGE FIXED INCOME QP TRUST—See Deutsche Bank Aktiengesellschaft; *Int'l*, pg. 2060
DEUTSCHE COLOMBIA S.A.—See Deutsche Bank Aktiengesellschaft; *Int'l*, pg. 2060
DEUTSCHE CUSTODY N.V.—See Deutsche Bank Aktiengesellschaft; *Int'l*, pg. 2060
DEUTSCHE DOKA SCHALUNGSTECHNIK GMBH—See Umdasch Group AG; *Int'l*, pg. 8022
DEUTSCHE EDELSTAHLWERKE GMBH—See Swiss Steel Holding AG; *Int'l*, pg. 7373
DEUTSCHE EFFECTEN- UND WECHSEL-BETEILIGUNGSGESELLSCHAFT AG.; *Int'l*, pg. 2065
DEUTSCHE EIGENHEIM UNION AG; *Int'l*, pg. 2065
DEUTSCHE EINKAUFS-CENTER MANAGEMENT G.M.B.H—See ECE Projektmanagement GmbH & Co KG; *Int'l*, pg. 2288
DEUTSCHE ENERGIE-AGENTUR GMBH—See KfW Group; *Int'l*, pg. 4148
DEUTSCHE EQUITIES INDIA PRIVATE LIMITED—See Deutsche Bank Aktiengesellschaft; *Int'l*, pg. 2060
DEUTSCHE EUROSHOP AG; *Int'l*, pg. 2065
DEUTSCHE EUROSHOP MANAGEMENT GMBH—See Deutsche EuroShop AG; *Int'l*, pg. 2065
DEUTSCHE FIDUCIARY SERVICES (SUISSE) SA—See Deutsche Bank Aktiengesellschaft; *Int'l*, pg. 2060
DEUTSCHE FISHFANG UNION GMBH—See Samherji hf; *Int'l*, pg. 6505
DEUTSCHE FOAMGLAS GMBH—See Owens Corning; *U.S. Public*, pg. 1626
DEUTSCHE FORFAIT GMBH—See DF Deutsche Forfait AG; *Int'l*, pg. 2094
DEUTSCHE FUTURES SINGAPORE PTE LTD—See Deutsche Bank Aktiengesellschaft; *Int'l*, pg. 2060
DEUTSCHE GAMMA GMBH—See Gilde Buy Out Partners B.V.; *Int'l*, pg. 2974
DEUTSCHE GAMMA GMBH—See Parcom Capital Management B.V.; *Int'l*, pg. 5740
DEUTSCHE GESELLSCHAFT FUR HUMANPLASMA MBH—See Octapharma AG; *Int'l*, pg. 5522
DEUTSCHE GIESSDRAHT GMBH—See Aurubis AG; *Int'l*, pg. 715
DEUTSCHE GOODYEAR GMBH—See The Goodyear Tire & Rubber Company; *U.S. Public*, pg. 2083
DEUTSCHE GRAMMOPHON GMBH—See Universal Music Group N.V.; *Int'l*, pg. 8080
DEUTSCHE GROUP SERVICES PTY LIMITED—See Deutsche Bank Aktiengesellschaft; *Int'l*, pg. 2060
DEUTSCHE GRUNDBESITZ-ANLAGEGESELLSCHAFT MIT BESCHRANKTER HAFTUNG—See Deutsche Bank Aktiengesellschaft; *Int'l*, pg. 2060
DEUTSCHE GRUNDBESITZ BETEILIGUNGSGESELLSCHAFT MBH—See Deutsche Bank Aktiengesellschaft; *Int'l*, pg. 2060
DEUTSCHE GRUNDSTUECKSAUKTIONEN AG; *Int'l*, pg. 2065
DEUTSCHE HOLDINGS (MALTA) LTD.—See Deutsche Bank Aktiengesellschaft; *Int'l*, pg. 2060
DEUTSCHE HOMOOPATHIE-UNION DHU ARZNEIMITTEL GMBH & CO. KG—See Dr. Willmar Schwabe GmbH & Co. KG; *Int'l*, pg. 2195
DEUTSCHE HYPOTHEKENBANK (ACTIEN-GESELLSCHAFT); *Int'l*, pg. 2065
DEUTSCHE IMMOBILIEN LEASING GMBH—See Deutsche Bank Aktiengesellschaft; *Int'l*, pg. 2060
DEUTSCHE INDUSTRIE REIT-AG; *Int'l*, pg. 2065
DEUTSCHE INTENSIVPFLEGE HOLDING B.V.—See Groupe Bruxelles Lambert SA; *Int'l*, pg. 3099
DEUTSCHE INTERNATIONAL CORPORATE SERVICES (IRELAND) LTD.—See Deutsche Bank Aktiengesellschaft; *Int'l*, pg. 2060
DEUTSCHE INTERNATIONAL CORPORATE SERVICES LIMITED—See Deutsche Bank Aktiengesellschaft; *Int'l*, pg. 2060
DEUTSCHE INTERNATIONAL FINANCE (IRELAND) LIMITED—See Deutsche Bank Aktiengesellschaft; *Int'l*, pg. 2060
DEUTSCHE INTERNATIONAL TRUST CORPORATION (CI) LIMITED—See Deutsche Bank Aktiengesellschaft; *Int'l*, pg. 2060

DEUTSCHE INDUSTRIE REIT-AG

DEUTSCHE INTERNET IMMOBILIEN AUKTIONEN GMBH—See Deutsche Grundstueckauktionen AG; *Int'l*, pg. 2065

DEUTSCHE INVERSIONES LIMITADA—See Deutsche Bank Aktiengesellschaft; *Int'l*, pg. 2060

DEUTSCHE INVEST CAPITAL PARTNERS GMBH; *Int'l*, pg. 2066

DEUTSCHE INVESTITIONS- UND ENTWICKLUNGSGE-SELLSCHAFT MBH—See KfW Group; *Int'l*, pg. 4148

DEUTSCHE INVESTMENTS INDIA PRIVATE LIMITED—See Deutsche Bank Aktiengesellschaft; *Int'l*, pg. 2060

DEUTSCHE INVEST MITTELSTAND GMBH—See Deutsche Invest Capital Partners GmbH; *Int'l*, pg. 2066

DEUTSCHE INVESTOR SERVICES PRIVATE LIMITED—See Deutsche Bank Aktiengesellschaft; *Int'l*, pg. 2060

DEUTSCHE KONSUM REIT-AG; *Int'l*, pg. 2066

DEUTSCHE KRANKENVERSICHERUNG AG—See Munchener Ruckversicherungs AG; *Int'l*, pg. 5087

DEUTSCHE KREDITBANK AG—See BayernLB Holding AG; *Int'l*, pg. 913

DEUTSCHE LAGERHAUS BETEILIGUNGS GMBH U. CO KG—See Immofinanz AG; *Int'l*, pg. 3628

DEUTSCHE LAGERHAUS GMBH U. CO KG—See Immofinanz AG; *Int'l*, pg. 3628

DEUTSCHE LAGERHAUS NEUNZEHNTE OBJEKT GMBH & CO KG—See Immofinanz AG; *Int'l*, pg. 3628

DEUTSCHE LAGERHAUS POING GMBH U. CO KG—See Immofinanz AG; *Int'l*, pg. 3628

DEUTSCHE LAND PLC; *Int'l*, pg. 2066

DEUTSCHE LEBENSVERSICHERUNGS-AG—See Allianz SE; *Int'l*, pg. 352

DEUTSCHE LUFTHANSA AG; *Int'l*, pg. 2066

DEUTSCHE MANAGED INVESTMENTS LIMITED—See Deutsche Bank Aktiengesellschaft; *Int'l*, pg. 2060

DEUTSCHE MESSE AG; *Int'l*, pg. 2071

DEUTSCHE MESSE INTERACTIVE GMBH—See Deutsche Messe AG; *Int'l*, pg. 2071

DEUTSCHE METROHM GMBH & CO. KG—See Metrohm AG; *Int'l*, pg. 4862

DEUTSCHE METROHM PROZESSANALYTIK GMBH & CO. KG—See Metrohm AG; *Int'l*, pg. 4862

DEUTSCHE MITTELSTANDSHOLDING GMBH; *Int'l*, pg. 2071

DEUTSCHE NANOSCHICHT GMBH—See BASF SE; *Int'l*, pg. 883

DEUTSCHE NEDERLAND N.V.—See Deutsche Bank Aktiengesellschaft; *Int'l*, pg. 2060

DEUTSCHE NEW ZEALAND LIMITED—See Deutsche Bank Aktiengesellschaft; *Int'l*, pg. 2060

DEUTSCH ENGINEERED CONNECTING DEVICES—See TE Connectivity Ltd.; *Int'l*, pg. 7494

DEUTSCHE NICKEL AMERICA INC.—See Deutsche Nickel GmbH; *Int'l*, pg. 2071

DEUTSCHE NICKEL GMBH; *Int'l*, pg. 2071

DEUTSCHE NIEDERLASSUNG DER FRIDAY INSURANCE S.A.—See Baloise Holding AG; *Int'l*, pg. 811

DEUTSCHE NOMINEES LIMITED—See Deutsche Bank Aktiengesellschaft; *Int'l*, pg. 2060

DEUTSCHE OPPENHEIM FAMILY OFFICE AG—See Deutsche Bank Aktiengesellschaft; *Int'l*, pg. 2060

DEUTSCHE OSSTEM GMBH—See MBK Partners Ltd.; *Int'l*, pg. 4753

DEUTSCHE OSSTEM GMBH—See Unison Capital, Inc.; *Int'l*, pg. 8061

DEUTSCHE PAPIER—See KPP Group Holdings Co., Ltd.; *Int'l*, pg. 4297

DEUTSCHE PFANDBRIEFBANK AG - ESCHBORN—See Hypo Real Estate Holding AG; *Int'l*, pg. 3553

DEUTSCHE PFANDBRIEFBANK AG—See Hypo Real Estate Holding AG; *Int'l*, pg. 3553

DEUTSCHE PFANDBRIEFBANK - CENTRAL & EASTERN EUROPE—See Hypo Real Estate Holding AG; *Int'l*, pg. 3553

DEUTSCHE PFANDBRIEFBANK - LONDON—See Hypo Real Estate Holding AG; *Int'l*, pg. 3553

DEUTSCHE PFANDBRIEFBANK - MADRID—See Hypo Real Estate Holding AG; *Int'l*, pg. 3553

DEUTSCHE PFANDBRIEFBANK - MILAN—See Hypo Real Estate Holding AG; *Int'l*, pg. 3553

DEUTSCHE PFANDBRIEFBANK - PARIS—See Hypo Real Estate Holding AG; *Int'l*, pg. 3553

DEUTSCHE PIRELLI REIFEN HOLDING GMBH—See China National Chemical Corporation; *Int'l*, pg. 1528

DEUTSCHE POST ADRESS GMBH—See Deutsche Post AG; *Int'l*, pg. 2079

DEUTSCHE POST AG; *Int'l*, pg. 2071

DEUTSCHE POSTBANK AG—See Deutsche Post AG; *Int'l*, pg. 2080

DEUTSCHE POST BETEILIGUNGEN HOLDING GMBH—See Deutsche Post AG; *Int'l*, pg. 2079

DEUTSCHE POST COM GMBH—See Deutsche Post AG; *Int'l*, pg. 2079

DEUTSCHE POST CUSTOMER SERVICE CENTER GMBH—See Deutsche Post AG; *Int'l*, pg. 2079

DEUTSCHE POST DHL BETEILIGUNGEN GMBH—See Deutsche Post AG; *Int'l*, pg. 2079

DEUTSCHE POST DHL CORPORATE REAL ESTATE MANAGEMENT GMBH—See Deutsche Post AG; *Int'l*, pg. 2079

DEUTSCHE POST DHL INHOUSE CONSULTING GMBH—See Deutsche Post AG; *Int'l*, pg. 2079

DEUTSCHE POST DHL RESEARCH AND INNOVATION GMBH—See Deutsche Post AG; *Int'l*, pg. 2079

DEUTSCHE POST DIREKT GMBH—See Deutsche Post AG; *Int'l*, pg. 2079

DEUTSCHE POST GEMEINNUTZIGE GESELLSCHAFT FUR SICHERE UND VERTRAULICHE KOMMUNIKATION IM INTERNET MBH—See Deutsche Post AG; *Int'l*, pg. 2079

DEUTSCHE POST GLOBAL MAIL (AUSTRALIA) PTY LTD.—See Deutsche Post AG; *Int'l*, pg. 2079

DEUTSCHE POST GLOBAL MAIL B.V.—See Deutsche Post AG; *Int'l*, pg. 2079

DEUTSCHE POST GLOBAL MAIL (FRANCE) SAS—See Deutsche Post AG; *Int'l*, pg. 2079

DEUTSCHE POST GLOBAL MAIL GMBH—See Deutsche Post AG; *Int'l*, pg. 2079

DEUTSCHE POST GLOBAL MAIL LTD.—See Deutsche Post AG; *Int'l*, pg. 2079

DEUTSCHE POST GLOBAL MAIL (SWITZERLAND) AG—See Deutsche Post AG; *Int'l*, pg. 2079

DEUTSCHE POST GLOBAL MAIL (UK) LTD.—See Deutsche Post AG; *Int'l*, pg. 2079

DEUTSCHE POST GRUNDSTUCKS- VERMIETUNGSGE-SELLSCHAFT BETA MBH—See Deutsche Post AG; *Int'l*, pg. 2079

DEUTSCHE POST IMMOBILIEN GMBH—See Deutsche Post AG; *Int'l*, pg. 2079

DEUTSCHE POST INVESTMENTS GMBH—See Deutsche Post AG; *Int'l*, pg. 2079

DEUTSCHE POST IT BRIEF GMBH—See Deutsche Post AG; *Int'l*, pg. 2079

DEUTSCHE POST IT SERVICES GMBH—See Deutsche Post AG; *Int'l*, pg. 2079

DEUTSCHE POST PENSIONSFONDS AG—See Deutsche Post AG; *Int'l*, pg. 2079

DEUTSCHE POST PENSIONS-TREUHAND GMBH & CO. KG—See Deutsche Post AG; *Int'l*, pg. 2079

DEUTSCHE POST REINSURANCE S.A.—See Deutsche Post AG; *Int'l*, pg. 2079

DEUTSCHE POST SHOP HANNOVER GMBH—See Deutsche Post AG; *Int'l*, pg. 2079

DEUTSCHE POST ZAHLUNGSDIENSTE GMBH—See Deutsche Post AG; *Int'l*, pg. 2079

DEUTSCHE PROVENTUS AG—See Swiss Life Holding; *Int'l*, pg. 7370

DEUTSCHE REAL ESTATE AG—See Summit Real Estate Holdings Ltd.; *Int'l*, pg. 7302

DEUTSCHE ROCKWOOL GMBH & CO. KG—See ROCKWOOL A/S; *Int'l*, pg. 6379

DEUTSCHE ROCKWOOL MINERALWOLL GMBH & CO. OHG—See ROCKWOOL A/S; *Int'l*, pg. 6379

DEUTSCHER ROHSTOFF AG; *Int'l*, pg. 2083

DEUTSCHER RING BAUSPARKASSE AKTIENGESELLSCHAFT—See BAWAG Group AG; *Int'l*, pg. 900

DEUTSCHER RING BETEILIGUNGSHOLDING GMBH—See Baloise Holding AG; *Int'l*, pg. 811

DEUTSCHER RING FINANCIAL SERVICES GMBH—See Baloise Holding AG; *Int'l*, pg. 811

DEUTSCHER RING KRANKENVERSICHERUNGSVEREIN A.G.—See SIGNAL IDUNA Gruppe; *Int'l*, pg. 6910

DEUTSCHER RING SACHVERSICHERUNGS-AG—See Baloise Holding AG; *Int'l*, pg. 811

DEUTSCHER SPARKASSEN- UND GIROVERBAND E.V.; *Int'l*, pg. 2085

DEUTSCHER STRASSEN-DIENST GMBH—See K+S Aktiengesellschaft; *Int'l*, pg. 4039

DEUTSCHE RUCKVERSICHERUNG AG; *Int'l*, pg. 2083

DEUTSCHE RUCKVERSICHERUNG SWITZERLAND LTD.—See Deutsche Ruckversicherung AG; *Int'l*, pg. 2083

DEUTSCHE SACHCAPITAL GMBH—See MPC Munchmeyer Petersen & Co. GmbH; *Int'l*, pg. 5061

DEUTSCHES ALTENHEIM, INC.; *U.S. Private*, pg. 1217

DEUTSCHE SB-KAUF AG—See Metro AG; *Int'l*, pg. 4857

DEUTSCHE SCHIFFSBANK AG—See Commerzbank AG; *Int'l*, pg. 1717

DEUTSCHE SCHLAUCHBOOT GMBH & CO. KG—See ONEX Corporation; *Int'l*, pg. 5580

DEUTSCHE SECURITIES ASIA LIMITED—See Deutsche Bank Aktiengesellschaft; *Int'l*, pg. 2061

DEUTSCHE SECURITIES CORREDORES DE BOLSA LTDA.—See Deutsche Bank Aktiengesellschaft; *Int'l*, pg. 2061

DEUTSCHE SECURITIES INC.—See Deutsche Bank Aktiengesellschaft; *Int'l*, pg. 2061

DEUTSCHE SECURITIES (INDIA) PRIVATE LIMITED—See Deutsche Bank Aktiengesellschaft; *Int'l*, pg. 2060

DEUTSCHE SECURITIES ISRAEL LTD.—See Deutsche Bank Aktiengesellschaft; *Int'l*, pg. 2061

DEUTSCHE SECURITIES KOREA CO—See Deutsche Bank Aktiengesellschaft; *Int'l*, pg. 2061

CORPORATE AFFILIATIONS

DEUTSCHE SECURITIES MENKUL DEGERLER A.S.—See Deutsche Bank Aktiengesellschaft; *Int'l*, pg. 2061

DEUTSCHE SECURITIES (PROPRIETARY) LIMITED—See Deutsche Bank Aktiengesellschaft; *Int'l*, pg. 2061

DEUTSCHE SECURITIES, S.A. DE C.V.—See Deutsche Bank Aktiengesellschaft; *Int'l*, pg. 2059

DEUTSCHE SHELL HOLDING GMBH—See Shell plc; *Int'l*, pg. 6797

DEUTSCHES INSTITUT FUR ALTERSVORSORGE GMBH—See Deutsche Bank Aktiengesellschaft; *Int'l*, pg. 2061

DEUTSCHES INSTITUT FUR BETRIEBSWIRTSCHAFT GMBH—See DEKRA e.V.; *Int'l*, pg. 2009

DEUTSCHE STEINZEUG AMERICA INC.—See Deutsche Steinzeug Cremer & Breuer AG; *Int'l*, pg. 2083

DEUTSCHE STEINZEUG CREMER & BREUER AG; *Int'l*, pg. 2083

DEUTSCHE STEINZEUG ITALIA S.R.L.—See Deutsche Steinzeug Cremer & Breuer AG; *Int'l*, pg. 2083

DEUTSCHE STIFTUNGSTRUST GMBH—See Deutsche Bank Aktiengesellschaft; *Int'l*, pg. 2061

DEUTSCHE STRUCTURED FINANCE GMBH & CO. ALPHARD KG—See Advent International Corporation; *U.S. Private*, pg. 96

DEUTSCHE STRUCTURED FINANCE GMBH & CO. ALPHARD KG—See Centerbridge Partners, L.P.; *U.S. Private*, pg. 812

DEUTSCHE STRUCTURED FINANCE GMBH & CO. DENEB KG—See Advent International Corporation; *U.S. Private*, pg. 96

DEUTSCHE STRUCTURED FINANCE GMBH & CO. DENEB KG—See Centerbridge Partners, L.P.; *U.S. Private*, pg. 812

DEUTSCHE STRUCTURED FINANCE GMBH & CO. TITAN KG—See Advent International Corporation; *U.S. Private*, pg. 96

DEUTSCHE STRUCTURED FINANCE GMBH & CO. TITAN KG—See Centerbridge Partners, L.P.; *U.S. Private*, pg. 812

DEUTSCHE STRUCTURED FINANCE GMBH—See Advent International Corporation; *U.S. Private*, pg. 96

DEUTSCHE STRUCTURED FINANCE GMBH—See Centerbridge Partners, L.P.; *U.S. Private*, pg. 812

DEUTSCHE TELECOM AG—See Deutsche Telekom AG; *Int'l*, pg. 2083

DEUTSCHE TELEFON STANDARD GMBH—See NFON AG; *Int'l*, pg. 5253

DEUTSCHE TELEKOM AG; *Int'l*, pg. 2083

DEUTSCHE TELEKOM FRANCE—See Deutsche Telekom AG; *Int'l*, pg. 2083

DEUTSCHE TELEKOM SA/NV—See Deutsche Telekom AG; *Int'l*, pg. 2083

DEUTSCHE TERRANOVA INDUSTRIE—See Compagnie de Saint-Gobain SA; *Int'l*, pg. 1723

DEUTSCHE THOMSON OHG—See Vantiva SA; *Int'l*, pg. 8130

DEUTSCHE TITAN GMBH—See ThyssenKrupp AG; *Int'l*, pg. 7729

DEUTSCHE TRANSFESA GMBH—See Deutsche Bahn AG; *Int'l*, pg. 2051

DEUTSCHE TRANSPORT-COMPAGNIE ERICH BOGDAN GMBH & CO. KG; *Int'l*, pg. 2085

DEUTSCHE TRUSTEE COMPANY LIMITED—See Deutsche Bank Aktiengesellschaft; *Int'l*, pg. 2061

DEUTSCHE TRUSTEE SERVICES (INDIA) PRIVATE LIMITED—See Deutsche Bank Aktiengesellschaft; *Int'l*, pg. 2061

DEUTSCHE UMSCHLAGGESELLSCHAFT SCHIENE-STRASSE (DUSS) MBH—See Deutsche Bahn AG; *Int'l*, pg. 2051

DEUTSCHE VAN RIETSCHOTEN & HOUWENS GMBH—See Electricite de France S.A.; *Int'l*, pg. 2351

DEUTSCHE VORTEX GMBH & CO. KG—See The Poul Due Jensen Foundation; *Int'l*, pg. 7674

DEUTSCHE WERTPAPIERSERVICE BANK AG; *Int'l*, pg. 2085

DEUTSCHE WOHNEN MANAGEMENT GMBH—See Deutsche Wohnen SE; *Int'l*, pg. 2085

DEUTSCHE WOHNEN SE; *Int'l*, pg. 2085

DEUTSCHE WOHN-INKASSO GMBH—See Vonovia SE; *Int'l*, pg. 8305

DEUTSCHE ZEPPELIN REEDEREI GMBH—See Zeppelin GmbH; *Int'l*, pg. 8637

DEUTSCHE ZIFFERBLATT MANUFAKTUR GMBH—See The Swatch Group Ltd.; *Int'l*, pg. 7691

DEUTSCH-GRIECHISCHE INDUSTRIE- UND HANDELSKAMMER—See Messe Munchen GmbH; *Int'l*, pg. 4841

DEUTSCH-HOLANDISCHE TABAKGESELLSCHAFT MBH—See Universal Corporation; *U.S. Public*, pg. 2254

DEUTSCH-HOLLANDISCHE TABAKGESELLSCHAFT MBH & CO. KG—See Blackstone Inc.; *U.S. Public*, pg. 356

DEUTSCH-HOLLANDISCHE TABAKGESELLSCHAFT MBH—See Universal Corporation; *U.S. Public*, pg. 2254

COMPANY NAME INDEX

DEUTSCH, INC.—See The Interpublic Group of Companies, Inc.; *U.S. Public*, pg. 2090
DEUTSCH INDIA POWER CONNECTORS (PVT.) LTD.—See TE Connectivity Ltd.; *Int'l*, pg. 7494
DEUTSCH INDUSTRIAL PRODUCTS DIVISION—See TE Connectivity Ltd.; *Int'l*, pg. 7494
DEUTSCH ISRAEL LTD.—See TE Connectivity Ltd.; *Int'l*, pg. 7494
DEUTSCH JAPAN LIMITED—See TE Connectivity Ltd.; *Int'l*, pg. 7494
DEUTSCH LA—See The Interpublic Group of Companies, Inc.; *U.S. Public*, pg. 2091
DEUTSCH-MALAYSISCHE INDUSTRIE- UND HANDELSKAMMER—See Messe Munchen GmbH; *Int'l*, pg. 4841
DEUTSCHMEDIA—See The Interpublic Group of Companies, Inc.; *U.S. Public*, pg. 2092
DEUTSCH MOTORS INC.; *Int'l*, pg. 2049
DEUTSCH NEW YORK—See Attivo group; *Int'l*, pg. 696
DEUTSCHWEIN CLASSICS GMBH & CO. KG—See Hawesko Holding AG; *Int'l*, pg. 3288
DEUTZ AG; *Int'l*, pg. 2085
DEUTZ ASIA-PACIFIC (PTE) LTD.—See DEUTZ AG; *Int'l*, pg. 2086
DEUTZ AUSTRALIA (PTY) LTD.—See DEUTZ AG; *Int'l*, pg. 2086
DEUTZ AUSTRIA GMBH—See DEUTZ AG; *Int'l*, pg. 2086
DEUTZ BELGIUM N.V.—See DEUTZ AG; *Int'l*, pg. 2086
DEUTZ BENELUX B.V.—See DEUTZ AG; *Int'l*, pg. 2086
DEUTZ BETEILLIGUNG GMBH—See DEUTZ AG; *Int'l*, pg. 2086
DEUTZ CORPORATION—See DEUTZ AG; *Int'l*, pg. 2086
DEUTZ CS S.R.O.—See DEUTZ AG; *Int'l*, pg. 2086
DEUTZ DITER S.A.—See DEUTZ AG; *Int'l*, pg. 2086
DEUTZ DO BRASIL LTDA.—See DEUTZ AG; *Int'l*, pg. 2086
DEUTZ FRANCE S.A.—See DEUTZ AG; *Int'l*, pg. 2086
DEUTZ ITALY S.R.L.—See DEUTZ AG; *Int'l*, pg. 2086
DEUTZ NETHERLANDS B.V.—See DEUTZ AG; *Int'l*, pg. 2086
DEUTZ ROMANIA S.R.L.—See DEUTZ AG; *Int'l*, pg. 2086
DEUTZ SICHERHEIT GESELLSCHAFT FUR INDUSTRIESERVICE MBH—See DEUTZ AG; *Int'l*, pg. 2086
DEUTZ SPAIN S.A.—See DEUTZ AG; *Int'l*, pg. 2086
DEUTZ UK LTD.—See DEUTZ AG; *Int'l*, pg. 2086
DEV9, LLC—See Nortal AS; *Int'l*, pg. 5438
DEVA BIKAS BANK LIMITED; *Int'l*, pg. 2086
DEVA GOLD SA—See Eldorado Gold Corporation; *Int'l*, pg. 2347
DEVA HOLDING A.S.—See Eastpharma Ltd.; *Int'l*, pg. 2274
DEVA HOLDINGS (NZ) LTD.—See Eastpharma Ltd.; *Int'l*, pg. 2275
DEVA INC.—See Tod's S.p.A.; *Int'l*, pg. 7772
DEVAL SPA—See Enel S.p.A.; *Int'l*, pg. 2411
DEVANEY ENERGY INC.; *U.S. Private*, pg. 1217
DEVANLAY SA—See Maus Freres S.A.; *Int'l*, pg. 4732
DEVAN LOWE INC.; *U.S. Private*, pg. 1217
DEVARANA SPA CO., LTD.—See Dusit Thani Public Company Limited; *Int'l*, pg. 2234
DEVAR, INC.; *U.S. Private*, pg. 1217
DEVASHRI NIRMAN LLP—See Goa Carbon Ltd.; *Int'l*, pg. 3018
DEVAULT PACKING COMPANY, INC.—See Trivest Partners, LP; *U.S. Private*, pg. 4240
DEVAX, INC.—See Biosensors International Group, Ltd.; *Int'l*, pg. 1041
DEVBLISS GMBH—See Verlagsgruppe Georg von Holtzbrinck GmbH; *Int'l*, pg. 8169
DEVBRIDGE CANADA ULC—See Cognizant Technology Solutions Corporation; *U.S. Public*, pg. 524
DEVBRIDGE GROUP LLC; *U.S. Private*, pg. 1217
DEVBRIDGE UK LTD.—See Cognizant Technology Solutions Corporation; *U.S. Public*, pg. 524
DEVCARE SOLUTIONS; *U.S. Private*, pg. 1217
DEVCLEVER LIMITED—See Veative Group plc; *Int'l*, pg. 8143
DEVCON CONSTRUCTION INCORPORATED; *U.S. Private*, pg. 1217
DEVCON S.A.—See T&M Phaedra Public Company Ltd.; *Int'l*, pg. 7395
DEVCONSULTANTS LIMITED—See Ramboll Gruppen A/S; *Int'l*, pg. 6197
DEVCON (TCI) LTD.; *U.S. Private*, pg. 1217
DEVCOOL INC.—See Securekloud Technologies Ltd.; *Int'l*, pg. 6674
DEVCO PARTNERS OY; *Int'l*, pg. 2086
DEV DIGITAL LLC; *U.S. Private*, pg. 1217
DEVEKO KLIMAATBEHEERSING B.V.—See CENTROTEC SE; *Int'l*, pg. 1414
DEVELCON; *U.S. Private*, pg. 2086
DEVELIA S.A.; *Int'l*, pg. 2087
DEVELICA DEUTSCHLAND LIMITED; *Int'l*, pg. 2087
DEVELOPERS INVESTORS, INC.—See W.C. Bradley Co.; *U.S. Private*, pg. 4419
DEVELOP GLOBAL LTD.; *Int'l*, pg. 2087
DEVELOPING EXCELLENCE PTY. LIMITED—See Academies Australasia Group Limited; *Int'l*, pg. 77

DEVELOPINTELLIGENCE LLC—See Pluralsight, Inc.; *U.S. Public*, pg. 1699
DEVELOPMENT 83 PTE. LTD.—See TEE International Limited; *Int'l*, pg. 7519
DEVELOPMENT ADVANCE SOLUTION CO., LTD.; *Int'l*, pg. 2087
DEVELOPMENTAL PATHWAYS, INC.; *U.S. Private*, pg. 1217
DEVELOPMENTAL RESOURCES CORPORATION; *U.S. Private*, pg. 1218
DEVELOPMENTAL SERVICES OF NORTHWEST KANSAS, INC.; *U.S. Private*, pg. 1218
DEVELOPMENTAL STUDIES CENTER; *U.S. Private*, pg. 1218
DEVELOPMENT ALTERNATIVES, INC.; *U.S. Private*, pg. 1217
DEVELOPMENT AND ENGINEERING NETHERLANDS B.V.—See OMRON Corporation; *Int'l*, pg. 5564
DEVELOPMENT BANK OF JAPAN, INC.; *Int'l*, pg. 2087
DEVELOPMENT BANK OF KAZAKHSTAN JSC—See National Managing Holding Baiterek JSC; *Int'l*, pg. 5161
THE DEVELOPMENT BANK OF SINGAPORE, LTD.—See DBS Group Holdings Ltd.; *Int'l*, pg. 1988
DEVELOPMENT CAPITAL BANK JSC; *Int'l*, pg. 2088
DEVELOPMENT CORPORATION FOR ISRAEL; *U.S. Private*, pg. 1217
DEVELOPMENT CORP.—See Synergis Technologies Group; *U.S. Private*, pg. 3903
DEVELOPMENT COUNSELLORS INTERNATIONAL, LTD.; *U.S. Private*, pg. 1217
DEVELOPMENT DESIGN GROUP INC.—See Brown Craig Turner; *U.S. Private*, pg. 667
DEVELOPMENT DIMENSIONS INTERNATIONAL INC.; *U.S. Private*, pg. 1217
DEVELOPMENT ENTERPRISES HOLDING COMPANY K.S.C.—See Kuwait Finance House K.S.C.; *Int'l*, pg. 4344
DEVELOPMENT FINANCE COMPANY OF UGANDA LTD.; *Int'l*, pg. 2088
DEVELOPMENT HOMES, INC.; *U.S. Private*, pg. 1217
DEVELOPMENT INVESTMENT CONSTRUCTION HOI AN JSC; *Int'l*, pg. 2088
DEVELOPMENT INVESTMENT CONSTRUCTION JSC; *Int'l*, pg. 2088
DEVELOPMENT OF NEW ALIMOS MARINA S.A.—See ELLAKTOR S.A.; *Int'l*, pg. 2365
DEVELOPMENT PARTNER AG—See Gateway Real Estate AG; *Int'l*, pg. 2889
DEVELOPMENT PARTNER IMMOBILIEN CONSULTING GMBH—See Gateway Real Estate AG; *Int'l*, pg. 2889
DEVELOPMENT SECURITIES ESTATES PLC—See U and I Group PLC; *Int'l*, pg. 7996
DEVELOPMENT SECURITIES (INVESTMENTS) PLC—See U and I Group PLC; *Int'l*, pg. 7996
DEVELOPMENT SECURITIES (PADDINGTON) LIMITED—See U and I Group PLC; *Int'l*, pg. 7996
DEVELOPMENT SECURITIES (SOUTHAMPTON A) LIMITED—See U and I Group PLC; *Int'l*, pg. 7996
DEVELOPMENT VENTURES GROUP, INC.—See Kajima Corporation; *Int'l*, pg. 4054
DEVELOPMENT WORKS FOOD CO; *Int'l*, pg. 2088
DEVELOP NORTH PLC; *Int'l*, pg. 2087
DEVELOPPEMENT ACTIVITES CHIMIQUES DISTRIBUTION SA; *Int'l*, pg. 2088
DEVELOPPEMENTS IMMOBILIERS ET COMMERCIAUX S.A.—See Accor S.A.; *Int'l*, pg. 91
DEVEN AD—See Solvay S.A.; *Int'l*, pg. 7078
DEVENS RECYCLING CENTER, LLC—See Republic Services, Inc.; *U.S. Public*, pg. 1786
DEVEREAUX MOTOR SALES INCORPORATED; *U.S. Private*, pg. 1218
DEVERE CONSTRUCTION COMPANY INC.; *U.S. Private*, pg. 1218
DE VERE GROUP LIMITED; *Int'l*, pg. 1997
DEVEREUX FLORIDA—See The Devereux Foundation, Inc.; *U.S. Private*, pg. 4020
THE DEVEREUX FOUNDATION, INC.; *U.S. Private*, pg. 4020
DEVERILL BLACK & COMPANY LIMITED—See Quilter plc; *Int'l*, pg. 6162
DEVERNOIS SA; *Int'l*, pg. 2088
DEVERO, INC.—See GI Manager L.P.; *U.S. Private*, pg. 1693
DEVERO, INC.—See TA Associates, Inc.; *U.S. Private*, pg. 3916
DEVERON CORP.—See Greencastle Resources Ltd.; *Int'l*, pg. 3073
DEVERSIFY HEALTH AB; *Int'l*, pg. 2088
DE-VERWALTUNGSGMBH—See ThyssenKrupp AG; *Int'l*, pg. 7724
THE DEVES INSURANCE PUBLIC COMPANY LIMTED—See The Crown Property Bureau; *Int'l*, pg. 7636
DEVESYS TECHNOLOGIES, INC.—See Bragg Gaming Group Inc.; *Int'l*, pg. 1136
DEVEX RESOURCES LIMITED; *Int'l*, pg. 2088
DEV GMBH—See VINCI S.A.; *Int'l*, pg. 8216
DEV HARI EXPORTS INDIA LTD.; *Int'l*, pg. 2086
DEVIANTART, INC.—See Wix.com Ltd.; *Int'l*, pg. 8440

DEVON ENERGY CORPORATION

DEVICE 4U SDN. BHD.—See AWC Berhad; *Int'l*, pg. 752
DEVICEANYWHERE; *U.S. Private*, pg. 1218
DEVICE ENG CO., LTD.—See ESPEC Corp.; *Int'l*, pg. 2505
DEVICE LINK CORPORATE—See Japan Industrial Partners, Inc.; *Int'l*, pg. 3889
DEVICELOCK, INC.—See Acronis Inc.; *U.S. Private*, pg. 66
DEVICES SALES TECHNOLOGY CO., LTD.—See Willtec Co., Ltd.; *Int'l*, pg. 8420
DEVICIX LLC—See Nortech Systems Incorporated; *U.S. Public*, pg. 1536
DEVICORE MEDICAL PRODUCTS INC.—See Danaher Corporation; *U.S. Public*, pg. 626
DEVICOR MEDICAL EUROPE GMBH—See Danaher Corporation; *U.S. Public*, pg. 626
DEVICOR MEDICAL PRODUCTS, INC.—See Danaher Corporation; *U.S. Public*, pg. 628
DEVILBISS AUTOMOTIVE REFINISHING—See Carlisle Companies Incorporated; *U.S. Public*, pg. 436
DEVILBISS HEALTHCARE GMBH—See Medical Depot, Inc.; *U.S. Private*, pg. 2654
DEVILBISS HEALTHCARE LLC—See Medical Depot, Inc.; *U.S. Private*, pg. 2654
DEVILBISS HEALTHCARE LTD—See Medical Depot, Inc.; *U.S. Private*, pg. 2654
DEVILBISS HEALTHCARE PTY LTD—See Medical Depot, Inc.; *U.S. Private*, pg. 2655
DEVILBISS HEALTHCARE S.A.S.—See Medical Depot, Inc.; *U.S. Private*, pg. 2655
DEVILBISS RANSBURG DE MEXICO, S. DE R.L. DE C.V.—See Carlisle Companies Incorporated; *U.S. Public*, pg. 436
DEVIL DOG MANUFACTURING CO., INC.—See General Sportswear Co. Inc.; *U.S. Private*, pg. 1667
DEVILLE INVESTMENT, INC.; *U.S. Private*, pg. 1218
DEVILLE RECTIFICATION S.A.S.—See voestalpine AG; *Int'l*, pg. 8288
DEVILS ARENA ENTERTAINMENT LLC—See Devils Holdings, LLC; *U.S. Private*, pg. 1218
DEVILS HOLDINGS, LLC; *U.S. Private*, pg. 1218
DEVINE CIVIL CONTRACTING PTY LTD.—See ACS, Actividades de Construccion y Servicios, S.A.; *Int'l*, pg. 113
DEVINE COMMUNICATIONS CORP.; *U.S. Private*, pg. 1218
THE DEVINE GROUP, INC.; *U.S. Private*, pg. 4020
DEVINE IMPEX LIMITED; *Int'l*, pg. 2089
DEVINE LIMITED—See ACS, Actividades de Construccion y Servicios, S.A.; *Int'l*, pg. 113
DEVINE, MILLIMET & BRANCH PROFESSIONAL ASSOCIATION; *U.S. Private*, pg. 1218
DEVINE & PETERS INTERMODAL; *U.S. Private*, pg. 1218
DEVINEY CONSTRUCTION CO., INC.; *U.S. Private*, pg. 1218
DEV INFORMATION TECHNOLOGY PVT. LTD.; *Int'l*, pg. 2086
DEV INFO-TECH NORTH AMERICA LIMITED—See DEV Information Technology Pvt. Ltd.; *Int'l*, pg. 2086
DEVIN OIL CO. INC.; *U.S. Private*, pg. 1218
DEVIR FAKTORING A.S.; *Int'l*, pg. 2089
DEVITA INTERNATIONAL, INC.; *U.S. Private*, pg. 1218
DEVITO GROUP; *U.S. Private*, pg. 1218
DEVITO/VERDI; *U.S. Private*, pg. 1218
DE VITRITE FABRIEK (THE VITRITE WORKS) B.V.—See Koninklijke Philips N.V.; *Int'l*, pg. 4267
DEVITT & FORAND CONTRACTORS INC.; *Int'l*, pg. 2089
DEVJO INDUSTRIES, INC.; *Int'l*, pg. 2089
DEVKI GROUP OF COMPANIES; *Int'l*, pg. 2089
DEVKI LEASING & FINANCE PRIVATE LIMITED; *Int'l*, pg. 2089
DEVK SERVICE GMBH; *Int'l*, pg. 2089
DEV LABTECH VENTURE LTD.; *Int'l*, pg. 2086
DEV LAND AND HOUSING PRIVATE LIMITED—See Manas Properties Limited; *Int'l*, pg. 4667
DEVLIN ELECTRONICS LIMITED; *Int'l*, pg. 2089
DEVMOUNTAIN, LLC—See Strategic Education, Inc.; *U.S. Public*, pg. 1954
DEVMYND SOFTWARE INC.; *U.S. Private*, pg. 1218
DEVNYA CEMENT JSC—See Heidelberg Materials AG; *Int'l*, pg. 3316
DEVOE AUTOMOTIVE GROUP; *U.S. Private*, pg. 1218
DEVOLD AMT AS—See SAERTEX GmbH & Co. KG; *Int'l*, pg. 6467
DEVOLD OF NORWAY AS—See Flakk Holding AS; *Int'l*, pg. 2697
DEVOLL HYDROPOWER SH.A.—See Statkraft AS; *Int'l*, pg. 7185
DEVON ARL CORPORATION—See Canadian Natural Resources Ltd.; *Int'l*, pg. 1284
DEVON BANK; *U.S. Private*, pg. 1219
DEVON CANADA CORPORATION—See Canadian Natural Resources Ltd.; *Int'l*, pg. 1284
DEVON CANADA—See Canadian Natural Resources Ltd.; *Int'l*, pg. 1284
DEVON ENERGY CORPORATION; *U.S. Public*, pg. 657
DEVON ENERGY PRODUCTION COMPANY, L.P.—See Devon Energy Corporation; *U.S. Public*, pg. 657

DEVONIAN HEALTH GROUP, INC.

DEVONIAN HEALTH GROUP, INC.; *Int'l*, pg. 2089
DEVON INNOVATIONS PVT. LTD.—See Opto Circuits (India) Limited; *Int'l*, pg. 5605
DEVON LIFESTYLE LTD.—See Koda Ltd.; *Int'l*, pg. 4225
DEVON MIDSTREAM PARTNERS, L.P.—See Devon Energy Corporation; *U.S. Public*, pg. 657
DEVON NEC CORPORATION—See Canadian Natural Resources Ltd.; *Int'l*, pg. 1284
DEVON OEI OPERATING, INC—See Devon Energy Corporation; *U.S. Public*, pg. 657
DEVONPORT ROYAL DOCKYARD LIMITED—See Babcock International Group PLC; *Int'l*, pg. 792
DEVON ROYCE, INC.—See International Business Machines Corporation; *U.S. Public*, pg. 1148
DEVONSHIRE CAPITAL LTD.; *Int'l*, pg. 2089
DEVONSHIRE DIAGNOSTIC CENTRE LIMITED—See HCA Healthcare, Inc.; *U.S. Public*, pg. 995
DEVONSHIRE GMBH—See Chatham Asset Management, LLC; *U.S. Private*, pg. 863
DEVONSHIRE INDUSTRIES LIMITED; *Int'l*, pg. 2089
DEVONSHIRE INVESTORS, INC.—See FMR LLC; *U.S. Private*, pg. 1554
DEVONSHIRE SP. Z O.O—See Chatham Asset Management, LLC; *U.S. Private*, pg. 863
DEVONSHIRE SWITZERLAND HOLDINGS GMBH—See RTX Corporation; *U.S. Public*, pg. 1823
DE VONS JEWELERS; *U.S. Private*, pg. 1181
DEVON-TECH TECHNOLOGY CO., LTD.—See ViTrox Corporation Berhad; *Int'l*, pg. 8262
DEVORE & JOHNSON, INC.—See Reece Limited; *Int'l*, pg. 6249
DEVOTEAM A/S—See Devoteam SA; *Int'l*, pg. 2089
DEVOTEAM BELGIUM SA/NV—See Devoteam SA; *Int'l*, pg. 2089
DEVOTEAM CONSULTING GMBH—See Devoteam SA; *Int'l*, pg. 2089
DEVOTEAM DAVINCI AS—See Devoteam SA; *Int'l*, pg. 2089
DEVOTEAM GENESIS AG—See Devoteam SA; *Int'l*, pg. 2089
DEVOTEAM GMBH—See Devoteam SA; *Int'l*, pg. 2089
DEVOTEAM GUIDANCE S.A.—See Devoteam SA; *Int'l*, pg. 2090
DEVOTEAM INFORMATION TECHNOLOGY & CONSULTANCY AS—See Devoteam SA; *Int'l*, pg. 2090
DEVOTEAM INTEGRA—See Devoteam SA; *Int'l*, pg. 2090
DEVOTEAM ITALIA S.R.L.—See Devoteam SA; *Int'l*, pg. 2090
DEVOTEAM MANAGEMENT CONSULTING NV—See Devoteam SA; *Int'l*, pg. 2090
DEVOTEAM MEXICO, S.A. DE C.V.—See Devoteam SA; *Int'l*, pg. 2090
DEVOTEAM MIDDLE EAST—See Devoteam SA; *Int'l*, pg. 2090
DEVOTEAM MOROCCO—See Devoteam SA; *Int'l*, pg. 2090
DEVOTEAM NEDERLAND BV—See Devoteam SA; *Int'l*, pg. 2090
DEVOTEAM NETHERLANDS BV—See Devoteam SA; *Int'l*, pg. 2090
DEVOTEAM NV—See Devoteam SA; *Int'l*, pg. 2090
DEVOTEAM OSICONSULT GMBH—See Devoteam SA; *Int'l*, pg. 2090
DEVOTEAM POLSKA SP. Z O.O.—See Devoteam SA; *Int'l*, pg. 2090
DEVOTEAM QUAINT AB—See Devoteam SA; *Int'l*, pg. 2090
DEVOTEAM SA—See Devoteam SA; *Int'l*, pg. 2090
DEVOTEAM SA; *Int'l*, pg. 2089
DEVOTEAM SECURA—See Devoteam SA; *Int'l*, pg. 2090
DEVOTEAM SPAIN—See Devoteam SA; *Int'l*, pg. 2090
DEVOTEAM S.R.O.—See Devoteam SA; *Int'l*, pg. 2090
DEVOTEAM TECHNOLOGY CONSULTING SARL—See Devoteam SA; *Int'l*, pg. 2090
DEVOTEAM TELECOM AS—See Devoteam SA; *Int'l*, pg. 2090
DEVOTEAM TELIGENT—See Devoteam SA; *Int'l*, pg. 2090
DEVOTEAM UK LTD.—See Devoteam SA; *Int'l*, pg. 2090
DEVOTED CONSTRUCTION LTD; *Int'l*, pg. 2090
DEVOTION ENERGY GROUP LIMITED; *Int'l*, pg. 2090
DEVOTO HERMANOS S.A.—See Companhia Brasileira de Distribuicao; *Int'l*, pg. 1746
DEVPORT AB; *Int'l*, pg. 2090
DEVRIES PUBLIC RELATIONS—See The Interpublic Group of Companies, Inc.; *U.S. Public*, pg. 2090
DE VRIJE ENERGIE PRODUCENT B.V.—See UGI Corporation; *U.S. Public*, pg. 2222
DEVRO ASIA LTD.—See RETHMANN AG & Co. KG; *Int'l*, pg. 6309
DEVRO B.V.—See RETHMANN AG & Co. KG; *Int'l*, pg. 6310
DEVRO INC.—See RETHMANN AG & Co. KG; *Int'l*, pg. 6310
DEVRO K.K.—See RETHMANN AG & Co. KG; *Int'l*, pg. 6310
DEVRO LTD.—See RETHMANN AG & Co. KG; *Int'l*, pg. 6310

DEVRO (NANTONG) TECHNOLOGY CO. LIMITED—See RETHMANN AG & Co. KG; *Int'l*, pg. 6309
DEVRO NEW HOLDINGS LIMITED—See RETHMANN AG & Co. KG; *Int'l*, pg. 6310
DEVRO PLC—See RETHMANN AG & Co. KG; *Int'l*, pg. 6309
DEVRO PTY. LTD.—See RETHMANN AG & Co. KG; *Int'l*, pg. 6310
DEVRO PTY. LTD.—See RETHMANN AG & Co. KG; *Int'l*, pg. 6310
DEVRO (SCOTLAND) LTD.—See RETHMANN AG & Co. KG; *Int'l*, pg. 6309
DEVRO S.R.O.—See RETHMANN AG & Co. KG; *Int'l*, pg. 6310
DE VROOMEN BULB CO., INC.; *U.S. Private*, pg. 1181
DEVRY/BECKER EDUCATIONAL DEVELOPMENT CORP.—See Adtalem Global Education Inc.; *U.S. Public*, pg. 43
DEVRY CANADA, LLC—See Adtalem Global Education Inc.; *U.S. Public*, pg. 43
DEVRY EDUCACIONAL DO BRASIL S/A—See Adtalem Global Education Inc.; *U.S. Public*, pg. 43
DEVRY/NEW YORK, INC.—See Adtalem Global Education Inc.; *U.S. Public*, pg. 43
DEVRY UNIVERSITY—See Adtalem Global Education Inc.; *U.S. Public*, pg. 43
DEVSISTERS CO., LTD.; *Int'l*, pg. 2090
DEVSOURCE TECHNOLOGY SOLUTIONS, LLC; *U.S. Private*, pg. 1219
DEVVSTREAM CORP; *U.S. Public*, pg. 657
DEVVSTREAM HOLDINGS INC.—See DevvStream Corp.; *U.S. Public*, pg. 657
DEVYANI INTERNATIONAL LIMITED; *Int'l*, pg. 2090
DEVYSER AB—See Devyser Diagnostics AB; *Int'l*, pg. 2091
DEVYSER DIAGNOSTICS AB; *Int'l*, pg. 2091
DEVYSER FRANCE S.A.S.—See Devyser Diagnostics AB; *Int'l*, pg. 2091
DEVYSER GMBH—See Devyser Diagnostics AB; *Int'l*, pg. 2091
DEVYSER IBERIA S.L.—See Devyser Diagnostics AB; *Int'l*, pg. 2091
DEVYSER S.R.L.—See Devyser Diagnostics AB; *Int'l*, pg. 2091
DE WAFELBAKKERS, LLC—See Brynwood Partners Management LLC; *U.S. Private*, pg. 674
DEWAG 1. OBJEKTGESELLSCHAFT MBH—See Equity Residential; *U.S. Public*, pg. 791
DEWAG MANAGEMENT GMBH—See Equity Residential; *U.S. Public*, pg. 791
DEWAL INDUSTRIES, INC.—See Rogers Corporation; *U.S. Public*, pg. 1808
DEWALT INDUSTRIAL TOOL COMPANY—See Stanley Black & Decker, Inc.; *U.S. Public*, pg. 1932
DEWALT INDUSTRIAL TOOLS S.P.A.—See Stanley Black & Decker, Inc.; *U.S. Public*, pg. 1932
DEWAN AUTOMATIVE ENGINEERING LTD.—See Dewan Farooque Motors Limited; *Int'l*, pg. 2091
DEWAN FAROOQUE MOTORS LIMITED; *Int'l*, pg. 2091
DEWAN HOUSING FINANCE CORPORATION LIMITED—See Piramal Enterprises Ltd.; *Int'l*, pg. 5874
DEWAN KHALID TEXTILE MILLS LIMITED; *Int'l*, pg. 2091
DEWAN MUSHTAQ TEXTILE MILLS LIMITED—See Dewan Farooque Motors Limited; *Int'l*, pg. 2091
DEWAN SALMAN FIBRE LIMITED; *Int'l*, pg. 2091
DEWAN SUGAR MILLS LIMITED—See Dewan Farooque Motors Limited; *Int'l*, pg. 2091
DEWAN TEXTILE MILL LIMITED; *Int'l*, pg. 2091
DEWAS SOYA LTD.—See Hind Syntex Limited; *Int'l*, pg. 3397
DEWAVRIN GROUPE; *Int'l*, pg. 2091
DEWAYNE'S QUALITY METAL COATINGS, LLC.; *U.S. Private*, pg. 1219
THE DEWBERRY COMPANIES INC.; *U.S. Private*, pg. 4020
DEWBERRY & DAVIS, INC.—See Dewberry LLC; *U.S. Private*, pg. 1219
DEWBERRY-GOODKIND, INC.—See Dewberry LLC; *U.S. Private*, pg. 1219
DEWBERRY LLC; *U.S. Private*, pg. 1219
DEWBERRY REDPOINT LTD; *Int'l*, pg. 2091
DEWBERRY TECHNOLOGIES, INC.—See Dewberry LLC; *U.S. Private*, pg. 1219
DEWB-IT BETEILIGUNGSGESELLSCHAFT MBH—See Deutsche Effecten- und Wechsel-Beteiligungsgesellschaft AG.; *Int'l*, pg. 2065
DEW ENGINEERING AND DEVELOPMENT ULC—See CoorsTek, Inc.; *U.S. Private*, pg. 1044
DEWERT ANTRIEBS- UND SYSTEMTECHNIK GMBH—See Phoenix Mecano AG; *Int'l*, pg. 5852
DEWERT AUSTRALIA PTY LTD.—See Phoenix Mecano AG; *Int'l*, pg. 5852
DEWERT MOTORIZED SYSTEMS INC—See Phoenix Mecano AG; *Int'l*, pg. 5852
DEWERTOKIN AB—See Phoenix Mecano AG; *Int'l*, pg. 5852
DEWERTOKIN AG—See Phoenix Mecano AG; *Int'l*, pg. 5852

DEWERTOKIN DO BRASIL LTDA.—See Phoenix Mecano AG; *Int'l*, pg. 5852
DEWERTOKIN GMBH—See Phoenix Mecano AG; *Int'l*, pg. 5852
DEWERTOKIN KFT.—See Phoenix Mecano AG; *Int'l*, pg. 5852
DEWERTOKIN SERVICES GMBH—See Phoenix Mecano AG; *Int'l*, pg. 5852
DEWERTOKIN TECHNOLOGY GROUP CO., LTD.—See Phoenix Mecano AG; *Int'l*, pg. 5852
DEWESOFT CHINA LTD.—See TKH Group N.V.; *Int'l*, pg. 7765
DEWESOFT CO., LTD.—See TKH Group N.V.; *Int'l*, pg. 7765
DEWESOFT D.O.O.—See TKH Group N.V.; *Int'l*, pg. 7765
DEWESOFT LLC—See TKH Group N.V.; *Int'l*, pg. 7765
DEWE SOLUTIONS PTE LTD—See TKH Group N.V.; *Int'l*, pg. 7765
DEWETRON BENELUX B.V.—See TKH Group N.V.; *Int'l*, pg. 7765
DEWETRON ELEKTRONISCHE MESSGERATE GESELLSCHAFT M.B.H.—See TKH Group N.V.; *Int'l*, pg. 7765
DEWETRON FINLAND OY—See TKH Group N.V.; *Int'l*, pg. 7765
DEWETRON GMBH—See TKH Group N.V.; *Int'l*, pg. 7765
DEWETRON, INC.—See TKH Group N.V.; *Int'l*, pg. 7765
DEWETRON KOREA LTD.—See TKH Group N.V.; *Int'l*, pg. 7765
DEWETRON-PRAHA SPOL. S.R.O.—See TKH Group N.V.; *Int'l*, pg. 7765
DEWETRON SCHWEIZ AG—See TKH Group N.V.; *Int'l*, pg. 7765
DEWETRON TEST & MEASUREMENT EQUIPMENT (BEIJING) CO. LTD.—See TKH Group N.V.; *Int'l*, pg. 7763
DEWETRON TEST & MEASUREMENT EQUIPMENT (SHANGHAI) CO. LTD.—See TKH Group N.V.; *Int'l*, pg. 7763
DEWETRON U.K. LTD.—See TKH Group N.V.; *Int'l*, pg. 7765
DEWEY CHEMICAL INC.—See Toyota Tsusho Corporation; *Int'l*, pg. 7879
DEWEY COMMUNICATIONS, INC.; *U.S. Private*, pg. 1219
DEWEY CORPORATION; *U.S. Private*, pg. 1219
THE DEWEY ELECTRONICS CORPORATION; *U.S. Public*, pg. 2066
DEWEY FORD INC.; *U.S. Private*, pg. 1219
DEWEY JORDAN INC.; *U.S. Private*, pg. 1219
DEWEY SERVICES INCORPORATED; *U.S. Private*, pg. 1219
DEWEY SQUARE GROUP—See WPP plc; *Int'l*, pg. 8469
DEWEY SQUARE TOWER ASSOCIATES, LLC—See MetLife, Inc.; *U.S. Public*, pg. 1430
DEWHURST GROUP PLC; *Int'l*, pg. 2091
DEWHURST (HONG KONG) LTD—See Dewhurst Group plc; *Int'l*, pg. 2091
DEWHURST (HUNGARY) KFT—See Dewhurst Group plc; *Int'l*, pg. 2091
DEWHURST LTD.—See Dewhurst Group plc; *Int'l*, pg. 2091
DEWHURST UK MANUFACTURING LTD—See Dewhurst Group plc; *Int'l*, pg. 2091
DE WIJNBEURS—See Union InVivo - Union de Cooperatives Agricoles; *Int'l*, pg. 8053
DEWILDT CAR SALES LIMITED; *Int'l*, pg. 2091
DEWILS INDUSTRIES; *U.S. Private*, pg. 1219
DEWINTER HOLDINGS, LLC.—See New Heritage Capital LLC; *U.S. Private*, pg. 2896
DE WIT LAS- EN SNIJTECHNIEK BV—See ABIRD Holding BV; *Int'l*, pg. 62
DEWITT & ASSOCIATES, INC.—See South Barnes Development Co.; *U.S. Private*, pg. 3719
DEWITT & COMPANY INCORPORATED—See General Atlantic Service Company, L.P.; *U.S. Private*, pg. 1662
DEWITT & COMPANY INCORPORATED—See HgCapital Trust plc; *Int'l*, pg. 3376
THE DEWITT COMPANY, INC.; *U.S. Private*, pg. 4021
DE WITTE LIETAER INTERNATIONAL TEXTILES NV—See AUNDE Achter & Ebels GmbH; *Int'l*, pg. 705
DEWITT EXCAVATION, LLC—See Sterling Infrastructure, Inc.; *U.S. Public*, pg. 1946
DEWITT HOSPITAL & NURSING HOME; *U.S. Private*, pg. 1219
DEWITT MACKALL CROUNSE & MOORE S.C.—See DeWitt Ross & Stevens S.C.; *U.S. Private*, pg. 1219
DEWITT REHABILITATION & NURSING CENTER, INC.—See Cassena Care LLC; *U.S. Private*, pg. 784
DEWITT ROSS & STEVENS S.C.; *U.S. Private*, pg. 1219
DEW JAPAN CO., LTD.—See TKH Group N.V.; *Int'l*, pg. 7765
DEWOLF CHEMICAL INC.; *U.S. Private*, pg. 1219
DEWOLFF, BOBERG & ASSOCIATES INC.; *U.S. Private*, pg. 1220
DEWPOINT, INC.; *U.S. Private*, pg. 1220
DEWYNTERS ADVERTISING INC.—See The First Artist Company Ltd.; *Int'l*, pg. 7643
DEWYNTERS LIMITED—See The First Artist Company Ltd.; *Int'l*, pg. 7643
DEXATEK TECHNOLOGY LTD.—See Ennoconn Corporation; *Int'l*, pg. 2443

COMPANY NAME INDEX

DEXCLUSIVE; *U.S. Private*, pg. 1220
DEXCO, LTD.—See Takaoka Toko Co., Ltd.; *Int'l*, pg. 7431
DEXCOM DEUTSCHLAND GMBH—See DexCom Inc; *U.S. Public*, pg. 657
DEXCOM INC; *U.S. Public*, pg. 657
DEXCOM INTERNATIONAL LTD.—See DexCom Inc; *U.S. Public*, pg. 657
DEXCOM SUISSE GMBH—See DexCom Inc; *U.S. Public*, pg. 657
DEXCOM (UK) LIMITED—See DexCom Inc; *U.S. Public*, pg. 657
DEXCO POLYMERS, L.P.—See TSRC Corporation; *Int'l*, pg. 7952
DEXELANCE S.P.A.; *Int'l*, pg. 2091
DEXERIALS AMERICA CORPORATION—See Development Bank of Japan, Inc.; *Int'l*, pg. 2087
DEXERIALS CORPORATION—See Development Bank of Japan, Inc.; *Int'l*, pg. 2087
DEXERIALS EUROPE B.V.—See Development Bank of Japan, Inc.; *Int'l*, pg. 2087
DEXERIALS HONG KONG LIMITED—See Development Bank of Japan, Inc.; *Int'l*, pg. 2087
DEXERIALS KOREA CORPORATION—See Development Bank of Japan, Inc.; *Int'l*, pg. 2087
DEXERIALS (SHENZHEN) CORPORATION—See Development Bank of Japan, Inc.; *Int'l*, pg. 2087
DEXERIALS SINGAPORE PTE. LTD.—See Development Bank of Japan, Inc.; *Int'l*, pg. 2087
DEXERIALS (SUZHOU) CO., LTD.—See Development Bank of Japan, Inc.; *Int'l*, pg. 2087
DEXERIALS TAIWAN CORPORATION—See Development Bank of Japan, Inc.; *Int'l*, pg. 2087
DEXIA BANK DENMARK A/S—See Dexia SA; *Int'l*, pg. 2092
DEXIA BANK NEDERLAND N.V.—See Dexia SA; *Int'l*, pg. 2092
DEXIA CLF BANQUE S.A—See Dexia SA; *Int'l*, pg. 2092
DEXIA CREDIOP S.P.A.—See Dexia SA; *Int'l*, pg. 2092
DEXIA CREDIT LOCAL SA—See Dexia SA; *Int'l*, pg. 2092
DEXIA CREDIT LOCAL—See Dexia SA; *Int'l*, pg. 2092
DEXIA CREDIT; *U.S. Private*, pg. 1220
DEXIA DELAWARE LLC—See Dexia SA; *Int'l*, pg. 2092
DEXIA EPARGNE PENSION SA—See Dexia SA; *Int'l*, pg. 2092
DEXIA FINANCE SA—See Dexia SA; *Int'l*, pg. 2092
DEXIA INGENIERIE SOCIALE S.A—See Dexia SA; *Int'l*, pg. 2092
DEXIA KOMMUNALBANK DEUTSCHLAND AG—See Helaba Landesbank Hessen-Thuringen; *Int'l*, pg. 3327
DEXIA KOMMUNALKREDIT BANK AG—See Dexia SA; *Int'l*, pg. 2092
DEXIA KOMMUNALKREDIT BULGARIA EOOD—See Dexia SA; *Int'l*, pg. 2092
DEXIA REAL ESTATE CAPITAL MARKETS—See Dexia SA; *Int'l*, pg. 2092
DEXIA SABADELL BANCO LOCAL SA—See Dexia SA; *Int'l*, pg. 2092
DEXIA SA; *Int'l*, pg. 2092
DEXIA SOCIETE DE CREDIT SA—See Dexia SA; *Int'l*, pg. 2092
DEX IMAGING, INC.—See Sycamore Partners Management, LP; *U.S. Private*, pg. 3896
DEXIN CHINA HOLDINGS CO., LTD.; *Int'l*, pg. 2092
DEXIN SERVICES GROUP LIMITED; *Int'l*, pg. 2093
DEXION ASIA LIMITED—See Amotiv Limited; *Int'l*, pg. 431
DEXION ASIA SDN. BHD.—See Tech-Link Storage Engineering Pte Ltd.; *Int'l*, pg. 7502
DEXION (AUSTRALIA) PTY. LTD.—See Corporacion Gestamp SL; *Int'l*, pg. 1804
DEXION (AUSTRALIA) PTY. LTD.—See Tech-Link Storage Engineering Pte Ltd.; *Int'l*, pg. 7502
DEXION CHINA—See Tech-Link Storage Engineering Pte Ltd.; *Int'l*, pg. 7502
DEXION COMINO LTD.—See Corporacion Gestamp SL; *Int'l*, pg. 1804
DEXION COMMERCIAL (NEW ZEALAND) LIMITED—See Amotiv Limited; *Int'l*, pg. 431
DEXION GMBH—See Corporacion Gestamp SL; *Int'l*, pg. 1804
DEXION INTEGRATED SYSTEMS PTY LIMITED—See Tech-Link Storage Engineering Pte Ltd.; *Int'l*, pg. 7502
DEXION KFT.—See Corporacion Gestamp SL; *Int'l*, pg. 1804
DEXION (NEW ZEALAND) LIMITED—See Tech-Link Storage Engineering Pte Ltd.; *Int'l*, pg. 7502
DEXION NV—See Corporacion Gestamp SL; *Int'l*, pg. 1804
DEXION POLSKA SP. Z.O.O.—See Corporacion Gestamp SL; *Int'l*, pg. 1804
DEXION S.R.O.—See Corporacion Gestamp SL; *Int'l*, pg. 1804
DEXKO GLOBAL, INC.—See Brookfield Corporation; *Int'l*, pg. 1175
DEXMA SENSORS S.L—See Herbalife Nutrition Ltd.; *Int'l*, pg. 3359
DEX MEDIA - ALBUQUERQUE—See Thryv Holdings, Inc.; *U.S. Public*, pg. 2157
DEX MEDIA BRE LLC—See Thryv Holdings, Inc.; *U.S. Public*, pg. 2157
DEX MEDIA - CHICAGO—See Thryv Holdings, Inc.; *U.S. Public*, pg. 2157
DEX MEDIA - DENVER—See Thryv Holdings, Inc.; *U.S. Public*, pg. 2157
DEX MEDIA HOLDINGS, INC.—See Thryv Holdings, Inc.; *U.S. Public*, pg. 2157
DEX MEDIA, INC. - EVERETT—See Thryv Holdings, Inc.; *U.S. Public*, pg. 2157
DEX MEDIA, INC. - FORT WAYNE—See Thryv Holdings, Inc.; *U.S. Public*, pg. 2157
DEXMET CORPORATION—See PPG Industries, Inc.; *U.S. Public*, pg. 1707
DEX ONE SERVICE, INC.—See Thryv Holdings, Inc.; *U.S. Public*, pg. 2157
D EXPOSITO & PARTNERS, LLC; *U.S. Private*, pg. 1136
DEXSON ELECTRIC SA—See Schneider Electric SE; *Int'l*, pg. 6626
DEX SUPPLY CHAIN SERVICES COOPERATIE N.V.—See Data Exchange Corporation; *U.S. Private*, pg. 1163
DEX SUPPLY CHAIN SERVICES LIMITED—See Data Exchange Corporation; *U.S. Private*, pg. 1163
DEXTECH MEDICAL AB; *Int'l*, pg. 2093
DEXTER APACHE HOLDINGS, INC.; *U.S. Private*, pg. 1220
DEXTER ATC FIELD SERVICES LLC—See GI Manager L.P.; *U.S. Private*, pg. 1691
DEXTER AXLE COMPANY—See Brookfield Corporation; *Int'l*, pg. 1175
DEXTER AXLE DIVISION - ALBION—See Brookfield Corporation; *Int'l*, pg. 1175
DEXTER AXLE DIVISION - ELKHART—See Brookfield Corporation; *Int'l*, pg. 1175
DEXTER AXLE DIVISION - EL RENO—See Brookfield Corporation; *Int'l*, pg. 1175
DEXTER AXLE DIVISION - FREMONT—See Brookfield Corporation; *Int'l*, pg. 1175
DEXTER AXLE DIVISION - MONTICELLO—See Brookfield Corporation; *Int'l*, pg. 1175
DEXTER CHASSIS GROUP—See Brookfield Corporation; *Int'l*, pg. 1176
DEXTER CONSTRUCTION COMPANY LIMITED—See Municipal Enterprises Limited; *Int'l*, pg. 5093
DEXTER FIELD SERVICES; *U.S. Private*, pg. 1220
DEXTER FINANCIAL SERVICES, INC.—See Dexter Apache Holdings, Inc.; *U.S. Private*, pg. 1220
DEXTER GROUP HOLDINGS LLC—See General Atlantic Service Company, L.P.; *U.S. Private*, pg. 1663
DEXTER GROUP HOLDINGS LLC—See Stone Point Capital LLC; *U.S. Private*, pg. 3825
DEXTER HOSPITAL LLC—See Southeast Missouri Hospital Association; *U.S. Private*, pg. 3726
DEXTER HYSOL AEROSPACE LLC—See Henkel AG & Co. KGaA; *Int'l*, pg. 3353
DEXTER LAUNDRY INC.—See Dexter Apache Holdings, Inc.; *U.S. Private*, pg. 1220
DEXTER MAGNETIC TECHNOLOGIES, INC.—See Tinicum Enterprises, Inc.; *U.S. Private*, pg. 4174
DEXTER MAGNETIC TECHNOLOGIES, INC. - SYOSSET—See Tinicum Enterprises, Inc.; *U.S. Private*, pg. 4174
DEXTERRA GROUP INC.; *Int'l*, pg. 2093
DEXTER-RUSSELL INC.—See Hyde Manufacturing Company; *U.S. Private*, pg. 2016
DEXTER SHOE COMPANY—See Berkshire Hathaway Inc.; *U.S. Public*, pg. 299
DEXTER SHOE COMPANY—See Berkshire Hathaway Inc.; *U.S. Public*, pg. 299
DEXTERS LONDON LIMITED; *Int'l*, pg. 2093
DEXTER STUDIOS CO., LTD; *Int'l*, pg. 2093
DEXTON BUSINESS SOLUTIONS; *Int'l*, pg. 2093
DEXTRAN PRODUCTS LIMITED—See Biospectra Inc.; *U.S. Private*, pg. 563
DEXTRO ENERGY GMBH & CO. KG—See Zertus GmbH; *Int'l*, pg. 8639
DEXUS ASSET MANAGEMENT LIMITED—See DEXUS; *Int'l*, pg. 2093
DEXUS CONVENIENCE RETAIL REIT—See DEXUS; *Int'l*, pg. 2093
DEXUS HOLDINGS PTY LIMITED—See DEXUS; *Int'l*, pg. 2093
DEXUS INDUSTRIA REIT—See DEXUS; *Int'l*, pg. 2093
DEXUS; *Int'l*, pg. 2093
DEXXON BELGIUM S.A.—See Dexxon Groupe SA; *Int'l*, pg. 2093
DEXXON GMBH—See Dexxon Groupe SA; *Int'l*, pg. 2093
DEXXON GROUPE SA; *Int'l*, pg. 2093
DEXXON ITALIA SPA—See Dexxon Groupe SA; *Int'l*, pg. 2093
DEYAAR DEVELOPMENT PJSC; *Int'l*, pg. 2093
DEYAAR FACILITIES MANAGEMENT LLC—See Deyaar Development PJSC; *Int'l*, pg. 2093
DEYA ELEVATOR SERVICES, INC.; *U.S. Private*, pg. 1220
DEYANG HAOHUA QINGPING LINKUANG CO., LTD.—See China National Chemical Corporation; *Int'l*, pg. 1527
DEYTA LLC.; *U.S. Private*, pg. 1220
DEYUN HOLDING LTD.; *Int'l*, pg. 2093
DEZA, A.S.—See Agrofert Holding, a.s.; *Int'l*, pg. 219
DEZER PROPERTIES, INC.; *U.S. Private*, pg. 1220
DEZHAN HEALTH CO., LTD.; *Int'l*, pg. 2094
DEZHOU HONGLIN ELECTRONIC CO., LTD.—See InvesTech Holdings Limited; *Int'l*, pg. 3778
DEZHOU JINGCHEN AUTOMOTIVE ELECTRONIC CO., LTD.—See InvesTech Holdings Limited; *Int'l*, pg. 3778
DEZHOU SHIHUA CHEMICAL CO., LTD.—See China National Chemical Corporation; *Int'l*, pg. 1527
DEZHOU UNITED PETROLEUM TECHNOLOGY CORP.—See Yantai Jereh Oilfield Services Group Co., Ltd.; *Int'l*, pg. 8565
DEZHOU ZHONGYU GAS CO., LTD.—See Zhongyu Energy Holdings Limited; *Int'l*, pg. 8675
DEZURIK, INC.—See Granite Equity Partners LLC; *U.S. Private*, pg. 1755
DFA AUSTRALIA LIMITED—See Dimensional Fund Advisors LP; *U.S. Private*, pg. 1233
DFA INVESTMENT DIMENSIONS GROUP INC.—See Dimensional Fund Advisors LP; *U.S. Private*, pg. 1233
DF-AP#1, LLC—See Dean Foods Company; *U.S. Private*, pg. 1183
DFA - TRANSPORT UND LOGISTIK GMBH—See Aurelius Equity Opportunities SE & Co. KGaA; *Int'l*, pg. 708
DFB PHARMACEUTICALS, INC.; *U.S. Private*, pg. 1220
DFB-REISEBUERO GMBH—See Global Business Travel Group, Inc.; *U.S. Public*, pg. 940
DF CAPITAL BANK LIMITED—See Distribution Finance Capital Holdings plc; *Int'l*, pg. 2136
DFCC BANK PLC; *Int'l*, pg. 2094
DFCC CONSULTING (PVT) LIMITED—See DFCC Bank PLC; *Int'l*, pg. 2094
DFCC VARDHANA BANK LIMITED—See DFCC Bank PLC; *Int'l*, pg. 2094
DFC GLOBAL CORP.—See Lone Star Global Acquisitions, LLC; *U.S. Private*, pg. 2487
D.F. CHASE INC.; *U.S. Private*, pg. 1142
DFCITY GROUP BERHAD; *Int'l*, pg. 2094
D.F. CONCERTS LIMITED—See Live Nation Entertainment, Inc.; *U.S. Public*, pg. 1328
D&F CONSTRUCTION, INC.; *U.S. Private*, pg. 1137
D & F CONTROL SYSTEMS—See Investor AB; *Int'l*, pg. 3786
DFC RESIDUAL CORP.—See Deutsche Bank Aktiengesellschaft; *Int'l*, pg. 2057
DFCU BANK LIMITED—See Development Finance Company of Uganda Ltd.; *Int'l*, pg. 2088
DF DEUTSCHE FORFAIT AG PAKISTAN (PVT.) LTD.—See DF Deutsche Forfait AG; *Int'l*, pg. 2094
DF DEUTSCHE FORFAIT AG; *Int'l*, pg. 2094
DF DEUTSCHE FORFAIT AMERICAS INC.—See DF Deutsche Forfait AG; *Int'l*, pg. 2094
DF DEUTSCHE FORFAIT S.R.O—See DF Deutsche Forfait AG; *Int'l*, pg. 2094
D&F DISTRIBUTORS INC.—See DXP Enterprises, Inc.; *U.S. Public*, pg. 697
DF DO BRASIL DESENVOLVIMIENTO DE PROJETOS LTDA—See Duro Felguera, S.A.; *Int'l*, pg. 2228
DFDS A/S; *Int'l*, pg. 2094
DFDS DENIZCILIK VE TASIMACILIK A.S.—See DFDS A/S; *Int'l*, pg. 2094
DFDS (DEUTSCHLAND) GMBH—See DFDS A/S; *Int'l*, pg. 2094
DFDS KOLETRANSPORT A/S—See DFDS A/S; *Int'l*, pg. 2094
DFDS LOGISTICS AB—See DFDS A/S; *Int'l*, pg. 2094
DFDS LOGISTICS AS—See DFDS A/S; *Int'l*, pg. 2094
DFDS LOGISTICS BV—See DFDS A/S; *Int'l*, pg. 2094
DFDS LOGISTICS GMBH—See DFDS A/S; *Int'l*, pg. 2094
DFDS LOGISTICS INTERMODAL A/S—See DFDS A/S; *Int'l*, pg. 2094
DFDS LOGISTICS (IRELAND) LTD.—See DFDS A/S; *Int'l*, pg. 2094
DFDS LOGISTICS LIMITED—See DFDS A/S; *Int'l*, pg. 2094
DFDS LOGISTICS NIJMEGEN B.V.—See DFDS A/S; *Int'l*, pg. 2094
DFDS LOGISTICS NV—See DFDS A/S; *Int'l*, pg. 2094
DFDS LOGISTICS OU—See DFDS A/S; *Int'l*, pg. 2094
DFDS LOGISTICS OY—See DFDS A/S; *Int'l*, pg. 2094
DFDS LOGISTICS POLSKA SP. Z O.O.—See DFDS A/S; *Int'l*, pg. 2094
DFDS LOGISTICS SARL—See DFDS A/S; *Int'l*, pg. 2094
DFDS LOGISTICS SERVICES NV—See DFDS A/S; *Int'l*, pg. 2094
DFDS LOGISTICS S.P.A.—See DFDS A/S; *Int'l*, pg. 2094
DFDS LOGISTICS WIJCHEN B.V.—See DFDS A/S; *Int'l*, pg. 2095
DFDS LOGISTICS WINTERSWIJK B.V.—See DFDS A/S; *Int'l*, pg. 2095
DFDS POLSKA SP. Z.O.O.—See DFDS A/S; *Int'l*, pg. 2095
DFDS SEAWAYS AB—See DFDS A/S; *Int'l*, pg. 2095
DFDS SEAWAYS AS—See DFDS A/S; *Int'l*, pg. 2095
DFDS SEAWAYS BALTIC GMBH—See DFDS A/S; *Int'l*, pg. 2095
DFDS SEAWAYS GMBH—See DFDS A/S; *Int'l*, pg. 2095

DFDS A/S

DFDS SEAWAYS HISPANIA S.L.—See DFDS A/S; *Int'l*, pg. 2095
DFDS SEAWAYS HOLDING AB—See DFDS A/S; *Int'l*, pg. 2095
DFDS SEAWAYS IJMUIDEN BV—See DFDS A/S; *Int'l*, pg. 2095
DFDS SEAWAYS LTD.—See DFDS A/S; *Int'l*, pg. 2095
DFDS SEAWAYS NEWCASTLE LTD.—See DFDS A/S; *Int'l*, pg. 2095
DFDS SEAWAYS NV—See DFDS A/S; *Int'l*, pg. 2095
DFDS SEAWAYS OU—See DFDS A/S; *Int'l*, pg. 2095
DFDS SEAWAYS S.A.S.—See DFDS A/S; *Int'l*, pg. 2095
DFDS SEAWAYS SIA—See DFDS A/S; *Int'l*, pg. 2095
DFDS SEAWAYS TERMINALS BV—See DFDS A/S; *Int'l*, pg. 2095
DFDS SIA—See DFDS A/S; *Int'l*, pg. 2095
DFDS STEVEDORING A/S—See DFDS A/S; *Int'l*, pg. 2095
DFE FAHRZEUGELEKTRIK GMBH—See Draexlmaier Gruppe; *Int'l*, pg. 2198
DF ELASTOMER SOLUTIONS LDA.—See Mutares SE & Co. KGaA; *Int'l*, pg. 5104
D&F EQUIPMENT SALES INC.; *U.S. Private*, pg. 1137
DFF CORP.—See CORE Industrial Partners, LLC; *U.S. Private*, pg. 1048
DFG CANADA, INC.—See Lone Star Global Acquisitions, LLC; *U.S. Private*, pg. 2487
DFG CONFECTIONARY LLC.; *U.S. Private*, pg. 1220
DFI AMERICA, LLC—See DFI Inc.; *Int'l*, pg. 2095
DFI CO.,LTD.—See DFI Inc.; *Int'l*, pg. 2095
DFI HOME FURNISHINGS TAIWAN LTD—See Jardine Matheson Holdings Limited; *Int'l*, pg. 3909
DFI INC.; *Int'l*, pg. 2095
DFI LUCKY PRIVATE LTD—See Jardine Matheson Holdings Limited; *Int'l*, pg. 3909
DFIND AB—See Randstad N.V.; *Int'l*, pg. 6202
DFIND AS—See Randstad N.V.; *Int'l*, pg. 6202
DFIND CONSULTING AS—See Randstad N.V.; *Int'l*, pg. 6201
DFIND IT AB—See Randstad N.V.; *Int'l*, pg. 6202
DFINE, INC.—See Merit Medical Systems, Inc.; *U.S. Public*, pg. 1425
DFI RETAIL GROUP HOLDINGS LIMITED—See Jardine Matheson Holdings Limited; *Int'l*, pg. 3909
DFJ JAIC VENTURE PARTNERS, LLC—See Japan Asia Investment Co., Ltd.; *Int'l*, pg. 3886
DFJ TAMIR FISHMAN VENTURES; *Int'l*, pg. 2095
D.F. KING & CO., INC.—See Pacific Equity Partners Pty. Limited; *Int'l*, pg. 5688
D.F. KING (EUROPE) LIMITED—See Pacific Equity Partners Pty. Limited; *Int'l*, pg. 5689
DF KING WORLDWIDE—See The Riverside Company; *U.S. Private*, pg. 4108
DFL HOLDINGS PTY LTD; *Int'l*, pg. 2095
D-FLIGHT S.P.A.—See ENAV S.p.A.; *Int'l*, pg. 2396
DFL INFRASTRUCTURE FINANCE LIMITED; *Int'l*, pg. 2095
DFL LEASE CO. LTD.—See Resona Holdings, Inc.; *Int'l*, pg. 6297
D-FLOW TECHNOLOGY, AB—See Badger Meter, Inc.; *U.S. Public*, pg. 263
DFM DOORS SP. Z O.O.—See Mercor S.A.; *Int'l*, pg. 4833
DFM FOODS LIMITED; *Int'l*, pg. 2095
DF MOMPRESA, S.A.U.—See Duro Felguera, S.A.; *Int'l*, pg. 2228
DFM ZANAM - LEGMET SP. Z O.O.—See KGHM Polska Miedz S.A.; *Int'l*, pg. 4148
DFNN, INC.; *Int'l*, pg. 2096
DFO, LLC—See Denny's Corporation; *U.S. Public*, pg. 654
DFP HOLDINGS LIMITED; *Int'l*, pg. 2096
DF POWER SYSTEMS PRIVATE LIMITED—See TD Power Systems Limited; *Int'l*, pg. 7486
D.F. PRAY INC.; *U.S. Private*, pg. 1142
DFP RECRUITMENT HOLDINGS PTY. LTD.—See Will Group, Inc.; *Int'l*, pg. 8412
DFR GOLD INC.; *Int'l*, pg. 2096
DF RICHARD INC.; *U.S. Private*, pg. 1220
DFR SOLUTIONS, LLC—See ANSYS, Inc.; *U.S. Public*, pg. 139
DFS AUSTRALIA PTY. LTD.—See LVMH Moet Hennessy Louis Vuitton SE; *Int'l*, pg. 4601
DFS B.V.—See Dell Technologies Inc.; *U.S. Public*, pg. 649
DFS COTAI LIMITADA—See LVMH Moet Hennessy Louis Vuitton SE; *Int'l*, pg. 4591
DFS DRAXLMAIER FAHRZEUGSYSTEME GMBH—See Draexlmaier Gruppe; *Int'l*, pg. 2198
DFS FLOORING, INC.; *U.S. Private*, pg. 1220
DFS FURNITURE LTD.; *Int'l*, pg. 2096
DFS GROUP L.P.—See LVMH Moet Hennessy Louis Vuitton SE; *Int'l*, pg. 4601
DFS GROUP LTD.—See LVMH Moet Hennessy Louis Vuitton SE; *Int'l*, pg. 4600
DFS GROUP LTD. - USA—See LVMH Moet Hennessy Louis Vuitton SE; *Int'l*, pg. 4601
DFS HONG KONG LTD.—See LVMH Moet Hennessy Louis Vuitton SE; *Int'l*, pg. 4601
DF SHUMPERT OIL CO.; *U.S. Private*, pg. 1220
DFS INDIA PRIVATE LTD—See LVMH Moet Hennessy Louis Vuitton SE; *Int'l*, pg. 4600
DFS JAPAN KK—See LVMH Moet Hennessy Louis Vuitton SE; *Int'l*, pg. 4601
DFS KOREA LTD.—See LVMH Moet Hennessy Louis Vuitton SE; *Int'l*, pg. 4601
DFS NEW ZEALAND LTD.—See LVMH Moet Hennessy Louis Vuitton SE; *Int'l*, pg. 4601
DFS SAIPAN LIMITED—See LVMH Moet Hennessy Louis Vuitton SE; *Int'l*, pg. 4601
DFS SEOUL LTD—See LVMH Moet Hennessy Louis Vuitton SE; *Int'l*, pg. 4600
DFS SERVICES LLC—See Discover Financial Services; *U.S. Public*, pg. 668
DFS TAIWAN LTD—See LVMH Moet Hennessy Louis Vuitton SE; *Int'l*, pg. 4601
D.F. STAUFFER BISCUIT CO., INC.—See Meiji Holdings Co., Ltd.; *Int'l*, pg. 4800
DFS VENTURE SINGAPORE (PTE) LTD—See LVMH Moet Hennessy Louis Vuitton SE; *Int'l*, pg. 4600
DFS VIETNAM LLC—See LVMH Moet Hennessy Louis Vuitton SE; *Int'l*, pg. 4600
DFT COMMUNICATIONS CORPORATION; *U.S. Private*, pg. 1220
DFT DEUTSCHE FLACHEN-TECHNIK INDUSTRIEBODEN GMBH—See L. Possehl & Co. mbH; *Int'l*, pg. 4382
DF TITLE, LLC—See Dream Finders Homes, Inc.; *U.S. Public*, pg. 687
DFU ANALYSENSERVICE GMBH—See NORD Holding Unternehmensbeteiligungsgesellschaft mbH; *Int'l*, pg. 5416
DFU SERVICE GMBH—See NORD Holding Unternehmensbeteiligungsgesellschaft mbH; *Int'l*, pg. 5416
DFV DEUTSCHE FAMILIENVERSICHERUNG AG; *Int'l*, pg. 2096
DFW CAMPER CORRAL INC.; *U.S. Private*, pg. 1220
DFW CAPITAL PARTNERS; *U.S. Private*, pg. 1220
DFW MOVERS & ERECTORS INC.; *U.S. Private*, pg. 1221
DFW PRINTING COMPANY, INC.—See DallasNews Corporation; *U.S. Public*, pg. 621
DF YOUNG AUSTRALIA PTY LTD—See Daniel F. Young, Inc.; *U.S. Private*, pg. 1154
DFZ CAPITAL BERHAD—See Atlan Holdings Berhad; *Int'l*, pg. 673
DFZ TUSSENHOLDING N.V.—See Achmea B.V.; *Int'l*, pg. 103
DG3 ASIA LIMITED—See Diversified Global Graphics Group, LLC; *U.S. Private*, pg. 1242
DG3 EUROPE LTD.—See Diversified Global Graphics Group, LLC; *U.S. Private*, pg. 1242
DG3 JAPAN LIMITED—See Diversified Global Graphics Group, LLC; *U.S. Private*, pg. 1242
DG3 MANILA LTD.—See Diversified Global Graphics Group, LLC; *U.S. Private*, pg. 1242
DG3 NORTH AMERICA, INC.—See Diversified Global Graphics Group, LLC; *U.S. Private*, pg. 1242
DGA S.A.; *Int'l*, pg. 2096
DGB ASIA BERHAD; *Int'l*, pg. 2096
DGB ASSET MANAGEMENT CO., LTD.—See DGB Financial Group Co., Ltd.; *Int'l*, pg. 2096
DGB CAPITAL LTD.—See DGB Financial Group Co., Ltd.; *Int'l*, pg. 2096
DGB CREDIT INFORMATION CO., LTD.—See DGB Financial Group Co., Ltd.; *Int'l*, pg. 2096
DGB FINANCIAL GROUP CO., LTD.; *Int'l*, pg. 2096
DGB GROUP N.V.; *Int'l*, pg. 2096
DGB LUGGAGE & LEATHER LLC; *U.S. Private*, pg. 1221
D & G BRICE CONTRACTORS, INC.; *U.S. Private*, pg. 1136
DGC ENVIRONMENTAL SERVICES, INC.—See DFW Capital Partners; *U.S. Private*, pg. 1221
DG COMMUNICATIONS, INC.—See Digital Garage, Inc.; *Int'l*, pg. 2121
DGE INC.—See FEV GmbH; *Int'l*, pg. 2648
DGENX CO., LTD. - GUNSAN PLANT—See Dgenx Co., Ltd.; *Int'l*, pg. 2096
DGENX CO., LTD.; *Int'l*, pg. 2096
D&G EQUIPMENT CO., INC.; *U.S. Private*, pg. 1137
D&G EQUIPMENT INC.; *U.S. Private*, pg. 1137
DG FINANCIAL TECHNOLOGY, INC.—See Digital Garage, Inc.; *Int'l*, pg. 2122
DG FOODS, LLC; *U.S. Private*, pg. 1221
DGH INVESTMENT COMPANY LTD.—See Dabbagh Group Holding Company Ltd.; *Int'l*, pg. 1902
DGH SDN. BHD.—See Pappajack Berhad; *Int'l*, pg. 5733
DGI COMMUNICATIONS, LLC—See Kirkwood Printing Company, Inc.; *U.S. Private*, pg. 2315
DGI MENARD INC.—See VINCI S.A.; *Int'l*, pg. 8231
DG INNOVATE PLC; *Int'l*, pg. 2096
DG INTERNATIONAL OIL COMPANY LTD.—See Dabbagh Group Holding Company Ltd.; *Int'l*, pg. 1902
DGI SUPPLY—See DoALL Company; *U.S. Private*, pg. 1250
DGIT SYSTEMS PTY. LTD.—See CSG Systems International, Inc.; *U.S. Public*, pg. 601
D.G. JENKINS DEVELOPMENT CORP.; *U.S. Private*, pg. 1142
DG KHAN CEMENT COMPANY LIMITED—See Nishat Mills Ltd.; *Int'l*, pg. 5363
DGL GROUP LIMITED; *Int'l*, pg. 2096
DGL INTERNATIONAL (SINGAPORE) PTE. LTD.—See Nippon Paint Holdings Co., Ltd.; *Int'l*, pg. 5325
D&G MACHINE PRODUCTS INC.; *U.S. Private*, pg. 1137
DGMB CASINO, LLC; *U.S. Private*, pg. 1221
DG MEDIOS SPA—See Live Nation Entertainment, Inc.; *U.S. Public*, pg. 1328
DGM GROWERS LTD—See Fresca Group Limited; *Int'l*, pg. 2774
DGM INDIA INTERNET MARKETING PRIVATE LIMITED—See Dentsu Group Inc.; *Int'l*, pg. 2038
DG MOBILE, INC.—See Digital Garage, Inc.; *Int'l*, pg. 2122
DGN SERVICE GMBH—See Deutsche Apotheker- und Arztebank eG; *Int'l*, pg. 2049
DG-NVO LOGISTICS.CO., LTD.—See Yongtaiyun Chemical Logistics Co., Ltd.; *Int'l*, pg. 8597
DGO GOLD LIMITED—See Gold Road Resources Limited; *Int'l*, pg. 3026
DGO GROBHANDEL GMBH—See AGRAVIS Raiffeisen AG; *Int'l*, pg. 215
DG PACKAGING (THAILAND) CO., LTD.—See Triple i Logistics Public Company Limited; *Int'l*, pg. 7926
DGP CO.,LTD.; *Int'l*, pg. 2097
DGR GLOBAL LIMITED; *Int'l*, pg. 2097
DGS BUSINESS SERVICES SP. Z O.O.—See Demant A/S; *Int'l*, pg. 2023
DGS (CHINA) CO LTD.—See DGS Druckguss Systeme AG; *Int'l*, pg. 2097
D.G.S. CONSTRUCTION COMPANY LTD.; *Int'l*, pg. 1900
DGS DRUCKGUSS SYSTEME AG; *Int'l*, pg. 2097
DGS DRUCKGUSS SYSTEME S.R.O.—See DGS Druckguss Systeme AG; *Int'l*, pg. 2097
DGSHAPE CORPORATION—See Roland DG Corporation; *Int'l*, pg. 6391
DGS RETAIL, INC.—See San Francisco Equity Partners; *U.S. Private*, pg. 3540
DGT ASSOCIATES, INC.; *U.S. Private*, pg. 1221
DG TECHNOLOGY CONSULTING, LLC; *U.S. Private*, pg. 1221
D&G TECHNOLOGY HOLDING CO., LTD.; *Int'l*, pg. 1899
DGTL HOLDINGS INC.; *Int'l*, pg. 2097
DGWB; *U.S. Private*, pg. 1221
DG WHITEFIELD LLC—See Korea Electric Power Corporation; *Int'l*, pg. 4283
D.G. YUENGLING & SON INCORPORATED; *U.S. Private*, pg. 1142
DHAANYA SEEDS LIMITED—See Tata Sons Limited; *Int'l*, pg. 7468
DHABRIYA POLYWOOD LIMITED; *Int'l*, pg. 2097
D.H. ADAMS COMPANY, INC. - LEOMINSTER—See D.H. Adams Company, Inc.; *U.S. Private*, pg. 1142
D.H. ADAMS COMPANY, INC.; *U.S. Private*, pg. 1142
DHA GROUP INC.—See ASGN Incorporated; *U.S. Public*, pg. 210
DHAKA BANK PLC; *Int'l*, pg. 2097
DHAKA BANK SECURITIES LIMITED—See Dhaka Bank PLC; *Int'l*, pg. 2097
DHAKA ELECTRIC SUPPLY COMPANY LIMITED; *Int'l*, pg. 2097
DHAKA INSURANCE LIMITED; *Int'l*, pg. 2097
DHAKA STOCK EXCHANGE LTD.; *Int'l*, pg. 2097
DHALIWAL LABS; *U.S. Private*, pg. 1221
DHAMECHA GROUP, INC.; *Int'l*, pg. 2098
DHAMPUR BIO ORGANICS LIMITED; *Int'l*, pg. 2098
DHAMPURE SPECIALTY SUGARS LTD; *Int'l*, pg. 2098
DHAMPUR SUGAR MILLS LIMITED; *Int'l*, pg. 2098
DHANADA CORPORATION LIMITED; *Int'l*, pg. 2098
DHANADA EDUCATION PVT. LTD.—See DHANADA CORPORATION LIMITED; *Int'l*, pg. 2098
DHANADA ENGINEERING PVT. LTD.—See DHANADA CORPORATION LIMITED; *Int'l*, pg. 2098
DHANALAXMI ROTO SPINNERS LTD.; *Int'l*, pg. 2098
DHANASHREE ELECTRONICS LIMITED; *Int'l*, pg. 2098
DHANI HEALTHCARE LIMITED—See Dhani Services Ltd.; *Int'l*, pg. 2098
DHANI LOANS & SERVICES LIMITED—See Dhani Services Ltd.; *Int'l*, pg. 2098
DHANI SERVICES LTD.; *Int'l*, pg. 2098
DHANLAXMI BANK LTD.; *Int'l*, pg. 2098
DHANLAXMI COTEX LTD.; *Int'l*, pg. 2098
DHANLAXMI FABRICS LTD.; *Int'l*, pg. 2098
DHANLEELA INVESTMENTS & TRADING COMPANY LIMITED; *Int'l*, pg. 2098
DHANUKA AGRITECH LIMITED; *Int'l*, pg. 2098
DHANUKA REALTY LTD.; *Int'l*, pg. 2098
DHANVANTARI BOTANICALS, PVT., LTD.—See Avesthagen Limited; *Int'l*, pg. 740
DHANVANTRI JEEVAN REKHA LTD.; *Int'l*, pg. 2098
DHANVARSHA FINVEST LIMITED; *Int'l*, pg. 2098
DHANYA AGROINDUSTRIAL PVT. LTD.—See Ecom Agroindustrial Corporation Ltd.; *Int'l*, pg. 2296
DHANYA AGROINDUSTRIAL PVT. LTD..—See Ecom Agroindustrial Corporation Ltd.; *Int'l*, pg. 2296
DHAP LTD—See Leggett & Platt, Incorporated; *U.S. Public*, pg. 1301
THE DHARAMSI MORARJI CHEMICAL CO. LTD.; *Int'l*, pg. 7636
DHARANI FINANCE LIMITED; *Int'l*, pg. 2098

DHARANI SUGARS & CHEMICALS LIMITED; *Int'l*, pg. 2099
DHARANI SUGARS & CHEMICALS LIMITED - UNIT - III—See DHARANI SUGARS & CHEMICALS LIMITED; *Int'l*, pg. 2099
DHARANI SUGARS & CHEMICALS LIMITED - UNIT - II—See DHARANI SUGARS & CHEMICALS LIMITED; *Int'l*, pg. 2099
DHARANI SUGARS & CHEMICALS LIMITED - UNIT - I—See DHARANI SUGARS & CHEMICALS LIMITED; *Int'l*, pg. 2099
DHARMAJ CROP GUARD LIMITED; *Int'l*, pg. 2099
THE DHARMAWANGSA—See Chow Tai Fook Enterprises Limited; *Int'l*, pg. 1585
DHARNI CAPITAL SERVICES LIMITED; *Int'l*, pg. 2099
DH ASIA INVESTMENT PTE. LTD.—See Daiwa House Industry Co., Ltd.; *Int'l*, pg. 1945
DHATRE UDYOG LIMITED; *Int'l*, pg. 2099
DHAUTOWARE CO LTD; *Int'l*, pg. 2099
DHB CAPITAL CORP.; *U.S. Public*, pg. 657
DHB-COMPONENTES AUTOMOTIVOS, S.A.—See General Motors Company; *U.S. Public*, pg. 924
D&H CANADA ULC—See D&H Distributing Co., Inc.; *U.S. Private*, pg. 1137
DH CAPITAL, LLC—See Citizens Financial Group, Inc.; *U.S. Public*, pg. 505
DH CAROLINA MANAGEMENT LLC—See Hyatt Hotels Corporation; *U.S. Public*, pg. 1076
DHC CORPORATION—See ORIX Corporation; *Int'l*, pg. 5633
DHC CORPORATION—See Chubb Limited; *Int'l*, pg. 1591
D&H CO., LTD.—See Aisan Industry Co., Ltd.; *Int'l*, pg. 250
DHC SOFTWARE CO., LTD.; *Int'l*, pg. 2099
DHC SOLVENT CHEMIE GMBH—See BP plc; *Int'l*, pg. 1131
DHC SUPPLIES INC.; *U.S. Private*, pg. 1221
DHC SUPPLY, LLC—See High Tide, Inc.; *Int'l*, pg. 3386
DHCU COMMUNITY CREDIT UNION; *U.S. Private*, pg. 1221
DHC USA INC.—See ORIX Corporation; *Int'l*, pg. 5633
D.H. CYPROTELS PLC—See Libra Holidays Group Public Ltd.; *Int'l*, pg. 4486
DH (DALIAN) ADMINISTRATIVE MANAGEMENT CONSULTING CENTER CO., LTD.—See Daiwa House Industry Co., Ltd.; *Int'l*, pg. 1945
DH DBHL MANAGEMENT LLC—See Hyatt Hotels Corporation; *U.S. Public*, pg. 1077
DH DEL MAR MANAGEMENT LLC—See Hyatt Hotels Corporation; *U.S. Public*, pg. 1077
DH DENMARK HOLDING APS—See Danaher Corporation; *U.S. Public*, pg. 625
D&H DISTRIBUTING CO., INC.; *U.S. Private*, pg. 1137
DH ENCHANTMENT, INC.; *U.S. Public*, pg. 657
DHENIN—See FAYAT SAS; *Int'l*, pg. 2625
DHENU BUILDCON INFRA LIMITED; *Int'l*, pg. 2099
DH EUROPE FINANCE SA—See Danaher Corporation; *U.S. Public*, pg. 625
DHFL PRAMERICA ASSET MANAGERS PRIVATE LIMITED—See Prudential Financial, Inc.; *U.S. Public*, pg. 1732
DHFL VYSYA HOUSING FINANCE LTD.—See Piramal Enterprises Ltd.; *Int'l*, pg. 5874
DHG INC.—See Finn Corporation; *U.S. Private*, pg. 1510
DHG PHARMACEUTICAL JOINT STOCK COMPANY—See Taisho Pharmaceutical Holdings Co., Ltd; *Int'l*, pg. 7417
D H GRIFFIN CONSTRUCTION CO. LLC—See D.H. Griffin Wrecking Co. Inc.; *U.S. Private*, pg. 1142
D. H. GRIFFIN CONTRACTING CO., INC—See D.H. Griffin Wrecking Co. Inc.; *U.S. Private*, pg. 1142
D.H. GRIFFIN CO.; *U.S. Private*, pg. 1140
D.H. GRIFFIN OF TEXAS, INC—See D.H. Griffin Wrecking Co. Inc.; *U.S. Private*, pg. 1142
D.H. GRIFFIN WRECKING CO. INC. - ASHEVILLE DIVISION—See D.H. Griffin Wrecking Co. Inc.; *U.S. Private*, pg. 1142
D.H. GRIFFIN WRECKING CO. INC. - CRUSHING DIVISION—See D.H. Griffin Wrecking Co. Inc.; *U.S. Private*, pg. 1142
D.H. GRIFFIN WRECKING CO. INC.; *U.S. Private*, pg. 1142
DHHI GERMANY GMBH—See Dalian Huarui Heavy Industry Group Co., Ltd.; *Int'l*, pg. 1952
DH HOLDINGS CO., LTD.; *Int'l*, pg. 2097
DH HOLDINGS CORP.—See Danaher Corporation; *U.S. Public*, pg. 625
DHH SPA; *Int'l*, pg. 2099
DHI ACQUISITION CORP.; *U.S. Private*, pg. 1221
DHI COMMUNITIES, INC.—See D.R. Horton, Inc.; *U.S. Public*, pg. 619
DHI COMPUTING SERVICE INCORPORATED; *U.S. Private*, pg. 1221
DHIC - PIONEER HILL, LLC—See D.R. Horton, Inc.; *U.S. Public*, pg. 619
DHIC - RIDGEWOOD, LLC—See D.R. Horton, Inc.; *U.S. Public*, pg. 619
DHI GROUP, INC.; *U.S. Public*, pg. 657
D-HILL SDN. BHD.—See Knusford Berhad; *Int'l*, pg. 4214

D. HILTON ASSOCIATES, INC.; *U.S. Private*, pg. 1140
DHI MINERALS LTD.—See Gold Royalty Corp.; *Int'l*, pg. 3026
DHI MORTGAGE COMPANY GP, INC.—See D.R. Horton, Inc.; *U.S. Public*, pg. 619
DHI MORTGAGE COMPANY LTD.—See D.R. Horton, Inc.; *U.S. Public*, pg. 619
DHIMYOTIS SAS—See Tessi S.A.; *Int'l*, pg. 7574
D & H INDIA LIMITED; *Int'l*, pg. 1898
D & H INDIA LIMITED - UNIT LL—See D & H India Limited; *Int'l*, pg. 1898
THE DHIPAYA INSURANCE PUBLIC COMPANY LIMITED—See Krung Thai Bank Public Company Limited; *Int'l*, pg. 4308
DHIR - AMBER CREEK, LLC—See D.R. Horton, Inc.; *U.S. Public*, pg. 619
DHIR - ARABELLA, LLC—See D.R. Horton, Inc.; *U.S. Public*, pg. 619
DHIR - BRIDGE HARBOR, LLC—See D.R. Horton, Inc.; *U.S. Public*, pg. 619
DHIR - BROOKSIDE AT PLEASANT VALLEY, LLC—See D.R. Horton, Inc.; *U.S. Public*, pg. 619
DHIR - CEDAR STATION, LLC—See D.R. Horton, Inc.; *U.S. Public*, pg. 620
DHIR - CYPRESS BAY, LLC—See D.R. Horton, Inc.; *U.S. Public*, pg. 620
DHIR - FOUNTAIN PARK, LLC—See D.R. Horton, Inc.; *U.S. Public*, pg. 620
DHIR - LAKESHORE VILLAGES, LLC—See D.R. Horton, Inc.; *U.S. Public*, pg. 620
DHIR - MILLBROOK PARK, LLC—See D.R. Horton, Inc.; *U.S. Public*, pg. 620
DHIR - RIVERSTONE AT WESTPOINTE, LLC—See D.R. Horton, Inc.; *U.S. Public*, pg. 620
DHISCO ELECTRONIC DISTRIBUTION, INC.—See H.I.G. Capital, LLC; *U.S. Private*, pg. 1829
DHISCO, INC.—See H.I.G. Capital, LLC; *U.S. Private*, pg. 1829
DHI TITLE OF ALABAMA, INC.—See D.R. Horton, Inc.; *U.S. Public*, pg. 619
DHI TITLE OF ARIZONA, INC.—See D.R. Horton, Inc.; *U.S. Public*, pg. 619
DHI TITLE OF MINNESOTA, INC.—See D.R. Horton, Inc.; *U.S. Public*, pg. 619
DHI TITLE OF NEVADA, INC.—See D.R. Horton, Inc.; *U.S. Public*, pg. 619
DHI TITLE OF OHIO, LLC—See D.R. Horton, Inc.; *U.S. Public*, pg. 619
DHI TITLE OF WASHINGTON, INC.—See D.R. Horton, Inc.; *U.S. Public*, pg. 619
DHI TITLE—See D.R. Horton, Inc.; *U.S. Public*, pg. 619
DHIVEHI RAAJJEYGE GULHUN PLC—See Bahrain Telecommunications Company BSC; *Int'l*, pg. 801
DHIYAFA HOLDING COMPANY S.A.L.—See Kuwait Projects Company (Holding) K.S.C.P.; *Int'l*, pg. 4347
DHJ INTERLINING LIMITED—See Chargeurs SA; *Int'l*, pg. 1450
DHJ INTERNATIONAL—See Chargeurs SA; *Int'l*, pg. 1449
DHJ (MALAYSIA) SDN BHD—See Chargeurs SA; *Int'l*, pg. 1450
DHK AUTOMOTIVE GMBH—See MBB SE; *Int'l*, pg. 4751
DH KIRKLAND MANAGEMENT LLC—See Hyatt Hotels Corporation; *U.S. Public*, pg. 1077
DHK SOLUTION CORPORATION—See Disco Corporation; *Int'l*, pg. 2131
DHL 2-MANN-HANDLING GMBH—See Deutsche Post AG; *Int'l*, pg. 2072
DHL AIR LIMITED—See Deutsche Post AG; *Int'l*, pg. 2073
DHL AIRWAYS GMBH—See Deutsche Post AG; *Int'l*, pg. 2073
DHL ANALYTICAL, INC—See Sentinel Capital Partners, L.L.C.; *U.S. Private*, pg. 3609
DHL ASIA PACIFIC SHARED SERVICES SDN. BHD.—See Deutsche Post AG; *Int'l*, pg. 2073
DHL AUTOMOTIVE GMBH—See Deutsche Post AG; *Int'l*, pg. 2073
DHL AVIATION (FRANCE) SAS—See Deutsche Post AG; *Int'l*, pg. 2072
DHL AVIATION (NETHERLANDS) B.V.—See Deutsche Post AG; *Int'l*, pg. 2073
DHL AVIATION (NIGERIA) LTD.—See Deutsche Post AG; *Int'l*, pg. 2072
DHL AVIATION NV / SA—See Deutsche Post AG; *Int'l*, pg. 2073
DHL AVIATION (UK) LIMITED—See Deutsche Post AG; *Int'l*, pg. 2073
DHL (BAHAMAS) LIMITED—See Deutsche Post AG; *Int'l*, pg. 2072
DHL (BOLIVIA) SRL—See Deutsche Post AG; *Int'l*, pg. 2072
DHL (BVI) LTD.—See Deutsche Post AG; *Int'l*, pg. 2072
DHL BWLOG GMBH—See Deutsche Post AG; *Int'l*, pg. 2072
DHL CORPORATE SERVICES SC MEXICO—See Deutsche Post AG; *Int'l*, pg. 2073
DHL (COSTA RICA) S.A.—See Deutsche Post AG; *Int'l*, pg. 2073
DHL CUSTOMS BROKERAGE LTD.—See Deutsche Post AG; *Int'l*, pg. 2073

DHL DANZAS AIR & OCEAN (CANADA) INC.—See Deutsche Post AG; *Int'l*, pg. 2073
DHL DANZAS AIR & OCEAN NORTH AMERICA—See Deutsche Post AG; *Int'l*, pg. 2073
DHL DANZAS AIR & OCEAN—See Deutsche Post AG; *Int'l*, pg. 2073
DHL DE EL SALVADOR S.A. DE C.V.—See Deutsche Post AG; *Int'l*, pg. 2076
DHL DOMINICANA S.A.—See Deutsche Post AG; *Int'l*, pg. 2076
DHL ECOMMERCE (MALAYSIA) SDN. BHD.—See Deutsche Post AG; *Int'l*, pg. 2078
DHL ECOMMERCE (SINGAPORE) PTE. LTD.—See Deutsche Post AG; *Int'l*, pg. 2078
DHL EGYPT W.L.L.—See Deutsche Post AG; *Int'l*, pg. 2073
DHL EKSPRES (SLOVENIJA), D.O.O.—See Deutsche Post AG; *Int'l*, pg. 2073
DHL ELANCOURT SARL—See Deutsche Post AG; *Int'l*, pg. 2072
DHL EMPLOYEE BENEFIT FUND OFP—See Deutsche Post AG; *Int'l*, pg. 2072
DHL EXEL SLOVAKIA, S.R.O.—See Deutsche Post AG; *Int'l*, pg. 2072
DHL EXEL SUPPLY CHAIN EUSKAL-LOG, S.L.U.—See Deutsche Post AG; *Int'l*, pg. 2073
DHL EXEL SUPPLY CHAIN HUNGARY LIMITED—See Deutsche Post AG; *Int'l*, pg. 2073
DHL EXEL SUPPLY CHAIN PHILS., INC.—See Deutsche Post AG; *Int'l*, pg. 2073
DHL EXEL SUPPLY CHAIN PORTUGAL, S.A.—See Deutsche Post AG; *Int'l*, pg. 2072
DHL EXEL SUPPLY CHAIN (SPAIN), S.L.U.—See Deutsche Post AG; *Int'l*, pg. 2073
DHL EXEL SUPPLY CHAIN (SWEDEN) AB—See Deutsche Post AG; *Int'l*, pg. 2073
DHL EXEL SUPPLY CHAIN TRADE (POLAND) SP.Z.O.O.—See Deutsche Post AG; *Int'l*, pg. 2073
DHL EXPRESS ADUANAS PERU S.A.C.—See Deutsche Post AG; *Int'l*, pg. 2074
DHL EXPRESS ADUANAS VENEZUELA C.A.—See Deutsche Post AG; *Int'l*, pg. 2074
DHL EXPRESS (ARGENTINA) S.A.—See Deutsche Post AG; *Int'l*, pg. 2073
DHL EXPRESS A/S—See Deutsche Post AG; *Int'l*, pg. 2074
DHL EXPRESS (AUSTRALIA) PTY LTD.—See Deutsche Post AG; *Int'l*, pg. 2073
DHL EXPRESS (AUSTRIA) GMBH—See Deutsche Post AG; *Int'l*, pg. 2073
DHL EXPRESS BARCELONA SPAIN S.L.—See Deutsche Post AG; *Int'l*, pg. 2074
DHL EXPRESS (BRAZIL) LTDA—See Deutsche Post AG; *Int'l*, pg. 2074
DHL EXPRESS (BRUNEI) SDN. BHD.—See Deutsche Post AG; *Int'l*, pg. 2074
DHL EXPRESS BULGARIA EOOD—See Deutsche Post AG; *Int'l*, pg. 2074
DHL EXPRESS (CAMBODIA) LTD.—See Deutsche Post AG; *Int'l*, pg. 2074
DHL EXPRESS (CANADA) LTD.—See Deutsche Post AG; *Int'l*, pg. 2072
DHL EXPRESS (CHILE) LTDA.—See Deutsche Post AG; *Int'l*, pg. 2074
DHL EXPRESS COLOMBIA LTDA.—See Deutsche Post AG; *Int'l*, pg. 2072
DHL EXPRESS CYPRUS—See Deutsche Post AG; *Int'l*, pg. 2074
DHL EXPRESS (CZECH REPUBLIC) S.R.O.—See Deutsche Post AG; *Int'l*, pg. 2074
DHL EXPRESS (ECUADOR) S.A.—See Deutsche Post AG; *Int'l*, pg. 2072
DHL EXPRESS (EL SALVADOR) S.A. DE C.V.—See Deutsche Post AG; *Int'l*, pg. 2074
DHL EXPRESS ESTONIA AS—See Deutsche Post AG; *Int'l*, pg. 2074
DHL EXPRESS (FIJI) LTD.—See Deutsche Post AG; *Int'l*, pg. 2074
DHL EXPRESS (FINLAND) OY—See Deutsche Post AG; *Int'l*, pg. 2072
DHL EXPRESS (FRANCE) SAS—See Deutsche Post AG; *Int'l*, pg. 2074
DHL EXPRESS GERMANY GMBH—See Deutsche Post AG; *Int'l*, pg. 2073
DHL EXPRESS (HELLAS) S.A.—See Deutsche Post AG; *Int'l*, pg. 2074
DHL EXPRESS (HONG KONG) LTD—See Deutsche Post AG; *Int'l*, pg. 2074
DHL EXPRESS HUNGARY FORWARDING AND SERVICES LLC—See Deutsche Post AG; *Int'l*, pg. 2074
DHL EXPRESS HUNGARY LTD.—See Deutsche Post AG; *Int'l*, pg. 2074
DHL EXPRESS IBERIA S.L.—See Deutsche Post AG; *Int'l*, pg. 2074
DHL EXPRESS (ICELAND) EHF—See Deutsche Post AG; *Int'l*, pg. 2074
DHL EXPRESS (INDIA) PVT. LTD.—See Deutsche Post AG; *Int'l*, pg. 2074

DHL EXPRESS INTERNATIONAL (THAILAND) LTD.—See Deutsche Post AG; *Int'l*, pg. 2074
DHL EXPRESS (IRELAND) LTD.—See Deutsche Post AG; *Int'l*, pg. 2074
DHL EXPRESS LAOS SOLE COMPANY LIMITED—See Deutsche Post AG; *Int'l*, pg. 2072
DHL EXPRESS LATVIA SIA—See Deutsche Post AG; *Int'l*, pg. 2072
DHL EXPRESS LDA—See Deutsche Post AG; *Int'l*, pg. 2074
DHL EXPRESS (LUXEMBOURG) S.A.—See Deutsche Post AG; *Int'l*, pg. 2074
DHL EXPRESS (MACAU) LTD.—See Deutsche Post AG; *Int'l*, pg. 2074
DHL EXPRESS MACEDONIA D.O.O.E.L.—See Deutsche Post AG; *Int'l*, pg. 2072
DHL EXPRESS (MALAYSIA) SDN. BHD.—See Deutsche Post AG; *Int'l*, pg. 2072
DHL EXPRESS MAROC S.A.—See Deutsche Post AG; *Int'l*, pg. 2074
DHL EXPRESS MEXICO, S.A. DE C.V.—See Deutsche Post AG; *Int'l*, pg. 2074
DHL EXPRESS NAVARRA SPAIN, S.L.—See Deutsche Post AG; *Int'l*, pg. 2074
DHL EXPRESS NEPAL PVT. LTD.—See Deutsche Post AG; *Int'l*, pg. 2074
DHL EXPRESS (NETHERLANDS) B.V.—See Deutsche Post AG; *Int'l*, pg. 2074
DHL EXPRESS (NORWAY) AS—See Deutsche Post AG; *Int'l*, pg. 2074
DHL EXPRESS (PAPUA NEW GUINEA) LTD.—See Deutsche Post AG; *Int'l*, pg. 2072
DHL EXPRESS PERU S.A.C.—See Deutsche Post AG; *Int'l*, pg. 2074
DHL EXPRESS (PHILIPPINES) CORP.—See Deutsche Post AG; *Int'l*, pg. 2074
DHL EXPRESS (POLAND) SP.Z.O.O.—See Deutsche Post AG; *Int'l*, pg. 2074
DHL EXPRESS PORTUGAL, LDA.—See Deutsche Post AG; *Int'l*, pg. 2074
DHL EXPRESS (RWANDA) LIMITED—See Deutsche Post AG; *Int'l*, pg. 2072
DHL EXPRESS (SCHWEIZ) AG—See Deutsche Post AG; *Int'l*, pg. 2074
DHL EXPRESS SERVICES (FRANCE) SAS—See Deutsche Post AG; *Int'l*, pg. 2074
DHL EXPRESS (SINGAPORE) PTE LTD.—See Deutsche Post AG; *Int'l*, pg. 2074
DHL EXPRESS (SLOVAKIA), SPOL. S R. O.—See Deutsche Post AG; *Int'l*, pg. 2074
DHL EXPRESS SPAIN S.L.—See Deutsche Post AG; *Int'l*, pg. 2072
DHL EXPRESS S.R.L.—See Deutsche Post AG; *Int'l*, pg. 2074
DHL EXPRESS (SWEDEN) AB—See Deutsche Post AG; *Int'l*, pg. 2074
DHL EXPRESS (TAIWAN) CORP.—See Deutsche Post AG; *Int'l*, pg. 2074
DHL EXPRESS (THAILAND) LIMITED—See Deutsche Post AG; *Int'l*, pg. 2074
DHL EXPRESS (UK) LIMITED—See Deutsche Post AG; *Int'l*, pg. 2074
DHL EXPRESS, UNIPESSOAL, LDA.—See Deutsche Post AG; *Int'l*, pg. 2072
DHL EXPRESS (USA), INC.—See Deutsche Post AG; *Int'l*, pg. 2074
DHL EXPRESS VALENCIA SPAIN S.L.—See Deutsche Post AG; *Int'l*, pg. 2074
DHL FINANCE SERVICES B.V.—See Deutsche Post AG; *Int'l*, pg. 2074
DHL FINLAND—See Deutsche Post AG; *Int'l*, pg. 2073
DHL FLETES AEREOS, C.A.—See Deutsche Post AG; *Int'l*, pg. 2074
DHL FOOD LOGISTICS EGYPT LTD.—See Deutsche Post AG; *Int'l*, pg. 2072
DHL FOODLOGISTICS GMBH—See Deutsche Post AG; *Int'l*, pg. 2072
DHL FOOD SERVICES GMBH—See Deutsche Post AG; *Int'l*, pg. 2075
DHL FREIGHT (BELGIUM) NV—See Deutsche Post AG; *Int'l*, pg. 2075
DHL FREIGHT CZ S.R.O.—See Deutsche Post AG; *Int'l*, pg. 2072
DHL FREIGHT DENMARK A/S—See Deutsche Post AG; *Int'l*, pg. 2072
DHL FREIGHT D.O.O.—See Deutsche Post AG; *Int'l*, pg. 2072
DHL FREIGHT ESTONIA AS—See Deutsche Post AG; *Int'l*, pg. 2075
DHL FREIGHT FINLAND OY—See Deutsche Post AG; *Int'l*, pg. 2075
DHL FREIGHT (FRANCE) SAS—See Deutsche Post AG; *Int'l*, pg. 2072
DHL FREIGHT GERMANY HOLDING GMBH—See Deutsche Post AG; *Int'l*, pg. 2072
DHL FREIGHT GMBH—See Deutsche Post AG; *Int'l*, pg. 2075
DHL FREIGHT HUNGARY FORWARDING AND LOGISTICS LTD.—See Deutsche Post AG; *Int'l*, pg. 2075
DHL FREIGHT (NETHERLANDS) B.V.—See Deutsche Post AG; *Int'l*, pg. 2075
DHL FREIGHT PORTUGAL, UNIPESSOAL LDA.—See Deutsche Post AG; *Int'l*, pg. 2072
DHL FREIGHT ROMANIA S.R.L.—See Deutsche Post AG; *Int'l*, pg. 2072
DHL FREIGHT SERVICES (NETHERLANDS) B.V.—See Deutsche Post AG; *Int'l*, pg. 2072
DHL FREIGHT SLOVAKIA, S.R.O.—See Deutsche Post AG; *Int'l*, pg. 2072
DHL FREIGHT SPAIN, S.L.—See Deutsche Post AG; *Int'l*, pg. 2075
DHL FREIGHT (SWEDEN) AB—See Deutsche Post AG; *Int'l*, pg. 2075
DHL FREIGHT TASIMACILIK VE LOJISTIK HIZMETLERI A.S.—See Deutsche Post AG; *Int'l*, pg. 2072
DHL GBS (UK) LIMITED—See Deutsche Post AG; *Int'l*, pg. 2075
DHL (GHANA) LIMITED—See Deutsche Post AG; *Int'l*, pg. 2073
DHL GLOBAL EVENT LOGISTICS GMBH—See Deutsche Post AG; *Int'l*, pg. 2072
DHL GLOBAL FORWARDING ADUANAS PERU S.A.—See Deutsche Post AG; *Int'l*, pg. 2075
DHL GLOBAL FORWARDING (ARGENTINA) S.A.—See Deutsche Post AG; *Int'l*, pg. 2075
DHL GLOBAL FORWARDING (AUSTRALIA) PTY LTD.—See Deutsche Post AG; *Int'l*, pg. 2075
DHL GLOBAL FORWARDING (AUSTRIA) GMBH—See Deutsche Post AG; *Int'l*, pg. 2075
DHL GLOBAL FORWARDING BAHRAIN WLL—See Deutsche Post AG; *Int'l*, pg. 2072
DHL GLOBAL FORWARDING (BELGIUM) NV—See Deutsche Post AG; *Int'l*, pg. 2075
DHL GLOBAL FORWARDING (CAMEROON) PLC—See Deutsche Post AG; *Int'l*, pg. 2072
DHL GLOBAL FORWARDING (CANADA) INC.—See Deutsche Post AG; *Int'l*, pg. 2075
DHL GLOBAL FORWARDING (CHILE) S.A.—See Deutsche Post AG; *Int'l*, pg. 2075
DHL GLOBAL FORWARDING & CO. LLC—See Deutsche Post AG; *Int'l*, pg. 2075
DHL GLOBAL FORWARDING (COLOMBIA) LTDA.—See Deutsche Post AG; *Int'l*, pg. 2075
DHL GLOBAL FORWARDING COTE D'IVOIRE SA—See Deutsche Post AG; *Int'l*, pg. 2075
DHL GLOBAL FORWARDING CUSTOMS, LLC—See Deutsche Post AG; *Int'l*, pg. 2072
DHL GLOBAL FORWARDING (CZ) S. R. O.—See Deutsche Post AG; *Int'l*, pg. 2075
DHL GLOBAL FORWARDING (DENMARK) A/S—See Deutsche Post AG; *Int'l*, pg. 2075
DHL GLOBAL FORWARDING D.O.O. BELGRADE—See Deutsche Post AG; *Int'l*, pg. 2072
DHL GLOBAL FORWARDING (ECUADOR) S.A.—See Deutsche Post AG; *Int'l*, pg. 2075
DHL GLOBAL FORWARDING EGYPT S.A.E.—See Deutsche Post AG; *Int'l*, pg. 2075
DHL GLOBAL FORWARDING (FINLAND) OY—See Deutsche Post AG; *Int'l*, pg. 2075
DHL GLOBAL FORWARDING (GABON) SA—See Deutsche Post AG; *Int'l*, pg. 2075
DHL GLOBAL FORWARDING GMBH—See Deutsche Post AG; *Int'l*, pg. 2075
DHL GLOBAL FORWARDING (GUATEMALA) S.A.—See Deutsche Post AG; *Int'l*, pg. 2075
DHL GLOBAL FORWARDING HELLAS S.A.—See Deutsche Post AG; *Int'l*, pg. 2075
DHL GLOBAL FORWARDING (HONG KONG) LIMITED—See Deutsche Post AG; *Int'l*, pg. 2075
DHL GLOBAL FORWARDING HUNGARY KFT.—See Deutsche Post AG; *Int'l*, pg. 2075
DHL GLOBAL FORWARDING (IRELAND) LIMITED—See Deutsche Post AG; *Int'l*, pg. 2075
DHL GLOBAL FORWARDING (ITALY) S. P. A.—See Deutsche Post AG; *Int'l*, pg. 2075
DHL GLOBAL FORWARDING (KUWAIT) COMPANY WLL—See Deutsche Post AG; *Int'l*, pg. 2075
DHL GLOBAL FORWARDING LANKA (PRIVATE) LIMITED—See Deutsche Post AG; *Int'l*, pg. 2075
DHL GLOBAL FORWARDING LEBANON S.A.L.—See Deutsche Post AG; *Int'l*, pg. 2075
DHL GLOBAL FORWARDING (LUXEMBOURG) S.A.—See Deutsche Post AG; *Int'l*, pg. 2075
DHL GLOBAL FORWARDING MANAGEMENT (ASIA PACIFIC) PTE. LTD.—See Deutsche Post AG; *Int'l*, pg. 2076
DHL GLOBAL FORWARDING MANAGEMENT GMBH—See Deutsche Post AG; *Int'l*, pg. 2072
DHL GLOBAL FORWARDING (MAURITIUS) LTD.—See Deutsche Post AG; *Int'l*, pg. 2072
DHL GLOBAL FORWARDING (MEXICO) S.A. DE C.V.—See Deutsche Post AG; *Int'l*, pg. 2075
DHL GLOBAL FORWARDING (NETHERLANDS) B.V.—See Deutsche Post AG; *Int'l*, pg. 2075
DHL GLOBAL FORWARDING (NEW ZEALAND) LIMITED—See Deutsche Post AG; *Int'l*, pg. 2075
DHL GLOBAL FORWARDING (NICARAGUA) S.A.—See Deutsche Post AG; *Int'l*, pg. 2075
DHL GLOBAL FORWARDING NIGERIA LIMITED—See Deutsche Post AG; *Int'l*, pg. 2072
DHL GLOBAL FORWARDING PAKISTAN (PRIVATE) LIMITED—See Deutsche Post AG; *Int'l*, pg. 2076
DHL GLOBAL FORWARDING PERU S.A.—See Deutsche Post AG; *Int'l*, pg. 2076
DHL GLOBAL FORWARDING (PHILIPPINES) INC.—See Deutsche Post AG; *Int'l*, pg. 2076
DHL GLOBAL FORWARDING PORTUGAL, LDA.—See Deutsche Post AG; *Int'l*, pg. 2076
DHL GLOBAL FORWARDING PORTUGAL, UNIPESSOAL, LDA.—See Deutsche Post AG; *Int'l*, pg. 2072
DHL GLOBAL FORWARDING (SENEGAL) S.A.—See Deutsche Post AG; *Int'l*, pg. 2075
DHL GLOBAL FORWARDING SP. Z.O.O.—See Deutsche Post AG; *Int'l*, pg. 2076
DHL GLOBAL FORWARDING (SWEDEN) AB—See Deutsche Post AG; *Int'l*, pg. 2075
DHL GLOBAL FORWARDING TASIMACILIK A.S.—See Deutsche Post AG; *Int'l*, pg. 2076
DHL GLOBAL FORWARDING (THAILAND) LIMITED—See Deutsche Post AG; *Int'l*, pg. 2072
DHL GLOBAL FORWARDING (UGANDA) LIMITED—See Deutsche Post AG; *Int'l*, pg. 2075
DHL GLOBAL FORWARDING (UK) LIMITED—See Deutsche Post AG; *Int'l*, pg. 2075
DHL GLOBAL FORWARDING VENEZUELA, C.A.—See Deutsche Post AG; *Int'l*, pg. 2075
DHL GLOBAL FORWARDING ZIMBABWE LTD.—See Deutsche Post AG; *Int'l*, pg. 2072
DHL GLOBAL MAIL (JAPAN) K. K.—See Deutsche Post AG; *Int'l*, pg. 2076
DHL GLOBAL MAIL (SINGAPORE) PTE. LTD.—See Deutsche Post AG; *Int'l*, pg. 2076
DHL GLOBAL MAIL—See Deutsche Post AG; *Int'l*, pg. 2076
DHL GLOBAL MAIL UK—See Deutsche Post AG; *Int'l*, pg. 2072
DHL GLOBAL MANAGEMENT GMBH—See Deutsche Post AG; *Int'l*, pg. 2072
DHL GLOBAL MATCH (BELGIUM) N.V.—See Deutsche Post AG; *Int'l*, pg. 2072
DHL GROUP SERVICES NV/SA—See Deutsche Post AG; *Int'l*, pg. 2073
DHL HOLDING (FRANCE) SAS—See Deutsche Post AG; *Int'l*, pg. 2076
DHL HOLDINGS (USA), INC.—See Deutsche Post AG; *Int'l*, pg. 2076
DHL HOME DELIVERY GMBH—See Deutsche Post AG; *Int'l*, pg. 2076
DHL HRADFLUTNINGAR EHF—See Deutsche Post AG; *Int'l*, pg. 2076
DHL HUB LEIPZIG GMBH—See Deutsche Post AG; *Int'l*, pg. 2076
DHL INFORMATION SERVICES (EUROPE) S.R.O.—See Deutsche Post AG; *Int'l*, pg. 2076
DHL INTERNATIONAL (ALGERIE) S.A.R.L.—See Deutsche Post AG; *Int'l*, pg. 2076
DHL INTERNATIONAL ANTILLES SARL—See Deutsche Post AG; *Int'l*, pg. 2073
DHL INTERNATIONAL (BEOGRADE) D.O.O.—See Deutsche Post AG; *Int'l*, pg. 2076
DHL INTERNATIONAL BOTSWANA (PTY) LTD.—See Deutsche Post AG; *Int'l*, pg. 2073
DHL INTERNATIONAL (BRUNEI) SDN BHD—See Deutsche Post AG; *Int'l*, pg. 2076
DHL INTERNATIONAL B.S.C. (C)—See Deutsche Post AG; *Int'l*, pg. 2076
DHL INTERNATIONAL B.V.—See Deutsche Post AG; *Int'l*, pg. 2076
DHL INTERNATIONAL CAMEROON SARL—See Deutsche Post AG; *Int'l*, pg. 2076
DHL INTERNATIONAL (CONGO) SPRL—See Deutsche Post AG; *Int'l*, pg. 2076
DHL INTERNATIONAL COTE D'IVOIRE SARL—See Deutsche Post AG; *Int'l*, pg. 2076
DHL INTERNATIONAL D.O.O.—See Deutsche Post AG; *Int'l*, pg. 2077
DHL INTERNATIONAL EXPRESS (FRANCE) SAS—See Deutsche Post AG; *Int'l*, pg. 2076
DHL INTERNATIONAL (GAMBIA) LTD.—See Deutsche Post AG; *Int'l*, pg. 2076
DHL INTERNATIONAL GMBH—See Deutsche Post AG; *Int'l*, pg. 2073
DHL INTERNATIONAL HELLAS S.A.—See Deutsche Post AG; *Int'l*, pg. 2076
DHL INTERNATIONAL KAZAKHSTAN, TOO—See Deutsche Post AG; *Int'l*, pg. 2076
DHL INTERNATIONAL LTD.—See Deutsche Post AG; *Int'l*, pg. 2076
DHL INTERNATIONAL LTD.—See Deutsche Post AG; *Int'l*, pg. 2076
DHL INTERNATIONAL MADAGASCAR SA—See Deutsche Post AG; *Int'l*, pg. 2076
DHL INTERNATIONAL MALAWI LTD.—See Deutsche Post AG; *Int'l*, pg. 2076
DHL INTERNATIONAL MAURITANIE SARL—See Deutsche Post AG; *Int'l*, pg. 2073

COMPANY NAME INDEX

DHL INTERNATIONAL (NIGERIA) LTD.—See Deutsche Post AG; *Int'l*, pg. 2076
DHL INTERNATIONAL (PTY) LTD.—See Deutsche Post AG; *Int'l*, pg. 2076
DHL INTERNATIONAL REUNION SARL—See Deutsche Post AG; *Int'l*, pg. 2073
DHL INTERNATIONAL ROMANIA SRL—See Deutsche Post AG; *Int'l*, pg. 2077
DHL INTERNATIONAL S.A./N.V.—See Deutsche Post AG; *Int'l*, pg. 2073
DHL INTERNATIONAL-SARAJEVO D.O.O.—See Deutsche Post AG; *Int'l*, pg. 2077
DHL INTERNATIONAL SENEGAL SARL—See Deutsche Post AG; *Int'l*, pg. 2077
DHL INTERNATIONAL S.R.L.—See Deutsche Post AG; *Int'l*, pg. 2077
DHL INTERNATIONAL (THAILAND) LTD.—See Deutsche Post AG; *Int'l*, pg. 2073
DHL INTERNATIONAL (UGANDA) LTD.—See Deutsche Post AG; *Int'l*, pg. 2076
DHL INTERNATIONAL (UK) LTD.—See Deutsche Post AG; *Int'l*, pg. 2076
DHL INTL (BULGARIA) E.O.O.D.—See Deutsche Post AG; *Int'l*, pg. 2077
DHL INTL (SLOVAKIA) SPOL. S R.O.—See Deutsche Post AG; *Int'l*, pg. 2077
DHL ISC (HONG KONG) LIMITED—See Deutsche Post AG; *Int'l*, pg. 2076
DHL (ISRAEL) LTD.—See Deutsche Post AG; *Int'l*, pg. 2073
DHL (JAMAICA) LTD—See Deutsche Post AG; *Int'l*, pg. 2073
DHL JAPAN, INC.—See Deutsche Post AG; *Int'l*, pg. 2077
DHL KEELLS (PRIVATE) LIMITED—See Deutsche Post AG; *Int'l*, pg. 2077
DHL KOREA LTD.—See Deutsche Post AG; *Int'l*, pg. 2077
DHL KUWAIT CO. LTD—See Deutsche Post AG; *Int'l*, pg. 2077
DHL LAO LIMITED—See Deutsche Post AG; *Int'l*, pg. 2077
DHL (LATVIA) SIA—See Deutsche Post AG; *Int'l*, pg. 2073
DHL LESOTHO (PROPRIETARY) LTD.—See Deutsche Post AG; *Int'l*, pg. 2077
DHL LOGISTICA D.O.O.—See Deutsche Post AG; *Int'l*, pg. 2077
DHL LOGISTICS (CAMBODIA) LTD.—See Deutsche Post AG; *Int'l*, pg. 2077
DHL LOGISTICS GHANA LTD.—See Deutsche Post AG; *Int'l*, pg. 2078
DHL LOGISTICS OOO—See Deutsche Post AG; *Int'l*, pg. 2077
DHL LOGISTICS (SCHWEIZ) AG—See Deutsche Post AG; *Int'l*, pg. 2077
DHL LOGISTICS (SLOVAKIA), SPOL. S R. O.—See Deutsche Post AG; *Int'l*, pg. 2077
DHL LOGISTICS TANZANIA LIMITED—See Deutsche Post AG; *Int'l*, pg. 2077
DHL LOGISTICS (UKRAINE) LTD.—See Deutsche Post AG; *Int'l*, pg. 2077
DHL LOGISTIK SERVICE GMBH—See Deutsche Post AG; *Int'l*, pg. 2078
DHL LOJISTIK HIZMETLERI A.S.—See Deutsche Post AG; *Int'l*, pg. 2077
DHL MANAGEMENT (SCHWEIZ) AG—See Deutsche Post AG; *Int'l*, pg. 2077
DHL (MAURITIUS) LTD.—See Deutsche Post AG; *Int'l*, pg. 2073
DHL METROPOLITAN LOGISTICS SC MEXICO S.A. DE C.V.—See Deutsche Post AG; *Int'l*, pg. 2078
D HLM NOTRE LOGIS; *Int'l*, pg. 1899
DHL MOZAMBIQUE LDA.—See Deutsche Post AG; *Int'l*, pg. 2077
DHL (NAMIBIA) (PTY) LTD.—See Deutsche Post AG; *Int'l*, pg. 2073
DHL NETWORK OPERATIONS (USA), INC.—See Deutsche Post AG; *Int'l*, pg. 2078
DHL OF CURACAO N.V.—See Deutsche Post AG; *Int'l*, pg. 2079
DH LOGISTIC PROPERTY VIETNAM CO., LTD.—See Daiwa House Industry Co., Ltd.; *Int'l*, pg. 1945
DHL PAKET GMBH—See Deutsche Post AG; *Int'l*, pg. 2078
DHL PAKISTAN (PRIVATE) LIMITED—See Deutsche Post AG; *Int'l*, pg. 2077
DHL PANAMA S.A.—See Deutsche Post AG; *Int'l*, pg. 2077
DHL (PARAGUAY) S.R.L.—See Deutsche Post AG; *Int'l*, pg. 2073
DHL PARCEL PORTUGAL, UNIPESSOAL LDA.—See Deutsche Post AG; *Int'l*, pg. 2078
DHL PENSIONS INVESTMENT FUND LIMITED—See Deutsche Post AG; *Int'l*, pg. 2077
DHL PIPELIFE LOGISTIK GMBH—See Deutsche Post AG; *Int'l*, pg. 2077
DHL QUALITY CARGO AS—See Deutsche Post AG; *Int'l*, pg. 2077
DHL RAIL AB—See Deutsche Post AG; *Int'l*, pg. 2077
DHL SAINGHIN SARL—See Deutsche Post AG; *Int'l*, pg. 2077

DHL SANDOUVILLE SARL—See Deutsche Post AG; *Int'l*, pg. 2078
DHL, S.A.—See Deutsche Post AG; *Int'l*, pg. 2076
DHL SC TRANSPORT SASU—See Deutsche Post AG; *Int'l*, pg. 2078
DHL SERVICES LIMITED—See Deutsche Post AG; *Int'l*, pg. 2077
DHL SERVICES LOGISTIQUES SAS—See Deutsche Post AG; *Int'l*, pg. 2077
DHL-SINOTRANS INTERNATIONAL AIR COURIER LTD.—See China Merchants Group Limited; *Int'l*, pg. 1522
DHL SOLUTIONS (BELGIUM) NV—See Deutsche Post AG; *Int'l*, pg. 2077
DHL SOLUTIONS FASHION GMBH—See Deutsche Post AG; *Int'l*, pg. 2077
DHL SOLUTIONS GMBH—See Deutsche Post AG; *Int'l*, pg. 2077
DHL SOLUTIONS GROSSGUT GMBH—See Deutsche Post AG; *Int'l*, pg. 2077
DHL SOLUTIONS RETAIL GMBH—See Deutsche Post AG; *Int'l*, pg. 2077
DHL SOLUTIONS (USA), INC.—See Deutsche Post AG; *Int'l*, pg. 2077
DHL STOCK EXPRESS SAS—See Deutsche Post AG; *Int'l*, pg. 2077
DHL SUPPLY CHAIN (AUSTRALIA) PTY LIMITED—See Deutsche Post AG; *Int'l*, pg. 2077
DHL SUPPLY CHAIN (BELGIUM) NV—See Deutsche Post AG; *Int'l*, pg. 2077
DHL SUPPLY CHAIN (CHILE) S.A.—See Deutsche Post AG; *Int'l*, pg. 2077
DHL SUPPLY CHAIN (DENMARK) A / S—See Deutsche Post AG; *Int'l*, pg. 2078
DHL SUPPLY CHAIN (FINLAND) OY—See Deutsche Post AG; *Int'l*, pg. 2077
DHL SUPPLY CHAIN INC.—See Deutsche Post AG; *Int'l*, pg. 2078
DHL SUPPLY CHAIN (IRELAND) LIMITED—See Deutsche Post AG; *Int'l*, pg. 2077
DHL SUPPLY CHAIN K. K.—See Deutsche Post AG; *Int'l*, pg. 2078
DHL SUPPLY CHAIN (KOREA) LTD.—See Deutsche Post AG; *Int'l*, pg. 2078
DHL SUPPLY CHAIN MANAGEMENT GMBH—See Deutsche Post AG; *Int'l*, pg. 2078
DHL SUPPLY CHAIN (NEW ZEALAND) LIMITED—See Deutsche Post AG; *Int'l*, pg. 2078
DHL SUPPLY CHAIN (NORWAY) AS—See Deutsche Post AG; *Int'l*, pg. 2078
DHL SUPPLY CHAIN (POLAND) SP. Z O.O.—See Deutsche Post AG; *Int'l*, pg. 2078
DHL SUPPLY CHAIN SINGAPORE PTE. LTD.—See Deutsche Post AG; *Int'l*, pg. 2078
DHL SUPPLY CHAIN (SOUTH AFRICA) (PTY) LTD.—See Deutsche Post AG; *Int'l*, pg. 2078
DHL SUPPLY CHAIN (VIETNAM) LIMITED—See Deutsche Post AG; *Int'l*, pg. 2078
DHL SWAZILAND (PROPRIETARY) LTD.—See Deutsche Post AG; *Int'l*, pg. 2078
DHL (TANZANIA) LTD.—See Deutsche Post AG; *Int'l*, pg. 2072
DHL TRADE FAIRS AND EVENTS (UK) LIMITED—See Deutsche Post AG; *Int'l*, pg. 2078
DHL TRADE FAIRS & EVENTS GMBH—See Deutsche Post AG; *Int'l*, pg. 2078
DHL-TRANSPORTADORES RAPIDOS INTERNACIONAIS LDA.—See Deutsche Post AG; *Int'l*, pg. 2078
DHL (URUGUAY) S.R.L.—See Deutsche Post AG; *Int'l*, pg. 2073
DHL VERWALTUNGS GMBH—See Deutsche Post AG; *Int'l*, pg. 2078
DHL-VNPT EXPRESS LTD.—See Deutsche Post AG; *Int'l*, pg. 2078
DHL VOIGT INTERNATIONAL GMBH—See Deutsche Post AG; *Int'l*, pg. 2078
DHL WAHL INTERNATIONAL GMBH—See Deutsche Post AG; *Int'l*, pg. 2078
DHL WORLDWIDE EXPRESS (BANGLADESH) PRIVATE LIMITED—See Deutsche Post AG; *Int'l*, pg. 2078
DHL WORLDWIDE EXPRESS CAMBODIA LTD—See Deutsche Post AG; *Int'l*, pg. 2078
DHL WORLDWIDE EXPRESS CARGO LLC—See Deutsche Post AG; *Int'l*, pg. 2078
DHL WORLDWIDE EXPRESS, INC—See Deutsche Post AG; *Int'l*, pg. 2078
DHL WORLDWIDE EXPRESS KENYA LTD.—See Deutsche Post AG; *Int'l*, pg. 2078
DHL WORLDWIDE EXPRESS LOGISTICS NV /SA—See Deutsche Post AG; *Int'l*, pg. 2078
DHL WORLDWIDE EXPRESS (PH) CORP.—See Deutsche Post AG; *Int'l*, pg. 2078
DHL WORLDWIDE EXPRESS (PNG) LTD.—See Deutsche Post AG; *Int'l*, pg. 2078
DHL WORLDWIDE EXPRESS TASIMACILIK VE TICARET A.S.—See Deutsche Post AG; *Int'l*, pg. 2078
DHL YEMEN LTD.—See Deutsche Post AG; *Int'l*, pg. 2078
D&H MANUFACTURING COMPANY—See ONEX Corporation; *Int'l*, pg. 5578

D & H MASONRY, INC.; *U.S. Private*, pg. 1136
DH MISSION BAY MANAGEMENT LLC—See Hyatt Hotels Corporation; *U.S. Public*, pg. 1077
DH MISSION PALMS MANAGEMENT LLC—See Hyatt Hotels Corporation; *U.S. Public*, pg. 1077
DHOBY GHAUT HOLDINGS SDN. BHD.—See Pappajack Berhad; *Int'l*, pg. 5733
DHOBY GHAUT (KAPAR) SDN. BHD.—See Pappajack Berhad; *Int'l*, pg. 5733
DHOBY GHAUT (M) SDN. BHD.—See Pappajack Berhad; *Int'l*, pg. 5733
DHOBY GHAUT (SEL) SDN. BHD.—See Pappajack Berhad; *Int'l*, pg. 5733
DHOFAR BEVERAGE AND FOOD STUFF COMPANY S.A.O.G; *Int'l*, pg. 2099
DHOFAR CATTLE FEED COMPANY SAOG; *Int'l*, pg. 2099
DHOFAR FISHERIES & FOOD INDUSTRIES COMPANY S.A.O.G.; *Int'l*, pg. 2099
DHOFAR INSURANCE COMPANY S.A.O.G; *Int'l*, pg. 2099
DHOFAR INTERNATIONAL DEVELOPMENT & INVESTMENT HOLDING COMPANY S.A.O.G; *Int'l*, pg. 2099
DHOFAR POULTRY COMPANY SAOG; *Int'l*, pg. 2099
DHOFAR TOURISM COMPANY SAOG; *Int'l*, pg. 2100
DHOFAR UNIVERSITY; *Int'l*, pg. 2100
DHOLLANDIA FRANCE; *Int'l*, pg. 2100
D. HONORE CONSTRUCTION, INC.; *U.S. Private*, pg. 1140
DHOOT INDUSTRIAL FINANCE LIMITED - SAMPOORNA TRADERS DIVISION—See Dhoot Industrial Finance Limited; *Int'l*, pg. 2100
DHOOT INDUSTRIAL FINANCE LIMITED; *Int'l*, pg. 2100
DHOSPAAK CO., LTD.—See Thai Beverage Public Company Limited; *Int'l*, pg. 7589
DHOUSE PATTANA PUBLIC COMPANY LIMITED; *Int'l*, pg. 2100
D.H. PACE COMPANY INC.—See E.E. Newcomer Enterprises Inc.; *U.S. Private*, pg. 1305
DHPC TECHNOLOGIES, INC.—See Veritas Capital Fund Management, LLC; *U.S. Private*, pg. 4363
DHP INDIA LIMITED.; *Int'l*, pg. 2100
DH PRIVATE EQUITY PARTNERS LLP; *Int'l*, pg. 2097
DH REALTY PARTNERS INC.; *U.S. Private*, pg. 1221
DHR FINLAND OY—See Danaher Corporation; *U.S. Public*, pg. 625
DHR HOLDING INDIA PVT. LTD.—See Danaher Corporation; *U.S. Public*, pg. 625
DH RICHMOND MANAGEMENT LLC—See Hyatt Hotels Corporation; *U.S. Public*, pg. 1077
DHR INTERNATIONAL, INC. - MILWAUKEE—See DHR International, Inc.; *U.S. Private*, pg. 1221
DHR INTERNATIONAL, INC. - NEW YORK—See DHR International, Inc.; *U.S. Private*, pg. 1221
DHR INTERNATIONAL, INC.; *U.S. Private*, pg. 1221
DH ROSLYN MANAGEMENT LLC—See Hyatt Hotels Corporation; *U.S. Public*, pg. 1077
DH RSC MANAGEMENT LLC—See Hyatt Hotels Corporation; *U.S. Public*, pg. 1077
DHRUVA CAPITAL SERVICES LIMITED; *Int'l*, pg. 2100
DHRUV CONSULTANCY SERVICES LIMITED; *Int'l*, pg. 2100
DHRUV ESTATES LIMITED; *Int'l*, pg. 2100
DHRUV WELLNESS LIMITED; *Int'l*, pg. 2100
DH SAN ANTONIO MANAGEMENT LLC—See Hyatt Hotels Corporation; *U.S. Public*, pg. 1077
DHS CONSULTING, LLC—See Accenture plc; *Int'l*, pg. 86
DH SCOTTSDALE MANAGEMENT LLC—See Hyatt Hotels Corporation; *U.S. Public*, pg. 1077
DH SEATTLE MANAGEMENT LLC—See Hyatt Hotels Corporation; *U.S. Public*, pg. 1077
DH SJ MANAGEMENT LLC—See Hyatt Hotels Corporation; *U.S. Public*, pg. 1077
DHS OIL INTERNATIONAL PTY LTD—See Imdex Limited; *Int'l*, pg. 3623
DHS OIL INTERNATIONAL PTY LTD—See Lime Rock Partners, LLC; *U.S. Private*, pg. 2456
DHSTEEL; *Int'l*, pg. 2100
DH STOWE MANAGEMENT LLC—See Hyatt Hotels Corporation; *U.S. Public*, pg. 1077
DH SUNRIVER MANAGEMENT LLC—See Hyatt Hotels Corporation; *U.S. Public*, pg. 1077
DH TAHOE MANAGEMENT LLC—See Hyatt Hotels Corporation; *U.S. Public*, pg. 1077
DHT HOLDINGS, INC.; *Int'l*, pg. 2100
DHT MANAGEMENT AS—See DHT Holdings, Inc.; *Int'l*, pg. 2100
DHT MANAGEMENT S.A.M.—See DHT Holdings, Inc.; *Int'l*, pg. 2100
DHT SHIP MANAGEMENT (SINGAPORE) PTE. LTD.—See DHT Holdings, Inc.; *Int'l*, pg. 2100
DHU IBERICA, S.A.—See Dr. Willmar Schwabe GmbH & Co. KG; *Int'l*, pg. 2195
D&H UNITED FUELING SOLUTIONS, INC.; *U.S. Private*, pg. 1137
DHUNSERI INVESTMENTS LIMITED; *Int'l*, pg. 2100
DHUNSERI TEA & INDUSTRIES LTD.; *Int'l*, pg. 2100
D'HUY ENGINEERING, INC. (DEI)—See H.I.G. Capital, LLC; *U.S. Private*, pg. 1827

DHV ENGINEERING CONSULTANCY CO. LTD.—See Koninklijke HaskoningDHV Groep B.V.; *Int'l*, pg. 4266
DHV HOLDINGS USA INC.—See Koninklijke HaskoningDHV Groep B.V.; *Int'l*, pg. 4266
DHV HYDROPROJEKT SP. Z O.O.—See Koninklijke HaskoningDHV Groep B.V.; *Int'l*, pg. 4266
DHV, S.A.—See Koninklijke HaskoningDHV Groep B.V.; *Int'l*, pg. 4266
DH WASHINGTON MANAGEMENT LLC—See Hyatt Hotels Corporation; *U.S. Public*, pg. 1077
DH WEST LOOP MANAGEMENT—See Hyatt Hotels Corporation; *U.S. Public*, pg. 1077
DH WILD DUNES MANAGEMENT LLC—See Hyatt Hotels Corporation; *U.S. Public*, pg. 1077
DHX INCORPORATED; *U.S. Private*, pg. 1221
DHX MEDIA LTD.; *Int'l*, pg. 2100
DHX MEDIA LTD. - TORONTO—See DHX Media Ltd.; *Int'l*, pg. 2101
DHX MEDIA LTD. - VANCOUVER—See DHX Media Ltd.; *Int'l*, pg. 2101
DHYAANI TILE & MARBLEZ LIMITED; *Int'l*, pg. 2101
DH YORK MANAGEMENT LLC—See Hyatt Hotels Corporation; *U.S. Public*, pg. 1077
DIA AQUA SOLUTIONS CO., INC.—See Mitsubishi Gas Chemical Company, Inc.; *Int'l*, pg. 4948
DIAB ASIA PACIFIC PTE LTD—See Ratos AB; *Int'l*, pg. 6218
DIAB A/S—See Ratos AB; *Int'l*, pg. 6218
DIAB AUSTRALIA PTY. LTD.—See Ratos AB; *Int'l*, pg. 6218
DIAB COMPOSITE MATERIAL TECHNOLOGY (KUNSHAN) CO. LTD.—See Ratos AB; *Int'l*, pg. 6218
DIABDIS SP. Z O.O.—See NEUCA S.A.; *Int'l*, pg. 5218
DIAB ECUADOR S.A.—See Ratos AB; *Int'l*, pg. 6218
DIAB ENGINEERING CONSULTANTS—See NRW Holdings Limited; *Int'l*, pg. 5475
DIAB ENGINEERING PTY. LTD.—See NRW Holdings Limited; *Int'l*, pg. 5475
DIABETER B.V.—See Medtronic plc; *Int'l*, pg. 4787
DIABETES MANAGEMENT & SUPPLIES LLC—See AdaptHealth Corp.; *U.S. Public*, pg. 38
DIABETES MEDICAL SUPPLY CENTER OF THE MIDLANDS—See AdaptHealth Corp.; *U.S. Public*, pg. 38
DIABETES RESEARCH & WELLNESS FOUNDATION; *U.S. Private*, pg. 1222
DIABETES SELF-MANAGEMENT CENTER, INC.—See UnitedHealth Group Incorporated; *U.S. Public*, pg. 2244
DIABETES SPECIALTY CENTER, LLC—See Advent International Corporation; *U.S. Private*, pg. 104
DIABETICSUPPLIES.COM, INC.; *U.S. Private*, pg. 1222
DIAB GMBH—See Ratos AB; *Int'l*, pg. 6218
DIAB INC.—See Ratos AB; *Int'l*, pg. 6218
DIAB INTERNATIONAL AB—See Ratos AB; *Int'l*, pg. 6218
DIABLO DIALYSIS, LLC—See DaVita Inc.; *U.S. Public*, pg. 638
DIABLO FOODS; *U.S. Private*, pg. 1222
DIABLO MEDIA LLC; *U.S. Private*, pg. 1222
DIABLO RESOURCES LIMITED; *Int'l*, pg. 2101
DIABLO SUBARU; *U.S. Private*, pg. 1222
DIABLO VALLEY PACKAGING INC.—See Keystone Group, L.P.; *U.S. Private*, pg. 2297
DIAB LTD—See Ratos AB; *Int'l*, pg. 6218
DIAB MIDDLE EAST—See Ratos AB; *Int'l*, pg. 6218
DIAB SALES AB—See Ratos AB; *Int'l*, pg. 6218
DIAB SA—See Ratos AB; *Int'l*, pg. 6218
DIAB SPAIN S.L.—See Ratos AB; *Int'l*, pg. 6218
DIAB SPA—See Ratos AB; *Int'l*, pg. 6218
DIAB SP. Z O.O.—See Ratos AB; *Int'l*, pg. 6218
DIACEUTICS PLC; *Int'l*, pg. 2101
DIA CHEMICAL CO., LTD.—See Kaneka Corporation; *Int'l*, pg. 4067
DIACOM CORPORATION—See Nova Capital Management Limited; *Int'l*, pg. 5450
DIA CONSULTANTS CO., LTD.—See DN HOLDINGS CO.,LTD; *Int'l*, pg. 2147
DIACON TECHNOLOGIES LIMITED—See Lonza Group AG; *Int'l*, pg. 4553
DIAC SALAF S.A.; *Int'l*, pg. 2101
DIADEIS NEW YORK, LLC—See HPS Investment Partners, LLC; *U.S. Private*, pg. 1997
DIA DENTAL AESTHETICS INTERNATIONAL INC.; *Int'l*, pg. 2101
DIADORA AMERICA, INC.—See Diadora Invicta; *Int'l*, pg. 2101
DIADORA INVICTA; *Int'l*, pg. 2101
DIADROM HOLDING AB; *Int'l*, pg. 2101
DIA ECOTECH HIROSHIMA CO., LTD.—See Mitsubishi Heavy Industries, Ltd.; *Int'l*, pg. 4953
DIA ENTERPRISE LIMITED—See Nippon Filcon Co., Ltd.; *Int'l*, pg. 5317
DIAEXPERT GMBH—See Ypsomed Holding AG; *Int'l*, pg. 8605
DIA-FRAG INDUSTRIA E COMERCIO DE MOTOPECAS LTDA.—See Westinghouse Air Brake Technologies Corporation; *U.S. Public*, pg. 2357
DIAGENODE CO., LTD.—See Hologic, Inc.; *U.S. Public*, pg. 1044

DIAGENODE SA—See Hologic, Inc.; *U.S. Public*, pg. 1044
DIAGENODE SPA—See Hologic, Inc.; *U.S. Public*, pg. 1044
DIAGEO BRANDS BV—See Diageo plc; *Int'l*, pg. 2102
DIAGEO CANADA, INC.—See Diageo plc; *Int'l*, pg. 2102
DIAGEO CANADA INC.—See Diageo plc; *Int'l*, pg. 2102
DIAGEO CANADA INC.—See Diageo plc; *Int'l*, pg. 2102
DIAGEO CAPITAL BV—See Diageo plc; *Int'l*, pg. 2102
DIAGEO CAPITAL PLC—See Diageo plc; *Int'l*, pg. 2102
DIAGEO COLOMBIA S.A.—See Diageo plc; *Int'l*, pg. 2102
DIAGEO GREAT BRITAIN LIMITED—See Diageo plc; *Int'l*, pg. 2102
DIAGEO HOLDINGS LTD.—See Diageo plc; *Int'l*, pg. 2102
DIAGEO INDIA PRIVATE LIMITED—See Diageo plc; *Int'l*, pg. 2102
DIAGEO INVESTMENT CORPORATION—See Diageo plc; *Int'l*, pg. 2102
DIAGEO IRELAND—See Diageo plc; *Int'l*, pg. 2102
DIAGEO JAPAN K.K—See Diageo plc; *Int'l*, pg. 2102
DIAGEO KIRIN CO., LTD.—See Kirin Holdings Company, Limited; *Int'l*, pg. 4187
DIAGEO KOREA COMPANY LIMITED—See Diageo plc; *Int'l*, pg. 2102
DIAGEO MOET HENNESSY (THAILAND) LIMITED—See LVMH Moet Hennessy Louis Vuitton SE; *Int'l*, pg. 4599
DIAGEO NORTH AMERICA INC.—See Diageo plc; *Int'l*, pg. 2102
DIAGEO NORTH AMERICA, INC.—See Diageo plc; *Int'l*, pg. 2102
DIAGEO NORTH AMERICA INC.—See Diageo plc; *Int'l*, pg. 2102
DIAGEO NORTH AMERICA—See Diageo plc; *Int'l*, pg. 2102
DIAGEO NORTH AMERICA—See Diageo plc; *Int'l*, pg. 2102
DIAGEO NORTH AMERICA—See Diageo plc; *Int'l*, pg. 2102
DIAGEO NORTHERN IRELAND—See Diageo plc; *Int'l*, pg. 2102
DIAGEO PLC; *Int'l*, pg. 2101
DIAGEO SCOTLAND LIMITED—See Diageo plc; *Int'l*, pg. 2102
DIAGEO UK—See Diageo plc; *Int'l*, pg. 2102
DIAGEO USVI INC.—See Diageo plc; *Int'l*, pg. 2102
DIAGNOS INC.; *Int'l*, pg. 2103
DIAGNOS POLAND SP. Z O.O.—See Diagnos Inc.; *Int'l*, pg. 2103
DIAGNOSTIC AND THERAPEUTIC CENTER OF ATHENS-HYGEIA S.A.; *Int'l*, pg. 2103
DIAGNOSTICA STAGO, INC.—See Diagnostica Stago S.A.S.; *Int'l*, pg. 2103
DIAGNOSTICA STAGO S.A.S.; *Int'l*, pg. 2103
DIAGNOSTIC CLINIC MED GROUP; *U.S. Private*, pg. 1222
DIAGNOSTIC CLINIC OF LONGVIEW—See Community Health Systems, Inc.; *U.S. Public*, pg. 552
DIAGNOSTIC CLINIC—See GuideWell Mutual Holding Corporation; *U.S. Private*, pg. 1813
DIAGNOSTIC CONSULTING NETWORK, INC.; *U.S. Private*, pg. 1222
DIAGNOSTIC ENDOSCOPY CENTER, LLC—See KKR & Co. Inc.; *U.S. Public*, pg. 1245
DIAGNOSTIC GRIFOLS, S.A.—See Grifols, S.A.; *Int'l*, pg. 3084
DIAGNOSTIC GROUP LLC—See Demant A/S; *Int'l*, pg. 2023
DIAGNOSTIC HYBRIDS, INC.—See QuidelOrtho Corporation; *U.S. Public*, pg. 1757
DIAGNOSTIC IMAGING ASSOCIATES—See RadNet, Inc.; *U.S. Public*, pg. 1761
DIAGNOSTIC IMAGING OF BRANDYWINE VALLEY, LP—See Community Health Systems, Inc.; *U.S. Public*, pg. 552
DIAGNOSTIC LABORATORY OF OKLAHOMA LLC—See Quest Diagnostics, Inc.; *U.S. Public*, pg. 1755
DIAGNOSTIC MEDICAL SYSTEMS S.A.; *Int'l*, pg. 2103
DIAGNOSTIC MEDLAB—See Sonic Healthcare Limited; *Int'l*, pg. 7097
DIAGNOSTICNI CENTER BLED D.O.O.—See Pozavarovalnica Sava, d.d.; *Int'l*, pg. 5949
DIAGNOSTICOS DA AMERICA S.A.; *Int'l*, pg. 2103
DIAGNOSTICO Y ASISTENCIA MEDICA S.A. I.P.S. DINAMICA—See Grupo de Inversiones Suramericana S.A.; *Int'l*, pg. 3125
DIAGNOSTIC PATHOLOGY SERVICES, INC.—See Quest Diagnostics, Inc.; *U.S. Public*, pg. 1755
DIAGNOSTIC PATHOLOGY SERVICES, P.C.—See Quest Diagnostics, Inc.; *U.S. Public*, pg. 1755
DIAGNOSTIC REFERENCE SERVICES INC.—See Quest Diagnostics, Inc.; *U.S. Public*, pg. 1755
DIAGNOSTICS & DESIGNS INC.; *U.S. Private*, pg. 1222
DIAGNOSTIC SERVICES, INC.—See Laboratory Corporation of America Holdings; *U.S. Public*, pg. 1286
DIAGNOSTICS RESEARCH GROUP, LLC—See IMA Group Management Company, LLC; *U.S. Private*, pg. 2044
DIAGNOSTIC SYSTEMS GMBH—See HORIBA Ltd; *Int'l*, pg. 3475

DIAGNOSTIX LTD.—See Thermo Fisher Scientific Inc.; *U.S. Public*, pg. 2148
DIAGNOSTYKA SP. Z O.O.—See Mid Europa Partners LLP; *Int'l*, pg. 4882
DIAGNOSYS FERNDOWN LIMITED—See Astronics Corporation; *U.S. Public*, pg. 217
DIAGNOSYS GMBH—See Astronics Corporation; *U.S. Public*, pg. 217
DIAGNOSYS SYSTEMS, INC.—See Astronics Corporation; *U.S. Public*, pg. 217
DIAGNOTES, INC.—See DrFirst.com, Inc.; *U.S. Private*, pg. 1277
DIA-GO B.V.—See Eurofins Scientific S.E.; *Int'l*, pg. 2536
DIAGOLD DESIGNS LIMITED—See Goldiam International Limited; *Int'l*, pg. 3033
DIAGONAL BIO AB; *Int'l*, pg. 2103
DIAGONAL TELEVISION, S.L.—See LOV Group Invest SAS; *Int'l*, pg. 4564
DIAGRAPH CORPORATION SDN. BHD—See Illinois Tool Works Inc.; *U.S. Public*, pg. 1102
DIAGRAPH MARKING & STENCILING PRODUCTS GROUP—See Illinois Tool Works Inc.; *U.S. Public*, pg. 1102
DIAGRAPH MEXICO, S.A. DE C.V.—See Illinois Tool Works Inc.; *U.S. Public*, pg. 1102
DIAGRAPH—See Illinois Tool Works Inc.; *U.S. Public*, pg. 1102
DIAKINISIS S.A.—See ELGEKA S.A.; *Int'l*, pg. 2359
DIAKOPTO INC.—See ANSYS, Inc.; *U.S. Public*, pg. 139
DIAL800; *U.S. Private*, pg. 1222
DIALAB OY—See Ifolor AG; *Int'l*, pg. 3599
DIAL A.D.; *Int'l*, pg. 2103
DIALCOM24 SP. Z O.O.; *Int'l*, pg. 2104
DIAL COMMUICATIONS GLOBAL MEDIA, LLC—See Cumulus Media Inc.; *U.S. Public*, pg. 610
DIAL COMPANIES CORPORATION; *U.S. Private*, pg. 1222
DIAL EQUITIES INC.—See Dial Companies Corporation; *U.S. Private*, pg. 1222
DIALES; *Int'l*, pg. 2104
DIALFORHEALTH INDIA LTD.—See Zydus Lifesciences Limited; *Int'l*, pg. 8700
DIAL FORSIKRING A/S—See Sampo plc; *Int'l*, pg. 6508
DIAL FORSIKRING A/S—See Sampo plc; *Int'l*, pg. 6508
DIALIGHT ASIA PTE. LTD.—See Dialight plc; *Int'l*, pg. 2104
DIALIGHT BTI A/S—See Dialight plc; *Int'l*, pg. 2104
DIALIGHT CORPORATION—See Dialight plc; *Int'l*, pg. 2104
DIALIGHT EUROPE LIMITED—See Dialight plc; *Int'l*, pg. 2104
DIALIGHT PLC; *Int'l*, pg. 2104
DIAL INDUSTRIES INCORPORATED; *U.S. Private*, pg. 1222
DIAL INTERNATIONAL, INC.—See Henkel AG & Co. KGaA; *Int'l*, pg. 3353
DIALL ALLIANCE LLC.—See Zoltav Resources Inc.; *Int'l*, pg. 8688
DIAL MANUFACTURING INC.—See Dial Industries Incorporated; *U.S. Private*, pg. 1222
DIALMARK, LLC—See The Beekman Group, LLC; *U.S. Private*, pg. 3993
DIALOG AXIATA PLC—See Axiata Group Berhad; *Int'l*, pg. 768
DIALOG BROADBAND NETWORKS (PRIVATE) LIMITED—See Axiata Group Berhad; *Int'l*, pg. 768
DIALOGCONCEPTS, INC.—See Agital Holdings, LLC; *U.S. Private*, pg. 128
DIALOG E & C SDN. BHD.—See Dialog Group Berhad; *Int'l*, pg. 2104
DIALOG ESECO SDN. BHD.—See Dialog Group Berhad; *Int'l*, pg. 2104
DIALOG FINANCE PLC; *Int'l*, pg. 2104
DIALOG GMBH—See Orbis SE; *Int'l*, pg. 5614
DIALOG GROUP BERHAD; *Int'l*, pg. 2104
DIALOGIC CORPORATION—See Novacap Management Inc.; *Int'l*, pg. 5453
DIALOGIC DISTRIBUTION LIMITED—See Novacap Management Inc.; *Int'l*, pg. 5453
DIALOGIC DO BRASIL COMERCIO DE EQUIPAMENTOS PARA TELECOMUNICACAO LTDA.—See Novacap Management Inc.; *Int'l*, pg. 5454
DIALOGIC D.O.O.—See Novacap Management Inc.; *Int'l*, pg. 5454
DIALOGIC INC.—See Novacap Management Inc.; *Int'l*, pg. 5453
DIALOGIC JAPAN, INC.—See Novacap Management Inc.; *Int'l*, pg. 5453
DIALOGIC MANUFACTURING LIMITED—See Novacap Management Inc.; *Int'l*, pg. 5453
DIALOGIC NETWORKS ESPANA SRL—See Novacap Management Inc.; *Int'l*, pg. 5453
DIALOGIC NETWORKS (ISRAEL) LTD.—See Novacap Management Inc.; *Int'l*, pg. 5453
DIALOGIC NETWORKS SDN BHD—See Novacap Management Inc.; *Int'l*, pg. 5454
DIALOGIC RUS LLC—See Novacap Management Inc.; *Int'l*, pg. 5454

DIALOGIC SARL—See Novacap Management Inc.; *Int'l*, pg. 5454
DIALOGIC SINGAPORE PTE. LIMITED—See Novacap Management Inc.; *Int'l*, pg. 5454
DIALOGIC (UK) LIMITED—See Novacap Management Inc.; *Int'l*, pg. 5453
DIALOG INTERNATIONAL (L) LTD.—See Dialog Group Berhad; *Int'l*, pg. 2104
DIA LOGISTICS (M) SDN. BHD.—See Mitsubishi Logistics Corporation; *Int'l*, pg. 4962
DIALOG, LLC—See Clarivate PLC; *Int'l*, pg. 1649
DIALOG SEMICONDUCTOR B.V.—See Renesas Electronics Corporation; *Int'l*, pg. 6275
DIALOG SEMICONDUCTOR GMBH—See Renesas Electronics Corporation; *Int'l*, pg. 6275
DIALOG SEMICONDUCTOR INC—See Renesas Electronics Corporation; *Int'l*, pg. 6275
DIALOG SEMICONDUCTOR (ITALY) S.R.L.—See Renesas Electronics Corporation; *Int'l*, pg. 6275
DIALOG SEMICONDUCTOR KK—See Renesas Electronics Corporation; *Int'l*, pg. 6275
DIALOG SEMICONDUCTOR PLC—See Renesas Electronics Corporation; *Int'l*, pg. 6275
DIALOG SEMICONDUCTOR TRADING (SHANGHAI) LIMITED—See Renesas Electronics Corporation; *Int'l*, pg. 6275
DIALOG SEMICONDUCTOR (UK) LIMITED—See Renesas Electronics Corporation; *Int'l*, pg. 6275
DIALOG SERVICES, INC.—See Dialog Group Berhad; *Int'l*, pg. 2104
DIALOG SERVICES PTY. LTD.—See Dialog Group Berhad; *Int'l*, pg. 2104
DIALOG SISTEMI S.R.L.—See Relatech S.p.A.; *Int'l*, pg. 6260
DIALOG TECHNIVAC LTD.—See Dialog Group Berhad; *Int'l*, pg. 2104
DIALOGUE MARKETING, INC.; *U.S. Private*, pg. 1222
DIALOGUE—See WPP plc; *Int'l*, pg. 8463
DIALOGUE SYSTEM INC.; *U.S. Private*, pg. 1222
DIAL ONE WOLFEDALE ELECTRIC LTD.; *Int'l*, pg. 2103
DIAL REALTY CORP—See Dial Companies Corporation; *U.S. Private*, pg. 1222
DIAL TEMPORARY HELP SERVICE; *U.S. Private*, pg. 1222
DIALYSE-ZENTRUM HAMBURG OST GMBH—See DaVita Inc.; *U.S. Public*, pg. 638
DIALYSIS CARE CENTER OF PALM COAST LLC—See Nautic Partners, LLC; *U.S. Private*, pg. 2869
THE DIALYSIS CENTER OF ATTLEBORO, LLC—See Nautic Partners, LLC; *U.S. Private*, pg. 2871
THE DIALYSIS CENTER OF GARY - MERRILLVILLE, LLC—See Nautic Partners, LLC; *U.S. Private*, pg. 2871
THE DIALYSIS CENTER OF HAMMOND, LLC—See Nautic Partners, LLC; *U.S. Private*, pg. 2871
DIALYSIS CENTER OF MILLEDGEVILLE, LLC—See Nautic Partners, LLC; *U.S. Private*, pg. 2869
THE DIALYSIS CENTER OF NORTH PHILADELPHIA, LLC—See Nautic Partners, LLC; *U.S. Private*, pg. 2871
THE DIALYSIS CENTER OF PORTAGE, LLC—See Nautic Partners, LLC; *U.S. Private*, pg. 2871
THE DIALYSIS CENTER OF SCHERERVILLE, LLC—See Nautic Partners, LLC; *U.S. Private*, pg. 2871
DIALYSIS CENTER OF WAKEFIELD LLC—See Nautic Partners, LLC; *U.S. Private*, pg. 2869
DIALYSIS CENTER OF WESTERLY LLC—See Nautic Partners, LLC; *U.S. Private*, pg. 2869
DIALYSIS CENTER OF WESTERN MASSACHUSETTS LLC—See Nautic Partners, LLC; *U.S. Private*, pg. 2869
DIALYSIS CENTER OF WEST ORANGE LLC—See Nautic Partners, LLC; *U.S. Private*, pg. 2869
DIALYSIS CENTER OF WEST WARWICK LLC—See Nautic Partners, LLC; *U.S. Private*, pg. 2869
DIALYSIS CENTER OF WOONSOCKET LLC—See Nautic Partners, LLC; *U.S. Private*, pg. 2869
DIALYSIS CLINIC, INC.; *U.S. Private*, pg. 1222
DIALYSIS OF DES MOINES, LLC—See DaVita Inc.; *U.S. Public*, pg. 638
DIALYSIS SERVICES OF LONDON, LLC—See Nautic Partners, LLC; *U.S. Private*, pg. 2869
DIALYSIS SERVICES OF PINEVILLE, LLC—See Nautic Partners, LLC; *U.S. Private*, pg. 2870
DIALYSIS SPECIALISTS OF DALLAS, INC.—See DaVita Inc.; *U.S. Public*, pg. 638
THE DIALYSIS UNIT OF CENTER CITY PHILADELPHIA, LLC—See Nautic Partners, LLC; *U.S. Private*, pg. 2871
DIAMANT ART CORP.; *Int'l*, pg. 2104
DIAMANT BOART PHILIPPINES, INC.—See Lepanto Consolidated Mining Company; *Int'l*, pg. 4466
DIAMANTE FILMS; *U.S. Private*, pg. 1222
DIAMANT GEBAUDEREINIGUNGSDIENST GMBH—See MEDIQON Group AG; *Int'l*, pg. 4780
DIAMANT INFRASTRUCTURE LIMITED; *Int'l*, pg. 2104
DIAMCOR MINING INC.; *Int'l*, pg. 2104
DIAM AUSTRALIA PTY. LTD—See Ardian SAS; *Int'l*, pg. 555
DIAM DEUTSCHLAND GMBH—See Ardian SAS; *Int'l*, pg. 555
DIAM DISPLAY (CHINA) CO., LTD.—See Ardian SAS; *Int'l*, pg. 555

DIAMED AG—See Bio-Rad Laboratories, Inc.; *U.S. Public*, pg. 334
DIAMED BENELUX, N.V.—See Bio-Rad Laboratories, Inc.; *U.S. Public*, pg. 333
DIAMED DEUTSCHLAND GMBH—See Bio-Rad Laboratories, Inc.; *U.S. Public*, pg. 334
DIAMED DIAGNOSTIKA DEUTSCHLAND G.M.B.H.—See Bio-Rad Laboratories, Inc.; *U.S. Public*, pg. 333
DIAMED FENNICA OY—See Bio-Rad Laboratories, Inc.; *U.S. Public*, pg. 333
DIAMED FRANCE S.A.—See Bio-Rad Laboratories, Inc.; *U.S. Public*, pg. 334
DIAMED (G.B.) LIMITED—See Bio-Rad Laboratories, Inc.; *U.S. Public*, pg. 333
DIAMED G.M.B.H.—See Bio-Rad Laboratories, Inc.; *U.S. Public*, pg. 333
DIAMED HOLDING AG—See Bio-Rad Laboratories, Inc.; *U.S. Public*, pg. 333
DIAMEDICA THERAPEUTICS INC.; *U.S. Public*, pg. 658
DIAMEDIC IMPORT—See HORIBA Ltd; *Int'l*, pg. 3475
DIAMEDIX CORPORATION—See Transasia Bio-Medicals Ltd.; *Int'l*, pg. 7896
DIAMED LATINO AMERICA S.A.—See Bio-Rad Laboratories, Inc.; *U.S. Public*, pg. 334
DIAMED OSTERREICH GMBH—See Bio-Rad Laboratories, Inc.; *U.S. Public*, pg. 334
DIAMED (SCHWEIZ) G.M.B.H.—See Bio-Rad Laboratories, Inc.; *U.S. Public*, pg. 333
DIAMET CORPORATION—See Mitsubishi Materials Corporation; *Int'l*, pg. 4963
DIAMET KLANG (MALAYSIA) SDN. BHD.—See Mitsubishi Materials Corporation; *Int'l*, pg. 4963
DIAMIC CO., LTD.—See Mitsubishi Paper Mills Limited; *Int'l*, pg. 4967
DIAMINES AND CHEMICALS LIMITED; *Int'l*, pg. 2104
DIAM INTERNATIONAL SAS—See Ardian SAS; *Int'l*, pg. 555
DIAM JAPAN K.K.—See Ardian SAS; *Int'l*, pg. 555
DIA MOLDING CO., LTD.—See Mitsubishi Chemical Group Corporation; *Int'l*, pg. 4931
DIAMOND AGENCY, INC.; *Int'l*, pg. 2105
DIAMOND AIRBORNE SENSING GMBH—See Diamond Aircraft Industries Gmbh; *Int'l*, pg. 2105
DIAMOND AIRCRAFT INDUSTRIES GMBH; *Int'l*, pg. 2105
DIAMOND AIRCRAFT INDUSTRIES INC.—See Wanfeng Auto Holding Group Co., Ltd.; *Int'l*, pg. 8340
DIAMOND AIR SERVICE INCORPORATION.—See Mitsubishi Heavy Industries, Ltd.; *Int'l*, pg. 4953
DIAMOND ALTERNATIVE ENERGY, LLC—See Valero Energy Corporation; *U.S. Public*, pg. 2272
DIAMOND ANIMAL HEALTH, INC.—See Mars, Incorporated; *U.S. Private*, pg. 2588
DIAMOND ASSET FINANCE COMPANY LIMITED—See Mitsubishi HC Capital Inc.; *Int'l*, pg. 4950
DIAMOND ASSET SERVICE COMPANY LIMITED—See Mitsubishi HC Capital Inc.; *Int'l*, pg. 4951
DIAMOND AUTOMATIONS INC.—See FPS Food Processing Systems B.V.; *Int'l*, pg. 2757
DIAMONDBACK AUTOMOTIVE ACCESSORIES INC.; *U.S. Private*, pg. 1224
DIAMONDBACK DRUGS, LLC—See Tailwind Capital Group, LLC; *U.S. Private*, pg. 3924
DIAMONDBACK ENERGY, INC.; *U.S. Public*, pg. 658
DIAMONDBACK E&P LLC—See Diamondback Energy, Inc.; *U.S. Public*, pg. 658
DIAMONDBACK TRUCK COVERS—See DiamondBack Automotive Accessories Inc.; *U.S. Private*, pg. 1224
DIAMOND BAR HIGHLANDER—See Alden Global Capital LLC; *U.S. Private*, pg. 158
DIAMOND BAR OUTDOORS, INC.—See Nova Lifestyle, Inc.; *U.S. Public*, pg. 1547
DIAMOND B CONSTRUCTION CO., LLC; *U.S. Private*, pg. 1222
DIAMOND BLADE WAREHOUSE INC.—See Granite Creek Capital Partners, LLC; *U.S. Private*, pg. 1755
DIAMOND BRAND CANVAS PRODUCTS CO., INC.; *U.S. Private*, pg. 1222
DIAMOND BRANDS INCORPORATED; *U.S. Private*, pg. 1222
DIAMOND BUILDING PRODUCTS PUBLIC COMPANY LIMITED; *Int'l*, pg. 2105
THE DIAMOND BUS COMPANY LIMITED—See Rotala Group Limited; *Int'l*, pg. 6402
DIAMOND CASTLE HOLDINGS, LLC; *U.S. Private*, pg. 1222
DIAMOND CHAIN COMPANY—See The Timken Company; *U.S. Public*, pg. 2132
DIAMOND CHAIN UK LTD—See The Timken Company; *U.S. Public*, pg. 2132
DIAMOND CHEMICAL CO., INC.; *U.S. Private*, pg. 1222
DIAMOND COACH CORPORATION; *U.S. Private*, pg. 1223
DIAMOND COMIC DISTRIBUTORS, INC.; *U.S. Private*, pg. 1223
DIAMOND COMPANY OF ARMENIA; *Int'l*, pg. 2105
DIAMOND CONSTRUCTION EQUIPMENT CORPORATION—See Mitsubishi Corporation; *Int'l*, pg. 4938

DIAMOND CRYSTAL BRANDS, INC.—See Peak Rock Capital LLC; *U.S. Private*, pg. 3123
DIAMOND CRYSTAL BREMEN, LLC—See Peak Rock Capital LLC; *U.S. Private*, pg. 3124
DIAMOND DETECTIVE AGENCY INC.; *U.S. Private*, pg. 1223
DIAMOND DINING CO., LTD.—See DD Holdings Co., Ltd.; *Int'l*, pg. 1993
DIAMOND DISCOVERIES INTERNATIONAL CORP.; *U.S. Public*, pg. 658
THE DIAMOND DISTRICT LLC; *U.S. Private*, pg. 4021
DIAMOND DRILLING CORPORATION OF THE PHILIPPINES—See Lepanto Consolidated Mining Company; *Int'l*, pg. 4466
DIAMOND DRUGS, INC.; *U.S. Private*, pg. 1223
DIAMOND ELECTRIC HOLDINGS CO., LTD.; *Int'l*, pg. 2105
DIAMOND ELECTRIC MFG. CO., LTD.; *Int'l*, pg. 2105
DIAMOND ELECTRONICS LLC—See Pye-Barker Fire & Safety, LLC; *U.S. Private*, pg. 3309
DIAMOND ENGINEERING CO., LTD.—See NIPPON CARBIDE INDUSTRIES CO., INC.; *Int'l*, pg. 5311
DIAMOND ENGINEERING COMPANY; *U.S. Private*, pg. 1223
DIAMOND ENGINEERING (DALIAN) CO., LTD.—See NIPPON CARBIDE INDUSTRIES CO., INC.; *Int'l*, pg. 5311
DIAMOND EQUIPMENT INC.; *U.S. Private*, pg. 1223
DIAMOND ESTATES WINES & SPIRITS, INC.; *Int'l*, pg. 2105
DIAMOND F.C. PARTNERS, CO., LTD.—See Mitsubishi Heavy Industries, Ltd.; *Int'l*, pg. 4953
DIAMOND FIELDS NAMIBIA (PTY) LTD.—See DFR Gold Inc.; *Int'l*, pg. 2096
DIAMOND FLOWER INFORMATION (NL) B.V.—See DFI Inc.; *Int'l*, pg. 2095
DIAMOND FOOD MARKETS INC.; *U.S. Private*, pg. 1223
DIAMOND FOODS, LLC—See Campbell Soup Company; *U.S. Public*, pg. 427
DIAMOND FRUIT GROWERS INC.; *U.S. Private*, pg. 1223
DIAMOND FURNITURE INC.; *U.S. Private*, pg. 1223
DIAMOND GAME ENTERPRISES, INC.—See Flutter Entertainment plc; *Int'l*, pg. 2715
DIAMOND GAME ENTERPRISES—See Pollard Banknote Limited; *Int'l*, pg. 5910
DIAMOND GEAR COMPANY, LTD.—See SHV Holdings N.V.; *Int'l*, pg. 6871
DIAMOND GENERAL INSURANCE LIMITED—See NICOZDIAMOND INSURANCE LIMITED; *Int'l*, pg. 5273
DIAMOND GENERATING ASIA, LIMITED—See Mitsubishi Corporation; *Int'l*, pg. 4938
DIAMOND GENERATING CORPORATION MEXICO, S. DE R. L. DE C.V.—See Mitsubishi Corporation; *Int'l*, pg. 4938
DIAMOND GENERATING CORP.—See Mitsubishi Corporation; *Int'l*, pg. 4938
DIAMOND GENERATING EUROPE BV—See Mitsubishi Corporation; *Int'l*, pg. 4938
DIAMOND GENERATING EUROPE LIMITED—See Mitsubishi Corporation; *Int'l*, pg. 4938
DIAMOND GROUP INC.; *U.S. Private*, pg. 1223
THE DIAMOND GROUP INC.; *U.S. Private*, pg. 4021
DIAMOND GT SERVICE EUROPE S.R.L.—See Mitsubishi Heavy Industries, Ltd.; *Int'l*, pg. 4953
DIAMOND GYPSUM, LLC—See Arcosa, Inc.; *U.S. Public*, pg. 186
DIAMOND HARDWOODS & ARCHITECTURAL PRODUCTS, INC.—See Hardwoods Distribution Inc.; *Int'l*, pg. 3273
DIAMONDHEAD BEACH RESORT—See SunStream, Inc.; *U.S. Private*, pg. 3873
DIAMONDHEAD CASINO CORPORATION; *U.S. Public*, pg. 659
DIAMOND HEALTHCARE CORPORATION—See Markel Group Inc.; *U.S. Public*, pg. 1368
DIAMOND HILL CAPITAL MANAGEMENT, INC.—See Diamond Hill Investment Group, Inc.; *U.S. Public*, pg. 658
DIAMOND HILL INVESTMENT GROUP, INC.; *U.S. Public*, pg. 658
DIAMOND HILL PLYWOOD COMPANY—See The Palmer-Donavin Manufacturing Company, Inc.; *U.S. Private*, pg. 4090
DIAMOND HOME HARDWARE & GARDEN, LLC—See Kodiak Building Partners LLC; *U.S. Private*, pg. 2336
DIAMOND HONDA OF GLENDALE; *U.S. Private*, pg. 1223
DIAMOND HOTELS AND RESORTS S.A.—See The Mabetex Group; *Int'l*, pg. 7665
DIAMOND INDUSTRIES LIMITED; *Int'l*, pg. 2105
DIAMOND INFOSYSTEMS LTD; *Int'l*, pg. 2105
DIAMOND INNOVATIONS, INC. - PACIFIC HEADQUARTERS—See KKR & Co. Inc.; *U.S. Public*, pg. 1253
DIAMOND INNOVATIONS, INC.—See KKR & Co. Inc.; *U.S. Public*, pg. 1252
DIAMOND INNOVATIONS INTERNATIONAL, INC. - EUROPEAN HEADQUARTERS—See KKR & Co. Inc.; *U.S. Public*, pg. 1253

DIAMOND INFOSYSTEMS LTD

CORPORATE AFFILIATIONS

DIAMOND INNOVATIONS INTERNATIONAL SALES—See KKR & Co. Inc.; *U.S. Public,* pg. 1253
DIAMOND INTERNATIONAL TRUCKS (GP) LTD.—See Diamond International Trucks Ltd.; *Int'l,* pg. 2105
DIAMOND INTERNATIONAL TRUCKS LTD.; *Int'l,* pg. 2105
DIAMOND JACKS CASINO & HOTEL—See The Cordish Companies; *U.S. Private,* pg. 4015
DIAMOND JO, LLC—See Boyd Gaming Corporation; *U.S. Public,* pg. 377
DIAMOND JO WORTH, LLC—See Boyd Gaming Corporation; *U.S. Public,* pg. 377
DIAMOND KEY INTERNATIONAL PTY. LTD; *Int'l,* pg. 2105
DIAMOND K RANCH LLC—See Valero Energy Corporation; *U.S. Public,* pg. 2272
DIAMOND LAKE 1994 L.L.C.—See United Natural Foods, Inc.; *U.S. Public,* pg. 2231
DIAMOND LAKE MINERALS, INC.; *U.S. Public,* pg. 658
DIAMOND LANE, INC.; *U.S. Private,* pg. 1223
DIAMONDLEASE LLC—See Al Habtoor Group LLC; *Int'l,* pg. 278
DIAMOND LINE K.K.—See Mitsui O.S.K. Lines, Ltd.; *Int'l,* pg. 4989
DIAMOND MANAGEMENT & TECHNOLOGY CONSULTANTS PRIVATE LIMITED—See PricewaterhouseCoopers Pvt. Ltd.; *Int'l,* pg. 5972
DIAMOND MANUFACTURING COMPANY; *U.S. Private,* pg. 1223
DIAMOND MARKETING SOLUTIONS GROUP, INC.—See Aquiline Capital Partners LLC; *U.S. Private,* pg. 304
DIAMOND MATERIALS CO., LTD.—See Diamond Building Products Public Company Limited; *Int'l,* pg. 2105
DIAMOND MATERIALS TECH, INC.—See Groupe BPCE; *Int'l,* pg. 3097
DIAMOND MEAT PROCESSING L.L.C.—See Siniora Food Industries P.L.C.; *Int'l,* pg. 6945
DIAMOND MIND INC.; *U.S. Private,* pg. 1223
DIAMOND NATION, LLC; *U.S. Private,* pg. 1223
DIAMOND OFFICE SERVICE CO., LTD.—See Mitsubishi Heavy Industries, Ltd.; *Int'l,* pg. 4953
DIAMOND OFFSHORE DEVELOPMENT COMPANY—See Loews Corporation; *U.S. Public,* pg. 1340
DIAMOND OFFSHORE DRILLING, INC.; *U.S. Public,* pg. 658
DIAMOND PAPER BOX COMPANY; *U.S. Private,* pg. 1223
DIAMOND PAPER CORPORATION—See Gould Paper Corporation; *U.S. Private,* pg. 1745
DIAMOND PARKING INC.—See Diamond Parking Services LLC; *U.S. Private,* pg. 1223
DIAMOND PARKING SERVICES LLC; *U.S. Private,* pg. 1223
DIAMOND P ENTERPRISES, INC.; *U.S. Private,* pg. 1223
DIAMOND PERFORATED METALS, INC.—See Gibraltar Industries, Inc.; *U.S. Public,* pg. 935
DIAMOND PLASTICS CORPORATION; *U.S. Private,* pg. 1223
DIAMOND POINT A.S.—See Allianz SE; *Int'l,* pg. 352
DIAMOND POWER AUSTRALIA PTY., LTD.—See Babcock & Wilcox Enterprises, Inc.; *U.S. Public,* pg. 262
DIAMOND POWER CENTRAL & EASTERN EUROPE S.R.O.—See Babcock & Wilcox Enterprises, Inc.; *U.S. Public,* pg. 262
DIAMOND POWER CORPORATION—See Chubu Electric Power Co., Inc.; *Int'l,* pg. 1593
DIAMOND POWER FINLAND OY—See Babcock & Wilcox Enterprises, Inc.; *U.S. Public,* pg. 262
DIAMOND POWER GERMANY GMBH—See Babcock & Wilcox Enterprises, Inc.; *U.S. Public,* pg. 262
DIAMOND POWER INFRASTRUCTURE LTD.; *Int'l,* pg. 2105
DIAMOND POWER INTERNATIONAL, INC.—See Babcock & Wilcox Enterprises, Inc.; *U.S. Public,* pg. 262
DIAMOND POWER MACHINE (HUBEI) CO., INC.—See Babcock & Wilcox Enterprises, Inc.; *U.S. Public,* pg. 262
DIAMOND POWER SERVICES S.E.A. LTD.—See Babcock & Wilcox Enterprises, Inc.; *U.S. Public,* pg. 262
DIAMOND POWER SPECIALTY COMPANY—See Babcock & Wilcox Enterprises, Inc.; *U.S. Public,* pg. 262
DIAMOND POWER SPECIALTY LTD.—See Babcock & Wilcox Enterprises, Inc.; *U.S. Public,* pg. 262
DIAMOND POWER SPECIALTY (PTY) LTD.—See Babcock & Wilcox Enterprises, Inc.; *U.S. Public,* pg. 262
DIAMOND POWER SWEDEN AB—See Babcock & Wilcox Enterprises, Inc.; *U.S. Public,* pg. 262
DIAMOND PRODUCTS COMPANY—See Diamond Vogel Paint, Inc.; *U.S. Private,* pg. 1224
DIAMOND PROPANE, INC.—See Ferrellgas Partners, L.P.; *U.S. Public,* pg. 829
DIAMOND PUBLIC RELATIONS; *U.S. Private,* pg. 1223
DIAMOND QUARTZITE PROCESSING (PTY) LTD—See Raubex Group Limited; *Int'l,* pg. 6221
DIAMOND REALTY INVESTMENTS, INC.—See Mitsubishi Corporation; *Int'l,* pg. 4938
DIAMOND REALTY MANAGEMENT INC.—See Mitsubishi Corporation; *Int'l,* pg. 4938

DIAMOND RESORTS CORPORATION—See Apollo Global Management, Inc.; *U.S. Public,* pg. 150
DIAMOND RESORTS CORPORATION—See Reverence Capital Partners LLC; *U.S. Private,* pg. 3415
DIAMOND RESORTS HOLDINGS, LLC—See Apollo Global Management, Inc.; *U.S. Public,* pg. 150
DIAMOND RESORTS HOLDINGS, LLC—See Reverence Capital Partners LLC; *U.S. Private,* pg. 3415
DIAMOND RESORTS INTERNATIONAL, INC.—See Apollo Global Management, Inc.; *U.S. Public,* pg. 150
DIAMOND RESORTS INTERNATIONAL, INC.—See Reverence Capital Partners LLC; *U.S. Private,* pg. 3415
DIAMONDROCK DC M STREET TENANT, LLC—See DiamondRock Hospitality Company; *U.S. Public,* pg. 659
DIAMONDROCK HOSPITALITY COMPANY; *U.S. Public,* pg. 659
DIAMONDROCK SAN DIEGO TENANT, LLC—See DiamondRock Hospitality Company; *U.S. Public,* pg. 659
DIAMOND SA; *Int'l,* pg. 2105
DIAMONDS DIRECT ONLINE USA, LLC; *U.S. Private,* pg. 1224
DIAMONDS DIRECT USA OF INDIANAPOLIS, INC.—See Diamonds Direct Online USA, LLC; *U.S. Private,* pg. 1224
DIAMOND SERVICES CORPORATION; *U.S. Private,* pg. 1224
DIAMOND SHARP SERVICES, INC.—See Birch Hill Equity Partners Management Inc.; *Int'l,* pg. 1046
DIAMOND SIMULATION GMBH—See Diamond Aircraft Industries Gmbh; *Int'l,* pg. 2105
DIAMOND SOFTWARE, INC.; *U.S. Private,* pg. 1224
DIAMOND SOLUTIONS, INC.; *U.S. Private,* pg. 1224
DIAMOND SPARKLING LIMITED—See Daido Group Ltd; *Int'l,* pg. 1920
DIAMOND SPORTS GROUP, LLC—See Sinclair, Inc.; *U.S. Public,* pg. 1885
DIAMOND S SHIPPING GROUP, INC.; *U.S. Private,* pg. 1224
DIAMOND STATE INSURANCE COMPANY—See Paine Schwartz Partners, LLC; *U.S. Private,* pg. 3075
DIAMOND STATE TRUCKING, INC.—See OEP Capital Advisors, L.P.; *U.S. Private,* pg. 2999
DIAMOND STATE VENTURES, LLC; *U.S. Private,* pg. 1224
DIAMOND'S TRANSFER LTD—See Armour Transportation Systems; *Int'l,* pg. 575
DIAMOND TANKER PTE. LTD.—See Mitsubishi Corporation; *Int'l,* pg. 4938
DIAMOND TECHNOLOGY ENTERPRISES, INC.; *U.S. Private,* pg. 1224
DIAMOND TOOL AND ABRASIVES INC.—See Nautic Partners, LLC; *U.S. Private,* pg. 2871
DIAMOND TOOL COATING, LLC—See Sandvik AB; *Int'l,* pg. 6529
DIAMOND TOOLS GROUP B.V.—See Torqx Capital Partners B.V.; *Int'l,* pg. 7830
DIAMOND TRADING COMPANY—See Anglo American PLC; *Int'l,* pg. 462
DIAMOND TRANSPORTATION SERVICES INC.—See Mobico Group PLC; *Int'l,* pg. 5009
DIAMOND TRANSPORTATION SYSTEMS; *U.S. Private,* pg. 1224
DIAMOND TRAVEL CO., LTD.—See Mitsubishi Heavy Industries, Ltd.; *Int'l,* pg. 4953
DIAMOND/TRIUMPH AUTO GLASS INC.; *U.S. Private,* pg. 1224
DIAMOND TRUST BANK BURUNDI S.A.—See Diamond Trust Bank Kenya Limited; *Int'l,* pg. 2106
DIAMOND TRUST BANK KENYA LIMITED; *Int'l,* pg. 2105
DIAMOND TRUST BANK TANZANIA LTD—See Aga Khan Development Network; *Int'l,* pg. 199
DIAMOND TRUST BANK UGANDA LIMITED—See Diamond Trust Bank Kenya Limited; *Int'l,* pg. 2106
DIAMOND TRUST BANK UGANDA LTD—See Aga Khan Development Network; *Int'l,* pg. 199
DIAMOND VALLEY HONDA GROUP, LLC.; *U.S. Private,* pg. 1224
DIAMOND VALLEY PORK PTY LTD—See QAF Limited; *Int'l,* pg. 6131
DIAMOND VISION SYSTEMS DIVISION—See Hyosung Heavy Industries Corp.; *Int'l,* pg. 3552
DIAMOND V MILLS, INC.; *U.S. Private,* pg. 1224
DIAMOND VOGEL PAINT, INC.; *U.S. Private,* pg. 1224
DIAMOND WIPES INTERNATIONAL, INC.; *U.S. Private,* pg. 1224
DIAMOND WIRELESS LLC—See BCE Inc.; *Int'l,* pg. 927
DIAMOND WIRE SPRING COMPANY; *U.S. Private,* pg. 1224
DIAMOND W SUPPLY CO.—See Tarkett S.A.; *Int'l,* pg. 7463
DIAMOND WTG ENGINEERING & SERVICES, INC.—See Mitsubishi Heavy Industries, Ltd.; *Int'l,* pg. 4953
DIA MOULDING SLOVAKIA S.R.O.—See Mitsubishi Chemical Group Corporation; *Int'l,* pg. 4931
DIAM TUNISIA SARL—See Ardian SAS; *Int'l,* pg. 555
DIAM TURKIYE—See Ardian SAS; *Int'l,* pg. 555
DIAM UK LTD—See Ardian SAS; *Int'l,* pg. 555
DIANA DOLLS FASHIONS INC; *Int'l,* pg. 2106

DIANA E. KELLY, INC.; *U.S. Private,* pg. 1224
DIANA FERRARI (AUSTRALIA) PTY LTD—See Fusion Retail Brands, Pty. Ltd.; *Int'l,* pg. 2849
DIANA FOOD CANADA INC.—See Symrise AG; *Int'l,* pg. 7380
DIANA FOOD CHILE SPA—See Symrise AG; *Int'l,* pg. 7380
DIANA FOOD LIMITED—See Symrise AG; *Int'l,* pg. 7380
DIANA FOOD SAS—See Symrise AG; *Int'l,* pg. 7380
DIANAGAS - SOC. DISTRIB. DE GAS NATURAL DE EVORA, S.A.—See Galp Energia SGPS, S.A.; *Int'l,* pg. 2875
DIANA ISAAC RETIREMENT VILLAGE LIMITED—See Ryman Healthcare Ltd.; *Int'l,* pg. 6439
DIANALABS SA—See Sonic Healthcare Limited; *Int'l,* pg. 7097
DIANAL AMERICA, INC.—See Mitsubishi Chemical Group Corporation; *Int'l,* pg. 4933
DIANA NATURALS INC.—See Symrise AG; *Int'l,* pg. 7380
DIANA PETFOOD (CHUZHOU) COMPANY LIMITED—See Symrise AG; *Int'l,* pg. 7380
DIANA PET FOOD COLOMBIA S.A.S.—See Symrise AG; *Int'l,* pg. 7380
DIANAPLANTSCIENCES INC.—See Symrise AG; *Int'l,* pg. 7380
DIANA PROPERTY SP. Z.O.O.—See CPI Property Group, S.A.; *Int'l,* pg. 1825
DIANA S.A.S.—See Symrise AG; *Int'l,* pg. 7380
DIANA SHIPPING INC.; *Int'l,* pg. 2106
DIANAS MEXICAN FOOD PRODUCTS; *U.S. Private,* pg. 1224
DIANA TEA COMPANY LIMITED; *Int'l,* pg. 2106
DIANA UNICHARM JOINT STOCK COMPANY—See Unicharm Corporation; *Int'l,* pg. 8032
DIAN DIAGNOSTICS GROUP CO., LTD.; *Int'l,* pg. 2106
DIANE SAUER CHEVROLET, INC.; *U.S. Private,* pg. 1224
DIANE VON FURSTENBERG COUTURE—See D.V.F. Studio; *U.S. Private,* pg. 1143
DIANGUANG EXPLOSION-PROOF TECHNOLOGY CO., LTD.; *Int'l,* pg. 2106
DIANI CONSTRUCTION; *U.S. Private,* pg. 1224
DIANNE'S FINE DESSERTS, INC.—See Wanxiang America Capital, LLC; *U.S. Private,* pg. 4436
DIANOMI INC.—See Dianomi Plc; *Int'l,* pg. 2106
DIANOMI PLC; *Int'l,* pg. 2106
DIANON SYSTEMS, INC.—See Laboratory Corporation of America Holdings; *U.S. Public,* pg. 1286
DIANON SYSTEMS, INC.—See Laboratory Corporation of America Holdings; *U.S. Public,* pg. 1286
DIANON SYSTEMS, INC.—See Laboratory Corporation of America Holdings; *U.S. Public,* pg. 1286
DIANTHUS THERAPEUTICS, INC.; *U.S. Public,* pg. 659
DIANTUS WATCH SA—See The Swatch Group Ltd.; *Int'l,* pg. 7691
DIAPAC LTD.—See Mistras Group, Inc.; *U.S. Public,* pg. 1451
DIAPA S.L.—See A.A.G. STUCCHI s.r.l.; *Int'l,* pg. 22
DIA PLAZA CO., LTD.—See Mitsubishi Materials Corporation; *Int'l,* pg. 4963
DIA PLUS MINUS HANDELSGESELLSCHAFT MBH—See Zur Rose Group AG; *Int'l,* pg. 8696
DIAPOLYACRYLATE CO., LTD.—See Mitsubishi Chemical Group Corporation; *Int'l,* pg. 4931
DIA PORTUGAL SUPERMERCADOS SA—See Carrefour SA; *Int'l,* pg. 1345
DIA RESIBON (THAILAND) CO., LTD.—See Noritake Co., Limited; *Int'l,* pg. 5428
DIARIO 20 MINUTOS SL—See Schibsted ASA; *Int'l,* pg. 6616
DIARIO EL CORREO, S.A.U.—See Vocento, S.A.; *Int'l,* pg. 8284
DIA RIX CORPORATION—See Mitsubishi Chemical Group Corporation; *Int'l,* pg. 4931
DIARYGOLD ASIA LIMITED—See Dairygold Co-Operative Society Ltd; *Int'l,* pg. 1940
DIARYGOLD DEUTSCHLAND HANDLESGESELLSCHAFT MBH—See Dairygold Co-Operative Society Ltd; *Int'l,* pg. 1940
DIASALT CORP.—See Mitsubishi Materials Corporation; *Int'l,* pg. 4963
DIAS DE SOUSA S.A.—See HORIBA Ltd; *Int'l,* pg. 3475
DIASFIN SA; *Int'l,* pg. 2106
DI ASIA INC.—See Dream Incubator Inc.; *Int'l,* pg. 2202
DIASORIN AB—See DiaSorin S.p.A.; *Int'l,* pg. 2106
DIASORIN AUSTRALIA (PTY) LTD.—See DiaSorin S.p.A.; *Int'l,* pg. 2106
DIASORIN CANADA INC.—See DiaSorin S.p.A.; *Int'l,* pg. 2106
DIASORIN CZECH S.R.O.—See DiaSorin S.p.A.; *Int'l,* pg. 2106
DIASORIN DEUTSCHLAND GMBH—See DiaSorin S.p.A.; *Int'l,* pg. 2106
DIASORIN IBERIA S.A.—See DiaSorin S.p.A.; *Int'l,* pg. 2106
DIASORIN INC.—See DiaSorin S.p.A.; *Int'l,* pg. 2106
DIASORIN ITALIA S.P.A.—See DiaSorin S.p.A.; *Int'l,* pg. 2106
DIASORIN LTDA—See DiaSorin S.p.A.; *Int'l,* pg. 2106
DIASORIN LTD.—See DiaSorin S.p.A.; *Int'l,* pg. 2106

COMPANY NAME INDEX

DIASORIN MEXICO S.A DE C.V.—See DiaSorin S.p.A.; *Int'l*, pg. 2106
DIASORIN MOLECULAR LLC—See DiaSorin S.p.A.; *Int'l*, pg. 2106
DIASORIN POLAND SP. Z O.O.—See DiaSorin S.p.A.; *Int'l*, pg. 2106
DIASORIN S.A/N.V.—See DiaSorin S.p.A.; *Int'l*, pg. 2106
DIASORIN S.A.—See DiaSorin S.p.A.; *Int'l*, pg. 2106
DIASORIN S.P.A.; *Int'l*, pg. 2106
DIASPARK INC.; *U.S. Private*, pg. 1224
DIASTEIN CO., LTD.—See Mitsubishi Heavy Industries, Ltd.; *Int'l*, pg. 4953
DIA-STRON INC.—See Judges Scientific plc; *Int'l*, pg. 4021
DIA-STRON LIMITED—See Judges Scientific plc; *Int'l*, pg. 4021
DIA SYSTEMS CORPORATION—See Mitsubishi Logistics Corporation; *Int'l*, pg. 4962
DIATEC AG—See Demant A/S; *Int'l*, pg. 2023
DIATEC DIAGNOSTICS GMBH—See Demant A/S; *Int'l*, pg. 2023
DIATECH INC.—See COLTENE Holding AG; *Int'l*, pg. 1706
DIATEC SARL—See HORIBA Ltd; *Int'l*, pg. 3475
DIATEC SPAIN, S.L.U.—See Demant A/S; *Int'l*, pg. 2023
DIATEC S.R.L.—See ANDRITZ AG; *Int'l*, pg. 455
DIATEX CO., LTD.—See Mitsubishi Chemical Group Corporation; *Int'l*, pg. 4931
DIATHERIX LABORATORIES, LLC—See Eurofins Scientific S.E.; *Int'l*, pg. 2536
DIATHEVA SRL—See SOL S.p.A.; *Int'l*, pg. 7067
DIA TIANTIAN (SHANGHAI) MANAGEMENT CONSULTING SERVICE CO. LTD—See Carrefour SA; *Int'l*, pg. 1344
DIATOMJ A/S—See Indutrade AB; *Int'l*, pg. 3678
DIATREME RESOURCES LIMITED; *Int'l*, pg. 2106
DIATRON MEDICINAI INSTRUMENTUMOK LABORATORIUMI DIAGNOSZTIKAI FEJLESZTO-GYARTO ZRT.—See Stratec SE; *Int'l*, pg. 7235
DIATRON MI ZRT.—See Stratec SE; *Int'l*, pg. 7235
DIATRON (US), INC.—See Stratec SE; *Int'l*, pg. 7235
DIAVAC LIMITED—See Nabtesco Corporation; *Int'l*, pg. 5119
DIAVERUM AB—See Bridgepoint Group Plc; *Int'l*, pg. 1153
DIAVERUM HUNGARY—See Baxter International Inc.; *U.S. Public*, pg. 281
DIAVERUM S.A.—See Bridgepoint Group Plc; *Int'l*, pg. 1153
DIAVERUM SPAIN—See Bridgepoint Group Plc; *Int'l*, pg. 1153
DIAVERUM URUGUAY—See Bridgepoint Group Plc; *Int'l*, pg. 1153
DIA.VI.PE.THI.V SA—See Viohalco SA/NV; *Int'l*, pg. 8243
DIAXON ABEE—See HELLENiQ ENERGY Holdings S.A.; *Int'l*, pg. 3334
DIAXON SA—See HELLENiQ ENERGY Holdings S.A.; *Int'l*, pg. 3334
DIAZ FRITZ ISABEL GENERAL CONTRACTORS; *U.S. Private*, pg. 1225
DIAZ WHOLESALE & MANUFACTURING CO., INC.; *U.S. Private*, pg. 1225
DIAZYME LABORATORIES, INC.—See General Atomics; *U.S. Private*, pg. 1663
DIBA INDUSTRIES, INC.—See Halma plc; *Int'l*, pg. 3231
DIBA INDUSTRIES LTD.—See Halma plc; *Int'l*, pg. 3231
DIBA JAPAN KK—See Halma plc; *Int'l*, pg. 3231
DIB BANK KENYA LTD.—See Dubai Islamic Bank PSJ; *Int'l*, pg. 2219
DIB CAPITAL LIMITED—See Dubai Islamic Bank PSJ; *Int'l*, pg. 2220
DIBEC B.V.—See Ronesans Holding A.S.; *Int'l*, pg. 6396
DI BELLA COFFEE, LLC—See Retail Food Group Limited; *Int'l*, pg. 6305
DIBERT VALVE & FITTING CO. INC.; *U.S. Private*, pg. 1225
DIBONA, BORNSTEIN & RANDOM, INC.; *U.S. Private*, pg. 1225
D&I BRIDGMAN AND SON LTD—See Mole Valley Farmers Ltd; *Int'l*, pg. 5021
DICALITE CORPORATION—See RGP Holding, Inc.; *U.S. Private*, pg. 3420
DICALITE EUROPE NORD, S.A.—See RGP Holding, Inc.; *U.S. Private*, pg. 3420
DICALITE HOLDINGS INC.—See RGP Holding, Inc.; *U.S. Private*, pg. 3420
DIC ALKYLPHENOL SINGAPORE PTE., LTD.—See DIC Corporation; *Int'l*, pg. 2107
DI CANIO ORGANIZATION INC.; *U.S. Private*, pg. 1221
DI CANIO RESIDENTIAL COMMUNITIES INC—See Di Canio Organization Inc.; *U.S. Private*, pg. 1221
DICAPTA CORP.; *U.S. Private*, pg. 1225
DICAR, INC.; *U.S. Private*, pg. 1225
DI CARLO DISTRIBUTORS INC.; *U.S. Private*, pg. 1222
DIC ASIA PACIFIC PTE LTD.—See DIC Corporation; *Int'l*, pg. 2107
DIC ASSET AG; *Int'l*, pg. 2107
DIC AUSTRALIA PTY LTD.—See DIC Corporation; *Int'l*, pg. 2107
DIC BERLIN GMBH R & D LABORATORY—See DIC Corporation; *Int'l*, pg. 2107

DIC (CHINA) CO., LTD.—See DIC Corporation; *Int'l*, pg. 2107
DICCICCO BATTISTA COMMUNICATIONS; *U.S. Private*, pg. 1225
DIC COLORANTS TAIWAN CO., LTD.—See DIC Corporation; *Int'l*, pg. 2107
DIC COLOR COATINGS, INC.—See DIC Corporation; *Int'l*, pg. 2107
DIC COLOR DESIGN, INC.—See DIC Corporation; *Int'l*, pg. 2107
DIC COMPOUNDS (MALAYSIA) SDN. BHD.—See DIC Corporation; *Int'l*, pg. 2107
DIC CORPORATION; *Int'l*, pg. 2107
DIC COVESTRO POLYMER LTD.—See DIC Corporation; *Int'l*, pg. 2107
DIC DA LAT INVESTMENT & TRADING JOINT STOCK COMPANY—See DIC Investment and Trading Joint Stock Company; *Int'l*, pg. 2111
DIC DA NANG INVESTMENT & TRADING JOINT STOCK COMPANY—See DIC Investment and Trading Joint Stock Company; *Int'l*, pg. 2111
DIC DECOR, INC.—See DIC Corporation; *Int'l*, pg. 2107
DIC - DONG TIEN JOINT STOCK COMPANY; *Int'l*, pg. 2107
DICE CAREERS GMBH—See DHI Group, Inc.; *U.S. Public*, pg. 657
DICE CAREERS LIMITED—See DHI Group, Inc.; *U.S. Public*, pg. 658
DICE CAREER SOLUTIONS, INC.—See DHI Group, Inc.; *U.S. Public*, pg. 658
DICE COMMUNICATIONS, INC.—See Waterfield Technologies, Inc.; *U.S. Private*, pg. 4453
DICE DANUBE INTEGRATED CIRCUIT ENGINEERING GMBH & CO. KG—See Infineon Technologies AG; *Int'l*, pg. 3686
DICE INC.—See DHI Group, Inc.; *U.S. Public*, pg. 658
DICENEXT INC.—See Daiwa House Industry Co., Ltd.; *Int'l*, pg. 1946
DICENTRAL CORP.—See Welsh, Carson, Anderson & Stowe; *U.S. Private*, pg. 4480
DIC EP CORP.—See DIC Corporation; *Int'l*, pg. 2107
DIC EPOXY (MALAYSIA) SDN. BHD.—See DIC Corporation; *Int'l*, pg. 2107
DICERNA PHARMACEUTICALS, INC.; *U.S. Public*, pg. 659
DICE SPORT & CASUAL WEAR S.A.E.; *Int'l*, pg. 2111
DIC ESTATE CO., LTD.—See DIC Corporation; *Int'l*, pg. 2107
DICE THERAPEUTICS, INC.—See Eli Lilly & Company; *U.S. Public*, pg. 731
DIC EUROPE GMBH—See DIC Corporation; *Int'l*, pg. 2107
DIC EUROPE - UK—See DIC Corporation; *Int'l*, pg. 2107
DIC FILTEC, INC.—See DIC Corporation; *Int'l*, pg. 2108
DIC FINE CHEMICALS PRIVATE LIMITED—See DIC Corporation; *Int'l*, pg. 2108
DIC GRAPHICS CHIA LUNG CORP.—See DIC Corporation; *Int'l*, pg. 2108
DIC GRAPHICS CORPORATION - CHIBA PLANT—See DIC Corporation; *Int'l*, pg. 2108
DIC GRAPHICS CORPORATION - GUNMA PLANT—See DIC Corporation; *Int'l*, pg. 2108
DIC GRAPHICS CORPORATION - HOKURIKU PLANT—See DIC Corporation; *Int'l*, pg. 2108
DIC GRAPHICS CORPORATION - KANSAI PLANT—See DIC Corporation; *Int'l*, pg. 2108
DIC GRAPHICS CORPORATION - KASHIMA PLANT—See DIC Corporation; *Int'l*, pg. 2108
DIC GRAPHICS CORPORATION - KOMAKI PLANT—See DIC Corporation; *Int'l*, pg. 2108
DIC GRAPHICS CORPORATION—See DIC Corporation; *Int'l*, pg. 2108
DIC GRAPHICS CORPORATION - TOKYO PLANT—See DIC Corporation; *Int'l*, pg. 2108
DIC GRAPHICS (DONGGUAN) LTD.—See DIC Corporation; *Int'l*, pg. 2108
DIC GRAPHICS (GUANGZHOU) LTD.—See DIC Corporation; *Int'l*, pg. 2108
DIC GRAPHICS (HONG KONG) LTD.—See DIC Corporation; *Int'l*, pg. 2108
DIC GRAPHICS (SHENYANG) CO., LTD.—See DIC Corporation; *Int'l*, pg. 2108
DIC GRAPHICS TAIYUAN CO., LTD.—See DIC Corporation; *Int'l*, pg. 2108
DIC GRAPHICS (THAILAND) CO., LTD.—See DIC Corporation; *Int'l*, pg. 2108
DIC (GUANGZHOU) CO., LTD.—See DIC Corporation; *Int'l*, pg. 2107
DICHTELEMENTE HALLITE GMBH—See Compagnie Generale des Etablissements Michelin SCA; *Int'l*, pg. 1745
DICHTOMATIK A.B.—See Freudenberg SE; *Int'l*, pg. 2783
DICHTOMATIK AMERICAS, LP—See Freudenberg SE; *Int'l*, pg. 2783
DICHTOMATIK B.V.—See Freudenberg SE; *Int'l*, pg. 2783
DICHTOMATIK CANADA, INC.—See Freudenberg SE; *Int'l*, pg. 2783
DICHTOMATIK (CHINA) CO., LTD.—See Freudenberg SE; *Int'l*, pg. 2783

DICHTOMATIK HANDELSGESELLSCHAFT MBH—See Freudenberg SE; *Int'l*, pg. 2783
DICHTOMATIK KFT.—See Freudenberg SE; *Int'l*, pg. 2783
DICHTOMATIK LTD.—See Freudenberg SE; *Int'l*, pg. 2783
DICHTOMATIK S.A.S. DI EXTERNA ITALIA S.R.L.—See Freudenberg SE; *Int'l*, pg. 2783
DICHTOMATIK S.A.S—See Freudenberg SE; *Int'l*, pg. 2783
DICHTOMATIK S.R.L.—See Freudenberg SE; *Int'l*, pg. 2783
DICHTOMATIK VERTRIEBSGESELLSCHAFT FUR TECHNISCHE DICHTUNGEN MBH—See Freudenberg SE; *Int'l*, pg. 2783
DICHTUNGSPARTNER HAMBURG GMBH; *Int'l*, pg. 2111
DIC IMAGING PRODUCTS USA INC.—See DIC Corporation; *Int'l*, pg. 2108
DIC INDIA LTD; *Int'l*, pg. 2111
DIC INTERIOR CO., LTD.—See DIC Corporation; *Int'l*, pg. 2108
DIC INTERNATIONAL AUSTRALIA PTY. LTD.—See DIC Corporation; *Int'l*, pg. 2108
DIC INTERNATIONAL (THAILAND) CO., LTD.—See DIC Corporation; *Int'l*, pg. 2108
DIC INTERNATIONAL (USA), LLC—See DIC Corporation; *Int'l*, pg. 2108
DIC INVESTMENT AND TRADING JOINT STOCK COMPANY; *Int'l*, pg. 2111
DIC KAKO, INC.—See DIC Corporation; *Int'l*, pg. 2108
DICK ANDERSON CONSTRUCTION; *U.S. Private*, pg. 1225
DICK BLICK COMPANY—See Dick Blick Holdings Inc.; *U.S. Private*, pg. 1225
DICK BLICK HOLDINGS INC.; *U.S. Private*, pg. 1225
DICK BRANTMEIER FORD INC.—See Van Horn Automotive Group, Inc.; *U.S. Private*, pg. 4340
DICK BROWNING, INC.; *U.S. Private*, pg. 1225
DICK BRUHN INCORPORATED; *U.S. Private*, pg. 1225
DICK CAMPAGNI'S CAPITAL FORD; *U.S. Private*, pg. 1225
DICK CLARK PRODUCTIONS, INC.—See Valence Media Group; *U.S. Private*, pg. 4331
DICK CLARK RESTAURANTS, INC.—See Valence Media Group; *U.S. Private*, pg. 4331
DICK DEAN ECONOMY CARS INC.; *U.S. Private*, pg. 1225
DICK DEVOE BUICK CADILLAC—See DeVoe Automotive Group; *U.S. Private*, pg. 1219
DICK DYER & ASSOCIATES, INC.; *U.S. Private*, pg. 1225
DICK DYER TOYOTA; *U.S. Private*, pg. 1226
DICK EDWARDS FORD LINCOLN MERCURY; *U.S. Private*, pg. 1226
DICKENS BOOKS LTD.; *U.S. Private*, pg. 1226
DICKENSHIED CRAVILLION INSURANCE SERVICES, INC.—See Seeman Holtz Property & Casualty, LLC; *U.S. Private*, pg. 3598
DICKENSON-RUSSELL CONTURA, LLC—See Alpha Metallurgical Resources, Inc.; *U.S. Public*, pg. 82
DICKENS PUBLISHING LTD.—See Pelangi Publishing Group Bhd; *Int'l*, pg. 5781
DICKER DATA FINANCIAL SERVICES PTY LTD—See Dicker Data Limited; *Int'l*, pg. 2111
DICKER DATA LIMITED; *Int'l*, pg. 2111
DICKER DATA NEW ZEALAND LTD.—See Dicker Data Limited; *Int'l*, pg. 2111
DICKERSON & BOWEN, INC.—See Granite Construction Incorporated; *U.S. Public*, pg. 957
DICKERSON FLORIDA, INC.—See The Dickerson Group, Inc.; *U.S. Private*, pg. 4021
THE DICKERSON GROUP, INC.; *U.S. Private*, pg. 4021
DICKERSON & NIEMAN REALTORS, INC.; *U.S. Private*, pg. 1226
DICKERSON REALTY CORPORATION—See The Dickerson Group, Inc.; *U.S. Private*, pg. 4021
DICKEY INC.; *U.S. Private*, pg. 1226
DICKEY-JOHN CORPORATION—See Churchill Equity, Inc.; *U.S. Private*, pg. 895
DICKEY-JOHN INTERNATIONAL LTD.—See Churchill Equity, Inc.; *U.S. Private*, pg. 895
DICKEY'S BARBECUE RESTAURANTS, INC.; *U.S. Private*, pg. 1227
DICKEYVILLE TELEPHONE, LLC—See Telephone & Data Systems, Inc.; *U.S. Public*, pg. 1998
DICK GENTHE CHEVROLET; *U.S. Private*, pg. 1226
DICK GORE'S RV WORLD INC.; *U.S. Private*, pg. 1226
DICK GREENFIELD DODGE INC.; *U.S. Private*, pg. 1226
DICK HUVAERE'S RICHMOND CHRYSLER DODGE INC.; *U.S. Private*, pg. 1226
DICKINSON BRANDS, INC.; *U.S. Private*, pg. 1227
DICKINSON CAMERON CONSTRUCTION COMPANY, INC.; *U.S. Private*, pg. 1227
DICKINSON CENTER, INC.; *U.S. Private*, pg. 1227
DICKINSON FINANCIAL CORPORATION; *U.S. Private*, pg. 1227
DICKINSON FLEET SERVICES LLC—See Cox Enterprises, Inc.; *U.S. Private*, pg. 1075
DICKINSON HUSSMAN ARCHITECTS, P.C.—See BLDD Architects, Inc.; *U.S. Private*, pg. 580
DICKINSON LEGG INC.—See Garbuio S.p.A.; *Int'l*, pg. 2883

DICKINSON FINANCIAL CORPORATION

CORPORATE AFFILIATIONS

DICKINSON LEGG LTD.—See Garbuio S.p.A.; *Int'l*, pg. 2883
DICKINSON, MACKAMAN, TYLER & HAGEN, P.C.; *U.S. Private*, pg. 1227
DICKINSON & MORRIS LIMITED—See Samworth Brothers Ltd.; *Int'l*, pg. 6519
DICKINSON PRESS, INC.; *U.S. Private*, pg. 1227
DICKINSON THEATRES INC.; *U.S. Private*, pg. 1227
DICKINSON WRIGHT PLLC; *U.S. Private*, pg. 1227
DIC KITANIHON POLYMER CO., LTD.—See DIC Corporation; *Int'l*, pg. 2108
DICK JONES COMMUNICATIONS, LLC—See Renovus Capital Partners; *U.S. Private*, pg. 3399
THE DICKLER CORP.; *U.S. Private*, pg. 1227
DICKMAN SUPPLY INCORPORATED; *U.S. Private*, pg. 1227
DICK MASHETER FORD, INC.; *U.S. Private*, pg. 1226
DICK MOORE INC.; *U.S. Private*, pg. 1226
DICK MYERS CHRYSLER DODGE JEEP; *U.S. Private*, pg. 1226
DICK NORRIS BUICK PONTIAC GMC; *U.S. Private*, pg. 1226
DICKON HALL FOODS (PTY) LTD.—See Libstar Holdings Ltd.; *Int'l*, pg. 4487
DIC KOREA CORP.—See DIC Corporation; *Int'l*, pg. 2108
DICK POE CHRYSLER-PLYMOUTH INC.; *U.S. Private*, pg. 1226
DICK POE MOTORS LP; *U.S. Private*, pg. 1226
DICK SCOTT DODGE INC.—See Dick Scott Motor Mall Inc.; *U.S. Private*, pg. 1226
DICK SCOTT MOTOR MALL INC.; *U.S. Private*, pg. 1226
DICK'S COUNTRY CHRYSLER JEEP DODGE; *U.S. Private*, pg. 1226
DICK SMITH AUTOMOTIVE GROUP; *U.S. Private*, pg. 1226
DICK SMITH AUTO SALES INC.—See Dick Smith Automotive Group; *U.S. Private*, pg. 1226
DICK SMITH ELECTRONICS FRANCHISING PTY. LTD.—See Anchorage Capital Partners Pty. Limited; *Int'l*, pg. 448
DICK SMITH ELECTRONICS LIMITED—See Anchorage Capital Partners Pty. Limited; *Int'l*, pg. 448
DICK SMITH FORD—See Dick Smith Automotive Group; *U.S. Private*, pg. 1226
DICK SMITH HOLDINGS LIMITED—See Anchorage Capital Partners Pty. Limited; *Int'l*, pg. 448
DICK SMITH INFINITI INC.—See Dick Smith Automotive Group; *U.S. Private*, pg. 1226
DICK SMITH NISSAN INC.—See Dick Smith Automotive Group; *U.S. Private*, pg. 1226
DICK SMITH NISSAN OF LEXINGTON—See Dick Smith Automotive Group; *U.S. Private*, pg. 1226
DICK SMITH (WHOLESALE) PTY. LTD.—See Anchorage Capital Partners Pty. Limited; *Int'l*, pg. 448
DICKSON CONCEPTS (INTERNATIONAL) LIMITED; *Int'l*, pg. 2112
DICKSON CONCEPTS LIMITED—See Dickson Concepts (International) Limited; *Int'l*, pg. 2112
DICKSON CONCEPTS (RETAIL) LIMITED—See Dickson Concepts (International) Limited; *Int'l*, pg. 2112
DICKSON EXPRESS COMPANY LIMITED—See Dickson Concepts (International) Limited; *Int'l*, pg. 2112
DICKSON INDUSTRIES, LLC; *U.S. Private*, pg. 1227
DICKSON INTERIOR DESIGN LIMITED—See Dickson Concepts (International) Limited; *Int'l*, pg. 2112
DICKSON INVESTMENTS (H.K.) LIMITED—See Dickson Concepts (International) Limited; *Int'l*, pg. 2112
DICKSON (SHANGHAI) COMPANY LIMITED—See Dickson Concepts (International) Limited; *Int'l*, pg. 2112
THE DICKSON SHOP SDN. BHD.—See Dickson Concepts (International) Limited; *Int'l*, pg. 2112
DICKSON'S, INC.—See Templeton Coal Company, Inc.; *U.S. Private*, pg. 3963
DICKSON TESTING COMPANY, INC.—See Berkshire Hathaway Inc.; *U.S. Public*, pg. 314
THE DICKSON TRADING (TAIWAN) CO., LTD.—See Dickson Concepts (International) Limited; *Int'l*, pg. 2112
DICKSON/UNIGAGE, INC.—See May River Capital, LLC; *U.S. Private*, pg. 2620
DICKSON WAREHOUSING LIMITED—See Jacobson Pharma Corporation Limited; *Int'l*, pg. 3865
DICK'S SANITATION SERVICE, INC.—See Waste Connections, Inc.; *Int'l*, pg. 8352
DICK'S SPORTING GOODS, INC.; *U.S. Public*, pg. 659
DICK'S SPORTING GOODS PARK—See Kroenke Sports & Entertainment, LLC; *U.S. Private*, pg. 2352
DICKSTEIN ASSOCIATES AGENCY LLC—See Kelso & Company, L.P.; *U.S. Private*, pg. 2279
DICKTEN MASCH PLASTICS—See Techniplas, LLC; *U.S. Private*, pg. 3954
DICK VANDYKE INCORPORATED; *U.S. Private*, pg. 1226
DIC KYUSHU POLYMER CO., LTD.—See DIC Corporation; *Int'l*, pg. 2108
DIC LANKA (PRIVATE) LTD.—See DIC Corporation; *Int'l*, pg. 2108
DIC LIFETEC CO., LTD.—See DIC Corporation; *Int'l*, pg. 2108
DIC MACHINERY & PRINTER'S SUPPLIES, INC.—See DIC Corporation; *Int'l*, pg. 2108

DIC (MALAYSIA) SDN. BHD.—See DIC Corporation; *Int'l*, pg. 2107
DIC MATERIAL INC.—See DIC Corporation; *Int'l*, pg. 2108
DIC MOLDING, INC.—See DIC Corporation; *Int'l*, pg. 2108
DIC NEW ZEALAND LTD.—See DIC Corporation; *Int'l*, pg. 2108
DIC NO. 4 JOINT STOCK COMPANY—See Development Investment Construction JSC; *Int'l*, pg. 2088
DICOCCO FAMILY'S ST. JUDE SHOP, INC.; *U.S. Private*, pg. 1227
DICOMAC LTDA.—See Quinenco S.A.; *Int'l*, pg. 6163
DICOM EXPRESS INC.—See International Distributions Services plc; *Int'l*, pg. 3747
DICOM, INC.; *U.S. Private*, pg. 1227
DI COM SOFTWARE CORP.—See The Carlyle Group Inc.; *U.S. Public*, pg. 2045
DICON FIBEROPTICS, INC.; *U.S. Private*, pg. 1227
DICON INVESTMENT LLC—See Alpha Dhabi Holding PJSC; *Int'l*, pg. 367
DIC ONSITE GMBH—See DIC Asset AG; *Int'l*, pg. 2107
DICOPAY AB—See Schibsted ASA; *Int'l*, pg. 6616
DICOPEL, INC.—See Arrow Electronics, Inc.; *U.S. Public*, pg. 199
DICOR CORPORATION, INC.—See Thor Industries, Inc.; *U.S. Public*, pg. 2156
DI CORP.; *Int'l*, pg. 2101
DI CORP. - THE DONGTAN PLANT—See DI Corp.; *Int'l*, pg. 2101
DIC PAKISTAN LTD.—See DIC Corporation; *Int'l*, pg. 2108
DIC PERFORMANCE RESINS GMBH—See DIC Corporation; *Int'l*, pg. 2108
DIC PHILIPPINES, INC.—See DIC Corporation; *Int'l*, pg. 2108
DIC PLASTICS, INC.—See DIC Corporation; *Int'l*, pg. 2108
DIC PROPERTIES LLC—See Eighteen Seventy Corporation; *U.S. Private*, pg. 1347
DIC (SHANGHAI) CO., LTD.—See DIC Corporation; *Int'l*, pg. 2107
DIC SOUTH ASIA PRIVATE LIMITED—See DIC Corporation; *Int'l*, pg. 2108
DIC SYNTHETIC RESINS (ZHONGSHAN) CO., LTD.—See DIC Corporation; *Int'l*, pg. 2108
DIC (TAIWAN) LTD.—See DIC Corporation; *Int'l*, pg. 2107
DICTOR CAPITAL CORPORATION; *U.S. Private*, pg. 1227
DIC TRADING (HK) LTD.—See DIC Corporation; *Int'l*, pg. 2108
DIC (VIETNAM) CO., LTD.—See DIC Corporation; *Int'l*, pg. 2107
DIC ZHANGJIAGANG CHEMICALS CO., LTD.—See DIC Corporation; *Int'l*, pg. 2108
D.I.D ASIA CO., LTD.—See Daido Kogyo Co., Ltd.; *Int'l*, pg. 1920
DID CO., LTD.—See DAEWON Chemical Co., Ltd.; *Int'l*, pg. 1910
D.I.D CO., LTD.—See Daido Kogyo Co., Ltd.; *Int'l*, pg. 1920
D.ID CORPORATION; *Int'l*, pg. 1901
DID EUROPE S.R.L.—See Daido Kogyo Co., Ltd.; *Int'l*, pg. 1920
DI DEUTSCHE IMMOBILIEN TREUHANDGESELLSCHAFT MBH—See Deutsche Bank Aktiengesellschaft; *Int'l*, pg. 2057
DI DEUTSCHLAND.IMMOBILIEN AG—See MLP SE; *Int'l*, pg. 5004
DIDIER BELGIUM N.V.—See RHI Magnesita N.V.; *Int'l*, pg. 6325
DIDIER-WERKE AG—See RHI Magnesita N.V.; *Int'l*, pg. 6325
DIDI GLOBAL INC.; *Int'l*, pg. 2112
DIDIM E&F; *Int'l*, pg. 2112
DIDION MILLING INC.; *U.S. Private*, pg. 1227
DIDIT.COM, INC.; *U.S. Private*, pg. 1227
DIDLAKE, INC.; *U.S. Private*, pg. 1228
DID MALAYSIA SDN. BHD.—See Daido Kogyo Co., Ltd.; *Int'l*, pg. 1920
DI DONG IL CORPORATION; *Int'l*, pg. 2101
D.I.D PHILIPPINES INC.—See Daido Kogyo Co., Ltd.; *Int'l*, pg. 1920
DIDRICK MEDICAL, INC.; *U.S. Private*, pg. 1228
DIDR.MEHN-ANDERSEN AS—See Mauna Kea Technologies SA; *Int'l*, pg. 4732
D.I.D VIETNAM CO., LTD.—See Daido Kogyo Co., Ltd.; *Int'l*, pg. 1920
DIE ALPENPUMPE GMBH—See BERGER Holding GmbH; *Int'l*, pg. 979
DIEBOLD ATM CIHAZLARI SANAYI VE TICARET A.S.—See Diebold Nixdorf, Inc.; *U.S. Public*, pg. 659
DIEBOLD AUSTRALIA PTY. LTD.—See Diebold Nixdorf, Inc.; *U.S. Public*, pg. 659
DIEBOLD BELGIUM—See Diebold Nixdorf, Inc.; *U.S. Public*, pg. 660
DIEBOLD BOLIVIA S.R. L.—See Diebold Nixdorf, Inc.; *U.S. Public*, pg. 660
DIEBOLD BRASIL LTDA—See Diebold Nixdorf, Inc.; *U.S. Public*, pg. 660
THE DIEBOLD COMPANY OF CANADA LIMITED—See Diebold Nixdorf, Inc.; *U.S. Public*, pg. 661

DIEBOLD-CORP SYSTEMS SDN BHD—See Diebold Nixdorf, Inc.; *U.S. Public*, pg. 661
DIEBOLD FRANCE—See Diebold Nixdorf, Inc.; *U.S. Public*, pg. 660
DIEBOLD GLASCOCK ADVERTISING, INC.; *U.S. Private*, pg. 1228
DIEBOLD GLOBAL FINANCE CORP—See Diebold Nixdorf, Inc.; *U.S. Public*, pg. 659
DIEBOLD HUNGARY LTD.—See Diebold Nixdorf, Inc.; *U.S. Public*, pg. 660
DIEBOLD INFORMATION AND SECURITY SYSTEMS, LLC—See Diebold Nixdorf, Inc.; *U.S. Public*, pg. 660
DIEBOLD INTERNATIONAL LIMITED—See Diebold Nixdorf, Inc.; *U.S. Public*, pg. 660
DIEBOLD LATIN AMERICA HOLDING COMPANY, LLC—See Diebold Nixdorf, Inc.; *U.S. Public*, pg. 660
DIEBOLD LATIN AMERICA OPERATIONAL HEADQUARTERS—See Diebold Nixdorf, Inc.; *U.S. Public*, pg. 660
DIEBOLD LUXEMBOURG—See Diebold Nixdorf, Inc.; *U.S. Public*, pg. 660
DIEBOLD MEXICO HOLDING COMPANY, INC.—See Diebold Nixdorf, Inc.; *U.S. Public*, pg. 660
DIEBOLD MEXICO, S.A. DE C.V.—See Diebold Nixdorf, Inc.; *U.S. Public*, pg. 660
DIEBOLD NIXDORF AB—See Diebold Nixdorf, Inc.; *U.S. Public*, pg. 660
DIEBOLD NIXDORF AG—See Diebold Nixdorf, Inc.; *U.S. Public*, pg. 660
DIEBOLD NIXDORF AG—See Diebold Nixdorf, Inc.; *U.S. Public*, pg. 660
DIEBOLD NIXDORF AUSTRALIA PTY. LTD.—See Diebold Nixdorf, Inc.; *U.S. Public*, pg. 660
DIEBOLD NIXDORF BUSINESS ADMINISTRATION CENTER GMBH—See Diebold Nixdorf, Inc.; *U.S. Public*, pg. 661
DIEBOLD NIXDORF B.V.B.A—See Diebold Nixdorf, Inc.; *U.S. Public*, pg. 660
DIEBOLD NIXDORF B.V.—See Diebold Nixdorf, Inc.; *U.S. Public*, pg. 660
DIEBOLD NIXDORF EURL—See Diebold Nixdorf, Inc.; *U.S. Public*, pg. 661
DIEBOLD NIXDORF GLOBAL SOLUTIONS B.V.—See Diebold Nixdorf, Inc.; *U.S. Public*, pg. 660
DIEBOLD NIXDORF GMBH—See Diebold Nixdorf, Inc.; *U.S. Public*, pg. 660
DIEBOLD NIXDORF (HONG KONG) LTD.—See Diebold Nixdorf, Inc.; *U.S. Public*, pg. 661
DIEBOLD NIXDORF, INC.; *U.S. Public*, pg. 659
DIEBOLD NIXDORF INDIA PRIVATE LIMITED—See Diebold Nixdorf, Inc.; *U.S. Public*, pg. 660
DIEBOLD NIXDORF INFORMATION SYSTEMS (SHANGHAI) CO. LTD.—See Diebold Nixdorf, Inc.; *U.S. Public*, pg. 661
DIEBOLD NIXDORF KFT.—See Diebold Nixdorf, Inc.; *U.S. Public*, pg. 661
DIEBOLD NIXDORF MIDDLE EAST FZ-LLC—See Diebold Nixdorf, Inc.; *U.S. Public*, pg. 661
DIEBOLD NIXDORF MYANMAR LIMITED—See Diebold Nixdorf, Inc.; *U.S. Public*, pg. 660
DIEBOLD NIXDORF OY—See Diebold Nixdorf, Inc.; *U.S. Public*, pg. 661
DIEBOLD NIXDORF PORTUGAL UNIPESSOAL, LDA.—See Diebold Nixdorf, Inc.; *U.S. Public*, pg. 660
DIEBOLD NIXDORF RETAIL SOLUTIONS S.R.O.—See Diebold Nixdorf, Inc.; *U.S. Public*, pg. 660
DIEBOLD NIXDORF S.A.—See Diebold Nixdorf, Inc.; *U.S. Public*, pg. 661
DIEBOLD NIXDORF SAS—See Diebold Nixdorf, Inc.; *U.S. Public*, pg. 660
DIEBOLD NIXDORF SINGAPORE PTE. LTD.—See Diebold Nixdorf, Inc.; *U.S. Public*, pg. 661
DIEBOLD NIXDORF SL—See Diebold Nixdorf, Inc.; *U.S. Public*, pg. 660
DIEBOLD NIXDORF SOUTH AFRICA (PTY) LTD.—See Diebold Nixdorf, Inc.; *U.S. Public*, pg. 660
DIEBOLD NIXDORF SP. Z.O.O.—See Diebold Nixdorf, Inc.; *U.S. Public*, pg. 661
DIEBOLD NIXDORF S.R.L.—See Diebold Nixdorf, Inc.; *U.S. Public*, pg. 660
DIEBOLD NIXDORF SRL—See Diebold Nixdorf, Inc.; *U.S. Public*, pg. 660
DIEBOLD NIXDORF S.R.O. (CZECH REPUBLIC)—See Diebold Nixdorf, Inc.; *U.S. Public*, pg. 661
DIEBOLD NIXDORF S.R.O. (SLOVAKIA)—See Diebold Nixdorf, Inc.; *U.S. Public*, pg. 661
DIEBOLD NIXDORF S.R.O.—See Diebold Nixdorf, Inc.; *U.S. Public*, pg. 661
DIEBOLD NIXDORF TAIWAN LTD.—See Diebold Nixdorf, Inc.; *U.S. Public*, pg. 661
DIEBOLD NIXDORF TECHNOLOGIES LLC—See Diebold Nixdorf, Inc.; *U.S. Public*, pg. 660
DIEBOLD NIXDORF TECHNOLOGY GMBH—See Diebold Nixdorf, Inc.; *U.S. Public*, pg. 661
DIEBOLD NIXDORF TEKNOLOJI A.S.—See Diebold Nixdorf, Inc.; *U.S. Public*, pg. 661
DIEBOLD NIXDORF (THAILAND) COMPANY LIMITED—See Diebold Nixdorf, Inc.; *U.S. Public*, pg. 660

COMPANY NAME INDEX

DIEBOLD NIXDORF (UK) LIMITED—See Diebold Nixdorf, Inc.; *U.S. Public*, pg. 661
DIEBOLD NIXDORF VIETNAM COMPANY LIMITED—See Diebold Nixdorf, Inc.; *U.S. Public*, pg. 660
DIEBOLD OF NEVADA, INC.—See Diebold Nixdorf, Inc.; *U.S. Public*, pg. 660
DIEBOLD OLTP—See Diebold Nixdorf, Inc.; *U.S. Public*, pg. 660
DIEBOLD PACIFIC, LIMITED—See Diebold Nixdorf, Inc.; *U.S. Public*, pg. 660
DIEBOLD PARAGUAY—See Diebold Nixdorf, Inc.; *U.S. Public*, pg. 660
DIEBOLD SELF-SERVICE SOLUTIONS INDUSTRIAL AND SERVICING ROM SRL.—See Diebold Nixdorf, Inc.; *U.S. Public*, pg. 660
DIEBOLD SOFTWARE SOLUTIONS, INC.—See Diebold Nixdorf, Inc.; *U.S. Public*, pg. 661
DIEBOLD (THAILAND) CO., LTD.—See Diebold Nixdorf, Inc.; *U.S. Public*, pg. 659
DIEBOLD URUGUAY S.A.—See Diebold Nixdorf, Inc.; *U.S. Public*, pg. 661
DIEBOLD VIETNAM COMPANY LIMITED—See Diebold Nixdorf, Inc.; *U.S. Public*, pg. 661
DIECKERHOFF GUSS GMBH—See Georgsmarienhutte Holding GmbH; *Int'l*, pg. 2940
DIECKMANN ARZNEIMITTEL GMBH—See Merck & Co., Inc.; *U.S. Public*, pg. 1416
DIECRAFT AUSTRALIA PTY. LTD.—See Tupperware Brands Corporation; *U.S. Public*, pg. 2204
DIE CUTS WITH A VIEW; *U.S. Private*, pg. 1228
DIE DRAUSSENWERBER GMBH—See JCDecaux S.A.; *Int'l*, pg. 3920
DIEDRICH MANUFACTURING, INC.—See City Capital Advisors, LLC; *U.S. Private*, pg. 905
DIEDRICHS & ASSOCIATES, INC.; *U.S. Private*, pg. 1228
D-I-E ELEKTRO AG—See CEZ, a.s.; *Int'l*, pg. 1427
DIE ERSTE IMMOBILIENVERMIETUNGSGESELLSCHAFT M.B.H.—See Erste Group Bank AG; *Int'l*, pg. 2498
DIEFENTHAL HOLDINGS, LLC; *U.S. Private*, pg. 1228
DIEFFENBACHER ASIA PACIFIC SDN. BHD.—See Dieffenbacher Holding GmbH & Co. KG; *Int'l*, pg. 2114
DIEFFENBACHER AUSTRALASIA PTY. LTD.—See Dieffenbaohor Holding GmbH & Co. KG; *Int'l*, pg. 2114
DIEFFENBACHER CUSTOMER SUPPORT, LLC—See Dieffenbacher Holding GmbH & Co. KG; *Int'l*, pg. 2114
DIEFFENBACHER CZ HYDRAULICKE LISY, S.R.O—See Dieffenbacher Holding GmbH & Co. KG; *Int'l*, pg. 2114
DIEFFENBACHER DO BRASIL CONSTRUCAO DE MAQUINAS E INSTALACOES LTDA.—See Dieffenbacher Holding GmbH & Co. KG; *Int'l*, pg. 2114
DIEFFENBACHER HOLDING GMBH & CO. KG; *Int'l*, pg. 2114
DIEFFENBACHER INDIA PVT. LTD.—See Dieffenbacher Holding GmbH & Co. KG; *Int'l*, pg. 2114
DIEFFENBACHER MACHINERY (CHANGZHOU) CO., LTD.—See Dieffenbacher Holding GmbH & Co. KG; *Int'l*, pg. 2114
DIEFFENBACHER MACHINERY SERVICES (BEIJING) CO., LTD.—See Dieffenbacher Holding GmbH & Co. KG; *Int'l*, pg. 2114
DIEFFENBACHER MASCHINENFABRIK GMBH—See Dieffenbacher Holding GmbH & Co. KG; *Int'l*, pg. 2114
DIEFFENBACHER NORTH AMERICA, INC.—See Dieffenbacher Holding GmbH & Co. KG; *Int'l*, pg. 2114
DIEFFENBACHER PANELBOARD OY—See Dieffenbacher Holding GmbH & Co. KG; *Int'l*, pg. 2114
DIEFFENBACHER SCHENCK PANEL GMBH—See Dieffenbacher Holding GmbH & Co. KG; *Int'l*, pg. 2114
DIEFFENBACHER SYSTEM-AUTOMATION GMBH—See Dieffenbacher Holding GmbH & Co. KG; *Int'l*, pg. 2114
DIEFFENBACHER USA, INC.—See Dieffenbacher Holding GmbH & Co. KG; *Int'l*, pg. 2114
DIEGEM-KENNEDY; *Int'l*, pg. 2114
DIEGO PELLICER WORLDWIDE, INC.; *U.S. Public*, pg. 661
DIEGO PLUS EDUCATION CORPORATION; *U.S. Private*, pg. 1228
DIEHL AEROSPACE GMBH—See Diehl Stiftung & Co. KG; *Int'l*, pg. 2114
DIEHL AEROSPACE GMBH—See Diehl Stiftung & Co. KG; *Int'l*, pg. 2114
DIEHL AEROSPACE GMBH—See Thales S.A.; *Int'l*, pg. 7602
DIEHL AEROSPACE GMBH—See Thales S.A.; *Int'l*, pg. 7602
DIEHL AEROSPACE, INC.—See Diehl Stiftung & Co. KG; *Int'l*, pg. 2114
DIEHL AEROSYSTEMS-HOLDING GMBH—See Diehl Stiftung & Co. KG; *Int'l*, pg. 2114
DIEHL AIRCABIN GMBH—See Diehl Stiftung & Co. KG; *Int'l*, pg. 2114
DIEHL AIRCABIN HUNGARY KFT.—See Diehl Stiftung & Co. KG; *Int'l*, pg. 2114
DIEHL AKO STIFTUNG & CO. KG—See Diehl Stiftung & Co. KG; *Int'l*, pg. 2114
DIEHL AUGE DECOUPAGE SAS—See Diehl Stiftung & Co. KG; *Int'l*, pg. 2114

DIEHL AVIATION GILCHING GMBH—See Diehl Stiftung & Co. KG; *Int'l*, pg. 2114
DIEHL COMFORT MODULES GMBH—See Diehl Stiftung & Co. KG; *Int'l*, pg. 2115
DIEHL CONNECTIVITY SOLUTIONS GMBH—See Diehl Stiftung & Co. KG; *Int'l*, pg. 2115
DIEHL CONTROLS MEXICO S.A. DE C.V.—See Diehl Stiftung & Co. KG; *Int'l*, pg. 2115
DIEHL CONTROLS (NANJING) CO. LTD.—See Diehl Stiftung & Co. KG; *Int'l*, pg. 2115
DIEHL CONTROLS NORTH AMERICA INC.—See Diehl Stiftung & Co. KG; *Int'l*, pg. 2115
DIEHL CONTROLS POLSKA SP. Z O.O.—See Diehl Stiftung & Co. KG; *Int'l*, pg. 2115
DIEHL DEFENCE GMBH & CO. KG—See Diehl Stiftung & Co. KG; *Int'l*, pg. 2115
DIEHL DO BRASIL METALURGICA LIMITADA—See Diehl Stiftung & Co. KG; *Int'l*, pg. 2115
DIEHL & EAGLE-PICHER GESELLSCHAFT MIT BESCHRANKTER HAFTUNG—See Diehl Stiftung & Co. KG; *Int'l*, pg. 2114
DIEHL & EAGLEPICHER GMBH—See GTCR LLC; *U.S. Private*, pg. 1805
DIEHL FORD INC.; *U.S. Private*, pg. 1228
DIEHL GAS METERING GMBH—See Diehl Stiftung & Co. KG; *Int'l*, pg. 2115
DIEHL METAL APPLICATIONS GMBH—See Diehl Stiftung & Co. KG; *Int'l*, pg. 2115
DIEHL METAL INDIA PRIVATE LIMITED—See Diehl Stiftung & Co. KG; *Int'l*, pg. 2115
DIEHL METALL (SHENZHEN) CO. LTD.—See Diehl Stiftung & Co. KG; *Int'l*, pg. 2115
DIEHL METALL STIFTUNG & CO. KG—See Diehl Stiftung & Co. KG; *Int'l*, pg. 2115
DIEHL METERING AB—See Diehl Stiftung & Co. KG; *Int'l*, pg. 2115
DIEHL METERING APS—See Diehl Stiftung & Co. KG; *Int'l*, pg. 2115
DIEHL METERING FZE—See Diehl Stiftung & Co. KG; *Int'l*, pg. 2115
DIEHL METERING GESMBH—See Diehl Stiftung & Co. KG; *Int'l*, pg. 2115
DIEHL METERING (JINAN) CO. LTD.—See Diehl Stiftung & Co. KG; *Int'l*, pg. 2115
DIEHL METERING LIMITED—See Diehl Stiftung & Co. KG; *Int'l*, pg. 2115
DIEHL METERING LLC—See Diehl Stiftung & Co. KG; *Int'l*, pg. 2115
DIEHL METERING S.A.S.—See Diehl Stiftung & Co. KG; *Int'l*, pg. 2115
DIEHL METERING S.L.—See Diehl Stiftung & Co. KG; *Int'l*, pg. 2115
DIEHL METERING SP. Z O.O.—See Diehl Stiftung & Co. KG; *Int'l*, pg. 2115
DIEHL METERING S.R.L.—See Diehl Stiftung & Co. KG; *Int'l*, pg. 2115
DIEHL METERING SYSTEMS GMBH—See Diehl Stiftung & Co. KG; *Int'l*, pg. 2115
DIEHL POWER ELECTRONIC SAS—See Diehl Stiftung & Co. KG; *Int'l*, pg. 2114
DIEHL REMSCHEID GMBH & CO—See Diehl Stiftung & Co. KG; *Int'l*, pg. 2115
DIEHL RETROFIT MISSILE SYSTEME GMBH—See Diehl Stiftung & Co. KG; *Int'l*, pg. 2115
DIEHL SERVICE MODULES GMBH—See Diehl Stiftung & Co. KG; *Int'l*, pg. 2115
DIEHL STIFTUNG & CO. KG; *Int'l*, pg. 2114
DIEHL SYNCHROTEC MANUFACTURING (WUXI) CO., LTD.—See Diehl Stiftung & Co. KG; *Int'l*, pg. 2115
DIEHL VENTURES GMBH—See Diehl Stiftung & Co. KG; *Int'l*, pg. 2115
DIEHL WERKZEUGBAU SEEBACH GMBH—See Diehl Stiftung & Co. KG; *Int'l*, pg. 2115
DIEHL WOODWORKING MACHINERY, INC.; *U.S. Private*, pg. 1228
DIEKRA SPEDITIONSGESELLSCHAFT MBH—See Smurfit Kappa Group plc; *Int'l*, pg. 7018
DIE LANDERBAHN CZ S.R.O.—See Ferrovie dello Stato Italiane S.p.A.; *Int'l*, pg. 2645
DIELECTRIC CORPORATION; *U.S. Private*, pg. 1228
DIELECTRIC, LLC—See Sinclair, Inc.; *U.S. Public*, pg. 1885
DIELECTRIC SCIENCES, INC.—See HEICO Corporation; *U.S. Public*, pg. 1020
DIELECTRICS INDUSTRIES INC.; *U.S. Private*, pg. 1228
DIELECTRO BALEAR S.A.—See Sonepar S.A.; *Int'l*, pg. 7092
DIELECTRO CANARIAS LA PALMA—See Sonepar S.A.; *Int'l*, pg. 7092
DIELINE CORP.—See Synergis Technologies Group; *U.S. Private*, pg. 3903
DIELINK—See Synergis Technologies Group; *U.S. Private*, pg. 3903
DIE MEHRWERTMACHER GMBH—See Bertelsmann SE & Co. KGaA; *Int'l*, pg. 992
DIEMOLDING CORPORATION; *U.S. Private*, pg. 1228
DIE-MOLD TOOL LTD.—See Mueller Industries, Inc.; *U.S. Public*, pg. 1484
DIENER BRICK COMPANY; *U.S. Private*, pg. 1228

DIETHELM KELLER HOLDING LIMITED

DIEN QUANG LAMP JSC; *Int'l*, pg. 2115
DIENUPURODAKUTSU INC.—See Daiwabo Holdings Co., Ltd.; *Int'l*, pg. 1949
DI. ENVIRO CORPORATION—See DI Corp.; *Int'l*, pg. 2101
DIEPHOLZ CHEVROLET CADILLAC INC.; *U.S. Private*, pg. 1228
DIERBERGS MARKETS INC.; *U.S. Private*, pg. 1228
DIERENARTSENPRAKTIJK NOP B.V—See CVS Group Plc; *Int'l*, pg. 1890
DIERENARTSENPRAKTIJK ZUID-WEST FRIESLAND B.V.—See CVS Group Plc; *Int'l*, pg. 1890
DIERENZIEKENHUIS DRACHTEN B.V.—See CVS Group Plc; *Int'l*, pg. 1890
DIERIG AG—See Dierig Holding AG; *Int'l*, pg. 2115
DIERIG HOLDING AG; *Int'l*, pg. 2115
DIERIG TEXTILWERKE GMBH—See Dierig Holding AG; *Int'l*, pg. 2115
DIERMEIER ENERGIE GMBH—See BayWa AG; *Int'l*, pg. 917
DIERREVI SPA—See CVC Capital Partners SICAV-FIS S.A.; *Int'l*, pg. 1882
DIE SCHWEIZERISCHE POST AG; *Int'l*, pg. 2112
DIESEKO GROUP B.V.—See SHV Holdings N.V.; *Int'l*, pg. 6871
DIESEL 24 LIMITED—See Edenred S.A.; *Int'l*, pg. 2307
DIESEL DISTRIBUTORS AUSTRALIA PTY LIMITED—See Bapcor Limited; *Int'l*, pg. 857
DIESEL DISTRIBUTORS LIMITED—See Bapcor Limited; *Int'l*, pg. 857
DIESELEC THISTLE GENERATORS LIMITED—See DCC plc; *Int'l*, pg. 1990
DIESEL ELECTRICA LDA.—See Honda Motor Co., Ltd.; *Int'l*, pg. 3460
DIESEL ELECTRIC SERVICES—See Milman Industries Inc.; *Int'l*, pg. 4897
DIESEL FORWARD, INC.; *U.S. Private*, pg. 1228
DIESEL INJECTION SERVICE CO., INC.; *U.S. Private*, pg. 1228
DIESEL LTD.—See Starwood Property Trust, Inc.; *U.S. Public*, pg. 1939
DIESEL MACHINERY INC.; *U.S. Private*, pg. 1229
DIESEL MARINE INTERNATIONAL DUBAI L.L.C.—See DMI UK Ltd.; *Int'l*, pg. 2146
DIESEL MARKETING SDN. BHD.—See Asia Brands Berhad; *Int'l*, pg. 610
DIESEL & MOTOR ENGINEERING PLC; *Int'l*, pg. 2115
DIESEL MOTOR NORDIC AB—See DEUTZ AG; *Int'l*, pg. 2086
DIESEL MOTOR NORDIC A/S—See DEUTZ AG; *Int'l*, pg. 2086
DIESEL PERFORMANCE INC.; *U.S. Private*, pg. 1229
DIESEL POWER EQUIPMENT COMPANY INCORPORATED; *U.S. Private*, pg. 1229
DIESEL POWER OPEN CAST MINING (PTY) LIMITED—See Vuwa Investments (Pty) Ltd; *Int'l*, pg. 8318
DIESEL RADIATOR CO.; *U.S. Private*, pg. 1229
DIESEL RECON COMPANY—See Cummins Inc.; *U.S. Public*, pg. 607
DIESEL RECON UK—See Cummins Inc.; *U.S. Public*, pg. 605
DIESEL SPA; *Int'l*, pg. 2116
DIE SERVICES INTERNATIONAL, LLC; *U.S. Private*, pg. 1228
DIESSEL AKTIENGESELLSCHAFT—See GEA Group Aktiengesellschaft; *Int'l*, pg. 2897
DIESSE SRL; *Int'l*, pg. 2116
DIESTE—See Omnicom Group Inc.; *U.S. Public*, pg. 1582
DIESTE—See Omnicom Group Inc.; *U.S. Public*, pg. 1582
DIE STONSDORFEREI W. KOERNER GMBH & CO. KG—See Berentzen-Gruppe AG; *Int'l*, pg. 978
DIET CENTER WORLDWIDE, INC.—See The Health Management Group, Inc.; *U.S. Private*, pg. 4043
DIETCOOK SHIRAOI CO., LTD.—See Kenko Mayonnaise Co., Ltd.; *Int'l*, pg. 4127
DIETCOOK SUPPLY CO., LTD.—See Kenko Mayonnaise Co., Ltd.; *Int'l*, pg. 4127
DIE-TECH INDUSTRIES, INC.; *U.S. Private*, pg. 1228
D'IETEREN AUTOMOTIVE S.A.—See s.a. D'Ieteren n.v.; *Int'l*, pg. 6448
DIETER HAFEMEISTER ERDBAU GMBH & CO—See ACS, Actividades de Construccion y Servicios, S.A.; *Int'l*, pg. 113
DIETERICH STANDARD INC.—See Emerson Electric Co.; *U.S. Public*, pg. 747
DIETER'S SOD SERVICE, INC.—See Agro-Iron, Inc.; *U.S. Private*, pg. 130
DIETHELM & CO. LTD.—See Diethelm Keller Holding Limited; *Int'l*, pg. 2117
DIETHELM KELLER BRANDS AG—See Diethelm Keller Holding Limited; *Int'l*, pg. 2117
DIETHELM KELLER HOLDING LIMITED; *Int'l*, pg. 2116
DIETHELM KELLER LOGISTICS LTD.—See Diethelm Keller Holding Limited; *Int'l*, pg. 2117
DIETHELM TRAVEL SRI LANKA—See Hemas Holdings PLC; *Int'l*, pg. 3340
DIETIKER AG—See The Federation of Migros Cooperatives; *Int'l*, pg. 7642

DIETHELM KELLER HOLDING LIMITED

DIETL INTERNATIONAL SERVICES, INC.—See ATL Partners, LLC; *U.S. Private*, pg. 369
DIETRICH DESIGN GROUP INC.—See Worthington Industries, Inc.; *U.S. Public*, pg. 2382
DIETRICH DESIGN GROUP INC.—See Worthington Industries, Inc.; *U.S. Public*, pg. 2382
THE DIETRICH FOUNDATION; *U.S. Private*, pg. 4021
DIETRICH INDUSTRIES, INC.—See Worthington Industries, Inc.; *U.S. Public*, pg. 2382
DIETRICH METAL FRAMING CANADA INC—See Worthington Industries, Inc.; *U.S. Public*, pg. 2382
DIETSMANN AD—See Dietsmann N.V.; *Int'l*, pg. 2117
DIETSMANN N.V.; *Int'l*, pg. 2117
DIETSWELL S.A.; *Int'l*, pg. 2117
DIETZEL GMBH; *Int'l*, pg. 2117
DIETZEL UNIVOLT DEUTSCHLAND GMBH—See Dietzel GmbH; *Int'l*, pg. 2117
DIETZGEN CORPORATION; *U.S. Private*, pg. 1229
DIETZ & KOLODENKO CO.; *U.S. Private*, pg. 1229
DIETZ & WATSON INC.; *U.S. Private*, pg. 1229
DIEVINI HOPP BIOTECH HOLDING GMBH & CO. KG; *Int'l*, pg. 2117
DIE WETHJE GMBH—See Pierer Konzerngesellschaft mbH; *Int'l*, pg. 5862
DIFC INVESTMENTS LLC; *Int'l*, pg. 2118
DIFCO, INC.—See LTL Holdings, Inc.; *U.S. Private*, pg. 2509
DIFCO LABORATORIES INCORPORATED—See Becton, Dickinson & Company; *U.S. Public*, pg. 292
DIFEO LEASING PARTNERSHIP—See Penske Automotive Group, Inc.; *U.S. Public*, pg. 1665
DIFEO PARTNERSHIP, LLC—See Penske Automotive Group, Inc.; *U.S. Public*, pg. 1665
DIFFERENCE CAPITAL FINANCIAL INC.; *Int'l*, pg. 2118
THE DIFFERENT DAIRY COMPANY LIMITED—See Donegal Investment Group Plc; *Int'l*, pg. 2163
DIFFER GROUP HOLDING CO., LTD.; *Int'l*, pg. 2118
DIFFFERENT GMBH—See Syzygy AG; *Int'l*, pg. 7394
DIFFULIVRE SA—See Vivendi SE; *Int'l*, pg. 8271
DIFFULIVRE SA—See Vivendi SE; *Int'l*, pg. 8272
DIFFUSION AUTOMOBILE CLERMONTAISE; *Int'l*, pg. 2118
DIFFUSION PHARMACEUTICALS LLC—See CervoMed Inc.; *U.S. Public*, pg. 476
DIFFUSION SARL—See Endress+Hauser (International) Holding AG; *Int'l*, pg. 2406
DIFFUTHERM B.V.—See Wurth Verwaltungsgesellschaft mbH; *Int'l*, pg. 8504
DIFGEN PHARMACEUTICALS PVT. LTD.; *Int'l*, pg. 2118
DIFIORE GROUP; *U.S. Private*, pg. 1229
DIF MANAGEMENT B.V.—See DIF Management Holding B.V.; *Int'l*, pg. 2117
DIF MANAGEMENT HOLDING B.V.; *Int'l*, pg. 2117
DIF ORGANVEREDLUNG GERHARD KUPERS GMBH & CO. KG—See Danish Crown AmbA; *Int'l*, pg. 1964
DIFUSION CENTRO DE INVESTIGACION Y PUBLICACIONES DE IDIOMAS, S.L.—See Ernst Klett AG; *Int'l*, pg. 2495
DIFUSION Y AUDIENCIAS—See Vivendi SE; *Int'l*, pg. 8268
DIFUSION Y AUDIENCIAS—See Vivendi SE; *Int'l*, pg. 8268
DIFUSORA LAROUSSE MEXICO SA DE CV—See Vivendi SE; *Int'l*, pg. 8271
DIGAGOGO VENTURES CORP.; *U.S. Private*, pg. 1229
DIGALOG SYSTEMS INC.; *U.S. Private*, pg. 1229
DIGATRADE FINANCIAL CORP.; *Int'l*, pg. 2118
DIGBY MORGAN (DIFC) LIMITED—See Randstad N.V.; *Int'l*, pg. 6201
DIGBY MORGAN—See Randstad N.V.; *Int'l*, pg. 6201
DIGCO UTILITY CONSTRUCTION, L.P.—See Quanta Services, Inc.; *U.S. Public*, pg. 1751
DIGENNARO COMMUNICATIONS; *U.S. Private*, pg. 1229
DIGERATI GROUP, LLC.; *U.S. Private*, pg. 1229
DIGERATI TECHNOLOGIES, INC.; *U.S. Public*, pg. 661
DIGESTIVE ENDOSCOPY CENTER, LLC—See KKR & Co. Inc.; *U.S. Public*, pg. 1245
DIGESTIVE HEALTH CENTER, LLC—See KKR & Co. Inc.; *U.S. Public*, pg. 1245
DIGGI MULTITRADE LIMITED; *Int'l*, pg. 2118
DIGIA FINLAND OY—See Digia Plc; *Int'l*, pg. 2118
DIGIA PLC; *Int'l*, pg. 2118
DIGIASIA CORP; *Int'l*, pg. 2118
DIGIA SWEDEN AB—See Digia Plc; *Int'l*, pg. 2118
DIGIB ASIA PACIFIC PTE. LTD.—See BRENNTAG SE; *Int'l*, pg. 1149
DIGI-BOOK JAPAN INC.—See TOPPAN Holdings Inc.; *Int'l*, pg. 7816
DIGIBOOKS4ALL S.A.—See Quality & Reliability S.A.; *Int'l*, pg. 6152
DIGICANN VENTURES INC; *Int'l*, pg. 2118
DIGICAP CO., LTD.; *Int'l*, pg. 2118
DIGICEL ARUBA—See Digicel Group Ltd.; *Int'l*, pg. 2119
DIGICEL (BARBADOS) LIMITED—See Digicel Group Ltd.; *Int'l*, pg. 2118
DIGICEL (BERMUDA) LIMITED—See Digicel Group Ltd.; *Int'l*, pg. 2118
DIGICEL BONAIRE—See Digicel Group Ltd.; *Int'l*, pg. 2119

DIGICEL (BVI) LIMITED—See Digicel Group Ltd.; *Int'l*, pg. 2118
DIGICEL CAYMAN LTD.—See Digicel Group Ltd.; *Int'l*, pg. 2119
DIGICEL CURACAO—See Digicel Group Ltd.; *Int'l*, pg. 2119
DIGICEL DOMINICA LTD.—See Digicel Group Ltd.; *Int'l*, pg. 2119
DIGICEL EL SALVADOR—See Digicel Group Ltd.; *Int'l*, pg. 2119
DIGICEL FIJI LTD—See Digicel Group Ltd.; *Int'l*, pg. 2119
DIGICEL GRENADA LTD.—See Digicel Group Ltd.; *Int'l*, pg. 2119
DIGICEL GROUP LTD.; *Int'l*, pg. 2118
DIGICEL GUYANA LTD.—See Digicel Group Ltd.; *Int'l*, pg. 2119
DIGICEL HAITI LTD.—See Digicel Group Ltd.; *Int'l*, pg. 2119
DIGICEL JAMAICA LTD.—See Digicel Group Ltd.; *Int'l*, pg. 2119
DIGICELL INTERNATIONAL, INC.; *U.S. Private*, pg. 1229
DIGICEL PANAMA LTD.—See Digicel Group Ltd.; *Int'l*, pg. 2118
DIGICEL (PNG) LIMITED—See Digicel Group Ltd.; *Int'l*, pg. 2118
DIGICEL SAMOA LIMITED—See Digicel Group Ltd.; *Int'l*, pg. 2119
DIGICEL (ST. LUCIA) LIMITED—See Digicel Group Ltd.; *Int'l*, pg. 2119
DIGICEL ST. VINCENT LIMITED—See Digicel Group Ltd.; *Int'l*, pg. 2119
DIGICEL (TONGA) LIMITED—See Digicel Group Ltd.; *Int'l*, pg. 2119
DIGICEL (TRINIDAD & TOBAGO) LIMITED—See Digicel Group Ltd.; *Int'l*, pg. 2119
DIGICEL TURKS & CAICOS LTD.—See Digicel Group Ltd.; *Int'l*, pg. 2119
DIGICEL VANUATU LTD.—See Digicel Group Ltd.; *Int'l*, pg. 2119
DIGICERT, INC.—See Clearlake Capital Group, L.P.; *U.S. Private*, pg. 934
DIGICERT, INC.—See Crosspoint Capital Partners LP; *U.S. Private*, pg. 1107
DIGICERT, INC.—See TA Associates, Inc.; *U.S. Private*, pg. 3915
DIGICHART INC.—See Constellation Software Inc.; *Int'l*, pg. 1774
DIGICO INC.—See National Amusements, Inc.; *U.S. Private*, pg. 2842
DIGICOM ELECTRONICS INC.—See Kaynes Technology India Limited; *Int'l*, pg. 4102
DIGI COMMUNICATIONS N.V; *Int'l*, pg. 2118
DIGI COMMUNICATION SYSTEME GMBH—See Alpiq Holding AG; *Int'l*, pg. 372
DIGICON CORPORATION; *U.S. Private*, pg. 1229
DIGICONTENT LIMITED; *Int'l*, pg. 2119
DIGICONTROL BENELUX B.V.—See Robert Bosch GmbH; *Int'l*, pg. 6360
DIGICORP, INC.—See Win, LLC; *U.S. Private*, pg. 4532
DIGIDIS S. L.—See mybet Holding SE; *Int'l*, pg. 5111
DIGIDOC S.R.L.—See I.M.A. Industria Macchine Automatiche S.p.A.; *Int'l*, pg. 3565
DIGIFEX AB—See AFRY AB; *Int'l*, pg. 194
DIGIFY, INC.—See GMA Network, Inc.; *Int'l*, pg. 3012
DIGIGRAM ASIA PTE LTD—See Transition Evergreen; *Int'l*, pg. 7901
DIGIGRAPH XPRESS LLC—See Next Page, Inc.; *U.S. Private*, pg. 2920
DIGIHAUL LIMITED—See Deutsche Post AG; *Int'l*, pg. 2080
DIGIHOST TECHNOLOGY, INC.; *Int'l*, pg. 2119
DIGI INTERNATIONAL GMBH—See Digi International Inc.; *U.S. Public*, pg. 662
DIGI INTERNATIONAL (HK) LTD.—See Digi International Inc.; *U.S. Public*, pg. 662
DIGI INTERNATIONAL INC.; *U.S. Public*, pg. 661
DIGI INTERNATIONAL KABUSHIKIKAISHA—See Digi International Inc.; *U.S. Public*, pg. 662
DIGI INTERNATIONAL LIMITED—See Digi International Inc.; *U.S. Public*, pg. 662
DIGI INTERNATIONAL SARL—See Digi International Inc.; *U.S. Public*, pg. 662
DIGI INTERNATIONAL—See Digi International Inc.; *U.S. Public*, pg. 662
DIGI INTERNATIONAL SPAIN S.A.—See Digi International Inc.; *U.S. Public*, pg. 662
DIGI-KEY CORPORATION; *U.S. Private*, pg. 1229
DIGI-KEY ELECTRONICS SHANGHAI COMPANY LTD.—See STMicroelectronics N.V.; *Int'l*, pg. 7217
DIGIKNOW, INC.—See Marcus Thomas LLC; *U.S. Private*, pg. 2573
DIGIKOO GMBH—See RWE AG; *Int'l*, pg. 6434
DIGIKORE STUDIOS LTD.—See Grauer & Weil India Limited; *Int'l*, pg. 3061
DIGILAB, INC.; *U.S. Private*, pg. 1229
DIGILAND PTE. LTD.—See New Silkroutes Group Limited; *Int'l*, pg. 5227
DIGILANT BRASIL—See Digilant, Inc.; *U.S. Private*, pg. 1229

CORPORATE AFFILIATIONS

DIGILANT B.V.—See Digilant, Inc.; *U.S. Private*, pg. 1229
DIGILANT, INC.; *U.S. Private*, pg. 1229
DIGILANT MADRID—See Digilant, Inc.; *U.S. Private*, pg. 1229
DIGILANT MEXICO—See Digilant, Inc.; *U.S. Private*, pg. 1229
DIGILIFE TECHNOLOGIES LIMITED; *Int'l*, pg. 2119
DIGILITI MONEY GROUP, INC.; *U.S. Private*, pg. 1229
DIGI M2M SOLUTIONS INDIA PVT. LTD.—See Digi International Inc.; *U.S. Public*, pg. 662
DIGIMARC CORPORATION; *U.S. Public*, pg. 662
DIGIMARC GMBH—See Digimarc Corporation; *U.S. Public*, pg. 662
DIGIMAX GLOBAL INC.; *Int'l*, pg. 2120
DIGIMAX SRL—See P-Duke Technology Co., Ltd.; *Int'l*, pg. 5681
DIGIMEDICAL SOLUTIONS, INC; *U.S. Private*, pg. 1229
DIGIMERGE TECHNOLOGIES INC.—See Teledyne Technologies Incorporated; *U.S. Public*, pg. 1993
DIGINEER, INC.; *U.S. Private*, pg. 1229
DIGINET GMBH & CO. KG—See CEWE Stiftung & Co. KGaA; *Int'l*, pg. 1425
DIGIOIA, GRAY & ASSOCIATES, LLC—See OceanSound Partners, LP; *U.S. Private*, pg. 2991
DIGIOP TECHNOLOGIES, LTD.—See GTCR LLC; *U.S. Private*, pg. 1802
DI GIORGIO CORPORATION—See Rose Partners LP; *U.S. Private*, pg. 3481
DIGIPATH LABS, INC.—See Hypha Labs, Inc.; *U.S. Public*, pg. 1079
DIGIPRINT AS—See Bergman & Beving AB; *Int'l*, pg. 980
DIGIRAD IMAGING SOLUTIONS, INC.—See Star Equity Holdings, Inc.; *U.S. Public*, pg. 1937
DIGISCRIBE INTERNATIONAL, LLC—See Longshore Capital Partners; *U.S. Private*, pg. 2493
DIGI-SIGN CERTIFICATION SERVICES LIMITED—See Tradelink Electronic Commerce Limited; *Int'l*, pg. 7888
DIGISPICE TECHNOLOGIES LTD.; *Int'l*, pg. 2120
DI & GI S.R.L.—See CTS Eventim AG & Co. KGAA; *Int'l*, pg. 1872
DIGISTAR CORPORATION BERHAD; *Int'l*, pg. 2120
DIGISTAR HOLDINGS SDN. BHD.—See Digistar Corporation Berhad; *Int'l*, pg. 2120
DIGISTICS PROPRIETARY LIMITED—See Super Group Limited; *Int'l*, pg. 7334
DIGITAALINEN ASUNTOKAUPPA DIAS OY—See Alma Media Corporation; *Int'l*, pg. 362
DIGITAL360 S.P.A.; *Int'l*, pg. 2123
DIGITAL 9 INFRASTRUCTURE PLC; *Int'l*, pg. 2120
DIGITAL ADVERTISING CONSORTIUM, INC.—See Hakuhodo DY Holdings Incorporated; *Int'l*, pg. 3220
DIGITAL AIR STRIKE INC.; *U.S. Private*, pg. 1229
DIGITAL.AI SOFTWARE, INC.—See TPG Capital, L.P.; *U.S. Public*, pg. 2173
DIGITAL ALLY, INC.; *U.S. Public*, pg. 662
DIGITAL AND DIRECT COMMUNICATIONS LIMITED—See Publicis Groupe S.A.; *Int'l*, pg. 6110
DIGITAL APPLIANCE CONTROLS DE MEXICO, S.A. DE C.V.—See SigmaTron International, Inc.; *U.S. Public*, pg. 1877
DIGITAL ARTEFACTS LLC—See GI Manager L.P.; *U.S. Private*, pg. 1692
DIGITAL ARTS AMERICA, INC.—See Digital Arts Inc.; *Int'l*, pg. 2120
DIGITAL ARTS ASIA PACIFIC PTE. LTD.—See Digital Arts Inc.; *Int'l*, pg. 2120
DIGITAL ARTS CONSULTING INC.—See Digital Arts Inc.; *Int'l*, pg. 2120
DIGITAL ARTS INC.; *Int'l*, pg. 2120
DIGITAL ASSET MONETARY NETWORK, INC.; *U.S. Public*, pg. 662
DIGITAL BALANCE AUSTRALIA PTY. LIMITED—See Ebiquity plc; *Int'l*, pg. 2285
DIGITAL BARRIERS PLC; *Int'l*, pg. 2120
DIGITAL BLUE DOG, INC.; *U.S. Private*, pg. 1230
DIGITAL BOARDWALK, INC.; *U.S. Private*, pg. 1230
DIGITALBOX PLC; *Int'l*, pg. 2123
DIGITALBRAINZ INC.; *U.S. Private*, pg. 1231
DIGITAL BRAND MEDIA & MARKETING GROUP, INC.; *U.S. Public*, pg. 662
DIGITAL BRANDS GROUP, INC.; *U.S. Public*, pg. 662
DIGITALBRIDGE GROUP, INC.; *U.S. Public*, pg. 664
DIGITAL BROS FRANCE S.A.R.L.—See Digital Bros SpA; *Int'l*, pg. 2120
DIGITAL BROS IBERIA S.L.—See Digital Bros SpA; *Int'l*, pg. 2120
DIGITAL BROS SPA; *Int'l*, pg. 2120
DIGITAL CHANGE INC.—See Allied Architects, Inc.; *Int'l*, pg. 356
DIGITAL CHARGING SOLUTION CORP.—See Bayerische Motoren Werke Aktiengesellschaft; *Int'l*, pg. 912
DIGITAL CHARGING SOLUTIONS GMBH—See Bayerische Motoren Werke Aktiengesellschaft; *Int'l*, pg. 912
DIGITAL CHECK CORP.; *U.S. Private*, pg. 1230
DIGITAL CHINA (CHINA) LIMITED—See Digital China Group Co., Ltd.; *Int'l*, pg. 2121
DIGITAL CHINA GROUP CO., LTD.; *Int'l*, pg. 2120
DIGITAL CHINA (HEFEI) COMPANY LIMITED—See Digital China Holdings Limited; *Int'l*, pg. 2121

COMPANY NAME INDEX

DIGITAL CHINA (HK) LIMITED—See Digital China Holdings Limited; *Int'l*, pg. 2121
DIGITAL CHINA HOLDINGS LIMITED; *Int'l*, pg. 2121
DIGITAL CHINA INFORMATION SERVICE GROUP CO., LTD.; *Int'l*, pg. 2121
DIGITAL CHINA LIMITED—See Digital China Holdings Limited; *Int'l*, pg. 2121
DIGITAL CHINA MACAO COMMERCIAL OFFSHORE LIMITED—See Digital China Holdings Limited; *Int'l*, pg. 2121
DIGITAL CHINA (SHENZHEN) LIMITED—See Digital China Holdings Limited; *Int'l*, pg. 2121
DIGITAL CHINA TECHNOLOGY LIMITED—See Digital China Holdings Limited; *Int'l*, pg. 2121
DIGITAL CHINA (ZHENGZHOU) LIMITED—See Digital China Holdings Limited; *Int'l*, pg. 2121
DIGITAL CHOCOLATE, INC.; *U.S. Private*, pg. 1230
DIGITAL CHOSUN INC.; *Int'l*, pg. 2121
DIGITAL CINEMA IMPLEMENTATION PARTNERS, LLC—See Cineworld Group plc; *Int'l*, pg. 1611
DIGITAL COLONY MANAGEMENT, LLC—See DigitalBridge Group, Inc.; *U.S. Public*, pg. 664
DIGITAL COLOR GRAPHICS; *U.S. Private*, pg. 1230
DIGITAL CONNECTIONS, INC.; *U.S. Private*, pg. 1230
DIGITAL CORE REIT LTD.—See Digital Realty Trust, Inc.; *U.S. Public*, pg. 663
DIGITAL CURRENCY SERVICES INC.; *U.S. Private*, pg. 1230
DIGITAL DAESUNG CO., LTD.; *Int'l*, pg. 2121
DIGITAL DEFENSE, INC.—See HGGC, LLC; *U.S. Private*, pg. 1929
DIGITAL DIMENSIONS, INC.—See DASI Solutions, LLC; *U.S. Private*, pg. 1162
DIGITAL DISPATCH INDIA PVT. LTD—See DDS Wireless International Inc.; *Int'l*, pg. 1994
DIGITAL DISPATCH (INTL) LTD—See DDS Wireless International Inc.; *Int'l*, pg. 1994
DIGITAL DISPATCH (ITL) PTE LTD—See DDS Wireless International Inc.; *Int'l*, pg. 1994
DIGITAL DISPATCH LIMITED PARTNERSHIP—See DDS Wireless International Inc.; *Int'l*, pg. 1994
DIGITAL DISPATCH LTD—See DDS Wireless International Inc.; *Int'l*, pg. 1994
DIGITAL DISPATCH SCANDINAVIA AB—See DDS Wireless International Inc.; *Int'l*, pg. 1994
DIGITAL DOGMA CORP.—See Harvest Partners L.P.; *U.S. Private*, pg. 1876
DIGITAL DOMAIN HOLDINGS LIMITED; *Int'l*, pg. 2121
DIGITAL DOMAIN PRODUCTIONS 3.0 (BC), LTD.—See Digital Domain Holdings Limited; *Int'l*, pg. 2121
DIGITAL EAST CORNELL, LLC—See Digital Realty Trust, Inc.; *U.S. Public*, pg. 663
DIGITAL ECONOMY DEVELOPMENT CENTER LLP—See Kazakhtelecom JSC; *Int'l*, pg. 4102
DIGITAL EGG INC.—See Dentsu Group Inc.; *Int'l*, pg. 2039
DIGITAL ELECTRONICS CORPORATION—See Schneider Electric SE; *Int'l*, pg. 6632
DIGITAL ENDOSCOPY GMBH—See Hoya Corporation; *Int'l*, pg. 3496
DIGITAL ENERGY WORLD; *U.S. Private*, pg. 1230
DIGITAL EVOLUTION GROUP LLC—See Dentsu Group Inc.; *Int'l*, pg. 2037
DIGITAL FACTORY CO., LTD.—See BEC World Public Company Limited; *Int'l*, pg. 936
DIGITAL FACTORY S.R.L.—See RCS MediaGroup S.p.A.; *Int'l*, pg. 6229
DIGITALFELD AG—See Rexel, S.A.; *Int'l*, pg. 6316
DIGITAL FILING SOLUTIONS, INC.—See Shazam, Inc.; *U.S. Private*, pg. 3628
DIGITAL FILM TECHNOLOGY GMBH—See Parter Capital Group GmbH; *Int'l*, pg. 5748
DIGITAL FILM TECHNOLOGY LLC—See Parter Capital Group GmbH; *Int'l*, pg. 5748
DIGITAL FILM TECHNOLOGY—See Parter Capital Group GmbH; *Int'l*, pg. 5748
DIGITAL FINANCIAL GROUP; *U.S. Private*, pg. 1230
DIGITAL FINANCIAL NETWORK INC.—See NewGround Resources; *U.S. Private*, pg. 2915
DIGITAL FOREST, INC.—See Halyard Capital Management, LLC; *U.S. Private*, pg. 1847
DIGITAL FRONTIER INC—See Tsuburaya Fields Holdings Inc.; *Int'l*, pg. 7955
DIGITAL FUEL, LLC; *U.S. Private*, pg. 1230
DIGITAL FURNITURE SDN. BHD.—See Jaycorp Berhad; *Int'l*, pg. 3915
DIGITAL FUSION INC.—See Kratos Defense & Security Solutions, Inc.; *U.S. Public*, pg. 1276
DIGITAL GARAGE, INC.; *Int'l*, pg. 2121
DIGITAL GARDEN INC.—See AOI TYO Holdings Inc.; *Int'l*, pg. 488
DIGITAL GATEWAY INC.; *U.S. Private*, pg. 1230
DIGITALGLOBE, INC.—See Advent International Corporation; *U.S. Private*, pg. 103
DIGITALGLOBE INTELLIGENCE SOLUTIONS, INC.—See Advent International Corporation; *U.S. Private*, pg. 103
DIGITALGLOBE INTERNATIONAL ASIA PACIFIC PTE. LTD.—See Advent International Corporation; *U.S. Private*, pg. 103

DIGITALGLOBE INTERNATIONAL, INC.—See Advent International Corporation; *U.S. Private*, pg. 103
DIGITALGLUE—See P2 Capital Partners, LLC; *U.S. Private*, pg. 3061
DIGITALGLUE—See Silver Lake Group, LLC; *U.S. Private*, pg. 3656
DIGITAL GOLF INC.—See Konami Group Corporation; *Int'l*, pg. 4245
DIGITAL GOLF SOLUTIONS SAS—See Comcast Corporation; *U.S. Public*, pg. 538
DIGITAL GRAPHICS INCORPORATION; *Int'l*, pg. 2122
DIGITAL GUARDIAN, INC.—See Fairhaven Capital Management, LLC; *U.S. Private*, pg. 1464
DIGITAL HANDS, LLC; *U.S. Private*, pg. 1230
DIGITAL HEALTH (PVT) LTD.—See Softlogic Holdings PLC; *Int'l*, pg. 7056
DIGITAL HEARING (UK) LTD.—See Demant A/S; *Int'l*, pg. 2023
DIGITAL HEARTS CO., LTD.—See Digital Hearts Holdings Co., Ltd.; *Int'l*, pg. 2122
DIGITAL HEARTS HOLDINGS CO., LTD.; *Int'l*, pg. 2122
DIGITAL HEARTS KOREA CO., LTD.—See Digital Hearts Holdings Co., Ltd.; *Int'l*, pg. 2122
DIGITAL HEARTS (THAILAND) CO., LTD.—See Digital Hearts Holdings Co., Ltd.; *Int'l*, pg. 2122
DIGITAL HEARTS USA INC.—See Digital Hearts Holdings Co., Ltd.; *Int'l*, pg. 2122
DIGITAL HOLDINGS, INC.; *Int'l*, pg. 2122
DIGITAL HOLLYWOOD INTERACTIVE LIMITED; *Int'l*, pg. 2122
DIGITAL HUB MIBE GMBH—See Dermapharm Holding SE; *Int'l*, pg. 2043
DIGITAL HUB PTE LTD—See Ban Leong Technologies Limited; *Int'l*, pg. 814
DIGITAL HYVE MARKETING LLC—See Butler/Till Media Services, Inc.; *U.S. Private*, pg. 697
DIGITALIA '08 S.R.L.—See Mediaset S.p.A.; *Int'l*, pg. 4773
DIGITAL IDENTITY INC.—See Orchestra Holdings, Inc.; *Int'l*, pg. 5615
DIGITAL ILLUSIONS CE AB—See Electronic Arts Inc.; *U.S. Public*, pg. 724
DIGITAL INFORMATION TECHNOLOGIES CORPORATION; *Int'l*, pg. 2122
DIGITAL INFUSION GMBH—See Asklepios Kliniken GmbH & Co. KGaA; *Int'l*, pg. 623
DIGITAL INSIGHT CORPORATION-PRODUCT DEVELOPMENT—See NCR Voyix Corporation.; *U.S. Public*, pg. 1502
DIGITAL INSIGHT CORPORATION—See NCR Voyix Corporation.; *U.S. Public*, pg. 1502
DIGITAL INSTINCT LLC—See Hellman & Friedman LLC; *U.S. Private*, pg. 1910
DIGITAL INSURANCE, LLC—See New Mountain Capital, LLC; *U.S. Private*, pg. 2901
DIGITAL INTELLIGENCE SYSTEMS, LLC; *U.S. Private*, pg. 1230
DIGITALIST CANADA LTD.—See Digitalist Group Oyj; *Int'l*, pg. 2123
DIGITALIST GROUP OYJ; *Int'l*, pg. 2123
DIGITAL KEYSTONE LIMITED—See Dunstan Thomas Group Limited; *Int'l*, pg. 2227
DIGITAL LABEL SOLUTIONS, LLC—See Genstar Capital, LLC; *U.S. Private*, pg. 1676
DIGITAL LAW & KENNETH—See Publicis Groupe S.A.; *Int'l*, pg. 6107
DIGITAL LEARNING MARKETPLACE PLC; *Int'l*, pg. 2122
DIGITAL LEASH, LLC—See Tiptree Inc.; *U.S. Public*, pg. 2159
DIGITAL LIFESTYLE OUTFITTERS—See Koninklijke Philips N.V.; *Int'l*, pg. 4269
DIGITAL LIGHTWAVE, INC.; *U.S. Public*, pg. 1230
DIGITAL LOCATIONS, INC.; *U.S. Public*, pg. 662
DIGITAL LUMENS, INC.—See Skyview Capital, LLC; *U.S. Private*, pg. 3686
DIGITAL MAGICS S.P.A.—See ZEST S.p.A.; *Int'l*, pg. 8639
DIGITAL MANAGEMENT, INC.—See OceanSound Partners, LP; *U.S. Private*, pg. 2990
DIGITAL MAP PRODUCTS, INC.—See Battery Ventures, L.P.; *U.S. Private*, pg. 489
DIGITAL MAP PRODUCTS, INC.—See Silver Lake Group, LLC; *U.S. Private*, pg. 3658
DIGITAL MATTER (PTY) LTD—See African Equity Empowerment Investmts Limited; *Int'l*, pg. 191
DIGITAL MEDIA CENTRE B.V.—See TVT Media; *Int'l*, pg. 7989
DIGITAL MEDIA ENTERPRISES LLC—See Chicken Soup for the Soul Entertainment, Inc.; *U.S. Public*, pg. 488
DIGITAL MEDIA HUB GMBH—See Bertelsmann SE & Co. KGaA; *Int'l*, pg. 992
DIGITAL MEDIA LAB INC.—See Kaga Electronics Co., Ltd.; *Int'l*, pg. 4048
DIGITAL MEDIA PROFESSIONALS INC.; *Int'l*, pg. 2122
DIGITAL MEDIA SOLUTIONS, INC.; *U.S. Public*, pg. 662
DIGITAL MEDIA SOLUTIONS, LLC—See Digital Media Solutions, Inc.; *U.S. Public*, pg. 663
DIGITAL MULTIMEDIA TECHNOLOGY CO., LTD.; *Int'l*, pg. 2122
DIGITAL NAUTIC SAS—See Beneteau S.A; *Int'l*, pg. 972

THE DIGITAL RING, LLC

DIGITAL NETWORKS GROUP, INC.—See ITOCHU Corporation; *Int'l*, pg. 3839
DIGITAL NEXT—See Oniva Online Group Europe AB; *Int'l*, pg. 5581
DIGITALOCEAN HOLDINGS, INC.; *U.S. Public*, pg. 665
DIGITAL ONE CONSULTING SP. Z O.O.; *Int'l*, pg. 2122
DIGITAL ONE LTD.—See Canada Pension Plan Investment Board; *Int'l*, pg. 1278
DIGITAL ONLINE MEDIA GMBH; *Int'l*, pg. 2123
DIGITALONUS INC.—See Mahindra & Mahindra Limited; *Int'l*, pg. 4647
DIGITAL OPERATIVE, INC.—See Transcosmos Inc.; *Int'l*, pg. 7898
DIGITAL OPTICS CO., LTD. - SEONGNAM FACTORY—See Noble M&B Co., Ltd.; *Int'l*, pg. 5397
DIGITAL OPTICS CO., LTD. - SIWHA FACTORY—See Noble M&B Co., Ltd.; *Int'l*, pg. 5397
DIGITALOPTICS CORPORATION ISRAEL LIMITED—See Adeia Inc.; *U.S. Public*, pg. 40
DIGITALOPTICS CORPORATION JAPAN GK—See Adeia Inc.; *U.S. Public*, pg. 40
DIGITALOPTICS CORPORATION KOREA LIMITED—See Adeia Inc.; *U.S. Public*, pg. 40
DIGITALOPTICS CORPORATION TAIWAN LIMITED—See Adeia Inc.; *U.S. Public*, pg. 40
DIGITAL PACIFIC PTY LTD—See Deluxe Corporation; *U.S. Public*, pg. 653
DIGITAL PAPER SOLUTIONS SDN. BHD.—See Key Alliance Group Berhad; *Int'l*, pg. 4144
DIGITAL PARADISE, INC.—See Millennium Global Holdings, Inc.; *Int'l*, pg. 4896
DIGITAL PAYMENTS PLC; *Int'l*, pg. 2123
DIGITAL PERIPHERAL SOLUTIONS, INC.; *U.S. Private*, pg. 1230
DIGITAL PHONE CO., LTD.—See Advanced Info Service Plc; *Int'l*, pg. 160
DIGITAL PHOTONICS CORP.—See Anderson Industrial Corporation; *Int'l*, pg. 450
DIGITAL PLANET COMMUNICATIONS, INC.—See UPSTACK, Inc.; *U.S. Private*, pg. 4312
DIGITAL PLUS INC.; *Int'l*, pg. 2123
DIGITALPOST INTERACTIVE, INC.; *U.S. Private*, pg. 1231
DIGITAL POWER CORPORATION—See Ault Alliance, Inc.; *U.S. Public*, pg. 227
DIGITAL PRINT IMPRESSIONS, INC.—See Merrick Industries Incorporated; *U.S. Private*, pg. 2675
DIGITAL PROJECTION LTD.—See Delta Electronics, Inc.; *Int'l*, pg. 2018
DIGITALPROJEKT 1 GMBH—See EWE Aktiengesellschaft; *Int'l*, pg. 2575
DIGITAL PROPERTY GUIDES LTD.—See Vivendi SE; *Int'l*, pg. 8271
DIGITAL PROSPECTORS CORP.; *U.S. Private*, pg. 1231
DIGITAL PUBLISHING INITIATIVES JAPAN CO., LTD.—See Media Do Co., Ltd.; *Int'l*, pg. 4770
DIGITAL PUBLISHING SOLUTIONS, INC.—See Diversified Global Graphics Group, LLC; *U.S. Private*, pg. 1242
DIGITAL PULP; *U.S. Private*, pg. 1231
DIGITAL REALTY AUSTRIA GMBH—See Digital Realty Trust, Inc.; *U.S. Public*, pg. 663
DIGITAL REALTY SWITZERLAND GMBH—See Digital Realty Trust, Inc.; *U.S. Public*, pg. 663
DIGITAL REALTY TRUST, INC.; *U.S. Public*, pg. 663
DIGITAL REALTY TRUST, L.P.—See Digital Realty Trust, Inc.; *U.S. Public*, pg. 663
DIGITAL RECEIVER TECHNOLOGY INC.—See The Boeing Company; *U.S. Public*, pg. 663
DIGITAL RESULT GMBH—See Bertrandt AG; *Int'l*, pg. 998
DIGITAL RFQ LTD.—See Nukkleus Inc.; *U.S. Public*, pg. 1555
THE DIGITAL RING, LLC; *U.S. Private*, pg. 4021
DIGITAL RISK, LLC—See Blackstone Inc.; *U.S. Public*, pg. 356
DIGITAL RIVER GMBH—See Siris Capital Group, LLC; *U.S. Private*, pg. 3672
DIGITAL RIVER, INC.—See Siris Capital Group, LLC; *U.S. Private*, pg. 3672
DIGITAL RIVER IRELAND LIMITED—See Siris Capital Group, LLC; *U.S. Private*, pg. 3672
DIGITAL RIVER ONLINE GAMES—See Siris Capital Group, LLC; *U.S. Private*, pg. 3672
DIGITAL ROADS, INC.—See Advanced Network Management, Inc.; *U.S. Public*, pg. 91
DIGITAL ROOM, LLC—See Sycamore Partners Management, LP; *U.S. Private*, pg. 3895
DIGITAL SANDBOX, INC.—See Edgewater Services, LLC; *U.S. Private*, pg. 1335
DIGITAL SCANNING CORPORATION PTE LTD—See DGB Asia Berhad; *Int'l*, pg. 2096
DIGITAL SECURITY CONTROLS, INC.—See Johnson Controls International plc; *Int'l*, pg. 3987
DIGITAL SECURITY CONTROLS—See Johnson Controls International plc; *Int'l*, pg. 3988
DIGITAL SPECIALTY CHEMICALS LIMITED—See Entegris, Inc.; *U.S. Public*, pg. 776
DIGITAL SPICE CORPORATION—See Altech Corporation; *Int'l*, pg. 389
DIGITAL SPIRIT GMBH—See IDOX PLC; *Int'l*, pg. 3596

THE DIGITAL RING, LLC

CORPORATE AFFILIATIONS

DIGITAL STORAGE INCORPORATED—See Dexxon Groupe SA; *Int'l*, pg. 2093
DIGITAL STORM, INC.; *U.S. Private*, pg. 1231
DIGITAL STORM SRL—See Sesa S.p.A.; *Int'l*, pg. 6728
DIGITAL TECH INC.—See Coolpad Group Limited; *Int'l*, pg. 1789
DIGITAL TELECOMMUNICATIONS PHILS., INC.—See PLDT Inc.; *Int'l*, pg. 5896
DIGITALTOWN, INC.; *U.S. Public*, pg. 666
DIGITAL TRADE AND TRANSPORTATION NETWORK LIMITED—See Tradelink Electronic Commerce Limited; *Int'l*, pg. 7888
DIGITAL TRAFFIC SYSTEMS, INC.—See Sterling Partners; *U.S. Private*, pg. 3806
DIGITAL TRANSCRIPTION SYSTEM, INC.—See Travis Business Systems Inc.; *U.S. Private*, pg. 4214
DIGITAL TURBINE (EMEA) LTD.—See Digital Turbine, Inc.; *U.S. Public*, pg. 664
DIGITAL TURBINE, INC.; *U.S. Public*, pg. 663
DIGITALUM N.V.—See Alan Allman Associates SA; *Int'l*, pg. 290
DIGITAL UNITED, INC.; *Int'l*, pg. 2123
DIGITAL UNLIMITED GROUP LTD.—See Accenture plc; *Int'l*, pg. 87
DIGITAL UTILITIES VENTURES, INC.; *U.S. Public*, pg. 664
DIGITAL VALUE S.P.A.; *Int'l*, pg. 2123
DIGITAL VIDEO NETWORKS LLC—See Marlin Equity Partners, LLC; *U.S. Private*, pg. 2583
DIGITAL VIDEO SYSTEMS, INC.; *U.S. Private*, pg. 1231
DIGITAL VIRGO ESPANA—See Digital Virgo Group SAS; *Int'l*, pg. 2123
DIGITAL VIRGO GROUP SAS; *Int'l*, pg. 2123
DIGITAL VIRGO S.A.—See Digital Virgo Group SAS; *Int'l*, pg. 2123
DIGITAL VIRGO SAS—See Digital Virgo Group SAS; *Int'l*, pg. 2123
DIGITAL VISION SYSTEMS INC—See Image Systems AB; *Int'l*, pg. 3618
DIGITAL VISION SYSTEMS LTD.—See Image Systems AB; *Int'l*, pg. 3618
DIGITAL VOICE SYSTEMS, INC.; *U.S. Private*, pg. 1231
DIGITAL WEST NETWORKS, INC.—See Stonepeak Partners L.P.; *U.S. Private*, pg. 3829
DIGITAL WINTER, LLC—See Digital Realty Trust, Inc.; *U.S. Public*, pg. 663
DIGITAL WORKFORCE SERVICES PLC; *Int'l*, pg. 2123
DIGITAL WORKFORCE SP. Z O.O.—See Digital Workforce Services Plc; *Int'l*, pg. 2123
DIGITALX LIMITED; *Int'l*, pg. 2123
DIGITAL ZEN—See Barker/DZP; *U.S. Private*, pg. 475
DIGITAS GREATER CHINA—See Publicis Groupe S.A.; *Int'l*, pg. 6097
DIGITAS HEALTH LONDON—See Publicis Groupe S.A.; *Int'l*, pg. 6098
DIGITAS HEALTH—See Publicis Groupe S.A.; *Int'l*, pg. 6098
DIGITAS HEALTH—See Publicis Groupe S.A.; *Int'l*, pg. 6098
DIGITAS INC.—See Publicis Groupe S.A.; *Int'l*, pg. 6097
DIGITAS INC—See Publicis Groupe S.A.; *Int'l*, pg. 6098
DIGITAS INC—See Publicis Groupe S.A.; *Int'l*, pg. 6098
DIGITAS, INC.—See Publicis Groupe S.A.; *Int'l*, pg. 6098
DIGITASLBI FRANCE—See Publicis Groupe S.A.; *Int'l*, pg. 6098
DIGITASLBI - NEW YORK—See Publicis Groupe S.A.; *Int'l*, pg. 6098
DIGITASLBI—See Publicis Groupe S.A.; *Int'l*, pg. 6098
DIGITASLBI SPAIN—See Publicis Groupe S.A.; *Int'l*, pg. 6098
DIGITAS LONDON—See Publicis Groupe S.A.; *Int'l*, pg. 6098
DIGITECH COMPUTER LLC—See Investor AB; *Int'l*, pg. 3787
DIGITECH SA; *Int'l*, pg. 2123
DIGITECH SYSTEMS CO., LTD.; *Int'l*, pg. 2123
DIGITEK ELECTRONICS LTD.—See Jabil Inc.; *U.S. Public*, pg. 1180
DIGITEK SOFTWARE, INC.; *U.S. Private*, pg. 1231
DIGI-TEL COMMUNICATIONS, LLC; *U.S. Private*, pg. 1229
DIGITEL CORPORATION; *U.S. Private*, pg. 1231
DIGI TELECOMMUNICATIONS SDN BHD—See Celcom-Digi Berhad; *Int'l*, pg. 1391
DIGITEL MOBILE PHILS., INC.—See PLDT Inc.; *Int'l*, pg. 5896
DIGITEST ELEKTRONIK SERVICE GMBH; *Int'l*, pg. 2124
DIGITEX CANADA INC.—See Xerox Holdings Corporation; *U.S. Public*, pg. 2386
DIGITHERA S.R.L.—See Unifiedpost Group SA; *Int'l*, pg. 8043
DIGITOUCH S.P.A.; *Int'l*, pg. 2124
DIGI TRADE, S.R.O.—See Raiffeisen Bank International AG; *Int'l*, pg. 6184
DIGI TRADE, S.R.O.—See Raiffeisen-Holding Niederosterreich-Wien reg. Gen.m.b.H.; *Int'l*, pg. 6186
DIGITRAN—See Electro Switch Corporation; *U.S. Private*, pg. 1353
DIGITREE GROUP S.A.; *Int'l*, pg. 2124

DIGITRONIC GMBH; *Int'l*, pg. 2124
DIGITRON INSTRUMENTATION LIMITED—See British Rototherm Company Ltd.; *Int'l*, pg. 1171
DIGITS LLC—See Avalon Documents Services; *U.S. Private*, pg. 403
DIGITTRON TECHNOLOGIES, INC.—See Pivot International, Inc.; *U.S. Private*, pg. 3192
DIGITY COMPANIES, LLC; *U.S. Private*, pg. 1231
DIGIUM, INC.—See Sangoma Technologies Corporation; *Int'l*, pg. 6538
DIGIVIVE SERVICES PRIVATE LIMITED—See Media Matrix Worldwide Limited; *Int'l*, pg. 4771
DIGIWEB LTD.; *Int'l*, pg. 2124
DIGIWIN SOFTWARE CO., LTD.; *Int'l*, pg. 2124
DIGIWIN SOFTWARE (VIETNAM) CO., LTD.—See Digiwin Software Co., Ltd.; *Int'l*, pg. 2124
DIGNEY GRANT LIMITED—See Brown & Brown, Inc.; *U.S. Public*, pg. 400
DIGNEY YORK ASSOCIATES LLC—See Zurn Elkay Water Solutions Corporation; *U.S. Public*, pg. 2412
DIGNITANA AB; *Int'l*, pg. 2124
DIGNITANA INC.—See Dignitana AB; *Int'l*, pg. 2124
DIGNITAS TECHNOLOGIES, LLC; *U.S. Private*, pg. 1231
DIGNITY CARING FUNERAL SERVICES—See Dignity plc; *Int'l*, pg. 2124
DIGNITY CREMATORIA LIMITED—See Dignity plc; *Int'l*, pg. 2124
DIGNITY FUNERALS LIMITED—See Dignity plc; *Int'l*, pg. 2124
DIGNITY HEALTH MEDICAL GROUP NEVADA, LLC—See Catholic Health Initiatives; *U.S. Private*, pg. 789
DIGNITY HEALTH—See Catholic Health Initiatives; *U.S. Private*, pg. 789
DIGNITY HEALTH - SOUTHERN CALIFORNIA—See Catholic Health Initiatives; *U.S. Private*, pg. 789
DIGNITY PLC; *Int'l*, pg. 2124
DIGNITY SERVICES LTD.—See Dignity plc; *Int'l*, pg. 2124
DIGONEX TECHNOLOGIES, INC.—See Emmis Communications Corporation; *U.S. Public*, pg. 753
DIGRAPH TRANSPORT SUPPLIES LIMITED—See LKQ Corporation; *U.S. Public*, pg. 1334
DIGRAPH TRANSPORT SUPPLIES (TELFORD) LIMITED—See LKQ Corporation; *U.S. Public*, pg. 1334
D.I. GROUP—See LVMH Moet Hennessy Louis Vuitton SE; *Int'l*, pg. 4592
DIGRUN GRUN SL—See XL Energy Ltd.; *Int'l*, pg. 8535
DIGUANG INTERNATIONAL DEVELOPMENT COMPANY LTD.; *Int'l*, pg. 2124
DIHA DEUTSCHE INDUSTRIE- UND HANDELSVEREINIGUNG ALBANIEN—See Messe Munchen GmbH; *Int'l*, pg. 4841
DIHAG HOLDING GMBH; *Int'l*, pg. 2124
DIH HOLDING US, INC.; *U.S. Public*, pg. 666
DIHR ALI S.P.A.—See Ali Holding S.r.l; *Int'l*, pg. 321
DIIT GMBH—See Metall Zug AG; *Int'l*, pg. 4847
DIJAMANT A.D; *Int'l*, pg. 2125
DIJAYA DEVELOPMENT SDN. BHD.—See Tropicana Corporation Berhad; *Int'l*, pg. 7939
DIJAYA MANAGEMENT SERVICES SDN. BHD.—See Tropicana Corporation Berhad; *Int'l*, pg. 7939
DIJET GMBH—See DIJET Industrial Co., Ltd; *Int'l*, pg. 2125
DIJET INCORPORATED—See DIJET Industrial Co., Ltd; *Int'l*, pg. 2125
DIJET INDUSTRIAL CO., LTD - MIE PLANT—See DIJET Industrial Co., Ltd; *Int'l*, pg. 2125
DIJET INDUSTRIAL CO., LTD; *Int'l*, pg. 2125
DIJET INDUSTRIAL CO., LTD - TONDABAYASHI PLANT—See DIJET Industrial Co., Ltd; *Int'l*, pg. 2125
DIJION CO., LTD—See Chori Co., Ltd.; *Int'l*, pg. 1583
DIKAR S. COOP.—See Mondragon Corporation; *Int'l*, pg. 5028
DIKE LIEGENSCHAFTSVERWERTUNG GESELLSCHAFT M.B.H.—See PORR AG; *Int'l*, pg. 5922
DIK-OCEAN ADVERTISING CO., LTD.—See Bain Capital, LP; *U.S. Private*, pg. 428
DIKSATTRANSWORLD LIMITED; *Int'l*, pg. 2125
DIKSHA GREENS LTD.; *Int'l*, pg. 2125
DILA CAPITAL ACQUISITION CORP.; *U.S. Public*, pg. 666
DILAS DIODE LASER, INC.—See Coherent Corp.; *U.S. Public*, pg. 527
DILAS DIODENLASER GMBH—See Coherent Corp.; *U.S. Public*, pg. 527
DILAWRI GROUP OF COMPANIES; *Int'l*, pg. 2125
DILAX FRANCE SAS—See DZ BANK AG Deutsche Zentral-Genossenschaftsbank; *Int'l*, pg. 2244
DILAX INTELCOM AG—See DZ BANK AG Deutsche Zentral-Genossenschaftsbank; *Int'l*, pg. 2244
DILAX INTELCOM GMBH—See init innovation in traffic systems SE; *Int'l*, pg. 3704
DILAX INTELCOM IBERICA S.L.U.—See DZ BANK AG Deutsche Zentral-Genossenschaftsbank; *Int'l*, pg. 2244
DILAX SYSTEMS INC.—See DZ BANK AG Deutsche Zentral-Genossenschaftsbank; *Int'l*, pg. 2244
DILAX SYSTEMS UK LTD.—See DZ BANK AG Deutsche Zentral-Genossenschaftsbank; *Int'l*, pg. 2244
DI LEGNO INTERIORS NV—See KBC Group NV; *Int'l*, pg. 4104

DILEXIS S.A.—See Tia Maruca Argentina SA; *Int'l*, pg. 7736
DILGARD FROZEN FOODS INC.; *U.S. Private*, pg. 1231
DILIBEL SA—See Vivendi SE; *Int'l*, pg. 8272
DILIGENTA LIMITED—See Tata Sons Limited; *Int'l*, pg. 7469
DILIGENT CORPORATION—See Insight Venture Management, LLC; *U.S. Private*, pg. 2089
DILIGENT DELIVERY SYSTEMS; *U.S. Private*, pg. 1231
DILIGENT INDUSTRIES LIMITED; *Int'l*, pg. 2125
DILIGENT MEDIA CORPORATION LIMITED; *Int'l*, pg. 2125
DILIP BUILDCON LIMITED; *Int'l*, pg. 2125
DILJ D.O.O.—See Nexe Grupa d.d.; *Int'l*, pg. 5243
DILL AIR CONTROLS PRODUCTS, LLC—See Shanghai Baolong Automotive Corporation; *Int'l*, pg. 6762
DILLARD INVESTMENT CO., INC.—See Dillard's Inc.; *U.S. Public*, pg. 666
DILLARD'S FORT WORTH DIVISION—See Dillard's Inc.; *U.S. Public*, pg. 666
DILLARD'S INC.; *U.S. Public*, pg. 666
DILLARD'S SAINT LOUIS DIVISION—See Dillard's Inc.; *U.S. Public*, pg. 666
DILLARD'S SOUTHEAST DIVISION—See Dillard's Inc.; *U.S. Public*, pg. 666
DILLCO FLUID SERVICE, INC.—See Enservco Corporation; *U.S. Public*, pg. 775
DILLIE & KUHN, INC.—See Crestone Services Group LLC; *U.S. Private*, pg. 1097
DILLI INCORPORATED; *Int'l*, pg. 2125
DILLINGER ESPANA S.L.U.—See AG der Dillinger Huttenwerke; *Int'l*, pg. 197
DILLINGER FRANCE S.A.—See AG der Dillinger Huttenwerke; *Int'l*, pg. 197
DILLINGER HUTTE SERVICES B.V.—See AG der Dillinger Huttenwerke; *Int'l*, pg. 197
DILLINGER HUTTE VERTRIEB GMBH—See AG der Dillinger Huttenwerke; *Int'l*, pg. 197
DILLINGER INDIA STEEL SERVICE CENTER PRIVATE LTD.—See AG der Dillinger Huttenwerke; *Int'l*, pg. 197
DILLINGER INTERNATIONAL S.A.—See AG der Dillinger Huttenwerke; *Int'l*, pg. 197
DILLINGER ITALIA S.R.L.—See AG der Dillinger Huttenwerke; *Int'l*, pg. 197
DILLINGER MIDDLE EAST FZE—See AG der Dillinger Huttenwerke; *Int'l*, pg. 197
DILLINGER NEDERLAND B.V.—See AG der Dillinger Huttenwerke; *Int'l*, pg. 197
DILLINGER NORGE AS—See AG der Dillinger Huttenwerke; *Int'l*, pg. 197
DILING GROUP, INC.—See Comfort Systems USA, Inc.; *U.S. Public*, pg. 543
DILLING MECHANICAL CONTRACTORS, INC.; *U.S. Private*, pg. 1231
DILL INVESTMENTS, LLC; *U.S. Private*, pg. 1231
DILLISTONE GROUP PLC; *Int'l*, pg. 2125
DILLISTONE SOLUTIONS LIMITED—See Dillistone Group Plc; *Int'l*, pg. 2125
DILLISTONE SYSTEMS (AUSTRALIA) PTY LTD—See Dillistone Group Plc; *Int'l*, pg. 2125
DILLISTONE SYSTEMS (US) INC.—See Dillistone Group Plc; *Int'l*, pg. 2125
DILLMAN FARM; *U.S. Private*, pg. 1231
DILLMAN & UPTON, INC.; *U.S. Private*, pg. 1231
DILLON COMPANIES, INC.—See The Kroger Co.; *U.S. Public*, pg. 2107
DILLON PROVISION COMPANY INC.; *U.S. Private*, pg. 1231
DILLON SUPPLY COMPANY—See Descours & Cabaud SA; *Int'l*, pg. 2044
DILLON TRANSPORT INC.; *U.S. Private*, pg. 1231
DILLON TRANSPORT INC—See Dillon Transport Inc.; *U.S. Private*, pg. 1231
DILLON YARN CORPORATION; *U.S. Private*, pg. 1231
DILMAH CEYLON TEA SERVICES PLC; *Int'l*, pg. 2125
DILMAR OIL COMPANY INC. - ATLANTA PLANT—See Dilmar Oil Company Inc.; *U.S. Private*, pg. 1232
DILMAR OIL COMPANY INC. - CHARLESTON PLANT—See Dilmar Oil Company Inc.; *U.S. Private*, pg. 1232
DILMAR OIL COMPANY INC. - CHARLOTTE PLANT—See Dilmar Oil Company Inc.; *U.S. Private*, pg. 1232
DILMAR OIL COMPANY INC. - COLUMBIA PLANT—See Dilmar Oil Company Inc.; *U.S. Private*, pg. 1232
DILMAR OIL COMPANY INC. - HENDERSON PLANT—See Dilmar Oil Company Inc.; *U.S. Private*, pg. 1232
DILMAR OIL COMPANY INC. - LATTA PLANT—See Dilmar Oil Company Inc.; *U.S. Private*, pg. 1232
DILMAR OIL COMPANY INC.; *U.S. Private*, pg. 1232
DILMAR OIL COMPANY INC. - WILMINGTON PLANT—See Dilmar Oil Company Inc.; *U.S. Private*, pg. 1232
DILON TECHNOLOGIES LLC; *U.S. Private*, pg. 1232
DILWORTH HEARING LTD.—See Amplifon S.p.A.; *Int'l*, pg. 435
DILWORTH MANUFACTURING COMPANY; *U.S. Private*, pg. 1232

COMPANY NAME INDEX

DIMACO UK LIMITED—See Colruyt Group N.V.; *Int'l*, pg. 1705
DIMAGI, INC.; *U.S. Private*, pg. 1232
DIMAH CAPITAL INVESTMENT COMPANY-K.S.C.—See Al Imtiaz Investment Group Company- K.S.C.; *Int'l*, pg. 279
DIMALSA LOGISTICS INC.—See Deutsche Post AG; *Int'l*, pg. 2080
DIMA LTDA.; *Int'l*, pg. 2125
DIMARE FRESH, INC.; *U.S. Private*, pg. 1232
DIMARE FRESH—See DiMare Fresh, Inc.; *U.S. Private*, pg. 1232
DIMARK LTD; *Int'l*, pg. 2125
DIMAR MANUFACTURING CORPORATION; *U.S. Private*, pg. 1232
DIMBAY GMBH—See Storskogen Group AB; *Int'l*, pg. 7227
DIMCO-GRAY CORP.; *U.S. Private*, pg. 1232
DIMCO PLC; *Int'l*, pg. 2125
DIME ABSTRACT LLC—See Dime Community Bancshares, Inc.; *U.S. Public*, pg. 666
THE DIME BANK—See Dimeco Inc.; *U.S. Public*, pg. 666
DIME BANK; *U.S. Private*, pg. 1232
DIMECO INC.; *U.S. Public*, pg. 666
DIME COMMUNITY BANCSHARES, INC.; *U.S. Public*, pg. 666
DIME COMMUNITY BANK—See Dime Community Bancshares, Inc.; *U.S. Public*, pg. 666
DIMED S.A. DISTRIBUIDORA DE MEDICAMENTOS; *Int'l*, pg. 2125
DIMEL CASTILLA, S.A.—See Sonepar S.A.; *Int'l*, pg. 7092
DIMELING, SCHREIBER & PARK; *U.S. Private*, pg. 1232
DIMELO, SA—See RingCentral, Inc.; *U.S. Public*, pg. 1799
DIME MAGAZINE PUBLISHING CO., INC.—See Woven Digital, Inc.; *U.S. Private*, pg. 4571
DIMENSIIONS HEALTHCARE LLC—See IQVIA Holdings Inc.; *U.S. Public*, pg. 1168
DIMENSIONAL ASSOCIATES, LLC—See JDS Capital Management, Inc.; *U.S. Private*, pg. 2196
DIMENSIONAL EQUIPAMENTOS ELETRICOS LTDA.—See Sonepar S.A.; *Int'l*, pg. 7093
DIMENSIONAL FUND ADVISORS CANADA INC.—See Dimensional Fund Advisors LP; *U.S. Private*, pg. 1233
DIMENSIONAL FUND ADVISORS LP; *U.S. Private*, pg. 1233
DIMENSIONAL FUND ADVISORS LTD.—See Dimensional Fund Advisors LP; *U.S. Private*, pg. 1233
DIMENSIONAL GRAPHICS CORPORATION; *U.S. Private*, pg. 1233
DIMENSIONAL INSIGHT, INC.; *U.S. Private*, pg. 1233
DIMENSIONAL JAPAN LTD.—See Dimensional Fund Advisors LP; *U.S. Private*, pg. 1233
DIMENSION-ALL INC.—See Takamiya Co., Ltd.; *Int'l*, pg. 7430
DIMENSIONAL MACHINE WORKS LLC—See Pradeep Metals Limited; *Int'l*, pg. 5952
DIMENSIONAL MANAGEMENT CORP.—See Waud Capital Partners LLC; *U.S. Private*, pg. 4457
DIMENSIONAL MERCHANDISING, INC.; *U.S. Private*, pg. 1233
DIMENSIONAL MUSIC PUBLISHING, LLC—See JDS Capital Management, Inc.; *U.S. Private*, pg. 2196
DIMENSION CONSTRUCTION INC.; *U.S. Private*, pg. 1232
DIMENSION DATA ASIA PACIFIC PTE. LTD.—See Nippon Telegraph & Telephone Corporation; *Int'l*, pg. 5340
DIMENSION DATA AUSTRALIA PTY LIMITED—See Nippon Telegraph & Telephone Corporation; *Int'l*, pg. 5341
DIMENSION DATA AUSTRALIA—See Nippon Telegraph & Telephone Corporation; *Int'l*, pg. 5341
DIMENSION DATA AUSTRALIA—See Nippon Telegraph & Telephone Corporation; *Int'l*, pg. 5341
DIMENSION DATA AUSTRALIA—See Nippon Telegraph & Telephone Corporation; *Int'l*, pg. 5341
DIMENSION DATA AUSTRALIA—See Nippon Telegraph & Telephone Corporation; *Int'l*, pg. 5341
DIMENSION DATA (BEIJING) LIMITED—See Nippon Telegraph & Telephone Corporation; *Int'l*, pg. 5340
DIMENSION DATA BELGIUM NV/SA—See Nippon Telegraph & Telephone Corporation; *Int'l*, pg. 5341
DIMENSION DATA BRASIL—See Nippon Telegraph & Telephone Corporation; *Int'l*, pg. 5341
DIMENSION DATA CHINA/ HONG KONG LIMITED—See Nippon Telegraph & Telephone Corporation; *Int'l*, pg. 5341
DIMENSION DATA ESPANA SL—See Nippon Telegraph & Telephone Corporation; *Int'l*, pg. 5341
DIMENSION DATA ESPANA—See Nippon Telegraph & Telephone Corporation; *Int'l*, pg. 5341
DIMENSION DATA FRANCE SA—See Nippon Telegraph & Telephone Corporation; *Int'l*, pg. 5341
DIMENSION DATA FRANCE—See Nippon Telegraph & Telephone Corporation; *Int'l*, pg. 5341
DIMENSION DATA GERMANY AG & CO.—See Nippon Telegraph & Telephone Corporation; *Int'l*, pg. 5341
DIMENSION DATA GERMANY—See Nippon Telegraph & Telephone Corporation; *Int'l*, pg. 5342
DIMENSION DATA GERMANY—See Nippon Telegraph & Telephone Corporation; *Int'l*, pg. 5342

DIMENSION DATA GERMANY—See Nippon Telegraph & Telephone Corporation; *Int'l*, pg. 5342
DIMENSION DATA INDIA LIMITED—See Nippon Telegraph & Telephone Corporation; *Int'l*, pg. 5341
DIMENSION DATA INDIA LIMITED—See Nippon Telegraph & Telephone Corporation; *Int'l*, pg. 5341
DIMENSION DATA INDIA—See Nippon Telegraph & Telephone Corporation; *Int'l*, pg. 5341
DIMENSION DATA INDIA—See Nippon Telegraph & Telephone Corporation; *Int'l*, pg. 5341
DIMENSION DATA INDIA—See Nippon Telegraph & Telephone Corporation; *Int'l*, pg. 5341
DIMENSION DATA INDIA—See Nippon Telegraph & Telephone Corporation; *Int'l*, pg. 5341
DIMENSION DATA INDIA—See Nippon Telegraph & Telephone Corporation; *Int'l*, pg. 5341
DIMENSION DATA ITALIA—See Nippon Telegraph & Telephone Corporation; *Int'l*, pg. 5342
DIMENSION DATA ITALIA SRL—See Nippon Telegraph & Telephone Corporation; *Int'l*, pg. 5342
DIMENSION DATA JAPAN INC.—See Nippon Telegraph & Telephone Corporation; *Int'l*, pg. 5341
DIMENSION DATA KOREA INC.—See Nippon Telegraph & Telephone Corporation; *Int'l*, pg. 5341
DIMENSION DATA LIMITED—See Nippon Telegraph & Telephone Corporation; *Int'l*, pg. 5342
DIMENSION DATA LIMITED—See Nippon Telegraph & Telephone Corporation; *Int'l*, pg. 5342
DIMENSION DATA LIMITED—See Nippon Telegraph & Telephone Corporation; *Int'l*, pg. 5342
DIMENSION DATA LUXEMBOURG SA—See Nippon Telegraph & Telephone Corporation; *Int'l*, pg. 5342
DIMENSION DATA MEXICO—See Nippon Telegraph & Telephone Corporation; *Int'l*, pg. 5342
DIMENSION DATA NEDERLAND BV—See Nippon Telegraph & Telephone Corporation; *Int'l*, pg. 5342
DIMENSIION DATA NEW ZEALAND LIMITED—See Nippon Telegraph & Telephone Corporation; *Int'l*, pg. 5341
DIMENSION DATA NORTH AMERICA, INC. - ALPHARETTA—See Nippon Telegraph & Telephone Corporation; *Int'l*, pg. 5342
DIMENSION DATA NORTH AMERICA, INC. - CHARLOTTE—See Nippon Telegraph & Telephone Corporation; *Int'l*, pg. 5342
DIMENSION DATA NORTH AMERICA, INC. - HAUPPAUGE—See Nippon Telegraph & Telephone Corporation; *Int'l*, pg. 5342
DIMENSION DATA NORTH AMERICA, INC. - HERNDON—See Nippon Telegraph & Telephone Corporation; *Int'l*, pg. 5342
DIMENSION DATA NORTH AMERICA, INC. - RALEIGH—See Nippon Telegraph & Telephone Corporation; *Int'l*, pg. 5342
DIMENSION DATA NORTH AMERICA, INC. - SHELTON—See Nippon Telegraph & Telephone Corporation; *Int'l*, pg. 5342
DIMENSION DATA NORTH AMERICA, INC.—See Nippon Telegraph & Telephone Corporation; *Int'l*, pg. 5342
DIMENSION DATA NORTH AMERICA—See Nippon Telegraph & Telephone Corporation; *Int'l*, pg. 5342
DIMENSION DATA PHILIPPINES, INC.—See Nippon Telegraph & Telephone Corporation; *Int'l*, pg. 5341
DIMENSION DATA PLC—See Nippon Telegraph & Telephone Corporation; *Int'l*, pg. 5340
DIMENSION DATA PTY LIMITED—See Nippon Telegraph & Telephone Corporation; *Int'l*, pg. 5342
DIMENSION DATA (SINGAPORE) PTE. LTD.—See Nippon Telegraph & Telephone Corporation; *Int'l*, pg. 5341
DIMENSION DATA—See Nippon Telegraph & Telephone Corporation; *Int'l*, pg. 5340
DIMENSION DATA—See Nippon Telegraph & Telephone Corporation; *Int'l*, pg. 5340
DIMENSION DATA—See Nippon Telegraph & Telephone Corporation; *Int'l*, pg. 5341
DIMENSION DATA—See Nippon Telegraph & Telephone Corporation; *Int'l*, pg. 5341
DIMENSION DATA—See Nippon Telegraph & Telephone Corporation; *Int'l*, pg. 5342
DIMENSION DATA—See Nippon Telegraph & Telephone Corporation; *Int'l*, pg. 5342
DIMENSION DATA—See Nippon Telegraph & Telephone Corporation; *Int'l*, pg. 5342
DIMENSION DATA—See Nippon Telegraph & Telephone Corporation; *Int'l*, pg. 5342
DIMENSION DATA SWITZERLAND S.A.—See Nippon Telegraph & Telephone Corporation; *Int'l*, pg. 5342
DIMENSION DATA TAIWAN LIMITED—See Nippon Telegraph & Telephone Corporation; *Int'l*, pg. 5341
DIMENSION DATA (THAILAND) LIMITED—See Nippon Telegraph & Telephone Corporation; *Int'l*, pg. 5341
DIMENSION DATA VIETNAM LIMITED—See Nippon Telegraph & Telephone Corporation; *Int'l*, pg. 5341
DIMENSION DATA VIETNAM LIMITED—See Nippon Telegraph & Telephone Corporation; *Int'l*, pg. 5341
DIMENSION DESIGN; *U.S. Private*, pg. 1232
DIMENSION DEVELOPMENT COMPANY; *U.S. Private*, pg. 1232
DIMENSION ENERGY CO. LLC; *U.S. Private*, pg. 1232
DIMENSION-POLYANT GMBH—See Sioen Industries NV; *Int'l*, pg. 6959

DIMENSION-POLYANT INC.—See Sioen Industries NV; *Int'l*, pg. 6960
DIMENSION-POLYANT SAILCLOTH PTY. LTD.—See Sioen Industries NV; *Int'l*, pg. 6960
DIMENSION-POLYANT SAS—See Sioen Industries NV; *Int'l*, pg. 6960
DIMENSION-POLYANT (UK) LTD.—See Sioen Industries NV; *Int'l*, pg. 6959
DIMENSION SA—See Banque Cantonale de Geneve S.A.; *Int'l*, pg. 852
DIMENSIONS HEALTHCARE CORPORATION; *U.S. Private*, pg. 1233
DIMENSIONS HOLDINGS LLC—See GTCR LLC; *U.S. Private*, pg. 1806
DIMENSIONS JORDAN & EMIRATES COMMERCIAL INVESTMENTS CORPORATION; *Int'l*, pg. 2126
DIMENSIONS TRAINING SOLUTIONS LTD.; *Int'l*, pg. 2126
DIMENSION X CORPORATION; *U.S. Private*, pg. 1232
DIMENSI TIMAL SDN. BHD.—See MTD Capital Bhd.; *Int'l*, pg. 5070
DIMEO CONSTRUCTION COMPANY; *U.S. Private*, pg. 1233
DIMEO SCHNEIDER & ASSOCIATES LLC—See Aon plc; *Int'l*, pg. 495
DIMERCO DATA SYSTEM CORP.; *Int'l*, pg. 2126
DIMERCO EXPRESS CORPORATION; *Int'l*, pg. 2126
DIMERCO EXPRESS (TAIWAN) CORPORATION—See Dimerco Express Corporation; *Int'l*, pg. 2126
DIMERCO EXPRESS (TAIWAN) CORPORATION—See Dimerco Express Corporation; *Int'l*, pg. 2126
DIMERCO EXPRESS (TAIWAN) CORPORATION—See Dimerco Express Corporation; *Int'l*, pg. 2126
DIMERCO EXPRESS (TAIWAN) CORPORATION—See Dimerco Express Corporation; *Int'l*, pg. 2126
DIMERCO EXPRESS USA CORP.—See Dimerco Express Corporation; *Int'l*, pg. 2126
DIMERIX LIMITED; *Int'l*, pg. 2126
DIMETHAID IMMUNOLOGY INC.—See Searchlight Pharma, Inc.; *Int'l*, pg. 6666
DIMETHAID MANAGEMENT INC.—See Searchlight Pharma, Inc.; *Int'l*, pg. 6666
DIMET (SIAM) PUBLIC COMPANY LIMITED; *Int'l*, pg. 2126
DIMEX LLC—See Westlake Corporation; *U.S. Public*, pg. 2360
DIMEX TECHNICS S.A.—See London Security PLC; *Int'l*, pg. 4547
DIMITRA SA—See ELLAKTOR S.A.; *Int'l*, pg. 2365
DIMITROVGRADKHIMMASH JSC—See HMS Hydraulic Machines & Systems Group plc; *Int'l*, pg. 3432
DIMKO MITREV JSC; *Int'l*, pg. 2126
DIMMI LIFE HOLDINGS LIMITED; *Int'l*, pg. 2126
DIMMIT REGIONAL HOSPITAL; *U.S. Private*, pg. 1233
DIMMITT AUTOMOTIVE GROUP; *U.S. Private*, pg. 1233
DIMNICAR A.D.; *Int'l*, pg. 2126
DIMO CORP.—See Acorn Growth Companies, LC; *U.S. Private*, pg. 63
DIMOND FABRICATORS—See MDU Resources Group, Inc.; *U.S. Public*, pg. 1409
DIMONT & ASSOCIATES, LLC—See Metro Public Adjustment, Inc.; *U.S. Private*, pg. 2686
DIMO (PVT) LTD.—See Diesel & Motor Engineering PLC; *Int'l*, pg. 2116
DIMOS; *Int'l*, pg. 2126
DIMPCO LTD.—See The Glen Dimplex Group; *Int'l*, pg. 7649
DIMPLES' CO., LTD.—See World Holdings Co., Ltd.; *Int'l*, pg. 8457
DIMPLEX AS—See The Glen Dimplex Group; *Int'l*, pg. 7649
DIMPLEX CLEANING SYSTEMS—See The Glen Dimplex Group; *Int'l*, pg. 7649
DIMPLEX JAPAN LTD.—See The Glen Dimplex Group; *Int'l*, pg. 7649
DIMPLEX NORTH AMERICA LIMITED—See The Glen Dimplex Group; *Int'l*, pg. 7649
DIMPLEX THERMAL SOLUTIONS—See The Glen Dimplex Group; *Int'l*, pg. 7649
DIM PORTUGAL - IMPORTACAO E COMERCIALIZACAO, LDA.—See Hanesbrands Inc.; *U.S. Public*, pg. 982
DIM SUM LESSEE, INC.—See Pebblebrook Hotel Trust; *U.S. Public*, pg. 1660
DIN ACCIAI S.P.A.—See voestalpine AG; *Int'l*, pg. 8289
DINAIR AIRBRUSH MAKE-UP SYSTEM, INC.; *U.S. Private*, pg. 1233
DINAIR CLEAN AIR OY—See Daikin Industries, Ltd.; *Int'l*, pg. 1936
DINAIR EKONOMIFILTER AS—See Daikin Industries, Ltd.; *Int'l*, pg. 1936
DINAIR FILTON SIA—See Daikin Industries, Ltd.; *Int'l*, pg. 1936
DINAIR GROUP AB—See Daikin Industries, Ltd.; *Int'l*, pg. 1936
DINA IRON & STEEL LIMITED; *Int'l*, pg. 2126
DINAMIK ISI MAKINA YALITIM MALZEMELERI SANAYI VE TICARET A.S.; *Int'l*, pg. 2126
DINAONE CORPORATION—See LIXIL Group Corporation; *Int'l*, pg. 4534

**DINARA A.D.; ** *Int'l*, pg. 2126
DINARA GRADNJA A.D.; *Int'l*, pg. 2126
DINARA SERVIS AD; *Int'l*, pg. 2127
DIN DEL AB—See Eniro Group AB; *Int'l*, pg. 2439
DIN DEL FORSALJNING AB—See Eniro Group AB; *Int'l*, pg. 2439
DINDON FOODS CORP.; *U.S. Private*, pg. 1233
DINE BRANDS GLOBAL, INC.; *U.S. Public*, pg. 666
DINE CONTRACT CATERING LIMITED—See Compass Group PLC; *Int'l*, pg. 1751
DINE DEVELOPMENT CORPORATION; *U.S. Private*, pg. 1233
DINEEN CONSTRUCTION CORPORATION; *Int'l*, pg. 2127
DIN ELEKTRO KRAFT OOO—See Schneider Electric SE; *Int'l*, pg. 6626
DINEL SAS—See Schneider Electric SE; *Int'l*, pg. 6626
DINEO SA—See Sonepar S.A.; *Int'l*, pg. 7093
DINEOUT SA LTD.; *Int'l*, pg. 2127
DINE PENGER AS—See Schibsted ASA; *Int'l*, pg. 6618
DINERS CLUB ISRAEL LTD.—See IDB Development Corporation Ltd.; *Int'l*, pg. 3588
DINERS CLUB ITALIA S.R.L.—See Discover Financial Services; *U.S. Public*, pg. 668
DINERS CLUB (MALAYSIA) SDN. BHD.—See Johan Holdings Berhad; *Int'l*, pg. 3977
DINERS CLUB PTY LIMITED—See Citigroup Inc.; *U.S. Public*, pg. 502
DINERS CLUB (SINGAPORE) PTE. LTD.—See Ezy Net Pte Ltd.; *Int'l*, pg. 2594
DINERS CLUB SPAIN, S.A.—See Banco Santander, S.A.; *Int'l*, pg. 825
DINERS CLUB UAE LLC—See Emirates NBD PJSC; *Int'l*, pg. 2381
DINERS WORLD TRAVEL (MALAYSIA) SDN. BHD.—See Johan Holdings Berhad; *Int'l*, pg. 3977
DINE S.A.B. DE C.V.; *Int'l*, pg. 2127
DINESH REMEDIES LTD.—See Shri Dinesh Mills Ltd.; *Int'l*, pg. 6865
DINEWISE, INC.; *U.S. Public*, pg. 667
DINEX, INC.—See Fuji Media Holdings, Inc.; *Int'l*, pg. 2813
DINGDANG HEALTH TECHNOLOGY GROUP LIMITED; *Int'l*, pg. 2127
DINGDONG (CAYMAN) LTD.; *Int'l*, pg. 2127
DING HE MINING HOLDINGS LIMITED; *Int'l*, pg. 2127
DINGLI CORPORATION LTD.; *Int'l*, pg. 2127
DIN GLOBAL CORP.; *U.S. Private*, pg. 1233
DINGLONG CULTURE CO., LTD.; *Int'l*, pg. 2127
DINGO RANGE PTY. LTD.—See Emerald Resources NL; *Int'l*, pg. 2378
DIN GOST TUV BERLIN BRANDENBURG GESELLSCHAFT FUR ZERTIFIZIERUNG IN EUROPA MBH—See TUV Rheinland Berlin-Brandenburg Pfalz e.V.; *Int'l*, pg. 7981
DINGS DYNAMICS CO.—See Venturedyne, Ltd.; *U.S. Private*, pg. 4358
DINGS MAGNETIC CO.—See Venturedyne, Ltd.; *U.S. Private*, pg. 4358
DINGWALL FORD SALES; *Int'l*, pg. 2127
DINGXING LIDA HAT MAKING CO., LTD.—See Hebei Lihua Hat Manufacturing Group Co., Ltd.; *Int'l*, pg. 3306
DINGXING LIDA HAT MAKING CO., LTD.—See The Japan Wool Textile Co., Ltd.; *Int'l*, pg. 7659
DINGYI GROUP INVESTMENT LIMITED; *Int'l*, pg. 2127
DING-YUE DEVELOPMENT CO., LTD.—See China Petrochemical Development Corp.; *Int'l*, pg. 1540
DINH TECHNICOM S.A—See Teleste Corporation; *Int'l*, pg. 7541
DINH TELECOM S.A—See Teleste Corporation; *Int'l*, pg. 7541
DI-NIKKO ENGINEERING CO., LTD.; *Int'l*, pg. 2101
DI-NIKKO ENGINEERING CO., LTD. - TODOROKU FACTORY—See Di-Nikko Engineering Co., Ltd.; *Int'l*, pg. 2101
DINI SPHERIS; *U.S. Private*, pg. 1233
DINIT D.O.O.—See Discover Financial Services; *U.S. Public*, pg. 668
DIN LEATHER(PVT) LTD.—See Din Textile Mills Ltd.; *Int'l*, pg. 2126
DINNG CREATIVE, INC.—See LifeVantage Corporation; *U.S. Public*, pg. 1313
DINNOSANTE—See L'Air Liquide S.A.; *Int'l*, pg. 4374
DINOCO OIL, INC.; *U.S. Private*, pg. 1233
DINOCRATES GROUP LLC; *U.S. Private*, pg. 1233
DINO ENERGY CORPORATION; *Int'l*, pg. 2127
DINOL GMBH—See Wurth Verwaltungsgesellschaft mbH; *Int'l*, pg. 8504
DINOL U.S. INC.—See Wurth Verwaltungsgesellschaft mbH; *Int'l*, pg. 8511
DINONA, INC.—See Kumho HT, Inc.; *Int'l*, pg. 4330
DINO POLSKA SA; *Int'l*, pg. 2127
DINOS CECILE CO., LTD.—See Fuji Media Holdings, Inc.; *Int'l*, pg. 2813
DINOVITE INC.—See The Carlyle Group Inc.; *U.S. Public*, pg. 2049
D-IN PACK COMPANY LIMITED—See The Siam Cement Public Company Limited; *Int'l*, pg. 7682
DINS HOKKAIDO CO., LTD.—See Daiei Kankyo Co., Ltd.; *Int'l*, pg. 1924

DINS KANSAI CO., LTD.—See Daiei Kankyo Co., Ltd.; *Int'l*, pg. 1924
DINS MIRAI CO., LTD.—See Daiei Kankyo Co., Ltd.; *Int'l*, pg. 1924
DINSMORE & SHOHL LLP; *U.S. Private*, pg. 1233
DINTEC AGROQUIMICA PRODUTOS QUIMICOS, LDA.—See Corteva, Inc.; *U.S. Public*, pg. 581
DIN TEXTILE MILLS LTD.; *Int'l*, pg. 2126
DINUBA AUTO CENTER, INC.—See General Motors Company; *U.S. Public*, pg. 924
DINUCCIO LTD.—See The New York Look Inc.; *U.S. Private*, pg. 4083
DIO CORPORATION; *Int'l*, pg. 2127
DIODES CO. LTD.—See Diodes Incorporated; *U.S. Public*, pg. 667
DIODES FABTECH INC.—See Diodes Incorporated; *U.S. Public*, pg. 667
DIODES INCORPORATED; *U.S. Public*, pg. 667
DIODES JAPAN K.K.—See Diodes Incorporated; *U.S. Public*, pg. 667
DIODES TAIWAN S.A.R.L—See Diodes Incorporated; *U.S. Public*, pg. 667
DIODES ZETEX GMBH—See Diodes Incorporated; *U.S. Public*, pg. 667
DIODES ZETEX NEUHAUS GMBH—See Diodes Incorporated; *U.S. Public*, pg. 667
DIODES ZETEX SEMICONDUCTORS LTD—See Diodes Incorporated; *U.S. Public*, pg. 667
DIOGENE S.R.L.—See Itway S.p.A.; *Int'l*, pg. 3846
DIOGEN SA—See Societe Anonyme d'Explosifs et de Produits Chimiques; *Int'l*, pg. 7035
DIO IMPLANT AUSTRALIA PTY LTD.—See DIO Corporation; *Int'l*, pg. 2127
DIOKI D.D.; *Int'l*, pg. 2127
DIOK ONE AG; *Int'l*, pg. 2127
DIO, LLC; *U.S. Private*, pg. 1234
DIONEX AUSTRIA GMBH—See Thermo Fisher Scientific Inc.; *U.S. Public*, pg. 2146
DIONEX BENELUX B.V.—See Thermo Fisher Scientific Inc.; *U.S. Public*, pg. 2146
DIONEX BRASIL INSTRUMENTOS CIENTIFICOS LTDA—See Thermo Fisher Scientific Inc.; *U.S. Public*, pg. 2146
DIONEX (CHINA) ANALYTICAL LTD—See Thermo Fisher Scientific Inc.; *U.S. Public*, pg. 2146
DIONEX CHINA LTD.—See Thermo Fisher Scientific Inc.; *U.S. Public*, pg. 2146
DIONEX CORPORATION—See Thermo Fisher Scientific Inc.; *U.S. Public*, pg. 2146
DIONEX DENMARK A/S—See Thermo Fisher Scientific Inc.; *U.S. Public*, pg. 2146
DIONEX GMBH—See Thermo Fisher Scientific Inc.; *U.S. Public*, pg. 2146
DIONEX HOLDING GMBH—See Thermo Fisher Scientific Inc.; *U.S. Public*, pg. 2146
DIONEX INDIA PVT. LTD—See Thermo Fisher Scientific Inc.; *U.S. Public*, pg. 2146
DIONEX IRELAND LIMITED—See Thermo Fisher Scientific Inc.; *U.S. Public*, pg. 2146
DIONEX KOREA LTD.—See Thermo Fisher Scientific Inc.; *U.S. Public*, pg. 2146
DIONEX PTY LTD—See Thermo Fisher Scientific Inc.; *U.S. Public*, pg. 2146
DIONEX SINGAPORE PTE LTD.—See Thermo Fisher Scientific Inc.; *U.S. Public*, pg. 2146
DIONEX SOFTRON GMBH—See Thermo Fisher Scientific Inc.; *U.S. Public*, pg. 2146
DIONEX S.P.A.—See Thermo Fisher Scientific Inc.; *U.S. Public*, pg. 2146
DIONEX SWEDEN AB—See Thermo Fisher Scientific Inc.; *U.S. Public*, pg. 2146
DIONEX (SWITZERLAND) AG—See Thermo Fisher Scientific Inc.; *U.S. Public*, pg. 2146
DIONEX TAIWAN LTD.—See Thermo Fisher Scientific Inc.; *U.S. Public*, pg. 2146
DIONEX (U.K.) LTD.—See Thermo Fisher Scientific Inc.; *U.S. Public*, pg. 2146
DION GLOBAL SOLUTIONS (ASIA PACIFIC) PTY LTD.—See Dion Global Solutions Limited; *Int'l*, pg. 2127
DION GLOBAL SOLUTIONS LIMITED; *Int'l*, pg. 2127
DION GLOBAL SOLUTIONS (NZ) LTD.—See Dion Global Solutions Limited; *Int'l*, pg. 2127
DIONIC INDUSTRIAL & TRADING S.A; *Int'l*, pg. 2127
DIONIC TRADING LTD—See Dionic Industrial & Trading S.A; *Int'l*, pg. 2128
DION INTERNATIONAL TRUCKS LLC; *U.S. Private*, pg. 1234
DIONO, INC.; *U.S. Private*, pg. 1234
DION'S QUIK MARTS INC—See Alimentation Couche-Tard Inc.; *Int'l*, pg. 328
DION TRANSACTION SOLUTIONS GMBH—See DPE Deutsche Private Equity GmbH; *Int'l*, pg. 2188
DIOPSYS, INC.—See LumiThera, Inc.; *U.S. Private*, pg. 2514
DIOPTICS MEDICAL PRODUCTS INC.—See EssilorLuxottica SA; *Int'l*, pg. 2513
DIOREM—See Capgemini SE; *Int'l*, pg. 1305
DIORK A.D.; *Int'l*, pg. 2128

DIOS EXPLORATION INC.; *Int'l*, pg. 2128
DIOS FASTIGHETER AB; *Int'l*, pg. 2128
DIOSNA CS S.R.O.—See Hillenbrand, Inc.; *U.S. Public*, pg. 1036
DIOSNA DIERKS & SOHNE GMBH—See Hillenbrand, Inc.; *U.S. Public*, pg. 1036
DIOS RIOS PARTNERS, LP; *U.S. Private*, pg. 1234
DIOSYNTH PRODUTOS FARMO-QUIMICOS LTDA.—See Merck & Co., Inc.; *U.S. Public*, pg. 1416
DIPACO, INC.—See Diesel Forward, Inc.; *U.S. Private*, pg. 1228
DIPASQUA ENTERPRISES, INC.; *U.S. Private*, pg. 1234
DIP CORPORATION; *Int'l*, pg. 2128
DIPCRAFT MANUFACTURING COMPANY; *U.S. Private*, pg. 1234
DIPECO AG—See Mondi plc; *Int'l*, pg. 5026
DIPHARMA FRANCIS S.R.L.; *Int'l*, pg. 2128
DIPL. ING. FUST AG—See Coop-Gruppe Genossenschaft; *Int'l*, pg. 1790
DIPL. ING. K. DIETZEL GMBH; *Int'l*, pg. 2128
DIPL.-ING.REINHOLD EGGERS GMBH—See Ushio, Inc.; *Int'l*, pg. 8097
DIPLOMA GROUP LIMITED; *Int'l*, pg. 2128
DIPLOMA PLC; *Int'l*, pg. 2128
DIPLOMA PROPERTIES PTY. LTD.—See Diploma Group Limited; *Int'l*, pg. 2128
DIPLOMAT GEORGIA, LLC—See Diplomat Holdings Ltd.; *Int'l*, pg. 2129
DIPLOMAT HOLDINGS LTD.; *Int'l*, pg. 2129
DIPLOMAT HOTEL CORPORATION; *U.S. Private*, pg. 1234
DIPLOMAT NEW ZEALAND LIMITED—See Diplomat Holdings Ltd.; *Int'l*, pg. 2129
DIPLOMAT NORGE AS—See Ratos AB; *Int'l*, pg. 6220
DIPLOMAT PARTS PTE LTD—See Jardine Matheson Holdings Limited; *Int'l*, pg. 3910
DIPLOMAT PHARMACY, INC.—See UnitedHealth Group Incorporated; *U.S. Public*, pg. 2247
DIPLOMAT PROSJEKT AS—See Ratos AB; *Int'l*, pg. 6220
DIPLOMAT RISK SERVICES—See Diplomat Hotel Corporation; *U.S. Private*, pg. 1234
DIPLOM-IS AS—See TINE SA; *Int'l*, pg. 7753
DIPNA PHARMACHEM LIMITED; *Int'l*, pg. 2129
DIPOL BALTIJA SIA—See BRENNTAG SE; *Int'l*, pg. 1149
DIPPED PRODUCTS PLC—See Hayleys PLC; *Int'l*, pg. 3291
DIPPIN' DOTS AUSTRALIA PTY. LTD.—See J&J Snack Foods Corporation; *U.S. Public*, pg. 1179
DIPPIN' DOTS FRANCHISING, LLC—See J&J Snack Foods Corporation; *U.S. Public*, pg. 1179
DIPPIN' DOTS, LLC—See J&J Snack Foods Corporation; *U.S. Public*, pg. 1179
DIPRA SA—See Thermador Groupe; *Int'l*, pg. 7707
DIP TECH LTD.—See American Securities LLC; *U.S. Private*, pg. 251
DIPULA INCOME FUND LIMITED; *Int'l*, pg. 2129
DIQU TECH PRIVATE LIMITED—See Aiphone Co., Ltd.; *Int'l*, pg. 235
DIRAD TECHNOLOGIES, INC.—See Telecloud, LLC; *U.S. Private*, pg. 3960
DIRAFROST FROZEN FRUIT INDUSTRY N.V.—See AGRANA Beteiligungs-AG; *Int'l*, pg. 214
DIRAFROST MAROC SARL—See AGRANA Beteiligungs-AG; *Int'l*, pg. 214
D & I RAILROAD—See L.G. Everist Inc.; *U.S. Private*, pg. 2366
DIRAMIC INSURANCE LIMITED—See OMV Aktiengesellschaft; *Int'l*, pg. 5567
DIRANA LIEGENSCHAFTSVERWERTUNGSGESELLSCHAFT M.B.H.—See UniCredit S.p.A.; *Int'l*, pg. 8040
DIRCKS ASSOCIATES; *U.S. Private*, pg. 1234
DIRCKS MOVING SERVICES, INC.; *U.S. Private*, pg. 1234
DIREC CO., LTD.—See Dai Nippon Printing Co., Ltd.; *Int'l*, pg. 1915
DIRECCT AG—See Baader Bank AG; *Int'l*, pg. 791
DIRECIONAL ENGENHARIA S.A.; *Int'l*, pg. 2129
DIRECLOGIX CORP—See CDW Corporation; *U.S. Public*, pg. 462
DIREC MACHINE TOOL LLC—See Quaser Machine Tools, Inc.; *Int'l*, pg. 6156
DIRECT ACCIDENT MANAGEMENT LIMITED—See Anexo Group Plc; *Int'l*, pg. 459
DIRECT AGENTS, INC.; *U.S. Private*, pg. 1234
DIRECT ANALYTICS GMBH—See Bertelsmann SE & Co. KGaA; *Int'l*, pg. 992
DIRECTA PLUS PLC; *Int'l*, pg. 2130
DIRECT ASIA INSURANCE (SINGAPORE) PTE LIMITED—See Hiscox Ltd.; *Int'l*, pg. 3407
DIRECT ASIA (THAILAND) CO., LTD.—See Hiscox Ltd.; *Int'l*, pg. 3407
DIRECTA SIM S.P.A.; *Int'l*, pg. 2130
DIRECT ASSURANCE—See AXA S.A.; *Int'l*, pg. 759
DIRECT AUTO FINANCIAL SERVICES LIMITED—See Vanquis Banking Group plc; *Int'l*, pg. 8130
DIRECT AUTOMOTIVE GROUP, LLC.; *U.S. Private*, pg. 1234
DIRECT BENEFITS, INC.—See Genstar Capital, LLC; *U.S. Private*, pg. 1674

COMPANY NAME INDEX

DIRECT BRANDS, INC.—See Pride Tree Holdings, Inc.; *U.S. Private*, pg. 3260
DIRECTBUY, INC.; *U.S. Private*, pg. 1236
DIRECT CABINET SALES INC.—See Express Kitchens; *U.S. Private*, pg. 1451
DIRECT CAPITAL CORPORATION—See First Citizens BancShares, Inc.; *U.S. Public*, pg. 841
DIRECT CHASSISLINK, INC.—See Apollo Global Management, Inc.; *U.S. Public*, pg. 150
DIRECT CHASSIS LLC—See China International Marine Containers (Group) Co., Ltd.; *Int'l*, pg. 1511
DIRECT CHECK REDEMPTION CENTER, INC.; *U.S. Private*, pg. 1234
DIRECT CHECKS UNLIMITED SALES, INC—See Deluxe Corporation; *U.S. Public*, pg. 653
DIRECT COMMUNICATION SOLUTIONS, INC.; *U.S. Public*, pg. 667
DIRECT COMPANIES, LLC; *U.S. Private*, pg. 1234
DIRECT CONNECT AUSTRALIA PTY. LTD.—See Snowy Hydro Limited; *Int'l*, pg. 7028
DIRECT CONNECT GROUP (DCG) LLC; *U.S. Private*, pg. 1235
DIRECT CONNECT LLC; *U.S. Private*, pg. 1235
DIRECT CONVERSION AB—See Varex Imaging Corporation; *U.S. Public*, pg. 2275
DIRECT CONVERSION GMBH—See Varex Imaging Corporation; *U.S. Public*, pg. 2275
DIRECT CREDIT ATLANTIC INC.—See QC Holdings, Inc.; *U.S. Private*, pg. 1742
DIRECT DATA CORPORATION; *U.S. Private*, pg. 1235
DIRECT DENTAL SUPPLY CO.—See Patterson Companies, Inc.; *U.S. Public*, pg. 1653
DIRECT DIGITAL HOLDINGS, INC.; *U.S. Public*, pg. 667
DIRECT DISTRIBUTORS INC.; *U.S. Private*, pg. 1235
DIRECT DRIVE SYSTEMS, INC.—See TechnipFMC plc; *Int'l*, pg. 7507
DIRECT EATS, INC.; *U.S. Private*, pg. 1235
DIRECTEC CORPORATION; *U.S. Private*, pg. 1236
DIRECTECH LLC; *U.S. Private*, pg. 1236
DIRECTED CAPITAL RESOURCES, LLC; *U.S. Private*, pg. 1236
DIRECTED ELECTRONICS CANADA, INC.—See Charlesbank Capital Partners, LLC; *U.S. Private*, pg. 855
DIRECTED ENERGY, INC—See Berkeley Nucleonics Corp.; *U.S. Private*, pg. 532
DIRECTED ENERGY SOLUTIONS; *U.S. Private*, pg. 1236
DIRECT EDGE CAMPAIGNS, LLC; *U.S. Private*, pg. 1235
DIRECT EDI, INC.—See SPS Commerce, Inc.; *U.S. Public*, pg. 1920
DIRECTED SERVICES LLC—See Voya Financial, Inc.; *U.S. Public*, pg. 2312
DIRECT EFFECT MEDIA SERVICES, INC.; *U.S. Private*, pg. 1236
DIRECTEL HOLDINGS LIMITED; *Int'l*, pg. 2130
DIRECTEMPLOYERS ASSOCIATION, INC.; *U.S. Private*, pg. 1236
DIRECT ENERGIE SA; *Int'l*, pg. 2129
DIRECT ENERGY BUSINESS, LLC—See NRG Energy, Inc.; *U.S. Public*, pg. 1549
DIRECT ENERGY BUSINESS MARKETING, LLC—See NRG Energy, Inc.; *U.S. Public*, pg. 1549
DIRECT ENERGY BUSINESS MARKETING, LLC - SOUTHEAST REGION—See NRG Energy, Inc.; *U.S. Public*, pg. 1549
DIRECT ENERGY, LP—See NRG Energy, Inc.; *U.S. Public*, pg. 1549
DIRECT ENERGY MARKETING LIMITED—See NRG Energy, Inc.; *U.S. Public*, pg. 1549
DIRECT ENERGY MARKETING LTD. - CANADA HOME SERVICES—See NRG Energy, Inc.; *U.S. Public*, pg. 1549
DIRECT ENERGY NEW YORK CORPORATION—See NRG Energy, Inc.; *U.S. Public*, pg. 1549
DIRECT ENERGY PURCHASING LIMITED—See Inspired PLC; *Int'l*, pg. 3720
DIRECT ENERGY RESOURCES PARTNERSHIP—See NRG Energy, Inc.; *U.S. Public*, pg. 1549
DIRECT ENERGY SERVICES, LLC—See NRG Energy, Inc.; *U.S. Public*, pg. 1549
DIRECT EXTERIORS, INC.; *U.S. Private*, pg. 1235
DIRECT FN LTD.—See National Technology Group; *Int'l*, pg. 5164
DIRECT FUELS LLC—See Sunoco LP; *U.S. Public*, pg. 1965
DIRECTFX SOLUTIONS INC.; *U.S. Private*, pg. 1235
DIRECT GENERAL CORPORATION—See The Allstate Corporation; *U.S. Public*, pg. 2033
DIRECTGROUP BERTELSMANN—See Bertelsmann SE & Co. KGaA; *Int'l*, pg. 992
DIRECT HEALTHCARE LTD; *Int'l*, pg. 2129
DIRECT HOLDINGS AMERICAS INC.—See Mosaic Media Investment Partners LLC; *U.S. Private*, pg. 2792
DIRECT HOLDINGS LIBRARIES INC.—See Mosaic Media Investment Partners LLC; *U.S. Private*, pg. 2792
DIRECTI GROUP; *Int'l*, pg. 2130
DIRECT IME CORP.—See GIC Pte. Ltd.; *Int'l*, pg. 2964
DIRECT IME CORP.—See Leonard Green & Partners, L.P.; *U.S. Private*, pg. 2426

THE DIRECT IMPACT COMPANY—See WPP plc; *Int'l*, pg. 8468
DIRECT IMPACT, INC.; *U.S. Private*, pg. 1235
DIRECT INFORMATION FZC—See Directi Group; *Int'l*, pg. 2130
DIRECT INNOVATIONS; *U.S. Private*, pg. 1235
DIRECT INSURANCE - FINANCIAL INVESTMENTS LTD.—See Zur Shamir Holdings Ltd.; *Int'l*, pg. 8697
DIRECT INTERNET LIMITED—See Tata Sons Limited; *Int'l*, pg. 7469
DIRECT INVESTMENT HOLDINGS GROUP, INC.; *U.S. Private*, pg. 1235
DIRECTIONAL CAPITAL LLC; *U.S. Private*, pg. 1236
DIRECTIONAL FURNITURE—See Tomlinson/Erwin-Lambeth, Inc.; *U.S. Private*, pg. 4184
DIRECTION DES FILIALES OUTRE-MER—See Sonepar SA; *Int'l*, pg. 7090
THE DIRECTIONS GROUP, LLC—See EK Health Services, Inc.; *U.S. Private*, pg. 1348
DIRECT IT CANADA INC.; *Int'l*, pg. 2129
DIRECT LENDING PARTNER—See Don Wenner Home Selling, Inc.; *U.S. Private*, pg. 1259
DIRECT LIFE & PENSION SERVICES LIMITED—See LSL Property Services plc; *Int'l*, pg. 4570
DIRECT LINE COMMUNICATIONS; *U.S. Private*, pg. 1235
DIRECT LINE GROUP LIMITED—See Direct Line Insurance Group plc; *Int'l*, pg. 2129
DIRECT LINE INSURANCE GROUP PLC; *Int'l*, pg. 2129
DIRECT LINE INSURANCE PLC—See Direct Line Insurance Group plc; *Int'l*, pg. 2129
DIRECT LINE SALES LIMITED—See Rentokil Initial plc; *Int'l*, pg. 6286
DIRECT LINK USA LLC—See Fuling Global Inc.; *Int'l*, pg. 2842
DIRECT LINK WORLDWIDE COMPANY LTD.—See PostNord AB; *Int'l*, pg. 5940
DIRECT LINK WORLDWIDE DISTRIBUTION PTE. LTD—See PostNord AB; *Int'l*, pg. 5940
DIRECT LINK WORLDWIDE GMBH—See PostNord AB; *Int'l*, pg. 5940
DIRECT LINK WORLDWIDE INC.—See PostNord AB; *Int'l*, pg. 5940
DIRECT LINK WORLDWIDE LTD.—See PostNord AB; *Int'l*, pg. 5940
DIRECT LINK WORLDWIDE PTY. LTD—See PostNord AB; *Int'l*, pg. 5940
DIRECT MACHINERY SALES CORP.—See Laundrylux Inc.; *U.S. Private*, pg. 2398
DIRECT MAIL COMPANY AG—See Die Schweizerische Post AG; *Int'l*, pg. 2112
DIRECT MAIL EXPRESS, INC.; *U.S. Private*, pg. 1235
DIRECT MAIL LOGISTIK AG—See Die Schweizerische Post AG; *Int'l*, pg. 2112
DIRECT MARKETING CENTER; *U.S. Private*, pg. 1235
DIRECT MARKETING MIX, INC.; *Int'l*, pg. 2130
DIRECT MARKETING SOLUTIONS, INC.; *U.S. Private*, pg. 1235
DIRECT MATIN PLUS—See Financière de L'Odet; *Int'l*, pg. 2667
DIRECT MEDIA MILLARD, INC.—See CCMP Capital Advisors, LP; *U.S. Private*, pg. 800
DIRECT MEDICAL DATA MARKETING CORP.—See DMD-Connects Services Inc.; *Int'l*, pg. 2143
DIRECT MEDICAL LTD COMPANY—See SOL S.p.A.; *Int'l*, pg. 7067
DIRECT MEDICAL SUPPLY, LLC—See KKR & Co. Inc.; *U.S. Public*, pg. 1249
DIRECTMED PARTS & SERVICE LLC—See NMS Capital Services, LLC; *U.S. Private*, pg. 2931
DIRECT MOTORLINE LIMITED—See Highway Insurance Holdings Plc; *Int'l*, pg. 3389
DIRECT NICKEL LIMITED; *Int'l*, pg. 2130
DIRECT ONLINE MARKETING, LLC; *U.S. Private*, pg. 1235
DIRECTORS AIR CORPORATION—See Directors Investment Group Inc.; *U.S. Private*, pg. 1236
DIRECTORS HOLDING CORPORATION—See Directors Investment Group Inc.; *U.S. Private*, pg. 1236
DIRECTORS INVESTMENT GROUP INC.; *U.S. Private*, pg. 1236
DIRECT PACK, INC.—See PMC Capital Partners, LLC; *U.S. Private*, pg. 3217
DIRECT PARTNER SOLUTIONS, INC.; *U.S. Private*, pg. 1235
DIRECT PARTNERS—See Omnicom Group Inc.; *U.S. Public*, pg. 1582
DIRECT PARTNERS—See Omnicom Group Inc.; *U.S. Public*, pg. 1583
DIRECTPATH, LLC—See CNO Financial Group, Inc.; *U.S. Public*, pg. 520
DIRECT PETROLEUM BULGARIA EOOD—See TransAtlantic Petroleum Ltd.; *U.S. Public*, pg. 2179
DIRECT PHARMACY SERVICE, INC.; *U.S. Private*, pg. 1235
DIRECT PLASTICS GROUP, LTD.—See Apollo Global Management, Inc.; *U.S. Public*, pg. 153
DIRECT POWER AND WATER CORPORATION—See Preformed Line Products Company; *U.S. Public*, pg. 1714

DIRKSEN SCREW PRODUCTS CO.

DIRECT PRINTER SERVICE GMBH—See ECO Supplies Europe AB; *Int'l*, pg. 2292
DIRECT RADIOGRAPHY CORP.—See Hologic, Inc.; *U.S. Public*, pg. 1044
DIRECT REDUCTION IRON COMPANY—See Al-Tuwairqi Group; *Int'l*, pg. 289
DIRECT RESPONSE ACADEMY; *U.S. Private*, pg. 1235
DIRECT RESPONSE CORPORATION—See Kemper Corporation; *U.S. Public*, pg. 1221
DIRECT RESPONSE DECKS INC.—See Marketshare Publications, Inc.; *U.S. Private*, pg. 2581
THE DIRECT RESPONSE GROUP, LLC; *U.S. Private*, pg. 4021
DIRECT RESPONSE INSURANCE ADMINISTRATIVE SERVICES, INC.; *U.S. Private*, pg. 1235
DIRECT RESPONSE MEDIA GROUP INC.; *Int'l*, pg. 2130
DIRECT RESPONSE SERVICE SA—See Teleperformance SE; *Int'l*, pg. 7540
DIRECT RESPONSE (THAILAND) LTD.—See The Interpublic Group of Companies, Inc.; *U.S. Public*, pg. 2092
DIRECT SCAFFOLD SUPPLY, INC.—See Highlander Partners, LP; *U.S. Private*, pg. 1939
DIRECT SEAFOODS COLCHESTER—See The Bidvest Group Limited; *Int'l*, pg. 7622
DIRECT SEAFOODS LONDON—See The Bidvest Group Limited; *Int'l*, pg. 7622
DIRECT SELLING ACQUISITION CORP.; *U.S. Public*, pg. 667
DIRECT SERVICES GUTERSLOH GMBH—See Bertelsmann SE & Co. KGaA; *Int'l*, pg. 992
DIRECT SOURCE SPECIAL PRODUCTS, INC.; *Int'l*, pg. 2130
DIRECT SOURCE SUPPLY, INC.—See Myers Industries, Inc.; *U.S. Public*, pg. 1488
DIRECT SOURCING GROUP PTE. LTD.—See Li & Fung Limited; *Int'l*, pg. 4479
DIRECT SOUTH INC.; *U.S. Private*, pg. 1235
DIRECT TECHNOLOGIES, INC.—See GI Manager L.P.; *U.S. Private*, pg. 1692
DIRECT TITLE SOLUTIONS, INC.; *U.S. Private*, pg. 1235
DIRECT TRAVEL, INC.—See ABRY Partners, LLC; *U.S. Private*, pg. 41
DIRECT VAPOR LLC—See Turning Point Brands, Inc.; *U.S. Public*, pg. 2205
DIRECTV ARGENTINA, S.A.—See AT&T Inc.; *U.S. Public*, pg. 220
DIRECTV COLOMBIA, LTDA.—See AT&T Inc.; *U.S. Public*, pg. 220
DIRECTV CUSTOMER SERVICES, INC.—See AT&T Inc.; *U.S. Public*, pg. 220
DIRECTV ENTERPRISES, LLC—See AT&T Inc.; *U.S. Public*, pg. 220
DIRECT VET MARKETING, INC.—See Clayton, Dubilier & Rice, LLC; *U.S. Private*, pg. 921
DIRECT VET MARKETING, INC.—See TPG Capital, L.P.; *U.S. Public*, pg. 2170
DIRECTV LATIN AMERICA, LLC—See AT&T Inc.; *U.S. Public*, pg. 220
DIRECTV, LLC—See AT&T Inc.; *U.S. Public*, pg. 220
DIRECTV PERU S.R.L.—See AT&T Inc.; *U.S. Public*, pg. 220
DIRECTV SPORTS NET PITTSBURGH, LLC—See AT&T Inc.; *U.S. Public*, pg. 220
DIRECTV TRINIDAD LIMITED—See AT&T Inc.; *U.S. Public*, pg. 220
DIRECT WEB ADVERTISING, INC.; *U.S. Private*, pg. 1236
DIRECT WINES LIMITED; *Int'l*, pg. 2130
DIRECT WONEN N V; *Int'l*, pg. 2130
DI REGIE SAS—See LVMH Moet Hennessy Louis Vuitton SE; *Int'l*, pg. 4591
DIREKTBANK N.V.—See ABN AMRO Group N.V.; *Int'l*, pg. 65
DIREKTMEDIA 121 OY—See Ratos AB; *Int'l*, pg. 6216
DIREKTMEDIA SVERIGE AB—See Ratos AB; *Int'l*, pg. 6216
DIREKTNA BANKA A.D.; *Int'l*, pg. 2130
DIREKTRONIK AB—See Lagercrantz Group AB; *Int'l*, pg. 4394
DIREKTSERVICE COMMERZ GMBH—See Commerzbank AG; *Int'l*, pg. 1717
THE DIREXION FUNDS—See Rafferty Holdings, LLC; *U.S. Private*, pg. 3345
DIREXXIS LLC—See Broadridge Financial Solutions, Inc.; *U.S. Public*, pg. 391
DIRHAM CONSTRUCTION LTD; *Int'l*, pg. 2130
DIRIGO PINES RETIREMENT COMMUNITY LLC—See Chicago Pacific Founders; *U.S. Private*, pg. 878
DIR INFORMATION SYSTEMS CO., LTD.—See Daiwa Securities Group Inc.; *Int'l*, pg. 1947
DIRINGER S.A.—See Iep Invest SA; *Int'l*, pg. 3597
DIRITEKS DIRILIS TEKSTIL SANAYI VE TICARET A.S.; *Int'l*, pg. 2130
DIRK BECKER ENTERTAINMENT GMBH—See CTS Eventim AG & Co. KGaA; *Int'l*, pg. 1872
DIRK INDIA PRIVATE LIMITED—See Adani Enterprises Limited; *Int'l*, pg. 125
DIRKSEN SCREW PRODUCTS CO.; *U.S. Private*, pg. 1236

DIRON WIRTSCHAFTSINFORMATIK GMBH & CO. KG—See CEWE Stiftung & Co. KGaA; *Int'l*, pg. 1425
DIRSON ENTERPRISES, INC; *U.S. Private*, pg. 1236
THE DIRT DOCTORS, LLC—See SiteOne Landscape Supply, Inc.; *U.S. Public*, pg. 1889
DIRTT ENVIRONMENTAL SOLUTIONS LTD.; *Int'l*, pg. 2130
DIRUI INDUSTRIAL CO., LTD.; *Int'l*, pg. 2130
DISABATINO CONSTRUCTION COMPANY INC.; *U.S. Private*, pg. 1237
DISABILITY MANAGEMENT SERVICES INC; *U.S. Private*, pg. 1237
DISABILITY RIGHTS CALIFORNIA; *U.S. Private*, pg. 1237
DISABILITY RIGHTS TEXAS; *U.S. Private*, pg. 1237
DISABILITY SERVICES, INC.—See Dungarvin, Inc.; *U.S. Private*, pg. 1289
DISABILITY SERVICES OF THE SOUTHWEST; *U.S. Private*, pg. 1237
DISABLED SPORTS USA, INC.—See Adaptive Sports USA, Inc.; *U.S. Private*, pg. 76
DISABLED VETERANS NATIONAL FOUNDATION; *U.S. Private*, pg. 1237
DISA DESTILARIA ITAUNAS S/A—See Infinity Bio-Energy Ltd.; *Int'l*, pg. 3687
DISA DIGITAL SAFETY PTE. LTD.—See DISA LIMITED; *Int'l*, pg. 2131
DISA EQUIPMENT (PTY) LTD.—See Invicta Holdings Limited; *Int'l*, pg. 3788
DISA GLOBAL SOLUTIONS, INC.—See Audax Group, Limited Partnership; *U.S. Private*, pg. 387
DIS AG—See Adecco Group AG; *Int'l*, pg. 141
DISA INDIA LTD—See Altor Equity Partners AB; *Int'l*, pg. 395
DISA INDUSTRIE AG—See Altor Equity Partners AB; *Int'l*, pg. 395
DISA INDUSTRIES A/S—See Altor Equity Partners AB; *Int'l*, pg. 395
DISA INDUSTRIES INC.—See Georg Fischer AG; *Int'l*, pg. 2935
DISA LIMITED; *Int'l*, pg. 2131
DISA MEDINOTEC PROPRIETARY LIMITED—See Medinotec Inc.; *Int'l*, pg. 4778
DISARM THERAPEUTICS INC.—See Eli Lilly & Company; *U.S. Public*, pg. 731
DIS ARTWORKS CO., LTD.—See Daiwabo Holdings Co., Ltd.; *Int'l*, pg. 1949
DISASTER PREPAREDNESS SYSTEMS, INC.; *Int'l*, pg. 2131
DISASTER RECOVERY SERVICES LIMITED—See Iron Mountain Incorporated; *U.S. Public*, pg. 1172
DISASTER RESTORATION SERVICES; *U.S. Private*, pg. 1237
DISBROWE CHEVROLET BUICK GMC CADILLAC; *Int'l*, pg. 2131
DISCA BETEILIGUNGSGESELLSCHAFT MBH—See Deutsche Bank Aktiengesellschaft; *Int'l*, pg. 2057
DISC BRAKES AUSTRALIA PTY LTD—See Amotiv Limited; *Int'l*, pg. 431
DISCERN, LLC—See New Mountain Capital, LLC; *U.S. Private*, pg. 2904
DISC GRAPHICS INC.—See Dunsirn Partners LLC; *U.S. Private*, pg. 1291
DISC GRAPHICS INC.—See Pfingsten Partners, LLC; *U.S. Private*, pg. 3164
DISC GRAPHICS LABEL GROUP INC.—See Dunsirn Partners LLC; *U.S. Private*, pg. 1291
DISC GRAPHICS LABEL GROUP INC.—See Pfingsten Partners, LLC; *U.S. Private*, pg. 3164
DIS-CHEM AIRPORT JUNCTION PROPRIETARY LIMITED—See Dis-Chem Pharmacies Ltd.; *Int'l*, pg. 2130
DIS-CHEM BALLITO JUNCTION PROPRIETARY LIMITED—See Dis-Chem Pharmacies Ltd.; *Int'l*, pg. 2130
DIS-CHEM BALLITO LIFESTYLE PROPRIETARY LIMITED—See Dis-Chem Pharmacies Ltd.; *Int'l*, pg. 2131
DIS-CHEM FERNDALE PROPRIETARY LIMITED—See Dis-Chem Pharmacies Ltd.; *Int'l*, pg. 2131
DIS-CHEM FESTIVAL MALL PROPRIETARY LIMITED—See Dis-Chem Pharmacies Ltd.; *Int'l*, pg. 2131
DIS-CHEM FLAMEWOOD VALUE CENTRE PROPRIETARY LIMITED—See Dis-Chem Pharmacies Ltd.; *Int'l*, pg. 2131
DIS-CHEM GLEN FAIR PROPRIETARY LIMITED—See Dis-Chem Pharmacies Ltd.; *Int'l*, pg. 2131
DIS-CHEM GOODWOOD PROPRIETARY LIMITED—See Dis-Chem Pharmacies Ltd.; *Int'l*, pg. 2131
DIS-CHEM JUBILEE PROPRIETARY LIMITED—See Dis-Chem Pharmacies Ltd.; *Int'l*, pg. 2131
DIS-CHEM KRUGERSDORP PROPRIETARY LIMITED—See Dis-Chem Pharmacies Ltd.; *Int'l*, pg. 2131
DIS-CHEM MAMS MALL PROPRIETARY LIMITED—See Dis-Chem Pharmacies Ltd.; *Int'l*, pg. 2131
DIS-CHEM MAPONYA PROPRIETARY LIMITED—See Dis-Chem Pharmacies Ltd.; *Int'l*, pg. 2131

DIS-CHEM MEGA MALL PROPRIETARY LIMITED—See Dis-Chem Pharmacies Ltd.; *Int'l*, pg. 2131
DIS-CHEM PHARMACIES LTD.; *Int'l*, pg. 2130
DIS-CHEM SWAKOPMUND PROPRIETARY LIMITED—See Dis-Chem Pharmacies Ltd.; *Int'l*, pg. 2131
DIS-CHEM THE GALLERIA AMANZIMTOTI PROPRIETARY LIMITED—See Dis-Chem Pharmacies Ltd.; *Int'l*, pg. 2131
DIS-CHEM THREE RIVERS PROPRIETARY LIMITED—See Dis-Chem Pharmacies Ltd.; *Int'l*, pg. 2131
DIS-CHEM TLC DE WIEKUS PROPRIETARY LIMITED—See Dis-Chem Pharmacies Ltd.; *Int'l*, pg. 2131
DIS-CHEM WALVIS BAY PROPRIETARY LIMITED—See Dis-Chem Pharmacies Ltd.; *Int'l*, pg. 2131
DIS-CHEM WERNHILL PROPRIETARY LIMITED—See Dis-Chem Pharmacies Ltd.; *Int'l*, pg. 2131
DIS-CHEM WORCESTER PROPRIETARY LIMITED—See Dis-Chem Pharmacies Ltd.; *Int'l*, pg. 2131
DISCIPLE DESIGN—See Thompson & Company Marketing Communications; *U.S. Private*, pg. 4158
DISCLOSURE INNOVATION INC.—See TAKARA & COMPANY LTD.; *Int'l*, pg. 7431
DISCMAKERS, INC.; *U.S. Private*, pg. 1237
DISC MEDICINE, INC.; *U.S. Public*, pg. 668
DISCO ASSOCIATES INC.—See Graybar Electric Company, Inc.; *U.S. Private*, pg. 1760
DISCO CORPORATION - CHINO PLANT—See Disco Corporation; *Int'l*, pg. 2131
DISCO CORPORATION - KURE PLANT—See Disco Corporation; *Int'l*, pg. 2132
DISCO CORPORATION - KUWABATA PLANT—See Disco Corporation; *Int'l*, pg. 2132
DISCO CORPORATION; *Int'l*, pg. 2131
DISCO HI-TEC AMERICA, INC.—See Disco Corporation; *Int'l*, pg. 2132
DISCO HI-TEC CHINA CO., LTD.—See Disco Corporation; *Int'l*, pg. 2131
DISCO HI-TEC CZECH S.R.O.—See Disco Corporation; *Int'l*, pg. 2132
DISCO HI-TEC EUROPE GMBH—See Disco Corporation; *Int'l*, pg. 2132
DISCO HI-TEC FRANCE SARL—See Disco Corporation; *Int'l*, pg. 2132
DISCO HI-TEC KOREA CORPORATION—See Disco Corporation; *Int'l*, pg. 2132
DISCO HI-TEC (MALAYSIA) SDN. BHD.—See Disco Corporation; *Int'l*, pg. 2132
DISCO HI-TEC MOROCCO SARL—See Disco Corporation; *Int'l*, pg. 2132
DISCO HI-TEC PHILIPPINES, INC.—See Disco Corporation; *Int'l*, pg. 2132
DISCO HI-TEC (SINGAPORE) PTE. LTD.—See Disco Corporation; *Int'l*, pg. 2132
DISCO HI-TEC TAIWAN CO., LTD.—See Disco Corporation; *Int'l*, pg. 2132
DISCO HI-TEC (THAILAND) CO., LTD.—See Disco Corporation; *Int'l*, pg. 2132
DISCO HI-TEC UK LTD.—See Disco Corporation; *Int'l*, pg. 2132
DISCO HI-TEC (VIETNAM) CO., LTD.—See Disco Corporation; *Int'l*, pg. 2131
DISCO, INC.—See Cellucap Manufacturing Co.; *U.S. Private*, pg. 807
DISCOM ELEKTRONISCHE SYSTEME UND KOMPONENTEN GMBH—See Spectris Plc; *Int'l*, pg. 7130
DISCO S.A.—See Cencosud S.A.; *Int'l*, pg. 1400
DISCO-SEA EUROPE S.R.L.—See Disco Corporation; *Int'l*, pg. 2132
DISCO TECHNOLOGY (SHANGHAI) CO., LTD.—See Disco Corporation; *Int'l*, pg. 2132
DISCOUNT CAPITAL LTD.—See ImageSat International (ISI) Ltd.; *Int'l*, pg. 3618
DISCOUNT CAR & TRUCK RENTALS LTD.—See Enterprise Holdings, Inc.; *U.S. Private*, pg. 1403
DISCOUNT CAR WASH INC.; *U.S. Private*, pg. 1237
DISCOUNT CLEANING PRODUCTS; *U.S. Private*, pg. 1237
DISCOUNT COFFEE.COM, INC.; *U.S. Private*, pg. 1237
DISCOUNT DANCE SUPPLY; *U.S. Private*, pg. 1237
DISCOUNT DRAINAGE SUPPLIES, LLC—See Winsupply, Inc.; *U.S. Private*, pg. 4545
DISCOUNT DRUG MART INC.; *U.S. Private*, pg. 1237
DISCOUNT ELECTRONICS; *U.S. Private*, pg. 1237
DISCOUNT EMPORIUM INC.; *U.S. Private*, pg. 1237
DISCOUNT FENCE SUPPLY, INC.; *U.S. Private*, pg. 1237
DISCOUNT FOODS INC.; *U.S. Private*, pg. 1237
DISCOUNT INVESTMENT CORP. LTD.—See IDB Development Corporation Ltd.; *Int'l*, pg. 3588
DISCOUNT LABELS, INC.—See Cenveo, Inc.; *U.S. Private*, pg. 834
DISCOUNTLIGHTINGSALE.COM—See Butler's Electric Supply; *U.S. Private*, pg. 697
DISCOUNTMUGS.COM—See BEL USA LLC; *U.S. Private*, pg. 516
DISCOUNT OFFICE ITEMS, INC.—See The ODP Corporation; *U.S. Public*, pg. 2117

DISCOUNT RAMPS.COM, LLC—See Rotunda Capital Partners LLC; *U.S. Private*, pg. 3488
DISCOUNT SCHOOL SUPPLY—See Brentwood Associates; *U.S. Private*, pg. 646
DISCOUNT SMOKE SHOP MISSOURI INC; *U.S. Private*, pg. 1237
DISCOUNT TELECOM S&V GMBH—See 3U Holding AG; *Int'l*, pg. 10
DISCOUNT TOBACCO OUTLET INC.; *U.S. Private*, pg. 1237
DISCOUNT TWO WAY RADIO CORPORATION; *U.S. Private*, pg. 1237
DISCOUNT VEHICLES AUSTRALIA PTY LTD—See carsales.com Limited; *Int'l*, pg. 1347
DISCOVER BANK—See Discover Financial Services; *U.S. Public*, pg. 668
DISCOVER CARD—See Discover Financial Services; *U.S. Public*, pg. 668
DISCOVER ECHO INC.—See BICO Group AB; *Int'l*, pg. 1019
DISCOVER ENGLISH PTY LTD—See Academies Australasia Group Limited; *Int'l*, pg. 77
DISCOVER FINANCIAL SERVICES; *U.S. Public*, pg. 668
DISCOVER HOME LOANS, INC.—See Discover Financial Services; *U.S. Public*, pg. 668
DISCOVERIE GROUP PLC; *Int'l*, pg. 2132
DISCOVER MAGAZINE—See Kalmbach Publishing Co.; *U.S. Private*, pg. 2257
DISCOVERORG, LLC—See TA Associates, Inc.; *U.S. Private*, pg. 3915
DISCOVER ORIENT HOLIDAYS SDN. BHD.—See Meta Bright Group Berhad; *Int'l*, pg. 4843
DISCOVERREADY, LLC—See GI Manager, L.P.; *U.S. Private*, pg. 1692
DISCOVER STUDENT LOANS—See Discover Financial Services; *U.S. Public*, pg. 668
DISCOVERTURE SOLUTIONS LLC—See Larsen & Toubro Limited; *Int'l*, pg. 4419
DISCOVER WELLNESS SOLUTIONS INC.; *Int'l*, pg. 2132
DISCOVERX CORP.; *U.S. Private*, pg. 1237
DISCOVERY AIR DEFENCE SERVICES INC.—See Clairvest Group Inc.; *Int'l*, pg. 1641
DISCOVERY AIR INC.—See Clairvest Group Inc.; *Int'l*, pg. 1641
DISCOVERY ALASKA LIMITED; *Int'l*, pg. 2134
DISCOVERY ALLIANCE, LLC—See Capital Southwest Corporation; *U.S. Public*, pg. 432
DISCOVERY ASIA SALES PRIVATE LIMITED—See Warner Bros. Discovery, Inc.; *U.S. Public*, pg. 2326
DISCOVERY BAY BEACH HOTEL—See Marketing & Reservations International Ltd.; *Int'l*, pg. 4696
DISCOVERY BEHAVIORAL HEALTH, INC; *U.S. Private*, pg. 1237
DISCOVERY BENEFITS, INC.—See WEX, Inc.; *U.S. Public*, pg. 2364
DISCOVERYBIOMED INC.—See Eurofins Scientific S.E.; *Int'l*, pg. 2536
DISCOVERY CAPITAL CORPORATION; *Int'l*, pg. 2134
THE DISCOVERY CHANNEL—See BCE Inc.; *Int'l*, pg. 927
DISCOVERY CLINICAL RESEARCH, INC.—See KKR & Co. Inc.; *U.S. Public*, pg. 1245
DISCOVERY COMMUNICATIONS BENELUX BV—See Warner Bros. Discovery, Inc.; *U.S. Public*, pg. 2326
DISCOVERY COMMUNICATIONS DEUTSCHLAND GMBH & CO. KG—See Warner Bros. Discovery, Inc.; *U.S. Public*, pg. 2326
DISCOVERY COMMUNICATIONS INDIA—See Warner Bros. Discovery, Inc.; *U.S. Public*, pg. 2326
DISCOVERY COMMUNICATIONS, LLC—See Warner Bros. Discovery, Inc.; *U.S. Public*, pg. 2326
DISCOVERY COMMUNICATIONS NORDIC APS—See Warner Bros. Discovery, Inc.; *U.S. Public*, pg. 2326
DISCOVERY COMPUTERS & WIRELESS INC.; *Int'l*, pg. 2134
DISCOVERY CONTENT VERWALTUNGS GMBH—See Warner Bros. Discovery, Inc.; *U.S. Public*, pg. 2326
DISCOVERY-CORP ENTERPRISES INC.; *Int'l*, pg. 2134
DISCOVERY COVE—See United Parks & Resorts Inc.; *U.S. Public*, pg. 2234
DISCOVERY DATA HOLDINGS INC.—See Deutsche Borse AG; *Int'l*, pg. 2063
DISCOVERY DOOR, INC.—See Platinum Equity, LLC; *U.S. Private*, pg. 3208
DISCOVERY EDUCATION EUROPE LTD.—See Clearlake Capital Group, L.P.; *U.S. Private*, pg. 934
DISCOVERY EDUCATION, INC.—See Clearlake Capital Group, L.P.; *U.S. Private*, pg. 934
DISCOVERY ENERGY CORP.; *U.S. Public*, pg. 668
DISCOVERY ENERGY SA PTY LTD—See Discovery Energy Corp.; *U.S. Public*, pg. 668
DISCOVERY FLEET CORPORATION—See Discovery World Corporation; *Int'l*, pg. 2134
DISCOVERY FOODS LTD.; *Int'l*, pg. 2134
DISCOVERY FORD BURLINGTON LTD.; *Int'l*, pg. 2134
DISCOVERY HARBOUR RESOURCES CORP.; *Int'l*, pg. 2134
DISCOVERY HEALTH (PROPRIETARY) LIMITED—See Discovery Limited; *Int'l*, pg. 2134

DISCOVERY HEALTH RECORD SOLUTIONS, LLC—See Silverhawk Capital Partners, LLC; *U.S. Private*, pg. 3663
DISCOVERY HOMES; *U.S. Private*, pg. 1238
DISCOVERY HONDA; *Int'l*, pg. 2134
DISCOVERY HOUSE-LT, INC.—See Acadia Healthcare Company, Inc.; *U.S. Public*, pg. 28
DISCOVERY HOUSE TV, INC.—See Acadia Healthcare Company, Inc.; *U.S. Public*, pg. 28
DISCOVERY HOUSE-UC, INC.—See Acadia Healthcare Company, Inc.; *U.S. Public*, pg. 28
DISCOVERY HOUSE WC, INC.—See Acadia Healthcare Company, Inc.; *U.S. Public*, pg. 28
DISCOVERY, INC. - DETROIT OFFICE—See Warner Bros. Discovery, Inc.; *U.S. Public*, pg. 2326
DISCOVERY, INC. - NEW YORK OFFICE—See Warner Bros. Discovery, Inc.; *U.S. Public*, pg. 2326
DISCOVERY LATIN AMERICA, L.L.C.—See Warner Bros. Discovery, Inc.; *U.S. Public*, pg. 2326
DISCOVERY LEARNING INC.—See Multi-Health Systems, Inc.; *U.S. Private*, pg. 2812
DISCOVERY LIFE SCIENCES, LLC; *U.S. Private*, pg. 1238
DISCOVERY LIMITED; *Int'l*, pg. 2134
DISCOVERY METALS CORP.; *Int'l*, pg. 2134
DISCOVERY MINERALS LTD.; *U.S. Public*, pg. 668
DISCOVERY MINING SERVICES LTD.—See Clairvest Group Inc.; *Int'l*, pg. 1641
DISCOVERY NETWORKS DANMARK—See Warner Bros. Discovery, Inc.; *U.S. Public*, pg. 2326
DISCOVERY NETWORKS FINLAND OY—See Warner Bros. Discovery, Inc.; *U.S. Public*, pg. 2326
DISCOVERY NETWORKS INTERNATIONAL HOLDINGS LTD.—See Warner Bros. Discovery, Inc.; *U.S. Public*, pg. 2326
DISCOVERY NETWORKS, S.L.—See Warner Bros. Discovery, Inc.; *U.S. Public*, pg. 2326
DISCOVERY NETWORKS SWEDEN AB—See Warner Bros. Discovery, Inc.; *U.S. Public*, pg. 2326
DISCOVERY NZ LIMITED—See Warner Bros. Discovery, Inc.; *U.S. Public*, pg. 2326
DISCOVERY ONE INVESTMENT CORP.; *Int'l*, pg. 2134
DISCOVERY PLACE, INC.; *U.S. Private*, pg. 1238
DISCOVERY POLSKA SP. Z.O.O.—See Warner Bros. Discovery, Inc.; *U.S. Public*, pg. 2326
DISCOVERY PRODUCTIONS, LLC—See Warner Bros. Discovery, Inc.; *U.S. Public*, pg. 2326
DISCOVERY RESEARCH LABORATORIES—See Shionogi & Co., Ltd.; *Int'l*, pg. 6851
DISCOVERY RIDGE RESOURCES, INC.; *Int'l*, pg. 2134
DISCOVERY SERVICES LLC; *U.S. Private*, pg. 1238
DISCOVERY TECHNOLOGY INTERNATIONAL, INC.; *U.S. Private*, pg. 1238
DISCOVERY TECHNOLOGY PTY LTD—See Data#3 Limited; *Int'l*, pg. 1977
DISCOVERY-THE FINANCIAL INFORMATION GROUP, INC.; *U.S. Private*, pg. 1238
DISCOVERY TOURS (SABAH) SDN BHD—See Warisan TC Holdings Berhad; *Int'l*, pg. 8345
DISCOVERY TOYS, LLC—See Eos International, Inc.; *U.S. Private*, pg. 1411
DISCOVERY WETLANDS SDN. BHD.—See Gamuda Berhad; *Int'l*, pg. 2879
DISCOVERY WORLD CORPORATION; *Int'l*, pg. 2134
DISCOVERY WORLD TRAVEL, INC.; *U.S. Private*, pg. 1238
DISCOVEX RESOURCES LIMITED; *Int'l*, pg. 2134
DISCRETIX, INC.—See Discretix Technologies Ltd.; *Int'l*, pg. 2135
DISCRETIX TECHNOLOGIES K.K.—See Discretix Technologies Ltd.; *Int'l*, pg. 2135
DISCRETIX TECHNOLOGIES LTD.; *Int'l*, pg. 2134
DISCRETIX TECHNOLOGIES LTD.—See Discretix Technologies Ltd.; *Int'l*, pg. 2135
DISCTRONICS TEXAS INC.; *U.S. Private*, pg. 1238
DISCUS DENTAL AUSTRIA GMBH—See Koninklijke Philips N.V.; *Int'l*, pg. 4267
DISCUS DENTAL EUROPE B.V.—See Koninklijke Philips N.V.; *Int'l*, pg. 4267
DISCUS INTERNATIONAL, LLC—See Koninklijke Philips N.V.; *Int'l*, pg. 4267
DISDERO LUMBER CO. INC.—See Tumac Lumber Co. Inc.; *U.S. Private*, pg. 4258
DIS DRAXLMAIER INDUSTRIAL SOLUTIONS GMBH—See Draexlmaier Gruppe; *Int'l*, pg. 2198
DISEC CO., LTD—See Core Corporation; *Int'l*, pg. 1797
DISEGNO CERAMICA SRL—See Mittel S.p.A.; *Int'l*, pg. 4994
DISENOS CONSTRUCCIONES Y FABRICACIONES HISPANOAMERICANAS, S.A.—See Applied Industrial Technologies, Inc.; *U.S. Public*, pg. 171
DISENOS Y PROYECTOS TECNICOS SA; *Int'l*, pg. 2135
DI-SEP SYSTEMS INTERNATIONAL—See RLR, Inc.; *U.S. Private*, pg. 3451
DISGUISE INC.—See JAKKS Pacific, Inc.; *U.S. Public*, pg. 1186
DISHA RESOURCES LIMITED; *Int'l*, pg. 2135
DISHMAN CARBOGEN AMCIS LIMITED; *Int'l*, pg. 2135

DISHMAN EUROPE LIMITED—See Dishman Carbogen Amcis Limited; *Int'l*, pg. 2135
DISHMAN INTERNATIONAL TRADE (SHANGHAI) CO., LTD.—See Dishman Carbogen Amcis Limited; *Int'l*, pg. 2135
DISHMAN JAPAN LTD.—See Dishman Carbogen Amcis Limited; *Int'l*, pg. 2135
DISHMAN NETHERLANDS B.V.—See Dishman Carbogen Amcis Limited; *Int'l*, pg. 2135
DISHMAN PHARMACEUTICALS & CHEMICALS (SHANGHAI) CO. LTD.—See Dishman Carbogen Amcis Limited; *Int'l*, pg. 2135
DISHMAN PHARMA SOLUTIONS AG.—See Dishman Carbogen Amcis Limited; *Int'l*, pg. 2135
DISHMAN SWITZERLAND LTD.—See Dishman Carbogen Amcis Limited; *Int'l*, pg. 2135
DISHMAN USA INC.—See Dishman Carbogen Amcis Limited; *Int'l*, pg. 2135
DISHNET WIRELESS LIMITED—See Maxis Berhad; *Int'l*, pg. 4742
DISH NETWORK CORPORATION—See EchoStar Corporation; *U.S. Public*, pg. 711
DISH NETWORK L.L.C.—See EchoStar Corporation; *U.S. Public*, pg. 711
DISH NETWORK SERVICE, L.L.C.—See EchoStar Corporation; *U.S. Public*, pg. 711
DISHOLDER 3, INC.—See The Walt Disney Company; *U.S. Public*, pg. 2138
DISHONE SATELLITE; *U.S. Private*, pg. 1238
DISH PLUS GMBH—See Metro AG; *Int'l*, pg. 4857
DISH TV INDIA LTD; *Int'l*, pg. 2135
D&I SILICA, LLC—See Atlas Energy Solutions Inc.; *U.S. Public*, pg. 224
DISITRON INDUSTRIES, INC.; *U.S. Private*, pg. 1238
DISKFAKTORY.COM—See Innovative Diversified Technologies Inc.; *U.S. Private*, pg. 2082
DISKOMAT AB—See Gosta Torssell Holding AB; *Int'l*, pg. 3043
DISKUS WERKE AG; *Int'l*, pg. 2135
DISMA REIZEN EINDHOVEN B.V.—See TUI AG; *Int'l*, pg. 7964
DISMA REIZEN OOSTERHOUT/BEINS TRAVEL B.V.—See TUI AG; *Int'l*, pg. 7964
DISMAS CHARITIES, INC.; *U.S. Private*, pg. 1238
DISMO FRANCE S.A.S.—See Rexel, S.A.; *Int'l*, pg. 6316
DISMO; *Int'l*, pg. 2135
DISNEY CANADA, INC.—See The Walt Disney Company; *U.S. Public*, pg. 2138
DISNEY CONSUMER PRODUCTS, INC.—See The Walt Disney Company; *U.S. Public*, pg. 2138
DISNEY CRUISE VACATIONS INC.—See The Walt Disney Company; *U.S. Public*, pg. 2138
DISNEY DESTINATIONS, LLC—See The Walt Disney Company; *U.S. Public*, pg. 2138
DISNEY ENTERPRISES, INC.—See The Walt Disney Company; *U.S. Public*, pg. 2138
DISNEY INTERACTIVE MEDIA GROUP—See The Walt Disney Company; *U.S. Public*, pg. 2138
DISNEY INTERACTIVE STUDIOS—See The Walt Disney Company; *U.S. Public*, pg. 2138
DISNEYLAND HOTELS—See The Walt Disney Company; *U.S. Public*, pg. 2138
DISNEYLAND RESORTS—See The Walt Disney Company; *U.S. Public*, pg. 2138
DISNEY MAGIC COMPANY LIMITED—See The Walt Disney Company; *U.S. Public*, pg. 2139
DISNEY PUBLISHING WORLDWIDE, INC.—See The Walt Disney Company; *U.S. Public*, pg. 2138
DISNEY SHOPPING, INC.—See The Walt Disney Company; *U.S. Public*, pg. 2138
DISNEY STORE INC.—See The Walt Disney Company; *U.S. Public*, pg. 2138
DISNEY THEATRICAL PRODUCTIONS—See The Walt Disney Company; *U.S. Public*, pg. 2139
DISNEY VACATION CLUB—See The Walt Disney Company; *U.S. Public*, pg. 2138
DISNEY WORLDWIDE SERVICES, INC.—See The Walt Disney Company; *U.S. Public*, pg. 2139
DISO MADRID S.L.R.—See General Motors Company; *U.S. Public*, pg. 927
DISORDERLY KIDS, LLC; *U.S. Private*, pg. 1238
DISOSWAY, INC.; *U.S. Private*, pg. 1238
DISPANO—See Compagnie de Saint-Gobain SA; *Int'l*, pg. 1723
DISPATCH BROADCAST GROUP—See The Dispatch Printing Company; *U.S. Private*, pg. 4021
THE DISPATCH PRINTING COMPANY; *U.S. Private*, pg. 4021
THE DISPATCH PUBLISHING COMPANY, INC.—See Gannett Co., Inc.; *U.S. Public*, pg. 905
DISPATCH PUBLISHING COMPANY, INC—See Paxton Media Group LLC; *U.S. Private*, pg. 3116
DISPATCH TECHNOLOGIES, INC.; *U.S. Private*, pg. 1238
DISPATCH TRANSPORTATION INC.; *U.S. Private*, pg. 1238
DISPENDIX GMBH—See BICO Group AB; *Int'l*, pg. 1019
DISPENSER BEVERAGES INC.; *U.S. Private*, pg. 1238
DISPENSER SERVICES INC.; *U.S. Private*, pg. 1238

DISPENSERS OPTICAL SERVICE CORPORATION; *U.S. Private*, pg. 1238
DISPENSE SYSTEMS INTERNATIONAL—See Aalberts N.V.; *Int'l*, pg. 34
DISPENSING DYNAMICS INTERNATIONAL; *U.S. Private*, pg. 1238
DISPLAY ART PLC; *Int'l*, pg. 2135
DISPLAY BOYS; *U.S. Private*, pg. 1238
DISPLAY INDUSTRIES, LLC; *U.S. Private*, pg. 1238
DISPLAYLINK CORP.—See Synaptics Incorporated; *U.S. Public*, pg. 1969
DISPLAYLINK (UK) LIMITED—See Synaptics Incorporated; *U.S. Public*, pg. 1969
DISPLAY PACK INC.; *U.S. Private*, pg. 1239
DISPLAY TECH CO., LTD.; *Int'l*, pg. 2135
DISPLAY TECHNOLOGIES, LLC—See Berkshire Hathaway Inc.; *U.S. Public*, pg. 309
DISPLAY UKRAINE LLC—See Ratos AB; *Int'l*, pg. 6218
DISPLAY WAYS LTD.—See Foga System International AB; *Int'l*, pg. 2720
DISPOMED DIABETES SERVICE NEDERLAND—See Advent International Corporation; *U.S. Private*, pg. 104
DISPOSABLE LAB SAS—See Eurofins Scientific S.E.; *Int'l*, pg. 2536
DISPOSABLE SOFT GOODS LIMITED—See DSG International Limited; *Int'l*, pg. 2210
DISPOSABLE SOFT GOODS (MALAYSIA) SDN. BHD.—See DSG International Limited; *Int'l*, pg. 2210
DISPOSABLE SOFT GOODS (S) PTE. LTD.—See DSG International Limited; *Int'l*, pg. 2210
DISPOSABLE SOFT GOODS (ZHONGSHAN) LIMITED—See Unicharm Corporation; *Int'l*, pg. 8032
DISPUTESUITE.COM, LLC; *U.S. Private*, pg. 1239
DISQUS, INC.—See Zeta Interactive Corporation; *U.S. Private*, pg. 4603
DISRUPTIVE CAPITAL ACQUISITION COMPANY LIMITED; *Int'l*, pg. 2135
DIS SERVICE & SOLUTION CO., LTD.—See Daiwabo Holdings Co., Ltd.; *Int'l*, pg. 1949
DIS SERVICE & SUPPORT CO., LTD.—See Daiwabo Holdings Co., Ltd.; *Int'l*, pg. 1949
DIS SOLUTION CO., LTD.—See Daiwabo Holdings Co., Ltd.; *Int'l*, pg. 1949
DISSTON COMPANY—See CAL SDI, INC.; *U.S. Private*, pg. 715
DISTAL INC.—See Gordon Food Service Inc.; *U.S. Private*, pg. 1743
DISTANT LANDS TRADING CO.—See ITO EN Ltd; *Int'l*, pg. 3834
DISTA, S.A.—See Eli Lilly & Company; *U.S. Public*, pg. 731
DISTEC GMBH—See Prismaflex International SA; *Int'l*, pg. 5982
DISTECH CONTROLS ENERGY SERVICES INC.—See Acuity Brands, Inc.; *U.S. Public*, pg. 37
DISTECH CONTROLS INC.—See Acuity Brands, Inc.; *U.S. Public*, pg. 37
DISTECH CONTROLS POLEN SP. Z O.O.—See Acuity Brands, Inc.; *U.S. Public*, pg. 37
DISTECH CONTROLS PORTUGAL DOMEBUS—See Acuity Brands, Inc.; *U.S. Public*, pg. 37
DISTECH CONTROLS PTE LTD—See Acuity Brands, Inc.; *U.S. Public*, pg. 37
DISTECH CONTROLS SAS—See Acuity Brands, Inc.; *U.S. Public*, pg. 37
DISTECH SYSTEMS, INC.—See Gleason Corporation; *U.S. Private*, pg. 1708
DISTEFANO TECHNOLOGY & MANUFACTURING—See Behlen Mfg. Co.; *U.S. Private*, pg. 515
DISTEK INTEGRATION, INC.; *U.S. Private*, pg. 1239
DISTELL GROUP HOLDINGS LIMITED—See L'Arche Green N.V.; *Int'l*, pg. 4376
DISTELL NAMIBIA LIMITED—See L'Arche Green N.V.; *Int'l*, pg. 4376
DISTELL SWAZILAND LIMITED—See L'Arche Green N.V.; *Int'l*, pg. 4376
DISTICO SA—See The Swatch Group Ltd.; *Int'l*, pg. 7691
DISTILERIA BAGO, INC.—See Top Frontier Investment Holdings, Inc.; *Int'l*, pg. 7811
THE DISTILLATA COMPANY; *U.S. Private*, pg. 4021
DISTILLEERDERIJEN ERVEN LUCAS BOLS BV—See Lucas Bols B.V.; *Int'l*, pg. 4573
DISTILLERIE DE LA GROIE SARL—See LVMH Moet Hennessy Louis Vuitton SE; *Int'l*, pg. 4599
DISTILLERIE MERLET & FILS SARL; *Int'l*, pg. 2135
DISTILLERIES COMPANY OF SRI LANKA PLC; *Int'l*, pg. 2135
DISTILLERIE STOCK USA LTD.—See CVC Capital Partners SICAV-FIS S.A.; *Int'l*, pg. 1888
DISTIL PLC; *Int'l*, pg. 2135
DISTIMO HOLDING B.V.—See App Annie Ltd.; *Int'l*, pg. 519
DISTINCT INFRASTRUCTURE GROUP INC.; *Int'l*, pg. 2135
DISTINCTIVE DESIGNS FURNITURE, INC.; *Int'l*, pg. 2135
DISTINCTIVE FLOORING LIMITED—See Victoria Plc; *Int'l*, pg. 8188
DISTINCTIVE FOODS LLC.; *U.S. Private*, pg. 1239

DISTINCTIVE FOODS LLC.

DISTINCTIVE INSURANCE—See Genstar Capital, LLC; *U.S. Private*, pg. 1674
DISTINCTIVE KITCHENS & BATHS, INC.—See The Sterling Group, L.P.; *U.S. Private*, pg. 4122
DISTINCT MOTION SDN. BHD.—See Sasbadi Holdings Berhad; *Int'l*, pg. 6582
THE DISTINGUISHED PROGRAM GROUP; *U.S. Private*, pg. 4021
DISTIT AB; *Int'l*, pg. 2136
DISTOKEN ACQUISITION CORPORATION; *Int'l*, pg. 2136
DISTORTIONS UNLIMITED CORP; *U.S. Private*, pg. 1239
DIS-TRAN PACKAGED SUBSTATIONS, LLC—See Crest Industries, LLC; *U.S. Private*, pg. 1096
DIS-TRAN STEEL FABRICATION, LLC—See Crest Industries, LLC; *U.S. Private*, pg. 1096
DIS-TRAN STEEL POLE, LLC—See Crest Industries, LLC; *U.S. Private*, pg. 1096
DIS-TRAN WOOD PRODUCTS, LLC—See Crest Industries, LLC; *U.S. Private*, pg. 1096
DISTRELEC GESELLSCHAFT MBH—See Pema Holding AG; *Int'l*, pg. 5784
DISTRELEC ITALIA SRL—See Pema Holding AG; *Int'l*, pg. 5784
DISTRIBION, INC.—See DallasNews Corporation; *U.S. Public*, pg. 621
DISTRIBO GMBH—See Sartorius AG; *Int'l*, pg. 6578
DISTRIBORG FRANCE SAS—See PAI Partners S.A.S.; *Int'l*, pg. 5700
DISTRIBORG GROUPE SA—See PAI Partners S.A.S.; *Int'l*, pg. 5700
DISTRIBUCIONES ALIADAS, S.A.—See Promotora de Informaciones S.A.; *Int'l*, pg. 5995
DISTRIBUCIONES UQUIFA S.A.S.—See Abbott Laboratories; *U.S. Public*, pg. 19
DISTRIBUIDORA ALFA, S.A.—See Grupo Televisa, S.A.B.; *Int'l*, pg. 3136
DISTRIBUIDORA AUTOMATRIZ ARGENTINA SA—See Inchcape plc; *Int'l*, pg. 3647
DISTRIBUIDORA AUTOMOTRIZ MARUBENI LTDA.—See Marubeni Corporation; *Int'l*, pg. 4705
DISTRIBUIDORA BENDIX CVS (DE) MEXICO SA DE CV—See Knorr-Bremse AG; *Int'l*, pg. 4210
DISTRIBUIDORA BOLIVARIANA, S.A.—See Grupo Televisa, S.A.B.; *Int'l*, pg. 3136
DISTRIBUIDORA CAFE MONTANA S.A.—See Segafredo Zanetti S.p.A.; *Int'l*, pg. 6682
DISTRIBUIDORA COATS DE GUATEMALA S.A.—See Coats Group plc; *Int'l*, pg. 1682
DISTRIBUIDORA CUMMINS CENTROAMERICA COSTA RICA, S.DE R.L.—See Cummins Inc.; *U.S. Public*, pg. 607
DISTRIBUIDORA CUMMINS CENTROAMERICA EL SALVADOR, S.DE R.L.—See Cummins Inc.; *U.S. Public*, pg. 607
DISTRIBUIDORA CUMMINS CENTROAMERICA GUATEMALA, LTDA.—See Cummins Inc.; *U.S. Public*, pg. 607
DISTRIBUIDORA CUMMINS CENTROAMERICA HONDURAS, S.DE R.L.—See Cummins Inc.; *U.S. Public*, pg. 607
DISTRIBUIDORA CUMMINS DE PANAMA, S. DE R.L.—See Cummins Inc.; *U.S. Public*, pg. 607
DISTRIBUIDORA CUMMINS S.A. SUCURSAL BOLIVIA—See Cummins Inc.; *U.S. Public*, pg. 607
DISTRIBUIDORA DE ENERGIA ELECTRICA DEL BAGES SA—See Enel S.p.A.; *Int'l*, pg. 2412
DISTRIBUIDORA DE GAS DEL CENTRO S.A.; *Int'l*, pg. 2136
DISTRIBUIDORA DE PRODUTOS DE PETROLEO IPIRANGA S.A.—See Ultrapar Participacoes S.A.; *Int'l*, pg. 8019
DISTRIBUIDORA E IMPORTADORA ALSEA, S. A. DE C.V.—See Alsea, S.A.B. de C.V.; *Int'l*, pg. 379
DISTRIBUIDORA FGB MEXICANAS S.A. DE C.V.—See Koninklijke DSM N.V.; *Int'l*, pg. 4266
DISTRIBUIDORA INTERNACIONAL DE ALIMENTACION S.A.—See LetterOne Holdings S.A.; *Int'l*, pg. 4470
DISTRIBUIDORA JAFRA DE COSMETICOS LTDA.—See Vorwerk & Co. KG; *Int'l*, pg. 8307
DISTRIBUIDORA KORMA, S.A. DE C.V.—See PPG Industries, Inc.; *U.S. Public*, pg. 1707
DISTRIBUIDORA LOS ANDES, S.A.—See Grupo Televisa, S.A.B.; *Int'l*, pg. 3136
DISTRIBUIDORA PAPELERA, S.A.—See Iberpapel Gestion SA; *Int'l*, pg. 3574
DISTRIBUIDORA SANTIAGO—See Sonepar S.A.; *Int'l*, pg. 7092
DISTRIBUIDORAS UNIDAS, S.A.—See Grupo Televisa, S.A.B.; *Int'l*, pg. 3136
DISTRIBUJDORA YAKULT GADARAJARA, S.A.DE C.V.—See Yakult Honsha Co., Ltd.; *Int'l*, pg. 8546
DISTRIBUTECH INC.—See Redfin Corporation; *U.S. Public*, pg. 1770
DISTRIBUTECH—See Redfin Corporation; *U.S. Public*, pg. 1770
DISTRIBUTECH—See Redfin Corporation; *U.S. Public*, pg. 1770
DISTRIBUTECH - SOUTHWEST REGION—See Redfin Corporation; *U.S. Public*, pg. 1770

DISTRIBUTEL COMMUNICATIONS LIMITED; *Int'l*, pg. 2136
DISTRIBUTIE ENERGIE ELECTRICA ROMANIA S.A.—See Societatea Energetica Electrica S.A.; *Int'l*, pg. 7034
DISTRIBUTIE ENERGIE OLTENIA S.A.—See CEZ, a.s.; *Int'l*, pg. 1427
DISTRIBUTION 2000 INC.; *U.S. Private*, pg. 1239
DISTRIBUTION 20/20—See Richelieu Hardware Ltd.; *Int'l*, pg. 6330
DISTRIBUTION ALTERNATIVES, INC.; *U.S. Private*, pg. 1239
DISTRIBUTION AMERICA, INC.; *U.S. Private*, pg. 1239
DISTRIBUTION AND WAREHOUSING NETWORK LIMITED; *Int'l*, pg. 2136
DISTRIBUTION AUTOMOBILES & MATERIELS EN ALGERIE, SPA—See Toyota Tsusho Corporation; *Int'l*, pg. 7876
DISTRIBUTION CONSTRUCTION, LLC—See Clayton, Dubilier & Rice, LLC; *U.S. Private*, pg. 919
DISTRIBUTION CONTROL SYSTEMS CARIBE, INC.—See ESCO Technologies, Inc.; *U.S. Public*, pg. 793
DISTRIBUTION COOPERATIVE INC; *U.S. Private*, pg. 1239
DISTRIBUTION FINANCE CAPITAL HOLDINGS PLC; *Int'l*, pg. 2136
DISTRIBUTION INNOVATION AS—See Schibsted ASA; *Int'l*, pg. 6616
DISTRIBUTION INTERNATIONAL, INC.—See TopBuild Corp.; *U.S. Public*, pg. 2163
DISTRIBUTION MARCEL DION INC.; *Int'l*, pg. 2136
DISTRIBUTION & MARKING SERVICES, INC.; *U.S. Private*, pg. 1239
DISTRIBUTION NOW FZE—See DNOW Inc.; *U.S. Public*, pg. 671
DISTRIBUTION ROYALTY INC.; *U.S. Private*, pg. 1239
DISTRIBUTIONS 20-20 INC—See Richelieu Hardware Ltd.; *Int'l*, pg. 6330
DISTRIBUTION SANITAIRE CHAUFFAGE SAS—See Compagnie de Saint-Gobain SA; *Int'l*, pg. 1723
DISTRIBUTION SERVICES A/S—See PostNord AB; *Int'l*, pg. 5940
DISTRIBUTION SERVICES, INC.—See Chatham Asset Management, LLC; *U.S. Private*, pg. 860
DISTRIBUTION SERVICES OF AMERICA, INC.; *U.S. Private*, pg. 1239
DISTRIBUTIONS JRV INC. - LIFTING DIVISION—See Distributions JRV Inc.; *Int'l*, pg. 2137
DISTRIBUTIONS JRV INC.; *Int'l*, pg. 2137
DISTRIBUTION SOLUTIONS GROUP, INC.; *U.S. Public*, pg. 668
DISTRIBUTION SOLUTIONS INTERNATIONAL, INC.—See Thermo Fisher Scientific Inc.; *U.S. Public*, pg. 2146
DISTRIBUTION TECHNOLOGY LTD.; *Int'l*, pg. 2136
DISTRIBUTION TRUCKING COMPANY—See The Kroger Co.; *U.S. Public*, pg. 2107
DISTRIBUTION UNLIMITED, INC.—See Galesi Group; *U.S. Private*, pg. 1637
DISTRIBUTION VIDEO & AUDIO, INC.; *U.S. Private*, pg. 1239
DISTRIBUTIVE EDUCATION CLUBS OF AMERICA, INC.; *U.S. Private*, pg. 1239
DISTRIBUTIVNI CENTAR A.D.; *Int'l*, pg. 2137
DISTRIBUTOR CORPORATION OF NEW ENGLAND INC.; *U.S. Private*, pg. 1239
DISTRIBUTOR RESOURCE MANAGEMENT, INC.—See Meal Ticket; *U.S. Private*, pg. 2647
DISTRIBUTOR SERVICE INC.; *U.S. Private*, pg. 1239
DISTRIBUTORS WAREHOUSE INC.; *U.S. Private*, pg. 1239
DISTRICON GMBH—See Oakley Capital Limited; *Int'l*, pg. 5504
DISTRICT COPPER CORP.; *Int'l*, pg. 2137
DISTRICT MEDICAL GROUP INC.; *U.S. Private*, pg. 1239
DISTRICT MINES LTD.; *Int'l*, pg. 2137
DISTRICT OF COLUMBIA PRIMARY CARE ASSOCIATION; *U.S. Private*, pg. 1239
DISTRICT PHOTO INC.; *U.S. Private*, pg. 1239
DISTRIGAS OF MASSACHUSETTS LLC—See ENGIE SA; *Int'l*, pg. 2428
DISTRIGAZ CONFORT SRL—See ENGIE SA; *Int'l*, pg. 2431
DISTRILABO S.A.S.—See Thermador Groupe; *Int'l*, pg. 7707
DISTRIMEDIA SERVICES B.V.—See RDA Holding Co.; *U.S. Private*, pg. 3363
DISTRIMONDO AG—See Bunzl plc; *Int'l*, pg. 1218
DISTRIPARK.COM SP. Z O.O.—See PCC SE; *Int'l*, pg. 5767
DISTRIPARK GMBH—See PCC SE; *Int'l*, pg. 5767
DISTRIPLAST SAS—See Beaulieu International Group NV; *Int'l*, pg. 934
DISTRI POND INVEST N.V.—See Kingspan Group PLC; *Int'l*, pg. 4178
DISTRISUD SA—See Vivendi SE; *Int'l*, pg. 8275
DISTRITO CASTELLANA NORTE, S.A.—See Banco Bilbao Vizcaya Argentaria, S.A.; *Int'l*, pg. 817

CORPORATE AFFILIATIONS

DISTRIVAL SA—See Carrefour SA; *Int'l*, pg. 1345
DISTRUPOL B.V.—See One Rock Capital Partners, LLC; *U.S. Private*, pg. 3022
DISTRUPOL IRELAND LIMITED—See One Rock Capital Partners, LLC; *U.S. Private*, pg. 3022
DISTRUPOL LIMITED—See One Rock Capital Partners, LLC; *U.S. Private*, pg. 3022
DISTRUPOL NORDIC AB—See One Rock Capital Partners, LLC; *U.S. Private*, pg. 3022
DISTTECH, LLC—See Ontario Municipal Employees Retirement System; *Int'l*, pg. 5584
D.I. SUPPLY INC.—See Drury Inn Inc.; *U.S. Private*, pg. 1280
DISWAY SA; *Int'l*, pg. 2137
DISYS TECHNOLOGIES LTD.—See Lindab International AB; *Int'l*, pg. 4503
D.I. SYSTEM CO., LTD.; *Int'l*, pg. 1900
DITAS DENIZ ISLETMECILIGI VE TANKERCILIGI A.S.—See Koc Holding A.S.; *Int'l*, pg. 4223
DITAS DOGAN YEDEK PARCA IMALAT VE TEKNIK A.S.; *Int'l*, pg. 2137
DITCH WITCH EQUIPMENT CO. INC.—See The Pape Group, Inc.; *U.S. Private*, pg. 4090
DITCH WITCH EQUIPMENT OF TENNESSE INC.; *U.S. Private*, pg. 1240
DITCH WITCH MINNESOTA INC.; *U.S. Private*, pg. 1240
DITCH WITCH OF HOUSTON—See Bluestem Equity, Ltd.; *U.S. Private*, pg. 598
DITCH WITCH OF SOUTH TEXAS—See Bluestem Equity, Ltd.; *U.S. Private*, pg. 598
DITCH WITCH SALES INC.; *U.S. Private*, pg. 1240
DIT CO., LTD.—See Future Corporation; *Int'l*, pg. 2853
DIT CORPORATION; *U.S. Private*, pg. 1240
DITEC D.D. LAZIO S.R.L.—See ASSA ABLOY AB; *Int'l*, pg. 639
DITEC D.D. LOMBARDIA S.R.L.—See ASSA ABLOY AB; *Int'l*, pg. 639
DITEC ENTREMATIC CANADA INC.—See ASSA ABLOY AB; *Int'l*, pg. 639
DITEC ENTREMATIC US INC—See ASSA ABLOY AB; *Int'l*, pg. 639
DITEC ESPANA S.L.U.—See ASSA ABLOY AB; *Int'l*, pg. 639
DITECH FINANCIAL LLC—See Rithm Capital Corp.; *U.S. Public*, pg. 1800
DITECH HOLDING CORPORATION; *U.S. Private*, pg. 1240
DITECH NETWORKS, INC.—See Microsoft Corporation; *U.S. Public*, pg. 1442
DI.TECH S.P.A.—See Sesa S.p.A.; *Int'l*, pg. 6728
DITECPESA, S.A.—See Ferrovial S.A.; *Int'l*, pg. 2644
DITEC S.P.A.—See ASSA ABLOY AB; *Int'l*, pg. 639
DITEC SWISS S.A.—See ASSA ABLOY AB; *Int'l*, pg. 639
DITEC TUR GMBH—See ASSA ABLOY AB; *Int'l*, pg. 639
DITEK CORPORATION; *U.S. Private*, pg. 1240
DITEMSA, S.A. DE C.V.; *Int'l*, pg. 2137
DIT GROUP LIMITED; *Int'l*, pg. 2137
DITMAS OIL ASSOCIATES INC.—See Gaseteria Oil Corp.; *U.S. Private*, pg. 1648
DIT-MCO INTERNATIONAL—See Commerce Bancshares, Inc.; *U.S. Public*, pg. 544
DITO, LLC; *U.S. Private*, pg. 1240
DITSCH USA LLC—See Fomento Economico Mexicano, S.A.B. de C.V.; *Int'l*, pg. 2724
DITTBORN & UNZUETA MRM—See The Interpublic Group of Companies, Inc.; *U.S. Public*, pg. 2098
DITT DISTRIKT AS—See Eniro Group AB; *Int'l*, pg. 2439
DITTMAR LUMBER CORP.; *U.S. Private*, pg. 1240
DITTOE PUBLIC RELATIONS, INC.; *U.S. Private*, pg. 1240
DITTO SALES INC.; *U.S. Private*, pg. 1240
DITULO OFFICE (PTY) LIMITED—See The Bidvest Group Limited; *Int'l*, pg. 7624
DIURNAL EUROPE B.V.—See Neurocrine Biosciences Inc.; *U.S. Public*, pg. 1510
DIURNAL GROUP PLC—See Neurocrine Biosciences Inc.; *U.S. Public*, pg. 1510
DIURNAL LIMITED—See IP Group plc; *Int'l*, pg. 3795
DIVA ACQUISITION CORP.—See Steven Madden, Ltd.; *U.S. Public*, pg. 1947
DIVABOX SAS—See Inter Parfums, Inc.; *U.S. Public*, pg. 1140
DIVA CORPORATION OF AMERICA—See Avant Corporation; *Int'l*, pg. 735
DIVA CORPORATION OF UK—See Avant Corporation; *Int'l*, pg. 735
DIVA LABORATORIES LTD.; *Int'l*, pg. 2137
DIVA LIMOUSINE LTD.; *U.S. Private*, pg. 1240
DIVALL INSURED INCOME PROPERTIES 2 LIMITED PARTNERSHIP; *U.S. Private*, pg. 1240
DIVAL SAFETY EQUIPMENT INC.; *U.S. Private*, pg. 1240
DIVAN AS—See Koc Holding A.S.; *Int'l*, pg. 4223
DIVANE BROS. ELECTRIC COMPANY; *U.S. Private*, pg. 1240
DIVAN TURIZM ISLETMELERI A.S.—See Koc Holding A.S.; *Int'l*, pg. 4223
DIVAR CHEMICALS, INC.; *U.S. Private*, pg. 1240
DIVA TRADE A.D.; *Int'l*, pg. 2137
DIVCO CONSTRUCTION CORP.; *U.S. Private*, pg. 1240

COMPANY NAME INDEX DIVERSIFIED DATA COMMUNICATIONS
Company Index

DIV DEUTSCHE IMMOBILIENFONDS GMBH—See Helaba Landesbank Hessen-Thuringen; *Int'l*, pg. 3327
DIVE N SURF; *U.S. Private*, pg. 1240
DIVERGENT ENERGY SERVICES CORP.; *Int'l*, pg. 2137
DIVERGER LIMITED—See Count Limited; *Int'l*, pg. 1817
DIVERSA FUNDS MANAGEMENT PTY LTD—See Sargon Capital Pty Ltd.; *Int'l*, pg. 6577
DIVERSANT, LLC; *U.S. Private*, pg. 1240
DIVERSAPACK, LLC—See Universal Packaging Systems, Inc.; *U.S. Private*, pg. 4306
DIVERSA PTY LTD—See Sargon Capital Pty Ltd.; *Int'l*, pg. 6577
DIVERSCO INC.—See ABM Industries, Inc.; *U.S. Public*, pg. 26
DIVERSCO SUPPLY INC.; *Int'l*, pg. 2137
DIVERSE COMPUTER MARKETERS, INC.—See SB Financial Group, Inc.; *U.S. Public*, pg. 1842
DIVERSE DEVELOPMENT GROUP, INC.; *U.S. Private*, pg. 1240
DIVERSE ENERGY SYSTEMS LLC—See Turnbridge Capital, LLC; *U.S. Private*, pg. 4260
DIVERSEID PRODUCTS OF FLORIDA LLC; *U.S. Private*, pg. 1241
THE DIVERSE INCOME TRUST PLC; *Int'l*, pg. 7636
DIVERSE LABELLING CONSULTANTS (PTY) LTD—See Berry Global Group, Inc; *U.S. Public*, pg. 324
DIVERSE LYNX, LLC; *U.S. Private*, pg. 1240
DIVERSE OPTICS, INC.; *U.S. Private*, pg. 1241
DIVERSE SOLUTIONS, INC.—See Zillow Group, Inc.; *U.S. Public*, pg. 2405
DIVERSE SUPPLY CHAIN SDN. BHD.—See 9R Limited; *Int'l*, pg. 17
DIVERSE SUPPLY CHAIN (SG) PTE. LTD.—See 9R Limited; *Int'l*, pg. 17
DIVERSEY ACTING OFF-SHORE CAPITAL MANAGEMENT LIMITED LIABILITY COMPANY—See Sealed Air Corporation; *U.S. Public*, pg. 1852
DIVERSEY AUSTRIA TRADING GMBH—See Platinum Equity, LLC; *U.S. Private*, pg. 3204
DIVERSEY BELGIUM BVBA—See Platinum Equity, LLC; *U.S. Private*, pg. 3204
DIVERSEY BRASIL INDUSTRIA QUIMICA LTDA.—See Sealed Air Corporation; *U.S. Public*, pg. 1852
DIVERSEY B.V.—See Platinum Equity, LLC; *U.S. Private*, pg. 3204
DIVERSEY CANADA, INC.—See Platinum Equity, LLC; *U.S. Private*, pg. 3204
DIVERSEY CARE—See Platinum Equity, LLC; *U.S. Private*, pg. 3204
DIVERSEY CESKA REPUBLIKA S.R.O.—See Platinum Equity, LLC; *U.S. Private*, pg. 3204
DIVERSEY DANMARK APS—See Sealed Air Corporation; *U.S. Public*, pg. 1852
DIVERSEY DE ARGENTINA S.A.—See Platinum Equity, LLC; *U.S. Private*, pg. 3204
DIVERSEY DEUTSCHLAND GMBH & CO. OHG—See Platinum Equity, LLC; *U.S. Private*, pg. 3204
DIVERSEY EASTERN & CENTRAL AFRICA LIMITED—See Platinum Equity, LLC; *U.S. Private*, pg. 3204
DIVERSEY EGYPT LIMITED—See Sealed Air Corporation; *U.S. Public*, pg. 1852
DIVERSEY ESPANA PRODUCTION, S.L.—See Sealed Air Corporation; *U.S. Public*, pg. 1852
DIVERSEY ESPANA, S.L.—See Platinum Equity, LLC; *U.S. Private*, pg. 3204
DIVERSEY EUROPE B.V.—See Platinum Equity, LLC; *U.S. Private*, pg. 3204
DIVERSEY (FRANCE) S.A.S.—See Platinum Equity, LLC; *U.S. Private*, pg. 3204
DIVERSEY FRANCE SERVICES S.A.S.—See Sealed Air Corporation; *U.S. Public*, pg. 1852
DIVERSEY GERMANY PRODUCTION OHG—See Sealed Air Corporation; *U.S. Public*, pg. 1852
DIVERSEY HELLAS SOCIETE ANONYME CLEANING AND TRADING SYSTEMS—See Sealed Air Corporation; *U.S. Public*, pg. 1852
DIVERSEY HOLDINGS, LTD.—See Platinum Equity, LLC; *U.S. Private*, pg. 3204
DIVERSEY HONG KONG LIMITED—See Platinum Equity, LLC; *U.S. Private*, pg. 3204
DIVERSEY HUNGARY MANUFACTURE AND TRADE LIMITED LIABILITY COMPANY—See Sealed Air Corporation; *U.S. Public*, pg. 1852
DIVERSEY HYGIENE (TAIWAN) LTD.—See Platinum Equity, LLC; *U.S. Private*, pg. 3204
DIVERSEY HYGIENE (THAILAND) CO., LTD.—See Sealed Air Corporation; *U.S. Public*, pg. 1852
DIVERSEY, INC.—See Platinum Equity, LLC; *U.S. Private*, pg. 3204
DIVERSEY INDIA PRIVATE LIMITED—See Sealed Air Corporation; *U.S. Public*, pg. 1852
DIVERSEY ISRAEL LTD.—See Sealed Air Corporation; *U.S. Public*, pg. 1852
DIVERSEY ITALY PRODUCTION S.R.L.—See Sealed Air Corporation; *U.S. Public*, pg. 1852
DIVERSEY JAMAICA LIMITED—See Sealed Air Corporation; *U.S. Public*, pg. 1852
DIVERSEY KIMYA SANAYI VE TICARET A.S.—See Sealed Air Corporation; *U.S. Public*, pg. 1852
DIVERSEY KOREA CO., LTD.—See Platinum Equity, LLC; *U.S. Private*, pg. 3204
DIVERSEY LIMITED—See Platinum Equity, LLC; *U.S. Private*, pg. 3204
DIVERSEY LLC—See Sealed Air Corporation; *U.S. Public*, pg. 1853
DIVERSEY (MALAYSIA) SDN. BHD.—See Sealed Air Corporation; *U.S. Public*, pg. 1852
DIVERSEY MAROC S.A.—See Sealed Air Corporation; *U.S. Public*, pg. 1853
DIVERSEY NETHERLANDS PRODUCTION B.V.—See Sealed Air Corporation; *U.S. Public*, pg. 1853
DIVERSEY NEW ZEALAND LIMITED—See Sealed Air Corporation; *U.S. Public*, pg. 1853
DIVERSEY PERU S.A.C.—See Sealed Air Corporation; *U.S. Public*, pg. 1853
DIVERSEY PHILIPPINES, INC.—See Sealed Air Corporation; *U.S. Public*, pg. 1853
DIVERSEY POLSKA SP. Z O.O.—See Platinum Equity, LLC; *U.S. Private*, pg. 3204
DIVERSEY PORTUGAL - SISTEMAS DE HIGIENE E LIMPEZA, UNIPESSOAL, LDA.—See Sealed Air Corporation; *U.S. Public*, pg. 1853
DIVERSEY (PRIVATE) LIMITED—See Sealed Air Corporation; *U.S. Public*, pg. 1852
DIVERSEY ROMANIA S.R.L.—See Sealed Air Corporation; *U.S. Public*, pg. 1853
DIVERSEY SINGAPORE PTY. LTD.—See Sealed Air Corporation; *U.S. Public*, pg. 1853
DIVERSEY SLOVAKIA, S.R.O.—See Sealed Air Corporation; *U.S. Public*, pg. 1853
DIVERSEY SOUTH AFRICA (PTY.) LTD.—See Sealed Air Corporation; *U.S. Public*, pg. 1853
DIVERSEY S.R.L.—See Platinum Equity, LLC; *U.S. Private*, pg. 3204
DIVERSEY SUOMI OY—See Sealed Air Corporation; *U.S. Public*, pg. 1853
DIVERSEY SVERIGE AB—See Sealed Air Corporation; *U.S. Public*, pg. 1853
DIVERSEY SWEDEN SERVICES AB—See Sealed Air Corporation; *U.S. Public*, pg. 1853
DIVERSEY SWITZERLAND PRODUCTION GMBH—See Sealed Air Corporation; *U.S. Public*, pg. 1853
DIVERSEY TRADING (SHANGHAI) CO., LTD.—See Platinum Equity, LLC; *U.S. Private*, pg. 3204
DIVERSICARE AFTON OAKS, LLC—See Diversicare Healthcare Services, Inc.; *U.S. Public*, pg. 669
DIVERSICARE BRIARCLIFF, LLC—See Diversicare Healthcare Services, Inc.; *U.S. Public*, pg. 669
DIVERSICARE CLINTON, LLC—See Diversicare Healthcare Services, Inc.; *U.S. Public*, pg. 669
DIVERSICARE ESTATES, LLC—See Diversicare Healthcare Services, Inc.; *U.S. Public*, pg. 669
DIVERSICARE HARTFORD, LLC—See Diversicare Healthcare Services, Inc.; *U.S. Public*, pg. 669
DIVERSICARE HEALTHCARE SERVICES, INC.; *U.S. Public*, pg. 669
DIVERSICARE HILLCREST, LLC—See Diversicare Healthcare Services, Inc.; *U.S. Public*, pg. 669
DIVERSICARE HUMBLE, LLC—See Diversicare Healthcare Services, Inc.; *U.S. Public*, pg. 669
DIVERSICARE KATY, LLC—See Diversicare Healthcare Services, Inc.; *U.S. Public*, pg. 669
DIVERSICARE LEASING CORP.—See Diversicare Healthcare Services, Inc.; *U.S. Public*, pg. 669
DIVERSICARE MANAGEMENT SERVICES CO.—See Diversicare Healthcare Services, Inc.; *U.S. Public*, pg. 669
DIVERSICARE NORMANDY TERRACE, LLC—See Diversicare Healthcare Services, Inc.; *U.S. Public*, pg. 669
DIVERSICARE OF ARAB, LLC—See Diversicare Healthcare Services, Inc.; *U.S. Public*, pg. 669
DIVERSICARE OF BATESVILLE, LLC—See Diversicare Healthcare Services, Inc.; *U.S. Public*, pg. 669
DIVERSICARE OF BESSEMER, LLC—See Diversicare Healthcare Services, Inc.; *U.S. Public*, pg. 669
DIVERSICARE OF BIG SPRINGS, LLC—See Diversicare Healthcare Services, Inc.; *U.S. Public*, pg. 669
DIVERSICARE OF BOAZ, LLC—See Diversicare Healthcare Services, Inc.; *U.S. Public*, pg. 669
DIVERSICARE OF BRADFORD PLACE, LLC—See Diversicare Healthcare Services, Inc.; *U.S. Public*, pg. 669
DIVERSICARE OF BROOKHAVEN, LLC—See Diversicare Healthcare Services, Inc.; *U.S. Public*, pg. 669
DIVERSICARE OF CHANUTE, LLC—See Diversicare Healthcare Services, Inc.; *U.S. Public*, pg. 669
DIVERSICARE OF CHATEAU, LLC—See Diversicare Healthcare Services, Inc.; *U.S. Public*, pg. 669
DIVERSICARE OF COUNCIL GROVE, LLC—See Diversicare Healthcare Services, Inc.; *U.S. Public*, pg. 669
DIVERSICARE OF EUPORA, LLC—See Diversicare Healthcare Services, Inc.; *U.S. Public*, pg. 669
DIVERSICARE OF FOLEY, LLC—See Diversicare Healthcare Services, Inc.; *U.S. Public*, pg. 669
DIVERSICARE OF HAYSVILLE, LLC—See Diversicare Healthcare Services, Inc.; *U.S. Public*, pg. 669
DIVERSICARE OF HUEYTOWN, LLC—See Diversicare Healthcare Services, Inc.; *U.S. Public*, pg. 669
DIVERSICARE OF HUTCHINSON, LLC—See Diversicare Healthcare Services, Inc.; *U.S. Public*, pg. 669
DIVERSICARE OF LANETT, LLC—See Diversicare Healthcare Services, Inc.; *U.S. Public*, pg. 669
DIVERSICARE OF LARNED, LLC—See Diversicare Healthcare Services, Inc.; *U.S. Public*, pg. 669
DIVERSICARE OF MANSFIELD, LLC—See Diversicare Healthcare Services, Inc.; *U.S. Public*, pg. 669
DIVERSICARE OF MERIDIAN, LLC—See Diversicare Healthcare Services, Inc.; *U.S. Public*, pg. 669
DIVERSICARE OF MONTGOMERY, LLC—See Diversicare Healthcare Services, Inc.; *U.S. Public*, pg. 669
DIVERSICARE OF NICHOLASVILLE, LLC—See Diversicare Healthcare Services, Inc.; *U.S. Public*, pg. 669
DIVERSICARE OF ONEONTA, LLC—See Diversicare Healthcare Services, Inc.; *U.S. Public*, pg. 669
DIVERSICARE OF OXFORD, LLC—See Diversicare Healthcare Services, Inc.; *U.S. Public*, pg. 669
DIVERSICARE OF PELL CITY, LLC—See Diversicare Healthcare Services, Inc.; *U.S. Public*, pg. 669
DIVERSICARE OF PROVIDENCE, LLC—See Diversicare Healthcare Services, Inc.; *U.S. Public*, pg. 669
DIVERSICARE OF RIPLEY, LLC—See Diversicare Healthcare Services, Inc.; *U.S. Public*, pg. 670
DIVERSICARE OF RIVERCHASE, LLC—See Diversicare Healthcare Services, Inc.; *U.S. Public*, pg. 670
DIVERSICARE OF RIVERSIDE, LLC—See Diversicare Healthcare Services, Inc.; *U.S. Public*, pg. 670
DIVERSICARE OF SEDGWICK, LLC—See Diversicare Healthcare Services, Inc.; *U.S. Public*, pg. 670
DIVERSICARE OF SELMA, LLC—See Diversicare Healthcare Services, Inc.; *U.S. Public*, pg. 670
DIVERSICARE OF SENECA PLACE, LLC—See Diversicare Healthcare Services, Inc.; *U.S. Public*, pg. 670
DIVERSICARE OF SIENA WOODS, LLC—See Diversicare Healthcare Services, Inc.; *U.S. Public*, pg. 670
DIVERSICARE OF ST. JOSEPH, LLC—See Diversicare Healthcare Services, Inc.; *U.S. Public*, pg. 670
DIVERSICARE OF ST. THERESA, LLC—See Diversicare Healthcare Services, Inc.; *U.S. Public*, pg. 670
DIVERSICARE OF TUPELO, LLC—See Diversicare Healthcare Services, Inc.; *U.S. Public*, pg. 670
DIVERSICARE OF TYLERTOWN, LLC—See Diversicare Healthcare Services, Inc.; *U.S. Public*, pg. 670
DIVERSICARE OF WINFIELD, LLC—See Diversicare Healthcare Services, Inc.; *U.S. Public*, pg. 670
DIVERSICARE THERAPY SERVICES, LLC—See Diversicare Healthcare Services, Inc.; *U.S. Public*, pg. 669
DIVERSICARE TREEMONT, LLC—See Diversicare Healthcare Services, Inc.; *U.S. Public*, pg. 669
DIVERSICARE WINDSOR HOUSE, LLC—See Diversicare Healthcare Services, Inc.; *U.S. Public*, pg. 669
DIVERSICARE YORKTOWN, LLC—See Diversicare Healthcare Services, Inc.; *U.S. Public*, pg. 669
DIVERSIFIED AERO SERVICES, INC.; *U.S. Private*, pg. 1241
DIVERSIFIED AIR SYSTEMS INC.; *U.S. Private*, pg. 1241
DIVERSIFIED AUTOMATION, INC.—See Triton Advisers Limited; *Int'l*, pg. 7933
DIVERSIFIED AUTOMOTIVE INC.; *U.S. Private*, pg. 1241
DIVERSIFIED BUSINESS COMMUNICATIONS CANADA—See Diversified Communications; *U.S. Private*, pg. 1241
DIVERSIFIED BUSINESS COMMUNICATIONS—See Diversified Communications; *U.S. Private*, pg. 1241
DIVERSIFIED BUSINESS COMMUNICATIONS UK—See Diversified Communications; *U.S. Private*, pg. 1241
DIVERSIFIED CABINET DISTRIBUTORS—See Masco Corporation; *U.S. Public*, pg. 1390
DIVERSIFIED CAPITAL CREDIT CORP.; *U.S. Private*, pg. 1241
DIVERSIFIED CHEMICAL TECHNOLOGIES INC.; *U.S. Private*, pg. 1241
DIVERSIFIED CHEMICAL TECHNOLOGIES OPERATING COMPANY INC.—See Diversified Chemical Technologies Inc.; *U.S. Private*, pg. 1241
DIVERSIFIED CLINICAL SERVICES, INC.; *U.S. Private*, pg. 1241
DIVERSIFIED COATINGS INC.; *U.S. Private*, pg. 1241
DIVERSIFIED COMMUNICATIONS INDIA—See Diversified Communications; *U.S. Private*, pg. 1241
DIVERSIFIED COMMUNICATIONS; *U.S. Private*, pg. 1241
DIVERSIFIED COMPUTER SUPPLIES; *U.S. Private*, pg. 1241
DIVERSIFIED CONTRACTORS, INC.—See Prysmian S.p.A.; *Int'l*, pg. 6011
DIVERSIFIED CONTROLS & SYSTEMS, INC.; *U.S. Private*, pg. 1241
DIVERSIFIED CPC INTERNATIONAL, INC.—See Sumitomo Corporation; *Int'l*, pg. 7273
DIVERSIFIED DATA COMMUNICATIONS; *U.S. Private*, pg. 1242
DIVERSIFIED DENTAL SERVICES INC—See Principal Financial Group, Inc.; *U.S. Public*, pg. 1720
DIVERSIFIED DESIGN INC.—See Beers & Hoffman, Ltd.; *U.S. Private*, pg. 514

DIVERSIFIED DATA COMMUNICATIONS
CORPORATE AFFILIATIONS

DIVERSIFIED DISTRIBUTION SYSTEMS, LLC—See Bunzl plc; *Int'l*, pg. 1218
DIVERSIFIED DYNAMICS CORPORATION; *U.S. Private*, pg. 1242
DIVERSIFIED ELECTRONICS INC.; *U.S. Private*, pg. 1242
DIVERSIFIED ENERGY COMPANY PLC; *U.S. Public*, pg. 670
DIVERSIFIED ENERGY HOLDINGS, INC.; *U.S. Public*, pg. 670
DIVERSIFIED EVENTS HONG KONG—See Diversified Communications; *U.S. Private*, pg. 1241
DIVERSIFIED EXECUTIVE SYSTEMS, INC.; *U.S. Private*, pg. 1242
DIVERSIFIED EXHIBITIONS AUSTRALIA—See Diversified Communications; *U.S. Private*, pg. 1241
DIVERSIFIED FASTENING SYSTEMS; *U.S. Private*, pg. 1242
DIVERSIFIED FOOD & SEASONING INC.; *U.S. Private*, pg. 1242
DIVERSIFIED FOODSERVICE SUPPLY, INC.—See New Mountain Capital, LLC; *U.S. Private*, pg. 2901
DIVERSIFIED FREIGHT SYSTEM CORPORATION—See Dimerco Express Corporation; *Int'l*, pg. 2126
DIVERSIFIED FREIGHT SYSTEM PHILIPPINES CORPORATION—See Dimerco Express Corporation; *Int'l*, pg. 2126
DIVERSIFIED GAS & OIL CORPORATION—See Diversified Energy Company PLC; *U.S. Public*, pg. 670
DIVERSIFIED GLASS SERVICES; *U.S. Private*, pg. 1242
DIVERSIFIED GLOBAL GRAPHICS GROUP, LLC; *U.S. Private*, pg. 1242
DIVERSIFIED GROUP LLC; *U.S. Private*, pg. 1242
DIVERSIFIED HEALTH CARE MANAGEMENT, INC.—See ModuleMD LLC; *U.S. Private*, pg. 2764
DIVERSIFIED HEALTHCARE TRUST; *U.S. Public*, pg. 670
DIVERSIFIED HUMAN RESOURCES, INC.—See Paychex, Inc.; *U.S. Public*, pg. 1655
DIVERSIFIED INDUSTRIAL STAFFING; *U.S. Private*, pg. 1242
DIVERSIFIED INSURANCE SOLUTIONS, INC.; *U.S. Private*, pg. 1242
DIVERSIFIED INTERIORS OF EL PASO INC.; *U.S. Private*, pg. 1242
DIVERSIFIED INTERNATIONAL LOGISTICS PTE. LTD.—See Dimerco Express Corporation; *Int'l*, pg. 2126
DIVERSIFIED INTERNATIONAL SCIENCES CORPORATION; *U.S. Private*, pg. 1242
DIVERSIFIED LABELING SOLUTIONS, INC.; *U.S. Private*, pg. 1243
DIVERSIFIED LIGHTING ASSOCIATES INC.; *U.S. Private*, pg. 1243
DIVERSIFIED MAINTENANCE SYSTEMS, LLC; *U.S. Private*, pg. 1243
DIVERSIFIED MANUFACTURING CORPORATION—See San Francisco Equity Partners; *U.S. Private*, pg. 3540
DIVERSIFIED MARKETING GROUP, INC.; *U.S. Private*, pg. 1243
DIVERSIFIED MEDICAL STAFFING, LLC; *U.S. Private*, pg. 1243
DIVERSIFIED MEMBERS CREDIT UNION; *U.S. Private*, pg. 1243
DIVERSIFIED MILLWORK INC.—See Palo Duro Hardwoods Inc.; *U.S. Private*, pg. 3082
DIVERSIFIED MORTGAGE, INC.; *U.S. Private*, pg. 1243
DIVERSIFIED OIL & GAS HOLDINGS, LTD.; *U.S. Public*, pg. 670
DIVERSIFIED PARATRANSIT INC.; *U.S. Private*, pg. 1243
DIVERSIFIED PLASTICS CORPORATION; *U.S. Private*, pg. 1243
DIVERSIFIED PRODUCTION SERVICES, LLC—See Live Nation Entertainment, Inc.; *U.S. Public*, pg. 1328
DIVERSIFIED PROJECT MANAGEMENT, INC.—See STV Group, Inc.; *U.S. Private*, pg. 3845
DIVERSIFIED PROPERTY FUND LTD—See Resilient REIT Limited; *Int'l*, pg. 6296
DIVERSIFIED PROTECTION SYSTEMS INC.—See GTCR LLC; *U.S. Private*, pg. 1802
DIVERSIFIED RESTAURANT HOLDINGS, INC.—See ICV Partners, LLC; *U.S. Private*, pg. 2034
DIVERSIFIED ROYALTY CORP.; *Int'l*, pg. 2137
DIVERSIFIED SCIENTIFIC SERVICES, INC.—See Perma-Fix Environmental Services, Inc.; *U.S. Public*, pg. 1676
DIVERSIFIED SEARCH, LLC; *U.S. Private*, pg. 1243
DIVERSIFIED SECURITY SOLUTIONS, INC.—See Kratos Defense & Security Solutions, Inc.; *U.S. Public*, pg. 1276
DIVERSIFIED SERVICE OPTIONS INC.—See GuideWell Mutual Holding Corporation; *U.S. Private*, pg. 1813
DIVERSIFIED SILICONE PRODUCTS, INC.—See Rogers Corporation; *U.S. Public*, pg. 1808
DIVERSIFIED SPECIALTIES, INC.; *U.S. Private*, pg. 1243
DIVERSIFIED SUPPLY INC.; *U.S. Private*, pg. 1243
DIVERSIFIED TECHNICAL SYSTEMS, INC.—See Vishay Precision Group, Inc.; *U.S. Public*, pg. 2303
DIVERSIFIED TECHNOLOGY CONSULTANTS, INC.; *U.S. Private*, pg. 1243

DIVERSIFIED TECHNOLOGY INC.—See Ergon, Inc.; *U.S. Private*, pg. 1417
DIVERSIFIED TECHNOLOGY SOLUTIONS INTERNATIONAL, INC.—See Nippon Telegraph & Telephone Corporation; *Int'l*, pg. 5344
DIVERSIFIED TECHNOLOGY SOLUTIONS INTERNATIONAL, INC.—See Nippon Telegraph & Telephone Corporation; *Int'l*, pg. 5344
DIVERSIFIED ULBRICH OF CANADA—See Ulbrich Stainless Steel & Special Metals, Inc.; *U.S. Private*, pg. 4275
DIVERSIFIED ULBRICH OF CANADA—See Ulbrich Stainless Steel & Special Metals, Inc.; *U.S. Private*, pg. 4275
DIVERSIFIED UNITED INVESTMENT LIMITED; *Int'l*, pg. 2137
DIVERSIFIED UTILITY SERVICES, INC.; *U.S. Private*, pg. 1243
DIVERSIFIED WOODCRAFTS, INC.—See JBC Holding Co.; *U.S. Private*, pg. 2193
DIVERSIS CAPITAL, LLC; *U.S. Private*, pg. 1244
DIVERSITAK, INC.—See Diversified Chemical Technologies, Inc.; *U.S. Private*, pg. 1241
DIVERSITECH CORPORATION—See Partners Group Holding AG; *Int'l*, pg. 5749
DIVERSITECH EQUIPMENT & SALES (1984) LTD.—See Absolent Air Care Group AB; *Int'l*, pg. 70
DIVERTCO USA INC.—See Divestco Inc.; *Int'l*, pg. 2137
DIVERZIFY—See ACON Investments, LLC; *U.S. Private*, pg. 62
THE DIVE SHOP, INC.; *U.S. Private*, pg. 4021
DIVESTCO INC.; *Int'l*, pg. 2137
DIVFEX BERHAD—See Insas Berhad; *Int'l*, pg. 3718
DIVGI TORQTRANSFER SYSTEMS—See BorgWarner Inc.; *U.S. Public*, pg. 370
DIV GRUPA DOO; *Int'l*, pg. 2137
DIVI ARUBA BEACH RESORT; *Int'l*, pg. 2137
DIVID AB—See Systemair AB; *Int'l*, pg. 7391
DIVIDE DRIVES, INC.; *U.S. Public*, pg. 670
DIVIDELLA AG—See Korber AG; *Int'l*, pg. 4280
DIVIDEND 15 SPLIT CORP. II—See Quadravest Capital Management Inc.; *Int'l*, pg. 6149
DIVIDEND 15 SPLIT CORP.—See Quadravest Capital Management Inc.; *Int'l*, pg. 6149
DIVIDEND CAPITAL ADVISORS LLC—See Prologis, Inc.; *U.S. Public*, pg. 1726
DIVIDEND GROWTH SPLIT CORP.—See Brompton Funds Limited; *Int'l*, pg. 1173
DIVIDEND & INCOME FUND; *U.S. Public*, pg. 670
DIVIDEND SELECT 15 CORP.—See Quadravest Capital Management Inc.; *Int'l*, pg. 6149
DIVIDEND SWEDEN AB; *Int'l*, pg. 2137
DIVIDUM OY—See CapMan PLC; *Int'l*, pg. 1315
DIVIHN INTEGRATION INC.; *U.S. Private*, pg. 1244
DIVI HOTELS, INC.; *U.S. Private*, pg. 1244
DIVIMOVE GMBH—See Bertelsmann SE & Co. KGaA; *Int'l*, pg. 994
DIVINE CORPORATION; *U.S. Private*, pg. 1244
DIVINUS FABRICS LIMITED; *Int'l*, pg. 2137
DIVIRGILIO INSURANCE & FINANCIAL GROUP; *U.S. Private*, pg. 1244
DIVISAO TURBINAS SOLAR S.A. DE C.V.—See Caterpillar, Inc.; *U.S. Public*, pg. 453
DIVISION 5 LLC—See Rodgers Metal Craft, Inc.; *U.S. Private*, pg. 3470
DIVISION EQUIPEMENTS DASSAULT (DED)—See Groupe Industriel Marcel Dassault S.A.; *Int'l*, pg. 3105
DIVISIONS, INC.—See Roark Capital Group Inc.; *U.S. Private*, pg. 3454
THE DIVISION—See The Interpublic Group of Companies, Inc.; *U.S. Public*, pg. 2102
DIVI'S LABORATORIES EUROPE AG—See Divis Laboratories Limited; *Int'l*, pg. 2138
DIVIS LABORATORIES LIMITED; *Int'l*, pg. 2137
DIVIS LABORATORIES (USA) INC.—See Divis Laboratories Limited; *Int'l*, pg. 2138
DIVISO GRUPO FINANCIERO S.A.; *Int'l*, pg. 2138
DIVOSTA BUILDING, LLC—See PulteGroup, Inc.; *U.S. Public*, pg. 1737
DIV SERVICES SDN. BHD.—See Dialog Group Berhad; *Int'l*, pg. 2104
DIVURGENT; *U.S. Private*, pg. 1244
DIVVYPAY, LLC—See BILL HOLDINGS, INC.; *U.S. Public*, pg. 331
DIVX, LLC—See SoftBank Group Corp.; *Int'l*, pg. 7052
DIVYASHAKTI LIMITED; *Int'l*, pg. 2138
DIWANG INDUSTRIAL HOLDINGS LIMITED; *Int'l*, pg. 2138
DIW INSTANDHALTUNG GMBH—See STRABAG SE; *Int'l*, pg. 7230
DIW INSTANDHALTUNG GMBH—See STRABAG SE; *Int'l*, pg. 7230
DIX 1898, INC; *U.S. Private*, pg. 1244
DIX & EATON INCORPORATED; *U.S. Private*, pg. 1244
DIXID—See Alten S.A.; *Int'l*, pg. 390
DIXIE BEDDING CORPORATION; *U.S. Private*, pg. 1244
DIXIE BRANDS, INC.; *U.S. Private*, pg. 1244
DIXIE BUICK GMC TRUCK INC.; *U.S. Private*, pg. 1244

DIXIE CARPET INSTALLATIONS INC.—See The Sterling Group, L.P.; *U.S. Private*, pg. 4122
DIXIE CHEMICAL COMPANY, INC.—See DX Holding Company Inc.; *U.S. Private*, pg. 1296
DIXIE CONSTRUCTION PRODUCTS INC.; *U.S. Private*, pg. 1245
DIXIE CONSUMER PRODUCTS LLC—See Koch Industries, Inc.; *U.S. Private*, pg. 2327
DIXIE DIAMOND MANUFACTURING, INC.; *U.S. Private*, pg. 1245
DIXIE DYE & CHEMICAL INC.—See Exact Color Systems, LLC; *U.S. Private*, pg. 1445
DIXIE ELECTRIC COOPERATIVE; *U.S. Private*, pg. 1245
DIXIE ELECTRIC, INC.—See Motorcar Parts of America, Inc.; *U.S. Public*, pg. 1477
DIXIE ELECTRIC LLC—See First Reserve Management, L.P.; *U.S. Private*, pg. 1525
DIXIE ELECTRIC LTD.—See Motorcar Parts of America, Inc.; *U.S. Public*, pg. 1477
DIXIE ELECTRIC MEMBERSHIP CORP.; *U.S. Private*, pg. 1245
DIXIE ELECTRIC POWER ASSOCIATION; *U.S. Private*, pg. 1245
DIXIE ESCALANTE RURAL ELECTRIC ASSOCIATION, INC.; *U.S. Private*, pg. 1245
DIXIE GAS & OIL CORPORATION; *U.S. Private*, pg. 1245
DIXIE GOLD INC.; *Int'l*, pg. 2138
THE DIXIE GROUP, INC.; *U.S. Public*, pg. 2067
DIXIE HEALTH, INC.; *U.S. Private*, pg. 1245
DIXIE HOMECRAFTERS INC.; *U.S. Private*, pg. 1245
DIXIELAND PRODUCE INC.; *U.S. Private*, pg. 1245
DIXIE LANDSCAPE CO. INC.; *U.S. Private*, pg. 1245
DIXIELINE BUILDERS FUND CONTROL, INC.—See Builders FirstSource, Inc.; *U.S. Public*, pg. 410
DIXIELINE LUMBER & HOME CENTERS—See Builders FirstSource, Inc.; *U.S. Public*, pg. 410
DIXIE MACHINE & FABRICATING CO.—See Dallas Industries, Inc.; *U.S. Private*, pg. 1149
DIXIE MEDICAL INC.; *U.S. Private*, pg. 1245
DIXIE METAL PRODUCTS INC.; *U.S. Private*, pg. 1245
DIXIE MOTORS, INC.; *U.S. Private*, pg. 1245
DIXIE NUMERICS LLC; *U.S. Private*, pg. 1245
DIXIE OIL COMPANY; *U.S. Private*, pg. 1245
DIXIE PACIFIC MANUFACTURING CO.—See Ingersoll Rand Inc.; *U.S. Public*, pg. 1120
DIXIE PAPER COMPANY; *U.S. Private*, pg. 1245
DIXIE PIPELINE COMPANY LLC—See Enterprise Products Partners L.P.; *U.S. Public*, pg. 778
DIXIE PIPE SALES, LP; *U.S. Public*, pg. 1245
DIXIE PLYWOOD AND LUMBER COMPANY; *U.S. Private*, pg. 1245
DIXIE POLY DRUM CORPORATION; *U.S. Private*, pg. 1245
DIXIE PRINTING & PACKAGING, LLC—See Kollman Label Group, LLC; *U.S. Private*, pg. 2341
DIXIE REEL & BOX CO.—See Lone Star Corrugated Container Corporation; *U.S. Private*, pg. 2484
DIXIE RESTAURANTS INC.; *U.S. Private*, pg. 1245
DIXIE RV SUPERSTORE; *U.S. Private*, pg. 1245
DIXIE SALES COMPANY INC.; *U.S. Private*, pg. 1245
DIXIE STAMPEDE LP; *U.S. Private*, pg. 1245
DIXIE TOGA SA—See Amcor plc; *U.S. Public*, pg. 418
DIXIE WHITE HOUSE NURSING HOME, LLC—See Omega Healthcare Investors, Inc.; *U.S. Public*, pg. 1571
DIXON BROS. INC.; *U.S. Private*, pg. 1245
DIXON BROTHERS INC.; *U.S. Private*, pg. 1245
DIXON ELECTRIC LTD.—See Sonepar S.A.; *Int'l*, pg. 7091
DIXON EUROPE, LTD.—See F.I.L.A. - Fabbrica Italiana Lapis ed Affini S.p.A.; *Int'l*, pg. 2596
DIXON FISHERIES INC.; *U.S. Private*, pg. 1246
DIXON GROUP CANADA LIMITED—See Dixon Valve & Coupling Company; *U.S. Private*, pg. 1246
DIXON GROUP EUROPE LTD—See Dixon Valve & Coupling Company; *U.S. Private*, pg. 1246
DIXON HEALTH CARE CENTER—See Omega Healthcare Investors, Inc.; *U.S. Public*, pg. 1571
DIXON HOMES—See TAMAWOOD LIMITED; *Int'l*, pg. 7449
DIXON, HUBARD, FEINOUR & BROWN, INC.—See Atlantic Union Bankshares Corporation; *U.S. Public*, pg. 223
DIXON MIDLAND LIGHTING CO.; *U.S. Private*, pg. 1246
DIXON NETWORKS CORPORATION; *Int'l*, pg. 2138
DIXON PUMPS, INC.—See Madison Dearborn Partners, LLC; *U.S. Private*, pg. 2542
DIXON, R B HOLDINGS LTD.; *Int'l*, pg. 2138
DIXON RIVER APARTMENTS, L.P.—See Apartment Investment and Management Company; *U.S. Public*, pg. 144
DIXONS B.V.—See KKR & Co. Inc.; *U.S. Public*, pg. 1261
DIXONS CARPHONE COE S.R.O.—See Currys plc; *Int'l*, pg. 1879
DIXON SCHWABL ADVERTISING; *U.S. Private*, pg. 1246
DIXON SCHWABL INC.; *U.S. Private*, pg. 1246
DIXONS DEUTSCHLAND GMBH—See Currys plc; *Int'l*, pg. 1879
DIXON-SHANE LLC—See Amneal Pharmaceuticals, Inc.; *U.S. Public*, pg. 125

COMPANY NAME INDEX

DIXONS OF WESTERHOPE—See Air Products & Chemicals, Inc.; *U.S. Public*, pg. 66
DIXON STATIONERY COMPANY LTD.—See F.I.L.A. - Fabbrica Italiana Lapis ed Affini S.p.A.; *Int'l*, pg. 2596
DIXON SYSTEMS PTY LTD—See TAMAWOOD LIMITED; *Int'l*, pg. 7449
DIXON TECHNOLOGIES (INDIA) LIMITED; *Int'l*, pg. 2138
DIXON TICONDEROGA ART ULC—See F.I.L.A. - Fabbrica Italiana Lapis ed Affini S.p.A.; *Int'l*, pg. 2596
DIXON TICONDEROGA COMPANY—See F.I.L.A. - Fabbrica Italiana Lapis ed Affini S.p.A.; *Int'l*, pg. 2596
DIXON TICONDEROGA DE MEXICO, S.A. DE C.V.—See F.I.L.A. - Fabbrica Italiana Lapis ed Affini S.p.A.; *Int'l*, pg. 2596
DIXON TICONDEROGA INC.—See F.I.L.A. - Fabbrica Italiana Lapis ed Affini S.p.A.; *Int'l*, pg. 2596
DIXON VALVE & COUPLING COMPANY - DIXON BRASS DIVISION—See Dixon Valve & Coupling Company; *U.S. Private*, pg. 1246
DIXON VALVE & COUPLING COMPANY - DIXON POWHATAN DIVISION—See Dixon Valve & Coupling Company; *U.S. Private*, pg. 1246
DIXON VALVE & COUPLING COMPANY - DIXON QUICK COUPLING DIVISION—See Dixon Valve & Coupling Company; *U.S. Private*, pg. 1246
DIXON VALVE & COUPLING COMPANY - DIXON SANITARY DIVISION—See Dixon Valve & Coupling Company; *U.S. Private*, pg. 1246
DIXON VALVE & COUPLING COMPANY - DIXON SPECIALTY HOSE DIVISION—See Dixon Valve & Coupling Company; *U.S. Private*, pg. 1246
DIXON VALVE & COUPLING COMPANY; *U.S. Private*, pg. 1246
DIXTAL TECNOLOGIA INDUSTRIA E COMERCIO LTDA.—See Koninklijke Philips N.V.; *Int'l*, pg. 4267
DIXY GROUP AO; *Int'l*, pg. 2138
DIYAR AL MUHARRAQ COMPANY W.L.L.—See Kuwait Finance House K.S.C.; *Int'l*, pg. 4344
DIY GROUP, INC.; *U.S. Private*, pg. 1246
DIYIXIAN.COM LIMITED—See Tsinghua Holdings Co., Ltd.; *Int'l*, pg. 7951
DIY MASTER PTY. LTD.—See Xplore Wealth Limited; *Int'l*, pg. 8538
DIY PRODUCTS ASIA LTD.—See Wurth Verwaltungsgesellschaft mbH; *Int'l*, pg. 8504
DIZBI PRIVATE LIMITED; *Int'l*, pg. 2138
DIZON COPPER-SILVER MINES, INC.; *Int'l*, pg. 2138
DIZZ FINANCE PLC; *Int'l*, pg. 2138
D.J. BRONSON INC.; *U.S. Private*, pg. 1142
DJ CARMICHAEL PTY LIMITED—See WH Ireland Group PLC; *Int'l*, pg. 8396
D&J CONSTRUCTION COMPANY INC.; *U.S. Private*, pg. 1137
D. & J. DAMKALIDIS S.A.—See Leifheit AG; *Int'l*, pg. 4446
DJD/GOLDEN ADVERTISING, INC.; *U.S. Private*, pg. 1246
D&J ENTERPRISES INC.; *U.S. Private*, pg. 1137
DJERRIWARRH INVESTMENTS LIMITED; *Int'l*, pg. 2138
DJ FRANTEXTIL AB—See New Wave Group AB; *Int'l*, pg. 5229
DJ GALVANIZING—See ArcelorMittal S.A.; *Int'l*, pg. 544
DJ GALVANIZING—See JFE Holdings, Inc.; *Int'l*, pg. 3937
DJ INTERNATIONAL INCORPORATED; *U.S. Private*, pg. 1246
DJI OPCO LLC—See S&P Global Inc.; *U.S. Public*, pg. 1830
DJJD, INC.—See Pamplona Capital Management LLP; *Int'l*, pg. 5711
DJK EUROPE GMBH—See Daiichi Jitsugyo Co. Ltd.; *Int'l*, pg. 1927
DJK FACTORY SOLUTIONS (PHILIPPINES), INC.—See Daiichi Jitsugyo Co. Ltd.; *Int'l*, pg. 1927
DJK GLOBAL MEXICO, S.A. DE C.V.—See Daiichi Jitsugyo Co. Ltd.; *Int'l*, pg. 1927
DJK INNOVALUE CORPORATION—See Daiichi Jitsugyo Co. Ltd.; *Int'l*, pg. 1927
DJK RESIDENTIAL—See Madison Dearborn Partners, LLC; *U.S. Private*, pg. 2542
DJK SOLAR SOLUTION CO., LTD.—See Daiichi Jitsugyo Co. Ltd.; *Int'l*, pg. 1927
DJK (TAIWAN) CORP.—See Daiichi Jitsugyo Co. Ltd.; *Int'l*, pg. 1927
DJ-LA LLC; *U.S. Private*, pg. 1246
DJ LEASING LLC; *U.S. Private*, pg. 1246
DJM ASSET MANAGEMENT, LLC—See Gordon Brothers Group, LLC; *U.S. Private*, pg. 1742
DJ MATIC N.V.—See Stingray Group Inc.; *Int'l*, pg. 7215
DJ MEDIAPRINT & LOGISTICS LTD.; *Int'l*, pg. 2138
DJM SALES & MARKETING; *U.S. Private*, pg. 1246
DJO ASIA-PACIFIC LTD.—See Enovis Corporation; *U.S. Public*, pg. 772
DJO BENELUX B.V.B.A.—See Enovis Corporation; *U.S. Public*, pg. 772
DJO CANADA INC.—See Enovis Corporation; *U.S. Public*, pg. 772
DJO FRANCE, S.A.S.—See Enovis Corporation; *U.S. Public*, pg. 772
DJO GLOBAL, INC—See Enovis Corporation; *U.S. Public*, pg. 772

DJO GLOBAL SWITZERLAND SARL—See Enovis Corporation; *U.S. Public*, pg. 772
DJO IBERICA PRODUCTOS ORTOPEDICOS S.L.—See Enovis Corporation; *U.S. Public*, pg. 772
DJO ITALIA SRL—See Enovis Corporation; *U.S. Public*, pg. 772
DJO, LLC—See Enovis Corporation; *U.S. Public*, pg. 772
DJO NORDIC AB—See Enovis Corporation; *U.S. Public*, pg. 772
DJO ORTHOPAEDIC SOUTH AFRICA PTY. LTD.—See Enovis Corporation; *U.S. Public*, pg. 772
DJ ORTHOPEDICS DE MEXICO SA DE CV—See Enovis Corporation; *U.S. Public*, pg. 772
DJ ORTHOPEDICS DEUTSCHLAND—See Enovis Corporation; *U.S. Public*, pg. 772
DJOSER B.V.—See Cox & Kings Limited; *Int'l*, pg. 1822
DJOSER-DIVANTOURA BVBA—See Cox & Kings Limited; *Int'l*, pg. 1822
DJO SURGICAL—See Enovis Corporation; *U.S. Public*, pg. 772
DJO UK LTD.—See Enovis Corporation; *U.S. Public*, pg. 772
D.J. POWERS COMPANY INC.; *U.S. Private*, pg. 1142
DJ PRECISION CO., LTD.—See I-PEX Inc.; *Int'l*, pg. 3563
DJR HOLDING CO.; *U.S. Private*, pg. 1247
DJ ROOFING SUPPLY INC.; *U.S. Private*, pg. 1246
DJS ADVERTISING; *U.S. Private*, pg. 1247
D&J SALES CO. LLC; *U.S. Private*, pg. 1137
DJS ANTIBODIES LTD.—See AbbVie Inc.; *U.S. Public*, pg. 24
DJS INTERNATIONAL SERVICES INC.—See BDP International Inc.; *U.S. Private*, pg. 502
D&J (STEELS) LIMITED—See Original Steel Services Limited; *Int'l*, pg. 5630
D & J TILE COMPANY, INC.; *U.S. Private*, pg. 1136
DJURO DJAKOVIC MONTAGE GMBH—See Bilfinger SE; *Int'l*, pg. 1028
DJURSLANDS BANK A/S; *Int'l*, pg. 2138
DKABIO CO., LTD.—See MetaAge Corporation; *Int'l*, pg. 4844
DK ADVERTISING (HK) LTD.—See Bain Capital, LP; *U.S. Private*, pg. 428
D. KAY LEONARD, INC.—See LMS Reinforcing Steel Group; *Int'l*, pg. 4538
DK AZTEC CO., LTD.; *Int'l*, pg. 2138
DKB CODE FACTORY GMBH—See BayernLB Holding AG; *Int'l*, pg. 913
DK BETON A/S—See Heidelberg Materials AG; *Int'l*, pg. 3310
DKB FINANCE GMBH—See BayernLB Holding AG; *Int'l*, pg. 913
DKB GRUNDBESITZVERMITTLUNG GMBH—See BayernLB Holding AG; *Int'l*, pg. 913
DKB HOUSEHOLD SWITZERLAND AG—See Diethelm Keller Holding Limited; *Int'l*, pg. 2116
DKB IMMOBILIEN BETEILIGUNGS GMBH—See BayernLB Holding AG; *Int'l*, pg. 913
DKB IT-SERVICES GMBH—See BayernLB Holding AG; *Int'l*, pg. 913
DKB SERVICE GMBH—See BayernLB Holding AG; *Int'l*, pg. 913
DKB WOHNEN GMBH—See BayernLB Holding AG; *Int'l*, pg. 913
DKB WOHNIMMOBILIEN BETEILIGUNGS GMBH & CO. KG—See Helaba Landesbank Hessen-Thuringen; *Int'l*, pg. 3327
DKC DEKA KOMMUNAL CONSULT GMBH—See DekaBank; *Int'l*, pg. 2005
DK CEMENT A/S—See Heidelberg Materials AG; *Int'l*, pg. 3310
D&K COATING TECHNOLOGIES, INC.—See D&K Group, Inc.; *U.S. Private*, pg. 1138
DK COMPANY A/S; *Int'l*, pg. 2138
DK CONSULTING, LLC; *U.S. Private*, pg. 1247
DK CROWN HOLDINGS INC.—See DraftKings Inc.; *U.S. Public*, pg. 687
D&K CUSTOM MACHINE DESIGN INC.—See D&K Group, Inc.; *U.S. Private*, pg. 1138
DK&D CO., LTD.; *Int'l*, pg. 2138
DK ELECTRONIC MATERIALS, INC.; *Int'l*, pg. 2138
D&K ENGINEERING, INC.—See The Burke Porter Group; *U.S. Private*, pg. 4003
D.K. ENTERPRISES GLOBAL LIMITED; *Int'l*, pg. 1901
DKE TECHNOLOGY SDN. BHD.—See Mynews Holdings Berhad; *Int'l*, pg. 5113
D&K EUROPE LTD.—See D&K Group, Inc.; *U.S. Private*, pg. 1138
DK-FH INC.—See DraftKings Inc.; *U.S. Public*, pg. 687
DK FOOT & CASUAL; *U.S. Private*, pg. 1247
D.K FORD SALES; *Int'l*, pg. 1901
DKG CAPITAL, INC.—See Emry Capital Group, Inc.; *U.S. Private*, pg. 1388
D&K GROUP, INC.; *U.S. Private*, pg. 1138
DKH, INCORPORATED; *U.S. Private*, pg. 1247
D&K HOLDINGS L.L.C.—See Independent Petroleum Group Company S.A.K.; *Int'l*, pg. 3650
D & K IMPLEMENT LLC; *U.S. Private*, pg. 1136
DK INDUSTRIAL SOLUTIONS, LLC—See Diethelm Keller Holding Limited; *Int'l*, pg. 2116

D&K INTERNATIONAL INC.—See D&K Group, Inc.; *U.S. Private*, pg. 1138
DKK AMERICA MATERIALS, INC.—See Daiichi Kigenso Kagaku Kogyo Co., Ltd.; *Int'l*, pg. 1928
DKK CO., LTD.; *Int'l*, pg. 2139
DKK LOGISTICS CORPORATION—See Daiichi Kigenso Kagaku Kogyo Co., Ltd.; *Int'l*, pg. 1928
DKK MANUFACTURING (THAILAND) CO., LTD.—See DKK Co., Ltd.; *Int'l*, pg. 2139
DKK OF AMERICA, INC.—See DKK Co., Ltd.; *Int'l*, pg. 2139
DK KOREA CO., LTD.—See DAIICHIKOUSHO CO., LTD.; *Int'l*, pg. 1930
DKK (SHANGHAI) MATERIALS TRADING CO., LTD.—See Daiichi Kigenso Kagaku Kogyo Co., Ltd.; *Int'l*, pg. 1928
DKK (THAILAND) CO., LTD.—See DKK Co., Ltd.; *Int'l*, pg. 2139
DKK THAI MATERIALS TRADING CO., LTD.—See Daiichi Kigenso Kagaku Kogyo Co., Ltd.; *Int'l*, pg. 1928
DKK-TOA ALICE CORPORATION—See DKK-TOA Corporation; *Int'l*, pg. 2139
DKK-TOA ANALYTICA CORPORATION—See DKK-TOA Corporation; *Int'l*, pg. 2139
DKK-TOA CORPORATION; *Int'l*, pg. 2139
DKK-TOA IWATE CORPORATION—See DKK-TOA Corporation; *Int'l*, pg. 2139
DK-LOK CORPORATION; *Int'l*, pg. 2139
DKLS CONSTRUCTION SDN BHD—See DKLS Industries Berhad; *Int'l*, pg. 2139
DKLS DEVELOPMENT SDN. BHD.—See DKLS Industries Berhad; *Int'l*, pg. 2139
DKLS ENERGY SDN. BHD.—See DKLS Industries Berhad; *Int'l*, pg. 2139
DKLS EQUITY SDN BHD—See DKLS Industries Berhad; *Int'l*, pg. 2139
DKLS INDUSTRIES BERHAD; *Int'l*, pg. 2139
DKLS MARKETING SDN. BHD.—See DKLS Industries Berhad; *Int'l*, pg. 2139
DKLS PRECAST SYSTEM SDN BHD—See DKLS Industries Berhad; *Int'l*, pg. 2139
DKLS PREMIERHOME SDN BHD—See DKLS Industries Berhad; *Int'l*, pg. 2139
DKLS QUARRY & PREMIX SDN. BHD.—See DKLS Industries Berhad; *Int'l*, pg. 2139
DKLS SIGNATUREHOMES SDN. BHD.—See DKLS Industries Berhad; *Int'l*, pg. 2139
DKM—See Groupe Legris Industries; *Int'l*, pg. 3106
DK MUSIC PUBLISHING CO., LTD.—See DAIICHIKOUSHO CO., LTD.; *Int'l*, pg. 1930
DKN FINANCIAL GROUP LIMITED—See Insignia Financial Ltd.; *Int'l*, pg. 3719
DKN HOTEL LLC; *U.S. Private*, pg. 1247
DK PUBLISHING—See Bertelsmann SE & Co. KGaA; *Int'l*, pg. 991
DKR CAPITAL INC.; *U.S. Private*, pg. 1247
DK RENTAL N.V.—See Loxam SAS; *Int'l*, pg. 4566
DKS CO. LTD.; *Int'l*, pg. 2139
DKS DRAXLMAIER KUNSTSTOFFSYSTEME GMBH—See Draexlmaier Gruppe; *Int'l*, pg. 2198
DKSH AUSTRALIA PTY. LTD.—See Diethelm Keller Holding Limited; *Int'l*, pg. 2116
DKSH (CAMBODIA) LTD.—See Diethelm Keller Holding Limited; *Int'l*, pg. 2116
DKSH CORPORATE SHARED SERVICES CENTER SDN. BHD.—See Diethelm Keller Holding Limited; *Int'l*, pg. 2116
DKSH (FRANCE) S.A.—See Diethelm Keller Holding Limited; *Int'l*, pg. 2116
DKSH GMBH—See Diethelm Keller Holding Limited; *Int'l*, pg. 2116
DKSH GREAT BRITAIN LTD.—See Diethelm Keller Holding Limited; *Int'l*, pg. 2116
DKSH GUAM, INC.—See Diethelm Keller Holding Limited; *Int'l*, pg. 2116
DKSH HOLDING LIMITED—See Diethelm Keller Holding Limited; *Int'l*, pg. 2116
DKSH HOLDINGS (ASIA) SDN. BHD.—See Diethelm Keller Holding Limited; *Int'l*, pg. 2116
DKSH HOLDINGS (MALAYSIA) BERHAD—See Diethelm Keller Holding Limited; *Int'l*, pg. 2116
DKSH HONG KONG LTD.—See Diethelm Keller Holding Limited; *Int'l*, pg. 2116
D. K. SHIFFLET & ASSOCIATES, LTD.—See EagleTree Capital, LP; *U.S. Private*, pg. 1311
DKSH INDIA PVT. LTD.—See Diethelm Keller Holding Limited; *Int'l*, pg. 2116
DKSH JAPAN K.K.—See Diethelm Keller Holding Limited; *Int'l*, pg. 2116
DKSH KOREA LTD.—See Diethelm Keller Holding Limited; *Int'l*, pg. 2116
DKSH LAOS COMPANY LIMITED—See HORIBA Ltd.; *Int'l*, pg. 3475
DKSH LOGISTICS LTD.—See Diethelm Keller Holding Limited; *Int'l*, pg. 2116
DKSH LUXURY AND LIFESTYLE EUROPE GMBH—See Diethelm Keller Holding Limited; *Int'l*, pg. 2116
DKSH MALAYSIA SDN. BHD.—See Diethelm Keller Holding Limited; *Int'l*, pg. 2116

DKS CO., LTD.

DKSH MANAGEMENT LTD.—See Diethelm Keller Holding Limited; *Int'l*, pg. 2116
DKSH MANAGEMENT PTE LTD.—See Diethelm Keller Holding Limited; *Int'l*, pg. 2116
DKSH NETHERLANDS B.V.—See Diethelm Keller Holding Limited; *Int'l*, pg. 2116
DKSH NEW ZEALAND LTD.—See Diethelm Keller Holding Limited; *Int'l*, pg. 2116
DKSH PHARMACEUTICAL (SHANGHAI) LTD.—See Diethelm Keller Holding Limited; *Int'l*, pg. 2116
DKSH PHILIPPINES INC.—See Diethelm Keller Holding Limited; *Int'l*, pg. 2116
DKSH (SHANGHAI) CO., LTD.—See Warburg Pincus LLC; *U.S. Private*, pg. 4437
DKSH SHANGHAI LTD.—See Diethelm Keller Holding Limited; *Int'l*, pg. 2117
DKSH SINGAPORE PTE LTD.—See Diethelm Keller Holding Limited; *Int'l*, pg. 2117
DKSH SWITZERLAND LTD.—See Diethelm Keller Holding Limited; *Int'l*, pg. 2116
DKSH TAIWAN LTD.—See Diethelm Keller Holding Limited; *Int'l*, pg. 2116
DKSH TECHNOLOGY SDN. BHD.—See Diethelm Keller Holding Limited; *Int'l*, pg. 2117
DKSH (THAILAND) LIMITED—See Diethelm Keller Holding Limited; *Int'l*, pg. 2116
DKSH VIETNAM CO. LTD.—See Diethelm Keller Holding Limited; *Int'l*, pg. 2117
DK-SPEC INC.; *Int'l*, pg. 2139
DKS (SHANGHAI) INTERNATIONAL TRADING CO., LTD.—See DKS Co. Ltd.; *Int'l*, pg. 2139
DKS SYSTEMS, LLC; *U.S. Private*, pg. 1247
DK TECH; *Int'l*, pg. 2138
DKT INTERNATIONAL, INC., *U.S. Private*, pg. 1247
D-K TRADING CORP.; *U.S. Private*, pg. 1139
DK TURBINES, LLC.—See Kalitta Air, LLC; *U.S. Private*, pg. 2257
DKTV A/S—See Arbejdsmarkedets Tillaegspension; *Int'l*, pg. 537
DKTV A/S—See Macquarie Group Limited; *Int'l*, pg. 4626
DKTV A/S—See PFA Holding A/S; *Int'l*, pg. 5835
DKTV A/S—See PKA A/S; *Int'l*, pg. 5887
DK UIL (TIANJIN) ELECTRONICS CO., LTD—See Dongkuk Steel Mill Co., Ltd.; *Int'l*, pg. 2169
DK UNC CO., LTD.—See Dongkuk Steel Mill Co., Ltd.; *Int'l*, pg. 2169
DKV - ALPHA VERMOGENSVERWALTUNGS GMBH—See Munchener Ruckversicherungs AG; *Int'l*, pg. 5086
DKV BELGIUM S.A./N.V.—See Munchener Ruckversicherungs AG; *Int'l*, pg. 5087
DKV - BETA VERMOGENSVERWALTUNGS GMBH—See Munchener Ruckversicherungs AG; *Int'l*, pg. 5086
DKV DEUTSCHE KRANKENVERSICHERUNG AKTIENGESELLSCHAFT—See Munchener Ruckversicherungs AG; *Int'l*, pg. 5086
DK VINA CO., LTD.—See DK&D Co., Ltd.; *Int'l*, pg. 2139
DKV LUXEMBOURG SA—See Munchener Ruckversicherungs AG; *Int'l*, pg. 5087
DKV RESIDENZ AM TIBUSPLATZ GGMBH—See Munchener Ruckversicherungs AG; *Int'l*, pg. 5086
DKV-RESIDENZ IN DER CONTRESCARPE GMBH—See Munchener Ruckversicherungs AG; *Int'l*, pg. 5086
DKV SERVICIOS, S.A.—See Munchener Ruckversicherungs AG; *Int'l*, pg. 5086
DKW COMMUNICATIONS INC.; *U.S. Private*, pg. 1247
DK WILD & COMPANY LIMITED—See Epiris Managers LLP; *Int'l*, pg. 2461
DLALA BROKERAGE AND INVESTMENTS HOLDING COMPANY Q.S.C; *Int'l*, pg. 2140
DLALA ISLAMIC BROKERAGE COMPANY (W.L.L)—See Dlala Brokerage and Investments Holding Company Q.S.C; *Int'l*, pg. 2140
DLALA REAL ESTATE S.P.C.—See Dlala Brokerage and Investments Holding Company Q.S.C; *Int'l*, pg. 2140
DLA PIPER AUSTRALIA - MELBOURNE—See DLA Piper Global; *Int'l*, pg. 2140
DLA PIPER AUSTRALIA—See DLA Piper Global; *Int'l*, pg. 2140
DLA PIPER BAZ NLD SPA; *Int'l*, pg. 2140
DLA PIPER (CANADA) LLP—See DLA Piper Global; *Int'l*, pg. 2140
DLA PIPER DENMARK LAW FIRM P/S—See DLA Piper Global; *Int'l*, pg. 2140
DLA PIPER GALLASTEGUI Y LOZANO—See DLA Piper Global; *Int'l*, pg. 2140
DLA PIPER GLOBAL; *Int'l*, pg. 2140
DLA PIPER INTERNATIONAL LLP—See DLA Piper Global; *Int'l*, pg. 2140
DLA PIPER KUWAIT—See DLA Piper Global; *Int'l*, pg. 2140
DLA PIPER LLP (US)—See DLA Piper Global; *Int'l*, pg. 2140
DLA PIPER LLP (US) - WASHINGTON, D.C.—See DLA Piper Global; *Int'l*, pg. 2140
DLA PIPER RUS LTD.—See DLA Piper Global; *Int'l*, pg. 2140
DLA PIPER UK LLP—See DLA Piper Global; *Int'l*, pg. 2140
D'LAURO & RODGERS, INC.; *U.S. Private*, pg. 1139

D. LAZZARONI & C. S.P.A.; *Int'l*, pg. 1900
D L BECK INC.; *U.S. Private*, pg. 1136
DLB INC.; *U.S. Private*, pg. 1247
D.L. BUILDING MATERIALS INC.—See GMS Inc.; *U.S. Public*, pg. 947
DLC ASIA LTD.; *Int'l*, pg. 2140
DL CHEMICAL CO. LTD.—See Daelim Industrial Co., Ltd.; *Int'l*, pg. 1908
DLC HOLDINGS CORP.; *Int'l*, pg. 2140
DLC INC.—See Odyssey Investment Partners, LLC; *U.S. Private*, pg. 2994
DLC INTEGRATED MARKETING CORP.—See WPP plc; *Int'l*, pg. 8489
DLC MANAGEMENT CORP.; *U.S. Private*, pg. 1247
DLCO AUSTRALIA ARCHITECTURAL GLASS FITTINGS PTY. LTD.—See MHG Glass Pty Ltd; *Int'l*, pg. 4872
DL CONSTRUCTION CO., LTD.; *Int'l*, pg. 2140
D.L. COUCH WALLCOVERING, INC.; *U.S. Private*, pg. 1142
D.L. DEEKS INSURANCE SERVICES INC.—See Intact Financial Corporation; *Int'l*, pg. 3727
D.L. DEEKS INSURANCE SERVICES INC.—See Tryg A/S; *Int'l*, pg. 7946
DL E&C CO., LTD.—See Daelim Industrial Co., Ltd.; *Int'l*, pg. 1908
DLE INC.; *Int'l*, pg. 2140
DLE OUEST—See Eiffage S.A.; *Int'l*, pg. 2330
DLE OUTRE-MER—See Eiffage S.A.; *Int'l*, pg. 2330
DLE SPECIALITES—See Eiffage S.A.; *Int'l*, pg. 2330
D.L. EVANS BANCORP; *U.S. Private*, pg. 1142
D.L. EVANS BANK—See D.L. Evans Bancorp; *U.S. Private*, pg. 1142
DLF AKRUTI INFO PARKS (PUNE) LIMITED—See DLF Limited; *Int'l*, pg. 2141
D. L. FALK CONSTRUCTION INC.; *U.S. Private*, pg. 1140
DLF AMBA; *Int'l*, pg. 2140
DLF CYBER CITY DEVELOPERS LIMITED—See DLF Limited; *Int'l*, pg. 2141
DLF EMPORIO LIMITED—See DLF Limited; *Int'l*, pg. 2141
DLF ESTATE DEVELOPERS LIMITED—See DLF Limited; *Int'l*, pg. 2141
DLF FINANCIAL SERVICES LIMITED—See DLF Limited; *Int'l*, pg. 2141
DLF GOLF RESORT LIMITED—See DLF Limited; *Int'l*, pg. 2141
DLF HOME DEVELOPERS LIMITED—See DLF Limited; *Int'l*, pg. 2141
DLF INFO CITY DEVELOPERS (CHENNAI) LTD.—See DLF Limited; *Int'l*, pg. 2141
DLF INTERNATIONAL HOLDINGS PTE LIMITED—See DLF Limited; *Int'l*, pg. 2141
DLF LIMITED; *Int'l*, pg. 2141
D&L FOUNDRY, INC.; *U.S. Private*, pg. 1138
DLF PROJECTS LIMITED—See DLF Limited; *Int'l*, pg. 2141
DLF PROMENADE LIMITED—See DLF Limited; *Int'l*, pg. 2141
DLF RECREATIONAL FOUNDATION LIMITED—See DLF Limited; *Int'l*, pg. 2141
DLF RETAIL DEVELOPERS LIMITED—See DLF Limited; *Int'l*, pg. 2141
DLF SEEDS A/S; *Int'l*, pg. 2141
DLF UNIVERSAL LIMITED—See DLF Limited; *Int'l*, pg. 2141
DLF UTILITIES LIMITED—See DLF Limited; *Int'l*, pg. 2141
DLG EXHIBITIONS & EVENTS CORP LTD.; *Int'l*, pg. 2141
DLG HANBIT CO., LTD.—See Duc Long Gia Lai Group JSC; *Int'l*, pg. 2222
DLG LEGAL SERVICES LIMITED—See Direct Line Insurance Group plc; *Int'l*, pg. 2129
D.L.G.L. LTD.; *Int'l*, pg. 1901
DLHBOWLES, INC.—See Apollo Global Management, Inc.; *U.S. Public*, pg. 146
DLH COTE D'IVOIRE S.A—See Scandinavian Investment Group A/S; *Int'l*, pg. 6612
DLH FINLAND OY—See Scandinavian Investment Group A/S; *Int'l*, pg. 6612
DLH FRANCE S.A.S.—See Scandinavian Investment Group A/S; *Int'l*, pg. 6612
DLH FUEL COMPANY MBH—See Deutsche Lufthansa AG; *Int'l*, pg. 2066
DLH HOLDINGS CORP.; *U.S. Public*, pg. 670
DLH NEDERLAND B.V.—See Scandinavian Investment Group A/S; *Int'l*, pg. 6612
DLH NORGE AS—See Scandinavian Investment Group A/S; *Int'l*, pg. 6612
DL HOLDINGS GROUP LIMITED; *Int'l*, pg. 2140
DLH POLAND SP. Z O.O.—See Grupa Grass Sp. z o.o.; *Int'l*, pg. 3116
DLH PROCUREMENT CAMEROUN S.A.R.L.—See Scandinavian Investment Group A/S; *Int'l*, pg. 6612
DLH SLOVAKIA S.R.O.—See Grupa Grass Sp. z o.o.; *Int'l*, pg. 3116
DLH SOLUTIONS, INC.—See DLH Holdings Corp.; *U.S. Public*, pg. 670
DLI ASIA PACIFIC PTE. LTD.—See Dai-ichi Life Holdings, Inc.; *Int'l*, pg. 1917
DLIGHT BVBA—See BASF SE; *Int'l*, pg. 883

D&L INDUSTRIES, INC.; *Int'l*, pg. 1899
D-LINK CORPORATION, INC.; *Int'l*, pg. 1900
D-LINK (DEUTSCHLAND) GMBH—See D-Link Corporation, Inc.; *Int'l*, pg. 1900
D-LINK (INDIA) LTD—See D-Link Corporation, Inc.; *Int'l*, pg. 1900
D-LINK MALAYSIA SDN. BHD.—See D-Link Corporation, Inc.; *Int'l*, pg. 1900
D-LINK SYSTEMS, INC.—See D-Link Corporation, Inc.; *Int'l*, pg. 1900
D'LIVE CO., LTD.; *Int'l*, pg. 1899
D. L. KENNEY GENERAL CONTRACTORS INC.; *U.S. Private*, pg. 1140
DLKW LOWE—See The Interpublic Group of Companies, Inc.; *U.S. Public*, pg. 2091
D & L LEASING, INC.—See Lykins Companies, Inc.; *U.S. Private*, pg. 2520
D.L. LEE & SONS INC.; *U.S. Private*, pg. 1142
D&L LICHTPLANUNG GMBH—See ITAB Shop Concept AB; *Int'l*, pg. 3827
DL MARTIN CO.; *U.S. Private*, pg. 1247
D/L MOTOR COMPANY—See AutoNation, Inc.; *U.S. Public*, pg. 234
D/L MOTOR COMPANY—See AutoNation, Inc.; *U.S. Public*, pg. 234
DLOCAL LTD.; *Int'l*, pg. 2141
DLO CORP.—See The Walt Disney Company; *U.S. Public*, pg. 2140
DLOG GESELLSCHAFT FUR ELEKTRONISCHE DATENTECHNIK MBH—See Advantech Co., Ltd.; *Int'l*, pg. 164
D'LONG INTERNATIONAL STRATEGIC INVESTMENT CO., LTD.—See China CITIC Financial Asset Management Co., Ltd.; *Int'l*, pg. 1489
DLORAH, INC.—See National American University Holdings, Inc.; *U.S. Public*, pg. 1493
D&L PARTS CO. INC.; *U.S. Private*, pg. 1138
DLP BUILDERS—See Don Wenner Home Selling, Inc.; *U.S. Private*, pg. 1259
DLP CAPITAL ADVISORS—See Don Wenner Home Selling, Inc.; *U.S. Private*, pg. 1259
DLP CARDIAC PARTNERS, LLC—See Apollo Global Management, Inc.; *U.S. Public*, pg. 155
DLP CARDIOLOGY ASSOCIATES, LLC—See Apollo Global Management, Inc.; *U.S. Public*, pg. 155
DLP CENTRAL CAROLINA FAMILY MEDICINE, LLC—See Apollo Global Management, Inc.; *U.S. Public*, pg. 155
DLP CONEMAUGH MEMORIAL MEDICAL CENTER, LLC—See Apollo Global Management, Inc.; *U.S. Public*, pg. 155
DLP CONEMAUGH MINERS MEDICAL CENTER, LLC—See Apollo Global Management, Inc.; *U.S. Public*, pg. 155
DLP CONEMAUGH PHYSICIAN PRACTICES, LLC—See Apollo Global Management, Inc.; *U.S. Public*, pg. 155
DLP FRYE REGIONAL MEDICAL CENTER, LLC—See Apollo Global Management, Inc.; *U.S. Public*, pg. 155
DLP HARRIS REGIONAL HOSPITAL, LLC—See Apollo Global Management, Inc.; *U.S. Public*, pg. 155
DLP HEALTHCARE, LLC—See Apollo Global Management, Inc.; *U.S. Public*, pg. 155
DLP INTERACTIVE MEDIA—See Don Wenner Home Selling, Inc.; *U.S. Private*, pg. 1259
DLP MARIA PARHAM MEDICAL CENTER, LLC—See Apollo Global Management, Inc.; *U.S. Public*, pg. 155
DLP MARIA PARHAM PHYSICIAN PRACTICES, LLC—See Apollo Global Management, Inc.; *U.S. Public*, pg. 155
DLP MARQUETTE GENERAL HOSPITAL, LLC—See Apollo Global Management, Inc.; *U.S. Public*, pg. 155
DLP MARQUETTE PHYSICIAN PRACTICES, INC.—See Apollo Global Management, Inc.; *U.S. Public*, pg. 155
D.L. PORTER CONSTRUCTORS INC.; *U.S. Private*, pg. 1142
DLP PERSON URGENT CARE, LLC—See Apollo Global Management, Inc.; *U.S. Public*, pg. 155
DLP REAL ESTATE CAPITAL INC.; *U.S. Private*, pg. 1247
DLP REALTY PROPERTY MANAGEMENT—See Don Wenner Home Selling, Inc.; *U.S. Private*, pg. 1259
DLP REALTY—See Don Wenner Home Selling, Inc.; *U.S. Private*, pg. 1259
DLP RESOURCES INC.; *Int'l*, pg. 2141
DL PROPERTIES LTD—See Keppel Corporation Limited; *Int'l*, pg. 4130
DLP RUTHERFORD PHYSICIAN PRACTICES, LLC—See Apollo Global Management, Inc.; *U.S. Public*, pg. 155
DLP RUTHERFORD REGIONAL HEALTH SYSTEM, LLC—See Apollo Global Management, Inc.; *U.S. Public*, pg. 155
DLP SWAIN COUNTY HOSPITAL, LLC—See Apollo Global Management, Inc.; *U.S. Public*, pg. 155
DLP WESTERN CAROLINA PHYSICIAN PRACTICES, LLC—See Apollo Global Management, Inc.; *U.S. Public*, pg. 155
DLP WILMED NURSING CARE AND REHABILITATION CENTER, LLC—See Apollo Global Management, Inc.; *U.S. Public*, pg. 155
DLP WILSON PHYSICIAN PRACTICES, LLC—See Apollo Global Management, Inc.; *U.S. Public*, pg. 155

COMPANY NAME INDEX

DL RADIATORS SRL—See Stelrad Group plc; *Int'l*, pg. 7204
DLR GROUP INC.—See DLR Holding, LLC; *U.S. Private*, pg. 1247
DLR GROUP (SHANGHAI) ARCHITECTURAL DESIGN CONSULTING CO., LTD.—See DLR Holding, LLC; *U.S. Private*, pg. 1247
DLR HOLDING, LLC; *U.S. Private*, pg. 1247
DLSA AUTOMOBILES; *Int'l*, pg. 2141
DLS ARGENTINA LIMITED—See Archer Limited; *Int'l*, pg. 548
DLS-EURASIA TOO—See dls Land und See Speditionsgesellschaft mbH; *Int'l*, pg. 2141
DLSI SA; *Int'l*, pg. 2142
DLS LAND UND SEE SPEDITIONSGESELLSCHAFT MBH; *Int'l*, pg. 2141
DLSM INCORPORATED; *U.S. Private*, pg. 1247
DL SOFTWARE; *Int'l*, pg. 2140
DLS-RUSSIJA, LTD—See dls Land und See Speditionsgesellschaft mbH; *Int'l*, pg. 2141
DLS TRANS LTD. SP. Z O.O.—See dls Land und See Speditionsgesellschaft mbH; *Int'l*, pg. 2141
D&L SUPPLY INC.; *U.S. Private*, pg. 1138
DLT ASA; *Int'l*, pg. 2142
D.L. THURROTT INC.—See INSCO, Inc.; *U.S. Private*, pg. 2085
DLT RESOLUTION INC.; *U.S. Public*, pg. 670
DLT SOLUTIONS, LLC—See TD Synnex Corp; *U.S. Public*, pg. 1985
DLUBAK SPECIALTY GLASS CORPORATION—See Grey Mountain Partners, LLC; *U.S. Private*, pg. 1784
DLVA, INC.; *U.S. Private*, pg. 1248
DLV IMMOBILIEN LEASING GESELLSCHAFT M.B.H.—See UniCredit S.p.A.; *Int'l*, pg. 8037
DL WINDY ACRES, LLC—See Constellation Energy Corporation; *U.S. Public*, pg. 572
DLX INDUSTRIES, INC.—See Royal Industries, Inc.; *U.S. Private*, pg. 3492
DM9 JAYME SYFU INC.—See Dentsu Group Inc.; *Int'l*, pg. 2036
DMA ENTERPRISES; *U.S. Private*, pg. 1248
D. MAG (KUNSHAN) NEW MATERIAL TECHNOLOGY CO., LTD.—See Giant Manufacturing Co., Ltd.; *Int'l*, pg. 2961
DMA HOLDINGS, INC.; *U.S. Private*, pg. 1248
D-MAIL DIRECT S.R.L.—See Netweek S.p.A.; *Int'l*, pg. 5217
D-MAIL S.R.O.—See Netweek S.p.A.; *Int'l*, pg. 5217
D-MAIL VENDA DIRECTA S.A.—See Netweek S.p.A.; *Int'l*, pg. 5217
DMA MASCHINEN UND ANLAGENBAU GMBH & CO. KG—See L. Possehl & Co. mbH; *Int'l*, pg. 4382
DMA MEDIA LTD.; *Int'l*, pg. 2142
D MARINE INVESTMENT HOLDING B.V.—See Dogus Holding AS; *Int'l*, pg. 2154
D-MARKET ELECTRONIC SERVICES & TRADING; *Int'l*, pg. 1900
D MARTONE INDUSTRIES INC.—See AJD Holding Co.; *U.S. Private*, pg. 144
D MASONS SOFTWARE, LLC—See SPS Commerce, Inc.; *U.S. Public*, pg. 1920
DMAX LTD.—See Isuzu Motors Limited; *Int'l*, pg. 3825
DMB DIRECT MAIL BIEL-BIENNE AG—See Die Schweizerische Post AG; *Int'l*, pg. 2112
DMB DR. DIETER MURMANN BETEILIGUNGSGESELLSCHAFT MBH; *Int'l*, pg. 2142
DMBGROUP, LLC—See Data443 Risk Mitigation, Inc.; *U.S. Public*, pg. 635
DMBM LLC; *U.S. Private*, pg. 1248
D.M. BOWMAN INCORPORATED—See Bowman Group LLP; *U.S. Private*, pg. 626
DMB PROPERTY VENTURE LP; *U.S. Private*, pg. 1248
DMC ADVERTISING & DIRECT MARKETING, INC.; *U.S. Private*, pg. 1248
DMCARD CARTOES DE CREDITO S.A.; *Int'l*, pg. 2142
DM CASTING TECHNOLOGY (THAILAND) CO., LTD.—See Daido Metal Corporation; *Int'l*, pg. 1921
DMC BEVERAGE CORP.; *U.S. Private*, pg. 1248
DMC CARDIOVASCULAR INSTITUTE—See Tenet Healthcare Corporation; *U.S. Public*, pg. 2015
DMC CONSTRUCTION, INC.; *U.S. Private*, pg. 1248
THE DMC CORPORATION—See Bernard Krief Consultants SA; *Int'l*, pg. 986
DMC DIGITAL MOTOR CONTROL GMBH—See Addtech AB; *Int'l*, pg. 132
DMC EDUCATION & RESEARCH—See Tenet Healthcare Corporation; *U.S. Public*, pg. 2015
DMC ENTERPRISES INC.; *U.S. Private*, pg. 1248
DMC GLOBAL INC.; *U.S. Public*, pg. 671
DMCI HOLDINGS, INC.; *Int'l*, pg. 2142
DMC IMAGING, L.L.C.—See Tenet Healthcare Corporation; *U.S. Public*, pg. 2003
DMCI MINING CORPORATION—See DMCI Holdings, Inc.; *Int'l*, pg. 2142
DMC INTERNATIONAL IMAGING LTD.—See Airbus SE; *Int'l*, pg. 243
DMCI POWER CORPORATION—See DMCI Holdings, Inc.; *Int'l*, pg. 2143

DMC-MEMPHIS, INC.—See Acadia Healthcare Company, Inc.; *U.S. Public*, pg. 28
DMC MINING SERVICES CORPORATION—See KGHM Polska Miedz S.A.; *Int'l*, pg. 4149
DMC MINING SERVICES—See KGHM Polska Miedz S.A.; *Int'l*, pg. 4149
DMC-NORTHERN PETROLEUM CHEMICALS JOINT STOCK COMPANY; *Int'l*, pg. 2142
D&M CONSULTING ENGINEERS, INC.—See AECOM; *U.S. Public*, pg. 51
D.M. CONSUNJI, INC.—See DMCI Holdings, Inc.; *Int'l*, pg. 2142
DMC SRL—See Fullsix S.p.A.; *Int'l*, pg. 2843
DMCS/SOURCELINK INC.; *U.S. Private*, pg. 1248
DMC SURGERY HOSPITAL—See Tenet Healthcare Corporation; *U.S. Public*, pg. 2015
DMC SWEEPING, LLC—See Warburg Pincus LLC; *U.S. Private*, pg. 4440
DMC (USA) CORPORATION—See Antofagasta plc; *Int'l*, pg. 484
DMDCONNECTS SERVICES INC.; *Int'l*, pg. 2143
DMD DATA SYSTEMS, INC.; *U.S. Private*, pg. 1248
D.M. DISPOSAL CO., INC.—See Waste Connections, Inc.; *Int'l*, pg. 8353
DMD PRODUCTS, LLC; *U.S. Private*, pg. 1248
DM-DROGERIE MARKT GMBH & CO. KG; *Int'l*, pg. 2142
DME ALLIANCE, INC.—See O'Neal Inc.; *U.S. Private*, pg. 2979
DME ALMY SA—See Financiere de L'Odet; *Int'l*, pg. 2667
D MECATRONICS, INC.; *Int'l*, pg. 1899
D-M-E (CHINA) LIMITED—See Hillenbrand, Inc.; *U.S. Public*, pg. 1036
D-MEC LTD.—See JSR Corp.; *Int'l*, pg. 4013
DME COMPANY LLC—See Hillenbrand, Inc.; *U.S. Public*, pg. 1037
DME CORPORATION—See Astronics Corporation; *U.S. Public*, pg. 217
DMED BIOPHARMACEUTICAL CO. LTD.; *Int'l*, pg. 2143
DMEDIA COMMERCE SPA—See Netweek S.p.A.; *Int'l*, pg. 5217
DMEDIA GROUP S.P.A.—See Netweek S.p.A.; *Int'l*, pg. 5217
DME EUROPE C.V.B.A.—See Hillenbrand, Inc.; *U.S. Public*, pg. 1037
DMEGC GERMANY GMBH—See Hengdian Group DMEGC Magnetics Co., Ltd.; *Int'l*, pg. 3346
DMEGC JAPAN CORPORATION LIMITED—See Hengdian Group DMEGC Magnetics Co., Ltd.; *Int'l*, pg. 3346
DMEGC SOLAR USA, LLC—See Hengdian Group DMEGC Magnetics Co., Ltd.; *Int'l*, pg. 3346
DMEGC UK SOLAR PV—See Hengdian Group DMEGC Magnetics Co., Ltd.; *Int'l*, pg. 3346
D-M-E MOLD TECHNOLOGY (SHENZHEN) COMPANY LTD.—See Hillenbrand, Inc.; *U.S. Public*, pg. 1036
D-M-E NORMALIEN GMBH—See Hillenbrand, Inc.; *U.S. Public*, pg. 1036
DME OF CANADA, LTD.—See Hillenbrand, Inc.; *U.S. Public*, pg. 1037
DMEP CORPORATION; *U.S. Private*, pg. 1248
D.M. FIGLEY CO. INC.; *U.S. Private*, pg. 1142
DMF INC.; *U.S. Private*, pg. 1248
DMG AMERICA INC.—See DMG MORI Co., Ltd.; *Int'l*, pg. 2145
DMG BANCSHARES, INC.; *U.S. Private*, pg. 1248
DMG BLOCKCHAIN SOLUTIONS INC.; *Int'l*, pg. 2143
DMG CORPORATION; *U.S. Private*, pg. 1248
DMG ECOLINE GMBH—See DMG MORI Co., Ltd.; *Int'l*, pg. 2144
D&M GENERAL CONTRACTING, INC.; *U.S. Private*, pg. 1138
DMG EQUIPMENT COMPANY, LLC—See Vulcan Materials Company; *U.S. Public*, pg. 2313
DMG EVENTS ASIA PACIFIC PTE LTD.—See Daily Mail & General Trust plc; *Int'l*, pg. 1937
DMG EVENTS (CANADA) INC.—See Daily Mail & General Trust plc; *Int'l*, pg. 1937
DMG EVENTS (DUBAI) LIMITED—See Daily Mail & General Trust plc; *Int'l*, pg. 1937
DMG EVENTS EGYPT INC.—See Daily Mail & General Trust plc; *Int'l*, pg. 1937
DMG EVENTS LIMITED—See Daily Mail & General Trust plc; *Int'l*, pg. 1937
DMG EVENTS, LLC—See Daily Mail & General Trust plc; *Int'l*, pg. 1937
DMG EVENTS (USA) INC. - DIGITAL MARKETING—See Daily Mail & General Trust plc; *Int'l*, pg. 1937
DMG EVENTS (USA) INC.—See Daily Mail & General Trust plc; *Int'l*, pg. 1937
DMG GMBH—See IRCE S.p.A.; *Int'l*, pg. 3806
DMG INCORPORATED; *U.S. Private*, pg. 1248
DMG INFORMATION US INC.—See Daily Mail & General Trust plc; *Int'l*, pg. 1937
DMG MORI ACADEMY GMBH—See DMG MORI Co., Ltd.; *Int'l*, pg. 2143
DMG MORI AKTIENGESELLSCHAFT—See DMG MORI Co., Ltd.; *Int'l*, pg. 2143
DMG MORI AUSTRALIA PTY. LTD.—See DMG MORI Co., Ltd.; *Int'l*, pg. 2144

DMG MORI AUSTRIA GMBH—See DMG MORI Co., Ltd.; *Int'l*, pg. 2143
DMG MORI BELUX BVBA - SPRL—See DMG MORI Co., Ltd.; *Int'l*, pg. 2143
DMG MORI BERLIN GMBH—See DMG MORI Co., Ltd.; *Int'l*, pg. 2143
DMG MORI BIELEFELD GMBH—See DMG MORI Co., Ltd.; *Int'l*, pg. 2143
DMG MORI BRASIL—See DMG MORI Co., Ltd.; *Int'l*, pg. 2143
DMG MORI B.U.G. CO., LTD.—See DMG MORI Co., Ltd.; *Int'l*, pg. 2144
DMG MORI CASTECH CO., LTD.—See DMG MORI Co., Ltd.; *Int'l*, pg. 2144
DMG MORI CO., LTD. - PLANT 1—See DMG MORI Co., Ltd.; *Int'l*, pg. 2144
DMG MORI CO., LTD.; *Int'l*, pg. 2143
DMG MORI CZECH S.R.O.—See DMG MORI Co., Ltd.; *Int'l*, pg. 2144
DMG MORI CZECH, S.R.O.—See DMG MORI Co., Ltd.; *Int'l*, pg. 2143
DMG MORI DENMARK APS—See DMG MORI Co., Ltd.; *Int'l*, pg. 2143
DMG MORI DEUTSCHLAND GMBH—See DMG MORI Co., Ltd.; *Int'l*, pg. 2143
DMG MORI DIGITAL CO., LTD.—See DMG MORI Co., Ltd.; *Int'l*, pg. 2144
DMG MORI ELLISON TECHNOLOGIES—See Ellison Technologies Inc.; *U.S. Private*, pg. 1374
DMG MORI EUROPE AG—See DMG MORI Co., Ltd.; *Int'l*, pg. 2143
DMG MORI FINLAND OY AB—See DMG MORI Co., Ltd.; *Int'l*, pg. 2144
DMG MORI FRANCE - HAUTE-SAVOIE—See DMG MORI Co., Ltd.; *Int'l*, pg. 2144
DMG MORI FRANCE - LYON—See DMG MORI Co., Ltd.; *Int'l*, pg. 2144
DMG MORI FRANCE S.A.S.—See DMG MORI Co., Ltd.; *Int'l*, pg. 2143
DMG MORI FRANKFURT GMBH—See DMG MORI Co., Ltd.; *Int'l*, pg. 2143
DMG MORI GLOBAL MARKETING GMBH—See DMG MORI Co., Ltd.; *Int'l*, pg. 2144
DMG MORI GLOBAL SERVICE MILLING GMBH—See DMG MORI Co., Ltd.; *Int'l*, pg. 2144
DMG MORI GLOBAL SERVICE TURNING GMBH—See DMG MORI Co., Ltd.; *Int'l*, pg. 2144
DMG MORI GREECE LTD.—See DMG MORI Co., Ltd.; *Int'l*, pg. 2144
DMG MORI HAMBURG GMBH—See DMG MORI Co., Ltd.; *Int'l*, pg. 2143
DMG MORI HILDEN GMBH—See DMG MORI Co., Ltd.; *Int'l*, pg. 2143
DMG MORI HUNGARY KFT.—See DMG MORI Co., Ltd.; *Int'l*, pg. 2144
DMG MORI IBERICA S.L.U.—See DMG MORI Co., Ltd.; *Int'l*, pg. 2144
DMG MORI INDIA PVT. LTD.—See DMG MORI Co., Ltd.; *Int'l*, pg. 2143
DMG MORI ISTANBUL MAKINE TICARET VE SERVIS LIMITED SIRKETI—See DMG MORI Co., Ltd.; *Int'l*, pg. 2144
DMG MORI ITALIA S.R.L.—See DMG MORI Co., Ltd.; *Int'l*, pg. 2144
DMG MORI KOREA CO., LTD.—See DMG MORI Co., Ltd.; *Int'l*, pg. 2144
DMG MORI MACHINE TOOLS TRADING CO., LTD.—See DMG MORI Co., Ltd.; *Int'l*, pg. 2144
DMG MORI (MALAYSIA) SDN. BHD.—See DMG MORI Co., Ltd.; *Int'l*, pg. 2145
DMG MORI MIDDLE EAST FZE—See DMG MORI Co., Ltd.; *Int'l*, pg. 2144
DMG MORI MUNCHEN GMBH—See DMG MORI Co., Ltd.; *Int'l*, pg. 2143
DMG MORI NETHERLANDS B.V.—See DMG MORI Co., Ltd.; *Int'l*, pg. 2144
DMG MORI NORWAY AS—See DMG MORI Co., Ltd.; *Int'l*, pg. 2144
DMG MORI PHILIPPINES INC.—See DMG MORI Co., Ltd.; *Int'l*, pg. 2144
DMG MORI POLSKA SP. Z O.O.—See DMG MORI Co., Ltd.; *Int'l*, pg. 2144
DMG MORI ROMANIA S.R.L.—See DMG MORI Co., Ltd.; *Int'l*, pg. 2144
DMG MORI SALES & SERVICE CO., LTD.—See DMG MORI Co., Ltd.; *Int'l*, pg. 2145
DMG MORI SCHWEIZ AG—See DMG MORI Co., Ltd.; *Int'l*, pg. 2144
DMG MORI SEIKI CANADA INC.—See DMG MORI Co., Ltd.; *Int'l*, pg. 2144
DMG MORI SEIKI CO., LTD. - NARA CAMPUS NO. 1 PLANT—See DMG MORI Co., Ltd.; *Int'l*, pg. 2145
DMG MORI SEIKI CO., LTD. - NARA CAMPUS NO. 2 PLANT—See DMG MORI Co., Ltd.; *Int'l*, pg. 2145
DMG MORI SEIKI INDIA PVT. LTD.—See DMG MORI Co., Ltd.; *Int'l*, pg. 2145
DMG MORI SEIKI (THAILAND) CO., LTD.—See DMG MORI Co., Ltd.; *Int'l*, pg. 2145

DMG MORI CO., LTD.

CORPORATE AFFILIATIONS

DMG MORI SINGAPORE PTE. LTD.—See DMG MORI Co., Ltd.; *Int'l*, pg. 2145
DMG MORI SOFTWARE SOLUTIONS GMBH—See DMG MORI Co., Ltd.; *Int'l*, pg. 2144
DMG MORI SPARE PARTS GMBH—See DMG MORI Co., Ltd.; *Int'l*, pg. 2144
DMG MORI STUTTGART GMBH—See DMG MORI Co., Ltd.; *Int'l*, pg. 2145
DMG MORI SWEDEN AB—See DMG MORI Co., Ltd.; *Int'l*, pg. 2145
DMG MORI TAIWAN CO. LTD.—See DMG MORI Co., Ltd.; *Int'l*, pg. 2145
DMG MORI (THAILAND) CO., LTD.—See DMG MORI Co., Ltd.; *Int'l*, pg. 2143
DMG MORI UK LIMITED—See DMG MORI Co., Ltd.; *Int'l*, pg. 2144
DMG MORI USA, INC.—See DMG MORI Co., Ltd.; *Int'l*, pg. 2145
DMG MORI USED MACHINES CO., LTD.—See DMG MORI Co., Ltd.; *Int'l*, pg. 2145
DMG MORI USED MACHINES GMBH—See DMG MORI Co., Ltd.; *Int'l*, pg. 2144
DMG MORI VIET NAM CO., LTD.—See DMG MORI Co., Ltd.; *Int'l*, pg. 2145
DMG VERTRIEBS UND SERVICE GMBH DECKEL MAHO GILDEMEISTER—See DMG MORI Co., Ltd.; *Int'l*, pg. 2143
DM HEALTHCARE MANAGEMENT SERVICES LLC; *Int'l*, pg. 2142
D&M HOLDINGS U.S. INC.—See Bain Capital, LP; *U.S. Private*, pg. 438
DMH REALTY, LLC—See Pacific Oak Strategic Opportunity REIT, Inc.; *U.S. Public*, pg. 1632
DMI ADMINISTRATIVE SERVICES S.A.—See Dar Al-Maal Al-Islami Trust; *Int'l*, pg. 1971
DMI AUTOMOTIVE INC.—See DMI UK Ltd.; *Int'l*, pg. 2145
DMI CANADA, INC.—See Otter Tail Corporation; *U.S. Public*, pg. 1624
DMI CORP.; *U.S. Private*, pg. 1248
DMI DALIAN LTD—See DMI UK Ltd.; *Int'l*, pg. 2145
DMI DIESEL OFFSHORE (S) PTE LTD.—See DMI UK Ltd.; *Int'l*, pg. 2145
DMI DISTRIBUTION INC.; *U.S. Private*, pg. 1248
DMI FURNITURE, INC.—See Flexsteel Industries, Inc.; *U.S. Public*, pg. 853
DMI GUANGZHOU LTD—See DMI UK Ltd.; *Int'l*, pg. 2145
DMI INTERNATIONAL B.V.—See Aebi Schmidt Holding AG; *Int'l*, pg. 170
DMI MARINE INC.—See DMI UK Ltd.; *Int'l*, pg. 2145
DMI NANTONG LTD—See DMI UK Ltd.; *Int'l*, pg. 2145
D&M, INC.—See Cross Marketing Group Inc.; *Int'l*, pg. 1856
D & M INDUSTRIES, INC.; *U.S. Private*, pg. 1136
DMI SCANDINAVIA AS—See DMI UK Ltd.; *Int'l*, pg. 2145
DMI SOURCING COMPANY, LLC—See Flexsteel Industries, Inc.; *U.S. Public*, pg. 853
DMI TECHNOLOGY CORP.—See Delany Capital Management Corp.; *U.S. Private*, pg. 1194
DMI TILE & MARBLE CO. INC.; *U.S. Private*, pg. 1248
DMITRIY & COMPANY LLC—See RH; *U.S. Public*, pg. 1796
DMI UK LTD.; *Int'l*, pg. 2145
DMI WOLFGANG DRECHSLER GMBH—See DMI UK Ltd.; *Int'l*, pg. 2145
DMI YOUNG & CUNNINGHAM LTD.—See DMI UK Ltd.; *Int'l*, pg. 2145
DMJ & CO., PLLC; *U.S. Private*, pg. 1249
DMJ & CO., PLLC—See DMJ & Co., PLLC; *U.S. Private*, pg. 1249
DMK ASSOCIATES, INC.; *U.S. Private*, pg. 1249
DMK DEUTSCHES MILCHKONTOR GMBH; *Int'l*, pg. 2146
DMK DRILLING FLUIDS LTD.; *Int'l*, pg. 2146
DMK EIS GMBH—See DMK Deutsches Milchkontor GmbH; *Int'l*, pg. 2146
DMK MEXICO, S.A. DE C.V.—See Palmer International, Inc.; *U.S. Private*, pg. 3081
DMK PHARMACEUTICALS CORPORATION; *U.S. Public*, pg. 671
DM LABEL GROUP—See Avery Dennison Corporation; *U.S. Public*, pg. 244
D.M. LOVITT INSURANCE AGENCY—See GTCR LLC; *U.S. Private*, pg. 1802
DMM SALES SDN. BHD.—See MBM Resources Berhad; *Int'l*, pg. 4754
DMN3/DALLAS—See DMN3; *U.S. Private*, pg. 1249
DMN3; *U.S. Private*, pg. 1249
DMN LTD.—See The Gores Group, LLC; *U.S. Private*, pg. 4034
DM NOVAFOAM LTD.—See Daicel Corporation; *Int'l*, pg. 1918
DMOA CO., LTD; *Int'l*, pg. 2146
DM OPTICS LTD.—See Yokogawa Electric Corporation; *Int'l*, pg. 8592
DMOS DRESDEN MOS DESIGN GMBH—See ELMOS Semiconductor AG; *Int'l*, pg. 2368
DMP CORPORATION—See Element Solutions Inc.; *U.S. Public*, pg. 725

DM PETROLEUM OPERATIONS COMPANY—See Jacobs Engineering Group, Inc.; *U.S. Public*, pg. 1185
DM PLC; *Int'l*, pg. 2142
D&M PREMIUM SOUND SOLUTIONS, LLC—See Masimo Corporation; *U.S. Public*, pg. 1392
DM PRODUCTIONS B.V.—See PostNL N.V.; *Int'l*, pg. 5940
D&M PROFESSIONAL—See Bain Capital, LP; *U.S. Private*, pg. 438
DMR DEMIRBAG ELEKTRIK MALZEMELERI TICARET ANONIM SIRKETI—See Schneider Electric SE; *Int'l*, pg. 6626
DMR HYDROENGINEERING & INFRASTRUCTURES LTD.; *Int'l*, pg. 2146
DMR MECHANICAL, LLC.; *U.S. Private*, pg. 1249
DMR SEALS LIMITED—See Diploma PLC; *Int'l*, pg. 2128
DMS CO., LTD.; *Int'l*, pg. 2146
DMS FACILITY SERVICES INC.; *U.S. Private*, pg. 1249
DMS HEALTH TECHNOLOGIES, INC.; *U.S. Private*, pg. 1249
DM SHIPPING LTD—See d'Amico International Shipping S.A.; *Int'l*, pg. 1899
DM SHIVTEX, INC.; *U.S. Public*, pg. 1248
DMS IMAGING SA; *Int'l*, pg. 2146
DMS INC.; *Int'l*, pg. 2146
DMS INK—See Revitalize Capital; *U.S. Private*, pg. 3416
DMS INTERNATIONAL INCORPORATED—See NBA Quantum PLC; *Int'l*, pg. 5179
DMS KOREA CO., LTD.—See Daido Metal Corporation; *Int'l*, pg. 1921
DMS MOLDES MEXICO S.A. DE C.V.—See Daido Steel Co., Ltd.; *Int'l*, pg. 1922
DM SOLUTIONS CO., LTD; *Int'l*, pg. 2142
DMSS SOFTWARE LTDA.; *Int'l*, pg. 2146
D.M. STOLTZFUS & SON INC.; *U.S. Private*, pg. 1142
DMST PTY LIMITED—See SubZero Group Limited; *Int'l*, pg. 7250
DMT CONSULTING LIMITED—See TUV NORD AG; *Int'l*, pg. 7980
DMT CONSULTING PRIVATE LIMITED—See TUV NORD AG; *Int'l*, pg. 7980
DMT DEMMINER MASCHINENBAU TECHNIK GMBH; *Int'l*, pg. 2146
D.M. TEXTILE MILLS LIMITED; *Int'l*, pg. 1901
DMT GEOSCIENCES LTD.—See TUV NORD AG; *Int'l*, pg. 7980
DMT GEOSURVEY SPOL. S.R.O.—See TUV NORD AG; *Int'l*, pg. 7980
DMT GMBH & CO. KG—See TUV NORD AG; *Int'l*, pg. 7980
DMT INGENIEURE GMBH—See Per Aarsleff Holding A/S; *Int'l*, pg. 5795
DMT-KAI BATLA PTY. LTD.—See TUV NORD AG; *Int'l*, pg. 7980
D&M TOOL CORPORATION—See Specialty Manufacturers, Inc.; *U.S. Private*, pg. 3750
DMT PETROLOGIC GMBH—See TUV NORD AG; *Int'l*, pg. 7980
DM TRANS, LLC; *U.S. Private*, pg. 1248
D & M TRUSS CO. INC.—See Tibbetts Lumber Co., LLC; *U.S. Private*, pg. 4166
DMT SERVICES INC.; *U.S. Private*, pg. 1249
DMT SOLUTIONS GLOBAL CORPORATION—See Platinum Equity, LLC; *U.S. Private*, pg. 3202
DMT VERWALTUNGSGESELLSCHAFT MBH—See TUV NORD AG; *Int'l*, pg. 7980
DMW CORPORATION - HOUSTON BRANCH—See DMW Corporation; *Int'l*, pg. 2147
DMW CORPORATION INDIA PRIVATE LIMITED—See DMW Corporation; *Int'l*, pg. 2147
DMW CORPORATION - MISHIMA PLANT—See DMW Corporation; *Int'l*, pg. 2147
DMW CORPORATION; *Int'l*, pg. 2146
DMW ELECTRICAL INSTRUMENTATION INC.; *Int'l*, pg. 2147
DM WENCESLAO & ASSOCIATES, INC.; *Int'l*, pg. 2142
DMW&H; *U.S. Private*, pg. 1249
DMW WORLDWIDE LLC; *U.S. Private*, pg. 1249
DMX TECHNOLOGIES GROUP LIMITED; *Int'l*, pg. 2147
DMY SQUARED TECHNOLOGY GROUP, INC.; *U.S. Public*, pg. 671
DNA BRAND MECHANICS; *U.S. Private*, pg. 1249
DNA BRANDS, INC.; *U.S. Public*, pg. 671
DNA CHIP RESEARCH INC.; *Int'l*, pg. 2147
DNA DIAGNOSTICS CENTER, INC.—See GHO Capital Partners LLP; *Int'l*, pg. 2959
DNA DIRECT, INC.—See The Cigna Group; *U.S. Public*, pg. 2062
DNA ELECTRONICS, INC.—See Genting Berhad; *Int'l*, pg. 2928
DNA ELECTRONICS, INC.—See Genting Berhad; *Int'l*, pg. 2928
DNA ELECTRONICS LTD.—See Genting Berhad; *Int'l*, pg. 2928
DNA GENOTEK INC.—See OraSure Technologies, Inc.; *U.S. Public*, pg. 1614
DNA HOLDINGS CORPORATION; *Int'l*, pg. 2147
DNA INVESTMENT JOINT STOCK CORPORATION; *Int'l*, pg. 2147

DNAKE XIAMEN INTELLIGENT TECHNOLOGY CO., LTD.; *Int'l*, pg. 2147
DNA LABORATORIES SDN. BHD.—See Revvity, Inc.; *U.S. Public*, pg. 1794
DNA LABS—See Sonic Healthcare Limited; *Int'l*, pg. 7097
DNA LANDMARKS INC.—See BASF SE; *Int'l*, pg. 877
DNAL CO., LTD.—See BTS Group Holdings Public Company Limited; *Int'l*, pg. 1205
DNA LINK INC.; *Int'l*, pg. 2147
DNA LINK USA, INC.—See DNA Link Inc.; *Int'l*, pg. 2147
D NALOZBE D.D.; *Int'l*, pg. 2147
DNA MODEL MANAGEMENT LLC; *U.S. Private*, pg. 1249
DNA OY—See Telenor ASA; *Int'l*, pg. 7538
DNA RESPONSE, INC.—See Bluewater Media LLC; *U.S. Private*, pg. 598
DNATA FOR AIRPORT SERVICES LTD.—See The Emirates Group; *Int'l*, pg. 7640
DNATA INC.—See The Emirates Group; *Int'l*, pg. 7639
DNATA INTERNATIONAL PVT LTD—See The Emirates Group; *Int'l*, pg. 7639
DNATA LIMITED—See The Emirates Group; *Int'l*, pg. 7639
DNATA NEWREST SOUTH AFRICA—See Newrest Group International S.A.S.; *Int'l*, pg. 5237
DNATA PW AIRPORT LOGISTICS LLC—See The Emirates Group; *Int'l*, pg. 7639
DNATA SINGAPORE PTE LTD—See The Emirates Group; *Int'l*, pg. 7639
DNATA—See The Emirates Group; *Int'l*, pg. 7639
DNATA SWITZERLAND AG—See The Emirates Group; *Int'l*, pg. 7640
DNATA TRAVEL (UK) LIMITED—See The Emirates Group; *Int'l*, pg. 7640
DNA TESTING CENTERS, CORP.; *Int'l*, pg. 2147
DNA TESTING CENTRES OF CANADA, LTD.—See DNA Testing Centers, Corp.; *Int'l*, pg. 2147
DN AUTOMOTIVE CORPORATION; *Int'l*, pg. 2147
DN AUTOMOTIVE GERMANY GMBH—See DN Automotive Corporation; *Int'l*, pg. 2147
DN AUTOMOTIVE VMS LIMITED—See DN Automotive Corporation; *Int'l*, pg. 2147
DNB ASIA AS; *Int'l*, pg. 2147
DNB ASSET MANAGEMENT AS—See DNB Bank ASA; *Int'l*, pg. 2147
DNB AUTO FINANCE OY—See DNB Bank ASA; *Int'l*, pg. 2147
DNB BANK ASA; *Int'l*, pg. 2147
DNB BANK POLSKA S.A.—See DNB Bank ASA; *Int'l*, pg. 2147
DNB BOLIGKREDITT AS—See DNB Bank ASA; *Int'l*, pg. 2147
DNB EIENDOM AS—See DNB Bank ASA; *Int'l*, pg. 2148
DNB FINANCIAL CORPORATION—See S&T Bancorp, Inc.; *U.S. Public*, pg. 1832
DNB LIVSFORSIKRING AS—See DNB Bank ASA; *Int'l*, pg. 2148
DNB LUXEMBOURG S.A.—See DNB Bank ASA; *Int'l*, pg. 2148
DNB MARKETS, INC.—See DNB Bank ASA; *Int'l*, pg. 2148
DNB NAERINGSEIENDOM AS—See DNB Bank ASA; *Int'l*, pg. 2148
DNB NAERINGSMEGLING AS—See DNB Bank ASA; *Int'l*, pg. 2148
DNB SWEDEN AB—See DNB Bank ASA; *Int'l*, pg. 2148
DNB (UK) LIMITED—See DNB Bank ASA; *Int'l*, pg. 2148
DNCA FINANCE S.P.A—See Groupe BPCE; *Int'l*, pg. 3093
DNCA LUXEMBOURG SA—See Groupe BPCE; *Int'l*, pg. 3094
DNC MEDIA CO., LTD.; *Int'l*, pg. 2148
D-NEE COSMETICS CO., LTD.—See Arata Corporation; *Int'l*, pg. 536
DNEG NORTH AMERICA INC.—See Prime Focus Limited; *Int'l*, pg. 5977
DNEG PLC—See Prime Focus Limited; *Int'l*, pg. 5977
DNE GROUP LTD.; *U.S. Private*, pg. 1249
D&N ELECTRIC COMPANY; *U.S. Private*, pg. 1138
DNEPROVAGONMASH LTD.—See Dniprovagonmash JSC; *Int'l*, pg. 2148
DNEX DRILLING TECH & OILFIELD SERVICES SDN. BHD.—See Dagang NeXchange Berhad; *Int'l*, pg. 1912
DNEX SEMICONDUCTOR SDN. BHD.—See Dagang NeXchange Berhad; *Int'l*, pg. 1912
DNEX TECHNOLOGY SDN. BHD.—See Dagang NeXchange Berhad; *Int'l*, pg. 1912
DNF CO., LTD - DNF ULSAN PLANT—See DNF Co., Ltd.; *Int'l*, pg. 2148
DNF CO LTD - ELECTRONIC MATERIAL DIVISION—See DNF Co., Ltd.; *Int'l*, pg. 2148
DNF CO LTD - FINE CHEMICAL DIVISION—See DNF Co., Ltd.; *Int'l*, pg. 2148
DNF CO., LTD.; *Int'l*, pg. 2148
DN GLOBAL HOME CARE LTDA—See SOL S.p.A.; *Int'l*, pg. 7067
DNH MEDICAL MANAGEMENT, INC.—See DaVita Inc.; *U.S. Public*, pg. 637
DN HOLDINGS CO.,LTD; *Int'l*, pg. 2147
DNI CORP.; *U.S. Private*, pg. 1249
DNI GROUP, LLC—See Inabata & Co. Ltd.; *Int'l*, pg. 3643
DNI METALS INC.; *Int'l*, pg. 2148

COMPANY NAME INDEX

DNIPROAZOT JSC; *Int'l*, pg. 2148
DNIPROVAGONMASH JSC; *Int'l*, pg. 2148
DNI RETAIL (PTY) LTD.—See Lesaka Technologies, Inc.; *Int'l*, pg. 4468
D.N.K. CO., LTD.—See Dai Nippon Printing Co., Ltd.; *Int'l*, pg. 1914
DNKH LOGISTICS PTE LTD—See Chasen Holdings Limited; *Int'l*, pg. 1457
DN LIGHTING CO., LTD.—See Dai Nippon Toryo Co., Ltd.; *Int'l*, pg. 1916
DNN CORP.—See ESW Capital, LLC; *U.S. Private*, pg. 1430
DNO ASA; *Int'l*, pg. 2148
D'NONCE (JOHORE) SDN. BHD.—See D'nonce Technology Bhd.; *Int'l*, pg. 1899
D'NONCE (KELANTAN) SDN. BHD.—See D'nonce Technology Bhd.; *Int'l*, pg. 1900
D'NONCE (K.L) SDN. BHD.—See D'nonce Technology Bhd.; *Int'l*, pg. 1900
D'NONCE (M) SDN. BHD.—See D'nonce Technology Bhd.; *Int'l*, pg. 1900
D'NONCE TECHNOLOGY BHD.; *Int'l*, pg. 1899
DNO NORGE AS—See DNO ASA; *Int'l*, pg. 2148
DNO NORTH SEA PLC; *Int'l*, pg. 2148
DNO TECHNICAL SERVICES AS—See DNO ASA; *Int'l*, pg. 2148
DNOW AUSTRALIA PTY. LTD.—See DNOW Inc.; *U.S. Public*, pg. 671
DNOW CANADA ULC—See DNOW Inc.; *U.S. Public*, pg. 671
DNOW DE MEXICO S DE RL DE CV—See DNOW Inc.; *U.S. Public*, pg. 671
DNOW INC.; *U.S. Public*, pg. 671
DNOW L.P.—See DNOW Inc.; *U.S. Public*, pg. 671
DNO YEMEN AS—See DNO ASA; *Int'l*, pg. 2148
DNP (AMERICA), INC.—See Dai Nippon Printing Co., Ltd.; *Int'l*, pg. 1914
DNP AMERICA, LLC—See Dai Nippon Printing Co., Ltd.; *Int'l*, pg. 1914
DNP ART COMMUNICATIONS CO., LTD.—See Dai Nippon Printing Co., Ltd.; *Int'l*, pg. 1914
DNP AV CENTER CO., LTD.—See Dai Nippon Printing Co., Ltd.; *Int'l*, pg. 1914
DNP BUSINESS CONSULTING (SHANGHAI) CO., LTD.—See Dai Nippon Printing Co., Ltd.; *Int'l*, pg. 1914
DNP CHUBU CO., LTD.—See Dai Nippon Printing Co., Ltd.; *Int'l*, pg. 1914
DNP COLOR TECHNO KAMEYAMA CO., LTD.—See Dai Nippon Printing Co., Ltd.; *Int'l*, pg. 1914
DNP CORPORATION USA—See Dai Nippon Printing Co., Ltd.; *Int'l*, pg. 1914
DNP DATA TECHNO CO., LTD.—See Dai Nippon Printing Co., Ltd.; *Int'l*, pg. 1914
DNP DATA TECHNO KANSAI CO., LTD.—See Dai Nippon Printing Co., Ltd.; *Int'l*, pg. 1914
DNP DENMARK A/S—See Dai Nippon Printing Co., Ltd.; *Int'l*, pg. 1914
DNP DIGITALCOM CO., LTD.—See Dai Nippon Printing Co., Ltd.; *Int'l*, pg. 1914
DNP DIGITAL SOLUTIONS CO., LTD.—See Dai Nippon Printing Co., Ltd.; *Int'l*, pg. 1914
DNP ELECTRONICS AMERICA, LLC—See Dai Nippon Printing Co., Ltd.; *Int'l*, pg. 1914
DNP ELLIO CO., LTD.—See Dai Nippon Printing Co., Ltd.; *Int'l*, pg. 1914
DNP ENGINEERING CO., LTD.—See Dai Nippon Printing Co., Ltd.; *Int'l*, pg. 1914
DNP FACILITY SERVICES CO., LTD.—See Dai Nippon Printing Co., Ltd.; *Int'l*, pg. 1914
DNP FINE CHEMICALS CO., LTD.—See Dai Nippon Printing Co., Ltd.; *Int'l*, pg. 1914
DNP FINE CHEMICALS UTSUNOMIYA CO., LTD.—See Dai Nippon Printing Co., Ltd.; *Int'l*, pg. 1914
DNP FINE ELECTRONICS CO., LTD.—See Dai Nippon Printing Co., Ltd.; *Int'l*, pg. 1914
DNP FOTOLUSIO CO., LTD.—See Dai Nippon Printing Co., Ltd.; *Int'l*, pg. 1914
DNP GRAPHICA CO., LTD.—See Dai Nippon Printing Co., Ltd.; *Int'l*, pg. 1914
DNP HARTAJAYA SDN BHD—See Wing Tai Holdings Limited; *Int'l*, pg. 8427
DNP HOKKAIDO CO., LTD.—See Dai Nippon Printing Co., Ltd.; *Int'l*, pg. 1914
DNP HOLDING USA CORPORATION—See Dai Nippon Printing Co., Ltd.; *Int'l*, pg. 1914
DNP HOSO CO., LTD.—See Dai Nippon Printing Co., Ltd.; *Int'l*, pg. 1914
DNP HUMAN SERVICES CO., LTD.—See Dai Nippon Printing Co., Ltd.; *Int'l*, pg. 1914
DNP HYPERTECH CO., LTD.—See Dai Nippon Printing Co., Ltd.; *Int'l*, pg. 1914
DNP ID SYSTEM CO., LTD.—See Dai Nippon Printing Co., Ltd.; *Int'l*, pg. 1914
DNP IMAGINGCOMM AMERICA CORPORATION—See Dai Nippon Printing Co., Ltd.; *Int'l*, pg. 1914
DNP IMAGINGCOMM AMERICA CORPORATION—See Dai Nippon Printing Co., Ltd.; *Int'l*, pg. 1914
DNP IMAGINGCOMM ASIA SDN. BHD.—See Dai Nippon Printing Co., Ltd.; *Int'l*, pg. 1914

DNP IMAGINGCOMM EUROPE B.V.—See Dai Nippon Printing Co., Ltd.; *Int'l*, pg. 1914
DNP IMAGING COMMUNICATION (SHANGHAI) CO., LTD.—See Dai Nippon Printing Co., Ltd.; *Int'l*, pg. 1914
DNP INFORMATION SYSTEMS CO., LTD.—See Dai Nippon Printing Co., Ltd.; *Int'l*, pg. 1914
DNP INTERNATIONAL CO. INC.; *U.S. Private*, pg. 1249
DNP INTERNATIONAL TRADING (SHANGHAI) CO., LTD.—See Dai Nippon Printing Co., Ltd.; *Int'l*, pg. 1914
DNP LAND SDN BHD—See Wing Tai Holdings Limited; *Int'l*, pg. 8427
DNP LOGISTICS CO., LTD.—See Dai Nippon Printing Co., Ltd.; *Int'l*, pg. 1915
DNP LSI DESIGN CO., LTD.—See Dai Nippon Printing Co., Ltd.; *Int'l*, pg. 1914
DNP MEDIA ART CO., LTD.—See Dai Nippon Printing Co., Ltd.; *Int'l*, pg. 1915
DNP MEDIA CREATE CO., LTD.—See Dai Nippon Printing Co., Ltd.; *Int'l*, pg. 1915
DNP MEDIA SUPPORT CO., LTD.—See Dai Nippon Printing Co., Ltd.; *Int'l*, pg. 1915
DNP MICRO TECHNICA CO., LTD.—See Dai Nippon Printing Co., Ltd.; *Int'l*, pg. 1915
DNP MULTI PRINT CO., LTD.—See Dai Nippon Printing Co., Ltd.; *Int'l*, pg. 1915
DNP NISHI NIPPON CO., LTD.—See Dai Nippon Printing Co., Ltd.; *Int'l*, pg. 1915
DNP PHOTO IMAGING CO., LTD.—See Dai Nippon Printing Co., Ltd.; *Int'l*, pg. 1915
DNP PHOTO IMAGING EUROPE SAS—See Dai Nippon Printing Co., Ltd.; *Int'l*, pg. 1915
DNP PHOTO IMAGING JAPAN CO., LTD.—See Dai Nippon Printing Co., Ltd.; *Int'l*, pg. 1915
DNP PHOTO IMAGING RUSSIA LLC—See Dai Nippon Printing Co., Ltd.; *Int'l*, pg. 1915
DNP PHOTOMASK EUROPE S.P.A.—See Dai Nippon Printing Co., Ltd.; *Int'l*, pg. 1915
DNP PLANNING NETWORK CO., LTD.—See Dai Nippon Printing Co., Ltd.; *Int'l*, pg. 1915
DNP PLASTIC MOLDING (SHANGHAI) CO., LTD.—See Dai Nippon Printing Co., Ltd.; *Int'l*, pg. 1915
DNP PRECISION DEVICES CO., LTD.—See Dai Nippon Printing Co., Ltd.; *Int'l*, pg. 1915
DNP PROPERTY MANAGEMENT SDN BHD—See Wing Tai Holdings Limited; *Int'l*, pg. 8427
DNP SELECT INCOME FUND INC.; *U.S. Public*, pg. 671
DNP SHIKOKU CO., LTD.—See Dai Nippon Printing Co., Ltd.; *Int'l*, pg. 1915
DNP (SINGAPORE) PTE. LTD.—See Dai Nippon Printing Co., Ltd.; *Int'l*, pg. 1914
DNP SP TECH CO., LTD.—See Dai Nippon Printing Co., Ltd.; *Int'l*, pg. 1915
DNP TAMURA PLASTIC CO., LTD.—See Dai Nippon Printing Co., Ltd.; *Int'l*, pg. 1915
DNP TECHNOPACK CO., LTD.—See Dai Nippon Printing Co., Ltd.; *Int'l*, pg. 1915
DNP TECHNOPACK TOKAI CO., LTD.—See Dai Nippon Printing Co., Ltd.; *Int'l*, pg. 1915
DNP TECHNOPACK YOKOHAMA CO., LTD.—See Dai Nippon Printing Co., Ltd.; *Int'l*, pg. 1915
DNP TECHNO POLYMER CO., LTD.—See Dai Nippon Printing Co., Ltd.; *Int'l*, pg. 1915
DNP TOHOKU CO., LTD.—See Dai Nippon Printing Co., Ltd.; *Int'l*, pg. 1915
DNP TOTAL PROCESS MAEBASHI CO., LTD.—See Dai Nippon Printing Co., Ltd.; *Int'l*, pg. 1915
DNP TOTAL PROCESS NAGAOKA CO., LTD.—See Dai Nippon Printing Co., Ltd.; *Int'l*, pg. 1915
DNP TRADING CO., LTD.—See Dai Nippon Printing Co., Ltd.; *Int'l*, pg. 1915
DNP (UK) CO. LTD.—See Dai Nippon Printing Co., Ltd.; *Int'l*, pg. 1914
DNP UNIPROCESS CO., LTD.—See Dai Nippon Printing Co., Ltd.; *Int'l*, pg. 1915
DNR PRESSURE WELDING LTD.—See Quanta Services, Inc.; *U.S. Public*, pg. 1751
DNS CAPITAL, LLC; *U.S. Private*, pg. 1249
DNS ELECTRONICS, LLC—See Screen Holdings Co., Ltd.; *Int'l*, pg. 6654
DNS FEATS (TAIWAN) CO., LTD—See Screen Holdings Co., Ltd.; *Int'l*, pg. 6654
DN TANKS, INC.; *U.S. Private*, pg. 1249
DNT BUSINESS SERVICE CO., LTD.—See Dai Nippon Toryo Co., Ltd.; *Int'l*, pg. 1916
DNT CONSTRUCTION, LLC; *U.S. Private*, pg. 1249
DNT CORPORATION; *U.S. Private*, pg. 1249
DNT KANSAI MEXICANA S.A. DE C.V.—See Dai Nippon Toryo Co., Ltd.; *Int'l*, pg. 1916
DNT PAINT (MALAYSIA) SDN. BHD.—See Dai Nippon Toryo Co., Ltd.; *Int'l*, pg. 1916
DNT SANYO CHEMICAL CO., LTD.—See Dai Nippon Toryo Co., Ltd.; *Int'l*, pg. 1916
DNT SERVICE CO., LTD.—See Dai Nippon Toryo Co., Ltd.; *Int'l*, pg. 1916
DNT (SHANGHAI) CO., LTD.—See Dai Nippon Toryo Co., Ltd.; *Int'l*, pg. 1916
DNT SINGAPORE PTE. LTD.—See Dai Nippon Toryo Co., Ltd.; *Int'l*, pg. 1916
DN TYRE & RUBBER PLC; *Int'l*, pg. 2147

DOBER CHEMICAL CORP.

DNV ALESUND—See DNV GL Group AS; *Int'l*, pg. 2148
DNV BERGEN—See DNV GL Group AS; *Int'l*, pg. 2148
DNV BUSINESS ASSURANCE INDIA PRIVATE LTD—See DNV GL Group AS; *Int'l*, pg. 2148
DNV CERTIFICATION—See DNV GL Group AS; *Int'l*, pg. 2151
DNV EIENDOM—See DNV GL Group AS; *Int'l*, pg. 2148
DNV FLORO—See DNV GL Group AS; *Int'l*, pg. 2148
DNV FORDE—See DNV GL Group AS; *Int'l*, pg. 2148
DNV FREDRIKSTAD—See DNV GL Group AS; *Int'l*, pg. 2148
DNV GL BUSINESS ASSURANCE DENMARK A/S—See DNV GL Group AS; *Int'l*, pg. 2149
DNV GL CYPRUS LTD.—See DNV GL Group AS; *Int'l*, pg. 2149
DNV GL GROUP AS; *Int'l*, pg. 2148
DNV GL - LITHUANIA—See DNV GL Group AS; *Int'l*, pg. 2149
DNV GL SE - HAMBURG—See DNV GL Group AS; *Int'l*, pg. 2149
DNV GL SE—See DNV GL Group AS; *Int'l*, pg. 2148
DNV GL—See DNV GL Group AS; *Int'l*, pg. 2151
DNV GL—See DNV GL Group AS; *Int'l*, pg. 2151
DNV HAUGESUND—See DNV GL Group AS; *Int'l*, pg. 2150
DNV INC.—See DNV GL Group AS; *Int'l*, pg. 2151
DNV KRISTIANSAND S—See DNV GL Group AS; *Int'l*, pg. 2150
DNV KRISTIANSUND N—See DNV GL Group AS; *Int'l*, pg. 2150
DNV MARITIME NORTH AMERICA NEW ORLEANS—See DNV GL Group AS; *Int'l*, pg. 2151
DNV PORSGRUNN—See DNV GL Group AS; *Int'l*, pg. 2150
DNV REGION NORGE AS—See DNV GL Group AS; *Int'l*, pg. 2150
DNV REGION NORGE AS—See DNV GL Group AS; *Int'l*, pg. 2150
DNV SOFTWARE USA—See DNV GL Group AS; *Int'l*, pg. 2151
DNV STORD—See DNV GL Group AS; *Int'l*, pg. 2151
DNV TROMSO—See DNV GL Group AS; *Int'l*, pg. 2151
DNV ULSTEINVIK—See DNV GL Group AS; *Int'l*, pg. 2151
DNXCORP SE; *Int'l*, pg. 2151
DNX DRILLING INC.—See Incitec Pivot Limited; *Int'l*, pg. 3647
DOALL COMPANY; *U.S. Private*, pg. 1250
DOAN BUICK; *U.S. Private*, pg. 1250
DOAN CHEVROLET LLC; *U.S. Private*, pg. 1250
DOAN DODGE CHRYSLER JEEP RAM FIAT—See West Herr Automotive Group, Inc.; *U.S. Private*, pg. 4485
DOAN PYRAMID LLC; *U.S. Private*, pg. 1250
DOAN VIET CO. LTD—See Doppelmayr Group; *Int'l*, pg. 2174
DOAN XA PORT JSC; *Int'l*, pg. 2152
DOAPP, INC.—See Vista Equity Partners, LLC; *U.S. Private*, pg. 4399
DOAR COMMUNICATIONS INC.; *U.S. Private*, pg. 1250
DOBA LLC; *U.S. Private*, pg. 1250
DOBANK SPA; *Int'l*, pg. 2152
DOBBIES GARDEN CENTRES LIMITED—See Hattington Capital LLP; *Int'l*, pg. 3285
DOBBIES GARDEN CENTRES LIMITED—See Midlothian Capital Partners Limited; *Int'l*, pg. 4886
DOBBIES GROVELANDS—See Hattington Capital LLP; *Int'l*, pg. 3285
DOBBIES GROVELANDS—See Midlothian Capital Partners Limited; *Int'l*, pg. 4887
DOBBS APPAREL—See David Dobbs Enterprises Inc.; *U.S. Private*, pg. 1169
DOBBS BROTHERS MANAGEMENT; *U.S. Private*, pg. 1250
DOBBS BUSINESS PRODUCTS—See David Dobbs Enterprises Inc.; *U.S. Private*, pg. 1169
DOBBS FORD, INC.—See AutoNation, Inc.; *U.S. Public*, pg. 234
DOBBS FORD OF MEMPHIS, INC.—See AutoNation, Inc.; *U.S. Public*, pg. 234
DOBBS MOBILE BAY, INC.—See AutoNation, Inc.; *U.S. Public*, pg. 234
DOBBS MOBILE BAY, INC.—See AutoNation, Inc.; *U.S. Public*, pg. 234
DOBBS MOTORS OF ARIZONA, INC.—See AutoNation, Inc.; *U.S. Public*, pg. 234
DOBBS MOTORS OF ARIZONA, INC.—See AutoNation, Inc.; *U.S. Public*, pg. 234
DOBBS TEMPORARY SERVICES, INC.; *U.S. Private*, pg. 1250
DOBBS TIRE & AUTO CENTERS, INC.; *U.S. Private*, pg. 1250
DOBER CHEMICAL CORP. - GLENWOOD PLANT—See Dober Chemical Corp.; *U.S. Private*, pg. 1250
DOBER CHEMICAL CORP. - MIDLOTHIAN PLANT—See Dober Chemical Corp.; *U.S. Private*, pg. 1250
DOBER CHEMICAL CORP.; *U.S. Private*, pg. 1250
DOBLE ENGINEERING COMPANY—See ESCO Technologies, Inc.; *U.S. Public*, pg. 793
DOBLE LEMKE GMBH—See ESCO Technologies, Inc.; *U.S. Public*, pg. 793

DOBER CHEMICAL CORP.

DOBLE POWERTEST LIMITED—See ESCO Technologies, Inc.; *U.S. Public*, pg. 793
DOBLER CONSULTING INC.; *U.S. Private*, pg. 1250
DOBLETHOMAS & ASSOCIATES, INC.—See Laco Associates, Inc.; *U.S. Private*, pg. 2372
DOBLE TRANSINOR AS—See ESCO Technologies, Inc.; *U.S. Public*, pg. 793
DOBOJINVEST A.D.; *Int'l*, pg. 2152
DOBOJKA A.D.; *Int'l*, pg. 2153
DOBOTEX ITALIA SRL—See Kering S.A.; *Int'l*, pg. 4136
DOBOTEX UK LTD—See Kering S.A.; *Int'l*, pg. 4136
DOBRINSKI OF KINGFISHER, INC.; *U.S. Private*, pg. 1250
DOBROPLAST FABRYKA OKIEN SP. Z O.O.—See Arbonia AG; *Int'l*, pg. 538
DOBRUDZHA HOLDING AD; *Int'l*, pg. 2153
DOBSON FLOORS INC.; *U.S. Private*, pg. 1250
DOBY VERROLEC FZE—See Heitkamp & Thumann KG; *Int'l*, pg. 3326
DOBY VERROLEC LTD—See Heitkamp & Thumann KG; *Int'l*, pg. 3326
DOCAPOST—See La Poste S.A.; *Int'l*, pg. 4388
DOCASAP, INC.—See UnitedHealth Group Incorporated; *U.S. Public*, pg. 2240
DO CA SRL—See Savino Del Bene S.p.A.; *Int'l*, pg. 6600
DOCAVENUE SASU—See Cegedim S.A.; *Int'l*, pg. 1390
DOC CARE AB—See Lundbeckfonden; *Int'l*, pg. 4583
DOCCHECK AG; *Int'l*, pg. 2153
DOCCHECK MEDIZINBEDARF & LOGISTIK GMBH—See DocCheck AG; *Int'l*, pg. 2153
DOC DORTMUNDER OBERFLACHENCENTRUM GMBH—See ThyssenKrupp AG; *Int'l*, pg. 7731
DOCEBO FRANCE S.A.S.—See Docebo, Inc.; *Int'l*, pg. 2153
DOCEBO, INC.; *Int'l*, pg. 2153
DOCEBO NA INC.—See Docebo, Inc.; *Int'l*, pg. 2153
DOCEBO S.P.A.—See Docebo, Inc.; *Int'l*, pg. 2153
DOCEBO UK LTD.—See Docebo, Inc.; *Int'l*, pg. 2153
DOCEO OFFICE SOLUTIONS, LLC; *U.S. Private*, pg. 1251
DOC GENERICI S.R.L.—See Intermediate Capital Group plc; *Int'l*, pg. 3742
DOCGO INC.; *U.S. Public*, pg. 672
DOCHTER LUMBER & SAWMILL, INC.; *U.S. Private*, pg. 1251
DOCIRCLE INC.; *U.S. Private*, pg. 1251
DOCKER, INC.; *U.S. Private*, pg. 1251
DOCKERS BRAND—See Levi Strauss & Co.; *U.S. Public*, pg. 1308
DOCKING BANCSHARES, INC.; *U.S. Private*, pg. 1251
DOCKING SOLUTION & SERVICE GMBH—See Sanwa Holdings Corporation; *Int'l*, pg. 6560
DOCK LEVELER MANUFACTURING; *U.S. Private*, pg. 1251
DOCK-N-LOCK LLC; *U.S. Private*, pg. 1251
DOCK PRODUCTS CANADA—See ASSA ABLOY AB; *Int'l*, pg. 633
DOCK RESINS CORPORATION—See Lifecore Biomedical, Inc.; *U.S. Public*, pg. 1312
DOCKSIDE SERVICES, INC.—See ATAR Capital, LLC; *U.S. Private*, pg. 364
DOCKSIDE SERVICES, INC—See ModivCare, Inc.; *U.S. Public*, pg. 1455
DOCK TELEMARKETING, S.A.—See Melia Hotels International, S.A.; *Int'l*, pg. 4809
DOCKWISE LTD.—See HAL Trust N.V.; *Int'l*, pg. 3226
DOCKWISE YACHT TRANSPORT, LLC—See Spliethoff's Bevrachtingskantoor B.V.; *Int'l*, pg. 7141
DOCKYARD GENERAL ENGINEERING SERVICES (PVT) LTD. - MARINE & INDUSTRIAL HARDWARE DIVISION—See Colombo Dockyard PLC; *Int'l*, pg. 1702
DOCKYARD GENERAL ENGINEERING SERVICES (PVT) LTD.—See Colombo Dockyard PLC; *Int'l*, pg. 1702
DOCLOGIX JSC—See Alna AB; *Int'l*, pg. 364
DOCMAGIC, INC.; *U.S. Private*, pg. 1251
DOCMED TECHNOLOGY PTE. LTD.—See Hyphens Pharma International Limited; *Int'l*, pg. 3553
DOCMETRIC GMBH—See PAO Severstal; *Int'l*, pg. 5731
DOCMORRIS N.V.—See Zur Rose Group AG; *Int'l*, pg. 8696
DO & CO AIRLINE CATERING AUSTRIA GMBH—See DO & CO Aktiengesellschaft; *Int'l*, pg. 2151
DO & CO AKTIENGESELLSCHAFT; *Int'l*, pg. 2151
DO & CO ALBERTINA GMBH—See DO & CO Aktiengesellschaft; *Int'l*, pg. 2152
DO & CO BERLIN GMBH—See DO & CO Aktiengesellschaft; *Int'l*, pg. 2152
DO & CO CATERING-CONSULT & BETEILIGUNGS GMBH—See DO & CO Aktiengesellschaft; *Int'l*, pg. 2152
DO & CO CATERING & LOGISTICS AUSTRIA GMBH—See DO & CO Aktiengesellschaft; *Int'l*, pg. 2152
DO & CO CHICAGO CATERING, INC.—See DO & CO Aktiengesellschaft; *Int'l*, pg. 2152
DOCO CREDIT UNION; *U.S. Private*, pg. 1251
DO & CO EVENT & AIRLINE CATERING LTD—See DO & CO Aktiengesellschaft; *Int'l*, pg. 2152

DO & CO EVENT AUSTRIA GMBH—See DO & CO Aktiengesellschaft; *Int'l*, pg. 2152
DO & CO FRANKFURT GMBH—See DO & CO Aktiengesellschaft; *Int'l*, pg. 2152
DO & CO GASTRONOMIE GMBH—See DO & CO Aktiengesellschaft; *Int'l*, pg. 2152
DO & CO HOTEL MUNCHEN GMBH—See DO & CO Aktiengesellschaft; *Int'l*, pg. 2152
DO & CO IM HAAS HAUS RESTAURANTBETRIEBS GMBH—See DO & CO Aktiengesellschaft; *Int'l*, pg. 2152
DO & CO IM PLATINUM RESTAURANTBETRIEBS GMBH—See DO & CO Aktiengesellschaft; *Int'l*, pg. 2152
DO & CO INTERNATIONAL CATERING LTD—See DO & CO Aktiengesellschaft; *Int'l*, pg. 2152
DO & CO KYIV LLC—See DO & CO Aktiengesellschaft; *Int'l*, pg. 2152
DO & CO LOS ANGELES, INC.—See DO & CO Aktiengesellschaft; *Int'l*, pg. 2152
DO & CO LOUNGE GMBH—See DO & CO Aktiengesellschaft; *Int'l*, pg. 2152
DOCOMO BEIJING COMMUNICATIONS LABORATORIES CO., LTD.—See Nippon Telegraph & Telephone Corporation; *Int'l*, pg. 5349
DOCOMO CAPITAL, INC.—See Nippon Telegraph & Telephone Corporation; *Int'l*, pg. 5349
DOCOMO COMMUNICATIONS LABORATORIES EUROPE GMBH—See Nippon Telegraph & Telephone Corporation; *Int'l*, pg. 5349
DOCOMO CS HOKKAIDO, INC.—See Nippon Telegraph & Telephone Corporation; *Int'l*, pg. 5342
DOCOMO CS, INC.—See Nippon Telegraph & Telephone Corporation; *Int'l*, pg. 5349
DOCOMO DATACOM, INC.—See Nippon Telegraph & Telephone Corporation; *Int'l*, pg. 5342
DOCOMO DIGITAL GERMANY GMBH—See Bango Plc; *Int'l*, pg. 836
DOCOMO DIGITAL LIMITED—See Bango Plc; *Int'l*, pg. 836
DOCOMO ENGINEERING CHUGOKU, INC.—See Nippon Telegraph & Telephone Corporation; *Int'l*, pg. 5349
DOCOGO ENGINEERING HOKKAIDO INC.—See Nippon Telegraph & Telephone Corporation; *Int'l*, pg. 5349
DOCOMO ENGINEERING KANSAI, INC.—See Nippon Telegraph & Telephone Corporation; *Int'l*, pg. 5349
DOCOMO ENGINEERING SHIKOKU INC.—See Nippon Telegraph & Telephone Corporation; *Int'l*, pg. 5349
DOCOMO ENGINEERING TOKAI INC.—See Nippon Telegraph & Telephone Corporation; *Int'l*, pg. 5349
DOCOMO EUROPE LIMITED—See Nippon Telegraph & Telephone Corporation; *Int'l*, pg. 5349
DOCOMO GACCO, INC.—See Nippon Telegraph & Telephone Corporation; *Int'l*, pg. 5342
DOCOMO I KYUSHU INC.—See Nippon Telegraph & Telephone Corporation; *Int'l*, pg. 5350
DOCOMO INNOVATIONS, INC.—See Nippon Telegraph & Telephone Corporation; *Int'l*, pg. 5349
DOCOMO INTERTOUCH AUSTRALIA PTY. LTD.—See Nippon Telegraph & Telephone Corporation; *Int'l*, pg. 5350
DOCOMO INTERTOUCH PTE. LTD.—See Nippon Telegraph & Telephone Corporation; *Int'l*, pg. 5350
DOCOMO MOBILE INC.—See Nippon Telegraph & Telephone Corporation; *Int'l*, pg. 5349
DOCOMO MOBILEMEDIA KANSAI, INC.—See Nippon Telegraph & Telephone Corporation; *Int'l*, pg. 5349
DOCOMO MOBILE TOKAI INC.—See Nippon Telegraph & Telephone Corporation; *Int'l*, pg. 5349
DOCOMO MONEX HOLDINGS, INC.—See Monex Group, Inc.; *Int'l*, pg. 5032
DOCOMO PACIFIC, INC.—See Nippon Telegraph & Telephone Corporation; *Int'l*, pg. 5349
DOCOMO PACIFIC(SAIPAN), INC.—See Nippon Telegraph & Telephone Corporation; *Int'l*, pg. 5342
DOCOMO SERVICE CHUGOKU, INC.—See Nippon Telegraph & Telephone Corporation; *Int'l*, pg. 5350
DOCOMO SERVICE HOKKAIDO INC.—See Nippon Telegraph & Telephone Corporation; *Int'l*, pg. 5350
DOCOMO SERVICE HOKURIKU INC.—See Nippon Telegraph & Telephone Corporation; *Int'l*, pg. 5350
DOCOMO SERVICE INC.—See Nippon Telegraph & Telephone Corporation; *Int'l*, pg. 5349
DOCOMO SERVICE KANSAI INC.—See Nippon Telegraph & Telephone Corporation; *Int'l*, pg. 5350
DOCOMO SERVICE KYUSHU INC.—See Nippon Telegraph & Telephone Corporation; *Int'l*, pg. 5350
DOCOMO SERVICE SHIKOKU INC.—See Nippon Telegraph & Telephone Corporation; *Int'l*, pg. 5350
DOCOMO SERVICE TOHOKU INC.—See Nippon Telegraph & Telephone Corporation; *Int'l*, pg. 5350
DOCOMO SERVICE TOKAI INC.—See Nippon Telegraph & Telephone Corporation; *Int'l*, pg. 5350
DOCOMO SUPPORT CO., LTD.—See Nippon Telegraph & Telephone Corporation; *Int'l*, pg. 5350
DOCOMO SYSTEMS, INC.—See Nippon Telegraph & Telephone Corporation; *Int'l*, pg. 5350
DOCOMO TAMETAN, INC.—See Nippon Telegraph & Telephone Corporation; *Int'l*, pg. 5350

CORPORATE AFFILIATIONS

DOCOMO TECHNOLOGY, INC.—See Nippon Telegraph & Telephone Corporation; *Int'l*, pg. 5350
DO & CO MUNCHEN GMBH—See DO & CO Aktiengesellschaft; *Int'l*, pg. 2152
DO & CO MUSEUM CATERING LTD—See DO & CO Aktiengesellschaft; *Int'l*, pg. 2152
DO & CO NEW YORK CATERING, INC.—See DO & CO Aktiengesellschaft; *Int'l*, pg. 2152
DOCON TECHNOLOGIES PRIVATE LIMITED; *Int'l*, pg. 2153
DO & CO PARTY-SERVICE & CATERING GMBH—See DO & CO Aktiengesellschaft; *Int'l*, pg. 2152
DO & CO PASTRY GMBH—See DO & CO Aktiengesellschaft; *Int'l*, pg. 2152
DO & CO POLAND SP. Z O.O.—See DO & CO Aktiengesellschaft; *Int'l*, pg. 2152
DO & CO SALZBURG RESTAURANTS & BETRIEBS GMBH—See DO & CO Aktiengesellschaft; *Int'l*, pg. 2152
DO & CO SERVICE GMBH—See DO & CO Aktiengesellschaft; *Int'l*, pg. 2152
DOCPHIN, INC.—See HealthTap, Inc.; *U.S. Private*, pg. 1898
DOCPLANNER GROUP; *Int'l*, pg. 2153
DOCPOINT SOLUTIONS, LLC—See Konica Minolta, Inc.; *Int'l*, pg. 4257
DOC POPCORN FRANCHISING, INC.; *U.S. Private*, pg. 1251
DOCSCENTRE PTY. LTD.—See Sequoia Financial Group Limited; *Int'l*, pg. 6719
DOCSCORP PTY. LIMITED—See Freedom Solutions Group, L.L.C.; *U.S. Private*, pg. 1604
DOCS DRUGS LTD.; *U.S. Private*, pg. 1251
DOCS FOOD STORES INC.; *U.S. Private*, pg. 1251
DOCS GLOBAL INC.—See ICON plc; *Int'l*, pg. 3584
DOCS INTERNATIONAL BELGIUM N.V.—See ICON plc; *Int'l*, pg. 3584
DOCS INTERNATIONAL BV—See ICON plc; *Int'l*, pg. 3584
DOCS INTERNATIONAL POLAND SP. Z O.O.—See ICON plc; *Int'l*, pg. 3584
DOCS INTERNATIONAL SWEDEN AB—See ICON plc; *Int'l*, pg. 3584
DOC-TECH, INC.—See DocMagic, Inc.; *U.S. Private*, pg. 1251
DOCTER OPTICS ASIA LTD.—See Hella GmbH & Co. KGaA; *Int'l*, pg. 3331
DOCTER OPTICS INC.—See Hella GmbH & Co. KGaA; *Int'l*, pg. 3331
DOCTER OPTICS SE—See Hella GmbH & Co. KGaA; *Int'l*, pg. 3331
DOCTIPHARMA SAS—See Zur Rose Group AG; *Int'l*, pg. 8696
DOCTISSIMO SAS—See Television Francaise 1 S.A.; *Int'l*, pg. 7542
DOCTOR ANYWHERE PTE LTD.; *Int'l*, pg. 2153
DOCTORBASE, INC.—See Kareo, Inc.; *U.S. Private*, pg. 2262
DOCTOR BRAMBLETT ROAD, LLC—See Waste Management, Inc.; *U.S. Public*, pg. 2331
DOCTOR CARE ANYWHERE GROUP PLC; *Int'l*, pg. 2153
DOCTOR CARE ANYWHERE LIMITED—See Doctor Care Anywhere Group PLC; *Int'l*, pg. 2153
DOCTOR DIABETIC SUPPLY, INC.—See Bertram Capital Management, LLC; *U.S. Private*, pg. 540
DOCTORDIRECTORY.COM, LLC—See Ziff Davis, Inc.; *U.S. Public*, pg. 2404
DOCTORDOCTOR PTY LIMITED—See Sonic Healthcare Limited; *Int'l*, pg. 7097
DOCTORGLASSES CHAIN CO LTD; *Int'l*, pg. 2153
DOCTOR NET, INC.—See Noritsu Koki Co., Ltd.; *Int'l*, pg. 5429
DOCTORS ADMINISTRATIVE SOLUTIONS, LLC; *U.S. Private*, pg. 1251
DOCTOR'S ASSOCIATES INC.; *U.S. Private*, pg. 1251
DOCTOR'S BEST, INC.—See Xiamen Kingdomway Group Company; *Int'l*, pg. 8525
DOCTORS BILLING SERVICE, INC.—See KKR & Co. Inc.; *U.S. Public*, pg. 1249
DOCTOR'S CHOICE HOME CARE, INC.; *U.S. Private*, pg. 1251
THE DOCTORS COMPANY INSURANCE SERVICES—See The Doctors Company; *U.S. Private*, pg. 4021
THE DOCTORS COMPANY/NORTHWEST PHYSICIANS—See The Doctors Company; *U.S. Private*, pg. 4022
THE DOCTORS COMPANY—See The Doctors Company; *U.S. Private*, pg. 4021
THE DOCTORS COMPANY; *U.S. Private*, pg. 4021
DOCTORS EXCHANGE, INC.—See Ebix Inc.; *U.S. Public*, pg. 710
THE DOCTORS (HASTINGS) LIMITED—See Green Cross Health Limited; *Int'l*, pg. 3070
DOCTORS HOSPITAL (CONROE), INC.—See HCA Healthcare, Inc.; *U.S. Public*, pg. 995

COMPANY NAME INDEX

DOCTORS HOSPITAL NORTH AUGUSTA IMAGING CENTER, LLC—See HCA Healthcare, Inc.; *U.S. Public*, pg. 995
DOCTORS HOSPITAL OF AUGUSTA, LLC—See HCA Healthcare, Inc.; *U.S. Public*, pg. 995
DOCTORS HOSPITAL OF AUGUSTA NEUROLOGY, LLC—See HCA Healthcare, Inc.; *U.S. Public*, pg. 995
DOCTORS HOSPITAL OF MANTECA, INC.—See Tenet Healthcare Corporation; *U.S. Public*, pg. 2003
DOCTORS HOSPITAL OF SARASOTA—See HCA Healthcare, Inc.; *U.S. Public*, pg. 995
DOCTORS' HOSPITAL OF SHREVEPORT—See Universal Health Services, Inc.; *U.S. Public*, pg. 2260
DOCTORS HOSPITAL PHYSICIAN SERVICES, LLC—See Quorum Health Corporation; *U.S. Private*, pg. 3329
DOCTORS HOSPITAL—See Baptist Health South Florida, Inc.; *U.S. Private*, pg. 471
THE DOCTORS (HUAPAI) LIMITED—See Green Cross Health Limited; *Int'l*, pg. 3070
THE DOCTORS LABORATORY LIMITED—See Sonic Healthcare Limited; *Int'l*, pg. 7099
THE DOCTORS LABORATORY (MANCHESTER) LIMITED—See Sonic Healthcare Limited; *Int'l*, pg. 7099
THE DOCTORS' LIFE INSURANCE COMPANY INC.—See The Doctors Company; *U.S. Private*, pg. 4022
THE DOCTORS' MANAGEMENT COMPANY—See The Doctors Company; *U.S. Private*, pg. 4022
DOCTORS MEDICAL CENTER OF MODESTO, INC.—See Tenet Healthcare Corporation; *U.S. Public*, pg. 2003
DOCTORS' MEMORIAL HOSPITAL INC.; *U.S. Private*, pg. 1251
DOCTOR'S NATURAL; *U.S. Private*, pg. 1251
DOCTORS.NET.UK LIMITED—See Sony Group Corporation; *Int'l*, pg. 7102
THE DOCTORS (NEW LYNN) LIMITED—See Green Cross Health Limited; *Int'l*, pg. 3070
DOCTORS OUTPATIENT CENTER FOR SURGERY, LLC—See Tenet Healthcare Corporation; *U.S. Public*, pg. 2002
DOCTORS OUTPATIENT SURGICENTER, LTD.—See Tenet Healthcare Corporation; *U.S. Public*, pg. 2010
DOCTORS PARK SURGERY CENTER, LLC—See KKR & Co. Inc.; *U.S. Public*, pg. 1245
DOCTORS' PREFERRED, INC.—See Eagle Publishing Inc.; *U.S. Private*, pg. 1310
DOCTORS RESOURCE SPECIALISTS, LLC—See Riverside Partners, LLC; *U.S. Private*, pg. 3446
DOCTORS SAME DAY SURGERY CENTER, INC.—See HCA Healthcare, Inc.; *U.S. Public*, pg. 995
DOCTORS SAME DAY SURGERY CENTER, LTD.—See HCA Healthcare, Inc.; *U.S. Public*, pg. 995
THE DOCTORS (WHANGAPARAOA) LIMITED—See Green Cross Health Limited; *Int'l*, pg. 3070
DOCUFY GMBH—See Heidelberger Druckmaschinen AG; *Int'l*, pg. 3321
DOCUGRAPHICS, LLC; *U.S. Private*, pg. 1252
DOCU GROUP DEUTSCHE HOLDING GMBH—See Apax Partners LLP; *Int'l*, pg. 502
DOCU GROUP DEUTSCHE HOLDING GMBH—See TowerBrook Capital Partners, L.P.; *U.S. Private*, pg. 4195
DOCUGROUP PAPIR SZOLGALTATO KORLATOLT FELELOSSEGU TARSASAG—See Iron Mountain Incorporated; *U.S. Public*, pg. 1172
DOCU GROUP SWEDEN AB—See Stirling Square Capital Partners LLP; *Int'l*, pg. 7216
DOCU I SVERIGE AB—See Segulah Advisor AB; *Int'l*, pg. 6684
DOCULEGAL, LLC—See Adecco Group AG; *Int'l*, pg. 141
DOCULYNX, INC.—See The HiGro Group LLC; *U.S. Private*, pg. 4052
DOCUMED LTD.—See CSL Limited; *Int'l*, pg. 1866
DOCUMENT CAPTURE TECHNOLOGIES INC.; *U.S. Private*, pg. 1252
DOCUMENT CENTER INC—See Nimonik, Inc.; *Int'l*, pg. 5297
DOCUMENT ESSENTIALS LLC—See Doceo Office Solutions, LLC; *U.S. Private*, pg. 1251
DOCUMENT SERVICE CENTER GMBH.—See RWS Holdings plc; *Int'l*, pg. 6436
DOCUMENT SOLUTIONS LLC—See Modern Office Methods Inc.; *U.S. Private*, pg. 2762
DOCUMENT STORAGE CORPORATION—See Berkshire Partners LLC; *U.S. Private*, pg. 534
DOCUPACE TECHNOLOGIES LLC—See Financial Technology Ventures Management Co. LLC; *U.S. Private*, pg. 1508
DOCUPHASE LLC—See LoneTree Capital LLC; *U.S. Private*, pg. 2490
DOCUPLEX, INC.; *U.S. Private*, pg. 1252
DOCUSIGN BRASIL PARTICIPACOES LTDA.—See DocuSign, Inc.; *U.S. Public*, pg. 672
DOCUSIGN BRASIL SOLUCOES EM TECNOLOGIA LTDA.—See DocuSign, Inc.; *U.S. Public*, pg. 672
DOCUSIGN FRANCE SAS—See DocuSign, Inc.; *U.S. Public*, pg. 672
DOCUSIGN, INC.; *U.S. Public*, pg. 672
DOCUSIGN INTERNATIONAL (ASIA-PACIFIC) PRIVATE LIMITED—See DocuSign, Inc.; *U.S. Public*, pg. 672

DOCUSIGN UK LIMITED—See DocuSign, Inc.; *U.S. Public*, pg. 672
DOCUSOFT SP. Z O.O.—See Arcus S.A.; *Int'l*, pg. 553
DOCUSOURCE INC.; *U.S. Private*, pg. 1252
DOCUSOURCE OF NC, LLC; *U.S. Private*, pg. 1252
DOCUSOURCE PRINT MANAGEMENT; *U.S. Private*, pg. 1252
DOCUTAP INC.—See Warburg Pincus LLC; *U.S. Private*, pg. 4438
DOCUTAR IRATRENDEZO ES TAROLO SZOLGALTATO KFT.—See Iron Mountain Incorporated; *U.S. Public*, pg. 1173
DOCUTEK SOLUTION, INC.—See SYSTEX Corporation; *Int'l*, pg. 7393
DOCUTREND; *U.S. Private*, pg. 1252
DO DAY DREAM PCL; *Int'l*, pg. 2152
DOD BIOTECH PUBLIC COMPANY LIMITED; *Int'l*, pg. 2153
DODD DIESEL INC.; *U.S. Private*, pg. 1252
DO DEUTSCHE OFFICE AG—See alstria office REIT-AG; *Int'l*, pg. 383
DODGE CHRYSLER JEEP OF WINTER HAVEN, INC.; *U.S. Private*, pg. 1252
DODGE CITY AUTO—See AutoCanada Inc.; *Int'l*, pg. 726
DODGE CITY COOPERATIVE EXCHANGE INC.; *U.S. Private*, pg. 1252
DODGE CITY DAILY GLOBE—See Gannett Co., Inc.; *U.S. Public*, pg. 901
DODGE COMMUNICATIONS, INC.—See Myelin Health Communications, Inc.; *U.S. Private*, pg. 2824
DODGE COMPANY INC.; *U.S. Private*, pg. 1252
DODGE DATA & ANALYTICS LLC—See Symphony Technology Group, LLC; *U.S. Private*, pg. 3900
DODGE INDUSTRIAL AUSTRALIA PTY LTD.—See RBC Bearings Incorporated; *U.S. Public*, pg. 1766
DODGE INDUSTRIAL CANADA INC.—See RBC Bearings Incorporated; *U.S. Public*, pg. 1766
DODGE INDUSTRIAL INDIA PRIVATE LIMITED—See RBC Bearings Incorporated; *U.S. Public*, pg. 1766
DODGE MANUFACTURING COMPANY—See ABB Ltd.; *Int'l*, pg. 51
DODGE MECHANICAL POWER TRANSMISSION MEXICO, S. DE R.L. DE C.V.—See RBC Bearings Incorporated; *U.S. Public*, pg. 1766
DODGE MOVING & STORAGE COMPANY INCORPORATED; *U.S. Private*, pg. 1252
DODGEN INDUSTRIES INC.; *U.S. Private*, pg. 1252
DODGE OF BELLEVUE, INC.—See AutoNation, Inc.; *U.S. Public*, pg. 234
DODGE OF BURNSVILLE, INC.; *U.S. Private*, pg. 1252
DODGER INDUSTRIES INC—See The Greene Company of Virginia Inc.; *U.S. Private*, pg. 4039
DODGEVILLE AGRI-SERVICE INC.—See Vita Plus Corporation; *U.S. Private*, pg. 4405
DODIN CAMPENON BERNARD SAS—See VINCI S.A.; *Int'l*, pg. 8230
DODIN GUADELOUPE SAS—See VINCI S.A.; *Int'l*, pg. 8216
DODIN QUEBEC INC.—See VINCI S.A.; *Int'l*, pg. 8216
DODLA DAIRY LIMITED; *Int'l*, pg. 2153
DO DO FASHION LIMITED—See Tungtex (Holdings) Co. Ltd.; *Int'l*, pg. 7972
DODONI PORTFOLIO INVESTMENTS PUBLIC COMPANY LTD.—See Elma Holdings Public Company Ltd; *Int'l*, pg. 2367
DODONI S.A.—See SI Capital Partners Ltd; *Int'l*, pg. 6874
DODSAL ENGINEERING & CONSTRUCTION PTE. LIMITED—See The Dodsal Group; *Int'l*, pg. 7636
THE DODSAL GROUP; *Int'l*, pg. 7636
DODSON ADVERTISING; *U.S. Private*, pg. 1252
DODSON AVIATION INCORPORATED—See Dodson International, Inc.; *U.S. Private*, pg. 1252
DODSON BROTHERS EXTERMINATING COMPANY, INC.; *U.S. Private*, pg. 1252
DODSON ENGINEERED PRODUCTS, INC.—See Core & Main, Inc.; *U.S. Public*, pg. 576
THE DODSON GROUP, INC.; *U.S. Private*, pg. 4022
DODSON INTERNATIONAL, INC.; *U.S. Private*, pg. 1252
DODSON INTERNATIONAL PARTS INC.—See Dodson International, Inc.; *U.S. Private*, pg. 1252
DODSON STEEL PRODUCTS INC.; *U.S. Private*, pg. 1252
DOE-ANDERSON; *U.S. Private*, pg. 1252
DOEDIJNS AUTOMOTIVE B.V.—See IK Investment Partners Limited; *Int'l*, pg. 3609
DOEDIJNS CONTROLS B.V.—See IK Investment Partners Limited; *Int'l*, pg. 3609
DOEDIJNS GROUP INTERNATIONAL B.V.—See IK Investment Partners Limited; *Int'l*, pg. 3609
DOEDIJNS HYDRAULICS B.V.—See IK Investment Partners Limited; *Int'l*, pg. 3609
DOEDIJNS PNEUMATICS B.V.—See IK Investment Partners Limited; *Int'l*, pg. 3609
DOEHLER AUSTRALIA PTY LTD—See Dohler GmbH; *Int'l*, pg. 2156
DOEHLER BUKOVINA LLC—See Dohler GmbH; *Int'l*, pg. 2156
DOEHLER GEORGIA, LTD.—See Dohler GmbH; *Int'l*, pg. 2156

DOEHLER INDIA PVT. LTD.—See Dohler GmbH; *Int'l*, pg. 2155
DOEHLER ITALIA S.R.L.—See Dohler GmbH; *Int'l*, pg. 2155
DOEHLER KAZAKHSTAN LLP—See Dohler GmbH; *Int'l*, pg. 2155
DOEHLER MEXICO S.A. DE C.V.—See Dohler GmbH; *Int'l*, pg. 2155
DOEHLER NATURAL FOOD & BEVERAGE INGREDIENTS (BANGKOK) CO., LTD.—See Dohler GmbH; *Int'l*, pg. 2156
DOEHLER NATURAL FOOD & BEVERAGE INGREDIENTS (JINSHAN) CO. LTD.—See Dohler GmbH; *Int'l*, pg. 2155
DOEHLER NF & BI—See Dohler GmbH; *Int'l*, pg. 2155
DOEHLER NORTH AMERICA—See Dohler GmbH; *Int'l*, pg. 2155
DOEHLER NZ LTD.—See Dohler GmbH; *Int'l*, pg. 2156
DOEHLER TASHKENT—See Dohler GmbH; *Int'l*, pg. 2155
DOEHLER UKRAINE LTD—See Dohler GmbH; *Int'l*, pg. 2155
DOEI CORPORATION—See Yaskawa Electric Corporation; *Int'l*, pg. 8569
DOE INDUSTRIES SDN. BHD.—See C.I. Holdings Berhad; *Int'l*, pg. 1243
DOE & INGALLS, INC.; *U.S. Private*, pg. 1252
DOE & INGALLS MANAGEMENT, LLC—See Thermo Fisher Scientific Inc.; *U.S. Public*, pg. 2146
DOE & INGALLS OF FLORIDA OPERATING LLC—See Thermo Fisher Scientific Inc.; *U.S. Public*, pg. 2146
DOEPKER INDUSTRIES LTD.; *Int'l*, pg. 2153
DOEREN MAYHEW & CO., P.C.; *U.S. Private*, pg. 1252
DOERFER CORPORATION; *U.S. Private*, pg. 1252
DOERING COMPANY, LLC; *U.S. Private*, pg. 1253
DOERLE FOOD SERVICES, LLC—See Sysco Corporation; *U.S. Public*, pg. 1973
DOERR ASSOCIATES; *U.S. Private*, pg. 1253
DOERRENBERG SPECIAL STEELS TAIWAN LTD.—See Gesco AG; *Int'l*, pg. 2945
DOERS EDUCATION ASEAN LIMITED; *U.S. Private*, pg. 1253
DOERS WINDOW MANUFACTURING, LLC—See Koch Industries, Inc.; *U.S. Private*, pg. 2332
THE DOE RUN COMPANY—See The Renco Group Inc.; *U.S. Private*, pg. 4104
DOE RUN PERU S.R.L.—See The Renco Group Inc.; *U.S. Private*, pg. 4104
DOEXTRA CRM SOLUTIONS, LLC—See TAC Partners, Inc.; *U.S. Private*, pg. 3920
DOF ASA; *Int'l*, pg. 2153
DOFASCO TUBULAR PRODUCTS—See ArcelorMittal S.A.; *Int'l*, pg. 544
DOFASCO USA INC.—See ArcelorMittal S.A.; *Int'l*, pg. 544
DOF GROUP ASA; *Int'l*, pg. 2154
DO FINANCIAL SERVICE CO., LTD.—See Sumitomo Mitsui Financial Group, Inc.; *Int'l*, pg. 7294
DOF INC.—See Dentsu Group Inc.; *Int'l*, pg. 2040
DO-FLUORIDE NEW MATERIALS CO LTD; *Int'l*, pg. 2152
DOF MANAGEMENT ARGENTINA S.A.—See DOF Group ASA; *Int'l*, pg. 2154
DOF MANAGEMENT AUSTRALIA PTY LTD—See DOF ASA; *Int'l*, pg. 2154
DOF SUBSEA AS—See DOF ASA; *Int'l*, pg. 2154
DOF SUBSEA AUSTRALIAN PTY.—See DOF ASA; *Int'l*, pg. 2154
DOF SUBSEA US INC.—See DOF ASA; *Int'l*, pg. 2154
DOFU DONAUFUTTER GMBH—See AGRAVIS Raiffeisen AG; *Int'l*, pg. 215
DOGA CZ S.R.O.—See Doga; *Int'l*, pg. 2154
DOGA FZ—See Doga; *Int'l*, pg. 2154
DOGA INDUSTRIES—See Doga; *Int'l*, pg. 2154
DOGAN BURDA DERGI YAYINCILIK VE PAZARLAMA A.S.; *Int'l*, pg. 2154
DOGANER ALCI MADENCILIK ENERJI ITHALAT IHRACAT PAZARLAMA TICARET VE SANAYI A.S.—See Compagnie de Saint-Gobain SA; *Int'l*, pg. 1723
DOGAN GAZETECILIK A.S.—See Adil Bey Holding A.S.; *Int'l*, pg. 148
DOGAN SIRKETLER GRUBU HOLDING A.S.—See Adil Bey Holding A.S.; *Int'l*, pg. 148
DOGA; *Int'l*, pg. 2154
DOG DOG BOY; *U.S. Private*, pg. 1253
DOG EAT DOG ADVERTISING; *U.S. Private*, pg. 1253
DOGFISH HEAD CRAFT BREWERY, INC.—See The Boston Beer Company, Inc.; *U.S. Public*, pg. 2041
DOGGER AB—See BHG Group AB; *Int'l*, pg. 1014
DOGGETT EQUIPMENT SERVICES, LTD.; *U.S. Private*, pg. 1253
DOGGETT HEAVY MACHINERY SERVICES—See Doggett Equipment Services, Ltd.; *U.S. Private*, pg. 1253
DOGGETT MACHINERY SERVICES—See Doggett Equipment Services, Ltd.; *U.S. Private*, pg. 1253
DOGGY AB—See NDX UAB; *Int'l*, pg. 5182
DOGI INTERNATIONAL FABRICS, S.A—See Sherpa Capital SL; *Int'l*, pg. 6826
DOGIN BUSINESS SERVICE, LTD.—See Hokuhoku Financial Group, Inc.; *Int'l*, pg. 3444
DOGIN CARD CO., LTD.—See Hokuhoku Financial Group, Inc.; *Int'l*, pg. 3444

DOG LAKE CONSTRUCTION, INC.   CORPORATE AFFILIATIONS

DOG LAKE CONSTRUCTION, INC.; *U.S. Private*, pg. 1253
DOGNESS (INTERNATIONAL) CORPORATION; *Int'l*, pg. 1898
D & O GREEN TECHNOLOGIES BERHAD; *Int'l*, pg. 1898
DOGTAS KELEBEK MOBILYA SANAYI VE TICARET A.S.; *Int'l*, pg. 2154
DOGTIME MEDIA, INC.—See Evolve Media, LLC; *U.S. Private*, pg. 1443
DOGTOPIA; *U.S. Private*, pg. 1253
DOGUSAN BORU SANAYII VE TICARET A.S.; *Int'l*, pg. 2155
DOGUS DIDIM MARINA ISLETMELERI VE TICARET A.S.—See Dogus Holding AS; *Int'l*, pg. 2154
DOGUS GAYRIMENKUL YATIRIM ORTAKLIGI A.S.; *Int'l*, pg. 2154
DOGUS HOLDING AS; *Int'l*, pg. 2154
DOGUS MUSTERI SISTEMLERI A.S.—See Dogus Holding AS; *Int'l*, pg. 2154
DOGUS OTOMOTIV SERVIS VE TICARET A.S.; *Int'l*, pg. 2155
DOGUS OTO PAZARLAMA VE TICARET A.S.—See Dogus Holding AS; *Int'l*, pg. 2154
DOGUS SAGLIKLI YASAM VE DANISMANLIK HIZMETLERI TICARET A.S.—See Dogus Holding AS; *Int'l*, pg. 2154
DOGUS SIGORTA ARACILIK HIZMETLERI A.S.—See Dogus Holding AS; *Int'l*, pg. 2154
DOGUS TELEKOMUNIKASYON HIZMETLERI A.S.—See Dogus Holding AS; *Int'l*, pg. 2154
DOGUS YAYIN GRUBU A.S.—See Dogus Holding AS; *Int'l*, pg. 2154
DOGWOOD SOLAR, LLC—See Duke Energy Corporation; *U.S. Public*, pg. 690
DOGWOOD STATE BANK; *U.S. Public*, pg. 672
DOHA BANK ASSURANCE COMPANY W.L.L—See Doha Bank Q.S.C.; *Int'l*, pg. 2155
DOHA BANK Q.S.C.; *Int'l*, pg. 2155
DOHA INSURANCE GROUP QPSC; *Int'l*, pg. 2155
DOHA INTERNATIONAL AIRPORT—See Qatar Investment Authority; *Int'l*, pg. 6134
DOHA MODERN CARPENTARY CO. W.L.L—See Taleb Group; *Int'l*, pg. 7446
DOHENY ENTERPRISES INC.; *U.S. Private*, pg. 1253
DOHERTY & ASSOCIATES LTD.—See AGF Management Limited; *Int'l*, pg. 206
DOHERTY EMPLOYER SERVICES—See Paychex, Inc.; *U.S. Public*, pg. 1655
DOHERTY EMPLOYMENT GROUP, INC.; *U.S. Private*, pg. 1253
DOHERTY ENTERPRISES, INC.; *U.S. Private*, pg. 1253
DOHERTY FORD; *U.S. Private*, pg. 1253
DOHERTY STAFFING SOLUTIONS—See Doherty Employment Group, Inc.; *U.S. Private*, pg. 1253
DOHLE HANDELSGRUPPE HOLDING GMBH & CO. KG; *Int'l*, pg. 2155
DOHLER AMERICA LATINA LTDA.—See Dohler GmbH; *Int'l*, pg. 2155
DOHLER AUSTRIA GMBH—See Dohler GmbH; *Int'l*, pg. 2156
DOHLER COLOMBIA S.A.S—See Dohler GmbH; *Int'l*, pg. 2155
DOHLER CZ S.R.O.—See Dohler GmbH; *Int'l*, pg. 2155
DOHLER DINTER UKRAINE SKALA LTD.—See Dohler GmbH; *Int'l*, pg. 2155
DOHLER EAST AFRICA LTD.—See Dohler GmbH; *Int'l*, pg. 2156
DOHLER EGYPT FOR THE PRODUCTION OF NATURAL FOOD & BEVERAGE INGREDIENTS S.A.E.—See Dohler GmbH; *Int'l*, pg. 2155
DOHLER EISLEBEN GMBH—See Dohler GmbH; *Int'l*, pg. 2156
DOHLER ESPANA NATURAL BEVERAGE INGREDIENTS S.L.—See Dohler GmbH; *Int'l*, pg. 2155
DOHLER FOOD & BEVERAGE INGREDIENTS RIZHAO CO. LTD.—See Dohler GmbH; *Int'l*, pg. 2155
DOHLER FOOD & BEVERAGE INGREDIENTS SHANGHAI CO. LTD.—See Dohler GmbH; *Int'l*, pg. 2155
DOHLER FRANCE S.A.R.L.—See Dohler GmbH; *Int'l*, pg. 2155
DOHLER GIDA SAN. VE TIC. LTD. STI.—See Dohler GmbH; *Int'l*, pg. 2155
DOHLER GMBH; *Int'l*, pg. 2155
DOHLER GMBH—See Dohler GmbH; *Int'l*, pg. 2156
DOHLER HOLLAND B.V.—See Dohler GmbH; *Int'l*, pg. 2155
DOHLER HUNGARIA KFT.—See Dohler GmbH; *Int'l*, pg. 2155
DOHLER IRANIAN LIMITED—See Dohler GmbH; *Int'l*, pg. 2156
DOHLER JAPAN K.K.—See Dohler GmbH; *Int'l*, pg. 2156
DOHLER MARMARA—See Dohler GmbH; *Int'l*, pg. 2156
DOHLER MIDDLE EAST LTD.—See Dohler GmbH; *Int'l*, pg. 2156
DOHLER-MILNE ASEPTICS LLC—See Dohler GmbH; *Int'l*, pg. 2156
DOHLER-MILNE ASEPTICS LLC—See Wyckoff Farms, Incorporated; *U.S. Private*, pg. 4575

DOHLER NEUENKIRCHEN GMBH—See Dohler GmbH; *Int'l*, pg. 2156
DOHLER NEUSS GMBH—See Dohler GmbH; *Int'l*, pg. 2156
DOHLER POLSKA SP. Z O.O.—See Dohler GmbH; *Int'l*, pg. 2156
DOHLER ROGGEL B.V.—See Dohler GmbH; *Int'l*, pg. 2156
DOHLER ROMANIA S.R.L.—See Dohler GmbH; *Int'l*, pg. 2156
DOHLER S.A.; *Int'l*, pg. 2156
DOHLER SCANDINAVIA A/S—See Dohler GmbH; *Int'l*, pg. 2156
DOHLER SCHWEIZ AG—See Dohler GmbH; *Int'l*, pg. 2156
DOHLER SOFIA EOOD—See Dohler GmbH; *Int'l*, pg. 2156
DOHLER SOUTH AFRICA (PTY) LTD.—See Dohler GmbH; *Int'l*, pg. 2156
DOHLER (UK) LIMITED—See Dohler GmbH; *Int'l*, pg. 2155
DOHLER WEST AFRICA—See Dohler GmbH; *Int'l*, pg. 2155
THE DOHMEN COMPANY FOUNDATION—See Dohmen Co.; *U.S. Private*, pg. 1254
DOHMEN CO.; *U.S. Private*, pg. 1253
DOHMEN INVESTMENT GROUP, LLC—See Dohmen Co.; *U.S. Private*, pg. 1254
DOHMEYER HOLDING BVBA—See Air Water Inc.; *Int'l*, pg. 240
DOHOD INVESTMENT COMPANY JSC; *Int'l*, pg. 2156
&DO HOLDINGS CO., LTD.; *Int'l*, pg. 1
DOHOME ENERGY COMPANY LIMITED—See DoHome Public Company Limited; *Int'l*, pg. 2156
DOHOME GROUP COMPANY LIMITED—See DoHome Public Company Limited; *Int'l*, pg. 2156
DOHOME PUBLIC COMPANY LIMITED; *Int'l*, pg. 2156
THE DOHRING GROUP, INC.; *U.S. Private*, pg. 4022
DOHRMANN INSURANCE AGENCY INC.—See Genstar Capital, LLC; *U.S. Private*, pg. 1674
DOHRN TRANSFER COMPANY; *U.S. Private*, pg. 1254
DOHWA ENGINEERING CO., LTD.; *Int'l*, pg. 2156
DOIG CORPORATION; *U.S. Private*, pg. 1254
DO INFINITE DREAM COMPANY LIMITED—See Do Day Dream PCL; *Int'l*, pg. 2152
DOING STEEL, INC.; *U.S. Private*, pg. 1254
DO IT AGAIN CORP.; *U.S. Public*, pg. 672
DO IT BEST CORP.; *U.S. Private*, pg. 1249
DOIT CO., LTD.—See Pan Pacific International Holdings Corporation; *Int'l*, pg. 5715
DO-IT CORPORATION; *U.S. Private*, pg. 1250
DO IT!—See Omnicom Group Inc.; *U.S. Public*, pg. 1594
DOKA ALGERIE SARL—See Umdasch Group AG; *Int'l*, pg. 8022
DOKA BELFORM IOOO—See Umdasch Group AG; *Int'l*, pg. 8022
DOKA BRASIL LTDA.—See Umdasch Group AG; *Int'l*, pg. 8022
DOKA BULGARIA EOOD—See Umdasch Group AG; *Int'l*, pg. 8022
DOKA CANADA LTD.—See Umdasch Group AG; *Int'l*, pg. 8022
DOKA CHILE LIMITADA—See Umdasch Group AG; *Int'l*, pg. 8022
DOKA CHINA LTD.—See Umdasch Group AG; *Int'l*, pg. 8022
DOKA DANMARK APS—See Umdasch Group AG; *Int'l*, pg. 8022
DOKA DREVO S.R.O.—See Umdasch Group AG; *Int'l*, pg. 8022
DOKA EESTI OU.—See Umdasch Group AG; *Int'l*, pg. 8022
DOKA EMIRATES LLC—See Umdasch Group AG; *Int'l*, pg. 8022
DOKA ESPANA S.A.—See Umdasch Group AG; *Int'l*, pg. 8022
DOKA FINLAND OY—See Umdasch Group AG; *Int'l*, pg. 8022
DOKA FORMWORK AUSTRALIA PTY LTD.—See Umdasch Group AG; *Int'l*, pg. 8022
DOKA FORMWORK MALAYSIA SND. BHD.—See Umdasch Group AG; *Int'l*, pg. 8022
DOKA FORMWORK NIGERIA LTD.—See Umdasch Group AG; *Int'l*, pg. 8022
DOKA FORMWORK PTE. LTD.—See Umdasch Group AG; *Int'l*, pg. 8022
DOKA FORMWORK (SHANGHAI) CO., LTD.—See Umdasch Group AG; *Int'l*, pg. 8022
DOKA FRANCE SAS—See Umdasch Group AG; *Int'l*, pg. 8022
DOKA GMBH—See Umdasch Group AG; *Int'l*, pg. 8022
DOKA GULF FZE—See Umdasch Group AG; *Int'l*, pg. 8022
DOKA HELLAS A.E.—See Umdasch Group AG; *Int'l*, pg. 8022
DOKA HRVATSKA D.O.O.—See Umdasch Group AG; *Int'l*, pg. 8022
DOKA INDIA PVT. LTD.—See Umdasch Group AG; *Int'l*, pg. 8022

DOKA INDUSTRIE GMBH—See Umdasch Group AG; *Int'l*, pg. 8022
DOKA IRELAND LTD.—See Umdasch Group AG; *Int'l*, pg. 8022
DOKA ISRAEL LTD.—See Umdasch Group AG; *Int'l*, pg. 8022
DOKA ITALIA S.P.A.—See Umdasch Group AG; *Int'l*, pg. 8022
DOKA JAPAN K.K.—See Umdasch Group AG; *Int'l*, pg. 8022
DOKA JORDAN LLC—See Umdasch Group AG; *Int'l*, pg. 8022
DOKA KALIP-ISKELE A.S.—See Umdasch Group AG; *Int'l*, pg. 8022
DOKA KOREA LTD.—See Umdasch Group AG; *Int'l*, pg. 8022
DOKA LATVIA SIA—See Umdasch Group AG; *Int'l*, pg. 8022
DOKA LIETUVA UAB—See Umdasch Group AG; *Int'l*, pg. 8022
DOKA MAROC SARL AU—See Umdasch Group AG; *Int'l*, pg. 8022
DOKA MEXICO S. DE R.L. DE C.V.—See Umdasch Group AG; *Int'l*, pg. 8022
DOKA MOCAMBIQUE LTD.—See Umdasch Group AG; *Int'l*, pg. 8023
DOKA MUSCAT LLC—See Umdasch Group AG; *Int'l*, pg. 8023
DOKA NEDERLAND BV—See Umdasch Group AG; *Int'l*, pg. 8023
DOKA NORGE AS—See Umdasch Group AG; *Int'l*, pg. 8023
DOKA N.V.—See Umdasch Group AG; *Int'l*, pg. 8023
DOKA PANAMA S.A.—See Umdasch Group AG; *Int'l*, pg. 8023
DOKA PERU S.A.C.—See Umdasch Group AG; *Int'l*, pg. 8023
DOKA POLSKA SP. Z.O.O.—See Umdasch Group AG; *Int'l*, pg. 8023
DOKA PORTUGAL LDA.—See Umdasch Group AG; *Int'l*, pg. 8023
DOKA QATAR LLC—See Umdasch Group AG; *Int'l*, pg. 8023
DOKA ROMANIA S.R.L.—See Umdasch Group AG; *Int'l*, pg. 8023
DOKA RUS OOO—See Umdasch Group AG; *Int'l*, pg. 8023
DOKA SAUDI ARABIA COMPANY LLC—See Umdasch Group AG; *Int'l*, pg. 8023
DOKA SCHWEIZ AG—See HIAG Immobilen Holding AG; *Int'l*, pg. 3382
DOKA SCHWEIZ AG—See Umdasch Group AG; *Int'l*, pg. 8023
DOKA SERB D.O.O.—See Umdasch Group AG; *Int'l*, pg. 8023
DOKA SLOVAKIA S.R.O.—See Umdasch Group AG; *Int'l*, pg. 8023
DOKA SLOVENIJA D.O.O.—See Umdasch Group AG; *Int'l*, pg. 8023
DOKA SOUTH AFRICA (PTY) LTD.—See Umdasch Group AG; *Int'l*, pg. 8023
DOKA SVERIGE AB—See Umdasch Group AG; *Int'l*, pg. 8023
DOKA TUNISIA LTD.—See Umdasch Group AG; *Int'l*, pg. 8023
DOKA UK LTD.—See Umdasch Group AG; *Int'l*, pg. 8023
DOKA USA LTD.—See Umdasch Group AG; *Int'l*, pg. 8023
DOKA WAWASAN TKH HOLDINGS BERHAD; *Int'l*, pg. 2156
DOKAY LIMITED—See Hang Lung Group Limited; *Int'l*, pg. 3244
DOKER-PORT SP. Z O.O.—See Deutsche Bahn AG; *Int'l*, pg. 2051
DOKIC NTK A.D.; *Int'l*, pg. 2156
DOKKA FASTENERS AS—See Wurth Verwaltungsgesellschaft mbH; *Int'l*, pg. 8504
DOKKA FASTENERS A/S—See Wurth Verwaltungsgesellschaft mbH; *Int'l*, pg. 8504
DOKTAS DOKUMCULUK TICARET VE SANAYI A.S—See Parsan Makina Parcalari Sanayii AS; *Int'l*, pg. 5747
DOKTAS METAL SANAYI VE TICARTE A.S.; *Int'l*, pg. 2156
DOLA INTERNATIONAL CORP.; *U.S. Private*, pg. 1254
THE DOLAN COMPANY; *U.S. Private*, pg. 4022
DOLAN CONSTRUCTION INC.; *U.S. Private*, pg. 1254
DOLAN GMBH—See Dralon GmbH; *Int'l*, pg. 2200
DOLAN-JENNER INDUSTRIES INC.—See Danaher Corporation; *U.S. Public*, pg. 626
DOLAN NORTHWEST LLC; *U.S. Private*, pg. 1254
DOLAN'S OF CONCORD; *U.S. Private*, pg. 1254
DOLAT INVESTMENTS LTD.; *Int'l*, pg. 2156
DOLBY AUSTRALIA PTY. LTD.—See Dolby Laboratories, Inc.; *U.S. Public*, pg. 672
DOLBY INTERNATIONAL AB—See Dolby Laboratories, Inc.; *U.S. Public*, pg. 672
DOLBY LABORATORIES, INC.; *U.S. Public*, pg. 672
DOLBY LABORATORIES LICENSING CORPORATION—See Dolby Laboratories, Inc.; *U.S. Public*, pg. 672

COMPANY NAME INDEX

DOLBY MEDICAL HOME RESPIRATORY CARE LTD.—See SOL S.p.A.; *Int'l*, pg. 7067
DOLCE EUROPA—See International Gourmet Foods Inc.; *U.S. Private*, pg. 2117
DOLCE & GABBANA DO BRASIL COMERICO, IMPORTACAO E PARTICIPACOES LTDA.—See Dolce & Gabbana S.R.L.; *Int'l*, pg. 2157
DOLCE & GABBANA HONG KONG LTD—See Dolce & Gabbana S.R.L.; *Int'l*, pg. 2157
DOLCE & GABBANA JAPAN K.K.—See Dolce & Gabbana S.R.L.; *Int'l*, pg. 2157
DOLCE & GABBANA SHANGHAI CO., LTD.—See Dolce & Gabbana S.R.L.; *Int'l*, pg. 2157
DOLCE & GABBANA S.R.L. - INCISA IN VAL D'ARNO FACILITY—See Dolce & Gabbana S.R.L.; *Int'l*, pg. 2157
DOLCE & GABBANA S.R.L. - LONATE POZZOLO FACILITY—See Dolce & Gabbana S.R.L.; *Int'l*, pg. 2157
DOLCE & GABBANA S.R.L.; *Int'l*, pg. 2157
DOLCE & GABBANA USA, INC.—See Dolce & Gabbana S.R.L.; *Int'l*, pg. 2157
DOLCE VITA HOLDINGS, INC.—See Steven Madden, Ltd.; *U.S. Public*, pg. 1947
DOLCIS BV—See Macintosh Retail Group NV; *Int'l*, pg. 4622
DOLCO PACKAGING—See Genstar Capital, LLC; *U.S. Private*, pg. 1678
DOLCO PACKAGING—See Genstar Capital, LLC; *U.S. Private*, pg. 1678
DOLDEMEDIEN VERLAG GMBH—See WEKA Holding GmbH & Co.KG; *Int'l*, pg. 8371
DOLD FOODS—See Hormel Foods Corporation; *U.S. Public*, pg. 1054
DOLD KALTFLIESSPRESSTEILE GMBH—See Gevelot S.A.; *Int'l*, pg. 2954
DOLEAC ELECTRIC COMPANY INCORPORATED; *U.S. Private*, pg. 1254
DOLE BERRY COMPANY—See Dole plc; *Int'l*, pg. 2157
DOLE DECIDUOUS—See Dole plc; *Int'l*, pg. 2157
DOLE EUROPE SAS—See Dole plc; *Int'l*, pg. 2157
DOLE EXOTICS B.V.—See Dole plc; *Int'l*, pg. 2157
DOLE FOOD CO., INC. - HAWAII—See Dole plc; *Int'l*, pg. 2157
DOLE FOOD COMPANY, INC.—See Dole plc; *Int'l*, pg. 2157
DOLE FOODS OF CANADA LTD.—See Dole plc; *Int'l*, pg. 2157
DOLE FRESH FRUIT COMPANY—See Dole plc; *Int'l*, pg. 2157
DOLE FRESH FRUIT EUROPE OHG—See Dole plc; *Int'l*, pg. 2157
DOLE FRESH VEGETABLES, INC.—See Dole plc; *Int'l*, pg. 2157
DOLE HELLAS LTD.—See Dole plc; *Int'l*, pg. 2157
DOLE HOLDING COMPANY, LLC—See Dole plc; *Int'l*, pg. 2157
DOLE INTERNATIONAL HOLDINGS, INC.—See ITOCHU Corporation; *Int'l*, pg. 3836
DOLE JAPAN, INC.—See ITOCHU Corporation; *Int'l*, pg. 3836
DOLE LANKA (PRIVATE) LIMITED—See ITOCHU Corporation; *Int'l*, pg. 3836
DOLE NORDIC AB—See Dole plc; *Int'l*, pg. 2157
DOLE NORDIC A/S—See Dole plc; *Int'l*, pg. 2157
DOLE PACKAGED FOODS EUROPE SAS—See ITOCHU Corporation; *Int'l*, pg. 3836
DOLE PACKAGED FOODS, LLC—See ITOCHU Corporation; *Int'l*, pg. 3836
DOLE PACKAGED FROZEN FOODS—See ITOCHU Corporation; *Int'l*, pg. 3836
DOLE PHILIPPINES, INC.—See ITOCHU Corporation; *Int'l*, pg. 3836
DOLE PLC; *Int'l*, pg. 2157
DOLESE BROS. CO.; *U.S. Private*, pg. 1254
DOLE SOUTH AFRICA (PTY), LTD.—See Dole plc; *Int'l*, pg. 2157
DOLE THAILAND LTD.—See ITOCHU Corporation; *Int'l*, pg. 3836
DOLET HILLS LIGNITE COMPANY—See American Electric Power Company, Inc.; *U.S. Public*, pg. 100
DOLE TROPICAL PRODUCTS LATIN AMERICA, LTD.—See Dole plc; *Int'l*, pg. 2158
DOLEX DOLLAR EXPRESS, INC.—See Palladium Equity Partners, LLC; *U.S. Private*, pg. 3077
DOLEX ENVIOS, S.A. DE C.V.—See Palladium Equity Partners, LLC; *U.S. Private*, pg. 3077
DOLFIN FINANCIAL (UK) LTD.—See Dolfin Group Ltd.; *Int'l*, pg. 2158
DOLFIN GROUP LTD.; *Int'l*, pg. 2158
DOLFIN RUBBERS LTD.; *Int'l*, pg. 2158
DOLKAM SUJA A.S.; *Int'l*, pg. 2158
DOLLARAMA INC.; *Int'l*, pg. 2158
DOLLAR BANK, FEDERAL SAVINGS BANK—See Dollar Mutual Bancorp; *U.S. Private*, pg. 1254
DOLLAR BANK INSURANCE AGENCY, INC.—See Dollar Mutual Bancorp; *U.S. Private*, pg. 1254
DOLLAR BANK LEASING CORP.—See Dollar Mutual Bancorp; *U.S. Private*, pg. 1254

DOLLAR DAZE INC.; *U.S. Private*, pg. 1254
DOLLAR FINANCIAL CZECH REPUBLIC S.R.O.—See Lone Star Global Acquisitions, LLC; *U.S. Private*, pg. 2487
DOLLAR FINANCIAL GROUP, INC.—See Lone Star Global Acquisitions, LLC; *U.S. Private*, pg. 2487
DOLLAR FINANCIAL U.S., INC.—See Lone Star Global Acquisitions, LLC; *U.S. Private*, pg. 2487
DOLLAR GENERAL CORPORATION; *U.S. Public*, pg. 672
DOLLAR INDUSTRIES LIMITED; *Int'l*, pg. 2158
DOLLAR MUTUAL BANCORP; *U.S. Private*, pg. 1254
DOLLAR SHAVE CLUB, INC.—See Unilever PLC; *Int'l*, pg. 8047
DOLLAR SWEETS COMPANY PTY LTD; *Int'l*, pg. 2158
DOLLAR THRIFTY AUTOMOTIVE GROUP CANADA INC.—See Hertz Global Holdings, Inc.; *U.S. Public*, pg. 1029
DOLLAR THRIFTY AUTOMOTIVE GROUP, INC.—See Hertz Global Holdings, Inc.; *U.S. Public*, pg. 1029
DOLLAR TREE DISTRIBUTION, INC.—See Dollar Tree, Inc.; *U.S. Public*, pg. 672
DOLLAR TREE, INC.; *U.S. Public*, pg. 672
DOLLAR TREE MANAGEMENT, INC.—See Dollar Tree, Inc.; *U.S. Public*, pg. 672
DOLLAR TREE STORES, INC.—See Dollar Tree, Inc.; *U.S. Public*, pg. 672
DOLLAR UNION LIMITED—See Chinese Estates Holdings Limited; *Int'l*, pg. 1569
DOLL CAPITAL MANAGEMENT; *U.S. Private*, pg. 1254
DOLLFUS MIEG & CIE, S.A.—See Bernard Krief Consultants SA; *Int'l*, pg. 986
DOLLKEN PROFILES GMBH—See Surteco Group SE; *Int'l*, pg. 7344
DOLLKEN SP.Z O.O.—See Surteco Group SE; *Int'l*, pg. 7345
DOLLY INC.; *U.S. Private*, pg. 1254
DOLLY VARDEN SILVER CORPORATION; *Int'l*, pg. 2159
DOLMAR GMBH—See Makita Corporation; *Int'l*, pg. 4657
DOLNOSLASKA FABRYKA MASZYN ZANAM - LEGMET SP. Z O.O.—See KGHM Polska Miedz S.A.; *Int'l*, pg. 4148
DOLNOSLASKA SPOLKA GAZOWNICTWA SP. Z O.O.—See Polskie Gornictwo Naftowe i Gazownictwo S.A.; *Int'l*, pg. 5912
DOLNOSLASKIE CENTRUM HURTU ROLNO-SPOZYWCZEGO SA; *Int'l*, pg. 2159
DOLOMATRIX PHILIPPINES INC.; *Int'l*, pg. 2159
DOLOMITE AB—See Invacare Corporation; *U.S. Private*, pg. 2130
DOLOMITE BERHAD—See Dolomite Corporation Berhad; *Int'l*, pg. 2159
DOLOMITE CORPORATION BERHAD; *Int'l*, pg. 2159
DOLOMITE FRANCHI S.P.A.—See RHI Magnesita N.V.; *Int'l*, pg. 6325
DOLOMITE INDUSTRIES COMPANY SDN. BHD.—See Dolomite Corporation Berhad; *Int'l*, pg. 2159
DOLOMITE PRODUCTS COMPANY INC.—See CRH plc; *Int'l*, pg. 1847
DOLOMITE PROPERTIES SDN. BHD.—See Dolomite Corporation Berhad; *Int'l*, pg. 2159
DOLOMITE READYMIXED CONCRETE SDN. BHD.—See Dolomite Corporation Berhad; *Int'l*, pg. 2159
DOLOMIT JSC—See Novolipetski Metallurgicheski Komb OAO; *Int'l*, pg. 5466
DOLOVO U RESTRUKTURIRANJU A.D.; *Int'l*, pg. 2159
DOLPHIN DEBIT ACCESS, LLC—See Euronet Worldwide, Inc.; *U.S. Public*, pg. 797
DOLPHIN DELIVERY LTD.; *Int'l*, pg. 2159
DOLPHIN DESIGN SAS—See Soitec S.A.; *Int'l*, pg. 7060
DOLPHIN ENGINEERING PTE. LTD.—See UMS Holdings Limited; *Int'l*, pg. 8027
DOLPHIN ENTERTAINMENT, INC.; *U.S. Public*, pg. 672
DOLPHIN HOTELS PLC; *Int'l*, pg. 2159
DOLPHIN IMAGING SYSTEMS, LLC—See Patterson Companies, Inc.; *U.S. Public*, pg. 1653
DOLPHIN, INC.—See Karsten Manufacturing Corporation; *U.S. Private*, pg. 2263
DOLPHIN INTEGRATION INC.—See Soitec S.A.; *Int'l*, pg. 7060
DOLPHIN INTERCONNECT SOLUTIONS AS; *Int'l*, pg. 2159
DOLPHIN INTERCONNECT SOLUTIONS NA INC.—See Dolphin Interconnect Solutions AS; *Int'l*, pg. 2159
DOLPHIN INTERNATIONAL BERHAD—See Asia Poly Holdings Berhad; *Int'l*, pg. 615
DOLPHIN INTERNATIONAL INC.; *U.S. Private*, pg. 1255
DOLPHIN LINE INCORPORATED; *U.S. Private*, pg. 1255
DOLPHIN MALL ASSOCIATES LLC—See Simon Property Group, Inc.; *U.S. Public*, pg. 1881
DOLPHIN MEDICAL SERVICES LTD.; *Int'l*, pg. 2159
DOLPHIN NURSERIES (TOOTING) LTD.—See Bain Capital, LP; *U.S. Private*, pg. 437
DOLPHIN OFFSHORE ENTERPRISES (INDIA) LTD; *Int'l*, pg. 2159
DOLPHINS ENTERPRISES, LLC; *U.S. Private*, pg. 1255
DOLPHIN SERVICES, LLC—See Gulf Island Fabrication, Inc.; *U.S. Public*, pg. 975

DOME PUBLISHING COMPANY, INC.

DOLPHIN SHIPPING NEW ZEALAND LIMITED—See OPTIMUS GROUP Co., Ltd.; *Int'l*, pg. 5605
THE DOLPHIN—See Alden Global Capital LLC; *U.S. Private*, pg. 158
THE DOLSEN COMPANIES, INC.; *U.S. Private*, pg. 4022
DOMA B.V.—See Unilever PLC; *Int'l*, pg. 8044
DOMACOM LIMITED; *Int'l*, pg. 2159
DOM AG SICHERHEITSTECHNIK—See Groupe SFPI SA; *Int'l*, pg. 3111
DOMA HOLDINGS, INC.; *U.S. Public*, pg. 673
DOMAILLE ENGINEERING, LLC—See Onward Capital LLC; *U.S. Private*, pg. 3028
DOMAILLE ENGINEERING, LLC—See Thompson Street Capital Manager LLC; *U.S. Private*, pg. 4161
DOMAIN ACTIVE PTY LIMITED—See Enero Group Limited; *Int'l*, pg. 2423
DOMAIN ASSOCIATES LLC; *U.S. Private*, pg. 1255
DOMAINE CARNEROS—See Taittinger SA; *Int'l*, pg. 7418
DOMAINE CHANDON AUSTRALIA PTY LTD—See LVMH Moet Hennessy Louis Vuitton SE; *Int'l*, pg. 4599
DOMAINE CHANDON, INC.—See LVMH Moet Hennessy Louis Vuitton SE; *Int'l*, pg. 4599
DOMAINE DE BELLEVUE SAS—See VINCI S.A.; *Int'l*, pg. 8216
DOMAINE POWER HOLDINGS LIMITED—See Hainan Traffic Administration Holding Co., Ltd.; *Int'l*, pg. 3213
DOMAINES JEAN MARTELL—See Pernod Ricard S.A.; *Int'l*, pg. 5810
DOMAIN HOLDINGS AUSTRALIA LIMITED—See Nine Entertainment Co. Holdings Limited; *Int'l*, pg. 5298
DOMAIN INC.; *U.S. Private*, pg. 1255
DOMAINMARKET.COM LLC; *U.S. Private*, pg. 1255
DOMAIN MEDIA CORP.; *U.S. Private*, pg. 1255
DOMAIN MENADA SP. Z.O.O.—See Marie Brizard Wine & Spirits S.A.; *Int'l*, pg. 4693
DOMAIN PORTO CARRAS S.A.—See Technical Olympic SA; *Int'l*, pg. 7506
THE DOMAIN RETIREMENT COUNTRY CLUB PTY. LTD.—See Brookfield Corporation; *Int'l*, pg. 1186
DOMAIN ROBOT ENTERPRISES INC.—See United Internet AG; *Int'l*, pg. 8069
DOMAINS BY PROXY, LLC—See KKR & Co. Inc.; *U.S. Public*, pg. 1252
DOMAINS BY PROXY, LLC—See Silver Lake Group, LLC; *U.S. Private*, pg. 3657
DOMAINS BY PROXY, LLC—See TCMI, Inc.; *U.S. Private*, pg. 3943
DOMAIN TECHNOLOGY PARTNERS, INC.—See Frontenac Company LLC; *U.S. Private*, pg. 1613
DOMAINZ LTD—See 5G Networks Limited; *Int'l*, pg. 13
DOMAN BUILDING MATERIALS GROUP LTD.—See The Futura Corporation; *Int'l*, pg. 7647
DOMANI STUDIOS LLC—See Publicis Groupe S.A.; *Int'l*, pg. 6097
DOMANI WEALTH, LLC—See Savant Capital, LLC; *U.S. Private*, pg. 3556
DOMANTIS LTD.—See GSK plc; *Int'l*, pg. 3145
DOMARI & ASSOCIATES, INC.; *U.S. Private*, pg. 1255
DOMAT CONTROL SYSTEM S.R.O.—See CEZ, a.s.; *Int'l*, pg. 1427
DOMAT CONTROL SYSTEM S.R.O.—See CEZ, a.s.; *Int'l*, pg. 1427
DOMBRACHT AUSTRIA GMBH—See Aloys F. Dornbracht GmbH & Co. KG; *Int'l*, pg. 365
DOM CAMERA & COMPANY, LLC; *U.S. Private*, pg. 1255
DOMCOLLECT INTERNATIONAL GMBH—See United Internet AG; *Int'l*, pg. 8069
DOMCOLLECT WORLDWIDE INTELLECTUAL PROPERTY AG—See United Internet AG; *Int'l*, pg. 8069
DOM CONSTRUCTION SP. Z O.O.—See Dom Development S.A.; *Int'l*, pg. 2159
DOMCURA AKTIENGESELLSCHAFT—See MLP SE; *Int'l*, pg. 5004
DOM DEUTSCHE ONLINE MEDIEN GMBH—See Carl Bennet AB; *Int'l*, pg. 1332
DOM DEVELOPMENT S.A.; *Int'l*, pg. 2159
DOM DEVELOPMENT WROCLAW SP. Z O.O.—See Dom Development S.A.; *Int'l*, pg. 2159
DOME CORPORATION NORTH AMERICA; *U.S. Private*, pg. 1255
DOMECQ BODEGAS—See Pernod Ricard S.A.; *Int'l*, pg. 5810
DOME DIALYSIS, LLC—See DaVita Inc.; *U.S. Public*, pg. 638
DOME EQUITIES, LLC; *U.S. Private*, pg. 1255
DOME GOLD MINES LIMITED; *Int'l*, pg. 2159
DOME HEADWEAR CO.; *U.S. Private*, pg. 1255
DOME INVESTMENTS PUBLIC COMPANY LTD.—See A. Tsokkos Hotels Public Ltd.; *Int'l*, pg. 22
DOMENECH HERMANOS S.A.U—See Beaulieu International Group NV; *Int'l*, pg. 934
DOMENICK & ASSOCIATES—See Bryn Mawr Bank Corporation; *U.S. Public*, pg. 408
DOME PUBLISHING COMPANY, INC.; *U.S. Private*, pg. 1255
DOMER GMBH & CO. KG STANZ- UND UMFORMTECHNOLOGIE—See Gesco AG; *Int'l*, pg. 2945

DOMESCO MEDICAL JOINT STOCK CORPORATION

DOMESCO MEDICAL JOINT STOCK CORPORATION; *Int'l*, pg. 2159
DOMES PHARMA SA; *Int'l*, pg. 2159
DOMESTIC CASTING COMPANY, LLC; *U.S. Private*, pg. 1255
DOMESTIC FUELS & LUBES—See Domestic Industries Inc.; *U.S. Private*, pg. 1255
DOMESTIC & GENERAL GROUP LIMITED—See CVC Capital Partners SICAV-FIS S.A.; *Int'l*, pg. 1883
DOMESTIC & GENERAL INSURANCE PLC—See CVC Capital Partners SICAV-FIS S.A.; *Int'l*, pg. 1883
DOMESTIC & GENERAL INSURANCE SERVICES LIMITED—See CVC Capital Partners SICAV-FIS S.A.; *Int'l*, pg. 1883
DOMESTIC & GENERAL SERVICE GMBH—See CVC Capital Partners SICAV-FIS S.A.; *Int'l*, pg. 1883
DOMESTIC & GENERAL SERVICES LIMITED—See CVC Capital Partners SICAV-FIS S.A.; *Int'l*, pg. 1883
DOMESTIC INDUSTRIES INC.; *U.S. Private*, pg. 1255
DOMESTIC INDUSTRIES OF VIRGINIA INC.—See Domestic Industries Inc.; *U.S. Private*, pg. 1255
DOMESTIC LINEN SUPPLY & LAUNDRY COMPANY; *U.S. Private*, pg. 1256
DOMESTIC UNIFORM RENTAL CO—See Domestic Linen Supply & Laundry Company; *U.S. Private*, pg. 1256
DOMETIC ASIA CO. LTD.—See Dometic Group AB; *Int'l*, pg. 2160
DOMETIC AUSTRIA GMBH—See Dometic Group AB; *Int'l*, pg. 2160
DOMETIC BENELUX B.V.—See Dometic Group AB; *Int'l*, pg. 2160
DOMETIC DENMARK A/S—See Dometic Group AB; *Int'l*, pg. 2160
DOMETIC DEUTSCHLAND GMBH—See Dometic Group AB; *Int'l*, pg. 2160
DOMETIC FINLAND OY—See Dometic Group AB; *Int'l*, pg. 2160
DOMETIC GERMANY GMBH—See Dometic Group AB; *Int'l*, pg. 2160
DOMETIC GERMANY MPS GMBH—See Dometic Group AB; *Int'l*, pg. 2160
DOMETIC GMBH—See Dometic Group AB; *Int'l*, pg. 2160
DOMETIC GROUP AB; *Int'l*, pg. 2160
DOMETIC INTERNATIONAL AB—See Dometic Group AB; *Int'l*, pg. 2160
DOMETIC ITALY S.R.L.—See Dometic Group AB; *Int'l*, pg. 2160
DOMETIC KK—See Dometic Group AB; *Int'l*, pg. 2160
DOMETIC KOREA CO., LTD.—See Dometic Group AB; *Int'l*, pg. 2160
DOMETIC MIDDLE EAST FZCO—See Dometic Group AB; *Int'l*, pg. 2160
DOMETIC MX, S DE RL DE CV—See Dometic Group AB; *Int'l*, pg. 2160
DOMETIC NEW ZEALAND LTD.—See Dometic Group AB; *Int'l*, pg. 2160
DOMETIC NORWAY AS—See Dometic Group AB; *Int'l*, pg. 2160
DOMETIC POLAND SPOLKA Z OGRANICZONA ODPOWIEDZIALNOSCIA—See Dometic Group AB; *Int'l*, pg. 2160
DOMETIC PTE. LTD.—See Dometic Group AB; *Int'l*, pg. 2160
DOMETIC (PTY) LTD.—See Dometic Group AB; *Int'l*, pg. 2160
DOMETIC RUS LIMITED LIABILITY COMPANY—See Dometic Group AB; *Int'l*, pg. 2160
DOMETIC S.A.S—See Dometic Group AB; *Int'l*, pg. 2160
DOMETIC SCANDINAVIA AB—See Dometic Group AB; *Int'l*, pg. 2160
DOMETIC SEITZ AB—See Dometic Group AB; *Int'l*, pg. 2160
DOMETIC (SHENZHEN) TRADING CO, LTD.—See Dometic Group AB; *Int'l*, pg. 2160
DOMETIC SLOVAKIA S.R.O.—See Dometic Group AB; *Int'l*, pg. 2160
DOMETIC SPAIN SL—See Dometic Group AB; *Int'l*, pg. 2160
DOMETIC SWITZERLAND AG—See Dometic Group AB; *Int'l*, pg. 2160
DOMETIC UK AWNINGS LTD.—See Dometic Group AB; *Int'l*, pg. 2160
DOMETIC UK BLIND SYSTEMS LTD.—See Dometic Group AB; *Int'l*, pg. 2160
DOMEXPORT INC.; *Int'l*, pg. 2161
DOMEX TECHNOLOGY CORPORATION—See Standard Foods Corporation; *Int'l*, pg. 7168
DOMIA GROUP SA—See IK Investment Partners Limited; *Int'l*, pg. 3609
DOMICIL CITY GMBH—See Yihua Lifestyle Technology Co., Ltd.; *Int'l*, pg. 8582
DOMICILE MANAGEMENT SERVICES, INC.—See United Airlines Holdings, Inc.; *U.S. Public*, pg. 2228
DOMICIL MOEBEL GMBH—See Yihua Lifestyle Technology Co., Ltd.; *Int'l*, pg. 8582
DOMICIL PTE LTD—See Yihua Lifestyle Technology Co., Ltd.; *Int'l*, pg. 8582
DOMI ENVIRONMENTAL SOLUTIONS CO., LTD.—See Penta-Ocean Construction Co., Ltd.; *Int'l*, pg. 5788

DOMIKI AKINITON S.A.—See Domiki Kritis S.A.; *Int'l*, pg. 2161
DOMIKI KRITIS S.A.; *Int'l*, pg. 2161
DOMINANCE INDUSTRIES, INC.—See Owens Corning; *U.S. Public*, pg. 1626
DOMINANT ENTERPRISE BERHAD; *Int'l*, pg. 2161
DOMINANT OPTO TECHNOLOGIES JAPAN KK—See D & O Green Technologies Berhad; *Int'l*, pg. 1898
DOMINANT OPTO TECHNOLOGIES KOREA INC.—See D & O Green Technologies Berhad; *Int'l*, pg. 1898
DOMINANT OPTO TECHNOLOGIES NORTH AMERICA, INC.—See D & O Green Technologies Berhad; *Int'l*, pg. 1898
DOMINANT OPTO TECHNOLOGIES SDN. BHD.—See D & O Green Technologies Berhad; *Int'l*, pg. 1898
DOMINANT OPTO TECHNOLOGIES (SHANGHAI) CO., LTD.—See D & O Green Technologies Berhad; *Int'l*, pg. 1898
DOMINANT SEMICONDUCTORS (EUROPE GMBH)—See D & O Green Technologies Berhad; *Int'l*, pg. 1898
DOMINANT SEMICONDUCTORS KOREA INC.—See D & O Green Technologies Berhad; *Int'l*, pg. 1898
DOMINARI FINANCIAL INC.—See Alkido Pharma Inc.; *U.S. Public*, pg. 63
DOMINARI SECURITIES LLC—See Alkido Pharma Inc.; *U.S. Public*, pg. 63
DOMINICA ELECTRICITY SERVICES LTD.—See Emera, Inc.; *Int'l*, pg. 2377
DOMINICANA PORTER NOVELLI—See Omnicom Group Inc.; *U.S. Public*, pg. 1590
DOMINICAN COMMUNICATIONS CORP.; *U.S. Private*, pg. 1256
DOMINICAN HOSPITAL—See Catholic Health Initiatives; *U.S. Private*, pg. 789
DOMINICAN OAKS CORPORATION—See Catholic Health Initiatives; *U.S. Private*, pg. 789
DOMINICAN SISTERS FAMILY HEALTH SERVICE; *U.S. Private*, pg. 1256
DOMINICA SERVICES, INC.—See Adtalem Global Education Inc.; *U.S. Public*, pg. 43
DOMINICK & DOMINICK—See B. Riley Financial, Inc.; *U.S. Public*, pg. 260
DOMINIE PRESS INC.—See Pearson plc; *Int'l*, pg. 5777
DOMINION AIR & MACHINERY CO.; *U.S. Private*, pg. 1256
DOMINION BIOLOGICALS LTD.—See Werfen Life Group, S.A.U.; *Int'l*, pg. 8379
DOMINION BUILDING PRODUCTS—See ASSA ABLOY AB; *Int'l*, pg. 637
DOMINION CAPITAL, INC.—See Dominion Energy, Inc.; *U.S. Public*, pg. 673
DOMINION CAROLINA SALES INC.; *U.S. Private*, pg. 1256
DOMINION CITRUS LIMITED—See Dominion Holding Corporation; *Int'l*, pg. 2161
DOMINION CITRUS WHOLESALE—See Dominion Holding Corporation; *Int'l*, pg. 2161
DOMINION CLEARINGHOUSE—See Dominion Energy, Inc.; *U.S. Public*, pg. 674
DOMINION COAL CORPORATION—See SunCoke Energy, Inc.; *U.S. Public*, pg. 1963
DOMINION COVE POINT LNG LP—See Dominion Energy, Inc.; *U.S. Public*, pg. 673
DOMINION DIAGNOSTICS, LLC—See Riverside Partners, LLC; *U.S. Private*, pg. 3446
DOMINION DIAMOND (INDIA) PRIVATE LIMITED—See Burgundy Diamond Mines Limited; *Int'l*, pg. 1224
DOMINION DIGITAL, INC.; *U.S. Private*, pg. 1256
DOMINION EAST OHIO ENERGY—See Dominion Energy, Inc.; *U.S. Public*, pg. 673
DOMINION ELECTRIC SUPPLY COMPANY, INC.; *U.S. Private*, pg. 1256
DOMINION ENERGY BRAYTON POINT, LLC—See Dominion Energy, Inc.; *U.S. Public*, pg. 673
DOMINION ENERGY HOLDINGS, INC.—See Dominion Energy, Inc.; *U.S. Public*, pg. 673
DOMINION ENERGY, INC.—See Dominion Energy, Inc.; *U.S. Public*, pg. 674
DOMINION ENERGY, INC.; *U.S. Public*, pg. 673
DOMINION ENERGY KEWAUNEE, INC.—See Dominion Energy, Inc.; *U.S. Public*, pg. 674
DOMINION ENERGY MIDSTREAM PARTNERS, LP—See Dominion Energy, Inc.; *U.S. Public*, pg. 674
DOMINION ENERGY QUESTAR CORPORATION—See Dominion Energy, Inc.; *U.S. Public*, pg. 674
DOMINION ENERGY QUESTAR PIPELINE, LLC—See Southwest Gas Holdings, Inc.; *U.S. Public*, pg. 1913
DOMINION ENERGY SOLUTIONS, INC.—See Dominion Energy, Inc.; *U.S. Public*, pg. 674
DOMINION ENERGY SOUTH CAROLINA, INC.—See Dominion Energy, Inc.; *U.S. Public*, pg. 674
DOMINION ENGINEERING, INC.—See Bernhard Capital Partners Management, LP; *U.S. Public*, pg. 536
DOMINION ENTERPRISES—See Irish Times; *U.S. Private*, pg. 2138
DOMINION ENTERTAINMENT, INC.—See K-Tel International Inc.; *Int'l*, pg. 4042
DOMINION EQUITY LLC; *U.S. Private*, pg. 1256

DOMINION FARM PRODUCE LIMITED—See Dominion Holding Corporation; *Int'l*, pg. 2161
DOMINION FERTILITY—See Webster Equity Partners, LLC; *U.S. Private*, pg. 4467
DOMINION GAS ASIA PACIFIC PTE LIMITED—See Mitsubishi Chemical Group Corporation; *Int'l*, pg. 4936
DOMINION GENERATION CORPORATION—See Dominion Energy, Inc.; *U.S. Public*, pg. 674
THE DOMINION GOLF GROUP—See Arcis Equity Partners LLC; *U.S. Private*, pg. 312
DOMINION HOLDING CORPORATION; *Int'l*, pg. 2161
DOMINION HOLDINGS, INC.—See BDO Unibank, Inc.; *Int'l*, pg. 930
DOMINION HOME PROTECTION SERVICES, INC.—See Dominion Energy, Inc.; *U.S. Public*, pg. 674
DOMINION HOMES, INC.; *U.S. Private*, pg. 1256
DOMINION HOPE GAS—See Dominion Energy, Inc.; *U.S. Public*, pg. 674
DOMINION HOSPITAL—See HCA Healthcare, Inc.; *U.S. Public*, pg. 995
DOMINION HOSPITAL—See HCA Healthcare, Inc.; *U.S. Public*, pg. 995
DOMINION INTERIOR SUPPLY CORPORATION—See American Securities LLC; *U.S. Private*, pg. 248
DOMINION INVESTMENTS, INC.—See Dominion Energy, Inc.; *U.S. Public*, pg. 674
DOMINION KINCAID GENERATION L.L.C.—See Dominion Energy, Inc.; *U.S. Public*, pg. 674
DOMINION KINGS PLACE LLC—See UDR, Inc.; *U.S. Public*, pg. 2218
DOMINION LEASING SOFTWARE LLC—See Banyan Software, Inc.; *U.S. Private*, pg. 470
DOMINION LENDING CENTRES INC.; *Int'l*, pg. 2161
DOMINION MINERALS CORP.; *U.S. Private*, pg. 1256
DOMINION MINERALS LIMITED; *Int'l*, pg. 2161
DOMINION MOTORS; *Int'l*, pg. 2161
DOMINION NICKEL ALLOYS LTD.; *Int'l*, pg. 2161
DOMINION NUCLEAR CONNECTICUT, INC.—See Dominion Energy, Inc.; *U.S. Public*, pg. 674
THE DOMINION OF CANADA GENERAL INSURANCE COMPANY—See The Travelers Companies, Inc.; *U.S. Public*, pg. 2136
DOMINION OILFIELD SERVICES LIMITED—See Mitsubishi Chemical Group Corporation; *Int'l*, pg. 4936
DOMINION PAVING & SEALING, INC.—See Shoreline Equity Partners, LLC; *U.S. Private*, pg. 3641
DOMINION PAYROLL SERVICES; *U.S. Private*, pg. 1256
DOMINION PRIVATIZATION FLORIDA, LLC—See Dominion Energy, Inc.; *U.S. Public*, pg. 674
DOMINION PRIVATIZATION TEXAS, LLC—See Dominion Energy, Inc.; *U.S. Public*, pg. 674
DOMINION PROPERTIES INC.; *U.S. Private*, pg. 1256
DOMINION RESOURCES BLACK WARRIOR TRUST; *U.S. Public*, pg. 674
DOMINION SURE SEAL LTD.; *Int'l*, pg. 2161
DOMINION SYSTEMS, INC.—See Anderson Anderson & Brown LLP; *Int'l*, pg. 450
DOMINION TECHNICAL SOLUTIONS, INC.—See Dominion Energy, Inc.; *U.S. Public*, pg. 674
DOMINION TEXTILE (USA), LLC—See Berry Global Group, Inc; *U.S. Public*, pg. 321
DOMINION TRANSMISSION, INC.—See Dominion Energy, Inc.; *U.S. Public*, pg. 674
DOMINION VALLLEY COUNTRY CLUB—See Apollo Global Management, Inc.; *U.S. Public*, pg. 149
DOMINION VIDEO SATELLITE INC.; *U.S. Private*, pg. 1256
DOMINION VILLAGE AT CHESAPEAKE—See AlerisLife Inc.; *U.S. Private*, pg. 160
DOMINION WAREHOUSING & DISTRIBUTION SERVICES LTD.; *Int'l*, pg. 2161
DOMINION WIRE AND CABLES LTD.—See Prysmian S.p.A.; *Int'l*, pg. 6011
DOMINIQUE DUTSCHER SAS; *Int'l*, pg. 2161
DOMINIQUE PRUDENT SAS; *Int'l*, pg. 2161
DOMINIQUE'S LIVESTOCK MARKET; *U.S. Private*, pg. 1256
DOMINO AMJET B.V.—See Brother Industries, Ltd.; *Int'l*, pg. 1197
DOMINO AMJET IBERICA SAU—See Brother Industries, Ltd.; *Int'l*, pg. 1197
DOMINO ASIA PTE. LTD.—See Brother Industries, Ltd.; *Int'l*, pg. 1197
DOMINO CHINA LIMITED—See Brother Industries, Ltd.; *Int'l*, pg. 1197
DOMINO CODING LTD.—See EAC Invest AS; *Int'l*, pg. 2261
DOMINO DATA LAB, INC.; *U.S. Private*, pg. 1256
DOMINO DEUTSCHLAND GMBH—See Brother Industries, Ltd.; *Int'l*, pg. 1197
DOMINO FOODS - ARABI SUGAR REFINERY—See Florida Crystals Corporation; *U.S. Private*, pg. 1548
DOMINO FOODS - BALTIMORE SUGAR REFINERY—See Florida Crystals Corporation; *U.S. Private*, pg. 1548
DOMINO GRAPH TECH AG—See Brother Industries, Ltd.; *Int'l*, pg. 1197
DOMINO HIGHVOLTAGE SUPPLY INC.—See Quanta Services, Inc.; *U.S. Public*, pg. 1751

COMPANY NAME INDEX

DOMINO HOLDINGS FRANCE SARL—See Philip Morris International Inc.; *U.S. Public*, pg. 1687
DOMINO KOREA LIMITED—See Brother Industries, Ltd.; *Int'l*, pg. 1197
DOMINO LASER GMBH—See Brother Industries, Ltd.; *Int'l*, pg. 1197
DOMINO NORTH AMERICA—See Brother Industries, Ltd.; *Int'l*, pg. 1197
DOMINO PRINT AND APPLY AB—See Brother Industries, Ltd.; *Int'l*, pg. 1197
DOMINO PRINTECH INDIA LLP—See Brother Industries, Ltd.; *Int'l*, pg. 1197
DOMINO PRINTING MEXICO SA DE CV—See Brother Industries, Ltd.; *Int'l*, pg. 1197
DOMINO PRINTING SCIENCES PLC—See Brother Industries, Ltd.; *Int'l*, pg. 1197
DOMINO PRINTING SOLUTIONS INC.—See Brother Industries, Ltd.; *Int'l*, pg. 1197
DOMINO PRINTING TECHNOLOGY LTD.—See Brother Industries, Ltd.; *Int'l*, pg. 1198
DOMINO SAS—See Brother Industries, Ltd.; *Int'l*, pg. 1197
DOMINO'S IP HOLDER LLC—See Domino's Pizza, Inc.; *U.S. Public*, pg. 674
DOMINO—See Omnicom Group Inc.; *U.S. Public*, pg. 1575
DOMINOS PIZZA BELGIUM S.P.R.L.—See Domino's Pizza Enterprises Ltd.; *Int'l*, pg. 2162
DOMINO'S PIZZA DEUTSCHLAND GMBH—See Domino's Pizza Enterprises Ltd.; *Int'l*, pg. 2162
DOMINO'S PIZZA DISTRIBUTION LLC—See Domino's Pizza, Inc.; *U.S. Public*, pg. 675
DOMINO'S PIZZA ENTERPRISES LTD.; *Int'l*, pg. 2162
DOMINO'S PIZZA GERMANY GMBH—See Domino's Pizza Group plc; *Int'l*, pg. 2162
DOMINO'S PIZZA GROUP LIMITED—See Domino's Pizza Group plc; *Int'l*, pg. 2162
DOMINO'S PIZZA GROUP PLC; *Int'l*, pg. 2162
DOMINO'S PIZZA, INC.; *U.S. Public*, pg. 674
DOMINO'S PIZZA INTERNATIONAL LLC—See Domino's Pizza, Inc.; *U.S. Public*, pg. 675
DOMINO'S PIZZA (ISLE OF MAN) LIMITED—See Domino's Pizza Group plc; *Int'l*, pg. 2162
DOMINO'S PIZZA LLC—See Domino's Pizza, Inc.; *U.S. Public*, pg. 675
DOMINO'S PIZZA NEDERLAND B.V.—See Domino's Pizza Enterprises Ltd.; *Int'l*, pg. 2162
DOMINO'S PIZZA NETHERLANDS B.V.—See Domino's Pizza Enterprises Ltd.; *Int'l*, pg. 2162
DOMINO'S PIZZA NEW ZEALAND LIMITED—See Domino's Pizza Enterprises Ltd.; *Int'l*, pg. 2162
DOMINO UK LTD.—See Brother Industries, Ltd.; *Int'l*, pg. 1198
DOMINOVAS ENERGY CORPORATION; *U.S. Public*, pg. 675
DOMINUS CAPITAL, L.P.; *U.S. Private*, pg. 1256
DOM INWESTYCYJNY BRE BANKU SA—See Commerzbank AG; *Int'l*, pg. 1719
DOM INWESTYCYJNY XELION SP. Z O.O.—See Bank Polska Kasa Opieki Spolka Akcyjna; *Int'l*, pg. 849
DOMINY OIL INC.; *U.S. Private*, pg. 1257
DOMIS S.A.—See Somfy SA; *Int'l*, pg. 7085
DOMITYS SAS—See Nexity SA; *Int'l*, pg. 5244
DOMIZIL BAUTRAGER GMBH—See STRABAG SE; *Int'l*, pg. 7230
DOM MAKLERSKI BZ WBK S.A.—See Banco Santander, S.A.; *Int'l*, pg. 826
DOM-METALUX S.A.S.—See Groupe SFPI SA; *Int'l*, pg. 3111
DOMMO EMPREENDIMENTOS IMOBILIARIOS SA—See Oi S.A.; *Int'l*, pg. 5533
DOMMO ENERGIA S.A.—See Petro Rio S.A.; *Int'l*, pg. 5825
DOM-NEDERLAND—See Groupe SFPI SA; *Int'l*, pg. 3111
DOMNICK HUNTER GROUP LTD.—See Parker Hannifin Corporation; *U.S. Public*, pg. 1645
DOMNICK HUNTER-RL (THAILAND) CO., LTD.—See RS Group plc; *Int'l*, pg. 6417
DOMO CAPROLEUNA GMBH—See Domo NV; *Int'l*, pg. 2162
DOMO CHEMICAL GMBH; *Int'l*, pg. 2162
DOMOFINANCE SA—See BNP Paribas SA; *Int'l*, pg. 1090
DOMO, INC.; *U.S. Public*, pg. 675
DOMOLIFE S.R.L.—See Mitsubishi Chemical Group Corporation; *Int'l*, pg. 4937
DOMO NV; *Int'l*, pg. 2162
DOMOPLAN BAUGESELLSCHAFT MBH—See Bauunternehman Echterhoff GmbH & Co. KG; *Int'l*, pg. 898
DOMOPLEX LTD—See Viohalco SA/NV; *Int'l*, pg. 8243
DOMO RECORDS, INC.; *U.S. Private*, pg. 1257
DO MORE GOOD LLC; *U.S. Private*, pg. 1250
DOMOTEC SA—See Ariston Thermo S.p.A.; *Int'l*, pg. 567
DOMO WELLNESS ROMANIA SRL—See Harvia Oyj; *Int'l*, pg. 3281
DOM POLSKA SP.Z.O.O.—See Groupe SFPI SA; *Int'l*, pg. 3111
COMPRO, S.A.S.—See Groupe Adeo S.A.; *Int'l*, pg. 3091
DOMRETOR OY—See Atria Plc; *Int'l*, pg. 694
DOM.RF JSC; *Int'l*, pg. 2159

DOMS APS—See Vontier Corporation; *U.S. Public*, pg. 2308
DOM S.A.R.L.—See Groupe SFPI SA; *Int'l*, pg. 3111
DOM SICHERHEITSTECHNIK GMBH & CO. KG—See Groupe SFPI SA; *Int'l*, pg. 3111
DOM SICHERHEITSTECHNIK GMBH & CO. KG—See Groupe SFPI SA; *Int'l*, pg. 3111
DOMS INDUSTRIES PVT. LTD.—See F.I.L.A. - Fabbrica Italiana Lapis ed Affini S.p.A.; *Int'l*, pg. 2596
DOMSJO FABRIKER AB—See The Aditya Birla Group; *Int'l*, pg. 7610
DOMTAR ASIA LIMITED—See PT Sinar Mas Group; *Int'l*, pg. 6073
DOMTAR A.W. LLC—See PT Sinar Mas Group; *Int'l*, pg. 6073
DOMTAR CORPORATION - KAMLOOPS MILL—See PT Sinar Mas Group; *Int'l*, pg. 6073
DOMTAR CORPORATION—See PT Sinar Mas Group; *Int'l*, pg. 6072
DOMTAR CORPORATION - WINDSOR MILL—See PT Sinar Mas Group; *Int'l*, pg. 6073
DOMTAR-HAWESVILLE—See PT Sinar Mas Group; *Int'l*, pg. 6073
DOMTAR, INC.—See PT Sinar Mas Group; *Int'l*, pg. 6073
DOMTAR INDUSTRIES-ASHDOWN MILL—See PT Sinar Mas Group; *Int'l*, pg. 6073
DOMTAR INDUSTRIES—See PT Sinar Mas Group; *Int'l*, pg. 6073
DOMTAR-JOHNSONBURG—See PT Sinar Mas Group; *Int'l*, pg. 6073
DOMTAR-KINGSPORT—See PT Sinar Mas Group; *Int'l*, pg. 6073
DOMTAR-MARLBORO—See PT Sinar Mas Group; *Int'l*, pg. 6073
DOMTAR PACIFIC PAPERS ULC—See PT Sinar Mas Group; *Int'l*, pg. 6073
DOMTAR PAPER COMPANY, LLC—See PT Sinar Mas Group; *Int'l*, pg. 6073
DOMTAR PERSONAL CARE ABSORBENT HYGIENE INC.—See PT Sinar Mas Group; *Int'l*, pg. 6073
DOMTAR PERSONAL CARE EUROPE, S.L.U.—See PT Sinar Mas Group; *Int'l*, pg. 6073
DOMTAR-PLYMOUTH—See PT Sinar Mas Group; *Int'l*, pg. 6073
DOMTAR-ROTHSCHILD—See PT Sinar Mas Group; *Int'l*, pg. 6073
DOMTECH, INC.; *Int'l*, pg. 2162
DOMUSA CALEFACCION, S.COOP.—See Mondragon Corporation; *Int'l*, pg. 5028
DOMUS AUREA GMBH—See Carl Schaefer GmbH & Co. KG; *Int'l*, pg. 1333
DOMUS CLEAN REINIGUNGS GMBH—See UniCredit S.p.A.; *Int'l*, pg. 8040
DOMUS FACILITY MANAGEMENT GMBH—See UniCredit S.p.A.; *Int'l*, pg. 8040
DOMUS FIN S.A.; *Int'l*, pg. 2162
DOMUS INC.; *U.S. Private*, pg. 1257
DOMUS NOVA S.P.A.—See Garofalo Health Care SpA; *Int'l*, pg. 2886
DOM VILLE SERVICES; *Int'l*, pg. 2159
DO MY OWN PEST CONTROL; *U.S. Private*, pg. 1250
DOM ZDROJOWY SP. Z O.O—See INPRO S.A.; *Int'l*, pg. 3717
DONA ANA TITLE COMPANY, INC.—See First American Financial Corporation; *U.S. Public*, pg. 835
DONACO INTERNATIONAL LIMITED; *Int'l*, pg. 2162
DONAGHYS AUSTRALIA PTY LTD—See Donaghys Limited; *Int'l*, pg. 2163
DONAGHYS LIMITED - DUNEDIN FACTORY—See Donaghys Limited; *Int'l*, pg. 2163
DONAGHYS LIMITED; *Int'l*, pg. 2163
DON AGRO INTERNATIONAL LIMITED; *Int'l*, pg. 2162
DONAHUE DURHAM & NOONAN PC—See Carmody Torrance Sandak & Hennessey LLP; *U.S. Private*, pg. 766
DONAHUE SCHRIBER REALTY GROUP, INC.—See First Washington Realty Inc.; *U.S. Private*, pg. 1530
DONALD B REMMEY INC.; *U.S. Private*, pg. 1259
DONALD B. RICE TIRE CO. INC.; *U.S. Private*, pg. 1259
DONALD BRUCE & CO.; *U.S. Private*, pg. 1259
DONALD B. SMITH INCORPORATED; *U.S. Private*, pg. 1259
DONALD C. BOWERS INSURANCE, INC.—See Farmers National Banc Corp.; *U.S. Public*, pg. 822
DONALD DANFORTH PLANT SCIENCE CENTER; *U.S. Private*, pg. 1259
DONALD F DICKERSON ASSOCIATES—See Coffman Engineers, Inc.; *U.S. Private*, pg. 961
DONALD J. FAGER & ASSOCIATES; *U.S. Private*, pg. 1260
DONALD J PLINER OF FLORIDA, INC.—See Castanea Partners, Inc.; *U.S. Private*, pg. 784
DONALD L. BLOUNT & ASSOCIATES, INC.—See Leidos Holdings, Inc.; *U.S. Public*, pg. 1304
DONALD MINERAL SANDS PTY. LTD.—See Astron Corporation Limited; *U.S. Public*, pg. 662
DONALD R. HARVEY, INC.; *U.S. Private*, pg. 1260
DONALDSON AUSTRALASIA PTY. LTD.—See Donaldson Company, Inc.; *U.S. Public*, pg. 675

DONALDSON (CHINA) TRADING CO., LTD.—See Donaldson Company, Inc.; *U.S. Public*, pg. 675
DONALDSON CO., INC.—See Donaldson Company, Inc.; *U.S. Public*, pg. 675
DONALDSON COLOMBIA S.A.S.—See Donaldson Company, Inc.; *U.S. Public*, pg. 675
DONALDSON COMPANY, INC.; *U.S. Public*, pg. 675
DONALDSON EUROPE, B.V.B.A.—See Donaldson Company, Inc.; *U.S. Public*, pg. 675
DONALDSON FAR EAST LTD.—See Donaldson Company, Inc.; *U.S. Public*, pg. 676
DONALDSON FILTER COMPONENTS LTD.—See Donaldson Company, Inc.; *U.S. Public*, pg. 675
DONALDSON FILTRATION (ASIA PACIFIC) PTE. LTD.—See Donaldson Company, Inc.; *U.S. Public*, pg. 676
DONALDSON FILTRATION DEUTSCHLAND GMBH—See Donaldson Company, Inc.; *U.S. Public*, pg. 675
DONALDSON FILTRATION (GB) LTD.—See Donaldson Company, Inc.; *U.S. Public*, pg. 675
DONALDSON FILTRATION MAGYARORSZAG KFT.—See Donaldson Company, Inc.; *U.S. Public*, pg. 675
DONALDSON FILTRATION MALAYSIA SDN BHD—See Donaldson Company, Inc.; *U.S. Public*, pg. 676
DONALDSON FILTRATION NORWAY A.S.—See Donaldson Company, Inc.; *U.S. Public*, pg. 675
DONALDSON FILTRATION OSTERREICH, GMBH—See Donaldson Company, Inc.; *U.S. Public*, pg. 675
DONALDSON FILTRATION SYSTEMS (PTY.) LTD.—See Donaldson Company, Inc.; *U.S. Public*, pg. 675
DONALDSON FILTROS IBERICA S.L.—See Donaldson Company, Inc.; *U.S. Public*, pg. 675
DONALDSON FRANCE, S.A.S.—See Donaldson Company, Inc.; *U.S. Public*, pg. 675
DONALDSON GMBH—See Donaldson Company, Inc.; *U.S. Public*, pg. 675
DONALDSON IBERICA SOLUCIONES EN FILTRACION, S.L.—See Donaldson Company, Inc.; *U.S. Public*, pg. 675
DONALDSON KOREA CO., LTD.—See Donaldson Company, Inc.; *U.S. Public*, pg. 676
DONALDSON NEDERLAND B.V.—See Donaldson Company, Inc.; *U.S. Public*, pg. 675
DONALDSON PLASTIC SURGERY, LLC; *U.S. Private*, pg. 1260
DONALDSON S.A. DE C.V.—See Donaldson Company, Inc.; *U.S. Public*, pg. 676
DONALDSON SCANDINAVIA A.P.S.—See Donaldson Company, Inc.; *U.S. Public*, pg. 675
DONALDSON SCHWEIZ GMBH—See Donaldson Company, Inc.; *U.S. Public*, pg. 675
DONALDSON (WUXI) FILTERS CO., LTD.—See Donaldson Company, Inc.; *U.S. Public*, pg. 675
DONALD WARDLE & SON LTD—See Co-operative Group Limited; *Int'l*, pg. 1679
DONALD WARD LIMITED; *Int'l*, pg. 2163
DONALSONVILLE HOSPITAL, INC.; *U.S. Private*, pg. 1260
DONAN SHOKUHIN CO., LTD.—See Meiji Holdings Co., Ltd.; *Int'l*, pg. 4800
DONATECH CORPORATION; *U.S. Private*, pg. 1260
DONATELLE PLASTICS, INC.—See DuPont de Nemours, Inc.; *U.S. Public*, pg. 692
DONATELLO INTERMEDIAZIONE SRL—See Assicurazioni Generali S.p.A.; *Int'l*, pg. 643
DONATH BURSON-MARSTELLER S.R.O.—See WPP plc; *Int'l*, pg. 8468
DONATI SOLLEVAMENTI S.R.L.—See Konecranes Plc; *Int'l*, pg. 4253
DONAT IT GMBH—See Adecco Group AG; *Int'l*, pg. 140
DONATOR BERATUNGS GMBH—See Allianz SE; *Int'l*, pg. 352
DONATOS PIZZERIA CORPORATION; *U.S. Private*, pg. 1260
DONATWALD+HAQUE; *U.S. Private*, pg. 1260
DONAU KIES VERWALTUNGS GMBH—See Heidelberg Materials AG; *Int'l*, pg. 3310
DONAU-MORTEL GMBH & CO. KG—See BERGER Holding GmbH; *Int'l*, pg. 979
DONAU VERSICHERUNGS AG—See Vienna Insurance Group AG Wiener Versicherung Gruppe; *Int'l*, pg. 8194
DONAU-WASSERKRAFT AKTIENGESELLSCHAFT—See E.ON SE; *Int'l*, pg. 2252
DONAUZENTRUM BESITZ- U. VERMIETUNGS GMBH—See Unibail-Rodamco-Westfield SE; *Int'l*, pg. 8029
DONAU ZENTRUM BETRIEBSFUHRUNGSGES.M.B.H.—See Unibail-Rodamco-Westfield SE; *Int'l*, pg. 8029
DON-A-VEE CHRYSLER JEEP INC.; *U.S. Private*, pg. 1259
DONBASENERGO PJSC; *Int'l*, pg. 2163
DON BESSETTE MOTORS, INC.; *U.S. Private*, pg. 1257
DON BEST SPORTS CORPORATION—See Light & Wonder, Inc.; *U.S. Public*, pg. 1314
DON BEYER MOTORS INC.; *U.S. Private*, pg. 1257
DON BLACKBURN & COMPANY; *U.S. Private*, pg. 1257
DON BOSCO B.V.B.A.—See s.a. D'Ieteren n.v.; *Int'l*, pg. 6448

DON BLACKBURN & COMPANY

DON BOURGEOIS & FILS CONTRACTEUR INC—See EBC Inc.; *Int'l*, pg. 2284
DON BROWN AUTOMOTIVE GROUP; *U.S. Private*, pg. 1257
DON-BUR (BODIES & TRAILERS) LTD; *Int'l*, pg. 2162
DONBY SHIPPERS SUPPLY, CO.—See Benchmark Industrial, Inc.; *U.S. Private*, pg. 524
DONCAFE INTERNATIONAL DOO—See Strauss Group Ltd.; *Int'l*, pg. 7238
DON CAMERON & ASSOCIATES, INC.—See Radiant Logistics, Inc.; *U.S. Public*, pg. 1759
DONCASTER CITATION SERVICE CENTRE LIMITED—See Textron Inc.; *U.S. Public*, pg. 2028
THE DONCASTER RACECOURSE MANAGEMENT COMPANY LIMITED—See Reuben Brothers SA; *Int'l*, pg. 6311
DONCASTERS GROUP LTD.—See Dubai Holding LLC; *Int'l*, pg. 2218
DONCASTER—See Tanner Companies, LP; *U.S. Private*, pg. 3931
DONCASTERS TRUCAST LTD.—See Dubai Holding LLC; *Int'l*, pg. 2218
DONCASTER VETS4PETS LIMITED—See Pets at Home Group Plc; *Int'l*, pg. 5833
DON CESAR RESORT HOTEL LTD.—See Loews Corporation; *U.S. Public*, pg. 1340
DON CHALMERS FORD INC; *U.S. Private*, pg. 1257
THE DON CHAPIN CO. INC.; *U.S. Private*, pg. 4022
DON C. MUSICK CONSTRUCTION CO., INC.; *U.S. Private*, pg. 1257
DON CO., LTD.—See Yoshinoya Holdings Co., Ltd.; *Int'l*, pg. 8600
DON DAVIS AUTO GROUP, INC.; *U.S. Private*, pg. 1257
DON DAVIS BAY CITY—See Don Davis Dealerships, Inc.; *U.S. Private*, pg. 1257
DON DAVIS DEALERSHIPS, INC.; *U.S. Private*, pg. 1257
DON DAVIS FORD, INC.—See Don Davis Auto Group, Inc.; *U.S. Private*, pg. 1257
DON DAVIS MOTOR CO., INC.—See Don Davis Dealerships, Inc.; *U.S. Private*, pg. 1257
DONDELINGER CHEVROLET CADILLAC; *U.S. Private*, pg. 1260
DONDLINGER & SONS CONSTRUCTION CO. INC.; *U.S. Private*, pg. 1260
DONDLINGER & SONS CONSTRUCTION CO. INC.-TEXAS—See Dondlinger & Sons Construction Co. Inc.; *U.S. Private*, pg. 1260
DON DOCKSTEADER MOTORS LTD; *Int'l*, pg. 2162
DONEAR INDUSTRIES LTD; *Int'l*, pg. 2163
D-ONE CO., LTD.—See Pan Pacific International Holdings Corporation; *Int'l*, pg. 5715
DONE & DUSTED GROUP LIMITED; *Int'l*, pg. 2163
DONE+DUSTED INC—See Done & Dusted Group Limited; *Int'l*, pg. 2163
DONE & DUSTED PRODUCTIONS, INC.—See Done & Dusted Group Limited; *Int'l*, pg. 2163
DONEGAL CONSTRUCTION CORPORATION—See SurfaceCycle, Inc.; *U.S. Private*, pg. 3884
DONEGAL DEMOCRAT LTD—See JPIMedia Holdings Limited; *Int'l*, pg. 4006
DONEGAL FINANCIAL SERVICES CORPORATION—See Northwest Bancshares, Inc.; *U.S. Public*, pg. 1541
DONEGAL GROUP INC.; *U.S. Public*, pg. 676
DONEGAL INSURANCE GROUP—See Donegal Group Inc.; *U.S. Public*, pg. 676
DONEGAL INSURANCE GROUP—See Donegal Group Inc.; *U.S. Public*, pg. 676
DONEGAL INVESTMENT GROUP PLC; *Int'l*, pg. 2163
DONEGAL MUTUAL INSURANCE COMPANY—See Donegal Group Inc.; *U.S. Public*, pg. 676
DONEGAL POTATOES LIMITED—See Donegal Investment Group Plc; *Int'l*, pg. 2163
DONE INFORMATION OY—See Revenio Group Oyj; *Int'l*, pg. 6312
DON E. KEITH TRANSPORTATION, LLC; *U.S. Private*, pg. 1257
DONELAN'S SUPERMARKETS, INC.; *U.S. Private*, pg. 1260
THE DONERAIL GROUP LP; *U.S. Private*, pg. 4022
DONER CANADA, INC.—See Doner; *U.S. Private*, pg. 1260
DONER CANADA, INC.—See Doner; *U.S. Private*, pg. 1260
DONER CARDWELL HAWKINS—See Doner; *U.S. Private*, pg. 1260
DON ERICKSON INC.; *U.S. Private*, pg. 1257
DONER PARTNERS LLC—See Stagwell, Inc.; *U.S. Public*, pg. 1926
DONER; *U.S. Private*, pg. 1260
DONER—See Doner; *U.S. Private*, pg. 1260
DONER—See Doner; *U.S. Private*, pg. 1260
DONER—See Doner; *U.S. Private*, pg. 1260
DONESI D.O.O.—See Delivery Hero SE; *Int'l*, pg. 2013
DONESI D.O.O.—See Delivery Hero SE; *Int'l*, pg. 2013
DONE SOFTWARE SOLUTIONS OY—See Revenio Group Oyj; *Int'l*, pg. 6312
DONETSK ELECTROMETALLURGICAL PLANT PJSC—See Mechel PAO; *Int'l*, pg. 4766
DONETSKKOKS PJSC; *Int'l*, pg. 2163

DON FOLK CHEVROLET KELOWNA; *Int'l*, pg. 2162
DON FRANKLIN FORD LINCOLN LLC; *U.S. Private*, pg. 1257
DONG-A AMERICA CORP—See Dong-A Socio Holdings Co., Ltd.; *Int'l*, pg. 2164
DONG A ELTEK CO., LTD.; *Int'l*, pg. 2163
DONGA FOOD CO., LTD.—See Sajodongaone Co., Ltd.; *Int'l*, pg. 6485
DONGAH GEOLOGICAL ENGINEERING CO., LTD. - EUMSEONG PLANT—See DongAh Geological Engineering Co., Ltd.; *Int'l*, pg. 2165
DONGAH GEOLOGICAL ENGINEERING CO., LTD.; *Int'l*, pg. 2165
DONG-AH GEOLOGICAL ENGINEERING COMPANY LIMITED—See DongAh Geological Engineering Co., Ltd.; *Int'l*, pg. 2165
DONGAH GEOLOGICAL ENGINEERING INDIA PRIVATE LTD.—See DongAh Geological Engineering Co., Ltd.; *Int'l*, pg. 2165
DONG AH TIRE & RUBBER CO., LTD. - BUKJEONG PLANT—See DN Automotive Corporation; *Int'l*, pg. 2147
DONG-A HWASUNG CO., LTD.; *Int'l*, pg. 2164
DONGA HWASUNG MEXICO, S.A. DE C.V.—See Dong-A Hwasung Co., Ltd.; *Int'l*, pg. 2164
DONG-A HWA SUNG TECHNOLOGY(WUXI) CO., LTD.—See Dong-A Hwasung Co., Ltd.; *Int'l*, pg. 2164
DONG-A INDIA AUTOMOTIVE PVT. LTD.—See Dong-A Hwasung Co., Ltd.; *Int'l*, pg. 2164
DONG A LAND JOINT STOCK COMPANY—See Phu Nhuan Jewelry Joint Stock Company; *Int'l*, pg. 5857
DONG ANH INVESTMENT, CONSTRUCTION AND BUILDING MATERIAL JOINT STOCK COMPANY—See Infrastructure Development and Construction Corporation; *Int'l*, pg. 3697
DONGA ONE CORPORATION - BUSAN FACTORY—See Sajodongaone Co., Ltd.; *Int'l*, pg. 6485
DONGA ONE CORPORATION - INCHEON FACTORY—See Sajodongaone Co., Ltd.; *Int'l*, pg. 6486
DONGA ONE CORPORATION - WONJU FACTORY—See Sajodongaone Co., Ltd.; *Int'l*, pg. 6486
DONG-A OTSUKA CO., LTD.—See Otsuka Holdings Co., Ltd.; *Int'l*, pg. 5659
DONG A PAINT JSC; *Int'l*, pg. 2163
DONG A PLASTIC GROUP JSC; *Int'l*, pg. 2163
DONG-A POLAND SP.Z O.O—See Dong-A Hwasung Co., Ltd.; *Int'l*, pg. 2164
DONG-A SOCIO HOLDINGS CO., LTD.; *Int'l*, pg. 2164
DONG-A ST CO., LTD.—See Dong-A Socio Holdings Co., Ltd.; *Int'l*, pg. 2165
DONGBANG AGRO CORP.; *Int'l*, pg. 2165
DONG BANG NOVOFERM INC—See Sanwa Holdings Corporation; *Int'l*, pg. 6560
DONGBANG SHIP MACHINERY CO., LTD.; *Int'l*, pg. 2165
DONG BANG TRANSPORT LOGISTICS CO., LTD.; *Int'l*, pg. 2163
DONGBEI SPECIAL STEEL GROUP CO., LTD.—See Jiangsu Shagang Group Ltd.; *Int'l*, pg. 3954
DONGBU ASSET MANAGEMENT CO., LTD.—See Dongbu Group; *Int'l*, pg. 2165
DONGBU CAPITAL CO., LTD.—See Dongbu Group; *Int'l*, pg. 2166
DONGBU CORP - CONSTRUCTION—See Dongbu Group; *Int'l*, pg. 2166
DONGBU CORP. - LOGISTICS—See Dongbu Group; *Int'l*, pg. 2166
DONGBU CORPORATION—See Dongbu Group; *Int'l*, pg. 2166
DONGBU DAEWOO ELECTRONICS JAPAN CO., LTD.—See Dongbu Group; *Int'l*, pg. 2165
DONGBU ENGINEERING CO., LTD.—See Dongbu Group; *Int'l*, pg. 2166
DONGBU EXPRESS CO., LTD.—See Dongwon Enterprise Co., Ltd.; *Int'l*, pg. 2170
DONGBU FINE CHEMICAL CO., LTD.—See Dongbu Group; *Int'l*, pg. 2166
DONGBU GROUP; *Int'l*, pg. 2165
DONGBU HITEK CO., LTD.—See Dongbu Group; *Int'l*, pg. 2166
DONGBU HITEK FABRICATION 1—See Dongbu Group; *Int'l*, pg. 2166
DONGBU HITEK FABRICATION 2—See Dongbu Group; *Int'l*, pg. 2166
DONGBU INC.—See Dongbu Group; *Int'l*, pg. 2166
DONGBUKA NO 12 SHIP INVESTMENT CO., LTD.; *Int'l*, pg. 2166
DONGBUKA NO.13 SHIP INVESTMENT CO., LTD.; *Int'l*, pg. 2166
DONGBU LIFE INSURANCE CO., LTD.—See Dongbu Group; *Int'l*, pg. 2165
DONGBU LIGHTEC EUROPE LTD.—See GeumVit Corp.; *Int'l*, pg. 2954
DONGBU LIGHTEC JAPAN CO., LTD—See GeumVit Corp.; *Int'l*, pg. 2954
DONGBU LIGHTEC USA INC—See GeumVit Corp.; *Int'l*, pg. 2954
DONGBU LIGHTEC (YANTAI) CO., LTD—See GeumVit Corp.; *Int'l*, pg. 2954

CORPORATE AFFILIATIONS

DONGBU METAL CO., LTD.—See Dongbu Group; *Int'l*, pg. 2166
DONGBU ORGANIC FOODS—See Dongbu Group; *Int'l*, pg. 2166
DONGBU SAVINGS BANK CO., LTD.—See Dongbu Group; *Int'l*, pg. 2166
DONGBU SOLAR CO., LTD.—See Dongbu Group; *Int'l*, pg. 2166
DONGBU STEEL CO.,LTD.—See Dongbu Group; *Int'l*, pg. 2166
DONGBU TECHNOLOGY INSTITUTE—See Dongbu Group; *Int'l*, pg. 2166
DONG DO MARINE JOINT STOCK COMPANY; *Int'l*, pg. 2163
DONGDO SHIP REPAIR CO. LTD—See Dong Do Marine Joint Stock Company; *Int'l*, pg. 2163
DONG-EE-JIAO CO., LTD.; *Int'l*, pg. 2165
DONG ENERGY SALES (UK) LTD.—See Orsted AS; *Int'l*, pg. 5644
DONGES STEELTEC GMBH—See Mutares SE & Co. KGaA; *Int'l*, pg. 5104
DONGFANG CITY HOLDING GROUP COMPANY LIMITED; *U.S. Private*, pg. 1260
DONGFANG DIGICOM TECHNOLOGY (GUANGDONG) CO., LTD.—See Guangdong Dongfang Science & Technology Co., Ltd.; *Int'l*, pg. 3153
DONGFANG ELECTRIC CORPORATION LIMITED; *Int'l*, pg. 2166
DONGFANG ELECTRIC (WUHAN) NUCLEAR EQUIPEMENT CO., LTD.—See Dongfang Electric Corporation Limited; *Int'l*, pg. 2166
DONGFANG ELECTRONICS CO., LTD.; *Int'l*, pg. 2166
DONGFENG AUTOMOBILE CO., LTD.—See Dongfeng Motor Corporation; *Int'l*, pg. 2166
DONGFENG BROSE AUTOMOTIVE SYSTEM CO., LTD.—See Brose Fahrzeugteile GmbH & Co. KG; *Int'l*, pg. 1196
DONGFENG COMMERCIAL VEHICLE (MALAYSIA) SDN BHD—See MWE Holdings Berhad; *Int'l*, pg. 5110
DONGFENG CUMMINS ENGINE CO., LTD.—See Cummins Inc.; *U.S. Public*, pg. 607
DONGFENG CUMMINS ENGINE CO., LTD.—See Dongfeng Motor Corporation; *Int'l*, pg. 2166
DONGFENG ELECTRIC VEHICLE CO., LTD.—See Dongfeng Motor Corporation; *Int'l*, pg. 2166
DONGFENG ELECTRONIC TECHNOLOGY CO., LTD.; *Int'l*, pg. 2166
DONGFENG HONDA AUTOMOBILE CO., LTD.—See Honda Motor Co., Ltd.; *Int'l*, pg. 3460
DONGFENG ISEKI AGRICULTURAL MACHINERY CO., LTD.—See Iseki & Co., Ltd.; *Int'l*, pg. 3814
DONGFENG ISEKI AGRICULTURAL MACHINERY (HUBEI) CO., LTD.—See Dongfeng Motor Corporation; *Int'l*, pg. 2166
DONGFENG KASAI (DALIAN) AUTOMOTIVE TRIM SYSTEMS CO., LTD.—See Kasai Kogyo Co., Ltd.; *Int'l*, pg. 4086
DONGFENG KASAI (WUHAN) ROOF TRIM SYSTEMS CO., LTD.—See Kasai Kogyo Co., Ltd.; *Int'l*, pg. 4086
DONGFENG KASAI (XIANGYANG) AUTOMOTIVE TRIM SYSTEMS CO., LTD.—See Kasai Kogyo Co., Ltd.; *Int'l*, pg. 4086
DONGFENG MOTOR CORPORATION; *Int'l*, pg. 2166
DONGFENG MOTOR GROUP CO. LTD.—See Dongfeng Motor Corporation; *Int'l*, pg. 2166
DONGFENG NISSAN AUTO FINANCE CO., LTD.—See Nissan Motor Co., Ltd.; *Int'l*, pg. 5367
DONGFENG NISSAN PASSENGER VEHICLE COMPANY—See Nissan Motor Co., Ltd.; *Int'l*, pg. 5367
DONGFENG PEUGEOT CITROEN AUTO FINANCE CO., LTD.—See Stellantis N.V.; *Int'l*, pg. 7201
DONGFENG PEUGEOT CITROEN AUTOMOBILE COMPANY LTD.—See Dongfeng Motor Corporation; *Int'l*, pg. 2166
DONGFENG SCI-TECH GROUP CO., LTD.; *Int'l*, pg. 2166
DONGFENG UNIPRES HOT STAMPING CORPORATION—See Unipres Corporation; *Int'l*, pg. 8056
DONGGUAN ACE TECHNOLOGY CO., LTD.—See Ace Technologies Corp.; *Int'l*, pg. 95
DONGGUAN ADVANCED ELECTRONIC TECHNOLOGY CO. LTD.—See Shanghai Putailai New Energy Technology Co., Ltd.; *Int'l*, pg. 6777
DONGGUAN ADVANCED MATERIAL TECHNOLOGY CO. LTD.—See Shanghai Putailai New Energy Technology Co., Ltd.; *Int'l*, pg. 6777
DONGGUAN AEON TECH CO., LTD.—See Wha Yu Industrial Co., Ltd.; *Int'l*, pg. 8396
DONGGUAN AITAJI NEW MATERIAL CO., LTD.—See Suzhou Hengmingda Electronic Technology Co., Ltd.; *Int'l*, pg. 7350
DONGGUAN ALPS ELECTRONICS CO., LTD.—See Alps Alpine Co., Ltd.; *Int'l*, pg. 376
DONGGUAN AMPEREX ELECTRONICS TECHNOLOGY CO., LTD.—See TDK Corporation; *Int'l*, pg. 7487
DONGGUAN AOHAI TECHNOLOGY CO., LTD.; *Int'l*, pg. 2167

COMPANY NAME INDEX

DONGGUAN AOZE AUTOMOBILE SALES SERVICES CO., LTD.—See China ZhengTong Auto Services Holdings Limited; *Int'l*, pg. 1566

DONGGUAN BENSON AUTOMOBILE GLASS COMPANY LIMITED—See Xinyi Glass Holdings Limited; *Int'l*, pg. 8534

DONGGUAN BOTON FLAVOR & FRAGRANCES COMPANY LIMITED—See China Boton Group Company Limited; *Int'l*, pg. 1487

DONGGUAN BOTON FLAVORS & FRAGRANCES COMPANY LIMITED—See China Boton Group Company Limited; *Int'l*, pg. 1487

DONGGUAN CHANGAN QPL ELECTRONICS MANUFACTURING COMPANY LIMITED—See QPL International Holdings Limited; *Int'l*, pg. 6147

DONGGUAN CHAO BA BATTERIES CO., LTD.—See Gold Peak Technology Group Limited; *Int'l*, pg. 3025

DONGGUAN CHAOYE PRECISION EQUIPMENT CO., LTD.—See Funeng Oriental Equipment Technology Co., Ltd.; *Int'l*, pg. 2846

DONGGUAN CHAOZHI NEW MATERIALS CO., LTD.—See Guangdong Dtech Technology Co., Ltd.; *Int'l*, pg. 3154

DONG GUAN CHENG DA METAL PRODUCT COMPANY LIMITED—See COXON Precise Industrial Co., Ltd.; *Int'l*, pg. 1823

DONG GUAN CHENG GUANG METAL PRODUCTS CO., LTD.—See AVY Precision Technology, Inc.; *Int'l*, pg. 751

DONGGUAN CHENGQU DAIICHI PRECISION MOLD CO., LTD.—See Minebea Mitsumi Inc.; *Int'l*, pg. 4902

DONGGUAN CHENGYUE COMPUTER FITTINGS CO., LTD.—See Shin Zu Shing Co., Ltd.; *Int'l*, pg. 6838

DONG GUAN CHENSONG PLASTIC & MOULD—See COXON Precise Industrial Co., Ltd.; *Int'l*, pg. 1823

DONGGUAN CHILISIN ELECTRONICS CO., LTD.—See Yageo Corporation; *Int'l*, pg. 8545

DONGGUAN CHITWING TECHNOLOGY CO LTD; *Int'l*, pg. 2167

DONGGUAN CHUN YIK PAPER WARE FACTORY LIMITED—See Hop Fung Group Holdings Ltd; *Int'l*, pg. 3473

DONGGUAN CITY JMO OPTICAL CO., LTD.—See Zhong Yang Technology Co., Ltd.; *Int'l*, pg. 8672

DONGGUAN CITY PRECIMET TRADING CO LTD—See Technic Incorporated; *U.S. Private*, pg. 3953

DONGGUAN CITY SYNPOWER CO., LTD.—See Sungwoo Techron Co., Ltd.; *Int'l*, pg. 7316

DONGGUAN CITY YONGWEI TECHNOLOGY CO., LTD.—See Veken Technology Co., Ltd.; *Int'l*, pg. 8148

DONGGUAN CLARION ORIENT ELECTRONICS CO., LTD.—See FORVIA SE; *Int'l*, pg. 2745

DONGGUAN CLEANERA CLEANROOM PRODUCTS COMPANY LIMITED—See Kossan Rubber Industries Bhd; *Int'l*, pg. 4291

DONGGUAN COILS ELECTRONIC CO. LTD.—See CEC International Holdings Limited; *Int'l*, pg. 1372

DONGGUAN COSMOS PLASTICS PRODUCTS COMPANY LTD—See Cosmos Machinery Enterprises Limited; *Int'l*, pg. 1813

DONGGUAN DAEJOO ELECTRONIC MATERIALS CO., LTD.—See Daejoo Electronic Materials Co., Ltd.; *Int'l*, pg. 1907

DONG GUAN DAI-ICHI SEIKO MOLD & PLASTICS CO., LTD.—See I-PEX Inc.; *Int'l*, pg. 3563

DONG GUAN DAINICHI CHEMICAL MANUFACTURING CO., LTD.—See Dainichiseika Color & Chemicals Mfg. Co., Ltd.; *Int'l*, pg. 1939

DONGGUAN DEVELOPMENT (HOLDINGS) CO., LTD.; *Int'l*, pg. 2167

DONGGUAN DHL SUPPLY CHAIN CO., LTD.—See Deutsche Post AG; *Int'l*, pg. 2078

DONGGUAN DINGTAIXIN ELEC. CO., LTD.—See Guangdong Dtech Technology Co., Ltd.; *Int'l*, pg. 3154

DONGGUAN DINGTONG PRECISION METAL CO., LTD.; *Int'l*, pg. 2167

DONGGUAN DONGBU TOYOTA AUTO SALES & SERVICES CO., LTD.—See China MeiDong Auto Holdings Limited; *Int'l*, pg. 1519

DONGGUAN DONGFA TEAC AUDIO CO., LTD.—See Evolution Capital Management LLC; *U.S. Private*, pg. 1443

DONGGUAN DONGMA ELECTRONIC COMPANY—See Moatech Co., Ltd.; *Int'l*, pg. 5007

DONGGUAN DONGMEI THREAD MFG. CO. LTD.—See The Kroger Co.; *U.S. Public*, pg. 2108

DONGGUAN DONGMEI TOYOTA AUTO SALES & SERVICES CO., LTD.—See China MeiDong Auto Holdings Limited; *Int'l*, pg. 1519

DONGGUAN DPT ELECTRONICS CO., LTD.—See Wuhu Token Sciences Co., Ltd.; *Int'l*, pg. 8502

DONGGUAN EDENSOFT LIMITED—See Edensoft Holdings Limited; *Int'l*, pg. 2308

DONGGUAN EONTEC CO., LTD.; *Int'l*, pg. 2167

DONG GUAN E-RUN ELECTRONIC PRODUCT LTD.—See Bright Led Electronics Corp.; *Int'l*, pg. 1161

DONGGUAN EVERWIN PRECISION TECHNOLOGY CO., LTD.—See Shenzhen Everwin Precision Technology Co., Ltd.; *Int'l*, pg. 6809

DONGGUAN FANCHANG CURTAIN PRODUCT CO., LTD.—See Nien Made Enterprise Co., Ltd.; *Int'l*, pg. 5280

DONGGUAN FENG GANG CASTFAST METAL & PLASTICS CO., LTD.—See Karrie International Holdings Limited; *Int'l*, pg. 4085

DONGGUAN FENG GANG CASTON METAL & PLASTICS CO., LTD.—See Karrie International Holdings Limited; *Int'l*, pg. 4085

DONGGUAN FOUND CHAIN IOT CO., LTD.—See Everspring Industry Co., Ltd.; *Int'l*, pg. 2569

DONGGUAN FRONTIER ELECTRONICS CO., LTD.—See Prosperity Dielectrics Co., Ltd.; *Int'l*, pg. 6002

DONGGUAN FUKOKU RUBBER & PLASTICS INDUSTRY CO., LTD.—See Fukoku Co., Ltd.; *Int'l*, pg. 2838

DONGGUAN FUQIANG ELECTRONICS CO., LTD.—See Cheng Eui Precision Industry Co., Ltd.; *Int'l*, pg. 1465

DONGGUAN FUTABA METAL PRODUCTS CO., LTD.—See Futaba Industrial Co., Ltd.; *Int'l*, pg. 2851

DONGGUANG CITY MING LOONG PAPER CO., LTD.—See Cheng Loong Corp.; *Int'l*, pg. 1466

DONGGUAN GEM ELECTRONICS & METAL CO., LTD.—See Gem Terminal Ind. Co., Ltd.; *Int'l*, pg. 2915

DONG GUANG KDK ALUMINUM FOIL MANUFACTURE LTD.—See Nippon Chemi-Con Corporation; *Int'l*, pg. 5312

DONGGUAN GOLDEN SUN ABRASIVES CO., LTD.; *Int'l*, pg. 2167

DONGGUAN G-PRO COMPUTER CO., LTD.—See Lite-On Technology Corporation; *Int'l*, pg. 4525

DONGGUAN GUANFENG AUTO CO., LTD.—See China MeiDong Auto Holdings Limited; *Int'l*, pg. 1519

DONG GUANG YING HUA PRECISION METAL CO., LTD.—See AVY Precision Technology, Inc.; *Int'l*, pg. 751

DONGGUAN HANGHUA-HARIMA PAPER CHEMICALS CO., LTD.—See Harima Chemicals Group, Inc.; *Int'l*, pg. 3276

DONGGUAN HEITKAMP & THUMANN METAL PRODUCTS LTD—See Heitkamp & Thumann KG; *Int'l*, pg. 3326

DONG GUAN HIROSAWA AUTOMOTIVE TRIM CO., LTD.—See Hiroca Holdings Ltd.; *Int'l*, pg. 3404

DONGGUAN HONGFUHANHAO NEW METERIAL TECHNOLOGY CO., LTD.—See Shenzhen Hongfuhan Technology Co., Ltd.; *Int'l*, pg. 6812

DONG GUAN HONG YUEN ELECTRONICS LTD.—See China Aerospace International Holdings Limited; *Int'l*, pg. 1481

DONGGUAN HONMYUE TEXTILE LIMITED—See Honmyue Enterprise Co., Ltd.; *Int'l*, pg. 3472

DONGGUAN HSU FU CHI FOODS COMPANY LIMITED—See Nestle S.A.; *Int'l*, pg. 5202

DONGGUAN HUAJIA SURFACE TECHNOLOGY CO., LTD.—See PPG Industries, Inc.; *U.S. Public*, pg. 1707

DONGGUAN HUA YI BRASS PRODUCTS CO., LTD.—See Solartech International Holdings Limited; *Int'l*, pg. 7070

DONGGUAN HUMEN WANSHIH ELECTRONIC CO., LTD.—See Wanshih Electronics Co., Ltd.; *Int'l*, pg. 8342

DONGGUAN IM DIGITAL ELECTRONICS CO. LTD—See IM Co., Ltd.; *Int'l*, pg. 3617

DONGGUAN INABATA ENGINEERING PLASTICS CO., LTD.—See Inabata & Co. Ltd.; *Int'l*, pg. 3643

DONGGUAN INKEL ELECTRONICS CO LTD—See INKEL Corporation; *Int'l*, pg. 3705

DONGGUAN INOAC (F.K.) METAL & ELASTOMER CO., LTD.—See INOAC Corporation; *Int'l*, pg. 3714

DONGGUAN INOAC KENJOU AUTOMOTIVE CO., LTD.—See INOAC Corporation; *Int'l*, pg. 3714

DONGGUAN INOAC METAL & ELASTOMER CO., LTD.—See INOAC Corporation; *Int'l*, pg. 3714

DONGGUAN INOAC POLYMER CO., LTD.—See INOAC Corporation; *Int'l*, pg. 3714

DONG GUAN JARLLY ELECTRONICS CO., LTD.—See Jarllytec Co., Ltd.; *Int'l*, pg. 3911

DONGGUAN JETCROWN TECHNOLOGY LIMITED—See Deswell Industries, Inc.; *Int'l*, pg. 2047

DONGGUAN JFE SHOJI STEEL PRODUCTS CO., LTD.—See JFE Holdings, Inc.; *Int'l*, pg. 3936

DONGGUAN JIAHONG ELECTRONICS CO., LTD.—See CHIALIN Precision Industrial Co., Ltd.; *Int'l*, pg. 1475

DONGGUAN JIA XIN HANDBAG COMPANY LIMITED—See Lee & Man Chemical Company Limited; *Int'l*, pg. 4439

DONGGUAN JIEXUNTENG PRECISION ELECTRONIC SCIENCE & TECHNOLOGY CO., LTD.—See Zhejiang Yonggui Electric Equipment Co., Ltd.; *Int'l*, pg. 8667

DONGGUAN JINNJIXING PRECISION OPTICAL CO., LTD.—See CHIALIN Precision Industrial Co., Ltd.; *Int'l*, pg. 1475

DONGGUAN JINRONG AUTO PARTS CO., LTD.—See Tianjin Jinrong Tianyu Precision Machinery, Inc.; *Int'l*, pg. 7739

DONGGUAN JMO OPTICAL CO.,LTD.—See Zhong Yang Technology Co., Ltd.; *Int'l*, pg. 8672

DONGGUAN JPT OPTICAL TECHNOLOGY CO., LTD.—See Shenzhen JPT Opto-Electronics Co., Ltd.; *Int'l*, pg. 6815

DONGGUAN JUNG SHING WIRE CO., LTD.—See Jung Shing Wire Co., Ltd.; *Int'l*, pg. 4026

DONGGUAN KAILAI ELECTRONIC CO., LTD.—See Ying-Tong Telecommunication Co., Ltd.; *Int'l*, pg. 8584

DONGGUAN KEWEI MEDICAL INSTRUMENT CO., LTD.—See MicroPort Scientific Corporation; *Int'l*, pg. 4880

DONGGUAN KEYSTONE ELECTRIC WIRE & CABLE CO. LTD.—See Prysmian S.p.A.; *Int'l*, pg. 6011

DONGGUAN KEYSTONE ELECTRIC WIRE & CABLE CO, LTD.—See Prysmian S.p.A.; *Int'l*, pg. 6011

DONGGUAN KFC CO., LTD.—See Yum China Holdings, Inc.; *U.S. Public*, pg. 2399

DONGGUAN KHUAN HUANG PRECISE MOLD PLASTIC CO., LTD.—See Syncmold Enterprise Corp.; *Int'l*, pg. 7382

DONGGUAN KINGSUN OPTOELECTRONIC CO., LTD.; *Int'l*, pg. 2167

DONGGUAN KOHOKU ELECTRONICS CO., LTD.—See Kohoku Kogyo Co., Ltd.; *Int'l*, pg. 4229

DONGGUAN KRP DEVELOPMENT COMPANY LIMITED—See Karrie International Holdings Limited; *Int'l*, pg. 4085

DONGGUAN KWAN HONG ELECTRONICS CO. LTD.—See Deswell Industries, Inc.; *Int'l*, pg. 2047

DONGGUAN LEADER ELECTRONICS INC.—See Leader Electronics Inc.; *Int'l*, pg. 4433

DONGGUAN LEEWAY FOOTWEAR COMPANY LIMITED—See Caleres, Inc.; *U.S. Public*, pg. 422

DONGGUAN LIAOBU SCAS AUTOMOBILE SALES SERVICES CO., LTD.—See China ZhengTong Auto Services Holdings Limited; *Int'l*, pg. 1566

DONGGUAN LIESHENG ELECTRONIC TECHNOLOGY CO., LTD.; *Int'l*, pg. 2167

DONGGUAN LILLY PAINT INDUSTRIES LIMITED—See The Sherwin-Williams Company; *U.S. Public*, pg. 2129

DONGGUAN LITENG FOODS CO., LTD.—See Thai Beverage Public Company Limited; *Int'l*, pg. 7589

DONG-GUAN LI YUAN ELECTRONICS CO., LTD.—See Everspring Industry Co., Ltd.; *Int'l*, pg. 2569

DONGGUAN LUXON ELECTRONICS CORP.—See Kai-emei Electronic Corp.; *Int'l*, pg. 4051

DONGGUAN MAXHON INTERNET OF THINGS TECHNOLOGY CO., LTD.—See MYS Group Co., Ltd.; *Int'l*, pg. 5114

DONGGUAN MEMTECH ELECTRONIC PRODUCTS CO., LTD.—See Memtech International Ltd; *Int'l*, pg. 4814

DONGGUAN MEMTECH LENS TECHNOLOGIES CO., LTD.—See Memtech International Ltd; *Int'l*, pg. 4814

DONGGUAN MEMTECH OPTICAL & MAGNETIC CO., LTD. - MORGAN HILL BRANCH—See Dongguan Memtech Optical & Magnetic Co., Ltd.; *Int'l*, pg. 2167

DONGGUAN MEMTECH OPTICAL & MAGNETIC CO., LTD.; *Int'l*, pg. 2167

DONGGUAN MING LOONG PAPER CO., LTD.—See Cheng Loong Corp.; *Int'l*, pg. 1466

DONGGUAN MOLEX SOUTH-CHINA CONNECTOR CO. LTD.—See Koch Industries, Inc.; *U.S. Private*, pg. 2334

DONGGUAN MURATA ELECTRONICS CO., LTD.—See Murata Manufacturing Co., Ltd.; *Int'l*, pg. 5097

DONGGUAN MYS ENVIRONMENTAL PROTECTION & TECHNOLOGY COMPANY LTD.—See MYS Group Co., Ltd.; *Int'l*, pg. 5114

DONGGUAN NEW ISLAND PRINTING CO., LTD.—See China Huajun Group Limited; *Int'l*, pg. 1509

DONGGUAN NEW ORIENT TECHNOLOGY CO., LTD.—See Shanghai Hongda New Material Co., LTD.; *Int'l*, pg. 6770

DONGGUAN NICCA NEW MATERIAL CO., LTD.—See Nicca Chemical Co., Ltd.; *Int'l*, pg. 5263

DONGGUAN NIFCO CO., LTD.—See Nifco Inc.; *Int'l*, pg. 5281

DONG GUAN NIKON SURVEYING INSTRUMENTS CO., LTD.—See Nikon Corporation; *Int'l*, pg. 5292

DONGGUAN NISSEI ELECTRONICS CO., LTD.—See Nippon Seiki Co., Ltd.; *Int'l*, pg. 5329

DONGGUAN NISSIN PLASTIC PRODUCTS CO., LTD.—See Wong's Kong King International (Holdings) Limited; *Int'l*, pg. 8447

DONGGUAN NISTAR TRANSMITTING TECHNOLOGY CO., INC.—See Baosheng Science & Technology Innovation Co., Ltd; *Int'l*, pg. 856

DONGGUAN NVT TECHNOLOGY CO., LTD.—See TDK Corporation; *Int'l*, pg. 7487

DONGGUAN PAIHO POWDER COATING CO., LTD.—See Taiwan Paiho Limited; *Int'l*, pg. 7422

DONGGUAN PAIHO TEXTILE LIMITED—See Taiwan Paiho Limited; *Int'l*, pg. 7422

DONGGUAN PICO EXHIBITION SERVICES CO LIMITED—See Pico Far East Holdings Limited; *Int'l*, pg. 5860

DONGGUAN PIOLAX CO., LTD.—See Piolax Inc.; *Int'l*, pg. 5871

DONGGUAN POLY YULAN GRAND THEATRE MANAGEMENT CORPORATION LIMITED—See Poly Culture Group Corporation Limited; *Int'l*, pg. 5913

DONGGUAN POSSEHL ELECTRONICS CO. LTD.—See L. Possehl & Co. mbH; *Int'l*, pg. 4384
DONGGUAN QUAN SHENG ELECTRIC CO., LTD.—See Powertech Industrial Co., Ltd.; *Int'l*, pg. 5948
DONGGUAN QUICKMIND HANDBAG FACTORY CO., LTD.—See Wah Sun Handbags International Holdings Limited; *Int'l*, pg. 8330
DONGGUAN QUNHAN ELECTRONICS CO.,LTD.—See CviLux Corporation; *Int'l*, pg. 1889
DONGGUAN RECHI COMPRESSOR CO., LTD.—See Rechi Precision Co., Ltd.; *Int'l*, pg. 6235
DONGGUAN RICOH ELEMEX OFFICE MACHINE CO., LTD.—See Ricoh Company, Ltd.; *Int'l*, pg. 6334
DONGGUAN RURAL COMMERCIAL BANK CO., LTD.; *Int'l*, pg. 2167
DONGGUAN SALIPT CO., LTD.—See ChangYuan Group Ltd.; *Int'l*, pg. 1444
DONGGUAN SAMSUNG SDI CO., LTD.—See Samsung Group; *Int'l*, pg. 6514
DONGGUAN SCAS AUTOMOBILE SALES SERVICES CO., LTD.—See China ZhengTong Auto Services Holdings Limited; *Int'l*, pg. 1566
DONGGUAN SHATIN LAKE SIDE TEXTILES PRINTING & DYEING CO., LTD.—See Fountain Set (Holdings) Limited; *Int'l*, pg. 2754
DONG GUAN SHEN MAO SOLDERING TIN CO., LTD.—See Shenmao Technology Inc.; *Int'l*, pg. 6802
DONG GUAN SHENYANG SOLDER MATERIAL CO., LTD.—See Shenmao Technology Inc.; *Int'l*, pg. 6803
DONGGUAN SHIBAURA ELECTRONICS CO., LTD.—See Shibaura Electronics Co., Ltd.; *Int'l*, pg. 6827
DONGGUAN SHILONG KYOCERA CO., LTD.—See KYOCERA Corporation; *Int'l*, pg. 4355
DONGGUAN SHINHINT AUDIO TECHNOLOGY LIMITED—See Jintai Energy Holdings Limited; *Int'l*, pg. 3970
DONGGUAN SHINWHA INTERTEK CORP.—See Shinwha Intertek Corporation; *Int'l*, pg. 6850
DONGGUAN SHUN ON ELECTRONICS CO., LTD.—See Shun On Electronic Co., Ltd.; *Int'l*, pg. 6869
DONGGUAN SIZHING ELECTRONIC CO., LTD.—See Surface Mount Technology (Holdings) Limited; *Int'l*, pg. 7343
DONGGUAN STEEL WEALTH METAL CO., LTD.—See Golik Holdings Limited; *Int'l*, pg. 3036
DONGGUAN SUMIDA (TAI PING) ELECTRIC CO., LTD.—See Sumida Corporation; *Int'l*, pg. 7261
DONGGUAN SUMIKINBUSSAN METAL PRODUCTS CO., LTD.—See Nippon Steel Corporation; *Int'l*, pg. 5337
DONGGUAN SUMIKO ELECTRONIC PASTE CO., LTD.—See Sumitomo Metal Mining Co., Ltd.; *Int'l*, pg. 7291
DONGGUAN SUPERIOR MANUFACTURING TECHNOLOGY CO. LTD.—See Surface Mount Technology (Holdings) Limited; *Int'l*, pg. 7343
DONGGUAN SURPASS STRUCTURE CERAMICS CO., LTD.—See Shenzhen Sunlord Electronics Co., Ltd.; *Int'l*, pg. 6822
DONGGUAN SWELL AUTO PARTS CO., LTD.—See Guangdong Hongtu Technology (Holdings) Co., Ltd.; *Int'l*, pg. 3156
DONGGUAN TAICA HIROSAWA TECHNOLOGIES CO., LTD.—See Hiroca Holdings Ltd.; *Int'l*, pg. 3404
DONGGUAN TAISOL ELECTRONICS CO., LTD.—See TaiSol Electronics Co., Ltd.; *Int'l*, pg. 7418
DONGGUAN TARRY ELECTRONICS CO., LTD.; *Int'l*, pg. 2167
DONGGUAN TEAC ELECTRONICS CO., LTD.—See Evolution Capital Management LLC; *U.S. Private*, pg. 1443
DONGGUAN TETSUWA METALS CO., LTD.—See Hanwa Co., Ltd.; *Int'l*, pg. 3262
DONGGUAN TEXWINCA TEXTILE & GARMENT LTD—See Texwinca Holdings Limited; *Int'l*, pg. 7584
DONGGUAN TONGLI TRADING CO., LTD.—See Tatung Company; *Int'l*, pg. 7475
DONG GUAN TOP NATION ELECTRONIC LIMITED—See Yao Sheng Electronics Co., Ltd.; *Int'l*, pg. 8566
DONGGUAN TRANSPOWER ELECTRIC PRODUCTS CO., LTD.—See TE Connectivity Ltd.; *Int'l*, pg. 7494
DONGGUAN UNION TOOL LTD.—See Union Tool Co.; *Int'l*, pg. 8054
DONGGUAN UNIVERSAL CLASSICAL MATERIAL LTD.—See China Resources Building Materials Technology Holdings Limited; *Int'l*, pg. 1548
DONGGUAN UNZA CONSUMER PRODUCTS LTD.—See Wipro Limited; *Int'l*, pg. 8432
DONGGUAN VANKE REAL ESTATE COMPANY LIMITED—See China Vanke Co., Ltd.; *Int'l*, pg. 1562
DONGGUAN VEKEN BATTERY CO., LTD.—See Veken Technology Co., Ltd.; *Int'l*, pg. 8148
DONGGUAN VEKEN NEW ENERGY SCIENCE & TECHNOLOGY CO.—See Veken Technology Co., Ltd.; *Int'l*, pg. 8148
DONGGUAN WALSIN TECHNOLOGY ELECTRONICS CO., LTD—See Walsin Technology Corporation; *Int'l*, pg. 8335
DONGGUAN WALSIN WIRE & CABLE LTD.—See Walsin Lihwa Corporation; *Int'l*, pg. 8334

DONGGUAN WEI BAO SPORTS EQUIPMENT CO., LTD.—See WW Holding Inc; *Int'l*, pg. 8516
DONGGUAN WEIHANG ELECTRICAL PRODUCT COMPANY LIMITED—See Zhongzheng International Company Limited; *Int'l*, pg. 8677
DONGGUAN WEI HUA HANDBAG COMPANY LIMITED—See Lee & Man Chemical Company Limited; *Int'l*, pg. 4439
DONGGUAN WELL SHIN ELECTRONIC PRODUCTS CO., LTD.—See Well Shin Technology Co., Ltd.; *Int'l*, pg. 8373
DONGGUAN WIDEHOLD METAL COMPANY LIMITED—See Golik Holdings Limited; *Int'l*, pg. 3036
DONGGUAN WINNERWAY INDUSTRY ZONE LTD.; *Int'l*, pg. 2167
DONGGUAN WISE ALLY INDUSTRIAL CO., LTD.—See Wise Ally International Holdings Limited; *Int'l*, pg. 8435
DONGGUAN WONDERFUL PACKAGING COMPANY LIMITED—See Amcor plc; *Int'l*, pg. 418
DONGGUAN WONG'S KONG KING ELECTRONICS CO., LIMITED—See Wong's Kong King International (Holdings) Limited; *Int'l*, pg. 8447
DONGGUAN YEONG GUAN FOUNDRY CO., LTD.—See Yeong Guan Energy Technology Group Co., Ltd.; *Int'l*, pg. 8577
DONG GUAN YEONG GUAN MOULD FACTORY CO., LTD.—See Yeong Guan Energy Technology Group Co., Ltd.; *Int'l*, pg. 8577
DONGGUAN YIHEDA AUTOMATION CO., LTD.; *Int'l*, pg. 2167
DONGGUAN YINGTONG WIRE CO., LTD.—See YingTong Telecommunication Ltd.; *Int'l*, pg. 8584
DONGGUAN YIZHAO ELECTRONIC CO., LTD.—See Wenzhou Yihua Connector Co., Ltd.; *Int'l*, pg. 8378
DONGGUAN YOKOWO CAR COMPONENTS CO., LTD.—See YOKOWO Co., Ltd.; *Int'l*, pg. 8595
DONGGUAN YOKOWO COMMUNICATION COMPONENTS CO., LTD.—See YOKOWO Co., Ltd.; *Int'l*, pg. 8595
DONGGUAN YOKOWO ELECTRONICS CO., LTD.—See YOKOWO Co., Ltd.; *Int'l*, pg. 8595
DONGGUAN YORKEY OPTICAL MACHINERY COMPONENTS LTD.—See YORKEY OPTICAL INTERNATIONAL (CAYMAN) LTD; *Int'l*, pg. 8599
DONGGUAN YOUXUN ELECTRONICS CO., LTD.—See Alpha Networks Inc.; *Int'l*, pg. 369
DONGGUAN YULONG TELECOMMUNICATION TECH CO., LTD.—See Coolpad Group Limited; *Int'l*, pg. 1789
DONGGUAN YUTONG OPTICAL TECHNOLOGY CO., LTD.; *Int'l*, pg. 2167
DONGGUAN ZENSEE PRINTING LIMITED—See Q P Group Holdings Limited; *Int'l*, pg. 6129
DONGGUAN ZHENGDE CONNECTOR CO., LTD.—See Wenzhou Yihua Connector Co., Ltd.; *Int'l*, pg. 8378
DONGGUAN ZHENGTONG KAIDI AUTOMOBILE SALES SERVICES CO., LTD.—See China ZhengTong Auto Services Holdings Limited; *Int'l*, pg. 1566
DONG GUAN ZHONG JIA ELECTRONICS CO. LTD.—See IQ Group Holdings Berhad; *Int'l*, pg. 3803
DONGGUAN ZHONGTIAN AUTOMATION TECHNOLOGY CO., LTD.—See Ningbo Cixing Co., Ltd.; *Int'l*, pg. 5301
DONGGUAN ZHONGXING ELECTRONICS CO., LTD.—See Ningbo Sunrise Elc Technology Co., Ltd.; *Int'l*, pg. 5306
DONG HAI JOINT STOCK COMPANY; *Int'l*, pg. 2163
DONGHEE CZECH S.R.O.—See DH Holdings Co., Ltd.; *Int'l*, pg. 2097
DONGHEE RUS LLC—See DH Holdings Co., Ltd.; *Int'l*, pg. 2097
DONGHEE SLOVAKIA S.R.O.—See DH Holdings Co., Ltd.; *Int'l*, pg. 2097
DONGHIA INC.—See Kravet, Inc.; *U.S. Private*, pg. 2350
DONGHUA (HONG KONG) LIMITED—See Shanghai Dasheng Agriculture Finance Technology Co., Ltd.; *Int'l*, pg. 6764
DONGHUA MACHINERY LTD.—See Cosmos Machinery Enterprises Limited; *Int'l*, pg. 1813
DONGHUA TESTING TECHNOLOGY CO., LTD.; *Int'l*, pg. 2167
DONG HUNG INVESTMENT DEVELOPMENT CONSULTANCY JOINT STOCK COMPANY LIMITED—See AEON Co., Ltd.; *Int'l*, pg. 177
DONGHWA CONTAINER TRANSPORTATION SERVICE CO., LTD.—See China International Marine Containers (Group) Co., Ltd.; *Int'l*, pg. 1511
DONGHWA CORPORATION—See Yujin Co., Ltd.; *Int'l*, pg. 8611
DONGHWA TELECOM CO. LTD—See Chunghwa Telecom Co.; *Int'l*, pg. 1598
DONGIL-BANDO CO.—See Bando Chemical Industries, Ltd.; *Int'l*, pg. 830
DONGILI INVESTMENT GROUP, INC.; *U.S. Private*, pg. 1260
DONGIL INDUSTRIES, LTD.—See Dongil Metal Co., Ltd.; *Int'l*, pg. 2167
DONGIL METAL CO., LTD. - DASAN FACTORY—See Cheil Grinding Wheel Ind, Ltd.; *Int'l*, pg. 1460
DONGIL METAL CO., LTD. - OGYE FACTORY—See Dongil Metal Co., Ltd.; *Int'l*, pg. 2167

DONGIL METAL CO., LTD.; *Int'l*, pg. 2167
DONGIL RUBBER BELT AMERICA, INC.—See DRB Holding Co., Ltd.; *Int'l*, pg. 2201
DONGIL RUBBER BELT JAPAN CO., LTD.—See DRB Holding Co., Ltd.; *Int'l*, pg. 2201
DONGIL RUBBER BELT SLOVAKIA, S.R.O.—See DRB Holding Co., Ltd.; *Int'l*, pg. 2201
DONGIL RUBBER BELT VIETNAM CO., LTD.—See DRB Holding Co., Ltd.; *Int'l*, pg. 2201
DONG-IL SHIMADZU CORP.—See DI Corp.; *Int'l*, pg. 2101
DONGIL STEEL CO., LTD.; *Int'l*, pg. 2168
DONG IL STEEL MFG CO., LTD.; *Int'l*, pg. 2163
DONGIL TECHNOLOGY LTD.; *Int'l*, pg. 2168
DONGJIANG ENVIRONMENTAL COMPANY LIMITED; *Int'l*, pg. 2168
DONGJIN SEMICHEM CO., LTD. - BALAN PLANT—See Dongjin Semichem Co., Ltd.; *Int'l*, pg. 2168
DONGJIN SEMICHEM CO., LTD. - INCHEON PLANT—See Dongjin Semichem Co., Ltd.; *Int'l*, pg. 2168
DONGJIN SEMICHEM CO., LTD. - SHIWHA PLANT—See Dongjin Semichem Co., Ltd.; *Int'l*, pg. 2168
DONGJIN SEMICHEM CO., LTD.; *Int'l*, pg. 2168
DONGJIN SEMICHEM ORDOS CITY TECHNOLOGY CO., LTD.—See Dongjin Semichem Co., Ltd.; *Int'l*, pg. 2168
DONGJIN SEMICHEM TECHNOLOGY (QIDONG) CO., LTD.—See Dongjin Semichem Co., Ltd.; *Int'l*, pg. 2168
DONGJIN SEMICHEM (XI'AN) SEMICONDUCTOR MATERIALS CO., LTD.—See Dongjin Semichem Co., Ltd.; *Int'l*, pg. 2168
DONGKOO BIO & PHARMA CO., LTD.; *Int'l*, pg. 2168
DONG KOOK LIFESCIENCE CO., LTD.—See Dongkook Pharmaceutical Co., Ltd.; *Int'l*, pg. 2168
DONGKOOK PHARMACEUTICAL CO., LTD.; *Int'l*, pg. 2168
DONGKUK CORPORATION—See Dongkuk Steel Mill Co., Ltd.; *Int'l*, pg. 2169
DONGKUK INDUSTRIES CO., LTD. - POHANG FACTORY—See Dongkuk Industries Co., Ltd.; *Int'l*, pg. 2168
DONGKUK INDUSTRIES CO., LTD. - SIHEUNG FACTORY—See Dongkuk Industries Co., Ltd.; *Int'l*, pg. 2168
DONGKUK INDUSTRIES CO., LTD.; *Int'l*, pg. 2168
DONGKUK INTERNATIONAL, INC.—See Dongkuk Steel Mill Co., Ltd.; *Int'l*, pg. 2169
DONGKUK REFRACTORIES & STEEL CO., LTD.; *Int'l*, pg. 2168
DONGKUK S&C CO., LTD. - DK WIND POWER PLANT—See Dongkuk S&C Co., Ltd.; *Int'l*, pg. 2169
DONGKUK S&C CO., LTD.; *Int'l*, pg. 2168
DONGKUK STEEL CHINA CO., LTD.—See Dongkuk Steel Mill Co., Ltd.; *Int'l*, pg. 2169
DONGKUK STEEL INDIA PRIVATE LIMITED—See Dongkuk Steel Mill Co., Ltd.; *Int'l*, pg. 2169
DONGKUK STEEL MEXICO, S.A. DE C.V.—See Dongkuk Steel Mill Co., Ltd.; *Int'l*, pg. 2169
DONGKUK STEEL MILL CO., LTD. - BUSAN WORKS—See Dongkuk Steel Mill Co., Ltd.; *Int'l*, pg. 2169
DONGKUK STEEL MILL CO., LTD. - DANGJIN WORKS—See Dongkuk Steel Mill Co., Ltd.; *Int'l*, pg. 2169
DONGKUK STEEL MILL CO., LTD. - INCHEON WORKS—See Dongkuk Steel Mill Co., Ltd.; *Int'l*, pg. 2169
DONGKUK STEEL MILL CO., LTD. - POHANG WORKS—See Dongkuk Steel Mill Co., Ltd.; *Int'l*, pg. 2169
DONGKUK STEEL MILL CO., LTD.; *Int'l*, pg. 2169
DONGKUK STEEL THAILAND LTD.—See Dongkuk Steel Mill Co., Ltd.; *Int'l*, pg. 2169
DONGLAI COATING TECHNOLOGY SHANGHAI CO., LTD.; *Int'l*, pg. 2169
DONGMAN ENTERTAINMENT CORP.—See NAVER Corporation; *Int'l*, pg. 5174
DONGMA PALM INDUSTIRES (ZHANGJIAGANG) CO. LTD.—See Kwantas Corporation Berhad; *Int'l*, pg. 4350
DONG NAI MARITIME SERVICES JOINT STOCK COMPANY—See Dong Nai Port; *Int'l*, pg. 2164
DONG NAI PAINT CORPORATION; *Int'l*, pg. 2163
DONGNAI PLASTIC JSC; *Int'l*, pg. 2169
DONG NAI PORT; *Int'l*, pg. 2164
DONG NAI ROOFSHEET & CONSTRUCTION MATERIAL JOINT STOCK COMPANY; *Int'l*, pg. 2164
DONGNAM CHEMICAL CO., LTD.; *Int'l*, pg. 2169
DONGNAN ELECTRONICS CO., LTD.; *Int'l*, pg. 2169
DONGPENG HOLDINGS COMPANY LIMITED; *Int'l*, pg. 2169
DONG PHU RUBBER JOINT STOCK COMPANY; *Int'l*, pg. 2164
DON GRESSWELL LTD.—See Wall Family Enterprise, Inc.; *U.S. Private*, pg. 4430
DONGRUI FOOD GROUP CO., LTD.; *Int'l*, pg. 2169
DONGSEO CONSTRUCTION CO., LTD.—See Daesang Corporation; *Int'l*, pg. 1909
DONGSHENG PHARMACEUTICAL INTERNATIONAL CO., LTD.; *Int'l*, pg. 2169

COMPANY NAME INDEX

DONGSHIN ENGINEERING & CONSTRUCTION CO., LTD.; *Int'l*, pg. 2169
DONG SUH CHEMICAL CO., LTD.—See Kumkang Kind; *Int'l*, pg. 4331
DONG-SUH CHEMICAL IND. CO., LTD.—See Kumkang Kind; *Int'l*, pg. 4331
DONG SUH COMPANIES INC.; *Int'l*, pg. 2164
DONG-SUH FOODS CORPORATION—See Mondelez International, Inc.; *U.S. Public*, pg. 1461
DONG SUNG AMERICA INC.—See Dongsung Chemical Co., Ltd.; *Int'l*, pg. 2169
DONGSUNG BIOPOL CO., LTD.—See Dongsung Chemical Co., Ltd.; *Int'l*, pg. 2170
DONGSUNG BIORANE CO., LTD.—See Dongsung Chemical Co., Ltd.; *Int'l*, pg. 2170
DONGSUNG CHEMICAL CO., LTD. - SIHWA FACTORY—See Dongsung Chemical Co., Ltd.; *Int'l*, pg. 2170
DONGSUNG CHEMICAL CO., LTD. - SINPYEONG FACTORY—See Dongsung Chemical Co., Ltd.; *Int'l*, pg. 2170
DONGSUNG CHEMICAL CO., LTD.; *Int'l*, pg. 2169
DONGSUNG CHEMICAL CO., LTD. - YEOCHEON FACTORY—See Dongsung Chemical Co., Ltd.; *Int'l*, pg. 2170
DONGSUNG ECORE CO., LTD.—See Dongsung Chemical Co., Ltd.; *Int'l*, pg. 2170
DONGSUNG FINETEC CO., LTD.; *Int'l*, pg. 2170
DONGSUNG FINETEC INTERNATIONAL, INC.—See DONGSUNG FINETEC CO., LTD.; *Int'l*, pg. 2170
DONGSUNG HOLDINGS CO., LTD.—See Dongsung Chemical Co., Ltd.; *Int'l*, pg. 2170
DONGSUNG METAL CO., LTD.—See Daido Metal Corporation; *Int'l*, pg. 1921
DONGSUNG NSC COMPANY LTD.; *Int'l*, pg. 2170
DONGSUNG NSC VIETNAM COMPANY LTD.—See Dongsung NSC Company Ltd.; *Int'l*, pg. 2170
DONG SUNG PHARMACEUTICAL COMPANY LTD. - ASAN FACTORY—See Dong Sung Pharmaceutical Company Ltd.; *Int'l*, pg. 2164
DONG SUNG PHARMACEUTICAL COMPANY LTD.; *Int'l*, pg. 2164
DONGSUNG TCS CO., LTD.—See SG Private Equity Co., Ltd.; *Int'l*, pg. 6741
DONGTAI CHINA GLASS SPECIAL GLASS COMPANY LIMITED—See China Glass Holdings Limited; *Int'l*, pg. 1504
DONG THUAN TOURISM JOINT-STOCK COMPANY—See Tin Nghia Corp.; *Int'l*, pg. 7752
DONGWHA AUSTRALIA HOLDINGS PTY LTD.—See DONGWHA HOLDINGS CO., LTD.; *Int'l*, pg. 2170
DONGWHA DUBAI—See DONGWHA HOLDINGS CO., LTD.; *Int'l*, pg. 2170
DONG WHA G&P CORPORATION—See DONG WHA PHARM CO., LTD.; *Int'l*, pg. 2164
DONGWHA HOLDINGS CO., LTD.; *Int'l*, pg. 2170
DONGWHA HONG KONG INTERNATIONAL CO LTD—See DONGWHA HOLDINGS CO., LTD.; *Int'l*, pg. 2170
DONGWHA INDIA PRIVATE LIMITED—See DONGWHA HOLDINGS CO., LTD.; *Int'l*, pg. 2170
DONGWHA MALAYSIA HOLDINGS SDN. BHD. - KULIM PLANT—See DONGWHA HOLDINGS CO., LTD.; *Int'l*, pg. 2170
DONGWHA MALAYSIA HOLDINGS SDN. BHD. - MERBOK PLANT—See DONGWHA HOLDINGS CO., LTD.; *Int'l*, pg. 2170
DONGWHA MALAYSIA HOLDINGS SDN. BHD. - NILAI PLANT—See DONGWHA HOLDINGS CO., LTD.; *Int'l*, pg. 2170
DONGWHA MALAYSIA HOLDINGS SDN. BHD.—See DONGWHA HOLDINGS CO., LTD.; *Int'l*, pg. 2170
DONG WHA PHARM CO., LTD.; *Int'l*, pg. 2164
DONGWHA SHENZHEN—See DONGWHA HOLDINGS CO., LTD.; *Int'l*, pg. 2170
DONGWON AUTOPART TECHNOLOGY ALABAMA L.L.C—See Dongwon Metal Co., Ltd.; *Int'l*, pg. 2171
DONGWON DEVELOPMENT CO., LTD.; *Int'l*, pg. 2170
DONGWON ENTERPRISE CO., LTD.; *Int'l*, pg. 2170
DONGWON FARMS—See Dongwon Enterprise Co., Ltd.; *Int'l*, pg. 2170
DONGWON F&B CO., LTD - GANGJIN FACTORY—See Dongwon Enterprise Co., Ltd.; *Int'l*, pg. 2170
DONGWON F&B CO., LTD JEONGEUP FACTORY—See Dongwon Enterprise Co., Ltd.; *Int'l*, pg. 2170
DONGWON F&B CO., LTD.—See Dongwon Enterprise Co., Ltd.; *Int'l*, pg. 2170
DONGWON F&B CO., LTD SUWON FACTORY—See Dongwon Enterprise Co., Ltd.; *Int'l*, pg. 2170
DONGWON F&B (SHANGHAI) CO., LTD.—See Dongwon Enterprise Co., Ltd.; *Int'l*, pg. 2170
DONG WON FISHERIES CO., LTD.; *Int'l*, pg. 2164
DONGWON HOME FOOD CO., LTD.—See Dongwon Enterprise Co., Ltd.; *Int'l*, pg. 2170
DONGWON INDUSTRIES CO., LTD.—See Dongwon Enterprise Co., Ltd.; *Int'l*, pg. 2171
DONGWON JAPAN CO., LTD.—See Dongwon Enterprise Co., Ltd.; *Int'l*, pg. 2170
DONGWON METAL CO., LTD. - ASAN PLANT—See Dongwon Metal Co., Ltd.; *Int'l*, pg. 2171
DONGWON METAL CO., LTD. - KYUNGSAN PLANT—See Dongwon Metal Co., Ltd.; *Int'l*, pg. 2171
DONGWON METAL CO., LTD.; *Int'l*, pg. 2171
DONGWON OLEV CORP.—See Dongwon Enterprise Co., Ltd.; *Int'l*, pg. 2171
DONGWON SYSTEMS CORP.—See Dongwon Enterprise Co., Ltd.; *Int'l*, pg. 2171
DONGWON WINEPLUS CO. LTD.—See Dongwon Enterprise Co., Ltd.; *Int'l*, pg. 2171
DONGWOO FARM TO TABLE CO., LTD.; *Int'l*, pg. 2171
DONGWOO FINE-CHEM CO., LTD.—See Sumitomo Chemical Company, Limited; *Int'l*, pg. 7264
DONGWOON ANATECH CO., LTD.; *Int'l*, pg. 2171
DONGWU CEMENT INTERNATIONAL LIMITED; *Int'l*, pg. 2171
DONGXING INTERNATIONAL INC.; *Int'l*, pg. 2171
DONGXING SECURITIES CO., LTD.; *Int'l*, pg. 2171
DONGXU OPTOELECTRONIC TECHNOLOGY CO., LTD.; *Int'l*, pg. 2171
DONG YANG ENERGY CO., LTD.—See Dongyang Engineering & Construction Corp.; *Int'l*, pg. 2171
DONGYANG ENGINEERING & CONSTRUCTION CORP.; *Int'l*, pg. 2171
DONGYANG E&P INC.; *Int'l*, pg. 2171
DONGYANG EXPRESS CORP.; *Int'l*, pg. 2171
DONGYANG GANGCHUL CO., LTD - 1ST FACTORY—See Aluko Co., Ltd; *Int'l*, pg. 400
DONGYANG GANGCHUL CO., LTD - 2ND FACTORY—See Aluko Co., Ltd; *Int'l*, pg. 400
DONGYANG GANGCHUL CO., LTD - 5TH FACTORY—See Aluko Co., Ltd; *Int'l*, pg. 400
DONGYANG PARAGON CO., LTD.—See Dongyang Engineering & Construction Corp.; *Int'l*, pg. 2171
DONG YANG P&F CO., LTD - GIMPO FACTORY—See DYPNF CO.,LTD; *Int'l*, pg. 2243
DONGYANG PISTON CO., LTD.; *Int'l*, pg. 2171
DONGYANG PISTON USA INC.—See Dongyang Piston Co., Ltd.; *Int'l*, pg. 2172
DONG YANG S.TEC CO., LTD.; *Int'l*, pg. 2164
DONG YANG STEEL PIPE CO., LTD. - CHUNGJU FACTORY—See Dong Yang Steel Pipe Co., Ltd.; *Int'l*, pg. 2164
DONG YANG STEEL PIPE CO., LTD.; *Int'l*, pg. 2164
DONGYANG TECH CO., LTD.—See Dongyang Piston Co., Ltd.; *Int'l*, pg. 2172
DONGYING DAQIAO LVDA LANDSCAPE CO., LTD.—See Zhewen Interactive Group Co Ltd; *Int'l*, pg. 8671
DONGYING HI-TECH SPRING CHEMICAL CO., LTD.—See HaiKe Chemical Group Ltd; *Int'l*, pg. 3211
DONGYING KECHUANG BIOCHEMICAL ENGINEERING CO., LTD.—See Zhewen Interactive Group Co Ltd; *Int'l*, pg. 8671
DONGYING KEDA ELECTRIC ENGINEERING CO., LTD.—See Zhewen Interactive Group Co Ltd; *Int'l*, pg. 8671
DONGYING KEYING REAL ESTATE CO., LTD.—See Zhewen Interactive Group Co Ltd; *Int'l*, pg. 8671
DONGYING YELLOW RIVER BRIDGE CO., LTD.—See Zhewen Interactive Group Co Ltd; *Int'l*, pg. 8671
DONGYING ZHONGKE LOW CARBON TECHNOLOGY SERVICE CO., LTD.—See Zhewen Interactive Group Co Ltd; *Int'l*, pg. 8671
DONG YI RI SHENG HOME DECORATION GROUP COMPANY LIMITED; *Int'l*, pg. 2164
DONGYUE GROUP LIMITED; *Int'l*, pg. 2172
DONGZHU ECOLOGICAL ENVIRONMENT PROTECTION CO., LTD.; *Int'l*, pg. 2172
DONHAD PTY. LTD.—See Valmont Industries, Inc.; *U.S. Public*, pg. 2273
DON HALL GM SUPERCENTER; *U.S. Private*, pg. 1257
DON HATTAN CHEVROLET, INC.; *U.S. Private*, pg. 1257
DON HEATH'S AUTO HAUS, INC.; *U.S. Private*, pg. 1257
DON HILL AUTOMOTIVE ASSOCIATES INC.; *U.S. Private*, pg. 1257
DON HILL PONTIAC JEEP INC.—See Don Hill Automotive Associates Inc.; *U.S. Private*, pg. 1257
DON HINDS FORD INC.; *U.S. Private*, pg. 1258
DON HUMBERTO SPA—See The AES Corporation; *U.S. Public*, pg. 2031
DONIHE GRAPHICS, INC.—See Champion Industries, Inc.; *U.S. Public*, pg. 478
DON JACOBS AUTOMOTIVE INC.; *U.S. Private*, pg. 1258
DON JACOBS IMPORTS, INC.; *U.S. Private*, pg. 1258
DON JACOBS TOYOTA; *U.S. Private*, pg. 1258
DON JAGODA ASSOCIATES, INC.; *U.S. Private*, pg. 1258
DON JAGODA ASSOCIATES, INC.—See Don Jagoda Associates, Inc.; *U.S. Private*, pg. 1258
DON JOHNSON MOTORS INC.; *U.S. Private*, pg. 1258
DON JOHNSON MOTORS INC.; *U.S. Private*, pg. 1258
DON JOSEPH INCORPORATED; *U.S. Private*, pg. 1258
DON K CHEVROLET INC.; *U.S. Private*, pg. 1258
THE DONKEY BARN, LLC—See Godspeed Capital Management LP; *U.S. Private*, pg. 1725
DONKEYREPUBLIC HOLDING A/S; *Int'l*, pg. 2172
DONKI THAILAND CO., LTD.—See Pan Pacific International Holdings Corporation; *Int'l*, pg. 5715

DON KRUEGER CONSTRUCTION CO.; *U.S. Private*, pg. 1258
DON KYATT SPARE PARTS (QLD) PTY LTD—See Bapcor Limited; *Int'l*, pg. 857
DON-LEE DISTRIBUTORS INC.; *U.S. Private*, pg. 1259
DONLEN CORPORATION—See Apollo Global Management, Inc.; *U.S. Public*, pg. 147
DONLEN FSHCO COMPANY—See Hertz Global Holdings, Inc.; *U.S. Public*, pg. 1029
DONLEY FORD LINCOLN INC.; *U.S. Private*, pg. 1260
DONLEY'S, INC.; *U.S. Private*, pg. 1260
DON & LOW LTD—See Thrace Plastics Holding and Commercial S.A.; *Int'l*, pg. 7720
DONMAR CAR SALES LTD; *Int'l*, pg. 2172
DON-MAR CREATIONS INC.; *U.S. Private*, pg. 1259
DON MART CLOTHES INC.—See Charles Navasky & Company; *U.S. Private*, pg. 853
DON MASSEY CADILLAC LONE TREE—See Sonic Automotive, Inc.; *U.S. Public*, pg. 1902
DON M. BARRON CONTRACTORS INC.; *U.S. Private*, pg. 1258
DON MCCUE CHEVROLET & GEO INC.; *U.S. Private*, pg. 1258
DON MCCUE CHEVROLET; *U.S. Private*, pg. 1258
DON MCGILL TOYOTA OF HOUSTON; *U.S. Private*, pg. 1258
DON MEALEY CHEVROLET, INC.—See AutoNation, Inc.; *U.S. Public*, pg. 234
DON MEALEY CHEVROLET, INC.—See AutoNation, Inc.; *U.S. Public*, pg. 234
DON MEALEY IMPORTS, INC.—See AutoNation, Inc.; *U.S. Public*, pg. 234
DON MEALEY MAZDA; *U.S. Private*, pg. 1258
DON MEDLIN CO.; *U.S. Private*, pg. 1258
DON MIGUEL MEXICAN FOODS, INC.—See Grupo Herdez, S.A.B. de C.V.; *Int'l*, pg. 3130
DON MIGUEL MEXICAN FOODS, INC.—See Hormel Foods Corporation; *U.S. Public*, pg. 1054
DON MILLER SUBARU EAST; *U.S. Private*, pg. 1258
DON MILLS SURGICAL UNIT LTD.—See CareRx Corporation; *Int'l*, pg. 1325
DON MOORE NISSAN; *U.S. Private*, pg. 1258
DONNAFUGATA RESORT, S.R.L.—See Minor International PCL; *Int'l*, pg. 4911
THE DONNA KARAN COMPANY LLC—See G-III Apparel Group, Ltd.; *U.S. Public*, pg. 894
THE DONNA KARAN COMPANY LLC—See G-III Apparel Group, Ltd.; *U.S. Public*, pg. 894
THE DONNA KARAN COMPANY STORE LLC—See G-III Apparel Group, Ltd.; *U.S. Public*, pg. 894
DONNA KARAN INTERNATIONAL INC.—See G-III Apparel Group, Ltd.; *U.S. Public*, pg. 893
DONNA KARAN (ITALY) SRL—See G-III Apparel Group, Ltd.; *U.S. Public*, pg. 893
DONNA KARAN SERVICE COMPANY BV—See G-III Apparel Group, Ltd.; *U.S. Public*, pg. 893
DONNA SAYLERS' FABULOUS-FURS; *U.S. Private*, pg. 1260
DONNELLEY FINANCIAL, LLC—See Donnelley Financial Solutions, Inc.; *U.S. Public*, pg. 677
DONNELLEY FINANCIAL SOLUTIONS CANADA CORPORATION—See Donnelley Financial Solutions, Inc.; *U.S. Public*, pg. 677
DONNELLEY FINANCIAL SOLUTIONS, INC.; *U.S. Public*, pg. 676
DONNELLEY FINANCIAL SOLUTIONS UK LIMITED—See Donnelley Financial Solutions, Inc.; *U.S. Public*, pg. 677
DONNELLEY TRANSLATION SERVICES (SHANGHAI) CO., LTD.—See Donnelley Financial Solutions, Inc.; *U.S. Public*, pg. 677
DONNELLON MCCARTHY INC.; *U.S. Private*, pg. 1261
DONNELL SYSTEMS INC.; *U.S. Private*, pg. 1260
DONNERWOOD MEDIA, INC.; *U.S. Private*, pg. 1261
DONNINGTON PACKAGING SUPPLIES LTD—See Sequana SA; *Int'l*, pg. 6719
DONNINI ENTERPRISES INC.; *U.S. Private*, pg. 1261
DONN PRODUCTS (PTY) LTD—See Compagnie de Saint-Gobain SA; *Int'l*, pg. 1725
DONN SOUTH AFRICA (PTY) LTD—See Compagnie de Saint-Gobain SA; *Int'l*, pg. 1725
D'ONOFRIO & SON LANDSCAPING, INC.; *U.S. Private*, pg. 1139
THE DONOHOE COMPANIES, INC.; *U.S. Private*, pg. 4022
DONOHOE CONSTRUCTION COMPANY—See The Donohoe Companies, Inc.; *U.S. Private*, pg. 4022
DONOHOE DEVELOPMENT COMPANY—See The Donohoe Companies, Inc.; *U.S. Private*, pg. 4022
DONOHOE HOSPITALITY SERVICES, LLC—See The Donohoe Companies, Inc.; *U.S. Private*, pg. 4022
DONOHOE REAL ESTATE SERVICES—See The Donohoe Companies, Inc.; *U.S. Private*, pg. 4023
DONOHOO CHEVROLET, LLC; *U.S. Private*, pg. 1261
DONOHUE COMMERCIAL SERVICE INC.—See United Mechanical, Inc.; *U.S. Private*, pg. 4294
DONOR ALLIANCE, INC.; *U.S. Private*, pg. 1261
DONORIA SPOLKA AKCYJNA—See Howden Group Holdings Limited; *Int'l*, pg. 3493

DONOR NETWORK OF ARIZONA

DONOR NETWORK OF ARIZONA; *U.S. Private*, pg. 1261
DONOVAN ADVERTISING & MARKETING SERVICES; *U.S. Private*, pg. 1261
DONOVAN ENTERPRISES; *U.S. Private*, pg. 1261
DONOVAN FARMERS ELEVATOR COOP; *U.S. Private*, pg. 1261
DONOVAN MARINE INC.; *U.S. Private*, pg. 1261
DONPON; *Int'l*, pg. 2172
DON PRESLEY AUCTIONS; *U.S. Private*, pg. 1258
DON QUIJOTE HONOLULU—See Pan Pacific International Holdings Corporation; *Int'l*, pg. 5715
DON QUIJOTE USA CO., LTD.—See Pan Pacific International Holdings Corporation; *Int'l*, pg. 5715
DON REID FORD, INC.; *U.S. Private*, pg. 1258
DON RINGLER CHEVROLET CO. INC.; *U.S. Private*, pg. 1258
DON ROBERTO JEWELERS INC.; *U.S. Private*, pg. 1258
DON SAHONG POWER COMPANY LTD.—See Mega First Corporation Berhad; *Int'l*, pg. 4792
DON'S APPLIANCES LLC—See Kodiak Building Partners LLC; *U.S. Private*, pg. 2336
DON'S AUTOMOTIVE MALL, INC.—See Stellex Capital Management LP; *U.S. Private*, pg. 3800
DONS & BENS INC.—See Gabriel's Holdings Ltd.; *U.S. Private*, pg. 1632
DON'S BROOKLYN CHEVROLET, INC.; *U.S. Private*, pg. 1259
DON'S BUILDING SUPPLY, L.P.—See CRH plc; *Int'l*, pg. 1847
DONSCO, INC.; *U.S. Private*, pg. 1261
DON SEBASTIANI & SONS; *U.S. Private*, pg. 1258
DON SEELYE FORD INC.; *U.S. Private*, pg. 1259
DON'S FARM SUPPLY, INC.; *U.S. Private*, pg. 1259
DONSKOY FACTORY OF RADIOCOMPONENTS OJSC; *Int'l*, pg. 2172
DON SMALL & SONS OIL DISTRIBUTING CO. INC.; *U.S. Private*, pg. 1259
DON'S MOBILE GLASS INC.; *U.S. Private*, pg. 1259
DON'S PHOTO SHOP LTD.; *Int'l*, pg. 2162
DON'S TRUCK SALES INC.; *U.S. Private*, pg. 1259
DON-THAKER CLEANING SERVICES PTE. LIMITED—See OCS Group Limited; *Int'l*, pg. 5521
DON THORNTON CADILLAC SAAB, INC.; *U.S. Private*, pg. 1259
DON'T LOOK BACK LESSEE, LLC—See Pebblebrook Hotel Trust; *U.S. Public*, pg. 1660
DONT NOD ENTERTAINMENT SA; *Int'l*, pg. 2172
THE DONUM ESTATE, INC—See A. Racke GmbH; *Int'l*, pg. 21
DONUTCINO PTY LTD.—See Retail Food Group Limited; *Int'l*, pg. 6305
DONUT MANAGEMENT INC.; *U.S. Private*, pg. 1261
DONUTS INC.—See Ethos Capital, LLC; *U.S. Private*, pg. 1432
DON VALLEY VOLKSWAGEN LTD.; *Int'l*, pg. 2162
DON WALTER KITCHEN DISTRIBUTORS; *U.S. Private*, pg. 1259
DONWAY FORD SALES LTD.; *Int'l*, pg. 2172
DON WENNER HOME SELLING, INC.; *U.S. Private*, pg. 1259
DON WESSEL HONDA; *U.S. Private*, pg. 1259
DON WHEATON CHEVROLET BUICK GMC LTD.; *Int'l*, pg. 2162
DON WILLIAMSON NISSAN; *U.S. Private*, pg. 1259
DON YOUNG COMPANY INCORPORATED; *U.S. Private*, pg. 1259
DONZE CADRANS SA—See Kering S.A.; *Int'l*, pg. 4134
DONZI MARINE CORPORATION—See American Marine Holdings, LLC; *U.S. Private*, pg. 240
DOODAD; *U.S. Private*, pg. 1261
DOODEH SANATI PARS COMPANY; *Int'l*, pg. 2172
DOODYCALLS FRANCHISING, LLC—See Apax Partners LLP; *Int'l*, pg. 502
DOODY MECHANICAL, INC.—See APi Group Corporation; *Int'l*, pg. 514
DOOK MEDIA GROUP LIMITED.; *Int'l*, pg. 2172
DOOLEY CHEMICALS LLC—See Piedmont Chemical Industries, Inc.; *U.S. Private*, pg. 3177
DOOLEYMACK CONSTRUCTORS INC.; *U.S. Private*, pg. 1261
DOOLEY OIL INC.; *U.S. Private*, pg. 1261
DOOLEY'S PETROLEUM INCORPORATED; *U.S. Private*, pg. 1261
DOOLITTLE DISTRIBUTING INC.; *U.S. Private*, pg. 1261
DOOLITTLE OIL CO. INC.; *U.S. Private*, pg. 1261
DOOLITTLES RESTAURANTS; *U.S. Private*, pg. 1261
DOONAN SPECIALIZED TRAILER, LLC; *U.S. Private*, pg. 1261
DOONAN TRUCK & EQUIPMENT OF WICHITA, INC.; *U.S. Private*, pg. 1261
DOONEY & BOURKE, INC.; *U.S. Private*, pg. 1261
D. O. O. ORMESTER-SECURITY—See Ormester Vagyonvedelmi Nyrt; *Int'l*, pg. 5641
DOORBOT; *U.S. Private*, pg. 1262
DOOR COMPONENTS, INC.; *U.S. Private*, pg. 1261
DOOR COMPONENTS, L.P.—See Platinum Equity, LLC; *U.S. Private*, pg. 3208
DOOR CONTROL, INC.—See Sanwa Holdings Corporation; *Int'l*, pg. 6560

DOOR COUNTY COOPERATIVE INC.; *U.S. Private*, pg. 1261
DOORDASH, INC.; *U.S. Public*, pg. 677
DOOR ENGINEERING AND MANUFACTURING LLC—See Audax Group, Limited Partnership; *U.S. Private*, pg. 386
DOOR GALLERY MFG. INC.; *U.S. Private*, pg. 1262
DOORLINK MANUFACTURING, INC.; *U.S. Private*, pg. 1262
DOORMATION, INC.; *U.S. Private*, pg. 1262
THE DOOR MILL, INC.—See Bain Capital, LP; *U.S. Private*, pg. 450
DOORN-DJIL YOORDANING MINING AND CONSTRUCTION PTY LTD—See Macmahon Holdings Limited; *Int'l*, pg. 4623
DOOR PRO AMERICA, LLC—See Rotunda Capital Partners LLC; *U.S. Private*, pg. 3488
DOORS AKADEMI EGITIM VE DANISMANLIK HIZMETLERI A.S.—See Dogus Holding AS; *Int'l*, pg. 2154
DOORS INCORPORATED; *U.S. Private*, pg. 1262
DOORS MOVEMENT TECHNOLOGY S.L.—See Tecnolama S.A.; *Int'l*, pg. 7516
DOOR-STOP INTERNATIONAL LIMITED—See Owens Corning; *U.S. Public*, pg. 1626
DOOR STORE FURNITURE; *U.S. Private*, pg. 1262
DOORS ULUSLARARASI YONETIM DANISMANLIGI TICARET A.S.—See Dogus Holding AS; *Int'l*, pg. 2154
DOOR SYSTEMS INC.—See ASSA ABLOY AB; *Int'l*, pg. 639
DOOR TO DOOR ORGANICS INC.; *U.S. Private*, pg. 1262
DOORWAYS PTY. LTD.—See ASSA ABLOY AB; *Int'l*, pg. 638
DOOSAN ADVERTISING COMPANY—See Doosan Corporation; *Int'l*, pg. 2172
DOOSAN ATS AMERICA, LLC—See Doosan Corporation; *Int'l*, pg. 2172
DOOSAN BABCOCK ENERGY GERMANY GMBH—See Doosan Corporation; *Int'l*, pg. 2172
DOOSAN BEARS INC.—See Doosan Corporation; *Int'l*, pg. 2172
DOOSAN BOBCAT CHILE S.A.—See Doosan Corporation; *Int'l*, pg. 2172
DOOSAN BOBCAT CHINA CO., LTD.—See Doosan Corporation; *Int'l*, pg. 2172
DOOSAN BOBCAT EMEA S.R.O.—See Doosan Corporation; *Int'l*, pg. 2172
DOOSAN BOBCAT GLOBAL COLLABORATION CENTER, INC.—See Doosan Corporation; *Int'l*, pg. 2172
DOOSAN BOBCAT INC—See Doosan Corporation; *Int'l*, pg. 2172
DOOSAN BOBCAT KOREA CO., LTD.—See Doosan Corporation; *Int'l*, pg. 2173
DOOSAN BOBCAT SINGAPORE PTE. LTD.—See Doosan Corporation; *Int'l*, pg. 2173
DOOSAN CHINA FINANCIAL LEASING CORP.—See Doosan Corporation; *Int'l*, pg. 2173
DOOSAN CORPORATION - IKSAN FACTORY—See Doosan Corporation; *Int'l*, pg. 2173
DOOSAN CORPORATION - JEUNGPYEONG FACTORY—See Doosan Corporation; *Int'l*, pg. 2173
DOOSAN CORPORATION; *Int'l*, pg. 2172
DOOSAN CUVEX CO., LTD.—See Q Capital Partners Co., Ltd; *Int'l*, pg. 6129
DOOSAN CUVEX CO., LTD.—See Shinyoung Securities Co., Ltd.; *Int'l*, pg. 6851
DOOSAN CUVEX CO., LTD.—See Woori Financial Group Inc.; *Int'l*, pg. 8454
DOOSAN DIGITAL INNOVATION AMERICA LLC—See Doosan Corporation; *Int'l*, pg. 2173
DOOSAN ELECTRO-MATERIALS AMERICA, LLC—See Doosan Corporation; *Int'l*, pg. 2173
DOOSAN ELECTRO-MATERIALS (CHANGSHU) CO., LTD.—See Doosan Corporation; *Int'l*, pg. 2173
DOOSAN ELECTRO-MATERIALS (SHENZHEN) LIMITED—See Doosan Corporation; *Int'l*, pg. 2173
DOOSAN ELECTRO-MATERIALS SINGAPORE PTE CO., LTD.—See Doosan Corporation; *Int'l*, pg. 2173
DOOSAN ELECTRO-MATERIALS SINGAPORE PTE LTD—See Doosan Corporation; *Int'l*, pg. 2173
DOOSAN ELECTRO-MATERIALS VIETNAM CO., LTD.—See Doosan Corporation; *Int'l*, pg. 2173
DOOSAN ENERBILITY—See Doosan Corporation; *Int'l*, pg. 2173
DOOSAN ENGINEERING & CONSTRUCTION CO., LTD. - DOOSAN VINA (CPE PLANT)—See Q Capital Partners Co., Ltd; *Int'l*, pg. 6129
DOOSAN ENGINEERING & CONSTRUCTION CO., LTD. - DOOSAN VINA (CPE PLANT)—See Shinyoung Securities Co., Ltd.; *Int'l*, pg. 6851
DOOSAN ENGINEERING & CONSTRUCTION CO., LTD. - DOOSAN VINA (CPE PLANT)—See Woori Financial Group Inc.; *Int'l*, pg. 8454
DOOSAN ENGINEERING & CONSTRUCTION CO., LTD.—See Q Capital Partners Co., Ltd; *Int'l*, pg. 6129
DOOSAN ENGINEERING & CONSTRUCTION CO., LTD.—See Shinyoung Securities Co., Ltd.; *Int'l*, pg. 6851

CORPORATE AFFILIATIONS

DOOSAN ENGINEERING & CONSTRUCTION CO., LTD.—See Woori Financial Group Inc.; *Int'l*, pg. 8453
DOOSAN ENPURE LTD.—See SKion GmbH; *Int'l*, pg. 6990
DOOSAN FUEL CELL CO LTD.; *U.S. Private*, pg. 1262
DOOSAN GRIDTECH LLC—See Doosan Corporation; *Int'l*, pg. 2173
DOOSAN H2 INNOVATION CO., LTD.—See Doosan Corporation; *Int'l*, pg. 2173
DOOSAN HEAVY INDUSTRIES AMERICA LLC—See Doosan Corporation; *Int'l*, pg. 2173
DOOSAN HEAVY INDUSTRIES JAPAN CORP.—See Doosan Corporation; *Int'l*, pg. 2173
DOOSAN HEAVY INDUSTRIES VIETNAM CO., LTD.—See Doosan Corporation; *Int'l*, pg. 2173
DOOSAN HF CONTROLS CORP.—See E2S Co., Ltd.; *Int'l*, pg. 2261
DOOSAN INDUSTRIAL DEVELOPMENT CO., LTD.—See Doosan Corporation; *Int'l*, pg. 2173
DOOSAN INDUSTRIAL VEHICLE AMERICA CORP.—See Doosan Corporation; *Int'l*, pg. 2173
DOOSAN INDUSTRIAL VEHICLE EUROPE N.V.—See Doosan Corporation; *Int'l*, pg. 2173
DOOSAN INDUSTRIAL VEHICLE U.K. LTD.—See Doosan Corporation; *Int'l*, pg. 2173
DOOSAN INFRACORE AMERICA CORPORATION—See HD Hyundai Infracore Co., Ltd.; *Int'l*, pg. 3299
DOOSAN INFRACORE CHINA CO., LTD.—See Doosan Corporation; *Int'l*, pg. 2173
DOOSAN INFRACORE (CHINA) INVESTMENT CO., LTD.—See Doosan Corporation; *Int'l*, pg. 2173
DOOSAN INFRACORE GERMANY GMBH—See HD Hyundai Infracore Co., Ltd.; *Int'l*, pg. 3300
DOOSAN INFRACORE INDIA PRIVATE CO., LTD.—See HD Hyundai Infracore Co., Ltd.; *Int'l*, pg. 3300
DOOSAN INFRACORE NORTH AMERICA LLC—See Doosan Corporation; *Int'l*, pg. 2173
DOOSAN INFRACORE XINJIANG MACHINERY CO., LTD.—See HD Hyundai Infracore Co., Ltd.; *Int'l*, pg. 3300
DOOSAN INTERNATIONAL AUSTRALIA PTY LTD—See Doosan Corporation; *Int'l*, pg. 2173
DOOSAN INTERNATIONAL SOUTH AFRICA PTY LTD—See Doosan Corporation; *Int'l*, pg. 2173
DOOSAN INTERNATIONAL UK LTD.—See Doosan Corporation; *Int'l*, pg. 2173
DOOSAN LENTJES GMBH—See Doosan Corporation; *Int'l*, pg. 2173
DOOSAN LOGISTICS EUROPE GMBH—See Doosan Corporation; *Int'l*, pg. 2173
DOOSAN LOGISTICS SOLUTION CO., LTD.—See Doosan Corporation; *Int'l*, pg. 2173
DOOSAN MAGAZINE—See Doosan Corporation; *Int'l*, pg. 2173
DOOSAN MECATEC CO., LTD.—See Doosan Corporation; *Int'l*, pg. 2173
DOOSAN MOBILITY INNOVATION INC.—See Doosan Corporation; *Int'l*, pg. 2173
DOOSAN MOBILITY INNOVATION (SHENZHEN) CO. LTD.—See Doosan Corporation; *Int'l*, pg. 2173
DOOSAN POWER SYSTEMS ARABIA COMPANY LIMITED—See Doosan Corporation; *Int'l*, pg. 2173
DOOSAN POWER SYSTEMS CO., LTD.—See Doosan Corporation; *Int'l*, pg. 2173
DOOSAN POWER SYSTEMS INDIA PRIVATE LTD.—See Doosan Corporation; *Int'l*, pg. 2173
DOOSAN ROBOTICS INC.—See Doosan Corporation; *Int'l*, pg. 2173
DOOSAN SKODA POWER S.R.O—See Doosan Corporation; *Int'l*, pg. 2173
DOOSAN TESNA INC; *Int'l*, pg. 2174
DOOSAN TOWER CORPORATION—See Doosan Corporation; *Int'l*, pg. 2173
DOOSAN TURBOMACHINERY SERVICES INC.—See Doosan Corporation; *Int'l*, pg. 2174
DOOSAN VINA HAIPHONG CO., LTD.—See Doosan Corporation; *Int'l*, pg. 2173
D.O.O. TCS S.E. EUROPE—See TCS TurControlSysteme AG; *Int'l*, pg. 7486
D.O.O. TEHNOALAT—See August Rueggeberg GmbH & Co. KG PFERD-Werkzeuge; *Int'l*, pg. 703
DO OUTDOORS, LLC—See BDT Capital Partners, LLC; *U.S. Private*, pg. 503
DOOVLE LIMITED; *Int'l*, pg. 2174
DOOYOO GMBH—See Vivendi SE; *Int'l*, pg. 8278
DOOZER SOFTWARE, INC.—See Management Analysis & Utilization, Inc.; *U.S. Private*, pg. 2560
DOPACO, INC.—See Pactiv Evergreen Inc.; *U.S. Public*, pg. 1633
DOPAK INC.—See KKR & Co. Inc.; *U.S. Public*, pg. 1242
DOPLA S.P.A.; *Int'l*, pg. 2174
DOPPELMAYR ANDORRA S.A.—See Doppelmayr Group; *Int'l*, pg. 2174
DOPPELMAYR A/S—See Doppelmayr Group; *Int'l*, pg. 2174
DOPPELMAYR AUSTRALIA PTY. LTD.—See Doppelmayr Group; *Int'l*, pg. 2174
DOPPELMAYR BRASIL SISTEMAS DE TRANSPORTE LTDA.—See Doppelmayr Group; *Int'l*, pg. 2174

COMPANY NAME INDEX

DOPPELMAYR CABLE CAR GMBH—See Doppelmayr Group; *Int'l*, pg. 2174
DOPPELMAYR CANADA LTD.—See Doppelmayr Group; *Int'l*, pg. 2174
DOPPELMAYR CHILE HOLDING SPA—See Doppelmayr Group; *Int'l*, pg. 2174
DOPPELMAYR COLOMBIA S.A.S.—See Doppelmayr Group; *Int'l*, pg. 2174
DOPPELMAYR DO BRASIL SISTEMAS DE TRANSPORTE LTDA.—See Doppelmayr Group; *Int'l*, pg. 2175
DOPPELMAYR FINN OY—See Doppelmayr Group; *Int'l*, pg. 2174
DOPPELMAYR FRANCE S.A.—See Doppelmayr Group; *Int'l*, pg. 2174
DOPPELMAYR GROUP; *Int'l*, pg. 2174
DOPPELMAYR HOLDING AG—See Doppelmayr Group; *Int'l*, pg. 2174
DOPPELMAYR INDIA PRIVATE LIMITED—See Doppelmayr Group; *Int'l*, pg. 2174
DOPPELMAYR ITALIA SRL—See Doppelmayr Group; *Int'l*, pg. 2174
DOPPELMAYR LANOVE DRAHY, SPOL. S R O.—See Doppelmayr Group; *Int'l*, pg. 2175
DOPPELMAYR LIFTS (NZ) LTD.—See Doppelmayr Group; *Int'l*, pg. 2174
DOPPELMAYR MEXICO S.A. DE C.V.—See Doppelmayr Group; *Int'l*, pg. 2174
DOPPELMAYR NEW ZEALAND LTD.—See Doppelmayr Group; *Int'l*, pg. 2174
DOPPELMAYR PANAMA CORP.—See Doppelmayr Group; *Int'l*, pg. 2174
DOPPELMAYR PERU S.A.C.—See Doppelmayr Group; *Int'l*, pg. 2174
DOPPELMAYR POLSKA SP Z O.O.—See Doppelmayr Group; *Int'l*, pg. 2174
DOPPELMAYR PORTUGAL UNIPESSOLA, LDA.—See Doppelmayr Group; *Int'l*, pg. 2174
DOPPELMAYR SCANDINAVIA AB—See Doppelmayr Group; *Int'l*, pg. 2174
DOPPELMAYR SEILBAHNEN GMBH—See Doppelmayr Group; *Int'l*, pg. 2174
DOPPELMAYR SKIDALYFTUR HF.—See Doppelmayr Group; *Int'l*, pg. 2174
DOPPELMAYR SKIOALYFTUR EHF—See Doppelmayr Group; *Int'l*, pg. 2174
DOPPELMAYR SOUTH CAUCASUS—See Doppelmayr Group; *Int'l*, pg. 2174
DOPPELMAYR TRANSPORT TECHNOLOGY GMBH—See Doppelmayr Group; *Int'l*, pg. 2174
DOPPELMAYR TURKEY ASANSOR TELEFERIK VE KABLOLU TASIMA SISTEMLERI INS. TAAH. LTD. STI—See Doppelmayr Group; *Int'l*, pg. 2175
DOPPELMAYR TURKEY ASANSOR TELEFERIK VE KABLOLU TASIYICI SISTEMLER INS. TAAH. LTD. STI.—See Doppelmayr Group; *Int'l*, pg. 2175
DOPPELMAYR USA, INC—See Doppelmayr Group; *Int'l*, pg. 2175
DOPPELMAYR VIETNAM CO. LTD.—See Doppelmayr Group; *Int'l*, pg. 2175
DORA CONSTRUCTION LIMITED; *Int'l*, pg. 2175
DORADO CORPORATION; *U.S. Private*, pg. 1262
DORADO OIL COMPANY; *U.S. Private*, pg. 1262
DORAL BUICK, PONTIAC, GMC; *U.S. Private*, pg. 1262
DORAL GROUP RENEWABLE ENERGY RSRCS LTD.; *Int'l*, pg. 2175
DORAL-HY, LLC—See Lithia Motors, Inc.; *U.S. Public*, pg. 1322
DORAL INTERNATIONAL INC.; *Int'l*, pg. 2175
DOR ALON ENERGY IN ISRAEL (1988) LTD; *Int'l*, pg. 2175
DORAL PTY. LTD.—See Iwatani Corporation; *Int'l*, pg. 3850
DORAL STEEL INC.; *U.S. Private*, pg. 1262
DORAL-VW, LLC—See Lithia Motors, Inc.; *U.S. Public*, pg. 1322
DORANCO, INC.; *U.S. Private*, pg. 1262
DORAS S.A.—See Samse SA; *Int'l*, pg. 6508
DORATO TOOLS AB—See J2L Holding AB; *Int'l*, pg. 3859
DORAVILLE RECYCLING PLANT—See Greif Inc.; *U.S. Public*, pg. 966
DORAVILLE TRANSFER STATION, LLC—See Waste Management, Inc.; *U.S. Public*, pg. 2331
DORAY MINERALS LIMITED—See Red 5 Limited; *Int'l*, pg. 6243
D.O.R.C. DUTCH OPHTHALMIC RESEARCH CENTER (INTERNATIONAL) B.V.—See Carl-Zeiss-Stiftung; *Int'l*, pg. 1333
DORCHESTER BANNER—See Independent Newspapers, Inc.; *U.S. Private*, pg. 2060
DORCHESTER CAPITAL PARTNERS ASP FUND, A SERIES OF ALTERNATIVE STRATEGIES PLATFORM, LLC—See Wells Fargo & Company; *U.S. Public*, pg. 2343
DORCHESTER GROUP OF COMPANIES; *Int'l*, pg. 2175
DORCHESTER HOUSE MULTI-SERVICE CENTER; *U.S. Private*, pg. 1262
DORCHESTER INSURANCE COMPANY—See Topa Equities Ltd, Inc.; *U.S. Private*, pg. 4186
DORCHESTER MINERALS, L.P.; *U.S. Public*, pg. 677

DORCHESTER PUBLISHING CO., INC.; *U.S. Private*, pg. 1262
DORCHESTER VETS4PETS LIMITED—See Pets at Home Group Plc; *Int'l*, pg. 5833
DORCY INTERNATIONAL H.K LTD—See Dorcy International Inc.; *U.S. Private*, pg. 1262
DORCY INTERNATIONAL INC.; *U.S. Private*, pg. 1262
DORCY PACIFIC PTY LTD—See Dorcy International Inc.; *U.S. Private*, pg. 1262
DORDOGNE ENROBES SAS—See VINCI S.A.; *Int'l*, pg. 8216
DORE & ASSOCIATES CONTRACTING, INC.; *U.S. Private*, pg. 1262
DORE COPPER MINING CORPORATION; *Int'l*, pg. 2175
DOREEN POWER GENERATIONS & SYSTEMS LIMITED; *Int'l*, pg. 2175
DOREL BELGIUM SA—See Dorel Industries, Inc.; *Int'l*, pg. 2176
DOREL CONSULTING (SHANGHAI) CO., LTD.—See Dorel Industries, Inc.; *Int'l*, pg. 2176
DOREL FRANCE S.A.—See Dorel Industries, Inc.; *Int'l*, pg. 2176
DOREL GERMANY GMBH—See Dorel Industries, Inc.; *Int'l*, pg. 2176
DOREL HISPANIA SA—See Dorel Industries, Inc.; *Int'l*, pg. 2176
DOREL HOME FURNISHINGS, INC.—See Dorel Industries, Inc.; *Int'l*, pg. 2176
DOREL HOME PRODUCTS—See Dorel Industries, Inc.; *Int'l*, pg. 2176
DOREL INDUSTRIES, INC.; *Int'l*, pg. 2175
DOREL ITALIA SPA—See Dorel Industries, Inc.; *Int'l*, pg. 2176
DOREL JUVENILE GROUP, INC.—See Dorel Industries, Inc.; *Int'l*, pg. 2176
DOREL NETHERLANDS—See Dorel Industries, Inc.; *Int'l*, pg. 2176
DOREL SUISSE SARL—See Dorel Industries, Inc.; *Int'l*, pg. 2176
DOREL (UK) LTD.—See Dorel Industries, Inc.; *Int'l*, pg. 2176
DOREMI LABS, INC.—See Dolby Laboratories, Inc.; *U.S. Public*, pg. 672
DOREMUS (HONG KONG)—See Omnicom Group Inc.; *U.S. Public*, pg. 1583
DOREMUS LONDON—See Omnicom Group Inc.; *U.S. Public*, pg. 1583
DOREMUS (SAN FRANCISCO)—See Omnicom Group Inc.; *U.S. Public*, pg. 1583
DOREMUS—See Omnicom Group Inc.; *U.S. Public*, pg. 1583
DORE UNDERWRITING SERVICES LIMITED—See Stone Point Capital LLC; *U.S. Private*, pg. 3821
DOREY ELECTRIC COMPANY; *U.S. Private*, pg. 1262
DORFHOTEL GESMBH—See TUI AG; *Int'l*, pg. 7964
DORFIN INC.; *Int'l*, pg. 2176
DORF-KETAL CHEMICALS INDIA PVT. LTD.; *Int'l*, pg. 2176
DORFMAN-PACIFIC COMPANY; *U.S. Private*, pg. 1262
DORGE MEDIC SA—See Bastide le Confort Medical SA; *Int'l*, pg. 888
DORIA ENTERPRISES INC.; *U.S. Private*, pg. 1262
DORIAN DRAKE INTERNATIONAL, INC.; *U.S. Private*, pg. 1262
DORIAN LPG (DK) APS—See Dorian LPG Ltd.; *U.S. Public*, pg. 677
DORIAN LPG LTD.; *U.S. Public*, pg. 677
D'ORIANO S.A.—See Orsero S.p.A.; *Int'l*, pg. 5644
DORIC GROUP HOLDINGS PTY LTD—See Alisthe Investments Pty Ltd; *Int'l*, pg. 329
DORIC NIMROD AIR ONE LIMITED; *Int'l*, pg. 2176
DORIC NIMROD AIR THREE LIMITED; *Int'l*, pg. 2177
DORIC NIMROD AIR TWO LIMITED; *Int'l*, pg. 2177
DORIEMUS PLC; *Int'l*, pg. 2177
DORIGHT CO., LTD.; *Int'l*, pg. 2177
DORIGNAC'S FOOD CENTER INC.; *U.S. Private*, pg. 1263
DORILTON CAPITAL ADVISORS LLC; *U.S. Private*, pg. 1263
DORI MEDIA AMERICA INC.—See Dori Media Group Ltd.; *Int'l*, pg. 2176
DORI MEDIA CONTENIDOS S.A.—See Dori Media Group Ltd.; *Int'l*, pg. 2176
DORI MEDIA DISTRIBUTION ARGENTINA S.A.—See Dori Media Group Ltd.; *Int'l*, pg. 2176
DORI MEDIA DISTRIBUTION GMBH—See Dori Media Group Ltd.; *Int'l*, pg. 2176
DORI MEDIA GROUP LTD.; *Int'l*, pg. 2176
DORI MEDIA INTERNATIONAL GMBH—See Dori Media Group Ltd.; *Int'l*, pg. 2176
DORI MEDIA OT LTD.—See Dori Media Group Ltd.; *Int'l*, pg. 2176
DORI MEDIA SPIKE LTD.—See Dori Media Group Ltd.; *Int'l*, pg. 2176
DORINCO REINSURANCE COMPANY—See Dow Inc.; *U.S. Public*, pg. 683
DORLING KINDERSLEY AUSTRALIA PTY LTD—See Pearson plc; *Int'l*, pg. 5776

DORLING KINDERSLEY LTD.—See Bertelsmann SE & Co. KGaA; *Int'l*, pg. 991
DORLING KINDERSLEY PUBLISHING INC—See Pearson plc; *Int'l*, pg. 5777
DORLING KINDERSLEY PUBLISHING PRIVATE LIMITED—See Bertelsmann SE & Co. KGaA; *Int'l*, pg. 992
DORLING KINDERSLEY VERLAG GMBH—See Pearson plc; *Int'l*, pg. 5775
DORLYL SNC—See Arkema S.A.; *Int'l*, pg. 571
DORMAC PTY. LTD.; *Int'l*, pg. 2177
DORMA DOOR CONTROLS LIMITED—See dormakaba Holding AG; *Int'l*, pg. 2178
DORMA DOOR CONTROLS PTY LTD—See dormakaba Holding AG; *Int'l*, pg. 2178
DORMA DOOR SYSTEMS D.O.O.—See dormakaba Holding AG; *Int'l*, pg. 2178
DOR-MAE INDUSTRIES; *U.S. Private*, pg. 1262
DORMAEL SLAAPKAMERS B.V.—See Beter Bed Holding N.V.; *Int'l*, pg. 1002
DORMA-GLAS GMBH—See dormakaba Holding AG; *Int'l*, pg. 2178
DORMA GULF DOOR CONTROLS FZE—See dormakaba Holding AG; *Int'l*, pg. 2178
DORMA HUEPPE PTY. LTD.—See dormakaba Holding AG; *Int'l*, pg. 2177
DORMA HUPPE ASIA SDN. BHD.—See dormakaba Holding AG; *Int'l*, pg. 2177
DORMA HUPPE AUSTRIA GMBH—See dormakaba Holding AG; *Int'l*, pg. 2178
DORMA HUPPE RAUMTRENNSYSTEME GMBH + CO. KG—See dormakaba Holding AG; *Int'l*, pg. 2178
DORMA INDIA PRIVATE LIMITED—See dormakaba Holding AG; *Int'l*, pg. 2178
DORMA ITALIANA S.R.L.—See dormakaba Holding AG; *Int'l*, pg. 2178
DORMAKABA ACCESS INDONESIA, PT—See dormakaba Holding AG; *Int'l*, pg. 2178
DORMAKABA AUSTRALIA PTY. LTD.—See dormakaba Holding AG; *Int'l*, pg. 2178
DORMAKABA AUSTRIA GMBH—See dormakaba Holding AG; *Int'l*, pg. 2178
DORMAKABA AUSTRIA GMBH—See dormakaba Holding AG; *Int'l*, pg. 2178
DORMAKABA BELGIUM N.V.—See dormakaba Holding AG; *Int'l*, pg. 2178
DORMAKABA BRASIL SOLUCOES DE ACESSO LTDA.—See dormakaba Holding AG; *Int'l*, pg. 2178
DORMAKABA BULGARIA EOOD—See dormakaba Holding AG; *Int'l*, pg. 2178
DORMAKABA CESKO S.R.O—See dormakaba Holding AG; *Int'l*, pg. 2178
DORMAKABA DANMARK A/S—See dormakaba Holding AG; *Int'l*, pg. 2178
DORMAKABA DEUTSCHLAND GMBH—See dormakaba Holding AG; *Int'l*, pg. 2178
DORMAKABA DEUTSCHL & GMBH—See dormakaba Holding AG; *Int'l*, pg. 2178
DORMAKABA EAD GMBH—See dormakaba Holding AG; *Int'l*, pg. 2178
DORMAKABA ESPANA S.A.U.—See dormakaba Holding AG; *Int'l*, pg. 2178
DORMAKABA EURASIA LLC—See dormakaba Holding AG; *Int'l*, pg. 2178
DORMAKABA FRANCE S.A.S—See dormakaba Holding AG; *Int'l*, pg. 2178
DORMAKABA GULF FZE—See dormakaba Holding AG; *Int'l*, pg. 2179
DORMAKABA HOLDING AG; *Int'l*, pg. 2177
DORMAKABA HOLDING AUSTRALIA PTY. LTD.—See dormakaba Holding AG; *Int'l*, pg. 2178
DORMAKABA HOLDING GMBH & CO. KGAA—See dormakaba Holding AG; *Int'l*, pg. 2178
DORMAKABA HRVATSKA D.O.O.—See dormakaba Holding AG; *Int'l*, pg. 2178
DORMAKABA IRELAND LTD.—See dormakaba Holding AG; *Int'l*, pg. 2178
DORMAKABA ITALIA SRL—See dormakaba Holding AG; *Int'l*, pg. 2179
DORMAKABA JAPAN CO., LTD.—See dormakaba Holding AG; *Int'l*, pg. 2179
DORMAKABA KAPI VE GUVENLIK SISTEMLERI SANAYI VE TICARET A.S.—See dormakaba Holding AG; *Int'l*, pg. 2178
DORMAKABA KENYA LIMITED—See dormakaba Holding AG; *Int'l*, pg. 2179
DORMAKABA KOREA INC.—See dormakaba Holding AG; *Int'l*, pg. 2179
DORMAKABA LUXEMBOURG S.A.—See dormakaba Holding AG; *Int'l*, pg. 2179
DORMAKABA MAGYARORSZAG ZRT.—See dormakaba Holding AG; *Int'l*, pg. 2178
DORMAKABA MALAYSIA SDN. BHD.—See dormakaba Holding AG; *Int'l*, pg. 2179
DORMAKABA MAROC SARL—See dormakaba Holding AG; *Int'l*, pg. 2179
DORMAKABA MIDDLE EAST LLC—See dormakaba Holding AG; *Int'l*, pg. 2178

DORMAKABA HOLDING AG

DORMAKABA NEDERLAND B.V.—See dormakaba Holding AG; *Int'l*, pg. 2179
DORMAKABA NORGE AS—See dormakaba Holding AG; *Int'l*, pg. 2179
DORMAKABA PHILIPPINES INC.—See dormakaba Holding AG; *Int'l*, pg. 2179
DORMAKABA POLSKA SP. Z O.O.—See dormakaba Holding AG; *Int'l*, pg. 2179
DORMAKABA PORTUGAL S.A.U.—See dormakaba Holding AG; *Int'l*, pg. 2179
DORMAKABA PORTUGAL, UNIPESSOAL LDA.—See dormakaba Holding AG; *Int'l*, pg. 2179
DORMAKABA PRODUCTION MALAYSIA SDN. BHD.—See dormakaba Holding AG; *Int'l*, pg. 2179
DORMAKABA ROMANIA S.R.L.—See dormakaba Holding AG; *Int'l*, pg. 2179
DORMAKABA SCHWEIZ AG—See dormakaba Holding AG; *Int'l*, pg. 2179
DORMAKABA SINGAPORE PTE LTD—See dormakaba Holding AG; *Int'l*, pg. 2179
DORMAKABA SLOVENSKO S.R.O.—See dormakaba Holding AG; *Int'l*, pg. 2179
DORMAKABA SOUTH AFRICA PTY LTD—See dormakaba Holding AG; *Int'l*, pg. 2179
DORMAKABA SUOMI OY—See dormakaba Holding AG; *Int'l*, pg. 2179
DORMAKABA SVERIGE AB—See dormakaba Holding AG; *Int'l*, pg. 2179
DORMAKABA (THAILAND) LTD.—See dormakaba Holding AG; *Int'l*, pg. 2178
DORMAKABA UK HOLDING LIMITED—See dormakaba Holding AG; *Int'l*, pg. 2179
DORMAKABA UK LIMITED - HITCHIN OFFICE—See dormakaba Holding AG; *Int'l*, pg. 2179
DORMAKABA UK LIMITED - TIVERTON OFFICE—See dormakaba Holding AG; *Int'l*, pg. 2179
DORMAKABA USA INC.—See dormakaba Holding AG; *Int'l*, pg. 2179
DORMAKABA ZRT.—See dormakaba Holding AG; *Int'l*, pg. 2179
DORMAN BROTHERS, LLC—See J.R. Simplot Company; *U.S. Private*, pg. 2170
DORMAN INDUSTRIES, LLC; *U.S. Private*, pg. 1263
DORMANKO DERTIG (PTY) LTD.—See AFGRI Limited; *Int'l*, pg. 188
DORMAN LONG TECHNOLOGY LTD—See The Cleveland Group of Companies Limited; *Int'l*, pg. 7633
DORMAN LONG UK LTD—See The Cleveland Group of Companies Limited; *Int'l*, pg. 7633
DORMAN LONG ZALCON LTD—See The Cleveland Group of Companies Limited; *Int'l*, pg. 7633
DORMANN + WINKELS GMBH—See VINCI S.A.; *Int'l*, pg. 8216
DORMAN PRODUCTS, INC.; *U.S. Public*, pg. 677
DORMAN SMITH SWITCHGEAR LIMITED—See TE Connectivity Ltd.; *Int'l*, pg. 7496
DORMAN SMITH SWITCHGEAR LLC—See TE Connectivity Ltd.; *Int'l*, pg. 7496
DORMAN TRADING COMPANY, INC.—See Miami International Holdings, Inc.; *U.S. Private*, pg. 2697
DORMA ROMANIA S.R.L.—See dormakaba Holding AG; *Int'l*, pg. 2178
DORMA UKRAINE LLC—See dormakaba Holding AG; *Int'l*, pg. 2178
DORMEO NORTH AMERICAN, LLC—See Sinomax Group Limited; *Int'l*, pg. 6953
DORMER TOOLS AB—See Sandvik AB; *Int'l*, pg. 6534
DORMER TOOLS - FRANCE—See Sandvik AB; *Int'l*, pg. 6534
DORMER TOOLS - ITALY—See Sandvik AB; *Int'l*, pg. 6534
DORMER TOOLS LTD.—See Sandvik AB; *Int'l*, pg. 6534
DORMER TOOLS S.A.—See Sandvik AB; *Int'l*, pg. 6534
DORMONT MANUFACTURING CO.—See Watts Water Technologies, Inc.; *U.S. Public*, pg. 2338
DORMVILTRE AB—See Trelleborg AB; *Int'l*, pg. 7910
DORNACOM SA; *Int'l*, pg. 2179
DORNBIRNER SPARKASSE BANK AG; *Int'l*, pg. 2179
DORNBRACHT AMERICAS INC.—See Aloys F. Dornbracht GmbH & Co. KG; *Int'l*, pg. 365
DORNBRACHT ASIA PACIFIC LTD.—See Aloys F. Dornbracht GmbH & Co. KG; *Int'l*, pg. 365
DORNBRACHT ESPANA S.L.—See Aloys F. Dornbracht GmbH & Co. KG; *Int'l*, pg. 365
DORNBRACHT FRANCE SARL—See Aloys F. Dornbracht GmbH & Co. KG; *Int'l*, pg. 365
DORNBRACHT INDIA PRIVATE LIMITED—See Aloys F. Dornbracht GmbH & Co. KG; *Int'l*, pg. 365
DORNBRACHT INTERNATIONAL HOLDING GMBH—See Aloys F. Dornbracht GmbH & Co. KG; *Int'l*, pg. 365
DORNBRACHT ITALIA S.R.L.—See Aloys F. Dornbracht GmbH & Co. KG; *Int'l*, pg. 365
DORNBRACHT NEDERLAND BV—See Aloys F. Dornbracht GmbH & Co. KG; *Int'l*, pg. 365
DORNBRACHT NORDIC A/S—See Aloys F. Dornbracht GmbH & Co. KG; *Int'l*, pg. 365
DORNBRACHT SCHWEIZ AG—See Aloys F. Dornbracht GmbH & Co. KG; *Int'l*, pg. 365
DORNBRACHT (SHANGHAI) COMMERCIAL LTD.—See Aloys F. Dornbracht GmbH & Co. KG; *Int'l*, pg. 365
DORNBRACHT SOUTH EAST ASIA PTE LTD.—See Aloys F. Dornbracht GmbH & Co. KG; *Int'l*, pg. 365
DORNBRACHT TURKEY—See Aloys F. Dornbracht GmbH & Co. KG; *Int'l*, pg. 365
DORNBRACHT UK LTD.—See Aloys F. Dornbracht GmbH & Co. KG; *Int'l*, pg. 365
DORNER MANUFACTURING CORP.; *U.S. Private*, pg. 1263
DORNERWORKS, LTD.; *U.S. Private*, pg. 1263
DORNEY PARK & WILDWATER KINGDOM—See Six Flags Entertainment Corporation; *U.S. Public*, pg. 1890
DORN HOMES, INC.—See American Southern Homes, LLC; *U.S. Private*, pg. 255
DORNIER CONSULTING GMBH—See Airbus SE; *Int'l*, pg. 242
DORNIER GMBH—See Airbus SE; *Int'l*, pg. 242
DORNIER MEDTECH AMERICA—See Airbus SE; *Int'l*, pg. 242
DORNIER MEDTECH EUROPE GMBH—See Airbus SE; *Int'l*, pg. 242
DORNOCH MEDICAL SYSTEMS, INC.—See Zimmer Biomet Holdings, Inc.; *U.S. Public*, pg. 2406
DORNOD AUTO ZAM JOINT STOCK COMPANY; *Int'l*, pg. 2179
DORO AB; *Int'l*, pg. 2179
DORO A/S, NORWAY—See Doro AB; *Int'l*, pg. 2179
DORO HONG KONG LTD—See Doro AB; *Int'l*, pg. 2179
DOROM SRL—See Teva Pharmaceutical Industries, Ltd.; *Int'l*, pg. 7580
DORON PRECISION SYSTEMS, INC.; *U.S. Private*, pg. 1263
DORO SAS—See Doro AB; *Int'l*, pg. 2179
DOROTHY LANE MARKETS INC.—See *U.S. Private*, pg. 1263
DOROTHY LEO INC.; *U.S. Private*, pg. 1263
DOROUD CEMENT COMPANY—See Fars & Khuzestan Cement Co.; *Int'l*, pg. 2620
DORRENBECK EDELSTAHL GMBH—See Gesco AG; *Int'l*, pg. 2945
DORRENBERG SPECIAL STEELS PTE. LTD.—See Gesco AG; *Int'l*, pg. 2945
DORRENBERG TRATAMIENTOS TERMICOS SL—See Gesco AG; *Int'l*, pg. 2945
DORRIES SCHARMANN TECHNOLOGIE GMBH—See Starrag Group Holding AG; *Int'l*, pg. 7179
DORRIES SCHARMANN TECHNOLOGIE SERVICE CENTER GMBH & CO KG—See Starrag Group Holding AG; *Int'l*, pg. 7179
THE DORRIS LUMBER & MOULDING CO.; *U.S. Private*, pg. 4023
DORSAVI LTD; *Int'l*, pg. 2179
DORSCH CONSULT ABU DHABI—See RAG-Stiftung; *Int'l*, pg. 6178
DORSCH CONSULT ASIA CO., LTD.—See RAG-Stiftung; *Int'l*, pg. 6178
DORSCH CONSULT (INDIA) PRIVATE LTD.—See RAG-Stiftung; *Int'l*, pg. 6178
DORSCH HOLDING GMBH—See RAG-Stiftung; *Int'l*, pg. 6178
DORSCH INTERNATIONAL CONSULTANTS GMBH—See RAG-Stiftung; *Int'l*, pg. 6178
DORSCH QATAR LLC—See RAG-Stiftung; *Int'l*, pg. 6178
DORSEL BAZ LTD.; *Int'l*, pg. 2180
DORSETT BROS CONCRETE SUPPLY, INC.; *U.S. Private*, pg. 1263
DORSETT BUKIT BINTANG SDN. BHD.—See Far East Consortium International Limited; *Int'l*, pg. 2615
DORSETT HOSPITALITY INTERNATIONAL LIMITED—See Far East Consortium International Limited; *Int'l*, pg. 2615
DORSETT HOSPITALITY INTERNATIONAL (SINGAPORE) PTE. LIMITED—See Far East Consortium International Limited; *Int'l*, pg. 2615
DORSETT & JACKSON INC.; *U.S. Private*, pg. 1263
DORSETT REGENCY HOTEL (M) SDN. BHD.—See Far East Consortium International Limited; *Int'l*, pg. 2615
DORSETT TECHNOLOGIES INC.—See MMF Capital Management LLC; *U.S. Private*, pg. 2754
THE DORSEY GROUP INC.; *Int'l*, pg. 7637
DORSEY & WHITNEY LLP; *U.S. Private*, pg. 1263
DORSEY, WRIGHT & ASSOCIATES, LLC—See Nasdaq, Inc.; *U.S. Public*, pg. 1491
DORT FINANCIAL CREDIT UNION; *U.S. Private*, pg. 1264
DORTMUNDER GUSSASPHALT GMBH & CO. KG; *Int'l*, pg. 2180
DORTONICS, INC.—See Sag Harbor Industries, Inc.; *U.S. Private*, pg. 3525
DORUK FAKTORING A.S.; *Int'l*, pg. 2180
DORUK FINANSMAN A.S.—See Adil Bey Holding A.S.; *Int'l*, pg. 148
DORVIN LEIS COMPANY INC.; *U.S. Private*, pg. 1264
DOSAGE 2000 S.A.R.L.—See Nordson Corporation; *U.S. Public*, pg. 1532
DOSAL CAPITAL, LLC; *U.S. Private*, pg. 1264
DOSANKO CORP.—See JFLA Holdings Inc.; *Int'l*, pg. 3939
DOSATRON INTERNATIONAL SAS—See Ingersoll Rand Inc.; *U.S. Public*, pg. 1118

CORPORATE AFFILIATIONS

DOSEAID PTY LTD—See EBOS Group Limited; *Int'l*, pg. 2285
DOSEME LLC—See Nautic Partners, LLC; *U.S. Private*, pg. 2871
DOSENBACH OCHSNER AG—See Deichmann SE; *Int'l*, pg. 2005
DOSEOLOGY SCIENCES INC.; *Int'l*, pg. 2180
DO SERVICE CO., LTD.—See AEON Co., Ltd.; *Int'l*, pg. 177
DOS GRINGOS INC.; *U.S. Private*, pg. 1264
DOSHIN RUBBER PRODUCTS (M) SDN. BHD.—See Kossan Rubber Industries Bhd; *Int'l*, pg. 4291
DOSHISHA CO., LTD.; *Int'l*, pg. 2180
DOSH SOFTWARE LTD—See Bain Capital, LP; *U.S. Private*, pg. 442
DOSIK, INC.—See Encompass Health Corporation; *U.S. Public*, pg. 755
DOSIS ALFA BT.—See PHOENIX Pharmahandel GmbH & Co. KG; *Int'l*, pg. 5854
DOSITEC SISTEMAS SL—See Dover Corporation; *U.S. Public*, pg. 678
DOSJAN TEMIR JOLY JSC; *Int'l*, pg. 2180
DOSKOCIL MANUFACTURING COMPANY INC.—See Platinum Equity, LLC; *U.S. Private*, pg. 3202
DOSMAR OY—See Amplex AB; *Int'l*, pg. 433
DOSMATIC U.S.A., INC.—See Dover Corporation; *U.S. Public*, pg. 679
DOS: PUNTOS DDB—See Omnicom Group Inc.; *U.S. Public*, pg. 1582
DOSS AVIATION, INC.—See L3Harris Technologies, Inc.; *U.S. Public*, pg. 1281
DOSSETT PONTIAC CADILLAC GMC; *U.S. Private*, pg. 1264
DOSSIER SYSTEMS, INC.—See Advanced Manufacturing Control Systems Ltd.; *Int'l*, pg. 160
DOSS, LTD.; *U.S. Private*, pg. 1264
DOSTER CONSTRUCTION COMPANY INC.; *U.S. Private*, pg. 1264
DOSTER WAREHOUSE INC.; *U.S. Private*, pg. 1264
DOST STEELS LIMITED; *Int'l*, pg. 2180
DOSU MAYA MAYACILIK AS—See Compagnie des Levures Lesaffre SA; *Int'l*, pg. 1738
DOTBOX LLC—See Stagwell, Inc.; *U.S. Public*, pg. 1926
DOTCMS INC.; *U.S. Private*, pg. 1265
DOTCOM DISTRIBUTION—See Ryder System, Inc.; *U.S. Public*, pg. 1828
DOT COMMODITY, INC.—See Rakuten Group, Inc.; *Int'l*, pg. 6195
DOTDASH MEREDITH, INC.—See IAC Inc.; *U.S. Public*, pg. 1082
DOTDIGITAL EMEA LIMITED—See dotdigital Group PLC; *Int'l*, pg. 2180
DOTDIGITAL GROUP PLC; *Int'l*, pg. 2180
DOTDIGITAL POLAND SP. Z O.O—See dotdigital Group PLC; *Int'l*, pg. 2180
DOTECO S.P.A.—See Piovan SpA; *Int'l*, pg. 5872
D OTEL MARMARIS TURIZM ISLETMECILIGI TICARET VE SANAYI A.S.—See Dogus Holding AS; *Int'l*, pg. 2154
DOT FAMILY HOLDINGS LLC; *U.S. Private*, pg. 1264
DOT FOODS, INC.; *U.S. Private*, pg. 1264
DOT GF CO., LTD.—See FreakOut Holdings, Inc.; *Int'l*, pg. 2767
DOTHAN CHRYSLER DODGE JEEP RAM; *U.S. Private*, pg. 1265
THE DOTHAN EAGLE—See Lee Enterprises, Incorporated; *U.S. Public*, pg. 1299
DOTHAN GLASS CO. INC.; *U.S. Private*, pg. 1265
DO THANH TECHNOLOGY CORPORATION; *Int'l*, pg. 2152
DOTHAN SECURITY INC.; *U.S. Private*, pg. 1265
DOTHOME, LLC.—See National Association of Realtors; *U.S. Private*, pg. 2847
DOTLOOP, LLC—See Zillow Group, Inc.; *U.S. Public*, pg. 2405
DOTMAILER LIMITED—See dotdigital Group PLC; *Int'l*, pg. 2180
DOTMATICS, INC—See Insight Venture Management, LLC; *U.S. Private*, pg. 2090
DOT MOBILE SDN BHD—See Digilife Technologies Limited; *Int'l*, pg. 2119
THE DOT NET FACTORY LLC; *U.S. Private*, pg. 4023
DOTPHOTO, INC.; *U.S. Private*, pg. 1265
DOT PRINTER, INC.; *U.S. Private*, pg. 1265
DOT RESOURCES LTD.; *Int'l*, pg. 2180
DOTS GESELLSCHAFT FUR SOFTWAREENTWICKLUNG MBH—See Konica Minolta, Inc.; *Int'l*, pg. 4257
DOTS, INC.—See Irving Place Capital Management, L.P.; *U.S. Private*, pg. 2141
DOTSTAY S.P.A.; *Int'l*, pg. 2180
DOTSTER, INC.; *U.S. Private*, pg. 1265
DOTTED LINE COMMUNICATIONS; *U.S. Private*, pg. 1265
DOTTED LINE COMMUNICATIONS—See Dotted Line Communications; *U.S. Private*, pg. 1265
DOTTIKON ES AMERICA, INC.—See Dottikon ES Holding AG; *Int'l*, pg. 2180
DOTTIKON ES HOLDING AG; *Int'l*, pg. 2180

COMPANY NAME INDEX

DOTTIKON EXCLUSIVE SYNTHESIS AG—See Dottikon ES Holding AG; *Int'l*, pg. 2180
DOTTI PTY. LTD.—See Premier Investments Limited; *Int'l*, pg. 5960
DOT TRANSPORTATION, INC.—See Dot Foods, Inc.; *U.S. Private*, pg. 1264
DOTWALK, INC.—See ServiceNow, Inc.; *U.S. Public*, pg. 1872
DOTY MACHINE WORKS, INC.—See Miller Mechanical Services, Inc.; *U.S. Private*, pg. 2735
DOUBLE 8 FOODS INC.; *U.S. Private*, pg. 1265
DOUBLE A (1991) PUBLIC COMPANY LIMITED; *Int'l*, pg. 2180
DOUBLE AA BUILDERS, LTD.; *U.S. Private*, pg. 1265
DOUBLE A ALIZAY—See Double A (1991) Public Company Limited; *Int'l*, pg. 2180
DOUBLE A INTERNATIONAL BUSINESS (BEIJING) CO., LTD.—See Double A (1991) Public Company Limited; *Int'l*, pg. 2180
DOUBLE A INTERNATIONAL BUSINESS (GUANGZHOU) CO., LTD.—See Double A (1991) Public Company Limited; *Int'l*, pg. 2180
DOUBLE A INTERNATIONAL BUSINESS KOREA LTD—See Double A (1991) Public Company Limited; *Int'l*, pg. 2181
DOUBLE A INTERNATIONAL BUSINESS (SHANGHAI) CO., LTD—See Double A (1991) Public Company Limited; *Int'l*, pg. 2181
DOUBLE A INTERNATIONAL HONG KONG LIMITED—See Double A (1991) Public Company Limited; *Int'l*, pg. 2181
DOUBLE A INTERNATIONAL NETWORK (AUSTRALIA) PTY LTD—See Double A (1991) Public Company Limited; *Int'l*, pg. 2181
DOUBLE A INTERNATIONAL NETWORK B.V.—See Double A (1991) Public Company Limited; *Int'l*, pg. 2181
DOUBLE A INTERNATIONAL NETWORK CO., LTD—See Double A (1991) Public Company Limited; *Int'l*, pg. 2181
DOUBLE A INTERNATIONAL NETWORK CO. (PRIVATE) LIMITED—See Double A (1991) Public Company Limited; *Int'l*, pg. 2181
DOUBLE A INTERNATIONAL NETWORK (M) SDN BHD—See Double A (1991) Public Company Limited; *Int'l*, pg. 2181
DOUBLE A INTERNATIONAL NETWORK (PHILIPPINES) INC.—See Double A (1991) Public Company Limited; *Int'l*, pg. 2181
DOUBLE A PULP AND PAPER COMPANY LIMITED—See Double A (1991) Public Company Limited; *Int'l*, pg. 2181
DOUBLE ARROW AUSTRALIA PTY LTD.—See Zhejiang Double Arrow Rubber Co., Ltd.; *Int'l*, pg. 8651
DOUBLE A SERBIA. DOUBLE A INTERNATIONAL NETWORK COMPANY LIMITED—See Double A (1991) Public Company Limited; *Int'l*, pg. 2181
DOUBLE A TRAILER SALES INC.; *U.S. Private*, pg. 1265
DOUBLE BARREL ENVIRONMENTAL SERVICES INCORPORATED; *U.S. Private*, pg. 1265
DOUBLE B FOODS, INC.—See Atlantic Street Capital Management LLC; *U.S. Private*, pg. 374
DOUBLE BOGEY, LLC—See PENN Entertainment, Inc.; *U.S. Public*, pg. 1662
DOUBLE BOND CHEMICAL IND. CO., LTD.; *Int'l*, pg. 2181
THE DOUBLE B PARTNERSHIP—See Boston Properties, Inc.; *U.S. Public*, pg. 373
DOUBLE CHANCE PROPERTIES PTE LTD—See Second Chance Properties Ltd.; *Int'l*, pg. 6672
DOUBLE CHECK CO. INC.; *U.S. Private*, pg. 1265
DOUBLE CHEESE CORPORATION; *U.S. Private*, pg. 1265
DOUBLE-COLA CO.-USA; *U.S. Private*, pg. 1266
DOUBLECOOL B.V.—See LCI Industries; *U.S. Public*, pg. 1296
DOUBLE CROWN RESOURCES INC.; *U.S. Private*, pg. 1265
DOUBLEDAY AUSTRALIA PTY LTD—See Bertelsmann SE & Co. KGaA; *Int'l*, pg. 992
DOUBLEDAY BOOK CLUB—See Bertelsmann SE & Co. KGaA; *Int'l*, pg. 992
DOUBLEDAY CANADA LIMITED—See Pride Tree Holdings, Inc.; *U.S. Private*, pg. 3260
DOUBLEDAY NEW ZEALAND LTD.—See Bertelsmann SE & Co. KGaA; *Int'l*, pg. 992
DOUBLEDAY—See Bertelsmann SE & Co. KGaA; *Int'l*, pg. 990
DOUBLE DECKER LANES—See Bowlero Corp; *U.S. Public*, pg. 376
DOUBLE DELAWARE INC.; *U.S. Private*, pg. 1265
DOUBLE D FOODS—See Downs Food Group; *U.S. Private*, pg. 1269
DOUBLE DIAMOND COMPANIES—See Double Delaware Inc.; *U.S. Private*, pg. 1265
DOUBLE DIAMOND DELAWARE INC.; *U.S. Private*, pg. 1265
DOUBLE DOWN HOLDINGS INC.; *U.S. Private*, pg. 1265

DOUBLEDOWN INTERACTIVE CO., LTD.—See DoubleUGames Co., Ltd.; *Int'l*, pg. 2181
DOUBLE DOWN INTERACTIVE LLC—See DoubleUGames Co., Ltd.; *Int'l*, pg. 2181
DOUBLEDRAGON CORPORATION; *Int'l*, pg. 2181
DOUBLE EAGLE STEEL COATING COMPANY—See United States Steel Corporation; *U.S. Public*, pg. 2236
DOUBLE E COMPANY, LLC—See River Associates Investments, LLC; *U.S. Private*, pg. 3443
DOUBLE FINE PRODUCTIONS—See Microsoft Corporation; *U.S. Public*, pg. 1439
DOUBLE FLOWERING CAMMELIA CO., LTD—See HACHI-BAN CO., LTD.; *Int'l*, pg. 3203
DOUBLE G COATINGS COMPANY, L.P.—See Cleveland-Cliffs, Inc.; *U.S. Public*, pg. 514
DOUBLE G COATINGS COMPANY, L.P.—See United States Steel Corporation; *U.S. Public*, pg. 2236
DOUBLE G COATINGS, INC.—See United States Steel Corporation; *U.S. Public*, pg. 2236
DOUBLE GRADE NON-WOVEN INDUSTRIES SDN. BHD.—See Tek Seng Holdings Berhad; *Int'l*, pg. 7526
DOUBLE HAPPINESS TYRE INDUSTRIAL CO, LTD—See China National Chemical Corporation; *Int'l*, pg. 1527
DOUBLE H BOOT COMPANY—See Berkshire Hathaway Inc.; *U.S. Public*, pg. 299
DOUBLE L GROUP LTD.; *U.S. Private*, pg. 1265
DOUBLELINE CAPITAL LP; *U.S. Private*, pg. 1266
DOUBLELINE GROUP LP—See DoubleLine Capital LP; *U.S. Private*, pg. 1266
DOUBLELINE INCOME SOLUTIONS FUND—See DoubleLine Capital LP; *U.S. Private*, pg. 1266
DOUBLELINE INCOME SOLUTIONS TRUST—See Bank of Montreal; *Int'l*, pg. 846
DOUBLE LINE, INC.; *U.S. Private*, pg. 1265
DOUBLELINE OPPORTUNISTIC CREDIT FUND—See DoubleLine Capital LP; *U.S. Private*, pg. 1266
DOUBLE MEDICAL TECHNOLOGY INC.; *Int'l*, pg. 2181
DOUBLE NEGATIVE CANADA PRODUCTIONS LIMITED—See Prime Focus Limited; *Int'l*, pg. 5977
DOUBLE P CORPORATION; *U.S. Private*, pg. 1266
DOUBLEPOSITIVE MARKETING GROUP, INC.—See Aquiline Capital Partners LLC; *U.S. Private*, pg. 304
DOUBLE QUICK INC.—See First Reserve Management, L.P.; *U.S. Private*, pg. 1526
DOUBLE R BRAND FOODS LLC.; *U.S. Private*, pg. 1266
DOUBLE STANDARD INC.; *Int'l*, pg. 2181
DOUBLE STAR DRILLING (1998) LTD; *Int'l*, pg. 2181
DOUBLESTAR TIRE, INC.—See Qingdao Doublestar Co., Ltd.; *Int'l*, pg. 6142
DOUBLE TAKE LLC—See Take-Two Interactive Software, Inc.; *U.S. Public*, pg. 1979
DOUBLE-TAKE SOFTWARE SAS—See Open Text Corporation; *Int'l*, pg. 5596
DOUBLE-TEAM BUSINESS PLANS LLC; *U.S. Private*, pg. 1266
DOUBLE THREE CO., LTD.—See Land & Houses Public Company Limited; *Int'l*, pg. 4403
DOUBLETREE BY HILTON METROPOLITAN-NEW YORK CITY—See Highgate Hotels, L.P.; *U.S. Public*, pg. 1938
DOUBLETREE BY HILTON - SOUTH BEND—See Hotel Group International, Inc.; *U.S. Private*, pg. 1989
DOUBLETREE HOTEL DENVER/BOULDER—See Hilton Worldwide Holdings Inc.; *U.S. Public*, pg. 1040
DOUBLETREE HOTEL WILMINGTON—See Hilton Worldwide Holdings Inc.; *U.S. Public*, pg. 1040
DOUBLETREE LLC—See Hilton Worldwide Holdings Inc.; *U.S. Public*, pg. 1040
DOUBLETREE SPOKANE CITY CENTER LLC—See Park Hotels & Resorts Inc.; *U.S. Public*, pg. 1638
DOUBLEUGAMES CO., LTD.; *Int'l*, pg. 2181
DOUBLEVERIFY HOLDINGS, INC.; *U.S. Public*, pg. 677
DOUBLEVIEW GOLD CORP; *Int'l*, pg. 2181
DOUCET & ASSOCIATES, INC.—See Goldberg Lindsay & Co., LLC; *U.S. Private*, pg. 1729
DOUCETTE HOMES, INC.; *U.S. Private*, pg. 1266
DOUCETTE REALTY LTD.; *Int'l*, pg. 2181
DOUG ASHY BUILDING MATERIALS INC.; *U.S. Private*, pg. 1266
DOUG ASHY BUILDING MATERIALS OF RAYNE INC.—See Doug Ashy Building Materials Inc.; *U.S. Private*, pg. 1266
DOUG ASHY BUILDING MATERIALS OF VILLE PLATTE INC.—See Doug Ashy Building Materials Inc.; *U.S. Private*, pg. 1266
DOUG HENRY BUICK GMC, INC.; *U.S. Private*, pg. 1266
DOUG HENRY CHEVROLET INC.; *U.S. Private*, pg. 1266
THE DOUGHERTY COMPANY INC.—See GI Manager L.P.; *U.S. Private*, pg. 1693
THE DOUGHERTY COMPANY INC.—See Summit Partners, L.P.; *U.S. Private*, pg. 3856
DOUGHERTY EQUIPMENT CO. INC.; *U.S. Private*, pg. 1266
DOUGHERTY FINANCIAL GROUP LLC; *U.S. Private*, pg. 1266
DOUGHERTY GLASS COMPANY—See Dothan Glass Co. Inc.; *U.S. Private*, pg. 1265
DOUGHERTY'S HOLDINGS, INC.—See Dougherty's Pharmacy, Inc.; *U.S. Private*, pg. 1266

DOUGLAS N. HIGGINS INC.

DOUGHERTY'S PHARMACY, INC.—See Dougherty's Pharmacy, Inc.; *U.S. Private*, pg. 1266
DOUGHERTY'S PHARMACY, INC.; *U.S. Private*, pg. 1266
DOUG HOLLYHAND CONSTRUCTION CO.; *U.S. Private*, pg. 1266
DOUGLAS ARCHITECTS, INC—See TBA Studio Architecture, A Professional Corporation; *U.S. Private*, pg. 3941
DOUGLAS AUTOTECH CORPORATION—See JTEKT Corporation; *Int'l*, pg. 4017
DOUGLAS AVERY & ASSOCIATES, LTD.—See Select Medical Holdings Corporation; *U.S. Public*, pg. 1858
DOUGLAS BARWICK INC.—See Canerector Inc.; *Int'l*, pg. 1290
DOUGLAS BARWICK—See Canerector Inc.; *Int'l*, pg. 1290
DOUGLAS CHERO S.P.A.—See Schlumberger Limited; *U.S. Public*, pg. 1844
DOUGLAS C LANE & ASSOCIATES, INC.—See Clayton, Dubilier & Rice, LLC; *U.S. Private*, pg. 923
DOUGLAS C LANE & ASSOCIATES, INC.—See Stone Point Capital LLC; *U.S. Private*, pg. 3824
DOUGLAS COMPANIES INC.; *U.S. Private*, pg. 1266
THE DOUGLAS COMPANY, INC.; *U.S. Private*, pg. 4023
DOUGLAS CORPORATION; *U.S. Private*, pg. 1267
DOUGLAS COSMETICS GMBH—See CVC Capital Partners SICAV-FIS S.A.; *Int'l*, pg. 1883
DOUGLAS COUNTY FARMERS COOP; *U.S. Private*, pg. 1267
DOUGLAS COUNTY INSURANCE SERVICES; *U.S. Private*, pg. 1267
DOUGLAS CROSSING RETIREMENT COMMUNITY INC.—See Extendicare Inc.; *Int'l*, pg. 2591
DOUGLAS DYNAMICS FINANCE COMPANY—See Douglas Dynamics, Inc.; *U.S. Public*, pg. 677
DOUGLAS DYNAMICS, INC.; *U.S. Public*, pg. 677
DOUGLAS EINKAUFS- UND SERVICEGESELLSCHAFT MBH & CO. KG—See CVC Capital Partners SICAV-FIS S.A.; *Int'l*, pg. 1883
DOUGLAS ELECTRIC COOPERATIVE, INC.; *U.S. Private*, pg. 1267
DOUGLAS ELLIMAN INC.; *U.S. Public*, pg. 677
DOUGLAS ELLIMAN, LLC—See Japan Tobacco Inc.; *Int'l*, pg. 3907
DOUGLAS ELLIMAN PROPERTY MANAGEMENT—See Japan Tobacco Inc.; *Int'l*, pg. 3907
DOUGLAS ELLIMAN REALTY, LLC—See Japan Tobacco Inc.; *Int'l*, pg. 3907
DOUGLAS EMMETT 1998, LLC—See Douglas Emmett, Inc.; *U.S. Public*, pg. 678
DOUGLAS EMMETT BUILDERS—See Douglas Emmett, Inc.; *U.S. Public*, pg. 678
DOUGLAS EMMETT, INC.; *U.S. Public*, pg. 677
DOUGLAS EMMETT MANAGEMENT HAWAII, LLC—See Douglas Emmett, Inc.; *U.S. Public*, pg. 678
DOUGLAS EMMETT MANAGEMENT, INC.—See Douglas Emmett, Inc.; *U.S. Public*, pg. 678
DOUGLAS EMMETT MANAGEMENT, LLC—See Douglas Emmett, Inc.; *U.S. Public*, pg. 678
DOUGLAS EMMETT REALTY FUND, LLC—See Douglas Emmett, Inc.; *U.S. Public*, pg. 678
DOUGLAS GARDENS COMMUNITY MENTAL HEALTH CENTER OF MIAMI BEACH; *U.S. Private*, pg. 1267
DOUGLAS GILL INTERNATIONAL LIMITED—See POP Capital LLC; *U.S. Private*, pg. 3228
DOUGLAS GMBH—See CVC Capital Partners SICAV-FIS S.A.; *Int'l*, pg. 1883
DOUGLAS-GUARDIAN SERVICES CORPORATION; *U.S. Private*, pg. 1267
DOUGLAS HEALTH SERVICE LLC—See Silverhawk Capital Partners, LLC; *U.S. Private*, pg. 3663
DOUGLAS INSURANCE AGENCY, INC.—See New York Community Bancorp, Inc.; *U.S. Public*, pg. 1512
DOUGLAS INSURANCE BROKERS LIMITED—See Brown & Brown, Inc.; *U.S. Public*, pg. 400
DOUGLAS, KNIGHT & ASSOCIATES, INC.; *U.S. Private*, pg. 1267
DOUGLAS LABORATORIES; *U.S. Private*, pg. 1267
DOUGLAS LAKE CATTLE CO.; *Int'l*, pg. 2181
DOUGLAS LIGHTING CONTROLS, INC.—See Panasonic Holdings Corporation; *Int'l*, pg. 5717
DOUGLAS LUMBER CORPORATION—See Builders FirstSource, Inc.; *U.S. Public*, pg. 410
DOUGLAS MACHINE, INC.; *U.S. Private*, pg. 1267
DOUGLAS MACHINES CORPORATION—See CNL Strategic Capital Management LLC; *U.S. Private*, pg. 952
DOUGLAS MANUFACTURING CO, INC.—See Rulmeca Corporation; *U.S. Private*, pg. 3503
DOUGLAS MOTORS CORPORATION; *U.S. Private*, pg. 1267
DOUGLAS MOTORS INC.; *U.S. Private*, pg. 1267
DOUGLAS N. HIGGINS INC.; *U.S. Private*, pg. 1267
DOUGLAS PARFUMERIJE D.O.O.—See CVC Capital Partners SICAV-FIS S.A.; *Int'l*, pg. 1883
DOUGLAS POLSKA SP. Z O.O.—See CVC Capital Partners SICAV-FIS S.A.; *Int'l*, pg. 1883
DOUGLAS PRODUCTS & PACKAGING COMPANY LLC—See Brightstar Capital Partners, L.P.; *U.S. Private*, pg. 653
DOUGLAS/QUIKUT—See Berkshire Hathaway Inc.; *U.S. Public*, pg. 300

DOUGLASS COLONY GROUP, INC.

CORPORATE AFFILIATIONS

DOUGLASS COLONY GROUP, INC.; *U.S. Private,* pg. 1267
DOUGLASS DISTRIBUTING COMPANY INC.; *U.S. Private,* pg. 1267
DOUGLASS HANLY MOIR PATHOLOGY PTY LIMITED—See Sonic Healthcare Limited; *Int'l,* pg. 7097
DOUGLASS ORTHOPEDIC & SPINE REHABILITATION, INC.; *U.S. Private,* pg. 1267
THE DOUGLAS STEAM SAW MILL & TIMBER COMPANY LIMITED—See Haldane Fisher Ltd.; *Int'l,* pg. 3227
DOUGLAS STEEL FABRICATING CORPORATION; *U.S. Private,* pg. 1267
DOUGLAS STEEL SUPPLY CO.; *U.S. Private,* pg. 1267
DOUGLAS STEPHEN PLASTICS, INC.; *U.S. Private,* pg. 1267
THE DOUGLAS STEWART COMPANY INC.; *U.S. Private,* pg. 4023
DOUGLAS TELECOMMUNICATIONS; *U.S. Private,* pg. 1267
DOUGLAS THEATRE CO.; *U.S. Private,* pg. 1267
DOUGLAS TOBACCO PRODUCTS CO.—See Douglas Companies Inc.; *U.S. Private,* pg. 1266
DOUGLAS VIDEO WAREHOUSE; *U.S. Private,* pg. 1267
DOUGLAS WILSON COMPANIES; *U.S. Private,* pg. 1267
DOUG MARSHALL CHEVROLET CORVETTE CADILLAC; *Int'l,* pg. 2181
DOUG RILEY ENTERPRISES INC.; *U.S. Private,* pg. 1266
DOUG VEERKAMP GENERAL ENGINEERING, INC.; *U.S. Private,* pg. 1266
DOUJA PROMOTION GROUPE ADDOHA SA; *Int'l,* pg. 2181
DOUMAK INC.; *U.S. Private,* pg. 1268
DOUMOB; *Int'l,* pg. 2182
DOUNOR SAS—See Berry Global Group, Inc; *U.S. Public,* pg. 321
DOUNREAY SITE RESTORATION LIMITED—See Babcock International Group PLC; *Int'l,* pg. 792
DOURON, INC.; *U.S. Private,* pg. 1268
DOUSHEN BEIJING EDUCATION & TECHNOLOGY INC.; *Int'l,* pg. 2182
DOUTERLOIGNE N.V.—See CRH plc; *Int'l,* pg. 1844
DOUTOR COFFEE CO., LTD.—See Doutor-Nichires Holdings Co., Ltd.; *Int'l,* pg. 2182
DOUTOR-NICHIRES HOLDINGS CO., LTD.; *Int'l,* pg. 2182
DOUTORS REASSURANCE S.A.—See UCB S.A.; *Int'l,* pg. 8011
DOUWE EGBERTS COFFEE SYSTEMS BVBA—See JAB Holding Company S.a.r.l.; *Int'l,* pg. 3862
DOUWE EGBERTS COFFEE SYSTEMS LTD—See JAB Holding Company S.a.r.l.; *Int'l,* pg. 3863
DOUWE EGBERTS COFFEE TREATMENT & SUPPLY BV—See JAB Holding Company S.a.r.l.; *Int'l,* pg. 3862
DOUWE EGBERTS N.V.—See JAB Holding Company S.a.r.l.; *Int'l,* pg. 3862
DOUWE EGBERTS OPERATING SERVICE BVBA—See JAB Holding Company S.a.r.l.; *Int'l,* pg. 3862
DOUWE EGBERTS PROFESSIONAL GERMANY GMBH—See JAB Holding Company S.a.r.l.; *Int'l,* pg. 3862
DOUWE EGBERTS VAN NELLE PARTICIPATIONS BV—See JAB Holding Company S.a.r.l.; *Int'l,* pg. 3863
DOUWES INTERNATIONAL B.V—See Indutrade AB; *Int'l,* pg. 3679
DOUX SA—See Avril SCA; *Int'l,* pg. 750
DOUYU INTERNATIONAL HOLDINGS LIMITED; *Int'l,* pg. 2182
DOUZONE BIZON CO., LTD.; *Int'l,* pg. 2182
DOVA PHARMACEUTICALS, INC.—See Swedish Orphan Biovitrum AB; *Int'l,* pg. 7365
DOVARRI, INC.; *U.S. Private,* pg. 1268
DOVE CONTRACTING, INC.; *U.S. Private,* pg. 1268
DOVE DATA PRODUCTS INC.; *U.S. Private,* pg. 1268
DOVE ELECTRONIC COMPONENTS; *U.S. Private,* pg. 1268
DOVE EQUIPMENT—See ICAFe, Inc.; *U.S. Private,* pg. 2029
DOVELL & WILLIAMS, INC.; *U.S. Private,* pg. 1268
DOVEL TECHNOLOGIES, INC.—See Veritas Capital Fund Management, LLC; *U.S. Private,* pg. 4362
DOVENMUEHLE FUNDING INC.—See Dovenmuehle Mortgage Inc.; *U.S. Private,* pg. 1268
DOVENMUEHLE INSURANCE AGENCY INC.—See Dovenmuehle Mortgage Inc.; *U.S. Private,* pg. 1268
DOVENMUEHLE MORTGAGE INC.; *U.S. Private,* pg. 1268
DOVER ARTIFICIAL LIFT INTERNATIONAL, LLC—See Dover Corporation; *U.S. Public,* pg. 679
DOVER ARTIFICIAL LIFT, LLC—See Dover Corporation; *U.S. Public,* pg. 679
DOVER ARTIFICIAL LIFT PTY LTD—See Dover Corporation; *U.S. Public,* pg. 679
DOVER ASIA TRADING PRIVATE LTD.—See Dover Corporation; *U.S. Public,* pg. 679
DOVER BMCS ACQUISITION CORP.—See Dover Corporation; *U.S. Public,* pg. 679
DOVER CHEMICAL CORPORATION—See ICC Industries, Inc.; *U.S. Private,* pg. 2029

DOVER CHEMICAL—See ICC Industries, Inc.; *U.S. Private,* pg. 2029
DOVER COMMUNICATION TECHNOLOGIES, INC.—See Dover Corporation; *U.S. Public,* pg. 679
DOVER CORPORATION (CANADA) LIMITED—See Dover Corporation; *U.S. Public,* pg. 679
DOVER CORPORATION REGIONAL HEADQUARTERS—See Dover Corporation; *U.S. Public,* pg. 679
DOVER CORPORATION; *U.S. Public,* pg. 678
DOVER DOWNS GAMING & ENTERTAINMENT, INC.—See Bally's Corporation; *U.S. Public,* pg. 268
DOVER DOWNS, INC—See Bally's Corporation; *U.S. Public,* pg. 268
DOVER ENERGY AUTOMATION, LLC—See Dover Corporation; *U.S. Public,* pg. 679
DOVER ENERGY, INC.—See Dover Corporation; *U.S. Public,* pg. 679
DOVER ENGINEERED SYSTEMS, INC.—See Dover Corporation; *U.S. Public,* pg. 679
DOVER ENGINEERED SYSTEMS UK LTD—See Dover Corporation; *U.S. Public,* pg. 679
DOVER FLOUR HALIFAX—See Excelsior Cooperative Avicole; *Int'l,* pg. 2578
DOVER FLOUR MILLS LTD.—See Excelsior Cooperative Avicole; *Int'l,* pg. 2578
DOVER FLUIDS UK LTD—See Dover Corporation; *U.S. Public,* pg. 680
DOVER FRANCE HOLDINGS, S.A.S.—See Dover Corporation; *U.S. Public,* pg. 680
DOVER FUELING SOLUTIONS UK LIMITED—See Dover Corporation; *U.S. Public,* pg. 680
DOVERIE UNITED HOLDING AD; *Int'l,* pg. 2182
DOVER INTERNATIONAL SPEEDWAY, INC.—See Sonic Financial Corporation; *U.S. Private,* pg. 3713
DOVER LUXEMBOURG FINANCE S.A.R.L.—See Dover Corporation; *U.S. Public,* pg. 680
DOVER MOTORSPORTS, INC.—See Sonic Financial Corporation; *U.S. Private,* pg. 3713
THE DOVER OPHTHALMOLOGY ASC, LLC—See KKR & Co. Inc.; *U.S. Public,* pg. 1247
DOVER PCS HOLDING LLC—See Dover Corporation; *U.S. Public,* pg. 680
DOVER PUBLICATIONS, INC.—See Atlas Holdings, LLC; *U.S. Private,* pg. 377
DOVER PUMP SOLUTIONS GROUP (EUROPE) GMBH—See Dover Corporation; *U.S. Public,* pg. 680
DOVER PUMP SOLUTIONS GROUP—See Dover Corporation; *U.S. Public,* pg. 680
DOVER REFRIGERATION & FOOD EQUIPMENT, INC.—See Dover Corporation; *U.S. Public,* pg. 680
DOVER REHABILITATION & LIVING CENTER—See Apollo Global Management, Inc.; *U.S. Public,* pg. 156
DOVER SADDLERY, INC.—See Webster Equity Partners, LLC; *U.S. Private,* pg. 4467
DOVER (SHANGHAI) TRADING COMPANY—See Dover Corporation; *U.S. Public,* pg. 679
DOVER-SHERBORN PRESS—See Gannett Co., Inc.; *U.S. Public,* pg. 902
DOVER—See Danaher Corporation; *U.S. Public,* pg. 626
DOVER SOUTHEAST ASIA (THAILAND) LTD.—See Dover Corporation; *U.S. Public,* pg. 681
DOVER SPAIN HOLDINGS, S.L.—See Dover Corporation; *U.S. Public,* pg. 681
DOVER (SUZHOU) INDUSTRIAL EQUIPMENT MANUFACTURING CO., LTD.—See Dover Corporation; *U.S. Public,* pg. 680
DOVETAIL INSURANCE CORP.—See Marsh & McLennan Companies, Inc.; *U.S. Public,* pg. 1374
DOVETAIL MANAGING GENERAL AGENCY CORPORATION—See Marsh & McLennan Companies, Inc.; *U.S. Public,* pg. 1374
DOVETAIL PROMOTION PARTNERS; *U.S. Private,* pg. 1268
DOVETAIL PUBLIC RELATIONS; *U.S. Private,* pg. 1268
DOVETAIL SERVICES (UK) LIMITED—See British Broadcasting Corporation; *Int'l,* pg. 1169
DOVETAIL SOLUTIONS INC.; *U.S. Private,* pg. 1268
DOVETAIL; *U.S. Private,* pg. 1268
DOVISTA A/S—See VKR Holding A/S; *Int'l,* pg. 8281
DOVISTA POLSKA SP. Z O.O.—See VKR Holding A/S; *Int'l,* pg. 8281
DOVISTA UK LTD.—See VKR Holding A/S; *Int'l,* pg. 8281
DOVITECH A/S—See Addtech AB; *Int'l,* pg. 132
DOVRE CANADA LTD.—See Dovre Group Plc; *Int'l,* pg. 2182
DOVRE GROUP ENERGY AS—See Dovre Group Plc; *Int'l,* pg. 2182
DOVRE GROUP INC.—See Dovre Group Plc; *Int'l,* pg. 2182
DOVRE GROUP PLC; *Int'l,* pg. 2182
DOWA ADVANCED MATERIALS (SHANGHAI) CO., LTD.—See Dowa Holdings Co., Ltd.; *Int'l,* pg. 2183
DOWA ECO-SYSTEM CO., LTD.—See Dowa Holdings Co., Ltd.; *Int'l,* pg. 2182
DOWA ELECTRONIC MATERIALS CO., LTD.—See Dowa Holdings Co., Ltd.; *Int'l,* pg. 2183
DOWA ELECTRONICS MATERIALS OKAYAMA CO., LTD.—See Dowa Holdings Co., Ltd.; *Int'l,* pg. 2183

DOWA ENVIRONMENTAL ENGINEERING (SUZHOU) CO., LTD.—See Dowa Holdings Co., Ltd.; *Int'l,* pg. 2183
DOWA ENVIRONMENTAL MANAGEMENT CO., LTD.—See Dowa Holdings Co., Ltd.; *Int'l,* pg. 2183
DOWA F-TEC CO., LTD.—See Dowa Holdings Co., Ltd.; *Int'l,* pg. 2183
DOWA F-TEC (SINGAPORE) PTE. LTD.—See Dowa Holdings Co., Ltd.; *Int'l,* pg. 2183
DOWA GALLIUM WAX SALES CO., LTD.—See Dowa Holdings Co., Ltd.; *Int'l,* pg. 2183
DOW AGROSCIENCES AUSTRALIA LIMITED—See Corteva, Inc.; *U.S. Public,* pg. 581
DOW AGROSCIENCES B.V.-PHILIPPINES—See Corteva, Inc.; *U.S. Public,* pg. 582
DOW AGROSCIENCES B.V.—See Corteva, Inc.; *U.S. Public,* pg. 581
DOW AGROSCIENCES CANADA INC. - SASKATOON—See Corteva, Inc.; *U.S. Public,* pg. 582
DOW AGROSCIENCES CANADA INC.—See Corteva, Inc.; *U.S. Public,* pg. 582
DOW AGROSCIENCES CHILE S.A.—See Corteva, Inc.; *U.S. Public,* pg. 582
DOW AGROSCIENCES COSTA RICA S.A.—See Corteva, Inc.; *U.S. Public,* pg. 582
DOW AGROSCIENCES DE MEXICO S.A. DE C.V.—See Corteva, Inc.; *U.S. Public,* pg. 582
DOW AGROSCIENCES IBERICA S.A.—See Corteva, Inc.; *U.S. Public,* pg. 582
DOW AGROSCIENCES INDIA PVT. LTD.—See Corteva, Inc.; *U.S. Public,* pg. 582
DOW AGROSCIENCES INDUSTRIAL LTDA.—See Corteva, Inc.; *U.S. Public,* pg. 582
DOW AGROSCIENCES (MALAYSIA) SDN BHD—See Corteva, Inc.; *U.S. Public,* pg. 581
DOW AGROSCIENCES (NZ) LIMITED—See Corteva, Inc.; *U.S. Public,* pg. 581
DOW AGROSCIENCES PACIFIC LIMITED—See Corteva, Inc.; *U.S. Public,* pg. 582
DOW AGROSCIENCES PARAGUAY S.A.—See Corteva, Inc.; *U.S. Public,* pg. 582
DOW AGROSCIENCES POLSKA SP Z.O.O.—See Corteva, Inc.; *U.S. Public,* pg. 582
DOW AGROSCIENCES SOUTHERN AFRICA (PROPRIETARY) LIMITED—See Corteva, Inc.; *U.S. Public,* pg. 582
DOW AGROSCIENCES SWITZERLAND S.A.—See Corteva, Inc.; *U.S. Public,* pg. 582
DOW AGROSCIENCES TAIWAN LTD.—See Corteva, Inc.; *U.S. Public,* pg. 582
DOW AGROSCIENCES TECHNOLOGY GMBH—See Corteva, Inc.; *U.S. Public,* pg. 582
DOW AGROSCIENCES (THAILAND) LTD.—See Corteva, Inc.; *U.S. Public,* pg. 582
DOWA HD EUROPE GMBH—See Dowa Holdings Co., Ltd.; *Int'l,* pg. 2182
DOWA HIGHTECH CO., LTD.—See Dowa Holdings Co., Ltd.; *Int'l,* pg. 2183
DOWA HOLDINGS CO., LTD.; *Int'l,* pg. 2182
DOWA INTERNATIONAL CORPORATION—See Dowa Holdings Co., Ltd.; *Int'l,* pg. 2183
DOWA IP CREATION CO., LTD.—See Dowa Holdings Co., Ltd.; *Int'l,* pg. 2183
DOWA KOHSAN CO., LTD.—See Dowa Holdings Co., Ltd.; *Int'l,* pg. 2183
DOWAKSA ILERI KOMPOZIT MALZEMELER SAN. LTD. STI.—See Aksa Akrilik Kimya Sanayii A.S.; *Int'l,* pg. 264
DOWAKSA SWITZERLAND GMBH—See Aksa Akrilik Kimya Sanayii A.S.; *Int'l,* pg. 264
DOWAKSA USA LLC—See Aksa Akrilik Kimya Sanayii A.S.; *Int'l,* pg. 264
DOWAL PLUMBING SUPPLY CO INC—See F.W. Webb Company; *U.S. Private,* pg. 1457
DOWA MANAGEMENT SERVICES CO., LTD.—See Dowa Holdings Co., Ltd.; *Int'l,* pg. 2183
DOWA METAL CO., LTD.—See Dowa Holdings Co., Ltd.; *Int'l,* pg. 2183
DOWA METALS & MINING AMERICA, INC.—See Dowa Holdings Co., Ltd.; *Int'l,* pg. 2183
DOWA METALS & MINING CO., LTD.—See Dowa Holdings Co., Ltd.; *Int'l,* pg. 2183
DOWA METALS & MINING (THAILAND) CO., LTD.—See Dowa Holdings Co., Ltd.; *Int'l,* pg. 2183
DOWA METALTECH CO., LTD.—See Dowa Holdings Co., Ltd.; *Int'l,* pg. 2183
DOWA METALTECH (THAILAND) CO., LTD.—See Dowa Holdings Co., Ltd.; *Int'l,* pg. 2183
DOWA METANIX CO., LTD.—See Dowa Holdings Co., Ltd.; *Int'l,* pg. 2183
DOWA NEW MATERIALS (SHANGHAI) CO., LTD.—See Dowa Holdings Co., Ltd.; *Int'l,* pg. 2183
DOWA POWER DEVICE CO., LTD.—See Dowa Holdings Co., Ltd.; *Int'l,* pg. 2183
DOWA PRECISION CO., LTD.—See Dowa Holdings Co., Ltd.; *Int'l,* pg. 2183
DOWA PRECISION (THAILAND) CO., LTD.—See Dowa Holdings Co., Ltd.; *Int'l,* pg. 2183

COMPANY NAME INDEX

DOWA SEMICONDUCTOR AKITA CO., LTD.—See Dowa Holdings Co., Ltd.; *Int'l*, pg. 2183
DOWA TECHNO ENGINEERING CO., LTD.—See Dowa Holdings Co., Ltd.; *Int'l*, pg. 2184
DOWA TECHNOLOGY CO., LTD.—See Dowa Holdings Co., Ltd.; *Int'l*, pg. 2184
DOWA TECHNO-RESEARCH CO., LTD.—See Dowa Holdings Co., Ltd.; *Int'l*, pg. 2184
DOWA TECNO-RESEACH CO., LTD.—See Dowa Holdings Co., Ltd.; *Int'l*, pg. 2184
DOWA THERMOTECH CO., LTD.—See Dowa Holdings Co., Ltd.; *Int'l*, pg. 2184
DOWA THERMOTECH MEXICO S.A. DE C.V.—See Dowa Holdings Co., Ltd.; *Int'l*, pg. 2184
DOWA THERMOTECH (THAILAND) CO., LTD.—See Dowa Holdings Co., Ltd.; *Int'l*, pg. 2184
DOWA THT AMERICA, INC.—See Dowa Holdings Co., Ltd.; *Int'l*, pg. 2183
DOWA-TSUUN CO., LTD.—See Dowa Holdings Co., Ltd.; *Int'l*, pg. 2183
DOW AUSTRIA GESELLSCHAFT M.B.H—See Dow Inc.; *U.S. Public*, pg. 683
DOW BELGIUM B.V.B.A—See Dow Inc.; *U.S. Public*, pg. 684
DOW BENELUX B.V.—See Dow Inc.; *U.S. Public*, pg. 685
DOW BRASIL INDUSTRIA E COMERCIO DE PRODUTOS QUIMICOS LTDA.—See Dow Inc.; *U.S. Public*, pg. 683
DOW BRASIL SUDESTE INDUSTRIAL LTDA.—See Dow Inc.; *U.S. Public*, pg. 683
DOW CHEMICAL (AUSTRALIA) PTY LTD.—See Dow Inc.; *U.S. Public*, pg. 683
DOW CHEMICAL BANGLADESH PRIVATE LIMITED—See Dow Inc.; *U.S. Public*, pg. 683
DOW CHEMICAL CANADA ULC—See Dow Inc.; *U.S. Public*, pg. 683
DOW CHEMICAL CANADA ULC—See Dow Inc.; *U.S. Public*, pg. 683
DOW CHEMICAL CANADA ULC—See Dow Inc.; *U.S. Public*, pg. 683
DOW CHEMICAL (CHINA) INVESTMENT COMPANY LIMITED—See Dow Inc.; *U.S. Public*, pg. 683
THE DOW CHEMICAL CO. - BAYPORT PLANT—See Dow Inc.; *U.S. Public*, pg. 686
THE DOW CHEMICAL CO. - HAYWARD PLANT—See Dow Inc.; *U.S. Public*, pg. 686
THE DOW CHEMICAL COMPANY - KNOXVILLE PLANT—See Dow Inc.; *U.S. Public*, pg. 686
DOW CHEMICAL COMPANY LIMITED—See Dow Inc.; *U.S. Public*, pg. 684
THE DOW CHEMICAL COMPANY - LOUISIANA OPERATIONS—See Dow Inc.; *U.S. Public*, pg. 686
THE DOW CHEMICAL COMPANY - MARIETTA—See Dow Inc.; *U.S. Public*, pg. 686
THE DOW CHEMICAL COMPANY-MIDLAND—See Dow Inc.; *U.S. Public*, pg. 686
THE DOW CHEMICAL COMPANY - NORWICH—See Dow Inc.; *U.S. Public*, pg. 686
THE DOW CHEMICAL COMPANY - RUSSELLVILLE—See Dow Inc.; *U.S. Public*, pg. 686
THE DOW CHEMICAL COMPANY—See Dow Inc.; *U.S. Public*, pg. 683
THE DOW CHEMICAL COMPANY - TEXAS OPERATIONS—See Dow Inc.; *U.S. Public*, pg. 686
THE DOW CHEMICAL COMPANY - WASHINGTON, DC—See Dow Inc.; *U.S. Public*, pg. 686
DOW CHEMICAL (GUANGZHOU) COMPANY LIMITED—See Dow Inc.; *U.S. Public*, pg. 684
DOW CHEMICAL IBERICA S.A.—See Dow Inc.; *U.S. Public*, pg. 684
DOW CHEMICAL INTER-AMERICAN LIMITED—See Dow Inc.; *U.S. Public*, pg. 684
DOW CHEMICAL INTERNATIONAL PVT. LTD.—See Dow Inc.; *U.S. Public*, pg. 684
DOW CHEMICAL JAPAN LIMITED—See Dow Inc.; *U.S. Public*, pg. 684
DOW CHEMICAL KOREA LIMITED—See Dow Inc.; *U.S. Public*, pg. 684
DOW CHEMICAL (MALAYSIA) SDN. BHD.—See Dow Inc.; *U.S. Public*, pg. 684
DOW CHEMICAL (NZ) LIMITED—See Dow Inc.; *U.S. Public*, pg. 683
DOW CHEMICAL PACIFIC LIMITED—See Dow Inc.; *U.S. Public*, pg. 684
DOW CHEMICAL PACIFIC (SINGAPORE) PTE LTD.—See Dow Inc.; *U.S. Public*, pg. 684
DOW CHEMICAL PHILIPPINES, INC.—See Dow Inc.; *U.S. Public*, pg. 684
DOW CHEMICAL ROMANIA S.R.L.—See Dow Inc.; *U.S. Public*, pg. 684
DOW CHEMICAL ROMANIA S.R.L.—See Dow Inc.; *U.S. Public*, pg. 685
DOW CHEMICAL (SICHUAN) CO., LTD.—See Dow Inc.; *U.S. Public*, pg. 683
DOW CHEMICAL SILICONES KOREA, LTD.—See Dow Inc.; *U.S. Public*, pg. 684
DOW CHEMICAL TAIWAN LIMITED—See Dow Inc.; *U.S. Public*, pg. 684
DOW CHEMICAL THAILAND LTD.—See Dow Inc.; *U.S. Public*, pg. 684

DOW CHEMICAL VIETNAM LLC—See Dow Inc.; *U.S. Public*, pg. 684
DOW CHEMICAL (ZHANGJIAGANG) CO., LTD.—See Dow Inc.; *U.S. Public*, pg. 683
DOWCO, INC.—See Patrick Industries, Inc.; *U.S. Public*, pg. 1652
DOW CORNING AUSTRALIA PTY LTD—See Dow Inc.; *U.S. Public*, pg. 684
DOW CORNING SINGAPORE PTE. LTD.—See Dow Inc.; *U.S. Public*, pg. 684
DOW CORNING TORAY SILICON CO., LTD.—See Dow Inc.; *U.S. Public*, pg. 684
DOW CORNING TORAY SILICON CO., LTD.—See Toray Industries, Inc.; *Int'l*, pg. 7823
DOWD ASSOCIATES INC.—See RFE Investment Partners; *U.S. Private*, pg. 3420
DOW DEUTSCHLAND ANLAGENGESELLSCHAFT MBH—See Stirling Square Capital Partners LLP; *Int'l*, pg. 7216
DOW DEUTSCHLAND ANLAGENGESELLSCHAFT MBH—See Dow Inc.; *U.S. Public*, pg. 684
DOW DEUTSCHLAND BETEILIGUNGSGESELLSCHAFT MBH—See Dow Inc.; *U.S. Public*, pg. 684
DOWD & GUILD, INC.; *U.S. Private*, pg. 1268
DOWDING INDUSTRIES, INC.; *U.S. Private*, pg. 1268
DOWDING & MILLS LIMITED—See Sulzer Ltd.; *Int'l*, pg. 7257
DOW DIVERSIFIED, INC.—See H2I Group, Inc.; *U.S. Private*, pg. 1837
DOW EGYPT SERVICES LIMITED—See Dow Inc.; *U.S. Public*, pg. 684
DOW EUROPE GMBH—See Dow Inc.; *U.S. Public*, pg. 684
DOW EUROPE HOLDINGS B.V.—See Dow Inc.; *U.S. Public*, pg. 685
DOW FINANCIAL HOLDINGS INC.—See Dow Inc.; *U.S. Public*, pg. 684
DOW FRANCE S.A.S.—See Dow Inc.; *U.S. Public*, pg. 685
DOW FRANCE S.A.S.—See Dow Inc.; *U.S. Public*, pg. 685
DOW HELLAS SA—See Dow Inc.; *U.S. Public*, pg. 685
DOW HOLDINGS LLC—See Dow Inc.; *U.S. Public*, pg. 684
THE DOW HOTEL COMPANY LLC; *U.S. Private*, pg. 4023
DOW HUNGARY LTD.—See Dow Inc.; *U.S. Public*, pg. 685
DOW INC.; *U.S. Public*, pg. 683
DOW INTERBRANCH B.V.—See Dow Inc.; *U.S. Public*, pg. 685
DOW INTERNATIONAL HOLDINGS COMPANY—See Dow Inc.; *U.S. Public*, pg. 684
DOW INTERNATIONAL HOLDINGS S.A.—See Dow Inc.; *U.S. Public*, pg. 684
DOW INVESTMENT ARGENTINA S.R.L.—See Dow Inc.; *U.S. Public*, pg. 685
DOW ITALIA DIVISIONE COMMERCIALE S.R.L—See Dow Inc.; *U.S. Public*, pg. 685
DOW ITALIA S.R.L.—See Dow Inc.; *U.S. Public*, pg. 685
DOW ITALIA S.R.L.—See Dow Inc.; *U.S. Public*, pg. 685
DOW JONES BUSINESS & RELATIONSHIP INTELLIGENCE CANADA—See News Corporation; *U.S. Public*, pg. 1518
DOW JONES BUSINESS & RELATIONSHIP INTELLIGENCE—See News Corporation; *U.S. Public*, pg. 1518
DOW JONES CANADA, INC.—See News Corporation; *U.S. Public*, pg. 1518
DOW JONES & COMPANY, INC.—See News Corporation; *U.S. Public*, pg. 1518
DOW JONES ENTERPRISE MEDIA—See News Corporation; *U.S. Public*, pg. 1518
DOW JONES INTERNATIONAL LTD.—See News Corporation; *U.S. Public*, pg. 1518
DOW JONES NEDERLAND BV—See News Corporation; *U.S. Public*, pg. 1518
DOW JONES NEWS GMBH—See News Corporation; *U.S. Public*, pg. 1518
DOW JONES NEWSWIRES—See News Corporation; *U.S. Public*, pg. 1518
DOW JONES PUBLISHING COMPANY (ASIA), INC.—See News Corporation; *U.S. Public*, pg. 1518
DOWLAIS GROUP PLC; *Int'l*, pg. 2184
DOW LEWIS MOTORS, INC.; *U.S. Private*, pg. 1268
DOWLING AARON INCORPORATED—See Fennemore Craig, P.C.; *U.S. Private*, pg. 1495
DOWLING CAPITAL MANAGEMENT, LLC; *U.S. Private*, pg. 1268
DOWLING CONSULTING GROUP, INC.—See Technology Recovery Group Ltd.; *U.S. Private*, pg. 3955
DOWLING CONSULTING PTY LTD—See Nomura Research Institute, Ltd.; *Int'l*, pg. 5413
DOWLING GRAPHICS, INC.; *U.S. Private*, pg. 1268
DOWLING & O'NEIL INSURANCE AGENCY, INC.—See ABRY Partners, LLC; *U.S. Private*, pg. 43
DOWLING & POPE ADVERTISING INC.; *U.S. Private*, pg. 1268

DOWLING & YAHNKE, LLC—See CI Financial Corporation; *Int'l*, pg. 1601
DOW MANAGEMENT COMPANY, INC.; *U.S. Private*, pg. 1268
DOW MATERIAL SCIENCES LTD.—See Dow Inc.; *U.S. Public*, pg. 683
DOW MATERIALS SCIENCE SAUDI ARABIA LIMITED—See Dow Inc.; *U.S. Public*, pg. 685
DOW MOTORS (OTTAWA) LIMITED; *Int'l*, pg. 2182
DOWN2EARTH CAPITAL NV; *Int'l*, pg. 2184
DOWN2EARTH PARTNERS NV—See Down2Earth Capital NV; *Int'l*, pg. 2184
DOWN 2 FISH CHARTERS, LLC—See Arvana Inc.; *U.S. Public*, pg. 208
DOWN EAST COMMUNITY HOSPITAL; *U.S. Private*, pg. 1269
DOWNEAST CONCEPTS INC.; *U.S. Private*, pg. 1269
DOWNEAST ENERGY—See NGL Energy Partners LP; *U.S. Public*, pg. 1527
DOWNEAST PENSION SERVICES, INC.—See NBT Bancorp Inc.; *U.S. Public*, pg. 1500
DOWNEAST PENSION SERVICES, INC.—See NBT Bancorp Inc.; *U.S. Public*, pg. 1501
DOWNEAST TOYOTA BMW INC.; *U.S. Private*, pg. 1269
DOWNER AUSTRALIA PTY LTD—See Downer EDI Limited; *Int'l*, pg. 2185
DOWNER CLADDING SYSTEMS LTD.—See Eleco Plc; *Int'l*, pg. 2347
DOWNER CONSTRUCTION (FIJI) LIMITED—See Downer EDI Limited; *Int'l*, pg. 2185
DOWNER EDI ENGINEERING - CONTRACTING / POWER SYSTEMS—See Downer EDI Limited; *Int'l*, pg. 2185
DOWNER EDI ENGINEERING GROUP PTY LIMITED—See Downer EDI Limited; *Int'l*, pg. 2185
DOWNER EDI ENGINEERING HOLDINGS PTY LTD—See Downer EDI Limited; *Int'l*, pg. 2185
DOWNER EDI ENGINEERING - PROJECTS PTY LTD—See Downer EDI Limited; *Int'l*, pg. 2185
DOWNER EDI ENGINEERING (S) PTE LTD—See Downer EDI Limited; *Int'l*, pg. 2185
DOWNER EDI ENGINEERING TRANSMISSION PTY LTD—See Downer EDI Limited; *Int'l*, pg. 2185
DOWNER EDI GROUP INSURANCE PTE. LTD.—See Downer EDI Limited; *Int'l*, pg. 2185
DOWNER EDI GROUP (NZ) LTD—See Downer EDI Limited; *Int'l*, pg. 2185
DOWNER EDI LIMITED; *Int'l*, pg. 2185
DOWNER EDI MINING HOLDING PTY LTD.—See Downer EDI Limited; *Int'l*, pg. 2185
DOWNER EDI MINING - MINERALS EXPLORATION PTY LTD—See Downer EDI Limited; *Int'l*, pg. 2185
DOWNER EDI MINING PTY LTD.—See Downer EDI Limited; *Int'l*, pg. 2185
DOWNER EDI RAIL PTY LTD—See Downer EDI Limited; *Int'l*, pg. 2185
DOWNER EDI SERVICES PTY LTD—See Downer EDI Limited; *Int'l*, pg. 2185
DOWNER EDI (USA) PTY LTD—See Downer EDI Limited; *Int'l*, pg. 2185
DOWNER EDI WORKS PTY LTD.—See Downer EDI Limited; *Int'l*, pg. 2186
DOWNER ENGINEERING POWER PTY LIMITED—See Downer EDI Limited; *Int'l*, pg. 2186
DOWNER GROUP FINANCE PTY LIMITED—See Downer EDI Limited; *Int'l*, pg. 2186
DOWNER HOLDINGS PTY LTD—See Downer EDI Limited; *Int'l*, pg. 2186
DOWNER MBL PTY LIMITED—See Downer EDI Limited; *Int'l*, pg. 2186
DOWNER NEW ZEALAND LIMITED—See Downer EDI Limited; *Int'l*, pg. 2186
DOWNER PIPETECH PTY. LIMITED—See Downer EDI Limited; *Int'l*, pg. 2186
DOWNER PTE LTD—See Downer EDI Limited; *Int'l*, pg. 2186
DOWNES & READER HARDWOOD CO., INC.—See Hardwoods Distribution Inc.; *Int'l*, pg. 3273
DOWNEY CARE CENTER CORP.—See The Ensign Group, Inc.; *U.S. Public*, pg. 2070
DOWNEY FORD SALES; *Int'l*, pg. 2186
DOWNEY-GOODLEIN ELEVATOR CORP.—See KONE Oyj; *Int'l*, pg. 4247
DOWNEY OIL CO. INC.; *U.S. Private*, pg. 1269
DOWNING CONSTRUCTION, INC.; *U.S. Private*, pg. 1269
DOWNING DISPLAYS INC.; *U.S. Private*, pg. 1269
DOWNING-FRYE REALTY, LNC.; *U.S. Private*, pg. 1269
DOWNING LLP; *Int'l*, pg. 2186
DOWNING ONE VCT PLC; *Int'l*, pg. 2186
DOWNING RENEWABLES & INFRASTRUCTURE TRUST PLC; *Int'l*, pg. 2186
DOWNING STRATEGIC MICRO-CAP INVESTMENT TRUST PLC; *Int'l*, pg. 2186
DOWNING TWO VCT PLC; *Int'l*, pg. 2187
DOWNLANDS LIABILITY MANAGEMENT LTD.—See Apollo Global Management, Inc.; *U.S. Public*, pg. 148
DOWN-LITE PRODUCTS INC.; *U.S. Private*, pg. 1269
DOWNRIVER CENTERS, INC.—See DaVita Inc.; *U.S. Public*, pg. 638

DOWNRIVER DODGE, INC.—See Stellantis N.V.; *Int'l*, pg. 7200
DOWNS CONSTRUCTION LTD.; *Int'l*, pg. 2187
DOWNS CRANE & HOIST CO, INC.; *U.S. Private*, pg. 1269
DOWNS FOOD GROUP; *U.S. Private*, pg. 1269
DOWNSTREAM—See PAG Capital; *Int'l*, pg. 5697
DOWNSVIEW CHRYSLER PLYMOUTH (1964) LTD.; *Int'l*, pg. 2187
DOWNSVIEW DRYWALL CONTRACTING; *Int'l*, pg. 2187
DOWNSVIEW HEATING & AIR CONDITIONING; *Int'l*, pg. 2187
DOWNTOWN ACTION MARKETING—See Omnicom Group Inc.; *U.S. Public*, pg. 1596
DOWNTOWN AUTO CENTER; *U.S. Private*, pg. 1269
DOWNTOWN BUSINESS IMPROVEMENT DISTRICT CORPORATION; *U.S. Private*, pg. 1269
DOWNTOWN DAYTON SPECIAL IMPROVEMENT DISTRICT INC.; *U.S. Private*, pg. 1269
DOWNTOWN FORD SALES INC; *U.S. Private*, pg. 1269
DOWNTOWN HOUSTON DIALYSIS CENTER, L.P.—See DaVita Inc.; *U.S. Public*, pg. 638
DOWNTOWN L.A. MOTORS, LP; *U.S. Private*, pg. 1269
DOWNTOWN LA NISSAN MOTORS; *U.S. Private*, pg. 1269
DOWNTOWN MARRIOTT HOTEL—See Raphael Hotel Group; *U.S. Private*, pg. 3355
DOWNTOWN PARTNERS CHICAGO—See Omnicom Group Inc.; *U.S. Public*, pg. 1583
DOWNTOWN PONTIAC BUICK (1983) LIMITED; *Int'l*, pg. 2187
DOWNTOWN PROPERTIES OWNER,LLC—See Nippon Telegraph & Telephone Corporation; *Int'l*, pg. 5342
DOWNTOWN REPORTING LLC; *U.S. Private*, pg. 1269
DOWNTOWN TRAVEL SERVICES PTE LTD—See Tan Chong International Limited; *Int'l*, pg. 7453
DOWN UNDER ANSWERS, LLC; *U.S. Private*, pg. 1269
DOWN UNDER CONSTRUCTION, LLC—See Hylan Datacom & Electrical, LLC; *U.S. Private*, pg. 2018
DOWNUNDER GEOSOLUTIONS (AMERICA) LLC—See DUG Technology Ltd.; *Int'l*, pg. 2223
DOWNUNDER GEOSOLUTIONS (ASIA) SDN. BHD.—See DUG Technology Ltd.; *Int'l*, pg. 2223
DOWNUNDER GEOSOLUTIONS (LONDON) PTY LTD.—See DUG Technology Ltd.; *Int'l*, pg. 2223
DOW OLEFINVERBUND GMBH—See Dow Inc.; *U.S. Public*, pg. 684
DOW PERFORMANCE MATERIALS (AUSTRALIA) PTY. LTD.—See Dow Inc.; *U.S. Public*, pg. 685
DOW PERU S.A.—See Dow Inc.; *U.S. Public*, pg. 685
DOW PHARMACEUTICAL SCIENCES, INC.—See Bausch Health Companies Inc.; *Int'l*, pg. 898
DOW PIPE LINE COMPANY—See Dow Inc.; *U.S. Public*, pg. 684
DOW PIPE LINE COMPANY—See Dow Inc.; *U.S. Public*, pg. 684
DOW PIPE LINE COMPANY—See Dow Inc.; *U.S. Public*, pg. 684
DOW PIPE LINE COMPANY—See Dow Inc.; *U.S. Public*, pg. 684
DOW POLSKA SP.Z.O.O.—See Dow Inc.; *U.S. Public*, pg. 685
DOW PORTUGAL - PRODUTOS QUIMICOS UNIPESSOAL, LDA.—See Dow Inc.; *U.S. Public*, pg. 685
DOW QUIMICA CHILENA S.A.—See Dow Inc.; *U.S. Public*, pg. 685
DOW QUIMICA DE COLOMBIA S.A.—See Dow Inc.; *U.S. Public*, pg. 685
DOW QUIMICA MEXICANA S.A. DE C.V.—See Dow Inc.; *U.S. Public*, pg. 685
DOW (SHANGHAI) HOLDING CO., LTD.—See Dow Inc.; *U.S. Public*, pg. 683
DOW SILICONES BELGIUM SPRL—See Dow Inc.; *U.S. Public*, pg. 685
DOW SILICONES CORPORATION - KENDALLVILLE SITE—See Dow Inc.; *U.S. Public*, pg. 684
DOW SILICONES CORPORATION—See Dow Inc.; *U.S. Public*, pg. 684
DOW SILICONES DEUTSCHLAND GMBH—See Dow Inc.; *U.S. Public*, pg. 685
DOW SILICONES (SHANGHAI) CO., LTD.—See Dow Inc.; *U.S. Public*, pg. 685
DOW SILICONES UK LIMITED—See Dow Inc.; *U.S. Public*, pg. 685
DOW SILICONES (ZHANGJIAGANG) CO., LTD.—See Dow Inc.; *U.S. Public*, pg. 685
DOW SILOXANES (ZHANGJIAGANG) CO., LTD.—See Dow Inc.; *U.S. Public*, pg. 685
DOW SOUTHERN AFRICA (PTY) LTD.—See Dow Inc.; *U.S. Public*, pg. 685
DOW SVERIGE AB—See Dow Inc.; *U.S. Public*, pg. 685
DOW TORAY CO., LTD.—See Dow Inc.; *U.S. Public*, pg. 683
DOW TURKIYE KIMYA SANAYI VE TICARET LTD STI—See Dow Inc.; *U.S. Public*, pg. 685
DOWTY AEROSPACE PROPELLERS, REPAIR & OVERHAUL—See General Electric Company; *U.S. Public*, pg. 918
DOWTY AUTOMOTIVE—See Trelleborg AB; *Int'l*, pg. 7911
DOWTY PROPELLERS—See General Electric Company; *U.S. Public*, pg. 918
DOW VENEZUELA, C.A.—See Corteva, Inc.; *U.S. Public*, pg. 582
DOW VERWALTUNGSGESELLSCHAFT MBH—See Dow Inc.; *U.S. Public*, pg. 685
DOWWAY HOLDINGS LTD.; *Int'l*, pg. 2187
DOW WOLFF CELLULOSICS GMBH & CO. KG—See Stirling Square Capital Partners LLP; *Int'l*, pg. 7216
DOW WOLFF CELLULOSICS LLC—See Stirling Square Capital Partners LLP; *Int'l*, pg. 7216
DOXA AB; *Int'l*, pg. 2187
DOXA INSURANCE HOLDINGS LLC; *U.S. Private*, pg. 1269
DOXEE CZECH S.R.O.—See Doxee S.p.A; *Int'l*, pg. 2187
DOXEE S.P.A; *Int'l*, pg. 2187
DOXIM INC.—See GI Manager L.P.; *U.S. Private*, pg. 1692
DOXIMITY, INC.; *U.S. Public*, pg. 686
DOYEN INTERNATIONAL HOLDINGS LIMITED; *Int'l*, pg. 2187
DOYLE CHEVROLET-SUBARU; *U.S. Private*, pg. 1270
DOYLE ELECTRIC SERVICES INC.; *U.S. Private*, pg. 1270
DOYLE EQUIPMENT COMPANY INC.; *U.S. Private*, pg. 1270
DOYLE GROUP INC.; *U.S. Private*, pg. 1270
DOYLE HOTELS (HOLDINGS) LIMITED; *Int'l*, pg. 2187
DOYLE MOBILE HOMES PARTS, INC.—See Berkshire Hathaway Inc.; *U.S. Public*, pg. 304
DOYLE SECURITY SYSTEMS INC.—See Doyle Group Inc.; *U.S. Private*, pg. 1270
DOYLE SYSTEMS; *U.S. Private*, pg. 1270
DOYLE WEALTH MANAGEMENT, INC.; *U.S. Private*, pg. 1270
DOYON, LIMITED; *U.S. Private*, pg. 1270
DOYON UNIVERSAL SERVICES, LLC—See Sodexo, S.A.; *Int'l*, pg. 7047
DOYON UTILITIES, LLC; *U.S. Private*, pg. 1270
DOZA DERD A.D.; *Int'l*, pg. 2187
THE DOZIER COMPANY; *U.S. Private*, pg. 4023
DOZ S.A.—See CEPD N.V.; *Int'l*, pg. 1420
D. P. ABHUSHAN LTD.; *Int'l*, pg. 1900
DPA GROUP N.V.—See Gilde Equity Management (GEM) Benelux Partners B.V.; *Int'l*, pg. 2975
DP AIRCRAFT I LIMITED; *Int'l*, pg. 2187
DPA MICROPHONES A/S—See RCF Group SpA; *Int'l*, pg. 6228
DPA MICROPHONES, INC.—See RCF Group SpA; *Int'l*, pg. 6228
DPA MICROPHONES LTD.—See RCF Group SpA; *Int'l*, pg. 6228
D-PATRICK INC.; *U.S. Private*, pg. 1139
D.P. BROWN OF DETROIT INC.—See Genuine Parts Company; *U.S. Public*, pg. 933
DPC DASH LTD.; *Int'l*, pg. 2187
DPC FOSHAN CO., LTD.—See Stick Investment Co., Ltd.; *Int'l*, pg. 7215
DP CHEMICALS CO., LTD.—See Omni-Plus System Limited; *Int'l*, pg. 5563
DP CHEMICALS VIETNAM CO., LTD.—See Omni-Plus System Limited; *Int'l*, pg. 5563
DPC INDUSTRIES INC.—See DX Holding Company Inc.; *U.S. Private*, pg. 1296
DPC MASCHINEN VERTRIEB GMBH—See Alamo Group Inc.; *U.S. Public*, pg. 71
DPCM CAPITAL, INC.—See D-Wave Quantum Inc.; *Int'l*, pg. 1900
DPC NANTONG CO., LTD.—See Stick Investment Co., Ltd.; *Int'l*, pg. 7215
DP+COMPANY; *U.S. Private*, pg. 1270
DPC POLSKA SP. Z O.O. W LIKWIDACJI—See Siemens Aktiengesellschaft; *Int'l*, pg. 6886
DP DATA SYSTEMS LIMITED; *Int'l*, pg. 2187
DPD DYNAMIC PARCEL DISTRIBUTION GMBH & CO. KG—See PostNord AB; *Int'l*, pg. 5940
DPDGROUP UK LTD.—See La Poste S.A.; *Int'l*, pg. 4388
DP DISTRIBUTION LLC—See Bain Capital, LP; *U.S. Private*, pg. 440
DPD PARCEL HOLDING A/S—See PostNord AB; *Int'l*, pg. 5940
D.P. EATON ELECTRIC—See Eaton Corporation plc; *Int'l*, pg. 2279
DPECO CO., LTD.; *Int'l*, pg. 2188
DPE DEUTSCHE PRIVATE EQUITY GMBH; *Int'l*, pg. 2187
DPE DEUTSCHE PRIVATE EQUITY MANAGEMENT III GMBH—See DPE Deutsche Private Equity GmbH; *Int'l*, pg. 2187
DP EURASIA N.V.—See Jubilant Bhartia Group; *Int'l*, pg. 4020
DPEX LOGISTICS PTE LTD—See Japan Post Holdings Co., Ltd.; *Int'l*, pg. 3900
DPEX WORLDWIDE EXPRESS (S) PTE. LTD.—See Japan Post Holdings Co., Ltd.; *Int'l*, pg. 3900
DPEX WORLDWIDE (HK) LIMITED—See Japan Post Holdings Co., Ltd.; *Int'l*, pg. 3900
DPFC S.A.R.L.—See Domino's Pizza Enterprises Ltd.; *Int'l*, pg. 2162
DP FESTO—See Festo AG & Co. KG; *Int'l*, pg. 2646
DP FOX VENTURES, LLC; *U.S. Private*, pg. 1270
DPG BV; *Int'l*, pg. 2188
DPG MEDIA BV—See DPG Media Group NV; *Int'l*, pg. 2188
DPG MEDIA GROUP NV; *Int'l*, pg. 2188
D-PHARM LTD.; *Int'l*, pg. 1900
DPH ASIA LTD—See Dichtungspartner Hamburg GmbH; *Int'l*, pg. 2111
DPH HOLDINGS CORPORATION—See Aptiv PLC; *Int'l*, pg. 524
DPH (SOUTH AFRICA) INDUSTRIAL, MINING & AUTOMOTIVE SUPPLIES (PTY) LTD—See Dichtungspartner Hamburg GmbH; *Int'l*, pg. 2111
DPH TURKEY—See Dichtungspartner Hamburg GmbH; *Int'l*, pg. 2111
DPI ALLIANCE PTE. LTD.—See DPI Holdings Berhad; *Int'l*, pg. 2189
DPI CHEMICALS SDN. BHD.—See DPI Holdings Berhad; *Int'l*, pg. 2189
DPI HOLDINGS BERHAD; *Int'l*, pg. 2189
DPI HOLDINGS (PROPRIETARY) LIMITED—See DISTRIBUTION AND WAREHOUSING NETWORK LIMITED; *Int'l*, pg. 2136
DPI, INC.; *U.S. Private*, pg. 1270
DPI LABORATORY SERVICES LIMITED—See Q P Group Holdings Limited; *Int'l*, pg. 6129
DPI MID ATLANTIC—See KeHE Distributors, LLC; *U.S. Private*, pg. 2273
DPI MIDWEST—See KeHE Distributors, LLC; *U.S. Private*, pg. 2273
DPI NORTHWEST—See KeHE Distributors, LLC; *U.S. Private*, pg. 2273
DPI PLASTICS (PROPRIETARY) LIMITED—See DISTRIBUTION AND WAREHOUSING NETWORK LIMITED; *Int'l*, pg. 2136
DPI PLASTICS SDN. BHD.—See DPI Holdings Berhad; *Int'l*, pg. 2189
DP IRAN CO.; *Int'l*, pg. 2187
DPI ROCKY MOUNTAIN—See KeHE Distributors, LLC; *U.S. Private*, pg. 2273
DPI SPECIALTY FOODS, INC.—See KeHE Distributors, LLC; *U.S. Private*, pg. 2273
DPI WEST—See KeHE Distributors, LLC; *U.S. Private*, pg. 2273
DPJ CLOTHING LTD.—See Bombay Rayon Fashions Limited; *Int'l*, pg. 1104
DP JUB DELNISKA DRUZBA POOBLASCENKA D.D.—See Nippon Paint Holdings Co., Ltd.; *Int'l*, pg. 5325
DP KRKA UKRAINA—See Krka, d.d., Novo Mesto; *Int'l*, pg. 4302
D PLAST-EFTEC A.S.—See EMS-Chemie Holding AG; *Int'l*, pg. 2393
D PLAST-EFTEC NN—See EMS-Chemie Holding AG; *Int'l*, pg. 2393
D PLAST-EFTEC UA—See EMS-Chemie Holding AG; *Int'l*, pg. 2393
DPL ENERGY RESOURCES, INC.—See Interstate Gas Supply Inc.; *U.S. Private*, pg. 2124
DPL INC.—See The AES Corporation; *U.S. Public*, pg. 2031
DPM FRAGRANCE—See The Thymes, LLC; *U.S. Private*, pg. 4127
DPM MELLON LLC—See The Bank of New York Mellon Corporation; *U.S. Public*, pg. 2037
DPNK CO., LTD; *Int'l*, pg. 2189
DPNL BV—See DuPont de Nemours, Inc.; *U.S. Public*, pg. 692
DP OSRAM UKRAINE—See ams AG; *Int'l*, pg. 438
DP PIZZA LIMITED—See DP Poland PLC; *Int'l*, pg. 2187
DP POLAND PLC; *Int'l*, pg. 2187
DPP RESTAURANTS LIMITED—See Apollo Global Management, Inc.; *U.S. Public*, pg. 164
DPRA INCORPORATED; *U.S. Private*, pg. 1271
DPRA Inc.—See OakLeaf Software, Inc.; *U.S. Private*, pg. 2985
DPR CONSTRUCTION, INC.; *U.S. Private*, pg. 1270
DPR CONSTRUCTION; *U.S. Private*, pg. 1270
DP REALTY LIMITED—See Domino's Pizza Group plc; *Int'l*, pg. 2162
DPREVIEW.COM LTD.—See Amazon.com, Inc.; *U.S. Public*, pg. 91
DPR GROUP, INC.; *U.S. Private*, pg. 1270
DPR GROUP, INC.—See DPR Group, Inc.; *U.S. Private*, pg. 1271
DPR HARDIN CONSTRUCTION COMPANY, LLC—See DPR Construction, Inc.; *U.S. Private*, pg. 1270
DPS BRIDGE WORKS CO., LTD.—See Mitsui E&S Holdings Co., Ltd.; *Int'l*, pg. 4984
DPS BRISTOL (HOLDINGS) LTD.; *Int'l*, pg. 2189
DP SCHENKER—See Deutsche Bahn AG; *Int'l*, pg. 2052
DPS CHILE COMERCIAL LIMITADA—See Bunzl plc; *Int'l*, pg. 1218
DP SERVICE LLC—See Dynaxys LLC; *U.S. Private*, pg. 1300
DP SERVICE S.R.L.—See Codere S.A.; *Int'l*, pg. 1688
D.P.S.I. DIGITAL PRODUCTION SOLUTIONS ISRAEL LTD.—See IDT Corporation; *U.S. Public*, pg. 1093
DPSI INC.; *U.S. Private*, pg. 1271
DPS RESOURCES BERHAD; *Int'l*, pg. 2189

COMPANY NAME INDEX

DPSS LASERS, INC.—See The Jordan Company, L.P.; *U.S. Private*, pg. 4060
DPS TELECOM; *U.S. Private*, pg. 1271
D.P. SUPPLY B.V—See DMK Deutsches Milchkontor GmbH; *Int'l*, pg. 2146
DP SUPPLY GMBH—See DMK Deutsches Milchkontor GmbH; *Int'l*, pg. 2146
DPS VIETNAM TRADING & DISTRIBUTION PARTS CO., LTD.—See THK CO., LTD.; *Int'l*, pg. 7711
DPT CONSULTING GROUP, INC.; *U.S. Private*, pg. 1271
DPT LABORATORIES, LTD.—See RoundTable Healthcare Management, Inc.; *U.S. Private*, pg. 3489
DPT LAKEWOOD, INC.—See RoundTable Healthcare Management, Inc.; *U.S. Private*, pg. 3489
DPV DEUTSCHER PRESSEVERTRIEB GMBH—See Bertelsmann SE & Co. KGaA; *Int'l*, pg. 992
DPV DRUCK UND PAPIERVEREDELUNG GMBH; *Int'l*, pg. 2189
DP WINCH—See Dover Corporation; *U.S. Public*, pg. 679
D P WIRES LTD.; *Int'l*, pg. 1899
DPWN HOLDINGS (USA), INC.—See Deutsche Post AG; *Int'l*, pg. 2079
DP WORLD AMERICAS RO, INC.—See Dubai World Corporation; *Int'l*, pg. 2220
DP WORLD ANTWERP N.V.—See Dubai World Corporation; *Int'l*, pg. 2220
DP WORLD AUSTRALIA LIMITED—See Corsair Capital, LLC; *U.S. Private*, pg. 1059
DP WORLD CALLAO S.R.L.—See Dubai World Corporation; *Int'l*, pg. 2220
DP WORLD (CANADA) INC.—See Dubai World Corporation; *Int'l*, pg. 2220
DP WORLD CARGO SERVICES (PTY) LIMITED—See Dubai World Corporation; *Int'l*, pg. 2220
DP WORLD FUJAIRAH FZE—See Dubai World Corporation; *Int'l*, pg. 2220
DP WORLD FZE—See Dubai World Corporation; *Int'l*, pg. 2220
DP WORLD GERMERSHEIM, GMBH AND CO. KG—See Dubai World Corporation; *Int'l*, pg. 2220
DP WORLD LIMITED—See Dubai World Corporation; *Int'l*, pg. 2220
DP WORLD MARITIME COOPERATIEVE U.A.—See Dubai World Corporation; *Int'l*, pg. 2221
DP WORLD PLC—See Dubai World Corporation; *Int'l*, pg. 2220
DP WORLD PRIVATE LIMITED—See Dubai World Corporation; *Int'l*, pg. 2221
DP WORLD—See Dubai World Corporation; *Int'l*, pg. 2220
DP WORLD TARRAGONA S.A.—See Dubai World Corporation; *Int'l*, pg. 2221
DP WORLD YARIMCA LIMAN ISLETMELERI ANONIM SIRKETI—See Dubai World Corporation; *Int'l*, pg. 2221
DPZ ARGENTINA—See Acento Advertising, Inc.; *U.S. Private*, pg. 58
DPZ-DUAILIBI, PETIT, ZARAGOZA, PROPAGANDA S.A.—See Acento Advertising, Inc.; *U.S. Private*, pg. 58
DPZ-RIO DE JANEIRO—See Acento Advertising, Inc.; *U.S. Private*, pg. 58
DQE COMMUNICATIONS LLC—See GI Manager L.P.; *U.S. Private*, pg. 1692
DQE ENERGY SERVICES—See Macquarie Group Limited; *Int'l*, pg. 4627
DQ HOLDINGS (AUSTRALIA) PTY LTD—See Dril-Quip, Inc.; *U.S. Public*, pg. 687
D&Q JEWELLERY CO., LTD.—See Festaria Holdings Co., Ltd.; *Int'l*, pg. 2646
DRAABE INDUSTRIETECHNIK GMBH—See Meier Capital AG; *Int'l*, pg. 4799
DRA ADVISORS LLC; *U.S. Private*, pg. 1271
DR. ABIDI PHARMACEUTICALS PJSC; *Int'l*, pg. 2190
DRACE GEOCISA, S.A.—See ACS, Actividades de Construccion y Servicios, S.A.; *Int'l*, pg. 111
DRACE INFRAESTRUCTURAS, S.A.—See ACS, Actividades de Construccion y Servicios, S.A.; *Int'l*, pg. 111
DRACE MEDIO AMBIENTE, S.A.—See ACS, Actividades de Construccion y Servicios, S.A.; *Int'l*, pg. 111
DRACO ELECTRONICS, LLC—See Wanshih Electronics Co., Ltd.; *Int'l*, pg. 8342
DRACO, INC.; *U.S. Private*, pg. 1271
DRA CONSULTANTS LIMITED; *Int'l*, pg. 2196
DRACO PCB PUBLIC COMPANY LIMITED—See Chin Poon Industrial Co., Ltd.; *Int'l*, pg. 1480
DRA DEBT RECOVERY AGENCY B.V.—See Munchener Ruckversicherungs AG; *Int'l*, pg. 5086
DRAEGER ARABIA CO. LTD.—See Draegerwerk AG & Co. KGaA; *Int'l*, pg. 2196
DRAEGER AUSTRALIA PTY. LTD.—See Draegerwerk AG & Co. KGaA; *Int'l*, pg. 2196
DRAEGER CANADA LTD.—See Draegerwerk AG & Co. KGaA; *Int'l*, pg. 2196
DRAEGER COLOMBIA SA—See Draegerwerk AG & Co. KGaA; *Int'l*, pg. 2196
DRAEGER CONSTRUCTION INC.; *U.S. Private*, pg. 1271
DRAEGER CROATIA D.O.O.—See Draegerwerk AG & Co. KGaA; *Int'l*, pg. 2196
DRAEGER HELLAS A.E.—See Draegerwerk AG & Co. KGaA; *Int'l*, pg. 2196

DRAEGER HONG KONG LIMITED—See Draegerwerk AG & Co. KGaA; *Int'l*, pg. 2196
DRAEGER, INC.—See Draegerwerk AG & Co. KGaA; *Int'l*, pg. 2197
DRAEGER INDIA PRIVATE LIMITED—See Draegerwerk AG & Co. KGaA; *Int'l*, pg. 2196
DRAEGER IRELAND LTD.—See Draegerwerk AG & Co. KGaA; *Int'l*, pg. 2196
DRAEGER ITALIA S.P.A.—See Draegerwerk AG & Co. KGaA; *Int'l*, pg. 2196
DRAEGER KOREA CO., LTD.—See Draegerwerk AG & Co. KGaA; *Int'l*, pg. 2196
DRAEGER LEASING INC.—See Draeger Oil Co. Inc.; *U.S. Private*, pg. 1271
DRAEGER MALAYSIA SDN. BHD.—See Draegerwerk AG & Co. KGaA; *Int'l*, pg. 2196
DRAEGER MAROC SARLAU—See Draegerwerk AG & Co. KGaA; *Int'l*, pg. 2196
DRAEGER MEDICAL BULGARIA EOOD—See Draegerwerk AG & Co. KGaA; *Int'l*, pg. 2196
DRAEGER MEDICAL HISPANIA S.A.—See Draegerwerk AG & Co. KGaA; *Int'l*, pg. 2196
DRAEGER MEDICAL ITALIANA S.P.A.—See Draegerwerk AG & Co. KGaA; *Int'l*, pg. 2196
DRAEGER MEDICAL SOUTH AFRICA (PTY) LTD—See Draegerwerk AG & Co. KGaA; *Int'l*, pg. 2196
DRAEGER MEDICAL TAIWAN LTD.—See Draegerwerk AG & Co. KGaA; *Int'l*, pg. 2196
DRAEGER MEDICAL (THAILAND) LTD.—See Draegerwerk AG & Co. KGaA; *Int'l*, pg. 2196
DRAEGER MEDICAL UK LTD.—See Draegerwerk AG & Co. KGaA; *Int'l*, pg. 2196
DRAEGER MEDIKAL TICARET VE SERVIS ANONIM SIRKETI—See Draegerwerk AG & Co. KGaA; *Int'l*, pg. 2196
DRAEGER MYANMAR LIMITED—See Draegerwerk AG & Co. KGaA; *Int'l*, pg. 2196
DRAEGER NEW ZEALAND LIMITED—See Draegerwerk AG & Co. KGaA; *Int'l*, pg. 2196
DRAEGER OIL CO. INC.; *U.S. Private*, pg. 1271
DRAEGER OOO—See Draegerwerk AG & Co. KGaA; *Int'l*, pg. 2196
DRAEGER PANAMA COMERCIAL, S. DE R.L.—See Draegerwerk AG & Co. KGaA; *Int'l*, pg. 2196
DRAEGER PANAMA S. DE R.L.—See Draegerwerk AG & Co. KGaA; *Int'l*, pg. 2197
DRAEGER PERU S.A.C.—See Draegerwerk AG & Co. KGaA; *Int'l*, pg. 2197
DRAEGER PHILIPPINES CORPORATION—See Draegerwerk AG & Co. KGaA; *Int'l*, pg. 2197
DRAEGER SAFETY AUSTRIA GMBH—See Draegerwerk AG & Co. KGaA; *Int'l*, pg. 2197
DRAEGER SAFETY BULGARIA EOOD—See Draegerwerk AG & Co. KGaA; *Int'l*, pg. 2197
DRAEGER SAFETY CANADA LTD.—See Draegerwerk AG & Co. KGaA; *Int'l*, pg. 2197
DRAEGER SAFETY EQUIPMENT (CHINA) CO., LTD.—See Draegerwerk AG & Co. KGaA; *Int'l*, pg. 2197
DRAEGER SAFETY INDIA PVT. LTD.—See Draegerwerk AG & Co. KGaA; *Int'l*, pg. 2197
DRAEGER SAFETY KORUNMA TEKNOLOJILERI ANONIM SIRKETI—See Draegerwerk AG & Co. KGaA; *Int'l*, pg. 2197
DRAEGER SAFETY LTD.—See Draegerwerk AG & Co. KGaA; *Int'l*, pg. 2197
DRAEGER SAFETY NEDERLAND B V—See Draegerwerk AG & Co. KGaA; *Int'l*, pg. 2197
DRAEGER SAFETY NORGE A/S—See Draegerwerk AG & Co. KGaA; *Int'l*, pg. 2197
DRAEGER SAFETY PACIFIC LTD.—See Draegerwerk AG & Co. KGaA; *Int'l*, pg. 2197
DRAEGER SAFETY S.A. DE C.V.—See Draegerwerk AG & Co. KGaA; *Int'l*, pg. 2197
DRAEGER SAFETY S.A.—See Draegerwerk AG & Co. KGaA; *Int'l*, pg. 2197
DRAEGER SAFETY (SCHWEIZ) AG—See Draegerwerk AG & Co. KGaA; *Int'l*, pg. 2197
DRAEGER SAFETY SWEDEN AB—See Draegerwerk AG & Co. KGaA; *Int'l*, pg. 2197
DRAEGER SAFETY (THAILAND) LTD.—See Draegerwerk AG & Co. KGaA; *Int'l*, pg. 2197
DRAEGER SAFETY UK LTD.—See Draegerwerk AG & Co. KGaA; *Int'l*, pg. 2197
DRAEGER SINGAPORE PTE LTD.—See Draegerwerk AG & Co. KGaA; *Int'l*, pg. 2197
DRAEGER'S SUPER MARKETS INC.; *U.S. Private*, pg. 1271
DRAEGER TEHNIKA D.O.O.—See Draegerwerk AG & Co. KGaA; *Int'l*, pg. 2197
DRAEGER VIETNAM CO., LTD.—See Draegerwerk AG & Co. KGaA; *Int'l*, pg. 2197
DRAEGERWERK AG & CO. KGAA; *Int'l*, pg. 2196
DRAEXLMAIER AUTOMOTIVE OF AMERICA, LLC—See Draexlmaier Gruppe; *Int'l*, pg. 2198
DRAEXLMAIER AUTOMOTIVE SYSTEMS (THAILAND) CO., LTD.—See Draexlmaier Gruppe; *Int'l*, pg. 2198
DRAEXLMAIER GRUPPE; *Int'l*, pg. 2198

DR. AGARWAL'S EYE HOSPITAL LIMITED

DRAEXLMAIER (SHENYANG) AUTOMOTIVE COMPONENTS CO., LTD.—See Draexlmaier Gruppe; *Int'l*, pg. 2198
DRAFT BEER SERVICES OF ATLANTA, INC.—See Falconhead Capital, LLC; *U.S. Private*, pg. 1467
DRAFTFCB AD FABRIKA—See The Interpublic Group of Companies, Inc.; *U.S. Public*, pg. 2092
DRAFTFCB CANADA INC.—See The Interpublic Group of Companies, Inc.; *U.S. Public*, pg. 2092
DRAFTFCB CAPE TOWN—See The Interpublic Group of Companies, Inc.; *U.S. Public*, pg. 2092
DRAFTFCB DURBAN—See The Interpublic Group of Companies, Inc.; *U.S. Public*, pg. 2092
DRAFTFCB HEALTHCARE—See The Interpublic Group of Companies, Inc.; *U.S. Public*, pg. 2092
DRAFTFCB JOHANNESBURG—See The Interpublic Group of Companies, Inc.; *U.S. Public*, pg. 2092
DRAFTFCB MA—See The Interpublic Group of Companies, Inc.; *U.S. Public*, pg. 2092
DRAFTFCB PARTNERS WERBEAGENTUR GES.M.B.H.—See The Interpublic Group of Companies, Inc.; *U.S. Public*, pg. 2092
DRAFTFCB RUSSIA—See The Interpublic Group of Companies, Inc.; *U.S. Public*, pg. 2092
DRAFTFCB SHIMONI FINKELSTEIN—See The Interpublic Group of Companies, Inc.; *U.S. Public*, pg. 2092
DRAFTFCB—See The Interpublic Group of Companies, Inc.; *U.S. Public*, pg. 2092
DRAFTFCB—See The Interpublic Group of Companies, Inc.; *U.S. Public*, pg. 2092
DRAFTFCB—See The Interpublic Group of Companies, Inc.; *U.S. Public*, pg. 2092
DRAFTFCB (THAILAND) LTD.—See The Interpublic Group of Companies, Inc.; *U.S. Public*, pg. 2092
DRAFTFCB ULKA—See The Interpublic Group of Companies, Inc.; *U.S. Public*, pg. 2092
DRAFTFCB ULKA—See The Interpublic Group of Companies, Inc.; *U.S. Public*, pg. 2092
DRAFTFCB ULKA—See The Interpublic Group of Companies, Inc.; *U.S. Public*, pg. 2092
DRAFTFCB ULKA—See The Interpublic Group of Companies, Inc.; *U.S. Public*, pg. 2092
DRAFTFCB ULKA—See The Interpublic Group of Companies, Inc.; *U.S. Public*, pg. 2092
DRAFTFCB WEST—See The Interpublic Group of Companies, Inc.; *U.S. Public*, pg. 2093
DRAFTFCB WEST—See The Interpublic Group of Companies, Inc.; *U.S. Public*, pg. 2093
DRAFT INC.; *U.S. Public*, pg. 2199
DRAFTKINGS HOLDINGS INC.—See DraftKings Inc.; *U.S. Public*, pg. 687
DRAFTKINGS INC.; *U.S. Public*, pg. 687
DRAGADOS CANADA, INC.—See ACS, Actividades de Construccion y Servicios, S.A.; *Int'l*, pg. 111
DRAGADOS GULF CONSTRUCTION, LTDA.—See ACS, Actividades de Construccion y Servicios, S.A.; *Int'l*, pg. 111
DRAGADOS INVERSIONES USA, S.L.—See ACS, Actividades de Construccion y Servicios, S.A.; *Int'l*, pg. 111
DRAGADOS OFFSHORE DE MEJICO KU-A2, S.A DE C.V.—See ACS, Actividades de Construccion y Servicios, S.A.; *Int'l*, pg. 111
DRAGADOS OFFSHORE, S.A.—See ACS, Actividades de Construccion y Servicios, S.A.; *Int'l*, pg. 111
DRAGADOS S.A.—See ACS, Actividades de Construccion y Servicios, S.A.; *Int'l*, pg. 111
DRAGADOS UK LIMITED—See ACS, Actividades de Construccion y Servicios, S.A.; *Int'l*, pg. 111
DRAGADOS USA INC.—See ACS, Actividades de Construccion y Servicios, S.A.; *Int'l*, pg. 111
DRAGAMEX SA DE CV—See HAL Trust N.V.; *Int'l*, pg. 3226
DRAGANFLY, INC.; *Int'l*, pg. 2199
DRAGANFLY INVESTMENTS LIMITED; *Int'l*, pg. 2199
DRAGAPOR DRAGAGENS DE PORTUGAL S.A.—See HAL Trust N.V.; *Int'l*, pg. 3226
DR. AGARWAL'S EYE HOSPITAL LIMITED; *Int'l*, pg. 2190
DRAGENOPHARM APOTHEKER PUSCHL GMBH & CO. KG—See BC Partners LLP; *Int'l*, pg. 922
DRAGER ARGENTINA SA—See Draegerwerk AG & Co. KGaA; *Int'l*, pg. 2197
DRAGER AUSTRIA GMBH—See Draegerwerk AG & Co. KGaA; *Int'l*, pg. 2197
DRAGER CHILE LTDA.—See Draegerwerk AG & Co. KGaA; *Int'l*, pg. 2197
DRAGER DANMARK A/S—See Draegerwerk AG & Co. KGaA; *Int'l*, pg. 2197
DRAGER DO BRASIL LTDA.—See Draegerwerk AG & Co. KGaA; *Int'l*, pg. 2198
DRAGER FRANCE SAS—See Draegerwerk AG & Co. KGaA; *Int'l*, pg. 2197
DRAGER GEBAUDE UND SERVICE GMBH—See Draegerwerk AG & Co. KGaA; *Int'l*, pg. 2197
DRAGER HISPANIA S.A.U.—See Draegerwerk AG & Co. KGaA; *Int'l*, pg. 2197
DRAGER IRELAND LTD.—See Draegerwerk AG & Co. KGaA; *Int'l*, pg. 2197

DRAGER MEDICAL ANSY GMBH—See Draegerwerk AG & Co. KGaA; *Int'l*, pg. 2197
DRAGER MEDICAL BELGIUM NV—See Draegerwerk AG & Co. KGaA; *Int'l*, pg. 2197
DRAGER MEDICAL CROATIA D.O.O.—See Draegerwerk AG & Co. KGaA; *Int'l*, pg. 2197
DRAGER MEDICAL DEUTSCHLAND GMBH—See Draegerwerk AG & Co. KGaA; *Int'l*, pg. 2197
DRAGER MEDICAL EQUIPMENT (SHANGHAI) CO., LTD.—See Draegerwerk AG & Co. KGaA; *Int'l*, pg. 2197
DRAGER MEDICAL HISPANIA SA—See Draegerwerk AG & Co. KGaA; *Int'l*, pg. 2197
DRAGER MEDICAL HUNGARY KFT.—See Draegerwerk AG & Co. KGaA; *Int'l*, pg. 2197
DRAGER MEDICAL ROMANIA SRL—See Draegerwerk AG & Co. KGaA; *Int'l*, pg. 2197
DRAGER MSI GMBH—See Draegerwerk AG & Co. KGaA; *Int'l*, pg. 2197
DRAGER NEDERLAND B.V.—See Draegerwerk AG & Co. KGaA; *Int'l*, pg. 2197
DRAGER NORGE AS—See Draegerwerk AG & Co. KGaA; *Int'l*, pg. 2197
DRAGER PORTUGAL, LDA.—See Draegerwerk AG & Co. KGaA; *Int'l*, pg. 2197
DRAGER ROMANIA SRL—See Draegerwerk AG & Co. KGaA; *Int'l*, pg. 2197
DRAGER SAFETY AG & CO. KGAA—See Draegerwerk AG & Co. KGaA; *Int'l*, pg. 2197
DRAGER SAFETY BELGIUM N.V.—See Draegerwerk AG & Co. KGaA; *Int'l*, pg. 2197
DRAGER SAFETY DANMARK A/S—See Draegerwerk AG & Co. KGaA; *Int'l*, pg. 2197
DRAGER SAFETY D.O.O.—See Draegerwerk AG & Co. KGaA; *Int'l*, pg. 2198
DRAGER SAFETY HISPANIA SA—See Draegerwerk AG & Co. KGaA; *Int'l*, pg. 2197
DRAGER SAFETY HUNGARIA KFT.—See Draegerwerk AG & Co. KGaA; *Int'l*, pg. 2198
DRAGER SAFETY ROMANIA SRL—See Draegerwerk AG & Co. KGaA; *Int'l*, pg. 2198
DRAGER SCHWEIZ AG—See Draegerwerk AG & Co. KGaA; *Int'l*, pg. 2198
DRAGER SLOVENIJA D.O.O.—See Draegerwerk AG & Co. KGaA; *Int'l*, pg. 2198
DRAGER SLOVENSKO S.R.O.—See Draegerwerk AG & Co. KGaA; *Int'l*, pg. 2198
DRAGER SOUTH AFRICA (PTY) LTD.—See Draegerwerk AG & Co. KGaA; *Int'l*, pg. 2198
DRAGER SUOMI OY—See Draegerwerk AG & Co. KGaA; *Int'l*, pg. 2198
DRAGER SVERIGE AB—See Draegerwerk AG & Co. KGaA; *Int'l*, pg. 2198
DRAGER TGM GMBH—See Draegerwerk AG & Co. KGaA; *Int'l*, pg. 2198
DRAGESHOLM AB—See Carl Bennet AB; *Int'l*, pg. 1331
DRAGISA BRASOVAN TRUDBENIK A.D.; *Int'l*, pg. 2199
DRAGO ENTERTAINMENT SA; *Int'l*, pg. 2199
DRAGON ALFA CEMENT LIMITED—See Fomento de Construcciones y Contratas, S.A.; *Int'l*, pg. 2722
DRAGONBOX FINLAND OY—See The Goldman Sachs Group, Inc.; *U.S. Public*, pg. 2082
DRAGON CLAW USA INC.; *U.S. Private*, pg. 1271
DRAGON CROWN GROUP HOLDINGS LIMITED; *Int'l*, pg. 2199
DRAGONEER INVESTMENT GROUP, LLC; *U.S. Private*, pg. 1271
DRAGON ESP, LTD.; *U.S. Private*, pg. 1271
DRAGONFLY CAPITAL CORP.; *Int'l*, pg. 2199
DRAGONFLY ENERGY HOLDINGS CORP.; *U.S. Public*, pg. 687
DRAGONFLY FILM & TV LIMITED—See LOV Group Invest SAS; *Int'l*, pg. 4565
DRAGONFLY GF CO., LTD.; *Int'l*, pg. 2199
DRAGONFLY TECHNOLOGIES PTY. LTD.—See Black Box Limited; *Int'l*, pg. 1058
DRAGON FRONTIER SDN. BHD.—See Oriental Holdings Berhad; *Int'l*, pg. 5624
DRAGON GROUP INTERNATIONAL LIMITED—See ASTI Holdings Limited; *Int'l*, pg. 655
DRAGON HILL FINANCIAL SERVICES LIMITED—See Wuling Motors Holdings Limited; *Int'l*, pg. 8503
DRAGON INNOVATION, INC.—See Avnet, Inc.; *U.S. Public*, pg. 252
DRAGON JADE INTERNATIONAL LIMITED; *Int'l*, pg. 2199
DRAGONJET CORPORATION - DRAGONJET KAOHSIUNG PLANT—See Lite-On Technology Corporation; *Int'l*, pg. 4525
DRAGONJET CORPORATION - DRAGONJET VIETNAM PLANT—See Lite-On Technology Corporation; *Int'l*, pg. 4525
DRAGONJET CORPORATION—See Lite-On Technology Corporation; *Int'l*, pg. 4525
DRAGON KING GROUP HOLDINGS LIMITED; *Int'l*, pg. 2199
DRAGONLAND TECHNOLOGY PTE LTD—See Keppel Corporation Limited; *Int'l*, pg. 4130

DRAGON LEGEND ENTERTAINMENT (CANADA) INC.; *Int'l*, pg. 2199
DRAGON LOGISTICS CO., LTD.—See Sumitomo Corporation; *Int'l*, pg. 7268
DRAGON MINING; *Int'l*, pg. 2199
DRAGON MINING (SWEDEN) AB—See Dragon Mining; *Int'l*, pg. 2199
DRAGON MOUNTAIN GOLD LIMITED; *Int'l*, pg. 2199
DRAGON OIL PLC—See Emirates National Oil Company Limited; *Int'l*, pg. 2381
DRAGONPLAY LTD—See Light & Wonder, Inc.; *U.S. Public*, pg. 1314
DRAGON POLYMERS INC.; *U.S. Private*, pg. 1271
DRAGON PORTLAND LIMITED—See Fomento de Construcciones y Contratas, S.A.; *Int'l*, pg. 2722
DRAGON PRODUCTS COMPANY, LLC—See Grupo Empresarial Kaluz S.A. de C.V.; *Int'l*, pg. 3127
DRAGON PRODUCTS LTD.—See Modern Group, Ltd.; *U.S. Private*, pg. 2761
DRAGON RISE GROUP HOLDINGS LIMITED; *Int'l*, pg. 2199
DRAGON STEEL CORPORATION—See China Steel Corporation; *Int'l*, pg. 1555
DRAGON SWEATER & SPINNING LIMITED; *Int'l*, pg. 2199
DRAGONTAIL SYSTEMS LIMITED—See Dragontail Systems Limited; *Int'l*, pg. 2200
DRAGONTAIL SYSTEMS LIMITED; *Int'l*, pg. 2200
DRAGONTAIL SYSTEMS USA INC.—See Dragontail Systems Limited; *Int'l*, pg. 2200
DRAGON UKRAINIAN PROPERTIES & DEVELOPMENT PLC; *Int'l*, pg. 2199
DRAGONWAVE HFCL INDIA PRIVATE LIMITED—See HFCL Limited; *Int'l*, pg. 3375
DRAGONWAVE MEXICO S.A. DE C.V.—See Transform-X, Inc.; *U.S. Private*, pg. 4208
DRAGONWAVE-X CANADA, INC.—See COMSovereign Holding Corp.; *U.S. Public*, pg. 562
DRAGONWAVE-X—See Transform-X, Inc.; *U.S. Private*, pg. 4208
DRAGOS, INC.; *U.S. Private*, pg. 1272
DRAGO SUPPLY COMPANY INC.—See Genuine Parts Company; *U.S. Public*, pg. 933
DRAGOY GROSSIST AS—See Austevoll Seafood ASA; *Int'l*, pg. 717
DRA GROUP HOLDINGS PROPRIETARY LIMITED; *Int'l*, pg. 2196
DRAGSBAEK A/S—See Orkla ASA; *Int'l*, pg. 5637
DRAHOTA COMMERCIAL LLC.; *U.S. Private*, pg. 1272
DRAHOTA CONSTRUCTION CO—See Federal Contracting Inc; *U.S. Private*, pg. 1487
DRAHTWERK FRIEDR. LOTTERS GMBH & CO. KG; *Int'l*, pg. 2200
DRAHTWERK LUISENTHAL GMBH—See Saarstahl AG; *Int'l*, pg. 6461
DRAHTWERK ST. INGBERT GMBH—See Saarstahl AG; *Int'l*, pg. 6461
DR. AICHHORN GMBH; *Int'l*, pg. 2190
DRAIEH GENERA TRADING CO. WLL—See DAMAC Group; *Int'l*, pg. 1955
DRAINAGE SYSTEMS DUBLIN LIMITED—See Grafton Group plc; *Int'l*, pg. 3050
DRAINTECH S.R.L.—See Interpump Group S.p.A.; *Int'l*, pg. 3755
DRAKA BELGIUM N.V.—See Prysmian S.p.A.; *Int'l*, pg. 6010
DRAKA CABLES (HONG KONG) LIMITED—See Prysmian S.p.A.; *Int'l*, pg. 6010
DRAKA COMTEQ GERMANY GMBH & CO. KG—See Prysmian S.p.A.; *Int'l*, pg. 6010
DRAKA DISTRIBUTION ABERDEEN LIMITED—See Prysmian S.p.A.; *Int'l*, pg. 6010
DRAKA KABEL SVERIGE AB—See Prysmian S.p.A.; *Int'l*, pg. 6010
DRAKA KABELY S.R.O.—See Prysmian S.p.A.; *Int'l*, pg. 6010
DRAKA UK LTD.—See Prysmian S.p.A.; *Int'l*, pg. 6010
DRAKE AIR, INC.—See AMETEK, Inc.; *U.S. Public*, pg. 117
DRAKE AUSTRALIA PTY LTD—See Drake New Zealand Ltd.; *Int'l*, pg. 2200
DRAKE CEMENT, LLC—See Union Andina de Cementos S.A.A.; *Int'l*, pg. 8050
DRAKE CIRCUS CENTRE LIMITED—See The British Land Company PLC; *Int'l*, pg. 7628
DRAKE COOPER INC.; *U.S. Private*, pg. 1272
DRAKE ENTERPRISES LTD.; *U.S. Private*, pg. 1272
DRAKE, INC.; *U.S. Private*, pg. 1272
DRAKE INDUSTRIES, INC.—See Cubbison Company; *U.S. Private*, pg. 1120
DRAKE MANUFACTURING SERVICE CO., LLC—See Uni-World Capital, L.P.; *U.S. Private*, pg. 4281
DRAKE & MORGAN LIMITED; *Int'l*, pg. 2200
DRAKE NEW ZEALAND LTD.; *Int'l*, pg. 2200
DRAKEN INTERNATIONAL INC.; *U.S. Private*, pg. 1272
DRAKENSBERG GARDENS GOLF & SPA RESORT—See Gooderson Leisure Corporation; *Int'l*, pg. 3039
DRAKE RESOURCES LIMITED; *Int'l*, pg. 2200

DRAKES BAY FUNDRAISING, INC.—See Next Generation Fundraising, Inc.; *U.S. Private*, pg. 2920
DRAKE & SCULL INTERNATIONAL L.L.C.—See Drake & Scull International PJSC; *Int'l*, pg. 2200
DRAKE & SCULL INTERNATIONAL PJSC; *Int'l*, pg. 2200
DRAKE-WILLIAMS STEEL INC.; *U.S. Private*, pg. 1272
DRAKKAR & ASSOCIES INC.; *Int'l*, pg. 2200
DRAKKAR MAK INC.—See Drakkar & Associes Inc.; *Int'l*, pg. 2200
DRAKONTAS LLC; *U.S. Private*, pg. 1272
DRALON GMBH; *Int'l*, pg. 2200
DRAMA INC.—See NAVER Corporation; *Int'l*, pg. 5174
DRAMAR ANDALUCIA TRATAMIENTO DE MARPOLES, S.L.U.—See ACS, Actividades de Construccion y Servicios, S.A.; *Int'l*, pg. 111
THE DRAMBUIE LIQUEUR COMPANY LTD.—See William Grant & Sons Ltd.; *Int'l*, pg. 8413
DRAMMEN KINO AS—See Egmont Fonden; *Int'l*, pg. 2325
DRANCO CONSTRUCTION LIMITED; *Int'l*, pg. 2200
DRANETZ TECHNOLOGIES INC.—See METRAWATT International GmbH; *Int'l*, pg. 4856
DRAPER CHEVROLET COMPANY; *U.S. Private*, pg. 1272
DRAPER HOLDINGS BUSINESS TRUST; *U.S. Private*, pg. 1272
DRAPER INC.; *U.S. Private*, pg. 1272
DRAPER KNITTING CO., INC.; *U.S. Private*, pg. 1272
DRAPER & KRAMER, INCORPORATED—See DKH, Incorporated; *U.S. Private*, pg. 1247
DRAPER & KRAMER REALTY ADVISORS, INC.—See DKH, Incorporated; *U.S. Private*, pg. 1247
DRAPER & KRAMER RETIREMENT PROPERTY SERVICES—See DKH, Incorporated; *U.S. Private*, pg. 1247
DRAPER OAKWOOD TECHNOLOGY ACQUISITION, INC.—See Rebonz Holding Limited; *Int'l*, pg. 6249
DRAPERS & DAMONS, LLC—See Bluestem Brands, Inc.; *U.S. Private*, pg. 598
DRAPER VALLEY FARMS INC.—See Perdue Farms Incorporated; *U.S. Private*, pg. 3147
DRAPERYCRAFTERS INC.—See Frank Kasmir & Associates Inc.; *U.S. Private*, pg. 1595
DRAPHIX, LLC; *U.S. Private*, pg. 1272
DRASEIKIU KARJERAS UAB—See SigmaRoc Plc; *Int'l*, pg. 6909
DRA TAGGART, LLC—See DRA Group Holdings Proprietary Limited; *Int'l*, pg. 2196
DRA TAGGART SITE SERVICES, LLC—See DRA Group Holdings Proprietary Limited; *Int'l*, pg. 2196
DR. AUGUST OETKER KG; *Int'l*, pg. 2190
DRAVENSA C.A.—See HAL Trust N.V.; *Int'l*, pg. 3226
DRAVON MEDICAL, INC.; *U.S. Private*, pg. 1272
DRAWBRIDGE GLOBAL MACRO ADVISORS LLC—See SoftBank Group Corp.; *Int'l*, pg. 7052
DRAW CONNECT LIMITED—See Marsh & McLennan Companies, Inc.; *U.S. Public*, pg. 1374
DRAW CREATE LIMITED—See Marsh & McLennan Companies, Inc.; *U.S. Public*, pg. 1374
DRAW DISTANCE S.A.; *Int'l*, pg. 2200
DRAWER BOX SPECIALTIES INC.—See Renovo Capital, LLC; *U.S. Private*, pg. 3399
DRAWER BOX SPECIALTIES INC.—See The Rosewood Corporation; *U.S. Private*, pg. 4112
DRAWING BOARD—See Taylor Corporation; *U.S. Private*, pg. 3938
DRAWIN VERTRIEBS-GMBH—See Wacker Chemie AG; *Int'l*, pg. 8323
DRAX BIOMASS INTERNATIONAL INC.—See Drax Group plc; *Int'l*, pg. 2200
DRAX GENERATION ENTERPRISE LIMITED—See Vitol Holding B.V.; *Int'l*, pg. 8260
DRAX GROUP PLC; *Int'l*, pg. 2200
DRAX POWER LIMITED—See Drax Group plc; *Int'l*, pg. 2200
DRAYTEK CORPORATION; *Int'l*, pg. 2200
DRAYTEK GMBH—See DrayTek Corporation; *Int'l*, pg. 2200
DRAYTON RICHDALE CORP.; *U.S. Private*, pg. 1272
DRAYTON VALLEY FORD SALES LTD; *Int'l*, pg. 2201
DR. BABOR GMBH & CO. KG; *Int'l*, pg. 2190
DRB AVIATION CONSULTANTS INC.—See Temasek Holdings (Private) Limited; *Int'l*, pg. 7552
DRB-HICOM AUTO SOLUTIONS SDN BHD—See DRB-HICOM Berhad; *Int'l*, pg. 2201
DRB-HICOM BERHAD; *Int'l*, pg. 2201
DRB-HICOM COMMERCIAL VEHICLES SDN. BHD.—See DRB-HICOM Berhad; *Int'l*, pg. 2201
DRB-HICOM EZ-DRIVE SDN. BHD.—See DRB-HICOM Berhad; *Int'l*, pg. 2201
DRB HOLDING CO., LTD.; *Int'l*, pg. 2201
DRB INDUSTRIAL CO., LTD.—See DRB Holding Co., Ltd.; *Int'l*, pg. 2201
D&R BOATS INC.; *U.S. Private*, pg. 1138
DR. BOCK INDUSTRIES AG; *Int'l*, pg. 2190
DRB SYSTEMS, LLC—See New Mountain Capital, LLC; *U.S. Public*, pg. 2900
DRC ENGINEERING PTE. LTD.—See Grandshores Technology Group Limited; *Int'l*, pg. 3058
DRC HEALTH SYSTEMS, L.P.—See Encompass Health Corporation; *U.S. Public*, pg. 755

COMPANY NAME INDEX

DR CHUA'S FAMILY CLINIC PTE. LTD.—See New Silkroutes Group Limited; *Int'l*, pg. 5227
DRC INC.; *U.S. Private*, pg. 1272
DR CORPORATION LIMITED; *Int'l*, pg. 2189
DRC SYSTEMS INDIA PRIVATE LIMITED—See Infibeam Avenues Limited; *Int'l*, pg. 3684
DR. D.A. DELIS AG—See BASF SE; *Int'l*, pg. 883
DRD CO., LTD.—See Persol Holdings Co., Ltd.; *Int'l*, pg. 5819
DRDGOLD LIMITED; *Int'l*, pg. 2202
DRD NORTHWEST LLC; *U.S. Private*, pg. 1272
DREADNOUGHT RESOURCES LTD.; *Int'l*, pg. 2202
DREAMAX TELIVISION INC—See TBS Holdings, Inc.; *Int'l*, pg. 7481
DREAMBABY N.V.—See Colruyt Group N.V.; *Int'l*, pg. 1705
DREAM BOX LEARNING INC.—See Clearlake Capital Group, L.P.; *U.S. Private*, pg. 934
DREAMBRANDS, INC.; *U.S. Private*, pg. 1275
DREAM CENTER FOUNDATION, A CALIFORNIA NONPROFIT CORP.; *U.S. Private*, pg. 1272
DREAMCIS INC.—See Hangzhou Tigermed Consulting Co., Ltd.; *Int'l*, pg. 3251
DREAM CREATION LTD—See Perfectech International Holdings Limited; *Int'l*, pg. 5799
DREAM DERMATOLOGY COMPANY LIMITED—See Do Day Dream PCL; *Int'l*, pg. 2152
DREAM DINING CORP.—See TORIDOLL Holdings Corporation; *Int'l*, pg. 7828
DREAMEAST GROUP LIMITED; *Int'l*, pg. 2203
DREAM FINDERS HOMES, INC.; *U.S. Public*, pg. 687
DREAM FINDERS HOMES LLC; *U.S. Private*, pg. 1275
DREAMFLY PRODUCTIONS CORPORATION; *U.S. Private*, pg. 1275
DREAMFOLKS SERVICES LTD.; *Int'l*, pg. 2203
DREAMGATE (SINGAPORE) PTE. LTD.—See RGB International Bhd.; *Int'l*, pg. 6319
DREAMGEAR, LLC; *U.S. Private*, pg. 1275
DREAM GLOBAL REAL ESTATE INVESTMENT TRUST—See Blackstone Inc.; *U.S. Public*, pg. 350
DREAMHACK SPORTS GAMES A/S—See Modern Times Group MTG AB; *Int'l*, pg. 5014
DREAMHAUS GMBH—See CTS Eventim AG & Co. KGAA; *Int'l*, pg. 1872
DREAM HOMES & DEVELOPMENT CORP.; *U.S. Public*, pg. 687
DREAM HOMES LIMITED; *U.S. Private*, pg. 1275
DREAM HOP CO.,LTD.—See PCA Corporation; *Int'l*, pg. 5766
DREAM HOSTEL SK SRO—See Safestay Plc; *Int'l*, pg. 6470
DREAM HOSTEL SP. Z O.O.—See Safestay Plc; *Int'l*, pg. 6470
DREAM IMPACT TRUST; *Int'l*, pg. 2202
DREAM INCUBATOR INC.; *Int'l*, pg. 2202
DREAM INCUBATOR (VIETNAM) JOINT STOCK COMPANY—See Dream Incubator Inc.; *Int'l*, pg. 2202
DREAM INDUSTRIAL REAL ESTATE INVESTMENT TRUST—See Dream Unlimited Corp.; *Int'l*, pg. 2203
DREAM INKO CO., LTD.—See Dream International Ltd; *Int'l*, pg. 2202
DREAM INTERNATIONAL LTD; *Int'l*, pg. 2202
DREAM INTERNATIONAL USA, INC—See Dream International Ltd; *Int'l*, pg. 2202
DREAM JOB MYANMAR LTD.—See Will Group, Inc.; *Int'l*, pg. 8412
DREAMLAND CORPORATION (MALAYSIA) SDN. BHD.—See FACB Industries Incorporated Berhad; *Int'l*, pg. 2600
DREAMLAND N.V.—See Colruyt Group N.V.; *Int'l*, pg. 1705
DREAM LIFE SCIENCE (PVT.) LIMITED—See Raigam Marketing Services (Pvt) Ltd.; *Int'l*, pg. 6188
DREAM OFFICE REAL ESTATE INVESTMENT TRUST—See Dream Unlimited Corp.; *Int'l*, pg. 2203
DREAM PHARMA CORP.—See Hanwha Group; *Int'l*, pg. 3264
DREAM POLISHERS, INC.; *U.S. Private*, pg. 1275
DREAM PRODUCTS SDN. BHD.—See FACB Industries Incorporated Berhad; *Int'l*, pg. 2600
DREAMSCAPE NETWORKS LIMITED; *Int'l*, pg. 2203
DREAMS CORPORATION—See Kaga Electronics Co., Ltd.; *Int'l*, pg. 4048
DREAMS LTD.—See Tempur Sealy International, Inc.; *U.S. Public*, pg. 1999
DREAMSTALK STUDIOS INC.—See StarDyne Technologies Inc.; *Int'l*, pg. 7176
DREAMSTYLE REMODELING, INC.; *U.S. Private*, pg. 1275
DREAMTECH CO., LTD.; *Int'l*, pg. 2203
DREAM T ENTERTAINMENT CO., LTD.; *Int'l*, pg. 2203
DREAM UNLIMITED CORP.; *Int'l*, pg. 2203
DREAM-UP TOMAMAE CO., LTD.—See Electric Power Development Co., Ltd.; *Int'l*, pg. 2349
DREAMUS COMPANY; *Int'l*, pg. 2203
DREAM VINA CO., LTD.—See Dream International Ltd; *Int'l*, pg. 2202
DREAM VISION CO., LTD.; *Int'l*, pg. 2203
DREAMWEAR, INC.; *U.S. Private*, pg. 1275

DREAMWORKS ANIMATION, LLC—See Comcast Corporation; *U.S. Public*, pg. 539
DREAMWORKS LLC—See National Amusements, Inc.; *U.S. Private*, pg. 2842
DREAMWORLD LIMITED; *Int'l*, pg. 2203
DREBO AMERICA, INC.—See Techtronic Industries Co., Ltd.; *Int'l*, pg. 7513
DREBO WERKZEUGFABRIK GMBH—See Techtronic Industries Co., Ltd.; *Int'l*, pg. 7513
DRECO ENERGY SERVICES ULC—See NOV, Inc.; *U.S. Public*, pg. 1544
DRECOM CO., LTD.; *Int'l*, pg. 2203
DREDGING CORPORATION OF INDIA LTD; *Int'l*, pg. 2203
DREDGING INTERNATIONAL ASIA PACIFIC (PTE) LTD—See Ackermans & van Haaren NV; *Int'l*, pg. 105
DREDGING INTERNATIONAL NV—See Ackermans & van Haaren NV; *Int'l*, pg. 105
DREDGING SUPPLY COMPANY INC.; *U.S. Private*, pg. 1275
DRE DRAEXLMAIER ELEKTROTEK S.R.O.—See Draexlmaier Gruppe; *Int'l*, pg. 2198
DREEBIT GMBH—See Dr. Ing. K. Busch GmbH; *Int'l*, pg. 2193
THE DREES COMPANY, INC.; *U.S. Private*, pg. 4023
DREES HOMES—See The Drees Company, Inc.; *U.S. Private*, pg. 4023
DREES PREFERRED COLLECTION, INC.—See The Drees Company, Inc.; *U.S. Private*, pg. 4023
DREES & SOMMER BELGIUM S.P.R.L—See Drees & Sommer SE; *Int'l*, pg. 2204
DREES & SOMMER BERLIN GMBH—See Drees & Sommer SE; *Int'l*, pg. 2204
DREES & SOMMER COLOGNE GMBH—See Drees & Sommer SE; *Int'l*, pg. 2204
DREES & SOMMER DRESDEN GMBH—See Drees & Sommer SE; *Int'l*, pg. 2204
DREES & SOMMER ESPANA S.L.—See Drees & Sommer SE; *Int'l*, pg. 2204
DREES & SOMMER FRANCE SARL—See Drees & Sommer SE; *Int'l*, pg. 2204
DREES & SOMMER HAMBURG GMBH—See Drees & Sommer SE; *Int'l*, pg. 2204
DREES & SOMMER ITALIA ENGINEERING S.R.L.—See Drees & Sommer SE; *Int'l*, pg. 2204
DREES & SOMMER LEIPZIG GMBH—See Drees & Sommer SE; *Int'l*, pg. 2204
DREES & SOMMER LUXEMBOURG SARL—See Drees & Sommer SE; *Int'l*, pg. 2204
DREES & SOMMER NETHERLANDS B.V.—See Drees & Sommer SE; *Int'l*, pg. 2204
DREES & SOMMER NORDIC A/S—See Drees & Sommer SE; *Int'l*, pg. 2204
DREES & SOMMER POLSKA SP.Z.O.O.—See Drees & Sommer SE; *Int'l*, pg. 2204
DREES & SOMMER PROJECT MANAGEMENT & CONSULTING (BEIJING) CO., LTD.—See Drees & Sommer SE; *Int'l*, pg. 2204
DREES & SOMMER PROJEKTMANAGEMENT UND BAUTECHNISCHE BERATUNG GMBH—See Drees & Sommer SE; *Int'l*, pg. 2204
DREES & SOMMER ROMANIA S.R.L—See Drees & Sommer SE; *Int'l*, pg. 2204
DREES & SOMMER RUSSIA & CIS—See Drees & Sommer SE; *Int'l*, pg. 2204
DREES & SOMMER SCHWEIZ GMBH—See Drees & Sommer SE; *Int'l*, pg. 2204
DREES & SOMMER SE; *Int'l*, pg. 2203
DREES & SOMMER TURKIYE LTD.—See Drees & Sommer SE; *Int'l*, pg. 2204
DREES & SOMMER UK LTD.—See Drees & Sommer SE; *Int'l*, pg. 2204
DREES & SOMMER UKRAINE—See Drees & Sommer SE; *Int'l*, pg. 2204
DREES & SOMMER ULM GMBH—See Drees & Sommer SE; *Int'l*, pg. 2204
DREFA IMMOBILIEN MANAGEMENT GMBH—See DREFA Media Holding GmbH; *Int'l*, pg. 2204
DREFA MEDIA HOLDING GMBH; *Int'l*, pg. 2204
DR EGON ZEHNDER & PARTNER AG—See Egon Zehnder International Inc.; *U.S. Private*, pg. 1344
DR.E.GRAUB AG—See AGRAVIS Raiffeisen AG; *Int'l*, pg. 215
DR. E. HACKHOFER EDV-SOFTWAREBERATUNG GESELLSCHAFT M.B.H.—See UNIQA Insurance Group AG; *Int'l*, pg. 8057
DREI-BANKEN-VERSICHERUNGS AG—See Bank fur Tirol und Vorarlberg Ag; *Int'l*, pg. 838
DREIDOPPEL GMBH—See IREKS GmbH; *Int'l*, pg. 3806
DREIECK FIDUCIARIA SA—See EFG International AG; *Int'l*, pg. 2320
DREIFIVE AG—See TX Group AG; *Int'l*, pg. 7992
DREIFIVE GMBH—See TX Group AG; *Int'l*, pg. 7992
DREIFIVE (SWITZERLAND) AG—See TX Group AG; *Int'l*, pg. 7992
DRE INC.—See Jordan Industries, Inc.; *U.S. Private*, pg. 2235
DREISBACH ENTERPRISES INC.; *U.S. Private*, pg. 1275

DREWEX S.A.

DREISILKER ELECTRIC MOTORS INC.; *U.S. Private*, pg. 1276
DREISON INTERNATIONAL, INC.; *U.S. Private*, pg. 1276
DREMEL—See Robert Bosch GmbH; *Int'l*, pg. 6364
DRESCHER ASOCIADOS SRL—See Atlas Copco AB; *Int'l*, pg. 683
DRESCHER FULL-SERVICE VERSAND GMBH—See Exela Technologies, Inc.; *U.S. Public*, pg. 806
DRESDNER AUFZUGSDIENST GMBH—See KONE Oyj; *Int'l*, pg. 4247
DRESDNER BANK AG—See Commerzbank AG; *Int'l*, pg. 1717
DRESDNER BANK MEXICO S.A.—See Commerzbank AG; *Int'l*, pg. 1718
DRESDNER BANK ZAO—See Commerzbank AG; *Int'l*, pg. 1718
DRESDNER CHAUFFEUR SERVICE 8X8 GMBH—See Bertelsmann SE & Co. KGaA; *Int'l*, pg. 992
DRESDNER DRUCK- UND VERLAGSHAUS GMBH & CO. KG—See Bertelsmann SE & Co. KGaA; *Int'l*, pg. 994
DRESDNER KLEINWORT DEUTSCHLAND GMBH—See Commerzbank AG; *Int'l*, pg. 1717
DRESDNER KLEINWORT FRANCE SA—See Commerzbank AG; *Int'l*, pg. 1717
DRESDNER KLEINWORT LIMITED—See Commerzbank AG; *Int'l*, pg. 1718
DRESDNER KLEINWORT PFANDBRIEFE INVESTMENTS, INC.—See Bank of America Corporation; *U.S. Public*, pg. 272
DRESDNER KLEINWORT SHANGHAI—See Commerzbank AG; *Int'l*, pg. 1718
DRESDNER KLEINWORT—See Commerzbank AG; *Int'l*, pg. 1717
DRESDNER KUHLANLAGENBAU GMBH—See Dussmann Stiftung & Co. KGaA; *Int'l*, pg. 2234
DRESEARCH FAHRZEUGELEKTRONIK GMBH—See init innovation in traffic systems SE; *Int'l*, pg. 3704
DRESHER DIALYSIS, LLC—See DaVita Inc.; *U.S. Public*, pg. 638
DRESNER ALLEN CARON—See Dresner Corporate Services Inc.; *U.S. Private*, pg. 1276
DRESNER CORPORATE SERVICES INC.; *U.S. Private*, pg. 1276
DRESSANDER BHC INC.—See Simplicity Financial Marketing Holdings Inc.; *U.S. Private*, pg. 3667
DRESSED FOR SALE AUSTRALIA PTY. LTD.—See Johns Lyng Group Limited; *Int'l*, pg. 3984
DRESSEL GMBH—See Korber AG; *Int'l*, pg. 4281
DRESSER & ASSOCIATES, INC.—See Net@Work, Inc.; *U.S. Private*, pg. 2886
DRESSER-RAND AS—See Siemens Energy AG; *Int'l*, pg. 6901
DRESSER-RAND CANADA, INC.—See Siemens Energy AG; *Int'l*, pg. 6901
DRESSER-RAND CO. - BURLINGTON—See Siemens Energy AG; *Int'l*, pg. 6901
DRESSER-RAND COMPANY LTD.—See Siemens Energy AG; *Int'l*, pg. 6901
DRESSER-RAND COMPANY—See Siemens Energy AG; *Int'l*, pg. 6901
DRESSER-RAND CO. - OLEAN—See Siemens Energy AG; *Int'l*, pg. 6901
DRESSER-RAND CO. - PAINTED POST—See Siemens Energy AG; *Int'l*, pg. 6901
DRESSER-RAND CO. - WELLSVILLE—See Siemens Energy AG; *Int'l*, pg. 6901
DRESSER-RAND GMBH—See Siemens Energy AG; *Int'l*, pg. 6901
DRESSER-RAND GROUP INC.—See Siemens Energy AG; *Int'l*, pg. 6901
DRESSER-RAND S.A.—See Siemens Energy AG; *Int'l*, pg. 6901
DRESSER-RAND SERVICES, LLC—See Siemens Energy AG; *Int'l*, pg. 6901
DRESSER-RAND TRINIDAD & TOBAGO LIMITED—See Siemens Energy AG; *Int'l*, pg. 6901
DRESSER-RAND (UK) LTD.—See Siemens Energy AG; *Int'l*, pg. 6901
DRESS FOR SUCCESS WORLDWIDE; *U.S. Private*, pg. 1276
DRESSLER TRUCK SERVICE INC.; *U.S. Private*, pg. 1276
DRESSMART GMBH—See New Wave Group AB; *Int'l*, pg. 5229
DRESSTA CO., LTD.—See Guangxi Liugong Machinery Co., Ltd.; *Int'l*, pg. 3163
DRESS YOUR BODY SA—See The Swatch Group Ltd.; *Int'l*, pg. 7691
DREVER INTERNATIONAL S.A.—See SMS Holding GmbH; *Int'l*, pg. 7015
DREW AMEROID (SINGAPORE) PTE. LTD.—See Court Square Capital Partners, L.P.; *U.S. Private*, pg. 1068
DREW CHILD DEVELOPMENT CORPORATION; *U.S. Private*, pg. 1276
DREWEX S.A.; *Int'l*, pg. 2204
DREW FOAM COMPANIES, INC.—See Wynnchurch Capital, L.P.; *U.S. Private*, pg. 4577
DREW MARINE GERMANY GMBH—See Court Square Capital Partners, L.P.; *U.S. Private*, pg. 1068

DREW MARINE INTERNATIONAL B.V.—See Court Square Capital Partners, L.P.; *U.S. Private*, pg. 1069
DREW MARINE JAPAN G.K.—See Court Square Capital Partners, L.P.; *U.S. Private*, pg. 1069
DREW MARINE SIGNAL AND SAFETY UK LTD—See Court Square Capital Partners, L.P.; *U.S. Private*, pg. 1069
DREW MARINE USA, INC.—See Court Square Capital Partners, L.P.; *U.S. Private*, pg. 1068
DREW OIL COMPANY, INC.; *U.S. Private*, pg. 1276
DREW PEARSON INTERNATIONAL (EUROPE) LTD.—See Mainland Headwear Holdings Ltd.; *Int'l*, pg. 4651
DREW SCIENTIFIC, INC.—See Transasia Bio-Medicals Ltd.; *Int'l*, pg. 7896
DREW SHOE CORPORATION—See Wexford Capital Limited Partnership; *U.S. Private*, pg. 4502
DREW'S LLC—See Frontenac Company LLC; *U.S. Private*, pg. 1614
DREW SMITH HOMES LIMITED—See Vistry Group PLC; *Int'l*, pg. 8255
DREW TECHNOLOGIES INC.—See Searchlight Capital Partners, L.P.; *U.S. Private*, pg. 3590
DREXEL BUILDING SUPPLY; *U.S. Private*, pg. 1276
DREXEL CHEMICAL COMPANY INC.; *U.S. Private*, pg. 1276
DREXELINE FOODS LLP; *U.S. Private*, pg. 1276
DREXEL METALS CORPORATION; *U.S. Private*, pg. 1276
DREXEL UNIVERSITY; *U.S. Private*, pg. 1276
DREYCO INC.; *U.S. Private*, pg. 1276
DREYER MEDICAL GROUP, LTD.—See Advocate Health Care Network; *U.S. Private*, pg. 111
DREYER & REINBOLD INC.; *U.S. Private*, pg. 1277
DREYER'S GRAND ICE CREAM HOLDINGS, INC.—See Nestle S.A.; *Int'l*, pg. 5208
DREYER'S GRAND ICE CREAM—See Nestle S.A.; *Int'l*, pg. 5208
DREYFUS ASHBY INC.; *U.S. Private*, pg. 1277
THE DREYFUS CORPORATION—See The Bank of New York Mellon Corporation; *U.S. Public*, pg. 2038
DREYFUS MUNICIPAL INFRASTRUCTURE FUND, INC.; *U.S. Private*, pg. 1277
DR. FALK PHARMA BENELUX B.V.—See Dr. Falk Pharma GmbH; *Int'l*, pg. 2191
DR. FALK PHARMA ESPANA S.L.—See Dr. Falk Pharma GmbH; *Int'l*, pg. 2191
DR. FALK PHARMA GMBH; *Int'l*, pg. 2190
DR. FALK PHARMA LLC—See Dr. Falk Pharma GmbH; *Int'l*, pg. 2191
DR FALK PHARMA UK LTD—See Dr. Falk Pharma GmbH; *Int'l*, pg. 2190
DR FINSTERER UND KONIGS INKASSO GMBH—See Altor Equity Partners AB; *Int'l*, pg. 396
DRFIRST.COM, INC.; *U.S. Private*, pg. 1277
DR. FODISCH UMWELTMESSTECHNIK AG—See NORD Holding Unternehmensbeteiligungsgesellschaft mbH; *Int'l*, pg. 5416
DR. FOODS, INC.; *Int'l*, pg. 2191
DR. FRANZ FEURSTEIN GMBH—See delfortgroup AG; *Int'l*, pg. 2013
DR. FRESH, LLC—See Perrigo Company plc; *Int'l*, pg. 5812
DR. FRITZ FAULHABER GMBH & CO. KG; *Int'l*, pg. 2191
DRG & ASSOCIATES, INC.; *U.S. Private*, pg. 1277
DRGEM CORP.; *Int'l*, pg. 2204
D & R GENERAL CONTRACTING & DESIGN, INC.; *U.S. Private*, pg. 1136
DR. GERHARD MANN CHEM.-PHARM. FABRIK GESELLSCHAFT MIT BESCHRANKTER HAFTUNG—See Bausch Health Companies Inc.; *Int'l*, pg. 897
DR. GERHARD MANN CHEM.-PHARM. FABRIK GMBH—See Bausch Health Companies Inc.; *Int'l*, pg. 897
DRG INTERNATIONAL, INC.—See OriGene Technologies, Inc.; *U.S. Private*, pg. 3042
DR. GRAPHX—See Tukaiz LLC; *U.S. Private*, pg. 4257
DRG TECHNOLOGIES; *U.S. Private*, pg. 1277
DR. HABEEBULLAH LIFE SCIENCES LIMITED; *Int'l*, pg. 2191
DRH CAMBRIDGE HOMES, INC.—See D.R. Horton, Inc.; *U.S. Public*, pg. 620
DRH CONSTRUCTION, INC.—See D.R. Horton, Inc.; *U.S. Public*, pg. 620
DR. HELMUT ROTHENBERGER HOLDING GMBH; *Int'l*, pg. 2191
D&R HENDERSON PTY. LTD.; *Int'l*, pg. 1899
DRH HOLDINGS JOINT STOCK COMPANY; *Int'l*, pg. 2204
DR. HOEFER-JANKER GMBH & CO. KLINIK KG—See Mercurius Health SA; *Int'l*, pg. 4834
DR. HONLE AG; *Int'l*, pg. 2192
D.R. HORTON - COLORADO, LLC—See D.R. Horton, Inc.; *U.S. Public*, pg. 619
D.R. HORTON/CONTINENTAL SERIES—See D.R. Horton, Inc.; *U.S. Public*, pg. 619
D.R. HORTON - CROWN, LLC—See D.R. Horton, Inc.; *U.S. Public*, pg. 619

D.R. HORTON - GEORGIA, LLC—See D.R. Horton, Inc.; *U.S. Public*, pg. 619
D.R. HORTON HOMES—See D.R. Horton, Inc.; *U.S. Public*, pg. 619
D.R. HORTON, INC. -CHICAGO—See D.R. Horton, Inc.; *U.S. Public*, pg. 619
D.R. HORTON, INC. - CONROE OFFICE—See D.R. Horton, Inc.; *U.S. Public*, pg. 619
D.R. HORTON, INC. - DFW EAST DIVISION OFFICE—See D.R. Horton, Inc.; *U.S. Public*, pg. 619
D.R. HORTON, INC. - FRESNO—See D.R. Horton, Inc.; *U.S. Public*, pg. 619
D.R. HORTON, INC. - HUNTSVILLE—See D.R. Horton, Inc.; *U.S. Public*, pg. 619
D.R. HORTON, INC. - MINNESOTA—See D.R. Horton, Inc.; *U.S. Public*, pg. 619
D.R. HORTON, INC. - SAN ANTONIO OFFICE—See D.R. Horton, Inc.; *U.S. Public*, pg. 619
D.R. HORTON, INC. - SEATTLE OFFICE—See D.R. Horton, Inc.; *U.S. Public*, pg. 619
D.R. HORTON, INC.; *U.S. Public*, pg. 619
D.R. HORTON, INC—See D.R. Horton, Inc.; *U.S. Public*, pg. 619
D.R. HORTON - INDIANA, LLC—See D.R. Horton, Inc.; *U.S. Public*, pg. 619
D.R. HORTON INSURANCE AGENCY, INC.—See D.R. Horton, Inc.; *U.S. Public*, pg. 619
D.R. HORTON - IOWA, LLC—See D.R. Horton, Inc.; *U.S. Public*, pg. 619
D.R. HORTON REALTY, LLC—See D.R. Horton, Inc.; *U.S. Public*, pg. 619
D.R. HORTON—See D.R. Horton, Inc.; *U.S. Public*, pg. 619
DRH SOUTHWEST CONSTRUCTION, INC.—See D.R. Horton, Inc.; *U.S. Public*, pg. 620
DRH TUCSON CONSTRUCTION, INC.—See D.R. Horton, Inc.; *U.S. Public*, pg. 620
DRI ADVANCED TEST SYSTEMS INC.—See AB Dynamics plc; *Int'l*, pg. 39
DRI CAPITAL INC.—See Persis Holdings Limited; *Int'l*, pg. 5818
DRI COMPANIES; *U.S. Private*, pg. 1277
DRICONEQ AB—See Mincon Group PLC; *Int'l*, pg. 4900
DRICONEQ PRODUCTION AB—See Mincon Group PLC; *Int'l*, pg. 4900
DRI CORPORATION; *U.S. Private*, pg. 1277
DRI-EAZ PRODUCTS, INC.—See RPM International Inc.; *U.S. Public*, pg. 1816
DRI-EAZ PRODUCTS LIMITED—See RPM International Inc.; *U.S. Public*, pg. 1816
DRI ENTERPRISES LTD.; *U.S. Private*, pg. 1277
DRIESSEN WATER I INC.; *U.S. Private*, pg. 1277
DRIFT EXPLORATION DRILLING INC.—See Orbit Garant Drilling Inc.; *Int'l*, pg. 5614
DRIFTLESS GLEN DISTILLERY LLC; *U.S. Private*, pg. 1277
DRIFT SUPERSAND (PROPRIETARY) LIMITED—See Consolidated Infrastructure Group Limited; *Int'l*, pg. 1771
DRIFTWOOD CATERING, LLC; *U.S. Private*, pg. 1277
DRIFTWOOD DAIRY HOLDING CORPORATION—See Vietnam Dairy Products Joint Stock Company; *Int'l*, pg. 8198
DRIFTWOOD DAIRY—See Vietnam Dairy Products Joint Stock Company; *Int'l*, pg. 8198
DRIFTWOOD GARDEN CENTER; *U.S. Private*, pg. 1277
DRIFTWOOD HOSPITALITY MANAGEMENT, LLC; *U.S. Private*, pg. 1277
DRIFTWOOD LNG LLC—See Woodside Energy Group Ltd; *Int'l*, pg. 8450
DRIGGS CORPORATION; *U.S. Private*, pg. 1277
DRILLCUT LIMITED—See GLORY FLAME HOLDINGS LIMITED; *Int'l*, pg. 3009
DRILLERS SERVICE, LLC—See Franklin Electric Co., Inc.; *U.S. Public*, pg. 878
DRILLHOLE SURVEYING INSTRUMENTS (PTY) LTD—See Imdex Limited; *Int'l*, pg. 3623
DRILL INC.—See Dentsu Group Inc.; *Int'l*, pg. 2039
DRILLING ENGINEERS INC.—See Terracon Consultants, Inc.; *U.S. Private*, pg. 3970
DRILLING EQUIPMENT AND CHEMICAL COMPANY—See The Olayan Group; *Int'l*, pg. 7672
DRILLING & PRODUCTION RESOURCES, INC.—See Parker Hannifin Corporation; *U.S. Public*, pg. 1641
DRILLING RESEARCH & DEVELOPMENT CORPORATION—See Weatherford International plc; *U.S. Public*, pg. 2339
DRILLING TOOLS AUSTRALIA PTY. LTD.—See Robit Plc; *Int'l*, pg. 6370
DRILLING TOOLS INTERNATIONAL CORP.; *U.S. Public*, pg. 688
DRILLING TOOLS INTERNATIONAL, INC.—See Drilling Tools International Corp.; *U.S. Public*, pg. 688
DRILLISCH LOGISTIK GMBH—See United Internet AG; *Int'l*, pg. 8069
DRILLISCH ONLINE GMBH—See United Internet AG; *Int'l*, pg. 8069
DRILLISCH TELECOM GMBH—See United Internet AG; *Int'l*, pg. 8069

DRILLOT CORPORATION; *U.S. Private*, pg. 1277
DRILL RIGS AUSTRALIA PTY. LTD.—See Perenti Global Limited; *Int'l*, pg. 5798
DRILLSCAN EUROPE SAS—See Helmerich & Payne, Inc.; *U.S. Public*, pg. 1024
DRILLSCAN SAS—See Helmerich & Payne, Inc.; *U.S. Public*, pg. 1024
DRILLSCAN US, INC.—See Helmerich & Payne, Inc.; *U.S. Public*, pg. 1024
DRILLSPOT; *U.S. Private*, pg. 1277
DRIL-QUIP ASIA PACIFIC PTE LTD—See Dril-Quip, Inc.; *U.S. Public*, pg. 687
DRIL-QUIP DO BRASIL LTDA—See Dril-Quip, Inc.; *U.S. Public*, pg. 687
DRIL-QUIP (EUROPE) LIMITED—See Dril-Quip, Inc.; *U.S. Public*, pg. 687
DRIL-QUIP (EUROPE) LIMITED—See Dril-Quip, Inc.; *U.S. Public*, pg. 687
DRIL-QUIP (EUROPE) LIMITED—See Dril-Quip, Inc.; *U.S. Public*, pg. 687
DRIL-QUIP (EUROPE) LIMITED—See Dril-Quip, Inc.; *U.S. Public*, pg. 687
DRIL-QUIP, INC.; *U.S. Public*, pg. 687
DRIL-QUIP LONDON—See Dril-Quip, Inc.; *U.S. Public*, pg. 687
DRIL-QUIP NEW ORLEANS—See Dril-Quip, Inc.; *U.S. Public*, pg. 687
DRIL-QUIP (NIGERIA) LTD—See Dril-Quip, Inc.; *U.S. Public*, pg. 687
DRIL-QUIP TIW MEXICO S.A. DE C.V.—See Dril-Quip, Inc.; *U.S. Public*, pg. 687
DRILTECH GEOTECHNICAL ENGINEERING LIMITED—See Chinney Alliance Group Limited; *Int'l*, pg. 1570
DRI MARK PRODUCTS, INC.; *U.S. Private*, pg. 1277
DRIMM SAS—See Groupe Seche SAS; *Int'l*, pg. 3110
DRINA OSIGURANJE A.D.; *Int'l*, pg. 2204
DRINA RESOURCES D.O.O.—See Terra Balcanica Resources Corporation; *Int'l*, pg. 7566
DRINA TRANS A.D.; *Int'l*, pg. 2204
DRING AIR CONDITIONING & HEATING, LP; *U.S. Private*, pg. 1277
DRINGENBERG GMBH BETRIEBSEINRICHTUNGEN—See Wurth Verwaltungsgesellschaft mbH; *Int'l*, pg. 8504
DRINGENBERG POLSKA SP. Z O.O.—See Wurth Verwaltungsgesellschaft mbH; *Int'l*, pg. 8504
DR. ING. GOSSLING MASCHINENFABRIK GMBH; *Int'l*, pg. 2192
DR. ING. H.C. F. PORSCHE AG—See Porsche Automobil Holding SE; *Int'l*, pg. 5926
DR. ING. K. BUSCH GMBH; *Int'l*, pg. 2192
DRINKALL DEAN (LONDON) LIMITED—See Paragon Entertainment Limited; *Int'l*, pg. 5736
DRINKFINITY USA, INC.—See PepsiCo, Inc.; *U.S. Public*, pg. 1668
DRINKS HUB ASIA PTE LTD—See Atlan Holdings Berhad; *Int'l*, pg. 674
DRINKSTAR GMBH—See Symrise AG; *Int'l*, pg. 7380
DRINKSTATION, INC.—See PepsiCo, Inc.; *U.S. Public*, pg. 1668
DRIP FERTIGATION RESEARCH CO., LTD.—See OAT Agrio Co., Ltd.; *Int'l*, pg. 5507
DRI RELAYS INC.—See TE Connectivity Ltd.; *Int'l*, pg. 7494
THE DRISCOLL AGENCY, INC.—See Cross Financial Corporation; *U.S. Private*, pg. 1105
DRISCOLL'S, INC; *U.S. Private*, pg. 1277
DRISCOLL'S OF FLORIDA, INC.—See Driscoll's, Inc; *U.S. Private*, pg. 1278
DRISHA INSTITUTE FOR JEWISH EDUCATION, INC.; *U.S. Private*, pg. 1278
DRISHTICON INC.; *U.S. Private*, pg. 1278
DRI-THE VOICE OF THE DEFENSE BAR; *U.S. Private*, pg. 1277
DRITTE ADLER REAL ESTATE GMBH & CO. KG—See ADLER Group SA; *Int'l*, pg. 150
DRITTE CORSA VERWALTUNGSGESELLSCHAFT GMBH—See Mallinckrodt Public Limited Company; *Int'l*, pg. 4663
DRITTE KORSCHENBROICHER ARMATUREN GMBH—See Pentair plc; *Int'l*, pg. 5789
DRITTE TENVA PROPERTY GMBH NETTETAL—See Avnet, Inc.; *U.S. Public*, pg. 252
DRIVE AUTO, LLC—See Sinclair, Inc.; *U.S. Public*, pg. 1885
DRIVECLEVER A/S—See MEKO AB; *Int'l*, pg. 4805
DRIVE INDIA ENTERPRISE SOLUTIONS LIMITED—See TVS Logistics Services Ltd.; *Int'l*, pg. 7989
DRIVE INSURANCE HOLDINGS, INC.—See The Progressive Corporation; *U.S. Public*, pg. 2124
DRIVEITAWAY HOLDINGS, INC.; *U.S. Public*, pg. 688
DRIVE KAWASAKI BRISTOL—See DRIVE Motor Retail Limited; *Int'l*, pg. 2204
DRIVEK ITALIA S.R.L.—See Motork Plc; *Int'l*, pg. 5054
DRIVEKORE INC.; *U.S. Private*, pg. 1278
DRIVELINES NW, INC.—See Platinum Equity, LLC; *U.S. Private*, pg. 3209

COMPANY NAME INDEX

DRIVELINK NETWORK LIMITED—See The Logistics Partnership LLP; *Int'l*, pg. 7664
DRIVELOG GMBH—See Robert Bosch GmbH; *Int'l*, pg. 6360
DRIVE MOTOR RETAIL LIMITED; *Int'l*, pg. 2204
DRIVE MOTOR RETAIL LIMITED—See General Motors Company; *U.S. Public*, pg. 928
DRIVEN ASIA-PACIFIC PTE. LTD.—See WEDS CO., LTD.; *Int'l*, pg. 8367
DRIVEN BRANDS HOLDINGS INC.; *U.S. Public*, pg. 688
DRIVEN BRANDS, INC.—See Roark Capital Group Inc.; *U.S. Private*, pg. 3454
DRIVEN BY RIIDE DATA LTD.—See MBH Corporation Plc; *Int'l*, pg. 4752
DRIVEN DELIVERIES, INC.—See Stem Holdings, Inc.; *U.S. Public*, pg. 1945
DRIVE NEW JERSEY INSURANCE COMPANY—See The Progressive Corporation; *U.S. Public*, pg. 2124
DRIVEN, INC.; *U.S. Private*, pg. 1278
DRIVENMEDIA; *U.S. Private*, pg. 1278
DRIVENOW BELGIUM S.P.R.L.—See Bayerische Motoren Werke Aktiengesellschaft; *Int'l*, pg. 912
DRIVENOW ITALY S.R.L.—See Bayerische Motoren Werke Aktiengesellschaft; *Int'l*, pg. 912
DRIVE-O-RAMA INC.; *U.S. Private*, pg. 1278
DRIVER CONSULT LIMITED—See Diales; *Int'l*, pg. 2104
DRIVER CONSULT (OMAN) LLC—See Diales; *Int'l*, pg. 2104
DRIVERGE VEHICLE INNOVATIONS, LLC.; *U.S. Private*, pg. 1278
DRIVER-HARRIS COMPANY; *U.S. Private*, pg. 1278
DRIVER HELLAS C.S.A.—See China National Chemical Corporation; *Int'l*, pg. 1528
DRIVER ITALIA S.P.A.—See China National Chemical Corporation; *Int'l*, pg. 1528
DRIVER PIPELINE COMPANY INC.; *U.S. Private*, pg. 1278
DRIVER PROJECT SERVICES (UAE) LLC—See Diales; *Int'l*, pg. 2104
DRIVERS ALERT, LLC—See MidOcean Partners, LLP; *U.S. Private*, pg. 2717
DRIVERS HISTORY; *U.S. Private*, pg. 1278
DRIVERSIDE, INC.—See Advance Auto Parts, Inc.; *U.S. Public*, pg. 44
DRIVER TRAINING & SOLUTIONS, LLC.—See TransSystem Inc.; *U.S. Private*, pg. 4206
DRIVER TRETT (CANADA) LTD.—See Diales; *Int'l*, pg. 2104
DRIVER TRETT (HONG KONG) LTD.—See Diales; *Int'l*, pg. 2104
DRIVER TRETT (SINGAPORE) PTE. LTD.—See Diales; *Int'l*, pg. 2104
THE DRIVERY GMBH—See Hella GmbH & Co. KGaA; *Int'l*, pg. 3332
DRIVE & SAVE PROPRIETARY LIMITED—See Karooooo Ltd.; *Int'l*, pg. 4085
DRIVESAVERS DATA RECOVERY, INC.; *U.S. Private*, pg. 1278
DRIVES & CONVEYORS INC.; *U.S. Private*, pg. 1278
DRIVESERVICE SRL—See FLY Srl; *Int'l*, pg. 2715
DRIVE SHACK INC.; *U.S. Public*, pg. 688
DRIVE SHACK ORLANDO LLC—See Drive Shack Inc.; *U.S. Public*, pg. 688
DRIVESHAFT PARTS PTY. LTD.—See Invicta Holdings Limited; *Int'l*, pg. 3788
DRIVE SOURCE INTERNATIONAL, INC.—See TGP Investments, LLC; *U.S. Private*, pg. 3979
DRIVETECH (UK) LIMITED—See TowerBrook Capital Partners, L.P.; *U.S. Private*, pg. 4194
DRIVETECH (UK) LIMITED—See Warburg Pincus LLC; *U.S. Private*, pg. 4436
DRIVETEST, LLC.—See Mercedes-Benz Group AG; *Int'l*, pg. 4824
DRIVETIME AUTOMOTIVE GROUP, INC.; *U.S. Private*, pg. 1278
DRIVETRAIN AUSTRALIA PTY. LTD.—See Engenco Limited; *Int'l*, pg. 2427
DRIVE TRAIN INDUSTRIES, INC.; *U.S. Private*, pg. 1278
DRIVETRAIN PHILIPPINES INC.—See Engenco Limited; *Int'l*, pg. 2427
DRIVETRAIN POWER AND PROPULSION PTY. LTD.—See Engenco Limited; *Int'l*, pg. 2427
DRIVETRAIN SINGAPORE PTE. LTD.—See Engenco Limited; *Int'l*, pg. 2427
DRIVE VAUXHALL ALDERSHOT—See DRIVE Motor Retail Limited; *Int'l*, pg. 2204
DRIVE VAUXHALL BRISTOL—See DRIVE Motor Retail Limited; *Int'l*, pg. 2204
DRIVE VAUXHALL BURY ST. EDMUNDS—See DRIVE Motor Retail Limited; *Int'l*, pg. 2204
DRIVE VAUXHALL CLEVEDON—See DRIVE Motor Retail Limited; *Int'l*, pg. 2204
DRIVE VAUXHALL HAVERHILL—See DRIVE Motor Retail Limited; *Int'l*, pg. 2204
DRIVEWAY FINANCE CORPORATION—See Lithia Motors, Inc.; *U.S. Public*, pg. 1322
DRIVEWAY MOTORS, LLC—See Lithia Motors, Inc.; *U.S. Public*, pg. 1322

DRIVEWAY SOFTWARE CORP.—See Earnix Ltd.; *Int'l*, pg. 2267
DRIVHUSET AB—See Addtech AB; *Int'l*, pg. 132
THE DRIVING FORCE, INC.; *Int'l*, pg. 7637
DRIVING PLUS LIMITED—See Staffline Group PLC; *Int'l*, pg. 7162
DRIV-LOK, INC.; *U.S. Private*, pg. 1278
DR. JAY'S INC.; *U.S. Private*, pg. 1271
DR. JOSEF RAABE SLOVENSKO, S. R. O.—See Ernst Klett AG; *Int'l*, pg. 2495
DR JOSEF RAABE SPOLKA WYDAWNICZA SP. Z O.O.—See Ernst Klett AG; *Int'l*, pg. 2495
DR. KLEINE PHARMA GMBH—See Oakley Capital Limited; *Int'l*, pg. 5504
DR KULICH PHARMA S.R.O.—See Fagron NV; *Int'l*, pg. 2603
DR. KURT WOLFF GMBH & CO. KG; *Int'l*, pg. 2194
DR LALCHANDANI LABS LTD.; *Int'l*, pg. 2189
DR. LAL PATH LABS BANGLADESH PRIVATE LIMITED—See Dr. Lal PathLabs Ltd.; *Int'l*, pg. 2194
DR. LAL PATHLABS LTD.; *Int'l*, pg. 2194
DR. LAL PATHLABS NEPAL PRIVATE LIMITED—See Dr. Lal PathLabs Ltd.; *Int'l*, pg. 2194
DR. LANGE NEDERLAND B.V.—See Danaher Corporation; *U.S. Public*, pg. 626
D&R LATHIAN LLC; *U.S. Private*, pg. 1138
DR. LAUK & DR. BREITLING GMBH—See Eurofins Scientific S.E.; *Int'l*, pg. 2536
DR. LEONARD HEALTH CARE CATALOG; *U.S. Private*, pg. 1271
DRL GROUP LTD.—See American Food Distributors; *U.S. Private*, pg. 234
D & R LOWE CATERING SUPPLIES (PTY) LIMITED—See The Bidvest Group Limited; *Int'l*, pg. 7624
DR. MACH GMBH & CO. KG; *Int'l*, pg. 2194
D&R MACHINE COMPANY, INC.—See CORE Industrial Partners, LLC; *U.S. Private*, pg. 1048
DR MAGNET S.R.O.—See Centene Corporation; *U.S. Public*, pg. 468
DR MARCUS COONEY & ASSOCIATES PTE LTD—See Qualitas Medical Group Limited; *Int'l*, pg. 6151
DR. MARTENS AIRWAIR USA LLC—See Permira Advisers LLP; *Int'l*, pg. 5808
DR. MAX BDC, S.R.O.—See Penta Investments Limited; *Int'l*, pg. 5788
DR. MAX SP. Z O.O.—See Penta Investments Limited; *Int'l*, pg. 5788
DR+ MEDICAL & PAINCARE MARSILING—See Singapore Paincare Holdings Limited; *Int'l*, pg. 6941
DR. MERTENS EDELSTAHLHANDEL GMBH—See ThyssenKrupp AG; *Int'l*, pg. 7724
DRM INC.; *U.S. Private*, pg. 1278
DRM PARTNERS, INC.; *U.S. Private*, pg. 1279
DRM SISTEME ELECTRICE SRL—See Draexlmaier Gruppe; *Int'l*, pg. 2198
DROBO, INC.—See StorCentric, Inc.; *U.S. Private*, pg. 3831
DROEGE GROUP AG; *Int'l*, pg. 2204
DR. OETKER VERLAG KG—See Dr. August Oetker KG; *Int'l*, pg. 2190
DROFUS AB—See Nemetschek SE; *Int'l*, pg. 5195
DROFUS AS—See Nemetschek SE; *Int'l*, pg. 5195
DROFUS PTY. LTD.—See Nemetschek SE; *Int'l*, pg. 5195
DROGA5, LLC—See Accenture plc; *Int'l*, pg. 88
DROGA5—See Accenture plc; *Int'l*, pg. 88
DROGA CHOCOLATES, LLC—See Hilton Grand Vacations Inc.; *U.S. Public*, pg. 1039
DROGA KOLINSKA D.D.—See ATLANTIC GRUPA d.d.; *Int'l*, pg. 675
DROGARIA MAIS ECONOMICA S.A.—See Brazil Pharma S.A.; *Int'l*, pg. 1143
DROGARIA ONOFRE LTDA.—See Raia Drogasil S.A.; *Int'l*, pg. 6182
DROGHEDA INDEPENDENT COMPANY LIMITED—See Mediahuis Partners NV; *Int'l*, pg. 4772
DROGHEDA INDEPENDENT COMPANY LIMITED—See VP Exploitatie N.V.; *Int'l*, pg. 8311
DROGHERIA E ALIMENTARI SPA—See McCormick & Company, Incorporated; *U.S. Public*, pg. 1404
DROGOBYCH TRUCK CRANE PLANT PJSC; *Int'l*, pg. 2205
DROGOMEX SP. Z O.O.—See CRH plc; *Int'l*, pg. 1844
DROGUERIA DE LA VILLA INC.—See FMC Inc.; *U.S. Private*, pg. 1554
DROISYS INC.; *U.S. Private*, pg. 1279
DR. O.K. WACK CHEMIE GMBH; *Int'l*, pg. 2194
DROMEAS S.A; *Int'l*, pg. 2205
DROMOST SP. Z.O.O.—See PBG S.A.; *Int'l*, pg. 5765
DRONCO FRANCE SARL—See Jason Industries, Inc.; *U.S. Private*, pg. 2189
DRONCO GMBH—See Jason Industries, Inc.; *U.S. Private*, pg. 2189
DRONCO SCANDINAVIA AB—See Jason Industries, Inc.; *U.S. Private*, pg. 2189
DRON & DICKSON LTD.; *Int'l*, pg. 2205
DRONEACHARYA AERIAL INNOVATIONS LIMITED; *Int'l*, pg. 2206
DRONE DELIVERY CANADA CORP.; *Int'l*, pg. 2205

DR. REDDY'S LABORATORIES LIMITED

DRONE GUARDER, INC.—See Video River Networks, Inc.; *U.S. Public*, pg. 2297
DRONEMATRIX N.V.—See Nordic Unmanned ASA; *Int'l*, pg. 5423
DRONESEED CO.; *U.S. Private*, pg. 1279
DRONE SERVICES USA, INC.; *U.S. Private*, pg. 1279
DRONESHIELD LIMITED; *Int'l*, pg. 2206
DRONEUP LLC; *U.S. Private*, pg. 1279
DRONE USA, LLC—See Bantec, Inc.; *U.S. Public*, pg. 275
DRONE VOLT SA; *Int'l*, pg. 2206
DROPBOX, INC.; *U.S. Public*, pg. 688
DROPLETS, INC.—See Vivox, Inc.; *U.S. Private*, pg. 4406
DROPMYSITE PTE. LTD.—See Dropsuite Limited; *Int'l*, pg. 2206
DROPOFF, INC.; *U.S. Private*, pg. 1279
DROP S.A.; *Int'l*, pg. 2206
DROP STOP, LLC; *U.S. Private*, pg. 1279
DROPSUITE LIMITED; *Int'l*, pg. 2206
DROR ORTHO-DESIGN, INC.; *U.S. Public*, pg. 688
DROSED S.A.—See LDC SA; *Int'l*, pg. 4430
DROSED—See LDC SA; *Int'l*, pg. 4430
DROSED SUROWIEC—See LDC SA; *Int'l*, pg. 4431
DROUBAY AUTOMOTIVE GROUP INCORPORATED; *U.S. Private*, pg. 1279
DROVERS ID PTY LTD—See Merck & Co., Inc.; *U.S. Public*, pg. 1416
DROZAPOL-PROFIL S.A.; *Int'l*, pg. 2206
DR. PARK AVE.; *U.S. Private*, pg. 1271
DR. PAUL LOHMANN GMBH KG; *Int'l*, pg. 2194
DRP CONSULTING, INC.—See Twining Inc.; *U.S. Private*, pg. 4266
DR. PENG TELECOM & MEDIA GROUP CO., LTD.; *Int'l*, pg. 2194
DR. PEPPER BOTTLING CO. ELK CITY; *U.S. Private*, pg. 1271
DR. PEPPER/SEVEN UP BOTTLING GROUP MIDWEST DIVISION—See JAB Holding Company S.a.r.l.; *Int'l*, pg. 3862
DR. PEPPER/SEVEN-UP BOTTLING GROUP OF ST. LOUIS—See JAB Holding Company S.a.r.l.; *Int'l*, pg. 3862
DR. PEPPER/SEVEN UP BOTTLING GROUP—See JAB Holding Company S.a.r.l.; *Int'l*, pg. 3862
DR. PEPPER/SEVEN UP BOTTLING GROUP—See JAB Holding Company S.a.r.l.; *Int'l*, pg. 3862
DR. PEPPER/SEVEN UP, INC.—See JAB Holding Company S.a.r.l.; *Int'l*, pg. 3862
DR. PEPPER/SEVEN UP MANUFACTURING COMPANY—See JAB Holding Company S.a.r.l.; *Int'l*, pg. 3862
DR PEPPER SNAPPLE GROUP, INC.—See JAB Holding Company S.a.r.l.; *Int'l*, pg. 3862
DR PEPPER SNAPPLE GROUP, INC. - WILLIAMSON—See JAB Holding Company S.a.r.l.; *Int'l*, pg. 3862
DR. PHIL COSMETICS INC.—See KOSE Corporation; *Int'l*, pg. 4290
DR POWER LLC—See Dead River Company; *U.S. Private*, pg. 1182
DR. PROGRAM CO., LTD.—See Taisho Pharmaceutical Holdings Co., Ltd; *Int'l*, pg. 7417
DR. REDDY'S LABORATORIES (AUSTRALIA) PTY. LIMITED—See Dr. Reddy's Laboratories Limited; *Int'l*, pg. 2195
DR. REDDY'S LABORATORIES (EU) LIMITED—See Dr. Reddy's Laboratories Limited; *Int'l*, pg. 2195
DR. REDDY'S LABORATORIES, INC.—See Dr. Reddy's Laboratories Limited; *Int'l*, pg. 2195
DR. REDDY'S LABORATORIES LIMITED; *Int'l*, pg. 2194
DR. REDDY'S LABORATORIES LLC—See Dr. Reddy's Laboratories Limited; *Int'l*, pg. 2195
DR. REDDY'S LABORATORIES LOUISIANA LLC—See Dr. Reddy's Laboratories Limited; *Int'l*, pg. 2195
DR. REDDY'S LABORATORIES NEW YORK, INC—See Dr. Reddy's Laboratories Limited; *Int'l*, pg. 2195
DR. REDDY'S LABORATORIES (PROPRIETARY) LIMITED—See Dr. Reddy's Laboratories Limited; *Int'l*, pg. 2195
DR. REDDY'S LABORATORIES ROMANIA SRL—See Dr. Reddy's Laboratories Limited; *Int'l*, pg. 2195
DR. REDDY'S LABORATORIES—See Dr. Reddy's Laboratories Limited; *Int'l*, pg. 2195
DR. REDDY'S LABORATORIES TENNESSEE LLC—See NMC Health PLC; *Int'l*, pg. 5392
DR. REDDY'S NEW ZEALAND LTD.—See Dr. Reddy's Laboratories Limited; *Int'l*, pg. 2195
DRS C3 & AVIATION COMPANY—See Leonardo S.p.A.; *Int'l*, pg. 4458
DRS C3 SYSTEMS, INC.—See Leonardo S.p.A.; *Int'l*, pg. 4459
DRS C3 SYSTEMS, INC.—See Leonardo S.p.A.; *Int'l*, pg. 4459
DRS C3 SYSTEMS, INC.—See Leonardo S.p.A.; *Int'l*, pg. 4459
DRS C3 SYSTEMS, LLC—See Leonardo S.p.A.; *Int'l*, pg. 4459
DRS CENGEN, LLC—See Leonardo S.p.A.; *Int'l*, pg. 4459
DR. SCHELLER COSMETICS AG—See JAB Holding Company S.a.r.l.; *Int'l*, pg. 3860

DR. SCHELLER COSMETICS POLSKA SP. Z O.O.—See JAB Holding Company S.a.r.l.; *Int'l*, pg. 3860
DR. SCHMIDT INTRAOCULARLINSEN GMBH—See HumanOptics AG; *Int'l*, pg. 3530
DR. SCHMITT GMBH—See MLP SE; *Int'l*, pg. 5004
DR SCHNABEL GMBH—See SGL Carbon SE; *Int'l*, pg. 6741
DR. SCHUMACHER GMBH; *Int'l*, pg. 2195
DRS COMPANY LIMITED—See Mitsubishi HC Capital Inc.; *Int'l*, pg. 4950
DRS CONSOLIDATED CONTROLS, INC.—See Leonardo S.p.A.; *Int'l*, pg. 4459
DRS DATA & IMAGING SYSTEMS INC—See Leonardo S.p.A.; *Int'l*, pg. 4459
DRS DATA & RESEARCH SERVICES PLC; *Int'l*, pg. 2206
DRS DATA SERVICES LIMITED—See DRS Data & Research Services Plc; *Int'l*, pg. 2206
DRS DEFENSE SOLUTIONS, LLC—See Leonardo S.p.A.; *Int'l*, pg. 4459
DRS DEFENSE TECHNICAL SERVICES, INC.—See Leonardo S.p.A.; *Int'l*, pg. 4459
DRS DILIP ROADLINES LTD.; *Int'l*, pg. 2206
DRS. ELLIS, ROJAS, ROSS & DEBS, INC.—See KKR & Co. Inc.; *U.S. Public*, pg. 1245
DRS ENVIRONMENTAL SYSTEMS, INC.—See Charlesbank Capital Partners, LLC; *U.S. Private*, pg. 855
DRS FERMONT—See Leonardo S.p.A.; *Int'l*, pg. 4459
DR. SHRINK, INC.; *U.S. Private*, pg. 1271
DRS ICAS LLC—See Leonardo S.p.A.; *Int'l*, pg. 4459
DRS IMAGING SERVICES, LLC—See The HiGro Group LLC; *U.S. Private*, pg. 4052
DRS INTEGRATED DEFENSE SYSTEMS AND SERVIES GROUP—See Leonardo S.p.A.; *Int'l*, pg. 4459
DRSMILE IBERIA S.L.—See Straumann Holding AG; *Int'l*, pg. 7237
DRSMILE ITALIA S.R.L.—See Straumann Holding AG; *Int'l*, pg. 7237
D.R. SMITH CO., INC.—See H.I.G. Capital, LLC; *U.S. Private*, pg. 1833
DR SMOOTHIE BRANDS—See Highlander Partners, LP.; *U.S. Private*, pg. 1939
DRS PIVOTAL POWER—See Leonardo S.p.A.; *Int'l*, pg. 4459
DRS POWER & CONTROL TECHNOLOGIES, INC.—See Leonardo S.p.A.; *Int'l*, pg. 4459
DRS POWER SOLUTIONS—See Leonardo S.p.A.; *Int'l*, pg. 4459
DRS POWER TECHNOLOGY, INC.—See Leonardo S.p.A.; *Int'l*, pg. 4459
DRS PRODUCT RETURNS LLC—See Leading Ridge Management, LLC; *U.S. Private*, pg. 2406
DRS RSTA, INC.—See Leonardo S.p.A.; *Int'l*, pg. 4459
DRS SIGNAL SOLUTIONS, INC.—See Leonardo S.p.A.; *Int'l*, pg. 4459
DRS SONETICOM INC—See Leonardo S.p.A.; *Int'l*, pg. 4459
DRS SURVEILLANCE SUPPORT SYSTEMS, INC.—See Leonardo S.p.A.; *Int'l*, pg. 4459
DRS SUSTAINMENT SYSTEMS, INC.—See Leonardo S.p.A.; *Int'l*, pg. 4459
DRS TECHNICAL SERVICES, INC.—See Leonardo S.p.A.; *Int'l*, pg. 4459
DRS TECHNOLOGIES CANADA LTD.—See DEV Information Technology Pvt. Ltd.; *Int'l*, pg. 2086
DRS TEST & ENERGY MANAGEMENT, LLC—See Leonardo S.p.A.; *Int'l*, pg. 4459
DR. SULAIMAN AL HABIB MEDICAL SERVICES GROUP COMPANY; *Int'l*, pg. 2195
DRT AMERICA, INC.—See Firmenich International SA; *Int'l*, pg. 2681
DRT-ANTHEA AROMA CHEMICALS PRIVATE LIMITED—See Firmenich International SA; *Int'l*, pg. 2679
DRT CYBER INC.—See VersaBank; *Int'l*, pg. 8173
DRTECH CORPORATION - DRTECH KOREA FACTORY—See DRTECH Corporation; *Int'l*, pg. 2206
DRTECH CORPORATION; *Int'l*, pg. 2206
DRTECH EUROPE GMBH—See DRTECH Corporation; *Int'l*, pg. 2206
DR. TECHN. JOSEF ZELISKO, FABRIK FUR ELEKTROTECHNIK UND MASCHINENBAU GES.MBH—See Knorr-Bremse AG; *Int'l*, pg. 4210
DR. TECHN. JOSEF ZELISKO GMBH—See Knorr-Bremse AG; *Int'l*, pg. 4211
DRTECH NORTH AMERICA INC—See DRTECH Corporation; *Int'l*, pg. 2206
DRTECH SHANGHAI CO, LTD—See DRTECH Corporation; *Int'l*, pg. 2206
DR. THEISS NATURWAREN GMBH; *Int'l*, pg. 2195
DR. THEISS NATURWAREN SARL—See Dr. Theiss Naturwaren GmbH; *Int'l*, pg. 2195
DR. THOMAS + PARTNER GMBH & CO. KG; *Int'l*, pg. 2195
DRT MFG. COMPANY; *U.S. Private*, pg. 1279
DR. TORRENTS, S.L.—See Tootsie Roll Industries, Inc.; *U.S. Public*, pg. 2163
DRT PINOVA INC.—See Firmenich International SA; *Int'l*, pg. 2679

DRT SPECIALTY CHEMICALS (WUXI) CO., LTD.—See Firmenich International SA; *Int'l*, pg. 2681
DRT STRATEGIES, INC.; *U.S. Private*, pg. 1279
DRT TRANSPORTATION; *U.S. Private*, pg. 1279
DRTV.AGENCY GMBH—See The Social Chain AG; *Int'l*, pg. 7687
DRUART S.A.—See Ackermans & van Haaren NV; *Int'l*, pg. 105
DRU BELGIUM—See DRU Verwarming B.V.; *Int'l*, pg. 2206
DRUCK.AT DRUCK- UND HANDELSGESELLSCHAFT GMBH—See Cimpress plc; *Int'l*, pg. 1609
DRUCKERFACHMANN.DE GMBH—See Droege Group AG; *Int'l*, pg. 2205
DRUCKFARBEN HELLAS A.E.B.E.—See Windmoeller & Hoelscher KG; *Int'l*, pg. 8425
DRUCKFARBEN HELLAS S.A.; *Int'l*, pg. 2206
DRUCKFARBEN ROMANIA S.R.L.—See Druckfarben Hellas S.A.; *Int'l*, pg. 2206
DRUCK- UND SPRITZGUSSWERK HETTICH GMBH & CO. KG—See Hettich Holding GmbH & Co. oHG; *Int'l*, pg. 3365
DRUG ABUSE AND COMPREHENSIVE COORDINATING OFFICE, INC.; *U.S. Private*, pg. 1279
DRUGASAR LTD.—See DRU Verwarming B.V.; *Int'l*, pg. 2206
DRUG DEV INC.—See IQVIA Holdings Inc.; *U.S. Public*, pg. 1168
DRUG EMPORIUM—See Gibson Merchandise Group Inc.; *U.S. Private*, pg. 1696
DRUG INFORMATION ASSOCIATION; *U.S. Private*, pg. 1279
DRUG PLASTICS CLOSURES—See Drug Plastics & Glass Co. Inc.; *U.S. Private*, pg. 1279
DRUG PLASTICS & GLASS CO. INC.; *U.S. Private*, pg. 1279
DRUG SAFETY ALLIANCE, INC.—See Clayton, Dubilier & Rice, LLC; *U.S. Private*, pg. 927
DRUGSTORE CHAMPS-ELYSEES SNC—See Publicis Groupe S.A.; *Int'l*, pg. 6098
DRUGSTORE.COM, INC.—See Walgreens Boots Alliance, Inc.; *U.S. Public*, pg. 2324
DRUG TRANSPORT INC.; *U.S. Private*, pg. 1279
DRUID CAPITAL PARTNERS, LLC; *U.S. Private*, pg. 1279
DRUID GROUP LIMITED—See Sopra Steria Group S.A.; *Int'l*, pg. 7111
DRUID RIDGE CEMETERY—See Service Corporation International; *U.S. Public*, pg. 1871
THE DRUKER COMPANY, LTD.; *U.S. Private*, pg. 4023
DRUKWERKDEAL.NL PRODUCTIE B.V.—See Cimpress plc; *Int'l*, pg. 1609
DRULEY ENTERPRISES INC.; *U.S. Private*, pg. 1279
DRUM HILL FORD, INC.; *U.S. Private*, pg. 1279
DRUM HOUSING ASSOCIATION LIMITED—See Radian Group Limited; *Int'l*, pg. 6174
DRUM INCOME PLUS REIT PLC—See Pollen Street Limited; *Int'l*, pg. 5910
DRUMMOND BANKING COMPANY; *U.S. Private*, pg. 1279
DRUMMOND COMMUNITY BANK—See Drummond Banking Company; *U.S. Private*, pg. 1279
DRUMMOND COMPANY, INC. - ABC COKE DIVISION—See Drummond Company, Inc.; *U.S. Private*, pg. 1280
DRUMMOND COMPANY, INC.; *U.S. Private*, pg. 1280
DRUMMONDS LIMITED—See Liffey Mills Ltd.; *Int'l*, pg. 4495
DRUMMOND VENTURES CORP.; *Int'l*, pg. 2206
DRUMZ PLC; *Int'l*, pg. 2206
DRUPAL CONNECT; *U.S. Private*, pg. 1280
DRURY COMMUNICATIONS LIMITED; *Int'l*, pg. 2206
DRURY DEVELOPMENT CORP.; *U.S. Private*, pg. 1280
DRURY DEVELOPMENT—See Drury Development Corp.; *U.S. Private*, pg. 1280
DRURY HOTELS COMPANY, LLC—See Drury Inn Inc.; *U.S. Private*, pg. 1280
DRURY INN INC.; *U.S. Private*, pg. 1280
DRURY INN POPLAR BLUFF INC.—See Drury Inn Inc.; *U.S. Private*, pg. 1280
DRURY INNS INC.—See Drury Inn Inc.; *U.S. Private*, pg. 1280
DRURY INN & SUITES STADIUM—See Drury Inn Inc.; *U.S. Private*, pg. 1280
DRURY SOUTH, INC.—See Drury Inn Inc.; *U.S. Private*, pg. 1280
DRURY SOUTHWEST, INC.—See Drury Inn Inc.; *U.S. Private*, pg. 1280
DRURY SURGERY LIMITED—See Green Cross Health Limited; *Int'l*, pg. 3070
DRUSTVENI STANDARD CAJAVEC A.D.; *Int'l*, pg. 2206
DRUSTVO ZA POSREDOVANJE U OSIGURANJU—See Willis Towers Watson Public Limited Company; *Int'l*, pg. 8414
DRUSTVO ZA UPRAVUVANJE SO ZADOLZITELNI I DOBOVOLIN PENZISKO FONDOVI SAVA PENZISKO DRUSTVO A.D—See Pozavarovalnica Sava, d.d.; *Int'l*, pg. 5949
DRU VERWARMING B.V.; *Int'l*, pg. 2206
DRUZHBA AD; *Int'l*, pg. 2206

DRUZHBA-NOVA ALLC—See Kernel Holding S.A.; *Int'l*, pg. 4137
DRVNA INDUSTRIJA SPACVA D.D; *Int'l*, pg. 2206
DR. VON FROREICH - BIOSCIENTIA GMBH—See Sonic Healthcare Limited; *Int'l*, pg. 7097
DR WARREN E SMITH COMMUNITY MENTAL HEALTH MENTAL RETARDATION & SUBSTANCE ABUSE CENTERS; *U.S. Private*, pg. 1271
DRW - DELITZSCHER ANLAGENBAU GMBH—See VINCI S.A.; *Int'l*, pg. 8216
DRW HOLDINGS, LLC; *U.S. Private*, pg. 1280
DR. WILLIAM MERTENS GMBH—See Swiss Steel Holding AG; *Int'l*, pg. 7373
DR. WILLMAR SCHWABE GMBH & CO. KG; *Int'l*, pg. 2195
DR. WILLMAR SCHWABE INDIA PVT. LTD.—See Dr. Willmar Schwabe GmbH & Co. KG; *Int'l*, pg. 2195
DRW INVESTMENTS (UK) LTD.—See DRW Holdings, LLC; *U.S. Private*, pg. 1280
DR. W. KOLB AG—See Kuala Lumpur Kepong Berhad; *Int'l*, pg. 4318
DR. W. KOLB HOLDING AG—See Kuala Lumpur Kepong Berhad; *Int'l*, pg. 4318
DR. W. KOLB NETHERLANDS BV—See Kuala Lumpur Kepong Berhad; *Int'l*, pg. 4318
DR. WOLMAN GMBH—See BASF SE; *Int'l*, pg. 883
DR.WU SKINCARE CO., LTD.; *Int'l*, pg. 2196
DRX DISTRIBUTION MANAGEMENT, INC.—See Pacific Equity Partners Pty. Limited; *Int'l*, pg. 5689
DRYCE ITALIA S.R.L.—See Mitsubishi Chemical Group Corporation; *Int'l*, pg. 4937
DRY CELL & STORAGE BATTERY JSC; *Int'l*, pg. 2206
DRYCE S.R.L.—See Mitsubishi Chemical Group Corporation; *Int'l*, pg. 4936
DRYCLEAN USA DEVELOPMENT CORP—See EVI Industries, Inc.; *U.S. Public*, pg. 803
DRYCLEAN USA LICENSE CORP—See EVI Industries, Inc.; *U.S. Public*, pg. 803
DRYCO CONSTRUCTION, INC.; *U.S. Private*, pg. 1280
DRYCO LLC—See I Squared Capital Advisors (US) LLC; *U.S. Private*, pg. 2021
DRYCO LLC—See TDR Capital LLP; *Int'l*, pg. 7490
DRY CREEK STRUCTURES; *U.S. Private*, pg. 1280
DRY CREEK SURGERY CENTER, LLC—See UnitedHealth Group Incorporated; *U.S. Public*, pg. 2240
DRYDEN MUTUAL INSURANCE COMPANY; *U.S. Private*, pg. 1281
DRYDEN & PALMER COMPANY—See Founders Equity, Inc.; *U.S. Private*, pg. 1581
DRYDOCKS WORLD LLC—See Dubai World Corporation; *Int'l*, pg. 2222
DRYDON EQUIPMENT, INC.—See DXP Enterprises, Inc.; *U.S. Public*, pg. 697
DRYERTECH INDUSTRIES LTD.; *Int'l*, pg. 2207
DRYFIX GMBH—See Wienerberger AG; *Int'l*, pg. 8405
DRY FLY CAPITAL LLC; *U.S. Private*, pg. 1280
DRYFRUIT FACTORY LLP—See Span Divergent Ltd.; *Int'l*, pg. 7124
DRY ICE CORP.—See American Compressed Gases Inc.; *U.S. Private*, pg. 227
DRY LAKE WIND POWER II, LLC—See Iberdrola, S.A.; *Int'l*, pg. 3570
DRYLOCK TECHNOLOGIES NV; *Int'l*, pg. 2207
DRYMALLA CONSTRUCTION COMPANY; *U.S. Private*, pg. 1281
DRYMASTER RESTORATION—See BMS CAT, Inc.; *U.S. Private*, pg. 601
DRYMIX LTD.—See United Basalt Products Limited; *Int'l*, pg. 8065
DRYPATROL, LLC—See FirstService Corporation; *Int'l*, pg. 2691
DRY-PRO BASEMENT SYSTEMS, INC.; *U.S. Private*, pg. 1280
DRYSDALE PROPERTIES LTD—See Bank of Cyprus Holdings Public Limited Company; *Int'l*, pg. 842
DRYSDALES INC.—See Boot Barn Holdings, Inc.; *U.S. Public*, pg. 368
DRYSHIPS INC.; *Int'l*, pg. 2207
DRYSON AB—See Litorina Capital Management AB; *Int'l*, pg. 4528
DRY STORAGE CORPORATION; *U.S. Private*, pg. 1280
DRY SYSTEMS TECHNOLOGIES, INC.—See Alpha Natural Resources, Inc.; *U.S. Private*, pg. 199
DRYTAC CORPORATION; *U.S. Private*, pg. 1281
DRYVE INC.; *U.S. Private*, pg. 1281
DRYVIT HOLDINGS, INC.—See RPM International Inc.; *U.S. Public*, pg. 1819
DRYVIT SYSTEMS CANADA LTD.—See RPM International Inc.; *U.S. Public*, pg. 1819
DRYVIT SYSTEMS, INC.—See RPM International Inc.; *U.S. Public*, pg. 1819
DRYVIT SYSTEMS USA (EUROPE) SP. Z O.O.—See RPM International Inc.; *U.S. Public*, pg. 1819
DRYVIT UK LIMITED—See RPM International Inc.; *U.S. Public*, pg. 1819
DS4 SAL.—See EuroGroup Laminations S.p.A.; *Int'l*, pg. 2552
DSA FINANCIAL CORP.; *U.S. Public*, pg. 688

COMPANY NAME INDEX

DS ALL CO., LTD—See Thonburi Healthcare Group PCL; *Int'l*, pg. 7716
DS ALL CO., LTD.—See Thonburi Healthcare Group PCL; *Int'l*, pg. 7716
D&S ANASTOPOULOS SA; *Int'l*, pg. 1899
DSA ONCORE; *U.S. Private*, pg. 1281
DSA-SOFTWARE, INC.—See Distribution Services of America, Inc.; *U.S. Private*, pg. 1239
DSA TECHNOLOGIES INC.—See Executech Utah, LLC; *U.S. Private*, pg. 1447
DSB CO., LTD.—See Nomura Research Institute, Ltd.; *Int'l*, pg. 5413
THE D.S. BROWN COMPANY—See Gibraltar Industries, Inc.; *U.S. Public*, pg. 936
D-SCAN INC.—See Levi Strauss & Co.; *U.S. Public*, pg. 1309
DS CAPITAL, LLC; *U.S. Private*, pg. 1281
D&S CAR WASH EQUIPMENT CO.; *U.S. Private*, pg. 1138
DSC (DILEONARDO SIANO CASERTA) ADVERTISING; *U.S. Private*, pg. 1281
DS CHEMPORT (AUSTRALIA) PTY LTD—See FUJIFILM Holdings Corporation; *Int'l*, pg. 2821
DS CHEMPORT (MALAYSIA) SDN. BHD.—See FUJIFILM Holdings Corporation; *Int'l*, pg. 2821
DSCI, LLC—See Siris Capital Group, LLC; *U.S. Private*, pg. 3674
DSC INVESTMENT INC.; *Int'l*, pg. 2209
DSC LIMITED; *U.S. Private*, pg. 1281
D+S COMMUNICATION CENTER MANAGEMENT GMBH—See Stroer SE & Co. KGaA; *Int'l*, pg. 7242
DS CONTAINERS INC.—See Daiwa Can Company; *Int'l*, pg. 1944
D.S. CORPORATION—See Yamaha Corporation; *Int'l*, pg. 8549
DS CORP.—See Thor Industries, Inc.; *U.S. Public*, pg. 2156
DSC/PURGATORY LLC; *U.S. Private*, pg. 1281
D SCREENS SIA—See AS Ekspress Grupp; *Int'l*, pg. 589
DSCS HOLDINGS LLC; *U.S. Private*, pg. 1281
DSC SYSTEMS (M) SDN. BHD.—See DGB Asia Berhad; *Int'l*, pg. 2096
DSD BRUCKENBAU GMBH—See Pirson Montage SA; *Int'l*, pg. 5875
DS DEFENDINGER AG—See Uzin Utz AG; *Int'l*, pg. 8103
DS DEUTSCHLAND GMBH—See Dassault Systemes S.A.; *Int'l*, pg. 1974
DSD FERROMETALCO SAE—See Pirson Montage SA; *Int'l*, pg. 5875
DSD HILGERS STAHLBAU GMBH—See Pirson Montage SA; *Int'l*, pg. 5875
DS DIGITAL PRIVATE LIMITED—See S Chand & Company Limited; *Int'l*, pg. 6442
DSD INDUSTRIE ROHRTECHNIK GMBH—See Pirson Montage SA; *Int'l*, pg. 5875
DSD INTERNATIONAL CONTRACTORS S.A.R.L.—See Pirson Montage SA; *Int'l*, pg. 5875
D&S DISTRIBUTION INC.; *U.S. Private*, pg. 1138
DSD, LTD.—See Disco Corporation; *Int'l*, pg. 2131
DSD MONTAGETECHNIK GMBH—See Pirson Montage SA; *Int'l*, pg. 5875
DSD NOELL GMBH—See Pirson Montage SA; *Int'l*, pg. 5875
DSD STEEL BULGARIA LTD.—See Pirson Montage SA; *Int'l*, pg. 5875
DSD STEEL CONSTRUCTION AG—See Pirson Montage SA; *Int'l*, pg. 5875
DSD STEEL GROUP GMBH—See Pirson Montage SA; *Int'l*, pg. 5875
DSEC CO., LTD.; *Int'l*, pg. 2209
DSE DEVELOPMENT LTD.—See Caledonia Investments plc; *Int'l*, pg. 1262
DSE DIREKT-SERVICE-ENERGIE GMBH—See ENGIE SA; *Int'l*, pg. 2429
DSE DIREKT-SERVICE-ENERGIE GMBH—See E.ON SE; *Int'l*, pg. 2257
DSE DIREKT-SERVICE-ENERGIE GMBH—See Vattenfall AB; *Int'l*, pg. 8137
DSE DRAXLMAIER SYSTEMY ELEKTRYCZNE SP. Z O.O.—See Draexlmaier Gruppe; *Int'l*, pg. 2198
DSE INC.—See National Presto Industries, Inc; *U.S. Public*, pg. 1497
DSE (NZ) LIMITED—See Woolworths Group Limited; *Int'l*, pg. 8451
DS FINANCE CO., LTD.—See Screen Holdings Co., Ltd.; *Int'l*, pg. 6654
DS-FRANCE S.A.S.—See Danish Crown AmbA; *Int'l*, pg. 1964
DSFU GMBH—See Samherji hf; *Int'l*, pg. 6504
DS FURNITURE MANUFACTURER SDN BHD—See Design Studio Group Ltd.; *Int'l*, pg. 2045
DSG-CANUSA GMBH & CO. KG—See ShawCor Ltd.; *Int'l*, pg. 6791
DSG-CANUSA ITALIA S.R.L.—See ShawCor Ltd.; *Int'l*, pg. 6791
DSG-CANUSA POLSKA SP. Z.O.O.—See ShawCor Ltd.; *Int'l*, pg. 6791
DSG-CANUSA—See ShawCor Ltd.; *Int'l*, pg. 6791
DSG-CANUSA—See ShawCor Ltd.; *Int'l*, pg. 6791

DSG ENERGY LIMITED—See DCC plc; *Int'l*, pg. 1990
DSG GLOBAL INC.; *Int'l*, pg. 2209
DSG, INC.—See Signant Health MGT LLP; *U.S. Private*, pg. 3649
DSG INTERNATIONAL BELGIUM BVBA—See Currys plc; *Int'l*, pg. 1879
DSG INTERNATIONAL LIMITED; *Int'l*, pg. 2209
DSG INTERNATIONAL (THAILAND) PUBLIC COMPANY LIMITED—See DSG International Limited; *Int'l*, pg. 2209
DSG (MALAYSIA) SDN. BHD.—See DSG International Limited; *Int'l*, pg. 2209
DSG MANUFACTURING MALAYSIA SDN. BHD.—See Depa PLC; *Int'l*, pg. 2040
DSG PROJECTS MALAYSIA SDN. BHD.—See Depa PLC; *Int'l*, pg. 2040
DS GRAPHICS INC.; *U.S. Private*, pg. 1281
DSG RETAIL LIMITED—See Currys plc; *Int'l*, pg. 1879
DSG (THAILAND) CO., LTD.—See Depa PLC; *Int'l*, pg. 2040
DS HEALTHCARE GROUP, INC.; *U.S. Private*, pg. 1281
DSH FLOORING LIMITED—See Brickability Group plc; *Int'l*, pg. 1151
DS HOLDING-GMBH—See The Social Chain AG; *Int'l*, pg. 7687
DS HULL COMPANY INCORPORATED; *U.S. Private*, pg. 1281
DSI ASIA/PACIFIC—See Nextworld, LLC; *U.S. Private*, pg. 2921
DSI AUTOMOTIVE PRODUCTS—See DSI, Inc.; *U.S. Private*, pg. 1281
DSI/DATASOURCE, INC.—See The Graham Group, Inc.; *U.S. Private*, pg. 4037
DSI DISTRIBUTING, INC.; *U.S. Private*, pg. 1281
DSI, DOCUMENT SOLUTIONS, INC.; *U.S. Private*, pg. 1281
DSI/DYNAMATIC CORPORATION; *U.S. Private*, pg. 1281
DSI EMEA LTD.—See Nextworld, LLC; *U.S. Private*, pg. 2921
DSI EUROPE GMBH—See Vishay Precision Group, Inc.; *U.S. Public*, pg. 2303
DSI FZE—See Schoeller-Bleckmann Oilfield Equipment AG; *Int'l*, pg. 6637
DSI GETRANKEARMATUREN GMBH & CO. KG—See Aalberts N.V.; *Int'l*, pg. 34
DSI HOLDING GMBH—See Triton Advisers Limited; *Int'l*, pg. 7929
DSI, INC.; *U.S. Private*, pg. 1281
DSI INTERNATIONAL LUXEMBOURG SARL—See Triton Advisers Limited; *Int'l*, pg. 7929
DSI-ITI, LLC—See American Securities LLC; *U.S. Private*, pg. 249
DS IMPACT GMBH—See The Social Chain AG; *Int'l*, pg. 7687
D.S. INDUSTRIES LIMITED; *Int'l*, pg. 1901
DSI SCHAUM CHEMIE SP. Z O.O.—See Sandvik AB; *Int'l*, pg. 6529
DSIT SOLUTIONS LTD.—See Acorn Energy, Inc.; *U.S. Public*, pg. 36
DSI TUNNELING LLC—See Frank Calandra, Inc.; *U.S. Private*, pg. 1594
DSI UNDERGROUND ARGENTINA S.A.—See Sandvik AB; *Int'l*, pg. 6529
DSI UNDERGROUND AUSTRALIA PTY. LIMITED—See Sandvik AB; *Int'l*, pg. 6529
DSI UNDERGROUND AUSTRIA GMBH—See Sandvik AB; *Int'l*, pg. 6529
DSI UNDERGROUND CANADA LTD.—See Sandvik AB; *Int'l*, pg. 6529
DSI UNDERGROUND CHEMICALS SP. Z O.O.—See Sandvik AB; *Int'l*, pg. 6529
DSI UNDERGROUND CHILE SPA—See Sandvik AB; *Int'l*, pg. 6529
DSI UNDERGROUND COLOMBIA S.A.S.—See Sandvik AB; *Int'l*, pg. 6529
DSI UNDERGROUND GMBH—See Sandvik AB; *Int'l*, pg. 6529
DSI UNDERGROUND MEROL SP. Z O.O.—See Sandvik AB; *Int'l*, pg. 6529
DSI UNDERGROUND MEXICO S.A. DE C.V.—See Sandvik AB; *Int'l*, pg. 6529
DSI UNDERGROUND PERU S.A.C.—See Sandvik AB; *Int'l*, pg. 6529
DSI UNDERGROUND POLAND SP. Z O.O.—See Sandvik AB; *Int'l*, pg. 6529
DSI UNDERGROUND SPAIN S.A.U.—See Sandvik AB; *Int'l*, pg. 6529
DSI UNDERGROUND SYSTEM BRASIL INDUSTRIA E COMERCIO LTDA.—See Sandvik AB; *Int'l*, pg. 6529
DSI UNDERGROUND SYSTEMS, INC. - CAMBRIDGE—See Triton Advisers Limited; *Int'l*, pg. 7929
DSI UNDERGROUND SYSTEMS, INC. - MARTINSBURG—See Triton Advisers Limited; *Int'l*, pg. 7929
DSI UNDERGROUND SYSTEMS, INC.—See Triton Advisers Limited; *Int'l*, pg. 7929
DSI UNDERGROUND UK HOLDINGS LTD.—See Sandvik AB; *Int'l*, pg. 6529

DS MEDIALABS

DSI UNDERGROUND UK LTD.—See Sandvik AB; *Int'l*, pg. 6529
DSI UNDERGROUND VENTILATION SYSTEMS SPA—See Sandvik AB; *Int'l*, pg. 6529
DSK BANK—See OTP Bank Plc; *Int'l*, pg. 5657
DSK CO., LTD.; *Int'l*, pg. 2210
DSK HYP AG—See Skandinaviska Enskilda Banken AB; *Int'l*, pg. 6977
DSL DEFENCE SERVICE LOGISTICS GMBH—See Krauss-Maffei Wegmann GmbH & Co. KG; *Int'l*, pg. 4300
DSLEXTREME.COM INC.—See Broadvoice, Inc.; *U.S. Private*, pg. 660
DS LOGISTICS CO., LTD.—See Osaka Soda Co., Ltd.; *Int'l*, pg. 5646
DSM ADVANCED POLYESTERS EMMEN BV—See Koninklijke DSM N.V.; *Int'l*, pg. 4262
DSM AGRO SERVICES BV—See Koninklijke DSM N.V.; *Int'l*, pg. 4262
DS MARKETING GMBH—See The Social Chain AG; *Int'l*, pg. 7687
DSM BELGIUM NV—See Koninklijke DSM N.V.; *Int'l*, pg. 4262
DSM BIO-BASED PRODUCTS & SERVICES BV—See Koninklijke DSM N.V.; *Int'l*, pg. 4263
DSM BIOMEDICAL BV—See Koninklijke DSM N.V.; *Int'l*, pg. 4263
DSM BIOMEDICAL INC.—See Koninklijke DSM N.V.; *Int'l*, pg. 4263
DSM CAPUA SPA—See Koninklijke DSM N.V.; *Int'l*, pg. 4262
DSM CENTRAL EUROPE SRO—See Koninklijke DSM N.V.; *Int'l*, pg. 4262
DSM CHEMICAL TECHNOLOGY R&D BV—See Koninklijke DSM N.V.; *Int'l*, pg. 4262
DSM CHINA HOLDING AG—See Koninklijke DSM N.V.; *Int'l*, pg. 4264
DSM CHINA HOLDING I BV—See Koninklijke DSM N.V.; *Int'l*, pg. 4263
DSM CHINA HOLDING II BV—See Koninklijke DSM N.V.; *Int'l*, pg. 4263
DSM (CHINA) LTD.—See Roche Holding AG; *Int'l*, pg. 6373
DSM CHINA LTD—See Koninklijke DSM N.V.; *Int'l*, pg. 4264
DSM COMMERCIAL COORDINATION & PARTICIPATIONS BV—See Koninklijke DSM N.V.; *Int'l*, pg. 4262
DSM COMPUTER GMBH—See Avnet, Inc.; *U.S. Public*, pg. 252
DSM CORPORATE INSURANCES AG—See Koninklijke DSM N.V.; *Int'l*, pg. 4262
DSM CZECH REPUBLIC—See Koninklijke DSM N.V.; *Int'l*, pg. 4262
DSM DAB BV—See Koninklijke DSM N.V.; *Int'l*, pg. 4262
DSM DELFT BV—See Koninklijke DSM N.V.; *Int'l*, pg. 4263
DSM DELFT PERMIT BV—See Koninklijke DSM N.V.; *Int'l*, pg. 4263
DSM DEMOLITION LIMITED—See Metric Capital Partners LLP; *Int'l*, pg. 4856
DSM DESOTECH BV—See Koninklijke DSM N.V.; *Int'l*, pg. 4262
DSM DESOTECH (CHINA) HOLDING BV—See Koninklijke DSM N.V.; *Int'l*, pg. 4262
DSM DEUTSCHLAND GMBH—See Koninklijke DSM N.V.; *Int'l*, pg. 4262
DSM DYNEEMA B.V.—See Koninklijke DSM N.V.; *Int'l*, pg. 4262
DSM DYNEEMA LLC—See Koninklijke DSM N.V.; *Int'l*, pg. 4262
DSM EASTERN EUROPE, LLC—See Koninklijke DSM N.V.; *Int'l*, pg. 4262
DS MEDIALABS; *U.S. Private*, pg. 1281
DSME E&R LTD.—See Hanwha Ocean Co., Ltd.; *Int'l*, pg. 3266
DSM ENGINEERING MATERIALS—See Koninklijke DSM N.V.; *Int'l*, pg. 4262
DSM ENGINEERING PLASTIC PRODUCTS—See Koninklijke DSM N.V.; *Int'l*, pg. 4262
DSM ENGINEERING PLASTICS BV—See Koninklijke DSM N.V.; *Int'l*, pg. 4262
DSM ENGINEERING PLASTICS (CHINA) BV—See Koninklijke DSM N.V.; *Int'l*, pg. 4262
DSM ENGINEERING PLASTICS (EMMEN) BV—See Koninklijke DSM N.V.; *Int'l*, pg. 4262
DSM ENGINEERING PLASTICS INC—See Koninklijke DSM N.V.; *Int'l*, pg. 4262
DSM ENGINEERING PLASTICS INTERNATIONAL BV—See Koninklijke DSM N.V.; *Int'l*, pg. 4262
DSM ENGINEERING PLASTICS—See Koninklijke DSM N.V.; *Int'l*, pg. 4262
DSM ENGINEERING PLASTICS TAIWAN PTE. LTD.—See Koninklijke DSM N.V.; *Int'l*, pg. 4262
DSM ESPANA SA—See Koninklijke DSM N.V.; *Int'l*, pg. 4263
DSM EXECUTIVE SERVICES BV—See Koninklijke DSM N.V.; *Int'l*, pg. 4263
DSM EXPERT CENTER BV—See Koninklijke DSM N.V.; *Int'l*, pg. 4263

DS MEDIALABS

DSM FINANCE BV—See Koninklijke DSM N.V.; *Int'l*, pg. 4263
DSM-FIRMENICH AG; *Int'l*, pg. 2210
DSM FOOD SPECIALTIES AUSTRALIA PTY LTD.—See Koninklijke DSM N.V.; *Int'l*, pg. 4263
DSM FOOD SPECIALTIES B.V.—See Koninklijke DSM N.V.; *Int'l*, pg. 4263
DSM FOOD SPECIALTIES CHINA HOLDING 1 BV—See Koninklijke DSM N.V.; *Int'l*, pg. 4263
DSM FOOD SPECIALTIES GERMANY GMBH—See Koninklijke DSM N.V.; *Int'l*, pg. 4263
DSM FOOD SPECIALTIES ITALY SPA—See Koninklijke DSM N.V.; *Int'l*, pg. 4263
DSM FOOD SPECIALTIES LTD. STI.—See Koninklijke DSM N.V.; *Int'l*, pg. 4263
DSM FOOD SPECIALTIES MELTAGEL BV—See Koninklijke DSM N.V.; *Int'l*, pg. 4263
DSM FOOD SPECIALTIES MEXICANA S.A. DE C.V.—See Koninklijke DSM N.V.; *Int'l*, pg. 4263
DSM FOOD SPECIALTIES POLAND SP. Z O.O.—See Koninklijke DSM N.V.; *Int'l*, pg. 4263
DSM FOOD SPECIALTIES (SHANGHAI) LTD—See Koninklijke DSM N.V.; *Int'l*, pg. 4263
DSM FOOD SPECIALTIES—See Koninklijke DSM N.V.; *Int'l*, pg. 4263
DSM FOOD SPECIALTIES SUPERDEX SAS—See Koninklijke DSM N.V.; *Int'l*, pg. 4263
DSM FOOD SPECIALTIES USA, INC.—See Koninklijke DSM N.V.; *Int'l*, pg. 4263
DSM FRANCE S.A.—See Koninklijke DSM N.V.; *Int'l*, pg. 4263
DSM FUNCTIONAL MATERIALS—See Koninklijke DSM N.V.; *Int'l*, pg. 4263
DSM GIST FRANCE SAS—See Koninklijke DSM N.V.; *Int'l*, pg. 4263
DSM GIST SERVICES BV—See Koninklijke DSM N.V.; *Int'l*, pg. 4263
DSM HIGH PERFORMANCE POLYETHYLENES BV—See Koninklijke DSM N.V.; *Int'l*, pg. 4262
DSM HOLDING COMPANY USA, INC.—See Koninklijke DSM N.V.; *Int'l*, pg. 4263
DSM ICD PARTICIPATIONS BV—See Koninklijke DSM N.V.; *Int'l*, pg. 4262
DSM IDEMITSU CORP. LTD.—See Idemitsu Kosan Co., Ltd.; *Int'l*, pg. 3590
DSM IDEMITSU CORP. LTD.—See Koninklijke DSM N.V.; *Int'l*, pg. 4263
DSM INDIA PRIVATE LIMITED—See Koninklijke DSM N.V.; *Int'l*, pg. 4262
DSM INDUSTRIAL SERVICES BV—See Koninklijke DSM N.V.; *Int'l*, pg. 4264
DSM INFORMATION & COMMUNICATION TECHNOLOGY—See Koninklijke DSM N.V.; *Int'l*, pg. 4263
DSM INNOVATION CENTER BV—See Koninklijke DSM N.V.; *Int'l*, pg. 4263
DSM INNOVATION INC.—See Koninklijke DSM N.V.; *Int'l*, pg. 4264
DSM INNOVATIVE SYNTHESIS BV—See Koninklijke DSM N.V.; *Int'l*, pg. 4264
DSM INTERNATIONAL BV—See Koninklijke DSM N.V.; *Int'l*, pg. 4264
DSM INTERNATIONAL PARTICIPATIONS BV—See Koninklijke DSM N.V.; *Int'l*, pg. 4264
DSM IP ASSETS BV—See Koninklijke DSM N.V.; *Int'l*, pg. 4264
DSM ITALIA S.R.L.—See Koninklijke DSM N.V.; *Int'l*, pg. 4264
DSM JAPAN KK—See Koninklijke DSM N.V.; *Int'l*, pg. 4264
DSM KREFELD AUSSENWERBUNG GMBH—See Stroer SE & Co. KGaA; *Int'l*, pg. 7242
DSM LIFE SCIENCE PRODUCTS INTERNATIONAL GMBH—See Koninklijke DSM N.V.; *Int'l*, pg. 4264
DSM LOTTOSERVICE GMBH—See mybet Holding SE; *Int'l*, pg. 5111
DSM NEDERLAND BV—See Koninklijke DSM N.V.; *Int'l*, pg. 4264
DSM NUTRITIONAL PRODUCTS AG—See Koninklijke DSM N.V.; *Int'l*, pg. 4264
DSM NUTRITIONAL PRODUCTS AG—See Koninklijke DSM N.V.; *Int'l*, pg. 4264
DSM NUTRITIONAL PRODUCTS AG—See Koninklijke DSM N.V.; *Int'l*, pg. 4264
DSM NUTRITIONAL PRODUCTS ARGENTINA SA—See Koninklijke DSM N.V.; *Int'l*, pg. 4264
DSM NUTRITIONAL PRODUCTS ASIA PACIFIC PTE LTD.—See Koninklijke DSM N.V.; *Int'l*, pg. 4264
DSM NUTRITIONAL PRODUCTS A/S—See Koninklijke DSM N.V.; *Int'l*, pg. 4264
DSM NUTRITIONAL PRODUCTS AUSTRALIA PTY LTD.—See Koninklijke DSM N.V.; *Int'l*, pg. 4264
DSM NUTRITIONAL PRODUCTS CANADA INC - CAMBRIDGE PREMIX PLANT—See Koninklijke DSM N.V.; *Int'l*, pg. 4264
DSM NUTRITIONAL PRODUCTS CANADA INC. - HIGH RIVER PREMIX PLANT—See Koninklijke DSM N.V.; *Int'l*, pg. 4264
DSM NUTRITIONAL PRODUCTS CANADA INC.—See Koninklijke DSM N.V.; *Int'l*, pg. 4264
DSM NUTRITIONAL PRODUCTS CHILE SA - PUERTO VARAS PREMIX PLANT—See Koninklijke DSM N.V.; *Int'l*, pg. 4264
DSM NUTRITIONAL PRODUCTS CHILE SA—See Koninklijke DSM N.V.; *Int'l*, pg. 4264
DSM NUTRITIONAL PRODUCTS CHINA BV—See Koninklijke DSM N.V.; *Int'l*, pg. 4264
DSM NUTRITIONAL PRODUCTS CHINA HOLDING BV—See Koninklijke DSM N.V.; *Int'l*, pg. 4265
DSM NUTRITIONAL PRODUCTS CHINA HOLDING GMBH—See Koninklijke DSM N.V.; *Int'l*, pg. 4264
DSM NUTRITIONAL PRODUCTS COLOMBIA SA - FEED PREMIX PLANT—See Koninklijke DSM N.V.; *Int'l*, pg. 4264
DSM NUTRITIONAL PRODUCTS COLOMBIA SA - FOOD/PHARMACEUTICAL PREMIX PLANT—See Koninklijke DSM N.V.; *Int'l*, pg. 4264
DSM NUTRITIONAL PRODUCTS COLOMBIA SA—See Koninklijke DSM N.V.; *Int'l*, pg. 4264
DSM NUTRITIONAL PRODUCTS ECUADOR SA—See Koninklijke DSM N.V.; *Int'l*, pg. 4264
DSM NUTRITIONAL PRODUCTS EUROPE AG—See Koninklijke DSM N.V.; *Int'l*, pg. 4264
DSM NUTRITIONAL PRODUCTS FRANCE SAS - PREMIX PLANT—See Koninklijke DSM N.V.; *Int'l*, pg. 4264
DSM NUTRITIONAL PRODUCTS FRANCE SAS—See Koninklijke DSM N.V.; *Int'l*, pg. 4264
DSM NUTRITIONAL PRODUCTS GMBH—See Koninklijke DSM N.V.; *Int'l*, pg. 4265
DSM NUTRITIONAL PRODUCTS HELLAS LTD. - PREMIX PLANT—See Koninklijke DSM N.V.; *Int'l*, pg. 4265
DSM NUTRITIONAL PRODUCTS HELLAS LTD.—See Koninklijke DSM N.V.; *Int'l*, pg. 4265
DSM NUTRITIONAL PRODUCTS HUNGARY LTD—See Koninklijke DSM N.V.; *Int'l*, pg. 4265
DSM NUTRITIONAL PRODUCTS IBERIA SA—See Koninklijke DSM N.V.; *Int'l*, pg. 4265
DSM NUTRITIONAL PRODUCTS INDIA PVT. LTD.—See Koninklijke DSM N.V.; *Int'l*, pg. 4265
DSM NUTRITIONAL PRODUCTS INDIA PVT. LTD. - THANE PREMIX PLANT—See Koninklijke DSM N.V.; *Int'l*, pg. 4265
DSM NUTRITIONAL PRODUCTS LLC—See Koninklijke DSM N.V.; *Int'l*, pg. 4265
DSM NUTRITIONAL PRODUCTS MEXICO SA DE CV—See Koninklijke DSM N.V.; *Int'l*, pg. 4265
DSM NUTRITIONAL PRODUCTS NEDERLAND BV—See Koninklijke DSM N.V.; *Int'l*, pg. 4265
DSM NUTRITIONAL PRODUCTS NV—See Koninklijke DSM N.V.; *Int'l*, pg. 4265
DSM NUTRITIONAL PRODUCTS PERU SA - LIMA PREMIX PLANT—See Koninklijke DSM N.V.; *Int'l*, pg. 4265
DSM NUTRITIONAL PRODUCTS PERU SA—See Koninklijke DSM N.V.; *Int'l*, pg. 4265
DSM NUTRITIONAL PRODUCTS PHILIPPINES, INC.—See Koninklijke DSM N.V.; *Int'l*, pg. 4265
DSM NUTRITIONAL PRODUCTS ROMANIA SRL—See Koninklijke DSM N.V.; *Int'l*, pg. 4265
DSM NUTRITIONAL PRODUCTS RUS LLC—See Koninklijke DSM N.V.; *Int'l*, pg. 4265
DSM NUTRITIONAL PRODUCTS—See Koninklijke DSM N.V.; *Int'l*, pg. 4264
DSM NUTRITIONAL PRODUCTS SOUTH AFRICA (PTY) LTD.—See Koninklijke DSM N.V.; *Int'l*, pg. 4265
DSM NUTRITIONAL PRODUCTS SP. Z.O.O.—See Koninklijke DSM N.V.; *Int'l*, pg. 4265
DSM NUTRITIONAL PRODUCTS TATARSTAN HOLDING BV—See Koninklijke DSM N.V.; *Int'l*, pg. 4265
DSM NUTRITIONAL PRODUCTS U.K. LIMITED—See Koninklijke DSM N.V.; *Int'l*, pg. 4265
DSM NUTRITIONAL PRODUCTS URUGUAY SA - MONTEVIDEO PREMIX PLANT—See Koninklijke DSM N.V.; *Int'l*, pg. 4265
DSM NUTRITIONAL PRODUCTS URUGUAY SA—See Koninklijke DSM N.V.; *Int'l*, pg. 4265
DSM NUTRITIONAL PRODUCTS VENEZUELA SA—See Koninklijke DSM N.V.; *Int'l*, pg. 4265
DSM NUTRITIONAL PRODUCTS VIETNAM LTD.—See Koninklijke DSM N.V.; *Int'l*, pg. 4265
DSM NYLATRON BV—See Koninklijke DSM N.V.; *Int'l*, pg. 4262
DSM PENSION SERVICES BV—See Koninklijke DSM N.V.; *Int'l*, pg. 4265
DSM PLASTOMERS BV—See Koninklijke DSM N.V.; *Int'l*, pg. 4265
DSM POLAND SP. Z.O.O.—See Koninklijke DSM N.V.; *Int'l*, pg. 4265
DSM POLYMERS INTERNATIONAL BV—See Koninklijke DSM N.V.; *Int'l*, pg. 4266
DSM PS EXECUTIVE CENTERS—See Koninklijke DSM N.V.; *Int'l*, pg. 4263
DSM SCANDINAVIA AB—See Koninklijke DSM N.V.; *Int'l*, pg. 4266
DSM SCHADEVERZEKERINGSMIJ NV—See Koninklijke DSM N.V.; *Int'l*, pg. 4265
DSM SERVICES MEXICO SA DE CV—See Koninklijke DSM N.V.; *Int'l*, pg. 4265

CORPORATE AFFILIATIONS

DSM SERVICES USA, INC.—See Koninklijke DSM N.V.; *Int'l*, pg. 4263
DSM SINGAPORE INDUSTRIAL PTE LTD.—See Koninklijke DSM N.V.; *Int'l*, pg. 4264
DSM SINOCHEM PHARMACEUTICALS NETHERLANDS B.V.—See Bain Capital, LP; *U.S. Private*, pg. 439
DSM SOURCING BV—See Koninklijke DSM N.V.; *Int'l*, pg. 4266
DSM SOUTH AMERICA LTDA—See Koninklijke DSM N.V.; *Int'l*, pg. 4266
DSM SPECIALTY COMPOUNDS N.V.—See Koninklijke DSM N.V.; *Int'l*, pg. 4262
DSM SUCCINIC ACID B.V.—See Koninklijke DSM N.V.; *Int'l*, pg. 4263
DSM TECHNOLOGY CONSULTANTS LLC—See Court Square Capital Partners, L.P.; *U.S. Private*, pg. 1070
DSM TRADING (SHANGHAI) CO LTD.—See Koninklijke DSM N.V.; *Int'l*, pg. 4266
DSM VENTURING & BUSINESS DEVELOPMENT—See Koninklijke DSM N.V.; *Int'l*, pg. 4266
DSM VENTURING BV—See Koninklijke DSM N.V.; *Int'l*, pg. 4264
DSM VITAMINS (CHANGCHUN) LTD.—See Koninklijke DSM N.V.; *Int'l*, pg. 4265
DSM VITAMINS (HUNAN) LTD.—See Koninklijke DSM N.V.; *Int'l*, pg. 4265
DSM VITAMINS (SHANGHAI) LTD.—See Koninklijke DSM N.V.; *Int'l*, pg. 4265
DS NET CO., LTD.—See TKH Group N.V.; *Int'l*, pg. 7765
DSNL CO LTD; *Int'l*, pg. 2210
DSNR MEDIA GROUP; *Int'l*, pg. 2210
DSO FLUID HANDLING CO., INC.—See Audax Group, Limited Partnership; *U.S. Private*, pg. 388
DSOFT TECHNOLOGY COMPANY—See Chiulista Services, Inc.; *U.S. Private*, pg. 887
DSPACE GMBH; *Int'l*, pg. 2210
DSPACE INC.—See dSPACE GmbH; *Int'l*, pg. 2210
DSPACE JAPAN K.K.—See dSPACE GmbH; *Int'l*, pg. 2210
DSPACE LTD.—See dSPACE GmbH; *Int'l*, pg. 2210
DSPACE MECHATRONIC CONTROL TECHNOLOGY (SHANGHAI) CO., LTD.—See dSPACE GmbH; *Int'l*, pg. 2210
DSPACE SARL—See dSPACE GmbH; *Int'l*, pg. 2210
DSP BEYOND PTY LTD—See LOV Group Invest SAS; *Int'l*, pg. 4564
DSP BLACKROCK INVESTMENT MANAGERS PRIVATE LIMITED—See BlackRock, Inc.; *U.S. Public*, pg. 345
DSP BLACKROCK INVESTMENT MANAGERS PRIVATE LIMITED—See Synaptics Incorporated; *U.S. Public*, pg. 1969
DSP BUILDERS INC.; *U.S. Private*, pg. 1281
DSP CLINICAL RESEARCH; *U.S. Private*, pg. 1281
DSP CO., LTD.—See DHSteel; *Int'l*, pg. 2100
DSP DESIGN LTD—See Season Group International Co., Ltd.; *Int'l*, pg. 6666
DSP DISTRIBUTION SERVICE CO., LTD.—See Sumitomo Chemical Company, Limited; *Int'l*, pg. 7267
DSPG EDINBURGH LTD.—See Synaptics Incorporated; *U.S. Public*, pg. 1969
DSP GOKYO FOOD & CHEMICAL CO., LTD.—See Sumitomo Chemical Company, Limited; *Int'l*, pg. 7267
DSP GROUP HK LIMITED—See Synaptics Incorporated; *U.S. Public*, pg. 1969
DSP GROUP, INC.—See Synaptics Incorporated; *U.S. Public*, pg. 1969
DSP GROUP LTD.—See Synaptics Incorporated; *U.S. Public*, pg. 1969
DSP GROUP (SHENZHEN) LIMITED—See Synaptics Incorporated; *U.S. Public*, pg. 1969
DS PHARMA ANIMAL HEALTH CO., LTD.—See Sumitomo Chemical Company, Limited; *Int'l*, pg. 7267
DS PHARMA BIOMEDICAL CO., LTD.—See Sumitomo Chemical Company, Limited; *Int'l*, pg. 7267
DS PHARMACY, INC.—See Walgreens Boots Alliance, Inc.; *U.S. Public*, pg. 2323
DSP LABS LIMITED—See Mitek Systems, Inc.; *U.S. Public*, pg. 1452
D SPORTS MERCHANDISING INC.—See Dentsu Group Inc.; *Int'l*, pg. 2034
DS PRODUKTE GMBH—See The Social Chain AG; *Int'l*, pg. 7687
DS PROJECT MANAGEMENT SDN BHD—See Design Studio Group Ltd.; *Int'l*, pg. 2045
DS PROPERTY DEVELOPMENTS LIMITED—See U and I Group PLC; *Int'l*, pg. 7996
DSP SINGAPORE HOLDINGS PTE. LTD.—See DuPont de Nemours, Inc.; *U.S. Public*, pg. 692
DSP TECHNOLOGY INDIAN PRIVATE LIMITED—See Synaptics Incorporated; *U.S. Public*, pg. 1969
DSP TECHNOLOGY—See Synaptics Incorporated; *U.S. Public*, pg. 1969
DSQUARED INTERNATIONAL, LLC; *U.S. Private*, pg. 1281
D SQUARE ENERGY LLC; *U.S. Private*, pg. 1136
DSR CORP. - GWANGYANG STAINLESS STEEL FACTORY—See DSR Corp.; *Int'l*, pg. 2210
DSR CORP.; *Int'l*, pg. 2210
D&S RESIDENTIAL SERVICES, LP—See Comvest Group Holdings LLC; *U.S. Private*, pg. 1007

COMPANY NAME INDEX

DSR INTERNATIONAL CORP—See DSR Corp.; *Int'l*, pg. 2210
DSR MANAGEMENT, INC.; *U.S. Private*, pg. 1281
DSRM GROUP PLC—See Tata Sons Limited; *Int'l*, pg. 7472
DSRM NATIONAL BANK—See Valero Energy Corporation; *U.S. Public*, pg. 2272
DSR QINGDAO LIMITED—See DSR Corp.; *Int'l*, pg. 2210
DSR TAIKO BERHAD; *Int'l*, pg. 2210
DSR TRADING CORP—See DSR Wire Corporation; *Int'l*, pg. 2210
DSR WIRE CORPORATION; *Int'l*, pg. 2210
DSR WIRE CORPORATION - SUNCHEON FACTORY 1—See DSR Wire Corporation; *Int'l*, pg. 2210
DSR WIRE CORPORATION - SUNCHEON FACTORY 2—See DSR Wire Corporation; *Int'l*, pg. 2210
DSR WIRE CORPORATION - YULCHON FACTORY—See DSR Wire Corporation; *Int'l*, pg. 2210
DSS ADMINISTRATIVE GROUP, INC.—See DSS, Inc.; *U.S. Public*, pg. 689
D S S COMPANY—See MDU Resources Group, Inc.; *U.S. Public*, pg. 1410
DSS DIGITAL INC.—See Proof Authentication Corporation; *U.S. Private*, pg. 3284
DS SERVICES OF AMERICA, INC. - CRYSTAL SPRINGS—See Primo Water Corporation; *U.S. Public*, pg. 1718
DS SERVICES OF AMERICA, INC. - DEEP ROCK WATER CO.—See Primo Water Corporation; *U.S. Public*, pg. 1718
DS SERVICES OF AMERICA, INC. - HINCKLEY SPRINGS—See Primo Water Corporation; *U.S. Public*, pg. 1718
DS SERVICES OF AMERICA, INC. - MOUNT OLYMPUS—See Primo Water Corporation; *U.S. Public*, pg. 1718
DS SERVICES OF AMERICA, INC.—See Primo Water Corporation; *U.S. Public*, pg. 1718
DSSI LLC; *U.S. Private*, pg. 1282
DSS, INC.; *U.S. Public*, pg. 689
D-SS INC.—See Datasection Inc.; *Int'l*, pg. 1979
DSS INTERNATIONAL INC.—See DSS, Inc.; *U.S. Public*, pg. 689
DS SMITH AD—See DS Smith Plc; *Int'l*, pg. 2209
DS SMITH AMBALAJ A.S.—See DS Smith Plc; *Int'l*, pg. 2207
DS SMITH BELISCE CROATIA D.O.O.—See DS Smith Plc; *Int'l*, pg. 2207
DS SMITH BULGARIA S.A.—See DS Smith Plc; *Int'l*, pg. 2207
DS SMITH CORREX—See DS Smith Plc; *Int'l*, pg. 2207
DS SMITH CORRUGATED PACKAGING LTD—See DS Smith Plc; *Int'l*, pg. 2208
DS SMITH DUCAPLAST—See DS Smith Plc; *Int'l*, pg. 2207
DS SMITH HAMBURG DISPLAY GMBH—See DS Smith Plc; *Int'l*, pg. 2207
DS SMITH INOS PAPIR SERVIS D.O.O.—See DS Smith Plc; *Int'l*, pg. 2207
DS SMITH KAYSERSBERG S.A.S.—See DS Smith Plc; *Int'l*, pg. 2207
DS SMITH PACKAGING ALES SAS—See DS Smith Plc; *Int'l*, pg. 2207
DS SMITH PACKAGING ARENSHAUSEN MIVEPA GMBH—See DS Smith Plc; *Int'l*, pg. 2207
DS SMITH PACKAGING ARNSTADT GMBH—See DS Smith Plc; *Int'l*, pg. 2207
DS SMITH PACKAGING AUSTRIA GMBH—See DS Smith Plc; *Int'l*, pg. 2207
DS SMITH PACKAGING BALTIC HOLDING OY—See DS Smith Plc; *Int'l*, pg. 2207
DS SMITH PACKAGING BELGIUM N.V.—See DS Smith Plc; *Int'l*, pg. 2207
DS SMITH PACKAGING BH D.O.O.—See DS Smith Plc; *Int'l*, pg. 2207
DS SMITH PACKAGING CESKA REPUBLICA S.R.O.—See DS Smith Plc; *Int'l*, pg. 2208
DS SMITH PACKAGING CZECH REPUBLIC S.R.O.—See DS Smith Plc; *Int'l*, pg. 2207
DS SMITH PACKAGING DENMARK A/S—See DS Smith Plc; *Int'l*, pg. 2208
DS SMITH PACKAGING DEUTSCHLAND STIFTUNG & CO. KG—See DS Smith Plc; *Int'l*, pg. 2208
DS SMITH PACKAGING DPF SAS—See DS Smith Plc; *Int'l*, pg. 2207
DS SMITH PACKAGING DURTAL SAS—See DS Smith Plc; *Int'l*, pg. 2207
DS SMITH PACKAGING ESTONIA AS—See DS Smith Plc; *Int'l*, pg. 2207
DS SMITH PACKAGING FEGERSHEIM SAS—See DS Smith Plc; *Int'l*, pg. 2207
DS SMITH PACKAGING FINLAND OY—See DS Smith Plc; *Int'l*, pg. 2208
DS SMITH PACKAGING FRANCE—See DS Smith Plc; *Int'l*, pg. 2208
DS SMITH PACKAGING FUZESABONY KFT.—See DS Smith Plc; *Int'l*, pg. 2207
DS SMITH PACKAGING GALICIA S.A.—See DS Smith Plc; *Int'l*, pg. 2207

DS SMITH PACKAGING GHIMBAV SRL—See DS Smith Plc; *Int'l*, pg. 2208
DS SMITH PACKAGING-HOLLY SPRINGS, LLC—See DS Smith Plc; *Int'l*, pg. 2208
DS SMITH PACKAGING ITALIA—See DS Smith Plc; *Int'l*, pg. 2208
DS SMITH PACKAGING ITALIA SPA—See DS Smith Plc; *Int'l*, pg. 2208
DS SMITH PACKAGING KAYPAC SAS—See DS Smith Plc; *Int'l*, pg. 2208
DS SMITH PACKAGING LAROUSSE SAS—See DS Smith Plc; *Int'l*, pg. 2208
DS SMITH PACKAGING LTD.—See DS Smith Plc; *Int'l*, pg. 2208
DS SMITH PACKAGING LUCENA, S.L.—See DS Smith Plc; *Int'l*, pg. 2208
DS SMITH PACKAGING MANNHEIM—See DS Smith Plc; *Int'l*, pg. 2208
DS SMITH PACKAGING MEHUN-CIM SASU—See DS Smith Plc; *Int'l*, pg. 2208
DS SMITH PACKAGING NEDERLAND BV—See DS Smith Plc; *Int'l*, pg. 2208
DS SMITH PACKAGING PAKKAUSJALOSTE OY—See DS Smith Plc; *Int'l*, pg. 2208
DS SMITH PACKAGING POLAND SP. Z O.O.—See DS Smith Plc; *Int'l*, pg. 2208
DS SMITH PACKAGING PORTUGAL, S.A.—See DS Smith Plc; *Int'l*, pg. 2208
DS SMITH PACKAGING ROMANIA S.R.L.—See DS Smith Plc; *Int'l*, pg. 2208
DS SMITH PACKAGING SLOVAKIA S.R.O.—See DS Smith Plc; *Int'l*, pg. 2208
DS SMITH PACKAGING SUD EST SASU—See DS Smith Plc; *Int'l*, pg. 2208
DS SMITH PACKAGING SWEDEN AB—See DS Smith Plc; *Int'l*, pg. 2208
DS SMITH PACKAGING SWITZERLAND AG—See DS Smith Plc; *Int'l*, pg. 2208
DS SMITH PACKAGING SYSTEMS SAS—See DS Smith Plc; *Int'l*, pg. 2208
DS SMITH PACKAGING VELIN SASU—See DS Smith Plc; *Int'l*, pg. 2208
DS SMITH PAPER COULLONS SAS—See DS Smith Plc; *Int'l*, pg. 2208
DS SMITH PAPER DEUTSCHLAND GMBH—See DS Smith Plc; *Int'l*, pg. 2208
DS SMITH PAPER ITALIA SRL—See DS Smith Plc; *Int'l*, pg. 2208
DS SMITH PAPER KAYSERSBERG SAS—See DS Smith Plc; *Int'l*, pg. 2208
DS SMITH PAPER LIMITED—See DS Smith Plc; *Int'l*, pg. 2208
DS SMITH PAPER LTD - HIGHER KINGS PAPER MILL—See DS Smith Plc; *Int'l*, pg. 2208
DS SMITH PAPER LTD - HOLLINS PAPER MILL—See DS Smith Plc; *Int'l*, pg. 2208
DS SMITH PAPER LTD - WANSBROUGH PAPER MILL—See DS Smith Plc; *Int'l*, pg. 2208
DS SMITH PAPER ROUEN SAS—See DS Smith Plc; *Int'l*, pg. 2209
DS SMITH PAPER VIANA, S.A.—See DS Smith Plc; *Int'l*, pg. 2209
DS SMITH PAPER ZARNESTI. S.R.L.—See DS Smith Plc; *Int'l*, pg. 2209
DS SMITH PLASTICS LTD.—See Sealed Air Corporation; *U.S. Public*, pg. 1853
DS SMITH PLC - KARTOTEX PLANT—See DS Smith Plc; *Int'l*, pg. 2209
DS SMITH PLC; *Int'l*, pg. 2207
DS SMITH POLSKA S.A.—See DS Smith Plc; *Int'l*, pg. 2207
DS SMITH RECYCLING BENELUX B.V.—See DS Smith Plc; *Int'l*, pg. 2209
DS SMITH RECYCLING DEUTSCHLAND GMBH—See DS Smith Plc; *Int'l*, pg. 2209
DS SMITH RECYCLING GROUP—See DS Smith Plc; *Int'l*, pg. 2209
DS SMITH RECYCLING ITALIA SRL—See DS Smith Plc; *Int'l*, pg. 2209
DS SMITH RECYCLING SPAIN S.A.—See DS Smith Plc; *Int'l*, pg. 2209
DS SMITH RECYCLING UK LIMITED—See DS Smith Plc; *Int'l*, pg. 2209
DS SMITH REPLEN—See Sealed Air Corporation; *U.S. Public*, pg. 1853
DS SMITH RIVATEX—See DS Smith Plc; *Int'l*, pg. 2207
DS SMITH SLOVAKIA S.R.O.—See DS Smith Plc; *Int'l*, pg. 2207
DS SMITH SLOVENIJA D.O.O.—See DS Smith Plc; *Int'l*, pg. 2209
DS SMITH TRISS S.R.O.—See DS Smith Plc; *Int'l*, pg. 2209
DS SMITH UNIJAPAPIR CROATIA D.O.O.—See DS Smith Plc; *Int'l*, pg. 2209
DS SMITH VERPACKUNG + DISPLAY VERTRIEBSGESELLSCHAFT MBH—See DS Smith Plc; *Int'l*, pg. 2208
DS SMITH WITZENHAUSEN MILL—See DS Smith Plc; *Int'l*, pg. 2208

DS SMITH WORLDWIDE DISPENSERS—See Sealed Air Corporation; *U.S. Public*, pg. 1853
DS SPEDITION GMBH; *Int'l*, pg. 2209
DSS SUSTAINABLE SOLUTIONS SWITZERLAND SA; *Int'l*, pg. 2210
DSS-USF PHX LLC—See United Renewable Energy Co., Ltd.; *Int'l*, pg. 8073
DSTAR ELECTRONIC COMPANY LIMITED—See WPG Holdings Limited; *Int'l*, pg. 8460
DST CO., LTD.; *Int'l*, pg. 2210
DST DEFENCE SERVICE TRACKS GMBH—See Diehl Stiftung & Co. KG; *Int'l*, pg. 2114
DS TECHNOLOGIES INC.—See Densan System Co., Ltd.; *Int'l*, pg. 2028
DS TECHNOLOGY (USA), INC.—See Starrag Group Holding AG; *Int'l*, pg. 7179
DST GLOBAL SOLUTIONS LLC—See SS&C Technologies Holdings, Inc.; *U.S. Public*, pg. 1923
DST GLOBAL SOLUTIONS S.A. (PROPRIETARY) LTD—See SS&C Technologies Holdings, Inc.; *U.S. Public*, pg. 1923
DST GLOBAL SOLUTIONS SHANGHAI LIMITED—See SS&C Technologies Holdings, Inc.; *U.S. Public*, pg. 1923
DST HEALTH SOLUTIONS, INC.—See SS&C Technologies Holdings, Inc.; *U.S. Public*, pg. 1923
DSTILLERY; *U.S. Private*, pg. 1282
DST INDUSTRIES, INC.; *U.S. Private*, pg. 1282
DS TOMBRAS—See Charles Tombras Advertising, Inc.; *U.S. Private*, pg. 854
DST SYSTEMS, INC.—See SS&C Technologies Holdings, Inc.; *U.S. Public*, pg. 1923
DSTV MEDIA SALES PROPRIETARY LIMITED—See MultiChoice Group Limited; *Int'l*, pg. 5083
D'STYLE, INC.—See HNI Corporation; *U.S. Public*, pg. 1043
DSU LEASING, INC.—See DSU Peterbilt & GMC Truck, Inc.; *U.S. Private*, pg. 1282
DSU PETERBILT & GMC TRUCK, INC.; *U.S. Private*, pg. 1282
DSU RENTAL—See DSU Peterbilt & GMC Truck, Inc.; *U.S. Private*, pg. 1282
DSV AIR AND SEA FOR LOGISTICS SERVICES COMPANY W.L.L.—See DSV A/S; *Int'l*, pg. 2212
DSV AIR & SEA AB—See DSV A/S; *Int'l*, pg. 2211
DSV AIR & SEA AG—See DSV A/S; *Int'l*, pg. 2211
DSV AIR & SEA A/S—See DSV A/S; *Int'l*, pg. 2211
DSV AIR & SEA AS—See DSV A/S; *Int'l*, pg. 2211
DSV AIR & SEA AS—See DSV A/S; *Int'l*, pg. 2211
DSV AIR & SEA CO. LTD.—See DSV A/S; *Int'l*, pg. 2211
DSV AIR & SEA CO., LTD.—See DSV A/S; *Int'l*, pg. 2211
DSV AIR & SEA CO. LTD.—See DSV A/S; *Int'l*, pg. 2211
DSV AIR & SEA CO., LTD.—See DSV A/S; *Int'l*, pg. 2211
DSV AIR & SEA DOMINICANA, S.R.L.—See DSV A/S; *Int'l*, pg. 2211
DSV AIR & SEA D.O.O.—See DSV A/S; *Int'l*, pg. 2212
DSV AIR & SEA GMBH—See DSV A/S; *Int'l*, pg. 2211
DSV AIR & SEA (HUNGARY) LTD.—See DSV A/S; *Int'l*, pg. 2211
DSV AIR & SEA INC.—See DSV A/S; *Int'l*, pg. 2211
DSV AIR & SEA INC.—See DSV A/S; *Int'l*, pg. 2211
DSV AIR & SEA INC.—See DSV A/S; *Int'l*, pg. 2211
DSV AIR & SEA INTERNATIONAL PRIVATE LIMITED—See DSV A/S; *Int'l*, pg. 2211
DSV AIR & SEA JSC—See DSV A/S; *Int'l*, pg. 2211
DSV AIR & SEA LIMITED—See DSV A/S; *Int'l*, pg. 2211
DSV AIR & SEA LIMITED—See DSV A/S; *Int'l*, pg. 2211
DSV AIR & SEA LIMITED—See DSV A/S; *Int'l*, pg. 2211
DSV AIR & SEA LIMITED—See DSV A/S; *Int'l*, pg. 2211
DSV AIR & SEA LIMITED—See DSV A/S; *Int'l*, pg. 2211
DSV AIR & SEA LIMITED—See DSV A/S; *Int'l*, pg. 2211
DSV AIR & SEA LLC—See DSV A/S; *Int'l*, pg. 2211
DSV AIR & SEA LTD.—See DSV A/S; *Int'l*, pg. 2211
DSV AIR & SEA LTD.—See DSV A/S; *Int'l*, pg. 2211
DSV AIR & SEA LTD.—See DSV A/S; *Int'l*, pg. 2211
DSV AIR & SEA LTD.—See DSV A/S; *Int'l*, pg. 2211
DSV AIR & SEA LTD.—See DSV A/S; *Int'l*, pg. 2211
DSV AIR & SEA NV—See DSV A/S; *Int'l*, pg. 2211
DSV AIR & SEA OOD—See DSV A/S; *Int'l*, pg. 2211
DSV AIR & SEA OY—See DSV A/S; *Int'l*, pg. 2211
DSV AIR & SEA PA INC.—See DSV A/S; *Int'l*, pg. 2211
DSV AIR & SEA PAKISTAN (SMC-PRIVATE) LIMITED—See DSV A/S; *Int'l*, pg. 2211
DSV AIR & SEA PORTUGAL, LDA—See DSV A/S; *Int'l*, pg. 2211
DSV AIR & SEA (PR) INC.—See DSV A/S; *Int'l*, pg. 2211
DSV AIR & SEA PTE. LTD—See DSV A/S; *Int'l*, pg. 2211
DSV AIR & SEA (PTY) LIMITED—See DSV A/S; *Int'l*, pg. 2211
DSV AIR & SEA PTY. LTD.—See DSV A/S; *Int'l*, pg. 2211
DSV AIR & SEA PVT. LTD.—See DSV A/S; *Int'l*, pg. 2211
DSV AIR & SEA S.A. DE C.V.—See DSV A/S; *Int'l*, pg. 2212
DSV AIR & SEA S.A.—See DSV A/S; *Int'l*, pg. 2211
DSV AIR & SEA S.A.—See DSV A/S; *Int'l*, pg. 2212
DSV AIR & SEA S.A.—See DSV A/S; *Int'l*, pg. 2212
DSV AIR & SEA S.A.—See DSV A/S; *Int'l*, pg. 2212
DSV AIR & SEA S.A.—See DSV A/S; *Int'l*, pg. 2212

DSU PETERBILT & GMC TRUCK, INC.

CORPORATE AFFILIATIONS

DSV AIR & SEA SAS—See DSV A/S; *Int'l*, pg. 2212
DSV AIR & SEA S.A.S.—See DSV A/S; *Int'l*, pg. 2212
DSV AIR & SEA S.A.U.—See DSV A/S; *Int'l*, pg. 2212
DSV AIR & SEA SDN. BHD.—See DSV A/S; *Int'l*, pg. 2212
DSV AIR & SEA—See DSV A/S; *Int'l*, pg. 2211
DSV AIR & SEA SP. Z.O.O—See DSV A/S; *Int'l*, pg. 2212
DSV AIR & SEA SRL—See DSV A/S; *Int'l*, pg. 2212
DSV AIR & SEA S.R.O.—See DSV A/S; *Int'l*, pg. 2212
DSV AIR & SEA W.L.L.—See DSV A/S; *Int'l*, pg. 2211
DSV AIR SERVICES S.A.—See DSV A/S; *Int'l*, pg. 2212
DSV A/S; *Int'l*, pg. 2210
DSV COMMERCIALS LTD.—See DSV A/S; *Int'l*, pg. 2212
DSV DRAXLMAIER SYSTEMVERKABELUNGEN GMBH—See Draexlmaier Gruppe; *Int'l*, pg. 2198
DSV HELLAS S.A.—See DSV A/S; *Int'l*, pg. 2212
DSV HRVATSKA D.O.O.—See DSV A/S; *Int'l*, pg. 2212
DSV HUNGARIA KFT—See DSV A/S; *Int'l*, pg. 2212
DSV INSURANCE A/S—See DSV A/S; *Int'l*, pg. 2212
DSV INTERNATIONAL HAVA VE DENIZ TASIMACILIGI LTD.SIRKETI—See DSV A/S; *Int'l*, pg. 2212
DSV LOGISTICS CO., LTD.—See DSV A/S; *Int'l*, pg. 2212
DSV LOGISTICS LLC—See DSV A/S; *Int'l*, pg. 2212
DSV LOGISTICS SA—See DSV A/S; *Int'l*, pg. 2212
DSV OSTERREICH SPEDITION GMBH—See DSV A/S; *Int'l*, pg. 2212
DSV PANALPINA MARINE SHIPPING W.L.L.—See DSV A/S; *Int'l*, pg. 2212
DSV ROAD AB—See DSV A/S; *Int'l*, pg. 2212
DSV ROAD AB—See DSV A/S; *Int'l*, pg. 2212
DSV ROAD A.S.—See DSV A/S; *Int'l*, pg. 2212
DSV ROAD AS—See DSV A/S; *Int'l*, pg. 2212
DSV ROAD AS—See DSV A/S; *Int'l*, pg. 2212
DSV ROAD B.V.—See DSV A/S; *Int'l*, pg. 2212
DSV ROAD DOOEL SKOPJE—See DSV A/S; *Int'l*, pg. 2212
DSV ROAD D.O.O.—See DSV A/S; *Int'l*, pg. 2213
DSV ROAD EOOD—See DSV A/S; *Int'l*, pg. 2212
DSV ROAD GMBH—See DSV A/S; *Int'l*, pg. 2212
DSV ROAD HOLDING A/S—See DSV A/S; *Int'l*, pg. 2212
DSV ROAD, INC.—See DSV A/S; *Int'l*, pg. 2213
DSV ROAD, INC.—See DSV A/S; *Int'l*, pg. 2213
DSV ROAD LIMITED—See DSV A/S; *Int'l*, pg. 2212
DSV ROAD LTD.—See DSV A/S; *Int'l*, pg. 2212
DSV ROAD NV—See DSV A/S; *Int'l*, pg. 2212
DSV ROAD OOO—See DSV A/S; *Int'l*, pg. 2212
DSV ROAD OY—See DSV A/S; *Int'l*, pg. 2212
DSV ROAD S.A.—See DSV A/S; *Int'l*, pg. 2212
DSV ROAD S.A.U.—See DSV A/S; *Int'l*, pg. 2212
DSV ROAD & SOLUTIONS A.S.—See DSV A/S; *Int'l*, pg. 2212
DSV ROAD SP. Z.O.O—See DSV A/S; *Int'l*, pg. 2212
DSV ROAD S.R.L.—See DSV A/S; *Int'l*, pg. 2212
DSV ROAD TRANSPORT, INC.—See DSV A/S; *Int'l*, pg. 2212
DSV SAKHALIN, OOO—See DSV A/S; *Int'l*, pg. 2213
DSV S.A.—See DSV A/S; *Int'l*, pg. 2213
DSV SGPS, LDA.—See DSV A/S; *Int'l*, pg. 2213
DSV SLOVAKIA, S.R.O.—See DSV A/S; *Int'l*, pg. 2213
DSV SOLUTIONS 2 BV—See DSV A/S; *Int'l*, pg. 2213
DSV SOLUTIONS AB—See DSV A/S; *Int'l*, pg. 2213
DSV SOLUTIONS A/S—See DSV A/S; *Int'l*, pg. 2213
DSV SOLUTIONS AS—See DSV A/S; *Int'l*, pg. 2213
DSV SOLUTIONS (AUTOMOTIVE) NV—See DSV A/S; *Int'l*, pg. 2213
DSV SOLUTIONS BRASIL SERVICOS DE LOGISTICA LTDA.—See DSV A/S; *Int'l*, pg. 2213
DSV SOLUTIONS B.V.—See DSV A/S; *Int'l*, pg. 2213
DSV SOLUTIONS (DORDRECHT) B.V.—See DSV A/S; *Int'l*, pg. 2213
DSV SOLUTIONS FOR LOGISTICS SERVICES COMPANY LLC—See DSV A/S; *Int'l*, pg. 2213
DSV SOLUTIONS GMBH—See DSV A/S; *Int'l*, pg. 2213
DSV SOLUTIONS GROUP GMBH—See DSV A/S; *Int'l*, pg. 2213
DSV SOLUTIONS INC.—See DSV A/S; *Int'l*, pg. 2213
DSV SOLUTIONS LDA.—See DSV A/S; *Int'l*, pg. 2213
DSV SOLUTIONS LTD.—See DSV A/S; *Int'l*, pg. 2213
DSV SOLUTIONS (MOERDIJK) B.V.—See DSV A/S; *Int'l*, pg. 2213
DSV SOLUTIONS NEDERLAND B.V.—See DSV A/S; *Int'l*, pg. 2213
DSV SOLUTIONS NV—See DSV A/S; *Int'l*, pg. 2213
DSV SOLUTIONS OOO—See DSV A/S; *Int'l*, pg. 2213
DSV SOLUTIONS OY—See DSV A/S; *Int'l*, pg. 2213
DSV SOLUTIONS PTE. LTD.—See DSV A/S; *Int'l*, pg. 2213
DSV SOLUTIONS PUURS NV—See DSV A/S; *Int'l*, pg. 2213
DSV SOLUTIONS S.A.E.—See DSV A/S; *Int'l*, pg. 2213
DSV SOLUTIONS S.A.S.—See DSV A/S; *Int'l*, pg. 2213
DSV SOLUTIONS S.A.U.—See DSV A/S; *Int'l*, pg. 2213
DSV SOLUTIONS SP. Z.O.O.—See DSV A/S; *Int'l*, pg. 2213
DSV SOLUTIONS SRL—See DSV A/S; *Int'l*, pg. 2213
DSV SOUTH AFRICA (PTY) LTD.—See DSV A/S; *Int'l*, pg. 2213
DSV S.P.A.—See DSV A/S; *Int'l*, pg. 2213
DSV STUTTGART GMBH & CO. KG—See DSV A/S; *Int'l*, pg. 2213

DSV TRANSITARIOS LDA.—See DSV A/S; *Int'l*, pg. 2213
DSV TRANSPORT AS—See DSV A/S; *Int'l*, pg. 2213
DSV TRANSPORT D.O.O.—See DSV A/S; *Int'l*, pg. 2213
DSV TRANSPORT INTERNATIONAL S.A.—See DSV A/S; *Int'l*, pg. 2213
DSV TRANSPORT LTD.—See DSV A/S; *Int'l*, pg. 2213
DSV TRANSPORT SIA—See DSV A/S; *Int'l*, pg. 2213
DSV TRANSPORT UAB—See DSV A/S; *Int'l*, pg. 2213
DSV TRANSPORT (US), INC.—See DSV A/S; *Int'l*, pg. 2213
DSV UKRAINE—See DSV A/S; *Int'l*, pg. 2213
DSV-UTI EGYPT LTD.—See DSV A/S; *Int'l*, pg. 2213
DSW CAPITAL PLC; *Int'l*, pg. 2216
DS WELLFOODS CO.,LTD.—See Osaka Soda Co., Ltd.; *Int'l*, pg. 5646
DS WELLNESS & HEALTH MANAGEMENT LIMITED—See Feiyang International Holdings Group Limited; *Int'l*, pg. 2632
DSWISS, INC.; *Int'l*, pg. 2216
D.S. WOLF GROUP INTERNATIONAL, LLC; *U.S. Private*, pg. 1142
DSW RESTAURANTS INC.—See Drury Inn Inc.; *U.S. Private*, pg. 1280
DSW SHOE WAREHOUSE, INC.—See Schottenstein Stores Corporation; *U.S. Private*, pg. 3569
DSYS INC; *U.S. Private*, pg. 1282
DTAC NETWORK CO., LTD.—See Charoen Pokphand Group Co., Ltd.; *Int'l*, pg. 1453
DTAP @ DUO PTE. LTD.—See Republic Healthcare Ltd.; *Int'l*, pg. 6295
DTAP @ HOLLAND V PTE. LTD.—See Republic Healthcare Ltd.; *Int'l*, pg. 6295
DTAP @ SOMERSET PTE. LTD.—See Republic Healthcare Ltd.; *Int'l*, pg. 6295
DTB-DEUTSCHE BIOGAS AG; *Int'l*, pg. 2216
DTB DEUTSCHE TECHNIKBERATUNG GMBH—See Ceconomy AG; *Int'l*, pg. 1373
DT CAPITAL LIMITED; *Int'l*, pg. 2216
D.T. CARSON ENTERPRISES INC.; *U.S. Private*, pg. 1142
DT&C CO., LTD.; *Int'l*, pg. 2216
DTC COMMUNICATIONS, INC.—See Advent International Corporation; *U.S. Private*, pg. 99
DTC COMPUTER SUPPLIES, INC.; *U.S. Private*, pg. 1282
DTC DYNAMIC TEST CENTER AG—See Pilatus Aircraft Ltd.; *Int'l*, pg. 5866
D.T.C. ENTERPRISE PUBLIC COMPANY LIMITED; *Int'l*, pg. 1901
D.T.C. INDUSTRIES PUBLIC COMPANY LIMITED; *Int'l*, pg. 1901
D.T. CIRCUIT TECHNOLOGY CO., LTD.—See Japan Industrial Partners, Inc.; *Int'l*, pg. 3889
DT CLOUD ACQUISITION CORP.; *Int'l*, pg. 2216
DTCOM - DIRECT TO COMPANY S/A; *Int'l*, pg. 2216
DTC SURGERY CENTER, LLC—See UnitedHealth Group Incorporated; *U.S. Public*, pg. 2240
DT DEVELOPMENT VIETNAM LLC—See Daiwa House Industry Co., Ltd.; *Int'l*, pg. 1945
DTD LTD—See Sargon Capital Pty Ltd.; *Int'l*, pg. 6577
DT DOBIE KENYA—See Toyota Tsusho Corporation; *Int'l*, pg. 7876
DTECH LABS, INC.—See Elliott Management Corporation; *U.S. Private*, pg. 1368
DTECH LABS, INC.—See Veritas Capital Fund Management, LLC; *U.S. Private*, pg. 4362
D-TECH OPTOELECTRONICS INC.—See GCS Holdings, Inc.; *Int'l*, pg. 2895
DTE ELECTRIC COMPANY—See DTE Energy Company; *U.S. Public*, pg. 689
DTE ENERGY COMPANY; *U.S. Public*, pg. 689
DTE ENERGY TRADING, INC.—See DTE Energy Company; *U.S. Public*, pg. 689
DTE GAS COMPANY—See DTE Energy Company; *U.S. Public*, pg. 689
DT ELECTRONIC MANUFACTURING (BEIJING) CO., LTD.—See Detection Technology Oyj; *Int'l*, pg. 2047
DT ELECTRONIC TECHNOLOGY (WUXI) CO., LTD.—See Detection Technology Oyj; *Int'l*, pg. 2047
D-TERRA SOLUTIONS LLC—See DeBartolo Holdings, LLC; *U.S. Private*, pg. 1186
DTE STAMPEN A/S—See Dansk Traeemballage A/S; *Int'l*, pg. 1969
DTF (H.K.) LTD.—See Detection Technology Oyj; *Int'l*, pg. 2048
DT FINE ELECTRONICS CO., LTD.—See Dai Nippon Printing Co., Ltd.; *Int'l*, pg. 1915
DTF TAX-FREE INCOME 2028 TERM FUND INC.; *U.S. Public*, pg. 689
DTG2GO, LLC—See Delta Apparel, Inc.; *U.S. Public*, pg. 652
DTG ENTERPRISES, INC.—See Macquarie Group Limited; *Int'l*, pg. 4624
DTG OPERATIONS, INC.—See Hertz Global Holdings, Inc.; *U.S. Public*, pg. 1029
DTG SUPPLY, LLC—See Hertz Global Holdings, Inc.; *U.S. Public*, pg. 1029
DTG VERPACKUNGSLOGISTIK GMBH—See Deufol SE; *Int'l*, pg. 2048
DTHERA SCIENCES; *U.S. Public*, pg. 689

DT HI LOAD AUSTRALIA PTY. LTD.—See Perenti Global Limited; *Int'l*, pg. 5798
DTI DIVERSITECH, INC.—See Bureau Veritas S.A.; *Int'l*, pg. 1221
DTI GROUP LTD; *Int'l*, pg. 2217
DTIQ TECHNOLOGIES, INC.; *U.S. Private*, pg. 1282
DTK OCEANIC LIMITED—See STX Corporation; *Int'l*, pg. 7245
DTL DONAU-TANKLAGERGESELLSCHAFT MBH & CO. KG—See BayWa AG; *Int'l*, pg. 917
DTLR HOLDING, INC.—See Bruckmann, Rosser, Sherrill & Co., LLC; *U.S. Private*, pg. 671
DTL TRANSPORTATION INC.; *U.S. Private*, pg. 1282
D.T. MCCALL & SONS; *U.S. Private*, pg. 1142
DT MIDSTREAM, INC.; *U.S. Public*, pg. 689
DTM PACKAGING, LLC—See Granite Equity Partners LLC; *U.S. Private*, pg. 1755
DTM SYSTEMS INC.; *Int'l*, pg. 2217
DTN, LLC—See TBG Treuhand Partner AG; *Int'l*, pg. 7480
DTOS INTERNATIONAL EAST AFRICA (K) LIMITED—See Ireland Blyth Limited; *Int'l*, pg. 3806
DTOS LTD.—See Ireland Blyth Limited; *Int'l*, pg. 3806
DTOS TRUSTEES LTD.—See Ireland Blyth Limited; *Int'l*, pg. 3807
DTP TERRASSEMENT SA—See Bouygues S.A.; *Int'l*, pg. 1123
DTR DRAXLMAIER SISTEME TEHNICE ROMANIA S.R.L.—See Draexlmaier Gruppe; *Int'l*, pg. 2198
DT REAL ESTATE, LLC—See Hilton Worldwide Holdings Inc.; *U.S. Public*, pg. 1040
DTRIC INSURANCE COMPANY, LIMITED—See MS&AD Insurance Group Holdings, Inc.; *Int'l*, pg. 5065
D-TRIX NV—See DPG Media Group NV; *Int'l*, pg. 2189
DTRT HEALTH ACQUISITION CORP.; *U.S. Public*, pg. 689
D-TRUST GMBH—See Bundesdruckerei GmbH; *Int'l*, pg. 1215
DTR VMS ITALY S.R.L.—See DN Automotive Corporation; *Int'l*, pg. 2147
DTR VMS ITALY S.R.L.—See KKR & Co. Inc.; *U.S. Public*, pg. 1260
DTS (ASIA) LIMITED—See Xperi Inc.; *U.S. Public*, pg. 2392
DTS BETEILIGUNGEN GMBH & CO. KG—See MBB SE; *Int'l*, pg. 4751
DTS BETEILIGUNGEN VERWALTUNGS GMBH—See MBB SE; *Int'l*, pg. 4751
DTS CLOUD SECURITY MONEPE—See MBB SE; *Int'l*, pg. 4751
DTS COMPANIES INC.; *U.S. Private*, pg. 1282
DTS CORPORATION; *Int'l*, pg. 2217
DTS FLUID POWER LLC; *U.S. Private*, pg. 1282
DTS GUANGZHOU—See Xperi Inc.; *U.S. Public*, pg. 2392
DTS, INC.—See Xperi Inc.; *U.S. Public*, pg. 2391
DTS INSIGHT CORPORATION—See DTS Corporation; *Int'l*, pg. 2217
DTS IT AG—See MBB SE; *Int'l*, pg. 4751
DTS JAPAN KK—See Xperi Inc.; *U.S. Public*, pg. 2392
DTS LICENSING LIMITED—See Xperi Inc.; *U.S. Public*, pg. 2392
DTS LICENSING PTE. LTD.—See Xperi Inc.; *U.S. Public*, pg. 2392
DTS, LLC—See Xperi Inc.; *U.S. Public*, pg. 2392
DTS LOGISTICS LLC—See DTS Companies Inc.; *U.S. Private*, pg. 1282
DTS (SHANGHAI) CORPORATION—See DTS Corporation; *Int'l*, pg. 2217
DTS SOFTWARE VIETNAM CO., LTD.—See DTS Corporation; *Int'l*, pg. 2217
DTS SYSTEME GMBH—See MBB SE; *Int'l*, pg. 4751
DTS SYSTEME MUNSTER GMBH—See MBB SE; *Int'l*, pg. 4751
DTS SYSTEME WIEN GMBH—See MBB SE; *Int'l*, pg. 4751
DTSV INC.; *U.S. Private*, pg. 1282
DTS WASHINGTON LLC—See Xperi Inc.; *U.S. Public*, pg. 2392
DTS WEST CORPORATION—See DTS Corporation; *Int'l*, pg. 2217
DTV NETWORK SYSTEMS, INC.—See AT&T Inc.; *U.S. Public*, pg. 220
DTV SERVICES LIMITED—See British Broadcasting Corporation; *Int'l*, pg. 1169
DTV SERVICES LIMITED—See Comcast Corporation; *U.S. Public*, pg. 541
DTV SERVICES LIMITED—See National Grid plc; *Int'l*, pg. 5157
DTXS SILK ROAD INVESTMENT HOLDINGS COMPANY LIMITED; *Int'l*, pg. 2217
DTZ ZADELHOFF V.O.F.—See Ontario Teachers' Pension Plan; *Int'l*, pg. 5589
DTZ ZADELHOFF V.O.F.—See PAG Asia Capital Ltd.; *Int'l*, pg. 5696
DTZ ZADELHOFF V.O.F.—See TPG Capital, L.P.; *U.S. Public*, pg. 2173
DUAGON AG—See Deutsche Beteiligungs AG; *Int'l*, pg. 2063
DUAL AUSTRALIA PTY LIMITED—See Howden Group Holdings Limited; *Int'l*, pg. 3493

COMPANY NAME INDEX

DUAL AUTOMOTIVE TECHNOLOGIES (SHANGHAI) CO., LTD.—See DUAL Co. Ltd; *Int'l*, pg. 2217
DUAL BORGSTENA TEXTILE PORTUGAL UNIPESSOAL, LDA.—See DUAL Co. Ltd; *Int'l*, pg. 2217
DUAL CO. LTD - DUAL ASAN PLANT—See DUAL Co. Ltd; *Int'l*, pg. 2217
DUAL CO. LTD - DUAL BANWOUL PLANT—See DUAL Co. Ltd; *Int'l*, pg. 2217
DUAL CO. LTD - DUAL GANGHWA PLANT—See DUAL Co. Ltd; *Int'l*, pg. 2217
DUAL CO. LTD - DUAL ULSAN PLANT—See DUAL Co. Ltd; *Int'l*, pg. 2217
DUAL CO. LTD; *Int'l*, pg. 2217
DUAL COMMERCIAL LLC—See Howden Group Holdings Limited; *Int'l*, pg. 3493
DUAL CORPORATE RISKS LIMITED—See Howden Group Holdings Limited; *Int'l*, pg. 3493
DUAL DEUTSCHLAND GMBH—See Howden Group Holdings Limited; *Int'l*, pg. 3493
DUAL DRIVE TECHNOLOGIES, LTD.—See Energy Transfer LP; *U.S. Public*, pg. 762
DUAL ENGRAVING PTY. LTD.—See Dewhurst Group plc; *Int'l*, pg. 2091
DUAL GROUP AMERICAS INC—See Howden Group Holdings Limited; *Int'l*, pg. 3493
DUAL IBERICA RIESGOS PROFESIONALES S.A.—See Howden Group Holdings Limited; *Int'l*, pg. 3493
DUAL INTERNATIONAL LIMITED—See Howden Group Holdings Limited; *Int'l*, pg. 3493
DUALIS GMBH IT SOLUTION—See Durr AG; *Int'l*, pg. 2230
DUALIS GMBH—See Durr AG; *Int'l*, pg. 2230
DUAL ITALIA S.P.A—See Howden Group Holdings Limited; *Int'l*, pg. 3493
DUALITE SALES & SERVICE, INC.; *U.S. Private*, pg. 1282
DUAL LITE MANUFACTURING INC.—See Hubbell Incorporated; *U.S. Public*, pg. 1066
DUAL MOOLSAN CO., LTD—See DUAL Co. Ltd; *Int'l*, pg. 2217
DUAL NEW ZEALAND LIMITED—See Howden Group Holdings Limited; *Int'l*, pg. 3493
DUAL SPECIALTY UNDERWRITERS INC.—See Howden Group Holdings Limited; *Int'l*, pg. 3493
DUALTAP CO., LTD.; *Int'l*, pg. 2217
DUAL TEMP COMPANY, INC.; *U.S. Private*, pg. 1282
DUAL UNDERWRITING AGENCY (HONG KONG) LIMITED—See Howden Group Holdings Limited; *Int'l*, pg. 3493
DUAL UNDERWRITING AGENCY (SINGAPORE) PTE. LIMITED—See Howden Group Holdings Limited; *Int'l*, pg. 3493
DUANE MORRIS LLP; *U.S. Private*, pg. 1282
DUANE READE HOLDINGS, INC.—See Walgreens Boots Alliance, Inc.; *U.S. Public*, pg. 2323
DUANE READE, INC.—See Walgreens Boots Alliance, Inc.; *U.S. Public*, pg. 2323
DUANE READE INTERNATIONAL, LLC—See Walgreens Boots Alliance, Inc.; *U.S. Public*, pg. 2323
DUANE READE REALTY, INC.—See Walgreens Boots Alliance, Inc.; *U.S. Public*, pg. 2323
DUANE SAMMONS INSURANCE CENTER, INC.—See Stone Point Capital LLC; *U.S. Private*, pg. 3818
DUARTE, INC.; *U.S. Private*, pg. 1283
DU-ART FILM LABORATORIES INC.; *U.S. Private*, pg. 1282
DU-ART FILM LABS, INC.; *U.S. Public*, pg. 689
DUBAI AEROSPACE ENTERPRISE LTD; *Int'l*, pg. 2218
DUBAI AIRPORT FREE ZONE—See ManpowerGroup Inc.; *U.S. Public*, pg. 1357
DUBAI AL AHLIA TRANSPORT L.L.C—See Gulf General Investment Company PSC; *Int'l*, pg. 3180
DUBAI CIVIL ENGINEERING EST—See Al Hamad Contracting Company LLC; *Int'l*, pg. 278
DUBAI CRANES & TECHNICAL SERVICES LTD.—See Dubai Investments PJSC; *Int'l*, pg. 2219
DUBAI DUTY FREE—See Investment Corporation of Dubai; *Int'l*, pg. 3785
DUBAI EXPRESS LLC—See The Emirates Group; *Int'l*, pg. 7639
DUBAI FINANCIAL GROUP—See Dubai Holding LLC; *Int'l*, pg. 2218
DUBAI FINANCIAL MARKET PJSC—See Investment Corporation of Dubai; *Int'l*, pg. 3785
DUBAI FINANCIAL SERVICES AUTHORITY; *Int'l*, pg. 2218
DUBAI GROUP—See Dubai Holding LLC; *Int'l*, pg. 2218
DUBAI HOLDING LLC; *Int'l*, pg. 2218
DUBAI INSURANCE COMPANY (PSC); *Int'l*, pg. 2218
DUBAI INSURANCE GROUP—See Dubai Holding LLC; *Int'l*, pg. 2218
DUBAI INTERNATIONAL CAPITAL, LLC—See Dubai Holding LLC; *Int'l*, pg. 2218
DUBAI INTERNATIONAL DRIVING CENTER (DIDC)—See Dubai Investments PJSC; *Int'l*, pg. 2219
DUBAI INTERNATIONAL FINANCIAL CENTRE.—See National Bank of Egypt; *Int'l*, pg. 5152
DUBAI INVESTMENT GROUP—See Dubai Holding LLC; *Int'l*, pg. 2218

DUBAI INVESTMENTS PARK DEVELOPMENT COMPANY LLC—See Dubai Investments PJSC; *Int'l*, pg. 2219
DUBAI INVESTMENTS PJSC; *Int'l*, pg. 2219
DUBAI INVESTMENTS REAL ESTATE COMPANY—See Dubai Investments PJSC; *Int'l*, pg. 2219
DUBAI ISLAMIC BANK PRINTING PRESS LLC—See Dubai Islamic Bank PSJ; *Int'l*, pg. 2220
DUBAI ISLAMIC BANK PSJ; *Int'l*, pg. 2219
DUBAI ISLAMIC FINANCIAL SERVICES L.L.C.—See Dubai Islamic Bank PSJ; *Int'l*, pg. 2220
DUBAI ISLAMIC INSURANCE & REINSURANCE COMPANY P.S.C; *Int'l*, pg. 2220
DUBAI MARITIME CITY LLC—See Dubai World Corporation; *Int'l*, pg. 2221
DUBAI MERCANTILE EXCHANGE LIMITED—See CME Group, Inc.; *U.S. Public*, pg. 516
DUBAI MERCANTILE EXCHANGE LIMITED—See Dubai Holding LLC; *Int'l*, pg. 2218
DUBAI NATIONAL INSURANCE & REINSURANCE PSC; *Int'l*, pg. 2220
DUBAI PETROLEUM COMPANY—See ConocoPhillips; *U.S. Public*, pg. 568
DUBAI PROPERTIES GROUP LLC—See Dubai Holding LLC; *Int'l*, pg. 2218
DUBAI PROPERTIES—See Dubai Holding LLC; *Int'l*, pg. 2218
DUBAI REFRESHMENTS (P.S.C.) - DUBAI MAIN PRODUCTION FACILITY—See Dubai Refreshments (P.S.C.); *Int'l*, pg. 2220
DUBAI REFRESHMENTS (P.S.C.); *Int'l*, pg. 2220
DUBAI TOURISM & COMMERCE MARKETING; *Int'l*, pg. 2220
DUBAI TRADE FZE—See Dubai World Corporation; *Int'l*, pg. 2221
DUBAI WORLD CORPORATION; *Int'l*, pg. 2220
DUBAL HOLDING L.L.C—See Investment Corporation of Dubai; *Int'l*, pg. 3785
DUBAR INDUSTRIA E COMERCIO DE BEBIDAS LTDA—See Marie Brizard Wine & Spirits S.A.; *Int'l*, pg. 4693
DUBBER CORPORATION LIMITED; *Int'l*, pg. 2222
DUBEK LTD.; *Int'l*, pg. 2222
DU BELL LUMBER CO.; *U.S. Private*, pg. 1282
DUBICKI ROBNI MAGAZIN A.D.; *Int'l*, pg. 2222
DUBILIER & COMPANY, INC.; *U.S. Private*, pg. 1283
DUBIN CLARK & COMPANY, INC.; *U.S. Private*, pg. 1283
THE DUBIN GROUP, INC.—See HireQuest, Inc.; *U.S. Public*, pg. 1042
DUBLIN & ASSOCIATES, INC.; *U.S. Private*, pg. 1283
DUBLIN BUICK GMC; *U.S. Private*, pg. 1283
THE DUBLIN BUSINESS SCHOOL LIMITED—See Graham Holdings Company; *U.S. Public*, pg. 956
DUBLIN CONSTRUCTION COMPANY, INC.; *U.S. Private*, pg. 1283
DUBLIN DIALYSIS CENTER, LLC—See Nautic Partners, LLC; *U.S. Private*, pg. 2870
DUBLIN DOG COMPANY, INC.—See Prospect Hill Growth Partners, L.P.; *U.S. Private*, pg. 3288
DUBLIN FERRYPORT TERMINALS—See Irish Continental Group plc; *Int'l*, pg. 3809
DUBLIN INSURANCE SERVICES, INC.—See Aon plc; *Int'l*, pg. 496
DUBLIN INTERNAL MEDICINE PC—See St. Luke's Health Network, Inc.; *U.S. Private*, pg. 3773
DUBLIN MILLWORK CO. INC.—See Strait & Lamp Lumber Co. Inc.; *U.S. Private*, pg. 3833
DUBLIN SAN RAMON SERVICES DISTRICT; *U.S. Private*, pg. 1283
DUBLIN SURGERY CENTER, LLC—See UnitedHealth Group Incorporated; *U.S. Public*, pg. 2240
DUBLIN TRIUMPH—See Triumph Motorcycles Limited; *Int'l*, pg. 7936
DUBOIS CHEMICALS, INC.—See Altas Partners LP; *Int'l*, pg. 386
DUBOIS TELEPHONE EXCHANGE, INC.—See Range Telephone Cooperative Inc.; *U.S. Private*, pg. 3354
DUBOIS WOOD PRODUCTS INC.; *U.S. Private*, pg. 1283
DUBOKO PLAVETNILO UGLJAN PROJEKTANT D.O.O.—See Cubus Lux Plc; *Int'l*, pg. 1876
DUBORGH SKADEFORSIKRING A/S—See Intact Financial Corporation; *Int'l*, pg. 3727
DUBORGH SKADEFORSIKRING A/S—See Tryg A/S; *Int'l*, pg. 7946
DUBOSE & ASSOCIATES INSURANCE COMPANY—See Colonial Savings, F.A.; *U.S. Private*, pg. 972
DUBOSE NATIONAL ENERGY SERVICES, INC.—See Reliance Steel & Aluminum Co.; *U.S. Public*, pg. 1779
DUBOSE STEEL INC.—See Russel Metals Inc.; *Int'l*, pg. 6430
DU BOULAY CONTRACTS LTD.—See MBH Corporation Plc; *Int'l*, pg. 4752
DUB PUBLISHING, INC. - DUB SHOP—See DUB Publishing, Inc.; *U.S. Private*, pg. 1283
DUB PUBLISHING, INC.; *U.S. Private*, pg. 1283
DUBRAC TP; *Int'l*, pg. 2222
DUBRASKI & ASSOCIATES INSURANCE SERVICES, LLC—See Kelso & Company, L.P.; *U.S. Private*, pg. 2279
DUBREUIL AUTOMOBILES; *Int'l*, pg. 2222

DUBROOK CONCRETE, INC.—See Vulcan Materials Company; *U.S. Public*, pg. 2314
DUBROVACKA INVESTICIJSKA GRUPA D.O.O.—See INSTITUT IGH d.d.; *Int'l*, pg. 3723
DUBUG NO 7 INC.; *U.S. Private*, pg. 1283
DUBUIS ET CIE S.A.S.—See Stanley Black & Decker, Inc.; *U.S. Public*, pg. 1932
DUBUIS HEALTH SYSTEM, INC.; *U.S. Private*, pg. 1283
DUBUQUE BANK & TRUST COMPANY—See Heartland Financial USA, Inc.; *U.S. Public*, pg. 1018
DUBUQUE RACING ASSOCIATION LTD.; *U.S. Private*, pg. 1283
DUBUQUE STAMPING & MANUFACTURING INC.; *U.S. Private*, pg. 1283
DUBUS INDUSTRIES; *Int'l*, pg. 2222
DUCAPLAST S.A.S—See DS Smith Plc; *Int'l*, pg. 2209
DUCART INTERNATIONAL PAPER, LTD.; *Int'l*, pg. 2223
DUCATEX S.A.; *Int'l*, pg. 2223
DUCATI MOTOR HOLDING S.P.A.—See Porsche Automobil Holding SE; *Int'l*, pg. 5926
DUCATI NORTH AMERICA INC.—See Porsche Automobil Holding SE; *Int'l*, pg. 5926
DUCATI SEATTLE, LLC; *U.S. Private*, pg. 1283
DUCATT NV; *Int'l*, pg. 2223
DUC GIANG CHEMICALS GROUP JOINT STOCK COMPANY; *Int'l*, pg. 2222
DUCHATEAU FLOORS; *U.S. Private*, pg. 1284
DUCHEMBIO CO., LTD.; *Int'l*, pg. 2223
DUCHOSSOIS CAPITAL MANAGEMENT LLC—See The Duchossois Group, Inc.; *U.S. Private*, pg. 4023
THE DUCHOSSOIS GROUP, INC.; *U.S. Private*, pg. 4023
DUCHY INDEPENDENT FINANCIAL ADVISERS LIMITED—See Tavistock Investments PLC; *Int'l*, pg. 7477
DUCKBACK PRODUCTS—See The Sherwin-Williams Company; *U.S. Public*, pg. 2127
DUCK CREEK TECHNOLOGIES, INC.—See Vista Equity Partners, LLC; *U.S. Private*, pg. 4396
DUCK DUCK MOOSE, INC.—See Khan Academy, Inc.; *U.S. Private*, pg. 2301
DUCKER FSG HOLDINGS LLC; *U.S. Private*, pg. 1284
DUCKER WORLDWIDE LLC—See Ducker FSG Holdings LLC; *U.S. Private*, pg. 1284
DUCKETT CREEK SEWER DISTRICT; *U.S. Private*, pg. 1284
THE DUCKHORN PORTFOLIO, INC.; *U.S. Public*, pg. 2067
DUCKHORN WINE COMPANY—See TSG Consumer Partners LLC; *U.S. Private*, pg. 4253
DUCKREY ENTERPRISES INC.; *U.S. Private*, pg. 1284
DUCK RIVER ELECTRIC MEMBERSHIP CORPORATION; *U.S. Private*, pg. 1284
DUCKS CO.—See FP Corporation; *Int'l*, pg. 2756
DUCKS UNLIMITED, INC.; *U.S. Private*, pg. 1284
DUCK SYSTEMS CO., LTD.—See The Keihin Co., Ltd.; *Int'l*, pg. 7662
DUCKTRAP RIVER OF MAINE LLC—See Mowi ASA; *Int'l*, pg. 5059
DUCKYANG INDUSTRY CO., LTD.; *Int'l*, pg. 2223
DUCLARKEE, INC.; *U.S. Private*, pg. 1284
DUC LONG GIA LAI GROUP JSC; *Int'l*, pg. 2222
DUCLOUX SA—See VINCI S.A.; *Int'l*, pg. 8216
DU-CO CERAMICS COMPANY; *U.S. Private*, pg. 1282
DUCO INC.—See TechnipFMC plc; *Int'l*, pg. 7508
DUCOMMUN AEROSTRUCTURES INC.—See Ducommun Incorporated; *U.S. Public*, pg. 690
DUCOMMUN AEROSTRUCTURES, LLC—See Ducommun Incorporated; *U.S. Public*, pg. 690
DUCOMMUN AEROSTRUCTURES NEW YORK, INC.—See Ducommun Incorporated; *U.S. Public*, pg. 690
DUCOMMUN AEROSTRUCTURES—See Ducommun Incorporated; *U.S. Public*, pg. 690
DUCOMMUN AEROSTRUCTURES—See Ducommun Incorporated; *U.S. Public*, pg. 690
DUCOMMUN INCORPORATED; *U.S. Public*, pg. 689
DUCOMMUN—See Ducommun Incorporated; *U.S. Public*, pg. 690
DUCON INFRATECHNOLOGIES LIMITED—See Telidyne Inc.; *U.S. Public*, pg. 1998
DUCON TECHNOLOGIES INC.; *U.S. Private*, pg. 1284
DUCO SPECIALITY COATINGS (PTY) LIMITED—See AECI Limited; *Int'l*, pg. 171
DUC S.A.—See Plukon Food Group BV; *Int'l*, pg. 5898
DUC THANH WOOD PROCESSING JSC; *Int'l*, pg. 2223
DUCTIL STEEL S.A.—See Invest Nikarom Srl; *Int'l*, pg. 3775
DUCTMANN LTD.—See Lindab International AB; *Int'l*, pg. 4503
DUCTMATE INDUSTRIES INC.; *U.S. Private*, pg. 1284
DUCTOR IMPLANTACAO DE PROJETOS LTDA.—See TUV Rheinland Berlin-Brandenburg Pfalz e.V.; *Int'l*, pg. 7981
DUCTSOX CORPORATION—See Rite-Hite Holding Corporation; *U.S. Private*, pg. 3442
DUCTS UNLIMITED MECHANICAL SYSTEMS, INC.; *U.S. Private*, pg. 1284
DUCTTESTERS, INC.—See Gallant Capital Partners, LLC; *U.S. Public*, pg. 1639

DUCTS UNLIMITED MECHANICAL SYSTEMS, INC.

DUDA FARM FRESH FOOD—See A. Duda & Sons Inc.; *U.S. Private*, pg. 23
DUDA MOBILE INC.; *U.S. Private*, pg. 1284
DUDA RANCHES - DUDA SOD DIVISION—See A. Duda & Sons Inc.; *U.S. Private*, pg. 23
DUDDELL'S HONG KONG LIMITED—See Jia Group Holdings Limited; *Int'l*, pg. 3941
DUDEK & BOCK S. DE R.L. DE C.V.—See Dudek & Bock Spring Manufacturing Company; *U.S. Private*, pg. 1284
DUDEK & BOCK SPRING MANUFACTURING COMPANY; *U.S. Private*, pg. 1284
DUDEK INSURANCE AGENCY GROUP—See ABRY Partners, LLC; *U.S. Private*, pg. 42
DUDICK, INC.—See RPM International Inc.; *U.S. Public*, pg. 1818
DUDIGITAL GLOBAL LIMITED; *Int'l*, pg. 2223
DUDLEY BUILDING SOCIETY; *Int'l*, pg. 2223
DUDLEY INDUSTRIES LTD—See Rentokil Initial plc; *Int'l*, pg. 6286
DUDLEY PRODUCTS INC.; *U.S. Private*, pg. 1284
DUDLEY SUPERMARKET INC.; *U.S. Private*, pg. 1284
DUDNYK ADVERTISING & PUBLIC RELATIONS, INC.—See Dudnyk Enterprises, Ltd.; *U.S. Private*, pg. 1284
DUDNYK ENTERPRISES, LTD.; *U.S. Private*, pg. 1284
DUEA MOTOR COMPANY INC.; *U.S. Private*, pg. 1284
DUEARITY AB; *Int'l*, pg. 2223
DUE DILIGENCE CORPORATION—See Houlihan Lokey, Inc.; *U.S. Public*, pg. 1055
DUELCO A/S—See Addtech AB; *Int'l*, pg. 132
DUER CAROLINA COIL, INC.—See American Securities LLC; *U.S. Private*, pg. 249
DUERKOPP ADLER AG—See Shang Gong Group Co., Ltd.; *Int'l*, pg. 6760
DUERKOPP ADLER (DA) TRADING (SHANGHAI) CO., LTD—See Shang Gong Group Co., Ltd.; *Int'l*, pg. 6760
DUERR CYPLAN LIMITED—See Durr AG; *Int'l*, pg. 2230
DUESENBERG TECHNOLOGIES INC.; *Int'l*, pg. 2223
DUET ACQUISITION CORP.; *Int'l*, pg. 2223
DUET GROUP—See CK Hutchison Holdings Limited; *Int'l*, pg. 1636
DUET INDIA HOTELS (BANGALORE) PRIVATE LTD—See InterContinental Hotels Group PLC; *Int'l*, pg. 3736
DUET INVESTMENT HOLDINGS LIMITED—See CK Hutchison Holdings Limited; *Int'l*, pg. 1636
DUFAYLITE DEVELOPMENTS LIMITED; *Int'l*, pg. 2223
DUFERCO INTERNATIONAL TRADING HOLDING SA—See HBIS Group Co., Ltd.; *Int'l*, pg. 3295
DUFERCO S.A.; *Int'l*, pg. 2223
DUFERCO STEEL INC.—See Duferco S.A.; *Int'l*, pg. 2223
DUFERCOSTEEL PROCESSING (PTY) LTD—See HBIS Group Co., Ltd.; *Int'l*, pg. 3295
DUFF AUTO SALES, INC—See Sutherlin Automotive Group, LLC; *U.S. Private*, pg. 3887
DUFFE GRAIN INC.; *U.S. Private*, pg. 1284
DUFFEK SAND & GRAVEL INC.; *U.S. Private*, pg. 1284
DUFFERIN AGGREGATES BUTLER PIT—See CRH plc; *Int'l*, pg. 1843
DUFFERIN CONCRETE - KITCHENER—See CRH plc; *Int'l*, pg. 1843
DUFFERIN CONCRETE—See CRH plc; *Int'l*, pg. 1843
DUFFERIN CONSTRUCTION COMPANY—See CRH plc; *Int'l*, pg. 1843
DUFFEY COMMUNICATIONS, INC.; *U.S. Private*, pg. 1285
DUFFIELD ASSOCIATES INC.—See Round Table Capital Management, LP; *U.S. Private*, pg. 3488
DUFFIN MANUFACTURING COMPANY—See Geberit AG; *Int'l*, pg. 2904
DUFF-NORTON—See Columbus McKinnon Corporation; *U.S. Public*, pg. 536
DUFF & PHELPS B.V.—See Permira Advisers LLP; *Int'l*, pg. 5807
DUFF & PHELPS CANADA LIMITED—See Permira Advisers LLP; *Int'l*, pg. 5807
DUFF & PHELPS GMBH—See Permira Advisers LLP; *Int'l*, pg. 5807
DUFF & PHELPS INVESTMENT MANAGEMENT CO—See Virtus Investment Partners, Inc.; *U.S. Public*, pg. 2300
DUFF & PHELPS K.K.—See Permira Advisers LLP; *Int'l*, pg. 5807
DUFF & PHELPS, LTD.—See Permira Advisers LLP; *Int'l*, pg. 5807
DUFF & PHELPS SAS—See Permira Advisers LLP; *Int'l*, pg. 5807
DUFF & PHELPS (SWITZERLAND) SA—See Permira Advisers LLP; *Int'l*, pg. 5807
DUFF & PHELPS UTILITY AND INFRASTRUCTURE FUND INC.; *U.S. Public*, pg. 690
DUFFY MECHANICAL CORP.—See EMCOR Group, Inc.; *U.S. Public*, pg. 736
DUFFY & SHANLEY, INC.; *U.S. Private*, pg. 1285
DUFFY'S HOLDINGS INC.; *U.S. Private*, pg. 1285
DUFFYS NAPA VALLEY REHAB, LLC—See Acadia Healthcare Company, Inc.; *U.S. Public*, pg. 23
DUFFY'S SPORTS GRILL—See Duffy's Holdings Inc.; *U.S. Private*, pg. 1285

DUFIEUX INDUSTRIE S.A.S.—See Evolem S.A.; *Int'l*, pg. 2572
DUFOUR ADVERTISING; *U.S. Private*, pg. 1285
DUFOUR S.A.; *Int'l*, pg. 2223
DUFOUR SISTERON—See La cooperative Arterris SCA; *Int'l*, pg. 4387
DUFRITAL SPA—See Avolta AG; *Int'l*, pg. 749
DUFRY BABASEL MULHOUSE LTD.—See Avolta AG; *Int'l*, pg. 749
DUFRY FRANCE SA—See Avolta AG; *Int'l*, pg. 749
DUFRY HOLDINGS & INVESTMENTS AG—See Avolta AG; *Int'l*, pg. 749
DUFRY MANAGEMENT LTD.—See Avolta AG; *Int'l*, pg. 749
DUFRY SAMNAUN LTD.—See Avolta AG; *Int'l*, pg. 749
DUFRY SHOP FINANCE LIMITED SRL.—See Avolta AG; *Int'l*, pg. 749
DUFU INDUSTRIES SERVICES PTE LTD—See Dufu Technology Corp. Berhad; *Int'l*, pg. 2223
DUFU TECHNOLOGY CORP. BERHAD; *Int'l*, pg. 2223
DUGA A.D.; *Int'l*, pg. 2224
DUGA HOLDING AD; *Int'l*, pg. 2224
DUGAN & MEYERS CONSTRUCTION SERVICES, LTD.—See Baker Concrete Construction, Inc.; *U.S. Private*, pg. 456
DUGAN & MEYERS LLC—See Baker Concrete Construction, Inc.; *U.S. Private*, pg. 455
DUGAN & MEYERS LLC—See Baker Concrete Construction, Inc.; *U.S. Private*, pg. 456
DUGAN OIL CO. INC.; *U.S. Private*, pg. 1285
DUGAN PRODUCTION CORP.; *U.S. Private*, pg. 1285
DUGARD MIDDLE EAST—See C Dugard Ltd; *Int'l*, pg. 1238
DUGARD RUS LLC—See C Dugard Ltd; *Int'l*, pg. 1238
DU GESELLSCHAFT FUR ARBEITNEHMERUBERLASSUNG MBH—See Unilever PLC; *Int'l*, pg. 8044
DUGGAL COLOR PROJECTS INC.; *U.S. Private*, pg. 1285
DUGGAL VISUAL SOLUTIONS, INC.; *U.S. Private*, pg. 1285
DUGGAN CONTRACTING CORPORATION; *U.S. Private*, pg. 1285
DUGGAN INDUSTRIES, INC.; *U.S. Private*, pg. 1285
DUGGAN & MARCON INC.—See Marcon & Boyer Inc.; *U.S. Private*, pg. 2572
THE DUGGAN RHODES GROUP; *U.S. Private*, pg. 4023
DUG TECHNOLOGY LTD.; *Int'l*, pg. 2223
DUHIG AND CO. INC.; *U.S. Private*, pg. 1285
DUIBA GROUP LIMITED; *Int'l*, pg. 2224
DUING D.O.O.—See 2G Energy AG; *Int'l*, pg. 5
DUININCK COMPANIES LLC; *U.S. Private*, pg. 1285
DU INTERNATIONAL INC.; *U.S. Private*, pg. 1282
DUISBURGER VERSORGUNGS- UND VERKEHRSGESELLSCHAFT MBH; *Int'l*, pg. 2224
DUJODWALA PAPER CHEMICALS LIMITED; *Int'l*, pg. 2224
DUKA & BOSNA D.D.; *Int'l*, pg. 2224
DUKAL CORPORATION; *U.S. Private*, pg. 1285
DUKANE CORPORATION-AUDIO VISUAL DIVISION—See Dukane Corporation; *U.S. Private*, pg. 1285
DUKANE CORPORATION; *U.S. Private*, pg. 1285
DUKANE CORPORATION-ULTRASONICS DIVISION—See Dukane Corporation; *U.S. Private*, pg. 1285
DUKANE INTELLIGENT ASSEMBLY SOLUTIONS—See Dukane Corporation; *U.S. Private*, pg. 1285
DUKANE SEACOM, INC.—See HEICO Corporation; *U.S. Public*, pg. 1020
DUKAT MLIJECNA INDUSTRIJA D.D.—See Groupe Lactalis SA; *Int'l*, pg. 3105
DUKE AUTOMOTIVE CORP.; *U.S. Private*, pg. 1285
DUKE CAPITAL CORPORATION—See Duke Energy Corporation; *U.S. Public*, pg. 690
DUKE CONCRETE PRODUCTS INC.—See The Fort Miller Group Inc.; *U.S. Private*, pg. 4029
DUKE ENERGY AMERICAS, LLC—See Duke Energy Corporation; *U.S. Public*, pg. 690
DUKE ENERGY BUSINESS SERVICES LLC—See Duke Energy Corporation; *U.S. Public*, pg. 690
DUKE ENERGY CAROLINAS, LLC—See Duke Energy Corporation; *U.S. Public*, pg. 690
DUKE ENERGY CAROLINAS, LLC—See Duke Energy Corporation; *U.S. Public*, pg. 690
DUKE ENERGY CORPORATION; *U.S. Public*, pg. 690
DUKE ENERGY CORP. - SENECA—See Duke Energy Corporation; *U.S. Public*, pg. 690
DUKE ENERGY FLORIDA, LLC—See Duke Energy Corporation; *U.S. Public*, pg. 690
DUKE ENERGY GENERATION SERVICES—See Duke Energy Corporation; *U.S. Public*, pg. 690
DUKE ENERGY INDIANA, LLC—See Duke Energy Corporation; *U.S. Public*, pg. 690
DUKE ENERGY INTERNATIONAL, LLC—See Duke Energy Corporation; *U.S. Public*, pg. 690
DUKE ENERGY KENTUCKY, INC.—See Duke Energy Corporation; *U.S. Public*, pg. 690
DUKE ENERGY NGL SERVICES LP—See Duke Energy Corporation; *U.S. Public*, pg. 690

CORPORATE AFFILIATIONS

DUKE ENERGY NORTH AMERICA, LLC—See Duke Energy Corporation; *U.S. Public*, pg. 690
DUKE ENERGY OHIO, INC.—See Duke Energy Corporation; *U.S. Public*, pg. 690
DUKE ENERGY OHIO, INC—See Duke Energy Corporation; *U.S. Public*, pg. 690
DUKE ENERGY PROGRESS, LLC—See Duke Energy Corporation; *U.S. Public*, pg. 691
DUKE ENERGY RENEWABLE SERVICES, LLC—See Duke Energy Corporation; *U.S. Public*, pg. 691
DUKE ENERGY ROYAL, LLC—See Duke Energy Corporation; *U.S. Public*, pg. 691
DUKE GRAPHICS, INC.—See Heeter Printing Co., Inc.; *U.S. Private*, pg. 1903
DUKE/HULFISH, LLC—See Prologis, Inc.; *U.S. Public*, pg. 1727
DUKE MANUFACTURING COMPANY, INC.; *U.S. Private*, pg. 1285
DUKE MANUFACTURING COMPANY, INC. - ST. LOUIS FACTORY—See Duke Manufacturing Company, Inc.; *U.S. Private*, pg. 1285
DUKE MANUFACTURING C.R. S.R.O.—See Duke Manufacturing Company, Inc.; *U.S. Private*, pg. 1285
DUKEMOUNT CAPITAL PLC; *Int'l*, pg. 2224
DUKE OFFSHORE LIMITED; *Int'l*, pg. 2224
DUKE OIL SERVICES (UK) LTD—See Nigerian National Petroleum Corporation; *Int'l*, pg. 5282
DUKE REALTY CORPORATION—See Prologis, Inc.; *U.S. Public*, pg. 1726
DUKE REALTY LIMITED PARTNERSHIP—See Prologis, Inc.; *U.S. Public*, pg. 1726
DUKE REALTY OHIO—See Prologis, Inc.; *U.S. Public*, pg. 1726
DUKE ROYALTY LIMITED; *Int'l*, pg. 2224
DUKES ACE HARDWARE INC.; *U.S. Private*, pg. 1286
DUKES AEROSPACE, INC.—See TransDigm Group Incorporated; *U.S. Public*, pg. 2182
DUKES LUMBER CO. INC.; *U.S. Private*, pg. 1286
DUKES PHYSICIAN SERVICES, LLC—See Community Health Systems, Inc.; *U.S. Public*, pg. 552
DUKE STREET CAPITAL LIMITED; *Int'l*, pg. 2224
DUKETON MINING LIMITED; *Int'l*, pg. 2224
DUKE UNIVERSITY; *U.S. Private*, pg. 1285
DUKIN INDUSTRIES CO., LTD.—See Daikin Industries, Ltd.; *Int'l*, pg. 1935
DUKLA STROJIRNY, S.R.O.—See Safichem Group AG; *Int'l*, pg. 6471
DUKSAN HI-METAL CO., LTD.; *Int'l*, pg. 2224
DUK SAN NEOLUX CO., LTD.; *Int'l*, pg. 2224
DUKSAN TECHOPIA CO., LTD.; *Int'l*, pg. 2224
DUKSHINEPC CO., LTD.; *Int'l*, pg. 2224
DUKSUNG CO., LTD. - INCHEON FACTORY—See Duksung Co., Ltd.; *Int'l*, pg. 2224
DUKSUNG CO., LTD. - OSAN FACTORY—See Duksung Co., Ltd.; *Int'l*, pg. 2224
DUKSUNG CO., LTD. - PYEONGTAEK FACTORY—See Duksung Co., Ltd.; *Int'l*, pg. 2224
DUKSUNG CO., LTD.; *Int'l*, pg. 2224
DULAI FRUITS ENTERPRISE SDN. BHD.—See PLS Plantations Berhad; *Int'l*, pg. 5898
DULAMIA COTTON SPINNING MILLS LTD.; *Int'l*, pg. 2224
DULANY INDUSTRIES INC.; *U.S. Private*, pg. 1286
DULCICH, INC.; *U.S. Private*, pg. 1286
DULCINEA FARMS, LLC—See Arable Capital Partners LLC; *U.S. Private*, pg. 307
DULHUNTY POLES PTY LTD—See Energy Technologies Limited; *Int'l*, pg. 2423
DULHUNTY POWER (AUST) PTY LIMITED—See Energy Technologies Limited; *Int'l*, pg. 2423
DULHUNTY POWER (NZ) LIMITED—See Energy Technologies Limited; *Int'l*, pg. 2423
DULHUNTY POWER (THAILAND) LIMITED—See Energy Technologies Limited; *Int'l*, pg. 2423
DULLES MOTORCARS; *U.S. Private*, pg. 1286
DULL OLSON WEEKES ARCHITECTS, INC.—See ARCADIS N.V.; *Int'l*, pg. 542
DULUTH CHRYSLER JEEP DODGE & RAM; *U.S. Private*, pg. 1286
DULUTH HOLDINGS INC.; *U.S. Public*, pg. 691
DULUTH NEWS TRIBUNE—See Forum Communications Company; *U.S. Private*, pg. 1577
DULUTH REGIONAL CARE CENTER; *U.S. Private*, pg. 1286
DULUTH STORAGE, LLC—See Nelnet, Inc.; *U.S. Public*, pg. 1504
DULUX BOTSWANA (PTY) LIMITED—See Akzo Nobel N.V.; *Int'l*, pg. 273
DULUXGROUP LIMITED—See Nippon Paint Holdings Co., Ltd.; *Int'l*, pg. 5325
DULUX HOLDINGS (PNG) LIMITED—See Nippon Paint Holdings Co., Ltd.; *Int'l*, pg. 5325
DULUX HOLDINGS PTY LTD—See Nippon Paint Holdings Co., Ltd.; *Int'l*, pg. 5325
DULUX LIMITED—See Akzo Nobel N.V.; *Int'l*, pg. 274
DULUX PAINTS IRELAND LTD.—See Akzo Nobel N.V.; *Int'l*, pg. 270
DULUX PAINTS ZA—See Akzo Nobel N.V.; *Int'l*, pg. 274

COMPANY NAME INDEX DUNDEE CORPORATION

Company Index

DULUX SWAZILAND (PTY) LIMITED—See Akzo Nobel N.V.; *Int'l*, pg. 274
DUMA-BANDZINK GMBH—See SMS Holding GmbH; *Int'l*, pg. 7015
DUMAC BUSINESS SYSTEMS, INC.; *U.S. Private*, pg. 1286
DUMAC INC.; *U.S. Private*, pg. 1286
DUMAS AUTOMOBILES; *Int'l*, pg. 2224
DUMAS CONCEPTS IN BUILDING; *U.S. Private*, pg. 1287
DUMAS CO-OP; *U.S. Private*, pg. 1286
DUMAS COTTON WAREHOUSE INC.; *U.S. Private*, pg. 1287
DUMAZULU LODGE & TRADITIONAL VILLAGE—See Gooderson Leisure Corporation; *Int'l*, pg. 3039
DUMEZ-GTM CALEDONIE—See VINCI S.A.; *Int'l*, pg. 8230
DUMEZ GTM SAS—See VINCI S.A.; *Int'l*, pg. 8216
DUMEZ ILE-DE-FRANCE—See VINCI S.A.; *Int'l*, pg. 8216
DUMEZ LAGORSSE—See VINCI S.A.; *Int'l*, pg. 8216
DUMMEN ORANGE HOLDING B.V.; *Int'l*, pg. 2225
DU-MONT COMPANY INCORPORATED; *U.S. Private*, pg. 1282
DUMONT GROUP INCORPORATED; *U.S. Private*, pg. 1287
DUMORE CORPORATION - DUMORE MOTORS UNIT—See Ilion Capital Partners; *U.S. Private*, pg. 2041
DUMORE CORPORATION—See Ilion Capital Partners; *U.S. Private*, pg. 2041
DUNA ASZFALT ZTR; *Int'l*, pg. 2225
DUNA-DRAVA CEMENT KFT.—See Heidelberg Materials AG; *Int'l*, pg. 3310
DUNAFIN KFT.—See delfortgroup AG; *Int'l*, pg. 2013
DUNA HOUSE HOLDING PUBLIC COMPANY LIMITED; *Int'l*, pg. 2225
DUNAN MICROSTAQ, INC.—See Zhejiang Dun'An Artificial Environment Co., Ltd.; *Int'l*, pg. 8651
DUNAN PRICISION, INC.—See Zhejiang Dun'An Artificial Environment Co., Ltd.; *Int'l*, pg. 8651
DUNA PLAZA ZRT—See BNP Paribas SA; *Int'l*, pg. 1090
DUNAPREF SA; *Int'l*, pg. 2225
DUNAV A.D. GROCKA; *Int'l*, pg. 2225
DUNAV A.D.; *Int'l*, pg. 2225
DUNAVANT ENTERPRISES, INC.; *U.S. Private*, pg. 1287
DUNAVANT ENTERPRISES—See Dunavant Enterprises, Inc.; *U.S. Private*, pg. 1287
DUNAV OSIGURANJE AD BANJA LUKA; *Int'l*, pg. 2225
DUNAVPREVOZ A.D.; *Int'l*, pg. 2225
DUNAV RE A.D.; *Int'l*, pg. 2225
DUNAWAY ASSOCIATES, LLC; *U.S. Private*, pg. 1287
DUNBAR ARMORED INC.—See The Brink's Company; *U.S. Public*, pg. 2043
DUNBAR FUNERAL HOME—See Service Corporation International; *U.S. Public*, pg. 1871
DUNBAR STONE COMPANY; *U.S. Private*, pg. 1287
DUNBARTON CORPORATION—See CGF Industries, Inc.; *U.S. Private*, pg. 844
DUNBIA GROUP; *Int'l*, pg. 2225
DUN & BRADSTREET (AUSTRALIA) PTY. LTD.—See Archer Capital Pty. Ltd.; *Int'l*, pg. 547
DUN & BRADSTREET BELGIUM N.V.—See Cannae Holdings, Inc.; *U.S. Public*, pg. 429
DUN & BRADSTREET BELGIUM N.V.—See CC Capital Partners, LLC; *U.S. Private*, pg. 798
DUN & BRADSTREET BELGIUM N.V.—See Intercontinental Exchange, Inc.; *U.S. Public*, pg. 1142
DUN & BRADSTREET B.V.—See Cannae Holdings, Inc.; *U.S. Public*, pg. 429
DUN & BRADSTREET B.V.—See CC Capital Partners, LLC; *U.S. Private*, pg. 798
DUN & BRADSTREET B.V.—See Intercontinental Exchange, Inc.; *U.S. Public*, pg. 1142
DUN & BRADSTREET CANADA BV—See Cannae Holdings, Inc.; *U.S. Public*, pg. 429
DUN & BRADSTREET CANADA BV—See CC Capital Partners, LLC; *U.S. Private*, pg. 798
DUN & BRADSTREET CANADA BV—See Intercontinental Exchange, Inc.; *U.S. Public*, pg. 1142
DUN & BRADSTREET CANADA LTD.—See Cannae Holdings, Inc.; *U.S. Public*, pg. 429
DUN & BRADSTREET CANADA LTD.—See CC Capital Partners, LLC; *U.S. Private*, pg. 798
DUN & BRADSTREET CANADA LTD.—See Intercontinental Exchange, Inc.; *U.S. Public*, pg. 1142
DUN & BRADSTREET CIS—See Cannae Holdings, Inc.; *U.S. Public*, pg. 429
DUN & BRADSTREET CIS—See CC Capital Partners, LLC; *U.S. Private*, pg. 798
DUN & BRADSTREET CIS—See Intercontinental Exchange, Inc.; *U.S. Public*, pg. 1142
THE DUN & BRADSTREET CORPORATION—See Cannae Holdings, Inc.; *U.S. Public*, pg. 429
THE DUN & BRADSTREET CORPORATION—See CC Capital Partners, LLC; *U.S. Private*, pg. 798
THE DUN & BRADSTREET CORPORATION—See Intercontinental Exchange, Inc.; *U.S. Public*, pg. 1141
DUN & BRADSTREET CREDIBILITY CORP.—See Cannae Holdings, Inc.; *U.S. Public*, pg. 429
DUN & BRADSTREET CREDIBILITY CORP.—See CC Capital Partners, LLC; *U.S. Private*, pg. 798
DUN & BRADSTREET CREDIBILITY CORP.—See Intercontinental Exchange, Inc.; *U.S. Public*, pg. 1142
DUN & BRADSTREET (D&B) MALAYSIA SDN. BHD.—See Credit Bureau Asia Limited; *Int'l*, pg. 1835
DUN & BRADSTREET DENMARK A/S—See Ratos AB; *Int'l*, pg. 6216
DUN & BRADSTREET DEUTSCHLAND GMBH—See Ratos AB; *Int'l*, pg. 6216
DUN & BRADSTREET ESTONIA AS—See Dun & Bradstreet Holdings, Inc.; *U.S. Public*, pg. 691
DUN & BRADSTREET EUROPE, LTD.—See Cannae Holdings, Inc.; *U.S. Public*, pg. 429
DUN & BRADSTREET EUROPE, LTD.—See CC Capital Partners, LLC; *U.S. Private*, pg. 798
DUN & BRADSTREET EUROPE, LTD.—See Intercontinental Exchange, Inc.; *U.S. Public*, pg. 1142
DUN & BRADSTREET FINLAND OY—See Ratos AB; *Int'l*, pg. 6216
DUN & BRADSTREET FRANCE SA—See Base D'Informations Legales Holding S.A.S.; *Int'l*, pg. 871
DUN & BRADSTREET (HK) LTD.—See Cannae Holdings, Inc.; *U.S. Public*, pg. 429
DUN & BRADSTREET (HK) LTD.—See CC Capital Partners, LLC; *U.S. Private*, pg. 798
DUN & BRADSTREET (HK) LTD.—See Intercontinental Exchange, Inc.; *U.S. Public*, pg. 1141
DUN & BRADSTREET HOLDINGS, INC.; *U.S. Public*, pg. 691
DUN & BRADSTREET, INC. - CREDIT SERVICES—See Cannae Holdings, Inc.; *U.S. Public*, pg. 429
DUN & BRADSTREET, INC. - CREDIT SERVICES—See CC Capital Partners, LLC; *U.S. Private*, pg. 798
DUN & BRADSTREET, INC. - CREDIT SERVICES—See Intercontinental Exchange, Inc.; *U.S. Public*, pg. 1142
DUN & BRADSTREET INFORMATION SERVICES GMBH—See Ratos AB; *Int'l*, pg. 6216
DUN & BRADSTREET INFORMATION SERVICES INDIA PVT LTD.—See Cannae Holdings, Inc.; *U.S. Public*, pg. 429
DUN & BRADSTREET INFORMATION SERVICES INDIA PVT LTD.—See CC Capital Partners, LLC; *U.S. Private*, pg. 798
DUN & BRADSTREET INFORMATION SERVICES INDIA PVT LTD.—See Intercontinental Exchange, Inc.; *U.S. Public*, pg. 1142
DUN & BRADSTREET INTERNATIONAL CONSULTANT (SHANGHAI) LTD.—See Cannae Holdings, Inc.; *U.S. Public*, pg. 429
DUN & BRADSTREET INTERNATIONAL CONSULTANT (SHANGHAI) LTD.—See CC Capital Partners, LLC; *U.S. Private*, pg. 798
DUN & BRADSTREET INTERNATIONAL CONSULTANT (SHANGHAI) LTD.—See Intercontinental Exchange, Inc.; *U.S. Public*, pg. 1142
DUN & BRADSTREET INVESTMENTS LIMITED—See Cannae Holdings, Inc.; *U.S. Public*, pg. 429
DUN & BRADSTREET INVESTMENTS LIMITED—See CC Capital Partners, LLC; *U.S. Private*, pg. 798
DUN & BRADSTREET INVESTMENTS LIMITED—See Intercontinental Exchange, Inc.; *U.S. Public*, pg. 1142
DUN & BRADSTREET (ISRAEL) LTD.—See Cannae Holdings, Inc.; *U.S. Public*, pg. 429
DUN & BRADSTREET (ISRAEL) LTD.—See CC Capital Partners, LLC; *U.S. Private*, pg. 798
DUN & BRADSTREET (ISRAEL) LTD.—See Intercontinental Exchange, Inc.; *U.S. Public*, pg. 1141
DUN & BRADSTREET LTD.—See Cannae Holdings, Inc.; *U.S. Public*, pg. 429
DUN & BRADSTREET LTD.—See CC Capital Partners, LLC; *U.S. Private*, pg. 798
DUN & BRADSTREET LTD.—See Intercontinental Exchange, Inc.; *U.S. Public*, pg. 1142
DUN & BRADSTREET NETPROSPEX—See Cannae Holdings, Inc.; *U.S. Public*, pg. 429
DUN & BRADSTREET NETPROSPEX—See CC Capital Partners, LLC; *U.S. Private*, pg. 798
DUN & BRADSTREET NETPROSPEX—See Intercontinental Exchange, Inc.; *U.S. Public*, pg. 1142
DUN & BRADSTREET (NEW ZEALAND) LTD.—See Archer Capital Pty. Ltd.; *Int'l*, pg. 547
DUN & BRADSTREET POLAND SP. Z O.O.—See Ratos AB; *Int'l*, pg. 6216
DUN & BRADSTREET SCHWEIZ AG—See Ratos AB; *Int'l*, pg. 6216
DUN & BRADSTREET (SINGAPORE) PTE. LTD.—See Cannae Holdings, Inc.; *U.S. Public*, pg. 429
DUN & BRADSTREET (SINGAPORE) PTE. LTD.—See CC Capital Partners, LLC; *U.S. Private*, pg. 798
DUN & BRADSTREET (SINGAPORE) PTE. LTD.—See Intercontinental Exchange, Inc.; *U.S. Public*, pg. 1142
DUN & BRADSTREET SLOVAKIA, S.R.O.—See Dun & Bradstreet Holdings, Inc.; *U.S. Public*, pg. 691
DUN & BRADSTREET SPA—See Cannae Holdings, Inc.; *U.S. Public*, pg. 429
DUN & BRADSTREET SPA—See CC Capital Partners, LLC; *U.S. Private*, pg. 798
DUN & BRADSTREET SPA—See Intercontinental Exchange, Inc.; *U.S. Public*, pg. 1142
DUN & BRADSTREET SPOL S.R.O.—See Ratos AB; *Int'l*, pg. 6216
DUN & BRADSTREET SVERIGE AB—See Ratos AB; *Int'l*, pg. 6216
DUN & BRADSTREET TECHNOLOGIES & DATA SERVICES PRIVATE LIMITED—See Cannae Holdings, Inc.; *U.S. Public*, pg. 429
DUN & BRADSTREET TECHNOLOGIES & DATA SERVICES PRIVATE LIMITED—See CC Capital Partners, LLC; *U.S. Private*, pg. 798
DUN & BRADSTREET TECHNOLOGIES & DATA SERVICES PRIVATE LIMITED—See Intercontinental Exchange, Inc.; *U.S. Public*, pg. 1142
DUN & BRADSTREET (VIETNAM) LLC—See Cannae Holdings, Inc.; *U.S. Public*, pg. 429
DUN & BRADSTREET (VIETNAM) LLC—See CC Capital Partners, LLC; *U.S. Private*, pg. 798
DUN & BRADSTREET (VIETNAM) LLC—See Intercontinental Exchange, Inc.; *U.S. Public*, pg. 1142
DUNCAN AVIATION INC.; *U.S. Private*, pg. 1287
DUNCAN BOLT; *U.S. Private*, pg. 1287
DUNCAN BROTHERS LIMITED—See Camellia Plc; *Int'l*, pg. 1271
DUNCAN CHANNON; *U.S. Private*, pg. 1287
DUNCAN CO.; *U.S. Private*, pg. 1287
DUNCAN CREEK INC.—See Mason Companies, Inc.; *U.S. Private*, pg. 2602
DUNCAN/DAY ADVERTISING; *U.S. Private*, pg. 1288
DUNCAN DISPOSAL SYSTEMS LLC—See BC Partners LLP; *Int'l*, pg. 924
DUNCAN ENGINEERING LIMITED; *Int'l*, pg. 2225
DUNCAN ENTERPRISES—See Duncan Financial Corporation; *U.S. Private*, pg. 1287
DUNCAN FARMACEUTICA, S.A.—See GSK plc; *Int'l*, pg. 3148
DUNCAN FINANCIAL CORPORATION; *U.S. Private*, pg. 1287
DUNCAN FOX S.A.; *Int'l*, pg. 2225
DUNCAN FREIGHTLINER, INC.—See Lonestar Freightliner Group, Ltd.; *U.S. Private*, pg. 2489
DUNCAN HAMILTON & CO LIMITED; *Int'l*, pg. 2225
DUNCAN INDUSTRIAL SOLUTIONS INC.—See TruArc Partners, L.P.; *U.S. Private*, pg. 4245
DUNCAN KITCHEN GRIPS INC.—See Browne & Co.; *Int'l*, pg. 1198
DUNCAN LAWRIE (IOM) LIMITED—See Camellia Plc; *Int'l*, pg. 1271
DUNCAN LAWRIE LIMITED—See Camellia Plc; *Int'l*, pg. 1271
DUNCAN LAWRIE OFFSHORE SERVICES LIMITED—See Camellia Plc; *Int'l*, pg. 1271
DUNCAN LAWRIE—See Camellia Plc; *Int'l*, pg. 1271
DUNCAN OIL COMPANY; *U.S. Private*, pg. 1287
DUNCAN OIL COMPANY; *U.S. Private*, pg. 1287
DUNCAN-PARNELL, INC.; *U.S. Private*, pg. 1288
DUNCAN-PARNELL—See Duncan-Parnell, Inc.; *U.S. Private*, pg. 1288
DUNCAN-PARNELL—See Duncan-Parnell, Inc.; *U.S. Private*, pg. 1288
DUNCAN-PARNELL—See Duncan-Parnell, Inc.; *U.S. Private*, pg. 1288
DUNCAN-PARNELL—See Duncan-Parnell, Inc.; *U.S. Private*, pg. 1288
DUNCAN-PARNELL—See Duncan-Parnell, Inc.; *U.S. Private*, pg. 1288
DUNCAN PHARMACEUTICALS PHILIPPINES INC.—See GSK plc; *Int'l*, pg. 3145
DUNCAN REGIONAL HOSPITAL; *U.S. Private*, pg. 1287
DUNCAN SEAWALL, DOCK & BOAT LIFT, LLC; *U.S. Private*, pg. 1287
DUNCAN SOLUTIONS, INC.—See Navient Corporation; *U.S. Public*, pg. 1500
DUNCAN SUPPLY CO. INC.; *U.S. Private*, pg. 1288
DUNCAN SYSTEMS INC.—See LCI Industries; *U.S. Public*, pg. 1295
DUNCAN TOYS COMPANY—See Nordic Group of Companies, Ltd.; *U.S. Private*, pg. 2936
DUNCAN-WILLIAMS, INC.; *U.S. Private*, pg. 1288
DUNCASTER LIFECARE COMMUNITY; *U.S. Private*, pg. 1288
DUNDALK DEMOCRAT LTD—See JPIMedia Holdings Limited; *Int'l*, pg. 4006
DUNDAS DATA VISUALIZATION, INC.—See TA Associates, Inc.; *U.S. Private*, pg. 3915
DUNDAS MINERALS LIMITED; *Int'l*, pg. 2225
DUNDAS STAR NEWS INC.—See Torstar Corporation; *Int'l*, pg. 7831
DUNDEE 360 REAL ESTATE CORPORATION—See Dundee Corporation; *Int'l*, pg. 2225
DUNDEE BANK—See Mackey Banco, Inc.; *U.S. Private*, pg. 2537
DUNDEE BREWING CO.—See Florida Ice and Farm Co. S.A.; *Int'l*, pg. 2707
DUNDEE CITRUS GROWERS ASSOCIATION; *U.S. Private*, pg. 1288
DUNDEE CORPORATION; *Int'l*, pg. 2225

DUNDEE CORPORATION

DUNDEE ENERGY LIMITED—See Dundee Corporation; *Int'l*, pg. 2225
DUNDEE INSURANCE AGENCY LTD—See The Bank of Nova Scotia; *Int'l*, pg. 7616
DUNDEE PRECIOUS METALS INC.; *Int'l*, pg. 2226
DUNDEE PRECIOUS METALS KRUMOVGRAD EAD—See Dundee Precious Metals Inc.; *Int'l*, pg. 2226
DUNDEE PRECIOUS METALS - SOFIA—See Dundee Precious Metals Inc.; *Int'l*, pg. 2226
DUNDEE PRECIOUS METALS TSUMEB (PTY) LTD—See Sinomine Resource Group Co.; *Int'l*, pg. 6953
DUNDEE REALTY MANAGEMENT (B.C.) CORP.—See Dundee Corporation; *Int'l*, pg. 2226
DUNDEE REALTY MANAGEMENT CORPORATION—See Dundee Corporation; *Int'l*, pg. 2225
DUNDEE REALTY MANAGEMENT (SASK) CORP.—See Dundee Corporation; *Int'l*, pg. 2226
DUNDEE REALTY USA INC.—See Dundee Corporation; *Int'l*, pg. 2226
DUNDEE RESOURCES LTD.—See Dundee Corporation; *Int'l*, pg. 2226
DUNDEE SUSTAINABLE TECHNOLOGIES INC.; *Int'l*, pg. 2226
DUNDEE VETS4PETS LIMITED—See Pets at Home Group Plc; *Int'l*, pg. 5833
DUNDEEWEALTH INC.—See The Bank of Nova Scotia; *Int'l*, pg. 7616
DUNDON CAPITAL ACQUISITION CORPORATION; *U.S. Private*, pg. 1288
DUNDRUM TOWN CENTRE MANAGEMENT LIMITED—See Hammerson plc; *Int'l*, pg. 3238
THE DUNE COMPANY OF IMPERIAL VALLEY INC.; *U.S. Private*, pg. 4023
DUNE COMPANY OF YUMA LLC; *U.S. Private*, pg. 1288
DUNEDIN CAPITAL PARTNERS LIMITED—See Dunedin Enterprise Investment Trust PLC; *Int'l*, pg. 2226
DUNEDIN CITY MOTORS LTD—See The Colonial Motor Company Limited; *Int'l*, pg. 7634
DUNEDIN ENTERPRISE INVESTMENT TRUST PLC; *Int'l*, pg. 2226
DUNEDIN INCOME GROWTH INVESTMENT TRUST PLC; *Int'l*, pg. 2226
DUNELM GROUP PLC; *Int'l*, pg. 2226
DUNELM (SOFT FURNISHINGS) LIMITED—See Dunelm Group plc; *Int'l*, pg. 2226
DUNE MEDICAL DEVICES—See Dilon Technologies LLC; *U.S. Private*, pg. 1232
DUNE MERCANTILE LIMITED; *Int'l*, pg. 2226
DUNES POINT CAPITAL, LLC; *U.S. Private*, pg. 1288
DUNGAN ENGINEERING PA; *U.S. Private*, pg. 1289
DUNGARVIN, INC.; *U.S. Private*, pg. 1289
DUNHAM & ASSOCIATES INVESTMENT COUNCIL, INC.; *U.S. Private*, pg. 1289
DUNHAM-BUSH, INC.—See Berjaya Corporation Berhad; *Int'l*, pg. 984
DUNHAM-BUSH (MALAYSIA) BERHAD—See Berjaya Corporation Berhad; *Int'l*, pg. 984
DUNHAM ENGINEERING—See Tailwind Capital Group, LLC; *U.S. Private*, pg. 3924
DUNHAM EXPRESS CORPORATION; *U.S. Private*, pg. 1289
DUNHAM-PRICE INC.; *U.S. Private*, pg. 1289
DUNHAM RUBBER & BELTING CORP.—See Platte River Ventures, LLC; *U.S. Private*, pg. 3211
DUNHAM'S ATHLEISURE CORPORATION; *U.S. Private*, pg. 1289
DUNHILL HOMES, LLC; *U.S. Private*, pg. 1289
DUNHILL INTERNATIONAL LIST CO., INC.; *U.S. Private*, pg. 1289
DUNHOUR AGENCY, INC.—See World Insurance Associates LLC; *U.S. Private*, pg. 4565
DUNI AB; *Int'l*, pg. 2226
DUNI AG—See Duni AB; *Int'l*, pg. 2226
DUNI A/S—See Duni AB; *Int'l*, pg. 2226
DUNI BENELUX B.V.—See Duni AB; *Int'l*, pg. 2226
DUNI BENELUX B.V.—See Duni AB; *Int'l*, pg. 2226
DUNI BETEILIGUNGSGESELLSCHAFT MBH—See Duni AB; *Int'l*, pg. 2226
DUNI & CO. KG—See Duni AB; *Int'l*, pg. 2226
DUNI (CZ) S.R.O.—See Duni AB; *Int'l*, pg. 2226
DUNIEC BROS. LTD.; *Int'l*, pg. 2226
DUNI EFF SP. Z O.O.—See Duni AB; *Int'l*, pg. 2226
DUNI GMBH—See Duni AB; *Int'l*, pg. 2226
DUNI IBERICA S.L.—See Duni AB; *Int'l*, pg. 2226
DUNI LTD.—See Duni AB; *Int'l*, pg. 2227
DUNI OY—See Duni AB; *Int'l*, pg. 2226
DUNI SALES POLAND SP. Z O.O.—See Duni AB; *Int'l*, pg. 2227
DUNI VERWALTUNGS GMBH—See Duni AB; *Int'l*, pg. 2226
DUNI ZAO—See Duni AB; *Int'l*, pg. 2227
DUNK & BRIGHT FURNITURE CO.; *U.S. Private*, pg. 1289
DUNKELBERGER ENGINEERING & TESTING, INC. - SARASOTA OFFICE—See Terracon Consultants, Inc.; *U.S. Private*, pg. 3970
DUNKELBERGER ENGINEERING & TESTING, INC.—See Terracon Consultants, Inc.; *U.S. Private*, pg. 3970

DUNKERMOTOREN FRANCE SAS—See AMETEK, Inc.; *U.S. Public*, pg. 120
DUNKERMOTOREN ITALIA S.R.L.—See AMETEK, Inc.; *U.S. Public*, pg. 120
DUNKERMOTOREN SUBOTICA D.O.O.—See AMETEK, Inc.; *U.S. Public*, pg. 120
DUNKERMOTOREN TAICANG CO., LTD.—See AMETEK, Inc.; *U.S. Public*, pg. 120
DUNKERMOTOREN USA INC.—See AMETEK, Inc.; *U.S. Public*, pg. 120
DUNKERQUE LNG SAS—See AXA S.A.; *Int'l*, pg. 757
DUNKERQUE LNG SAS—See Electricite de France S.A.; *Int'l*, pg. 2350
DUNKERQUE LNG SAS—See Publigas; *Int'l*, pg. 6114
DUNKIN' BRANDS GROUP, INC.—See Roark Capital Group Inc.; *U.S. Private*, pg. 3455
DUNKIN' BRANDS, INC.—See Roark Capital Group Inc.; *U.S. Private*, pg. 3455
DUNKIN & BUSH INC.; *U.S. Private*, pg. 1289
DUNKIN' DONUTS LLC—See Roark Capital Group Inc.; *U.S. Private*, pg. 3455
DUNKIN'S DIAMONDS; *U.S. Private*, pg. 1289
DUNKIRK POWER LLC—See NRG Energy, Inc.; *U.S. Public*, pg. 1550
DUNKIRK SPECIALTY STEEL, LLC—See Universal Stainless & Alloy Products, Inc.; *U.S. Public*, pg. 2262
DUNKLEY INTERNATIONAL—See Cherry Central Cooperative, Inc.; *U.S. Private*, pg. 874
DUNLAP & CO., INC.; *U.S. Private*, pg. 1289
DUNLAP INDUSTRIES INC.; *U.S. Private*, pg. 1290
DUNLAP & KYLE CO. INC.; *U.S. Private*, pg. 1289
DUNLAP MANUFACTURING CO.—See The Vernon Company; *U.S. Private*, pg. 4130
DUNLAP OIL COMPANY INC.; *U.S. Private*, pg. 1290
DUNLAP SALES, INC.; *U.S. Private*, pg. 1290
DUNLAPSLK, P.C.; *U.S. Private*, pg. 1290
DUNLAW OPTICAL LABORATORIES INC.—See EssilorLuxottica SA; *Int'l*, pg. 2513
DUNLOP AIRCRAFT TYRES LIMITED—See Liberty Hall Capital Partners, L.P.; *U.S. Private*, pg. 2444
DUNLOP AUTO TYRES PVT. LIMITED—See Ruia Group; *Int'l*, pg. 6426
DUNLOP BTL LTD.—See SSE Plc; *Int'l*, pg. 7155
DUNLOP CONVEYOR BELTING GHANA LIMITED—See Compagnie Generale des Etablissements Michelin SCA; *Int'l*, pg. 1742
DUNLOP CONVEYOR BELTING POLSKA SP.ZO.O—See Compagnie Generale des Etablissements Michelin SCA; *Int'l*, pg. 1742
DUNLOP GOLF CLUB CORP.—See Sumitomo Rubber Industries, Ltd.; *Int'l*, pg. 7298
DUNLOP GOODYEAR TIRES LTD.—See Sumitomo Rubber Industries, Ltd.; *Int'l*, pg. 7298
DUNLOP GRUND UND SERVICE VERWALTUNGS GMBH—See The Goodyear Tire & Rubber Company; *U.S. Public*, pg. 2083
DUNLOP HOME PRODUCTS, LTD.—See Sumitomo Rubber Industries, Ltd.; *Int'l*, pg. 7298
DUNLOPILLO DEUTSCHLAND GMBH—See Bettzeit GmbH; *Int'l*, pg. 1004
DUNLOP OIL & MARINE LTD.—See Continental Aktiengesellschaft; *Int'l*, pg. 1781
DUNLOP POLYMERS PVT. LTD.—See Ruia Group; *Int'l*, pg. 6426
DUNLOP SERVICE B.V.—See Compagnie Generale des Etablissements Michelin SCA; *Int'l*, pg. 1742
DUNLOP SLAZENGER GROUP LTD.; *Int'l*, pg. 2227
DUNLOP SPORTS ENTERPRISES LTD.—See Sumitomo Rubber Industries, Ltd.; *Int'l*, pg. 7299
DUNLOP SPORTS KOREA CO., LTD.—See Sumitomo Rubber Industries, Ltd.; *Int'l*, pg. 7299
DUNLOP SPORTS LIMITED - ICHIJIMA FACTORY—See Sumitomo Rubber Industries, Ltd.; *Int'l*, pg. 7299
DUNLOP SPORTS MARKETING CO., LTD.—See Sumitomo Rubber Industries, Ltd.; *Int'l*, pg. 7299
DUNLOP SPORTS WELLNESS CO. LTD.—See Sumitomo Rubber Industries, Ltd.; *Int'l*, pg. 7300
DUNLOP SRIXON SPORTS ASIA SDN. BHD.—See Sumitomo Rubber Industries, Ltd.; *Int'l*, pg. 7299
DUNLOP SRIXON SPORTS HONG KONG CO., LTD.—See Sumitomo Rubber Industries, Ltd.; *Int'l*, pg. 7299
DUNLOP SRIXON SPORTS MANUFACTURING (THAILAND) CO., LTD.—See Sumitomo Rubber Industries, Ltd.; *Int'l*, pg. 7299
DUNLOP SRIXON SPORTS SOUTH AFRICA (PTY.) LTD.—See Sumitomo Rubber Industries, Ltd.; *Int'l*, pg. 7299
DUNLOP SRIXON SPORTS (THAILAND) CO., LTD.—See Sumitomo Rubber Industries, Ltd.; *Int'l*, pg. 7299
DUNLOP TECH GMBH—See Sumitomo Rubber Industries, Ltd.; *Int'l*, pg. 7299
DUNLOP TIRE (THAILAND) CO., LTD.—See Sumitomo Rubber Industries, Ltd.; *Int'l*, pg. 7299
DUNMORE CORPORATION/BREWSTER—See Steel Partners Holdings L.P.; *U.S. Public*, pg. 1942
DUNMORE CORPORATION—See Steel Partners Holdings L.P.; *U.S. Public*, pg. 1942

CORPORATE AFFILIATIONS

DUNMORE EUROPE GMBH—See Steel Partners Holdings L.P.; *U.S. Public*, pg. 1942
DUNMORE LLLP—See Enstar Group Limited; *Int'l*, pg. 2448
DUNMORE MATERIALS—See Haines & Kibblehouse Inc.; *U.S. Private*, pg. 1841
DUNNAGE ENGINEERING INC.; *U.S. Private*, pg. 1290
DUNN & BERGER, INC.—See Aveanna Healthcare Holdings Inc.; *U.S. Public*, pg. 242
DUNN BLUE PRINT COMPANY; *U.S. Private*, pg. 1290
DUNN BROS COFFEE, INC.—See Gala Capital Partners, LLC; *U.S. Private*, pg. 1635
DUNN & CO. INC.; *U.S. Private*, pg. 1290
DUNN CONSTRUCTION COMPANY, INC.; *U.S. Private*, pg. 1290
DUNN&CO.; *U.S. Private*, pg. 1290
DUNNDATA COMPANY; *U.S. Private*, pg. 1290
DUNN-EDWARDS CORPORATION—See Nippon Paint Holdings Co., Ltd.; *Int'l*, pg. 5325
DUNN ELECTRIC CO.; *U.S. Private*, pg. 1290
DUNNE MANNING INC.; *U.S. Private*, pg. 1290
DUNNHUMBY AUSTRALIA PTY LIMITED—See Tesco PLC; *Int'l*, pg. 7571
DUNNHUMBY BRASIL CONSULTORA LTDA—See Tesco PLC; *Int'l*, pg. 7571
DUNNHUMBY CHILE SPA—See Tesco PLC; *Int'l*, pg. 7571
DUNNHUMBY CONSULTING SERVICES INDIA PRIVATE LIMITED—See Tesco PLC; *Int'l*, pg. 7571
DUNNHUMBY IRELAND LIMITED—See Tesco PLC; *Int'l*, pg. 7571
DUNNHUMBY (KOREA) LIMITED—See Tesco PLC; *Int'l*, pg. 7571
DUNNHUMBY LIMITED—See Tesco PLC; *Int'l*, pg. 7572
DUNNHUMBY NEW ZEALAND LIMITED—See Tesco PLC; *Int'l*, pg. 7571
DUNNHUMBY SPAIN S.L.—See Tesco PLC; *Int'l*, pg. 7571
DUNNHUMBY (THAILAND) LIMITED—See Tesco PLC; *Int'l*, pg. 7571
DUNNING MOTOR SALES, INC.; *U.S. Private*, pg. 1290
DUNN INSURANCE, INC.—See Aquiline Capital Partners LLC; *U.S. Private*, pg. 305
DUNN LUMBER COMPANY INCORPORATED; *U.S. Private*, pg. 1290
DUNN LUMBER NORTHWEST INC.—See Dunn Lumber Company Incorporated; *U.S. Private*, pg. 1290
DUNN MANUFACTURING CORPORATION; *U.S. Private*, pg. 1290
DUNN PAPER, INC.—See Arbor Private Investment Company, LLC; *U.S. Private*, pg. 309
DUNN-RITE PRODUCTS, INC.; *U.S. Private*, pg. 1290
DUNN ROADBUILDERS LLC; *U.S. Private*, pg. 1290
DUNNS (LONG SUTTON) LTD; *Int'l*, pg. 2227
DUNN SOLUTIONS GROUP, INC.—See Kaar Technologies India Pvt Ltd.; *Int'l*, pg. 4045
DUNN'S SPORTING GOODS CO. INC.; *U.S. Private*, pg. 1290
DUNN TIRE LLC; *U.S. Private*, pg. 1290
DUNOD EDITEUR SA—See Vivendi SE; *Int'l*, pg. 8272
DUNPHEY & ASSOCIATES SUPPLY CO.—See Watsco, Inc.; *U.S. Public*, pg. 2336
DUNSFORD FINANCE PLANNING PTY. LTD.—See Azimut Holding SpA; *Int'l*, pg. 779
DUNSFORD FINANCIAL PLANNING PTY. LTD.—See Azimut Holding SpA; *Int'l*, pg. 779
DUNS INVESTING CORPORATION—See Cannae Holdings, Inc.; *U.S. Public*, pg. 429
DUNS INVESTING CORPORATION—See CC Capital Partners, LLC; *U.S. Private*, pg. 798
DUNS INVESTING CORPORATION—See Intercontinental Exchange, Inc.; *U.S. Public*, pg. 1142
DUNSIRN PARTNERS LLC; *U.S. Private*, pg. 1290
DUNSNET, LLC—See Cannae Holdings, Inc.; *U.S. Public*, pg. 429
DUNSNET, LLC—See CC Capital Partners, LLC; *U.S. Private*, pg. 798
DUNSNET, LLC—See Intercontinental Exchange, Inc.; *U.S. Public*, pg. 1142
DUNSTAN THOMAS CONSULTING LIMITED—See Dunstan Thomas Group Limited; *Int'l*, pg. 2227
DUNSTAN THOMAS ENERGY LIMITED—See Dunstan Thomas Group Limited; *Int'l*, pg. 2227
DUNSTAN THOMAS GROUP LIMITED; *Int'l*, pg. 2227
DUNSTAN THOMAS HOLDINGS LIMITED—See Dunstan Thomas Group Limited; *Int'l*, pg. 2227
DUNTON BROTHERS LTD.—See Michelmersh Brick Holdings PLC; *Int'l*, pg. 4875
DUNWELL COMPUTERS OF CALIFORNIA—See PC Warehouse Investment Inc.; *U.S. Private*, pg. 3119
DUNWOODY VILLAGE; *U.S. Private*, pg. 1291
DUNXIN FINANCIAL HOLDINGS LTD; *Int'l*, pg. 2227
DUNYA VARLIK YONETIM A.S.; *Int'l*, pg. 2227
DUOBACK CO., LTD; *Int'l*, pg. 2227
DUO BANK OF CANADA—See Centerbridge Partners, L.P.; *U.S. Private*, pg. 814
DUOC HAU GIANG PHARMACEUTICAL JSC—See Taisho Pharmaceutical Holdings Co., Ltd; *Int'l*, pg. 7417
DUODEC Z IMMOBILIEN LEASING GESELLSCHAFT M.B.H.—See UniCredit S.p.A.; *Int'l*, pg. 8037

COMPANY NAME INDEX

DUO DOGS, INC.; *U.S. Private*, pg. 1291
DUO-FAST CORPORATION—See Illinois Tool Works Inc.; *U.S. Public*, pg. 1102
DUO-FAST DE ESPANA S.A.—See Illinois Tool Works Inc.; *U.S. Public*, pg. 1102
DUO-FAST, INC.; *U.S. Private*, pg. 1291
DUO-FAST KOREA CO. LTD.—See Illinois Tool Works Inc.; *U.S. Public*, pg. 1102
DUO-FAST LLC—See Illinois Tool Works Inc.; *U.S. Public*, pg. 1102
DUO-FORM PLASTICS; *U.S. Private*, pg. 1291
DUOLINE TECHNOLOGY—See Robroy Industries Inc.; *U.S. Private*, pg. 3463
DUOLINGO, INC.; *U.S. Public*, pg. 691
DUOLUN TECHNOLOGY CO., LTD.; *Int'l*, pg. 2227
DUONG HIEU TRADING & MINING JSC; *Int'l*, pg. 2227
DUOPHARMA BIOTECH BERHAD—See Batu Kawan Berhad; *Int'l*, pg. 891
DUOPHARMA BIOTECH BERHAD—See Permodalan Nasional Berhad; *Int'l*, pg. 5809
DUO PR; *U.S. Private*, pg. 1291
DUO SECURITY LLC—See Cisco Systems, Inc.; *U.S. Public*, pg. 499
DUO SOFTWARE (PVT.) LIMITED—See Duo World, Inc.; *U.S. Public*, pg. 691
DUOS TECHNOLOGIES GROUP, INC.; *U.S. Public*, pg. 692
DUOTECH SERVICES, INC—See Bernhard Capital Partners Management, LP; *U.S. Private*, pg. 537
DUO WORLD, INC.; *U.S. Public*, pg. 691
DUOYUAN GLOBAL WATER INC.—See Duoyuan Investments Limited; *Int'l*, pg. 2227
DUOYUAN INVESTMENTS LIMITED; *Int'l*, pg. 2227
DUOYUAN PRINTING, INC.—See Duoyuan Investments Limited; *Int'l*, pg. 2227
DUPACO COMMUNITY CREDIT UNION; *U.S. Private*, pg. 1291
DU PAGE AIRPORT AUTHORITY; *U.S. Private*, pg. 1282
DUPAGE CREDIT UNION; *U.S. Private*, pg. 1291
DUPAGE DODGE CHRYSLER JEEP, INC.; *U.S. Private*, pg. 1291
DUPAGE MACHINE PRODUCTS, INC.; *U.S. Private*, pg. 1291
DU PAGE PRECISION PRODUCTS CO.; *U.S. Private*, pg. 1282
DUPAMIJ HOLDING GMBH—See Heidelberg Materials AG; *Int'l*, pg. 3310
DUPAR CONTROLS INC.—See Dewhurst Group plc; *Int'l*, pg. 2091
DU PAREIL AU MEME SA; *Int'l*, pg. 2217
DUPHIL INC.; *U.S. Private*, pg. 1291
DUPLESSIS BUICK GMC TRUCK, INC.; *U.S. Private*, pg. 1291
DUPLEX SA; *Int'l*, pg. 2227
DUPLICATOR SALES & SERVICE INC.; *U.S. Private*, pg. 1291
DUPLI-COLOR PRODUCTS COMPANY—See The Sherwin-Williams Company; *U.S. Public*, pg. 2127
DUPLI ENVELOPES & GRAPHICS - MALVERN—See Matt Industries Inc.; *U.S. Private*, pg. 2613
DUPLIN MARKETING COMPANY, LLC—See WH Group Limited; *Int'l*, pg. 8395
DUPLI PRINT SAS; *Int'l*, pg. 2227
DUPLO MEDIA AS—See Schibsted ASA; *Int'l*, pg. 6617
DUPLO USA CORPORATION; *U.S. Private*, pg. 1291
DUPNITSA-TABAC AD; *Int'l*, pg. 2227
DUPONT AGRICULTURAL CHEMICALS LTD, SHANGHAI—See FMC Corporation; *U.S. Public*, pg. 861
DUPONT AGRICULTURAL PRODUCTS—See Corteva, Inc.; *U.S. Public*, pg. 582
DUPONT AGRICULTURE & NUTRITION—See Corteva, Inc.; *U.S. Public*, pg. 582
DU PONT APOLLO (SHENZHEN) LIMITED—See DuPont de Nemours, Inc.; *U.S. Public*, pg. 692
DUPONT-ASAHI FLASH SPUN PRODUCTS CO., LTD.—See Asahi Kasei Corporation; *Int'l*, pg. 596
DUPONT ASIA PACIFIC LIMITED—See Dow Inc.; *U.S. Public*, pg. 685
DUPONT ASTURIAS, S.L.—See Corteva, Inc.; *U.S. Public*, pg. 583
DUPONT (AUSTRALIA) LTD.—See Corteva, Inc.; *U.S. Public*, pg. 582
DU PONT (AUSTRALIA) PTY LTD.—See DuPont de Nemours, Inc.; *U.S. Public*, pg. 692
DUPONT BEDU TRANSPORTS—See SNCF; *Int'l*, pg. 7025
DUPONT CAPITAL MANAGEMENT CORPORATION—See Corteva, Inc.; *U.S. Public*, pg. 583
DU PONT CHINA HOLDING COMPANY LTD.—See DuPont de Nemours, Inc.; *U.S. Public*, pg. 692
DUPONT (CHINA) RESEARCH & DEVELOPMENT AND MANAGEMENT CO., LTD.—See DuPont de Nemours, Inc.; *U.S. Public*, pg. 692
DUPONT COMMUNITY CREDIT UNION; *U.S. Private*, pg. 1291
DU PONT DE NEMOURS (BELGIUM) BVBA—See DuPont de Nemours, Inc.; *U.S. Public*, pg. 692
DUPONT DE NEMOURS (DEUTSCHLAND) GMBH—See DuPont de Nemours, Inc.; *U.S. Public*, pg. 693
DUPONT DE NEMOURS (FRANCE) S.A.S, CERNAY PLANT—See Corteva, Inc.; *U.S. Public*, pg. 584
DUPONT DE NEMOURS, INC.; *U.S. Public*, pg. 693
DUPONT DE NEMOURS KENYA LIMITED—See International Flavors & Fragrances Inc.; *U.S. Public*, pg. 1151
DUPONT DE NEMOURS (LUXEMBOURG) SARL—See DuPont de Nemours, Inc.; *U.S. Public*, pg. 693
DUPONT DE NEMOURS (NEDERLAND) B.V.—See DuPont de Nemours, Inc.; *U.S. Public*, pg. 693
DUPONT DE NEMOURS SOUTH AFRICA (PTY) LTD.—See Corteva, Inc.; *U.S. Public*, pg. 584
DUPONT DEUTSCHLAND HOLDING GMBH & CO. KG—See DuPont de Nemours, Inc.; *U.S. Public*, pg. 692
DUPONT DO BRASIL S.A.—See Corteva, Inc.; *U.S. Public*, pg. 584
DU PONT FAR EAST, INC.—See Corteva, Inc.; *U.S. Public*, pg. 582
DUPONT FILAMENTS EUROPE, B.V.—See Celanese Corporation; *U.S. Public*, pg. 465
DUPONT HELLAS S.A.—See Corteva, Inc.; *U.S. Public*, pg. 582
DUPONT IBERICA, S.L.—See Corteva, Inc.; *U.S. Public*, pg. 584
DUPONT KABUSHIKI KAISHA—See DuPont de Nemours, Inc.; *U.S. Public*, pg. 692
DUPONT (KOREA) INC.—See DuPont de Nemours, Inc.; *U.S. Public*, pg. 692
DUPONT & LEOSK ENTERPRISES SDN BHD; *Int'l*, pg. 2227
DUPONT MAGYARORSZAG KFT—See Corteva, Inc.; *U.S. Public*, pg. 582
DUPONT MEXICO, S.A. DE C.V.—See DuPont de Nemours, Inc.; *U.S. Public*, pg. 693
DU PONT-MGC CO., LTD.—See Mitsubishi Gas Chemical Company, Inc.; *Int'l*, pg. 4948
DUPONT MITSUI FLUOROCHEMICALS CO., LTD.—See DuPont de Nemours, Inc.; *U.S. Public*, pg. 692
DUPONT MITSUI FLUOROCHEMICALS CO., LTD.—See Mitsui Chemicals, Inc.; *Int'l*, pg. 4981
DUPONT MITSUI POLYCHEMICALS CO., LTD.—See DuPont de Nemours, Inc.; *U.S. Public*, pg. 692
DUPONT MITSUI POLYCHEMICALS CO., LTD.—See Mitsui Chemicals, Inc.; *Int'l*, pg. 4981
DUPONT NUTRITION BIOSCIENCES APS—See DuPont de Nemours, Inc.; *U.S. Public*, pg. 692
DUPONT NUTRITION BIOSCIENCES - BRABRAND—See DuPont de Nemours, Inc.; *U.S. Public*, pg. 692
DUPONT NUTRITION & BIOSCIENCES IBERICA S.L.U.—See DuPont de Nemours, Inc.; *U.S. Public*, pg. 692
DUPONT NUTRITION MANUFACTURING UK LIMITED—See DuPont de Nemours, Inc.; *U.S. Public*, pg. 693
DUPONT PAKISTAN OPERATIONS (PVT.) LIMITED—See DuPont de Nemours, Inc.; *U.S. Public*, pg. 693
DUPONT PERFORMANCE SOLUTIONS (SINGAPORE) PTE. LTD.—See Celanese Corporation; *U.S. Public*, pg. 465
DUPONT PERFORMANS COZUMLERI ENDUSTRIYEL URUNLER TICARET LIMITED SIRKETI—See Celanese Corporation; *U.S. Public*, pg. 465
DUPONT POLAND SP Z O.O.—See Corteva, Inc.; *U.S. Public*, pg. 582
DUPONT PUBLISHING, INC.—See GMF Capital LLC; *U.S. Private*, pg. 1722
DUPONT REGISTRY—See GMF Capital LLC; *U.S. Private*, pg. 1722
DUPONT ROMANIA S.R.L.—See Corteva, Inc.; *U.S. Public*, pg. 582
DUPONT, S.A. DE C.V.—See DuPont de Nemours, Inc.; *U.S. Public*, pg. 693
DUPONT SINGAPORE PTE. LTD.—See Corteva, Inc.; *U.S. Public*, pg. 584
DUPONT SPECIALTY PRODUCTS GMBH & CO. KG—See DuPont de Nemours, Inc.; *U.S. Public*, pg. 693
DUPONT SPECIALTY PRODUCTS INDIA PRIVATE LIMITED—See DuPont de Nemours, Inc.; *U.S. Public*, pg. 693
DUPONT STYLO CORPORATION—See DuPont de Nemours, Inc.; *U.S. Public*, pg. 693
DUPONT STYRO CORPORATION—See DuPont de Nemours, Inc.; *U.S. Public*, pg. 693
DUPONT TAIWAN LTD.—See DuPont de Nemours, Inc.; *U.S. Public*, pg. 693
DUPONT TEIJIN FILMS CHINA LTD.—See DuPont de Nemours, Inc.; *U.S. Public*, pg. 693
DUPONT TEIJIN FILMS CHINA LTD.—See Teijin Limited; *Int'l*, pg. 7522
DUPONT (THAILAND) LIMITED—See Corteva, Inc.; *U.S. Public*, pg. 582
DU PONT-TORAY CO., LTD.—See DuPont de Nemours, Inc.; *U.S. Public*, pg. 692
DU PONT-TORAY CO., LTD.—See Toray Industries, Inc.; *Int'l*, pg. 7823

DURALEE MULTIFABRICS, INC.

DUPONT TURKEY ENDUSTRI URUNLERI LIMITED SIRKETI—See Corteva, Inc.; *U.S. Public*, pg. 582
DUPONT UENTROP GMBH—See DuPont de Nemours, Inc.; *U.S. Public*, pg. 693
DUPONT (U.K.) INDUSTRIAL LIMITED—See DuPont de Nemours, Inc.; *U.S. Public*, pg. 692
DUPONT (U.K.) LTD.—See Corteva, Inc.; *U.S. Public*, pg. 582
DUPONT UKRAINE LLC—See Corteva, Inc.; *U.S. Public*, pg. 584
DUPONT WASHINGTON WORKS—See Corteva, Inc.; *U.S. Public*, pg. 584
THE DUPPS COMPANY; *U.S. Private*, pg. 4024
THE DUPPS COMPANY THERMAL TECHNOLOGY DIV.—See The Dupps Company; *U.S. Private*, pg. 4024
DUPREE, INC.; *U.S. Private*, pg. 1291
DUPRE ENERGY SERVICES, LLC; *U.S. Private*, pg. 1291
DUPREE PLUMBING COMPANY; *U.S. Private*, pg. 1291
DUPRE LOGISTICS, LLC; *U.S. Private*, pg. 1291
DUPRE MINERALS LIMITED—See Goodwin PLC; *Int'l*, pg. 3041
DUPREY LIMITED—See National Electronics Holdings Limited; *Int'l*, pg. 5156
DUPUY STORAGE & FORWARDING LLC—See Ridgewood Infrastructure LLC; *U.S. Private*, pg. 3433
DUPUY STORAGE & FORWARDING LLC—See Savage Services Corporation; *U.S. Private*, pg. 3555
DUQUESNE LIGHT COMPANY—See Macquarie Group Limited; *Int'l*, pg. 4627
DUQUESNE LIGHT HOLDINGS, INC.—See Macquarie Group Limited; *Int'l*, pg. 4627
DUQUETTE CONSTRUCTION; *Int'l*, pg. 2227
DURA ART STONE INC.; *U.S. Private*, pg. 1291
DURA AUTOMOTIVE—See MiddleGround Management, LP; *U.S. Private*, pg. 2711
DURA AUTOMOTIVE SYSTEMS, INC.—See MiddleGround Management, LP; *U.S. Private*, pg. 2711
DURABAG COMPANY INC.; *U.S. Private*, pg. 1292
DURA-BOND BEARING CO.—See Melling Tool Company Inc.; *U.S. Private*, pg. 2662
DURA-BOND INDUSTRIES INC.; *U.S. Private*, pg. 1292
DURABON SDN BHD—See IJM Corporation Berhad; *Int'l*, pg. 3608
DURABOOK AMERICAS INC.—See Twinhead International Corp.; *Int'l*, pg. 7990
DURABUILT WINDOWS & DOORS; *Int'l*, pg. 2228
THE DURACELL COMPANY—See Berkshire Hathaway Inc.; *U.S. Public*, pg. 316
DURACLEAN INTERNATIONAL, INC.; *U.S. Private*, pg. 1292
DURA COAT PRODUCTS, INC.—See Axalta Coating Systems Ltd.; *U.S. Public*, pg. 255
DURA COAT PRODUCTS OF ALABAMA, INC.—See Axalta Coating Systems Ltd.; *U.S. Public*, pg. 255
DURACO INDUSTRIES, INC.—See Hines Corporation; *U.S. Private*, pg. 1949
DURACO SPECIALTY TAPES LLC—See OpenGate Capital Management, LLC; *U.S. Private*, pg. 3030
DURAFERRO INDUSTRIA E COMERCIO LTDA.—See Bardella S.A. Industrias Mecanicas; *Int'l*, pg. 864
DURAFIBER TECHNOLOGIES (DFT), INC. - SALISBURY PLANT—See Sun Capital Partners, Inc.; *U.S. Private*, pg. 3859
DURAFIBER TECHNOLOGIES (DFT), INC. - SHELBY FACILITY—See Sun Capital Partners, Inc.; *U.S. Private*, pg. 3859
DURAFIBER TECHNOLOGIES (DFT), INC.—See Sun Capital Partners, Inc.; *U.S. Private*, pg. 3859
DURAFIBER TECHNOLOGIES (DFT), INC. - WINNSBORO PLANT—See Sun Capital Partners, Inc.; *U.S. Private*, pg. 3859
DURA-FIBRE, LLC.—See Dunsirn Partners LLC; *U.S. Private*, pg. 1290
DURAFLAME, INC.; *U.S. Private*, pg. 1292
DURAFLEX INC.; *U.S. Private*, pg. 1292
DURAFLEX LTD.—See Masco Corporation; *U.S. Public*, pg. 1391
DURAGAS, S.A.—See Repsol, S.A.; *Int'l*, pg. 6292
DURAGROUP LLC; *U.S. Private*, pg. 1292
DURALAMP S.P.A—See 3F Filippi SpA; *Int'l*, pg. 7
DURALED LIGHTING TECHNOLOGIES CORP.—See Unity Opto Technology Co., Ltd.; *Int'l*, pg. 8076
DURALEE MULTIFABRICS, INC.; *U.S. Private*, pg. 1292
DURA-LINE CORPORATION—See Grupo Empresarial Kaluz S.A. de C.V.; *Int'l*, pg. 3127
DURA-LINE CORP. - SPARKS PLANT—See Grupo Empresarial Kaluz S.A. de C.V.; *Int'l*, pg. 3127
DURA-LINE HOLDINGS, INC.—See Grupo Empresarial Kaluz S.A. de C.V.; *Int'l*, pg. 3127
DURALIT—See Grupo Empresarial Kaluz S.A. de C.V.; *Int'l*, pg. 3126
DURAL LEEDS PTY. LTD.—See 3G Capital Partners L.P.; *U.S. Public*, pg. 12
DURALLOY AG—See Aalberts N.V.; *Int'l*, pg. 34
DURALLOY SUD GMBH—See Aalberts N.V.; *Int'l*, pg. 34
DURALOY TECHNOLOGY—See Park Corp.; *U.S. Private*, pg. 3096

DURALEE MULTIFABRICS, INC.

CORPORATE AFFILIATIONS

DURA MEDICAL, INC.—See HCA Healthcare, Inc.; *U.S. Public*, pg. 995
DURAMED INC.—See Can B Corp.; *U.S. Public*, pg. 428
DURAMERICA BROKERAGE INC; *U.S. Private*, pg. 1292
DURA-METAL PRODUCTS CORP.—See KKR & Co. Inc.; *U.S. Public*, pg. 1252
DURAMETAL, S.A.—See Cie Automotive S.A.; *Int'l*, pg. 1604
DURA-MILL INC.—See Sandvik AB; *Int'l*, pg. 6534
DURAMOLD CASTINGS INC; *U.S. Private*, pg. 1292
DURANCE GRANULATS; *Int'l*, pg. 2228
DURAND BUILDERS SERVICE INC.; *U.S. Private*, pg. 1292
DURAND GLASS MANUFACTURING CO.—See Jacques Georges Durand Industries, S.A.; *Int'l*, pg. 3866
DURAN DOGAN BASIM VE AMBALAJ SANAYI A.S.; *Int'l*, pg. 2228
DURAND PRODUCTS, LLC—See Lyon & Dittrich Holding Company; *U.S. Private*, pg. 2522
DURAND SA; *Int'l*, pg. 2228
DURAND SERVICES; *Int'l*, pg. 2228
DURAND WAYLAND INC.; *U.S. Private*, pg. 1292
DURANGO BOOT COMPANY, LLC—See Rocky Brands, Inc.; *U.S. Public*, pg. 1807
DURANGO COCA-COLA BOTTLING CO.; *U.S. Private*, pg. 1292
DURANGO DIALYSIS CENTER, LLC—See DaVita Inc.; *U.S. Public*, pg. 638
DURANGO RESOURCES INC.; *Int'l*, pg. 2228
DURANGO SWITZERLAND B.V.—See Kardan N.V.; *Int'l*, pg. 4079
DURAN OIL CO; *U.S. Private*, pg. 1292
DURANT BANCORP, INC.; *U.S. Private*, pg. 1292
DURANTE RENTALS, LLC—See Clairvest Group Inc.; *Int'l*, pg. 1641
DURANTE S.P.A.—See Sesa S.p.A.; *Int'l*, pg. 6728
DURANT H.M.A., LLC—See Community Health Systems, Inc.; *U.S. Public*, pg. 552
DURANT PLASTICS & MANUFACTURING, INC.; *U.S. Private*, pg. 1292
DURA PLASTIC PRODUCTS, INC.—See Tigre S.A; *Int'l*, pg. 7747
DURAPOWER MANUFACTURING (PTY) LIMITED—See Power Development Services (Pty) Limited; *Int'l*, pg. 5945
DURASERV CORP; *U.S. Private*, pg. 1293
DURA SOFTWARE, INC.—See Dura Software Series A Qof LLC; *U.S. Private*, pg. 1292
DURA SOFTWARE SERIES A QOF LLC; *U.S. Private*, pg. 1291
DURASOL AWNINGS, INC.—See BAT S.p.A.; *Int'l*, pg. 888
DURA SOLETANCHE BACHY MOZAMBIQUE, LDA.—See VINCI S.A.; *Int'l*, pg. 8216
DURA SOLETANCHE BACHY PTY LTD.—See VINCI S.A.; *Int'l*, pg. 8234
DURA SUPREME LLC—See GHK Capital Partners LP; *U.S. Private*, pg. 1690
DURATECH INDUSTRIES INC.; *U.S. Private*, pg. 1293
DURATEC LIMITED; *Int'l*, pg. 2228
DURATEL S.P.A.—See EcoTec s.r.l.; *Int'l*, pg. 2300
DURATEX NORTH AMERICA INC.—See Itausa - Investimentos Itau S.A.; *Int'l*, pg. 3831
DURATEX S.A.—See Itausa - Investimentos Itau S.A.; *Int'l*, pg. 3831
DURATHERM WINDOW CORPORATION—See Westny Building Products Co.; *U.S. Private*, pg. 4500
DURATIONAL CAPITAL MANAGEMENT, LP; *U.S. Private*, pg. 1293
DURA UNDERCUSHIONS LTD.; *Int'l*, pg. 2228
DURAVANT LLC—See Warburg Pincus LLC; *U.S. Private*, pg. 4437
DURAVENT, INC.—See Egeria Capital Management B.V.; *Int'l*, pg. 2323
DURAWOOD PRODUCTS, INC.; *U.S. Private*, pg. 1293
DURAY/J.F. DUNCAN INDUSTRIES, INC.; *U.S. Private*, pg. 1293
DURBAL METALLWARENFABRIK GMBH—See The Timken Company; *U.S. Public*, pg. 2133
DURBAN COAL TERMINALS COMPANY PTY. LTD.—See The Bidvest Group Limited; *Int'l*, pg. 7624
THE DURBIN GROUP, LLC—See The Goldman Sachs Group, Inc.; *U.S. Public*, pg. 2080
DURBIN PLC—See Uniphar Plc; *Int'l*, pg. 8056
DURCON COMPANY OF POLAND SP. Z O.O.—See Clayton, Dubilier & Rice, LLC; *U.S. Private*, pg. 930
DURCON, LLC—See Clayton, Dubilier & Rice, LLC; *U.S. Private*, pg. 930
DURDACH BROS. INC.; *U.S. Private*, pg. 1293
DURDANS HOSPITAL; *Int'l*, pg. 2228
DURECOM CO., LTD.—See Hancom, Inc.; *Int'l*, pg. 3242
DURECT CORPORATION; *U.S. Public*, pg. 694
DUREX INC.; *U.S. Private*, pg. 1293
DUREX LIMITED—See Reckitt Benckiser Group plc; *Int'l*, pg. 6236
DUREX PRODUCTS INC.—See The Weir Group PLC; *Int'l*, pg. 7699
DUREZ CANADA CO., LTD.—See Sumitomo Bakelite Co., Ltd.; *Int'l*, pg. 7262

DURFEE-BUFFINTON INSURANCE AGENCY INC.—See World Insurance Associates LLC; *U.S. Private*, pg. 4565
DURGA BEARINGS CO. PVT. LTD.—See THK CO., LTD.; *Int'l*, pg. 7711
DURGA BEARINGS (MUMBAI) CO. PVT. LTD.—See THK CO., LTD.; *Int'l*, pg. 7711
THE DURHAM BULLS BASEBALL CLUB, INC.—See Capitol Broadcasting Company, Inc.; *U.S. Private*, pg. 743
DURHAM COCA COLA BOTTLING CO.; *U.S. Private*, pg. 1293
DURHAM CO.; *U.S. Private*, pg. 1293
DURHAM DISTILLERY LLC—See Constellation Brands, Inc.; *U.S. Public*, pg. 571
DURHAM GEO-ENTERPRISES INCORPORATED; *U.S. Private*, pg. 1293
DURHAM GEO SLOPE INDICATOR—See Durham Geo-Enterprises Incorporated; *U.S. Private*, pg. 1293
DURHAM GROUP—See Cashman & Katz Integrated Communications; *U.S. Private*, pg. 783
THE DURHAM HERALD CO.—See Paxton Media Group LLC; *U.S. Private*, pg. 3116
DURHAM JONES & PINEGAR, P.C.—See Dentons Group; *U.S. Private*, pg. 1207
DURHAM NUCLEAR IMAGING INC.—See WELL Health Technologies Corp.; *Int'l*, pg. 8372
DURHAM PECAN COMPANY, INC.; *U.S. Private*, pg. 1293
DURHAM PUMP, INC.; *U.S. Private*, pg. 1293
DURHAM SCHOOL SERVICES, L.P.—See Mobico Group PLC.; *Int'l*, pg. 5009
DURHAM SCHOOL SERVICES, REGIONAL OFFICE—See Mobico Group PLC; *Int'l*, pg. 5009
DURHAM SCHOOL SERVICES—See Mobico Group PLC; *Int'l*, pg. 5009
DURHAM TEES VALLEY AIRPORT LIMITED—See Peel Holdings Ltd.; *Int'l*, pg. 5779
DUR HOSPITALITY CO.; *Int'l*, pg. 2227
DURI AB—See Ratos AB; *Int'l*, pg. 6218
DURIENSEGAS - SOC. DISTRIB. DE GAS NATURAL DO DOURO, S.A.—See Galp Energia SGPS, S.A.; *Int'l*, pg. 2875
DURING DO BRASIL LTDA.—See L. Possehl & Co. mbH; *Int'l*, pg. 4382
DURING MX S.A.—See L. Possehl & Co. mbH; *Int'l*, pg. 4382
DURING SCHWEISSTECHNIK GMBH—See L. Possehl & Co. mbH; *Int'l*, pg. 4382
DURISOL RAALTE B.V.; *Int'l*, pg. 2228
DURITZAS ENTERPRISES INC.; *U.S. Private*, pg. 1293
DURKEE-MOWER, INC.; *U.S. Private*, pg. 1293
DURKIN EQUIPMENT CO. INC.—See Midwest Automation Inc.; *U.S. Private*, pg. 2720
DURKIN GROUP & ASSOCIATES LLC—See Gordon Brothers Group, LLC; *U.S. Private*, pg. 1742
DURLOCK S.A.—See Etex SA/NV; *Int'l*, pg. 2521
DURMAN COLOMBIA SAS—See Aliaxis S.A./N.V.; *Int'l*, pg. 323
DURMAN ESQUIVEL DE MEXICO S.A. DE CV—See Aliaxis S.A./N.V.; *Int'l*, pg. 324
DURMAN ESQUIVEL GUATEMALA S.A.—See Aliaxis S.A./N.V.; *Int'l*, pg. 324
DURMAN ESQUIVEL PUERTO RICO CORP.—See Aliaxis S.A./N.V.; *Int'l*, pg. 324
DURMAN ESQUIVEL S.A.—See Aliaxis S.A./N.V.; *Int'l*, pg. 324
DURMONT TEPPICHBODENFABRIK GMBH—See Pierer Konzerngesellschaft mbH; *Int'l*, pg. 5862
DURO ART INDUSTRIES, INC.; *U.S. Private*, pg. 1293
DURO BAG MANUFACTURING CO. - BROWNSVILLE—See Apollo Global Management, Inc.; *U.S. Public*, pg. 153
DURO BAG MANUFACTURING CO. - ELIZABETH—See Apollo Global Management, Inc.; *U.S. Public*, pg. 153
DURO BAG MANUFACTURING COMPANY—See Apollo Global Management, Inc.; *U.S. Public*, pg. 153
DURO BAG MANUFACTURING CO. - RICHWOOD—See Apollo Global Management, Inc.; *U.S. Public*, pg. 153
DUROC AB; *Int'l*, pg. 2229
DUROC ENGINEERING I GOTEBORG AB—See Duroc AB; *Int'l*, pg. 2229
DUROC ENGINEERING I HELSINGBORG AB—See Duroc AB; *Int'l*, pg. 2229
DUROC ENGINEERING I UMEA AB—See Duroc AB; *Int'l*, pg. 2229
DUROCHER AUTO SALES INC.; *U.S. Private*, pg. 1294
DUROCHER MARINE—See Kokosing Construction Company, Inc.; *U.S. Private*, pg. 2340
DUROCHER TV & APPLIANCE INC.; *U.S. Private*, pg. 1294
DUROC LASER COATING AB—See Duc Long Gia Lai Group JSC; *Int'l*, pg. 2222
DUROC MACHINE TOOL AB—See Duroc AB; *Int'l*, pg. 2229
DUROC MACHINE TOOL AS—See Duroc AB; *Int'l*, pg. 2229
DUROC MACHINE TOOL OU—See Duroc AB; *Int'l*, pg. 2229

DUROC MACHINE TOOL SIA—See Duroc AB; *Int'l*, pg. 2229
DUROCRAFT DESIGN MANUFACTURING INC.—See Craftmade International, Inc.; *U.S. Private*, pg. 1082
DUROC RAIL AB—See Duroc AB; *Int'l*, pg. 2229
DUROC TOOLING I OLOFSTROM AB—See Duroc AB; *Int'l*, pg. 2229
DURO DAKOVIC ELEKTROMONT D.D.—See Duro Dakovic Holding d.d.; *Int'l*, pg. 2228
DURO DAKOVIC ENERGETIKA I INFRASTRUKTURA D.O.O.—See Duro Dakovic Holding d.d.; *Int'l*, pg. 2228
DURO DAKOVIC HOLDING D.D.; *Int'l*, pg. 2228
DURO DAKOVIC INZENJERING D.D.—See Duro Dakovic Holding d.d.; *Int'l*, pg. 2228
DURO DAKOVIC MONTAZA D.D.—See Bilfinger SE; *Int'l*, pg. 1028
DURO DAKOVIC PROIZVODNJA OPREME D.O.O.—See Duro Dakovic Holding d.d.; *Int'l*, pg. 2228
DURO DAKOVIC SLOBODNA ZONA D.O.O.—See Duro Dakovic Holding d.d.; *Int'l*, pg. 2228
DURO DAKOVIC SPECIJALNA VOZILA D.D.—See Duro Dakovic Holding d.d.; *Int'l*, pg. 2228
DURO DAKOVIC STROJNA OBRADA D.O.O.—See Duro Dakovic Holding d.d.; *Int'l*, pg. 2228
DURO DAKOVIC TERMOENERGETSKA POSTROJENJA D.O.O.; *Int'l*, pg. 2228
DURO DE MEXICO, S.A. DE C.V.; *Int'l*, pg. 2228
DURO DYNE CORPORATION; *U.S. Private*, pg. 1293
DURODYNE INC.—See Eaton Corporation plc; *Int'l*, pg. 2279
DURO ELECTRIC, LLC—See MDU Resources Group, Inc.; *U.S. Public*, pg. 1410
DURO FELGUERA INDUSTRIAL PROJECTS CONSULTING CO., LTD.—See Duro Felguera, S.A.; *Int'l*, pg. 2228
DURO FELGUERA OIL & GAS S.A.—See Duro Felguera, S.A.; *Int'l*, pg. 2228
DURO FELGUERA PLANTAS INDUSTRIALES, S.A.U.—See Duro Felguera, S.A.; *Int'l*, pg. 2228
DURO FELGUERA, S.A.; *Int'l*, pg. 2228
DURO INDUSTRIES INC.; *U.S. Private*, pg. 1293
DURO-LAST ROOFING, INC.; *U.S. Private*, pg. 1293
DURO-LIFE CORPORATION—See Tricor Pacific Capital, Inc.; *Int'l*, pg. 7920
DURO METAL INDUSTRIAL (M) SDN. BHD.—See Mayu Global Group Berhad; *Int'l*, pg. 4747
DURON, INC.—See The Sherwin-Williams Company; *U.S. Public*, pg. 2127
DURON ONTARIO LTD.; *Int'l*, pg. 2230
DUROPACK D.O.O.—See DS Smith Plc; *Int'l*, pg. 2209
DUROPACK GMBH—See DS Smith Plc; *Int'l*, pg. 2209
DUROPACK KRUSEVAC A. D.—See DS Smith Plc; *Int'l*, pg. 2209
DUROPACK LTD; *Int'l*, pg. 2230
DUROPACK STARPACK KFT.—See DS Smith Plc; *Int'l*, pg. 2209
DUROPACK STEMI LTD.—See DS Smith Plc; *Int'l*, pg. 2209
DUROPACK TRAKIA PAPIR S.A.—See DS Smith Plc; *Int'l*, pg. 2209
DUROPACK TURPAK OBALY A.S.—See DS Smith Plc; *Int'l*, pg. 2209
DUROPAL GMBH—See Pfleiderer GmbH; *Int'l*, pg. 5836
DUROPLY INDUSTRIES LTD.; *Int'l*, pg. 2230
DURO SALAJ A.D.; *Int'l*, pg. 2229
DUROSPAN CO., LTD.—See Vanachai Group Public Company Limited; *Int'l*, pg. 8128
DUROS S.A.; *Int'l*, pg. 2230
DUROTECH, INC.; *U.S. Private*, pg. 1294
DUR-O-WAL INC.—See Dayton Superior Corporation; *U.S. Private*, pg. 1178
DUROX COMPANY—See Westinghouse Air Brake Technologies Corporation; *U.S. Public*, pg. 2357
DURR AFRICA (PTY.) LTD.—See Durr AG; *Int'l*, pg. 2230
DURR AG; *Int'l*, pg. 2230
DURR AIS S.A. DE C.V.—See Durr AG; *Int'l*, pg. 2230
DURR ANLAGENBAU GMBH—See Durr AG; *Int'l*, pg. 2231
DURRANS RMS (PTY) LTD—See James Durrans & Sons Limited; *Int'l*, pg. 3875
DURRANTS LTD.—See Exponent Private Equity LLP; *Int'l*, pg. 2589
DURR ASSEMBLY PRODUCTS GMBH—See Durr AG; *Int'l*, pg. 2231
DURR BRASIL LTDA.—See Durr AG; *Int'l*, pg. 2231
DURR DE MEXICO S.A. DE C.V.—See Durr AG; *Int'l*, pg. 2232
DURR DENTAL AG—See Air Techniques, Inc.; *U.S. Private*, pg. 140
DURR ECOCLEAN GMBH—See Shenyang Blue Silver Industry Automatic Equipment Co., Ltd.; *Int'l*, pg. 6803
DURR ECOCLEAN INC—See Durr AG; *Int'l*, pg. 2231
DURR ECOCLEAN S.A.S.—See Durr AG; *Int'l*, pg. 2231
DURRETT SHEPPARD STEEL COMPANY, INC.—See Reliance Steel & Aluminum Co.; *U.S. Public*, pg. 1779
DURR INC.—See Durr AG; *Int'l*, pg. 2231
DURR INDIA PRIVATE LTD.—See Durr AG; *Int'l*, pg. 2231
DURR IT SERVICE GMBH—See Durr AG; *Int'l*, pg. 2231
DURR JAPAN K.K.—See Durr AG; *Int'l*, pg. 2231

COMPANY NAME INDEX

DURR KOREA INC.—See Durr AG; *Int'l*, pg. 2231
DURR LTD.—See Durr AG; *Int'l*, pg. 2231
DURR MECHANICAL CONSTRUCTION INC.; *U.S. Private*, pg. 1294
DURR MEGTEC LLC—See Durr AG; *Int'l*, pg. 2231
DURR PAINTSHOP SYSTEMS ENGINEERING (SHANGHAI) CO. LTD.—See Durr AG; *Int'l*, pg. 2231
DURR POLAND SP. Z O.O.—See Durr AG; *Int'l*, pg. 2231
DURRPOL SP.Z.O.O.—See Durr AG; *Int'l*, pg. 2232
DURR SOMAC GMBH—See Durr AG; *Int'l*, pg. 2231
DURR SOUTH AFRICA (PTY.) LTD—See Durr AG; *Int'l*, pg. 2231
DURR SYSTEMS CANADA INC.—See Durr AG; *Int'l*, pg. 2231
DURR SYSTEMS CZECH REPUBLIC A.S.—See Durr AG; *Int'l*, pg. 2231
DURR SYSTEMS GMBH—See Durr AG; *Int'l*, pg. 2231
DURR SYSTEMS GMBH—See Durr AG; *Int'l*, pg. 2231
DURR SYSTEMS INC. - PLYMOUTH—See Durr AG; *Int'l*, pg. 2231
DURR SYSTEMS, INC.—See Durr AG; *Int'l*, pg. 2231
DURR SYSTEMS MAKINE MUHENDISLIK PROJE ITHALAT VE IHRACAT LTD—See Durr AG; *Int'l*, pg. 2231
DURR SYSTEMS (MALAYSIA) SDN. BHD.—See Durr AG; *Int'l*, pg. 2231
DURR SYSTEMS MAROC SARL AU—See Durr AG; *Int'l*, pg. 2231
DURR SYSTEM SPAIN SA—See Durr AG; *Int'l*, pg. 2231
DURR SYSTEMS S.A.S.—See Durr AG; *Int'l*, pg. 2231
DURR SYSTEMS SLOVAKIA SPOL. S R.O.—See Durr AG; *Int'l*, pg. 2231
DURR SYSTEMS—See Durr AG; *Int'l*, pg. 2231
DURR SYSTEMS SPAIN—See Durr AG; *Int'l*, pg. 2231
DURR SYSTEMS WOLFSBURG GMBH—See Durr AG; *Int'l*, pg. 2231
DURR (THAILAND) CO., LTD.—See Durr AG; *Int'l*, pg. 2230
DURR UNIVERSAL EUROPE LTD.—See Durr AG; *Int'l*, pg. 2231
DURR UNIVERSAL, INC.—See Durr AG; *Int'l*, pg. 2231
DURR UNIVERSAL S. DE R.L. DE C.V.—See Durr AG; *Int'l*, pg. 2231
DURR VIETNAM COMPANY LIMITED—See Durr AG; *Int'l*, pg. 2232
D-URSO ENTERPRISES INC.; *U.S. Private*, pg. 1139
DURST-BAU GMBH—See ACS, Actividades de Construccion y Servicios, S.A.; *Int'l*, pg. 113
DURST CORPORATION; *U.S. Private*, pg. 1294
DURSTMULLER GMBH—See Arcure; *Int'l*, pg. 552
DURST—See Regal Rexnord Corporation; *U.S. Public*, pg. 1773
DURWEST CONSTRUCTION MANAGEMENT; *Int'l*, pg. 2234
DUSA PHARMACEUTICALS, INC.—See Sun Pharmaceutical Industries Ltd.; *Int'l*, pg. 7307
DUSCHPRODUKTER SWEDEN AB—See Volati AB; *Int'l*, pg. 8300
DUSCHY MARKETING OU—See Volati AB; *Int'l*, pg. 8300
DUSHORE CONSTRUCTION MATERIALS—See Haines & Kibblehouse Inc.; *U.S. Private*, pg. 1841
DUSIT EXCELLENCE CO., LTD.—See Dusit Thani Public Company Limited; *Int'l*, pg. 2234
DUSIT THANI FREEHOLD & LEASEHOLD REIT; *Int'l*, pg. 2234
DUSIT THANI PHILIPPINES, INC.—See Dusit Thani Public Company Limited; *Int'l*, pg. 2234
DUSIT THANI PUBLIC COMPANY LIMITED; *Int'l*, pg. 2234
DUSK GROUP LIMITED; *Int'l*, pg. 2234
DUSKIN CO., LTD.; *Int'l*, pg. 2234
DUSKIN SERVE KYUSU CO., LTD.—See Duskin Co., Ltd.; *Int'l*, pg. 2234
DUSKIN SERVE TAIWAN CO.—See Uni-President Enterprises Corporation; *Int'l*, pg. 8028
DUSKIN SERVE TOHOKU CO., LTD.—See Duskin Co., Ltd.; *Int'l*, pg. 2234
DUSKIN SERVE TOKAI HOKURIKU CO., LTD.—See Duskin Co., Ltd.; *Int'l*, pg. 2234
DUSK NEW ZEALAND LIMITED—See Dusk Group Limited; *Int'l*, pg. 2234
DUSLO, A.S.—See Agrofert Holding, a.s.; *Int'l*, pg. 219
DUSSELDORFER PRIVATBRAUEREI FRANKENHEIM GMBH & CO. KG—See Warsteiner Brauerei Haus Cramer KG; *Int'l*, pg. 8346
DUSSINVEST2 BETEILIGUNGSGESELLSCHAFT MBH—See Erste Abwicklungsanstalt AoR; *Int'l*, pg. 2497
DUSSMANN GULF LLC—See Dussmann Stiftung & Co. KGaA; *Int'l*, pg. 2234
DUSSMANN KULTURKINDERGARTEN GEMEINNUTZIGE GMBH—See Dussmann Stiftung & Co. KGaA; *Int'l*, pg. 2234
DUSSMANN MIDDLE EAST GMBH—See Dussmann Stiftung & Co. KGaA; *Int'l*, pg. 2234
DUSSMANN PROPERTY MANAGEMENT (SHANGHAI) CO. LTD.—See Dussmann Stiftung & Co. KGaA; *Int'l*, pg. 2234
DUSSMANN SERVICE DEUTSCHLAND GMBH—See Dussmann Stiftung & Co. KGaA; *Int'l*, pg. 2234

DUSSMANN SERVICE S.R.L.—See Dussmann Stiftung & Co. KGaA; *Int'l*, pg. 2234
DUSSMANN STIFTUNG & CO. KGAA; *Int'l*, pg. 2234
DUSTEX LLC—See Insight Equity Holdings LLC; *U.S. Private*, pg. 2086
DUST FREE, LP—See CSW Industrials, Inc.; *U.S. Public*, pg. 601
DUSTIN AB—See Altor Equity Partners AB; *Int'l*, pg. 394
DUSTIN A/S—See Dustin Group AB; *Int'l*, pg. 2235
DUSTIN FINLAND OY—See Dustin Group AB; *Int'l*, pg. 2235
DUSTIN GROUP AB; *Int'l*, pg. 2235
DUSTIN NORWAY AS—See Dustin Group AB; *Int'l*, pg. 2235
DUSTROL INC.; *U.S. Private*, pg. 1294
DUST-TEX HONOLULU, INC.—See Hakuyosha Company Ltd.; *Int'l*, pg. 3222
DUSTY RHODES FORD SALES INCORPORATED; *U.S. Private*, pg. 1294
DUSTYS CAMPER WORLD, LLC—See Camping World Holdings, Inc.; *U.S. Public*, pg. 427
DUTAILIER LTD.—See Groupe Dutailier Inc.; *Int'l*, pg. 3102
DUTALAND BERHAD; *Int'l*, pg. 2235
DUTA PLANTATIONS SDN. BHD.—See DutaLand Berhad; *Int'l*, pg. 2235
DUTA SECURITY SDN. BHD.—See Global Oriental Berhad; *Int'l*, pg. 3000
DUTA TECHNIC SDN. BHD.—See HeiTech Padu Berhad; *Int'l*, pg. 3326
DUTCH-BANGLA BANK PLC; *Int'l*, pg. 2235
DUTCH BRAND MANAGEMENT BV—See Bjorn Borg AB; *Int'l*, pg. 1054
DUTCH BROS. COFFEE, LLC; *U.S. Private*, pg. 1294
DUTCH BROS INC.; *U.S. Public*, pg. 694
DUTCH CHEVROLET BUICK; *U.S. Private*, pg. 1294
DUTCH CONTACT CENTERS B.V.—See Teleperformance SE; *Int'l*, pg. 7540
DUTCH DEFENSE VEHICLE SYSTEMS B.V.—See Krauss-Maffei Wegmann GmbH & Co. KG; *Int'l*, pg. 4300
DUTCHDELTA FINANCE SARL—See E.ON SE; *Int'l*, pg. 2252
DUTCH ENTERPRISES INC.; *U.S. Private*, pg. 1294
DUTCHESS COUNTY AGRICULTURAL SOCIETY, INC.; *U.S. Private*, pg. 1294
DUTCHESS QUARRY & SUPPLY CO., INC.—See Peckham Industries, Inc.; *U.S. Private*, pg. 3127
DUTCHESS TERMINALS INC.; *U.S. Private*, pg. 1294
DUTCH GOLD HONEY INC.; *U.S. Private*, pg. 1294
DUTCH HERITAGE GARDENS; *U.S. Private*, pg. 1294
DUTCH ID B.V.—See ASR Nederland N.V.; *Int'l*, pg. 632
DUTCH LADY MILK INDUSTRIES BERHAD—See Zuivelcooperatie FrieslandCampina U.A.; *Int'l*, pg. 8694
DUTCH LANKA TRAILER MANUFACTURERS LTD—See United Motors Lanka PLC; *Int'l*, pg. 8071
DUTCH LANKA TRAILERS MANUFACTURES LLC—See Tata Sons Limited; *Int'l*, pg. 7468
DUTCHLEASE B.V.—See Pon Holdings B.V.; *Int'l*, pg. 5918
DUTCH LIGHT PRO B.V.—See Midwich Group Plc; *Int'l*, pg. 4887
DUTCH MADE; *U.S. Private*, pg. 1294
DUTCHMAN HOSPITALITY GROUP, INC.; *U.S. Private*, pg. 1294
DUTCH MAS B.V.—See RHI Magnesita N.V.; *Int'l*, pg. 6325
DUTCHMASTER NURSERIES LTD.; *Int'l*, pg. 2235
DUTCHMEN MANUFACTURING, INC.—See Thor Industries, Inc.; *U.S. Public*, pg. 2156
DUTCHMEN MANUFACTURING, INC.—See Thor Industries, Inc.; *U.S. Public*, pg. 2156
DUTCH MILLER CHEVROLET INC.; *U.S. Private*, pg. 1294
DUTCH MILLER KIA; *U.S. Private*, pg. 1294
DUTCH OIL COMPANY INC.; *U.S. Private*, pg. 1294
DUTCH OPHTHALMIC USA, INC.—See Carl-Zeiss-Stiftung; *Int'l*, pg. 1333
DUTCH OVEN GOLD GROUP INC.; *Int'l*, pg. 2235
DUTCH POINT CREDIT UNION; *U.S. Private*, pg. 1294
DUTCH POWER COMPANY B.V.—See Alamo Group Inc.; *U.S. Public*, pg. 71
DUTCH PRIME FOODS INC.; *U.S. Private*, pg. 1294
DUTCH QUALITY STONE, INC.—See Seven Group Holdings Limited; *Int'l*, pg. 6733
DUTCH SPACE B.V.—See Airbus SE; *Int'l*, pg. 245
DUTCH VALLEY AUTO WORKS; *U.S. Private*, pg. 1294
DUTCH VALLEY FOOD COMPANY, INC.—See Weis Markets, Inc.; *U.S. Public*, pg. 2342
DUTCHWAY FARM MARKET INC.; *U.S. Private*, pg. 1294
DUTCO MCCONNELL DOWELL QATAR LLC—See Aveng Limited; *Int'l*, pg. 738
DUTCO TENNANT AQUA-TERRA LLC—See KS Energy Limited; *Int'l*, pg. 4309
DUTECH HOLDINGS LIMITED; *Int'l*, pg. 2235
DUTEXDOR; *Int'l*, pg. 2235
DUTRAC COMMUNITY CREDIT UNION; *U.S. Private*, pg. 1295
THE DUTRA GROUP INC.; *U.S. Private*, pg. 4024

DUTRO COMPANY; *U.S. Private*, pg. 1295
DUTRO FORD LINCOLN MERCURY INC.; *U.S. Private*, pg. 1295
DUTRON POLYMERS LIMITED; *Int'l*, pg. 2235
DUTSCHER SCIENTIFIC LTD—See Dominique Dutscher SAS; *Int'l*, pg. 2161
DUTTON-FORSHAW MOTOR CO., LTD.—See Lookers plc; *Int'l*, pg. 4555
DUTTON-LAINSON COMPANY; *U.S. Private*, pg. 1295
DUTTON MILL VILLAGE, LLC—See Sun Communities, Inc.; *U.S. Public*, pg. 1961
DUTTON PLUMBING, INC.—See Baum Capital Partners Management LLC; *U.S. Private*, pg. 490
DUTY FREE CARIBBEAN HOLDINGS LTD.—See Avolta AG; *Int'l*, pg. 749
DUTY FREE CARIBBEAN HOLDINGS LTD.—See Cave Shepherd & Co., Ltd.; *Int'l*, pg. 1362
DUTY FREE DUBAI PORTS FZE—See The Emirates Group; *Int'l*, pg. 7639
DUTY FREE INTERNATIONAL LIMITED—See Atlan Holdings Berhad; *Int'l*, pg. 673
DUVAL ACURA—See Scott-McRae Automotive Group Inc.; *U.S. Private*, pg. 3578
DUVALCO B.V.—See Sevens Atelier Limited; *Int'l*, pg. 6734
DUVAL CONTAINER COMPANY—See Kelso & Company, L.P.; *U.S. Private*, pg. 2278
DUVALCO VALVES & FITTINGS PTE. LTD.—See Sevens Atelier Limited; *Int'l*, pg. 6734
DUVAL ELECTRICITE SAS—See VINCI S.A.; *Int'l*, pg. 8216
DUVAL GUILLAUME ANTWERP—See Publicis Groupe S.A.; *Int'l*, pg. 6098
DUVAL GUILLAUME BRUSSELS—See Publicis Groupe S.A.; *Int'l*, pg. 6098
DUVAL GUILLAUME CORPORATE—See Publicis Groupe S.A.; *Int'l*, pg. 6098
DUVAL LEASE SERVICE, LLC—See John Wood Group PLC; *Int'l*, pg. 3983
DUVAL MOTOR COMPANY INC.—See Scott-McRae Automotive Group Inc.; *U.S. Private*, pg. 3578
DUVAL MOTORS AT THE AVENUES INC—See Scott-McRae Automotive Group Inc.; *U.S. Private*, pg. 3578
DUVAL PRECISION GRINDING INC.—See Peter Pan Bus Lines, Inc.; *U.S. Private*, pg. 3159
DUVALTEX INC.; *Int'l*, pg. 2236
DUVAN A.D.; *Int'l*, pg. 2236
DUVAN A.D.; *Int'l*, pg. 2236
DUVAN CACAK A.D.; *Int'l*, pg. 2236
DUVAN PROMET A.D.; *Int'l*, pg. 2236
DUVANSKA INDUSTRIJA A.D.; *Int'l*, pg. 2236
DUVAPLAST A.D.; *Int'l*, pg. 2236
DUVEL MOORTGAT FRANCE SARL—See Fibemi NV; *Int'l*, pg. 2651
DUVEL MOORTGAT NV—See Fibemi NV; *Int'l*, pg. 2651
DUVEL MOORTGAT SHANGHAI LTD—See Fibemi NV; *Int'l*, pg. 2651
DUVEL MOORTGAT UK LTD—See Fibemi NV; *Int'l*, pg. 2651
DUVEL MOORTGAT USA, LTD.—See Fibemi NV; *Int'l*, pg. 2652
DUVENJIAN; *U.S. Private*, pg. 1295
DUVIMEX BELGIUM BVBA—See Wurth Verwaltungsgesellschaft mbH; *Int'l*, pg. 8504
DUVINE ADVENTURES, INC.—See Lindblad Expeditions Holdings, Inc.; *U.S. Public*, pg. 1319
DUXBURY HARDWARE CORP.; *U.S. Private*, pg. 1295
DUXFORD FINANCIAL, INC.—See Brookfield Corporation; *Int'l*, pg. 1183
DUX INDUSTRIES LTD—See Aliaxis S.A./N.V.; *Int'l*, pg. 324
DUX MANUFACTURING LIMITED—See Noritz Corporation; *Int'l*, pg. 5429
DUXTON FARMS LIMITED; *Int'l*, pg. 2236
DUXTON HOTELS INTERNATIONAL PTY LTD—See Low Keng Huat (Singapore) Limited; *Int'l*, pg. 4566
DUXTON WATER LIMITED; *Int'l*, pg. 2236
DUXWARE, LLC—See i3 Verticals, Inc.; *U.S. Public*, pg. 1081
DUYEN HAI HANOI MULTIMODAL TRANSPORT CO., LTD—See TCO Holdings Joint Stock Company; *Int'l*, pg. 7484
DUYEN HAI MANUFACTURING & TRADING CO., LTD.—See TCO Holdings Joint Stock Company; *Int'l*, pg. 7484
DUYEN HAI PHU THO TRANSPORT CO., LTD.—See TCO Holdings Joint Stock Company; *Int'l*, pg. 7484
DUYEN HAI PHU THO TRANSPORT CO., LTD—See TCO Holdings Joint Stock Company; *Int'l*, pg. 7484
DUYEN HAI ROAD TRANSPORT CO., LTD.—See TCO Holdings Joint Stock Company; *Int'l*, pg. 7484
DUYEN HAI ROAD TRANSPORT CO., LTD—See TCO Holdings Joint Stock Company; *Int'l*, pg. 7484
DUYEN HAI TRANSPORT CO., LTD.—See TCO Holdings Joint Stock Company; *Int'l*, pg. 7484
DUYEN HAI TRANSPORT CO., LTD—See TCO Holdings Joint Stock Company; *Int'l*, pg. 7484
DUYNIE HOLDING B.V.—See Royal Cosun U.A.; *Int'l*, pg. 6411

DUXTON WATER LIMITED

DUYVIS B.V.—See PepsiCo, Inc.; *U.S. Public*, pg. 1668
DUYVIS PRODUCTION B.V.—See PepsiCo, Inc.; *U.S. Public*, pg. 1668
DUZEY A.S.—See Koc Holding A.S.; *Int'l*, pg. 4223
DUZEY TUKETIM MALLARI SANAYI PAZARLAMA A.S.—See Koc Holding A.S.; *Int'l*, pg. 4223
DUZHE PUBLISHING & MEDIA CO., LTD.; *Int'l*, pg. 2236
DV.8 SAATCHI & SAATCHI—See Publicis Groupe S.A.; *Int'l*, pg. 6108
DVA - DEUTSCHE VERKEHRS-ASSEKURANZ-VERMITTLUNGS GMBH—See Marsh & McLennan Companies, Inc.; *U.S. Public*, pg. 1374
DVA - DEUTSCHE VERKEHRS-ASSEKURANZ-VERMITTLUNGS GMBH—See Deutsche Bahn AG; *Int'l*, pg. 2051
DVA - DEUTSCHE VERKEHRS-ASSEKURANZ-VERMITTLUNGS GMBH—See DEVK Service GmbH; *Int'l*, pg. 2089
DVA - DEUTSCHE VERKEHRS-ASSEKURANZ-VERMITTLUNGS GMBH—See Marsh & McLennan Companies, Inc.; *U.S. Public*, pg. 1379
DVA HEALTHCARE OF MASSACHUSETTS, INC.—See DaVita Inc.; *U.S. Public*, pg. 637
DVA HEALTHCARE OF NEW LONDON, LLC—See DaVita Inc.; *U.S. Public*, pg. 637
DVA HEALTHCARE OF NORWICH, LLC—See DaVita Inc.; *U.S. Public*, pg. 637
DVA HEALTHCARE OF PENNSYLVANIA, INC.—See DaVita Inc.; *U.S. Public*, pg. 637
DVA HEALTHCARE OF TUSCALOOSA, LLC—See DaVita Inc.; *U.S. Public*, pg. 637
DVA HEALTHCARE RENAL CARE, INC.—See DaVita Inc.; *U.S. Public*, pg. 637
DVA LABORATORY SERVICES, INC.—See DaVita Inc.; *U.S. Public*, pg. 637
D. VAN NOOIJEN B.V.—See Aderans Co., Ltd.; *Int'l*, pg. 143
D. VAN NOOIJEN B.V.—See Aderans Co., Ltd.; *Int'l*, pg. 143
DVA RENAL HEALTHCARE, INC.—See DaVita Inc.; *U.S. Public*, pg. 637
DV ASSET MANAGEMENT EAD—See Vienna Insurance Group AG Wiener Versicherung Gruppe; *Int'l*, pg. 8194
DVA/WASHINGTON UNIVERSITY HEALTHCARE OF GREATER ST. LOUIS, LLC—See DaVita Inc.; *U.S. Public*, pg. 637
DVB BANK AMERICA N.V.—See DZ BANK AG Deutsche Zentral-Genossenschaftsbank; *Int'l*, pg. 2243
DVB BANK N.V.—See Mitsubishi UFJ Financial Group, Inc.; *Int'l*, pg. 4968
DVB BANK SE—See Mitsubishi UFJ Financial Group, Inc.; *Int'l*, pg. 4968
DVB CAPITAL MARKETS LLC—See Mitsubishi UFJ Financial Group, Inc.; *Int'l*, pg. 4968
DVB GROUP MERCHANT BANK (ASIA) LTD—See Mitsubishi UFJ Financial Group, Inc.; *Int'l*, pg. 4968
DVB INVESTMENT MANAGEMENT N.V.—See DZ BANK AG Deutsche Zentral-Genossenschaftsbank; *Int'l*, pg. 2243
D.V. BROWN & ASSOCIATES, INC.; *U.S. Private*, pg. 1143
DVBS, INC.—See Moody's Corporation; *U.S. Public*, pg. 1467
DVB TRANSPORT FINANCE LTD—See Mitsubishi UFJ Financial Group, Inc.; *Int'l*, pg. 4968
DVB TRANSPORT (US) LLC—See DZ BANK AG Deutsche Zentral-Genossenschaftsbank; *Int'l*, pg. 2243
DV CARE NETHERLANDS B.V.—See DaVita Inc.; *U.S. Public*, pg. 637
DV CONSTRUCTION SA—See Bouygues S.A.; *Int'l*, pg. 1122
DVDO, INC.—See Lattice Semiconductor Corporation; *U.S. Public*, pg. 1294
D&V ELECTRONICS LTD—See Motorcar Parts of America, Inc.; *U.S. Public*, pg. 1477
D&V ELECTRONIC TECHNOLOGY (SHANGHAI) CO., LTD—See Motorcar Parts of America, Inc.; *U.S. Public*, pg. 1477
DVELE, INC.; *U.S. Private*, pg. 1295
D.V.F. STUDIO; *U.S. Private*, pg. 1143
DVH HOSPITAL ALLIANCE, LLC—See Universal Health Services, Inc.; *U.S. Public*, pg. 2257
DVHP INC.; *U.S. Private*, pg. 1295
D'VINE WINE, INC.—See Handcrafted Wines, LLC; *U.S. Private*, pg. 1852
DVIRIA NANO TECH SDN. BHD.—See Ho Wah Genting Berhad; *Int'l*, pg. 3435
DVL GROUP, INC.; *U.S. Private*, pg. 1295
DVL SEIGENTHALER, INC.—See Ruder Finn Group, Inc.; *U.S. Private*, pg. 3501
DVL SMITH LIMITED—See Enero Group Limited; *Int'l*, pg. 2423
DVMC PROPERTIES, LLC—See Universal Health Realty Income Trust; *U.S. Public*, pg. 2255
DVN MEDIENSERVICE GMBH & CO. KG—See Pearson plc; *Int'l*, pg. 5778
D'VONTZ; *U.S. Private*, pg. 1139
DV POWER LIMITED—See Mobicon Group Limited; *Int'l*, pg. 5009

DVR ITALIA S.R.L.—See Sesa S.p.A.; *Int'l*, pg. 6728
DVS DRAXLMAIER VERDRAHTUNGSSYSTEME GMBH—See Draexlmaier Gruppe; *Int'l*, pg. 2198
DVS EQUIPAMENTOS DE PROTECAO INDIVIDUAL LTDA.—See Bunzl plc; *Int'l*, pg. 1218
DVS FOOTWEAR INTERNATIONAL, LLC—See Elan-Polo Inc.; *U.S. Private*, pg. 1350
DVS INDUSTRIES PRIVATE LIMITED—See MM Forgings Limited; *Int'l*, pg. 5004
DVS LIMITED—See Fletcher Building Limited; *Int'l*, pg. 2699
DVS LTD.—See Midwich Group Plc; *Int'l*, pg. 4887
DVSM LLC; *U.S. Private*, pg. 1295
DV-SYSTEM—See Cefla S.C.; *Int'l*, pg. 1389
DVV MEDIA GROUP GMBH—See Rheinische-Bergische Verlagsgesellschaft mbH; *Int'l*, pg. 6321
DVV MEDIA INTERNATIONAL LTD.—See Rheinische-Bergische Verlagsgesellschaft mbH; *Int'l*, pg. 6321
DVX, INC.; *Int'l*, pg. 2236
DWA, INC.; *U.S. Private*, pg. 1295
DWAIN TAYLOR CHEVROLET-BUICK-GMC; *U.S. Private*, pg. 1295
D. WALDNER COMPANY, INC.; *U.S. Private*, pg. 1140
DWA MEDIA; *U.S. Private*, pg. 1295
DWANGO CO., LTD.—See Kadokawa Corporation; *Int'l*, pg. 4047
DWARF INC.—See AOI TYO Holdings Inc.; *Int'l*, pg. 488
DWARF TECHNOLOGY HOLDINGS, INC.; *Int'l*, pg. 2236
DWARIKESH SUGAR INDUSTRIES LTD; *Int'l*, pg. 2236
D-WAVE QUANTUM INC.; *Int'l*, pg. 1900
D-WAVE SYSTEMS INC.—See D-Wave Quantum Inc.; *Int'l*, pg. 1900
DWAYNE LANES CHRYSLER DODGE JEEP RAM; *U.S. Private*, pg. 1295
DW BETON GMBH—See Bain Capital, LP; *U.S. Private*, pg. 438
DWC 3.0 S.P.A.; *Int'l*, pg. 2236
D.W. CAMPBELL-COBB PKWY, INC.—See D.W. Campbell, Inc.; *U.S. Private*, pg. 1143
D.W. CAMPBELL, INC.; *U.S. Private*, pg. 1143
D.W. CAMPBELL OF ATLANTA, INC.—See D.W. Campbell, Inc.; *U.S. Private*, pg. 1143
D.W. CAMPBELL OF DUNWOODY, INC.—See D.W. Campbell, Inc.; *U.S. Private*, pg. 1143
D.W. CAMPBELL OF KENNESAW, INC.—See D.W. Campbell, Inc.; *U.S. Private*, pg. 1143
D.W. CAMPBELL OF MARIETTA, INC.—See D.W. Campbell, Inc.; *U.S. Private*, pg. 1143
DWC CONSTRUCTION COMPANY, INC.; *U.S. Private*, pg. 1295
DWC LAW FIRM PS—See Aeon Law PLLC; *U.S. Private*, pg. 117
D.W. DICKEY & SONS INC. - COLUMBIANA PLANT—See D.W. Dickey & Sons Inc.; *U.S. Private*, pg. 1143
D.W. DICKEY & SONS INC. - EAST LIVERPOOL CONCRETE PLANT—See D.W. Dickey & Sons Inc.; *U.S. Private*, pg. 1143
D.W. DICKEY & SONS INC. - LISBON CONCRETE PLANT—See D.W. Dickey & Sons Inc.; *U.S. Private*, pg. 1143
D.W. DICKEY & SONS INC.; *U.S. Private*, pg. 1143
D.W. DICKEY & SONS INC. - STEUBENVILLE PLANT—See D.W. Dickey & Sons Inc.; *U.S. Private*, pg. 1143
D&W DIESEL INC.; *U.S. Private*, pg. 1138
DW DIGITAL WIRELESS INC—See DDS Wireless International Inc.; *Int'l*, pg. 1994
DW DISTRIBUTION L.L.C.—See National Amusements, Inc.; *U.S. Private*, pg. 2842
DWELL ADELAIDE STUDENT LIVING PTY. LTD.—See Centurion Corporation Limited; *Int'l*, pg. 1417
DWELL US STUDENT LIVING LLC—See Centurion Corporation Limited; *Int'l*, pg. 1417
D. WESTERN THERAPEUTICS INSTITUTE, INC.; *Int'l*, pg. 1900
DWEWANG INTERNATIONAL CORP.—See BERICAP GmbH & Co. KG; *Int'l*, pg. 981
DWF GROUP PLC—See Inflexion Private Equity Partners LLP; *Int'l*, pg. 3689
DW FILMS L.L.C.—See National Amusements, Inc.; *U.S. Private*, pg. 2842
D&W FINE PACK LLC - FORT CALHOUN—See Mid Oaks Investments LLC; *U.S. Private*, pg. 2706
D&W FINE PACK LLC - FOUNTAIN INN—See Mid Oaks Investments LLC; *U.S. Private*, pg. 2706
D&W FINE PACK LLC - LAKE ZURICH—See Mid Oaks Investments LLC; *U.S. Private*, pg. 2706
D&W FINE PACK LLC—See Mid Oaks Investments LLC; *U.S. Private*, pg. 2706
DWF OF BOISE—See Denver Wholesale Florists Company; *U.S. Private*, pg. 1208
DWF OF CINCINNATI, INC.—See Denver Wholesale Florists Company; *U.S. Private*, pg. 1208
DWF OF DALLAS—See Denver Wholesale Florists Company; *U.S. Private*, pg. 1208
DWF OF FLINT INC.—See Denver Wholesale Florists Company; *U.S. Private*, pg. 1208
DWF OF MILWAUKEE, INC.—See Denver Wholesale Florists Company; *U.S. Private*, pg. 1208

CORPORATE AFFILIATIONS

DWF OF NORTH KANSAS CITY—See Denver Wholesale Florists Company; *U.S. Private*, pg. 1208
DWF OF OMAHA—See Denver Wholesale Florists Company; *U.S. Private*, pg. 1208
DWF OF SAINT LOUIS, INC.—See Denver Wholesale Florists Company; *U.S. Private*, pg. 1208
DWF OF SALT LAKE, INC.—See Denver Wholesale Florists Company; *U.S. Private*, pg. 1208
DWF OF TOLEDO—See Denver Wholesale Florists Company; *U.S. Private*, pg. 1208
DWF PENSION TRUSTEES LIMITED—See Inflexion Private Equity Partners LLP; *Int'l*, pg. 3689
DWFRITZ AUTOMATION INC.—See Balmoral Funds LLC; *U.S. Private*, pg. 461
DWFRITZ INTERNATIONAL, INC.—See Sandvik AB; *Int'l*, pg. 6529
DWF SEATAC—See Denver Wholesale Florists Company; *U.S. Private*, pg. 1208
DWIGHT CAPITAL LLC; *U.S. Private*, pg. 1295
DWIGHT W. ANDRUS INSURANCE INC.—See Hellman & Friedman LLC; *U.S. Private*, pg. 1908
DWITIYA TRADING LIMITED; *Int'l*, pg. 2236
DWK DRAHTWERK KOLN GMBH—See Saarstahl AG; *Int'l*, pg. 6461
DWK LIFE SCIENCES GMBH—See OEP Capital Advisors, L.P.; *U.S. Private*, pg. 2999
DWL USA INC.—See Compumedics Limited; *Int'l*, pg. 1757
DW MANAGEMENT SERVICES, LLC; *Int'l*, pg. 2236
D & W MANUFACTURING CO., INC.; *U.S. Private*, pg. 1136
D.W. MCMILLAN MEMORIAL HOSPITAL—See United-Health Group Incorporated; *U.S. Public*, pg. 2244
DWNET TECHNOLOGY (SUZHOU) LIMITED—See SerComm Corporation; *Int'l*, pg. 6722
D.W. NEWCOMER'S SONS FUNERAL HOMES—See Service Corporation International; *U.S. Public*, pg. 1871
D.W. NICHOLSON CORPORATION; *U.S. Private*, pg. 1143
DWOLLA INC.; *U.S. Private*, pg. 1296
DWORSHER DIALYSIS, LLC—See DaVita Inc.; *U.S. Public*, pg. 638
D & W PAINTING INC.; *U.S. Private*, pg. 1136
D & W PAPER TUBE, INC.—See Sonoco Products Company; *U.S. Public*, pg. 1904
DW PLASTICS NV—See Sealed Air Corporation; *U.S. Public*, pg. 1853
DWR - DEUTSCHE GESELLSCHAFT FUR WEISSBLECHRECYCLING MBH—See ThyssenKrupp AG; *Int'l*, pg. 7724
DW RICHARDS SONS INC.; *U.S. Private*, pg. 1295
DWS ALTERNATIVES GLOBAL LIMITED—See Deutsche Bank Aktiengesellschaft; *Int'l*, pg. 2057
DWS ASSET MANAGEMENT (KOREA) COMPANY LIMITED—See Deutsche Bank Aktiengesellschaft; *Int'l*, pg. 2057
DWS (AUSTRIA) INVESTMENTGESELLSCHAFT MBH—See Deutsche Bank Aktiengesellschaft; *Int'l*, pg. 2057
DWS CH AG—See Deutsche Bank Aktiengesellschaft; *Int'l*, pg. 2057
DW SCHWELLEN GMBH—See Bain Capital, LP; *U.S. Private*, pg. 438
DWS DISTRIBUTORS, INC.—See Deutsche Bank Aktiengesellschaft; *Int'l*, pg. 2057
DWS FAR EASTERN INVESTMENTS LIMITED—See Deutsche Bank Aktiengesellschaft; *Int'l*, pg. 2057
DWS FINANZ-SERVICE GMBH—See Deutsche Bank Aktiengesellschaft; *Int'l*, pg. 2057
DWS GROUP GMBH & CO. KGAA; *Int'l*, pg. 2236
DWS GRUNDBESITZ GMBH—See Deutsche Bank Aktiengesellschaft; *Int'l*, pg. 2057
DWS HOLDING & SERVICE GMBH—See Deutsche Bank Aktiengesellschaft; *Int'l*, pg. 2057
DWS INVESTMENT GMBH—See Deutsche Bank Aktiengesellschaft; *Int'l*, pg. 2057
DWS INVESTMENT S.A. LUXEMBOURG—See Deutsche Bank Aktiengesellschaft; *Int'l*, pg. 2057
DWS INVESTMENT S.A.—See Deutsche Bank Aktiengesellschaft; *Int'l*, pg. 2057
DWS INVESTMENTS AUSTRALIA LIMITED—See Deutsche Bank Aktiengesellschaft; *Int'l*, pg. 2057
DWS INVESTMENTS DISTRIBUTORS, INC.—See Deutsche Bank Aktiengesellschaft; *Int'l*, pg. 2057
DWS INVESTMENTS HONG KONG LIMITED—See Deutsche Bank Aktiengesellschaft; *Int'l*, pg. 2057
DWS INVESTMENTS SERVICE COMPANY—See Deutsche Bank Aktiengesellschaft; *Int'l*, pg. 2057
DWS INVESTMENTS S.G.I.I.C.—See Deutsche Bank Aktiengesellschaft; *Int'l*, pg. 2057
DWS INVESTMENTS SHANGHAI LIMITED—See Deutsche Bank Aktiengesellschaft; *Int'l*, pg. 2057
DWS INVESTMENTS SINGAPORE LIMITED—See DWS Group GmbH & Co. KGAA; *Int'l*, pg. 2236
DWS LIMITED; *Int'l*, pg. 2236
DWS MUNICIPAL INCOME TRUST; *U.S. Public*, pg. 694
DWS POLSKA TFI S.A.—See Deutsche Bank Aktiengesellschaft; *Int'l*, pg. 2057
DWS STRATEGIC MUNICIPAL INCOME TRUST; *U.S. Public*, pg. 694

COMPANY NAME INDEX

DW STUDIOS PRODUCTIONS L.L.C.—See National Amusements, Inc.; *U.S. Private*, pg. 2842
DW SYSTEMBAU GMBH—See Bain Capital, LP; *U.S. Private*, pg. 438
DW TELEVISION L.L.C.—See National Amusements, Inc.; *U.S. Private*, pg. 2842
DWT HOLDING B.V.—See ShawCor Ltd.; *Int'l*, pg. 6791
D. W. VAN DYKE & CO. OF CONNECTICUT INC.—See DDR Holdings Inc.; *U.S. Private*, pg. 1181
DWWA INC.; *U.S. Private*, pg. 1296
DW WINDSOR GROUP LIMITED—See Luceco PLC; *Int'l*, pg. 4573
D.W. WINDSOR LIMITED—See Luceco PLC; *Int'l*, pg. 4573
DWW WOOLWORTH DEUTSCHLAND GMBH & CO. KG—See Argyll Partners Ltd.; *Int'l*, pg. 563
THE DWYER GROUP, INC.—See Harvest Partners L.P.; *U.S. Private*, pg. 1877
DWYER INSTRUMENTS, LLC—See Arcline Investment Management LP; *U.S. Private*, pg. 313
DWYER INSTRUMENTS LTD—See Arcline Investment Management LP; *U.S. Private*, pg. 313
DWYER INSTRUMENTS PTY LTD—See Arcline Investment Management LP; *U.S. Private*, pg. 313
DWYER KITCHENS—See Dwyer Products Corporation; *U.S. Private*, pg. 1296
DWYER PRODUCTS CORPORATION; *U.S. Private*, pg. 1296
DWZ INDUSTRIES SDN BHD—See MClean Technologies Berhad; *Int'l*, pg. 4759
DX ANTENNA CO., LTD.—See Elecom Co., Ltd.; *Int'l*, pg. 2348
DXB ACL AIRSHOP DWC LLC—See Ranger Aerospace LLC; *U.S. Private*, pg. 3354
DXB ENTERTAINMENTS PJSC; *Int'l*, pg. 2237
DXC CONNECT PTY LTD—See DXC Technology Company; *U.S. Public*, pg. 696
DXC ECLIPSE PTY LTD—See DXC Technology Company; *U.S. Public*, pg. 695
DXC INSURANCE SOLUTIONS AUSTRALIA PTY LTD—See DXC Technology Company; *U.S. Public*, pg. 696
DXCM SWEDEN AB—See DexCom Inc; *U.S. Public*, pg. 667
DXC TECHNOLOGY AUSTRALIA HOLDINGS PTY LIMITED—See DXC Technology Company; *U.S. Public*, pg. 695
DXC TECHNOLOGY AUSTRALIA PTY. LIMITED—See DXC Technology Company; *U.S. Public*, pg. 695
DXC TECHNOLOGY AUSTRALIA PTY. LIMITED—See DXC Technology Company; *U.S. Public*, pg. 696
DXC TECHNOLOGY BALTIC UAB—See DXC Technology Company; *U.S. Public*, pg. 696
DXC TECHNOLOGY BULGARIA E.O.O.D.—See DXC Technology Company; *U.S. Public*, pg. 695
DXC TECHNOLOGY COMPANY; *U.S. Public*, pg. 694
DXC TECHNOLOGY DANMARK A/S—See DXC Technology Company; *U.S. Public*, pg. 695
DXC TECHNOLOGY DEUTSCHLAND GMBH—See DXC Technology Company; *U.S. Public*, pg. 695
DXC TECHNOLOGY HONG KONG LIMITED—See DXC Technology Company; *U.S. Public*, pg. 695
DXC TECHNOLOGY SARL—See DXC Technology Company; *U.S. Public*, pg. 696
DXC TECHNOLOGY SCANDIHEALTH A/S—See DXC Technology Company; *U.S. Public*, pg. 695
DXC TECHNOLOGY SERVICES VIETNAM COMPANY LIMITED—See DXC Technology Company; *U.S. Public*, pg. 696
DXC TECHNOLOGY SLOVAKIA S.R.O—See DXC Technology Company; *U.S. Public*, pg. 695
DXC TECHNOLOGY SWITZERLAND GMBH—See DXC Technology Company; *U.S. Public*, pg. 695
DXC TECHONOLOGY INFORMATION SERVICES SLOVAKIA S.R.O.—See DXC Technology Company; *U.S. Public*, pg. 696
DXC TECHONOLOGY NORGE AS—See DXC Technology Company; *U.S. Public*, pg. 695
DXC UNITED PTY. LIMITED—See DXC Technology Company; *U.S. Public*, pg. 695
DX DISTRIBUTORS INC.—See DX Holding Company Inc.; *U.S. Private*, pg. 1296
DX DONAUPLEX BETRIEBSGES.MBH—See Unibail-Rodamco-Westfield SE; *Int'l*, pg. 8029
DX (GROUP) PLC—See H.I.G. Capital, LLC; *U.S. Private*, pg. 1828
DX HOLDING COMPANY INC.; *U.S. Private*, pg. 1296
DXI CAPITAL CORP.; *Int'l*, pg. 2237
DXI INDUSTRIES INC.—See DX Holding Company Inc.; *U.S. Private*, pg. 1296
DX MAIL—See Freightways Group Limited; *Int'l*, pg. 2771
DXN COMFORT TOURS SDN. BHD.—See DXN Holdings Bhd.; *Int'l*, pg. 2237
DXN HERBAL MANUFACTURING (INDIA) PRIVATE LIMITED—See DXN Holdings Bhd.; *Int'l*, pg. 2237
DXN HOLDINGS BHD.; *Int'l*, pg. 2237
DXN INDUSTRIES (M) SDN. BHD.—See DXN Holdings Bhd.; *Int'l*, pg. 2237

DXN INTERNATIONAL (AUSTRALIA) PTY. LTD.—See DXN Holdings Bhd.; *Int'l*, pg. 2237
DXN INTERNATIONAL (HONG KONG) LIMITED—See DXN Holdings Bhd.; *Int'l*, pg. 2237
DXN INTERNATIONAL PAKISTAN (PRIVATE) LIMITED—See DXN Holdings Bhd.; *Int'l*, pg. 2237
DXN INTERNATIONAL PERU S.A.C.—See DXN Holdings Bhd.; *Int'l*, pg. 2237
DXN LIMITED; *Int'l*, pg. 2237
DXN MARKETING SDN. BHD.—See DXN Holdings Bhd.; *Int'l*, pg. 2237
DXN PHARMACEUTICAL SDN. BHD.—See DXN Holdings Bhd.; *Int'l*, pg. 2237
DXN (SINGAPORE) PTE LTD—See DXN Holdings Bhd.; *Int'l*, pg. 2237
DXP ENTERPRISES, INC.; *U.S. Public*, pg. 697
DX SERVICE COMPANY INC.—See DX Holding Company Inc.; *U.S. Private*, pg. 1296
DXS LTD.—See QIAGEN N.V.; *Int'l*, pg. 6139
DXSTORM.COM INC.; *Int'l*, pg. 2237
DX & VX CO.; *Int'l*, pg. 2237
DY4 SYSTEMS, INC.—See Curtiss-Wright Corporation; *U.S. Public*, pg. 612
DY6 METALS LTD.; *Int'l*, pg. 2237
DYACO CANADA INC.—See Dyaco International Inc.; *Int'l*, pg. 2238
DYACO EUROPE GMBH—See Dyaco International Inc.; *Int'l*, pg. 2238
DYACO GERMANY GMBH—See Dyaco International Inc.; *Int'l*, pg. 2238
DYACO INTERNATIONAL INC. - MAIN FACTORY—See Dyaco International Inc.; *Int'l*, pg. 2238
DYACO INTERNATIONAL INC.; *Int'l*, pg. 2237
DYACO JAPAN CO., LTD.—See Dyaco International Inc.; *Int'l*, pg. 2238
DYACO (SHANGHAI) TRADING CO., LTD.—See Dyaco International Inc.; *Int'l*, pg. 2238
DYADIC INTERNATIONAL, INC.; *U.S. Public*, pg. 698
DYADIC NEDERLAND B.V.—See Dyadic International, Inc.; *U.S. Public*, pg. 698
DYAL CAPITAL PARTNERS—See Blue Owl Capital Inc.; *U.S. Public*, pg. 364
DY AMERICA INC.—See DY Corporation; *Int'l*, pg. 2237
DY AUTO CORPORATION—See DY Corporation; *Int'l*, pg. 2237
DYCASA S.A.—See ACS, Actividades de Construccion y Servicios, S.A.; *Int'l*, pg. 111
DYCENT BIOTECH (SHANGHAI) CO. LTD.; *Int'l*, pg. 2238
DYCKERHOFF BASAL BETONMORTEL B.V.—See Buzzi SpA; *Int'l*, pg. 1230
DYCKERHOFF BASAL NEDERLAND B.V.—See Buzzi SpA; *Int'l*, pg. 1230
DYCKERHOFF GMBH—See Buzzi SpA; *Int'l*, pg. 1230
DYCKERHOFF POLSKA SP. Z O.O.—See Buzzi SpA; *Int'l*, pg. 1230
DYCOM INDUSTRIES, INC.; *U.S. Public*, pg. 698
DYCORE B.V.—See CRH plc; *Int'l*, pg. 1844
DY CORPORATION; *Int'l*, pg. 2237
DYDEN CORPORATION—See Sumitomo Electric Industries, Ltd.; *Int'l*, pg. 7277
DYDO BEVERAGE SHIZUOKA, INC.—See DyDo Group Holdings, Inc.; *Int'l*, pg. 2238
DYDO DRINCO INC.—See DyDo Group Holdings, Inc.; *Int'l*, pg. 2238
DYDO DRINCO TURKEY ICECEK SATIS VE PAZARLAMA A.S.—See DyDo Group Holdings, Inc.; *Int'l*, pg. 2238
DYDO GROUP HOLDINGS, INC.; *Int'l*, pg. 2238
DYE & DURHAM LIMITED; *Int'l*, pg. 2238
DYEHARD FAN SUPPLY, LLC—See Teall Capital Partners, LLC; *U.S. Private*, pg. 3948
DYENOMITE, LLC; *U.S. Private*, pg. 1296
DYER AUTO AUCTION INC.; *U.S. Private*, pg. 1296
DYER BANK & TRUST—See Wintrust Financial Corporation; *U.S. Public*, pg. 2375
DYER CONSTRUCTION COMPANY, INC.; *U.S. Private*, pg. 1296
DYER GRAIN—See Green Plains Inc.; *U.S. Public*, pg. 963
DYER HOLDINGS PTY. LTD.; *Int'l*, pg. 2238
DYERSBURG ELECTRIC SYSTEM; *U.S. Private*, pg. 1296
DYERSBURG HOSPITAL CORPORATION—See Community Health Systems, Inc.; *U.S. Public*, pg. 553
DYERSVILLE DIE CAST—See Joseph L. Ertl, Inc.; *U.S. Private*, pg. 2237
DYESOL AUSTRALIA PTY. LTD.—See Greatcell Solar Ltd.; *Int'l*, pg. 3067
DYESOL INDUSTRIES PTY. LTD.—See Greatcell Solar Ltd.; *Int'l*, pg. 3067
DYESOL UK LTD.—See Greatcell Solar Ltd.; *Int'l*, pg. 3067
DYFED STEELS LIMITED; *Int'l*, pg. 2238
DYFLEX CO. LTD.—See Sika AG; *Int'l*, pg. 6917
DY IKSAN—See DY Corporation; *Int'l*, pg. 2237
DY INNOVATE CORPORATION—See DY Corporation; *Int'l*, pg. 2237
DYKAB I LULEA AB—See Endur ASA; *Int'l*, pg. 2410
DYKAB VARV & MEK AB—See Endur ASA; *Int'l*, pg. 2409
DYKA B.V.—See Tessenderlo Group NV; *Int'l*, pg. 7573

DYKA GMBH—See Tessenderlo Group NV; *Int'l*, pg. 7573
DYKA PLASTICS N.V.—See Tessenderlo Group NV; *Int'l*, pg. 7573
DYKA POLSKA SP.Z.O.O.—See Tessenderlo Group NV; *Int'l*, pg. 7573
DYKA SAS—See Tessenderlo Group NV; *Int'l*, pg. 7573
DYKA SK S.R.O.—See Tessenderlo Group NV; *Int'l*, pg. 7573
DYKA S.R.L.—See Tessenderlo Group NV; *Int'l*, pg. 7573
DYKA S.R.O—See Tessenderlo Group NV; *Int'l*, pg. 7573
DYKA TUBE S.A.S.—See Tessenderlo Group NV; *Int'l*, pg. 7573
DYKE INDUSTRY, INC.; *U.S. Private*, pg. 1296
DYKEMA ARCHITECTS INC.; *U.S. Private*, pg. 1296
DYKEMA GOSSETT PLLC; *U.S. Private*, pg. 1296
DYKES LUMBER COMPANY INC.; *U.S. Private*, pg. 1296
DYKNOW; *U.S. Private*, pg. 1296
DYKSTRA CONSTRUCTION, INC.—See MidOcean Partners, LLP; *U.S. Private*, pg. 2716
DYLAND BV—See Carlsberg A/S; *Int'l*, pg. 1340
DYLOAN BOND FACTORY S.R.L.—See Pattern SpA; *Int'l*, pg. 5760
DYMATIC CHEMICALS INC.; *Int'l*, pg. 2238
DYMATIZE ENTERPRISES, INC.—See Post Holdings, Inc.; *U.S. Public*, pg. 1703
DYMAX CORP.; *U.S. Private*, pg. 1296
DYMEDEX CONSULTING, LLC—See Bain Capital, LP; *U.S. Private*, pg. 432
DYM ENERGY CORPORATION; *U.S. Private*, pg. 1296
DYMIN STEEL INC.; *Int'l*, pg. 2238
DYMON ASIA CAPITAL (SINGAPORE) PTE. LTD; *Int'l*, pg. 2238
DYMONT INSTALLATION OY—See Instalco AB; *Int'l*, pg. 3721
DYMOS CZECH REPUBLIC S.R.O.—See Hyundai Motor Company; *Int'l*, pg. 3558
DYMUN + COMPANY, INC.—See NFM Group Inc.; *U.S. Private*, pg. 2923
DYN365, INC.; *U.S. Private*, pg. 1296
DYNABOOK AMERICAS, INC.—See Hon Hai Precision Industry Co., Ltd.; *Int'l*, pg. 3457
DYNABOOK EUROPE GMBH—See Hon Hai Precision Industry Co., Ltd.; *Int'l*, pg. 3457
DYNABOOK FRANCE—See Hon Hai Precision Industry Co., Ltd.; *Int'l*, pg. 3457
DYNABOOK INC.—See Hon Hai Precision Industry Co., Ltd.; *Int'l*, pg. 3457
DYNABOOK SINGAPORE PTE. LTD—See Hon Hai Precision Industry Co., Ltd.; *Int'l*, pg. 3457
DYNABOOK - UK—See Hon Hai Precision Industry Co., Ltd.; *Int'l*, pg. 3457
DYNABRADE DO BRASIL LTDA.—See Dynabrade, Inc.; *U.S. Private*, pg. 1297
DYNABRADE EUROPE S.A.R.L.—See Dynabrade, Inc.; *U.S. Private*, pg. 1297
DYNABRADE, INC.; *U.S. Private*, pg. 1297
DYNABRADE INDIA ABRASIVE POWER TOOLS PVT. LTD.—See Dynabrade, Inc.; *U.S. Private*, pg. 1297
DYNABRADE INTERNATIONAL SALES CORPORATION—See Dynabrade, Inc.; *U.S. Private*, pg. 1297
DYNA-BRITE LIGHTING, INC.; *U.S. Private*, pg. 1297
DYNACARE CANADA INC.—See Laboratory Corporation of America Holdings; *U.S. Public*, pg. 1286
DYNACARE COMPANY—See Laboratory Corporation of America Holdings; *U.S. Public*, pg. 1286
DYNACARE INC.—See Laboratory Corporation of America Holdings; *U.S. Public*, pg. 1286
DYNACARE NORTHWEST INC.—See Laboratory Corporation of America Holdings; *U.S. Public*, pg. 1286
DYNACAST DE MEXICO, S.A. DE C.V.—See Partners Group Holding AG; *Int'l*, pg. 5749
DYNACAST DEUTSCHLAND GMBH—See Partners Group Holding AG; *Int'l*, pg. 5749
DYNACAST ESPANA S.A.—See Partners Group Holding AG; *Int'l*, pg. 5749
DYNACAST INTERNATIONAL INC.—See Partners Group Holding AG; *Int'l*, pg. 5749
DYNACAST INTERNATIONAL INC. - TOOLING DIVISION—See Partners Group Holding AG; *Int'l*, pg. 5749
DYNACAST OSTERREICH GMBH—See Partners Group Holding AG; *Int'l*, pg. 5749
DYNACAST - PETERBOROUGH—See Partners Group Holding AG; *Int'l*, pg. 5749
DYNACAST (SHANGHAI) LTD.—See Partners Group Holding AG; *Int'l*, pg. 5749
DYNACAST (SINGAPORE) PTE LTD—See Partners Group Holding AG; *Int'l*, pg. 5749
DYNAC CORPORATION—See Suntory Holdings Limited; *Int'l*, pg. 7326
DYNACERT GMBH—See dynaCERT Inc.; *Int'l*, pg. 2239
DYNACERT INC.; *Int'l*, pg. 2239
DYNAC HOLDINGS CORPORATION—See Suntory Holdings Limited; *Int'l*, pg. 7326
DYNACO EUROPE NV—See ASSA ABLOY AB; *Int'l*, pg. 639
DYNACO INC.; *U.S. Private*, pg. 1297
DYNACOLOR CO., LTD.; *Int'l*, pg. 2239

DYNACOLOR CO., LTD.

DYNACON, INC.—See Forum Energy Technologies, Inc.; *U.S. Public*, pg. 873
DYNACONS SYSTEMS & SOLUTIONS LTD.; *Int'l*, pg. 2239
DYNA CONTRACTING; *U.S. Private*, pg. 1297
DYNACOR GROUP INC.; *Int'l*, pg. 2239
DYNACO USA INC.—See KBC Group NV; *Int'l*, pg. 4104
DYNACQ HEALTHCARE, INC.; *U.S. Private*, pg. 1297
DYNACRAFT—See PACCAR Inc.; *U.S. Public*, pg. 1630
DYNACRAFT—See PACCAR Inc.; *U.S. Public*, pg. 1630
DYNAC SDN. BHD.; *Int'l*, pg. 2238
DYNACTION SA; *Int'l*, pg. 2239
DYNAC UK LTD.—See Dynac Sdn. Bhd.; *Int'l*, pg. 2238
DYNACURE SA; *Int'l*, pg. 2239
DYNA-EMPIRE, INC.; *U.S. Private*, pg. 1297
DYNAENERGETICS GMBH & CO. KG—See DMC Global Inc.; *U.S. Public*, pg. 671
DYNAFOND SA; *Int'l*, pg. 2239
DYNAGAS LNG PARTNERS LP; *Int'l*, pg. 2239
DYNAGREEN ENVIRONMENTAL PROTECTION GROUP CO., LTD.; *Int'l*, pg. 2239
DYNAGRID CONSTRUCTION GROUP, LLC—See Brown Brothers Harriman & Co.; *U.S. Private*, pg. 667
DYNAGRI S.A.R.L—See KWS SAAT SE & Co. KGaA; *Int'l*, pg. 4352
DYNA GROUP INTERNATIONAL INC.; *U.S. Public*, pg. 699
DYNA IMAGE CORPORATION—See Diodes Incorporated; *U.S. Public*, pg. 667
DYNAIR INC.—See Carlisle Companies Incorporated; *U.S. Public*, pg. 436
DYNALCO CONTROLS CORPORATION—See Crane NXT, Co.; *U.S. Public*, pg. 589
DYNALECTRIC COMPANY OF COLORADO—See EMCOR Group, Inc.; *U.S. Public*, pg. 736
DYNALECTRIC COMPANY OF NEVADA—See EMCOR Group, Inc.; *U.S. Public*, pg. 736
DYNALECTRIC COMPANY OF OHIO—See EMCOR Group, Inc.; *U.S. Public*, pg. 736
DYNALECTRIC COMPANY—See EMCOR Group, Inc.; *U.S. Public*, pg. 736
DYNALECTRIC - FLORIDA—See EMCOR Group, Inc.; *U.S. Public*, pg. 736
DYNALECTRIC - GEORGIA—See EMCOR Group, Inc.; *U.S. Public*, pg. 736
DYNALECTRIC - LOS ANGELES—See EMCOR Group, Inc.; *U.S. Public*, pg. 736
DYNALECTRIC - OREGON—See EMCOR Group, Inc.; *U.S. Public*, pg. 736
DYNALECTRIC - SAN DIEGO—See EMCOR Group, Inc.; *U.S. Public*, pg. 736
DYNALENE INC.; *U.S. Private*, pg. 1297
DYNALIFEDX—See Laboratory Corporation of America Holdings; *U.S. Public*, pg. 1286
DYNA-LIFT, INC.; *U.S. Private*, pg. 1297
DYNALINK MODEMS LTD.—See Casa Systems, Inc.; *U.S. Private*, pg. 778
DYNALINQ BV—See bpost NV/SA; *Int'l*, pg. 1133
DYNAMAC CORPORATION—See Dynamac International Inc.; *U.S. Private*, pg. 1297
DYNA-MAC ENGINEERING SERVICES PTE LTD—See Hanwha Group; *Int'l*, pg. 3264
DYNA-MAC ENGINEERING SERVICES PTE LTD—See Hanwha Ocean Co., Ltd.; *Int'l*, pg. 3266
DYNA-MAC HOLDINGS LTD.—See Hanwha Group; *Int'l*, pg. 3264
DYNA-MAC HOLDINGS LTD.—See Hanwha Ocean Co., Ltd.; *Int'l*, pg. 3266
DYNAMAC INTERNATIONAL INC.; *U.S. Private*, pg. 1297
DYNA-MAC OFFSHORE SERVICES PTE. LTD.—See Hanwha Group; *Int'l*, pg. 3264
DYNA-MAC OFFSHORE SERVICES PTE. LTD.—See Hanwha Ocean Co., Ltd.; *Int'l*, pg. 3266
DYNAMATIC LIMITED UK—See Dynamatic Technologies Limited; *Int'l*, pg. 2239
DYNAMATIC TECHNOLOGIES LIMITED; *Int'l*, pg. 2239
DYNAM BUSINESS SUPPORT CO., LTD.—See Dynam Japan Holdings, Co., Ltd.; *Int'l*, pg. 2239
DYNAM CO., LTD.—See Dynam Japan Holdings, Co., Ltd.; *Int'l*, pg. 2239
DYNAMEDIA OF AMERICA, INC.; *U.S. Private*, pg. 1297
DYNA METAL CO., LTD.—See Daido Metal Corporation; *Int'l*, pg. 1921
DYNAMEX CANADA CORP.—See TFI International Inc.; *Int'l*, pg. 7586
DYNAMEX INC.—See TFI International Inc.; *Int'l*, pg. 7586
DYNAMEX OPERATIONS EAST, INC.—See TFI International Inc.; *Int'l*, pg. 7586
DYNAM HONG KONG CO., LIMITED—See Dynam Japan Holdings, Co., Ltd.; *Int'l*, pg. 2239
DYNAMIC AIR INC.; *U.S. Private*, pg. 1297
DYNAMIC AIRMASTER (HONG KONG) LIMITED—See Japan Post Holdings Co., Ltd.; *Int'l*, pg. 3900
DYNAMIC APEX MACAO COMMERCIAL OFFSHORE LIMITED—See Ju Teng International Holdings Limited; *Int'l*, pg. 4020
DYNAMIC ARCHITECTURES LIMITED; *Int'l*, pg. 2240
DYNAMIC ARCHITECTURAL WINDOWS & DOORS INC.; *Int'l*, pg. 2240

DYNAMICARD, INC.; *U.S. Private*, pg. 1299
DYNAMIC ASSETS MANAGEMENT COMPANY (LUXEMBOURG) SA—See Banque Profil de Gestion SA; *Int'l*, pg. 854
DYNAMIC AUTOMATION; *U.S. Private*, pg. 1297
DYNAMIC BRANDS; *U.S. Private*, pg. 1297
DYNAMIC BUILDERS INC.; *U.S. Private*, pg. 1297
DYNAMIC BUILDING CORP.; *U.S. Private*, pg. 1297
DYNAMIC CABLES LIMITED; *Int'l*, pg. 2240
DYNAMIC CERTIFICATION LABORATORIES—See Vibration Mountings & Controls, Inc.; *U.S. Private*, pg. 4376
DYNAMIC CHEMICAL PTE. LTD.—See Ancom Nylex Berhad; *Int'l*, pg. 449
DYNAMIC CHEMICAL TRADING PTE LTD—See Nylex (Malaysia) Berhad; *Int'l*, pg. 5500
DYNAMIC COLOURS LIMITED; *Int'l*, pg. 2240
DYNAMIC COMPUTER CORPORATION; *U.S. Private*, pg. 1297
DYNAMIC COMPUTING SERVICES CORP.; *U.S. Private*, pg. 1297
DYNAMIC COMPUTING TECHNOLOGY CO., LTD.—See Hon Hai Precision Industry Co., Ltd.; *Int'l*, pg. 3456
DYNAMIC CONCEPTS INC.; *U.S. Private*, pg. 1297
DYNAMIC CONCEPTS, INC.—See Millennium Engineering & Integration Company; *U.S. Private*, pg. 2731
DYNAMIC CONTROLS HS, INC.—See RTX Corporation; *U.S. Public*, pg. 1821
DYNAMIC CONTROLS, INC.—See Daikin Industries, Ltd.; *Int'l*, pg. 1936
DYNAMIC CONTROLS, LTD.—See Allient Inc.; *U.S. Public*, pg. 80
DYNAMIC COOKING SYSTEMS, INC.—See Haier Smart Home Co., Ltd.; *Int'l*, pg. 3210
DYNAMIC DECISIONS INC.; *U.S. Private*, pg. 1298
DYNAMIC DENTAL PARTNERS INC—See Huron Capital Partners LLC; *U.S. Private*, pg. 2012
DYNAMIC DESIGN CO., LTD.; *Int'l*, pg. 2240
DYNAMIC DESIGN SOLUTIONS, INC.; *U.S. Private*, pg. 1298
DYNAMIC DIES INC.; *U.S. Private*, pg. 1298
DYNAMIC DISPLAYS, INC.; *U.S. Private*, pg. 1298
DYNAMIC DRILL & BLAST PTY. LTD.—See Dynamic Group Holdings Limited; *Int'l*, pg. 2240
DYNAMIC ELECTRONICS CO., LTD.; *Int'l*, pg. 2240
DYNAMIC ELECTRONICS (HUANGSHI) CO., LTD.—See Dynamic Electronics Co., Ltd.; *Int'l*, pg. 2240
DYNAMIC ELECTRONICS (KUNSHAN) CO., LTD.—See Dynamic Electronics Co., Ltd.; *Int'l*, pg. 2240
DYNAMIC ENERGY, INC.—See Mechel PAO; *Int'l*, pg. 4766
DYNAMIC ENGINEERING INC.; *U.S. Private*, pg. 1298
DYNAMIC EUROPE LTD.—See Invacare Corporation; *U.S. Private*, pg. 2130
DYNAMIC EVER INVESTMENTS LIMITED—See USI Corporation; *Int'l*, pg. 8098
DYNAMIC FASTENER SERVICE INC.; *U.S. Private*, pg. 1298
DYNAMIC FLUID CONTROL (PTY) LTD.—See Aveng Limited; *Int'l*, pg. 738
DYNAMIC FOODS—See Food Management Partners, Inc.; *U.S. Private*, pg. 1561
DYNAMIC GEOSOLUTIONS 2008 LTD—See New Jcm Group CO., Ltd; *Int'l*, pg. 5226
DYNAMIC GLASS, LLC—See Platform Partners LLC; *U.S. Private*, pg. 3200
DYNAMIC GRAPHICS INC.—See Bertelsmann SE & Co. KGaA; *Int'l*, pg. 990
DYNAMIC GROUP HOLDINGS LIMITED; *Int'l*, pg. 2240
DYNAMIC HEALTHIER CONSULTANT; *U.S. Private*, pg. 1298
DYNAMIC HOLDINGS LIMITED; *Int'l*, pg. 2240
DYNAMIC HOMES, INC.; *U.S. Private*, pg. 1298
DYNAMIC HYDROCARBONS LTD.; *U.S. Private*, pg. 1298
DYNAMIC INDUSTRIES LIMITED; *Int'l*, pg. 2240
DYNAMIC INSTRUMENTS INC.—See Technology for Energy Corporation; *U.S. Private*, pg. 3955
DYNAMIC INTERNATIONAL USA, INC.; *U.S. Private*, pg. 1298
DYNAMIC IT SOLUTIONS CO., LTD.—See SCGJWD Logistics Public Company Limited; *Int'l*, pg. 6614
DYNAMIC LANGUAGE CENTER, LTD.; *U.S. Private*, pg. 1298
DYNAMIC LAUNDRY SYSTEMS, INC.—See BDT Capital Partners, LLC; *U.S. Private*, pg. 502
DYNAMIC LIVING, INC.; *U.S. Private*, pg. 1298
DYNAMIC LOGIC—See Bain Capital, LP; *U.S. Private*, pg. 448
DYNAMIC LOGIC—See Bain Capital, LP; *U.S. Private*, pg. 448
DYNAMIC LOGIC—See Bain Capital, LP; *U.S. Private*, pg. 448
DYNAMIC LOGIC—See Bain Capital, LP; *U.S. Private*, pg. 448
DYNAMIC LOGISTICS (HONG KONG) LTD—See Japan Post Holdings Co., Ltd.; *Int'l*, pg. 3900
DYNAMIC LOGISTIX, LLC; *U.S. Private*, pg. 1298
DYNAMIC MACHINERY LTD.—See Quaser Machine Tools, Inc.; *Int'l*, pg. 6156

DYNAMIC MANAGEMENT COMPANY LLC; *U.S. Private*, pg. 1298
DYNAMIC MANUFACTURING SOLUTIONS, LLC—See Ultra Clean Holdings, Inc.; *U.S. Public*, pg. 2223
DYNAMIC MARKETING, INC.; *U.S. Private*, pg. 1298
DYNAMIC MARKETING SDN. BHD.—See YTL Corporation Berhad; *Int'l*, pg. 8606
DYNAMIC MARK LIMITED—See Shui On Company Limited; *Int'l*, pg. 6869
DYNAMIC MECHANICAL CONTRACTORS INC.; *U.S. Private*, pg. 1298
DYNAMIC MEDIA TIRANA—See Omnicom Group Inc.; *U.S. Public*, pg. 1575
DYNAMIC MEDICAL SYSTEMS, INC.—See Invacare Corporation; *U.S. Private*, pg. 2130
DYNAMIC METALS LIMITED; *Int'l*, pg. 2240
DYNAMIC METHODS; *U.S. Private*, pg. 1298
DYNAMIC MICROSTEPPERS LIMITED; *Int'l*, pg. 2240
DYNAMIC MOBILE IMAGING; *U.S. Private*, pg. 1298
DYNAMIC NETWORK SERVICES, INC.—See Oracle Corporation; *U.S. Public*, pg. 1611
DYNAMIC OFFSHORE RESOURCES, LLC—See SandRidge Energy, Inc.; *U.S. Public*, pg. 1839
DYNAMIC PAINT PRODUCTS INC.—See Centre Lane Partners, LLC; *U.S. Private*, pg. 828
DYNAMIC PCB ELECTRONICS CO., LTD.—See Dynamic Electronics Co., Ltd.; *Int'l*, pg. 2240
DYNAMIC PORTFOLIO MANAGEMENT & SERVICES LIMITED; *Int'l*, pg. 2240
DYNAMIC PRECISION GROUP—See AeroEquity Partners, LLC; *U.S. Private*, pg. 118
DYNAMIC PRECISION GROUP—See The Carlyle Group Inc.; *U.S. Public*, pg. 2046
DYNAMIC PROGRESS INTERNATIONAL LIMITED—See Alltronics Holdings Limited; *Int'l*, pg. 361
DYNAMIC & PROTO CIRCUITS INC.; *Int'l*, pg. 2239
DYNAMIC QUEST, INC.—See Spire Capital Partners, LLC; *U.S. Private*, pg. 3757
DYNAMIC RECYCLING; *U.S. Private*, pg. 1298
DYNAMIC REPROGRAPHICS, INC.—See Thomas Reprographics, Inc.; *U.S. Private*, pg. 4157
DYNAMIC RESEARCH, INC.—See AB Dynamics plc; *Int'l*, pg. 39
DYNAMIC RESOURCE GROUP, INC.; *U.S. Private*, pg. 1298
DYNAMIC RESOURCES, INC.; *U.S. Private*, pg. 1299
DYNAMIC RISK ASSESSMENT SYSTEMS, INC.—See Eddyfi NDT, Inc.; *Int'l*, pg. 2304
DYNAMIC ROBOTIC SOLUTIONS AB—See AIP, LLC; *U.S. Private*, pg. 137
DYNAMIC ROBOTIC SOLUTIONS GMBH—See AIP, LLC; *U.S. Private*, pg. 137
DYNAMIC ROBOTIC SOLUTIONS, INC.—See AIP, LLC; *U.S. Private*, pg. 137
DYNAMICS BUSINESS SOLUTIONS S.R.L.—See Sesa S.p.A.; *Int'l*, pg. 6728
DYNAMIC SEALING TECHNOLOGIES, INC.—See Kadant Inc.; *U.S. Public*, pg. 1212
DYNAMIC SECURITY INC.; *U.S. Private*, pg. 1299
DYNAMIC SERVICES & SECURITY LIMITED; *Int'l*, pg. 2240
DYNAMICSIGNALS LLC; *U.S. Private*, pg. 1299
DYNAMICS MARKETING INC.; *U.S. Private*, pg. 1299
DYNAMIC SOLUTIONS GROUP INC.; *U.S. Private*, pg. 1299
DYNAMIC SOLUTIONS WORLDWIDE, LLC—See Vestar Capital Partners, LLC; *U.S. Private*, pg. 4372
DYNAMIC SOURCE MANUFACTURING INC.; *Int'l*, pg. 2240
DYNAMIC SPECIALTY VEHICLES LTD.; *Int'l*, pg. 2241
DYNAMICS RESOURCES INC.—See Sverica Capital Management LP; *U.S. Private*, pg. 3889
DYNAMIC SUPPLIES PTY. LTD.; *Int'l*, pg. 2241
DYNAMIC SYSTEMS HOLDINGS, INC.; *Int'l*, pg. 2241
DYNAMIC SYSTEMS INC.—See FGI Group Inc.; *U.S. Private*, pg. 1501
DYNAMIC SYSTEMS, INC.; *U.S. Private*, pg. 1299
DYNAMIC SYSTEMS, INC.—See Vishay Precision Group, Inc.; *U.S. Public*, pg. 2303
DYNAMIC SYSTEMS TECHNOLOGY, INC.; *U.S. Private*, pg. 1299
DYNAMIC TEAM SPORTS INC.; *U.S. Private*, pg. 1299
DYNAMIC TECHNOLOGIES GROUP INC.; *Int'l*, pg. 2241
DYNAMIC TECHNOLOGY SUPPLIES COMPANY LTD.; *Int'l*, pg. 2241
DYNAMIC TIRE CORP.; *Int'l*, pg. 2241
DYNAMIC TOOLING SERVICES (PRIVATE) LIMITED—See Chien Wei Precise Technology Co., Ltd.; *Int'l*, pg. 1477
DYNAMIC VENDING, INC.—See Compass Group PLC; *Int'l*, pg. 1751
DYNAMIC WEB MARKETING B.V.—See LeoVegas AB; *Int'l*, pg. 4466
DYNAMIC WEB TRAINING PTY LTD—See SEEK Limited; *Int'l*, pg. 6678
DYNAMIC WHEEL CO PTY LIMITED—See National Tyre & Wheel Limited; *Int'l*, pg. 5164
DYNAMIC WORKFORCE SOLUTIONS, LLC—See Madison Dearborn Partners, LLC; *U.S. Private*, pg. 2540

DYNAMIC WORKFORCE SOLUTIONS - TEXAS, LLC—See Madison Dearborn Partners, LLC; *U.S. Private*, pg. 2540
DYNAMIC WORLDWIDE WEST, INC.—See Dynamic International USA, Inc.; *U.S. Private*, pg. 1298
DYNA-MIG MFG. OF STRATFORD INC.—See F-Tech Inc.; *Int'l*, pg. 2595
DYNAMIK PUMPEN GMBH—See KSB SE & Co. KGaA; *Int'l*, pg. 4310
DYNAMITE BAITS LTD.—See Rapala VMC Oyj; *Int'l*, pg. 6209
DYNAMITE PLANT FOOD—See Florikan ESA LLC; *U.S. Private*, pg. 1551
DYNAMIT; *U.S. Private*, pg. 1299
DYNAMIX BALWAS GROUP OF COMPANIES; *Int'l*, pg. 2241
DYNAMIX GROUP INC.; *U.S. Private*, pg. 1299
DYNAMIX MECHANICAL, LLC; *U.S. Private*, pg. 1299
DYNAM JAPAN HOLDINGS, CO., LTD.; *Int'l*, pg. 2239
DYNAMO AMUSEMENT, INC.; *Int'l*, pg. 2241
DYNAMO DEVELOPMENT, INC.—See TechMagic; *Int'l*, pg. 7505
DYNAMORE NORDIC AB—See ANSYS, Inc.; *U.S. Public*, pg. 139
DYNAPAC CO., LTD. - FUKUSHIMA PLANT—See Dynapac Co., Ltd.; *Int'l*, pg. 2241
DYNAPAC CO., LTD. - KANIE PLANT—See Dynapac Co., Ltd.; *Int'l*, pg. 2241
DYNAPAC CO., LTD. - KAWAGOE PLANT—See Dynapac Co., Ltd.; *Int'l*, pg. 2241
DYNAPAC CO., LTD. - MATSUMOTO PLANT—See Dynapac Co., Ltd.; *Int'l*, pg. 2241
DYNAPAC CO., LTD. - MIYOSHI PLANT—See Dynapac Co., Ltd.; *Int'l*, pg. 2241
DYNAPAC CO., LTD. - SHIZUOKA PLANT—See Dynapac Co., Ltd.; *Int'l*, pg. 2241
DYNAPAC CO., LTD.; *Int'l*, pg. 2241
DYNAPAC CO., LTD. - TSUKUBA PLANT—See Dynapac Co., Ltd.; *Int'l*, pg. 2241
DYNAPAC COMPACTION EQUIPMENT AB—See FAYAT SAS; *Int'l*, pg. 2624
DYNAPAC DO BRASIL IND. COM LTDA.—See FAYAT SAS; *Int'l*, pg. 2624
DYNAPAC FRANCE SAS—See FAYAT SAS; *Int'l*, pg. 2624
DYNAPAC GF (MALAYSIA) SDN.BHD—See Dynapac Co., Ltd.; *Int'l*, pg. 2241
DYNAPAC GMBH—See FAYAT SAS; *Int'l*, pg. 2624
DYNAPAC (HAI PHONG) CO., LTD.—See Dynapac Co., Ltd.; *Int'l*, pg. 2241
DYNAPAC (HANOI) CO., LTD.—See Dynapac Co., Ltd.; *Int'l*, pg. 2241
DYNAPAC (HK) LTD.—See Dynapac Co., Ltd.; *Int'l*, pg. 2241
DYNAPACK INTERNATIONAL TECHNOLOGY CORPORATION; *Int'l*, pg. 2242
DYNAPACK (SUCHOU) CO., LTD.—See Dynapack International Technology Corporation; *Int'l*, pg. 2242
DYNAPAC (M) SDN. BHD.—See Dynapac Co., Ltd.; *Int'l*, pg. 2241
DYNAPAC (SUZHOU) CO., LTD.—See Dynapac Co., Ltd.; *Int'l*, pg. 2241
DYNAPAC (SZ) LTD.—See Dynapac Co., Ltd.; *Int'l*, pg. 2241
DYNAPAR CORPORATION—See Fortive Corporation; *U.S. Public*, pg. 870
DYNAPATH SYSTEMS, INC.; *U.S. Private*, pg. 1299
DYNAPLAST SA—See Groupe Guillin SA; *Int'l*, pg. 3103
DYNAPOWER COMPANY, LLC—See Sensata Technologies Holding plc; *U.S. Public*, pg. 1865
DYNAPRESSE MARKETING SA—See Vivendi SE; *Int'l*, pg. 8275
DYNARDO AUSTRIA GMBH—See ANSYS, Inc.; *U.S. Public*, pg. 139
DYNARDO (DYNAMIC SOFTWARE & ENGINEERING) GMBH—See ANSYS, Inc.; *U.S. Public*, pg. 139
DYNA RECHI (JIUJIANG) CO., LTD.—See China Steel Corporation; *Int'l*, pg. 1555
DYNARESOURCE, INC.; *U.S. Public*, pg. 699
DYNAREX CORP; *U.S. Private*, pg. 1299
DYNARIC, INC.; *U.S. Private*, pg. 1299
DYNASIL CORPORATION OF AMERICA; *U.S. Private*, pg. 1299
DYNASIL - SYNTHETIC FUSED SILICA—See Dynasil Corporation of America; *U.S. Private*, pg. 1299
DYNASIS INTEGRATED SYSTEMS CORP.—See Perpetual Capital, LLC; *U.S. Private*, pg. 3153
DYNASIVE ENTERPRISE SDN BHD—See IJM Corporation Berhad; *Int'l*, pg. 3608
DYNASOUND, INC.—See AMETEK, Inc.; *U.S. Public*, pg. 119
DYNASPAN FURNITURE SDN. BHD.—See Eurospan Holdings Berhad; *Int'l*, pg. 2558
DYNASPLINT SYSTEMS INC.; *U.S. Private*, pg. 1300
DYNASTAR HOLDINGS, INC.; *U.S. Public*, pg. 699
DYNASTIC LION SDN BHD—See Nadayu Properties Berhad; *Int'l*, pg. 5123
DYNASTREAM INNOVATIONS INC.—See Garmin Ltd.; *Int'l*, pg. 2885

DYNASTY AEROTECH INTERNATIONAL CORP.—See China Airlines Ltd.; *Int'l*, pg. 1482
DYNASTY CERAMIC PUBLIC COMPANY LIMITED; *Int'l*, pg. 2242
DYNASTY CONSOLIDATED INDUSTRIES INCORPORATED; *U.S. Private*, pg. 1300
DYNASTY EQUITY PARTNERS MANAGEMENT, LLC; *U.S. Private*, pg. 1300
DYNASTY FARMS, INC.—See Pacific International Marketing, Inc.; *U.S. Private*, pg. 3068
DYNASTY FASHIONS, INC.; *U.S. Private*, pg. 1300
DYNASTY FINE WINES GROUP LIMITED; *Int'l*, pg. 2242
DYNASTY FOOTWEAR LTD; *U.S. Private*, pg. 1300
DYNASTY GOLD CORP.; *Int'l*, pg. 2242
DYNASTY HOLIDAYS, INC.—See China Airlines Ltd.; *Int'l*, pg. 1482
DYNASTY HOTEL OF HAWAII, INC—See China Airlines Ltd.; *Int'l*, pg. 1481
DYNASTY MODULAR FURNITURES PRIVATE LIMITED—See Dhabriya Polywood Limited; *Int'l*, pg. 2097
DYNASTY PROPERTIES CO., LTD.—See China Airlines Ltd.; *Int'l*, pg. 1481
DYNASTY RESOURCES LIMITED; *Int'l*, pg. 2242
DYNASTY TECHNOLOGY GROUP S.A.—See Diebold Nixdorf, Inc.; *U.S. Public*, pg. 660
DYNASTY TRAVEL INTERNATIONAL PTE. LTD.—See JTB Corp.; *Int'l*, pg. 4015
DYNASTY VIEW SDN. BHD.—See Seleksi Juang Sdn Bhd; *Int'l*, pg. 6700
DYNASYNERGY SERVICES SDN. BHD.—See OCK Group Berhad; *Int'l*, pg. 5520
DYNASYS S.A.S.—See Thoma Bravo, L.P.; *U.S. Private*, pg. 4151
DYNASYS TECHNOLOGY & ENGINEERING SDN. BHD.—See Shin Yang Shipping Corporation Berhad; *Int'l*, pg. 6838
DYNATA, LLC - LEHI—See Court Square Capital Partners, L.P.; *U.S. Private*, pg. 1069
DYNATA, LLC—See Court Square Capital Partners, L.P.; *U.S. Private*, pg. 1069
DYNATEC DRILLING, INC.; *U.S. Private*, pg. 1300
DYNATECH FURNACES PVT. LTD.—See AMG Critical Materials N.V.; *Int'l*, pg. 425
DYNATECH INTERNATIONAL CORP.; *U.S. Private*, pg. 1300
DYNATECT MANUFACTURING, INC.—See 3i Group plc; *Int'l*, pg. 8
DYNATECT POLYCLUTCH—See 3i Group plc; *Int'l*, pg. 8
DYNATEK, INC.—See K.K. Birla Group; *Int'l*, pg. 4044
DYNATEM, INC.—See Eurotech S.p.A.; *Int'l*, pg. 2558
DYNA TEN CORPORATION—See Comfort Systems USA, Inc.; *U.S. Public*, pg. 544
DYNA TEN MAINTENANCE SERVICES, LLC—See Comfort Systems USA, Inc.; *U.S. Public*, pg. 544
DYNATEX INTERNATIONAL; *U.S. Private*, pg. 1300
DYNATEX NV—See Sioen Industries NV; *Int'l*, pg. 6960
DYNATRACE ASIA PACIFIC LIMITED—See Dynatrace, Inc.; *U.S. Public*, pg. 700
DYNATRACE ASIA-PACIFIC PTY. LTD.—See Dynatrace, Inc.; *U.S. Public*, pg. 700
DYNATRACE A/S—See KKR & Co. Inc.; *U.S. Public*, pg. 1240
DYNATRACE AUSTRIA GMBH—See Dynatrace, Inc.; *U.S. Public*, pg. 700
DYNATRACE BV—See Dynatrace, Inc.; *U.S. Public*, pg. 700
DYNATRACE BV—See KKR & Co. Inc.; *U.S. Public*, pg. 1240
DYNATRACE DE MEXICO—See Dynatrace, Inc.; *U.S. Public*, pg. 700
DYNATRACE FINLAND OY—See KKR & Co. Inc.; *U.S. Public*, pg. 1240
DYNATRACE, INC.; *U.S. Public*, pg. 699
DYNATRACE INDIA SOFTWARE OPERATIONS PVT. LTD.—See Dynatrace, Inc.; *U.S. Public*, pg. 700
DYNATRACE IRELAND LIMITED—See Dynatrace, Inc.; *U.S. Public*, pg. 700
DYNATRACE LIMITED—See KKR & Co. Inc.; *U.S. Public*, pg. 1240
DYNATRACE LLC—See Dynatrace, Inc.; *U.S. Public*, pg. 700
DYNATRACE SARL—See KKR & Co. Inc.; *U.S. Public*, pg. 1240
DYNATRACE SP. Z.O.O—See Dynatrace, Inc.; *U.S. Public*, pg. 700
DYNA TRAINING PROPRIETARY LIMITED—See Workforce Holdings Ltd.; *Int'l*, pg. 8455
DYNATRONICS CORPORATION; *U.S. Public*, pg. 700
DYNATRON INDUSTRIAL CO., LTD—See TOA Corporation; *Int'l*, pg. 7768
DYNAT VERSCHLUSSTECHNIK GMBH—See YKK Corporation; *Int'l*, pg. 8588
DYNAVAX EUROPE GMBH—See Dynavax Technologies Corporation; *U.S. Public*, pg. 700
DYNAVAX GMBH—See Dynavax Technologies Corporation; *U.S. Public*, pg. 700
DYNAVAX TECHNOLOGIES CORPORATION; *U.S. Public*, pg. 700

DYNAVEST PTE. LTD.; *Int'l*, pg. 2242
DYNAVEST TECHNOLOGIES (SUZHOU) CO, LTD—See Dynavest Pte. Ltd.; *Int'l*, pg. 2242
DYNAVEST (THAILAND) CO, LTD—See Dynavest Pte. Ltd.; *Int'l*, pg. 2242
DYNAVISION LTD.; *Int'l*, pg. 2242
DYNAWARE ASIA PACIFIC PTE. LTD.—See Dynatrace, Inc.; *U.S. Public*, pg. 700
DYNAX AMERICA CORPORATION—See Exedy Corporation; *Int'l*, pg. 2580
DYNAX CORPORATION—See Exedy Corporation; *Int'l*, pg. 2580
DYNAX INDUSTRY (SHANGHAI) CO., LTD.—See Exedy Corporation; *Int'l*, pg. 2580
DYNAXYS LLC; *U.S. Private*, pg. 1300
DYNCORP AEROSPACE OPERATIONS LTD.—See Cerberus Capital Management, L.P.; *U.S. Private*, pg. 838
DYNCORP INTERNATIONAL LLC—See Cerberus Capital Management, L.P.; *U.S. Private*, pg. 838
DYN DIAGNOSTICS LTD.—See HORIBA Ltd.; *Int'l*, pg. 3475
DYNEA (GUANGDONG) CO., LTD.—See AICA Kogyo Company, Limited; *Int'l*, pg. 229
DYNEA (NANJING) CO., LTD.—See AICA Kogyo Company, Limited; *Int'l*, pg. 229
DYNEA N.V.—See Ackermans & van Haaren NV; *Int'l*, pg. 106
DYNEA PAKISTAN LIMITED - GADOON UNIT—See Dynea Pakistan Limited; *Int'l*, pg. 2242
DYNEA PAKISTAN LIMITED - HUB UNIT—See Dynea Pakistan Limited; *Int'l*, pg. 2242
DYNEA PAKISTAN LIMITED; *Int'l*, pg. 2242
DYNEA (SHANGHAI) CO., LTD.—See AICA Kogyo Company, Limited; *Int'l*, pg. 229
DYNEFF ESPAGNE SL—See AnAn International Limited; *Int'l*, pg. 446
DYNEFF SAS—See AnAn International Limited; *Int'l*, pg. 446
DYNEGY, INC.—See Vistra Corp.; *U.S. Public*, pg. 2306
DYNEGY MARKETING AND TRADE, LLC—See Vistra Corp.; *U.S. Public*, pg. 2306
DYNEGY MIDWEST GENERATION, LLC—See Vistra Corp.; *U.S. Public*, pg. 2306
DYNEGY NORTH AMERICA, INC.—See Energy Capital Partners Management, LP; *U.S. Private*, pg. 1394
DYNELYTICS AG; *Int'l*, pg. 2242
DYNEMIC PRODUCTS LTD.; *Int'l*, pg. 2242
DYNEON GMBH—See 3M Company; *U.S. Public*, pg. 5
DYNEON GMBH—See 3M Company; *U.S. Public*, pg. 8
DYNE SYSTEMS, INC.—See Taylor Dynamometer, Inc.; *U.S. Private*, pg. 3939
DYNE THERAPEUTICS, INC.; *U.S. Public*, pg. 700
DYNETICS INC.—See Leidos Holdings, Inc.; *U.S. Public*, pg. 1304
DYNEX CAPITAL, INC.; *U.S. Public*, pg. 700
DYNEX ENERGY SA; *Int'l*, pg. 2242
DYNEX EXTRUSIONS LTD—See Aliaxis S.A./N.V.; *Int'l*, pg. 324
DYNEX POWER INC.—See Zhuzhou CRRC Times Electric Co. Ltd.; *Int'l*, pg. 8679
DYNEX SEMICONDUCTOR LIMITED—See Zhuzhou CRRC Times Electric Co. Ltd.; *Int'l*, pg. 8679
DYNEX TECHNOLOGIES, INC.—See Telegraph Hill Partners Management Company, LLC; *U.S. Private*, pg. 3960
DYNIC CORPORATION - FUJI FACTORY—See Dynic Corporation; *Int'l*, pg. 2242
DYNIC CORPORATION - MOKA FACTORY—See Dynic Corporation; *Int'l*, pg. 2242
DYNIC CORPORATION - OJI FACTORY—See Dynic Corporation; *Int'l*, pg. 2242
DYNIC CORPORATION - SHIGA FACTORY—See Dynic Corporation; *Int'l*, pg. 2242
DYNIC CORPORATION; *Int'l*, pg. 2242
DYNIC FACTORY SERVICE CO., LTD.—See Dynic Corporation; *Int'l*, pg. 2242
DYNIC (HK) LTD.—See Dynic Corporation; *Int'l*, pg. 2242
DYNIC INTERNATIONAL TRADING (SHANGHAI) CO., LTD.—See Dynic Corporation; *Int'l*, pg. 2242
DYNIC JUNO CO., LTD.—See Dynic Corporation; *Int'l*, pg. 2243
DYNIC SINGAPORE PTE. LTD.—See Dynic Corporation; *Int'l*, pg. 2243
DYNIC (UK) LTD.—See Dynic Corporation; *Int'l*, pg. 2242
DYNIC USA CORPORATION—See Dynic Corporation; *Int'l*, pg. 2243
DYNISCO EUROPE GMBH—See Roper Technologies, Inc.; *U.S. Public*, pg. 1811
DYNISCO INSTRUMENTS LLC—See Roper Technologies, Inc.; *U.S. Public*, pg. 1811
DYNISCO INSTRUMENTS S.A.R.L.—See Roper Technologies, Inc.; *U.S. Public*, pg. 1811
DYNISCO SHANGHAI SENSOR AND INSTRUMENT CO., LTD.—See Roper Technologies, Inc.; *U.S. Public*, pg. 1811
DYNISCO SPOL, SRO—See Roper Technologies, Inc.; *U.S. Public*, pg. 1811
DYNISCO S.R.L.—See Roper Technologies, Inc.; *U.S. Public*, pg. 1811

DYNIC CORPORATION

DYNISCO-VIATRAN INSTRUMENT SDN BHD—See Roper Technologies, Inc.; *U.S. Public*, pg. 1811
DYNIS LLC.; *U.S. Private*, pg. 1300
DYNITEC GMBH—See Diehl Stiftung & Co. KG; *Int'l*, pg. 2115
DYN MARINE SERVICES OF VIRGINIA LLC—See Cerberus Capital Management, L.P.; *U.S. Private*, pg. 838
DYNNIQ ENERGY B.V.—See Heijmans N.V.; *Int'l*, pg. 3322
DYNNIQ GROUP B.V.—See Egeria Capital Management B.V.; *Int'l*, pg. 2323
DYNNIQ NEDERLAND BV—See Egeria Capital Management B.V.; *Int'l*, pg. 2323
DYNNIQ PEEK TRAFFIC B.V.—See Egeria Capital Management B.V.; *Int'l*, pg. 2323
DYNNIQ UK LTD—See Egeria Capital Management B.V.; *Int'l*, pg. 2323
DYNOJET RESEARCH, INC.—See Irving Place Capital Management, L.P.; *U.S. Private*, pg. 2141
DYNOJET RESEARCH, INC.—See New Value Capital LLC; *U.S. Private*, pg. 2907
DYNOMIGHTY DESIGN; *U.S. Private*, pg. 1300
DYNO NOBEL ASIA PACIFIC LIMITED—See Incitec Pivot Limited; *Int'l*, pg. 3647
DYNO NOBEL CANADA, INC.—See Incitec Pivot Limited; *Int'l*, pg. 3647
DYNO NOBEL EXPLOSIVOS CHILE LIMITADA—See Incitec Pivot Limited; *Int'l*, pg. 3647
DYNO NOBEL HOLDINGS USA, INC.—See Incitec Pivot Limited; *Int'l*, pg. 3647
DYNO NOBEL, INC.—See Incitec Pivot Limited; *Int'l*, pg. 3647
DYNO NOBEL MORANBAH PTY LTD—See Incitec Pivot Limited; *Int'l*, pg. 3647
DYNO NOBEL MOURA PTY LIMITED—See Incitec Pivot Limited; *Int'l*, pg. 3647
DYNO NOBEL NITROGEN, INC.—See Incitec Pivot Limited; *Int'l*, pg. 3648
DYNO NOBEL SWEDEN AB—See Orica Limited; *Int'l*, pg. 5620
DYNO NOBEL TRANSPORTATION INC.—See Incitec Pivot Limited; *Int'l*, pg. 3648
DYNO OIL CO. INC.; *U.S. Private*, pg. 1300
DYNPORT VACCINE COMPANY LLC—See General Dynamics Corporation; *U.S. Public*, pg. 913
DYN; *U.S. Private*, pg. 1296
DYNTEK, INC.; *U.S. Public*, pg. 700
DYNTEK INC.—See DynTek, Inc.; *U.S. Public*, pg. 700
DYO BOYA FABRIKALARI SANAYI VE TICARET AS; *Int'l*, pg. 2243
DYOMO CORPORATION—See Brightcom Group Ltd.; *Int'l*, pg. 1162
DYONYX, L.P.; *U.S. Private*, pg. 1300
DYPNF CO.,LTD; *Int'l*, pg. 2243
DY POWER CORPORATION—See DY Corporation; *Int'l*, pg. 2237
DY POWER SYSTEMS (M) SDN. BHD.—See Stick Investment Co., Ltd.; *Int'l*, pg. 7215
DYRUP A/S—See PPG Industries, Inc.; *U.S. Public*, pg. 1707
DYRUP GMBH—See PPG Industries, Inc.; *U.S. Public*, pg. 1707
DYRUP SAS—See PPG Industries, Inc.; *U.S. Public*, pg. 1707
DYRUP SP. Z.O.O.—See PPG Industries, Inc.; *U.S. Public*, pg. 1707
DYSART CORPORATION; *U.S. Private*, pg. 1300
DYSBOX SA—See Sonepar S.A.; *Int'l*, pg. 7093
DYSON DIECASTING—See The Alumasc Group plc; *Int'l*, pg. 7613
DYSON, DYSON & DUNN INC.; *U.S. Private*, pg. 1300
DYSON GROUP PLC; *Int'l*, pg. 2243
THE DYSON GROUP; *Int'l*, pg. 7637
DYSON INC.—See Dyson Ltd.; *Int'l*, pg. 2243
THE DYSON-KISSNER-MORAN CORPORATION; *U.S. Private*, pg. 4024
DYSON LTD.; *Int'l*, pg. 2243
DYSONS INC.; *U.S. Private*, pg. 1300
DYSTAR ANILINAS TEXTEIS UNIPESSOAL, LDA.—See Kiri Industries Ltd.; *Int'l*, pg. 4186
DYSTAR BENELUX—See Kiri Industries Ltd.; *Int'l*, pg. 4186
DYSTAR BOEHME AFRICA (PTY) LTD.—See Kiri Industries Ltd.; *Int'l*, pg. 4186
DYSTAR CAROLINA CHEMICAL—See Kiri Industries Ltd.; *Int'l*, pg. 4186
DYSTAR CHINA LDT.—See Kiri Industries Ltd.; *Int'l*, pg. 4186
DYSTAR DE MEXICO S. DE R.L. DE C.V—See Kiri Industries Ltd.; *Int'l*, pg. 4186
DYSTAR FOAM CONTROL—See Kiri Industries Ltd.; *Int'l*, pg. 4186
DYSTAR FRANCE S.A.R.L.—See Kiri Industries Ltd.; *Int'l*, pg. 4186
DYSTAR HILTON DAVIS—See Kiri Industries Ltd.; *Int'l*, pg. 4186
DYSTAR HISPANIA, S.L., SOCIEDAD UNIPERSONAL—See Kiri Industries Ltd.; *Int'l*, pg. 4186
DYSTAR INDIA PRIVATE LIMITED—See Kiri Industries Ltd.; *Int'l*, pg. 4186
DYSTAR INDUSTRIA E COMERCIO DE PRODUTOS QUIMICOS LTDA.—See Kiri Industries Ltd.; *Int'l*, pg. 4186
DYSTAR ITALIA S.R.L.—See Kiri Industries Ltd.; *Int'l*, pg. 4186
DYSTAR JAPAN LTD.—See Kiri Industries Ltd.; *Int'l*, pg. 4186
DYSTAR KOREA LTD.—See Kiri Industries Ltd.; *Int'l*, pg. 4186
DYSTAR L.P.—See Kiri Industries Ltd.; *Int'l*, pg. 4186
DYSTAR PAKISTAN (PVT.) LTD.—See Kiri Industries Ltd.; *Int'l*, pg. 4186
DYSTAR (SHANGHAI) TRADING CO., LTD.—See Kiri Industries Ltd.; *Int'l*, pg. 4186
DYSTAR SINGAPORE PTE. LTD.—See Kiri Industries Ltd.; *Int'l*, pg. 4186
DYSTAR TAIWAN LTD.—See Kiri Industries Ltd.; *Int'l*, pg. 4186
DYSTAR TEXTILFARBEN GMBH—See Kiri Industries Ltd.; *Int'l*, pg. 4186
DYSTAR THAI LTD.—See Kiri Industries Ltd.; *Int'l*, pg. 4186
DYTECNA ENGINEERING LTD—See Dytecna Limited; *Int'l*, pg. 2243
DYTECNA LIMITED; *Int'l*, pg. 2243
DY TERMINAL LTD.—See Singamas Container Holdings Limited; *Int'l*, pg. 6939
DYTON (CHONGQING) SWITCHGEAR CO., LTD.—See Tianjin Benefo Tejing Electric Co., Ltd.; *Int'l*, pg. 7738
DYTRAN INSTRUMENTS, INC.—See Spectris Plc; *Int'l*, pg. 7130
DYVENTIVE INC.; *U.S. Private*, pg. 1300
DYWIDAG -HOLDING GMBH—See STRABAG SE; *Int'l*, pg. 7230
DYWIDAG INTERNATIONAL GMBH—See STRABAG SE; *Int'l*, pg. 7230
DYWIDAG SAUDI ARABIA CO. LTD.—See STRABAG SE; *Int'l*, pg. 7230
DYWIDAG-SYSTEMS INTERNATIONAL A/S—See Triton Advisers Limited; *Int'l*, pg. 7929
DYWIDAG-SYSTEMS INTERNATIONAL B.V.—See Triton Advisers Limited; *Int'l*, pg. 7929
DYWIDAG-SYSTEMS INTERNATIONAL CANADA LTD. - EASTERN DIVISION—See Triton Advisers Limited; *Int'l*, pg. 7929
DYWIDAG-SYSTEMS INTERNATIONAL CANADA LTD. - WESTERN DIVISION—See Triton Advisers Limited; *Int'l*, pg. 7929
DYWIDAG-SYSTEMS INTERNATIONAL FAR EAST LTD.—See Triton Advisers Limited; *Int'l*, pg. 7929
DYWIDAG-SYSTEMS INTERNATIONAL GMBH—See Triton Advisers Limited; *Int'l*, pg. 7929
DYWIDAG-SYSTEMS INTERNATIONAL GMBH—See Triton Advisers Limited; *Int'l*, pg. 7929
DYWIDAG-SYSTEMS INTERNATIONAL LTD.—See Triton Advisers Limited; *Int'l*, pg. 7929
DYWIDAG-SYSTEMS INTERNATIONAL N.V.—See Triton Advisers Limited; *Int'l*, pg. 7929
DYWIDAG-SYSTEMS INTERNATIONAL PTY. LTD.—See Triton Advisers Limited; *Int'l*, pg. 7929
DYWIDAG-SYSTEMS INTERNATIONAL USA, INC. - LONG BEACH—See Triton Advisers Limited; *Int'l*, pg. 7929
DYWIDAG-SYSTEMS INTERNATIONAL USA, INC.—See Triton Advisers Limited; *Int'l*, pg. 7929
DYWIDAG-SYSTEMS INTERNATIONAL USA, INC. - TUCKER—See Triton Advisers Limited; *Int'l*, pg. 7929
DYWIDAG-SYSTEMS KOREA CO. LTD—See Triton Advisers Limited; *Int'l*, pg. 7929
DYWITECH CO. LTD.—See Triton Advisers Limited; *Int'l*, pg. 7929
DYWIT S.P.A.—See Triton Advisers Limited; *Int'l*, pg. 7929
DZ BANK AG DEUTSCHE ZENTRAL-GENOSSENSCHAFTSBANK; *Int'l*, pg. 2243
DZ BANK IRELAND PLC—See DZ BANK AG Deutsche Zentral-Genossenschaftsbank; *Int'l*, pg. 2243
DZ BANK NEW YORK BRANCH—See DZ BANK AG Deutsche Zentral-Genossenschaftsbank; *Int'l*, pg. 2243
DZ BANK POLSKA—See DZ BANK AG Deutsche Zentral-Genossenschaftsbank; *Int'l*, pg. 2243
DZ BANK SAO PAULO REPRESENTACAO LTDA.—See DZ BANK AG Deutsche Zentral-Genossenschaftsbank; *Int'l*, pg. 2243
DZB DRUCKZENTRUM BERN AG—See TX Group AG; *Int'l*, pg. 7991
DZ COMPLIANCEPARTNER GMBH—See DZ BANK AG Deutsche Zentral-Genossenschaftsbank; *Int'l*, pg. 2243
DZD SLOVENSKO SPOL S.R.O.—See NIBE Industrier AB; *Int'l*, pg. 5260
DZD STROJIRNA S.R.O.—See NIBE Industrier AB; *Int'l*, pg. 5260
DZERZHYNSKY PJSC; *Int'l*, pg. 2245
DZETA CONSEIL SAS; *Int'l*, pg. 2245
DZ FINANCIAL MARKETS LLC—See DZ BANK AG Deutsche Zentral-Genossenschaftsbank; *Int'l*, pg. 2243
DZ HYP AG—See DZ BANK AG Deutsche Zentral-Genossenschaftsbank; *Int'l*, pg. 2244

CORPORATE AFFILIATIONS

DZI AN MECHANOELECTRIC JSC; *Int'l*, pg. 2245
DZI - GENERAL INSURANCE JSC—See KBC Group NV; *Int'l*, pg. 4106
DZI INSURANCE PLC—See KBC Group NV; *Int'l*, pg. 4106
DZ IMMOBILIEN+TREUHAND GMBH—See DZ BANK AG Deutsche Zentral-Genossenschaftsbank; *Int'l*, pg. 2244
DZINE FOOD SOLUTIONS CO., LTD.—See Charoen Pokphand Foods Public Company Limited; *Int'l*, pg. 1452
D&Z LIMITED—See Morgan Stanley; *U.S. Public*, pg. 1471
D & Z MEDIA ACQUISITION CORP.; *U.S. Public*, pg. 619
DZ PRIVATBANK S.A.—See DZ BANK AG Deutsche Zentral-Genossenschaftsbank; *Int'l*, pg. 2244
DZ PRIVATBANK (SCHWEIZ) AG—See DZ BANK AG Deutsche Zentral-Genossenschaftsbank; *Int'l*, pg. 2244
DZ PRIVATBANK SINGAPORE LTD—See DZ BANK AG Deutsche Zentral-Genossenschaftsbank; *Int'l*, pg. 2244
DZS INC.; *U.S. Public*, pg. 700
DZS JAPAN INC—See DZS Inc.; *U.S. Public*, pg. 701
DZ SOLUTIONS; *U.S. Private*, pg. 1300
DZSP 21 LLC—See Parsons Corporation; *U.S. Public*, pg. 1650
DZS SOFTWARE SOLUTIONS, INC.—See WDB Holdings Co., Ltd.; *Int'l*, pg. 8362
DZUKA COMMUNICATIONS—See The Interpublic Group of Companies, Inc.; *U.S. Public*, pg. 2093
DZ VERSICHERUNGSVERMITTLUNG GESELLSCHAFT MBH—See DZ BANK AG Deutsche Zentral-Genossenschaftsbank; *Int'l*, pg. 2244
DZWIGI SP. Z O.O.—See Jastrzebska Spolka Weglowa S.A.; *Int'l*, pg. 3913

E

E-18 LIMITED—See Reliance - ADA Group Limited; *Int'l*, pg. 6262
E1 CONTAINER TERMINAL CORP.—See E1 Corporation; *Int'l*, pg. 2260
E1 CORPORATION; *Int'l*, pg. 2260
E1 ENTERTAINMENT U.S. LP; *U.S. Private*, pg. 1307
E1 TELEVISION INTERNATIONAL LTD.—See Lions Gate Entertainment Corp.; *Int'l*, pg. 4520
E1 TELEVISION PRODUCTIONS INC—See Lions Gate Entertainment Corp.; *Int'l*, pg. 4520
E21CORP; *U.S. Private*, pg. 1308
E24 AG—See Mountain Capital Management AG; *Int'l*, pg. 5057
E24 NAERINGSLIV AS—See Schibsted ASA; *Int'l*, pg. 6618
E2AMP; *U.S. Private*, pg. 1308
E2B TEKNOLOGIES; *U.S. Private*, pg. 1308
E2E NETWORKS LIMITED; *Int'l*, pg. 2260
E2IP TECHNOLOGIES; *Int'l*, pg. 2261
E2MAX CENTRE PTE LTD—See Cathay Organisation Holdings Ltd; *Int'l*, pg. 1360
E2M TECHNOLOGIES B.V.—See Amphenol Corporation; *U.S. Public*, pg. 130
E2M TECHNOLOGIES INC.—See Amphenol Corporation; *U.S. Public*, pg. 131
E2OPEN AG—See Insight Venture Management, LLC; *U.S. Private*, pg. 2090
E2OPEN CHINA—See Insight Venture Management, LLC; *U.S. Private*, pg. 2090
E2OPEN, LLC—See Insight Venture Management, LLC; *U.S. Private*, pg. 2090
E2OPEN LTD.—See Insight Venture Management, LLC; *U.S. Private*, pg. 2090
E2OPEN MALAYSIA—See Insight Venture Management, LLC; *U.S. Private*, pg. 2090
E2OPEN PARENT HOLDINGS, INC.—See Insight Venture Management, LLC; *U.S. Private*, pg. 2090
E2 RECRUITING, INC.; *U.S. Private*, pg. 1308
E2S CO., LTD.; *Int'l*, pg. 2261
E3 CO., LTD.—See Envipro Holdings Inc.; *Int'l*, pg. 2454
E3 DIAGNOSTICS INC.—See Demant A/S; *Int'l*, pg. 2025
E-3 ELECTRICAL; *U.S. Private*, pg. 1302
E3 ENERGIE EFFIZIENZ EXPERTEN GMBH—See BayWa AG; *Int'l*, pg. 917
E3 FEDERAL SOLUTIONS, LLC—See NewSpring Capital LLC; *U.S. Private*, pg. 2918
E3 GROUP SA—See Grupo Arbulu S.L.; *Int'l*, pg. 3120
E3 HLK AG—See BKW AG; *Int'l*, pg. 1055
E3 LITHIUM LTD.; *Int'l*, pg. 2261
E3 SYSTEMS ITALY—See Grupo Arbulu S.L.; *Int'l*, pg. 3120
E3 SYSTEMS MALTA—See Grupo Arbulu S.L.; *Int'l*, pg. 3120
E3 SYSTEMS USA—See Grupo Arbulu S.L.; *Int'l*, pg. 3120
E4E BUSINESS SOLUTIONS INDIA PRIVATE LIMITED—See e4e Inc.; *U.S. Private*, pg. 1308
E4E FINANCIAL SERVICES—See e4e Inc.; *U.S. Private*, pg. 1308
E4E HEALTHCARE SERVICES PVT. LTD.—See e4e Inc.; *U.S. Private*, pg. 1308
E4E INC.; *U.S. Private*, pg. 1308
E4E SOLUTIONS; *U.S. Private*, pg. 1308
E4 HEALTH LLC—See GuideWell Mutual Holding Corporation; *U.S. Private*, pg. 1814

COMPANY NAME INDEX

E4 SERVICES, LLC—See McLarty Capital Partners UK LLP; *U.S. Private*, pg. 2640
E4U A.S.; *Int'l*, pg. 2261
E7 PTY LTD—See Bentley Systems, Inc.; *U.S. Public*, pg. 297
EAA COVERED BOND BANK PLC—See Erste Abwicklungsanstalt AoR; *Int'l*, pg. 2497
EAAGADS LTD.; *Int'l*, pg. 2261
EAA JAPAN K.K.—See Erste Abwicklungsanstalt AoR; *Int'l*, pg. 2497
E. AARON ENTERPRISES INC.—See Aaron Group of Companies; *U.S. Private*, pg. 32
EAB ELEKTROANLAGENBAU GMBH RHEIN/MAIN—See CEZ, a.s.; *Int'l*, pg. 1427
EAB ENGINEERING AS—See Schlumberger Limited; *U.S. Public*, pg. 1844
EAB GLOBAL, INC.; *U.S. Private*, pg. 1308
EAB GROUP OYJ; *Int'l*, pg. 2261
EABI CONSULTING SAS—See ManpowerGroup Inc.; *U.S. Public*, pg. 1360
EA CABLE ASSEMBLIES (HONGKONG) CO., LIMITED—See BizLink Holding Inc.; *Int'l*, pg. 1053
EACCESS LLC—See Elliott Management Corporation; *U.S. Private*, pg. 1368
EACCESS LLC—See Veritas Capital Fund Management, LLC; *U.S. Private*, pg. 4362
EACCESS SOLUTIONS, INC.; *U.S. Private*, pg. 1308
EAC CHEMICALS SINGAPORE PTE. LTD.—See EAC Invest AS; *Int'l*, pg. 2261
EAC CONSUMER PRODUCTS LTD. APS—See EAC Invest AS; *Int'l*, pg. 2261
EACHAIRN AEROSPACE HOLDINGS LIMITED—See Melrose Industries PLC; *Int'l*, pg. 4812
EAC INVEST AS; *Int'l*, pg. 2261
EACM ADVISORS LLC—See The Bank of New York Mellon Corporation; *U.S. Public*, pg. 2037
EAC NETWORK; *U.S. Private*, pg. 1308
EACO CORPORATION; *U.S. Public*, pg. 701
EA.COM—See Electronic Arts Inc.; *U.S. Public*, pg. 724
EACOM TIMBER CORPORATION—See Interfor Corporation; *Int'l*, pg. 3740
E&A CONTRACTORS PTY. LTD.—See E&A Limited; *Int'l*, pg. 2246
EAC (PHILIPPINES) INC.—See EAC Invest AS; *Int'l*, pg. 2261
EAC PRODUCT DEVELOPMENT SOLUTIONS; *U.S. Private*, pg. 1308
EA DIGITAL ILLUSIONS CE AB—See Electronic Arts Inc.; *U.S. Public*, pg. 724
EADS ATR S.A.—See Airbus SE; *Int'l*, pg. 246
EADS CANADA, INC.—See Airbus SE; *Int'l*, pg. 245
EADS CASA—See Airbus SE; *Int'l*, pg. 246
EADS CHILE—See Airbus SE; *Int'l*, pg. 246
EADS CHINA—See Airbus SE; *Int'l*, pg. 246
THE EADS COMPANY; *U.S. Private*, pg. 4024
EADS COMPOSITES AQUITAINE—See Airbus SE; *Int'l*, pg. 246
EADS COMPOSITES ATLANTIC LIMITED—See Airbus SE; *Int'l*, pg. 245
EADS DEFENSE & SECURITY NETWORKS—See Airbus SE; *Int'l*, pg. 246
EADS DISTRIBUTION, LLC—See Applied Industrial Technologies, Inc.; *U.S. Public*, pg. 171
EADS FRANCE S.A.S. - INNOVATION WORKS—See Airbus SE; *Int'l*, pg. 246
EADS FRANCE S.A.S.—See Airbus SE; *Int'l*, pg. 246
EADS INDIA PVT LTD—See Airbus SE; *Int'l*, pg. 246
EADS INDONESIA—See Airbus SE; *Int'l*, pg. 246
EADS KOREA CO., LTD.—See Airbus SE; *Int'l*, pg. 246
EADS MEXICO, S.A. DE C.V.—See Airbus SE; *Int'l*, pg. 246
EADS MULTICOMS—See Airbus SE; *Int'l*, pg. 246
EADS NORWAY NUF—See Airbus SE; *Int'l*, pg. 246
EADS REAL ESTATE TAUFKIRCHEN GMBH & CO. KG—See Airbus SE; *Int'l*, pg. 242
EADS SECURE NETWORKS—See Airbus SE; *Int'l*, pg. 246
EADS SINGAPORE PTE LTD—See Airbus SE; *Int'l*, pg. 247
EADS SODERN NORTH AMERICA, INC.—See Airbus SE; *Int'l*, pg. 243
EADS SOGERMA SERVICES—See TAT Services SASU; *Int'l*, pg. 7466
EADS SOUTH AFRICA PTY. LTD.—See Airbus SE; *Int'l*, pg. 246
EADS SUPPLY & SERVICES, INC.—See Airbus SE; *Int'l*, pg. 243
EADS SYSTEMS & DEFENSE ELECTRONICS—See Airbus SE; *Int'l*, pg. 246
EADS TAIWAN CO., LTD—See Airbus SE; *Int'l*, pg. 246
EADS THAILAND—See Airbus SE; *Int'l*, pg. 246
EADS TURKEY—See Airbus SE; *Int'l*, pg. 246
EA ELEKTROARMATUREN AG—See Knill Holding GmbH; *Int'l*, pg. 4208
EA ENGINEERING, P.C.—See EA Engineering, Science & Technology, Inc.; *U.S. Private*, pg. 1308
EA ENGINEERING, SCIENCE, AND TECHNOLOGY (MI), PLC.—See EA Engineering, Science & Technology, Inc.; *U.S. Private*, pg. 1308

EA ENGINEERING, SCIENCE & TECHNOLOGY, INC.; *U.S. Private*, pg. 1308
EAF COMPUTER SERVICE SUPPLIES GMBH—See eaf Holding GmbH; *Int'l*, pg. 2262
EAF FRANCE SA—See discoverIE Group plc; *Int'l*, pg. 2133
EAF HOLDING GMBH; *Int'l*, pg. 2262
EAGA INSURANCE SERVICES LIMITED—See Carillion plc; *Int'l*, pg. 1331
EAGAN INSURANCE AGENCY, INC.—See Galiot Insurance Services, Inc.; *U.S. Private*, pg. 1638
EAGAN PRODUCTS, LLC—See Leggett & Platt, Incorporated; *U.S. Public*, pg. 1302
EAGARS FUNERALS LIMITED—See Propel Funeral Partners Limited; *Int'l*, pg. 5997
EAG-BETEILIGUNGS AG; *Int'l*, pg. 2263
EAGERS AUTOMOTIVE LIMITED; *Int'l*, pg. 2263
EAGERS NOMINEES PTY LTD—See Eagers Automotive Limited; *Int'l*, pg. 2264
EAGERS RETAIL PTY LTD—See Eagers Automotive Limited; *Int'l*, pg. 2264
E.A. GIBSON SHIPBROKERS LIMITED; *Int'l*, pg. 2250
EAG LABORATORIES GMBH—See Eurofins Scientific S.E.; *Int'l*, pg. 2549
EAGLE ACTUATOR COMPONENTS GMBH & CO. KG—See Eagle Industry Co., Ltd.; *Int'l*, pg. 2265
EAGLE ADJUSTING SERVICES, INC.—See SE Capital, LLC; *U.S. Private*, pg. 3582
EAGLE ADVANTAGE SOLUTIONS, INC.—See Constellation Software Inc.; *Int'l*, pg. 1774
EAGLE AERIAL SYSTEMS, INC.—See AgEagle Aerial Systems Inc.; *U.S. Public*, pg. 60
EAGLE AFFILIATES, INC.—See Injectron Corporation; *U.S. Private*, pg. 2077
EAGLE AIR MAINTENANCE LIMITED—See Air New Zealand Limited; *Int'l*, pg. 239
EAGLE AIRWAYS LIMITED—See Air New Zealand Limited; *Int'l*, pg. 239
EAGLE APPLIED SCIENCES, LLC.—See Bristol Bay Native Corporation; *U.S. Private*, pg. 656
EAGLE ASSET MANAGEMENT (CP) LIMITED—See Great Eagle Holdings Limited; *Int'l*, pg. 3064
EAGLE ASSET MANAGEMENT, INC.—See Raymond James Financial, Inc.; *U.S. Public*, pg. 1763
EAGLE ASSOCIATES INC.; *U.S. Private*, pg. 1308
EAGLE AVIATION INC.; *U.S. Private*, pg. 1308
EAGLE AVIATION SERVICES, INC.—See American Airlines Group Inc.; *U.S. Public*, pg. 96
EAGLE BANCORP, INC.; *U.S. Public*, pg. 701
EAGLE BANCORP MONTANA, INC.; *U.S. Public*, pg. 701
EAGLEBANK—See Eagle Bancorp, Inc.; *U.S. Public*, pg. 701
EAGLE BANK; *U.S. Private*, pg. 1308
EAGLE BAY RESOURCES CORP.; *Int'l*, pg. 2264
EAGLE BIDCO 2018 LIMITED—See KKR & Co. Inc.; *U.S. Public*, pg. 1256
EAGLE BUICK GMC, INC.; *U.S. Private*, pg. 1308
EAGLE BULK EUROPE A/S—See Star Bulk Carriers Corp.; *Int'l*, pg. 7173
EAGLE BULK EUROPE GMBH—See Star Bulk Carriers Corp.; *Int'l*, pg. 7173
EAGLE BULK PTE. LTD.—See Star Bulk Carriers Corp.; *Int'l*, pg. 7173
EAGLE BULK SHIPPING INC.—See Star Bulk Carriers Corp.; *Int'l*, pg. 7173
EAGLEBURGMANN AUSTRALASIA PTY. LTD. - MELBOURNE—See Eagle Industry Co., Ltd.; *Int'l*, pg. 2265
EAGLEBURGMANN AUSTRALASIA PTY. LTD. - MELBOURNE—See Freudenberg SE; *Int'l*, pg. 2783
EAGLEBURGMANN AUSTRALASIA PTY. LTD.—See Eagle Industry Co., Ltd.; *Int'l*, pg. 2265
EAGLEBURGMANN AUSTRALASIA PTY. LTD.—See Freudenberg SE; *Int'l*, pg. 2783
EAGLEBURGMANN AUSTRIA GMBH—See Freudenberg SE; *Int'l*, pg. 2783
EAGLEBURGMANN BELGIUM BVBA—See Freudenberg SE; *Int'l*, pg. 2783
EAGLEBURGMANN BREDAN S.R.O.—See Freudenberg SE; *Int'l*, pg. 2783
EAGLEBURGMANN BT S.P.A.—See Freudenberg SE; *Int'l*, pg. 2783
EAGLEBURGMANN CANADA INC.—See Freudenberg SE; *Int'l*, pg. 2783
EAGLEBURGMANN COLOMBIA, S.A.S.—See Freudenberg SE; *Int'l*, pg. 2783
EAGLEBURGMANN CZECH S.R.O.—See Freudenberg SE; *Int'l*, pg. 2783
EAGLEBURGMANN DE VENEZUELA, C.A.—See Freudenberg SE; *Int'l*, pg. 2784
EAGLEBURGMANN DO BRASIL VEDACOES INDUSTRIAS LTDA.—See Freudenberg SE; *Int'l*, pg. 2784
EAGLEBURGMANN ENDUSTRIYEL SIZDIRMALIK SANAYI VE TICARET LTD. STI.—See Freudenberg SE; *Int'l*, pg. 2783
EAGLEBURGMANN ESPEY GMBH—See Freudenberg SE; *Int'l*, pg. 2783
EAGLEBURGMANN FRANCE S.A.S.—See Freudenberg SE; *Int'l*, pg. 2783

EAGLECARE INC.

EAGLEBURGMANN GERMANY GMBH & CO. KG—See Freudenberg SE; *Int'l*, pg. 2783
EAGLEBURGMANN HUNGARIA KFT.—See Freudenberg SE; *Int'l*, pg. 2784
EAGLEBURGMANN IBERICA S. A.—See Freudenberg SE; *Int'l*, pg. 2784
EAGLEBURGMANN INDIA PVT. LTD.—See Eagle Industry Co., Ltd.; *Int'l*, pg. 2265
EAGLEBURGMANN INDIA PVT. LTD.—See Eagle Industry Co., Ltd.; *Int'l*, pg. 2265
EAGLEBURGMANN INDIA PVT. LTD.—See Freudenberg SE; *Int'l*, pg. 2784
EAGLEBURGMANN INDIA PVT. LTD.—See Freudenberg SE; *Int'l*, pg. 2784
EAGLEBURGMANN INDUSTRIES LP—See Freudenberg SE; *Int'l*, pg. 2784
EAGLEBURGMANN INDUSTRIES RUSSIA—See Freudenberg SE; *Int'l*, pg. 2784
EAGLEBURGMANN INDUSTRIES UK LP—See Freudenberg SE; *Int'l*, pg. 2784
EAGLEBURGMANN ITALIA S.R.L.—See Freudenberg SE; *Int'l*, pg. 2784
EAGLEBURGMANN JAPAN CO., LTD.—See Eagle Industry Co., Ltd.; *Int'l*, pg. 2265
EAGLEBURGMANN JAPAN CO., LTD.—See Freudenberg SE; *Int'l*, pg. 2784
EAGLEBURGMANN KE A/S—See Freudenberg SE; *Int'l*, pg. 2784
EAGLEBURGMANN KE, INC.—See Freudenberg SE; *Int'l*, pg. 2784
EAGLEBURGMANN KE PTE. LTD.—See Freudenberg SE; *Int'l*, pg. 2784
EAGLEBURGMANN KE PVT. LTD.—See Freudenberg SE; *Int'l*, pg. 2784
EAGLEBURGMANN KOREA LTD.—See Freudenberg SE; *Int'l*, pg. 2784
EAGLEBURGMANN (MALAYSIA) SDN BHD—See Freudenberg SE; *Int'l*, pg. 2784
EAGLEBURGMANN MEXICO S.A. DE C.V.—See Freudenberg SE; *Int'l*, pg. 2784
EAGLEBURGMANN MIDDLE EAST FZE—See Freudenberg SE; *Int'l*, pg. 2784
EAGLEBURGMANN NETHERLANDS B.V.—See Freudenberg SE; *Int'l*, pg. 2784
EAGLEBURGMANN NEW ZEALAND, LTD.—See Eagle Industry Co., Ltd.; *Int'l*, pg. 2265
EAGLEBURGMANN NEW ZEALAND, LTD.—See Freudenberg SE; *Int'l*, pg. 2784
EAGLEBURGMANN NORWAY A/S—See Freudenberg SE; *Int'l*, pg. 2784
EAGLEBURGMANN NOVA MAGNETICS LTD.—See Freudenberg SE; *Int'l*, pg. 2784
EAGLEBURGMANN OOO—See Freudenberg SE; *Int'l*, pg. 2784
EAGLEBURGMANN PHILIPPINES INC.—See Freudenberg SE; *Int'l*, pg. 2784
EAGLEBURGMANN POLAND SP. Z O.O.—See Freudenberg SE; *Int'l*, pg. 2784
EAGLEBURGMANN PRODUCTION CENTER JUDENBURG GMBH—See Freudenberg SE; *Int'l*, pg. 2784
EAGLEBURGMANN PRODUCTION CENTER S.A. DE C.V.—See Freudenberg SE; *Int'l*, pg. 2784
EAGLEBURGMANN RO SRL—See Freudenberg SE; *Int'l*, pg. 2784
EAGLEBURGMANN SAUDI ARABIA CO. LTD.—See Freudenberg SE; *Int'l*, pg. 2784
EAGLEBURGMANN SEALS SOUTH AFRICA (PTY) LTD.—See Freudenberg SE; *Int'l*, pg. 2784
EAGLEBURGMANN SINGAPORE PTE. LTD—See Freudenberg SE; *Int'l*, pg. 2784
EAGLEBURGMANN SWEDEN AB—See Freudenberg SE; *Int'l*, pg. 2784
EAGLEBURGMANN SWEDEN AB—See Freudenberg SE; *Int'l*, pg. 2784
EAGLEBURGMANN (SWITZERLAND) AG—See Freudenberg SE; *Int'l*, pg. 2783
EAGLEBURGMANN TAIWAN CORPORATION—See Freudenberg SE; *Int'l*, pg. 2784
EAGLEBURGMANN (THAILAND) CO., LTD.—See Freudenberg SE; *Int'l*, pg. 2784
EAGLEBURGMANN VIETNAM COMPANY LTD.—See Freudenberg SE; *Int'l*, pg. 2784
EAGLEBURGMANN (WUXI) CO. LTD.—See Freudenberg SE; *Int'l*, pg. 2783
EAGLE BUSINESS SOLUTIONS INC.; *U.S. Private*, pg. 1308
EAGLE BUTTON CO., INC.; *U.S. Private*, pg. 1308
EAGLE CANADA, INC.—See Wilks Brothers LLC; *U.S. Private*, pg. 4521
EAGLECARE INC.; *U.S. Private*, pg. 1311
EAGLE CEMENT CORPORATION—See Top Frontier Investment Holdings, Inc.; *Int'l*, pg. 7811
EAGLE CLAIMS SERVICES, INC.—See CorVel Corporation; *U.S. Public*, pg. 585
EAGLECLAW MIDSTREAM VENTURES, LLC—See Kayne Anderson Capital Advisors, L.P.; *U.S. Private*, pg. 2267
EAGLE COACH COMPANY—See J.B. Poindexter & Co., Inc.; *U.S. Private*, pg. 2158

EAGLECARE INC.

EAGLE COMMERCIAL CONSTRUCTION, LLC—See Markel Group Inc.; *U.S. Public*, pg. 1367
EAGLE COMMERCIAL REALTY, LLC—See Markel Group Inc.; *U.S. Public*, pg. 1367
EAGLE COMMUNICATIONS INC.; *U.S. Private*, pg. 1308
EAGLE COMPRESSORS INC.—See Paratech, Inc.; *U.S. Private*, pg. 3093
EAGLE COMTRONICS INC.; *U.S. Private*, pg. 1308
EAGLE CONSTRUCTION OF VA., LLC—See Markel Group Inc.; *U.S. Public*, pg. 1367
EAGLE COPTERS AUSTRALASIA PTY. LTD.—See Eagle Copters Ltd.; *Int'l*, pg. 2264
EAGLE COPTERS LTD.; *Int'l*, pg. 2264
EAGLE COPTERS SOUTH AMERICA S.A.—See Eagle Copters Ltd.; *Int'l*, pg. 2264
EAGLE CORNICE CO. INC.—See Altas Partners LP; *Int'l*, pg. 386
EAGLE CORPORATION; *U.S. Private*, pg. 1309
EAGLE CREEK EUROPE, LTD.—See V. F. Corporation; *U.S. Public*, pg. 2268
EAGLE CREEK, INC.—See V. F. Corporation; *U.S. Public*, pg. 2268
EAGLE CREEK SIDING, LLC—See Bain Capital, LP; *U.S. Private*, pg. 450
EAGLE CREEK SOFTWARE SERVICES, INC.—See Atos SE; *Int'l*, pg. 692
EAGLE CREST HOMES, INC.—See Chief Industries, Inc.; *U.S. Private*, pg. 881
EAGLE CRUSHER CO. INC.; *U.S. Private*, pg. 1309
EAGLE DAIRY DIRECT LLC—See Dairy Farmers of America, Inc.; *U.S. Private*, pg. 1146
EAGLE DIRECT, INC.—See National Amusements, Inc.; *U.S. Private*, pg. 2841
EAGLE DISPOSAL OF PA INC.—See Waste Connections, Inc.; *Int'l*, pg. 8352
EAGLE DISTRIBUTING CO. INC.; *U.S. Private*, pg. 1309
EAGLE DISTRIBUTING OF SHREVEPORT; *U.S. Private*, pg. 1309
EAGLE EDUCATION & TRAINING LIMITED—See Graham Holdings Company; *U.S. Public*, pg. 954
EAGLE ELEVATOR CO., INC.—See 3Phase Elevator Corp; *U.S. Private*, pg. 13
EAGLE ENERGY INC.; *Int'l*, pg. 2264
EAGLE ENGINEERING AEROSPACE CO., LTD.—See Eagle Industry Co., Ltd.; *Int'l*, pg. 2265
EAGLE ENGINEERING AEROSPACE KOREA CO., LTD.—See Eagle Industry Co., Ltd.; *Int'l*, pg. 2265
EAGLE ENGINEERING AEROSPACE SINGAPORE PTE. LTD.—See Eagle Industry Co., Ltd.; *Int'l*, pg. 2265
EAGLE ENGINEERING AEROSPACE TAIWAN CO., LTD.—See Eagle Industry Co., Ltd.; *Int'l*, pg. 2265
EAGLE ENGINEERING, INC.—See Arsenal Capital Management LP; *U.S. Private*, pg. 338
EAGLE ENTERPRISE, INC.—See General Dynamics Corporation; *U.S. Public*, pg. 913
EAGLE ENTERPRISES INC.—See W W Capital Corporation; *U.S. Private*, pg. 4417
EAGLE ENVIRONMENTAL CONSULTING, INC—See Sun Capital Partners, Inc.; *U.S. Private*, pg. 3859
EAGLE EQUIPMENT COMPANY INC.—See Kenny Pipe & Supply, Inc.; *U.S. Private*, pg. 2286
EAGLE EXPLORATION CO.; *U.S. Public*, pg. 702
EAGLE EYE SOLUTIONS GROUP PLC; *Int'l*, pg. 2264
EAGLE EYE SOLUTIONS LTD—See Eagle Eye Solutions Group PLC; *Int'l*, pg. 2264
EAGLE EYE SOLUTIONS (NORTH) LTD.—See Eagle Eye Solutions Group PLC; *Int'l*, pg. 2264
EAGLE EYE SURGERY AND LASER CENTER, LLC—See KKR & Co. Inc.; *U.S. Public*, pg. 1245
EAGLE FAB; *U.S. Private*, pg. 1309
EAGLE FAMILY FOODS GROUP LLC—See Kelso & Company, L.P.; *U.S. Private*, pg. 2278
EAGLE FILTERS GROUP OYJ; *Int'l*, pg. 2264
EAGLE FINANCIAL BANCORP, INC.—See LCNB Corp.; *U.S. Public*, pg. 1296
EAGLE FINANCIAL SERVICES, INC.; *U.S. Public*, pg. 702
EAGLE FOOTBALL GROUP; *Int'l*, pg. 2264
EAGLE FORD ENVIRONMENTAL SERVICES, LLC—See Texcom, Inc.; *U.S. Public*, pg. 2027
EAGLE FORD OIL AND GAS CORP; *U.S. Public*, pg. 702
EAGLE FORD RECLAMATION COMPANY, LLC—See Waste Connections, Inc.; *Int'l*, pg. 8354
EAGLE FOUR EQUITIES LLC; *U.S. Private*, pg. 1309
EAGLE FUND SERVICES, INC.—See Raymond James Financial, Inc.; *U.S. Public*, pg. 1764
EAGLE GAS MARKETING COMPANY—See Mustang Fuel Corporation; *U.S. Private*, pg. 2819
EAGLE GRAPHICS; *U.S. Private*, pg. 1309
EAGLE GRAPHITE INCORPORATED; *Int'l*, pg. 2264
THE EAGLE GROUP; *U.S. Private*, pg. 4024
EAGLE GROWTH AND INCOME OPPORTUNITIES FUND; *U.S. Private*, pg. 1309
EAGLE HARBOR HEALTHCARE, INC.—See The Ensign Group, Inc.; *U.S. Public*, pg. 2070
EAGLE HEALTH HOLDINGS LIMITED; *Int'l*, pg. 2264
EAGLE HERALD PUBLISHING LLC—See Adams Publishing Group, LLC; *U.S. Private*, pg. 74

EAGLE HIGHCAST CO., LTD.—See Eagle Industry Co., Ltd.; *Int'l*, pg. 2265
EAGLE HOLDING EUROPE B.V.—See Eagle Industry Co., Ltd.; *Int'l*, pg. 2265
EAGLE HOME MORTGAGE LLC—See Lennar Corporation; *U.S. Public*, pg. 1306
EAGLE HOMES INC.; *U.S. Private*, pg. 1309
EAGLE-I HOLDINGS PLC; *Int'l*, pg. 2266
EAGLE INDUSTRIES LLC; *U.S. Private*, pg. 1309
EAGLE INDUSTRY CO., LTD. - OKAYAMA FACTORY—See Eagle Industry Co., Ltd.; *Int'l*, pg. 2265
EAGLE INDUSTRY CO., LTD. - SAITAMA FACTORY—See Eagle Industry Co., Ltd.; *Int'l*, pg. 2265
EAGLE INDUSTRY CO., LTD.; *Int'l*, pg. 2264
EAGLE INDUSTRY FRANCE S.A.S.—See Eagle Industry Co., Ltd.; *Int'l*, pg. 2265
EAGLE INDUSTRY HOKKAIDO CO., LTD.—See Eagle Industry Co., Ltd.; *Int'l*, pg. 2265
EAGLE INDUSTRY HUNGARY KFT.—See Eagle Industry Co., Ltd.; *Int'l*, pg. 2265
EAGLE INDUSTRY SALES (SHANGHAI) CO., LTD.—See Eagle Industry Co., Ltd.; *Int'l*, pg. 2265
EAGLE INDUSTRY TAIWAN CORPORATION—See Eagle Industry Co., Ltd.; *Int'l*, pg. 2265
EAGLE INDUSTRY (WUXI) CO., LTD.—See Eagle Industry Co., Ltd.; *Int'l*, pg. 2265
EAGLE INFRASTRUCTURE SERVICES, INC.; *U.S. Private*, pg. 1309
EAGLE INSURANCE COMPANY LTD.; *Int'l*, pg. 2266
EAGLE INSURANCE LIMITED—See Ireland Blyth Limited; *Int'l*, pg. 3807
EAGLE INTERNATIONAL INSTITUTE INC.—See NIIT Limited; *Int'l*, pg. 5288
EAGLE INTERNATIONAL LLC—See Tennant Company; *U.S. Public*, pg. 2016
EAGLE INTERTRANS COMPANY LIMITED—See WP Energy PCL; *Int'l*, pg. 8460
EAGLE INVESTMENT SERVICES INC.—See Eagle Financial Services, Inc.; *U.S. Public*, pg. 702
EAGLE IRON WORKS, LLC—See McLanahan Corporation; *U.S. Private*, pg. 2640
EAGLE LEASING COMPANY; *U.S. Private*, pg. 1309
EAGLE LIFE INSURANCE COMPANY—See Brookfield Reinsurance Ltd.; *U.S. Public*, pg. 1193
EAGLE LIGHTING (AUSTRALIA) PTY LTD—See Fagerhult Group AB; *Int'l*, pg. 2602
EAGLE LIGHTING GEORGE PROPRIETARY LIMITED—See The Bidvest Group Limited; *Int'l*, pg. 7624
EAGLELINE ACQUISITION CORP.; *U.S. Private*, pg. 1311
EAGLE LNG PARTNERS LLC—See Ferus Inc.; *Int'l*, pg. 2646
EAGLE MANAGED CARE CORP.—See New Rite Aid, LLC; *U.S. Private*, pg. 2905
EAGLE MANUFACTURING COMPANY; *U.S. Private*, pg. 1309
EAGLE MANUFACTURING GROUP; *U.S. Private*, pg. 1309
EAGLE MANUFACTURING LLC—See Linamar Corporation; *Int'l*, pg. 4500
EAGLE MARINE INDUSTRIES INC.; *U.S. Private*, pg. 1310
EAGLE MATERIALS INC.; *U.S. Public*, pg. 702
EAGLEMED LLC—See KKR & Co. Inc.; *U.S. Public*, pg. 1252
EAGLE METAL PROCESSING & RECYCLING INC—See Eagle Manufacturing Group; *U.S. Private*, pg. 1309
EAGLE MOBILE HOME CENTER INC.; *U.S. Private*, pg. 1310
EAGLEMOSS PUBLICATIONS LTD; *Int'l*, pg. 2266
EAGLE MOUNTAIN MINING LIMITED; *Int'l*, pg. 2266
EAGLE MOVING SYSTEMS INC—See Ambassador Van Lines Inc.; *U.S. Private*, pg. 217
EAGLE NATIONAL STEEL LTD; *U.S. Private*, pg. 1310
EAGLE NEWSPAPERS INC.; *U.S. Private*, pg. 1310
EAGLE NEW ZEALAND LIMITED—See Eagle Industry Co., Ltd.; *Int'l*, pg. 2265
EAGLE NICE DEVELOPMENT LIMITED—See Eagle Nice (International) Holdings Ltd.; *Int'l*, pg. 2266
EAGLE NICE (INTERNATIONAL) HOLDINGS LTD.; *Int'l*, pg. 2266
EAGLE NORTH HOLDINGS INC; *Int'l*, pg. 2266
EAGLE ONE GOLF PRODUCTS—See U.S. Eagle Corporation; *U.S. Private*, pg. 4270
EAGLE OPERATING CORP.—See RFE Investment Partners; *U.S. Private*, pg. 3419
EAGLE OTTAWA BRASIL INDUSTRIA E BENEFICIAMENTO DE COUROS LTDA.—See Lear Corporation; *U.S. Public*, pg. 1296
EAGLE OTTAWA CHINA LTD.—See Lear Corporation; *U.S. Public*, pg. 1296
EAGLE OTTAWA HUNGARY KFT.—See Lear Corporation; *U.S. Public*, pg. 1296
EAGLE OTTAWA LLC—See Lear Corporation; *U.S. Public*, pg. 1296
EAGLE OTTAWA NORTH AMERICA, LLC—See Lear Corporation; *U.S. Public*, pg. 1296

CORPORATE AFFILIATIONS

EAGLE OTTAWA (THAILAND) CO., LTD.—See Lear Corporation; *U.S. Public*, pg. 1296
EAGLE OTTAWA U.K. LTD.—See Lear Corporation; *U.S. Public*, pg. 1296
EAGLE PACKAGING INC.—See Anheuser-Busch InBev SA/NV; *Int'l*, pg. 465
EAGLE PERFORMANCE PRODUCTS, INC.—See Wendel SA; *Int'l*, pg. 8376
EAGLE PHARMACEUTICALS, INC.; *U.S. Public*, pg. 702
EAGLEPICHER TECHNOLOGIES, LLC—See GTCR LLC; *U.S. Private*, pg. 1805
EAGLE PIPELINE CONSTRUCTION, INC.—See John Wood Group PLC; *Int'l*, pg. 3984
EAGLE PLAINS RESOURCES LTD.; *Int'l*, pg. 2266
EAGLE POINT CREDIT COMPANY INC.; *U.S. Public*, pg. 703
EAGLE POINT INCOME COMPANY INC.; *U.S. Public*, pg. 703
EAGLE POINT SOFTWARE CORPORATION; *U.S. Private*, pg. 1310
EAGLE POWER & EQUIPMENT CORP.; *U.S. Private*, pg. 1310
EAGLE PRESS & EQUIPMENT CO. LIMITED—See Isgec Heavy Engineering Ltd.; *Int'l*, pg. 3817
EAGLE PRESS, INC.; *U.S. Private*, pg. 1310
EAGLE PRINTING COMPANY; *U.S. Private*, pg. 1310
EAGLE PRIVATE CAPITAL, LLC; *U.S. Private*, pg. 1310
EAGLE PRODUCT INSPECTION LIMITED—See Mettler-Toledo International, Inc.; *U.S. Public*, pg. 1432
EAGLE PRODUCT INSPECTION LLC—See Mettler-Toledo International, Inc.; *U.S. Public*, pg. 1432
EAGLE PRODUCTIVITY SOLUTIONS; *U.S. Private*, pg. 1310
EAGLE PROFESSIONAL RESOURCES INC.—See Cornell Capital LLC; *U.S. Private*, pg. 1051
EAGLE PROFESSIONAL RESOURCES INC.—See TorQuest Partners Inc.; *Int'l*, pg. 7830
EAGLE PROPRIETARY INVESTMENTS LIMITED—See National Industries Group Holding S.A.K.; *Int'l*, pg. 5159
EAGLE PUBLISHING INC. - EAGLES FINANCIAL PUBLICATIONS DIVISION—See Eagle Publishing Inc.; *U.S. Private*, pg. 1310
EAGLE PUBLISHING INC.; *U.S. Private*, pg. 1310
EAGLE PUBLISHING INC. - THE HUMAN EVENTS GROUP DIVISION—See Eagle Publishing Inc.; *U.S. Private*, pg. 1310
EAGLE RAY TECHNOLOGIES GROUP—See Carl Marks & Co., Inc.; *U.S. Private*, pg. 763
EAGLE REALTY GROUP, LLC—See Western & Southern Financial Group, Inc.; *U.S. Private*, pg. 4490
EAGLE REALTY OF VIRGINIA, LLC—See Markel Group Inc.; *U.S. Public*, pg. 1368
EAGLE RIDGE APARTMENTS CALIFORNIA, LLC—See RAIT Financial Trust; *U.S. Private*, pg. 3348
EAGLE RIDGE LANDFILL, LLC—See BC Partners LLP; *Int'l*, pg. 924
EAGLE RIDGE RESORT, LLC; *U.S. Private*, pg. 1310
EAGLERIES JAPAN CO., LTD.—See Eaglerise Electric & Electronic (China) Co., Ltd.; *Int'l*, pg. 2266
EAGLERISE E&E INC.—See Eaglerise Electric & Electronic (China) Co., Ltd.; *Int'l*, pg. 2266
EAGLERISE E&E (USA), INC.—See Eaglerise Electric & Electronic (China) Co., Ltd.; *Int'l*, pg. 2266
EAGLERISE ELECTRIC & ELECTRONIC (CHINA) CO., LTD.; *Int'l*, pg. 2266
EAGLERISE ELECTRIC & ELECTRONIC (JIAN) CO., LTD.—See Eaglerise Electric & Electronic (China) Co., Ltd.; *Int'l*, pg. 2266
EAGLERISE-MAGROOTS TECHNOLOGY SHENZHEN CORPORATION LIMITED—See Eaglerise Electric & Electronic (China) Co., Ltd.; *Int'l*, pg. 2266
EAGLE RIVER CHRYSLER LTD.; *Int'l*, pg. 2266
EAGLE ROCK AGGREGATES, INC.—See Vulcan Materials Company; *U.S. Public*, pg. 2314
EAGLE ROCK DISTRIBUTING COMPANY; *U.S. Private*, pg. 1310
EAGLE ROCK NORTH DISTRIBUTING COMPANY—See Eagle Rock Distributing Company; *U.S. Private*, pg. 1310
EAGLE SALES COMPANY INCORPORATED; *U.S. Private*, pg. 1310
EAGLE SEALING RESEARCH & DEVELOPMENT (WUXI) CO., LTD.—See Eagle Industry Co., Ltd.; *Int'l*, pg. 2265
EAGLE SHIPMANAGEMENT PTE LTD—See Petroliam Nasional Berhad; *Int'l*, pg. 5829
EAGLE SHIPPING INTERNATIONAL (USA) LLC—See Star Bulk Carriers Corp.; *Int'l*, pg. 7173
EAGLES HOLDINGS PTE. LTD.—See Symphony International Holdings Limited; *Int'l*, pg. 7379
EAGLES INVESTMENT SYSTEMS LLC—See The Bank of New York Mellon Corporation; *U.S. Public*, pg. 2037
EAGLE'S MARK INC.; *U.S. Private*, pg. 1311
EAGLES PERSONAL MANAGEMENT COMPANY—See Live Nation Entertainment, Inc.; *U.S. Public*, pg. 1328
EAGLE STAR LIFE ASSURANCE CO. LTD.—See Zurich Insurance Group Limited; *Int'l*, pg. 8697
EAGLE STAR MALTA LTD.—See Zurich Insurance Group Limited; *Int'l*, pg. 8697

COMPANY NAME INDEX

EAGLESTONE, LLC—See Aterian Investment Management, L.P.; *U.S. Private*, pg. 366
EAGLE SUPPORT SERVICES CORPORATION; *U.S. Private*, pg. 1310
EAGLE SYSTEMS INC.; *U.S. Private*, pg. 1311
EAGLE SYSTEMS & SERVICES, INC.; *U.S. Private*, pg. 1310
EAGLE TECHNOLOGIES GROUP; *U.S. Private*, pg. 1311
EAGLE TECHNOLOGY, INC.—See Silversmith Management, L.P.; *U.S. Private*, pg. 3664
EAGLE TELEVISION SALES—See iHeartMedia, Inc.; *U.S. Public*, pg. 1096
EAGLE TEST SYSTEMS, INC.—See Teradyne, Inc.; *U.S. Public*, pg. 2018
EAGLE TRANSPORTATION LLC—See Gryphon Investors, LLC; *U.S. Private*, pg. 1799
EAGLE TRANSPORT CORPORATION; *U.S. Private*, pg. 1311
EAGLETREE CAPITAL, LP; *U.S. Private*, pg. 1311
EAGLE-TRIBUNE PUBLISHING COMPANY INC.—See The Retirement Systems of Alabama; *U.S. Private*, pg. 4105
EAGLE VALLEY TELEPHONE COMPANY—See Arvig Enterprises, Inc.; *U.S. Private*, pg. 344
EAGLE VALLEY TELEPHONE COMPANY—See Blue Earth Valley Communications; *U.S. Private*, pg. 588
EAGLE VALLEY TELEPHONE COMPANY—See Nuvera Communications, Inc.; *U.S. Public*, pg. 1556
EAGLE VAN LINES INC.—See Coleman American Companies, Inc.; *U.S. Private*, pg. 967
EAGLE VENEER INC.; *U.S. Private*, pg. 1311
EAGLE VETRINARY TECHNOLOGY CO., LTD.; *Int'l*, pg. 2266
EAGLE VET. TECH CO., LTD.; *Int'l*, pg. 2266
EAGLEVIEW TECHNOLOGIES, INC.—See Vista Equity Partners, LLC; *U.S. Private*, pg. 4396
EAGLEVILLE HOSPITAL; *U.S. Private*, pg. 1312
EAGLE VISION, INC.—See Audax Group, Limited Partnership; *U.S. Private*, pg. 388
EAGLE WELLNESS, LLC—See Eagle Publishing Inc.; *U.S. Private*, pg. 1310
EAGLE WELL SERVICING DIVISION—See Western Energy Services Corp.; *Int'l*, pg. 8388
EAGLE WINDOW & DOOR, INC.—See Andersen Corporation; *U.S. Private*, pg. 276
EAGLE & WISE SERVICE S.R.L.—See Gruppo MutuiOnline S.p.A; *Int'l*, pg. 3141
EAGLEWOOD VILLAGE, LLC—See Regional Health Properties, Inc.; *U.S. Public*, pg. 1775
EAGLE:XM; *U.S. Private*, pg. 1311
EAGON ENERGY CO., LTD.—See Eagon Holdings Co., Ltd.; *Int'l*, pg. 2266
EAGON GREEN TECH CO., LTD.—See Eagon Holdings Co., Ltd.; *Int'l*, pg. 2266
EAGON HOLDINGS CO., LTD.; *Int'l*, pg. 2266
EAGON INDUSTRIAL CO., LTD.; *Int'l*, pg. 2267
EAGON LAUTARO S.A.—See Eagon Holdings Co., Ltd.; *Int'l*, pg. 2266
EAGON PACIFIC PLANTATION LTD.—See Eagon Holdings Co., Ltd.; *Int'l*, pg. 2266
EAGON USA CORP.—See Eagon Industrial Co., Ltd.; *Int'l*, pg. 2267
EAGON WINDOWS & DOORS SYSTEM CO., LTD.—See Eagon Holdings Co., Ltd.; *Int'l*, pg. 2266
E.A. & H. HILDRETH INC.; *U.S. Private*, pg. 1304
EA HOLDINGS BERHAD; *Int'l*, pg. 2261
E.A. HUGHES & CO., INC.—See Solomon-Page Group LLC; *U.S. Private*, pg. 3710
EAI DESIGN SERVICES, LLC—See ViaSat, Inc.; *U.S. Public*, pg. 2291
EAI-EMBRAER AVIATION INTERNATIONAL—See Embraer S.A.; *Int'l*, pg. 2375
EA, INC.—See Cresset Asset Management, LLC; *U.S. Private*, pg. 1095
E&A INDUSTRIES, INC.; *U.S. Private*, pg. 1301
EAI PARTNERSHIP LP; *U.S. Private*, pg. 1312
EAI TECHNOLOGIES, LLC; *U.S. Private*, pg. 1312
E.A. JUFFALI & BROTHERS COMPANY; *Int'l*, pg. 2250
EAKES INC.; *U.S. Private*, pg. 1312
EAKIN-YOUNGENTOB ASSOCIATES INC.; *U.S. Private*, pg. 1312
E&A LIMITED; *Int'l*, pg. 2246
EALIXIR, INC.; *U.S. Public*, pg. 703
E.A.L MAN HIN & SONS LTD.—See Honda Motor Co., Ltd.; *Int'l*, pg. 3460
E&A MARKETS INC.; *U.S. Private*, pg. 1301
EAM CORPORATION—See PT Sinar Mas Group; *Int'l*, pg. 6073
EAM GMBH & CO. KG; *Int'l*, pg. 2267
EAM MOSCA CANADA LTD—See Mosca AG; *Int'l*, pg. 5050
EAM MOSCA CORPORATION—See Mosca AG; *Int'l*, pg. 5050
EAM-MOSCA DE MEXICO S DE RL DE CV—See Mosca AG; *Int'l*, pg. 5050
EAM NELSON HOLDING, LLC—See Entergy Corporation; *U.S. Public*, pg. 777
EA MSC SDN. BHD.—See EA Holdings Berhad; *Int'l*, pg. 2261

EAM SOLAR ASA; *Int'l*, pg. 2267
EAO AG; *Int'l*, pg. 2267
EAO AUTOMOTIVE GMBH & CO. KG—See EAO AG; *Int'l*, pg. 2267
EAO BENELUX B.V.—See EAO AG; *Int'l*, pg. 2267
EAO CORPORATION—See EAO AG; *Int'l*, pg. 2267
EAO FAR EAST LTD.—See EAO AG; *Int'l*, pg. 2267
EAO FRANCE SAS—See EAO AG; *Int'l*, pg. 2267
EAO (GUANGZHOU) LIMITED—See EAO AG; *Int'l*, pg. 2267
EAO JAPAN CO. LTD.—See EAO AG; *Int'l*, pg. 2267
EAO LIMITED—See EAO AG; *Int'l*, pg. 2267
EAO LUMITAS GMBH—See EAO AG; *Int'l*, pg. 2267
EAO SCHWEIZ AG—See EAO AG; *Int'l*, pg. 2267
EAO SVENSKA AB—See EAO AG; *Int'l*, pg. 2267
EAO SWITCH CORPORATION—See EAO AG; *Int'l*, pg. 2267
EAO VERKAUF (SCHWEIZ) AG—See EAO AG; *Int'l*, pg. 2267
EA PALM NETWORK CO., LTD.—See Energy Absolute Public Company Limited; *Int'l*, pg. 2422
E.A. PATTEN CO., LLC—See Stanley Black & Decker, Inc.; *U.S. Public*, pg. 1932
EAPEC HIROSHIMA CO., LTD.—See Chudenko Corporation; *Int'l*, pg. 1594
EA PHARMA CO., LTD.—See Eisai Co., Ltd.; *Int'l*, pg. 2334
EA PHENOMIC—See Electronic Arts Inc.; *U.S. Public*, pg. 724
E.A.P.S. - EMPRESA DE ANALISE, PREVENCAO E SEGURANCA, S.A.—See Caixa Geral de Depositos S.A.; *Int'l*, pg. 1260
EARCANAL—See Marcegaglia S.p.A.; *Int'l*, pg. 4688
EARGO, INC.—See Patient Square Capital, L.P.; *U.S. Private*, pg. 3106
EARHART PETROLEUM INC.; *U.S. Private*, pg. 1312
EARL & BROWN COMPANY; *U.S. Private*, pg. 1312
EARL DUDLEY ASSOCIATES INC.; *U.S. Private*, pg. 1312
EARLE M. JORGENSEN CANADA, INC.—See Reliance Steel & Aluminum Co.; *U.S. Public*, pg. 1779
EARLE M. JORGENSEN CANADA, INC.—See Reliance Steel & Aluminum Co.; *U.S. Public*, pg. 1780
EARLE M. JORGENSEN CO. - HONING CENTER/TULSA—See Reliance Steel & Aluminum Co.; *U.S. Public*, pg. 1780
EARLE M. JORGENSEN COMPANY—See Reliance Steel & Aluminum Co.; *U.S. Public*, pg. 1779
EARLE M. JORGENSEN CO. - SPECIALTY TUBING/ELDRIDGE—See Reliance Steel & Aluminum Co.; *U.S. Public*, pg. 1780
EARL ENTERPRISES; *U.S. Private*, pg. 1312
EARL G. GRAVES LTD.; *U.S. Private*, pg. 1312
EARL G. GRAVES PUBLISHING CO., INC.—See Earl G. Graves Ltd.; *U.S. Private*, pg. 1312
EARLHAM SAVINGS BANK; *U.S. Private*, pg. 1313
EARL & LORAINE MILLER CHILDREN'S HOSPITAL—See Memorial Health Services; *U.S. Private*, pg. 2663
EARL MAY SEED & NURSERY L.C.; *U.S. Private*, pg. 1313
EARL R. MARTIN, INC.; *U.S. Private*, pg. 1313
EARL SHILTON BUILDING SOCIETY; *Int'l*, pg. 2267
EARL TINDOL FORD INC.; *U.S. Private*, pg. 1313
EARL T. WADHAMS INC.—See Wadhams Enterprises Inc.; *U.S. Private*, pg. 4424
EARL W. COLVARD INC.; *U.S. Private*, pg. 1313
EARL W. JOHNSTON ROOFING INC.—See Dunes Point Capital, LLC; *U.S. Private*, pg. 1288
EARLY AGE CO., LTD.; *Int'l*, pg. 2267
EARLY AMERICAN HISTORY AUCTIONS, INC.; *U.S. Private*, pg. 1313
EARLYBIRDCAPITAL INC.; *U.S. Private*, pg. 1313
EARLYBIRD FARM (PTY) LTD.—See Astral Foods Limited; *Int'l*, pg. 658
EARLY BIRDS S.A.S.—See CrownPeak Technology, Inc.; *U.S. Private*, pg. 1113
EARLY, CASSIDY & SCHILLING, LLC—See GTCR LLC; *U.S. Private*, pg. 1803
EARLYDETECT INC.; *U.S. Private*, pg. 1314
EARLY EQUITY PLC; *Int'l*, pg. 2267
EARLY GROWTH FINANCIAL SERVICES, LLC—See Escalon Services Inc.; *U.S. Private*, pg. 1424
EARLY LEARNING CENTRE LIMITED—See The Entertainer (Amersham) Ltd.; *Int'l*, pg. 7640
EARLY LEARNING COALITION OF ALACHUA COUNTY; *U.S. Private*, pg. 1313
EARLY LEARNING COALITION OF BREVARD COUNTY, INC.; *U.S. Private*, pg. 1313
EARLY LEARNING COALITION OF BROWARD COUNTY, INC.; *U.S. Private*, pg. 1313
EARLY LEARNING COALITION OF DUVAL, INC.; *U.S. Private*, pg. 1313
THE EARLY LEARNING COALITION OF FLAGLER AND VOLUSIA COUNTIES, INC.; *U.S. Private*, pg. 4024
EARLY LEARNING COALITION OF INDIAN RIVER, MARTIN & OKEECHOBEE COUNTIES, INC.; *U.S. Private*, pg. 1313
EARLY LEARNING COALITION OF LAKE COUNTY; *U.S. Private*, pg. 1313

EARLY LEARNING COALITION OF MANATEE COUNTY, INC.; *U.S. Private*, pg. 1313
EARLY LEARNING COALITION OF MIAMI-DADE/MONROE; *U.S. Private*, pg. 1313
EARLY LEARNING COALITION OF NORTHWEST FLORIDA, INC.; *U.S. Private*, pg. 1313
EARLY LEARNING COALITION OF OSCEOLA COUNTY, INC.; *U.S. Private*, pg. 1313
EARLY LEARNING COALITION OF PALM BEACH COUNTY, INC.; *U.S. Private*, pg. 1313
EARLY LEARNING COALITION OF PINELLAS COUNTY, INC.; *U.S. Private*, pg. 1313
EARLY LEARNING COALITION OF SOUTHWEST FLORIDA, INC.; *U.S. Private*, pg. 1313
EARLY LEARNING COALITION OF THE BIG BEND REGION; *U.S. Private*, pg. 1313
EARLY LEARNING COALITION OF THE NATURE COAST, INC.; *U.S. Private*, pg. 1313
EARLY LEARNING GROUP GMBH—See Splendid Medien AG; *Int'l*, pg. 7140
EARLYPAY LTD.; *Int'l*, pg. 2267
EARLY START AUSTRALIA PTY LTD.—See Madison Dearborn Partners, LLC; *U.S. Private*, pg. 2540
EARLY TIMES DISTILLERS COMPANY—See Brown-Forman Corporation; *U.S. Public*, pg. 403
EARLY WARNING NETWORK PTY. LTD.—See Aeeris Limited; *Int'l*, pg. 173
EARLY WARNING SERVICES, LLC—See Wells Fargo & Company; *U.S. Public*, pg. 2343
EARLY WARNING SYSTEM GMBH—See Federation Internationale de Football Association; *Int'l*, pg. 2631
EARLYWORKS CO., LTD.; *Int'l*, pg. 2267
EARN-A-CAR, INC.; *Int'l*, pg. 2267
EARN CMO LLC—See Ellington Credit Company Management LLC; *U.S. Public*, pg. 734
EARNEST & ASSOCIATES, LLC; *U.S. Private*, pg. 1314
EARNEST MACHINE PRODUCTS CO.; *U.S. Private*, pg. 1314
EARNHARDT CHRYSLER-JEEP—See Earnhardt's Auto Centers; *U.S. Private*, pg. 1314
EARNHARDT DODGE—See Earnhardt's Auto Centers; *U.S. Private*, pg. 1314
EARNHARDT FORD—See Earnhardt's Auto Centers; *U.S. Private*, pg. 1314
EARNHARDT HONDA—See Earnhardt's Auto Centers; *U.S. Private*, pg. 1314
EARNHARDT'S AUTO CENTERS; *U.S. Private*, pg. 1314
EARNHARDT TOYOTA SCION; *U.S. Private*, pg. 1314
EARNIX LTD.; *Int'l*, pg. 2267
EARN MORTGAGE LLC—See Ellington Credit Company Management LLC; *U.S. Public*, pg. 734
EARP DISTRIBUTION CENTER; *U.S. Private*, pg. 1314
EAR PROFESSIONALS INTERNATIONAL CORPORATION—See UnitedHealth Group Incorporated; *U.S. Public*, pg. 2240
EARPRO S.A.—See Midwich Group Plc; *Int'l*, pg. 4887
EARTH2EARTH PROPRIETARY LIMITED—See Groupe Seche SAS; *Int'l*, pg. 3110
EARTH911, INC.—See Quest Resource Holding Corporation; *U.S. Public*, pg. 1756
EARTH & AEROSPACE MANUFACTURING IND. CO. LTD; *Int'l*, pg. 2267
EARTH ALIVE CLEAN TECHNOLOGIES INC.; *Int'l*, pg. 2268
EARTHBOUND FARM, LLC—See Danone; *Int'l*, pg. 1967
EARTH BROTHERS, LTD.—See Performance Food Group Company; *U.S. Public*, pg. 1675
EARTH CLASS MAIL, INC.—See LegalZoom.com, Inc.; *U.S. Public*, pg. 1301
EARTHCOLOR, INC.—See Mittera Group, Inc.; *U.S. Private*, pg. 2751
EARTH CONSULTING GROUP, INC.; *U.S. Private*, pg. 1314
EARTH CONTACT PRODUCTS, LLC.; *U.S. Private*, pg. 1314
EARTHCORE INDUSTRIES LLC.; *U.S. Private*, pg. 1314
EARTH CORPORATION; *Int'l*, pg. 2268
EARTH CORPORATION—See Earth Corporation; *Int'l*, pg. 2268
EARTHDIGITAL—See Mittera Group, Inc.; *U.S. Private*, pg. 2751
EARTH ENVIRONMENTAL SERVICE CO., LTD.—See Earth Corporation; *Int'l*, pg. 2268
EARTH EXPLORATION, INC.—See Terracon Consultants, Inc.; *U.S. Private*, pg. 3970
EARTH FARE, INC.; *U.S. Private*, pg. 1314
EARTH FRIENDLY PRODUCTS—See Venus Laboratories Inc.; *U.S. Private*, pg. 4358
EARTH GEN-BIOFUEL INC.; *U.S. Public*, pg. 703
EARTHGRAINS BAKING CO. INC.—See Grupo Bimbo, S.A.B. de C.V.; *Int'l*, pg. 3122
EARTH HOME PRODUCTS (MALAYSIA) SDN. BHD.—See Earth Corporation; *Int'l*, pg. 2268
EARTH INC.; *U.S. Private*, pg. 1314
EARTH INFINITY CO., LTD.; *Int'l*, pg. 2268
EARTHINTEGRATE—See Mittera Group, Inc.; *U.S. Private*, pg. 2751
EARTHLAB LUXEMBOURG S.A.—See Leonardo S.p.A.; *Int'l*, pg. 4458

EARTHLABS INC.

EARTHLABS INC.; *Int'l*, pg. 2268
EARTH LIFE SCIENCES, INC.; *U.S. Public*, pg. 703
EARTHLINK BUSINESS, LLC—See Windstream Holdings, Inc.; *U.S. Public*, pg. 2373
EARTHLINK HOLDINGS, LLC—See Windstream Holdings, Inc.; *U.S. Public*, pg. 2373
EARTHLINK, LLC—See Trive Capital Inc.; *U.S. Private*, pg. 4239
EARTHLITE, LLC—See Branford Castle, Inc.; *U.S. Private*, pg. 639
EARTH MECHANICS, INC.; *U.S. Private*, pg. 1314
EARTHMINDED BENELUX NV—See Greif Inc.; *U.S. Public*, pg. 967
EARTHMINDED FRANCE S.A.S.—See Greif Inc.; *U.S. Public*, pg. 967
EARTHMINDED FRANCE—See Greif Inc.; *U.S. Public*, pg. 969
EARTHMINDED GERMANY GMBH—See Greif Inc.; *U.S. Public*, pg. 967
EARTH MINDED LLC—See Greif Inc.; *U.S. Public*, pg. 967
EARTHMINDED NETHERLANDS B.V.—See Greif Inc.; *U.S. Public*, pg. 967
EARTHMOVER CREDIT UNION; *U.S. Private*, pg. 1314
EARTHMOVERS LANDFILL, LLC—See Waste Management, Inc.; *U.S. Public*, pg. 2331
EARTH NETWORKS, INC.—See Union Park Capital; *U.S. Private*, pg. 4284
EARTH-PANDA ADVANCE MAGNETIC MATERIAL CO., LTD.; *Int'l*, pg. 2268
EARTH-PANDA (BAOTOU) CO., LTD.—See Earth-Panda Advance Magnetic Material Co., Ltd.; *Int'l*, pg. 2268
EARTH-PANDA CO., LTD.—See Earth-Panda Advance Magnetic Material Co., Ltd.; *Int'l*, pg. 2268
EARTH-PANDA JAPAN CO., LTD.—See Earth-Panda Advance Magnetic Material Co., Ltd.; *Int'l*, pg. 2268
EARTH-PANDA MAGNETIC APPLICATION TECH CO., LTD.—See Earth-Panda Advance Magnetic Material Co., Ltd.; *Int'l*, pg. 2268
EARTH-PANDA (SUZHOU) CO., LTD.—See Earth-Panda Advance Magnetic Material Co., Ltd.; *Int'l*, pg. 2268
EARTH-PANDA (SUZHOU) MAGNET CO., LTD.—See Earth-Panda Advance Magnetic Material Co., Ltd.; *Int'l*, pg. 2268
EARTH-PANDA (TIANJIN) ELECTRICAL CO., LTD.—See Earth-Panda Advance Magnetic Material Co., Ltd.; *Int'l*, pg. 2268
EARTH PET CO., LTD.—See Earth Corporation; *Int'l*, pg. 2268
EARTHPORTFX LIMITED—See Foreign Currency Direct PLC; *Int'l*, pg. 2731
EARTHPORT MIDDLE EAST LTD.—See Earthport Plc; *Int'l*, pg. 2268
EARTHPORT PLC; *Int'l*, pg. 2268
EARTHQUAKE MEDIA, LLC; *U.S. Private*, pg. 1314
EARTHRISE NUTRITIONAL LLC—See DIC Corporation; *Int'l*, pg. 2109
EARTH SCIENCE ANALYTICS AS—See Equinor ASA; *Int'l*, pg. 2484
EARTH SCIENCE DIVISION—See American Excelsior Company; *U.S. Private*, pg. 232
EARTH SCIENCE TECH, INC.; *U.S. Public*, pg. 703
EARTHSEARCH COMMUNICATIONS, INC.—See EAST COAST DIVERSIFIED CORPORATION; *U.S. Private*, pg. 1316
EARTH SENSE ENERGY SYSTEMS INC.; *U.S. Private*, pg. 1314
EARTH SERVICES & ABATEMENT, INC.; *U.S. Private*, pg. 1314
EARTH SIGNAL PROCESSING LTD.; *Int'l*, pg. 2268
EARTH'S OWN FOOD COMPANY INC.—See Agrifoods International Cooperative LTD; *Int'l*, pg. 217
EARTHSTAFF GMBH—See Cordant Group PLC; *Int'l*, pg. 1795
EARTH STAHL & ALLOYS LTD.; *Int'l*, pg. 2268
EARTHSTONE ENERGY, LLC—See Permian Resources Corp; *U.S. Public*, pg. 1677
EARTH SUPPLIED PRODUCTS LLC; *U.S. Private*, pg. 1314
EARTH SYSTEM SCIENCE CO., LTD.—See Founder's Consultants Holdings, Inc.; *Int'l*, pg. 2753
EARTH TAMURA ELECTRONIC (MYANMAR) CO., LTD.—See Tamura Corporation; *Int'l*, pg. 7451
EARTHTECH CONTRACTING, INC.—See Kinderhook Industries, LLC; *U.S. Private*, pg. 2307
EARTH TECH ENVIRONMENT PUBLIC COMPANY LIMITED—See Better World Green Public Company Limited; *Int'l*, pg. 1003
EARTHTECHNICA CO., LTD.—See Kawasaki Heavy Industries, Ltd.; *Int'l*, pg. 4095
EARTHTECHNICA CO., LTD. - YACHIYO WORKS—See Kawasaki Heavy Industries, Ltd.; *Int'l*, pg. 4095
EARTHTECHNICA M&S CO., LTD.—See Kawasaki Heavy Industries, Ltd.; *Int'l*, pg. 4095
EARTH (THAILAND) CO., LTD.—See Earth Corporation; *Int'l*, pg. 2268
EARTH THEBAULT—See Mittera Group, Inc.; *U.S. Private*, pg. 2751
EARTH TOOL COMPANY, LLC—See The Toro Company; *U.S. Public*, pg. 2135

EARTHTRON LLC; *U.S. Private*, pg. 1314
EARTHWISE BAG COMPANY, INC.—See Bunzl plc; *Int'l*, pg. 1217
EARTHWISE ENVIRONMENTAL, INC.—See Nolan Capital, Inc.; *U.S. Private*, pg. 2934
EARTHWISE MINERALS CORP.; *Int'l*, pg. 2268
EARTHWORKS INDUSTRIES INC.; *Int'l*, pg. 2269
EARTHWORKS PACIFIC INC.; *U.S. Private*, pg. 1315
EARUM PHARMACEUTICALS LIMITED; *Int'l*, pg. 2269
EASA S.A.—See Etex SA/NV; *Int'l*, pg. 2521
EASAT ANTENNAS LTD.—See Goodwin PLC; *Int'l*, pg. 3041
EASAT RADAR SYSTEMS LIMITED—See Goodwin PLC; *Int'l*, pg. 3041
EASE2PAY N.V.; *Int'l*, pg. 2269
EASE INC.—See Luminate Capital Management, Inc.; *U.S. Private*, pg. 2514
EASELEY KNITWEAR LIMITED—See Yangtzekiang Garment Limited; *Int'l*, pg. 8561
EASEMYTRIP THAI CO., LTD.—See Easy Trip Planners Limited; *Int'l*, pg. 2276
EASEMYTRIP TOURS LLC—See Easy Trip Planners Limited; *Int'l*, pg. 2276
EASI-EDGE LIMITED—See Billington Holdings Plc; *Int'l*, pg. 1031
EASIGAS (PTY.) LTD.—See Rubis SCA; *Int'l*, pg. 6423
EASI INDUSTRIAL SUPPLIES LIMITED—See ANSA McAL Limited; *Int'l*, pg. 477
EASIOPTION BPO SERVICES PRIVATE LTD.—See J.C. Flowers & Co. LLC; *U.S. Private*, pg. 2160
EASIOPTION LTD.—See J.C. Flowers & Co. LLC; *U.S. Private*, pg. 2160
EASIPROCESS PRIVATE LTD.—See J.C. Flowers & Co. LLC; *U.S. Private*, pg. 2160
EASIYO PRODUCTS (UK) LIMITED—See Inner Mongolia Yili Industrial Group Co., Ltd.; *Int'l*, pg. 3708
EASLEY COMBINED UTILITY SYSTEM; *U.S. Private*, pg. 1315
EASLEY & RIVERS INC.; *U.S. Private*, pg. 1315
EASMUNT PAVING, INC.—See Advanced Pavement Group Corp.; *U.S. Private*, pg. 92
EASO BOLSA, S.A.—See Banco de Sabadell, S.A.; *Int'l*, pg. 821
EASOM AUTOMATION SYSTEMS, INC.—See Lincoln Electric Holdings, Inc.; *U.S. Public*, pg. 1317
EASON & CO PUBLIC COMPANY LTD.; *Int'l*, pg. 2269
EASSON HOLDINGS LIMITED; *Int'l*, pg. 2269
EASSONS TRANSPORT LIMITED; *Int'l*, pg. 2269
EASS SDN. BHD.—See EA Holdings Berhad; *Int'l*, pg. 2261
EAST 33 LIMITED; *Int'l*, pg. 2269
EAST 74TH STREET HOLDINGS, INC.—See Steel Partners Holdings L.P.; *U.S. Public*, pg. 1942
EAST AFRICA COMMERCIAL & SHIPPING CO., LTD.—See Financiere de L'Odet; *Int'l*, pg. 2667
EAST AFRICA METALS INC.; *Int'l*, pg. 2269
EAST AFRICAN BREWERIES LIMITED—See Diageo plc; *Int'l*, pg. 2102
EAST AFRICAN CABLES LIMITED; *Int'l*, pg. 2269
EAST AFRICAN PORTLAND CEMENT COMPANY LIMITED; *Int'l*, pg. 2269
EAST AIR CORPORATION; *U.S. Private*, pg. 1315
EASTAI TECHNOLOGY (M) SDN. BHD.—See Tong-Tai Machine Tool Co., Ltd.; *Int'l*, pg. 7806
EAST ALABAMA MEDICAL CENTER HOMECARE, LLC—See UnitedHealth Group Incorporated; *U.S. Public*, pg. 2244
EAST ARKANSAS AREA AGENCY ON AGING; *U.S. Private*, pg. 1315
EAST ARKANSAS VIDEO INC.—See Wehco Media, Inc.; *U.S. Private*, pg. 4469
EASTAR OFFSHORE PTE. LTD.—See Alam Maritim Resources Berhad; *Int'l*, pg. 290
EAST ASCENSION TELEPHONE COMPANY LLC—See RTC Holdings, L.L.C.; *U.S. Private*, pg. 3498
EAST ASIA HOLDINGS INVESTMENT LIMITED; *Int'l*, pg. 2269
EAST ASIA PROPERTY AGENCY CO., LTD.—See The Bank of East Asia, Limited; *Int'l*, pg. 7615
EAST ASIA SECURITIES COMPANY LIMITED—See The Bank of East Asia, Limited; *Int'l*, pg. 7615
EAST ASIA STRATEGIC HOLDINGS LIMITED—See The Bank of East Asia, Limited; *Int'l*, pg. 7615
THE EAST ASIATIC 2010 (THAILAND) COMPANY LTD.—See EAC Invest AS; *Int'l*, pg. 2262
EAST ASIATIC TIMBER (HOLLAND) B.V.—See Scandinavian Investment Group A/S; *Int'l*, pg. 6612
EAST BALKAN PROPERTIES PLC; *Int'l*, pg. 2269
EAST BALT COMMISSARY LLC—See Grupo Bimbo, S.A.B. de C.V.; *Int'l*, pg. 3122
EAST BALT FRANCE S.A.R.L.—See Grupo Bimbo, S.A.B. de C.V.; *Int'l*, pg. 3122
EAST BALTIMORE DEVELOPMENT INC.; *U.S. Private*, pg. 1315
EAST BALT, INC.—See Grupo Bimbo, S.A.B. de C.V.; *Int'l*, pg. 3122
EAST BALT ITALIA S.R.L.—See Grupo Bimbo, S.A.B. de C.V.; *Int'l*, pg. 3122

EASTBANK TEXTILES, LLC—See Inman Holding Co. Inc.; *U.S. Private*, pg. 2079
EAST BAY BMW; *U.S. Private*, pg. 1315
EAST BAY CLARKLIFT INC.; *U.S. Private*, pg. 1315
EAST BAY COMMUNITY FOUNDATION; *U.S. Private*, pg. 1315
EASTBAY EQUITIES INC.—See State Street Capital Realty, LLC; *U.S. Private*, pg. 3793
EASTBAY FOOT LOCKER.COM—See Foot Locker, Inc.; *U.S. Public*, pg. 863
EAST BAY FORD TRUCK SALES, INC.; *U.S. Private*, pg. 1315
EAST BAY INSURANCE AGENCY INC.; *U.S. Private*, pg. 1315
EAST BAY INTEGRATED CARE; *U.S. Private*, pg. 1315
EAST BAY MUNICIPAL UTILITY DISTRICT; *U.S. Private*, pg. 1315
EAST BAY NEWSPAPERS—See Alden Global Capital LLC; *U.S. Private*, pg. 155
EAST BAY RV; *U.S. Private*, pg. 1315
EAST BAY TIRE CO.; *U.S. Private*, pg. 1315
EAST BAY ZOOLOGICAL SOCIETY; *U.S. Private*, pg. 1315
EAST BERGEN IMAGING, LLC—See RadNet, Inc.; *U.S. Public*, pg. 1761
EASTBIZ CORP.; *U.S. Private*, pg. 1319
EASTBOND (HONG KONG) LIMITED—See National Electronics Holdings Limited; *Int'l*, pg. 5156
EAST BOSTON NEIGHBORHOOD HEALTH CENTER CORP.; *U.S. Private*, pg. 1315
EAST BOSTON SAVINGS BANK—See Meridian Bancorp, Inc.; *U.S. Public*, pg. 1424
EASTBRIDGE GROUP; *Int'l*, pg. 2271
EASTBRIDGE INVESTMENTS PLC; *Int'l*, pg. 2271
EASTBROOK HOMES INC.; *U.S. Private*, pg. 1319
EAST BRUNSWICK STUART LLC—See The Great Atlantic & Pacific Tea Company, Inc.; *U.S. Private*, pg. 4038
EAST BRUNSWICK SURGERY CENTER, LLC—See UnitedHealth Group Incorporated; *U.S. Public*, pg. 2240
EAST BUILDTECH LTD; *Int'l*, pg. 2269
EAST BUY HOLDING LIMITED; *Int'l*, pg. 2269
EAST CAMBRIDGE SAVINGS BANK INC.; *U.S. Private*, pg. 1315
EAST CAMPUS REALTY, LLC—See Mutual of Omaha Insurance Company; *U.S. Private*, pg. 2820
EAST CAPE RACING (PTY) LIMITED—See PHUMELELA GAMING AND LEISURE LIMITED; *Int'l*, pg. 5858
EAST CAROLINA ENVIRONMENTAL, LLC—See Republic Services, Inc.; *U.S. Public*, pg. 1786
EAST CENTRAL ENERGY; *U.S. Private*, pg. 1315
EAST CENTRAL IOWA COOP; *U.S. Private*, pg. 1315
EAST CENTRAL OKLAHOMA ELECTRIC COOPERATIVE, INC.; *U.S. Private*, pg. 1316
EAST CENTRAL/SELECT SIRES—See Select Sires Inc.; *U.S. Private*, pg. 3601
EAST CHICAGO MACHINE TOOL CORPORATION—See Kadant Inc.; *U.S. Public*, pg. 1212
EAST CHINA ENGINEERING SCIENCE & TECHNOLOGY CO., LTD.; *Int'l*, pg. 2269
EAST CHINA GRID COMPANY LIMITED—See State Grid Corporation of China; *Int'l*, pg. 7182
EAST COAST AIR & HEAT, LLC—See Del-Air Heating, Air Conditioning & Refrigeration Corp.; *U.S. Private*, pg. 1193
EAST COAST AUTO TRANSPORT INCORPORATED; *U.S. Private*, pg. 1316
EAST COAST AVIATION LLC; *U.S. Private*, pg. 1316
EAST COAST BENEFIT PLANS, INC.—See New Mountain Capital, LLC; *U.S. Private*, pg. 2901
EAST COAST CATERING LIMITED—See Compass Group PLC; *Int'l*, pg. 1751
EAST COAST CATERING (NS) LIMITED—See Compass Group PLC; *Int'l*, pg. 1751
EAST COAST DIVERSIFIED CORPORATION; *U.S. Private*, pg. 1316
EAST COAST FLEET SERVICE CORPORATION—See CSI Holdings III, LLC; *U.S. Private*, pg. 1117
EAST COAST FURNITECH PUBLIC COMPANY LIMITED; *Int'l*, pg. 2269
EAST COAST LOT & PAVEMENT MAINTENANCE CORP.—See Cerberus Capital Management, L.P.; *U.S. Private*, pg. 839
EAST COAST LUMBER COMPANY INC.; *U.S. Private*, pg. 1316
EAST COAST LUMBER & SUPPLY CO. INC.; *U.S. Private*, pg. 1316
EAST COAST MANUFACTURING SDN. BHD.—See Engtex Group Berhad; *Int'l*, pg. 2436
EAST COAST METAL DISTRIBUTORS—See Watsco, Inc.; *U.S. Public*, pg. 2336
EAST COAST METALS SDN. BHD.—See Engtex Group Berhad; *Int'l*, pg. 2436
EAST COAST OILS AND FATS LTD—See Mohammed Enterprises Tanzania Limited; *Int'l*, pg. 5018
EAST COAST RIGGING & CONTRACTING COMPANY, INC.—See Incorp Holdings, LLC; *U.S. Private*, pg. 2054
EAST COAST SEAFOOD INC.—See American Holdco Inc.; *U.S. Private*, pg. 236

COMPANY NAME INDEX

EASTCOAST SOLUTIONS AB—See Precise Biometrics AB; *Int'l*, pg. 5957
EAST COAST SPRINKLER SUPPLY; *U.S. Private*, pg. 1316
EASTCOAST STEEL LIMITED; *Int'l*, pg. 2271
EAST COAST TRAFFIC CONTROLLERS PTY. LTD.—See Teaminvest Private Group Limited; *Int'l*, pg. 7501
EAST COAST TRANSPORT AND LOGISTICS, LLC—See P.A.M. Transportation Services, Inc.; *U.S. Public*, pg. 1629
EAST COAST WAREHOUSE & DISTRIBUTION CORP.—See Romark Logistics, Inc.; *U.S. Private*, pg. 3476
EAST COLOMBIA S.A.—See Cencosud S.A.; *Int'l*, pg. 1400
EASTCO MANAGEMENT CORPORATION; *U.S. Private*, pg. 1319
EAST COMMUNICATIONS COMPANY LIMITED—See TOKAI Holdings Corporation; *Int'l*, pg. 7779
EASTCOM NETWORK CO., LTD.—See Eastern communications Co., LTD.; *Int'l*, pg. 2272
EASTCOMPEACE (INDIA) CO., LTD.—See Eastcompeace Technology Co., Ltd.; *Int'l*, pg. 2271
EASTCOMPEACE (RUSSIA) CO., LTD.—See Eastcompeace Technology Co., Ltd.; *Int'l*, pg. 2271
EASTCOMPEACE (SINGAPORE) CO., LTD.—See Eastcompeace Technology Co., Ltd.; *Int'l*, pg. 2271
EASTCOMPEACE SMART CARD (BANGLADESH) CO., LTD.—See Eastcompeace Technology Co., Ltd.; *Int'l*, pg. 2271
EASTCOMPEACE TECHNOLOGY CO., LTD.; *Int'l*, pg. 2271
EASTCOMTRANS LLP; *Int'l*, pg. 2271
EAST CONTINENTAL SUPPLIES LLC—See Bain Capital, LP; *U.S. Private*, pg. 440
EAST COOPER COASTAL FAMILY PHYSICIANS, L.L.C.—See Tenet Healthcare Corporation; *U.S. Public*, pg. 2003
EAST COOPER COMMUNITY HOSPITAL, INC.—See Tenet Healthcare Corporation; *U.S. Public*, pg. 2008
EAST COOPER HYPERBARICS, L.L.C.—See Tenet Healthcare Corporation; *U.S. Public*, pg. 2003
EAST COOPER OBGYN, L.L.C.—See Tenet Healthcare Corporation; *U.S. Public*, pg. 2003
EAST COOPER PRIMARY CARE PHYSICIANS, L.L.C.—See Tenet Healthcare Corporation; *U.S. Public*, pg. 2003
EAST COUNTY PREOWNED SUPERSTORE; *U.S. Private*, pg. 1316
EAST-COURT FORD LINCOLN SALES; *Int'l*, pg. 2271
EAST COURT PROPERTIES LLC.; *U.S. Private*, pg. 1316
EAST DELTA FLOUR MILLS; *Int'l*, pg. 2270
EASTDIL SECURED, LLC—See Temasek Holdings (Private) Limited; *Int'l*, pg. 7547
EAST DUBUQUE NITROGEN FERTILIZERS, LLC—See Icahn Enterprises L.P.; *U.S. Public*, pg. 1084
EASTECH ELECTRONICS (HK) LIMITED—See Eastern Asia Technology Ltd.; *Int'l*, pg. 2271
EASTECH ELECTRONICS (SG) PTE. LTD.—See Eastern Holding Limited; *Int'l*, pg. 2272
EASTECH ELECTRONICS (TAIWAN) INC.—See Eastern Asia Technology Ltd.; *Int'l*, pg. 2271
EASTECH (HUIZHOU) CO., LTD.—See Eastern Holding Limited; *Int'l*, pg. 2272
EASTECH INNOVATIONS (TW) INC.—See Eastern Holding Limited; *Int'l*, pg. 2272
EASTECH MICROACOUSTICS (HK) LIMITED—See Eastern Holding Limited; *Int'l*, pg. 2272
EASTECH (SG) PTE. LTD.—See Eastern Holding Limited; *Int'l*, pg. 2272
EASTECH SYSTEMS (HUIYANG) CO., LTD.—See Eastern Holding Limited; *Int'l*, pg. 2272
EASTELE TECHNOLOGY CHINA LIMITED—See Avnet, Inc.; *U.S. Public*, pg. 252
EAST EL PASO PHYSICIANS' MEDICAL CENTER, LLC—See Tenet Healthcare Corporation; *U.S. Public*, pg. 2010
EAST END ASPHALT COMPANY LIMITED—See Polaris Holding Company Limited; *Int'l*, pg. 5907
EAST END DIALYSIS CENTER, INC.—See DaVita Inc.; *U.S. Public*, pg. 638
EAST ENERGY RESOURCES LIMITED; *Int'l*, pg. 2270
EAST ENGINEERING LTD OY—See AFRY AB; *Int'l*, pg. 195
EASTERDAY FARMS PRODUCE CO.; *U.S. Private*, pg. 1319
EASTER ENTERPRISES, INC.; *U.S. Private*, pg. 1319
EASTERLIN PECAN CO. INC.; *U.S. Private*, pg. 1319
EASTERLY GOVERNMENT PROPERTIES, INC.; *U.S. Public*, pg. 703
EASTERN AERO MARINE INC.; *U.S. Private*, pg. 1319
EASTERN AIRWAYS (UK) LIMITED—See Bristow Group, Inc.; *U.S. Public*, pg. 387
EASTERN ALABAMA RAILWAY, LLC—See Brookfield Infrastructure Partners L.P.; *Int'l*, pg. 1191
EASTERN ALABAMA RAILWAY, LLC—See GIC Pte. Ltd.; *Int'l*, pg. 2965
EASTERN ALLIANCE INSURANCE COMPANY—See ProAssurance Corporation; *U.S. Public*, pg. 1723

EASTERN ALUMINUM SUPPLY-A RICHARDS COMPANY—See Richards Building Supply Company; *U.S. Private*, pg. 3428
EASTERN ALUMINUM SUPPLY OF VIRGINIA, A RICHARDS COMPANY—See Richards Building Supply Company; *U.S. Private*, pg. 3428
EASTERN ASIA INDUSTRIES SDN. BHD—See Eastern Asia Technology Ltd.; *Int'l*, pg. 2271
EASTERN ASIA TECHNOLOGY (HK) LIMITED—See Eastern Asia Technology Ltd.; *Int'l*, pg. 2271
EASTERN ASIA TECHNOLOGY LTD.; *Int'l*, pg. 2271
EASTERN BANANA ESTATES LIMITED—See PanJam Investment Limited; *Int'l*, pg. 5728
EASTERN BANK PLC; *Int'l*, pg. 2271
EASTERN BANKSHARES, INC.; *U.S. Public*, pg. 703
EASTERN BANK—See Eastern Bankshares, Inc.; *U.S. Public*, pg. 704
EASTERN BAY ENERGY TRUST; *Int'l*, pg. 2271
EASTERN CARIBBEAN AMALGAMATED BANK; *Int'l*, pg. 2272
EASTERN CARIBBEAN CENTRAL BANK; *Int'l*, pg. 2272
EASTERN CARIBBEAN GAS PIPELINE CO LTD—See National Gas Company of Trinidad & Tobago Limited; *Int'l*, pg. 5157
EASTERN CARIBBEAN SECURITIES EXCHANGE; *Int'l*, pg. 2272
EASTERN COALFIELDS LIMITED—See Coal India Limited; *Int'l*, pg. 1680
EASTERN COAL SUPPLIES LIMITED—See Galilee Energy Limited; *Int'l*, pg. 2873
THE EASTERN COLORADO BANK—See Weed Investment Group, Inc.; *U.S. Private*, pg. 4469
EASTERN COMMERCIAL LEASING PUBLIC COMPANY LIMITED; *Int'l*, pg. 2272
EASTERN COMMUNICATIONS CO., LTD.; *Int'l*, pg. 2272
EASTERN COMPANY—See Chemical Industries Holding Company; *Int'l*, pg. 1461
THE EASTERN COMPANY; *U.S. Public*, pg. 2069
EASTERN COMPUTER SERVICE INC.—See Cooperative Holdings Inc.; *Int'l*, pg. 1042
EASTERN CONCRETE MATERIALS, INC.—See Vulcan Materials Company; *U.S. Public*, pg. 2314
EASTERN CONNECTION OPERATING INC.—See International Distributions Services plc; *Int'l*, pg. 3747
EASTERN CONSTRUCTION COMPANY LIMITED; *Int'l*, pg. 2272
EASTERN CONTRACTOR SERVICES, LIMITED LIABILITY COMPANY—See Installed Building Products, Inc.; *U.S. Public*, pg. 1132
EASTERN CONTROLS INC.; *U.S. Private*, pg. 1319
EASTERN DATA, INC.; *U.S. Private*, pg. 1319
EASTERN DRAGON EXPRESS (H.K.) LTD—See HPI AG; *Int'l*, pg. 3500
EASTERN DRAGON FILM CO., LTD—See China Poly Group Corporation; *Int'l*, pg. 1541
EASTERN ENERGY AUSTRALIA PTY LIMITED—See Santos Limited; *Int'l*, pg. 6559
EASTERN ENERGY GAS HOLDINGS, LLC—See Dominion Energy, Inc.; *U.S. Public*, pg. 674
EASTERN ENGINEERED WOOD PRODUCTS; *U.S. Private*, pg. 1319
EASTERN ENVIRONMENT SOLUTIONS, CORP.; *Int'l*, pg. 2272
EASTERN ETCHING & MANUFACTURING CO.; *U.S. Private*, pg. 1319
EASTERN EXPLORATION PTY LTD—See DGR Global Limited; *Int'l*, pg. 2097
EASTERN EXTERIOR WALL SYSTEMS INC.—See Marcon & Boyer Inc.; *U.S. Private*, pg. 2572
EASTERN FARMERS COOPERATIVE; *U.S. Private*, pg. 1319
EASTERN FEDERAL CORP.; *U.S. Private*, pg. 1319
EASTERN FISH COMPANY—See Marubeni Corporation; *Int'l*, pg. 4706
EASTERN GASES LIMITED; *Int'l*, pg. 2272
EASTERN GOLDFIELDS EXPLORATION (PTY) LTD—See Vantage Goldfields Limited; *Int'l*, pg. 8130
EASTERN GOLDFIELDS, INC.; *U.S. Public*, pg. 704
EASTERN GOLD JADE CO., LTD.; *Int'l*, pg. 2272
EASTERN HARVESTERS LTD.—See Claas KGaA mbH; *Int'l*, pg. 1641
EASTERN HEATING & COOLING, INC.—See Comfort Systems USA, Inc.; *U.S. Public*, pg. 544
EASTERN HOLDING LIMITED; *Int'l*, pg. 2272
EASTERN HOLDING NV—See Resilux NV; *Int'l*, pg. 6296
EASTERN HOLDINGS LTD.; *Int'l*, pg. 2272
EASTERN HOME SHOPPING & LEISURE CO., LTD.—See Eastern Media International Corporation; *Int'l*, pg. 2273
EASTERN HOUSING LIMITED; *Int'l*, pg. 2272
EASTERN IDAHO RAILROAD—See Kinder Morgan, Inc.; *U.S. Public*, pg. 1233
EASTERN IDAHO REGIONAL MEDICAL CENTER—See HCA Healthcare, Inc.; *U.S. Public*, pg. 995
EASTERN ILLINI ELECTRIC COOPERATIVE; *U.S. Private*, pg. 1319
EASTERN INDUSTRIAL AUTOMATION; *U.S. Private*, pg. 1319

EASTERN OIL COMPANY

EASTERN INDUSTRIAL ESTATE COMPANY LIMITED—See WHA Corporation Public Company Limited; *Int'l*, pg. 8396
EASTERN INDUSTRIAL LTD., SHANGHAI—See The Eastern Company; *U.S. Public*, pg. 2069
EASTERN INDUSTRIAL & OILFIELD SERVICES COMPANY—See Senergy Holding Company K.P.S.C.; *Int'l*, pg. 6707
EASTERN INDUSTRIAL SUPPLIES INC.; *U.S. Private*, pg. 1320
EASTERN INDUSTRIES, INC. - BETHLEHEM PLANT—See New Enterprise Stone & Lime Co., Inc.; *U.S. Private*, pg. 2895
EASTERN INDUSTRIES, INC.—See New Enterprise Stone & Lime Co., Inc.; *U.S. Private*, pg. 2895
EASTERN INDUSTRIES—See Precision Punch Corporation; *U.S. Private*, pg. 3246
EASTERN INSTRUMENT LABORATORIES, INC.; *U.S. Private*, pg. 1320
EASTERN INSULATION COMPANY—See A.H. Algosaibi & Bros.; *Int'l*, pg. 24
EASTERN INSURANCE COMPANY LIMITED; *Int'l*, pg. 2272
EASTERN INSURANCE GROUP, LLC—See Arthur J. Gallagher & Co.; *U.S. Public*, pg. 204
EASTERN INSURANCE HOLDINGS, INC.—See ProAssurance Corporation; *U.S. Public*, pg. 1723
EASTERN IOWA LIGHT & POWER COOPERATIVE INC.; *U.S. Private*, pg. 1320
EASTERN IOWA TIRE CO. INC.; *U.S. Private*, pg. 1320
EASTERN JASON FABRICATION SERVICES PTE LTD—See Federal International (2000) Ltd; *Int'l*, pg. 2630
EASTERN KENTUCKY CONCENTRATED EMPLOYMENT PROGRAM, INC.; *U.S. Private*, pg. 1320
EASTERN LAND MANAGEMENT (ELM); *U.S. Private*, pg. 1320
EASTERN LIFT TRUCK CO. INC.; *U.S. Private*, pg. 1320
EASTERN LOGICA INFOWAY LTD.; *Int'l*, pg. 2273
EASTERN LONG ISLAND HOSPITAL; *U.S. Private*, pg. 1320
EASTERN LUBRICANTS BLENDERS LIMITED; *Int'l*, pg. 2273
EASTERN MAINE HEALTHCARE SYSTEMS; *U.S. Private*, pg. 1320
EASTERN MANAGED PRINT NETWORK, LLC - FAIRPORT—See Xerox Holdings Corporation; *U.S. Public*, pg. 2387
EASTERN MANAGED PRINT NETWORK, LLC—See Xerox Holdings Corporation; *U.S. Public*, pg. 2387
EASTERN MANAGEMENT COMPANY; *U.S. Private*, pg. 1320
EASTERN MARINE SERVICES LIMITED—See China National Offshore Oil Corp.; *Int'l*, pg. 1533
EASTERN MARINE SERVICES LIMITED—See Trico Marine Services, Inc.; *U.S. Private*, pg. 4229
EASTERN MARINE SYSTEM CO., LTD.—See Azuma Shipping Co., Ltd.; *Int'l*, pg. 782
EASTERN MARKETING CORPORATION—See Energy Corporation of America; *U.S. Private*, pg. 1394
EASTERN MEDIA INTERNATIONAL CORPORATION; *Int'l*, pg. 2273
EASTERN MEDITERRANEAN RESOURCES (SLOVAKIA) SRO—See Atalaya Mining plc; *Int'l*, pg. 665
EASTERN MERCHANTS PLC; *Int'l*, pg. 2273
EASTERN METAL OF ELMIRA INC.; *U.S. Private*, pg. 1320
EASTERN METALS LIMITED; *Int'l*, pg. 2273
EASTERN METAL SUPPLY INC. - EASTERN ARCHITECTURAL SYSTEMS DIVISION—See Clayton, Dubilier & Rice, LLC; *U.S. Private*, pg. 920
EASTERN METAL SUPPLY INC.—See Wynnchurch Capital, L.P.; *U.S. Private*, pg. 4577
EASTERN METAL SUPPLY TEXAS INC.—See Wynnchurch Capital, L.P.; *U.S. Private*, pg. 4577
EASTERN MICHIGAN BANK—See Eastern Michigan Financial Corp; *U.S. Public*, pg. 704
EASTERN MICHIGAN FINANCIAL CORP; *U.S. Public*, pg. 704
EASTERN MINING D.O.O—See Adriatic Metals plc; *Int'l*, pg. 153
EASTERN MOTORS LLC—See Al Fahim Group; *Int'l*, pg. 277
EASTERN MOTORS LTD.—See Bridgestone Corporation; *Int'l*, pg. 1159
EASTERN MOUNTAIN SPORTS, LLC—See GoDigital Media Group, LLC; *U.S. Private*, pg. 1724
EASTERN MUNICIPAL WATER DISTRICT INC.; *U.S. Private*, pg. 1320
EASTERN NATIONAL BANK INC.; *U.S. Private*, pg. 1320
EASTERN NATIONAL OILFIELD SERVICES CO.—See Senergy Holding Company K.P.S.C.; *Int'l*, pg. 6707
EASTERN NATIONAL; *U.S. Private*, pg. 1320
EASTERN NIAGARA HEALTH SERVICES; *U.S. Private*, pg. 1320
EASTERN NOVA CO., LTD.—See Honda Motor Co., Ltd.; *Int'l*, pg. 3460
EASTERN OIL COMPANY; *U.S. Private*, pg. 1320

EASTERN OIL COMPANY

EASTERN OIL WELL SERVICE COMPANY—See PrimeEnergy Resources Corporation; *U.S. Public*, pg. 1717
EASTERN OMNI CONSTRUCTORS INC.; *U.S. Private*, pg. 1320
EASTERN OPTICAL LABORATORIES LTD.—See EssilorLuxottica SA; *Int'l*, pg. 2512
EASTERN & ORIENTAL BERHAD; *Int'l*, pg. 2271
EASTERN & ORIENTAL HOTEL SDN. BHD.—See Eastern & Oriental Berhad; *Int'l*, pg. 2271
EASTERN ORTHODOX MANAGEMENT CORP.; *U.S. Private*, pg. 1320
EASTERN OUTFITTERS, INC.—See Frasers Group plc; *Int'l*, pg. 2765
EASTERN PACIFIC INDUSTRIAL CORPORATION BERHAD—See Terengganu Incorporated Sdn. Bhd.; *Int'l*, pg. 7564
EASTERN PENN SUPPLY COMPANY (EPSCO); *U.S. Private*, pg. 1320
EASTERN PENNSYLVANIA BUSINESS JOURNAL—See Journal Publications, Inc.; *U.S. Private*, pg. 2238
EASTERN PETROCHEMICAL CO.—See Saudi Basic Industries Corporation; *Int'l*, pg. 6590
EASTERN PIONEER DRIVING SCHOOL CO., LTD.; *Int'l*, pg. 2273
EASTERN PIPELINE CORP.—See Energy Corporation of America; *U.S. Private*, pg. 1394
EASTERN PLATINUM LIMITED; *Int'l*, pg. 2273
EASTERN POLYMER GROUP PUBLIC COMPANY LIMITED; *Int'l*, pg. 2273
EASTERN POLYPACK CO., LTD.—See Eastern Polymer Group Public Company Limited; *Int'l*, pg. 2273
EASTERN POULTRY DISTRIBUTORS INC.; *U.S. Private*, pg. 1320
EASTERN POWER GROUP PUBLIC COMPANY LIMITED; *Int'l*, pg. 2273
EASTERN PRETECH (MALAYSIA) SDN. BHD. - BERANANG FACTORY—See YTL Corporation Berhad; *Int'l*, pg. 8606
EASTERN PRETECH (MALAYSIA) SDN. BHD. - SEELONG FACTORY—See YTL Corporation Berhad; *Int'l*, pg. 8606
EASTERN PRETECH (MALAYSIA) SDN. BHD.—See YTL Corporation Berhad; *Int'l*, pg. 8606
EASTERN PRETECH (MALAYSIA) SDN. BHD. - SUNGAI PETANI FACTORY—See YTL Corporation Berhad; *Int'l*, pg. 8606
EASTERN PRODUCE CAPE (PTY) LIMITED—See Camellia Plc; *Int'l*, pg. 1271
EASTERN PRODUCE KENYA LIMITED—See Camellia Plc; *Int'l*, pg. 1271
EASTERN PRODUCE SOUTH AFRICA (PTY) LIMITED—See Camellia Plc; *Int'l*, pg. 1271
EASTERN PROPANE GAS, INC.—See Eastern Propane Gas, Inc.; *U.S. Private*, pg. 1321
EASTERN PROPANE GAS, INC.; *U.S. Private*, pg. 1321
EASTERN PROVINCE CEMENT COMPANY; *Int'l*, pg. 2273
EASTERN PUBLISHING PTE LTD—See Eastern Holdings Ltd.; *Int'l*, pg. 2272
EASTERN REFRIGERATION, CO.—See Ares Management Corporation; *U.S. Public*, pg. 189
EASTERN REFRIGERATION SUPPLY CO.; *Int'l*, pg. 2273
EASTERN RESEARCH SERVICES INC.; *U.S. Private*, pg. 1321
EASTERN RESOURCES, INC.—See Black Diamond Financial Group, LLC; *U.S. Private*, pg. 571
EASTERN RESOURCES LIMITED; *Int'l*, pg. 2273
EASTERN RURAL PTY LTD—See Elders Limited; *Int'l*, pg. 2346
EASTERN SALT (PVT.) LIMITED.—See Raigam Marketing Services (Pvt) Ltd.; *Int'l*, pg. 6188
EASTERNS AUTOMOTIVE GROUP; *U.S. Private*, pg. 1321
EASTERN SAVINGS BANK, FSB; *U.S. Private*, pg. 1321
EASTERN SEABOARD ENVIRONMENTAL COMPLEX CO., LTD.—See Dowa Holdings Co., Ltd.; *Int'l*, pg. 2183
EASTERN SEA LAEM CHABANG TERMINAL CO., LTD.—See Thanachart Capital PCL; *Int'l*, pg. 7607
EASTERN SECURITY, INC.—See Allied Universal Manager LLC; *U.S. Public*, pg. 190
EASTERN SECURITY & PROTECTION SERVICES, INC.; *Int'l*, pg. 2274
EASTERN SHIPBUILDING GROUP, INC.; *U.S. Private*, pg. 1321
EASTERN SHORE MARKETS, INC.—See Camellia Food Stores, Inc.; *U.S. Private*, pg. 728
EASTERN SHORE NATURAL GAS COMPANY—See Chesapeake Utilities Corporation; *U.S. Public*, pg. 485
EASTERN SIERRA PROPANE—See Ferrellgas Partners, L.P.; *U.S. Public*, pg. 829
EASTERN SILK INDUSTRIES LIMITED; *Int'l*, pg. 2274
EASTERN SILK MILLS INC.; *U.S. Private*, pg. 1321
EASTERN SKATEBOARD SUPPLY INC.; *U.S. Private*, pg. 1321
EASTERN SLEEP PRODUCTS COMPANY INC.; *U.S. Private*, pg. 1321

EASTERN SOFTWARE SYSTEMS PVT. LTD.—See Beyondsoft Corporation; *Int'l*, pg. 1005
EASTERN SOFTWARE SYSTEMS PVT. LTD.—See Beyondsoft Corporation; *Int'l*, pg. 1006
EASTERN SOFTWARE SYSTEMS PVT. LTD.—See Beyondsoft Corporation; *Int'l*, pg. 1006
EASTERN SOFTWARE SYSTEMS PVT. LTD.—See Beyondsoft Corporation; *Int'l*, pg. 1006
EASTERN SOLDAR ENGINEERING & CONSTRUCTION SDN. BHD.—See Harbour-Link Group Berhad; *Int'l*, pg. 3272
EASTERN SOLDAR (SINGAPORE) PTE. LTD.—See Harbour-Link Group Berhad; *Int'l*, pg. 3272
EASTERN STAR GAS LIMITED—See Santos Limited; *Int'l*, pg. 6559
EASTERN STAR REAL ESTATE PUBLIC COMPANY LIMITED; *Int'l*, pg. 2274
EASTERN STATES ASSOCIATES INC.; *U.S. Private*, pg. 1321
EASTERN STATES COMPONENTS, INC.; *U.S. Private*, pg. 1321
EASTERN STATES MINE SUPPLY CO.—See Raleigh Mine & Industrial Supply, Inc.; *U.S. Private*, pg. 3349
EASTERN STEEL CORP.; *U.S. Private*, pg. 1321
EASTERN STEEL SDN BHD; *Int'l*, pg. 2274
EASTERN SUGAR BV—See Suddeutsche Zuckerruben-Verwertungs-Genossenschaft eG; *Int'l*, pg. 7252
EASTERN SUGAR BV—See Tate & Lyle PLC; *Int'l*, pg. 7473
EASTERN TECHNICAL ENGINEERING PUBLIC CO., LTD.; *Int'l*, pg. 2274
EASTERN TECHNOLOGIES, INC.; *U.S. Private*, pg. 1321
EASTERN TEXTILE COMPANY—See Al Abdullatif Industrial Investment Company; *Int'l*, pg. 275
EASTERN TITLE AGENCY, INC.—See Hovnanian Enterprises, Inc.; *U.S. Public*, pg. 1056
EASTERN TRADE MEDIA PTE LTD—See Eastern Holdings Ltd.; *Int'l*, pg. 2272
EASTERN TREADS LIMITED; *Int'l*, pg. 2274
EASTERN WATER RESOURCES DEVELOPMENT & MANAGEMENT PUBLIC COMPANY LIMITED; *Int'l*, pg. 2274
EASTERNWELL GROUP PTY LIMITED—See Apollo Global Management, Inc.; *U.S. Public*, pg. 166
EASTERNWELL WA PTY LIMITED—See Apollo Global Management, Inc.; *U.S. Public*, pg. 166
EASTERN WIN METALS & MACHINERY PTE LTD—See HupSteel Limited; *Int'l*, pg. 3538
EASTER-OWENS ELECTRIC COMPANY—See Crusoe Energy Systems LLC; *U.S. Private*, pg. 1114
EASTERSEALS ARC OF NORTHEAST INDIANA, INC.; *U.S. Private*, pg. 1321
EASTER SEALS CENTRAL TEXAS; *U.S. Private*, pg. 1319
EASTERS INC.; *U.S. Private*, pg. 1321
EASTER UNLIMITED INC.; *U.S. Private*, pg. 1319
EASTEX CRUDE COMPANY; *U.S. Private*, pg. 1321
EASTEX DODGE OF BEAUMONT INC.—See Southeast Texas Classic Automotive; *U.S. Private*, pg. 3726
EASTEX TELEPHONE COOPERATIVE; *U.S. Private*, pg. 1321
EASTEY ENTERPRISES INC.—See Engage Technologies Corp.; *U.S. Private*, pg. 1397
EAST FALLS FAMILY MEDICINE, LLC—See HCA Healthcare, Inc.; *U.S. Public*, pg. 995
EASTFIELD ASSOCIATES, LLC—See Mountain Development Corp.; *U.S. Private*, pg. 2799
EASTFIELD RESOURCES LTD.; *Int'l*, pg. 2274
EAST FLORIDA CARENOW URGENT CARE, LLC—See HCA Healthcare, Inc.; *U.S. Public*, pg. 995
EAST FLORIDA EMERGENCY PHYSICIAN GROUP, LLC—See HCA Healthcare, Inc.; *U.S. Public*, pg. 995
EAST FLORIDA HOSPITALISTS, LLC—See HCA Healthcare, Inc.; *U.S. Public*, pg. 995
EAST FLORIDA PRIMARY CARE, LLC—See HCA Healthcare, Inc.; *U.S. Public*, pg. 995
EAST FT. LAUDERDALE, LLC—See DaVita Inc.; *U.S. Public*, pg. 638
EAST GARRISON PARTNERS I, LLC—See Brookfield Corporation; *Int'l*, pg. 1183
EASTGATE BIOTECH CORP.; *Int'l*, pg. 2274
EASTGATE CHRYSLER JEEP, INC.; *U.S. Private*, pg. 1321
EASTGATE PHARMACEUTICALS, INC.—See EastGate Biotech Corp.; *Int'l*, pg. 2274
EASTGATE PHYSICAL THERAPY, LIMITED PARTNERSHIP—See U.S. Physical Therapy, Inc.; *U.S. Public*, pg. 2214
EASTGATE SAFARIS & TRANSFERS—See Cullinan Holdings Limited; *Int'l*, pg. 1877
EASTGATE STORAGE, LLC—See CBL & Associates Properties, Inc.; *U.S. Public*, pg. 458
EAST GEORGIA REGIONAL MEDICAL CENTER, LLC—See Community Health Systems, Inc.; *U.S. Public*, pg. 553
EAST GOSFORD & DISTRICTS FINANCIAL SERVICES LTD.—See Bendigo & Adelaide Bank Ltd.; *Int'l*, pg. 971
THE EAST GREENWICH PENDULUM—See R.I.S.N. Operations Inc.; *U.S. Private*, pg. 3336

CORPORATE AFFILIATIONS

EAST GROUP CO., LTD.; *Int'l*, pg. 2270
EASTGROUP PROPERTIES, INC.; *U.S. Public*, pg. 704
EASTHAM ENTERPRISES INC.; *U.S. Private*, pg. 1321
EASTHAM FORGE INC.—See Eastham Enterprises Inc.; *U.S. Private*, pg. 1322
EASTHAMPTON SAVINGS BANK—See Hometown Financial Group, Inc.; *U.S. Private*, pg. 1975
EASTHAM, WATSON, DALE & FORNEY, LLP—See Schouest, Bamdas, Soshea & BenMaier, PLLC; *U.S. Private*, pg. 3569
EAST HARDWOOD CO. INC.; *U.S. Private*, pg. 1316
EAST HARLEM COUNCIL FOR HUMAN SERVICES, INC.; *U.S. Private*, pg. 1316
EAST HAVEN BUILDERS SUPPLY, INC.—See Bain Capital, LP; *U.S. Private*, pg. 450
EAST HAVEN LANDSCAPE PRODUCTS—See SiteOne Landscape Supply, Inc.; *U.S. Public*, pg. 1889
EAST HILLS CHEVROLET GEO; *U.S. Private*, pg. 1316
EAST HOUSTON MEDICAL PLAZA, LLC—See Ventas, Inc.; *U.S. Public*, pg. 2278
EAST IDAHO CREDIT UNION; *U.S. Private*, pg. 1316
EAST INDIANA TREATMENT CENTER, LLC—See Acadia Healthcare Company, Inc.; *U.S. Public*, pg. 28
EAST INDIA SECURITIES LIMITED; *Int'l*, pg. 2270
EAST INDIA TRAVEL COMPANY, INC.—See Cox & Kings Limited; *Int'l*, pg. 1822
EAST ISLES REINSURANCE, LTD.—See W.R. Berkley Corporation; *U.S. Public*, pg. 2317
EAST JAPAN BELT PRODUCTS, INC.—See Bando Chemical Industries, Ltd.; *Int'l*, pg. 830
EAST JAPAN FOODS CO.,LTD.—See Hanwa Co., Ltd.; *Int'l*, pg. 3262
EAST JAPAN MARKETING & COMMUNICATIONS, INC.; *Int'l*, pg. 2270
EAST JAPAN RAILWAY COMPANY - NEW YORK OFFICE—See East Japan Railway Company; *Int'l*, pg. 2270
EAST JAPAN RAILWAY COMPANY; *Int'l*, pg. 2270
EAST JEAN LIMITED—See Giordano International Limited; *Int'l*, pg. 2977
EAST JEFFERSON GENERAL HOSPITAL AUXILIARY, INC.; *U.S. Private*, pg. 1316
EAST JERSEY RAILROAD AND TERMINAL COMPANY—See Macquarie Group Limited; *Int'l*, pg. 4624
EAST KANSAS AGRI ENERGY LLC; *U.S. Public*, pg. 703
EAST KENT ROAD CAR COMPANY LTD.—See Stagecoach Group plc; *Int'l*, pg. 7163
EAST KENTUCKY POWER COOPERATIVE; *U.S. Private*, pg. 1316
EAST KILBRIDE SOUTH VETS4PETS LIMITED—See Pets at Home Group Plc; *Int'l*, pg. 5833
THE EASTLAKE COMPANY—See J.G. Boswell Co., Inc.; *U.S. Private*, pg. 2165
EAST LAKE FOUNDATION; *U.S. Private*, pg. 1316
EAST LAKE, LLC; *U.S. Private*, pg. 1316
EASTLAKE STUDIO INC.—See geniant, LLC; *U.S. Private*, pg. 1671
EAST LANCASHIRE NEWSPAPERS LTD—See JPIMedia Holdings Limited; *Int'l*, pg. 4006
EASTLAND INSURANCE COMPANY LIMITED; *Int'l*, pg. 2274
EASTLAND MALL, LLC—See CBL & Associates Properties, Inc.; *U.S. Public*, pg. 458
EASTLAND SHOE CORPORATION; *U.S. Private*, pg. 1322
EASTLAND TITLE SERVICE LLC—See Strattam Capital, LLC; *U.S. Private*, pg. 3837
EASTLAN RESOURCES LLC; *U.S. Private*, pg. 1322
EAST LAWN PALMS MORTUARY & CEMETERY—See Service Corporation International; *U.S. Public*, pg. 1869
EASTLINK CABLE SYSTEMS—See Bragg Group of Companies; *Int'l*, pg. 1136
EASTLINK—See Bragg Group of Companies; *Int'l*, pg. 1136
EAST LOS ANGELES COMMUNITY UNION; *U.S. Private*, pg. 1316
EAST MAIN FOODS INC.; *U.S. Private*, pg. 1316
EASTMAIN RESOURCES INC.—See Fury Gold Mines Limited; *Int'l*, pg. 2848
EASTMAN CHEMICAL ADVANCED MATERIALS B.V.—See Eastman Chemical Company; *U.S. Public*, pg. 704
EASTMAN CHEMICAL ASIA PACIFIC PTE. LTD.—See Eastman Chemical Company; *U.S. Public*, pg. 704
EASTMAN CHEMICAL BARCELONA, S.L.—See Eastman Chemical Company; *U.S. Public*, pg. 704
EASTMAN CHEMICAL B.V.—See Eastman Chemical Company; *U.S. Public*, pg. 704
EASTMAN CHEMICAL B.V., THE HAGUE, ZUG BRANCH—See Eastman Chemical Company; *U.S. Public*, pg. 704
EASTMAN CHEMICAL CANADA, INC.—See Eastman Chemical Company; *U.S. Public*, pg. 704
EASTMAN CHEMICAL (CHINA) CO., LTD.—See Eastman Chemical Company; *U.S. Public*, pg. 704
EASTMAN CHEMICAL (CHINA) CO., LTD.—See Eastman Chemical Company; *U.S. Public*, pg. 704

COMPANY NAME INDEX

EASTMAN CHEMICAL COMPANY FOUNDATION, INC.—See Eastman Chemical Company; *U.S. Public*, pg. 704
EASTMAN CHEMICAL COMPANY INVESTMENTS, INC.—See Eastman Chemical Company; *U.S. Public*, pg. 704
EASTMAN CHEMICAL COMPANY; *U.S. Public*, pg. 704
EASTMAN CHEMICAL COMPANY—See Eastman Chemical Company; *U.S. Public*, pg. 704
EASTMAN CHEMICAL COMPANY SOUTH CAROLINA OPERATIONS—See Eastman Chemical Company; *U.S. Public*, pg. 704
EASTMAN CHEMICAL DO BRASIL LTDA.—See Eastman Chemical Company; *U.S. Public*, pg. 705
EASTMAN CHEMICAL GERMANY GMBH—See Eastman Chemical Company; *U.S. Public*, pg. 705
EASTMAN CHEMICAL GMBH—See Eastman Chemical Company; *U.S. Public*, pg. 704
EASTMAN CHEMICAL HTF GMBH—See Eastman Chemical Company; *U.S. Public*, pg. 704
EASTMAN CHEMICAL IBERICA, S.L.—See Eastman Chemical Company; *U.S. Public*, pg. 704
EASTMAN CHEMICAL INDIA PRIVATE LIMITED—See Eastman Chemical Company; *U.S. Public*, pg. 704
EASTMAN CHEMICAL INTERNATIONAL AG—See Eastman Chemical Company; *U.S. Public*, pg. 704
EASTMAN CHEMICAL INTERNATIONAL GMBH—See Eastman Chemical Company; *U.S. Public*, pg. 705
EASTMAN CHEMICAL ITALIA S.R.L.—See Eastman Chemical Company; *U.S. Public*, pg. 704
EASTMAN CHEMICAL JAPAN LIMITED—See Eastman Chemical Company; *U.S. Public*, pg. 705
EASTMAN CHEMICAL KOREA LTD.—See Eastman Chemical Company; *U.S. Public*, pg. 705
EASTMAN CHEMICAL (MALAYSIA) SDN. BHD.—See Eastman Chemical Company; *U.S. Public*, pg. 704
EASTMAN CHEMICAL MIDDELBURG, B.V.—See Eastman Chemical Company; *U.S. Public*, pg. 705
EASTMAN CHEMICAL (NANJING) CO., LTD.—See Eastman Chemical Company; *U.S. Public*, pg. 704
EASTMAN CHEMICAL PRODUCTS SINGAPORE PTE. LTD.—See Eastman Chemical Company; *U.S. Public*, pg. 705
EASTMAN CHEMICAL RESINS, INC.—See Eastman Chemical Company; *U.S. Public*, pg. 705
EASTMAN CHEMICAL SINGAPORE PTE. LTD.—See Eastman Chemical Company; *U.S. Public*, pg. 705
EASTMAN CHEMICAL TEXAS CITY, INC.—See Eastman Chemical Company; *U.S. Public*, pg. 705
EASTMAN CHEMICAL URUAPAN, S.A. DE C.V.—See Eastman Chemical Company; *U.S. Public*, pg. 705
EASTMAN CHEMICAL WORKINGTON LIMITED—See Eastman Chemical Company; *U.S. Public*, pg. 705
EASTMAN COGENERATION L.P.—See Eastman Chemical Company; *U.S. Public*, pg. 705
EASTMAN COMPANY UK LIMITED—See Eastman Chemical Company; *U.S. Public*, pg. 705
EASTMAN CREDIT UNION; *U.S. Private*, pg. 1322
EASTMAN ESPANA S.L.—See Eastman Chemical Company; *U.S. Public*, pg. 705
EASTMAN FIBERS KOREA, LTD.—See Eastman Chemical Company; *U.S. Public*, pg. 705
EASTMAN FRANCE S.A.R.L.—See Eastman Chemical Company; *U.S. Public*, pg. 705
EASTMAN INDUSTRIES; *U.S. Private*, pg. 1322
EASTMAN KODAK COMPANY, SMALL SALES AND CUST SERV OFFICE—See Eastman Kodak Company; *U.S. Public*, pg. 707
EASTMAN KODAK COMPANY; *U.S. Public*, pg. 706
EASTMAN KODAK HOLDINGS B.V.—See Eastman Kodak Company; *U.S. Public*, pg. 706
EASTMAN KODAK INTERNATIONAL CAPITAL COMPANY, INC.—See Eastman Kodak Company; *U.S. Public*, pg. 707
EASTMAN KODAK PRINTING—See Eastman Kodak Company; *U.S. Public*, pg. 707
EASTMAN MACHINE COMPANY; *U.S. Private*, pg. 1322
EASTMAN MAZZUCCHELLI PLASTICS (SHENZHEN) COMPANY LIMITED—See Eastman Chemical Company; *U.S. Public*, pg. 705
EASTMAN MFG JAPAN LTD.—See Eastman Chemical Company; *U.S. Public*, pg. 705
EASTMAN PARK MICROGRAPHICS, INC. - DALLAS—See Eastman Park Micrographics, Inc.; *U.S. Private*, pg. 1322
EASTMAN PARK MICROGRAPHICS, INC.; *U.S. Private*, pg. 1322
EASTMAN RADIO SALES—See iHeartMedia, Inc.; *U.S. Public*, pg. 1096
EASTMAN SERVICIOS CORPORATIVOS, S.A. DE C.V.—See Eastman Chemical Company; *U.S. Public*, pg. 705
EASTMAN (SHANGHAI) CHEMICAL COMMERCIAL CO., LTD.—See Eastman Chemical Company; *U.S. Public*, pg. 704
EASTMAN SHUANGWEI FIBERS COMPANY LIMITED—See Eastman Chemical Company; *U.S. Public*, pg. 705

EASTMAN SPECIALTIES AS—See Eastman Chemical Company; *U.S. Public*, pg. 705
EASTMAN SPECIALTIES CORPORATION—See Eastman Chemical Company; *U.S. Public*, pg. 705
EASTMAN SPECIALTIES OU—See Eastman Chemical Company; *U.S. Public*, pg. 705
EASTMAN STAPLES LIMITED; *Int'l*, pg. 2274
EAST MANUFACTURING CORP.—See Fultra SAPI de CV; *Int'l*, pg. 2843
EAST MAUI IRRIGATION CO., LTD.—See Alexander & Baldwin, Inc.; *U.S. Public*, pg. 75
EAST MEADOW PLAZA REGENCY, LLC—See Regency Centers Corporation; *U.S. Public*, pg. 1774
EAST MESA INDEPENDENT—See Independent Newspapers, Inc.; *U.S. Private*, pg. 2060
EAST MIDLANDS INTERNATIONAL AIRPORT LIMITED—See The Manchester Airport Group plc; *Int'l*, pg. 7665
EAST MIDLANDS NEWSPAPERS LTD—See JPIMedia Holdings Limited; *Int'l*, pg. 4006
EAST MIDLANDS TRAINS LIMITED—See Stagecoach Group plc; *Int'l*, pg. 7163
EAST MISSISSIPPI ELECTRIC POWER ASSOCIATION; *U.S. Private*, pg. 1316
EAST MOLINE METAL PRODUCTS COMPANY; *U.S. Private*, pg. 1316
EAST MONEY INFORMATION CO., LTD.; *Int'l*, pg. 2270
EAST MORGAN HOLDINGS, INC.; *U.S. Public*, pg. 703
EAST MUSKEGON ROOFING & SHEET METAL COMPANY; *U.S. Private*, pg. 1317
EASTNINE AB; *Int'l*, pg. 2274
EAST OCEAN OILS & GRAINS INDUSTRIES; *Int'l*, pg. 2270
EAST OF CHICAGO PIZZA CO.; *U.S. Private*, pg. 1317
EAST OF HUDSON WATERSHED CORPORATION; *U.S. Private*, pg. 1317
THE EAST OHIO GAS COMPANY—See Enbridge Inc.; *Int'l*, pg. 2397
EAST OHIO LUMBER CO. INC.; *U.S. Private*, pg. 1317
EAST OIL & GAS PRODUCTION COMPANY—See National Iranian Oil Company; *Int'l*, pg. 5160
EAST OLYMPIC POULTRY INC.; *U.S. Private*, pg. 1317
EASTON BASEBALL/SOFTBALL INC.—See Fairfax Financial Holdings Limited; *Int'l*, pg. 2605
EASTON BASEBALL/SOFTBALL INC.—See Power Corporation of Canada; *Int'l*, pg. 5944
EASTON BLOCK & SUPPLY—See Haines & Kibblehouse Inc.; *U.S. Private*, pg. 1841
EASTON COACH CO.; *U.S. Private*, pg. 1322
EASTONE CENTURY TECHNOLOGY CO., LTD.; *Int'l*, pg. 2274
THE EASTON GROUP; *U.S. Private*, pg. 4024
EASTON JOURNAL—See Gannett Co., Inc.; *U.S. Public*, pg. 902
EASTON PHARMACEUTICALS, INC.; *Int'l*, pg. 2274
EASTON PRESS—See MBI, Inc.; *U.S. Private*, pg. 2624
EASTON PUBLISHING CO.—See Advance Publications, Inc.; *U.S. Private*, pg. 86
EASTON PUBLISHING CO.—See Advance Publications, Inc.; *U.S. Private*, pg. 86
EASTON SANDERSON & COMPANY; *U.S. Private*, pg. 1322
EASTON WORKS CO., LTD.—See Macnica Holdings, Inc.; *Int'l*, pg. 4624
EAST ORANGE GENERAL HOSPITAL—See Leonard Green & Partners, L.P.; *U.S. Private*, pg. 2428
EAST OREGONIAN PUBLISHING CO.; *U.S. Private*, pg. 1317
EAST OREGONIAN—See East Oregonian Publishing Co.; *U.S. Private*, pg. 1317
EAST ORLANDO HEALTH & REHAB CENTER INC; *U.S. Private*, pg. 1317
EAST OTTER TAIL TELEPHONE COMPANY INC.—See Arvig Enterprises, Inc.; *U.S. Private*, pg. 345
EASTPACK AVOCADO COMPANY LIMITED—See EastPack Limited; *Int'l*, pg. 2274
EASTPACK LIMITED; *Int'l*, pg. 2274
EAST PALO ALTO TENNIS & TUTORING; *U.S. Private*, pg. 1317
EAST PASADENA WATER CO.—See American Water Works Company, Inc.; *U.S. Public*, pg. 112
EAST PENN MANUFACTURING CO., INC.; *U.S. Private*, pg. 1317
EAST PENN RAILROAD, LLC—See 3i Group plc; *Int'l*, pg. 9
EAST PFLUGERVILLE MEDICAL CENTER LLC—See Adeptus Health Inc.; *U.S. Public*, pg. 78
EASTPHARMA LTD.; *Int'l*, pg. 2274
EAST PIPES INTEGRATED COMPANY FOR INDUSTRY; *Int'l*, pg. 2270
EASTPLAST CO., LTD.—See Thai Metal Drum Mfg. Public Co., Ltd.; *Int'l*, pg. 7593
EAST POINTE HOSPITAL, INC.—See HCA Healthcare, Inc.; *U.S. Public*, pg. 995
EASTPORT HOLDINGS, INC.; *U.S. Private*, pg. 1322
EAST PORTLAND SURGERY CENTER, LLC—See Tenet Healthcare Corporation; *U.S. Public*, pg. 2010
EASTPRINT, INC.—See East West Manufacturing, LLC; *U.S. Private*, pg. 1319

EAST PROFIT INTERNATIONAL LTD.—See Promate Electronic Co., Ltd.; *Int'l*, pg. 5992
EAST RAND PLASTICS (PTY) LTD.—See Transpaco Ltd.; *Int'l*, pg. 7904
EAST REAL ESTATE CO., LTD.—See Kajima Corporation; *Int'l*, pg. 4054
THE EASTRIDGE GROUP, INC.; *U.S. Private*, pg. 4024
EASTRIDGE PERSONNEL OF LAS VEGAS—See The Eastridge Group, Inc.; *U.S. Private*, pg. 4024
EASTRIDGE TECHNOLOGY, INC.—See SHI International Corp.; *U.S. Private*, pg. 3635
EAST RIVER ELECTRIC POWER COOPERATIVE; *U.S. Private*, pg. 1317
EASTROC BEVERAGE GROUP CO., LTD.; *Int'l*, pg. 2275
EAST SHORE AIRCRAFT LLC—See Stifel Financial Corp.; *U.S. Public*, pg. 1949
EAST SHORE HOSPITAL PTE LTD—See Khazanah Nasional Berhad; *Int'l*, pg. 4152
EAST SHORE RESORT; *U.S. Private*, pg. 1317
EASTSIBERIAN PLC; *Int'l*, pg. 2275
EAST SIDE CLINICAL LABORATORY, INC.—See Sonic Healthcare Limited; *Int'l*, pg. 7098
EASTSIDE DISTILLING, INC.; *U.S. Public*, pg. 708
EASTSIDE DODGE CHRYSLER JEEP LTD.; *Int'l*, pg. 2275
EAST SIDE FINANCIAL, INC.; *U.S. Public*, pg. 703
EASTSIDE FLOOR SERVICES LTD.; *U.S. Private*, pg. 1322
EASTSIDE FLOOR SUPPLIES, LTD.—See Eastside Floor Services Ltd.; *U.S. Private*, pg. 1322
EASTSIDE FOODS INC.; *U.S. Private*, pg. 1322
EASTSIDE HEART AND VASCULAR, LLC—See HCA Healthcare, Inc.; *U.S. Public*, pg. 995
EAST SIDE HOTEL SERVICES, INC.—See Marriott International, Inc.; *U.S. Public*, pg. 1370
EAST SIDE HOUSE, INC.; *U.S. Private*, pg. 1317
EAST SIDE LUMBERYARD SUPPLY CO.; *U.S. Private*, pg. 1317
EAST SIDE MARKET PLACE INC.; *U.S. Private*, pg. 1317
EASTSIDE MEDICAL CENTER—See HCA Healthcare, Inc.; *U.S. Public*, pg. 1012
EAST SIDE PLATING INC.; *U.S. Private*, pg. 1317
EASTSIDE RETIREMENT ASSOCIATION; *U.S. Private*, pg. 1322
EASTSIDE URGENT CARE LLC—See HCA Healthcare, Inc.; *U.S. Public*, pg. 995
EASTSPRING AL-WARA' INVESTMENTS BERHAD—See Prudential plc; *Int'l*, pg. 6009
EASTSPRING ASSET MANAGEMENT KOREA CO. LTD.—See Prudential plc; *Int'l*, pg. 6009
EASTSPRING INVESTMENT MANAGEMENT (SHANGHAI) COMPANY LIMITED—See Prudential plc; *Int'l*, pg. 6009
EASTSPRING INVESTMENTS BERHAD—See Prudential plc; *Int'l*, pg. 6009
EASTSPRING INVESTMENTS FUND MANAGEMENT LIMITED LIABILITY COMPANY—See Prudential plc; *Int'l*, pg. 6009
EASTSPRING INVESTMENTS (HONG KONG) LIMITED—See Prudential plc; *Int'l*, pg. 6009
EASTSPRING INVESTMENTS INCORPORATED—See Prudential plc; *Int'l*, pg. 6009
EASTSPRING INVESTMENT (SINGAPORE) LTD.—See Prudential plc; *Int'l*, pg. 6009
EASTSPRING INVESTMENTS LIMITED—See Prudential plc; *Int'l*, pg. 6009
EASTSPRING INVESTMENTS (LUXEMBOURG) S.A.—See Prudential plc; *Int'l*, pg. 6009
EASTSPRING SECURITIES INVESTMENT TRUST CO., LTD.—See Prudential plc; *Int'l*, pg. 6009
EAST SPRINGS INTERNATIONAL N.V—See Nestle S.A.; *Int'l*, pg. 5202
EAST STAR RESOURCES PLC; *Int'l*, pg. 2270
EAST STONE ACQUISITION CORPORATION; *U.S. Public*, pg. 703
EAST SYNERGY LIMITED—See Eastern Asia Technology Ltd.; *Int'l*, pg. 2271
EAST TEAK FINE HARDWOODS, INC.; *U.S. Private*, pg. 1317
EAST TEAK FINE HARDWOODS, INC.—See East Teak Fine Hardwoods, Inc.; *U.S. Private*, pg. 1317
EAST TELECOM, LLC—See KT Corporation; *Int'l*, pg. 4314
EAST TENDER OPTOELECTRONICS CORPORATION—See Sesoda Corporation; *Int'l*, pg. 6729
EAST TENNESSEE CHILDREN'S HOSPITAL; *U.S. Private*, pg. 1318
EAST TENNESSEE CLINIC CORP.—See Community Health Systems, Inc.; *U.S. Public*, pg. 553
EAST TENNESSEE FOUNDATION; *U.S. Private*, pg. 1318
EAST TENNESSEE MATERIALS AND ENERGY CORPORATION—See Perma-Fix Environmental Services, Inc.; *U.S. Public*, pg. 1676
EAST TENNESSEE NATURAL GAS, LLC—See Enbridge Inc.; *Int'l*, pg. 2397
EAST TENNESSEE NISSAN MORRISTOWN; *U.S. Private*, pg. 1318

EAST TENNESSEE RAILWAY, L.P.—See Brookfield Infrastructure Partners L.P.; *Int'l*, pg. 1191
EAST TENNESSEE RAILWAY, L.P.—See GIC Pte. Ltd.; *Int'l*, pg. 2965
EAST TEXAS BANCSHARES, INC.; *U.S. Private*, pg. 1318
EAST TEXAS COMMUNITIES FOUNDATION, INC.; *U.S. Private*, pg. 1318
EAST TEXAS ELECTRIC COOPERATIVE, INC.; *U.S. Private*, pg. 1318
EAST TEXAS FIBER LINE, INC.—See Consolidated Communications Holdings, Inc.; *U.S. Public*, pg. 570
EAST TEXAS FINANCIAL CORPORATION; *U.S. Private*, pg. 1318
EAST TEXAS INTEGRATED CIRCUITS, INC.—See Broadcom Inc.; *U.S. Public*, pg. 388
EAST TEXAS MACK SALES LLC; *U.S. Private*, pg. 1318
EAST TEXAS PROFESSIONAL CREDIT UNION; *U.S. Private*, pg. 1318
EAST TEXAS SUPPORT SERVICES, INC.; *U.S. Private*, pg. 1318
EAST TRENCHERS S.R.L.—See TESMEC S.p.A.; *Int'l*, pg. 7572
EAST VALLEY ENDOSCOPY, LLC—See KKR & Co. Inc.; *U.S. Public*, pg. 1245
EAST VALLEY TRIBUNE—See EOS Publishing, LLC; *U.S. Private*, pg. 1411
EASTVIEW FUEL OILS LIMITED—See Valero Energy Corporation; *U.S. Public*, pg. 2272
EASTWARD COMPANIES, INC.; *U.S. Private*, pg. 1322
EASTWAY PLYMOUTH CHRYSLER LTD; *Int'l*, pg. 2275
EAST WEST AGRO AB; *Int'l*, pg. 2270
EAST & WEST ALUM CRAFT LTD.; *Int'l*, pg. 2269
EAST WEST BANCORP, INC.; *U.S. Public*, pg. 703
EAST WEST BANK (CHINA) LIMITED—See East West Bancorp, Inc.; *U.S. Public*, pg. 703
EAST WEST BANKING CORPORATION—See Filinvest Development Corporation; *Int'l*, pg. 2663
EAST WEST BANK—See East West Bancorp, Inc.; *U.S. Public*, pg. 703
EASTWEST BIOSCIENCE, INC.; *Int'l*, pg. 2275
EAST WEST CONNECTION, INC.; *U.S. Private*, pg. 1318
EAST WEST COPOLYMER LLC; *U.S. Private*, pg. 1318
EAST-WEST DISTRIBUTING CO.—See Walgreens Boots Alliance, Inc.; *U.S. Public*, pg. 2323
EAST WEST ENERGY LTD.; *U.S. Private*, pg. 1318
EAST WEST HOLDINGS LIMITED; *Int'l*, pg. 2270
EAST WEST INDUSTRIAL ENGINEERING CO. INC; *U.S. Private*, pg. 1318
EAST WEST INSURANCE COMPANY LIMITED; *Int'l*, pg. 2270
EAST WEST LIFE ASSURANCE COMPANY LIMITED; *Int'l*, pg. 2270
EAST WEST MANUFACTURING, LLC; *U.S. Private*, pg. 1318
EASTWEST MARKETING GROUP, LLC; *U.S. Private*, pg. 1322
EAST WEST PARTNERS MANAGEMENT CO.; *U.S. Private*, pg. 1319
EAST WEST PARTNERS; *U.S. Private*, pg. 1319
EAST WEST PETROLEUM CORP.; *Int'l*, pg. 2270
EASTWEST PUBLIC RELATIONS—See Omnicom Group Inc.; *U.S. Public*, pg. 1578
EAST WEST RESORT MANAGEMENT—See East West Partners; *U.S. Private*, pg. 1319
EAST WEST SURGERY CENTER, L.P.—See Tenet Healthcare Corporation; *U.S. Public*, pg. 2010
EAST WEST TEA COMPANY, LLC; *U.S. Private*, pg. 1319
EASTWIND MARITIME SA INC.; *U.S. Private*, pg. 1322
EASTWOOD BIO-MEDICAL CANADA INC.; *Int'l*, pg. 2275
THE EASTWOOD COMPANY—See Kian Capital Partners, LLC; *U.S. Private*, pg. 2302
EASTWOOD HOMES; *U.S. Private*, pg. 1322
EASTWOOD INSURANCE SERVICES; *U.S. Private*, pg. 1322
EAST YORKSHIRE MOTOR SERVICES LIMITED—See GLOBALVIA Inversiones, S.A.U.; *Int'l*, pg. 3005
EAST YORKSHIRE MOTOR SERVICES LIMITED—See Kinetic Group Services Pty Ltd.; *Int'l*, pg. 4167
EASUN CAPITAL MARKETS LIMITED; *Int'l*, pg. 2275
EASUN REYROLLE LTD; *Int'l*, pg. 2275
E.A. SWEEN COMPANY; *U.S. Private*, pg. 1304
EA SWISS SARL—See Electronic Arts Inc.; *U.S. Public*, pg. 724
EASYACCESS FINANCIAL SERVICES LIMITED; *Int'l*, pg. 2276
EASYAIRCONDITIONING GROUP LIMITED—See Beijer Ref AB; *Int'l*, pg. 944
EASY APIOMAT GMBH—See Easy Software AG; *Int'l*, pg. 2275
EASYBACKGROUNDS, INC.—See Audax Group, Limited Partnership; *U.S. Private*, pg. 387
EASYBANK AG—See BAWAG Group AG; *Int'l*, pg. 900
EASYBELL GMBH—See ecotel communication ag; *Int'l*, pg. 2300
EASY BIO PHILIPPINES, INC.—See Easy Holdings Co., Ltd.; *Int'l*, pg. 2275
EASY BROKING ONLINE LTD.—See PSC Insurance Group Limited; *Int'l*, pg. 6016

EASY BUY PLUS, INC; *U.S. Private*, pg. 1323
EASYCALL COMMUNICATIONS PHILIPPINES, INC.; *Int'l*, pg. 2276
EASYCAMP B.V.—See Cox & Kings Limited; *Int'l*, pg. 1822
EASY CLICK WORLDWIDE NETWORK TECHNOLOGY CO., LTD.; *Int'l*, pg. 2275
EASY DATE HOLDINGS LTD; *Int'l*, pg. 2275
EASYDENTIC (FRANCE)—See SafeTIC S.A.; *Int'l*, pg. 6470
EASYDIS—See Finatis SA; *Int'l*, pg. 2670
EASY DOES IT INC.; *U.S. Private*, pg. 1323
EASY DRIVE S.R.L.—See Stellantis N.V.; *Int'l*, pg. 7196
EASY FIELD SERVICES S.A.—See TRSB Groupe SA; *Int'l*, pg. 7940
EASYFILL AB; *Int'l*, pg. 2276
EASYFINANCIAL SERVICES INC.—See goeasy Ltd.; *Int'l*, pg. 3021
EASY FINCORP LIMITED; *Int'l*, pg. 2275
EASYFOOD A/S—See Orkla ASA; *Int'l*, pg. 5637
EASY GARDENER PRODUCTS, INC.—See Centre Lane Partners, LLC; *U.S. Private*, pg. 827
EASYGRASS LLC—See Sentinel Capital Partners, L.L.C.; *U.S. Private*, pg. 3609
EASY HEAT EUROPE B.V.—See Emerson Electric Co.; *U.S. Public*, pg. 740
EASY HEAT, INC.—See Emerson Electric Co.; *U.S. Public*, pg. 740
EASY HEAT, INC.—See Emerson Electric Co.; *U.S. Public*, pg. 740
EASY HEAT LTD.—See Emerson Electric Co.; *U.S. Public*, pg. 740
EASY HOLDINGS CO., LTD.; *Int'l*, pg. 2275
EASYHOME NEW RETAIL GROUP CO., LTD.; *Int'l*, pg. 2276
EASYHOME U.S. LTD.—See goeasy Ltd.; *Int'l*, pg. 3021
EASYHOTEL FRANCE SAS—See easyHotel plc; *Int'l*, pg. 2276
EASYHOTEL PLC; *Int'l*, pg. 2276
EASYHOTEL SPAIN S.L.U.—See easyHotel plc; *Int'l*, pg. 2276
EASY ICE, LLC—See Freeman Spogli & Co. Incorporated; *U.S. Private*, pg. 1606
EASY INTERNATIONAL CONSULTING GMBH—See Easy Software AG; *Int'l*, pg. 2275
EASYIO ENGINEERING PTE LTD.; *Int'l*, pg. 2276
EASYJET AIRLINE COMPANY LIMITED—See easyJet plc; *Int'l*, pg. 2276
EASYJET PLC; *Int'l*, pg. 2276
EASYKNIT GLOBAL COMPANY LIMITED—See Easyknit International Holdings Ltd.; *Int'l*, pg. 2276
EASYKNIT INTERNATIONAL HOLDINGS LTD.; *Int'l*, pg. 2276
EASYKNIT PROPERTIES MANAGEMENT LIMITED—See Easyknit International Holdings Ltd.; *Int'l*, pg. 2276
EASY-LASER AB—See Indutrade AB; *Int'l*, pg. 3678
EASYLEASING GMBH—See BAWAG Group AG; *Int'l*, pg. 900
EASYLINK SERVICES FRANCE SARL—See Open Text Corporation; *Int'l*, pg. 5597
EASYLINK SERVICES INTERNATIONAL CORPORATION—See Open Text Corporation; *Int'l*, pg. 5597
EASYLINK SERVICES INTERNATIONAL LTD.—See Open Text Corporation; *Int'l*, pg. 5597
EASYLINK SERVICES—See Open Text Corporation; *Int'l*, pg. 5597
EASYLOG SAS—See WiseTech Global Limited; *Int'l*, pg. 8437
EASY MARKET S.P.A.—See TUI AG; *Int'l*, pg. 7964
EASYMEDMOBILE INDIA PRIVATE LTD.—See Easy Technologies, Inc.; *Int'l*, pg. 2276
EASYMED TECHNOLOGIES, INC.—See Easy Technologies Inc.; *Int'l*, pg. 2276
EASY MIX SDN. BHD.—See Bina Puri Holdings Bhd; *Int'l*, pg. 1032
EASY MONEY GROUP (EMG); *U.S. Private*, pg. 1323
EASY ONE FINANCIAL GROUP LTD.; *Int'l*, pg. 2275
EASYPAY (PROPRIETARY) LIMITED—See Lesaka Technologies, Inc.; *Int'l*, pg. 4468
EASY PICKINS INC.; *U.S. Private*, pg. 1323
EASYPSIM LTD.—See Swisscom AG; *Int'l*, pg. 7373
EASYRIDERS, LLC—See Paisano Publications, LLC; *U.S. Private*, pg. 3076
EASYSCRIPTS CUTLER BAY, LLC—See Elevance Health, Inc.; *U.S. Public*, pg. 729
EASYSCRIPTS HIALEAH LLC—See Elevance Health, Inc.; *U.S. Public*, pg. 729
EASYSCRIPTS, LLC—See Elevance Health, Inc.; *U.S. Public*, pg. 730
EASYSCRIPTS WESTCHESTER, LLC—See Elevance Health, Inc.; *U.S. Public*, pg. 729
EASYSEAT, LLC; *U.S. Private*, pg. 1323
EASY SMART GROUP HOLDINGS LIMITED; *Int'l*, pg. 2275
EASYSOFT-SOFTWARE E SISTEMAS SA—See 3i Group plc; *Int'l*, pg. 8
EASY SOFTWARE AG; *Int'l*, pg. 2275
EASY SOFTWARE (ASIA PACIFIC) PTE. LTD.—See Easy Software AG; *Int'l*, pg. 2275

EASY SOFTWARE DEUTSCHLAND GMBH—See Easy Software AG; *Int'l*, pg. 2275
EASY SOFTWARE GMBH—See Easy Software AG; *Int'l*, pg. 2276
EASY SOFTWARE INC.—See Easy Software AG; *Int'l*, pg. 2276
EASY SOFTWARE TURKIYE LTD. STI.—See Easy Software AG; *Int'l*, pg. 2276
EASY SOFTWARE (UK) PLC—See Easy Software AG; *Int'l*, pg. 2275
EASY SOUND RECORDING CO.—See Welk Music Group Inc.; *U.S. Private*, pg. 4474
EASYSPACE LIMITED—See iomart Group plc; *Int'l*, pg. 3792
EASY STREET INSURANCE, LLC—See Integrity Marketing Group LLC; *U.S. Private*, pg. 2103
EASY SUN SDN. BHD.—See ES Ceramics Technology Bhd; *Int'l*, pg. 2500
EASY TECHNOLOGIES INC.; *Int'l*, pg. 2276
EASY TIGER PRODUCTIONS PTY LTD.—See Bertelsmann SE & Co. KGaA; *Int'l*, pg. 992
EASY TRIP PLANNERS LIMITED; *Int'l*, pg. 2276
EASYTURF—See Tarkett S.A.; *Int'l*, pg. 7463
EASY VISIBLE SUPPLY CHAIN MANAGEMENT CO., LTD.; *Int'l*, pg. 2276
EASY VISION—See EssilorLuxottica SA; *Int'l*, pg. 2512
EASYVISTA GMBH—See Eurazeo SE; *Int'l*, pg. 2528
EASYVISTA HOLDING SAS—See Eurazeo SE; *Int'l*, pg. 2528
EASYVISTA INC.—See Eurazeo SE; *Int'l*, pg. 2528
EASYVISTA ITALY—See Eurazeo SE; *Int'l*, pg. 2528
EASYVISTA PORTUGAL S.A.—See Eurazeo SE; *Int'l*, pg. 2528
EASYVISTA, S.A.—See Eurazeo SE; *Int'l*, pg. 2528
EASYVISTA SARL—See Eurazeo SE; *Int'l*, pg. 2528
EASYVISTA SL—See Eurazeo SE; *Int'l*, pg. 2528
EASYVISTA SPAIN—See Eurazeo SE; *Int'l*, pg. 2528
EASYVISTA SRL—See Eurazeo SE; *Int'l*, pg. 2528
EASYVISTA UNITED KINGDOM—See Eurazeo SE; *Int'l*, pg. 2528
EASY WAY FOOD STORES INC.; *U.S. Private*, pg. 1323
EASYWELL BIOMEDICALS, INC.; *Int'l*, pg. 2277
EAT24, LLC—See Just Eat Takeaway.com N.V.; *Int'l*, pg. 4030
EAT & BEYOND GLOBAL HOLDINGS INC.; *Int'l*, pg. 2277
E A TECHNICAL SERVICES, INC.—See Dycom Industries, Inc.; *U.S. Public*, pg. 698
E.A TECHNIQUE (M) BHD; *Int'l*, pg. 2250
EATEL CONSTRUCTION CO., INC.—See RTC Holdings, L.L.C.; *U.S. Private*, pg. 3498
EATELCORP INC.—See RTC Holdings, L.L.C.; *U.S. Private*, pg. 3498
EATEM CORP.—See Linsalata Capital Partners, Inc.; *U.S. Private*, pg. 2463
EATERIES, INC.; *U.S. Private*, pg. 1323
EATGOOD SWEDEN AB; *Int'l*, pg. 2277
EAT HERE BRANDS, LLC; *U.S. Private*, pg. 1323
EATHERLY CONSTRUCTORS INC.; *U.S. Private*, pg. 1323
EAT&HOLDINGS CO.,LTD; *Int'l*, pg. 2277
EATING RECOVERY CENTER; *U.S. Private*, pg. 1323
EAT LTD—See JAB Holding Company S.a.r.l.; *Int'l*, pg. 3863
EATMORE SPROUTS AND GREENS LTD.; *Int'l*, pg. 2277
EAT'N PARK HOSPITALITY GROUP, INC.; *U.S. Private*, pg. 1323
EATON AEROSPACE LLC - CONVEYANCE SYSTEMS DIVISION, JACKSON—See Eaton Corporation plc; *Int'l*, pg. 2279
EATON AEROSPACE LLC - ELECTRICAL SENSING & CONTROLS DIVISION, COSTA MESA—See Eaton Corporation plc; *Int'l*, pg. 2279
EATON AEROSPACE LLC - ELECTRICAL SENSING & CONTROLS DIVISION, GLENOLDEN—See Eaton Corporation plc; *Int'l*, pg. 2279
EATON AEROSPACE LLC - ELECTRICAL SENSING & CONTROLS DIVISION, GRAND RAPIDS—See Eaton Corporation plc; *Int'l*, pg. 2279
EATON AEROSPACE LLC - ELECTRICAL SENSING & CONTROLS DIVISION, SARASOTA—See Eaton Corporation plc; *Int'l*, pg. 2279
EATON AEROSPACE LLC - FUEL SYSTEMS DIVISION, CLEVELAND—See Eaton Corporation plc; *Int'l*, pg. 2279
EATON AEROSPACE LLC - HYDRAULIC SYSTEMS DIVISION, JACKSON—See Eaton Corporation plc; *Int'l*, pg. 2279
EATON AEROSPACE LLC - HYDRAULIC SYSTEMS DIVISION, LOS ANGELES—See Eaton Corporation plc; *Int'l*, pg. 2279
EATON AEROSPACE LLC—See Eaton Corporation plc; *Int'l*, pg. 2279
EATON AUTOMOTIVE COMPONENTS SPOLKA Z O.O.—See Eaton Corporation plc; *Int'l*, pg. 2279
EATON AUTOMOTIVE G.M.B.H.—See Eaton Corporation plc; *Int'l*, pg. 2279
EATON AUTOMOTIVE SYSTEMS SPOLKA Z O.O.—See Eaton Corporation plc; *Int'l*, pg. 2279

COMPANY NAME INDEX

EATON CONTROLS, S. DE R.L. DE C.V.—See Eaton Corporation plc; *Int'l*, pg. 2279
EATON CONTROLS (UK) LIMITED—See Eaton Corporation plc; *Int'l*, pg. 2279
EATON CORP. - AIRFLEX—See Eaton Corporation plc; *Int'l*, pg. 2279
EATON CORP. - ELECTRICAL SECTOR, AMERICAS—See Eaton Corporation plc; *Int'l*, pg. 2279
EATON CORP. - ELECTRICAL SECTOR, COLUMBUS—See Eaton Corporation plc; *Int'l*, pg. 2279
EATON CORP. - ELECTRICAL SECTOR, POWER QUALITY USA—See Eaton Corporation plc; *Int'l*, pg. 2279
EATON CORP. - ELECTRICAL SECTOR, WATERTOWN—See Eaton Corporation plc; *Int'l*, pg. 2279
EATON CORP. - ENGINE AIR MANAGEMENT—See Eaton Corporation plc; *Int'l*, pg. 2280
EATON CORP. - FLUID CONNECTORS—See Eaton Corporation plc; *Int'l*, pg. 2280
EATON CORP. - GOLF GRIP—See Eaton Corporation plc; *Int'l*, pg. 2280
EATON CORP. - INDUSTRIAL CONTROLS—See Eaton Corporation plc; *Int'l*, pg. 2280
EATON CORPORATION PLC; *Int'l*, pg. 2277
EATON CORPORATION—See Eaton Corporation plc; *Int'l*, pg. 2277
EATON CORP. - SUPERCHARGERS—See Eaton Corporation plc; *Int'l*, pg. 2280
EATON CORP. - TRANSMISSIONS—See Eaton Corporation plc; *Int'l*, pg. 2280
EATON CORP. - VEHICLE GROUP, AUTOMOTIVE DIVISION—See Eaton Corporation plc; *Int'l*, pg. 2280
EATON CORP. - VEHICLE GROUP, BELMOND PLANT—See Eaton Corporation plc; *Int'l*, pg. 2280
EATON CORP. - VEHICLE GROUP, KEARNEY PLANT—See Eaton Corporation plc; *Int'l*, pg. 2280
EATON CORP. - VEHICLE GROUP—See Eaton Corporation plc; *Int'l*, pg. 2280
EATON CORP. - VEHICLE GROUP, TRUCK DIVISION—See Eaton Corporation plc; *Int'l*, pg. 2280
EATON CYLINDER—See Eaton Corporation plc; *Int'l*, pg. 2280
EATON ELECTRICAL CANADA—See Eaton Corporation plc; *Int'l*, pg. 2279
EATON ELECTRICAL LTD.—See Eaton Corporation plc; *Int'l*, pg. 2281
EATON ELECTRICAL MEXICO - GUADALAJARA SALES OFFICE—See Eaton Corporation plc; *Int'l*, pg. 2280
EATON ELECTRICAL MEXICO - MONTERREY SALES OFFICE—See Eaton Corporation plc; *Int'l*, pg. 2280
EATON ELECTRICAL S.A.—See Eaton Corporation plc; *Int'l*, pg. 2279
EATON ELECTRICAL, S.A.—See Eaton Corporation plc; *Int'l*, pg. 2280
EATON ELECTRICAL SYSTEMS LIMITED—See Eaton Corporation plc; *Int'l*, pg. 2280
EATON ELECTRIC APS—See Eaton Corporation plc; *Int'l*, pg. 2281
EATON ELECTRIC HOLDINGS LLC—See Eaton Corporation plc; *Int'l*, pg. 2280
EATON ELECTRIC LIMITED—See Eaton Corporation plc; *Int'l*, pg. 2281
EATON ELECTRIC SALES S.A.S.—See Eaton Corporation plc; *Int'l*, pg. 2281
EATON ELECTRIC SIA—See Eaton Corporation plc; *Int'l*, pg. 2280
EATON ELECTRIC (SOUTH AFRICA) PTY LTD.—See Eaton Corporation plc; *Int'l*, pg. 2280
EATON ELECTRIC SPRL—See Eaton Corporation plc; *Int'l*, pg. 2280
EATON ELEKTRIK TICARET LIMITED SIRKETI—See Eaton Corporation plc; *Int'l*, pg. 2280
EATON ELEKTROTECHNIKA S.R.O.—See Eaton Corporation plc; *Int'l*, pg. 2280
EATON ENTERPRISES (HUNGARY) KFT.—See Eaton Corporation plc; *Int'l*, pg. 2280
EATON FEDERAL SAVINGS BANK; *U.S. Private*, pg. 1323
EATON FILTRATION LLC - RONNINGEN-PETTER—See Eaton Corporation plc; *Int'l*, pg. 2280
EATON FILTRATION LLC—See Eaton Corporation plc; *Int'l*, pg. 2280
EATON FILTRATION (SHANGHAI) CO. LTD.—See Eaton Corporation plc; *Int'l*, pg. 2280
EATONFORM INC.; *U.S. Private*, pg. 1323
EATON FZE—See Eaton Corporation plc; *Int'l*, pg. 2280
EATON GERMANY GMBH - AEROSPACE GROUP, CONVEYANCE SYSTEMS—See Eaton Corporation plc; *Int'l*, pg. 2279
EATON GERMANY GMBH—See Eaton Corporation plc; *Int'l*, pg. 2281
EATON GMBH—See Eaton Corporation plc; *Int'l*, pg. 2281
EATON HOLDING INVESTMENTS GMBH & CO. KG—See Eaton Corporation plc; *Int'l*, pg. 2281
EATON HOLDING SE & CO. KG—See Eaton Corporation plc; *Int'l*, pg. 2280
EATON HOLEC AB—See Eaton Corporation plc; *Int'l*, pg. 2280

EATON HYDRAULICS LLC - BEREA—See Eaton Corporation plc; *Int'l*, pg. 2280
EATON HYDRAULICS LLC—See Eaton Corporation plc; *Int'l*, pg. 2280
EATON INDUSTRIAL SYSTEMS PRIVATE LIMITED—See Eaton Corporation plc; *Int'l*, pg. 2281
EATON INDUSTRIES (BELGIUM) BVBA—See Eaton Corporation plc; *Int'l*, pg. 2281
EATON INDUSTRIES (CANADA) COMPANY—See Eaton Corporation plc; *Int'l*, pg. 2281
EATON INDUSTRIES (COLOMBIA) S.A.S.—See Eaton Corporation plc; *Int'l*, pg. 2281
EATON INDUSTRIES (EGYPT) LTD.—See Eaton Corporation plc; *Int'l*, pg. 2281
EATON INDUSTRIES EOOD—See Eaton Corporation plc; *Int'l*, pg. 2281
EATON INDUSTRIES (FRANCE) S.A.S.—See Eaton Corporation plc; *Int'l*, pg. 2281
EATON INDUSTRIES GMBH—See Eaton Corporation plc; *Int'l*, pg. 2281
EATON INDUSTRIES II G.M.B.H.—See Eaton Corporation plc; *Int'l*, pg. 2281
EATON INDUSTRIES (JAPAN) LTD.—See Eaton Corporation plc; *Int'l*, pg. 2280
EATON INDUSTRIES MANUFACTURING GMBH—See Eaton Corporation plc; *Int'l*, pg. 2281
EATON INDUSTRIES (NETHERLANDS) B.V. - HYDRAULICS DIVISION—See Eaton Corporation plc; *Int'l*, pg. 2281
EATON INDUSTRIES (NETHERLANDS) B.V.—See Eaton Corporation plc; *Int'l*, pg. 2281
EATON INDUSTRIES PRIVATE LIMITED—See Eaton Corporation plc; *Int'l*, pg. 2281
EATON INDUSTRIES PTY. LTD.—See Eaton Corporation plc; *Int'l*, pg. 2281
EATON INDUSTRIES, S. DE R.L. DE C.V.—See Eaton Corporation plc; *Int'l*, pg. 2281
EATON INDUSTRIES (SHANGHAI) CO., LTD.—See Eaton Corporation plc; *Int'l*, pg. 2281
EATON INTERNATIONAL INDUSTRIES NIGERIA LIMITED—See Eaton Corporation plc; *Int'l*, pg. 2281
EATON INVESTMENTS CO., LTD.—See Eaton Corporation plc; *Int'l*, pg. 2281
EATON LIMITED - FUEL & MOTION CONTROL SYSTEMS DIVISION—See Eaton Corporation plc; *Int'l*, pg. 2279
EATON LTDA. - FLUID POWER DIVISION, GUARATINGUETA PLANT—See Eaton Corporation plc; *Int'l*, pg. 2280
EATON LTD. - HYDRAULIC SYSTEMS—See Eaton Corporation plc; *Int'l*, pg. 2280
EATON MANUFACTURING GMBH—See Eaton Corporation plc; *Int'l*, pg. 2281
EATON MEDC LIMITED—See Eaton Corporation plc; *Int'l*, pg. 2281
EATON METAL PRODUCTS COMPANY; *U.S. Private*, pg. 1323
EATON MORTGAGE, LLC—See Wells Fargo & Company; *U.S. Public*, pg. 2343
EATON OFFICE SUPPLY CO., INC.; *U.S. Private*, pg. 1323
EATON ONTARIO SALES—See Eaton Corporation plc; *Int'l*, pg. 2279
EATON PARTNERS, LLC - SAN DIEGO—See Stifel Financial Corp.; *U.S. Public*, pg. 1949
EATON PARTNERS, LLC—See Stifel Financial Corp.; *U.S. Public*, pg. 1949
EATON PARTNERS (UK) LLP—See Stifel Financial Corp.; *U.S. Public*, pg. 1949
EATON PHOENIXTEC MMPL CO.,LTD.—See Eaton Corporation plc; *Int'l*, pg. 2281
EATON POWER QUALITY AB—See Eaton Corporation plc; *Int'l*, pg. 2281
EATON POWER QUALITY COMPANY—See Eaton Corporation plc; *Int'l*, pg. 2279
EATON POWER QUALITY LIMITED—See Eaton Corporation plc; *Int'l*, pg. 2281
EATON POWER QUALITY OY—See Eaton Corporation plc; *Int'l*, pg. 2281
EATON POWER QUALITY S.A.—See Eaton Corporation plc; *Int'l*, pg. 2279
EATON POWER SOLUTIONS LTDA.—See Eaton Corporation plc; *Int'l*, pg. 2279
EATON POWER SOLUTIONS - MEXICO & CENTRAL AMERICA—See Eaton Corporation plc; *Int'l*, pg. 2280
EATON RESIDENCES MANAGEMENT LIMITED—See Great Eagle Holdings Limited; *Int'l*, pg. 3064
EATON S.A.—See Eaton Corporation plc; *Int'l*, pg. 2281
EATON STEEL CORPORATION; *U.S. Private*, pg. 1323
EATON TECHNOLOGIES G.M.B.H.—See Eaton Corporation plc; *Int'l*, pg. 2281
EATON TECHNOLOGIES LIMITED—See Eaton Corporation plc; *Int'l*, pg. 2281
EATON TECHNOLOGIES, S. DE R.L. DE C.V.—See Eaton Corporation plc; *Int'l*, pg. 2281
EATONTOWN MONMOUTH MALL LLC—See Vornado Realty Trust; *U.S. Public*, pg. 2310
EATON TRUCK COMPONENTS (PTY.) LIMITED—See Eaton Corporation plc; *Int'l*, pg. 2280

EATON VANCE ACQUISITIONS—See Morgan Stanley; *U.S. Public*, pg. 1471
EATON VANCE CALIFORNIA MUNICIPAL INCOME TRUST; *U.S. Public*, pg. 708
EATON VANCE CORP.—See Morgan Stanley; *U.S. Public*, pg. 1471
EATON VANCE DISTRIBUTORS, INC.—See Morgan Stanley; *U.S. Public*, pg. 1471
EATON VANCE ENHANCED EQUITY INCOME FUND; *U.S. Public*, pg. 708
EATON VANCE ENHANCED EQUITY INCOME II; *U.S. Public*, pg. 708
EATON VANCE FLOATING-RATE 2022 TARGET TERM TRUST; *U.S. Public*, pg. 708
EATON VANCE FLOATING-RATE INCOME PLUS FUND; *U.S. Public*, pg. 708
EATON VANCE FLOATING-RATE INCOME TRUST; *U.S. Public*, pg. 708
EATON VANCE INVESTMENT COUNSEL—See Morgan Stanley; *U.S. Public*, pg. 1471
EATON VANCE LIMITED DURATION INCOME FUND; *U.S. Public*, pg. 708
EATON VANCE MANAGEMENT (INTERNATIONAL) LIMITED—See Morgan Stanley; *U.S. Public*, pg. 1472
EATON VANCE MANAGEMENT—See Morgan Stanley; *U.S. Public*, pg. 1472
EATON VANCE MUNICIPAL BOND FUND; *U.S. Public*, pg. 708
EATON VANCE MUNICIPAL INCOME 2028 TERM TRUST—See Morgan Stanley; *U.S. Public*, pg. 1472
EATON VANCE MUNICIPAL INCOME TRUST; *U.S. Public*, pg. 708
EATON VANCE NATIONAL MUNICIPAL OPPORTUNITIES TRUST; *U.S. Public*, pg. 708
EATON VANCE RISK-MANAGED DIVERSIFIED EQUITY INCOME FUND; *U.S. Public*, pg. 708
EATON VANCE SENIOR FLOATING-RATE TRUST; *U.S. Public*, pg. 708
EATON VANCE SENIOR INCOME TRUST; *U.S. Public*, pg. 708
EATON VANCE SHORT DURATION DIVERSIFIED INCOME FUND; *U.S. Public*, pg. 708
EATON VANCE TAX-ADVANTAGED DIVIDEND INCOME FUND; *U.S. Public*, pg. 708
EATON VANCE TAX-ADVANTAGED GLOBAL DIVIDEND INCOME FUND; *U.S. Public*, pg. 709
EATON VANCE TAX-ADVANTAGED GLOBAL DIVIDEND OPPORTUNITIES FUND; *U.S. Public*, pg. 709
EATON VANCE TAX-MANAGED BUY-WRITE INCOME FUND; *U.S. Public*, pg. 709
EATON VANCE TAX-MANAGED BUY-WRITE OPPORTUNITIES FUND; *U.S. Public*, pg. 709
EATON VANCE TAX-MANAGED DIVERSIFIED EQUITY INCOME FUND; *U.S. Public*, pg. 709
EATON VANCE TAX MANAGED GLOBAL BUY WRITE OPPORTUNITIES FUND; *U.S. Public*, pg. 708
EATON VANCE TAX-MANAGED GLOBAL DIVERSIFIED EQUITY INCOME FUND; *U.S. Public*, pg. 709
EATON VANCE WATEROAK ADVISORS—See Morgan Stanley; *U.S. Public*, pg. 1472
EAT & TRAVEL WEEKLY COMPANY LIMITED—See Next Digital Limited; *Int'l*, pg. 5248
EAT WALK CO., LTD—See create restaurants holdings inc.; *Int'l*, pg. 1832
EATWARE INC.; *Int'l*, pg. 2282
EAT WELL INC.; *U.S. Private*, pg. 1323
EAT WELL INVESTMENT GROUP INC.; *Int'l*, pg. 2277
EATZI'S TEXAS BEVERAGE CORP.; *U.S. Private*, pg. 1323
EAU CLAIRE PRESS COMPANY—See Adams Publishing Group, LLC; *U.S. Private*, pg. 75
EAU ET FEU—See Carrier Global Corporation; *U.S. Public*, pg. 441
EAU ET FORCE—See Veolia Environnement S.A.; *Int'l*, pg. 8155
EAUKER MINERALS CORP.; *U.S. Private*, pg. 1323
EAU MINERALE NATURELLE DE PLANCOET SOURCE SASSAY S.A.S.—See Societe des Eaux Minerales d'Ogeu SAS; *Int'l*, pg. 7038
EAU TECHNOLOGIES, INC.; *U.S. Public*, pg. 709
E AUTOMOTIVE INC.; *Int'l*, pg. 2245
EAUX DE MARSEILLE—See Veolia Environnement S.A.; *Int'l*, pg. 8155
EAUX MINERALES DE RIBEAUVILLE SA—See S.A. Spadel N.V.; *Int'l*, pg. 6448
EAUX VIVES WATER INC.—See Morgan Stanley; *U.S. Public*, pg. 1472
EAV BETEILIGUNGS-GMBH—See E.ON SE; *Int'l*, pg. 2256
EAVES BURLINGTON, LLC—See AvalonBay Communities, Inc.; *U.S. Public*, pg. 240
EAVES CREEKSIDE SOLAR, LLC—See AvalonBay Communities, Inc.; *U.S. Public*, pg. 240
EAVES HUNTINGTON BEACH—See AvalonBay Communities, Inc.; *U.S. Public*, pg. 240
EAVS SA; *Int'l*, pg. 2282
EBAA IRON, INC.; *U.S. Private*, pg. 1323
EBA COMMUNICATIONS - BEIJING—See Omnicom Group Inc.; *U.S. Public*, pg. 1578

EBA COMMUNICATIONS LTD—See Omnicom Group Inc.; *U.S. Public*, pg. 1578
EBA COMMUNICATIONS - SHANGHAI—See Omnicom Group Inc.; *U.S. Public*, pg. 1578
EBAGS, LLC—See Samsonite International S.A.; *Int'l*, pg. 6510
EBAJITSU CO., LTD.—See Ebara Jitsugyo Co., Ltd.; *Int'l*, pg. 2284
E-BAND COMMUNICATIONS, LLC—See Moseley Associates, Inc.; *U.S. Private*, pg. 2793
EBANG INTERNATIONAL HOLDINGS INC.; *Int'l*, pg. 2282
EBANNER SOLUTION SDN. BHD.—See eprint Group Limited; *Int'l*, pg. 2465
EBARA AGENCY CO., LTD.—See Ebara Corporation; *Int'l*, pg. 2282
EBARA-BENGUET, INC.—See Benguet Corporation; *Int'l*, pg. 974
EBARA-BENGUET, INC.—See Ebara Corporation; *Int'l*, pg. 2283
EBARA BOMBAS AMERICA DO SUL LTDA.—See Ebara Corporation; *Int'l*, pg. 2282
EBARA BOMBAS COLOMBIA S.A.S.—See Ebara Corporation; *Int'l*, pg. 2283
EBARA-BYRON JACKSON, LTD.—See Ebara Corporation; *Int'l*, pg. 2283
EBARA CORPORATION; *Int'l*, pg. 2282
EBARA DENSAN (KUNSHAN) MFG. CO., LTD.—See Ebara Corporation; *Int'l*, pg. 2283
EBARA DENSAN LTD.—See Ebara Corporation; *Int'l*, pg. 2282
EBARA DENSAN (QINGDAO) TECHNOLOGY CO., LTD.—See Ebara Corporation; *Int'l*, pg. 2283
EBARA-DENSAN TAIWAN MANUFACTURING CO., LTD.—See Ebara Corporation; *Int'l*, pg. 2283
EBARA EARNEST CO., LTD.—See Ebara Corporation; *Int'l*, pg. 2282
EBARA-ELLIOTT SERVICE (TAIWAN) CO., LTD.—See Ebara Corporation; *Int'l*, pg. 2284
EBARA ENGINEERING SINGAPORE PTE. LTD.—See Ebara Corporation; *Int'l*, pg. 2283
EBARA ENVIRONMENTAL PLANT CO., LTD.—See Ebara Corporation; *Int'l*, pg. 2283
EBARA ESPANA BOMBAS S.A.—See Ebara Corporation; *Int'l*, pg. 2283
EBARA FAN & BLOWER CO., LTD.—See Ebara Corporation; *Int'l*, pg. 2283
EBARA FIELD TECH. CORPORATION—See Ebara Corporation; *Int'l*, pg. 2283
EBARA FLUID MACHINERY KOREA CO., LTD.—See Ebara Corporation; *Int'l*, pg. 2283
EBARA FOODS INDUSTRY, INC. - GUNMA FACTORY—See Ebara Foods Industry, Inc.; *Int'l*, pg. 2284
EBARA FOODS INDUSTRY, INC.; *Int'l*, pg. 2284
EBARA FOODS INDUSTRY, INC. - TOCHIGI FACTORY—See Ebara Foods Industry, Inc.; *Int'l*, pg. 2284
EBARA FOODS INDUSTRY, INC. - TSUYAMA FACTORY—See Ebara Foods Industry, Inc.; *Int'l*, pg. 2284
EBARA FOODS (SHANGHAI) CO., LTD.—See Ebara Foods Industry, Inc.; *Int'l*, pg. 2284
EBARA GREAT PUMPS CO., LTD.—See Ebara Corporation; *Int'l*, pg. 2283
EBARA HAI DUONG COMPANY LTD.—See Ebara Corporation; *Int'l*, pg. 2283
EBARA HAMADA BLOWER CO., LTD.—See Ebara Corporation; *Int'l*, pg. 2282
EBARA INDUSTRIAS MECANICAS E COMERCIO LTDA.—See Ebara Corporation; *Int'l*, pg. 2283
EBARA INTERNATIONAL CORP.—See Ebara Corporation; *Int'l*, pg. 2283
EBARA JITSUGYO CO., LTD.; *Int'l*, pg. 2284
EBARA JITSUGYO POWER CO., LTD.—See Ebara Jitsugyo Co., Ltd.; *Int'l*, pg. 2284
EBARA MACHINERY CHINA CO., LTD.—See Ebara Corporation; *Int'l*, pg. 2283
EBARA MACHINERY INDIA PRIVATE LIMITED—See Ebara Corporation; *Int'l*, pg. 2283
EBARA MACHINERY ZIBO CO., LTD.—See Ebara Corporation; *Int'l*, pg. 2283
EBARA MATERIAL CO., LTD.—See Ebara Corporation; *Int'l*, pg. 2283
EBARA MEISTER CO., LTD.—See Ebara Corporation; *Int'l*, pg. 2283
EBARA POMPY POLSKA SP. Z O.O.—See Ebara Corporation; *Int'l*, pg. 2283
EBARA PRECISION MACHINERY EUROPE GMBH—See Ebara Corporation; *Int'l*, pg. 2283
EBARA PRECISION MACHINERY KOREA INC—See Ebara Corporation; *Int'l*, pg. 2283
EBARA PRECISION MACHINERY TAIWAN INCORPORATED—See Ebara Corporation; *Int'l*, pg. 2283
EBARA PUMP INDUSTRIES P.J.S.—See Ebara Corporation; *Int'l*, pg. 2283
EBARA PUMPS AUSTRALIA PTY. LTD.—See Ebara Corporation; *Int'l*, pg. 2283

EBARA PUMPS EUROPE S.P.A.—See Ebara Corporation; *Int'l*, pg. 2283
EBARA PUMPS MALAYSIA SDN. BHD.—See Ebara Corporation; *Int'l*, pg. 2283
EBARA PUMPS MEXICO, S.A. DE C.V.—See Ebara Corporation; *Int'l*, pg. 2283
EBARA PUMPS MIDDLE EAST FZE—See Ebara Corporation; *Int'l*, pg. 2283
EBARA PUMPS PHILIPPINES, INC.—See Ebara Corporation; *Int'l*, pg. 2283
EBARA PUMPS RUS LIMITED LIABILITY COMPANY—See Ebara Corporation; *Int'l*, pg. 2282
EBARA PUMPS SAUDI ARABIA LLC—See Ebara Corporation; *Int'l*, pg. 2283
EBARA PUMPS SOUTH AFRICA (PTY) LTD.—See Ebara Corporation; *Int'l*, pg. 2283
EBARA QINGDAO CO. LTD.—See Ebara Corporation; *Int'l*, pg. 2283
EBARA REFRIGERATION EQUIPMENT & SYSTEMS (CHINA) CO., LTD.—See Ebara Corporation; *Int'l*, pg. 2283
EBARA REFRIGERATION EQUIPMENT & SYSTEMS CO., LTD.—See Ebara Corporation; *Int'l*, pg. 2283
EBARA SHOHNAN SPORTS CENTER INC.—See Ebara Corporation; *Int'l*, pg. 2282
EBARA TECHNOLOGIES INC.—See Ebara Corporation; *Int'l*, pg. 2283
EBARA (THAILAND) LIMITED—See Ebara Corporation; *Int'l*, pg. 2282
EBARA THERMAL SYSTEMS (THAILAND) CO., LTD.—See Ebara Corporation; *Int'l*, pg. 2283
EBARA VIETNAM PUMP COMPANY LIMITED—See Ebara Corporation; *Int'l*, pg. 2283
EBARA YOSHIKURA HYDRO-TECH CO., LTD.—See Ebara Corporation; *Int'l*, pg. 2283
EBASE CO., LTD.; *Int'l*, pg. 2284
EBA S.L.—See Grupo Empresarial San Jose, S.A.; *Int'l*, pg. 3128
EBATES, INC.—See Rakuten Group, Inc.; *Int'l*, pg. 6195
EBAY CANADA LIMITED—See eBay Inc.; *U.S. Public*, pg. 709
EBAY CORPORATE SERVICES GMBH—See eBay Inc.; *U.S. Public*, pg. 709
EBAY GMARKET CO., LTD.—See eBay Inc.; *U.S. Public*, pg. 709
EBAY GMBH—See eBay Inc.; *U.S. Public*, pg. 709
EBAY INC.; *U.S. Public*, pg. 709
EBAY INSURANCE SERVICES, INC.—See eBay Inc.; *U.S. Public*, pg. 709
EBAY KOREA CO., LTD.—See Shinsegae Inc.; *Int'l*, pg. 6848
EBAY MARKETING (THAILAND) COMPANY LIMITED—See eBay Inc.; *U.S. Public*, pg. 709
EBAY MOTORS INDIA PRIVATE LIMITED—See eBay Inc.; *U.S. Public*, pg. 709
EBAY SINGAPORE SERVICES PRIVATE LIMITED—See eBay Inc.; *U.S. Public*, pg. 709
EBAY SPAIN INTERNATIONAL, S.L.—See eBay Inc.; *U.S. Public*, pg. 709
EBAY TAIWAN COMPANY LTD.—See eBay Inc.; *U.S. Public*, pg. 709
EB BAKERY OF BEIJING CO., LTD.—See Grupo Bimbo, S.A.B. de C.V.; *Int'l*, pg. 3122
EB BAKERY OF SHENYANG CO., LTD.—See Grupo Bimbo, S.A.B. de C.V.; *Int'l*, pg. 3122
EBB AUTO CO. INC.; *U.S. Private*, pg. 1323
E.B. BERGER INCORPORATED; *U.S. Private*, pg. 1304
EBBGATE INVESTMENTS LIMITED—See Barclays PLC; *Int'l*, pg. 862
EBB HOTELBETRIEBS GMBH—See Erste Group Bank AG; *Int'l*, pg. 2498
THE E.B. BRADLEY CO., INC.; *U.S. Public*, pg. 4024
EBBTIDE CORPORATION; *U.S. Private*, pg. 1323
EBBY HALLIDAY REAL ESTATE, INC.—See Berkshire Hathaway Inc.; *U.S. Public*, pg. 306
EBC HR & PAYROLL SOLUTIONS, INC.; *U.S. Private*, pg. 1323
EBC INC.; *Int'l*, pg. 2284
EBC INC.; *U.S. Private*, pg. 1323
EBCO GENERAL CONTRACTORS; *U.S. Private*, pg. 1324
EBCO INC.; *U.S. Private*, pg. 1324
EBCO INDUSTRIES LTD.; *Int'l*, pg. 2284
E.B. CREASY & COMPANY PLC; *Int'l*, pg. 2251
EBD GMBH—See Informa plc; *Int'l*, pg. 3691
EBD GROUP GMBH—See Informa plc; *Int'l*, pg. 3691
E-B DISPLAY CO., INC.; *U.S. Private*, pg. 1302
EBECS BUSINESS SOLUTIONS (IRELAND) LIMITED—See DXC Technology Company; *U.S. Public*, pg. 697
EBECS COMPANY LIMITED—See DXC Technology Company; *U.S. Public*, pg. 697
EBECS LIMITED—See Blackstone Inc.; *U.S. Public*, pg. 356
E. BEFFA S.A.—See Akzo Nobel N.V.; *Int'l*, pg. 274
EBEHAKO GMBH—See VINCI S.A.; *Int'l*, pg. 8236
EB ELEKTRO AS—See Addtech AB; *Int'l*, pg. 132
THE EBELING GROUP, INC.; *U.S. Private*, pg. 4025

EBEL, SIGNORELLI & WELKE LLC; *U.S. Private*, pg. 1324
EBEL WATCHES S.A.—See Movado Group, Inc.; *U.S. Public*, pg. 1479
EBENCHMARKERS LTD.—See Informa plc; *Int'l*, pg. 3692
EBEN DESIGN, INC.; *U.S. Private*, pg. 1324
EBENEZER MEDICAL OUTREACH, INC.; *U.S. Private*, pg. 1324
EBENEZER RAILCAR SERVICES—See ERS Industries Inc.; *U.S. Private*, pg. 1423
E-BEN GMBH & CO. KG—See HEAG Sudhessische Energie AG; *Int'l*, pg. 3302
EBENISTERIE ST-URBAIN LTEE; *Int'l*, pg. 2284
EBENSBURG POWER CO.—See Babcock & Wilcox Enterprises, Inc.; *U.S. Public*, pg. 263
EBERHARD HARDWARE MANUFACTURING LTD.—See The Eastern Company; *U.S. Public*, pg. 2069
EBERHARD MANUFACTURING DIVISION—See The Eastern Company; *U.S. Public*, pg. 2069
EBERHARD POHNER UNTERNEHMEN FUR HOCH- UND TIEFBAU GMBH—See STRABAG SE; *Int'l*, pg. 7230
EBERLE CONTROLS GMBH—See Schneider Electric SE; *Int'l*, pg. 6631
EBERLE DESIGN, INC.—See Vance Street Capital LLC; *U.S. Private*, pg. 4342
EBERLESTOCK USA LLC; *U.S. Private*, pg. 1324
EBERLE VIVIAN, INC.—See Liberty Mutual Holding Company Inc.; *U.S. Private*, pg. 2445
EBERSPACHER MIKUNI CLIMATE CONTROL SYSTEMS CORPORATION—See Mikuni Corporation; *Int'l*, pg. 4893
EBERTLANG DISTRIBUTION GMBH—See Harald Quandt Holding GmbH; *Int'l*, pg. 3270
EBERT NORMAN BRADY ARCHITECTS PA—See LS3P Associates Ltd.; *U.S. Private*, pg. 2508
EBEST SPECIAL PURPOSE ACQUISITION 3 COMPANY; *Int'l*, pg. 2285
EBET GAMING SYSTEMS PTY LIMITED—See Tabcorp Holdings Limited; *Int'l*, pg. 7401
EBET, INC.—See Tabcorp Holdings Limited; *Int'l*, pg. 7401
EBET, INC.; *U.S. Public*, pg. 709
EBET SYSTEMS PTY LIMITED—See Tabcorp Holdings Limited; *Int'l*, pg. 7401
EBEWE PHARMA GES.MBH NFG. KG—See Sandoz Group AG; *Int'l*, pg. 6526
EB GIDA SANAYI VE TICARET LTD. SIRKETI—See Grupo Bimbo, S.A.B. de C.V.; *Int'l*, pg. 3122
E&B GIFTWARE LLC—See Cortec Group Management Services, LLC; *U.S. Private*, pg. 1060
EB HOLDINGS CORP.—See WEX, Inc.; *U.S. Public*, pg. 2364
E.B. HORN CO.; *U.S. Private*, pg. 1304
EBI ASIA PACIFIC PTE LTD—See Eagle Industry Co., Ltd.; *Int'l*, pg. 2265
EBI FOODS LIMITED—See Kerry Group plc; *Int'l*, pg. 4138
EBI INTERNATIONAL, INC.—See Everything Blockchain, Inc.; *U.S. Public*, pg. 802
EBI, LLC—See Zimmer Biomet Holdings, Inc.; *U.S. Public*, pg. 2406
EBI MEDICAL SYSTEMS, LLC—See Zimmer Biomet Holdings, Inc.; *U.S. Public*, pg. 2406
EBIOX LIMITED; *Int'l*, pg. 2285
EBI PATIENT CARE, INC.—See Zimmer Biomet Holdings, Inc.; *U.S. Public*, pg. 2406
EBIQUITY ASSOCIATES LIMITED—See Brookfield Corporation; *Int'l*, pg. 1179
EBIQUITY ASSOCIATES LIMITED—See Elliott Management Corporation; *U.S. Private*, pg. 1372
EBIQUITY GERMANY GMBH—See Ebiquity plc; *Int'l*, pg. 2285
EBIQUITY ITALIA S.R.L.—See Ebiquity plc; *Int'l*, pg. 2285
EBIQUITY ITALY MEDIA ADVISOR S.R.L.—See Ebiquity plc; *Int'l*, pg. 2285
EBIQUITY MARSH LIMITED—See Ebiquity plc; *Int'l*, pg. 2285
EBIQUITY PLC; *Int'l*, pg. 2285
EBIQUITY PTE. LIMITED—See Ebiquity plc; *Int'l*, pg. 2285
EBIQUITY RUSSIA OOO—See Ebiquity plc; *Int'l*, pg. 2285
EBIQUITY SAS—See Ebiquity plc; *Int'l*, pg. 2285
EBI SA—See Ecobank Transnational Incorporated; *Int'l*, pg. 2293
E BISMEDIA S.P.A.—See Swisscom AG; *Int'l*, pg. 7373
EBIT INFORMATION SYSTEMS; *U.S. Private*, pg. 1324
EBITO CHEMIEBETEILIGUNGEN AG—See Clariant AG; *Int'l*, pg. 1648
EBIX AUSTRALIA PTY., LTD.—See Ebix Inc.; *U.S. Public*, pg. 710
EBIX AUSTRALIA (VIC) PTY. LTD.—See Ebix Inc.; *U.S. Public*, pg. 710
EBIX BPO DIVISION—See Ebix Inc.; *U.S. Public*, pg. 710
EBIXCASH WORLD MONEY LTD.—See Ebix Inc.; *U.S. Public*, pg. 710
EBIX CONSULTING—See Ebix Inc.; *U.S. Public*, pg. 710
EBIX EUROPE LIMITED—See Ebix Inc.; *U.S. Public*, pg. 710
EBIXEXCHANGE—See Ebix Inc.; *U.S. Public*, pg. 710
EBIX INC.; *U.S. Public*, pg. 709

COMPANY NAME INDEX

EBIX LATIN AMERICA TECHNOLOGIA E CONSULTORIA LTDA—See Ebix Inc.; *U.S. Public*, pg. 710
EBIXLIFE INC.—See Ebix Inc.; *U.S. Public*, pg. 710
EBIX NEW ZEALAND—See Ebix Inc.; *U.S. Public*, pg. 710
EBIX SINGAPORE PTE LTD—See Ebix Inc.; *U.S. Public*, pg. 710
EBIZAUTOS; *U.S. Private*, pg. 1324
EBJ FOODS CORP.; *U.S. Private*, pg. 1324
EBLENS LP—See Prospect Hill Growth Partners, L.P.; *U.S. Private*, pg. 3288
EBLOCK, INC.—See E Automotive Inc.; *Int'l*, pg. 2245
EBL PARTNERS LLC; *U.S. Private*, pg. 1324
E.B. MAWSON AND SONS PTY. LTD.—See CRH plc; *Int'l*, pg. 1842
EB MAWSON & SONS PTY LTD; *Int'l*, pg. 2282
EBMS; *U.S. Private*, pg. 1324
E&B NATURAL RESOURCES; *U.S. Private*, pg. 1301
EBN B.V.; *Int'l*, pg. 2285
EBNER GMBH & CO. KG; *Int'l*, pg. 2285
EBNOTHER ELEKTRO AG—See Burkhalter Holding AG; *Int'l*, pg. 1224
EBN SINA MEDICAL W.L.L.—See Aamal Company Q.S.C.; *Int'l*, pg. 36
EBOHR LUXURIES INTERNATIONAL CO., LIMITED—See Citychamp Watch & Jewellery Group Limited; *Int'l*, pg. 1629
E. BOINEAU & COMPANY; *U.S. Private*, pg. 1303
E. BON BUILDING MATERIALS COMPANY LIMITED—See E. Bon Holdings Ltd; *Int'l*, pg. 2250
E. BON HOLDINGS LTD; *Int'l*, pg. 2249
EBONITE INTERNATIONAL INCORPORATED; *U.S. Private*, pg. 1324
EBOOKERS LIMITED—See Expedia Group, Inc.; *U.S. Public*, pg. 810
EBOOK INITIATIVE JAPAN CO., LTD.; *Int'l*, pg. 2285
E-BOOK SYSTEMS EUROPE—See E-Book Systems Pte. Ltd.; *Int'l*, pg. 2247
E-BOOK SYSTEMS INC.—See E-Book Systems Pte. Ltd.; *Int'l*, pg. 2247
E-BOOK SYSTEMS K. K.—See E-Book Systems Pte. Ltd.; *Int'l*, pg. 2247
E-BOOK SYSTEMS PTE. LTD.; *Int'l*, pg. 2247
EBOOK TECHNOLOGIES, INC.—See Alphabet Inc.; *U.S. Public*, pg. 84
EBOS GROUP LIMITED; *Int'l*, pg. 2285
EBOS GROUP PTY LIMITED—See EBOS Group Limited; *Int'l*, pg. 2285
EBOS HEALTH & SCIENCE PTY LIMITED—See EBOS Group Limited; *Int'l*, pg. 2285
E. BOWMAN & SONS LTD; *Int'l*, pg. 2250
EBP AB—See AB Volvo; *Int'l*, pg. 42
EB PHARMA, LLC—See Eiger BioPharmaceuticals, Inc.; *U.S. Public*, pg. 721
EBP MONEY PTY. LTD.—See FSA Group Limited; *Int'l*, pg. 2798
EBP SUPPLY SOLUTIONS; *U.S. Private*, pg. 1324
EBQUICKSTART, LLC; *U.S. Private*, pg. 1324
EBRAHIM K. KANOO COMPANY B.S.C - AUTO PAINT DIVISION—See Ebrahim K. Kanoo Company B.S.C.; *Int'l*, pg. 2286
EBRAHIM K. KANOO COMPANY B.S.C. - KANOO AUTOMOTIVE EQUIPMENT DIVISION—See Ebrahim K. Kanoo Company B.S.C.; *Int'l*, pg. 2286
EBRAHIM K. KANOO COMPANY B.S.C - KANOO IT DIVISION—See Ebrahim K. Kanoo Company B.S.C.; *Int'l*, pg. 2286
EBRAHIM K. KANOO COMPANY B.S.C - KANOO VEHICLE LEASING DIVISION—See Ebrahim K. Kanoo Company B.S.C.; *Int'l*, pg. 2286
EBRAHIM K. KANOO COMPANY B.S.C - OILS & LUBRICANTS DIVISION—See Ebrahim K. Kanoo Company B.S.C.; *Int'l*, pg. 2286
EBRAHIM K. KANOO COMPANY B.S.C - SECURITY 1 DIVISION—See Ebrahim K. Kanoo Company B.S.C.; *Int'l*, pg. 2286
EBRAHIM K. KANOO COMPANY B.S.C.; *Int'l*, pg. 2286
EBRAHIM K. KANOO COMPANY B.S.C. - TYRE DIVISION—See Ebrahim K. Kanoo Company B.S.C.; *Int'l*, pg. 2286
EBRAINS, INC.; *Int'l*, pg. 2286
E. BRAUDE (LONDON) LTD.—See NIBE Industrier AB; *Int'l*, pg. 5260
EB-RESTAURANTSBETRIEBE GES.M.B.H.—See Erste Group Bank AG; *Int'l*, pg. 2498
EBREVIA, INC.—See Donnelley Financial Solutions, Inc.; *U.S. Public*, pg. 677
E.BRICKS VENTURES; *Int'l*, pg. 2251
EBRIDGE BUSINESS SOLUTIONS LLC; *U.S. Private*, pg. 1324
E-BRIDGE BV—See Randstad N.V.; *Int'l*, pg. 6201
EBRIDGE, INC.; *U.S. Private*, pg. 1324
EBRO FOODS S.A.; *Int'l*, pg. 2286
EBROFROST DENMARK A/S—See Ebro Foods S.A.; *Int'l*, pg. 2286
EBROFROST DENMARK A/S—See Ebro Foods S.A.; *Int'l*, pg. 2286
EBROFROST GERMANY GMBH—See Ebro Foods S.A.; *Int'l*, pg. 2286

EBROFROST UK LTD.—See Ebro Foods S.A.; *Int'l*, pg. 2286
EBRO INDIA PRIVATE LIMITED—See Ebro Foods S.A.; *Int'l*, pg. 2286
EBROKER GROUP LTD.; *Int'l*, pg. 2287
EBROKER SYSTEMS LIMITED—See eBroker Group Ltd.; *Int'l*, pg. 2287
EBRO TILDA PRIVATE LIMITED—See Ebro Foods S.A.; *Int'l*, pg. 2286
EBR SYSTEMS, INC.; *U.S. Private*, pg. 1324
EBRYIT INC.; *U.S. Private*, pg. 1324
EBS ASSOCIATES, INC.—See OUT OF THE BOXTECHNOLOGY; *U.S. Private*, pg. 3051
EBSCO CANADA LTD.—See EBSCO Industries, Inc.; *U.S. Private*, pg. 1324
EBSCO DEVELOPMENT COMPANY, INC—See EBSCO Industries, Inc.; *U.S. Private*, pg. 1324
EBSCO INCOME PROPERTIES LLC—See EBSCO Industries, Inc.; *U.S. Private*, pg. 1324
EBSCO INDUSTRIES, INC. - EBSCO CREATIVE CONCEPTS DIVISION—See EBSCO Industries, Inc.; *U.S. Private*, pg. 1325
EBSCO INDUSTRIES, INC. - EBSCO MEDIA DIVISION—See EBSCO Industries, Inc.; *U.S. Private*, pg. 1325
EBSCO INDUSTRIES, INC. - EBSCO RECEPTION ROOM SUBSCRIPTION SERVICES DIVISION—See EBSCO Industries, Inc.; *U.S. Private*, pg. 1325
EBSCO INDUSTRIES, INC. - EBSCO RESEARCH DIVISION—See EBSCO Industries, Inc.; *U.S. Private*, pg. 1325
EBSCO INDUSTRIES, INC. - KNIGHT & HALE DIVISION—See EBSCO Industries, Inc.; *U.S. Private*, pg. 1325
EBSCO INDUSTRIES, INC. - NSC INTERNATIONAL DIVISION—See EBSCO Industries, Inc.; *U.S. Private*, pg. 1325
EBSCO INDUSTRIES, INC. - PRADCO FISHING DIVISION—See EBSCO Industries, Inc.; *U.S. Private*, pg. 1325
EBSCO INDUSTRIES, INC. - PUBLISHER PROMOTION AND FULFILLMENT DIVISION—See EBSCO Industries, Inc.; *U.S. Private*, pg. 1325
EBSCO INDUSTRIES, INC.; *U.S. Private*, pg. 1324
EBSCO INDUSTRIES, INC. - STEWART SIGNS DIVISION—See EBSCO Industries, Inc.; *U.S. Private*, pg. 1325
EBSCO INDUSTRIES, INC. - SUBSCRIPTION SERVICES DIVISION—See EBSCO Industries, Inc.; *U.S. Private*, pg. 1325
EBSCO INDUSTRIES, INC. - VULCAN INDUSTRIES DIVISION—See EBSCO Industries, Inc.; *U.S. Private*, pg. 1325
EBSCO INDUSTRIES WESTWOOD—See EBSCO Industries, Inc.; *U.S. Private*, pg. 1325
EBSCO INFORMATION SERVICES—See EBSCO Industries, Inc.; *U.S. Private*, pg. 1325
EBSCO INTERNATIONAL INC.—See EBSCO Industries, Inc.; *U.S. Private*, pg. 1325
EBSCO SIGNS & DISPLAYS—See EBSCO Industries, Inc.; *U.S. Private*, pg. 1325
EBSCO TELESERVICES—See EBSCO Industries, Inc.; *U.S. Private*, pg. 1325
EBS D.A.C.—See AIB Group plc; *Int'l*, pg. 228
EBS DEALING RESOURCES INC—See CME Group, Inc.; *U.S. Public*, pg. 516
EBS DEALING RESOURCES INTERNATIONAL LIMITED—See CME Group, Inc.; *U.S. Public*, pg. 516
EBS DEALING RESOURCES JAPAN LIMITED—See CME Group, Inc.; *U.S. Public*, pg. 516
EBS/FORAN INSURANCE & ADVISORY SERVICES, INC.—See Aon plc; *Int'l*, pg. 496
EBS HEALTHCARE, INC.—See Rothschild & Co SCA; *Int'l*, pg. 6403
EBS MORTGAGE FINANCE—See AIB Group plc; *Int'l*, pg. 228
EBSO, INC.; *U.S. Private*, pg. 1325
EBSO, INC.—See EBSO, Inc.; *U.S. Private*, pg. 1325
EBS PENSIONEER TRUSTEES LIMITED—See Embark Group Limited; *Int'l*, pg. 2374
EBS PENSION LIMITED—See Embark Group Limited; *Int'l*, pg. 2374
EBS-RAY PUMPS PTY. LTD.—See Dover Corporation; *U.S. Public*, pg. 681
EBS-RMSCO, INC.—See The Lifetime Healthcare Companies; *U.S. Public*, pg. 4070
EBS SELF-ADMINISTERED PERSONAL PENSION PLAN TRUSTEES LIMITED—See Embark Group Limited; *Int'l*, pg. 2374
EBS SERVICE CO LIMITED—See CME Group, Inc.; *U.S. Public*, pg. 516
EB SUB, INC.—See EPIRUS Biopharmaceuticals, Inc.; *U.S. Private*, pg. 1413
EBS WOHNUNGSGESELLSCHAFT MBH—See Vienna Insurance Group AG Wiener Versicherung Gruppe; *Int'l*, pg. 8194
EBTEC CORPORATION—See Aquasium Technology Limited; *Int'l*, pg. 528
EB TECH CO., LTD.; *Int'l*, pg. 2282

E.B. TECNICA MEXICANA, S.A. DE C.V.—See Zurn Elkay Water Solutions Corporation; *U.S. Public*, pg. 2412
EBT ENGINEERING PTE. LTD.—See PEC Ltd.; *Int'l*, pg. 5778
EBTH, INC.; *U.S. Private*, pg. 1326
E B TRANS SA; *Int'l*, pg. 2246
EBT TECHNOLOGY, INC.—See Koninklijke Philips N.V.; *Int'l*, pg. 4267
EBTTIKAR TECHNOLOGY COMPANY—See National Technology Group; *Int'l*, pg. 5164
E-BUILDER, INC.—See Trimble, Inc.; *U.S. Public*, pg. 2193
EBULB, INC.; *U.S. Private*, pg. 1326
EBULLION, INC.; *Int'l*, pg. 2287
EBUREAU LLC—See TransUnion; *U.S. Public*, pg. 2185
EBUSCO HOLDING N.V.; *Int'l*, pg. 2287
E-BUSINESS INTERNATIONAL INC (E-BI); *U.S. Private*, pg. 1302
EBUSINESS STRATEGIS, LLC; *U.S. Private*, pg. 1326
EBU UMFORMTECHNIK GMBH—See Xuzhou Metalforming Machine Group Co., Ltd; *Int'l*, pg. 8541
EBUYS, INC.—See Schottenstein Stores Corporation; *U.S. Private*, pg. 3569
EBV-BETEILIGUNGS GMBH—See Erste Group Bank AG; *Int'l*, pg. 2498
EBV ELECTROLINK (PTY) LTD—See Avnet, Inc.; *U.S. Public*, pg. 251
EBV ELEKTRONIK APS—See Avnet, Inc.; *U.S. Public*, pg. 252
EBV ELEKTRONIK D.O.O.—See Avnet, Inc.; *U.S. Public*, pg. 252
EBV ELEKTRONIK, DRUZBA ZA POSREDOVANJE D.O.O.—See Avnet, Inc.; *U.S. Public*, pg. 252
EBV ELEKTRONIK EOOD—See Avnet, Inc.; *U.S. Public*, pg. 252
EBV ELEKTRONIK FRANCE SAS—See Avnet, Inc.; *U.S. Public*, pg. 252
EBV ELEKTRONIK GMBH & CO. KG—See Avnet, Inc.; *U.S. Public*, pg. 251
EBV ELEKTRONIK GMBH & CO. KG—See Avnet, Inc.; *U.S. Public*, pg. 252
EBV-ELEKTRONIK GMBH—See Avnet, Inc.; *U.S. Public*, pg. 252
EBV ELEKTRONIK ISRAEL (2008) LTD.—See Avnet, Inc.; *U.S. Public*, pg. 252
EBV ELEKTRONIK KFT—See Avnet, Inc.; *U.S. Public*, pg. 251
EBV ELEKTRONIK LTD.—See Avnet, Inc.; *U.S. Public*, pg. 251
EBV ELEKTRONIK M—See Avnet, Inc.; *U.S. Public*, pg. 251
EBV ELEKTRONIK OU—See Avnet, Inc.; *U.S. Public*, pg. 252
EBV ELEKTRONIK SAS—See Avnet, Inc.; *U.S. Public*, pg. 252
EBV ELEKTRONIK SPAIN S.L.—See Avnet, Inc.; *U.S. Public*, pg. 252
EBV ELEKTRONIK SPOL. S.R.O.—See Avnet, Inc.; *U.S. Public*, pg. 251
EBV ELEKTRONIK SP. Z O.O.—See Avnet, Inc.; *U.S. Public*, pg. 252
EBV ELEKTRONIK SP. Z O.O.—See Avnet, Inc.; *U.S. Public*, pg. 252
EBV ELEKTRONIK S.R.L.—See Avnet, Inc.; *U.S. Public*, pg. 251
EBV ELEKTRONIK S.R.L.—See Avnet, Inc.; *U.S. Public*, pg. 252
EBV ELEKTRONIK S.R.O.—See Avnet, Inc.; *U.S. Public*, pg. 252
EBV ELEKTRONIK TICARET LTD.—See Avnet, Inc.; *U.S. Public*, pg. 251
EBV ELEKTRONIK TOV—See Avnet, Inc.; *U.S. Public*, pg. 252
EBV ELEKTRONIK TOV—See Avnet, Inc.; *U.S. Public*, pg. 252
EBV ELEKTRONIK, UNIPESSOAL LDA.—See Avnet, Inc.; *U.S. Public*, pg. 252
EBV EXPLOSIVES ENVIRONMENTAL COMPANY—See EQT AB; *Int'l*, pg. 2467
EBV - LEASING GESELLSCHAFT M.B.H. & CO. KG—See Erste Group Bank AG; *Int'l*, pg. 2498
E.B. WALL + ASSOCIATES; *U.S. Private*, pg. 1304
EBW ELECTRONICS, INC.; *U.S. Private*, pg. 1326
EBX GROUP LTD.; *Int'l*, pg. 2287
EBY-BROWN COMPANY, LLC—See Performance Food Group Company; *U.S. Public*, pg. 1674
EBY-BROWN CO.—See Performance Food Group Company; *U.S. Public*, pg. 1674
EBY-BROWN CO.—See Performance Food Group Company; *U.S. Public*, pg. 1674
EBY-BROWN CO.—See Performance Food Group Company; *U.S. Public*, pg. 1674
EBY-BROWN CO.—See Performance Food Group Company; *U.S. Public*, pg. 1674
EBY-BROWN MID-ATLANTIC—See Performance Food Group Company; *U.S. Public*, pg. 1674
EBY BROWN OHIO—See Performance Food Group Company; *U.S. Public*, pg. 1674
EBY CORPORATION; *U.S. Private*, pg. 1326

EBY CORPORATION

EBY GEWERBEOBJEKT GMBH—See E.ON SE; *Int'l*, pg. 2256
EBYLINE, INC.—See IZEA Worldwide, Inc.; *U.S. Public*, pg. 1179
EBY PORT 3 GMBH—See E.ON SE; *Int'l*, pg. 2256
EBY PORT 5 GMBH—See E.ON SE; *Int'l*, pg. 2256
EC2E—See Industrielle De Controle Et D Equipement; *Int'l*, pg. 3675
ECAD SOLUTIONS CO., LTD.—See NITTO KOGYO CORPORATION; *Int'l*, pg. 5387
E. CALLSEN & CO. A.S.—See BERICAP GmbH & Co. KG; *Int'l*, pg. 981
ECA MARCELLUS TRUST I—See Energy Corporation of America; *U.S. Private*, pg. 1394
ECA MARKETING, INC.—See Aon plc; *Int'l*, pg. 496
ECA MEDICAL INSTRUMENTS—See LongueVue Capital, LLC; *U.S. Private*, pg. 2493
EC AMERICA, INC.—See Arrow Electronics, Inc.; *U.S. Public*, pg. 200
ECAMP GMBH—See Cox & Kings Limited; *Int'l*, pg. 1822
ECAMPUSCASH INC.; *U.S. Private*, pg. 1326
E+CANCERCARE—See Kohlberg & Company, LLC; *U.S. Private*, pg. 2339
E-CAN OILFIELD SERVICES L.P.—See Mullen Group Ltd.; *Int'l*, pg. 5080
ECAPITAL ADVISORS, LLC; *U.S. Private*, pg. 1326
ECAPS AB—See GomSpace Group AB; *Int'l*, pg. 3037
E-CARBON FAR EAST LTD.—See Westinghouse Air Brake Technologies Corporation; *U.S. Public*, pg. 2357
ECARD S.A.; *Int'l*, pg. 2287
ECARGO HOLDINGS LIMITED; *Int'l*, pg. 2287
ECARX HOLDINGS, INC.; *Int'l*, pg. 2287
ECASA, S.A.—See The Bank of Nova Scotia; *Int'l*, pg. 7618
ECA S.A.—See Groupe Gorge S.A.; *Int'l*, pg. 3103
E CASH FINTECH LIMITED—See Minerva Group Holding Limited; *Int'l*, pg. 4908
ECA SP Z.O.O.—See Willis Towers Watson Public Limited Company; *Int'l*, pg. 8414
E.C. AVIATION SERVICES, INC.—See Gentex Corporation; *U.S. Public*, pg. 931
E.C. BARTON & CO. DESIGN CENTER—See E.C. Barton & Company; *U.S. Private*, pg. 1304
E.C. BARTON & COMPANY; *U.S. Private*, pg. 1304
ECB BANCORP, INC.; *U.S. Public*, pg. 710
ECB BROKERAGE—See E.C. Barton & Company; *U.S. Private*, pg. 1304
ECB CORP.; *U.S. Private*, pg. 1326
ECBEING CORP.—See Softcreate Holdings Corp.; *Int'l*, pg. 7054
E.C. BIRCH PROPRIETARY LIMITED; *Int'l*, pg. 2251
E.C.B N.V.—See Allcargo Logistics Limited; *Int'l*, pg. 333
ECCA HOLDINGS PTY LTD—See Groupe Bruxelles Lambert SA; *Int'l*, pg. 3100
ECC CAPITAL CORPORATION; *U.S. Public*, pg. 710
ECC DO BRASIL CIA DE SEGUROS—See Embraer S.A.; *Int'l*, pg. 2375
ECCELSA AVIATION S.R.L.—See Meridiana S.p.A.; *Int'l*, pg. 4835
EC CHEMICAL TECHNOLOGIES (S) PTE. LTD.—See Sulzer Ltd.; *Int'l*, pg. 7256
ECCHO RIGHTS AB—See CJ Corporation; *Int'l*, pg. 1633
ECC INSURANCE BROKERS, INC.—See Brown & Brown, Inc.; *U.S. Public*, pg. 400
ECC LEASING COMPANY LTD.—See Embraer S.A.; *Int'l*, pg. 2375
ECCLESIASTICAL INSURANCE OFFICE PLC; *Int'l*, pg. 2288
ECCO AUTO WORLD CORPORATION; *Int'l*, pg. 2288
ECCO BALTIC SIA—See Ecco Sko A/S; *Int'l*, pg. 2288
ECCO DOMANI USA INC.; *U.S. Private*, pg. 1326
ECCO EMEA SALES SE—See Ecco Sko A/S; *Int'l*, pg. 2288
ECCO EQUIPMENT CORPORATION; *U.S. Private*, pg. 1326
ECCO III ENTERPRISES, INC.; *U.S. Private*, pg. 1326
ECCO LEATHER B.V.—See Ecco Sko A/S; *Int'l*, pg. 2288
ECCOLET (PORTUGAL) FABRICA DE SAPATOS, LDA.—See Ecco Sko A/S; *Int'l*, pg. 2288
EC COMPANY INC.; *U.S. Private*, pg. 1326
EC CONCIERGE CORPORATION—See Canon Inc.; *Int'l*, pg. 1293
ECCO SAFETY GROUP; *U.S. Private*, pg. 1326
ECCO SERVICIOS DE PERSONAL SA DE CV—See Adecco Group AG; *Int'l*, pg. 141
ECCO SHOE PRODUCTION PTE. LTD.—See Ecco Sko A/S; *Int'l*, pg. 2288
ECCO SHOES CANADA, INC.—See Ecco Sko A/S; *Int'l*, pg. 2288
ECCO SHOES (NZ) LIMITED—See Ecco Sko A/S; *Int'l*, pg. 2288
ECCO SHOES PACIFIC PTY. LTD.—See Ecco Sko A/S; *Int'l*, pg. 2288
ECCO SKO A/S; *Int'l*, pg. 2288
ECCO TANNERY HOLDING (SINGAPORE) PTE. LTD.—See Ecco Sko A/S; *Int'l*, pg. 2288
ECCO (THAILAND) CO., LTD.—See Ecco Sko A/S; *Int'l*, pg. 2288
E.C. COTTLE INC.; *U.S. Private*, pg. 1304

ECCO USA INC.—See Ecco Sko A/S; *Int'l*, pg. 2288
ECCO (XIAMEN) CO. LTD.—See Ecco Sko A/S; *Int'l*, pg. 2288
EC CREDIT CONTROL (AUST) PTY LIMITED—See Turners Automotive Group Limited; *Int'l*, pg. 7979
EC CREDIT CONTROL (NZ) LIMITED—See Turners Automotive Group Limited; *Int'l*, pg. 7979
ECC WEST TENNESSEE MC, LLC—See Anderson Regional Health System; *U.S. Private*, pg. 277
ECDC ENVIRONMENTAL L.C.; *U.S. Private*, pg. 1326
EC DRIVER & ASSOCIATES, INC.—See AECOM; *U.S. Public*, pg. 51
ECE CO., LTD.—See Ebara Corporation; *Int'l*, pg. 2282
ECE FLATMEDIA GMBH—See Stroer SE & Co. KGaA; *Int'l*, pg. 7242
ECE I, LLC—See EPR Properties; *U.S. Public*, pg. 784
ECE INDUSTRIES LIMITED - ELEVATOR DIVISION—See ECE Industries Limited; *Int'l*, pg. 2288
ECE INDUSTRIES LIMITED - METER DIVISION—See ECE Industries Limited; *Int'l*, pg. 2288
ECE INDUSTRIES LIMITED; *Int'l*, pg. 2288
ECE ITALIA S.R.L.—See ECE Projektmanagement GmbH & Co KG; *Int'l*, pg. 2288
ECE-LAMDA HELLAS S.A.—See Lamda Development SA; *Int'l*, pg. 4401
ECENARRO, S.COOP.—See Mondragon Corporation; *Int'l*, pg. 5028
E&C ENGINEERING CORPORATION—See CTCI Corporation; *Int'l*, pg. 1870
E-CENTIVES, INC.—See Invenda Corporation; *U.S. Private*, pg. 2131
ECE PROJEKTMANAGEMENT AUSTRIA GMBH—See ECE Projektmanagement GmbH & Co KG; *Int'l*, pg. 2288
ECE PROJEKTMANAGEMENT BUDAPEST KFT.—See ECE Projektmanagement GmbH & Co KG; *Int'l*, pg. 2288
ECE PROJEKTMANAGEMENT GMBH & CO KG; *Int'l*, pg. 2288
ECE PROJEKTMANAGEMENT POLSKA SP. Z.O.O.—See ECE Projektmanagement GmbH & Co KG; *Int'l*, pg. 2288
ECE PROJEKTMANAGEMENT PRAHA S.R.O.—See ECE Projektmanagement GmbH & Co KG; *Int'l*, pg. 2288
ECE PROJEKTMANAGEMENT SLOVAKIA S.R.O.—See ECE Projektmanagement GmbH & Co KG; *Int'l*, pg. 2288
ECE REAL ESTATE PARTNERS G.M.B.H.—See ECE Projektmanagement GmbH & Co KG; *Int'l*, pg. 2288
ECE REAL ESTATE PARTNERS S.A.R.L.—See ECE Projektmanagement GmbH & Co KG; *Int'l*, pg. 2288
E.C. ERNST, INC.—See The Philadelphia Bourse, Inc.; *U.S. Private*, pg. 4094
E.C. ERNST SOUTH EAST—See The Philadelphia Bourse, Inc.; *U.S. Private*, pg. 4094
ECE RUSSLAND OOO—See ECE Projektmanagement GmbH & Co KG; *Int'l*, pg. 2288
ECESSA CORPORATION—See TheIPGuys.Net LLC; *U.S. Private*, pg. 4141
ECE TURKIYE PROJE YONETIMI A.S.—See ECE Projektmanagement GmbH & Co KG; *Int'l*, pg. 2288
EC EUROPA IMMOBILIEN FONDS NR. 3 GMBH & CO. KG—See Deutsche Bank Aktiengesellschaft; *Int'l*, pg. 2061
EC FANS & DRIVES, LLC—See Epec Engineered Technologies; *U.S. Private*, pg. 1412
ECF GROUP B.V.—See Chepri Holding B.V.; *Int'l*, pg. 1471
E.CF SAS—See Groupe BPCE; *Int'l*, pg. 3095
ECG MANAGEMENT CONSULTANTS, INC.—See Gryphon Investors, LLC; *U.S. Private*, pg. 1798
E.C. GRIFFITH CO.; *U.S. Private*, pg. 1304
EC GROCER PTE. LTD.—See Cab Cakaran Corporation Berhad; *Int'l*, pg. 1245
ECHANNELING PLC; *Int'l*, pg. 2289
ECHANNELLING PLC—See Sri Lanka Telecom PLC; *Int'l*, pg. 7150
EC HEALTHCARE; *Int'l*, pg. 2287
E-CHECK HOLDINGS, INC.; *U.S. Private*, pg. 1302
ECHELON ASIA PACIFIC LTD.—See Renesas Electronics Corporation; *Int'l*, pg. 6275
ECHELON AUSTRALIA PTY LIMITED—See Marsh & McLennan Companies, Inc.; *U.S. Public*, pg. 1374
ECHELON BIOSCIENCES INC—See Avista Capital Partners, L.P.; *U.S. Private*, pg. 409
ECHELON CORPORATION—See Renesas Electronics Corporation; *Int'l*, pg. 6275
ECHELON EUROPE LTD.—See Renesas Electronics Corporation; *Int'l*, pg. 6275
ECHELON FRANCE, S.A.R.L.—See Renesas Electronics Corporation; *Int'l*, pg. 6275
ECHELON GENERAL INSURANCE COMPANY AUTOMOBILE DIVISION—See CAA Club Group; *Int'l*, pg. 1245
ECHELON GENERAL INSURANCE COMPANY NICHE PRODUCTS DIVISION—See CAA Club Group; *Int'l*, pg. 1245
ECHELON GENERAL INSURANCE COMPANY—See CAA Club Group; *Int'l*, pg. 1245

CORPORATE AFFILIATIONS

ECHELON JAPAN, K.K.—See Renesas Electronics Corporation; *Int'l*, pg. 6275
ECHELON REAL ESTATE SERVICES LLC; *U.S. Private*, pg. 1326
ECHEVERRIA IZQUIERDO S.A.; *Int'l*, pg. 2289
ECHEZABAL & ASSOCIATES, INC.—See Peak Rock Capital LLC; *U.S. Private*, pg. 3124
ECHMI S.A.; *Int'l*, pg. 2289
ECHO 24, INC.; *U.S. Private*, pg. 1327
ECHO AUTOMOTIVE, INC.; *U.S. Private*, pg. 1327
ECHO BAY MINERALS COMPANY—See Kinross Gold Corporation; *Int'l*, pg. 4182
ECHO CENTER CO., LTD.—See Nippon Steel Corporation; *Int'l*, pg. 5337
ECHO DATA GROUP INC.—See Fort Point Capital, LLC; *U.S. Private*, pg. 1574
THE ECHO DESIGN GROUP, INC.; *U.S. Private*, pg. 4025
ECHO ELECTRONICS COMPANY LIMITED—See Echo International Holdings Group Limited; *Int'l*, pg. 2289
ECHO ENERGY PLC; *Int'l*, pg. 2289
ECHO ENGINEERING & PRODUCTION SUPPLIES, INC.; *U.S. Private*, pg. 1327
ECHO FARMS GOLF & COUNTRY CLUB, INC.—See Matrix Development Group Inc.; *U.S. Private*, pg. 2612
ECHO GIKEN CO., LTD.—See Kurabo Industries Ltd.; *Int'l*, pg. 4335
ECHO GLOBAL LOGISTICS, INC.—See The Jordan Company, L.P.; *U.S. Private*, pg. 4060
ECHO GROUP, INC.; *U.S. Private*, pg. 1327
ECHO HEALTH, INC; *U.S. Private*, pg. 1327
ECHO INCORPORATED—See Yamabiko Corporation; *Int'l*, pg. 8547
ECHO INDUSTRY CORPORATION—See Yamabiko Corporation; *Int'l*, pg. 8547
ECHOING HILLS VILLAGE, INC.; *U.S. Private*, pg. 1327
ECHO INTERNATIONAL CO.; *U.S. Private*, pg. 1327
ECHO INTERNATIONAL HOLDINGS GROUP LIMITED; *Int'l*, pg. 2289
ECHO INVESTMENT S.A.; *Int'l*, pg. 2289
ECHOIQ LIMITED; *Int'l*, pg. 2289
ECHO LAKE FARM PRODUCE COMPANY INC.—See Elkin Co.; *U.S. Private*, pg. 1363
ECHOLINE S.A.S.—See Karnov Group AB; *Int'l*, pg. 4084
ECHO, LLC; *U.S. Private*, pg. 1327
ECHO LOCUM TENENS, INC.—See UnitedHealth Group Incorporated; *U.S. Public*, pg. 2240
ECHOLS OIL COMPANY; *U.S. Private*, pg. 1327
ECHOMAIL, INC.; *U.S. Private*, pg. 1327
ECHO MAINTENANCE, LLC; *U.S. Private*, pg. 1327
ECHO MANAGED SERVICES LTD.—See Arjun Infrastructure Partners Limited; *Int'l*, pg. 568
ECHO MARKETING CO., LTD.; *Int'l*, pg. 2289
ECHONOVA S.R.L.—See TCS TurControlSysteme AG; *Int'l*, pg. 7485
ECHOPARK AL, LLC—See Sonic Automotive, Inc.; *U.S. Public*, pg. 1902
ECHOPARK AUTOMOTIVE, INC.—See Sonic Automotive, Inc.; *U.S. Public*, pg. 1902
ECHOPARK GA, LLC—See Sonic Automotive, Inc.; *U.S. Public*, pg. 1902
ECHO PUBLISHING & PRINTING—See Shivers Trading & Operating Company; *U.S. Private*, pg. 3638
ECHO PUBLISHING & PRINTING—See Shivers Trading & Operating Company; *U.S. Private*, pg. 3638
ECHO ROCK VENTURES INC.; *U.S. Private*, pg. 1327
ECHO—See HealthStream, Inc.; *U.S. Public*, pg. 1017
ECHOSPHERE L.L.C.—See EchoStar Corporation; *U.S. Public*, pg. 711
ECHOSTAR BROADCASTING CORPORATION—See EchoStar Corporation; *U.S. Public*, pg. 711
ECHOSTAR CORPORATION; *U.S. Public*, pg. 711
ECHOSTAR DATA NETWORKS CORPORATION—See EchoStar Corporation; *U.S. Public*, pg. 711
ECHOSTAR INTERNATIONAL CORPORATION—See EchoStar Corporation; *U.S. Public*, pg. 711
ECHOSTAR MOBILE LIMITED—See EchoStar Corporation; *U.S. Public*, pg. 711
ECHOSTAR SATELLITE OPERATING CORPORATION—See EchoStar Corporation; *U.S. Public*, pg. 711
ECHOSTAR SATELLITE SERVICES LLC—See EchoStar Corporation; *U.S. Public*, pg. 711
ECHOSTAR TECHNOLOGIES LLC—See EchoStar Corporation; *U.S. Public*, pg. 711
ECHOSTAR UKRAINE, LLC—See EchoStar Corporation; *U.S. Public*, pg. 711
ECHO SYSTEMS—See Echo Group, Inc.; *U.S. Private*, pg. 1327
ECHO THERAPEUTICS, INC.; *U.S. Public*, pg. 710
ECHO TORRE LAZUR—See The Interpublic Group of Companies, Inc.; *U.S. Public*, pg. 2102
ECHO TRADING CO., LTD.; *Int'l*, pg. 2289
ECHO VALLEY MEATS, INC.; *U.S. Private*, pg. 1327
ECICS LIMITED—See IFS Capital Limited; *Int'l*, pg. 3599
ECI ENVIROCOATINGS (CANADA) INC.—See ECL EnviroClean Ventures Ltd.; *Int'l*, pg. 2291
E-CIE VIE S.A.—See Assicurazioni Generali S.p.A.; *Int'l*, pg. 2289
ECI PARTNERS LLP; *Int'l*, pg. 2289

ECI SCREEN PRINT INC.—See J.N. White Associates, Inc.; *U.S. Private*, pg. 2169
ECI SOFTWARE SOLUTIONS, INC.—See Apax Partners LLP; *Int'l*, pg. 503
ECI—See Electronic Commerce Inc.; *U.S. Private*, pg. 1355
ECIT ACCOUNT A/S—See TowerBrook Capital Partners, L.P.; *U.S. Private*, pg. 4194
ECIT ADVISORY AB—See TowerBrook Capital Partners, L.P.; *U.S. Private*, pg. 4194
ECI TAIWAN CO., LTD.—See Expeditors International of Washington, Inc.; *U.S. Public*, pg. 810
ECIT AKTIVAPLUSS AS—See TowerBrook Capital Partners, L.P.; *U.S. Private*, pg. 4195
ECIT AROS A/S—See TowerBrook Capital Partners, L.P.; *U.S. Private*, pg. 4194
ECIT AS—See TowerBrook Capital Partners, L.P.; *U.S. Private*, pg. 4194
ECIT AUTOGEAR AS—See TowerBrook Capital Partners, L.P.; *U.S. Private*, pg. 4194
ECIT CAPSTONE AS—See TowerBrook Capital Partners, L.P.; *U.S. Private*, pg. 4194
ECIT CONSULTA AS—See TowerBrook Capital Partners, L.P.; *U.S. Private*, pg. 4194
ECI TECHNOLOGY HOLDINGS LIMITED; *Int'l*, pg. 2289
ECI TECHNOLOGY INTERNATIONAL, INC.—See KLA Corporation; *U.S. Public*, pg. 1267
ECI TELECOM AMERICAS INC.—See Ribbon Communications Inc.; *U.S. Public*, pg. 1797
ECI TELECOM GMBH—See Ribbon Communications Inc.; *U.S. Public*, pg. 1797
ECI TELECOM IBERICA S.A.—See Ribbon Communications Inc.; *U.S. Public*, pg. 1797
ECI TELECOM LTD. - CHINA—See Ribbon Communications Inc.; *U.S. Public*, pg. 1797
ECI TELECOM LTD.—See Ribbon Communications Inc.; *U.S. Public*, pg. 1796
ECI TELECOM (PHILIPPINES), INC.—See Ribbon Communications Inc.; *U.S. Public*, pg. 1797
ECI TELECOM (SINGAPORE)—See Ribbon Communications Inc.; *U.S. Public*, pg. 1797
ECI TELECOM—See Ribbon Communications Inc.; *U.S. Public*, pg. 1797
ECI TELECOM UKRAINE LLC—See Ribbon Communications Inc.; *U.S. Public*, pg. 1797
ECIT LILLEHAMMER AS—See TowerBrook Capital Partners, L.P.; *U.S. Private*, pg. 4194
ECIT MARKETING AS—See TowerBrook Capital Partners, L.P.; *U.S. Private*, pg. 4194
ECIT NORMANN & OYGARDEN AS—See TowerBrook Capital Partners, L.P.; *U.S. Private*, pg. 4194
ECIT PERITUS AS—See TowerBrook Capital Partners, L.P.; *U.S. Private*, pg. 4194
ECIT RAD & REGNSKAP AS—See TowerBrook Capital Partners, L.P.; *U.S. Private*, pg. 4195
ECIT SERVICES AB—See TowerBrook Capital Partners, L.P.; *U.S. Private*, pg. 4195
ECIT SOLUTIONS A/S—See TowerBrook Capital Partners, L.P.; *U.S. Private*, pg. 4195
ECIT SOLUTIONS DI AS—See TowerBrook Capital Partners, L.P.; *U.S. Private*, pg. 4195
ECIT SOLUTIONS ITS AS—See TowerBrook Capital Partners, L.P.; *U.S. Private*, pg. 4195
ECIT SOLUTIONS ONE AS—See TowerBrook Capital Partners, L.P.; *U.S. Private*, pg. 4195
ECIT SOLUTIONS PRO AB—See TowerBrook Capital Partners, L.P.; *U.S. Private*, pg. 4195
ECIT STORD AS—See TowerBrook Capital Partners, L.P.; *U.S. Private*, pg. 4195
ECIT TRONDHEIM AS—See TowerBrook Capital Partners, L.P.; *U.S. Private*, pg. 4195
ECIT VEIBY AKONTO AS—See TowerBrook Capital Partners, L.P.; *U.S. Private*, pg. 4195
ECIT WLCOM AS—See TowerBrook Capital Partners, L.P.; *U.S. Private*, pg. 4195
E-CITY BIOSCOPE ENTERTAINMENT PVT LTD—See Essel Corporate Resources Pvt. Ltd.; *Int'l*, pg. 2509
E-CITY PROPERTY MANAGEMENT & SERVICES PVT. LTD.—See Essel Corporate Resources Pvt. Ltd.; *Int'l*, pg. 2509
ECKA GRANULES AUSTRALIA PTY. LTD.—See Palladium Equity Partners, LLC; *U.S. Private*, pg. 3078
ECKA GRANULES GERMANY GMBH - ESSEN BEARING TECHNOLOGIES—See Palladium Equity Partners, LLC; *U.S. Private*, pg. 3078
ECKA GRANULES GERMANY GMBH—See Palladium Equity Partners, LLC; *U.S. Private*, pg. 3078
ECKA GRANULES INTL. TRADING (SHANGHAI) CO. LTD.—See Palladium Equity Partners, LLC; *U.S. Private*, pg. 3078
ECKA GRANULES ITALIA SRL—See Palladium Equity Partners, LLC; *U.S. Private*, pg. 3078
ECKA GRANULES JAPAN CO. LTD.—See Palladium Equity Partners, LLC; *U.S. Private*, pg. 3078
ECKA GRANULES METAL POWDERS LTD.—See Palladium Equity Partners, LLC; *U.S. Private*, pg. 3078
ECKA GRANULES OF AMERICA L.P.—See Palladium Equity Partners, LLC; *U.S. Private*, pg. 3078

ECKARDS HOME IMPROVEMENTS; *U.S. Private*, pg. 1327
ECKARDT ELECTRIC COMPANY, INC.; *U.S. Private*, pg. 1327
ECKART AMERICA CORPORATION—See SKion GmbH; *Int'l*, pg. 6988
ECKART ASIA LIMITED—See SKion GmbH; *Int'l*, pg. 6989
ECKART ASIA LIMITED—See SKion GmbH; *Int'l*, pg. 6989
ECKART ASIA LTD.—See SKion GmbH; *Int'l*, pg. 6988
ECKART BENELUX B.V.—See SKion GmbH; *Int'l*, pg. 6989
ECKART COLD STORAGE CO. INC.; *U.S. Private*, pg. 1327
ECKART DE MEXICO INDUSTRIES, S.R.L. DE C.V.—See SKion GmbH; *Int'l*, pg. 6989
ECKART & FINARD, INC.—See Bertram Capital Management, LLC; *U.S. Private*, pg. 540
ECKART FRANCE S.A.—See SKion GmbH; *Int'l*, pg. 6989
ECKART GMBH & CO. KG—See SKion GmbH; *Int'l*, pg. 6988
ECKART ITALIA S.R.L.—See SKion GmbH; *Int'l*, pg. 6989
ECKART LLC; *U.S. Private*, pg. 1327
ECKART PIGMENTS KY—See SKion GmbH; *Int'l*, pg. 6989
ECKART SHANGHAI CO. LTD.—See SKion GmbH; *Int'l*, pg. 6988
ECKART SWITZERLAND SA—See SKion GmbH; *Int'l*, pg. 6989
ECKART UK LTD.—See SKion GmbH; *Int'l*, pg. 6989
ECKART ZHUHAI CO. LTD.—See SKion GmbH; *Int'l*, pg. 6989
ECKEL INDUSTRIES INC.; *U.S. Private*, pg. 1327
ECKELMANN AG; *Int'l*, pg. 2289
ECKELMANN AUTOMATION TECHNOLOGY (SHANGHAI) CO., LTD.—See Eckelmann AG; *Int'l*, pg. 2289
ECKELMANN INDUSTRIAL AUTOMATION TECHNOLOGIES (BEIJING) CO., LTD.—See Eckelmann AG; *Int'l*, pg. 2290
ECKELMANN S.R.O.—See Eckelmann AG; *Int'l*, pg. 2290
ECKELT GLAS GMBH—See Compagnie de Saint-Gobain SA; *Int'l*, pg. 1723
ECKENROD FORD LINCOLN MERCURY OF CULLMAN, INC.; *U.S. Private*, pg. 1327
ECK ENTERPRISES LLC; *U.S. Private*, pg. 1327
ECKER CENTER FOR BEHAVIORAL HEALTH; *U.S. Private*, pg. 1327
ECKER ENTERPRISES INC.; *U.S. Private*, pg. 1328
ECKERT COLD STORAGE COMPANY; *U.S. Private*, pg. 1328
ECKERT SEAMANS CHERIN & MELLOTT, LLC; *U.S. Private*, pg. 1328
ECKERT'S ORCHARDS; *U.S. Private*, pg. 1328
ECKERT & ZIEGLER ANALYTICS, LNC.—See Eckert & Ziegler Strahlen- und Medizintechnik AG; *Int'l*, pg. 2290
ECKERT & ZIEGLER BEBIG DO BRASIL LTDA.—See Eckert & Ziegler Strahlen- und Medizintechnik AG; *Int'l*, pg. 2290
ECKERT & ZIEGLER BEBIG GMBH—See Eckert & Ziegler Strahlen- und Medizintechnik AG; *Int'l*, pg. 2290
ECKERT & ZIEGLER BEBIG LTD.—See Eckert & Ziegler Strahlen- und Medizintechnik AG; *Int'l*, pg. 2290
ECKERT & ZIEGLER BEBIG SARL—See Eckert & Ziegler Strahlen- und Medizintechnik AG; *Int'l*, pg. 2290
ECKERT & ZIEGLER BEBIG S.A.—See Eckert & Ziegler Strahlen- und Medizintechnik AG; *Int'l*, pg. 2290
ECKERT & ZIEGLER CESIO S.R.O.—See Eckert & Ziegler Strahlen- und Medizintechnik AG; *Int'l*, pg. 2290
ECKERT & ZIEGLER CHEMOTRADE GMBH—See Eckert & Ziegler Strahlen- und Medizintechnik AG; *Int'l*, pg. 2290
ECKERT & ZIEGLER EURO-PET BERLIN GMBH—See Eckert & Ziegler Strahlen- und Medizintechnik AG; *Int'l*, pg. 2290
ECKERT & ZIEGLER EUROTOPE GMBH—See Eckert & Ziegler Strahlen- und Medizintechnik AG; *Int'l*, pg. 2290
ECKERT & ZIEGLER F-CON DEUTSCHLAND GMBH—See Eckert & Ziegler Strahlen- und Medizintechnik AG; *Int'l*, pg. 2290
ECKERT & ZIEGLER F-CON EUROPE GMBH—See Eckert & Ziegler Strahlen- und Medizintechnik AG; *Int'l*, pg. 2290
ECKERT & ZIEGLER IBERIA S.L.—See Eckert & Ziegler Strahlen- und Medizintechnik AG; *Int'l*, pg. 2290
ECKERT & ZIEGLER ISOTOPE PRODUCTS, GMBH—See Eckert & Ziegler Strahlen- und Medizintechnik AG; *Int'l*, pg. 2290
ECKERT & ZIEGLER ISOTOPE PRODUCTS, INC.—See Eckert & Ziegler Strahlen- und Medizintechnik AG; *Int'l*, pg. 2290
ECKERT & ZIEGLER ITALIA S.R.L.—See Eckert & Ziegler Strahlen- und Medizintechnik AG; *Int'l*, pg. 2290
ECKERT & ZIEGLER NUCLITEC GMBH—See Eckert & Ziegler Strahlen- und Medizintechnik AG; *Int'l*, pg. 2290
ECKERT & ZIEGLER STRAHLEN- UND MEDIZINTECHNIK AG; *Int'l*, pg. 2290
ECKERT & ZIEGLER UMWELTDIENSTE GMBH—See Eckert & Ziegler Strahlen- und Medizintechnik AG; *Int'l*, pg. 2290
ECKER WINDOW CORPORATION; *U.S. Private*, pg. 1328

ECKES AG; *Int'l*, pg. 2290
ECKES-GRANINI AUSTRIA GMBH—See Eckes AG; *Int'l*, pg. 2290
ECKES-GRANINI DEUTSCHLAND GMBH—See Eckes AG; *Int'l*, pg. 2290
ECKES-GRANINI FINLAND OY AB—See Eckes AG; *Int'l*, pg. 2291
ECKES-GRANINI FRANCE SNC—See Eckes AG; *Int'l*, pg. 2290
ECKES-GRANINI GROUP GMBH—See Eckes AG; *Int'l*, pg. 2290
ECKES-GRANINI IBERICA S.A.U.—See Eckes AG; *Int'l*, pg. 2291
ECKES-GRANINI (SUISSE) S.A.—See Eckes AG; *Int'l*, pg. 2290
ECKHARD GARBE GMBH—See Heidelberg Materials AG; *Int'l*, pg. 3310
ECKHART & COMPANY, INC.—See BindTech LLC; *U.S. Private*, pg. 560
ECK INDUSTRIES, INC.; *U.S. Private*, pg. 1327
ECKLER ENGINEERING INC—See H.I.G. Capital, LLC; *U.S. Private*, pg. 1827
ECKLEY ASPHALT—See Haines & Kibblehouse Inc.; *U.S. Private*, pg. 1841
ECKMAN CONSTRUCTION COMPANY, INC.; *U.S. Private*, pg. 1328
EC KNOXVILLE REALTY, LLC—See Ventas, Inc.; *U.S. Public*, pg. 2278
ECKOH PLC; *Int'l*, pg. 2291
ECKOH UK LIMITED—See Eckoh plc; *Int'l*, pg. 2291
ECK SUPPLY COMPANY—See Sonepar S.A.; *Int'l*, pg. 7093
E-CLASS EDUCATION SYSTEM LTD—See Sundaram Multi Pap Limited; *Int'l*, pg. 7312
ECLAT ENTERPRISE LTD.—See Eclat Textile Co., Ltd.; *Int'l*, pg. 2291
ECLAT FABRICS (VIETNAM) CO., LTD.—See Eclat Textile Co., Ltd.; *Int'l*, pg. 2291
ECLAT FOREVER MACHINERY CO., LTD.; *Int'l*, pg. 2291
ECLAT HEALTH SOLUTIONS INC.—See Gulf Capital PJSC; *Int'l*, pg. 3180
ECLAT PHARMACEUTICALS, LLC—See AVADEL PHARMACEUTICALS PLC; *Int'l*, pg. 734
ECLAT TEXTILE (CAMBODIA) CO., LTD.—See Eclat Textile Co., Ltd.; *Int'l*, pg. 2291
ECLAT TEXTILE CO., LTD.; *Int'l*, pg. 2291
ECLAT TEXTILE (COMBODIA) CO., LTD.—See Eclat Textile Co., Ltd.; *Int'l*, pg. 2291
ECLAT TEXTILE (VIETNAM) CO., LTD.—See Eclat Textile Co., Ltd.; *Int'l*, pg. 2291
ECLC OF NEW JERSEY; *U.S. Private*, pg. 1328
ECL DEVELOPMENTS LIMITED—See Empire Company Limited; *Int'l*, pg. 2387
ECL ENVIROCLEAN VENTURES LTD.; *Int'l*, pg. 2291
ECLERX LIMITED—See eClerx Services Ltd; *Int'l*, pg. 2291
ECLERX SERVICES LTD; *Int'l*, pg. 2291
ECL FINANCE LIMITED—See Edelweiss Financial Services Ltd.; *Int'l*, pg. 2306
ECLINICALWORKS, LLC; *U.S. Private*, pg. 1328
ECLINIX HOLDINGS LIMITED—See Aidigong Maternal & Child Health Limited; *Int'l*, pg. 231
ECLI PRODUCTS, LLC—See Quaker Chemical Corporation; *U.S. Public*, pg. 1745
ECLIPSE ADVANTAGE, LLC—See LSCG Management, Inc.; *U.S. Private*, pg. 2508
ECLIPSE AEROSPACE, INC.; *U.S. Private*, pg. 1328
ECLIPSE CASH SYSTEMS, LLC—See Further Global Capital Management, L.P.; *U.S. Private*, pg. 1625
ECLIPSE ENERGY INC.—See Gateway Energy Company, LLC; *U.S. Private*, pg. 1650
ECLIPSE ENERGY UK PLC—See Vattenfall AB; *Int'l*, pg. 8136
ECLIPSE ENGINEERING, P.C.—See Cushing Terrell; *U.S. Private*, pg. 1127
ECLIPSE FOUNDATION GROUP, INC.—See Orbital Infrastructure Group, Inc.; *U.S. Public*, pg. 1615
ECLIPSE GOLD MINING CORPORATION—See Northern Vertex Mining Corp.; *Int'l*, pg. 5445
ECLIPSE INC.—See Honeywell International Inc.; *U.S. Public*, pg. 1047
ECLIPSE IOR SERVICES, LLC—See Flotek Industries, Inc.; *U.S. Public*, pg. 853
ECLIPSE MARKETING GROUP, INC.—See Radiall S.A.; *Int'l*, pg. 6174
ECLIPSE METALS LTD.; *Int'l*, pg. 2291
ECLIPSE MOBILE ELECTRONICS—See Denso Corporation; *Int'l*, pg. 2030
ECLIPSE RESIDENTIAL MORTGAGE INVESTMENT CORPORATION; *Int'l*, pg. 2291
ECLIPSE RESOURCES - OHIO, LLC—See Expand Energy Corporation; *U.S. Public*, pg. 808
ECLIPSE SOFTWARE SYSTEMS LLC—See Bestpass, Inc.; *U.S. Private*, pg. 544
ECLIPSE SP LLC—See Danir Resources AB; *Int'l*, pg. 1963
ECLIPSE TRANSLATIONS LIMITED—See RWS Holdings plc; *Int'l*, pg. 6436

ECLIPTEK, LLC—See ILSI America LLC; *U.S. Private*, pg. 2043
EC LOGISTIK GMBH—See OBB-Holding AG; *Int'l*, pg. 5509
E.CL S.A.—See ENGIE SA; *Int'l*, pg. 2434
ECLUSIVE LLC—See Nautic Partners, LLC; *U.S. Private*, pg. 2274
ECL WESTERN HOLDINGS LIMITED—See Empire Company Limited; *Int'l*, pg. 2387
ECM ASSET MANAGEMENT LIMITED—See Wells Fargo & Company; *U.S. Public*, pg. 2343
ECMC FOUNDATION; *U.S. Private*, pg. 1328
ECMD, INC.; *U.S. Private*, pg. 1328
ECM ENERGY SERVICES, INC.; *U.S. Private*, pg. 1328
ECM EQUITY CAPITAL MANAGEMENT GMBH; *Int'l*, pg. 2291
ECM EUROPE S.R.L.—See Teledata Marine Solutions Ltd; *Int'l*, pg. 7530
ECM GREENTECH SASU—See ECM Technologies SAS; *Int'l*, pg. 2292
ECM INDUSTRIES, LLC—See nVent Electric plc; *Int'l*, pg. 5498
ECM INGENIEUR-UNTERNEHMEN FUR ENERGIE- UND UMWELTTECHNIK GMBH—See Alpiq Holding AG; *Int'l*, pg. 372
ECM ING.UNTERNEHMEN FUR ENERGIE-UND UMWELTTECHNIK GMBH—See Alpiq Holding AG; *Int'l*, pg. 372
EC-MISSION VERDE, LLC—See Equity Residential; *U.S. Public*, pg. 791
ECMK LIMITED—See Insight Venture Management, LLC; *U.S. Private*, pg. 2089
ECMK LIMITED—See Stone Point Capital LLC; *U.S. Private*, pg. 3822
ECM LIMITED—See Sonepar S.A.; *Int'l*, pg. 7093
ECM MARITIME SERVICES, LLC—See Teledata Marine Solutions Ltd; *Int'l*, pg. 7530
ECMM SERVICES INC.—See Hon Hai Precision Industry Co., Ltd.; *Int'l*, pg. 3456
ECMOHO LIMITED; *Int'l*, pg. 2292
E C MOORE COMPANY; *U.S. Private*, pg. 1300
ECMP (PTY) LTD—See Stefanutti Stocks Holdings Limited; *Int'l*, pg. 7192
ECM PRINTING—See Adams Publishing Group, LLC; *U.S. Private*, pg. 75
ECM PUBLISHERS, INC.—See Adams Publishing Group, LLC; *U.S. Private*, pg. 75
ECM REAL ESTATE INVESTMENTS A.G.; *Int'l*, pg. 2292
ECMS, INC.—See L.N. Curtis & Sons; *U.S. Private*, pg. 2366
ECM-SUN GROUP, LLC—See Adams Publishing Group, LLC; *U.S. Private*, pg. 75
ECM TECHNOLOGIES SAS; *Int'l*, pg. 2292
ECM TRANSPORTATION, INC.; *U.S. Private*, pg. 1328
ECM (USA), INC.—See ECM Technologies SAS; *Int'l*, pg. 2292
ECN AUTOMATION EL SALVADOR S.A. DE C.V.—See Endress+Hauser (International) Holding AG; *Int'l*, pg. 2406
ECN CAPITAL CORP.; *Int'l*, pg. 2292
ECNET (HONG KONG) LIMITED—See Blackstone Inc.; *U.S. Public*, pg. 357
ECNET KABUSHIKI KAISHA—See Blackstone Inc.; *U.S. Public*, pg. 357
ECNET LIMITED—See Blackstone Inc.; *U.S. Public*, pg. 357
ECNET (M) SDN. BHD.—See Blackstone Inc.; *U.S. Public*, pg. 357
ECNET (SHANGHAI) CO. LTD.—See Blackstone Inc.; *U.S. Public*, pg. 357
ECNET SYSTEMS (THAILAND) COMPANY LIMITED—See Blackstone Inc.; *U.S. Public*, pg. 357
ECNG ENERGY LIMITED PARTNERSHIP—See AltaGas Ltd.; *Int'l*, pg. 384
ECO360, LLC—See RiskOn International, Inc.; *U.S. Public*, pg. 1799
ECOACT S.A.S.—See Atos SE; *Int'l*, pg. 692
ECOAGRI ASIA LTD.—See AlFarm Ltd.; *Int'l*, pg. 231
ECO ALLIANCE CO., LTD.—See Seino Holdings Co., Ltd.; *Int'l*, pg. 6690
ECOANALYSTS, INC.; *U.S. Private*, pg. 1329
ECO ANALYTICS AG—See Indutrade AB; *Int'l*, pg. 3678
ECO ANIMAL HEALTH GROUP PLC; *Int'l*, pg. 2292
ECO ANIMAL HEALTH LIMITED—See ECO Animal Health Group plc; *Int'l*, pg. 2292
ECOARK, INC.—See RiskOn International, Inc.; *U.S. Public*, pg. 1799
ECOASSET SOLUTIONS, LLC—See Lykes Brothers Inc.; *U.S. Private*, pg. 2519
ECOAST SALES SOLUTIONS, LTD.; *U.S. Private*, pg. 1329
ECO (ATLANTIC) OIL & GAS LTD.; *Int'l*, pg. 2292
ECOATM, LLC—See Apollo Global Management, Inc.; *U.S. Public*, pg. 150
ECO-BAGS PRODUCTS, INC.; *U.S. Private*, pg. 1328
ECOBALT SOLUTIONS INC.—See Jervois Global Limited; *Int'l*, pg. 3932
ECOBANK BENIN LIMITED—See Ecobank Transnational Incorporated; *Int'l*, pg. 2293

ECOBANK BURKINA FASO S.A.—See Ecobank Transnational Incorporated; *Int'l*, pg. 2293
ECOBANK BURUNDI S.A.—See Ecobank Transnational Incorporated; *Int'l*, pg. 2293
ECOBANK CAMEROON S.A.—See Ecobank Transnational Incorporated; *Int'l*, pg. 2293
ECOBANK CAPE VERDE LTD.—See Ecobank Transnational Incorporated; *Int'l*, pg. 2293
ECOBANK CENTRAFRIQUE—See Ecobank Transnational Incorporated; *Int'l*, pg. 2293
ECOBANK CHAD LTD.—See Ecobank Transnational Incorporated; *Int'l*, pg. 2293
ECOBANK CONGO BRAZZAVILLE LIMITED—See Ecobank Transnational Incorporated; *Int'l*, pg. 2294
ECOBANK CONGO RDC LIMITED—See Ecobank Transnational Incorporated; *Int'l*, pg. 2294
ECOBANK COTE D'IVOIRE S.A.—See Ecobank Transnational Incorporated; *Int'l*, pg. 2294
ECOBANK DEVELOPMENT CORPORATION—See Ecobank Transnational Incorporated; *Int'l*, pg. 2294
ECOBANK GABON S.A.—See Ecobank Transnational Incorporated; *Int'l*, pg. 2294
ECOBANK GAMBIA LIMITED—See Ecobank Transnational Incorporated; *Int'l*, pg. 2294
ECOBANK GHANA LIMITED—See Ecobank Transnational Incorporated; *Int'l*, pg. 2294
ECOBANK GUINEA BISSAU S.A.—See Ecobank Transnational Incorporated; *Int'l*, pg. 2294
ECOBANK GUINEA EQUATORIALE LTD.—See Ecobank Transnational Incorporated; *Int'l*, pg. 2294
ECOBANK GUINEA LTD.—See Ecobank Transnational Incorporated; *Int'l*, pg. 2294
ECOBANK KENYA LIMITED—See Ecobank Transnational Incorporated; *Int'l*, pg. 2294
ECOBANK LIBERIA LIMITED—See Ecobank Transnational Incorporated; *Int'l*, pg. 2294
ECOBANK MALAWI LIMITED—See Ecobank Transnational Incorporated; *Int'l*, pg. 2294
ECOBANK MICRO FINANCE SIERRA LEONE S.L.—See Ecobank Transnational Incorporated; *Int'l*, pg. 2294
ECOBANK MOZAMBIQUE S.A.—See Ecobank Transnational Incorporated; *Int'l*, pg. 2294
ECOBANK NIGERIA PLC—See Ecobank Transnational Incorporated; *Int'l*, pg. 2294
ECOBANK RWANDA PLC—See Ecobank Transnational Incorporated; *Int'l*, pg. 2294
ECOBANK SAO TOME S.A.—See Ecobank Transnational Incorporated; *Int'l*, pg. 2294
ECOBANK SENEGAL LTD.—See Ecobank Transnational Incorporated; *Int'l*, pg. 2294
ECOBANK SIERRA LEONE LIMITED—See Ecobank Transnational Incorporated; *Int'l*, pg. 2294
ECOBANK TANZANIA LIMITED—See Ecobank Transnational Incorporated; *Int'l*, pg. 2294
ECOBANK TCHAD S.A.—See Ecobank Transnational Incorporated; *Int'l*, pg. 2294
ECOBANK TOGO S.A.—See Ecobank Transnational Incorporated; *Int'l*, pg. 2294
ECOBANK TRANSNATIONAL INCORPORATED; *Int'l*, pg. 2293
ECOBANK UGANDA LIMITED—See Ecobank Transnational Incorporated; *Int'l*, pg. 2294
ECOBANK ZAMBIA LIMITED—See Ecobank Transnational Incorporated; *Int'l*, pg. 2294
ECOBANK ZIMBABWE LIMITED—See Ecobank Transnational Incorporated; *Int'l*, pg. 2294
ECOBAT S.R.O.—See Energizer Holdings, Inc.; *U.S. Public*, pg. 761
ECOBEE TECHNOLOGIES ULC—See Generac Holdings Inc.; *U.S. Public*, pg. 913
ECOBIOGESTION SAS—See Compagnie des Alpes S.A.; *Int'l*, pg. 1738
ECOBIO HOLDINGS CO., LTD.; *Int'l*, pg. 2294
ECOBOARD INDUSTRIES LTD; *Int'l*, pg. 2294
ECO-BORASTAPETER AB—See Litorina Capital Management AB; *Int'l*, pg. 4528
ECO BOTANIC SDN. BHD.—See Eco World Development Group Berhad; *Int'l*, pg. 2293
ECOBUILD PRODUCTS PTE LTD—See GPS Alliance Holdings Limited; *Int'l*, pg. 3047
ECOBUILT HOLDINGS BERHAD; *Int'l*, pg. 2294
ECO BUSINESS PARK 1 SDN. BHD.—See Eco World Development Group Berhad; *Int'l*, pg. 2293
ECO BUSINESS PARK 2 SDN. BHD.—See Eco World Development Group Berhad; *Int'l*, pg. 2293
ECOCAB CO., LTD.; *Int'l*, pg. 2294
ECOCA INDUSTRIAL CO., LTD.—See Fair Friend Group; *Int'l*, pg. 2604
ECOCASH HOLDINGS ZIMBABWE LIMITED; *Int'l*, pg. 2294
ECO CENTRAL LTD—See Christchurch City Holdings Ltd.; *Int'l*, pg. 1586
ECOCHEM N.V.—See Thermo Fisher Scientific Inc.; *U.S. Public*, pg. 2146
ECOCITYSERVICE CORPORATION—See Bain Capital, LP; *U.S. Private*, pg. 434
ECOCIVIL ELECTROMUR G.E., S.L.—See ACS, Actividades de Construccion y Servicios, S.A.; *Int'l*, pg. 111

ECOCLEAN GMBH—See Shenyang Blue Silver Industry Automatic Equipment Co., Ltd.; *Int'l*, pg. 6803
ECO CONSTRUCTION & MAINTENANCE MANAGEMENT, LLC; *U.S. Private*, pg. 1328
E CO CONSULTANTS, INC.—See Littlejohn & Co., LLC; *U.S. Private*, pg. 2469
ECODEAL-GESTAO INTEGRAL DE RESIDUOS INDUSTRIAIS, S.A.—See Fomento de Construcciones y Contratas, S.A.; *Int'l*, pg. 2722
ECODE LANKA SOFTWARE (PRIVATE) LIMITED—See STERIS plc; *Int'l*, pg. 7209
ECO DE LOS ANDES S.A.—See Nestle S.A.; *Int'l*, pg. 5202
ECO DEPOT, INC.; *U.S. Public*, pg. 711
ECODE SOLUTIONS, LLC—See UnitedHealth Group Incorporated; *U.S. Public*, pg. 2253
ECODYNE HEAT EXCHANGERS, INC.—See Berkshire Hathaway Inc.; *U.S. Public*, pg. 311
ECODYNE LIMITED—See Berkshire Hathaway Inc.; *U.S. Public*, pg. 311
ECOEMISSIONS SOLUTIONS, INC.; *U.S. Private*, pg. 1329
ECO ENERGIETECHNIK GMBH—See UGI Corporation; *U.S. Public*, pg. 2222
ECO ENERGY COMPANY LIMITED—See Henderson Land Development Co. Ltd.; *Int'l*, pg. 3344
ECOENERGY INSIGHTS LIMITED—See Carrier Global Corporation; *U.S. Public*, pg. 443
ECO ENERGY PUMPS, INC.; *U.S. Private*, pg. 1328
ECOENER, S.A.; *Int'l*, pg. 2295
ECO ENGINEERING, INC.; *U.S. Private*, pg. 1328
ECO FARMS SALES INC.; *U.S. Private*, pg. 1328
ECOFIBRE LIMITED; *Int'l*, pg. 2295
ECOFI INVESTISSEMENT SA—See Groupe BPCE; *Int'l*, pg. 3094
ECOFIN GLOBAL UTILITIES & INFRASTRUCTURE TRUST PLC; *Int'l*, pg. 2295
ECOFIN U.S. RENEWABLES INFRASTRUCTURE TRUST PLC; *Int'l*, pg. 2295
ECOFIRST CONSOLIDATED BHD; *Int'l*, pg. 2295
ECO-FIRST KFT.—See MOL Magyar Olaj- es Gazipari Nyrt.; *Int'l*, pg. 5019
ECOFIRST PRODUCTS SDN BHD—See EcoFirst Consolidated Bhd; *Int'l*, pg. 2295
ECOFIRST SERVICES PRIVATE LIMITED—See Tata Sons Limited; *Int'l*, pg. 7468
ECOFLAM BRUCIATORI S.P.A.—See Ariston Holding N.V.; *Int'l*, pg. 567
ECOFLO FIELD SERVICES, LLC—See Republic Services, Inc.; *U.S. Public*, pg. 1786
ECO FRIENDLY FOOD PROCESSING PARK LTD.; *Int'l*, pg. 2292
ECOFROZ S.A.—See Air Water Inc.; *Int'l*, pg. 240
ECOFYS GERMANY GMBH—See Bain Capital, LP; *U.S. Private*, pg. 432
ECOFYS INVESTMENTS B.V.—See Bain Capital, LP; *U.S. Private*, pg. 432
ECOFYS UK LIMITED—See Bain Capital, LP; *U.S. Private*, pg. 432
ECOFYS WTTS B.V.—See Bain Capital, LP; *U.S. Private*, pg. 432
ECOGEN EUROPE LTD.—See Redhawk Holdings Corp.; *U.S. Public*, pg. 1770
ECQ GLASS PRODUCTION, LLC—See Koch Industries, Inc.; *U.S. Private*, pg. 2332
ECOGRAF LIMITED; *Int'l*, pg. 2295
ECOGRAS SAS—See Veolia Environnement S.A.; *Int'l*, pg. 8159
ECO GREEN CITY SDN. BHD.—See Avaland Berhad; *Int'l*, pg. 734
ECOGREEN ENERGY LUCKNOW PRIVATE LIMITED—See Zheneng Jinjiang Environment Holding Company Limited; *Int'l*, pg. 8669
ECOGREEN ENERGY PRIVATE LIMITED—See Zheneng Jinjiang Environment Holding Company Limited; *Int'l*, pg. 8669
ECOGREEN FINE CHEMICALS B.V.—See EcoGreen International Group Limited; *Int'l*, pg. 2295
ECOGREEN FINE CHEMICALS LIMITED—See EcoGreen International Group Limited; *Int'l*, pg. 2295
ECOGREEN INTERNATIONAL GROUP LIMITED; *Int'l*, pg. 2295
ECOGREEN MANUFACTURING—See EcoGreen International Group Limited; *Int'l*, pg. 2295
ECOGROUP INC.; *U.S. Private*, pg. 1329
E. COHEN AND COMPANY; *U.S. Private*, pg. 1303
ECOHOME FINANCIAL INC.—See Simply Group; *Int'l*, pg. 6934
ECO-HOME PANEL CO., LTD.—See Sala Corporation; *Int'l*, pg. 6490
ECO HORIZON SDN. BHD.—See Eco World Development Group Berhad; *Int'l*, pg. 2293
ECO HOTELS UK PLC.—See Red Ribbon Asset Management PLC; *Int'l*, pg. 6245
ECO HUILE SA—See Aurea, S.A.; *Int'l*, pg. 707
ECO INDUSTRIAL SERVICES COMPANY LIMITED—See Frasers Property Limited; *Int'l*, pg. 2766
ECO INNOVATION GROUP, INC.; *U.S. Public*, pg. 712

ECO INNOVATION INC.—See Konoike Transport Co., Ltd.; *Int'l*, pg. 4274
ECOINTERACTIVE, LLC—See KKR & Co. Inc.; *U.S. Public*, pg. 1267
ECOLAB AB—See Ecolab Inc.; *U.S. Public*, pg. 713
ECOLAB APS—See Ecolab Inc.; *U.S. Public*, pg. 713
ECOLAB ARGENTINA S.R.L.—See Ecolab Inc.; *U.S. Public*, pg. 713
ECOLAB ASIA PACIFIC PTE. LTD.—See Ecolab Inc.; *U.S. Public*, pg. 713
ECOLAB AS—See Ecolab Inc.; *U.S. Public*, pg. 713
ECOLAB A/S—See Ecolab Inc.; *U.S. Public*, pg. 713
ECOLAB B.V.B.A./S.P.R.L.—See Ecolab Inc.; *U.S. Public*, pg. 713
ECOLAB B.V.—See Ecolab Inc.; *U.S. Public*, pg. 713
ECOLAB CANADA—See Ecolab Inc.; *U.S. Public*, pg. 713
ECOLAB (CHINA) INVESTMENT CO., LTD.—See Ecolab Inc.; *U.S. Public*, pg. 712
ECOLAB COLOMBIA S.A.—See Ecolab Inc.; *U.S. Public*, pg. 713
ECOLAB CO.—See Ecolab Inc.; *U.S. Public*, pg. 713
ECOLAB CREDIT UNION—See Ecolab Inc.; *U.S. Public*, pg. 713
ECOLAB DEUTSCHLAND GMBH—See Ecolab Inc.; *U.S. Public*, pg. 713
ECOLAB D.O.O.—See Ecolab Inc.; *U.S. Public*, pg. 714
ECOLAB EAST AFRICA (KENYA) LIMITED—See Ecolab Inc.; *U.S. Public*, pg. 713
ECOLAB ECUADOR CIA. LTDA.—See Ecolab Inc.; *U.S. Public*, pg. 713
ECOLAB ENGINEERING GMBH—See Ecolab Inc.; *U.S. Public*, pg. 713
ECOLAB EOOD—See Ecolab Inc.; *U.S. Public*, pg. 713
ECOLAB EUROPE GMBH—See Ecolab Inc.; *U.S. Public*, pg. 713
ECOLAB EXPORT GMBH—See Ecolab Inc.; *U.S. Public*, pg. 713
ECOLAB G.K.—See Ecolab Inc.; *U.S. Public*, pg. 713
ECOLAB GLOBAL INSTITUTIONAL GROUP—See Ecolab Inc.; *U.S. Public*, pg. 713
ECOLAB GMBH—See Ecolab Inc.; *U.S. Public*, pg. 713
ECOLAB (GUAM) LLC—See Ecolab Inc.; *U.S. Public*, pg. 712
ECOLAB HISPANO-PORTUGUESA S.L.—See Ecolab Inc.; *U.S. Public*, pg. 713
ECOLAB HOLDING ITALY SRL—See Ecolab Inc.; *U.S. Public*, pg. 713
ECOLAB HYGIENE D.O.O.—See Ecolab Inc.; *U.S. Public*, pg. 713
ECOLAB HYGIENE KFT.—See Ecolab Inc.; *U.S. Public*, pg. 713
ECOLAB HYGIENE S.R.O.—See Ecolab Inc.; *U.S. Public*, pg. 713
ECOLAB HYGIENE SYSTEMS GMBH—See Ecolab Inc.; *U.S. Public*, pg. 713
ECOLAB INC.; *U.S. Public*, pg. 712
ECOLAB KOREA LTD.—See Ecolab Inc.; *U.S. Public*, pg. 713
ECOLAB LIMITED—See Ecolab Inc.; *U.S. Public*, pg. 713
ECOLAB LIMITED—See Ecolab Inc.; *U.S. Public*, pg. 713
ECOLAB LIMITED—See Ecolab Inc.; *U.S. Public*, pg. 713
ECOLAB LIMITED—See Ecolab Inc.; *U.S. Public*, pg. 713
ECOLAB LIMITED—See Ecolab Inc.; *U.S. Public*, pg. 713
ECOLAB LIMITED—See Ecolab Inc.; *U.S. Public*, pg. 713
ECOLAB LLC—See Ecolab Inc.; *U.S. Public*, pg. 713
ECOLAB LTD.—See Ecolab Inc.; *U.S. Public*, pg. 713
ECOLAB MANUFACTURING INC.—See Ecolab Inc.; *U.S. Public*, pg. 713
ECOLAB MAROC S.A.—See Ecolab Inc.; *U.S. Public*, pg. 713
ECOLAB MAROC SOCIETE A RESPONSABILITE LIMITEE D'ASSOCIE UNIQUE—See Ecolab Inc.; *U.S. Public*, pg. 713
ECOLAB NEW ZEALAND LTD.—See Ecolab Inc.; *U.S. Public*, pg. 713
ECOLAB NL 10 B.V.—See Ecolab Inc.; *U.S. Public*, pg. 713
ECOLABONE B.V.—See Ecolab Inc.; *U.S. Public*, pg. 714
ECOLAB PEST ELIMINATION—See Ecolab Inc.; *U.S. Public*, pg. 713
ECOLAB PEST FRANCE SAS—See Ecolab Inc.; *U.S. Public*, pg. 714
ECOLAB PRODUCTION BELGIUM BVBA—See Ecolab Inc.; *U.S. Public*, pg. 714
ECOLAB PTE. LTD.—See Ecolab Inc.; *U.S. Public*, pg. 714
ECOLAB (PTY) LTD.—See Ecolab Inc.; *U.S. Public*, pg. 712
ECOLAB PTY. LTD.—See Ecolab Inc.; *U.S. Public*, pg. 714
ECOLAB QUIMICA LTDA.—See Ecolab Inc.; *U.S. Public*, pg. 713
ECOLAB, S.A. DE C.V.—See Ecolab Inc.; *U.S. Public*, pg. 714
ECOLAB S. A.—See Ecolab Inc.; *U.S. Public*, pg. 714
ECOLAB S.A.—See Ecolab Inc.; *U.S. Public*, pg. 714
ECOLAB SAS—See Ecolab Inc.; *U.S. Public*, pg. 714
ECOLAB (SCHWEIZ) GMBH—See Ecolab Inc.; *U.S. Public*, pg. 713

ECOLAB, S. DE R.L. DE C.V.—See Ecolab Inc.; *U.S. Public*, pg. 714
ECOLAB SDN BHD—See Ecolab Inc.; *U.S. Public*, pg. 714
ECOLAB SERVICES ARGENTINA S.R.L.—See Ecolab Inc.; *U.S. Public*, pg. 714
ECOLAB SERVICES POLAND SP. Z O O—See Ecolab Inc.; *U.S. Public*, pg. 714
ECOLAB SNC—See Ecolab Inc.; *U.S. Public*, pg. 714
ECOLAB SP. Z O.O.—See Ecolab Inc.; *U.S. Public*, pg. 714
ECOLAB S.R.L.—See Ecolab Inc.; *U.S. Public*, pg. 714
ECOLAB SRL—See Ecolab Inc.; *U.S. Public*, pg. 714
ECOLAB SRL—See Ecolab Inc.; *U.S. Public*, pg. 714
ECOLAB S.R.O.—See Ecolab Inc.; *U.S. Public*, pg. 714
ECOLAB (TRINIDAD & TOBAGO)UNLIMITED—See Ecolab Inc.; *U.S. Public*, pg. 713
ECOLAB USA INC. - FOOD & BEVERAGE PROCESSING—See Ecolab Inc.; *U.S. Public*, pg. 714
ECOLAB USA INC.—See Ecolab Inc.; *U.S. Public*, pg. 714
ECOLAB USA INC. - TUCSON—See Ecolab Inc.; *U.S. Public*, pg. 714
ECOLAB VIETNAM COMPANY LIMITED—See Ecolab Inc.; *U.S. Public*, pg. 714
ECOLAB Y COMPANIA COLECTIVA DE RESPONSABILIDAD LIMITADA—See Ecolab Inc.; *U.S. Public*, pg. 714
E.COLESGROUP PTY LTD—See Coles Group Limited; *Int'l*, pg. 1698
ECOLIBRIUM SOLAR, INC.—See Tenex Capital Management, L.P.; *U.S. Private*, pg. 3966
ECOLINK INTELLIGENT TECHNOLOGY, INC.—See Universal Electronics, Inc.; *U.S. Public*, pg. 2255
ECOLITE BIOTECH MANUFACTURING SDN. BHD.—See Sunzen Biotech Berhad; *Int'l*, pg. 7333
ECOLITE MANUFACTURING CO. INC.; *U.S. Private*, pg. 1329
ECOLIVEGREEN CORP.; *U.S. Private*, pg. 1329
ECOLLEGE INC—See Pearson plc; *Int'l*, pg. 5778
ECOLOCAP SOLUTIONS INC.; *U.S. Public*, pg. 717
ECOLOC NV—See RPM International Inc.; *U.S. Public*, pg. 1816
ECO LOG ENVIRONMENTAL RISK INFORMATION SERVICES LTD.—See GVIC Communications Corp.; *Int'l*, pg. 3189
ECOLOGIA Y TECNICAS SANITARIAS, S.L.—See ACS, Actividades de Construccion y Servicios, S.A.; *Int'l*, pg. 111
ECOLOGICAL FIBERS INC.; *U.S. Private*, pg. 1329
ECOLOGICALLY SOUND MEDICAL SERVICES—See Federated Healthcare Supply Holdings, Inc.; *U.S. Private*, pg. 1491
ECOLOGIC BRANDS, INC.—See Jabil Inc.; *U.S. Public*, pg. 1180
ECOLOGIC ENERGY SOLUTIONS, LLC—See Installed Building Products, Inc.; *U.S. Public*, pg. 1132
ECOLOGIX RESOURCES GROUP, INC.; *U.S. Public*, pg. 717
ECOLOGY ACTION OF SANTA CRUZ; *U.S. Private*, pg. 1329
ECOLOGY AND ENVIRONMENT, INC.—See WSP Global, Inc.; *Int'l*, pg. 8495
ECOLOGY AND ENVIRONMENT OF SAUDI ARABIA CO., LTD.—See WSP Global, Inc.; *Int'l*, pg. 8496
ECOLOGY AUTO WRECKING INC.; *U.S. Private*, pg. 1329
ECOLOGY BUILDING SOCIETY; *Int'l*, pg. 2295
ECOLOGY CONTROL INDUSTRIES, INC—See Ecology Control Industries, Inc.; *U.S. Private*, pg. 1329
ECOLOGY CONTROL INDUSTRIES, INC.; *U.S. Private*, pg. 1329
ECOLOGY & ENVIRONMENT ARGENTINA—See WSP Global, Inc.; *Int'l*, pg. 8496
ECOLOGY & ENVIRONMENT DO BRASIL LTDA.—See WSP Global, Inc.; *Int'l*, pg. 8496
ECOLOGY & ENVIRONMENT ENGINEERING, INC.—See WSP Global, Inc.; *Int'l*, pg. 8496
ECOLOPAC CO., LTD.—See Teikoku Tsushin Kogyo Co., Ltd.; *Int'l*, pg. 7524
ECOLUMBER S.A.; *Int'l*, pg. 2295
ECOLUTIONS CARBON INDIA PVT. LTD.—See ecolutions GmbH & Co. KGaA; *Int'l*, pg. 2295
ECOLUTIONS GMBH & CO. KGAA; *Int'l*, pg. 2295
ECOLUTIONS NEW ENERGY INVESTMENT CO., LTD.—See ecolutions GmbH & Co. KGaA; *Int'l*, pg. 2295
ECOMAC GEBRAUCHTMASCHINEN GMBH—See Krones AG; *Int'l*, pg. 4305
ECOM AGROINDUSTRIAL ASIA PTE LTD—See Ecom Agroindustrial Corporation Ltd.; *Int'l*, pg. 2296
ECOM AGROINDUSTRIAL ASIA PTE. LTD.—See Ecom Agroindustrial Corporation Ltd.; *Int'l*, pg. 2296
ECOM AGROINDUSTRIAL CORP. LTD—See Ecom Agroindustrial Corporation Ltd.; *Int'l*, pg. 2296
ECOM AGROINDUSTRIAL CORPORATION LTD.; *Int'l*, pg. 2295
ECOM AGROTRADE LIMITED—See Ecom Agroindustrial Corporation Ltd.; *Int'l*, pg. 2296
ECO MAJESTIC DEVELOPMENT SDN. BHD.—See Eco World Development Group Berhad; *Int'l*, pg. 2293

ECOMAL AUSTRIA GES.MBH—See Vishay Intertechnology, Inc.; *U.S. Public*, pg. 2302
ECOMAL CESKA REPUBLIKA S.R.O.—See Vishay Intertechnology, Inc.; *U.S. Public*, pg. 2302
ECOMAL DEUTSCHLAND GMBH—See Vishay Intertechnology, Inc.; *U.S. Public*, pg. 2302
ECOMAL ELEKTRONSKE KOMPONENTE D.O.O.—See Vishay Intertechnology, Inc.; *U.S. Public*, pg. 2302
ECOMAL EUROPE GMBH—See Vishay Intertechnology, Inc.; *U.S. Public*, pg. 2302
ECOMAL FINLAND OY—See Vishay Intertechnology, Inc.; *U.S. Public*, pg. 2302
ECOMAL FRANCE S.A.—See Vishay Intertechnology, Inc.; *U.S. Public*, pg. 2302
ECOMAL HUNGARY KFT.—See Vishay Intertechnology, Inc.; *U.S. Public*, pg. 2302
ECOMAL IBERIA S.A.U.—See Vishay Intertechnology, Inc.; *U.S. Public*, pg. 2302
ECOMAL ITALY SRL—See Vishay Intertechnology, Inc.; *U.S. Public*, pg. 2302
ECOMAL NEDERLAND BV—See Vishay Intertechnology, Inc.; *U.S. Public*, pg. 2302
ECOMAL POLAND SP. Z O.O.—See Vishay Intertechnology, Inc.; *U.S. Public*, pg. 2302
ECOMAL SCHWEIZ A.G.—See Vishay Intertechnology, Inc.; *U.S. Public*, pg. 2302
ECOMAL SWEDEN AB—See Vishay Intertechnology, Inc.; *U.S. Public*, pg. 2302
ECOMAL UK LTD.—See Vishay Intertechnology, Inc.; *U.S. Public*, pg. 2302
ECOMANAGE CORPORATION—See Hitachi Zosen Corporation; *Int'l*, pg. 3410
ECOMARK ENERGY, INC.; *U.S. Private*, pg. 1329
ECOM ATLANTIC, INC; *U.S. Private*, pg. 1329
ECOMAX, INC.—See Clark Orient (BVI) Ltd.; *Int'l*, pg. 1650
ECOMB AB; *Int'l*, pg. 2296
ECO MEADOWS SDN. BHD.—See Eco World Development Group Berhad; *Int'l*, pg. 2293
ECO MEDI GLOVE SDN BHD—See Riverstone Holdings Limited; *Int'l*, pg. 6353
ECOMEMBRANE LLC—See Ecomembrane S.p.A.; *Int'l*, pg. 2296
ECOMEMBRANE S.P.A.; *Int'l*, pg. 2296
ECO MERIDIAN SDN BHD—See S P Setia Berhad; *Int'l*, pg. 6443
ECO-METERING—See ENGIE SA; *Int'l*, pg. 2429
E-COMETRUE INC.; *Int'l*, pg. 2247
ECOMIAM SA; *Int'l*, pg. 2296
ECOMIC CO LTD; *Int'l*, pg. 2296
ECOMITZ LLC; *U.S. Private*, pg. 1329
ECOM JAPAN LTD—See Ecom Agroindustrial Corporation Ltd.; *Int'l*, pg. 2296
ECOM LOGISTIK GMBH—See Pelikan International Corporation Berhad; *Int'l*, pg. 5783
E-COMMERCE CHINA DANGDANG INC.; *Int'l*, pg. 2247
E-COMMERCE EXCHANGE INC.; *U.S. Private*, pg. 1302
ECOMMERCE PARTNERS; *U.S. Private*, pg. 1329
ECOMM GROUP, INC.—See Commerce Group Corp.; *U.S. Public*, pg. 545
ECOMMISSION FINANCIAL SERVICES, INC.—See Lightyear Capital LLC; *U.S. Private*, pg. 2454
E-COMMODITIES HOLDINGS LIMITED; *Int'l*, pg. 2247
E COMMUNICATIONS SYSTEMS INC.; *U.S. Private*, pg. 1300
ECOMNETS, INC.; *U.S. Private*, pg. 1329
ECOMOTT, INC.; *Int'l*, pg. 2296
ECOMPANY INTERNATIONAL B.V.—See Kingenta Ecological Engineering Group Co., Ltd.; *Int'l*, pg. 4172
ECOMPANYSTORE, INC.; *U.S. Private*, pg. 1329
ECOMPEX, INC.; *U.S. Private*, pg. 1329
E-COMPLISH LLC; *U.S. Private*, pg. 1302
ECOM PRODUCTS GROUP CORPORATION; *U.S. Public*, pg. 717
ECOMSYSTEMS, INC.; *U.S. Private*, pg. 1329
ECOM TRADING (SHANGHAI) CO. LTD.—See Ecom Agroindustrial Corporation Ltd.; *Int'l*, pg. 2296
ECOM USA, INC., USA—See Ecom Agroindustrial Corporation Ltd.; *Int'l*, pg. 2296
ECONACH HOLDINGS CO., LTD.; *Int'l*, pg. 2296
ECON AMBULANCE SERVICES PTE LTD—See China Healthcare Limited; *Int'l*, pg. 1507
ECON CARESKILL TRAINING CENTRE PTE LTD—See China Healthcare Limited; *Int'l*, pg. 1507
E-CONCERT SOLUTIONS—See Apollo Global Management, Inc.; *U.S. Public*, pg. 151
E-CONCERT SOLUTIONS—See Apollo Global Management, Inc.; *U.S. Public*, pg. 151
ECONDITION GMBH—See Investment AB Latour; *Int'l*, pg. 3781
ECONECOL INC.—See Envipro Holdings Inc.; *Int'l*, pg. 2454
ECONERGY RENEWABLE ENERGY LTD.; *Int'l*, pg. 2296
ECONET GLOBAL LTD.—See Econet Wireless Zimbabwe Limited; *Int'l*, pg. 2297
ECONET INSURANCE (PRIVATE) LIMITED—See EcoCash Holdings Zimbabwe Limited; *Int'l*, pg. 2294
ECONET LIFE (PRIVATE) LIMITED—See EcoCash Holdings Zimbabwe Limited; *Int'l*, pg. 2294

ECONET (SUZHOU) LIMITED—See MediaTek Inc.; *Int'l*, pg. 4773
ECONET WIRELESS (PVT) LTD—See Econet Wireless Zimbabwe Limited; *Int'l*, pg. 2297
ECONET WIRELESS ZIMBABWE LIMITED; *Int'l*, pg. 2296
ECONFRAME BERHAD; *Int'l*, pg. 2297
E-CON GAS, INC—See UGI Corporation; *U.S. Public*, pg. 2221
ECON HEALTHCARE (M) SDN BHD—See China Healthcare Limited; *Int'l*, pg. 1507
ECON MEDICARE CENTRE PTE LTD—See China Healthcare Limited; *Int'l*, pg. 1507
ECON MEDICARE CENTRE SDN BHD—See China Healthcare Limited; *Int'l*, pg. 1507
ECONOCARIBE CONSOLIDATORS INC.—See Allcargo Logistics Limited; *Int'l*, pg. 334
ECONOCOM AUSTRIA GMBH—See Econocom Group SA; *Int'l*, pg. 2297
ECONOCOM BRASIL S.A.—See Econocom Group SA; *Int'l*, pg. 2297
ECONOCOM DEUTSCHLAND GMBH—See Econocom Group SA; *Int'l*, pg. 2297
ECONOCOM DIGITAL FINANCE LIMITED—See Econocom Group SA; *Int'l*, pg. 2297
ECONOCOM DIGITAL SECURITY SAS—See Atos SE; *Int'l*, pg. 692
ECONOCOM FINANCE SNC—See Econocom Group SA; *Int'l*, pg. 2297
ECONOCOM FINANCIAL SERVICES INTERNATIONAL BV—See Econocom Group SA; *Int'l*, pg. 2297
ECONOCOM FRANCE SAS—See Econocom Group SA; *Int'l*, pg. 2297
ECONOCOM GROUP SA; *Int'l*, pg. 2297
ECONOCOM INTERNATIONAL ITALIA SPA—See Econocom Group SA; *Int'l*, pg. 2297
ECONOCOM LEASE SA/NV—See Econocom Group SA; *Int'l*, pg. 2297
ECONOCOM LOCATION SAS—See Econocom Group SA; *Int'l*, pg. 2297
ECONOCOM LTD.—See Econocom Group SA; *Int'l*, pg. 2297
ECONOCOM LUXEMBOURG SA—See Econocom Group SA; *Int'l*, pg. 2297
ECONOCOM MANAGED SERVICES SA/NV—See Econocom Group SA; *Int'l*, pg. 2298
ECONOCOM MANAGED SERVICES SAS—See Econocom Group SA; *Int'l*, pg. 2297
ECONOCOM MAROC SARL—See Econocom Group SA; *Int'l*, pg. 2297
ECONOCOM NEDERLAND BV—See Econocom Group SA; *Int'l*, pg. 2297
ECONOCOM POLSKA SP Z.O.O—See Econocom Group SA; *Int'l*, pg. 2297
ECONOCOM PRODUCTS AND SOLUTIONS SAS—See Econocom Group SA; *Int'l*, pg. 2297
ECONOCOM PRODUCTS & SOLUTIONS BELUX SA/NV—See Econocom Group SA; *Int'l*, pg. 2297
ECONOCOM PRODUCTS & SOLUTIONS S.L.—See Econocom Group SA; *Int'l*, pg. 2297
ECONOCOM PSF SA—See Econocom Group SA; *Int'l*, pg. 2297
ECONOCOM PUBLIC BV—See Econocom Group SA; *Int'l*, pg. 2298
ECONOCOM RE SA LUXEMBOURG—See Econocom Group SA; *Int'l*, pg. 2298
ECONOCOM SA—See Econocom Group SA; *Int'l*, pg. 2298
ECONOCOM SAS—See Econocom Group SA; *Int'l*, pg. 2298
ECONOCOM SERVICIOS SA—See Econocom Group SA; *Int'l*, pg. 2298
ECONOCOM TELECOM BV—See Econocom Group SA; *Int'l*, pg. 2298
ECONOCOM TELECOM SERVICES SAS—See Econocom Group SA; *Int'l*, pg. 2298
ECONOFFICE PRODUCTS & SUPPLIES, INC.; *U.S. Private*, pg. 1329
ECONOHOMES, LLC; *U.S. Private*, pg. 1329
ECONOLITE CANADA, INC.—See Econolite Group, Inc.; *U.S. Private*, pg. 1330
ECONOLITE CONTROL PRODUCTS, INC.—See Econolite Group, Inc.; *U.S. Private*, pg. 1330
ECONOLITE GROUP, INC.; *U.S. Private*, pg. 1330
ECONOLODGE CO., LTD.—See Heeton Holdings Limited; *Int'l*, pg. 3307
ECONO LUBE N' TUNE INC.—See Roark Capital Group Inc.; *U.S. Private*, pg. 3454
ECONOMEDIA; *Int'l*, pg. 2298
THE ECONOMICAL INSURANCE GROUP—See The Economical Insurance Group; *Int'l*, pg. 7637
THE ECONOMICAL INSURANCE GROUP; *Int'l*, pg. 7637
ECONOMICAL INSURANCE—See The Economical Insurance Group; *Int'l*, pg. 7637
ECONOMICAL SUPER MARKET INCORPORATED; *U.S. Private*, pg. 1330
ECONOMIC DATA RESEARCH B.V.—See Munchener Ruckversicherungs AG; *Int'l*, pg. 5088
ECONOMIC DATA RESOURCES B.V.—See Munchener Ruckversicherungs AG; *Int'l*, pg. 5088

THE ECONOMIC DEVELOPMENT CORPORATION OF KANSAS CITY, MISSOURI; *U.S. Private*, pg. 4025
ECONOMIC INSTITUTE AD BANJA LUKA; *Int'l*, pg. 2298
ECONOMIC INVESTMENT TRUST LIMITED; *Int'l*, pg. 2298
ECONOMIC OPPORTUNITY AUTHORITY FOR SAVANNAH-CHATHAM COUNTY, INC.; *U.S. Private*, pg. 1330
ECONOMIC PACKAGING CORPORATION; *U.S. Private*, pg. 1330
ECONOMIC RESEARCH SERVICES INC.—See Exela Technologies, Inc.; *U.S. Public*, pg. 806
ECONOMICS PARTNERS, LLC—See Ryan, LLC; *U.S. Private*, pg. 3511
ECONOMIC ZONES WORLD COMPANY—See Dubai World Corporation; *Int'l*, pg. 2222
THE ECONOMIST GROUP (ASIA/PACIFIC) LIMITED—See The Economist Group Limited; *Int'l*, pg. 7637
THE ECONOMIST GROUP FRANCE S.A.R.L—See The Economist Group Limited; *Int'l*, pg. 7637
THE ECONOMIST GROUP LIMITED; *Int'l*, pg. 7637
THE ECONOMIST GROUP (LUXEMBOURG) LIMITED—See The Economist Group Limited; *Int'l*, pg. 7637
THE ECONOMIST GROUP SINGAPORE PTE LIMITED—See The Economist Group Limited; *Int'l*, pg. 7637
THE ECONOMIST GROUP (SWITZERLAND) SA—See The Economist Group Limited; *Int'l*, pg. 7637
THE ECONOMIST INTELLIGENCE UNIT, NA, INC—See The Economist Group Limited; *Int'l*, pg. 7637
THE ECONOMIST NEWSPAPER GROUP, INC—See The Economist Group Limited; *Int'l*, pg. 7637
THE ECONOMIST NEWSPAPER LIMITED—See The Economist Group Limited; *Int'l*, pg. 7637
THE ECONOMY ADVERTISING COMPANY INC.; *U.S. Private*, pg. 4025
ECONOMY AUTO OUTLET; *U.S. Private*, pg. 1330
THE ECONOMY BANK N V—See BNP Paribas SA; *Int'l*, pg. 1093
ECONOMY CASH & CARRY INC.; *U.S. Private*, pg. 1330
ECONOMY FOODS, INC.—See Sysco Corporation; *U.S. Public*, pg. 1973
ECONOMY LOCKER STORAGE CO. INC.; *U.S. Private*, pg. 1330
ECONOMY PAVING CO. INC.; *U.S. Private*, pg. 1330
ECONOMY PROPANE CORP.; *U.S. Private*, pg. 1330
ECONOMY REFRIGERATION HEATING VENTILATION SUPPLY CORP.; *U.S. Private*, pg. 1330
ECONOMY WHEELS LTD; *Int'l*, pg. 2298
ECONO-PRINT INC.; *U.S. Private*, pg. 1329
ECONO PRODUCTS INC.; *U.S. Private*, pg. 1329
ECONOQUALITY FREIGHT FORWARDERS, INC.—See M.B.R. Industries, Inc.; *U.S. Private*, pg. 2528
ECONOS CO., LTD.; *Int'l*, pg. 2298
ECONOSERVE SOLUTIONS, LLC—See Riverside Partners, LLC; *U.S. Private*, pg. 3446
ECONO TRADE (INDIA) LIMITED; *Int'l*, pg. 2297
ECONPILE HOLDINGS BERHAD; *Int'l*, pg. 2298
ECON PRECAST PTE. LTD.—See Koon Holdings Limited; *Int'l*, pg. 4278
ECON PRECAST SDN. BHD.—See Koon Holdings Limited; *Int'l*, pg. 4278
ECON SOLUTIONS GMBH—See MVV Energie AG; *Int'l*, pg. 5109
ECON SOUTH, LLC—See Land South Holdings, LLC; *U.S. Private*, pg. 2384
E CONSTRUCTION GROUP INC.; *U.S. Private*, pg. 1300
E-CONSULTANCY.COM LIMITED—See Centaur Media plc; *Int'l*, pg. 1402
ECONTACTLIVE, INC.; *U.S. Private*, pg. 1330
E CONTRACTORS USA, LLC; *U.S. Private*, pg. 1300
ECONTROLS GROUP, INC.—See Genisys Controls, LLC; *U.S. Private*, pg. 1671
ECO ORO MINERALS CORP.; *Int'l*, pg. 2292
ECOPACK, D.O.O.—See Comet Umetni brusi in nekovine, d.d.; *Int'l*, pg. 1711
ECOPACK LTD; *Int'l*, pg. 2298
ECOPAC (U.K.) LIMITED—See Macfarlane Group PLC; *Int'l*, pg. 4621
ECO-PAK, LLC—See The Townsend Corporation; *U.S. Private*, pg. 4127
ECO-PAN, INC.—See Concrete Pumping Holdings, Inc.; *U.S. Public*, pg. 566
ECO-PAN LIMITED—See Concrete Pumping Holdings, Inc.; *U.S. Public*, pg. 566
ECO PAPER JP CO., LTD.—See Japan Pulp and Paper Company Limited; *Int'l*, pg. 3903
ECOPARC DE BARCELONA S.A.—See ACS, Actividades de Construccion y Servicios, S.A.; *Int'l*, pg. 111
EC OPCO WASHINGTON TOWNSHIP, LLC—See Ventas, Inc.; *U.S. Public*, pg. 2278
EC OPCO XENIA, LLC—See Ventas, Inc.; *U.S. Public*, pg. 2278
ECOPETROL OLEO E GAS DO BRASIL LTDA.—See Ecopetrol S.A.; *Int'l*, pg. 2298
ECOPETROL S.A.; *Int'l*, pg. 2298

ECOPETROL USA, INC.—See Ecopetrol S.A.; *Int'l*, pg. 2298
ECO - PHU HOLDING—See Derichebourg S.A.; *Int'l*, pg. 2041
ECOPILHAS LDA.—See Energizer Holdings, Inc.; *U.S. Public*, pg. 761
ECOPLAN CO., LTD.—See Founder's Consultants Holdings, Inc.; *Int'l*, pg. 2753
ECO PLANT SERVICES CO., LTD.—See The Siam Cement Public Company Limited; *Int'l*, pg. 7682
ECOPLASTIC CORPORATION; *Int'l*, pg. 2299
ECOPLAST LTD.; *Int'l*, pg. 2299
ECOPLUS, INC.; *U.S. Public*, pg. 717
ECOPOLIFIX SRL—See Ring International Holding AG; *Int'l*, pg. 6343
ECO-PORT KYUSHU CO., LTD.—See Japan Pulp and Paper Company Limited; *Int'l*, pg. 3903
ECOPORTO KOPER, D.O.O.—See Luka Koper d.d.; *Int'l*, pg. 4576
ECO POWER CO., LTD.—See Cosmo Energy Holdings Co., Ltd.; *Int'l*, pg. 1812
ECOPPIA SCIENTIFIC LTD.; *Int'l*, pg. 2299
ECO PRINT CENTER NV—See DPG Media Group NV; *Int'l*, pg. 2188
ECOPRO BM CO., LTD.; *Int'l*, pg. 2299
ECOPRO CO., LTD.; *Int'l*, pg. 2299
ECO PRODUCCIONES, S.A. DE C.V.—See Grupo Televisa, S.A.B.; *Int'l*, pg. 3136
ECO-PRODUCTS, INC.—See Apollo Global Management, Inc.; *U.S. Public*, pg. 154
ECOPRO HN CO., LTD.; *Int'l*, pg. 2299
ECO PURE PREMIUM WATER COMPANY LIMITED—See Simonds Farsons Cisk plc; *Int'l*, pg. 6932
ECORA RESOURCES PLC; *Int'l*, pg. 2299
ECORA SOFTWARE CORPORATION—See ESW Capital, LLC; *U.S. Private*, pg. 1430
ECORDATI RARE DISEASES GERMANY GMBH—See Recordati S.p.A.; *Int'l*, pg. 6239
ECORE CO., LTD.—See Itochu Enex Co., Ltd.; *Int'l*, pg. 3841
ECOREC SRL—See Derichebourg S.A.; *Int'l*, pg. 2042
ECO-RECYCLE CO., LTD.—See Dowa Holdings Co., Ltd.; *Int'l*, pg. 2184
ECO RECYCLING LIMITED.; *Int'l*, pg. 2292
ECORE INTERNATIONAL INC.; *U.S. Private*, pg. 1330
ECOREM—See ABO-Group NV/SA; *Int'l*, pg. 66
ECOREXPERIENCE, INC.; *U.S. Private*, pg. 1330
ECORODOVIAS INFRAESTRUCTURA E LOGISTICA S.A.—See Argo Finanziaria S.p.A.; *Int'l*, pg. 562
E& CORPORATION CO., LTD.; *Int'l*, pg. 2246
E.C. ORTIZ & CO., LLP; *U.S. Private*, pg. 1304
ECORUB AB; *Int'l*, pg. 2299
ECO SAFE SYSTEMS USA, INC.; *U.S. Public*, pg. 712
ECO SANCTUARY SDN. BHD.—See Eco World Development Group Berhad; *Int'l*, pg. 2293
ECOSAVE HOLDINGS LIMITED; *Int'l*, pg. 2299
ECOSCAPES COMPOSITES, LLC—See Innovative Composites International, Inc.; *Int'l*, pg. 3712
ECOSCIENCE INTERNATIONAL BERHAD; *Int'l*, pg. 2299
ECOSCIENCES, INC.; *U.S. Public*, pg. 717
ECO SCIENCE SOLUTIONS, INC.; *U.S. Private*, pg. 1328
ECO'S CO., LTD; *Int'l*, pg. 2293
ECOSECURITIES GROUP PLC; *Int'l*, pg. 2299
ECOSECURITIES, LTD.—See EcoSecurities Group plc; *Int'l*, pg. 2299
ECO SECURITIZADORA DE DIREITOS CREDITORIOS DO AGRONEGOCIO S.A.; *Int'l*, pg. 2292
ECO SERVICES OPERATIONS CORP.—See Ecovyst Inc.; *U.S. Public*, pg. 717
ECOSERV LLC; *U.S. Private*, pg. 1330
ECOSESTO SPA—See Falck S.p.A.; *Int'l*, pg. 2610
ECO-SHIFT POWER CORP.; *Int'l*, pg. 2293
ECOS HOKUEI CORP.—See EXEO Group Inc.; *Int'l*, pg. 2583
ECOSIAN CO., LTD.—See HanmiGlobal Co., LTD.; *Int'l*, pg. 3257
ECOSISTEMAS DIGITALES S.A.S.—See Bancolombia S.A.; *Int'l*, pg. 828
ECOSITE OY—See Elisa Corporation; *Int'l*, pg. 2361
ECO SKY SDN. BHD.—See Eco World Development Group Berhad; *Int'l*, pg. 2293
ECOSLOPS SA; *Int'l*, pg. 2299
ECOSMART NEDERLAND B.V.—See Renewi plc; *Int'l*, pg. 6278
ECOSMART UNION SA—See Purcari Wineries Public Company Limited; *Int'l*, pg. 6121
ECOSMART US, LLC—See The Riverside Company; *U.S. Private*, pg. 4108
ECOSON B.V.—See Darling Ingredients Inc.; *U.S. Public*, pg. 634
ECOSORT, L.L.C.—See Waste Connections, Inc.; *Int'l*, pg. 8353
ECOSPHERE TECHNOLOGIES, INC.; *U.S. Private*, pg. 1330
ECO SPINDLES (PVT) LTD—See BPPL Holdings PLC; *Int'l*, pg. 1133
ECOSPRAY TECHNOLOGIES S.R.L.—See Carnival Corporation; *U.S. Public*, pg. 438
ECOSSE ENERGY CORP.; *Int'l*, pg. 2300

COMPANY NAME INDEX

ECOST.COM, INC.—See Insight Enterprises, Inc.; *U.S. Public*, pg. 1130
ECO-STIM ENERGY SOLUTIONS, INC.; *U.S. Public*, pg. 712
ECO SUMMER SDN. BHD.—See Eco World Development Group Berhad; *Int'l*, pg. 2293
ECOSUNTEK S.P.A.; *Int'l*, pg. 2300
ECO SUPPLIES EUROPE AB; *Int'l*, pg. 2292
ECOSWAY KOREA, INC.—See Berjaya Corporation Berhad; *Int'l*, pg. 984
ECOSWAY MEXICO, S.A. DE C.V.—See Berjaya Corporation Berhad; *Int'l*, pg. 985
ECOSWAY RUS LLC—See Berjaya Corporation Berhad; *Int'l*, pg. 985
ECOSYL PRODUCTS LTD—See Volac International Limited; *Int'l*, pg. 8300
ECOSYNTHETIX, INC.; *Int'l*, pg. 2300
ECOSYNTHETIX LTD.—See EcoSynthetix, Inc.; *Int'l*, pg. 2300
ECOS YONEZAWA CO., LTD.—See Takuma Co., Ltd.; *Int'l*, pg. 7442
ECO-SYSTEM AKITA CO., LTD.—See Dowa Holdings Co., Ltd.; *Int'l*, pg. 2183
ECO-SYSTEM CHIBA CO., LTD.—See Dowa Holdings Co., Ltd.; *Int'l*, pg. 2184
ECOSYSTEM CONSULTING SERVICE, INC.—See GZA GeoEnvironmental Inc.; *U.S. Private*, pg. 1822
ECO-SYSTEM HANAOKA CO., LTD.—See Dowa Holdings Co., Ltd.; *Int'l*, pg. 2184
ECO-SYSTEM JAPAN CO., LTD.—See Dowa Holdings Co., Ltd.; *Int'l*, pg. 2184
ECO-SYSTEM KOSAKA CO., LTD.—See Dowa Holdings Co., Ltd.; *Int'l*, pg. 2184
ECO-SYSTEM OKAYAMA CO., LTD.—See Dowa Holdings Co., Ltd.; *Int'l*, pg. 2184
ECO-SYSTEM RECYCLING CO., LTD.—See Dowa Holdings Co., Ltd.; *Int'l*, pg. 2184
ECO-SYSTEM SANYO CO., LTD.—See Dowa Holdings Co., Ltd.; *Int'l*, pg. 2184
ECO SYSTEMS LTD.; *Int'l*, pg. 2292
ECOTEAM, LLC—See Thompson Street Capital Manager LLC; *U.S. Private*, pg. 4161
ECOTEC GMBH—See Zech Group SE; *Int'l*, pg. 8628
ECO TECH CONTRACTORS INC.; *U.S. Private*, pg. 1328
ECOTECH ENTERPRISES INC.—See Hawkins, Inc.; *U.S. Public*, pg. 989
ECOTECH MARINE; *U.S. Private*, pg. 1330
ECOTEC S.R.L.; *Int'l*, pg. 2300
ECO-TEK GROUP INC.; *Int'l*, pg. 2293
ECO-TEK HOLDINGS LIMITED; *Int'l*, pg. 2293
ECOTEL COMMUNICATION AG; *Int'l*, pg. 2300
ECOTEL PRIVATE GMBH—See ecotel communication ag; *Int'l*, pg. 2300
ECO TERRACES SDN. BHD.—See Eco World Development Group Berhad; *Int'l*, pg. 2293
ECOTERRES S.A.—See Ackermans & van Haaren NV; *Int'l*, pg. 105
ECOTHERM INSULATION (UK) LIMITED—See Kingspan Group PLC; *Int'l*, pg. 4176
ECOTONE, INC.—See L2 Capital Partners; *U.S. Private*, pg. 2367
ECOTONE—See PAI Partners S.A.S.; *Int'l*, pg. 5700
ECO TOURS ASIA SDN. BHD.—See Salcon Berhad; *Int'l*, pg. 6492
ECOTRICITY GROUP LTD.; *Int'l*, pg. 2300
ECO TROPICS DEVELOPMENT SDN. BHD.—See Eco World Development Group Berhad; *Int'l*, pg. 2293
ECOULT—See East Penn Manufacturing Co., Inc.; *U.S. Private*, pg. 1317
ECOURIER UK LTD.; *Int'l*, pg. 2300
ECOVACS ROBOTICS CO., LTD.; *Int'l*, pg. 2300
ECOVA, INC.—See ENGIE SA; *Int'l*, pg. 2431
ECOVAL TECHNOLOGY SAS—See Electricite de France S.A.; *Int'l*, pg. 2350
ECOVATION, INC.—See Ecolab Inc.; *U.S. Public*, pg. 714
ECOVER BELGIUM NV; *Int'l*, pg. 2300
ECO VOLT CO.,LTD.; *Int'l*, pg. 2292
ECOVYST CATALYST TECHNOLOGIES UK LTD.—See Ecovyst Inc.; *U.S. Public*, pg. 717
ECOVYST INC.; *U.S. Public*, pg. 717
ECOWATER CANADA LTD.—See Berkshire Hathaway Inc.; *U.S. Public*, pg. 311
ECOWATER SYSTEMS LLC—See Berkshire Hathaway Inc.; *U.S. Public*, pg. 311
ECO WAVE POWER GLOBAL AB; *Int'l*, pg. 2292
ECO-WIND CONSTRUCTION S.A.—See CEZ, a.s.; *Int'l*, pg. 1427
ECOWIND D.O.O.—See BayWa AG; *Int'l*, pg. 917
ECOWIND HANDELS- & WARTUNGS-GMBH—See BayWa AG; *Int'l*, pg. 917
ECO WINDOW SYSTEMS LLC—See Koch Industries, Inc.; *U.S. Public*, pg. 2332
ECOWISE AUSTRALIA PTY LTD—See ALS Limited; *Int'l*, pg. 378
ECOWISE ENVIRONMENTAL PTY LTD—See ALS Limited; *Int'l*, pg. 378
ECOWISE HOLDINGS LIMITED - CO-GEN BIOMASS POWER PLANT—See ecoWise Holdings Limited; *Int'l*, pg. 2300

ECOWISE HOLDINGS LIMITED; *Int'l*, pg. 2300
ECOWISE MARINA POWER PTE. LTD.—See ecoWise Holdings Limited; *Int'l*, pg. 2300
ECOWISE SOLUTIONS PTE. LTD.—See ecoWise Holdings Limited; *Int'l*, pg. 2300
ECOWOOD CO. LTD.—See Bunka Shutter Co., Ltd.; *Int'l*, pg. 1216
ECO WORLD-BALLYMORE EMBASSY GARDENS COMPANY LIMITED—See Eco World International Berhad; *Int'l*, pg. 2293
ECO WORLD-BALLYMORE LONDON CITY ISLAND COMPANY LIMITED—See Eco World International Berhad; *Int'l*, pg. 2293
ECO WORLD DEVELOPMENT GROUP BERHAD; *Int'l*, pg. 2293
ECO WORLD DEVELOPMENT MANAGEMENT (BBCC) SDN. BHD.—See Eco World Development Group Berhad; *Int'l*, pg. 2293
ECO WORLD INTERNATIONAL BERHAD; *Int'l*, pg. 2293
ECO WORLD INTERNATIONAL MARKETING SDN BHD—See Eco World International Berhad; *Int'l*, pg. 2293
ECO WORLD SYDNEY DEVELOPMENT PTY. LTD.—See Eco World International Berhad; *Int'l*, pg. 2293
ECOXY AS—See Nordic Unmanned ASA; *Int'l*, pg. 5423
ECO/Y&R, S.A—See WPP plc; *Int'l*, pg. 8491
ECPARK PTE. LTD.—See Tsukada Global Holdings Inc.; *Int'l*, pg. 7956
ECP-CENTRAL AFRICA—See Emerging Capital Partners (ECP); *U.S. Private*, pg. 1381
ECP COLLESTRADA S.R.L.—See Eurocommercial Properties N.V.; *Int'l*, pg. 2534
ECP EMERGING GROWTH LIMITED; *Int'l*, pg. 2300
ECP ENERGIECONTRACTING GMBH—See Robert Bosch GmbH; *Int'l*, pg. 6360
ECP ENVIRONMENTAL GROWTH OPPORTUNITIES CORP.; *U.S. Public*, pg. 717
ECPH MANAGEMENT INC.; *U.S. Private*, pg. 1330
ECP INCORPORATED—See Daubert Industries, Inc.; *U.S. Private*, pg. 1167
ECP KARLSKRONA AB—See Eurocommercial Properties N.V.; *Int'l*, pg. 2534
E.C.P. LIMITED—See Edenred S.A.; *Int'l*, pg. 2307
ECP MORABERG K.B.—See Eurocommercial Properties N.V.; *Int'l*, pg. 2534
ECP-MOROCCO—See Emerging Capital Partners (ECP); *U.S. Private*, pg. 1381
ECP-NIGERIA—See Emerging Capital Partners (ECP); *U.S. Private*, pg. 1381
ECP-NORTH AFRICA—See Emerging Capital Partners (ECP); *U.S. Private*, pg. 1381
EC POHL & CO PTY. LTD.—See Global Masters Fund Limited; *Int'l*, pg. 2999
EC POWER, LLC; *U.S. Private*, pg. 1326
EC POWER SYSTEMS; *U.S. Private*, pg. 1326
ECP-PARIS—See Emerging Capital Partners (ECP); *U.S. Private*, pg. 1381
ECP-SOUTHERN AFRICA—See Emerging Capital Partners (ECP); *U.S. Private*, pg. 1381
ECP-WEST AFRICA—See Emerging Capital Partners (ECP); *U.S. Private*, pg. 1381
ECR AG—See H2APEX Group SCA; *Int'l*, pg. 3199
ECR BELGIUM BVBA—See Beijer Ref AB; *Int'l*, pg. 944
ECRC; *Int'l*, pg. 2301
E-CREDIBLE CO., LTD.; *Int'l*, pg. 2247
EC&R ENERGY MARKETING, LLC—See E.ON SE; *Int'l*, pg. 2252
EC RESEARCH CORP.—See Cross Marketing Group Inc.; *Int'l*, pg. 1856
ECRID, INC.; *U.S. Public*, pg. 717
ECRI INSTITUTE; *U.S. Private*, pg. 1330
ECR INTERNATIONAL, INC.—See TerraVest Industries, Inc.; *Int'l*, pg. 7568
ECRI; *U.S. Private*, pg. 1330
ECR ITALY SPA—See Beijer Ref AB; *Int'l*, pg. 944
ECRM IMAGING SYSTEMS-CHINA—See ECRM Imaging Systems, Inc.; *U.S. Private*, pg. 1330
ECRM IMAGING SYSTEMS-HONG KONG—See ECRM Imaging Systems, Inc.; *U.S. Private*, pg. 1330
ECRM IMAGING SYSTEMS, INC.; *U.S. Private*, pg. 1330
ECR MINERALS PLC; *Int'l*, pg. 2301
EC&R NA SOLAR PV, LLC—See E.ON SE; *Int'l*, pg. 2256
EC&R NEDERLAND B.V.—See Beijer Ref AB; *Int'l*, pg. 944
ECRON ACUNOVA LIMITED—See TAKE Solutions Limited; *Int'l*, pg. 7436
ECRONOVA POLYMER GMBH—See Michelman Inc.; *U.S. Private*, pg. 2699
EC&R PANTHER CREEK WIND FARM III, LLC—See E.ON SE; *Int'l*, pg. 2256
EC&R PANTHER CREEK WIND FARM I&II, LLC—See E.ON SE; *Int'l*, pg. 2256
EC&R PAPALOTE CREEK II, LLC—See E.ON SE; *Int'l*, pg. 2256
EC&R PAPALOTE CREEK I, LLC—See E.ON SE; *Int'l*, pg. 2256
EC&R QSE, LLC—See E.ON SE; *Int'l*, pg. 2256
EC&R SERVICES, LLC—See E.ON SE; *Int'l*, pg. 2256
ECRUSH.COM, INC.—See The Hearst Corporation; *U.S. Private*, pg. 4046

ECRYPT TECHNOLOGIES, INC.; *U.S. Private*, pg. 1331
ECS ASTAR SDN BHD—See VSTECS Holdings Limited; *Int'l*, pg. 8315
ECSAT D.O.O.—See Sopra Steria Group S.A.; *Int'l*, pg. 7109
ECS BIZTECH LIMITED; *Int'l*, pg. 2301
ECS CABLE PROTECTION SP. Z O.O.—See Illinois Tool Works Inc.; *U.S. Public*, pg. 1103
ECSC GROUP PLC—See Daisy Group Limited; *Int'l*, pg. 1943
ECS CHINA TECHNOLOGY (SHANGHAI) COMPANY LIMITED—See VSTECS Holdings Limited; *Int'l*, pg. 8314
E&CS CO., LTD.—See Tobishima Corporation; *Int'l*, pg. 7771
ECS COMPUTERS ASIA PTE LTD—See VSTECS Holdings Limited; *Int'l*, pg. 8314
E.C.S. D.O.O.—See Illinois Tool Works Inc.; *U.S. Public*, pg. 1102
ECS ELECTRICAL CABLE SUPPLY LTD.; *Int'l*, pg. 2301
ECS - ENERGY CONSULTING SERVICES—See ENGIE SA; *Int'l*, pg. 2434
ECS ENGINEERING & CONSTRUCTION LIMITED; *Int'l*, pg. 2301
EC SERVICES—See Danbury AeroSpace, Inc.; *U.S. Private*, pg. 1153
EC SERWIS SP. Z O.O.—See E.ON SE; *Int'l*, pg. 2256
ECS EUROPEAN CONSTRUCTION SERVICES GMBH—See STRABAG SE; *Int'l*, pg. 7230
ECS FEDERAL, LLC—See ASGN Incorporated; *U.S. Public*, pg. 210
ECS HOLDINGS LIMITED—See VSTECS Holdings Limited; *Int'l*, pg. 8314
ECSI, LLC—See SynTerra Corp.; *U.S. Private*, pg. 3905
ECS INC.; *U.S. Private*, pg. 1331
ECS, INC.—See Coffman Engineers, Inc.; *U.S. Private*, pg. 961
ECS INDO PTE LTD.—See VSTECS Holdings Limited; *Int'l*, pg. 8314
ECS INDUSTRIAL COMPUTER CO., LTD.—See Elitegroup Computer Systems Co., Ltd.; *Int'l*, pg. 2363
ECS INFOCOM (PHILS) PTE LTD.—See VSTECS Holdings Limited; *Int'l*, pg. 8314
ECSI; *U.S. Private*, pg. 1331
ECS IT BERHAD; *Int'l*, pg. 2301
ECS KU SDN BHD—See VSTECS Holdings Limited; *Int'l*, pg. 8315
ECS KUSH SDN BHD—See VSTECS Holdings Limited; *Int'l*, pg. 8314
ECS LIMITED; *Int'l*, pg. 2301
EC SOLUTIONS INC.—See Alan Allman Associates SA; *Int'l*, pg. 290
EC SOURCE SERVICES, LLC—See MasTec, Inc.; *U.S. Public*, pg. 1393
EC SOURCING GROUP INC.—See Simfoni, Inc.; *U.S. Private*, pg. 3665
ECS PERICOMP SDN BHD—See VSTECS Holdings Limited; *Int'l*, pg. 8315
ECSPONENT SOUTH AFRICA (PTY) LTD—See Afristrat Investment Holdings Limited; *Int'l*, pg. 193
ECS TECHNOLOGY CHINA LTD.—See VSTECS Holdings Limited; *Int'l*, pg. 8315
ECS TECHNOLOGY COMPANY LIMITED—See VSTECS Holdings Limited; *Int'l*, pg. 8315
ECS TECHNOLOGY (GUANGZHOU) COMPANY LIMITED—See VSTECS Holdings Limited; *Int'l*, pg. 8315
ECS TECHNOLOGY (HK) CO., LIMITED—See VSTECS Holdings Limited; *Int'l*, pg. 8315
ECS TELECOM CO., LTD.; *Int'l*, pg. 2301
E.C. STYBERG ENGINEERING CO., INC.; *U.S. Private*, pg. 1305
ECTEON, INC.—See Rothschild & Co SCA; *Int'l*, pg. 6403
ECTEON, INC.—See TA Associates, Inc.; *U.S. Private*, pg. 3917
ECT FINANCE LTD.—See Environmental Clean Technologies Limited; *Int'l*, pg. 2454
ECT HOLDINGS CORP.—See Deutsche Bank Aktiengesellschaft; *Int'l*, pg. 2061
ECTYCELL SASU—See Cellectis S.A.; *Int'l*, pg. 1393
ECUACENTAIR CIA. LTDA.—See World Kinect Corporation; *U.S. Public*, pg. 2380
ECUACENTAIR S.A.—See World Kinect Corporation; *U.S. Public*, pg. 2380
ECUAESTIBAS S.A.—See Quinenco S.A.; *Int'l*, pg. 6163
ECU AIR N.V.—See Allcargo Logistics Limited; *Int'l*, pg. 333
ECUATORIANA DE SAL Y PRODUCTOS QUIMICOS C.A.—See K+S Aktiengesellschaft; *Int'l*, pg. 4040
ECU AUSTRALIA PTY LTD.—See Allcargo Logistics Limited; *Int'l*, pg. 333
ECU ELECTRONIC INDUSTRY CO., LTD.—See Anhui Sun-Create Electronics Co., Ltd.; *Int'l*, pg. 469
ECUHOLD N.V.—See Allcargo Logistics Limited; *Int'l*, pg. 333
ECU INTERNATIONAL N.V.—See Allcargo Logistics Limited; *Int'l*, pg. 333
ECU INTERNATIONAL—See Allcargo Logistics Limited; *Int'l*, pg. 334

E.C. STYBERG ENGINEERING CO., INC. CORPORATE AFFILIATIONS

ECU LINE ABU DHABI LLC—See Allcargo Logistics Limited; *Int'l*, pg. 333
ECU LINE ALGERIE S.A.R.L.—See Allcargo Logistics Limited; *Int'l*, pg. 333
ECU-LINE CANADA INC.—See Allcargo Logistics Limited; *Int'l*, pg. 334
ECU LINE CHILE S.A.—See Allcargo Logistics Limited; *Int'l*, pg. 333
ECU LINE CHINA LTD.—See Allcargo Logistics Limited; *Int'l*, pg. 333
ECU LINE COTE D'IVOIRE SARL—See Allcargo Logistics Limited; *Int'l*, pg. 333
ECU-LINE CZECH S.R.O.—See Allcargo Logistics Limited; *Int'l*, pg. 334
ECU LINE DE COLOMBIA S.A—See Allcargo Logistics Limited; *Int'l*, pg. 334
ECU LINE DEL ECUADOR S.A.—See Allcargo Logistics Limited; *Int'l*, pg. 333
ECU LINE DOHA W.L.L.—See Allcargo Logistics Limited; *Int'l*, pg. 333
ECU LINE EGYPT LTD.—See Allcargo Logistics Limited; *Int'l*, pg. 333
ECU-LINE (GERMANY) GMBH—See Allcargo Logistics Limited; *Int'l*, pg. 334
ECU-LINE GUANGZHOU LTD.—See Allcargo Logistics Limited; *Int'l*, pg. 334
ECU LINE GUATEMALA S.A.—See Allcargo Logistics Limited; *Int'l*, pg. 333
ECU-LINE HONG KONG LTD.—See Allcargo Logistics Limited; *Int'l*, pg. 334
ECU LINE JAPAN LTD.—See Allcargo Logistics Limited; *Int'l*, pg. 333
ECU-LINE MALTA LTD.—See Allcargo Logistics Limited; *Int'l*, pg. 334
ECU LINE MAROC S.A.—See Allcargo Logistics Limited; *Int'l*, pg. 333
ECU LINE MIDDLEEAST LLC—See Allcargo Logistics Limited; *Int'l*, pg. 333
ECU-LINE N.V.—See Allcargo Logistics Limited; *Int'l*, pg. 334
ECU-LINE PANAMA S.A.—See Allcargo Logistics Limited; *Int'l*, pg. 334
ECU-LINE PARAGUAY SA—See Allcargo Logistics Limited; *Int'l*, pg. 333
ECU-LINE PERU S.A.—See Allcargo Logistics Limited; *Int'l*, pg. 334
ECU LINE PHILIPPINES INC.—See Allcargo Logistics Limited; *Int'l*, pg. 333
ECU LINE ROMANIA S.R.L.—See Allcargo Logistics Limited; *Int'l*, pg. 334
ECU LINE ROTTERDAM B.V.—See Allcargo Logistics Limited; *Int'l*, pg. 333
ECU LINE S.A. (PTY) LTD.—See Allcargo Logistics Limited; *Int'l*, pg. 333
ECU-LINE SAUDI ARABIA LLC—See Allcargo Logistics Limited; *Int'l*, pg. 334
ECU LINE SINGAPORE PTE. LTD.—See Allcargo Logistics Limited; *Int'l*, pg. 333
ECU-LINE SPAIN S.L.—See Allcargo Logistics Limited; *Int'l*, pg. 333
ECU LINE (THAILAND) CO.LTD.—See Allcargo Logistics Limited; *Int'l*, pg. 334
ECU LOGISTICS S.A.—See Allcargo Logistics Limited; *Int'l*, pg. 333
ECUMED PETROLEUM LIMITED—See Zenith Energy Ltd.; *Int'l*, pg. 8633
ECUMENICAL ENTERPRISES INC.; *U.S. Private*, pg. 1331
ECUMEN; *U.S. Private*, pg. 1331
ECU NORDIC OY—See Allcargo Logistics Limited; *Int'l*, pg. 333
ECUPHAR BV—See Animalcare Group plc; *Int'l*, pg. 471
ECUPHAR GMBH—See Animalcare Group plc; *Int'l*, pg. 471
ECUPHAR NV/SA—See Animalcare Group plc; *Int'l*, pg. 471
ECUPHAR VETERINARIA SL—See Animalcare Group plc; *Int'l*, pg. 471
ECURV INC.—See Exelon Corporation; *U.S. Public*, pg. 807
ECUSTA CREDIT UNION—See Champion Credit Union; *U.S. Private*, pg. 846
EC UTBILDNING AB—See AcadeMedia AB; *Int'l*, pg. 75
ECUTEC BARCELONA S.L.—See Erich Netzsch GmbH & Co. Holding KG; *Int'l*, pg. 2491
ECU TRUCKING, INC.—See Allcargo Logistics Limited; *Int'l*, pg. 333
ECU WORLDWIDE CEE S.R.L.—See Allcargo Logistics Limited; *Int'l*, pg. 333
ECU WORLDWIDE (CYPRUS) LTD.—See Allcargo Logistics Limited; *Int'l*, pg. 334
ECU WORLDWIDE ITALY S.R.L.—See Allcargo Logistics Limited; *Int'l*, pg. 334
ECU WORLDWIDE (KENYA) LTD.—See Allcargo Logistics Limited; *Int'l*, pg. 334
ECU WORLDWIDE LANKA (PRIVATE) LTD.—See Allcargo Logistics Limited; *Int'l*, pg. 334
ECU WORLDWIDE LOGISTICS DO BRAZIL LTDA—See Allcargo Logistics Limited; *Int'l*, pg. 334

ECU WORLDWIDE (MALAYSIA) SDN BHD—See Allcargo Logistics Limited; *Int'l*, pg. 334
ECU WORLDWIDE (MAURITIUS) LTD.—See Allcargo Logistics Limited; *Int'l*, pg. 334
ECU WORLDWIDE MEXICO SA DE CV—See Allcargo Logistics Limited; *Int'l*, pg. 334
ECU WORLDWIDE NEW ZEALAND LTD.—See Allcargo Logistics Limited; *Int'l*, pg. 334
ECU WORLDWIDE (POLAND) SP ZOO—See Allcargo Logistics Limited; *Int'l*, pg. 334
ECU WORLDWIDE (SOUTH AFRICA) PTY LTD—See Allcargo Logistics Limited; *Int'l*, pg. 334
ECU WORLDWIDE TURKEY TASIMACILIK LIMITED SIRKETI—See Allcargo Logistics Limited; *Int'l*, pg. 334
ECVISION (SHENZHEN) CO. LTD.—See Insight Venture Management, LLC; *U.S. Private*, pg. 2087
ECV—See Eiffage S.A.; *Int'l*, pg. 2329
E.C. WASTE, INC.—See Post Capital Partners, LLC; *U.S. Private*, pg. 3234
EC WORLD REIT; *Int'l*, pg. 2287
E-CYCLE LLC; *U.S. Private*, pg. 1302
ECYCLERS, LLC—See The Kane Company; *U.S. Private*, pg. 4064
ECZACIBASI ASSET MANAGEMENT CO.—See Eczacibasi Holding A.S.; *Int'l*, pg. 2301
ECZACIBASI-BAXTER HASTANE URUNLERI SANAYI VE TICARET A.S.—See Baxter International Inc.; *U.S. Public*, pg. 281
ECZACIBASI-BAXTER HOSPITAL SUPPLY CO.—See Eczacibasi Holding A.S.; *Int'l*, pg. 2301
ECZACIBASI GIRISIM CO.—See Eczacibasi Holding A.S.; *Int'l*, pg. 2301
ECZACIBASI HIJYEN URUNLERI SANAYI VE TICARET A.S.—See Eczacibasi Holding A.S.; *Int'l*, pg. 2301
ECZACIBASI HOLDING A.S.; *Int'l*, pg. 2301
ECZACIBASI INVESTMENT HOLDING CO.—See Eczacibasi Holding A.S.; *Int'l*, pg. 2301
ECZACIBASI-LINCOLN ELECTRIC ASKAYNAK CO.—See Eczacibasi Holding A.S.; *Int'l*, pg. 2301
ECZACIBASI MONROL NUKLEER URUNLER SAN. VE TIC. A.S.—See Eczacibasi Holding A.S.; *Int'l*, pg. 2301
ECZACIBASI OCCUPATIONAL HEALTH AND SAFETY SERVICES—See Eczacibasi Holding A.S.; *Int'l*, pg. 2301
ECZACIBASI PHARMACEUTICAL & INDUSTRIAL INVESTMENT CO.—See Eczacibasi Holding A.S.; *Int'l*, pg. 2301
ECZACIBASI YAPI GERECLERI SANAYI VE TICARET A.S.—See Eczacibasi Holding A.S.; *Int'l*, pg. 2301
ECZACIBASI YATIRIM HOLDING ORTAKLIGI A.S.; *Int'l*, pg. 2302
EC ZIELONA GORA S.A.—See Zespol Elektrocieplowni Wroclawskich KOGENERACJA S.A.; *Int'l*, pg. 8639
EDA ATTIKIS S.A.—See Italgas S.p.A.; *Int'l*, pg. 3828
EDAC AERO ROTATING COMPONENTS—See Hanwha Group; *Int'l*, pg. 3264
EDAC SYSTEMS INC.; *U.S. Private*, pg. 1332
E-DA DEVELOPMENT CORP.—See Yieh Phui Enterprise Co., Ltd.; *Int'l*, pg. 8581
EDAFOLOGIA Y RESTAURACION DEL ENTORNO GALLEGO, S.L.—See ACS, Actividades de Construccion y Servicios, S.A.; *Int'l*, pg. 111
EDAG DO BRASIL LTDA.—See ATON GmbH; *Int'l*, pg. 689
EDAG ENGINEERING AB—See ATON GmbH; *Int'l*, pg. 688
EDAG ENGINEERING CZ SPOL. S.R.O.—See ATON GmbH; *Int'l*, pg. 688
EDAG ENGINEERING & DESIGN INDIA PRIV. LTD.—See ATON GmbH; *Int'l*, pg. 688
EDAG ENGINEERING GMBH—See ATON GmbH; *Int'l*, pg. 688
EDAG ENGINEERING GROUP AG—See ATON GmbH; *Int'l*, pg. 688
EDAG ENGINEERING POLSKA SP.Z.O.O.—See ATON GmbH; *Int'l*, pg. 688
EDAG ENGINEERING SCHWEIZ GMBH—See ATON GmbH; *Int'l*, pg. 689
EDAG ENGINEERING S.R.L.—See ATON GmbH; *Int'l*, pg. 689
EDAG HOLDING SDN. BHD.—See ATON GmbH; *Int'l*, pg. 689
EDAG HUNGARY KFT.—See ATON GmbH; *Int'l*, pg. 689
EDAG INC.—See ATON GmbH; *Int'l*, pg. 689
EDAG ITALIA S.R.L.—See ATON GmbH; *Int'l*, pg. 689
EDAG JAPAN CO., LTD.—See ATON GmbH; *Int'l*, pg. 689
EDAG MEXICO, S.A. DE C.V.—See ATON GmbH; *Int'l*, pg. 689
EDAG NETHERLANDS B.V.—See ATON GmbH; *Int'l*, pg. 689
EDAG PRODUCTION SOLUTION CZ S.R.O.—See ATON GmbH; *Int'l*, pg. 689
EDAG PRODUCTION SOLUTIONS GMBH & CO. KG—See ATON GmbH; *Int'l*, pg. 689
EDAG PRODUCTION SOLUTIONS INDIA PRIV. LTD.—See ATON GmbH; *Int'l*, pg. 689
EDAG PRODUCTION SOLUTIONS KOREA LTD.—See ATON GmbH; *Int'l*, pg. 689

EDAG TECHNOLOGIES INDIA PRIV. LTD.—See ATON GmbH; *Int'l*, pg. 689
EDAN DIAGNOSTICS, INC.—See Edan Instruments, Inc.; *Int'l*, pg. 2303
EDAN INSTRUMENTS GMBH—See Edan Instruments, Inc.; *Int'l*, pg. 2303
EDAN INSTRUMENTS, INC.; *Int'l*, pg. 2303
EDAN MEDICAL INDIA PRIVATE LTD.—See Edan Instruments, Inc.; *Int'l*, pg. 2304
EDAN MEDICAL (UK) LTD.—See Edan Instruments, Inc.; *Int'l*, pg. 2304
EDAP GMBH—See EDAP TMS S.A.; *Int'l*, pg. 2304
EDAP RUSSIA—See EDAP TMS S.A.; *Int'l*, pg. 2304
EDAP TECHNOMED CO. LTD.—See EDAP TMS S.A.; *Int'l*, pg. 2304
EDAP TECHNOMED INC.—See EDAP TMS S.A.; *Int'l*, pg. 2304
EDAP TECHNOMED ITALIA SRL—See EDAP TMS S.A.; *Int'l*, pg. 2304
EDAP TECHNOMED (M) SDN BHD—See EDAP TMS S.A.; *Int'l*, pg. 2304
EDAP TECHNOMED SDN BHD—See EDAP TMS S.A.; *Int'l*, pg. 2304
EDAPTIVE SYSTEMS, LLC—See The Carlyle Group Inc.; *U.S. Public*, pg. 2048
EDAP TMS FRANCE S.A.—See EDAP TMS S.A.; *Int'l*, pg. 2304
EDAP TMS GMBH—See EDAP TMS S.A.; *Int'l*, pg. 2304
EDAP TMS KOREA—See EDAP TMS S.A.; *Int'l*, pg. 2304
EDAP TMS S.A.; *Int'l*, pg. 2304
EDARA L.L.C.—See Emirates NBD PJSC; *Int'l*, pg. 2382
EDARAN IT SERVICES SDN. BHD.—See Edran Berhad; *Int'l*, pg. 2315
EDARAN OTOMOBIL NASIONAL BERHAD—See DRB-HICOM Berhad; *Int'l*, pg. 2201
EDARAN PRECISION INDIA PRIVATE LIMITED—See YBS International Berhad; *Int'l*, pg. 8574
EDARAN PRECISION INDUSTRIES SDN. BHD.—See YBS International Berhad; *Int'l*, pg. 8574
EDARAN RESOURCES PTE. LTD.—See YBS International Berhad; *Int'l*, pg. 8574
EDARAN TAN CHONG MOTOR SDN. BHD.—See Tan Chong Motor Holdings Berhad; *Int'l*, pg. 7453
EDARAN TRADE NETWORK SDN. BHD.—See Edran Berhad; *Int'l*, pg. 2315
EDARON INC.; *U.S. Private*, pg. 1332
EDATEL S.A. E.S.P.—See Millicom International Cellular S.A.; *Int'l*, pg. 4896
ED A. WILSON INC.—See Tenir Investments Inc.; *U.S. Private*, pg. 3967
EDAX—See AMETEK, Inc.; *U.S. Public*, pg. 117
ED BELL CONSTRUCTION COMPANY INC.—See Ed Bell Investments Company Inc.; *U.S. Private*, pg. 1331
ED BELL INVESTMENTS COMPANY INC.; *U.S. Private*, pg. 1331
EDB INVESTMENTS PTE. LTD.; *Int'l*, pg. 2304
ED BOZARTH CHEVROLET AND BUICK, INC.; *U.S. Private*, pg. 1331
ED BOZARTH CHEVROLET COMPANY, INC.; *U.S. Private*, pg. 1331
ED BROKING MIAMI INC.—See BGC Group, Inc.; *U.S. Public*, pg. 328
ED BROWN DISTRIBUTORS—See EVI Industries, Inc.; *U.S. Public*, pg. 803
E.D. BULLARD COMPANY; *U.S. Private*, pg. 1305
EDCC BANK LTD.—See Ecobank Transnational Incorporated; *Int'l*, pg. 2293
EDC COMMUNICATIONS LIMITED—See Mill Road Capital Management LLC; *U.S. Private*, pg. 2730
EDC CONSULTING LLC; *U.S. Private*, pg. 1332
EDC EUROPEAN EXCAVATOR DESIGN CENTER BETEILIGUNGS-GMBH—See Caterpillar, Inc.; *U.S. Public*, pg. 452
EDC EUROPEAN EXCAVATOR DESIGN CENTER VERWALTUNGS GMBH—See Caterpillar, Inc.; *U.S. Public*, pg. 450
EDC, INC.—See Metallus Inc.; *U.S. Public*, pg. 1427
EDC INVESTMENT CORPORATION—See Ecobank Transnational Incorporated; *Int'l*, pg. 2294
EDC IRELAND—See Chevron Corporation; *U.S. Public*, pg. 487
EDCO DISPOSAL CORPORATION; *U.S. Private*, pg. 1332
EDCO, INC.—See Exco Technologies Limited; *Int'l*, pg. 2580
EDCO INVESTMENT B.V.—See Enka Insaat ve Sanayi A.S.; *Int'l*, pg. 2440
EDCO LLC; *U.S. Private*, pg. 1332
E.D. COLLIER & SON—See Bateman Brothers Lumber Co., Inc.; *U.S. Private*, pg. 486
EDCON HOLDINGS LIMITED; *Int'l*, pg. 2304
EDCON LIMITED—See Edcon Holdings Limited; *Int'l*, pg. 2304
ED CONTACT SRL—See Leonardo S.p.A.; *Int'l*, pg. 4458
EDCOR DRILLING SERVICES INC.—See Sparton Resources Inc.; *Int'l*, pg. 7127
EDCO WASTE & RECYCLING SERVICES INC.—See EDCO Disposal Corporation; *U.S. Private*, pg. 1332
E.D. CRANE & ASSOCIATES; *U.S. Private*, pg. 1305

COMPANY NAME INDEX

EDC STOCKBROKERS LIMITED—See Ecobank Transnational Incorporated; *Int'l*, pg. 2294
EDC WIND ENERGY HOLDINGS, INC.—See First Gen Corporation; *Int'l*, pg. 2684
EDDA WIND ASA; *Int'l*, pg. 2304
EDD HELMS ELECTRICAL, INC.—See Edd Helms Group, Inc.; *U.S. Public*, pg. 717
EDD HELMS GROUP, INC.; *U.S. Public*, pg. 717
EDD HELMS MCDONALD AIR CONDITIONING, INC.—See Edd Helms Group, Inc.; *U.S. Public*, pg. 717
EDDIE BAUER, INC.—See Leonard Green & Partners, L.P.; *U.S. Private*, pg. 2424
EDDIE BAUER JAPAN, INC.—See Leonard Green & Partners, L.P.; *U.S. Private*, pg. 2424
EDDIE BAUER JAPAN, INC.—See Otto GmbH & Co. KG; *Int'l*, pg. 5663
EDDIE BRYANT ENTERPRISES INC.; *U.S. Private*, pg. 1332
EDDIE GILSTRAP MOTORS INCORPORATED; *U.S. Private*, pg. 1332
EDDIES TIRE SERVICE INC.; *U.S. Private*, pg. 1332
EDDIE STOBART LIMITED—See DBAY Advisors Limited; *Int'l*, pg. 1986
EDDIE STOBART LOGISTICS PLC—See DBAY Advisors Limited; *Int'l*, pg. 1986
EDDIE STOBART PROMOTIONS LIMITED—See DBAY Advisors Limited; *Int'l*, pg. 1986
EDDIES TRUCK SALES INCORPORATED; *U.S. Private*, pg. 1332
EDDING AG; *Int'l*, pg. 2304
EDDING ARGENTINA SA—See Edding AG; *Int'l*, pg. 2304
EDDING BENELUX BV—See Edding AG; *Int'l*, pg. 2304
EDDING COLOMBIA SAS—See Edding AG; *Int'l*, pg. 2304
EDDING EXPRESSIVE SKIN GMBH—See Edding AG; *Int'l*, pg. 2304
EDDING FRANCE SAS—See Edding AG; *Int'l*, pg. 2304
EDDING HELLAS LTD.—See Edding AG; *Int'l*, pg. 2304
EDDING INTERNATIONAL GMBH—See Edding AG; *Int'l*, pg. 2304
EDDING OFIS VE KIRTASIYE—See Edding AG; *Int'l*, pg. 2304
EDDING UK LTD.—See Edding AG; *Int'l*, pg. 2304
EDDING VERTRIEB GMBH—See Edding AG; *Int'l*, pg. 2304
EDD INVESTMENT CO.; *U.S. Private*, pg. 1332
EDDL—See Vivendi SE; *Int'l*, pg. 8272
EDDS SUPPLIES INC.; *U.S. Private*, pg. 1332
EDDYFI NDT, INC.; *Int'l*, pg. 2304
EDDY GROUP LIMITED; *Int'l*, pg. 2304
EDDY PACKING CO., INC.—See Insight Equity Holdings LLC; *U.S. Private*, pg. 2086
EDDY'S TOYOTA OF WICHITA INC.; *U.S. Private*, pg. 1332
EDECLINSEYSYSTEM CO.,LTD.—See Fuji Corporation; *Int'l*, pg. 2809
EDECO TOOLS AB—See Indutrade AB; *Int'l*, pg. 3678
ED & EDDIE'S ICE CREAM—See DeBartolo Holdings, LLC; *U.S. Private*, pg. 1186
EDEIS S.A.S.—See Ciclad SA; *Int'l*, pg. 1603
EDEKA ZENTRALE AG & CO. KG; *Int'l*, pg. 2305
EDELAP S.A.—See Techint S.p.A.; *Int'l*, pg. 7503
EDELBROCK CORPORATION; *U.S. Private*, pg. 1332
EDELBROCK FOUNDRY CORP.—See Edelbrock Corporation; *U.S. Private*, pg. 1332
EDEL GERMANY GMBH—See Edel SE & Co. KGaA; *Int'l*, pg. 2305
EDELGRAPHIT GMBH—See AMG Critical Materials N.V.; *Int'l*, pg. 425
EDELIGHT GMBH—See Hubert Burda Media Holding Kommanditgesellschaft; *Int'l*, pg. 3520
EDELMAN BEIJING—See Daniel J. Edelman, Inc.; *U.S. Private*, pg. 1155
EDELMAN FINANCIAL ENGINES, LLC—See Hellman & Friedman LLC; *U.S. Private*, pg. 1908
EDELMAN FINANCIAL SERVICES, LLC—See Hellman & Friedman LLC; *U.S. Private*, pg. 1907
EDELMAN HONG KONG—See Daniel J. Edelman, Inc.; *U.S. Private*, pg. 1155
EDELMAN LEATHER, LLC—See MillerKnoll, Inc.; *U.S. Public*, pg. 1447
EDELMANN (BEIJING) CO., LTD.—See Edelmann GmbH; *Int'l*, pg. 2305
EDELMANN (BEIJING) PHARMACEUTICAL PACKAGING & PRINTING, LTD.—See Edelmann GmbH; *Int'l*, pg. 2305
EDELMANN BITTERFELD GMBH—See Edelmann GmbH; *Int'l*, pg. 2305
EDELMANN BRAZIL EMBALAGENS LTDA.—See Edelmann GmbH; *Int'l*, pg. 2305
EDELMANN FRANCE—See Edelmann GmbH; *Int'l*, pg. 2305
EDELMANN GMBH; *Int'l*, pg. 2305
EDELMANN HUNGARY PACKAGING ZRT.—See Edelmann GmbH; *Int'l*, pg. 2305
EDELMANN LEAFLET SOLUTIONS GMBH—See Edelmann GmbH; *Int'l*, pg. 2305
EDELMANN NORDERSTEDT GMBH—See Edelmann GmbH; *Int'l*, pg. 2305
EDELMANN PACKAGING INDIA PRIVATE LIMITED—See Edelmann GmbH; *Int'l*, pg. 2305
EDELMANN PACKAGING MEXICO S.A. DE C.V.—See Edelmann GmbH; *Int'l*, pg. 2305
EDELMANN PHARMADRUCK GMBH—See Edelmann GmbH; *Int'l*, pg. 2305
EDELMANN POLAND SP.Z O.O.—See Edelmann GmbH; *Int'l*, pg. 2305
EDELMANN SCOTT, INC.; *U.S. Private*, pg. 1332
EDELMANN USA, INC. - PULASKI—See Edelmann GmbH; *Int'l*, pg. 2305
EDELMANN USA, INC.—See Edelmann GmbH; *Int'l*, pg. 2305
EDELMANN WUPPERTAL GMBH—See Edelmann GmbH; *Int'l*, pg. 2306
EDELMAN RUSSIA—See Daniel J. Edelman, Inc.; *U.S. Private*, pg. 1155
EDELMAN—See Daniel J. Edelman, Inc.; *U.S. Private*, pg. 1154
EDELMAN—See Daniel J. Edelman, Inc.; *U.S. Private*, pg. 1154
EDELMAN—See Daniel J. Edelman, Inc.; *U.S. Private*, pg. 1154
EDELMAN—See Daniel J. Edelman, Inc.; *U.S. Private*, pg. 1154
EDELMAN—See Daniel J. Edelman, Inc.; *U.S. Private*, pg. 1154
EDELMAN—See Daniel J. Edelman, Inc.; *U.S. Private*, pg. 1154
EDELMAN—See Daniel J. Edelman, Inc.; *U.S. Private*, pg. 1154
EDELMAN—See Daniel J. Edelman, Inc.; *U.S. Private*, pg. 1154
EDELMAN—See Daniel J. Edelman, Inc.; *U.S. Private*, pg. 1155
EDELMAN—See Daniel J. Edelman, Inc.; *U.S. Private*, pg. 1155
EDELMAN—See Daniel J. Edelman, Inc.; *U.S. Private*, pg. 1155
EDELMAN—See Daniel J. Edelman, Inc.; *U.S. Private*, pg. 1155
EDELMAN—See Daniel J. Edelman, Inc.; *U.S. Private*, pg. 1155
EDELMAN—See Daniel J. Edelman, Inc.; *U.S. Private*, pg. 1155
EDELMAN—See Daniel J. Edelman, Inc.; *U.S. Private*, pg. 1155
EDELMAN—See Daniel J. Edelman, Inc.; *U.S. Private*, pg. 1155
EDELMAN—See Daniel J. Edelman, Inc.; *U.S. Private*, pg. 1155
EDELMAN—See Daniel J. Edelman, Inc.; *U.S. Private*, pg. 1155
EDELMAN—See Daniel J. Edelman, Inc.; *U.S. Private*, pg. 1155
EDELMAN—See Daniel J. Edelman, Inc.; *U.S. Private*, pg. 1155
EDELMAN—See Daniel J. Edelman, Inc.; *U.S. Private*, pg. 1155
EDELMAN—See Daniel J. Edelman, Inc.; *U.S. Private*, pg. 1155
EDELMAN SOUTH AFRICA—See Daniel J. Edelman, Inc.; *U.S. Private*, pg. 1155
EDELMAN SOUTHWEST - DALLAS—See Daniel J. Edelman, Inc.; *U.S. Private*, pg. 1155
EDELMAN SOUTHWEST—See Daniel J. Edelman, Inc.; *U.S. Private*, pg. 1155
EDELMAN S.R.L.—See Daniel J. Edelman, Inc.; *U.S. Private*, pg. 1155
EDEL MEDIA & ENTERTAINMENT GMBH—See Edel SE & Co. KGaA; *Int'l*, pg. 2305
EDEL MUSICA VERTRIEBS GMBH—See Edel SE & Co. KGaA; *Int'l*, pg. 2305
EDEL MUSIC S.A.—See Edel SE & Co. KGaA; *Int'l*, pg. 2305
EDEL RECORDS FINLAND OY—See Edel SE & Co. KGaA; *Int'l*, pg. 2305
EDEL RECORDS GMBH—See Edel SE & Co. KGaA; *Int'l*, pg. 2305
EDEL RECORDS (SWITZERLAND) AG—See Edel SE & Co. KGaA; *Int'l*, pg. 2305
EDELSA GRUPO DIDASCALIA S.A.—See Vivendi SE; *Int'l*, pg. 8272
EDEL SE & CO. KGAA; *Int'l*, pg. 2305
EDELSTAHLWERKE BUDERUS NEDERLAND B.V.—See voestalpine AG; *Int'l*, pg. 8288
EDEL UK RECORDS LTD.—See Edel SE & Co. KGaA; *Int'l*, pg. 2305
EDELWEISS AIR AG—See Deutsche Lufthansa AG; *Int'l*, pg. 2070
EDELWEISS BROKING LIMITED—See Edelweiss Financial Services Ltd.; *Int'l*, pg. 2306
EDELWEISS CAPITAL (SINGAPORE) PTE. LIMITED—See Edelweiss Financial Services Ltd.; *Int'l*, pg. 2306
EDELWEISS CUSTODIAL SERVICES LIMITED—See Edelweiss Financial Services Ltd.; *Int'l*, pg. 2306
EDELWEISS FINANCIAL PRODUCTS AND SOLUTIONS LIMITED—See Edelweiss Financial Services Ltd.; *Int'l*, pg. 2306
EDELWEISS FINANCIAL SERVICES INC.—See Edelweiss Financial Services Ltd.; *Int'l*, pg. 2306
EDELWEISS FINANCIAL SERVICES LTD.; *Int'l*, pg. 2306
EDELWEISS GENERAL INSURANCE COMPANY LIMITED—See Edelweiss Financial Services Ltd.; *Int'l*, pg. 2306
EDELWEISS INSURANCE BROKERS LIMITED—See Edelweiss Financial Services Ltd.; *Int'l*, pg. 2306
EDELWEISS MULTI STRATEGY FUND ADVISORS LLP—See Edelweiss Financial Services Ltd.; *Int'l*, pg. 2306
EDELWEISS SECURITIES LIMITED—See Edelweiss Financial Services Ltd.; *Int'l*, pg. 2306
EDELWEISS TOKIO LIFE INSURANCE COMPANY LIMITED—See Edelweiss Financial Services Ltd.; *Int'l*, pg. 2306
EDENA S.A.—See Phoenix Beverages Limited; *Int'l*, pg. 5849
EDEN AUTOMOTIVE INVESTMENTS LIMITED; *Int'l*, pg. 2306
EDEN BRACKNELL—See Eden Automotive Investments Limited; *Int'l*, pg. 2306
EDENBRIDGE HEALTHCARE LIMITED—See EMIS Group plc; *Int'l*, pg. 2383
EDEN CAPITAL MANAGEMENT LLC; *U.S. Private*, pg. 1333
EDEN CATERING SDN. BHD.—See Eden Inc. Berhad; *Int'l*, pg. 2306
EDEN COMPANY, INC.; *U.S. Private*, pg. 1333
EDEN CRYOGENICS LLC; *U.S. Private*, pg. 1333
EDEN DAILY NEWS—See Lee Enterprises, Incorporated; *U.S. Public*, pg. 1299
EDENDERRY POWER LIMITED—See Bord na Mona Plc; *Int'l*, pg. 1113
EDEN EMPIRE INC.; *Int'l*, pg. 2306
E&D ENERGIE- UND DIENSTLEISTUNGS GMBH & CO. KG—See EWE Aktiengesellschaft; *Int'l*, pg. 2575
EDEN FARM LIMITED—See Kitwave Group Plc; *Int'l*, pg. 4196
EDEN FOODS INC.; *U.S. Private*, pg. 1333
EDEN (FRANCE)—See SafeTIC S.A.; *Int'l*, pg. 6470
EDEN (GM) LIMITED—See General Motors Company; *U.S. Public*, pg. 928
EDENHALL LIMITED—See Marshalls plc; *Int'l*, pg. 4702
EDEN HOTEL LANKA PLC—See LOLC Holdings PLC; *Int'l*, pg. 4545
EDEN HOUSING, INC.; *U.S. Private*, pg. 1333
EDEN HOUSING MANAGEMENT, INC.—See Eden Housing, Inc.; *U.S. Private*, pg. 1333
EDEN INC. BERHAD; *Int'l*, pg. 2306
EDEN INDUSTRIES (UK) LIMITED—See Berkshire Hathaway Inc.; *U.S. Public*, pg. 311
EDEN INNOVATIONS LTD.; *Int'l*, pg. 2306
EDEN INTERNATIONAL SA; *Int'l*, pg. 2306
EDENKOOL PTE LTD—See Far East Group Limited; *Int'l*, pg. 2616
EDEN MEDICAL CENTER—See Sutter Health; *U.S. Private*, pg. 3887
EDEN OIL CO. INC.; *U.S. Private*, pg. 1333
EDENRED ARGENTINA—See Edenred S.A.; *Int'l*, pg. 2307
EDENRED AUSTRIA GMBH—See Edenred S.A.; *Int'l*, pg. 2307
EDENRED BELGIUM SA—See Edenred S.A.; *Int'l*, pg. 2307
EDENRED BULGARIA AD—See Edenred S.A.; *Int'l*, pg. 2307
EDENRED CORPORATE PAYMENT SAS—See Edenred S.A.; *Int'l*, pg. 2307
EDENRED CZ S.R.O—See Edenred S.A.; *Int'l*, pg. 2307
EDENRED DEUTSCHLAND GMBH—See Edenred S.A.; *Int'l*, pg. 2307
EDENRED EMPLOYEE BENEFITS UK LTD—See Edenred S.A.; *Int'l*, pg. 2307
EDENRED ESPANA S.A.—See Edenred S.A.; *Int'l*, pg. 2307

EDEN OIL CO. INC.
CORPORATE AFFILIATIONS

EDENRED FINLAND OY—See Edenred S.A.; *Int'l*, pg. 2307

EDENRED FINLAND OY—See Edenred S.A.; *Int'l*, pg. 2307

EDENRED HONG-KONG LIMITED—See Edenred S.A.; *Int'l*, pg. 2307

EDENRED INCENTIVES & MOTIVATION LTD—See Edenred S.A.; *Int'l*, pg. 2307

EDENRED INCENTIVES & REWARDS DEUTSCHLAND—See Edenred S.A.; *Int'l*, pg. 2307

EDENRED (INDIA) PVT LTD—See Edenred S.A.; *Int'l*, pg. 2307

EDENRED ITALIA FIN S.R.L—See Edenred S.A.; *Int'l*, pg. 2308

EDENRED ITALIA SRL—See Edenred S.A.; *Int'l*, pg. 2308

EDENRED JAPAN CO., LTD.—See Edenred S.A.; *Int'l*, pg. 2308

EDENRED LIBAN—See Edenred S.A.; *Int'l*, pg. 2308

EDENRED MAGYARORSZAG KFT—See Edenred S.A.; *Int'l*, pg. 2308

EDENRED MAROC SAS—See Edenred S.A.; *Int'l*, pg. 2308

EDENRED MD S.R.L.—See Edenred S.A.; *Int'l*, pg. 2308

EDENRED MEXICO—See Edenred S.A.; *Int'l*, pg. 2308

EDENRED NORTH AMERICA INC.—See Edenred S.A.; *Int'l*, pg. 2308

EDENRED PERU SA—See Edenred S.A.; *Int'l*, pg. 2308

EDENRED POLSKA SP. Z O.O—See Edenred S.A.; *Int'l*, pg. 2308

EDENRED PORTUGAL LDA—See Edenred S.A.; *Int'l*, pg. 2308

EDENRED PTE LIMITED—See Edenred S.A.; *Int'l*, pg. 2308

EDENRED ROMANIA SRL—See Edenred S.A.; *Int'l*, pg. 2308

EDENRED SAL—See Edenred S.A.; *Int'l*, pg. 2308

EDENRED S.A.; *Int'l*, pg. 2307

EDENRED SHANGHAI (CHINA)—See Edenred S.A.; *Int'l*, pg. 2308

EDENRED SINGAPORE PTE. LTD.—See Edenred S.A.; *Int'l*, pg. 2308

EDENRED SLOVAKIA, S.R.O—See Edenred S.A.; *Int'l*, pg. 2308

EDENRED SUISSE SA—See Edenred S.A.; *Int'l*, pg. 2308

EDENRED SWEDEN AB—See Edenred S.A.; *Int'l*, pg. 2308

EDENRED TRAVEL LIMITED—See Edenred S.A.; *Int'l*, pg. 2308

EDENRED UK—See Edenred S.A.; *Int'l*, pg. 2308

EDENRED VOUCHERS DEUTSCHLAND—See Edenred S.A.; *Int'l*, pg. 2308

EDEN RESEARCH PLC; *Int'l*, pg. 2307

EDEN RETIREMENT CENTER INC.; *U.S. Private*, pg. 1333

EDEN SERVICES, INC.—See Hilton Grand Vacations Inc.; *U.S. Public*, pg. 1040

EDEN SHUR-FINE—See C&S Wholesale Grocers, Inc.; *U.S. Private*, pg. 704

EDENS INDUSTRIAL PARK, INC.—See Bee Street Holdings LLC; *U.S. Private*, pg. 513

EDENSLEEP NEW ZEALAND LIMITED—See ResMed Inc.; *U.S. Public*, pg. 1790

EDENSOFT HOLDINGS LIMITED; *Int'l*, pg. 2308

EDEN SPRINGS (DENMARK) A/S—See Eden International SA; *Int'l*, pg. 2306

EDEN SPRINGS ESPANA S.A.—See Eden International SA; *Int'l*, pg. 2307

EDEN SPRINGS ESPANA S.A.U—See Primo Water Corporation; *U.S. Public*, pg. 1718

EDEN SPRINGS (ESTONIA) OU—See Eden International SA; *Int'l*, pg. 2306

EDEN SPRINGS INTERNATIONAL S.A.—See Primo Water Corporation; *U.S. Public*, pg. 1718

EDEN SPRINGS LATVIA SIA—See Eden International SA; *Int'l*, pg. 2307

EDEN SPRINGS (NEDERLAND) BV—See Eden International SA; *Int'l*, pg. 2306

EDEN SPRINGS (NORWAY) A/S—See Eden International SA; *Int'l*, pg. 2306

EDEN SPRINGS OY FINLAND—See Eden International SA; *Int'l*, pg. 2306

EDEN SPRINGS (POLAND) SP. Z O.O.—See Eden International SA; *Int'l*, pg. 2306

EDEN SPRINGS PORTUGAL SA—See Eden International SA; *Int'l*, pg. 2306

EDEN SPRINGS SCANDINAVIA AB—See Primo Water Corporation; *U.S. Public*, pg. 1718

EDEN SPRINGS SP. Z O.O.—See Primo Water Corporation; *U.S. Public*, pg. 1718

EDEN SPRINGS (SWEDEN) AB—See Eden International SA; *Int'l*, pg. 2306

EDEN SPRINGS (SWITZERLAND) SA—See Eden International SA; *Int'l*, pg. 2306

EDEN SPRINGS (UK) LIMITED—See Eden International SA; *Int'l*, pg. 2307

EDENS REALTY, INC.; *U.S. Private*, pg. 1333

EDEN STONE CO. INC.; *U.S. Private*, pg. 1333

EDENTON MOTORS INC.; *U.S. Private*, pg. 1333

EDENTREE INVESTMENT MANAGEMENT LIMITED—See Ecclesiastical Insurance Office plc; *Int'l*, pg. 2288

EDEN & TYE INC.; *U.S. Private*, pg. 1333

EDENVILLE ENERGY PLC; *Int'l*, pg. 2308

EDEN WATER & COFFEE DEUTSCHLAND GMBH—See Eden International SA; *Int'l*, pg. 2307

E-DEODAR ROBOT EQUIPMENT CO., LTD.—See Ningbo Techmation Co., Ltd.; *Int'l*, pg. 5306

EDEREL SPORT INC.; *U.S. Private*, pg. 1333

EDER FLAG MANUFACTURING CO.; *U.S. Private*, pg. 1333

EDERRA, S.A.—See Banco de Sabadell, S.A.; *Int'l*, pg. 821

EDESA BIOTECH, INC.; *Int'l*, pg. 2308

EDESIA INC.; *U.S. Private*, pg. 1333

E. DESIGN INSURANCE CO., LTD.—See Tokio Marine Holdings, Inc.; *Int'l*, pg. 7782

EDESIX LIMITED—See Motorola Solutions, Inc.; *U.S. Public*, pg. 1477

ED ETNYRE & CO. INC.—See Etnyre International Ltd. Inc.; *U.S. Private*, pg. 1432

EDEXCEL CHINA LTD—See Pearson plc; *Int'l*, pg. 5775

EDEXPERTS; *U.S. Private*, pg. 1333

ED FAGAN INC.; *U.S. Private*, pg. 1331

EDF BELGIUM SA—See Electricite de France S.A.; *Int'l*, pg. 2350

EDF CONSULTING, INC.—See Llorente & Cuenca Madrid, S.L.; *Int'l*, pg. 4535

EDF DEMASZ PARTNER KFT—See Electricite de France S.A.; *Int'l*, pg. 2350

EDF ENERGIES NOUVELLES S.A.—See Electricite de France S.A.; *Int'l*, pg. 2350

EDF ENERGY PLC—See Electricite de France S.A.; *Int'l*, pg. 2350

EDF ENERGY UK LTD—See Electricite de France S.A.; *Int'l*, pg. 2350

EDF EUROPE S.R.L.—See Guangdong Dongfang Science & Technology Co., Ltd.; *Int'l*, pg. 3153

EDF HOLDING SAS—See Electricite de France S.A.; *Int'l*, pg. 2350

EDF INTERNATIONAL SA—See Electricite de France S.A.; *Int'l*, pg. 2350

EDF INVEST; *Int'l*, pg. 2308

EDF LUMINUS NV—See Electricite de France S.A.; *Int'l*, pg. 2350

E D & F MAN ASIA PTE LIMITED—See ED&F Man Holdings Limited; *Int'l*, pg. 2302

E D & F MAN ASIA PTE LIMITED & SVG INTERMOL—See ED&F Man Holdings Limited; *Int'l*, pg. 2302

E D & F MAN BRASIL S.A.—See ED&F Man Holdings Limited; *Int'l*, pg. 2302

ED&F MAN CAPITAL MARKETS HONG KONG LIMITED—See ED&F Man Holdings Limited; *Int'l*, pg. 2303

E D & F MAN CAPITAL MARKETS INC.—See ED&F Man Holdings Limited; *Int'l*, pg. 2302

ED&F MAN CAPITAL MARKETS MENA LIMITED—See ED&F Man Holdings Limited; *Int'l*, pg. 2303

E D & F MAN COMERCIO S.A. DE C.V.—See ED&F Man Holdings Limited; *Int'l*, pg. 2302

ED&F MAN COMMODITIES EGYPT LIMITED—See ED&F Man Holdings Limited; *Int'l*, pg. 2303

E D & F MAN COMMODITIES INDIA PVT LIMITED—See ED&F Man Holdings Limited; *Int'l*, pg. 2302

E D & F MAN COMMODITIES SP Z OO—See ED&F Man Holdings Limited; *Int'l*, pg. 2302

E D & F MAN DEUTSCHLAND GMBH—See ED&F Man Holdings Limited; *Int'l*, pg. 2302

E D & F MAN ESPANA, S.A.—See ED&F Man Holdings Limited; *Int'l*, pg. 2302

ED & F MAN GULF DMCC—See ED&F Man Holdings Limited; *Int'l*, pg. 2302

ED&F MAN HOLDINGS LIMITED; *Int'l*, pg. 2302

ED&F MAN INGREDIENTS S.R.O.—See ED&F Man Holdings Limited; *Int'l*, pg. 2303

E D & F MAN KOREA LIMITED—See ED&F Man Holdings Limited; *Int'l*, pg. 2302

E D & F MAN LIQUID PRODUCTS BELGIUM N.V.—See ED&F Man Holdings Limited; *Int'l*, pg. 2302

ED&F MAN LIQUID PRODUCTS CZECH REPUBLIC S.R.O.—See ED&F Man Holdings Limited; *Int'l*, pg. 2303

E D & F MAN LIQUID PRODUCTS EUROPE BV—See ED&F Man Holdings Limited; *Int'l*, pg. 2302

E D & F MAN LIQUID PRODUCTS INC—See ED&F Man Holdings Limited; *Int'l*, pg. 2302

E D & F MAN LIQUID PRODUCTS IRELAND LIMITED—See ED&F Man Holdings Limited; *Int'l*, pg. 2302

E D & F MAN LIQUID PRODUCTS ITALIA S.R.L.—See ED&F Man Holdings Limited; *Int'l*, pg. 2302

ED&F MAN LIQUID PRODUCTS LLC—See ED&F Man Holdings Limited; *Int'l*, pg. 2303

ED&F MAN LIQUID PRODUCTS NEDERLAND B.V.—See ED&F Man Holdings Limited; *Int'l*, pg. 2303

ED&F MAN LIQUID PRODUCTS UK—See ED&F Man Holdings Limited; *Int'l*, pg. 2303

E D & F MAN MALAYSIA SDN. BHD.—See ED&F Man Holdings Limited; *Int'l*, pg. 2302

ED&F MAN MOCAMBIQUE LIMITADA—See ED&F Man Holdings Limited; *Int'l*, pg. 2303

E D & F MAN MOZAMBIQUE LTDA—See ED&F Man Holdings Limited; *Int'l*, pg. 2302

E D & F MAN NICARAGUA LIMITED—See ED&F Man Holdings Limited; *Int'l*, pg. 2302

E D & F MAN PERU S.A.C.—See ED&F Man Holdings Limited; *Int'l*, pg. 2302

E D & F MAN PHILIPPINES INC.—See ED&F Man Holdings Limited; *Int'l*, pg. 2302

E D & F MAN PORTUGAL, LDA—See ED&F Man Holdings Limited; *Int'l*, pg. 2302

E D & F MAN (SHANGHAI) CO., LIMITED—See ED&F Man Holdings Limited; *Int'l*, pg. 2302

E D & F MAN SUCRE SARL—See ED&F Man Holdings Limited; *Int'l*, pg. 2302

E D & F MAN SUGAR BULGARIA—See ED&F Man Holdings Limited; *Int'l*, pg. 2302

E D & F MAN SUGAR INC—See ED&F Man Holdings Limited; *Int'l*, pg. 2302

ED&F MAN TERMINALS IRELAND LIMITED—See ED&F Man Holdings Limited; *Int'l*, pg. 2303

ED&F MAN TERMINALS UK LIMITED—See ED&F Man Holdings Limited; *Int'l*, pg. 2303

E D & F MAN TRGOVINA D.O.O.—See ED&F Man Holdings Limited; *Int'l*, pg. 2302

E D & F MAN URUGUAY SA—See ED&F Man Holdings Limited; *Int'l*, pg. 2302

ED&F MAN VENEZUELA S.A.—See ED&F Man Holdings Limited; *Int'l*, pg. 2303

EDF POLSKA SP. Z O.O.—See Electricite de France S.A.; *Int'l*, pg. 2350

EDF PRODUCTION UK LTD—See Electricite de France S.A.; *Int'l*, pg. 2350

EDF RENEWABLES, INC.—See Electricite de France S.A.; *Int'l*, pg. 2350

EDF TRADING LIMITED—See Electricite de France S.A.; *Int'l*, pg. 2350

EDF TRADING NORTH AMERICA, LLC—See Electricite de France S.A.; *Int'l*, pg. 2350

EDG AG—See Infront ASA; *Int'l*, pg. 3699

EDGAR AMBIENT MEDIA GROUP GMBH—See Stroer SE & Co. KGaA; *Int'l*, pg. 7242

EDGAR BOETTCHER MASON CONTRACTORS; *U.S. Private*, pg. 1333

EDGAR, DUNN & COMPANY (EDC)—See Auriemma Consulting Group, Inc.; *U.S. Private*, pg. 393

EDGARIZING SOLUTIONS, INC.; *U.S. Private*, pg. 1333

EDGAR KLEINE KAPUNKT GMBH—See EssilorLuxottica SA; *Int'l*, pg. 2515

EDGAR ONLINE—See Donnelley Financial Solutions, Inc.; *U.S. Public*, pg. 677

EDGAR P BENJAMIN HEALTHCARE CENTER, INC.; *U.S. Private*, pg. 1333

EDGARS STORES LIMITED; *Int'l*, pg. 2308

ED. GARVEY & COMPANY - FRANKLIN—See Orora Limited; *Int'l*, pg. 5643

ED. GARVEY & COMPANY - LOS ANGELES—See Orora Limited; *Int'l*, pg. 5643

ED. GARVEY & COMPANY - MILWAUKEE—See Orora Limited; *Int'l*, pg. 5643

ED. GARVEY & COMPANY—See Orora Limited; *Int'l*, pg. 5643

ED. GARVEY & COMPANY - STURTEVANT—See Orora Limited; *Int'l*, pg. 5643

EDGE ADHESIVES, INC.—See Gladstone Management Corporation; *U.S. Private*, pg. 1705

EDGEAQ, LLC—See Summit Partners, L.P.; *U.S. Private*, pg. 3856

EDGEAQ, LLC—See The Jordan Company, L.P.; *U.S. Private*, pg. 4062

EDGE ASSET MANAGEMENT INC—See Principal Financial Group, Inc.; *U.S. Public*, pg. 1720

EDGE AUTONOMY SLO, LLC—See AE Industrial Partners, LP; *U.S. Private*, pg. 112

EDGE BIOSYSTEMS, INC.—See StoneCalibre, LLC; *U.S. Private*, pg. 3828

EDGEBUILDER, INC.—See Star Equity Holdings, Inc.; *U.S. Public*, pg. 1937

EDGE CAPITAL PARTNERS, LLC; *U.S. Private*, pg. 1333

EDGE CENTRES PTY LTD; *Int'l*, pg. 2309

EDGE COMMERCIAL REAL ESTATE LLC—See KLNB, LLC; *U.S. Private*, pg. 2320

EDGE COMMUNICATIONS, INC.; *U.S. Private*, pg. 1334

EDGE CONSTRUCTION SUPPLY, LLC—See NEFCO Corp.; *U.S. Private*, pg. 2880

EDGECORE, LLC—See Eastport Holdings, Inc.; *U.S. Private*, pg. 1322

EDGECRAFT CORPORATION—See The Legacy Companies; *U.S. Private*, pg. 4069

EDGE DATA SOLUTIONS, INC.; *U.S. Public*, pg. 717

EDGE DEVELOPMENT, INC.; *U.S. Private*, pg. 1334

EDGE ELECTRONICS INC.; *U.S. Private*, pg. 1334

EDGE ELECTRONICS TRADING LLC—See Midwich Group Plc; *Int'l*, pg. 4887

EDGE FINANCIAL, INC.; *U.S. Private*, pg. 1334

COMPANY NAME INDEX

EDGE FRANCHISING CO., LIMITED—See NaaS Technology Inc.; *Int'l*, pg. 5118
EDGE GLOBAL LIMITED; *Int'l*, pg. 2309
EDGE GROUP LIMITED; *Int'l*, pg. 2309
EDGE HOMES GROUP LTD.—See Sumitomo Forestry Co., Ltd.; *Int'l*, pg. 7285
EDGE HOMES LLC—See Sumitomo Forestry Co., Ltd.; *Int'l*, pg. 7286
EDGE HOSTING, LLC—See DataBank, Ltd.; *U.S. Private*, pg. 1164
EDGE INVESTMENT MANAGEMENT LIMITED—See Edge Group Limited; *Int'l*, pg. 2309
EDGEIQ, INC.—See DXC Technology Company; *U.S. Public*, pg. 696
EDGELINK, LLC; *U.S. Private*, pg. 1334
EDGEMATE, INC.; *U.S. Private*, pg. 1334
EDGEMODE, INC.; *U.S. Public*, pg. 717
EDGEMONT GOLD CORP.; *Int'l*, pg. 2309
EDGE NATURAL RESOURCES LLC; *U.S. Private*, pg. 1334
EDGE NETWORK SERVICES LIMITED—See Meta Platforms, Inc.; *U.S. Public*, pg. 1427
EDGEN GROUP INC.—See Sumitomo Corporation; *Int'l*, pg. 7273
EDGEN MURRAY CORP. - HOUSTON OFFICE—See Sumitomo Corporation; *Int'l*, pg. 7273
EDGEN MURRAY CORPORATION—See Sumitomo Corporation; *Int'l*, pg. 7273
EDGEN MURRAY DO BRASIL LIMITADA—See Sumitomo Corporation; *Int'l*, pg. 7273
EDGEN MURRAY EUROPE LIMITED—See Sumitomo Corporation; *Int'l*, pg. 7273
EDGEN MURRAY FRANCE S.A.S.—See Sumitomo Corporation; *Int'l*, pg. 7273
EDGEN MURRAY FZE—See Sumitomo Corporation; *Int'l*, pg. 7273
EDGEN MURRAY (INDIA) PVT, LTD—See Sumitomo Corporation; *Int'l*, pg. 7273
EDGEN MURRAY PTE. LTD.—See Sumitomo Corporation; *Int'l*, pg. 7273
EDGENTA ENERGY PROJECTS SDN. BHD.—See Khazanah Nasional Berhad; *Int'l*, pg. 4153
EDGENTA ENVIRONMENTAL & MATERIAL TESTING SDN BHD—See Khazanah Nasional Berhad; *Int'l*, pg. 4153
EDGENTA FACILITIES SDN. BHD.—See Khazanah Nasional Berhad; *Int'l*, pg. 4153
EDGENTA HEALTHCARE MANAGEMENT SDN BHD—See Khazanah Nasional Berhad; *Int'l*, pg. 4153
EDGENTA HEALTHTRONICS SDN. BHD.—See Khazanah Nasional Berhad; *Int'l*, pg. 4153
EDGENTA MEDISERVE SDN. BHD.—See Khazanah Nasional Berhad; *Int'l*, pg. 4153
EDGENTA PROPEL BERHAD—See Khazanah Nasional Berhad; *Int'l*, pg. 4153
EDGENTA TOWNSHIP MANAGEMENT SERVICES SDN. BHD.—See Khazanah Nasional Berhad; *Int'l*, pg. 4153
EDGE PERFORMANCE VCT PLC—See Edge Group Limited; *Int'l*, pg. 2309
EDGE PHYSICAL THERAPY, LIMITED PARTNERSHIP—See U.S. Physical Therapy, Inc.; *U.S. Public*, pg. 2214
THE EDGE PICTURE CO., LTD.—See Zinc Media Group plc; *Int'l*, pg. 8684
EDGE PRODUCTS; *U.S. Private*, pg. 1334
EDGEROCK TECHNOLOGIES, LLC—See BGSF, Inc.; *U.S. Public*, pg. 330
EDGERTON FORGE, INC.—See Avis Industrial Corporation; *U.S. Private*, pg. 407
EDGERTON HOSPITAL AND HEALTH SERVICES INC.; *U.S. Private*, pg. 1334
EDGES ELECTRICAL GROUP; *U.S. Private*, pg. 1334
EDGE SERVICES, INC.; *U.S. Private*, pg. 1334
EDGE SOLUTIONS INC.; *U.S. Private*, pg. 1334
EDGESOURCE CORPORATION; *U.S. Private*, pg. 1334
EDGESTONE CAPITAL PARTNERS INC.; *Int'l*, pg. 2309
EDGE SYSTEMS INTERMEDIATE, LLC—See The Beauty Health Company; *U.S. Public*, pg. 2038
EDGE SYSTEMS, LLC—See The Beauty Health Company; *U.S. Public*, pg. 2038
EDGE SYSTEMS, LLC; *U.S. Private*, pg. 1334
EDGE TECH CORP.; *U.S. Private*, pg. 1334
EDGETECH EUROPE GMBH—See Quanex Building Products Corp.; *U.S. Public*, pg. 1749
EDGE TECHNOLOGY GROUP, LLC—See Court Square Capital Partners, L.P.; *U.S. Private*, pg. 1070
EDGETECH (UK) LTD—See Quanex Building Products Corp.; *U.S. Public*, pg. 1749
EDGE TESTING SOLUTIONS LIMITED—See Eurofins Scientific S.E.; *Int'l*, pg. 2539
EDGE TOTAL INTELLIGENCE INC.; *Int'l*, pg. 2309
EDGEVIEW PARTNERS L.P.—See Piper Sandler Companies; *U.S. Public*, pg. 1694
EDGEWARE AB; *Int'l*, pg. 2309
EDGEWARE COMPUTERS, INC.; *U.S. Private*, pg. 1334
EDGEWARE INC.—See Edgeware AB; *Int'l*, pg. 2309
EDGEWATER ASSOCIATES LIMITED—See Manx Financial Group PLC; *Int'l*, pg. 4680
EDGEWATER AUTOMATION, LLC—See Manders Industries B.V.; *Int'l*, pg. 4668
EDGEWATER BANCORP, INC.—See United Federal Credit Union; *U.S. Private*, pg. 4292
EDGEWATER BANK—See United Federal Credit Union; *U.S. Private*, pg. 4292
EDGEWATER BEACH RESORT MANAGEMENT, INC.; *U.S. Private*, pg. 1334
EDGEWATER CAPITAL PARTNERS, L.P.; *U.S. Private*, pg. 1334
EDGEWATER COMMERCIAL CONSTRUCTION, INC.; *U.S. Private*, pg. 1335
EDGEWATER CONSTRUCTION SERVICES, LLC; *U.S. Private*, pg. 1335
EDGEWATER EXPLORATION, INC.; *Int'l*, pg. 2309
EDGEWATER HOTEL & CASINO—See Marnell Corrao Associates, Inc.; *U.S. Private*, pg. 2586
EDGEWATER POWER BOATS, LLC—See Nimbus Group AB; *Int'l*, pg. 5297
EDGEWATER SERVICES, LLC; *U.S. Private*, pg. 1335
EDGEWATER SYSTEMS FOR BALANCED LIVING; *U.S. Private*, pg. 1335
EDGEWATER TECHNOLOGY (DELAWARE), INC.—See Alithya Group, Inc.; *Int'l*, pg. 329
EDGEWATER TECHNOLOGY-RANZAL & ASSOCIATES—See Alithya Group, Inc.; *Int'l*, pg. 329
EDGEWATER WIRELESS SYSTEMS INC.; *Int'l*, pg. 2309
EDGEWAVE INC.—See GoSecure Inc.; *U.S. Private*, pg. 1744
EDGEWEBHOSTING INC.; *U.S. Private*, pg. 1335
EDGEWELL PERSONAL CARE COMPANY; *U.S. Public*, pg. 717
EDGEWELL PERSONAL CARE ITALY S.P.A.—See Edgewell Personal Care Company; *U.S. Public*, pg. 718
EDGEWELL PERSONAL CARE, LLC—See Edgewell Personal Care Company; *U.S. Public*, pg. 718
EDGEWELL PERSONAL CARE - ORMOND BEACH—See Edgewell Personal Care Company; *U.S. Public*, pg. 718
EDGEWISE NETWORKS INC.—See Zscaler, Inc.; *U.S. Public*, pg. 2411
EDGEWISE THERAPEUTICS, INC.; *U.S. Public*, pg. 718
EDGEWOOD CENTER FOR CHILDREN AND FAMILIES; *U.S. Private*, pg. 1335
EDGEWOOD COMPANIES; *U.S. Private*, pg. 1335
EDGEWOOD LIFECARE COMMUNITY; *U.S. Private*, pg. 1335
EDGEWOOD MOBILE HOMES INC.; *U.S. Private*, pg. 1335
EDGEWOOD PARTNERS INSURANCE CENTER—See Keystone Group, L.P.; *U.S. Private*, pg. 2297
EDGEWOOD PROPERTIES INC.; *U.S. Private*, pg. 1336
EDGEWOOD VILLAGE MARKET INC.; *U.S. Private*, pg. 1336
EDGIL ASSOCIATES, INC.—See Gladifi; *U.S. Private*, pg. 1704
EDGILE, LLC—See Wipro Limited; *Int'l*, pg. 8432
EDGIO, INC.; *U.S. Public*, pg. 718
E & D GMBH—See Koninklijke Philips N.V.; *Int'l*, pg. 4267
EDG PARTNERS, LLC; *U.S. Private*, pg. 1333
EDGREN MOTOR COMPANY, INC.—See AutoNation, Inc.; *U.S. Public*, pg. 234
EDGREN MOTOR COMPANY, INC.—See AutoNation, Inc.; *U.S. Public*, pg. 234
EDG/SW HOLDINGS LLC; *U.S. Private*, pg. 1333
EDGWARE ENERGY LIMITED—See RWE AG; *Int'l*, pg. 6434
ED HICKS IMPORTS, LTD.; *U.S. Private*, pg. 1331
EDIA CO., LTD.; *Int'l*, pg. 2309
E.DIALOG GMBH—See E.ON SE; *Int'l*, pg. 2260
EDIBLE ARRANGEMENTS INTERNATIONAL, INC.; *U.S. Private*, pg. 1336
EDIBLE GARDEN AG INCORPORATED; *U.S. Public*, pg. 719
EDIBLE GARDEN CORP.—See Unrivaled Brands, Inc.; *U.S. Public*, pg. 2263
EDIBLE OIL COMPANY (D) LLC—See Al Ghurair Investment LLC; *Int'l*, pg. 278
EDIBLES REX; *U.S. Private*, pg. 1336
EDICIONES DIGITALES HOY, S.L.U.—See Vocento, S.A.; *Int'l*, pg. 8284
EDICIONES GRAZALEMA, S.L.—See Promotora de Informaciones S.A.; *Int'l*, pg. 5995
EDICIONES LAROUSSE ARGENTINA SA—See Vivendi SE; *Int'l*, pg. 8273
EDICIONES LAROUSSE S.A. DE C.V.—See Vivendi SE; *Int'l*, pg. 8273
EDICIONES SANTILLANA INC.—See Promotora de Informaciones S.A.; *Int'l*, pg. 5995
EDICIONES SANTILLANA, S.A.—See Promotora de Informaciones S.A.; *Int'l*, pg. 5995
EDICIONES SANTILLANA, S.A.—See Promotora de Informaciones S.A.; *Int'l*, pg. 5995
EDICIONES XERAIS DE GALICIA SA—See Vivendi SE; *Int'l*, pg. 8271
EDICIONS OBRADOIRO, S.L.—See Promotora de Informaciones S.A.; *Int'l*, pg. 5995
EDICIONS VORAMAR, S.A.—See Promotora de Informaciones S.A.; *Int'l*, pg. 5995
EDICOES INAPA, LDA.—See Inapa - Investimentos, Participacoes e Gestao, SA; *Int'l*, pg. 3645
EDICO FINANCIAL PRESS SERVICES LIMITED—See EDICO Holdings Limited; *Int'l*, pg. 2309
EDICO HOLDINGS LIMITED; *Int'l*, pg. 2309
EDICT EGAMING GMBH—See Gauselmann AG; *Int'l*, pg. 2891
EDICTO GMBH—See VITA 34 AG; *Int'l*, pg. 8257
EDIFECS, INC.; *U.S. Private*, pg. 1336
EDIFICE, INC.; *U.S. Private*, pg. 1336
EDIFIER TECHNOLOGY CO., LTD.; *Int'l*, pg. 2309
EDIFINANCE PARTICIPATIONS SAS—See Vivendi SE; *Int'l*, pg. 8271
EDIFIST LEARNING INC.—See Canon Inc.; *Int'l*, pg. 1296
EDIFIXIO S.A.S.—See Atos SE; *Int'l*, pg. 692
EDIF—See Vivendi SE; *Int'l*, pg. 8271
EDIFY ACQUISITION CORP.; *U.S. Public*, pg. 719
EDIFY MULTIMEDIA GROUP LLC; *U.S. Public*, pg. 1336
EDI GMBH—See Nordson Corporation; *U.S. Public*, pg. 1532
EDI HEALTH GROUP; *U.S. Public*, pg. 1336
EDILE SAN FELICE S.P.A.; *Int'l*, pg. 2309
EDIL.GI SRL; *Int'l*, pg. 2309
EDILIANS SASU—See Groupe Bruxelles Lambert SA; *Int'l*, pg. 3100
EDILIT S.R.L.—See Etex SA/NV; *Int'l*, pg. 2521
EDILIZIACROBATICA FRANCE SAS—See EdiliziAcrobatica S.p.A.; *Int'l*, pg. 2309
EDILIZIACROBATICA IBERICA S.L.—See EdiliziAcrobatica S.p.A.; *Int'l*, pg. 2310
EDILIZIACROBATICA S.P.A.; *Int'l*, pg. 2309
EDILON SEDRA BV—See The James Walker Group Ltd; *Int'l*, pg. 7657
EDI, LTD.—See Ross & Baruzzini, Inc.; *U.S. Private*, pg. 3485
EDIMAX COMPUTER COMPANY—See Edimax Technology Co., Ltd.; *Int'l*, pg. 2310
EDIMAX TECHNOLOGY AUSTRALIA PTY. LTD.—See Edimax Technology Co., Ltd.; *Int'l*, pg. 2310
EDIMAX TECHNOLOGY CO., LTD.; *Int'l*, pg. 2310
EDIMAX TECHNOLOGY EUROPE B.V.—See Edimax Technology Co., Ltd.; *Int'l*, pg. 2310
EDIMAX TECHNOLOGY MEA FZE—See Edimax Technology Co., Ltd.; *Int'l*, pg. 2310
EDIMAX TECHNOLOGY POLAND SP. Z O.O.—See Edimax Technology Co., Ltd.; *Int'l*, pg. 2310
EDIMAX TECHNOLOGY (SE ASIA) PTE. LTD.—See Edimax Technology Co., Ltd.; *Int'l*, pg. 2310
EDIMAX TECHNOLOGY (UK) LTD.—See Edimax Technology Co., Ltd.; *Int'l*, pg. 2310
EDIMENSIONAL, INC.; *U.S. Private*, pg. 1336
ED IMMOBILIEN GMBH & CO. KG—See EnBW Energie Baden-Wurttemberg AG; *Int'l*, pg. 2398
EDIMPRESA-EDITORA LDA.—See Impresa SGPS S.A.; *Int'l*, pg. 3637
EDIM S.P.A.—See Robert Bosch GmbH; *Int'l*, pg. 6360
ED INA D.O.O.—See Electricite de France S.A.; *Int'l*, pg. 2350
ED INA D.O.O.—See INA-Industrija Nafte, d.d.; *Int'l*, pg. 3642
EDINA REALTY, INC.—See Berkshire Hathaway Inc.; *U.S. Public*, pg. 306
EDINA REALTY—See Berkshire Hathaway Inc.; *U.S. Public*, pg. 306
EDINA REALTY TITLE—See Berkshire Hathaway Inc.; *U.S. Public*, pg. 306
EDINBURGH AIRPORT LIMITED—See BlackRock, Inc.; *U.S. Public*, pg. 346
EDINBURGH BUTTERFLY & INSECT WORLD—See Hattington Capital LLP; *Int'l*, pg. 3285
EDINBURGH BUTTERFLY & INSECT WORLD—See Midlothian Capital Partners Limited; *Int'l*, pg. 4887
THE EDINBURGH CENTRE FOR CARBON MANAGEMENT LIMITED—See CVC Capital Partners SICAV-FIS S.A.; *Int'l*, pg. 1882
THE EDINBURGH INVESTMENT TRUST PLC—See Invesco Ltd.; *U.S. Public*, pg. 1163
EDINBURGH MEDICAL SERVICES LIMITED—See Tenet Healthcare Corporation; *U.S. Public*, pg. 2002
EDINBURGH PARK (LIVERPOOL) MANAGEMENT COMPANY LIMITED—See Persimmon plc; *Int'l*, pg. 5815
EDINBURGH PETROLEUM EQUIPMENT LIMITED—See Weatherford International plc; *U.S. Public*, pg. 2339
THE EDINBURGH SALMON COMPANY LTD.—See Loch Duart Ltd.; *Int'l*, pg. 4540
THE EDINBURGH WOOLLEN MILL LTD.; *Int'l*, pg. 7637
EDINBURGH WORLDWIDE INVESTMENT TRUST PLC; *Int'l*, pg. 2310
EDINTSVO AD; *Int'l*, pg. 2310
ED INVEST S.A.; *Int'l*, pg. 2302
EDION CORPORATION; *Int'l*, pg. 2310
EDION EAST CORPORATION—See EDION Corporation; *Int'l*, pg. 2310
EDION HOUSE SYSTEM CORPORATION—See EDION Corporation; *Int'l*, pg. 2310
EDION X VENTURES CORPORATION—See EDION Corporation; *Int'l*, pg. 2310

EDIP (EDITION-DIFFUSION-IMPRESSION-PUBLICITE); *Int'l*, pg. 2310
EDIP GAYRIMENKUL YATIRIM SANAYI VE TICARET A.S.; *Int'l*, pg. 2310
EDI POLOGNE S.A.—See Vivendi SE; *Int'l*, pg. 8274
EDIPRESSE ASIA LTD—See Edipresse SA; *Int'l*, pg. 2310
EDIPRESSE AS ROMANIA SRL—See Edipresse SA; *Int'l*, pg. 2310
EDIPRESSE-KONLIGA ZAO—See Edipresse SA; *Int'l*, pg. 2310
EDIPRESSE POLSKA SA—See Edipresse SA; *Int'l*, pg. 2310
EDIPRESSE SA; *Int'l*, pg. 2310
EDIPRESSE UKRAINE LLC—See Edipresse SA; *Int'l*, pg. 2310
EDI RAIL (MARYBOROUGH) PTY LTD.—See Downer EDI Limited; *Int'l*, pg. 2186
E-DIRECT CORP—See Accton Technology Corporation; *Int'l*, pg. 94
EDIS COMPANY; *U.S. Private*, pg. 1336
E.DISCOM TELEKOMMUNIKATION GMBH—See E.ON SE; *Int'l*, pg. 2260
EDISCOVERY INC.—See ArcherHall, LLC; *U.S. Private*, pg. 311
EDISERVICIOS MADRID 2000 S.L.U.—See RCS MediaGroup S.p.A.; *Int'l*, pg. 6229
E.DISNATUR ERNEUERBARE ENERGIEN GMBH—See E.ON SE; *Int'l*, pg. 2260
EDISON BANCSHARES, INC.; *U.S. Private*, pg. 1336
EDISON CAPITAL—See Edison International; *U.S. Public*, pg. 719
EDISON CHOUEST OFFSHORE, LLC; *U.S. Private*, pg. 1336
EDISON ELECTRIC INSTITUTE; *U.S. Private*, pg. 1336
EDISON FINANCIAL ULC—See Rocket Companies, Inc.; *U.S. Public*, pg. 1804
EDISON FITNESS GROUP LLC—See Planet Fitness, Inc.; *U.S. Public*, pg. 1697
EDISON INTERNATIONAL; *U.S. Public*, pg. 719
EDISON LEARNING, INC.—See Liberty Partners, L.P.; *U.S. Private*, pg. 2446
EDISON LITHIUM CORP.; *Int'l*, pg. 2310
EDISON LITHOGRAPHING & PRINTING CORP.; *U.S. Private*, pg. 1336
EDISON MALL, LLC—See Washington Prime Group Inc.; *U.S. Private*, pg. 4448
EDISON MEDIA RESEARCH; *U.S. Private*, pg. 1336
EDISON MISSION GROUP INC.—See Edison International; *U.S. Public*, pg. 719
EDISON NATIONAL BANK—See Edison Bancshares, Inc.; *U.S. Public*, pg. 1336
EDISON O&M SERVICES—See Edison International; *U.S. Public*, pg. 719
EDISON OPTO CORP.; *Int'l*, pg. 2311
EDISON OPTO (DONG GUAN) CO., LTD.—See Edison Opto Corp.; *Int'l*, pg. 2311
EDISON OPTO USA CORPORATION—See Edison Opto Corp.; *Int'l*, pg. 2311
EDISON PROPERTIES, LLC; *U.S. Private*, pg. 1337
EDISON RENEWABLE ENERGY, INC.—See Edison International; *U.S. Public*, pg. 719
EDISON S.P.A.—See Electricite de France S.A.; *Int'l*, pg. 2350
EDISON VENTURE PARTNERS LLC; *U.S. Private*, pg. 1337
E.DISTHERM ENERGIELOSUNGEN GMBH—See E.ON SE; *Int'l*, pg. 2260
E.DISTHERM WARMEDIENSTLEISTUNGEN GMBH—See E.ON SE; *Int'l*, pg. 2260
EDISTO DIALYSIS, LLC—See DaVita Inc.; *U.S. Public*, pg. 638
EDISTO ELECTRIC COOPERATIVE; *U.S. Private*, pg. 1337
EDISTON PROPERTY INVESTMENT COMPANY PLC; *Int'l*, pg. 2311
EDISTRIBUCION REDES DIGITALES SL—See Enel S.p.A.; *Int'l*, pg. 2411
E! DISTRIBUTION, L.L.C.—See Comcast Corporation; *U.S. Public*, pg. 538
EDISUN POWER EUROPE AG; *Int'l*, pg. 2311
EDISUN POWER SWITZERLAND LTD.—See Edisun Power Europe AG; *Int'l*, pg. 2311
EDIT'66 SAE—See HAL Trust N.V.; *Int'l*, pg. 3224
EDIT'66 SAS—See HAL Trust N.V.; *Int'l*, pg. 3224
EDITA BOBERGS AB—See Nordic Morning Plc; *Int'l*, pg. 5422
EDITA FOOD INDUSTRIES SAE; *Int'l*, pg. 2311
EDIT AGENCY LIMITED—See Kin and Carta plc; *Int'l*, pg. 4164
EDITA PRIMA OY—See Nordic Morning Plc; *Int'l*, pg. 5422
EDITA PUBLISHING OY—See Nordic Morning Plc; *Int'l*, pg. 5422
EDITA SA—See TX Group AG; *Int'l*, pg. 7991
EDITAS MEDICINE INC; *U.S. Public*, pg. 719
EDITA VASTRA AROS AB—See Nordic Morning Plc; *Int'l*, pg. 5422
EDITEK, INC.; *U.S. Private*, pg. 1337
EDITION LTD.; *Int'l*, pg. 2311

EDITIONS ATLAS (FRANCE) S.A.S.—See De Agostini S.p.A.; *Int'l*, pg. 1994
EDITIONS BORDAS—See Czech Media Invest as; *Int'l*, pg. 1898
EDITIONS CASTERMAN S.A.—See Madrigall SA; *Int'l*, pg. 4635
EDITIONS DES DEUX TERRES SAS—See Vivendi SE; *Int'l*, pg. 8272
EDITIONS DU MONITEUR—See Bridgepoint Group Plc; *Int'l*, pg. 1155
EDITIONS DURAND-SALABERT-ESCHIG—See Universal Music Group N.V.; *Int'l*, pg. 8081
EDITIONS DU RENOUVEAU PEDAGOGIQUE INC—See Pearson plc; *Int'l*, pg. 5775
EDITIONS DU SIGNE SA; *Int'l*, pg. 2311
EDITIONS FLAMMARION LTEE—See Madrigall SA; *Int'l*, pg. 4635
EDITIONS GALLIMARD SA—See Madrigall SA; *Int'l*, pg. 4635
EDITIONS GRANADA SA; *Int'l*, pg. 2311
EDITIONS GRASSET ET FASQUELLE S.A.—See Vivendi SE; *Int'l*, pg. 8272
EDITIONS HATIER—See Vivendi SE; *Int'l*, pg. 8272
EDITIONS J'AI LU S.A.—See Madrigall SA; *Int'l*, pg. 4635
EDITIONS JEAN-CLAUDE LATTES SNC—See Vivendi SE; *Int'l*, pg. 8271
EDITIONS LAMY—See Wolters Kluwer n.v.; *Int'l*, pg. 8444
EDITIONS LAROUSSE SAS—See Vivendi SE; *Int'l*, pg. 8272
EDITIONS LEFEBVRE SARRUT SA; *Int'l*, pg. 2311
EDITIONS MAISON DES LANGUES S.A.R.L.—See Ernst Klett AG; *Int'l*, pg. 2495
EDITIONS MUSICALES FRANCOIS 1ER—See Vivendi SE; *Int'l*, pg. 8275
EDITIONS NATHAN—See Czech Media Invest as; *Int'l*, pg. 1898
EDITIONS PRIVAT SA; *Int'l*, pg. 2311
EDITIONS RAABE S.A.R.L.—See Ernst Klett AG; *Int'l*, pg. 2495
EDITIONS STOCK SAS—See Vivendi SE; *Int'l*, pg. 8271
EDITION WILHELM HANSEN—See Music Sales Corporation; *U.S. Private*, pg. 2818
EDITIS SAS—See Czech Media Invest as; *Int'l*, pg. 1898
EDITORA ABRIL—See Vivendi SE; *Int'l*, pg. 8274
EDITORA ANUNTIS SEGUNDAMANO ONLINE DO BRAZIL LTDA—See Schibsted ASA; *Int'l*, pg. 6616
EDITORA ATICA S.A.—See Cogna Educacao S.A.; *Int'l*, pg. 1695
EDITORA MODERNA, LTDA.—See Promotora de Informaciones S.A.; *Int'l*, pg. 5995
EDITORA OBJETIVA LTDA.—See Promotora de Informaciones S.A.; *Int'l*, pg. 5995
EDITORA SALVAT DO BRASIL LTDA.—See Vivendi SE; *Int'l*, pg. 8271
EDITORIAL BARCANOVA SA—See Vivendi SE; *Int'l*, pg. 8272
EDITORIAL C&P S.A.S.—See Grupo Televisa, S.A.B.; *Int'l*, pg. 3136
EDITORIAL DEL PUEBLO VASCO S.A.—See RCS MediaGroup S.p.A.; *Int'l*, pg. 6229
EDITORIALE FVG SPA—See Giovanni Agnelli B.V.; *Int'l*, pg. 2978
EDITORIALE GIORGIO MONDADORI SPA—See Cairo Communication S.p.A.; *Int'l*, pg. 1253
EDITORIALE LA CRONACA S.R.L—See Netweek S.p.A.; *Int'l*, pg. 5217
EDITORIALE LA NUOVA SARDEGNA SPA—See Giovanni Agnelli B.V.; *Int'l*, pg. 2978
EDITORIALE METROPOLI SPA—See Giovanni Agnelli B.V.; *Int'l*, pg. 2978
EDITORIALE VENETO S.R.L.—See RCS MediaGroup S.p.A.; *Int'l*, pg. 6229
EDITORIAL GYJ TELEVISA, S.A. DE C.V.—See Grupo Televisa, S.A.B.; *Int'l*, pg. 3136
EDITORIAL LA RAZON S.A.—See Grupo Clarin S.A.; *Int'l*, pg. 3125
EDITORIAL MACMILLAN DE VENEZUELA S.A.—See Verlagsgruppe Georg von Holtzbrinck GmbH; *Int'l*, pg. 8170
EDITORIAL MOTORPRESS-TELEVISA, S.A. DE C.V.—See Grupo Televisa, S.A.B.; *Int'l*, pg. 3136
EDITORIAL PLANETA DE AGOSTINI, SA—See De Agostini S.p.A.; *Int'l*, pg. 1994
EDITORIAL SANTILLANA, S.A. DE C.V.—See Promotora de Informaciones S.A.; *Int'l*, pg. 5995
EDITORIAL SANTILLANA, S.A.—See Promotora de Informaciones S.A.; *Int'l*, pg. 5995
EDITORIAL SANTILLANA, S.A.—See Promotora de Informaciones S.A.; *Int'l*, pg. 5995
EDITORIAL SANTILLANA, S.A.—See Promotora de Informaciones S.A.; *Int'l*, pg. 5995
EDITORIAL SANTILLANA, S.A.—See Promotora de Informaciones S.A.; *Int'l*, pg. 5995
EDITORIAL TELEVISA COLOMBIA CULTURAL, S.A.—See Grupo Televisa, S.A.B.; *Int'l*, pg. 3136
EDITORIAL TELEVISA INTERNATIONAL, S.A.—See Grupo Televisa, S.A.B.; *Int'l*, pg. 3136
EDITORIAL TELEVISA S.A. DE C.V.—See Grupo Televisa, S.A.B.; *Int'l*, pg. 3136

EDITORIUM AS—See Eniro Group AB; *Int'l*, pg. 2439
EDITRICE IL GIORNO S.P.A.—See Monrif S.p.A.; *Int'l*, pg. 5035
EDITRICE LA STAMPA S.P.A.—See Stellantis N.V.; *Int'l*, pg. 7200
EDITRICE VIMERCATESE S.R.L.—See Netweek S.p.A.; *Int'l*, pg. 5217
EDITSHARE, LLC—See ParkerGale, LLC; *U.S. Private*, pg. 3098
EDIZIONE PROPERTY S.P.A.—See Edizione S.r.l.; *Int'l*, pg. 2311
EDIZIONE S.R.L.; *Int'l*, pg. 2311
ED KELLUM & SON APPLIANCE CO.; *U.S. Private*, pg. 1331
ED KENLEY FORD, INC.; *U.S. Private*, pg. 1331
ED KIRBY ADVENTURE; *U.S. Private*, pg. 1331
ED LEARN FORD LINCOLN LTD.; *Int'l*, pg. 2302
EDLEUN, INC.—See Ontario Teachers' Pension Plan; *Int'l*, pg. 5587
EDL FASTENERS LTD.—See Wurth Verwaltungsgesellschaft mbH; *Int'l*, pg. 8504
EDL GROUP OPERATIONS PTY LTD—See CK Hutchison Holdings Limited; *Int'l*, pg. 1636
EDL HOTELS SCA—See The Walt Disney Company; *U.S. Public*, pg. 2139
EDL MASSMAN, LLC—See Granite Equity Partners LLC; *U.S. Private*, pg. 1755
EDL NGD (WA) PTY LTD—See CK Hutchison Holdings Limited; *Int'l*, pg. 1636
EDLOGICAL GROUP CORP.; *U.S. Private*, pg. 1337
EDLONG CORPORATION; *U.S. Private*, pg. 1337
EDLP MARKETING, LDA.—See Edel SE & Co. KGaA; *Int'l*, pg. 2305
EDL PROPERTIES LIMITED—See Empee Distilleries Limited; *Int'l*, pg. 2385
E.D. LUCE PACKAGING—See O. Berk Company L.L.C.; *U.S. Private*, pg. 2981
EDLUND COMPANY, INC.; *U.S. Private*, pg. 1337
EDMAC EUROPE N.V.—See Atlas Copco AB; *Int'l*, pg. 682
EDM AMERICAS, INC.—See Rainbow HoldCo Limited; *Int'l*, pg. 6190
EDM AMERICAS; *U.S. Private*, pg. 1337
EDMAR CLEANING CORP.; *U.S. Private*, pg. 1337
EDMARK GMC PONTIAC BUICK, INC.; *U.S. Private*, pg. 1337
ED MARTIN ACURA; *U.S. Private*, pg. 1331
ED MARTIN CHEVY CADILLAC; *U.S. Private*, pg. 1331
EDMC MARKETING AND ADVERTISING, INC.—See Dream Center Foundation, a California Nonprofit Corp.; *U.S. Private*, pg. 1273
EDMEN COMMUNITY STAFFING SOLUTIONS PTY LTD—See PeopleIn Limited; *Int'l*, pg. 5794
EDMENTUM, INC.—See The Vistria Group, LP; *U.S. Private*, pg. 4131
EDMESTON AB—See Metso Oyj; *Int'l*, pg. 4865
EDMI ELECTRONICS SDN BHD—See Osaki Electric Co., Ltd.; *Int'l*, pg. 5647
EDMI EUROPE LIMITED—See Osaki Electric Co., Ltd.; *Int'l*, pg. 5647
EDMI GAS PTY LTD—See Osaki Electric Co., Ltd.; *Int'l*, pg. 5647
EDMI INDIA PVT. LTD.—See Osaki Electric Co., Ltd.; *Int'l*, pg. 5647
EDMI INTERNATIONAL TRADING (SHANGHAI) CO., LTD—See Osaki Electric Co., Ltd.; *Int'l*, pg. 5647
EDMI LIMITED—See Osaki Electric Co., Ltd.; *Int'l*, pg. 5647
EDMI METERS SDN BHD—See Osaki Electric Co., Ltd.; *Int'l*, pg. 5647
ED MINIAT, INC.; *U.S. Private*, pg. 1331
EDMI NZ LIMITED—See Osaki Electric Co., Ltd.; *Int'l*, pg. 5647
EDMI PHILIPPINES INC.—See Osaki Electric Co., Ltd.; *Int'l*, pg. 5647
EDMI PTY LTD—See Osaki Electric Co., Ltd.; *Int'l*, pg. 5647
EDMI (SHENZHEN) CO., LTD.—See Osaki Electric Co., Ltd.; *Int'l*, pg. 5647
ED MITCHELL INC.; *U.S. Private*, pg. 1331
EDMI VIETNAM COMPANY LIMITED—See Osaki Electric Co., Ltd.; *Int'l*, pg. 5647
EDM MACHINING SOLUTIONS (M) SDN. BHD.—See Toyo Ventures Holdings Berhad; *Int'l*, pg. 7860
EDMODO, INC.—See NetDragon Websoft Holdings Limited; *Int'l*, pg. 5213
EDMOND DE ROTHSCHILD ADVISORY MANAGEMENT (BEIJING) CO., LTD.—See Edmond de Rothschild Holding S.A.; *Int'l*, pg. 2313
EDMOND DE ROTHSCHILD ASSET MANAGEMENT CHILE S.A.—See Edmond de Rothschild Holding S.A.; *Int'l*, pg. 2313
EDMOND DE ROTHSCHILD ASSET MANAGEMENT (C.I.) LIMITED—See Edmond de Rothschild Holding S.A.; *Int'l*, pg. 2313
EDMOND DE ROTHSCHILD ASSET MANAGEMENT (LUXEMBOURG) SA—See Edmond de Rothschild Holding S.A.; *Int'l*, pg. 2313

COMPANY NAME INDEX

EDMOND DE ROTHSCHILD ASSET MANAGEMENT—See Edmond de Rothschild Holding S.A.; *Int'l*, pg. 2313
EDMOND DE ROTHSCHILD ASSET MANAGEMENT (SUISSE) SA—See Edmond de Rothschild Holding S.A.; *Int'l*, pg. 2313
EDMOND DE ROTHSCHILD (BAHAMAS) LTD.—See Edmond de Rothschild Holding S.A.; *Int'l*, pg. 2312
EDMOND DE ROTHSCHILD CORPORATE FINANCE—See Edmond de Rothschild Holding S.A.; *Int'l*, pg. 2313
EDMOND DE ROTHSCHILD ENTERPRISES PATRIMONIALES CROISSANCE—See Edmond de Rothschild Holding S.A.; *Int'l*, pg. 2313
EDMOND DE ROTHSCHILD ENTERPRISES PATRIMONIALES—See Edmond de Rothschild Holding S.A.; *Int'l*, pg. 2313
EDMOND DE ROTHSCHILD (EUROPE) SA/NV—See Edmond de Rothschild Holding S.A.; *Int'l*, pg. 2312
EDMOND DE ROTHSCHILD HOLDING S.A.; *Int'l*, pg. 2312
EDMOND DE ROTHSCHILD INVESTMENT PARTNERS (HONG KONG) LTD.—See Edmond de Rothschild Holding S.A.; *Int'l*, pg. 2313
EDMOND DE ROTHSCHILD INVESTMENT PARTNERS (SHANGHAI) LTD.—See Edmond de Rothschild Holding S.A.; *Int'l*, pg. 2313
EDMOND DE ROTHSCHILD INVESTMENT SERVICES LIMITED—See Edmond de Rothschild Holding S.A.; *Int'l*, pg. 2312
EDMOND DE ROTHSCHILD (ISRAEL) LTD.—See Edmond de Rothschild Holding S.A.; *Int'l*, pg. 2313
EDMOND DE ROTHSCHILD (LUGANO) S.A.—See Edmond de Rothschild Holding S.A.; *Int'l*, pg. 2313
EDMOND DE ROTHSCHILD (MONACO) LTD.—See Edmond de Rothschild Holding S.A.; *Int'l*, pg. 2313
EDMOND DE ROTHSCHILD PRIVATE EQUITY MANAGEMENT LTD.—See Edmond de Rothschild Holding S.A.; *Int'l*, pg. 2312
EDMOND DE ROTHSCHILD PRIVATE EQUITY PARTNERS (ISRAEL) LTD.—See Edmond de Rothschild Holding S.A.; *Int'l*, pg. 2313
EDMOND DE ROTHSCHILD (UK) LIMITED—See Edmond de Rothschild Holding S.A.; *Int'l*, pg. 2313
EDMOND GENERAL SURGERY, LLC—See HCA Healthcare, Inc.; *U.S. Public*, pg. 995
EDMOND PHARMA S.R.L.—See Recipharm AB; *Int'l*, pg. 6235
EDMOND PHYSICIAN SERVICES, LLC—See HCA Healthcare, Inc.; *U.S. Public*, pg. 995
EDMOND PODIATRY ASSOCIATES, LLC—See HCA Healthcare, Inc.; *U.S. Public*, pg. 995
EDMONDS CHEVROLET BUICK GMC; *Int'l*, pg. 2313
EDMONDS ENGINEERING, INC.—See The Dewberry Companies Inc.; *U.S. Private*, pg. 4020
EDMONDSONS LIMITED—See Brown & Brown, Inc.; *U.S. Public*, pg. 400
EDMONSON ELECTRIC, LLC—See IES Holdings, Inc.; *U.S. Public*, pg. 1094
EDMONTON BANCSHARES INC.; *U.S. Private*, pg. 1337
EDMONTON JOURNAL GROUP INC.—See Chatham Asset Management, LLC; *U.S. Private*, pg. 861
EDMONTON JOURNAL—See Chatham Asset Management, LLC; *U.S. Private*, pg. 861
EDMONTON KENWORTH LTD. - KENWORTH FORT MCMURRAY DIVISION—See Edmonton Kenworth Ltd.; *Int'l*, pg. 2313
EDMONTON KENWORTH LTD. - KENWORTH LEDUC DIVISION—See Edmonton Kenworth Ltd.; *Int'l*, pg. 2313
EDMONTON KENWORTH LTD. - KENWORTH LLOYDMINSTER DIVISION—See Edmonton Kenworth Ltd.; *Int'l*, pg. 2313
EDMONTON KENWORTH LTD.; *Int'l*, pg. 2313
EDMONTON STATE BANK—See Edmonton Bancshares Inc.; *U.S. Private*, pg. 1337
THE EDMONTON SUN—See Chatham Asset Management, LLC; *U.S. Private*, pg. 861
EDM RECORDS MANAGEMENT LIMITED—See Rainbow HoldCo Limited; *Int'l*, pg. 6190
EDM SUPPLIES, INC.—See Global EDM Supplies, Inc.; *U.S. Private*, pg. 1713
EDM-TOOLS (M) SDN. BHD.—See Toyo Ventures Holdings Berhad; *Int'l*, pg. 7860
EDM-TOOLS (PENANG) SDN. BHD.—See Toyo Ventures Holdings Berhad; *Int'l*, pg. 7860
ED MULLINAX FORD, LLC—See AutoNation, Inc.; *U.S. Public*, pg. 234
EDMUND BELL & CO., LIMITED—See Redwood Distribution Ltd.; *Int'l*, pg. 6249
EDMUND HILLARY RETIREMENT VILLAGE LIMITED—See Ryman Healthcare Ltd.; *Int'l*, pg. 6439
EDMUND INDUSTRIAL OPTICS INC.; *U.S. Private*, pg. 1337
EDMUND KIM INTERNATIONAL INC.; *U.S. Private*, pg. 1337
EDMUND KIM PRODUCTIONS GROUP—See Edmund Kim International Inc.; *U.S. Private*, pg. 1338

EDMUND OPTICS CHINA CO. LTD.—See Edmund Industrial Optics Inc.; *U.S. Private*, pg. 1337
EDMUND OPTICS GMBH—See Edmund Industrial Optics Inc.; *U.S. Private*, pg. 1337
EDMUND OPTICS JAPAN LTD.—See Edmund Industrial Optics Inc.; *U.S. Private*, pg. 1337
EDMUND OPTICS KOREA LTD.—See Edmund Industrial Optics Inc.; *U.S. Private*, pg. 1337
EDMUND OPTICS LTD.—See Edmund Industrial Optics Inc.; *U.S. Private*, pg. 1337
EDMUND OPTICS SINGAPORE PTE. LTD.—See Edmund Industrial Optics Inc.; *U.S. Private*, pg. 1337
EDMUND OPTICS—See Edmund Industrial Optics Inc.; *U.S. Private*, pg. 1337
EDMUNDS, INC.; *U.S. Private*, pg. 1338
EDMUNDS MANUFACTURING COMPANY; *U.S. Private*, pg. 1338
EDMUND TIE & COMPANY (SEA) PTE. LTD.; *Int'l*, pg. 2313
EDMUND TIE & COMPANY (THAILAND) CO, LTD.—See Edmund Tie & Company (SEA) Pte. Ltd.; *Int'l*, pg. 2313
EDNA VALLEY VINEYARD—See E. & J. Gallo Winery; *U.S. Private*, pg. 1303
ED NETZE GMBH—See EnBW Energie Baden-Wurttemberg AG; *Int'l*, pg. 2398
EDNEY DISTRIBUTING COMPANY; *U.S. Private*, pg. 1338
EDNIL D.O.O. SARAJEVO—See KKR & Co. Inc.; *U.S. Public*, pg. 1254
EDNIL D.O.O. SARAJEVO—See The Goldman Sachs Group, Inc.; *U.S. Public*, pg. 2079
EDOARDOS MARTIN, S.A.B. DE C.V.; *Int'l*, pg. 2313
E.D. OATES PTY. LTD.—See Freudenberg SE; *Int'l*, pg. 2783
EDOB ABWICKLUNGS AG—See Regent, L.P.; *U.S. Private*, pg. 3387
EDOC ACQUISITION CORP.—See Australian Oilseeds Holdings Limited; *Int'l*, pg. 722
EDOCTUM PERU S.A.C.—See Tega Industries Limited; *Int'l*, pg. 7521
EDOCTUM S.A.—See Tega Industries Limited; *Int'l*, pg. 7521
EDO CULTURAL CENTER CO., LTD.—See Ichishin Holdings Co., Ltd.; *Int'l*, pg. 3581
EDOCUMENT RESOURCES, LLC—See KYOCERA Corporation; *Int'l*, pg. 4357
EDOGAWA DANBORU CO., LTD.—See Rengo Co., Ltd.; *Int'l*, pg. 6279
EDOGAWA METALS CO., LTD.—See TPR Co., Ltd.; *Int'l*, pg. 7883
EDO INTERACTIVE, INC.—See Augeo Affinity Marketing, Inc.; *U.S. Private*, pg. 392
EDOKO FOOD IMPORTERS LTD.; *Int'l*, pg. 2313
E-DOME A. S.—See CEZ, a.s.; *Int'l*, pg. 1429
EDOM ELECTRONIC TECHNOLOGY (SHANGHAI) CO., LTD.—See EDOM Technology Co., Ltd.; *Int'l*, pg. 2313
E-DOMIZIL AG—See HomeToGo SE; *Int'l*, pg. 3456
E-DOMIZIL GMBH—See HomeToGo SE; *Int'l*, pg. 3456
EDOM TECHNOLOGY CO., LTD.; *Int'l*, pg. 2313
EDOM TECHNOLOGY JAPAN CO., LTD.—See EDOM Technology Co., Ltd.; *Int'l*, pg. 2313
EDOM TECHNOLOGY (SHANGHAI) LTD.—See EDOM Technology Co., Ltd.; *Int'l*, pg. 2313
EDOM TRADING (SHENZHEN) LTD.—See EDOM Technology Co., Ltd.; *Int'l*, pg. 2313
EDON CONSTRUCTION COMPANY, INC.; *U.S. Private*, pg. 1338
EDON FARMERS COOPERATIVE ASSOCIATION; *U.S. Private*, pg. 1338
EDOSAKI KYOEI INDUSTRIES CO., LTD.—See Uchida Yoko Co., Ltd.; *Int'l*, pg. 8012
EDOTCO BANGLADESH CO. LTD.—See Axiata Group Berhad; *Int'l*, pg. 768
EDOTCO GROUP SDN BHD—See Axiata Group Berhad; *Int'l*, pg. 768
EDOTCO MYANMAR LIMITED—See Sojitz Corporation; *Int'l*, pg. 7061
EDOTCO TOWERS (BANGLADESH) LIMITED—See Axiata Group Berhad; *Int'l*, pg. 768
EDOTFOODS, INC.—See Dot Foods, Inc.; *U.S. Private*, pg. 1265
EDOT LLC—See CyberAdvisors, Inc.; *U.S. Private*, pg. 1133
EDOUARD ROUSSEAU S.A.S.—See Thermador Groupe; *Int'l*, pg. 7707
EDO WESTERN CORP.—See L3Harris Technologies, Inc.; *U.S. Public*, pg. 1279
EDPAC INTERNATIONAL LTD.—See Munters Group AB; *Int'l*, pg. 5094
EDPA KIMYA SAN. VE TIC. A.S.; *Int'l*, pg. 2315
EDPA TEKSTIL TICARET A.S.; *Int'l*, pg. 2315
EDPA USA, INC.; *U.S. Private*, pg. 1338
EDP DISTRIBUICAO DE ENERGIA, S.A.—See EDP - Energias de Portugal, S.A.; *Int'l*, pg. 2314
EDP DISTRIBUICAO—See EDP - Energias de Portugal, S.A.; *Int'l*, pg. 2314
EDP - ENERGIAS DE PORTUGAL, S.A.; *Int'l*, pg. 2314
EDP - ENERGIAS DO BRASIL S.A.—See EDP - Energias de Portugal, S.A.; *Int'l*, pg. 2314

THE EDRINGTON GROUP

ED PERRY AUTO PARTS COMPANY, INC.; *U.S. Private*, pg. 1331
EDP ESCELSA - ESPIRITO SANTO CENTRAIS ELETRICAS S.A.—See EDP - Energias de Portugal, S.A.; *Int'l*, pg. 2314
EDP ESPIRITO SANTO DISTRIBUICAO DE ENERGIA S.A.—See EDP - Energias de Portugal, S.A.; *Int'l*, pg. 2314
EDP EUROPE—See Engineered Data Products, LLC; *U.S. Private*, pg. 1398
EDP GAS.COM - COMERCIO DE GAS NATURAL, S.A.—See EDP - Energias de Portugal, S.A.; *Int'l*, pg. 2314
EDP GAS SERVICO UNIVERSAL, S.A.—See EDP - Energias de Portugal, S.A.; *Int'l*, pg. 2314
EDP GAS - S.G.P.S., S.A.—See REN - Redes Energeticas Nacionais SGPS, S.A.; *Int'l*, pg. 6272
EDP GEOSCIENCES—See Soil & Materials Engineers, Inc.; *U.S. Private*, pg. 3706
EDP - GESTAO DA PRODUCAO DE ENERGIA, S.A.—See EDP - Energias de Portugal, S.A.; *Int'l*, pg. 2314
EDP INOVACAO, S.A.—See EDP - Energias de Portugal, S.A.; *Int'l*, pg. 2314
EDPO, LLC; *U.S. Private*, pg. 1338
EDP - PROJECTOS S.G.P.S., S.A.—See EDP - Energias de Portugal, S.A.; *Int'l*, pg. 2314
EDP RENEWABLES CANADA, LTD—See EDP - Energias de Portugal, S.A.; *Int'l*, pg. 2314
EDP RENEWABLES NORTH AMERICA, L.L.C.—See EDP - Energias de Portugal, S.A.; *Int'l*, pg. 2314
EDP RENEWABLES POLSKA, SP. Z O.O.—See EDP - Energias de Portugal, S.A.; *Int'l*, pg. 2314
EDP RENOVAVEIS S.A.—See EDP - Energias de Portugal, S.A.; *Int'l*, pg. 2314
ED PRODUCTS LTD.—See Amphenol Corporation; *U.S. Public*, pg. 130
EDP SERVICOS - SISTEMAS PARA A QUALIDADE E EFICIENCIA ENERGETICA, S.A.—See EDP - Energias de Portugal, S.A.; *Int'l*, pg. 2314
EDP SERVINER - SERVICOS DE ENERGIA, S.A.—See EDP - Energias de Portugal, S.A.; *Int'l*, pg. 2314
E.D. PUBLICATIONS, INC.—See RCI Hospitality Holdings, Inc.; *U.S. Public*, pg. 1767
E. D. PUBLICATIONS, INC.—See RCI Hospitality Holdings, Inc.; *U.S. Public*, pg. 1767
EDRAN BERHAD; *Int'l*, pg. 2315
EDRASIS - C. PSALLIDAS S.A.; *Int'l*, pg. 2315
EDR AUBURN, LLC—See Greystar Real Estate Partners, LLC; *U.S. Private*, pg. 1785
EDRI-EL ISRAEL ASSETS LTD.; *Int'l*, pg. 2315
EDRINGTON DENMARK A/S—See The Edrington Group; *Int'l*, pg. 7637
EDRINGTON FINLAND OY—See The Edrington Group; *Int'l*, pg. 7637
THE EDRINGTON GROUP - EDRINGTON AMERICAS CENTRAL & CANADA DIVISION—See The Edrington Group; *Int'l*, pg. 7638
THE EDRINGTON GROUP - EDRINGTON AMERICAS NORTHEAST DIVISION—See The Edrington Group; *Int'l*, pg. 7638
THE EDRINGTON GROUP - EDRINGTON AMERICAS SOUTH DIVISION—See The Edrington Group; *Int'l*, pg. 7638
THE EDRINGTON GROUP - EDRINGTON AMERICAS WEST DIVISION—See The Edrington Group; *Int'l*, pg. 7638
THE EDRINGTON GROUP; *Int'l*, pg. 7637
EDRINGTON HONG KONG LTD—See The Edrington Group; *Int'l*, pg. 7637
EDRINGTON KOREA LTD.—See The Edrington Group; *Int'l*, pg. 7637
EDRINGTON NORWAY AS—See The Edrington Group; *Int'l*, pg. 7638
EDRINGTON SHANGHAI LTD.—See The Edrington Group; *Int'l*, pg. 7638
EDRINGTON SINGAPORE PTE LTD—See The Edrington Group; *Int'l*, pg. 7638
EDRINGTON SWEDEN AB—See The Edrington Group; *Int'l*, pg. 7638
EDRINGTON TAIWAN LTD.—See The Edrington Group; *Int'l*, pg. 7638
EDRIVE ACTUATORS, INC.—See Graham Holdings Company; *U.S. Public*, pg. 955
EDRIVING, LLC—See Vista Equity Partners, LLC; *U.S. Private*, pg. 4401
EDR MANAGEMENT INC.—See Greystar Real Estate Partners, LLC; *U.S. Private*, pg. 1785
EDRO ENGINEERING, INC.—See voestalpine AG; *Int'l*, pg. 8291
EDRO SPECIALTY STEELS GMBH—See voestalpine AG; *Int'l*, pg. 8291
EDRO SPECIALTY STEELS, INC.—See voestalpine AG; *Int'l*, pg. 8291
EDR SYRACUSE, LLC—See Greystar Real Estate Partners, LLC; *U.S. Private*, pg. 1785
EDSAL MANUFACTURING COMPANY, INC.—See Monomoy Capital Partners LLC; *U.S. Private*, pg. 2772

EDSA SHANGRI-LA HOTEL & RESORT, INC.—See Shangri-La Asia Limited; *Int'l*, pg. 6783
EDSA; *U.S. Private*, pg. 1338
ED SAS—See Carrefour SA; *Int'l*, pg. 1345
EDSBYNS INDUSTRI AB—See Snap-on Incorporated; *U.S. Public*, pg. 1897
EDSCHA AAPICO AUTOMOTIVE CO., LTD.—See Acek Desarrollo y Gestion Industrial SL; *Int'l*, pg. 96
EDSCHA AUTOMOTIVE HAUZENBERG GMBH—See Acek Desarrollo y Gestion Industrial SL; *Int'l*, pg. 96
EDSCHA AUTOMOTIVE HENGERSBERG GMBH—See Acek Desarrollo y Gestion Industrial SL; *Int'l*, pg. 96
EDSCHA AUTOMOTIVE KAMENICE S.R.O.—See VBG Group AB; *Int'l*, pg. 8138
EDSCHA AUTOMOTIVE MICHIGIAN INC.—See Acek Desarrollo y Gestion Industrial SL; *Int'l*, pg. 96
EDSCHA BRIEY, S.A.S.—See Acek Desarrollo y Gestion Industrial SL; *Int'l*, pg. 96
EDSCHA BURGOS, S.A.—See Acek Desarrollo y Gestion Industrial SL; *Int'l*, pg. 96
EDSCHA DO BRASIL, LTDA.—See Acek Desarrollo y Gestion Industrial SL; *Int'l*, pg. 96
EDSCHA ENGINEERING FRANCE S.A.S—See Acek Desarrollo y Gestion Industrial SL; *Int'l*, pg. 96
EDSCHA ENGINEERING, GMBH.—See Acek Desarrollo y Gestion Industrial SL; *Int'l*, pg. 96
EDSCHA HOLDING GMBH—See Acek Desarrollo y Gestion Industrial SL; *Int'l*, pg. 96
EDSCHA HRADEC S.R.O.—See Acek Desarrollo y Gestion Industrial SL; *Int'l*, pg. 96
EDSCHA PHA LTD.—See Acek Desarrollo y Gestion Industrial SL; *Int'l*, pg. 96
EDSCHA SANTANDER, S.L.—See Acek Desarrollo y Gestion Industrial SL; *Int'l*, pg. 96
EDSCHA VELKY MEDER S.R.O.—See Acek Desarrollo y Gestion Industrial SL; *Int'l*, pg. 96
ED SCHMIDT PONTIAC - GMC TRUCK, INC.; *U.S. Private*, pg. 1331
ED SCHULTS CHEVROLET CADILLAC; *U.S. Private*, pg. 1331
EDSCO FASTENERS, LLC—See Commercial Metals Company; *U.S. Public*, pg. 546
EDS DOO BELGRADE—See Public Power Corporation S.A.; *Int'l*, pg. 6095
EDS DOO SKOPJE—See Public Power Corporation S.A.; *Int'l*, pg. 6095
ED'S EASY DINER GROUP LIMITED; *Int'l*, pg. 2303
ED SEIFRIED CONSTRUCTION, INC.; *U.S. Private*, pg. 1331
EDSERV SOFTSYSTEMS LIMITED; *Int'l*, pg. 2315
ED SHULTS CHEVROLET, INC.—See Shults Management Group, Inc.; *U.S. Private*, pg. 3644
ED SHULTS OF WARREN, INC.; *U.S. Private*, pg. 1332
ED SIMAL & ASSOCIATES INC.; *U.S. Private*, pg. 1332
EDSIM LEATHER CO. INC.; *U.S. Private*, pg. 1338
EDSINC.; *U.S. Private*, pg. 1338
E.D.S. INTERNATIONAL LIMITED—See Veritas Capital Fund Management, LLC; *U.S. Private*, pg. 4364
E.D.S.I. SAS—See Kudelski S.A.; *Int'l*, pg. 4323
EDS MANUFACTURING, INCORPORATED—See Yazaki Corporation; *Int'l*, pg. 8572
EDS MANUFACTURING INC.; *U.S. Private*, pg. 1338
EDS MEDIA AG—See Die Schweizerische Post AG; *Int'l*, pg. 2112
E.D. SMITH FOODS, LTD.—See TreeHouse Foods, Inc.; *U.S. Public*, pg. 2187
EDSON FINANCIAL INC.—See Krystal Infinity LLC; *U.S. Private*, pg. 2354
EDS-R GMBH; *Int'l*, pg. 2315
ED'S SUPPLY COMPANY INC.—See Gryphon Investors, LLC; *U.S. Private*, pg. 1798
ED STAUB & SONS PETROLEUM INC.; *U.S. Private*, pg. 1332
ED STAUB & SONS—See Ed Staub & Sons Petroleum Inc.; *U.S. Private*, pg. 1332
E.D. SUPPLY CO. INC.; *U.S. Private*, pg. 1305
ED TAYLOR CONSTRUCTION INC.; *U.S. Private*, pg. 1332
ED & TECH INTERNATIONAL LIMITED; *Int'l*, pg. 2302
EDTECHX HOLDINGS ACQUISITION CORP.; *Int'l*, pg. 2315
EDT-EUROPE APS—See Emerging Display Tech; *Int'l*, pg. 2379
ED TILLMAN AUTO SALES INC.; *U.S. Private*, pg. 1332
EDT-JAPAN CORP.—See Emerging Display Tech; *Int'l*, pg. 2379
EDTRIN GROUP LIMITED; *Int'l*, pg. 2315
EDTS, LLC—See WDIT, Incorporated; *U.S. Private*, pg. 4462
EDUARD HACHMANN GESELLSCHAFT MIT BESCHRANKTER HAFTUNG—See STRABAG SE; *Int'l*, pg. 7230
EDUARD KETTNER; *Int'l*, pg. 2315
EDUARD MERKLE GMBH & CO KG—See Omya (Schweiz) AG; *Int'l*, pg. 5570
EDUCACTIVA, S.A.C.—See Promotora de Informaciones S.A.; *Int'l*, pg. 5995
EDUCARE GLOBAL ACADEMY PTE. LTD.—See Ascendo International Holdings Pte. Ltd.; *Int'l*, pg. 602

EDUCARE HUMAN CAPITAL PRIVATE LIMITED—See Ascendo International Holdings Pte. Ltd.; *Int'l*, pg. 602
EDUCATE 360 LLC—See Morgan Stanley; *U.S. Public*, pg. 1474
EDUCATED DESIGN & DEVELOPMENT, INC.; *U.S. Private*, pg. 1338
EDUCATE, INC.—See Sterling Partners; *U.S. Private*, pg. 3807
EDUCATE ONLINE, INC.—See Sterling Partners; *U.S. Private*, pg. 3807
EDUCATION ADVANCED, INC.—See Serent Capital Management Company, LLC; *U.S. Private*, pg. 3613
EDUCATION AFFILIATES INC.—See JLL Partners, LLC; *U.S. Private*, pg. 2212
EDUCATIONAL BOOK JSC; *Int'l*, pg. 2315
EDUCATIONAL BOOK JSC; *Int'l*, pg. 2315
EDUCATIONAL BOOK JSC; *Int'l*, pg. 2315
EDUCATIONAL COMMISSION FOR FOREIGN MEDICAL GRADUATES; *U.S. Private*, pg. 1339
EDUCATIONAL COMMUNITY CREDIT UNION; *U.S. Private*, pg. 1339
EDUCATIONAL CREDIT MANAGEMENT CO.; *U.S. Private*, pg. 1339
EDUCATIONAL DATA SYSTEMS, INC.; *U.S. Private*, pg. 1339
EDUCATIONAL DEVELOPERS, INC.; *U.S. Private*, pg. 1339
EDUCATIONAL DEVELOPMENT CORPORATION - HOME BUSINESS DIVISION—See Educational Develop; *U.S. Public*, pg. 720
EDUCATIONAL DEVELOPMENT CORPORATION - PUBLISHING DIVISION—See Educational Develop; *U.S. Public*, pg. 720
EDUCATIONAL DEVELOPMENT CORPORATION; *U.S. Public*, pg. 719
EDUCATIONAL EMPLOYEES CREDIT UNION; *U.S. Private*, pg. 1339
EDUCATIONAL ENTERPRISES AUSTRALIA PTY LTD.—See Navitas Limited; *Int'l*, pg. 5176
EDUCATIONAL FUNDING OF THE SOUTH; *U.S. Private*, pg. 1339
EDUCATIONAL HOLDING GROUP K.S.C.P.—See Boubyan Petrochemical Co. KSC; *Int'l*, pg. 1119
EDUCATIONAL HOUSING SERVICES; *U.S. Private*, pg. 1339
EDUCATIONAL INSIGHTS, INC.—See Learning Resources, Inc.; *U.S. Private*, pg. 2408
EDUCATIONAL MEDIA FOUNDATION; *U.S. Private*, pg. 1339
EDUCATIONAL OUTFITTERS, LLC; *U.S. Private*, pg. 1339
EDUCATIONAL SERVICES OF AMERICA; *U.S. Private*, pg. 1339
EDUCATIONAL TECHNOLOGY ARABIA COMPANY LIMITED—See HAK Algahtani Group of Companies; *Int'l*, pg. 3219
EDUCATIONAL TELEVISION ASSOCIATION; *U.S. Private*, pg. 1339
EDUCATIONAL TESTING SERVICE INC.; *U.S. Private*, pg. 1339
EDUCATIONAL TREND SDN. BHD.—See HeiTech Padu Berhad; *Int'l*, pg. 3326
EDUCATION CARTOGRAPHY & ILLUSTRATION JSC; *Int'l*, pg. 2315
EDUCATION CENTRE OF THE SLOVENIAN ELECTRIC POWER AUTHORITY—See Elektro Slovenia d.o.o.; *Int'l*, pg. 2357
EDUCATIONCITY INC.—See The Vistria Group, LP; *U.S. Private*, pg. 4131
EDUCATION CONNECTION; *U.S. Private*, pg. 1338
EDUCATION CORPORATION OF AMERICA; *U.S. Private*, pg. 1338
EDUCATION DEVELOPMENT CENTER INC.; *U.S. Private*, pg. 1338
EDUCATIONDYNAMICS, LLC—See Renovus Capital Partners; *U.S. Private*, pg. 3399
EDUCATION EXPERIENCES, INC.—See MidOcean Partners, LLP; *U.S. Private*, pg. 2716
EDUCATION FIRST; *U.S. Private*, pg. 1338
EDUCATION GROWTH LLC; *U.S. Private*, pg. 1339
EDUCATION HOLDINGS 1—See IAC Inc.; *U.S. Public*, pg. 1083
EDUCATION MANAGEMENT CORPORATION—See Dream Center Foundation, a California Nonprofit Corp.; *U.S. Private*, pg. 1272
EDUCATION MANAGEMENT SOLUTIONS, INC—See Collegis LLC; *U.S. Private*, pg. 968
EDUCATION MEDIA & PUBLISHING GROUP (CHINA) LIMITED; *Int'l*, pg. 2315
EDUCATION NETWORKS OF AMERICA, INC.—See ZelnickMedia Corp.; *U.S. Private*, pg. 4600
EDUCATIONPARTNER CO LTD; *Int'l*, pg. 2315
EDUCATION PERSONNEL HOLDCO LIMITED—See Intermediate Capital Group plc; *Int'l*, pg. 3742
EDUCATION PIONEERS; *U.S. Private*, pg. 1339
EDUCATION PLACEMENT GROUP LIMITED—See Sovereign Capital Partners LLP; *Int'l*, pg. 7121
EDUCATION-PLUS, INC.; *U.S. Private*, pg. 1339

EDUCATION REALTY TRUST, INC.—See Greystar Real Estate Partners, LLC; *U.S. Private*, pg. 1785
EDUCATION SERVICE CENTER REGION 12; *U.S. Private*, pg. 1339
EDUCATION SERVICE CENTER REGION II; *U.S. Private*, pg. 1339
EDUCATION TECHNOLOGY PARTNERS; *U.S. Private*, pg. 1339
THE EDUCATION TRUST; *U.S. Private*, pg. 4025
EDUCATION UMBRELLA LTD.—See Aurelius Equity Opportunities SE & Co. KGaA; *Int'l*, pg. 708
EDUCATIONWORKS; *U.S. Private*, pg. 1340
EDUCATORS INSURANCE AGENCY, INC.—See The Hanover Insurance Group, Inc.; *U.S. Public*, pg. 2087
EDUCATORS PREFERRED CORPORATION—See Aon plc; *Int'l*, pg. 496
EDUCAUSE; *U.S. Private*, pg. 1340
EDUCERE, LLC; *U.S. Private*, pg. 1340
EDUCOM CORPORATION—See EQT AB; *Int'l*, pg. 2467
EDUCOMP SOLUTIONS, LTD.; *Int'l*, pg. 2315
EDUCOM S.R.L.—See IQVIA Holdings Inc.; *U.S. Public*, pg. 1168
EDUCURIOUS PARTNERS; *U.S. Private*, pg. 1340
EDUEXEL INFOTAINMENT LIMITED; *Int'l*, pg. 2316
EDUGLOBAL AUSTRALIA PTY LTD.—See Navitas Limited; *Int'l*, pg. 5176
EDUGRADE AB—See Hexatronic Group AB; *Int'l*, pg. 3370
EDUGRADE SE—See Hexatronic Group AB; *Int'l*, pg. 3370
EDUGROUPE—See Neurones S.A.; *Int'l*, pg. 5219
EDULAB, INC.; *Int'l*, pg. 2316
EDULENCE CORPORATION—See Fundos Group LLC; *U.S. Private*, pg. 1623
EDULENCE CORPORATION—See Trinity Private Equity Group, LLC; *U.S. Private*, pg. 4235
EDUMATICS CORPORATION INC.—See Educomp Solutions, Ltd.; *Int'l*, pg. 2315
EDUN APPAREL LTD.; *Int'l*, pg. 2316
EDUNIVERSAL SA; *Int'l*, pg. 2316
EDU-PERFORMANCE CANADA INC.—See DGTL Holdings Inc.; *Int'l*, pg. 2097
EDU-PERFORMANCE EUROPE—See DGTL Holdings Inc.; *Int'l*, pg. 2097
EDU-PERFORMANCE MEXICO—See DGTL Holdings Inc.; *Int'l*, pg. 2097
EDUPOINT EDUCATIONAL SYSTEMS, LLC; *U.S. Private*, pg. 1340
EDUSERVE INTERNATIONAL LIMITED—See i-Control Holdings Limited; *Int'l*, pg. 3563
EDUSPEC HOLDINGS BERHAD; *Int'l*, pg. 2316
EDUTAINMENTLIVE, LLC; *U.S. Private*, pg. 1340
EDUTECH LAB AP PRIVATE LIMITED—See EduLab, Inc.; *Int'l*, pg. 2316
EDUTECH LAB, INC.—See EduLab, Inc.; *Int'l*, pg. 2316
EDUTOR TECHNOLOGIES INDIA PRIVATE LIMITED—See S Chand & Company Limited; *Int'l*, pg. 6442
EDUTUTOR OY—See BHG Group AB; *Int'l*, pg. 1014
EDVANCE INTERNATIONAL HOLDINGS LIMITED; *Int'l*, pg. 2316
EDVANCE TECHNOLOGY (HONG KONG) LIMITED—See Edvance International Holdings Limited; *Int'l*, pg. 2316
EDVANCE TECHNOLOGY (SINGAPORE) PTE. LTD.—See Edvance International Holdings Limited; *Int'l*, pg. 2316
EDVANTAGE GROUP HOLDINGS LIMITED; *Int'l*, pg. 2316
EDVANTAGE INSTITUTE AUSTRALIA PTY. LTD.—See Edvantage Group Holdings Limited; *Int'l*, pg. 2316
EDVANTAGE INSTITUTE (SINGAPORE) PTE. LTD.—See Edvantage Group Holdings Limited; *Int'l*, pg. 2316
EDVANTAGES; *U.S. Private*, pg. 1340
EDVENSWA ENTERPRISES LIMITED; *Int'l*, pg. 2316
EDVENTURECO PTY LTD—See AWN Holdings Limited; *Int'l*, pg. 753
EDVIRT AB—See Sandvik AB; *Int'l*, pg. 6529
EDVISORS NETWORK, INC.; *U.S. Private*, pg. 1340
ED VOYLES DEALERSHIPS; *U.S. Private*, pg. 1332
ED WALTON CONSTRUCTION CO.; *U.S. Private*, pg. 1332
EDWARD APPFEL CO; *U.S. Private*, pg. 1340
EDWARD BARBER & COMPANY LIMITED—See Triton Advisers Limited; *Int'l*, pg. 7934
EDWARD B. BEHARRY & CO. LTD.; *Int'l*, pg. 2316
EDWARD B. HOWLIN INC.; *U.S. Private*, pg. 1340
EDWARD BILLINGTON & SON LTD.; *Int'l*, pg. 2316
EDWARD B. O'REILLY & ASSOCIATES, INC.; *U.S. Private*, pg. 1340
EDWARD C. LEVY CO.; *U.S. Private*, pg. 1340
EDWARD DILLON & CO. LTD.; *Int'l*, pg. 2316
EDWARD DON & COMPANY—See Sysco Corporation; *U.S. Public*, pg. 1973
EDWARD E. HALL & COMPANY—See One80 Intermediaries LLC; *U.S. Private*, pg. 3024
EDWARD EHRBAR INC.; *U.S. Private*, pg. 1340
EDWARD FIELDS, INCORPORATED—See Tai Ping Carpets International Limited; *Int'l*, pg. 7408
EDWARD HEALTH VENTURES—See Edward Hospital & Health Services; *U.S. Private*, pg. 1341

COMPANY NAME INDEX E.E. REED CONSTRUCTION, L.P.

Company Index

EDWARD HOSPITAL & HEALTH SERVICES; *U.S. Private*, pg. 1341
EDWARD HOSPITAL INC.—See Edward Hospital & Health Services; *U.S. Private*, pg. 1341
EDWARD H. WOLF & SONS INC.; *U.S. Private*, pg. 1340
EDWARD H. WOLF & SONS INC.—See Edward H. Wolf & Sons Inc.; *U.S. Private*, pg. 1341
EDWARD J. QUIGLEY ASSOCIATES; *U.S. Private*, pg. 1341
EDWARD KELLER (PHILIPPINES) INC.—See Diethelm Keller Holding Limited; *Int'l*, pg. 2116
EDWARD KRAEMER & SONS INC.; *U.S. Private*, pg. 1341
EDWARD LESKE CO.; *U.S. Private*, pg. 1341
EDWARD LOWE FOUNDATION; *U.S. Private*, pg. 1341
EDWARD MARC BRANDS, LLC—See Promise Holdings, LLC; *U.S. Private*, pg. 3283
EDWARD M. KENNEDY COMMUNITY HEALTH CENTER, INC.; *U.S. Private*, pg. 1341
EDWARDO'S RESTAURANT, INC.—See Bravo Restaurants Inc.; *U.S. Private*, pg. 641
EDWARD R. JAMES PARTNERS, LLC; *U.S. Private*, pg. 1341
EDWARD ROSE BUILDING COMPANY—See Edward Rose Company; *U.S. Private*, pg. 1341
EDWARD ROSE COMPANY; *U.S. Private*, pg. 1341
EDWARD ROSE & SONS, LLC—See Edward Rose Company; *U.S. Private*, pg. 1341
EDWARD SAGEL FUNERAL DIRECTION, INC.—See Service Corporation International; *U.S. Public*, pg. 1869
EDWARDS BROTHERS - CAROLINA—See Edwards Brothers, Inc.; *U.S. Private*, pg. 1341
EDWARDS BROTHERS, INC.; *U.S. Private*, pg. 1341
EDWARDS BUILDING CENTER, INC.—See Angeles Equity Partners, LLC; *U.S. Private*, pg. 282
EDWARDS BUILDING CENTER, INC.—See Clearlake Capital Group, L.P.; *U.S. Private*, pg. 934
EDWARDS BUSINESS MACHINES INC.; *U.S. Private*, pg. 1341
EDWARDS CAPITAL, LLC; *U.S. Private*, pg. 1341
EDWARDS CHEVROLET - 280, INC.; *U.S. Private*, pg. 1342
EDWARDS CHEVROLET CO., INC.; *U.S. Private*, pg. 1342
EDWARDS CONSTRUCTION SERVICES INC.—See REX Engineering Group, Inc.; *U.S. Private*, pg. 3417
EDWARDS CONTRACTING—See Reding Gravel & Excavating Co., Inc.; *U.S. Private*, pg. 3379
EDWARDS DEVELOPMENT CORPORATION; *U.S. Private*, pg. 1342
EDWARDS DOORS SYSTEMS LIMITED; *Int'l*, pg. 2316
EDWARDS ELECTRICAL & MECHANICAL, INC.—See Comfort Systems USA, Inc.; *U.S. Public*, pg. 544
EDWARDS ENGINEERING, INC.; *U.S. Private*, pg. 1342
EDWARDS GARAGE LTD.; *Int'l*, pg. 2317
EDWARDS GMBH—See Atlas Copco AB; *Int'l*, pg. 682
EDWARDS GROOM SAUNDERS—See The Engine Group; *Int'l*, pg. 7640
EDWARDS GROUP LIMITED—See Atlas Copco AB; *Int'l*, pg. 682
EDWARDS INDIA PRIVATE LTD.—See Atlas Copco AB; *Int'l*, pg. 682
EDWARDS INDUSTRIES, LLC; *U.S. Private*, pg. 1342
EDWARDS ISRAEL VACUUM LTD.—See Atlas Copco AB; *Int'l*, pg. 682
EDWARDS JAPAN LIMITED—See Atlas Copco AB; *Int'l*, pg. 682
EDWARDS JET CENTER; *U.S. Private*, pg. 1342
EDWARDS KOREA LTD.—See Atlas Copco AB; *Int'l*, pg. 682
EDWARDS LIFESCIENCES AG—See Edwards Lifesciences Corporation; *U.S. Public*, pg. 720
EDWARDS LIFESCIENCES (ASIA) PTE., LTD.—See Edwards Lifesciences Corporation; *U.S. Public*, pg. 720
EDWARDS LIFESCIENCES ASSET MANAGEMENT CORPORATION—See Edwards Lifesciences Corporation; *U.S. Public*, pg. 720
EDWARDS LIFESCIENCES A/S—See Edwards Lifesciences Corporation; *U.S. Public*, pg. 720
EDWARDS LIFESCIENCES AUSTRIA GMBH—See Edwards Lifesciences Corporation; *U.S. Public*, pg. 720
EDWARDS LIFESCIENCES (CANADA) INC.—See Edwards Lifesciences Corporation; *U.S. Public*, pg. 720
EDWARDS LIFESCIENCES COMERCIO E INDUSTRIA DE PRODUTOS MEDICO-CIRURGICOS LTDA.—See Edwards Lifesciences Corporation; *U.S. Public*, pg. 720
EDWARDS LIFESCIENCES CORPORATION OF PUERTO RICO—See Edwards Lifesciences Corporation; *U.S. Public*, pg. 720
EDWARDS LIFESCIENCES CORPORATION; *U.S. Public*, pg. 720
EDWARDS LIFESCIENCES COSTA RICA, S.R.L.—See Edwards Lifesciences Corporation; *U.S. Public*, pg. 720
EDWARDS LIFESCIENCES CZECH REPUBLIC S.R.O.—See Edwards Lifesciences Corporation; *U.S. Public*, pg. 720
EDWARDS LIFESCIENCES DR—See Edwards Lifesciences Corporation; *U.S. Public*, pg. 720
EDWARDS LIFESCIENCES HELLAS, EPE—See Edwards Lifesciences Corporation; *U.S. Public*, pg. 720
EDWARDS LIFESCIENCES (INDIA) PRIVATE LIMITED—See Edwards Lifesciences Corporation; *U.S. Public*, pg. 720
EDWARDS LIFESCIENCES IRELAND, LIMITED—See Edwards Lifesciences Corporation; *U.S. Public*, pg. 720
EDWARDS LIFESCIENCES (ISRAEL) LTD—See Edwards Lifesciences Corporation; *U.S. Public*, pg. 720
EDWARDS LIFESCIENCES ITALIA SPA—See Edwards Lifesciences Corporation; *U.S. Public*, pg. 720
EDWARDS LIFESCIENCES (JAPAN) LIMITED—See Edwards Lifesciences Corporation; *U.S. Public*, pg. 720
EDWARDS LIFESCIENCES KOREA CO., LTD.—See Edwards Lifesciences Corporation; *U.S. Public*, pg. 720
EDWARDS LIFESCIENCES LIMITED—See Edwards Lifesciences Corporation; *U.S. Public*, pg. 720
EDWARDS LIFESCIENCES (MALAYSIA) SDN. BHD.—See Edwards Lifesciences Corporation; *U.S. Public*, pg. 720
EDWARDS LIFESCIENCES MEXICO, S.A. DE C.V.—See Edwards Lifesciences Corporation; *U.S. Public*, pg. 721
EDWARDS LIFESCIENCES NORDIC AB—See Edwards Lifesciences Corporation; *U.S. Public*, pg. 721
EDWARDS LIFESCIENCES (POLAND) LTD.—See Edwards Lifesciences Corporation; *U.S. Public*, pg. 720
EDWARDS LIFESCIENCES (PORTUGAL) COMERCIO E DISTRIBUICAO DE DISPOSITIVOS MEDICOS, LDA.—See Edwards Lifesciences Corporation; *U.S. Public*, pg. 720
EDWARDS LIFESCIENCES (PROPRIETARY) LTD—See Edwards Lifesciences Corporation; *U.S. Public*, pg. 720
EDWARDS LIFESCIENCES PTY. LIMITED—See Edwards Lifesciences Corporation; *U.S. Public*, pg. 721
EDWARDS LIFESCIENCES SALES CORPORATION—See Edwards Lifesciences Corporation; *U.S. Public*, pg. 721
EDWARDS LIFESCIENCES SALES (ISRAEL) LTD.—See Edwards Lifesciences Corporation; *U.S. Public*, pg. 721
EDWARDS LIFESCIENCES SAS—See Edwards Lifesciences Corporation; *U.S. Public*, pg. 721
EDWARDS LIFESCIENCES SERVICES GMBH—See Edwards Lifesciences Corporation; *U.S. Public*, pg. 721
EDWARDS LIFESCIENCES (SHANGHAI) MEDICAL PRODUCTS CO., LTD.—See Edwards Lifesciences Corporation; *U.S. Public*, pg. 720
EDWARDS LIFESCIENCES (SINGAPORE) PTE LTD—See Edwards Lifesciences Corporation; *U.S. Public*, pg. 720
EDWARDS LIFESCIENCES S.L.—See Edwards Lifesciences Corporation; *U.S. Public*, pg. 721
EDWARDS LIFESCIENCES—See Edwards Lifesciences Corporation; *U.S. Public*, pg. 720
EDWARDS LIFESCIENCES S.P.R.L.—See Edwards Lifesciences Corporation; *U.S. Public*, pg. 721
EDWARDS LIFESCIENCES (TAIWAN) CORPORATION—See Edwards Lifesciences Corporation; *U.S. Public*, pg. 720
EDWARDS LIFESCIENCES (THAILAND) LTD.—See Edwards Lifesciences Corporation; *U.S. Public*, pg. 720
EDWARDS LIFESCIENCES WORLD TRADE (SHANGHAI) CO., LTD.—See Edwards Lifesciences Corporation; *U.S. Public*, pg. 721
EDWARDS LTD.—See Atlas Copco AB; *Int'l*, pg. 682
EDWARD'S MANUFACTURING CO, INC.—See Tenex Capital Management, L.P.; *U.S. Private*, pg. 3966
EDWARDS/MOONEY & MOSES, LLC—See Installed Building Products, Inc.; *U.S. Public*, pg. 1132
EDWARD'S OIL CO. INC.; *U.S. Private*, pg. 1341
EDWARDS PUBLICATIONS INC.; *U.S. Private*, pg. 1342
THE EDWARD S. QUIRK CO., INC.; *U.S. Private*, pg. 4025
EDWARDS REPORTING INC.—See Huseby, LLC; *U.S. Private*, pg. 2013
EDWARDS ROTORCRAFT SOLUTIONS INC—See Textron Inc.; *U.S. Public*, pg. 2028
EDWARDS SALES CORPORATION; *U.S. Private*, pg. 1342
EDWARDS SAS—See Atlas Copco AB; *Int'l*, pg. 682
EDWARDS (SHANGHAI) MEDICAL PRODUCTS CO., LTD.—See Edwards Lifesciences Corporation; *U.S. Public*, pg. 720
EDWARDS S.P.A.—See Atlas Copco AB; *Int'l*, pg. 682
EDWARDS S.R.O.—See Atlas Copco AB; *Int'l*, pg. 682
EDWARDS TECHNOLOGIES SINGAPORE PTE. LTD.—See Atlas Copco AB; *Int'l*, pg. 682
THE EDWARD SUROVELL COMPANY—See Hanna Holdings, Inc.; *U.S. Private*, pg. 1854
EDWARDS VACUO LTDA—See Atlas Copco AB; *Int'l*, pg. 682
EDWARDS VACUUM, LLC—See Atlas Copco AB; *Int'l*, pg. 682
EDWARDSVILLE AMBULATORY SURGERY CENTER, L.L.C.—See Quorum Health Corporation; *U.S. Private*, pg. 3329
EDWARDSVILLE PUBLISHING COMPANY, LLC—See The Hearst Corporation; *U.S. Private*, pg. 4047
EDWARD THOMAS TRADING COMPANY; *U.S. Private*, pg. 1341
EDWARD W. SCOTT ELECTRIC CO.; *U.S. Private*, pg. 1341
EDWARD W. SPARROW HOSPITAL ASSOCIATION—See University of Michigan; *U.S. Private*, pg. 4309
EDWIN B. STIMPSON COMPANY, INC.; *U.S. Private*, pg. 1342
EDWIN CO., LTD.—See ITOCHU Corporation; *Int'l*, pg. 3836
EDWIN DEUTGEN, KUNSTOFFTECHNIK GMBH—See Amphenol Corporation; *U.S. Public*, pg. 130
EDWIN GOULD SERVICES FOR CHILDREN AND FAMILIES; *U.S. Private*, pg. 1342
EDWIN L. HEIM COMPANY INC.; *U.S. Private*, pg. 1342
EDWIN WATTS GOLF SHOPS, LLC—See Sun Capital Partners, Inc.; *U.S. Private*, pg. 3859
ED WITTMEIER FORD INC.; *U.S. Private*, pg. 1332
EDX AUSTRALIA PTY LIMITED—See Equifax Inc.; *U.S. Public*, pg. 785
EDX, INC.—See 2U, Inc.; *U.S. Public*, pg. 3
EDX INFORMATION SYSTEMS, INC.; *U.S. Private*, pg. 1342
EDX WIRELESS, INC.; *U.S. Private*, pg. 1342
EDYNAMICS SOLUTIONS LTD; *Int'l*, pg. 2317
EDY'S GRAND ICE CREAM COMPANY—See Nestle S.A.; *Int'l*, pg. 5208
EDY'S GRAND ICE CREAM MIDWEST REGION—See Nestle S.A.; *Int'l*, pg. 5208
ED. ZUBLIN AG—See STRABAG SE; *Int'l*, pg. 7230
E&E ACQUIRING LLC; *U.S. Private*, pg. 1301
E.E. AUSTIN & SON INC.; *U.S. Private*, pg. 1305
EEB KABELTECHNIK GMBH—See TKH Group N.V.; *Int'l*, pg. 7763
E.E. BLACK, LTD.—See Tutor Perini Corporation; *U.S. Public*, pg. 2206
EEBOO CORPORATION; *U.S. Private*, pg. 1343
EEC ACQUISITION LLC—See Wind Point Advisors LLC; *U.S. Private*, pg. 4536
EEC, INCORPORATED; *U.S. Private*, pg. 1343
EECO, INC.—See Emerson Electric Co.; *U.S. Public*, pg. 742
EECOL ELECTRIC ULC—See WESCO International, Inc.; *U.S. Public*, pg. 2351
E&E CO., LTD.; *U.S. Private*, pg. 1301
E&E COMPONENTS (HK) LIMITED—See Everlight Electronics Co., Ltd.; *Int'l*, pg. 2567
EECON CONSTRUCTION SERVICES; *U.S. Private*, pg. 1343
EECO—See Transico Incorporated; *U.S. Private*, pg. 4208
EECO SWITCH (UK)—See Transico Incorporated; *U.S. Private*, pg. 4208
EE CRUZ & COMPANY INC.—See ACS, Actividades de Construccion y Servicios, S.A.; *Int'l*, pg. 113
E&E ENTERPRISES GLOBAL, INC.; *U.S. Private*, pg. 1301
E&E EXHIBITS; *U.S. Private*, pg. 1301
EE-FIT PTY LIMITED—See Fletcher Building Limited; *Int'l*, pg. 2701
EEGEES INC.—See Eastbridge Group; *Int'l*, pg. 2271
EEG ENTERPRISES, INC.—See Ai-Media Technologies Limited; *Int'l*, pg. 227
EE&G ENVIRONMENTAL SERVICES, LLC; *U.S. Private*, pg. 1342
E E HOOD & SONS CONSTRUCTION; *U.S. Private*, pg. 1300
EE-HWA CONSTRUCTION CO., LTD.; *Int'l*, pg. 2317
EEI-CONSTRUCTION DIVISION—See EEI Corporation; *Int'l*, pg. 2317
EEI CONSTRUCTION & MARINE CORP.—See EEI Corporation; *Int'l*, pg. 2317
EEI CORPORATION; *Int'l*, pg. 2317
EEI GLOBAL, INC.; *U.S. Private*, pg. 1343
EEI HOLDING CORPORATION; *U.S. Private*, pg. 1343
EEII AG; *Int'l*, pg. 2317
EEI INDIA ENERGY PRIVATE LIMITED—See Ningbo Techmation Co., Ltd.; *Int'l*, pg. 5306
EEI POWER CORP.—See EEI Corporation; *Int'l*, pg. 2317
EEJA AMERICA INC.—See Tanaka Holdings Co., Ltd.; *Int'l*, pg. 7455
EEKA FASHION HOLDINGS LIMITED; *Int'l*, pg. 2317
EEK CO., LTD.—See SOLXYZ Co., Ltd.; *Int'l*, pg. 7083
EE LIMITED—See BT Group plc; *Int'l*, pg. 1203
EEMAX, INC.—See The Riverside Company; *U.S. Private*, pg. 4108
EEMERGE, INC.—See SL Green Realty Corp.; *U.S. Public*, pg. 1894
EEMS ITALIA S.P.A; *Int'l*, pg. 2317
EEM TECNOLOGIAS DE ACCIONAMIENTO Y CONTROL, S.A.—See Hydac International GmbH; *Int'l*, pg. 3544
E ENERGY ADAMS, LLC—See NGL Energy Partners LP; *U.S. Public*, pg. 1527
E-ENERGY CORPORATION—See Sojitz Corporation; *Int'l*, pg. 7066
EENERGY GROUP PLC; *Int'l*, pg. 2317
E-ENERGY VENTURES INC.; *Int'l*, pg. 2247
E.E. NEWCOMER ENTERPRISES INC.; *U.S. Private*, pg. 1305
E! ENTERTAINMENT TELEVISION, LLC—See Comcast Corporation; *U.S. Public*, pg. 539
E.E. REED CONSTRUCTION, L.P.; *U.S. Private*, pg. 1305

E.E. SCHENCK COMPANY

E.E. SCHENCK COMPANY; *U.S. Private*, pg. 1305
E. ESCHER INC.; *U.S. Private*, pg. 1303
EESCO DISTRIBUTION—See WESCO International, Inc.; *U.S. Public*, pg. 2351
EE SIN PAPER PRODUCTS PTE. LTD.—See Muda Holdings Berhad; *Int'l*, pg. 5076
EES LEASING LLC—See Archrock, Inc.; *U.S. Public*, pg. 186
E & E SOLUTIONS INC.—See Dowa Holdings Co., Ltd.; *Int'l*, pg. 2184
EES, S.A. DE C.V.—See Johnson & Johnson; *U.S. Public*, pg. 1195
EESTECH, INC.; *Int'l*, pg. 2317
E&E STEEL, INC.—See Rolled Steel Products Corporation; *U.S. Private*, pg. 3474
EESTERLINE SENSORS SERVICES AMERICAS, INC.—See TransDigm Group Incorporated; *U.S. Public*, pg. 2180
EESTI AJALEHED AS—See AS Ekspress Grupp; *Int'l*, pg. 590
EESTI ENERGIA AS; *Int'l*, pg. 2317
EESTI ENERGIA TEHNOLOOGIATOOSTUS AS—See Eesti Energia AS; *Int'l*, pg. 2317
EESTI POLEVKIVI AS—See Eesti Energia AS; *Int'l*, pg. 2317
EESTI TELEKOM—See Telia Company AB; *Int'l*, pg. 7543
EET. EUROPARTS AB—See FSN Capital Partners AS; *Int'l*, pg. 2799
EET EUROPARTS A/S—See FSN Capital Partners AS; *Int'l*, pg. 2799
EET EUROPARTS AS—See FSN Capital Partners AS; *Int'l*, pg. 2799
EET EUROPARTS BV—See FSN Capital Partners AS; *Int'l*, pg. 2799
EET EUROPARTS B.V.—See FSN Capital Partners AS; *Int'l*, pg. 2799
EET EUROPARTS EGYPT—See FSN Capital Partners AS; *Int'l*, pg. 2799
EET EUROPARTS GMBH—See FSN Capital Partners AS; *Int'l*, pg. 2799
EET EUROPARTS GMBH—See FSN Capital Partners AS; *Int'l*, pg. 2799
EET EUROPARTS GMBH—See FSN Capital Partners AS; *Int'l*, pg. 2799
EET EUROPARTS LTD—See FSN Capital Partners AS; *Int'l*, pg. 2799
EET EUROPARTS OY—See FSN Capital Partners AS; *Int'l*, pg. 2799
EET EUROPARTS (PTY) LTD—See FSN Capital Partners AS; *Int'l*, pg. 2799
EET EUROPARTS S.A.—See FSN Capital Partners AS; *Int'l*, pg. 2799
EET EUROPARTS SP. Z O.O.—See FSN Capital Partners AS; *Int'l*, pg. 2799
EET EUROPARTS S.R.L.—See FSN Capital Partners AS; *Int'l*, pg. 2799
EET EUROPARTS S.R.O.—See FSN Capital Partners AS; *Int'l*, pg. 2799
EET FRANCE SAS—See FSN Capital Partners AS; *Int'l*, pg. 2799
EET PORTUGAL—See FSN Capital Partners AS; *Int'l*, pg. 2799
EEVS INSIGHT LIMITED—See APC Technology Group plc; *Int'l*, pg. 508
EEW ENERGY FROM WASTE DELFZIJL B.V.—See Beijing Enterprises Holdings Limited; *Int'l*, pg. 950
EEW ENERGY FROM WASTE GMBH—See Beijing Enterprises Holdings Limited; *Int'l*, pg. 950
EEW ENERGY FROM WASTE GOPPINGEN GMBH—See Beijing Enterprises Holdings Limited; *Int'l*, pg. 950
EEW ENERGY FROM WASTE GROSSRASCHEN GMBH—See Beijing Enterprises Holdings Limited; *Int'l*, pg. 950
EEW ENERGY FROM WASTE HANNOVER GMBH—See Beijing Enterprises Holdings Limited; *Int'l*, pg. 950
EEW ENERGY FROM WASTE HELMSTEDT GMBH—See Beijing Enterprises Holdings Limited; *Int'l*, pg. 950
EEW ENERGY FROM WASTE HERINGEN GMBH—See Beijing Enterprises Holdings Limited; *Int'l*, pg. 950
EEW ENERGY FROM WASTE PREMNITZ GMBH—See Beijing Enterprises Holdings Limited; *Int'l*, pg. 950
EEW ENERGY FROM WASTE SAARBRUCKEN GMBH—See Beijing Enterprises Holdings Limited; *Int'l*, pg. 950
EEW ENERGY FROM WASTE STAPELFELD GMBH—See Beijing Enterprises Holdings Limited; *Int'l*, pg. 950
EEW GMBH—See MB Holding Company LLC; *Int'l*, pg. 4750
EEW HOLDING GMBH—See Beijing Enterprises Holdings Limited; *Int'l*, pg. 950
E.E. WINE INC.; *U.S. Private*, pg. 1305
EEX ASIA PTE. LIMITED—See Deutsche Borse AG; *Int'l*, pg. 2064
E.E. ZIMMERMAN COMPANY—See Zimmerman Holding Company; *U.S. Private*, pg. 4605
EF2I SAS—See VINCI S.A.; *Int'l*, pg. 8216
EFA AUTOMAZIONE S.P.A.—See Relatech S.p.A.; *Int'l*, pg. 6260

EFACEC ALGERIE EURL.—See Efacec Capital, SGPS, S.A.; *Int'l*, pg. 2318
EFACEC ANGOLA, LDA.—See Efacec Capital, SGPS, S.A.; *Int'l*, pg. 2318
EFACEC ASIA PACIFICO, LTD.—See Efacec Capital, SGPS, S.A.; *Int'l*, pg. 2318
EFACEC CAPITAL, SGPS, S.A.; *Int'l*, pg. 2318
EFACEC CENTRAL EUROPE, LTD.—See Efacec Capital, SGPS, S.A.; *Int'l*, pg. 2318
EFACEC CHILE, SA—See Efacec Capital, SGPS, S.A.; *Int'l*, pg. 2318
EFACEC CONTRACTING CENTRAL EUROPE GMBH—See Efacec Capital, SGPS, S.A.; *Int'l*, pg. 2318
EFACEC C&S MV COMPONENTS PVT. LTD.—See Efacec Capital, SGPS, S.A.; *Int'l*, pg. 2318
EFACEC DO BRASIL, LTDA.—See Efacec Capital, SGPS, S.A.; *Int'l*, pg. 2318
EFACEC ENGENHARIA E SISTEMAS, S.A.—See Efacec Capital, SGPS, S.A.; *Int'l*, pg. 2318
EFACEC EQUIPOS ELECTRICOS, S.L.—See Efacec Capital, SGPS, S.A.; *Int'l*, pg. 2318
EFACEC MARKETING INTERNACIONAL, SA—See Efacec Capital, SGPS, S.A.; *Int'l*, pg. 2318
EFACEC MAROC SARLAU—See Efacec Capital, SGPS, S.A.; *Int'l*, pg. 2318
EFACEC MOZAMBIQUE, LDA.—See Efacec Capital, SGPS, S.A.; *Int'l*, pg. 2318
EFACEC PRAHA S.R.O.—See Efacec Capital, SGPS, S.A.; *Int'l*, pg. 2318
EFACEC SERVICOS CORPORATIVOS, SA—See Efacec Capital, SGPS, S.A.; *Int'l*, pg. 2318
EFACEC SINGAPORE PTE., LTD—See Efacec Capital, SGPS, S.A.; *Int'l*, pg. 2318
EFACEC SISTEMAS ESPANA, S.L.—See Efacec Capital, SGPS, S.A.; *Int'l*, pg. 2318
EFACEC TUNIS—See Efacec Capital, SGPS, S.A.; *Int'l*, pg. 2318
EFACEC USA, INC.—See Efacec Capital, SGPS, S.A.; *Int'l*, pg. 2318
E FACTOR EXPERIENCES LIMITED; *Int'l*, pg. 2246
EFACTOR GROUP CORP.; *U.S. Private*, pg. 1343
EFAD REAL ESTATE COMPANY; *Int'l*, pg. 2318
EFA, INC.—See Sherpa Capital SL; *Int'l*, pg. 6826
EFANOR INVESTIMENTOS, SGPS, SA; *Int'l*, pg. 2318
EFASHIONS SOLUTIONS, LLC; *U.S. Private*, pg. 1343
EFAX.COM INC.—See Ziff Davis, Inc.; *U.S. Public*, pg. 2404
EFB ELEKTRONIK AUSTRIA GMBH—See TKH Group N.V.; *Int'l*, pg. 7763
EFB ELEKTRONIK GMBH—See TKH Group N.V.; *Int'l*, pg. 7763
EFB ELEKTRONIK LTD—See TKH Group N.V.; *Int'l*, pg. 7763
EFB NORDICS A/S—See TKH Group N.V.; *Int'l*, pg. 7763
EFC DEVELOPMENTS LTD.—See Executive Flight Centre Fuel Services Ltd.; *Int'l*, pg. 2580
EFC FINLAND OY—See Lagercrantz Group AB; *Int'l*, pg. 4394
EFC (I) LIMITED; *Int'l*, pg. 2319
EFC INTERNATIONAL INC.; *U.S. Private*, pg. 1343
EF CMO LLC—See Ellington Management Group, L.L.C.; *U.S. Private*, pg. 1364
EFCO CORPORATION—See Apogee Enterprises, Inc.; *U.S. Public*, pg. 145
EFCO CORP.—See Wilian Holding Co., Inc.; *U.S. Private*, pg. 4520
EFCO INC.—See Park-Ohio Holdings Corp.; *U.S. Public*, pg. 1638
EFCO MALAYSIA SDN. BHD.—See Wilian Holding Co., Inc.; *U.S. Private*, pg. 4520
EFD INDUCAO BRASIL LTD.—See Arendals Fossekompani ASA; *Int'l*, pg. 558
EFD INDUCTION AB—See Arendals Fossekompani ASA; *Int'l*, pg. 558
EFD INDUCTION AS—See Arendals Fossekompani ASA; *Int'l*, pg. 558
EFD INDUCTION CO. LTD.—See Arendals Fossekompani ASA; *Int'l*, pg. 558
EFD INDUCTION GES.M.B.H—See Arendals Fossekompani ASA; *Int'l*, pg. 558
EFD INDUCTION GMBH—See Arendals Fossekompani ASA; *Int'l*, pg. 558
EFD INDUCTION GROUP AS—See Arendals Fossekompani ASA; *Int'l*, pg. 559
EFD INDUCTION INC.—See Arendals Fossekompani ASA; *Int'l*, pg. 558
EFD INDUCTION K.K.—See Arendals Fossekompani ASA; *Int'l*, pg. 558
EFD INDUCTION LTDA.—See Arendals Fossekompani ASA; *Int'l*, pg. 559
EFD INDUCTION LTD.—See Arendals Fossekompani ASA; *Int'l*, pg. 559
EFD INDUCTION MARCOUSSIS S.A.—See Arendals Fossekompani ASA; *Int'l*, pg. 559
EFD INDUCTION PVT. LTD.—See Arendals Fossekompani ASA; *Int'l*, pg. 559
EFD INDUCTION S.A—See Arendals Fossekompani ASA; *Int'l*, pg. 559

CORPORATE AFFILIATIONS

EFD INDUCTION (SHANGHAI) CO. LTD.—See Arendals Fossekompani ASA; *Int'l*, pg. 558
EFD INDUCTION SL—See Arendals Fossekompani ASA; *Int'l*, pg. 559
EFD INDUCTION SP. Z O.O—See Arendals Fossekompani ASA; *Int'l*, pg. 559
EFD INDUCTION SRL—See Arendals Fossekompani ASA; *Int'l*, pg. 559
EFEKTO CARE (PTY) LTD—See Ascendis Health Limited; *Int'l*, pg. 601
EFENDOS GLOBAL, INC.; *U.S. Private*, pg. 1343
EFE NEWS SERVICES (US) INC.—See Agencia EFE, S.A.; *Int'l*, pg. 205
EFESAN DEMIR SANAYI VE TICARET A.S.—See Efesan Group; *Int'l*, pg. 2319
EFESAN GROUP; *Int'l*, pg. 2319
EFESANPORT—See Efesan Group; *Int'l*, pg. 2319
EFES BREWERIES INTERNATIONAL N.V.—See Anadolu Efes Biracilik ve Malt Sanayii A.S.; *Int'l*, pg. 445
EFES DEUTSCHLAND GMBH—See Anadolu Efes Biracilik ve Malt Sanayii A.S.; *Int'l*, pg. 445
EFESIS SCHLEIFTECHNIK GMBH—See Compagnie de Saint-Gobain SA; *Int'l*, pg. 1730
EFESO CONSULTING S.A.—See Eurazeo SE; *Int'l*, pg. 2528
EFES PAZARLAMA VE DAGITIM TICARET A.S.—See Anadolu Efes Biracilik ve Malt Sanayii A.S.; *Int'l*, pg. 445
EFES TURIZM ISLETMELERI A.S.—See AG Anadolu Grubu Holding A.S.; *Int'l*, pg. 197
EFES VARLIK YONETIM A.S.—See Turkiye Is Bankasi A.S.; *Int'l*, pg. 7976
EFES VITANTA MOLDOVA BREWERY S.A.—See Anadolu Efes Biracilik ve Malt Sanayii A.S.; *Int'l*, pg. 445
EFFBE-CZ S.R.O.—See Woco Industrietechnik GmbH; *Int'l*, pg. 8442
EFFBE FRANCE S.A.S.—See Woco Industrietechnik GmbH; *Int'l*, pg. 8441
EFFECTA KOINE S.R.L.—See Trevisan Cometal SpA; *Int'l*, pg. 7917
EFFECT CO., LTD.—See People, Dreams & Technologies Group Co., Ltd.; *Int'l*, pg. 5793
EFFECTIVE ENVIRONMENTAL, INC.; *U.S. Private*, pg. 1343
EFFECTIVE LIFESTYLE PRIVATE LIMITED—See Safa Systems & Technologies Limited; *Int'l*, pg. 6468
EFFECTIVE PEOPLE A/S—See Learning Technologies Group plc; *Int'l*, pg. 4435
EFFECTIVE SPEND LLC; *U.S. Private*, pg. 1343
EFFECT-SYSTEM S.A.—See Lubawa S.A.; *Int'l*, pg. 4572
EFFEFF FRANCE S.A.S.—See ASSA ABLOY AB; *Int'l*, pg. 641
EFFEPIEFFE S.R.L.—See CompuGroup Medical SE & Co. KGaA; *Int'l*, pg. 1756
EFFER S.P.A.—See Cargotec Corporation; *Int'l*, pg. 1327
EFFIA S.A.—See SNCF; *Int'l*, pg. 7025
EFFIA—See SNCF; *Int'l*, pg. 7026
EFFICIENCE - MGI—See Safran SA; *Int'l*, pg. 6473
EFFICIENCY ENGINEERING INC.—See Kontrol Technologies Corp.; *Int'l*, pg. 4276
EFFICIENCY ENTERPRISES INC.—See Breakthru Beverage Group, LLC; *U.S. Private*, pg. 643
EFFICIENCY FOR LNG APPLICATIONS, S.L.—See Enagas, S.A.; *Int'l*, pg. 2396
EFFICIENCY PRODUCTION INCORPORATED; *U.S. Private*, pg. 1343
EFFICIENT COLLABORATIVE RETAIL MARKETING COMPANY LLC—See TruArc Partners, L.P.; *U.S. Private*, pg. 4245
EFFICIENT DRIVETRAINS INC.—See Cummins Inc.; *U.S. Public*, pg. 607
EFFICIENT E-SOLUTIONS BERHAD; *Int'l*, pg. 2319
EFFICIENT FRONTIER TECHNOLOGY INDIA PRIVATE LIMITED—See Adobe Inc.; *U.S. Public*, pg. 42
EFFICIENT GROUP LIMITED—See Apex Fund Services Holdings Ltd.; *Int'l*, pg. 510
EFFICIENTIA S.A.—See Companhia Energetica de Minas Gerais - CEMIG; *Int'l*, pg. 1747
EFFICIENT LIGHTING CONSULTANTS, INC.; *U.S. Private*, pg. 1343
EFFICIENT MARKET ADVISORS—See Cantor Fitzgerald, L.P.; *U.S. Private*, pg. 736
EFFICIENT SELECT (PTY) LTD—See Apex Fund Services Holdings Ltd.; *Int'l*, pg. 510
EFFICIENT WORKFLOW SOLUTIONS LLC—See Constellation Software Inc.; *Int'l*, pg. 1773
EFFICIO SOLUTIONS, INC.—See ShareBuilders, Inc.; *U.S. Private*, pg. 3626
EFFICO PORTUGAL—See BNP Paribas SA; *Int'l*, pg. 1090
EFFILAB S.A.S—See Solocal Group; *Int'l*, pg. 7074
EFFILIO AG—See Bossard Holding AG; *Int'l*, pg. 1117
EFFILUX GMBH—See Optex Group Co., Ltd.; *Int'l*, pg. 5601
EFFILUX S.A.S.—See Optex Group Co., Ltd.; *Int'l*, pg. 5601
EFFINGHAM EQUITY INC.; *U.S. Private*, pg. 1343
EFFINGHAM SURGICAL PARTNERS, LLC—See Tenet Healthcare Corporation; *U.S. Public*, pg. 2010
EFFINGHAM TRUCK SALES INC.; *U.S. Private*, pg. 1343

EFFINGO TEXTILE & TRADING LIMITED; *Int'l*, pg. 2319
EFFITEC SA—See Romande Energie Holding S.A.; *Int'l*, pg. 6394
EFFIZIENZCLOUD GMBH—See EnBW Energie Baden-Wurttemberg AG; *Int'l*, pg. 2401
EFFNET AB—See Tessin Nordic Holding AB; *Int'l*, pg. 7575
EFFORTLESS IT LLC; *U.S. Private*, pg. 1343
EFFOX, INC.—See CECO Environmental Corp.; *U.S. Public*, pg. 463
EF FURNITURE SDN BHD—See Lii Hen Industries Bhd.; *Int'l*, pg. 4497
EFFYIS,INC.—See Hotto Link Inc.; *Int'l*, pg. 3490
EFG AG—See EFG International AG; *Int'l*, pg. 2319
EFG ASESORIAS FINANCIERAS SPA—See EFG International AG; *Int'l*, pg. 2320
EFG ASSET MANAGEMENT (AMERICAS) CORP.—See EFG International AG; *Int'l*, pg. 2320
EFG ASSET MANAGEMENT HOLDING AG—See EFG International AG; *Int'l*, pg. 2320
EFG ASSET MANAGEMENT (HONG KONG) LTD.—See EFG International AG; *Int'l*, pg. 2320
EFG ASSET MANAGEMENT (SINGAPORE) PTE. LTD.—See EFG International AG; *Int'l*, pg. 2320
EFG ASSET MANAGEMENT (SWITZERLAND) S.A.—See EFG International AG; *Int'l*, pg. 2320
EFG ASSET MANAGEMENT (UK) LTD.—See EFG International AG; *Int'l*, pg. 2320
EFG ASSET MANAGERS SAM—See EFG International AG; *Int'l*, pg. 2320
EFG AUTO LEASING E.O.O.D.—See Eurobank Ergasias Services and Holdings S.A.; *Int'l*, pg. 2532
EFG BANK AB—See EFG International AG; *Int'l*, pg. 2320
EFG BANK AG—See EFG International AG; *Int'l*, pg. 2320
EFG BANK AG—See EFG International AG; *Int'l*, pg. 2320
EFG BANK EUROPEAN FINANCIAL GROUP SA; *Int'l*, pg. 2319
EFG BANK (GIBRALTAR) LTD—See EFG International AG; *Int'l*, pg. 2320
EFG BANK LTD.—See EFG International AG; *Int'l*, pg. 2320
EFG BANK (LUXEMBOURG) SA—See EFG International AG; *Int'l*, pg. 2320
EFG BANK (LUXEMBOURG) S.A.—See EFG International AG; *Int'l*, pg. 2320
EFG BANK (MONACO)—See EFG International AG; *Int'l*, pg. 2320
EFG BANK & TRUST (BAHAMAS) LTD.—See EFG International AG; *Int'l*, pg. 2320
EFG BANK VON ERNST AG—See EFG International AG; *Int'l*, pg. 2320
EFG BANQUE PRIVEE SA—See EFG International AG; *Int'l*, pg. 2320
EFG BUSINESS SERVICES D.O.O. BEOGRAD—See Eurobank Ergasias Services and Holdings S.A.; *Int'l*, pg. 2532
EFG CAPITAL ASESORES FINANCIEROS S.A.C.—See EFG International AG; *Int'l*, pg. 2320
EFG CAPITAL INTERNATIONAL CORP.—See EFG International AG; *Int'l*, pg. 2320
EFG EUROBANK FINANCE S.A.—See Eurobank Ergasias Services and Holdings S.A.; *Int'l*, pg. 2532
EFG EUROBANK PROPERTY SERVICES S.A.—See Eurobank Ergasias Services and Holdings S.A.; *Int'l*, pg. 2532
EFG HARRIS ALLDAY—See EFG International AG; *Int'l*, pg. 2320
EFG HERMES FINANCIAL MANAGEMENT (EGYPT) LTD—See EFG Holding; *Int'l*, pg. 2319
EFG-HERMES INVESTMENT BANKING—See EFG Holding; *Int'l*, pg. 2319
EFG - HERMES JORDAN COMPANY—See EFG Holding; *Int'l*, pg. 2319
EFG - HERMES KENYA LTD.—See EFG Holding; *Int'l*, pg. 2319
EFG-HERMES LEASING COMPANY—See EFG Holding; *Int'l*, pg. 2319
EFG- HERMES OMAN LLC—See EFG Holding; *Int'l*, pg. 2319
EFG HERMES PAKISTAN LIMITED—See EFG Holding; *Int'l*, pg. 2319
EFG- HERMES UAE LLC—See EFG Holding; *Int'l*, pg. 2319
EFG HERMES UAE LTD—See EFG Holding; *Int'l*, pg. 2319
EFG - HERMES UK LIMITED—See EFG Holding; *Int'l*, pg. 2319
EFG HERMES USA, INC.—See EFG Holding; *Int'l*, pg. 2319
EFG HOLDING; *Int'l*, pg. 2319
EFG INDEPENDENT FINANCIAL ADVISERS—See EFG International AG; *Int'l*, pg. 2320
EFG INDEPENDENT FINANCIAL ADVISORS LTD—See EFG International AG; *Int'l*, pg. 2320
EFG INTERNATIONAL AG; *Int'l*, pg. 2319
EFG INVESTMENT BANK—See EFG International AG; *Int'l*, pg. 2320
EFG LEASING A.D. BELGRADE—See Eurobank Ergasias Services and Holdings S.A.; *Int'l*, pg. 2532

EFG LEASING IFN S.A.—See Eurobank Ergasias Services and Holdings S.A.; *Int'l*, pg. 2532
EFG LEASING POLAND SP. Z O.O—See Eurobank Ergasias Services and Holdings S.A.; *Int'l*, pg. 2532
EFG OFFSHORE LIMITED—See EFG International AG; *Int'l*, pg. 2320
EFG OFICINA DE REPRESENTACION URUGUAY SA—See EFG International AG; *Int'l*, pg. 2320
EFG (PANAMA) S.A.—See EFG International AG; *Int'l*, pg. 2319
EFG PLATTS FIELLO LIMITED—See EFG International AG; *Int'l*, pg. 2320
EFG PLATTS FLELLO LTD—See EFG International AG; *Int'l*, pg. 2320
EFG PRIVATE BANK (CHANNEL ISLANDS) LIMITED—See EFG International AG; *Int'l*, pg. 2320
EFG PRIVATE BANK LIMITED—See EFG International AG; *Int'l*, pg. 2320
EFG PROPERTY SERVICES D.O.O. BELGRADE—See Eurobank Ergasias Services and Holdings S.A.; *Int'l*, pg. 2532
EFG PROPERTY SERVICES POLSKA SP.Z.O.O.—See Eurobank Ergasias Services and Holdings S.A.; *Int'l*, pg. 2532
EFG PROPERTY SERVICES UKRAINE LLC—See Eurobank Ergasias Services and Holdings S.A.; *Int'l*, pg. 2532
EFG RETAIL SERVICES IFN S.A.—See Eurobank Ergasias Services and Holdings S.A.; *Int'l*, pg. 2532
EFG SA—See EFG International AG; *Int'l*, pg. 2320
EFG SECURITIES BULGARIA E.A.D.—See Eurobank Ergasias Services and Holdings S.A.; *Int'l*, pg. 2532
EFG WEALTH MANAGEMENT (BERMUDA) LTD.—See EFG International AG; *Int'l*, pg. 2320
EFG WEALTH MANAGEMENT (CANADA) LIMITED—See EFG International AG; *Int'l*, pg. 2321
EFG WEALTH MANAGEMENT (CAYMAN) LTD.—See EFG International AG; *Int'l*, pg. 2321
EFG WEALTH MANAGEMENT (INDIA) PRIVATE LIMITED—See EFG International AG; *Int'l*, pg. 2321
EFG WEALTH SOLUTIONS (SINGAPORE) LTD.—See EFG International AG; *Int'l*, pg. 2321
EF HUTTON AMERICA, INC.; *U.S. Public*, pg. 721
EF HUTTON CORP.; *U.S. Private*, pg. 1343
EFI BELGIUM BVBA—See Siris Capital Group, LLC; *U.S. Private*, pg. 3672
EFI BRAZIL LTDA.—See Siris Capital Group, LLC; *U.S. Private*, pg. 3672
EFI (CANADA), INC.—See Siris Capital Group, LLC; *U.S. Private*, pg. 3672
EFI CRETAPRINT S.L.—See Siris Capital Group, LLC; *U.S. Private*, pg. 3672
EFI CRETAPRINT, S.L.—See Siris Capital Group, LLC; *U.S. Private*, pg. 3672
EFI ELECTRONICS EUROPE SL—See Schneider Electric SE; *Int'l*, pg. 6626
EFI GLOBAL CANADA—See The Carlyle Group Inc.; *U.S. Public*, pg. 2053
EFI GLOBAL, INC.—See The Carlyle Group Inc.; *U.S. Public*, pg. 2053
EFI K.K.—See Siris Capital Group, LLC; *U.S. Private*, pg. 3672
E-FILE MASTERS LLC—See Metrofile Holdings Limited; *Int'l*, pg. 4861
EFI LTD—See Safwood S.p.A.; *Int'l*, pg. 6477
E FINANCE CONSULTING REPLY S.R.L.—See Reply S.p.A.; *Int'l*, pg. 6291
EFINANCIALCAREERS GMBH—See DHI Group, Inc.; *U.S. Public*, pg. 658
EFINANCIAL, LLC; *U.S. Private*, pg. 1343
EF INSTITUTE FOR CULTURAL EXCHANGE INC.; *U.S. Private*, pg. 1343
EFIRD CHRYSLER JEEP DODGE; *U.S. Private*, pg. 1343
EF&I SERVICES CORP.—See Willcrest Partners; *U.S. Private*, pg. 4521
EF JOHNSON TECHNOLOGIES, INC.—See JVCKENWOOD Corporation; *Int'l*, pg. 4032
EF KENILWORTH LLC—See I Squared Capital Advisors (US) LLC; *U.S. Private*, pg. 2025
EFKON AG—See STRABAG SE; *Int'l*, pg. 7230
EFKON BULGARIA LTD.—See STRABAG SE; *Int'l*, pg. 7230
EFKON INDIA PRIVATE LIMITED—See STRABAG SE; *Int'l*, pg. 7230
EFKON ROMANIA SRL—See STRABAG SE; *Int'l*, pg. 7230
E.F. LACROSSE SALES INC.; *U.S. Private*, pg. 1305
EFLEETS CORPORATION; *U.S. Private*, pg. 1343
EFL EXPRESS PRIVATE LIMITED—See Expolanka Holdings PLC; *Int'l*, pg. 2589
EFL GLOBAL B.V.—See Expolanka Holdings PLC; *Int'l*, pg. 2589
EFL MALAYSIA SDN. BHD.—See Expolanka Holdings PLC; *Int'l*, pg. 2589
EFL MAURITIUS LIMITED—See Shapoorji Pallonji & Co. Ltd.; *Int'l*, pg. 6788
EFLUX SINGAPORE PTE LTD—See Hyflux Ltd; *Int'l*, pg. 3548

EFM LOGISTICS PTY. LTD.—See Singapore Post Limited; *Int'l*, pg. 6942
E.F. MOORE INC.; *U.S. Private*, pg. 1305
EF MORTGAGE LLC—See Ellington Management Group, L.L.C.; *U.S. Private*, pg. 1364
EFM SALES COMPANY—See Vari Corporation; *U.S. Private*, pg. 4346
EF NOVA OSELYA LLC—See Dragon Ukrainian Properties & Development Plc; *Int'l*, pg. 2199
EFO FINANCIAL GROUP LLC; *U.S. Private*, pg. 1343
EFOLDER, INC.; *U.S. Private*, pg. 1343
EF-ON INC.; *Int'l*, pg. 2318
EFORA ENERGY LTD.—See Public Investment Corporation (SOC) Limited; *Int'l*, pg. 6094
EFORCITY CORPORATION; *U.S. Private*, pg. 1343
EFORE AB—See Inission AB; *Int'l*, pg. 3703
EFORE (SUZHOU) AUTOMOTIVE TECHNOLOGY CO., LTD.—See Inission AB; *Int'l*, pg. 3703
EFORE (SUZHOU) ELECTRONICS CO., LTD.—See Inission AB; *Int'l*, pg. 3703
EFORE TELECOM FINLAND OY—See Shenzhen Kexin Communication Technologies Co., Ltd; *Int'l*, pg. 6815
E FOR L AIM PUBLIC COMPANY LIMITED; *Int'l*, pg. 2246
EFORT EUROPE S.R.L—See EFORT Intelligent Equipment Co., Ltd.; *Int'l*, pg. 2321
EFORT FRANCE S.A.S—See EFORT Intelligent Equipment Co., Ltd.; *Int'l*, pg. 2321
E FORTIFY ASIA SDN. BHD.—See Multi-Chem Limited; *Int'l*, pg. 5082
EFORT INTELLIGENT EQUIPMENT CO., LTD.; *Int'l*, pg. 2321
EF OXNARD LLC—See I Squared Capital Advisors (US) LLC; *U.S. Private*, pg. 2025
EFP CORPORATION—See J.B. Poindexter & Co., Inc.; *U.S. Private*, pg. 2158
EFPZ—See The Interpublic Group of Companies, Inc.; *U.S. Public*, pg. 2093
EFRAME, LLC; *U.S. Private*, pg. 1344
EFRAME SDN. BHD.—See OSK Holdings Berhad; *Int'l*, pg. 5651
E-FREIGHT COURIER, LLC—See MED-STAT USA LLC; *U.S. Private*, pg. 2650
EFRONT D.O.O.—See BlackRock, Inc.; *U.S. Public*, pg. 347
EFRONT FINANCIAL SOLUTIONS INC.—See BlackRock, Inc.; *U.S. Public*, pg. 347
EFRONT GMBH—See BlackRock, Inc.; *U.S. Public*, pg. 347
EFRONT HONG KONG LIMITED—See BlackRock, Inc.; *U.S. Public*, pg. 347
EFRONT (JERSEY) LIMITED—See BlackRock, Inc.; *U.S. Public*, pg. 347
EFRONT KABUSHIKI KAISHA—See BlackRock, Inc.; *U.S. Public*, pg. 347
EFRONT LTD.—See BlackRock, Inc.; *U.S. Public*, pg. 347
EFRONT SASU—See BlackRock, Inc.; *U.S. Public*, pg. 347
EFRONT SINGAPORE PTE. LTD.—See BlackRock, Inc.; *U.S. Public*, pg. 347
EFRONT SOFTWARE LUXEMBOURG S.A R.L.—See BlackRock, Inc.; *U.S. Public*, pg. 347
EFRONT SOLUTIONS FINANCEIERES INC.—See BlackRock, Inc.; *U.S. Public*, pg. 347
EFS INTERNATIONAL BV—See Econocom Group SA; *Int'l*, pg. 2297
EF SOLUTIONS LLC—See Allianz SE; *Int'l*, pg. 352
EFT CANADA INC.; *Int'l*, pg. 2321
EFTC OPERATING CORPORATION—See Benchmark Electronics, Inc.; *U.S. Public*, pg. 296
EFTEC AG—See EMS-Chemie Holding AG; *Int'l*, pg. 2393
EFTEC ASIA PTE. LTD.—See EMS-Chemie Holding AG; *Int'l*, pg. 2393
EFTEC BRASIL LTDA.—See EMS-Chemie Holding AG; *Int'l*, pg. 2393
EFTEC (CHANGSHU) AUTOMOTIVE MATERIALS LIMITED—See EMS-Chemie Holding AG; *Int'l*, pg. 2393
EFTEC (CHANGSHU) ENGINEERING CO., LTD.—See EMS-Chemie Holding AG; *Int'l*, pg. 2393
EFTEC CHINA LTD.—See EMS-Chemie Holding AG; *Int'l*, pg. 2393
EFTEC (CZECH REPUBLIC) A.S.—See EMS-Chemie Holding AG; *Int'l*, pg. 2393
EFTEC (ELABUGA) OOO—See EMS-Chemie Holding AG; *Int'l*, pg. 2393
EFTEC ENGINEERING AB—See EMS-Chemie Holding AG; *Int'l*, pg. 2393
EFTEC ENGINEERING GMBH—See EMS-Chemie Holding AG; *Int'l*, pg. 2393
EFTEC (INDIA) PVT. LTD.—See EMS-Chemie Holding AG; *Int'l*, pg. 2393
EFTEC LTD.—See EMS-Chemie Holding AG; *Int'l*, pg. 2393
EFTEC MARKET GMBH—See EMS-Chemie Holding AG; *Int'l*, pg. 2393
EFTEC MEXICO S.A. DE C.V.—See EMS-Chemie Holding AG; *Int'l*, pg. 2393

EFT CANADA INC.

CORPORATE AFFILIATIONS

EFTEC (NIZHNIY NOVGOROD) OOO—See EMS-Chemie Holding AG; *Int'l*, pg. 2393
EFTEC NORTH AMERICA, L.L.C.—See EMS-Chemie Holding AG; *Int'l*, pg. 2393
EFTEC N.V.—See EMS-Chemie Holding AG; *Int'l*, pg. 2393
EFTEC-PLACOSA—See EMS-Chemie Holding AG; *Int'l*, pg. 2393
EFTEC (ROMANIA) S.R.L.—See EMS-Chemie Holding AG; *Int'l*, pg. 2393
EFTEC S.A.R.L.—See EMS-Chemie Holding AG; *Int'l*, pg. 2394
EFTEC S.A.—See EMS-Chemie Holding AG; *Int'l*, pg. 2394
EFTEC (SHANGHAI) SERVICES CO., LTD.—See EMS-Chemie Holding AG; *Int'l*, pg. 2393
EFTEC SHROFF INDIA LIMITED—See EMS-Chemie Holding AG; *Int'l*, pg. 2394
EFTEC (THAILAND) CO. LTD.—See EMS-Chemie Holding AG; *Int'l*, pg. 2393
EFTEL PTY LIMITED—See Aware Super Pty Ltd; *Int'l*, pg. 752
EFTEL PTY LIMITED—See Macquarie Group Limited; *Int'l*, pg. 4629
EFTEN CAPITAL AS; *Int'l*, pg. 2321
EFTEN REAL ESTATE FUND III AS; *Int'l*, pg. 2321
EFTPOS NEW ZEALAND LIMITED—See British Columbia Investment Management Corp.; *Int'l*, pg. 1170
EFTPOS NEW ZEALAND LIMITED—See Francisco Partners Management, LP; *U.S. Private*, pg. 1592
EFT SOLUTIONS HOLDINGS LIMITED; *Int'l*, pg. 2321
EFT SOLUTIONS PTY LTD—See ComfortDelGro Corporation Limited; *Int'l*, pg. 1712
EFT-USLUGE D.O.O—See Euronet Worldwide, Inc.; *U.S. Public*, pg. 797
EFU GENERAL INSURANCE LTD - CENTRAL DIVISION—See EFU General Insurance Ltd.; *Int'l*, pg. 2321
EFU GENERAL INSURANCE LTD.; *Int'l*, pg. 2321
EFULFILLMENT SERVICE, INC., *U.S. Private*, pg. 1344
EFU LIFE ASSURANCE LIMITED; *Int'l*, pg. 2321
EFUN TECHNOLOGY CO., LTD.; *Int'l*, pg. 2322
EFUSION CO., LTD.—See ASJ Inc.; *Int'l*, pg. 621
EFUSION SOLUTIONS PTE. LTD.; *Int'l*, pg. 2322
E-FUTURE CO., LTD.; *Int'l*, pg. 2247
EFUTURE HOLDING INC.—See Beijing Shiji Information Technology Co., Ltd.; *Int'l*, pg. 956
EFW INC.—See Elbit Systems Limited; *Int'l*, pg. 2344
EFX DE COSTA RICA, S.A.—See Equifax Inc.; *U.S. Public*, pg. 786
EFX GLOBAL KL SDN BHD—See Enerflex Ltd.; *Int'l*, pg. 2418
EFX MEDIA—See Yes& Holdings, LLC; *U.S. Private*, pg. 4588
EGAA OFFSET A/S—See Bong AB; *Int'l*, pg. 1107
EGAIN COMMUNICATIONS BV—See eGain Corporation; *U.S. Public*, pg. 721
EGAIN COMMUNICATIONS LTD.—See eGain Corporation; *U.S. Public*, pg. 721
EGAIN COMMUNICATIONS LTD.—See eGain Corporation; *U.S. Public*, pg. 721
EGAIN COMMUNICATIONS PVT. LTD.—See eGain Corporation; *U.S. Public*, pg. 721
EGAIN COMMUNICATIONS SRL—See eGain Corporation; *U.S. Public*, pg. 721
EGAIN CORPORATION; *U.S. Public*, pg. 721
EGAIN FRANCE S.A.R.L.—See eGain Corporation; *U.S. Public*, pg. 721
EGALAX-EMPIA TECHNOLOGY, INC.; *Int'l*, pg. 2322
EGANA 2, S.L.—See Cie Automotive S.A.; *Int'l*, pg. 1604
EGAN AUTOMATION, INC.—See The Egan Companies; *U.S. Private*, pg. 4025
THE EGAN COMPANIES; *U.S. Private*, pg. 4025
EGAN ELECTRICAL CONTRACTORS—See The Egan Companies; *U.S. Private*, pg. 4025
EGAN MECHANICAL CONTRACTORS INC.—See The Egan Companies; *U.S. Private*, pg. 4025
EGAN VISUAL INC.; *Int'l*, pg. 2322
EGASCA, S.A.—See Citizen Watch Co., Ltd.; *Int'l*, pg. 1625
EG A/S—See Francisco Partners Management, LP; *U.S. Private*, pg. 1589
EGAT PUBLIC COMPANY LIMITED; *Int'l*, pg. 2322
EGAZ-DEGAZ FOLDGAZELOSZTO ZRT.—See ENGIE SA; *Int'l*, pg. 2431
EGBERT CORP.—See Materion Corporation; *U.S. Public*, pg. 1395
EG CAPITAL GROUP, LLC; *U.S. Private*, pg. 1344
EGC CRITICAL COMPONENTS—See Compagnie Generale des Etablissements Michelin SCA; *Int'l*, pg. 1745
THE EGC GROUP; *U.S. Private*, pg. 4025
EGCO COGENERATION CO., LTD.—See Electricity Generating Public Co., Ltd.; *Int'l*, pg. 2352
EGCO ENGINEERING AND SERVICE CO. LTD—See EGAT Public Company Limited; *Int'l*, pg. 2322
EGCO ENGINEERING & SERVICE CO., LTD—See Electricity Generating Public Co., Ltd.; *Int'l*, pg. 2352
EGCO GREEN ENERGY CO., LTD.—See Electricity Generating Public Co., Ltd.; *Int'l*, pg. 2352

EG COMPONETS NORWAY AS—See Amplex AB; *Int'l*, pg. 434
EGCOM TARA CO. LTD.—See Eastern Water Resources Development & Management Public Company Limited; *Int'l*, pg. 2274
EGCO PEARL CO., LTD.—See Electricity Generating Public Co., Ltd.; *Int'l*, pg. 2352
EG CORPORATION; *Int'l*, pg. 2322
EGC, SA—See Mutares SE & Co. KGaA; *Int'l*, pg. 5105
EGE CARPETS DACH GMBH—See Egetaepper A/S; *Int'l*, pg. 2324
EGE CARPETS NORWAY AS—See Egetaepper A/S; *Int'l*, pg. 2324
EGE CARPETS SWEDEN AB—See Egetaepper A/S; *Int'l*, pg. 2324
EGE CARPETS UK LTD.—See Egetaepper A/S; *Int'l*, pg. 2324
EGE CONTRACT A/S—See Egetaepper A/S; *Int'l*, pg. 2324
EGEDIS SAS—See TotalEnergies SE; *Int'l*, pg. 7835
EGE ENDUSTRI VE TICARET AS; *Int'l*, pg. 2322
EGE GROUP LTD.—See Nayax Ltd.; *Int'l*, pg. 5178
EGE GUBRE SANAYI A.S.; *Int'l*, pg. 2322
EGELCRAFT, LLC—See Sun Communities, Inc.; *U.S. Public*, pg. 1961
EG ELECTRONICS AB—See Amplex AB; *Int'l*, pg. 434
EGELI & CO ENERJI YATIRIMLARI A.S.; *Int'l*, pg. 2322
EGELI & CO TARIM GIRISIM SERMAYESI YATIRIM ORTAKLIGI AS; *Int'l*, pg. 2322
EGELI & CO. YATIRIM HOLDING A.S.; *Int'l*, pg. 2322
EGE LIMAN ISLETMELERI A.S.—See Global Yatirim Holding A.S.; *Int'l*, pg. 3002
EGEMIN AUTOMATION INC.; *U.S. Private*, pg. 1344
EGENCIA AUSTRALIA PTY. LTD.—See Expedia Group, Inc.; *U.S. Public*, pg. 809
EGENCIA GMBH—See Expedia Group, Inc.; *U.S. Public*, pg. 809
EGENCIA UK LTD.—See Expedia Group, Inc.; *U.S. Public*, pg. 809
EGENERA, INC.; *U.S. Private*, pg. 1344
E - GEOS SPA—See Leonardo S.p.A.; *Int'l*, pg. 4458
EGEPLAST EGE PLASTIK SAN VE TIC. A.S.; *Int'l*, pg. 2322
EGE PROFIL AS—See Deceuninck NV; *Int'l*, pg. 2000
EGE PROFIL TICARET VE SANAYI AS—See Deceuninck NV; *Int'l*, pg. 2000
EGE PROFIL TIC. VE SAN. A.S.—See Deceuninck NV; *Int'l*, pg. 2000
EGERIA CAPITAL MANAGEMENT B.V; *Int'l*, pg. 2323
EGER MARTINIQUE SAS—See VINCI S.A.; *Int'l*, pg. 8217
EGERNSUND TEGL A.M.B.A.—See Wienerberger AG; *Int'l*, pg. 8405
EGER PROPERTIES—See Owens Corning; *U.S. Public*, pg. 1626
EGERSUND GROUP AS; *Int'l*, pg. 2323
EGERSUND HEROY AS—See Egersund Group AS; *Int'l*, pg. 2323
EGERSUND ICELAND EHF—See Egersund Group AS; *Int'l*, pg. 2323
EGERSUND TRADING AS—See Egersund Group AS; *Int'l*, pg. 2323
EGE SERAMIK AMERICA INC.—See Ege Seramik Sanayi ve Ticaret A.S.; *Int'l*, pg. 2322
EGE SERAMIK IC VE DIS TICARET A.S.—See Ege Seramik Sanayi ve Ticaret A.S.; *Int'l*, pg. 2322
EGE SERAMIK SANAYI VE TICARET A.S.; *Int'l*, pg. 2322
EGETAEPPER A/S; *Int'l*, pg. 2324
EGE-TAV EGE TARIM HAYVANCILIK YATIRIM TICARET VE SANAYI ANONIM SIRKETI—See NH Foods Ltd.; *Int'l*, pg. 5256
EGETIS THERAPEUTICS AB; *Int'l*, pg. 2324
EGEV SAS—See VINCI S.A.; *Int'l*, pg. 8217
E.G. FORREST COMPANY INC.; *U.S. Private*, pg. 1305
EGF THERAMED HEALTH CORP.; *Int'l*, pg. 2324
EGG AND CITI UK CONSUMER—See Citigroup Inc.; *U.S. Public*, pg. 503
EGGBOROUGH POWER LTD—See Energeticky a Prumyslovy Holding, a.s.; *Int'l*, pg. 2420
EGGED BULGARIA—See Egged Israel Transport Cooperative Society Ltd.; *Int'l*, pg. 2324
EGGED HOLDING—See Egged Israel Transport Cooperative Society Ltd.; *Int'l*, pg. 2324
EGGED ISRAEL TRANSPORT COOPERATIVE SOCIETY LTD.; *Int'l*, pg. 2324
EGG ELECTRIC INC.; *U.S. Private*, pg. 1344
EGGELHOF INCORPORATED; *U.S. Private*, pg. 1344
EGGER AUSTRALASIA PTY LIMITED—See Fritz Egger GmbH & Co.; *Int'l*, pg. 2793
EGGER BALTIC UAB—See Fritz Egger GmbH & Co.; *Int'l*, pg. 2793
EGGER BARONY LTD.—See Fritz Egger GmbH & Co.; *Int'l*, pg. 2793
EGGER BENELUX GCV—See Fritz Egger GmbH & Co.; *Int'l*, pg. 2793
EGGER BESCHICHTUNGSWERK MARIENMUNSTER GMBH & CO. KG - BEVERN PLANT—See Fritz Egger GmbH & Co.; *Int'l*, pg. 2793

EGGER BESCHICHTUNGSWERK MARIENMUNSTER GMBH & CO. KG—See Fritz Egger GmbH & Co.; *Int'l*, pg. 2793
EGGER CZ S.R.O.—See Fritz Egger GmbH & Co.; *Int'l*, pg. 2793
EGGER HOLZWERKSTOFFE BRILON GMBH & CO. KG—See Fritz Egger GmbH & Co.; *Int'l*, pg. 2793
EGGER HOLZWERKSTOFFE SCHWEIZ GMBH—See Fritz Egger GmbH & Co.; *Int'l*, pg. 2793
EGGER HOLZWERKSTOFFE WISMAR GMBH & CO. KG—See Fritz Egger GmbH & Co.; *Int'l*, pg. 2793
EGGER KUNSTSTOFFE GMBH & CO. KG—See Fritz Egger GmbH & Co.; *Int'l*, pg. 2793
EGGER ORMAN URUNLERI A.S.—See Fritz Egger GmbH & Co.; *Int'l*, pg. 2793
EGGER POLSKA SP. Z.O.O.—See Fritz Egger GmbH & Co.; *Int'l*, pg. 2793
EGGER PRODUCTOS DE MADERA LIMITADA—See Fritz Egger GmbH & Co.; *Int'l*, pg. 2793
EGGER RETAIL PRODUCTS FRANCE S.A.S.—See Fritz Egger GmbH & Co.; *Int'l*, pg. 2793
EGGER RETAIL PRODUCTS GMBH & CO. KG—See Fritz Egger GmbH & Co.; *Int'l*, pg. 2793
EGGER-ROL SA—See Fritz Egger GmbH & Co.; *Int'l*, pg. 2794
EGGER ROMANIA SRL—See Fritz Egger GmbH & Co.; *Int'l*, pg. 2793
EGGER RS DOO—See Fritz Egger GmbH & Co.; *Int'l*, pg. 2793
EGGER SCANDINAVIA APS—See Fritz Egger GmbH & Co.; *Int'l*, pg. 2794
EGGERS INDUSTRIES INC.—See VT Industries, Inc.; *U.S. Private*, pg. 4415
EGGER TURKIYE LTD.—See Fritz Egger GmbH & Co.; *Int'l*, pg. 2794
EGGER (UK) LIMITED—See Fritz Egger GmbH & Co.; *Int'l*, pg. 2793
EGGFREE CAKE BOX LTD.—See Cake Box Holdings plc; *Int'l*, pg. 1260
EGGING CO; *U.S. Private*, pg. 1344
EGGLAND'S BEST, INC.; *U.S. Private*, pg. 1344
EGGMANN FREY AG—See Mobico Group PLC; *Int'l*, pg. 5008
THE EGGO COMPANY—See Kellanova; *U.S. Public*, pg. 1218
EGGPLANT GROUP LIMITED—See Keysight Technologies, Inc.; *U.S. Public*, pg. 1227
EGGPLANT—See Keysight Technologies, Inc.; *U.S. Public*, pg. 1227
EGGRICULTURE FOODS LTD.; *Int'l*, pg. 2324
EGGSMART CORPORATION—See Chairman's Brands Corporation; *Int'l*, pg. 1437
EG HEALTHCARE, INC.—See Excelsior Medical Co., Ltd.; *Int'l*, pg. 2579
EGHTESAD NOVIN BANK; *Int'l*, pg. 2324
EGI COOLING SYSTEMS TRADING (BEIJING) CO.—See Triton Advisers Limited; *Int'l*, pg. 7930
EGIDE SA; *Int'l*, pg. 2324
EGIDE USA, INC.—See Egide SA; *Int'l*, pg. 2324
EGIDE USA, LLC—See Egide SA; *Int'l*, pg. 2324
EGIDIO GALBANI SPA—See Groupe Lactalis SA; *Int'l*, pg. 3106
EGI INSURANCE MANAGERS INC.—See ICPEI Holdings Inc.; *Int'l*, pg. 3586
EGIL ENG & CO. AS—See Addtech AB; *Int'l*, pg. 133
EG INDUSTRIES BERHAD; *Int'l*, pg. 2322
EGING PHOTOVOLTAIC EUROPE GMBH—See EGing Photovoltaic Technology Co., Ltd.; *Int'l*, pg. 2324
EGING PHOTOVOLTAIC TECHNOLOGY CO., LTD.; *Int'l*, pg. 2324
EGING PHOTOVOLTAIC TECHNOLOGY CO., LTD.—See EGing Photovoltaic Technology Co., Ltd.; *Int'l*, pg. 2324
EGIS ALGERIE S.P.A.—See Caisse des Depots et Consignations; *Int'l*, pg. 1257
EGIS AVIA SA—See Caisse des Depots et Consignations; *Int'l*, pg. 1257
EGIS BDPA SA—See Caisse des Depots et Consignations; *Int'l*, pg. 1257
EGIS BEIJING INDUSTRIAL TECHNICAL CO., LTD.—See Caisse des Depots et Consignations; *Int'l*, pg. 1257
EGIS BULGARIA EOOD—See Les Laboratoires Servier SAS; *Int'l*, pg. 4467
EGIS CAMEROUN—See Caisse des Depots et Consignations; *Int'l*, pg. 1257
EGIS CAPITAL PARTNERS LLC; *U.S. Private*, pg. 1344
EGIS D.O.O. BEOGRAD—See Groupe Egis S.A.; *Int'l*, pg. 3102
EGIS EASYTRIP SERVICES SA—See Caisse des Depots et Consignations; *Int'l*, pg. 1257
EGIS EAU SA—See Caisse des Depots et Consignations; *Int'l*, pg. 1257
EGIS EMIRATES LLC—See Groupe Egis S.A.; *Int'l*, pg. 3102
EGIS EYSER SA—See Caisse des Depots et Consignations; *Int'l*, pg. 1257
EGIS GEOPLAN PVT. LTD.—See Caisse des Depots et Consignations; *Int'l*, pg. 1257

COMPANY NAME INDEX

EGIS GYOGYSZERGYAR NYRT - EGIS PLC LACTA PLANT—See Les Laboratoires Servier SAS; *Int'l*, pg. 4468
EGIS GYOGYSZERGYAR NYRT—See Les Laboratoires Servier SAS; *Int'l*, pg. 4467
EGIS ILACLARI (TURKEY) LTD.—See Les Laboratoires Servier SAS; *Int'l*, pg. 4467
EGIS INDIA CONSULTING ENGINEERS PRIVATE LIMITED—See Caisse des Depots et Consignations; *Int'l*, pg. 1257
EGIS INTERNATIONAL S.A.—See Caisse des Depots et Consignations; *Int'l*, pg. 1257
EGIS KENYA LIMITED—See Caisse des Depots et Consignations; *Int'l*, pg. 1257
EGIS LAGAN SERVICES LTD.—See Groupe Egis S.A.; *Int'l*, pg. 3102
EGISMEX, S. DE R.L. DE C.V.—See Groupe Egis S.A.; *Int'l*, pg. 3102
EGIS PARKING SERVICES B.V.—See Groupe Egis S.A.; *Int'l*, pg. 3102
EGIS PHARMACEUTICALS PLC—See Les Laboratoires Servier SAS; *Int'l*, pg. 4468
EGIS POLAND SP. Z O.O.—See Caisse des Depots et Consignations; *Int'l*, pg. 1257
EGIS POLSKA DYSTRYBUCJA LTD.—See Les Laboratoires Servier SAS; *Int'l*, pg. 4468
EGIS PRAHA SPOL.S.R.O.—See Les Laboratoires Servier SAS; *Int'l*, pg. 4468
EGIS PROJECTS ASIA PACIFIC PTY LTD—See Caisse des Depots et Consignations; *Int'l*, pg. 1257
EGIS PROJECTS CANADA INC.—See Caisse des Depots et Consignations; *Int'l*, pg. 1258
EGIS PROJECTS IRELAND LTD—See Caisse des Depots et Consignations; *Int'l*, pg. 1258
EGIS PROJECTS PHILIPPINES, INC.—See Caisse des Depots et Consignations; *Int'l*, pg. 1258
EGIS PROJECTS POLSKA SP. Z O.O.—See Caisse des Depots et Consignations; *Int'l*, pg. 1258
EGIS RAIL KSA—See Groupe Egis S.A.; *Int'l*, pg. 3102
EGIS RAIL S.A.—See Caisse des Depots et Consignations; *Int'l*, pg. 1258
EGIS ROAD OPERATION CROATIA D.O.O.—See Caisse des Depots et Consignations; *Int'l*, pg. 1258
EGIS ROAD OPERATION INDIA PRIVATE LIMITED—See Caisse des Depots et Consignations; *Int'l*, pg. 1258
EGIS ROAD OPERATION M40 LTD.—See Groupe Egis S.A.; *Int'l*, pg. 3102
EGIS ROAD OPERATION PORTUGAL S.A.—See Groupe Egis S.A.; *Int'l*, pg. 3102
EGIS ROAD & TUNNEL OPERATION IRELAND LIMITED—See Groupe Egis S.A.; *Int'l*, pg. 3102
EGIS ROMANIA SA—See Groupe Egis S.A.; *Int'l*, pg. 3102
EGIS RUS LLC—See Les Laboratoires Servier SAS; *Int'l*, pg. 4468
EGIS S.A.—See Caisse des Depots et Consignations; *Int'l*, pg. 1257
EGIS TUNEL ISLETMECILIGI A.S.—See Groupe Egis S.A.; *Int'l*, pg. 3102
EGIS UKRAINA LLC—See Caisse des Depots et Consignations; *Int'l*, pg. 1258
EGIZII ELECTRIC, INC.—See EEI Holding Corporation; *U.S. Private*, pg. 1343
EG KOMMUNEINFORMATION A/S—See Francisco Partners Management, LP; *U.S. Private*, pg. 1589
EG LABO SAS - LABORATOIRES EUROGENERICS SAS—See Bain Capital, LP; *U.S. Private*, pg. 443
EG LABO SAS - LABORATOIRES EUROGENERICS SAS—See Cinven Limited; *Int'l*, pg. 1613
EGLENTOWICZ WRECKING LLC; *U.S. Private*, pg. 1344
EGL GENETIC DIAGNOSTICS LLC—See Eurofins Scientific S.E.; *Int'l*, pg. 2536
EGL HOLDINGS COMPANY LIMITED; *Int'l*, pg. 2324
EGL MANAGEMENT SERVICES PTY LIMITED—See The Environmental Group Limited; *Int'l*, pg. 7640
E GLOBAL DRILLING CORP—See Energold Drilling Corp.; *Int'l*, pg. 2421
EGLOBAL; *U.S. Private*, pg. 1344
E-GLOBE S.P.A.; *Int'l*, pg. 2247
E.G.L. RESOURCES, INC.—See PBEX, LLC; *U.S. Private*, pg. 3118
EGLS CO., LTD.; *Int'l*, pg. 2324
E. GLUCK CORP.; *U.S. Private*, pg. 1304
EG METAL CORPORATION—See EG Corporation; *Int'l*, pg. 2322
EGMF KENYA—See George Forrest International S.A.; *Int'l*, pg. 2938
EGMONT ADMINISTRATION A/S—See Egmont Fonden; *Int'l*, pg. 2325
EGMONT AS—See Egmont Fonden; *Int'l*, pg. 2325
EGMONT BULGARIA EAD—See Egmont Fonden; *Int'l*, pg. 2325
EGMONT CREATIVE A/S—See Egmont Fonden; *Int'l*, pg. 2325
EGMONT CREATIVE CENTER A/S—See Egmont Fonden; *Int'l*, pg. 2325
EGMONT CR S.R.O.—See Egmont Fonden; *Int'l*, pg. 2325
EGMONT D.O.O.—See Egmont Fonden; *Int'l*, pg. 2325
EGMONT EHAPA COMIC COLLECTION GMBH—See Egmont Fonden; *Int'l*, pg. 2325
EGMONT EHAPA MEDIA GMBH—See Egmont Fonden; *Int'l*, pg. 2325
EGMONT EHAPA VERLAG GMBH—See Egmont Fonden; *Int'l*, pg. 2325
EGMONT ESTONIA AS—See Egmont Fonden; *Int'l*, pg. 2325
EGMONT FONDEN; *Int'l*, pg. 2325
EGMONT HOLDING AB—See Egmont Fonden; *Int'l*, pg. 2325
EGMONT HOLDING OY—See Egmont Fonden; *Int'l*, pg. 2325
EGMONT HUNGARY KFT.—See Egmont Fonden; *Int'l*, pg. 2325
EGMONT IMAGINATION A/S—See Egmont Fonden; *Int'l*, pg. 2325
EGMONT INTERNATIONAL HOLDING A/S—See Egmont Fonden; *Int'l*, pg. 2325
EGMONT KARNAN AB—See Egmont Fonden; *Int'l*, pg. 2325
EGMONT KIDS MEDIA NORDIC AS—See Egmont Fonden; pg. 2326
EGMONT LATVIJA SIA—See Egmont Fonden; *Int'l*, pg. 2325
EGMONT POLSKA SP. Z O.O.—See Egmont Fonden; *Int'l*, pg. 2325
EGMONT PRINTING SERVICE A/S—See Egmont Fonden; *Int'l*, pg. 2326
EGMONT PUBLISHING KIDS AB—See Egmont Fonden; *Int'l*, pg. 2326
EGMONT PUBLISHING MAGASINER A/S—See Egmont Fonden; *Int'l*, pg. 2325
EGMONT PUBLISHING SUBSIDIARY AB—See Egmont Fonden; *Int'l*, pg. 2326
EGMONT SERBIA—See Egmont Fonden; *Int'l*, pg. 2326
EGMONT SERIEFORLAGET A/S—See Egmont Fonden; *Int'l*, pg. 2325
EGMONT SERIEFORLAGET AS—See Egmont Fonden; *Int'l*, pg. 2325
EGMONT SOURCING (HK) LTD.—See Egmont Fonden; *Int'l*, pg. 2325
EGMONT TIDSKRIFTER AB—See Egmont Fonden; *Int'l*, pg. 2325
EGMONT TIDSKRIFTER BM AB—See Egmont Fonden; *Int'l*, pg. 2325
EGMONT UK LTD.—See Charlesbank Capital Partners, LLC; *U.S. Private*, pg. 854
EGMONT UKRAINE LLC—See Egmont Fonden; *Int'l*, pg. 2325
EGMONT US INC.—See Egmont Fonden; *Int'l*, pg. 2325
EGMONT VERLAGSGESELLSCHAFTEN MBH—See Egmont Fonden; *Int'l*, pg. 2325
EG NORGE AS—See Francisco Partners Management, LP; *U.S. Private*, pg. 1589
EGNYTE INC.; *U.S. Private*, pg. 1344
EGOKIEFER AG—See Arbonia AG; *Int'l*, pg. 538
EGOKIEFER SA—See Arbonia AG; *Int'l*, pg. 538
EGOLF AG STRASSEN- UND TIEFBAU—See Strabag SE; *Int'l*, pg. 7230
EGOLF MOTORS, INC.; *U.S. Private*, pg. 1344
EGO MOVEMENT STUTTGART, GMBH—See TVS Motor Company Ltd.; *Int'l*, pg. 7989
EGON SENGER GMBH—See Senger Holding GmbH; *Int'l*, pg. 6708
EGON VON RUVILLE GMBH—See INA-Holding Schaeffler GmbH & Co. KG; *Int'l*, pg. 3639
EGON ZEHNDER ASSOCIES S.A.—See Egon Zehnder International Inc.; *U.S. Private*, pg. 1344
EGON ZEHNDER INTERNACIONAL DE MEXICO S.A. DE C.V.—See Egon Zehnder International Inc.; *U.S. Private*, pg. 1344
EGON ZEHNDER INTERNATIONAL B.V.—See Egon Zehnder International Inc.; *U.S. Private*, pg. 1344
EGON ZEHNDER INTERNATIONAL CHILE S.A.—See Egon Zehnder International Inc.; *U.S. Private*, pg. 1345
EGON ZEHNDER INTERNATIONAL CO., LTD.—See Egon Zehnder International Inc.; *U.S. Private*, pg. 1345
EGON ZEHNDER INTERNATIONAL CONSULTORES LDA.—See Egon Zehnder International Inc.; *U.S. Private*, pg. 1345
EGON ZEHNDER INTERNATIONAL GES.M.B.H.—See Egon Zehnder International Inc.; *U.S. Private*, pg. 1345
EGON ZEHNDER INTERNATIONAL GMBH—See Egon Zehnder International Inc.; *U.S. Private*, pg. 1345
EGON ZEHNDER INTERNATIONAL GMBH—See Egon Zehnder International Inc.; *U.S. Private*, pg. 1345
EGON ZEHNDER INTERNATIONAL GMBH—See Egon Zehnder International Inc.; *U.S. Private*, pg. 1345
EGON ZEHNDER INTERNATIONAL GMBH—See Egon Zehnder International Inc.; *U.S. Private*, pg. 1345
EGON ZEHNDER INTERNATIONAL GMBH—See Egon Zehnder International Inc.; *U.S. Private*, pg. 1345
EGON ZEHNDER INTERNATIONAL GMBH—See Egon Zehnder International Inc.; *U.S. Private*, pg. 1345
EGON ZEHNDER INTERNATIONAL INC.; *U.S. Private*, pg. 1344
EGON ZEHNDER INTERNATIONAL (ISRAEL) LTD.—See Egon Zehnder International Inc.; *U.S. Private*, pg. 1344
EGON ZEHNDER INTERNATIONAL KFT.—See Egon Zehnder International Inc.; *U.S. Private*, pg. 1345
EGON ZEHNDER INTERNATIONAL LTDA.—See Egon Zehnder International Inc.; *U.S. Private*, pg. 1345
EGON ZEHNDER INTERNATIONAL LTDA.—See Egon Zehnder International Inc.; *U.S. Private*, pg. 1345
EGON ZEHNDER INTERNATIONAL LTD.—See Egon Zehnder International Inc.; *U.S. Private*, pg. 1345
EGON ZEHNDER INTERNATIONAL (M) SDN BHD—See Egon Zehnder International Inc.; *U.S. Private*, pg. 1344
EGON ZEHNDER INTERNATIONAL OY—See Egon Zehnder International Inc.; *U.S. Private*, pg. 1345
EGON ZEHNDER INTERNATIONAL PTE LTD.—See Egon Zehnder International Inc.; *U.S. Private*, pg. 1345
EGON ZEHNDER INTERNATIONAL PTY LTD.—See Egon Zehnder International Inc.; *U.S. Private*, pg. 1345
EGON ZEHNDER INTERNATIONAL PTY LTD.—See Egon Zehnder International Inc.; *U.S. Private*, pg. 1345
EGON ZEHNDER INTERNATIONAL PVT. LTD.—See Egon Zehnder International Inc.; *U.S. Private*, pg. 1345
EGON ZEHNDER INTERNATIONAL PVT. LTD.—See Egon Zehnder International Inc.; *U.S. Private*, pg. 1345
EGON ZEHNDER INTERNATIONAL S.A.—See Egon Zehnder International Inc.; *U.S. Private*, pg. 1345
EGON ZEHNDER INTERNATIONAL S.A.—See Egon Zehnder International Inc.; *U.S. Private*, pg. 1345
EGON ZEHNDER INTERNATIONAL S.A.—See Egon Zehnder International Inc.; *U.S. Private*, pg. 1345
EGON ZEHNDER INTERNATIONAL S.A.—See Egon Zehnder International Inc.; *U.S. Private*, pg. 1345
EGON ZEHNDER INTERNATIONAL S.A.—See Egon Zehnder International Inc.; *U.S. Private*, pg. 1345
EGON ZEHNDER INTERNATIONAL (SHANGHAI) COMPANY LIMITED—See Egon Zehnder International Inc.; *U.S. Private*, pg. 1344
EGON ZEHNDER INTERNATIONAL S.L.—See Egon Zehnder International Inc.; *U.S. Private*, pg. 1345
EGON ZEHNDER INTERNATIONAL S.L.—See Egon Zehnder International Inc.; *U.S. Private*, pg. 1345
EGON ZEHNDER INTERNATIONAL S.P.A.—See Egon Zehnder International Inc.; *U.S. Private*, pg. 1345
EGON ZEHNDER INTERNATIONAL SP. Z O.O.—See Egon Zehnder International Inc.; *U.S. Private*, pg. 1345
EGON ZEHNDER LUXEMBOURG S.A.—See Egon Zehnder International Inc.; *U.S. Private*, pg. 1345
EGO PRODUCTIONS SASU—See Mediawan SA; *Int'l*, pg. 4774
EGOV STRATEGIES LLC—See Wonderware, Inc.; *U.S. Private*, pg. 4556
EG PENNER BUILDING CENTRES; *Int'l*, pg. 2322
EGP, INC.; *U.S. Private*, pg. 1345
EGP INVEST, SPOL. S R.O.—See CEZ, a.s.; *Int'l*, pg. 1429
EG POTECH CO. LTD—See EG Corporation; *Int'l*, pg. 2322
EG POWER ELECTRONICS (INDIA) PVT. LTD.—See Amplex AB; *Int'l*, pg. 434
E'GRAND CO., LTD.; *Int'l*, pg. 2247
E-GRAPHICS—See Omnicom Group Inc.; *U.S. Public*, pg. 1594
EGREEN CO., LTD.; *Int'l*, pg. 2326
EG RETAIL & MEDIE—See Francisco Partners Management, LP; *U.S. Private*, pg. 1589
EGR EXPLORATION LTD.; *Int'l*, pg. 2326
EGR INTERNATIONAL, INC.; *U.S. Private*, pg. 1345
EGRO SUISSE AG—See Ali Holding S.r.l.; *Int'l*, pg. 321
EGROUP, INC.; *U.S. Private*, pg. 1345
EG S.A.—See Bain Capital, LP; *U.S. Private*, pg. 443
EG S.A.—See Cinven Limited; *Int'l*, pg. 1613
EGS AUTOMATION GMBH—See AMETEK, Inc.; *U.S. Public*, pg. 120
EGS CO., LTD.—See Sumitomo Chemical Company, Limited; *Int'l*, pg. 7264
EGS COMERCIALIZADORA MEXICO, S. DE R.L. DE C.V.—See Emerson Electric Co.; *U.S. Public*, pg. 740
EGS ELECTRIC GROUP CANADA LTD.—See Emerson Electric Co.; *U.S. Public*, pg. 740
EGS ENCLOSURES & CONTROLS—See Emerson Electric Co.; *U.S. Public*, pg. 740
EG (SHANGHAI) COMMERCIAL CO., LTD.—See Amplex AB; *Int'l*, pg. 434
EGS HOLDINGS, LLC—See Entergy Corporation; *U.S. Public*, pg. 777
EG SIERRA L.L.C.; *U.S. Private*, pg. 1344
EGS, INC.; *U.S. Private*, pg. 1346
EGS INTERNATIONAL INC.; *U.S. Private*, pg. 1345
EG SOLUTIONS LTD.—See Verint Systems Inc.; *U.S. Public*, pg. 2281
EG S.P.A.—See Bain Capital, LP; *U.S. Private*, pg. 443
EG S.P.A.—See Cinven Limited; *Int'l*, pg. 1613
EG SVERIGE AB—See Francisco Partners Management, LP; *U.S. Private*, pg. 1589
EG SYSTEMS LLC; *U.S. Private*, pg. 1344
EG SYSTEMS, LLC—See TruGreen Limited Partnership; *U.S. Private*, pg. 4249
EG TECH CORP.—See EG Corporation; *Int'l*, pg. 2322
E.G. TECHNOLOGY MANAGEMENT CORPORATION—See IWASAKI ELECTRIC Co., Ltd.; *Int'l*, pg. 3849

EG SYSTEMS LLC

EGTON MEDICAL INFORMATION SYSTEMS LTD. - EGTON DIVISION—See EMIS Group plc; *Int'l*, pg. 2382
EGT PRINTING SOLUTIONS, LLC—See Chatham Asset Management, LLC; *U.S. Private*, pg. 862
EG-TRADING OY—See Kingspan Group PLC; *Int'l*, pg. 4178
EG TRANSPORTATION SERVICES LLC—See Unrivaled Brands, Inc.; *U.S. Public*, pg. 2263
EGT—See Orange S.A.; *Int'l*, pg. 5608
EGUANA GMBH—See Eguana Technologies Inc.; *Int'l*, pg. 2326
EGUANA TECHNOLOGIES INC.; *Int'l*, pg. 2326
EGUARANTEE; *Int'l*, pg. 2327
E-GUARDIAN, INC.; *Int'l*, pg. 2247
EGUMBALL, INC.; *U.S. Private*, pg. 1346
EGURIDAD PRIVADA ACTIVE SECURITY COMPANY A.S.C. CIA. LTDA.—See Bain Capital, LP; *U.S. Private*, pg. 434
EG UTILITY A/S—See Francisco Partners Management, LP; *U.S. Private*, pg. 1589
EGUZKIA-NHK, S.A.—See NHK Spring Co., Ltd.; *Int'l*, pg. 5257
EG+ WORLDWIDE—See Omnicom Group Inc.; *U.S. Public*, pg. 1596
EGW TEMPORARIES INC.; *U.S. Private*, pg. 1346
EGW UTILITIES, INC.; *U.S. Private*, pg. 1346
EGW WOHNBAU GEMEINNUTZIGE GES.M.B.H.—See Vienna Insurance Group AG Wiener Versicherung Gruppe; *Int'l*, pg. 8194
EGYM GMBH; *Int'l*, pg. 2327
EGYPTAIR CARGO—See EgyptAir Holding Company; *Int'l*, pg. 2327
EGYPTAIR HOLDING COMPANY; *Int'l*, pg. 2327
EGYPTAIR MAINTENANCE & ENGINEERING—See EgyptAir Holding Company; *Int'l*, pg. 2327
EGYPT ALUMINIUM COMPANY; *Int'l*, pg. 2327
EGYPT FOR INFORMATION DISSEMINATION—See Cairo & Alexandria Stock Exchanges; *Int'l*, pg. 1253
EGYPT FOR POULTRY; *Int'l*, pg. 2327
EGYPT FREE SHOPS CO.; *Int'l*, pg. 2327
EGYPTIAN ARABIAN CMAR SECURITIES BROKERAGE; *Int'l*, pg. 2327
EGYPTIAN CHEMICAL INDUSTRIES CO. (KIMA)—See Chemical Industries Holding Company; *Int'l*, pg. 1461
EGYPTIAN CO. FOR SHOES (BATA)—See Chemical Industries Holding Company; *Int'l*, pg. 1461
THE EGYPTIAN COMPANY FOR FACTORING S.A.E.—See Kuwait Projects Company (Holding) K.S.C.P.; *Int'l*, pg. 4347
THE EGYPTIAN COMPANY FOR PIPES & CEMENT PRODUCTS CO. (SIEGWART)—See Chemical Industries Holding Company; *Int'l*, pg. 1462
EGYPTIAN DAIRY AND FOODSTUFF COMPANY—See Saudi Dairy & Foodstuff Co. Ltd.; *Int'l*, pg. 6593
EGYPTIAN ELECTRIC COOPERATIVE ASSOCIATION—See Touchstone Energy Cooperative, Inc.; *U.S. Private*, pg. 4192
EGYPTIAN FERTILIZERS COMPANY—See OCI N.V.; *Int'l*, pg. 5519
EGYPTIAN FINANCIAL & INDUSTRIAL CO.; *Int'l*, pg. 2327
EGYPTIAN FOR DEVELOPING BUILDING MATERIALS; *Int'l*, pg. 2327
EGYPTIAN GULF BANK; *Int'l*, pg. 2327
EGYPTIAN GYPSUM COMPANY LTD.—See Orascom Construction PLC; *Int'l*, pg. 5613
EGYPTIAN INTERNATIONAL INDUSTRIAL MINERALS S.A.E.—See Gruppo Minerali Maffei S.p.A.; *Int'l*, pg. 3140
EGYPTIAN INTERNATIONAL MEDICAL CENTER S.A.E—See Kuwait Projects Company (Holding) K.S.C.P.; *Int'l*, pg. 4346
EGYPTIAN INTERNATIONAL MOTORS EGYPT—See Mannai Corporation QPSC; *Int'l*, pg. 4674
EGYPTIAN INTERNATIONAL PHARMACEUTICAL INDUSTRIES COMPANY; *Int'l*, pg. 2327
EGYPTIAN IRON & STEEL COMPANY—See Metallurgical Industries Company (EJSC); *Int'l*, pg. 4848
EGYPTIAN KUWAITI HOLDING; *Int'l*, pg. 2327
EGYPTIAN LIFE TAKAFUL—See Fairfax Financial Holdings Limited; *Int'l*, pg. 2607
EGYPTIAN MEDIA PRODUCTION CITY SAE; *Int'l*, pg. 2327
EGYPTIAN PETROLEUM HH RIG MANUFACTURING S.A.E CO.—See Honghua Group Ltd; *Int'l*, pg. 3470
EGYPTIAN RESORTS COMPANY; *Int'l*, pg. 2327
EGYPTIANS ABROAD INVESTMENT & DEVELOPMENT CO.; *Int'l*, pg. 2327
EGYPTIAN SAUDI FINANCE BANK—See Al Baraka Banking Group B.S.C.; *Int'l*, pg. 276
EGYPTIANS FOR HOUSING & DEVELOPMENT CO.; *Int'l*, pg. 2327
EGYPTIAN SMART CARDS COMPANY—See Brookfield Corporation; *Int'l*, pg. 1189
EGYPTIAN STARCH & GLUCOSE COMPANY—See Cairo Three A Group; *Int'l*, pg. 1253

EGYPTIAN TRANSPORTATION & LOGISTICS COMPANY—See Egyptian Transport & Commercial Services Company S.A.E.; *Int'l*, pg. 2327
EGYPTIAN TRANSPORT & COMMERCIAL SERVICES COMPANY S.A.E.; *Int'l*, pg. 2327
EGYPTIAN VEHICLES MANUFACTURING CO. S.A.E.—See Ghabbour Auto S.A.E.; *Int'l*, pg. 2958
EGYPT KUWAIT HOLDING CO. S.A.E; *Int'l*, pg. 2327
EGYPT LIFE TAKAFUL INSURANCE COMPANY, S.A.E.—See Fairfax Financial Holdings Limited; *Int'l*, pg. 2607
EGYPT & MIDDLE EAST IMPORT-EXPORT LTD. CO.—See Aiphone Co., Ltd.; *Int'l*, pg. 235
EGYPT OTSUKA PHARMACEUTICAL CO., S.A.E.—See Otsuka Holdings Co., Ltd.; *Int'l*, pg. 5659
EGYTEC CABLES COMPANY—See El Sewedy Electric Company; *Int'l*, pg. 2341
EGYTRANS DEPOT SOLUTIONS COMPANY—See Egyptian Transport & Commercial Services Company S.A.E.; *Int'l*, pg. 2327
EHANG HOLDINGS LIMITED; *Int'l*, pg. 2327
E.HARDING & SONS LIMITED—See A. M. Castle & Co.; *U.S. Public*, pg. 11
EHARMONY.COM, INC.—See ProSiebenSat.1 Media SE; *Int'l*, pg. 6000
EHARVEST—See Farms.com Ltd.; *Int'l*, pg. 2620
EHAVE, INC.; *U.S. Public*, pg. 721
E. HAWLE ARMATURENWERKE GMBH; *Int'l*, pg. 2250
EH BAARE CORPORATION; *U.S. Private*, pg. 1346
EHB LOGISTICS CO., LTD.—See KKR & Co. Inc.; *U.S. Public*, pg. 1258
E&H CERTIFIED PUBLIC ACCOUNTANTS & MANAGEMENT CONSULTANTS P.C.—See Mbe Cpas LLP; *U.S. Private*, pg. 2624
EHC GLOBAL - BAESWEILER PLANT—See Prysmian S.p.A.; *Int'l*, pg. 6010
EHC GLOBAL, INC.—See Prysmian S.p.A.; *Int'l*, pg. 6010
EHC GLOBAL - SHANGHAI PLANT—See Prysmian S.p.A.; *Int'l*, pg. 6010
EHC INC.; *U.S. Private*, pg. 1346
EH COFFEE INC.—See PlantX Life Inc.; *Int'l*, pg. 5891
E&H CO., LTD.; *Int'l*, pg. 2247
EH CONSTRUCTION LLC; *U.S. Private*, pg. 1346
EHD ADVISORY SERVICES, INC.—See Savant Capital, LLC; *U.S. Private*, pg. 3556
EHD TECHNOLOGIES, LLC—See Groupe Crit, S.A.; *Int'l*, pg. 3101
EHEALTH, INC.; *U.S. Public*, pg. 721
EHEALTHINSURANCE SERVICES, INC.—See eHealth, Inc.; *U.S. Public*, pg. 721
EHEALTH SOLUTIONS, INC.—See ResMed Inc.; *U.S. Public*, pg. 1790
EHEALTH-TEC GMBH—See Zur Rose Group AG; *Int'l*, pg. 8697
EHE, INC.—See UM Holdings Limited; *U.S. Private*, pg. 4278
EH EUROPE GMBH—See EnerSys; *U.S. Public*, pg. 766
EHG EISENHOLDING GMBH—See Mercedes-Benz Group AG; *Int'l*, pg. 4824
E.H. HAMILTON TRUCKING SERVICE; *U.S. Private*, pg. 1305
EHHI HOLDINGS, INC.—See Encompass Health Corporation; *U.S. Public*, pg. 755
EHI CAR SERVICES LIMITED; *Int'l*, pg. 2328
THE EHIME BANK, LTD.; *Int'l*, pg. 7638
EHIME GAIYA FUND CORPORATION LIMITED—See The Ehime Bank, Ltd.; *Int'l*, pg. 7638
EHIME HOSPITAL PERTNERS CO., LTD.—See Taisei Corporation; *Int'l*, pg. 7415
EHIME-JCB CO., LTD.—See The Ehime Bank, Ltd.; *Int'l*, pg. 7638
EHIME KAIUN CO., LTD.—See Sankyu, Inc.; *Int'l*, pg. 6543
EHIME KOBAYASHI PHARMACEUTICAL CO., LTD.—See Kobayashi Pharmaceutical Co., Ltd.; *Int'l*, pg. 4216
EHI MODULAR COMPANY, INC.—See Innovative Building Systems LLC; *U.S. Private*, pg. 2082
EHINGER-SCHWARZ GMBH & CO. KG; *Int'l*, pg. 2328
EHISA CONSTRUCCIONES Y OBRAS, S.A.U.—See Elecnor, S.A.; *Int'l*, pg. 2347
EHL AG—See CRH plc; *Int'l*, pg. 1844
EHLERDING MOTORSPORTS INC.; *U.S. Private*, pg. 1346
EHL IMMOBILIEN GMBH; *Int'l*, pg. 2328
EHL IMMOBILIEN MANAGEMENT GMBH—See EHL Immobilien GmbH; *Int'l*, pg. 2328
E HOLDINGS, LLC—See Comcast Corporation; *U.S. Public*, pg. 538
E-HOME HOUSEHOLD SERVICE HOLDINGS LIMITED; *Int'l*, pg. 2248
EHOTEL AG; *Int'l*, pg. 2328
E-HOUSE (CHINA) ENTERPRISE HOLDINGS LTD.; *Int'l*, pg. 2248
E-HOUSE (CHINA) HOLDINGS LIMITED; *Int'l*, pg. 2248
EHP ECZACIBASI HEALTH CARE PRODUCTS JOINT STOCK CO.—See Eczacibasi Holding A.S.; *Int'l*, pg. 2301
EH PROPERTY MANAGEMENT PTE LTD—See Enviro-Hub Holdings Ltd.; *Int'l*, pg. 2454

E+HPS ENGINEERING (SUZHOU) CO., LTD.—See Ellipsiz Ltd.; *Int'l*, pg. 2366
E+HPS PTE. LTD—See Ellipsiz Ltd.; *Int'l*, pg. 2366
EH PUBLISHING, INC.; *U.S. Private*, pg. 1346
EHRENSTRAHLE & CO. I STOCKHOLM AB—See Omnicom Group Inc.; *U.S. Public*, pg. 1581
EHRFELD MIKROTECHNIK BTS GMBH—See Bayer Aktiengesellschaft; *Int'l*, pg. 906
EHRHARDT, KEEFE, STEINER & HOTTMAN, P.C.; *U.S. Private*, pg. 1346
EHRHARDT TOOL & MACHINE, LLC—See Dunes Point Capital, LLC; *U.S. Private*, pg. 1288
EHRLICH FOOD COMPANY INC.; *U.S. Private*, pg. 1346
EHRLICH WERKZEUG & GERATEBAU GMBH—See Amphenol Corporation; *U.S. Public*, pg. 130
EHRMANN AG; *Int'l*, pg. 2328
EHS LENS PHILIPPINES, INC.—See Hoya Corporation; *Int'l*, pg. 3494
EHS TECHNOLOGIES CORP.; *U.S. Private*, pg. 1346
E&H STEEL CORPORATION; *U.S. Private*, pg. 1301
EHS TRAINING & SERVICES CO., LTD.—See Thai Union Group Public Company Limited; *Int'l*, pg. 7596
E&H TRANSPORT NETWORK INC.; *U.S. Private*, pg. 1301
E-HUALU (FUJIAN) INFORMATION TECHNOLOGY CO., LTD.—See Beijing E-Hualu Information Technology Co., Ltd.; *Int'l*, pg. 949
E-HUALU INTEGRATION TECHNOLOGY CO., LTD.—See Beijing E-Hualu Information Technology Co., Ltd.; *Int'l*, pg. 949
E-HUALU (JILIN) INFORMATION TECHNOLOGY CO., LTD.—See Beijing E-Hualu Information Technology Co., Ltd.; *Int'l*, pg. 949
E-HUALU (LESHAN) INVESTMENT DEVELOPMENT CO., LTD.—See Beijing E-Hualu Information Technology Co., Ltd.; *Int'l*, pg. 949
E-HUALU (QUANZHOU) INVESTMENT DEVELOPMENT CO., LTD.—See Beijing E-Hualu Information Technology Co., Ltd.; *Int'l*, pg. 949
E-HUALU (SHANDONG) INFORMATION TECHNOLOGY CO., LTD.—See Beijing E-Hualu Information Technology Co., Ltd.; *Int'l*, pg. 949
E-HUALU (TIANJIN) INFORMATION TECHNOLOGY CO., LTD.—See Beijing E-Hualu Information Technology Co., Ltd.; *Int'l*, pg. 949
E-HUALU (TIANJIN) INTERNATIONAL TRADE COMPANY—See Beijing E-Hualu Information Technology Co., Ltd.; *Int'l*, pg. 949
EHV POWER ULC—See Quanta Services, Inc.; *U.S. Public*, pg. 1751
EHWA TECHNOLOGIES INFORMATION CO. LTD.; *Int'l*, pg. 2328
EHW (SEYCHELLES) LTD.—See Honda Motor Co., Ltd.; *Int'l*, pg. 3460
EHY CONSTRUCTION & ENGINEERING COMPANY LIMITED—See MECOM Power & Construction Limited; *Int'l*, pg. 4767
EI AUTOSERVIS A.D.; *Int'l*, pg. 2328
EIBC (P) LTD—See THK CO., LTD.; *Int'l*, pg. 7711
EIC ACTIVITIES PTY LTD—See ACS, Actividades de Construccion y Servicios, S.A.; *Int'l*, pg. 111
EI CERAMICS LLC—See S K Bajoria Group; *Int'l*, pg. 6442
EICHENBAUM/ASSOCIATES, INC.; *U.S. Private*, pg. 1346
EICHER MOTORS LIMITED; *Int'l*, pg. 2328
EICHLER HUNGARIA KFT.—See Meier Capital AG; *Int'l*, pg. 4799
EIC INTERNATIONAL CO., LTD.—See Electronics Industry Public Company Limited; *Int'l*, pg. 2354
EICKHOFF AUSTRALIA PTY. LTD—See Eickhoff Maschinenfabrik GmbH; *Int'l*, pg. 2328
EICKHOFF BERGBAUTECHNIK GMBH—See Eickhoff Maschinenfabrik GmbH; *Int'l*, pg. 2328
EICKHOFF CORPORATION—See Eickhoff Maschinenfabrik GmbH; *Int'l*, pg. 2328
EICKHOFF (G.B.) LTD.—See Eickhoff Maschinenfabrik GmbH; *Int'l*, pg. 2328
EICKHOFF GIESSEREI GMBH—See Eickhoff Maschinenfabrik GmbH; *Int'l*, pg. 2328
EICKHOFF INDUSTRIE-ANLAGENBAU UDN MONTAGEN GMBH—See Georgsmarienhutte Holding GmbH; *Int'l*, pg. 2940
EICKHOFF MASCHINENFABRIK GMBH; *Int'l*, pg. 2328
EICKHOFF MINING TECHNOLOGY GMBH—See Eickhoff Maschinenfabrik GmbH; *Int'l*, pg. 2328
EICKHOFF POLONIA LTD.—See Eickhoff Maschinenfabrik GmbH; *Int'l*, pg. 2328
EICKHOFF PTY LTD—See Eickhoff Maschinenfabrik GmbH; *Int'l*, pg. 2328
EICL LIMITED; *Int'l*, pg. 2328
EICO INC.; *U.S. Private*, pg. 1346
EI COMPANIES; *U.S. Private*, pg. 1346
EIC SECURITIES LTD.—See Eastern Insurance Company Limited; *Int'l*, pg. 2273
EIC SEMICONDUCTOR, INC.—See Electronics Industry Public Company Limited; *Int'l*, pg. 2354
EIDAI CO., LTD.; *Int'l*, pg. 2328
EIDAI KAKO CO., LTD.; *Int'l*, pg. 2328

COMPANY NAME INDEX

EIDAI STAFF SERVICE CO., LTD.—See Eidai Co., Ltd.; *Int'l*, pg. 2328
EIDAI VIETNAM CO., LTD.—See Eidai Co., Ltd.; *Int'l*, pg. 2328
EIDE BAILLY LLP; *U.S. Private*, pg. 1346
EIDEN COMMUNICATIONS CO., LTD.—See EDION Corporation; *Int'l*, pg. 2310
EIDER S.A.S.—See Calida Holding AG; *Int'l*, pg. 1264
EIDESVIK AS—See Eidesvik Holding A/S; *Int'l*, pg. 2329
EIDESVIK HOLDING A/S; *Int'l*, pg. 2328
EIDESVIK OFFSHORE ASA; *Int'l*, pg. 2329
EIDOS LTD.—See Square Enix Holdings Co. Ltd.; *Int'l*, pg. 7147
EIDOS S.R.L.—See L. Possehl & Co. mbH; *Int'l*, pg. 4382
EIDOS THERAPEUTICS, INC.—See BridgeBio Pharma, Inc.; *U.S. Public*, pg. 381
E.I.D. - PARRY (INDIA) LIMITED—See The Murugappa Group, Ltd.; *Int'l*, pg. 7668
EID PASSPORT, INC.; *U.S. Private*, pg. 1346
EIDP, INC.—See Corteva, Inc.; *U.S. Public*, pg. 582
EID S.A.S.—See Beijer Ref AB; *Int'l*, pg. 944
THE EIDSON GROUP, LLC—See Avison Young (Canada) Inc.; *Int'l*, pg. 745
E.I. DUPONT CANADA COMPANY—See Corteva, Inc.; *U.S. Public*, pg. 584
E.I. DUPONT CANADA - THETFORD INC.—See DuPont de Nemours, Inc.; *U.S. Public*, pg. 693
E.I. DUPONT DE NEMOURS & CO.—See Corteva, Inc.; *U.S. Public*, pg. 584
E.I. DUPONT DE NEMOURS & CO.—See Corteva, Inc.; *U.S. Public*, pg. 584
E.I. DUPONT DE NEMOURS & CO.—See Corteva, Inc.; *U.S. Public*, pg. 584
E.I. DUPONT DE NEMOURS & CO.—See Corteva, Inc.; *U.S. Public*, pg. 584
E.I. DUPONT INDIA PRIVATE LIMITED—See Corteva, Inc.; *U.S. Public*, pg. 584
EIE AB—See Indutrade AB; *Int'l*, pg. 3678
EIE MASKIN AB—See Indutrade AB; *Int'l*, pg. 3678
EIE MASKIN AS—See Indutrade AB; *Int'l*, pg. 3678
EIENDOMSMEGLER 1 INNLANDET AS—See Sparebank 1 Oestlandet; *Int'l*, pg. 7125
EIENDOMSSELSKAPET DRONNING MAUDS GATE 15 AS—See Eksportfinans ASA; *Int'l*, pg. 2340
EIENDOMSSIKRING AS—See Lasservice AS; *Int'l*, pg. 4421
EIENDOMSSPAR ASA; *Int'l*, pg. 2329
EIFFAGE CONSTRUCTION ALSACE FRANCHE COMTE S.N.C—See Eiffage S.A.; *Int'l*, pg. 2329
EIFFAGE CONSTRUCTION ARTOIS HAINAUT S.N.C.—See Eiffage S.A.; *Int'l*, pg. 2329
EIFFAGE CONSTRUCTION AUVERGNE SNC—See Eiffage S.A.; *Int'l*, pg. 2329
EIFFAGE CONSTRUCTION BASSE NORMANDIE—See Eiffage S.A.; *Int'l*, pg. 2329
EIFFAGE CONSTRUCTION BOURGOGNE—See Eiffage S.A.; *Int'l*, pg. 2329
EIFFAGE CONSTRUCTION BRETAGNE S.N.C—See Eiffage S.A.; *Int'l*, pg. 2329
EIFFAGE CONSTRUCTION CENTRE—See Eiffage S.A.; *Int'l*, pg. 2329
EIFFAGE CONSTRUCTION CHAMPAGNE—See Eiffage S.A.; *Int'l*, pg. 2329
EIFFAGE CONSTRUCTION COTE D AZUR S.N.C—See Eiffage S.A.; *Int'l*, pg. 2329
EIFFAGE CONSTRUCTION LIMOUSIN—See Eiffage S.A.; *Int'l*, pg. 2329
EIFFAGE CONSTRUCTION LORRAINE S.N.C—See Eiffage S.A.; *Int'l*, pg. 2329
EIFFAGE CONSTRUCTION MATERIEL—See Eiffage S.A.; *Int'l*, pg. 2329
EIFFAGE CONSTRUCTION METALLIQUE S.A.—See Eiffage S.A.; *Int'l*, pg. 2329
EIFFAGE CONSTRUCTION MIDI PYRENEES S.N.C—See Eiffage S.A.; *Int'l*, pg. 2329
EIFFAGE CONSTRUCTION NORD—See Eiffage S.A.; *Int'l*, pg. 2329
EIFFAGE CONSTRUCTION PARIS PATRIMOINE—See Eiffage S.A.; *Int'l*, pg. 2329
EIFFAGE CONSTRUCTION PROVENCE S.N.C—See Eiffage S.A.; *Int'l*, pg. 2330
EIFFAGE CONSTRUCTION RHONE-ALPES S.N.C.—See Eiffage S.A.; *Int'l*, pg. 2330
EIFFAGE CONSTRUCTION SERVICES—See Eiffage S.A.; *Int'l*, pg. 2330
EIFFAGE CONSTRUCTION—See Eiffage S.A.; *Int'l*, pg. 2329
EIFFAGE CONSTRUCTION VAL DE SEINE S.N.C—See Eiffage S.A.; *Int'l*, pg. 2330
EIFFAGE DEUTSCHLAND BAUHOLDING GMBH—See Eiffage S.A.; *Int'l*, pg. 2330
EIFFAGE ENERGIA S.L—See Eiffage S.A.; *Int'l*, pg. 2330
EIFFAGE ENERGIE CENTRE-EST—See Eiffage S.A.; *Int'l*, pg. 2330
EIFFAGE ENERGIE ELECTRONIQUE S.A.S.—See Eiffage S.A.; *Int'l*, pg. 2330
EIFFAGE ENERGIE ILE-DE-FRANCE—See Eiffage S.A.; *Int'l*, pg. 2330
EIFFAGE ENERGIE NORD—See Eiffage S.A.; *Int'l*, pg. 2330

EIFFAGE ENERGIE POITOU-CHARENTES S.A.S.—See Eiffage S.A.; *Int'l*, pg. 2330
EIFFAGE ENERGIE S.A.S.—See Eiffage S.A.; *Int'l*, pg. 2330
EIFFAGE ENERGIE THERMIE S.A.S.—See Eiffage S.A.; *Int'l*, pg. 2330
EIFFAGE ENERGIE TRANSPORT & DISTRIBUTION S.A.S.—See Eiffage S.A.; *Int'l*, pg. 2330
EIFFAGE ENERGIE VAL DE LOIRE S.A.S.—See Eiffage S.A.; *Int'l*, pg. 2330
EIFFAGE GENIE CIVIL—See Eiffage S.A.; *Int'l*, pg. 2330
EIFFAGE IMMOBILIER POLSKA SP. Z OO—See Eiffage S.A.; *Int'l*, pg. 2330
EIFFAGE IMMOBILIER—See Eiffage S.A.; *Int'l*, pg. 2330
EIFFAGE INFRAESTRUCTURAS—See Eiffage S.A.; *Int'l*, pg. 2331
EIFFAGE INFRA-NORDWEST GMBH—See Eiffage S.A.; *Int'l*, pg. 2330
EIFFAGE INFRA-WEST GMBH—See Eiffage S.A.; *Int'l*, pg. 2331
EIFFAGE INTERNATIONAL S.A.—See Eiffage S.A.; *Int'l*, pg. 2331
EIFFAGE POLSKA BUDOWNICTWO SA—See Eiffage S.A.; *Int'l*, pg. 2330
EIFFAGE POLSKA KOLEJE SP. Z O.O.—See Eiffage S.A.; *Int'l*, pg. 2330
EIFFAGE S.A.; *Int'l*, pg. 2329
EIFFAGE TRAVAUX PUBLICS EST—See Eiffage S.A.; *Int'l*, pg. 2331
EIFFAGE TRAVAUX PUBLICS MEDITERRANEE—See Eiffage S.A.; *Int'l*, pg. 2331
EIFFAGE TRAVAUX PUBLICS NORD S.N.C—See Eiffage S.A.; *Int'l*, pg. 2331
EIFFAGE TRAVAUX PUBLICS OUEST S.N.C—See Eiffage S.A.; *Int'l*, pg. 2331
EIFFAGE TRAVAUX PUBLICS RESEAUX—See Eiffage S.A.; *Int'l*, pg. 2331
EIFFAGE TRAVAUX PUBLICS SAS—See Eiffage S.A.; *Int'l*, pg. 2330
EIFFAGE TRAVAUX PUBLICS SUD OUEST S.N.C—See Eiffage S.A.; *Int'l*, pg. 2331
EIFFEL DEUTSCHLAND STAHLTECHNOLOGIE GMBH - DUISBURG—See Certina Holding AG; *Int'l*, pg. 1423
EIFFEL DEUTSCHLAND STAHLTECHNOLOGIE GMBH—See Certina Holding AG; *Int'l*, pg. 1423
EIFFEL INDUSTRIE S.A.S—See Eiffage S.A.; *Int'l*, pg. 2331
EIF KC LANDFILL GAS, LLC—See Enpower Corp.; *U.S. Private*, pg. 1401
EIF SDN. BHD.—See Expeditors International of Washington, Inc.; *U.S. Public*, pg. 810
EIGENBRODT AB—See Axel Johnson Gruppen AB; *Int'l*, pg. 763
EIGENBRODT WIDNI BALTIC OU—See Axel Johnson Gruppen AB; *Int'l*, pg. 763
EIGENBRODT WIDNI OY—See Axel Johnson Gruppen AB; *Int'l*, pg. 763
EIGEN FABRIKAAT BU—See Omnicom Group Inc.; *U.S. Public*, pg. 1580
EIGENMANN AG—See Burkhalter Holding AG; *Int'l*, pg. 1224
EIGENSONNE GMBH—See Amia Energy GmbH; *Int'l*, pg. 426
EIGER BIOPHARMACEUTICALS, INC.; *U.S. Public*, pg. 721
EIG GLOBAL (CHINA) CO. LTD.—See Esthetics International Group Berhad; *Int'l*, pg. 2518
EIG GLOBAL ENERGY (ASIA) LTD.—See Affiliated Managers Group, Inc.; *U.S. Public*, pg. 54
EIG GLOBAL ENERGY (AUSTRALIA) PTY. LTD.—See Affiliated Managers Group, Inc.; *U.S. Public*, pg. 54
EIG GLOBAL ENERGY (BRASIL) REPRESENTACOES LTDA.—See Affiliated Managers Group, Inc.; *U.S. Public*, pg. 54
EIG GLOBAL ENERGY (EUROPE) LTD.—See Affiliated Managers Group, Inc.; *U.S. Public*, pg. 54
EIG GLOBAL ENERGY KOREA, LTD.—See Affiliated Managers Group, Inc.; *U.S. Public*, pg. 54
EIG GLOBAL ENERGY PARTNERS, LLC; *U.S. Private*, pg. 1347
EIG GLOBAL (HK) LTD.—See Esthetics International Group Berhad; *Int'l*, pg. 2518
EIG GLOBAL PTE LTD—See Esthetics International Group Berhad; *Int'l*, pg. 2518
EIGHT CAPITAL PARTNERS PLC; *Int'l*, pg. 2331
EIGHT CAPITAL—See Dundee Corporation; *Int'l*, pg. 2226
EIGHTCO HOLDINGS INC.; *U.S. Public*, pg. 721
EIGHT CROSSINGS; *U.S. Private*, pg. 1347
EIGHTEEN SEVENTY CORPORATION; *U.S. Private*, pg. 1347
EIGHTEEN SEVENTY STRAND CORP.; *U.S. Private*, pg. 1347
EIGHTEEN SOUND S.R.L.—See B&C Speakers SpA; *Int'l*, pg. 784
THE EIGHTEENTH BANK, LIMITED—See Fukuoka Financial Group, Inc.; *Int'l*, pg. 2840
THE EIGHTEENTH CARD CO., LTD.—See Fukuoka Financial Group, Inc.; *Int'l*, pg. 2840

THE EIGHTEENTH LEASE CO., LTD.—See Fukuoka Financial Group, Inc.; *Int'l*, pg. 2840
THE EIGHTEENTH SOFTWARE CO., LTD.—See Fukuoka Financial Group, Inc.; *Int'l*, pg. 2840
EIGHT ELEVEN SERVICES SDN. BHD.—See NV Multi Asia Sdn. Bhd.; *Int'l*, pg. 5497
EIGHTH GATE CAPITAL MANAGEMENT PTY LTD—See Ingenia Communities Group; *Int'l*, pg. 3701
EIGHT NORTHERN INDIAN PUEBLOS COUNCIL, INC.; *U.S. Private*, pg. 1347
EIGHT O'CLOCK COFFEE—See Tata Sons Limited; *Int'l*, pg. 7470
EIGHT PEAKS GROUP LTD.; *Int'l*, pg. 2331
EIGHT ROADS VENTURES—See FMR LLC; *U.S. Private*, pg. 1554
THE EIGHTS GROUP PTY LTD.; *Int'l*, pg. 7638
EIGHT TO GO LLC.; *U.S. Private*, pg. 1347
EIGHTY EIGHT OIL CO.—See True Companies; *U.S. Private*, pg. 4247
EIGHTY JEWELLERS LIMITED; *Int'l*, pg. 2331
EIGHTYTHREE CORPORATION—See Hibino Corporation; *Int'l*, pg. 3383
EIGNABJARG EHF.—See Arion Bank hf.; *Int'l*, pg. 565
EIGNARHALDSFELAGIO LANDEY EHF.—See Arion Bank hf.; *Int'l*, pg. 565
EIG PHARMA ASIA SDN. BHD.—See Esthetics International Group Berhad; *Int'l*, pg. 2518
EIHAB TRAVELS LLC—See Oman Holdings International Company SAOG; *Int'l*, pg. 5559
EIH ASSOCIATED HOTELS LIMITED; *Int'l*, pg. 2332
EIHO PRODUCE CORPORATION—See Nippon Television Holdings Inc.; *Int'l*, pg. 5356
EIH PLC; *Int'l*, pg. 2332
EII INC.; *U.S. Private*, pg. 1347
EIJI CORPORATION—See Murakami Corporation; *Int'l*, pg. 5095
EIJSINK B.V.—See Metro AG; *Int'l*, pg. 4857
EIKA, S. COOP.—See Mondragon Corporation; *Int'l*, pg. 5029
EIK BANK P/F; *Int'l*, pg. 2332
EIKENBERRY CORPORATION; *U.S. Private*, pg. 1347
EIKEN CHEMICAL CO. LTD.; *Int'l*, pg. 2332
EIKEN CHINA CO., LTD.—See EIKEN CHEMICAL CO. LTD.; *Int'l*, pg. 2332
EIKEN INDUSTRIES CO., LTD.; *Int'l*, pg. 2332
EIKEN SHOJI CO., LTD.—See Riken Vitamin Co., Ltd.; *Int'l*, pg. 6341
EIK FASTEIGNAFELAG HF; *Int'l*, pg. 2332
EIKICHI KAIUN CO., LTD.—See Senko Group Holdings Co., Ltd.; *Int'l*, pg. 6709
EIKMASKIN AS—See AGCO Corporation; *U.S. Public*, pg. 58
EIKO CO., LTD.—See Medipal Holdings Corporation; *Int'l*, pg. 4779
EIKO CO., LTD.—See TOSNET Corporation; *Int'l*, pg. 7832
EIKO LIFESCIENCES LIMITED; *Int'l*, pg. 2332
EIKO SERVICE CO., LTD.—See Sumitomo Chemical Company, Limited; *Int'l*, pg. 7267
EIKO SHIPPING CO., LTD.—See Senko Group Holdings Co., Ltd.; *Int'l*, pg. 6709
EILDON CAPITAL LIMITED—See CVC Limited; *Int'l*, pg. 1889
EILEEN FISHER, INC.; *U.S. Private*, pg. 1347
EILERS FINANCIAL SERVICES, INC.—See Aon plc; *Int'l*, pg. 496
EILLOC PTY LTD.—See Nylex Limited; *Int'l*, pg. 5500
EIMC, L.L.C.—See Engle Martin & Associates, LLC; *U.S. Private*, pg. 1399
EIMCO ELECON INDIA LTD; *Int'l*, pg. 2332
THE EIMCO- K.C.P.LTD—See KCP Sugar & Industries Corporation Ltd; *Int'l*, pg. 4110
E.I. MEDICAL IMAGING; *U.S. Private*, pg. 1305
EIMO TECHNOLOGIES INC.—See Nissha Co., Ltd.; *Int'l*, pg. 5371
EIMSKIPAFELAG ISLANDS HF.; *Int'l*, pg. 2332
EIMSKIP—See Eimskipafelag Islands Hf.; *Int'l*, pg. 2332
EIMSKIP UK LTD.—See Eimskipafelag Islands Hf.; *Int'l*, pg. 2332
EIMSKIP USA INC.—See Eimskipafelag Islands Hf.; *Int'l*, pg. 2332
EINBECKER BRAUHAUS AG; *Int'l*, pg. 2332
EINDEC CORPORATION LIMITED; *Int'l*, pg. 2332
EINDHOVEN AIRPORT N.V.—See Schiphol Group NV; *Int'l*, pg. 6621
EINDHOVENS DAGBLAD B.V.—See DPG Media Group NV; *Int'l*, pg. 2189
EINFOCHIPS, INC.—See eInfochips Limited; *Int'l*, pg. 2332
E-INFOCHIPS KK—See Arrow Electronics, Inc.; *U.S. Public*, pg. 199
EINFOCHIPS LIMITED; *Int'l*, pg. 2332
E-INFOCHIPS PRIVATE LIMITED—See Arrow Electronics, Inc.; *U.S. Public*, pg. 200
EINHELL ARGENTINA S. A—See Einhell Germany AG; *Int'l*, pg. 2332
EINHELL AUSTRALIA PTY. LTD.—See Einhell Germany AG; *Int'l*, pg. 2332
EINHELL BENELUX B.V.—See Einhell Germany AG; *Int'l*, pg. 2332

EINHELL BIH D.O.O.—See Einhell Germany AG; *Int'l*, pg. 2333
EINHELL BRASIL COM. DISTR. FERR. E EQUIP. LTDA—See Ancora Chumbadores Ltda.; *Int'l*, pg. 449
EINHELL BULGARIA LTD.—See Einhell Germany AG; *Int'l*, pg. 2333
EINHELL CHILE S.A.—See Einhell Germany AG; *Int'l*, pg. 2333
EINHELL COLOMBIA S.A.S.—See Einhell Germany AG; *Int'l*, pg. 2333
EINHELL CROATIA D.O.O—See Einhell Germany AG; *Int'l*, pg. 2333
EINHELL DENMARK APS—See Einhell Germany AG; *Int'l*, pg. 2333
EINHELL D. O. O.—See Einhell Germany AG; *Int'l*, pg. 2332
EINHELL ESPANA—See Einhell Germany AG; *Int'l*, pg. 2333
EINHELL FINLAND OY—See Einhell Germany AG; *Int'l*, pg. 2333
EINHELL FRANCE S.A.S.—See Einhell Germany AG; *Int'l*, pg. 2333
EINHELL GERMANY AG; *Int'l*, pg. 2332
EINHELL HELLAS S.A.—See Einhell Germany AG; *Int'l*, pg. 2333
EINHELL HOLDING GESELLSCHAFT M.B.H.—See Einhell Germany AG; *Int'l*, pg. 2333
EINHELL HUNGARIA LTD.—See Einhell Germany AG; *Int'l*, pg. 2333
EINHELL INTRATEK MUHENDISLIK VE DIS TICARET A.S.—See Einhell Germany AG; *Int'l*, pg. 2333
EINHELL ITALIA S.R.L.—See Einhell Germany AG; *Int'l*, pg. 2333
EINHELL MIDDLE EAST TRADING FZC—See Einhell Germany AG; *Int'l*, pg. 2333
EINHELL NORDIC APS—See Einhell Germany AG; *Int'l*, pg. 2333
EINHELL NORWAY AS—See Einhell Germany AG; *Int'l*, pg. 2333
EINHELL OSTERREICH GESELLSCHAFT MBH—See Einhell Germany AG; *Int'l*, pg. 2333
EINHELL POLSKA SP. Z.O.O.—See Einhell Germany AG; *Int'l*, pg. 2333
EINHELL PORTUGAL - COMERCIO INT., LDA.—See Einhell Germany AG; *Int'l*, pg. 2333
EINHELL PORTUGAL LDA.—See Einhell Germany AG; *Int'l*, pg. 2333
EINHELL ROMANIA S.R.L.—See Einhell Germany AG; *Int'l*, pg. 2333
EINHELL SAS—See Einhell Germany AG; *Int'l*, pg. 2333
EINHELL SAS—See Einhell Germany AG; *Int'l*, pg. 2333
EINHELL SCHWEIZ AG—See Einhell Germany AG; *Int'l*, pg. 2333
EINHELL SKANDINAVIA APS—See Einhell Germany AG; *Int'l*, pg. 2333
EINHELL SLOVAKIA S.R.O.—See Einhell Germany AG; *Int'l*, pg. 2333
EINHELL TURKEY DIS TICARET A.S.—See Einhell Germany AG; *Int'l*, pg. 2333
EINHELL UK LTD.—See Einhell Germany AG; *Int'l*, pg. 2333
EINHELL UKRAINE TOV—See Einhell Germany AG; *Int'l*, pg. 2333
EINHELL UNICORE S.R.O.—See Einhell Germany AG; *Int'l*, pg. 2333
EINHORN YAFFEE & PRESCOTT; *U.S. Private*, pg. 1347
E INK CORPORATION—See E Ink Holdings, Inc,; *Int'l*, pg. 2246
E INK HOLDINGS, INC,; *Int'l*, pg. 2246
EINSAMOBILE GMBH—See mobilezone holding ag; *Int'l*, pg. 5011
EINSTEIN BROTHERS BAGELS; *U.S. Private*, pg. 1347
EINSTEIN MONTGOMERY SURGERY CENTER, LLC—See Tenet Healthcare Corporation; *U.S. Public*, pg. 2010
EINSTEIN & NOAH CORP.—See JAB Holding Company S.a.r.l.; *Int'l*, pg. 3861
EINSTEIN NOAH RESTAURANT GROUP, INC.—See JAB Holding Company S.a.r.l.; *Int'l*, pg. 3861
EINSTRUCTION CORP.—See Centre Lane Partners, LLC; *U.S. Private*, pg. 828
E-INSURE SERVICES, INC.—See Hellman & Friedman LLC; *U.S. Private*, pg. 1908
E INVESTMENT & DEVELOPMENT CO., LTD.; *Int'l*, pg. 2246
EION INC.; *Int'l*, pg. 2334
EIPII EXPORTS PVT LTD.—See Bliss Gvs Pharma Ltd.; *Int'l*, pg. 1063
EI POWER TECHNOLOGIES SDN. BHD.—See OCK Group Berhad; *Int'l*, pg. 5520
EIQNETWORKS, INC.; *U.S. Private*, pg. 1347
EIQON AS—See AF Gruppen ASA; *Int'l*, pg. 184
EIRCOM HOLDINGS (IRELAND) LIMITED; *Int'l*, pg. 2334
EIRCOM LIMITED—See eircom Holdings (Ireland) Limited; *Int'l*, pg. 2334
EIRGENIX EUROPE GMBH—See EirGenix, Inc.; *Int'l*, pg. 2334
EIRGENIX, INC.; *Int'l*, pg. 2334

EIRGEN PHARMA LTD.—See OPKO Health, Inc.; *U.S. Public*, pg. 1608
EIRICH FRANCE SAS—See Maschinenfabrik Gustav Eirich GmbH & Co KG; *Int'l*, pg. 4720
EIRICH GROUP CHINA LTD.—See Maschinenfabrik Gustav Eirich GmbH & Co KG; *Int'l*, pg. 4720
EIRICH INDIA PVT. LTD.—See Maschinenfabrik Gustav Eirich GmbH & Co KG; *Int'l*, pg. 4720
EIRICH INDUSTRIAL LTDA.—See Maschinenfabrik Gustav Eirich GmbH & Co KG; *Int'l*, pg. 4720
EIRICH MACHINERY JIANGYIN (EMJ) CO., LTD.—See Maschinenfabrik Gustav Eirich GmbH & Co KG; *Int'l*, pg. 4720
EIRICH MACHINES INC.—See Maschinenfabrik Gustav Eirich GmbH & Co KG; *Int'l*, pg. 4720
EI RISK MANAGEMENT CORP.—See Ei Companies; *U.S. Private*, pg. 1346
EISA - EMPRESA INTERAGRICOLA S.A.—See Ecom Agroindustrial Corporation Ltd.; *Int'l*, pg. 2296
EISAGOGIKI EMPORIKI ELLADOS A.E.—See Audio Group Greece B.V.; *Int'l*, pg. 701
EISAI AB—See Eisai Co., Ltd.; *Int'l*, pg. 2335
EISAI AUSTRALIA PTY. LTD.—See Eisai Co., Ltd.; *Int'l*, pg. 2334
EISAI B.V.—See Eisai Co., Ltd.; *Int'l*, pg. 2335
EISAI CHINA HOLDINGS LTD.—See Eisai Co., Ltd.; *Int'l*, pg. 2334
EISAI CHINA INC.—See Eisai Co., Ltd.; *Int'l*, pg. 2334
EISAI CHINA INC. - SUZHOU FACTORY—See Eisai Co., Ltd.; *Int'l*, pg. 2334
EISAI CLINICAL RESEARCH SINGAPORE PTE LTD.—See Eisai Co., Ltd.; *Int'l*, pg. 2334
EISAI CO., LTD. - KASHIMA PLANT—See Eisai Co., Ltd.; *Int'l*, pg. 2335
EISAI CO., LTD.; *Int'l*, pg. 2334
EISAI CORPORATION OF NORTH AMERICA—See Eisai Co., Ltd.; *Int'l*, pg. 2335
EISAI DISTRIBUTION CO., LTD.—See Eisai Co., Ltd.; *Int'l*, pg. 2335
EISAI EUROPE LTD.—See Eisai Co., Ltd.; *Int'l*, pg. 2335
EISAI FARMACEUTICA S.A.—See Eisai Co., Ltd.; *Int'l*, pg. 2335
EISAI FARMACEUTICA, UNIPESSOAL LDA.—See Eisai Co., Ltd.; *Int'l*, pg. 2335
EISAI FOOD & CHEMICALS CO., LTD.—See Eisai Co., Ltd.; *Int'l*, pg. 2335
EISAI GESMBH—See Eisai Co., Ltd.; *Int'l*, pg. 2335
EISAI HONG KONG CO., LTD.—See Eisai Co., Ltd.; *Int'l*, pg. 2335
EISAI INC. - ANDOVER RESEARCH LABORATORY—See Eisai Co., Ltd.; *Int'l*, pg. 2335
EISAI INC. - RESEARCH TRIANGLE PARK—See Eisai Co., Ltd.; *Int'l*, pg. 2335
EISAI INC.—See Eisai Co., Ltd.; *Int'l*, pg. 2335
EISAI KOREA, INC.—See Eisai Co., Ltd.; *Int'l*, pg. 2335
EISAI LABORATORIOS LTDA.—See Eisai Co., Ltd.; *Int'l*, pg. 2335
EISAI LABORATORIOS, S. DE R.L. DE C.V.—See Eisai Co., Ltd.; *Int'l*, pg. 2335
EISAI (LIAONING) PHARMACEUTICAL CO., LTD.—See Eisai Co., Ltd.; *Int'l*, pg. 2334
EISAI LIMITED—See Eisai Co., Ltd.; *Int'l*, pg. 2335
EISAI LTD.—See Eisai Co., Ltd.; *Int'l*, pg. 2335
EISAI (MALAYSIA) SDN. BHD.—See Eisai Co., Ltd.; *Int'l*, pg. 2334
EISAI MANUFACTURING LTD.—See Eisai Co., Ltd.; *Int'l*, pg. 2335
EISAI PHARMA AG—See Eisai Co., Ltd.; *Int'l*, pg. 2335
EISAI PHARMACEUTICALS INDIA PRIVATE LTD.—See Eisai Co., Ltd.; *Int'l*, pg. 2335
EISAI PHARMATECHNOLOGY & MANUFACTURING PVT. LTD.—See Eisai Co., Ltd.; *Int'l*, pg. 2335
EISAI R&D MANAGEMENT CO., LTD.—See Eisai Co., Ltd.; *Int'l*, pg. 2335
EISAI SA/NV—See Eisai Co., Ltd.; *Int'l*, pg. 2335
EISAI S.A.S.—See Eisai Co., Ltd.; *Int'l*, pg. 2335
EISAI SEIKAKEN CO., LTD.—See Lawson, Inc.; *Int'l*, pg. 4426
EISAI (SINGAPORE) PTE. LTD.—See Eisai Co., Ltd.; *Int'l*, pg. 2334
EISAI S.R.L.—See Eisai Co., Ltd.; *Int'l*, pg. 2335
EISAI (SUZHOU) TRADING CO., LTD.—See Eisai Co., Ltd.; *Int'l*, pg. 2334
EISAI TAIWAN, INC.—See Eisai Co., Ltd.; *Int'l*, pg. 2335
EISAI (THAILAND) MARKETING CO., LTD.—See Eisai Co., Ltd.; *Int'l*, pg. 2334
EISAI VIETNAM CO., LTD.—See Eisai Co., Ltd.; *Int'l*, pg. 2335
EISBAR SPORTMODEN GMBH—See Tyrol Equity AG; *Int'l*, pg. 7996
EIS DE MEXICO—See Genuine Parts Company; *U.S. Public*, pg. 932
EIS ECZACIBASI ILAC, SINAI VE FINANSAL YATIRIMLAR SANAYI VE TICARET A.S.—See Eczacibasi Holding A.S.; *Int'l*, pg. 2301
E.I.S. ELECTRONICS GMBH—See Littelfuse, Inc.; *U.S. Public*, pg. 1326
THE EISEN AGENCY; *U.S. Private*, pg. 4025

EISENBAHN-SIEDLUNGSGESELLSCHAFT STUTTGART GGMBH—See Vonovia SE; *Int'l*, pg. 8305
EISENBAU KRAMER GMBH - LITTFELD PLANT—See Eisenbau Kramer GmbH; *Int'l*, pg. 2336
EISENBAU KRAMER GMBH - RECKLINGHAUSEN PLANT—See Eisenbau Kramer GmbH; *Int'l*, pg. 2336
EISENBAU KRAMER GMBH; *Int'l*, pg. 2336
EISENBERG INTERNATIONAL CORPORATION; *U.S. Private*, pg. 1347
EISEN-BIBLIOTHEK STIFTUNG DER GEORG FISCHER AG—See Georg Fischer AG; *Int'l*, pg. 2935
EISENMAN ASSOCIATES INC.; *U.S. Private*, pg. 1347
EISENMANN AG; *Int'l*, pg. 2336
EISENMANN CORPORATION—See Eisenmann AG; *Int'l*, pg. 2336
EISENMANN DO BRASIL EQUIPAMENTOS INDUSTRIAIS LTDA.—See Eisenmann AG; *Int'l*, pg. 2336
EISENMANN FRANCE SARL—See Eisenmann AG; *Int'l*, pg. 2336
EISENMANN INDIA PVT. LTD.—See Eisenmann AG; *Int'l*, pg. 2336
EISENMANN INGENIERIA S.A.—See Eisenmann AG; *Int'l*, pg. 2336
EISENMANN ITALIA S.R.L.—See Eisenmann AG; *Int'l*, pg. 2336
EISENMANN S.A. DE C.V.—See Eisenmann AG; *Int'l*, pg. 2336
EISENMANN SHANGHAI CO., LTD.—See Eisenmann AG; *Int'l*, pg. 2336
EISENMANN SURFACE FINISHING SYSTEMS INDIA PVT. LTD.—See Eisenmann AG; *Int'l*, pg. 2336
EISENMANN THERMAL SOLUTIONS GMBH & CO. KG—See Eisenmann AG; *Int'l*, pg. 2336
EISENMANN U.K. LTD.—See Eisenmann AG; *Int'l*, pg. 2336
EISENMETALL HANDELSGESELLSCHAFT MBH—See ThyssenKrupp AG; *Int'l*, pg. 7724
EISENSCHUTZGESELLSCHAFT M.B.H.—See PORR AG; *Int'l*, pg. 5922
EISEN- UND HUTTENWERKE AG—See ThyssenKrupp AG; *Int'l*, pg. 7724
EISENWERK ARNSTADT GMBH—See DIHAG Holding GmbH; *Int'l*, pg. 2124
EISENWERK ERLA GMBH—See Dynamatic Technologies Limited; *Int'l*, pg. 2239
EISENWERK ERZGEBIRGE 1566 GMBH—See Prevent DEV GmbH; *Int'l*, pg. 5967
EIS FABRICO—See Audax Group, Limited Partnership; *U.S. Private*, pg. 387
EISHIN JIDOSHA KOGYO CO., LTD.—See Mercedes-Benz Group AG; *Int'l*, pg. 4824
EI SHO GEN CO., LTD.—See Kirin Holdings Company, Limited; *Int'l*, pg. 4187
EISHOGEN CO., LTD.—See Kirin Holdings Company, Limited; *Int'l*, pg. 4187
EISHOKU-MEDIX, INC.—See Compass Group PLC; *Int'l*, pg. 1751
EIS HOLDINGS, LLC—See Sun Capital Partners, Inc.; *U.S. Private*, pg. 3859
E.I. SIGNATURE INVESTMENTS LIMITED; *Int'l*, pg. 2251
EIS, INC.—See Audax Group, Limited Partnership; *U.S. Private*, pg. 387
EIS, INC.—See Audax Group, Limited Partnership; *U.S. Private*, pg. 387
EIS, INC.—See Audax Group, Limited Partnership; *U.S. Private*, pg. 387
EIS INC—See Audax Group, Limited Partnership; *U.S. Private*, pg. 387
EIS, INC. - TEMPE—See Audax Group, Limited Partnership; *U.S. Private*, pg. 387
EISO ENTERPRISE CO., LTD.; *Int'l*, pg. 2336
E.I.SOL CO., LTD.—See SOLXYZ Co., Ltd.; *Int'l*, pg. 7083
EIS OPTICS LIMITED—See Materion Corporation; *U.S. Public*, pg. 1395
EIS OPTICS (SHANGHAI) LIMITED—See Materion Corporation; *U.S. Public*, pg. 1395
E.I. SPECTRA, LLC—See BelHealth Investment Partners LLC; *U.S. Private*, pg. 517
EIS PORTUGAL SERVICIOS DE CATERING LDA.—See Newrest Group International S.A.S.; *Int'l*, pg. 5236
EISS BROTHERS, INC.—See Stellex Capital Management LP; *U.S. Private*, pg. 3800
EISSMANN AUTOMOTIVE CESKA REPUBLIKA S.R.O.—See Eissmann Automotive Deutschland GmbH; *Int'l*, pg. 2336
EISSMANN AUTOMOTIVE DE MEXICO S.A. DE C.V.—See Eissmann Automotive Deutschland GmbH; *Int'l*, pg. 2336
EISSMANN AUTOMOTIVE DETROIT DEVELOPMENT, LLC—See Eissmann Automotive Deutschland GmbH; *Int'l*, pg. 2336
EISSMANN AUTOMOTIVE DEUTSCHLAND GMBH; *Int'l*, pg. 2336
EISSMANN AUTOMOTIVE HUNGARIA KFT.—See Eissmann Automotive Deutschland GmbH; *Int'l*, pg. 2336
EISSMANN AUTOMOTIVE NORTH AMERICA, INC.—See Eissmann Automotive Deutschland GmbH; *Int'l*, pg. 2336

COMPANY NAME INDEX

EISSMANN AUTOMOTIVE SLOVENSKO S.R.O—See Eissmann Automotive Deutschland GmbH; *Int'l*, pg. 2336
EISSMANN COTESA GMBH—See Eissmann Automotive Deutschland GmbH; *Int'l*, pg. 2336
EISSMANN INDIVIDUAL GMBH—See Eissmann Automotive Deutschland GmbH; *Int'l*, pg. 2336
EISYS, INC.—See GEO Holdings Corporation; *Int'l*, pg. 2932
EISYS LTD.—See OTP Bank Plc; *Int'l*, pg. 5657
EISYS S.P.A.—See Thales S.A.; *Int'l*, pg. 7598
EITA ELECTRIC SDN. BHD.—See Eita Resources Berhad; *Int'l*, pg. 2336
EITA ELEVATOR (MALAYSIA) SDN. BHD.—See Eita Resources Berhad; *Int'l*, pg. 2336
EITA POWER SYSTEM SDN. BHD.—See Eita Resources Berhad; *Int'l*, pg. 2336
EITA RESEARCH & DEVELOPMENT SDN. BHD.—See Eita Resources Berhad; *Int'l*, pg. 2336
EITA RESOURCES BERHAD; *Int'l*, pg. 2336
EITA-SCHNEIDER (MFG) SDN. BHD.—See Eita Resources Berhad; *Int'l*, pg. 2336
EITA TECHNOLOGIES (MALAYSIA) SDN. BHD.—See Eita Resources Berhad; *Int'l*, pg. 2336
EITA TECHNOLOGIES PTE. LTD.—See Eita Resources Berhad; *Int'l*, pg. 2336
EITECH AB—See VINCI S.A.; *Int'l*, pg. 8217
EITECH ELECTRO AB—See VINCI S.A.; *Int'l*, pg. 8217
EI-TECHNOLOGIES FRANCE SAS—See Cognizant Technology Solutions Corporation; *U.S. Public*, pg. 524
EIT ENVIRONMENTAL DEVELOPMENT GROUP CO., LTD.; *Int'l*, pg. 2336
EITOPIA CO., LTD.—See Toray Industries, Inc.; *Int'l*, pg. 7823
EI TOWERS S.P.A.; *Int'l*, pg. 2328
EIT PROFESSIONALS CORP.; *U.S. Private*, pg. 1348
E-IT PROFESSIONALS INDIA PVT. LTD.—See eIT Professionals Corp.; *U.S. Private*, pg. 1348
EIT SPRENDIMAI UAB—See Atea ASA; *Int'l*, pg. 667
EIVA A/S—See Sonardyne International Ltd.; *Int'l*, pg. 7089
EIVA-SAFEX AS—See Mitsubishi Chemical Group Corporation; *Int'l*, pg. 4936
EIWA CHEMICAL IND. CO., LTD.—See Mitsubishi Gas Chemical Company, Inc.; *Int'l*, pg. 4948
EIWA CORPORATION; *Int'l*, pg. 2337
EIWA INTERNATIONAL INC.; *U.S. Private*, pg. 1348
EIWA METAL CO., LTD.—See Kanematsu Corporation; *Int'l*, pg. 4068
EIX DIAGONAL CONCESSIONARIA DE LA GENERALITAT DE CATALUNYA, S.A.—See ACS, Actividades de Construccion y Servicios, S.A.; *Int'l*, pg. 111
EIZEN CORPORATION CO., LTD.—See Wavelock Holdings Co., Ltd.; *Int'l*, pg. 8359
EIZO AUSTRIA GMBH—See EIZO Corporation; *Int'l*, pg. 2337
EIZO CORPORATION; *Int'l*, pg. 2337
EIZO DISPLAY TECHNOLOGIES (SUZHOU) CO., LTD.—See EIZO Corporation; *Int'l*, pg. 2337
EIZO ENGINEERING CORPORATION—See EIZO Corporation; *Int'l*, pg. 2337
EIZO EUROPE GMBH—See EIZO Corporation; *Int'l*, pg. 2337
EIZO GMBH—See EIZO Corporation; *Int'l*, pg. 2337
EIZO INC.—See EIZO Corporation; *Int'l*, pg. 2337
EIZO LIMITED—See EIZO Corporation; *Int'l*, pg. 2337
EIZO NANAO AG—See EIZO Corporation; *Int'l*, pg. 2337
EIZO NANAO MS CORPORATION—See EIZO Corporation; *Int'l*, pg. 2337
EIZO NORDIC AB—See EIZO Corporation; *Int'l*, pg. 2337
EIZO SUPPORT NETWORK CORPORATION—See EIZO Corporation; *Int'l*, pg. 2337
EIZO TECHNOLOGIES GMBH—See EIZO Corporation; *Int'l*, pg. 2337
EJ2 COMMUNICATIONS, INC.; *U.S. Private*, pg. 1348
EJ4, LLC—See Waud Capital Partners LLC; *U.S. Private*, pg. 4457
EJADA FOR FINANCIAL INVESTMENTS PLC; *Int'l*, pg. 2337
EJADAH ASSET MANAGEMENT GROUP L.L.C—See Dubai Holding LLC; *Int'l*, pg. 2218
E.J. BARTELLS CO.; *U.S. Private*, pg. 1305
E. J. BEAN & CO.—See James Fisher & Sons Public Limited Company; *Int'l*, pg. 3875
EJB PAVING & MATERIALS CO.—See New Enterprise Stone & Lime Co., Inc.; *U.S. Private*, pg. 2895
E.J. BRENEMAN, LP.; *U.S. Private*, pg. 1305
E.J. DEL MONTE CORP.; *U.S. Private*, pg. 1305
EJECTA MARKETING LTD.; *Int'l*, pg. 2337
EJECTT INC; *Int'l*, pg. 2337
EJE (HONG KONG) HOLDINGS LIMITED; *Int'l*, pg. 2337
EJ ELECTRIC INSTALLATION CO.; *U.S. Private*, pg. 1348
EJENDOMSAKTIESELSKABET AF 4. MARTS 1982—See Carlsberg A/S; *Int'l*, pg. 1340
EJENDOMSSELSKABET AF 1. JUNI 1986 A/S—See Sydbank A/S; *Int'l*, pg. 7377
EJESUR S.A.—See BNP Paribas SA; *Int'l*, pg. 1090
EJE TBWA—See Omnicom Group Inc.; *U.S. Public*, pg. 1598

EJF ACQUISITION CORP.; *U.S. Public*, pg. 721
EJF CAPITAL LLC; *U.S. Private*, pg. 1348
EJF INVESTMENTS LTD.; *Int'l*, pg. 2337
E. & J. GALLO WINERY; *U.S. Private*, pg. 1303
EJ GROUP, INC.; *U.S. Private*, pg. 1348
E.J. HARRISON & SONS INC.; *U.S. Private*, pg. 1306
E & J HEALTH CARE, LLC—See Centerbridge Partners, L.P.; *U.S. Private*, pg. 813
EJ HOLDINGS INC.; *Int'l*, pg. 2337
EJL ALSACE SAS—See VINCI S.A.; *Int'l*, pg. 8217
E&J LAWRENCE CORP.; *U.S. Private*, pg. 1301
EJL LORRAINE SAS—See VINCI S.A.; *Int'l*, pg. 8217
EJM DEVELOPMENT CO.; *U.S. Private*, pg. 1348
EJM ENGINEERING, INC.—See GI Manager L.P.; *U.S. Private*, pg. 1691
EJM PIPE SERVICES INC.; *U.S. Private*, pg. 1348
E. JORDAN BROOKES CO. INC.; *U.S. Private*, pg. 1304
EJOY AUSTRALIA PTY. LTD.—See Teco Electric & Machinery Co., Ltd.; *Int'l*, pg. 7517
E.J. POPE & SON. INC.—See Haymaker Acquisition Corp.; *U.S. Private*, pg. 1885
EJR ERICH JAEGER ROZNOV S.R.O.—See AdCapital AG; *Int'l*, pg. 126
EJ'S SHOES INC.; *U.S. Private*, pg. 1348
E.J. THOMAS COMPANY; *U.S. Private*, pg. 1306
E.J. VESTCO INDUSTRIES, LLC; *U.S. Private*, pg. 1306
E.J. VICTOR INC.; *U.S. Private*, pg. 1306
E.J. WELCH COMPANY INC.; *U.S. Private*, pg. 1306
EJWORKS CORPORATION—See PC DEPOT CORPORATION; *Int'l*, pg. 5765
EKACHAI MEDICAL CARE PCL; *Int'l*, pg. 2338
EKA CHEMICALS (AUSTRALIA) PTY LTD—See GIC Pte. Ltd.; *Int'l*, pg. 2968
EKA CHEMICALS (AUSTRALIA) PTY LTD—See The Carlyle Group Inc.; *U.S. Public*, pg. 2051
EKA CHEMICALS CANADA, INC.—See GIC Pte. Ltd.; *Int'l*, pg. 2968
EKA CHEMICALS CANADA, INC.—See The Carlyle Group Inc.; *U.S. Public*, pg. 2051
EKA CHEMICALS DO BRASIL S.A.—See GIC Pte. Ltd.; *Int'l*, pg. 2968
EKA CHEMICALS DO BRASIL S.A.—See The Carlyle Group Inc.; *U.S. Public*, pg. 2051
EKA CHEMICALS (GUANGZHOU) CO., LTD.—See GIC Pte. Ltd.; *Int'l*, pg. 2968
EKA CHEMICALS (GUANGZHOU) CO., LTD.—See The Carlyle Group Inc.; *U.S. Public*, pg. 2051
EKA D.O.O.—See Knorr-Bremse AG; *Int'l*, pg. 4210
EKA FOODSTUFF SDN. BHD.—See EKA Noodles Berhad; *Int'l*, pg. 2338
EKAHAU, INC.; *U.S. Private*, pg. 1348
EKAHAU OY—See Ziff Davis, Inc.; *U.S. Public*, pg. 2403
EKAM LEASING & FINANCE CO. LTD.; *Int'l*, pg. 2338
E-KANCELARIA GRUPA PRAWNO-FINANSOWA S.A.; *Int'l*, pg. 2248
EKA NOODLES BERHAD; *Int'l*, pg. 2338
EKANSH CONCEPTS LIMITED; *Int'l*, pg. 2338
EKARAT ENGINEERING PUBLIC COMPANY LIMITED; *Int'l*, pg. 2338
E-KART ELECTRONIC CARD SYSTEMS CO.—See Eczacibasi Holding A.S.; *Int'l*, pg. 2301
EKASER, S.A. DE C.V.—See ElringKlinger AG; *Int'l*, pg. 2369
EKATI DIAMOND MINE—See Burgundy Diamond Mines Limited; *Int'l*, pg. 1224
EKATO RUHR- UND MISCHTECHNIK GMBH; *Int'l*, pg. 2338
E.K. BAILEY CONSTRUCTION, INC.; *U.S. Private*, pg. 1306
EKB CONTAINER LOGISTIK GMBH & CO. KG—See CTS Spedition GmbH; *Int'l*, pg. 1874
EKB ELEKTRO UND KUNSTSTOFFTECHNIK GMBH—See Draexlmaier Gruppe; *Int'l*, pg. 2198
EKB GROEP B.V.—See Eiffage S.A.; *Int'l*, pg. 2329
EKB ZUID B.V.—See TKH Group N.V.; *Int'l*, pg. 7763
EK CHOR CHINA MOTORCYCLE CO., LTD.—See Charoen Pokphand Group Co., Ltd.; *Int'l*, pg. 1453
EKC INTERNATIONAL FZE—See Everest Kanto Cylinder Limited; *Int'l*, pg. 2564
EKC TECHNOLOGY, INC.—See DuPont de Nemours, Inc.; *U.S. Public*, pg. 693
EK DESIGN SERVICES, INC.—See Jacobs Engineering Group, Inc.; *U.S. Public*, pg. 1184
EKENNIS SOFTWARE SERVICE LTD.; *Int'l*, pg. 2338
E-KENT GECIS SISTEMLERI VE BILETLEME TEKNOLOJILERI A.S.—See Aktif Yatirim Bankasi A.S.; *Int'l*, pg. 267
EKF DIAGNOSTICS HOLDINGS PLC; *Int'l*, pg. 2338
EKF DIAGNOSTICS INC.—See EKF Diagnostics Holdings PLC; *Int'l*, pg. 2338
EK HEALTH SERVICES, INC.; *U.S. Private*, pg. 1348
EKI ENERGY SERVICES LIMITED; *Int'l*, pg. 2338
EKIMAE REAL ESTATE CO., LTD.—See Relo Group, Inc.; *Int'l*, pg. 6265
E. KINAST DISTRIBUTORS INC—See Richelieu Hardware Ltd.; *Int'l*, pg. 6331
EKINOPS BELGIUM NV—See Ekinops S.A.; *Int'l*, pg. 2338
EKINOPS CORPORATION—See Ekinops S.A.; *Int'l*, pg. 2338

EKINOPS ESPANA SRL.—See Ekinops S.A.; *Int'l*, pg. 2338
EKINOPS FRANCE SA—See Ekinops S.A.; *Int'l*, pg. 2338
EKINOPS INDIA PVT. LTD.—See Ekinops S.A.; *Int'l*, pg. 2338
EKINOPS ITALIA SRL.—See Ekinops S.A.; *Int'l*, pg. 2338
EKINOPS S.A.; *Int'l*, pg. 2338
EKIP-98 HOLDING AD; *Int'l*, pg. 2338
EKI POWER TRADING PRIVATE LIMITED—See EKI Energy Services Limited; *Int'l*, pg. 2338
EKI RETAIL SERVICE HANKYU HANSHIN CO., LTD.—See Hankyu Hanshin Holdings Inc.; *Int'l*, pg. 3255
EKISUI HOUSE REAL ESTATE CHUBU, LTD.—See Sekisui House, Ltd.; *Int'l*, pg. 6697
EKITAN & CO., LTD.; *Int'l*, pg. 2338
EKIZ KIMYA SANAYI VE TICARET A.S.; *Int'l*, pg. 2338
EKIZ YAG VE SABUN SANAYI A.S.; *Int'l*, pg. 2338
EKK EAGLE AMERICA INC.—See Eagle Industry Co., Ltd.; *Int'l*, pg. 2265
EKK EAGLE ASIA PACIFIC PTE. LTD.—See Eagle Industry Co., Ltd.; *Int'l*, pg. 2265
EKK EAGLE INDUSTRY ASIA-PACIFIC PTE. LTD.—See Eagle Industry Co., Ltd.; *Int'l*, pg. 2265
EKK EAGLE INDUSTRY MEXICO S.A. DE C.V.—See Eagle Industry Co., Ltd.; *Int'l*, pg. 2265
EKK EAGLE PRODUCTS INDIA PVT. LTD.—See Eagle Industry Co., Ltd.; *Int'l*, pg. 2265
EKK EAGLE (THAILAND) CO. LTD.—See Eagle Industry Co., Ltd.; *Int'l*, pg. 2265
EKK, INC.—See Eagle Industry Co., Ltd.; *Int'l*, pg. 2265
EKK SALES EUROPE B.V.—See Eagle Industry Co., Ltd.; *Int'l*, pg. 2265
EKLANDIA FASTIGHETS AB—See Castellum AB; *Int'l*, pg. 1356
E. KLINK A/S—See Per Aarsleff Holding A/S; *Int'l*, pg. 5795
EKLUNDS INC.; *U.S. Private*, pg. 1348
E.K. MACHINE CO., INC.; *U.S. Private*, pg. 1306
EKM GLOBAL LIMITED—See TD Synnex Corp; *U.S. Public*, pg. 1985
EK MITTELSTANDSFINANZIERUNGS AG—See Global Equity Partners Beteiligungs-Management AG; *Int'l*, pg. 2996
EKO ABEE—See HELLENiQ ENERGY Holdings S.A.; *Int'l*, pg. 3334
EKO BULGARIA EAD—See HELLENiQ ENERGY Holdings S.A.; *Int'l*, pg. 3334
EKOCORP PLC.; *Int'l*, pg. 2339
E KOCREF CR-REIT CO., LTD.; *Int'l*, pg. 2246
EKO ENERGETIKA DOO—See ERA d.o.o.; *Int'l*, pg. 2488
EKO EXPORT S.A.; *Int'l*, pg. 2338
EKO FAGEL FISK O MITTEMELLAN AB—See Sysco Corporation; *U.S. Public*, pg. 1973
EKO FAKTORING A.S.; *Int'l*, pg. 2339
EKOF FLOTATION GMBH—See KHD Humboldt Wedag International AG; *Int'l*, pg. 4154
EKO GEORGIA LTD—See HELLENiQ ENERGY Holdings S.A.; *Int'l*, pg. 3334
EKO HOLDING SA—See Eurocash S.A.; *Int'l*, pg. 2533
EKO INTERNATIONAL CORP.; *U.S. Public*, pg. 721
EKO-KOM, A.S.; *Int'l*, pg. 2339
EKOL LOJISTIK AS—See Abu Dhabi Investment Company; *Int'l*, pg. 72
EKOMAK ENDUSTRIYEL KOMPRESOR MAKINE SANAYIVETICARET A.S—See Atlas Copco AB; *Int'l*, pg. 682
EKOMI INC.; *U.S. Private*, pg. 1348
EKOMI, LTD.—See The Goldman Sachs Group, Inc.; *U.S. Public*, pg. 2081
EKONE OYSTER CO.—See Taylor United Inc.; *U.S. Private*, pg. 3940
EKONEX D.O.O.—See Nexe Grupa d.d.; *Int'l*, pg. 5243
EKONO HOMES LTD.—See Alam Group of Companies; *Int'l*, pg. 289
EKOPAK NV; *Int'l*, pg. 2339
EKOPARTNERIT TURKU OY—See Fortum Oyj; *Int'l*, pg. 2740
EKOPATH METROPOLIS LAB SERVICES PRIVATE LIMITED—See Metropolis Healthcare Ltd.; *Int'l*, pg. 4863
EKORNES ASA—See QuMei Home Furnishings Group Co., Ltd.; *Int'l*, pg. 6166
EKORNES ASIA PTE LTD—See QuMei Home Furnishings Group Co., Ltd.; *Int'l*, pg. 6166
EKORNES FETSUND AS—See QuMei Home Furnishings Group Co., Ltd.; *Int'l*, pg. 6166
EKORNES IBERICA SL—See QuMei Home Furnishings Group Co., Ltd.; *Int'l*, pg. 6166
EKORNES INC.—See QuMei Home Furnishings Group Co., Ltd.; *Int'l*, pg. 6166
EKORNES KK—See QuMei Home Furnishings Group Co., Ltd.; *Int'l*, pg. 6166
EKORNES LATIN AMERICA LTDA—See QuMei Home Furnishings Group Co., Ltd.; *Int'l*, pg. 6166
EKORNES LTD—See QuMei Home Furnishings Group Co., Ltd.; *Int'l*, pg. 6166
EKORNES MOEBELVERTRIEBS GMBH—See QuMei Home Furnishings Group Co., Ltd.; *Int'l*, pg. 6166

EKOPAK NV
CORPORATE AFFILIATIONS

EKORNES S.A.R.L.—See QuMei Home Furnishings Group Co., Ltd.; *Int'l*, pg. 6166
EKORNES SKANDINAVIA AS—See QuMei Home Furnishings Group Co., Ltd.; *Int'l*, pg. 6166
EKORNES SP. Z.O.O.—See QuMei Home Furnishings Group Co., Ltd.; *Int'l*, pg. 6166
EKOSEM-AGRAR GMBH; *Int'l*, pg. 2339
EKOSEM AGRARPROJEKTE GMBH—See Ekosem-Agrar GmbH; *Int'l*, pg. 2339
EKO SERBIA AD—See HELLENiQ ENERGY Holdings S.A.; *Int'l*, pg. 3334
EKOSTAV A.S; *Int'l*, pg. 2339
EKOTAB AD KOCHERINOVO; *Int'l*, pg. 2339
EKOTECHNIKA AG; *Int'l*, pg. 2339
EKOTON+ JSC; *Int'l*, pg. 2339
EKOTRANS BOGDANKA SP. Z.O.O.—See Lubelski Wegiel BOGDANKA Spolka Akcyjna; *Int'l*, pg. 4572
EKOTROPE INC.; *U.S. Private*, pg. 1348
EKOVENT AB—See Lindab International AB; *Int'l*, pg. 4503
EKOVEST BERHAD; *Int'l*, pg. 2339
EKO-WARK SP. Z.O.O.—See Kardan N.V.; *Int'l*, pg. 4079
EKOWOOD IBERICA SL—See TSH Resources Berhad; *Int'l*, pg. 7950
EKOWOOD INTERNATIONAL BERHAD—See TSH Resources Berhad; *Int'l*, pg. 7950
EKOWOOD MALAYSIA SDN. BHD.—See TSH Resources Berhad; *Int'l*, pg. 7950
EKOWOOD (USA) INC.—See TSH Resources Berhad; *Int'l*, pg. 7950
EKO YU AD—See HELLENiQ ENERGY Holdings S.A.; *Int'l*, pg. 3334
EKPO FUEL CELL TECHNOLOGIES GMBH—See ElringKlinger AG; *Int'l*, pg. 2369
EK POWER SOLUTIONS AB—See Addtech AB; *Int'l*, pg. 133
E.K. RILEY INVESTMENTS, LLC—See LPL Financial Holdings Inc.; *U.S. Public*, pg. 1343
EKS ASIA LTD.—See Eks France; *Int'l*, pg. 2339
EKSA SP. Z.O.O.—See Prysmian S.p.A.; *Int'l*, pg. 6010
EKS FRANCE; *Int'l*, pg. 2339
EKS GROUP LLC; *U.S. Private*, pg. 1348
EKS INTERNATIONAL SWEDEN AB—See Eks France; *Int'l*, pg. 2339
EKS INTERNATIONAL (UK) LTD.—See Eks France; *Int'l*, pg. 2339
EKSO BIONICS (EMEA)—See Ekso Bionics Holdings, Inc.; *U.S. Public*, pg. 722
EKSO BIONICS HOLDINGS, INC.; *U.S. Public*, pg. 722
EKSONS CORPORATION BERHAD; *Int'l*, pg. 2339
EKSPAN LIMITED—See RPM International Inc.; *U.S. Public*, pg. 1816
EKSPORTFINANS ASA; *Int'l*, pg. 2340
EKSPRES BANK AS—See BNP Paribas SA; *Int'l*, pg. 1090
EKSPRESS MEEDIA AS—See AS Ekspress Grupp; *Int'l*, pg. 590
EKSPRES YATIRIM MENKUL DEGERLER A.S.—See Net Holding A.S.; *Int'l*, pg. 5211
EK SUCCESS LTD.—See GTCR LLC; *U.S. Private*, pg. 1806
EKT ENERGIE UND KOMMUNAL-TECHNOLOGIE GMBH—See Stadtwerke Hannover AG; *Int'l*, pg. 7161
EKTER S.A.; *Int'l*, pg. 2340
EKTTITAB HOLDING COMPANY S.A.K.C.; *Int'l*, pg. 2340
EKUITI NASIONAL BERHAD; *Int'l*, pg. 2340
E.KUNDENSERVICE NETZ GMBH—See E.ON SE; *Int'l*, pg. 2260
E-KURASHI CO., LTD.—See Chubu Electric Power Co., Inc.; *Int'l*, pg. 1593
EKVE SDN BHD—See Ahmad Zaki Resources Berhad; *Int'l*, pg. 225
EKVIA S.R.O.—See Orkla ASA; *Int'l*, pg. 5637
EKWB D.O.O.; *Int'l*, pg. 2340
EKWIENOX LIMITED; *Int'l*, pg. 2340
ELAA FOR TRAVEL, TOURISM & SHIPPING LTD.—See Seera Group Holding Co.; *Int'l*, pg. 6679
ELABO GMBH—See Zech Group SE; *Int'l*, pg. 8628
ELABORADORA DE SUBPRODUTOS DE ORIGEM ANIMAL DO BRASIL LTDA.—See Danish Crown AmbA; *Int'l*, pg. 1965
ELAC SONAR GMBH—See Cohort plc; *Int'l*, pg. 1696
EL-AD GROUP, LTD.; *U.S. Private*, pg. 1349
ELAF ISLAMIC BANK; *Int'l*, pg. 2342
ELAGHMORE GP LLP; *Int'l*, pg. 2342
EL AGUILA, COMPANIA DE SEGUROS, S.A. DE C.V.—See American Financial Group, Inc.; *U.S. Public*, pg. 103
ELAH HOLDINGS, INC.; *U.S. Public*, pg. 722
ELAHI COTTON MILLS LIMITED; *Int'l*, pg. 2342
EL AHRAM FOR PACKING S.A.E.; *Int'l*, pg. 2340
ELAINE, INC.; *U.S. Private*, pg. 1349
ELAINE SECURITIES PLC; *Int'l*, pg. 2342
ELAIS UNILEVER HELLAS SA—See Unilever PLC; *Int'l*, pg. 8044
ELAJO ENGINEERING AB—See VINCI S.A.; *Int'l*, pg. 8217
EL AL AIRLINES LTD.; *Int'l*, pg. 2340
EL AL ISRAEL AIRLINES, LTD.—See El Al Airlines Ltd.; *Int'l*, pg. 2340

ELAM CONSTRUCTION, INC.—See Summit Materials, Inc.; *U.S. Public*, pg. 1960
ELAMEX, S.A. DE C.V.—See Accel, S.A.B. de C.V.; *Int'l*, pg. 79
ELAMOTORS TOYOTA TSUSHO (S.I.) LTD.—See Toyota Tsusho Corporation; *Int'l*, pg. 7876
ELANA AGRICULTURAL LAND FUND REIT; *Int'l*, pg. 2343
ELANA AGROCREDIT; *Int'l*, pg. 2343
ELAN A.D.; *Int'l*, pg. 2342
ELAN-AUSY GMBH—See Randstad N.V.; *Int'l*, pg. 6201
ELAN CHEMICAL COMPANY INC.; *U.S. Private*, pg. 1349
ELANCO AH PORTUGAL, UNIPESSOAL LDA—See Elanco Animal Health Incorporated; *U.S. Public*, pg. 722
ELANCO ANIMAL HEALTH INCORPORATED; *U.S. Public*, pg. 722
ELANCO ANIMAL HEALTH, KOREA, LTD.—See Elanco Animal Health Incorporated; *U.S. Public*, pg. 722
ELANCO ANIMAL HEALTH UK LIMITED—See Eli Lilly & Company; *U.S. Public*, pg. 731
ELANCO ARGENTINA S.R.L.—See Elanco Animal Health Incorporated; *U.S. Public*, pg. 722
ELANCO - AUGUSTA TECHNOLOGY CENTER—See Elanco Animal Health Incorporated; *U.S. Public*, pg. 722
ELANCO AUSTRALASIA PTY. LTD.—See Eli Lilly & Company; *U.S. Public*, pg. 731
ELANCO BELGIUM BVBA—See Elanco Animal Health Incorporated; *U.S. Public*, pg. 722
ELANCO CANADA LIMITED—See Eli Lilly & Company; *U.S. Public*, pg. 731
ELANCO CENTRE DE RECHERCHE SANTE ANIMALE SA—See Novartis AG; *Int'l*, pg. 5457
ELANCO CHILE SPA—See Elanco Animal Health Incorporated; *U.S. Public*, pg. 722
ELANCO COLOMBIA S.A.S.—See Elanco Animal Health Incorporated; *U.S. Public*, pg. 722
ELANCO DENMARK APS—See Elanco Animal Health Incorporated; *U.S. Public*, pg. 722
ELANCO DEUTSCHLAND GMBH—See Eli Lilly & Company; *U.S. Public*, pg. 731
ELANCO FRANCE S.A.S.—See Eli Lilly & Company; *U.S. Public*, pg. 731
ELANCO GESELLSCHAFT M.B.H.—See Elanco Animal Health Incorporated; *U.S. Public*, pg. 722
ELANCO HAYVAN SAGLIGI LIMITED SIRKETI—See Elanco Animal Health Incorporated; *U.S. Public*, pg. 722
ELANCO HUNGARY KFT.—See Elanco Animal Health Incorporated; *U.S. Public*, pg. 722
ELANCO INDIA PRIVATE LIMITED—See Eli Lilly & Company; *U.S. Public*, pg. 731
ELANCO ITALIA S.P.A.—See Eli Lilly & Company; *U.S. Public*, pg. 731
ELANCO MALAYSIA SDN. BHD.—See Elanco Animal Health Incorporated; *U.S. Public*, pg. 722
ELANCO NEDERLAND B.V.—See Eli Lilly & Company; *U.S. Public*, pg. 731
ELANCO NEW ZEALAND—See Elanco Animal Health Incorporated; *U.S. Public*, pg. 722
ELAN CONSTRUCTION LIMITED; *Int'l*, pg. 2342
ELANCO PHILIPPINES INC.—See Elanco Animal Health Incorporated; *U.S. Public*, pg. 723
ELANCO PRODUCTS LIMITED—See Elanco Animal Health Incorporated; *U.S. Public*, pg. 723
ELAN CORPORATION—See Sony Group Corporation; *Int'l*, pg. 7102
ELANCO SALUD ANIMAL SA DE CV—See Eli Lilly & Company; *U.S. Public*, pg. 731
ELANCO SAUDE ANIMAL LTDA.—See Eli Lilly & Company; *U.S. Public*, pg. 731
ELANCO (SHANGHAI) ANIMAL HEALTH CO., LTD.—See Eli Lilly & Company; *U.S. Public*, pg. 731
ELANCO S.R.L.—See Elanco Animal Health Incorporated; *U.S. Public*, pg. 723
ELANCO (TAIWAN) ANIMAL HEALTH CO. LTD.—See Eli Lilly & Company; *U.S. Public*, pg. 731
ELANCO (THAILAND) LTD.—See Eli Lilly & Company; *U.S. Public*, pg. 731
ELANCO TIERGESUNDHEIT AG—See Eli Lilly & Company; *U.S. Public*, pg. 731
ELANCO UK AH LIMITED—See Eli Lilly & Company; *U.S. Public*, pg. 731
ELANCO US, INC.—See Eli Lilly & Company; *U.S. Public*, pg. 731
ELANCO VALQUIMICA S.A.—See Elanco Animal Health Incorporated; *U.S. Public*, pg. 723
ELANCO VIETNAM COMPANY LIMITED—See Elanco Animal Health Incorporated; *U.S. Public*, pg. 723
E-LAND APPAREL LTD; *Int'l*, pg. 2248
E-LAND CO., LTD.—See Shanghai Newtouch Software Co., Ltd.; *Int'l*, pg. 6776
ELAND ENERGY INC.; *U.S. Private*, pg. 1350
ELAND ENGINEERING, INC.—See Comvest Group Holdings LLC; *U.S. Private*, pg. 1007
ELANDERS AB—See Carl Bennet AB; *Int'l*, pg. 1331
ELANDERS (BEIJING) PRINTING COMPANY LTD—See Carl Bennet AB; *Int'l*, pg. 1331

ELANDERS DIGITALTRYCK AB—See Carl Bennet AB; *Int'l*, pg. 1331
ELANDERS GUMMESSONS AB—See Carl Bennet AB; *Int'l*, pg. 1331
ELANDERS HINDSON LTD.—See Carl Bennet AB; *Int'l*, pg. 1331
ELANDERS HUNGARY KFT—See Carl Bennet AB; *Int'l*, pg. 1331
ELANDERS ITALY S.R.L—See Carl Bennet AB; *Int'l*, pg. 1331
ELANDERS LTD—See Carl Bennet AB; *Int'l*, pg. 1331
ELANDERS NOVUM AB, STOCKHOLM—See Carl Bennet AB; *Int'l*, pg. 1331
ELANDERS POLSKA SP. Z.O.O.—See Carl Bennet AB; *Int'l*, pg. 1331
ELANDERS REPRODUCAO DE IMAGENS LTDA—See Carl Bennet AB; *Int'l*, pg. 1331
ELANDERS—See Carl Bennet AB; *Int'l*, pg. 1331
ELANDERS STOCKHOLM—See Carl Bennet AB; *Int'l*, pg. 1331
ELANDERS SVENSKT TRYCK AB—See Carl Bennet AB; *Int'l*, pg. 1331
ELANDERS SVERIGE AB—See Carl Bennet AB; *Int'l*, pg. 1331
ELANDERS UK LTD.—See Carl Bennet AB; *Int'l*, pg. 1331
ELANDERSUSA, LLC—See Carl Bennet AB; *Int'l*, pg. 1331
E-LAND FASHION CHINA HOLDINGS, LIMITED—See E-Land World Ltd.; *Int'l*, pg. 2248
E-LAND INTERNATIONAL FASHION (SHANGHAI) CO., LTD.—See E-Land World Ltd.; *Int'l*, pg. 2248
ELAND OIL & GAS (NIGERIA) LIMITED—See Seplat Energy Plc; *Int'l*, pg. 6718
ELAND OIL & GAS PLC—See Seplat Energy Plc; *Int'l*, pg. 6718
E-LAND WORLD LTD.; *Int'l*, pg. 2248
ELANGO INDUSTRIES LIMITED; *Int'l*, pg. 2343
ELAN GROUP INC.—See Principal Financial Group, Inc.; *U.S. Public*, pg. 1721
ELAN GROUP LTD.—See ManpowerGroup Inc.; *U.S. Public*, pg. 1357
ELAN GROWTH PARTNERS, LLC; *U.S. Private*, pg. 1349
ELAN (H.K.) MICROELECTRONIC CORP.—See ELAN Microelectronic Corp.; *Int'l*, pg. 2342
ELAN (H.K.) MICROELECTRONICS CORP.—See ELAN Microelectronic Corp.; *Int'l*, pg. 2342
ELAN INCORPORATED FZE—See Time Technoplast Limited; *Int'l*, pg. 7751
ELAN INDUSTRIES—See Etam Developpement SCA; *Int'l*, pg. 2520
ELAN INFORMATION TECHNOLOGY GROUP.—See ELAN Microelectronic Corp.; *Int'l*, pg. 2342
ELAN IT RESOURCE A/S—See ManpowerGroup Inc.; *U.S. Public*, pg. 1357
ELAN I.T. RESOURCE SAS—See ManpowerGroup Inc.; *U.S. Public*, pg. 1357
ELAN IT SERVICES GMBH—See ManpowerGroup Inc.; *U.S. Public*, pg. 1357
ELANIX BIOTECHNOLOGIES AG; *Int'l*, pg. 2343
ELAN MARKETING, INC.—See Xerox Holdings Corporation; *U.S. Public*, pg. 2387
ELAN MICROELECTRONIC CORP SHANGHAI LTD.—See ELAN Microelectronic Corp.; *Int'l*, pg. 2342
ELAN MICROELECTRONIC CORP.; *Int'l*, pg. 2342
ELAN MICROELECTRONICS (SHANGHAI) CO., LTD.—See ELAN Microelectronic Corp.; *Int'l*, pg. 2342
ELAN MICROELECTRONICS (SHENZHEN) CO., LTD.—See ELAN Microelectronic Corp.; *Int'l*, pg. 2342
ELANOR INVESTORS GROUP; *Int'l*, pg. 2343
ELANOR RETAIL PROPERTY FUND; *Int'l*, pg. 2343
ELAN PARTNERS; *U.S. Private*, pg. 1350
ELAN PHARMA INTERNATIONAL LIMITED—See Perrigo Company plc; *Int'l*, pg. 5812
ELAN-POLO INC.; *U.S. Private*, pg. 1350
ELANTAS BECK GMBH—See SKion GmbH; *Int'l*, pg. 6987
ELANTAS BECK INDIA LTD.—See SKion GmbH; *Int'l*, pg. 6987
ELANTAS DEATECH S.R.L.—See SKion GmbH; *Int'l*, pg. 6987
ELANTAS EUROPE GMBH—See SKion GmbH; *Int'l*, pg. 6989
ELANTAS EUROPE SRL.—See SKion GmbH; *Int'l*, pg. 6989
ELANTAS GMBH—See SKion GmbH; *Int'l*, pg. 6987
ELANTAS ISOLANTES ELETRICOS DO BRASIL LTDA.—See SKion GmbH; *Int'l*, pg. 6987
ELANTAS ITALIA S.R.L.—See SKion GmbH; *Int'l*, pg. 6987
ELANTAS MALAYSIA SDN. BHD.—See SKion GmbH; *Int'l*, pg. 6989
ELANTAS PDG, INC.—See SKion GmbH; *Int'l*, pg. 6987
ELANTAS (TONGLING) CO. LTD.—See SKion GmbH; *Int'l*, pg. 6987
ELANTAS (ZHUHAI) CO. LTD.—See SKion GmbH; *Int'l*, pg. 6987
ELANTIS PREMIUM FUNDING (NZ) LIMITED—See Arthur J. Gallagher & Co.; *U.S. Public*, pg. 203
ELARA INVESTMENTS SP. Z.O.O.—See CPD S.A.; *Int'l*, pg. 1824
ELARA LEITSTELLENTECHNIK GMBH—See Frequentis AG; *Int'l*, pg. 2773

COMPANY NAME INDEX

ELARDUSPARK SHOPPING CENTRE (PTY) LIMITED—See Octodec Investments Limited; *Int'l*, pg. 5523
ELARG AGRICULTURAL LAND OPPORTUNITY FUND REIT; *Int'l*, pg. 2343
ELAS GEOTECNICA SRL—See Societa Esercizi Commerciali Industriali; *Int'l*, pg. 7034
ELASIS-SOCIETA CONSORTILE PER AZIONI—See Stellantis N.V.; *Int'l*, pg. 7198
ELAS NV—See Haco N.V.; *Int'l*, pg. 3204
ELASTEC/AMERICAN MARINE, INC.; *U.S. Private*, pg. 1350
ELASTEC S.R.L—See Merck & Co., Inc.; *U.S. Public*, pg. 1416
ELASTICBOX INC.—See Lumen Technologies, Inc.; *U.S. Public*, pg. 1346
ELASTIC N.V.; *U.S. Public*, pg. 723
ELASTICSEARCH (BEIJING) INFORMATION TECHNOLOGY CO., LTD.—See Elastic N.V.; *U.S. Public*, pg. 723
ELASTICSEARCH B.V.—See Elastic N.V.; *U.S. Public*, pg. 723
ELASTICSEARCH KK—See Elastic N.V.; *U.S. Public*, pg. 723
ELASTICSEARCH KOREA LIMITED—See Elastic N.V.; *U.S. Public*, pg. 723
ELASTICSEARCH PTY. LTD.—See Elastic N.V.; *U.S. Public*, pg. 723
ELASTIC STOP NUT CORPORATION OF AMERICA—See KKR & Co. Inc.; *U.S. Public*, pg. 1262
ELASTIC THERAPY, LLC—See Enovis Corporation; *U.S. Public*, pg. 772
ELASTIKA PIRELLI C.S.A.—See China National Chemical Corporation; *Int'l*, pg. 1528
ELASTOGRAN FRANCE S.A.S—See BASF SE; *Int'l*, pg. 883
ELASTOGRAN GMBH—See BASF SE; *Int'l*, pg. 883
ELASTOGRAN INNOVATIONSPROJEKTE BETEILIGUNGSGESELLSCHAFT MBH—See BASF SE; *Int'l*, pg. 883
ELASTOGRAN ITALIA S.P.A—See BASF SE; *Int'l*, pg. 883
ELASTOGRAN LAGOMAT NORDIC AB—See BASF SE; *Int'l*, pg. 883
ELASTOGRAN UK LIMITED—See BASF SE; *Int'l*, pg. 883
ELASTOMERIC ENGINEERING CO. LTD.—See HEXPOL AB; *Int'l*, pg. 3372
ELASTOMEROS DE CANTABRIA S.A.—See Trelleborg AB; *Int'l*, pg. 7911
ELASTOMEROS TECNICOS MOLDEADOS, INC.—See Park-Ohio Holdings Corp.; *U.S. Public*, pg. 1639
ELASTOMEROS TECNICOS MOLDEADOS, S. DE R. L. DE C.V.—See Park-Ohio Holdings Corp.; *U.S. Public*, pg. 1638
ELASTOMER SOLUTIONS GMBH—See Mutares SE & Co. KGaA; *Int'l*, pg. 5104
ELASTOMER SOLUTIONS MAROC S.A.R.L—See Mutares SE & Co. KGaA; *Int'l*, pg. 5104
ELASTOMER SOLUTIONS MEXICO S. DE R.L. DE C.V.—See Mutares SE & Co. KGaA; *Int'l*, pg. 5104
ELASTOMER SOLUTIONS S.R.O.—See Mutares SE & Co. KGaA; *Int'l*, pg. 5104
ELASTOMIX CO., LTD.—See JSR Corp.; *Int'l*, pg. 4013
ELASTOMIX (FOSHAN) CO., LTD.—See JSR Corp.; *Int'l*, pg. 4013
ELASTOMIX MEXICO, S.A. DE C.V.—See JSR Corp.; *Int'l*, pg. 4013
ELASTOMIX (THAILAND) CO., LTD.—See JSR Corp.; *Int'l*, pg. 4013
ELASTO S.A.—See General Motors Company; *U.S. Public*, pg. 924
ELASTO VALVE RUBBER PRODUCTS INC.—See Devjo Industries, Inc.; *Int'l*, pg. 2089
ELASTRAK S.A.—See ELTRAK S.A.; *Int'l*, pg. 2371
ELASTRON S.A.; *Int'l*, pg. 2343
ELATE GROUP, INC.; *U.S. Private*, pg. 1350
ELATE HOLDINGS LIMITED; *Int'l*, pg. 2343
ELATERAL, INC.—See Elateral Ltd.; *Int'l*, pg. 2343
ELATERAL LTD.; *Int'l*, pg. 2343
ELAU SARL—See Schneider Electric SE; *Int'l*, pg. 6626
ELAUT GERMANY GMBH—See Elaut International N.V.; *Int'l*, pg. 2343
ELAUT INTERNATIONAL N.V.; *Int'l*, pg. 2343
ELAUT N.V.—See Elaut International N.V.; *Int'l*, pg. 2343
ELAUT SPAIN SL—See Elaut International N.V.; *Int'l*, pg. 2343
ELAUT USA, INC.—See Elaut International N.V.; *Int'l*, pg. 2343
ELAUWIT LLC; *U.S. Private*, pg. 1350
ELAVON CANADA COMPANY—See U.S. Bancorp; *U.S. Public*, pg. 2212
ELAVON EUROPEAN HOLDINGS B.V.—See U.S. Bancorp; *U.S. Public*, pg. 2212
ELAVON EUROPEAN HOLDINGS C.V.—See U.S. Bancorp; *U.S. Public*, pg. 2212
ELAVON FINANCIAL SERVICES DAC—See U.S. Bancorp; *U.S. Public*, pg. 2212
ELAVON, INC.—See U.S. Bancorp; *U.S. Public*, pg. 2212
ELAYAWAY, INC.; *U.S. Private*, pg. 1350

ELBA HR INSAN KAYNAKLARI EGITIM VE DANISMANLIK A.S.—See Logo Yazilim Sanayi ve Ticaret A.S.; *Int'l*, pg. 4543
ELBAR INDUSTRIAL LIMITED; *Int'l*, pg. 2344
E&L BATTERY & IGNITION CO.—See Hahn Automotive Warehouse, Inc.; *U.S. Private*, pg. 1840
ELB CAPITAL INVESTMENTS (PTY) LIMITED—See ELB Group Limited; *Int'l*, pg. 2343
ELBE-CESCO INC.—See The Union Group; *U.S. Private*, pg. 4129
ELBECO INCORPORATED—See Lakeland Industries, Inc.; *U.S. Public*, pg. 1288
ELBE-FLUGZEUGWERKE GMBH—See Temasek Holdings (Private) Limited; *Int'l*, pg. 7552
ELBE HOLDING GMBH & CO. KG—See Brd. Klee A/S; *Int'l*, pg. 1143
ELBEKIES GMBH—See VINCI S.A.; *Int'l*, pg. 8219
ELBE LEADING TECHNOLOGY SOLUTIONS LTD.—See Quaser Machine Tools, Inc.; *Int'l*, pg. 6156
ELBENERGIE GMBH—See E.ON SE; *Int'l*, pg. 2257
ELB ENGINEERING SERVICES (PTY) LIMITED—See ELB Group Limited; *Int'l*, pg. 2343
ELBE NORMARK AS—See Rapala VMC Oyj; *Int'l*, pg. 6209
ELB EQUIPMENT HOLDINGS LIMITED—See ELB Group Limited; *Int'l*, pg. 2343
ELB EQUIPMENT LIMITED - CONSTRUCTION EQUIPMENT DIVISION—See ELB Group Limited; *Int'l*, pg. 2343
ELB EQUIPMENT LIMITED - EARTHMOVING EQUIPMENT DIVISION—See ELB Group Limited; *Int'l*, pg. 2343
ELB EQUIPMENT LIMITED - MINING & QUARRYING EQUIPMENT DIVISION—See ELB Group Limited; *Int'l*, pg. 2343
ELB EQUIPMENT LIMITED—See ELB Group Limited; *Int'l*, pg. 2343
ELBE RIJN LLOYD B.V.—See OT Logistics S.A.; *Int'l*, pg. 5656
ELBERTA CRATE & BOX CO.; *U.S. Private*, pg. 1350
ELBERTON DIALYSIS FACILITY, INC.—See DaVita Inc.; *U.S. Public*, pg. 638
ELBERTON MANUFACTURING COMPANY INCORPORATED; *U.S. Private*, pg. 1350
ELBEST SECURITY SP. Z O.O.—See PGE Polska Grupa Energetyczna S.A.; *Int'l*, pg. 5837
ELBEST SP. Z O.O.—See PGE Polska Grupa Energetyczna S.A.; *Int'l*, pg. 5837
ELB GROUP LIMITED; *Int'l*, pg. 2343
ELBI OF AMERICA INC—See Elbi S.P.A.; *Int'l*, pg. 2344
ELBISCO HOLDING S.A.; *Int'l*, pg. 2344
ELBISCO INDUSTRIAL & COMMERCIAL S.A.—See Elbisco Holding S.A.; *Int'l*, pg. 2344
ELBI S.P.A.; *Int'l*, pg. 2344
ELBIS SP. Z O.O.—See Elektrownia Belchatow S.A.; *Int'l*, pg. 2357
ELBIT IMAGING LTD.; *Int'l*, pg. 2344
ELBIT MEDICAL TECHNOLOGIES LTD.; *Int'l*, pg. 2344
ELBIT SECURITY SYSTEMS LTD.—See Elbit Systems Limited; *Int'l*, pg. 2344
ELBIT SYSTEMS CYCLONE LTD.—See Elbit Systems Limited; *Int'l*, pg. 2344
ELBIT SYSTEMS ELECTRO-OPTICS ELOP LTD.—See Elbit Systems Limited; *Int'l*, pg. 2344
ELBIT SYSTEMS EW AND SIGINT - ELISRA LTD—See Elbit Systems Limited; *Int'l*, pg. 2344
ELBIT SYSTEMS LAND AND C4I LTD.—See Elbit Systems Limited; *Int'l*, pg. 2344
ELBIT SYSTEMS LIMITED; *Int'l*, pg. 2344
ELBIT SYSTEMS OF AMERICA, LLC—See Elbit Systems Limited; *Int'l*, pg. 2344
ELBIT SYSTEMS OF AUSTRALIA PTY LTD.—See Elbit Systems Limited; *Int'l*, pg. 2345
ELBKIND REPLY GMBH—See Reply S.p.A.; *Int'l*, pg. 6291
ELBKLASSIK KONZERTE GMBH—See DEAG Deutsche Entertainment AG; *Int'l*, pg. 1998
ELBOW RIVER MARKETING LTD.—See Parkland Corporation; *Int'l*, pg. 5743
ELB POWER SYSTEMS LIMITED—See ELB Group Limited; *Int'l*, pg. 2343
ELBRIDGE INVESTMENTS (CYPRUS) LTD.; *Int'l*, pg. 2345
ELBROMPLAST S.A.—See Plastiques du Val de Loire S.A.; *Int'l*, pg. 5892
ELBROOK CASH & CARRY LTD.; *Int'l*, pg. 2345
ELBTAL PLASTICS GMBH & CO. KG—See KAP Beteiligungs-AG; *Int'l*, pg. 4076
ELBTAL TIEFKUHLKOST VERTRIEBS GMBH—See FRoSTA AG; *Int'l*, pg. 2797
EL BURRITO MEXICAN FOOD PRODUCTS CORP.—See House Foods Group Inc.; *Int'l*, pg. 3490
ELCA HOLDING SA; *Int'l*, pg. 2345
ELCA INFORMATION TECHNOLOGY LTD.—See ELCA Holding SA; *Int'l*, pg. 2345
EL CAJON FORD; *U.S. Private*, pg. 1348
EL CAMINO RESOURCES LLC; *U.S. Private*, pg. 1348
EL CAMINO TRAILWAYS; *U.S. Private*, pg. 1348
EL CAPITAN PRECIOUS METALS INC.; *U.S. Public*, pg. 722

ELC TECHNOLOGIES

ELCAR FENCE & SUPPLY CO.; *U.S. Private*, pg. 1350
ELCA TECHNOLOGIES S.R.L.—See Cefla S.C.; *Int'l*, pg. 1390
ELCAT INC.; *U.S. Private*, pg. 1350
ELC GROUP CONSULTING AND ENGINEERING INC.—See Koninklijke HaskoningDHV Groep B.V.; *Int'l*, pg. 4266
ELCH GMBH—See Henkel AG & Co. KGaA; *Int'l*, pg. 3348
EL CHICO RESTAURANTS, INC.—See Cracken, Harkey & Co., LLC; *U.S. Private*, pg. 1081
ELCID INVESTMENTS LIMITED; *Int'l*, pg. 2345
EL CID LAND & CATTLE INC.—See Allsup Enterprises Inc.; *U.S. Private*, pg. 194
EL CLASIFICADO; *U.S. Private*, pg. 1348
ELC MANAGEMENT LLC—See The Estee Lauder Companies Inc.; *U.S. Public*, pg. 2073
ELCO AUSTRIA GMBH—See Ariston Holding N.V.; *Int'l*, pg. 567
ELCO BURNERS B.V.—See Ariston Holding N.V.; *Int'l*, pg. 567
ELCO BURNERS GMBH—See Ariston Holding N.V.; *Int'l*, pg. 567
EL-CO CERAM INC.—See S.C. EL-CO S.A.; *Int'l*, pg. 6451
ELCO CONTRACTING & SERVICES (1973) LTD.—See Elco Limited; *Int'l*, pg. 2345
THE ELCO CORP.—See Bain Capital, LP; *U.S. Private*, pg. 441
ELCO DE COLOMBIA SAS—See Regal Rexnord Corporation; *U.S. Public*, pg. 1773
ELCO DIRECT LIMITED—See Bremworth Limited; *Int'l*, pg. 1145
ELCO DO BRAZIL LTDA.—See Regal Rexnord Corporation; *U.S. Public*, pg. 1773
EL-CO D.O.O.—See S.C. EL-CO S.A.; *Int'l*, pg. 6451
ELCO E-TRADE SRL—See Regal Rexnord Corporation; *U.S. Public*, pg. 1773
ELCO EUROPE GMBH—See KYOCERA Corporation; *Int'l*, pg. 4355
ELCOFLEX (SUZHOU) CO., LTD.—See Career Technology (MFG.) Co., Ltd.; *Int'l*, pg. 1323
ELCOGRAF S.P.A.—See Pozzoni S.p.A.; *Int'l*, pg. 5949
ELCO HEATING SOLUTIONS LIMITED—See Ariston Holding N.V.; *Int'l*, pg. 567
ELCO HOLLAND B.V.—See Elco Limited; *Int'l*, pg. 2345
ELCO INC.; *U.S. Private*, pg. 1350
ELCO LABORATORIES INC.; *U.S. Private*, pg. 1350
ELCO LANDMARK RESIDENTIAL HOLDINGS LLC—See Elco Limited; *Int'l*, pg. 2345
ELCO LEASING LIMITED—See Commerzbank AG; *Int'l*, pg. 1718
ELCO LIMITED; *Int'l*, pg. 2345
ELCOME INTERNATIONAL LLC—See Daeyang Electric Co., Ltd.; *Int'l*, pg. 1911
EL COMERCIO, S.A.—See Vocento, S.A.; *Int'l*, pg. 8284
ELCOM INC.—See Yazaki Corporation; *Int'l*, pg. 8572
ELCOM INC.; *U.S. Private*, pg. 1350
ELCOM INTERNATIONAL, INC.; *U.S. Private*, pg. 1350
ELCOMMUNICATION SWEDEN AB—See Storskogen Group AB; *Int'l*, pg. 7227
ELCO MOTORS ASIA PTE LIMITED—See Regal Rexnord Corporation; *U.S. Public*, pg. 1773
ELCOM PLUS JSC—See ELCOM Technology Communications Corporation; *Int'l*, pg. 2345
ELCOMTEC CO., LTD; *Int'l*, pg. 2345
ELCOM TECHNOLOGY COMMUNICATIONS CORPORATION; *Int'l*, pg. 2345
ELCOM TECHNOLOGY PTY LTD; *Int'l*, pg. 2345
ELCON CORPORATION; *U.S. Private*, pg. 1350
ELCON INC.; *U.S. Private*, pg. 1350
EL CONQUISTADOR MAH II LLC—See MetLife, Inc.; *U.S. Public*, pg. 1430
EL CONQUISTADOR RESORT—See Blackstone Inc.; *U.S. Public*, pg. 351
EL COQUI LANDFILL COMPANY, INC.—See Waste Management, Inc.; *U.S. Public*, pg. 2331
ELCORA ADVANCED MATERIALS CORP.; *Int'l*, pg. 2346
ELCOR INC.—See Mueller Electric Company; *U.S. Private*, pg. 2810
EL CORREO DIGITAL, S.L.—See Vocento, S.A.; *Int'l*, pg. 8284
EL CORTE INGLES LIFE, PENSIONS AND INSURANCE, S.A.—See El Corte Ingles, S.A.; *Int'l*, pg. 2340
EL CORTE INGLES, S.A. COMPUTERS—See El Corte Ingles, S.A.; *Int'l*, pg. 2340
EL CORTE INGLES, S.A.; *Int'l*, pg. 2340
ELCO SP. Z O.O.—See Immofinanz AG; *Int'l*, pg. 3628
ELCOT CAPITAL MANAGEMENT LIMITED; *Int'l*, pg. 2346
ELCOTHERMA FINLAND OY AB—See Schneider Electric SE; *Int'l*, pg. 6627
ELCOTHERM AG—See Ariston Thermo S.p.A.; *Int'l*, pg. 567
EL COTO DE RIOJA S.A.—See Baron de Ley, S.A.; *Int'l*, pg. 867
ELCO USA, INC.—See KYOCERA Corporation; *Int'l*, pg. 4359
ELC TECHNOLOGIES; *U.S. Private*, pg. 1350

839

ELDA ELTRA S.A.—See Schneider Electric SE; *Int'l*, pg. 6626
ELDAN ELECTRONIC CO. LTD.; *Int'l*, pg. 2346
ELDAN TRANSPORTATION LTD.; *Int'l*, pg. 2346
ELDAV INVESTMENT LTD.; *Int'l*, pg. 2346
ELDEC CORPORATION—See Crane NXT, Co.; *U.S. Public*, pg. 589
ELDEC ELECTRONICS LTD.—See Crane NXT, Co.; *U.S. Public*, pg. 591
ELDEC FRANCE S.A.R.L.—See Crane NXT, Co.; *U.S. Public*, pg. 589
ELDECO HOUSING & INDUSTRIES LTD; *Int'l*, pg. 2346
ELDECO, INC.—See Comfort Systems USA, Inc.; *U.S. Public*, pg. 544
EL-DELTA COMPANY—See Chemical Industries Holding Company; *Int'l*, pg. 1461
ELDER AUTO, INC.—See Elder Automotive Group; *U.S. Private*, pg. 1350
ELDER AUTOMOTIVE GROUP OF TAMPA BAY, INC.—See Elder Automotive Group; *U.S. Private*, pg. 1350
ELDER AUTOMOTIVE GROUP; *U.S. Private*, pg. 1350
THE ELDER-BEERMAN STORES CORP.—See The Bon Ton Stores, Inc.; *U.S. Public*, pg. 2041
ELDER FORD OF TAMPA, LLC—See Elder Automotive Group; *U.S. Private*, pg. 1350
ELDER HOME OPTIONS, L.L.C.—See Amedisys, Inc.; *U.S. Public*, pg. 93
ELDERHOSTEL, INC.; *U.S. Private*, pg. 1351
ELDER-JONES, INC.; *U.S. Private*, pg. 1351
ELDERLEE, INC.—See REH Holdings Inc.; *U.S. Private*, pg. 3389
ELDER MANUFACTURING COMPANY, INC.; *U.S. Private*, pg. 1351
ELDER PHARMACEUTICALS LTD.; *Int'l*, pg. 2346
ELDER PROJECTS LIMITED; *Int'l*, pg. 2346
ELDER RESEARCH INC.; *U.S. Private*, pg. 1351
ELDER SALES & SERVICE INC.; *U.S. Private*, pg. 1351
ELDERSERVE, INC.; *U.S. Private*, pg. 1351
ELDER SERVICES OF CAPE COD & THE ISLANDS, INC.; *U.S. Private*, pg. 1351
ELDERS FINE FOODS (SHANGHAI) COMPANY—See Elders Limited; *Int'l*, pg. 2346
ELDERS INSURANCE (UNDERWRITING AGENCY) PTY LIMITED—See QBE Insurance Group Limited; *Int'l*, pg. 6136
ELDERS LIMITED; *Int'l*, pg. 2346
ELDERSOURCE; *U.S. Private*, pg. 1351
ELDERS REAL ESTATE (QLD) PTY. LTD.—See Elders Limited; *Int'l*, pg. 2346
ELDERS REAL ESTATE (TASMANIA) PTY. LTD.—See Elders Limited; *Int'l*, pg. 2346
ELDERS REAL ESTATE (WA) PTY. LTD.—See Elders Limited; *Int'l*, pg. 2346
ELDERS RURAL SERVICES AUSTRALIA LIMITED—See Elders Limited; *Int'l*, pg. 2346
ELDERS RURAL SERVICES LIMITED—See Elders Limited; *Int'l*, pg. 2346
ELDERSTREET INVESTMENTS LTD.; *Int'l*, pg. 2346
ELDERWOOD ADMINISTRATIVE SERVICES, LLC—See Post Acute Partners, LLC; *U.S. Private*, pg. 3234
ELDERWOOD AT TONAWANDA—See Post Acute Partners, LLC; *U.S. Private*, pg. 3234
ELDFELL INVESTMENTS LIMITED—See Barclays PLC; *Int'l*, pg. 862
ELDIAR FURNITURE MANUFACTURING AND DECORATION L.L.C.—See Depa PLC; *Int'l*, pg. 2041
EL DIARIO LA PRENSA—See S.A. La Nacion; *Int'l*, pg. 6448
EL. D. MOUZAKIS S.A.; *Int'l*, pg. 2341
ELDOLED B.V.—See Acuity Brands, Inc.; *U.S. Public*, pg. 37
ELDON AB—See nVent Electric plc; *Int'l*, pg. 5498
ELDON A/S—See nVent Electric plc; *Int'l*, pg. 5498
ELDON CS ENCLOSURES PVT LIMITED—See nVent Electric plc; *Int'l*, pg. 5498
ELDON C. STUTSMAN INC.; *U.S. Private*, pg. 1351
ELDON DANMARK—See nVent Electric plc; *Int'l*, pg. 5498
ELDON ELECTRIC LTD—See nVent Electric plc; *Int'l*, pg. 5498
ELDON ESPANA S.A.U.—See nVent Electric plc; *Int'l*, pg. 5498
ELDON GMBH—See nVent Electric plc; *Int'l*, pg. 5498
ELDON HOLDING AB—See nVent Electric plc; *Int'l*, pg. 5498
ELDON INTERNATIONAL S.A.—See nVent Electric plc; *Int'l*, pg. 5498
ELDON N.V.—See nVent Electric plc; *Int'l*, pg. 5498
ELDOON LIMITED—See Cafe de Coral Holdings Limited; *Int'l*, pg. 1250
EL DORADO AMMONIA L.L.C.—See LSB Industries, Inc.; *U.S. Public*, pg. 1344
ELDORADO ARTESIAN SPRINGS, INC.; *U.S. Private*, pg. 1351
ELDORADO AT SANTA FE—See AMREP Corporation; *U.S. Public*, pg. 133
EL DORADO BROADCASTERS; *U.S. Private*, pg. 1348
EL DORADO BROADCASTERS—See El Dorado Broadcasters; *U.S. Private*, pg. 1348

EL DORADO CHEMICAL COMPANY—See LSB Industries, Inc.; *U.S. Public*, pg. 1344
EL DORADO FURNITURE CORP.; *U.S. Private*, pg. 1349
ELDORADO GOLD CORPORATION; *Int'l*, pg. 2346
ELDORADO, INC.—See Boyd Gaming Corporation; *U.S. Public*, pg. 377
EL DORADO INVESTMENT COMPANY—See Pinnacle West Capital Corporation; *U.S. Public*, pg. 1692
EL DORADO MOBILE HOMES INC.; *U.S. Private*, pg. 1349
EL DORADO MOTORS INC.; *U.S. Private*, pg. 1349
ELDORADO NATIONAL (CALIFORNIA), INC.—See AIP, LLC; *U.S. Private*, pg. 135
ELDORADO NATIONAL (KANSAS), INC.—See AIP, LLC; *U.S. Private*, pg. 135
EL DORADO NEWSPAPERS—See Chatham Asset Management, LLC; *U.S. Private*, pg. 866
EL DORADO NEWS-TIMES—See Wehco Media, Inc.; *U.S. Private*, pg. 4470
EL DORADO NITRIC LLC—See LSB Industries, Inc.; *U.S. Public*, pg. 1344
ELDORADO RESORTS LLC—See Caesars Entertainment, Inc.; *U.S. Public*, pg. 420
EL DORADO SAVINGS BANK, F.S.B.; *U.S. Private*, pg. 1349
ELDORADO STONE—See Seven Group Holdings Limited; *Int'l*, pg. 6733
ELDORADO STONE OPERATIONS LLC—See Seven Group Holdings Limited; *Int'l*, pg. 6733
EL DORADO TIMES—See Gannett Co., Inc.; *U.S. Public*, pg. 901
EL DORADO UTILITIES, INC.—See AMREP Corporation; *U.S. Public*, pg. 133
ELDORA MOUNTAIN RESORT—See Powdr Corp.; *U.S. Private*, pg. 3236
ELDRA B.V.—See TKH Group N.V.; *Int'l*, pg. 7763
ELDRA KUNSTSTOFFTECHNIK GMBH—See Draexlmaier Gruppe; *Int'l*, pg. 2198
ELDRIDGE ELECTRIC CO.; *U.S. Private*, pg. 1351
ELDRIDGE INDUSTRIES LLC; *U.S. Private*, pg. 1351
ELDRIDGE SUPPLY COMPANY; *U.S. Private*, pg. 1351
ELDRIST DIALYSIS, LLC—See DaVita Inc.; *U.S. Public*, pg. 638
E-LEAD ELECTRONIC CO., LTD.; *Int'l*, pg. 2248
E-LEAD ELECTRONIC TECHNOLOGY (JIANGSU) CO., LTD.—See E-Lead Electronic Co., Ltd.; *Int'l*, pg. 2248
E-LEAD ELECTRONIC (THAILAND) CO., LTD.—See E-Lead Electronic Co., Ltd.; *Int'l*, pg. 2248
ELEARNING BROTHERS, LLC—See Fundos Group LLC; *U.S. Private*, pg. 1623
ELEARNING BROTHERS, LLC—See Trinity Private Equity Group, LLC; *U.S. Private*, pg. 4235
E-LEARNING SAS—See John Wiley & Sons, Inc.; *U.S. Public*, pg. 1192
E-LEATHER LTD.; *Int'l*, pg. 2248
ELEBELLE (PROPRIETARY) LTD—See L'Oreal S.A.; *Int'l*, pg. 4378
ELEB-EMBRAER—See Embraer S.A.; *Int'l*, pg. 2375
ELECDOR, S.A.—See Elecnor, S.A.; *Int'l*, pg. 2347
ELEC & ELTEK COMPANY (MACAO COMMERCIAL OFFSHORE) LIMITED—See Kingboard Holdings Limited; *Int'l*, pg. 4170
ELEC & ELTEK (GUANGZHOU) ELECTRONIC COMPANY LIMITED—See Kingboard Holdings Limited; *Int'l*, pg. 4170
ELEC & ELTEK INTERNATIONAL COMPANY LIMITED—See Kingboard Holdings Limited; *Int'l*, pg. 4170
ELEC & ELTEK INTERNATIONAL HOLDINGS LIMITED—See Kingboard Holdings Limited; *Int'l*, pg. 4170
ELEC & ELTEK (THAILAND) LIMITED—See Kingboard Holdings Limited; *Int'l*, pg. 4170
ELECNOR CHILE, S.A.—See Elecnor, S.A.; *Int'l*, pg. 2347
ELECNOR DEIMOS—See Indra Sistemas, S.A.; *Int'l*, pg. 3660
ELECNOR HAWKEYE, LLC—See Elecnor, S.A.; *Int'l*, pg. 2347
ELECNOR, S.A.; *Int'l*, pg. 2347
ELECO BAUPRODUKTE—See Eleco Plc; *Int'l*, pg. 2347
ELECOM CO., LTD.; *Int'l*, pg. 2348
ELECON ENGINEERING COMPANY LTD.; *Int'l*, pg. 2348
ELECON MIDDLE EAST FZCO—See Elecon Engineering Company Ltd.; *Int'l*, pg. 2348
ELECON SINGAPORE PTE. LIMITED—See Elecon Engineering Company Ltd.; *Int'l*, pg. 2348
ELECON US TRANSMISSION LIMITED—See Elecon Engineering Company Ltd.; *Int'l*, pg. 2348
ELECO PLC; *Int'l*, pg. 2347
ELECO PRODUITS S.A.S.—See Dr. Honle AG; *Int'l*, pg. 2192
ELECOSOFT BV—See Eleco Plc; *Int'l*, pg. 2348
ELECO SOFTWARE GMBH—See Eleco Plc; *Int'l*, pg. 2348
ELECO SOFTWARE LIMITED—See Eleco Plc; *Int'l*, pg. 2347
ELECO TIMBER FRAME LTD.—See Eleco Plc; *Int'l*, pg. 2348
ELEC OUEST SAS—See VINCI S.A.; *Int'l*, pg. 8217

ELECPRO USA INC.—See DEA General Aviation Holding Co., Ltd.; *Int'l*, pg. 1997
ELECSTER OYJ; *Int'l*, pg. 2348
ELECSTER (TIANJIN) ASEPTIC PACKAGING CO. LTD.—See Elecster Oyj; *Int'l*, pg. 2348
ELECSYS CORPORATION—See Lindsay Corporation; *U.S. Public*, pg. 1319
ELECSYS DIVISION—See DCX-CHOL Enterprises, Inc.; *U.S. Private*, pg. 1180
ELECTA VENTURES S.R.L.—See Azimut Holding SpA; *Int'l*, pg. 779
ELECTECH DISTRIBUTION SYSTEMS PTE. LTD.—See Sunrise Shares Holdings Ltd.; *Int'l*, pg. 7322
ELEC-TECH INTERNATIONAL CO., LTD.; *Int'l*, pg. 2347
ELECTION SERVICES CORPORATION; *U.S. Private*, pg. 1351
ELECTION SYSTEMS & SOFTWARE INC.—See Lee Enterprises, Incorporated; *U.S. Public*, pg. 1298
ELECTION SYSTEMS & SOFTWARE INC.—See McCarthy Group, LLC; *U.S. Private*, pg. 2626
ELECTOCHEM SOLUTIONS, INC.—See Integer Holdings Corporation; *U.S. Public*, pg. 1134
ELECTORI CO., LTD.—See Hibino Corporation; *Int'l*, pg. 3383
ELECTRA AIR CONDITIONING INDUSTRIES 2006 LIMITED—See Elco Limited; *Int'l*, pg. 2345
ELECTRA AMERICA, INC.—See Elco Limited; *Int'l*, pg. 2345
ELECTRA BATTERY MATERIALS CORPORATION; *Int'l*, pg. 2348
ELECTRABEL BLUE SKY INVESTMENTS SCRL—See ENGIE SA; *Int'l*, pg. 2431
ELECTRABEL CUSTOMER SOLUTIONS N.V./S.A—See ENGIE SA; *Int'l*, pg. 2431
ELECTRABEL FRANCE S.A.—See ENGIE SA; *Int'l*, pg. 2431
ELECTRABEL GREEN PROJECTS FLANDERS SCRL—See ENGIE SA; *Int'l*, pg. 2432
ELECTRABEL NEDERLAND RETAIL N.V.—See ENGIE SA; *Int'l*, pg. 2431
ELECTRABEL S.A.—See ENGIE SA; *Int'l*, pg. 2431
ELECTRA BICYCLE COMPANY, LLC—See Trek Bicycle Corporation; *U.S. Private*, pg. 4217
ELECTRA-BOX DIAGNOSTICA AB—See Addtech AB; *Int'l*, pg. 133
ELECTRA-BOX DIAGNOSTICA APS—See Addtech AB; *Int'l*, pg. 133
ELECTRA-BOX DIAGNOSTICA A/S—See Addtech AB; *Int'l*, pg. 133
ELECTRA-BOX DIAGNOSTICA OY—See Addtech AB; *Int'l*, pg. 133
ELECTRA BUIN SA—See Burkhalter Holding AG; *Int'l*, pg. 1224
ELECTRA CONSUMER PRODUCTS (1970) LTD.—See Elco Limited; *Int'l*, pg. 2345
ELECTRA DEUTSCHLAND GMBH—See PGE Polska Grupa Energetyczna S.A.; *Int'l*, pg. 5837
ELECTRA-FINISH, INC.—See PPG Industries, Inc.; *U.S. Public*, pg. 1707
ELECTRA FORM INDUSTRIES—See Wentworth Technologies Co. Ltd.; *Int'l*, pg. 8377
ELECTRA HELLA'S S.A.—See Hella GmbH & Co. KGaA; *Int'l*, pg. 3331
ELECTRA INFORMATION SYSTEMS, INC.—See Symphony Technology Group, LLC; *U.S. Private*, pg. 3900
ELECTRA LINK INC.; *U.S. Private*, pg. 1352
ELECTRA LTD.—See Elco Limited; *Int'l*, pg. 2345
ELECTRAMECCANICA VEHICLES CORP.—See XOS, INC.; *U.S. Public*, pg. 2391
ELECTRA REAL ESTATE LTD.—See Elco Limited; *Int'l*, pg. 2345
ELECTRA STONE LTD.; *Int'l*, pg. 2348
ELECTRATHERM, INC.—See BITZER SE; *Int'l*, pg. 1052
ELECTRAWATCH INC.—See Austal Limited; *Int'l*, pg. 716
ELECTRAWINDS SE; *Int'l*, pg. 2348
ELECTRECORD SA; *Int'l*, pg. 2348
ELECTREN, S.A.—See ACS, Actividades de Construccion y Servicios, S.A.; *Int'l*, pg. 111
ELECTREON WIRELESS LTD.; *Int'l*, pg. 2348
ELECTRI-CABLE ASSEMBLIES, INC.—See Graham Holdings Company; *U.S. Public*, pg. 955
ELECTRICA CONQUENSE, S.A.—See Iberdrola, S.A.; *Int'l*, pg. 3571
ELECTRICA DE LA RIBERA DEL EBRO, S.A.—See EDP - Energias de Portugal, S.A.; *Int'l*, pg. 2314
ELECTRICA FURNIZARE SA—See Societatea Energetica Electrica S.A.; *Int'l*, pg. 7034
ELECTRICAL APPLIANCE OUTLET LIMITED—See AO World PLC; *Int'l*, pg. 487
ELECTRICAL COMPONENTS INTERNATIONAL, INC.—See Cerberus Capital Management, L.P.; *U.S. Private*, pg. 838
ELECTRICAL COMPONENTS INTERNATIONAL—See Cerberus Capital Management, L.P.; *U.S. Private*, pg. 838
ELECTRICAL CONSTRUCTION & MAINTENANCE AUSTRALIA PTY LTD - FABRICATION FACILITY—See Electrical Construction & Maintenance Australia Pty Ltd; *Int'l*, pg. 2349

COMPANY NAME INDEX

ELECTRICAL CONSTRUCTION & MAINTENANCE AUSTRALIA PTY LTD; *Int'l*, pg. 2349
ELECTRICAL CONTRACTORS, INC.; *U.S. Private*, pg. 1352
ELECTRICAL & CONTROL SPECIALISTS LTD—See Forges Tardieu Ltd; *Int'l*, pg. 2733
ELECTRICAL CORP. AMERICA INC.; *U.S. Private*, pg. 1352
ELECTRICAL DESIGN & CONTROL CO. INC.—See DASCAN Industrial Controls; *Int'l*, pg. 1973
ELECTRICAL DISTRIBUTING INC.; *U.S. Private*, pg. 1353
ELECTRICAL DISTRIBUTORS; *U.S. Private*, pg. 1353
ELECTRICAL ENGINEERING & EQUIPMENT COMPANY INC.; *U.S. Private*, pg. 1353
ELECTRICAL ENGINEERING & SERVICE CO., INC.—See ABB Ltd.; *Int'l*, pg. 56
ELECTRICAL EQUIPMENT COMPANY; *U.S. Private*, pg. 1353
ELECTRICAL EQUIPMENT COMPANY—See Electrical Equipment Company; *U.S. Private*, pg. 1353
ELECTRICAL EQUIPMENT JOINT STOCK COMPANY; *Int'l*, pg. 2349
ELECTRICAL GEODESICS, INC.—See Telegraph Hill Partners Management Company, LLC; *U.S. Private*, pg. 3960
ELECTRICAL HOME-AIDS PTY LTD—See Godfreys Group Limited; *Int'l*, pg. 3019
ELECTRICAL INDUSTRIES COMPANY; *Int'l*, pg. 2349
ELECTRICAL INSIGHTS LLC—See Tsubakimoto Chain Co.; *Int'l*, pg. 7954
ELECTRICAL INSULATION SUPPLIERS DE MEXICO, S.A. DE C.V.—See Genuine Parts Company; *U.S. Public*, pg. 932
ELECTRICAL INSURANCE TRUSTEES; *U.S. Private*, pg. 1353
ELECTRICAL POWER PRODUCTS INC—See Electro Management Corporation; *U.S. Private*, pg. 1353
ELECTRICAL POWER PRODUCTS INC.; *U.S. Private*, pg. 1353
ELECTRICAL REBUILDERS SALES INC.; *U.S. Private*, pg. 1353
ELECTRICAL RELIABILITY SERVICES, INC.—See Emerson Electric Co.; *U.S. Public*, pg. 746
ELECTRICAL RELIABILITY SERVICES, INC.—See Emerson Electric Co.; *U.S. Public*, pg. 746
ELECTRICAL RELIABILITY SERVICES, INC.—See Emerson Electric Co.; *U.S. Public*, pg. 746
ELECTRICAL RELIABILITY SERVICES, INC.—See Emerson Electric Co.; *U.S. Public*, pg. 746
ELECTRICAL RELIABILITY SERVICES, INC.—See Emerson Electric Co.; *U.S. Public*, pg. 746
ELECTRICAL RELIABILITY SERVICES, INC.—See Emerson Electric Co.; *U.S. Public*, pg. 746
ELECTRICAL RELIABILITY SERVICES, INC.—See Emerson Electric Co.; *U.S. Public*, pg. 746
ELECTRICAL SALES INC.—See Winsupply, Inc.; *U.S. Private*, pg. 4545
ELECTRICAL SUPPLIES INC.; *U.S. Private*, pg. 1353
ELECTRICAL SYSTEMS AND INSTRUMENTATION, INC.; *U.S. Private*, pg. 1353
ELECTRICAL SYSTEMS INC.—See Monico Inc.; *U.S. Private*, pg. 2770
ELECTRICAL TEST INSTRUMENT, LLC; *U.S. Private*, pg. 1353
ELECTRICAL WHOLESALE SERVICES PTY LTD—See Sonepar S.A.; *Int'l*, pg. 7090
ELECTRICAL WHOLESALE SUPPLY CO. INC.; *U.S. Private*, pg. 1353
ELECTRICAL WHOLESALE SUPPLY CO. UTAH; *U.S. Private*, pg. 1353
ELECTRICA PUNTILLA SA; *Int'l*, pg. 2349
ELECTRIC ARTISTS, INC.; *U.S. Private*, pg. 1352
ELECTRICA SERV SA—See Societatea Energetica Electrica S.A.; *Int'l*, pg. 7035
ELECTRIC BOAT CORPORATION—See General Dynamics Corporation; *U.S. Public*, pg. 915
THE ELECTRIC CAR COMPANY; *U.S. Private*, pg. 4025
ELECTRIC CAR DISTRIBUTORS INC.; *U.S. Private*, pg. 1352
ELECTRIC CENTER EURL—See SMC Corporation; *Int'l*, pg. 7003
ELECTRIC CITY PRINTING COMPANY—See Chatham Asset Management, LLC; *U.S. Private*, pg. 862
ELECTRIC CLOUD INC.; *U.S. Private*, pg. 1352
ELECTRIC COATING TECHNOLOGIES, LLC—See Aurora Capital Group, LLC; *U.S. Private*, pg. 393
ELECTRIC CONDUIT CONSTRUCTION CO.; *U.S. Private*, pg. 1352
ELECTRIC CONNECTOR TECHNOLOGY CO., LTD. - CARLSBAD BRANCH—See Electric Connector Technology Co., Ltd.; *Int'l*, pg. 2348
ELECTRIC CONNECTOR TECHNOLOGY CO., LTD.; *Int'l*, pg. 2348
ELECTRIC CONTROL SYSTEMS AUTOMATION AS—See Addtech AB; *Int'l*, pg. 133
ELECTRIC ENERGY, INC.—See Ameren Corporation; *U.S. Public*, pg. 94
ELECTRIC FETUS COMPANY; *U.S. Private*, pg. 1352

ELECTRIC FEVER COMPANY (HONG KONG)—See Sonepar S.A.; *Int'l*, pg. 7091
ELECTRIC FIXTURE & SUPPLY COMPANY INC.; *U.S. Private*, pg. 1352
ELECTRIC FUEL BATTERY CORPORATION—See Greenbriar Equity Group, L.P.; *U.S. Private*, pg. 1775
ELECTRIC FUEL INFRASTRUCTURE SWEDEN 2 AB—See DistIT AB; *Int'l*, pg. 2136
ELECTRIC GLASS FIBER AMERICA LLC—See Nippon Electric Glass Co., Ltd.; *Int'l*, pg. 5314
ELECTRIC GLASS FIBER NL, B.V.—See Nippon Electric Glass Co., Ltd.; *Int'l*, pg. 5314
ELECTRIC GLASS FIBER UK, LTD.—See Nippon Electric Glass Co., Ltd.; *Int'l*, pg. 5314
ELECTRIC GLASS (GUANGZHOU) CO., LTD.—See Nippon Electric Glass Co., Ltd.; *Int'l*, pg. 5314
ELECTRIC GLASS (KOREA) CO., LTD.—See Nippon Electric Glass Co., Ltd.; *Int'l*, pg. 5314
ELECTRIC GLASS (NANJING) CO., LTD.—See Nippon Electric Glass Co., Ltd.; *Int'l*, pg. 5314
ELECTRIC GLASS (SHANGHAI) CO., LTD.—See Nippon Electric Glass Co., Ltd.; *Int'l*, pg. 5314
ELECTRIC GLASS (XIAMEN) CO., LTD.—See Nippon Electric Glass Co., Ltd.; *Int'l*, pg. 5314
ELECTRIC GUARD DOG, LLC—See TruArc Partners, L.P.; *U.S. Private*, pg. 4245
ELECTRIC GUITAR PLC; *Int'l*, pg. 2349
ELECTRIC H2O, INC.—See Global Water Technologies, Inc.; *U.S. Public*, pg. 945
ELECTRICIDAD DE LA PAZ, S.A.—See Iberdrola, S.A.; *Int'l*, pg. 3571
ELECTRIC INSURANCE COMPANY—See Fairfax Financial Holdings Limited; *Int'l*, pg. 2608
ELECTRICITE DE FRANCE S.A.; *Int'l*, pg. 2350
ELECTRICITE DE STRASBOURG; *Int'l*, pg. 2352
ELECTRICITE DE TAHITI—See ENGIE SA; *Int'l*, pg. 2431
ELECTRICITE ET EAUX DE MADAGASCAR SA; *Int'l*, pg. 2352
ELECTRICITE G. BUGNARD SA—See BKW AG; *Int'l*, pg. 1055
ELECTRICITE MILLOT SAS—See VINCI S.A.; *Int'l*, pg. 8217
ELECTRICITY DISTRIBUTION SERVICES LIMITED—See James Fisher & Sons Public Limited Company; *Int'l*, pg. 3875
ELECTRICITY GENERATING PUBLIC CO., LTD.; *Int'l*, pg. 2352
ELECTRIC KHODRO SHARGH COMPANY; *Int'l*, pg. 2349
ELECTRIC LAST MILE SOLUTIONS, INC.—See Mullen Automotive, Inc.; *U.S. Public*, pg. 1486
ELECTRIC MACHINERY COMPANY LLC—See WEG S.A.; *Int'l*, pg. 8367
THE ELECTRIC MAIL COMPANY—See Ziff Davis, Inc.; *U.S. Public*, pg. 2404
THE ELECTRIC MATERIALS COMPANY INC.—See United Stars Inc.; *U.S. Private*, pg. 4298
ELECTRIC MELTING SERVICES COMPANY, LTD.—See Indel, Inc.; *U.S. Private*, pg. 2055
ELECTRIC MIRROR, INC.; *U.S. Private*, pg. 1352
ELECTRIC MOBILITY CORPORATION; *U.S. Private*, pg. 1352
ELECTRIC MOTION COMPANY INC.; *U.S. Private*, pg. 1352
ELECTRIC MOTOR & CONTRACTING CO., INC.; *U.S. Private*, pg. 1352
ELECTRIC MOTOR REPAIR COMPANY; *U.S. Private*, pg. 1352
ELECTRIC MOTOR SALES & SUPPLY CO.; *U.S. Private*, pg. 1352
ELECTRIC MOTOR SERVICE INC.; *U.S. Private*, pg. 1352
ELECTRIC MOTOR SERVICE—See Tri-State Armature & Electric Works, Inc.; *U.S. Private*, pg. 4223
ELECTRI-CORD MANUFACTURING CO.; *U.S. Private*, pg. 1352
ELECTRIC POWER DEVELOPMENT CO., LTD.; *Int'l*, pg. 2349
ELECTRIC POWER ENGINEERS, LLC—See Lime Rock Partners, LLC; *U.S. Private*, pg. 2456
ELECTRIC POWER TECHNOLOGY LIMITED; *Int'l*, pg. 2349
ELECTRIC RESEARCH & MANUFACTURING COOPERATIVE, INC. (ERMCO)—See Arkansas Electric Cooperatives, Inc.; *U.S. Private*, pg. 325
ELECTRIC ROYALTIES LTD.; *Int'l*, pg. 2349
ELECTRIC SERVICE & SALES, INC.—See Tencarva Machinery Company, LLC; *U.S. Private*, pg. 3965
ELECTRIC SPECIALTIES COMPANY—See Per Mar Security Services; *U.S. Private*, pg. 3146
ELECTRIC SUPPLY CO.; *U.S. Private*, pg. 1352
ELECTRIC SUPPLY & EQUIPMENT CO. INC.; *U.S. Private*, pg. 1352
ELECTRIC SUPPLY, INC.; *U.S. Private*, pg. 1352
ELECTRIC SUPPLY, INC.; *U.S. Private*, pg. 1352
ELECTRIC TIME CO., INC.; *U.S. Private*, pg. 1352
ELECTRIC TORQUE MACHINES, INC.—See Graco, Inc.; *U.S. Public*, pg. 953
ELECTRIC TRACTOR CORP.; *Int'l*, pg. 2349

ELECTROFILM MFG. CO.

ELECTRIC UTILITY SUPPLY CO.—See Rural Electric Supply Cooperative Inc.; *U.S. Private*, pg. 3504
ELECTRIC WORD PLC; *Int'l*, pg. 2349
ELECTRIFICATION COALITION; *U.S. Private*, pg. 1353
ELECTRIQ POWER HOLDINGS, INC.; *U.S. Public*, pg. 723
ELECTRIUM SALES LIMITED—See Siemens Aktiengesellschaft; *Int'l*, pg. 6886
ELECTRIX, INC.—See Light Fantastic Realty, Inc.; *U.S. Private*, pg. 2452
ELECTRIX LIMITED—See VINCI S.A.; *Int'l*, pg. 8217
ELECTRIX PTY LIMITED—See VINCI S.A.; *Int'l*, pg. 8237
ELECTRO ACO ALTONA S.A.; *Int'l*, pg. 2352
ELECTRO ADAPTER; *U.S. Private*, pg. 1353
ELECTRO ANDINA LTDA—See Legrand S.A.; *Int'l*, pg. 4444
ELECTROAPARATAJ S.A.; *Int'l*, pg. 2353
ELECTRO-ARCO S.A.—See Lincoln Electric Holdings, Inc.; *U.S. Public*, pg. 1317
ELECTROARGES SA; *Int'l*, pg. 2353
ELECTRO-BIOLOGY, LLC—See Zimmer Biomet Holdings, Inc.; *U.S. Public*, pg. 2406
ELECTRO BRAND, INC.; *U.S. Private*, pg. 1353
ELECTRO CABLE EGYPT—See Pioneers Holding Company; *Int'l*, pg. 5872
ELECTRO CABLES EGYPT CO.—See Pioneers Holding Company; *Int'l*, pg. 5872
ELECTRO-CENTRE SAS—See Societe BIC S.A.; *Int'l*, pg. 7037
ELECTRO-CERAMICS (THAILAND) CO., LTD.—See NIPPON CARBIDE INDUSTRIES CO., INC.; *Int'l*, pg. 5311
ELECTRO CHEMICAL FINISHING CO.; *U.S. Private*, pg. 1353
ELECTROCHEM SOLUTIONS, INC. - BEAVERTON DESIGN & DEVELOPMENT CENTER—See Integer Holdings Corporation; *U.S. Public*, pg. 1134
ELECTROCHEM SOLUTIONS, LLC—See Aterian Investment Management, L.P.; *U.S. Private*, pg. 366
ELECTRO-COATINGS OF CALIFORNIA INC.—See Acme Holdings, Inc.; *U.S. Private*, pg. 61
ELECTRO-COATINGS OF IOWA, INC.—See Acme Holdings, Inc.; *U.S. Private*, pg. 61
ELECTRO-COATINGS OF TEXAS, INC.—See Acme Holdings, Inc.; *U.S. Private*, pg. 61
ELECTROCOM, INC.—See General Dynamics Corporation; *U.S. Public*, pg. 913
ELECTRO-COMMUNICATIONS CO.; *U.S. Private*, pg. 1354
ELECTROCOMPONENTS FRANCE SARL—See RS Group plc; *Int'l*, pg. 6417
ELECTROCOMPONENTS UK LIMITED—See RS Group plc; *Int'l*, pg. 6417
ELECTRO COMPOSITES (2008) ULC—See Hubbell Incorporated; *U.S. Public*, pg. 1067
ELECTROCOM S.A.—See Aiphone Co., Ltd.; *Int'l*, pg. 235
ELECTROCONDUCTORES DE HONDURAS, S.A.—See Prysmian S.p.A.; *Int'l*, pg. 6011
ELECTROCONSTRUCTIA ELCO ALBA IULIA SA; *Int'l*, pg. 2353
ELECTROCONSTRUCTIA ELCO SA; *Int'l*, pg. 2353
ELECTROCONSTRUCTIA ELCO TIMISOARA S.A.; *Int'l*, pg. 2353
ELECTROCORE, INC.; *U.S. Public*, pg. 723
ELECTROCRAFT ARKANSAS, INC.—See Delany Capital Management Corp.; *U.S. Private*, pg. 1194
ELECTROCRAFT, INC.—See Delany Capital Management Corp.; *U.S. Private*, pg. 1194
ELECTROCRAFT MICHIGAN, INC.—See Delany Capital Management Corp.; *U.S. Private*, pg. 1194
ELECTROCRAFT NEW HAMPSHIRE, INC.—See Delany Capital Management Corp.; *U.S. Private*, pg. 1194
ELECTROCUBE INCORPORATED; *U.S. Private*, pg. 1354
ELECTRODES, INC.; *U.S. Private*, pg. 1354
ELECTRODOMESTICOS TAURUS SL—See Taurus Group; *Int'l*, pg. 7476
ELECTRO-DRAAD B.V.—See TKH Group N.V.; *Int'l*, pg. 7763
ELECTRODYNAMICS INC—See L3Harris Technologies, Inc.; *U.S. Public*, pg. 1281
ELECTRO ENTERPRISES, INC.—See Audax Group, Limited Partnership; *U.S. Private*, pg. 388
ELECTRO FIBER TECHNOLOGIES LLC—See James Cropper Plc; *Int'l*, pg. 3875
ELECTROFILM MANUFACTURING COMPANY LLC—See ITT Inc.; *U.S. Public*, pg. 1177
ELECTROFILM MFG. CO.; *U.S. Private*, pg. 1354
ELECTROGAS, S.A.—See REN - Redes Energeticas Nacionais SGPS, S.A.; *Int'l*, pg. 6272
ELECTRO GAZ SERVICE SA—See Brookfield Corporation; *Int'l*, pg. 1188
ELECTROGAZ—See PJSC Gazprom; *Int'l*, pg. 5879
ELECTROGEN INTERNATIONAL LTD.—See The Manitowoc Company, Inc.; *U.S. Public*, pg. 2111
ELECTROHOLD BULGARIA EOOD—See Eurohold Bulgaria AD; *Int'l*, pg. 2553
ELECTROHOLD SALES AD—See Eurohold Bulgaria AD; *Int'l*, pg. 2553
ELECTROHOLD TRADE EAD—See Eurohold Bulgaria AD; *Int'l*, pg. 2553

ELECTROFILM MFG. CO.

ELECTROID CO—See Valcor Engineering Corporation; *U.S. Private*, pg. 4330
ELECTROIMPACT INC.; *U.S. Private*, pg. 1354
ELECTROLAN SA—See Sonepar S.A.; *Int'l*, pg. 7090
ELECTROL CO.—See Innovative Manufacturing Solutions Corp.; *U.S. Private*, pg. 2082
ELECTROLINE LTD—See Amplex AB; *Int'l*, pg. 434
ELECTROLOCK INC.; *U.S. Private*, pg. 1354
ELECTROLOR SAS—See VINCI S.A.; *Int'l*, pg. 8217
ELECTROL SPECIALTIES, INC.; *U.S. Private*, pg. 1354
ELECTROLUBE LIMITED—See Element Solutions Inc.; *U.S. Public*, pg. 726
ELECTROLUX AG—See AB Electrolux; *Int'l*, pg. 39
ELECTROLUX APPLIANCES S.P.A.—See AB Electrolux; *Int'l*, pg. 39
ELECTROLUX ARGENTINA S.A.—See AB Electrolux; *Int'l*, pg. 39
ELECTROLUX ASSOCIATED COMPANY B.V.—See AB Electrolux; *Int'l*, pg. 39
ELECTROLUX A.S.—See AB Electrolux; *Int'l*, pg. 39
ELECTROLUX AUSTRIA GMBH—See AB Electrolux; *Int'l*, pg. 39
ELECTROLUX BELGIUM N.V.—See AB Electrolux; *Int'l*, pg. 39
ELECTROLUX CANADA CORP.—See Bissell Homecare, Inc.; *U.S. Private*, pg. 566
ELECTROLUX CEE G.M.B.H.—See AB Electrolux; *Int'l*, pg. 39
ELECTROLUX CENTRAL AND EASTERN EUROPE GES. M.B.H. NFG. KG.—See AB Electrolux; *Int'l*, pg. 39
ELECTROLUX CENTRAL VACUUM SYSTEMS—See Bissell Homecare, Inc.; *U.S. Private*, pg. 566
ELECTROLUX COMERCIAL VENEZUELA C.A—See AB Electrolux; *Int'l*, pg. 39
ELECTROLUX DE CHILE S.A.—See AB Electrolux; *Int'l*, pg. 41
ELECTROLUX DE COLOMBIA S.A.—See AB Electrolux; *Int'l*, pg. 41
ELECTROLUX DEL PARAGUAY S.A.—See AB Electrolux; *Int'l*, pg. 41
ELECTROLUX DEL PERU S.A.—See AB Electrolux; *Int'l*, pg. 41
ELECTROLUX DEUTSCHLAND GMBH—See AB Electrolux; *Int'l*, pg. 39
ELECTROLUX DO BRASIL SA—See AB Electrolux; *Int'l*, pg. 39
ELECTROLUX D.O.O.—See AB Electrolux; *Int'l*, pg. 41
ELECTROLUX ESPANA S.A.—See AB Electrolux; *Int'l*, pg. 39
ELECTROLUX ESTONIA LTD—See AB Electrolux; *Int'l*, pg. 39
ELECTROLUX (FAR EAST) LTD.—See AB Electrolux; *Int'l*, pg. 39
ELECTROLUX FILTER AB—See AB Electrolux; *Int'l*, pg. 40
ELECTROLUX FLOOR CARE AND SMALL APPLIANCES AB—See AB Electrolux; *Int'l*, pg. 40
ELECTROLUX FRANCE S.A.—See AB Electrolux; *Int'l*, pg. 40
ELECTROLUX (HANGZHOU) DOMESTIC APPLIANCES CO. LTD—See AB Electrolux; *Int'l*, pg. 39
ELECTROLUX HAUSGERATE G.M.B.H.—See AB Electrolux; *Int'l*, pg. 40
ELECTROLUX HAUSGERATE GMBH—See AB Electrolux; *Int'l*, pg. 40
ELECTROLUX HEMPRODUKTER AB—See AB Electrolux; *Int'l*, pg. 40
ELECTROLUX HOLDING AG—See AB Electrolux; *Int'l*, pg. 40
ELECTROLUX HOME APPLIANCES SDN BHD—See AB Electrolux; *Int'l*, pg. 40
ELECTROLUX HOME CARE PRODUCTS CANADA—See Bissell Homecare, Inc.; *U.S. Private*, pg. 566
ELECTROLUX HOME CARE PRODUCTS, INC.—See Bissell Homecare, Inc.; *U.S. Private*, pg. 566
ELECTROLUX HOME PRODUCTS AS—See AB Electrolux; *Int'l*, pg. 40
ELECTROLUX HOME PRODUCTS CORPORATION N.V.—See AB Electrolux; *Int'l*, pg. 40
ELECTROLUX HOME PRODUCTS DENMARK A/S—See AB Electrolux; *Int'l*, pg. 40
ELECTROLUX HOME PRODUCTS ESPANA S.A.—See AB Electrolux; *Int'l*, pg. 40
ELECTROLUX HOME PRODUCTS, INC. - ANDERSON—See Bissell Homecare, Inc.; *U.S. Private*, pg. 566
ELECTROLUX HOME PRODUCTS, INC. - SAINT CLOUD—See Bissell Homecare, Inc.; *U.S. Private*, pg. 566
ELECTROLUX HOME PRODUCTS, INC.—See Bissell Homecare, Inc.; *U.S. Private*, pg. 566
ELECTROLUX HOME PRODUCTS, INC. - WEBSTER CITY—See Bissell Homecare, Inc.; *U.S. Private*, pg. 566
ELECTROLUX HOME PRODUCTS (NEDERLAND) B.V.—See AB Electrolux; *Int'l*, pg. 40
ELECTROLUX HOME PRODUCTS NORWAY AS—See AB Electrolux; *Int'l*, pg. 40
ELECTROLUX HOME PRODUCTS PTY. LTD.—See AB Electrolux; *Int'l*, pg. 40
ELECTROLUX HOME PRODUCTS UK—See AB Electrolux; *Int'l*, pg. 41
ELECTROLUX IRELAND LTD—See AB Electrolux; *Int'l*, pg. 40
ELECTROLUX ITALIA S.P.A.—See AB Electrolux; *Int'l*, pg. 40
ELECTROLUX JAPAN LTD.—See AB Electrolux; *Int'l*, pg. 40
ELECTROLUX-JUNO KUCHENTECHNIK GMBH—See AB Electrolux; *Int'l*, pg. 41
ELECTROLUX LAUNDRY SYSTEMS DENMARK A/S—See AB Electrolux; *Int'l*, pg. 40
ELECTROLUX LAUNDRY SYSTEMS SWEDEN AB—See AB Electrolux; *Int'l*, pg. 40
ELECTROLUX LDA—See AB Electrolux; *Int'l*, pg. 40
ELECTROLUX LEHEL HUTOGEPGYAR KFT—See AB Electrolux; *Int'l*, pg. 40
ELECTROLUX LJUBLJANA D.O.O.—See AB Electrolux; *Int'l*, pg. 40
ELECTROLUX (MALAYSIA) HOLDINGS SDN. BHD.—See AB Electrolux; *Int'l*, pg. 40
ELECTROLUX NORTH AMERICA, INC.—See AB Electrolux; *Int'l*, pg. 40
ELECTROLUX (NZ) LIMITED—See AB Electrolux; *Int'l*, pg. 39
ELECTROLUX OUTDOOR PRODUCTS A/S—See AB Electrolux; *Int'l*, pg. 40
ELECTROLUX PHILLIPPINES, INC.—See AB Electrolux; *Int'l*, pg. 40
ELECTROLUX PLC—See AB Electrolux; *Int'l*, pg. 41
ELECTROLUX POLAND SPOLKA Z.O.O.—See AB Electrolux; *Int'l*, pg. 40
ELECTROLUX PROFESSIONAL AB; *Int'l*, pg. 2353
ELECTROLUX PROFESSIONAL AG—See Electrolux Professional AB; *Int'l*, pg. 2353
ELECTROLUX PROFESSIONAL AS—See AB Electrolux; *Int'l*, pg. 40
ELECTROLUX PROFESSIONAL BV—See AB Electrolux; *Int'l*, pg. 40
ELECTROLUX PROFESSIONAL GMBH—See AB Electrolux; *Int'l*, pg. 40
ELECTROLUX PROFESSIONAL, INC.—See AB Electrolux; *Int'l*, pg. 40
ELECTROLUX PROFESSIONAL LTD—See AB Electrolux; *Int'l*, pg. 40
ELECTROLUX PROFESSIONAL OY—See AB Electrolux; *Int'l*, pg. 41
ELECTROLUX PROFESSIONAL S.P.A.—See AB Electrolux; *Int'l*, pg. 40
ELECTROLUX PROFESSIONNEL SAS—See AB Electrolux; *Int'l*, pg. 40
ELECTROLUX PTY. LTD.—See AB Electrolux; *Int'l*, pg. 40
ELECTROLUX ROMANIA SA—See AB Electrolux; *Int'l*, pg. 40
ELECTROLUX S.E.A. PRIVATE LTD.—See AB Electrolux; *Int'l*, pg. 40
ELECTROLUX SLOVAKIA S.R.O. O.Z.—See AB Electrolux; *Int'l*, pg. 41
ELECTROLUX THAILAND CO. LTD.—See AB Electrolux; *Int'l*, pg. 41
ELECTROLUX UKRAINE LLC—See AB Electrolux; *Int'l*, pg. 41
ELECTROLUX ZANUSSI ITALIA SPA—See AB Electrolux; *Int'l*, pg. 41
ELECTROMACH B.V.—See R. STAHL AG; *Int'l*, pg. 6169
ELECTRO-MAG INC.—See Graybar Electric Company, Inc.; *U.S. Private*, pg. 1760
ELECTROMAGNETICA S.A.; *Int'l*, pg. 2353
ELECTROMAGNETIC GEOSERVICES ASA; *Int'l*, pg. 2353
ELECTRO MAGNETIC MARINE EXPLORATION TECHNOLOGIES (EMMET) ZAO—See Fugro N.V.; *Int'l*, pg. 2805
ELECTROMAGS AUTMOTIVE PRODUCTS PRIVATE LIMITED—See The Bombay Burmah Trading Corporation Limited; *Int'l*, pg. 7627
ELECTRO MANAGEMENT CORPORATION; *U.S. Private*, pg. 1353
ELECTROMANUFACTURAS, S. DE R.L. DE C.V.—See Eaton Corporation plc; *Int'l*, pg. 2278
ELECTRO MART LIMITED—See Daikin Industries, Ltd.; *Int'l*, pg. 1935
ELECTROMASHINA JSC—See Russian Technologies State Corporation; *Int'l*, pg. 6431
ELECTRO-MATIC PRODUCTS, INC.—See Electro-Matic Ventures, Inc.; *U.S. Private*, pg. 1354
ELECTRO-MATIC VENTURES, INC.; *U.S. Private*, pg. 1354
ELECTROMATIK FZCO—See TCS TurControlSysteme AG; *Int'l*, pg. 7485
ELECTRO-MECHANICAL CORPORATION—See Graycliff Partners LP; *U.S. Private*, pg. 1760
ELECTRO MECHANICAL SYSTEMS LTD.; *Int'l*, pg. 2352
ELECTROMECH TECHNOLOGIES—See TransDigm Group Incorporated; *U.S. Public*, pg. 2182
ELECTRO MEDICAL GROUP PTY. LTD.—See Paragon Care Limited; *Int'l*, pg. 5736

CORPORATE AFFILIATIONS

ELECTRO MEDICAL INSTRUMENTS BV—See Amplifon S.p.A.; *Int'l*, pg. 435
ELECTROMEDICAL PRODUCTS INTERNATIONAL, INC.—See Tillery Capital LLC; *U.S. Private*, pg. 4171
ELECTROMEDICAL TECHNOLOGIES, INC.; *U.S. Public*, pg. 723
ELECTROMEDICIONES KAINOS S.A.—See METRAWATT International GmbH; *Int'l*, pg. 4855
ELECTROMED, INC.; *U.S. Public*, pg. 723
ELECTROMET CORPORATION; *U.S. Private*, pg. 1354
ELECTRO-METHODS, INC.; *U.S. Private*, pg. 1354
ELECTRO-METRICS CORPORATION; *U.S. Private*, pg. 1354
ELECTROMINING SA; *Int'l*, pg. 2353
ELECTROMONTAGE SAS—See VINCI S.A.; *Int'l*, pg. 8217
ELECTRO-MOTIVE CANADA CO.—See Caterpillar, Inc.; *U.S. Public*, pg. 453
ELECTRO-MOTIVE DIESEL, INC.—See Caterpillar, Inc.; *U.S. Public*, pg. 453
ELECTRO-MOTIVE TECHNICAL CONSULTING CO. (BEIJING) LTD.—See Caterpillar, Inc.; *U.S. Public*, pg. 452
ELECTROMUR, S.A.—See ACS, Actividades de Construccion y Servicios, S.A.; *Int'l*, pg. 111
ELECTRON BEAM TECHNOLOGIES, INC.; *U.S. Private*, pg. 1355
ELECTRON ETTO S.R.O.—See NIBE Industrier AB; *Int'l*, pg. 5260
ELECTRON HOUSE (OVERSEAS) LIMITED—See Avnet, Inc.; *U.S. Public*, pg. 253
ELECTRONICA CLARION, S.A. DE C.V.—See FORVIA SE; *Int'l*, pg. 2745
ELECTRONICA CLARION, S.A. DE C.V.—See FORVIA SE; *Int'l*, pg. 2745
ELECTRONICA NSC DE MEXICO, S.A. DE C.V.—See Texas Instruments Incorporated; *U.S. Public*, pg. 2025
ELECTRONICA OLFER S.L.—See P-Duke Technology Co., Ltd.; *Int'l*, pg. 5681
ELECTRONIC ARTS BELGIUM—See Electronic Arts Inc.; *U.S. Public*, pg. 724
ELECTRONIC ARTS (CANADA), INC.—See Electronic Arts Inc.; *U.S. Public*, pg. 724
ELECTRONIC ARTS CZECH REPUBLIC S.R.O.—See Electronic Arts Inc.; *U.S. Public*, pg. 724
ELECTRONIC ARTS GMBH—See Electronic Arts Inc.; *U.S. Public*, pg. 724
ELECTRONIC ARTS HK LIMITED—See Electronic Arts Inc.; *U.S. Public*, pg. 724
ELECTRONIC ARTS INC.; *U.S. Public*, pg. 723
ELECTRONIC ARTS ITALIA S.R.L.—See Electronic Arts Inc.; *U.S. Public*, pg. 724
ELECTRONIC ARTS NORWAY AS—See Electronic Arts Inc.; *U.S. Public*, pg. 724
ELECTRONIC ARTS POLSKA SP.Z.O.O.—See Electronic Arts Inc.; *U.S. Public*, pg. 724
ELECTRONIC ARTS PROPRIETARY LIMITED—See Electronic Arts Inc.; *U.S. Public*, pg. 724
ELECTRONIC ARTS PUBLISHING SARL—See Electronic Arts Inc.; *U.S. Public*, pg. 724
ELECTRONIC ARTS ROMANIA SRL—See Electronic Arts Inc.; *U.S. Public*, pg. 724
ELECTRONIC ARTS SOFTWARE S.L.—See Electronic Arts Inc.; *U.S. Public*, pg. 724
ELECTRONIC ARTS SWEDEN AB—See Electronic Arts Inc.; *U.S. Public*, pg. 724
ELECTRONIC ARTS UK LTD.—See Electronic Arts Inc.; *U.S. Public*, pg. 724
ELECTRONIC ASSEMBLY PRODUCTS, LTD.—See ViTrox Corporation Berhad; *Int'l*, pg. 8262
ELECTRONIC BUSINESS SYSTEM; *Int'l*, pg. 2354
ELECTRONIC CASH SYSTEMS, INC.; *U.S. Private*, pg. 1355
ELECTRONIC CHECK SERVICES INC; *U.S. Private*, pg. 1355
ELECTRONIC CIRCUIT DESIGNS PTY. LIMITED—See Inventis Limited; *Int'l*, pg. 3773
ELECTRONIC CLEARING HOUSE, INC.—See Intuit Inc.; *U.S. Public*, pg. 1160
ELECTRONIC COMMERCE INC; *U.S. Private*, pg. 1355
ELECTRONIC COMPONENT SALES INC.—See Taiwan Line Tek Electronic Co., Ltd.; *Int'l*, pg. 7422
ELECTRONIC CONTRACTING COMPANY; *U.S. Private*, pg. 1355
ELECTRONIC CONTROLS DESIGN; *U.S. Private*, pg. 1355
ELECTRONIC CONTROL SECURITY INC.; *U.S. Public*, pg. 724
ELECTRONIC CONTROL SYSTEMS, INC.—See Huron Capital Partners LLC; *U.S. Private*, pg. 2011
ELECTRONIC CUSTOM DISTRIBUTORS, INC.—See Resideo Technologies, Inc.; *U.S. Public*, pg. 1789
ELECTRONIC DATA CARRIERS INC.; *U.S. Private*, pg. 1355
ELECTRONIC DATA INNOVATION GROUP EDIG AB—See Ratos AB; *Int'l*, pg. 6216
ELECTRONIC DATA, LLC—See Arora Engineers, Inc.; *U.S. Private*, pg. 334
ELECTRONIC DATA MAGNETICS, INC.; *U.S. Private*, pg. 1355

COMPANY NAME INDEX

ELECTRONIC DATA PAYMENT SYSTEMS; *U.S. Private*, pg. 1355
ELECTRONIC DATA SYSTEMSBELGIUM BVBA—See HP Inc.; *U.S. Public*, pg. 1062
ELECTRONIC DATA SYSTEMS INTERNATIONAL B.V.—See Veritas Capital Fund Management, LLC; *U.S. Private*, pg. 4364
ELECTRONIC DESIGN FOR INDUSTRY, INC.—See Turnbridge Capital, LLC; *U.S. Private*, pg. 4260
ELECTRONIC DESIGN, INC.—See Fulham & Co., Inc.; *U.S. Private*, pg. 1620
ELECTRONIC DRIVES & CONTROLS; *U.S. Private*, pg. 1355
ELECTRONIC ENGINEERING CO.; *U.S. Private*, pg. 1355
ELECTRONIC ENTERTAINMENT DESIGN & RESEARCH—See The NPD Group, Inc.; *U.S. Private*, pg. 4085
ELECTRONIC ENVIRONMENTS CORP.; *U.S. Private*, pg. 1355
ELECTRONIC EVOLUTIONS, INC.—See Ultimate Technologies Group, Inc.; *U.S. Private*, pg. 4277
THE ELECTRONIC EXPRESS INC.; *U.S. Private*, pg. 4025
ELECTRONIC FUNDS SOURCE LLC - CHANHASSEN—See WEX, Inc.; *U.S. Public*, pg. 2364
ELECTRONIC FUNDS SOURCE LLC—See WEX, Inc.; *U.S. Public*, pg. 2364
ELECTRONIC HARNESSES (U.K.) LTD.—See Sumitomo Electric Industries, Ltd.; *Int'l*, pg. 7277
ELECTRONIC HEALTHCARE NETWORK ACCREDITATION COMMISSION; *U.S. Private*, pg. 1355
ELECTRONIC INDUSTRIES ALLIANCE INC.; *U.S. Private*, pg. 1355
ELECTRONIC INDUSTRIES CORPORATION; *U.S. Private*, pg. 1355
ELECTRONIC INDUSTRIES CO.; *Int'l*, pg. 2354
ELECTRONIC INK—See LiquidHub, Inc.; *U.S. Private*, pg. 2466
ELECTRONIC INSTRUMENTATION & TECHNOLOGY; *U.S. Private*, pg. 1355
ELECTRONIC KNOWLEDGE INTERCHANGE CO.; *U.S. Private*, pg. 1355
ELECTRONIC MAINTENANCE COMPANY INCORPORATED; *U.S. Private*, pg. 1355
ELECTRONIC MANUFACTURING TECHNOLOGY, LLC—See Elbit Systems Limited; *Int'l*, pg. 2345
ELECTRONIC MEDIA SYSTEMS, INC.—See DigitalBridge Group, Inc.; *U.S. Public*, pg. 664
ELECTRONIC MICRO SYSTEMS INC—See Halma plc; *Int'l*, pg. 3231
ELECTRONIC MODULAR SERVICES LIMITED—See Carrier Global Corporation; *U.S. Public*, pg. 443
ELECTRONIC MUSICAL INSTRUMENTS ROLAND SCANDINAVIA A/S—See Roland Corporation; *Int'l*, pg. 6390
ELECTRONIC NETWORK SYSTEMS, INC.—See UnitedHealth Group Incorporated; *U.S. Public*, pg. 2248
ELECTRONICPARTNER AUSTRIA GMBH—See ElectronicPartner Handel SE; *Int'l*, pg. 2354
ELECTRONICPARTNER BELGIE N.V.—See ElectronicPartner Handel SE; *Int'l*, pg. 2354
ELECTRONICPARTNER GMBH—See ElectronicPartner Handel SE; *Int'l*, pg. 2354
ELECTRONICPARTNER HANDEL SE; *Int'l*, pg. 2354
ELECTRONICPARTNER NEDERLAND B.V.—See ElectronicPartner Handel SE; *Int'l*, pg. 2354
ELECTRONICPARTNER SCHWEIZ AG—See ElectronicPartner Handel SE; *Int'l*, pg. 2354
ELECTRONIC PAYMENT EXCHANGE, INC.—See North American Bancard, LLC; *U.S. Private*, pg. 2940
ELECTRONIC PAYMENT PROVIDERS, INC.—See Repay Holdings Corporation; *U.S. Public*, pg. 1784
ELECTRONIC PAYMENTS, INC.; *U.S. Private*, pg. 1355
ELECTRONIC PAYMENT SYSTEMS GLOBAL—See The Celler Organization; *U.S. Private*, pg. 4006
ELECTRONIC PAYMENT SYSTEMS, LLC; *U.S. Private*, pg. 1355
ELECTRONIC PRODUCTS MAGAZINE—See The Hearst Corporation; *U.S. Private*, pg. 4045
ELECTRONIC RECYCLERS INTERNATIONAL, INC.; *U.S. Private*, pg. 1356
ELECTRONIC REGISTRY SYSTEMS, INC.—See Health Catalyst, Inc.; *U.S. Public*, pg. 1014
ELECTRONICS BOUTIQUE AUSTRALIA PTY. LTD.—See GameStop Corp.; *U.S. Public*, pg. 895
ELECTRONICS BOUTIQUE CANADA INC.—See GameStop Corp.; *U.S. Public*, pg. 895
ELECTRONICS CO., LTD.—See UJU ELECTRONICS Co., Ltd.; *Int'l*, pg. 8016
ELECTRONIC SECURITY DEVICES, INC.—See ASSA ABLOY AB; *Int'l*, pg. 639
ELECTRONIC SERVICES CORPORATION OF AMERICA; *U.S. Private*, pg. 1356
ELECTRONIC SERVITOR PUBLICATION NETWORK, INC.; *U.S. Public*, pg. 724
ELECTRONICS FOR IMAGING AB—See Siris Capital Group, LLC; *U.S. Private*, pg. 3672

ELECTRONICS FOR IMAGING AUSTRALIA PTY. LTD.—See Siris Capital Group, LLC; *U.S. Private*, pg. 3672
ELECTRONICS FOR IMAGING B.V.—See Siris Capital Group, LLC; *U.S. Private*, pg. 3672
ELECTRONICS FOR IMAGING GMBH—See Siris Capital Group, LLC; *U.S. Private*, pg. 3673
ELECTRONICS FOR IMAGING, INC. - ARIZONA—See Siris Capital Group, LLC; *U.S. Private*, pg. 3672
ELECTRONICS FOR IMAGING, INC. - GEORGIA—See Siris Capital Group, LLC; *U.S. Private*, pg. 3672
ELECTRONICS FOR IMAGING, INC. - INKJET SOLUTIONS—See Siris Capital Group, LLC; *U.S. Private*, pg. 3672
ELECTRONICS FOR IMAGING, INC. - LEBANON—See Siris Capital Group, LLC; *U.S. Private*, pg. 3672
ELECTRONICS FOR IMAGING, INC. - MASSACHUSETTS—See Siris Capital Group, LLC; *U.S. Private*, pg. 3672
ELECTRONICS FOR IMAGING, INC. - PITTSBURGH—See Siris Capital Group, LLC; *U.S. Private*, pg. 3672
ELECTRONICS FOR IMAGING, INC.—See Siris Capital Group, LLC; *U.S. Private*, pg. 3672
ELECTRONICS FOR IMAGING INDIA PRIVATE LIMITED—See Siris Capital Group, LLC; *U.S. Private*, pg. 3672
ELECTRONICS FOR IMAGING ITALIA SRL—See Siris Capital Group, LLC; *U.S. Private*, pg. 3673
ELECTRONICS FOR IMAGING JAPAN YK—See Siris Capital Group, LLC; *U.S. Private*, pg. 3673
ELECTRONICS FOR IMAGING KOREA CO., LTD.—See Siris Capital Group, LLC; *U.S. Private*, pg. 3672
ELECTRONICS FOR IMAGING UNITED KINGDOM LIMITED—See Siris Capital Group, LLC; *U.S. Private*, pg. 3673
ELECTRONICS INDUSTRY PUBLIC COMPANY LIMITED; *Int'l*, pg. 2354
ELECTRONICS INTEGRATION TECHNOLOGY, INC.—See Technology Dynamics, Inc.; *U.S. Private*, pg. 3955
ELECTRONICS LINE 3000 LTD.—See RISCO Ltd.; *Int'l*, pg. 6349
ELECTRONICS MANUFACTURING SOLUTIONS—See Benchmark Electronics, Inc.; *U.S. Public*, pg. 296
ELECTRONICS MARKETING GROUP; *U.S. Private*, pg. 1356
ELECTRONICS MART INDIA LIMITED; *Int'l*, pg. 2354
ELECTRONICS STAMPING CORP.; *U.S. Private*, pg. 1356
ELECTRONIC SUPPLY COMPANY—See H.I.G. Capital, LLC; *U.S. Private*, pg. 1827
ELECTRONIC SYSTEMS, INC.—See Xerox Holdings Corporation; *U.S. Public*, pg. 2389
ELECTRONIC SYSTEMS PROTECTION, INC.; *U.S. Private*, pg. 1356
ELECTRONIC SYSTEMS TECHNOLOGY, INC.; *U.S. Public*, pg. 724
ELECTRONIC TECHNOLOGIES INTERNATIONAL, INC.; *U.S. Private*, pg. 1356
ELECTRONIC TELE-COMMUNICATIONS, INC.; *U.S. Public*, pg. 725
ELECTRONIC THEATRE CONTROLS ASIA—See Electronic Theatre Controls, Inc.; *U.S. Private*, pg. 1356
ELECTRONIC THEATRE CONTROLS GMBH—See Electronic Theatre Controls, Inc.; *U.S. Private*, pg. 1356
ELECTRONIC THEATRE CONTROLS, INC.; *U.S. Private*, pg. 1356
ELECTRONIC THEATRE CONTROLS LTD.—See Electronic Theatre Controls, Inc.; *U.S. Private*, pg. 1356
ELECTRONIC TOLL COLLECTION (PTY) LTD.—See Kapsch-Group Beteiligungs GmbH; *Int'l*, pg. 4077
ELECTRONIC TRAFFIC, S.A.—See ACS, Actividades de Construccion y Servicios, S.A.; *Int'l*, pg. 112
ELECTRONIC TRANSACTION CONSULTANTS, LLC—See Quarterhill Inc.; *Int'l*, pg. 6155
ELECTRONIC TRANSACTION GROUP NORDIC HOLDING AB—See British Columbia Investment Management Corp.; *Int'l*, pg. 1170
ELECTRONIC TRANSACTION GROUP NORDIC HOLDING AB—See Francisco Partners Management, LP; *U.S. Private*, pg. 1592
ELECTRONIC TRANSFER, INC.; *U.S. Private*, pg. 1356
ELECTRONIC WARFARE ASSOCIATES-CANADA, LTD.—See Intertek Group plc; *Int'l*, pg. 3762
ELECTRONIC WARFARE ASSOCIATES, INC.—See Sagewind Capital LLC; *U.S. Private*, pg. 3527
ELECTRON ITALIA S.R.L.—See Leonardo S.p.A.; *Int'l*, pg. 4460
ELECTRONIZET SA—See Ackermans & van Haaren NV; *Int'l*, pg. 105
ELECTRON LIBRE PRODUCTIONS SARL—See Vivendi SE; *Int'l*, pg. 8275
ELECTRON MEC S.A.R.L; *Int'l*, pg. 2353
ELECTRON MEC S.A.R.L; *Int'l*, pg. 2354
ELECTRON MICROSCOPY SCIENCES, INC.—See The Graham Group, Inc.; *U.S. Private*, pg. 4037
ELECTRO-OIL INTERNATIONAL A/S—See Ferguson plc; *Int'l*, pg. 2638

ELECTRO TECHNIK INDUSTRIES

ELECTROOP S.A—See Jenoptik AG; *Int'l*, pg. 3928
ELECTRO-OPTICAL INDUSTRIES, LLC—See HGH Infrared Systems Inc.; *U.S. Private*, pg. 1930
ELECTRO OPTICAL SYSTEMS NORDIC AB—See EOS GmbH Electro Optical Systems; *Int'l*, pg. 2458
ELECTRO OPTIC SYSTEMS HOLDINGS LIMITED; *Int'l*, pg. 2353
ELECTRO OPTIC SYSTEMS PTY LIMITED—See Electro Optic Systems Holdings Limited; *Int'l*, pg. 2353
ELECTRO-OPTIX, INC.; *U.S. Private*, pg. 1354
ELECTROPAC CO., INC.—See Mass Design, Inc.; *U.S. Private*, pg. 2603
ELECTROPALMA—See Rubis SCA; *Int'l*, pg. 6423
ELECTROPAR LTD.—See Preformed Line Products Company; *U.S. Public*, pg. 1714
ELECTRO PARTES DE MATAMOROS, S.A. DE C.V.—See The Hines Group, Inc.; *U.S. Private*, pg. 4053
ELECTROPHORETICS LTD.—See Proteome Sciences plc; *Int'l*, pg. 6004
ELECTROPLAST SA—See Sonepar S.A.; *Int'l*, pg. 7093
ELECTROPLATING ENGINEERS OF JAPAN LTD.—See Tanaka Holdings Co., Ltd.; *Int'l*, pg. 7455
ELECTROPRECIZIA S.A.; *Int'l*, pg. 2354
ELECTRO PRIME INC.; *U.S. Private*, pg. 1353
ELECTROPRIVOD LTD.; *Int'l*, pg. 2354
ELECTRO PUNO SAA; *Int'l*, pg. 2353
ELECTROPURA, S.R.L. DE C.V.—See PepsiCo, Inc.; *U.S. Public*, pg. 1668
ELECTROPUTERE S.A.; *Int'l*, pg. 2354
ELECTROPUTERE VFU PASCANI S.A.; *Int'l*, pg. 2354
ELECTROQUIL, S.A.—See I Squared Capital Advisors (US) LLC; *U.S. Private*, pg. 2025
ELECTROQUIMICA DEL NOROESTE, S.A.—See Jose de Mello, SGPS, S.A.; *Int'l*, pg. 4001
ELECTRO QUIMICA MEXICANA S.A. DE C.V.—See FMC Corporation; *U.S. Public*, pg. 861
ELECTRO RENT (BEIJING) TEST & MEASUREMENT EQUIPMENT RENTAL CO., LTD.—See Platinum Equity, LLC; *U.S. Private*, pg. 3202
ELECTRO RENT CORPORATION (EASTERN REGIONAL OFFICE)—See Platinum Equity, LLC; *U.S. Private*, pg. 3202
ELECTRO RENT CORPORATION—See Platinum Equity, LLC; *U.S. Private*, pg. 3202
ELECTRO RENT EUROPE NV—See Platinum Equity, LLC; *U.S. Private*, pg. 3202
ELECTROREP-ENERGY PRODUCTS; *U.S. Private*, pg. 1356
ELECTROREP, INC.—See Forward Solutions; *U.S. Private*, pg. 1578
ELECTRO-REPS INC.; *U.S. Private*, pg. 1354
ELECTROROUTE HOLDINGS LIMITED—See Mitsubishi Corporation; *Int'l*, pg. 4938
ELECTRO-SCIENCE LABORATORIES, LLC—See American Securities LLC; *U.S. Private*, pg. 251
ELECTRO SCIENTIFIC INDUSTRIES EUROPE LTD.—See MKS Instruments, Inc.; *U.S. Public*, pg. 1452
ELECTRO SCIENTIFIC INDUSTRIES, INC.—See MKS Instruments, Inc.; *U.S. Public*, pg. 1452
ELECTRO SCIENTIFIC INDUSTRIES JAPAN CO., LTD.—See MKS Instruments, Inc.; *U.S. Public*, pg. 1452
ELECTRO SCIENTIFIC INDUSTRIES SINGAPORE PTE LTD.—See MKS Instruments, Inc.; *U.S. Public*, pg. 1452
ELECTRO-SENSORS, INC.; *U.S. Public*, pg. 723
ELECTROSERVICE AB—See AB Electrolux; *Int'l*, pg. 41
ELECTRO-SERV (PVT.) LTD.—See SMC Corporation; *Int'l*, pg. 7003
ELECTROSOFT SERVICES INC; *U.S. Private*, pg. 1356
ELECTROSONIC, INC.—See Helvar Merca Oy AB; *Int'l*, pg. 3339
ELECTRO SONIC INC.; *Int'l*, pg. 2353
ELECTROSONIC, INC.; *U.S. Private*, pg. 1356
ELECTRO STANDARDS LABORATORIES INC.; *U.S. Private*, pg. 1353
ELECTRO STATIC TECHNOLOGY—See Illinois Tool Works Inc.; *U.S. Public*, pg. 1103
ELECTROSTEEL ALGERIE SPA—See Electrosteel Castings Ltd; *Int'l*, pg. 2354
ELECTROSTEEL CASTINGS GULF FZE.—See Electrosteel Castings Ltd; *Int'l*, pg. 2354
ELECTROSTEEL CASTINGS LTD; *Int'l*, pg. 2354
ELECTROSTEEL CASTINGS (UK) LIMITED—See Electrosteel Castings Ltd; *Int'l*, pg. 2354
ELECTROSTEEL EUROPE S.A.—See Electrosteel Castings Ltd; *Int'l*, pg. 2354
ELECTROSTEEL USA, LLC—See Electrosteel Castings Ltd; *Int'l*, pg. 2354
ELECTRO SUR ESTE SAA; *Int'l*, pg. 2353
ELECTRO SWITCH CORPORATION; *U.S. Private*, pg. 1353
ELECTROSWITCH ELECTRONIC PRODUCTS—See Electro Switch Corporation; *U.S. Private*, pg. 1353
ELECTROSWITCH SWITCHES & RELAYS—See Electro Switch Corporation; *U.S. Private*, pg. 1354
ELECTRO TECHNIK INDUSTRIES; *U.S. Private*, pg. 1354

ELECTRO TECHNIK INDUSTRIES

ELECTROTECNICA FAMAR S.A.C.I.I.E.—See Mirgor S.A.C.I.F.I.A.; *Int'l*, pg. 4919
ELECTROTEK CONCEPTS, INC.—See METRAWATT International GmbH; *Int'l*, pg. 4856
ELECTROTEL S.A.; *Int'l*, pg. 2354
ELECTROTHERM INDIA LTD - ELECTRIC VEHICLE DIVISION—See Electrotherm India Ltd; *Int'l*, pg. 2354
ELECTROTHERM INDIA LTD - ELECTROTHERM RENEWABLES—See Electrotherm India Ltd; *Int'l*, pg. 2354
ELECTROTHERM INDIA LTD - ENGINEERING & PROJECT DIVISION—See Electrotherm India Ltd; *Int'l*, pg. 2355
ELECTROTHERM INDIA LTD; *Int'l*, pg. 2354
ELECTRO THERM S.A.S—See NIBE Industrier AB; *Int'l*, pg. 5260
ELECTROVAYA COMPANY—See Electrovaya Inc.; *Int'l*, pg. 2355
ELECTROVAYA CORP.,—See Electrovaya Inc.; *Int'l*, pg. 2355
ELECTROVAYA INC.; *Int'l*, pg. 2355
ELECTROVAYA USA INC.—See Electrovaya Inc.; *Int'l*, pg. 2355
ELECTRO VIDRO S.A.—See Seves S.p.A.; *Int'l*, pg. 6736
ELECTROVOZ KURASTYRU ZAUYTY LLP—See Alstom S.A.; *Int'l*, pg. 383
ELECTRO-WIRE INC.—See Audax Group, Limited Partnership; *U.S. Private*, pg. 387
ELECTROX LASER LIMITED—See The 600 Group PLC; *Int'l*, pg. 7609
ELECTROZEMPER S.A.—See F.W. Thorpe plc; *Int'l*, pg. 2597
ELECTRUM AUTOMATION AB—See Addtech AB; *Int'l*, pg. 133
ELECTRUM SPECIAL ACQUISITION CORPORATION; *U.S. Private*, pg. 1356
ELECVEN CONSTRUCCIONES, S.A.—See Elecnor, S.A.; *Int'l*, pg. 2347
ELEDON PHARMACEUTICALS, INC.; *U.S. Public*, pg. 725
ELEFANTEN PORTUGUESA LDA. INDUSTRIA DE CALCADO—See Freudenberg SE; *Int'l*, pg. 2785
ELEFANTRISTE A/S—See Lagercrantz Group AB; *Int'l*, pg. 4394
ELEFIRST SCIENCE AND TECHNOLOGY CO., LTD.; *Int'l*, pg. 2355
E.LEGAL TECHNOLOGY SOLUTIONS LIMITED—See The Ince Group Plc; *Int'l*, pg. 7654
ELEGANCE GMBH—See Puccini Holding GmbH; *Int'l*, pg. 6115
ELEGANCE OPTICAL INTERNATIONAL HOLDINGS LTD.; *Int'l*, pg. 2355
ELEGANCE OPTICAL INVESTMENTS LIMITED—See Elegance Optical International Holdings Ltd.; *Int'l*, pg. 2355
ELEGANCE OPTICAL MANUFACTORY LIMITED—See Elegance Optical International Holdings Ltd.; *Int'l*, pg. 2355
ELEGANT FOOTWEAR LIMITED—See Quetta Group of Companies LLC; *Int'l*, pg. 6161
ELEGANT ILLUSIONS, INC., *U.S. Private*, pg. 1356
ELEGANT LANDSCAPES PTY LIMITED—See Nutrien Ltd.; *Int'l*, pg. 5493
ELEGANT MARBLES & GRANI INDUSTRIES LTD.; *Int'l*, pg. 2355
ELEGANT RESORTS LTD.—See Seera Group Holding Co.; *Int'l*, pg. 6679
ELEGANZA TILES, INC.; *U.S. Private*, pg. 1356
ELEGIA FORMATION, SAS—See Editions Lefebvre Sarrut SA; *Int'l*, pg. 2311
ELEGRITY, INC.—See iManage LLC; *U.S. Private*, pg. 2046
ELE INTERNATIONAL, INC—See Danaher Corporation; *U.S. Public*, pg. 626
ELE INTERNATIONAL—See Danaher Corporation; *U.S. Public*, pg. 626
ELEISON COMPOSITES, LLC—See Innovative Composites International, Inc.; *Int'l*, pg. 3712
ELEISON PHARMACEUTICALS INC.; *U.S. Private*, pg. 1356
ELEJOR - CENTRAIS ELETRIÇAS DO RIO JORDAO S.A.—See Companhia Paranaense de Energia; *Int'l*, pg. 1748
ELEKDIRECT LIMITED—See AO World PLC; *Int'l*, pg. 487
ELEKEIROZ S.A.—See H.I.G. Capital, LLC; *U.S. Private*, pg. 1828
ELEKEM LTD.—See Ensinger GmbH; *Int'l*, pg. 2447
ELEKTA AB; *Int'l*, pg. 2355
ELEKTA ASIA LTD—See Elekta AB; *Int'l*, pg. 2355
ELEKTA BMEI (BEIJING) MEDICAL EQUIPMENT CO., LTD—See Elekta AB; *Int'l*, pg. 2355
ELEKTA B.V.—See Elekta AB; *Int'l*, pg. 2355
ELEKTA GMBH—See Elekta AB; *Int'l*, pg. 2355
ELEKTA GMBH—See Elekta AB; *Int'l*, pg. 2355
ELEKTA HELLAS EPE—See Elekta AB; *Int'l*, pg. 2355
ELEKTA / IMPAC MEDICAL SYSTEMS, INC.—See Elekta AB; *Int'l*, pg. 2355
ELEKTA IMPAC SOFTWARE—See Elekta AB; *Int'l*, pg. 2356

ELEKTA INC.—See Elekta AB; *Int'l*, pg. 2355
ELEKTA INSTRUMENT AB—See Elekta AB; *Int'l*, pg. 2355
ELEKTA INSTRUMENT (SHANGHAI) LTD—See Elekta AB; *Int'l*, pg. 2355
ELEKTA KK.—See Elekta AB; *Int'l*, pg. 2355
ELEKTA LIMITED—See Elekta AB; *Int'l*, pg. 2355
ELEKTA LIMITED—See Elekta AB; *Int'l*, pg. 2355
ELEKTA LLC—See Elekta AB; *Int'l*, pg. 2355
ELEKTA LTD.—See Elekta AB; *Int'l*, pg. 2355
ELEKTA MEDICAL SA DE CV—See Elekta AB; *Int'l*, pg. 2355
ELEKTA MEDICAL S.A.—See Elekta AB; *Int'l*, pg. 2355
ELEKTA MEDICAL SYSTEMS COMERCIO E PRESTACAO DE SERVICOS PARA RADIOLOGIA, RADIOCIRURGIA E RADIOTERAPIA LTDA.—See Elekta AB; *Int'l*, pg. 2355
ELEKTA MEDICAL SYSTEMS INDIA PVT. LTD.—See Elekta AB; *Int'l*, pg. 2355
ELEKTA MEDICAL SYSTEMS SRL—See Elekta AB; *Int'l*, pg. 2356
ELEKTA MEDIKAL SISTEMLER TICARET A.S.—See Elekta AB; *Int'l*, pg. 2356
ELEKTA NEUROMAG OY—See Elekta AB; *Int'l*, pg. 2356
ELEKTA PTE LTD.—See Elekta AB; *Int'l*, pg. 2356
ELEKTA PTY. LTD.—See Elekta AB; *Int'l*, pg. 2356
ELEKTA (PTY) LTD (SOUTHERN AFRICA)—See Elekta AB; *Int'l*, pg. 2355
ELEKTA S.A./N.V.—See Elekta AB; *Int'l*, pg. 2356
ELEKTA SA—See Elekta AB; *Int'l*, pg. 2356
ELEKTA SERVICES S.R.O.—See Elekta AB; *Int'l*, pg. 2356
ELEKTA SOLUTIONS AB—See Elekta AB; *Int'l*, pg. 2356
ELEKTA S.P.A.—See Elekta AB; *Int'l*, pg. 2356
ELEKTA SP.Z.O.O—See Elekta AB; *Int'l*, pg. 2356
ELEKTOR INDUSTRIES INC.; *U.S. Private*, pg. 1357
ELEKTRA BREGENZ AG—See Koc Holding A.S.; *Int'l*, pg. 4223
ELEKTRAM SPOL. S R.O.—See Sonepar S.A.; *Int'l*, pg. 7090
ELEKTRA NORESTE S.A.—See Empresas Publicas de Medellin ESP; *Int'l*, pg. 2392
ELEKTRA RECORDS—See Access Industries, Inc.; *U.S. Private*, pg. 52
ELEKTRARNA POCERADY, A.S.—See CEZ, a.s.; *Int'l*, pg. 1427
ELEKTRARNY OPATOVICE, A.S.—See J&T Finance Group SE; *Int'l*, pg. 3854
ELEKTRICA SOLUZIONA S.A. (ROMANIA)—See Indra Sistemas, S.A.; *Int'l*, pg. 3660
ELEKTRILEVI OU—See Eesti Energia AS; *Int'l*, pg. 2317
ELEKTRIM-MEGADEX S.A.—See Elektrim S.A.; *Int'l*, pg. 2356
ELEKTRIM S.A.; *Int'l*, pg. 2356
ELEKTRIM-VOLT S.A.—See Elektrim S.A.; *Int'l*, pg. 2356
ELEKTRISKA AB DELTA—See Schneider Electric SE; *Int'l*, pg. 6626
ELEKTRISK AS—See Instalco AB; *Int'l*, pg. 3721
ELEKTRISOLA ATESINA S.R.L.—See Elektrisola Dr. Gerd Schildbach GmbH & Co. KG; *Int'l*, pg. 2356
ELEKTRISOLA COMPANY LIMITED—See Elektrisola Dr. Gerd Schildbach GmbH & Co. KG; *Int'l*, pg. 2356
ELEKTRISOLA DR. GERD SCHILDBACH GMBH & CO. KG; *Int'l*, pg. 2356
ELEKTRISOLA FEINDRAHT AG—See Elektrisola Dr. Gerd Schildbach GmbH & Co. KG; *Int'l*, pg. 2356
ELEKTRISOLA FRANCE SA—See Elektrisola Dr. Gerd Schildbach GmbH & Co. KG; *Int'l*, pg. 2356
ELEKTRISOLA (HANGZHOU) CO., LTD.—See Elektrisola Dr. Gerd Schildbach GmbH & Co. KG; *Int'l*, pg. 2356
ELEKTRISOLA INC.—See Elektrisola Dr. Gerd Schildbach GmbH & Co. KG; *Int'l*, pg. 2356
ELEKTRISOLA INDIA PVT. LTD.—See Elektrisola Dr. Gerd Schildbach GmbH & Co. KG; *Int'l*, pg. 2356
ELEKTRISOLA KOREA CO. LTD.—See Elektrisola Dr. Gerd Schildbach GmbH & Co. KG; *Int'l*, pg. 2356
ELEKTRISOLA (M) SDN. BHD.—See Elektrisola Dr. Gerd Schildbach GmbH & Co. KG; *Int'l*, pg. 2356
ELEKTRISOLA S.A. DE C.V.—See Elektrisola Dr. Gerd Schildbach GmbH & Co. KG; *Int'l*, pg. 2356
ELEKTRIZITAETSWERK MINDEN-RAVENSBERG—See E.ON SE; *Int'l*, pg. 2253
ELEKTRIZITATSWERK AACH EG,—See EnBW Energie Baden-Wurttemberg AG; *Int'l*, pg. 2398
ELEKTRIZITATSWERK DER STADT ZURICH; *Int'l*, pg. 2356
ELEKTRIZITATSWERK WEISSENHORN AG—See EnBW Energie Baden-Wurttemberg AG; *Int'l*, pg. 2398
ELEKTRO ARBER AG—See Burkhalter Holding AG; *Int'l*, pg. 1224
ELEKTROAUTOMATIK I SVERIGE AB—See Storskogen Group AB; *Int'l*, pg. 7227
ELEKTRO-BAU AG ROTHRIST—See Burkhalter Holding AG; *Int'l*, pg. 1225
ELEKTROBIT AUSTRIA GMBH—See Continental Aktiengesellschaft; *Int'l*, pg. 1783
ELEKTROBIT AUTOMOTIVE AMERICAS INC.—See Continental Aktiengesellschaft; *Int'l*, pg. 1783
ELEKTROBIT AUTOMOTIVE GMBH—See Continental Aktiengesellschaft; *Int'l*, pg. 1783

CORPORATE AFFILIATIONS

ELEKTROBIT AUTOMOTIVE SOFTWARE (SHANGHAI) CO., LTD.—See Continental Aktiengesellschaft; *Int'l*, pg. 1783
ELEKTROBIT FRANCE SAS—See Continental Aktiengesellschaft; *Int'l*, pg. 1783
ELEKTROBIT NIPPON K.K.—See Continental Aktiengesellschaft; *Int'l*, pg. 1783
ELEKTROBIT TECHNOLOGIES OY—See Bittium Oyj; *Int'l*, pg. 1050
ELEKTRO BURKHALTER AG—See Burkhalter Holding AG; *Int'l*, pg. 1224
ELEKTRO-CENTRALEN ENTREPRENAD HISINGS BACKA AB—See Instalco AB; *Int'l*, pg. 3721
ELEKTRO CHRISTOFFEL, ZNL DER CAVIEZEL AG—See Burkhalter Holding AG; *Int'l*, pg. 1224
ELEKTROCIEPLOWNIA BEDZIN S.A.—See RWE AG; *Int'l*, pg. 6434
ELEKTROCIEPLOWNIA CHORZOW ELCHO SP. Z.O.O.—See CEZ, a.s.; *Int'l*, pg. 1426
ELEKTRO-DECKER GMBH—See CEZ, a.s.; *Int'l*, pg. 1427
ELEKTRODISTRIBUCIJA DOOEL—See EVN AG; *Int'l*, pg. 2571
ELEKTRODIZALICA A.D.; *Int'l*, pg. 2357
ELEKTRO-DYNAMO AB—See Axel Johnson Gruppen AB; *Int'l*, pg. 763
ELEKTRO ELCO AB—See OEM International AB; *Int'l*, pg. 5528
ELEKTRO ELECTRICIDADE E SERVICOS, S.A.—See Iberdrola, S.A.; *Int'l*, pg. 3571
ELEKTROENERGETICKE MONTAZE, A. S.—See Stredoslovenska Energetika, A.S.; *Int'l*, pg. 7239
ELEKTRO FEUZ AG—See BKW AG; *Int'l*, pg. 1055
ELEKTRO GRUPA D.D.; *Int'l*, pg. 2356
ELEKTRO GUTZWILLER AG—See Burkhalter Holding AG; *Int'l*, pg. 1224
ELEKTRO HUNZIKER AG—See Burkhalter Holding AG; *Int'l*, pg. 1224
ELEKTROHUUS VON ALLMEN AG—See Burkhalter Holding AG; *Int'l*, pg. 1225
ELEKTROIMPORTOREN AS; *Int'l*, pg. 2357
ELEKTRO INDUSTRIJSKA SERVISNA MREZA A.D.; *Int'l*, pg. 2357
ELEKTRO KALIN AG—See Burkhalter Holding AG; *Int'l*, pg. 1224
ELEKTROKARBON A.S.—See HTC holding a.s.; *Int'l*, pg. 3508
ELEKTROKERAMIK SONNEBERG GMBH—See Seves S.p.A.; *Int'l*, pg. 6736
ELEKTROKONTAKT GMBH—See Nexans S.A.; *Int'l*, pg. 5241
ELEKTROKONTAKT SRL DE CV—See Nexans S.A.; *Int'l*, pg. 5240
ELEKTROKOPPAR AB—See IK Investment Partners Limited; *Int'l*, pg. 3609
ELEKTROKRAJINA A.D. BANJA LUKA; *Int'l*, pg. 2357
ELEKTRO MACK GMBH; *Int'l*, pg. 2357
ELEKTRO-MATERIAL AG—See Rexel, S.A.; *Int'l*, pg. 6316
ELEKTROMETAL AD; *Int'l*, pg. 2357
ELEKTROMETAL A.D.; *Int'l*, pg. 2357
ELEKTRO-METALL EXPORT GMBH—See TransDigm Group Incorporated; *U.S. Public*, pg. 2182
ELEKTROMONT A.D.; *Int'l*, pg. 2357
ELEKTROMONTAZ KRAKOW S.A.—See PROCHEM S.A.; *Int'l*, pg. 5986
ELEKTROMOTORENWERK GRUNHAIN GMBH—See MS Industrie AG; *Int'l*, pg. 5065
ELEKTRONABAVA D.O.O.—See Rexel, S.A.; *Int'l*, pg. 6316
ELEKTRO NAEGELIN AG—See BKW AG; *Int'l*, pg. 1055
ELEKTRON COMPONENTS CORPORATION—See Checkit plc; *Int'l*, pg. 1459
ELEKTRON COMPONENTS LTD.—See Checkit plc; *Int'l*, pg. 1459
ELEKTRON COMPONENTS TUNISIE SARL—See Checkit plc; *Int'l*, pg. 1459
ELEKTRONIKA SLOVENSKO A.S.—See Schneider Electric SE; *Int'l*, pg. 6627
ELEKTRO NIKLAUS AG—See Burkhalter Holding AG; *Int'l*, pg. 1224
ELEKTRONISCHE FAHRWERKSYSTEME GMBH—See Adecco Group AG; *Int'l*, pg. 140
ELEKTRO PIZOL AG—See Burkhalter Holding AG; *Int'l*, pg. 1224
ELEKTROPORCELAN A.D.; *Int'l*, pg. 2357
ELEKTROPORCELAN ARANDELOVAC A.D.; *Int'l*, pg. 2357
ELEKTRORAZPREDELENIE YUG EAD—See EVN AG; *Int'l*, pg. 2571
ELEKTRO REDES S.A.—See Iberdrola, S.A.; *Int'l*, pg. 3572
ELEKTROREMONT D.D.; *Int'l*, pg. 2357
ELEKTRO RUEGG AG—See Burkhalter Holding AG; *Int'l*, pg. 1224
ELEKTRO SCHMIDLIN AG—See Burkhalter Holding AG; *Int'l*, pg. 1225
ELEKTROSERVIS A.D.; *Int'l*, pg. 2357
ELEKTRO SIEGRIST AG—See Burkhalter Holding AG; *Int'l*, pg. 1225
ELEKTROS, INC.; *Int'l*, pg. 2357

COMPANY NAME INDEX

ELEKTROSKANDIA AB—See Sonepar S.A.; *Int'l*, pg. 7090
ELEKTROSKANDIA LATVIA—See Rexel, S.A.; *Int'l*, pg. 6316
ELEKTROSKANDIA LTD.—See Rexel, S.A.; *Int'l*, pg. 6316
ELEKTROSKANDIA NORGE AS—See Rexel, S.A.; *Int'l*, pg. 6316
ELEKTROSKANDIA POLSKA S.A.—See Rexel, S.A.; *Int'l*, pg. 6317
ELEKTROSKANDIA SUOMI OY—See Rexel, S.A.; *Int'l*, pg. 6316
ELEKTRO SLOVENIA D.O.O.; *Int'l*, pg. 2357
ELEKTRO STAMPFL AG—See Burkhalter Holding AG; *Int'l*, pg. 1225
ELEKTRO STILLER GMBH—See Alpiq Holding AG; *Int'l*, pg. 372
ELEKTRO-TECHNIK-PFISTERER-GMBH—See CEZ, a.s.; *Int'l*, pg. 1427
ELEKTROTERMIJA LTD.—See NIBE Industrier AB; *Int'l*, pg. 5260
ELEKTROTIM S.A.; *Int'l*, pg. 2357
ELEKTROVEZE PROIZVODNJA A.D.; *Int'l*, pg. 2357
ELEKTROWERK WEISWEILER GMBH—See Afarak Group SE; *Int'l*, pg. 185
ELEKTRO WINTER AG—See BKW AG; *Int'l*, pg. 1055
ELEKTROWNIA BELCHATOW S.A.; *Int'l*, pg. 2357
ELEKTROWNIA KOZIENICE S.A.—See ENEA S.A.; *Int'l*, pg. 2410
ELEKTROWNIA SKAWINA S.A.—See CEZ, a.s.; *Int'l*, pg. 1427
ELEKTROWNIE WIATROWE LUBIECHOVO SP. Z.O.O.—See CEZ, a.s.; *Int'l*, pg. 1427
ELEKTROWNIE WODNE SP. Z O.O.—See ENEA S.A.; *Int'l*, pg. 2410
ELEKTRO ZURICHSEE AG—See Burkhalter Holding AG; *Int'l*, pg. 1225
EL & EL WOOD PRODUCTS CORP.—See Metrie Canada Limited; *Int'l*, pg. 4856
ELEMATEC CORPORATION—See Toyota Tsusho Corporation; *Int'l*, pg. 7876
ELEMATEC CZECH S.R.O.—See Toyota Tsusho Corporation; *Int'l*, pg. 7876
ELEMATEC ELECTRONICS (DALIAN) CO., LTD.—See Toyota Tsusho Corporation; *Int'l*, pg. 7877
ELEMATEC HONG KONG LIMITED—See Toyota Tsusho Corporation; *Int'l*, pg. 7077
ELEMATEC INTERNATIONAL TRADING (SHENZHEN) CO., LTD.—See Toyota Tsusho Corporation; *Int'l*, pg. 7877
ELEMATEC KOREA CO., LTD.—See Toyota Tsusho Corporation; *Int'l*, pg. 7877
ELEMATEC PHILIPPINES, INC.—See Toyota Tsusho Corporation; *Int'l*, pg. 7877
ELEMATEC (QINGDAO) TRADING CO., LTD.—See Toyota Tsusho Corporation; *Int'l*, pg. 7876
ELEMATEC (SHANGHAI) TRADING CO., LTD.—See Toyota Tsusho Corporation; *Int'l*, pg. 7876
ELEMATEC SINGAPORE (PTE.) LTD.—See Toyota Tsusho Corporation; *Int'l*, pg. 7877
ELEMATEC TAIWAN CORPORATION—See Toyota Tsusho Corporation; *Int'l*, pg. 7876
ELEMATEC (THAILAND) CO., LTD.—See Toyota Tsusho Corporation; *Int'l*, pg. 7877
ELEMATEC (TIANJIN) INTERNATIONAL TRADING CO., LTD.—See Toyota Tsusho Corporation; *Int'l*, pg. 7876
ELEMATEC TRADING (DALIAN) CO., LTD.—See Toyota Tsusho Corporation; *Int'l*, pg. 7877
ELEMATEC TRADING INDIA PRIVATE LIMITED—See Toyota Tsusho Corporation; *Int'l*, pg. 7877
ELEMATEC USA CORPORATION—See Toyota Tsusho Corporation; *Int'l*, pg. 7877
ELEMATEC VIETNAM CO., LTD.—See Toyota Tsusho Corporation; *Int'l*, pg. 7876
ELEMENT14 ASIA PTE. LTD.—See Avnet, Inc.; *U.S. Public*, pg. 253
ELEMENT14 CO., LTD.—See Avnet, Inc.; *U.S. Public*, pg. 253
ELEMENT14 HOLDING BV—See Avnet, Inc.; *U.S. Public*, pg. 253
ELEMENT14 INDIA PVT LIMITED—See Avnet, Inc.; *U.S. Public*, pg. 253
ELEMENT14 LIMITED—See Avnet, Inc.; *U.S. Public*, pg. 253
ELEMENT14 LIMITED—See Avnet, Inc.; *U.S. Public*, pg. 253
ELEMENT14 PTE LTD—See Avnet, Inc.; *U.S. Public*, pg. 253
ELEMENT14 PTE. LTD.—See Avnet, Inc.; *U.S. Public*, pg. 253
ELEMENT14 PTY LTD—See Avnet, Inc.; *U.S. Public*, pg. 253
ELEMENT14. S. DE R.L. DE C.V—See Avnet, Inc.; *U.S. Public*, pg. 253
ELEMENT14 SDN. BHD.—See Avnet, Inc.; *U.S. Public*, pg. 254
ELEMENT 14 SP. ZOO—See Avnet, Inc.; *U.S. Public*, pg. 253
ELEMENT 21 GOLF CANADA INC—See American Rare Earths & Materials, Corp.; *Int'l*, pg. 423
ELEMENT 25 LIMITED; *Int'l*, pg. 2357

ELEMENT 29 RESOURCES INC.; *Int'l*, pg. 2357
ELEMENT 78 LLC; *U.S. Private*, pg. 1357
ELEMENT79 GOLD CORP.; *Int'l*, pg. 2358
ELEMENT AG—See CRH plc; *Int'l*, pg. 1844
ELEMENTAL ALTUS ROYALTIES CORP.; *Int'l*, pg. 2358
ELEMENTAL ENERGIES HOLDINGS LIMITED; *Int'l*, pg. 2358
ELEMENTAL HEALTHCARE LIMITED—See Surgical Innovations Group Plc; *Int'l*, pg. 7344
ELEMENTAL HOLDING S.A.; *Int'l*, pg. 2358
ELEMENT ALPHA SA; *Int'l*, pg. 2358
ELEMENTAL RESOURCE MANAGEMENT LTD.—See Elemental Holding S.A.; *Int'l*, pg. 2358
ELEMENTAL TECHNOLOGIES, INC.; *U.S. Private*, pg. 1357
ELEMENTAL USA INC.—See Elemental Holding S.A.; *Int'l*, pg. 2358
ELEMENTARY ENERGY LIMITED—See Triple Point Energy Transition Plc; *Int'l*, pg. 7927
ELEMENT BLUE LLC—See Delta-v Capital, LLC; *U.S. Private*, pg. 1202
ELEMENT CARE; *U.S. Private*, pg. 1357
ELEMENT CLEVELAND—See Temasek Holdings (Private) Limited; *Int'l*, pg. 7547
ELEMENT DATA, INC.; *U.S. Private*, pg. 1357
ELEMENT FLEET MANAGEMENT CORPORATION MEXICO S.A. DE C.V—See Element Fleet Management Corporation; *Int'l*, pg. 2358
ELEMENT FLEET MANAGEMENT CORPORATION; *Int'l*, pg. 2358
ELEMENT GLOBAL, INC.; *U.S. Public*, pg. 725
ELEMENTIA S.A.—See Grupo Empresarial Kaluz S.A. de C.V.; *Int'l*, pg. 3126
ELEMENTIS CHROMIUM, LP—See Elementis plc; *Int'l*, pg. 2359
ELEMENTIS CHROMIUM—See Elementis plc; *Int'l*, pg. 2359
ELEMENTIS LTP, LT—See Elementis plc; *Int'l*, pg. 2359
ELEMENTIS PHARMA GMBH—See Elementis plc; *Int'l*, pg. 2359
ELEMENTIS PLC; *Int'l*, pg. 2358
ELEMENTIS S.E.A. (MALAYSIA) SDN BHD—See Elementis plc; *Int'l*, pg. 2359
ELEMENTIS SPECIALTIES, INC.—See Elementis plc; *Int'l*, pg. 2359
ELEMENT K PRESS LLC—See Charterhouse Capital Partners LLP; *Int'l*, pg. 1456
ELEMENT LEXINGTON—See Marriott International, Inc.; *U.S. Public*, pg. 1372
ELEMENT LIFESTYLE RETIREMENT INC.; *Int'l*, pg. 2358
ELEMENT LIGHTING DESIGN LIMITED—See e Lighting Group Holdings Limited; *Int'l*, pg. 2246
ELEMENT MARKETS LLC—See TPG Capital, L.P.; *U.S. Public*, pg. 2177
ELEMENT MATERIALS TECHNOLOGY AB - KARLSKOGA—See Temasek Holdings (Private) Limited; *Int'l*, pg. 7547
ELEMENT MATERIALS TECHNOLOGY AB—See Temasek Holdings (Private) Limited; *Int'l*, pg. 7547
ELEMENT MATERIALS TECHNOLOGY B.V.—See Temasek Holdings (Private) Limited; *Int'l*, pg. 7547
ELEMENT MATERIALS TECHNOLOGY - CINCINNATI—See Temasek Holdings (Private) Limited; *Int'l*, pg. 7547
ELEMENT MATERIALS TECHNOLOGY LABORATORY SOLUTIONS UK LIMITED—See Temasek Holdings (Private) Limited; *Int'l*, pg. 7547
ELEMENT MATERIALS TECHNOLOGY LTD.—See Temasek Holdings (Private) Limited; *Int'l*, pg. 7547
ELEMENT MATERIALS TECHNOLOGY WARWICK LTD—See Temasek Holdings (Private) Limited; *Int'l*, pg. 7547
ELEMENT METECH AB—See Temasek Holdings (Private) Limited; *Int'l*, pg. 7547
ELEMENT METECH AB—See Temasek Holdings (Private) Limited; *Int'l*, pg. 7547
ELEMENT METECH A/S—See Temasek Holdings (Private) Limited; *Int'l*, pg. 7547
ELEMENT METECH GMBH—See Temasek Holdings (Private) Limited; *Int'l*, pg. 7547
ELEMENT METECH OY—See Temasek Holdings (Private) Limited; *Int'l*, pg. 7547
ELEMENT NATIONAL MANAGEMENT COMPANY; *U.S. Private*, pg. 1357
ELEMENT NUTRITIONAL SCIENCES INC.; *Int'l*, pg. 2358
ELEMENTOS LIMITED; *Int'l*, pg. 2359
ELEMENT PARTNERS, LLC; *U.S. Private*, pg. 1357
ELEMENT PAYMENT SERVICES, INC.; *U.S. Private*, pg. 1357
ELEMENT RANCHO DOMINGUEZ—See Temasek Holdings (Private) Limited; *Int'l*, pg. 7547
ELEMENT RISK MANAGEMENT LLC; *U.S. Private*, pg. 1357
ELEMENT RULE CO., LTD.—See Adastria Co., Ltd.; *Int'l*, pg. 126
ELEMENTS BEHAVIORAL HEALTH, INC.; *U.S. Private*, pg. 1357
ELEMENTS FOR WOMEN, INC.; *U.S. Private*, pg. 1357

ELEMENTS HEALTH INVESTORS, LLC; *U.S. Private*, pg. 1357
ELEMENT SIX ABRASIVES HOLDINGS LIMITED—See Anglo American PLC; *Int'l*, pg. 462
ELEMENT SIX GMBH—See Anglo American PLC; *Int'l*, pg. 462
ELEMENT SIX LIMITED—See Anglo American PLC; *Int'l*, pg. 462
ELEMENT SIX LIMITED—See Anglo American PLC; *Int'l*, pg. 462
ELEMENT SIX (PRODUCTION) PROPRIETARY LIMITED—See Anglo American PLC; *Int'l*, pg. 462
ELEMENT SIX S.A.—See Anglo American PLC; *Int'l*, pg. 462
ELEMENT SIX TECHNOLOGIES LIMITED—See Anglo American PLC; *Int'l*, pg. 462
ELEMENT SIX TECHNOLOGIES (OR) CORP.—See Anglo American PLC; *Int'l*, pg. 462
ELEMENT SIX TECHNOLOGIES US CORPORATION—See Anglo American PLC; *Int'l*, pg. 462
ELEMENT SIX TRADING (SHANGHAI) CO., LTD.—See Anglo American PLC; *Int'l*, pg. 462
ELEMENT SIX (UK) LIMITED—See Anglo American PLC; *Int'l*, pg. 462
ELEMENT SIX U.S. CORPORATION—See Anglo American PLC; *Int'l*, pg. 462
ELEMENT SKATEBOARDS, INC.—See Leonard Green & Partners, L.P.; *U.S. Private*, pg. 2424
ELEMENTS, LLC; *U.S. Private*, pg. 1357
ELEMENTS OF HEALTH AND WELLNESS, INC.—See ASC Global Inc.; *U.S. Private*, pg. 345
ELEMENT SOLUTIONS INC.; *U.S. Public*, pg. 725
ELEMENT SOLUTIONS, LLC—See Hinduja Global Solutions Ltd.; *Int'l*, pg. 3398
ELEMENT—See The Engine Group; *Int'l*, pg. 7640
ELEMENT TECHNICAL SERVICES INC.; *Int'l*, pg. 2358
ELEMENT VEHICLE MANAGEMENT SERVICES, LLC—See Element Fleet Management Corporation; *Int'l*, pg. 2358
ELEMENT WHEELS; *U.S. Private*, pg. 1357
ELEME PETROCHEMICALS COMPANY LTD—See Nigerian National Petroleum Corporation; *Int'l*, pg. 5282
ELEMETAL REFINING, LLC; *U.S. Private*, pg. 1357
ELEMICA, INC.—See Eurazeo SE; *Int'l*, pg. 2528
ELEMICA INTERNATIONAL B.V.—See Eurazeo SE; *Int'l*, pg. 2528
ELEMICA INTERNATIONAL INC.—See Eurazeo SE; *Int'l*, pg. 2528
ELEMIS LIMITED—See L'Occitane Groupe S.A.; *Int'l*, pg. 4378
ELEMKA S.A.—See Metlen Energy & Metals S.A.; *Int'l*, pg. 4854
ELEMUS LLC—See Danto Holdings Corporation; *Int'l*, pg. 1969
ELENA'S FOOD SPECIALTIES, INC.—See ADF Foods Ltd.; *Int'l*, pg. 145
ELENBAAS COMPANY; *U.S. Private*, pg. 1357
EL ENCANTO INCORPORATED; *U.S. Private*, pg. 1349
EL ENCANTO INC.—See LVMH Moet Hennessy Louis Vuitton SE; *Int'l*, pg. 4591
ELENCO ELECTRONICS, INC.; *U.S. Private*, pg. 1357
ELENCO LIGHTING AB—See Fagerhult Group AB; *Int'l*, pg. 2602
ELENGY S.A.—See ENGIE SA; *Int'l*, pg. 2428
ELENICA AD; *Int'l*, pg. 2359
EL.EN. S.P.A.; *Int'l*, pg. 2341
ELENSYS CO., LTD.; *Int'l*, pg. 2359
ELENTEC CO,. LTD.; *Int'l*, pg. 2359
ELENTEC INDIA TECHNOLOGIES PVT. LTD. - CHARGER FACTORY—See Elentec co,. Ltd.; *Int'l*, pg. 2359
ELENTEC INDIA TECHNOLOGIES PVT. LTD.—See Elentec co,. Ltd.; *Int'l*, pg. 2359
ELEPHANT CAPITAL PLC; *Int'l*, pg. 2359
ELEPHANT HILL CAPITAL, INC.; *Int'l*, pg. 2359
ELEPHANT HOLDINGS LIMITED—See Pokfulam Development Company Limited; *Int'l*, pg. 5905
ELEPHANT INSURANCE COMPANY—See Admiral Group plc; *Int'l*, pg. 151
ELEPHANT INSURANCE SERVICES LLC—See Admiral Group plc; *Int'l*, pg. 151
ELEPHANT NONWOVENS - NAO TECIDOS U.P., LDA.—See Aktieselskabet Schouw & Co.; *Int'l*, pg. 265
ELEPHANT OIL CORP.; *U.S. Private*, pg. 1358
ELEPRENEURS U.S., LLC—See Sharing Services Global Corporation; *U.S. Public*, pg. 1873
ELEROM S.A. ROMAN; *Int'l*, pg. 2359
ELESA S.P.A.—See Brd. Klee A/S; *Int'l*, pg. 1143
ELES-GEN, D.O.O.—See Elektro Slovenia d.o.o.; *Int'l*, pg. 2357
ELES S.P.A.; *Int'l*, pg. 2359
ELESYS NORTH AMERICA INC.—See Honda Motor Co., Ltd.; *Int'l*, pg. 3460
ELET.CA—See Marcegaglia S.p.A.; *Int'l*, pg. 4688
ELETROBRAS ELETRONORTE—See Centrais Elétricas Brasileiras S.A.; *Int'l*, pg. 1403
ELETROBRAS TERMONUCLEAR SA—See Centrais Elétricas Brasileiras S.A.; *Int'l*, pg. 1403

ELES S.P.A.

ELETRONOR DISTRIBUIDORA DE MATERIAIS ELETRICOS LTDA—See Sonepar S.A.; *Int'l*, pg. 7093
ELETROPAULO METROPOLITANA ELETRICIDADE DE SAO PAULO S.A.—See Enel S.p.A.; *Int'l*, pg. 2412
ELETROSUL CENTRAIS ELETRICAS S.A.—See Centrais Eletricas Brasileiras S.A.; *Int'l*, pg. 1403
ELETT CORPORATION—See Toyota Industries Corporation; *Int'l*, pg. 7866
ELETTO (THAILAND) CO. LTD.—See NITTO KOGYO CORPORATION; *Int'l*, pg. 5387
ELETTRA INVESTIMENTI SPA—See CogenInfra SpA; *Int'l*, pg. 1694
ELETTRO CELIO SA—See Burkhalter Holding AG; *Int'l*, pg. 1225
ELETTROINGROSS S.P.A.—See Sonepar S.A.; *Int'l*, pg. 7092
ELETTRONICA BIO MEDICALE S.P.A.—See Permira Advisers LLP; *Int'l*, pg. 5808
ELETTRONICA CIMONE SRL—See Beghelli S.p.A.; *Int'l*, pg. 941
ELETTRONICA INDUSTRIALE S.P.A.—See Mediaset S.p.A.; *Int'l*, pg. 4773
ELETTRONICA SANTERNO S.P.A.—See Enertronica Santerno S.p.A.; *Int'l*, pg. 2425
ELETTROPIEMME S.R.L.—See Gefran S.p.A.; *Int'l*, pg. 2912
ELEV8 BRANDS, INC.; *U.S. Public*, pg. 728
ELEVAATE LIMITED—See Charlesbank Capital Partners, LLC; *U.S. Private*, pg. 855
ELEVACITY U.S., LLC—See Sharing Services Global Corporation; *U.S. Public*, pg. 1873
ELEVADORES ATLAS SCHINDLER S.A.—See Schindler Holding AG; *Int'l*, pg. 6618
ELEVADORES OTIS LTDA.—See Otis Worldwide Corporation; *U.S. Public*, pg. 1623
ELEVADORES OTIS, S.A. DE C.V.—See Otis Worldwide Corporation; *U.S. Public*, pg. 1623
ELEVADORES OTIS S/A—See Otis Worldwide Corporation; *U.S. Public*, pg. 1623
ELEVADORES SCHINDLER S.A. DE C.V.—See Schindler Holding AG; *Int'l*, pg. 6618
ELEVAIR S.A.—See Emerson Electric Co.; *U.S. Public*, pg. 743
ELEVANCE HEALTH, INC.; *U.S. Public*, pg. 728
ELEVANCE RENEWABLE SCIENCES, INC.; *U.S. Private*, pg. 1358
ELEVATE CREDIT, INC.—See Park Cities Asset Management LLC; *U.S. Private*, pg. 3095
ELEVATE CREDIT INTERNATIONAL LIMITED—See Park Cities Asset Management LLC; *U.S. Private*, pg. 3095
ELEVATE ENTERTAINMENT, INC.; *U.S. Private*, pg. 1358
ELEVATE HOLDINGS, INC.; *U.S. Private*, pg. 1358
ELEVATE ORAL CARE, LLC; *U.S. Private*, pg. 1358
ELEVATE STAFFING, INC.; *U.S. Private*, pg. 1358
ELEVATE TECHNOLOGY SOLUTIONS; *U.S. Private*, pg. 1358
ELEVATE TEXTILES INC.—See Platinum Equity, LLC; *U.S. Private*, pg. 3203
ELEVATE URANIUM LTD.; *Int'l*, pg. 2359
ELEVATION, INC.; *U.S. Private*, pg. 1358
ELEVATION MARKETING; *U.S. Private*, pg. 1358
ELEVATION ONCOLOGY, INC.; *U.S. Public*, pg. 731
ELEVATION PARTNERS; *U.S. Private*, pg. 1358
ELEVATIONS CREDIT UNION; *U.S. Private*, pg. 1358
ELEVATION; *U.S. Private*, pg. 1358
ELEVATION—See Elevation; *U.S. Private*, pg. 1358
ELEVATIVE NETWORKS LLC—See Rimstorm, Inc.; *U.S. Private*, pg. 3437
ELEVATOR CAR SYSTEM—See Schindler Holding AG; *Int'l*, pg. 6618
ELEVATOR EQUIPMENT CORPORATION; *U.S. Private*, pg. 1358
ELEVATOR ESCALATOR SERVICES LIMITED—See Schindler Holding AG; *Int'l*, pg. 6619
ELEVATORI BARI S.R.L.—See KONE Oyj; *Int'l*, pg. 4247
ELEVATOR MAINTENANCE & REPAIR, INC.—See KONE Oyj; *Int'l*, pg. 4249
ELEVATOR MEDIA CO., LTD.—See Japan Elevator Service Holdings Co., Ltd.; *Int'l*, pg. 3888
ELEVATOR RESEARCH MANUFACTURING CORP.—See Dewhurst Group plc; *Int'l*, pg. 2091
ELEVATOR SERVICE LLC—See Carroll Capital LLC; *U.S. Private*, pg. 773
ELEVATORS UNLIMITED, INC.—See KONE Oyj; *Int'l*, pg. 4249
ELEVEN INC.—See Bluefocus Intelligent Communications Group Co., Ltd.; *Int'l*, pg. 1071
ELEVEN (LANGFANG) AUTO ACCESSORIES CO., LTD.—See WEDS CO., LTD.; *Int'l*, pg. 8367
ELEVENTH DAY ENTERTAINMENT INC.; *U.S. Private*, pg. 1358
ELE VERTEILNETZ GMBH—See RWE AG; *Int'l*, pg. 6434
ELEVION GMBH—See CEZ, a.s.; *Int'l*, pg. 1427
ELEVION GROUP B.V.—See CEZ, a.s.; *Int'l*, pg. 1427
ELEXA CONSUMER PRODUCTS INC.; *U.S. Private*, pg. 1358
ELEXCEL CORPORATION—See DKS Co. Ltd.; *Int'l*, pg. 2140

ELEX CEMCAT AG—See ThyssenKrupp AG; *Int'l*, pg. 7724
ELEXIS AG—See SMS Holding GmbH; *Int'l*, pg. 7016
ELEXO S.A.—See Atos SE; *Int'l*, pg. 692
ELEXPRESSEN I LUND AB—See Instalco AB; *Int'l*, pg. 3721
ELEXXION AG; *Int'l*, pg. 2359
ELEY GUILD HARDY ARCHITECTS, PA; *U.S. Private*, pg. 1358
ELEY LIMITED—See Lloyds Banking Group plc; *Int'l*, pg. 4537
ELFAB LIMITED—See Halma plc; *Int'l*, pg. 3231
ELFAC A/S—See Lagercrantz Group AB; *Int'l*, pg. 4394
ELFA TRADING COMPANY INC.; *U.S. Private*, pg. 1359
E.L.F. BEAUTY, INC.; *U.S. Public*, pg. 701
ELF BUSINESS ENERGY—See TotalEnergies SE; *Int'l*, pg. 7841
ELF BUSINESS ENERGY—See TotalEnergies SE; *Int'l*, pg. 7841
EL FENIX CORPORATION; *U.S. Private*, pg. 1349
ELFEN SERVICE GMBH—See United Labels AG; *Int'l*, pg. 8070
ELFETEX SPOL. S R.O.—See Wurth Verwaltungsgesellschaft mbH; *Int'l*, pg. 8504
E-L FINANCIAL CORPORATION LIMITED; *Int'l*, pg. 2248
ELF ON THE SHELF, THE; *U.S. Private*, pg. 1359
EL FORGE LTD - APPUR DIVISION—See El Forge Ltd; *Int'l*, pg. 2340
EL FORGE LTD - HOSUR DIVISION—See El Forge Ltd; *Int'l*, pg. 2341
EL FORGE LTD; *Int'l*, pg. 2340
ELF PETROLEUM NIGERIA LTD.—See TotalEnergies SE; *Int'l*, pg. 7840
ELFS BROKERAGE LLC—See Janel Corporation; *U.S. Public*, pg. 1187
ELFTE BASF PROJEKTENTWICKLUNGSGESELL-SCHAFT MBH—See BASF SE; *Int'l*, pg. 883
ELFVERSON & CO. AB—See CORTICEIRA AMORIM, S.G.P.S., S.A.; *Int'l*, pg. 1807
ELGA AB—See Illinois Tool Works Inc.; *U.S. Public*, pg. 1103
ELGA AKTIEBOLAG—See Illinois Tool Works Inc.; *U.S. Public*, pg. 1103
ELGA BERKEFELD GMBH—See Veolia Environnement S.A.; *Int'l*, pg. 8161
ELGA CREDIT UNION; *U.S. Private*, pg. 1359
ELGAEUROPE S.R.L.—See Tokyo Ohka Kogyo Co., Ltd.; *Int'l*, pg. 7793
ELGA LABWATER LLC—See Veolia Environnement S.A.; *Int'l*, pg. 8163
ELGAR ELECTRIC LTD.; *Int'l*, pg. 2359
ELGAS AUTOGAS PTY LIMITED—See Linde plc; *Int'l*, pg. 4505
ELG CANADA, INC.—See Franz Haniel & Cie. GmbH; *Int'l*, pg. 2762
ELG CARBON FIBRE LTD.—See Franz Haniel & Cie. GmbH; *Int'l*, pg. 2762
ELG CARRS STAINLESS STEELS—See Franz Haniel & Cie. GmbH; *Int'l*, pg. 2763
ELGEKA FERFELIS ROMANIA S.A.—See ELGEKA S.A.; *Int'l*, pg. 2359
ELGEKA S.A.; *Int'l*, pg. 2359
EL GEZIRAH HOTELS TOURISM—See Accor S.A.; *Int'l*, pg. 91
ELG FZE—See UnitedHealth Group Incorporated; *U.S. Public*, pg. 2240
ELG HANIEL GMBH—See Franz Haniel & Cie. GmbH; *Int'l*, pg. 2762
ELG HANIEL METALS LTD—See Franz Haniel & Cie. GmbH; *Int'l*, pg. 2763
ELGIA, INC.; *U.S. Private*, pg. 1359
ELGI BUILDING PRODUCTS LTD.—See Super Spinning Mills Ltd; *Int'l*, pg. 7335
ELGI COMPRESSORES DO BRAZIL LTDA—See ELGI Equipments Limited; *Int'l*, pg. 2360
ELGI COMPRESSORS (M) SDN. BHD.—See ELGI Equipments Limited; *Int'l*, pg. 2359
ELGI COMPRESSORS TRADING (SHANGHAI) CO., LTD—See ELGI Equipments Limited; *Int'l*, pg. 2360
ELGI COMPRESSORS USA INC.—See ELGI Equipments Limited; *Int'l*, pg. 2360
ELGI ELECTRIC & INDUSTRIES LTD.—See Super Spinning Mills Ltd; *Int'l*, pg. 7335
ELGI EQUIPMENTS AUSTRALIA PTY LTD.—See ELGI Equipments Limited; *Int'l*, pg. 2360
ELGI EQUIPMENTS LIMITED - PRESSURE VESSEL DIVISION—See ELGI Equipments Limited; *Int'l*, pg. 2360
ELGI EQUIPMENTS LIMITED; *Int'l*, pg. 2359
ELGI EQUIPMENTS LTD.—See ELGI Equipments Limited; *Int'l*, pg. 2360
ELGI EQUIPMENTS PTY LTD.—See ELGI Equipments Limited; *Int'l*, pg. 2360
ELGI EQUIPMENTS (ZHEJIANG) LIMITED—See ELGI Equipments Limited; *Int'l*, pg. 2360
ELGIE SAS—See VINCI S.A.; *Int'l*, pg. 8217
ELGIGANTEN AKTIEBOLAG—See Currys plc; *Int'l*, pg. 1879
ELGIGANTEN A/S—See Currys plc; *Int'l*, pg. 1879

CORPORATE AFFILIATIONS

ELGI GULF FZE—See ELGI Equipments Limited; *Int'l*, pg. 2360
ELGIN-BUTLER BRICK COMPANY; *U.S. Private*, pg. 1359
ELGIN DAIRY FOODS, INC.; *U.S. Private*, pg. 1359
ELG INDIA PRIVATE LIMITED—See Franz Haniel & Cie. GmbH; *Int'l*, pg. 2763
ELGIN EQUIPMENT GROUP, LLC; *U.S. Private*, pg. 1359
ELGIN FASTENER GROUP—See MW Industries, Inc.; *U.S. Private*, pg. 2822
ELGIN INDUSTRIES INC.; *U.S. Private*, pg. 1359
ELGIN MOLDED PLASTICS INC.; *U.S. Private*, pg. 1359
ELGIN NATIONAL INDUSTRIES, INC.—See Brookfield Corporation; *Int'l*, pg. 1181
ELGIN RIVERBOAT RESORT—See Caesars Entertainment, Inc.; *U.S. Public*, pg. 420
ELGIN SWEEPER COMPANY—See Federal Signal Corporation; *U.S. Public*, pg. 826
ELGIN SWEEPING SERVICES, INC.; *U.S. Private*, pg. 1359
ELGI RUBBER COMPANY BV—See Elgi Rubber Company Limited; *Int'l*, pg. 2360
ELGI RUBBER COMPANY LIMITED - CINCINNATI RETREAD SYSTEMS DIVISION—See Elgi Rubber Company Limited; *Int'l*, pg. 2360
ELGI RUBBER COMPANY LIMITED; *Int'l*, pg. 2360
ELGI RUBBER COMPANY LLC—See Elgi Rubber Company Limited; *Int'l*, pg. 2360
ELGI SOFTWARE & TECHNOLOGIES LTD.—See Super Spinning Mills Ltd; *Int'l*, pg. 7335
ELGI TREADS (I) LTD.—See Super Spinning Mills Ltd; *Int'l*, pg. 7335
ELGITREAD (USA) LLC—See ELGI Equipments Limited; *Int'l*, pg. 2360
ELGI ULTRA INDUSTRIES LTD.—See Super Spinning Mills Ltd; *Int'l*, pg. 7335
ELG LEGIMA SPOL. S.R.O.—See Franz Haniel & Cie. GmbH; *Int'l*, pg. 2763
ELG METALS, INC.—See Franz Haniel & Cie. GmbH; *Int'l*, pg. 2763
ELG METALS, INC.—See Franz Haniel & Cie. GmbH; *Int'l*, pg. 2763
ELG METALS, INC. - SOUTHERN DIVISION—See Franz Haniel & Cie. GmbH; *Int'l*, pg. 2763
ELG METALS, INC. - WEST COAST DIVISION—See Franz Haniel & Cie. GmbH; *Int'l*, pg. 2763
ELG METALS TAIWAN CORPORATION—See Franz Haniel & Cie. GmbH; *Int'l*, pg. 2763
ELG OIL LLC—See Energy Transfer LP; *U.S. Public*, pg. 763
ELGO IRRIGATION LTD.—See Trans-Resources, Inc.; *U.S. Private*, pg. 4206
ELGOOD-MAYO CORP.—See OceanSound Partners, LP; *U.S. Private*, pg. 2991
ELGOOD OY—See Addtech AB; *Int'l*, pg. 133
ELG RECYCLING PROCESSORS PTY LTD—See Franz Haniel & Cie. GmbH; *Int'l*, pg. 2763
EL GROUP LIMITED—See Stonegate Pub Company Limited; *Int'l*, pg. 7222
ELG UTICA ALLOYS (HARTFORD), INC.—See ELG Utica Alloys, Inc.; *U.S. Private*, pg. 1359
ELG UTICA ALLOYS (HARTFORD), INC.—See Franz Haniel & Cie. GmbH; *Int'l*, pg. 2763
ELG UTICA ALLOYS, INC.; *U.S. Private*, pg. 1359
ELG UTICA ALLOYS LTD—See Franz Haniel & Cie. GmbH; *Int'l*, pg. 2763
E.L. HAMM & ASSOCIATES INC.; *U.S. Private*, pg. 1306
ELHART DODGE NISSAN HYUNDAI—See Elhart Management Corp.; *U.S. Private*, pg. 1359
ELHART MANAGEMENT CORP.; *U.S. Private*, pg. 1359
ELHART PONTIAC-GMC-TRUCK INC.—See Elhart Management Corp.; *U.S. Private*, pg. 1359
E.L. HARVEY & SONS INC.—See Waste Connections, Inc.; *Int'l*, pg. 8352
ELHIM ISKRA JSC; *Int'l*, pg. 2360
ELHO BV; *Int'l*, pg. 2360
E.L. HOLLINGSWORTH & CO.; *U.S. Private*, pg. 1306
ELH WBN WAGGONBAU NIESKY GMBH—See Budamar Logistics AS; *Int'l*, pg. 1210
ELH WBN WAGGONBAU NIESKY GMBH—See Optifin Invest s.r.o.; *Int'l*, pg. 5603
ELIA ASSET SA—See Elia Group SA; *Int'l*, pg. 2360
ELIADA HOMES, INC.; *U.S. Private*, pg. 1360
ELIA ENGINEERING SA—See Elia Group SA; *Int'l*, pg. 2360
ELIA GRID INTERNATIONAL GMBH—See Elia Group SA; *Int'l*, pg. 2360
ELIA GRID INTERNATIONAL LLC—See Elia Group SA; *Int'l*, pg. 2360
ELIA GRID INTERNATIONAL NV/SA—See Elia Group SA; *Int'l*, pg. 2360
ELIA GRID INTERNATIONAL PTE. LTD.—See Elia Group SA; *Int'l*, pg. 2360
ELIA GROUP SA; *Int'l*, pg. 2360
ELIAHU INSURANCE COMPANY LTD.—See Shlomo Eliahu Holdings Ltd.; *Int'l*, pg. 6857
ELIANCE (PTY) LIMITED; *Int'l*, pg. 2360
ELIANE S/A - REVESTIMENTOS CERAMICOS—See Mohawk Industries, Inc.; *U.S. Public*, pg. 1457

COMPANY NAME INDEX

ELIAN SOLUTIONS SRL—See Bittnet Systems SA Bucuresti; *Int'l*, pg. 1050
ELIAS ARTS LLC—See Seaport Capital, LLC; *U.S. Private*, pg. 3586
ELIAS BROTHERS GROUP PAINTING & CONTRACTING, INC.; *U.S. Private*, pg. 1360
ELIASSEN GROUP, LLC—See Stone Point Capital LLC; *U.S. Private*, pg. 3823
ELIAS WILF CORPORATION; *U.S. Private*, pg. 1360
ELICA FRANCE S.A.S.—See Elica S.p.A.; *Int'l*, pg. 2361
ELICA GROUP POLSKA—See Elica S.p.A.; *Int'l*, pg. 2361
ELICAMEX—See Elica S.p.A.; *Int'l*, pg. 2361
ELICA PB WHIRLPOOL KITCHEN APPLIANCES PRIVATE LIMITED—See Whirlpool Corporation; *U.S. Public*, pg. 2367
ELICA S.P.A.; *Int'l*, pg. 2360
ELICA TRADING LLC—See Elica S.p.A.; *Int'l*, pg. 2361
E LICENSE INC.—See Toyota Tsusho Corporation; *Int'l*, pg. 7879
ELICERA THERAPEUTICS AB; *Int'l*, pg. 2361
ELICERE INC; *U.S. Private*, pg. 1360
ELICIO THERAPEUTICS, INC; *U.S. Public*, pg. 734
ELIDATA S.R.L.—See CAD IT S.p.A.; *Int'l*, pg. 1247
ELIEM THERAPEUTICS, INC.; *U.S. Public*, pg. 734
ELIE TAHARI, LTD.; *U.S. Private*, pg. 1360
ELIFE HOLDINGS LIMITED; *Int'l*, pg. 2361
E-LIFE MALL CORPORATION; *Int'l*, pg. 2248
ELIF GLOBAL PACKAGING S.A.E.—See Huhtamaki India Limited; *Int'l*, pg. 3524
ELIF GLOBAL S.A.—See Huhtamaki India Limited; *Int'l*, pg. 3524
ELIF HOLDING ANONIM SIRKETI—See Huhtamaki Oyj; *Int'l*, pg. 3524
ELIF HOLDING ANONIM SIRKET—See Huhtamaki India Limited; *Int'l*, pg. 3524
ELIF TRADING SRL—See Nicolas Correa S.A.; *Int'l*, pg. 5272
E LIGHTING GROUP HOLDINGS LIMITED; *Int'l*, pg. 2246
ELI GLOBAL, LLC; *U.S. Private*, pg. 1359
ELIGO S.P.A.; *Int'l*, pg. 2361
ELIKO EX-IMPORT INC.; *U.S. Private*, pg. 1360
ELILARIO ITALIA S.P.A.—See Inversiones Aereas S.L.; *Int'l*, pg. 3774
ELI LILLY AND COMPANY (INDIA) PVT. LTD.—See Eli Lilly & Company; *U.S. Public*, pg. 733
ELI LILLY AND COMPANY (IRELAND) LTD.—See Eli Lilly & Company; *U.S. Public*, pg. 733
ELI LILLY AND COMPANY (N.Z.) LIMITED—See Eli Lilly & Company; *U.S. Public*, pg. 732
ELI LILLY AND COMPANY (TAIWAN), INC.—See Eli Lilly & Company; *U.S. Public*, pg. 732
ELI LILLY ASIA, INC.—See Eli Lilly & Company; *U.S. Public*, pg. 732
ELI LILLY ASIAN OPERATIONS, LIMITED—See Eli Lilly & Company; *U.S. Public*, pg. 732
ELI LILLY ASIA PACIFIC SSC SDN BHD—See Eli Lilly & Company; *U.S. Public*, pg. 732
ELI LILLY AUSTRALIA PTY. LIMITED—See Eli Lilly & Company; *U.S. Public*, pg. 732
ELI LILLY BENELUX, S.A.—See Eli Lilly & Company; *U.S. Public*, pg. 732
ELI LILLY B-H D.O.O.—See Eli Lilly & Company; *U.S. Public*, pg. 732
ELI LILLY CANADA, INC.—See Eli Lilly & Company; *U.S. Public*, pg. 732
ELI LILLY & COMPANY (INDIA) PVT. LTD.—See Eli Lilly & Company; *U.S. Public*, pg. 731
ELI LILLY & COMPANY LIMITED—See Eli Lilly & Company; *U.S. Public*, pg. 732
ELI LILLY & COMPANY; *U.S. Public*, pg. 731
ELI LILLY CORK LIMITED—See Eli Lilly & Company; *U.S. Public*, pg. 732
ELI LILLY CR S.R.O.—See Eli Lilly & Company; *U.S. Public*, pg. 732
ELI LILLY CR S.R.O.—See Eli Lilly & Company; *U.S. Public*, pg. 732
ELI LILLY DANMARK A/S—See Eli Lilly & Company; *U.S. Public*, pg. 732
ELI LILLY DE MEXICO S.A. DE C.V.—See Eli Lilly & Company; *U.S. Public*, pg. 732
ELI LILLY DO BRASIL LTDA.—See Eli Lilly & Company; *U.S. Public*, pg. 733
ELI LILLY EGYPT—See Eli Lilly & Company; *U.S. Public*, pg. 732
ELI LILLY EXPORT S.A.—See Eli Lilly & Company; *U.S. Public*, pg. 732
ELI LILLY FARMACEVTSKA DRUZBA, D.O.O.—See Eli Lilly & Company; *U.S. Public*, pg. 733
ELI LILLY FARMACEVTSKA DRUZBA, D.O.O.—See Eli Lilly & Company; *U.S. Public*, pg. 733
ELI LILLY FINANCE, S.A.—See Eli Lilly & Company; *U.S. Public*, pg. 732
ELI LILLY GES.M.B.H.—See Eli Lilly & Company; *U.S. Public*, pg. 732
ELI LILLY GMBH—See Eli Lilly & Company; *U.S. Public*, pg. 733
ELI LILLY GROUP LIMITED—See Eli Lilly & Company; *U.S. Public*, pg. 732
ELI LILLY HRVATSKA D.O.O.—See Eli Lilly & Company; *U.S. Public*, pg. 732
ELI LILLY INTERAMERICA, INC.—See Eli Lilly & Company; *U.S. Public*, pg. 732
ELI LILLY INTERAMERICA INC., Y COMPANIA LIMITADA—See Eli Lilly & Company; *U.S. Public*, pg. 732
ELI LILLY INTERNATIONAL CORPORATION—See Eli Lilly & Company; *U.S. Public*, pg. 732
ELI LILLY ISRAEL LTD.—See Eli Lilly & Company; *U.S. Public*, pg. 732
ELI LILLY ITALIA, S.P.A.—See Eli Lilly & Company; *U.S. Public*, pg. 732
ELI LILLY ITALIA SPA—See Eli Lilly & Company; *U.S. Public*, pg. 732
ELI LILLY JAPAN K.K.—See Eli Lilly & Company; *U.S. Public*, pg. 732
ELI LILLY LITHUANIA UAB—See Eli Lilly & Company; *U.S. Public*, pg. 732
ELI LILLY (MALAYSIA) SDN. BHD.—See Eli Lilly & Company; *U.S. Public*, pg. 731
ELI LILLY (MALAYSIA) SDN. BHD.—See Eli Lilly & Company; *U.S. Public*, pg. 731
ELI LILLY (M) SDN. BHD.—See Eli Lilly & Company; *U.S. Public*, pg. 732
ELI LILLY NEDERLAND B.V.—See Eli Lilly & Company; *U.S. Public*, pg. 732
ELI LILLY NORGE A.S.—See Eli Lilly & Company; *U.S. Public*, pg. 733
ELI LILLY NORGE A.S.—See Eli Lilly & Company; *U.S. Public*, pg. 733
ELI LILLY PAKISTAN (PVT.) LTD.—See Eli Lilly & Company; *U.S. Public*, pg. 732
ELI LILLY (PHILIPPINES), INCORPORATED—See Eli Lilly & Company; *U.S. Public*, pg. 731
ELI LILLY (PHILIPPINES), INCORPORATED—See Eli Lilly & Company; *U.S. Public*, pg. 731
ELI LILLY POLSKA SP. Z.O.O. (LTD.)—See Eli Lilly & Company; *U.S. Public*, pg. 732
ELI LILLY ROMANIA SRL—See Eli Lilly & Company; *U.S. Public*, pg. 733
ELI LILLY (S.A.) (PROPRIETARY) LIMITED—See Eli Lilly & Company; *U.S. Public*, pg. 732
ELI LILLY SAUDI ARABIA LIMITED—See Eli Lilly & Company; *U.S. Public*, pg. 733
ELI LILLY (SINGAPORE) PTE. LTD.—See Eli Lilly & Company; *U.S. Public*, pg. 732
ELI LILLY SLOVAKIA SRO—See Eli Lilly & Company; *U.S. Public*, pg. 732
ELI LILLY SPAIN HOLDING ETVE, S.L.—See Eli Lilly & Company; *U.S. Public*, pg. 732
ELI LILLY (SUISSE) S.A.—See Eli Lilly & Company; *U.S. Public*, pg. 732
ELI LILLY SUZHOU PHARMACEUTICAL CO. LTD.—See Eli Lilly & Company; *U.S. Public*, pg. 732
ELI LILLY SWEDEN AB—See Eli Lilly & Company; *U.S. Public*, pg. 733
ELI LILLY TRADING (SHANGHAI) COMPANY LIMITED—See Eli Lilly & Company; *U.S. Public*, pg. 733
ELI LILLY VOSTOK SA—See Eli Lilly & Company; *U.S. Public*, pg. 733
ELI LILLY Y COMPANIA DE MEXICO, S.A. DE C.V.—See Eli Lilly & Company; *U.S. Public*, pg. 733
ELI LILLY Y COMPANIA DE VENEZUELA, S.A.—See Eli Lilly & Company; *U.S. Public*, pg. 733
ELIMINATOR CUSTOM BOATS INC.; *U.S. Private*, pg. 1360
ELIM PARK BAPTIST HOME INC.; *U.S. Private*, pg. 1360
ELINA TEJARAT KAVIR TRADING COMPANY—See A.A.G. STUCCHI s.r.l.; *Int'l*, pg. 22
ELIN EBG TRACTION GMBH—See Siemens Aktiengesellschaft; *Int'l*, pg. 6886
EL-INFO I VAXJO AB—See SmartCraft ASA; *Int'l*, pg. 7002
ELINI BVBA; *Int'l*, pg. 2361
ELINI DESIGNS CORP.—See Elini BVBA; *Int'l*, pg. 2361
ELIN MOTOREN GMBH—See Voith GmbH & Co. KGaA; *Int'l*, pg. 8297
ELINOIL S.A.; *Int'l*, pg. 2361
ELINSTALLATIONER I KARLSHAMN AB—See Instalco AB; *Int'l*, pg. 3721
ELIN TECHNICAL SA—See ELINOIL S.A.; *Int'l*, pg. 2361
ELIN VERD S.A.; *Int'l*, pg. 2361
ELINX CORPORATION; *U.S. Public*, pg. 734
ELIO MOTORS, INC; *U.S. Public*, pg. 734
ELION CLEAN ENERGY CO.; *Int'l*, pg. 2361
ELION ENTERPRISES AS—See Telia Company AB; *Int'l*, pg. 7543
ELIOR SCA—See Charterhouse Capital Partners LLP; *Int'l*, pg. 1455
ELIPS LIFE AG—See Swiss Re Ltd.; *Int'l*, pg. 7371
ELIPSLIFE EMEA HOLDING B.V.—See Swiss Re Ltd.; *Int'l*, pg. 7372
ELIPTICON WOOD PRODUCTS, INC.; *U.S. Private*, pg. 1360
ELIQUO WATER GROUP GMBH—See SKion GmbH; *Int'l*, pg. 6989
ELI RESEARCH INDIA PVT. LTD.—See Eli Global, LLC; *U.S. Private*, pg. 1359
ELI RESEARCH, LLC—See Eli Global, LLC; *U.S. Private*, pg. 1359
ELISA CAMLINE HOLDING GMBH—See Elisa Corporation; *Int'l*, pg. 2361
ELISA CORPORATION; *Int'l*, pg. 2361
ELISA EESTI AS—See Elisa Corporation; *Int'l*, pg. 2361
ELISA SANTA MONICA OY—See Elisa Corporation; *Int'l*, pg. 2361
ELISA SENIORENSTIFT ASCHAFFENBURG GMBH—See Clariane SE; *Int'l*, pg. 1643
ELISA SENIORENSTIFT GMBH—See Clariane SE; *Int'l*, pg. 1643
ELISA VIDERA NORGE AS—See Elisa Corporation; *Int'l*, pg. 2361
ELISA VIDERA OY—See Elisa Corporation; *Int'l*, pg. 2361
ELISA VIDERA SPAIN S.L—See Elisa Corporation; *Int'l*, pg. 2361
ELISA VIDERA UK LTD.—See Elisa Corporation; *Int'l*, pg. 2361
ELIS BREAD (ELI ZABAR) INC.; *U.S. Private*, pg. 1360
ELI'S CHEESECAKE COMPANY; *U.S. Private*, pg. 1360
ELIS DANMARK A/S—See Eurazeo SE; *Int'l*, pg. 2528
ELISHA TECHNOLOGIES INC—See Orscheln Group; *U.S. Private*, pg. 3045
ELIS NEDERLAND B.V.—See Eurazeo SE; *Int'l*, pg. 2528
ELIS NORGE AS—See Eurazeo SE; *Int'l*, pg. 2528
ELIS S.A.—See Eurazeo SE; *Int'l*, pg. 2528
ELIS TEXTIL SERVICE AB—See Eurazeo SE; *Int'l*, pg. 2528
EL ISTIFA SA—See Groupe BPCE; *Int'l*, pg. 3094
ELIT CZ, SPOL S.R.O.—See LKQ Corporation; *U.S. Public*, pg. 1334
ELITE ADVANCED LASER CORPORATION; *Int'l*, pg. 2362
ELITE AEROSPACE GROUP, INC.; *U.S. Private*, pg. 1360
ELITE ALUMINUM CORPORATION; *U.S. Private*, pg. 1360
ELITE BMW; *Int'l*, pg. 2362
ELITE BUILDER SERVICES, INC.—See Live Ventures Incorporated; *U.S. Public*, pg. 1332
ELITE CARE INCORPORATED—See Patient Square Capital, L.P.; *U.S. Private*, pg. 3107
ELITE CENTURY HOLDINGS LIMITED—See Maxnerva Technology Services Ltd.; *Int'l*, pg. 4742
ELITECH FRANCE SAS—See Bruker Corporation; *U.S. Public*, pg. 406
ELITECHGROUP AUSTRALIA PTY. LTD.—See Bruker Corporation; *U.S. Public*, pg. 406
ELITECHGROUP B.V.—See Bruker Corporation; *U.S. Public*, pg. 406
ELITECHGROUP CLINICAL SYSTEMS SAS—See Bruker Corporation; *U.S. Public*, pg. 406
ELITECHGROUP INC.—See Bruker Corporation; *U.S. Public*, pg. 406
ELITECHGROUP MOLECULAR DIAGNOSTICS—See Bruker Corporation; *U.S. Public*, pg. 406
ELITECHGROUP (NZ) LIMITED—See Bruker Corporation; *U.S. Public*, pg. 406
ELITECH GROUP SAS—See Bruker Corporation; *U.S. Public*, pg. 406
ELITECHGROUP S.P.A.—See Bruker Corporation; *U.S. Public*, pg. 406
ELITECH LTDA.—See Bruker Corporation; *U.S. Public*, pg. 406
ELITECH MICROBIO SAS—See Bruker Corporation; *U.S. Public*, pg. 406
ELITECH SA/NV—See Bruker Corporation; *U.S. Public*, pg. 406
ELITECH SR D.O.O.—See Bruker Corporation; *U.S. Public*, pg. 406
ELITECH UK LIMITED—See Bruker Corporation; *U.S. Public*, pg. 406
ELITE CME INC; *U.S. Private*, pg. 1360
ELITE CNC MACHINING, INC.; *U.S. Private*, pg. 1360
ELITE COLLECTIONS, INC.; *U.S. Private*, pg. 1360
ELITE COLOR ENVIRONMENTAL RESOURCES SCIENCE & TECHNOLOGY CO., LTD.; *Int'l*, pg. 2362
E-LITECOM CO., LTD.; *Int'l*, pg. 2249
ELITE COMMERCIAL REIT; *Int'l*, pg. 2362
ELITE COMPRESSION SERVICES, LLC—See Archrock, Inc.; *U.S. Public*, pg. 186
ELITE COMPUTER CONSULTANTS LP; *U.S. Private*, pg. 1360
ELITECON INTERNATIONAL LIMITED; *Int'l*, pg. 2363
ELITE CORE ENTERPRISES LLC; *U.S. Private*, pg. 1360
ELITE CRETE SYSTEMS INC.; *U.S. Private*, pg. 1360
ELITE CUSTOM BUILDERS LLC; *U.S. Private*, pg. 1360
ELITE CUSTOM EXTERIORS, INC.; *U.S. Private*, pg. 1360
ELITE DANS. ARASTIRMA GELISTIRME REK. VE HLK. ILS. TIC. A.S—See Loras Holding A.S.; *Int'l*, pg. 4557
ELITE ELECTRONIC MATERIAL CO., LTD. - KUNSHAN PLANT—See Elite Material Co., Ltd.; *Int'l*, pg. 2362
ELITE ELECTRONIC MATERIAL (KUNSHAN) CO., LTD.—See Elite Material Co., Ltd.; *Int'l*, pg. 2362
ELITE ELECTRONIC MATERIAL (ZHONGSHAN) CO., LTD.—See Elite Material Co., Ltd.; *Int'l*, pg. 2362
ELITE EMAIL INC.; *Int'l*, pg. 2362

ELITE EMAIL INC.

ELITE FINANCING GROUP, LLC—See Fathom Holdings Inc.; *U.S. Public*, pg. 824
ELITE FLOORING & DESIGN INC.; *U.S. Private*, pg. 1361
ELITE FOAM, LLC—See Leggett & Platt, Incorporated; *U.S. Public*, pg. 1302
ELITE FOREIGN TRADING INC.—See Everlight Chemical Industrial Co.; *Int'l*, pg. 2567
ELITE GROUNDS, L.C.—See Stratton & Bratt Landscapes, LLC; *U.S. Private*, pg. 3837
ELITEGROUP COMPUTER SYSTEMS CO., LTD.; *Int'l*, pg. 2363
ELITEGROUP COMPUTER SYSTEMS (HK) CO., LTD.—See Elitegroup Computer Systems Co., Ltd.; *Int'l*, pg. 2363
ELITEGROUP COMPUTER SYSTEMS (JAPAN) CO., LTD.—See Elitegroup Computer Systems Co., Ltd.; *Int'l*, pg. 2363
THE ELITE GROUP LLC—See ABRY Partners, LLC; *U.S. Private*, pg. 42
ELITE GROUP PROPRIETARY LIMITED—See African Dawn Capital Limited; *Int'l*, pg. 191
ELITE HAVENS LTD.—See Dusit Thani Public Company Limited; *Int'l*, pg. 2234
ELITE HEALTH SYSTEMS HOLDINGS INC.—See Elite Health Systems Inc.; *U.S. Public*, pg. 734
ELITE HEALTH SYSTEMS INC.; *U.S. Public*, pg. 734
ELITE HEARING LLC—See Amplifon S.p.A.; *Int'l*, pg. 435
ELITE HOME HEALTH OF HOLIDAY ISLAND—See UnitedHealth Group Incorporated; *U.S. Public*, pg. 2245
ELITE HOMES—See Berkshire Hathaway Inc.; *U.S. Public*, pg. 304
ELITE HOME SUPPLIES—See Hendricks Holding Company, Inc.; *U.S. Private*, pg. 1914
ELITE HUMAN CAPITAL GROUP; *U.S. Private*, pg. 1361
ELITE HUMAN RESOURCE MANAGEMENT CO., LTD.—See BES Engineering Corporation; *Int'l*, pg. 998
ELITE INFORMATION SYSTEMS, INC.—See Thomson Reuters Corporation; *Int'l*, pg. 7715
ELITE INFORMATION SYSTEMS, INC.—See Thomson Reuters Corporation; *Int'l*, pg. 7715
ELITE INSURANCE GROUP, INC.—See Porch Group, Inc.; *U.S. Public*, pg. 1702
ELITE INSURANCE PARTNERS, LLC; *U.S. Private*, pg. 1361
ELITE KSB HOLDINGS LIMITED; *Int'l*, pg. 2362
ELITE LABORATORIES, INC.—See Elite Pharmaceuticals, Inc.; *U.S. Public*, pg. 734
ELITE LEGACY EDUCATION LTD.—See Legacy Education Alliance, Inc.; *U.S. Public*, pg. 1301
ELITE LICENSING COMPANY S.A.—See Elite World S.A.; *Int'l*, pg. 2362
ELITE LIFT TRUCK INC.—See Tym Corporation; *Int'l*, pg. 7994
ELITE LIMOUSINE PLUS, INC.; *U.S. Private*, pg. 1361
ELITE LINE SERVICES, INC.—See Daifuku Co., Ltd.; *Int'l*, pg. 1925
ELITE LOGISTICS, LLC; *U.S. Private*, pg. 1361
ELITE MACHINERY PTE LTD.—See THK CO., LTD.; *Int'l*, pg. 7711
ELITE MANAGEMENT S.A.—See Elite World S.A.; *Int'l*, pg. 2362
ELITE MANUFACTURING TECHNOLOGIES, INC.—See CORE Industrial Partners, LLC; *U.S. Private*, pg. 1048
ELITE MARKET LLC; *U.S. Private*, pg. 1361
ELITE MASONRY, INC.; *U.S. Private*, pg. 1361
ELITE MATERIAL CO., LTD. - HSINCHU PLANT—See Elite Material Co., Ltd.; *Int'l*, pg. 2362
ELITE MATERIAL CO., LTD.; *Int'l*, pg. 2362
ELITE MATERIAL CO., LTD. - TAOYUAN PLANT—See Elite Material Co., Ltd.; *Int'l*, pg. 2362
ELITE MEDIA, INC.; *U.S. Private*, pg. 1361
ELITEMEDIANET GMBH—See ProSiebenSat.1 Media SE; *Int'l*, pg. 6000
ELITE MEETINGS INTERNATIONAL, LLC—See Blackstone Inc.; *U.S. Public*, pg. 353
ELITE MERCHANT SOLUTIONS; *U.S. Private*, pg. 1361
ELITE MODEL MANAGEMENT AMSTERDAM B.V.—See Elite World S.A.; *Int'l*, pg. 2362
ELITE MODEL MANAGEMENT BRATISLAVA SRO.—See Elite World S.A.; *Int'l*, pg. 2362
ELITE MODEL MANAGEMENT COPENHAGEN—See Elite World S.A.; *Int'l*, pg. 2362
ELITE MODEL MANAGEMENT CORPORATION; *U.S. Private*, pg. 1361
ELITE MODEL MANAGEMENT LONDON LTD.—See Elite World S.A.; *Int'l*, pg. 2362
ELITE MODEL MANAGEMENT PRAGUE SRO—See Elite World S.A.; *Int'l*, pg. 2362
ELITE MODEL MANAGEMENT SARL—See Elite World S.A.; *Int'l*, pg. 2362
ELITE MODEL MANAGEMENT SARL—See Elite World S.A.; *Int'l*, pg. 2363
ELITE MODULAR LEASING & SALES, INC.—See WillScot Mobile Mini Holdings Corp.; *U.S. Private*, pg. 2372
ELITE ONE SOURCE NUTRISCIENCES—See Ampersand Management LLC; *U.S. Private*, pg. 265
ELITE ORTHOPAEDICS OF EL PASO, PLLC—See HCA Healthcare, Inc.; *U.S. Public*, pg. 995
ELITE ORTHOPAEDICS OF IRVING, PLLC—See HCA Healthcare, Inc.; *U.S. Public*, pg. 995
ELITE ORTHOPAEDICS PTE. LTD.—See Alliance Healthcare Group Limited; *Int'l*, pg. 340
ELITE PACIFIC, LLC; *U.S. Private*, pg. 1361
ELITE PAPER TRADING SDN. BHD.—See Kobay Technology Bhd.; *Int'l*, pg. 4216
ELITE PERFORMANCE HOLDING CORP.; *U.S. Private*, pg. 1361
ELITE PHARMACEUTICALS, INC.; *U.S. Public*, pg. 734
ELITE PIZZA TEXAS, LLC; *U.S. Private*, pg. 1361
ELITE PROPERTIES OF AMERICA, INC.; *U.S. Private*, pg. 1361
ELITE RADIO & ENGINEERING CO., LTD.—See Daikin Industries, Ltd.; *Int'l*, pg. 1935
ELITE RECRUITING GROUP LLC; *U.S. Private*, pg. 1361
ELITE RESEARCH, INC.—See Elite Pharmaceuticals, Inc.; *U.S. Public*, pg. 734
ELITE RETAILS SERVICES INC.; *U.S. Private*, pg. 1361
ELITE ROADS; *U.S. Private*, pg. 1361
ELITE SAFELITE AUTO GLASS—See s.a. D'Ieteren n.v.; *Int'l*, pg. 6448
ELITE SALES PROCESSING, INC.—See Reinsurance Group of America, Inc.; *U.S. Public*, pg. 1777
ELITE SEMICONDUCTOR MICROELECTRONICS TECHNOLOGY INC.; *Int'l*, pg. 2362
ELITE SEWING MACHINE MFG. CO., LTD.—See AISIN Corporation; *Int'l*, pg. 253
ELITESOFT GLOBAL INC.; *U.S. Private*, pg. 1362
ELITE SPICE, INC.; *U.S. Private*, pg. 1361
ELITE SPORTSWEAR & AWARDS LTD.; *Int'l*, pg. 2362
ELITE SPORTSWEAR, L.P.; *U.S. Private*, pg. 1361
ELITE STAFFING INC; *U.S. Private*, pg. 1361
ELITE STORAGE SOLUTIONS INC.—See Nucor Corporation; *U.S. Public*, pg. 1553
ELITE STORAGE SOLUTIONS—See Nucor Corporation; *U.S. Public*, pg. 1553
ELITE STOR CAPITAL PARTNERS, LLC—See Benjamin Macfarland Company, LLC; *U.S. Private*, pg. 526
ELITE SUPPLY PARTNERS INC.—See Russel Metals Inc.; *Int'l*, pg. 6430
ELITE SURFACE TECHNOLOGIES PTY. LTD.; *Int'l*, pg. 2362
ELITE SURGICAL AFFILIATES—See Nobilis Health Corp.; *U.S. Private*, pg. 2932
ELITE TEAM REALTY & PROPERTY MANAGEMENT; *U.S. Private*, pg. 1361
ELITE TECHNOLOGY INC.; *U.S. Private*, pg. 1361
ELITETELE.COM HOLDINGS PLC; *Int'l*, pg. 2363
ELITE TOOLING LIMITED—See Tivoly S.A.; *Int'l*, pg. 7762
ELITE TOOLS LTD.—See Atlantic China Welding Consumables, Inc.; *Int'l*, pg. 674
ELITE TRAVEL MANAGEMENT GROUP; *U.S. Private*, pg. 1361
ELITE UNDERWRITING LIMITED—See Highway Insurance Holdings Plc; *Int'l*, pg. 3389
ELITE VIEW DEVELOPMENT LTD.—See PINE Technology Holdings Limited; *Int'l*, pg. 5868
ELITE-WEILER POOLS, INC.; *U.S. Private*, pg. 1362
ELITE WORKWEAR UK LIMITED; *Int'l*, pg. 2362
ELITE WORLD S.A.; *Int'l*, pg. 2362
ELITFONSTER AB—See Ratos AB; *Int'l*, pg. 6218
ELIT GROUP GMBH—See LKQ Corporation; *U.S. Public*, pg. 1334
ELITISE LLC—See COMSovereign Holding Corp.; *U.S. Public*, pg. 562
ELIT POLSKA SP. Z O.O.—See LKQ Corporation; *U.S. Public*, pg. 1334
ELIT SLOVAKIA S.R.O.—See LKQ Corporation; *U.S. Public*, pg. 1334
ELIT UKRAINE LLC—See LKQ Corporation; *U.S. Public*, pg. 1334
ELITYS CONSULTING SARL—See Alten S.A.; *Int'l*, pg. 390
ELIVISION CO., LTD.; *Int'l*, pg. 2363
ELIWELL CONTROLS SRL—See Schneider Electric SE; *Int'l*, pg. 6627
ELIXENS AMERICA INC.—See Elixens S.A.; *Int'l*, pg. 2363
ELIXENS S.A.; *Int'l*, pg. 2363
ELIXENS UK LTD—See Elixens S.A.; *Int'l*, pg. 2363
ELIXINOL BV—See Elixinol Wellness Limited; *Int'l*, pg. 2363
ELIXINOL WELLNESS LIMITED; *Int'l*, pg. 2363
ELIXIR CAPITAL LTD.; *Int'l*, pg. 2363
ELIXIR DOOR COMPANY - DIVISION 81—See Elixir Industries; *U.S. Private*, pg. 1362
ELIXIR ENERGY LIMITED; *Int'l*, pg. 2363
ELIXIR EQUITIES PRIVATE LIMITED—See Elixir Capital Ltd.; *Int'l*, pg. 2363
ELIXIR INDUSTRIES, CARGO TRAILER INDUSTRY—See Elixir Industries; *U.S. Private*, pg. 1362
ELIXIR INDUSTRIES - DIVISION 27—See Elixir Industries; *U.S. Private*, pg. 1362
ELIXIR INDUSTRIES—See Elixir Industries; *U.S. Private*, pg. 1362
ELIXIR INDUSTRIES; *U.S. Private*, pg. 1362
ELIXIR INDUSTRIES—See Elixir Industries; *U.S. Private*, pg. 1362
ELIXIR INDUSTRIES—See Elixir Industries; *U.S. Private*, pg. 1362
ELIXIR INDUSTRIES—See Elixir Industries; *U.S. Private*, pg. 1362
ELIXIR INDUSTRIES—See Elixir Industries; *U.S. Private*, pg. 1362
ELIXIR INDUSTRIES, WACO DIV—See Elixir Industries; *U.S. Private*, pg. 1362
ELIXIR INSURANCE COMPANY—See New Rite Aid, LLC; *U.S. Private*, pg. 2905
ELIXIRR, INC.—See Elixirr International plc; *Int'l*, pg. 2363
ELIXIRR INTERNATIONAL PLC; *Int'l*, pg. 2363
ELIX VINTAGE RESIDENCIAL SOCIMI S.A.—See Allianz SE; *Int'l*, pg. 352
ELIZABETHAN HOLDINGS LIMITED—See Deutsche Bank Aktiengesellschaft; *Int'l*, pg. 2061
ELIZABETH ARDEN (AUSTRALIA) PTY LTD.—See MacAndrews & Forbes Incorporated; *U.S. Private*, pg. 2533
ELIZABETH ARDEN (CANADA) LIMITED—See MacAndrews & Forbes Incorporated; *U.S. Private*, pg. 2533
ELIZABETH ARDEN (DENMARK) APS—See MacAndrews & Forbes Incorporated; *U.S. Private*, pg. 2533
ELIZABETH ARDEN, INC.—See MacAndrews & Forbes Incorporated; *U.S. Private*, pg. 2533
ELIZABETH ARDEN INTERNATIONAL HOLDING, INC.—See MacAndrews & Forbes Incorporated; *U.S. Private*, pg. 2533
ELIZABETH ARDEN INTERNATIONAL S.A.R.L.—See MacAndrews & Forbes Incorporated; *U.S. Private*, pg. 2533
ELIZABETH ARDEN KOREA YUHAN HOESA—See MacAndrews & Forbes Incorporated; *U.S. Private*, pg. 2533
ELIZABETH ARDEN (NEW ZEALAND) LIMITED—See MacAndrews & Forbes Incorporated; *U.S. Private*, pg. 2533
ELIZABETH ARDEN (SOUTH AFRICA) (PTY) LTD.—See MacAndrews & Forbes Incorporated; *U.S. Private*, pg. 2533
ELIZABETH ARDEN (UK) LTD.—See MacAndrews & Forbes Incorporated; *U.S. Private*, pg. 2533
ELIZABETH CARBIDE DIE CO. INC.—See Operio Group, LLC; *U.S. Public*, pg. 3032
ELIZABETH CHRISTIAN PUBLIC RELATIONS LLC; *U.S. Private*, pg. 1362
ELIZABETH GLASER PEDIATRIC AIDS FOUNDATION; *U.S. Private*, pg. 1362
ELIZABETH HALL & ASSOCIATES, INC.; *U.S. Private*, pg. 1362
ELIZABETH-HATA INTERNATIONAL—See Operio Group, LLC; *U.S. Public*, pg. 3032
ELIZABETH MORELAND CONSULTING, INC.—See Stone Point Capital LLC; *U.S. Private*, pg. 3825
ELIZABETH RIVER CROSSINGS OPCO, LLC—See Macquarie Group Limited; *Int'l*, pg. 4627
ELIZABETH RIVER CROSSINGS OPCO, LLC—See Skanska AB; *Int'l*, pg. 6978
ELIZABETH RIVER TERMINALS LLC—See Kinder Morgan, Inc.; *U.S. Public*, pg. 1233
ELIZABETH TAVERN PTY. LTD.—See Woolworths Group Limited; *Int'l*, pg. 8452
ELIZABETH TELEPHONE COMPANY—See Madison Dearborn Partners, LLC; *U.S. Private*, pg. 2540
ELIZABETHTON TWINS BASEBALL CLUB—See Pohlad Companies; *U.S. Private*, pg. 3221
ELIZABETHTOWN GAS COMPANY—See JPMorgan Chase & Co.; *U.S. Public*, pg. 1210
ELIZA BRYANT VILLAGE; *U.S. Private*, pg. 1362
ELIZA CORPORATION—See Veritas Capital Fund Management, LLC; *U.S. Private*, pg. 4362
ELIZADE NIGERIA LIMITED; *Int'l*, pg. 2363
ELIZA TINSLEY LTD.; *Int'l*, pg. 2363
ELIZUR CORP.; *U.S. Private*, pg. 1362
ELJER, INC.—See Sun Capital Partners, Inc.; *U.S. Private*, pg. 3858
ELJET AVIATION SERVICES; *U.S. Private*, pg. 1362
ELJOSA TRAVEL & TOURS PROPRIETARY LIMITED—See Frontier Transport Holdings Limited; *Int'l*, pg. 2796
ELKA BETEILIGUNGS GMBH; *Int'l*, pg. 2364
EL KAHERA HOUSING—See Pioneers Holding Company; *Int'l*, pg. 5872
ELKAN-VOGEL INC.—See Theodore Presser Co.; *U.S. Private*, pg. 4141
ELKAPSLING AB—See Lagercrantz Group AB; *Int'l*, pg. 4394
ELK ASSOCIATES FUNDING CORPORATION—See Ameritrans Capital Corporation; *U.S. Public*, pg. 115
ELKAY ELECTRICAL—See ABB Ltd.; *Int'l*, pg. 52
ELKAY INTERIOR SYSTEMS—See Zurn Elkay Water Solutions Corporation; *U.S. Public*, pg. 2412
ELKAY MANUFACTURING COMPANY—See Zurn Elkay Water Solutions Corporation; *U.S. Public*, pg. 2412
ELKAY PLASTICS COMPANY, INC.; *U.S. Private*, pg. 1363
ELK BRAND MANUFACTURING CO.; *U.S. Private*, pg. 1362

COMPANY NAME INDEX

ELK CAPITAL CORPORATION—See Ameritrans Capital Corporation; *U.S. Public*, pg. 115
ELK CORPORATION; *Int'l*, pg. 2363
ELK CORPORATION—See Canon Inc.; *Int'l*, pg. 1296
ELKCORP.—See GAF Materials Corporation; *U.S. Private*, pg. 1633
ELK CREEK LAWN & TREE CARE, LLC—See Senske Lawn & Tree Care, Inc.; *U.S. Private*, pg. 3608
ELK CREEK RESOURCES CORP.—See NioCorp Developments Ltd.; *U.S. Public*, pg. 1530
ELK-DESA CAPITAL SDN. BHD.—See IOI Corporation Berhad; *Int'l*, pg. 3792
ELK-DESA FURNITURE SDN. BHD.—See ELK-Desa Resources Bhd; *Int'l*, pg. 2364
ELK-DESA RESOURCES BHD; *Int'l*, pg. 2363
ELKEM ASA-CARBON DIVISION—See China National Chemical Corporation; *Int'l*, pg. 1527
ELKEM ASA - MATERIALS DIVISION—See China National Chemical Corporation; *Int'l*, pg. 1527
ELKEM ASA - SILICON DIVISION—See China National Chemical Corporation; *Int'l*, pg. 1527
ELKEM ASA—See China National Chemical Corporation; *Int'l*, pg. 1527
ELKEM BJOLVEFOSSEN—See China National Chemical Corporation; *Int'l*, pg. 1527
ELKEME S.A.—See Viohalco SA/NV; *Int'l*, pg. 8243
ELKEM ICELAND—See China National Chemical Corporation; *Int'l*, pg. 1527
ELKEM JAPAN K.K.—See China National Chemical Corporation; *Int'l*, pg. 1527
ELKEM LTD.—See China National Chemical Corporation; *Int'l*, pg. 1527
ELKEM MARNES KVARTSITTBRUDD—See China National Chemical Corporation; *Int'l*, pg. 1527
ELKEM METAL CANADA INC.—See China National Chemical Corporation; *Int'l*, pg. 1527
ELKEM METALS CANADA INC.-HAMILTON—See China National Chemical Corporation; *Int'l*, pg. 1527
ELKEM SILICON MATERIALS USA—See China National Chemical Corporation; *Int'l*, pg. 1527
ELKEM TANA—See China National Chemical Corporation; *Int'l*, pg. 1527
ELKEM THAMSHAVN—See China National Chemical Corporation; *Int'l*, pg. 1527
ELKFORD INDUSTRIES LTD.—See Vortex Resource Group Ltd.; *Int'l*, pg. 8174
ELK GROUP INTERNATIONAL, INC.; *U.S. Private*, pg. 1362
ELK GROVE DIALYSIS CENTER, LLC—See DaVita Inc.; *U.S. Public*, pg. 638
ELK GROVE PARK DISTRICT; *U.S. Private*, pg. 1362
ELKHART BRASS MANUFACTURING COMPANY, INC.—See The Sterling Group, L.P.; *U.S. Private*, pg. 4122
THE ELKHART COOPERATIVE EQUITY EXCHANGE; *U.S. Private*, pg. 4025
ELKHART GENERAL HOSPITAL, INC.—See Beacon Health System, Inc.; *U.S. Private*, pg. 504
ELKHART GRAIN COMPANY; *U.S. Private*, pg. 1363
ELKHART PLASTICS, INC.; *U.S. Private*, pg. 1363
ELKHART PRODUCTS CORP.-ELKHART PLANT—See Mueller Industries, Inc.; *U.S. Public*, pg. 1484
ELKHART PRODUCTS CORPORATION-INDUSTRIAL DIVISION—See Mueller Industries, Inc.; *U.S. Public*, pg. 1484
ELKHART PRODUCTS CORPORATION—See Mueller Industries, Inc.; *U.S. Public*, pg. 1484
ELKHART PRODUCTS LIMITED—See Aalberts N.V.; *Int'l*, pg. 34
THE ELK HORN COAL COMPANY LLC—See Wexford Capital Limited Partnership; *U.S. Private*, pg. 4502
ELKHORN CONSTRUCTION INC.—See John Wood Group PLC; *Int'l*, pg. 3984
ELKHORN HOLDINGS INC.—See John Wood Group PLC; *Int'l*, pg. 3984
ELKHORN-LUEPTOW'S INC.; *U.S. Private*, pg. 1363
ELKHORN OPERATING CO. INC.; *U.S. Private*, pg. 1363
ELKHORN RURAL PUBLIC POWER DISTRICT; *U.S. Private*, pg. 1363
ELKIN CO.; *U.S. Private*, pg. 1363
ELKINGTON CHINA LIMITED—See The Alumasc Group plc; *Int'l*, pg. 7613
ELKINGTON GATIC—See The Alumasc Group plc; *Int'l*, pg. 7613
ELKINS CONSTRUCTORS, INC.; *U.S. Private*, pg. 1363
ELKINS FORD LAND; *U.S. Private*, pg. 1363
ELKINS INTER-MOUNTAIN CO. INC.—See The Nutting Company, Inc.; *U.S. Private*, pg. 4086
ELKJOP NORDIC AS—See Currys plc; *Int'l*, pg. 1879
ELKO AB—See Schneider Electric SE; *Int'l*, pg. 6626
ELKO AS—See Schneider Electric SE; *Int'l*, pg. 6626
ELKO C.E., S.A.—See Arrow Electronics, Inc.; *U.S. Public*, pg. 199
ELKO EHF.—See Festi hf; *Int'l*, pg. 2646
EL KOEI CO., LTD.—See Nippon Koei Co., Ltd.; *Int'l*, pg. 5321
ELKOK A.D.; *Int'l*, pg. 2364
ELKOME GROUP OY—See Addtech AB; *Int'l*, pg. 133
ELKOME OY—See Addtech AB; *Int'l*, pg. 133

ELKOM SOLUTIONS GMBH—See MEDIQON Group AG; *Int'l*, pg. 2364
ELKON ELEKTRIK SANAYI VE TICARET AS—See Electricite de France S.A.; *Int'l*, pg. 2351
ELKONTAKT I BORAS AB—See Instalco AB; *Int'l*, pg. 3721
ELKOP S.A.; *Int'l*, pg. 2364
ELK ORTHOBIOLOGICS LIMITED; *Int'l*, pg. 2363
ELK PETROLEUM INC—See ELK Petroleum Limited; *Int'l*, pg. 2363
ELK PETROLEUM LIMITED; *Int'l*, pg. 2363
ELK PREMIUM BUILDING PRODUCTS, INC.—See GAF Materials Corporation; *U.S. Private*, pg. 1633
EL KRAFT TEKNIK & KONSULT I SALA AB—See Instalco AB; *Int'l*, pg. 3721
ELK REGIONAL HEALTH CENTER; *U.S. Private*, pg. 1362
ELK RIVER FORD MERCURY, INC.; *U.S. Private*, pg. 1362
ELK RIVER LANDFILL, INC.—See Waste Management, Inc.; *U.S. Public*, pg. 2331
ELK RIVER MACHINE CO.—See The Cretex Companies, Inc.; *U.S. Private*, pg. 4016
ELK RIVER PUBLIC UTILITY DISTRICT; *U.S. Private*, pg. 1363
ELK RIVER WIND FARM, LLC.—See Iberdrola, S.A.; *Int'l*, pg. 3570
ELK RUN COAL COMPANY, INC.—See Alpha Natural Resources, Inc.; *U.S. Private*, pg. 198
ELK SUPPLY COMPANY; *U.S. Private*, pg. 1363
ELKTON GAS COMPANY—See Chesapeake Utilities Corporation; *U.S. Public*, pg. 485
ELK VALLEY HEALTH SERVICES, LLC—See UnitedHealth Group Incorporated; *U.S. Public*, pg. 2244
ELK VALLEY PROFESSIONAL AFFILIATES, INC.—See UnitedHealth Group Incorporated; *U.S. Public*, pg. 2244
ELKVIEW MINE LIMITED PARTNERSHIP—See Teck Resources Limited; *Int'l*, pg. 7514
ELLAHI INTERNATIONAL (PVT) LTD.—See Nagina Group; *Int'l*, pg. 5128
ELLAH LAKES PLC.; *Int'l*, pg. 2364
ELLAKTOR S.A.; *Int'l*, pg. 2364
ELLA MOSS—See GMM Capital LLC; *U.S. Private*, pg. 1722
ELLARD LIMITED—See Indutrade AB; *Int'l*, pg. 3678
ELLA'S KITCHEN (BRANDS) LIMITED—See The Hain Celestial Group, Inc.; *U.S. Public*, pg. 2086
ELLA'S KITCHEN GROUP LIMITED—See The Hain Celestial Group, Inc.; *U.S. Public*, pg. 2086
ELLBA EASTERN (PTE) LTD.—See BASF SE; *Int'l*, pg. 878
ELLBA EASTERN (PTE) LTD.—See Shell plc; *Int'l*, pg. 6798
ELLCON-NATIONAL INC.; *U.S. Private*, pg. 1363
ELLCOT SPINNING MILLS LIMITED—See Nagina Group; *Int'l*, pg. 5129
ELLEAIR BUSINESS SUPPORT CO., LTD.—See Daio Paper Corporation; *Int'l*, pg. 1940
ELLEAIR INTERNATIONAL KOREA CO., LTD.—See Daio Paper Corporation; *Int'l*, pg. 1940
ELLEAIR INTERNATIONAL (THAILAND) CO., LTD.—See Daio Paper Corporation; *Int'l*, pg. 1940
ELLEAIR PAPER CO., LTD.—See Daio Paper Corporation; *Int'l*, pg. 1940
ELLEAIR PRODUCT CO., LTD.—See Daio Paper Corporation; *Int'l*, pg. 1940
ELLEAIR TEXEL CORPORATION—See Daio Paper Corporation; *Int'l*, pg. 1940
ELLE.COM—See Vivendi SE; *Int'l*, pg. 8274
ELLE DECOR—See The Hearst Corporation; *U.S. Private*, pg. 4046
ELLE DRIVER SAS—See Wild Bunch AG; *Int'l*, pg. 8409
ELLE INTERNATIONAL SA—See Vivendi SE; *Int'l*, pg. 8271
ELLENBARRIE INDUSTRIAL GASES LTD.—See Air Water Inc.; *Int'l*, pg. 240
ELLENBEE-LEGGETT COMPANY INC.; *U.S. Private*, pg. 1363
ELLENDALE ELECTRIC COMPANY, INC.; *U.S. Private*, pg. 1363
ELLEN PHILIP ASSOCIATES, INC.—See Integrated Software Solutions, Inc.; *U.S. Private*, pg. 2101
ELLENSBURG TELEPHONE COMPANY—See Consolidated Communications Holdings, Inc.; *U.S. Public*, pg. 570
ELLENTON ICE & SPORTS COMPLEX, LLC; *U.S. Private*, pg. 1363
ELLENVILLE REGIONAL HOSPITAL; *U.S. Private*, pg. 1363
ELL ENVIRONMENTAL HOLDINGS LIMITED; *Int'l*, pg. 2364
ELLERINE HOLDINGS LTD.; *Int'l*, pg. 2365
ELLERMAN INVESTMENTS LTD.; *Int'l*, pg. 2365
ELLERSTON ASIAN INVESTMENTS LIMITED; *Int'l*, pg. 2365
ELLERSTON GLOBAL INVESTMENTS LIMITED; *Int'l*, pg. 2365

ELLERY HOMESTYLES, LLC—See Trivest Partners, LP; *U.S. Private*, pg. 4240
ELLE—See The Hearst Corporation; *U.S. Private*, pg. 4046
ELLETT BROTHERS, INC.; *U.S. Private*, pg. 1363
ELLEVATE FINANCIAL, INC.; *U.S. Private*, pg. 1363
ELLEVATE FINANCIAL LLC—See Ellevate Financial, Inc.; *U.S. Private*, pg. 1363
ELLE VERLAG GMBH—See Vivendi SE; *Int'l*, pg. 8274
ELLEX AUSTRALIA PTY. LTD.—See Lumibird Group; *Int'l*, pg. 4578
ELLEX DEUTSCHLAND GMBH—See Ellex Medical Lasers Limited; *Int'l*, pg. 2365
ELLEX (JAPAN) CORPORATION—See Ellex Medical Lasers Limited; *Int'l*, pg. 2365
ELLEX MEDICAL LASERS LIMITED; *Int'l*, pg. 2365
ELLEX MEDICAL PTY LTD.—See Ellex Medical Lasers Limited; *Int'l*, pg. 2365
ELLEX SERVICES EUROPE S.A.R.L—See Ellex Medical Lasers Limited; *Int'l*, pg. 2365
ELLEX (USA) INC.—See Ellex Medical Lasers Limited; *Int'l*, pg. 2365
ELLICOTT DEVELOPMENT CO.; *U.S. Private*, pg. 1363
ELLICOTT DREDGE ENTERPRISES, LLC—See Markel Group Inc.; *U.S. Public*, pg. 1368
ELLICOTT DREDGES, LLC—See Markel Group Inc.; *U.S. Public*, pg. 1368
ELLICOTT KIDNEY CENTER, LLC—See Nautic Partners, LLC; *U.S. Private*, pg. 2870
ELLICOTT PAINT CO. INC.; *U.S. Private*, pg. 1363
ELLIE MAE, INC.—See Intercontinental Exchange, Inc.; *U.S. Public*, pg. 1142
ELLIES ELECTRONICS (BLOEMFONTEIN)(PTY) LTD—See Ellies Holdings Limited; *Int'l*, pg. 2366
ELLIES ELECTRONICS (CAPE)(PTY) LTD—See Ellies Holdings Limited; *Int'l*, pg. 2366
ELLIES ELECTRONICS (NATAL)(PTY) LTD—See Ellies Holdings Limited; *Int'l*, pg. 2366
ELLIES ELECTRONICS (NELSPRUIT)(PTY) LTD—See Ellies Holdings Limited; *Int'l*, pg. 2366
ELLIES ELECTRONICS (PIETERSBURG)(PTY) LTD—See Ellies Holdings Limited; *Int'l*, pg. 2366
ELLIES HOLDINGS LIMITED; *Int'l*, pg. 2365
ELLIES (PTY) LTD—See Ellies Holdings Limited; *Int'l*, pg. 2366
ELLIMAC PRIME HOLDINGS INC.—See Cosco Capital, Inc.; *Int'l*, pg. 1809
ELLINAS FINANCE PUBLIC COMPANY LTD; *Int'l*, pg. 2366
ELLINGTON CREDIT COMPANY MANAGEMENT LLC; *U.S. Public*, pg. 734
ELLINGTON FINANCIAL INC.—See Ellington Management Group, L.L.C.; *U.S. Private*, pg. 1364
ELLINGTON FINANCIAL OPERATING PARTNERSHIP LLC—See Ellington Management Group, L.L.C.; *U.S. Private*, pg. 1364
ELLINGTON HOUSING INC.; *U.S. Private*, pg. 1363
ELLINGTON MANAGEMENT GROUP, L.L.C.; *U.S. Private*, pg. 1364
ELLINIKI TECHNODOMIKI ANEMOS S.A—See ELLAKTOR S.A.; *Int'l*, pg. 2365
ELLINIKI TECHNODOMIKI ENERGIAKI S.A—See ELLAKTOR S.A.; *Int'l*, pg. 2365
ELLIO LLC; *U.S. Private*, pg. 1364
ELLIOT ELECTRIC COMPANY INC.—See Davis H. Elliot Company Inc.; *U.S. Private*, pg. 1173
ELLIOT ENGINEERING, INC.—See Davis H. Elliot Company Inc.; *U.S. Private*, pg. 1173
THE ELLIOT GROUP LLC; *U.S. Private*, pg. 4025
ELLIOTT ADVISORS (UK) LIMITED—See Elliott Management Corporation; *U.S. Private*, pg. 1364
ELLIOTT ASSOCIATES, L.P.—See Elliott Management Corporation; *U.S. Private*, pg. 1365
ELLIOTT AVIATION, INC.; *U.S. Private*, pg. 1364
ELLIOTT BULK SERVICES, LLC—See Elliott Oil Co. Inc.; *U.S. Private*, pg. 1373
ELLIOTT CHEVROLET, INC.; *U.S. Private*, pg. 1364
ELLIOTT COMPANY; *U.S. Private*, pg. 1364
ELLIOTT COMPANY—See Ebara Corporation; *Int'l*, pg. 2284
ELLIOTT DAVIS DECOSIMO, LLC; *U.S. Private*, pg. 1364
ELLIOTT EBARA SINGAPORE PTE. LTD.—See Ebara Corporation; *Int'l*, pg. 2284
ELLIOTT EBARA TURBOMACHINERY CORPORATION—See Ebara Corporation; *Int'l*, pg. 2284
ELLIOTT ELECTRIC SUPPLY; *U.S. Private*, pg. 1364
ELLIOTT EQUIPMENT COMPANY INCORPORATED; *U.S. Private*, pg. 1364
ELLIOTT EQUIPMENT COMPANY; *U.S. Private*, pg. 1364
ELLIOTT & FRANTZ INC.; *U.S. Private*, pg. 1364
ELLIOTT GROUP HOLDINGS, INC.—See Ebara Corporation; *Int'l*, pg. 2284
ELLIOTT HARDWARE INC.; *U.S. Private*, pg. 1364
ELLIOTT-HARTMAN AGENCY—See ABRY Partners, LLC; *U.S. Private*, pg. 42
ELLIOTT HOMES INC.; *U.S. Private*, pg. 1364
ELLIOTT HOMES INC.—See Solitaire Homes, Inc.; *U.S. Private*, pg. 3709

ELLIOTT INTERNATIONAL, L.P.—See Elliott Management Corporation; *U.S. Private*, pg. 1365
ELLIOTT INVESTMENT MANAGEMENT L.P.—See Elliott Management Corporation; *U.S. Private*, pg. 1365
ELLIOTT LUCCA—See Indonesian Imports, Inc.; *U.S. Private*, pg. 2064
ELLIOTT MACHINE WORKS, INC.—See Stellar Industries Inc.; *U.S. Private*, pg. 3799
ELLIOTT MANAGEMENT CORPORATION; *U.S. Private*, pg. 1364
ELLIOTT MANUFACTURING COMPANY, INC.—See Granite Equity Partners LLC; *U.S. Private*, pg. 1755
ELLIOTT MASTUURA CANADA INC.—See Nicolas Correa S.A.; *Int'l*, pg. 5273
ELLIOTT MATSUURA CANADA, INC.; *Int'l*, pg. 2366
ELLIOTT OIL CO. INC.; *U.S. Private*, pg. 1373
ELLIOTT SAWMILLING COMPANY, INC.—See Canfor Corporation; *Int'l*, pg. 1291
ELLIOTT'S HARDWARE, INC.—See Tyndale Advisors, LLC; *U.S. Private*, pg. 4268
ELLIOTT SPECIAL RISKS LP—See Markel Group Inc.; *U.S. Public*, pg. 1368
ELLIOTT STONE CO., INC.—See TorQuest Partners Inc.; *Int'l*, pg. 7830
ELLIOTT TAPE INC.; *U.S. Private*, pg. 1373
ELLIOTT TURBOMACHINERY CANADA, INC.—See Ebara Corporation; *Int'l*, pg. 2284
ELLIOTT TURBOMACHINERY LTD.—See Ebara Corporation; *Int'l*, pg. 2284
ELLIOTT TURBOMACHINERY S.A.—See Ebara Corporation; *Int'l*, pg. 2284
ELLIOTT/WILSON CAPITOL TRUCKS LLC; *U.S. Private*, pg. 1373
ELLIOTT WILSON INSURANCE, LLC—See Shore Bancshares, Inc.; *U.S. Public*, pg. 1875
ELLIPSIZ COMMUNICATIONS LTD.; *Int'l*, pg. 2366
ELLIPSIZ COMMUNICATIONS (NZ) LIMITED—See Ellipsiz Ltd.; *Int'l*, pg. 2366
ELLIPSIZ COMMUNICATIONS TAIWAN LTD—See Ellipsiz Ltd.; *Int'l*, pg. 2366
ELLIPSIZ DSS PTE. LTD.—See Ellipsiz Ltd.; *Int'l*, pg. 2366
ELLIPSIZ INETEST (SHANGHAI) CO., LTD—See Ellipsiz Ltd.; *Int'l*, pg. 2366
ELLIPSIZ INETEST (SUZHOU) CO., LTD.—See Ellipsiz Ltd.; *Int'l*, pg. 2366
ELLIPSIZ LTD.; *Int'l*, pg. 2366
ELLIPSIZ SECOND SOURCE INC—See Ellipsiz Ltd.; *Int'l*, pg. 2366
ELLIPSIZ SEMILAB (SHANGHAI) CO., LTD—See Ellipsiz Ltd.; *Int'l*, pg. 2366
ELLIPSIZ (SHANGHAI) INTERNATIONAL LTD—See Ellipsiz Ltd.; *Int'l*, pg. 2366
ELLIPSIZ SINGAPORE PTE LTD—See Ellipsiz Ltd.; *Int'l*, pg. 2366
ELLIPTIC LABORATORIES ASA; *Int'l*, pg. 2366
ELLIS BROTHERS INC.; *U.S. Private*, pg. 1374
ELLIS CAPITAL, LLC—See Ellis, McQuary, Stanley & Associates LLC; *U.S. Private*, pg. 1374
ELLIS COFFEE COMPANY; *U.S. Private*, pg. 1374
ELLIS & COMPANY LTD.—See A.A.G. STUCCHI s.r.l.; *Int'l*, pg. 23
ELLIS CONSTRUCTION SPECIALTIES; *U.S. Private*, pg. 1374
ELLIS COUNTY LANDFILL TX, LP—See Republic Services, Inc.; *U.S. Public*, pg. 1786
ELLISDON CONSTRUCTION INC.—See EllisDon Corporation; *Int'l*, pg. 2366
ELLISDON CONSTRUCTION INC.—See EllisDon Corporation; *Int'l*, pg. 2366
ELLISDON CONSTRUCTION SERVICES INC.—See EllisDon Corporation; *Int'l*, pg. 2366
ELLISDON CORPORATION; *Int'l*, pg. 2366
ELLISDON CORPORATION—See EllisDon Corporation; *Int'l*, pg. 2366
ELLISDON CORPORATION—See EllisDon Corporation; *Int'l*, pg. 2367
ELLISDON CORPORATION—See EllisDon Corporation; *Int'l*, pg. 2367
ELLISDON CORPORATION—See EllisDon Corporation; *Int'l*, pg. 2367
ELLISDON SERVICES INC.—See EllisDon Corporation; *Int'l*, pg. 2367
ELLIS & EASTERN COMPANY—See MDU Resources Group, Inc.; *U.S. Public*, pg. 1410
ELLIS HOLDING CO.; *U.S. Private*, pg. 1374
ELLIS HOME OXYGEN & MEDICAL EQUIPMENT, INC.—See AdaptHealth Corp.; *U.S. Public*, pg. 38
ELLIS HOSIERY MILLS INC.; *U.S. Private*, pg. 1374
ELLIS, MCQUARY, STANLEY & ASSOCIATES LLC; *U.S. Private*, pg. 1374
ELLIS MEARES & SON INC.; *U.S. Private*, pg. 1374
ELLISON BAKERY INC—See MidOcean Partners, LLP; *U.S. Private*, pg. 2717
THE ELLISON CO. INC.; *U.S. Private*, pg. 4025
ELLISON MEDIA COMPANY; *U.S. Private*, pg. 1374
ELLISON NURSING GROUP, LLC; *U.S. Private*, pg. 1374
ELLISON SURFACE TECHNOLOGIES, INC.—See Bodycote plc; *Int'l*, pg. 1098
ELLISON TECHNOLOGIES INC.; *U.S. Private*, pg. 1374

ELLISON TECHNOLOGIES, INC.—See Ellison Technologies Inc.; *U.S. Private*, pg. 1374
ELLISON TECHNOLOGIES, INC.—See Ellison Technologies Inc.; *U.S. Private*, pg. 1374
ELLISON TRAVEL & TOURS LTD.; *Int'l*, pg. 2367
ELLIS POTTERY INC.; *U.S. Private*, pg. 1374
ELLIS, RICHARD CB & REICHLE KLEIN; *U.S. Private*, pg. 1374
ELLIS SKINNER COMPANY, INC.; *U.S. Private*, pg. 1374
ELLIS STEEL COMPANY INC.; *U.S. Private*, pg. 1374
ELLIS STONE CONSTRUCTION COMPANY; *U.S. Private*, pg. 1374
ELLIS-WALKER BUILDERS, INC.; *U.S. Private*, pg. 1374
ELLIS & WATTS GLOBAL INDUSTRIES, LLC—See Berkshire Hathaway Inc.; *U.S. Public*, pg. 312
ELLMAN INTERNATIONAL, LLC—See Clayton, Dubilier & Rice, LLC; *U.S. Private*, pg. 922
ELLO FURNITURE MANUFACTURING CO.; *U.S. Private*, pg. 1374
ELLOMAY CAPITAL LTD.; *Int'l*, pg. 2367
ELLORA ENERGY INC.—See Exxon Mobil Corporation; *U.S. Public*, pg. 814
ELLOS AB—See Nordic Capital AB; *Int'l*, pg. 5420
ELLOS FINLAND OY—See Nordic Capital AB; *Int'l*, pg. 5420
ELLSIN ENVIRONMENTAL LTD. - ELLSIN PLANT 1—See Environmental Waste International Inc.; *Int'l*, pg. 2455
ELLSIN ENVIRONMENTAL LTD.—See Environmental Waste International Inc.; *Int'l*, pg. 2455
ELLSWORTH COOPERATIVE CREAMERY; *U.S. Private*, pg. 1375
ELLSWORTH COOP; *U.S. Private*, pg. 1374
ELLSWORTH CORPORATION; *U.S. Private*, pg. 1375
ELLSWORTH CORPORATION; *U.S. Private*, pg. 1375
ELLSWORTH FALLS LUMBER CO. INC.; *U.S. Private*, pg. 1375
ELLSWORTH HANDCRAFTED BICYCLES, INC.—See BST NanoCarbon LLC; *U.S. Private*, pg. 675
ELLSWORTH PAULSEN CONSTRUCTION CO.—See ACS, Actividades de Construccion y Servicios, S.A.; *Int'l*, pg. 113
ELLUCIAN COMPANY L.P. - MALVERN—See Vista Equity Partners, LLC; *U.S. Private*, pg. 4396
ELLUCIAN COMPANY L.P.—See Blackstone Inc.; *U.S. Public*, pg. 353
ELLUCIAN COMPANY L.P.—See Vista Equity Partners, LLC; *U.S. Private*, pg. 4396
ELLUMEN INC.; *U.S. Private*, pg. 1375
ELLWEE AB; *Int'l*, pg. 2367
ELLWOOD CHROME CRANKSHAFT COMPANY—See Ellwood Group, Inc.; *U.S. Private*, pg. 1375
ELLWOOD CITY FORGE—See Ellwood Group, Inc.; *U.S. Private*, pg. 1375
ELLWOOD CRANKSHAFT & MACHINE COMPANY, LLC—See Ellwood Group, Inc.; *U.S. Private*, pg. 1375
ELLWOOD ENGINEERED CASTING CO—See Ellwood Group, Inc.; *U.S. Private*, pg. 1375
ELLWOOD GROUP, INC.; *U.S. Private*, pg. 1375
ELLWOOD MILL PRODUCTS—See Ellwood Group, Inc.; *U.S. Private*, pg. 1375
ELLWOOD NATIONAL CRANKSHAFT CO—See Ellwood Group, Inc.; *U.S. Private*, pg. 1375
ELLWOOD NATIONAL CRANKSHAFT SERVICES—See Ellwood Group, Inc.; *U.S. Private*, pg. 1375
ELLWOOD NATIONAL FORGE COMPANY, LLC—See Ellwood Group, Inc.; *U.S. Private*, pg. 1375
ELLWOOD QUALITY STEELS COMPANY—See Ellwood Group, Inc.; *U.S. Private*, pg. 1375
ELLWOOD ROSE MACHINE, INC.—See Ellwood Group, Inc.; *U.S. Private*, pg. 1375
ELLWOOD SPECIALTY STEEL COMPANY, LLC—See Ellwood Group, Inc.; *U.S. Private*, pg. 1375
ELLWOOD TEXAS FORGE—See Ellwood Group, Inc.; *U.S. Private*, pg. 1375
ELMA ASIA PACIFIC PTE. LTD.—See Elma Electronic AG; *Int'l*, pg. 2367
ELMA BUSTRONIC CORP.—See Elma Electronic AG; *Int'l*, pg. 2367
ELMA CO., LTD.—See Gunze Limited; *Int'l*, pg. 3185
ELMA ELECTRONIC AG; *Int'l*, pg. 2367
ELMA ELECTRONIC FRANCE SASU—See Elma Electronic AG; *Int'l*, pg. 2367
ELMA ELECTRONIC GMBH—See Elma Electronic AG; *Int'l*, pg. 2367
ELMA ELECTRONIC GMBH—See Elma Electronic AG; *Int'l*, pg. 2367
ELMA ELECTRONIC INC.—See Elma Electronic AG; *Int'l*, pg. 2367
ELMA ELECTRONIC ISRAEL LTD—See Elma Electronic AG; *Int'l*, pg. 2367
ELMA ELECTRONIC ROMANIA SRL—See Elma Electronic AG; *Int'l*, pg. 2367
ELMA ELECTRONIC TECHNOLOGY (SHANGHAI) CO., LTD.—See Elma Electronic AG; *Int'l*, pg. 2367
ELMA ELECTRONIC UK LTD.—See Elma Electronic AG; *Int'l*, pg. 2367
ELMA HANS SCHMIDBAUER GMBH & CO. KG; *Int'l*, pg. 2367

ELMA HOLDINGS PUBLIC COMPANY LTD; *Int'l*, pg. 2367
ELMA INSTRUMENTS A/S—See Indutrade AB; *Int'l*, pg. 3678
ELMARCO S.R.O.—See BNP Paribas SA; *Int'l*, pg. 1089
ELMAR ENGINEERING LIMITED—See NOV, Inc.; *U.S. Public*, pg. 1544
ELMAR FAR EAST PTY LTD—See NOV, Inc.; *U.S. Public*, pg. 1544
ELMAR SERVICES LIMITED—See NOV, Inc.; *U.S. Public*, pg. 1544
ELMAR SERVICES PTY LTD—See NOV, Inc.; *U.S. Public*, pg. 1544
ELMA SCHMIDBAUER SUISSE AG—See Elma Hans Schmidbauer GmbH & Co. KG; *Int'l*, pg. 2367
EL-MASRY INDUSTRIAL SERVICES LLC—See Hydac International GmbH; *Int'l*, pg. 3544
ELMASU A.S.—See Goltas Cimento A.S.; *Int'l*, pg. 3037
ELMATAS A.S.—See Goltas Cimento A.S.; *Int'l*, pg. 3037
ELMAT - SCHLAGHECK GMBH & CO. KG; *Int'l*, pg. 2367
EL MAZRAA—See Poulina Group Holding S.A.; *Int'l*, pg. 5942
ELM CHEVROLET COMPANY, INC.; *U.S. Private*, pg. 1375
ELMC HOLDINGS, LLC; *U.S. Private*, pg. 1376
ELM CITY SALES INC.; *U.S. Private*, pg. 1375
ELM COMPUTER TECHNOLOGIES LIMITED—See Beijing Teamsun Technology Co., Ltd.; *Int'l*, pg. 958
ELM CORPORATION—See Future Corporation; *Int'l*, pg. 2853
ELMCO SALES INC.—See Acorn Engineering Company, Inc.; *U.S. Private*, pg. 63
ELM CREEK PARTNERS; *U.S. Private*, pg. 1375
ELM CREEK WIND II, LLC—See Iberdrola, S.A.; *Int'l*, pg. 3570
ELMCROFT OF FLORENCE, LP—See Senior Care, Inc.; *U.S. Private*, pg. 3606
ELMDALE MANAGEMENT GROUP, LLC.—See Elmdale Partners, LLC; *U.S. Private*, pg. 1376
ELMDALE PARTNERS, LLC; *U.S. Private*, pg. 1376
ELME ALEXANDRIA LLC—See Elme Communities; *U.S. Public*, pg. 735
ELME COMMUNITIES; *U.S. Public*, pg. 734
ELME CONYERS LLC—See Elme Communities; *U.S. Public*, pg. 735
ELMEC ROMANIA SRL—See Folli Follie S.A.; *Int'l*, pg. 2721
ELMED CO., LTD.—See Nichi-Iko Pharmaceutical Co., Ltd.; *Int'l*, pg. 5266
E&L MEDICAL SYSTEMS GMBH—See NEXUS AG; *Int'l*, pg. 5250
ELME DRUID HILLS LLC—See Elme Communities; *U.S. Public*, pg. 735
ELME DULLES LLC—See Elme Communities; *U.S. Public*, pg. 735
ELME EAGLES LANDING 860 LLC—See Elme Communities; *U.S. Public*, pg. 735
ELME GERMANTOWN LLC—See Elme Communities; *U.S. Public*, pg. 735
ELME HERNDON LLC—See Elme Communities; *U.S. Public*, pg. 735
ELMEK ELEKTROMEKANIK SANAYI VE TICARET ANONIM SIRKETI AS—See ABB Ltd.; *Int'l*, pg. 51
ELME KENMORE LLC—See Elme Communities; *U.S. Public*, pg. 735
ELME LEESBURG LLC—See Elme Communities; *U.S. Public*, pg. 735
ELME MANASSAS LLC—See Elme Communities; *U.S. Public*, pg. 735
ELME MARIETTA LLC—See Elme Communities; *U.S. Public*, pg. 735
ELME MESSER GAAS A.S.—See Messer Group GmbH; *Int'l*, pg. 4842
ELME MESSER METALURGS LSEZ SIA—See Messer Group GmbH; *Int'l*, pg. 4842
ELME MESSER UKRAINE—See Messer Group GmbH; *Int'l*, pg. 4842
ELME METALL FINLAND OY—See BLRT Grupp AS; *Int'l*, pg. 1065
ELME METALL LATVIA SIA—See BLRT Grupp AS; *Int'l*, pg. 1065
ELME METALL LITHUANIA, UAB—See BLRT Grupp AS; *Int'l*, pg. 1065
ELME METALL OU—See BLRT Grupp AS; *Int'l*, pg. 1065
ELME METALL POLAND SP. Z O.O.—See BLRT Grupp AS; *Int'l*, pg. 1065
ELME METALL RUSSIA—See BLRT Grupp AS; *Int'l*, pg. 1065
ELMENDORF STRATEGIES LLC—See Home Front Communications, LLC; *U.S. Private*, pg. 1971
ELMEN ENTERPRISES INC. - MENOMINEE—See Elmen Enterprises; *U.S. Private*, pg. 1376
ELMEN ENTERPRISES; *U.S. Private*, pg. 1376
ELMEN SP. Z O.O.—See PGE Polska Grupa Energetyczna S.A.; *Int'l*, pg. 5837
ELME PARAMOUNT LLC—See Elme Communities; *U.S. Public*, pg. 735
ELME PARK ADAMS APARTMENTS LLC—See Elme Communities; *U.S. Public*, pg. 735

COMPANY NAME INDEX

ELMERA GROUP ASA; *Int'l*, pg. 2367
ELMER BANCORP, INC.; *U.S. Public*, pg. 735
ELMER BUCHTA TRUCKING, LLC; *U.S. Private*, pg. 1376
ELMER CANDY CORPORATION; *U.S. Private*, pg. 1376
ELME RIVERSIDE APARTMENTS LLC—See Elme Communities; *U.S. Public*, pg. 735
ELME ROOSEVELT TOWERS LLC—See Elme Communities; *U.S. Public*, pg. 735
ELMERS CRANE AND DOZER INC.; *U.S. Private*, pg. 1376
ELMER SMITH OIL COMPANY; *U.S. Private*, pg. 1376
ELMER'S PRODUCTS CANADA, CORPORATION—See Newell Brands Inc.; *U.S. Public*, pg. 1514
ELMER'S PRODUCTS, INC.—See Newell Brands Inc.; *U.S. Public*, pg. 1514
ELMER'S RESTAURANTS, INC.; *U.S. Private*, pg. 1376
ELMER'S & TOAGOSEI CO.—See Toagosei Co. Ltd.; *Int'l*, pg. 7770
ELME SANDY SPRINGS LLC—See Elme Communities; *U.S. Public*, pg. 735
ELMETEC (PVT) LIMITED—See Johnson and Phillips (Pakistan) Limited; *Int'l*, pg. 3985
ELME TROVE LLC—See Elme Communities; *U.S. Public*, pg. 735
ELMET TECHNOLOGIES INC.; *U.S. Private*, pg. 1376
ELME WATKINS MILL LLC—See Elme Communities; *U.S. Public*, pg. 735
ELME WELLINGTON LLC—See Elme Communities; *U.S. Public*, pg. 735
EL MEX SALINES CO.—See Chemical Industries Holding Company; *Int'l*, pg. 1461
ELME YALE WEST LLC—See Elme Communities; *U.S. Public*, pg. 735
ELM FORD-MERCURY INC.; *U.S. Private*, pg. 1375
ELM GLOBAL LOGISTICS; *U.S. Private*, pg. 1375
ELM GROVE DODGE CHRYSLER JEEP INC.; *U.S. Private*, pg. 1375
ELMHURST AUTO GROUP; *U.S. Private*, pg. 1376
ELMHURST BMW—See Elmhurst Auto Group; *U.S. Private*, pg. 1376
ELMHURST-CHICAGO STONE CO; *U.S. Private*, pg. 1376
ELMHURST DAIRY, INC.; *U.S. Private*, pg. 1376
ELMHURST GROUP; *U.S. Private*, pg. 1376
ELMHURST MEMORIAL HEALTHCARE; *U.S. Private*, pg. 1376
ELMHURST TOYOTA—See Elmhurst Auto Group; *U.S. Private*, pg. 1376
EL MILAGRO INCORPORATED; *U.S. Private*, pg. 1349
EL MILANILLO, S.A.—See Banco Bilbao Vizcaya Argentaria, S.A.; *Int'l*, pg. 817
EL MIRADOR SURGERY CENTER, L.L.C.—See Tenet Healthcare Corporation; *U.S. Public*, pg. 2005
ELMIRA SAVINGS BANK—See Community Bank System, Inc.; *U.S. Public*, pg. 550
ELM KRAGELUND AS—See Sdiptech AB; *Int'l*, pg. 6658
ELM LLC; *U.S. Private*, pg. 1376
ELMO GREER & SONS INC.; *U.S. Private*, pg. 1376
EL-MOHANDES JOTUN S.A.E.—See Jotun A/S; *Int'l*, pg. 4002
ELMO LEATHER AB—See Rino Mastrotto Group S.p.A.; *Int'l*, pg. 6345
ELMONT A.D.; *Int'l*, pg. 2367
EL MONTE AUTO SERVICES LLC—See Car Pros Automotive Group, Inc.; *U.S. Private*, pg. 747
EL MONTE RENTS INC.—See Tourism Holdings Limited; *Int'l*, pg. 7848
ELMONT INWESTYCJE SP. Z O.O—See PROCHEM S.A.; *Int'l*, pg. 5986
EL MOR CHEVROLET; *U.S. Private*, pg. 1349
ELMORE GROUP LTD.; *U.S. Private*, pg. 1376
ELMORE INTEREST INC.; *U.S. Private*, pg. 1376
EL-MOR ELECTRIC INSTALLATION & SERVICES (1986) LTD.—See Inter-Gamma Investment Company Ltd.; *Int'l*, pg. 3735
ELMORE LTD.; *Int'l*, pg. 2367
ELMORE TOYOYA; *U.S. Private*, pg. 1377
ELMOS CENTRAL IT SERVICES GMBH & CO. KG—See ELMOS Semiconductor AG; *Int'l*, pg. 2368
ELMOS JAPAN K.K.—See ELMOS Semiconductor AG; *Int'l*, pg. 2368
ELMOS KOREA LTD—See ELMOS Semiconductor AG; *Int'l*, pg. 2368
ELMOS N.A. INC—See ELMOS Semiconductor AG; *Int'l*, pg. 2368
ELMO SOFTWARE LIMITED—See K1 Investment Management, LLC; *U.S. Private*, pg. 2252
ELMOS SEMICONDUCTOR AG; *Int'l*, pg. 2368
ELMOS SEMICONDUCTOR SINGAPORE PTE. LTD.—See ELMOS Semiconductor AG; *Int'l*, pg. 2368
ELMOS SEMICONDUCTOR SUD GMBH—See ELMOS Semiconductor AG; *Int'l*, pg. 2368
ELMOS SEMICONDUCTOR TECHNOLOGY (SHANGHAI) CO., LTD.—See ELMOS Semiconductor AG; *Int'l*, pg. 2368
ELMOTEC STATOMAT GMBH—See INA-Holding Schaeffler GmbH & Co. KG; *Int'l*, pg. 3639
ELM PLATING CO.; *U.S. Private*, pg. 1376

ELMS ENDOSCOPY CENTER, LLC—See KKR & Co. Inc.; *U.S. Public*, pg. 1245
THE ELMS GROUP LIMITED—See Insig AI plc; *Int'l*, pg. 3718
ELMSHORNER NACHRICHTEN—See Axel Springer SE; *Int'l*, pg. 766
ELMS STANSTED LIMITED—See Group 1 Automotive, Inc.; *U.S. Public*, pg. 971
ELM STREET TECHNOLOGY LLC; *U.S. Private*, pg. 1376
EL MUNDO TV—See RCS MediaGroup S.p.A.; *Int'l*, pg. 6229
E.L. MUSTEE & SONS, INC.; *U.S. Private*, pg. 1306
ELMWOOD COUNTRY CLUB, INC.—See Ridgewood Real Estate Partners, LLC; *U.S. Private*, pg. 3434
ELNA AMERICA, INC.—See Taiyo Yuden Company Ltd.; *Int'l*, pg. 7426
ELNA CO., LTD. - SHIGA FACTORY—See Taiyo Yuden Company Ltd.; *Int'l*, pg. 7426
ELNA CO., LTD. - SHIRAKAWA FACTORY—See Taiyo Yuden Company Ltd.; *Int'l*, pg. 7426
ELNA CO., LTD.—See Taiyo Yuden Company Ltd.; *Int'l*, pg. 7426
ELNA COMPONENTS CO., LTD.—See Taiyo Yuden Company Ltd.; *Int'l*, pg. 7426
ELNA ELECTRONICS (S) PTE. LTD.—See Taiyo Yuden Company Ltd.; *Int'l*, pg. 7426
ELNA (HK) CO., LTD.—See Taiyo Yuden Company Ltd.; *Int'l*, pg. 7426
ELNA INTERNTIONAL CORP. SA—See Janome Sewing Machine Co., Ltd.; *Int'l*, pg. 3880
ELNA MATSUMOTO CO., LTD.—See Taiyo Yuden Company Ltd.; *Int'l*, pg. 7426
ELNA PCB (M) SDN. BHD.—See Taiyo Yuden Company Ltd.; *Int'l*, pg. 7426
ELNA PRINTED CIRCUITS CO., LTD.—See Global Brands Manufacture Ltd.; *Int'l*, pg. 2993
ELNA (SHANGHAI) CO., LTD.—See Taiyo Yuden Company Ltd.; *Int'l*, pg. 7426
ELNA-SONIC SDN. BHD.—See Taiyo Yuden Company Ltd.; *Int'l*, pg. 7426
EL NASR CLOTHING & TEXTILES CO.; *Int'l*, pg. 2341
EL NASR COMPANY FOR FERTILIZERS & CHEMICAL INDUSTRIES—See Chemical Industries Holding Company; *Int'l*, pg. 1461
EL NASR FOR MANUFACTURING AGRICULTURAL CROPS S.A.E.; *Int'l*, pg. 2341
EL-NASR SALINE COMPANY—See Chemical Industries Holding Company; *Int'l*, pg. 1462
EL NASSER ELECTRIC & ELECTRONIC APPARATUS CO.—See Chemical Industries Holding Company; *Int'l*, pg. 1461
EL NASSR COMPANY FOR RUBBER PRODUCTS (NARUBEEN)—See Chemical Industries Holding Company; *Int'l*, pg. 1461
ELNA TOHOKU CO., LTD.—See Taiyo Yuden Company Ltd.; *Int'l*, pg. 7426
ELNET TECHNOLOGIES LIMITED; *Int'l*, pg. 2368
EL-NILE CO. FOR PHARMACEUTICALS & CHEMICAL INDUSTRIES; *Int'l*, pg. 2341
EL NORTE DE CASTILLA S.A.—See Vocento, S.A.; *Int'l*, pg. 8284
EL NUEVO HERALD—See Chatham Asset Management, LLC; *U.S. Private*, pg. 867
ELOA CALIFORNIA ACQUISITION CORP.—See EssilorLuxottica SA; *Int'l*, pg. 2513
E-LOAN, INC.—See Popular, Inc.; *U.S. Public*, pg. 1702
EL OBOUR PAINTS & CHEMICAL INDUSTRIES CO.—See Paints and Chemicals Industries Company S.A.E.; *Int'l*, pg. 5702
EL OBOUR REAL ESTATE INVESTMENT; *Int'l*, pg. 2341
ELOCAL USA LLC—See Brookfield Corporation; *Int'l*, pg. 1189
THE ELOCEN GROUP LLC; *U.S. Private*, pg. 4025
ELOCOAT B.V.—See Ferd AS; *Int'l*, pg. 2635
ELODRIVE GMBH; *Int'l*, pg. 2368
ELOF HANSSON AB; *Int'l*, pg. 2368
ELOF HANSSON AB-SUC.—See Elof Hansson AB; *Int'l*, pg. 2368
ELOF HANSSON (AUSTRALIA) PTY LTD—See Elof Hansson AB; *Int'l*, pg. 2368
ELOF HANSSON FIBER LLC—See Elof Hansson AB; *Int'l*, pg. 2368
ELOF HANSSON INC. - FIBER DIVISION—See Elof Hansson AB; *Int'l*, pg. 2368
ELOF HANSSON INC.—See Elof Hansson AB; *Int'l*, pg. 2368
ELOF HANSSON (INDIA) PVT LTD—See Elof Hansson AB; *Int'l*, pg. 2368
ELOF HANSSON INTERNATIONAL AB—See Elof Hansson AB; *Int'l*, pg. 2368
ELOF HANSSON K.K.—See Elof Hansson AB; *Int'l*, pg. 2368
ELOF HANSSON LTDA—See Elof Hansson AB; *Int'l*, pg. 2368
ELOF HANSSON PAPER & BOARD, INC.—See Elof Hansson AB; *Int'l*, pg. 2368
ELOF HANSSON PULP AND PAPER LTD—See Elof Hansson AB; *Int'l*, pg. 2368

ELONG POWER HOLDING LIMITED

ELOF HANSSON PULP & PAPER SINGAPORE PTE LTD—See Elof Hansson AB; *Int'l*, pg. 2368
ELOGICOMNET MOROCCO DISTRIBUTION SARL—See Logicom Public Ltd; *Int'l*, pg. 4542
E-LOGI CORPORATION—See EDION Corporation; *Int'l*, pg. 2310
ELOGICS SYSTEM COMPANY-S.P.C—See Privatization Holding Company K.S.C.C.; *Int'l*, pg. 5984
E-LOGISTICS N.V.—See Colruyt Group N.V.; *Int'l*, pg. 1705
E-LOGIT CO., LTD.; *Int'l*, pg. 2249
ELOIGNE COMPANY—See Xcel Energy Inc.; *U.S. Public*, pg. 2385
ELOISE B. KYPER FUNERAL HOME, INC.—See Axar Capital Management L.P.; *U.S. Private*, pg. 411
ELO LIFE SYSTEMS, INC.—See Precision BioSciences, Inc.; *U.S. Public*, pg. 1713
ELOMA GMBH—See Ali Holding S.r.l; *Int'l*, pg. 322
EL-O-MATIC BENELUX BV—See Emerson Electric Co.; *U.S. Public*, pg. 750
EL-O-MATIC GMBH—See Emerson Electric Co.; *U.S. Public*, pg. 743
EL-O-MATIC LIMITED—See Emerson Electric Co.; *U.S. Public*, pg. 743
ELOMATIC OY; *Int'l*, pg. 2368
EL-O-MATIC USA, INC.—See Emerson Electric Co.; *U.S. Public*, pg. 746
EL-O-MATIC VALVE ACTUATORS (F.E.) PTE. LTD.—See Emerson Electric Co.; *U.S. Public*, pg. 743
ELOMECH ELEKTROANLAGEN GMBH—See Eiffage S.A.; *Int'l*, pg. 2331
ELON AB; *Int'l*, pg. 2368
ELONEX; *Int'l*, pg. 2368
ELONG, INC. - CHENGDU—See Tencent Holdings Limited; *Int'l*, pg. 7559
ELONG, INC. - CHENGDU—See Trip.com Group Ltd.; *Int'l*, pg. 7926
ELONG, INC. - GUANGZHOU—See Tencent Holdings Limited; *Int'l*, pg. 7559
ELONG, INC. - GUANGZHOU—See Trip.com Group Ltd.; *Int'l*, pg. 7926
ELONG, INC. - HANGZHOU—See Tencent Holdings Limited; *Int'l*, pg. 7559
ELONG, INC. - HANGZHOU—See Trip.com Group Ltd.; *Int'l*, pg. 7926
ELONG, INC. - NANJING—See Tencent Holdings Limited; *Int'l*, pg. 7559
ELONG, INC. - NANJING—See Trip.com Group Ltd.; *Int'l*, pg. 7926
ELONG, INC. - SHANGHAI OFFICE—See Tencent Holdings Limited; *Int'l*, pg. 7559
ELONG, INC. - SHANGHAI OFFICE—See Trip.com Group Ltd.; *Int'l*, pg. 7926
ELONG, INC. - SHENZHEN—See Tencent Holdings Limited; *Int'l*, pg. 7559
ELONG, INC. - SHENZHEN—See Trip.com Group Ltd.; *Int'l*, pg. 7926
ELONG, INC.—See Tencent Holdings Limited; *Int'l*, pg. 7559
ELONG, INC.—See Trip.com Group Ltd.; *Int'l*, pg. 7926
ELONG, INC. - WUHAN—See Tencent Holdings Limited; *Int'l*, pg. 7559
ELONG, INC. - WUHAN—See Trip.com Group Ltd.; *Int'l*, pg. 7926
ELONG POWER HOLDING LIMITED; *Int'l*, pg. 2369
ELOPAK AB—See Ferd AS; *Int'l*, pg. 2635
ELOPAK AS - MARKET UNIT—See Ferd AS; *Int'l*, pg. 2636
ELOPAK A/S—See Ferd AS; *Int'l*, pg. 2635
ELOPAK B.V.—See Ferd AS; *Int'l*, pg. 2635
ELOPAK B.V.—See Ferd AS; *Int'l*, pg. 2636
ELOPAK B.V.—See Ferd AS; *Int'l*, pg. 2636
ELOPAK DENMARK AS—See Ferd AS; *Int'l*, pg. 2635
ELOPAK D.O.O.—See Ferd AS; *Int'l*, pg. 2636
ELOPAK EQS GMBH—See Ferd AS; *Int'l*, pg. 2636
ELOPAK FRANCE B.V.—See Ferd AS; *Int'l*, pg. 2635
ELOPAK GES.M.B.H—See Ferd AS; *Int'l*, pg. 2635
ELOPAK GMBH—See Ferd AS; *Int'l*, pg. 2635
ELOPAK HUNGARY—See Ferd AS; *Int'l*, pg. 2635
ELOPAK, INC.—See Ferd AS; *Int'l*, pg. 2636
ELOPAK ISRAEL AS—See Ferd AS; *Int'l*, pg. 2636
ELOPAK LTD.—See Ferd AS; *Int'l*, pg. 2635
ELOPAK MALAYSIA SDN BHD—See Ferd AS; *Int'l*, pg. 2635
ELOPAK OBEIKAN LTD.—See Ferd AS; *Int'l*, pg. 2635
ELOPAK OY—See Ferd AS; *Int'l*, pg. 2635
ELOPAK PRODUCTION SERVICES GMBH & CO KG—See Ferd AS; *Int'l*, pg. 2636
ELOPAK S.A.—See Ferd AS; *Int'l*, pg. 2635
ELOPAK—See Ferd AS; *Int'l*, pg. 2635
ELOPAK SOUTH AFRICA (PTY) LTD.—See Ferd AS; *Int'l*, pg. 2636
ELOPAK S.P.A.—See Ferd AS; *Int'l*, pg. 2636
ELOPAK SYSTEMS AG—See Ferd AS; *Int'l*, pg. 2635
ELOPAK UK LTD.—See Ferd AS; *Int'l*, pg. 2636
ELOPAK UKRAINE—See Ferd AS; *Int'l*, pg. 2636
ELOQUA, INC.—See Oracle Corporation; *U.S. Public*, pg. 1611

ELORE ENTERPRISES LLC—See The Carlyle Group Inc.; *U.S. Public*, pg. 2047
EL ORO LTD.; *Int'l*, pg. 2341
ELORO RESOURCES LTD.; *Int'l*, pg. 2369
ELOS ENVIRONMENTAL, LLC—See Bernhard Capital Partners Management, LP; *U.S. Private*, pg. 537
ELOS MEDTECH AB—See TA Associates, Inc.; *U.S. Private*, pg. 3918
ELOS MEDTECH PINOL A/S—See TA Associates, Inc.; *U.S. Private*, pg. 3918
ELOS MEDTECH TIANJIN CO. LTD.—See TA Associates, Inc.; *U.S. Private*, pg. 3918
ELOS MEDTECH TIMMERSDALA AB—See TA Associates, Inc.; *U.S. Private*, pg. 3918
ELO—See Auchan Holding S.A.; *Int'l*, pg. 699
ELO TOUCH SOLUTIONS ARGENTINA SA—See Crestview Partners, L.P.; *U.S. Private*, pg. 1098
ELO TOUCH SOLUTIONS (BELGIUM) NV—See Crestview Partners, L.P.; *U.S. Private*, pg. 1098
ELO TOUCH SOLUTIONS, INC. - ROCHESTER—See Crestview Partners, L.P.; *U.S. Private*, pg. 1098
ELO TOUCH SOLUTIONS, INC.—See Crestview Partners, L.P.; *U.S. Private*, pg. 1098
ELO TOUCH SOLUTIONS SINGAPORE PTE LTD—See Crestview Partners, L.P.; *U.S. Private*, pg. 1098
ELO TOUCH SYSTEMS ARGENTINA S.A.—See TE Connectivity Ltd.; *Int'l*, pg. 7494
ELOVENT AB—See Instalco AB; *Int'l*, pg. 3721
ELOVI VIETNAM JOINT STOCK COMPANY—See Morinaga Milk Industry Co., Ltd.; *Int'l*, pg. 5046
ELOWFAR CO., LTD.—See Tropical Canning (Thailand) Public Company Limited; *Int'l*, pg. 7939
ELOXX PHARMACEUTICALS, INC.; *U.S. Public*, pg. 735
ELOYALTY (CANADA) CORPORATION—See NICE Ltd.; *Int'l*, pg. 5265
ELOYALTY (UK) LIMITED—See NICE Ltd.; *Int'l*, pg. 5265
ELOY ESD SOLAR HOLDINGS, LLC—See The AES Corporation; *U.S. Public*, pg. 2031
ELPAC COMPONENTS—See MEGATRON Elektronik AG & Co.; *Int'l*, pg. 4794
EL PACHON S.A.—See Glencore plc; *Int'l*, pg. 2990
EL-PAGARNA I MALMO AB—See Instalco AB; *Int'l*, pg. 3721
EL PAK SP. Z O.O.—See Zespol Elektrowni Patnow-Adamow-Konin S.A.; *Int'l*, pg. 8639
ELPAS, INC.—See Halma plc; *Int'l*, pg. 3231
THE EL PASO ASC, L.P.—See KKR & Co. Inc.; *U.S. Public*, pg. 1247
EL PASO BEHAVIORAL HEALTH SYSTEM—See Universal Health Services, Inc.; *U.S. Public*, pg. 2257
EL PASO CENTER FOR GASTROINTESTINAL ENDOSCOPY, LLC—See Tenet Healthcare Corporation; *U.S. Public*, pg. 2002
EL PASO CGP COMPANY, L.L.C.—See Kinder Morgan, Inc.; *U.S. Public*, pg. 1232
EL PASO CNG COMPANY, L.L.C.—See Kinder Morgan, Inc.; *U.S. Public*, pg. 1232
EL PASO COMMUNICATION SYSTEMS, INC; *U.S. Private*, pg. 1349
EL PASO DAY SURGERY, LLC—See Tenet Healthcare Corporation; *U.S. Public*, pg. 2005
EL PASO DISPOSAL, LP—See Waste Connections, Inc.; *Int'l*, pg. 8353
EL PASO ELECTRIC COMPANY—See JPMorgan Chase & Co.; *U.S. Public*, pg. 1206
EL PASO HEALTHCARE SYSTEM, LTD.—See HCA Healthcare, Inc.; *U.S. Public*, pg. 995
EL PASO HEALTH, LLC—See Nautic Partners, LLC; *U.S. Private*, pg. 2870
EL PASO IRON & METAL I, LTD.—See W. Silver Recycling, Inc.; *U.S. Private*, pg. 4418
EL PASO LEGENDS, LTD—See American Realty Investors, Inc.; *U.S. Public*, pg. 108
EL PASO LLC—See Kinder Morgan, Inc.; *U.S. Public*, pg. 1232
EL PASO NATURAL GAS COMPANY, LLC—See Kinder Morgan, Inc.; *U.S. Public*, pg. 1232
EL PASO PIPELINE PARTNERS, L.P.—See Kinder Morgan, Inc.; *U.S. Public*, pg. 1232
EL PASO SPECIALTY HOSPITAL, LTD.—See Bain Capital, LP; *U.S. Private*, pg. 445
EL PASO SURGERY CENTERS, L.P.—See HCA Healthcare, Inc.; *U.S. Public*, pg. 995
EL PASO TIMES—See Gannett Co., Inc.; *U.S. Public*, pg. 899
EL PASO WATER UTILITIES; *U.S. Private*, pg. 1349
ELP CORPORATION; *Int'l*, pg. 2369
ELPEC AS—See Eesti Energia AS; *Int'l*, pg. 2317
EL.P.ET BALKANIKI S.A.—See HELLENiQ ENERGY Holdings S.A.; *Int'l*, pg. 3334
ELPET VALKANIKI SA—See HELLENiQ ENERGY Holdings S.A.; *Int'l*, pg. 3334
ELPHINSTONE PTY LTD; *Int'l*, pg. 2369
ELPHI S.R.L.—See VINCI S.A.; *Int'l*, pg. 8237
ELPHI VM SRL—See VINCI S.A.; *Int'l*, pg. 8217
ELPIDA MEMORY (EUROPE) SARL—See Micron Technology, Inc.; *U.S. Public*, pg. 1437
ELPIDA MEMORY (HONG KONG) CO., LTD.—See Micron Technology, Inc.; *U.S. Public*, pg. 1437

ELPIDA MEMORY (KOREA) CO., LTD.—See Micron Technology, Inc.; *U.S. Public*, pg. 1437
ELPIDA MEMORY (TAIWAN) CO., LTD.—See Micron Technology, Inc.; *U.S. Public*, pg. 1437
ELPIDA MEMORY (USA) INC.—See Micron Technology, Inc.; *U.S. Public*, pg. 1437
EL PIMIENTO (SPA)—See RWE AG; *Int'l*, pg. 6434
ELPIS SP. Z O.O.—See PCC SE; *Int'l*, pg. 5766
ELPITIYA PLANTATIONS PLC; *Int'l*, pg. 2369
ELPO AD; *Int'l*, pg. 2369
EL POLLO LOCO HOLDINGS, INC.—See Trimaran Capital Partners, LLC; *U.S. Private*, pg. 4232
EL POLLO LOCO INC.—See Trimaran Capital Partners, LLC; *U.S. Private*, pg. 4232
ELPOOL I UMEA AB—See Addnode Group AB; *Int'l*, pg. 130
EL POPOCATAPETL INDUSTRIES, INC.; *U.S. Private*, pg. 1349
ELPRECO SA—See CRH plc; *Int'l*, pg. 1844
ELPRESS AB—See Lagercrantz Group AB; *Int'l*, pg. 4394
ELPRESS A/S—See Lagercrantz Group AB; *Int'l*, pg. 4394
ELPRESS (BEIJING) ELECTRICAL COMPONENTS CO. LTD—See Lagercrantz Group AB; *Int'l*, pg. 4394
ELPRESS GMBH—See Lagercrantz Group AB; *Int'l*, pg. 4394
ELPRO ESTATES LIMITED—See Elpro International Ltd.; *Int'l*, pg. 2369
ELPRO INTERNATIONAL LTD.; *Int'l*, pg. 2369
EL & PROJEKTERING VETLANDA AB—See Storskogen Group AB; *Int'l*, pg. 7227
ELPRO SP. Z O.O.—See PROCHEM S.A.; *Int'l*, pg. 5987
EL PROVEEDOR TECNOLOGICO S.R.L.—See Komax Holding AG; *Int'l*, pg. 4240
EL PUERTO DE LIVERPOOL S.A.B. DE C.V.; *Int'l*, pg. 2341
ELQ S.A.; *Int'l*, pg. 2369
EL RAN FURNITURE; *Int'l*, pg. 2341
ELRAY RESOURCES, INC.; *U.S. Public*, pg. 735
EL REY MEXICAN PRODUCTS INC.; *U.S. Private*, pg. 1349
ELRING GASKETS (PTY) LTD.—See ElringKlinger AG; *Int'l*, pg. 2369
ELRING ITALIA S.R.L.—See ElringKlinger AG; *Int'l*, pg. 2369
ELRINGKLINGER ABSCHIRMTECHNIK (SCHWEIZ) AG—See ElringKlinger AG; *Int'l*, pg. 2369
ELRINGKLINGER AG; *Int'l*, pg. 2369
ELRINGKLINGER AUTOMOTIVE COMPONENTS (INDIA) PVT. LTD.—See ElringKlinger AG; *Int'l*, pg. 2369
ELRINGKLINGER AUTOMOTIVE MANUFACTURING, INC.—See ElringKlinger AG; *Int'l*, pg. 2369
ELRINGKLINGER CANADA, INC.—See ElringKlinger AG; *Int'l*, pg. 2369
ELRINGKLINGER CHINA, LTD.—See ElringKlinger AG; *Int'l*, pg. 2369
ELRINGKLINGER CHONGQING LTD.—See ElringKlinger AG; *Int'l*, pg. 2369
ELRING KLINGER DO BRASIL LTDA.—See ElringKlinger AG; *Int'l*, pg. 2369
ELRINGKLINGER ENGINEERED PLASTICS NORTH AMERICA, INC.—See ElringKlinger AG; *Int'l*, pg. 2369
ELRINGKLINGER ENGINEERED PLASTICS (QINGDAO) CO., LTD.—See ElringKlinger AG; *Int'l*, pg. 2369
ELRINGKLINGER ENGINEERED PLASTICS (QINGDAO) COMMERCIAL CO., LTD.—See ElringKlinger AG; *Int'l*, pg. 2369
ELRING KLINGER (GREAT BRITAIN) LTD.—See ElringKlinger AG; *Int'l*, pg. 2369
ELRINGKLINGER HOLDING USA, INC.—See ElringKlinger AG; *Int'l*, pg. 2369
ELRINGKLINGER ITALIA SRL—See ElringKlinger AG; *Int'l*, pg. 2369
ELRINGKLINGER KOREA CO., LTD.—See ElringKlinger AG; *Int'l*, pg. 2369
ELRINGKLINGER KUNSTSTOFFTECHNIK GMBH—See ElringKlinger AG; *Int'l*, pg. 2369
ELRINGKLINGER LOGISTIC SERVICE GMBH—See ElringKlinger AG; *Int'l*, pg. 2370
ELRING KLINGER MEXICO, S.A. DE C.V.—See ElringKlinger AG; *Int'l*, pg. 2369
ELRING KLINGER MOTORTECHNIK GMBH—See ElringKlinger AG; *Int'l*, pg. 2369
ELRING KLINGER, S.A.U.—See ElringKlinger AG; *Int'l*, pg. 2369
ELRINGKLINGER SOUTH AFRICA (PTY) LTD.—See ElringKlinger AG; *Int'l*, pg. 2370
ELRINGKLINGER SWITZERLAND AG—See ElringKlinger AG; *Int'l*, pg. 2370
ELRINGKLINGER TEXAS, LLC—See ElringKlinger AG; *Int'l*, pg. 2370
ELRINGKLINGER TR OTOMOTIV SANAYI VE TICARET A.S.—See ElringKlinger AG; *Int'l*, pg. 2370
ELRINGKLINGER USA, INC.—See ElringKlinger AG; *Int'l*, pg. 2370
ELRING PARTS LTD.—See ElringKlinger AG; *Int'l*, pg. 2370
EL RIO SANTA CRUZ NEIGHBORHOOD HEALTH CENTER, INC.; *U.S. Private*, pg. 1349

ELRO GROSSKUCHEN GMBH—See Illinois Tool Works Inc.; *U.S. Public*, pg. 1103
ELRON OY—See Elomatic Oy; *Int'l*, pg. 2368
ELRON VENTURES LTD; *Int'l*, pg. 2370
ELRO (U.K.) LIMITED—See Illinois Tool Works Inc.; *U.S. Public*, pg. 1103
ELRO-WERKE AG—See Illinois Tool Works Inc.; *U.S. Public*, pg. 1103
ELSACOM NV—See Leonardo S.p.A.; *Int'l*, pg. 4458
ELSA ERNI SYSTEM—See ERNI Electronics GmbH; *Int'l*, pg. 2494
ELSAG DATAMAT S.P.A.—See Leonardo S.p.A.; *Int'l*, pg. 4460
ELSAG NORTH AMERICA LLC—See Leonardo S.p.A.; *Int'l*, pg. 4460
EL & SAKERHET SORMLAND AB—See Instalco AB; *Int'l*, pg. 3721
ELSALYS BIOTECH SA—See Mediolanum Farmaceutici SpA; *Int'l*, pg. 4778
ELSAMEX BRASIL LTDA—See Infrastructure Leasing & Financial Services Limited; *Int'l*, pg. 3697
ELSAMEX INDIA PVT LIMITED—See Infrastructure Leasing & Financial Services Limited; *Int'l*, pg. 3697
ELSAMEX PORTUGAL S.A.—See Infrastructure Leasing & Financial Services Limited; *Int'l*, pg. 3698
ELSAN LTD.; *Int'l*, pg. 2370
ELSA SILGAN METAL PACKAGING S.A.—See Silgan Holdings, Inc.; *U.S. Public*, pg. 1878
ELSA - SILGAN METAL PACKAGING S.A.—See Silgan Holdings, Inc.; *U.S. Public*, pg. 1878
ELSA SOLUTIONS SPA; *Int'l*, pg. 2370
ELSCINT LIMITED—See Elbit Imaging Ltd.; *Int'l*, pg. 2344
ELSEA INCORPORATED; *U.S. Private*, pg. 1377
ELSECO LIMITED; *Int'l*, pg. 2370
ELSE FRANCE S.A.S.—See JAB Holding Company S.a.r.l.; *Int'l*, pg. 3861
EL SEGUNDO POWER II LLC—See NRG Energy, Inc.; *U.S. Public*, pg. 1550
ELSENER-KLIMA AG—See Poenina Holding AG; *Int'l*, pg. 5903
ELSER & AUCONE, INC.; *U.S. Private*, pg. 1377
ELSEVIER (AUSTRALIA) PTY. LIMITED—See RELX plc; *Int'l*, pg. 6268
ELSEVIER B.V.—See RELX plc; *Int'l*, pg. 6268
ELSEVIER EDITORA LTDA—See RELX plc; *Int'l*, pg. 6268
ELSEVIER HEALTH SCIENCES—See RELX plc; *Int'l*, pg. 6268
ELSEVIER INC. - CELL PRESS—See RELX plc; *Int'l*, pg. 6268
ELSEVIER INC.—See RELX plc; *Int'l*, pg. 6268
ELSEVIER INC.—See RELX plc; *Int'l*, pg. 6268
ELSEVIER INFORMATION SYSTEMS GMBH—See RELX plc; *Int'l*, pg. 6268
ELSEVIER IRELAND LIMITED—See RELX plc; *Int'l*, pg. 6268
ELSEVIER JAPAN KK—See RELX plc; *Int'l*, pg. 6268
ELSEVIER KOREA LLC—See RELX plc; *Int'l*, pg. 6268
ELSEVIER LIMITED—See RELX plc; *Int'l*, pg. 6268
ELSEVIER MASSON SAS—See RELX plc; *Int'l*, pg. 6269
ELSEVIER SERVICES IRELAND LTD.—See RELX plc; *Int'l*, pg. 6269
ELSEVIER SINGAPORE PTE. LTD.—See RELX plc; *Int'l*, pg. 6269
EL SEWEDY ELECTRIC COMPANY; *Int'l*, pg. 2341
ELSEY & ASSOCIATES SURETY INSURANCE AGENCY, INC.—See Marsh & McLennan Companies, Inc.; *U.S. Public*, pg. 1380
EL SHAMS PYRAMIDS CO. FOR HOTELS & TOURISTIC PROJECTS S.A.E.; *Int'l*, pg. 2341
ELSHIN INTERNATIONAL PTE LTD—See THK CO., LTD.; *Int'l*, pg. 7711
EL SILENCIO HOLDINGS, INC.—See Constellation Brands, Inc.; *U.S. Public*, pg. 571
ELSIM ELEKTROTEKNIK SISTEMLER SANAYI VE TICARET A.S.—See Regal Rexnord Corporation; *U.S. Public*, pg. 1772
ELSINORE READY MIX CO. INC.; *U.S. Private*, pg. 1377
ELSINORE SERVICES, INC.; *U.S. Private*, pg. 1377
ELSINORE VALLEY MUNICIPAL WATER DISTRICT; *U.S. Private*, pg. 1377
ELSMORE RESOURCES LIMITED; *Int'l*, pg. 2370
ELSNER ENGINEERING WORKS INC.; *U.S. Private*, pg. 1377
ELSOFT RESEARCH BERHAD; *Int'l*, pg. 2370
ELSOFT SYSTEMS SDN. BHD.—See Elsoft Research Berhad; *Int'l*, pg. 2370
ELSO HAZAI ENERGIA-PORTFOLIO PLC; *Int'l*, pg. 2370
EL SOL FOODS LLC—See Cacique, Inc.; *U.S. Private*, pg. 712
ELSPEC ANDINA S.A.S—See Elspec Engineering Ltd.; *Int'l*, pg. 2370
ELSPEC ENGINEERING INDIA PVT. LTD.—See Elspec Engineering Ltd.; *Int'l*, pg. 2370
ELSPEC ENGINEERING LTD.; *Int'l*, pg. 2370
ELSPEC LTD.—See Elspec Engineering Ltd.; *Int'l*, pg. 2370
ELSPEC NORTH AMERICA, INC.—See Elspec Engineering Ltd.; *Int'l*, pg. 2370

ELSPEC PORTUGAL LDA.—See Elspec Engineering Ltd.; *Int'l*, pg. 2370
ELSTA BV & CO. CV—See The AES Corporation; *U.S. Public*, pg. 2031
ELSTA MOSDORFER BOSNIA D.O.O.—See Knill Holding GmbH; *Int'l*, pg. 4208
ELSTA MOSDORFER D.O.O.—See Knill Holding GmbH; *Int'l*, pg. 4208
ELSTA MOSDORFER GMBH—See Knill Holding GmbH; *Int'l*, pg. 4208
ELSTER AMCO WATER, LLC—See Honeywell International Inc.; *U.S. Public*, pg. 1047
ELSTER AMERICAN METER COMPANY, LLC—See Honeywell International Inc.; *U.S. Public*, pg. 1047
ELSTER CANADIAN METER COMPANY, LLC—See Honeywell International Inc.; *U.S. Public*, pg. 1047
ELSTER GMBH—See Honeywell International Inc.; *U.S. Public*, pg. 1047
ELSTER GROUP GMBH—See Honeywell International Inc.; *U.S. Public*, pg. 1047
ELSTER-INSTROMET A/S—See Honeywell International Inc.; *U.S. Public*, pg. 1048
ELSTER INSTROMET GMBH—See Honeywell International Inc.; *U.S. Public*, pg. 1048
ELSTER INSTROMET PRODUCTION GMBH—See Honeywell International Inc.; *U.S. Public*, pg. 1048
ELSTER-INSTROMET VERTRIEBSGESELLSCHAFT M.B.H.—See Honeywell International Inc.; *U.S. Public*, pg. 1048
ELSTER METERING PTY LTD.—See Honeywell International Inc.; *U.S. Public*, pg. 1048
ELSTER N.V./S.A.—See Honeywell International Inc.; *U.S. Public*, pg. 1048
ELSTER SOLUTIONS LLC—See Honeywell International Inc.; *U.S. Public*, pg. 1048
ELSTER S.R.L.—See Honeywell International Inc.; *U.S. Public*, pg. 1048
ELSTER S.R.O.—See Honeywell International Inc.; *U.S. Public*, pg. 1047
ELSTER WATER METERING B.V.—See Honeywell International Inc.; *U.S. Public*, pg. 1048
ELSTER WATER METERING HOLDINGS LIMITED—See Honeywell International Inc.; *U.S. Public*, pg. 1048
ELSTER WATER METERING LTD.—See Honeywell International Inc.; *U.S. Public*, pg. 1048
ELSTON RICHARDS, INC.; *U.S. Private*, pg. 1377
EL SUPERIOR MEXICAN FOODS LLC.; *U.S. Private*, pg. 1349
ELSYS AB—See Investment AB Latour; *Int'l*, pg. 3781
ELSYSTEM I PERSTORP AB—See Addtech AB; *Int'l*, pg. 133
ELTAC XXI S.L.—See Hydrofarm Holdings Group, Inc.; *U.S. Public*, pg. 1079
ELTA - EMPRESA DE LISTAS TELEFONICAS DE ANGOLA—See Altice Europe N.V.; *Int'l*, pg. 393
ELTA INTELLIGENCE RADAR & AEW GROUP—See Israel Aerospace Industries Ltd.; *Int'l*, pg. 3822
ELTA-KABEL D.O.O.—See Telekomunikacije Republike Srpske a.d.; *Int'l*, pg. 7538
EL TALLER CREATIVO—See WPP plc; *Int'l*, pg. 8465
ELTA MD, INC.—See Colgate-Palmolive Company; *U.S. Public*, pg. 532
ELTANIN INCORPORADORA LTDA—See PDG Realty S.A. Empreendimentos e Participacoes; *Int'l*, pg. 5770
EL TAPATIO MARKETS INCORPORATED; *U.S. Private*, pg. 1349
ELTA TECHNOLOGY CO., LTD; *Int'l*, pg. 2370
ELTEC ELEKTRONIK AG—See CornerstoneCapital Verwaltungs AG; *Int'l*, pg. 1801
ELTECH A/S—See Addtech AB; *Int'l*, pg. 133
ELTECH AUTOMATION A/S—See Addtech AB; *Int'l*, pg. 133
ELTECH SOLUTIONS A/S—See Addtech AB; *Int'l*, pg. 133
ELTECO AS—See Addtech AB; *Int'l*, pg. 133
ELTEK ARGENTINA S.R.L.—See Delta Electronics, Inc.; *Int'l*, pg. 2017
ELTEK AS—See Delta Electronics, Inc.; *Int'l*, pg. 2017
ELTEK AUSTRALIA PTY LTD—See Delta Electronics, Inc.; *Int'l*, pg. 2017
ELTEK DEUTSCHLAND GMBH—See Delta Electronics, Inc.; *Int'l*, pg. 2017
ELTEK DISTRIBUTION SRL—See Aiphone Co., Ltd.; *Int'l*, pg. 235
ELTEK EGYPT ASA—See Delta Electronics, Inc.; *Int'l*, pg. 2017
ELTEK ENERGY INTERNATIONAL DE MEXICO S. DE R.L. DE C.V.—See Delta Electronics, Inc.; *Int'l*, pg. 2017
ELTEK ENERGY TECHNOLOGY LTD.—See Delta Electronics, Inc.; *Int'l*, pg. 2017
ELTEK EUROPE GMBH—See Nistec Ltd.; *Int'l*, pg. 5379
ELTEK INC.—See Delta Electronics, Inc.; *Int'l*, pg. 2017
ELTEK ITALIA S.R.L.—See Delta Electronics, Inc.; *Int'l*, pg. 2017
ELTEK LTD.—See Nistec Ltd.; *Int'l*, pg. 5379
ELTEK MONTAGE GMBH—See Delta Electronics, Inc.; *Int'l*, pg. 2017
EL-TEKNIK I GAVLE AB—See Bravida Holding AB; *Int'l*, pg. 1142

ELTEK PAKISTAN (PVT) LTD.—See Delta Electronics, Inc.; *Int'l*, pg. 2017
ELTEK PERU SRL—See Delta Electronics, Inc.; *Int'l*, pg. 2017
ELTEK POLSKA SP. Z O.O.—See Delta Electronics, Inc.; *Int'l*, pg. 2017
ELTEK POWER CO., LTD.—See Delta Electronics, Inc.; *Int'l*, pg. 2018
ELTEK POWER FRANCE SAS—See Delta Electronics, Inc.; *Int'l*, pg. 2017
ELTEK POWER INC.—See Delta Electronics, Inc.; *Int'l*, pg. 2017
ELTEK POWER (MALAYSIA) SDN. BHD—See Delta Electronics, Inc.; *Int'l*, pg. 2017
ELTEK POWER OY—See Delta Electronics, Inc.; *Int'l*, pg. 2017
ELTEK POWER PTE. LTD.—See Delta Electronics, Inc.; *Int'l*, pg. 2017
ELTEK POWER SWEDEN AB—See Delta Electronics, Inc.; *Int'l*, pg. 2017
ELTEK POWER (UK) LTD.—See Delta Electronics, Inc.; *Int'l*, pg. 2017
ELTEK SGS PVT. LTD.—See Delta Electronics, Inc.; *Int'l*, pg. 2017
ELTEK SISTEMAS DE ENERGIA INDUSTRIA E COMERCIO S.A.—See Delta Electronics, Inc.; *Int'l*, pg. 2017
ELTEK S.R.O.—See Delta Electronics, Inc.; *Int'l*, pg. 2017
ELTEK USA INC.—See Nistec Ltd.; *Int'l*, pg. 5379
ELTEL AB; *Int'l*, pg. 2370
EL TELAR INC.; *U.S. Private*, pg. 1349
ELTEL GROUP CORPORATION—See Eltel AB; *Int'l*, pg. 2370
ELTEL INFRANET GMBH—See Eltel AB; *Int'l*, pg. 2370
ELTEL NETWORKS A/S—See Eltel AB; *Int'l*, pg. 2370
ELTEL NETWORKS AS—See Eltel AB; *Int'l*, pg. 2370
ELTEL NETWORKS AS—See Tecnolines OU; *Int'l*, pg. 7516
ELTEL NETWORKS ENERGETYKA S.A.—See Mutares SE & Co. KGaA; *Int'l*, pg. 5104
ELTEL NETWORKS ENGINEERING S.A.—See Mutares SE & Co. KGaA; *Int'l*, pg. 5104
ELTEL NETWORKS GMBH—See Eltel AB; *Int'l*, pg. 2371
ELTEL NETWORKS INFRANET AB—See Eltel AB; *Int'l*, pg. 2370
ELTEL NETWORKS OY—See Eltel AB; *Int'l*, pg. 2371
ELTEL NETWORKS SIA—See Eltel AB; *Int'l*, pg. 2371
ELTEL NETWORKS TE AB—See Eltel AB; *Int'l*, pg. 2371
ELTEL NETWORKS TELECOM SP. Z O.O.—See Eltel AB; *Int'l*, pg. 2371
ELTEL SISA, ZNL DER ELEKTROHUUS VON ALLMEN AG—See Burkhalter Holding AG; *Int'l*, pg. 1225
ELTEL TECHNOLOGISTCS, LTD.—See Malam-Team Ltd.; *Int'l*, pg. 4659
ELTES CO., LTD.; *Int'l*, pg. 2371
ELTE; *Int'l*, pg. 2370
ELTEX-ELEKTROSTATIK-GESELLSCHAFT MIT BESCHRANKTER HAFTUNG—See Illinois Tool Works Inc.; *U.S. Public*, pg. 1103
ELTEX ENTERPRISES 2002 LTD.; *Int'l*, pg. 2371
ELTHERM ASIA-PACIFIC PTE. LTD.—See INDUS Holding AG; *Int'l*, pg. 3662
ELTHERM CANADA INC.—See INDUS Holding AG; *Int'l*, pg. 3662
ELTHERM GMBH—See INDUS Holding AG; *Int'l*, pg. 3662
ELTHERM ITALY SRL—See INDUS Holding AG; *Int'l*, pg. 3662
ELTHERM KAZAKHSTAN—See INDUS Holding AG; *Int'l*, pg. 3662
ELTHERM KAZAKHSTAN—See INDUS Holding AG; *Int'l*, pg. 3662
ELTHERM NORTH AFRICA SARL—See INDUS Holding AG; *Int'l*, pg. 3662
ELTHERM RUS LIMITED LIABILITY COMPANY—See INDUS Holding AG; *Int'l*, pg. 3662
ELTHERM SCHWEIZ AG—See INDUS Holding AG; *Int'l*, pg. 3662
ELTHERM (SHANGHAI) CO., LTD.—See INDUS Holding AG; *Int'l*, pg. 3662
ELTHERM SOUTH AFRICA (PTY) LTD.—See INDUS Holding AG; *Int'l*, pg. 3662
ELTHERM SPAIN, S.L.U.—See INDUS Holding AG; *Int'l*, pg. 3662
ELTHERM UK LTD.—See INDUS Holding AG; *Int'l*, pg. 3663
E.L. THOMPSON ASSOCIATES LLC; *U.S. Private*, pg. 1306
EL TIEMPO LATINO LLC—See Nash Holdings LLC; *U.S. Private*, pg. 2835
ELTM, L.P.—See Enbridge Inc.; *Int'l*, pg. 2397
ELTOFI AS—See W.P. Carey Inc.; *U.S. Public*, pg. 2315
ELTON ANDERSON ASSOCIATES—See Ghafari Associates, L.L.C.; *U.S. Private*, pg. 1690
ELTON CORPORATION D.O.O.—See ELTON INTERNATIONAL TRADING COMPANY S.A.; *Int'l*, pg. 2371
ELTON CORPORATION LTD—See ELTON INTERNATIONAL TRADING COMPANY S.A.; *Int'l*, pg. 2371
ELTON CORPORATION S.A.—See ELTON INTERNATIONAL TRADING COMPANY S.A.; *Int'l*, pg. 2371

ELTON INTERNATIONAL TRADING COMPANY S.A.; *Int'l*, pg. 2371
ELTOP PRAHA S.R.O.—See NIBE Industrier AB; *Int'l*, pg. 5260
EL TORITO JAPAN CO., LTD.—See Zensho Holdings Co., Ltd.; *Int'l*, pg. 8634
EL TORITO RESTAURANTS, INC.—See Z Capital Group, LLC; *U.S. Private*, pg. 4596
EL TORO EXPORT; *U.S. Private*, pg. 1349
EL TORO WATER DISTRICT; *U.S. Private*, pg. 1349
ELTOSCH GRAFIX AMERICA INC.—See Dr. Honle AG; *Int'l*, pg. 2192
ELTOSCH GRAFIX ASIA—See Dr. Honle AG; *Int'l*, pg. 2192
ELTOSCH-GRAFIX GMBH—See Dr. Honle AG; *Int'l*, pg. 2192
EL-TRADE SP. Z O.O.—See Warner Bros. Discovery, Inc.; *U.S. Public*, pg. 2326
ELTRA DIYEURONET BV—See Sonepar S.A.; *Int'l*, pg. 7090
ELTRAF, A.S.—See CEZ, a.s.; *Int'l*, pg. 1428
ELTRAK BULGARIA LTD.—See ELTRAK S.A.; *Int'l*, pg. 2371
ELTRAK S.A.; *Int'l*, pg. 2371
THE ELTRON COMPANY; *U.S. Private*, pg. 4025
THE ELTRON CO.—See The Eltron Company; *U.S. Private*, pg. 4025
ELTROTREC S.A.C.; *Int'l*, pg. 2371
ELTUR SERWIS SP. Z O.O.—See PGE Polska Grupa Energetyczna S.A.; *Int'l*, pg. 5837
ELTWIN A/S—See NIBE Industrier AB; *Int'l*, pg. 5260
ELTWIN SP. Z.O.O.—See NIBE Industrier AB; *Int'l*, pg. 5260
ELUMATEC AG—See Cifin S.r.l.; *Int'l*, pg. 1606
ELUMATEC ASIA PTE LTD.—See Cifin S.r.l.; *Int'l*, pg. 1606
ELUMATEC AUSTRALIA PTY. LTD.—See Cifin S.r.l.; *Int'l*, pg. 1606
ELUMATEC AUSTRIA GMBH—See Cifin S.r.l.; *Int'l*, pg. 1606
ELUMATEC BENELUX B.V.—See Cifin S.r.l.; *Int'l*, pg. 1606
ELUMATEC BULGARIA EOOD—See Cifin S.r.l.; *Int'l*, pg. 1606
ELUMATEC CHILE LIMITADA—See Cifin S.r.l.; *Int'l*, pg. 1606
ELUMATEC CZ S.R.O.—See Cifin S.r.l.; *Int'l*, pg. 1606
ELUMATEC DE AMERICA LATINA S.A.—See Cifin S.r.l.; *Int'l*, pg. 1606
ELUMATEC D.O.O.—See Cifin S.r.l.; *Int'l*, pg. 1606
ELUMATEC D.O.O.—See Cifin S.r.l.; *Int'l*, pg. 1606
ELUMATEC FRANCE S.A.S.—See Cifin S.r.l.; *Int'l*, pg. 1606
ELUMATEC INDIA PRIVATE LIMITED—See Cifin S.r.l.; *Int'l*, pg. 1606
ELUMATEC ITALIA S.R.L.—See Cifin S.r.l.; *Int'l*, pg. 1606
ELUMATEC KOREA CO. LTD.—See Cifin S.r.l.; *Int'l*, pg. 1606
ELUMATEC LITHUANIA UAB—See Cifin S.r.l.; *Int'l*, pg. 1606
ELUMATEC MACHINERY SHANGHAI CO. LTD.—See Cifin S.r.l.; *Int'l*, pg. 1606
ELUMATEC MAKINE VE SERVIS SAN. VE TIC. LTD. STI.—See Cifin S.r.l.; *Int'l*, pg. 1606
ELUMATEC MALAYSIA SDN BHD—See Cifin S.r.l.; *Int'l*, pg. 1606
ELUMATEC MASCHINEN D.O.O.—See Cifin S.r.l.; *Int'l*, pg. 1606
ELUMATEC MASCHINEN SH.P.K.—See Cifin S.r.l.; *Int'l*, pg. 1606
ELUMATEC MIDDLE EAST LLC—See Cifin S.r.l.; *Int'l*, pg. 1606
ELUMATEC NORGE AS—See Cifin S.r.l.; *Int'l*, pg. 1606
ELUMATEC NORTH AMERICA INC.—See Cifin S.r.l.; *Int'l*, pg. 1606
ELUMATEC POLSKA SP. Z O. O.—See Cifin S.r.l.; *Int'l*, pg. 1606
ELUMATEC ROMANIA SRL.—See Cifin S.r.l.; *Int'l*, pg. 1606
ELUMATEC SHENZHEN CO. LTD.—See Cifin S.r.l.; *Int'l*, pg. 1606
ELUMATEC SKANDINAVIEN AB—See Cifin S.r.l.; *Int'l*, pg. 1606
ELUMATEC SLOVENSKO, S.R.O.—See Cifin S.r.l.; *Int'l*, pg. 1606
ELUMATEC SOUTH AFRICA (PTY) LTD.—See Cifin S.r.l.; *Int'l*, pg. 1606
ELUMATEC SOUTH AFRICA (PTY) LTD.—See Cifin S.r.l.; *Int'l*, pg. 1606
ELUMATEC SWISS AG—See Cifin S.r.l.; *Int'l*, pg. 1606
ELUMATEC UNITED KINGDOM LTD.—See Cifin S.r.l.; *Int'l*, pg. 1606
ELUMEO SE; *Int'l*, pg. 2371
ELUMICOR; *U.S. Private*, pg. 1377
ELUMINATE, LLC—See Healthcare Services Group, Inc.; *U.S. Public*, pg. 1015
ELUM MUSIC COMPANY; *U.S. Private*, pg. 1377
E-LUNCH SRL—See Edenred S.A.; *Int'l*, pg. 2307
ELUOMENG LIMITED—See Avnet, Inc.; *U.S. Public*, pg. 253

ELUON CORPORATION

ELUON CORPORATION; *Int'l*, pg. 2371
ELUON INS CO., LTD.—See ELUON Corporation; *Int'l*, pg. 2371
ELUON LBS CORP.—See ELUON Corporation; *Int'l*, pg. 2371
ELUSOFT GMBH—See Cifin S.r.l.; *Int'l*, pg. 1606
ELUSYS THERAPEUTICS, INC.; *U.S. Private*, pg. 1377
ELUTIA INC.; *U.S. Public*, pg. 735
ELUXURY, LLC—See Culp, Inc.; *U.S. Public*, pg. 605
ELVACO AB—See Investment AB Latour; *Int'l*, pg. 3782
ELVACO A.D.—See Kompanija BOBAR d.o.o.; *Int'l*, pg. 4244
ELVA INTERNATIONAL INC.; *U.S. Public*, pg. 735
ELVAL COLOUR IBERICA S.L.U.—See Viohalco SA/NV; *Int'l*, pg. 8243
ELVALHALCOR S.A.—See Viohalco SA/NV; *Int'l*, pg. 8243
ELVEHAVN BRYGGE HUS G AS—See Peab AB; *Int'l*, pg. 5771
ELVERDI NORGE AS—See SmartCraft ASA; *Int'l*, pg. 7002
ELVE S.A.; *Int'l*, pg. 2371
ELVETHAM HEATH DEVELOPMENTS—See Persimmon plc; *Int'l*, pg. 5817
ELVETINO AG—See Schweizerische Bundesbahnen SBB AG; *Int'l*, pg. 6646
ELVEX CORPORATION—See Delta Plus Group; *Int'l*, pg. 2020
ELVEY GROUP LTD—See Hudaco Industries Limited; *Int'l*, pg. 3521
ELVEY SECURITY TECHNOLOGIES (PTY) LTD—See Hudaco Industries Limited; *Int'l*, pg. 3521
ELVIA REISEVERSICHERUNG AG—See Allianz SE; *Int'l*, pg. 342
ELVIA SOCIETE D'ASSURANCES DE VOYAGES—See Allianz SE; *Int'l*, pg. 342
ELVICTOR GROUP, INC.; *Int'l*, pg. 2371
ELVIEMEK LAND DEVELOPMENT - LOGISTICS PARKS - ENERGY - RECYCLING SA; *Int'l*, pg. 2371
ELVILA S.A.; *Int'l*, pg. 2371
ELVIP S.R.O.—See EL. D. MOUZAKIS S.A.; *Int'l*, pg. 2341
ELVIS COMMUNICATIONS LIMITED—See Next 15 Group plc; *Int'l*, pg. 5246
ELVIS PRESLEY ENTERPRISES, INC.—See Apollo Global Management, Inc.; *U.S. Public*, pg. 148
ELVISRIDGE CAPITAL, LLC; *U.S. Private*, pg. 1377
ELV MULTIMODAL C.A.—See Allcargo Logistics Limited; *Int'l*, pg. 333
EL WADI FOR INTERNATIONAL AND INVESTMENT DEVELOPMENT SAE; *Int'l*, pg. 2341
ELWA GHANA LTD.—See Allcargo Logistics Limited; *Int'l*, pg. 334
ELWEMA AUTOMOTIVE GMBH—See MAX Automation SE; *Int'l*, pg. 4733
ELW ENERGIEVERSORGUNG LEINEFELDE-WORBIS GMBH—See Stadtwerke Hannover AG; *Int'l*, pg. 7161
ELWOOD NATIONAL CRANKSHAFT SERVICES—See Ellwood Group, Inc.; *U.S. Private*, pg. 1375
ELWOOD PROFESSIONAL—See Elwood Staffing Services, Inc.; *U.S. Private*, pg. 1377
ELWOOD STAFFING SERVICES, INC. - GRAND RAPIDS—See Elwood Staffing Services, Inc.; *U.S. Private*, pg. 1377
ELWOOD STAFFING SERVICES, INC.; *U.S. Private*, pg. 1377
ELXSI CORPORATION—See SPX Technologies, Inc.; *U.S. Public*, pg. 1921
ELY GOLD ROYALTIES INC.—See Gold Royalty Corp.; *Int'l*, pg. 3026
ELYPSIS, INC.—See WineDirect, Inc.; *U.S. Private*, pg. 4540
ELYRIA FOUNDRY COMPANY LLC—See Silverhawk Capital Partners, LLC; *U.S. Private*, pg. 3663
ELYRIA MANUFACTURING CORP.; *U.S. Private*, pg. 1377
ELYSEE DEVELOPMENT CORP.; *Int'l*, pg. 2372
ELYS GAME TECHNOLOGY, CORP.; *Int'l*, pg. 2372
ELYSIAN BREWING COMPANY—See Anheuser-Busch InBev SA/NV; *Int'l*, pg. 465
ELYSIAN CAPITAL LLP; *Int'l*, pg. 2372
ELYSIS LIMITED PARTNERSHIP—See Rio Tinto plc; *Int'l*, pg. 6346
ELYSIUM CAPITAL MANAGEMENT, LLC; *U.S. Private*, pg. 1377
ELYSIUM DIGITAL LLC—See Aon plc; *Int'l*, pg. 493
ELYSIUM FUND MANAGEMENT LIMITED; *Int'l*, pg. 2372
ELZAY READY WEAR MANUFACTURING COMPANY; *Int'l*, pg. 2372
ELZINGA & VOLKERS, INC.; *U.S. Private*, pg. 1377
ELZINGA & VOLKERS PROFESSIONAL SERVICES INC.—See Elzinga & Volkers, Inc.; *U.S. Private*, pg. 1377
EMAAR DEVELOPMENT PJSC—See Emaar Properties PJSC; *Int'l*, pg. 2372
EMAAR DHA ISLAMABAD LIMITED—See Emaar Properties PJSC; *Int'l*, pg. 2372
EMAAR GIGA KARACHI LIMITED—See Emaar Properties PJSC; *Int'l*, pg. 2372
EMAAR HOSPITALITY GROUP LLC—See Emaar Properties PJSC; *Int'l*, pg. 2372
EMAAR HOTELS & RESORTS LLC—See Emaar Properties PJSC; *Int'l*, pg. 2372
EMAAR INDIA LIMITED—See Emaar Properties PJSC; *Int'l*, pg. 2372
EMAAR INTERNATIONAL JORDAN—See Emaar Properties PJSC; *Int'l*, pg. 2372
EMAAR INTERNATIONAL MALLS LLC—See Emaar Properties PJSC; *Int'l*, pg. 2372
EMAAR LEBANON S.A—See Emaar Properties PJSC; *Int'l*, pg. 2372
EMAAR MALLS GROUP LLC—See Emaar Properties PJSC; *Int'l*, pg. 2372
EMAAR MGF LAND LIMITED—See Emaar Properties PJSC; *Int'l*, pg. 2372
EMAAR MGF LAND LIMITED—See The Motor & General Finance Limited; *Int'l*, pg. 7668
EMAAR MISR FOR DEVELOPMENT S.A.E.; *Int'l*, pg. 2372
EMAAR PAKISTAN GROUP—See Emaar Properties PJSC; *Int'l*, pg. 2372
EMAAR PROPERTIES CANADA LTD—See Emaar Properties PJSC; *Int'l*, pg. 2372
EMAAR PROPERTIES PJSC; *Int'l*, pg. 2372
EMAAR RETAIL LLC—See Emaar Properties PJSC; *Int'l*, pg. 2372
EMAAR TECHNOLOGIES LLC—See Emaar Properties PJSC; *Int'l*, pg. 2373
EMAAR THE ECONOMIC CITY JSC; *Int'l*, pg. 2373
EMAAR TURKEY—See Emaar Properties PJSC; *Int'l*, pg. 2373
EMAAR USA—See Emaar Properties PJSC; *Int'l*, pg. 2373
E-MACHITOWN CO., LTD.—See Hikari Tsushin, Inc.; *Int'l*, pg. 3390
EMAC HOLDINGS LIMITED—See Promisia Healthcare Limited; *Int'l*, pg. 5994
EMA DESIGN AUTOMATION, INC.; *U.S. Private*, pg. 1377
E&M ADVERTISING; *U.S. Private*, pg. 1301
EMAE - EMPRESA METROPOLITANA DE AGUAS E ENERGIA S.A.; *Int'l*, pg. 2373
EMAGIC.COM LLC—See MGIC Investment Corporation; *U.S. Public*, pg. 1435
EMAGIN CORPORATION—See Samsung Group; *Int'l*, pg. 6511
EMAGINE GMBH; *Int'l*, pg. 2373
EMAGINE GMBH—See emagine GmbH; *Int'l*, pg. 2373
EMAGINE IT, INC.; *U.S. Private*, pg. 1378
E.MAGINE OPTICAL, INC.—See EssilorLuxottica SA; *Int'l*, pg. 2514
EMAG SOLUTIONS LLC—See Patriarch Partners, LLC; *U.S. Private*, pg. 3109
EMAILAGE CORP.—See RELX plc; *Int'l*, pg. 6267
EMAIL CONNECTION (PTY) LIMITED—See The Bidvest Group Limited; *Int'l*, pg. 7624
EMAILDIRECT; *U.S. Private*, pg. 1378
EMAILERI OY—See Enento Group Plc; *Int'l*, pg. 2415
EMA INDIA LTD.; *Int'l*, pg. 2372
EMAINT ENTERPRISES, LLC—See Fortive Corporation; *U.S. Public*, pg. 870
EMAK DEUTSCHLAND GMBH—See Emak S.p.A.; *Int'l*, pg. 2373
EMAK FRANCE SAS—See Emak S.p.A.; *Int'l*, pg. 2373
EMA KIMYA SISTEMLERI SANAYI VE TICARET A.S.—See Huntsman Corporation; *U.S. Public*, pg. 1073
EMAKINA AB—See EPAM Systems, Inc.; *U.S. Public*, pg. 783
EMAKINA BV—See Emakina Group S.A.; *Int'l*, pg. 2373
EMAKINA.CH LABEL.CH S.A.—See EPAM Systems, Inc.; *U.S. Public*, pg. 783
EMAKINA.CH SA.—See Emakina Group S.A.; *Int'l*, pg. 2373
EMAKINA.FR SA.—See Emakina Group S.A.; *Int'l*, pg. 2373
EMAKINA GROUP S.A.; *Int'l*, pg. 2373
EMAKINA.NL BV—See Emakina Group S.A.; *Int'l*, pg. 2373
EMAK S.P.A.; *Int'l*, pg. 2373
EMAK U.K. LTD.—See Emak S.p.A.; *Int'l*, pg. 2373
EMAK WORLDWIDE, INC.; *U.S. Private*, pg. 1378
EMALLIANCE IVANOVO—See PJSC EnergoMashinostroitelny Alliance; *Int'l*, pg. 5878
EMA LUBRICANTS CO. LTD.—See Exxon Mobil Corporation; *U.S. Public*, pg. 814
EMA LUBRICANTS CO. LTD.—See GIBCA Limited; *Int'l*, pg. 2962
EMAMI BANGLADESH LIMITED—See Emami Ltd; *Int'l*, pg. 2374
EMAMI GROUP; *Int'l*, pg. 2373
EMAMI INDO LANKA PVT LTD—See Emami Ltd; *Int'l*, pg. 2374
EMAMI INTERNATIONAL FZE—See Emami Ltd; *Int'l*, pg. 2374
EMAMI LTD; *Int'l*, pg. 2374
EMAMI OVERSEAS FZE—See Emami Ltd; *Int'l*, pg. 2374
EMAMI PAPER MILLS LTD.—See Emami Ltd; *Int'l*, pg. 2374
EMAMI REALTY LIMITED—See Emami Ltd; *Int'l*, pg. 2374
EMAMI REALTY LIMITED—See Emami Group; *Int'l*, pg. 2374

CORPORATE AFFILIATIONS

EMAMI RUS (LLC)—See Emami Ltd; *Int'l*, pg. 2374
E-MANAGEMENT; *U.S. Private*, pg. 1302
EMAN A.S.; *Int'l*, pg. 2374
EMANATE—See Omnicom Group Inc.; *U.S. Public*, pg. 1586
EMANCIPET CENTRAL AUSTIN—See Emancipet, Inc.; *U.S. Private*, pg. 1378
EMANCIPET, INC.; *U.S. Private*, pg. 1378
E MAN CONSTRUCTION COMPANY LIMITED—See Henderson Land Development Co. Ltd.; *Int'l*, pg. 3344
EMAN SOLUTIONS LLC—See eMan A.S.; *Int'l*, pg. 2374
EMANTRAS, INC.—See Learning Technologies Group plc; *Int'l*, pg. 4435
EMANUEL UNGARO; *Int'l*, pg. 2374
EMAP COMMUNICATIONS BV—See Apax Partners LLP; *Int'l*, pg. 507
EMAP COMMUNICATIONS BV—See The Scott Trust Limited; *Int'l*, pg. 7681
EMAP COMMUNICATIONS USA—See Apax Partners LLP; *Int'l*, pg. 507
EMAP COMMUNICATIONS USA—See The Scott Trust Limited; *Int'l*, pg. 7681
EMAP CONSTRUCTION NETWORKS LTD.—See Apax Partners LLP; *Int'l*, pg. 507
EMAP CONSTRUCTION NETWORKS LTD.—See The Scott Trust Limited; *Int'l*, pg. 7681
EMAP CONSTRUCT LTD.—See Apax Partners LLP; *Int'l*, pg. 507
EMAP CONSTRUCT LTD.—See The Scott Trust Limited; *Int'l*, pg. 7681
EMAP LIMITED—See Apax Partners LLP; *Int'l*, pg. 507
EMAP LIMITED—See The Scott Trust Limited; *Int'l*, pg. 7681
EMAP MACLAREN—See Apax Partners LLP; *Int'l*, pg. 507
EMAP MACLAREN—See The Scott Trust Limited; *Int'l*, pg. 7681
EMAP MAGAZINES LTD.—See Vivendi SE; *Int'l*, pg. 8274
EMAP PUBLIC SECTOR MANAGEMENT LTD.—See Apax Partners LLP; *Int'l*, pg. 507
EMAP PUBLIC SECTOR MANAGEMENT LTD.—See The Scott Trust Limited; *Int'l*, pg. 7681
EMA PUBLIC RELATIONS SERVICES—See Eric Mower and Associates, Inc.; *U.S. Private*, pg. 1419
EMARATECH—See Investment Corporation of Dubai; *Int'l*, pg. 3785
EMARAT EUROPE FAST BUILDING TECHNOLOGY SYSTEM FACTORY L.L.C—See National Marine Dredging Company PJSC; *Int'l*, pg. 5161
EMARKETER INC.—See Axel Springer SE; *Int'l*, pg. 766
EMARSYS BEIJING LIMITED—See SAP SE; *Int'l*, pg. 6566
EMARSYS EMARKETING SYSTEMS GMBH—See SAP SE; *Int'l*, pg. 6566
EMARSYS INTERACTIVE SERVICES GMBH—See SAP SE; *Int'l*, pg. 6566
EMARSYS NORTH AMERICA, INC.—See SAP SE; *Int'l*, pg. 6566
EMARSYS S.A.S.—See SAP SE; *Int'l*, pg. 6566
EMART INC.—See Shinsegae Inc.; *Int'l*, pg. 6848
EMAS AMC—See Ezra Holdings Ltd.; *Int'l*, pg. 2594
EMA S.A.R.; *Int'l*, pg. 2372
EMAS KIARA MARKETING SDN. BHD.—See MB World Group Berhad; *Int'l*, pg. 4751
EMAS KIARA SDN. BHD.; *Int'l*, pg. 2374
EMAS OFFSHORE LIMITED—See Ezra Holdings Ltd.; *Int'l*, pg. 2594
EMASON, INC.; *U.S. Private*, pg. 1378
EM-ASSIST, INC.—See Cardno Limited; *Int'l*, pg. 1322
EMASZ; *Int'l*, pg. 2374
EMATEC - CUERNAVACA PLANT—See Ematec II S. de R. L. de C.V.; *Int'l*, pg. 2374
EMATEC II S. DE R. L. DE C.V. - GUADALAJARA PLANT—See Ematec II S. de R. L. de C.V.; *Int'l*, pg. 2374
EMATEC II S. DE R. L. DE C.V. - GUADALUPE PLANT—See Ematec II S. de R. L. de C.V.; *Int'l*, pg. 2374
EMATEC II S. DE R. L. DE C.V. - HERMOSILLO PLANT—See Ematec II S. de R. L. de C.V.; *Int'l*, pg. 2374
EMATEC II S. DE R. L. DE C.V.; *Int'l*, pg. 2374
EMATS, INC.; *U.S. Private*, pg. 1378
E-MAX GROUP, INC.; *U.S. Private*, pg. 1302
EMBACH EHITUS OU—See Nordecon AS; *Int'l*, pg. 5418
EMBALAJES WINPAK DE MEXICO, S.A. DE C.V.—See Winpak Ltd.; *Int'l*, pg. 8429
EMBALLAGES LAURENT SAS—See International Paper Company; *U.S. Public*, pg. 1155
EMBANET ULC—See Pearson plc; *Int'l*, pg. 5775
EMBARCADERO CENTER ASSOCIATES—See Boston Properties, Inc.; *U.S. Public*, pg. 373
EMBARCADERO TECHNOLOGIES EUROPE LTD.—See HGGC, LLC; *U.S. Private*, pg. 1929
EMBARCADERO TECHNOLOGIES, INC.—See HGGC, LLC; *U.S. Private*, pg. 1929
EMBARK CORPORATION; *U.S. Private*, pg. 1378
EMBARK GROUP LIMITED; *Int'l*, pg. 2374
EMBARK TECHNOLOGY, INC.—See Applied Intuition, Inc.; *U.S. Private*, pg. 299

COMPANY NAME INDEX

EMBARQ COMMUNICATIONS, INC.—See Lumen Technologies, Inc.; *U.S. Public*, pg. 1346
EMBARQ MID-ATLANTIC MANAGEMENT SERVICES COMPANY—See Lumen Technologies, Inc.; *U.S. Public*, pg. 1346
EMBARQ MINNESOTA, INC.—See Lumen Technologies, Inc.; *U.S. Public*, pg. 1346
THE EMBARRAS RIVER BASIN AGENCY, INC.; *U.S. Private*, pg. 4025
EMBASSY BANCORP, INC.; *U.S. Public*, pg. 735
EMBASSY BANK—See Embassy Bancorp, Inc.; *U.S. Public*, pg. 736
EMBASSY DENTAL PROFESSIONALS, P.C.—See CPF Dental, LLC; *U.S. Private*, pg. 1080
EMBASSY INDUSTRIES, INC.—See Mestek, Inc.; *U.S. Public*, pg. 1426
EMBASSY OFFICE PARKS REIT; *Int'l*, pg. 2374
EMBASSY PROPERTY DEVELOPMENTS PVT. LTD.—See Blackstone Inc.; *U.S. Public*, pg. 350
EMBASSY SUITES CASINO SAN JUAN—See Hilton Worldwide Holdings Inc.; *U.S. Public*, pg. 1040
EMBASSY SUITES CHICAGO O'HARE-ROSEMONT—See The Dow Hotel Company LLC; *U.S. Private*, pg. 4023
EMBASSY SUITES MANAGEMENT LLC—See Hilton Worldwide Holdings Inc.; *U.S. Public*, pg. 1040
EMBASSY SUITES PHOENIX AIRPORT LLC—See Park Hotels & Resorts Inc.; *U.S. Public*, pg. 1638
EMB CO., LTD.; *Int'l*, pg. 2374
EMBECTA CORP.; *U.S. Public*, pg. 736
EMBEDDED HEALTH SOLUTIONS PTY. LTD.—See Careteq Limited; *Int'l*, pg. 1325
EMBEDICS LLC—See Kudelski S.A.; *Int'l*, pg. 4323
EMBED LIMITED—See Littelfuse, Inc.; *U.S. Public*, pg. 1326
EMBEDWAY TECHNOLOGIES (SHANGHAI) CORPORATION; *Int'l*, pg. 2374
EMBEE MOBILE, INC.—See Similarweb Ltd.; *Int'l*, pg. 6931
EMBEE PROCESSING, LLC—See All Metals Processing of Orange County, LLC; *U.S. Private*, pg. 171
EMBEGA, S. COOP.—See Mondragon Corporation; *Int'l*, pg. 5028
EMBELLENCE GROUP AB; *Int'l*, pg. 2374
EMDELTON LIMITED; *Int'l*, pg. 2374
EMBENTION SISTEMAS INTELIGENTES, S.A.; *Int'l*, pg. 2375
EMBER INFRASTRUCTURE MANAGEMENT, LP; *U.S. Private*, pg. 1378
EMBER RESOURCES INC.—See ARC Financial Corp.; *Int'l*, pg. 539
EMBER RESOURCES INC.—See Brookfield Corporation; *Int'l*, pg. 1187
EMBER RESOURCES INC.—See KERN Partners Ltd.; *Int'l*, pg. 4137
EMBER THERAPEUTICS, INC.; *U.S. Public*, pg. 736
EMBIL ILAC SANAYII LTD—See Insud Pharma, S.L.; *Int'l*, pg. 3725
EMBLA SYSTEMS LLC—See ArchiMed SAS; *Int'l*, pg. 548
EMBLAZE MOBILE LTD.—See B.S.D. Crown Ltd.; *Int'l*, pg. 790
EMBLEM CORP.—See Aleafia Health Inc.; *Int'l*, pg. 305
EMBLEM HEALTHCARE, INC.—See The Ensign Group, Inc.; *U.S. Public*, pg. 2070
EMBLEMHEALTH, INC.; *U.S. Private*, pg. 1378
EMBLEM, LLC; *U.S. Private*, pg. 1378
EMBOTELLADORA ANDINA S.A.; *Int'l*, pg. 2375
EMBOTELLADORA DE OCCIDENTE S.A. DE C.V.—See PepsiCo, Inc.; *U.S. Public*, pg. 1669
EMBOTELLADORA LAGUNERA, S.A. DE C.V.—See Arca Continental, S.A.B. de C.V.; *Int'l*, pg. 540
EMBOTELLADORA SAN LUIS, S.A. DE C.V.—See Arca Continental, S.A.B. de C.V.; *Int'l*, pg. 540
EMBOTELLADORAS CHILENAS UNIDAS S.A.—See L'Arche Green N.V.; *Int'l*, pg. 4377
EMBOTELLADORAS CHILENAS UNIDAS S.A.—See Quinenco S.A.; *Int'l*, pg. 6164
EMBRACE CHANGE ACQUISITION CORP.; *Int'l*, pg. 2375
EMBRACE FINANCIAL SERVICES LTD.—See LSL Property Services plc; *Int'l*, pg. 4570
EMBRACE GMBH—See Bertelsmann SE & Co. KGaA; *Int'l*, pg. 992
EMBRACE GROUP LIMITED—See D. E. Shaw & Co., L.P.; *U.S. Private*, pg. 1139
EMBRACE GROUP LIMITED—See Varde Partners, Inc.; *U.S. Private*, pg. 4346
EMBRACE HOME LOANS, INC.; *U.S. Private*, pg. 1378
EMBRACE PET INSURANCE AGENCY, LLC—See The Carlyle Group Inc.; *U.S. Public*, pg. 2050
EMBRACER GROUP AB; *Int'l*, pg. 2375
EMBRACE (UK) LIMITED—See D. E. Shaw & Co., L.P.; *U.S. Private*, pg. 1139
EMBRACE (UK) LIMITED—See Varde Partners, Inc.; *U.S. Private*, pg. 4346
EMBRACING HOSPICE—See The Riverside Company; *U.S. Private*, pg. 4107
EMBRACO EUROPE S.R.L.—See Whirlpool Corporation; *U.S. Public*, pg. 2367
EMBRACO INDUSTRIA DE COMPRESSORES E SOLUCOES EM REFRIGERACAO LTDA.—See Nidec Corporation; *Int'l*, pg. 5274
EMBRACO MEXICO, S. DE R.L. DE C.V.—See Nidec Corporation; *Int'l*, pg. 5274
EMBRACO NORTH AMERICA, INC.—See Nidec Corporation; *Int'l*, pg. 5275
EMBRACO RUS LLC—See Nidec Corporation; *Int'l*, pg. 5274
EMBRACO S.A.—See Whirlpool Corporation; *U.S. Public*, pg. 2368
EMBRACO SLOVAKIA S.R.O.—See Nidec Corporation; *Int'l*, pg. 5274
EMBRAER AIRCRAFT HOLDING INC.—See Embraer S.A.; *Int'l*, pg. 2375
EMBRAER AIRCRAFT MAINTENANCE SERVICES, INC.—See Embraer S.A.; *Int'l*, pg. 2375
EMBRAER AVIATION EUROPE SAS—See Embraer S.A.; *Int'l*, pg. 2375
EMBRAER AVIATION INTERNATIONAL SAS—See Embraer S.A.; *Int'l*, pg. 2375
EMBRAER CHINA—See Embraer S.A.; *Int'l*, pg. 2375
EMBRAER EXECUTIVE AIRCRAFT, INC.—See Embraer S.A.; *Int'l*, pg. 2375
EMBRAER EXECUTIVE JET SERVICES, LLC—See Embraer S.A.; *Int'l*, pg. 2375
EMBRAER S.A.; *Int'l*, pg. 2375
EMBRAER SERVICES, INC.—See Embraer S.A.; *Int'l*, pg. 2375
EMBRAER SPAIN HOLDING CO., SL—See Embraer S.A.; *Int'l*, pg. 2375
EMBRATEL PARTICIPACOES S.A.—See America Movil, S.A.B. de C.V.; *Int'l*, pg. 422
EMBREX DE MEXICO S. DE R.L. DE C.V.—See Zoetis, Inc.; *U.S. Public*, pg. 2410
EMBRUDIS; *Int'l*, pg. 2376
E&M BRUNNENBAU UND BOHRTECHNIK GMBH; *Int'l*, pg. 2247
EMBRY HOLDINGS LIMITED; *Int'l*, pg. 2376
EMBRYOME SCIENCES, INC.—See Lineage Cell Therapeutics, Inc.; *U.S. Public*, pg. 1320
EMBRYOTECH LABS INC.—See Astorg Partners S.A.S.; *Int'l*, pg. 656
EMBRY-RIDDLE AERONAUTICAL UNIVERSITY, ASIA LTD.—See Embry-Riddle Aeronautical University; *U.S. Private*, pg. 1379
EMBRY-RIDDLE AERONAUTICAL UNIVERSITY - PRESCOTT—See Embry-Riddle Aeronautical University; *U.S. Private*, pg. 1379
EMBRY-RIDDLE AERONAUTICAL UNIVERSITY; *U.S. Private*, pg. 1378
EMBS, INC.—See Intercontinental Exchange, Inc.; *U.S. Public*, pg. 1142
EMBUX TECHNOLOGY CO., LTD.—See NEXCOM International Co., Ltd.; *Int'l*, pg. 5242
EMC ADVISORY SERVICES LIMITED—See Lonsdale Capital Partners LLP; *Int'l*, pg. 4552
EMCAMPUS CO., LTD.—See Sala Corporation; *Int'l*, pg. 6490
EMC ANALYTICAL SERVICES, LLC; *U.S. Private*, pg. 1379
EMCASCO INSURANCE COMPANY—See Employers Mutual Casualty Company; *U.S. Private*, pg. 1387
EMC AUSTRALIA PTY LIMITED—See Dell Technologies Inc.; *U.S. Public*, pg. 650
EMC BRASIL SERVICOS DE TI LTDA—See Dell Technologies Inc.; *U.S. Public*, pg. 650
EMC CHILE S.A.—See Dell Technologies Inc.; *U.S. Public*, pg. 650
EMC COMPANY; *U.S. Private*, pg. 1379
EMC COMPUTER SYSTEMS AS, NORWAY—See Dell Technologies Inc.; *U.S. Public*, pg. 650
EMC COMPUTER SYSTEMS A/S—See Dell Technologies Inc.; *U.S. Public*, pg. 650
EMC COMPUTER SYSTEMS AUSTRIA GMBH—See Dell Technologies Inc.; *U.S. Public*, pg. 650
EMC COMPUTER SYSTEMS (BENELUX) B.V.—See Dell Technologies Inc.; *U.S. Public*, pg. 650
EMC COMPUTER SYSTEMS DANMARK A/S—See Dell Technologies Inc.; *U.S. Public*, pg. 650
EMC COMPUTER SYSTEMS (FE) LIMITED—See Dell Technologies Inc.; *U.S. Public*, pg. 650
EMC COMPUTER SYSTEMS FRANCE—See Dell Technologies Inc.; *U.S. Public*, pg. 650
EMC COMPUTER SYSTEMS ITALIA S.P.A—See Dell Technologies Inc.; *U.S. Public*, pg. 650
EMC COMPUTER-SYSTEMS OY—See Dell Technologies Inc.; *U.S. Public*, pg. 651
EMC COMPUTER SYSTEMS POLAND SP. Z O.O.—See Dell Technologies Inc.; *U.S. Public*, pg. 650
EMC COMPUTER SYSTEMS (SOUTH ASIA) PTE LTD—See Dell Technologies Inc.; *U.S. Public*, pg. 650
EMC COMPUTER SYSTEMS SPAIN, S.A.U.—See Dell Technologies Inc.; *U.S. Public*, pg. 650
EMC COMPUTER SYSTEMS VENEZUELA, S.A.—See Dell Technologies Inc.; *U.S. Public*, pg. 651
EMC CORPORATION OF CANADA—See Dell Technologies Inc.; *U.S. Public*, pg. 651

EMCORE CORPORATION

EMC CORPORATION OF CANADA—See Dell Technologies Inc.; *U.S. Public*, pg. 651
EMC CORPORATION - SANTA CLARA—See Dell Technologies Inc.; *U.S. Public*, pg. 651
EMC CORPORATION—See Dell Technologies Inc.; *U.S. Public*, pg. 650
EMC CORPORATION - SOUTHBOROUGH—See Dell Technologies Inc.; *U.S. Public*, pg. 651
EMC CZECH REPUBLIC S.R.O.—See Dell Technologies Inc.; *U.S. Public*, pg. 651
EMC DEL PERU S.A.—See Dell Technologies Inc.; *U.S. Public*, pg. 651
EMC DEUTSCHLAND GMBH—See Dell Technologies Inc.; *U.S. Public*, pg. 651
EMC INDUSTRIAL GROUP LIMITED—See Endress+Hauser (International) Holding AG; *Int'l*, pg. 2406
EMC INFORMATION SYSTEMS COLOMBIA LTDA.—See Dell Technologies Inc.; *U.S. Public*, pg. 651
EMC INFORMATION SYSTEMS N.V.—See Dell Technologies Inc.; *U.S. Public*, pg. 651
EMC INFORMATION SYSTEMS PAKISTAN (PRIVATE) LIMITED—See Dell Technologies Inc.; *U.S. Public*, pg. 651
EMC INFORMATION SYSTEMS SWEDEN AB—See Dell Technologies Inc.; *U.S. Public*, pg. 651
EMC INFORMATION SYSTEMS (THAILAND) LIMITED—See Dell Technologies Inc.; *U.S. Public*, pg. 651
EMC INSTYTUT MEDYCZNY S.A.—See Penta Investments Limited; *Int'l*, pg. 5788
EMC INSURANCE COMPANIES—See Employers Mutual Casualty Company; *U.S. Private*, pg. 1387
EMC INSURANCE GROUP INC.—See Employers Mutual Casualty Company; *U.S. Private*, pg. 1386
EMCLAIRE FINANCIAL CORP—See Farmers National Banc Corp.; *U.S. Public*, pg. 822
EMC LIMITED; *Int'l*, pg. 2376
EMC MANAGEMENT CONCEPTS—See EMC Analytical Services, LLC; *U.S. Private*, pg. 1379
EMC MORTGAGE CORP.—See JPMorgan Chase & Co.; *U.S. Public*, pg. 1206
EMC NEW ZEALAND CORPORATION LIMITED—See Dell Technologies Inc.; *U.S. Public*, pg. 650
EMCO CHEMICAL DISTRIBUTORS INC.; *U.S. Private*, pg. 1379
EMCO CORPORATION - BRITISH COLUMBIA—See Blackfriars Corp.; *U.S. Private*, pg. 575
EMCO CORPORATION—See Blackfriars Corp.; *U.S. Private*, pg. 575
EMCO ENTERPRISES, INC.—See Andersen Corporation; *U.S. Private*, pg. 275
EMCO FAMUO SRL—See KUHN Holding GmbH; *Int'l*, pg. 4326
EMCO HIGH VOLTAGE CORP.—See XP Power Limited; *Int'l*, pg. 8537
EMCO INC.; *U.S. Private*, pg. 1379
EMCO INDUSTRIES LIMITED; *Int'l*, pg. 2376
EMCO INTOS SPOL. S R.O.—See KUHN Holding GmbH; *Int'l*, pg. 4326
EMCO INTOS S.R.O.—See KUHN Holding GmbH; *Int'l*, pg. 4326
EMCO ITALIA SRL—See KUHN Holding GmbH; *Int'l*, pg. 4326
THE E&M CO., LTD.; *Int'l*, pg. 7637
EMCO LTD.; *Int'l*, pg. 2376
EMCO MAGDEBURG AG—See KUHN Holding GmbH; *Int'l*, pg. 4326
EMCO MAIER CORPORATION—See KUHN Holding GmbH; *Int'l*, pg. 4326
EMCO MAIER GES.M.B.H.—See KUHN Holding GmbH; *Int'l*, pg. 4326
EMCO MAIER GMBH & CO. KG—See KUHN Holding GmbH; *Int'l*, pg. 4326
EMCO MECOF SRL—See KUHN Holding GmbH; *Int'l*, pg. 4326
EMCOM ENTERTAINMENT CO., LTD.—See EMCOM Holdings Co., Ltd.; *Int'l*, pg. 2376
EMCOM HOLDINGS CO., LTD.; *Int'l*, pg. 2376
EMCOMP INTERNATIONAL AB—See Addtech AB; *Int'l*, pg. 133
EMCOMP SCANDINAVIA AB—See Addtech AB; *Int'l*, pg. 133
E&M COMPUTING LTD.—See First Israel Mezzanine Investors Ltd.; *Int'l*, pg. 2685
EMCON ASSOCIATES, INC.—See Ontario Teachers' Pension Plan; *Int'l*, pg. 5589
EMCON ASSOCIATES, INC.—See PAG Asia Capital Ltd.; *Int'l*, pg. 5696
EMCON ASSOCIATES, INC.—See TPG Capital, L.P.; *U.S. Public*, pg. 2173
EMCON EMANATION CONTROL LTD.—See AEA Investors LP; *U.S. Private*, pg. 113
EMCON TECHNOLOGIES HUNGARY HOLDINGS KFT—See FORVIA SE; *Int'l*, pg. 2745
EMCOR CONSTRUCTION SERVICES, INC.—See EMCOR Group, Inc.; *U.S. Public*, pg. 736
EMCORE CORPORATION; *U.S. Public*, pg. 739

855

EMCORE CORPORATION

EMCORE FIBER OPTICS, INC.—See EMCORE Corporation; *U.S. Public*, pg. 739
EMCOR FACILITIES KNOWLEDGE CENTER—See EMCOR Group, Inc.; *U.S. Public*, pg. 737
EMCOR FACILITIES SERVICES, INC.—See EMCOR Group, Inc.; *U.S. Public*, pg. 737
EMCOR FACILITIES SERVICES - SITE BASED SERVICES—See EMCOR Group, Inc.; *U.S. Public*, pg. 737
EMCOR GOVERNMENT SERVICES, INC.—See EMCOR Group, Inc.; *U.S. Public*, pg. 737
EMCOR GROUP, INC.; *U.S. Public*, pg. 736
EMCOR GROUP (UK) PLC—See EMCOR Group, Inc.; *U.S. Public*, pg. 737
EMCOR INTERNATIONAL, INC.—See EMCOR Group, Inc.; *U.S. Public*, pg. 737
EMCOR SERVICES AIRCOND CORPORATION—See EMCOR Group, Inc.; *U.S. Public*, pg. 737
EMCOR SERVICES ARC—See EMCOR Group, Inc.; *U.S. Public*, pg. 738
EMCOR SERVICES MESA INTEGRATED SOLUTIONS—See EMCOR Group, Inc.; *U.S. Public*, pg. 738
EMCOR SERVICES NEW YORK/NEW JERSEY—See EMCOR Group, Inc.; *U.S. Public*, pg. 737
EMCOR SERVICES NEW YORK/NEW JERSEY—See EMCOR Group, Inc.; *U.S. Public*, pg. 737
EMCOR SERVICES NORTHEAST, INC.—See EMCOR Group, Inc.; *U.S. Public*, pg. 738
EMCOR SERVICES TEAM MECHANICAL, INC.—See EMCOR Group, Inc.; *U.S. Public*, pg. 738
EMCOR SERVICES TEAM MECHANICAL, INC.—See EMCOR Group, Inc.; *U.S. Public*, pg. 738
EMCO TECH CONSTRUCTION CORP.; *U.S. Private*, pg. 1379
EMC OUTDOOR; *U.S. Private*, pg. 1379
EMCO WHEATON CORP.—See Ingersoll Rand Inc.; *U.S. Public*, pg. 1118
EMCO WHEATON GMBH—See Ingersoll Rand Inc.; *U.S. Public*, pg. 1118
EMCO WHEATON UK—See Ingersoll Rand Inc.; *U.S. Public*, pg. 1118
EMCO WHEATON USA, INC.—See Ingersoll Rand Inc.; *U.S. Public*, pg. 1118
EMC PUBLIC COMPANY LIMITED; *Int'l*, pg. 2376
EMC PUBLISHING, LLC; *U.S. Private*, pg. 1379
EMC SALES & MARKETING—See Dell Technologies Inc.; *U.S. Public*, pg. 651
EMC SCHOOL, LLC—See CIP Capital Fund, L.P.; *U.S. Private*, pg. 899
EMC SERVICES ELMILJOTEKNIK AB—See Saab AB; *Int'l*, pg. 6459
EMCS THAI CO. LTD.—See Thai Reinsurance Public Co., Ltd.; *Int'l*, pg. 7595
EMC UNDERWRITERS, LLC.—See Employers Mutual Casualty Company; *U.S. Private*, pg. 1387
EMDAY; *U.S. Private*, pg. 1379
EMD BIOSCIENCES, INC.—See Merck KGaA; *Int'l*, pg. 4830
EMDEON BUSINESS SERVICES LLC—See McKesson Corporation; *U.S. Public*, pg. 1407
EMDEON BUSINESS SERVICES—See McKesson Corporation; *U.S. Public*, pg. 1407
EMDEON BUSINESS SERVICES—See McKesson Corporation; *U.S. Public*, pg. 1407
EMD INTERNATIONAL HOLDINGS, INC.—See Caterpillar, Inc.; *U.S. Public*, pg. 452
EMDI (OVERSEAS) FZ LLC—See Ironwood Education Ltd.; *Int'l*, pg. 3811
EMD LOCOMOTIVE COMPANY DE MEXICO, S.A. DE C.V.—See Caterpillar, Inc.; *U.S. Public*, pg. 452
EMD MILLIPORE CORPORATION—See Merck KGaA; *Int'l*, pg. 4830
EMD MUSIC S.A.; *Int'l*, pg. 2376
EMDOOR INFORMATION CO., LTD.; *Int'l*, pg. 2376
EMD SERONO, INC.—See Merck KGaA; *Int'l*, pg. 4831
EMD SERONO RESEARCH & DEVELOPMENT INSTITUTE—See Merck KGaA; *Int'l*, pg. 4831
EMD SERONO RESEARCH INSTITUTE, INC.—See Merck KGaA; *Int'l*, pg. 4831
EMDS, INC.—See CompuGroup Medical SE & Co, KGaA; *Int'l*, pg. 1757
EMDT AMERICA INC.—See Kopin Corporation; *U.S. Public*, pg. 1271
EMD TECHNOLOGIES INCORPORATED—See HEICO Corporation; *U.S. Public*, pg. 1020
EME CAPITAL LLP; *Int'l*, pg. 2376
EMECO HOLDINGS LIMITED; *Int'l*, pg. 2376
EMECOLE METRO LLC—See Metropolitan Industries, Inc.; *U.S. Private*, pg. 2688
EMEDAPPS INC.—See Med Tech Solutions; *U.S. Private*, pg. 2650
EMEDASIA SDN. BHD.—See Hong Seng Consolidated Berhad; *Int'l*, pg. 3469
EMEDCO INC.—See Brady Corporation; *U.S. Public*, pg. 379
E MED FUTURE, INC; *U.S. Public*, pg. 701
EMEDGENE TECHNOLOGIES LTD.—See Illumina, Inc.; *U.S. Public*, pg. 1112

EMED HUMAN RESOURCES INDIA PRIVATE LIMITED—See Aster DM Healthcare Ltd.; *Int'l*, pg. 654
EMEDIA COMMUNICATIONS, LLC—See Ziff Davis, Inc.; *U.S. Public*, pg. 2404
EMEDIA GROUP INC; *U.S. Private*, pg. 1379
E MEDIA HOLDINGS LIMITED; *Int'l*, pg. 2246
EMEDIA INVESTMENTS PROPRIETARY LIMITED—See E Media Holdings Limited; *Int'l*, pg. 2246
E-MEDIA PLUS INC.; *U.S. Private*, pg. 1302
E-MEDIAT AG—See CSL Limited; *Int'l*, pg. 1867
EMED, LLC; *U.S. Private*, pg. 1379
EMED TARTESSUS S.L.U.—See Atalaya Mining plc; *Int'l*, pg. 665
EMEFCY LTD.—See Fluence Corporation Limited; *U.S. Public*, pg. 857
EMEIS BELGIUM—See Emeis SA; *Int'l*, pg. 2376
EMEI SHAN TOURISM COMPANY LIMITED; *Int'l*, pg. 2376
EMEIS SA; *Int'l*, pg. 2376
EMEK ELEKTRIK ENDUSTRISI A.S.; *Int'l*, pg. 2376
EME KFT.—See Orange1 Holding; *Int'l*, pg. 5611
EMEK USA INC.—See Emek Elektrik Endustrisi A.S.; *Int'l*, pg. 2376
E&M ELECTRIC & MACHINERY; *U.S. Private*, pg. 1301
EMEL MATERIAIS ELETRICOS SA—See Sonepar S.A.; *Int'l*, pg. 7093
EMEMORY TECHNOLOGY, INC.; *Int'l*, pg. 2377
EMEN INSTALLATION MATERIALS SDN BHD—See KVC Industrial Supplies Sdn. Bhd.; *Int'l*, pg. 4349
EMENITE LTD.—See Etex SA/NV; *Int'l*, pg. 2521
EMENTUM, INC.; *U.S. Private*, pg. 1379
EMERA BRUNSWICK PIPELINE CO LTD—See Emera, Inc.; *Int'l*, pg. 2377
EMERA (CARIBBEAN) INCORPORATED—See Emera, Inc.; *Int'l*, pg. 2377
EMERA ENERGY—See Emera, Inc.; *Int'l*, pg. 2377
EMERA, INC.; *Int'l*, pg. 2377
E-MERALCO VENTURES, INC.—See Manila Electric Company; *Int'l*, pg. 4671
EMERALD ACQUISITION, INC.—See Harbor Beach Capital, LLC; *U.S. Private*, pg. 1858
EMERALD AIRWAYS LTD.; *Int'l*, pg. 2377
EMERALD AR SYSTEMS; *U.S. Private*, pg. 1379
EMERALD BAY APARTMENTS NEVADA, LLC—See RAIT Financial Trust; *U.S. Private*, pg. 3348
EMERALD BIOAGRICULTURE CORP.; *U.S. Private*, pg. 1379
EMERALD CAPITAL CORP—See Pinetree Capital Ltd.; *Int'l*, pg. 5868
EMERALD CITY GRAPHICS, INC.—See Chatham Asset Management, LLC; *U.S. Private*, pg. 862
EMERALD COAST ASSOCIATES, INC.—See GeoPoint Surveying, Inc.; *U.S. Private*, pg. 1681
EMERALD COAST BEHAVIORAL HOSPITAL, LLC—See Universal Health Services, Inc.; *U.S. Public*, pg. 2257
EMERALD COAST SAS—See Leonard Green & Partners, L.P.; *U.S. Private*, pg. 2424
EMERALD COAST TRUSS, LLC—See Bain Capital, LP; *U.S. Private*, pg. 450
EMERALD COAST UTILITIES AUTHORITY; *U.S. Private*, pg. 1379
EMERALD COAST UTILITY SERVICES, INC.—See American States Water Company; *U.S. Public*, pg. 110
EMERALD COMPANIES, INC.; *U.S. Private*, pg. 1379
EMERALD CONSTRUCTION MANAGEMENT, INC.—See urban-gro, Inc.; *U.S. Public*, pg. 2266
EMERALD DATA SOLUTIONS, INC.; *U.S. Private*, pg. 1379
EMERALD ENERGY PLC—See Sinochem Corporation; *Int'l*, pg. 6949
EMERALD EXPOSITIONS, INC. - ALPHARETTA—See ONEX Corporation; *Int'l*, pg. 5579
EMERALD EXPOSITIONS, INC.—See ONEX Corporation; *Int'l*, pg. 5579
EMERALD FINANCIAL SERVICES, LLC—See H&R Block, Inc.; *U.S. Public*, pg. 976
EMERALD FOODS INC.; *U.S. Private*, pg. 1379
EMERALD HAVEN REALITY LIMITED—See Sundaram Clayton Ltd.; *Int'l*, pg. 7312
EMERALD HEALTH BOTANICALS, INC.—See Skye Bioscience, Inc.; *U.S. Public*, pg. 1892
EMERALD HEALTHCARE, INC.—See The Ensign Group, Inc.; *U.S. Public*, pg. 2070
EMERALD HEALTH SERVICES; *U.S. Private*, pg. 1379
EMERALD HEALTH THERAPEUTICS, INC.—See Skye Bioscience, Inc.; *U.S. Public*, pg. 1892
EMERALD HILLS FUNERAL HOME & MEMORIAL PARK—See Service Corporation International; *U.S. Public*, pg. 1871
EMERALD HOLDING, INC.—See ONEX Corporation; *Int'l*, pg. 5578
EMERALD ISLE EXPLORATIONS LTD.; *U.S. Private*, pg. 1379
EMERALD ISLE LANDSCAPING, INC.—See Osceola Capital Management, LLC; *U.S. Private*, pg. 3047
EMERALD KALAMA CHEMICAL B.V.—See LANXESS AG; *Int'l*, pg. 4414
EMERALD KALAMA CHEMICAL LIMITED—See LANXESS AG; *Int'l*, pg. 4414

CORPORATE AFFILIATIONS

EMERALD KALAMA CHEMICAL, LLC—See LANXESS AG; *Int'l*, pg. 4414
EMERALD LANDSCAPE COMPANY, INC.—See BrightView Holdings, Inc.; *U.S. Public*, pg. 384
EMERALD LANDSCAPE SERVICES, INC.—See StayGreen, LLC; *U.S. Private*, pg. 3794
EMERALD LEISURES LIMITED; *Int'l*, pg. 2377
EMERALD MEDICAL SERVICES PTE. LTD.—See IntriCon Corporation; *U.S. Public*, pg. 1159
EMERALD OIL, INC.; *U.S. Private*, pg. 1379
EMERALD PACKAGING, INC.; *U.S. Private*, pg. 1380
EMERALD PARK SDN. BHD.—See Gromutual Berhad; *Int'l*, pg. 3087
EMERALD PERFORMANCE MATERIALS, LLC—See LANXESS AG; *Int'l*, pg. 4414
EMERALD PLANTATION HOLDINGS LIMITED; *Int'l*, pg. 2377
EMERALD PRECISION ENGINEERING SDN. BHD.—See Advanced Systems Automation Limited; *Int'l*, pg. 162
EMERALD REALTY OF NORTHWEST FLORIDA, LLC—See D.R. Horton, Inc.; *U.S. Public*, pg. 620
EMERALD RESOURCES NL; *Int'l*, pg. 2378
EMERALD SAFARI RESORT (PTY) LIMITED—See Caesars Entertainment, Inc.; *U.S. Public*, pg. 420
EMERALD SERVICES INC.; *U.S. Private*, pg. 1380
EMERALD STAR LIMITED—See TUI AG; *Int'l*, pg. 7964
EMERALD STAY S.A.—See 029 Group SE; *Int'l*, pg. 1
EMERALD TECHNOLOGIES—See Crestview Partners, L.P.; *U.S. Private*, pg. 1098
EMERALD TECHNOLOGY VALUATIONS, LLC—See Gordon Brothers Group, LLC; *U.S. Private*, pg. 1742
EMERALD TEXTILES, LLC—See Pacific Avenue Capital Partners, LLC; *U.S. Private*, pg. 3065
EMERALD TREE FARM; *U.S. Private*, pg. 1380
EMERALD WB LLC—See Emerald Oil, Inc.; *U.S. Private*, pg. 1379
EMERA MAINE—See ENMAX Corporation; *Int'l*, pg. 2442
EMERAM CAPITAL PARTNERS GMBH; *Int'l*, pg. 2378
EMERA S.R.L.—See BayWa AG; *Int'l*, pg. 917
EMERAUDE S.A.S.—See Carlsberg A/S; *Int'l*, pg. 1340
EMERA UTILITY SERVICES INC.—See Emera, Inc.; *Int'l*, pg. 2377
EMERCE AFRICA (PTY.) LTD.—See SMA Solar Technology AG; *Int'l*, pg. 6999
EMERCE GMBH—See SMA Solar Technology AG; *Int'l*, pg. 6999
EMERCHANDISE GROUP LLC; *U.S. Private*, pg. 1380
EMERCON CONSTRUCTION INC.; *U.S. Private*, pg. 1380
EMEREN GROUP LTD; *U.S. Public*, pg. 739
EMERGE 180 INC.; *U.S. Private*, pg. 1380
EMERGE COMMERCE LTD.; *Int'l*, pg. 2378
EMERGE DIGITAL INC.; *U.S. Private*, pg. 1380
EMERGE, INC.; *U.S. Private*, pg. 1380
EMERGE IT SOLUTIONS, LLC; *U.S. Private*, pg. 1380
EMERGE MONITORING, INC.—See Track Group, Inc.; *U.S. Public*, pg. 2178
EMERGENCE CAPITAL PARTNERS; *U.S. Private*, pg. 1380
EMERGENCY24, INC.; *U.S. Private*, pg. 1380
EMERGENCY ASSISTANCE BEIJING CO., LTD.—See Emergency Assistance Japan Co., Ltd.; *Int'l*, pg. 2378
EMERGENCY ASSISTANCE JAPAN CO., LTD.; *Int'l*, pg. 2378
EMERGENCY ASSISTANCE JAPAN (SINGAPORE), PTE. LTD—See Emergency Assistance Japan Co., Ltd.; *Int'l*, pg. 2378
EMERGENCY ASSISTANCE JAPAN (U.S.A), INC.—See Emergency Assistance Japan Co., Ltd.; *Int'l*, pg. 2378
EMERGENCY ASSISTANCE THAILAND CO., LTD—See Emergency Assistance Japan Co., Ltd.; *Int'l*, pg. 2378
EMERGENCY COVERAGE CORPORATION—See Blackstone Inc.; *U.S. Public*, pg. 359
EMERGENCY ESSENTIALS INC.; *U.S. Private*, pg. 1380
EMERGENCY FOOD NETWORK; *U.S. Private*, pg. 1380
EMERGENCY MEDICAL CARE—See Medavie Blue Cross; *Int'l*, pg. 4768
EMERGENCY MEDICAL FOUNDATION; *U.S. Private*, pg. 1380
EMERGENCY MEDICAL TRANSPORT, INC.—See KKR & Co. Inc.; *U.S. Public*, pg. 1249
EMERGENCY MEDICINE CONSULTANTS, LTD.—See Blackstone Inc.; *U.S. Public*, pg. 359
EMERGENCY NURSES ASSOCIATION; *U.S. Private*, pg. 1380
EMERGENCY PHYSICIAN SOLUTIONS OF SOUTH FLORIDA, LLC—See KKR & Co, Inc.; *U.S. Public*, pg. 1245
EMERGENCY POWER SYSTEMS LIMITED—See Emerson Electric Co.; *U.S. Public*, pg. 743
EMERGENCY PROFESSIONAL SERVICES, PC—See KKR & Co. Inc.; *U.S. Public*, pg. 1245
EMERGENCY PSYCHIATRIC MEDICINE, PLLC—See HCA Healthcare, Inc.; *U.S. Public*, pg. 995
EMERGENCY RESPONSE TECHNOLOGIES, INC.—See Ilustrato Pictures International Inc.; *Int'l*, pg. 3616
EMERGENCY RESTORATION EXPERTS, LLC; *U.S. Private*, pg. 1380
EMERGENCY VISIONS; *U.S. Private*, pg. 1380

COMPANY NAME INDEX

EMERGENETICS INTERNATIONAL-ASIA (EGI-A)—See Emergenetics, LLC; *U.S. Private*, pg. 1381
EMERGENETICS INTERNATIONAL—See Emergenetics, LLC; *U.S. Private*, pg. 1381
EMERGENETICS, LLC; *U.S. Private*, pg. 1380
EMERGENT BIODEFENSE OPERATIONS LANSING LLC—See Emergent BioSolutions Inc.; *U.S. Public*, pg. 739
EMERGENT BIOSOLUTIONS CANADA INC.—See Emergent BioSolutions Inc.; *U.S. Public*, pg. 739
EMERGENT BIOSOLUTIONS, INC.; *U.S. Public*, pg. 739
EMERGENT BIOSOLUTIONS, INC.—See Emergent BioSolutions Inc.; *U.S. Public*, pg. 739
EMERGENT BIOSOLUTIONS UK LTD.—See Emergent BioSolutions Inc.; *U.S. Public*, pg. 739
EMERGENT CAPITAL, INC.; *U.S. Public*, pg. 1381
EMERGENT COLD LP—See Bay Grove Capital LLC; *U.S. Private*, pg. 492
EMERGENT COUNTERMEASURES INTERNATIONAL LTD.—See Emergent BioSolutions Inc.; *U.S. Public*, pg. 740
EMERGENT ENERGY PROPRIETARY LIMITED—See African Equity Empowerment Investmts Limited; *Int'l*, pg. 191
EMERGENT HEALTH CORP.; *U.S. Public*, pg. 740
EMERGENT INDUSTRIAL SOLUTIONS LIMITED; *Int'l*, pg. 2378
EMERGENT, LLC; *U.S. Private*, pg. 1381
EMERGENT MEDICAL ASSOCIATES; *U.S. Private*, pg. 1381
EMERGENT METALS CORP.; *Int'l*, pg. 2378
EMERGENT METHOD, LLC; *U.S. Private*, pg. 1381
EMERGENT PRODUCT DEVELOPMENT GAITHERSBURG INC.—See Emergent BioSolutions Inc.; *U.S. Public*, pg. 740
EMERGENT PRODUCT DEVELOPMENT SEATTLE LLC—See Emergent BioSolutions Inc.; *U.S. Public*, pg. 740
EMERGENT PROTECTIVE PRODUCTS USA INC—See Emergent BioSolutions Inc.; *U.S. Public*, pg. 740
EMERGENT SALES AND MARKETING GERMANY GMBH—See Emergent BioSolutions Inc.; *U.S. Public*, pg. 740
EMERGENT SALES AND MARKETING SINGAPORE PTE. LTD.—See Emergent BioSolutions Inc.; *U.S. Public*, pg. 740
EMERGEO SOLUTIONS WORLDWIDE INC.; *Int'l*, pg. 2378
EMERGER FERTILIZANTES S.A.—See Kovdorskiy GOK JSC; *Int'l*, pg. 4293
E.MERGE TECHNOLOGY ACQUISITION CORP.; *U.S. Public*, pg. 701
EMERGEVEST LIMITED; *Int'l*, pg. 2378
EMERGIA INC.; *Int'l*, pg. 2378
EMERGING CAPITAL PARTNERS (ECP); *U.S. Private*, pg. 1381
EMERGING DISPLAY TECHNOLOGIES CORP.; *Int'l*, pg. 2378
EMERGING DISPLAY TECHNOLOGIES CORP.—See Emerging Display Tech; *Int'l*, pg. 2379
EMERGING DISPLAY TECHNOLOGIES CO.—See Emerging Display Tech; *Int'l*, pg. 2379
EMERGING GLORY SDN BHD; *Int'l*, pg. 2379
EMERGING INVESTMENT PARTNERS; *Int'l*, pg. 2379
EMERGING MARKETS COMMUNICATIONS LLC—See PAR Capital Management, Inc.; *U.S. Private*, pg. 3089
EMERGING MARKETS HORIZON CORP.; *Int'l*, pg. 2379
EMERGING MARKETS PAYMENTS—See Emirates NBD PJSC; *Int'l*, pg. 2382
EMERGING MEDIA CORP.—See The Movie Studio, Inc.; *U.S. Public*, pg. 2116
EMERGING OPPORTUNITIES CORP.; *U.S. Private*, pg. 1381
EMERGINGSOFT CORP.—See Dean Evans & Associates, Inc.; *U.S. Private*, pg. 1183
EMERGING SOVEREIGN GROUP LLC; *U.S. Private*, pg. 1381
E-MERGING TECHNOLOGIES GROUP, INC.; *U.S. Private*, pg. 1302
EMERGING TOWNS & CITIES SINGAPORE LTD.; *Int'l*, pg. 2379
EMERGING VISION, INC.; *U.S. Private*, pg. 1381
EMERGING WORLD PHARMA, INC.; *U.S. Private*, pg. 1381
EMERGINT TECHNOLOGIES, INC.—See CACI International Inc.; *U.S. Public*, pg. 417
EMERGIS INC.—See TELUS CORPORATION; *Int'l*, pg. 7546
EMERGITECH, INC.—See Vista Equity Partners, LLC; *U.S. Private*, pg. 4395
EMERGN LIMITED; *Int'l*, pg. 2379
EMERGN LIMITED—See Emergn Limited; *Int'l*, pg. 2379
EMERGN LIMITED—See Emergn Limited; *Int'l*, pg. 2379
EMERGTECH BUSINESS SOLUTIONS, INC.; *U.S. Private*, pg. 1381
EMERGYCARE, INC.; *U.S. Private*, pg. 1381
EMERICARE SKYLYN PLACE LLC—See Brookdale Senior Living Inc.; *U.S. Public*, pg. 394

EMERICK CONSTRUCTION CO. INC.; *U.S. Private*, pg. 1381
EM ERIKSSON STEEL SERVICE CENTER AB—See SSAB AB; *Int'l*, pg. 7155
EMERIO AUSTRALIA PTY. LTD.—See Nippon Telegraph & Telephone Corporation; *Int'l*, pg. 5344
EMERIO GLOBESOFT PTE. LTD.—See Nippon Telegraph & Telephone Corporation; *Int'l*, pg. 5344
EMERIO (MALAYSIA) SDN. BHD.—See Nippon Telegraph & Telephone Corporation; *Int'l*, pg. 5344
EMERIO TECHNOLOGIES PRIVATE LIMITED—See Nippon Telegraph & Telephone Corporation; *Int'l*, pg. 5344
EMERIO (THAILAND) LTD.—See Nippon Telegraph & Telephone Corporation; *Int'l*, pg. 5344
EMERI-SKY SC LLC—See Brookdale Senior Living Inc.; *U.S. Public*, pg. 394
EMERISQUE BRANDS UK LIMITED; *Int'l*, pg. 2379
EMERITA RESOURCES CORP.; *Int'l*, pg. 2379
EMERITOL GRAND TERRACE LLC—See Brookdale Senior Living Inc.; *U.S. Public*, pg. 394
EMERITUS CORPORATION—See Brookdale Senior Living Inc.; *U.S. Public*, pg. 394
EMERITUS INTERNATIONAL REINSURANCE COMPANY LIMITED—See Zimre Holdings Limited; *Int'l*, pg. 8684
EMERITUSMERCED INC.—See Brookdale Senior Living Inc.; *U.S. Public*, pg. 394
EMERITUS REINSURANCE COMPANY LIMITED—See Zimre Holdings Limited; *Int'l*, pg. 8684
EMERITUS REINSURANCE ZAMBIA LIMITED—See Zimre Holdings Limited; *Int'l*, pg. 8684
EMERITUS RESEGGUROS, SA—See Zimre Holdings Limited; *Int'l*, pg. 8684
EMERIWEG DEERFIELD LLC—See Brookdale Senior Living Inc.; *U.S. Public*, pg. 394
EMERLING CHEVROLET INC.; *U.S. Private*, pg. 1381
EMERLING FORD, INC.; *U.S. Private*, pg. 1381
EMERPOWSYS, S. DE R.L. DE C.V.—See Emerson Electric Co.; *U.S. Public*, pg. 743
EMERSION SYSTEMS PTY LTD—See Novatti Group Limited; *Int'l*, pg. 5461
EMERSON AIR COMFORT PRODUCTS—See Emerson Electric Co.; *U.S. Public*, pg. 744
EMERSON APPLIANCE CONTROLS—See Emerson Electric Co.; *U.S. Public*, pg. 743
EMERSON ARGENTINA S.A.—See Emerson Electric Co.; *U.S. Public*, pg. 743
EMERSON ASIA PACIFIC PRIVATE LIMITED—See Emerson Electric Co.; *U.S. Public*, pg. 747
EMERSON AUTOMATION SOLUTIONS AS—See Emerson Electric Co.; *U.S. Public*, pg. 743
EMERSON AUTOMATION SOLUTIONS FINAL CONTROL GERMANY GMBH—See Emerson Electric Co.; *U.S. Public*, pg. 743
EMERSON AUTOMATION SOLUTIONS FINAL CONTROL HUNGARY KFT.—See Emerson Electric Co.; *U.S. Public*, pg. 748
EMERSON AUTOMATION SOLUTIONS FINAL CONTROL ITALIA S.R.L.—See Emerson Electric Co.; *U.S. Public*, pg. 743
EMERSON AUTOMATION SOLUTIONS FINAL CONTROL NETHERLANDS B.V.—See Emerson Electric Co.; *U.S. Public*, pg. 745
EMERSON AUTOMATION SOLUTIONS FINAL CONTROL POLSKA SP. Z O.O.—See Emerson Electric Co.; *U.S. Public*, pg. 743
EMERSON AUTOMATION SOLUTIONS FINALL CONTROL UK LTD.—See Pentair plc; *Int'l*, pg. 5789
EMERSON AUTOMATION SOLUTIONS - GERMANY—See Emerson Electric Co.; *U.S. Public*, pg. 743
EMERSON AUTOMATION SOLUTIONS GMBH—See Emerson Electric Co.; *U.S. Public*, pg. 743
EMERSON AUTOMATION SOLUTIONS INTELLIGENT PLATFORMS PRIVATE LIMITED—See Emerson Electric Co.; *U.S. Public*, pg. 749
EMERSON AUTOMATION SOLUTIONS IRELAND LIMITED—See Emerson Electric Co.; *U.S. Public*, pg. 743
EMERSON AUTOMATION SOLUTIONS - NETHERLANDS—See Emerson Electric Co.; *U.S. Public*, pg. 743
EMERSON AUTOMATION SOLUTIONS UK LIMITED—See Emerson Electric Co.; *U.S. Public*, pg. 743
EMERSON BEIJING INSTRUMENT CO. LTD.—See Emerson Electric Co.; *U.S. Public*, pg. 743
EMERSON BRAZIL—See Emerson Electric Co.; *U.S. Public*, pg. 743
EMERSON CLIMATE TECHNOLOGIES ARABIA LIMITED CO.—See Emerson Electric Co.; *U.S. Public*, pg. 743
EMERSON CLIMATE TECHNOLOGIES AUSTRALIA PTY. LTD.—See Emerson Electric Co.; *U.S. Public*, pg. 743
EMERSON CLIMATE TECHNOLOGIES FZE—See Emerson Electric Co.; *U.S. Public*, pg. 743
EMERSON CLIMATE TECHNOLOGIES GMBH—See Emerson Electric Co.; *U.S. Public*, pg. 743
EMERSON CLIMATE TECHNOLOGIES GMBH—See Emerson Electric Co.; *U.S. Public*, pg. 743

EMERSON ELECTRIC CO.

EMERSON CLIMATE TECHNOLOGIES, INC.—See Emerson Electric Co.; *U.S. Public*, pg. 743
EMERSON CLIMATE TECHNOLOGIES (INDIA) LIMITED—See Emerson Electric Co.; *U.S. Public*, pg. 743
EMERSON CLIMATE TECHNOLOGIES MEXICO SA DE CV—See Emerson Electric Co.; *U.S. Public*, pg. 744
EMERSON CLIMATE TECHNOLOGIES RETAIL SOLUTIONS EUROPE S.R.L.—See Emerson Electric Co.; *U.S. Public*, pg. 743
EMERSON CLIMATE TECHNOLOGIES RETAIL SOLUTIONS, INC.—See Emerson Electric Co.; *U.S. Public*, pg. 744
EMERSON CLIMATE TECHNOLOGIES SARL—See Emerson Electric Co.; *U.S. Public*, pg. 744
EMERSON CLIMATE TECHNOLOGIES (SHENYANG) REFRIGERATION CO., LTD.—See Emerson Electric Co.; *U.S. Public*, pg. 743
EMERSON CLIMATE TECHNOLOGIES - SOLUTIONS (SUZHOU) CO., LTD.—See Emerson Electric Co.; *U.S. Public*, pg. 743
EMERSON CLIMATE TECHNOLOGIES (SOUTH AFRICA) (PTY) LTD.—See Emerson Electric Co.; *U.S. Public*, pg. 743
EMERSON CLIMATE TECHNOLOGIES S.R.L.—See Emerson Electric Co.; *U.S. Public*, pg. 743
EMERSON CLIMATE TECHNOLOGIES, S.R.O.—See Emerson Electric Co.; *U.S. Public*, pg. 743
EMERSON CLIMATE TECHNOLOGIES (SUZHOU) CO., LTD.—See Emerson Electric Co.; *U.S. Public*, pg. 743
EMERSON CLIMATE TECHNOLOGIES (SUZHOU) RESEARCH & DEVELOPMENT CO., LTD.—See Emerson Electric Co.; *U.S. Public*, pg. 744
EMERSON CLIMATE TECHNOLOGIES - TRANSPORTATION SOLUTIONS APS—See Emerson Electric Co.; *U.S. Public*, pg. 743
EMERSON COMERCIO EM TECNOLOGIA DE CLIMATIZACAO LTDA—See Emerson Electric Co.; *U.S. Public*, pg. 744
EMERSON & CUMING—See Henkel AG & Co. KGaA; *Int'l*, pg. 3353
EMERSON & CUMING—See Henkel AG & Co. KGaA; *Int'l*, pg. 3353
EMERSON DEVELOPMENTS (HOLDINGS) LIMITED; *Int'l*, pg. 2379
EMERSON D.O.O.—See Emerson Electric Co.; *U.S. Public*, pg. 749
EMERSON EGYPT LLC—See Emerson Electric Co.; *U.S. Public*, pg. 744
EMERSON ELECTRIC (ASIA) LIMITED—See Emerson Electric Co.; *U.S. Public*, pg. 744
EMERSON ELECTRIC CANADA LIMITED—See Emerson Electric Co.; *U.S. Public*, pg. 744
EMERSON ELECTRIC (CHINA) HOLDING CO., LTD.—See Emerson Electric Co.; *U.S. Public*, pg. 744
EMERSON ELECTRIC (CHINA) HOLDINGS CO., LTD.—See Emerson Electric Co.; *U.S. Public*, pg. 744
EMERSON ELECTRIC CO. - HUMBOLDT—See Emerson Electric Co.; *U.S. Public*, pg. 744
EMERSON ELECTRIC CO. (INDIA) PRIVATE LTD.—See Emerson Electric Co.; *U.S. Public*, pg. 744
EMERSON ELECTRIC COMPANY (INDIA) PRIVATE LIMITED—See Emerson Electric Co.; *U.S. Public*, pg. 745
EMERSON ELECTRIC CO.; *U.S. Public*, pg. 740
EMERSON ELECTRIC DE MEXICO S.A. DE C.V.—See Emerson Electric Co.; *U.S. Public*, pg. 745
EMERSON ELECTRIC DO BRASIL LTDA—See Emerson Electric Co.; *U.S. Public*, pg. 745
EMERSON ELECTRIC KOREA LTD.—See Emerson Electric Co.; *U.S. Public*, pg. 745
EMERSON ELECTRIC (MALAYSIA) SDN. BHD.—See Emerson Electric Co.; *U.S. Public*, pg. 744
EMERSON ELECTRIC (M) SDN BHD—See Emerson Electric Co.; *U.S. Public*, pg. 744
EMERSON ELECTRIC NEDERLAND BV—See Emerson Electric Co.; *U.S. Public*, pg. 745
EMERSON ELECTRIC OVERSEAS FINANCE CORP.—See Emerson Electric Co.; *U.S. Public*, pg. 742
EMERSON ELECTRIC POLAND SP. Z O.O.—See Emerson Electric Co.; *U.S. Public*, pg. 745
EMERSON ELECTRIC (TAIWAN) COMPANY LIMITED—See Emerson Electric Co.; *U.S. Public*, pg. 744
EMERSON ELECTRIC (THAILAND) LIMITED—See Emerson Electric Co.; *U.S. Public*, pg. 744
EMERSON ELECTRIC U.K. LTD.—See Emerson Electric Co.; *U.S. Public*, pg. 745
EMERSON ELECTRIC (U.S.) HOLDING CORPORATION (CHILE) LIMITADA—See Emerson Electric Co.; *U.S. Public*, pg. 744
EMERSON ELECTRIC (U.S.) HOLDING CORPORATION—See Emerson Electric Co.; *U.S. Public*, pg. 742
EMERSON ELECTRONIC CONNECTOR AND COMPONENTS, S.A. DE C.V.—See Emerson Electric Co.; *U.S. Public*, pg. 745

EMERSON ELECTRIC CO.

EMERSON ENERGY SYSTEMS ARGENTINA S.A.—See Emerson Electric Co.; *U.S. Public*, pg. 745
EMERSON ENERGY SYSTEMS—See Emerson Electric Co.; *U.S. Public*, pg. 745
EMERSON ERESOURCE (XI'AN) CO., LTD.—See Emerson Electric Co.; *U.S. Public*, pg. 749
EMERSON FLOW CONTROLS—See Emerson Electric Co.; *U.S. Public*, pg. 744
EMERSON FZE—See Emerson Electric Co.; *U.S. Public*, pg. 745
EMERSON HARDWOOD COMPANY; *U.S. Private*, pg. 1382
EMERSON HOSPITAL; *U.S. Private*, pg. 1382
EMERSON INDUSTRIAL AUTOMATION BELGIUM NV—See Emerson Electric Co.; *U.S. Public*, pg. 745
EMERSON INDUSTRIAL AUTOMATION ITALY SPA—See Emerson Electric Co.; *U.S. Public*, pg. 745
EMERSON INDUSTRIAL AUTOMATION POLAND SP. Z.O.O.—See Emerson Electric Co.; *U.S. Public*, pg. 745
EMERSON INSTRUMENT & VALVE SERVICE—See Emerson Electric Co.; *U.S. Public*, pg. 748
EMERSON INSTRUMENT & VALVE SERVICES—See Emerson Electric Co.; *U.S. Public*, pg. 746
EMERSON INTERNATIONAL, INC.—See Emerson Developments (Holdings) Limited; *Int'l*, pg. 2379
EMERSON JAPAN, LTD., FUSITE DIVISION—See Emerson Electric Co.; *U.S. Public*, pg. 745
EMERSON JAPAN LTD.—See Emerson Electric Co.; *U.S. Public*, pg. 745
EMERSON JAPAN, LTD.—See Emerson Electric Co.; *U.S. Public*, pg. 745
EMERSON JUNKANG ENTERPRISE (SHANGHAI) CO., LTD.—See Emerson Electric Co.; *U.S. Public*, pg. 745
EMERSON LLC—See Emerson Electric Co.; *U.S. Public*, pg. 746
EMERSON MACHINERY & EQUIPMENT (SHENZHEN) CO., LTD.—See Emerson Electric Co.; *U.S. Public*, pg. 745
EMERSON MACHINERY HEALTH MANAGEMENT COMPANY—See Emerson Electric Co.; *U.S. Public*, pg. 746
EMERSON MATTRESS INC.; *U.S. Private*, pg. 1382
EMERSON MEXICO FINANCE, S.A. DE C.V. SOFOM, ENR—See Emerson Electric Co.; *U.S. Public*, pg. 745
EMERSON NETWORK POWER AB—See Emerson Electric Co.; *U.S. Public*, pg. 747
EMERSON NETWORK POWER AUSTRALIA PTY. LTD.—See Vertiv Holdings Co; *U.S. Public*, pg. 2288
EMERSON NETWORK POWER CO., LTD.—See Emerson Electric Co.; *U.S. Public*, pg. 747
EMERSON NETWORK POWER DO BRASIL LTDA—See Emerson Electric Co.; *U.S. Public*, pg. 745
EMERSON NETWORK POWER - EMBEDDED COMPUTING GMBH—See Emerson Electric Co.; *U.S. Public*, pg. 745
EMERSON NETWORK POWER, ENERGY SYSTEMS—See Vertiv Holdings Co; *U.S. Public*, pg. 2289
EMERSON NETWORK POWER ENTERPRISE SRL—See Emerson Electric Co.; *U.S. Public*, pg. 745
EMERSON NETWORK POWER GMBH—See Vertiv Holdings Co; *U.S. Public*, pg. 2288
EMERSON NETWORK POWER GUC SISTEMLERI LIMITED SIRKETI—See Emerson Electric Co.; *U.S. Public*, pg. 745
EMERSON NETWORK POWER HOLDING S.R.L.—See Vertiv Holdings Co; *U.S. Public*, pg. 2288
EMERSON NETWORK POWER INDUSTRIAL SYSTEMS SAS—See Emerson Electric Co.; *U.S. Public*, pg. 742
EMERSON NETWORK POWER ITALIA—See Vertiv Holdings Co; *U.S. Public*, pg. 2288
EMERSON NETWORK POWER ITALIA SRL—See Emerson Electric Co.; *U.S. Public*, pg. 742
EMERSON NETWORK POWER, LDA—See Vertiv Holdings Co; *U.S. Public*, pg. 2288
EMERSON NETWORK POWER, LIEBERT SERVICES, INC. - EDISON—See Vertiv Holdings Co; *U.S. Public*, pg. 2289
EMERSON NETWORK POWER, LIEBERT SERVICES, INC.—See Vertiv Holdings Co; *U.S. Public*, pg. 2289
EMERSON NETWORK POWER LTD.—See Vertiv Holdings Co; *U.S. Public*, pg. 2288
EMERSON NETWORK POWER (MALAYSIA) SDN. BHD.—See Vertiv Holdings Co; *U.S. Public*, pg. 2288
EMERSON NETWORK POWER PAKISTAN (PRIVATE) LIMITED—See Emerson Electric Co.; *U.S. Public*, pg. 745
EMERSON NETWORK POWER (PHILIPPINES), INC.—See Emerson Electric Co.; *U.S. Public*, pg. 745
EMERSON NETWORK POWER SAS—See Emerson Electric Co.; *U.S. Public*, pg. 742
EMERSON NETWORK POWER (SINGAPORE) PTE. LTD.—See Vertiv Holdings Co; *U.S. Public*, pg. 2288
EMERSON NETWORK POWER—See Vertiv Holdings Co; *U.S. Public*, pg. 2288
EMERSON NETWORK POWER—See Vertiv Holdings Co; *U.S. Public*, pg. 2288

EMERSON NETWORK POWER (SOUTH AFRICA) (PTY) LTD—See Emerson Electric Co.; *U.S. Public*, pg. 745
EMERSON NETWORK POWER SP. Z.O.O.—See Emerson Electric Co.; *U.S. Public*, pg. 745
EMERSON NETWORK POWER SURGE PROTECTION, INC.—See Vertiv Holdings Co; *U.S. Public*, pg. 2289
EMERSON NETWORK POWER SURGE PROTECTION, INC.—See Vertiv Holdings Co; *U.S. Public*, pg. 2289
EMERSON NETWORK POWER (THAILAND) CO. LTD.—See Vertiv Holdings Co; *U.S. Public*, pg. 2288
EMERSON NETWORK POWER (VIETNAM) CO., LTD.—See Emerson Electric Co.; *U.S. Public*, pg. 745
EMERSON OIL CO. INC.; *U.S. Private*, pg. 1382
EMERSON ORADEA S.R.L.—See Emerson Electric Co.; *U.S. Public*, pg. 745
EMERSON PACIFIC PTE. LTD.—See Emerson Electric Co.; *U.S. Public*, pg. 746
EMERSON PARADIGM HOLDING LLC—See Emerson Electric Co.; *U.S. Public*, pg. 746
EMERSON (PHILIPPINES) CORPORATION—See Emerson Electric Co.; *U.S. Public*, pg. 744
EMERSON PROCESS MANAGEMENT AB—See Emerson Electric Co.; *U.S. Public*, pg. 746
EMERSON PROCESS MANAGEMENT AG—See Emerson Electric Co.; *U.S. Public*, pg. 746
EMERSON PROCESS MANAGEMENT ASIA PACIFIC PTE LTD—See Emerson Electric Co.; *U.S. Public*, pg. 747
EMERSON PROCESS MANAGEMENT AS—See Emerson Electric Co.; *U.S. Public*, pg. 746
EMERSON PROCESS MANAGEMENT A/S—See Emerson Electric Co.; *U.S. Public*, pg. 746
EMERSON PROCESS MANAGEMENT AUSTRALIA PTY LIMITED—See Emerson Electric Co.; *U.S. Public*, pg. 747
EMERSON PROCESS MANAGEMENT BV—See Emerson Electric Co.; *U.S. Public*, pg. 747
EMERSON PROCESS MANAGEMENT CO., LTD.—See Emerson Electric Co.; *U.S. Public*, pg. 748
EMERSON PROCESS MANAGEMENT CSI—See Emerson Electric Co.; *U.S. Public*, pg. 746
EMERSON PROCESS MANAGEMENT DE COLOMBIA SAS—See Emerson Electric Co.; *U.S. Public*, pg. 749
EMERSON PROCESS MANAGEMENT DISTRIBUTION LTD.—See Emerson Electric Co.; *U.S. Public*, pg. 747
EMERSON PROCESS MANAGEMENT DISTRIBUTION N.V.—See Emerson Electric Co.; *U.S. Public*, pg. 746
EMERSON PROCESS MANAGEMENT EUROPE GMBH—See Emerson Electric Co.; *U.S. Public*, pg. 748
EMERSON PROCESS MANAGEMENT GMBH & CO. OHG—See Emerson Electric Co.; *U.S. Public*, pg. 746
EMERSON PROCESS MANAGEMENT GMBH & CO. OHG—See Emerson Electric Co.; *U.S. Public*, pg. 747
EMERSON PROCESS MANAGEMENT INSTRUMENT & VALVE SERVICES—See Emerson Electric Co.; *U.S. Public*, pg. 744
EMERSON PROCESS MANAGEMENT JAPAN LTD.—See Emerson Electric Co.; *U.S. Public*, pg. 746
EMERSON PROCESS MANAGEMENT KFT.—See Emerson Electric Co.; *U.S. Public*, pg. 747
EMERSON PROCESS MANAGEMENT, LDA—See Emerson Electric Co.; *U.S. Public*, pg. 748
EMERSON PROCESS MANAGEMENT LIMITED—See Emerson Electric Co.; *U.S. Public*, pg. 747
EMERSON PROCESS MANAGEMENT LIMITED—See Emerson Electric Co.; *U.S. Public*, pg. 747
EMERSON PROCESS MANAGEMENT LLLP—See Emerson Electric Co.; *U.S. Public*, pg. 748
EMERSON PROCESS MANAGEMENT LTDA.—See Emerson Electric Co.; *U.S. Public*, pg. 748
EMERSON PROCESS MANAGEMENT MAGYARORSZAG KFT.—See Emerson Electric Co.; *U.S. Public*, pg. 748
EMERSON PROCESS MANAGEMENT MOROCCO SARL—See Emerson Electric Co.; *U.S. Public*, pg. 744
EMERSON PROCESS MANAGEMENT NV—See Emerson Electric Co.; *U.S. Public*, pg. 748
EMERSON PROCESS MANAGEMENT OY—See Emerson Electric Co.; *U.S. Public*, pg. 747
EMERSON PROCESS MANAGEMENT POWER & WATER SOLUTIONS INDIA PRIVATE LIMITED—See Emerson Electric Co.; *U.S. Public*, pg. 748
EMERSON PROCESS MANAGEMENT POWER & WATER SOLUTIONS—See Emerson Electric Co.; *U.S. Public*, pg. 747
EMERSON PROCESS MANAGEMENT POWER & WATER SOLUTIONS SP. Z.O.O.—See Emerson Electric Co.; *U.S. Public*, pg. 748
EMERSON PROCESS MANAGEMENT QATAR S.S.Q.—See Emerson Electric Co.; *U.S. Public*, pg. 748
EMERSON PROCESS MANAGEMENT REGULATOR TECHNOLOGIES, INC.—See Emerson Electric Co.; *U.S. Public*, pg. 747
EMERSON PROCESS MANAGEMENT REGULATOR TECHNOLOGIES TULSA, LLC—See Emerson Electric Co.; *U.S. Public*, pg. 747
EMERSON PROCESS MANAGEMENT ROMANIA S.R.L.—See Emerson Electric Co.; *U.S. Public*, pg. 747

CORPORATE AFFILIATIONS

EMERSON PROCESS MANAGEMENT ROSEMOUNT INC.—See Emerson Electric Co.; *U.S. Public*, pg. 747
EMERSON PROCESS MANAGEMENT ROSEMOUNT INC—See Emerson Electric Co.; *U.S. Public*, pg. 747
EMERSON PROCESS MANAGEMENT ROSEMOUNT & MICRO MOTION DIVISION—See Emerson Electric Co.; *U.S. Public*, pg. 747
EMERSON PROCESS MANAGEMENT S.A.—See Emerson Electric Co.; *U.S. Public*, pg. 748
EMERSON PROCESS MANAGEMENT SAS—See Emerson Electric Co.; *U.S. Public*, pg. 749
EMERSON PROCESS MANAGEMENT SHARED SERVICES LIMITED—See Emerson Electric Co.; *U.S. Public*, pg. 747
EMERSON PROCESS MANAGEMENT, S.L.—See Emerson Electric Co.; *U.S. Public*, pg. 747
EMERSON PROCESS MANAGEMENT—See Emerson Electric Co.; *U.S. Public*, pg. 747
EMERSON PROCESS MANAGEMENT—See Emerson Electric Co.; *U.S. Public*, pg. 747
EMERSON PROCESS MANAGEMENT—See Emerson Electric Co.; *U.S. Public*, pg. 746
EMERSON PROCESS MANAGEMENT—See Emerson Electric Co.; *U.S. Public*, pg. 746
EMERSON PROCESS MANAGEMENT—See Emerson Electric Co.; *U.S. Public*, pg. 746
EMERSON PROCESS MANAGEMENT—See Emerson Electric Co.; *U.S. Public*, pg. 746
EMERSON PROCESS MANAGEMENT—See Emerson Electric Co.; *U.S. Public*, pg. 746
EMERSON PROCESS MANAGEMENT—See Emerson Electric Co.; *U.S. Public*, pg. 746
EMERSON PROCESS MANAGEMENT—See Emerson Electric Co.; *U.S. Public*, pg. 746
EMERSON PROCESS MANAGEMENT—See Emerson Electric Co.; *U.S. Public*, pg. 747
EMERSON PROCESS MANAGEMENT—See Emerson Electric Co.; *U.S. Public*, pg. 746
EMERSON PROCESS MANAGEMENT—See Emerson Electric Co.; *U.S. Public*, pg. 746
EMERSON PROCESS MANAGEMENT (SOUTH AFRICA) (PROPRIETARY) LTD.—See Emerson Electric Co.; *U.S. Public*, pg. 745
EMERSON PROCESS MANAGEMENT SP. Z.O.O.—See Emerson Electric Co.; *U.S. Public*, pg. 747
EMERSON PROCESS MANAGEMENT S.R.L.—See Emerson Electric Co.; *U.S. Public*, pg. 748
EMERSON PROCESS MANAGEMENT S.R.O.—See Emerson Electric Co.; *U.S. Public*, pg. 748
EMERSON PROCESS MANAGEMENT TICARET LIMITED SIRKETI—See Emerson Electric Co.; *U.S. Public*, pg. 747
EMERSON PROCESS MANAGEMENT UAB—See Emerson Electric Co.; *U.S. Public*, pg. 747
EMERSON PROCESS MANAGEMENT VALVE ACTUATION LLC—See Emerson Electric Co.; *U.S. Public*, pg. 748
EMERSON PROCESS MANAGEMENT, VALVE AUTOMATION DIVISION—See Emerson Electric Co.; *U.S. Public*, pg. 748
EMERSON PROCESS MANAGEMENT-VALVE AUTOMATION—See Emerson Electric Co.; *U.S. Public*, pg. 748
EMERSON PROCESS MANAGEMENT-VALVE AUTOMATION—See Emerson Electric Co.; *U.S. Public*, pg. 746
EMERSON PROCESS MANAGEMENT VIRGO VALVES, INC.—See Emerson Electric Co.; *U.S. Public*, pg. 749
EMERSON PROFESSIONAL TOOLS AG—See Emerson Electric Co.; *U.S. Public*, pg. 749
EMERSON PROFESSIONAL TOOLS (SHANGHAI) CO., LTD.—See Emerson Electric Co.; *U.S. Public*, pg. 749
EMERSON RADIO CORP.; *U.S. Public*, pg. 752
EMERSON REID LLC; *U.S. Private*, pg. 1382
EMERSON REMOTE AUTOMATION SOLUTIONS—See Emerson Electric Co.; *U.S. Public*, pg. 748
EMERSON RESOURCES, INC.—See Leonard Green & Partners, L.P.; *U.S. Private*, pg. 2426
EMERSON RETAIL SERVICES EUROPE GMBH—See Emerson Electric Co.; *U.S. Public*, pg. 744
EMERSON SALES (UK) LIMITED—See Emerson Electric Co.; *U.S. Public*, pg. 749
EMERSON SAUDI ARABIA LLC—See Emerson Electric Co.; *U.S. Public*, pg. 745
EMERSON S.R.L.—See Emerson Electric Co.; *U.S. Public*, pg. 745
EMERSON-SWAN INC.; *U.S. Private*, pg. 1382
EMERSON SWEDEN AB—See Emerson Electric Co.; *U.S. Public*, pg. 745
EMERSON (TAIWAN) LIMITED—See Emerson Electric Co.; *U.S. Public*, pg. 743
EMERSON TECHNOLOGIES GMBH & CO. OHG—See Emerson Electric Co.; *U.S. Public*, pg. 749
EMERSON (THAILAND) LIMITED—See Emerson Electric Co.; *U.S. Public*, pg. 743
EMERSON TOOL COMPANY—See Emerson Electric Co.; *U.S. Public*, pg. 749
EMERSON VENEZUELA C.A.—See Emerson Electric Co.; *U.S. Public*, pg. 749

COMPANY NAME INDEX

EMER S.P.A.—See Westport Fuel Systems Inc.; *Int'l*, pg. 8393
EMERY & ASSOCIATES; *U.S. Private*, pg. 1382
EMERY DISTRIBUTORS INC.; *U.S. Private*, pg. 1382
EMERY HOWARD PORTFOLIO MANAGEMENT, INC.—See Creative Planning, LLC; *U.S. Private*, pg. 1090
EMERY OLEOCHEMICALS RIKA SDN. BHD.—See New Japan Chemical Co., Ltd.; *Int'l*, pg. 5225
EMERY THOMPSON MACHINE SUPPLY CO.—See The Middleby Corporation; *U.S. Public*, pg. 2113
EMERY-WATERHOUSE COMPANY—See Ace Hardware Corporation; *U.S. Private*, pg. 56
EMERY WINSLOW SCALE COMPANY—See The A.H. Emery Company; *U.S. Private*, pg. 3980
EMESS DESIGN GROUP LLC—See Edg/Sw Holdings LLC; *U.S. Private*, pg. 1333
EMETALS LIMITED; *Int'l*, pg. 2380
EMETER CORPORATION—See Siemens Aktiengesellschaft; *Int'l*, pg. 6895
EM EVENT MARKETING AG—See DEAG Deutsche Entertainment AG; *Int'l*, pg. 1998
EMEX LLC—See O2 Investment Partners, LLC; *U.S. Private*, pg. 2982
EMF CAPITAL PARTNERS LIMITED; *Int'l*, pg. 2380
EMF CAPITAL (UK) LIMITED—See EMF Capital Partners Limited; *Int'l*, pg. 2380
EMF CORPORATION; *U.S. Private*, pg. 1382
EMFI SAS—See 3M Company; *U.S. Public*, pg. 8
EMFRONTIER INC.; *Int'l*, pg. 2380
EMG AUTOMATION GMBH—See SMS Holding GmbH; *Int'l*, pg. 7016
EMGEE CABLES & COMMUNICATIONS LTD.; *Int'l*, pg. 2380
EMGE FOODS, LLC—See Peer Foods Group, Inc.; *U.S. Private*, pg. 3128
EMG - ETHNIC MARKETING GROUP, INC.; *U.S. Private*, pg. 1382
EMG EUROMARINE ELECTRONICS GMBH—See Rheinmetall AG; *Int'l*, pg. 6321
EMGH LIMITED—See Sumitomo Corporation; *Int'l*, pg. 7273
EMG HOLDINGS LTD; *Int'l*, pg. 2380
EMG, INC.; *U.S. Private*, pg. 1382
EMG MOTOR GROUP LTD—See EMG Holdings Ltd; *Int'l*, pg. 2380
EMGP—See Caisse des Depots et Consignations; *Int'l*, pg. 1258
E.M. GRAY & SON INC.; *U.S. Private*, pg. 1306
EMGS AMERICAS INC.—See Electromagnetic Geoservices ASA; *Int'l*, pg. 2353
EMGS ASIA PACIFIC SDN BHD—See Electromagnetic Geoservices ASA; *Int'l*, pg. 2353
EMGS AS—See Electromagnetic Geoservices ASA; *Int'l*, pg. 2353
EMGS DO BRASIL LTDA.—See Electromagnetic Geoservices ASA; *Int'l*, pg. 2353
EMGS INTERNATIONAL BV—See Electromagnetic Geoservices ASA; *Int'l*, pg. 2353
EMHART GLASS GMBH—See Bucher Industries AG; *Int'l*, pg. 1208
EMHART GLASS INC—See Bucher Industries AG; *Int'l*, pg. 1208
EMHART GLASS INTERNATIONAL SA—See Bucher Industries AG; *Int'l*, pg. 1208
EMHART GLASS JAPAN CO LTD—See Bucher Industries AG; *Int'l*, pg. 1208
EMHART GLASS LTD.—See Bucher Industries AG; *Int'l*, pg. 1208
EMHART GLASS MANUFACTURING INC.—See Bucher Industries AG; *Int'l*, pg. 1208
EMHART GLASS MANUFACTURING INC.—See Bucher Industries AG; *Int'l*, pg. 1208
EMHART GLASS OOO—See Bucher Industries AG; *Int'l*, pg. 1208
EMHART GLASS PTE. LTD.—See Bucher Industries AG; *Int'l*, pg. 1208
EMHART GLASS S.A.—See Bucher Industries AG; *Int'l*, pg. 1208
EMHART GLASS SDN BHD—See Bucher Industries AG; *Int'l*, pg. 1208
EMHART GLASS S.R.L.—See Bucher Industries AG; *Int'l*, pg. 1208
EMHART GLASS SWEDEN AB—See Bucher Industries AG; *Int'l*, pg. 1209
EMHART GLASS VISION GMBH—See Bucher Industries AG; *Int'l*, pg. 1209
EMHART HARTTUNG A/S—See Stanley Black & Decker, Inc.; *U.S. Public*, pg. 1934
EMHART TEKNOLOGIES B.V.—See Stanley Black & Decker, Inc.; *U.S. Public*, pg. 1932
EMHART TEKNOLOGIES GMBH—See Stanley Black & Decker, Inc.; *U.S. Public*, pg. 1934
EMHART TEKNOLOGIES (INDIA) PRIVATE LIMITED—See Stanley Black & Decker, Inc.; *U.S. Public*, pg. 1934
EMHART TEKNOLOGIES LLC—See Stanley Black & Decker, Inc.; *U.S. Public*, pg. 1932

EM HOLDINGS LLC—See Sumitomo Corporation; *Int'l*, pg. 7273
EMH PARTNERS GMBH; *Int'l*, pg. 2380
EMIC EQUIPAMENTOS E SISTEMAS DE ENSAIO LTDA.—See Illinois Tool Works Inc.; *U.S. Public*, pg. 1103
EMICH SUBARU WEST, LLC—See AutoNation, Inc.; *U.S. Public*, pg. 234
EMICH SUBARU WEST, LLC—See AutoNation, Inc.; *U.S. Public*, pg. 235
EMICO ASIA SDN. BHD.—See Emico Holdings Berhad; *Int'l*, pg. 2380
EMICO DEVELOPMENT SDN. BHD.—See Emico Holdings Berhad; *Int'l*, pg. 2380
EMICO HOLDINGS BERHAD; *Int'l*, pg. 2380
EMICO MARKETING SDN. BHD.—See Emico Holdings Berhad; *Int'l*, pg. 2380
EMICO MELAKA SDN. BHD.—See Emico Holdings Berhad; *Int'l*, pg. 2380
EMICO PENANG SDN. BHD.—See Emico Holdings Berhad; *Int'l*, pg. 2380
EMI CORP.; *U.S. Private*, pg. 1382
EMIDA CORPORATION; *U.S. Private*, pg. 1382
EMIDA CORPORATION—See Emida Corporation; *U.S. Private*, pg. 1382
E-MID SIM S.P.A.—See CME Group, Inc.; *U.S. Public*, pg. 518
EMIDS TECHNOLOGIES PVT. LTD. CORP. HEADQUARTERS—See emids Technologies Pvt. Ltd. Corp.; *Int'l*, pg. 2380
EMIDS TECHNOLOGIES PVT. LTD. CORP.; *Int'l*, pg. 2380
EMI/DUBLIN—See EMI Strategic Marketing, Inc.; *U.S. Private*, pg. 1382
E.M.I. - EZER MORTGAGE INSURANCE COMPANY LTD.—See Harel Insurance Investments & Financial Services Ltd.; *Int'l*, pg. 3274
EMIGH HARDWARE CO.; *U.S. Private*, pg. 1382
EMIGRANT BANK—See New York Private Bank & Trust Corporation; *U.S. Public*, pg. 2911
EMIGRANT CAPITAL CORP.—See New York Private Bank & Trust Corporation; *U.S. Public*, pg. 2911
EMIGRANT FUNDING CORPORATION—See New York Private Bank & Trust Corporation; *U.S. Public*, pg. 2911
EMIGRANT MORTGAGE COMPANY, INC.—See New York Private Bank & Trust Corporation; *U.S. Private*, pg. 2911
EMI GROUP LIMITED—See Citigroup Inc.; *U.S. Public*, pg. 504
EMI HEALTH; *U.S. Private*, pg. 1382
EMI HOLDING, INC.—See Emmaus Life Sciences, Inc.; *U.S. Public*, pg. 752
EMILAB, SRL.—See I Squared Capital Advisors (US) LLC; *U.S. Private*, pg. 2022
EMILAB, SRL.—See TDR Capital LLP; *Int'l*, pg. 7491
EMILAMERICA, INC.—See Mohawk Industries, Inc.; *U.S. Public*, pg. 1457
EMILAM INDUSTRIES LLC—See NMC Health PLC; *Int'l*, pg. 5392
EMI LATIN AMERICA INC.—See Universal Music Group N.V.; *Int'l*, pg. 8081
EMIL CAPITAL PARTNERS LLC—See Tengelmann Warenhandelsgesellschaft KG; *Int'l*, pg. 7560
EMILCERAMICA S.R.L.—See Mohawk Industries, Inc.; *U.S. Public*, pg. 1457
EMIL FREY HOLDING AG; *Int'l*, pg. 2380
EMIL FREY NEDERLAND NV—See Emil Frey Holding AG; *Int'l*, pg. 2380
EMILGERMANY GMBH—See Mohawk Industries, Inc.; *U.S. Public*, pg. 1457
EMILIA DEVELOPMENT LTD.; *Int'l*, pg. 2380
EMILIA ROMAGNA FACTOR S.P.A.—See BPER BANCA S.p.A; *Int'l*, pg. 1132
EMILIO PUCCI HONG KONG CO LTD—See LVMH Moet Hennessy Louis Vuitton SE; *Int'l*, pg. 4591
EMILIO PUCCI LTD—See LVMH Moet Hennessy Louis Vuitton SE; *Int'l*, pg. 4600
EMILIO PUCCI S.R.L.—See LVMH Moet Hennessy Louis Vuitton SE; *Int'l*, pg. 4600
EMIL LUNDGREN AB—See VINCI S.A.; *Int'l*, pg. 8237
EMIL LUX GMBH & CO. KG—See Tengelmann Warenhandelsgesellschaft KG; *Int'l*, pg. 7560
EMIL MAYR HOCH- UND TIEFBAU GMBH—See PORR AG; *Int'l*, pg. 5922
EMIL MOESTUE AS—See Schneider Electric SE; *Int'l*, pg. 6625
EMIL MULLER GMBH—See BC Partners LLP; *Int'l*, pg. 923
EMIL NICKISCH GMBH—See Wurth Verwaltungsgesellschaft mbH; *Int'l*, pg. 8504
EMIL-RO LEASING S.P.A.—See BPER BANCA S.p.A; *Int'l*, pg. 1132
EMIL VON DUNGEN INC.; *U.S. Private*, pg. 1382
EMILY CORPORATION—See GMSS Holdings, LLC; *U.S. Private*, pg. 1723
EMI MUSIC PUBLISHING (BELGIUM) SA NV—See Blackstone Inc.; *U.S. Public*, pg. 349
EMI MUSIC PUBLISHING (BELGIUM) SA NV—See Jynwel Capital Limited; *Int'l*, pg. 4035

EMI MUSIC PUBLISHING (BELGIUM) SA NV—See Mubadala Investment Company PJSC; *Int'l*, pg. 5075
EMI MUSIC PUBLISHING (BELGIUM) SA NV—See Sony Group Corporation; *Int'l*, pg. 7104
EMI MUSIC PUBLISHING CANADA—See Blackstone Inc.; *U.S. Public*, pg. 349
EMI MUSIC PUBLISHING CANADA—See Jynwel Capital Limited; *Int'l*, pg. 4035
EMI MUSIC PUBLISHING CANADA—See Mubadala Investment Company PJSC; *Int'l*, pg. 5075
EMI MUSIC PUBLISHING CANADA—See Sony Group Corporation; *Int'l*, pg. 7104
EMI MUSIC PUBLISHING CESKA REPUBLIKA, A.S.—See Blackstone Inc.; *U.S. Public*, pg. 349
EMI MUSIC PUBLISHING CESKA REPUBLIKA, A.S.—See Jynwel Capital Limited; *Int'l*, pg. 4035
EMI MUSIC PUBLISHING CESKA REPUBLIKA, A.S.—See Mubadala Investment Company PJSC; *Int'l*, pg. 5075
EMI MUSIC PUBLISHING CESKA REPUBLIKA, A.S.—See Sony Group Corporation; *Int'l*, pg. 7104
EMI MUSIC PUBLISHING CHILE—See Blackstone Inc.; *U.S. Public*, pg. 349
EMI MUSIC PUBLISHING CHILE—See Jynwel Capital Limited; *Int'l*, pg. 4036
EMI MUSIC PUBLISHING CHILE—See Mubadala Investment Company PJSC; *Int'l*, pg. 5075
EMI MUSIC PUBLISHING CHILE—See Sony Group Corporation; *Int'l*, pg. 7104
EMI MUSIC PUBLISHING DENMARK A/S—See Blackstone Inc.; *U.S. Public*, pg. 349
EMI MUSIC PUBLISHING DENMARK A/S—See Jynwel Capital Limited; *Int'l*, pg. 4036
EMI MUSIC PUBLISHING DENMARK A/S—See Mubadala Investment Company PJSC; *Int'l*, pg. 5075
EMI MUSIC PUBLISHING DENMARK A/S—See Sony Group Corporation; *Int'l*, pg. 7104
EMI MUSIC PUBLISHING (GREECE) LLC—See Blackstone Inc.; *U.S. Public*, pg. 349
EMI MUSIC PUBLISHING (GREECE) LLC—See Jynwel Capital Limited; *Int'l*, pg. 4035
EMI MUSIC PUBLISHING (GREECE) LLC—See Mubadala Investment Company PJSC; *Int'l*, pg. 5075
EMI MUSIC PUBLISHING (GREECE) LLC—See Sony Group Corporation; *Int'l*, pg. 7104
EMI MUSIC PUBLISHING (HOLLAND) B.V.—See Blackstone Inc.; *U.S. Public*, pg. 349
EMI MUSIC PUBLISHING (HOLLAND) B.V.—See Jynwel Capital Limited; *Int'l*, pg. 4035
EMI MUSIC PUBLISHING (HOLLAND) B.V.—See Mubadala Investment Company PJSC; *Int'l*, pg. 5075
EMI MUSIC PUBLISHING (HOLLAND) B.V.—See Sony Group Corporation; *Int'l*, pg. 7104
EMI MUSIC PUBLISHING HONG KONG—See Blackstone Inc.; *U.S. Public*, pg. 349
EMI MUSIC PUBLISHING HONG KONG—See Jynwel Capital Limited; *Int'l*, pg. 4036
EMI MUSIC PUBLISHING HONG KONG—See Mubadala Investment Company PJSC; *Int'l*, pg. 5075
EMI MUSIC PUBLISHING HONG KONG—See Sony Group Corporation; *Int'l*, pg. 7104
EMI MUSIC PUBLISHING ITALIA SRL—See Blackstone Inc.; *U.S. Public*, pg. 349
EMI MUSIC PUBLISHING ITALIA SRL—See Jynwel Capital Limited; *Int'l*, pg. 4036
EMI MUSIC PUBLISHING ITALIA SRL—See Mubadala Investment Company PJSC; *Int'l*, pg. 5075
EMI MUSIC PUBLISHING ITALIA SRL—See Sony Group Corporation; *Int'l*, pg. 7104
EMI MUSIC PUBLISHING LTD.—See Blackstone Inc.; *U.S. Public*, pg. 349
EMI MUSIC PUBLISHING LTD.—See Jynwel Capital Limited; *Int'l*, pg. 4036
EMI MUSIC PUBLISHING LTD.—See Mubadala Investment Company PJSC; *Int'l*, pg. 5075
EMI MUSIC PUBLISHING LTD.—See Sony Group Corporation; *Int'l*, pg. 7104
EMI MUSIC PUBLISHING MALAYSIA SDN BHD—See Blackstone Inc.; *U.S. Public*, pg. 349
EMI MUSIC PUBLISHING MALAYSIA SDN BHD—See Jynwel Capital Limited; *Int'l*, pg. 4036
EMI MUSIC PUBLISHING MALAYSIA SDN BHD—See Mubadala Investment Company PJSC; *Int'l*, pg. 5075
EMI MUSIC PUBLISHING MALAYSIA SDN BHD—See Sony Group Corporation; *Int'l*, pg. 7104
EMI MUSIC PUBLISHING MEXICO—See Blackstone Inc.; *U.S. Public*, pg. 349
EMI MUSIC PUBLISHING MEXICO—See Jynwel Capital Limited; *Int'l*, pg. 4036
EMI MUSIC PUBLISHING MEXICO—See Mubadala Investment Company PJSC; *Int'l*, pg. 5075
EMI MUSIC PUBLISHING MEXICO—See Sony Group Corporation; *Int'l*, pg. 7104
EMI MUSIC PUBLISHING PORTUGAL—See Blackstone Inc.; *U.S. Public*, pg. 349
EMI MUSIC PUBLISHING PORTUGAL—See Jynwel Capital Limited; *Int'l*, pg. 4036
EMI MUSIC PUBLISHING PORTUGAL—See Mubadala Investment Company PJSC; *Int'l*, pg. 5075

EMIL VON DUNGEN INC.
CORPORATE AFFILIATIONS

EMI MUSIC PUBLISHING PORTUGAL—See Sony Group Corporation; *Int'l*, pg. 7104
EMI MUSIC PUBLISHING SCANDINAVIA AB—See Blackstone Inc.; *U.S. Public*, pg. 349
EMI MUSIC PUBLISHING SCANDINAVIA AB—See Jynwel Capital Limited; *Int'l*, pg. 4036
EMI MUSIC PUBLISHING SCANDINAVIA AB—See Mubadala Investment Company PJSC; *Int'l*, pg. 5075
EMI MUSIC PUBLISHING SCANDINAVIA AB—See Sony Group Corporation; *Int'l*, pg. 7104
EMI MUSIC PUBLISHING—See Blackstone Inc.; *U.S. Public*, pg. 349
EMI MUSIC PUBLISHING—See Jynwel Capital Limited; *Int'l*, pg. 4035
EMI MUSIC PUBLISHING—See Mubadala Investment Company PJSC; *Int'l*, pg. 5075
EMI MUSIC PUBLISHING—See Sony Group Corporation; *Int'l*, pg. 7104
EMI MUSIC PUBLISHING SPAIN—See Blackstone Inc.; *U.S. Public*, pg. 349
EMI MUSIC PUBLISHING SPAIN—See Jynwel Capital Limited; *Int'l*, pg. 4036
EMI MUSIC PUBLISHING SPAIN—See Mubadala Investment Company PJSC; *Int'l*, pg. 5075
EMI MUSIC PUBLISHING SPAIN—See Sony Group Corporation; *Int'l*, pg. 7104
EMINENCE BENELUX S.A.—See GMM Capital LLC; *U.S. Private*, pg. 1723
EMINENCE ENTERPRISE LIMITED—See Easyknit International Holdings Ltd.; *Int'l*, pg. 2276
EMINENCE ORGANIC SKIN CARE INC.; *Int'l*, pg. 2380
EMINENCE S.A.S.—See GMM Capital LLC; *U.S. Private*, pg. 1723
EMINENCE SPEAKER LLC.—See B&C Speakers SpA; *Int'l*, pg. 784
EMINENT ELECTRONIC TECHNOLOGY,CO., LTD.—See ELAN Microelectronic Corp.; *Int'l*, pg. 2342
EMINENT EUROPE B.V.—See TKH Group N.V.; *Int'l*, pg. 7764
EMINENT GOLD CORP.; *Int'l*, pg. 2380
EMINENT LUGGAGE CORP.; *Int'l*, pg. 2381
EMINENT PEDESTAL SDN. BHD—See Eastern & Oriental Berhad; *Int'l*, pg. 2271
EMINENT TECHNOLOGY SOLUTIONS, INC.; *U.S. Private*, pg. 1382
EMINIS AMBALAJ SANAYI VE TICARET A.S.; *Int'l*, pg. 2381
EMIN TEKNIK HORTUM VE MAKINE AS—See NIBE Industrier AB; *Int'l*, pg. 5260
E&M INTERNATIONAL, INC.—See Chenega Corporation; *U.S. Private*, pg. 872
EMI PANAMA S.A.—See Lundbeckfonden; *Int'l*, pg. 4580
EMIRA PROPERTY FUND; *Int'l*, pg. 2381
EMIRATE INTEGRATED TELECOMMUNICATIONS COMPANY PJSC; *Int'l*, pg. 2381
EMIRATES ADVANCED INVESTMENTS GROUP LLC; *Int'l*, pg. 2381
EMIRATES BUILDING SYSTEMS COMPANY LLC—See Dubai Investments PJSC; *Int'l*, pg. 2219
EMIRATES CEMENT LLC; *Int'l*, pg. 2381
EMIRATES CMS POWER COMPANY—See Abu Dhabi Water & Electricity Authority; *Int'l*, pg. 73
EMIRATES COLD STORAGE COMPANY—See Bhatia Brothers Group; *Int'l*, pg. 1014
EMIRATES CUISINE SOLUTIONS LLC—See The Emirates Group; *Int'l*, pg. 7639
EMIRATES DEFENCE INDUSTRIES COMPANY—See Mubadala Investment Company PJSC; *Int'l*, pg. 5074
EMIRATES DISTRICT COOLING COMPANY LLC—See Dubai Investments PJSC; *Int'l*, pg. 2219
EMIRATES DRIVING COMPANY PJSC; *Int'l*, pg. 2381
EMIRATES DRIVING INSTITUTE—See Belhasa Group of Companies; *Int'l*, pg. 964
EMIRATES ENVIRONMENTAL GROUP; *Int'l*, pg. 2381
EMIRATES EXTRUDED POLYSTYRENE LLC—See Dubai Investments PJSC; *Int'l*, pg. 2219
EMIRATES EXTRUSIONS FACTORY LLC—See Dubai Investments PJSC; *Int'l*, pg. 2218
EMIRATES FLIGHT CATERING COMPANY L.L.C.—See The Emirates Group; *Int'l*, pg. 7639
EMIRATES FLOAT GLASS LLC—See Dubai Investments PJSC; *Int'l*, pg. 2219
EMIRATES FOR INFORMATION TECHNOLOGY CO.—See Softlab S.p.A.; *Int'l*, pg. 7055
EMIRATES GAS LLC—See Emirates National Oil Company Limited; *Int'l*, pg. 2381
EMIRATES GATEWAY SECURITIES SERVICES LLC—See Alpha Dhabi Holding PJSC; *Int'l*, pg. 367
EMIRATES GLASS LLC—See Dubai Investments PJSC; *Int'l*, pg. 2219
EMIRATES GLOBAL ALUMINIUM PJSC; *Int'l*, pg. 2381
THE EMIRATES GROUP; *Int'l*, pg. 7638
EMIRATES HOTELS (AUSTRALIA) PTY LTD.—See The Emirates Group; *Int'l*, pg. 7639
EMIRATES INSURANCE COMPANY; *Int'l*, pg. 2381
EMIRATES INTERNATIONAL TELECOMMUNICATIONS LLC—See Dubai Holding LLC; *Int'l*, pg. 2219
EMIRATES INVESTMENT BANK P.J.S.C.—See Al-Futtaim Private Company LLC; *Int'l*, pg. 285

EMIRATES INVESTMENT & DEVELOPMENT COMPANY PSC; *Int'l*, pg. 2381
EMIRATES INVESTMENT SERVICES LTD—See Emirates NBD PJSC; *Int'l*, pg. 2382
EMIRATES ISLAMIC BANK PJSC; *Int'l*, pg. 2381
EMIRATES LEBANON BANK S.A.L.—See Bank of Sharjah P.S.C.; *Int'l*, pg. 848
EMIRATES LEISURE RETAIL (AUSTRALIA) PTY LTD.—See The Emirates Group; *Int'l*, pg. 7639
EMIRATES LEISURE RETAIL LLC—See The Emirates Group; *Int'l*, pg. 7639
EMIRATES LEISURE RETAIL (SINGAPORE) PTE. LTD.—See The Emirates Group; *Int'l*, pg. 7639
EMIRATES MOTOR CO.—See Al Fahim Group; *Int'l*, pg. 277
EMIRATES NATIONAL ELECTROMECHANICAL L.L.C.—See Finance House P.J.S.C.; *Int'l*, pg. 2664
EMIRATES NATIONAL OIL COMPANY LIMITED; *Int'l*, pg. 2381
EMIRATES NATIONAL OIL COMPANY SINGAPORE PTE LTD—See Emirates National Oil Company Limited; *Int'l*, pg. 2381
EMIRATES NBD ASSET MANAGEMENT LTD—See Emirates NBD PJSC; *Int'l*, pg. 2382
EMIRATES NBD BANK PJSC—See Emirates NBD PJSC; *Int'l*, pg. 2382
EMIRATES NBD CAPITAL KSA LLC—See Emirates NBD PJSC; *Int'l*, pg. 2382
EMIRATES NBD CAPITAL LTD.—See Emirates NBD PJSC; *Int'l*, pg. 2382
EMIRATES NBD PJSC; *Int'l*, pg. 2381
EMIRATES NBD SECURITIES LLC—See Emirates NBD PJSC; *Int'l*, pg. 2382
EMIRATES NBD TRUST COMPANY (JERSEY) LIMITED—See Emirates NBD PJSC; *Int'l*, pg. 2382
EMIRATES PETROLEUM PRODUCTS COMPANY LLC—See Emirates National Oil Company Limited; *Int'l*, pg. 2381
EMIRATES POST; *Int'l*, pg. 2382
EMIRATES PRE-INSULATED PIPES INDUSTRIES LLC—See National Central Cooling Company PJSC; *Int'l*, pg. 5155
EMIRATES PROPERTIES REIT; *Int'l*, pg. 2382
EMIRATES PROPERTY INVESTMENT CO.—See Al Fahim Group; *Int'l*, pg. 277
EMIRATES REEM INVESTMENTS COMPANY P.J.S.C; *Int'l*, pg. 2382
EMIRATES REIT (CEIC) PLC; *Int'l*, pg. 2382
EMIRATES SAFETY LABORATORY LLC—See Alpha Dhabi Holding PJSC; *Int'l*, pg. 367
EMIRATES STALLIONS PROPERTIES LLC—See International Holdings Company PJSC; *Int'l*, pg. 3750
EMIRATES STAR SERVICES LLC—See Mezzan Holding Co KSC; *Int'l*, pg. 4870
EMIRATES TECHNO CASTING FZE—See Pentair plc; *Int'l*, pg. 5789
EMIRATES TECHNO CASTING LLC—See Pentair plc; *Int'l*, pg. 5789
EMIRATES TECHNOLOGY COMPANY (EMITAC); *Int'l*, pg. 2382
EMIRATES TELECOMMUNICATIONS GROUP COMPAPNY PJSC; *Int'l*, pg. 2382
EMIRATES TELECOMMUNICATIONS & MARINE SERVICES FZE—See Emirates Telecommunications Group Company PJSC; *Int'l*, pg. 2382
EMIRATES THERMOSTONE FACTORY LLC—See Dubai Investments PJSC; *Int'l*, pg. 2219
EMIRATES WESTERN PETROLEUM SERVICES—See Senergy Holding Company K.P.S.C.; *Int'l*, pg. 6707
EMI RECORDED MUSIC AUSTRALIA PTY. LTD.—See Universal Music Group N.V.; *Int'l*, pg. 8081
EMI RECORDED MUSIC NORTH AMERICA—See Universal Music Group N.V.; *Int'l*, pg. 8081
EMI RECORDS (IRELAND) LTD.—See Universal Music Group N.V.; *Int'l*, pg. 8081
EMIRIAN S.A.I.C.F.I.R.—See Stanley Black & Decker, Inc.; *U.S. Public*, pg. 1932
EMIR OIL, LLP—See MIE Holdings Corporation; *Int'l*, pg. 4888
EMISENSE TECHNOLOGIES, LLC—See CoorsTek, Inc.; *U.S. Private*, pg. 1044
EMIS GROUP PLC; *Int'l*, pg. 2382
E. MISHAN & SONS, INC.; *U.S. Private*, pg. 1304
EMIS HEALTH—See EMIS Group plc; *Int'l*, pg. 2382
EMISPHERE TECHNOLOGIES, INC.—See Novo Nordisk Fonden; *Int'l*, pg. 5463
EMISSION ADVISORS, INC.—See AEGIS Hedging Solutions, LLC; *U.S. Private*, pg. 116
EMISSION PARTICLE SOLUTION SWEDEN AB—See De-Tai New Energy Group Limited; *Int'l*, pg. 2047
EMI STRATEGIC MARKETING, INC.; *U.S. Private*, pg. 1382
EMITEC AG—See Yokogawa Electric Corporation; *Int'l*, pg. 8592
EMITEC GESELLSCHAFT FUR EMISSIONSTECHNOLOGIE MBH—See INA-Holding Schaeffler GmbH & Co. KG; *Int'l*, pg. 3641
EMITEC JAPAN K.K.—See INA-Holding Schaeffler GmbH & Co. KG; *Int'l*, pg. 3641

EMITEC KOREA INC.—See INA-Holding Schaeffler GmbH & Co. KG; *Int'l*, pg. 3641
EMI TERTIAIRE SAS—See VINCI S.A.; *Int'l*, pg. 8217
EMIT S.A.—See Cantoni Motor S.A.; *Int'l*, pg. 1299
EMI-TUV SUD KFT.—See TUV SUD AG; *Int'l*, pg. 7984
EMIVEST AEROSPACE CORPORATION—See Emirates Investment & Development Company PSC; *Int'l*, pg. 2381
EMIVEST BERHAD; *Int'l*, pg. 2383
EMIVEST FEEDMILL VIETNAM CO., LIMITED—See Leong Hup International Berhad; *Int'l*, pg. 4461
EMJ CORPORATION; *U.S. Private*, pg. 1382
EMKA BENELUX B.V.—See EMKA-Beschlagteile GmbH & Co. KG; *Int'l*, pg. 2383
EMKA BESCHLAGTEILE AG—See EMKA-Beschlagteile GmbH & Co. KG; *Int'l*, pg. 2383
EMKA BESCHLAGTEILE GES.M.B.H.—See EMKA-Beschlagteile GmbH & Co. KG; *Int'l*, pg. 2383
EMKA-BESCHLAGTEILE GMBH & CO. KG; *Int'l*, pg. 2383
EMKA BESCHLAGTEILE IBERICA S.L.—See EMKA-Beschlagteile GmbH & Co. KG; *Int'l*, pg. 2383
EMKA BESCHLAGTEILE SRL—See EMKA-Beschlagteile GmbH & Co. KG; *Int'l*, pg. 2383
EMKA BOSNIA D.O.O.—See EMKA-Beschlagteile GmbH & Co. KG; *Int'l*, pg. 2383
EMKA FRANCE SA—See EMKA-Beschlagteile GmbH & Co. KG; *Int'l*, pg. 2383
EMKA HELLAS S.A.—See EMKA-Beschlagteile GmbH & Co. KG; *Int'l*, pg. 2383
EMKA INC.—See EMKA-Beschlagteile GmbH & Co. KG; *Int'l*, pg. 2383
EMKA INDIA PANEL ACCESSORIES PVT LTD—See EMKA-Beschlagteile GmbH & Co. KG; *Int'l*, pg. 2383
EMKA INDUSTRIAL HARDWARE CO. LTD.—See EMKA-Beschlagteile GmbH & Co. KG; *Int'l*, pg. 2383
EMKA ITALIA S.R.L.—See EMKA-Beschlagteile GmbH & Co. KG; *Int'l*, pg. 2383
EMKA JSC; *Int'l*, pg. 2383
EMKA KILIT SISTEMLERI METAL SAN. VE TIC. LTD. STI.—See EMKA-Beschlagteile GmbH & Co. KG; *Int'l*, pg. 2383
EMKA MEXICO BESCHLAGTEILE S. DE R.L. DE C.V.—See EMKA-Beschlagteile GmbH & Co. KG; *Int'l*, pg. 2383
EMKA MIDDLE EAST LLC—See EMKA-Beschlagteile GmbH & Co. KG; *Int'l*, pg. 2383
EMKA OKOVI D.O.O.—See EMKA-Beschlagteile GmbH & Co. KG; *Int'l*, pg. 2383
EMKA POLSKA SP. Z. O. O.—See EMKA-Beschlagteile GmbH & Co. KG; *Int'l*, pg. 2383
EMKA SCANDINAVIA AB—See EMKA-Beschlagteile GmbH & Co. KG; *Int'l*, pg. 2383
EMKAT SOLUTIONS, INC.; *U.S. Private*, pg. 1383
EMKA (UK) LTD.—See EMKA-Beschlagteile GmbH & Co. KG; *Int'l*, pg. 2383
EMKAY GLOBAL FINANCIAL SERVICES LIMITED; *Int'l*, pg. 2383
EMKAY, INC.; *U.S. Private*, pg. 1383
EMKAY TAPS & CUTTING TOOLS LTD.; *Int'l*, pg. 2383
EMK CONSULTANTS OF FLORIDA, INC.; *U.S. Private*, pg. 1383
EMKEY ENERGY, LLC; *U.S. Private*, pg. 1383
EMKON AUTOMATION GMBH—See OPTIMA Packaging Group GmbH; *Int'l*, pg. 5603
EM KOREA CO., LTD.; *Int'l*, pg. 2372
EMLAB P&K LLC—See Eurofins Scientific S.E.; *Int'l*, pg. 2536
EMLAK KATILIM VARLIK KIRALAMA A.S.; *Int'l*, pg. 2384
EMLAK KONUT ASANSOR SISTEMLERI SANAYI VE TICARET A.S.—See Emlak Konut Gayrimenkul Yatirim Ortakligi AS; *Int'l*, pg. 2384
EMLAK KONUT GAYRIMENKUL YATIRIM ORTAKLIGI AS; *Int'l*, pg. 2384
E.M. LAWRENCE LTD.; *U.S. Private*, pg. 1306
EML PAYMENTS LIMITED; *Int'l*, pg. 2383
EML PAYMENT SOLUTIONS LIMITED—See EML Payments Limited; *Int'l*, pg. 2383
EMMABODA GLAS AB—See Compagnie de Saint-Gobain SA; *Int'l*, pg. 1734
EMMA, INC.; *U.S. Private*, pg. 1383
EMMAR INVESTMENTS & REAL ESTATE DEVELOPMENT COMPANY; *Int'l*, pg. 2384
EMMA SAFETY FOOTWEAR B.V.—See Investment AB Latour; *Int'l*, pg. 3781
EMMAUS LIFE SCIENCES, INC.; *U.S. Public*, pg. 752
EMMAUS PACK S.R.L.—See Apollo Global Management, Inc.; *U.S. Public*, pg. 159
EMMA VILLAS S.P.A.; *Int'l*, pg. 2384
EMMBI INDUSTRIES LIMITED; *Int'l*, pg. 2384
EMMECOM S.R.L.—See Cassa Depositi e Prestiti S.p.A.; *Int'l*, pg. 1354
E&M MEDIA GROUP—See E&M Advertising; *U.S. Private*, pg. 1301
EMMEDI S.A.—See IVS Group S.A.; *Int'l*, pg. 3848
EMMEDI S.R.L.—See Sesa S.p.A.; *Int'l*, pg. 6728
EMMEGI DEUTSCHLAND GMBH—See Cifin S.r.l.; *Int'l*, pg. 1605

COMPANY NAME INDEX

EMMEGI DO BRASIL LTDA—See Cifin S.r.l.; *Int'l*, pg. 1606
EMMEGI IBERICA, S.A.—See Cifin S.r.l.; *Int'l*, pg. 1605
EMMEGI SCANDINAVIA AB—See Cifin S.r.l.; *Int'l*, pg. 1605
EMMEGI SCANDINAVIA AB—See Cifin S.r.l.; *Int'l*, pg. 1606
EMMEGISOFT SRL.—See Cifin S.r.l.; *Int'l*, pg. 1606
EMMEGI S.P.A.—See Cifin S.r.l.; *Int'l*, pg. 1605
EMMEGI SUISSE SA—See Cifin S.r.l.; *Int'l*, pg. 1606
EMMEGI (SUZHOU) CO., LTD.—See Cifin S.r.l.; *Int'l*, pg. 1605
EMMEGI TURK—See Cifin S.r.l.; *Int'l*, pg. 1606
EMMEGI (UK) LTD.—See Cifin S.r.l.; *Int'l*, pg. 1605
EMME INC.—See SimpleHealth, Inc.; *U.S. Private*, pg. 3667
EMME KIES + BETON AG—See Vicat S.A.; *Int'l*, pg. 8185
EMMENDINGER MASCHINENBAU GMBH; *Int'l*, pg. 2384
EMMER DEVELOPMENT CORP.; *U.S. Private*, pg. 1383
EMMERSON PLC; *Int'l*, pg. 2384
EMMERSON RESOURCES LIMITED; *Int'l*, pg. 2384
EMMERT INDUSTRIAL CORPORATION; *U.S. Private*, pg. 1383
THE EMMES COMPANY, LLC—See Behrman Brothers Management Corp.; *U.S. Private*, pg. 515
EMMESSAR BIOTECH & NUTRITION LTD.; *Int'l*, pg. 2384
EMMETI S.P.A.—See Rettig Group Ltd.; *Int'l*, pg. 6310
EMMETI UK LTD.—See Rettig Group Ltd.; *Int'l*, pg. 6310
EMMETSBURG BANK SHARES, INC.; *U.S. Private*, pg. 1383
EMMETSBURG FOOD PRIDE GROCERY & DELI INC.; *U.S. Private*, pg. 1383
EMMETSBURG PUBLISHING CO.—See The Nutting Company, Inc.; *U.S. Private*, pg. 4086
EMMI AG; *Int'l*, pg. 2384
EMMI BENELUX B.V.—See Emmi AG; *Int'l*, pg. 2384
EMMI CANADA INC.—See Emmi AG; *Int'l*, pg. 2384
EM MICROELECTRONIC-MARIN S.A.—See The Swatch Group Ltd.; *Int'l*, pg. 7691
EM MICROELECTRONIC - US INC.—See The Swatch Group Ltd.; *Int'l*, pg. 7693
EMMI DESSERT ITALIA S.P.A—See Emmi AG; *Int'l*, pg. 2384
EMMI DEUTSCHLAND GMBH—See Emmi AG; *Int'l*, pg. 2384
EMMI OSTERREICH GMBH—See Emmi AG; *Int'l*, pg. 2384
EMMI ROTH USA INC.—See Emmi AG; *Int'l*, pg. 2384
EMMI ROTH USA INC.—See Emmi AG; *Int'l*, pg. 2384
EMMIS AUSTIN RADIO BROADCASTING COMPANY, L.P.; *U.S. Private*, pg. 1383
EMMIS COMMUNICATIONS CORPORATION; *U.S. Public*, pg. 753
EMMIS INDIANA BROADCASTING, L.P.—See Emmis Communications Corporation; *U.S. Public*, pg. 753
EMMIS MEADOWLANDS CORPORATION—See Emmis Communications Corporation; *U.S. Public*, pg. 753
EMMI SOLUTIONS, LLC—See Wolters Kluwer n.v.; *Int'l*, pg. 8444
EMMIS OPERATING COMPANY—See Emmis Communications Corporation; *U.S. Public*, pg. 753
EMMIS PUBLISHING CORPORATION—See Emmis Communications Corporation; *U.S. Public*, pg. 753
EMMIS PUBLISHING, L.P.—See Emmis Communications Corporation; *U.S. Public*, pg. 753
EMMIS RADIO, L.L.C.—See Emmis Communications Corporation; *U.S. Public*, pg. 753
EMMI UK LIMITED—See Emmi AG; *Int'l*, pg. 2384
EMMONS BUSINESS INTERIORS LLC; *U.S. Private*, pg. 1383
EMMSONS ASIA PTE. LTD.—See Emmsons International Limited; *Int'l*, pg. 2385
EMMSONS INTERNATIONAL LIMITED; *Int'l*, pg. 2385
EMMTEC SERVICES B.V.—See GETEC Energie Holding GmbH; *Int'l*, pg. 2947
EMMY BUILDING CO. INC.; *U.S. Private*, pg. 1383
EMMY TECHNOLOGY DEVELOPMENT LIMITED—See China-Hong Kong Photo Products Holdings Limited; *Int'l*, pg. 1568
EMN ACQUISITION CORPORATION—See RMG Networks Holding Corporation; *U.S. Private*, pg. 3451
EMNET INC.; *Int'l*, pg. 2385
EMNET JAPAN CO., LTD.—See eMnet Inc.; *Int'l*, pg. 2385
EMNI CO., LTD; *Int'l*, pg. 2385
EMNOS GMBH—See Clayton, Dubilier & Rice, LLC; *U.S. Private*, pg. 926
EMNOS IBERIA S.L—See American Express Company; *U.S. Public*, pg. 102
EMNOS S.A.R.L.—See American Express Company; *U.S. Public*, pg. 102
EMNOS UK LTD.—See American Express Company; *U.S. Public*, pg. 102
EMNOS USA CORP.—See American Express Company; *U.S. Public*, pg. 102
EMO AS—See Sycamore Partners Management, LP; *U.S. Private*, pg. 3896
EMO AUSTRALASIA NZ LTD—See Emo-Trans Inc.; *U.S. Private*, pg. 1383

E-MOBILITY POWER CO., INC.—See Tokyo Electric Power Company Holdings, Incorporated; *Int'l*, pg. 7790
EMO ENERGY SOLUTIONS, LLC—See Lilker Associates Consulting Engineers, PC; *U.S. Private*, pg. 2455
EMO-FARM LTD.—See Bausch Health Companies Inc.; *Int'l*, pg. 897
E'MOLD HOLDING PTE. LTD.—See Accrelist Ltd.; *Int'l*, pg. 93
E'MOLD MANUFACTURING (KUNSHAN) CO., LTD.—See Accrelist Ltd.; *Int'l*, pg. 93
EMOLECULES, INC.—See Avista Capital Partners, L.P.; *U.S. Private*, pg. 409
EMOLEUM ROADS GROUP PTY LIMITED—See Downer EDI Limited; *Int'l*, pg. 2186
EMONECO, INC.; *U.S. Private*, pg. 1383
EMONEY ADVISOR, LLC—See FMR LLC; *U.S. Private*, pg. 1555
EMO OIL LIMITED—See DCC plc; *Int'l*, pg. 1990
EMORI & CO., (HONG KONG) LTD.—See Kowa Co., Ltd.; *Int'l*, pg. 4294
EMORI & CO., LTD.—See Kowa Co., Ltd.; *Int'l*, pg. 4293
EMORI ENGINEERING CO., LTD.—See Nicca Chemical Co., Ltd.; *Int'l*, pg. 5263
EMORI INFORMATION SYSTEM BLDG.—See Kowa Co., Ltd.; *Int'l*, pg. 4294
EMORI LOGISTICS CO., LTD.—See Kowa Co., Ltd.; *Int'l*, pg. 4294
EMORI PAINT CO., LTD.—See Kowa Co., Ltd.; *Int'l*, pg. 4294
EMORI POLAND SP. Z O.O.—See Kowa Co., Ltd.; *Int'l*, pg. 4294
EMORI (THAILAND) CO., LTD.—See Kowa Co., Ltd.; *Int'l*, pg. 4294
E. MORRIS COMMUNICATIONS, INC.; *U.S. Private*, pg. 1304
EMORTGAGE LOGIC, LLC—See Assurant, Inc.; *U.S. Public*, pg. 215
EMORY ALLIANCE CREDIT UNION—See Credit Union 1; *U.S. Private*, pg. 1091
EMORY BANCSHARES, INC.; *U.S. Private*, pg. 1383
EMORY ELECTRIC INC.; *U.S. Private*, pg. 1383
EMORY JOHNS CREEK HOSPITAL—See HCA Healthcare, Inc.; *U.S. Public*, pg. 995
EMOS LTD.—See AKRITAS S.A.; *Int'l*, pg. 264
EMO; *Int'l*, pg. 2385
E. MOSS, LIMITED—See Walgreens Boots Alliance, Inc.; *U.S. Public*, pg. 2322
EMOSS MOBILE SYSTEMS B.V.—See Precision Camshafts Limited; *Int'l*, pg. 5957
EMOTION KAYAKS, INC.—See Lifetime Products Inc.; *U.S. Private*, pg. 2451
EMOTIVA AUDIO CORPORATION—See Jade Design, Inc.; *U.S. Private*, pg. 2181
EMOTIVA PROFESSIONAL, LLC—See Jade Design, Inc.; *U.S. Private*, pg. 2181
E-MOTIVE DISPLAY PTE. LIMITED—See Halma plc; *Int'l*, pg. 3231
EMO TRANS (CANADA) FREIGHT LTD.—See Emo-Trans Inc.; *U.S. Private*, pg. 1383
EMO-TRANS GMBH—See Emo-Trans Inc.; *U.S. Private*, pg. 1383
EMO-TRANS INC.; *U.S. Private*, pg. 1383
EMO TRANS KOREA CO LTD—See Emo-Trans Inc.; *U.S. Private*, pg. 1383
EMO TRANS PERU S.A.C.—See Emo-Trans Inc.; *U.S. Private*, pg. 1383
EMOVA GROUP; *Int'l*, pg. 2385
EMOVE, INC.—See U-Haul Holding Company; *U.S. Public*, pg. 2211
EMOVIS OPERATIONS IRELAND LIMITED—See ACS, Actividades de Construccion y Servicios, S.A.; *Int'l*, pg. 112
EMOZE LTD.—See B.S.D. Crown Ltd.; *Int'l*, pg. 790
EMPACADORA ECUATORIANO DANESA (ECUADASA) S.A.—See EAC Invest AS; *Int'l*, pg. 2261
EMPACO EQUIPMENT CORP.; *U.S. Private*, pg. 1384
EMPAKK AS—See Christian Berner Tech Trade AB; *Int'l*, pg. 1586
EMPA S.A.—See Teixeira Duarte SA; *Int'l*, pg. 7525
EMPA STRUCTURES (PTY) LTD.—See Raubex Group Limited; *Int'l*, pg. 6221
EMPATH PARTNERS IN CARE; *U.S. Private*, pg. 1384
EMPAYAR INDERA SDN BHD—See Protasco Berhad; *Int'l*, pg. 6003
EMPCO-LITE INC.—See Elgin Molded Plastics Inc.; *U.S. Private*, pg. 1359
EMP. CONST. MOLLER Y PEREZ-COTAPOS S.A.; *Int'l*, pg. 2385
EMPEE DISTILLERIES LIMITED; *Int'l*, pg. 2385
EMPEE SUGARS & CHEMICALS LTD.; *Int'l*, pg. 2385
EMPEIRIA CAPITAL PARTNERS LLC; *U.S. Private*, pg. 1384
EMPEOPLE CREDIT UNION; *U.S. Private*, pg. 1384
EMPERADOR DISTILLERS, INC—See Alliance Global Group, Inc.; *Int'l*, pg. 339
EMPERADOR INC.—See Alliance Global Group, Inc.; *Int'l*, pg. 339
EMPERIA HOLDING S.A; *Int'l*, pg. 2385

EMPERIA INFO SP. Z O.O.—See Emperia Holding S.A; *Int'l*, pg. 2385
EMPERIAL AMERICAS, INC.; *U.S. Private*, pg. 1384
EMPEROR CAPITAL GROUP LIMITED; *Int'l*, pg. 2386
EMPEROR CULTURE GROUP LIMITED; *Int'l*, pg. 2386
EMPEROR ENERGY LIMITED; *Int'l*, pg. 2386
EMPEROR ENTERTAINMENT HOTEL LIMITED; *Int'l*, pg. 2386
EMPEROR GLOBAL RESOURCES LLC—See Shenzhen Emperor Technology Co., Ltd.; *Int'l*, pg. 6808
THE EMPEROR HOTEL LIMITED—See Emperor International Holdings Limited; *Int'l*, pg. 2386
EMPEROR INTERNATIONAL HOLDINGS LIMITED; *Int'l*, pg. 2386
EMPEROR METALS INC.; *Int'l*, pg. 2386
EMPEROR OIL LTD.; *Int'l*, pg. 2386
EMPEROR PAPER INDUSTRIES LTD.; *U.S. Private*, pg. 1384
EMPEROR'S KITCHEN SDN BHD—See JAB Holding Company S.a.r.l.; *Int'l*, pg. 3863
EMPEROR WATCH & JEWELLERY (HK) COMPANY LIMITED—See Emperor Watch & Jewellery Limited; *Int'l*, pg. 2386
EMPEROR WATCH & JEWELLERY LIMITED; *Int'l*, pg. 2386
EMP FRAS- UND MESSTECHNIK GMBH—See Fair Friend Group; *Int'l*, pg. 2604
EMP GLOBAL LLC; *U.S. Private*, pg. 1383
EMPHASIS SERVICES LIMITED—See AsianLogic Limited; *Int'l*, pg. 620
EMPHASYS COMPUTER SOLUTIONS, INC.—See Constellation Software Inc.; *Int'l*, pg. 1772
EMPHASYS SOFTWARE INC.—See Constellation Software Inc.; *Int'l*, pg. 1772
EMPHASYS TECHNOLOGIES, INC.—See Ocorian Limited; *Int'l*, pg. 5520
EMPHOR FZCO; *Int'l*, pg. 2386
EMPHYSYS, INC.—See Tecan Group AG; *Int'l*, pg. 7501
EMPICA LTD.; *Int'l*, pg. 2386
EMPIE, INC.; *U.S. Private*, pg. 1384
EMPI, INC.—See Enovis Corporation; *U.S. Public*, pg. 772
EMPIK SP. Z O.O.—See Penta Investments Limited; *Int'l*, pg. 5788
EMPILHADORES DE PORTUGAL (CENTRO) LDA—See Manitou BF S.A.; *Int'l*, pg. 4672
EMPIRE AERO CENTER—See Israel Aerospace Industries Ltd.; *Int'l*, pg. 3822
EMPIRE AEROSPACE—See Empire Airlines; *U.S. Private*, pg. 1384
EMPIRE AIRLINES; *U.S. Private*, pg. 1384
EMPIRE AUTOMATION SYSTEMS INC; *U.S. Private*, pg. 1384
EMPIRE BANCORP, INC.—See Flushing Financial Corporation; *U.S. Public*, pg. 860
EMPIRE BLUE CROSS & BLUE SHIELD—See Elevance Health, Inc.; *U.S. Public*, pg. 730
EMPIRE BUILDING & ENVIRONMENTAL SERVICES; *U.S. Private*, pg. 1384
EMPIRE BUILDING MATERIALS INC.; *U.S. Private*, pg. 1384
EMPIRE BUS SALES, LLC—See Beam Mack Sales & Service, Inc.; *U.S. Private*, pg. 506
EMPIRE CANDLE COMPANY, LLC; *U.S. Private*, pg. 1384
EMPIRECARE HEALTH ASSOCIATES, INC.—See The Ensign Group, Inc.; *U.S. Public*, pg. 2070
EMPIRE CHEESE, INC.—See The Great Lakes Cheese Co., Inc.; *U.S. Private*, pg. 4038
EMPIRE CITY IRON WORKS; *U.S. Private*, pg. 1384
EMPIRECLS WORLDWIDE CHAUFFEURED SERVICES—See GTS Holdings, Inc.; *U.S. Private*, pg. 1807
EMPIRE COMMERCIAL & INDUSTRIAL CORPORATION; *U.S. Private*, pg. 1384
EMPIRE COMPANY LIMITED; *Int'l*, pg. 2386
THE EMPIRE COMPANY, LLC—See Hardwoods Distribution Inc.; *Int'l*, pg. 3273
THE EMPIRE CRANE COMPANY, LLC—See Bigge Crane & Rigging Company; *U.S. Private*, pg. 555
EMPIRE CROSSING RETIREMENT COMMUNITY INC.—See Extendicare Inc.; *U.S. Private*, pg. 2591
EMPIRE DENMARK APS—See Kakel Max AB; *Int'l*, pg. 4056
EMPIRE DIAMOND CORPORATION; *U.S. Private*, pg. 1384
EMPIRE DIE CASTING CO., INC.; *U.S. Private*, pg. 1384
EMPIRE DISTRIBUTION (EUROPE) SPOLKA Z OGRANICZONA ODPOWIEDZIALNOSCIA—See Food Empire Holdings Limited; *Int'l*, pg. 2727
EMPIRE DISTRIBUTORS, INC. - AUGUSTA—See Berkshire Hathaway Inc.; *U.S. Public*, pg. 312
EMPIRE DISTRIBUTORS INC-CHARLOTTE—See Berkshire Hathaway Inc.; *U.S. Public*, pg. 312
EMPIRE DISTRIBUTORS, INC. - SAVANNAH—See Berkshire Hathaway Inc.; *U.S. Public*, pg. 312
EMPIRE DISTRIBUTORS, INC.—See Berkshire Hathaway Inc.; *U.S. Public*, pg. 312
EMPIRE DISTRIBUTORS, INC. - TIFTON—See Berkshire Hathaway Inc.; *U.S. Public*, pg. 312

EMPIRE DIE CASTING CO., INC.

EMPIRE DISTRIBUTORS OF NORTH CAROLINA INC. - RALEIGH—See Berkshire Hathaway Inc.; *U.S. Public*, pg. 312
EMPIRE DISTRIBUTORS OF NORTH CAROLINA, INC. - WILMINGTON—See Berkshire Hathaway Inc.; *U.S. Public*, pg. 312
EMPIRE DISTRIBUTORS OF TENNESSEE, INC.—See Berkshire Hathaway Inc.; *U.S. Public*, pg. 304
THE EMPIRE DISTRICT ELECTRIC COMPANY—See Algonquin Power & Utilities Corp.; *Int'l*, pg. 319
EMPIRE DISTRICT INDUSTRIES, INC.—See Algonquin Power & Utilities Corp.; *Int'l*, pg. 319
EMPIRE DIVERSIFIED ENERGY, INC.; *U.S. Public*, pg. 753
EMPIRED LTD; *Int'l*, pg. 2387
EMPIRE DYNAMIC STRUCTURES LTD.—See Dynamic Technologies Group Inc.; *Int'l*, pg. 2241
EMPIRE EAST LAND HOLDINGS, INC.—See Alliance Global Group, Inc.; *Int'l*, pg. 339
EMPIRE ELECTRIC ASSOCIATION, INC.; *U.S. Private*, pg. 1384
EMPIRE ELECTRIC MAINTENANCE & SERVICE, INC.—See The Carlyle Group Inc.; *U.S. Public*, pg. 2053
EMPIRE ENERGY CORPORATION INTERNATIONAL; *U.S. Private*, pg. 1384
EMPIRE ENERGY GROUP LIMITED; *Int'l*, pg. 2387
EMPIRE FIDELITY INVESTMENTS LIFE INSURANCE COMPANY—See FMR LLC; *U.S. Private*, pg. 1555
EMPIRE FIRE & MARINE INSURANCE CO.—See Zurich Insurance Group Limited; *Int'l*, pg. 8699
EMPIRE FOOD BROKERS INC.; *U.S. Private*, pg. 1384
EMPIRE FORD LINCOLN; *U.S. Private*, pg. 1385
EMPIRE GAS COMPANY INC.; *U.S. Private*, pg. 1385
EMPIRE GLOBAL GAMING, INC.; *U.S. Public*, pg. 753
EMPIRE HEALTHCHOICE ASSURANCE, INC.—See Elevance Health, Inc.; *U.S. Public*, pg. 730
EMPIRE HEALTHCHOICE HMO, INC.—See Elevance Health, Inc.; *U.S. Public*, pg. 730
EMPIRE HYDRAULIC SERVICE—See Empire Southwest LLC; *U.S. Private*, pg. 1385
EMPIRE HYUNDAI, INC.; *U.S. Private*, pg. 1385
EMPIRE INVESTMENT HOLDINGS, LLC; *U.S. Private*, pg. 1385
EMPIRE IRON WORKS LTD.—See Dynamic Technologies Group Inc.; *Int'l*, pg. 2241
EMPIRE KOSHER POULTRY, INC.—See Palisades Associates, Inc.; *U.S. Private*, pg. 3077
EMPIRE LEVEL MANUFACTURING CORP.—See Techtronic Industries Co., Ltd.; *Int'l*, pg. 7513
THE EMPIRE LIFE INSURANCE COMPANY—See E-L Financial Corporation Limited; *Int'l*, pg. 2248
EMPIRE LIFE INVESTMENTS INC.—See E-L Financial Corporation Limited; *Int'l*, pg. 2248
EMPIRE LIVESTOCK MARKETING LLC—See Dairy Farmers of America, Inc.; *U.S. Private*, pg. 1146
EMPIRE LUMBER COMPANY; *U.S. Private*, pg. 1385
EMPIRE MACHINERY—See Empire Southwest LLC; *U.S. Private*, pg. 1385
EMPIRE MAINTENANCE INDUSTRIES INC.; *Int'l*, pg. 2387
EMPIRE MANAGEMENT COMPANY; *U.S. Private*, pg. 1385
EMPIRE MERCHANTS, LLC - BROOKLYN—See Breakthru Beverage Group, LLC; *U.S. Private*, pg. 643
EMPIRE MERCHANTS, LLC—See Breakthru Beverage Group, LLC; *U.S. Private*, pg. 643
EMPIRE MERCHANTS NORTH, LLC—See Breakthru Beverage Group, LLC; *U.S. Private*, pg. 643
EMPIRE METALS CORP.; *Int'l*, pg. 2387
EMPIRE METALS LIMITED; *Int'l*, pg. 2387
EMPIRE NATIONAL BANK—See Flushing Financial Corporation; *U.S. Public*, pg. 860
EMPIRE NATURAL GAS CORPORATION; *U.S. Private*, pg. 1385
EMPIRE NISSAN INC.—See Romero Motors Corporation; *U.S. Private*, pg. 3476
EMPIRE OFFICE, INC; *U.S. Private*, pg. 1385
EMPIRE OF METALS LTD.—See Quaser Machine Tools, Inc.; *Int'l*, pg. 6156
EMPIRE OIL CO.—See Marathon Petroleum Corporation; *U.S. Public*, pg. 1363
EMPIRE OPTICAL OF CALIFORNIA INC—See EssilorLuxottica SA; *Int'l*, pg. 2513
EMPIRE PACKING COMPANY, L.P.; *U.S. Private*, pg. 1385
EMPIRE PAPER COMPANY; *U.S. Private*, pg. 1385
EMPIRE PETROLEUM CORPORATION; *U.S. Public*, pg. 753
EMPIRE PETROLEUM PARTNERS, LLC—See Haymaker Acquisition Corp.; *U.S. Private*, pg. 1885
EMPIRE PETROLEUM PARTNERS, LP—See Haymaker Acquisition Corp.; *U.S. Private*, pg. 1885
EMPIRE PIPE & SUPPLY CO., INC.; *U.S. Private*, pg. 1385
EMPIRE POST MEDIA, INC.; *U.S. Private*, pg. 1385
EMPIRE POWER SYSTEMS—See Empire Southwest LLC; *U.S. Private*, pg. 1385
EMPIRE PRECISION MACHINING—See Empire Southwest LLC; *U.S. Private*, pg. 1385
EMPIRE PROPERTIES; *U.S. Private*, pg. 1385
EMPIRE REALTY ASSOCIATES, INC.—See Pacific Union International, Inc.; *U.S. Private*, pg. 3071
EMPIRE RECYCLING CORP.; *U.S. Private*, pg. 1385
EMPIRE RESORTS, INC.; *U.S. Private*, pg. 1385
EMPIRE RESOURCES, INC.—See Ta Chen Stainless Pipe, Ltd.; *Int'l*, pg. 7399
EMPIRE RESOURCES LIMITED; *Int'l*, pg. 2387
EMPIRE RESOURCES PACIFIC LTD.—See Ta Chen Stainless Pipe, Ltd.; *Int'l*, pg. 7399
EMPIRE ROOFING, INC.—See Altas Partners LP; *Int'l*, pg. 386
EMPIRE SCREEN PRINTING, INC.; *U.S. Private*, pg. 1385
EMPIRE SERVICES, INC.—See Greenwave Technology Solutions, Inc.; *U.S. Public*, pg. 965
EMPIRE SERVICE SOLUTION CO., LTD.—See PTG Energy Public Company Limited; *Int'l*, pg. 6090
EMPIRE SILVER CO., INC.—See Lifetime Brands, Inc.; *U.S. Public*, pg. 1313
THE EMPIRE; *U.S. Private*, pg. 4026
EMPIRE SOUTHERN TIER EQUIPMENT CORP.—See Leuner Inc.; *U.S. Private*, pg. 2433
EMPIRE SOUTHWEST LLC; *U.S. Private*, pg. 1385
EMPIRE STAPLE CO.; *U.S. Private*, pg. 1385
EMPIRE STATE BANK—See ES Bancshares, Inc.; *U.S. Public*, pg. 793
EMPIRE STATE BUILDING COMPANY LLC—See Malkin Properties, L.L.C.; *U.S. Private*, pg. 2557
EMPIRE STATE CONTAINER INC—See Buckeye Corrugated Inc.; *U.S. Private*, pg. 677
EMPIRE STATE MINES, LLC—See Titan Mining Corp.; *Int'l*, pg. 7760
EMPIRE STATE REALTY OP, L.P.—See Empire State Realty Trust, Inc.; *U.S. Public*, pg. 753
EMPIRE STATE REALTY TRUST, INC.; *U.S. Public*, pg. 753
EMPIRE STATE RELIEF FUND; *U.S. Private*, pg. 1386
EMPIRE SWEDEN AB—See Kakel Max AB; *Int'l*, pg. 4056
EMPIRE THEATERS LIMITED—See Empire Company Limited; *Int'l*, pg. 2387
EMPIRE TODAY, LLC—See Charlesbank Capital Partners, LLC; *U.S. Private*, pg. 855
EMPIRE TRANSPORT—See Empire Southwest LLC; *U.S. Private*, pg. 1385
EMPIRE TRUCK LINES, INC.—See IMC Holding, LLC; *U.S. Private*, pg. 2046
EMPIRE TRUCK SALES INC—See GS&L Enterprises Incorporated; *U.S. Private*, pg. 1800
EMPIRE VISION CTR. INC.—See Highmark Health; *U.S. Private*, pg. 1940
EMPIRE WIRE & SUPPLY, LLC—See Audax Group, Limited Partnership; *U.S. Private*, pg. 387
EMPIRICA LLC—See ALS Limited; *Int'l*, pg. 378
EMPIRICAL SYSTEMS (M) SDN. BHD.—See KUB Malaysia Berhad; *Int'l*, pg. 4319
EMPIRIC STUDENT PROPERTY PLC; *Int'l*, pg. 2387
EMPIRIS LLC—See Bain Capital, LP; *U.S. Private*, pg. 432
EMPIRIX INC.—See Apax Partners LLP; *Int'l*, pg. 504
EMPLAL NORDESTE EMBALAGENS PLASTICAS LTDA.—See Amcor plc; *Int'l*, pg. 418
EMPLAL PARTICIPACOES S.A.—See Amcor plc; *Int'l*, pg. 418
EMP LATIN AMERICAN MANAGEMENT LLC—See EMP Global LLC; *U.S. Private*, pg. 1384
EMPLICITY; *U.S. Private*, pg. 1386
EMPLOCITY S.A.; *Int'l*, pg. 2387
EMPLOY-ABILITY UNLIMITED INC.; *U.S. Private*, pg. 1386
EMPLOY AMERICA, LLC; *U.S. Private*, pg. 1386
EMPLOYBRIDGE, LLC—See Apollo Global Management, Inc.; *U.S. Public*, pg. 151
EMPLOYEASE, INC.—See Automatic Data Processing, Inc.; *U.S. Public*, pg. 230
EMPLOYEE ASSISTANCE SERVICES, INC.—See Centene Corporation; *U.S. Public*, pg. 469
EMPLOYEE BENEFITS ADMINISTRATORS LTD.—See Alignvest Management Corporation; *Int'l*, pg. 327
EMPLOYEE BENEFITS INTERNATIONAL; *U.S. Private*, pg. 1386
EMPLOYEE & FAMILY RESOURCES INC.; *U.S. Private*, pg. 1386
EMPLOYEE OWNED HOLDINGS, INC.; *U.S. Private*, pg. 1386
EMPLOYEE PLANS, LLC—See Old National Bancorp; *U.S. Public*, pg. 1567
EMPLOYEESCREENIQ, INC.—See Caisse de Depot et Placement du Quebec; *Int'l*, pg. 1255
EMPLOYEESCREENIQ, INC.—See The Goldman Sachs Group, Inc.; *U.S. Public*, pg. 2081
EMPLOYEES LIFE COMPANY MUTUAL; *U.S. Private*, pg. 1386
EMPLOYEES OF MUNICIPAL & OTHER PUBLIC EMPLOYERS; *U.S. Private*, pg. 1386
EMPLOYEE SOLUTIONS; *U.S. Private*, pg. 1386
EMPLOYEES ONLY; *U.S. Private*, pg. 1386
EMPLOYER ADVANTAGE, LLC.—See G&A Outsourcing, Inc.; *U.S. Private*, pg. 1628

CORPORATE AFFILIATIONS

EMPLOYER FLEXIBLE MANAGEMENT, LLC; *U.S. Private*, pg. 1386
EMPLOYER FLEXIBLE—See Employer Flexible Management, LLC; *U.S. Private*, pg. 1386
EMPLOYER FLEXIBLE—See Employer Flexible Management, LLC; *U.S. Private*, pg. 1386
EMPLOYER MANAGEMENT SOLUTIONS, INC.; *U.S. Private*, pg. 1386
EMPLOYER'S COMP ASSOCIATES, INC.—See American Financial Group, Inc.; *U.S. Public*, pg. 103
EMPLOYERS COMPENSATION INSURANCE CO.—See Employers Holdings, Inc.; *U.S. Public*, pg. 754
EMPLOYERS DENTAL SERVICES, INC.—See Principal Financial Group, Inc.; *U.S. Public*, pg. 1720
EMPLOYER'S DEPOT INC.; *U.S. Private*, pg. 1386
EMPLOYER SERVICES CORPORATION—See Stone Point Capital LLC; *U.S. Private*, pg. 3822
EMPLOYERS GROUP, INC.—See Employers Holdings, Inc.; *U.S. Public*, pg. 754
EMPLOYERS HOLDINGS, INC.; *U.S. Public*, pg. 754
EMPLOYERS INSURANCE COMPANY OF NEVADA—See Employers Holdings, Inc.; *U.S. Public*, pg. 754
EMPLOYERS INSURANCE COMPANY OF WAUSAU—See Liberty Mutual Holding Company Inc.; *U.S. Private*, pg. 2445
EMPLOYERS MUTUAL CASUALTY COMPANY; *U.S. Private*, pg. 1386
EMPLOYERS RESOURCE MANAGEMENT INC.; *U.S. Private*, pg. 1387
EMPLOYERS SECURITY INSURANCE COMPANY—See ProAssurance Corporation; *U.S. Public*, pg. 1723
EMPLOYERS TEMPORARY SERVICE; *U.S. Private*, pg. 1387
EMPLOYERS UNITY INC.; *U.S. Private*, pg. 1387
EMPLOYMENT CONTROL INC.; *U.S. Private*, pg. 1387
EMPLOYMENT DEVELOPMENT, INC.; *U.S. Private*, pg. 1387
EMPLOYMENT ENTERPRISES INC.; *U.S. Private*, pg. 1387
EMPLOYMENT GROUP HOLDING CORP.; *U.S. Private*, pg. 1387
EMPLOYMENT GROUP INC.—See Employment Group Holding Corp.; *U.S. Private*, pg. 1387
EMPLOYMENT MANAGEMENT SYSTEMS PTY LTD.—See Rision Limited; *Int'l*, pg. 6350
EMPLOYMENT SCREENING SERVICES (ESS)—See Audax Group, Limited Partnership; *U.S. Private*, pg. 387
EMPLOYMENT SOLUTIONS; *U.S. Private*, pg. 1387
EMPLOYMENT TECHNOLOGIES CORPORATION; *U.S. Private*, pg. 1387
EMPLOYUS, LLC—See The Staffing Group Ltd.; *U.S. Private*, pg. 4120
EMP MANAGEMENT, LLC; *U.S. Private*, pg. 1384
EMP METALS CORP.; *Int'l*, pg. 2385
EMPO CORPORATION; *U.S. Private*, pg. 1387
EMP OF FRANKLIN INC.—See Elgin Molded Plastics Inc.; *U.S. Private*, pg. 1359
EMPORIA FOUNDRY INC.—See Campbell Foundry Company; *U.S. Private*, pg. 730
EMPORIA HOME CARE SERVICES, LLC—See Community Health Systems, Inc.; *U.S. Public*, pg. 553
EMPORIA HOSPITAL CORPORATION—See Bon Secours Mercy Health, Inc.; *U.S. Private*, pg. 612
EMPORIO ACAPULCO, S.A. DE C.V.—See Emporio Hotels & Resorts S.A. de C.V.; *Int'l*, pg. 2387
EMPORIOASIA LEO BURNETT—See Publicis Groupe S.A.; *Int'l*, pg. 6100
EMPORIO HOTELS & RESORTS S.A. DE C.V.; *Int'l*, pg. 2387
EMPORIO IXTAPA S.A. DE C.V., LIC.—See Emporio Hotels & Resorts S.A. de C.V.; *Int'l*, pg. 2387
EMPORIO MAZATLAN, S.A. DE C.V.—See Emporio Hotels & Resorts S.A. de C.V.; *Int'l*, pg. 2387
EMPORIO VERACRUZ S.A. DE C.V.—See Emporio Hotels & Resorts S.A. de C.V.; *Int'l*, pg. 2387
EMPORIO ZACATECAS, S.A. DE C.V.—See Emporio Hotels & Resorts S.A. de C.V.; *Int'l*, pg. 2387
EMPORIUM DRUG MART INC. OF AMARILLO—See Gibson Merchandise Group Inc.; *U.S. Private*, pg. 1696
EMPORIUM DRUG MART INC. OF LAFAYETTE—See Gibson Merchandise Group Inc.; *U.S. Private*, pg. 1696
EMPORIUM DRUG MART INC. OF LONGVIEW—See Gibson Merchandise Group Inc.; *U.S. Private*, pg. 1696
EMPORIUM DRUG MART INC. OF LUBBOCK—See Gibson Merchandise Group Inc.; *U.S. Private*, pg. 1696
EMPORIUM DRUG MART INC. OF SHREVEPORT—See Gibson Merchandise Group Inc.; *U.S. Private*, pg. 1696
EMPORIUM DRUG MART INC. OF TYLER—See Gibson Merchandise Group Inc.; *U.S. Private*, pg. 1696
EMPORIUM DRUG MART INC. OF WACO—See Gibson Merchandise Group Inc.; *U.S. Private*, pg. 1696
EMPORIUM HARDWOODS, LLC—See H.I.G. Capital, LLC; *U.S. Private*, pg. 1832
EMPORIUM PRESENTS—See Live Nation Entertainment, Inc.; *U.S. Public*, pg. 1328
EMPOS LTD.—See Synthos S.A.; *Int'l*, pg. 7387
EMPOWER CLINICS INC.; *Int'l*, pg. 2387

EMPOWERDX, INC.—See Eurofins Scientific S.E.; *Int'l*, pg. 2536
EMPOWERDX UMWELTANALYTIK DEUTSCHLAND GMBH—See Eurofins Scientific S.E.; *Int'l*, pg. 2536
EMPOWEREDBENEFITS, LLC—See Aflac Incorporated; *U.S. Public*, pg. 57
EMPOWERED PRODUCTS, INC.; *U.S. Private*, pg. 1387
EMPOWERED PRODUCTS NEVADA, INC.—See Empowered Products, Inc.; *U.S. Private*, pg. 1387
EMPOWERED VENTURES, INC.; *U.S. Private*, pg. 1387
EMPOWER ENERGIES, INC.—See General Motors Company; *U.S. Public*, pg. 924
EMPOWER INDIA LIMITED; *Int'l*, pg. 2388
EMPOWERING FINANCIAL SOLUTIONS, INC.—See Bluesphere Advisors LLC; *U.S. Private*, pg. 597
EMPOWERISK (PROPRIETARY) LIMITED—See Sebata Holdings; *Int'l*, pg. 6669
EMPOWER LIMITED—See Contact Energy Limited; *Int'l*, pg. 1778
EMPOWER MATERIALS, INC.—See Axess Corporation; *U.S. Private*, pg. 412
EMPOWER MEDIAMARKETING; *U.S. Private*, pg. 1387
EMPOWER OY—See AAC Capital Partners Holding B.V.; *Int'l*, pg. 31
EMPOWER RF SYSTEMS, INC.; *U.S. Private*, pg. 1387
EMPOWER SOFTWARE SOLUTIONS, INC.—See Hellman & Friedman LLC; *U.S. Private*, pg. 1910
EMPOWER SOLUTIONS, INC.—See Nippon Telegraph & Telephone Corporation; *Int'l*, pg. 5348
EMPOWER TECHNOLOGIES, INC.—See EMR Technology Solutions, Inc.; *U.S. Private*, pg. 1388
EMPRENDIMIENTOS DE VALOR S.A.—See Banco Bilbao Vizcaya Argentaria, S.A.; *Int'l*, pg. 817
EMPRESA AGRARIA AZUCARERA ANDAHUASI S.A.A.; *Int'l*, pg. 2388
EMPRESA AGRICOLA SAN JUAN SA; *Int'l*, pg. 2388
EMPRESA AMAZONENSE DE TRANSMISSAO DE ENERGIA S.A.—See Alupar Investimento S.A.; *Int'l*, pg. 401
EMPRESA CARIOCA DE PRODUTOS QUIMICOS S.A.—See Ultrapar Participacoes S.A.; *Int'l*, pg. 8019
EMPRESA CATARINENSE DE TRANSMISSAO DE ENERGIA S.A.—See Alupar Investimento S.A.; *Int'l*, pg. 401
EMPRESA CONCESSIONARIA DE RODOVIAS DO NORTE S.A. ECONORTE—See TPI - Triunfo Participacoes e Investimentos S.A.; *Int'l*, pg. 7883
EMPRESA CONSTRUCTORA BELFI SA; *Int'l*, pg. 2388
EMPRESA DE ALUMBRADO ELECTRICO DE CEUTA ENERGIA S.L.U.—See Enel S.p.A.; *Int'l*, pg. 2411
EMPRESA DE ALUMBRADO ELECTRICO DE CEUTA SA—See Enel S.p.A.; *Int'l*, pg. 2412
EMPRESA DE BLAS Y COMPANIA S.A.—See Deutsche Bahn AG; *Int'l*, pg. 2051
EMPRESA DE DESARROLLO PESQUERO DE CHILE S.A.—See Nissui Corporation; *Int'l*, pg. 5377
EMPRESA DE DISTRIBUCION ELECTRICA DE LIMA NORTE S.A.A.—See Enel S.p.A.; *Int'l*, pg. 2412
EMPRESA DE DISTRIBUCION ELECTRICA METRO OESTE, S.A.—See Naturgy Energy Group, S.A.; *Int'l*, pg. 5169
EMPRESA DE GENERACION ELECTRICA CHEVES S.A—See Statkraft AS; *Int'l*, pg. 7185
EMPRESA DE GENERACION ELECTRICA DEL SUR SA; *Int'l*, pg. 2388
EMPRESA DE GENERACION ELECTRICA SAN GABAN S.A.; *Int'l*, pg. 2388
EMPRESA DE GENERACION ELECTRICA S.A.—See Polaris Renewable Energy Inc.; *Int'l*, pg. 5908
EMPRESA DE LUZ Y FUERZA ELECTRICA DE ORURO, S.A.—See Iberdrola, S.A.; *Int'l*, pg. 3571
EMPRESA DE MEIOS AUDIOVISUAIS, LDA.—See Promotora de Informaciones S.A.; *Int'l*, pg. 5995
EMPRESA DE REFRACTARIOS COLOMBIANOS S.A.—See Platinum Equity, LLC; *U.S. Private*, pg. 3203
EMPRESA DE SERVICIOS SANITARIOS DE LOS LAGOS SA; *Int'l*, pg. 2388
EMPRESA DE SERVICOS E COMERCIALIZACAO DE ENERGIA ELETRICA S.A.—See Companhia Energetica de Minas Gerais - CEMIG; *Int'l*, pg. 1747
EMPRESA DE TELECOMUNICACIONES DE BOGOTA SA; *Int'l*, pg. 2388
EMPRESA DISTRIBUIDORA DE PAPELES Y CARTONES SPA—See Empresas CMPC S.A.; *Int'l*, pg. 2389
EMPRESA DISTRIBUIDORA SUR S.A.—See Enel S.p.A.; *Int'l*, pg. 2412
EMPRESA DISTRIBUIDORA Y COMERCIALIZADORA NORTE S.A.—See Grupo EMES S.A.; *Int'l*, pg. 3126
EMPRESA ELECTRICA CAMPICHE S.A.—See The AES Corporation; *U.S. Public*, pg. 2031
EMPRESA ELECTRICA DE ANTOFAGASTA S.A.—See State Grid Corporation of China; *Int'l*, pg. 7183
EMPRESA ELECTRICA DE MAGALLANES S.A.—See State Grid Corporation of China; *Int'l*, pg. 7183
EMPRESA ELECTRICA DE ORIENTE, S.A. DE C.V.—See The AES Corporation; *U.S. Public*, pg. 2031
EMPRESA ELECTRICA PEHUENCHE, S.A.—See Enel S.p.A.; *Int'l*, pg. 2413
EMPRESA ELECTRICA PILMAIQUEN S.A.; *Int'l*, pg. 2388

EMPRESA ELECTRICA SANTIAGO SPA—See The AES Corporation; *U.S. Public*, pg. 2031
EMPRESA ELECTRICIDAD DEL PERU-ELECTROPERU SA; *Int'l*, pg. 2388
EMPRESA ENERGETICA DO MATO GROSSO DO SUL S.A.—See EDP - Energias de Portugal, S.A.; *Int'l*, pg. 2314
EMPRESA FINANCIERA EDYFICAR S.A.—See Credicorp Ltd.; *Int'l*, pg. 1834
EMPRESA GENERAL DE INVERSIONES, S.A.; *Int'l*, pg. 2388
EMPRESA MARITIMA S.A.—See K+S Aktiengesellschaft; *Int'l*, pg. 4039
EMPRESA MIXTA DE AGUAS DE SANTA CRUZ DE TENERIFE, S.A.—See Sacyr, S.A.; *Int'l*, pg. 6465
EMPRESA NACIONAL DE COMERCIO REDITO E PARTICIPACOES, S.A.-ENCORPAR; *Int'l*, pg. 2388
EMPRESA NACIONAL DE ENERGIA ENEX S.A.—See Quinenco S.A.; *Int'l*, pg. 6163
EMPRESA NACIONAL DE EXPLOSIVOS SA—See Sigdo Koppers S.A.; *Int'l*, pg. 6907
EMPRESA NACIONAL DEL PETROLEO; *Int'l*, pg. 2388
EMPRESA NACIONAL DE TELECOMUNICACIONES S.A.—See Almendral S.A.; *Int'l*, pg. 364
EMPRESA PARA LA GESTION DE RESIDUOS INDUSTRIALES. S.A.—See Sociedad Estatal de Participaciones Industriales; *Int'l*, pg. 7031
EMPRESA PETROLERA CHACO S.A.—See BP plc; *Int'l*, pg. 1131
EMPRESA PETROLERA CHACO S.A.—See Bridas Corporation; *Int'l*, pg. 1152
EMPRESA PORTUGUESA DE CENARIOS, LDA.—See Promotora de Informaciones S.A.; *Int'l*, pg. 5995
EMPRESA REGIONAL DE SERVICIO PU DE EL SA; *Int'l*, pg. 2388
EMPRESARIA GROUP PLC; *Int'l*, pg. 2388
EMPRESARIA LIMITED—See Empresaria Group Plc; *Int'l*, pg. 2388
EMPRESAS AQUACHILE SA—See Agrosuper SA; *Int'l*, pg. 221
EMPRESAS BECHARA, INC.; *U.S. Private*, pg. 1388
EMPRESAS BERRIOS INC.; *U.S. Private*, pg. 1388
EMPRESAS CABLEVISION, S.A.B. DE C.V.—See Grupo Televisa, S.A.B.; *Int'l*, pg. 3136
EMPRESAS CABO DE HORNOS S.A.; *Int'l*, pg. 2389
EMPRESAS CMPC S.A.; *Int'l*, pg. 2389
EMPRESAS COPEC S.A.—See AntarChile S.A.; *Int'l*, pg. 481
EMPRESAS DE NARINO LTDA.—See ED&F Man Holdings Limited; *Int'l*, pg. 2303
EMPRESAS DE NARIO LTDA—See ED&F Man Holdings Limited; *Int'l*, pg. 2303
EMPRESAS HITES S.A.; *Int'l*, pg. 2390
EMPRESAS IANSA S.A.—See ED&F Man Holdings Limited; *Int'l*, pg. 2303
EMPRESAS ICA S.A.B. DE C.V.; *Int'l*, pg. 2390
EMPRESAS JUAN YARUR S.A.C.; *Int'l*, pg. 2391
EMPRESAS LA POLAR S.A.; *Int'l*, pg. 2391
EMPRESAS LIPIGAS SA; *Int'l*, pg. 2391
EMPRESAS PENTA S.A.; *Int'l*, pg. 2391
EMPRESAS PETROLEO IPIRANGA; *Int'l*, pg. 2391
EMPRESAS POLAR; *Int'l*, pg. 2391
EMPRESAS PUBLICAS DE MEDELLIN ESP; *Int'l*, pg. 2391
EMPRESAS PUBLICAS DE ORIENTE ANTIOQUENO S.A.—See Empresas Publicas de Medellin ESP; *Int'l*, pg. 2392
EMPRESAS PUERTORRIQUENAS DE DESARROLLO INC.; *U.S. Private*, pg. 1388
EMPRESAS SERRALLES INC.; *U.S. Private*, pg. 1388
EMPRESAS TAGAROPULOS, S.A.; *Int'l*, pg. 2392
EMPRESAS TRICOT SA; *Int'l*, pg. 2392
EMPRESAS Y CONTROLES EN COMUNICACIONES, S.A. DE C.V.—See America Movil, S.A.B. de C.V.; *Int'l*, pg. 421
EMPRESAS Y-NUINA, INC.; *U.S. Private*, pg. 1388
EMPRES AT ROCK SPRINGS, LLC—See Apollo Global Management, Inc.; *U.S. Public*, pg. 156
EMPRESS AMBULANCE SERVICE INC.; *U.S. Private*, pg. 1388
EMPRESS LOUISIANA PROPERTIES, L.P.—See Expand Energy Corporation; *U.S. Public*, pg. 808
EMPRESS MINING INC.; *Int'l*, pg. 2392
EMPRESS RESOURCES CORP.—See Big Ridge Gold Corp.; *Int'l*, pg. 1021
EMPRESS ROYALTY CORP.; *Int'l*, pg. 2392
EMPRISE BANK—See Emprise Financial Corporation; *U.S. Private*, pg. 1388
EMPRISE FINANCIAL CORPORATION; *U.S. Private*, pg. 1388
EMP SOLUTIONS, INC.; *U.S. Public*, pg. 753
EMP TECHNOLOGIES, LTD.—See Pyrotek Incorporated; *U.S. Private*, pg. 3310
EMPTEEZY BENELUX BVBA—See Empteezy Ltd; *Int'l*, pg. 2392
EMPTEEZY HOLLAND BV—See Empteezy Ltd; *Int'l*, pg. 2392
EMPTEEZY IBERICA S.L.—See Empteezy Ltd; *Int'l*, pg. 2392

EMPTEEZY ITALIA S.R.L.—See Empteezy Ltd; *Int'l*, pg. 2392
EMPTEEZY LTD; *Int'l*, pg. 2392
EMPTEEZY UAE FZE—See Empteezy Ltd; *Int'l*, pg. 2392
EMPTORIS, INC.—See International Business Machines Corporation; *U.S. Public*, pg. 1145
EMPYREAN BENEFIT SOLUTIONS, INC.; *U.S. Private*, pg. 1388
EMPYREAN CASHEWS LIMITED; *Int'l*, pg. 2392
EMPYREAN ENERGY PLC; *Int'l*, pg. 2392
EMPYREAN SERVICES LLC; *U.S. Private*, pg. 1388
EMPYREAN TECHNOLOGY CO., LTD.; *Int'l*, pg. 2392
EMPYRION WEALTH MANAGEMENT, INC.—See Genstar Capital, LLC; *U.S. Private*, pg. 1677
EMPYRION WEALTH MANAGEMENT, INC.—See Keystone Group, L.P.; *U.S. Private*, pg. 2298
EMQTEC AG; *Int'l*, pg. 2392
EM QUANTUM TECHNOLOGIES, INC.; *U.S. Public*, pg. 735
EMR CAPITAL PTY LTD; *Int'l*, pg. 2392
EMR EHF.—See Origo hf.; *Int'l*, pg. 5631
EMR EMERSON HOLDINGS (SWITZERLAND) GMBH—See Emerson Electric Co.; *U.S. Public*, pg. 743
EMRIC D.O.O.—See TietoEVRY Oyj; *Int'l*, pg. 7745
EMR LTD—See European Metal Recycling Limited; *Int'l*, pg. 2556
EMRO CO. LTD.; *Int'l*, pg. 2392
EMRO FINANCE IRELAND LIMITED—See BPER BANCA S.p.A; *Int'l*, pg. 1132
EM.RO. POPOLARE S.P.A.—See BPER BANCA S.p.A; *Int'l*, pg. 1132
EMR TECHNOLOGY SOLUTIONS, INC.; *U.S. Private*, pg. 1388
EMR US HOLDINGS LLC—See Emerson Electric Co.; *U.S. Public*, pg. 743
EMRY CAPITAL GROUP, INC.; *U.S. Private*, pg. 1388
EMS BRUEL & KJAER IBERICA S.A.—See EnviroSuite Limited; *Int'l*, pg. 2455
EMS BRUEL & KJAER TAIWAN LTD.—See EnviroSuite Limited; *Int'l*, pg. 2455
EMS-CHEMIE AG—See EMS-Chemie Holding AG; *Int'l*, pg. 2393
EMS-CHEMIE (CHINA) LTD.—See EMS-Chemie Holding AG; *Int'l*, pg. 2393
EMS-CHEMIE (DEUTSCHLAND) GMBH—See EMS-Chemie Holding AG; *Int'l*, pg. 2393
EMS-CHEMIE (FRANCE) S.A.—See EMS-Chemie Holding AG; *Int'l*, pg. 2393
EMS-CHEMIE HOLDING AG; *Int'l*, pg. 2393
EMS-CHEMIE (JAPAN) LTD.—See EMS-Chemie Holding AG; *Int'l*, pg. 2393
EMS-CHEMIE (KOREA) LTD.—See EMS-Chemie Holding AG; *Int'l*, pg. 2393
EMS-CHEMIE (NEUMUNSTER) GMBH CO. KG—See EMS-Chemie Holding AG; *Int'l*, pg. 2393
EMS-CHEMIE (NORTH AMERICA) INC.—See EMS-Chemie Holding AG; *Int'l*, pg. 2393
EMS-CHEMIE (PRODUKTION) AG—See EMS-Chemie Holding AG; *Int'l*, pg. 2393
EMS-CHEMIE (SUZHOU) LTD.—See EMS-Chemie Holding AG; *Int'l*, pg. 2393
EMS-CHEMIE (SWITZERLAND) AG—See EMS-Chemie Holding AG; *Int'l*, pg. 2393
EMS-CHEMIE (TAIWAN) LTD.—See EMS-Chemie Holding AG; *Int'l*, pg. 2393
EMS-CHEMIE (UK) LTD.—See EMS-Chemie Holding AG; *Int'l*, pg. 2393
EMSCHER LIPPE ENERGIE GMBH—See RWE AG; *Int'l*, pg. 6434
EMSCO INC.; *U.S. Private*, pg. 1388
EMSCO INC.; *U.S. Private*, pg. 1388
EMS CO., LTD—See EPS Holdings, Inc.; *Int'l*, pg. 2465
EMS CONSULTING - INTELLIGENT CHAOS; *U.S. Private*, pg. 1388
EMS DEVELOPMENT CORPORATION—See Advent International Corporation; *U.S. Private*, pg. 100
EMSEAL JOINT SYSTEMS, LTD.—See Sika AG; *Int'l*, pg. 6914
EMSEAS TEKNIK AB—See ad pepper media International NV; *Int'l*, pg. 122
EMSE, INC.—See Daburn Electronics & Cable Corp.; *U.S. Private*, pg. 1144
EMS ENERGY LIMITED; *Int'l*, pg. 2392
EMS ENTERTAINMENT (M) SDN BHD—See Event Marketing Service GmbH; *Int'l*, pg. 2562
EMSER TILE LLC; *U.S. Private*, pg. 1388
EMS EXHIBITS LAS VEGAS, INC.—See Event Marketing Service GmbH; *Int'l*, pg. 2562
EMS EXHIBITS MIAMI, LLC.—See Event Marketing Service GmbH; *Int'l*, pg. 2562
EMS EXHIBITS ORLANDO, LLC.—See Event Marketing Service GmbH; *Int'l*, pg. 2562
EMS-GRILTECH AG—See EMS-Chemie Holding AG; *Int'l*, pg. 2393
EM SHIPPING SDN. BHD.; *Int'l*, pg. 2372
EMSIG MANUFACTURING CORP.; *U.S. Private*, pg. 1388
EMS INDUSTRIAL INC.; *U.S. Private*, pg. 1388

EMS INDUSTRIAL INC.

EMS-INTERNATIONAL FINANCE (GUERNSEY) LTD.—See EMS-Chemie Holding AG; *Int'l*, pg. 2393
EMS INVIROTEL ENERGY MANAGEMENT PROPRIETARY LIMITED—See The Bidvest Group Limited; *Int'l*, pg. 7624
EMSL ANALYTICAL, INC.; *U.S. Private*, pg. 1388
EMSLAND-STARKE ASIA PACIFIC PTE LTD.—See Emsland-Starke GmbH; *Int'l*, pg. 2394
EMSLAND-STARKE GMBH GOLSSEN FACTORY—See Emsland-Starke GmbH; *Int'l*, pg. 2394
EMSLAND-STARKE GMBH KYRITZ FACTORY—See Emsland-Starke GmbH; *Int'l*, pg. 2394
EMSLAND-STARKE GMBH; *Int'l*, pg. 2394
EMSLAND-STARKE GMBH WIETZENDORF FACTORY—See Emsland-Starke GmbH; *Int'l*, pg. 2394
EMSLAND-STARKE LOGISTICS GMBH & CO. KG—See Emsland-Starke GmbH; *Int'l*, pg. 2394
EMS LIMITED; *Int'l*, pg. 2392
EMS LIVE ENTERTAINMENT GMBH—See Event Marketing Service GmbH; *Int'l*, pg. 2562
EMS MANAGEMENT, LLC—See KKR & Co. Inc.; *U.S. Public*, pg. 1251
EMS OFFSHORE PTE. LTD.—See EMS Energy Limited; *Int'l*, pg. 2392
EMSONIC CO., LTD.—See EXA E&C Inc.; *Int'l*, pg. 2576
EMSOR, SOCIEDAD DE RESPONSABILIDAD LIMITADA—See Hologic, Inc.; *U.S. Public*, pg. 1044
EMS-PATENT AG—See EMS-Chemie Holding AG; *Int'l*, pg. 2393
EMS-PATVAG S.R.O.—See Hirtenberger Holding GmbH; *Int'l*, pg. 3406
EMSR EUROTHERM GMBH—See Schneider Electric SE; *Int'l*, pg. 6627
EMS SAFETY SERVICES INC.—See Waud Capital Partners LLC; *U.S. Private*, pg. 4457
EMS SEVEN SEAS ASA—See Supreme Group BV; *Int'l*, pg. 7341
EMS SOFTWARE, LLC—See Fortive Corporation; *U.S. Public*, pg. 870
E.M. STAHL B.V.—See R. STAHL AG; *Int'l*, pg. 6169
EMSTANK GMBH—See Marquard & Bahls AG; *Int'l*, pg. 4699
EMS TECHNOLOGY SOLUTIONS, LLC; *U.S. Private*, pg. 1388
EMSTEEL BUILDING MATERIALS PJSC; *Int'l*, pg. 2394
EMS-UBE LTD.—See UBE Corporation; *Int'l*, pg. 8000
EMS-UBE LTD.—See EMS-Chemie Holding AG; *Int'l*, pg. 2393
EMS WATER PTE LTD—See EMS Energy Limited; *Int'l*, pg. 2392
EMS WIRING SYSTEMS PTE LTD; *Int'l*, pg. 2393
EM SYSTEMS CO., LTD.; *Int'l*, pg. 2372
EMTAC LABORATORIES PRIVATE LIMITED—See Vimta Labs Limited; *Int'l*, pg. 8209
EMT DISTRIBUTION PTY. LTD.—See Crayon Group Holding ASA; *Int'l*, pg. 1829
EMTE ANDORA, S.A.—See COMSA EMTE S.L.; *Int'l*, pg. 1761
EMTEC FEDERAL, INC.—See Kelso & Company, L.P.; *U.S. Private*, pg. 2278
EMTEC FEDERAL, INC.—See Kelso & Company, L.P.; *U.S. Private*, pg. 2278
EM-TEC GMBH—See Dover Corporation; *U.S. Public*, pg. 683
EM TECH CO., LTD.—See EO Technics Co., Ltd.; *Int'l*, pg. 2457
EMTEC INTERNATIONAL HOLDING GMBH—See Dexxon Groupe SA; *Int'l*, pg. 2093
EMTE CLEANROOM S.A.—See COMSA EMTE S.L.; *Int'l*, pg. 1761
EMTEC MAGNETICS IBERICA S.A.—See Dexxon Groupe SA; *Int'l*, pg. 2093
EMTEC MAGNETICS POLSKA SP. Z.O.O.—See Dexxon Groupe SA; *Int'l*, pg. 2093
EMTEC MAGNETICS (SCHWEIZ) GMBH—See Dexxon Groupe SA; *Int'l*, pg. 2093
EMTE INSTALACIONES—See COMSA EMTE S.L.; *Int'l*, pg. 1761
EMTEK (DONGGUAN) CO., LTD.—See EMTEK (Shenzhen) Co., Ltd.; *Int'l*, pg. 2394
EMTEK (GUANGZHOU) CO., LTD.—See EMTEK (Shenzhen) Co., Ltd.; *Int'l*, pg. 2394
EMTEK (NINGBO) CO., LTD.—See EMTEK (Shenzhen) Co., Ltd.; *Int'l*, pg. 2394
EMTEK PRODUCTS, INC.—See ASSA ABLOY AB; *Int'l*, pg. 639
EMTEK (SHENZHEN) CO., LTD.; *Int'l*, pg. 2394
EMTEK (SUZHOU) CO., LTD.—See EMTEK (Shenzhen) Co., Ltd.; *Int'l*, pg. 2394
EMTEK (WUHAN) CO., LTD.—See EMTEK (Shenzhen) Co., Ltd.; *Int'l*, pg. 2394
EMTE, LDA—See COMSA EMTE S.L.; *Int'l*, pg. 1761
EMTE ME ZONA FRANCA S.A.—See COMSA EMTE S.L.; *Int'l*, pg. 1761
EMTEQ EUROPE GMBH—See RTX Corporation; *U.S. Public*, pg. 1822
E.M.T.E. S.A.R.L.—See COMSA EMTE S.L.; *Int'l*, pg. 1761
EMT ESINDUSED AS—See Telia Company AB; *Int'l*, pg. 7543

EM TEST (SWITZERLAND) GMBH—See AMETEK, Inc.; *U.S. Public*, pg. 120
EM TEST (USA), INC.—See AMETEK, Inc.; *U.S. Public*, pg. 120
EMTEX SOFTWARE, INC.—See Pitney Bowes Inc.; *U.S. Public*, pg. 1694
E.M. THARP INC.; *U.S. Private*, pg. 1306
E.M. THOMAS MANAGEMENT INC.; *U.S. Private*, pg. 1306
EMT MISCHTECHNIK GMBH—See WAMGROUP S.p.A.; *Int'l*, pg. 8339
EM-TRACK MARINE ELECTRONICS LIMITED—See SRT Marine Systems plc; *Int'l*, pg. 7152
EMTROL-BUELL TECHNOLOGIES—See CECO Environmental Corp.; *U.S. Public*, pg. 463
EMTRON ELECTRONIC GMBH—See FORTEC Elektronik AG; *Int'l*, pg. 2738
EMUAMERICAS, LLC; *U.S. Private*, pg. 1388
EMU DESIGN (QLD) PTY. LTD.—See GBST Holdings Limited; *Int'l*, pg. 2893
EMUDHRA, INC.—See eMudhra Limited; *Int'l*, pg. 2394
EMUDHRA LIMITED; *Int'l*, pg. 2394
EMUGE-FRANKEN AB—See EMUGE-Werk Richard Glimpel GmbH & Co. KG; *Int'l*, pg. 2394
EMUGE-FRANKEN AB—See EMUGE-Werk Richard Glimpel GmbH & Co. KG; *Int'l*, pg. 2394
EMUGE-FRANKEN (BULGARIA) E.O.O.D.—See EMUGE-Werk Richard Glimpel GmbH & Co. KG; *Int'l*, pg. 2394
EMUGE-FRANKEN B.V.—See EMUGE-Werk Richard Glimpel GmbH & Co. KG; *Int'l*, pg. 2394
EMUGE-FRANKEN HASSAS KESICI TAKIM SANAYI LTD. STI.—See EMUGE-Werk Richard Glimpel GmbH & Co. KG; *Int'l*, pg. 2394
EMUGE-FRANKEN NASTROJE SPOL. S R.O.—See EMUGE-Werk Richard Glimpel GmbH & Co. KG; *Int'l*, pg. 2394
EMUGE-FRANKEN SARL—See EMUGE-Werk Richard Glimpel GmbH & Co. KG; *Int'l*, pg. 2394
EMUGE-FRANKEN SERVISNI CENTRUM, S.R.O.—See EMUGE-Werk Richard Glimpel GmbH & Co. KG; *Int'l*, pg. 2394
EMUGE-FRANKEN, S.L.—See EMUGE-Werk Richard Glimpel GmbH & Co. KG; *Int'l*, pg. 2394
EMUGE-FRANKEN S.R.L.—See EMUGE-Werk Richard Glimpel GmbH & Co. KG; *Int'l*, pg. 2394
EMUGE-FRANKEN TECHNIK—See EMUGE-Werk Richard Glimpel GmbH & Co. KG; *Int'l*, pg. 2394
EMUGE-FRANKEN TEHNIKA D.O.O.—See EMUGE-Werk Richard Glimpel GmbH & Co. KG; *Int'l*, pg. 2394
EMUGE-FRANKEN TOOLING SERVICE D.O.O.—See EMUGE-Werk Richard Glimpel GmbH & Co. KG; *Int'l*, pg. 2394
EMUGE-FRANKEN TOOLS ROMANIA SRL—See EMUGE-Werk Richard Glimpel GmbH & Co. KG; *Int'l*, pg. 2394
EMUGE-FRANKEN UK LIMITED—See EMUGE-Werk Richard Glimpel GmbH & Co. KG; *Int'l*, pg. 2394
EMUGE PRAZISIONSWERKZEUGE GMBH—See EMUGE-Werk Richard Glimpel GmbH & Co. KG; *Int'l*, pg. 2394
EMUGE-WERK RICHARD GLIMPEL GMBH & CO. KG; *Int'l*, pg. 2394
EMULATE THERAPEUTICS, INC.; *U.S. Public*, pg. 754
EMULITHE SAS—See VINCI S.A.; *Int'l*, pg. 8217
EMULSION TECHNOLOGY CO., LTD.—See JSR Corp.; *Int'l*, pg. 4013
EMUNDO GMBH—See Gofore PLC; *Int'l*, pg. 3022
EMU NL; *Int'l*, pg. 2394
EMURTEL, S.A.—See ACS, Actividades de Construccion y Servicios, S.A.; *Int'l*, pg. 112
EMUSIC.COM INC.—See TriPlay, Inc.; *U.S. Private*, pg. 4236
E-MU SYSTEMS, INC—See Creative Technology Ltd.; *Int'l*, pg. 1833
E-MUZYKA S.A.—See Penta Investments Limited; *Int'l*, pg. 5788
EMV CAPITAL LIMITED—See NetScientific plc; *Int'l*, pg. 5215
EMVIA LIVING GMBH—See Chequers SA; *Int'l*, pg. 1471
EMVISION MEDICAL DEVICES LTD.; *Int'l*, pg. 2395
EMWOOD LUMBER CO. INC.; *U.S. Private*, pg. 1388
EMW; *Int'l*, pg. 2395
EMX COMPANY LTD.—See Ameriprise Financial, Inc.; *U.S. Public*, pg. 114
EMX CONTROLS INC.; *U.S. Private*, pg. 1389
EMX ENTERPRISES LIMITED; *Int'l*, pg. 2395
EMX ROYALTY CORPORATION; *Int'l*, pg. 2395
EMX (USA) SERVICES CORP.—See EMX Royalty Corporation; *Int'l*, pg. 2395
EMYRIA LIMITED; *Int'l*, pg. 2395
EMZA VISUAL SENSE LTD.—See Synaptics Incorporated; *U.S. Public*, pg. 1969
ENA AICHI ELECTRIC CO., LTD.—See Aichi Electric Co., Ltd.; *Int'l*, pg. 229
ENABLE GAS GATHERING, LLC—See Energy Transfer LP; *U.S. Public*, pg. 763
ENABLE GAS TRANSMISSION, LLC—See Energy Transfer LP; *U.S. Public*, pg. 763

CORPORATE AFFILIATIONS

ENABLE GATHERING AND PROCESSING, LLC—See Energy Transfer LP; *U.S. Public*, pg. 763
ENABLE HOLDINGS, INC.; *U.S. Public*, pg. 754
ENABLE, INC.; *U.S. Private*, pg. 1389
ENABLE IPC CORP.; *U.S. Public*, pg. 754
ENABLEIT, LLC; *U.S. Private*, pg. 1389
ENABLE MEDIA LIMITED—See Siris Capital Group, LLC; *U.S. Private*, pg. 3675
ENABLE MIDSTREAM PARTNERS, LP—See Energy Transfer LP; *U.S. Public*, pg. 763
ENABLENCE TECHNOLOGIES INC.; *Int'l*, pg. 2395
ENABLENCE USA COMPONENTS, INC.—See Enablence Technologies Inc.; *Int'l*, pg. 2395
ENABLE OKLAHOMA INTRASTATE TRANSMISSION, LLC—See Energy Transfer LP; *U.S. Public*, pg. 763
ENABLE PRODUCTS, LLC—See Energy Transfer LP; *U.S. Public*, pg. 763
ENABLE SERVICES LTD—See Christchurch City Holdings Ltd.; *Int'l*, pg. 1586
ENABLES IT GROUP LIMITED; *Int'l*, pg. 2395
ENABLEWISE, LLC; *U.S. Private*, pg. 1389
ENABLING ASIA, INC.; *U.S. Public*, pg. 754
ENABLX, INC.; *U.S. Private*, pg. 1389
ENACON PARKING PTY LIMITED—See Mulpha International Bhd.; *Int'l*, pg. 5081
ENACT CONVEYANCING LIMITED—See First American Financial Corporation; *U.S. Public*, pg. 838
ENACT HOLDINGS, INC.—See Genworth Financial, Inc.; *U.S. Public*, pg. 933
ENACTUS; *U.S. Private*, pg. 1389
ENAGAS, S.A.; *Int'l*, pg. 2396
ENAIRE; *Int'l*, pg. 2396
ENALASYS CORP.; *U.S. Private*, pg. 1389
ENALPIN AG—See EnBW Energie Baden-Wurttemberg AG; *Int'l*, pg. 2398
ENALYZER A/S; *Int'l*, pg. 2396
ENAMELED STEEL; *U.S. Private*, pg. 1389
ENAMEL PRODUCTS SDN. BHD.—See Milux Corporation Berhad; *Int'l*, pg. 4897
ENANTA PHARMACEUTICALS, INC.; *U.S. Public*, pg. 754
ENANTIGEN THERAPEUTICS, INC.—See Arbutus Biopharma Corporation; *U.S. Public*, pg. 178
ENAP INC.; *U.S. Private*, pg. 1389
ENAP REFINERIAS SA—See Empresa Nacional del Petroleo; *Int'l*, pg. 2388
ENAP SA—See APS Energia SA; *Int'l*, pg. 522
ENAPTER AG; *Int'l*, pg. 2396
ENAQUA INC.—See The Poul Due Jensen Foundation; *Int'l*, pg. 7674
ENARTIS ARGENTINA S.A.—See Esseco Group SRL; *Int'l*, pg. 2509
ENARTIS CENTRAL EUROPE S.R.O.—See Esseco Group SRL; *Int'l*, pg. 2509
ENARTIS CHILE LTDA—See Esseco Group SRL; *Int'l*, pg. 2509
ENARTIS PACIFIC PTY LTD—See Esseco Group SRL; *Int'l*, pg. 2509
ENARTIS PORTUGAL UNIPESSOAL, LDA—See Esseco Group SRL; *Int'l*, pg. 2509
ENARTIS SEPSA S.A.U.—See Esseco Group SRL; *Int'l*, pg. 2509
ENARTIS SOUTH AFRICA LTD—See Esseco Group SRL; *Int'l*, pg. 2509
ENARTIS VINQUIRY INC.—See Esseco Group SRL; *Int'l*, pg. 2509
ENA TOKAI RIKA CO., LTD.—See Tokai Rika Co., Ltd.; *Int'l*, pg. 7780
ENAUTA PARTICIPACOES S.A.; *Int'l*, pg. 2396
ENAV S.P.A.; *Int'l*, pg. 2396
ENBASYS GMBH—See BDI - BioEnergy International AG; *Int'l*, pg. 929
ENBD REIT CEIC PLC; *Int'l*, pg. 2396
E.N. BEARD HARDWOOD LUMBER INC.; *U.S. Private*, pg. 1306
ENBEE TRADE & FINANCE LIMITED; *Int'l*, pg. 2396
ENB FINANCIAL CORP.; *U.S. Public*, pg. 754
ENBI GERMANY GMBH—See Platinum Equity, LLC; *U.S. Private*, pg. 3203
ENBI INDIANA, INC.—See Platinum Equity, LLC; *U.S. Private*, pg. 3203
ENBIO CO., LTD.; *Int'l*, pg. 2396
ENBIO ENGINEERING, INC.—See EnBio Holdings Inc.; *Int'l*, pg. 2396
ENBIO HOLDINGS INC.; *Int'l*, pg. 2396
ENBIO REAL ESTATE, INC.—See EnBio Holdings Inc.; *Int'l*, pg. 2396
ENBIOTIX, INC.—See Spexis Ltd; *Int'l*, pg. 7134
ENBI ROCHESTER, INC.—See Platinum Equity, LLC; *U.S. Private*, pg. 3203
E N BISSO & SON INC.; *U.S. Private*, pg. 1301
ENBI (ZHUHAI) INDUSTRIAL CO., LTD—See Platinum Equity, LLC; *U.S. Private*, pg. 3203
ENBRIDGE ENERGY COMPANY, INC.—See Enbridge Inc.; *Int'l*, pg. 2397
ENBRIDGE ENERGY MANAGEMENT, LLC—See Enbridge Inc.; *Int'l*, pg. 2397
ENBRIDGE ENERGY PARTNERS, L.P.—See Enbridge Inc.; *Int'l*, pg. 2397

COMPANY NAME INDEX

ENBRIDGE GAS INC.—See Enbridge Inc.; *Int'l*, pg. 2397
ENBRIDGE GAS NEW BRUNSWICK INC.—See Algonquin Power & Utilities Corp.; *Int'l*, pg. 319
ENBRIDGE G & P (NORTH TEXAS) L P—See Enbridge Inc.; *Int'l*, pg. 2397
ENBRIDGE INCOME FUND HOLDINGS INC.—See Enbridge Inc.; *Int'l*, pg. 2397
ENBRIDGE INC.; *Int'l*, pg. 2396
ENBRIDGE PIPELINE CORPORATION—See Enbridge Inc.; *Int'l*, pg. 2397
ENBRIDGE PIPELINES (ATHABASCA) INC.—See Enbridge Inc.; *Int'l*, pg. 2397
ENBRIDGE PIPELINES, INC.—See Enbridge Inc.; *Int'l*, pg. 2397
ENBW ASIA PACIFIC LTD.—See EnBW Energie Baden-Wurttemberg AG; *Int'l*, pg. 2398
ENBW BALTIC 1 GMBH & CO. KG—See EnBW Energie Baden-Wurttemberg AG; *Int'l*, pg. 2398
ENBW BALTIC 1 VERWALTUNGS GESELLSCHAFT MBH—See EnBW Energie Baden-Wurttemberg AG; *Int'l*, pg. 2398
ENBW BENELUX B.V.—See EnBW Energie Baden-Wurttemberg AG; *Int'l*, pg. 2398
ENBW BIOMASSE GMBH—See EnBW Energie Baden-Wurttemberg AG; *Int'l*, pg. 2398
ENBW ENERGIE BADEN-WURTTEMBERG AG; *Int'l*, pg. 2397
ENBW ENERGY FACTORY GMBH—See EnBW Energie Baden-Wurttemberg AG; *Int'l*, pg. 2398
ENBW ENERGYWATCHERS GMBH—See EnBW Energie Baden-Wurttemberg AG; *Int'l*, pg. 2398
ENBW GASNETZ GMBH—See EnBW Energie Baden-Wurttemberg AG; *Int'l*, pg. 2398
ENBW HOLDING A.S.—See EnBW Energie Baden-Wurttemberg AG; *Int'l*, pg. 2398
ENBW KERNKRAFT GMBH—See EnBW Energie Baden-Wurttemberg AG; *Int'l*, pg. 2398
ENBW KOMMUNALE BETEILIGUNGEN GMBH—See EnBW Energie Baden-Wurttemberg AG; *Int'l*, pg. 2398
ENBW KRAFTWERKE AG—See EnBW Energie Baden-Wurttemberg AG; *Int'l*, pg. 2398
ENBW MAINFRANKENPARK GMBH—See EnBW Energie Baden-Wurttemberg AG; *Int'l*, pg. 2398
ENBW NORTH AMERICA INC.—See EnBW Energie Baden-Wurttemberg AG; *Int'l*, pg. 2398
ENBW OMEGA DREIUNDZWANZIGSTE VERWALTUNGSGESELLSCHAFT MBH—See EnBW Energie Baden-Wurttemberg AG; *Int'l*, pg. 2398
ENBW OMEGA ELFTE VERWALTUNGSGESELLSCHAFT MBH—See EnBW Energie Baden-Wurttemberg AG; *Int'l*, pg. 2398
ENBW OMEGA SIEBZEHNTE VERWALTUNGSGESELLSCHAFT MBH—See EnBW Energie Baden-Wurttemberg AG; *Int'l*, pg. 2398
ENBW OSTWURTTEMBERG DONAURIES AG—See EnBW Energie Baden-Wurttemberg AG; *Int'l*, pg. 2398
ENBW PERSPEKTIVEN GMBH—See EnBW Energie Baden-Wurttemberg AG; *Int'l*, pg. 2398
ENBW SVERIGE AB—See EnBW Energie Baden-Wurttemberg AG; *Int'l*, pg. 2398
ENBW SYSTEME INFRASTRUKTUR SUPPORT GMBH—See EnBW Energie Baden-Wurttemberg AG; *Int'l*, pg. 2398
ENBW TRADING GMBH—See EnBW Energie Baden-Wurttemberg AG; *Int'l*, pg. 2398
ENBW VERTRIEB GMBH—See EnBW Energie Baden-Wurttemberg AG; *Int'l*, pg. 2398
ENCADRIA STAFFING SOLUTIONS, INC.—See Koch Industries, Inc.; *U.S. Private*, pg. 2327
ENCANA CORPORATION - EASTERN CANADA OFFICE—See Ovintiv Inc.; *U.S. Public*, pg. 1625
ENCANA CORPORATION—See Ovintiv Inc.; *U.S. Public*, pg. 1625
ENCANA GLOBAL HOLDINGS S.A R.L.—See Ovintiv Inc.; *U.S. Public*, pg. 1625
ENCANA MARKETING (USA) INC.—See Ovintiv Inc.; *U.S. Public*, pg. 1625
ENCANA OIL & GAS (USA) INC.—See Ovintiv Inc.; *U.S. Public*, pg. 1625
ENCANTO POTASH CORP.; *Int'l*, pg. 2401
ENCANTO RESOURCES LTD—See Encanto Potash Corp.; *Int'l*, pg. 2401
ENCANTO RESTAURANTS, INC; *U.S. Private*, pg. 1389
ENCAP FLATROCK MIDSTREAM—See EnCap Investments L.P.; *U.S. Private*, pg. 1389
ENCAP INVESTMENTS L.P.; *U.S. Private*, pg. 1389
ENCAP, LLC; *U.S. Private*, pg. 1390
ENCAPSYS LLC; *U.S. Private*, pg. 1390
ENCARE OF PENNYPACK, INC.—See Welltower Inc.; *U.S. Public*, pg. 2348
ENCASE PACKAGING PRIVATE LIMITED—See Vaibhav Global Limited; *Int'l*, pg. 8108
ENCASE REALTY PRIVATE LIMITED—See Oberoi Realty Limited; *Int'l*, pg. 5510
ENCASH ENTERTAINMENT LIMITED; *Int'l*, pg. 2401
ENCAVIS AG; *Int'l*, pg. 2401
ENCAVIS ASSET MANAGEMENT AG—See Encavis AG; *Int'l*, pg. 2401
ENCAVIS PORTFOLIO MANAGEMENT GMBH—See Encavis AG; *Int'l*, pg. 2401
ENCAVIS TECHNICAL SERVICES GMBH—See Encavis AG; *Int'l*, pg. 2401
ENC DIGITAL TECHNOLOGY CO., LTD.; *Int'l*, pg. 2401
ENCE, ENERGIA Y CELULOSA, S.A. - PONTEVEDRA MILL—See ENCE Energia y Celulosa, S.A.; *Int'l*, pg. 2401
ENCE ENERGIA Y CELULOSA, S.A.; *Int'l*, pg. 2401
ENCERATEC, INC.—See Japan Industrial Partners, Inc.; *Int'l*, pg. 3891
ENCHEM CO., LTD.; *Int'l*, pg. 2401
ENCHI CORPORATION—See Marathon Petroleum Corporation; *U.S. Public*, pg. 1364
ENCHO CO., LTD.; *Int'l*, pg. 2401
ENCHOICE, INC.; *U.S. Private*, pg. 1390
ENCI B.V.—See Heidelberg Materials AG; *Int'l*, pg. 3310
ENCI HOLDING N.V.—See Heidelberg Materials AG; *Int'l*, pg. 3309
ENCI-MAASBRICHT B.V.—See Heidelberg Materials AG; *Int'l*, pg. 3309
ENCIMA GLOBAL LLC—See Strategas Research Partners, LLC; *U.S. Private*, pg. 3834
ENCINITAS ENDOSCOPY CENTER, LLC—See Tenet Healthcare Corporation; *U.S. Public*, pg. 2010
ENCINITAS HERITAGE PARTNERS, LLC—See AlerisLife Inc.; *U.S. Private*, pg. 160
ENCINO ENVIRONMENTAL SERVICES, LLC; *U.S. Private*, pg. 1390
ENCISION INC.; *U.S. Public*, pg. 754
ENCITECH CONNECTORS AB—See Beijer Alma AB; *Int'l*, pg. 942
ENCLARA HEALTH, LLC—See Consonance Capital Partners LLC; *U.S. Private*, pg. 1023
ENCLARA PHARMACIA, INC.—See Humana, Inc.; *U.S. Public*, pg. 1069
ENCLAVE AT PINE GROVE, LLC—See Century Communities, Inc.; *U.S. Public*, pg. 475
ENCLOS CORP.—See C.H. Holdings, USA Inc.; *U.S. Private*, pg. 707
ENCODA SYSTEMS INC.—See Quad/Graphics, Inc.; *U.S. Public*, pg. 1744
ENCODE PACKAGING INDIA LIMITED; *Int'l*, pg. 2402
ENCO INDUSTRIES, INC.; *U.S. Private*, pg. 1390
ENCO MANUFACTURING CORP.; *U.S. Private*, pg. 1390
ENCOM GMBH—See Energoprojekt Holding a.d.; *Int'l*, pg. 2421
ENCOMPASS ASIA—See Encompass Digital Media; *U.S. Private*, pg. 1390
ENCOMPASS DIGITAL MEDIA, INC.—See Encompass Digital Media; *U.S. Private*, pg. 1390
ENCOMPASS DIGITAL MEDIA—See Encompass Digital Media; *U.S. Private*, pg. 1390
ENCOMPASS DIGITAL MEDIA—See Encompass Digital Media; *U.S. Private*, pg. 1390
ENCOMPASS DIGITAL MEDIA; *U.S. Private*, pg. 1390
ENCOMPASS ENERGY SERVICES, INC.; *U.S. Public*, pg. 754
ENCOMPASS GROUP AFFILIATES, INC.—See Bain Capital, LP; *U.S. Private*, pg. 444
ENCOMPASS GROUP LLC; *U.S. Private*, pg. 1390
ENCOMPASS GROUP LLC - TECHSTYLES DIVISION—See Encompass Group LLC; *U.S. Private*, pg. 1390
ENCOMPASS GROUP LLC - THE PILLOW FACTORY DIVISION—See Encompass Group LLC; *U.S. Private*, pg. 1390
ENCOMPASS HEALTH CORPORATION; *U.S. Public*, pg. 754
ENCOMPASS HEALTH DEACONESS REHABILITATION HOSPITAL, LLC—See Encompass Health Corporation; *U.S. Public*, pg. 755
ENCOMPASS HEALTH REHABILITATION HOSPITAL OF ALBUQUERQUE, LLC—See Encompass Health Corporation; *U.S. Public*, pg. 755
ENCOMPASS HEALTH REHABILITATION HOSPITAL OF ALTAMONTE SPRINGS, LLC—See Encompass Health Corporation; *U.S. Public*, pg. 755
ENCOMPASS HEALTH REHABILITATION HOSPITAL OF ALTOONA, LLC—See Encompass Health Corporation; *U.S. Public*, pg. 755
ENCOMPASS HEALTH REHABILITATION HOSPITAL OF BAKERSFIELD, LLC—See Encompass Health Corporation; *U.S. Public*, pg. 755
ENCOMPASS HEALTH REHABILITATION HOSPITAL OF BLUFFTON, LLC—See Encompass Health Corporation; *U.S. Public*, pg. 755
ENCOMPASS HEALTH REHABILITATION HOSPITAL OF BRAINTREE, LLC—See Encompass Health Corporation; *U.S. Public*, pg. 755
ENCOMPASS HEALTH REHABILITATION HOSPITAL OF CARDINAL HILL, LLC—See Encompass Health Corporation; *U.S. Public*, pg. 755
ENCOMPASS HEALTH REHABILITATION HOSPITAL OF CINCINNATI, LLC—See Encompass Health Corporation; *U.S. Public*, pg. 755
ENCOMPASS HEALTH REHABILITATION HOSPITAL OF DAYTON, LLC—See Encompass Health Corporation; *U.S. Public*, pg. 755
ENCOMPASS HEALTH REHABILITATION HOSPITAL OF EAST VALLEY, LLC—See Encompass Health Corporation; *U.S. Public*, pg. 755
ENCOMPASS HEALTH REHABILITATION HOSPITAL OF ERIE, LLC—See Encompass Health Corporation; *U.S. Public*, pg. 755
ENCOMPASS HEALTH REHABILITATION HOSPITAL OF FORT SMITH, LLC—See Encompass Health Corporation; *U.S. Public*, pg. 755
ENCOMPASS HEALTH REHABILITATION HOSPITAL OF FRANKLIN, LLC—See Encompass Health Corporation; *U.S. Public*, pg. 755
ENCOMPASS HEALTH REHABILITATION HOSPITAL OF FREDERICKSBURG, LLC—See Encompass Health Corporation; *U.S. Public*, pg. 755
ENCOMPASS HEALTH REHABILITATION HOSPITAL OF GADSDEN, LLC—See Encompass Health Corporation; *U.S. Public*, pg. 755
ENCOMPASS HEALTH REHABILITATION HOSPITAL OF GULFPORT, LLC—See Encompass Health Corporation; *U.S. Public*, pg. 755
ENCOMPASS HEALTH REHABILITATION HOSPITAL OF IOWA CITY, LLC—See Encompass Health Corporation; *U.S. Public*, pg. 755
ENCOMPASS HEALTH REHABILITATION HOSPITAL OF KINGSPORT, LLC—See Encompass Health Corporation; *U.S. Public*, pg. 755
ENCOMPASS HEALTH REHABILITATION HOSPITAL OF LAKEVIEW, LLC—See Encompass Health Corporation; *U.S. Public*, pg. 755
ENCOMPASS HEALTH REHABILITATION HOSPITAL OF LAS VEGAS, LLC—See Encompass Health Corporation; *U.S. Public*, pg. 755
ENCOMPASS HEALTH REHABILITATION HOSPITAL OF MIAMI, LLC—See Encompass Health Corporation; *U.S. Public*, pg. 755
ENCOMPASS HEALTH REHABILITATION HOSPITAL OF MODESTO, LLC—See Encompass Health Corporation; *U.S. Public*, pg. 755
ENCOMPASS HEALTH REHABILITATION HOSPITAL OF MONTGOMERY, INC.—See Encompass Health Corporation; *U.S. Public*, pg. 755
ENCOMPASS HEALTH REHABILITATION HOSPITAL OF NEW ENGLAND, LLC—See Encompass Health Corporation; *U.S. Public*, pg. 755
ENCOMPASS HEALTH REHABILITATION HOSPITAL OF NORTHERN KENTUCKY, LLC—See Encompass Health Corporation; *U.S. Public*, pg. 755
ENCOMPASS HEALTH REHABILITATION HOSPITAL OF NORTHERN VIRGINIA, LLC—See Encompass Health Corporation; *U.S. Public*, pg. 755
ENCOMPASS HEALTH REHABILITATION HOSPITAL OF OCALA, LLC—See Encompass Health Corporation; *U.S. Public*, pg. 755
ENCOMPASS HEALTH REHABILITATION HOSPITAL OF ROCK HILL, LLC—See Encompass Health Corporation; *U.S. Public*, pg. 755
ENCOMPASS HEALTH REHABILITATION HOSPITAL OF SAVANNAH, LLC—See Encompass Health Corporation; *U.S. Public*, pg. 755
ENCOMPASS HEALTH REHABILITATION HOSPITAL OF SHELBY COUNTY, LLC—See Encompass Health Corporation; *U.S. Public*, pg. 755
ENCOMPASS HEALTH REHABILITATION HOSPITAL OF SUGAR LAND, LLC—See Encompass Health Corporation; *U.S. Public*, pg. 755
ENCOMPASS HEALTH REHABILITATION HOSPITAL OF SUNRISE, LLC—See Encompass Health Corporation; *U.S. Public*, pg. 756
ENCOMPASS HEALTH REHABILITATION HOSPITAL OF TOLEDO, LLC—See Encompass Health Corporation; *U.S. Public*, pg. 756
ENCOMPASS HEALTH REHABILITATION HOSPITAL OF TUSTIN, L.P.—See Encompass Health Corporation; *U.S. Public*, pg. 756
ENCOMPASS HEALTH REHABILITATION HOSPITAL OF WESTERN MASSACHUSETTS, LLC—See Encompass Health Corporation; *U.S. Public*, pg. 756
ENCOMPASS HEALTH REHABILITATION HOSPITAL OF WESTERVILLE, LLC—See Encompass Health Corporation; *U.S. Public*, pg. 756
ENCOMPASS HEALTH REHABILITATION HOSPITAL OF YORK, LLC—See Encompass Health Corporation; *U.S. Public*, pg. 756
ENCOMPASS HOLDINGS, INC.; *U.S. Public*, pg. 759
ENCOMPASS HOME HEALTH OF AUSTIN, LLC—See Encompass Health Corporation; *U.S. Public*, pg. 756
ENCOMPASS HOME HEALTH OF COLORADO, LLC—See Encompass Health Corporation; *U.S. Public*, pg. 756
ENCOMPASS HOME HEALTH OF DFW, LLC—See Encompass Health Corporation; *U.S. Public*, pg. 756
ENCOMPASS HOME HEALTH OF THE MID ATLANTIC, LLC—See Encompass Health Corporation; *U.S. Public*, pg. 756
ENCOMPASS HOME HEALTH OF THE SOUTHEAST, LLC—See Encompass Health Corporation; *U.S. Public*, pg. 756

ENCOMPASS HOLDINGS, INC.

CORPORATE AFFILIATIONS

ENCOMPASS HOME HEALTH OF THE WEST, LLC—See Encompass Health Corporation; *U.S. Public*, pg. 756
ENCOMPASS HOSPICE OF THE WEST, LLC—See Encompass Health Corporation; *U.S. Public*, pg. 756
ENCOMPASS INSURANCE COMPANY—See The Allstate Corporation; *U.S. Public*, pg. 2033
ENCOMPASS LATIN AMERICA—See Encompass Digital Media; *U.S. Private*, pg. 1390
ENCOMPASS LENDING GROUP, LP—See Fathom Holdings Inc.; *U.S. Public*, pg. 824
ENCOMPASS LONDON—See Encompass Digital Media; *U.S. Private*, pg. 1390
ENCOMPASS LOS ANGELES—See Encompass Digital Media; *U.S. Private*, pg. 1390
ENCOMPASS OF FORT WORTH, LP—See Encompass Health Corporation; *U.S. Public*, pg. 756
ENCOMPASS OF WEST TEXAS, LP—See Encompass Health Corporation; *U.S. Public*, pg. 756
ENCOMPASS PARTS DISTRIBUTION, INC.—See Bain Capital, LP; *U.S. Private*, pg. 444
ENCOMPASS REHABILITATION HOSPITAL OF ABILENE, LLC—See Encompass Health Corporation; *U.S. Public*, pg. 756
ENCOMPASS REHABILITATION HOSPITAL OF DALLAS, LLC—See Encompass Health Corporation; *U.S. Public*, pg. 756
ENCOMPASS REHABILITATION HOSPITAL OF PEARLAND, LLC—See Encompass Health Corporation; *U.S. Public*, pg. 756
ENCOMPASS REHABILITATION HOSPITAL OF RICHARDSON, LLC—See Encompass Health Corporation; *U.S. Public*, pg. 756
ENCOMPASS REHABILITATION HOSPITAL OF ROUND ROCK, LLC—See Encompass Health Corporation; *U.S. Public*, pg. 756
ENCOMPASS REHABILITATION HOSPITAL OF THE MID-CITIES, LLC—See Encompass Health Corporation; *U.S. Public*, pg. 756
ENCOMPASS REHABILITATION HOSPITAL OF THE WOODLANDS, INC.—See Encompass Health Corporation; *U.S. Public*, pg. 756
ENCOMPASS REHABILITATION HOSPITAL THE VINTAGE, LLC—See Encompass Health Corporation; *U.S. Public*, pg. 756
ENCOMPASS SUPPLY CHAIN MANAGEMENT (CANADA) INC.—See Harwood Capital LLP; *Int'l*, pg. 3282
ENCOMPASS TEXTILES & INTERIORS—See Encompass Group LLC; *U.S. Private*, pg. 1390
ENCON GROUP INC.—See Marsh & McLennan Companies, Inc.; *U.S. Public*, pg. 1374
ENCONNEX LLC; *U.S. Private*, pg. 1390
ENCON SAFETY PRODUCTS—See Nautic Partners, LLC; *U.S. Private*, pg. 2872
ENCO PRODUCTS LIMITED—See GraceKennedy Limited; *Int'l*, pg. 3048
ENCORE ART GROUP; *Int'l*, pg. 2402
ENCORE ASSOCIATES INC.; *U.S. Private*, pg. 1390
ENCORE AUTOMATION LLC—See Taikisha Ltd.; *Int'l*, pg. 7413
ENCORE AVIATION LLC; *U.S. Private*, pg. 1390
ENCORE BANK, NATIONAL ASSOCIATION—See Ovation Holdings, Inc.; *U.S. Private*, pg. 3052
ENCORE BEVERAGE, LLC—See Cork Distributors, LLC; *U.S. Private*, pg. 1050
ENCORE BRANDS, INC.; *U.S. Private*, pg. 1391
ENCORE CAPITAL GROUP, INC.; *U.S. Public*, pg. 759
ENCORE CONSTRUCTION GROUP, INC.—See Garney Holding Company, Inc.; *U.S. Private*, pg. 1645
ENCORE CONSUMER CAPITAL LLC—See Encore Associates Inc.; *U.S. Private*, pg. 1390
ENCORE CRUISES—See H.I.S. Co., Ltd.; *Int'l*, pg. 3195
ENCORE DIGITAL MEDIA LIMITED—See Next 15 Group plc; *Int'l*, pg. 5246
ENCORE ELECTRONICS, INC.—See Allan R. Nelson Engineering (1997) Inc.; *Int'l*, pg. 332
ENCORE ENERGY CORP.; *Int'l*, pg. 2402
ENCORE ENERGY PARTNERS LP—See Grizzly Energy, LLC; *U.S. Public*, pg. 970
ENCORE FRUIT MARKETING INC.; *U.S. Private*, pg. 1391
ENCORE HOLLYWOOD—See Deluxe Corporation; *U.S. Public*, pg. 653
ENCORE HOMES LIMITED—See Guinness Northern Counties Ltd; *Int'l*, pg. 3174
ENCORE LAMI SDN. BHD.—See Ohishi Sangyo Co., Ltd.; *Int'l*, pg. 5532
ENCORE LUXURY COACH LEASING LLC; *U.S. Private*, pg. 1391
ENCORE METALS, INC.—See Reliance Steel & Aluminum Co.; *U.S. Public*, pg. 1781
ENCORE METALS—See Reliance Steel & Aluminum Co.; *U.S. Public*, pg. 1781
ENCORE METALS—See Reliance Steel & Aluminum Co.; *U.S. Public*, pg. 1781
ENCORE METALS—See Reliance Steel & Aluminum Co.; *U.S. Public*, pg. 1781
ENCORE METALS—See Reliance Steel & Aluminum Co.; *U.S. Public*, pg. 1781

ENCORE METALS—See Reliance Steel & Aluminum Co.; *U.S. Public*, pg. 1781
ENCORE MOTORCARS OF SARASOTA, INC.; *U.S. Private*, pg. 1391
ENCORE NETWORKS INC.; *U.S. Private*, pg. 1391
ENCORE PARTNERS LLC; *U.S. Private*, pg. 1391
ENCORE PRODUCTIONS, INC.—See Freeman Decorating Co.; *U.S. Private*, pg. 1605
ENCORE RECEIVABLE MANAGEMENT, INC.—See Concentrix Corporation; *U.S. Public*, pg. 565
ENCORE REDEVELOPMENT, LLC—See SUSI Partners AG; *Int'l*, pg. 7346
ENCORE REHABILITATION SERVICES LLC—See Revelstoke Capital Partners LLC; *U.S. Private*, pg. 3413
ENCORE SENIOR LIVING, LLC—See LCS Holdings Inc.; *U.S. Private*, pg. 2404
ENCORE TICKETS LTD.—See Great Hill Partners, L.P.; *U.S. Private*, pg. 1763
ENCORE UNLIMITED LLC—See Summit Partners, L.P.; *U.S. Private*, pg. 3856
ENCORE WIRE CORPORATION—See Prysmian S.p.A.; *Int'l*, pg. 6010
ENCORP BERHAD—See Lembaga Kemajuan Tanah Persekutuan; *Int'l*, pg. 4448
ENCOS GMBH ENGINEERING + CONSTRUCTION + SERVICE—See TUV NORD AG; *Int'l*, pg. 7980
ENCO SPOL. S R.O.; *Int'l*, pg. 2401
ENCOUNTERCARE SOLUTIONS, INC.; *U.S. Public*, pg. 760
ENCOUNTER RESOURCES LIMITED; *Int'l*, pg. 2402
ENCOUNTER TECHNOLOGIES, INC.; *U.S. Public*, pg. 760
ENCOURAGE TECHNOLOGIES CO., LTD.; *Int'l*, pg. 2402
ENCOWAY GMBH—See Lenze SE; *Int'l*, pg. 4454
ENCRES DUBUIT SA; *Int'l*, pg. 2402
ENCRISP, LLC; *U.S. Private*, pg. 1391
ENC TECHNOLOGY CO., LTD.—See Techwing Inc.; *Int'l*, pg. 7514
ENCYCLE/TEXAS, INC.—See Grupo Mexico, S.A.B. de C.V.; *Int'l*, pg. 3132
ENCYCLOPAEDIA BRITANNICA, INC.; *U.S. Private*, pg. 1391
ENCYSIVE PHARMACEUTICALS INC.—See Pfizer Inc.; *U.S. Public*, pg. 1679
ENDANET GMBH—See MVV Energie AG; *Int'l*, pg. 5108
ENDAT OY—See Clyde Blowers Capital IM LLP; *Int'l*, pg. 1665
ENDAVA DOOEL SKOPJE—See Endava plc; *Int'l*, pg. 2402
ENDAVA GMBH—See Endava plc; *Int'l*, pg. 2402
ENDAVA LIMITED—See Endava plc; *Int'l*, pg. 2402
ENDAVA LIMITED—See Endava plc; *Int'l*, pg. 2402
ENDAVA, LLC—See Endava plc; *Int'l*, pg. 2402
ENDAVA PLC; *Int'l*, pg. 2402
ENDAVA ROMANIA SRL—See Endava plc; *Int'l*, pg. 2402
ENDAVA ROMANIA SRL—See Endava plc; *Int'l*, pg. 2402
ENDAVA (US) LLC—See Endava plc; *Int'l*, pg. 2402
ENDEAVOR ACQUISITION CORP.; *U.S. Private*, pg. 1391
THE ENDEAVOR AGENCY LLC—See The Interpublic Group of Companies, Inc.; *U.S. Public*, pg. 2104
ENDEAVOR AIR, INC.—See Delta Air Lines, Inc.; *U.S. Public*, pg. 651
ENDEAVOR BUSINESS MEDIA LLC; *U.S. Private*, pg. 1391
ENDEAVOR COMMERCE, INC.—See Francisco Partners Management, LP; *U.S. Private*, pg. 1592
ENDEAVOR ENERGY RESOURCES LP; *U.S. Private*, pg. 1391
ENDEAVOR EXPERIENCES, LLC—See Silver Lake Group, LLC; *U.S. Private*, pg. 3654
ENDEAVOR GROUP HOLDINGS, INC.—See Silver Lake Group, LLC; *U.S. Private*, pg. 3653
ENDEAVOR INSURANCE SERVICES, INC.—See ABRY Partners, LLC; *U.S. Private*, pg. 43
ENDEAVOR IP, INC.; *U.S. Private*, pg. 1391
ENDEAVOR OPERATIONS PTY LTD—See Polymetals Resources Ltd.; *Int'l*, pg. 5915
ENDEAVOR PIPELINE, INC.—See GMX Resources Inc.; *U.S. Private*, pg. 1723
ENDEAVOR SCHOOLS, LLC; *U.S. Private*, pg. 1391
ENDEAVOR STREAMING, LLC—See William Morris Endeavor Entertainment, LLC; *U.S. Private*, pg. 4523
ENDEAVOUR AIR, INC.—See Delta Air Lines, Inc.; *U.S. Public*, pg. 652
ENDEAVOUR CH PTY LTD—See EBOS Group Limited; *Int'l*, pg. 2285
ENDEAVOUR FINANCIAL LTD.; *Int'l*, pg. 2402
ENDEAVOUR GROUP LIMITED; *Int'l*, pg. 2402
ENDEAVOUR MINERALS PTY LTD—See Impact Minerals Limited; *Int'l*, pg. 3630
ENDEAVOUR MINING PLC; *Int'l*, pg. 2402
ENDEAVOUR SILVER CORP.; *Int'l*, pg. 2402
ENDEAVOUR SOFTWARE TECHNOLOGIES INC.—See Genpact Limited; *Int'l*, pg. 2926
ENDEAVOUR SOFTWARE TECHNOLOGIES PRIVATE LIMITED—See Genpact Limited; *Int'l*, pg. 2926
ENDEAVOUR UNITED CO., LTD.—See Phoenix Capital Co., Ltd.; *Int'l*, pg. 5849
ENDEAVOUR VENTURES LIMITED; *Int'l*, pg. 2403

ENDECO OMEGA SINTO (PTY) LTD.—See Sintokogio Ltd.; *Int'l*, pg. 6958
ENDECOTTS INC.—See Verder International B.V.; *Int'l*, pg. 8166
ENDEKA CERAMICS S.A.—See American Securities LLC; *U.S. Private*, pg. 251
ENDEKA CERAMICS SPA—See American Securities LLC; *U.S. Private*, pg. 251
ENDEKA CERAMICS S.R.L.—See American Securities LLC; *U.S. Private*, pg. 251
ENDEKA GROUP, INC.—See DigitalBridge Group, Inc.; *U.S. Public*, pg. 664
ENDELL VETERINARY GROUP LIMITED—See CVS Group Plc; *Int'l*, pg. 1890
ENDEL SAS—See ENGIE SA; *Int'l*, pg. 2431
ENDEMOL ARGENTINA S.A.—See LOV Group Invest SAS; *Int'l*, pg. 4564
ENDEMOL BELGIE N.V.—See LOV Group Invest SAS; *Int'l*, pg. 4564
ENDEMOL BRAZIL—See LOV Group Invest SAS; *Int'l*, pg. 4564
ENDEMOL CHILE LDA.—See LOV Group Invest SAS; *Int'l*, pg. 4564
ENDEMOL COLOMBIA SA—See LOV Group Invest SAS; *Int'l*, pg. 4564
ENDEMOL DEUTSCHLAND GMBH—See LOV Group Invest SAS; *Int'l*, pg. 4564
ENDEMOL ESPANA HOLDING, S.L.—See LOV Group Invest SAS; *Int'l*, pg. 4564
ENDEMOL FICTION—See LOV Group Invest SAS; *Int'l*, pg. 4564
ENDEMOL FRANCE—See LOV Group Invest SAS; *Int'l*, pg. 4564
ENDEMOL GLOBO S.A.—See LOV Group Invest SAS; *Int'l*, pg. 4564
ENDEMOL INDIA—See LOV Group Invest SAS; *Int'l*, pg. 4563
ENDEMOL ITALIA HOLDING S.P.A.—See LOV Group Invest SAS; *Int'l*, pg. 4564
ENDEMOL MALAYSIA ENTERTAINMENT GROUP SDN—See LOV Group Invest SAS; *Int'l*, pg. 4564
ENDEMOL MEDYAPRODUCTION TICARET LIMITED—See LOV Group Invest SAS; *Int'l*, pg. 4564
ENDEMOL MIDDLE EAST PRODUCTIONS S.A.L.—See LOV Group Invest SAS; *Int'l*, pg. 4564
ENDEMOL MIDDLE EAST—See LOV Group Invest SAS; *Int'l*, pg. 4564
ENDEMOL MOSCOW—See LOV Group Invest SAS; *Int'l*, pg. 4564
ENDEMOL NEDERLAND, B.V.—See LOV Group Invest SAS; *Int'l*, pg. 4564
ENDEMOL NORDIC AB—See LOV Group Invest SAS; *Int'l*, pg. 4564
ENDEMOL POLAND—See LOV Group Invest SAS; *Int'l*, pg. 4564
ENDEMOL PORTUGAL LDA.—See LOV Group Invest SAS; *Int'l*, pg. 4564
ENDEMOL SHINE AUSTRALIA PTY LTD—See LOV Group Invest SAS; *Int'l*, pg. 4565
ENDEMOL SHINE GROUP SPV B.V.—See LOV Group Invest SAS; *Int'l*, pg. 4564
ENDEMOL SHINE NORDICS AB—See LOV Group Invest SAS; *Int'l*, pg. 4565
ENDEMOL SOUTH AFRICA (PTY) LTD.—See LOV Group Invest SAS; *Int'l*, pg. 4564
ENDEMOL SWEDEN AB—See LOV Group Invest SAS; *Int'l*, pg. 4564
ENDEMOL UK PLC—See LOV Group Invest SAS; *Int'l*, pg. 4564
ENDEMOL USA INC.—See LOV Group Invest SAS; *Int'l*, pg. 4564
ENDERLE GROUP, INC.; *U.S. Private*, pg. 1391
ENDERLEIN & CO. GMBH—See UniCredit S.p.A.; *Int'l*, pg. 8039
ENDERO OOO—See Know IT AB; *Int'l*, pg. 4212
ENDERO OY—See Know IT AB; *Int'l*, pg. 4212
ENDESA ARGENTINA SA—See Enel S.p.A.; *Int'l*, pg. 2413
ENDESA CEMSA SA—See Enel S.p.A.; *Int'l*, pg. 2413
ENDESA DESARROLLO SL—See Enel S.p.A.; *Int'l*, pg. 2412
ENDESA ECO SA—See Enel S.p.A.; *Int'l*, pg. 2413
ENDESA ENERGIA SA—See Enel S.p.A.; *Int'l*, pg. 2412
ENDESA FINANCIACION FILIALES SAU—See Enel S.p.A.; *Int'l*, pg. 2412
ENDESA GENERACION PORTUGAL, S.A.—See Enel S.p.A.; *Int'l*, pg. 2412
ENDESA GENERACION, S.A.—See Enel S.p.A.; *Int'l*, pg. 2412
ENDESA INGENIERIA SLU—See Enel S.p.A.; *Int'l*, pg. 2412
ENDESA IRELAND LTD—See SSE Plc; *Int'l*, pg. 7155
ENDESA NETWORK FACTORY SL—See Enel S.p.A.; *Int'l*, pg. 2412
ENDESA RED SA—See Enel S.p.A.; *Int'l*, pg. 2412
ENDESA, S.A.—See Enel S.p.A.; *Int'l*, pg. 2412
ENDESA SERVICIOS SL—See Enel S.p.A.; *Int'l*, pg. 2412
ENDESA X SERVICIOS SLU—See Enel S.p.A.; *Int'l*, pg. 2412
ENDESA X WAY S.L.—See Enel S.p.A.; *Int'l*, pg. 2412

ENDESCO SERVICES CORPORATION—See Gas Technology Institute; *U.S. Private*, pg. 1647
ENDEVIS, LLC—See My Job Matcher, Inc.; *U.S. Private*, pg. 2823
ENDEXX CORPORATION; *U.S. Public*, pg. 760
ENDGAME SYSTEMS, LLC; *U.S. Private*, pg. 1391
ENDI CORP.; *U.S. Public*, pg. 760
ENDICOTT CLAY PRODUCTS CO.; *U.S. Private*, pg. 1391
ENDICOTT GROUP EQUITY PARTNERS, L.P.; *U.S. Private*, pg. 1391
ENDICOTT INTERCONNECT TECHNOLOGIES, INC.; *U.S. Private*, pg. 1391
ENDINET B.V.—See Alliander N.V.; *Int'l*, pg. 341
ENDION MEDICAL HEALTHCARE, P.C.—See United-Health Group Incorporated; *U.S. Public*, pg. 2240
ENDLESS CHARGE, INC.; *U.S. Private*, pg. 1391
ENDLESS GAMES INC.—See Goliath International Holding BV; *Int'l*, pg. 3036
ENDLESS LLP; *Int'l*, pg. 2403
ENDLESS MOUNTAINS HEALTH SYSTEMS; *U.S. Private*, pg. 1391
ENDLESS POOLS, INC.—See Masco Corporation; *U.S. Public*, pg. 1392
ENDLESS SOLAR CORPORATION PTY LIMITED; *Int'l*, pg. 2403
ENDLESS YOUTH AND LIFE LLC—See Suarez Corporation Industries; *U.S. Private*, pg. 3846
ENDOCEUTICS INC.; *Int'l*, pg. 2405
ENDOCHOICE HOLDINGS, INC.—See Boston Scientific Corporation; *U.S. Public*, pg. 375
ENDOCHOICE, INC.—See Boston Scientific Corporation; *U.S. Public*, pg. 375
ENDOCYTE, INC.—See Novartis AG; *Int'l*, pg. 5457
ENDODENT INC—See COLTENE Holding AG; *Int'l*, pg. 1706
ENDO FINANCE PLC; *Int'l*, pg. 2403
ENDO FORGING (THAILAND) CO. LTD.—See Endo Manufacturing Co., Ltd.; *Int'l*, pg. 2405
ENDOGENE LTD.; *Int'l*, pg. 2405
ENDO HEALTH SOLUTIONS INC.—See Endo International plc; *Int'l*, pg. 2404
ENDO INTERNATIONAL PLC; *Int'l*, pg. 2403
ENDO LIGHTING ACCESSORIES INDIA PRIVATE LIMITED—See ENDO Lighting Corporation; *Int'l*, pg. 2404
ENDO LIGHTING CORPORATION; *Int'l*, pg. 2404
ENDO LIGHTING SE ASIA PTE. LTD—See ENDO Lighting Corporation; *Int'l*, pg. 2404
ENDO LIGHTING (THAILAND) PUBLIC COMPANY LTD.—See ENDO Lighting Corporation; *Int'l*, pg. 2404
ENDO LIGHTING VIETNAM CO. LTD.—See ENDO Lighting Corporation; *Int'l*, pg. 2404
ENDOLOGIX, INC.; *U.S. Private*, pg. 1392
ENDO MANAGEMENT LIMITED—See Endo International plc; *Int'l*, pg. 2404
ENDO MANUFACTURING CO., LTD.; *Int'l*, pg. 2405
ENDO METAL SLEEVE (THAILAND) CO., LTD.—See Endo Manufacturing Co., Ltd.; *Int'l*, pg. 2405
ENDOMINES AB; *Int'l*, pg. 2405
ENDOMINES OY—See Endomines AB; *Int'l*, pg. 2405
ENDONOVO THERAPEUTICS, INC.; *U.S. Public*, pg. 760
ENDO PHARMACEUTICALS SOLUTIONS INC. - NEW JERSEY—See Endo International plc; *Int'l*, pg. 2404
ENDO PHARMACEUTICALS SOLUTIONS INC.—See Endo International plc; *Int'l*, pg. 2404
ENDOR EHF.—See Hexatronic Group AB; *Int'l*, pg. 3370
ENDOR PRODUCTIONS LIMITED—See ProSiebenSat.1 Media SE; *Int'l*, pg. 6000
ENDOSCOPIC TECHNOLOGIES, LLC—See AtriCure, Inc.; *U.S. Public*, pg. 225
ENDOSCOPY ASC OF MIDDLE GEORGIA, LLC—See Tenet Healthcare Corporation; *U.S. Public*, pg. 2002
THE ENDOSCOPY CENTER OF EL PASO, L.P.—See KKR & Co. Inc.; *U.S. Public*, pg. 1247
ENDOSCOPY CENTER OF HACKENSACK, LLC—See Tenet Healthcare Corporation; *U.S. Public*, pg. 2010
THE ENDOSCOPY CENTER OF KNOXVILLE, L.P.—See KKR & Co. Inc.; *U.S. Public*, pg. 1247
ENDOSCOPY CENTER OF LAKE COUNTY LLC—See Tenet Healthcare Corporation; *U.S. Public*, pg. 2002
THE ENDOSCOPY CENTER OF SANTA FE, L.P.—See KKR & Co. Inc.; *U.S. Public*, pg. 1247
THE ENDOSCOPY CENTER OF SOUTHEAST TEXAS, L.P.—See KKR & Co. Inc.; *U.S. Public*, pg. 1247
ENDOSCOPY CENTER OF SOUTH SACRAMENTO, LLC—See Tenet Healthcare Corporation; *U.S. Public*, pg. 2002
THE ENDOSCOPY CENTER OF ST. THOMAS, L.P.—See KKR & Co. Inc.; *U.S. Public*, pg. 1247
THE ENDOSCOPY CENTER OF THE SOUTH BAY, L.P.—See KKR & Co. Inc.; *U.S. Public*, pg. 1247
THE ENDOSCOPY CENTER OF TOPEKA, L.P.—See KKR & Co. Inc.; *U.S. Public*, pg. 1247
THE ENDOSCOPY CENTER OF WASHINGTON D.C., L.P.—See KKR & Co. Inc.; *U.S. Public*, pg. 1247
THE ENDOSCOPY CENTER OF WEST CENTRAL OHIO, LLC—See Kelso & Company, L.P.; *U.S. Private*, pg. 2279
ENDOSCOPY CONSULTANTS, LLC—See WellStar Health System, Inc.; *U.S. Private*, pg. 4478
ENDOSCOPY DEVELOPMENT COMPANY LLC—See RoundTable Healthcare Management, Inc.; *U.S. Private*, pg. 3489
ENDOSCOPY OF PLANO, L.P.—See HCA Healthcare, Inc.; *U.S. Public*, pg. 995
ENDOSOLUTIONS, INC.—See Integra LifeSciences Holdings Corporation; *U.S. Public*, pg. 1135
ENDO STAINLESS STEEL (THAILAND) CO. LTD.—See Endo Manufacturing Co., Ltd.; *Int'l*, pg. 2405
ENDO STAINLESS STEEL (VIETNAM) CO., LTD.—See Endo Manufacturing Co., Ltd.; *Int'l*, pg. 2405
ENDOSTIM, INC.; *U.S. Private*, pg. 1392
ENDOTEC, INC.—See Cellumed Co., Ltd; *Int'l*, pg. 1395
ENDO THAI CO.LTD.—See Endo Manufacturing Co., Ltd.; *Int'l*, pg. 2405
ENDO-THERAPEUTICS, INC.; *U.S. Private*, pg. 1392
ENDO TRADE (BEIJING) CO., LTD.—See ENDO Lighting Corporation; *Int'l*, pg. 2404
ENDO TRADE (BEIJING) SHANGHAI CO., LTD—See ENDO Lighting Corporation; *Int'l*, pg. 2404
ENDO U.S. INC.—See Endo International plc; *Int'l*, pg. 2404
ENDPOINT CLINICAL—See Laboratory Corporation of America Holdings; *U.S. Public*, pg. 1286
ENDPOINT EXCHANGE, LLC—See Fidelity National Infor; *U.S. Public*, pg. 832
ENDRA LIFE SCIENCES INC.; *U.S. Public*, pg. 760
ENDRES MANUFACTURING CO, INC.; *U.S. Private*, pg. 1392
ENDRES PROCESSING LLC; *U.S. Private*, pg. 1392
ENDRESS AND HAUSER ARABIA LLC—See Endress+Hauser (International) Holding AG; *Int'l*, pg. 2406
ENDRESS+HAUSER AB—See Endress+Hauser (International) Holding AG; *Int'l*, pg. 2406
ENDRESS+HAUSER AG—See Endress+Hauser (International) Holding AG; *Int'l*, pg. 2406
ENDRESS+HAUSER ALGERIE SARL—See Endress+Hauser (International) Holding AG; *Int'l*, pg. 2406
ENDRESS+HAUSER ANALYTICAL INSTRUMENTS (SUZHOU) CO., LTD.—See Endress+Hauser (International) Holding AG; *Int'l*, pg. 2406
ENDRESS+HAUSER ARGENTINA S.A.—See Endress+Hauser (International) Holding AG; *Int'l*, pg. 2406
ENDRESS HAUSER A.S.—See Endress+Hauser (International) Holding AG; *Int'l*, pg. 2406
ENDRESS+HAUSER A/S—See Endress+Hauser (International) Holding AG; *Int'l*, pg. 2406
ENDRESS+HAUSER AS—See Endress+Hauser (International) Holding AG; *Int'l*, pg. 2406
ENDRESS+HAUSER AUSTRALIA PTY LTD.—See Endress+Hauser (International) Holding AG; *Int'l*, pg. 2406
ENDRESS+HAUSER (BALTIC) UAB—See Endress+Hauser (International) Holding AG; *Int'l*, pg. 2406
ENDRESS+HAUSER (BRASIL) INSTRUMENTACAO E AUTOMACAO LTDA—See Endress+Hauser (International) Holding AG; *Int'l*, pg. 2406
ENDRESS+HAUSER B.V.—See Endress+Hauser (International) Holding AG; *Int'l*, pg. 2406
ENDRESS+HAUSER CANADA LTD.—See Endress+Hauser (International) Holding AG; *Int'l*, pg. 2407
ENDRESS+HAUSER CHILE LTD.—See Endress+Hauser (International) Holding AG; *Int'l*, pg. 2407
ENDRESS+HAUSER (CHINA) AUTOMATION INSTRUMENTATION CO. LTD.—See Endress+Hauser (International) Holding AG; *Int'l*, pg. 2406
ENDRESS+HAUSER COLOMBIA S.A.S.—See Endress+Hauser (International) Holding AG; *Int'l*, pg. 2407
ENDRESS+HAUSER CONDUCTA GMBH+CO. KG—See Endress+Hauser (International) Holding AG; *Int'l*, pg. 2407
ENDRESS+HAUSER CONDUCTA, INC.—See Endress+Hauser (International) Holding AG; *Int'l*, pg. 2407
ENDRESS+HAUSER CONSULT AG—See Endress+Hauser (International) Holding AG; *Int'l*, pg. 2407
ENDRESS+HAUSER CONTROLE E AUTOMACAO LTDA.—See Endress+Hauser (International) Holding AG; *Int'l*, pg. 2407
ENDRESS+HAUSER CZECH S.R.O.—See Endress+Hauser (International) Holding AG; *Int'l*, pg. 2407
ENDRESS+HAUSER (DEUTSCHLAND) GMBH+CO. KG.—See Endress+Hauser (International) Holding AG; *Int'l*, pg. 2406
ENDRESS+HAUSER D.O.O.—See Endress+Hauser (International) Holding AG; *Int'l*, pg. 2407
ENDRESS+HAUSER ELEKTRONIK SAN.VE TIC. A.S.—See Endress+Hauser (International) Holding AG; *Int'l*, pg. 2407
ENDRESS+HAUSER FLOWTEC AG—See Endress+Hauser (International) Holding AG; *Int'l*, pg. 2407
ENDRESS+HAUSER FLOWTEC (BRASIL) FLUXOMETROS LTDA.—See Endress+Hauser (International) Holding AG; *Int'l*, pg. 2407
ENDRESS+HAUSER FLOWTEC (CHINA) CO., LTD.—See Endress+Hauser (International) Holding AG; *Int'l*, pg. 2407
ENDRESS+HAUSER FLOWTEC (INDIA) PVT. LTD.—See Endress+Hauser (International) Holding AG; *Int'l*, pg. 2407
ENDRESS+HAUSER GES.M.B.H.—See Endress+Hauser (International) Holding AG; *Int'l*, pg. 2407
ENDRESS+HAUSER GROUP SERVICES AG—See Endress+Hauser (International) Holding AG; *Int'l*, pg. 2407
ENDRESS+HAUSER (HELLAS) S.A.—See Endress+Hauser (International) Holding AG; *Int'l*, pg. 2406
ENDRESS+HAUSER (H.K.) LTD.—See Endress+Hauser (International) Holding AG; *Int'l*, pg. 2406
ENDRESS+HAUSER INC. - NORTHEAST REGIONAL CENTER—See Endress+Hauser (International) Holding AG; *Int'l*, pg. 2407
ENDRESS+HAUSER INC.—See Endress+Hauser (International) Holding AG; *Int'l*, pg. 2407
ENDRESS+HAUSER (INDIA) AUTOMATION INSTRUMENTATION PVT. LTD.—See Endress+Hauser (International) Holding AG; *Int'l*, pg. 2406
ENDRESS+HAUSER (INDIA) PVT. LTD.—See Endress+Hauser (International) Holding AG; *Int'l*, pg. 2406
ENDRESS+HAUSER INFOSERVE GMBH+CO. KG—See Endress+Hauser (International) Holding AG; *Int'l*, pg. 2407
ENDRESS+HAUSER INTERNATIONAL AG—See Endress+Hauser (International) Holding AG; *Int'l*, pg. 2407
ENDRESS+HAUSER (INTERNATIONAL) HOLDING AG; *Int'l*, pg. 2405
ENDRESS+HAUSER (IRELAND) LTD.—See Endress+Hauser (International) Holding AG; *Int'l*, pg. 2406
ENDRESS+HAUSER ITALIA S.P.A.—See Endress+Hauser (International) Holding AG; *Int'l*, pg. 2407
ENDRESS+HAUSER JAPAN CO.,LTD.—See Endress+Hauser (International) Holding AG; *Int'l*, pg. 2407
ENDRESS+HAUSER KOREA CO., LTD.—See Endress+Hauser (International) Holding AG; *Int'l*, pg. 2407
ENDRESS+HAUSER LTD.—See Endress+Hauser (International) Holding AG; *Int'l*, pg. 2407
ENDRESS+HAUSER MAGYARORSZAG FOLYAMATMUSZEREZESI KFT.—See Endress+Hauser (International) Holding AG; *Int'l*, pg. 2407
ENDRESS+HAUSER (MAGYARORSZAG) KFT.—See Endress+Hauser (International) Holding AG; *Int'l*, pg. 2406
ENDRESS+HAUSER MESSTECHNIK GMBH+CO. KG—See Endress+Hauser (International) Holding AG; *Int'l*, pg. 2407
ENDRESS + HAUSER MEXICO, S.A. DE C.V.—See Endress+Hauser (International) Holding AG; *Int'l*, pg. 2406
ENDRESS+HAUSER (M) SDN. BHD.—See Endress+Hauser (International) Holding AG; *Int'l*, pg. 2406
ENDRESS+HAUSER OY—See Endress+Hauser (International) Holding AG; *Int'l*, pg. 2407
ENDRESS+HAUSER PANAMA INC.—See Endress+Hauser (International) Holding AG; *Int'l*, pg. 2407
ENDRESS+HAUSER PHILIPPINES INC.—See Endress+Hauser (International) Holding AG; *Int'l*, pg. 2407
ENDRESS+HAUSER POLSKA SP. Z O.O.—See Endress+Hauser (International) Holding AG; *Int'l*, pg. 2407
ENDRESS+HAUSER PORTUGAL, LDA—See Endress+Hauser (International) Holding AG; *Int'l*, pg. 2407
ENDRESS & HAUSER PROCESS AUTOMATION (UAE) TRADING LLC—See Endress+Hauser (International) Holding AG; *Int'l*, pg. 2406
ENDRESS+HAUSER PROCESS SOLUTIONS AG—See Endress+Hauser (International) Holding AG; *Int'l*, pg. 2407
ENDRESS+HAUSER (PTY.) LTD.—See Endress+Hauser (International) Holding AG; *Int'l*, pg. 2406
ENDRESS+HAUSER (QATAR) L.L.C.—See Endress+Hauser (International) Holding AG; *Int'l*, pg. 2406
ENDRESS+HAUSER ROMANIA SRL—See Endress+Hauser (International) Holding AG; *Int'l*, pg. 2407
ENDRESS+HAUSER SA/NV—See Endress+Hauser (International) Holding AG; *Int'l*, pg. 2408

ENDRESS+HAUSER (INTERNATIONAL) HOLDING AG

ENDRESS+HAUSER SAS - CERNAY—See Endress+Hauser (International) Holding AG; *Int'l*, pg. 2408
ENDRESS+HAUSER SAS—See Endress+Hauser (International) Holding AG; *Int'l*, pg. 2408
ENDRESS+HAUSER (SCHWEIZ) AG—See Endress+Hauser (International) Holding AG; *Int'l*, pg. 2406
ENDRESS+HAUSER (SEA) PTE LTD.—See Endress+Hauser (International) Holding AG; *Int'l*, pg. 2406
ENDRESS+HAUSER SE+CO. KG.—See Endress+Hauser (International) Holding AG; *Int'l*, pg. 2408
ENDRESS+HAUSER SHANGHAI AUTOMATION EQUIPMENT CO. LTD.—See Endress+Hauser (International) Holding AG; *Int'l*, pg. 2408
ENDRESS+HAUSER SICESTHERM S.R.L.—See Endress+Hauser (International) Holding AG; *Int'l*, pg. 2408
ENDRESS+HAUSER (SLOVENIJA) D.O.O.—See Endress+Hauser (International) Holding AG; *Int'l*, pg. 2406
ENDRESS+HAUSER (SUZHOU) AUTOMATION INSTRUMENTATION CO., LTD.—See Endress+Hauser (International) Holding AG; *Int'l*, pg. 2406
ENDRESS+HAUSER SYSTEMPLAN GMBH—See Endress+Hauser (International) Holding AG; *Int'l*, pg. 2408
ENDRESS+HAUSER (THAILAND) LTD.—See Endress+Hauser (International) Holding AG; *Int'l*, pg. 2406
ENDRESS+HAUSER (UAE) LLC—See Endress+Hauser (International) Holding AG; *Int'l*, pg. 2406
ENDRESS+HAUSER (USA) AUTOMATION INSTRUMENTATION INC.—See Endress+Hauser (International) Holding AG; *Int'l*, pg. 2407
ENDRESS+HAUSER VENEZUELA S.A.—See Endress+Hauser (International) Holding AG; *Int'l*, pg. 2408
ENDRESS+HAUSER (VIETNAM) CO., LTD.—See Endress+Hauser (International) Holding AG; *Int'l*, pg. 2406
ENDRESS+HAUSER WETZER GMBH + CO. KG—See Endress+Hauser (International) Holding AG; *Int'l*, pg. 2408
ENDRESS+HAUSER WETZER INDIA PVT. LTD.—See Endress+Hauser (International) Holding AG; *Int'l*, pg. 2408
ENDRESS+HAUSER WETZER (SUZHOU) CO. LTD.—See Endress+Hauser (International) Holding AG; *Int'l*, pg. 2408
ENDRESS+HAUSER WETZER USA INC.—See Endress+Hauser (International) Holding AG; *Int'l*, pg. 2408
ENDRESS+HAUSER YAMANASHI CO. LTD.—See Endress+Hauser (International) Holding AG; *Int'l*, pg. 2408
ENDRESS Y HAUSER, S.A.—See Endress+Hauser (International) Holding AG; *Int'l*, pg. 2406
END RESULT COMPANY LLC—See Genstar Capital, LLC; *U.S. Private*, pg. 1678
ENDRICH BAUELEMENTE S.L.—See Endrich Bauelemente Vertriebs GmbH; *Int'l*, pg. 2409
ENDRICH BAUELEMENTE VERTRIEBS GMBH; *Int'l*, pg. 2409
ENDRICH GES.M.B.H—See Endrich Bauelemente Vertriebs GmbH; *Int'l*, pg. 2409
ENDRIES INTERNATIONAL, INC.—See MSD Capital, L.P.; *U.S. Private*, pg. 2807
ENDRISS GMBH—See Amadeus Fire AG; *Int'l*, pg. 405
END STAGE RENAL DISEASE NETWORK OF TEXAS, INC.—See Alliant Health Solutions; *U.S. Private*, pg. 184
ENDURANCE ACQUISITION CORP.; *U.S. Public*, pg. 760
ENDURANCE AMANN GMBH—See Affirma Capital Limited; *Int'l*, pg. 187
ENDURANCE ENERGY LTD.—See Warburg Pincus LLC; *U.S. Private*, pg. 4438
ENDURANCE ENGINEERING S.R.L.—See Affirma Capital Limited; *Int'l*, pg. 187
ENDURANCE EXPLORATION GROUP, INC.; *U.S. Public*, pg. 760
ENDURANCE F.O.A. S.P.A.—See Affirma Capital Limited; *Int'l*, pg. 187
ENDURANCE FONDALMEC S.P.A.—See Affirma Capital Limited; *Int'l*, pg. 187
ENDURANCE GOLD CORPORATION; *Int'l*, pg. 2410
ENDURANCE INTERNATIONAL GROUP HOLDINGS, INC.—See Clearlake Capital Group, L.P.; *U.S. Private*, pg. 934
ENDURANCE INTERNATIONAL GROUP HOLDINGS, INC.—See Siris Capital Group, LLC; *U.S. Private*, pg. 3673
THE ENDURANCE INTERNATIONAL GROUP, INC.—See Clearlake Capital Group, L.P.; *U.S. Private*, pg. 934
THE ENDURANCE INTERNATIONAL GROUP, INC.—See Siris Capital Group, LLC; *U.S. Private*, pg. 3673
ENDURANCE IT SERVICES; *U.S. Private*, pg. 1392
ENDURANCE MOTIVE SA; *Int'l*, pg. 2410

ENDURANCE OVERSEAS S.R.L.—See Affirma Capital Limited; *Int'l*, pg. 187
ENDURANCE S.R.L.—See Sesa S.p.A.; *Int'l*, pg. 6728
ENDURANCE TECHNOLOGIES, INC.—See Arsenal Capital Management LP; *U.S. Private*, pg. 339
ENDURANCE TECHNOLOGIES LIMITED—See Affirma Capital Limited; *Int'l*, pg. 187
ENDURANCE WEALTH MANAGEMENT, INC.—See Clayton, Dubilier & Rice, LLC; *U.S. Private*, pg. 923
ENDURANCE WEALTH MANAGEMENT, INC.—See Stone Point Capital LLC; *U.S. Private*, pg. 3824
ENDURANCE WORLDWIDE INSURANCE LIMITED—See Sompo Holdings, Inc.; *Int'l*, pg. 7087
ENDURA PLASTICS, INC.; *U.S. Private*, pg. 1392
ENDURA PRODUCTS INC.—See Owens Corning; *U.S. Public*, pg. 1626
ENDURA S.A.—See The Swatch Group Ltd.; *Int'l*, pg. 7691
ENDUR ASA; *Int'l*, pg. 2409
ENDURIS EXTRUSIONS, INC.; *U.S. Private*, pg. 1392
ENDUR MARITIME AS—See Endur ASA; *Int'l*, pg. 2410
ENDURO INDUSTRIES, INC.—See Black Diamond Capital Holdings, LLC; *U.S. Private*, pg. 570
ENDURO SYSTEMS, INC.; *U.S. Private*, pg. 1392
END USER SERVICES, INC.—See Ad-Base Group, Inc.; *U.S. Private*, pg. 72
ENDYMED LTD.; *Int'l*, pg. 2410
THE END ZONE, INC.—See RCI Hospitality Holdings, Inc.; *U.S. Public*, pg. 1767
ENEA AB; *Int'l*, pg. 2410
ENEABBA GAS LIMITED; *Int'l*, pg. 2410
ENEA BIOENERGIA SP. Z O.O.—See ENEA S.A.; *Int'l*, pg. 2410
ENEA CIEPLO SERWIS SP. Z O.O.—See ENEA S.A.; *Int'l*, pg. 2410
ENEA CIEPLO SP. Z O.O.—See ENEA S.A.; *Int'l*, pg. 2410
ENEA ELEKTROWNIA POLANIEC S.A.—See ENEA S.A.; *Int'l*, pg. 2410
ENEA GMBH—See Enea AB; *Int'l*, pg. 2410
ENEA INNOWACJE SP. Z O.O.—See ENEA S.A.; *Int'l*, pg. 2410
ENEA KK—See Enea AB; *Int'l*, pg. 2410
ENEA LOGISTYKA SP. Z O.O.—See ENEA S.A.; *Int'l*, pg. 2410
ENEA NETBRICKS SAS—See Enea AB; *Int'l*, pg. 2410
ENEA OPERATOR SP. Z O.O.—See ENEA S.A.; *Int'l*, pg. 2410
ENEA OSWIETLENIE SP. Z O.O.—See ENEA S.A.; *Int'l*, pg. 2410
ENEA POLANIEC SERWIS SP. Z O.O.—See ENEA S.A.; *Int'l*, pg. 2410
ENEA POLYHEDRA LTD—See Enea AB; *Int'l*, pg. 2410
ENEARC CO., LTD.—See Itochu Enex Co., Ltd.; *Int'l*, pg. 3841
ENEA S.A.; *Int'l*, pg. 2410
ENEA SERVICES ROMANIA SRL—See AROBS Transilvania Software S.A.; *Int'l*, pg. 577
ENEA SERWIS SP. Z O.O.—See ENEA S.A.; *Int'l*, pg. 2410
ENEA SOFTWARE (BEIJING) CO., LTD.—See Enea AB; *Int'l*, pg. 2410
ENEA SOFTWARE & SERVICES, INC—See Enea AB; *Int'l*, pg. 2410
ENEA SOFTWARE SRL—See Enea AB; *Int'l*, pg. 2410
ENEA TEKSCI INC.—See Enea AB; *Int'l*, pg. 2410
ENEA TRADING SP. Z O.O.—See ENEA S.A.; *Int'l*, pg. 2410
ENEA WYTWARZANIE SP. Z O.O.—See Lubelski Wegiel BOGDANKA Spolka Akcyjna; *Int'l*, pg. 4572
ENECAL PTE. LIMITED—See SPT Energy Group Inc.; *Int'l*, pg. 7146
ENECHANGE CO., LTD.—See EPCO Co., Ltd.; *Int'l*, pg. 2459
ENECO BELGIUM N.V.—See Eneco Holding N.V.; *Int'l*, pg. 2411
ENECO ENERGY LIMITED; *Int'l*, pg. 2411
ENECO HOLDING N.V.; *Int'l*, pg. 2411
ENECO REFRESH LIMITED; *Int'l*, pg. 2411
ENECO ZUID NEDERLAND B.V.—See Eneco Holding N.V.; *Int'l*, pg. 2411
ENECSYS LLC—See Enecsys plc; *Int'l*, pg. 2411
ENECSYS PLC; *Int'l*, pg. 2411
ENECSYS TAIWAN LIMITED—See Enecsys plc; *Int'l*, pg. 2411
ENEDO FINLAND OY—See Inission AB; *Int'l*, pg. 3703
ENEDO INC.—See Inission AB; *Int'l*, pg. 3703
ENEDO PLC—See Inission AB; *Int'l*, pg. 3703
ENEDO SARL—See Inission AB; *Int'l*, pg. 3703
ENEDO S.A.—See Inission AB; *Int'l*, pg. 3703
ENE (EAST COAST) SDN. BHD.—See MPHB Capital Berhad; *Int'l*, pg. 5061
ENE (EAST MALAYSIA) SDN. BHD.—See MPHB Capital Berhad; *Int'l*, pg. 5061
ENEFCO INTERNATIONAL, INC.—See Argosy Capital Group, LLC; *U.S. Private*, pg. 321
ENEFCO USA, INC. - GLOBALDIE DIVISION—See Argosy Capital Group, LLC; *U.S. Private*, pg. 321
ENEFCO USA, INC.—See Argosy Capital Group, LLC; *U.S. Private*, pg. 321
ENEFIT GREEN AS; *Int'l*, pg. 2411

CORPORATE AFFILIATIONS

ENEFIT OUTOTEC TECHNOLOGY OU—See Eesti Energia AS; *Int'l*, pg. 2317
ENEFIT SIA—See Eesti Energia AS; *Int'l*, pg. 2317
ENEFI VAGYONKEZELO NYRT; *Int'l*, pg. 2411
ENEGATE CO., LTD.—See Osaki Electric Co., Ltd.; *Int'l*, pg. 5647
ENEGATE - SAYO PLANT—See Osaki Electric Co., Ltd.; *Int'l*, pg. 5647
ENEGEX LIMITED; *Int'l*, pg. 2411
ENEIGHBORHOODS INC.—See Irish Times; *U.S. Private*, pg. 2138
ENEL AMERICAS S.A.—See Enel S.p.A.; *Int'l*, pg. 2412
ENEL BRASIL PARTICIPACOES LTDA—See Enel S.p.A.; *Int'l*, pg. 2413
ENEL BRASIL S.A.—See Enel S.p.A.; *Int'l*, pg. 2412
ENEL CHILE S.A.—See Enel S.p.A.; *Int'l*, pg. 2412
ENEL COLINA SA—See Enel S.p.A.; *Int'l*, pg. 2412
ENEL COVE FORT LLC—See Enel S.p.A.; *Int'l*, pg. 2412
ENEL DE COSTA RICA SA—See Enel S.p.A.; *Int'l*, pg. 2414
ENEL DISTRIBUCION CEAR S.A.—See Enel S.p.A.; *Int'l*, pg. 2412
ENEL DISTRIBUCION CHILE SA—See Enel S.p.A.; *Int'l*, pg. 2412
ENEL DISTRIBUCION CHILE SA—See Enel S.p.A.; *Int'l*, pg. 2412
ENEL DISTRIBUCION PERU SAA—See Enel S.p.A.; *Int'l*, pg. 2412
ENEL DISTRIBUZIONE S.P.A.—See Enel S.p.A.; *Int'l*, pg. 2412
ENEL ENERGIA S.P.A.—See Enel S.p.A.; *Int'l*, pg. 2412
ENEL F2I SOLARE ITALIA S.P.A.—See F2i - Fondi Italiani per le infrastrutture SGR S.p.A.; *Int'l*, pg. 2597
ENEL FINANCE INTERNATIONAL NV—See Enel S.p.A.; *Int'l*, pg. 2413
ENEL GENERACION CHILE S.A.—See Enel S.p.A.; *Int'l*, pg. 2413
ENEL GREEN POWER CANADA, INC.—See Enel S.p.A.; *Int'l*, pg. 2413
ENEL GREEN POWER CHILE LTDA.—See Enel S.p.A.; *Int'l*, pg. 2413
ENEL GREEN POWER COSTA RICA SA—See Enel S.p.A.; *Int'l*, pg. 2413
ENEL GREEN POWER ESPANA SL—See Enel S.p.A.; *Int'l*, pg. 2413
ENEL GREEN POWER FRANCE SAS—See Enel S.p.A.; *Int'l*, pg. 2413
ENEL GREEN POWER GUATEMALA SA—See Enel S.p.A.; *Int'l*, pg. 2413
ENEL GREEN POWER HELLAS SA—See Enel S.p.A.; *Int'l*, pg. 2413
ENEL GREEN POWER HELLAS SA—See Macquarie Group Limited; *Int'l*, pg. 4626
ENEL GREEN POWER MEXICO S DE RL DE CV—See Enel S.p.A.; *Int'l*, pg. 2413
ENEL GREEN POWER NORTH AMERICA, INC.—See Enel S.p.A.; *Int'l*, pg. 2413
ENEL GREEN POWER PANAMA SA—See Enel S.p.A.; *Int'l*, pg. 2413
ENEL GREEN POWER PERU SA—See Enel S.p.A.; *Int'l*, pg. 2413
ENEL GREEN POWER ROMANIA SRL—See Enel S.p.A.; *Int'l*, pg. 2413
ENEL GREEN POWER ROME VILLORESI SRL—See Enel S.p.A.; *Int'l*, pg. 2413
ENEL GREEN POWER S.P.A.—See Enel S.p.A.; *Int'l*, pg. 2413
ENEL GUATEMALA SA—See Enel S.p.A.; *Int'l*, pg. 2413
ENEL IBEROAMERICA SL—See Enel S.p.A.; *Int'l*, pg. 2413
ENEL LATIN AMERICA (CHILE) LTDA.—See Enel S.p.A.; *Int'l*, pg. 2414
ENEL LATINOAMERICA SA—See Enel S.p.A.; *Int'l*, pg. 2413
ENEL M&P SRL—See Enel S.p.A.; *Int'l*, pg. 2413
ENEL PANAMA SA—See Enel S.p.A.; *Int'l*, pg. 2413
ENEL PRODUZIONE S.P.A.—See Enel S.p.A.; *Int'l*, pg. 2412
ENEL SERVIZIO ELETTRICO SPA—See Enel S.p.A.; *Int'l*, pg. 2412
ENEL S.P.A.; *Int'l*, pg. 2411
ENEL STILLWATER LLC—See Enel S.p.A.; *Int'l*, pg. 2413
ENEL WASHINGTON DC LTD.—See Enel S.p.A.; *Int'l*, pg. 2413
ENEL X ARGENTINA SAU—See Enel S.p.A.; *Int'l*, pg. 2413
ENEL X AUSTRALIA (PTY) LTD.—See Enel S.p.A.; *Int'l*, pg. 2413
ENEL X BRASIL SA—See Enel S.p.A.; *Int'l*, pg. 2414
ENEL X JAPAN KK—See Enel S.p.A.; *Int'l*, pg. 2414
ENEL X KOREA LIMITED—See Enel S.p.A.; *Int'l*, pg. 2414
ENEL X NORTH AMERICA, INC.—See Enel S.p.A.; *Int'l*, pg. 2413
ENEL X WAY ROMANIA S.R.L.—See Enel S.p.A.; *Int'l*, pg. 2414
ENEMAERKE & PETERSEN A/S—See Hojgaard Holding A/S; *Int'l*, pg. 3442
ENE (MELAKA) SDN. BHD.—See MPHB Capital Berhad; *Int'l*, pg. 5061

COMPANY NAME INDEX

ENE (NEGERI SEMBILAN) SDN. BHD.—See MPHB Capital Berhad; *Int'l*, pg. 5062
EN ENGINEERING, LLC—See General Atlantic Service Company, L.P.; *U.S. Private*, pg. 1662
ENENSYS TECHNOLOGIES SA; *Int'l*, pg. 2415
ENENTO GROUP PLC; *Int'l*, pg. 2415
ENEOS CAREER SUPPORT CORPORATION—See ENEOS Holdings, Inc.; *Int'l*, pg. 2415
ENEOS CELLTECH CO., LTD.—See ENEOS Holdings, Inc.; *Int'l*, pg. 2415
ENEOS CORPORATION—See ENEOS Holdings, Inc.; *Int'l*, pg. 2415
ENEOS FRONTIER COMPANY, LIMITED—See ENEOS Holdings, Inc.; *Int'l*, pg. 2417
ENEOS GLOBE CORPORATION—See ENEOS Holdings, Inc.; *Int'l*, pg. 2415
ENEOS HOLDINGS, INC.; *Int'l*, pg. 2415
ENEOS INSURANCE SERVICE CORPORATION—See ENEOS Holdings, Inc.; *Int'l*, pg. 2415
ENEOS NUC CORPORATION—See Tecnos Japan Inc.; *Int'l*, pg. 7517
ENEOS REAL ESTATE CORPORATION—See ENEOS Holdings, Inc.; *Int'l*, pg. 2415
ENEOS TRADING COMPANY LIMITED—See ENEOS Holdings, Inc.; *Int'l*, pg. 2415
ENEOS WING CORPORATION—See ENEOS Holdings, Inc.; *Int'l*, pg. 2415
ENE (PENANG) SDN. BHD.—See MPHB Capital Berhad; *Int'l*, pg. 5062
ENE (PERAK) SDN. BHD.—See MPHB Capital Berhad; *Int'l*, pg. 5062
ENE PUBLICIDAD SA BARCELONA—See WPP plc; *Int'l*, pg. 8492
ENE PUBLICIDAD, S.A. MADRID—See WPP plc; *Int'l*, pg. 8492
ENER1 GROUP, INC.; *U.S. Private*, pg. 1392
ENER1, INC.—See Ener1 Group, Inc.; *U.S. Private*, pg. 1392
ENERACTIVE SOLUTIONS, LLC.—See Edison International; *U.S. Public*, pg. 719
ENERAQUA TECHNOLOGIES PLC; *Int'l*, pg. 2418
ENERBANK USA—See Regions Financial Corporation; *U.S. Public*, pg. 1776
ENERBOIS SA—See Romande Energie Holding S.A.; *Int'l*, pg. 0004
ENERCARE INC.—See Brookfield Infrastructure Partners L.P.; *Int'l*, pg. 1190
ENERCHEM INTERNATIONAL, INC.; *Int'l*, pg. 2418
ENERCHINA HOLDINGS LIMITED—See Sinolink Worldwide Holdings Limited; *Int'l*, pg. 6952
ENERCHINA RESOURCES LIMITED—See Oshidori International Holdings Limited; *Int'l*, pg. 5650
ENERCLEAR SERVICES INC.—See Corrosion & Abrasion Solutions Ltd.; *Int'l*, pg. 1806
ENERCO GROUP INCORPORATED; *U.S. Private*, pg. 1392
ENERCON ENGINEERING INC.; *U.S. Private*, pg. 1392
ENERCON INDUSTRIES CORPORATION; *U.S. Private*, pg. 1392
ENERCON SERVICES, INC.—See Brookfield Corporation; *Int'l*, pg. 1182
ENER-CORE, INC.; *U.S. Public*, pg. 760
ENERES CO., LTD.—See KDDI Corporation; *Int'l*, pg. 4111
ENEREV5 METALS INC.; *Int'l*, pg. 2418
ENERFAB, INC.; *U.S. Private*, pg. 1392
ENERFIN ENERVENTO, S.L.U.—See Elecnor, S.A.; *Int'l*, pg. 2347
ENERFIN RENEWABLES, LLC—See Elecnor, S.A.; *Int'l*, pg. 2347
ENERFIN RESOURCES LP; *U.S. Private*, pg. 1393
ENERFLEX AUSTRALASIA HOLDINGS PTY. LTD.—See Enerflex Ltd.; *Int'l*, pg. 2418
ENERFLEX ENERGY SYSTEMS INC.—See Enerflex Ltd.; *Int'l*, pg. 2418
ENERFLEX ENERGY SYSTEMS (WYOMING) INC.—See Enerflex Ltd.; *Int'l*, pg. 2418
ENERFLEX LTD.; *Int'l*, pg. 2418
ENERFLEX MENA LTD—See Enerflex Ltd.; *Int'l*, pg. 2418
ENERFLEX PROCESS PTY. LTD.—See Enerflex Ltd.; *Int'l*, pg. 2418
ENERFLEX PTE. LTD.—See Enerflex Ltd.; *Int'l*, pg. 2418
ENERFLEX SERVICE PTY. LTD.—See Enerflex Ltd.; *Int'l*, pg. 2418
ENERFLOW INDUSTRIES INC.—See NOV, Inc.; *U.S. Public*, pg. 1544
ENERFUND, LLC; *U.S. Private*, pg. 1393
ENERG2 TECHNOLOGIES, INC.—See BASF SE; *Int'l*, pg. 883
ENERGA S.A.—See Orlen S.A.; *Int'l*, pg. 5640
ENERGAS CORP.; *U.S. Private*, pg. 1393
ENERGAS LTD.—See L'Air Liquide S.A.; *Int'l*, pg. 4375
ENERGEAN ISRAEL FINANCE LTD.—See Energean plc; *Int'l*, pg. 2419
ENERGEAN ISRAEL TRANSMISSION LTD.—See Energean plc; *Int'l*, pg. 2419
ENERGEAN OIL & GAS S.A.—See Energean plc; *Int'l*, pg. 2419
ENERGEAN PLC; *Int'l*, pg. 2419
ENERGEIA A.S.; *Int'l*, pg. 2419

ENERGEN CORPORATION—See Diamondback Energy, Inc.; *U.S. Public*, pg. 658
ENERGEN OF VIRGINIA INC.; *U.S. Private*, pg. 1393
ENERGEN RESOURCES CORPORATION—See Diamondback Energy, Inc.; *U.S. Public*, pg. 658
ENERGENZE CONSULTING, LLC—See NV5 Global, Inc.; *U.S. Public*, pg. 1557
ENERGENZE CONSULTING LTD.—See NV5 Global, Inc.; *U.S. Public*, pg. 1557
ENERGETICKE CENTRUM S.R.O.—See CEZ, a.s.; *Int'l*, pg. 1427
ENERGETICKE OPRAVNY, A.S.—See CEZ, a.s.; *Int'l*, pg. 1427
ENERGETICKY A PRUMYSLOVY HOLDING, A.S.; *Int'l*, pg. 2419
ENERGETIC PAINTING & DRYWALL; *U.S. Private*, pg. 1393
ENERGETICS & ENERGY SAVINGS FUND - FEEI SPV; *Int'l*, pg. 2420
ENERGETIC SERVICES INC. - EDSON FACILITY—See Energetic Services Inc.; *Int'l*, pg. 2419
ENERGETIC SERVICES INC. - FORT NELSON FACILITY—See Energetic Services Inc.; *Int'l*, pg. 2419
ENERGETIC SERVICES INC. - GRANDE PRAIRIE FACILITY—See Energetic Services Inc.; *Int'l*, pg. 2419
ENERGETIC SERVICES INC.; *Int'l*, pg. 2419
ENERGETICS INCORPORATED-ARLINGTON—See TPG Capital, L.P.; *U.S. Public*, pg. 2176
ENERGETICS INCORPORATED—See TPG Capital, L.P.; *U.S. Public*, pg. 2176
ENERGETICS INCORPORATED-WASHINGTON—See TPG Capital, L.P.; *U.S. Public*, pg. 2176
ENERGETIKA CHROPYNE, A.S—See Agrofert Holding, a.s.; *Int'l*, pg. 219
ENERGETIKA CRNOMELJ D.O.O.—See Sava d.d.; *Int'l*, pg. 6595
ENERGETIKAI ES TAVKOZLESI HALOZATEPITO ES SZERELO KFT.—See E.ON SE; *Int'l*, pg. 2253
ENERGETIKA MALENOVICE, A.S.—See E.ON SE; *Int'l*, pg. 2257
ENERGETIKA SERVIS S.R.O.—See E.ON SE; *Int'l*, pg. 2256
ENERGETIKA VITKOVICE, A.S.—See CEZ, a.s.; *Int'l*, pg. 1428
ENERGETIKA Z.J. D.O.O.—See SOL S.p.A.; *Int'l*, pg. 7067
ENERGETIQ TECHNOLOGY, INC.—See Hamamatsu Photonics K.K.; *Int'l*, pg. 3235
ENERGETYKA DWORY SP. Z O.O.—See Synthos S.A.; *Int'l*, pg. 7387
ENERGETYKA POZNANSKA PRZEDSIEBIORSTWO USLUG ENERGETYCZNYCH ENERGOBUD LESZNO SP. Z O.O.—See ENEA S.A.; *Int'l*, pg. 2410
ENERGETYKA POZNANSKA ZAKLAD OBSLUGI SOCJALNEJ ENERGO-TOUR SP. Z O.O.—See ENEA S.A.; *Int'l*, pg. 2410
ENERGETYKA SP. Z O.O.—See KGHM Polska Miedz S.A.; *Int'l*, pg. 4148
ENERGIA ALTERNATIVA SRL—See Athena Investments A/S; *Int'l*, pg. 669
ENERGIA BUSINESS SERVICE CO., INC.—See The Chugoku Electric Power Co., Inc.; *Int'l*, pg. 7632
ENERGIA CEUTA XXI COMERCIALIZADORA DE REFERENCIA SA—See Enel S.p.A.; *Int'l*, pg. 2414
ENERGIA COMMUNICATIONS INC—See The Chugoku Electric Power Co., Inc.; *Int'l*, pg. 7632
ENERGIA DE CASABLANCA SA; *Int'l*, pg. 2420
ENERGIA DEL SUR S.A.—See ENGIE SA; *Int'l*, pg. 2434
ENERGIA E INDUSTRIA DE TOLEDO, S.A.—See EDP - Energias de Portugal, S.A.; *Int'l*, pg. 2314
ENERGIA INNOVACION Y DESARROLLO FOTOVOLTAICO S.A.; *Int'l*, pg. 2420
ENERGIAKI PINIAS 2 S.A.—See NAFPAKTOS TEXTILE INDUSTRY S.A.; *Int'l*, pg. 5124
ENERGIA LATINA SA; *Int'l*, pg. 2420
ENERGIA L&B PARTNERS CO., INC.—See The Chugoku Electric Power Co., Inc.; *Int'l*, pg. 7632
ENERGIA MINERALS (ITALIA) S.R.L—See Altamin Limited; *Int'l*, pg. 385
ENERGIA NUEVA ENERGIA LIMPIA MEXICO SRL DE CV—See Enel S.p.A.; *Int'l*, pg. 2414
ENERGIAOK SP. Z O.O.—See City Service SE; *Int'l*, pg. 1627
ENERGIAS AMBIENTALES DE NOVO, S.A.—See ACS, Actividades de Construccion y Servicios, S.A.; *Int'l*, pg. 112
ENERGIAS AMBIENTALES, S.A.—See ACS, Actividades de Construccion y Servicios, S.A.; *Int'l*, pg. 112
ENERGIA, SAS—See ENGIE SA; *Int'l*, pg. 2428
ENERGIAS DE GRAUS SL—See Enel S.p.A.; *Int'l*, pg. 2413
ENERGIA SMILE CO., INC.—See The Chugoku Electric Power Co., Inc.; *Int'l*, pg. 7632
ENERGIA VERDE SRL—See Athena Investments A/S; *Int'l*, pg. 669
ENERGIA/Y&R—See WPP plc; *Int'l*, pg. 8491
ENERGIA/Y&R—See WPP plc; *Int'l*, pg. 8491
ENERGIA ZACHOD SP. Z O.O—See San Leon Energy plc; *Int'l*, pg. 6521

ENERGIBYGG AS—See Bravida Holding AB; *Int'l*, pg. 1142
ENERGICA MOTOR COMPANY S.P.A.—See Ideanomics, Inc.; *U.S. Public*, pg. 1088
ENERGIE AG; *Int'l*, pg. 2420
ENERGIE DE SION REGION SA—See EnBW Energie Baden-Wurttemberg AG; *Int'l*, pg. 2398
ENERGIEDIENST AG—See EnBW Energie Baden-Wurttemberg AG; *Int'l*, pg. 2398
ENERGIEDIENST HOLDING AG—See EnBW Energie Baden-Wurttemberg AG; *Int'l*, pg. 2398
ENERGIEDIENST NETZE GMBH—See EnBW Energie Baden-Wurttemberg AG; *Int'l*, pg. 2398
ENERGIE DIRECT MINERALOLHANDELSGESMBH—See DCC plc; *Int'l*, pg. 1990
ENERGIE ELECTRIQUE DE TAHADDART SA—See Enel S.p.A.; *Int'l*, pg. 2414
ENERGIE ELECTRIQUE DU SIMPLON SA—See Alpiq Holding AG; *Int'l*, pg. 373
ENERGIEFINANZ GMBH—See EnBW Energie Baden-Wurttemberg AG; *Int'l*, pg. 2398
ENERGIE HOLDING A.S.—See Groupe BPCE; *Int'l*, pg. 3094
ENERGIEKONTOR AG; *Int'l*, pg. 2420
ENERGIEKONTOR UK LTD.—See Energiekontor AG; *Int'l*, pg. 2420
ENERGIEKONTOR US INC.—See Energiekontor AG; *Int'l*, pg. 2420
ENERGIE LLC—See ExeLED Holdings, Inc.; *U.S. Private*, pg. 1448
ENERGIELOSUNG GMBH—See E.ON SE; *Int'l*, pg. 2260
ENERGIENETZE BAYERN GMBH—See E.ON SE; *Int'l*, pg. 2257
ENERGIENETZE BERLIN GMBH—See RWE AG; *Int'l*, pg. 6434
ENERGIENETZE OFFENBACH GMBH—See MVV Energie AG; *Int'l*, pg. 5108
ENERGIENETZE SCHAAFHEIM GMBH—See E.ON SE; *Int'l*, pg. 2257
ENERGIEOBJEKTGESELLSCHAFT MBH-EOG—See E.ON SE; *Int'l*, pg. 2253
ENERGIEPARK TRELDER BERG GMBH—See Enovos International S.A.; *Int'l*, pg. 2444
ENERGIE-PENSIONS-MANAGEMENT GMBH—See Fortum Oyj; *Int'l*, pg. 2742
ENERGIEREVOLTE GMBH—See HWE AG; *Int'l*, pg. 6434
ENERGIE SAARLORLUX AG—See ENGIE SA; *Int'l*, pg. 2432
ENERGIES FRANCE S.A.S.—See RWE AG; *Int'l*, pg. 6434
ENERGIE STEIERMARK AG; *Int'l*, pg. 2420
ENERGIE STEIERMARK KUNDEN GMBH—See Energie Steiermark AG; *Int'l*, pg. 2420
ENERGIE STEIERMARK SERVICE GMBH—See Energie Steiermark AG; *Int'l*, pg. 2420
ENERGIESUDWEST NETZ GMBH—See Enovos International S.A.; *Int'l*, pg. 2444
ENERGIETECHNIK ESSEN GMBH—See Georgsmarienhutte Holding GmbH; *Int'l*, pg. 2940
ENERGIE- UND MEDIENVERSORGUNG SCHWARZA GMBH (EMS)—See Thuringer Energie AG; *Int'l*, pg. 7723
ENERGIE UND WASSER POTSDAM GMBH—See E.ON SE; *Int'l*, pg. 2257
ENERGIE UND WASSER WAHLSTEDT/BAD SEGEBERG GMBH & CO. KG—See E.ON SE; *Int'l*, pg. 2257
ENERGIEUNION GMBH—See EnBW Energie Baden-Wurttemberg AG; *Int'l*, pg. 2400
ENERGIEVERSORGUNG ALZENAU GMBH—See E.ON SE; *Int'l*, pg. 2257
ENERGIEVERSORGUNG GAILDORF OHG DER ENBW KOMMUNALE BETEILIGUNGEN GMBH—See EnBW Energie Baden-Wurttemberg AG; *Int'l*, pg. 2398
ENERGIEVERSORGUNG GERA GMBH—See ENGIE SA; *Int'l*, pg. 2431
ENERGIEVERSORGUNGSBETRIEB GERRY WEBER GMBH—See GERRY WEBER International AG; *Int'l*, pg. 2944
ENERGIEVERSUM GMBH & CO. KG—See EnBW Energie Baden-Wurttemberg AG; *Int'l*, pg. 2398
ENERGIEWACHT GROEP B.V.—See RWE AG; *Int'l*, pg. 6434
ENERGIEWACHT WEST NEDERLAND B.V.—See RWE AG; *Int'l*, pg. 6434
ENERGIEWERKE ROSTOCK AG—See E.ON SE; *Int'l*, pg. 2253
ENERGIEWONEN B.V.—See E.ON SE; *Int'l*, pg. 2257
ENERGIJA SK—See TCS TurControlSysteme AG; *Int'l*, pg. 7485
ENERGIJOS SKIRSTYMO OPERATORIUS AB—See UAB Ignitis grupe; *Int'l*, pg. 7998
ENERGIJOS TIEKIMAS SIA—See UAB Ignitis grupe; *Int'l*, pg. 7998
ENERGIJOS TIEKIMAS UAB—See UAB Ignitis grupe; *Int'l*, pg. 7998
ENERGILEC SAS—See VINCI S.A.; *Int'l*, pg. 8217
ENERGIPARTNER AS—See Alpiq Holding AG; *Int'l*, pg. 373
ENERGIS CO., LTD.—See Mitsubishi Heavy Industries, Ltd.; *Int'l*, pg. 4953

ENERGIS GMBH—See RWE AG; *Int'l*, pg. 6434
ENERGISMART NORGE AS—See Elmera Group ASA; *Int'l*, pg. 2367
ENERGISME S.A.; *Int'l*, pg. 2420
ENERGIS-NETZGESELLSCHAFT MBH—See RWE AG; *Int'l*, pg. 6436
ENERGIT S.P.A.—See Alpiq Holding AG; *Int'l*, pg. 373
ENERGIT SP. Z O.O.—See NEPI Rockcastle N.V.; *Int'l*, pg. 5200
ENERGIX RENEWABLE ENERGIES LTD.; *Int'l*, pg. 2420
ENERGIX US LLC—See Energix Renewable Energies Ltd.; *Int'l*, pg. 2420
ENERGIZER ARGENTINA S.A.—See Energizer Holdings, Inc.; *U.S. Public*, pg. 761
ENERGIZER AUSTRALIA PTY. LTD.—See Energizer Holdings, Inc.; *U.S. Public*, pg. 761
ENERGIZER BATTERY, INC.—See Energizer Holdings, Inc.; *U.S. Public*, pg. 761
ENERGIZER BATTERY MANUFACTURING, INC.—See Energizer Holdings, Inc.; *U.S. Public*, pg. 761
ENERGIZER CZECH SPOL.SR.O.—See Energizer Holdings, Inc.; *U.S. Public*, pg. 761
ENERGIZER DO BRASIL LTDA.—See Energizer Holdings, Inc.; *U.S. Public*, pg. 761
ENERGIZER GROUP AUSTRIA HANDELS GMBH—See Edgewell Personal Care Company; *U.S. Public*, pg. 718
ENERGIZER GROUP BELGIUM N.V.—See Energizer Holdings, Inc.; *U.S. Public*, pg. 761
ENERGIZER GROUP FRANCE SAS—See Edgewell Personal Care Company; *U.S. Public*, pg. 718
ENERGIZER GROUP HOLLAND B.V.—See Edgewell Personal Care Company; *U.S. Public*, pg. 718
ENERGIZER GROUP POLSKA SP. ZO.O—See Energizer Holdings, Inc.; *U.S. Public*, pg. 761
ENERGIZER GROUP PORTUGAL UNIPESSOAL, LDA.—See Edgewell Personal Care Company; *U.S. Public*, pg. 718
ENERGIZER GROUP SWEDEN AB—See Energizer Holdings, Inc.; *U.S. Public*, pg. 761
ENERGIZER GROUP VENEZUELA C.A.—See Edgewell Personal Care Company; *U.S. Public*, pg. 718
ENERGIZER HELLAS A.E.—See Energizer Holdings, Inc.; *U.S. Public*, pg. 761
ENERGIZER HOLDINGS, INC.; *U.S. Public*, pg. 760
ENERGIZER HONG KONG LIMITED—See Edgewell Personal Care Company; *U.S. Public*, pg. 718
ENERGIZER IRELAND LIMITED—See Energizer Holdings, Inc.; *U.S. Public*, pg. 761
ENERGIZER ITALY S.R.L.—See Energizer Holdings, Inc.; *U.S. Public*, pg. 761
ENERGIZER KOREA LTD.—See Energizer Holdings, Inc.; *U.S. Public*, pg. 761
ENERGIZER LLC—See Edgewell Personal Care Company; *U.S. Public*, pg. 718
ENERGIZER MALAYSIA SDN. BHD.—See Energizer Holdings, Inc.; *U.S. Public*, pg. 761
ENERGIZER MANAGEMENT HOLDING VERWALTUNGS GMBH—See Energizer Holdings, Inc.; *U.S. Public*, pg. 761
ENERGIZER MIDDLE EAST AND AFRICA LIMITED—See Energizer Holdings, Inc.; *U.S. Public*, pg. 761
ENERGIZER NZ LIMITED—See Energizer Holdings, Inc.; *U.S. Public*, pg. 761
ENERGIZER PERSONAL CARE, LLC—See Edgewell Personal Care Company; *U.S. Public*, pg. 718
ENERGIZER PHILIPPINES, INC.—See Energizer Holdings, Inc.; *U.S. Public*, pg. 761
ENERGIZER PUERTO RICO, INC.—See Edgewell Personal Care Company; *U.S. Public*, pg. 718
ENERGIZER SA—See Energizer Holdings, Inc.; *U.S. Public*, pg. 761
ENERGIZER-SCHICK TAIWAN LTD.—See Edgewell Personal Care Company; *U.S. Public*, pg. 718
ENERGIZER SINGAPORE PTE. LTD.—See Energizer Holdings, Inc.; *U.S. Public*, pg. 761
ENERGIZER (SOUTH AFRICA) LTD.—See Energizer Holdings, Inc.; *U.S. Public*, pg. 761
ENERGIZER (THAILAND) LIMITED—See Energizer Holdings, Inc.; *U.S. Public*, pg. 761
ENERGIZER TRADING LIMITED—See Energizer Holdings, Inc.; *U.S. Public*, pg. 761
ENERGOAPARATURA S.A.; *Int'l*, pg. 2420
ENERGOAQUA A.S.; *Int'l*, pg. 2421
ENERGOBALTIC SP. Z O.O.—See Grupa LOTOS S.A.; *Int'l*, pg. 3117
ENERGOCHEM A.S.—See Saficham Group AG; *Int'l*, pg. 6471
ENERGOCOM - VEGA DISTRIBUTION LLP—See Grieshaber Holding GmbH; *Int'l*, pg. 3083
ENERGO CONSULT L.L.C.—See Energoprojekt Holding a.d.; *Int'l*, pg. 2421
ENERGOGREEN RENEWABLES S.R.L.—See Fintel Energia Group S.p.A.; *Int'l*, pg. 2677
ENERGO GROUP LIMITED—See Enero Group Limited; *Int'l*, pg. 2424
ENERGOINSTAL S.A.; *Int'l*, pg. 2421
ENERGOINVEST AUTOMATIKA A.D.; *Int'l*, pg. 2421

ENERGOINVEST-DALEKOVODIZGRADNJA, D.D.; *Int'l*, pg. 2421
ENERGOINVEST, D.D.; *Int'l*, pg. 2421
ENERGOINVEST TVORNICA DALEKOVODNIH STUBOVA D.D.; *Int'l*, pg. 2421
ENERGOLD DE MEXICO S.A. DE C.V.—See Energold Drilling Corp.; *Int'l*, pg. 2421
ENERGOLD DRILLING CORP.; *Int'l*, pg. 2421
ENERGOMASHBANK, PLC; *Int'l*, pg. 2421
ENERGO-MERKUR LTD.—See MVM Magyar Villamos Muvek Zrt.; *Int'l*, pg. 5107
ENERGOMIAR SP. Z O.O.—See ENEA S.A.; *Int'l*, pg. 2410
ENERGOMONTAJ S.A. - ELECTRICAL, AUTOMATION & TELECOMMUNICATION INSTALLATIONS DIVISION—See Energomontaj S.A.; *Int'l*, pg. 2421
ENERGOMONTAJ S.A. - FEE—See Energomontaj S.A.; *Int'l*, pg. 2421
ENERGOMONTAJ S.A. - HIDRO DIVISION—See Energomontaj S.A.; *Int'l*, pg. 2421
ENERGOMONTAJ S.A.; *Int'l*, pg. 2421
ENERGOMONTAJ S.A. - THERMO DIVISION—See Energomontaj S.A.; *Int'l*, pg. 2421
ENERGO NIGERIJA LTD.—See Energoprojekt Holding a.d.; *Int'l*, pg. 2421
ENERGONOVA D.D.; *Int'l*, pg. 2421
ENERGOPARTNER SP. Z O.O.—See ENEA S.A.; *Int'l*, pg. 2410
ENERGOPETROL D.D.—See INA-Industrija Nafte, d.d.; *Int'l*, pg. 3642
ENERGOPOMIAR SP. Z.O.O.—See PGE Polska Grupa Energetyczna S.A.; *Int'l*, pg. 5837
ENERGOPOTOK LLP—See Kazakhstan Utility Systems LLP; *Int'l*, pg. 4102
ENERGO-PRO A.S.; *Int'l*, pg. 2420
ENERGO-PRO BULGARIA EAD—See ENERGO-PRO a.s.; *Int'l*, pg. 2420
ENERGO-PRO CAUCASUS LLC—See ENERGO-PRO a.s.; *Int'l*, pg. 2420
ENERGO-PRO CZECH S.R.O.—See ENERGO-PRO a.s.; *Int'l*, pg. 2420
ENERGO-PRO EAD—See ENERGO-PRO a.s.; *Int'l*, pg. 2420
ENERGO-PRO GEORGIA JSC—See ENERGO-PRO a.s.; *Int'l*, pg. 2420
ENERGO-PRO GRID AD—See E.ON SE; *Int'l*, pg. 2256
ENERGO-PRO GUNEY ELEKTRIK URETIM SAN. VE TIC. A.S.—See ENERGO-PRO a.s.; *Int'l*, pg. 2420
ENERGOPROJEKT ENERGODATA A.D.—See Energoprojekt Holding a.d.; *Int'l*, pg. 2421
ENERGOPROJEKT - ENTEL A.D.—See Energoprojekt Holding a.d.; *Int'l*, pg. 2421
ENERGOPROJEKT ENTEL COMPANY—See Energoprojekt Holding a.d.; *Int'l*, pg. 2421
ENERGOPROJEKT ENTEL L.L.C.—See Energoprojekt Holding a.d.; *Int'l*, pg. 2421
ENERGOPROJEKT ENTEL LTD.—See Energoprojekt Holding a.d.; *Int'l*, pg. 2421
ENERGOPROJEKT GARANT A.D.O.—See Energoprojekt Holding a.d.; *Int'l*, pg. 2421
ENERGOPROJEKT HIDROINZENJERING A.D.—See Energoprojekt Holding a.d.; *Int'l*, pg. 2422
ENERGOPROJEKT HOLDING A.D.; *Int'l*, pg. 2421
ENERGOPROJEKT HOLDING GUINEE S.A.—See Energoprojekt Holding a.d.; *Int'l*, pg. 2422
ENERGOPROJEKT INDUSTRIJA A.D.; *Int'l*, pg. 2422
ENERGOPROJEKT-KRAKOW S.A.—See Eltel AB; *Int'l*, pg. 2371
ENERGOPROJEKT NISKOGRADNJA JOINT STOCK CO.—See Energoprojekt Holding a.d.; *Int'l*, pg. 2422
ENERGOPROJEKT OPREMA A.D.—See Energoprojekt Holding a.d.; *Int'l*, pg. 2422
ENERGOPROJEKT URBANIZAM I ARHITEKTURA A.D.; *Int'l*, pg. 2422
ENERGOPROJEKT VISOKOGRADNJA A.D.; *Int'l*, pg. 2422
ENERGOREMONT BOBOV DOL EAD—See Dietsmann N.V.; *Int'l*, pg. 2117
ENERGOREMONT KOZLODUY EOOD—See Dietsmann N.V.; *Int'l*, pg. 2117
ENERGOREMONT RADNEVO EOOD—See Dietsmann N.V.; *Int'l*, pg. 2117
ENERGOREMONT RUSE AD—See Dietsmann N.V.; *Int'l*, pg. 2117
ENERGOSBYT PLUS JSC; *Int'l*, pg. 2422
ENERGOS DEUTSCHLAND GMBH—See E.ON SE; *Int'l*, pg. 2257
ENERGOTRANS, A.S.—See CEZ, a.s.; *Int'l*, pg. 1427
ENERGO CORPORATION; *U.S. Public*, pg. 762
ENERGO-UTECH S.A.—See PGE Polska Grupa Energetyczna S.A.; *Int'l*, pg. 5837
ENERGROUP HOLDINGS CORPORATION; *Int'l*, pg. 2422
ENERGULF RESOURCES INC.; *Int'l*, pg. 2422
ENERGY 11, L.P.; *U.S. Private*, pg. 1393
ENERGY 1 CORP.; *U.S. Private*, pg. 1393
ENERGY 21 A.S.—See Mid Europa Partners LLP; *Int'l*, pg. 4882
ENERGY 360 PTY. LTD.—See AGL Energy Limited; *Int'l*, pg. 211

ENERGY4U GMBH—See Atos SE; *Int'l*, pg. 692
ENERGY ABSOLUTE PUBLIC COMPANY LIMITED; *Int'l*, pg. 2422
ENERGY ABSORPTION SYSTEMS, INC.—See Trinity Industries, Inc.; *U.S. Public*, pg. 2193
ENERGY ACTION (AUSTRALIA) PTY LIMITED—See Energy Action Limited; *Int'l*, pg. 2422
ENERGY ACTION LIMITED; *Int'l*, pg. 2422
ENERGY ACUITY LLC—See Hellman & Friedman LLC; *U.S. Private*, pg. 1908
ENERGY AIR GMBH—See Fraport AG; *Int'l*, pg. 2764
ENERGY ALLIANCE TECHNOLOGY CORP.; *U.S. Private*, pg. 1393
ENERGY ALLOYS, LLC; *U.S. Private*, pg. 1393
ENERGY ALLOYS SERVICES, LLC—See Energy Alloys, LLC; *U.S. Private*, pg. 1393
ENERGY ALLOYS UK LTD.—See Energy Alloys, LLC; *U.S. Private*, pg. 1393
ENERGY ALTERNATIVES, INC.—See Dakota Electric Association; *U.S. Private*, pg. 1147
ENERGY AND WATER DEVELOPMENT CORP.; *U.S. Public*, pg. 762
ENERGY ANSWERS INTERNATIONAL, INC.; *U.S. Private*, pg. 1393
ENERGY ANSWERS INTERNATIONAL, LLC—See Energy Answers International, Inc.; *U.S. Private*, pg. 1393
ENERGY ASSETS GROUP LIMITED—See Astatine Investment Partners LLC; *U.S. Private*, pg. 360
ENERGYAUSTRALIA—See CLP Holdings Limited; *Int'l*, pg. 1663
ENERGYAUSTRALIA YALLOURN PTY. LTD.—See CLP Holdings Limited; *Int'l*, pg. 1663
ENERGY BBDO—See Omnicom Group Inc.; *U.S. Public*, pg. 1575
ENERGY BEVERAGE MANAGEMENT LLC—See Gulf Distributing Holdings LLC; *U.S. Private*, pg. 1816
ENERGY BEVERAGES LLC—See Monster Beverage Corporation; *U.S. Public*, pg. 1465
ENERGY BRANDS, INC.—See The Coca-Cola Company; *U.S. Public*, pg. 2064
ENERGY CAPITAL PARTNERS MANAGEMENT, LP; *U.S. Private*, pg. 1393
ENERGYCAP, LLC—See Resurgens Technology Partners, LLC; *U.S. Private*, pg. 3411
ENERGY CENTER HARRISBURG LLC—See BlackRock, Inc.; *U.S. Public*, pg. 345
ENERGY CENTER MINNEAPOLIS LLC—See BlackRock, Inc.; *U.S. Public*, pg. 345
ENERGY CENTER PAXTON LLC—See BlackRock, Inc.; *U.S. Public*, pg. 345
ENERGY CENTER PHOENIX LL—See BlackRock, Inc.; *U.S. Public*, pg. 345
ENERGY CENTER PITTSBURGH LLC—See BlackRock, Inc.; *U.S. Public*, pg. 345
ENERGY CENTRAL; *U.S. Private*, pg. 1394
ENERGY CONSULT GMBH—See PNE AG; *Int'l*, pg. 5901
ENERGY CONSULTING GROUP, LLC—See Quanta Services, Inc.; *U.S. Public*, pg. 1751
ENERGY CONSULTING SERVICES S.A.—See ENGIE SA; *Int'l*, pg. 2432
ENERGY CONSULT POLSKA SP.Z O.O.—See PNE AG; *Int'l*, pg. 5900
ENERGY CONSULT PRUFGESELLSCHAFT GMBH—See PNE AG; *Int'l*, pg. 5901
ENERGY CONSULT SVERIGE AB—See PNE AG; *Int'l*, pg. 5900
ENERGY CONTROL CONSULTANTS, INC.; *U.S. Private*, pg. 1394
ENERGY CONTROL, INC.—See ENGIE SA; *Int'l*, pg. 2428
ENERGY CONTROL SYSTEMS ENGINEERING INC.—See CODA Holdings, Inc.; *U.S. Private*, pg. 959
ENERGY CONVERSION SERVICES, INC.; *U.S. Private*, pg. 1394
THE ENERGY COOPERATIVE, INC.; *U.S. Private*, pg. 4026
ENERGY CORP OF AMERICA—See Energy Corporation of America; *U.S. Private*, pg. 1394
ENERGY CORPORATION OF AMERICA; *U.S. Private*, pg. 1394
ENERGY CORPORATION OF AMERICA—See Energy Corporation of America; *U.S. Private*, pg. 1395
ENERGY CORPORATION OF AMERICA—See Energy Corporation of America; *U.S. Private*, pg. 1395
ENERGY DATA LAB SP. Z O.O.—See Atende S.A.; *Int'l*, pg. 668
ENERGY-DELTA LTD.—See Synergon Holding PLC; *Int'l*, pg. 7384
ENERGY DESIGN SERVICE SYSTEMS; *U.S. Private*, pg. 1395
ENERGY DEVELOPMENT COMPANY LIMITED; *Int'l*, pg. 2422
ENERGY DEVELOPMENT CORPORATION (CHINA), INC.—See Chevron Corporation; *U.S. Public*, pg. 487
ENERGY DEVELOPMENT CORPORATION PERU S.A.C.—See First Gen Corporation; *Int'l*, pg. 2684
ENERGY DEVELOPMENT CORPORATION; *Int'l*, pg. 2422
ENERGY DEVELOPMENTS, INC.—See CK Hutchison Holdings Limited; *Int'l*, pg. 1637

COMPANY NAME INDEX

ENERGY DEVELOPMENTS LIMITED—See CK Hutchison Holdings Limited; *Int'l*, pg. 1636
ENERGY DEVELOPMENTS (UK) LIMITED—See CK Hutchison Holdings Limited; *Int'l*, pg. 1637
ENERGY DRILLING COMPANY; *U.S. Private*, pg. 1395
ENERGY EARTH LLC; *U.S. Private*, pg. 1395
ENERGY EARTH PUBLIC COMPANY LIMITED; *Int'l*, pg. 2422
ENERGY ENTERPRISE SOLUTIONS, LLC—See 1 Source Consulting, Inc.; *U.S. Private*, pg. 1
ENERGY & ENVIRONMENTAL ECONOMICS, INC.—See Willdan Group, Inc.; *U.S. Public*, pg. 2370
ENERGY & ENVIRONMENTAL SERVICE, INC.—See Enerlabs, Inc.; *U.S. Private*, pg. 1396
ENERGY EQUIPMENT & SUPPLY, INC.—See Ingersoll Rand Inc.; *U.S. Public*, pg. 1120
ENERGY EQUITY RESOURCES AJE LIMITED—See Panoro Energy ASA; *Int'l*, pg. 5729
ENERGY ERECTORS, INC.; *U.S. Private*, pg. 1395
ENERGY EXCHANGE OF SOUTHERN AFRICA PROPRIETARY LIMITED—See Remgro Limited; *Int'l*, pg. 6269
ENERGY & EXPLORATION PARTNERS, INC.; *U.S. Private*, pg. 1393
ENERGY & EXPLORATION PARTNERS, LLC—See Energy & Exploration Partners, Inc.; *U.S. Private*, pg. 1393
ENERGY EYE, INC.—See Somfy SA; *Int'l*, pg. 7085
ENERGY FINDERS, INC.; *U.S. Public*, pg. 762
ENERGY FOCUS, INC.; *U.S. Public*, pg. 762
THE ENERGY FOUNDATION; *U.S. Private*, pg. 4026
ENERGY FRONTIER—See Hokkaido Electric Power Co., Inc.; *Int'l*, pg. 3442
ENERGY FUELS INC.; *U.S. Public*, pg. 762
ENERGY HARDWARE HOLDINGS, INC.—See Barings BDC, Inc.; *U.S. Public*, pg. 276
ENERGY HOLDING NORWAY AS—See NRJ Group SA; *Int'l*, pg. 5474
ENERGY HOLDINGS, INC; *U.S. Public*, pg. 762
ENERGY HOLDINGS INTERNATIONAL, INC.; *U.S. Private*, pg. 1395
THE ENERGY HOUSE HOLDING COMPANY K.S.C.P.—See Kuwait Finance House K.S.C.; *Int'l*, pg. 4344
ENERGYICT N.V.—See Honeywell International Inc.; *U.S. Public*, pg. 1048
THE ENERGY INFORMATION CENTRE LTD.—See The Monarch Partnership Limited; *Int'l*, pg. 7668
ENERGY INSURANCE AGENCY, INC.—See The American Automobile Association, Inc.; *U.S. Private*, pg. 3985
ENERGY INTELLIGENCE CENTRE LTD—See The Monarch Partnership Limited; *Int'l*, pg. 7668
ENERGY INTELLIGENCE WORLDWIDE CORP, INC.; *U.S. Private*, pg. 1395
ENERGY INTERNATIONAL FOR PETROLEUM PROJECTS KCSC—See Fouad Alghanim & Sons Group of Companies; *Int'l*, pg. 2753
ENERGY INTERNATIONAL INVESTMENTS HOLDINGS LIMITED; *Int'l*, pg. 2422
ENERGYIQ LLC—See Thoma Bravo, L.P.; *U.S. Private*, pg. 4152
ENERGY LABS INC.—See Vertiv Holdings Co; *U.S. Public*, pg. 2289
ENERGY LAB S.P.A.; *Int'l*, pg. 2422
ENERGY LEADER BATTERIES INDIA PRIVATE LTD.—See EnerSys; *U.S. Public*, pg. 767
ENERGY LEADERS INCOME FUND—See Harvest Portfolios Group Inc.; *Int'l*, pg. 3281
ENERGYLED ELECTRONICS CORPORATION—See Ledtech Electronics Corporation; *Int'l*, pg. 4439
ENERGY LINE CORPORATION—See TOKAI Holdings Corporation; *Int'l*, pg. 7779
ENERGYLOGIC INC; *U.S. Private*, pg. 1396
ENERGY MAHANAKHON CO., LTD.—See Energy Absolute Public Company Limited; *Int'l*, pg. 2422
ENERGY MANAGEMENT CONTROL CORPORATION—See Huron Capital Partners LLC; *U.S. Private*, pg. 2011
ENERGY MANAGEMENT CORPORATION; *U.S. Private*, pg. 1395
ENERGY MANAGEMENT SERVICES INTERNATIONAL LLC—See Al Hassan Ghazi Ibrahim Shaker; *Int'l*, pg. 279
ENERGY MANUFACTURING COMPANY, INC.—See Ligon Industries LLC; *U.S. Private*, pg. 2455
ENERGY & MARINE UNDERWRITERS, INC.—See Brown & Brown, Inc.; *U.S. Public*, pg. 400
ENERGY MATE CO., LTD.—See Takuma Co., Ltd.; *Int'l*, pg. 7442
ENERGY MATERIAL TECHNOLOGY CO., LTD.—See Ningbo Ronbay New Energy Technology Co., Ltd.; *Int'l*, pg. 5305
ENERGY MATTERS PTY LTD—See SunEdison, Inc.; *U.S. Private*, pg. 3866
ENERGY MEDIA GMBH—See NRJ Group SA; *Int'l*, pg. 5474
ENERGY METALS AUSTRALIA PTY. LTD.—See Stavely Minerals Limited; *Int'l*, pg. 7186
ENERGY METALS LIMITED; *Int'l*, pg. 2422

THE ENERGY & MINERALS GROUP LP - DALLAS OFFICE—See The Energy & Minerals Group LP; *U.S. Private*, pg. 4026
THE ENERGY & MINERALS GROUP LP; *U.S. Private*, pg. 4026
ENERGYNET.COM, INC.; *U.S. Private*, pg. 1396
ENERGY NET GMBH—See Econocom Group SA; *Int'l*, pg. 2298
ENERGYNET (PVT) LTD.—See Hayleys PLC; *Int'l*, pg. 3291
ENERGY NORTH INCORPORATED; *U.S. Private*, pg. 1395
ENERGYNORTH PROPANE, INC.—See UGI Corporation; *U.S. Public*, pg. 2221
ENERGY NORTHWEST; *U.S. Private*, pg. 1395
ENERGY OGRE, LLC; *U.S. Private*, pg. 1395
ENERGY ONE LIMITED; *Int'l*, pg. 2423
ENERGY ONE LLC—See U.S. Energy Corp.; *U.S. Public*, pg. 2213
ENERGY OPERATORS, L. P.; *U.S. Private*, pg. 1395
ENERGY OPTIONS, INC.—See Huron Capital Partners LLC; *U.S. Private*, pg. 2011
ENERGYO SOLUTIONS INVEST AB; *Int'l*, pg. 2423
ENERGY OTTAWA INC.—See Hydro Ottawa Holding Inc.; *Int'l*, pg. 3546
ENERGY OUTREACH COLORADO; *U.S. Private*, pg. 1395
ENERGY OVERWATCH LLC; *U.S. Private*, pg. 1395
ENERGY PANEL STRUCTURES, INC.—See MacArthur Co.; *U.S. Private*, pg. 2534
ENERGYPATHWAYS PLC; *Int'l*, pg. 2423
ENERGY PETROLEUM CO. INC.; *U.S. Private*, pg. 1395
ENERGY PLUS HOLDINGS LLC—See NRG Energy, Inc.; *U.S. Public*, pg. 1550
ENERGY POOL DEVELOPPEMENT SAS—See Schneider Electric SE; *Int'l*, pg. 6626
ENERGY POOL INTERNATIONAL—See Schneider Electric SE; *Int'l*, pg. 6627
ENERGY & POWER SOLUTIONS, INC.; *U.S. Private*, pg. 1393
ENERGY POWER SYSTEMS AUSTRALIA PTY. LTD.; *Int'l*, pg. 2423
ENERGY POWER SYSTEMS PNG LIMITED—See Energy Power Systems Australia Pty. Ltd.; *Int'l*, pg. 2423
ENERGY & PROCESS CORP.—See Ferguson plc; *Int'l*, pg. 2637
ENERGY PROCESS TECHNOLOGY INC.; *U.S. Private*, pg. 1395
ENERGY PRODUCTION CORPORATION; *U.S. Private*, pg. 1395
ENERGY PRODUCTS INC.; *U.S. Private*, pg. 1395
ENERGY PROFESSIONALS, LLC; *U.S. Private*, pg. 1395
ENERGY PROSPECTING TECHNOLOGY USA, INC.—See New Jcm Group CO., Ltd; *Int'l*, pg. 5226
ENERGY REALTY, INC.—See CenterPoint Energy, Inc.; *U.S. Public*, pg. 472
ENERGY RECOMMERCE INC.—See Texas Instruments Incorporated; *U.S. Public*, pg. 2025
ENERGY RECOVERY, INC.; *U.S. Public*, pg. 762
ENERGY RESOURCES OF AUSTRALIA LTD.—See Rio Tinto plc; *Int'l*, pg. 6346
ENERGY RESOURCES OF AUSTRALIA—See Rio Tinto plc; *Int'l*, pg. 6346
ENERGY RETAILERS INC.; *U.S. Private*, pg. 1396
ENERGY REVENUE AMERICA, INC.; *U.S. Public*, pg. 762
ENERGY SAVERS OF GEORGIA, INC.—See NearU Services; *U.S. Private*, pg. 2877
ENERGY SAVE SYSTEM LTD.—See Nederman Holding AB; *Int'l*, pg. 5188
ENERGY SCIENCES, INC.—See IWASAKI ELECTRIC Co., Ltd.; *Int'l*, pg. 3849
ENERGY SERVICES GROUP INTERNATIONAL INC. (ESG); *U.S. Public*, pg. 1396
ENERGY SERVICES GROUP, LLC; *U.S. Private*, pg. 1396
ENERGY SERVICES HOLDINGS, LLC—See Cadent Energy Partners, LLC; *U.S. Private*, pg. 713
ENERGY SERVICES OF AMERICA CORPORATION; *U.S. Public*, pg. 762
ENERGY SOLUTION MANAGEMENT CO., LTD.—See Energy Absolute Public Company Limited; *Int'l*, pg. 2422
ENERGY SOLUTIONS CENTRE LLP—See Samruk-Energy JSC; *Int'l*, pg. 6508
ENERGYSOLUTIONS - DANBURY—See The Toronto-Dominion Bank; *Int'l*, pg. 7696
ENERGYSOLUTIONS FEDERAL EPC, INC.—See The Toronto-Dominion Bank; *Int'l*, pg. 7696
ENERGY SOLUTIONS INTERNATIONAL, INC.—See Emerson Electric Co.; *U.S. Public*, pg. 749
ENERGY SOLUTIONS INTERNATIONAL LTD.—See Emerson Electric Co.; *U.S. Public*, pg. 749
ENERGY SOLUTIONS INTERNATIONAL PRIVATE LIMITED—See Emerson Electric Co.; *U.S. Public*, pg. 749
ENERGY SOLUTIONS INTERNATIONAL SAS—See Emerson Electric Co.; *U.S. Public*, pg. 749
ENERGYSOLUTIONS, LLC—See The Toronto-Dominion Bank; *Int'l*, pg. 7696

ENERGYSOLUTIONS OF UTAH, INC.—See The Toronto-Dominion Bank; *Int'l*, pg. 7695
ENERGYSOLUTIONS SERVICES, INC.—See The Toronto-Dominion Bank; *Int'l*, pg. 7696
ENERGYSOLUTIONS, SPENT FUEL DIVISION, INC.—See The Toronto-Dominion Bank; *Int'l*, pg. 7696
ENERGY SOURCE, LLC—See Revolution Lighting Technologies, Inc.; *U.S. Public*, pg. 1793
ENERGY SOURCE NATURAL GAS SERVICES INC.; *Int'l*, pg. 2423
ENERGY SPECIALTY CONTRACTING, INC.—See The CapStreet Group LLC; *U.S. Private*, pg. 4005
ENERGY SPECTRUM SECURITIES CORPORATION; *U.S. Private*, pg. 1396
ENERGYS SANGYO CO., LTD.—See NGK Insulators, Ltd.; *Int'l*, pg. 5254
ENERGYS S.R.L.—See Piovan SpA; *Int'l*, pg. 5872
ENERGYST B.V.—See Caterpillar, Inc.; *U.S. Public*, pg. 452
ENERGY STEEL AND SUPPLY COMPANY—See Avingtrans plc; *Int'l*, pg. 743
ENERGY STEEL PRODUCTS, INC.—See Lone Star New Markets LP; *U.S. Private*, pg. 2489
ENERGY STEEL PRODUCTS—See Lone Star New Markets LP; *U.S. Private*, pg. 2489
ENERGY STEEL PRODUCTS—See Lone Star New Markets LP; *U.S. Private*, pg. 2489
ENERGY SUPPORT CORPORATION—See NGK Insulators, Ltd.; *Int'l*, pg. 5254
ENERGY SUR S.A.—See State Grid Corporation of China; *Int'l*, pg. 7183
ENERGY SYSTEMS CO.—See BlackRock, Inc.; *U.S. Public*, pg. 345
ENERGY SYSTEMS GROUP, LLC—See Brookfield Corporation; *Int'l*, pg. 1182
ENERGY TECHNIQUE LIMITED—See Volution Group plc; *Int'l*, pg. 8304
ENERGY TECHNOLOGIES INSTITUTE LLP—See Caterpillar, Inc.; *U.S. Public*, pg. 452
ENERGY TECHNOLOGIES LIMITED; *Int'l*, pg. 2423
ENERGY TRANSFER CRUDE MARKETING LLC—See Energy Transfer LP; *U.S. Public*, pg. 763
ENERGY TRANSFER DATA CENTER, LLC—See Energy Transfer LP; *U.S. Public*, pg. 763
ENERGY TRANSFER FUEL, LP—See Energy Transfer LP; *U.S. Public*, pg. 763
ENERGY TRANSFER GROUP, LLC—See Energy Transfer LP; *U.S. Public*, pg. 763
ENERGY TRANSFER LP; *U.S. Public*, pg. 762
ENERGY TRANSFER, LP—See Energy Transfer LP; *U.S. Public*, pg. 763
ENERGY TRANSFER OPERATING, L.P.—See Energy Transfer LP; *U.S. Public*, pg. 763
ENERGY TRANSFER PARTNERS, L.L.C.—See Energy Transfer LP; *U.S. Public*, pg. 763
ENERGY TRANSFER SOLUTIONS INC—See DVL Group, Inc.; *U.S. Private*, pg. 1295
ENERGY TRANSFER SOLUTIONS, LLC—See Madison Dearborn Partners, LLC; *U.S. Private*, pg. 2541
ENERGY TRANSFER TECHNOLOGIES, LTD.—See Energy Transfer LP; *U.S. Public*, pg. 763
ENERGY TRANSITION MINERALS LTD; *Int'l*, pg. 2423
ENERGY TRANSITION PARTNERS B.V.; *Int'l*, pg. 2423
ENERGY TRANSPORTATION INC.—See TriWest Capital Management Corp.; *Int'l*, pg. 7937
ENERGY TRUST OF OREGON, INC.; *U.S. Private*, pg. 1396
ENERGY UNITED ELECTRIC MEMBERSHIP CORPORATION; *U.S. Private*, pg. 1396
ENERGY USA INC.—See Marubeni Corporation; *Int'l*, pg. 4706
ENERGY VAULT HOLDINGS, INC.; *U.S. Public*, pg. 765
ENERGY VENTURES, LLC—See Enterprise Products Partners L.P.; *U.S. Public*, pg. 778
ENERGY WEST MONTANA, INC.—See First Reserve Management, L.P.; *U.S. Private*, pg. 1525
ENERGY WEST RESOURCES, INC.—See First Reserve Management, L.P.; *U.S. Private*, pg. 1525
ENERGYWORKS ARANDA, S.L.—See Iberdrola, S.A.; *Int'l*, pg. 3571
ENERGYWORKS CARBALLO, S.L.—See Iberdrola, S.A.; *Int'l*, pg. 3571
ENERGYWORKS CARTAGENA, S.L.—See Iberdrola, S.A.; *Int'l*, pg. 3571
ENERGYWORKS FONZ, S.L.—See Iberdrola, S.A.; *Int'l*, pg. 3571
ENERGYWORKS MONZON, S.L.—See Iberdrola, S.A.; *Int'l*, pg. 3571
ENERGYWORKS SAN MILLAN, S.L.—See Iberdrola, S.A.; *Int'l*, pg. 3571
ENERGYWORKS VENEZUELA, S.A.—See Iberdrola, S.A.; *Int'l*, pg. 3571
ENERGYWORKS VILLARROBLEDO, S.L.—See Iberdrola, S.A.; *Int'l*, pg. 3571
ENERGY WORLD CORPORATION LTD; *Int'l*, pg. 2423
ENERGY ZURICH (RADIO Z AG)—See NRJ Group SA; *Int'l*, pg. 5474
ENERGZET, A.S.—See Energeticky a Prumyslovy Holding, a.s.; *Int'l*, pg. 2419

ENERJISA BASKENT ELEKTRIK DAGITIM A.S.—See E.ON SE; *Int'l*, pg. 2257
ENERJISA BASKENT ELEKTRIK DAGITIM A.S.—See Haci Omer Sabanci Holding A.S.; *Int'l*, pg. 3204
ENERJISA ELECTRIK ENERJISI TOPTAN SATIS A.S.—See E.ON SE; *Int'l*, pg. 2257
ENERJISA ELECTRIK ENERJISI TOPTAN SATIS A.S.—See Haci Omer Sabanci Holding A.S.; *Int'l*, pg. 3204
ENERJISA ENERJI A.S.—See E.ON SE; *Int'l*, pg. 2257
ENERJISA ENERJI A.S.—See Haci Omer Sabanci Holding A.S.; *Int'l*, pg. 3204
ENERJISA ENERJI URETIM A.S. - CANAKKALE POWER PLANT—See E.ON SE; *Int'l*, pg. 2257
ENERJISA ENERJI URETIM A.S. - CANAKKALE POWER PLANT—See Haci Omer Sabanci Holding A.S.; *Int'l*, pg. 3204
ENERJISA ENERJI URETIM A.S. - KENTSA POWER PLANT—See E.ON SE; *Int'l*, pg. 2257
ENERJISA ENERJI URETIM A.S. - KENTSA POWER PLANT—See Haci Omer Sabanci Holding A.S.; *Int'l*, pg. 3204
ENERJISA ENERJI URETIM A.S. - MERSIN POWER PLANT—See E.ON SE; *Int'l*, pg. 2257
ENERJISA ENERJI URETIM A.S. - MERSIN POWER PLANT—See Haci Omer Sabanci Holding A.S.; *Int'l*, pg. 3204
ENERJISA ENERJI URETIM A.S.—See E.ON SE; *Int'l*, pg. 2257
ENERJISA ENERJI URETIM A.S.—See Haci Omer Sabanci Holding A.S.; *Int'l*, pg. 3204
ENERKEM INC.; *Int'l*, pg. 2423
ENERKON SOLAR INTERNATIONAL, INC.; *U.S. Public*, pg. 765
ENERLABS, INC.; *U.S. Private*, pg. 1396
ENERMARKET GMBH—See RWE AG; *Int'l*, pg. 6436
ENERMASCH HANDELS GMBH—See OOO Severgrupp; *Int'l*, pg. 5594
ENERMON S.A. DE C.V.—See Iberdrola, S.A.; *Int'l*, pg. 3571
ENERNEX LLC—See Cesi S.p.A.; *Int'l*, pg. 1424
ENERNOC GMBH—See Enel S.p.A.; *Int'l*, pg. 2413
ENERNOC KOREA LIMITED—See Enel S.p.A.; *Int'l*, pg. 2413
ENERNOC NEW ZEALAND LIMITED—See Enel S.p.A.; *Int'l*, pg. 2413
ENERNOC PTY LTD—See Enel S.p.A.; *Int'l*, pg. 2413
ENERNOC UK LIMITED—See Enel S.p.A.; *Int'l*, pg. 2413
ENERO GROUP LIMITED; *Int'l*, pg. 2423
ENERPAC AS—See Enerpac Tool Group Corp.; *U.S. Public*, pg. 765
ENERPAC BV—See Enerpac Tool Group Corp.; *U.S. Public*, pg. 765
ENERPAC CO. LTD.—See Enerpac Tool Group Corp.; *U.S. Public*, pg. 765
ENERPAC CORP.—See Enerpac Tool Group Corp.; *U.S. Public*, pg. 765
ENERPAC FRANCE S.A.S.—See Enerpac Tool Group Corp.; *U.S. Public*, pg. 765
ENERPAC HEAVY LIFTING TECHNOLOGY BV—See Enerpac Tool Group Corp.; *U.S. Public*, pg. 765
ENERPAC HYDRAULICS (INDIA) PVT. LTD.—See Enerpac Tool Group Corp.; *U.S. Public*, pg. 765
ENERPAC INTEGRATED SOLUTIONS B.V.—See Enerpac Tool Group Corp.; *U.S. Public*, pg. 765
ENERPAC LTD.—See Enerpac Tool Group Corp.; *U.S. Public*, pg. 765
ENERPAC MIDDLE EAST FZE—See Enerpac Tool Group Corp.; *U.S. Public*, pg. 765
ENERPAC—See Enerpac Tool Group Corp.; *U.S. Public*, pg. 765
ENERPAC S.P.A.—See Enerpac Tool Group Corp.; *U.S. Public*, pg. 765
ENERPAC TOOL GROUP CORP.; *U.S. Public*, pg. 765
ENERPEAK AG—See BKW AG; *Int'l*, pg. 1055
ENERPHASE INDUSTRIAL SOLUTIONS, INC.; *U.S. Private*, pg. 1396
ENERPIPE, INC—See Enerfab, Inc.; *U.S. Private*, pg. 1393
ENERPIPE LTD; *U.S. Private*, pg. 1396
ENERPLUS CORPORATION; *Int'l*, pg. 2424
ENERPLUS RESOURCES (USA) CORPORATION—See Enerplus Corporation; *Int'l*, pg. 2424
ENERPRO DE MEXICO, S.A. DE C.V.—See NOV, Inc.; *U.S. Public*, pg. 1544
ENERPRO PTE. LTD.—See JcbNEXT Berhad; *Int'l*, pg. 3920
ENERPULSE TECHNOLOGIES, INC.; *U.S. Private*, pg. 1396
ENERSENSE INTERNATIONAL OYJ; *Int'l*, pg. 2424
ENERSIZE OYJ; *Int'l*, pg. 2424
ENERSOL CO. LTD.—See PESTECH International Berhad; *Int'l*, pg. 5823
ENERSOL GMBH—See Shell plc; *Int'l*, pg. 6794
ENERSOURCE TECHNOLOGIES—See Hydro One Limited; *Int'l*, pg. 3546
ENERSPAR CORP.; *Int'l*, pg. 2424
ENERSUL INC.—See Berkshire Hathaway Inc.; *U.S. Public*, pg. 311

ENERSUL OPERATIONS—See Berkshire Hathaway Inc.; *U.S. Public*, pg. 311
ENERSUL TECHNOLOGIES—See Berkshire Hathaway Inc.; *U.S. Public*, pg. 311
ENERSYS AB—See EnerSys; *U.S. Public*, pg. 766
ENERSYS AD—See EnerSys; *U.S. Public*, pg. 766
ENERSYS ADVANCED SYSTEMS INC.—See EnerSys; *U.S. Public*, pg. 767
ENERSYS AE—See EnerSys; *U.S. Public*, pg. 766
ENERSYS A/S—See EnerSys; *U.S. Public*, pg. 766
ENERSYS AS—See EnerSys; *U.S. Public*, pg. 766
ENERSYS BVBA—See EnerSys; *U.S. Public*, pg. 767
ENERSYS BV—See EnerSys; *U.S. Public*, pg. 766
ENERSYS CANADA INC.—See EnerSys; *U.S. Public*, pg. 767
ENERSYS CORPORATION; *U.S. Private*, pg. 1396
ENERSYS DELAWARE INC.—See EnerSys; *U.S. Public*, pg. 767
ENERSYS DE MEXICO II, S DE R.L. DE CV—See EnerSys; *U.S. Public*, pg. 767
ENERSYS DE MEXICO, S.A. DE CV—See EnerSys; *U.S. Public*, pg. 767
ENERSYS ENERGY PRODUCTS INC.—See EnerSys; *U.S. Public*, pg. 767
ENERSYS EUROPE OY—See EnerSys; *U.S. Public*, pg. 766
ENERSYS HUNGARIA KFT.—See EnerSys; *U.S. Public*, pg. 767
ENERSYS INDIA BATTERIES PRIVATE LTD.—See EnerSys; *U.S. Public*, pg. 767
ENERSYS LLC—See EnerSys; *U.S. Public*, pg. 766
ENERSYS LTD.—See EnerSys; *U.S. Public*, pg. 766
ENERSYS MALAYSIA SDN BHD—See EnerSys; *U.S. Public*, pg. 767
ENERSYS MEXICO MANAGEMENT LLC—See EnerSys; *U.S. Public*, pg. 767
ENERSYS MOTIVE POWER—See EnerSys; *U.S. Public*, pg. 767
ENERSYS RESERVE POWER PTE. LTD.—See EnerSys; *U.S. Public*, pg. 767
ENERSYS S.A.R.L.—See EnerSys; *U.S. Public*, pg. 767
ENERSYS; *U.S. Public*, pg. 766
ENERSYS SOUTH EAST ASIA PTE. LTD.—See EnerSys; *U.S. Public*, pg. 767
ENERSYS SPRL—See EnerSys; *U.S. Public*, pg. 767
ENERSYS S.R.L.—See EnerSys; *U.S. Public*, pg. 767
ENERSYS S.R.O.—See EnerSys; *U.S. Public*, pg. 767
ENERSYS, S.R.O.—See EnerSys; *U.S. Public*, pg. 767
ENERSYSTEM ARGENTINA S.A.—See EnerSys; *U.S. Public*, pg. 767
ENERSYSTEM DO BRAZIL LTDA.—See EnerSys; *U.S. Public*, pg. 767
ENERTECH AB—See NIBE Industrier AB; *Int'l*, pg. 5260
ENERTEC HAMELN GMBH—See Stadtwerke Bielefeld GmbH; *Int'l*, pg. 7161
ENERTECH CAPITAL PARTNERS—See Safeguard Scientifics, Inc.; *U.S. Public*, pg. 1834
ENERTECH ENERGIE UND TECHNIK GMBH—See E.ON SE; *Int'l*, pg. 2253
ENERTECH GLOBAL LLC—See NIBE Industrier AB; *Int'l*, pg. 5260
ENERTECH GMBH—See NIBE Industrier AB; *Int'l*, pg. 5260
ENERTECHNIX, INC.—See Valmet Oyj; *Int'l*, pg. 8118
ENERTECH RESOURCES LLC—See ONEX Corporation; *Int'l*, pg. 5578
ENERTECH SPECIALTY CONTRACTING—See Irex Corporation; *U.S. Private*, pg. 2138
ENERTECK CORPORATION; *U.S. Public*, pg. 768
ENERTEC SYSTEMS 2001 LTD.—See Ault Alliance, Inc.; *U.S. Public*, pg. 227
ENERTEK, S.A. DE C.V.—See Iberdrola, S.A.; *Int'l*, pg. 3571
ENERTIME SAS; *Int'l*, pg. 2424
ENERTIS CHILE, SPA—See I Squared Capital Advisors (US) LLC; *U.S. Private*, pg. 2022
ENERTIS CHILE, SPA—See TDR Capital LLP; *Int'l*, pg. 7491
ENERTIS COLOMBIA S.A.S.—See I Squared Capital Advisors (US) LLC; *U.S. Private*, pg. 2022
ENERTIS COLOMBIA S.A.S.—See TDR Capital LLP; *Int'l*, pg. 7491
ENERTIS SOLAR, S.L.U.—See I Squared Capital Advisors (US) LLC; *U.S. Private*, pg. 2022
ENERTIS SOLAR, S.L.U.—See TDR Capital LLP; *Int'l*, pg. 7492
ENERTIS UK LIMITED—See I Squared Capital Advisors (US) LLC; *U.S. Private*, pg. 2022
ENERTIS UK LIMITED—See TDR Capital LLP; *Int'l*, pg. 7492
ENERTOPIA CORPORATION; *Int'l*, pg. 2424
ENERTORK LTD.; *Int'l*, pg. 2424
ENERTRADE—See EDP - Energias de Portugal, S.A.; *Int'l*, pg. 2314
ENERTRONICA SANTERNO S.P.A.; *Int'l*, pg. 2425
ENERVENT ZEHNDER OY—See Zehnder Group AG; *Int'l*, pg. 8630
ENERVEST, LTD.; *U.S. Private*, pg. 1396

ENERVEST MONROE GATHERING, LTD.—See EnerVest, Ltd.; *U.S. Private*, pg. 1397
ENERVEST OPERATING, LLC—See EnerVest, Ltd.; *U.S. Private*, pg. 1397
ENERVIT S.P.A.; *Int'l*, pg. 2425
ENERVOLUTION GMBH—See RWE AG; *Int'l*, pg. 6436
ENERWEB PROPRIETARY LIMITED—See Remgro Limited; *Int'l*, pg. 6269
ENERWISE GLOBAL TECHNOLOGIES, INC.—See LS Power Development, LLC; *U.S. Private*, pg. 2508
ENERZEA POWER SOLUTION PRIVATE LIMITED—See 2G Energy AG; *Int'l*, pg. 5
ENERZENT CO., LTD.; *Int'l*, pg. 2425
ENESA A.S.—See CEZ, a.s.; *Int'l*, pg. 1427
ENESCO CANADA CORPORATION—See Enesco, LLC; *U.S. Private*, pg. 1397
ENESCO FRANCE S.A.S.—See Enesco, LLC; *U.S. Private*, pg. 1397
ENESCO (HONG KONG) LTD.—See Enesco, LLC; *U.S. Private*, pg. 1397
ENESCO LIMITED—See Enesco, LLC; *U.S. Private*, pg. 1397
ENESCO, LLC; *U.S. Private*, pg. 1397
ENE (SELANGOR) SDN. BHD.—See MPHB Capital Berhad; *Int'l*, pg. 5062
ENESERVE CORPORATION—See Daiwa House Industry Co., Ltd.; *Int'l*, pg. 1946
ENESSANCE HOLDINGS CO., LTD.—See Idemitsu Kosan Co., Ltd.; *Int'l*, pg. 3590
ENE SYSTEMS INC.; *U.S. Private*, pg. 1392
ENE TECHNOLOGY INC.; *Int'l*, pg. 2410
ENETEC KYOTO CO., LTD—See Osaka Gas Co., Ltd.; *Int'l*, pg. 5645
ENETICA PTY LTD—See Dreamscape Networks Limited; *Int'l*, pg. 2203
ENETI INC.—See Cadeler A/S; *Int'l*, pg. 1247
ENETIQA A.S.—See Groupe BPCE; *Int'l*, pg. 3094
E-NET JAPAN CORP.; *Int'l*, pg. 2249
ENET SOLUTIONS - LOGICOM S.A.—See Logicom Public Ltd; *Int'l*, pg. 4542
ENETT INTERNATIONAL (SINGAPORE) PTE. LTD.—See WEX, Inc.; *U.S. Public*, pg. 2365
ENEV-AIR GMBH—See CENTROTEC SE; *Int'l*, pg. 1414
ENEVA S.A.; *Int'l*, pg. 2425
ENE VISION CO., LTD—See Toyota Tsusho Corporation; *Int'l*, pg. 7877
ENEVOLV, INC.—See Ginkgo Bioworks Holdings, Inc.; *U.S. Public*, pg. 938
ENEWALL LTD.—See Sika AG; *Int'l*, pg. 6914
ENEX ASSET MANAGEMENT CO., LTD.—See Itochu Enex Co., Ltd.; *Int'l*, pg. 3841
ENEX CLEAN POWER ENERGY CO., LTD.—See Itochu Enex Co., Ltd.; *Int'l*, pg. 3841
ENEX CO., LTD.; *Int'l*, pg. 2425
ENEX-DYNAMIC SDN. BHD.—See Fiamma Holdings Berhad; *Int'l*, pg. 2650
ENEX ENERGY CORP; *Int'l*, pg. 2425
ENEX INFRASTRUCTURE INVESTMENT CORP.; *Int'l*, pg. 2425
ENEXIO GERMANY GMBH—See Triton Advisers Limited; *Int'l*, pg. 7930
ENEXIO MANAGEMENT GMBH—See Triton Advisers Limited; *Int'l*, pg. 7930
ENEXIO UK LTD.—See Triton Advisers Limited; *Int'l*, pg. 7930
ENEXIO US LLC—See Triton Advisers Limited; *Int'l*, pg. 7930
ENEXIO WATER TECHNOLOGIES GMBH—See Triton Advisers Limited; *Int'l*, pg. 7930
ENEXIO WATER TECHNOLOGIES SP. Z O.O.—See Triton Advisers Limited; *Int'l*, pg. 7930
ENEXIO WATER TECHNOLOGIES S.R.O.—See Triton Advisers Limited; *Int'l*, pg. 7930
ENEX LIFE SERVICE CO., LTD.—See Itochu Enex Co., Ltd.; *Int'l*, pg. 3841
ENEX (MAURITIUS) LIMITED—See ENL Limited; *Int'l*, pg. 2442
ENEX OAKBRIDGE PTY LTD—See Glencore plc; *Int'l*, pg. 2990
ENEXOMA AG; *Int'l*, pg. 2425
ENEXON POLSKA SP. Z O.O.—See Wurth Verwaltungsgesellschaft mbH; *Int'l*, pg. 8504
ENEX PETROLEUM SALES NISHI-NIHON CO., LTD.—See Itochu Enex Co., Ltd.; *Int'l*, pg. 3841
EN-FAB INC.; *U.S. Private*, pg. 1389
ENFIELD EXPLORATION CORP.; *Int'l*, pg. 2425
ENFIELD HEALTHTRAX FITNESS & WELLNESS—See Healthtrax Inc.; *U.S. Private*, pg. 1898
ENFINITEC B.V.—See Acer Incorporated; *Int'l*, pg. 99
ENFINITY CORPORATION—See Enfinity N.V.; *Int'l*, pg. 2425
ENFINITY FRANCE SARL—See Enfinity N.V.; *Int'l*, pg. 2425
ENFINITY ITALIA SRL—See Enfinity N.V.; *Int'l*, pg. 2425
ENFINITY N.V.; *Int'l*, pg. 2425
ENFINITY PHILIPPINES RENEWABLE RESOURCES INC.—See Enfinity N.V.; *Int'l*, pg. 2425
ENFINITY THAILAND LIMITED—See Enfinity N.V.; *Int'l*, pg. 2425

COMPANY NAME INDEX — ENGINEERING EXCELLENCE INCORPORATED

ENFINITY WF SOLAR TRUST I—See Wells Fargo & Company; *U.S. Public*, pg. 2343
ENFIS LIGHTING—See Bould Opportunities PLC; *Int'l*, pg. 1119
ENFIS LIMITED—See Bould Opportunities PLC; *Int'l*, pg. 1119
ENFIS LTD.—See Bould Opportunities PLC; *Int'l*, pg. 1119
ENFLO LLC—See Odyssey Investment Partners, LLC; *U.S. Private*, pg. 2995
ENFO AB—See Enfo Oyj; *Int'l*, pg. 2425
ENFOCUS NV—See Danaher Corporation; *U.S. Public*, pg. 626
ENFO ENJOYIT INTERGRATION AB—See Enfo Oyj; *Int'l*, pg. 2425
ENFO OYJ; *Int'l*, pg. 2425
ENFORA, INC.—See Inseego Corp.; *U.S. Public*, pg. 1129
ENFO ZYSTEMS—See Enfo Oyj; *Int'l*, pg. 2425
E.NFRASTRUCTURE TECHNOLOGIES, INC.—See Zones, Inc.; *U.S. Private*, pg. 4608
ENFRASYS SAS—See VINCI S.A.; *Int'l*, pg. 8217
ENF TECHNOLOGY CO., LTD. - ASAN PLANT—See ENF Technology Co., Ltd.; *Int'l*, pg. 2425
ENF TECHNOLOGY CO., LTD.; *Int'l*, pg. 2425
ENF TECHNOLOGY CO., LTD. - ULSAN PLANT—See ENF Technology Co., Ltd.; *Int'l*, pg. 2425
ENF TECHNOLOGY GUANGZHOU CO., LTD.—See Korea Alcohol Industrial Co., Ltd.; *Int'l*, pg. 4282
ENFUSION, INC.; *U.S. Public*, pg. 768
ENFYN MANAGEMENT LIMITED—See ENL Limited; *Int'l*, pg. 2442
ENGAGE2EXCEL, INC.; *U.S. Private*, pg. 1397
ENGAGE2EXCEL RECRUITMENT SOLUTIONS—See Engage2Excel, Inc.; *U.S. Private*, pg. 1397
ENGAGE:BDR LIMITED; *Int'l*, pg. 2426
ENGAGE BEHAVIORAL HEALTH; *U.S. Private*, pg. 1397
ENGAGEDLY, INC.; *U.S. Private*, pg. 1397
ENGAGE HOSPITALITY LLC; *U.S. Private*, pg. 1397
ENGAGE IT SERVICES, INC.—See Providence St. Joseph Health; *U.S. Private*, pg. 3294
ENGAGEMENT LABS INC.—See DGTL Holdings Inc.; *Int'l*, pg. 2097
ENGAGE MOBILITY, INC.; *Int'l*, pg. 2426
ENGAGE PEO, LLC—See Kohlberg & Company, LLC; *U.S. Private*, pg. 2338
ENGAGEPOINT; *U.S. Private*, pg. 1397
ENGAGE PRINT, INC.—See Neuger Communications Group, Inc.; *U.S. Private*, pg. 2890
ENGAGE PR; *U.S. Private*, pg. 1397
ENGAGE PTY LTD.—See LivePerson, Inc.; *U.S. Public*, pg. 1332
ENGAGESMART, INC.—See Vista Equity Partners, LLC; *U.S. Private*, pg. 4402
ENGAGE; *U.S. Private*, pg. 1397
ENGAGE TECHNOLOGIES CORP.; *U.S. Private*, pg. 1397
ENGAGE TECHNOLOGIES, INC.—See Castlight Health, Inc.; *U.S. Public*, pg. 448
ENGAGE XR HOLDINGS PLC; *Int'l*, pg. 2426
ENGAUGE MARKETING, LLC - ATLANTA—See Publicis Groupe S.A.; *Int'l*, pg. 6114
ENGAUGE MARKETING, LLC - ORLANDO—See Publicis Groupe S.A.; *Int'l*, pg. 6114
ENGAUGE MARKETING, LLC - PITTSBURGH—See Publicis Groupe S.A.; *Int'l*, pg. 6114
ENGAUGE MARKETING, LLC—See Publicis Groupe S.A.; *Int'l*, pg. 6114
ENGCON AB; *Int'l*, pg. 2426
ENGCON AUSTRIA GMBH—See Engcon AB; *Int'l*, pg. 2426
ENGCON FRANCE S.A.S—See Engcon AB; *Int'l*, pg. 2426
ENGCON GERMANY GMBH—See Engcon AB; *Int'l*, pg. 2426
ENGCON IRELAND LTD.—See Engcon AB; *Int'l*, pg. 2426
ENGCON NORTH AMERICA INC.—See Engcon AB; *Int'l*, pg. 2426
ENGCON POLAND SP. Z O.O.—See Engcon AB; *Int'l*, pg. 2426
ENGCON UNITED KINGDOM LTD.—See Engcon AB; *Int'l*, pg. 2426
ENGECORPS ENGENHARIA S.A.—See Tecnica Y Proyectos S.A.; *Int'l*, pg. 7515
ENGELBERG TRANSPORTES INTERNACIONALES C.A.—See Deutsche Bahn AG; *Int'l*, pg. 2051
ENGELBERTH CONSTRUCTION INC.; *U.S. Private*, pg. 1397
ENGEL CONSTRUCTION & DEVELOPMENT GROUP; *Int'l*, pg. 2426
ENGEL DISTRIBUTION PTY LTD.—See Sawafuji Electric Co., Ltd.; *Int'l*, pg. 6602
ENGEL GENERAL DEVELOPERS LTD.—See Engel Construction & Development Group; *Int'l*, pg. 2426
ENGELHARD ARGANDA S.L.—See BASF SE; *Int'l*, pg. 883
ENGELHARD ENERGY CORPORATION—See BASF SE; *Int'l*, pg. 875
ENGELHARD METALS AG—See BASF SE; *Int'l*, pg. 875
ENGELHARD METALS LTD.—See BASF SE; *Int'l*, pg. 875
ENGELHARD PERU S.A.—See BASF SE; *Int'l*, pg. 883
ENGELHARD SOUTH AFRICA (PTY.) LTD.—See BASF SE; *Int'l*, pg. 883

ENGEL HOLDINGS INCORPORATED—See Brand Industrial Services, Inc.; *U.S. Private*, pg. 637
ENGELMANN SENSOR GMBH—See DPE Deutsche Private Equity GmbH; *Int'l*, pg. 2187
ENGELMANS BAKING CO.—See Shoreline Equity Partners, LLC; *U.S. Private*, pg. 3641
ENGEL & VOLKERS AMERICAS, INC.; *U.S. Private*, pg. 1397
ENGEMA LIGNES—See Ackermans & van Haaren NV; *Int'l*, pg. 105
ENGEMA MONTAGE—See Ackermans & van Haaren NV; *Int'l*, pg. 105
ENGEMA RAIL—See Ackermans & van Haaren NV; *Int'l*, pg. 105
ENGEMA SA/NV—See Ackermans & van Haaren NV; *Int'l*, pg. 105
ENGENCO LIMITED; *Int'l*, pg. 2426
ENGENE HOLDINGS INC.; *Int'l*, pg. 2427
ENGENHARIA/IEEPT/IETR—See Petroleo Brasileiro S.A. - PETROBRAS; *Int'l*, pg. 5827
ENGENIUM PTY LTD—See Resource Development Group Limited; *Int'l*, pg. 6302
ENGEN LIMITED—See Petroliam Nasional Berhad; *Int'l*, pg. 5829
ENGENT, INC.—See H.B. Fuller Company; *U.S. Public*, pg. 977
ENGERS KERAMIK GMBH & CO. KG—See Eczacibasi Holding A.S.; *Int'l*, pg. 2301
ENGEX, INC.; *U.S. Public*, pg. 768
ENGHOUSE INTERACTIVE—See Enghouse Systems Limited; *Int'l*, pg. 2427
ENGHOUSE INTERACTIVE—See Enghouse Systems Limited; *Int'l*, pg. 2427
ENGHOUSE NETWORKS (GERMANY) GMBH—See Enghouse Systems Limited; *Int'l*, pg. 2427
ENGHOUSE SYSTEMS LIMITED; *Int'l*, pg. 2427
ENGHOUSE TRANSPORTATION LLC—See Enghouse Systems Limited; *Int'l*, pg. 2427
ENGHOUSE (U.K.) LIMITED—See Enghouse Systems Limited; *Int'l*, pg. 2427
ENGIE AXIMA GERMANY GMBH—See ENGIE SA; *Int'l*, pg. 2428
ENGIE BRASIL ENERGIA SA—See ENGIE SA; *Int'l*, pg. 2432
ENGIE DEUTSCHLAND AG—See ENGIE SA; *Int'l*, pg. 2431
ENGIE ENERGIA PERU S.A.—See ENGIE SA; *Int'l*, pg. 2428
ENGIE ENERGIE NEDERLAND N.V.—See ENGIE SA; *Int'l*, pg. 2428
ENGIE ENERGY MARKETING NA, INC.—See ENGIE SA; *Int'l*, pg. 2428
ENGIE EPS S.A.—See ENGIE SA; *Int'l*, pg. 2429
ENGIE FIRE SERVICES AUSTRALIA PTY LIMITED—See ENGIE SA; *Int'l*, pg. 2431
ENGIE GAS & LNG HOLDINGS LLC—See ENGIE SA; *Int'l*, pg. 2428
ENGIE GAS & LNG LLC—See ENGIE SA; *Int'l*, pg. 2428
ENGIE INSIGHT SERVICES, INC.—See Avista Corporation; *U.S. Public*, pg. 249
ENGIE MECHANICAL SERVICES AUSTRALIA PTY LIMITED—See ENGIE SA; *Int'l*, pg. 2431
ENGIE NORTH AMERICA INC.—See ENGIE SA; *Int'l*, pg. 2428
ENGIE RESOURCES LLC—See ENGIE SA; *Int'l*, pg. 2428
ENGIE ROMANIA SA—See ENGIE SA; *Int'l*, pg. 2429
ENGIE SA; *Int'l*, pg. 2428
ENGIE SERVICES AUSTRALIA & NEW ZEALAND HOLDINGS PTY. LTD.—See ENGIE SA; *Int'l*, pg. 2431
ENGIE SERVICES INC.—See ENGIE SA; *Int'l*, pg. 2431
ENGIE SERVICES NEW ZEALAND LIMITED—See ENGIE SA; *Int'l*, pg. 2431
ENGIE SERVICES U.S. INC—See ENGIE SA; *Int'l*, pg. 2428
ENGILITY CORPORATION—See Science Applications International Corporation; *U.S. Public*, pg. 1848
ENGILITY HOLDINGS, INC.—See Science Applications International Corporation; *U.S. Public*, pg. 1848
ENGINE COMPANY ONE; *U.S. Private*, pg. 1397
ENGINE COMPONENTS, INC.—See Danbury AeroSpace, Inc.; *U.S. Private*, pg. 1152
ENGINE CONTROL SYSTEMS EUROPE AB—See CDTi Advanced Materials, Inc.; *U.S. Public*, pg. 462
ENGINE CONTROL SYSTEMS LIMITED—See CDTi Advanced Materials, Inc.; *U.S. Public*, pg. 462
ENGINE CONTROL SYSTEMS LTD.—See CDTi Advanced Materials, Inc.; *U.S. Public*, pg. 462
ENGINEERED ARRESTING SYSTEMS CORPORATION—See Curtiss-Wright Corporation; *U.S. Public*, pg. 612
ENGINEERED COMPONENTS CO; *U.S. Private*, pg. 1398
ENGINEERED CONCEPTS CONSULTING SERVICES INC.—See Terracon Consultants, Inc.; *U.S. Private*, pg. 3970
ENGINEERED CONTROLS INTERNATIONAL LLC - REGO CRYO-FLOW PRODUCTS DIVISION—See Windjammer Capital Investors, LLC; *U.S. Private*, pg. 4537

ENGINEERED CONTROLS INTERNATIONAL LLC—See Windjammer Capital Investors, LLC; *U.S. Private*, pg. 4537
ENGINEERED CUSTOM LUBRICANTS GMBH—See Quaker Chemical Corporation; *U.S. Public*, pg. 1745
ENGINEERED DATA PRODUCTS, LLC; *U.S. Private*, pg. 1398
ENGINEERED ENDEAVORS INC.—See Emerson Electric Co.; *U.S. Public*, pg. 749
ENGINEERED FABRICS CORPORATION—See Parker Hannifin Corporation; *U.S. Public*, pg. 1642
ENGINEERED FABRICS GROUP—See Trelleborg AB; *Int'l*, pg. 7912
ENGINEERED FLOORS, LLC; *U.S. Private*, pg. 1398
ENGINEERED FLUID INC.; *U.S. Private*, pg. 1398
ENGINEERED GLASS PRODUCTS LLC; *U.S. Private*, pg. 1398
ENGINEERED GLASS WALLS; *U.S. Private*, pg. 1398
ENGINEERED LININGS (PTY) LIMITED—See PSV Holdings Limited; *Int'l*, pg. 6018
ENGINEERED MACHINED PRODUCTS INC.—See Concentric AB; *Int'l*, pg. 1764
ENGINEERED MACHINERY, INC.—See Clayton, Dubilier & Rice, LLC; *U.S. Private*, pg. 926
ENGINEERED MATERIALS SOLUTIONS INC.—See Wickeder Westfalenstahl GmbH; *Int'l*, pg. 8401
ENGINEERED MATERIALS SOLUTIONS—See Wickeder Westfalenstahl GmbH; *Int'l*, pg. 8401
ENGINEERED METALS & COMPOSITES, INC.—See Patrick Industries, Inc.; *U.S. Public*, pg. 1652
ENGINEERED MOLDING TECHNOLOGY LLC—See Repligen Corporation; *U.S. Public*, pg. 1784
ENGINEERED PLASTIC COMPONENTS INC.; *U.S. Private*, pg. 1398
ENGINEERED PLASTICS COMPANY, LLC—See MacLean-Fogg Company; *U.S. Private*, pg. 2537
ENGINEERED PLASTICS INC.; *U.S. Private*, pg. 1398
ENGINEERED POLYMERS CORPORATION—See Imperial Plastics, Inc.; *U.S. Private*, pg. 2049
ENGINEERED POLYMER SOLUTIONS, INC.—See The Sherwin-Williams Company; *U.S. Public*, pg. 2129
ENGINEERED PRODUCTS INC—See Engineered Products, Inc.; *U.S. Private*, pg. 1398
ENGINEERED PRODUCTS, INC.; *U.S. Private*, pg. 1398
ENGINEERED PRODUCTS LLC—See Gower Corporation; *U.S. Private*, pg. 1747
ENGINEERED PRODUCTS—See The Pape Group, Inc.; *U.S. Private*, pg. 4090
ENGINEERED PROTECTION SYSTEMS, INC.; *U.S. Private*, pg. 1398
ENGINEERED SEAL PRODUCTS, INC.; *U.S. Private*, pg. 1398
ENGINEERED SOLUTIONS L.P.—See Enerpac Tool Group Corp.; *U.S. Public*, pg. 765
ENGINEERED SPECIALTY PRODUCTS, INC.; *U.S. Private*, pg. 1398
ENGINEERED SPECIALTY TEXTILES LLC; *U.S. Private*, pg. 1398
ENGINEERED SPRING PRODUCTS, INC.—See American Securities LLC; *U.S. Private*, pg. 249
ENGINEERED TAX SERVICES, INC; *U.S. Private*, pg. 1398
ENGINEERED WIRE PRODUCTS, INC.—See Contran Corporation; *U.S. Private*, pg. 1033
ENGINEER GOLD MINES LTD.; *Int'l*, pg. 2435
ENGINEERING AIDS SDN BHD; *Int'l*, pg. 2435
ENGINEERING AND INFORMATION TECHNOLOGIES, INC.; *U.S. Private*, pg. 1398
ENGINEERING ASSOCIATES, INC.—See Dycom Industries, Inc.; *U.S. Public*, pg. 698
ENGINEERING.COM INCORPORATED; *Int'l*, pg. 2435
ENGINEERING & COMPUTER SIMULATIONS, INC.; *U.S. Private*, pg. 1398
ENGINEERING & CONSTRUCTION INNOVATIONS INC.—See Patel Engineering Ltd.; *Int'l*, pg. 5755
ENGINEERING CONSTRUCTION TRAINING LTD—See Severfield Plc; *Int'l*, pg. 6734
ENGINEERING DESIGN & MANUFACTURING SERVICES, INC.—See Park-Ohio Holdings Corp.; *U.S. Public*, pg. 1639
ENGINEERING DESIGN TEAM, INC.—See HEICO Corporation; *U.S. Public*, pg. 1020
ENGINEERING DIVISION/COMMERCIAL AIRCRAFT GROUP—See Israel Aerospace Industries Ltd.; *Int'l*, pg. 3822
ENGINEERING ENGND OY—See MEYER WERFT GmbH; *Int'l*, pg. 4870
ENGINEERING & ENVIRONMENTAL CONSULTANTS, INC.—See Civil & Environmental Consultants, Inc.; *U.S. Private*, pg. 908
ENGINEERING & EQUIPMENT COMPANY INC.; *U.S. Private*, pg. 1398
ENGINEERING EXCELLENCE INCORPORATED; *U.S. Private*, pg. 1398
ENGINEERING INGEGNERIA INFORMATICA S.P.A. OSIMO—See Apax Partners LLP; *Int'l*, pg. 504
ENGINEERING INGEGNERIA INFORMATICA S.P.A.—See Apax Partners LLP; *Int'l*, pg. 504

ENGINEERING EXCELLENCE INCORPORATED

ENGINEERING INTERNATIONAL BELGIUM SA—See Apax Partners LLP; *Int'l*, pg. 504
ENGINEERING & MARINE SERVICES (PTE) LTD—See EMS Energy Limited; *Int'l*, pg. 2392
ENGINEERING.MO S.P.A—See Apax Partners LLP; *Int'l*, pg. 504
ENGINEERING NEWS-RECORD MAGAZINE—See BNP Media, Inc.; *U.S. Private*, pg. 602
ENGINEERING/REMEDIATION RESOURCES GROUP, INC.; *U.S. Private*, pg. 1399
ENGINEERING RESEARCH & CONSULTING INC.; *U.S. Private*, pg. 1398
ENGINEERING & RISK SERVICES CORPORATION—See Kajima Corporation; *Int'l*, pg. 4054
ENGINEERING & RISK SERVICES CORPORATION—See OYO Corporation; *Int'l*, pg. 5678
ENGINEERING SEISMOLOGY GROUP CANADA INC.—See Deep Imaging Technologies, Inc.; *U.S. Private*, pg. 1189
ENGINEERING SERVICE, INC.; *U.S. Private*, pg. 1399
ENGINEERING SERVICES INC.—See SuperRobotics Limited; *Int'l*, pg. 7339
ENGINEERING SERVICES NETWORK, INC.; *U.S. Private*, pg. 1399
ENGINEERING SERVICES & PRODUCTS COMPANY INC.; *U.S. Private*, pg. 1399
ENGINEERING STEEL BELGIUM SPRL—See Georgsmarienhutte Holding GmbH; *Int'l*, pg. 2940
ENGINEERING SYSTEM INTERNATIONAL GMBH—See Keysight Technologies, Inc.; *U.S. Public*, pg. 1226
ENGINEERING SYSTEM INTERNATIONAL SAS—See Keysight Technologies, Inc.; *U.S. Public*, pg. 1227
ENGINEERING SYSTEMS SOLUTIONS INC.; *U.S. Private*, pg. 1399
ENGINEERING WORLD HEALTH—See Engineers Without Borders-USA, Inc.; *U.S. Private*, pg. 1399
ENGINEERS AND CONSTRUCTORS INTERNATIONAL, INC.—See Mitsui E&S Holdings Co., Ltd.; *Int'l*, pg. 4984
ENGINEERS INDIA LTD.; *Int'l*, pg. 2435
ENGINEER SUPPLY, LLC—See ProClick Ventures, Inc.; *U.S. Private*, pg. 3272
ENGINEERS WITHOUT BORDERS-USA, INC.; *U.S. Private*, pg. 1399
THE ENGINE GROUP; *Int'l*, pg. 7640
ENGINE LEASE FINANCE CORPORATION—See Mitsubishi HC Capital Inc.; *Int'l*, pg. 4951
ENGINE MARKETING, LLC; *U.S. Private*, pg. 1397
ENGINE MONITOR, INC.—See MiddleGround Management, LP; *U.S. Private*, pg. 2712
ENGINE & PERFORMANCE WAREHOUSE, INC.—See National Auto Parts Warehouse, LLC; *U.S. Private*, pg. 2847
ENGINE REBUILDERS, INC.—See Reviva Inc.; *U.S. Private*, pg. 3416
THE ENGINE ROOM; *U.S. Private*, pg. 4026
ENGINES ENGINEERING S.R.L.; *Int'l*, pg. 2435
ENGINE—See The Engine Group; *Int'l*, pg. 7640
ENGINE SYSTEMS, INC.—See Kirby Corporation; *U.S. Public*, pg. 1235
ENGINETECH INC.; *U.S. Private*, pg. 1399
ENGINETICS AEROSPACE CORPORATION—See Standex International; *U.S. Public*, pg. 1930
ENGINE WAREHOUSE INC.; *U.S. Private*, pg. 1397
ENGINE YARD, INC.—See GFI Software S.A.; *Int'l*, pg. 2957
ENGINIA S.R.L.—See Carel Industries S.p.A.; *Int'l*, pg. 1324
ENGIN LIMITED—See Aware Super Pty Ltd; *Int'l*, pg. 752
ENGIN LIMITED—See Macquarie Group Limited; *Int'l*, pg. 4629
ENGINOVA SP. Z O.O.—See Tecnolama S.A.; *Int'l*, pg. 7516
ENGINUITY COMMUNICATIONS CORPORATION; *U.S. Private*, pg. 1399
ENGIS CORPORATION; *U.S. Private*, pg. 1399
ENGIS TECHNOLOGIES, INC; *Int'l*, pg. 2435
ENGIWEB SECURITY S.R.L.—See Apax Partners LLP; *Int'l*, pg. 504
ENG KAH CORPORATION BERHAD; *Int'l*, pg. 2425
ENG KAH ENTERPRISE (KL) SDN. BHD.—See Eng Kah Corporation Berhad; *Int'l*, pg. 2425
ENG KAH ENTERPRISE SDN. BHD.—See Eng Kah Corporation Berhad; *Int'l*, pg. 2425
ENG KONG CONTAINER AGENCIES (PTE) LTD—See Eng Kong Holdings Pte Ltd.; *Int'l*, pg. 2426
ENG KONG CONTAINER SERVICES (JOHOR) SDN BHD—See Eng Kong Holdings Pte Ltd.; *Int'l*, pg. 2426
ENG KONG CONTAINER SERVICES LTD—See Singamas Container Holdings Limited; *Int'l*, pg. 6939
ENG KONG CONTAINER SERVICES (PENANG) SDN BHD—See Eng Kong Holdings Pte Ltd.; *Int'l*, pg. 2426
ENG KONG CONTAINER SERVICES (SHENZHEN) COMPANY LIMITED—See Eng Kong Holdings Pte Ltd.; *Int'l*, pg. 2426
ENG KONG HOLDINGS PTE LTD.; *Int'l*, pg. 2425
ENGLANDER ENTERPRISES, INC.; *U.S. Private*, pg. 1399
ENGLANDER KNABE & ALLEN; *U.S. Private*, pg. 1399

ENGLAND, INC.—See La-Z-Boy Incorporated; *U.S. Public*, pg. 1285
ENGLAND LOGISTICS, INC.—See C.R. England, Inc.; *U.S. Private*, pg. 708
ENGLAND MOTOR CO. INC.; *U.S. Private*, pg. 1399
ENGLAND TIR GROUP—See Caisse des Depots et Consignations; *Int'l*, pg. 1258
ENGLEFIELD OIL COMPANY; *U.S. Private*, pg. 1399
THE ENGLE GROUP; *U.S. Private*, pg. 4026
ENGLE-HAMBRIGHT & DAVIES INC.; *U.S. Private*, pg. 1399
ENGLEKIRK INSTITUTIONAL—See Englekirk Partners Consulting Structural Engineers, Inc.; *U.S. Private*, pg. 1400
ENGLEKIRK PARTNERS CONSULTING STRUCTURAL ENGINEERS, INC.; *U.S. Private*, pg. 1400
ENGLEKIRK & SABOL, INC.—See Englekirk Partners Consulting Structural Engineers, Inc.; *U.S. Private*, pg. 1400
ENGLEKIRK SYSTEMS DEVELOPMENT, INC.—See Englekirk Partners Consulting Structural Engineers, Inc.; *U.S. Private*, pg. 1400
ENGLE MARTIN & ASSOCIATES, LLC; *U.S. Private*, pg. 1399
ENG LENG THAILAND CO., LTD.—See Hygieia Group Limited; *Int'l*, pg. 3549
ENGLEN MANUFACTURING SDN. BHD.—See Engtex Group Berhad; *Int'l*, pg. 2436
ENGLE, PAXSON & HAWTHORNE INSURANCE SERVICES, LLC—See ABRY Partners, LLC; *U.S. Private*, pg. 43
ENGLE PRINTING & PUBLISHING CO., INC.; *U.S. Private*, pg. 1399
ENGLER FINANCIAL GROUP, LLC—See Walker & Dunlop, Inc.; *U.S. Public*, pg. 2324
ENGLER & HARING GMBH—See KONE Oyj; *Int'l*, pg. 4247
ENGLER, MEIER & JUSTUS, INC.—See GMS Inc.; *U.S. Public*, pg. 947
ENGLERT INC.; *U.S. Private*, pg. 1400
THE ENGLEWOOD ASC, LLC—See KKR & Co. Inc.; *U.S. Public*, pg. 1247
ENGLEWOOD BANK & TRUST—See Crews Banking Corporation; *U.S. Private*, pg. 1099
ENGLEWOOD COMMUNITY HOSPITAL, INC.—See HCA Healthcare, Inc.; *U.S. Public*, pg. 996
ENGLEWOOD COMMUNITY HOSPITAL—See HCA Healthcare, Inc.; *U.S. Public*, pg. 996
ENGLEWOOD LAB, LLC; *U.S. Private*, pg. 1400
ENGLEWOOD LAB; *Int'l*, pg. 2435
ENGLEWOOD MERIDIAN LLC—See Brookdale Senior Living Inc.; *U.S. Public*, pg. 394
ENGLEWOOD TIRE DISTRIBUTORS, INC.; *U.S. Private*, pg. 1400
ENG LIAN HUP MANUFACTURING SDN. BHD.—See Engtex Group Berhad; *Int'l*, pg. 2436
ENG LIAN HUP TRADING SDN. BHD.—See Engtex Group Berhad; *Int'l*, pg. 2436
ENGLISH AMERICAN CONSTRUCTORS INC.—See Benning Construction Company Inc.; *U.S. Private*, pg. 528
ENGLISH + ASSOCIATES ARCHITECTS, INC.; *U.S. Private*, pg. 1400
ENGLISH COLOR & SUPPLY LLC; *U.S. Private*, pg. 1400
ENGLISH CONSTRUCTION CO. INC.—See W.C. English Incorporated; *U.S. Private*, pg. 4419
ENGLISH INTERNATIONAL SCHOOL PRAGUE—See Canada Pension Plan Investment Board; *Int'l*, pg. 1281
ENGLISH INTERNATIONAL SCHOOL PRAGUE—See EQT AB; *Int'l*, pg. 2470
ENGLISH LANGUAGE INSTITUTE/CHINA; *U.S. Private*, pg. 1400
ENGLISH LEASING LIMITED; *Int'l*, pg. 2435
ENGLISH NATIONAL OPERA; *Int'l*, pg. 2435
ENGLISH ROAD HOLDINGS, LLC—See Hubbell Incorporated; *U.S. Public*, pg. 1066
ENGLISH VILLAGE SALADS LIMITED—See Bakkavor Group plc; *Int'l*, pg. 806
ENGLOBAL CORPORATION; *U.S. Public*, pg. 768
ENGLOBAL U.S., INC.—See ENGlobal Corporation; *U.S. Public*, pg. 768
ENGLOBE CORP.—See Colliers International Group Inc.; *Int'l*, pg. 1701
ENGLUND MARINE SUPPLY CO. INC.; *U.S. Private*, pg. 1400
ENGMAB SARL—See Bristol-Myers Squibb Company; *U.S. Public*, pg. 386
ENGMAN-TAYLOR COMPANY INC.—See MSC Industrial Direct Co., Inc.; *U.S. Public*, pg. 1483
E-N-G MOBILE SYSTEMS, INC.—See PositiveID Corporation; *U.S. Private*, pg. 3233
ENGOLD MINES LTD.; *Int'l*, pg. 2435
ENGOTECH LIMITED—See Kee Shing Investment (BVI) Limited; *Int'l*, pg. 4115
ENGRAVING SOLUTIONS S.R.L.—See Korber AG; *Int'l*, pg. 4281
ENGRO CORPORATION LIMITED; *Int'l*, pg. 2435
ENGRO CORPORATION LIMITED; *Int'l*, pg. 2435
ENGRO ENERGY LIMITED—See Engro Corporation Limited; *Int'l*, pg. 2435

CORPORATE AFFILIATIONS

ENGRO ENFRASHARE (PRIVATE) LIMITED—See Engro Corporation Limited; *Int'l*, pg. 2435
ENGRO FERTILIZERS LIMITED—See Engro Corporation Limited; *Int'l*, pg. 2435
ENGRO FOODS LIMITED—See Zuivelcooperatie FrieslandCampina U.A.; *Int'l*, pg. 8693
ENGRO POLYMER & CHEMICALS LIMITED—See Engro Corporation Limited; *Int'l*, pg. 2435
ENGRO POWERGEN QADIRPUR LIMITED—See Engro Corporation Limited; *Int'l*, pg. 2435
EN+ GROUP INTERNATIONAL PJSC; *Int'l*, pg. 2395
EN+ GROUP LTD.; *Int'l*, pg. 2395
ENGRO VOPAK TERMINAL LTD—See Engro Corporation Limited; *Int'l*, pg. 2435
ENGRO VOPAK TERMINAL LTD—See Koninklijke Vopak N.V.; *Int'l*, pg. 4272
ENGS COMMERCIAL FINANCE CO.—See Mitsubishi HC Capital Inc.; *Int'l*, pg. 4951
ENG. SHABAH AL-SHAMMERY & PARTNERS CO.; *Int'l*, pg. 2426
ENG SOON ENGINEERING (1999) PTE LTD—See ES Group (Holdings) Limited; *Int'l*, pg. 2500
ENG SOON INVESTMENT PTE LTD—See ES Group (Holdings) Limited; *Int'l*, pg. 2500
ENGTEK INTERNATIONAL LIMITED—See Giovanni Agnelli B.V.; *Int'l*, pg. 2978
ENGTEK INTERNATIONAL LIMITED—See PrimeMovers Equity (S) Pte. Ltd.; *Int'l*, pg. 5979
ENG TEKNOLOGI HOLDINGS BHD.—See Giovanni Agnelli B.V.; *Int'l*, pg. 2978
ENG TEKNOLOGI HOLDINGS BHD.—See PrimeMovers Equity (S) Pte. Ltd.; *Int'l*, pg. 5979
ENG TEKNOLOGI SDN. BHD.—See Giovanni Agnelli B.V.; *Int'l*, pg. 2978
ENG TEKNOLOGI SDN. BHD.—See PrimeMovers Equity (S) Pte. Ltd.; *Int'l*, pg. 5979
ENGTEK PRECISION PHILIPPINES, INC.—See Giovanni Agnelli B.V.; *Int'l*, pg. 2978
ENGTEK PRECISION PHILIPPINES, INC.—See PrimeMovers Equity (S) Pte. Ltd.; *Int'l*, pg. 5979
ENGTEK (THAILAND) CO., LTD.—See Giovanni Agnelli B.V.; *Int'l*, pg. 2978
ENGTEK (THAILAND) CO., LTD.—See PrimeMovers Equity (S) Pte. Ltd.; *Int'l*, pg. 5979
ENGTEX DUCTILE IRON MARKETING SDN. BHD.—See Engtex Group Berhad; *Int'l*, pg. 2436
ENGTEX DUCTILE IRON PIPES INDUSTRY SDN. BHD.—See Engtex Group Berhad; *Int'l*, pg. 2436
ENGTEX GROUP BERHAD; *Int'l*, pg. 2436
ENGTEX INDUSTRIES SDN. BHD.—See Engtex Group Berhad; *Int'l*, pg. 2436
ENGTEX MARKETING SDN. BHD.—See Engtex Group Berhad; *Int'l*, pg. 2436
ENGTEX METALS SDN. BHD.—See Engtex Group Berhad; *Int'l*, pg. 2436
ENGTEX METALS (UTARA) SDN. BHD.—See Engtex Group Berhad; *Int'l*, pg. 2436
ENGTEX PIPE INDUSTRY SDN. BHD.—See Engtex Group Berhad; *Int'l*, pg. 2436
ENGTEX PROPERTIES SDN. BHD.—See Engtex Group Berhad; *Int'l*, pg. 2436
ENGTEX SDN BERHAD—See Engtex Group Berhad; *Int'l*, pg. 2436
ENGTEX STEEL INDUSTRIES SDN. BHD.—See Engtex Group Berhad; *Int'l*, pg. 2436
ENGVIEW LATIN AMERICA LTDA—See Sirma Group Holding JSC; *Int'l*, pg. 6962
ENGVIEW SYSTEMS CORP.—See Sirma Group Holding JSC; *Int'l*, pg. 6962
ENGYCO PLC; *Int'l*, pg. 2436
ENHABIT, INC.; *U.S. Public*, pg. 768
ENHANCECORP LIMITED—See HCA Healthcare, Inc.; *U.S. Public*, pg. 996
ENHANCED CAPITAL PARTNERS LLC; *U.S. Private*, pg. 1400
ENHANCED HYDROCARBON RECOVERY INC.—See HTC Purenergy Inc.; *Int'l*, pg. 3508
ENHANCED LANDSCAPE MANAGEMENT, LLC—See Landscape Developmental Inc.; *U.S. Private*, pg. 2387
ENHANCED MANUFACTURING SOLUTIONS, LLC—See American Computer Development, Inc.; *U.S. Private*, pg. 228
ENHANCED PETROLEUM SERVICES PARTNERSHIP - CHANDEL EQUIPMENT RENTALS DIVISION—See Ensign Energy Services Inc.; *Int'l*, pg. 2446
ENHANCED PETROLEUM SERVICES PARTNERSHIP—See Ensign Energy Services Inc.; *Int'l*, pg. 2446
ENHANCED POWDER COATING LTD.—See AZZ, Inc.; *U.S. Public*, pg. 259
ENHANCED RETAIL FUNDING, LLC—See Gordon Brothers Group, LLC; *U.S. Private*, pg. 1742
ENHANCED SECURITIES LIMITED—See G-Resources Group Limited; *Int'l*, pg. 2862
ENHANCED WELL TECHNOLOGIES AS—See EV Private Equity; *Int'l*, pg. 2560
ENHANCED WELL TECHNOLOGIES AS—See Shell plc; *Int'l*, pg. 6794
ENHANCE SKIN PRODUCTS INC.; *U.S. Public*, pg. 768

COMPANY NAME INDEX

ENHANCE TECHNOLOGIES (PVT) LTD.—See Daikin Industries, Ltd.; *Int'l*, pg. 1935
ENHANZ DCE, LLC—See Humana, Inc.; *U.S. Public*, pg. 1069
ENHERENT CORP.; *U.S. Public*, pg. 768
ENHERENT CORP.—See enherent Corp.; *U.S. Public*, pg. 768
ENHOPS, INC.—See Jeevan Scientific Technology Limited; *Int'l*, pg. 3927
ENHOPS SOLUTIONS PRIVATE LIMITED—See ProArch IT Solutions, Inc.; *U.S. Private*, pg. 3271
ENIA CARPETS NETHERLANDS B.V.—See Forbo Holding Ltd.; *Int'l*, pg. 2729
ENI ALGERIA PRODUCTION BV—See Eni S.p.A.; *Int'l*, pg. 2437
ENIA LIPOTECH SL—See Ascendis Health Limited; *Int'l*, pg. 601
ENI ANGOLA EXPLORATION—See Eni S.p.A.; *Int'l*, pg. 2437
ENI ARGENTINA EXPLORACION Y EXPLOTACION SA—See Eni S.p.A.; *Int'l*, pg. 2437
ENI AUSTRALIA LIMITED—See Eni S.p.A.; *Int'l*, pg. 2437
ENI AUSTRIA GMBH—See Eni S.p.A.; *Int'l*, pg. 2437
ENI AUSTRIA MARKETING GMBH—See Eni S.p.A.; *Int'l*, pg. 2437
ENI AUSTRIA TANKSTELLENBETRIEB GMBH—See Eni S.p.A.; *Int'l*, pg. 2437
ENIBLOCK S.A.; *Int'l*, pg. 2439
ENI BTC LTD—See Eni S.p.A.; *Int'l*, pg. 2437
ENI CESKA REPUBLIKA, S.R.O.—See Eni S.p.A.; *Int'l*, pg. 2437
ENICOR GMBH—See Haemonetics Corporation; *U.S. Public*, pg. 979
ENI CORPORATE UNIVERSITY SPA—See Eni S.p.A.; *Int'l*, pg. 2437
ENI CROATIA BV—See INA-Industrija Nafte, d.d.; *Int'l*, pg. 3642
ENICS AG—See Ahlstrom Capital Oy; *Int'l*, pg. 225
ENICS RAAHE OY—See Ahlstrom Capital Oy; *Int'l*, pg. 225
ENI DEUTSCHLAND GMBH—See Eni S.p.A.; *Int'l*, pg. 2437
ENI FINANCE INTERNATIONAL SA—See Eni S.p.A.; *Int'l*, pg. 2437
ENI FRANCE SARL—See Eni S.p.A.; *Int'l*, pg. 2437
ENI FUEL NORD SPA—See Eni S.p.A.; *Int'l*, pg. 2437
ENI GAS & POWER BELGIUM SA—See Eni S.p.A.; *Int'l*, pg. 2437
ENIGHETEN PERSONLIGASSISTANS AB—See Humana AB; *Int'l*, pg. 3530
ENIGMA-BULWARK, LIMITED; *U.S. Private*, pg. 1400
ENIGMA MINING LIMITED—See TNG Limited; *Int'l*, pg. 7767
ENIGMO, INC.—See Sony Group Corporation; *Int'l*, pg. 7107
ENI INDONESIA LTD.—See Eni S.p.A.; *Int'l*, pg. 2437
ENI INTERNATIONAL B.V.—See Eni S.p.A.; *Int'l*, pg. 2437
ENI INTERNATIONAL RESOURCES LTD—See Eni S.p.A.; *Int'l*, pg. 2437
ENI JPDA 06-105 PTY LTD—See Eni S.p.A.; *Int'l*, pg. 2437
ENIKON A.D.; *Int'l*, pg. 2439
ENILEC GESTION SARL—See LVMH Moet Hennessy Louis Vuitton SE; *Int'l*, pg. 4591
ENI MAGYARORSZAGON—See Eni S.p.A.; *Int'l*, pg. 2437
ENI OIL & GAS INC—See Eni S.p.A.; *Int'l*, pg. 2438
ENI PETROLEUM—See Eni S.p.A.; *Int'l*, pg. 2437
ENIPOWER MANTOVA SPA—See Eni S.p.A.; *Int'l*, pg. 2438
ENIPOWER SPA—See Eni S.p.A.; *Int'l*, pg. 2438
ENIPROGETTI SPA—See Eni S.p.A.; *Int'l*, pg. 2438
ENIRAM OY—See Wartsila Corporation; *Int'l*, pg. 8346
ENIRO 118 118 AB—See Eniro Group AB; *Int'l*, pg. 2439
ENIRO DANMARK A/S—See Eniro Group AB; *Int'l*, pg. 2439
ENIRO EMFAS AB—See Eniro Group AB; *Int'l*, pg. 2439
ENIRO GROUP AB; *Int'l*, pg. 2439
ENIRO GULA SIDORNA AB—See Eniro Group AB; *Int'l*, pg. 2439
ENIRO GULA SIDORNA FORSALJNING AB—See Eniro Group AB; *Int'l*, pg. 2439
ENIRO INTERNATIONAL AB—See Eniro Group AB; *Int'l*, pg. 2439
ENIRO NORGE AS—See Eniro Group AB; *Int'l*, pg. 2439
ENIRO NORWAY—See Eniro Group AB; *Int'l*, pg. 2439
ENIRO PASSAGEN AB—See Eniro Group AB; *Int'l*, pg. 2439
ENIRO SENTRAALI OY—See Eniro Group AB; *Int'l*, pg. 2439
ENIRO SVERIGE AB—See Eniro Group AB; *Int'l*, pg. 2439
ENIRO SVERIGE FORSALJNING AB—See Eniro Group AB; *Int'l*, pg. 2439
ENI SCHMIERTECHNIK GMBH—See Eni S.p.A.; *Int'l*, pg. 2437
ENISH INC.; *Int'l*, pg. 2439
ENISIAS CO., LTD.—See Cresco, Ltd.; *Int'l*, pg. 1840
ENI SLOVENSKO SPOL SRO—See Eni S.p.A.; *Int'l*, pg. 2437

ENI S.P.A. - GAS & POWER DIVISION—See Eni S.p.A.; *Int'l*, pg. 2437
ENI S.P.A. - REFINING & MARKETING DIVISION—See Eni S.p.A.; *Int'l*, pg. 2437
ENI S.P.A.; *Int'l*, pg. 2436
ENI SUISSE S.A.—See Eni S.p.A.; *Int'l*, pg. 2437
ENI TRADING & SHIPPING INC—See Eni S.p.A.; *Int'l*, pg. 2438
ENI TUNISIA BV—See Eni S.p.A.; *Int'l*, pg. 2437
ENI TURKMENISTAN LTD—See Eni S.p.A.; *Int'l*, pg. 2437
ENI UK LTD—See Eni S.p.A.; *Int'l*, pg. 2437
ENI ULT LTD—See Eni S.p.A.; *Int'l*, pg. 2437
ENI ULX LTD—See Eni S.p.A.; *Int'l*, pg. 2438
ENI USA INC—See Eni S.p.A.; *Int'l*, pg. 2438
ENI USA R&M CO INC—See Eni S.p.A.; *Int'l*, pg. 2438
ENI US OPERATING CO INC—See Eni S.p.A.; *Int'l*, pg. 2438
ENI VENEZUELA—See Eni S.p.A.; *Int'l*, pg. 2438
ENIZO SP. Z O.O.—See Energoinstal S.A.; *Int'l*, pg. 2421
EN-JAPAN INC.; *Int'l*, pg. 2395
ENJAZ ENERGY & PROJECTS CO.—See Al-Hejailan Group; *Int'l*, pg. 286
ENJAZ FOR DEVELOPMENT & MULTI PROJECTS COMPANY P.L.C.; *Int'l*, pg. 2439
ENJAZ PAYMENT SERVICES COMPANY LTD.—See BANK ALBILAD; *Int'l*, pg. 836
ENJET CO., LTD.; *Int'l*, pg. 2439
THE ENJOIYA GROUP, LLC; *U.S. Private*, pg. 4026
ENJOY LIFE NATURAL BRANDS, LLC—See Mondelez International, Inc.; *U.S. Public*, pg. 1461
ENJOYOR TECHNOLOGY CO., LTD.; *Int'l*, pg. 2439
ENJOY WELLNESS, S.L.—See Espiga Capital Gestion S.G.E.C.R, S.A.; *Int'l*, pg. 2506
ENKA ADAPAZARI POWER INVESTMENT B.V.—See Enka Insaat ve Sanayi A.S.; *Int'l*, pg. 2440
ENKA CONSTRUCTION & DEVELOPMENT B.V.—See Enka Insaat ve Sanayi A.S.; *Int'l*, pg. 2440
ENKA FINANSAL KIRALAMA A.S.—See Enka Insaat ve Sanayi A.S.; *Int'l*, pg. 2440
ENKA GEBZE POWER INVESTMENT B.V.—See Enka Insaat ve Sanayi A.S.; *Int'l*, pg. 2440
ENKA HOLDING B.V.—See Enka Insaat ve Sanayi A.S.; *Int'l*, pg. 2440
ENKA INSAAT VE SANAYI A.S.; *Int'l*, pg. 2439
ENKA INTERNATIONAL GMBH & CO. KG—See International Chemical Investors S.E.; *Int'l*, pg. 3745
ENKA ITALIA SRL—See International Chemical Investors S.E.; *Int'l*, pg. 3745
ENKA IZMIR POWER INVESTMENT B.V.—See Enka Insaat ve Sanayi A.S.; *Int'l*, pg. 2440
ENKA PAZARLAMA IHRACAT ITHALAT AS—See Enka Insaat ve Sanayi A.S.; *Int'l*, pg. 2440
ENKA POWER INVESTMENT B.V.—See Enka Insaat ve Sanayi A.S.; *Int'l*, pg. 2440
ENKA TC LLC—See Enka Insaat ve Sanayi A.S.; *Int'l*, pg. 2440
ENKA TEKNIK A.S.—See Enka Insaat ve Sanayi A.S.; *Int'l*, pg. 2440
ENKA TEKNIK GENEL MUTEAHHITLIK BAKIM ISLETME SEVK VE IDARE ANONIM SIRKETI—See Enka Insaat ve Sanayi A.S.; *Int'l*, pg. 2440
ENK CO., LTD.—See NK Co., Ltd.; *Int'l*, pg. 5390
ENK DRUCK & MEDIA GMBH; *Int'l*, pg. 2439
THE ENKEBOLL COMPANY; *U.S. Private*, pg. 4026
ENKEI AMERICA INC.; *U.S. Private*, pg. 1400
ENKEI WHEELS (INDIA) LTD.; *Int'l*, pg. 2440
ENKER D.D.; *Int'l*, pg. 2440
ENKLERESTART.NO AS—See TowerBrook Capital Partners, L.P.; *U.S. Private*, pg. 4195
ENKO CHEM, INC.; *U.S. Private*, pg. 1400
ENKOM ACTIVE OY—See Lagercrantz Group AB; *Int'l*, pg. 4394
ENKOM OY—See Lagercrantz Group AB; *Int'l*, pg. 4394
EN KONKATSU AGENT CO., LTD.—See en-japan Inc.; *Int'l*, pg. 2395
ENKOR D.O.O.—See BP plc; *Int'l*, pg. 1131
ENK PLC AUSTRALIAN REGIONAL OFFICE—See DMCI Holdings, Inc.; *Int'l*, pg. 2143
ENK PLC PHILIPPINES REGIONAL OFFICE—See DMCI Holdings, Inc.; *Int'l*, pg. 2143
ENK PLC—See DMCI Holdings, Inc.; *Int'l*, pg. 2142
ENKSZ ELSO NEMZETI KOZMUSZOLGALTATO ZRT.; *Int'l*, pg. 2440
ENLACE OPERATIVO S.A.—See Grupo de Inversiones Suramericana S.A.; *Int'l*, pg. 3125
ENLACES COMPUTACIONALES, S. DE R.L. DE C.V.—See Avnet, Inc.; *U.S. Public*, pg. 253
ENL AGRI LIMITED—See ENL Limited; *Int'l*, pg. 2441
ENL COMMERCIAL LIMITED—See ENL Limited; *Int'l*, pg. 2441
ENL FINANCE LIMITED—See ENL Limited; *Int'l*, pg. 2441
ENL FOUNDATION—See ENL Limited; *Int'l*, pg. 2441
ENL HOUSE LIMITED—See ENL Limited; *Int'l*, pg. 2441
ENLIGHTA INC.; *Int'l*, pg. 2442
ENLIGHT CORPORATION; *Int'l*, pg. 2442
ENLIGHTED ENERGY SYSTEMS PVT LTD—See Siemens Aktiengesellschaft; *Int'l*, pg. 6886
ENLIGHTED, INC.—See The Carlyle Group Inc.; *U.S. Public*, pg. 2046

ENLIGHTEN IT CONSULTING INC.—See Veritas Capital Fund Management, LLC; *U.S. Private*, pg. 4360
ENLIGHTEN IT CONSULTING LLC—See Huntington Ingalls Industries, Inc.; *U.S. Public*, pg. 1072
ENLIGHTENMENT CAPITAL LLC; *U.S. Private*, pg. 1400
ENLIGHT RENEWABLE ENERGY LTD.; *Int'l*, pg. 2442
ENLINK MIDSTREAM, INC.—See EnLink Midstream, LLC; *U.S. Public*, pg. 768
ENLINK MIDSTREAM, LLC; *U.S. Public*, pg. 768
ENLINK MIDSTREAM PARTNERS, LP—See EnLink Midstream, LLC; *U.S. Public*, pg. 768
ENLINX, LLC—See Port Logistics Group, Inc.; *U.S. Private*, pg. 3230
ENLIVEN THERAPEUTICS, INC; *U.S. Public*, pg. 768
ENLIVEX THERAPEUTICS LTD.; *Int'l*, pg. 2442
ENL LAND LTD—See ENL Limited; *Int'l*, pg. 2441
ENL LIMITED; *Int'l*, pg. 2440
ENLOE MEDICAL CENTER; *U.S. Private*, pg. 1401
ENLOW TRACTOR AUCTION, INC.; *U.S. Private*, pg. 1401
ENL PROPERTY LIMITED—See ENL Limited; *Int'l*, pg. 2441
ENLYTE GROUP, LLC—See Stone Point Capital LLC; *U.S. Private*, pg. 3823
ENMARK STATIONS, INC.—See Colonial Group, Inc.; *U.S. Private*, pg. 971
ENMAR TRADING LTD—See Enka Insaat ve Sanayi A.S.; *Int'l*, pg. 2440
ENMAX COMMERCIAL ENERGY MARKETING INC.—See ENMAX Corporation; *Int'l*, pg. 2442
ENMAX COMMERCIAL SERVICES INC.—See ENMAX Corporation; *Int'l*, pg. 2442
ENMAX CORPORATION; *Int'l*, pg. 2442
ENMAX ENCOMPASS INC.—See ENMAX Corporation; *Int'l*, pg. 2442
ENMAX ENERGY CORPORATION—See ENMAX Corporation; *Int'l*, pg. 2442
ENMAX ENERGY MARKETING INC.—See ENMAX Corporation; *Int'l*, pg. 2442
ENMAX GREEN POWER INC.—See ENMAX Corporation; *Int'l*, pg. 2442
ENMAX POWER CORPORATION—See ENMAX Corporation; *Int'l*, pg. 2442
ENMEX, S.A. DE C.V.—See Kerry Group plc; *Int'l*, pg. 4138
ENM HOLDINGS LIMITED; *Int'l*, pg. 2442
ENMOTIVE COMPANY LLC—See Gannett Co., Inc.; *U.S. Public*, pg. 896
ENMR PLATEAU TELECOM; *U.S. Private*, pg. 1401
ENNEN BROTHERS; *U.S. Private*, pg. 1401
ENN ENERGY HOLDINGS LIMITED; *Int'l*, pg. 2442
ENNET CORPORATION—See Nippon Telegraph & Telephone Corporation; *Int'l*, pg. 5343
ENNIA CARIBE HOLDING NV—See Banco di Caribe N.V.; *Int'l*, pg. 822
ENNIS BUSINESS FORMS OF KANSAS, INC.—See Ennis, Inc.; *U.S. Public*, pg. 769
ENNIS-FLINT, INC.—See PPG Industries, Inc.; *U.S. Public*, pg. 1707
ENNIS - FLINT NEW ZEALAND—See PPG Industries, Inc.; *U.S. Public*, pg. 1707
ENNIS FURNITURE CO. INC.; *U.S. Private*, pg. 1401
ENNIS, INC. - CHATHAM—See Ennis, Inc.; *U.S. Public*, pg. 769
ENNIS, INC. - COSHOCTON—See Ennis, Inc.; *U.S. Public*, pg. 769
ENNIS, INC. - DEWITT—See Ennis, Inc.; *U.S. Public*, pg. 769
ENNIS, INC. - ENNIS, TX—See Ennis, Inc.; *U.S. Public*, pg. 769
ENNIS, INC. - KNOXVILLE—See Ennis, Inc.; *U.S. Public*, pg. 769
ENNIS, INC. - MOULTRIE—See Ennis, Inc.; *U.S. Public*, pg. 769
ENNIS, INC. - PASO ROBLES—See Ennis, Inc.; *U.S. Public*, pg. 769
ENNIS, INC.; *U.S. Public*, pg. 768
ENNIS, INC. - WOLFE CITY—See Ennis, Inc.; *U.S. Public*, pg. 769
ENNIS PAINT INC.—See Brazos Private Equity Partners, LLC; *U.S. Private*, pg. 642
ENNIS, PELLUM & ASSOCIATES, CPAS; *U.S. Private*, pg. 1401
ENNIS POWER COMPANY LLC—See ENGIE SA; *Int'l*, pg. 2433
ENNIS STEEL INDUSTRIES INC.; *U.S. Private*, pg. 1401
ENNIS TRAFFIC SAFETY SOLUTIONS PTY LTD—See PPG Industries, Inc.; *U.S. Public*, pg. 1707
ENN NATURAL GAS CO., LTD.; *Int'l*, pg. 2442
ENNOBLE FINANCE, LLC—See CURO Group Holdings Corp.; *U.S. Public*, pg. 611
ENNOCONN CORPORATION; *Int'l*, pg. 2443
ENNOCONN (KUNSHAN) TECHNOLOGY CO., LTD.—See Ennoconn Corporation; *Int'l*, pg. 2443
ENNOCONN (SUZHOU) TECHNOLOGY CO., LTD.—See Ennoconn Corporation; *Int'l*, pg. 2443
ENNOGIE SOLAR GROUP A/S; *Int'l*, pg. 2443
ENNO ROGGEMANN GMBH & CO. KG; *Int'l*, pg. 2443
ENNOSTAR INC.; *Int'l*, pg. 2443

ENNOSTAR INC.

ENNOWYSE CORPORATION—See Ennoconn Corporation; *Int'l*, pg. 2443
ENNOX GROUP LTD.; *Int'l*, pg. 2444
ENNSVALLEY BAKERY LIMITED—See Unga Group PLC; *Int'l*, pg. 8027
ENNTE AS—See CCL Industries Inc.; *Int'l*, pg. 1368
ENOCELL OY—See Stora Enso Oyj; *Int'l*, pg. 7223
ENOCH PRATT FREE LIBRARY; *U.S. Private*, pg. 1401
ENOC PROCESSING COMPANY LLC—See Emirates National Oil Company Limited; *Int'l*, pg. 2381
ENODIS CORPORATION—See Ali Holding S.r.l.; *Int'l*, pg. 322
ENODIS FRANCE SA—See Ali Holding S.r.l.; *Int'l*, pg. 322
ENOGIA SA; *Int'l*, pg. 2444
ENOL SA—See HORIBA Ltd; *Int'l*, pg. 3475
EN OM FRA, S.A.—See Nova Ventures Group Corp.; *U.S. Private*, pg. 2966
ENOM, LLC—See Tucows, Inc.; *Int'l*, pg. 7963
ENOMOTO CO., LTD.; *Int'l*, pg. 2444
ENOMOTO HONG KONG CO.LTD.—See Enomoto Co., Ltd.; *Int'l*, pg. 2444
ENOMOTO PHILIPPINE MANUFACTURING INC.—See Enomoto Co., Ltd.; *Int'l*, pg. 2444
ENOMOTO PRECISION ENGINEERING (S) PTE.LTD.—See Enomoto Co., Ltd.; *Int'l*, pg. 2444
ENOP - ENGENHARIA E OBRAS PUBLICAS, LDA.—See CONDURIL, Engenharia S.A.; *Int'l*, pg. 1767
ENOPLASTIC SPA—See Cobepa S.A.; *Int'l*, pg. 1683
ENOR CORPORATION; *U.S. Private*, pg. 1401
E-NOR EMEA—See Dentsu Group Inc.; *Int'l*, pg. 2037
E-NOR LLC—See Dentsu Group Inc.; *Int'l*, pg. 2037
ENORM MINING LIMITED—See Thor Explorations Limited; *Int'l*, pg. 7717
ENO S.A.S.; *Int'l*, pg. 2444
ENOSERV, LLC—See ESCO Technologies, Inc.; *U.S. Public*, pg. 794
ENOSHIMA ELECTRIC RAILWAY CO., LTD.—See Odakyu Electric Railway Co., Ltd.; *Int'l*, pg. 5523
ENOTECA CO., LTD.—See Asahi Group Holdings Ltd.; *Int'l*, pg. 593
ENOTRIA GROUP LIMITED—See BlueGem Capital Partners LLP; *Int'l*, pg. 1071
EN OTSUKA PHARMACEUTICAL CO., LTD. - KITAKAMI PLANT—See Otsuka Holdings Co., Ltd.; *Int'l*, pg. 5659
EN OTSUKA PHARMACEUTICAL CO., LTD.—See Otsuka Holdings Co., Ltd.; *Int'l*, pg. 5659
ENOVA ELEKTRIK ENERJISI TOPTAN SATIS A.S.—See Nurol Holding A.S.; *Int'l*, pg. 5490
ENOVA ENERGY PRODUCTION INC.—See Nurol Holding A.S.; *Int'l*, pg. 5490
ENOVA ENERJI URETIM A.S.—See Nurol Holding A.S.; *Int'l*, pg. 5490
ENOVA ILLUMINATION, LLC; *U.S. Private*, pg. 1401
ENOVA INTERNATIONAL, INC.; *U.S. Public*, pg. 769
ENOVA SYSTEMS INC.; *U.S. Public*, pg. 770
ENOVATE MEDICAL, LLC—See The Sterling Group, L.P.; *U.S. Private*, pg. 4122
ENOVATION CONTROLS, LLC; *U.S. Private*, pg. 1401
ENOVATION CONTROLS, LTD.—See Helios Technologies, Inc.; *U.S. Public*, pg. 1023
ENOVAX PTE. LTD.—See PUC Berhad; *Int'l*, pg. 6115
E-NOVIA S.P.A.; *Int'l*, pg. 2249
ENOVIS CORPORATION; *U.S. Public*, pg. 770
ENOVITY, INC.—See Veolia Environnement S.A.; *Int'l*, pg. 8158
ENOVIX CORPORATION; *U.S. Public*, pg. 774
ENOVOS BALANCE DEUTSCHLAND GMBH—See Enovos International S.A.; *Int'l*, pg. 2444
ENOVOS DEUTSCHLAND SE—See Enovos International S.A.; *Int'l*, pg. 2444
ENOVOS INTERNATIONAL S.A.; *Int'l*, pg. 2444
ENOVOS LUXEMBOURG S.A.—See Enovos International S.A.; *Int'l*, pg. 2444
ENOX BIOPHARMA, INC.; *Int'l*, pg. 2444
ENPAC LLC; *U.S. Private*, pg. 1401
ENPAR SONDERWERKSTOFFE GMBH—See voestalpine AG; *Int'l*, pg. 8289
ENPHASE ENERGY AUSTRALIA PTY. LTD.—See Enphase Energy, Inc.; *U.S. Public*, pg. 774
ENPHASE ENERGY, INC.; *U.S. Public*, pg. 774
ENPHASE ENERGY NEW ZEALAND LIMITED—See Enphase Energy, Inc.; *U.S. Public*, pg. 774
ENPHASE ENERGY S.A.S.—See Enphase Energy, Inc.; *U.S. Public*, pg. 774
ENPHASE ENERGY S.R.L.—See Enphase Energy, Inc.; *U.S. Public*, pg. 774
ENPHASE ENERGY UK LIMITED—See Enphase Energy, Inc.; *U.S. Public*, pg. 774
ENPHASE SERVICE COMPANY, LLC—See Enphase Energy, Inc.; *U.S. Public*, pg. 774
ENPHASE SOLAR ENERGY PRIVATE LIMITED—See Enphase Energy, Inc.; *U.S. Public*, pg. 774
ENPHYS ACQUISITION CORP.; *U.S. Public*, pg. 774
EN PING KAM HING TEXTILE & DYEING CO., LTD.—See Kam Hing International Holdings Limited; *Int'l*, pg. 4059
ENPLAS CORPORATION - ENGINEERING PLASTICS PRODUCTS DIVISION—See ENPLAS CORPORATION; *Int'l*, pg. 2445
ENPLAS CORPORATION - KANUMA PLANT—See ENPLAS CORPORATION; *Int'l*, pg. 2445
ENPLAS CORPORATION - LED BUSINESS DIVISION—See ENPLAS CORPORATION; *Int'l*, pg. 2445
ENPLAS CORPORATION - PLASTIC OPTICS DIVISION—See ENPLAS CORPORATION; *Int'l*, pg. 2445
ENPLAS CORPORATION; *Int'l*, pg. 2444
ENPLAS HI-TECH (SINGAPORE) PTE. LTD.—See ENPLAS CORPORATION; *Int'l*, pg. 2445
ENPLAS (HONG KONG) LIMITED—See ENPLAS CORPORATION; *Int'l*, pg. 2444
ENPLAS HY-CAD ELECTRONIC (SHANGHAI) CO., LTD.—See ENPLAS CORPORATION; *Int'l*, pg. 2445
ENPLAS LABORATORIES, INC.—See ENPLAS CORPORATION; *Int'l*, pg. 2445
ENPLAS LIFE TECH, INC.—See ENPLAS CORPORATION; *Int'l*, pg. 2445
ENPLAS MICROTECH, INC.—See ENPLAS CORPORATION; *Int'l*, pg. 2445
ENPLAS NICHING TECHNOLOGY CORPORATION—See ENPLAS CORPORATION; *Int'l*, pg. 2445
ENPLAS PRECISION (MALAYSIA) SDN. BHD.—See ENPLAS CORPORATION; *Int'l*, pg. 2445
ENPLAS PRECISION (THAILAND) CO., LTD.—See ENPLAS CORPORATION; *Int'l*, pg. 2445
ENPLAS SEIKI CORPORATION—See ENPLAS CORPORATION; *Int'l*, pg. 2445
ENPLAS SEMICONDUCTOR PERIPHERAL CORPORATION—See ENPLAS CORPORATION; *Int'l*, pg. 2445
ENPLAS SEMICONDUCTOR PERIPHERALS PTE. LTD.—See ENPLAS CORPORATION; *Int'l*, pg. 2445
ENPLAS TESCO, INC.—See ENPLAS CORPORATION; *Int'l*, pg. 2445
ENPLAS (U.S.A.), INC.—See ENPLAS CORPORATION; *Int'l*, pg. 2445
ENPLAS (VIETNAM) CO., LTD.—See ENPLAS CORPORATION; *Int'l*, pg. 2445
ENPLUS LTD.; *Int'l*, pg. 2445
EN.PLUS GMBH—See CEZ, a.s.; *Int'l*, pg. 1427
EN POINTE GOV, INC.—See Din Global Corp.; *U.S. Private*, pg. 1233
EN POINTE TECHNOLOGIES, INC.—See Din Global Corp.; *U.S. Private*, pg. 1233
EN POINTE TECHNOLOGIES SALES, INC.—See Insight Enterprises, Inc.; *U.S. Public*, pg. 1130
ENPORION, INC.—See NB Ventures, Inc.; *U.S. Private*, pg. 2874
ENPOWER CORP.; *U.S. Private*, pg. 1401
ENPOWER MANAGEMENT CORP.—See Enpower Corp.; *U.S. Private*, pg. 1401
ENPOWER OPERATIONS CORP.—See Enpower Corp.; *U.S. Private*, pg. 1401
ENPRO ASSOCIATES, LLC—See Enpro Inc.; *U.S. Public*, pg. 774
ENPRO HOLDINGS, INC.—See Enpro Inc.; *U.S. Public*, pg. 774
ENPRO INC.; *U.S. Public*, pg. 774
ENPRO, INC.; *U.S. Private*, pg. 1401
ENPRO, LLC—See Essential Utilities Inc.; *U.S. Public*, pg. 795
ENPROTECH INDUSTRIAL TECHNOLOGIES, INC. VERSON, DANLY & NSD PARTS—See ITOCHU Corporation; *Int'l*, pg. 3838
ENQUERO, INC.—See Genpact Limited; *Int'l*, pg. 2926
ENQUEST PLC; *Int'l*, pg. 2445
ENQUICKFIX LIMITED—See ENL Limited; *Int'l*, pg. 2441
ENQUIRO SEARCH SOLUTIONS, INC.—See Yellow Pages Limited; *Int'l*, pg. 8576
ENQUIZIT INC.—See CDW Corporation; *U.S. Public*, pg. 462
ENRAD AB; *Int'l*, pg. 2445
ENRAF NONIUS IBERICA PORTUGAL, LDA.—See Prim S.A.; *Int'l*, pg. 5973
ENRAF NONIUS IBERICA, S.A.—See Prim S.A.; *Int'l*, pg. 5973
ENRA GROUP BERHAD; *Int'l*, pg. 2445
ENRA IOL SDN. BHD.—See ENRA Group Berhad; *Int'l*, pg. 2445
ENRA KIMIA SDN. BHD.—See ENRA Group Berhad; *Int'l*, pg. 2445
ENR ASSET MANAGEMENT INC.; *Int'l*, pg. 2445
ENRC LEASING BV—See Eurasian Natural Resources Corporation Limited; *Int'l*, pg. 2527
ENRC LOGISTICS LLP—See Eurasian Natural Resources Corporation Limited; *Int'l*, pg. 2527
ENRC MANAGEMENT (UK) LIMITED—See Eurasian Natural Resources Corporation Limited; *Int'l*, pg. 2527
ENRC MARKETING AG—See Eurasian Natural Resources Corporation Limited; *Int'l*, pg. 2527
ENRECOVER ENERGY RECOVERY SOLUTIONS PRIVATE LIMITED—See Refex Renewables & Infrastructure Limited; *Int'l*, pg. 6250
ENRG ELEMENTS LIMITED; *Int'l*, pg. 2445
ENRIC (BENGBU) COMPRESSOR CO., LTD.—See China International Marine Containers (Group) Co., Ltd.; *Int'l*, pg. 1511

CORPORATE AFFILIATIONS

ENRICH CONSULTING, INC.—See TA Associates, Inc.; *U.S. Private*, pg. 3917
ENRICH CONSULTING, INC.—See TPG Capital, L.P.; *U.S. Public*, pg. 2175
ENRICH TECH CO., LTD.—See Acter Co., Ltd.; *Int'l*, pg. 117
ENRIC (LANG FANG) ENERGY EQUIPMENT INTEGRATION CO., LTD.—See China International Marine Containers (Group) Co., Ltd.; *Int'l*, pg. 1511
ENRICO GIOTTI SPA—See McCormick & Company, Incorporated; *U.S. Public*, pg. 1404
E-NRJ SARL—See NRJ Group SA; *Int'l*, pg. 5474
ENROBES 34—See FAYAT SAS; *Int'l*, pg. 2625
ENROBES DE L'ONDAINE SAS—See VINCI S.A.; *Int'l*, pg. 8217
ENRO ENERGIE SE; *Int'l*, pg. 2445
ENROLL AMERICA; *U.S. Private*, pg. 1401
ENROLLCOM, INC.—See American Fidelity Corporation; *U.S. Private*, pg. 234
ENRO LUDWIGSFELDE ENERGIE GMBH—See EWE Aktiengesellschaft; *Int'l*, pg. 2575
ENROUTE EMERGENCY SYSTEMS—See Koch Industries, Inc.; *U.S. Private*, pg. 2330
EN ROUTE INTERNATIONAL AUSTRALIA PTY. LTD.—See The Emirates Group; *Int'l*, pg. 7639
EN ROUTE INTERNATIONAL GENERAL TRADING LLC—See The Emirates Group; *Int'l*, pg. 7639
EN ROUTE INTERNATIONAL LIMITED—See The Emirates Group; *Int'l*, pg. 7639
EN ROUTE INTERNATIONAL USA, INC.—See The Emirates Group; *Int'l*, pg. 7639
ENR RUSSIA INVEST SA; *Int'l*, pg. 2445
ENRU DEVELOPMENT B.V.—See Enka Insaat ve Sanayi A.S.; *Int'l*, pg. 2440
ENSA BH D.O.O.—See Sava d.d.; *Int'l*, pg. 6595
ENSAFE INC.; *U.S. Private*, pg. 1401
ENSAMBLADORES ELECTRONICOS DE MEXICO, S, DE R.L. DE C.V.—See RTX Corporation; *U.S. Public*, pg. 1822
ENSAR CORP.; *U.S. Private*, pg. 1401
ENSA STEEL INDUSTRIES LIMITED; *Int'l*, pg. 2445
ENSCICON CORPORATION; *U.S. Private*, pg. 1401
ENSCO ASIA PACIFIC PTE. LIMITED—See Valaris Limited; *Int'l*, pg. 8110
ENSCO ASIA PACIFIC (SINGAPORE) PTE. LTD.—See Valaris Limited; *Int'l*, pg. 8110
ENSCO AUSTRALIA PTY. LTD.—See Valaris Limited; *Int'l*, pg. 8110
ENSCO AVIONICS CANADA INC.—See Ensco Inc.; *U.S. Private*, pg. 1402
ENSCO AVIONICS, INC.—See Ensco Inc.; *U.S. Private*, pg. 1402
ENSCO DRILLING COMPANY (NIGERIA) LTD.—See Valaris Limited; *Int'l*, pg. 8110
ENSCO DRILLING (VENEZUELA), S.A.—See Valaris Limited; *Int'l*, pg. 8110
ENSCO GERUDI (M) SDN. BHD.—See Valaris Limited; *Int'l*, pg. 8110
ENSCO INCORPORATED—See Valaris Limited; *Int'l*, pg. 8110
ENSCO INC.; *U.S. Private*, pg. 1401
ENSCO OFFSHORE COMPANY - MARKETING & CONTRACTS—See Valaris Limited; *Int'l*, pg. 8110
ENSCO OFFSHORE LLC—See Valaris Limited; *Int'l*, pg. 8110
ENSCO OFFSHORE UK LTD.—See Valaris Limited; *Int'l*, pg. 8110
ENSCOPE PTY LTD—See Quanta Services, Inc.; *U.S. Public*, pg. 1751
ENSCO RAIL AUSTRALIA PTY LTD—See Ensco Inc.; *U.S. Private*, pg. 1402
ENSCO RAIL, INC.—See Ensco Inc.; *U.S. Private*, pg. 1402
ENSCO SERVICES LIMITED—See Valaris Limited; *Int'l*, pg. 8110
ENSCO—See Valaris Limited; *Int'l*, pg. 8110
ENSEADA—See Novonor S.A.; *Int'l*, pg. 5470
ENSEJOUR LTD.—See ENL Limited; *Int'l*, pg. 2441
ENSEMBLE EQUITY PTE., LTD.—See Project Planning Service Public Company Limited; *Int'l*, pg. 5991
ENSEMBLE HEALTH PARTNERS, INC.; *U.S. Private*, pg. 1402
ENSEMBLE SYSTEMS INC.; *Int'l*, pg. 2446
ENSENTA CORPORATION—See Jack Henry & Associates, Inc.; *U.S. Public*, pg. 1182
ENSEO INC; *U.S. Private*, pg. 1402
ENSER CORPORATION—See EnerSys; *U.S. Public*, pg. 767
ENSERVA GMBH—See Stadtwerke Solingen GmbH; *Int'l*, pg. 7162
ENSERVCO CORPORATION; *U.S. Public*, pg. 775
ENSERVE GROUP LIMITED—See Grovepoint Capital LLP; *Int'l*, pg. 3112
ENSERVE GROUP LIMITED—See Rubicon Partners Limited; *Int'l*, pg. 6422
ENSERVIO, INC.—See Vista Equity Partners, LLC; *U.S. Private*, pg. 4400
ENS GLOBAL CO., LTD.—See Sebang Co., Ltd.; *Int'l*, pg. 6669

COMPANY NAME INDEX

ENS GROUP, INC.; *U.S. Private*, pg. 1401
ENSHAM RESOURCES PTY. LTD.—See Idemitsu Kosan Co., Ltd.; *Int'l*, pg. 3590
ENSHU (CHINA) CORPORATION LTD.—See The Sumitomo Warehouse Co. Ltd.; *Int'l*, pg. 7689
ENSHU GMBH—See Enshu Limited; *Int'l*, pg. 2446
ENSHU INDIA PRIVATE LIMITED—See Enshu Limited; *Int'l*, pg. 2446
ENSHU KAMI KOGYO CO., LTD.—See Tomoku Co., Ltd.; *Int'l*, pg. 7801
ENSHU LIMITED - HAMAKITA FACTORY—See Enshu Limited; *Int'l*, pg. 2446
ENSHU LIMITED; *Int'l*, pg. 2446
ENSHU (QINGDAO) LIMITED—See Enshu Limited; *Int'l*, pg. 2446
ENSHU (QINGDAO) MACHINE CO., LTD.—See Enshu Limited; *Int'l*, pg. 2446
ENSHU SEIKO CO., LTD.—See Suzuki Motor Corporation; *Int'l*, pg. 7354
ENSHU SEINO TRANSPORTATION CO., LTD.—See Seino Holdings Co., Ltd.; *Int'l*, pg. 6690
ENSHU (THAILAND) LIMITED—See Enshu Limited; *Int'l*, pg. 2446
ENSHU TRUCK CO., LTD.—See The Sumitomo Warehouse Co. Ltd.; *Int'l*, pg. 7689
ENSHU TRUCK KANSAI CO., LTD.—See The Sumitomo Warehouse Co. Ltd.; *Int'l*, pg. 7689
ENSHU (USA) CORPORATION MEXICO R.O.W.I.—See Enshu Limited; *Int'l*, pg. 2446
ENSHU USA CORPORATION—See Enshu Limited; *Int'l*, pg. 2446
ENSHU VIETNAM CO., LTD.—See Enshu Limited; *Int'l*, pg. 2446
ENSIGHTEN, INC.; *U.S. Private*, pg. 1402
ENSIGN ARGENTINA S.A.—See Ensign Energy Services Inc.; *Int'l*, pg. 2446
ENSIGN AUSTRALIA PTY LIMITED—See Ensign Energy Services Inc.; *Int'l*, pg. 2446
THE ENSIGN-BICKFORD AEROSPACE & DEFENSE COMPANY—See Incitec Pivot Limited; *Int'l*, pg. 3648
ENSIGN-BICKFORD REALTY CORPORATION—See Incitec Pivot Limited; *Int'l*, pg. 3648
ENSIGN CHRYSLER DODGE JEEP; *Int'l*, pg. 2446
ENSIGN CLOVERDALE LLC—See The Ensign Group, Inc.; *U.S. Public*, pg. 2070
ENSIGN DE VENEZUELA C.A.—See Ensign Energy Services Inc.; *Int'l*, pg. 2447
ENSIGN DRILLING, INC.-NISKU OPERATIONS CENTRE—See Ensign Energy Services Inc.; *Int'l*, pg. 2446
ENSIGN DRILLING, INC.—See Ensign Energy Services Inc.; *Int'l*, pg. 2446
ENSIGN DRILLING PARTNERSHIP - ENCORE CORING & DRILLING DIVISION—See Ensign Energy Services Inc.; *Int'l*, pg. 2446
ENSIGN DRILLING PARTNERSHIP - ENGINEERING, PROCUREMENT & CONSTRUCTION DIVISION—See Ensign Energy Services Inc.; *Int'l*, pg. 2446
ENSIGN DRILLING PARTNERSHIP - ENSIGN ATLANTIC DIRECTIONAL SERVICES DIVISION—See Ensign Energy Services Inc.; *Int'l*, pg. 2446
ENSIGN DRILLING PARTNERSHIP - ENSIGN CANADIAN DRILLING DIVISION—See Ensign Energy Services Inc.; *Int'l*, pg. 2446
ENSIGN DRILLING PARTNERSHIP - ENSIGN DIRECTIONAL SERVICES DIVISION—See Ensign Energy Services Inc.; *Int'l*, pg. 2446
ENSIGN ENERGY SERVICES INC.; *Int'l*, pg. 2446
ENSIGN ENERGY SERVICES INTERNATIONAL LIMITED - EASTERN HEMISPHERE DIVISION—See Ensign Energy Services Inc.; *Int'l*, pg. 2446
ENSIGN ENERGY SERVICES INTERNATIONAL LIMITED—See Ensign Energy Services Inc.; *Int'l*, pg. 2446
ENSIGN EUROPA SP. Z.O.O.—See Ensign Energy Services Inc.; *Int'l*, pg. 2446
THE ENSIGN GROUP, INC.; *U.S. Public*, pg. 2069
ENSIGNIA CONSTRUCTION SDN. BHD.—See IGB Berhad; *Int'l*, pg. 3601
ENSIGN INTERNATIONAL ENERGY SERVICES INC. - LATIN AMERICA DIVISION—See Ensign Energy Services Inc.; *Int'l*, pg. 2446
ENSIGN INTERNATIONAL ENERGY SERVICES INC.—See Ensign Energy Services Inc.; *Int'l*, pg. 2446
ENSIGN INTERNATIONAL ENERGY SERVICES—See Ensign Energy Services Inc.; *Int'l*, pg. 2446
ENSIGN MONTGOMERY LLC—See The Ensign Group, Inc.; *U.S. Public*, pg. 2070
ENSIGN OPERATING COMPANY INC.—See Ensign Energy Services Inc.; *Int'l*, pg. 2446
ENSIGN PANORAMA LLC—See The Ensign Group, Inc.; *U.S. Public*, pg. 2071
ENSIGN PLEASANTON LLC—See The Ensign Group, Inc.; *U.S. Public*, pg. 2071
ENSIGN RIBBON BURNERS, LLC—See Lionheart Ventures; *U.S. Private*, pg. 2464
ENSIGN ROCKWELL SERVICES—See Ensign Energy Services Inc.; *Int'l*, pg. 2447

ENSIGN SANTA ROSA LLC—See The Ensign Group, Inc.; *U.S. Public*, pg. 2071
ENSIGN SONOMA LLC—See The Ensign Group, Inc.; *U.S. Public*, pg. 2071
ENSIGN UNITED STATES DRILLING (CALIFORNIA) INC. - ENSIGN CALIFORNIA WELL SERVICES DIVISION—See Ensign Energy Services Inc.; *Int'l*, pg. 2447
ENSIGN UNITED STATES DRILLING (CALIFORNIA) INC. - WEST COAST OILFIELD RENTALS DIVISON—See Ensign Energy Services Inc.; *Int'l*, pg. 2447
ENSIGN UNITED STATES DRILLING-CALIFORNIA—See Ensign Energy Services Inc.; *Int'l*, pg. 2447
ENSIGN UNITED STATES DRILLING INC. - ENSIGN DIRECTIONAL DRILLING SERVICES DIVISION—See Ensign Energy Services Inc.; *Int'l*, pg. 2447
ENSIGN UNITED STATES DRILLING INC. - ENSIGN WELL SERVICES DIVISION—See Ensign Energy Services Inc.; *Int'l*, pg. 2447
ENSIGN UNITED STATES DRILLING INC. - ROCKY MOUNTAIN OILFIELD RENTALS DIVISION—See Ensign Energy Services Inc.; *Int'l*, pg. 2447
ENSIGN UNITED STATES DRILLING, INC.—See Ensign Energy Services Inc.; *Int'l*, pg. 2447
ENSIGN US SOUTHERN DRILLING LLC—See Ensign Energy Services Inc.; *Int'l*, pg. 2447
ENSIGN WHITTIER WEST LLC—See The Ensign Group, Inc.; *U.S. Public*, pg. 2071
ENSIGN WILLITS LLC—See The Ensign Group, Inc.; *U.S. Public*, pg. 2071
ENSILICA INDIA PRIVATE LIMITED—See Ensilica Plc; *Int'l*, pg. 2447
ENSILICA PLC; *Int'l*, pg. 2447
ENSILIENCE CO., LTD.—See YFY, Inc.; *Int'l*, pg. 8579
ENSIL PTY. LTD.—See Nutrien Ltd.; *Int'l*, pg. 5492
ENSINGER ASIA HOLDING PTE LTD—See Ensinger GmbH; *Int'l*, pg. 2447
ENSINGER BUILDING PRODUCTS LTD.—See Ensinger GmbH; *Int'l*, pg. 2447
ENSINGER (CHINA) CO., LTD.—See Ensinger GmbH; *Int'l*, pg. 2447
ENSINGER COMPOSITES SCHWEIZ GMBH—See Ensinger GmbH; *Int'l*, pg. 2447
ENSINGER DANMARK A/S—See Ensinger GmbH; *Int'l*, pg. 2447
ENSINGER FRANCE S.A.R.L.—See Ensinger GmbH; *Int'l*, pg. 2447
ENSINGER GMBH; *Int'l*, pg. 2447
ENSINGER GROUP LIMITED—See Ensinger GmbH; *Int'l*, pg. 2447
ENSINGER-HYDE—See Ensinger GmbH; *Int'l*, pg. 2448
ENSINGER, INC.—See Ensinger GmbH; *Int'l*, pg. 2448
ENSINGER INDIA ENGINEERING PLASTICS PRIVATE LTD.—See Ensinger GmbH; *Int'l*, pg. 2447
ENSINGER INDUSTRIA DE PLASTICOS TECNICOS LTDA.—See Ensinger GmbH; *Int'l*, pg. 2447
ENSINGER ITALIA S.R.L.—See Ensinger GmbH; *Int'l*, pg. 2447
ENSINGER JAPAN CO., LTD.—See Ensinger GmbH; *Int'l*, pg. 2447
ENSINGER KOREA LTD.—See Ensinger GmbH; *Int'l*, pg. 2447
ENSINGER LIMITED—See Ensinger GmbH; *Int'l*, pg. 2447
ENSINGER MACHINING SA—See Ensinger GmbH; *Int'l*, pg. 2447
ENSINGER MALAYSIA—See Ensinger GmbH; *Int'l*, pg. 2447
ENSINGER PENN FIBRE INC.—See Ensinger GmbH; *Int'l*, pg. 2447
ENSINGER POLSKA SP. Z O.O.—See Ensinger GmbH; *Int'l*, pg. 2447
ENSINGER PRECISION COMPONENTS INC.—See Ensinger GmbH; *Int'l*, pg. 2447
ENSINGER PRECISION ENGINEERING LTD.—See Ensinger GmbH; *Int'l*, pg. 2448
ENSINGER S.A.—See Ensinger GmbH; *Int'l*, pg. 2448
ENSINGER (SHANGHAI) ENGINEERING PLASTICS CO., LTD.—See Ensinger GmbH; *Int'l*, pg. 2447
ENSINGER SINTIMID GMBH—See Ensinger GmbH; *Int'l*, pg. 2448
ENSINGER SPECIAL POLYMERS, INC.—See Ensinger GmbH; *Int'l*, pg. 2448
ENSINGER S.R.O.—See Ensinger GmbH; *Int'l*, pg. 2448
ENSINGER SWEDEN AB—See Ensinger GmbH; *Int'l*, pg. 2448
ENSINGER TECARIM GMBH—See Ensinger GmbH; *Int'l*, pg. 2448
ENSINGER TURKEY TEKNIK DANISMANLIK LTD. STI.—See Ensinger GmbH; *Int'l*, pg. 2448
ENSING TRUCK SERVICE INC—See En-Way Enterprises Inc.; *U.S. Private*, pg. 1389
ENS INTERNATIONAL PTY. LTD.—See AWN Holdings Limited; *Int'l*, pg. 753
ENSIS MANAGEMENT INC.—See Matrix Asset Management Inc.; *Int'l*, pg. 4728
ENSITE, INC.; *U.S. Private*, pg. 1402
ENSIVAL-MORET FRANCE SAS—See Sulzer Ltd.; *Int'l*, pg. 7257

ENSKILDA KAPITALFORVALTNING SEB AB—See Skandinaviska Enskilda Banken AB; *Int'l*, pg. 6977
ENSO FINANCIAL MANAGEMENT, LLP—See Bendigo Partners, LLC; *U.S. Private*, pg. 524
ENSO GROUP; *Int'l*, pg. 2448
ENSO INTERNATIONAL, INC.—See Stora Enso Oyj; *Int'l*, pg. 7224
ENSOL BIOSCIENCES, INC.; *Int'l*, pg. 2448
ENSONO GMBH—See KKR & Co. Inc.; *U.S. Public*, pg. 1244
ENSONO LIMITED—See KKR & Co. Inc.; *U.S. Public*, pg. 1244
ENSONO, LP—See KKR & Co. Inc.; *U.S. Public*, pg. 1244
ENSO OIL & GAS LTD.—See Enso Group; *Int'l*, pg. 2448
ENSOURCE, INC.—See Black Box Limited; *Int'l*, pg. 1058
ENSO WZHI PTE LIMITED—See Enso Group; *Int'l*, pg. 2448
ENSPERT INC.; *Int'l*, pg. 2448
ENSPIRE LEARNING, INC.; *U.S. Private*, pg. 1402
ENSSOLUTIONS GROUP INC.; *Int'l*, pg. 2448
ENSSOLUTIONS LTD.—See Enssolutions Group Inc.; *Int'l*, pg. 2448
ENSTAR AUSTRALIA LIMITED—See Enstar Group Limited; *Int'l*, pg. 2448
ENSTAR (EU) LIMITED—See Enstar Group Limited; *Int'l*, pg. 2448
ENSTAR GROUP LIMITED; *Int'l*, pg. 2448
ENSTAR HOLDINGS (US) LLC—See Enstar Group Limited; *Int'l*, pg. 2448
ENSTAR NATURAL GAS COMPANY—See AltaGas Ltd.; *Int'l*, pg. 384
ENSTAR NEW YORK, INC—See Enstar Group Limited; *Int'l*, pg. 2448
ENSTAR (US) INC.—See Enstar Group Limited; *Int'l*, pg. 2448
ENSTOA, INC.; *U.S. Private*, pg. 1402
ENSTOR INC.—See Iberdrola, S.A.; *Int'l*, pg. 3570
ENSTOR OPERATING COMPANY, LLC—See Iberdrola, S.A.; *Int'l*, pg. 3570
ENSTOR WAHA STORAGE AND TRANSPORTATION L.P.—See Iberdrola, S.A.; *Int'l*, pg. 3570
ENS TOYOTA; *Int'l*, pg. 2445
ENSTROM CANDIES, INC.; *U.S. Private*, pg. 1402
THE ENSTROM HELICOPTER CORP.—See Chongqing Helicopter Investment Co. Ltd.; *Int'l*, pg. 1579
ENSTYLE MANAGEMENT LIMITED—See ENL Limited; *Int'l*, pg. 2441
ENSUIKO SUGAR REFINING CO., LTD.; *Int'l*, pg. 2449
ENSURANCE LTD.; *Int'l*, pg. 2449
ENSURANCE UK LIMITED—See PSC Insurance Group Limited; *Int'l*, pg. 6016
ENSURANCE UNDERWRITING PTY. LIMITED—See Ensurance Ltd.; *Int'l*, pg. 2449
ENSURE ENGINEERING PTE. LTD.—See Nordic Group Limited; *Int'l*, pg. 5422
ENSURE GLOBAL CORP. LTD.; *Int'l*, pg. 2449
ENSURE IT SERVICES (PTY) LTD.—See Redington (India) Limited; *Int'l*, pg. 6247
ENSURE RECRUITMENT PTY LIMITED; *Int'l*, pg. 2449
ENSURE SERVICES ARABIA LLC—See Redington (India) Limited; *Int'l*, pg. 6247
ENSURE SERVICES BAHRAIN S.P.C.—See Redington (India) Limited; *Int'l*, pg. 6247
ENSURGE, INC.; *U.S. Public*, pg. 775
ENSURGE MICROPOWER ASA; *Int'l*, pg. 2449
ENSURITYGROUP, L.L.C.; *U.S. Private*, pg. 1402
ENSWERS INC.—See KT Corporation; *Int'l*, pg. 4314
ENSYNC, INC.; *U.S. Public*, pg. 775
ENSYNC SOLUTIONS, INC.—See Nextworld, LLC; *U.S. Private*, pg. 2921
ENSYST PTY LIMITED—See Temasek Holdings (Private) Limited; *Int'l*, pg. 7553
ENTACT, LLC—See J.F. Lehman & Company, Inc.; *U.S. Private*, pg. 2163
ENTAIN PLC; *Int'l*, pg. 2449
ENTALIZE CO., LTD.—See Pole To Win Holdings, Inc.; *Int'l*, pg. 5908
ENTAMEDIA LTD.—See Entatech UK Ltd.; *Int'l*, pg. 2450
ENTANET INTERNATIONAL LTD.—See Antin Infrastructure Partners SAS; *Int'l*, pg. 483
ENTAPACK PTY. LTD.—See Sealed Air Corporation; *U.S. Public*, pg. 1853
ENTAP LIMITED—See Platina Partners LLP; *Int'l*, pg. 5893
ENTARA CORPORATION; *U.S. Private*, pg. 1402
ENTASI SRL—See UniCredit S.p.A.; *Int'l*, pg. 8034
ENTASIS THERAPEUTICS HOLDINGS INC.—See Innoviva, Inc.; *U.S. Public*, pg. 1127
ENTAS NAKLIYAT VE TURIZM ANONIM SIRKETI—See Enka Insaat ve Sanayi A.S.; *Int'l*, pg. 2440
ENTATECH UK LTD.; *Int'l*, pg. 2450
ENTEC GESELLSCHAFT FUR ENDOKRINOLOGISCHE TECHNOLOGIE GMBH—See Bayer Aktiengesellschaft; *Int'l*, pg. 904
ENTEC GESELLSCHAFT FUR ENDOKRINOLOGISCHE TECHNOLOGIE MBH—See Bayer Aktiengesellschaft; *Int'l*, pg. 904
EN-TECH CORP.; *U.S. Private*, pg. 1389
ENTECH ENGINEERING INC.—See Entech Engineering Inc.; *U.S. Private*, pg. 1402

EN-TECH CORP.

ENTECH ENGINEERING INC.—See Entech Engineering Inc.; *U.S. Private*, pg. 1402
ENTECH ENGINEERING INC.—See Entech Engineering Inc.; *U.S. Private*, pg. 1402
ENTECH ENGINEERING INC.—See Entech Engineering Inc.; *U.S. Private*, pg. 1402
ENTECH ENGINEERING INC.; *U.S. Private*, pg. 1402
ENTECH INDUSTRIES PTY. LIMITED—See KKR & Co. Inc.; *U.S. Public*, pg. 1263
ENTECH SALES & SERVICE, INC.; *U.S. Private*, pg. 1402
ENTECH SA; *Int'l*, pg. 2450
ENTECH SOLAR, INC.; *U.S. Private*, pg. 1402
ENTEC POLYMERS, LLC—See Ravago Holding S.A.; *Int'l*, pg. 6222
ENTEC SERVICES, INC.; *U.S. Private*, pg. 1402
ENTEGA HAUSTECHNIK GMBH & CO. KG—See HEAG Sudhessische Energie AG; *Int'l*, pg. 3302
ENTEGART TEKNOLOJI COZUM VE HIZMETLERI A.S.—See Koc Holding A.S.; *Int'l*, pg. 4223
ENTEGEE INC.—See Adecco Group AG; *Int'l*, pg. 141
ENTEGRA BANK—See First Citizens BancShares, Inc.; *U.S. Public*, pg. 842
ENTEGRA FINANCIAL CORP.—See First Citizens BancShares, Inc.; *U.S. Public*, pg. 842
ENTEGRA LIMITED; *Int'l*, pg. 2450
ENTEGRA ROOF TILE CORP-POMPANO; *U.S. Private*, pg. 1403
ENTEGRA WASSERKRAFT AG—See Alpiq Holding AG; *Int'l*, pg. 373
ENTEGRIS CANADA LIMITED—See Entegris, Inc.; *U.S. Public*, pg. 776
ENTEGRIS GMBH—See Entegris, Inc.; *U.S. Public*, pg. 776
ENTEGRIS GP, INC.—See Entegris, Inc.; *U.S. Public*, pg. 776
ENTEGRIS, INC.; *U.S. Public*, pg. 776
ENTEGRIS JAPAN CO. LTD.—See Entegris, Inc.; *U.S. Public*, pg. 777
ENTEGRIS JAPAN HOLDING K.K.—See Entegris, Inc.; *U.S. Public*, pg. 776
ENTEGRIS-JETALON SOLUTIONS, INC.—See Entegris, Inc.; *U.S. Public*, pg. 777
ENTEGRIS KOREA LTD.—See Entegris, Inc.; *U.S. Public*, pg. 776
ENTEGRIS MALAYSIA SDN. BHD.—See Entegris, Inc.; *U.S. Public*, pg. 776
ENTEGRIS SAS—See Entegris, Inc.; *U.S. Public*, pg. 776
ENTEGRIS SINGAPORE PTE. LTD.—See Entegris, Inc.; *U.S. Public*, pg. 776
ENTEGRIS TAIWAN TECHNOLOGIES CO., LTD.—See Entegris, Inc.; *U.S. Public*, pg. 777
ENTEK HOLDING LLC; *U.S. Private*, pg. 1403
ENTEK INTERNATIONAL UK LTD.—See Entek Holding LLC; *U.S. Private*, pg. 1403
ENTEKRA, LLC—See Louisiana-Pacific Corporation; *U.S. Public*, pg. 1342
ENTELAR GROUP LIMITED—See Spark New Zealand Limited; *Int'l*, pg. 7126
EN-TEL COMMUNICATIONS LLC—See Windstream Holdings, Inc.; *U.S. Public*, pg. 2373
ENTELIOS AG—See Enel S.p.A.; *Int'l*, pg. 2413
ENTELOS, INC.—See Clearlake Capital Group, L.P.; *U.S. Private*, pg. 934
ENTEMANN'S BAKERY OUTLET—See Grupo Bimbo, S.A.B. de C.V.; *Int'l*, pg. 3122
ENTEMANN'S BAKERY—See Grupo Bimbo, S.A.B. de C.V.; *Int'l*, pg. 3122
ENTEMANN'S/OROWEAT—See Grupo Bimbo, S.A.B. de C.V.; *Int'l*, pg. 3122
ENTEMANN'S/OROWEAT—See Grupo Bimbo, S.A.B. de C.V.; *Int'l*, pg. 3122
ENTEMANN'S/OROWEAT—See Grupo Bimbo, S.A.B. de C.V.; *Int'l*, pg. 3122
ENTEMANN'S/OROWEAT—See Grupo Bimbo, S.A.B. de C.V.; *Int'l*, pg. 3122
ENTEMANN'S/OROWEAT—See Grupo Bimbo, S.A.B. de C.V.; *Int'l*, pg. 3122
ENTEN & ASSOCIATES, INC.; *U.S. Private*, pg. 1403
ENTEQ TECHNOLOGIES PLC; *Int'l*, pg. 2450
ENTEQ UPSTREAM USA INC.—See Enteq Technologies plc; *Int'l*, pg. 2450
ENTERA BIO LTD; *Int'l*, pg. 2450
ENTERACTIVE GMBH—See Splendid Medien AG; *Int'l*, pg. 7141
ENTER AIR SP ZOO; *Int'l*, pg. 2450
ENTERCOM BOSTON, LLC—See AUDACY, INC.; *U.S. Public*, pg. 226
ENTERCOM BUFFALO, LLC—See AUDACY, INC.; *U.S. Public*, pg. 226
ENTERCOM COLORADO, LLC—See AUDACY, INC.; *U.S. Public*, pg. 226
ENTERCOM CONNECTICUT, LLC—See AUDACY, INC.; *U.S. Public*, pg. 226
ENTERCOM DENVER, LLC—See AUDACY, INC.; *U.S. Public*, pg. 226
ENTERCOM FLORIDA, LLC—See AUDACY, INC.; *U.S. Public*, pg. 226

ENTERCOM GAINESVILLE, LLC—See AUDACY, INC.; *U.S. Public*, pg. 226
ENTERCOM GEORGIA, LLC—See AUDACY, INC.; *U.S. Public*, pg. 226
ENTERCOM GREENSBORO, LLC—See AUDACY, INC.; *U.S. Public*, pg. 226
ENTERCOM GREENVILLE, LLC—See AUDACY, INC.; *U.S. Public*, pg. 226
ENTERCOM ILLINOIS, LLC—See AUDACY, INC.; *U.S. Public*, pg. 226
ENTERCOM INDIANA, LLC—See AUDACY, INC.; *U.S. Public*, pg. 226
ENTERCOM KANSAS CITY, LLC—See AUDACY, INC.; *U.S. Public*, pg. 226
ENTERCOM LICENSE, LLC—See AUDACY, INC.; *U.S. Public*, pg. 226
ENTERCOM LOUISIANA, LLC—See AUDACY, INC.; *U.S. Public*, pg. 226
ENTERCOM MADISON, LLC—See AUDACY, INC.; *U.S. Public*, pg. 226
ENTERCOM MARYLAND, LLC—See AUDACY, INC.; *U.S. Public*, pg. 226
ENTERCOM MEDIA CORP.—See AUDACY, INC.; *U.S. Public*, pg. 226
ENTERCOM MIAMI, LLC—See AUDACY, INC.; *U.S. Public*, pg. 226
ENTERCOM MICHIGAN, LLC—See AUDACY, INC.; *U.S. Public*, pg. 226
ENTERCOM MILWAUKEE, LLC—See AUDACY, INC.; *U.S. Public*, pg. 226
ENTERCOM MINNESOTA, LLC—See AUDACY, INC.; *U.S. Public*, pg. 226
ENTERCOM NEVADA, LLC—See AUDACY, INC.; *U.S. Public*, pg. 226
ENTERCOM NEW ORLEANS, LLC—See AUDACY, INC.; *U.S. Public*, pg. 226
ENTERCOM NORFOLK, LLC—See AUDACY, INC.; *U.S. Public*, pg. 226
ENTERCOM NORTH CAROLINA, LLC—See AUDACY, INC.; *U.S. Public*, pg. 226
ENTERCOM OHIO, LLC—See AUDACY, INC.; *U.S. Public*, pg. 226
ENTERCOM OREGON, LLC—See AUDACY, INC.; *U.S. Public*, pg. 226
ENTERCOM PENNSYLVANIA, LLC—See AUDACY, INC.; *U.S. Public*, pg. 226
ENTERCOM PORTLAND, LLC—See AUDACY, INC.; *U.S. Public*, pg. 226
ENTERCOM RADIO, LLC—See AUDACY, INC.; *U.S. Public*, pg. 226
ENTERCOM ROCHESTER, LLC—See AUDACY, INC.; *U.S. Public*, pg. 226
ENTERCOM SAN DIEGO, LLC—See AUDACY, INC.; *U.S. Public*, pg. 226
ENTERCOM SEATTLE, LLC—See AUDACY, INC.; *U.S. Public*, pg. 226
ENTERCOM SOUTH CAROLINA, LLC—See AUDACY, INC.; *U.S. Public*, pg. 226
ENTERCOM TEXAS, LLC—See AUDACY, INC.; *U.S. Public*, pg. 226
ENTERCOM WASHINGTON DC, LLC—See AUDACY, INC.; *U.S. Public*, pg. 227
ENTERCOM WASHINGTON, LLC—See AUDACY, INC.; *U.S. Public*, pg. 227
ENTERCOM WICHITA, LLC—See AUDACY, INC.; *U.S. Public*, pg. 227
ENTERCOM WILKES-BARRE SCRANTON, LLC—See AUDACY, INC.; *U.S. Public*, pg. 227
ENTERCOM WISCONSIN, LLC—See AUDACY, INC.; *U.S. Public*, pg. 227
ENTEREX AMERICA LLC—See Enterex International Limited; *Int'l*, pg. 2451
ENTEREX EUROPE HOLDING B.V.—See Enterex International Limited; *Int'l*, pg. 2451
ENTEREX INTERNATIONAL LIMITED; *Int'l*, pg. 2450
ENTEREX POLSKA SP. Z O.O.—See Enterex International Limited; *Int'l*, pg. 2451
ENTERGY ARKANSAS, LLC—See Entergy Corporation; *U.S. Public*, pg. 777
ENTERGY CORPORATION; *U.S. Public*, pg. 777
ENTERGY LOUISIANA, LLC—See Entergy Corporation; *U.S. Public*, pg. 777
ENTERGY MISSISSIPPI, LLC—See Entergy Corporation; *U.S. Public*, pg. 777
ENTERGY NEW ORLEANS, LLC—See Entergy Corporation; *U.S. Public*, pg. 777
ENTERGY NUCLEAR FUELS COMPANY—See Entergy Corporation; *U.S. Public*, pg. 777
ENTERGY NUCLEAR GENERATION COMPANY—See Entergy Corporation; *U.S. Public*, pg. 777
ENTERGY NUCLEAR VERMONT YANKEE, LLC—See J.F. Lehman & Company, Inc.; *U.S. Private*, pg. 2164
ENTERGY POWER VENTURES, LLC—See Entergy Corporation; *U.S. Public*, pg. 777
ENTERGY TEXAS, INC.—See Entergy Corporation; *U.S. Public*, pg. 777
ENTERGY WHOLESALE COMMODITIES—See Entergy Corporation; *U.S. Public*, pg. 777

CORPORATE AFFILIATIONS

ENTERIS BIOPHARMA, INC.—See Carlson Capital, L.P.; *U.S. Private*, pg. 764
ENTERIX INC.—See Clinical Genomics Pty. Ltd.; *Int'l*, pg. 1659
ENTERNAL EDGE SDN. BHD.—See Batu Kawan Berhad; *Int'l*, pg. 891
ENTERO THERAPEUTICS, INC.; *U.S. Public*, pg. 777
ENTERPARTNERS CO., LTD; *Int'l*, pg. 2451
ENTERPRIME FINANCE SRL—See Capgemini SE; *Int'l*, pg. 1306
ENTERPRISE 4.0 TECHNOLOGY ACQUISITION CORP.; *U.S. Public*, pg. 777
ENTERPRISE BANCORP, INC.; *U.S. Public*, pg. 777
ENTERPRISE BANK AND TRUST COMPANY—See Enterprise Bancorp, Inc.; *U.S. Public*, pg. 778
ENTERPRISE BANK—See Enterprise Financial Services Group, Inc.; *U.S. Public*, pg. 778
ENTERPRISE BANK & TRUST—See Enterprise Financial Services Corp; *U.S. Public*, pg. 778
ENTERPRISE BUSINESS SYSTEM SOLUTION CO.—See Japan Industrial Partners, Inc.; *Int'l*, pg. 3889
ENTERPRISE CARE TELECONFERENCING (ASIA) PTY LTD.—See Siris Capital Group, LLC; *U.S. Private*, pg. 3673
ENTERPRISE CAR SALES—See Enterprise Holdings, Inc.; *U.S. Private*, pg. 1403
ENTERPRISE COMMUNITY PARTNERS, INC.; *U.S. Private*, pg. 1403
ENTERPRISE COMPUTING SOLUTIONS INC.; *U.S. Private*, pg. 1403
ENTERPRISE CRUDE OIL LLC—See Enterprise Products Partners L.P.; *U.S. Public*, pg. 778
ENTERPRISE CRUDE PIPELINE LLC—See Enterprise Products Partners L.P.; *U.S. Public*, pg. 778
ENTERPRISEDB CORPORATION—See Great Hill Partners, L.P.; *U.S. Private*, pg. 1763
ENTERPRISE DEVELOPMENT HOLDINGS LIMITED; *Int'l*, pg. 2451
ENTERPRISE DISTRIBUTION INC.; *U.S. Private*, pg. 1403
ENTERPRISE DIVERSIFIED, INC.—See ENDI Corp.; *U.S. Public*, pg. 760
ENTERPRISE ELECTRICAL, INC.; *U.S. Private*, pg. 1403
ENTERPRISE ELECTRONICS CORPORATION—See International Business Machines Corporation; *U.S. Public*, pg. 1151
ENTERPRISE ENERGY SERVICES INC.—See Enterprise Group, Inc.; *Int'l*, pg. 2451
THE ENTERPRISE EUROPE NETWORK LTD.—See Scottish Enterprise; *Int'l*, pg. 6653
ENTERPRISE FIELD SERVICES, LLC—See Enterprise Products Partners L.P.; *U.S. Public*, pg. 778
ENTERPRISE FINANCIAL GROUP, INC.; *U.S. Private*, pg. 1403
ENTERPRISE FINANCIAL SERVICES CORP; *U.S. Public*, pg. 778
ENTERPRISE FINANCIAL SERVICES GROUP, INC.; *U.S. Public*, pg. 778
ENTERPRISE FLEET MANAGEMENT EXCHANGE, INC.—See Deutsche Bank Aktiengesellschaft; *Int'l*, pg. 2061
ENTERPRISE FLEET SERVICES—See Enterprise Holdings, Inc.; *U.S. Private*, pg. 1403
ENTERPRISE FLEX-E-RENT—See Enterprise Holdings, Inc.; *U.S. Private*, pg. 1403
ENTERPRISE FLORIDA, INC.; *U.S. Private*, pg. 1403
ENTERPRISE FOODS (PTY) LIMITED—See Country Bird Holdings Limited; *Int'l*, pg. 1818
ENTERPRISE GATHERING LLC—See Enterprise Products Partners L.P.; *U.S. Public*, pg. 778
ENTERPRISE GROUP, INC.; *Int'l*, pg. 2451
ENTERPRISE GROUP PLC; *Int'l*, pg. 2451
ENTERPRISE GTM HOLDINGS L.P.—See Enterprise Products Partners L.P.; *U.S. Public*, pg. 778
ENTERPRISE HOLDING CORPORATION—See Securian Financial Group, Inc.; *U.S. Private*, pg. 3594
ENTERPRISE HOLDINGS, INC.; *U.S. Private*, pg. 1403
ENTERPRISE HOME LOANS—See Enterprise Financial Services Corp; *U.S. Public*, pg. 778
ENTERPRISE INFORMATION SERVICES, INC.—See Accenture plc; *Int'l*, pg. 85
ENTERPRISE INTEGRATION CORPORATION; *U.S. Private*, pg. 1404
ENTERPRISE INTEGRATION, INC.; *U.S. Private*, pg. 1404
ENTERPRISE INTERNATIONAL LIMITED; *Int'l*, pg. 2451
ENTERPRISE INTERNATIONAL OPERATIONS—See Enterprise Holdings, Inc.; *U.S. Private*, pg. 1403
ENTERPRISE INVESTMENT FUND SLHF; *Int'l*, pg. 2451
ENTERPRISE INVESTORS SP. Z O.O.; *Int'l*, pg. 2451
ENTERPRISE JBILLING SOFTWARE LTD.—See AppDirect Inc.; *U.S. Private*, pg. 296
ENTERPRISE/JWT—See WPP plc; *Int'l*, pg. 8479
ENTERPRISE LEASING COMPANY OF PHILADELPHIA, LLC—See Enterprise Holdings, Inc.; *U.S. Private*, pg. 1403
ENTERPRISE LEDGER—See Lee Enterprises, Incorporated; *U.S. Public*, pg. 1299

COMPANY NAME INDEX

ENTERPRISE LOGISTIC SERVICES LLC—See Enterprise Products Partners L.P.; *U.S. Public*, pg. 778
ENTERPRISE MARINE SERVICES LLC—See Enterprise Products Partners L.P.; *U.S. Public*, pg. 778
ENTERPRISE MASONRY CORPORATION; *U.S. Private*, pg. 1404
ENTERPRISE METALS LIMITED; *Int'l*, pg. 2452
ENTERPRISE NEWSMEDIA, LLC—See Gannett Co., Inc.; *U.S. Public*, pg. 896
ENTERPRISE OIL CO.—See AIP, LLC; *U.S. Private*, pg. 136
ENTERPRISE OIL NORGE AS—See Shell plc; *Int'l*, pg. 6796
ENTERPRISE ONSITE SERVICES CO.; *U.S. Private*, pg. 1404
ENTERPRISE PARKING SOLUTIONS LTD.—See Smart Parking Ltd.; *Int'l*, pg. 7000
ENTERPRISE PERFORMANCE SYSTEMS, INC.—See Roper Technologies, Inc.; *U.S. Public*, pg. 1813
ENTERPRISE PIPELINE COMPANY INC.—See Enterprise Group, Inc.; *Int'l*, pg. 2451
ENTERPRISE PRESS, INC.; *U.S. Private*, pg. 1404
ENTERPRISE PRODUCTS OPERATING LLC - BEATRICE OFFICE—See Enterprise Products Partners L.P.; *U.S. Public*, pg. 779
ENTERPRISE PRODUCTS OPERATING LLC—See Enterprise Products Partners L.P.; *U.S. Public*, pg. 778
ENTERPRISE PRODUCTS PARTNERS L.P.; *U.S. Public*, pg. 778
ENTERPRISE PROPERTIES INC.; *U.S. Private*, pg. 1404
ENTERPRISE PUBLISHING COMPANY, LLC—See Gannett Co., Inc.; *U.S. Public*, pg. 902
ENTERPRISE-RECORD—See Alden Global Capital LLC; *U.S. Private*, pg. 155
ENTERPRISE RECOVERY SYSTEMS, INC.—See Audax Group, Limited Partnership; *U.S. Private*, pg. 390
ENTERPRISE RENT-A-CAR CANADA CO.—See Enterprise Holdings, Inc.; *U.S. Private*, pg. 1403
ENTERPRISE RENT-A-CAR—See Enterprise Holdings, Inc.; *U.S. Private*, pg. 1403
ENTERPRISE RENT-A-TRUCK—See Enterprise Holdings, Inc.; *U.S. Private*, pg. 1403
ENTERPRISE RESOURCE PERFORMANCE, INC.—See ASGN Incorporated; *U.S. Public*, pg. 210
ENTERPRISE RISK STRATEGIES, LLC—See Mariner Wealth Advisors, LLC; *U.S. Private*, pg. 2575
ENTERPRISE SECURITY, INC.; *U.S. Private*, pg. 1404
ENTERPRISE SERVICES BELGIUM BVBA—See Veritas Capital Fund Management, LLC; *U.S. Private*, pg. 4364
ENTERPRISE SERVICES - EUROPE, MIDDLE EAST & AFRICA—See Veritas Capital Fund Management, LLC; *U.S. Private*, pg. 4363
ENTERPRISE SERVICES FRANCE SAS—See Veritas Capital Fund Management, LLC; *U.S. Private*, pg. 4364
ENTERPRISE SERVICES (HONG KONG) LIMITED—See Veritas Capital Fund Management, LLC; *U.S. Private*, pg. 4363
ENTERPRISE SERVICES INFORMATION SECURITY UK LIMITED—See Veritas Capital Fund Management, LLC; *U.S. Private*, pg. 4364
ENTERPRISE SERVICES ITALIA S.R.L.—See Veritas Capital Fund Management, LLC; *U.S. Private*, pg. 4364
ENTERPRISE SERVICES JAPAN, LTD.—See Veritas Capital Fund Management, LLC; *U.S. Private*, pg. 4364
ENTERPRISE SERVICES, LLC—See Veritas Capital Fund Management, LLC; *U.S. Private*, pg. 4363
ENTERPRISE SERVICES NEDERLAND B.V.—See DXC Technology Company; *U.S. Public*, pg. 696
ENTERPRISE SERVICES SVERIGE AB—See Veritas Capital Fund Management, LLC; *U.S. Private*, pg. 4364
ENTERPRISES INTERNATIONAL INC.; *U.S. Private*, pg. 1404
ENTERPRISE SOFTWORKS (PTY) LIMITED—See EOH HOLDINGS LIMITED; *Int'l*, pg. 2457
ENTERPRISE SOLUTIONS REALIZED; *U.S. Private*, pg. 1404
THE ENTERPRISE STRATEGY GROUP, INC.—See TechTarget, Inc.; *U.S. Public*, pg. 1989
ENTERPRISE SYSTEMS SOFTWARE LLC; *U.S. Private*, pg. 1404
ENTERPRISE TECHNOLOGY SERVICES LLC—See WestView Capital Partners, L.P.; *U.S. Private*, pg. 4501
ENTERPRISE TMS LLC—See C.H. Robinson Worldwide, Inc.; *U.S. Public*, pg. 415
ENTERPRISE TOOL & DIE, INC.; *U.S. Private*, pg. 1404
ENTERPRISE TRENCHLESS TECHNOLOGIES, INC—See Southwest Gas Holdings, Inc.; *U.S. Public*, pg. 1913
ENTERPRISE TRUST COMPANY—See Enterprise Financial Services Corp; *U.S. Public*, pg. 778
ENTERPRISE UNDERWRITING SVCS—See Managed Care of America Inc.; *U.S. Private*, pg. 2559
ENTERPRISE UNIVERSITY—See Enterprise Financial Services Corp; *U.S. Public*, pg. 778
ENTERPRISE VENTURES CORPORATION—See Concurrent Technologies Corporation; *U.S. Private*, pg. 1011
ENTERPRISE WEALTH SERVICES LLC—See Enterprise Bancorp, Inc.; *U.S. Public*, pg. 778
ENTERRA CORPORATION; *U.S. Public*, pg. 779
ENTERRA SOLUTIONS LLC—See glendonTodd Capital LLC; *U.S. Private*, pg. 1710
ENTERRISE CO. LTD.—See Capcom Co., Ltd.; *Int'l*, pg. 1302
ENTERSOFT BULGARIA EOOD—See Entersoft S.A.; *Int'l*, pg. 2452
ENTERSOFT MIDDLE EAST FZ LLC—See Entersoft S.A.; *Int'l*, pg. 2452
ENTERSOFT ROMANIA SOFTWARE SRL—See Entersoft S.A.; *Int'l*, pg. 2452
ENTERSOFT S.A.; *Int'l*, pg. 2452
THE ENTERTAINER (AMERSHAM) LTD.; *Int'l*, pg. 7640
ENTERTAINMENT ARTS RESEARCH, INC.; *U.S. Public*, pg. 779
ENTERTAINMENT BENEFITS GROUP, LLC; *U.S. Private*, pg. 1404
ENTERTAINMENT CRUISES INC.—See The Pritzker Group - Chicago, LLC; *U.S. Private*, pg. 4098
ENTERTAINMENT EARTH, INC.; *U.S. Private*, pg. 1404
ENTERTAINMENT ENGINEERING INC.; *U.S. Private*, pg. 1404
ENTERTAINMENT FOR ALL, LLC—See Comcast Corporation; *U.S. Public*, pg. 538
ENTERTAINMENT GAMING ASIA, INC.—See Melco International Development, Ltd.; *Int'l*, pg. 4808
ENTERTAINMENT GATEWAY GROUP CORP—See Globe Telecom, Inc.; *Int'l*, pg. 3006
ENTERTAINMENT HOLDINGS, INC.; *U.S. Private*, pg. 1404
ENTERTAINMENT LOGISTIX PTY. LTD.—See Helloworld Travel Limited; *Int'l*, pg. 3337
ENTERTAINMENT MAGPIE LIMITED; *Int'l*, pg. 2452
ENTERTAINMENT METALS INC.; *U.S. Private*, pg. 1404
ENTERTAINMENT NETWORK FRONTIER INC.—See GEO Holdings Corporation; *Int'l*, pg. 2932
ENTERTAINMENT NETWORK (INDIA) LIMITED—See Bennett, Coleman & Co. Ltd.; *Int'l*, pg. 975
ENTERTAINMENT NETWORK SCANDINAVIA AB—See Sony Group Corporation; *Int'l*, pg. 7105
ENTERTAINMENT ONE BENELUX B.V.—See Lions Gate Entertainment Corp.; *Int'l*, pg. 4520
ENTERTAINMENT ONE LIMITED PARTNERSHIP—See Lions Gate Entertainment Corp.; *Int'l*, pg. 4520
ENTERTAINMENT ONE LTD.—See Lions Gate Entertainment Corp.; *Int'l*, pg. 4520
ENTERTAINMENT PARTNERS GROUP INC.; *U.S. Private*, pg. 1404
ENTERTAINMENT PUBLICATIONS, LLC—See Afin Technologies Limited; *Int'l*, pg. 189
ENTERTAINMENT STUDIOS, INC.; *U.S. Private*, pg. 1405
ENTERTAINMENT STUDIOS MOTION PICTURES, LLC—See Entertainment Studios, Inc.; *U.S. Private*, pg. 1405
ENTERTAINMENT TECHNOLOGY PARTNERS LLC; *U.S. Private*, pg. 1405
ENTERTAINMENT TRANSPORTATION SPECIALISTS; *U.S. Private*, pg. 1405
ENTERTAINMENT WEEKLY INC.—See Meredith Corporation; *U.S. Public*, pg. 1422
ENTERWEB (PTY) LIMITED—See EOH HOLDINGS LIMITED; *Int'l*, pg. 2457
ENTERWORKS, INC.—See Symphony Technology Group, LLC; *U.S. Private*, pg. 3902
ENTEST GROUP, INC.; *Int'l*, pg. 2452
ENTE VASCO DE LA ENERGIA; *Int'l*, pg. 2450
ENTHALPY ANALYTICAL, INC.—See Montrose Environmental Corp.; *U.S. Private*, pg. 2777
ENTHEON BIOMEDICAL CORP.; *Int'l*, pg. 2452
ENTHEOS CAPITAL CORP.; *Int'l*, pg. 2452
ENTHONE GALVANOPLASTI SANAYL TICARET A.S.—See Element Solutions Inc.; *U.S. Public*, pg. 726
ENTHONE GMBH—See Element Solutions Inc.; *U.S. Public*, pg. 726
ENTHONE GMBH—See Element Solutions Inc.; *U.S. Public*, pg. 726
ENTHONE IBERICA S.A.—See Element Solutions Inc.; *U.S. Public*, pg. 726
ENTHONE INC.—See Element Solutions Inc.; *U.S. Public*, pg. 726
ENTHONE-OMI DE MEXICO S.A. DE C.V.—See Element Solutions Inc.; *U.S. Public*, pg. 726
ENTHONE SAS—See Element Solutions Inc.; *U.S. Public*, pg. 726
ENTHONE SDN BHD—See Element Solutions Inc.; *U.S. Public*, pg. 726
ENTHONE SP. Z.O.O.—See Element Solutions Inc.; *U.S. Public*, pg. 726
ENTHONE S.R.O.—See Element Solutions Inc.; *U.S. Public*, pg. 726
ENTHUSIAST GAMING HOLDINGS, INC.; *Int'l*, pg. 2452
ENTHUSIAST GAMING (TSR) INC.—See Enthusiast Gaming Holdings, Inc.; *Int'l*, pg. 2452
ENTIA BIOSCIENCES, INC.; *U.S. Private*, pg. 1405
ENTIE COMMERCIAL BANK, LTD.; *Int'l*, pg. 2452
ENTIERA, INC.—See Fair Isaac Corporation; *U.S. Public*, pg. 820
ENTIERA SOLUTIONS COMPANY LIMITED—See Fair Isaac Corporation; *U.S. Public*, pg. 820
ENTIGO CORPORATION; *U.S. Private*, pg. 1405
ENTIRE CONSTRUCTION PTE. LTD.—See Koon Holdings Limited; *Int'l*, pg. 4278
ENTIRE ENGINEERING PTE LTD—See Koon Holdings Limited; *Int'l*, pg. 4278
ENTIRE PRODUCTIONS, INC.; *U.S. Private*, pg. 1405
ENTIRE TECHNOLOGY CO., LTD.; *Int'l*, pg. 2452
ENTISYS SOLUTIONS, INC.; *U.S. Private*, pg. 1405
ENTITLE, INC.; *U.S. Private*, pg. 1405
ENTITLE INSURANCE COMPANY—See Radian Group, Inc.; *U.S. Public*, pg. 1759
ENTOLETER LLC; *U.S. Private*, pg. 1405
ENTOMO, INC.—See Insight Venture Management, LLC; *U.S. Private*, pg. 2090
EN TOOL & SUPPLY LIMITED—See Wentworth Technologies Co. Ltd.; *Int'l*, pg. 8377
ENTOPEST ENVIRONMENTAL SERVICES SDN. BHD.—See Ancom Nylex Berhad; *Int'l*, pg. 449
ENTOURAGE HEALTH CORP.; *Int'l*, pg. 2452
ENTOURAGE MINING INC.; *Int'l*, pg. 2452
ENTOURAGE YEARBOOKS; *U.S. Private*, pg. 1405
ENT PARTNERS LLC; *U.S. Private*, pg. 1402
ENTRA ASA; *Int'l*, pg. 2452
ENTR'ACTE SAS—See LDC SA; *Int'l*, pg. 4431
ENTRACTION HOLDING AB—See International Game Technology PLC; *Int'l*, pg. 3749
ENTRADAS EVENTIM S.A.—See CTS Eventim AG & Co. KGAA; *Int'l*, pg. 1872
ENTRADA THERAPEUTICS, INC.; *U.S. Public*, pg. 779
ENTRANCE CONTROLS INTEGRATED SECURITY—See Christenson Electric, Inc.; *U.S. Private*, pg. 890
ENTRANCE SOFTWARE; *U.S. Private*, pg. 1405
ENTRAVISION COMMUNICATIONS CORPORATION; *U.S. Public*, pg. 779
ENTRECAMPOS CUATRO SOCIMI SA; *Int'l*, pg. 2452
ENTREC CRANES & HEAVY HAUL (WESTERN) LTD.—See Berkshire Hathaway Inc.; *U.S. Public*, pg. 309
ENTRE COMPUTER SERVICES INC.; *U.S. Private*, pg. 1406
ENTREDA, INC.—See K1 Investment Management, LLC; *U.S. Private*, pg. 2252
ENTREE GOLD (US) INC.—See Entree Resources Ltd.; *Int'l*, pg. 2452
ENTREE LLC—See Entree Resources Ltd.; *Int'l*, pg. 2452
ENTREE RESOURCES LTD.; *Int'l*, pg. 2452
ENTREKEN ASSOCIATES, INC.; *U.S. Private*, pg. 1406
ENTREMONT S.A.—See BNP Paribas SA; *Int'l*, pg. 1090
ENTREMONT S.A.—See Frere-Bourgeois; *Int'l*, pg. 2773
ENTREPARTICULIERS.COM SA; *Int'l*, pg. 2453
ENTREPIX ASIA PTD., LTD.—See Amtech Systems, Inc.; *U.S. Public*, pg. 133
ENTREPOSAGE SUPERVISION—See Lassonde Industries, Inc.; *Int'l*, pg. 4421
ENTREPOSE ALGERIE EURL—See VINCI S.A.; *Int'l*, pg. 8217
ENTREPOSE ASIA SDN. BHD.—See VINCI S.A.; *Int'l*, pg. 8217
ENTREPOSE CHILE SPA—See VINCI S.A.; *Int'l*, pg. 8217
ENTREPOSE CONTRACTING S.A.—See VINCI S.A.; *Int'l*, pg. 8217
ENTREPOSE DE MEXICO S.A. DE C.V.—See VINCI S.A.; *Int'l*, pg. 8217
ENTREPOSE GROUP SAS—See VINCI S.A.; *Int'l*, pg. 8217
ENTREPOSE INDUSTRIES SAS—See VINCI S.A.; *Int'l*, pg. 8217
ENTREPOSE PROJETS S.A.S.—See VINCI S.A.; *Int'l*, pg. 8217
ENTREPOSE SERVICES S.A.S.—See VINCI S.A.; *Int'l*, pg. 8217
ENTREPOSTO MAQUINAS COMERCIO DE EQUIPAMENTO AGRICOLA E INDUSTRIAL S.A.—See Mitsubishi Heavy Industries, Ltd.; *Int'l*, pg. 4956
ENTREPOT A.C. L'ANGE-GARDIEN—See Lassonde Industries, Inc.; *Int'l*, pg. 4421
ENTREPOT FRIGO FARNHAM—See Lassonde Industries, Inc.; *Int'l*, pg. 4421
ENTREPOTS DE L'OCEAN S.A.S—See Nichirei Corporation; *Int'l*, pg. 5270
ENTREPOTS GODFROY S.A.S—See Nichirei Corporation; *Int'l*, pg. 5270
ENTREPRENDRE SA; *Int'l*, pg. 2453
ENTRE PRENEUR CO., LTD.—See FTGroup Co Ltd.; *Int'l*, pg. 2800
ENTREPRENEURIAL EQUITY PARTNERS, LLC; *U.S. Private*, pg. 1406
ENTREPRENEUR MEDIA, INC.; *U.S. Private*, pg. 1406
ENTREPRENEUR MEDIA SA (PTY) LTD.—See Entrepreneur Media, Inc.; *U.S. Private*, pg. 1406
ENTREPRENEUR UNIVERSE BRIGHT GROUP; *U.S. Public*, pg. 779
ENTREPRENORFIRMAET OSTERGAARD A/S—See Per Aarsleff Holding A/S; *Int'l*, pg. 5795
ENTREPRISE BODIN SAS—See VINCI S.A.; *Int'l*, pg. 8218
ENTREPRISE BOYER—See Ardian SAS; *Int'l*, pg. 555
ENTREPRISE D'ELECTRICITE DE PICARDIE SAS—See VINCI S.A.; *Int'l*, pg. 8218

ENTREPRISE D'ELECTRICITE ET D'EQUIPEMENT—See VINCI S.A.; *Int'l*, pg. 8237
ENTREPRISE DEMOUSELLE—See VINCI S.A.; *Int'l*, pg. 8237
ENTREPRISE DE TRAVAUX ELECTRIQUES VALETTE & CIE SAS—See VINCI S.A.; *Int'l*, pg. 8218
ENTREPRISE GABARRE SAS—See VINCI S.A.; *Int'l*, pg. 8218
ENTREPRISE GENERALE MALTA FORREST S.A.—See George Forrest International S.A.; *Int'l*, pg. 2938
ENTREPRISE GUIBAN ANTILLES—See Entreprise Guiban SA; *Int'l*, pg. 2453
ENTREPRISE GUIBAN SA; *Int'l*, pg. 2453
ENTREPRISE GUILLERM; *Int'l*, pg. 2453
ENTREPRISE MINIERE ET CHIMIQUE SA; *Int'l*, pg. 2453
ENTREPRISE PAUL CALIN; *Int'l*, pg. 2453
ENTREPRISE ROBERT THIBERT INC.; *Int'l*, pg. 2453
ENTREPRISES ET CHEMINS DE FER EN CHINE SA; *Int'l*, pg. 2453
ENTRETENIMIENTO GM DE MEXICO SA DE CV; *Int'l*, pg. 2453
ENTREX CARBON MARKET LLC—See Entrex Carbon Market, LLC; *U.S. Public*, pg. 779
ENTREX CARBON MARKET, LLC; *U.S. Public*, pg. 779
ENTRIX AMERICAS, SA—See Cardno Limited; *Int'l*, pg. 1323
ENTROPIE SAS—See Veolia Environnement S.A.; *Int'l*, pg. 8162
ENTROPIE SAS—See Veolia Environnement S.A.; *Int'l*, pg. 8161
ENTROPYSOFT S.A.S.—See Salesforce, Inc.; *U.S. Public*, pg. 1837
ENTRPRIZE CORPORATION; *U.S. Private*, pg. 1406
ENTR RATIONNELLE INSTALLATION ELECTRIQUE; *Int'l*, pg. 2452
ENTRUE BRASIL SERVICOS DE T.I. LTDA.—See LG Corp.; *Int'l*, pg. 4474
ENTRUST (EUROPE) LTD.—See DataCard Corporation; *U.S. Private*, pg. 1165
THE ENTRUST GROUP, INC.; *U.S. Private*, pg. 4026
ENTRUST, INC.; *U.S. Private*, pg. 1406
ENTRUST, INC.—See DataCard Corporation; *U.S. Private*, pg. 1165
ENTRUST INC.—See Prestige International Inc.; *Int'l*, pg. 5966
ENTRUST SECURITIES PLC; *Int'l*, pg. 2453
ENTRUST TECHNOLOGY CONSULTING SERVICES—See The Aldridge Company; *U.S. Private*, pg. 3983
ENTRUST WEALTH MANAGEMENT PTY LTD—See Euroz Hartleys Group Limited; *Int'l*, pg. 2559
ENTSERV SCHWEIZ GMBH—See DXC Technology Company; *U.S. Public*, pg. 696
ENTSORGA ENTSORGUNGS GMBH NFG KG—See Fomento de Construcciones y Contratas, S.A.; *Int'l*, pg. 2722
ENTSORGA WEST VIRGINIA LLC—See Renovare Environmental, Inc.; *U.S. Public*, pg. 1783
ENTSORGUNG GMBH—See VINCI S.A.; *Int'l*, pg. 8218
ENTSORGUNGSGESELLSCHAFT MBH FUR MECKLENBURG-VORPOMMERN—See L. Possehl & Co. mbH; *Int'l*, pg. 4382
ENTWICKLUNGSGESELLSCHAFT GUGLING VERWALTUNGS GMBH—See voestalpine AG; *Int'l*, pg. 8293
ENTWICKLUNGSGESELLSCHAFT UHLANDSTRASSE 187 GMBH & CO. KG—See Landesbank Baden-Wurttemberg; *Int'l*, pg. 4405
THE ENTWISTLE CO - DANVILLE FACILITY—See Brodart Co.; *U.S. Public*, pg. 661
THE ENTWISTLE CO.—See The Entwistle Co.; *U.S. Private*, pg. 4026
THE ENTWISTLE CO.; *U.S. Private*, pg. 4026
ENTX GROUP LLC; *U.S. Private*, pg. 1406
ENUSA INDUSTRIAS AVANZADAS S.A.—See Sociedad Estatal de Participaciones Industriales; *Int'l*, pg. 7031
ENVAC AB—See STENA AB; *Int'l*, pg. 7206
ENVA IRELAND LIMITED—See DCC plc; *Int'l*, pg. 1990
ENVAR ENGINEERS AND CONTRACTORS PTY. LTD.—See Downer EDI Limited; *Int'l*, pg. 2186
ENVASADORA DE AZUCAR, INC.—See Able Sales Company, Inc.; *U.S. Private*, pg. 39
ENVASES CENTRAL S.A.—See Embotelladora Andina S.A.; *Int'l*, pg. 2375
ENVASES CMF S.A.—See Embotelladora Andina S.A.; *Int'l*, pg. 2375
ENVASES DE ACERO, S.A. DE C.V.—See Air Products & Chemicals, Inc.; *U.S. Public*, pg. 66
ENVASES DEL ISTMO SA—See Ball Corporation; *U.S. Public*, pg. 267
ENVASES DEL PACIFICO S.A.; *Int'l*, pg. 2453
ENVASES ELOPAK S.A. DE C.V.—See Ferd AS; *Int'l*, pg. 2636
ENVASES GRAU, S.L.—See International Paper Company; *U.S. Public*, pg. 1155
ENVASES IMPRESOS S.A.—See Empresas CMPC S.A.; *Int'l*, pg. 2390
ENVASES MULTIPOA S.A. DE C.V.—See Illinois Tool Works Inc.; *U.S. Public*, pg. 1103

ENVASES UNIVERSALES REXAM DE CENTROAMERICA SA—See Ball Corporation; *U.S. Public*, pg. 267
ENVATO PTY LTD.—See Shutterstock, Inc.; *U.S. Public*, pg. 1876
ENVA UK LTD—See Exponent Private Equity LLP; *Int'l*, pg. 2589
ENV AUSTRALIA PTY. LTD.—See WSP Global, Inc.; *Int'l*, pg. 8497
ENVEA CHINA LTD.—See The Carlyle Group Inc.; *U.S. Public*, pg. 2046
ENVEA GLOBAL SAS—See The Carlyle Group Inc.; *U.S. Public*, pg. 2046
ENVEA GMBH—See The Carlyle Group Inc.; *U.S. Public*, pg. 2046
ENVEA INC.—See The Carlyle Group Inc.; *U.S. Public*, pg. 2046
ENVEA INDIA PVT LTD—See The Carlyle Group Inc.; *U.S. Public*, pg. 2046
ENVEA PROCESS GMBH—See The Carlyle Group Inc.; *U.S. Public*, pg. 2046
ENVEA UK LTD.—See The Carlyle Group Inc.; *U.S. Public*, pg. 2046
ENVE COMPOSITES LLC—See ANTA Sports Products Limited; *Int'l*, pg. 480
ENVELA CORPORATION; *U.S. Public*, pg. 779
ENVEL EUROPA S.A.—See Bong AB; *Int'l*, pg. 1107
ENVELOPPE QUEBEC (2008) INC.—See Supremex Inc.; *Int'l*, pg. 7341
ENVEN ENERGY CORPORATION—See Talos Energy Inc.; *U.S. Public*, pg. 1980
ENVERA SYSTEMS LLC—See Wind Point Advisors LLC; *U.S. Private*, pg. 4534
ENVERIC BIOSCIENCES, INC.; *U.S. Public*, pg. 780
ENVERITY ENGINEERING, LLC.; *U.S. Private*, pg. 1406
ENVERSA COMPANIES; *U.S. Private*, pg. 1406
ENVERUS, INC.—See Hellman & Friedman LLC; *U.S. Private*, pg. 1908
ENVERV INC.—See Semtech Corporation; *U.S. Public*, pg. 1864
ENVESTNET, INC.—See Bain Capital, LP; *U.S. Private*, pg. 439
ENVESTNET PORTFOLIO SOLUTIONS, INC.—See Bain Capital, LP; *U.S. Private*, pg. 439
ENVESTNET RETIREMENT SOLUTIONS, LLC—See Bain Capital, LP; *U.S. Private*, pg. 439
ENVIA MITTELDEUTSCHE ENERGIE AG—See RWE AG; *Int'l*, pg. 6436
ENVIANCE, INC.—See Thoma Bravo, L.P.; *U.S. Private*, pg. 4146
ENVIA NETZSERVICE GMBH—See RWE AG; *Int'l*, pg. 6434
ENVIA SYSTEMS, INC.—See General Motors Company; *U.S. Public*, pg. 924
ENVIA THERM GMBH—See RWE AG; *Int'l*, pg. 6436
ENVIA VERTEILNETZ GMBH—See RWE AG; *Int'l*, pg. 6436
ENVICONTROL-ENVITEC N.V.; *Int'l*, pg. 2453
ENVICOR; *U.S. Private*, pg. 1406
ENVICTUS INTERNATIONAL HOLDINGS LIMITED; *Int'l*, pg. 2453
ENVIONEER CO., LTD.; *Int'l*, pg. 2453
ENVIOS DE VALORES LA NACIONAL CORP.—See International Money Express Inc.; *U.S. Public*, pg. 1154
ENVIO TECHNOLOGY (SUQIAN) CO., LTD.—See Catcher Technology Co., Ltd.; *Int'l*, pg. 1359
ENVI-PAK A.S.; *Int'l*, pg. 2453
ENVIPCO AUTOMATEN GMBH—See Envipco Holding N.V.; *Int'l*, pg. 2453
ENVIPCO HOLDING N.V.; *Int'l*, pg. 2453
ENVIPCO PICKUP & PROCESSING SERVICES INC.—See Envipco Holding N.V.; *Int'l*, pg. 2453
ENVIPCO PORTUGAL UNIPESSOAL LDA.—See Envipco Holding N.V.; *Int'l*, pg. 2453
ENVIPCO SLOVAKIA S.R.O.—See Envipco Holding N.V.; *Int'l*, pg. 2453
ENVIPRO HOLDINGS INC.; *Int'l*, pg. 2453
ENVIPROSYSTEMS S.A.—See Edrasis - C. Psallidas S.A.; *Int'l*, pg. 2315
ENVIRA INGENIEROS ASESORES SL—See Eurofins Scientific S.E.; *Int'l*, pg. 2536
ENVIRATRENDS, INC.; *U.S. Private*, pg. 1406
ENVIRI CORPORATION; *U.S. Public*, pg. 780
ENVIRITE, INC.—See Republic Services, Inc.; *U.S. Public*, pg. 1788
ENVIRITE OF ILLINOIS, INC.—See Republic Services, Inc.; *U.S. Public*, pg. 1788
ENVIRITE OF PENNSYLVANIA, INC.—See Republic Services, Inc.; *U.S. Public*, pg. 1788
ENVIRITE TRANSPORTATION, LLC—See Republic Services, Inc.; *U.S. Public*, pg. 1788
ENVIROBURNERS OY—See Max Weishaupt GmbH; *Int'l*, pg. 4735
ENVIRO-CARE CO., INC.—See WAMGROUP S.p.A.; *Int'l*, pg. 8337
ENVIROCHEMIE ABWASSERREINIGUNGS GES.M.B.H.—See SKion GmbH; *Int'l*, pg. 6989
ENVIROCHEMIE AG—See SKion GmbH; *Int'l*, pg. 6989

ENVIROCHEMIE BULGARIA EOOD—See SKion GmbH; *Int'l*, pg. 6989
ENVIROCHEMIE BV—See SKion GmbH; *Int'l*, pg. 6989
ENVIROCHEMIE FZE—See SKion GmbH; *Int'l*, pg. 6989
ENVIROCHEMIE GMBH—See SKion GmbH; *Int'l*, pg. 6989
ENVIROCHEMIE POLSKA SP.Z O.O.—See SKion GmbH; *Int'l*, pg. 6989
ENVIROCHEMIE ROMANIA SRL—See SKion GmbH; *Int'l*, pg. 6989
ENVIROCHEMIE—See SKion GmbH; *Int'l*, pg. 6989
ENVIROCHEMIE TRATAMENTOS ESPECIALIZADOS LTDA.—See SKion GmbH; *Int'l*, pg. 6989
ENVIRO CLEAN PRODUCTS & SERVICES—See Enviro Clean Services LLC; *U.S. Private*, pg. 1406
ENVIRO CLEAN PRODUCTS & SERVICES—See Enviro Clean Services LLC; *U.S. Private*, pg. 1406
ENVIRO CLEAN PRODUCTS & SERVICES—See Enviro Clean Services LLC; *U.S. Private*, pg. 1406
ENVIRO CLEAN SERVICES LLC; *U.S. Private*, pg. 1406
ENVIROCOAT TECHNOLOGIES INC.—See ECL Enviro-Clean Ventures Ltd.; *Int'l*, pg. 2291
ENVIROCOMP LIMITED—See OCS Group Limited; *Int'l*, pg. 5521
ENVIROCON, INC.—See Washington Corporations; *U.S. Private*, pg. 4446
ENVIROCON, INC.—See Washington Corporations; *U.S. Private*, pg. 4446
ENVIROCON, INC.—See Washington Corporations; *U.S. Private*, pg. 4446
ENVIROCON, INC.—See Washington Corporations; *U.S. Private*, pg. 4446
ENVIROCON, INC.—See Washington Corporations; *U.S. Private*, pg. 4446
ENVIROCON, INC.—See Washington Corporations; *U.S. Private*, pg. 4446
ENVIROCON, INC.—See Washington Corporations; *U.S. Private*, pg. 4446
ENVIROCON, INC.—See Washington Corporations; *U.S. Private*, pg. 4446
ENVIROCON, INC.—See Washington Corporations; *U.S. Private*, pg. 4446
ENVIRO CONNEXIONS, INC.—See Waste Connections, Inc.; *Int'l*, pg. 8352
ENVIROCON TECHNOLOGIES, INC.; *U.S. Private*, pg. 1406
ENVIROCYCLE, INC.—See Republic Services, Inc.; *U.S. Public*, pg. 1786
ENVIRODYNE TECHNOLOGIES, INC.—See Prab, Inc.; *U.S. Private*, pg. 3241
ENVIRO ENERGY INTERNATIONAL HOLDINGS LIMITED; *Int'l*, pg. 2454
ENVIRO FALK AG—See SKion GmbH; *Int'l*, pg. 6990
ENVIROFALK GMBH—See SKion GmbH; *Int'l*, pg. 6989
ENVIROFLIGHT, LLC—See Darling Ingredients Inc.; *U.S. Public*, pg. 634
ENVIROFLO ENGINEERING LIMITED—See Ecolab Inc.; *U.S. Public*, pg. 714
ENVIROFONE LIMITED—See SK Inc.; *Int'l*, pg. 6971
ENVIROGEN GROUP NORTH AMERICA, INC.—See Promethean Investments LLP; *Int'l*, pg. 5993
ENVIROGEN GROUP S.A.—See Promethean Investments LLP; *Int'l*, pg. 5993
ENVIROGEN GROUP UK LIMITED—See Promethean Investments LLP; *Int'l*, pg. 5993
ENVIROGEN TECHNOLOGIES, INC.—See Promethean Investments LLP; *Int'l*, pg. 5993
ENVIROGEN WATER TECHNOLOGIES LTD.—See Promethean Investments LLP; *Int'l*, pg. 5993
ENVIROGOLD GLOBAL LIMITED; *Int'l*, pg. 2454
ENVIROGUARD PTY LTD—See Cleanaway Waste Management Limited; *Int'l*, pg. 1655
ENVIRQ-HUB HOLDINGS LTD.; *Int'l*, pg. 2454
ENVIROKINETICS INC.; *U.S. Private*, pg. 1406
ENVIROLOGIC AB; *Int'l*, pg. 2454
ENVIRO-LOG, INC.—See Summit Equity Group, LLC; *U.S. Private*, pg. 3854
ENVIROLOK, LLC—See Agrecol, LLC; *U.S. Private*, pg. 129
ENVIRO-METALS PTE LTD—See Enviro-Hub Holdings Ltd.; *Int'l*, pg. 2454
ENVIROMETAL TECHNOLOGIES, INC.; *Int'l*, pg. 2454
ENVIROMETRIC PROCESS CONTROLS; *U.S. Private*, pg. 1407
ENVIROMISSION LIMITED; *Int'l*, pg. 2454
ENVIRO-MULCH LAND CLEARING SOLUTIONS—See Petrowest Corp.; *Int'l*, pg. 5832
ENVIRONAMICS INC.; *U.S. Private*, pg. 1407
ENVIRONETX, LLC; *U.S. Private*, pg. 1407
ENVIRON GROUP (INVESTMENTS) PLC; *Int'l*, pg. 2454
ENVIRONICS COMMUNICATIONS INC.—See Environics Communications; *U.S. Private*, pg. 1407
ENVIRONICS COMMUNICATIONS; *U.S. Private*, pg. 1407
ENVIRONICS COMMUNICATIONS—See Environics Communications; *U.S. Private*, pg. 1407
ENVIRONICS COMUNICATIONS INC.—See Environics Communications; *U.S. Private*, pg. 1407
ENVIRONMATE TECH CORP.—See ESPEC Corp.; *Int'l*, pg. 2505
ENVIRONMENTAL AIR SYSTEMS, LLC—See Comfort Systems USA, Inc.; *U.S. Public*, pg. 544

COMPANY NAME INDEX

ENVIRONMENTAL ALLIANCE, INC.—See Montrose Environmental Group, Inc.; *U.S. Public*, pg. 1466
ENVIRONMENTAL ALTERNATIVES; *U.S. Private*, pg. 1407
ENVIRONMENTAL ANALYSIS CENTER CO., LTD.—See Daiki Axis Co., Ltd.; *Int'l*, pg. 1932
ENVIRONMENTAL AND LANDSCAPE SERVICES SDN. BHD.—See AWC Berhad; *Int'l*, pg. 752
ENVIRONMENTAL BIOTECH INTERNATIONAL, LLC; *U.S. Private*, pg. 1407
ENVIRONMENTAL BIOTECH LIMITED—See Franchise Brands plc; *Int'l*, pg. 2760
ENVIRONMENTAL CHEMICAL CORPORATION; *U.S. Private*, pg. 1407
ENVIRONMENTAL CHEMISTRY CONSULTING SERVICES, INC.—See Leonard Green & Partners, L.P.; *U.S. Private*, pg. 2426
ENVIRONMENTAL CHEMISTRY, INC.—See Montrose Environmental Group, Inc.; *U.S. Public*, pg. 1466
ENVIRONMENTAL CLEAN TECHNOLOGIES LIMITED; *Int'l*, pg. 2454
THE ENVIRONMENTAL CONSULTANCY LIMITED—See RPS Group plc; *Int'l*, pg. 6416
ENVIRONMENTAL CONSULTANTS, LLC—See Ember Infrastructure Management, LP; *U.S. Private*, pg. 1378
ENVIRONMENTAL CONSULTING & TECHNOLOGY, INC.; *U.S. Private*, pg. 1407
ENVIRONMENTAL CONTAINMENT CORPORATION; *U.S. Private*, pg. 1407
ENVIRONMENTAL CONTRACTORS OF ILLINOIS INC.—See William Charles, Ltd.; *U.S. Private*, pg. 4522
ENVIRONMENTAL CONTROL CENTER CO., LTD.; *Int'l*, pg. 2455
ENVIRONMENTAL CONTROLS CORP.; *U.S. Private*, pg. 1407
ENVIRONMENTAL DATA RESOURCES, INC.—See Daily Mail & General Trust plc; *Int'l*, pg. 1937
ENVIRONMENTAL DESIGN & CONSTRUCTION, LLC; *U.S. Private*, pg. 1407
ENVIRONMENTAL DESIGN, INC.—See Audax Group, Limited Partnership; *U.S. Private*, pg. 389
ENVIRONMENTAL EARTHSCAPES INCORPORATED; *U.S. Private*, pg. 1407
ENVIRONMENTAL ENERGY SERVICES, INC.; *U.S. Private*, pg. 1407
ENVIRONMENTAL ENGINEERING CONSULTANTS, INC.; *U.S. Private*, pg. 1407
ENVIRONMENTAL ENGINUITY GROUP LLC; *U.S. Private*, pg. 1407
ENVIRONMENTAL ENTERPRISES INC.; *U.S. Private*, pg. 1407
ENVIRONMENTAL EQUIPMENT & SERVICES; *U.S. Private*, pg. 1407
ENVIRONMENTAL FILTRATION TECHNOLOGIES LLC—See Nederman Holding AB; *Int'l*, pg. 5188
ENVIRONMENTAL FIRE PROTECTION, INC.; *U.S. Private*, pg. 1407
ENVIRONMENTAL GOVERNANCE LTD—See Jones Lang LaSalle Incorporated; *U.S. Public*, pg. 1203
THE ENVIRONMENTAL GROUP LIMITED; *Int'l*, pg. 7640
ENVIRONMENTAL HEALTH TESTING; *U.S. Private*, pg. 1408
ENVIRONMENTAL HOLDINGS GROUP, LLC.; *U.S. Private*, pg. 1408
ENVIRONMENTAL IMPACT ACQUISITION CORP.; *U.S. Public*, pg. 781
ENVIRONMENTAL INFRASTRUCTURE HOLDINGS CORP.; *U.S. Private*, pg. 1408
ENVIRONMENTAL INKS & COATINGS CORP.; *U.S. Private*, pg. 1408
ENVIRONMENTAL INTEGRATED SOLUTIONS LTD.—See CECO Environmental Corp.; *U.S. Public*, pg. 463
ENVIRONMENTAL INVESTMENT SERVICES ASIA LIMITED—See Somerley Capital Holdings Limited; *Int'l*, pg. 7084
ENVIRONMENTAL LABORATORIES BV—See Eurofins Scientific S.E.; *Int'l*, pg. 2536
ENVIRONMENTAL LABORATORY SERVICES LIMITED—See Eurofins Scientific S.E.; *Int'l*, pg. 2536
ENVIRONMENTAL LIGHTING CONCEPTS, INC.; *U.S. Private*, pg. 1408
ENVIRONMENTAL LUBRICANTS MANUFACTURING, INC.; *U.S. Private*, pg. 1408
ENVIRONMENTAL MANAGEMENT ALTERNATIVES, INC.—See Gryphon Investors, LLC; *U.S. Private*, pg. 1798
ENVIRONMENTAL MANAGEMENT CORPORATION—See American Water Works Company, Inc.; *U.S. Public*, pg. 112
ENVIRONMENTAL MANAGEMENT GROUP, INC.—See Promotora Ambiental S.A.B de C.V.; *Int'l*, pg. 5994
ENVIRONMENTAL MANAGEMENT RESOURCES, INC.; *U.S. Private*, pg. 1408
ENVIRONMENTAL MANAGEMENT SPECIALISTS, INC.—See Gryphon Investors, LLC; *U.S. Private*, pg. 1798
ENVIRONMENTAL MANUFACTURING SOLUTIONS, LLC; *U.S. Private*, pg. 1408

ENVIRONMENTAL MATERIALS LLC—See Clayton, Dubilier & Rice, LLC; *U.S. Private*, pg. 920
ENVIRONMENTAL PACKAGING TECHNOLOGIES HOLDINGS, INC.; *U.S. Public*, pg. 781
ENVIRONMENTAL PARTNERS, INC.—See TRC Companies, Inc.; *U.S. Private*, pg. 4215
ENVIRONMENTAL PEST SERVICE, LLC—See Rentokil Initial plc; *Int'l*, pg. 6286
ENVIRONMENTAL PLANNING GROUP, LLC—See Terracon Consultants, Inc.; *U.S. Private*, pg. 3971
ENVIRONMENTAL PRODUCTS & SERVICES OF VERMONT, INC.—See GenNx360 Capital Partners, L.P.; *U.S. Private*, pg. 1672
ENVIRONMENTAL PRODUCTS; *U.S. Private*, pg. 1408
ENVIRONMENTAL PROPERTY SERVICES LTD—See MITIE Group Plc; *Int'l*, pg. 4926
ENVIRONMENTAL RECYCLING TECHNOLOGIES; *U.S. Private*, pg. 1408
ENVIRONMENTAL RESEARCH & SOLUTIONS CO., LTD.—See CTI Engineering Co., Ltd.; *Int'l*, pg. 1871
ENVIRONMENTAL RESOURCE ASSOC., INC.—See Waters Corporation; *U.S. Public*, pg. 2334
ENVIRONMENTAL RESOURCES MANAGEMENT LIMITED—See Alberta Investment Management Corporation; *Int'l*, pg. 297
ENVIRONMENTAL RESOURCES MANAGEMENT LIMITED—See Ontario Municipal Employees Retirement System; *Int'l*, pg. 5584
ENVIRONMENTAL RESPONSE INC.—See Spray Systems Arizona Inc.; *U.S. Private*, pg. 3762
ENVIRONMENTAL SAMPLING SUPPLY, INC.—See Eurofins Scientific S.E.; *Int'l*, pg. 2536
ENVIRONMENTAL SCIENCE ASSOCIATES; *U.S. Private*, pg. 1408
ENVIRONMENTAL SCIENCE CORP.—See Leonard Green & Partners, L.P.; *U.S. Private*, pg. 2426
ENVIRONMENTAL SCIENTIFICS GROUP LTD.—See 3i Group plc; *Int'l*, pg. 8
ENVIRONMENTAL SERVICE LABORATORIES INC.; *U.S. Private*, pg. 1408
ENVIRONMENTAL SERVICE PROFESSIONALS, INC.; *U.S. Public*, pg. 781
ENVIRONMENTAL SERVICES GROUP LTD.—See 3i Group plc; *Int'l*, pg. 8
ENVIRONMENTAL SERVICES, INC.—See Terracon Consultants, Inc.; *U.S. Private*, pg. 3971
ENVIRONMENTAL SERVICES OF NORTH AMERICA, INC.; *U.S. Private*, pg. 1408
ENVIRONMENTAL SERVICES SPECIALISTS; *U.S. Private*, pg. 1408
ENVIRONMENTAL SOLAR DESIGN, INC.—See Sigora Solar, LLC; *U.S. Private*, pg. 3651
ENVIRONMENTAL SOLUTIONS GROUP—See Terex Corporation; *U.S. Public*, pg. 2019
ENVIRONMENTAL SOLUTIONS WORLDWIDE, INC.; *U.S. Public*, pg. 781
ENVIRONMENTAL SPECIALISTS, INC.—See ESI Contracting, Corp.; *U.S. Private*, pg. 1425
ENVIRONMENTAL STANDARDS, INC.—See Montrose Environmental Group, Inc.; *U.S. Public*, pg. 1466
ENVIRONMENTAL STRATEGY CONSULTANTS, INC.—See All4 LLC; *U.S. Private*, pg. 174
ENVIRONMENTAL STRESS SYSTEMS, INC.—See Chroma ATE Inc.; *Int'l*, pg. 1588
ENVIRONMENTAL SYSTEM PRODUCTS HOLDING; *U.S. Private*, pg. 1408
ENVIRONMENTAL SYSTEMS ASSOCIATES, INC.—See Brookfield Corporation; *Int'l*, pg. 1188
ENVIRONMENTAL SYSTEMS CORPORATION—See Fidelity Engineering LLC; *U.S. Private*, pg. 1502
ENVIRONMENTAL SYSTEMS RESEARCH INSTITUTE INC.; *U.S. Private*, pg. 1408
ENVIRONMENTAL TECHNICAL LABORATORIES, LTD.—See Nissan Chemical Corporation; *Int'l*, pg. 5366
ENVIRONMENTAL TECHNICAL LABORATORY, LTD.—See Nissan Chemical Corporation; *Int'l*, pg. 5366
ENVIRONMENTAL TECHNIQUES CORP.; *U.S. Private*, pg. 1409
ENVIRONMENTAL TECHNIQUES LIMITED—See New Mountain Capital, LLC; *U.S. Private*, pg. 2899
ENVIRONMENTAL TECHNOLOGY COMPANY—See Amano Corporation; *Int'l*, pg. 411
ENVIRONMENTAL TECHNOLOGY, INC.—See Arsenal Capital Management LP; *U.S. Private*, pg. 339
ENVIRONMENTAL TECTONICS CORPORATION; *U.S. Public*, pg. 781
ENVIRONMENTAL TESTING CORP.—See SGS SA; *Int'l*, pg. 6744
ENVIRONMENTAL TRUST COMPANY—See Waste Connections, Inc.; *Int'l*, pg. 8353
ENVIRONMENTAL TURF SERVICES INC.—See XFit Brands, Inc.; *U.S. Private*, pg. 2391
ENVIRONMENTAL WASTE INTERNATIONAL INC.; *Int'l*, pg. 2455
ENVIRONMENTAL WASTE MINIMIZATION INC.; *U.S. Private*, pg. 1409

ENVIRONMENTAL WASTE SOLUTIONS LLC; *U.S. Private*, pg. 1409
ENVIRONMENT AND GENERAL SERVICES, INC.—See APC Group, Inc.; *Int'l*, pg. 507
ENVIRONMENT ECOLOGY HOLDING COMPANY OF CHINA; *Int'l*, pg. 2454
ENVIRONMENT & ENERGY PUBLISHING, LLC—See Sinclair, Inc.; *U.S. Public*, pg. 1885
ENVIRONMENT FRIENDLY HOLDINGS CORP.; *Int'l*, pg. 2454
ENVIRONMENT FURNITURE, INC.—See Cisco Bros. Corp.; *U.S. Private*, pg. 900
ENVIRONMENT MANAGEMENT CORPORATION CO., LTD.—See SK Inc.; *Int'l*, pg. 6971
ENVIRONMENT-ONE CORPORATION—See Berkshire Hathaway Inc.; *U.S. Public*, pg. 314
ENVIRONMENT & POWER COMPANY LTD.—See JFE Holdings, Inc.; *Int'l*, pg. 3935
ENVIRONMENTS INC.; *U.S. Private*, pg. 1409
ENVIROPEST CONTROL SERVICES LTD.—See Rollins, Inc.; *U.S. Public*, pg. 1809
ENVIRO PLANT & ENGINEERING PTE. LTD.—See Sanli Environmental Limited; *Int'l*, pg. 6546
ENVIROPLEX, INC—See McGrath RentCorp.; *U.S. Public*, pg. 1407
ENVIROPURE SYSTEMS, INC.—See T&S Brass & Bronze Works, Inc.; *U.S. Private*, pg. 3910
ENVIRO-SAFE CONSULTING, LLC; *U.S. Private*, pg. 1406
ENVIROSAFE SERVICES OF OHIO, INC.—See J.F. Lehman & Company, Inc.; *U.S. Private*, pg. 2163
ENVIROSCALE, S.L.—See Soltec Power Holdings S.A.; *Int'l*, pg. 7076
ENVIROS CONSULTING LTD.—See Jacobs Engineering Group, Inc.; *U.S. Public*, pg. 1185
ENVIROSELL INC.—See Cross Marketing Group Inc.; *Int'l*, pg. 1856
ENVIROSELL JAPAN INC.—See Cross Marketing Group Inc.; *Int'l*, pg. 1856
ENVIROSERVE, INC.—See One Rock Capital Partners, LLC; *U.S. Private*, pg. 3022
ENVIROSERV HOLDINGS LIMITED—See Veolia Environnement S.A.; *Int'l*, pg. 8154
ENVIRO-SERV, INC.; *U.S. Public*, pg. 781
ENVIRO SHRED INC—See Greymart Metal Company Inc.; *U.S. Private*, pg. 1785
ENVIROSIGHT, LLC—See IDEX Corp; *U.S. Public*, pg. 1090
ENVIROSOIL LIMITED—See Municipal Enterprises Limited; *Int'l*, pg. 5093
ENVIROSOLUTIONS, INC.; *U.S. Private*, pg. 1409
ENVIROS, S. R. O.—See Jacobs Engineering Group, Inc.; *U.S. Public*, pg. 1185
ENVIROSTREAM AUSTRALIA PTY LTD—See Lithium Australia NL; *Int'l*, pg. 4526
ENVIROSTRUCT, LLC; *U.S. Private*, pg. 1409
ENVIROSUITE DENMARK APS—See EnviroSuite Limited; *Int'l*, pg. 2455
ENVIROSUITE LIMITED; *Int'l*, pg. 2455
ENVIROSUITE TAIWAN LTD.—See EnviroSuite Limited; *Int'l*, pg. 2455
ENVIROSYS LTD.—See HORIBA Ltd; *Int'l*, pg. 3475
ENVIROSYSTEMS INC.—See TorQuest Partners Inc.; *Int'l*, pg. 7830
ENVIRO TECH CHEMICAL SERVICES, INC.; *U.S. Private*, pg. 1406
ENVIROTECH DRIVE SYSTEMS, INC.—See Envirotech Vehicles, Inc.; *U.S. Public*, pg. 781
ENVIROTECH ENGINEERING & CONSULTING, INC.; *U.S. Private*, pg. 1409
ENVIRO TECH JAPAN CO., LTD.; *Int'l*, pg. 2454
ENVIROTECH LLC—See ITT Inc.; *U.S. Public*, pg. 1177
ENVIROTECHNOLOGIES INTERNATIONAL, INC.; *U.S. Public*, pg. 781
ENVIROTECH SERVICES INC.—See Monomoy Capital Partners LLC; *U.S. Private*, pg. 2772
ENVIRO TECH—See Dome Corporation North America; *U.S. Private*, pg. 1255
ENVIROTECH VEHICLES, INC.; *U.S. Public*, pg. 781
ENVIROTEK ENVIRONMENTAL & CONSTRUCTION SERVICES; *U.S. Private*, pg. 1409
ENVIROTEST CORP.—See Searchlight Capital Partners, L.P.; *U.S. Private*, pg. 3590
ENVIROTHERM GMBH—See Allied Resource Corporation; *U.S. Private*, pg. 187
ENVIROTRAC LTD.; *U.S. Private*, pg. 1409
ENVIROTROL, LLC—See Comfort Systems USA, Inc.; *U.S. Private*, pg. 544
ENVIROTROL PEST MANAGEMENT SYSTEMS INC.; *U.S. Private*, pg. 1409
ENVIROTROL PEST SOLUTIONS LLC—See Thompson Street Capital Manager LLC; *U.S. Private*, pg. 4161
ENVIROTROLSC, LLC—See Comfort Systems USA, Inc.; *U.S. Private*, pg. 544
ENVIROTRONICS ASIA SDN. BHD.—See Schunk GmbH; *Int'l*, pg. 6643
ENVIROTRONICS BEIJING INDUSTRY AND TRADE INC.—See Schunk GmbH; *Int'l*, pg. 6641

ENVIROTRONICS SINGAPORE PTE. LTD.—See Schunk GmbH; *Int'l*, pg. 6643
ENVIROVAULT L.P.—See TerraVest Industries, Inc.; *Int'l*, pg. 7568
ENVIROWASTE SA PROPRIETARY LIMITED—See Groupe Seche SAS; *Int'l*, pg. 3110
ENVIROWASTE SERVICES GROUP, INC.; *U.S. Private*, pg. 1409
ENVIROWASTE SERVICES LIMITED—See CK Hutchison Holdings Limited; *Int'l*, pg. 1637
ENVIROWORKS, INC.—See Fiskars Oyj Abp; *Int'l*, pg. 2693
ENVISAGE INFORMATION SYSTEMS, LLC; *U.S. Private*, pg. 1409
ENVISAGE TECHNOLOGIES, LLC; *U.S. Private*, pg. 1410
ENVISIONAL LIMITED—See HgCapital Trust plc; *Int'l*, pg. 3377
ENVISION BUSINESS CONSULTING, LLC.; *U.S. Private*, pg. 1410
ENVISION CAPITAL GROUP LLC; *U.S. Private*, pg. 1410
ENVISION CREDIT UNION; *U.S. Private*, pg. 1410
ENVISION ENERGY USA LIMITED—See Envision Group; *Int'l*, pg. 2455
ENVISION GROUP; *Int'l*, pg. 2455
ENVISION HEALTHCARE CLINICAL RESEARCH, INC.—See KKR & Co. Inc.; *U.S. Public*, pg. 1245
ENVISION HEALTHCARE CORPORATION—See KKR & Co. Inc.; *U.S. Public*, pg. 1244
ENVISION HEALTHCARE HOLDINGS, INC.—See KKR & Co. Inc.; *U.S. Public*, pg. 1249
ENVISION INSURANCE COMPANY—See New Rite Aid, LLC; *U.S. Private*, pg. 2905
ENVISIONIT MEDIA, INC.; *U.S. Private*, pg. 1410
ENVISION MEDICAL SOLUTIONS, LLC—See New Rite Aid, LLC; *U.S. Private*, pg. 2905
ENVISION PHARMACEUTICAL SERVICES, LLC—See New Rite Aid, LLC; *U.S. Private*, pg. 2905
ENVISION PHARMA INC.—See Ardian SAS; *Int'l*, pg. 555
ENVISION PHARMA INC.—See GHO Capital Partners LLP; *Int'l*, pg. 2959
ENVISION PHARMA LIMITED—See Ardian SAS; *Int'l*, pg. 555
ENVISION PHARMA LIMITED—See GHO Capital Partners LLP; *Int'l*, pg. 2959
ENVISION PHYSICIAN SERVICES, LLC—See KKR & Co. Inc.; *U.S. Public*, pg. 1249
ENVISION PLASTICS INDUSTRIES, LLC—See Loews Corporation; *U.S. Public*, pg. 1339
ENVISION; *U.S. Private*, pg. 1410
ENVISION TECHNOLOGY MARKETING GROUP, INC.; *U.S. Private*, pg. 1410
ENVISION TELEPHONY INC.; *U.S. Private*, pg. 1410
ENVISION UNLIMITED; *U.S. Private*, pg. 1410
ENVISIONWARE, INC.—See Constellation Software Inc.; *Int'l*, pg. 1775
ENVISTA FORENSICS, LLC—See Engle Martin & Associates, LLC; *U.S. Private*, pg. 1399
ENVISTA HOLDINGS CORPORATION; *U.S. Public*, pg. 781
ENVISTA, LLC.; *U.S. Private*, pg. 1410
ENVIT CAPITAL GROUP, INC.; *U.S. Public*, pg. 781
ENVITEC BIOGAS AG; *Int'l*, pg. 2455
ENVITEC BIOGAS BALTIC SIA—See EnviTec Biogas AG; *Int'l*, pg. 2455
ENVITEC BIOGAS BALTICS SIA—See EnviTec Biogas AG; *Int'l*, pg. 2455
ENVITEC BIOGAS CENTRAL EUROPE S.R.O.—See EnviTec Biogas AG; *Int'l*, pg. 2455
ENVITEC BIOGAS CHINA LTD.—See EnviTec Biogas AG; *Int'l*, pg. 2455
ENVITEC BIOGAS FRANCE S.A.R.L.—See EnviTec Biogas AG; *Int'l*, pg. 2455
ENVITEC BIOGAS NEDERLAND B.V.—See EnviTec Biogas AG; *Int'l*, pg. 2455
ENVITEC BIOGAS ROMANIA S.R.L—See EnviTec Biogas AG; *Int'l*, pg. 2455
ENVITEC BIOGAS SERVICE BALTIC SIA—See EnviTec Biogas AG; *Int'l*, pg. 2455
ENVITEC BIOGAS SOUTH EAST EUROPE LTD.—See EnviTec Biogas AG; *Int'l*, pg. 2455
ENVITEC BIOGAS S.R.L.—See EnviTec Biogas AG; *Int'l*, pg. 2455
ENVITEC BIOGAS UK LTD.—See EnviTec Biogas AG; *Int'l*, pg. 2455
ENVITEC GREEN POWER GMBH & CO. KG—See EnviTec Biogas AG; *Int'l*, pg. 2455
ENVITEC GREEN POWER VERWALTUNGS GMBH—See EnviTec Biogas AG; *Int'l*, pg. 2455
ENVITECH SDN. BHD.—See Salcon Berhad; *Int'l*, pg. 6492
ENVITEC SERVICE APS—See EnviTec Biogas AG; *Int'l*, pg. 2456
ENVITEC SERVICE GMBH—See EnviTec Biogas AG; *Int'l*, pg. 2456
ENVITEC SERVICE SARL—See EnviTec Biogas AG; *Int'l*, pg. 2456
ENVIVA INC.; *U.S. Public*, pg. 781
ENVIVA LP—See Enviva Inc.; *U.S. Public*, pg. 782

ENVIVA PELLETS AHOSKIE, LLC—See Enviva Inc.; *U.S. Public*, pg. 782
ENVIVA PELLETS AMORY, LLC—See Enviva Inc.; *U.S. Public*, pg. 782
ENVIVA PELLETS NORTHAMPTON, LLC—See Enviva Inc.; *U.S. Public*, pg. 782
ENVIVA PELLETS WIGGINS, LLC—See Enviva Inc.; *U.S. Public*, pg. 782
ENVIZION MEDICAL INC.; *U.S. Private*, pg. 1410
ENVIZION MEDICAL LTD.; *Int'l*, pg. 2456
ENVOI, LLC—See AiTi Global, Inc.; *U.S. Public*, pg. 87
ENVOLVE DENTAL OF TEXAS, INC.—See Centene Corporation; *U.S. Public*, pg. 468
ENVOLVE ENGINEERING, LLC—See HomeValet, Inc.; *U.S. Private*, pg. 1975
ENVOLVE INFRASTRUCTURE LTD.—See Renew Holdings plc; *Int'l*, pg. 6278
ENVOLVE OPTICAL, INC.—See Centene Corporation; *U.S. Public*, pg. 468
ENVOLVE PEOPLECARE, INC.—See Centene Corporation; *U.S. Public*, pg. 468
ENVOLVE PHARMACY SOLUTIONS, INC.—See Centene Corporation; *U.S. Public*, pg. 468
ENVOLVE VISION BENEFITS, INC.—See Centene Corporation; *U.S. Public*, pg. 468
ENVOLVE VISION, INC.—See Centene Corporation; *U.S. Public*, pg. 468
ENVOTECH-ILLINOIS L.L.C.—See Republic Services, Inc.; *U.S. Public*, pg. 1786
ENVOY AIR INC.—See American Airlines Group Inc.; *U.S. Public*, pg. 96
ENVOY AVIATION GROUP INC.—See American Airlines Group Inc.; *U.S. Public*, pg. 96
ENVOY SERVICES LIMITED—See Mastercard Incorporated; *U.S. Public*, pg. 1394
ENVOY SOLUTIONS LLC—See Kelso & Company, L.P.; *U.S. Private*, pg. 2279
ENVOY SOLUTIONS LLC—See Warburg Pincus LLC; *U.S. Private*, pg. 4436
ENVOY TECHNOLOGIES, INC.—See Blink Charging Co.; *U.S. Public*, pg. 361
ENVOY TEXTILES LTD.; *Int'l*, pg. 2456
ENV SERVICES, INC.—See Donaldson Company, Inc.; *U.S. Public*, pg. 676
ENVVENO MEDICAL CORPORATION; *U.S. Public*, pg. 782
ENVY LABS, LLC; *U.S. Private*, pg. 1410
ENVYSION, INC.—See Motorola Solutions, Inc.; *U.S. Public*, pg. 1477
ENWARE PTY. LTD.—See Watts Water Technologies, Inc.; *U.S. Public*, pg. 2337
ENWAVE CORPORATION; *Int'l*, pg. 2456
EN-WAY ENTERPRISES INC.; *U.S. Private*, pg. 1389
ENWEI PHARMACEUTICAL CO., LTD.; *Int'l*, pg. 2456
ENWELL ENERGY PLC; *Int'l*, pg. 2456
ENWESA OPERACIONES, S.A.—See Sociedad Estatal de Participaciones Industriales; *Int'l*, pg. 7032
EN WORLD HONG-KONG LIMITED.—See en-japan Inc.; *Int'l*, pg. 2395
EN WORLD JAPAN K.K.—See en-japan Inc.; *Int'l*, pg. 2395
EN WORLD KOREA CO., LTD—See en-japan Inc.; *Int'l*, pg. 2395
ENWRAP LOGISTIC & PACKAGING S.R.L.—See UFP Industries, Inc.; *U.S. Public*, pg. 2219
ENX GROUP LIMITED; *Int'l*, pg. 2456
ENX LEASING INVESTMENTS PROPRIETARY LIMITED—See enX Group Limited; *Int'l*, pg. 2456
ENXNET, INC.; *U.S. Private*, pg. 1410
ENYE LTD. CORPORATION—See BELIMO Holding AG; *Int'l*, pg. 965
ENYE MEDIA, LLC; *U.S. Private*, pg. 1410
ENYSE ENCLAVAMIENTOS Y SENALIZACION FERROVIARIA, S.A.—See ACS, Actividades de Construccion y Servicios, S.A.; *Int'l*, pg. 111
ENZA AIR PROPRIETARY LIMITED—See Ingersoll Rand Inc.; *U.S. Public*, pg. 1118
ENZA BIOTECH AB—See Croda International plc; *Int'l*, pg. 1852
ENZACOR PTY LIMITED—See BayWa AG; *Int'l*, pg. 919
ENZAFOODS NEW ZEALAND LIMITED—See BayWa AG; *Int'l*, pg. 919
ENZAFRUIT MARKETING LIMITED—See BayWa AG; *Int'l*, pg. 919
ENZAFRUIT NEW ZEALAND (CONTINENT) NV—See BayWa AG; *Int'l*, pg. 919
ENZAL CHEMICALS (INDIA) LTD.; *Int'l*, pg. 2456
ENZENE BIOSCIENCES LIMITED—See Alkem Laboratories Ltd.; *Int'l*, pg. 330
ENZO BIOCHEM, INC.; *U.S. Public*, pg. 782
ENZO CLINICAL LABS INC.—See Enzo Biochem, Inc.; *U.S. Public*, pg. 782
ENZO LIFE SCIENCES (ELS) AG—See Enzo Biochem Inc.; *U.S. Public*, pg. 782
ENZO LIFE SCIENCES—See Enzo Biochem Inc.; *U.S. Public*, pg. 782
ENZOLYTICS, INC.; *U.S. Public*, pg. 782
ENZON PHARMACEUTICALS, INC.; *U.S. Public*, pg. 782

ENZO THERAPEUTICS INC.—See Enzo Biochem Inc.; *U.S. Public*, pg. 782
ENZUMO CORPORATION PTY LTD—See Centrepoint Alliance Limited; *Int'l*, pg. 1412
ENZYCHEM LIFESCIENCES CORPORATION - JECHEON FACTORY—See Enzychem Lifesciences Corporation; *Int'l*, pg. 2456
ENZYCHEM LIFESCIENCES CORPORATION; *Int'l*, pg. 2456
ENZYCHEM LIFESCIENCES INC.—See Enzychem Lifesciences Corporation; *Int'l*, pg. 2456
ENZYMATICA AB; *Int'l*, pg. 2456
ENZYMATIC THERAPY INC.—See Dr. Willmar Schwabe GmbH & Co. KG; *Int'l*, pg. 2195
ENZYMEBIOSYSTEMS; *U.S. Private*, pg. 1410
ENZYME DEVELOPMENT CORPORATION; *U.S. Private*, pg. 1410
ENZYMEDICA, INC.; *U.S. Private*, pg. 1410
ENZYME ENVIRONMENTAL SOLUTIONS, INC.; *U.S. Private*, pg. 1410
ENZYME INNOVATION, INC.—See Advanced Enzyme Technologies Limited; *Int'l*, pg. 159
ENZYMES OF AMERICA HOLDING CORP.; *U.S. Public*, pg. 782
ENZYMOTEC USA, INC.—See International Flavors & Fragrances Inc.; *U.S. Public*, pg. 1151
EO2 S.A.; *Int'l*, pg. 2457
E&O CUSTOMER SERVICES SDN. BHD.—See Eastern & Oriental Berhad; *Int'l*, pg. 2271
EOFF ELECTRIC COMPANY—See Sonepar S.A.; *Int'l*, pg. 7093
EOFLOW CO., LTD.; *Int'l*, pg. 2457
EOG ARGENTINA S.R.L.—See EOG Resources, Inc.; *U.S. Public*, pg. 782
EOG RESOURCES CANADA, INC.—See EOG Resources, Inc.; *U.S. Public*, pg. 782
EOG RESOURCES, INC.; *U.S. Public*, pg. 782
EOG RESOURCES TRINIDAD LIMITED—See EOG Resources, Inc.; *U.S. Public*, pg. 782
EOG RESOURCES TRINIDAD LIMITED—See EOG Resources, Inc.; *U.S. Public*, pg. 782
EOG RESOURCES TRINIDAD NITRO UNLIMITED—See EOG Resources, Inc.; *U.S. Public*, pg. 782
EOG Y RESOURCES, INC.—See EOG Resources, Inc.; *U.S. Public*, pg. 782
EOH ABANTU (PTY) LIMITED—See Pan African Resources plc; *Int'l*, pg. 5713
E.O. HABHEGGER COMPANY INC.; *U.S. Private*, pg. 1306
EOH CONSULTING (PTY) LIMITED—See EOH HOLDINGS LIMITED; *Int'l*, pg. 2457
EOH CONSULTING SERVICES (EASTERN CAPE) (PTY) LIMITED—See EOH HOLDINGS LIMITED; *Int'l*, pg. 2457
EOH CONSULTING SERVICES (WESTERN CAPE) (PTY) LIMITED—See EOH HOLDINGS LIMITED; *Int'l*, pg. 2457
EOH HOLDINGS LIMITED; *Int'l*, pg. 2457
E. OHMAN J:OR AB; *Int'l*, pg. 2250
EOH MTHOMBO (PTY) LIMITED—See EOH HOLDINGS LIMITED; *Int'l*, pg. 2457
E.O. JOHNSON COMPANY, INC.; *U.S. Public*, pg. 1306
EOLE GENERATION SAS—See ENGIE SA; *Int'l*, pg. 2429
EOLE, INC.; *Int'l*, pg. 2457
EOLFI POLSKA SP. Z O.O.—See Veolia Environnement S.A.; *Int'l*, pg. 8153
EOLFI SA—See Veolia Environnement S.A.; *Int'l*, pg. 8153
EOLFI WIND HELLAS S.A.—See Veolia Environnement S.A.; *Int'l*, pg. 8153
EOLFLOR - PRODUCAO DE ENERGIA EO LICA LDA—See Enel S.p.A.; *Int'l*, pg. 2414
EOLICA ARLANZON, S.A.—See EDP - Energias de Portugal, S.A.; *Int'l*, pg. 2314
EOLICA DOBROGEA (SCHWEIZ) I. GMBH.—See Iberdrola, S.A.; *Int'l*, pg. 3571
EOLICA EL PEDREGOSO, S.L.—See AUDAX RENOVABLES, S.A.; *Int'l*, pg. 700
EOLICA GUADALTEBA, S.L.—See EDP - Energias de Portugal, S.A.; *Int'l*, pg. 2314
EOLICA POLCZYNO SP. Z O.O.—See Athena Investments A/S; *Int'l*, pg. 669
EOLIKI ZARAKA METAMORFOSSIS SA—See ELLAKTOR S.A.; *Int'l*, pg. 2365
EOL, INC.—See PRONEXUS INC.; *Int'l*, pg. 5996
EOLITE SYSTEMS, SAS—See MKS Instruments, Inc.; *U.S. Public*, pg. 1452
EOLO SRL—See ERG S.p.A.; *Int'l*, pg. 2491
EOLOS RUZGAR ENERJISI URETIM A.S.—See Parsan Makina Parcalari Sanayii AS; *Int'l*, pg. 5747
EOLUS NORTH AMERICA INC—See Eolus Vind AB; *Int'l*, pg. 2457
EOLUS VIND AB; *Int'l*, pg. 2457
EOM ACQUISITION CORP.—See AMCON Distributing Company; *U.S. Public*, pg. 93
EOMJIHOUSE INC.; *Int'l*, pg. 2457
EOM PHARMACEUTICAL HOLDINGS, INC.; *U.S. Public*, pg. 782
EOM PHARMACEUTICALS, INC.—See EOM Pharmaceutical Holdings, Inc.; *U.S. Public*, pg. 782

COMPANY NAME INDEX

E.ON ACADEMY GMBH—See E.ON SE; *Int'l*, pg. 2252
E.ON ANLAGENSERVICE GMBH—See E.ON SE; *Int'l*, pg. 2252
E.ON AUSTRIA GMBH—See E.ON SE; *Int'l*, pg. 2252
E.ON AVACON AG—See E.ON SE; *Int'l*, pg. 2252
E.ON AVACON VERTRIEB GMBH—See E.ON SE; *Int'l*, pg. 2252
E.ON AVACON WARME GMBH—See E.ON SE; *Int'l*, pg. 2252
E.ON BAYERN AG—See E.ON SE; *Int'l*, pg. 2252
E.ON BAYERN VERTRIEB GMBH—See E.ON SE; *Int'l*, pg. 2252
E.ON BAYERN WARME 1. BETEILIGUNGS-GMBH—See E.ON SE; *Int'l*, pg. 2252
E.ON BAYERN WARME GMBH—See E.ON SE; *Int'l*, pg. 2252
E.ON BELGIUM N.V.—See E.ON SE; *Int'l*, pg. 2252
E.ON BENELUX CCS PROJECT B.V.—See E.ON SE; *Int'l*, pg. 2252
E.ON BETEILIGUNGSVERWALTUNGS GMBH—See E.ON SE; *Int'l*, pg. 2252
E.ON BIOERDGAS GMBH—See E.ON SE; *Int'l*, pg. 2252
E.ON BIOFOR SVERIGE AB—See E.ON SE; *Int'l*, pg. 2255
E.ON BUILDING SERVICES ACADEMY—See E.ON SE; *Int'l*, pg. 2252
E.ON CESKA REPUBLIKA, S.R.O.—See E.ON SE; *Int'l*, pg. 2252
E.ON CLIMATE & RENEWABLES GMBH—See E.ON SE; *Int'l*, pg. 2252
E.ON CLIMATE & RENEWABLES ITALIA S.R.L.—See F2i - Fondi Italiani per le infrastrutture SGR S.p.A.; *Int'l*, pg. 2597
E.ON CLIMATE & RENEWABLES NORTH AMERICA LLC—See E.ON SE; *Int'l*, pg. 2252
E.ON CLIMATE & RENEWABLES UK BIOMASS LIMITED—See E.ON SE; *Int'l*, pg. 2256
E.ON CLIMATE & RENEWABLES UK LONDON ARRAY LIMITED—See E.ON SE; *Int'l*, pg. 2256
E.ON CLIMATE & RENEWABLES UK OFFSHORE WIND LIMITED—See E.ON SE; *Int'l*, pg. 2256
E.ON CLIMATE & RENEWABLES UK ROBIN RIGG WEST LIMITED—See E.ON SE; *Int'l*, pg. 2256
E.ON CLIMATE & RENEWABLES UK WIND LIMITED—See E.ON SE; *Int'l*, pg. 2256
E.ON COMERCIALIZADORA DE ULTIMO RECURSO S.L.—See E.ON SE; *Int'l*, pg. 2252
E.ON CZECH HOLDING AG—See E.ON SE; *Int'l*, pg. 2252
E.ON DANMARK A/S—See E.ON SE; *Int'l*, pg. 2252
E.ON DEL-DUNANTULI ARAMSZOLGALTATO ZRT.—See E.ON SE; *Int'l*, pg. 2253
E.ON DEL-DUNANTULI GAZSZOLGALTATO ZRT.—See E.ON SE; *Int'l*, pg. 2253
E.ON DIREKT GMBH—See E.ON SE; *Int'l*, pg. 2252
E.ON DISTRIBUCE, A.S.—See E.ON SE; *Int'l*, pg. 2252
E.ON DISTRIBUCIJA PLINA D.O.O.—See E.ON SE; *Int'l*, pg. 2252
E.ON DRIVE GMBH—See E.ON SE; *Int'l*, pg. 2252
EONE DIAGNOMICS GENOME CENTER CO., LTD.; *Int'l*, pg. 2458
E.ON EDIS AG—See E.ON SE; *Int'l*, pg. 2256
E.ON EDIS CONTRACTING GMBH—See E.ON SE; *Int'l*, pg. 2256
E-ONE, INC.—See AIP, LLC; *U.S. Private*, pg. 135
EON ELECTRIC LTD.; *Int'l*, pg. 2457
E.ON ELEKTRARNE S.R.O.—See E.ON SE; *Int'l*, pg. 2252
E.ON ELNAT STOCKHOLM AB—See E.ON SE; *Int'l*, pg. 2255
E.ON ELNAT SVERIGE AB—See E.ON SE; *Int'l*, pg. 2255
E.ON ENERGIAKERESKEDO KFT.—See E.ON SE; *Int'l*, pg. 2253
E.ON ENERGIA S.P.A—See F2i - Fondi Italiani per le infrastrutture SGR S.p.A.; *Int'l*, pg. 2597
E.ON ENERGIATERMELO KFT.—See E.ON SE; *Int'l*, pg. 2252
E.ON ENERGIE 31. BETEILIGUNGSGESELLSCHAFT MBH MUNCHEN—See E.ON SE; *Int'l*, pg. 2252
E.ON ENERGIE 39. BETEILIGUNGS-GMBH—See E.ON SE; *Int'l*, pg. 2252
E.ON ENERGIE AG—See E.ON SE; *Int'l*, pg. 2252
E.ON ENERGIE, A.S.—See E.ON SE; *Int'l*, pg. 2252
E.ON ENERGIE ODNAWIALNE SP. Z O.O.—See E.ON SE; *Int'l*, pg. 2252
E.ON ENERGIE ROMANIA S.A.—See E.ON SE; *Int'l*, pg. 2254
E.ON ENERGIHANDEL NORDIC AB—See E.ON SE; *Int'l*, pg. 2254
E.ON ENERGY INFRASTRUCTURE SOLUTIONS D.O.O.—See E.ON SE; *Int'l*, pg. 2253
E.ON ENERGY PROJECTS GMBH—See E.ON SE; *Int'l*, pg. 2253
E.ON ENERGY SALES GMBH—See E.ON SE; *Int'l*, pg. 2253
E.ON ENERGY—See E.ON SE; *Int'l*, pg. 2256
E.ON ENERGY TRADING BULGARIEN EOOD—See E.ON SE; *Int'l*, pg. 2254

E.ON ENERGY TRADING HOLDING GMBH—See E.ON SE; *Int'l*, pg. 2254
E.ON ENERGY TRADING NL STAFF COMPANY B.V.—See E.ON SE; *Int'l*, pg. 2254
E.ON ENERGY UK LIMITED—See E.ON SE; *Int'l*, pg. 2256
E.ON ENGINEERING GMBH—See E.ON SE; *Int'l*, pg. 2253
E.ON E&P—See E.ON SE; *Int'l*, pg. 2255
E.ON EROMUVEK TERMELO ES UZEMELTETO KFT—See E.ON SE; *Int'l*, pg. 2254
E.ON ESZAK-DUNANTULI ARAMSZOLGALTATO ZRT.—See E.ON SE; *Int'l*, pg. 2253
E.ON EUROPA, S.L.—See E.ON SE; *Int'l*, pg. 2252
E.ON FASTIGHETER SVERIGE AB—See E.ON SE; *Int'l*, pg. 2255
E.ON FERNWAERME GMBH—See E.ON SE; *Int'l*, pg. 2253
E.ON FIRST FUTURE ENERGY HOLDING B.V.—See E.ON SE; *Int'l*, pg. 2254
E.ON FORSALJNING SVERIGE AB—See E.ON SE; *Int'l*, pg. 2255
E.ON FRANCE MANAGEMENT S.A.S.—See E.ON SE; *Int'l*, pg. 2254
E.ON FRANCE S.A.S.—See E.ON SE; *Int'l*, pg. 2254
E.ON GASHANDEL SVERIGE AB—See E.ON SE; *Int'l*, pg. 2255
E.ON GASIFICATION DEVELOPMENT AB—See E.ON SE; *Int'l*, pg. 2255
E.ON GAS SVERIGE AB—See E.ON SE; *Int'l*, pg. 2255
E.ON GAZDASAGI SZOLGALTATO KFT.—See E.ON SE; *Int'l*, pg. 2254
E.ON GAZ DISTRIBUTIE S.A.—See E.ON SE; *Int'l*, pg. 2254
E.ON GRID SOLUTIONS GMBH—See E.ON SE; *Int'l*, pg. 2254
E.ON GRUGA GESCHAFTSFUHRUNGSGESELLSCHAFT MBH—See E.ON SE; *Int'l*, pg. 2254
E.ON GRUGA OBJEKTGESELLSCHAFT MBH & CO. KG—See E.ON SE; *Int'l*, pg. 2254
EON HADAPSAR INFRASTRUCTURE PVT. LTD.; *Int'l*, pg. 2458
E.ON HALOZATI SZOLGALTATO KFT.—See E.ON SE; *Int'l*, pg. 2253
E.ON HANSE VERTRIEB GMBH—See E.ON SE; *Int'l*, pg. 2254
E.ON HANSE WARME GMBH—See E.ON SE; *Int'l*, pg. 2254
E.ON HUMAN RESOURCES INTERNATIONAL GMBH—See E.ON SE; *Int'l*, pg. 2254
E.ON HUNGARIA ZRT.—See E.ON SE; *Int'l*, pg. 2253
E.ON IBERIA HOLDING GMBH—See E.ON SE; *Int'l*, pg. 2254
E.ON INHOUSE CONSULTING GMBH—See E.ON SE; *Int'l*, pg. 2254
E.ON INTERNATIONAL FINANCE B.V.—See E.ON SE; *Int'l*, pg. 2254
E.ON INVEST GMBH—See E.ON SE; *Int'l*, pg. 2254
E.ON IS FURSTENWALDE—See E.ON SE; *Int'l*, pg. 2253
E.ON IS GMBH—See E.ON SE; *Int'l*, pg. 2253
E.ON IS HUNGARY KFT.—See E.ON SE; *Int'l*, pg. 2253
E.ON ITALIA S.P.A.—See F2i - Fondi Italiani per le infrastrutture SGR S.p.A.; *Int'l*, pg. 2597
E.ON IT BULGARIA EOOD—See E.ON SE; *Int'l*, pg. 2254
E.ON IT HUNGARY KFT.—See E.ON SE; *Int'l*, pg. 2254
E.ON IT NETHERLANDS B.V.—See E.ON SE; *Int'l*, pg. 2254
E.ON IT SVERIGE AB—See E.ON SE; *Int'l*, pg. 2254
E.ON IT UK LIMITED—See E.ON SE; *Int'l*, pg. 2254
E.ON KAINUU OY—See E.ON SE; *Int'l*, pg. 2254
E.ON KARNKRAFT SVERIGE AB—See E.ON SE; *Int'l*, pg. 2255
E.ON KERNKRAFT GMBH—See E.ON SE; *Int'l*, pg. 2253
E.ON KOZEP-DUNANTULI GAZHALOZATI ZRT.—See E.ON SE; *Int'l*, pg. 2254
E.ON KRAFTWERKE GMBH—See E.ON SE; *Int'l*, pg. 2253
E.ON KRAFTWERKE GMBH—See E.ON SE; *Int'l*, pg. 2253
E.ON KUNDENSERVICE GMBH—See E.ON SE; *Int'l*, pg. 2254
E.ON KUNDSUPPORT SVERIGE AB—See E.ON SE; *Int'l*, pg. 2255
E-ONLINEDATA, LLC—See Global Payments Inc.; *U.S. Public*, pg. 943
EONMETALL GROUP BERHAD; *Int'l*, pg. 2458
EONMETALL INDUSTRIES SDN. BHD.—See Eonmetall Group Berhad; *Int'l*, pg. 2458
EONMETALL SYSTEMS SDN. BHD.—See Eonmetall Group Berhad; *Int'l*, pg. 2458
EONMETALL TECHNOLOGY SDN. BHD.—See Eonmetall Group Berhad; *Int'l*, pg. 2458
E.ON METERING GMBH—See E.ON SE; *Int'l*, pg. 2253
E.ON MITTE WARME GMBH—See E.ON SE; *Int'l*, pg. 2254
E.ON MOLDOVA-FURNIZARE—See E.ON SE; *Int'l*, pg. 2253
EON MOTORS GROUP SA; *Int'l*, pg. 2458
E.ON MYENERGY KFT.—See E.ON SE; *Int'l*, pg. 2254

EO PRODUCTS

E.ON NA CAPITAL LLC—See E.ON SE; *Int'l*, pg. 2254
E.ON NETZ GMBH—See E.ON SE; *Int'l*, pg. 2253
E.ON NEW BUILD & TECHNOLOGY GMBH—See E.ON SE; *Int'l*, pg. 2254
EON NRG LIMITED; *Int'l*, pg. 2458
E.ON PORTFOLIO SOLUTION GMBH—See E.ON SE; *Int'l*, pg. 2253
E.ON PRODUKTION DANMARK A/S—See E.ON SE; *Int'l*, pg. 2254
E.ON PRODUZIONE CENTRALE LIVORNO FERRARIS S.P.A.—See E.ON SE; *Int'l*, pg. 2255
E.ON REGENERABILE ROMANIA S.R.L—See E.ON SE; *Int'l*, pg. 2255
E.ON RENOVABLES, S.L.—See E.ON SE; *Int'l*, pg. 2252
E.ON RENOVAVEIS PORTUGAL, SGPS S.A.—See E.ON SE; *Int'l*, pg. 2255
E.ON RISK CONSULTING GMBH—See E.ON SE; *Int'l*, pg. 2255
E.ON ROMANIA S.R.L.—See E.ON SE; *Int'l*, pg. 2255
E.ON RUHRGAS AG—See E.ON SE; *Int'l*, pg. 2255
E.ON RUHRGAS AUSTRIA GMBH—See E.ON SE; *Int'l*, pg. 2255
E.ON RUHRGAS BBL B.V.—See E.ON SE; *Int'l*, pg. 2255
E.ON RUHRGAS DUTCH HOLDING B.V.—See E.ON SE; *Int'l*, pg. 2255
E.ON RUHRGAS E & P AGYPTEN GMBH—See E.ON SE; *Int'l*, pg. 2255
E.ON RUHRGAS E & P GMBH—See E.ON SE; *Int'l*, pg. 2255
E.ON RUHRGAS GGH GMBH—See E.ON SE; *Int'l*, pg. 2255
E.ON RUHRGAS GPA GMBH—See E.ON SE; *Int'l*, pg. 2255
E.ON RUHRGAS INTERNATIONAL AG—See E.ON SE; *Int'l*, pg. 2255
E.ON RUHRGAS PERSONALAGENTUR GMBH—See E.ON SE; *Int'l*, pg. 2255
E.ON RUHRGAS UK E&P LIMITED—See E.ON SE; *Int'l*, pg. 2255
E.ON RUSSIA HOLDING GMBH—See E.ON SE; *Int'l*, pg. 2255
E.ON SERVICE GMBH—See E.ON SE; *Int'l*, pg. 2255
E.ON SERVISNI, S.R.O.—See E.ON SE; *Int'l*, pg. 2255
E.ON SE; *Int'l*, pg. 2251
E-ON SOFTWARE SARL—See Bentley Systems, Inc.; *U.S. Public*, pg. 297
E.ON SUOMI OY—See E.ON SE; *Int'l*, pg. 2255
E.ON SVERIGE AB—See E.ON SE; *Int'l*, pg. 2255
E.ON SZOLGALTATO KFT.—See E.ON SE; *Int'l*, pg. 2253
EONTARR IT SOLUTIONS SDN. BHD.—See Eonmetall Group Berhad; *Int'l*, pg. 2458
E.ON THURINGER ENERGIE DRITTE VERMOGENSVERWALTUNGS-GMBH—See Thuringer Energie AG; *Int'l*, pg. 7723
E.ON TISZANTULI ARAMSZOLGALTATO RT.—See E.ON SE; *Int'l*, pg. 2253
E.ON TRADING NORDIC AB—See E.ON SE; *Int'l*, pg. 2255
E.ON TREND S.R.O.—See E.ON SE; *Int'l*, pg. 2256
E.ON UK CHP LIMITED—See E.ON SE; *Int'l*, pg. 2256
E.ON UK ENERGY SERVICES LIMITED—See E.ON SE; *Int'l*, pg. 2256
E.ON UK ENERGY SOLUTIONS LIMITED—See E.ON SE; *Int'l*, pg. 2256
E.ON UK HOLDING COMPANY LIMITED—See E.ON SE; *Int'l*, pg. 2256
E.ON UK PLC—See E.ON SE; *Int'l*, pg. 2256
E.ON UK POWER TECHNOLOGY LIMITED—See E.ON SE; *Int'l*, pg. 2256
E.ON UK PROPERTY SERVICES LIMITED—See E.ON SE; *Int'l*, pg. 2256
E.ON UK TECHNICAL SERVICES LIMITED—See E.ON SE; *Int'l*, pg. 2256
E.ON VARME DANMARK APS—See E.ON SE; *Int'l*, pg. 2252
E.ON VARMEKRAFT SVERIGE AB—See E.ON SE; *Int'l*, pg. 2255
E.ON VARME SVERIGE AB—See E.ON SE; *Int'l*, pg. 2255
E.ON VERTRIEB DEUTSCHLAND GMBH—See E.ON SE; *Int'l*, pg. 2256
E.ON VIND SVERIGE AB—See E.ON SE; *Int'l*, pg. 2255
E.ON WASSERKRAFT GMBH—See E.ON SE; *Int'l*, pg. 2253
E.ON WESTFALEN WESER 2. VERMOGENSVERWALTUNGS-GMBH—See E.ON SE; *Int'l*, pg. 2256
E.ON WESTFALEN WESER AG—See E.ON SE; *Int'l*, pg. 2253
E.ON WESTFALEN WESER VERTRIEB GMBH—See E.ON SE; *Int'l*, pg. 2253
E.ON ZWANZIGSTE VERWALTUNGS GMBH—See E.ON SE; *Int'l*, pg. 2256
EOPLEX LIMITED—See ASTI Holdings Limited; *Int'l*, pg. 655
EO PRODUCTS; *U.S. Private*, pg. 1410
E&O PROPERTY DEVELOPMENT BERHAD—See Eastern & Oriental Berhad; *Int'l*, pg. 2271
E&O PROPERTY (PENANG) SDN. BHD.—See Eastern & Oriental Berhad; *Int'l*, pg. 2271

EO PRODUCTS

E.O. RESOURCES, LLC—See Iberdrola, S.A.; *Int'l*, pg. 3570
EORIGINAL, INC—See Wolters Kluwer n.v.; *Int'l*, pg. 8445
EOS AIRLINES, INC.; *U.S. Private*, pg. 1410
EOS CANADA INC.—See Otto GmbH & Co. KG; *Int'l*, pg. 5662
EOSCENE CORPORATION; *U.S. Private*, pg. 1411
EOS CREDIREC SAS—See Otto GmbH & Co. KG; *Int'l*, pg. 5662
EOS DEFENSE SYSTEMS PTE LIMITED—See Electro Optic Systems Holdings Limited; *Int'l*, pg. 2353
EOS ELECTRO OPTICAL SYSTEMS LTD.—See EOS GmbH Electro Optical Systems; *Int'l*, pg. 2458
EOS ENERGY ENTERPRISES, INC.—See B. Riley Financial, Inc.; *U.S. Public*, pg. 260
EOS ENERGY STORAGE LLC—See B. Riley Financial, Inc.; *U.S. Public*, pg. 261
E&O SERVICES (SINGAPORE) LTD.—See LVMH Moet Hennessy Louis Vuitton SE; *Int'l*, pg. 4591
EOS GMBH ELECTRO OPTICAL SYSTEMS; *Int'l*, pg. 2458
EOS HOLDING GMBH—See Otto GmbH & Co. KG; *Int'l*, pg. 5662
EOS HOLDINGS INC.—See Otto GmbH & Co. KG; *Int'l*, pg. 5662
EOS HONG KONG LTD—See Otto GmbH & Co. KG; *Int'l*, pg. 5662
EOS IMAGE, INC.—See Alphatec Holdings, Inc.; *U.S. Public*, pg. 84
EOS IMAGING CANADA—See Alphatec Holdings, Inc.; *U.S. Public*, pg. 84
EOS IMAGING GMBH—See Alphatec Holdings, Inc.; *U.S. Public*, pg. 84
EOS IMAGING INC.—See Alphatec Holdings, Inc.; *U.S. Public*, pg. 84
EOS IMAGING S.A.—See Alphatec Holdings, Inc.; *U.S. Public*, pg. 84
EOS INC.; *Int'l*, pg. 2458
EOS INTERNATIONAL, INC.; *U.S. Private*, pg. 1411
EOS INTERNATIONAL—See SirsiDynix Corporation; *U.S. Private*, pg. 3675
EOS OF NORTH AMERICA, INC.—See EOS GmbH Electro Optical Systems; *Int'l*, pg. 2458
EOS OPTRONICS GMBH—See Electro Optic Systems Holdings Limited; *Int'l*, pg. 2353
EOS PARTNERS, L.P.; *U.S. Private*, pg. 1411
EOS PETRO, INC.; *U.S. Private*, pg. 1411
EOS PRODUCTS, LLC; *U.S. Private*, pg. 1411
EOS PUBLISHING, LLC; *U.S. Private*, pg. 1411
EOS SAUNATECHNIK GMBH—See Harvia Oyj; *Int'l*, pg. 3281
EOS SERVIZI FIDUCIARI SPA—See EFG International AG; *Int'l*, pg. 2320
EOS SINGAPORE PTE LTD—See EOS GmbH Electro Optical Systems; *Int'l*, pg. 2458
EOS SOLUTIONS UK PLC—See Otto GmbH & Co. KG; *Int'l*, pg. 5662
EOS SPACE SYSTEMS PTY LIMITED—See Electro Optic Systems Holdings Limited; *Int'l*, pg. 2353
EOS.S.R.L. ELECTRO OPTICAL SYSTEMS—See EOS GmbH Electro Optical Systems; *Int'l*, pg. 2458
EO STAL AB—See SSAB AB; *Int'l*, pg. 7155
EOS TECHNOLOGIES, INC.—See Electro Optic Systems Holdings Limited; *Int'l*, pg. 2353
E. OSTERMAN GAS SERVICE INC.; *U.S. Private*, pg. 1304
EOS.UPTRADE GMBH—See Siemens Aktiengesellschaft; *Int'l*, pg. 6901
EO TECHNICS CO., LTD.; *Int'l*, pg. 2457
EO TECHNICS CO., LTD.—See EO Technics Co., Ltd.; *Int'l*, pg. 2457
EO TECHNICS INDIA PVT. LTD—See EO Technics Co., Ltd.; *Int'l*, pg. 2457
EO TECHNICS INTERNATIONAL, INC.—See EO Technics Co., Ltd.; *Int'l*, pg. 2457
EO TECHNICS SINGAPORE PTE., LTD.—See EO Technics Co., Ltd.; *Int'l*, pg. 2457
EO TECHNICS TAIWAN CO., LTD.—See EO Technics Co., Ltd.; *Int'l*, pg. 2457
EOVATIONS, LLC—See UFP Industries, Inc.; *U.S. Public*, pg. 2219
EOWS MIDLAND COMPANY—See PrimeEnergy Resources Corporation; *U.S. Public*, pg. 1717
EP3OIL INC; *U.S. Public*, pg. 782
EPADYM S.A.—See ELLAKTOR S.A.; *Int'l*, pg. 2365
EPAG DOMAINSERVICES GMBH—See Tucows, Inc.; *Int'l*, pg. 7963
E. PAIRIS S.A.; *Int'l*, pg. 2250
EPA MANAGEMENT SDN BHD—See Johor Corporation; *Int'l*, pg. 3994
EPAM CONSULTING BV—See EPAM Systems, Inc.; *U.S. Public*, pg. 783
EPAM SISTEMOS—See EPAM Systems, Inc.; *U.S. Public*, pg. 783
EPAM SOLUTIONS, LLC—See EPAM Systems, Inc.; *U.S. Public*, pg. 783
EPAM SYSTEMS ARMENIA—See EPAM Systems, Inc.; *U.S. Public*, pg. 783
EPAM SYSTEMS BULGARIA EOOD—See EPAM Systems, Inc.; *U.S. Public*, pg. 783
EPAM SYSTEMS CANADA, LTD.—See EPAM Systems, Inc.; *U.S. Public*, pg. 783
EPAM SYSTEMS (CZECH REPUBLIC) S.R.O.—See EPAM Systems, Inc.; *U.S. Public*, pg. 783
EPAM SYSTEMS GMBH—See EPAM Systems, Inc.; *U.S. Public*, pg. 783
EPAM SYSTEMS (HONG KONG) LIMITED—See EPAM Systems, Inc.; *U.S. Public*, pg. 783
EPAM SYSTEMS, INC.; *U.S. Public*, pg. 783
EPAM SYSTEMS JAPAN G.K.—See EPAM Systems, Inc.; *U.S. Public*, pg. 783
EPAM SYSTEMS KFT—See EPAM Systems, Inc.; *U.S. Public*, pg. 783
EPAM SYSTEMS LLC—See EPAM Systems, Inc.; *U.S. Public*, pg. 783
EPAM SYSTEMS LTD.—See EPAM Systems, Inc.; *U.S. Public*, pg. 783
EPAM SYSTEMS NETHERLANDS B.V.—See EPAM Systems, Inc.; *U.S. Public*, pg. 783
EPAM SYSTEMS NORDIC AB—See EPAM Systems, Inc.; *U.S. Public*, pg. 783
EPAM SYSTEMS PLLC—See EPAM Systems, Inc.; *U.S. Public*, pg. 783
EPAM SYSTEMS (POLAND) SP. Z O.O.—See EPAM Systems, Inc.; *U.S. Public*, pg. 783
EPAM SYSTEMS PORTUGAL, UNIPESSOAL LDA.—See EPAM Systems, Inc.; *U.S. Public*, pg. 783
EPAM SYSTEMS (SWITZERLAND) GMBH—See EPAM Systems, Inc.; *U.S. Public*, pg. 783
E-PANGO SA; *Int'l*, pg. 2249
EPAN INDUSTRIES PTE LTD—See Asia Pacific Wire & Cable Corporation Limited; *Int'l*, pg. 614
EPAPYRUS, INC.; *Int'l*, pg. 2458
EPARK PET LIFE INC.—See extreme Co., Ltd.; *Int'l*, pg. 2592
EPARTNERS, INC.—See ePartners, Inc.; *U.S. Private*, pg. 1411
EPARTNERS, INC.; *U.S. Private*, pg. 1411
EPARTNERS LLC—See The Walt Disney Company; *U.S. Public*, pg. 2141
EPASA SHIPPING AGENCY SDN BHD—See Johor Corporation; *Int'l*, pg. 3994
E-PATH COMMUNICATIONS, INC.; *U.S. Private*, pg. 1302
EPATH LEARNING, INC.—See Welsh, Carson, Anderson & Stowe; *U.S. Private*, pg. 4479
E PATTI & SONS INC.; *U.S. Private*, pg. 1301
EPAULER CO., LTD.—See euglena Co., Ltd.; *Int'l*, pg. 2526
EPAX NORWAY AS—See Austevoll Seafood ASA; *Int'l*, pg. 717
E-PAY ASIA PTY. LTD.—See General Atlantic Service Company, L.P.; *U.S. Public*, pg. 1661
E-PAY AUSTRALIA PTY LTD—See Euronet Worldwide, Inc.; *U.S. Public*, pg. 799
EPAY AUSTRALIA PTY LTD—See Euronet Worldwide, Inc.; *U.S. Public*, pg. 799
E-PAY (M) SDN. BHD.—See General Atlantic Service Company, L.P.; *U.S. Public*, pg. 1661
EPAY NETHERLANDS B.V.—See Euronet Worldwide, Inc.; *U.S. Public*, pg. 799
EPAZZ, INC.; *U.S. Private*, pg. 1411
E.P. BARRUS LIMITED—See E.P. Barrus Ltd.; *Int'l*, pg. 2260
E.P. BARRUS LTD.; *Int'l*, pg. 2260
EPBF SA—See Groupe BPCE; *Int'l*, pg. 3094
EP BIOCOMPOSITES LIMITED; *Int'l*, pg. 2458
EPBIZ CO., LTD.—See EPS Holdings, Inc.; *Int'l*, pg. 2465
EPB; *U.S. Private*, pg. 1411
EPC ANDINA S.A.C—See Societe Anonyme d'Explosifs et de Produits Chimiques; *Int'l*, pg. 7035
EPC-BELGIQUE S.A—See Societe Anonyme d'Explosifs et de Produits Chimiques; *Int'l*, pg. 7035
EPC CAMEROUN—See Societe Anonyme d'Explosifs et de Produits Chimiques; *Int'l*, pg. 7035
EPC CANADA INC.—See Societe Anonyme d'Explosifs et de Produits Chimiques; *Int'l*, pg. 7035
EPC-COLUMBIA, INC.—See Engineered Plastic Components Inc.; *U.S. Private*, pg. 1398
EPC COTE D'IVOIRE—See Societe Anonyme d'Explosifs et de Produits Chimiques; *Int'l*, pg. 7035
EPC ESPANA—See Societe Anonyme d'Explosifs et de Produits Chimiques; *Int'l*, pg. 7035
EPC FRANCE—See Societe Anonyme d'Explosifs et de Produits Chimiques; *Int'l*, pg. 7035
EPC GABON—See Societe Anonyme d'Explosifs et de Produits Chimiques; *Int'l*, pg. 7035
EPC GUINEE—See Societe Anonyme d'Explosifs et de Produits Chimiques; *Int'l*, pg. 7035
EPC HUNGARY KFT—See Verra Mobility Corporation; *U.S. Public*, pg. 2286
EPC, INC.-EAST TROY—See Engineered Plastic Components Inc.; *U.S. Private*, pg. 1398
EPC JAPAN CORPORATION—See Societe Anonyme d'Explosifs et de Produits Chimiques; *Int'l*, pg. 7035
EP CLEVELAND, INC.—See Park-Ohio Holdings Corp.; *U.S. Public*, pg. 1639

CORPORATE AFFILIATIONS

EPC MAROC—See Societe Anonyme d'Explosifs et de Produits Chimiques; *Int'l*, pg. 7035
EPC NORGE AS—See Societe Anonyme d'Explosifs et de Produits Chimiques; *Int'l*, pg. 7035
EPCO CO., LTD.; *Int'l*, pg. 2458
EPCO (HK) LIMITED—See EPCO Co., Ltd.; *Int'l*, pg. 2459
EPCO (JILIN) LTD.—See EPCO Co., Ltd.; *Int'l*, pg. 2459
EP COMMODITIES, A.S.—See Energeticky a Prumyslovy Holding, a.s.; *Int'l*, pg. 2419
EP CONNECTORS GMBH—See AdCapital AG; *Int'l*, pg. 126
EP CONSULTING SERVICES CORPORATION—See Business Brain Showa-Ota Inc.; *Int'l*, pg. 1228
EPCOR ENERGY—See EPCOR Utilities, Inc.; *Int'l*, pg. 2459
EPCOR MERCHANT & CAPITAL, L.P.—See EPCOR Utilities, Inc.; *Int'l*, pg. 2459
EPCOR USA INC.—See EPCOR Utilities, Inc.; *Int'l*, pg. 2459
EPCOR UTILITIES, INC.; *Int'l*, pg. 2459
EPCOR WATER ARIZONA INC.—See EPCOR Utilities, Inc.; *Int'l*, pg. 2459
EPCOR WATER SERVICES, INC.—See EPCOR Utilities, Inc.; *Int'l*, pg. 2459
EPCOS AG—See TDK Corporation; *Int'l*, pg. 7487
EPCOS DO BRASIL LTDA.—See TDK Corporation; *Int'l*, pg. 7487
EPCOS ELECTRONIC COMPONENTS S.A.—See TDK Corporation; *Int'l*, pg. 7487
EPCOS ELEKTRONIKAI ALKATRESZ KFT.—See TDK Corporation; *Int'l*, pg. 7487
EPCO (SHENZHEN) LTD.—See EPCO Co., Ltd.; *Int'l*, pg. 2459
EPCOS, INC.—See TDK Corporation; *Int'l*, pg. 7487
EPCOS LIMITED—See TDK Corporation; *Int'l*, pg. 7487
EPCOS OHG—See TDK Corporation; *Int'l*, pg. 7487
EPCOS PTE LTD—See TDK Corporation; *Int'l*, pg. 7487
EPCOS S.R.O.—See TDK Corporation; *Int'l*, pg. 7487
EPCOS TECHNOLOGY (WUXI) CO., LTD.—See TDK Corporation; *Int'l*, pg. 7487
EPCOS (XIAOGAN) CO., LTD—See TDK Corporation; *Int'l*, pg. 7487
EPCOS (ZHUHAI FTZ) CO., LTD.—See TDK Corporation; *Int'l*, pg. 7487
EPC POWER CORP.—See Cleanhill Partners; *U.S. Private*, pg. 931
EPC POWER CORP.—See The Goldman Sachs Group, Inc.; *U.S. Public*, pg. 2076
EP-CRSU CO., LTD.—See EPS Holdings, Inc.; *Int'l*, pg. 2465
EPC S.A.—See PGE Polska Grupa Energetyczna S.A.; *Int'l*, pg. 5837
EPC SENEGAL SA—See Societe Anonyme d'Explosifs et de Produits Chimiques; *Int'l*, pg. 7035
EPCSOLUTIONS; *U.S. Private*, pg. 1411
EPC SVERIGE AB—See Societe Anonyme d'Explosifs et de Produits Chimiques; *Int'l*, pg. 7035
EPC-UK ADDITIVES—See Societe Anonyme d'Explosifs et de Produits Chimiques; *Int'l*, pg. 7035
EPC UNITED KINGDOM PLC—See Societe Anonyme d'Explosifs et de Produits Chimiques; *Int'l*, pg. 7035
EPDC COALTECH AND MARINE CO., LTD.—See Electric Power Development Co., Ltd.; *Int'l*, pg. 2349
EPDIS KENYA LIMITED—See Toyota Tsusho Corporation; *Int'l*, pg. 7876
EPDIS S.A.—See Toyota Tsusho Corporation; *Int'l*, pg. 7876
EPEAT, INC.; *U.S. Private*, pg. 1411
EPEC ENGINEERED TECHNOLOGIES; *U.S. Private*, pg. 1411
E P E CORP.—See Intervala, LLC; *U.S. Private*, pg. 2127
EPEC OY—See Ponsse Oyj; *Int'l*, pg. 5919
EPE-GOLDMAN BV—See Indutrade AB; *Int'l*, pg. 3678
EPE, INC—See Enstar Group Limited; *Int'l*, pg. 2448
EPELICAN.COM, INC.; *U.S. Private*, pg. 1412
EPENDION AB; *Int'l*, pg. 2459
EP ENERGY CORPORATION—See Access Industries, Inc.; *U.S. Private*, pg. 51
EP ENERGY CORPORATION—See Apollo Global Management, Inc.; *U.S. Public*, pg. 150
EP ENERGY CORPORATION—See Korea National Oil Corporation; *Int'l*, pg. 4286
EP ENERGY CORPORATION—See Riverstone Holdings LLC; *U.S. Private*, pg. 3447
EP ENERGY LLC—See Access Industries, Inc.; *U.S. Private*, pg. 51
EP ENERGY LLC—See Apollo Global Management, Inc.; *U.S. Public*, pg. 151
EP ENERGY LLC—See Korea National Oil Corporation; *Int'l*, pg. 4286
EP ENERGY LLC—See Riverstone Holdings LLC; *U.S. Private*, pg. 3447
EP ENERGY TRADING, A.S.—See Energeticky a Prumyslovy Holding, a.s.; *Int'l*, pg. 2420
EP ENGINEERED CLAYS CORPORATION—See Apollo Global Management, Inc.; *U.S. Public*, pg. 164
E-PERFECT IT LIMITED—See GET Holdings Limited; *Int'l*, pg. 2946
EPERLY SAS—See VINCI S.A.; *Int'l*, pg. 8218

COMPANY NAME INDEX

EPES CARRIERS INC.; *U.S. Private*, pg. 1412
EPES FREIGHT MANAGEMENT—See EPES Carriers Inc.; *U.S. Private*, pg. 1412
EPES LIMITED—See Invinity Energy Systems plc; *Int'l*, pg. 3789
EPES LOGISTICS SERVICES, INC.—See EPES Carriers Inc.; *U.S. Private*, pg. 1412
EPE SPECIAL OPPORTUNITIES LIMITED; *Int'l*, pg. 2459
EPES TRANSPORT SYSTEM, INC.—See EPES Carriers Inc.; *U.S. Private*, pg. 1412
E&P FINANCIAL GROUP LIMITED; *Int'l*, pg. 2247
EP-FORCE CO., LTD.—See EPS Holdings, Inc.; *Int'l*, pg. 2465
EPG COMMUNICATION HOLDINGS LIMITED—See IQVIA Holdings Inc.; *U.S. Public*, pg. 1168
EPG CONTROLS, INC.; *U.S. Private*, pg. 1412
E.P. GERBER & SONS INC.; *U.S. Private*, pg. 1306
EPG INNOVATION CENTER CO., LTD.—See Eastern Polymer Group Public Company Limited; *Int'l*, pg. 2273
E&P GLOBAL HOLDINGS LIMITED; *Int'l*, pg. 2247
E.P. GRAPHICS, INC.—See Dynamic Resource Group, Inc.; *U.S. Private*, pg. 1299
E.P. HENRY CORPORATION; *U.S. Private*, pg. 1306
EPHESOFT INC.—See Clearlake Capital Group, L.P.; *U.S. Private*, pg. 936
EPHESOFT INC.—See TA Associates, Inc.; *U.S. Private*, pg. 3916
EPH EUROPEAN PROPERTY HOLDINGS PLC; *Int'l*, pg. 2459
EPHIBIAN INC; *U.S. Private*, pg. 1412
EP-HOLDING GUINEE S.A.—See Energoprojekt Holding a.d.; *Int'l*, pg. 2421
EPHOX; *U.S. Private*, pg. 1412
EPHRAIM MCDOWELL HEALTH, INC.; *U.S. Private*, pg. 1412
EPHRAIM RESOURCES LIMITED; *Int'l*, pg. 2459
EPHRATA NATIONAL BANK—See ENB Financial Corp.; *U.S. Public*, pg. 754
EPHRICON WEB MARKETING LLC; *U.S. Private*, pg. 1412
EPIAS ENERJI PIYASALARI ISLETME A.S.—See Verusa Holding A.S.; *Int'l*, pg. 8175
EPI BIOTECH CO., LTD.; *Int'l*, pg. 2459
EPIC ADVISORS, INC.—See NBT Bancorp Inc.; *U.S. Public*, pg. 1501
EPIC AVIATION, LLC—See BlackRock, Inc.; *U.S. Public*, pg. 346
EPIC AVIATION, LLC—See Blackstone Inc.; *U.S. Public*, pg. 358
EPIC AVIATION, LLC—See Cascade Investment LLC; *U.S. Private*, pg. 780
EPIC BPIFRANCE; *Int'l*, pg. 2460
EPIC BROADBAND SOLUTIONS; *U.S. Private*, pg. 1412
EPIC CLOUD CO., LTD.—See MetaAge Corporation; *Int'l*, pg. 4844
EPIC COMMUNICATIONS, INC.—See Microwave Transmission Systems, Inc.; *U.S. Private*, pg. 2704
EPIC DATA LIMITED—See Sylogist Ltd.; *Int'l*, pg. 7378
EPIC DATA—See Sylogist Ltd.; *Int'l*, pg. 7378
EPIC DEVELOPMENT, INC.—See HCA Healthcare, Inc.; *U.S. Public*, pg. 995
EPIC DIVERSITY SDN BHD—See Chin Hin Group Berhad; *Int'l*, pg. 1480
EPIC ENERGY LTD. - NAVI MUMBAI WORKS—See Epic Energy Ltd.; *Int'l*, pg. 2460
EPIC ENERGY LTD.; *Int'l*, pg. 2460
EPICENTER NETWORK INC; *U.S. Private*, pg. 1413
EPIC ENTERPRISES INC—See PepsiCo, Inc.; *U.S. Public*, pg. 1668
EPICENTRE HOLDINGS LIMITED; *Int'l*, pg. 2460
EPICENTRE PTE. LTD.—See Epicentre Holdings Limited; *Int'l*, pg. 2460
EPICENTRE SOLUTIONS PTE. LTD.—See Epicentre Holdings Limited; *Int'l*, pg. 2460
EPICENTRE TECHNOLOGIES CORPORATION—See Illumina, Inc.; *U.S. Public*, pg. 1112
EPICENTRO DIGITAL LIMITED—See Pico Far East Holdings Limited; *Int'l*, pg. 5860
EPICEPT CORPORATION—See Immune Pharmaceuticals Inc.; *U.S. Public*, pg. 1113
EPICEPT GMBH—See Immune Pharmaceuticals Inc.; *U.S. Public*, pg. 1113
EPIC ETAILERS, LLC; *U.S. Private*, pg. 1412
EPIC GAMES INC.; *U.S. Private*, pg. 1412
EPIC GROUP—See Learning Technologies Group plc; *Int'l*, pg. 4435
EPIC HEALTH SERVICES, INC.—See Bain Capital, LP; *U.S. Private*, pg. 439
EPICHEM PTY LTD—See PharmAust Ltd.; *Int'l*, pg. 5841
EPIC HOLDINGS INC.—See Japan Tobacco Inc.; *Int'l*, pg. 3907
EPIC INSURANCE SOLUTIONS AGENCY LLC—See Fifth Third Bancorp; *U.S. Public*, pg. 833
EPIC LEARNING INC.—See Learning Technologies Group plc; *Int'l*, pg. 4435
EPI/CLEVELAND—See Engineered Products, Inc.; *U.S. Private*, pg. 1398

THE EPIC LIFE INSURANCE CO.—See Wisconsin Physicians Service Insurance Corporation; *U.S. Private*, pg. 4549
EPIC LOGISTICS, INC.—See EPES Carriers Inc.; *U.S. Private*, pg. 1412
EPIC LTD.—See Bahrain Telecommunications Company BSC; *Int'l*, pg. 801
EPIC MUSHTARI ENGINEERING SDN BHD—See Terengganu Incorporated Sdn. Bhd.; *Int'l*, pg. 7564
EPICORE BIONETWORKS INC.—See Archer-Daniels-Midland Company; *U.S. Public*, pg. 185
EPICOR EDI SOURCE, INC.—See Clayton, Dubilier & Rice, LLC; *U.S. Private*, pg. 922
EPICORE ECUADOR S.A.—See Archer-Daniels-Midland Company; *U.S. Public*, pg. 185
EPICOR INC.—See Xylem Inc.; *U.S. Public*, pg. 2393
EPICOR SOFTWARE (ASIA) PTE LTD.—See Clayton, Dubilier & Rice, LLC; *U.S. Private*, pg. 922
EPICOR SOFTWARE (BEIJING) COMPANY, LTD.—See Clayton, Dubilier & Rice, LLC; *U.S. Private*, pg. 922
EPICOR SOFTWARE CORPORATION-MINNEAPOLIS—See Clayton, Dubilier & Rice, LLC; *U.S. Private*, pg. 922
EPICOR SOFTWARE CORPORATION—See Clayton, Dubilier & Rice, LLC; *U.S. Private*, pg. 922
EPICOR SOFTWARE CPRUS LTD.—See Clayton, Dubilier & Rice, LLC; *U.S. Private*, pg. 922
EPICOR SOFTWARE CZECH S.R.O—See Clayton, Dubilier & Rice, LLC; *U.S. Private*, pg. 922
EPICOR SOFTWARE DEUTSCHLAND GMBH—See Clayton, Dubilier & Rice, LLC; *U.S. Private*, pg. 922
EPICOR SOFTWARE ESTONIA OU—See Clayton, Dubilier & Rice, LLC; *U.S. Private*, pg. 922
EPICOR SOFTWARE FINLAND OY—See Clayton, Dubilier & Rice, LLC; *U.S. Private*, pg. 922
EPICOR SOFTWARE HUNGARY KFT—See Clayton, Dubilier & Rice, LLC; *U.S. Private*, pg. 922
EPICOR SOFTWARE ITALIA S.R.L.—See Clayton, Dubilier & Rice, LLC; *U.S. Private*, pg. 922
EPICOR SOFTWARE JAPAN K.K.—See Clayton, Dubilier & Rice, LLC; *U.S. Private*, pg. 922
EPICOR SOFTWARE LATVIJA SIA—See Clayton, Dubilier & Rice, LLC; *U.S. Private*, pg. 922
EPICOR SOFTWARE (M) SDN BHD—See Clayton, Dubilier & Rice, LLC; *U.S. Private*, pg. 922
EPICOR SOFTWARE (NORTH ASIA) LTD.—See Clayton, Dubilier & Rice, LLC; *U.S. Private*, pg. 922
EPICOR SOFTWARE POLAND SP. Z O.O.—See Clayton, Dubilier & Rice, LLC; *U.S. Private*, pg. 922
EPICOR SOFTWARE (SEA) PTE LTD.—See Clayton, Dubilier & Rice, LLC; *U.S. Private*, pg. 922
EPICOR SOFTWARE (SHANGHAI) CO., LTD.—See Clayton, Dubilier & Rice, LLC; *U.S. Private*, pg. 922
EPICOR SOFTWARE SLOVAKIA, S.R.O.—See Clayton, Dubilier & Rice, LLC; *U.S. Private*, pg. 923
EPICOR SOFTWARE SRL—See Clayton, Dubilier & Rice, LLC; *U.S. Private*, pg. 922
EPICOR SOFTWARE UK, LTD.—See Clayton, Dubilier & Rice, LLC; *U.S. Private*, pg. 923
EPICOSITY; *U.S. Private*, pg. 1413
EPIC PERSONNEL PARTNERS LLC; *U.S. Private*, pg. 1412
EPIC PHARMA, LLC—See Humanwell Healthcare (Group) Co., Ltd.; *Int'l*, pg. 3530
EPIC PIPING, LLC—See Bernhard Capital Partners Management, LP; *U.S. Private*, pg. 537
EPIC PROPERTIES, INC.—See HCA Healthcare, Inc.; *U.S. Public*, pg. 995
EPIC PROVISIONS, LLC—See General Mills, Inc.; *U.S. Public*, pg. 921
EPICQUEST EDUCATION GROUP INTERNATIONAL LIMITED; *U.S. Public*, pg. 783
EPIC RECORDS GROUP—See Sony Group Corporation; *Int'l*, pg. 7103
EPIC REFERENCE LABS, INC.—See TPT Global Tech, Inc.; *U.S. Public*, pg. 2178
EPIC RESINS; *U.S. Private*, pg. 1412
EPIC RETIREMENT PLAN SERVICES, PORTLAND—See NBT Bancorp Inc.; *U.S. Public*, pg. 1501
EPICRYSTAL CORPORATION (CHANGZHOU) LTD.—See Ennostar Inc.; *Int'l*, pg. 2443
EPIC SEATS, INC.; *U.S. Private*, pg. 1412
EPIC STORES CORP.; *U.S. Private*, pg. 1412
EPIC SUISSE AG—See Alrov Properties & Lodgings Ltd.; *Int'l*, pg. 377
EPIC SUISSE PROPERTY MANAGEMENT GMBH—See Alrov Properties & Lodgings Ltd.; *Int'l*, pg. 377
EPIC SURGERY CENTERS, INC.—See HCA Healthcare, Inc.; *U.S. Public*, pg. 995
EPIC SYSTEMS CORPORATION; *U.S. Private*, pg. 1413
EPIC SYSTEMS, INC.; *U.S. Private*, pg. 1413
EPIC TECHNOLOGIES, LLC—See Natel Engineering Company, Inc.; *U.S. Private*, pg. 2838
EPIC THEATRES, INC.; *U.S. Private*, pg. 1413
THE EPICUREAN GROUP; *U.S. Private*, pg. 4026
EPICUREAN MANAGEMENT (ASIA) LIMITED—See Star Glory Holdings Company Limited; *Int'l*, pg. 7177
EPICURE CATERING CO., LTD.—See Dusit Thani Public Company Limited; *Int'l*, pg. 2234

EPICURE INVESTMENT MANAGEMENT LLC—See Qatar Insurance Company S.A.Q.; *Int'l*, pg. 6134
EPICURUS CORPORATION—See Yamaha Corporation; *Int'l*, pg. 8549
EPIC VENTURES SDN. BHD.—See Amverton Berhad; *Int'l*, pg. 442
EPIC WINE & SPIRITS; *U.S. Private*, pg. 1413
EPID RESEARCH OY—See IQVIA Holdings Inc.; *U.S. Public*, pg. 1168
EPI ENVIRONMENTAL PRODUCTS INC.—See EPI Environmental Technologies Inc.; *Int'l*, pg. 2460
EPI ENVIRONMENTAL PRODUCTS INC.—See EPI Environmental Technologies Inc.; *Int'l*, pg. 2460
EPI ENVIRONMENTAL TECHNOLOGIES INC.; *Int'l*, pg. 2459
EPI (EUROPE) LIMITED—See EPI Environmental Technologies Inc.; *Int'l*, pg. 2460
EPIGAN NV—See Soitec S.A.; *Int'l*, pg. 7060
EPIGENOMICS AG; *Int'l*, pg. 2460
EPIGENOMICS INC.—See Epigenomics AG; *Int'l*, pg. 2460
EPI (HOLDINGS) LIMITED; *Int'l*, pg. 2459
EPIKA FLEET SERVICES, INC.; *U.S. Private*, pg. 1413
EPI LABELERS LLC—See Leonard Green & Partners, L.P.; *U.S. Private*, pg. 2427
EPILEDS TECHNOLOGIES, INC.; *Int'l*, pg. 2460
EPILEPSY FOUNDATION OF AMERICA; *U.S. Private*, pg. 1413
EPILOG CORPORATION; *U.S. Private*, pg. 1413
EPINAL AUTO; *Int'l*, pg. 2460
EP INDUSTRIJA A.D.—See Energoprojekt Holding a.d.; *Int'l*, pg. 2421
EPINEX DIAGNOSTICS LABORATORIES, INC.—See Rennova Health, Inc.; *U.S. Public*, pg. 1783
EPION HEALTH, INC.—See Kyruus, Inc.; *U.S. Private*, pg. 2360
EPIOS—See VINCI S.A.; *Int'l*, pg. 8231
EPIPHANY DERMATOLOGY PA; *U.S. Private*, pg. 1413
EPIPHANY TECHNOLOGY ACQUISITION CORP.; *U.S. Public*, pg. 783
THE EPIPHONE COMPANY—See Gibson Brands, Inc.; *U.S. Public*, pg. 1696
EPIPHOTONICS CORP.—See Kohoku Kogyo Co., Ltd.; *Int'l*, pg. 4229
EPIPROCARE GMBH; *Int'l*, pg. 2460
EPIQ BANKRUPTCY SOLUTIONS, LLC—See Ontario Municipal Employees Retirement System; *Int'l*, pg. 5584
EPIQ CLASS ACTION & CLAIMS SOLUTIONS, INC.—See Ontario Municipal Employees Retirement System; *Int'l*, pg. 5584
EPIQ EDISCOVERY SOLUTIONS, INC.—See Ontario Municipal Employees Retirement System; *Int'l*, pg. 5584
EPIQ SYSTEMS, INC.—See Ontario Municipal Employees Retirement System; *Int'l*, pg. 5584
EPIQ SYSTEMS, LIMITED—See Ontario Municipal Employees Retirement System; *Int'l*, pg. 5584
EPIQ SYSTEMS LTD.—See Ontario Municipal Employees Retirement System; *Int'l*, pg. 5584
EPIREZ CONSTRUCTION PRODUCTS PTY LIMITED—See Illinois Tool Works Inc.; *U.S. Public*, pg. 1107
EPIRIS MANAGERS LLP; *Int'l*, pg. 2460
EPIROC AB; *Int'l*, pg. 2461
EPIROC ARGENTINA S.A.C.I.—See Epiroc AB; *Int'l*, pg. 2461
EPIROC ARMENIA LLC—See Epiroc AB; *Int'l*, pg. 2461
EPIROC AUSTRALIA PTY LTD.—See Epiroc AB; *Int'l*, pg. 2461
EPIROC B-H D.O.O.—See Epiroc AB; *Int'l*, pg. 2461
EPIROC BOLIVIA EQUIPOS Y SERVICIOS S.A.—See Epiroc AB; *Int'l*, pg. 2461
EPIROC BOTSWANA (PTY) LTD.—See Epiroc AB; *Int'l*, pg. 2461
EPIROC BRASIL COMERCIALIZACAO DE PRODUTOS E SERVICOS PARA MINERACAO E CONSTRUCAO LTDA.—See Epiroc AB; *Int'l*, pg. 2461
EPIROC BULGARIA EOOD—See Epiroc AB; *Int'l*, pg. 2461
EPIROC BURKINA FASO SARL—See Epiroc AB; *Int'l*, pg. 2461
EPIROC CANADA INC.—See Epiroc AB; *Int'l*, pg. 2461
EPIROC CENTRAL AMERICA S.A.—See Epiroc AB; *Int'l*, pg. 2462
EPIROC CENTRAL ASIA LLP—See Epiroc AB; *Int'l*, pg. 2462
EPIROC CHILE S.A.C.—See Epiroc AB; *Int'l*, pg. 2462
EPIROC COLOMBIA S.A.S.—See Epiroc AB; *Int'l*, pg. 2462
EPIROC CROATIA D.O.O.—See Epiroc AB; *Int'l*, pg. 2462
EPIROC CZECH REPUBLIC S.R.O.—See Epiroc AB; *Int'l*, pg. 2462
EPIROC DEUTSCHLAND GMBH—See Epiroc AB; *Int'l*, pg. 2462
EPIROC DRC SARL—See Epiroc AB; *Int'l*, pg. 2462
EPIROC DRILLING SOLUTIONS LLC—See Epiroc AB; *Int'l*, pg. 2462
EPIROC DRILLING TOOLS AB—See Epiroc AB; *Int'l*, pg. 2462
EPIROC DRILLING TOOLS LLC—See Epiroc AB; *Int'l*, pg. 2462

EPIROC AB

CORPORATE AFFILIATIONS

EPIROC EASTERN AFRICA LTD.—See Epiroc AB; *Int'l*, pg. 2462
EPIROC FINLAND OY AB—See Epiroc AB; *Int'l*, pg. 2462
EPIROC FRANCE S.A.S.—See Epiroc AB; *Int'l*, pg. 2462
EPIROC FVT INC.—See Epiroc AB; *Int'l*, pg. 2462
EPIROC HELLAS S.A.—See Epiroc AB; *Int'l*, pg. 2462
EPIROC HONG KONG LTD.—See Epiroc AB; *Int'l*, pg. 2462
EPIROC ITALIA S.R.L.—See Epiroc AB; *Int'l*, pg. 2462
EPIROC JAPAN KK—See Epiroc AB; *Int'l*, pg. 2462
EPIROC KOREA CO., LTD.—See Epiroc AB; *Int'l*, pg. 2462
EPIROC MAKINA AS—See Epiroc AB; *Int'l*, pg. 2462
EPIROC MALI SARL—See Epiroc AB; *Int'l*, pg. 2462
EPIROC MAROC SARL—See Epiroc AB; *Int'l*, pg. 2462
EPIROC MEXICO, S.A. DE C. V.—See Epiroc AB; *Int'l*, pg. 2462
EPIROC MEYCO AG—See Epiroc AB; *Int'l*, pg. 2462
EPIROC MIDDLE EAST FZE—See Epiroc AB; *Int'l*, pg. 2462
EPIROC MINERIA E INGENIERIA CIVIL ESPANA, S.L.U—See Epiroc AB; *Int'l*, pg. 2462
EPIROC MINING INDIA LTD.—See Epiroc AB; *Int'l*, pg. 2462
EPIROC MINING (NAMIBIA) (PTY) LTD.—See Epiroc AB; *Int'l*, pg. 2462
EPIROC MOCAMBIQUE LIMITADA—See Epiroc AB; *Int'l*, pg. 2462
EPIROC MONGOLIA LLC—See Epiroc AB; *Int'l*, pg. 2462
EPIROC NORGE AS—See Epiroc AB; *Int'l*, pg. 2462
EPIROC PERU S.A.—See Epiroc AB; *Int'l*, pg. 2462
EPIROC PHILIPPINES INC.—See Epiroc AB; *Int'l*, pg. 2462
EPIROC PORTUGAL UNIPESSOAL LDA—See Epiroc AB; *Int'l*, pg. 2462
EPIROC RUS LLC—See Epiroc AB; *Int'l*, pg. 2462
EPIROC SRBIJA A.D.—See Epiroc AB; *Int'l*, pg. 2462
EPIROC SWEDEN AB—See Epiroc AB; *Int'l*, pg. 2462
EPIROC TAJIKISTAN LLC—See Epiroc AB; *Int'l*, pg. 2462
EPIROC TANZANIA LTD.—See Epiroc AB; *Int'l*, pg. 2462
EPIROC TASHKENT LLC—See Epiroc AB; *Int'l*, pg. 2462
EPIROC (THAILAND) LTD.—See Epiroc AB; *Int'l*, pg. 2461
EPIROC TRADING CO., LTD.—See Epiroc AB; *Int'l*, pg. 2462
EPIROC UKRAINE LLC—See Epiroc AB; *Int'l*, pg. 2462
EPIROC USA LLC—See Epiroc AB; *Int'l*, pg. 2462
EPIROC ZAMBIA LTD.—See Epiroc AB; *Int'l*, pg. 2462
EPIROC ZIMBABWE (PRIVATE) LTD.—See Epiroc AB; *Int'l*, pg. 2462
EPIRUS BIOPHARMACEUTICALS, INC.; *U.S. Private*, pg. 1413
EPIRUS METALWORKS S.A.—See Viohalco SA/NV; *Int'l*, pg. 8243
EPIRUS SWITZERLAND GMBH—See EPIRUS Biopharmaceuticals, Inc.; *U.S. Private*, pg. 1413
EPI S.A.; *Int'l*, pg. 2460
EPISCOPAL CHURCH HOME & AFFILIATES LIFE CARE COMMUNITY INC.; *U.S. Private*, pg. 1413
EPISCOPAL COMMUNITIES & SERVICES; *U.S. Private*, pg. 1413
EPISCOPAL HEALTH FOUNDATION; *U.S. Private*, pg. 1413
EPISCOPAL RELIEF & DEVELOPMENT; *U.S. Private*, pg. 1413
EPISERVER AUSTRALIA PTY. LTD.—See Insight Venture Management, LLC; *U.S. Private*, pg. 2090
EPISERVER GROUP AB—See Insight Venture Management, LLC; *U.S. Private*, pg. 2090
EPISERVER INC.—See Insight Venture Management, LLC; *U.S. Private*, pg. 2090
EPISERVER PTY. LTD.—See Insight Venture Management, LLC; *U.S. Private*, pg. 2090
EPISIL HOLDINGS, INC.; *Int'l*, pg. 2463
EPISIL PRECISION INC.; *Int'l*, pg. 2463
EPISIL TECHNOLOGIES, INC.; *Int'l*, pg. 2463
EPISKIN SNC—See L'Oreal S.A.; *Int'l*, pg. 4378
EPISKY CORPORATION (XIAMEN) LTD.—See Ennostar Inc.; *Int'l*, pg. 2443
EPISTAR CORPORATION—See Ennostar Inc.; *Int'l*, pg. 2443
EPISTEME TRADING (SHANGHAI) CO., LTD—See Rohto Pharmaceutical Co. Ltd.; *Int'l*, pg. 6387
EPISTEM LIMITED—See Genedrive Plc; *Int'l*, pg. 2917
EPISURF MEDICAL AB; *Int'l*, pg. 2463
EPITAPH RECORDS; *U.S. Private*, pg. 1413
EPITEC GROUP INC.; *U.S. Private*, pg. 1413
EPITEX INC.—See Ushio, Inc.; *Int'l*, pg. 8097
EPITHERAPEUTICS APS—See Gilead Sciences, Inc.; *U.S. Public*, pg. 936
EPITOMICS HOLDINGS, INC.—See Danaher Corporation; *U.S. Public*, pg. 624
EPI-USE AMERICA; *U.S. Private*, pg. 1412
EPIWORKS, INC.—See Coherent Corp.; *U.S. Public*, pg. 528
EPIZYME, INC.—See Ipsen S.A.; *Int'l*, pg. 3798
EPKO INDUSTRIES INC.; *U.S. Private*, pg. 1413
EPLAN SERVICES INC.; *U.S. Private*, pg. 1414
EPLAN SOFTWARE & SERVICE GMBH & CO. KG—See Friedhelm Loh Stiftung & Co. KG; *Int'l*, pg. 2791

EPL ARCHIVES, SAS—See Avantor, Inc.; *U.S. Public*, pg. 242
EPLAY DIGITAL INC.; *Int'l*, pg. 2463
EPLDT, INC.—See PLDT Inc.; *Int'l*, pg. 5896
EPLDT VENTUS, INC.—See PLDT Inc.; *Int'l*, pg. 5896
E-PLEX LTD.; *Int'l*, pg. 2249
EPL FEED, LLC—See Elenbaas Company; *U.S. Private*, pg. 1357
EPL FEED, LLC—See Land O'Lakes, Inc.; *U.S. Private*, pg. 2383
EPL, INC.—See Lillo SpA; *Int'l*, pg. 4498
EPL LTD.—See Blackstone Inc.; *U.S. Public*, pg. 353
EPL PATHOLOGY ARCHIVES, LLC—See Avantor, Inc.; *U.S. Public*, pg. 242
E PLUS BUILDING PRODUCTS PTY. LTD.—See dormakaba Holding AG; *Int'l*, pg. 2177
EPLUS GROUP, INC.—See ePlus Inc.; *U.S. Public*, pg. 784
EPLUS INC.; *U.S. Public*, pg. 783
E-PLUS LIMITED; *Int'l*, pg. 2249
E-PLUS MOBILFUNK GMBH & CO. KG—See Telefonica, S.A.; *Int'l*, pg. 7535
E-PLUS NEDERLAND B.V.—See Koninklijke KPN N.V.; *Int'l*, pg. 4267
EPLUS—See ePlus Inc.; *U.S. Public*, pg. 784
EPLUS TECHNOLOGIES SDN. BHD.—See New Wave Holdings Ltd.; *Int'l*, pg. 5231
EPLUS TECHNOLOGY, INC—See ePlus Inc.; *U.S. Public*, pg. 784
EPMALL CO, LTD.—See Seiko Epson Corporation; *Int'l*, pg. 6686
EP MANAGEMENT CORPORATION—See Apollo Global Management, Inc.; *U.S. Public*, pg. 165
EP MANUFACTURING BHD.; *Int'l*, pg. 2458
EPMATE CO., LTD.—See EPS Holdings, Inc.; *Int'l*, pg. 2465
EPM BUS SOLUTIONS LIMITED—See Literacy Capital Plc; *Int'l*, pg. 4526
EPM CAPITAL MEXICO S.A. DE C.V.—See Empresas Publicas de Medellin ESP; *Int'l*, pg. 2391
EPM CHILE S.A.—See Empresas Publicas de Medellin ESP; *Int'l*, pg. 2392
EP MEDIATE CO., LTD.—See EPS Holdings, Inc.; *Int'l*, pg. 2465
EPMEDICAL CO., LTD.—See EPS Holdings, Inc.; *Int'l*, pg. 2465
EP MINERALS EUROPE GMBH & CO. KG—See Apollo Global Management, Inc.; *U.S. Public*, pg. 165
EP MINERALS, LLC—See Apollo Global Management, Inc.; *U.S. Public*, pg. 165
EP-MINT CO., LTD.—See EPS Holdings, Inc.; *Int'l*, pg. 2465
EPM SOLUTIONS, INC.; *U.S. Private*, pg. 1414
EPM SWISS PROPERTY MANAGEMENT AG—See Bilfinger SE; *Int'l*, pg. 1028
E-P:N MINKINREHU OY; *Int'l*, pg. 2249
EPOCH CHEMTRONICS CORP.; *Int'l*, pg. 2463
EPOCH CO. LTD.; *Int'l*, pg. 2463
EPOCH CORPORATION; *U.S. Private*, pg. 1414
EPOCH DESIGN LIMITED—See Writtle Holdings Limited; *Int'l*, pg. 8495
EPOCH ENERGY TECHNOLOGY SDN BHD; *Int'l*, pg. 2463
EPOCH INVESTMENT PARTNERS, INC.—See The Toronto-Dominion Bank; *Int'l*, pg. 7694
EPOCH MANAGEMENT, INC.—See Epoch Properties Inc.; *U.S. Private*, pg. 1414
EPOCH MATERIAL CO., LTD.—See Entegris, Inc.; *U.S. Public*, pg. 776
EPOCH NAGANO, CO., LTD.—See Nagano Keiki Co., Ltd.; *Int'l*, pg. 5125
EPOCH PROPERTIES INC.; *U.S. Private*, pg. 1414
EPOCH TECHNOLOGY CO., LTD.—See Air Water Inc.; *Int'l*, pg. 240
EPOLIN, LLC—See Arsenal Capital Management LP; *U.S. Private*, pg. 337
E-POLL MARKET RESEARCH; *U.S. Private*, pg. 1302
E&P O&M SERVICES SDN BHD—See Petroliam Nasional Berhad; *Int'l*, pg. 5829
EPON GOLF CORPORATION—See Endo Manufacturing Co., Ltd.; *Int'l*, pg. 2405
EPONK GROUP LTD.; *U.S. Private*, pg. 1414
EPONYMOUS ASSOCIATES LLC—See Steiner Equities Group LLC; *U.S. Private*, pg. 3798
EPOQ LOGISTIC DC K.S.—See Currys plc; *Int'l*, pg. 1879
EPOS CARD CO., LTD.—See Marui Group Co., Ltd.; *Int'l*, pg. 4713
EPOS CAT GMBH—See Adecco Group AG; *Int'l*, pg. 140
EPOS GROUP A/S—See Demant A/S; *Int'l*, pg. 2023
EPOS, S.A.—See Teixeira Duarte SA; *Int'l*, pg. 7525
EPOS SMALL AMOUNT & SHORT TERM INSURANCE CO., LTD.—See Marui Group Co., Ltd.; *Int'l*, pg. 4713
EPOST—See Canada Post Corporation; *Int'l*, pg. 1282
EPOWER METALS INC.; *Int'l*, pg. 2463
E-POWER RESOURCES INC.; *Int'l*, pg. 2249
E-POWER SUPPLY S.R.O.—See NEPI Rockcastle N.V.; *Int'l*, pg. 5200
EPOXY BASE ELECTRONIC MATERIAL CORPORATION LIMITED; *Int'l*, pg. 2463

EPOXYN PRODUCTS LLC—See OpenGate Capital Management, LLC; *U.S. Private*, pg. 3030
EPPENDORF AG; *Int'l*, pg. 2463
EPPENDORF ASIA PACIFIC SDN. BHD.—See Eppendorf AG; *Int'l*, pg. 2464
EPPENDORF AUSTRIA GMBH—See Eppendorf AG; *Int'l*, pg. 2464
EPPENDORF BELGIUM NV/SA—See Eppendorf AG; *Int'l*, pg. 2464
EPPENDORF BIOTECHNOLOGY INTERNATIONAL TRADE (SHANGHAI) COMPANY LTD.—See Eppendorf AG; *Int'l*, pg. 2464
EPPENDORF CANADA LTD.—See Eppendorf AG; *Int'l*, pg. 2464
EPPENDORF CHINA LTD.—See Eppendorf AG; *Int'l*, pg. 2464
EPPENDORF CHINA LTD.—See Eppendorf AG; *Int'l*, pg. 2464
EPPENDORF CO., LTD.—See Eppendorf AG; *Int'l*, pg. 2464
EPPENDORF CZECH & SLOVAKIA S.R.O.—See Eppendorf AG; *Int'l*, pg. 2464
EPPENDORF DO BRASIL LTDA.—See Eppendorf AG; *Int'l*, pg. 2464
EPPENDORF FRANCE S.A.R.L.—See Eppendorf AG; *Int'l*, pg. 2464
EPPENDORF IBERICA S.L.—See Eppendorf AG; *Int'l*, pg. 2464
EPPENDORF INDIA LTD.—See Eppendorf AG; *Int'l*, pg. 2464
EPPENDORF KOREA LTD.—See Eppendorf AG; *Int'l*, pg. 2464
EPPENDORF MIDDLE EAST FZ-LLC—See Eppendorf AG; *Int'l*, pg. 2464
EPPENDORF NORDIC APS—See Eppendorf AG; *Int'l*, pg. 2464
EPPENDORF NORGE AS—See Eppendorf AG; *Int'l*, pg. 2464
EPPENDORF NORTH AMERICA, INC.—See Eppendorf AG; *Int'l*, pg. 2464
EPPENDORF POLAND SP. ZO.O.—See Eppendorf AG; *Int'l*, pg. 2464
EPPENDORF RUSSIA OOO—See Eppendorf AG; *Int'l*, pg. 2464
EPPENDORF SCIENTIFIC, INC.—See Eppendorf AG; *Int'l*, pg. 2464
EPPENDORF SOUTH PACIFIC PTY. LTD.—See Eppendorf AG; *Int'l*, pg. 2464
EPPENDORF S.R.L.—See Eppendorf AG; *Int'l*, pg. 2464
EPPENDORF (THAILAND) CO. LTD.—See Eppendorf AG; *Int'l*, pg. 2464
EPPENDORF UK LTD.—See Eppendorf AG; *Int'l*, pg. 2464
EPPENDORF VERTRIEB DEUTSCHLAND GMBH—See Eppendorf AG; *Int'l*, pg. 2464
EPPENDORF ZENTRIFUGEN GMBH—See Eppendorf AG; *Int'l*, pg. 2464
EPPERSON & COMPANY INC.—See Genuine Parts Company; *U.S. Public*, pg. 933
EPPERSON WASTE DISPOSAL, INC.—See Republic Services, Inc.; *U.S. Public*, pg. 1786
EP-PHARMALINE CO., LTD.—See EPS Holdings, Inc.; *Int'l*, pg. 2465
EPPINGER MANUFACTURING CO.; *U.S. Private*, pg. 1414
EPPING FOREST YACHT CLUB—See Gate Petroleum Company; *U.S. Private*, pg. 1649
EPPING TRANSMISSION COMPANY, LLC—See Summit Midstream Partners, LP; *U.S. Public*, pg. 1960
EP POLYMERS (M) SDN BHD—See EP Manufacturing Bhd.; *Int'l*, pg. 2458
EPPOR-PACK SDN. BHD.—See Renotex Group Ltd.; *Int'l*, pg. 6285
EP POWER EUROPE, A.S.—See Energeticky a Prumyslovy Holding, a.s.; *Int'l*, pg. 2420
EPP PROFESSIONAL PUBLISHING GROUP GMBH—See Management Capital Holding AG; *Int'l*, pg. 4666
EPPSTEIN UHEN ARCHITECTS, INC.; *U.S. Private*, pg. 1414
EPRC LIMITED—See Hong Kong Economic Times Holdings Ltd; *Int'l*, pg. 3465
EPRCOMUNICAZIONE S.P.A.; *Int'l*, pg. 2465
EPRICE S.P.A.; *Int'l*, pg. 2465
EPRIM, A.S.—See CEZ, a.s.; *Int'l*, pg. 1428
E'PRIME AEROSPACE CORPORATION; *U.S. Private*, pg. 1302
EPRIMO GMBH—See RWE AG; *Int'l*, pg. 6436
EPRINT GROUP LIMITED; *Int'l*, pg. 2465
EPROCESS INTERNATIONAL S.A.—See Ecobank Transnational Incorporated; *Int'l*, pg. 2294
E PRODUCTION CO. LTD.—See Oriental Land Co., Ltd.; *Int'l*, pg. 5625
EPRODUCTION SOLUTIONS - CALIFORNIA—See Weatherford International plc; *U.S. Public*, pg. 2341
EPRODUCTION SOLUTIONS, INC.—See Weatherford International plc; *U.S. Public*, pg. 2341
EPRODUCTION SOLUTIONS—See Weatherford International plc; *U.S. Public*, pg. 2341
EPROFESSIONAL GMBH—See Axel Springer SE; *Int'l*, pg. 766

EPROLAB SA—See HORIBA Ltd; *Int'l*, pg. 3475
EPROMOS PROMOTIONAL PRODUCTS, INC.; *U.S. Private*, pg. 1414
EPRO N.V.—See Greenheart Group Limited; *Int'l*, pg. 3075
EPROPERTYSITES, LLC; *U.S. Private*, pg. 1414
EPRO SYSTEMS (HK) LIMITED—See Hang Tai Yue Group Holdings Limited; *Int'l*, pg. 3245
EPRO TELECOM HOLDINGS LIMITED—See ETS Group Limited; *Int'l*, pg. 2524
EPRO TELECOM—See PacificNet Inc.; *Int'l*, pg. 5692
EPROTEX, LLC—See Ascension Health Alliance; *U.S. Private*, pg. 346
EPR PROPERTIES; *U.S. Public*, pg. 784
EPRUF S.A.—See CEPD N.V.; *Int'l*, pg. 1420
EPSA HIMATIC GMBH—See Qingdao AInnovation Technology Group Co., Ltd.; *Int'l*, pg. 6142
EPS AMERICAS CORP.—See EPS Holdings, Inc.; *Int'l*, pg. 2465
EPS BIO TECHNOLOGY CORP.; *Int'l*, pg. 2465
EPS B.V.—See The Sherwin-Williams Company; *U.S. Public*, pg. 2127
EPS/CCA—See The Sherwin-Williams Company; *U.S. Public*, pg. 2129
EPS CHINA CO., LTD.—See EPS Holdings, Inc.; *Int'l*, pg. 2465
EPSCO INTERNATIONAL INC.—See Burelle S.A.; *Int'l*, pg. 1222
EPS CORP.; *U.S. Private*, pg. 1414
EPS CORP—See EPS Corp.; *U.S. Private*, pg. 1414
EPS CREATIVE HEALTH TECHNOLOGY GROUP LTD.—See EPS Holdings, Inc.; *Int'l*, pg. 2465
EPS DIGITAL-SHARE CO., LTD.—See EPS Holdings, Inc.; *Int'l*, pg. 2465
EPS EKISHIN CO., LTD.—See EPS Holdings, Inc.; *Int'l*, pg. 2465
EPS ELECTRICAL POWER DISTRIBUTION BOARD & SWITCHGEAR LTD—See Schneider Electric SE; *Int'l*, pg. 6626
EPSERVICE CO., LTD.—See Seiko Epson Corporation; *Int'l*, pg. 6688
EPS ETHYLEN-PIPELINE-SUD GMBH & CO. KG—See LyondellBasell Industries N.V.; *Int'l*, pg. 4608
EPS FINANCIAL, LLC—See Pathward Financial, Inc.; *U.S. Public*, pg. 1652
EPS GLOBAL RESEARCH PTE. LTD.—See EPS Holdings, Inc.; *Int'l*, pg. 2465
EPS HOLDINGS, INC.; *Int'l*, pg. 2465
EPSI GLOBAL RESEARCH (TAIWAN) CO., LTD.—See EPS Holdings, Inc.; *Int'l*, pg. 2465
EPSIIA CORPORATION—See Fiserv, Inc.; *U.S. Public*, pg. 850
EPSILON ASSOCIATI SGR S.P.A.—See Intesa Sanpaolo S.p.A.; *Int'l*, pg. 3765
EPSILON DATA MANAGEMENT, LLC—See Publicis Groupe S.A.; *Int'l*, pg. 6098
EPSILON DATA MANAGEMENT, LLC. - TORONTO—See Publicis Groupe S.A.; *Int'l*, pg. 6099
EPSILON ELECTRONICS INDUSTRY AND TRADE INC.—See Bozlu Holding; *Int'l*, pg. 1125
EPSILON ENERGY LTD.; *U.S. Public*, pg. 784
EPSILON ENERGY USA INC.—See Epsilon Energy Ltd.; *U.S. Public*, pg. 784
EPSILON EUROPE PLC—See Epsilon Net S.A.; *Int'l*, pg. 2466
EPSILON HEALTHCARE LTD.; *Int'l*, pg. 2466
EPSILON INSURANCE BROKING SERVICES PTY. LTD.—See BGC Group, Inc.; *U.S. Public*, pg. 328
EPSILON INTERNATIONAL, LLC—See Publicis Groupe S.A.; *Int'l*, pg. 6099
EPSILON INTERNATIONAL—See Publicis Groupe S.A.; *Int'l*, pg. 6099
EPSILON INTERNATIONAL—See Publicis Groupe S.A.; *Int'l*, pg. 6099
EPSILON INTERNATIONAL—See Publicis Groupe S.A.; *Int'l*, pg. 6099
EPSILON INTERNATIONAL—See Publicis Groupe S.A.; *Int'l*, pg. 6099
EPSILON INTERNATIONAL—See Publicis Groupe S.A.; *Int'l*, pg. 6099
EPSILON INTERNATIONAL—See Publicis Groupe S.A.; *Int'l*, pg. 6099
EPSILON INTERNATIONAL—See Publicis Groupe S.A.; *Int'l*, pg. 6099
EPSILON INTERNATIONAL—See Publicis Groupe S.A.; *Int'l*, pg. 6099
EPSILON KRAN GMBH—See Palfinger AG; *Int'l*, pg. 5707
EPSILON LANDAUER DOZIMETRI TEKNOLOJILERI SANAYI VE TICARET A.S.—See Bozlu Holding; *Int'l*, pg. 1125
EPSILON LANDAUER DOZIMETRI TEKNOLOJILERI SANAYI VE TICARET A.S.—See Fortive Corporation; *U.S. Public*, pg. 871
EPSILON NET S.A.; *Int'l*, pg. 2466
EPSILON PLASTICS, INC.—See Alpha Industries, Inc.; *U.S. Private*, pg. 197
EPSILON SA—See Die Schweizerische Post AG; *Int'l*, pg. 2113
EPSILON—See Publicis Groupe S.A.; *Int'l*, pg. 6099
EPSILON—See Publicis Groupe S.A.; *Int'l*, pg. 6099
EPSILON—See Publicis Groupe S.A.; *Int'l*, pg. 6099
EPSILON—See Publicis Groupe S.A.; *Int'l*, pg. 6099
EPSILON—See Publicis Groupe S.A.; *Int'l*, pg. 6099
EPSILON—See Publicis Groupe S.A.; *Int'l*, pg. 6099
EPSILON SYSTEMS SOLUTIONS; *U.S. Private*, pg. 1414
EPSILON TELECOMMUNICATIONS GMBH—See Gamma Communications PLC; *Int'l*, pg. 2878
EPSILON TEST SERVICES LIMITED—See The Bidvest Group Limited; *Int'l*, pg. 7622
EPSILON TRADING, INC.—See Delta Air Lines, Inc.; *U.S. Public*, pg. 652
EPSILOR-ELECTRIC FUEL LIMITED—See Greenbriar Equity Group, L.P.; *U.S. Private*, pg. 1775
EPSILYTE HOLDINGS LLC—See Balmoral Funds LLC; *U.S. Private*, pg. 461
EPS INTERNATIONAL (CHINA) CO., LTD.—See EPS Holdings, Inc.; *Int'l*, pg. 2465
EPS INTERNATIONAL CO., LTD.—See EPS Holdings, Inc.; *Int'l*, pg. 2465
EPS INTERNATIONAL KOREA LIMITED—See EPS Holdings, Inc.; *Int'l*, pg. 2465
EPS MARIA LANZENDORFERSTRASSE 17 ERRICHTUNGS- UND BETEILIGUNGS GMBH—See PORR AG; *Int'l*, pg. 5922
EPSODECUA CIA, LTDA.—See Seiko Epson Corporation; *Int'l*, pg. 6686
EP-SOGO CO., LTD.—See EPS Holdings, Inc.; *Int'l*, pg. 2465
EPSOM PROPERTIES LIMITED; *Int'l*, pg. 2466
EPSON AMERICA INC.—See Seiko Epson Corporation; *Int'l*, pg. 6686
EPSON AMERICA ROBOTICS DIVISION—See Seiko Epson Corporation; *Int'l*, pg. 6686
EPSON ARGENTINA, SRL—See Seiko Epson Corporation; *Int'l*, pg. 6686
EPSON AUSTRALIA PTY. LTD. (E.A.L.)—See Seiko Epson Corporation; *Int'l*, pg. 6687
EPSON CANADA LIMITED—See Seiko Epson Corporation; *Int'l*, pg. 6686
EPSON CHILE S.A.—See Seiko Epson Corporation; *Int'l*, pg. 6687
EPSON (CHINA) CO., LTD.—See Seiko Epson Corporation; *Int'l*, pg. 6686
EPSON COLOMBIA LTDA.—See Seiko Epson Corporation; *Int'l*, pg. 6687
EPSON COSTA RICA, S.A.—See Seiko Epson Corporation; *Int'l*, pg. 6687
EPSON DE MEXICO, S.A. DE C.V.—See Seiko Epson Corporation; *Int'l*, pg. 6687
EPSON DEUTSCHLAND GMBH—See Seiko Epson Corporation; *Int'l*, pg. 6687
EPSON DO BRASIL INDUSTRIA E COMERCIO LTDA.—See Seiko Epson Corporation; *Int'l*, pg. 6687
EPSON ELECTRONICS AMERICA—See Seiko Epson Corporation; *Int'l*, pg. 6687
EPSON ELECTRONICS OF AMERICA INC.—See Seiko Epson Corporation; *Int'l*, pg. 6686
EPSON EUROPE B.V.—See Seiko Epson Corporation; *Int'l*, pg. 6687
EPSON EUROPE ELECTRONICS GMBH—See Seiko Epson Corporation; *Int'l*, pg. 6687
EPSON FRANCE S.A. (E.F.S.)—See Seiko Epson Corporation; *Int'l*, pg. 6687
EPSON HONG KONG LTD.—See Seiko Epson Corporation; *Int'l*, pg. 6687
EPSON IBERICA, S.A.—See Seiko Epson Corporation; *Int'l*, pg. 6687
EPSON INDIA PVT. LTD.—See Seiko Epson Corporation; *Int'l*, pg. 6687
EPSON ITALIA S.P.A.—See Seiko Epson Corporation; *Int'l*, pg. 6687
EPSON KOREA CO., LTD.—See Seiko Epson Corporation; *Int'l*, pg. 6687
EPSON MALAYSIA SDN. BHD.—See Seiko Epson Corporation; *Int'l*, pg. 6687
EPSON MALAYSIA SDN. BHD.—See Seiko Epson Corporation; *Int'l*, pg. 6687
EPSON MEXICO, S.A. DE C.V.—See Seiko Epson Corporation; *Int'l*, pg. 6687
EPSON NEW ZEALAND LTD.—See Seiko Epson Corporation; *Int'l*, pg. 6687
EPSON PAULISTA LTDA.—See Seiko Epson Corporation; *Int'l*, pg. 6687
EPSON PERU, S.A.—See Seiko Epson Corporation; *Int'l*, pg. 6687
EPSON PHILIPPINES CORPORATION—See Seiko Epson Corporation; *Int'l*, pg. 6687
EPSON PORTLAND INC.—See Seiko Epson Corporation; *Int'l*, pg. 6686
EPSON PRECISION (HONG KONG) LTD.—See Seiko Epson Corporation; *Int'l*, pg. 6687
EPSON PRECISION (JOHOR) SDN. BHD.—See Seiko Epson Corporation; *Int'l*, pg. 6687
EPSON PRECISION MALAYSIA SDN. BHD.—See Seiko Epson Corporation; *Int'l*, pg. 6687
EPSON PRECISION (PHILIPPINES) INC.—See Seiko Epson Corporation; *Int'l*, pg. 6687
EPSON RESEARCH & DEVELOPMENT INC.—See Seiko Epson Corporation; *Int'l*, pg. 6686
EPSON (SHANGHAI) INFORMATION EQUIPMENT CO., LTD.—See Seiko Epson Corporation; *Int'l*, pg. 6686
EPSON SINGAPORE PTE., LTD. (ESP)—See Seiko Epson Corporation; *Int'l*, pg. 6687
EPSON TAIWAN TECHNOLOGY & TRADING LTD.—See Seiko Epson Corporation; *Int'l*, pg. 6687
EPSON TELFORD LTD.—See Seiko Epson Corporation; *Int'l*, pg. 6687
EPSON (THAILAND) CO., LTD.—See Seiko Epson Corporation; *Int'l*, pg. 6686
EPSON TOYOCOM CORPORATION—See Seiko Epson Corporation; *Int'l*, pg. 6687
EPSON TOYOCOM MALAYSIA SDN.BHD—See Seiko Epson Corporation; *Int'l*, pg. 6687
EPSON TOYOCOM (THAILAND) LTD.—See Seiko Epson Corporation; *Int'l*, pg. 6687
EPSON TOYOCOM (WUXI) CO.,LTD.—See Seiko Epson Corporation; *Int'l*, pg. 6687
EPSON (U.K.) LTD.—See Seiko Epson Corporation; *Int'l*, pg. 6686
EPSON VENEZUELA, S.A.—See Seiko Epson Corporation; *Int'l*, pg. 6687
EPSON VIETNAM CO., LTD.—See Seiko Epson Corporation; *Int'l*, pg. 6687
EPS POLSKA HOLDING SP. Z O.O.—See E.ON SE; *Int'l*, pg. 2256
EPS POLSKA SP. Z O.O.—See E.ON SE; *Int'l*, pg. 2256
EPS SETTLEMENTS GROUP INC.; *U.S. Private*, pg. 1414
EPS TAMUSSINOSTRASSE ERRICHTUNGS- UND BETEILIGUNGS GMBH—See PORR AG; *Int'l*, pg. 5922
EPSTEIN ARCHITECTURE & ENGINEERING SRL—See A. Epstein & Sons International, Inc.; *U.S. Private*, pg. 23
EPSTEIN BECKER & GREEN, P.C.; *U.S. Private*, pg. 1414
EPSTEIN CIVIL ENGINEERING, INC.—See A. Epstein & Sons International, Inc.; *U.S. Private*, pg. 23
EPSTEIN CONSTRUCTION INC.—See A. Epstein & Sons International, Inc.; *U.S. Private*, pg. 23
EPSTEIN SP. Z.O.O—See A. Epstein & Sons International, Inc.; *U.S. Private*, pg. 23
THE EPSTEN GROUP, INC.; *U.S. Private*, pg. 4026
EPS TIGERMED (SUZHOU) CO., LTD.—See EPS Holdings, Inc.; *Int'l*, pg. 2465
EPS TRIESTER STRASSE ERRICHTUNGS- UND BETEILIGUNGSVERWALTUNGS GMBH—See PORR AG; *Int'l*, pg. 5922
EP SUPPLY—See Reece Limited; *Int'l*, pg. 6249
EPSYS SAS—See Schneider Electric SE; *Int'l*, pg. 6627
EPTA AMERICA LLC—See Mondelez International, Inc.; *U.S. Public*, pg. 1461
EPTAM PRECISION SOLUTIONS—See Frazier & Company, Inc.; *U.S. Private*, pg. 1599
EPTA S.P.A.; *Int'l*, pg. 2466
EP TECHNOLOGY CORPORATION; *U.S. Private*, pg. 1411
EP&T GLOBAL LIMITED; *Int'l*, pg. 2458
EPTICORE MICROELECTRONICS (JIANGSU) CO., LTD.—See Shenzhen Fenda Technology Co., Ltd.; *Int'l*, pg. 6810
EPTING DISTRIBUTORS INC.; *U.S. Private*, pg. 1414
EPTISA SERVICIOS DE INGENIERIA S.A.—See ARCADIS N.V.; *Int'l*, pg. 541
EP TRADING CO., LTD.—See EPS Holdings, Inc.; *Int'l*, pg. 2465
EPTURA, INC.; *U.S. Private*, pg. 1414
EPT WATERPARKS, INC.—See EPR Properties; *U.S. Public*, pg. 784
EPUJA SPIRITECH LTD.; *Int'l*, pg. 2466
EPURAIR INC.—See Noveko International Inc.; *Int'l*, pg. 5461
EP URBANIZAM I ARH. A.D.—See Energoprojekt Holding a.d.; *Int'l*, pg. 2421
EPUREX FILMS GESCHAFTSFUHRUNGS-GMBH—See Bayer Aktiengesellschaft; *Int'l*, pg. 907
EPUREX FILMS GMBH & CO.KG—See Bayer Aktiengesellschaft; *Int'l*, pg. 907
EPURON EPE—See Kawa Capital Management, Inc.; *U.S. Private*, pg. 2266
EPURON GMBH—See Kawa Capital Management, Inc.; *U.S. Private*, pg. 2266
EPURON PTY LTD—See Kawa Capital Management, Inc.; *U.S. Private*, pg. 2266
EPURON SARL—See Kawa Capital Management, Inc.; *U.S. Private*, pg. 2266
EPURON S.A.S.—See ERG S.p.A.; *Int'l*, pg. 2491
EPURON SPAIN SLU—See Kawa Capital Management, Inc.; *U.S. Private*, pg. 2266
EP WEALTH ADVISORS, LLC; *U.S. Private*, pg. 1411
EPWIN GROUP PLC; *Int'l*, pg. 2466
EPWORTH MEDICAL IMAGING PTY LIMITED—See Sonic Healthcare Limited; *Int'l*, pg. 7097
EP YAMANASHI CO., LTD.—See EPS Holdings, Inc.; *Int'l*, pg. 2465

EPWIN GROUP PLC

EPYX FRANCE SAS—See Corpay, Inc.; *U.S. Public*, pg. 579
EPYX LIMITED—See Corpay, Inc.; *U.S. Public*, pg. 579
EQ1 GIVES, INC.; *U.S. Private*, pg. 1414
EQ ALABAMA, INC.—See Republic Services, Inc.; *U.S. Public*, pg. 1787
EQ BESTECH INC.—See SurplusGLOBAL, Inc.; *Int'l*, pg. 7344
EQB INC.; *Int'l*, pg. 2466
EQ CORP.—See Equilease Holding Corp.; *U.S. Private*, pg. 1415
EQ DETROIT, INC.—See Republic Services, Inc.; *U.S. Public*, pg. 1787
EQECAT, INC.—See American Bureau of Shipping; *U.S. Private*, pg. 226
EQ FLORIDA, INC.—See Republic Services, Inc.; *U.S. Public*, pg. 1787
EQGP HOLDINGS, LP—See EQT Corporation; *U.S. Public*, pg. 785
EQ HEALTH ACQUISITION CORP.; *U.S. Public*, pg. 784
EQHEALTH SOLUTIONS, LLC—See Apax Partners LLP; *Int'l*, pg. 504
EQ HOLDINGS, INC.—See Republic Services, Inc.; *U.S. Public*, pg. 1787
EQIN B.V.—See Value Enhancement Partners B.V.; *Int'l*, pg. 8124
EQ INC.; *Int'l*, pg. 2466
EQ INDIANA AUTO & TRUCK AUCTION INC.; *U.S. Private*, pg. 1414
EQ INDUSTRIAL SERVICES INC. - INDIANAPOLIS—See Republic Services, Inc.; *U.S. Public*, pg. 1788
EQ INDUSTRIAL SERVICES, INC.—See Republic Services, Inc.; *U.S. Public*, pg. 1788
EQIN N.V.—See Value Enhancement Partners B.V.; *Int'l*, pg. 8124
EQIOM BETONS—See CRH plc; *Int'l*, pg. 1843
EQIOM S.A.S. - GRAND-COURONNE GRINDING PLANT—See CRH plc; *Int'l*, pg. 1843
EQIOM S.A.S. - HEMING PLANT—See CRH plc; *Int'l*, pg. 1843
EQIOM S.A.S. - LA ROCHELLE GRINDING CENTER—See CRH plc; *Int'l*, pg. 1843
EQIOM S.A.S. - LUMBRES PLANT—See CRH plc; *Int'l*, pg. 1843
EQIOM S.A.S.—See CRH plc; *Int'l*, pg. 1843
EQ LABS, INC.; *U.S. Public*, pg. 784
EQ LIFE OY—See eQ Oyj; *Int'l*, pg. 2466
EQLIPSE TECHNOLOGIES—See Arlington Capital Partners LLC; *U.S. Private*, pg. 327
EQM MIDSTREAM PARTNERS, LP—See EQT Corporation; *U.S. Public*, pg. 785
EQM TECHNOLOGIES & ENERGY, INC.; *U.S. Public*, pg. 784
EQ NORTHEAST, INC.—See Republic Services, Inc.; *U.S. Public*, pg. 1788
EQ OKLAHOMA, INC.—See Republic Services, Inc.; *U.S. Public*, pg. 1788
EQOLOGY ASA; *Int'l*, pg. 2466
EQ OYJ; *Int'l*, pg. 2466
EQR-1500 MASS, LLC—See Equity Residential; *U.S. Public*, pg. 791
EQR-175 KENT AVENUE A, LLC—See Equity Residential; *U.S. Public*, pg. 791
EQR-228 WEST 71ST, LLC—See Equity Residential; *U.S. Public*, pg. 791
EQR-425 MASSACHUSETTS, LLC—See Equity Residential; *U.S. Public*, pg. 791
EQR-600 WASHINGTON, L.L.C.—See Equity Residential; *U.S. Public*, pg. 791
EQR-71 BROADWAY, LLC—See Equity Residential; *U.S. Public*, pg. 791
EQR-77 PARK AVENUE LLC—See Equity Residential; *U.S. Public*, pg. 791
EQR-ACADEMY VILLAGE, L.L.C.—See Equity Residential; *U.S. Public*, pg. 791
EQR-CAPE HOUSE I, LP—See Equity Residential; *U.S. Public*, pg. 791
EQ RESOURCE RECOVERY, INC.—See Republic Services, Inc.; *U.S. Public*, pg. 1788
EQ RESOURCES LIMITED; *Int'l*, pg. 2466
EQR-GALLERY APARTMENTS LIMITED PARTNERSHIP—See Equity Residential; *U.S. Public*, pg. 791
EQR-GATEWAY AT MALDEN CENTER, LLC—See Equity Residential; *U.S. Public*, pg. 791
EQR-GLO APARTMENTS, LLC—See Equity Residential; *U.S. Public*, pg. 791
EQR-HEIGHTS ON CAPITOL HILL LLC—See Equity Residential; *U.S. Public*, pg. 791
EQR-HERITAGE RIDGE, L.L.C.—See Equity Residential; *U.S. Public*, pg. 791
EQR-HUDSON CROSSING, LLC—See Equity Residential; *U.S. Public*, pg. 791
EQR-HUDSON POINTE, L.L.C.—See Equity Residential; *U.S. Public*, pg. 791
EQR-IVORY WOOD, L.L.C.—See Equity Residential; *U.S. Public*, pg. 791
EQR-KELVIN COURT, LLC—See Equity Residential; *U.S. Public*, pg. 791

EQR-KINGS COLONY, L.L.C.—See Equity Residential; *U.S. Public*, pg. 791
EQR-LEXINGTON FARM, L.L.C.—See Equity Residential; *U.S. Public*, pg. 791
EQR-LIBERTY TOWER, LLC—See Equity Residential; *U.S. Public*, pg. 791
EQR-LINDLEY, LLC—See Equity Residential; *U.S. Public*, pg. 791
EQR-LUNA UPPER WESTSIDE LLC—See Equity Residential; *U.S. Public*, pg. 791
EQR-MARK ON 8TH LLC—See Equity Residential; *U.S. Public*, pg. 791
EQR-METRO ON FIRST LLC—See Equity Residential; *U.S. Public*, pg. 791
EQR-MIDTOWN 24, LLC—See Equity Residential; *U.S. Public*, pg. 791
EQR-MILL CREEK, L.L.C.—See Equity Residential; *U.S. Public*, pg. 791
EQR-MIRAMAR LAKES, L.L.C.—See Equity Residential; *U.S. Public*, pg. 791
EQR-NORTHPARK, LLC—See Equity Residential; *U.S. Public*, pg. 791
EQR-NOTCH LLC—See Equity Residential; *U.S. Public*, pg. 791
EQR-OAK MILL, L.L.C.—See Equity Residential; *U.S. Public*, pg. 791
EQR-OAKS AT FALLS CHURCH, LLC—See Equity Residential; *U.S. Public*, pg. 791
EQR-PALM TRACE LANDING, L.L.C.—See Equity Residential; *U.S. Public*, pg. 791
EQR-PEGASUS, LLC—See Equity Residential; *U.S. Public*, pg. 791
EQR-RESERVE AT EISENHOWER LLC—See Equity Residential; *U.S. Public*, pg. 791
EQR-RIVERTOWER, LLC—See Equity Residential; *U.S. Public*, pg. 791
EQR-SIENA TERRACE, L.L.C.—See Equity Residential; *U.S. Public*, pg. 792
EQR-SKYLINE TERRACE LIMITED PARTNERSHIP—See Equity Residential; *U.S. Public*, pg. 792
EQR-SOUTHWOOD LIMITED PARTNERSHIP—See Equity Residential; *U.S. Public*, pg. 792
EQR-UWAJIMAYA VILLAGE, L.L.C.—See Equity Residential; *U.S. Public*, pg. 792
EQR-VANTAGE POINTE, LLC—See Equity Residential; *U.S. Public*, pg. 792
EQR-VIRGINIA SQUARE LLC—See Equity Residential; *U.S. Public*, pg. 792
EQR-WATERFORD PLACE, L.L.C.—See Equity Residential; *U.S. Public*, pg. 792
EQR-WELLINGTON GREEN, L.L.C.—See Equity Residential; *U.S. Public*, pg. 792
EQRX, INC.—See Revolution Medicines, Inc.; *U.S. Public*, pg. 1793
EQS ASIA LIMITED—See Thoma Bravo, L.P.; *U.S. Private*, pg. 4147
EQS GROUP AG—See Thoma Bravo, L.P.; *U.S. Private*, pg. 4147
EQS GROUP AG—See Thoma Bravo, L.P.; *U.S. Private*, pg. 4147
EQS GROUP GMBH—See Thoma Bravo, L.P.; *U.S. Private*, pg. 4147
EQS GROUP INC.—See Thoma Bravo, L.P.; *U.S. Private*, pg. 4147
EQS GROUP LTD.—See Thoma Bravo, L.P.; *U.S. Private*, pg. 4147
EQS GROUP SAS—See Thoma Bravo, L.P.; *U.S. Private*, pg. 4147
EQS GROUP S.R.L.—See Thoma Bravo, L.P.; *U.S. Private*, pg. 4147
EQS WEB TECHNOLOGIES PVT. LTD.—See Thoma Bravo, L.P.; *U.S. Private*, pg. 4147
EQT AB; *Int'l*, pg. 2467
EQT CORPORATION; *U.S. Public*, pg. 784
EQTEC PLC; *Int'l*, pg. 2483
EQT ENERGY, LLC—See EQT Corporation; *U.S. Public*, pg. 784
EQ TERMINAL SERVICES LLC—See Republic Services, Inc.; *U.S. Public*, pg. 1787
EQT FUND MANAGEMENT S.A.R.L.—See EQT AB; *Int'l*, pg. 2475
EQT FUNDS MANAGEMENT LTD—See EQT AB; *Int'l*, pg. 2475
EQ THE ENVIRONMENTAL QUALITY COMPANY—See Republic Services, Inc.; *U.S. Public*, pg. 1787
EQT MANAGEMENT S.A R.L.—See EQT AB; *Int'l*, pg. 2475
EQT NORTHERN EUROPE PRIVATE EQUITY FUNDS—See EQT AB; *Int'l*, pg. 2475
EQT PARTNERS AB—See EQT AB; *Int'l*, pg. 2467
EQT PARTNERS AG—See EQT AB; *Int'l*, pg. 2475
EQT PARTNERS ASIA LTD—See EQT AB; *Int'l*, pg. 2475
EQT PARTNERS A/S—See EQT AB; *Int'l*, pg. 2475
EQT PARTNERS AUSTRALIA PTY. LTD.—See EQT AB; *Int'l*, pg. 2475
EQT PARTNERS GMBH—See EQT AB; *Int'l*, pg. 2475
EQT PARTNERS INC.—See EQT AB; *Int'l*, pg. 2475
EQT PARTNERS JAPAN KK—See EQT AB; *Int'l*, pg. 2475

CORPORATE AFFILIATIONS

EQT PARTNERS KOREA CO., LTD.—See EQT AB; *Int'l*, pg. 2475
EQT PARTNERS NETHERLANDS B.V.—See EQT AB; *Int'l*, pg. 2475
EQT PARTNERS OY—See EQT AB; *Int'l*, pg. 2475
EQT PARTNERS SHANGHAI LTD—See EQT AB; *Int'l*, pg. 2475
EQT PARTNERS SINGAPORE PTE LTD—See EQT AB; *Int'l*, pg. 2475
EQT PARTNERS SPAIN S.L.U.—See EQT AB; *Int'l*, pg. 2475
EQT PARTNERS SP. Z O.O.—See EQT AB; *Int'l*, pg. 2475
EQT PARTNERS UK ADVISORS LLP—See EQT AB; *Int'l*, pg. 2475
EQT PRODUCTION COMPANY—See EQT Corporation; *U.S. Public*, pg. 784
EQT RE, LLC—See EQT Corporation; *U.S. Public*, pg. 784
EQT SCANDINAVIAN PARTNERS LTD.—See EQT AB; *Int'l*, pg. 2475
EQT SERVICES (UK) LIMITED—See EQT AB; *Int'l*, pg. 2475
EQUA BANK A.S.—See AnaCap Financial Partners LLP; *Int'l*, pg. 445
EQUAL CHANCE PROPERTIES PTE LTD—See Second Chance Properties Ltd.; *Int'l*, pg. 6672
EQUAL EARTH CORP.; *U.S. Private*, pg. 1415
EQUAL ENTERTAINMENT LLC; *U.S. Private*, pg. 1415
EQUAL EXPERTS DEVICES INC—See Equal Experts UK Ltd.; *Int'l*, pg. 2483
EQUAL EXPERTS INDIA PRIVATE LTD—See Equal Experts UK Ltd.; *Int'l*, pg. 2483
EQUAL EXPERTS UK LTD.; *Int'l*, pg. 2483
EQUALITY HOTEL MANAGEMENT SDN. BHD.—See HL Global Enterprises Limited; *Int'l*, pg. 3429
EQUALIZERCM; *U.S. Private*, pg. 1415
EQUALIZER FLANGE TOOL INNOVATION CO. LTD.—See Enerpac Tool Group Corp.; *U.S. Public*, pg. 765
EQUALIZER INTERNATIONAL INC.—See Enerpac Tool Group Corp.; *U.S. Public*, pg. 765
EQUAL JUSTICE WORKS; *U.S. Private*, pg. 1415
EQUALS GROUP PLC; *Int'l*, pg. 2483
EQUALS MONEY PLC—See Equals Group Plc; *Int'l*, pg. 2483
EQUALS S.A.—See StoneCo Ltd.; *Int'l*, pg. 7222
EQUALS THREE COMMUNICATIONS; *U.S. Private*, pg. 1415
EQUAMINERAL SA—See European Metals Holdings Limited; *Int'l*, pg. 2557
E-QUANTUM—See Valsef Group; *Int'l*, pg. 8123
EQUATE PETROCHEMICAL COMPANY K.S.C.C.—See Dow Inc.; *U.S. Public*, pg. 685
EQUATE PETROCHEMICAL COMPANY K.S.C.C.—See Kuwait Petroleum Corporation; *Int'l*, pg. 4346
EQUATERRA BV; *Int'l*, pg. 2483
EQUATERRA, INC.; *U.S. Private*, pg. 1415
EQUATION ENERGY PTE. LTD.—See DISA LIMITED; *Int'l*, pg. 2131
EQUATION RECYCLING PTE. LTD.—See DISA LIMITED; *Int'l*, pg. 2131
EQUATION RESOURCES PTE. LTD.—See DISA LIMITED; *Int'l*, pg. 2131
EQUATOR BEVERAGE COMPANY; *U.S. Public*, pg. 785
EQUATOR DESIGN, INC.—See Matthews International Corporation; *U.S. Public*, pg. 1399
EQUATORIAL COMMERCIAL BANK LIMITED—See Mwalimu Cooperative Savings & Credit Society Limited; *Int'l*, pg. 5110
EQUATORIAL ENERGIA ALAGOAS—See Equatorial Energia SA; *Int'l*, pg. 2484
EQUATORIAL ENERGIA SA; *Int'l*, pg. 2483
EQUATORIALE PTE. LTD.—See Swiber Holdings Limited; *Int'l*, pg. 7366
EQUATORIAL HOTEL MANAGEMENT PTE. LTD.—See HL Global Enterprises Limited; *Int'l*, pg. 3430
EQUATORIAL PARA—See Equatorial Energia SA; *Int'l*, pg. 2484
EQUATORIAL RESOURCES LIMITED; *Int'l*, pg. 2484
EQUATOR REINSURANCES LIMITED—See QBE Insurance Group Limited; *Int'l*, pg. 6136
EQUATOR (SCOTLAND) LTD.—See Matthews International Corporation; *U.S. Public*, pg. 1400
EQUBE GAMING LIMITED; *Int'l*, pg. 2484
EQUENSWORLDLINE SE—See Worldline SA; *Int'l*, pg. 8458
EQUIAN, LLC—See New Mountain Capital, LLC; *U.S. Private*, pg. 2902
EQUIAN, LLC—See UnitedHealth Group Incorporated; *U.S. Public*, pg. 2240
EQUIANT FINANCIAL SERVICES, INC.—See Concord Servicing Corp.; *U.S. Private*, pg. 1010
EQUIBASE COMPANY LLC; *U.S. Private*, pg. 1415
EQUICARE HEALTH INC.; *Int'l*, pg. 2484
EQUIFAX AMERICAS B.V.—See Equifax Inc.; *U.S. Public*, pg. 786
EQUIFAX ANALYTICS PRIVATE LIMITED—See Equifax Inc.; *U.S. Public*, pg. 785
EQUIFAX AUSTRALASIA GROUP SERVICES PTY LIMITED—See Equifax Inc.; *U.S. Public*, pg. 786

COMPANY NAME INDEX — EQUIPMENT & SYSTEMS FOR THE INDUSTRY

EQUIFAX AUSTRALIA COMMERCIAL SERVICES AND SOLUTIONS PTY LIMITED—See Equifax Inc.; *U.S. Public*, pg. 786
EQUIFAX AUSTRALIA PTY. LTD.—See Equifax Inc.; *U.S. Public*, pg. 786
EQUIFAX CANADA CO.—See Equifax Inc.; *U.S. Public*, pg. 786
EQUIFAX CANADIAN HOLDINGS CO.—See Equifax Inc.; *U.S. Public*, pg. 786
EQUIFAX COMMERCIAL SERVICES LTD.—See Equifax Inc.; *U.S. Public*, pg. 786
EQUIFAX DIRECT MARKETING SOLUTIONS, INC.—See Bread Financial Holdings Inc.; *U.S. Public*, pg. 381
EQUIFAX DO BRASIL HOLDINGS LTDA.—See Equifax Inc.; *U.S. Public*, pg. 786
EQUIFAX DO BRASIL LTDA.—See Equifax Inc.; *U.S. Public*, pg. 786
EQUIFAX INC.; *U.S. Public*, pg. 785
EQUIFAX INFORMATION SERVICES LLC—See Equifax Inc.; *U.S. Public*, pg. 786
EQUIFAX INFORMATION SERVICES OF PUERTO RICO, INC.—See Equifax Inc.; *U.S. Public*, pg. 786
EQUIFAX LTD.—See Equifax Inc.; *U.S. Public*, pg. 786
EQUIFAX NEW ZEALAND INFORMATION SERVICES AND SOLUTIONS LIMITED—See Equifax Inc.; *U.S. Public*, pg. 786
EQUIFAX PARAGUAY S.A.—See Equifax Inc.; *U.S. Public*, pg. 786
EQUIFAX PROPERTY DATA & ANALYTICS—See Equifax Inc.; *U.S. Public*, pg. 786
EQUIFAX SECURE UK LTD.—See Equifax Inc.; *U.S. Public*, pg. 786
EQUIFAX SPAIN HOLDINGS S.L.—See Equifax Inc.; *U.S. Public*, pg. 786
EQUIFAX SPECIAL SERVICES LLC—See Equifax Inc.; *U.S. Public*, pg. 786
EQUIFAX URUGUAY S.A.—See Equifax Inc.; *U.S. Public*, pg. 786
EQUIFAX WORKFORCE SOLUTIONS—See Equifax Inc.; *U.S. Public*, pg. 786
EQUIFAX WORKFORCE SOLUTIONS—See Equifax Inc.; *U.S. Public*, pg. 786
EQUIFAX WORKFORCE SOLUTIONS—See Equifax Inc.; *U.S. Public*, pg. 786
EQUIFAX WORKFORCE SOLUTIONS—See Equifax Inc.; *U.S. Public*, pg. 786
EQUIFLOR CORPORATION; *U.S. Private*, pg. 1415
EQUILAB, S.A. DE C.V.—See HORIBA Ltd; *Int'l*, pg. 3475
EQUILAR; *U.S. Private*, pg. 1415
EQUILEASE FINANCIAL SERVICES—See Equilease Holding Corp.; *U.S. Private*, pg. 1415
EQUILEASE HOLDING CORP.; *U.S. Private*, pg. 1415
EQUILIBRA S.R.L.—See Unilever PLC; *Int'l*, pg. 8044
EQUILIBRIUM CALIFICADORA DE RIESGO S.A.—See Moody's Corporation; *U.S. Public*, pg. 1467
EQUILIBRIUM CAPITAL MANAGEMENT LLC; *U.S. Private*, pg. 1415
EQUILIBRIUM CLASIFICADORA DE RIESGO S.A.—See Moody's Corporation; *U.S. Public*, pg. 1467
EQUILLIUM AUS PTY. LTD.—See Equillium, Inc.; *U.S. Public*, pg. 787
EQUILLIUM, INC.; *U.S. Public*, pg. 787
EQUIMARK-NFC DEVELOPMENT CORPORATION—See BDO Unibank, Inc.; *Int'l*, pg. 930
EQUIMAR SHIPHOLDINGS, LTD.—See B+H Ocean Carriers Ltd.; *Int'l*, pg. 784
EQUI=MEDIA LIMITED; *Int'l*, pg. 2484
EQUINE JOURNAL—See Shivers Trading & Operating Company; *U.S. Private*, pg. 3638
THE EQUINE NETWORK—See Active Interest Media, Inc.; *U.S. Private*, pg. 69
EQUINITI 360 CLINICAL LIMITED—See Siris Capital Group, LLC; *U.S. Private*, pg. 3673
EQUINITI DATA LIMITED—See Siris Capital Group, LLC; *U.S. Private*, pg. 3673
EQUINITI GATEWAY LIMITED—See Siris Capital Group, LLC; *U.S. Private*, pg. 3673
EQUINITI GROUP PLC—See Siris Capital Group, LLC; *U.S. Private*, pg. 3673
EQUINITI INDIA (PRIVATE) LIMITED—See Siris Capital Group, LLC; *U.S. Private*, pg. 3673
EQUINITI KYC SOLUTIONS B.V.—See Siris Capital Group, LLC; *U.S. Private*, pg. 3673
EQUINITI LIMITED—See Siris Capital Group, LLC; *U.S. Private*, pg. 3673
EQUINIX ASIA PACIFIC PTE. LTD.—See Equinix, Inc.; *U.S. Public*, pg. 787
EQUINIX AUSTRALIA PTY. LIMITED—See Equinix, Inc.; *U.S. Public*, pg. 787
EQUINIX (BULGARIA) DATA CENTERS EAD—See Equinix, Inc.; *U.S. Public*, pg. 787
EQUINIX CANADA LTD.—See Equinix, Inc.; *U.S. Public*, pg. 787
EQUINIX EUROPE, INC.—See Equinix, Inc.; *U.S. Public*, pg. 787
EQUINIX (GERMANY) ENTERPRISES GMBH—See Equinix, Inc.; *U.S. Public*, pg. 787
EQUINIX (GERMANY) GMBH—See Equinix, Inc.; *U.S. Public*, pg. 787

EQUINIX GROUP LTD—See Equinix, Inc.; *U.S. Public*, pg. 787
EQUINIX (HONG KONG) ENTERPRISES LIMITED—See Equinix, Inc.; *U.S. Public*, pg. 787
EQUINIX HONG KONG LIMITED—See Equinix, Inc.; *U.S. Public*, pg. 787
EQUINIX (IBX SERVICES) GMBH—See Equinix, Inc.; *U.S. Public*, pg. 787
EQUINIX, INC. - RESTON—See Equinix, Inc.; *U.S. Public*, pg. 788
EQUINIX, INC.; *U.S. Public*, pg. 787
EQUINIX (ITALY) ENTERPRISES S.R.L.—See Equinix, Inc.; *U.S. Public*, pg. 787
EQUINIX JAPAN K.K.—See Equinix, Inc.; *U.S. Public*, pg. 787
EQUINIX KOREA LLC—See Equinix, Inc.; *U.S. Public*, pg. 788
EQUINIX (LD10) LIMITED—See Equinix, Inc.; *U.S. Public*, pg. 787
EQUINIX (NETHERLANDS) HOLDINGS BV—See Equinix, Inc.; *U.S. Public*, pg. 787
EQUINIX OPERATING CO., LLC—See Equinix, Inc.; *U.S. Public*, pg. 788
EQUINIX (OTTAWA) GOVERNMENT LTD.—See Equinix, Inc.; *U.S. Public*, pg. 787
EQUINIX PERU S.R.L.—See Equinix, Inc.; *U.S. Public*, pg. 788
EQUINIX (REAL ESTATE) GMBH—See Equinix, Inc.; *U.S. Public*, pg. 787
EQUINIX SECURITY (CU1) LLC—See Equinix, Inc.; *U.S. Public*, pg. 788
EQUINIX SINGAPORE PTE. LTD.—See Equinix, Inc.; *U.S. Public*, pg. 787
EQUINIX (SWEDEN) AB—See Equinix, Inc.; *U.S. Public*, pg. 787
EQUINIX (SWITZERLAND) ENTERPRISES GMBH—See Equinix, Inc.; *U.S. Public*, pg. 787
EQUINIX (SWITZERLAND) GMBH—See Equinix, Inc.; *U.S. Public*, pg. 787
EQUINIX UK LIMITED—See Equinix, Inc.; *U.S. Public*, pg. 787
EQUINLAB SAC—See HORIBA Ltd; *Int'l*, pg. 3475
EQUINOR ALGERIA AS—See Equinor ASA; *Int'l*, pg. 2484
EQUINOR ANGOLA AS—See Equinor ASA; *Int'l*, pg. 2484
EQUINOR APSHERON AS—See Equinor ASA; *Int'l*, pg. 2484
EQUINOR ARGENTINA AS—See Equinor ASA; *Int'l*, pg. 2484
EQUINOR ASA; *Int'l*, pg. 2484
EQUINOR ASIA PACIFIC PTE. LTD.—See Equinor ASA; *Int'l*, pg. 2484
EQUINOR ASSET MANAGEMENT ASA—See Equinor ASA; *Int'l*, pg. 2484
EQUINOR AZERBAIJAN AS—See Equinor ASA; *Int'l*, pg. 2484
EQUINOR CANADA LTD.—See Equinor ASA; *Int'l*, pg. 2484
EQUINOR CHINA AS—See Equinor ASA; *Int'l*, pg. 2484
EQUINOR DANMARK A/S—See Equinor ASA; *Int'l*, pg. 2484
EQUINOR DEUTSCHLAND GMBH—See Equinor ASA; *Int'l*, pg. 2484
EQUINOR ENERGY AS—See Equinor ASA; *Int'l*, pg. 2484
EQUINOR ENERGY BELGIUM NV - MECHELEN OFFICE—See Equinor ASA; *Int'l*, pg. 2484
EQUINOR ENERGY BELGIUM NV—See Equinor ASA; *Int'l*, pg. 2484
EQUINOR ENERGY DO BRASIL LTDA—See Equinor ASA; *Int'l*, pg. 2484
EQUINOR E&P AMERICAS LP—See Equinor ASA; *Int'l*, pg. 2485
EQUINOR HOLDING NETHERLANDS B.V.—See Equinor ASA; *Int'l*, pg. 2484
EQUINOR INSURANCE AS—See Equinor ASA; *Int'l*, pg. 2484
EQUINOR MARKETING & TRADING (US) INC.—See Equinor ASA; *Int'l*, pg. 2485
EQUINOR NIGERIA ENERGY COMPANY LIMITED—See Chappal Energies Mauritius Limited; *Int'l*, pg. 1448
EQUINOR NORSK LNG AS—See Equinor ASA; *Int'l*, pg. 2484
EQUINOR POLSKA SP.ZO.O.—See Equinor ASA; *Int'l*, pg. 2484
EQUINOR REFINING DENMARK A/S—See Equinor ASA; *Int'l*, pg. 2484
EQUINOR SERVICE CENTER BELGIUM NV—See Equinor ASA; *Int'l*, pg. 2484
EQUINOR SOUTH KOREA CO., LTD.—See Equinor ASA; *Int'l*, pg. 2484
EQUINOR STORAGE DEUTSCHLAND GMBH—See Equinor ASA; *Int'l*, pg. 2484
EQUINOR TANZANIA AS—See Equinor ASA; *Int'l*, pg. 2484
EQUINOR TECHNOLOGY VENTURES AS—See Equinor ASA; *Int'l*, pg. 2484
EQUINOR UK LIMITED—See Equinor ASA; *Int'l*, pg. 2485
EQUINOR USA ONSHORE PROPERTIES INC.—See Equinor ASA; *Int'l*, pg. 2485

EQUINOR US HOLDINGS INC.—See Equinor ASA; *Int'l*, pg. 2485
EQUINOX BUSINESS SOLUTIONS; *U.S. Private*, pg. 1415
EQUINOX-COGNIZANT SARL—See Cognizant Technology Solutions Corporation; *U.S. Public*, pg. 524
EQUINOX CONSULTING SAS—See Cognizant Technology Solutions Corporation; *U.S. Public*, pg. 524
EQUINOXE KFT CG—See Beijer Ref AB; *Int'l*, pg. 944
EQUINOXE SOLUTIONS LIMITED—See Compass Group PLC; *Int'l*, pg. 1751
EQUINOX GOLD CORP.; *Int'l*, pg. 2485
EQUINOX IMPLANTS LLP—See Straumann Holding AG; *Int'l*, pg. 7237
EQUINOX RESOURCES LIMITED; *Int'l*, pg. 2485
EQUIOM (GUERNSEY) LIMITED—See Equiom (Isle of Man) Limited; *Int'l*, pg. 2485
EQUIOM (ISLE OF MAN) LIMITED; *Int'l*, pg. 2485
EQUIOM (JERSEY) LIMITED—See Equiom (Isle of Man) Limited; *Int'l*, pg. 2485
EQUIOM (MALTA) LIMITED—See Equiom (Isle of Man) Limited; *Int'l*, pg. 2485
EQUIOM MARINE & AVIATION SERVICES (JERSEY) LIMITED—See Equiom (Isle of Man) Limited; *Int'l*, pg. 2485
EQUIOM TRUST COMPANY (CYPRUS) LIMITED—See Equiom (Isle of Man) Limited; *Int'l*, pg. 2485
EQUION ENERGIA LIMITED—See Ecopetrol S.A.; *Int'l*, pg. 2298
EQUION ENERGIA LTD.—See Ecopetrol S.A.; *Int'l*, pg. 2298
EQUIPAGGIAMENTI ELETTRONICI INDUSTRIALI S.P.A.—See Ningbo Techmation Co., Ltd.; *Int'l*, pg. 5306
EQUIPAMENTOS CIENTIFICOS INSTRON LTD.—See Illinois Tool Works Inc.; *U.S. Public*, pg. 1108
EQUIPAMENTOS NGK-RINNAI, LTDA.—See Rinnai Corporation; *Int'l*, pg. 6344
EQUIPCERAMIC, S.A.; *Int'l*, pg. 2485
EQUIPCO INC.; *U.S. Private*, pg. 1415
E'QUIPE LTD.—See Kao Corporation; *Int'l*, pg. 4073
EQUIPEMENTS FDS INC.; *Int'l*, pg. 2485
EQUIPEMENTS PIERRE CHAMPIGNY LTEE; *Int'l*, pg. 2485
EQUIPEMENTS & SERVICE MAURITANIE SARL—See BIA Overseas S.A.; *Int'l*, pg. 1017
EQUIPEMENTS & SERVICES BIA—See BIA Overseas S.A.; *Int'l*, pg. 1017
EQUIPEMENTS & SERVICES NIAMEY—See BIA Overseas S.A.; *Int'l*, pg. 1017
EQUIPMAKE HOLDINGS PLC; *Int'l*, pg. 2485
EQUIPMAKE LIMITED—See Equipmake Holdings PLC; *Int'l*, pg. 2485
EQUIPMENT & CONTROLS, INC.; *U.S. Private*, pg. 1415
EQUIPMENT CO. W.L.L.—See Equipment Holding Company K.S.C.C.; *Int'l*, pg. 2485
EQUIPMENT DEPOT, INC.—See Pon Holdings B.V.; *Int'l*, pg. 5918
EQUIPMENT DEPOT KENTUCKY, INC.—See Pon Holdings B.V.; *Int'l*, pg. 5918
EQUIPMENT DEPOT LTD.—See Pon Holdings B.V.; *Int'l*, pg. 5918
EQUIPMENT DEPOT OF ILLINOIS, INC.—See Pon Holdings B.V.; *Int'l*, pg. 5919
EQUIPMENT DEPOT OHIO, INC.—See Pon Holdings B.V.; *Int'l*, pg. 5919
EQUIPMENT DEPOT PENNSYLVANIA, INC.—See Pon Holdings B.V.; *Int'l*, pg. 5919
EQUIPMENT DEPOT—See Pon Holdings B.V.; *Int'l*, pg. 5919
EQUIPMENTFACTS LLC—See Sandhills Publishing Company; *U.S. Private*, pg. 3543
EQUIPMENT FINANCE LIMITED—See Haier Smart Home Co., Ltd.; *Int'l*, pg. 3210
EQUIPMENT HOLDING COMPANY K.S.C.C.; *Int'l*, pg. 2485
EQUIPMENT INC.; *U.S. Private*, pg. 1415
EQUIPMENT MAINTENANCE SERVICES, INC.—See Sulzer Ltd.; *Int'l*, pg. 7257
EQUIPMENT MANAGEMENT GROUP, LLC—See BigRentz, Inc.; *U.S. Private*, pg. 556
EQUIPMENT RESEARCH GROUP PTY. LTD.—See carsales.com Limited; *Int'l*, pg. 1347
EQUIPMENT SALES AND RENTALS LTD—See Polaris Holding Company Limited; *Int'l*, pg. 5907
EQUIPMENT SALES CO.—See Fuji Corporation; *Int'l*, pg. 2809
EQUIPMENTS CELL CO., LTD.; *Int'l*, pg. 2485
EQUIPMENT SERVICES GROUP, INC.—See Gencor Industries, Inc.; *U.S. Public*, pg. 911
EQUIPMENT SPARE PARTS AFRICA (PTY) LTD.—See Invicta Holdings Limited; *Int'l*, pg. 3788
EQUIPMENT STORAGE & SERVICE INC.—See Ed Bell Investments Company Inc.; *U.S. Private*, pg. 1331
EQUIPMENT & SYSTEMS FOR THE INDUSTRY; *U.S. Private*, pg. 1415
EQUIPMENT TECHNOLOGY, LLC—See Palfinger AG; *Int'l*, pg. 5708

EQUIPMENT & SYSTEMS FOR THE INDUSTRY

EQUIPMENT TRADING SOLUTIONS GROUP, LLC—See Samsung BioLogics Co., Ltd.; *Int'l*, pg. 6510
EQUIPMENTWATCH—See Aurora Capital Group, LLC; *U.S. Private*, pg. 394
EQUIPMENT WORLD INC.; *Int'l*, pg. 2485
EQUIPO AUTOMOTRIZ AMERICANA S.A. DE C.V.—See Ningbo Joyson Electronic Corp.; *Int'l*, pg. 5303
EQUIPOS DE SENALIZACION Y CONTROL, S.A.—See ACS, Actividades de Construccion y Servicios, S.A.; *Int'l*, pg. 112
EQUIPOS NUCLEARES, S.A. (ENSA)—See Sociedad Estatal de Participaciones Industriales; *Int'l*, pg. 7032
EQUIPOS TERMO-METALICOS, S.A.—See Sociedad Estatal de Participaciones Industriales; *Int'l*, pg. 7032
EQUIPOS Y LABORATORIO DE COLOMBIA SAS—See HORIBA Ltd; *Int'l*, pg. 3475
EQUIPPP SOCIAL IMPACT TECHNOLOGIES LTD; *Int'l*, pg. 2485
EQUIPSYSTEMS, LLC; *U.S. Private*, pg. 1415
EQUIPTEST ENGINEERING PTE. LTD.—See Cohu, Inc.; *U.S. Public*, pg. 529
EQUIPT MANUFACTURING, INC.—See Hines Corporation; *U.S. Private*, pg. 1949
EQUIPTO ELECTRONICS CORP.; *U.S. Private*, pg. 1415
EQUIPTO, INC.—See Consolidated Storage Companies, Inc.; *U.S. Private*, pg. 1022
EQUISEARCH SERVICES INC.—See Palladian Capital Partners LLC; *U.S. Private*, pg. 3077
EQUISOFT INC.; *U.S. Private*, pg. 1415
EQUISOL LLC—See Environmental Infrastructure Holdings Corp.; *U.S. Private*, pg. 1408
EQUISOURCE HOTEL FUND I, LLP; *U.S. Private*, pg. 1416
EQUISPHERES INC.—See Zim Corporation; *Int'l*, pg. 8683
EQUIS STAFFING; *U.S. Private*, pg. 1415
EQUISTAR CHEMICALS LP—See LyondellBasell Industries N.V.; *Int'l*, pg. 4608
EQUISTAR CHEMICALS, LP—See LyondellBasell Industries N.V.; *Int'l*, pg. 4608
EQUISTAR GP, LLC—See LyondellBasell Industries N.V.; *Int'l*, pg. 4608
EQUISTONE PARTNERS EUROPE LIMITED; *Int'l*, pg. 2486
EQUISTONE PARTNERS EUROPE (SCHWEIZ) AG—See Equistone Partners Europe Limited; *Int'l*, pg. 2486
EQUISTONE PARTNERS GMBH—See Equistone Partners Europe Limited; *Int'l*, pg. 2486
EQUITABLE ADVISORS, LLC—See Equitable Holdings, Inc.; *U.S. Public*, pg. 789
EQUITABLE BANK—See Equitable Financial Corp.; *U.S. Public*, pg. 788
THE EQUITABLE BANK—See The Equitable Bank SSB; *U.S. Private*, pg. 4026
THE EQUITABLE BANK SSB; *U.S. Private*, pg. 4026
EQUITABLE ENERGY, LLC—See EQT Corporation; *U.S. Public*, pg. 784
EQUITABLE FINANCIAL CORP.; *U.S. Public*, pg. 788
EQUITABLE FINANCIAL LIFE INSURANCE COMPANY OF AMERICA—See Equitable Holdings, Inc.; *U.S. Public*, pg. 790
EQUITABLE FINANCIAL LIFE INSURANCE COMPANY; *U.S. Private*, pg. 1416
EQUITABLE HOLDINGS, INC.; *U.S. Public*, pg. 788
EQUITABLE LIFE & CASUALTY INSURANCE COMPANY; *U.S. Private*, pg. 1416
THE EQUITABLE LIFE INSURANCE COMPANY OF CANADA; *Int'l*, pg. 7640
EQUITABLE MINERAL & DEVELOPMENT INC.; *U.S. Private*, pg. 1416
EQUITABLE SAVINGS & LOAN ASSOCIATION; *U.S. Private*, pg. 1416
EQUITA GROUP S.P.A.; *Int'l*, pg. 2487
EQUITA LIMITED—See Capita plc; *Int'l*, pg. 1309
EQUITAL LTD.; *Int'l*, pg. 2487
EQUITAS HOLDINGS LIMITED; *Int'l*, pg. 2487
EQUITAS SMALL FINANCE BANK LIMITED—See Equitas Holdings Limited; *Int'l*, pg. 2488
EQUITES PROPERTY FUND LIMITED; *Int'l*, pg. 2488
THE EQUITIUM GROUP, LLC; *U.S. Private*, pg. 4026
EQUITIX INVESTMENT MANAGEMENT LIMITED; *Int'l*, pg. 2488
EQUITRAC CORPORATION—See Microsoft Corporation; *U.S. Public*, pg. 1442
EQUITRANS, LP—See EQT Corporation; *U.S. Public*, pg. 785
EQUITRANS MIDSTREAM CORPORATION—See EQT Corporation; *U.S. Public*, pg. 784
EQUI-TRAX ASSET SOLUTIONS LP—See Southwest Business Corporation; *U.S. Private*, pg. 3738
EQUITRUST GMBH—See E.R. CAPITAL HOLDING GmbH & Cie. KG; *Int'l*, pg. 2260
EQUITRUST LIFE INSURANCE COMPANY—See Magic Johnson Enterprises; *U.S. Private*, pg. 2546
EQUITRUST USA—See UDG, Inc.; *U.S. Public*, pg. 4274
EQUITY38, LLC; *U.S. Private*, pg. 1416
EQUITY & ADVISORY LTD.—See E&A Limited; *Int'l*, pg. 2247
EQUITY ANALYTICS, LLC—See Bank of America Corporation; *U.S. Public*, pg. 272

EQUITY APARTMENT MANAGEMENT, LLC—See Equity Residential; *U.S. Public*, pg. 792
EQUITY BANCSHARES, INC.; *U.S. Public*, pg. 790
EQUITY BANK LIMITED; *Int'l*, pg. 2488
EQUITY BANK—See Equity Bancshares, Inc.; *U.S. Public*, pg. 790
EQUITY CAPITAL MANAGEMENT, LLC; *U.S. Private*, pg. 1416
EQUITY COMMONWEALTH EQC—See Equity Commonwealth; *U.S. Public*, pg. 790
EQUITY COMMONWEALTH; *U.S. Public*, pg. 790
EQUITY CONCEPTS REALTY CORP.; *U.S. Private*, pg. 1416
EQUITY COOP LIVESTOCK SALES ASSOCIATION; *U.S. Private*, pg. 1416
EQUITY DISTRIBUTION ACQUISITION CORP.; *U.S. Public*, pg. 790
EQUITY DISTRIBUTION LLC—See Live Nation Entertainment, Inc.; *U.S. Public*, pg. 1328
EQUITY GROUP HOLDINGS PLC; *Int'l*, pg. 2488
EQUITY GROUP INVESTMENTS, LLC—See TowerBrook Capital Partners, L.P.; *U.S. Private*, pg. 4195
EQUITY GROUP KENTUCKY DIVISION LLC—See Tyson Foods, Inc.; *U.S. Public*, pg. 2209
EQUITY, INC.; *U.S. Private*, pg. 1416
EQUITY INSURANCE AGENCY, INC.—See Wells Fargo & Company; *U.S. Public*, pg. 2343
EQUITY INSURANCE GROUP LTD.—See The Ardonagh Group Limited; *Int'l*, pg. 7614
EQUITY INVESTMENT ADVISERS LIMITED—See Investment Research Group Limited; *Int'l*, pg. 3785
EQUITY INVESTMENT GROUP; *U.S. Private*, pg. 1416
EQUITY INVESTMENT SERVICES LTD—See Equity Bank Limited; *Int'l*, pg. 2488
EQUITY LIFESTYLE PROPERTIES, INC.; *U.S. Public*, pg. 790
EQUITY LOAN BROKING PTY LTD.—See Count Limited; *Int'l*, pg. 1817
EQUITY LOANS LLC.; *U.S. Private*, pg. 1416
EQUITY METALS CORPORATION; *Int'l*, pg. 2488
EQUITY METHODS, LLC—See Bank of America Corporation; *U.S. Public*, pg. 272
EQUITYMETRIX; *U.S. Private*, pg. 1416
EQUITY OFFICE MANAGEMENT, LLC—See Blackstone Inc.; *U.S. Public*, pg. 350
EQUITY ONE PLC—See Carson Cumberbatch PLC; *Int'l*, pg. 1347
EQUITY PARTNERS INSURANCE SERVICES, INC.—See One80 Intermediaries LLC; *U.S. Private*, pg. 3024
EQUITY POINT LISBOA UNIPESSOAL LDA.—See Safestay Plc; *Int'l*, pg. 6470
EQUITY POINT PRAGUE S.R.O—See Safestay Plc; *Int'l*, pg. 6470
EQUITY RESIDENTIAL MANAGEMENT, L.L.C.—See Equity Residential; *U.S. Public*, pg. 792
EQUITY RESIDENTIAL; *U.S. Public*, pg. 790
EQUITY SERVICES, INC.—See National Life Insurance Company; *U.S. Private*, pg. 2858
EQUITY STORY GROUP LTD.; *Int'l*, pg. 2488
EQUITY STORY PTY LTD.—See Equity Story Group Ltd.; *Int'l*, pg. 2488
EQUITYSTORY RS, LLC—See Thoma Bravo, L.P.; *U.S. Private*, pg. 4147
EQUITY SUD ADVISOR S.R.L.—See Meridie S.p.A.; *Int'l*, pg. 4836
EQUITY TITLE CO. INC.—See Anywhere Real Estate Inc.; *U.S. Public*, pg. 142
EQUITY TITLE COMPANY—See Anywhere Real Estate Inc.; *U.S. Public*, pg. 142
EQUITY TRANSPORTATION CO.; *U.S. Private*, pg. 1416
EQUITY TRUST COMPANY; *U.S. Private*, pg. 1416
EQUITY TRUSTEES LIMITED; *Int'l*, pg. 2488
EQUITY TWO PLC—See Carson Cumberbatch PLC; *Int'l*, pg. 1347
EQUITY VALUE INVESTMENTS NO.1 LIMITED—See Barclays PLC; *Int'l*, pg. 862
EQUIUS PARTNERS INC.—See TA Associates, Inc.; *U.S. Private*, pg. 3919
EQUIVEST GMBH & CO—See CBR Management GmbH; *Int'l*, pg. 1366
EQUIVIO INC.—See Microsoft Corporation; *U.S. Public*, pg. 1439
EQUOS RESEARCH CO., LTD.—See AISIN Corporation; *Int'l*, pg. 253
EQUOVIS GMBH—See AGRAVIS Raiffeisen AG; *Int'l*, pg. 215
E-QURE CORP.; *U.S. Private*, pg. 1302
EQUUS CAPITAL PARTNERS, LTD.; *U.S. Private*, pg. 1416
EQUUS COMPUTER SYSTEMS, INC.—See Equus, Holdings, Inc.; *U.S. Private*, pg. 1417
EQUUS GROUP, LLC; *U.S. Private*, pg. 1416
EQUUS HOLDINGS, INC.; *U.S. Private*, pg. 1417
EQUUS MINING LIMITED; *Int'l*, pg. 2488
EQUUS SOFTWARE, LLC; *U.S. Private*, pg. 1417
EQUUS TOTAL RETURN, INC.; *U.S. Public*, pg. 792
EQVA ASA; *Int'l*, pg. 2488
EQVITEC PARTNERS OY; *Int'l*, pg. 2488
ERAAYA LIFESPACES LIMITED; *Int'l*, pg. 2488

CORPORATE AFFILIATIONS

ERA BROKERS CONSOLIDATED - LAS VEGAS—See Brokers Consolidated, Inc.; *U.S. Private*, pg. 662
ERA BROKERS CONSOLIDATED - MESQUITE—See Brokers Consolidated, Inc.; *U.S. Private*, pg. 662
ERA CO., LTD.; *Int'l*, pg. 2488
ERADICO SERVICES, INC. - METRO NORTH SERVICE CENTER—See Rentokil Initial plc; *Int'l*, pg. 6287
ERADICO SERVICES, INC. - NORTHERN MICHIGAN SERVICE CENTER—See Rentokil Initial plc; *Int'l*, pg. 6287
ERADICO SERVICES, INC.—See Rentokil Initial plc; *Int'l*, pg. 6286
ERAD, INC.—See RadNet, Inc.; *U.S. Public*, pg. 1761
ERA D.O.O.; *Int'l*, pg. 2488
ERAE AUTOMOTIVE SYSTEMS CO.,LTD.—See Shanghai Aerospace Automobile Electromechanical Co., Ltd.; *Int'l*, pg. 6761
ERA ECOSYSTEM RESTORATION ASSOCIATES INC.—See Ostrom Climate Solutions Inc.; *Int'l*, pg. 5655
ERA FLIGHTSEEING LLC—See Bristow Group, Inc.; *U.S. Public*, pg. 387
ERA-FONSTER AB—See Ratos AB; *Int'l*, pg. 6220
ERA FRANCHISE SYSTEMS LLC—See Anywhere Real Estate Inc.; *U.S. Public*, pg. 141
ERAG ELEKTRIZITATSWERK RHEINAU AG—See EnBW Energie Baden-Wurttemberg AG; *Int'l*, pg. 2398
ERA HELICOPTERS, LLC—See Bristow Group, Inc.; *U.S. Public*, pg. 387
ERAJAYA DIGITAL RETAIL PTE. LTD.—See PT Erajaya Swasembada Tbk; *Int'l*, pg. 6038
ERAL CO., LTD.—See Nicca Chemical Co., Ltd.; *Int'l*, pg. 5263
ERA LEASING LLC—See Bristow Group, Inc.; *U.S. Public*, pg. 387
ERA MED LLC—See Bristow Group, Inc.; *U.S. Public*, pg. 387
ERAM EILIA, INC.—See Atlantic China Welding Consumables, Inc.; *Int'l*, pg. 674
ERAMET ALLOYS—See Eramet SA; *Int'l*, pg. 2488
ERAMET MANGANESE—See Eramet SA; *Int'l*, pg. 2489
ERAMET MARIETTA INC.—See Eramet SA; *Int'l*, pg. 2489
ERAMET NICKEL—See Eramet SA; *Int'l*, pg. 2489
ERAMET NORWAY A/S—See Eramet SA; *Int'l*, pg. 2489
ERAMET SA; *Int'l*, pg. 2488
ERANTOS, S.A.U.—See Sacyr, S.A.; *Int'l*, pg. 6465
ERA OGILVY PUBLIC RELATIONS CO. LTD.—See WPP plc; *Int'l*, pg. 8490
ERA PRODUCTS LIMITED—See Quanex Building Products Corp.; *U.S. Public*, pg. 1749
E-RAPTOR TECHNOLOGIES INC.—See Ilustrato Pictures International Inc.; *Int'l*, pg. 3616
ERARD SAS—See SCA Qualis; *Int'l*, pg. 6610
ERA REALTY NETWORK PTE. LTD.—See Morgan Stanley; *U.S. Public*, pg. 1471
ERA RESOURCES INC.; *Int'l*, pg. 2488
ERASCA, INC.; *U.S. Public*, pg. 792
ERASER DUST, INC.; *U.S. Private*, pg. 1417
ERASMUS ANTIQUARIAAT EN BOEKHANDEL B.V.—See Aurelius Equity Opportunities SE & Co. KGaA; *Int'l*, pg. 708
ERA S.P.A.—See LKQ Corporation; *U.S. Public*, pg. 1334
ERA S.R.L.—See LKQ Corporation; *U.S. Public*, pg. 1334
ERAS—See Checkalt, LLC; *U.S. Private*, pg. 869
ERASTEELE CHAMPAGNOLE—See Syntagma Capital Management SA; *Int'l*, pg. 7386
ERASTEEL INC.—See Eramet SA; *Int'l*, pg. 2489
ERASTEEL KLOSTER AB—See Syntagma Capital Management SA; *Int'l*, pg. 7386
ERASTEEL SAS- COMMENTRY PLANT—See Syntagma Capital Management SA; *Int'l*, pg. 7386
ERASTEEL SAS—See Syntagma Capital Management SA; *Int'l*, pg. 7386
ERASTEEL STUBS LTD.—See Syntagma Capital Management SA; *Int'l*, pg. 7386
ERA SUNRISE REALTY; *U.S. Private*, pg. 1417
ERA SUREWAY SDN. BHD.—See Sealink International Bhd; *Int'l*, pg. 6665
ERATAT LIFESTYLE LIMITED; *Int'l*, pg. 2489
ERA TECH COMMUNICATION PTE. LTD.—See PT Erajaya Swasembada Tbk; *Int'l*, pg. 6038
ERA TRAINING CENTER, LLC—See Bristow Group, Inc.; *U.S. Public*, pg. 388
ERA TRAINING CENTER, LLC—See Frasca International Inc.; *U.S. Private*, pg. 1599
ERAU EXTENDED CAMPUS COLLEGE OF CAREER EDUCATION—See Embry-Riddle Aeronautical University; *U.S. Private*, pg. 1379
ERA VALDIVIA CONTRACTORS, INC.; *U.S. Private*, pg. 1417
ERAWAN CHAOPHRAYA COMPANY LIMITED—See The Erawan Group Public Company Limited; *Int'l*, pg. 7640
THE ERAWAN GROUP PUBLIC COMPANY LIMITED; *Int'l*, pg. 7640
ERAWAN GROWTH MANAGEMENT COMPANY LIMITED—See The Erawan Group Public Company Limited; *Int'l*, pg. 7640
ERAWAN HOTEL PUBLIC COMPANY LIMITED—See The Erawan Group Public Company Limited; *Int'l*, pg. 7640

COMPANY NAME INDEX

ERAWAN NAKA COMPANY LIMITED—See The Erawan Group Public Company Limited; *Int'l*, pg. 7640
ERAWAN PHUKET COMPANY LIMITED—See The Erawan Group Public Company Limited; *Int'l*, pg. 7640
ERAWAN RAJDAMRI COMPANY LIMITED—See The Erawan Group Public Company Limited; *Int'l*, pg. 7640
ERAWAN SAMUI COMPANY LIMITED—See The Erawan Group Public Company Limited; *Int'l*, pg. 7640
ERAWAN TEXTILE CO., LTD.—See Saha Pathanapibul Public Company Limited; *Int'l*, pg. 6479
ERAYAK POWER SOLUTION GROUP INC.; *Int'l*, pg. 2489
ERBACON INVESTMENT HOLDINGS LIMITED; *Int'l*, pg. 2489
ERBA DIAGNOSTICS, INC.—See Transasia Bio-Medicals Ltd.; *Int'l*, pg. 7896
ERBA DIAGNOSTICS MANNHEIM GMBH—See Transasia Bio-Medicals Ltd.; *Int'l*, pg. 7895
ERB ELECTRIC CO.; *U.S. Private*, pg. 1417
ERB EQUIPMENT CO. INC.; *U.S. Private*, pg. 1417
ERB EQUIPMENT CO.—See Erb Equipment Co. Inc.; *U.S. Private*, pg. 1417
E.R. BERWALD ROOFING COMPANY; *U.S. Private*, pg. 1306
ERBE SA—See BNP Paribas SA; *Int'l*, pg. 1090
ERBE SA—See Frere-Bourgeois; *Int'l*, pg. 2773
ERB INDUSTRIES INC.; *U.S. Private*, pg. 1417
ERBORISTERIE D'ITALIA SRL—See Bioera S.p.A.; *Int'l*, pg. 1037
ERBOSAN ERCIYAS BORU SANAYII VE TICARET A.S.; *Int'l*, pg. 2489
ERBUD S.A.; *Int'l*, pg. 2489
E.R. CAPITAL HOLDING GMBH & CIE. KG; *Int'l*, pg. 2260
ERC INCORPORATED; *U.S. Private*, pg. 1417
ERCL LIMITED—See Getech Group plc; *Int'l*, pg. 2947
ERCO INTERIEURBOUW B.V.; *Int'l*, pg. 2489
ERCOM S.P.A.—See Luigi Lavazza S.p.A.; *Int'l*, pg. 4575
ERCON ASSOCIATES—See PMC Capital Partners, LLC; *U.S. Private*, pg. 3218
ERCO WORLDWIDE, INC.—See Birch Hill Equity Partners Management Inc.; *Int'l*, pg. 1046
ERCO WORLDWIDE—See Birch Hill Equity Partners Management Inc.; *Int'l*, pg. 1046
ERCO WORLDWIDE (USA) INC.—See Birch Hill Equity Partners Management Inc.; *Int'l*, pg. 1046
ERC PARTS INC.; *U.S. Private*, pg. 1417
ERC PROPERTIES INC.; *U.S. Private*, pg. 1417
ERCROS SA - ANIMAL FEED DIVISION - CARTAGENA FACTORY—See Ercros SA; *Int'l*, pg. 2489
ERCROS SA - ANIMAL FEED DIVISION - FLIX FACTORY—See Ercros SA; *Int'l*, pg. 2489
ERCROS SA - ANIMAL FEED DIVISION—See Ercros SA; *Int'l*, pg. 2489
ERCROS SA - BASIC CHEMICALS DIVISION - FLIX FACTORY—See Ercros SA; *Int'l*, pg. 2489
ERCROS SA - BASIC CHEMICALS DIVISION - SABINANIGO FACTORY—See Ercros SA; *Int'l*, pg. 2489
ERCROS SA - BASIC CHEMICALS DIVISION—See Ercros SA; *Int'l*, pg. 2489
ERCROS SA - BASIC CHEMICALS DIVISION - TARRAGONA FACTORY—See Ercros SA; *Int'l*, pg. 2489
ERCROS SA - BASIC CHEMICALS DIVISION - VILASECA I FACTORY—See Ercros SA; *Int'l*, pg. 2490
ERCROS SA - INTERMEDIATE CHEMICALS DIVISION - CERDANYOLA FACTORY—See Ercros SA; *Int'l*, pg. 2490
ERCROS SA - INTERMEDIATE CHEMICALS DIVISION—See Ercros SA; *Int'l*, pg. 2490
ERCROS SA - INTERMEDIATE CHEMICALS DIVISION - TORTOSA FACTORY—See Ercros SA; *Int'l*, pg. 2490
ERCROS SA - PHARMACEUTICAL DIVISION-FYSE—See Ercros SA; *Int'l*, pg. 2490
ERCROS SA - PLASTICS DIVISION—See Ercros SA; *Int'l*, pg. 2490
ERCROS SA; *Int'l*, pg. 2489
ERCROS SA - WATER TREATMENT DIVISION - SABINANIGO FACTORY—See Ercros SA; *Int'l*, pg. 2490
ERCROS SA - WATER TREATMENT DIVISION—See Ercros SA; *Int'l*, pg. 2490
ERDEMIR LOJISTIK A.S.—See Eregli Demir Ve Celik Fabrikalari T.A.S.; *Int'l*, pg. 2490
ERDEMIR MADENCILIK SANAYI VE TICARET A.S.—See Eregli Demir Ve Celik Fabrikalari T.A.S.; *Int'l*, pg. 2490
ERDEMIR MUHENDISLIK YONETIM VE DANISMANLIK HIZMETLERI A.S.—See Eregli Demir Ve Celik Fabrikalari T.A.S.; *Int'l*, pg. 2490
ERDEMIR ROMANIA S.R.L.—See Eregli Demir Ve Celik Fabrikalari T.A.S.; *Int'l*, pg. 2490
ERDENE MONGOL LLC—See Erdene Resource Development Corp.; *Int'l*, pg. 2490
ERDENE RESOURCE DEVELOPMENT CORP.; *Int'l*, pg. 2490
ERDENET MINING CORPORATION; *Int'l*, pg. 2490
ERDGAS-BETEILIGUNGSGESELLSCHAFT SUD MBH—See EnBW Energie Baden-Wurttemberg AG; *Int'l*, pg. 2399
ERDGAS SUDWEST GMBH—See EnBW Energie Baden-Wurttemberg AG; *Int'l*, pg. 2399

ERDLE PERFORATING COMPANY; *U.S. Private*, pg. 1417
ERDMAN HOLDINGS, INC.; *U.S. Private*, pg. 1417
ERDOL-ERDGASWORKOVER GMBH & CO. KG—See MB Holding Company LLC; *Int'l*, pg. 4750
ERDWARME PLUS GMBH—See NIBE Industrier AB; *Int'l*, pg. 5260
ERECORDING PARTNERS NETWORK, LLC—See Old Republic International Corporation; *U.S. Public*, pg. 1569
ERECO ZRT.—See Derichebourg S.A.; *Int'l*, pg. 2042
ERECRUITMENT SOLUTIONS SP. Z O.O.—See Grupa Pracuj S.A.; *Int'l*, pg. 3117
ERECT-A-LINE INC.—See Georgeco Inc.; *U.S. Private*, pg. 1684
ERECTION ELECTROMECHANICS TESTING JSC; *Int'l*, pg. 2490
EREDIVISIE BEHEER B.V.—See The Walt Disney Company; *U.S. Public*, pg. 2140
EREDIVISIE MEDIA & MARKETING C.V.—See The Walt Disney Company; *U.S. Public*, pg. 2140
EREGLI DEMIR VE CELIK FABRIKALARI T.A.S.; *Int'l*, pg. 2490
EREGLI TEKSTIL TURIZM SANAYI VE TICARET A.S.; *Int'l*, pg. 2490
EREINSURE.COM, INC.—See AmWINS Group, Inc.; *U.S. Private*, pg. 270
EREINSURE (UK) LIMITED—See AmWINS Group, Inc.; *U.S. Private*, pg. 270
E&R ENGINEERING CORP.; *Int'l*, pg. 2247
EREN GROUPE SA; *Int'l*, pg. 2490
E.REPUBLIC, INC.; *U.S. Private*, pg. 1307
ERESEARCHTECHNOLOGY GMBH—See Astorg Partners S.A.S.; *Int'l*, pg. 657
ERESEARCHTECHNOLOGY GMBH—See Nordic Capital AB; *Int'l*, pg. 5421
ERESEARCHTECHNOLOGY GMBH—See Novo Nordisk Fonden; *Int'l*, pg. 5465
ERESEARCHTECHNOLOGY, INC. - BRIDGEWATER—See Astorg Partners S.A.S.; *Int'l*, pg. 657
ERESEARCHTECHNOLOGY, INC. - BRIDGEWATER—See Nordic Capital AB; *Int'l*, pg. 5421
ERESEARCHTECHNOLOGY, INC. - BRIDGEWATER—See Novo Nordisk Fonden; *Int'l*, pg. 5465
ERESEARCHTECHNOLOGY, INC.—See Astorg Partners S.A.S.; *Int'l*, pg. 657
ERESEARCHTECHNOLOGY, INC.—See Nordic Capital AB; *Int'l*, pg. 5421
ERESEARCHTECHNOLOGY, INC.—See Novo Nordisk Fonden; *Int'l*, pg. 5465
ERESEARCHTECHNOLOGY LIMITED—See Astorg Partners S.A.S.; *Int'l*, pg. 657
ERESEARCHTECHNOLOGY LIMITED—See Nordic Capital AB; *Int'l*, pg. 5421
ERESEARCHTECHNOLOGY LIMITED—See Novo Nordisk Fonden; *Int'l*, pg. 5465
E REVOLUTION VENTURES, INC.; *U.S. Private*, pg. 1301
E-REWARDS, INC.; *U.S. Private*, pg. 1302
EREX CO., LTD.; *Int'l*, pg. 2490
ERFATOR PROJEKTLEDNING AB—See Bravida Holding AB; *Int'l*, pg. 1142
ERF WIRELESS, INC.; *U.S. Private*, pg. 1417
ERG CAP 3 REIT; *Int'l*, pg. 2490
ERG DEVELOPPEMENT FRANCE S.A.S.—See ERG S.p.A.; *Int'l*, pg. 2491
ERG EDELSTAHL RECYCLING GMBH—See CRONIMET Holding GmbH; *Int'l*, pg. 1854
ER&GE GMBH; *Int'l*, pg. 2488
ERG EOLICA ITALIA SRL—See ERG S.p.A.; *Int'l*, pg. 2491
ER&GE (UK) LIMITED—See ER&GE GmbH; *Int'l*, pg. 2488
ERG EXPLORATION JSC; *Int'l*, pg. 2490
ERGIS-RECYCLING SP. Z O.O.—See Ergis S.A.; *Int'l*, pg. 2491
ERGIS S.A.; *Int'l*, pg. 2491
ERGO ASIA MANAGEMENT PTE. LTD.—See Munchener Ruckversicherungs AG; *Int'l*, pg. 5086
ERGO ASIA PTY. LTD.—See Konica Minolta, Inc.; *Int'l*, pg. 4257
ERGO ASIGURARI DE VIATA SA—See Munchener Ruckversicherungs AG; *Int'l*, pg. 5087
ERGO AUSTRIA INTERNATIONAL AG—See Munchener Ruckversicherungs AG; *Int'l*, pg. 5086
THE ERGO BABY CARRIER, INC.—See Compass Diversified Holdings; *U.S. Public*, pg. 560
ERGOBABY EUROPE GMBH—See Compass Diversified Holdings; *U.S. Public*, pg. 560
ERGO COMPUTING UK LIMITED—See V.I.P. Computer Centre Limited; *Int'l*, pg. 8106
ERGO DIREKT LEBENSVERSICHERUNG AG—See Munchener Ruckversicherungs AG; *Int'l*, pg. 5086
ERGO ELETBIZTOSITO ZRT.—See Munchener Ruckversicherungs AG; *Int'l*, pg. 5086

ERGONOMIC GROUP INC.

ERGO (ERGONOMIC COMMUNICATIONS)—See The Interpublic Group of Companies, Inc.; *U.S. Public*, pg. 2091
ERGO-FIT GMBH & CO. KG; *Int'l*, pg. 2491
ERGO-FLEX TECHNOLOGIES, LLC; *U.S. Private*, pg. 1417
ERGO FUNDS AS—See Munchener Ruckversicherungs AG; *Int'l*, pg. 5086
ERGO GENERAL INSURANCE COMPANY S.A.—See Munchener Ruckversicherungs AG; *Int'l*, pg. 5086
ERGO GOURMET GMBH—See Munchener Ruckversicherungs AG; *Int'l*, pg. 5087
ERGO GRUBU HOLDING A.S.—See Munchener Ruckversicherungs AG; *Int'l*, pg. 5086
ERGO IMMOBILIEN-GMBH 14.VICTORIA & CO. KG—See Munchener Ruckversicherungs AG; *Int'l*, pg. 5086
ERGO IMMOBILIEN-GMBH 4. DKV & CO. KG—See Munchener Ruckversicherungs AG; *Int'l*, pg. 5086
ERGO IMMOBILIEN-GMBH 5. HAMBURG-MANNHEIMER & CO. KG—See Munchener Ruckversicherungs AG; *Int'l*, pg. 5086
ERGO IMMOBILIEN-GMBH 6. HAMBURG-MANNHEIMER & CO. KG—See Munchener Ruckversicherungs AG; *Int'l*, pg. 5086
ERGO IMMOBILIEN-GMBH 7. HAMBURG-MANNHEIMER & CO. KG—See Munchener Ruckversicherungs AG; *Int'l*, pg. 5086
ERGO IMMOBILIEN-VERWALTUNGS-GMBH—See Munchener Ruckversicherungs AG; *Int'l*, pg. 5086
ERGO INSURANCE NV/SA—See Munchener Ruckversicherungs AG; *Int'l*, pg. 5087
ERGO INSURANCE PTE. LTD.—See Munchener Ruckversicherungs AG; *Int'l*, pg. 5087
ERGO INSURANCE SERVICE GMBH—See Munchener Ruckversicherungs AG; *Int'l*, pg. 5087
ERGO INTERNATIONAL SERVICES GMBH—See Munchener Ruckversicherungs AG; *Int'l*, pg. 5086
ERGOISVICRE A.S.—See Munchener Ruckversicherungs AG; *Int'l*, pg. 5087
ERGO LATVIJA VERSICHERUNG AG—See Munchener Ruckversicherungs AG; *Int'l*, pg. 5086
ERGO LEBENSVERSICHERUNG AKTIENGESELLSCHAFT—See Munchener Ruckversicherungs AG; *Int'l*, pg. 5086
ERGO LIFE INSURANCE SE—See Munchener Ruckversicherungs AG; *Int'l*, pg. 5087
ERGOMAT, INC.—See SP Group A/S; *Int'l*, pg. 7122
ERGOMAT-NEDERLAND B.V.—See SP Group A/S; *Int'l*, pg. 7122
ERGOM DO BRASIL LTDA—See Stellantis N.V.; *Int'l*, pg. 7197
ERGOMED CLINICAL RESEARCH FZ LLC—See Permira Advisers LLP; *Int'l*, pg. 5804
ERGOMED CLINICAL RESEARCH LIMITED—See Permira Advisers LLP; *Int'l*, pg. 5804
ERGOMED CLINICAL RESEARCH LLC—See Permira Advisers LLP; *Int'l*, pg. 5804
ERGOMED D.O.O. NOVI SAD—See Permira Advisers LLP; *Int'l*, pg. 5804
ERGOMED D.O.O. SARAJEVO—See Permira Advisers LLP; *Int'l*, pg. 5804
ERGOMED GMBH—See Permira Advisers LLP; *Int'l*, pg. 5804
ERGOMED ISTRAZIVANJA ZAGREB D.O.O.—See Permira Advisers LLP; *Int'l*, pg. 5804
ERGOMED PLC—See Permira Advisers LLP; *Int'l*, pg. 5803
ERGOMED SPOLKA Z O.O.—See Permira Advisers LLP; *Int'l*, pg. 5804
ERGOMED VIRTUOSO SARL—See Permira Advisers LLP; *Int'l*, pg. 5804
ERGOM SOFFIAGGIO S.R.L.—See Stellantis N.V.; *Int'l*, pg. 7203
ERGON ASFALTOS MEXICO S. DE R.L. DE C.V.—See Ergon, Inc.; *U.S. Private*, pg. 1418
ERGON ASPHALT & EMULSIONS, INC.—See Ergon, Inc.; *U.S. Private*, pg. 1417
ERGON CAPITAL MANAGEMENT SA—See Groupe Bruxelles Lambert SA; *Int'l*, pg. 3099
ERGON CAPITAL MANAGEMENT SA—See Parcom Capital Management B.V.; *Int'l*, pg. 5739
ERGON ENERGY CORPORATION LIMITED; *Int'l*, pg. 2491
ERGON ENERGY PARTNERS, LP—See Ergon, Inc.; *U.S. Private*, pg. 1418
ERGON ENERGY TELECOMMUNICATIONS PTY LTD—See Ergon Energy Corporation Limited; *Int'l*, pg. 2491
ERGON EUROPE MEA, INC.—See Ergon, Inc.; *U.S. Private*, pg. 1418
ERGON, INC.; *U.S. Private*, pg. 1417
ERGON MARINE & INDUSTRIAL SUPPLY, INC.—See Ergon, Inc.; *U.S. Private*, pg. 1418
ERGON N.V.—See CRH plc; *Int'l*, pg. 1844
ERGON OIL PURCHASING, INC.—See Ergon, Inc.; *U.S. Private*, pg. 1418
ERGONOMIC GROUP INC.; *U.S. Private*, pg. 1418
ERGONOMICS AG—See Mountain Capital Management AG; *Int'l*, pg. 5057

891

ERGONOMIC GROUP INC.

ERGON POLAND SP. Z O.O.—See CRH plc; *Int'l*, pg. 1844
ERGON PROPERTIES, INC.—See Ergon, Inc.; *U.S. Private*, pg. 1418
ERGON REFINING, INC.—See Ergon, Inc.; *U.S. Private*, pg. 1418
ERGON-ST. JAMES, INC.—See Ergon, Inc.; *U.S. Private*, pg. 1418
ERGON TRUCKING, INC.—See Ergon, Inc.; *U.S. Private*, pg. 1418
ERGON WEST VIRGINIA, INC.—See Ergon, Inc.; *U.S. Private*, pg. 1418
ERGOPACK LLC—See Gr. Sarantis S.A.; *Int'l*, pg. 3047
ERGO PENSIONSFONDS AKTIENGESELLSCHAFT—See Munchener Ruckversicherungs AG; *Int'l*, pg. 5086
ERGO PENSIONSKASSE AG—See Munchener Ruckversicherungs AG; *Int'l*, pg. 5086
ERGO POISTOVNA, A.S.—See Munchener Ruckversicherungs AG; *Int'l*, pg. 5086
ERGO POJISTOVNA, A.S.—See Munchener Ruckversicherungs AG; *Int'l*, pg. 5087
ERGO PRIVATE CAPITAL GESUNDHEIT GMBH & CO. KG—See Munchener Ruckversicherungs AG; *Int'l*, pg. 5086
ERGO PRIVATE CAPITAL GMBH—See Munchener Ruckversicherungs AG; *Int'l*, pg. 5086
ERGO PRIVATE CAPITAL LEBEN GMBH & CO. KG—See Munchener Ruckversicherungs AG; *Int'l*, pg. 5086
ERGO PRIVATE EQUITY LEBEN GMBH—See Munchener Ruckversicherungs AG; *Int'l*, pg. 5086
ERGORESEARCH INC.—See Walter Capital Partners Inc.; *Int'l*, pg. 8336
ERGO RUSS VERSICHERUNG AG—See Munchener Ruckversicherungs AG; *Int'l*, pg. 5086
ERGO SCIENCE CORP.; *U.S. Private*, pg. 1417
ERGO SIGORTA A.S.—See Talanx AG; *Int'l*, pg. 7443
ERGO SIGORTA VE EMEKLILIK SATIS ARACILIK HIZMETLERI LIMITED SIRKETI—See Munchener Ruckversicherungs AG; *Int'l*, pg. 5086
ERGO SPECIALTY GMBH—See Munchener Ruckversicherungs AG; *Int'l*, pg. 5086
ERGOS TECHNOLOGY PARTNERS, INC.; *U.S. Private*, pg. 1418
ERGOTRON DEUTSCHLAND GMBH—See Melrose Industries PLC; *Int'l*, pg. 4812
ERGOTRON FRANCE SARL—See Melrose Industries PLC; *Int'l*, pg. 4812
ERGOTRON, INC.—See The Sterling Group, L.P.; *U.S. Private*, pg. 4122
ERGOTRON NEDERLAND B.V.—See The Sterling Group, L.P.; *U.S. Private*, pg. 4123
ERGO VERSICHERUNG AKTIENGESELLSCHAFT—See Munchener Ruckversicherungs AG; *Int'l*, pg. 5087
ERGO VERSICHERUNGSGRUPPE AG—See Munchener Ruckversicherungs AG; *Int'l*, pg. 5086
ERGO VERSICHERUNGS- UND FINANZIERUNGS-VERMITTLUNG GMBH—See Munchener Ruckversicherungs AG; *Int'l*, pg. 5087
ERGO VIDA SEGUROS Y REASEGUROS, SOCIEDAD ANONIMA—See Munchener Ruckversicherungs AG; *Int'l*, pg. 5088
ERGO ZIVLJENJSKA ZAVAROVALNICA D.D.—See Munchener Ruckversicherungs AG; *Int'l*, pg. 5087
ERGO ZIVOTNA POISTOVNA, A.S.—See Munchener Ruckversicherungs AG; *Int'l*, pg. 5087
ERGO ZIVOTNO OSIGURANJE D.D.—See Munchener Ruckversicherungs AG; *Int'l*, pg. 5088
ERG RENEW S.P.A.—See ERG S.p.A.; *Int'l*, pg. 2491
ERG S.A.; *Int'l*, pg. 2490
ERG S.P.A.; *Int'l*, pg. 2491
ERG WIND 6 S.R.L.—See ERG S.p.A.; *Int'l*, pg. 2491
ERG WIND SICILIA 3 S.R.L.—See ERG S.p.A.; *Int'l*, pg. 2491
ERGYCAPITAL S.P.A.—See Intek Group S.p.A.; *Int'l*, pg. 3732
ERGYTECH INC.—See Iberdrola, S.A.; *Int'l*, pg. 3570
ERHARD BMW OF BLOOMFIELD HILLS; *U.S. Private*, pg. 1419
ERHARD GMBH & CO. KG—See Triton Advisers Limited; *Int'l*, pg. 7934
ERHC ENERGY, INC; *U.S. Public*, pg. 792
E.R.H.S.A.; *Int'l*, pg. 2260
ERICA TANOV INC.; *U.S. Private*, pg. 1419
ERIC ELECTRONICS, INC.; *U.S. Private*, pg. 1419
ERICH HENKEL AUTOMOTIVE GROUP; *U.S. Private*, pg. 1419
ERICH JAEGER GMBH + CO. KG—See AdCapital AG; *Int'l*, pg. 126
ERICH JAEGER MEXICO, S. DE R.L.—See AdCapital AG; *Int'l*, pg. 126
ERICH JAEGER U.S.A. INC.—See AdCapital AG; *Int'l*, pg. 126
ERICH NETZSCH GMBH & CO. HOLDING KG; *Int'l*, pg. 2491
ERICHS ARMATUR AB—See AUMA Riester GmbH & Co. KG; *Int'l*, pg. 705
ERICHS ARMATUR AB—See Pentair plc; *Int'l*, pg. 5789
ERICH UTSCH AG; *Int'l*, pg. 2493

ERICH WEIT GMBH—See ThyssenKrupp AG; *Int'l*, pg. 7724
ERICH ZIEGLER GMBH—See Archer-Daniels-Midland Company; *U.S. Public*, pg. 185
ERICKSEN ADVERTISING & DESIGN, INC.; *U.S. Private*, pg. 1419
ERICKSEN NISSAN; *Int'l*, pg. 2493
ERICKSON ASSOCIATES, INC.; *U.S. Private*, pg. 1419
ERICKSON BUILDERS & CO.; *U.S. Private*, pg. 1419
ERICKSON BUILDING COMPONENTS, A CALIFORNIA LIMITED PARTNERSHIP—See Masco Corporation; *U.S. Public*, pg. 1390
ERICKSON BUILDING COMPONENTS, LLC—See Masco Corporation; *U.S. Public*, pg. 1390
ERICKSON CONSTRUCTION, LP—See Masco Corporation; *U.S. Public*, pg. 1390
ERICKSON FRAMING AZ LLC—See Asahi Kasei Corporation; *Int'l*, pg. 595
ERICKSON FRAMING OPERATIONS LLC—See Asahi Kasei Corporation; *Int'l*, pg. 596
ERICKSON GMC; *U.S. Private*, pg. 1419
ERICKSON INCORPORATED; *U.S. Private*, pg. 1419
ERICKSON LIVING MANAGEMENT, LLC—See Redwood Capital Investments, LLC; *U.S. Private*, pg. 3380
ERICKSON MACHINE TOOLS INC.—See The 600 Group PLC; *Int'l*, pg. 7609
ERICKSON METALS CORPORATION; *U.S. Private*, pg. 1420
ERICKSONS FLOORING & SUPPLY CO.; *U.S. Private*, pg. 1420
ERICKSON TRANSPORT CORPORATION; *U.S. Private*, pg. 1420
ERIC MOWER AND ASSOCIATES, INC. - ALBANY—See Eric Mower and Associates, Inc.; *U.S. Private*, pg. 1419
ERIC MOWER AND ASSOCIATES, INC. - ATLANTA—See Eric Mower and Associates, Inc.; *U.S. Private*, pg. 1419
ERIC MOWER AND ASSOCIATES, INC. - BOSTON—See Eric Mower and Associates, Inc.; *U.S. Private*, pg. 1419
ERIC MOWER AND ASSOCIATES, INC. - BUFFALO—See Eric Mower and Associates, Inc.; *U.S. Private*, pg. 1419
ERIC MOWER AND ASSOCIATES, INC. - CHARLOTTE—See Eric Mower and Associates, Inc.; *U.S. Private*, pg. 1419
ERIC MOWER AND ASSOCIATES, INC. - CINCINNATI—See Eric Mower and Associates, Inc.; *U.S. Private*, pg. 1419
ERIC MOWER AND ASSOCIATES, INC. - ROCHESTER—See Eric Mower and Associates, Inc.; *U.S. Private*, pg. 1419
ERIC MOWER AND ASSOCIATES, INC.; *U.S. Private*, pg. 1419
ERICO B.V.—See Pentair plc; *Int'l*, pg. 5789
ERICO D.O.O.—See Hisense Co., Ltd.; *Int'l*, pg. 3407
ERICO FRANCE SARL—See Pentair plc; *Int'l*, pg. 5789
ERICOM TELEKOMUNIKASYON VE ENERJI TEKNOLOJILERI A.S.; *Int'l*, pg. 2493
ERICO PRODUCTS AUSTRALIA PTY LIMITED—See Pentair plc; *Int'l*, pg. 5789
ERICPOL AB—See Ericpol Sp. z o.o.; *Int'l*, pg. 2493
ERICPOL SP. Z O.O.; *Int'l*, pg. 2493
ERICPOL TZOV—See Ericpol Sp. z o.o.; *Int'l*, pg. 2493
ERIC RAWLINS & CO., LTD.—See Brown & Brown, Inc.; *U.S. Public*, pg. 400
ERIC RYAN CORPORATION—See Renodis, Inc.; *U.S. Private*, pg. 3399
ERIC SCOTT LEATHERS LTD.; *U.S. Private*, pg. 1419
ERICSON INSURANCE SERVICES, LLC—See Arthur J. Gallagher & Co.; *U.S. Public*, pg. 204
ERICSON MANUFACTURING CO.; *U.S. Private*, pg. 1420
ERICSSON AB BRANCH OFFICE-DHAKA—See Telefonaktiebolaget LM Ericsson; *Int'l*, pg. 7531
ERICSSON AB LIBYA—See Telefonaktiebolaget LM Ericsson; *Int'l*, pg. 7531
ERICSSON AB—See Telefonaktiebolaget LM Ericsson; *Int'l*, pg. 7531
ERICSSON AB—See Telefonaktiebolaget LM Ericsson; *Int'l*, pg. 7531
ERICSSON AB—See Telefonaktiebolaget LM Ericsson; *Int'l*, pg. 7531
ERICSSON AB—See Telefonaktiebolaget LM Ericsson; *Int'l*, pg. 7531
ERICSSON AB—See Telefonaktiebolaget LM Ericsson; *Int'l*, pg. 7531
ERICSSON AB—See Telefonaktiebolaget LM Ericsson; *Int'l*, pg. 7531
ERICSSON AB—See Telefonaktiebolaget LM Ericsson; *Int'l*, pg. 7531
ERICSSON AG—See Telefonaktiebolaget LM Ericsson; *Int'l*, pg. 7531
ERICSSON ANTILLES—See Telefonaktiebolaget LM Ericsson; *Int'l*, pg. 7531
ERICSSON A/S—See Telefonaktiebolaget LM Ericsson; *Int'l*, pg. 7531
ERICSSON A/S—See Telefonaktiebolaget LM Ericsson; *Int'l*, pg. 7531
ERICSSON AUSTRALIA PTY. LTD.—See Telefonaktiebolaget LM Ericsson; *Int'l*, pg. 7531
ERICSSON AUSTRALIA PTY. LTD.- TREASURY—See Telefonaktiebolaget LM Ericsson; *Int'l*, pg. 7531

CORPORATE AFFILIATIONS

ERICSSON AUSTRIA GMBH—See Telefonaktiebolaget LM Ericsson; *Int'l*, pg. 7531
ERICSSON, BAHRAIN—See Telefonaktiebolaget LM Ericsson; *Int'l*, pg. 7534
ERICSSON BUSINESS COMMUNICATIONS NV/SA—See Telefonaktiebolaget LM Ericsson; *Int'l*, pg. 7531
ERICSSON BUSINESS CONSULTING ESPANA, S.A.—See Telefonaktiebolaget LM Ericsson; *Int'l*, pg. 7531
ERICSSON BUSINESS CONSULTING (M) SDN. BHD.—See Telefonaktiebolaget LM Ericsson; *Int'l*, pg. 7531
ERICSSON BUSINESS MOBILE NETWORKS—See Telefonaktiebolaget LM Ericsson; *Int'l*, pg. 7531
ERICSSON BUSINESS SYSTEMS AB (PRS)—See Telefonaktiebolaget LM Ericsson; *Int'l*, pg. 7531
ERICSSON CAMEROON—See Telefonaktiebolaget LM Ericsson; *Int'l*, pg. 7531
ERICSSON CANADA INCORPORATED—See Telefonaktiebolaget LM Ericsson; *Int'l*, pg. 7531
ERICSSON CANADA, INC.—See Telefonaktiebolaget LM Ericsson; *Int'l*, pg. 7531
ERICSSON CARIBBEAN, INC.—See Telefonaktiebolaget LM Ericsson; *Int'l*, pg. 7532
ERICSSON CHILE S.A.—See Telefonaktiebolaget LM Ericsson; *Int'l*, pg. 7532
ERICSSON (CHINA) COMMUNICATION CO., LTD.—See Telefonaktiebolaget LM Ericsson; *Int'l*, pg. 7531
ERICSSON (CHINA) COMPANY LTD.—See Telefonaktiebolaget LM Ericsson; *Int'l*, pg. 7531
ERICSSON COMMUNICATION SOLUTIONS PTE LTD.—See Telefonaktiebolaget LM Ericsson; *Int'l*, pg. 7532
ERICSSON COMMUNICATIONS—See Telefonaktiebolaget LM Ericsson; *Int'l*, pg. 7532
ERICSSON COMPANY FOR ELECTRONICS—See Telefonaktiebolaget LM Ericsson; *Int'l*, pg. 7532
ERICSSON CORPORATIA AO—See Telefonaktiebolaget LM Ericsson; *Int'l*, pg. 7532
ERICSSON CREDIT AB—See Telefonaktiebolaget LM Ericsson; *Int'l*, pg. 7532
ERICSSON DANMARK A/S—See Telefonaktiebolaget LM Ericsson; *Int'l*, pg. 7532
ERICSSON DE BOLIVIA TELECOMUNICACIONES S.A.—See Telefonaktiebolaget LM Ericsson; *Int'l*, pg. 7531
ERICSSON DE COLOMBIA S.A.—See Telefonaktiebolaget LM Ericsson; *Int'l*, pg. 7534
ERICSSON DE ECUADOR C.A.—See Telefonaktiebolaget LM Ericsson; *Int'l*, pg. 7534
ERICSSON DE EL SALVADOR S.A. DE C.V.—See Telefonaktiebolaget LM Ericsson; *Int'l*, pg. 7532
ERICSSON DEFENSE SYSTEMS PTY. LTD.—See Telefonaktiebolaget LM Ericsson; *Int'l*, pg. 7532
ERICSSON DE HONDURAS S.A.—See Telefonaktiebolaget LM Ericsson; *Int'l*, pg. 7531
ERICSSON DEL PARAGUAY—See Telefonaktiebolaget LM Ericsson; *Int'l*, pg. 7534
ERICSSON DE PANAMA S.A.—See Telefonaktiebolaget LM Ericsson; *Int'l*, pg. 7532
ERICSSON DIAX A/S—See Telefonaktiebolaget LM Ericsson; *Int'l*, pg. 7532
ERICSSON D.O.O.—See Telefonaktiebolaget LM Ericsson; *Int'l*, pg. 7534
ERICSSON EESTI AS—See Telefonaktiebolaget LM Ericsson; *Int'l*, pg. 7532
ERICSSON EGYPT LTD—See Telefonaktiebolaget LM Ericsson; *Int'l*, pg. 7531
ERICSSON ELECTRONIC SERVICES—See Telefonaktiebolaget LM Ericsson; *Int'l*, pg. 7532
ERICSSON ERISOFT AB—See Telefonaktiebolaget LM Ericsson; *Int'l*, pg. 7532
ERICSSON ESPANA S.A.—See Telefonaktiebolaget LM Ericsson; *Int'l*, pg. 7532
ERICSSON EUROLAB DEUTSCHLAND GMBH—See Telefonaktiebolaget LM Ericsson; *Int'l*, pg. 7532
ERICSSON FINANZ AG—See Telefonaktiebolaget LM Ericsson; *Int'l*, pg. 7532
ERICSSON FINA—See WPP plc; *Int'l*, pg. 8470
ERICSSON FRANCE S.A.—See Telefonaktiebolaget LM Ericsson; *Int'l*, pg. 7532
ERICSSON GMBH—See Telefonaktiebolaget LM Ericsson; *Int'l*, pg. 7532
ERICSSON HAITI—See Telefonaktiebolaget LM Ericsson; *Int'l*, pg. 7531
ERICSSON HELLAS S.A.—See Telefonaktiebolaget LM Ericsson; *Int'l*, pg. 7532
ERICSSON HOLDING INTERNATIONAL B.V.—See Telefonaktiebolaget LM Ericsson; *Int'l*, pg. 7532
ERICSSON HOLDING LTD.—See Telefonaktiebolaget LM Ericsson; *Int'l*, pg. 7532
ERICSSON HUNGARY LTD.—See Telefonaktiebolaget LM Ericsson; *Int'l*, pg. 7532
ERICSSON INC. - NEW YORK OFFICE—See Telefonaktiebolaget LM Ericsson; *Int'l*, pg. 7532
ERICSSON INC.—See Telefonaktiebolaget LM Ericsson; *Int'l*, pg. 7532
ERICSSON INDIA (PVT) LTD.—See Telefonaktiebolaget LM Ericsson; *Int'l*, pg. 7532

ERICSSON INVENTION LTD.—See Telefonaktiebolaget LM Ericsson; *Int'l*, pg. 7532
ERICSSON JAPAN K.K.—See Telefonaktiebolaget LM Ericsson; *Int'l*, pg. 7532
ERICSSON K.F.T.—See Telefonaktiebolaget LM Ericsson; *Int'l*, pg. 7532
ERICSSON KOREA LTD.—See Telefonaktiebolaget LM Ericsson; *Int'l*, pg. 7532
ERICSSON LEBANON COMMUNICATIONS SARL—See Telefonaktiebolaget LM Ericsson; *Int'l*, pg. 7531
ERICSSON LEBANON S.A.R.L.—See Telefonaktiebolaget LM Ericsson; *Int'l*, pg. 7532
ERICSSON LIMITED—See Telefonaktiebolaget LM Ericsson; *Int'l*, pg. 7532
ERICSSON LIMITED—See Telefonaktiebolaget LM Ericsson; *Int'l*, pg. 7532
ERICSSON LTD.—See Telefonaktiebolaget LM Ericsson; *Int'l*, pg. 7532
ERICSSON (MALAYSIA) SDN. BHD.—See Telefonaktiebolaget LM Ericsson; *Int'l*, pg. 7531
ERICSSON MANUFACTURING CO., LTD.—See Telefonaktiebolaget LM Ericsson; *Int'l*, pg. 7533
ERICSSON MICROWAVE SYSTEMS AB - BORAS—See Telefonaktiebolaget LM Ericsson; *Int'l*, pg. 7533
ERICSSON MICROWAVE SYSTEMS AB - GOTHENBURG—See Telefonaktiebolaget LM Ericsson; *Int'l*, pg. 7533
ERICSSON MICROWAVE SYSTEMS AB - KISTA—See Telefonaktiebolaget LM Ericsson; *Int'l*, pg. 7533
ERICSSON MICROWAVE SYSTEMS AB—See Telefonaktiebolaget LM Ericsson; *Int'l*, pg. 7533
ERICSSON MOBILE COMMUNICATIONS AB—See Telefonaktiebolaget LM Ericsson; *Int'l*, pg. 7533
ERICSSON MOBILE COMMUNICATIONS NORWAY—See Telefonaktiebolaget LM Ericsson; *Int'l*, pg. 7533
ERICSSON MOBILE COMMUNICATIONS—See Telefonaktiebolaget LM Ericsson; *Int'l*, pg. 7533
ERICSSON MOROCCO S.A.R.L.—See Telefonaktiebolaget LM Ericsson; *Int'l*, pg. 7533
ERICSSON NEDERLAND B.V.—See Telefonaktiebolaget LM Ericsson; *Int'l*, pg. 7533
ERICSSON NETWORK TECHNOLOGIES AB—See Telefonaktiebolaget LM Ericsson; *Int'l*, pg. 7533
ERICSSON NEW ZEALAND—See Telefonaktiebolaget LM Ericsson; *Int'l*, pg. 7533
ERICSSON NIKOLA TESLA D.D.—See Telefonaktiebolaget LM Ericsson; *Int'l*, pg. 7533
ERICSSON NV/SA—See Telefonaktiebolaget LM Ericsson; *Int'l*, pg. 7531
ERICSSON OMC LTD—See Telefonaktiebolaget LM Ericsson; *Int'l*, pg. 7533
ERICSSON PROJECT SERVICES (PTY) LTD.—See Telefonaktiebolaget LM Ericsson; *Int'l*, pg. 7533
ERICSSON RADIO SYSTEMS AB—See Telefonaktiebolaget LM Ericsson; *Int'l*, pg. 7533
ERICSSON REPUBLICA DOMINICANA—See Telefonaktiebolaget LM Ericsson; *Int'l*, pg. 7531
ERICSSON S.A.—See Telefonaktiebolaget LM Ericsson; *Int'l*, pg. 7533
ERICSSON SAUDI ARABIA—See Telefonaktiebolaget LM Ericsson; *Int'l*, pg. 7533
ERICSSON SENEGAL SARL—See Telefonaktiebolaget LM Ericsson; *Int'l*, pg. 7533
ERICSSON SLOVAKIA SPOL. S.R.O—See Telefonaktiebolaget LM Ericsson; *Int'l*, pg. 7531
ERICSSON SLOVENIA D.O.O.—See Telefonaktiebolaget LM Ericsson; *Int'l*, pg. 7533
ERICSSON SOUTH AFRICA (PTY) LTD.—See Telefonaktiebolaget LM Ericsson; *Int'l*, pg. 7533
ERICSSON S.P.A.—See Telefonaktiebolaget LM Ericsson; *Int'l*, pg. 7533
ERICSSON SPOL. S R. O.—See Telefonaktiebolaget LM Ericsson; *Int'l*, pg. 7533
ERICSSON SP. Z.O.O.—See Telefonaktiebolaget LM Ericsson; *Int'l*, pg. 7533
ERICSSON SUPPORT CENTRE SDN. BHD.—See Telefonaktiebolaget LM Ericsson; *Int'l*, pg. 7533
ERICSSON SVERIGE AB—See Telefonaktiebolaget LM Ericsson; *Int'l*, pg. 7533
ERICSSON TAIWAN LTD.—See Telefonaktiebolaget LM Ericsson; *Int'l*, pg. 7533
ERICSSON TELECOM AB—See Telefonaktiebolaget LM Ericsson; *Int'l*, pg. 7533
ERICSSON TELECOMMINICACOES, LDA.—See Telefonaktiebolaget LM Ericsson; *Int'l*, pg. 7533
ERICSSON TELECOMM. LANKA (PVT) LTD.—See Telefonaktiebolaget LM Ericsson; *Int'l*, pg. 7533
ERICSSON TELECOMMUNICACUES S.A.—See Telefonaktiebolaget LM Ericsson; *Int'l*, pg. 7533
ERICSSON TELECOMMUNICATIE B.V.—See Telefonaktiebolaget LM Ericsson; *Int'l*, pg. 7533
ERICSSON TELECOMMUNICATIONS, BULGARIA EOOD—See Telefonaktiebolaget LM Ericsson; *Int'l*, pg. 7533
ERICSSON TELECOMMUNICATIONS INC.—See Telefonaktiebolaget LM Ericsson; *Int'l*, pg. 7533
ERICSSON TELECOMMUNICATIONS PTE. LTD.—See Telefonaktiebolaget LM Ericsson; *Int'l*, pg. 7533

ERICSSON TELECOMMUNICATIONS ROMANIA S.A.R.L.—See Telefonaktiebolaget LM Ericsson; *Int'l*, pg. 7533
ERICSSON TELECOM S.A. DE C.V.—See Telefonaktiebolaget LM Ericsson; *Int'l*, pg. 7533
ERICSSON TELECOMUNICAZIONI—See Telefonaktiebolaget LM Ericsson; *Int'l*, pg. 7533
ERICSSON TELECOMUNICAZIONI S.P.A.—See Telefonaktiebolaget LM Ericsson; *Int'l*, pg. 7533
ERICSSON TELEKOMMUNIKATION GMBH & CO. KG—See Telefonaktiebolaget LM Ericsson; *Int'l*, pg. 7533
ERICSSON TELEVISION LTD.—See Telefonaktiebolaget LM Ericsson; *Int'l*, pg. 7532
ERICSSON TEMS AB—See Telefonaktiebolaget LM Ericsson; *Int'l*, pg. 7533
ERICSSON TEMS—See Telefonaktiebolaget LM Ericsson; *Int'l*, pg. 7532
ERICSSON THAILAND LTD.—See Telefonaktiebolaget LM Ericsson; *Int'l*, pg. 7533
ERICSSON TUNISIA—See Telefonaktiebolaget LM Ericsson; *Int'l*, pg. 7534
ERICSSON TURKIYE—See Telefonaktiebolaget LM Ericsson; *Int'l*, pg. 7531
ERICSSON VIETNAM COMPANY LTD—See Telefonaktiebolaget LM Ericsson; *Int'l*, pg. 7531
ERIDANIA SADAM SPA—See Societa Esercizi Commerciali Industriali; *Int'l*, pg. 7034
ERIDGE CAPITAL LIMITED; *Int'l*, pg. 2493
ERIDOMIC OY—See Stora Enso Oyj; *Int'l*, pg. 7225
ERIEBANK, A DIVISION OF CNB BANK—See CNB Financial Corporation; *U.S. Public*, pg. 519
ERIE BEARINGS CO. INC.; *U.S. Private*, pg. 1420
ERIE COCA-COLA BOTTLING COMPANY—See The Coca-Cola Company; *U.S. Public*, pg. 2064
ERIE COMMUNITY FOUNDATION; *U.S. Private*, pg. 1420
ERIE CONSTRUCTION MID-WEST INC.; *U.S. Private*, pg. 1420
ERIE COUNTY CABLEVISION—See Block Communications, Inc.; *U.S. Private*, pg. 582
ERIE COUNTY CARE MANAGEMENT, INC.; *U.S. Private*, pg. 1420
ERIE COUNTY HISTORICAL SOCIETY; *U.S. Private*, pg. 1420
ERIE COUNTY INVESTMENT CO.; *U.S. Private*, pg. 1420
ERIE COUNTY WATER AUTHORITY; *U.S. Private*, pg. 1420
ERIE FAMILY HEALTH CENTER; *U.S. Private*, pg. 1420
ERIE FAMILY LIFE INSURANCE COMPANY—See Erie Indemnity Company; *U.S. Public*, pg. 792
ERIE FOODS INTERNATIONAL, INC.; *U.S. Private*, pg. 1420
ERIE-HAVEN INC.; *U.S. Private*, pg. 1420
ERIE HOMES FOR CHILDREN AND ADULTS, INC.; *U.S. Private*, pg. 1420
ERIE INDEMNITY COMPANY; *U.S. Public*, pg. 792
ERIE INSURANCE COMPANY OF NEW YORK—See Erie Indemnity Company; *U.S. Public*, pg. 792
ERIE INSURANCE COMPANY—See Erie Indemnity Company; *U.S. Public*, pg. 792
ERIE INSURANCE PROPERTY & CASUALTY COMPANY—See Erie Indemnity Company; *U.S. Public*, pg. 792
ERIE MATERIALS INC.; *U.S. Private*, pg. 1420
ERIE MATERIALS INC.; *U.S. Private*, pg. 1420
ERIE & NIAGARA INSURANCE ASSOCIATION; *U.S. Private*, pg. 1420
ERIE PETROLEUM—See Reid Petroleum Corp.; *U.S. Private*, pg. 3391
ERIE PHILHARMONIC; *U.S. Private*, pg. 1420
ERIE SCIENTIFIC COMPANY OF PUERTO RICO—See Thermo Fisher Scientific Inc.; *U.S. Public*, pg. 2146
ERIE SCIENTIFIC LLC—See Thermo Fisher Scientific Inc.; *U.S. Public*, pg. 2146
ERIE STEEL, LTD.; *U.S. Private*, pg. 1420
ERIE TITLE AGENCY, INC.; *U.S. Private*, pg. 1420
ERIE TOOL & SUPPLY CO.—See Jergens Inc.; *U.S. Private*, pg. 2201
ERIEVIEW METAL TREATING CO.; *U.S. Private*, pg. 1421
ERIE-WATALA GLASS COMPANY LIMITED—See Thermo Fisher Scientific Inc.; *U.S. Public*, pg. 2146
ERIEZ MAGNETICS EUROPE LTD—See Eriez Manufacturing Co. Inc.; *U.S. Private*, pg. 1421
ERIEZ MAGNETICS INDIA PRIVATE LIMITED—See Eriez Manufacturing Co. Inc.; *U.S. Private*, pg. 1421
ERIEZ MANUFACTURING CO. INC. - ERIEZ FLOTATION DIVISION - CANADA—See Eriez Manufacturing Co. Inc.; *U.S. Private*, pg. 1421
ERIEZ MANUFACTURING CO. INC. - ERIEZ FLOTATION DIVISION - CHILE—See Eriez Manufacturing Co. Inc.; *U.S. Private*, pg. 1421
ERIEZ MANUFACTURING CO. INC. - ERIEZ FLOTATION DIVISION - PERU—See Eriez Manufacturing Co. Inc.; *U.S. Private*, pg. 1421
ERIEZ MANUFACTURING CO. INC.; *U.S. Private*, pg. 1421
ERI HOLDINGS CO., LTD.; *Int'l*, pg. 2491
ERIKA B-CURE LASER LTD.; *Int'l*, pg. 2493

ERIKA S.R.L.—See Onward Holdings Co., Ltd.; *Int'l*, pg. 5592
ERIK KELLAR PHOTOGRAPHY—See Osprey Capital LLC; *U.S. Private*, pg. 3048
ERIKLI SU VE MESRUBAT SANAYI VE TICARET A.S.—See Nestle S.A.; *Int'l*, pg. 5202
ERIKSBERG VILT & NATUR AB—See Mellby Gard Holding AB; *Int'l*, pg. 4811
ERIKS BV—See SHV Holdings N.V.; *Int'l*, pg. 6871
ERIK'S DELICAFE, INC.; *U.S. Private*, pg. 1421
ERIKSEN CHEVROLET-BUICK; *U.S. Private*, pg. 1421
ERIKSEN TRANSLATIONS, INC.; *U.S. Private*, pg. 1421
ERIKSEN TRANSLATIONS S.R.L.—See Eriksen Translations, Inc.; *U.S. Private*, pg. 1421
ERIKS GROUP NV—See SHV Holdings N.V.; *Int'l*, pg. 6871
ERIKS INDUSTRIAL SERVICES LTD.—See SHV Holdings N.V.; *Int'l*, pg. 6871
ERIKS MIDWEST—See LKCM Headwater Investments; *U.S. Private*, pg. 2475
ERIKS NORTH AMERICA, INC.—See LKCM Headwater Investments; *U.S. Private*, pg. 2475
ERIKS SEALS & PLASTICS, INC.—See LKCM Headwater Investments; *U.S. Private*, pg. 2475
ERIKS UK HOLDINGS LTD.—See SHV Holdings N.V.; *Int'l*, pg. 6871
ERIKS WEST, INC.—See LKCM Headwater Investments; *U.S. Private*, pg. 2475
ERIKS WEST—See LKCM Headwater Investments; *U.S. Private*, pg. 2475
ERIK THUN AB; *Int'l*, pg. 2493
ERIMA GMBH; *Int'l*, pg. 2493
ERIMAX, INC.; *U.S. Private*, pg. 1421
ERIMED INTERNATIONAL KB—See AdderaCare AB; *Int'l*, pg. 128
THE ERIN COMPANY; *U.S. Private*, pg. 4026
ERIN DODGE CHRYSLER LTD.; *Int'l*, pg. 2493
E & R INDUSTRIAL SALES, INC.—See Paradigm Capital Partners; *U.S. Private*, pg. 3089
ERIN ENGINEERING & RESEARCH INC.—See Gryphon Investors, LLC; *U.S. Private*, pg. 1798
ERIN INTERNATIONAL CO., LTD.—See Dynam Japan Holdings, Co., Ltd.; *Int'l*, pg. 2239
ERINMOTORWAY INVESTMENTS LIMITED; *Int'l*, pg. 2493
ERIN PARK AUTOMOTIVE PARTNERSHIP; *Int'l*, pg. 2493
ERINSTONE N.V.—See Sicon Ltd.; *Int'l*, pg. 6882
ERIN VENTURES INC.; *Int'l*, pg. 2493
ERISA FIDUCIARY ADVISORS, INC.—See Aon plc; *Int'l*, pg. 496
ERISBEG HOLDINGS LIMITED; *Int'l*, pg. 2493
ERISIM MUSTERI HIZMETLERI A.S.—See Turkiye Is Bankasi A.S.; *Int'l*, pg. 7976
ERIS LIFESCIENCES LIMITED; *Int'l*, pg. 2493
ERI SOLUTIONS, LLC; *U.S. Private*, pg. 1419
ERIS PHARMACEUTICALS AUSTRALIA PTY LTD.; *Int'l*, pg. 2493
ERIS TECHNOLOGY CO—See Diodes Incorporated; *U.S. Public*, pg. 667
ERISUD S.P.A.—See Telefonaktiebolaget LM Ericsson; *Int'l*, pg. 7534
ERITH GROUP; *Int'l*, pg. 2494
E. RITTER AGRIBUSINESS HOLDINGS, INC.—See E. Ritter & Company; *U.S. Private*, pg. 1304
E. RITTER AGRIBUSINESS HOLDINGS, INC.—See Grain Management, LLC; *U.S. Private*, pg. 1751
E. RITTER COMMUNICATIONS HOLDINGS, INC.—See E. Ritter & Company; *U.S. Private*, pg. 1304
E. RITTER COMMUNICATIONS HOLDINGS, INC.—See Grain Management, LLC; *U.S. Private*, pg. 1751
E. RITTER COMMUNICATIONS, INC.—See E. Ritter & Company; *U.S. Private*, pg. 1304
E. RITTER COMMUNICATIONS, INC.—See Grain Management, LLC; *U.S. Private*, pg. 1751
E. RITTER & COMPANY; *U.S. Private*, pg. 1304
E. RITTER FARM MANAGEMENT, INC.—See E. Ritter & Company; *U.S. Private*, pg. 1304
E. RITTER FARM MANAGEMENT, INC.—See Grain Management, LLC; *U.S. Private*, pg. 1751
E. RITTER TELEPHONE COMPANY—See E. Ritter & Company; *U.S. Private*, pg. 1304
E. RITTER TELEPHONE COMPANY—See Grain Management, LLC; *U.S. Private*, pg. 1751
ERIXX GMBH—See Ferrovie dello Stato Italiane S.p.A.; *Int'l*, pg. 2645
E.R. JAHNA INDUSTRIES INC.; *U.S. Private*, pg. 1306
E.R. JAPAN CORPORATION—See EDION Corporation; *Int'l*, pg. 2310
E.R.J. INSURANCE GROUP, INC.—See The Allstate Corporation; *U.S. Public*, pg. 2033
ERKA-AS—See Eroglu Holding AS; *Int'l*, pg. 2496
ERK PETROL YATIRIMLARI A.S.—See Vitol Holding B.V.; *Int'l*, pg. 8260
ERKUNT SANAYI A.S.—See Mahindra & Mahindra Limited; *Int'l*, pg. 4645
ERKUNT TRAKTOR SANAYII A.S.—See Mahindra & Mahindra Limited; *Int'l*, pg. 4645
ERLANGER BEHAVIORAL HEALTH, LLC—See Acadia Healthcare Company, Inc.; *U.S. Public*, pg. 28

ERLANGER HEALTH SYSTEM / CORPORATE AFFILIATIONS

ERLANGER HEALTH SYSTEM; *U.S. Private*, pg. 1421
ERLEBNIS AKADEMIE AG; *Int'l*, pg. 2494
ERLEBNIS BERGWERK MERKERS—See K+S Aktiengesellschaft; *Int'l*, pg. 4039
ERLENBACHER BACKWAREN GMBH—See Nestle S.A.; *Int'l*, pg. 5202
ERLIKON SA—See Viohalco SA/NV; *Int'l*, pg. 8243
ERLING HAUG AS—See Axel Johnson Gruppen AB; *Int'l*, pg. 764
ERL PHASE POWER TECHNOLOGIES LTD.—See Easun Reyrolle Ltd; *Int'l*, pg. 2275
ERLSON PRECISION COMPONENTS LIMITED—See GIL Investments Ltd.; *Int'l*, pg. 2973
ERMAN RETIREMENT ADVISORY, INC.—See Hellman & Friedman LLC; *U.S. Private*, pg. 1908
ER MARKETING; *U.S. Private*, pg. 1417
ER MARKS, INC.—See Qurate Retail, Inc.; *U.S. Public*, pg. 1757
ERMATEC MASCHINEN TECHNISCHE ANLAGEN GESELLSCHAFT M.B.H.—See STRABAG SE; *Int'l*, pg. 7230
ERMC II, L.P.—See Allied Universal Manager LLC; *U.S. Private*, pg. 191
ERMCO, INC.; *U.S. Private*, pg. 1421
ERM ELECTRONIC SYSTEMS LTD.—See ITURAN Location & Control Ltd.; *Int'l*, pg. 3844
ERMENEGILDO ZEGNA HOLDITALIA S.P.A.; *Int'l*, pg. 2494
ERMENEGILDO ZEGNA N.V.—See Investindustrial Acquisition Corp.; *Int'l*, pg. 3779
ERMES DEPARTMENT STORES LTD.—See N.K. Shacolas (Holdings) Ltd.; *Int'l*, pg. 5116
ERMEWA BERLIN—See Ermewa Interservices Sarl; *Int'l*, pg. 2494
ERMEWA FRANCE—See Ermewa Interservices Sarl; *Int'l*, pg. 2494
ERMEWA GENEVE—See Ermewa Interservices Sarl; *Int'l*, pg. 2494
ERMEWA INTERSERVICES SARL; *Int'l*, pg. 2494
ERMEWA LIMITED—See Ermewa Interservices Sarl; *Int'l*, pg. 2494
ERMEWA SRL—See Ermewa Interservices Sarl; *Int'l*, pg. 2494
ERMEWA S.R.L.—See Ermewa Interservices Sarl; *Int'l*, pg. 2494
THE ERM GROUP, INC.—See Alberta Investment Management Corporation; *Int'l*, pg. 297
THE ERM GROUP, INC.—See Ontario Municipal Employees Retirement System; *Int'l*, pg. 5584
ERM POWER LIMITED—See Shell plc; *Int'l*, pg. 6798
E.R.N. ELEKTRO-RECYCLING NORD GMBH—See Aurubis AG; *Int'l*, pg. 715
ERNEST BOREL (GUANGZHOU) CO., LTD.—See Citychamp Watch & Jewellery Group Limited; *Int'l*, pg. 1629
ERNEST BOREL HOLDINGS LIMITED—See Citychamp Watch & Jewellery Group Limited; *Int'l*, pg. 1629
ERNEST BOREL S.A.—See Citychamp Watch & Jewellery Group Limited; *Int'l*, pg. 1629
ERNEST DOE & SONS LIMITED; *Int'l*, pg. 2494
ERNEST HEALTH, INC.; *U.S. Private*, pg. 1421
ERNEST HENRY MINING PTY. LTD.—See Evolution Mining Limited; *Int'l*, pg. 2572
ERNEST JACKSON & CO LIMITED—See Mondelez International, Inc.; *U.S. Public*, pg. 1462
ERNEST JONES LIMITED—See Signet Jewelers Limited; *Int'l*, pg. 6911
ERNEST LOWE—See Hudaco Industries Limited; *Int'l*, pg. 3521
ERNEST MAIER, INC.; *U.S. Private*, pg. 1421
ERNEST MCCARTY FORD, INC.; *U.S. Private*, pg. 1421
ERNEST N. MORIAL CONVENTION CTR NEW ORLEANS; *U.S. Private*, pg. 1421
ERNEST PAPER PRODUCTS, INC. - FRESNO FACILITY—See Ernest Paper Products, Inc.; *U.S. Private*, pg. 1421
ERNEST PAPER PRODUCTS, INC. - HOUSTON FACILITY—See Ernest Paper Products, Inc.; *U.S. Private*, pg. 1422
ERNEST PAPER PRODUCTS, INC. - LAS VEGAS FACILITY—See Ernest Paper Products, Inc.; *U.S. Private*, pg. 1422
ERNEST PAPER PRODUCTS, INC. - PORTLAND FACILITY—See Ernest Paper Products, Inc.; *U.S. Private*, pg. 1422
ERNEST PAPER PRODUCTS, INC. - RALEIGH-DURHAM FACILITY—See Ernest Paper Products, Inc.; *U.S. Private*, pg. 1422
ERNEST PAPER PRODUCTS, INC. - RENO FACILITY—See Ernest Paper Products, Inc.; *U.S. Private*, pg. 1422
ERNEST PAPER PRODUCTS, INC. - SACRAMENTO FACILITY—See Ernest Paper Products, Inc.; *U.S. Private*, pg. 1422
ERNEST PAPER PRODUCTS, INC. - SAN DIEGO FACILITY—See Ernest Paper Products, Inc.; *U.S. Private*, pg. 1422
ERNEST PAPER PRODUCTS, INC.; *U.S. Private*, pg. 1421

ERNEST RUTHERFORD RETIREMENT VILLAGE LIMITED—See Ryman Healthcare Ltd.; *Int'l*, pg. 6439
ERNEST WILSONS & CO LIMITED—See Begbies Traynor Group plc; *Int'l*, pg. 940
ERNEX—See Bank of Montreal; *Int'l*, pg. 847
ERNEX—See Royal Bank of Canada; *Int'l*, pg. 6409
ERNI ASIA HOLDING PTE LTD—See ERNI Electronics GmbH; *Int'l*, pg. 2494
ERNI CABLE SYSTEMS AG—See ERNI Electronics GmbH; *Int'l*, pg. 2494
ERNIE BALL INC.; *U.S. Private*, pg. 1422
ERNIE GREEN INDUSTRIES, INC.; *U.S. Private*, pg. 1422
ERNI ELECTRONICS AG—See ERNI Electronics GmbH; *Int'l*, pg. 2494
ERNI ELECTRONICS CHINA—See ERNI Electronics GmbH; *Int'l*, pg. 2494
ERNI ELECTRONICS GMBH; *Int'l*, pg. 2494
ERNI ELECTRONICS, INC.—See ERNI Electronics GmbH; *Int'l*, pg. 2494
ERNI ELECTRONICS LTD.—See ERNI Electronics GmbH; *Int'l*, pg. 2494
ERNI ELECTRONIC SOLUTIONS GMBH—See FIDELITAS Industrieholding GmbH; *Int'l*, pg. 2654
ERNI ELECTRONICS (THAILAND) CO. LTD.—See ERNI Electronics GmbH; *Int'l*, pg. 2494
ERNIE PALMER, INC.; *U.S. Private*, pg. 1422
ERNIE VON SCHLEDORN LTD., INC.; *U.S. Private*, pg. 1422
ERNIE WILLIAMS LTD; *U.S. Private*, pg. 1422
ERNIE WILLIAMSON, INC.; *U.S. Private*, pg. 1422
ERNO LASZLO, INC.—See CITIC Group Corporation; *Int'l*, pg. 1619
ERNST AUTO CENTER INCORPORATED; *U.S. Private*, pg. 1423
ERNST DELLO GMBH & CO. KG; *Int'l*, pg. 2494
ERNST DIEGEL GMBH—See American Securities LLC; *U.S. Private*, pg. 252
ERNST & ENGBRING GMBH—See TKH Group N.V.; *Int'l*, pg. 7764
ERNST ENTERPRISES, INC.; *U.S. Private*, pg. 1423
ERNST GOHNER STIFTUNG; *Int'l*, pg. 2495
ERNSTING'S FAMILY GMBH & CO. KG; *Int'l*, pg. 2496
ERNST KLETT AG; *Int'l*, pg. 2495
ERNST KLETT VERTRIEBSGESELLSCHAFT—See Ernst Klett AG; *Int'l*, pg. 2495
ERNST RUSS AG; *Int'l*, pg. 2495
ERNST SCHAUSBERGER & CO GESELLSCHAFT M.B.H—See Mayr-Melnhof Karton AG; *Int'l*, pg. 4745
ERNST VON SCHLEDORN INC.; *U.S. Private*, pg. 1423
ERNST W. VELLEUER GMBH & CO. KG—See Beijer Alma AB; *Int'l*, pg. 942
ERNST & YOUNG GLOBAL LIMITED; *Int'l*, pg. 2494
ERNST & YOUNG GMBH WIRTSCHAFTSPRUFUNGSGESELLSCHAFT; *Int'l*, pg. 2494
ERNST & YOUNG INC.; *Int'l*, pg. 2494
ERNST & YOUNG J&M MANAGEMENT CONSULTING GMBH—See Ernst & Young GmbH Wirtschaftsprufungsgesellschaft; *Int'l*, pg. 2494
ERNST & YOUNG LLP; *Int'l*, pg. 2494
ERNST & YOUNG LLP; *U.S. Private*, pg. 1422
ERNST & YOUNG PVT LTD.; *Int'l*, pg. 2494
ERNTESEGEN NATURKOST GMBH—See Coop-Gruppe Genossenschaft; *Int'l*, pg. 1789
EROAD LIMITED; *Int'l*, pg. 2496
ERO COPPER CORP.; *Int'l*, pg. 2496
EROGLU GIYIM SAN. TIC. INC. - AKSARAY FACTORY—See Eroglu Holding AS; *Int'l*, pg. 2496
EROGLU GIYIM SAN. TIC. INC. - CORLU FACTORY—See Eroglu Holding AS; *Int'l*, pg. 2496
EROGLU GIYIM SAN. TIC. INC. - EGYPT FACTORY—See Eroglu Holding AS; *Int'l*, pg. 2496
EROGLU HOLDING AS; *Int'l*, pg. 2496
ERO MEAT COMPANY; *U.S. Private*, pg. 1423
ERONGO MARINE ENTERPRISES (PTY) LIMITED—See Oceana Group Limited; *Int'l*, pg. 5517
EROOMSYSTEM SPE, INC.—See eRoomSystem Technologies, Inc.; *U.S. Private*, pg. 1423
EROOMSYSTEM TECHNOLOGIES, INC.; *U.S. Private*, pg. 1423
EROPED TRADING LTD.—See A.A.G. STUCCHI s.r.l.; *Int'l*, pg. 22
EROS AUSTRALIA PVT. LTD.—See Eros International Plc; *Int'l*, pg. 2496
EROS DIGITAL FZ LLC—See Eros International Plc; *Int'l*, pg. 2497
EROS ELECTRICALS LLC—See Aiphone Co., Ltd.; *Int'l*, pg. 235
EROS ENTERTAINMENT, INC.—See Eros International Plc; *Int'l*, pg. 2496
EROS INTERNATIONAL LTD.—See Eros International Plc; *Int'l*, pg. 2496
EROS INTERNATIONAL MEDIA LTD.—See Eros International Plc; *Int'l*, pg. 2496
EROS INTERNATIONAL PLC; *Int'l*, pg. 2496
EROS INTERNATIONAL PTE LTD.—See Eros International Plc; *Int'l*, pg. 2496
EROS INTERNATIONAL USA INC.—See Eros International Plc; *Int'l*, pg. 2496
THE EROSION COMPANY; *U.S. Private*, pg. 4026

EROSKI S. COOP.—See Mondragon Corporation; *Int'l*, pg. 5028
EROS NETWORK LIMITED—See Eros International Plc; *Int'l*, pg. 2496
EROS (PACIFIC) PVT. LTD.—See Eros International Plc; *Int'l*, pg. 2496
EROS RESOURCES CORP.; *Int'l*, pg. 2497
EROS WORLDWIDE FZ LLC—See Eros International Plc; *Int'l*, pg. 2497
EROTIK ABWICKLUNGSGES AG; *Int'l*, pg. 2497
ERPA DIS TICARET PAZ. VE SAN LTD STI—See Eroglu Holding AS; *Int'l*, pg. 2496
ERP ANALYSTS, INC.; *U.S. Private*, pg. 1423
ERP INTERNATIONAL, LLC.; *U.S. Private*, pg. 1423
ERP IRON ORE, LLC; *U.S. Private*, pg. 1423
ERP OPERATING LIMITED PARTNERSHIP—See Equity Residential; *U.S. Public*, pg. 792
ERP POWER LLC—See Angeles Equity Partners, LLC; *U.S. Private*, pg. 282
E.R. PROBYN EXPORT LTD.—See E.R. Probyn Ltd.; *Int'l*, pg. 2260
E.R. PROBYN LTD.; *Int'l*, pg. 2260
ERPSOFT SYSTEMS LTD.; *Int'l*, pg. 2497
ERPSOFT SYSTEMS LTD.; *Int'l*, pg. 2497
ERP TECH S.P.A.—See BT Group plc; *Int'l*, pg. 1203
E.R. QUINN CO., INC.—See CVC Capital Partners SICAV-FIS S.A.; *Int'l*, pg. 1884
ERRAND SOLUTIONS, LLC; *U.S. Private*, pg. 1423
ERRANDS PLUS, INC.; *U.S. Private*, pg. 1423
ERRAWARRA RESOURCES LTD.; *Int'l*, pg. 2497
ERRECINQUE S.R.L. - BOLOGNA PLANT—See Errecinque S.r.l.; *Int'l*, pg. 2497
ERRECINQUE S,R.L. - COSENZA PLANT—See Errecinque S.r.l.; *Int'l*, pg. 2497
ERRECINQUE S.R.L.; *Int'l*, pg. 2497
ERRECINQUE S.R.L. - VOLPIANO PLANT—See Errecinque S.r.l.; *Int'l*, pg. 2497
ERRE DUE S.P.A.; *Int'l*, pg. 2497
ERREPLAST, S.R.L.—See La Seda de Barcelona, S.A.; *Int'l*, pg. 4389
ERRIA A/S; *Int'l*, pg. 2497
ERSA ASIA PACIFIC—See Kurtz Holding GmbH & Co. Beteiligungs KG; *Int'l*, pg. 4342
ERSA FRANCE—See Kurtz Holding GmbH & Co. Beteiligungs KG; *Int'l*, pg. 4343
ERSA GMBH—See Kurtz Holding GmbH & Co. Beteiligungs KG; *Int'l*, pg. 4342
ERSA NORTH AMERICA—See Kurtz Holding GmbH & Co. Beteiligungs KG; *Int'l*, pg. 4343
ERS AUSTRALIA PTY LTD—See Cleanaway Waste Management Limited; *Int'l*, pg. 1655
ERS DIGITAL, INC.—See ARC DOCUMENT SOLUTIONS, INC.; *U.S. Public*, pg. 179
ERSECO, INC.—See Erving Industries, Inc.; *U.S. Private*, pg. 1424
ERS GENOMICS LTD.—See CRISPR Therapeutics AG; *Int'l*, pg. 1850
ERSHIGS, INC.—See NOV, Inc.; *U.S. Public*, pg. 1544
ERS INDUSTRIES INC.; *U.S. Private*, pg. 1423
ERSKINE SYSTEMS LIMITED—See TT Electronics plc; *Int'l*, pg. 7959
ER SNELL CONTRACTOR INC.; *U.S. Private*, pg. 1417
ERS NEW ZEALAND LTD—See Capital Environment Holdings Limited; *Int'l*, pg. 1310
E. R. SQUIBB & SONS LIMITED—See Bristol-Myers Squibb Company; *U.S. Public*, pg. 386
ERS RAILWAYS B.V.—See Brookfield Infrastructure Partners L.P.; *Int'l*, pg. 1191
ERS RAILWAYS B.V.—See GIC Pte. Ltd.; *Int'l*, pg. 2965
ERS SINGAPORE PTE LTD—See Cleanaway Waste Management Limited; *Int'l*, pg. 1655
ERS—See FAYAT SAS; *Int'l*, pg. 2625
ERST ASIA PACIFIC PTE. LTD.—See ISDN Holdings Limited; *Int'l*, pg. 3813
ERSTE ABWICKLUNGSANSTALT AOR; *Int'l*, pg. 2497
ERSTE ALAPKEZELO ZRT.—See Erste Group Bank AG; *Int'l*, pg. 2498
ERSTE ASSET MANAGEMENT GMBH—See Erste Group Bank AG; *Int'l*, pg. 2498
ERSTE ASSET MANAGEMENT GMBH—See Erste Group Bank AG; *Int'l*, pg. 2498
ERSTE BANK AD NOVI SAD—See Erste Group Bank AG; *Int'l*, pg. 2498
ERSTE BANK AD PODGORICA—See Erste Group Bank AG; *Int'l*, pg. 2498
ERSTE BANK AG—See Erste Group Bank AG; *Int'l*, pg. 2498
ERSTE BANK D.D.—See Erste Group Bank AG; *Int'l*, pg. 2498
ERSTE BANK DER OESTERREICHISCHEN SPARKASSEN AG—See Erste Group Bank AG; *Int'l*, pg. 2498
ERSTE BANK HUNGARY NYRT.—See Erste Group Bank AG; *Int'l*, pg. 2498
ERSTE BANK (MALTA) LIMITED—See Erste Group Bank AG; *Int'l*, pg. 2498
ERSTE BIZTOSITASI ALKUSZ KFT.—See Vienna Insurance Group AG Wiener Versicherung Gruppe; *Int'l*, pg. 8194

ERSTE CARD CLUB D.D.—See Erste Group Bank AG; *Int'l*, pg. 2498
ERSTE CORPORATE FINANCE, A.S.—See Erste Group Bank AG; *Int'l*, pg. 2498
ERSTE DIGITAL GMBH—See Erste Group Bank AG; *Int'l*, pg. 2498
ERSTE DMD D.O.O.—See Erste Group Bank AG; *Int'l*, pg. 2498
ERSTE EUROPAISCHE PFANDBRIEF- UND KOMMUNALKREDITBANK AKTIENGESELLSCHAFT—See Commerzbank AG; *Int'l*, pg. 1718
ERSTE FAKTOR PENZUGYI SZOLGALTATO ZRT.—See Erste Group Bank AG; *Int'l*, pg. 2498
ERSTE FRANKFURTER HOIST GMBH—See Deutsche Bank Aktiengesellschaft; *Int'l*, pg. 2061
ERSTE GEMEINNUTZIGE WOHNUNGSGESELLSCHAFT HEIMSTATTE GESELLSCHAFT M.B.H.—See Vienna Insurance Group AG Wiener Versicherung Gruppe; *Int'l*, pg. 8194
ERSTE GROUP BANK AG; *Int'l*, pg. 2497
ERSTE GROUP PROCUREMENT—See Erste Group Bank AG; *Int'l*, pg. 2498
ERSTE KERESKEDOHAZ KFT.—See Erste Group Bank AG; *Int'l*, pg. 2498
ERSTE K-W-A BETEILIGUNGSGESELLSCHAFT MBH—See Bayer Aktiengesellschaft; *Int'l*, pg. 907
ERSTE NEKRETNINE D.O.O.—See Erste Group Bank AG; *Int'l*, pg. 2498
ERSTE ONSHORE WINDKRAFT BETEILIGUNGSGESELLSCHAFT MBH & CO. WINDPARK KRAHENBERG KG—See UniCredit S.p.A.; *Int'l*, pg. 8034
ERSTE ONSHORE WINDKRAFT BETEILIGUNGSGESELLSCHAFT MBH & CO. WINDPARK MOSE KG—See UniCredit S.p.A.; *Int'l*, pg. 8034
ERSTE OSIGURANJE VIENNA INSURANCE GROUP D.D.—See Vienna Insurance Group AG Wiener Versicherung Gruppe; *Int'l*, pg. 8194
ERSTE PRIVATE EQUITY LIMITED—See Erste Group Bank AG; *Int'l*, pg. 2498
ERSTE SECURITIES ISTANBUL MENKUL DEGERLER AS—See Erste Group Bank AG; *Int'l*, pg. 2498
ERSTE SECURITIES POLSKA S.A.—See Erste Group Bank AG; *Int'l*, pg. 2498
ERSTE-SPARINVEST KAPITALANLAGEGESELLSCHAFT M.B.H.—See Erste Group Bank AG; *Int'l*, pg. 2498
ERSTE & STEIERMARKISCHE BANK D.D.—See Erste Group Bank AG; *Int'l*, pg. 2498
ERSTE VIENNA INSURANCE GROUP BIZTOSITO ZRT—See Vienna Insurance Group AG Wiener Versicherung Gruppe; *Int'l*, pg. 8194
ERSTE WIENER WALZMUHLE VONWILLER GMBH—See Raiffeisen-Holding Niederosterreich-Wien reg. Gen.m.b.H.; *Int'l*, pg. 6185
ERST TECHNOLOGY GMBH—See Techniche Limited; *Int'l*, pg. 7506
E.R. STUEBNER CONSTRUCTION INC.; *U.S. Private*, pg. 1306
ERSU MEYVE VE GIDA SANAYI A.S.; *Int'l*, pg. 2499
ERTEX SOLAR TECHNIK GMBH—See VINCI S.A.; *Int'l*, pg. 8218
E & R TOOLING AND SOLUTIONS DE MEXICO, S. DE R.L. DE C.V.—See W.W. Grainger, Inc.; *U.S. Public*, pg. 2319
ERT SALES OF HAWAII INC.; *U.S. Private*, pg. 1423
ERTSOVERSLAGBEDRIJF EUROPOORT C.V.—See ThyssenKrupp AG; *Int'l*, pg. 7724
ERTUNNEL MAK. SAN. TIC. LTD. STI.—See MAHLE GmbH; *Int'l*, pg. 4648
ERTW GMBH—See Steilmann Holding AG; *Int'l*, pg. 7193
ERUPTR LLC—See H.I.G. Capital, LLC; *U.S. Private*, pg. 1829
ERV GMBH—See Alba SE; *Int'l*, pg. 293
ERVIN AMASTEEL DIVISION OF ERVIN INDUSTRIES INC.—See Ervin Industries, Inc.; *U.S. Private*, pg. 1423
ERVIN AMASTEEL DIV.—See Ervin Industries, Inc.; *U.S. Private*, pg. 1423
ERVIN AMASTEEL UK LP—See Ervin Industries, Inc.; *U.S. Private*, pg. 1423
ERVIN CABLE CONSTRUCTION, LLC—See Dycom Industries, Inc.; *U.S. Public*, pg. 698
ERVIN EQUIPMENT, INC.; *U.S. Private*, pg. 1423
ERVIN GERMANY GMBH—See Ervin Industries, Inc.; *U.S. Private*, pg. 1423
ERVING INDUSTRIES, INC.; *U.S. Private*, pg. 1424
ERVING PAPER PRODUCTS, INC.—See Erving Industries, Inc.; *U.S. Private*, pg. 1424
ERVIN INDUSTRIES, INC. - ERVIN TECHNOLOGIES DIVISION—See Ervin Industries, Inc.; *U.S. Private*, pg. 1423
ERVIN INDUSTRIES, INC.; *U.S. Private*, pg. 1423
ERVIN LEASING COMPANY—See Ervin Industries, Inc.; *U.S. Private*, pg. 1424
ERVIN MARKETING CREATIVE COMMUNICATIONS; *U.S. Private*, pg. 1424
ERVINS GROUP, LLC—See Acme Mills Co. Inc.; *U.S. Private*, pg. 61
E.R. WAGNER CASTERS AND WHEELS DIV.—See E.R. Wagner Manufacturing Co.; *U.S. Private*, pg. 1307

E.R. WAGNER MANUFACTURING CO. - ENGINEERED PRODUCTS DIVISION—See E.R. Wagner Manufacturing Co.; *U.S. Private*, pg. 1307
E.R. WAGNER MANUFACTURING CO.; *U.S. Private*, pg. 1306
ERWE IMMOBILIEN AG; *Int'l*, pg. 2500
ERWEKA GMBH; *Int'l*, pg. 2500
ERWIN BIICHELE GMBH & CO. KG—See Wurth Verwaltungsgesellschaft mbH; *Int'l*, pg. 8504
ERWIN BURBACH MASCHINENFABRIK GMBH—See Pentair plc; *Int'l*, pg. 5789
ERWIN HALDER KG; *Int'l*, pg. 2500
ERWIN HYMER CENTER BAD WALDSEE GMBH—See Thor Industries, Inc.; *U.S. Public*, pg. 2156
ERWIN HYMER CENTER STUTTGART GMBH—See Thor Industries, Inc.; *U.S. Public*, pg. 2156
ERWIN HYMER GROUP SE—See Thor Industries, Inc.; *U.S. Public*, pg. 2156
ERWIN HYMER GROUP STUTTGART GMBH—See Thor Industries, Inc.; *U.S. Public*, pg. 2156
ERWIN HYMER WORLD GMBH—See Thor Industries, Inc.; *U.S. Public*, pg. 2156
ERWIN JUNKER MACHINERY, INC.—See Otto Junker GmbH; *Int'l*, pg. 5664
ERWIN MULLER GRUPPE GMBH; *Int'l*, pg. 2500
ERWIN PEARL INC.; *U.S. Private*, pg. 1424
ERWIN PENLAND AND COMPANY—See Attivo group; *Int'l*, pg. 697
ERYAP CONSTRUCTION AND TRADE INC.—See Eroglu Holding AS; *Int'l*, pg. 2496
ERYMA SOGETREL GROUP; *Int'l*, pg. 2500
ERYTECH PHARMA, INC.—See PHAXIAM Therapeutics S.A.; *Int'l*, pg. 5843
ESAAR (INDIA) LIMITED; *Int'l*, pg. 2501
ESA ALLIANZ—See Allianz SE; *Int'l*, pg. 356
ESA ASSEMBLY PTE LTD—See Renaissance United Limited; *Int'l*, pg. 6273
ESAB AB—See Enovis Corporation; *U.S. Public*, pg. 770
ESAB AFRICA WELDING AND CUTTING (PROPRIETARY) LIMITED—See Enovis Corporation; *U.S. Public*, pg. 770
ESAB AG—See Enovis Corporation; *U.S. Public*, pg. 770
ESAB AKTIENGESELLSCHAFT—See Enovis Corporation; *U.S. Public*, pg. 770
ESAB APS—See Enovis Corporation; *U.S. Public*, pg. 770
ESAB ASIA/PACIFIC PTE. LTD.—See Enovis Corporation; *U.S. Public*, pg. 770
ESAB A/S—See Enovis Corporation; *U.S. Public*, pg. 770
ESAB AUTOMATION LTD.—See Enovis Corporation; *U.S. Public*, pg. 770
ESAB CORPORATION; *U.S. Public*, pg. 793
ESAB CUTTING SYSTEMS—See Enovis Corporation; *U.S. Public*, pg. 770
ESAB CUTTING SYSTEMS—See Enovis Corporation; *U.S. Public*, pg. 771
ESAB EGYPT—See Enovis Corporation; *U.S. Public*, pg. 770
ESAB FRANCE SAS—See Enovis Corporation; *U.S. Public*, pg. 770
ESAB GROUP CANADA, INC.—See Enovis Corporation; *U.S. Public*, pg. 770
THE ESAB GROUP, INC.—See Enovis Corporation; *U.S. Public*, pg. 771
ESAB GROUP (UK) LTD.—See Enovis Corporation; *U.S. Public*, pg. 770
ESAB IBERICA S.A.—See Enovis Corporation; *U.S. Public*, pg. 770
ESAB INDIA LTD.-KOLKATA—See Enovis Corporation; *U.S. Public*, pg. 770
ESAB INDIA LTD.—See Enovis Corporation; *U.S. Public*, pg. 770
ESAB INTERNATIONAL AB—See Enovis Corporation; *U.S. Public*, pg. 770
ESAB KFT—See Enovis Corporation; *U.S. Public*, pg. 770
ESAB (MALAYSIA) SDN BHD—See Enovis Corporation; *U.S. Public*, pg. 770
ESAB MEXICO S.A. DE C.V.—See Enovis Corporation; *U.S. Public*, pg. 770
ESAB MIDDLE EAST LLC—See Enovis Corporation; *U.S. Public*, pg. 771
ESAB MIDDLE EAST—See Enovis Corporation; *U.S. Public*, pg. 771
ESAB NEDERLAND B.V.—See Enovis Corporation; *U.S. Public*, pg. 771
ESAB OY—See Enovis Corporation; *U.S. Public*, pg. 771
ESAB PERSTORP AB—See Enovis Corporation; *U.S. Public*, pg. 771
ESAB RUSSIA BV—See Enovis Corporation; *U.S. Public*, pg. 770
ESAB S.A. INDUSTRIA E COMERCIO—See Enovis Corporation; *U.S. Public*, pg. 771
ESAB SALDATURA S.P.A.—See Enovis Corporation; *U.S. Public*, pg. 771
ESAB SEAH CORPORATION—See Enovis Corporation; *U.S. Public*, pg. 771
ESAB SLOVAKIA SRO—See Enovis Corporation; *U.S. Public*, pg. 771
ESAB SP.Z.O.O.—See Enovis Corporation; *U.S. Public*, pg. 771

ESAB SVERIGE AB—See Enovis Corporation; *U.S. Public*, pg. 771
ESAB (THAILAND) LTD.—See Enovis Corporation; *U.S. Public*, pg. 770
ESAB TYUMEN LIMITED LIABILITY COMPANY—See Enovis Corporation; *U.S. Public*, pg. 771
ESAB VAMBERK A.S.—See Enovis Corporation; *U.S. Public*, pg. 771
ESAB VAMBERK, S.R.O.—See Enovis Corporation; *U.S. Public*, pg. 771
ESAB WELDING & CUTTING GMBH—See Enovis Corporation; *U.S. Public*, pg. 772
ESAB WELDING & CUTTING PRODUCTS (SHANGHAI) CO LIMITED—See Enovis Corporation; *U.S. Public*, pg. 771
ESAB WELDING & CUTTING PRODUCTS—See Enovis Corporation; *U.S. Public*, pg. 771
ESAB WELDING & CUTTING PRODUCTS—See Enovis Corporation; *U.S. Public*, pg. 771
ESAB WELDING EQUIPMENT AB—See Enovis Corporation; *U.S. Public*, pg. 771
ESAB WELDING PRODUCTS (JIANGSU) CO LIMITED—See Enovis Corporation; *U.S. Public*, pg. 771
ESA CARGO & LOGISTICS GMBH—See Allianz SE; *Int'l*, pg. 352
ESAC, INC.; *U.S. Private*, pg. 1424
ESA CO., LTD.; *Int'l*, pg. 2500
ESACONTROL SRL—See FOS S.p.A.; *Int'l*, pg. 2748
ES ADVERTISING; *U.S. Private*, pg. 1424
ESA ELECTRONICS PTE LTD—See Renaissance United Limited; *Int'l*, pg. 6273
ESA ENVIRONMENTAL SPECIALISTS, INC.; *U.S. Private*, pg. 1424
ESA EUROSHIP ASSEKURADEURGESELLSCHAFT MBH & CO. KG—See Allianz SE; *Int'l*, pg. 350
ESA EUROSHIP GMBH—See Allianz SE; *Int'l*, pg. 356
ESAF – ESPIRITO SANTO ACTIVOS FINANCEIROS S.G.P.S., S.A.—See Novo Banco, S.A.; *Int'l*, pg. 5462
ESAKA LOGISTICS SERVICE CO., LTD.—See Senko Group Holdings Co., Ltd.; *Int'l*, pg. 6709
ESAKON ITALIA S.R.L.—See GPI S.p.A.; *Int'l*, pg. 3046
ESALEN INSTITUTE; *U.S. Private*, pg. 1424
ESALESTAX.COM, INC.—See Wolters Kluwer n.v.; *Int'l*, pg. 8445
ESALESTRACK—See Soleran, Inc.; *U.S. Private*, pg. 3709
ESA MCINTOSH LIMITED—See Havelock Europa PLC; *Int'l*, pg. 3287
E. SAM JONES DISTRIBUTOR INCORPORATED; *U.S. Private*, pg. 1304
ESAN ECZACIBASI INDUSTRIAL RAW MATERIALS CO.—See Eczacibasi Holding A.S.; *Int'l*, pg. 2301
ESANG NETWORKS CO., LTD.; *Int'l*, pg. 2501
ESAOTE ASIA PACIFIC DIAGNOSTIC PRIVATE LIMITED—See Esaote S.p.A.; *Int'l*, pg. 2501
ESAOTE BENELUX N.V.—See Esaote S.p.A.; *Int'l*, pg. 2501
ESAOTE BIOMEDICA DEUTSCHLAND GMBH—See Esaote S.p.A.; *Int'l*, pg. 2501
ESAOTE CHINA LTD.—See Esaote S.p.A.; *Int'l*, pg. 2501
ESAOTE ESPANA S.A.—See Esaote S.p.A.; *Int'l*, pg. 2501
ESAOTE EUROPE B.V.—See Esaote S.p.A.; *Int'l*, pg. 2501
ESAOTE FRANCE S.A.R.L.—See Esaote S.p.A.; *Int'l*, pg. 2501
ESAOTE HEALTHCARE DO BRASIL—See Esaote S.p.A.; *Int'l*, pg. 2501
ESAOTE LATINOAMERICA S.A.—See Esaote S.p.A.; *Int'l*, pg. 2501
ESAOTE MEDICAL SAS—See Esaote S.p.A.; *Int'l*, pg. 2501
ESAOTE NORTH AMERICA INC.—See Esaote S.p.A.; *Int'l*, pg. 2501
ESAOTE S.p.A.; *Int'l*, pg. 2501
ESAOTE UK—See Esaote S.p.A.; *Int'l*, pg. 2501
ESA PWA—See Environmental Science Associates; *U.S. Private*, pg. 1408
ESA RETAIL LIMITED—See The BDRC Group; *Int'l*, pg. 7620
ESAS GAYRIMENKUL—See ESAS Holding A.S.; *Int'l*, pg. 2501
ESAS HOLDING A.S.; *Int'l*, pg. 2501
ESASLIGRUP—See ESAS Holding A.S.; *Int'l*, pg. 2501
ESA S.R.O.—See KKR & Co. Inc.; *U.S. Public*, pg. 1258
E.SAT TV (PROPRIETARY) LIMITED—See Hosken Consolidated Investments Limited; *Int'l*, pg. 3485
ESAU & HUEBER GMBH.—See Buhler AG; *Int'l*, pg. 1212
ESAUTOMOTION S.P.A.; *Int'l*, pg. 2501
ESAVVY PTY LTD—See Empired Ltd; *Int'l*, pg. 2387
ES BANCSHARES, INC.; *U.S. Public*, pg. 793
ESBELT, S.A.—See Asgco Manufacturing, Inc.; *U.S. Private*, pg. 349
ESB-GEMEINNUTZIGE GESELLSCHAFT FUR BERUFLICHE BILDUNG MBH—See Asklepios Kliniken GmbH & Co. KGaA; *Int'l*, pg. 624
E.S. BOULOS COMPANY—See MYR Group Inc.; *U.S. Public*, pg. 1489
E.S. BOULOS COMPANY - UTILITIES DIVISION—See MYR Group Inc.; *U.S. Public*, pg. 1489

ES BANCSHARES, INC.

ESCADA AMERICA LLC—See Regent, L.P.; *U.S. Private*, pg. 3387
ESCADA BENELUX BV—See Regent, L.P.; *U.S. Private*, pg. 3387
ESCADA CANADA INC.—See Regent, L.P.; *U.S. Private*, pg. 3387
ESCADA FRANCE S.A.—See Regent, L.P.; *U.S. Private*, pg. 3387
ESCADA HONG KONG LTD.—See Regent, L.P.; *U.S. Private*, pg. 3387
ESCADA INNOVATIONS LTD.—See Siris Capital Group, LLC; *U.S. Private*, pg. 3673
ESCADA ITALIA S.R.L.—See Regent, L.P.; *U.S. Private*, pg. 3387
ESCADA JAPAN CO. LTD.—See Regent, L.P.; *U.S. Private*, pg. 3387
ESCADA KOREA LTD.—See Regent, L.P.; *U.S. Private*, pg. 3387
ESCADA MONTE CARLO S.A.M.—See Regent, L.P.; *U.S. Private*, pg. 3387
ESCADA PORTUGAL UNIPESSOAL LIMITADA—See Regent, L.P.; *U.S. Private*, pg. 3387
ESCADA SWITZERLAND LTD.—See Regent, L.P.; *U.S. Private*, pg. 3387
ESCADA TEXTILIEN-VERTRIEBSGES.M.B.H.—See Regent, L.P.; *U.S. Private*, pg. 3387
ESCADA UK LTD.—See Regent, L.P.; *U.S. Private*, pg. 3387
ESCAD MEDICAL GMBH—See STERIS plc; *Int'l*, pg. 7209
ESCALA BRAGA - SOCIEDADE GESTORA DO ESTABELECIMENTO, S.A.—See Jose de Mello, SGPS, S.A.; *Int'l*, pg. 4001
ESCALA COMUNICACAO & MARKETING LTDA.; *Int'l*, pg. 2501
ESCALADE, INCORPORATED; *U.S. Public*, pg. 793
ESCALADE SPORTS INC; *U.S. Private*, pg. 1424
ESCALADE SPORTS PLAYGROUND, INC.—See Escalade, Incorporated; *U.S. Public*, pg. 793
ESCALANTE GOLF, INC.; *U.S. Private*, pg. 1424
ESCALATE MEDIA HOLDINGS, LLC—See H.I.G. Capital, LLC; *U.S. Private*, pg. 1829
ESCALATE MEDIA, L.P.—See H.I.G. Capital, LLC; *U.S. Private*, pg. 1829
ESCALATE RETAIL, INC.—See Golden Gate Capital Management II, LLC; *U.S. Private*, pg. 1731
ESCALATUR VIAGENS, LDA.—See Barcelo Corporacion Empresarial S.A.; *Int'l*, pg. 859
ESCALA VILA FRANCA - SOCIEDADE GESTORA DO ESTABELECIMENTO, S.A.—See Jose de Mello, SGPS, S.A.; *Int'l*, pg. 4001
ESCALENT, INC.—See Symphony Technology Group, LLC; *U.S. Private*, pg. 3900
ESCALERAS, S. DE R.L. DE C.V.—See Cuprum S.A. de C.V.; *Int'l*, pg. 1878
ESCALON MEDICAL CORP.; *U.S. Public*, pg. 793
ESCALON MEDICAL IMAGING—See Escalon Medical Corp.; *U.S. Public*, pg. 793
ESCALON PENNSYLVANIA, INC.—See Escalon Medical Corp.; *U.S. Public*, pg. 793
ESCALON PREMIER BRANDS—See 3G Capital Inc.; *U.S. Private*, pg. 10
ESCALON PREMIER BRANDS—See Berkshire Hathaway Inc.; *U.S. Public*, pg. 318
ESCALON SERVICES INC.; *U.S. Private*, pg. 1424
ESCAMBIA COUNTY SCHOOL READINESS COALITION, INC.; *U.S. Private*, pg. 1424
ESCANABA & LAKE SUPERIOR RAILROAD CO.; *U.S. Private*, pg. 1424
ESCAPE HUNT GROUP LIMITED—See XP Factory Plc; *Int'l*, pg. 8537
ESCAPE MEDIA GROUP, INC.; *U.S. Private*, pg. 1425
ESCAPE MOBILE DIALOGUE L.T.D.—See InternetQ plc; *Int'l*, pg. 3754
ESCAPE POD; *U.S. Private*, pg. 1425
ESCAPES!—See Cooper Communities, Inc.; *U.S. Private*, pg. 1041
ESCAPE TECHNOLOGY GMBH—See 2Crsi SA; *Int'l*, pg. 4
ESCAPE TECHNOLOGY LTD.—See 2Crsi SA; *Int'l*, pg. 4
ESCAPOLOGY LLC; *U.S. Private*, pg. 1425
ESC CORPORATE SERVICES LTD.—See Information Services Corporation; *Int'l*, pg. 3695
E.S.C. ELECTRONICS CORP.; *U.S. Private*, pg. 1307
ESCENDENT, LLC; *U.S. Private*, pg. 1425
ESCENIC AS—See CCI Europe A/S; *Int'l*, pg. 1366
ES CERAMICS TECHNOLOGY BHD; *Int'l*, pg. 2500
ESCHA BAUELEMENTE GMBH; *Int'l*, pg. 2501
ESCHENBACH HOLDING GMBH—See Equistone Partners Europe Limited; *Int'l*, pg. 2486
ESCHENBACH OPTIK A/S—See Equistone Partners Europe Limited; *Int'l*, pg. 2486
ESCHENBACH OPTIK BV—See Equistone Partners Europe Limited; *Int'l*, pg. 2486
ESCHENBACH OPTIK GMBH—See Equistone Partners Europe Limited; *Int'l*, pg. 2486
ESCHENBACH OPTIK GMBH—See Equistone Partners Europe Limited; *Int'l*, pg. 2486
ESCHENBACH OPTIK OF AMERICA, INC.—See Equistone Partners Europe Limited; *Int'l*, pg. 2486

ESCHENBACH OPTIK OF JAPAN CO. LTD.—See Equistone Partners Europe Limited; *Int'l*, pg. 2486
ESCHENBACH OPTIK POLEN SP.Z.O.O.—See Equistone Partners Europe Limited; *Int'l*, pg. 2486
ESCHENBACH OPTIK S.A.R.L.—See Equistone Partners Europe Limited; *Int'l*, pg. 2486
ESCHENBACH OPTIK S.L.—See Equistone Partners Europe Limited; *Int'l*, pg. 2486
ESCHENBACH OPTIK SPOL S.R.O.—See Equistone Partners Europe Limited; *Int'l*, pg. 2486
ESCHENBACH OPTIK S.R.L.—See Equistone Partners Europe Limited; *Int'l*, pg. 2486
ESCHER ASIA PACIFIC PRIVATE LIMITED—See Escher Group Limited; *U.S. Private*, pg. 1425
ESCHER EUROPE LIMITED—See Escher Group Limited; *U.S. Private*, pg. 1425
ESCHER GROUP LIMITED; *U.S. Private*, pg. 1425
ESCHER PROCESS MODULES B.V.—See Iv-Groep b.v.; *Int'l*, pg. 3846
ESCHER UK LIMITED—See Escher Group Limited; *U.S. Private*, pg. 1425
ESCHMANN BETEILIGUNGSGESELLSCHAFT MBH—See voestalpine AG; *Int'l*, pg. 8292
ESCHMANN HOLDINGS LIMITED—See STERIS plc; *Int'l*, pg. 7210
ESCHMANN HOLDINGS PTE LIMITED—See STERIS plc; *Int'l*, pg. 7210
ESCHMANNSTAHL GMBH & CO. KG - REICHSHOF-WEHNRATH PLANT—See voestalpine AG; *Int'l*, pg. 8292
ESCHMANNSTAHL GMBH & CO. KG—See voestalpine AG; *Int'l*, pg. 8292
ESCHMANN TEXTURA INTERNACIONAL - TRANSFORMACAO DE FERRAMENTAS, UNIPESSOAL, LDA—See voestalpine AG; *Int'l*, pg. 8289
ESCHMANN TEXTURES INTERNATIONAL GMBH—See voestalpine AG; *Int'l*, pg. 8289
ESCHMANN VERMOGENSVERWALTUNG GMBH—See voestalpine AG; *Int'l*, pg. 8289
E. SCHNAPP & CO. WORKS LTD.; *Int'l*, pg. 2250
ESCHOLAR, LLC—See Constellation Software Inc.; *Int'l*, pg. 1774
ESC, INC.—See QXO, Inc.; *U.S. Public*, pg. 1758
ESCO AANDRIJVINGEN B.V.—See Esco Financial & Engineering Company S.A/N.V.; *Int'l*, pg. 2501
ESCO ANTRIEBSTECHNIK GMBH—See Esco Financial & Engineering Company S.A/N.V.; *Int'l*, pg. 2502
ESCOBAL JAPAN LTD.—See Kawasaki Kisen Kaisha, Ltd.; *Int'l*, pg. 4099
ESCO BENELUX N.V.—See K+S Aktiengesellschaft; *Int'l*, pg. 4042
ESCO BUCYRUS INC.—See The Weir Group PLC; *Int'l*, pg. 7699
E.S.CO. COMUNI SRL—See Enel S.p.A.; *Int'l*, pg. 2411
ESCO CORPORATION—See The Weir Group PLC; *Int'l*, pg. 7699
ESCO COUPLINGS (JINAN) LTD—See Esco Financial & Engineering Company S.A/N.V.; *Int'l*, pg. 2501
ESCO COUPLINGS N.V.—See Esco Financial & Engineering Company S.A/N.V.; *Int'l*, pg. 2501
ESCO COUPLINGS & TRANSMISSIONS PRIVATE LIMITED—See Esco Financial & Engineering Company S.A/N.V.; *Int'l*, pg. 2501
ESCO DRIVES & AUTOMATION N.V.—See Esco Financial & Engineering Company S.A/N.V.; *Int'l*, pg. 2501
ESCO ELECMETAL FUNDICION LIMITADA—See The Weir Group PLC; *Int'l*, pg. 7699
ESCO ENERGY SERVICES COMPANY—See The Southern Company; *U.S. Public*, pg. 2131
ESCO ENGINEERED PRODUCTS—See The Weir Group PLC; *Int'l*, pg. 7699
ESCO - EUROPEAN SALT COMPANY GMBH & CO. KG - BERNBURG PLANT—See K+S Aktiengesellschaft; *Int'l*, pg. 4039
ESCO - EUROPEAN SALT COMPANY GMBH & CO. KG - BORTH PLANT—See K+S Aktiengesellschaft; *Int'l*, pg. 4039
ESCO - EUROPEAN SALT COMPANY GMBH & CO. KG - BRAUNSCHWEIG-LUNEBURG PLANT—See K+S Aktiengesellschaft; *Int'l*, pg. 4039
ESCO FINANCIAL AND TRANSMISSIONS LTD.—See Esco Financial & Engineering Company S.A/N.V.; *Int'l*, pg. 2501
ESCO FINANCIAL & ENGINEERING COMPANY S.A/N.V.; *Int'l*, pg. 2501
ESCO FRANCE S.A.S.—See K+S Aktiengesellschaft; *Int'l*, pg. 4039
ESCO GLOBAL REALTY CORP.; *Int'l*, pg. 2502
ESCO GROUP; *U.S. Private*, pg. 1425
ESCO HOLDING FRANCE S.A.S—See K+S Aktiengesellschaft; *Int'l*, pg. 4042
ESCO HYDRA (UK) LIMITED—See The Weir Group PLC; *Int'l*, pg. 7699
ESCO INDUSTRIES INCORPORATED; *U.S. Private*, pg. 1425
ESCO INDUSTRIES, INC.; *U.S. Private*, pg. 1425
ESCO INTERNATIONAL GMBH—See K+S Aktiengesellschaft; *Int'l*, pg. 4042
ESCO LTD.; *U.S. Private*, pg. 1425

CORPORATE AFFILIATIONS

ESCO MARGINALEN AB; *Int'l*, pg. 2502
ESCO METALLBAUSYSTEME AUSTRIA GMBH—See VBH Holding AG; *Int'l*, pg. 8140
ESCO METALLBAUSYSTEME GMBH—See VBH Holding AG; *Int'l*, pg. 8140
ESCO MOCAMBIQUE S.A.—See The Weir Group PLC; *Int'l*, pg. 7699
ES-CON ASSET MANAGEMENT CO., LTD.—See ES-CON JAPAN Ltd.; *Int'l*, pg. 2500
ES-CON JAPAN LTD.; *Int'l*, pg. 2500
ESCON JAPAN REIT INVESTMENT CORP.—See ES-CON JAPAN Ltd.; *Int'l*, pg. 2500
ES-CON LIVING SERVICE LTD.—See ES-CON JAPAN Ltd.; *Int'l*, pg. 2500
ESCO NORDIC AB—See K+S Aktiengesellschaft; *Int'l*, pg. 4042
ESCO POLSKA SP.Z.O.O.—See VBH Holding AG; *Int'l*, pg. 8140
ESCO POWER N.V.—See Esco Financial & Engineering Company S.A/N.V.; *Int'l*, pg. 2501
ESCORP ASSET MANAGEMENT LIMITED; *Int'l*, pg. 2502
ESCORT, INC.—See Monomoy Capital Partners LLC; *U.S. Private*, pg. 2772
ESCORTS CAPITAL LIMITED—See Escorts Investment Bank Limited; *Int'l*, pg. 2502
ESCORTS CROP SOLUTION LIMITED—See Escorts Kubota Limited; *Int'l*, pg. 2502
ESCORTS FINANCE LIMITED—See Escorts Kubota Limited; *Int'l*, pg. 2502
ESCORTS HEART AND SUPER SPECIALITY INSTITUTE LIMITED—See Fortis Healthcare Limited; *Int'l*, pg. 2739
ESCORTS HEART INSTITUTE AND RESEARCH CENTRE LIMITED—See Fortis Healthcare Limited; *Int'l*, pg. 2739
ESCORTS HOSPITAL AND RESEARCH CENTRE LIMITED—See Fortis Healthcare Limited; *Int'l*, pg. 2739
ESCORTS INVESTMENT BANK LIMITED; *Int'l*, pg. 2502
ESCORTS KUBOTA LIMITED; *Int'l*, pg. 2502
ESCORTS SECURITIES LIMITED—See Escorts Kubota Limited; *Int'l*, pg. 2502
ESCORT TEKNOLOJI YATIRIM A.S.; *Int'l*, pg. 2502
ESCO RUS OOO—See VBH Holding AG; *Int'l*, pg. 8139
ESCO (SHANGHAI) TRADING CO., LTD.—See The Weir Group PLC; *Int'l*, pg. 7699
ESCO SPAIN S.L.—See K+S Aktiengesellschaft; *Int'l*, pg. 4042
ESCO SPECIALTY COATINGS (GUANGZHOU) CO., LTD.—See Eternal Materials Co., Ltd.; *Int'l*, pg. 2520
ESCOTA—See VINCI S.A.; *Int'l*, pg. 8230
ESCO TECHNOLOGIES HOLDING INC.—See ESCO Technologies, Inc.; *U.S. Public*, pg. 793
ESCO TECHNOLOGIES, INC.; *U.S. Public*, pg. 793
ESCO TRANSMISJA MOCY SP. Z O.O.—See Esco Financial & Engineering Company S.A/N.V.; *Int'l*, pg. 2501
ESCO TRANSMISSIONS N.V.—See Esco Financial & Engineering Company S.A/N.V.; *Int'l*, pg. 2502
ESCO TRANSMISSIONS S.A.—See Esco Financial & Engineering Company S.A/N.V.; *Int'l*, pg. 2502
ESCO VENTURES CO., LTD.—See Univentures Public Company Limited; *Int'l*, pg. 8077
ESCO VERWALTUNGS GMBH—See K+S Aktiengesellschaft; *Int'l*, pg. 4042
ESCOWA AB—See Castik Capital S.a.r.l.; *Int'l*, pg. 1356
ESCOY HOLDINGS BHD.—See Amalgamated Metal Corporation PLC; *Int'l*, pg. 408
ESCREEN CANADA ULC—See Abbott Laboratories; *U.S. Public*, pg. 19
ESCREEN, INC.—See Abbott Laboratories; *U.S. Public*, pg. 19
ESCRIT INC.; *Int'l*, pg. 2502
ESCROW AGENT JAPAN, INC.; *Int'l*, pg. 2502
ESCROW ASSOCIATES LLC—See NCC Group Plc; *Int'l*, pg. 5180
ESCROW.COM, INC.—See Freelancer Ltd.; *Int'l*, pg. 2770
ESCROW EUROPE AG—See NCC Group Plc; *Int'l*, pg. 5180
ESCROW EUROPE BV—See NCC Group Plc; *Int'l*, pg. 5180
ESCROW OPTIONS GROUP INC.; *U.S. Private*, pg. 1425
ESCRYPT GMBH EMBEDDED SECURITY—See Robert Bosch GmbH; *Int'l*, pg. 6368
ESCRYPT INC.—See Robert Bosch GmbH; *Int'l*, pg. 6367
ESC SERVICES, INC.—See Rockwell Automation, Inc.; *U.S. Public*, pg. 1805
ES CUBE CO., LTD.; *Int'l*, pg. 2500
ESCUDO CAPITAL CORPORATION; *Int'l*, pg. 2502
ESCUE WOOD PRESERVING, INC.—See Great Southern Wood Preserving, Incorporated; *U.S. Private*, pg. 1768
ESD BULGARIA LIMITED—See Invinity Energy Systems plc; *Int'l*, pg. 3789
ESD-CENTER AB.—See Addtech AB; *Int'l*, pg. 133
ESDEC BV; *Int'l*, pg. 2502
ESDEC USA—See Esdec BV; *Int'l*, pg. 2502
ESD ENERGIE SERVICE DEUTSCHLAND GMBH—See EnBW Energie Baden-Wurttemberg AG; *Int'l*, pg. 2398
ESD PARTNERS LIMITED—See Invinity Energy Systems plc; *Int'l*, pg. 3789
ESE BV—See Berry Global Group, Inc; *U.S. Public*, pg. 321

COMPANY NAME INDEX

ESEC AG—See BE Semiconductor Industries N.V.; *Int'l*, pg. 931
ESECLENDING (EUROPE) LIMITED—See PCP Enterprise, L.P.; *U.S. Private*, pg. 3121
ESECLENDING LLC—See PCP Enterprise, L.P.; *U.S. Private*, pg. 3121
ESE CONSULTANTS, INC.—See Toll Brothers, Inc.; *U.S. Public*, pg. 2161
ESE CONSULTANTS, INC.—See Toll Brothers, Inc.; *U.S. Public*, pg. 2161
ESE CONSULTANTS, INC.—See Toll Brothers, Inc.; *U.S. Public*, pg. 2161
ESEC (SINGAPORE) PTE. LTD.—See BE Semiconductor Industries N.V.; *Int'l*, pg. 931
ESECTOR, LTD.—See Computer Engineering & Consulting Ltd.; *Int'l*, pg. 1759
E-SECURE ASIA PTE. LTD.—See Multi-Chem Limited; *Int'l*, pg. 5082
E-SECURE (PTY) LIMITED—See EOH HOLDINGS LIMITED; *Int'l*, pg. 2457
ESE DIRECT LIMITED—See HC Slingsby PLC; *Int'l*, pg. 3297
E-SEEK, INC.—See Bundesdruckerei GmbH; *Int'l*, pg. 1216
E-SEEK, INC.—See Giesecke & Devrient GmbH; *Int'l*, pg. 2970
ESE ENERGY SDN. BHD.—See Harbour-Link Group Berhad; *Int'l*, pg. 3272
ESE ENTERTAINMENT, INC.; *Int'l*, pg. 2502
ESE EUROPE SP. Z O.O.—See ESE Entertainment, Inc.; *Int'l*, pg. 2502
ESE FRANCE SA—See Berry Global Group, Inc; *U.S. Public*, pg. 321
ESE GMBH—See Berry Global Group, Inc; *U.S. Public*, pg. 321
E-SEIKATSU CO., LTD.; *Int'l*, pg. 2249
ESE KFT—See Berry Global Group, Inc; *U.S. Public*, pg. 321
E.S. ELECTRI-CORD S. DE R.L. DE C.V.—See Electri-Cord Manufacturing Co.; *U.S. Private*, pg. 1352
ESENBOGA ELEKTRIK URETIM A.S.; *Int'l*, pg. 2502
ESENCIA GROUP; *Int'l*, pg. 2502
ESENCIA GROUP—See Esencia Group; *Int'l*, pg. 2502
ESENCIA GROUP—See Esencia Group; *Int'l*, pg. 2502
ESENDEX—See HgCapital Trust plc; *Int'l*, pg. 3376
ESENERGIA—See Mondragon Corporation; *Int'l*, pg. 5029
ESENER S.A.—See Veolia Environnement S.A.; *Int'l*, pg. 8158
ESENSE-LAB LTD; *Int'l*, pg. 2502
ESENSE LEARNING PRIVATE LIMITED—See Navneet Education Ltd; *Int'l*, pg. 5177
ESENTIRE, INC.; *Int'l*, pg. 2502
ESENTTIA MASTERBATCH LTDA.—See Ecopetrol S.A.; *Int'l*, pg. 2299
ESENTTIA S.A.—See Ecopetrol S.A.; *Int'l*, pg. 2299
E&S ENVIRONMENTAL SERVICES LTD—See Sun Capital Partners, Inc.; *U.S. Private*, pg. 3861
ESE NV—See Berry Global Group, Inc; *U.S. Public*, pg. 321
ESERVGLOBAL (HK) LIMITED—See Seamless Distribution Systems AB; *Int'l*, pg. 6665
ESERVGLOBAL HOLDINGS SAS—See Seamless Distribution Systems AB; *Int'l*, pg. 6665
ESERVGLOBAL NVSA—See Seamless Distribution Systems AB; *Int'l*, pg. 6665
ESERVGLOBAL (NZ) PTY LIMITED—See Seamless Distribution Systems AB; *Int'l*, pg. 6665
ESERVGLOBAL SAS—See Seamless Distribution Systems AB; *Int'l*, pg. 6665
ESERVGLOBAL TELECOM ROMANIA SRL—See Seamless Distribution Systems AB; *Int'l*, pg. 6665
ESERVGLOBAL UK LIMITED—See Seamless Distribution Systems AB; *Int'l*, pg. 6665
E SERVICES SINGAPORE PTE. LTD.—See Veritas Capital Fund Management, LLC; *U.S. Private*, pg. 4363
ESE SP. Z O.O.—See Berry Global Group, Inc; *U.S. Public*, pg. 321
ESET, LLC; *U.S. Private*, pg. 1425
ESET, SPOL. S.R.O.—See ESET, LLC; *U.S. Private*, pg. 1425
ESE WORLD BV—See Berry Global Group, Inc; *U.S. Public*, pg. 321
ESFAHAN'S MOBARAKEH STEEL COMPANY; *Int'l*, pg. 2503
ESFERA BUS S.L.—See Deutsche Bahn AG; *Int'l*, pg. 2051
ESFEROMATIC S.A.—See Sophia Capital S.A.; *Int'l*, pg. 7108
ES FIELD DELIVERY FRANCE SAS—See DXC Technology Company; *U.S. Public*, pg. 696
ES FIELD DELIVERY NEDERLAND B.V.—See DXC Technology Company; *U.S. Public*, pg. 696
ES FIELD DELIVERY SPAIN, S.L.U.—See DXC Technology Company; *U.S. Public*, pg. 696
ESFIN GESTION SA—See Groupe BPCE; *Int'l*, pg. 3094
E.S. FOX LIMITED; *Int'l*, pg. 2260
ESG CONSULTING INC.; *U.S. Private*, pg. 1425
ESG GLOBAL IMPACT CAPITAL INC.; *Int'l*, pg. 2503

ESG HOLDINGS, LTD.—See Advantage Partners LLP; *Int'l*, pg. 164
ESG INC.—See Goldwin, Inc.; *Int'l*, pg. 3035
ESGL HOLDINGS LIMITED; *Int'l*, pg. 2503
ES GLOBAL LTD; *Int'l*, pg. 2500
ESGOLD CORP.; *Int'l*, pg. 2503
ESG REPUBLIC; *U.S. Private*, pg. 1425
ES GROUP (HOLDINGS) LIMITED; *Int'l*, pg. 2500
ESGTI AG; *Int'l*, pg. 2503
ESG WOHNUNGSGESELLSCHAFT MBH VILLACH—See Vonovia SE; *Int'l*, pg. 8304
ESH ACQUISITION CORP.; *U.S. Public*, pg. 794
ESHA MEDIA RESEARCH LIMITED; *Int'l*, pg. 2503
ESHAREH ADVERTISING AGENCY—See The Interpublic Group of Companies, Inc.; *U.S. Public*, pg. 2099
ESHA RESEARCH INC.—See The Riverside Company; *U.S. Private*, pg. 4108
ESHARES, INC.; *U.S. Private*, pg. 1425
ESHELMAN COMPANY INC.; *U.S. Private*, pg. 1425
ESHEL TECHNOLOGY GROUP, INC.—See Arrow Electronics, Inc.; *U.S. Public*, pg. 199
ESHENBAUGH LAND COMPANY; *U.S. Private*, pg. 1425
ESH (HONG KONG) LIMITED—See Edvance International Holdings Limited; *Int'l*, pg. 2316
ESH HOSPITALITY, INC.—See Blackstone Inc.; *U.S. Public*, pg. 350
ESH HOSPITALITY, INC.—See Starwood Capital Group Global I, LLC; *U.S. Private*, pg. 3789
ESHIPPERS MANAGEMENT LTD.; *Int'l*, pg. 2503
ESHO - EMPRESA DE SERVICOS HOSPITALARES S.A—See UnitedHealth Group Incorporated; *U.S. Public*, pg. 2240
E & S HOME OF COLOR B.V.—See Dainichiseika Color & Chemicals Mfg. Co., Ltd.; *Int'l*, pg. 1939
E & S HOME OF COLOR, INC; *Int'l*, pg. 2245
ESHRAQ INVESTMENTS PJSC; *Int'l*, pg. 2503
ES HYDAGENT AB—See Indutrade AB; *Int'l*, pg. 3678
ESI ACQUISITION CORPORATION—See Applied Industrial Technologies, Inc.; *U.S. Public*, pg. 171
ESI ACQUISITION, INC.; *U.S. Private*, pg. 1425
ESI CANADA—See The Cigna Group; *U.S. Public*, pg. 2061
ESI CANADA—See The Cigna Group; *U.S. Public*, pg. 2061
ESI CED SERVICES—See Keysight Technologies, Inc.; *U.S. Public*, pg. 1226
ESI CHINA—See Keysight Technologies, Inc.; *U.S. Public*, pg. 1226
ESI COMPANIES INC.—See Mainco Investments Inc.; *U.S. Private*, pg. 2552
ESI CONTRACTING, CORP.; *U.S. Private*, pg. 1425
ESI CONTROLS LTD.—See Addtech AB; *Int'l*, pg. 133
ESI DAYTON—See MDU Resources Group, Inc.; *U.S. Public*, pg. 1410
ESI ELECTRONIC EQUIPMENT (SHANGHAI) CO., LTD.—See MKS Instruments, Inc.; *U.S. Public*, pg. 1452
ESI ENERGY SERVICES INC.—See Battery Mineral Resources Corp.; *Int'l*, pg. 890
ESI FRANCE SARL—See Keysight Technologies, Inc.; *U.S. Public*, pg. 1226
ESI GERMANY GMBH—See Keysight Technologies, Inc.; *U.S. Public*, pg. 1226
ESI GMBH—See Keysight Technologies, Inc.; *U.S. Public*, pg. 1226
ESIGN SOFTWARE GMBH—See Eleco Plc; *Int'l*, pg. 2348
ESIGNSYSTEMS—See DocMagic, Inc.; *U.S. Private*, pg. 1251
ESI GROUP HISPANIA, S.L.—See Keysight Technologies, Inc.; *U.S. Public*, pg. 1226
ESI GROUP NETHERLANDS—See Keysight Technologies, Inc.; *U.S. Public*, pg. 1226
ESI GROUP S.A.—See Keysight Technologies, Inc.; *U.S. Public*, pg. 1226
ESI GROUP USA; *U.S. Private*, pg. 1426
E.S.I. HOLDOING CORP.; *U.S. Private*, pg. 1307
ESI, INC.—See MDU Resources Group, Inc.; *U.S. Public*, pg. 1410
ESI INTERNATIONAL, INC.—See Providence Equity Partners L.L.C.; *U.S. Private*, pg. 3292
ESI INVESTMENT CO.—See Electro-Sensors, Inc.; *U.S. Public*, pg. 723
ESI ITALIA SRL—See Keysight Technologies, Inc.; *U.S. Public*, pg. 1226
ESI ITI GMBH—See Keysight Technologies, Inc.; *U.S. Public*, pg. 1226
ESI JAPAN LTD—See Keysight Technologies, Inc.; *U.S. Public*, pg. 1226
ESIKAS BETEILIGUNGSVERWALTUNGS GMBH—See PORR AG; *Int'l*, pg. 5922
ESI KOREA CO. LTD.—See MKS Instruments, Inc.; *U.S. Public*, pg. 1452
ESILICON CORPORATION—See Marvell Technology Group Ltd.; *Int'l*, pg. 4717
ESI MAIL ORDER PROCESSING, INC.—See The Cigna Group; *U.S. Public*, pg. 2061
ES IMMOBILIEN GMBH—See DXC Technology Company; *U.S. Public*, pg. 696
ES INDUSTRY CO LTD; *Int'l*, pg. 2500

ESI NORDICS AB—See Keysight Technologies, Inc.; *U.S. Public*, pg. 1226
ESI NORTH AMERICA, INC.—See Keysight Technologies, Inc.; *U.S. Public*, pg. 1226
E&S INTERNATIONAL ENTERPRISES INC.; *U.S. Private*, pg. 1301
E.S. INVESTMENTS, LLC; *U.S. Private*, pg. 1307
ESI PROCESS UK LIMITED—See Indutrade AB; *Int'l*, pg. 3678
ESI-PYROPHOTONICS LASERS, INC.—See MKS Instruments, Inc.; *U.S. Public*, pg. 1452
ESIR1, INC.; *U.S. Private*, pg. 1426
ESIS ACADEMY PTE. LTD.—See Chubb Limited; *Int'l*, pg. 1591
ESI SAS—See VINCI S.A.; *Int'l*, pg. 8218
ESIS CANADA, INC.—See Chubb Limited; *Int'l*, pg. 1592
ESI SERVICES TUNISIA SARL—See Keysight Technologies, Inc.; *U.S. Public*, pg. 1226
ESI SERVICES VIETNAM CO., LTD.—See Keysight Technologies, Inc.; *U.S. Public*, pg. 1226
ESIS, INC.—See Chubb Limited; *Int'l*, pg. 1591
ESI SOFTWARE PVT. LTD—See Keysight Technologies, Inc.; *U.S. Public*, pg. 1226
ESI SOUTH AMERICA COMERCIO E SERVICOS DE INFORMATICA LTDA—See Keysight Technologies, Inc.; *U.S. Public*, pg. 1227
ESIT ADVANCED SOLUTIONS INC.—See DXC Technology Company; *U.S. Public*, pg. 696
ESI TAIWAN—See MKS Instruments, Inc.; *U.S. Public*, pg. 1452
ESI TECHNOLOGIES B.V.—See Indutrade AB; *Int'l*, pg. 3678
ESI TECHNOLOGIES LTD.—See Indutrade AB; *Int'l*, pg. 3678
ESI UK LIMITED—See Keysight Technologies, Inc.; *U.S. Public*, pg. 1227
ESI US R&D, INC.—See Keysight Technologies, Inc.; *U.S. Public*, pg. 1227
ESI VENTURES LLC; *U.S. Private*, pg. 1426
E.S.I. WORLDWIDE, INC.—See E&S International Enterprises Inc.; *U.S. Private*, pg. 1301
E-SIXT GMBH & CO. KG—See Sixt SE; *Int'l*, pg. 6968
ESJOT GOLDENBERG; *Int'l*, pg. 2503
ESKANDAR LTD.; *Int'l*, pg. 2503
ESKANET S.A.—See WESCO International, Inc.; *U.S. Public*, pg. 2351
ESKA S.A.S—See Derichebourg S.A.; *Int'l*, pg. 2041
ESKATON; *U.S. Private*, pg. 1426
ESKAY MINING CORPORATION; *Int'l*, pg. 2503
ESKAY ROSENBAUER SDN. BHD.—See Rosenbauer International AG; *Int'l*, pg. 6399
ESKENAZI HEALTH FOUNDATION; *U.S. Private*, pg. 1426
ESKEN LIMITED; *Int'l*, pg. 2503
ESKER AUSTRALIA PTY. LTD.—See Esker S.A.; *Int'l*, pg. 2503
ESKER DOCUMENTS AUTOMATION ASIA PTE LTD—See Esker S.A.; *Int'l*, pg. 2503
ESKER GMBH—See Esker S.A.; *Int'l*, pg. 2503
ESKER IBERICA—See Esker S.A.; *Int'l*, pg. 2503
ESKER, INC.—See Esker S.A.; *Int'l*, pg. 2503
ESKER ITALIA S.R.L.—See Esker S.A.; *Int'l*, pg. 2503
ESKER LTD.—See Esker S.A.; *Int'l*, pg. 2503
ESKER S.A.; *Int'l*, pg. 2503
ESKIMO PIE CORPORATION—See Swisher Hygiene Inc.; *U.S. Private*, pg. 3894
ESKIMOS, INC.—See Arctic Slope Regional Corporation; *U.S. Private*, pg. 316
ESK INDIA COMMERCE & TRADE PVT. LTD.—See Sonepar S.A.; *Int'l*, pg. 7090
E.S. KLUFT & CO.—See Flex Equipos de Descanso SA; *Int'l*, pg. 2701
ESKMUIR PROPERTIES LTD; *Int'l*, pg. 2503
ESKMUIR SECURITIES LTD—See Eskmuir Properties Ltd; *Int'l*, pg. 2503
ESKO BRNO S.R.O—See Danaher Corporation; *U.S. Public*, pg. 626
ESKO BVBA—See Danaher Corporation; *U.S. Public*, pg. 626
ESKO-GRAPHICS BVBA—See Danaher Corporation; *U.S. Public*, pg. 626
ESKO-GRAPHICS GMBH—See Danaher Corporation; *U.S. Public*, pg. 626
ESKO GRAPHICS IMAGING GMBH—See Danaher Corporation; *U.S. Public*, pg. 626
ESKO-GRAPHICS INC.—See Danaher Corporation; *U.S. Public*, pg. 626
ESKO GRAPHICS KONGSBERG AS—See Danaher Corporation; *U.S. Public*, pg. 626
ESKO-GRAPHICS PTE LTD.—See Danaher Corporation; *U.S. Public*, pg. 626
ESKOLA LLC—See EMP Management, LLC; *U.S. Private*, pg. 1384
ESKOM HOLDINGS SOC LIMITED; *Int'l*, pg. 2503
ESKOPUU OY—See Ratos AB; *Int'l*, pg. 6220
ESKULAP SP. Z O.O.—See NEUCA S.A.; *Int'l*, pg. 5218
ESKYE SOLUTIONS, INC.; *U.S. Private*, pg. 1426
ESL DEFENCE LTD—See Textron Inc.; *U.S. Public*, pg. 2029

ESLEAD CORP.

ESLEAD CORP.; *Int'l*, pg. 2504
ESL FEDERAL CREDIT UNION—See Eastman Kodak Company; *U.S. Public*, pg. 706
ESLINGAR S.A.—See Delta Plus Group; *Int'l*, pg. 2020
ESLINK CLOUD COMPUTING CO., LTD.—See Goldcard Smart Group Co., Ltd.; *Int'l*, pg. 3027
ES-LINK CO., LTD.—See EPS Holdings, Inc;; *Int'l*, pg. 2465
ESLITE SPECTRUM CORP.; *Int'l*, pg. 2504
ESL PRELEVEMENT SAS—See Eurofins Scientific S.E.; *Int'l*, pg. 2536
ESL SHIPPING LTD—See Aspo Oyj; *Int'l*, pg. 631
ESL STEEL LIMITED—See Vedanta Resources Ltd; *Int'l*, pg. 8146
ESMACH S.P.A.—See Ali Holding S.r.l; *Int'l*, pg. 322
ESM ACQUISITION CORPORATION; *U.S. Public*, pg. 794
E&S MANUFACTURING, INC.—See Array Products Company, LLC; *U.S. Private*, pg. 334
ESMARK INCORPORATED; *U.S. Private*, pg. 1426
ESMARK INC.; *U.S. Private*, pg. 1426
ESMARK STEEL GROUP, LLC—See Esmark Incorporated; *U.S. Private*, pg. 1426
ESMART NETWORKS LIMITED—See Nexus Infrastructure plc; *Int'l*, pg. 5251
ESMECH EQUIPMENT PVT. LTD.—See SMS Holding GmbH; *Int'l*, pg. 7015
ESMG INC.—See Primco Management Inc.; *U.S. Private*, pg. 3261
ESM GROUP, INC. - ASHLAND CASTER DIVISION—See SKW Stahl-Metallurgie Holding AG; *Int'l*, pg. 6992
ESM GROUP, INC.—See SKW Stahl-Metallurgie Holding AG; *Int'l*, pg. 6992
ESMO CORPORATION; *Int'l*, pg. 2504
ESM PRODUCTIONS, LLC—See Live Nation Entertainment, Inc.; *U.S. Public*, pg. 1328
ESM TIANJIN CO. LTD.—See SKW Stahl-Metallurgie Holding AG; *Int'l*, pg. 6992
ESNAAD—See Abu Dhabi National Oil Company; *Int'l*, pg. 73
ESNAD COMPANY—See Alinma Bank; *Int'l*, pg. 329
ESNA - TEXAS—See KKR & Co. Inc.; *U.S. Public*, pg. 1262
ESN ENERGIESYSTEMENORD GMBH—See E.ON SE; *Int'l*, pg. 2257
ES NETWORKS CO., LTD.; *Int'l*, pg. 2500
ESN SICHERHEIT UND ZERTIFIZIERUNG GMBH—See E.ON SE; *Int'l*, pg. 2257
ES-O-EN CORP; *U.S. Private*, pg. 1424
ESOLAR, INC.—See Idealab Holdings, LLC; *U.S. Private*, pg. 2037
ESOL CO., LTD.; *Int'l*, pg. 2504
ESOL EUROPE S.A.S.—See Esol Co., Ltd.; *Int'l*, pg. 2504
ESOLUTION ARCHITECTS, INC.; *U.S. Private*, pg. 1426
E.SOLUTIONS GMBH—See Continental Aktiengesellschaft; *Int'l*, pg. 1783
ESOLUTIONS GROUP—See GHD Group Pty Ltd.; *Int'l*, pg. 2959
ESOLUTIONS, INC.—See Canada Pension Plan Investment Board; *Int'l*, pg. 1282
ESOLUTIONS, INC.—See EQT AB; *Int'l*, pg. 2481
E-SOLUTIONS INC.; *U.S. Private*, pg. 1303
E-SOLUTIONS LIMITED—See OCRA (Isle of Man) Limited; *Int'l*, pg. 5520
ESOME ADVERTISING TECHNOLOGIES GMBH—See ProSiebenSat.1 Media SE; *Int'l*, pg. 6000
ESOMET SAS—See BNP Paribas SA; *Int'l*, pg. 1091
ESON EUROPE S.R.O.—See Eson Precision Ind. Co., Ltd.; *Int'l*, pg. 2504
ESO NORD EST—See Emerson Electric Co.; *U.S. Public*, pg. 743
ESO NORMANDIE—See Emerson Electric Co.; *U.S. Public*, pg. 743
ESON PRECISION ENGINEERING (MALAYSIA) SDN. BHD.—See Eson Precision Ind. Co., Ltd.; *Int'l*, pg. 2504
ESON PRECISION ENGINEERING S.A. DE C.V.—See Eson Precision Ind. Co., Ltd.; *Int'l*, pg. 2504
ESON PRECISION IND. CO., LTD.; *Int'l*, pg. 2504
ESON SLOVAKIA A.S.—See Eson Precision Ind. Co., Ltd.; *Int'l*, pg. 2504
ESO OUEST SARL—See Emerson Electric Co.; *U.S. Public*, pg. 743
ESO PARTNERS L.P.; *Int'l*, pg. 2504
ESOR AFRICA (PTY) LIMITED—See Esor Limited; *Int'l*, pg. 2504
ESORFRANKI CIVILS (PTY) LIMITED—See Esor Limited; *Int'l*, pg. 2504
ESORFRANKI PIPELINES (PTY) LIMITED—See Esor Limited; *Int'l*, pg. 2504
ES ORIGINALS INC.; *U.S. Private*, pg. 1424
ESOR LIMITED; *Int'l*, pg. 2504
ESORO BETEILIGUNGSVERWALTUNGS GMBH & CO. KG—See PORR AG; *Int'l*, pg. 5922
ESO SOLUTIONS, INC.; *U.S. Private*, pg. 1426
ESO SUD EST SARL—See Emerson Electric Co.; *U.S. Public*, pg. 743
ESO SUD OUEST—See Emerson Electric Co.; *U.S. Public*, pg. 743

ESOTERIC COMPANY—See Evolution Capital Management LLC; *U.S. Private*, pg. 1443
ESOTERIX GENETIC COUNSELING, LLC—See Laboratory Corporation of America Holdings; *U.S. Public*, pg. 1286
ESOTERIX GENETIC LABORATORIES, LLC—See Laboratory Corporation of America Holdings; *U.S. Public*, pg. 1286
ESOTERIX, INC.—See Laboratory Corporation of America Holdings; *U.S. Public*, pg. 1286
ESOTIQ & HENDERSON SA; *Int'l*, pg. 2504
E SOURCE COMPANIES, LLC—See Align Capital Partners, LLC; *U.S. Private*, pg. 167
E-SOURCE, INC.; *U.S. Private*, pg. 1303
ESPACE ELEC S.A.S.—See Rexel, S.A.; *Int'l*, pg. 6316
ESPACE EXPANSION—See Unibail-Rodamco-Westfield SE; *Int'l*, pg. 8029
ESPACE MAISON LTEE—See United Basalt Products Limited; *Int'l*, pg. 8065
ESPACE MEDIA AG—See TX Group AG; *Int'l*, pg. 7991
ESPACE MEDIA GROUPE AG—See TX Group AG; *Int'l*, pg. 7991
ESPACES TV SA—See Ipsos S.A.; *Int'l*, pg. 3798
ESPACIO DE VINCULACION, A.C.—See Grupo Televisa, S.A.B.; *Int'l*, pg. 3136
ESPACIO LEON PROPCO S.L.U.—See Commerzbank AG; *Int'l*, pg. 1718
ESPACIO LLC—See Coteminas Companhia de Tecidos Norte de Minas; *Int'l*, pg. 1817
ESPACIO LLC—See Springs Global, Inc.; *U.S. Private*, pg. 3764
ESPA CORP, INC.—See KCI Holdings Inc.; *U.S. Private*, pg. 2269
ESPA-FINANCIAL ADVISORS GMBH—See Erste Group Bank AG; *Int'l*, pg. 2498
ESP AFRIKA PROPRIETARY LIMITED—See AYO Technology Solutions Ltd.; *Int'l*, pg. 775
ESPAIS SL—See Banco de Sabadell, S.A.; *Int'l*, pg. 821
ESPAMAD S.L.—See Wereldhave N.V.; *Int'l*, pg. 8378
ESPANOLA MERCANTILE CO.; *U.S. Private*, pg. 1426
ESPANORMED S.L.—See Zimmer Biomet Holdings, Inc.; *U.S. Public*, pg. 2406
ESPARMA GMBH—See Lindopharm GmbH; *Int'l*, pg. 4511
ESPARZA ADVERTISING; *U.S. Private*, pg. 1426
ESP ASSOCIATES, INC.—See Strength Capital Partners, LLC; *U.S. Private*, pg. 3839
ESP CLOTHING FINLAND OY—See Esprit Holdings Limited; *Int'l*, pg. 2506
ESP COMPUTER SERVICES, INC.; *U.S. Private*, pg. 1426
ESPEC (CHINA) LIMITED—See ESPEC Corp.; *Int'l*, pg. 2505
ESPEC CORP. - FUKUCHIYAMA PLANT—See ESPEC Corp.; *Int'l*, pg. 2505
ESPEC CORP.; *Int'l*, pg. 2505
ESPEC ENVIRONMENTAL CHAMBERS SALES & ENGINEERING LTD. STI.—See ESPEC Corp.; *Int'l*, pg. 2505
ESPEC ENVIRONMENTAL EQUIPMENT (SHANGHAI) CO, LTD.—See ESPEC Corp.; *Int'l*, pg. 2505
ESPEC EUROPE GMBH—See ESPEC Corp.; *Int'l*, pg. 2505
ESPECIALIDADES ASFALTICAS BITUMIX CVV S.A.—See VINCI S.A.; *Int'l*, pg. 8218
ESPECIALISTAS EN RESTAURANTES DE COMIDA ESTILO ASIATICA, S. A. DE C. V.—See Alsea, S.A.B. de C.V.; *Int'l*, pg. 379
ESPECIALISTAS EN SALUD-ESENSA S.A.S.—See DaVita Inc.; *U.S. Public*, pg. 638
ESPECIALIZADA Y PRIMARIA LHORTA-MANISES SA—See The British United Provident Association Limited; *Int'l*, pg. 7629
ESPEC KOREA CORP.—See ESPEC Corp.; *Int'l*, pg. 2505
ESPEC KYUSHU CORP.—See ESPEC Corp.; *Int'l*, pg. 2505
ESPEC MIC CORP.—See ESPEC Corp.; *Int'l*, pg. 2505
ESPEC NORTH AMERICA INC.—See ESPEC Corp.; *Int'l*, pg. 2505
ESPEC SOUTH EAST ASIA SDN. BHD.—See ESPEC Corp.; *Int'l*, pg. 2505
ESPEC TECHNO CORP.—See ESPEC Corp.; *Int'l*, pg. 2505
ESPEC TEST TECHNOLOGY (SHANGHAI) CO., LTD.—See ESPEC Corp.; *Int'l*, pg. 2505
ESPEE BIOPHARMA & FINECHEM, LLC; *U.S. Private*, pg. 1426
ESPEE GLOBAL HOLDINGS LLC—See Remus Pharmaceuticals Limited; *Int'l*, pg. 6272
ESPERA-BELGIUM B.V.B.A.—See ESPERA-WERKE GMBH; *Int'l*, pg. 2506
ESPERA IBERICA S.A.—See ESPERA-WERKE GMBH; *Int'l*, pg. 2506
ESPERA-NEDERLAND B.V.—See ESPERA-WERKE GMBH; *Int'l*, pg. 2506
ESPERANZA HEALTH CENTER; *U.S. Private*, pg. 1426
ESPERA S.A.R.L.—See ESPERA-WERKE GMBH; *Int'l*, pg. 2506
ESPERA SCHWEIZ GMBH—See ESPERA-WERKE GMBH; *Int'l*, pg. 2506
ESPERA-WERKE GMBH; *Int'l*, pg. 2505

CORPORATE AFFILIATIONS

ESPERION THERAPEUTICS, INC.; *U.S. Public*, pg. 794
ESPERITE N.V.; *Int'l*, pg. 2506
ESPERO BIOPHARMA, INC.; *U.S. Private*, pg. 1426
ESPERO PHARMACEUTICALS, INC.—See Espero Biopharma, Inc.; *U.S. Private*, pg. 1427
ESPEX BATTERIES LIMITED—See EXIDE INDUSTRIES LIMITED; *Int'l*, pg. 2585
ESPEY MFG. & ELECTRONICS CORP.; *U.S. Public*, pg. 794
ESPIAL GROUP INC.—See Enghouse Systems Limited; *Int'l*, pg. 2427
ESPIAL (UK) LIMITED—See Enghouse Systems Limited; *Int'l*, pg. 2427
ESPIGA CAPITAL GESTION S.G.E.C.R, S.A.; *Int'l*, pg. 2506
ESPIJNEIRA, PACHECO Y ASOCIADOS; *Int'l*, pg. 2506
ESPIRA ABOL AS—See AcadeMedia AB; *Int'l*, pg. 75
ESPIRA ARHAUG AS—See AcadeMedia AB; *Int'l*, pg. 75
ESPIRA ARKJAER AS—See AcadeMedia AB; *Int'l*, pg. 75
ESPIRA AROLIA AS—See AcadeMedia AB; *Int'l*, pg. 75
ESPIRA AROSFJELLET AS—See AcadeMedia AB; *Int'l*, pg. 75
ESPIRA BAGGERODBANEN AS—See AcadeMedia AB; *Int'l*, pg. 75
ESPIRA BJORGENE AS—See AcadeMedia AB; *Int'l*, pg. 75
ESPIRA BLAKSTAD AS—See AcadeMedia AB; *Int'l*, pg. 75
ESPIRA BRADALSFJELLET AS—See AcadeMedia AB; *Int'l*, pg. 75
ESPIRA BRASTEINTUNET AS—See AcadeMedia AB; *Int'l*, pg. 75
ESPIRA DRAGERSKOGEN AS—See AcadeMedia AB; *Int'l*, pg. 75
ESPIRA DVERGSNES AS—See AcadeMedia AB; *Int'l*, pg. 75
ESPIRA EIKENGA AS—See AcadeMedia AB; *Int'l*, pg. 75
ESPIRA EIKENOTTA NATURBARNEHAGE AS—See AcadeMedia AB; *Int'l*, pg. 75
ESPIRA EVANGTUNET AS—See AcadeMedia AB; *Int'l*, pg. 75
ESPIRA EVENTYRSKOGEN AS—See AcadeMedia AB; *Int'l*, pg. 75
ESPIRA EVJE AS—See AcadeMedia AB; *Int'l*, pg. 75
ESPIRA FASANVEIEN AS—See AcadeMedia AB; *Int'l*, pg. 75
ESPIRA FENSTAD AS—See AcadeMedia AB; *Int'l*, pg. 75
ESPIRA FINNAS AS—See AcadeMedia AB; *Int'l*, pg. 75
ESPIRA GARHAUG AS—See AcadeMedia AB; *Int'l*, pg. 75
ESPIRA GARTNERLOKKA AS—See AcadeMedia AB; *Int'l*, pg. 75
ESPIRA GASERUD AS—See AcadeMedia AB; *Int'l*, pg. 75
ESPIRA GJEMBLE AS—See AcadeMedia AB; *Int'l*, pg. 75
ESPIRA GREFSEN AS—See AcadeMedia AB; *Int'l*, pg. 75
ESPIRA GRONNESTOLEN AS—See AcadeMedia AB; *Int'l*, pg. 75
ESPIRA GRUPPEN AS—See AcadeMedia AB; *Int'l*, pg. 75
ESPIRA GULLHELLA AS—See AcadeMedia AB; *Int'l*, pg. 75
ESPIRA HALSNOY KLOSTER AS—See AcadeMedia AB; *Int'l*, pg. 75
ESPIRA HELLDALSASEN AS—See AcadeMedia AB; *Int'l*, pg. 75
ESPIRA HOLBEKK IDRETTSBARNEHAGE AS—See AcadeMedia AB; *Int'l*, pg. 75
ESPIRA HOLLUND AS—See AcadeMedia AB; *Int'l*, pg. 75
ESPIRA HOLUM AS—See AcadeMedia AB; *Int'l*, pg. 75
ESPIRA HOVSMARKA AS—See AcadeMedia AB; *Int'l*, pg. 75
ESPIRA HOYTORP FORT AS—See AcadeMedia AB; *Int'l*, pg. 75
ESPIRA HUSEBYPARKEN AS—See AcadeMedia AB; *Int'l*, pg. 75
ESPIRA JELOY AS—See AcadeMedia AB; *Int'l*, pg. 75
ESPIRA JUBERG AS—See AcadeMedia AB; *Int'l*, pg. 75
ESPIRA KARMSUND AS—See AcadeMedia AB; *Int'l*, pg. 75
ESPIRA KLOVERENGA AS—See AcadeMedia AB; *Int'l*, pg. 75
ESPIRA KNERTEN AS—See AcadeMedia AB; *Int'l*, pg. 75
ESPIRA KNIVEASEN AS—See AcadeMedia AB; *Int'l*, pg. 75
ESPIRA KRYSTALLVEIEN AS—See AcadeMedia AB; *Int'l*, pg. 75
ESPIRA KULTURSTIEN AS—See AcadeMedia AB; *Int'l*, pg. 75
ESPIRA KUNNSKAPSBYEN AS—See AcadeMedia AB; *Int'l*, pg. 75
ESPIRA KUVENTRAE AS—See AcadeMedia AB; *Int'l*, pg. 75
ESPIRA KYSTAD GARD AS—See AcadeMedia AB; *Int'l*, pg. 76
ESPIRA LINDESNES AS—See AcadeMedia AB; *Int'l*, pg. 76
ESPIRA LITLASUND AS—See AcadeMedia AB; *Int'l*, pg. 76
ESPIRA LOVESTAD AS—See AcadeMedia AB; *Int'l*, pg. 76
ESPIRA LURA AS—See AcadeMedia AB; *Int'l*, pg. 76
ESPIRA MARIENFRYD AS—See AcadeMedia AB; *Int'l*, pg. 76

COMPANY NAME INDEX

ESPIRA MARTHAHAUGEN AS—See AcadeMedia AB; *Int'l*, pg. 76
ESPIRA MOSTER AS—See AcadeMedia AB; *Int'l*, pg. 76
ESPIRA MURUVIK AS—See AcadeMedia AB; *Int'l*, pg. 76
ESPIRA MYRASKOGEN AS—See AcadeMedia AB; *Int'l*, pg. 76
ESPIRA NORDMO AS—See AcadeMedia AB; *Int'l*, pg. 76
ESPIRA NYKIRKE AS—See AcadeMedia AB; *Int'l*, pg. 76
ESPIRA OPAKER AS—See AcadeMedia AB; *Int'l*, pg. 76
ESPIRA OPSAHL AS—See AcadeMedia AB; *Int'l*, pg. 76
ESPIRA OREID AS—See AcadeMedia AB; *Int'l*, pg. 76
ESPIRA ORMDALEN AS—See AcadeMedia AB; *Int'l*, pg. 76
ESPIRA OSTREM AS—See AcadeMedia AB; *Int'l*, pg. 76
ESPIRA RA AS—See AcadeMedia AB; *Int'l*, pg. 76
ESPIRA RAMBJORA AS—See AcadeMedia AB; *Int'l*, pg. 76
ESPIRA REE AS—See AcadeMedia AB; *Int'l*, pg. 76
ESPIRA ROMHOLT AS—See AcadeMedia AB; *Int'l*, pg. 76
ESPIRA RUBBESTADNESET AS—See AcadeMedia AB; *Int'l*, pg. 76
ESPIRA SALAMONSKOGEN AS—See AcadeMedia AB; *Int'l*, pg. 76
ESPIRA SANDTOPPEN NATURBARNEHAGE AS—See AcadeMedia AB; *Int'l*, pg. 76
ESPIRA SANGEREIDASEN AS—See AcadeMedia AB; *Int'l*, pg. 76
ESPIRA SANUM AS—See AcadeMedia AB; *Int'l*, pg. 76
ESPIRA SCALA HUNDVAG AS—See AcadeMedia AB; *Int'l*, pg. 76
ESPIRA SCALA TASTA AS—See AcadeMedia AB; *Int'l*, pg. 76
ESPIRA SKAREDALEN AS—See AcadeMedia AB; *Int'l*, pg. 76
ESPIRA SKJERABERGET AS—See AcadeMedia AB; *Int'l*, pg. 76
ESPIRA SKOLEGATA AS—See AcadeMedia AB; *Int'l*, pg. 76
ESPIRA SLETTEN AS—See AcadeMedia AB; *Int'l*, pg. 76
ESPIRA SNURREFJELLET AS—See AcadeMedia AB; *Int'l*, pg. 76
ESPIRA SOLKNATTEN AS—See AcadeMedia AB; *Int'l*, pg. 76
ESPIRA SOLKROKEN AS—See AcadeMedia AB; *Int'l*, pg. 70
ESPIRA SPIREA AS—See AcadeMedia AB; *Int'l*, pg. 76
ESPIRA STEINSVIKEN AS—See AcadeMedia AB; *Int'l*, pg. 76
ESPIRA STJORDAL AS—See AcadeMedia AB; *Int'l*, pg. 76
ESPIRA STONGAFJELLET AS—See AcadeMedia AB; *Int'l*, pg. 76
ESPIRA SUNDBYFOSS AS—See AcadeMedia AB; *Int'l*, pg. 76
ESPIRA TAREMAREBY AS—See AcadeMedia AB; *Int'l*, pg. 76
ESPIRA TASTARUSTA AS—See AcadeMedia AB; *Int'l*, pg. 76
ESPIRA TAU AS—See AcadeMedia AB; *Int'l*, pg. 76
ESPIRA TJOSVOLL AS—See AcadeMedia AB; *Int'l*, pg. 76
ESPIRA TORSBERGSKOGEN AS—See AcadeMedia AB; *Int'l*, pg. 76
ESPIRA TORSHOVDALEN AS—See AcadeMedia AB; *Int'l*, pg. 76
ESPIRA TRISTILBAKKEN AS—See AcadeMedia AB; *Int'l*, pg. 76
ESPIRA TRYGSTAD AS—See AcadeMedia AB; *Int'l*, pg. 76
ESPIRA ULSETSKOGEN AS—See AcadeMedia AB; *Int'l*, pg. 76
ESPIRA ULVENVATNET AS—See AcadeMedia AB; *Int'l*, pg. 76
ESPIRA UND JOKI KINDERBETREUUNG GMBH—See AcadeMedia AB; *Int'l*, pg. 76
ESPIRA VANNVERKSDAMMEN AS—See AcadeMedia AB; *Int'l*, pg. 76
ESPIRA VARBAK ARCEN AS—See AcadeMedia AB; *Int'l*, pg. 76
ESPIRA VEDDERHEIA AS—See AcadeMedia AB; *Int'l*, pg. 76
ESPIRA VELDETUN AS—See AcadeMedia AB; *Int'l*, pg. 76
ESPIRE DENTAL PRACTICE, LLC; *U.S. Private*, pg. 1427
ESPIRE HOSPITALITY LIMITED; *Int'l*, pg. 2506
E-SPIRIT AG—See adesso SE; *Int'l*, pg. 144
E-SPIRIT INC.—See adesso SE; *Int'l*, pg. 144
ESPIRITO SANTO INFORMATICA, ACE—See Novo Banco, S.A.; *Int'l*, pg. 5462
ESPIRITO SANTO - UNIDADES DE SAUDE E DE APOIO A TERCEIRA IDADE, S.A.—See Fosun International Limited; *Int'l*, pg. 2751
ESPIRITO SANTO VENTURES - SOCIEDADE DE CAPITAL DE RISCO, S.A.—See Novo Banco, S.A.; *Int'l*, pg. 5462
E-SPIRIT SCHWEIZ AG—See adesso SE; *Int'l*, pg. 144
E-SPIRIT UK LTD.—See adesso SE; *Int'l*, pg. 144
ESPLANADE LIMITED; *Int'l*, pg. 2506
ESP LANDSCAPERS LTD.—See ENL Limited; *Int'l*, pg. 2441
E SPLIT CORP.; *Int'l*, pg. 2246

ESPN, INC.—See The Walt Disney Company; *U.S. Public*, pg. 2138
ESPN REGIONAL TELEVISION, INC.—See The Walt Disney Company; *U.S. Public*, pg. 2138
ESPN SPORTS MEDIA LIMITED—See BT Group plc; *Int'l*, pg. 1203
ESPOMEGA S. DE R.L. DE C.V—See Bunzl plc; *Int'l*, pg. 1218
ESPORTA GROUP LIMITED—See Virgin Management Limited; *Int'l*, pg. 8247
ESPORTA LIMITED—See Virgin Management Limited; *Int'l*, pg. 8247
ESPORTIA INTERNATIONAL INC.; *U.S. Private*, pg. 1427
ESPORTS ENTERTAINMENT GROUP, INC.; *Int'l*, pg. 2506
ESPOSITO SERVIZI ECOLOGICI SRL—See I.M.G. 2 s.r.l.; *Int'l*, pg. 3566
ESPO S.R.O.—See AdCapital AG; *Int'l*, pg. 126
ESPRAL INTERNATIONAL LTD.—See ENL Limited; *Int'l*, pg. 2441
ESPRAL LTD.—See ENL Limited; *Int'l*, pg. 2441
ESPREON LIMITED—See EQT AB; *Int'l*, pg. 2471
ESPRESSA COFFEE & WATER S.A.—See IVS Group S.A.; *Int'l*, pg. 3848
ESPRESSA C&W S.A.—See IVS Group S.A.; *Int'l*, pg. 3848
ESPRESSIF SYSTEMS SHANGHAI CO., LTD.; *Int'l*, pg. 2506
ESPRESSO PARTNERS INC.—See Wind Point Advisors LLC; *U.S. Private*, pg. 4536
ESPRINET S.P.A.; *Int'l*, pg. 2506
ESPRIT ASIA (DISTRIBUTION) LIMITED—See Esprit Holdings Limited; *Int'l*, pg. 2507
ESPRIT BELGIE RETAIL N.V.—See Esprit Holdings Limited; *Int'l*, pg. 2507
ESPRIT CANADA DISTRIBUTION LIMITED—See Esprit Holdings Limited; *Int'l*, pg. 2507
ESPRIT CANADA RETAIL LIMITED—See Esprit Holdings Limited; *Int'l*, pg. 2507
ESPRIT CANADA WHOLESALE INC.—See Esprit Holdings Limited; *Int'l*, pg. 2507
ESPRIT CARD SERVICES GMBH—See Esprit Holdings Limited; *Int'l*, pg. 2507
ESPRIT DE CORP DANMARK A/S—See Esprit Holdings Limited; *Int'l*, pg. 2507
ESPRIT DE CORP (FAR EAST) LIMITED—See Esprit Holdings Limited; *Int'l*, pg. 2507
ESPRIT DE CORP FRANCE S.A.S.—See Esprit Holdings Limited; *Int'l*, pg. 2507
ESPRIT DE CORP. (SPAIN) S.L.—See Esprit Holdings Limited; *Int'l*, pg. 2507
ESPRIT DE FRANCE SAS—See Compagnie Lebon SA; *Int'l*, pg. 1745
ESPRIT DESIGN & PRODUCT DEVELOPMENT GMBH—See Esprit Holdings Limited; *Int'l*, pg. 2507
ESPRIT EUROPE B.V.—See Esprit Holdings Limited; *Int'l*, pg. 2507
ESPRIT GB LIMITED—See Esprit Holdings Limited; *Int'l*, pg. 2507
ESPRIT GLOBAL IMAGE GMBH—See Esprit Holdings Limited; *Int'l*, pg. 2507
ESPRIT HANDELSGESELLSCHAFT MBH.—See Esprit Holdings Limited; *Int'l*, pg. 2507
ESPRIT HOLDINGS LIMITED; *Int'l*, pg. 2506
ESPRIT (HONG KONG) LIMITED—See Esprit Holdings Limited; *Int'l*, pg. 2507
ESPRIT INTERNATIONAL GP, INC.—See Esprit Holdings Limited; *Int'l*, pg. 2507
ESPRIT ITALY DISTRIBUTION S.R.L.—See Esprit Holdings Limited; *Int'l*, pg. 2507
ESPRIT LUXEMBOURG S.A.R.L.—See Esprit Holdings Limited; *Int'l*, pg. 2507
ESPRIT MACAO COMMERCIAL OFFSHORE LIMITED—See Esprit Holdings Limited; *Int'l*, pg. 2507
ESPRIT REGIONAL SERVICES LIMITED—See Esprit Holdings Limited; *Int'l*, pg. 2507
ESPRIT RETAIL B.V. & CO. KG.—See Esprit Holdings Limited; *Int'l*, pg. 2507
ESPRIT RETAIL PTE. LTD.—See Esprit Holdings Limited; *Int'l*, pg. 2507
ESPRIT SWITZERLAND DISTRIBUTION AG—See Esprit Holdings Limited; *Int'l*, pg. 2507
ESPRIT SWITZERLAND RETAIL AG—See Esprit Holdings Limited; *Int'l*, pg. 2507
ESPRIT TELECOM BV—See Liberty Global plc; *Int'l*, pg. 4484
ESPRIT US ONLINE SHOP LIMITED—See Esprit Holdings Limited; *Int'l*, pg. 2507
ESPRIX TECHNOLOGIES, LP; *U.S. Private*, pg. 1427
ESPRO ACOUSTIGUIDE SAS—See Espro Information Technologies Ltd.; *Int'l*, pg. 2507
ESPRO INFORMATION TECHNOLOGIES LTD.; *Int'l*, pg. 2507
ESP SYSTEX LTD.; *Int'l*, pg. 2505
ESP TECHONOLOGIES CORP.; *U.S. Private*, pg. 1426
THE ESPY CORP.—See Dover Corporation; *U.S. Public*, pg. 683
E-SQUARE CO., LTD.—See Ebara Corporation; *Int'l*, pg. 2282

ESQUIRE ASSIST LTD.—See Apax Partners LLP; *Int'l*, pg. 503
ESQUIRE BANK, NATIONAL ASSOCIATION—See Esquire Financial Holdings, Inc.; *U.S. Public*, pg. 794
ESQUIRE CHEF SDN BHD—See JAB Holding Company S.a.r.l.; *Int'l*, pg. 3863
ESQUIRE DEPOSITION SOLUTIONS, LLC - CHICAGO—See H.I.G. Capital, LLC; *U.S. Private*, pg. 1827
ESQUIRE DEPOSITION SOLUTIONS, LLC - LONG ISLAND—See H.I.G. Capital, LLC; *U.S. Private*, pg. 1827
ESQUIRE DEPOSITION SOLUTIONS, LLC - PHILADELPHIA—See H.I.G. Capital, LLC; *U.S. Private*, pg. 1827
ESQUIRE DEPOSITION SOLUTIONS, LLC - SAN DIEGO—See H.I.G. Capital, LLC; *U.S. Private*, pg. 1827
ESQUIRE DEPOSITION SOLUTIONS, LLC—See H.I.G. Capital, LLC; *U.S. Private*, pg. 1827
ESQUIRE DEPOSITION SOLUTIONS, LLC - WOODBRIDGE—See H.I.G. Capital, LLC; *U.S. Private*, pg. 1827
ESQUIRE FINANCIAL HOLDINGS, INC.; *U.S. Public*, pg. 794
ESQUIRE KNIT COMPOSITE LTD.; *Int'l*, pg. 2507
ESQUIRE MAGAZINE JAPAN, INC.—See Culture Convenience Club Co., Ltd.; *Int'l*, pg. 1877
ESQUIRE RADIO & ELECTRONICS INC.; *U.S. Private*, pg. 1427
ESQUIRES COFFEE HOUSES IRELAND LIMITED—See Cooks Coffee Company Limited; *Int'l*, pg. 1788
ESQUIRES COFFEE UK LIMITED—See Cooks Coffee Company Limited; *Int'l*, pg. 1788
ESQUIRE—See The Hearst Corporation; *U.S. Private*, pg. 4046
ESR ASSOCIATES INC—See ASM Technologies Limited; *Int'l*, pg. 627
ES REALISATIONS 2023 LIMITED—See Kingfisher plc; *Int'l*, pg. 4173
ESREY RESOURCES LTD; *Int'l*, pg. 2508
ESRG, LLC—See Caterpillar, Inc.; *U.S. Public*, pg. 452
ESR GROUP LIMITED; *Int'l*, pg. 2507
ESRI AUSTRALIA PTY. LTD.—See Boustead Singapore Limited; *Int'l*, pg. 1120
ESRI BELUX S.A.—See Environmental Systems Research Institute Inc.; *U.S. Private*, pg. 1408
ESRI BILGI SISTEMLERI MUHENDISLIK VE EGITIM, LTD.—See Environmental Systems Research Institute Inc.; *U.S. Private*, pg. 1408
ESRI BULGARIA LTD.—See Environmental Systems Research Institute Inc.; *U.S. Private*, pg. 1408
ESRI CANADA LIMITED—See Environmental Systems Research Institute Inc.; *U.S. Private*, pg. 1409
ESRI CHILE S.A.—See Environmental Systems Research Institute Inc.; *U.S. Private*, pg. 1409
ESRI CHINA (HONG KONG) LTD.—See Environmental Systems Research Institute Inc.; *U.S. Private*, pg. 1408
ESRI CHINA INFORMATION TECHNOLOGY CO. LTD—See Environmental Systems Research Institute Inc.; *U.S. Private*, pg. 1409
ESRI CIS LIMITED—See Environmental Systems Research Institute Inc.; *U.S. Private*, pg. 1408
ESRI DEUTSCHLAND GMBH—See Environmental Systems Research Institute Inc.; *U.S. Private*, pg. 1408
ESRI EASTERN AFRICA LTD.—See Environmental Systems Research Institute Inc.; *U.S. Private*, pg. 1409
ESRI FINLAND OY—See Environmental Systems Research Institute Inc.; *U.S. Private*, pg. 1409
ESRI ITALIA S.P.A.—See Environmental Systems Research Institute Inc.; *U.S. Private*, pg. 1409
ESRI JAPAN CORPORATION—See Environmental Systems Research Institute Inc.; *U.S. Private*, pg. 1409
ESRI KOREA, INC.—See Environmental Systems Research Institute Inc.; *U.S. Private*, pg. 1409
ESRI MALAYSIA SDN BHD—See Boustead Singapore Limited; *Int'l*, pg. 1120
ESRI MUSCAT CO. LLC—See Environmental Systems Research Institute Inc.; *U.S. Private*, pg. 1409
ESRI NEDERLAND B.V.—See Environmental Systems Research Institute Inc.; *U.S. Private*, pg. 1409
ESR INVESTMENT MANAGEMENT (S) PTE. LTD.; *Int'l*, pg. 2508
ESRI POLSKA SP. Z O.O.—See Environmental Systems Research Institute Inc.; *U.S. Private*, pg. 1409
ESRI PORTUGAL, S.A.—See Environmental Systems Research Institute Inc.; *U.S. Private*, pg. 1409
ESRI ROMANIA S.R.L.—See Environmental Systems Research Institute Inc.; *U.S. Private*, pg. 1409
ESRI RWANDA LTD.—See Environmental Systems Research Institute Inc.; *U.S. Private*, pg. 1409
ESRI SAUDI ARABIA LTD.—See Environmental Systems Research Institute Inc.; *U.S. Private*, pg. 1409
ESRI SCHWEIZ AG—See Environmental Systems Research Institute Inc.; *U.S. Private*, pg. 1409
ESRI SENEGAL SARL—See Environmental Systems Research Institute Inc.; *U.S. Private*, pg. 1409
ESRI SINGAPORE PTE LTD—See Boustead Singapore Limited; *Int'l*, pg. 1120

ESR INVESTMENT MANAGEMENT (S) PTE. LTD.

ESRI SOUTH AFRICA (PTY) LTD.—See Environmental Systems Research Institute Inc.; *U.S. Private*, pg. 1409
ESRI SOUTH ASIA PTE LTD—See Boustead Singapore Limited; *Int'l*, pg. 1120
ESRI SOUTH ASIA SDN. BHD.—See Boustead Singapore Limited; *Int'l*, pg. 1120
ESRI SUISSE SA—See Environmental Systems Research Institute Inc.; *U.S. Private*, pg. 1409
ESRI SVERIGE AB—See Environmental Systems Research Institute Inc.; *U.S. Private*, pg. 1409
ESRI (THAILAND) CO., LTD.—See Environmental Systems Research Institute Inc.; *U.S. Private*, pg. 1408
ESRI (UK) LTD.—See Environmental Systems Research Institute Inc.; *U.S. Private*, pg. 1408
ESRI UKRAINE LTD.—See Environmental Systems Research Institute Inc.; *U.S. Private*, pg. 1409
ESR KENDALL SQUARE REIT CO., LTD.; *Int'l*, pg. 2508
ESR-LOGOS REIT—See ESR Investment Management (S) Pte. Ltd.; *Int'l*, pg. 2508
ES ROBBINS CORPORATION; *U.S. Private*, pg. 1424
ESROCK PARTNERS; *U.S. Private*, pg. 1427
ESROC, LLC—See Great Hill Partners, L.P.; *U.S. Private*, pg. 1763
ESRT 1359 BROADWAY, L.L.C.—See Empire State Realty Trust, Inc.; *U.S. Public*, pg. 753
ESRT MH HOLDINGS, L.L.C.—See Empire State Realty Trust, Inc.; *U.S. Public*, pg. 753
ESSA ADVISORY SERVICES, LLC—See ESSA Bancorp, Inc.; *U.S. Public*, pg. 795
ESSA BANCORP, INC.; *U.S. Public*, pg. 794
ESSA BANK & TRUST—See ESSA Bancorp, Inc.; *U.S. Public*, pg. 795
ES SADOLIN AS—See Akzo Nobel N.V.; *Int'l*, pg. 274
ESSAI, INC.—See Advantest Corporation; *Int'l*, pg. 166
ESSA LIMITED—See ESAS Holding A.S.; *Int'l*, pg. 2501
ESSA PHARMA INC.; *Int'l*, pg. 2508
ESSAR ENERGY PLC—See Essar Global Limited; *Int'l*, pg. 2508
ESSAR EXPLORATION & PRODUCTION LTD.—See Essar Global Limited; *Int'l*, pg. 2508
ESSAR GLOBAL LIMITED; *Int'l*, pg. 2508
ESSAR INTERNATIONAL LTD.—See Essar Global Limited; *Int'l*, pg. 2508
ESSAR INVESTMENTS LTD.—See Essar Global Limited; *Int'l*, pg. 2508
ESSAR LAB MATE PVT LTD—See HORIBA Ltd; *Int'l*, pg. 3475
ESSAR OILFIELDS SERVICES LIMITED—See Essar Global Limited; *Int'l*, pg. 2508
ESSAR OILFIELDS SERVICES LIMITED—See Essar Shipping Limited; *Int'l*, pg. 2509
ESSAR PORTS LIMITED—See Essar Global Limited; *Int'l*, pg. 2508
ESSAR PORT & TERMINALS LTD.—See Essar Global Limited; *Int'l*, pg. 2508
ESSAR POWER LTD.—See Essar Global Limited; *Int'l*, pg. 2508
ESSAR SECURITIES LIMITED; *Int'l*, pg. 2508
ESSAR SHIPPING LIMITED; *Int'l*, pg. 2508
ESSAR STEEL LTD.—See Essar Global Limited; *Int'l*, pg. 2508
ESSAR STEEL MINNESOTA LLC—See Essar Global Limited; *Int'l*, pg. 2508
ESSAR TELEHOLDING LTD.—See Essar Global Limited; *Int'l*, pg. 2508
ESS ASIA LTD; *Int'l*, pg. 2508
ESSBIO SA; *Int'l*, pg. 2508
ESSCHEM INC.; *U.S. Private*, pg. 1427
ESSC HOLDINGS, INC.—See American Securities LLC; *U.S. Private*, pg. 249
ESSCO COLLINS LIMITED—See L3Harris Technologies, Inc.; *U.S. Public*, pg. 1281
ESSECO DO BRASIL INDUSTRIA E COMERCIO DE PRODUTOS QUIMICOS LTDA—See Esseco Group SRL; *Int'l*, pg. 2509
ESSECO GROUP SRL; *Int'l*, pg. 2509
ESSECO UK LIMITED—See Esseco Group SRL; *Int'l*, pg. 2509
ESSECO USA LLC—See Esseco Group SRL; *Int'l*, pg. 2509
ESSEDIESSE SOCIETA DI SERVIZI SPA—See Edizione S.r.l.; *Int'l*, pg. 2312
ESSEGI AUTOMATION S.R.L.—See Juki Corporation; *Int'l*, pg. 4022
ESSEGIBI FINANZIARIA S.P.A.—See Banco BPM S.p.A.; *Int'l*, pg. 818
ESSEGIBI PROMOZIONI IMMOBILIARI S.R.L.—See Banco BPM S.p.A.; *Int'l*, pg. 818
ESSEL CORPORATE RESOURCES PVT. LTD.; *Int'l*, pg. 2509
ESS ELECTRONICS TECHNOLOGY (SHENZHEN) CO., LTD.—See Imperium Partners Group, LLC; *U.S. Private*, pg. 2050
ESSEL FINANCE VKC FOREX LIMITED—See Ebix Inc.; *U.S. Public*, pg. 710
ESSEL INFRAPROJECTS LIMITED—See Essel Corporate Resources Pvt. Ltd.; *Int'l*, pg. 2509
ESSELTE AB—See ACCO Brands Corporation; *U.S. Public*, pg. 32
ESSELTE A/S—See ACCO Brands Corporation; *U.S. Public*, pg. 32
ESSELTE AS—See ACCO Brands Corporation; *U.S. Public*, pg. 32
ESSELTE BUSINESS BVBA—See ACCO Brands Corporation; *U.S. Public*, pg. 32
ESSELTE B.V.—See ACCO Brands Corporation; *U.S. Public*, pg. 32
ESSELTE DANMARK APS—See ACCO Brands Corporation; *U.S. Public*, pg. 32
ESSELTE KFT—See ACCO Brands Corporation; *U.S. Public*, pg. 32
ESSELTE LEITZ BURO MALZEMELERI SANAYI VE TICARET A.S.—See ACCO Brands Corporation; *U.S. Public*, pg. 33
ESSELTE LIMITED—See ACCO Brands Corporation; *U.S. Public*, pg. 33
ESSELTE OFFICE PRODUCTS GMBH—See ACCO Brands Corporation; *U.S. Public*, pg. 33
ESSELTE OFFICE PRODUCTS OY—See ACCO Brands Corporation; *U.S. Public*, pg. 33
ESSELTE OOO—See ACCO Brands Corporation; *U.S. Public*, pg. 33
ESSELTE POLSKA SP.Z.O.O.—See ACCO Brands Corporation; *U.S. Public*, pg. 33
ESSELTE SALES S.R.L—See ACCO Brands Corporation; *U.S. Public*, pg. 33
ESSELTE S.A. - PORTUGAL OFFICE—See ACCO Brands Corporation; *U.S. Public*, pg. 33
ESSELTE S.A.—See ACCO Brands Corporation; *U.S. Public*, pg. 33
ESSELTE S.P.A—See ACCO Brands Corporation; *U.S. Public*, pg. 33
ESSELTE SRO—See ACCO Brands Corporation; *U.S. Public*, pg. 33
ESSELTE SVERIGE AB—See ACCO Brands Corporation; *U.S. Public*, pg. 33
ESSELTE UK LTD.—See ACCO Brands Corporation; *U.S. Public*, pg. 33
ESSEL UTILITIES DISTRIBUTION COMPANY LTD—See Essel Corporate Resources Pvt. Ltd.; *Int'l*, pg. 2509
ESSEL VIDYUT VITARAN (GWALIOR) PVT. LTD.—See Essel Corporate Resources Pvt. Ltd.; *Int'l*, pg. 2509
ESSEL VIDYUT VITARAN (MUZAFFARPUR) LIMITED—See Essel Corporate Resources Pvt. Ltd.; *Int'l*, pg. 2509
ESSEL VIDYUT VITARAN (SAGAR) PRIVATE LIMITED—See Essel Corporate Resources Pvt. Ltd.; *Int'l*, pg. 2509
ESSEL VIDYUT VITARAN (UJJAIN) PVT. LTD.—See Essel Corporate Resources Pvt. Ltd.; *Int'l*, pg. 2509
ESSEM CORPORATION SDN BHD—See Daeyang Electric Co., Ltd.; *Int'l*, pg. 1911
ESSEMTEC AG—See Nano Dimension Ltd; *Int'l*, pg. 5142
ESSEN BIOSCIENCE, INC—See Sartorius AG; *Int'l*, pg. 6578
ESSEN BIOSCIENCE, INC.—See Sartorius AG; *Int'l*, pg. 6579
ESSENCE COMMUNICATIONS INC.; *U.S. Private*, pg. 1427
ESSENCE GLOBAL LIMITED—See WPP plc; *Int'l*, pg. 8463
ESSENCE INFORMATION TECHNOLOGY CO., LTD.; *Int'l*, pg. 2510
ESSENCE MAGAZINE—See Essence Communications Inc.; *U.S. Private*, pg. 1427
ESSENCEMEDIACOM HOLDINGS LIMITED—See WPP plc; *Int'l*, pg. 8463
ESSENCE METAL (ASIA) COMPANY LIMITED—See Lee Kee Holdings Limited; *Int'l*, pg. 4440
ESSENDANT CANADA, INC.—See Sycamore Partners Management, LP; *U.S. Private*, pg. 3896
ESSENDANT HONG KONG LIMITED—See Sycamore Partners Management, LP; *U.S. Private*, pg. 3897
ESSENDANT INC.—See Sycamore Partners Management, LP; *U.S. Private*, pg. 3896
ESSENDANT MANAGEMENT SERVICES LLC—See Sycamore Partners Management, LP; *U.S. Private*, pg. 3897
ESSENER TEERSCHOTTER GMBH—See VINCI S.A.; *Int'l*, pg. 8218
ESSEN HOUSE CO., LTD.—See Prima Meat Packers Ltd.; *Int'l*, pg. 5975
ESS ENN TIMBER AB; *Int'l*, pg. 2508
ESSENSYS PLC; *Int'l*, pg. 2510
ESSENT BELGIUM N.V.—See E.ON SE; *Int'l*, pg. 2257
ESSEN TECH CO., LTD.; *Int'l*, pg. 2510
ESSEN TECHNOLOGY (BEIJING) CO., LTD.—See Terumo Corporation; *Int'l*, pg. 7569
ESSENTEC INDUSTRIES CO., LTD.—See Zhejiang Yilida Ventilator Co., Ltd.; *Int'l*, pg. 8667
ESSENT GROUP LTD.; *Int'l*, pg. 2510
ESSENT GUARANTY, INC.—See Essent Group Ltd.; *Int'l*, pg. 2510
ESSENTIA ADVISORY PARTNERS, LLC—See EPAM Systems, Inc.; *U.S. Public*, pg. 783
ESSENTIA HEALTH; *U.S. Private*, pg. 1427
ESSENTIA INSTITUTE OF RURAL HEALTH; *U.S. Private*, pg. 1427
ESSENTIA INSURANCE COMPANY—See Markel Group Inc.; *U.S. Public*, pg. 1368
THE ESSENTIAL BAKING COMPANY; *U.S. Private*, pg. 4027
ESSENTIAL DATA CORPORATION; *U.S. Private*, pg. 1427
ESSENTIAL EMPLOYEE BENEFITS PROPRIETARY LIMITED—See Workforce Holdings Ltd.; *Int'l*, pg. 8455
ESSENTIAL ENERGY SERVICES LTD.—See Element Technical Services Inc.; *Int'l*, pg. 2358
ESSENTIAL ENERGY SERVICES LTD. - TRYTON RENTALS DIVISION—See Element Technical Services Inc.; *Int'l*, pg. 2358
ESSENTIAL FREIGHT SYSTEMS INC.; *U.S. Private*, pg. 1427
ESSENTIAL HOUSING INVESTMENT; *U.S. Private*, pg. 1427
ESSENTIALLY SPORTS MARKETING LIMITED—See Wasserman Media Group, LLC; *U.S. Private*, pg. 4450
ESSENTIAL METALS LIMITED; *Int'l*, pg. 2510
ESSENTIAL OILS OF TASMANIA PTY LTD—See Atlas Pearls Ltd.; *Int'l*, pg. 686
ESSENTIAL PERSONNEL, INC.; *U.S. Private*, pg. 1427
ESSENTIAL PHARMACEUTICAL CORP.; *U.S. Private*, pg. 1427
ESSENTIAL POWER SERVICES (PROPRIETARY) LIMITED—See Sebata Holdings; *Int'l*, pg. 6669
ESSENTIAL PROPERTIES REALTY TRUST, INC.; *U.S. Public*, pg. 795
ESSENTIAL SECURITY, INC.; *U.S. Private*, pg. 1427
ESSENTIAL UTILITIES INC.; *U.S. Public*, pg. 795
ESSENTIAL WHOLESALE; *U.S. Private*, pg. 1427
ESSENT N.V.—See E.ON SE; *Int'l*, pg. 2257
ESSENTRA (BANGOR) LTD.—See Essentra plc; *Int'l*, pg. 2511
ESSENTRA COMPONENTS B.V.—See Essentra plc; *Int'l*, pg. 2511
ESSENTRA COMPONENTS GMBH—See Essentra plc; *Int'l*, pg. 2511
ESSENTRA COMPONENTS JAPAN INC.—See Essentra plc; *Int'l*, pg. 2511
ESSENTRA COMPONENTS KFT—See Essentra plc; *Int'l*, pg. 2511
ESSENTRA COMPONENTS LTD.—See Essentra plc; *Int'l*, pg. 2511
ESSENTRA COMPONENT SOLUTIONS—See Essentra plc; *Int'l*, pg. 2511
ESSENTRA COMPONENTS (PTY) LTD.—See Essentra plc; *Int'l*, pg. 2511
ESSENTRA COMPONENTS SAS—See Essentra plc; *Int'l*, pg. 2511
ESSENTRA COMPONENTS S.R.O.—See Essentra plc; *Int'l*, pg. 2511
ESSENTRA CORPORATION—See Essentra plc; *Int'l*, pg. 2511
ESSENTRA EXTRUSION B.V.—See Essentra plc; *Int'l*, pg. 2511
ESSENTRA FILTER PRODUCTS LIMITED—See Essentra plc; *Int'l*, pg. 2511
ESSENTRA FILTER PRODUCTS S.A.—See Essentra plc; *Int'l*, pg. 2511
ESSENTRA (INDIA) PRIVATE LIMITED—See Essentra plc; *Int'l*, pg. 2511
ESSENTRA LIMITED—See Essentra plc; *Int'l*, pg. 2511
ESSENTRA MALAYSIA SDN. BHD.—See Essentra plc; *Int'l*, pg. 2511
ESSENTRA PACKAGING B.V.—See Essentra plc; *Int'l*, pg. 2511
ESSENTRA PACKAGING - CARDIFF—See Essentra plc; *Int'l*, pg. 2511
ESSENTRA PACKAGING GMBH—See Essentra plc; *Int'l*, pg. 2511
ESSENTRA PACKAGING INC.—See Essentra plc; *Int'l*, pg. 2511
ESSENTRA PACKAGING - NOTTINGHAM—See Essentra plc; *Int'l*, pg. 2511
ESSENTRA PACKAGING PTE. LIMITED—See Essentra plc; *Int'l*, pg. 2511
ESSENTRA PACKAGING & SECURITY LIMITED—See Essentra plc; *Int'l*, pg. 2511
ESSENTRA PACKAGING SRL—See Essentra plc; *Int'l*, pg. 2511
ESSENTRA PIPE PROTECTION TECHNOLOGIES—See Essentra plc; *Int'l*, pg. 2511
ESSENTRA PIPE PROTECTION TECHNOLOGIES—See Essentra plc; *Int'l*, pg. 2511
ESSENTRA PLC; *Int'l*, pg. 2510
ESSENTRA PTE. LTD.—See Essentra plc; *Int'l*, pg. 2511
ESSENTRA PTY. LTD.—See Essentra plc; *Int'l*, pg. 2511
ESSENTRA SP. Z O.O. ODDZIAL SKIFFY—See Essentra plc; *Int'l*, pg. 2511
ESSENTRA SP. Z O.O.—See Essentra plc; *Int'l*, pg. 2511
ESSENT RETAIL ENERGIE B.V.—See E.ON SE; *Int'l*, pg. 2257
ESSENTUKSKY PLANT OF MINERAL WATERS ON KMV LTD.—See PepsiCo, Inc.; *U.S. Public*, pg. 1668
ESSERE BENESSERE SPA; *Int'l*, pg. 2512
ESSERTEC GMBH—See SOPREMA SAS; *Int'l*, pg. 7111

COMPANY NAME INDEX

ESSER-WERKE GMBH & CO. KG—See Construction Forms, Inc.; *U.S. Private*, pg. 1023
ESSESS INC.—See Exelon Corporation; *U.S. Public*, pg. 806
ESSE-TI S.R.L.—See Investment AB Latour; *Int'l*, pg. 3781
ESSEX ANAVIA, L.P.—See Essex Property Trust, Inc.; *U.S. Public*, pg. 796
ESSEX BANK OF MARYLAND—See United Bankshares, Inc.; *U.S. Public*, pg. 2229
ESSEX BANK—See United Bankshares, Inc.; *U.S. Public*, pg. 2229
ESSEX BELLA VILLAGIO, L.P.—See Essex Property Trust, Inc.; *U.S. Public*, pg. 796
ESSEX BELLERIVE, L.P.—See Essex Property Trust, Inc.; *U.S. Public*, pg. 796
ESSEX BERNARD, L.P.—See Essex Property Trust, Inc.; *U.S. Public*, pg. 796
ESSEX BIO-TECHNOLOGY LIMITED; *Int'l*, pg. 2512
ESSEX BRIARWOOD, L.P.—See Essex Property Trust, Inc.; *U.S. Public*, pg. 796
ESSEX BRIDLE TRAILS, L.P.—See Essex Property Trust, Inc.; *U.S. Public*, pg. 796
ESSEX BRIGHTON RIDGE, L.P.—See Essex Property Trust, Inc.; *U.S. Public*, pg. 796
ESSEX BROWNELL—See LS Corp.; *Int'l*, pg. 4569
ESSEX BUILDERS CORP.; *U.S. Private*, pg. 1427
ESSEX CANYON OAKS APARTMENTS, L.P.—See Essex Property Trust, Inc.; *U.S. Public*, pg. 796
ESSEX CANYON POINTE, L.P.—See Essex Property Trust, Inc.; *U.S. Public*, pg. 796
ESSEX CARLYLE, L.P.—See Essex Property Trust, Inc.; *U.S. Public*, pg. 796
ESSEX CATALINA GARDENS, LLC—See Essex Property Trust, Inc.; *U.S. Public*, pg. 796
ESSEX CEMENT CO LLC—See Titan Cement Company S.A.; *Int'l*, pg. 7759
ESSEX CHEMIE AG—See Merck & Co., Inc.; *U.S. Public*, pg. 1416
ESSEX CONSTRUCTION, LLC—See Blunt Enterprises LLC; *U.S. Private*, pg. 600
ESSEX CORPORATION; *U.S. Private*, pg. 1427
ESSEX COUNTY COMMUNITY FOUNDATION; *U.S. Private*, pg. 1427
ESSEX CREDIT CORPORATION—See BNP Paribas SA; *Int'l*, pg. 1087
ESSEX DAVEY GLEN APARTMENTS, L.P.—See Essex Property Trust, Inc.; *U.S. Public*, pg. 796
ESSEX ELECTRICAL WHOLESALERS LTD.—See Manutan International SA; *Int'l*, pg. 4679
ESSEX ELECTRONICS (SINGAPORE) PTE LTD—See IPC Corporation Ltd.; *Int'l*, pg. 3796
ESSEX EQUITY MANAGEMENT, LLC; *U.S. Private*, pg. 1428
ESSEX ESPLANADE, L.P.—See Essex Property Trust, Inc.; *U.S. Public*, pg. 796
ESSEX FAIRWOOD POND, L.P.—See Essex Property Trust, Inc.; *U.S. Public*, pg. 796
ESSEX FM—See Global Radio Group Limited; *Int'l*, pg. 3000
ESSEX FOUNTAIN PARK APARTMENTS, L.P.—See Essex Property Trust, Inc.; *U.S. Public*, pg. 796
ESSEX FOX PLAZA, L.P.—See Essex Property Trust, Inc.; *U.S. Public*, pg. 796
ESSEX GRAIN PRODUCTS, INC.; *U.S. Private*, pg. 1428
ESSEX GROUP, INC.—See LS Corp.; *Int'l*, pg. 4569
ESSEX HAVER HILL, L.P.—See Essex Property Trust, Inc.; *U.S. Public*, pg. 796
ESSEX HUNTINGTON BREAKERS, L.P.—See Essex Property Trust, Inc.; *U.S. Public*, pg. 796
ESSEX INDUSTRIES, INC.; *U.S. Private*, pg. 1428
ESSEX INGLENOOK COURT, LLC—See Essex Property Trust, Inc.; *U.S. Public*, pg. 796
ESSEX INVESTMENT MANAGEMENT COMPANY, LLC; *U.S. Private*, pg. 1428
ESSEX KINGS ROAD, L.P.—See Essex Property Trust, Inc.; *U.S. Public*, pg. 796
ESSEX LABORATORIES INC.—See Firmenich International SA; *Int'l*, pg. 2680
ESSEX, LLC; *U.S. Private*, pg. 1428
ESSEX MANAGEMENT CORPORATION—See Essex Property Trust, Inc.; *U.S. Public*, pg. 796
ESSEX MANUFACTURING INC.; *U.S. Private*, pg. 1428
ESSEX MARBRISA LONG BEACH, L.P.—See Essex Property Trust, Inc.; *U.S. Public*, pg. 796
ESSEX MARINA CITY CLUB, L.P.—See Essex Property Trust, Inc.; *U.S. Public*, pg. 796
ESSEX MEDIPHARMA (ZHUHAI) COMPANY LIMITED—See Essex Bio-Technology Limited; *Int'l*, pg. 2512
ESSEX MINERALS, INC.; *Int'l*, pg. 2512
ESSEX MONTEREY VILLAS, L.P.—See Essex Property Trust, Inc.; *U.S. Public*, pg. 796
THE ESSEX NUFFIELD HOSPITAL—See Nuffield Health; *Int'l*, pg. 5487
ESSEX PARCWOOD APARTMENTS, L.P.—See Essex Property Trust, Inc.; *U.S. Public*, pg. 796
ESSEX PORTFOLIO, L.P.—See Essex Property Trust, Inc.; *U.S. Public*, pg. 796
ESSEX PROPERTY TRUST, INC.; *U.S. Public*, pg. 795

ESSEX REGENCY ESCUELA, L.P.—See Essex Property Trust, Inc.; *U.S. Public*, pg. 796
ESSEX REGENCY TOWER APARTMENTS, L.P.—See Essex Property Trust, Inc.; *U.S. Public*, pg. 796
ESSEX REXFORD, LLC—See Essex Property Trust, Inc.; *U.S. Public*, pg. 796
ESSEX SAMMAMISH VIEW, L.P.—See Essex Property Trust, Inc.; *U.S. Public*, pg. 796
ESSEX SANTEE COURT, L.P.—See Essex Property Trust, Inc.; *U.S. Public*, pg. 796
ESSEX SERVICES GROUP PLC; *Int'l*, pg. 2512
ESSEX STONEHEDGE VILLAGE, L.P.—See Essex Property Trust, Inc.; *U.S. Public*, pg. 796
ESSEX & SUFFOLK WATER LTD—See CK Hutchison Holdings Limited; *Int'l*, pg. 1637
ESSEX SUMMERHILL PARK, L.P.—See Essex Property Trust, Inc.; *U.S. Public*, pg. 796
ESSEX TECHNOLOGY GROUP, INC.—See Converge Technology Solutions Corp.; *Int'l*, pg. 1787
ESSEX THE COMMONS, L.P.—See Essex Property Trust, Inc.; *U.S. Public*, pg. 796
ESSEX THE POINTE, L.P.—See Essex Property Trust, Inc.; *U.S. Public*, pg. 796
ESSEX TIERRA VISTA, L.P.—See Essex Property Trust, Inc.; *U.S. Public*, pg. 796
ESSEX TOWNSHIP, L.P.—See Essex Property Trust, Inc.; *U.S. Public*, pg. 796
ESSEX VELO RAY, L.P.—See Essex Property Trust, Inc.; *U.S. Public*, pg. 796
ESSEX VISTA BELVEDERE, L.P.—See Essex Property Trust, Inc.; *U.S. Public*, pg. 796
ESSEX WANDERING CREEK, LLC—See Essex Property Trust, Inc.; *U.S. Public*, pg. 796
ESSEX WATERFORD, L.P.—See Essex Property Trust, Inc.; *U.S. Public*, pg. 796
ESSEX WHARFSIDE POINTE, L.P.—See Essex Property Trust, Inc.; *U.S. Public*, pg. 796
ESSEX WINDERMERE CORPORATION—See Northrop Grumman Corporation; *U.S. Public*, pg. 1540
ESSEX WOODLANDS MANAGEMENT, INC.; *U.S. Private*, pg. 1428
ESSEX X-RAY & MEDICAL EQUIPMENT LTD—See HEICO Corporation; *U.S. Public*, pg. 1020
ESS-FOOD AMBA—See Danish Crown AmbA; *Int'l*, pg. 1965
ESS-FOOD A/S—See Danish Crown AmbA; *Int'l*, pg. 1964
ESS-FOOD BRAZIL SERVICOS DE CONSULTORIA LTDA—See Danish Crown AmbA; *Int'l*, pg. 1964
ESS-FOOD HOLDING A/S—See Danish Crown AmbA; *Int'l*, pg. 1964
ESS-FOOD (SHANGHAI) TRADING CO. LTD—See Danish Crown AmbA; *Int'l*, pg. 1964
ESS GMBH—See Masco Corporation; *U.S. Public*, pg. 1390
ESS GROUP, INC.—See TRC Companies, Inc.; *U.S. Private*, pg. 4215
ESSIE COSMETICS, LTD.—See L'Oreal S.A.; *Int'l*, pg. 4380
ESSIE SUMMERS RETIREMENT VILLAGE LIMITED—See Ryman Healthcare Ltd.; *Int'l*, pg. 6439
ESSILOR AB—See EssilorLuxottica SA; *Int'l*, pg. 2512
ESSILOR ASIA PACIFIC PTE LTD.—See EssilorLuxottica SA; *Int'l*, pg. 2512
ESSILOR AUSTRIA GMBH—See EssilorLuxottica SA; *Int'l*, pg. 2512
ESSILOR CANADA LTD.—See EssilorLuxottica SA; *Int'l*, pg. 2512
ESSILOR DANMARK A.S.—See EssilorLuxottica SA; *Int'l*, pg. 2512
ESSILOR D.O.O—See EssilorLuxottica SA; *Int'l*, pg. 2512
ESSILOR EUROPEAN SHARED SERVICE CENTER LTD.—See EssilorLuxottica SA; *Int'l*, pg. 2512
ESSILOR GROUP THE NETHERLANDS B.V—See EssilorLuxottica SA; *Int'l*, pg. 2512
ESSILOR INDIA PVT LTD—See EssilorLuxottica SA; *Int'l*, pg. 2512
ESSILOR IRELAND LTD.—See EssilorLuxottica SA; *Int'l*, pg. 2513
ESSILOR LABORATORIES OF AMERICA, INC.—See EssilorLuxottica SA; *Int'l*, pg. 2513
ESSILOR LENS & SPECTS P LTD—See EssilorLuxottica SA; *Int'l*, pg. 2513
ESSILOR LOGISTIK GMBH—See EssilorLuxottica SA; *Int'l*, pg. 2513
ESSILOR LTD.—See EssilorLuxottica SA; *Int'l*, pg. 2513
ESSILORLUXOTTICA SA; *Int'l*, pg. 2512
ESSILOR MEXICO S.A DE CV—See EssilorLuxottica SA; *Int'l*, pg. 2513
ESSILOR NORGE A.S.—See EssilorLuxottica SA; *Int'l*, pg. 2513
ESSILOR OF AMERICA, INC.—See EssilorLuxottica SA; *Int'l*, pg. 2513
ESSILOR OPTICAL LABORATORY POLSKA SP. Z.O.O.—See EssilorLuxottica SA; *Int'l*, pg. 2513
ESSILOR POLONIA SP. Z O.O—See EssilorLuxottica SA; *Int'l*, pg. 2513
ESSILOR ROMANIA SRL—See EssilorLuxottica SA; *Int'l*, pg. 2513
ESSILOR S.A.—See EssilorLuxottica SA; *Int'l*, pg. 2513

ESSILOR SOUTH AFRICA (PTY) LTD.—See EssilorLuxottica SA; *Int'l*, pg. 2513
ESSINTIAL ENTERPRISE SOLUTIONS—See Global Equity Capital, LLC; *U.S. Private*, pg. 1714
ESSI SYSTEMS, INC.—See Accor S.A.; *Int'l*, pg. 91
ESSITY AKTIEBOLAG; *Int'l*, pg. 2516
ESSITY CANADA INC.—See Essity Aktiebolag; *Int'l*, pg. 2516
ESSITY CHILE SA—See Essity Aktiebolag; *Int'l*, pg. 2516
ESSITY CZECH REPUBLIC S.R.O.—See Essity Aktiebolag; *Int'l*, pg. 2517
ESSITY DENMARK A/S—See Essity Aktiebolag; *Int'l*, pg. 2517
ESSITY FRANCE SAS—See Essity Aktiebolag; *Int'l*, pg. 2517
ESSITY GERMANY GMBH—See Essity Aktiebolag; *Int'l*, pg. 2517
ESSITY HIJYEN URUNLERI SANAYI VE TICARET A.S.—See Essity Aktiebolag; *Int'l*, pg. 2517
ESSITY HUNGARY KFT—See Essity Aktiebolag; *Int'l*, pg. 2517
ESSITY ITALY S.P.A.—See Essity Aktiebolag; *Int'l*, pg. 2517
ESSITY NORWAY AS—See Essity Aktiebolag; *Int'l*, pg. 2517
ESSITY OPERATIONS POLAND SP. Z O.O.—See Essity Aktiebolag; *Int'l*, pg. 2517
ESSITY OPERATIONS WITZENHAUSEN GMBH—See Essity Aktiebolag; *Int'l*, pg. 2517
ESSITY POLAND SP. Z O.O.—See Essity Aktiebolag; *Int'l*, pg. 2517
ESSITY PROFESSIONAL HYGIENE NORTH AMERICA LLC—See Essity Aktiebolag; *Int'l*, pg. 2517
ESSITY SWITZERLAND AG—See Essity Aktiebolag; *Int'l*, pg. 2517
ESSIX BIOSCIENCES LIMITED; *Int'l*, pg. 2517
ESS LABORATORY—See Thielsch Engineering, Inc.; *U.S. Private*, pg. 4144
ESSLINGER-WOOTEN-MAXWELL REALTORS, INC.—See Berkshire Hathaway Inc.; *U.S. Public*, pg. 306
ESSMED AB—See Lumibird Group; *Int'l*, pg. 4578
ESS MOBILE OFFSHORE UNITS A/S—See Compass Group PLC; *Int'l*, pg. 1751
ESSMUELLER COMPANY; *U.S. Private*, pg. 1428
ESS NEXTIER INSURANCE GROUP, LLC—See IMA Financial Group, Inc.; *U.S. Private*, pg. 2043
ESSO AUSTRALIA PTY LTD—See Exxon Mobil Corporation; *U.S. Public*, pg. 814
ESSO BRASILEIRA DE PETROLEO LIMITADA—See Cosan S.A.; *Int'l*, pg. 1809
ESSO DEUTSCHLAND GMBH—See Exxon Mobil Corporation; *U.S. Public*, pg. 814
ESSO ERDGAS BETEILIGUNGSGESELLSCHAFT MBH—See Exxon Mobil Corporation; *U.S. Public*, pg. 814
ESSO EXPLORATION AND PRODUCTION GUYANA LIMITED—See Exxon Mobil Corporation; *U.S. Public*, pg. 814
ESSO ITALIANA S.R.L.—See Exxon Mobil Corporation; *U.S. Public*, pg. 814
ESSO NEDERLAND B.V.—See Exxon Mobil Corporation; *U.S. Public*, pg. 814
ESSO NORGE A.S.—See Exxon Mobil Corporation; *U.S. Public*, pg. 814
ESSO NORGE AS—See Exxon Mobil Corporation; *U.S. Public*, pg. 814
ESSO SOCIETE ANONYME FRANCAISE—See Exxon Mobil Corporation; *U.S. Public*, pg. 814
ESSO (THAILAND) PUBLIC COMPANY LIMITED—See Bangchak Corporation Public Company Limited; *Int'l*, pg. 832
ESSO TOWER—See Exxon Mobil Corporation; *U.S. Public*, pg. 816
ESSOX FINANCE S.R.O—See Societe Generale S.A.; *Int'l*, pg. 7039
ESSOX SRO—See Societe Generale S.A.; *Int'l*, pg. 7040
ESSROC SAN JUAN INC.—See Grupo Argos S.A.; *Int'l*, pg. 3121
ESS TECH, INC.; *U.S. Public*, pg. 794
ESS TECHNOLOGY, INC.—See Imperium Partners Group, LLC; *U.S. Private*, pg. 2050
ESS TECHNOLOGY INTERNATIONAL (KOREA) LTD.—See Imperium Partners Group, LLC; *U.S. Private*, pg. 2050
ESSTRA INDUSTRIES INC.; *Int'l*, pg. 2517
E/S STYROMATIC AB—See Bravida Holding AB; *Int'l*, pg. 1142
E.S. SUTTON INC.—See E.S. Sutton Inc.; *U.S. Private*, pg. 1307
E.S. SUTTON INC.; *U.S. Private*, pg. 1307
ESSVE PRODUKTER AB—See Bergman & Beving AB; *Int'l*, pg. 980
ES-SYSTEM NT SP. Z O.O.—See Triton Advisers Limited; *Int'l*, pg. 7931
ES-SYSTEM RZESZOW SP. Z O.O.—See Triton Advisers Limited; *Int'l*, pg. 7931
ES-SYSTEM S.A. - GDANSK DIVISION—See Triton Advisers Limited; *Int'l*, pg. 7931

ES-SYSTEM S.A. - KRAKOW CENTRALA DIVISION—See Triton Advisers Limited; *Int'l*, pg. 7931
ES-SYSTEM S.A. - LODZ DIVISION—See Triton Advisers Limited; *Int'l*, pg. 7931
ES-SYSTEM S.A. - MAZURY DIVISION—See Triton Advisers Limited; *Int'l*, pg. 7931
ES-SYSTEM S.A. - POZNAN DIVISION—See Triton Advisers Limited; *Int'l*, pg. 7931
ES-SYSTEM S.A. - SLASK DIVISION—See Triton Advisers Limited; *Int'l*, pg. 7931
ES-SYSTEM S.A.—See Triton Advisers Limited; *Int'l*, pg. 7931
ES-SYSTEM S.A. - WARSZAWA DIVISION—See Triton Advisers Limited; *Int'l*, pg. 7931
ES-SYSTEM S.A. - WROCLAW DIVISION—See Triton Advisers Limited; *Int'l*, pg. 7931
ES-SYSTEM SCANDINAVIA A.B.—See Triton Advisers Limited; *Int'l*, pg. 7931
ES-SYSTEM WILKASY SP. Z O.O.—See Triton Advisers Limited; *Int'l*, pg. 7931
ESTABELECIMENTOS SCIAL DO NORTE S.A.—See Camargo Correa S.A.; *Int'l*, pg. 1268
ESTABLECIMIENTOS ORTOPEDICOS PRIM, S.A.—See Prim S.A.; *Int'l*, pg. 5973
ESTABLISHMENT LABS HOLDINGS, INC.; *Int'l*, pg. 2517
ESTAB PLATT FRERES S.A.—See Carclo plc; *Int'l*, pg. 1321
ESTABROOK CORPORATION; *U.S. Private*, pg. 1428
ESTABROOK FORD LINCOLN MERCURY INC.; *U.S. Private*, pg. 1428
ESTACADO ENERGY LLC; *U.S. Private*, pg. 1428
ESTAC INDUSTRIAL AGENCIES LTD.—See Stemcor Holdings Limited; *Int'l*, pg. 7205
ESTACIONAMIENTOS Y SERVICIOS, S.A.—See H.I.G. Capital, LLC; *U.S. Private*, pg. 1827
ESTAD STAMPING & MANUFACTURING COMPANY; *U.S. Private*, pg. 1428
E-STAFF INSURANCE SERVICES CORPORATION—See Nihon Kohden Corporation; *Int'l*, pg. 5285
ESTA FINE COLOR CORPORATION—See Dainichiseika Color & Chemicals Mfg. Co., Ltd.; *Int'l*, pg. 1939
ESTALEIROS DO BRASIL LTDA.—See Toyo Engineering Corporation; *Int'l*, pg. 7853
ESTANCIA CAPITAL MANAGEMENT, LLC; *U.S. Private*, pg. 1428
ESTANFLUX S.A.—See Komax Holding AG; *Int'l*, pg. 4240
ESTAN ITALIA MINERALS SRL—See Eczacibasi Holding A.S.; *Int'l*, pg. 2301
E-STAR ALTERNATIVE PLC.; *Int'l*, pg. 2249
E-STARCO CO., LTD.; *Int'l*, pg. 2249
E-STAR COMMERCIAL MANAGEMENT COMPANY LIMITED; *Int'l*, pg. 2249
EST A.S.—See Asseco Poland S.A.; *Int'l*, pg. 641
ESTATELY, INC.—See Anywhere Real Estate Inc.; *U.S. Public*, pg. 142
ESTATE MANAGEMENT COMPANY JSC; *Int'l*, pg. 2517
E-STATE ONLINE CO., LTD.—See Tokyo Tatemono Co. Ltd.; *Int'l*, pg. 7796
THE ESTATES AT CARPENTERS; *U.S. Private*, pg. 4027
ESTATES WINDOWS LTD.; *U.S. Private*, pg. 1428
ESTATIA AG; *Int'l*, pg. 2517
E-STATION GREEN TECHNOLOGY GROUP CO., LIMITED; *Int'l*, pg. 2249
ESTAUGH; *U.S. Private*, pg. 1428
ESTAVAYER LAIT S.A.—See The Federation of Migros Cooperatives; *Int'l*, pg. 7642
ESTEC CORPORATION—See Foster Electric Co., Ltd.; *Int'l*, pg. 2749
ESTECH CORP.—See Dentsu Group Inc.; *Int'l*, pg. 2039
ES TECHNOLOGY LTD.—See Coherent Corp.; *U.S. Public*, pg. 528
ES TECH VENTURES, S.G.P.S., S.A.—See Novo Banco, S.A.; *Int'l*, pg. 5462
ESTEE LAUDER AG LACHEN—See The Estee Lauder Companies Inc.; *U.S. Public*, pg. 2073
ESTEE LAUDER CLINIQUE & ARAMIS—See The Estee Lauder Companies Inc.; *U.S. Public*, pg. 2073
THE ESTEE LAUDER COMPANIES INC.; *U.S. Public*, pg. 2073
ESTEE LAUDER COORDINATION CENTER BVBA—See The Estee Lauder Companies Inc.; *U.S. Public*, pg. 2073
ESTEE LAUDER COSMETICS LIMITED—See The Estee Lauder Companies Inc.; *U.S. Public*, pg. 2073
ESTEE LAUDER COSMETICS LTD.—See The Estee Lauder Companies Inc.; *U.S. Public*, pg. 2073
ESTEE LAUDER INC.—See The Estee Lauder Companies Inc.; *U.S. Public*, pg. 2073
ESTEE LAUDER—See The Estee Lauder Companies Inc.; *U.S. Public*, pg. 2073
ESTEE LAUDER S.R.L.—See The Estee Lauder Companies Inc.; *U.S. Public*, pg. 2073
ESTEEM BIO ORGANIC FOOD PROCESSING LTD; *Int'l*, pg. 2517
ESTEEM BROADCASTING, LLC; *U.S. Private*, pg. 1429
ESTEEM GLORY SDN. BHD.—See Eupe Corporation Berhad; *Int'l*, pg. 2526
ESTEIN & ASSOCIATES USA LTD.; *U.S. Private*, pg. 1429

ESTELLA JV CO LTD—See Keppel Corporation Limited; *Int'l*, pg. 4130
ESTELLE HOLDINGS CO., LTD.; *Int'l*, pg. 2517
ESTEL RAIL AUTOMATION SPA—See Siemens Aktiengesellschaft; *Int'l*, pg. 6886
EST ENERGETICS GMBH—See General Atomics; *U.S. Private*, pg. 1664
ESTENSON LOGISTICS LLC—See Hub Group, Inc.; *U.S. Public*, pg. 1065
ESTERAD INVESTMENT COMPANY BSC; *Int'l*, pg. 2518
THE ESTER-C COMPANY—See KKR & Co. Inc.; *U.S. Public*, pg. 1264
ESTERCHEM LTD.; *Int'l*, pg. 2518
ESTEREL TECHNOLOGIES GMBH—See ANSYS, Inc.; *U.S. Public*, pg. 139
ESTEREL TECHNOLOGIES, INC.—See ANSYS, Inc.; *U.S. Public*, pg. 139
ESTEREL TECHNOLOGIES, S.A.—See ANSYS, Inc.; *U.S. Public*, pg. 139
ESTERFORM PACKAGING LTD.; *Int'l*, pg. 2518
ESTER INDUSTRIES LTD; *Int'l*, pg. 2518
ESTERLE MOLD & MACHINE CO. INC.; *U.S. Private*, pg. 1429
ESTERLINE DEFENSE GROUP—See TransDigm Group Incorporated; *U.S. Public*, pg. 2180
ESTERLINE ENGINEERED MATERIALS-NMC AEROSPACE—See TransDigm Group Incorporated; *U.S. Public*, pg. 2181
ESTERLINE ENGINEERED MATERIALS—See TransDigm Group Incorporated; *U.S. Public*, pg. 2180
ESTERLINE SENSORS SERVICES AMERICAS, INC.—See TransDigm Group Incorporated; *U.S. Public*, pg. 2180
ESTERLINE SENSORS SERVICES AMERICAS, INC.—See TransDigm Group Incorporated; *U.S. Public*, pg. 2180
ESTERLINE SERVICES CHINA LTD.—See TransDigm Group Incorporated; *U.S. Public*, pg. 2180
ESTERLINE TECHNOLOGIES CORPORATION—See TransDigm Group Incorporated; *U.S. Public*, pg. 2180
ESTERO BAY CHEVROLET, INC—See Group 1 Automotive, Inc.; *U.S. Public*, pg. 971
ESTES CONSTRUCTION; *U.S. Private*, pg. 1429
ESTES-COX CORP.—See Hobbico, Inc.; *U.S. Private*, pg. 1958
ESTES EXPRESS LINES, INC. - ESTES LEVEL2 LOGISTICS DIVISION—See Estes Express Lines, Inc.; *U.S. Private*, pg. 1429
ESTES EXPRESS LINES, INC. - ESTES SPECIALIZED TRUCKLOAD AND DELIVERY SERVICES DIVISION—See Estes Express Lines, Inc.; *U.S. Private*, pg. 1429
ESTES EXPRESS LINES, INC. - ESTES SUREMOVE DIVISION—See Estes Express Lines, Inc.; *U.S. Private*, pg. 1429
ESTES EXPRESS LINES, INC.; *U.S. Private*, pg. 1429
ESTES FORWARDING WORLDWIDE LLC—See Estes Express Lines, Inc.; *U.S. Private*, pg. 1429
ESTES HEATING & AIR CONDITIONING, INC.; *U.S. Private*, pg. 1429
ESTES LEASING LLC—See Aim Leasing Co.; *U.S. Private*, pg. 132
ESTES PARK TRAIL-GAZETTE—See Alden Global Capital LLC; *U.S. Private*, pg. 157
ESTES—See Estes Express Lines, Inc.; *U.S. Private*, pg. 1429
E-STET; *U.S. Private*, pg. 1303
ESTEVE FARMA LDA.—See Laboratorios del Dr. Esteve, S.A.; *Int'l*, pg. 4390
ESTEVE HUAYI PHARMACEUTICAL CO., LTD.—See Laboratorios del Dr. Esteve, S.A.; *Int'l*, pg. 4390
ESTEVE PHARMACEUTICALS S.A.; *Int'l*, pg. 2518
ESTEVE S.P.A.—See Laboratorios del Dr. Esteve, S.A.; *Int'l*, pg. 4390
ESTEVES USA—See Torqx Capital Partners B.V.; *Int'l*, pg. 7830
ESTEX MANUFACTURING COMPANY; *U.S. Private*, pg. 1429
ESTEY-HOOVER INC. ADVERTISING-PUBLIC RELATIONS; *U.S. Private*, pg. 1429
EST GLOBAL APPAREL CO., LTD.; *Int'l*, pg. 2517
EST GROUP, INC.—See Curtiss-Wright Corporation; *U.S. Public*, pg. 612
ESTHELOGUE SRL—See El.En. S.p.A.; *Int'l*, pg. 2342
ESTHERVILLE PUBLICATIONS INC.—See The Nutting Company, Inc.; *U.S. Private*, pg. 4086
E.S. THE THIRD INC.; *U.S. Private*, pg. 1307
ESTHETICS AND WELLNESS INTERNATIONAL SDN. BHD.—See Esthetics International Group Berhad; *Int'l*, pg. 2518
ESTHETICS CONCEPT SDN.BHD.—See Esthetics International Group Berhad; *Int'l*, pg. 2518
ESTHETICS INTERNATIONAL GROUP BERHAD; *Int'l*, pg. 2518
ESTIA HEALTH LIMITED—See Bain Capital, LP; *U.S. Private*, pg. 431
ESTIC AMERICA, INC.—See Estic Corporation; *Int'l*, pg. 2518
ESTIC CORPORATION; *Int'l*, pg. 2518

ESTI CHEM A/S; *Int'l*, pg. 2518
ESTIC (THAILAND) CO., LTD.—See Estic Corporation; *Int'l*, pg. 2518
ESTILL MEDICAL TECHNOLOGIES, INC.; *U.S. Private*, pg. 1429
ESTIMA AG—See KDDL Limited; *Int'l*, pg. 4112
EST IMPRIMERIE; *Int'l*, pg. 2517
ESTLICK-GIRVIN & LEFEVER INC.; *U.S. Private*, pg. 1429
EST MAINTENANCE SERVICE SAS—See VINCI S.A.; *Int'l*, pg. 8218
ESTNATION INC.; *Int'l*, pg. 2518
ESTONIA AS FORTUM—See Fortum Oyj; *Int'l*, pg. 2740
ESTORE CORPORATION; *Int'l*, pg. 2518
ESTORIL SOL, SGPS, S.A.; *Int'l*, pg. 2518
ESTRADA HINOJOSA & CO., INC.—See Texas State Bankshares, Inc.; *U.S. Private*, pg. 3977
ESTRAVEL AS—See Finnair Plc; *Int'l*, pg. 2676
ESTRE AMBIENTAL S.A.; *Int'l*, pg. 2518
E STREET APPRAISAL MANAGEMENT LLC—See Rithm Capital Corp.; *U.S. Public*, pg. 1800
E STREET ENDOSCOPY, LLC—See UnitedHealth Group Incorporated; *U.S. Public*, pg. 2240
ESTRELLA AB—See Intersnack Group GmbH & Co. KG; *Int'l*, pg. 3760
ESTRELLA GROUP LTD; *Int'l*, pg. 2518
ESTRELLA IMMUNOPHARMA, INC.; *U.S. Public*, pg. 796
ESTRELLA INSURANCE INC.—See Stone Point Capital LLC; *U.S. Private*, pg. 3818
ESTRELLA INTERNATIONAL ENERGY SERVICES LTD.; *Int'l*, pg. 2518
ESTRELLA MOUNTAIN DIALYSIS, LLC—See Nautic Partners, LLC; *U.S. Private*, pg. 2870
ESTRELLA OY—See Intersnack Group GmbH & Co. KG; *Int'l*, pg. 3760
ESTRELLA RESOURCES (CHILE) SPA—See Estrella Resources Limited; *Int'l*, pg. 2519
ESTRELLA RESOURCES LIMITED; *Int'l*, pg. 2519
THE ESTRIDGE GROUP INC.; *U.S. Private*, pg. 4027
ESTRIMA S.P.A.; *Int'l*, pg. 2519
ESTRUCTURA, GRUPO DE ESTUDIOS ECONOMICOS, S.A.—See Promotora de Informaciones S.A.; *Int'l*, pg. 5995
ESTRUCTURAS METALICAS SINGULARES S.A.—See Siemens Energy AG; *Int'l*, pg. 6902
ESTSECURITY CORP.—See ESTsoft Corp; *Int'l*, pg. 2519
EST-SMT LLC—See ESPEC Corp.; *Int'l*, pg. 2505
ESTSOFT CORP; *Int'l*, pg. 2519
EST TOOLS CO., LTD.; *Int'l*, pg. 2517
ESTUARY INVESTMENT CORP.; *U.S. Private*, pg. 1429
ESTUDIO FERRERO ABOGADOS—See Philippi, Prietocarrizosa & Uria; *Int'l*, pg. 5845
ESTUN AUTOMATION CO., LTD.—See Nanjing Estun Automation Co., Ltd.; *Int'l*, pg. 5140
ESTUN INDUSTRIAL TECHNOLOGY EUROPE S.R.L.—See Nanjing Estun Automation Co., Ltd.; *Int'l*, pg. 5140
E-STYLE, LLC—See Qurate Retail, Inc.; *U.S. Public*, pg. 1758
E SUB LIMITED—See Heidelberg Materials AG; *Int'l*, pg. 3310
ESUCO BEHEER B.V.—See BASF SE; *Int'l*, pg. 883
ESUMEDICA - PRESTACAO DE CUIDADOS MEDICOS, S.A.—See Fosun International Limited; *Int'l*, pg. 2751
E.SUN BANK (CHINA), LTD.—See E. Sun Financial Holding Co., Ltd.; *Int'l*, pg. 2250
E.SUN COMMERCIAL BANK, LTD.—See E. Sun Financial Holding Co., Ltd.; *Int'l*, pg. 2250
E. SUN FINANCIAL HOLDING CO., LTD.; *Int'l*, pg. 2250
ESUN HOLDINGS LIMITED—See Lai Sun Group; *Int'l*, pg. 4396
E.SUN SECURITIES CO., LTD.—See E. Sun Financial Holding Co., Ltd.; *Int'l*, pg. 2250
E.SUN SECURITIES INVESTMENT TRUST CO., LTD.—See E. Sun Financial Holding Co., Ltd.; *Int'l*, pg. 2250
E.SUN VENTURE CAPITAL CORP.—See E. Sun Financial Holding Co., Ltd.; *Int'l*, pg. 2250
E-SUPPORTLINK, LTD.; *Int'l*, pg. 2249
ESURANCE INSURANCE SERVICES, INC.—See The Allstate Corporation; *U.S. Public*, pg. 2033
ESURANCE PROPERTY & CASUALTY INSURANCE COMPANY—See The Allstate Corporation; *U.S. Public*, pg. 2033
ESURE GROUP PLC—See Bain Capital, LP; *U.S. Private*, pg. 452
ESURE INSURANCE LTD.—See Bain Capital, LP; *U.S. Private*, pg. 453
ESVAGT A/S—See 3i Group plc; *Int'l*, pg. 8
ESVAGT A/S—See AMP Limited; *Int'l*, pg. 432
ESVAL SA; *Int'l*, pg. 2519
ESVIN ADVANCED TECHNOLOGIES LTD—See Seshasayee Paper & Boards Ltd; *Int'l*, pg. 6729
ESWATINI INSURANCE BROKERS (PTY) LIMITED—See Aon plc; *Int'l*, pg. 494
ESW CAPITAL, LLC; *U.S. Private*, pg. 1429
ESWEGEE VLIESSTOFF GMBH—See Hoftex Group AG; *Int'l*, pg. 3440

COMPANY NAME INDEX

ESW EXTEL SYSTEMS WEDEL GESELLSCHAFT FUR AUSRUSTUNG MBH—See Jenoptik AG; *Int'l*, pg. 3928
ESW GMBH I SENSORIK—See Jenoptik AG; *Int'l*, pg. 3928
ESW GMBH—See Jenoptik AG; *Int'l*, pg. 3928
ESW, INC.; *U.S. Private*, pg. 1431
E-SWITCH, INC.—See Stein Industries, Inc.; *U.S. Private*, pg. 3797
ESYS AUTOMATION, LLC—See Hitachi, Ltd.; *Int'l*, pg. 3423
ESYS TECHNOLOGIES PTE. LTD.—See Agnite Education Limited; *Int'l*, pg. 212
E-SYSTEM CORPORATION—See Canon Inc.; *Int'l*, pg. 1293
E SYSTEMS TECHNOLOGY; *U.S. Private*, pg. 1301
E-TABLE ONLINE RESTAURANT RESERVATION SERVICES SINGLE MEMBER P.C.—See Delivery Hero SE; *Int'l*, pg. 2013
ETABLISSEMENT D'ARGONAY—See Groupe Industriel Marcel Dassault S.A.; *Int'l*, pg. 3105
ETABLISSEMENT DE MARTIGNAS—See Groupe Industriel Marcel Dassault S.A.; *Int'l*, pg. 3105
ETABLISSEMENT DE MERIGNAC—See Groupe Industriel Marcel Dassault S.A.; *Int'l*, pg. 3105
ETABLISSEMENT D'ISTRES—See Groupe Industriel Marcel Dassault S.A.; *Int'l*, pg. 3105
ETABLISSEMENTEN VAN MOER N.V.—See V. F. Corporation; *U.S. Public*, pg. 2268
ETABLISSEMENT F.S. BIVOIS SARL—See Heidelberg Materials AG; *Int'l*, pg. 3310
ETABLISSEMENTS ALLIN; *Int'l*, pg. 2519
ETABLISSEMENTS BRANCHER S.A.S.—See Lennox International Inc.; *U.S. Public*, pg. 1307
ETABLISSEMENTS CAMILLE HOLTZ ET CIE S.A.—See Hornbach Holding AG & Co. KGaA; *Int'l*, pg. 3481
ETABLISSEMENTS CHARLES WILLE ET CIE S.A.—See ROCKWOOL A/S; *Int'l*, pg. 6380
ETABLISSEMENTS CHAZAUD; *Int'l*, pg. 2519
ETABLISSEMENTS CROUZET NV—See Schneider Electric SE; *Int'l*, pg. 6627
ETABLISSEMENTS EMILE GEORGET; *Int'l*, pg. 2519
ETABLISSEMENTS EMILE LLAU; *Int'l*, pg. 2519
ETABLISSEMENTS GASCHEAU; *Int'l*, pg. 2519
ETABLISSEMENTS GOUTOULY ET FILS; *Int'l*, pg. 2519
ETABLISSEMENTS HENRI PFIGNEN S.A.—See Tecnolama S.A.; *Int'l*, pg. 7516
ETABLISSEMENTS JEAN GRANIOU SAS—See VINCI S.A.; *Int'l*, pg. 8218
ETABLISSEMENTS J. SOUFFLET; *Int'l*, pg. 2519
ETABLISSEMENTS MARTINENQ; *Int'l*, pg. 2519
ETABLISSEMENTS MAUREL & PROM S.A.—See PT Pertamina (Persero); *Int'l*, pg. 6063
ETABLISSEMENTS PAUL PAULET SAS—See Thai Union Group Public Company Limited; *Int'l*, pg. 7596
ETABLISSEMENTS R. BLANCHET; *Int'l*, pg. 2519
ETABLISSEMENTS R. LEGRAND; *Int'l*, pg. 2519
ETABLISSEMENTS ROCHE ET COMPAGNIE; *Int'l*, pg. 2519
ETABLISSEMENTS VALLAROCHE SA—See Safran SA; *Int'l*, pg. 6473
ETABO ENERGIETECHNIK UND ANLAGENSERVICE GMBH—See ELKA Beteiligungs GmbH; *Int'l*, pg. 2364
ETAC AB—See Nordstjernan AB; *Int'l*, pg. 5425
ETAC ALARME SERVICES SECURITY SA—See Stanley Black & Decker, Inc.; *U.S. Public*, pg. 1932
ETAC AS—See Nordstjernan AB; *Int'l*, pg. 5425
ETAC A/S—See Nordstjernan AB; *Int'l*, pg. 5425
ETAC GMBH—See Nordstjernan AB; *Int'l*, pg. 5425
ETAC HOLLAND B.V.—See Nordstjernan AB; *Int'l*, pg. 5425
ETAC SUPPLY CENTER AB—See Nordstjernan AB; *Int'l*, pg. 5425
ETAC SVERIGE AB—See Nordstjernan AB; *Int'l*, pg. 5425
ETACTICS INC.; *U.S. Private*, pg. 1431
ETAC UK LIMITED—See Nordstjernan AB; *Int'l*, pg. 5425
ETA ELECTRIC INDUSTRY CO., LTD.; *Int'l*, pg. 2519
ETA ENERGIEBERATUNG GMBH—See Stadtwerke Munchen GmbH; *Int'l*, pg. 7162
ETA GLOBAL, INC.—See Copley Equity Partners,LLC; *U.S. Private*, pg. 1045
THE E-TAILING GROUP, INC.—See Astound Commerce Corp.; *U.S. Private*, pg. 361
ETAL GROUP AB—See Amplex AB; *Int'l*, pg. 434
ETAL GROUP (PVT.) LTD.—See Amplex AB; *Int'l*, pg. 434
ETAL, INC.—See Amplex AB; *Int'l*, pg. 434
ETALON GROUP PLC; *Int'l*, pg. 2520
ETALON-LENSPETSSMU CONSTRUCTION HOLDING COMPANY; *Int'l*, pg. 2520
ETAL (UK) LTD.—See Amplex AB; *Int'l*, pg. 434
ETAM DEVELOPPEMENT SCA; *Int'l*, pg. 2520
ETAMIC SA—See Jenoptik AG; *Int'l*, pg. 3928
ETAM ITALIA SRL—See Etam Developpement SCA; *Int'l*, pg. 2520
ETAM POLAND SP—See Etam Developpement SCA; *Int'l*, pg. 2520
ETAN INDUSTRIES INC.; *U.S. Private*, pg. 1431
ETANOMICS SERVICE GMBH—See Viessmann Werke GmbH & Co. KG; *Int'l*, pg. 8196
ETAO INTERNATIONAL CO., LTD.; *U.S. Public*, pg. 796

ETAP HOTELS LTD—See Accor S.A.; *Int'l*, pg. 91
ETA-POWER EUROPE LTD.—See Eta Electric Industry Co.; *Int'l*, pg. 2519
ETA S.A. MANUFACTURE HORLOGERE—See The Swatch Group Ltd.; *Int'l*, pg. 7691
ETA S.A.—See The Swatch Group Ltd.; *Int'l*, pg. 7691
ETAS AUTOMOTIVE INDIA PRIVATE LTD.—See Robert Bosch GmbH; *Int'l*, pg. 6362
ETAS AUTOMOTIVE TECHNOLOGY (SHANGHAI) CO., LTD.—See Robert Bosch GmbH; *Int'l*, pg. 6362
ETAS EMBEDDED SYSTEMS CANADA INC.—See Robert Bosch GmbH; *Int'l*, pg. 6360
ETAS GMBH—See Robert Bosch GmbH; *Int'l*, pg. 6362
ETAS, INC.—See Robert Bosch GmbH; *Int'l*, pg. 6362
ETAS K.K.—See Robert Bosch GmbH; *Int'l*, pg. 6362
ETAS KOREA CO., LTD.—See Robert Bosch GmbH; *Int'l*, pg. 6362
ETASK TECHNOLOGIES LIMITED; *Int'l*, pg. 2520
ETAS LTD.—See Robert Bosch GmbH; *Int'l*, pg. 6362
ETA S.P.A.—See Marcegaglia S.p.A.; *Int'l*, pg. 4688
ETAS S.A.S.—See Robert Bosch GmbH; *Int'l*, pg. 6362
ETA (THAILAND) CO. LTD.—See The Swatch Group Ltd.; *Int'l*, pg. 7691
ETA-USA INC.—See Eta Electric Industry Co., Ltd.; *Int'l*, pg. 2519
ETAVIS AG—See VINCI S.A.; *Int'l*, pg. 8237
ETAVIS ARNOLD AG—See VINCI S.A.; *Int'l*, pg. 8237
ETAVIS BARBONI+COLLAUD SA—See VINCI S.A.; *Int'l*, pg. 8218
ETAVIS BEUTLER AG—See VINCI S.A.; *Int'l*, pg. 8237
ETAVIS BROGER AG—See VINCI S.A.; *Int'l*, pg. 8237
ETAVIS EGLIN SA—See VINCI S.A.; *Int'l*, pg. 8218
ETAVIS ELCOM AG—See VINCI S.A.; *Int'l*, pg. 8218
ETAVIS ELETTRO-IMPIANTI SA—See VINCI S.A.; *Int'l*, pg. 8237
ETAVIS ELSA SA—See VINCI S.A.; *Int'l*, pg. 8218
ETAVIS ENGINEERING AG—See VINCI S.A.; *Int'l*, pg. 8237
ETAVIS GNS AG—See VINCI S.A.; *Int'l*, pg. 8237
ETAVIS GROSSENBACHER AG—See VINCI S.A.; *Int'l*, pg. 8237
ETAVIS JAG JAKOB AG—See VINCI S.A.; *Int'l*, pg. 8237
ETAVIS KRIEGEL+CO. AG—See VINCI S.A.; *Int'l*, pg. 8237
ETAVIS KRIEGEL+SCHAFFNER AG—See VINCI S.A.; *Int'l*, pg. 8237
ETAVIS MICATEL AG—See VINCI S.A.; *Int'l*, pg. 8237
ETAVIS SERVICES AG—See VINCI S.A.; *Int'l*, pg. 8237
ETAVIS TSA SA—See VINCI S.A.; *Int'l*, pg. 8237
E.T. BROWNE DRUG COMPANY, INC.; *U.S. Private*, pg. 1307
ET BUSINESS COLLEGE LIMITED—See Hong Kong Economic Times Holdings Ltd; *Int'l*, pg. 3465
ETC ENDURE ENERGY L.L.C.—See Energy Transfer LP; *U.S. Public*, pg. 763
ETC, ENVIRONMENTAL TEEN CONCEPTS—See Child Craft Industries, Inc.; *U.S. Private*, pg. 882
ETC FAYETTEVILLE OPERATING COMPANY, LLC—See Energy Transfer LP; *U.S. Public*, pg. 763
ETC FINANCE LIMITED—See New Century Group Hong Kong Limited; *Int'l*, pg. 5221
ETC GROUP INC—See DIF Management Holding B.V.; *Int'l*, pg. 2117
ETC HYDROCARBONS, LLC—See Energy Transfer LP; *U.S. Public*, pg. 763
ETC INC. INTERNATIONAL LOGISTICS; *U.S. Private*, pg. 1431
ETC INTERSTATE PROCUREMENT COMPANY, LLC—See Energy Transfer LP; *U.S. Public*, pg. 763
ETC M-A ACQUISITION LLC—See Energy Transfer LP; *U.S. Public*, pg. 763
ETCM (LABUAN) PTY. LTD.—See Tan Chong Motor Holdings Berhad; *Int'l*, pg. 7453
ETCM (MYANMAR) COMPANY LIMITED—See Tan Chong Motor Holdings Berhad; *Int'l*, pg. 7453
ETCM SA—See Eiffage S.A.; *Int'l*, pg. 2331
ETC NETWORKS LTD.-BROADCASTING DIVISION—See Essel Corporate Resources Pvt. Ltd.; *Int'l*, pg. 2510
ETC NETWORKS LTD.-EDUCATION DIVISION—See Essel Corporate Resources Pvt. Ltd.; *Int'l*, pg. 2510
ETC NETWORKS LTD.—See Essel Corporate Resources Pvt. Ltd.; *Int'l*, pg. 2510
ETCO DEVELOPMENT INC.; *U.S. Private*, pg. 1431
ETCO INCORPORATED; *U.S. Private*, pg. 1431
ETCON INC.; *U.S. Private*, pg. 1431
ETC-PZL AEROSPACE INDUSTRIES SP Z O.O.—See Environmental Tectonics Corporation; *U.S. Public*, pg. 781
ETC SIMULATION ADMS INNOVATION CENTER—See Environmental Tectonics Corporation; *U.S. Public*, pg. 781
ETEC ARABIA LIMITED—See SGC eTEC E&C Co., Ltd.; *Int'l*, pg. 6741
ETEC E&C (NANJING) CO., LTD.—See SGC eTEC E&C Co., Ltd.; *Int'l*, pg. 6741
ETEC E&C (SHANGHAI) CO., LTD.—See SGC eTEC E&C Co., Ltd.; *Int'l*, pg. 6741
ETECH, INC.; *U.S. Private*, pg. 1431

E-TECHNOLOGIES GROUP, LLC—See The Graham Group, Inc.; *U.S. Public*, pg. 4036
E-TECHNO LTD.—See Mitsubishi Heavy Industries, Ltd.; *Int'l*, pg. 4953
ETECH SOLUTIONS LIMITED—See Insight Venture Management, LLC; *U.S. Private*, pg. 2089
ETECH SOLUTIONS LIMITED—See Stone Point Capital LLC; *U.S. Private*, pg. 3823
ETECH SYSTEMS, INC.—See Hebert Kannegiesser GmbH; *Int'l*, pg. 3306
E-TECH TESTING SERVICES, INC.—See Trinity Industries, Inc.; *U.S. Public*, pg. 2193
ETEC MALAYSIA SDN. BHD.—See SGC eTEC E&C Co., Ltd.; *Int'l*, pg. 6741
ETE COMMON HOLDINGS, LLC—See Energy Transfer LP; *U.S. Public*, pg. 763
ETEC SA—See Ackermans & van Haaren NV; *Int'l*, pg. 105
ETELA ALBORZ INVESTMENT COMPANY—See Alborz Investment Company; *Int'l*, pg. 299
ETELA-KARJALAN LIIKUNTAKESKUS OY—See Pihlajalinna Oy; *Int'l*, pg. 5865
ETELECARE PHILIPPINES, INC.—See Concentrix Corporation; *U.S. Public*, pg. 565
ETEM BULGARIA SA—See Viohalco SA/NV; *Int'l*, pg. 8243
ETEM SYSTEMS SRL—See Viohalco SA/NV; *Int'l*, pg. 8243
ETEN INFORMATION SYSTEM CO., LTD.—See Acer Incorporated; *Int'l*, pg. 99
ETEQ COMPONENTS INTERNATIONAL PTE LTD.—See Arrow Electronics, Inc.; *U.S. Public*, pg. 199
ETEQ COMPONENTS PTE LTD.—See Arrow Electronics, Inc.; *U.S. Public*, pg. 199
ETEQ COMPONENTS PTE LTD.—See Arrow Electronics, Inc.; *U.S. Public*, pg. 199
ETERA CONSULTING LLC—See Quad-C Management, Inc.; *U.S. Private*, pg. 3315
ETERBRIGHT SOLAR CORPORATION—See Hiwin Technologies Corp.; *Int'l*, pg. 3427
ETERGE OPTO-ELECTRONICS CO., LTD.—See Zhong Yang Technology Co., Ltd.; *Int'l*, pg. 8672
ETERNA AG—See Citychamp Watch & Jewellery Group Limited; *Int'l*, pg. 1629
ETERNABOND, LLC—See H.B. Fuller Company; *U.S. Public*, pg. 977
ETERNA INDUSTRIES LIMITED—See Eterna Plc.; *Int'l*, pg. 2520
ETERNAL ASIA SUPPLY CHAIN MANAGEMENT LTD.; *Int'l*, pg. 2520
ETERNAL BEST INDUSTRIAL LIMITED; *Int'l*, pg. 2520
ETERNAL CHEMICAL (CHENGDU) CO., LTD.—See Eternal Materials Co., Ltd.; *Int'l*, pg. 2520
ETERNAL CHEMICAL CO., LTD. - LU-CHU PLANT—See China Petrochemical Development Corp.; *Int'l*, pg. 1540
ETERNAL CHEMICAL CO., LTD. - PING-NAN PLANT—See Eternal Materials Co., Ltd.; *Int'l*, pg. 2520
ETERNAL CHEMICAL CO., LTD. - TA-FA PLANT—See Eternal Materials Co., Ltd.; *Int'l*, pg. 2520
ETERNAL CHEMICAL (GUANGDONG) CO., LTD.—See Eternal Materials Co., Ltd.; *Int'l*, pg. 2520
ETERNAL CHEMICAL (GUANGZHOU) CO., LTD.—See Eternal Materials Co., Ltd.; *Int'l*, pg. 2520
ETERNAL CHEMICAL (JAPAN) CO., LTD.—See Eternal Materials Co., Ltd.; *Int'l*, pg. 2520
ETERNAL CHEMICAL (TIANJIN) CO., LTD.—See Eternal Materials Co., Ltd.; *Int'l*, pg. 2520
ETERNAL (CHINA) INVESTMENT CO., LTD.—See Eternal Materials Co., Ltd.; *Int'l*, pg. 2520
ETERNAL CO., LTD.—See Tokai Tokyo Financial Holdings, Inc.; *Int'l*, pg. 7781
ETERNAL ELECTRONIC MATERIAL (GUANGZHOU) CO., LTD.—See Eternal Materials Co., Ltd.; *Int'l*, pg. 2520
ETERNAL ELECTRONIC MATERIAL (THAILAND) CO., LTD.—See Eternal Materials Co., Ltd.; *Int'l*, pg. 2520
ETERNAL ELECTRONIC (SUZHOU) CO., LTD.—See Eternal Materials Co., Ltd.; *Int'l*, pg. 2520
ETERNAL ENERGY PUBLIC COMPANY LIMITED; *Int'l*, pg. 2520
ETERNAL MATERIALS CO., LTD.; *Int'l*, pg. 2520
ETERNAL MATERIALS (GUANGDONG) CO., LTD.—See Eternal Materials Co., Ltd.; *Int'l*, pg. 2520
ETERNAL MATERIALS (MALAYSIA) SDN. BHD.—See Eternal Materials Co., Ltd.; *Int'l*, pg. 2521
ETERNAL OPTICAL MATERIAL (SUZHOU) CO., LTD.—See Eternal Materials Co., Ltd.; *Int'l*, pg. 2521
ETERNAL PHOTOELECTRIC MATERIAL INDUSTRY (YINGKOU) CO., LTD.—See Eternal Materials Co., Ltd.; *Int'l*, pg. 2521
ETERNAL PHOTO ELECTRONIC MATERIALS (GUANGZHOU) CO., LTD.—See Eternal Materials Co., Ltd.; *Int'l*, pg. 2521
ETERNAL SAKATA INX CO. LTD.—See Sakata INX Corporation; *Int'l*, pg. 6487
ETERNAL SHOWA HIGHPOLYMER CO., LTD.—See Resonac Holdings Corporation; *Int'l*, pg. 6298
ETERNAL SPECIALTY CHEMICAL (ZHUHAI) CO., LTD.—See Eternal Materials Co., Ltd.; *Int'l*, pg. 2521

ETERNAL MATERIALS CO., LTD.

ETERNAL SPECIALTY MATERIALS (SUZHOU) CO., LTD.—See Eternal Materials Co., Ltd.; *Int'l*, pg. 2521
ETERNAL SPECIALTY MATERIALS (ZHUHAI) CO., LTD.—See Eternal Materials Co., Ltd.; *Int'l*, pg. 2521
ETERNAL SPEECH, INC.; *Int'l*, pg. 2521
ETERNAL SYNTHETIC RESINS (CHANGSHU) CO., LTD.—See Eternal Materials Co., Ltd.; *Int'l*, pg. 2521
ETERNAL TECHNOLOGY CORPORATION—See Eternal Materials Co., Ltd.; *Int'l*, pg. 2521
ETERNAL WORD TELEVISION NETWORK INC.; *U.S. Private*, pg. 1431
ETERNA PLC.; *Int'l*, pg. 2520
ETERNA THERAPEUTICS INC.; *U.S. Public*, pg. 797
ETERNIT ATLANTICO S.A.—See Grupo Empresarial Kaluz S.A. de C.V.; *Int'l*, pg. 3126
ETERNIT B.V.—See Etex SA/NV; *Int'l*, pg. 2521
ETERNIT COLOMBIANA S.A.—See Grupo Empresarial Kaluz S.A. de C.V.; *Int'l*, pg. 3127
ETERNIT ECUATORIANA—See Grupo Empresarial Kaluz S.A. de C.V.; *Int'l*, pg. 3127
ETERNIT GUANGZHOU BUILDING SYSTEMS CO. LTD.—See Etex SA/NV; *Int'l*, pg. 2521
ETERNIT KALUGA OOO—See Etex SA/NV; *Int'l*, pg. 2521
ETERNIT LTD.—See Etex SA/NV; *Int'l*, pg. 2521
ETERNIT NV—See Etex SA/NV; *Int'l*, pg. 2522
ETERNIT PACIFICO S.A.—See Grupo Empresarial Kaluz S.A. de C.V.; *Int'l*, pg. 3127
ETERNIT S.A.; *Int'l*, pg. 2521
ETERNIT S.A.S.—See Etex SA/NV; *Int'l*, pg. 2522
ETERNIT (SCHWEIZ) AG—See swisspor Management AG; *Int'l*, pg. 7374
ETERNIT WERKE LUDWIG HATSCHEK AG—See swisspor Management AG; *Int'l*, pg. 7374
ETERNITY GRAND LOGISTICS PUBLIC COMPANY LIMITED—See KKR & Co. Inc.; *U.S. Public*, pg. 1258
ETERNITY HEALTHCARE INC.—See Team Youn Bio Medicine International Corp. Limited; *Int'l*, pg. 7500
ETERNITY INVESTMENT LIMITED; *Int'l*, pg. 2521
ETERNITY SHIPPING COMPANY—See Euroseas Ltd.; *Int'l*, pg. 2558
ET EUROPE HOLDING BV—See Pareteum Corporation; *U.S. Public*, pg. 1637
ETEX BUILDING MATERIALS POLSKA SP. Z O.O.—See Etex SA/NV; *Int'l*, pg. 2522
ETEX CORPORATION—See Zimmer Biomet Holdings, Inc.; *U.S. Public*, pg. 2406
ETEX FARMACEUTICA LIMITADA—See GSK plc; *Int'l*, pg. 3145
ETEX SA/NV; *Int'l*, pg. 2521
ETEX TELEPHONE COOPERATIVE; *U.S. Private*, pg. 1431
E-TF1 S.A.S.—See Television Française 1 S.A.; *Int'l*, pg. 7542
ETF-EUROVIA TRAVAUX FERROVIAIRES S. A.—See VINCI S.A.; *Int'l*, pg. 8219
ETF LUXEMBOURG SA—See VINCI S.A.; *Int'l*, pg. 8217
ETF POLSKA SP. Z O.O.—See VINCI S.A.; *Int'l*, pg. 8217
ETFS ASIAN GOLD TRUST; *U.S. Private*, pg. 1431
ETF SAS—See VINCI S.A.; *Int'l*, pg. 8217
ETF SERVICES SAS—See VINCI S.A.; *Int'l*, pg. 8217
E.T.F.S. LLC—See Emirates NBD PJSC; *Int'l*, pg. 2381
ETFT ENVITEC FILTRATION TECHNIK GMBH—See EnviTec Biogas AG; *Int'l*, pg. 2455
ET FUEL PIPELINE, L.P.—See Energy Transfer LP; *U.S. Public*, pg. 763
ETGA GROUP LTD.; *Int'l*, pg. 2523
ETGAR INVESTMENT PORTFOLIO MANAGEMENT COMPANY OF THE MIZRAHI TEFAHOT GROUP LTD.—See Mizrahi Tefahot Bank Ltd.; *Int'l*, pg. 4997
ETGAR PORTFOLIO MANAGEMENT OF MIZRAHI TEFAHOT BANK LTD.—See Mizrahi Tefahot Bank Ltd.; *Int'l*, pg. 4996
ETG ENTWICKLUNGS- UND TECHNOLOGIE GESELLSCHAFT MBH—See Endress+Hauser (International) Holding AG; *Int'l*, pg. 2405
ETG ERZGEBIRGE TRANSPORTBETON GMBH—See STRABAG SE; *Int'l*, pg. 7230
ETG INTERNATIONAL LLC; *U.S. Private*, pg. 1431
ETHAN ALLEN (CANADA) INC.—See Ethan Allen Interiors Inc.; *U.S. Public*, pg. 797
ETHAN ALLEN DESIGN CENTER; *U.S. Private*, pg. 1431
ETHAN ALLEN GLOBAL, INC.—See Ethan Allen Interiors Inc.; *U.S. Public*, pg. 797
ETHAN ALLEN INTERIORS INC.; *U.S. Public*, pg. 797
ETHAN ALLEN INTERNATIONAL, BVBA—See Ethan Allen Interiors Inc.; *U.S. Public*, pg. 797
ETHAN ALLEN OPERATIONS, INC.—See Ethan Allen Interiors Inc.; *U.S. Public*, pg. 797
ETHAN ALLEN RETAIL, INC.—See Ethan Allen Interiors Inc.; *U.S. Public*, pg. 797
ETHANOL COMPANY LIMITED—See Press Corporation Plc; *Int'l*, pg. 5964
ETHANOL ENERGY A.S.—See Agrofert Holding, a.s.; *Int'l*, pg. 219
ETHANOL MANAGEMENT COMPANY LLC—See HF Sinclair Corporation; *U.S. Public*, pg. 1033
ETHANOL TECHNOLOGIES LIMITED; *Int'l*, pg. 2523
ETHEL M. CHOCOLATES, INC.—See Mars, Incorporated; *U.S. Private*, pg. 2589

ETHEMA HEALTH CORPORATION; *U.S. Public*, pg. 797
ETHERIDGE OIL COMPANY; *U.S. Private*, pg. 1431
ETHERIOS DESIGN SERVICES INC.—See Digi International Inc.; *U.S. Public*, pg. 662
ETHERNITY NETWORKS LTD.; *Int'l*, pg. 2523
ETHERSTACK INC.—See Etherstack PLC; *Int'l*, pg. 2523
ETHERSTACK JAPAN LIMITED—See Etherstack PLC; *Int'l*, pg. 2523
ETHERSTACK LIMITED—See Etherstack PLC; *Int'l*, pg. 2523
ETHERSTACK PLC; *Int'l*, pg. 2523
ETHERTRONICS INC.—See KYOCERA Corporation; *Int'l*, pg. 4359
ETHERTRONICS INC.—See KYOCERA Corporation; *Int'l*, pg. 4359
ETHERTRONICS INC.—See KYOCERA Corporation; *Int'l*, pg. 4359
ETHERWAN SYSTEMS INC.—See PHOENIX CONTACT GmbH & Co. KG; *Int'l*, pg. 5849
ETHIAS FINANCE SA/NV; *Int'l*, pg. 2523
ETHIAS SA—See Ethias Finance SA/NV; *Int'l*, pg. 2523
ETHICALCHEM—See Ethical Solutions, LLC; *U.S. Private*, pg. 1431
ETHICAL INTERNATIONAL TRADING & WAREHOUSING (SHANGHAI) CO., LTD.—See Everlight Chemical Industrial Co.; *Int'l*, pg. 2567
ETHICAL (QINGDAO) LTD.—See Everlight Chemical Industrial Co.; *Int'l*, pg. 2567
ETHICAL SOLUTIONS, LLC; *U.S. Private*, pg. 1431
ETHICAL TRADING COMPANY—See Everlight Chemical Industrial Co.; *Int'l*, pg. 2567
ETHICARE ADVISORS, INC.—See PCP Enterprise, L.P.; *U.S. Private*, pg. 3121
ETHICON ENDO-SURGERY (EUROPE) GMBH—See Johnson & Johnson; *U.S. Public*, pg. 1196
ETHICON ENDO-SURGERY INC—See Johnson & Johnson; *U.S. Public*, pg. 1195
ETHICON ENDO-SURGERY, LLC—See Johnson & Johnson; *U.S. Public*, pg. 1196
ETHICON GMBH—See Johnson & Johnson; *U.S. Public*, pg. 1196
ETHICON, INC.—See Johnson & Johnson; *U.S. Public*, pg. 1196
ETHICON, INC.—See Johnson & Johnson; *U.S. Public*, pg. 1195
ETHICON, INC.—See Johnson & Johnson; *U.S. Public*, pg. 1196
ETHICON IRELAND LIMITED—See Johnson & Johnson; *U.S. Public*, pg. 1196
ETHICON, LLC—See Johnson & Johnson; *U.S. Public*, pg. 1196
ETHICON SAS—See Johnson & Johnson; *U.S. Public*, pg. 1196
ETHIKA INVESTMENTS LLC; *U.S. Private*, pg. 1431
ETHIOPIAN AIRLINES ENTERPRISE; *Int'l*, pg. 2523
ETHIOPIAN COMMUNITY DEVELOPMENT COUNCIL, INC.; *U.S. Private*, pg. 1431
ETHIOPIA TANNERY SHARE COMPANY—See Pittards plc; *Int'l*, pg. 5876
ETHLAB S.R.L.—See Eurotech S.p.A.; *Int'l*, pg. 2558
ETHNIC COMMUNICATIONS PTY. LIMITED—See WPP plc; *Int'l*, pg. 8462
ETHNIKI FACTORS S.A.—See National Bank of Greece S.A.; *Int'l*, pg. 5153
ETHNIKI GENERAL INSURANCE (CYPRUS) LTD—See National Bank of Greece S.A.; *Int'l*, pg. 5153
ETHNIKI INSURANCE (CYPRUS) LTD—See National Bank of Greece S.A.; *Int'l*, pg. 5153
ETHNODATA S.A.—See National Bank of Greece S.A.; *Int'l*, pg. 5153
ETHNOMETRICS INC.—See Viad Corp.; *U.S. Public*, pg. 2291
E.T. HORN COMPANY INC.; *U.S. Private*, pg. 1307
ETHOS CAPITAL, LLC; *U.S. Private*, pg. 1432
ETHOS CAPITAL PARTNERS LIMITED; *Int'l*, pg. 2523
ETHOS ENERGY GROUP LIMITED—See John Wood Group PLC; *Int'l*, pg. 3983
ETHOS ENERGY GROUP LIMITED—See Siemens Energy AG; *Int'l*, pg. 6901
ETHOSENERGY POLAND S.A.—See Siemens Aktiengesellschaft; *Int'l*, pg. 6886
ETHOS INTERNATIONAL LIMITED—See John Swire & Sons Limited; *Int'l*, pg. 3979
ETHOS LIMITED; *Int'l*, pg. 2523
ETHOS PRIVATE EQUITY (PROPRIETARY) LIMITED—See TRG Management LP; *U.S. Private*, pg. 4219
ETHOS RISK SERVICES LLC; *U.S. Private*, pg. 1432
ETHOX CHEMICALS LLC—See Piedmont Chemical Industries, Inc.; *U.S. Private*, pg. 3177
ETHOZ GROUP LTD.—See ORIX Corporation; *Int'l*, pg. 5634
ETHOZ GROUP LTD.—See Tan Chong International Limited; *Int'l*, pg. 7453
ETHYLENE CHEMICAL CO., LTD.—See MORESCO Corporation; *Int'l*, pg. 5040
ETHYPHARM INC.—See PAI Partners S.A.S.; *Int'l*, pg. 5700

ETHYPHARM SAS—See PAI Partners S.A.S.; *Int'l*, pg. 5700
ETHYPHARM UK LTD.—See PAI Partners S.A.S.; *Int'l*, pg. 5700
ETHYPHARM USA CORP.—See PAI Partners S.A.S.; *Int'l*, pg. 5700
ETIBALTUS UAB—See Andlinger & Company, Inc.; *U.S. Private*, pg. 279
ETI B—See Andlinger & Company, Inc.; *U.S. Private*, pg. 278
ETICA ENTERTAINMENT INC.; *U.S. Private*, pg. 1432
THE ETICA GROUP INC.; *U.S. Public*, pg. 4027
ETICO PARTNERS, LLC—See Quaestus Holdings, LLC; *U.S. Private*, pg. 3316
E-TIC SISTEMES S.L.U.—See Alten S.A.; *Int'l*, pg. 390
ETI DE GMBH—See Andlinger & Company, Inc.; *U.S. Private*, pg. 278
ETI ELB S.R.O.—See Andlinger & Company, Inc.; *U.S. Private*, pg. 278
ETI ELEKTROELEMENT, D.D.—See Andlinger & Company, Inc.; *U.S. Private*, pg. 278
ETIENNE AIGNER, INC.—See The Hartstone Group Limited; *Int'l*, pg. 7652
ETIHAD AIRWAYS P.J.S.C.; *Int'l*, pg. 2523
ETIHAD ATHEEB TELECOM COMPANY—See Atheeb Group; *Int'l*, pg. 669
ETIHAD ATHEEB TELECOMMUNICATION CO; *Int'l*, pg. 2523
ETIHAD CAPITAL PJSC—See Naeem Holding; *Int'l*, pg. 5124
ETIHAD ETISALAT COMPANY; *Int'l*, pg. 2523
ETIHAD INTERNATIONAL HOSPITALITY LLC - SOLE PROPRIETORSHIP LLC—See Alpha Dhabi Holding PJSC; *Int'l*, pg. 367
ETIKA BEVERAGES SDN. BHD.—See Envictus International Holdings Limited; *Int'l*, pg. 2453
ETIKA DAIRIES NZ LIMITED—See Envictus International Holdings Limited; *Int'l*, pg. 2453
ETIKA DAIRIES SDN. BHD.—See Asahi Group Holdings Ltd.; *Int'l*, pg. 593
ETILAM S.A.—See ArcelorMittal S.A.; *Int'l*, pg. 545
ETILER GIDA VE TICARI YATIRIMLAR SAN VE TIC A.S.; *Int'l*, pg. 2523
ETIL SA—See Viohalco SA/NV; *Int'l*, pg. 8243
ETIMEX GMBH; *Int'l*, pg. 2523
ETIMEX PRIMARY PACKAGING GMBH—See Etimex GmbH; *Int'l*, pg. 2523
ETIMEX TECHNICAL COMPONENTS GMBH—See Etimex GmbH; *Int'l*, pg. 2523
ETIMEX USA, INC.—See Etimex GmbH; *Int'l*, pg. 2523
ETINPRO (BEIJING) CO., LTD.—See Beijing Kawin Technology Share-Holding Co., Ltd.; *Int'l*, pg. 954
ET INTERNATIONAL LTD; *U.S. Private*, pg. 1431
ETION CONNECT (PTY) LTD.—See Etion Limited; *Int'l*, pg. 2523
ETION LIMITED; *Int'l*, pg. 2523
ETIPACK AMERICA, INDUSTRIA, COMERCIO E REPRESENTACOES LTDA.—See L. Possehl & Co. mbH; *Int'l*, pg. 4382
ETIPACK B.V.—See L. Possehl & Co. mbH; *Int'l*, pg. 4382
ETIPACK S.P.A—See L. Possehl & Co. mbH; *Int'l*, pg. 4382
ETI POLAM SP.ZO.O.—See Andlinger & Company, Inc.; *U.S. Private*, pg. 278
ETIQA GENERAL INSURANCE BERHAD—See Malayan Banking Berhad; *Int'l*, pg. 4659
ETIQA GENERAL INSURANCE (CAMBODIA) PLC.—See Malayan Banking Berhad; *Int'l*, pg. 4659
ETIQA INSURANCE PTE. LTD.—See Malayan Banking Berhad; *Int'l*, pg. 4659
ETIQA INSURANCE & TAKAFUL BERHAD—See Malayan Banking Berhad; *Int'l*, pg. 4659
ETIQA LIFE & GENERAL ASSURANCE PHILIPPINES INC.—See Malayan Banking Berhad; *Int'l*, pg. 4660
ETIQA LIFE INSURANCE (CAMBODIA) PLC.—See Malayan Banking Berhad; *Int'l*, pg. 4660
ETIQA OFFSHORE INSURANCE (L) LTD.—See Malayan Banking Berhad; *Int'l*, pg. 4660
ETIQUETAS CCL S.A. DE C.V.—See CCL Industries Inc.; *Int'l*, pg. 1368
ETIREX SAS—See Spirax-Sarco Engineering plc; *Int'l*, pg. 7137
ETI SARAJEVO D.O.O.—See Andlinger & Company, Inc.; *U.S. Private*, pg. 278
ETI SOLID STATE LIGHTING INC.—See NVC International Holdings Limited; *Int'l*, pg. 5497
ETISON LLC; *U.S. Private*, pg. 1432
ETI UKRAINE LTD.—See Andlinger & Company, Inc.; *U.S. Private*, pg. 278
E-TIVITY CORPORATION (APAC) PTY. LTD.—See Tambla Limited; *Int'l*, pg. 7449
ETKIN EQUITIES; *U.S. Private*, pg. 1432
ETKON GMBH—See Straumann Holding AG; *Int'l*, pg. 7238
ETKON (SCHWEIZ) AG—See Straumann Holding AG; *Int'l*, pg. 7237
ETLA LIMITED—See Frencken Group Limited; *Int'l*, pg. 2772

COMPANY NAME INDEX

ETLA TECHNOLOGY (M) SDN.BHD.—See Frencken Group Limited; *Int'l*, pg. 2772
ETLA TECHNOLOGY (WUXI) CO.,LTD.—See Frencken Group Limited; *Int'l*, pg. 2772
E.T. MACKENZIE COMPANY INC.; *U.S. Private*, pg. 1307
E T MACKENZIE OF FLORIDA INC—See E.T. Mackenzie Company Inc.; *U.S. Private*, pg. 1307
ETM-ELECTROMATIC INC.; *U.S. Private*, pg. 1432
E-T-M ENTERPRISES INC.; *U.S. Private*, pg. 1303
ET MEXICO HOLDINGS II, S. DE R.L. DE C.V.—See Stellantis N.V.; *Int'l*, pg. 7201
ETM MANUFACTURING; *U.S. Private*, pg. 1432
ETM PROFESSIONAL CONTROL GMBH—See Siemens Aktiengesellschaft; *Int'l*, pg. 6886
ETM TRAVEL PTY LTD.—See Corporate Travel Management Limited; *Int'l*, pg. 1805
ETNA BIOTECH S.R.L.—See Zydus Lifesciences Limited; *Int'l*, pg. 8700
ETNA PRODUCTS CO. INC.; *U.S. Private*, pg. 1432
ETNA SHARED SERVICES; *U.S. Private*, pg. 1432
ET NET LIMITED—See Hong Kong Economic Times Holdings Ltd; *Int'l*, pg. 3465
ET NET NEWS AGENCY LIMITED—See Hong Kong Economic Times Holdings Ltd; *Int'l*, pg. 3465
ETNYRE INTERNATIONAL LTD. INC.; *U.S. Private*, pg. 1432
ETOBICOKE IRONWORKS LIMITED; *Int'l*, pg. 2524
ETO GRUPPE BETEILIGUNGEN GMBH; *Int'l*, pg. 2524
ETOL AROMA VE BAHARAT GIDA URUNLERI SAN.VE TIC.A.S.—See International Flavors & Fragrances Inc.; *U.S. Public*, pg. 1151
ETOL D.D.—See International Flavors & Fragrances Inc.; *U.S. Public*, pg. 1152
ETOL JVE D.O.O.—See International Flavors & Fragrances Inc.; *U.S. Public*, pg. 1152
E-TOLL SERVICES HUNGARY, KFT.—See W.A.G Payment Solutions Plc; *Int'l*, pg. 8321
ETOL RUS, LTD.—See International Flavors & Fragrances Inc.; *U.S. Public*, pg. 1152
ETOL SK S.R.O.—See International Flavors & Fragrances Inc.; *U.S. Public*, pg. 1152
ETOL UKRAJINA TZOV—See International Flavors & Fragrances Inc.; *U.S. Public*, pg. 1152
ETO MAGNETIC CORP.—See ETO GRUPPE Beteiligungen GmbH; *Int'l*, pg. 2524
ETON AB—See EQT AB; *Int'l*, pg. 2475
ETON BIOSCIENCE INC.—See Telesis Bio, Inc.; *U.S. Public*, pg. 1998
ETONE INDIA PRIVATE LIMITED—See Shilp Gravures Ltd; *Int'l*, pg. 6831
ETON PHARMACEUTICALS, INC.; *U.S. Public*, pg. 797
ETON PROPERTIES PHILIPPINES, INC.—See LT Group, Inc.; *Int'l*, pg. 4571
E-TON SOLAR TECH. CO., LTD.—See Inventec Corporation; *Int'l*, pg. 3773
ETO PRECISION (MALAYSIA) SDN. BHD.—See Kyokuto Boeki Kaisha, Ltd.; *Int'l*, pg. 4362
E-TOP UNION INC.—See LEAD DATA INC.; *Int'l*, pg. 4432
E-TOP (VIETNAM) CO., LTD.—See Eclat Textile Co., Ltd.; *Int'l*, pg. 2291
ETOS B.V.—See Koninklijke Ahold Delhaize N.V.; *Int'l*, pg. 4260
ETOS B.V.—See Koninklijke Ahold Delhaize N.V.; *Int'l*, pg. 4260
ETOS B.V.—See Koninklijke Ahold Delhaize N.V.; *Int'l*, pg. 4260
ETOS B.V.—See Koninklijke Ahold Delhaize N.V.; *Int'l*, pg. 4260
ETOWAH DIALYSIS, LLC—See DaVita Inc.; *U.S. Public*, pg. 638
E&T PLASTIC MANUFACTURING CO.; *U.S. Private*, pg. 1301
ETP TRANSMISSION AB—See Indutrade AB; *Int'l*, pg. 3678
ET PUBLISHING INTERNATIONAL, LLC—See Grupo Televisa, S.A.B.; *Int'l*, pg. 3136
ETR1 GROUP OU—See BHG Group AB; *Int'l*, pg. 1014
ETRA BALTI AS—See Oy Etra AB; *Int'l*, pg. 5676
E*TRADE BANK—See E*TRADE Financial Corporation; *U.S. Private*, pg. 1302
E*TRADE CAPITAL MANAGEMENT, LLC—See E*TRADE Financial Corporation; *U.S. Private*, pg. 1302
E*TRADE FINANCIAL CORPORATION; *U.S. Private*, pg. 1302
E*TRADE SECURITIES LLC—See E*TRADE Financial Corporation; *U.S. Private*, pg. 1302
ETRA ENERGIA S.R.L.—See Ascopiave S.p.A.; *Int'l*, pg. 603
ETRA INTERANDINA, S.A.—See ACS, Actividades de Construccion y Servicios, S.A.; *Int'l*, pg. 112
ETRA INVESTIGACION Y DESARROLLO, S.A.—See ACS, Actividades de Construccion y Servicios, S.A.; *Int'l*, pg. 112
ETRALUX, S.A.—See ACS, Actividades de Construccion y Servicios, S.A.; *Int'l*, pg. 112
ETRANORTE, S.A.—See ACS, Actividades de Construccion y Servicios, S.A.; *Int'l*, pg. 112
ETRANSERVICES, LLC; *U.S. Private*, pg. 1432

ETRANSMEDIA TECHNOLOGY INC.—See Northwell Health, Inc.; *U.S. Private*, pg. 2958
ETRANSMEDIA TECHNOLOGY INC.—See Pamplona Capital Management LLP; *Int'l*, pg. 5711
E-TRANZACT INTERNATIONAL PLC.; *Int'l*, pg. 2249
ETRATECH ASIA-PACIFIC ELECTRONICS (SHENZHEN) LTD.—See Gentherm Incorporated; *U.S. Public*, pg. 931
ETRATECH ASIA-PACIFIC LIMITED—See Gentherm Incorporated; *U.S. Public*, pg. 931
ETREA SA—See CSL Limited; *Int'l*, pg. 1866
ETREND HIGHTECH CORP.; *Int'l*, pg. 2524
ETRE REIT, LLC; *U.S. Private*, pg. 1432
E-TRIAL CO., LTD.—See EPS Holdings, Inc.; *Int'l*, pg. 2465
ETRIGUE CORPORATION; *U.S. Private*, pg. 1432
E-TRINITY N.V.—See Cegeka Groep NV; *Int'l*, pg. 1391
ETRION CORPORATION; *Int'l*, pg. 2524
ETRION SERVICES JAPAN KK—See Etrion Corporation; *Int'l*, pg. 2524
E-TRON CO., LTD; *Int'l*, pg. 2249
ETRONICS, INC.—See Foto Electric Supply Co., Inc.; *U.S. Private*, pg. 1579
ETROPAL JSC; *Int'l*, pg. 2524
ETRO S.P.A.; *Int'l*, pg. 2524
ETRO USA INC.—See Etro S.p.A.; *Int'l*, pg. 2524
ETROVISION TECHNOLOGY CO., LTD.—See Chung-Hsin Electric & Machinery Manufacturing Corp.; *Int'l*, pg. 1597
ETR; *U.S. Private*, pg. 1432
ETRURIA INFORMATICA SRL—See Banca Popolare dell'Etruria e del Lazio S.C.; *Int'l*, pg. 815
ETRUSCO GMBH—See Thor Industries, Inc.; *U.S. Public*, pg. 2156
ETRUSCUS RESOURCES CORP.; *Int'l*, pg. 2524
ETS ANTOINE FOURNIER—See Vicat S.A.; *Int'l*, pg. 8185
ETS EFFICIENT TECHNICAL SOLUTIONS GMBH—See CEZ, a.s.; *Int'l*, pg. 1427
ETS GEORGES RENAULT S.A.S.—See Atlas Copco AB; *Int'l*, pg. 678
ETS GROUP LIMITED; *Int'l*, pg. 2524
ETS HOLDINGS CO., LTD.; *Int'l*, pg. 2524
E.T. SIMONDS CONSTRUCTION COMPANY; *U.S. Private*, pg. 1307
ETS INGENIERIA SAS—See Hydac International GmbH; *Int'l*, pg. 3544
ETS INTERNATIONAL; *U.S. Private*, pg. 1432
ETS LINDGREN ENGINEERING INDIA PRIVATE LIMITED—See ESCO Technologies, Inc.; *U.S. Public*, pg. 793
ETS-LINDGREN GMBH—See ESCO Technologies, Inc.; *U.S. Public*, pg. 794
ETS-LINDGREN INC.—See ESCO Technologies, Inc.; *U.S. Public*, pg. 794
ETS LINDGREN JAPAN, INC.—See ESCO Technologies, Inc.; *U.S. Public*, pg. 794
ETS-LINDGREN LIMITED—See ESCO Technologies, Inc.; *U.S. Public*, pg. 794
ETS-LINDGREN, L.P.—See ESCO Technologies, Inc.; *U.S. Public*, pg. 793
ETS-LINDGREN OY—See ESCO Technologies, Inc.; *U.S. Public*, pg. 794
ETS. L. LACROIX FILS N.V—See Imperial Brands PLC; *Int'l*, pg. 3633
ETS MOUSSIER; *Int'l*, pg. 2524
ET SOFTWARE DEVELOPMENTS GMBH—See Fresenius Medical Care AG; *Int'l*, pg. 2774
ETS PIERRE KESS ET FILS S.A.—See The Brink's Company; *U.S. Public*, pg. 2043
ETS (PORTSMOUTH) LIMITED—See Addtech AB; *Int'l*, pg. 133
ETS RAOUL LENOIR SAS—See CVC Capital Partners SICAV-FIS S.A.; *Int'l*, pg. 1887
ETS RAYMOND BARRE; *Int'l*, pg. 2524
ETS S.A.S—See Montagne et Neige Developpement SA; *Int'l*, pg. 5035
ETS SZYMANSKI SAS—See Sonepar S.A.; *Int'l*, pg. 7090
ETSURYO CO., LTD.—See Mitsubishi Chemical Group Corporation; *Int'l*, pg. 4931
ETSY, INC.; *U.S. Public*, pg. 797
ETTAIN GROUP INC.—See ManpowerGroup Inc.; *U.S. Public*, pg. 1362
ET TECHTONICS, INC.—See Hill & Smith PLC; *Int'l*, pg. 3391
ETTE-CONSULTING OY—See Etteplan Oyj; *Int'l*, pg. 2524
ETTE-ENGINEERING OY—See Etteplan Oyj; *Int'l*, pg. 2524
ETTEPLAN B.V.—See Etteplan Oyj; *Int'l*, pg. 2524
ETTEPLAN CONSULTING (SHANGHAI) CO., LTD—See Etteplan Oyj; *Int'l*, pg. 2524
ETTEPLAN DENMARK A/S—See Etteplan Oyj; *Int'l*, pg. 2524
ETTEPLAN DESIGN CENTER OY—See Etteplan Oyj; *Int'l*, pg. 2524
ETTEPLAN DEUTSCHLAND GMBH—See Etteplan Oyj; *Int'l*, pg. 2524
ETTEPLAN ENGINEERING SOLUTIONS NETHERLANDS B.V.—See Etteplan Oyj; *Int'l*, pg. 2524

ETTEPLAN GERMANY GMBH—See Etteplan Oyj; *Int'l*, pg. 2524
ETTEPLAN INDUSTRITEKNIK AB—See Etteplan Oyj; *Int'l*, pg. 2525
ETTEPLAN INDUSTRY AB—See Etteplan Oyj; *Int'l*, pg. 2525
ETTEPLAN OYJ; *Int'l*, pg. 2524
ETTEPLAN—See Etteplan Oyj; *Int'l*, pg. 2524
ETTEPLAN SWEDEN AB—See Etteplan Oyj; *Int'l*, pg. 2525
ETTEPLAN TECHNICAL SYSTEMS AB—See Etteplan Oyj; *Int'l*, pg. 2525
ETTEPLAN TECHNOLOGY CENTER LTD.—See Etteplan Oyj; *Int'l*, pg. 2525
ETTEPLAN TECH POLAND S.A.—See Etteplan Oyj; *Int'l*, pg. 2525
ETTEPLAN USA INC.—See Etteplan Oyj; *Int'l*, pg. 2525
ETTIKETTOPRINTCOM AB—See Volati AB; *Int'l*, pg. 8300
ETTIKETTOPRINTCOM ATVIDABERG AB—See Volati AB; *Int'l*, pg. 8300
ETTLESON CADILLAC-BUICK-GMC, INC.; *U.S. Private*, pg. 1432
ETT LIMITED; *Int'l*, pg. 2524
ETTLINGER KUNSTSTOFFMASCHINEN GMBH—See Dover Corporation; *U.S. Public*, pg. 681
ETTLINGER NORTH AMERICA LP—See Dover Corporation; *U.S. Public*, pg. 681
ETT PROYECTOS S.A.—See AFRY AB; *Int'l*, pg. 195
ET TRADE LIMITED—See Hong Kong Economic Times Holdings Ltd; *Int'l*, pg. 3465
ETTYL LIMITED; *Int'l*, pg. 2525
ETUA OY—See Alma Media Corporation; *Int'l*, pg. 362
ETUBICS CORPORATION—See NantWorks, LLC; *U.S. Private*, pg. 2833
ETUDES INSTALLATIONS ET MAINTENANCE INDUSTRIELLES SAS; *Int'l*, pg. 2525
ETUDE WINES, INC—See Treasury Wine Estates Limited; *Int'l*, pg. 7909
ETUDIBEL S.A.—See Ascencio S.A.; *Int'l*, pg. 601
ETVA INDUSTRIAL PARKS S.A.—See Piraeus Financial Holdings S.A.; *Int'l*, pg. 5873
ETV-EROTERV RT.—See AFRY AB; *Int'l*, pg. 195
ETVISION MULTIMEDIA LIMITED—See Hong Kong Economic Times Holdings Ltd; *Int'l*, pg. 3465
E.TV (PROPRIETARY) LIMITED—See Hosken Consolidated Investments Limited; *Int'l*, pg. 3485
ET WATER SYSTEMS, INC.—See Jain Irrigation Systems Limited; *Int'l*, pg. 3872
ET WEALTH LIMITED—See Hong Kong Economic Times Holdings Ltd; *Int'l*, pg. 3465
ETX HOLDINGS, INC.—See Blue Point Capital Partners, LLC; *U.S. Private*, pg. 590
ETX INC.—See El Toro Export; *U.S. Private*, pg. 1349
ETYPE-OMNITECH LTD.—See Malam-Team Ltd.; *Int'l*, pg. 4659
ETZ D.D.—See INSTITUT IGH d.d.; *Int'l*, pg. 3723
ETZELWERK AG—See Schweizerische Bundesbahnen SBB AG; *Int'l*, pg. 6646
EUBANK FUNERAL HOME, INC.—See Service Corporation International; *U.S. Public*, pg. 1870
EUBIOCO S.A.—See CEPD N.V.; *Int'l*, pg. 1420
EUBIOLOGICS CO., LTD.; *Int'l*, pg. 2525
EUCA SANITIZING TECHNOLOGY COMPANY LIMITED—See Yips Chemical Holdings Limited; *Int'l*, pg. 8585
EUCATEX OF NORTH AMERICA, INC—See Eucatex S.A. Industria e Comercio; *Int'l*, pg. 2525
EUCATEX S.A. INDUSTRIA E COMERCIO - EUCATEX PAINTS AND VARNISHES PLANT—See Eucatex S.A. Industria e Comercio; *Int'l*, pg. 2525
EUCATEX S.A. INDUSTRIA E COMERCIO - FIBERBOARD FACILITY—See Eucatex S.A. Industria e Comercio; *Int'l*, pg. 2525
EUCATEX S.A. INDUSTRIA E COMERCIO - MDP AND LAMINATE FLOORING FACITLITY—See Eucatex S.A. Industria e Comercio; *Int'l*, pg. 2525
EUCATEX S.A. INDUSTRIA E COMERCIO - SEEDLINGS NURSERY UNIT—See Eucatex S.A. Industria e Comercio; *Int'l*, pg. 2525
EUCATEX S.A. INDUSTRIA E COMERCIO; *Int'l*, pg. 2525
EUCATEX TINTAS E VERNIZES LTDA.—See Eucatex S.A. Industria e Comercio; *Int'l*, pg. 2525
EUCERA SPA—See Monrif S.p.A.; *Int'l*, pg. 5035
EUCLID ADMIXTURE CANADA INC.—See RPM International Inc.; *U.S. Public*, pg. 1816
EUCLID ADVISORS LLC—See Virtus Investment Partners, Inc.; *U.S. Public*, pg. 2301
THE EUCLID CHEMICAL COMPANY—See RPM International Inc.; *U.S. Public*, pg. 1818
THE EUCLID CHEMICAL COMPANY—See RPM International Inc.; *U.S. Public*, pg. 1818
EUCLID INDUSTRIES INC.; *U.S. Private*, pg. 1432
EUCLID INSURANCE SERVICES, INC.; *U.S. Private*, pg. 1433
EUCLID LABS S.R.L.; *Int'l*, pg. 2525
EUCLID UNIVERSAL CORP.—See Jordan Industries, Inc.; *U.S. Private*, pg. 2235
EUCLYDE DATA CENTERS SAS—See I Squared Capital Advisors (US) LLC; *U.S. Private*, pg. 2025

EUCLYDE DC2—See I Squared Capital Advisors (US) LLC; *U.S. Private*, pg. 2025
EUCODIS BIOSCIENCE GMBH; *Int'l*, pg. 2525
EUCON CORPORATION; *U.S. Private*, pg. 1433
EUCON SHIPPING & TRANSPORT LTD.—See Irish Continental Group plc; *Int'l*, pg. 3809
EUCONUS FLUGZEUGLEASINGGESELLSCHAFT MBH—See Air Berlin PLC & Co. Luftverkehrs KG; *Int'l*, pg. 236
EUCRATES BIOMEDICAL ACQUISITION CORP.; *U.S. Public*, pg. 797
EUDA HEALTH HOLDINGS LIMITED; *Int'l*, pg. 2525
EUDA HEALTH LTD.—See EUDA Health Holdings Limited; *Int'l*, pg. 2526
EUE/SCREEN GEMS LTD.; *U.S. Private*, pg. 1433
EUFAULA DIALYSIS, LLC—See DaVita Inc.; *U.S. Public*, pg. 638
EUFORES, S.A.—See AntarChile S.A.; *Int'l*, pg. 481
EUFORES, S.A.—See Stora Enso Oyj; *Int'l*, pg. 7222
EUGENE ALLARD CUISINE ET TENDANCES; *Int'l*, pg. 2526
EUGENE ALLARD PRODUITS D'EMBALLAGE & D'ENTRETIEN INC—See Bain Capital, LP; *U.S. Private*, pg. 440
EUGENE BIRO CORP.; *U.S. Private*, pg. 1433
EUGENE B. SMITH & CO. INC.; *U.S. Private*, pg. 1433
EUGENE BURGER MANAGEMENT CORP.; *U.S. Private*, pg. 1433
EUGENE CORPORATION; *Int'l*, pg. 2526
EUGENE ENGINEERING CO. LIMITED—See Hitachi, Ltd.; *Int'l*, pg. 3412
EUGENE FREEZING & STORAGE CO.; *U.S. Private*, pg. 1433
EUGENE INVESTMENT & FUTURES CO., LTD.—See Eugene Investment & Securities Co., Ltd.; *Int'l*, pg. 2526
EUGENE INVESTMENT & SECURITIES CO., LTD.; *Int'l*, pg. 2526
EUGENE RACANELLI INC.; *U.S. Private*, pg. 1433
EUGENE SAND & GRAVEL, INC.—See CRH plc; *Int'l*, pg. 1847
EUGENE SPECIAL PURPOSE ACQUISITION 3 CO., LTD; *Int'l*, pg. 2526
EUGENE TECHNOLOGY CO., LTD.; *Int'l*, pg. 2526
EUGEN LAGLER GMBH; *Int'l*, pg. 2526
EUGLENA CO., LTD.; *Int'l*, pg. 2526
EUKALIN SPEZIAL-KLEBSTOFF FABRIK GMBH; *Int'l*, pg. 2526
EUKEDOS S.P.A.; *Int'l*, pg. 2526
EUKLEIA TRAINING LIMITED—See Learning Technologies Group plc; *Int'l*, pg. 4435
EUKLID SOFTWARE GMBH—See Mensch und Maschine Software SE; *Int'l*, pg. 4817
EULER GESTION—See Allianz SE; *Int'l*, pg. 352
EULER HERMES ACI—See Allianz SE; *Int'l*, pg. 352
EULER HERMES ACMAR SA—See Allianz SE; *Int'l*, pg. 352
EULER HERMES AKTIENGESELLSCHAFT—See Allianz SE; *Int'l*, pg. 352
EULER HERMES AUSTRALIA PTY LTD.—See Allianz SE; *Int'l*, pg. 352
EULER HERMES CESCOB SERVICE, S.R.O.—See Allianz SE; *Int'l*, pg. 352
EULER HERMES CESCOB UVEROVA POJISTOVNA A.S.—See Allianz SE; *Int'l*, pg. 352
EULER HERMES COLLECTIONS GMBH—See Allianz SE; *Int'l*, pg. 352
EULER HERMES COLLECTIONS SP. Z O.O.—See Allianz SE; *Int'l*, pg. 352
EULER HERMES COLLECTIONS UK LIMITED—See Allianz SE; *Int'l*, pg. 352
EULER HERMES COLOMBIA—See Allianz SE; *Int'l*, pg. 352
EULER HERMES CONSULTING (SHANGHAI) CO., LTD.—See Allianz SE; *Int'l*, pg. 352
EULER HERMES CREDIT INSURANCE NORDIC AB—See Allianz SE; *Int'l*, pg. 352
EULER HERMES CREDIT MANAGEMENT OOO—See Allianz SE; *Int'l*, pg. 352
EULER HERMES CREDIT MANAGEMENT SERVICES IRELAND LTD—See Allianz SE; *Int'l*, pg. 352
EULER HERMES CREDIT SERVICES (JP) LTD.—See Allianz SE; *Int'l*, pg. 352
EULER HERMES DANMARK—See Allianz SE; *Int'l*, pg. 352
EULER HERMES DEUTSCHLAND AG—See Allianz SE; *Int'l*, pg. 352
EULER HERMES EMPORIKI S.A.—See Allianz SE; *Int'l*, pg. 352
EULER HERMES EUROPE SA—See Allianz SE; *Int'l*, pg. 352
EULER HERMES FORDERUNGSMANAGEMENT GMBH—See Allianz SE; *Int'l*, pg. 352
EULER HERMES GROUP SA—See Allianz SE; *Int'l*, pg. 352
EULER HERMES HELLAS CREDIT INSURANCE SA—See Allianz SE; *Int'l*, pg. 352
EULER HERMES HOLDINGS UK PLC—See Allianz SE; *Int'l*, pg. 352

EULER HERMES HONG KONG SERVICE LIMITED—See Allianz SE; *Int'l*, pg. 353
EULER HERMES HONG KONG SERVICES LTD.—See Allianz SE; *Int'l*, pg. 352
EULER HERMES INDIA PVT. LTD.—See Allianz SE; *Int'l*, pg. 352
EULER HERMES IRELAND—See Allianz SE; *Int'l*, pg. 352
EULER HERMES KOREA NON-LIFE BROKER COMPANY LIMITED—See Allianz SE; *Int'l*, pg. 353
EULER HERMES MAGYAR KOVETELESKEZELO KFT.—See Allianz SE; *Int'l*, pg. 352
EULER HERMES MANAGEMENT UK LIMITED—See Allianz SE; *Int'l*, pg. 352
EULER HERMES NEW ZEALAND LTD.—See Allianz SE; *Int'l*, pg. 352
EULER HERMES NORGE—See Allianz SE; *Int'l*, pg. 352
EULER HERMES NORTH AMERICA INSURANCE COMPANY—See Allianz SE; *Int'l*, pg. 352
EULER HERMES RATING DEUTSCHLAND GMBH—See Allianz SE; *Int'l*, pg. 353
EULER HERMES RATING GMBH—See Allianz SE; *Int'l*, pg. 353
EULER HERMES REINSURANCE AG—See Allianz SE; *Int'l*, pg. 353
EULER HERMES RISK SERVICES UK LIMITED—See Allianz SE; *Int'l*, pg. 353
EULER HERMES RISK YONETIMI VE DANISMANLIK HIZMETLERI LIMITED SIRKETI—See Allianz SE; *Int'l*, pg. 353
EULER HERMES SEGUROS DE CREDITO SA—See Allianz SE; *Int'l*, pg. 353
EULER HERMES SEGUROS S.A.—See Allianz SE; *Int'l*, pg. 353
EULER HERMES SERVICE AB—See Allianz SE; *Int'l*, pg. 353
EULER HERMES SERVICES AG—See Allianz SE; *Int'l*, pg. 353
EULER HERMES SERVICES BELGIUM S.A.—See Allianz SE; *Int'l*, pg. 353
EULER HERMES SERVICES B.V.—See Allianz SE; *Int'l*, pg. 353
EULER HERMES SERVICES INDIA PRIVATE LIMITED—See Allianz SE; *Int'l*, pg. 353
EULER HERMES SERVICES ITALIA S.R.L.—See Allianz SE; *Int'l*, pg. 353
EULER HERMES SERVICII FINANCIARE S.R.L.—See Allianz SE; *Int'l*, pg. 353
EULER HERMES SERVICIOS S.A.—See Allianz SE; *Int'l*, pg. 353
EULER HERMES SERVICOS DE GESTAO DE RISCOS LTDA.—See Allianz SE; *Int'l*, pg. 353
EULER HERMES SFAC RECOUVREMENT S.A.S.—See Allianz SE; *Int'l*, pg. 353
EULER HERMES SFAC—See Allianz SE; *Int'l*, pg. 353
EULER HERMES SIGORTA A.S.—See Allianz SE; *Int'l*, pg. 353
EULER HERMES SINGAPORE SERVICES PTE LTD.—See Allianz SE; *Int'l*, pg. 353
EULER HERMES SUOMI—See Allianz SE; *Int'l*, pg. 353
EULER HERMES SVERIGE—See Allianz SE; *Int'l*, pg. 353
EULER HERMES TRADE CREDIT LIMITED—See Allianz SE; *Int'l*, pg. 353
EULER HERMES TRADE CREDIT UNDERWRITING AGENTS PTY LTD—See Allianz SE; *Int'l*, pg. 353
EULER HERMES UMA INC—See Allianz SE; *Int'l*, pg. 353
EULER HERMES WORLD AGENCY SASU—See Allianz SE; *Int'l*, pg. 353
EULER SFAC ASSET MANAGEMENT—See Allianz SE; *Int'l*, pg. 353
EUMECOM MEDIZIN INFORMATION FORTBILDING GMBH—See GSK plc; *Int'l*, pg. 3145
EUMOVIL—See WPP plc; *Int'l*, pg. 8472
EUMUNDI GROUP LIMITED; *Int'l*, pg. 2526
EUNETWORKS B.V.—See Stonepeak Partners L.P.; *U.S. Private*, pg. 3830
EUNETWORKS FIBER UK LIMITED—See Stonepeak Partners L.P.; *U.S. Private*, pg. 3830
EUNETWORKS GMBH—See Stonepeak Partners L.P.; *U.S. Private*, pg. 3830
EUNETWORKS GROUP LIMITED—See Stonepeak Partners L.P.; *U.S. Private*, pg. 3830
EUNETWORKS IRELAND - PRIVATE FIBER LIMITED—See Stonepeak Partners L.P.; *U.S. Private*, pg. 3830
EUNISELL INTERLINKED PLC; *Int'l*, pg. 2526
EUNISURE LTD.—See Edwards Capital, LLC; *U.S. Private*, pg. 1341
EUPE CORPORATION BERHAD; *Int'l*, pg. 2526
EUPEC PIPECOATINGS FRANCE S.A.—See Mutares SE & Co. KGaA; *Int'l*, pg. 5104
EUPE GOLF MANAGEMENT BHD.—See Eupe Corporation Berhad; *Int'l*, pg. 2526
EUPEN CABLE USA INC.; *U.S. Private*, pg. 1433
EUPHALT-HANDELSGESELLSCHAFT M.B.H.—See PORR AG; *Int'l*, pg. 5922
EUPHORA COMMUNICATIONS S.P.A.; *Int'l*, pg. 2526
EUPHORIA ACQUISITION, LLC—See Lincoln Educational Services Corporation; *U.S. Public*, pg. 1316

EURACON PHARMA GMBH—See Laboratorios del Dr. Esteve, S.A.; *Int'l*, pg. 4390
EURAFRICA BAUGESELLSCHAFT MBH—See ACS, Actividades de Construccion y Servicios, S.A.; *Int'l*, pg. 113
EURAFRIQUE—See Seaboard Corporation; *U.S. Public*, pg. 1850
EURALIS COOP; *Int'l*, pg. 2527
EURALIS ESPACES VERTS—See Euralis Coop; *Int'l*, pg. 2527
EURALIS SAATEN GMBH—See Euralis Coop; *Int'l*, pg. 2527
EURALIS SEMENCES SAS—See Euralis Coop; *Int'l*, pg. 2527
EURALIS SEMILLAS, S.A.—See Euralis Coop; *Int'l*, pg. 2527
EURALLIAGE SAS—See Jacquet Metal Service SA; *Int'l*, pg. 3866
EURALLUMINA SPA—See United Company RUSAL Plc; *Int'l*, pg. 8066
EURAMEX MANAGEMENT GROUP, LLC; *U.S. Private*, pg. 1433
EURAPHARMA S.A.—See Toyota Tsusho Corporation; *Int'l*, pg. 7876
EURARCO FRANCE S.A.—See Heidelberg Materials AG; *Int'l*, pg. 3316
EURASIA CAPITAL—See Silk Road Capital Ltd.; *Int'l*, pg. 6921
EURASIA CONSULT—See ARCADIS N.V.; *Int'l*, pg. 541
EURASIA DRILLING COMPANY LIMITED; *Int'l*, pg. 2527
EURASIA ENERGY LIMITED; *Int'l*, pg. 2527
EURASIA FONCIERE INVESTISSEMENTS SA; *Int'l*, pg. 2527
EURASIA FOOD SERVICE CO., LTD.—See Teco Electric & Machinery Co., Ltd.; *Int'l*, pg. 7518
EURASIA GROUPE SA; *Int'l*, pg. 2527
EURASIA MINING PLC; *Int'l*, pg. 2527
EURASIAN BANK JSC; *Int'l*, pg. 2527
EURASIAN BANK PJSC—See Eurasian Bank JSC; *Int'l*, pg. 2527
EURASIAN DEVELOPMENT BANK; *Int'l*, pg. 2527
EURASIAN NATURAL RESOURCES CORPORATION LIMITED; *Int'l*, pg. 2527
EURASIA TRAVEL CO., LTD.; *Int'l*, pg. 2527
EURAUCHAN SAS—See Auchan Holding S.A.; *Int'l*, pg. 699
EURAWASSER AUFBEREITUNGS- UND ENTSORGUNGSGESELLSCHAFT LEUNA MBH—See RETHMANN AG & Co. KG; *Int'l*, pg. 6306
EURAWASSER AUFBEREITUNGS- UND ENTSORGUNGSGESELLSCHAFT SAALE-UNSTRUT, MBH—See RETHMANN AG & Co. KG; *Int'l*, pg. 6306
EURAWASSER AUFBEREITUNGS- UND ENTSORGUNGS GMBH—See RETHMANN AG & Co. KG; *Int'l*, pg. 6306
EURAWASSER BETRIEBSFUHRUNGSGESELLSCHAFT MBH—See RETHMANN AG & Co. KG; *Int'l*, pg. 6306
EURAWASSER NORD GMBH—See RETHMANN AG & Co. KG; *Int'l*, pg. 6306
EURAZEO NORTH AMERICA INC.—See Eurazeo SE; *Int'l*, pg. 2528
EURAZEO PME SAS—See Eurazeo SE; *Int'l*, pg. 2528
EURAZEO SE; *Int'l*, pg. 2527
EURCO LTD.—See Belfius Bank SA/NV; *Int'l*, pg. 963
EURCO RE LTD.—See Belfius Bank SA/NV; *Int'l*, pg. 963
EURCO SA—See Belfius Bank SA/NV; *Int'l*, pg. 963
EUREAM GMBH—See Commerzbank AG; *Int'l*, pg. 1718
EUREC A/S—See BEWi ASA; *Int'l*, pg. 1004
EUREKA 4WD TRAINING PTY. LTD.—See Engenco Limited; *Int'l*, pg. 2427
EUREKA 93 INC.; *Int'l*, pg. 2530
EUREKA CHEMICAL COMPANY; *U.S. Private*, pg. 1433
EUREKA DESIGN PUBLIC COMPANY LIMITED; *Int'l*, pg. 2530
EUREKA EQUITY PARTNERS, L.P.; *U.S. Private*, pg. 1433
EUREKA FINANCIAL GROUP PTY. LTD.—See Azimut Holding SpA; *Int'l*, pg. 779
EUREKA FORBES LIMITED—See Shapoorji Pallonji & Co. Ltd.; *Int'l*, pg. 6788
EUREKA GROUP HOLDINGS LIMITED; *Int'l*, pg. 2530
EUREKA HOMESTEAD BANCORP, INC.; *U.S. Public*, pg. 797
EUREKA INDUSTRIES LIMITED; *Int'l*, pg. 2530
EUREKA LITHIUM CORP.; *Int'l*, pg. 2530
EUREKA MATERIALS CO—See Breedon Group plc; *Int'l*, pg. 1144
EUREKA PUMP AS—See HitecVision AS; *Int'l*, pg. 3425
EUREKA PUMP AS—See HitecVision AS; *Int'l*, pg. 3425
EUREKA PUMPS AMERICAS, INC.—See HitecVision AS; *Int'l*, pg. 3425
EUREKA PUMPS AS - KRISTIANSUND—See HitecVision AS; *Int'l*, pg. 3425
EUREKA PUMPS AS—See HitecVision AS; *Int'l*, pg. 3425
EUREKA PUMPS AS—See HitecVision AS; *Int'l*, pg. 3425
EUREKA PUMPS AS - SORUMSAND—See HitecVision AS; *Int'l*, pg. 3425
EUREKA PUMPS AS - TANANGER—See HitecVision AS; *Int'l*, pg. 3425

COMPANY NAME INDEX

EUREKA PUMPS KOREA—See HitecVision AS; *Int'l*, pg. 3425
EUREKA SAVINGS BANK; *U.S. Private*, pg. 1433
EUREKA SPRINGS HOSPITAL HOSPICE, LLC—See UnitedHealth Group Incorporated; *U.S. Public*, pg. 2245
EUREKA SPRINGS HOSPITAL, LLC—See UnitedHealth Group Incorporated; *U.S. Public*, pg. 2245
EUREKA STONE QUARRY INC.; *U.S. Private*, pg. 1433
EUREKA WATER PROBES; *U.S. Private*, pg. 1433
EUREKING SA; *Int'l*, pg. 2530
EUREKO RE N.V.—See Achmea B.V.; *Int'l*, pg. 103
EUREKO SIGORTA A.S.—See Achmea B.V.; *Int'l*, pg. 103
EURELECTRIC TUNISIE S.A.—See Prysmian S.p.A.; *Int'l*, pg. 6012
EUREMIS HOLDING SA; *Int'l*, pg. 2530
EURENCO BOFORS AB—See GIAT Industries S.A.; *Int'l*, pg. 2962
EURENCO BOFORS, INC.—See GIAT Industries S.A.; *Int'l*, pg. 2962
EURENCO—See GIAT Industries S.A.; *Int'l*, pg. 2962
EURENTA HOLDING GMBH—See OVB Holding AG; *Int'l*, pg. 5670
EURESA-LIFE S.A.—See P&V Assurances SCRL; *Int'l*, pg. 5681
EUREST BREMEN GMBH—See Compass Group PLC; *Int'l*, pg. 1751
EUREST COLECTIVIDADES SA—See Compass Group PLC; *Int'l*, pg. 1751
EUREST DEUTSCHLAND GMBH—See Compass Group PLC; *Int'l*, pg. 1751
EUREST ETTEREMUZEMELTETO KORLATOLT FELELOSSEGU TARSASAG—See Compass Group PLC; *Int'l*, pg. 1751
EUREST LUXEMBOURG S.A.—See Compass Group PLC; *Int'l*, pg. 1751
EUREST NEDERLAND BV—See Compass Group PLC; *Int'l*, pg. 1751
EUREST (PORTUGAL) - SOCIEDADE EUROPEIA DE RESTAURANTES, LDA.—See Compass Group PLC; *Int'l*, pg. 1751
EUREST PROPER MEALS DE MEXICO S.A. DE C.V.—See Compass Group PLC; *Int'l*, pg. 1751
EUREST RESTAURATIONSBETRIEBSGESELLSCHAFT M.B.H—See Compass Group PLC; *Int'l*, pg. 1752
EUREST ROM SRL—See Compass Group PLC; *Int'l*, pg. 1752
EUREST SERVICES B.V.—See Compass Group PLC; *Int'l*, pg. 1752
EUREST SERVICES GMBH—See Compass Group PLC; *Int'l*, pg. 1751
EUREST SERVICES, INC.—See Compass Group PLC; *Int'l*, pg. 1751
EUREST UK LIMITED—See Compass Group PLC; *Int'l*, pg. 1752
EUREX CLEARING AG—See Deutsche Borse AG; *Int'l*, pg. 2063
EUREX FRANKFURT AG—See Deutsche Borse AG; *Int'l*, pg. 2063
EUREX GLOBAL DERIVATIVES AG—See Deutsche Borse AG; *Int'l*, pg. 2063
EUREX REPO GMBH—See Deutsche Borse AG; *Int'l*, pg. 2063
EUREX ZURICH AG—See Deutsche Borse AG; *Int'l*, pg. 2063
EURISOL S.A.—See ThyssenKrupp AG; *Int'l*, pg. 7724
EURISO-TOP GMBH—See Otsuka Holdings Co., Ltd.; *Int'l*, pg. 5659
EURISO-TOP S.A.S—See Otsuka Holdings Co., Ltd.; *Int'l*, pg. 5659
EURIZON ASSET MANAGEMENT CROATIA D.O.O.—See Intesa Sanpaolo S.p.A.; *Int'l*, pg. 3765
EURIZON ASSET MANAGEMENT HUNGARY LTD.—See Intesa Sanpaolo S.p.A.; *Int'l*, pg. 3765
EURIZON CAPITAL S.A.—See Intesa Sanpaolo S.p.A.; *Int'l*, pg. 3765
EURIZON CAPITAL S.G.R. S.P.A.—See Intesa Sanpaolo S.p.A.; *Int'l*, pg. 3765
EURIZON FINANCIAL GROUP—See Intesa Sanpaolo S.p.A.; *Int'l*, pg. 3765
EURIZON MEDIA—See Horizon Media, Inc.; *U.S. Private*, pg. 1982
EURIZON SLJ CAPITAL LTD.—See Intesa Sanpaolo S.p.A.; *Int'l*, pg. 3765
EURL GAMES WORKSHOP—See Games Workshop Group PLC; *Int'l*, pg. 2877
EURL LIEBHERR ALGERIE—See Liebherr-International AG; *Int'l*, pg. 4488
EURL METITO ALGERIE—See Metito Holdings Ltd.; *Int'l*, pg. 4854
EURO ACCIDENT LIVFORSAKRING AB—See The Allstate Corporation; *U.S. Public*, pg. 2033
EUROADRIA D.O.O.—See MKT Print d.d.; *Int'l*, pg. 5003
EURO ADVANCED CARBON FIBER COMPOSITES GMBH—See Toray Industries, Inc.; *Int'l*, pg. 7823
EURO - AGRO WARSZAWA SP. Z O.O.—See Sika AG; *Int'l*, pg. 6917
EUROALARM ASSISTANCE PRAGUE, S.R.O.—See Munchener Ruckversicherungs AG; *Int'l*, pg. 5088

EURO-AMERICAN FOODS GROUP CO., INC.; *U.S. Private*, pg. 1433
EUROAMERICA SEGUROS DE VIDA, S.A.; *Int'l*, pg. 2532
EUROAPI SAS; *Int'l*, pg. 2532
EURO ARAB INSURANCE; *Int'l*, pg. 2532
EURO ASIA COLD CHAIN LOGISTIC CO., LTD.—See DFDS A/S; *Int'l*, pg. 2095
EURO ASIA EXPORTS LIMITED; *Int'l*, pg. 2530
EUROASIAN VENTURES FZE—See Manaksia Ltd; *Int'l*, pg. 4667
EURO ASIA PACKAGING (GUANGDONG) CO., LTD.—See China Aluminum Cans Holdings Limited; *Int'l*, pg. 1482
EUROASIA TOTAL LOGISTICS PUBLIC COMPANY LIMITED—See WICE Logistics Public Company Limited; *Int'l*, pg. 8401
EUROASIA TRANSPORT COMPANY LIMITED—See WICE Logistics Public Company Limited; *Int'l*, pg. 8401
EUROASSET ITALIA S.R.L.—See Commerzbank AG; *Int'l*, pg. 1718
EUROATLAS GESELLSCHAFT FUR LEISTUNGSELEKTRONIK GMBH—See L3Harris Technologies, Inc.; *U.S. Public*, pg. 1281
EURO AUCTIONS (UK) LTD.—See Gardrum Holdings Limited; *Int'l*, pg. 2884
EURO AUTOMATION S.R.L.—See EuroGroup Laminations S.p.A.; *Int'l*, pg. 2552
EUROAVIONICS GMBH—See HENSOLDT AG; *Int'l*, pg. 3355
EUROAVIONICS SCHW EIZ AG—See HENSOLDT AG; *Int'l*, pg. 3355
EUROAVIONICS UK LTD—See Super Group Limited; *Int'l*, pg. 7334
EUROAVIONICS USA LLC—See HENSOLDT AG; *Int'l*, pg. 3355
EUROAVIONICS US HOLDCO. INC.—See HENSOLDT AG; *Int'l*, pg. 3355
EUROBANK BULGARIA AD—See Eurobank Ergasias Services and Holdings S.A.; *Int'l*, pg. 2532
EUROBANK CYPRUS LTD.—See Eurobank Ergasias Services and Holdings S.A.; *Int'l*, pg. 2532
EUROBANK DIREKTNA A.D—See Eurobank Ergasias Services and Holdings S.A.; *Int'l*, pg. 2532
EUROBANK EFG A.D. BELGRADE—See Eurobank Ergasias Services and Holdings S.A.; *Int'l*, pg. 2532
EUROBANK EFG BUSINESS SERVICES S.A.—See Eurobank Ergasias Services and Holdings S.A.; *Int'l*, pg. 2532
EUROBANK EFG CYPRUS LTD.—See Eurobank Ergasias Services and Holdings S.A.; *Int'l*, pg. 2532
EUROBANK EFG EQUITIES INVESTMENT FIRM S.A.—See Eurobank Ergasias Services and Holdings S.A.; *Int'l*, pg. 2532
EUROBANK EFG FACTORS S.A.—See Eurobank Ergasias Services and Holdings S.A.; *Int'l*, pg. 2532
EUROBANK EFG FUND MANAGEMENT COMPANY (LUXEMBOURG) S.A.—See Eurobank Ergasias Services and Holdings S.A.; *Int'l*, pg. 2532
EUROBANK EFG MUTUAL FUNDS MANAGEMENT COMPANY S.A.—See Eurobank Ergasias Services and Holdings S.A.; *Int'l*, pg. 2532
EUROBANK ERGASIAS SERVICES AND HOLDINGS S.A.; *Int'l*, pg. 2532
EUROBANK FIN AND RENT S.A.—See Eurobank Ergasias Services and Holdings S.A.; *Int'l*, pg. 2532
EUROBANK LEASING SINGLE-MEMBER SA—See Eurobank Ergasias Services and Holdings S.A.; *Int'l*, pg. 2532
EUROBANK PRIVATE BANK LUXEMBOURG SA—See Eurobank Ergasias Services and Holdings S.A.; *Int'l*, pg. 2532
EURO BANK SPOLKA AKCYJNA—See Banco Comercial Portugues, S.A.; *Int'l*, pg. 820
EUROBATTERY MINERALS AB; *Int'l*, pg. 2533
EURO BAT TRI—See Floridienne SA; *Int'l*, pg. 2708
EUROBET ITALIA SRL—See Entain PLC; *Int'l*, pg. 2450
EUROBIO SCIENTIFIC SA; *Int'l*, pg. 2533
EUROBRIDGE CONSULTING BV—See Dr. Reddy's Laboratories Limited; *Int'l*, pg. 2195
EURO BROADCAST HIRE A/S—See Egmont Fonden; *Int'l*, pg. 2325
EURO BROKERS MEXICO S.A. DE C.V.—See BGC Group, Inc.; *U.S. Public*, pg. 328
EUROBROKERS S.A.; *Int'l*, pg. 2533
EUROBUD ASFALTY SP Z O.O.—See VINCI S.A.; *Int'l*, pg. 8218
EUROCABLE—See Nexans S.A.; *Int'l*, pg. 5240
EUROCAM AUSTRALIA PTY LTD—See LOV Group Invest SAS; *Int'l*, pg. 4564
EUROCAMP TRAVEL AG—See Cox & Kings Limited; *Int'l*, pg. 1822
EUROCAMP TRAVEL B.V.—See Cox & Kings Limited; *Int'l*, pg. 1822
EURO CAPITAL SAS—See Groupe BPCE; *Int'l*, pg. 3094
EUROCAPS LIMITED—See DCC plc; *Int'l*, pg. 1990
EUROCARB PRODUCTS LTD.—See Hayleys PLC; *Int'l*, pg. 3291
EUROCARD AB—See Skandinaviska Enskilda Banken AB; *Int'l*, pg. 6977

EUROCOM CORPORATION

EURO CARGO RAIL SAS—See Deutsche Bahn AG; *Int'l*, pg. 2051
EURO CAR PARTS (NORTHERN IRELAND) LIMITED—See LKQ Corporation; *U.S. Public*, pg. 1334
EUROCASH S.A.; *Int'l*, pg. 2533
EUROCASTLE INVESTMENT LIMITED; *Int'l*, pg. 2533
EUROCAVE S.A.—See SCA Qualis; *Int'l*, pg. 6610
EUROCELL BUILDING PLASTICS LTD.—See Tessenderlo Group NV; *Int'l*, pg. 7574
EUROCELL PLC—See Tessenderlo Group NV; *Int'l*, pg. 7574
EUROCELL PROFILES LTD.—See Tessenderlo Group NV; *Int'l*, pg. 7574
EURO-CENTER CAPE TOWN (PTY.) LTD.—See Munchener Ruckversicherungs AG; *Int'l*, pg. 5088
EURO-CENTER CHINA (HK) CO., LTD.—See Munchener Ruckversicherungs AG; *Int'l*, pg. 5088
EURO-CENTER, S.A.—See Munchener Ruckversicherungs AG; *Int'l*, pg. 5088
EURO-CENTER (THAILAND) CO. LTD.—See Munchener Ruckversicherungs AG; *Int'l*, pg. 5088
EURO CENTER TRADE S.R.O.—See AMBRA S.A.; *Int'l*, pg. 415
EURO-CENTER USA, INC.—See Munchener Ruckversicherungs AG; *Int'l*, pg. 5088
EURO-CENTER YEREL YARDIM HIZMETLERI LTD. STI—See Munchener Ruckversicherungs AG; *Int'l*, pg. 5088
EUROCENTRUM OFFICES SP. Z O.O.—See CPI Property Group, S.A.; *Int'l*, pg. 1825
EURO CERAMICS LTD; *Int'l*, pg. 2530
EUROCERAMIC TECHNOLOGIES CO., LTD.—See ES Ceramics Technology Bhd; *Int'l*, pg. 2500
EURO-CGA SDN. BHD.—See Minho (M) Berhad; *Int'l*, pg. 4910
EUROCHAIN MANUFACTURER SDN. BHD.—See Mintye Industries Bhd.; *Int'l*, pg. 4914
EURO CHAIRS MANUFACTURER (M) SDN BHD.—See Euro Holdings Berhad; *Int'l*, pg. 2531
EUROCHARM HOLDINGS CO., LTD.; *Int'l*, pg. 2533
EUROCHARM INNOVATION CO., LTD.—See Eurocharm Holdings Co., Ltd.; *Int'l*, pg. 2533
EURO CHEESE VERTRIEBS-GMBH—See DMK Deutsches Milchkontor GmbH; *Int'l*, pg. 2146
EUROCHEM AGRO ASIA PTE. LTD.—See Kovdorskiy GOK JSC; *Int'l*, pg. 4293
EUROCHEM AGRO GMBH—See EuroChem Mineral Chemical Company, OJSC; *Int'l*, pg. 2533
EUROCHEM AGRO HELLAS SA—See EuroChem Mineral Chemical Company, OJSC; *Int'l*, pg. 2533
EUROCHEM AGRO HUNGARY KFT—See Kovdorskiy GOK JSC; *Int'l*, pg. 4293
EUROCHEM AGRO IBERIA, S.L.—See EuroChem Mineral Chemical Company, OJSC; *Int'l*, pg. 2533
EUROCHEM AGRO SAS—See Kovdorskiy GOK JSC; *Int'l*, pg. 4293
EUROCHEM AGRO SPA—See Kovdorskiy GOK JSC; *Int'l*, pg. 4293
EUROCHEM ANTWERPEN NV—See EuroChem Mineral Chemical Company, OJSC; *Int'l*, pg. 2533
EUROCHEM - BELORECHENSKIE MINUDOBRENIA, LLC—See EuroChem Mineral Chemical Company, OJSC; *Int'l*, pg. 2533
EUROCHEM COMERCIO DE PRODUTOS QUIMICOS LTDA—See EuroChem Mineral Chemical Company, OJSC; *Int'l*, pg. 2534
EUROCHEM-FERTILIZERS, LLP—See Kovdorskiy GOK JSC; *Int'l*, pg. 4293
EUROCHEM MINERAL CHEMICAL COMPANY, OJSC; *Int'l*, pg. 2533
EURO CHEMO-PHARMA SDN BHD; *Int'l*, pg. 2531
EUROCHEM SERVICE POLSKA SP. Z O.O.—See BRENNTAG SE; *Int'l*, pg. 1149
EUROCHEM TRADING GMBH—See EuroChem Mineral Chemical Company, OJSC; *Int'l*, pg. 2533
EUROCHEM TRADING RUS, LLC—See Kovdorskiy GOK JSC; *Int'l*, pg. 4293
EUROCHEM TRADING USA CORP.—See EuroChem Mineral Chemical Company, OJSC; *Int'l*, pg. 2534
EUROCHEM-VOLGAKALIY, LLC—See Kovdorskiy GOK JSC; *Int'l*, pg. 4293
EUROCKOT LAUNCH SERVICES GMBH—See Airbus SE; *Int'l*, pg. 247
EUROCKOT LAUNCH SERVICES GMBH—See The Khrunichev State Research & Production Space Centre; *Int'l*, pg. 7662
EUROCLEAR FINLAND OY—See Euroclear S.A./N.V.; *Int'l*, pg. 2534
EUROCLEAR S.A./N.V.; *Int'l*, pg. 2534
EUROCLEAR SWEDEN AB—See Euroclear S.A./N.V.; *Int'l*, pg. 2534
EUROCLEAR UK & IRELAND—See Euroclear S.A./N.V.; *Int'l*, pg. 2534
EUROCLINICUM AS—See Tuffieh Funds SICAV Plc; *Int'l*, pg. 7963
EUROCLONE S.P.A.—See AddLife AB; *Int'l*, pg. 129
EUROCOIN GAMING B.V.—See Novomatic AG; *Int'l*, pg. 5467
EUROCOM CORPORATION; *Int'l*, pg. 2534

EUROCOMMERCIAL PROPERTIES AZUR S.A.R.L—See Eurocommercial Properties N.V.; *Int'l*, pg. 2534
EUROCOMMERCIAL PROPERTIES CAUMARTIN S.N.C.—See Eurocommercial Properties N.V.; *Int'l*, pg. 2534
EUROCOMMERCIAL PROPERTIES ITALIA S.R.L.—See Eurocommercial Properties N.V.; *Int'l*, pg. 2534
EUROCOMMERCIAL PROPERTIES LTD—See Eurocommercial Properties N.V.; *Int'l*, pg. 2534
EUROCOMMERCIAL PROPERTIES N.V.; *Int'l*, pg. 2534
EUROCOMMERCIAL PROPERTIES SWEDEN AB—See Eurocommercial Properties N.V.; *Int'l*, pg. 2534
EUROCOMPONENTES, S.A.—See Arrow Electronics, Inc.; *U.S. Public*, pg. 199
EURO-CONCEPT B.V.—See Nippon Concept Corporation; *Int'l*, pg. 5313
EURO CONCEPT ETANCHEITE—See VINCI S.A.; *Int'l*, pg. 8219
EUROCONSULTANTS S.A.; *Int'l*, pg. 2534
EUROCONSULT MOTT MACDONALD—See Mott MacDonald Group Ltd.; *Int'l*, pg. 5054
EUROCONSULT MOTT MACDONALD—See Mott MacDonald Group Ltd.; *Int'l*, pg. 5055
EUROCONTROL, S.A.—See Tecnicas Reunidas, S.A.; *Int'l*, pg. 7515
EUROCOPTER CHILE SA—See Airbus SE; *Int'l*, pg. 243
EUROCOPTER CHINA CO LTD—See Airbus SE; *Int'l*, pg. 243
EUROCOPTER DE MEXICO S.A.—See Airbus SE; *Int'l*, pg. 244
EUROCOPTER DEUTSCHLAND GMBH—See Airbus SE; *Int'l*, pg. 243
EUROCOPTER ESPANA SA—See Airbus SE; *Int'l*, pg. 244
EUROCOPTER INDIA PVT LTD—See Airbus SE; *Int'l*, pg. 244
EUROCOPTER JAPAN CO.—See Airbus SE; *Int'l*, pg. 244
EUROCOPTER JAPAN RG CO. LTD.—See Airbus SE; *Int'l*, pg. 244
EUROCOPTER KHDS LIMITED—See Airbus SE; *Int'l*, pg. 243
EUROCOPTER PHILIPPINES INC.—See Airbus SE; *Int'l*, pg. 244
EUROCOPTER SOUTH EAST ASIA PTE. LTD.—See Airbus SE; *Int'l*, pg. 244
EUROCOPTER SOUTHERN AFRICA PTY. LTD.—See Airbus SE; *Int'l*, pg. 244
EUROCOPTER UK LTD.—See Airbus SE; *Int'l*, pg. 244
EUROCOPTER VOSTOK—See Airbus SE; *Int'l*, pg. 243
EUROCORE GP S.A R.L.—See Prudential Financial, Inc.; *U.S. Public*, pg. 1731
EUROCOR GMBH—See Opto Circuits (India) Limited; *Int'l*, pg. 5605
EUROCORSET SA—See Van de Velde N.V.; *Int'l*, pg. 8125
EURO-COSLIGHT GMBH—See Coslight Technology International Group Limited; *Int'l*, pg. 1810
EURO COSMETIC S.P.A.—See Fine Foods & Pharmaceuticals N.T.M. S.p.A.; *Int'l*, pg. 2673
EUROCOUSTIC—See Compagnie de Saint-Gobain SA; *Int'l*, pg. 1723
EUROCRANE (CHINA) CO., LTD.; *Int'l*, pg. 2534
EURO CREATIVE TOURS (U.K) LTD.—See Japan Airlines Co., Ltd.; *Int'l*, pg. 3881
EUROCRETA S.A.—See Creta Farm S.A.; *Int'l*, pg. 1842
EUROCROSS ASSISTANCE NETHERLANDS B.V.—See Achmea B.V.; *Int'l*, pg. 103
EUROCROSS INTERNATIONAL CENTRAL EUROPE S.R.O.—See Achmea B.V.; *Int'l*, pg. 103
EUROC TEST EQUIPMENT (GUANGDONG) CO., LTD.—See IMV CORPORATION; *Int'l*, pg. 3638
EURO-CYCLES SA; *Int'l*, pg. 2531
EURO-CYNK GDYNIA SP. Z O.O.—See Stocznia Gdynia S.A.; *Int'l*, pg. 7220
EUROCYPRIA AIRLINES LTD—See Cyprus Airways Public Limited; *Int'l*, pg. 1897
EURODECOUPE S.A.S.—See AG der Dillinger Huttenwerke; *Int'l*, pg. 197
EURO DEPOT ESPANA S.A.U—See Kingfisher plc; *Int'l*, pg. 4173
EURODEV BV; *Int'l*, pg. 2534
EURODEV SARL—See EuroDev BV; *Int'l*, pg. 2534
EURODIA INDUSTRIE S.A.—See Tokuyama Corporation; *Int'l*, pg. 7787
EURODIAL-CENTRO DE NEFROLOGIA E DIALISE DE LEIRIA, S.A.—See DaVita Inc.; *U.S. Public*, pg. 638
EURODIFARM S.R.L.—See Deutsche Post AG; *Int'l*, pg. 2080
EURODIF SA—See Orano SA; *Int'l*, pg. 5611
EURODIS GMBH—See Osterreichische Post AG; *Int'l*, pg. 5653
EURO DISNEY ASSOCIES SCA—See The Walt Disney Company; *U.S. Public*, pg. 2139
EURO DISNEY COMMANDITE SAS—See The Walt Disney Company; *U.S. Public*, pg. 2139
EURO DISNEY S.C.A.—See The Walt Disney Company; *U.S. Public*, pg. 2139
EURODIS S.A.S.—See Vivendi SE; *Int'l*, pg. 8276

EURO DISTRIBUTORS SDN BHD—See Carlsberg A/S; *Int'l*, pg. 1340
EURODONTIC LIMITED—See The British United Provident Association Limited; *Int'l*, pg. 7629
EURODOUGH S.A.S.—See Power Corporation of Canada; *Int'l*, pg. 5945
EURODRILL GMBH.—See BAUER Aktiengesellschaft; *Int'l*, pg. 893
EURODRIP A.V.E.G.E.—See Temasek Holdings (Private) Limited; *Int'l*, pg. 7550
EURO-DRUCKSERVICE GMBH—See DPE Deutsche Private Equity GmbH; *Int'l*, pg. 2188
EURODRY LTD.; *Int'l*, pg. 2534
EURODYN SPRENGMITTEL GMBH—See Orica Limited; *Int'l*, pg. 5620
EURO EKSPERTS AD; *Int'l*, pg. 2531
EUROELETTRO HAMMOND S.P.A—See Hammond Power Solutions Inc.; *Int'l*, pg. 3239
EURO-ELZETT KFT.—See Groupe SFPI SA; *Int'l*, pg. 3111
EUROENERGY GROUP—See Marcegaglia S.p.A.; *Int'l*, pg. 4688
EURO ENGINEERING AG—See Adecco Group AG; *Int'l*, pg. 141
EUROESPES S.A.; *Int'l*, pg. 2534
EURO-EXCELLENCE INC.—See Vivendi SE; *Int'l*, pg. 8275
EUROEYES APS—See EuroEyes International Eye Clinic Limited; *Int'l*, pg. 2535
EUROEYES AUGENLASERZENTRUM BERLIN GMBH—See EuroEyes International Eye Clinic Limited; *Int'l*, pg. 2535
EUROEYES AUGENLASERZENTRUM BREMEN GMBH—See EuroEyes International Eye Clinic Limited; *Int'l*, pg. 2535
EUROEYES AUGENLASERZENTRUM CITY HAMBURG GMBH—See EuroEyes International Eye Clinic Limited; *Int'l*, pg. 2535
EUROEYES AUGENLASERZENTRUM HANNOVER GMBH—See EuroEyes International Eye Clinic Limited; *Int'l*, pg. 2535
EUROEYES AUGENLASERZENTRUM STUTTGART GMBH—See EuroEyes International Eye Clinic Limited; *Int'l*, pg. 2535
EUROEYES DEUTSCHLAND HOLDING GMBH & CO. KG—See EuroEyes International Eye Clinic Limited; *Int'l*, pg. 2535
EUROEYES HONG KONG CO. LIMITED—See EuroEyes International Eye Clinic Limited; *Int'l*, pg. 2535
EUROEYES INTERNATIONAL EYE CLINIC LIMITED; *Int'l*, pg. 2534
EUROFACTORY GMBH—See Konecranes Plc; *Int'l*, pg. 4251
EURO FASHION INNERS INTERNATIONAL PRIVATE LIMITED—See Rupa & Co Limited; *Int'l*, pg. 6428
EUROFASHION LTDA—See Cencosud S.A.; *Int'l*, pg. 1400
EUROFEEDERS LTD.—See Irish Continental Group plc; *Int'l*, pg. 3809
EUROFIGHTER GMBH—See Airbus SE; *Int'l*, pg. 247
EUROFIL POLSKA SP. Z O. O.—See Saarstahl AG; *Int'l*, pg. 6461
EUROFIMA; *Int'l*, pg. 2535
EUROFINANCE INVESTMENT COMPANY JSC; *Int'l*, pg. 2535
EURO-FINANCE LTD.; *Int'l*, pg. 2531
EUROFINANCE—See The Economist Group Limited; *Int'l*, pg. 7637
EUROFINS 1. VERWALTUNGSGESELLSCHAFT MBH—See Eurofins Scientific S.E.; *Int'l*, pg. 2536
EUROFINS 2. VERWALTUNGSGESELLSCHAFT MBH—See Eurofins Scientific S.E.; *Int'l*, pg. 2536
EUROFINS 3 OHMS SAS—See Eurofins Scientific S.E.; *Int'l*, pg. 2536
EUROFINS ABRAXIS, INC.—See Eurofins Scientific S.E.; *Int'l*, pg. 2536
EUROFINS ACMAA INSPECTIE B.V.—See Eurofins Scientific S.E.; *Int'l*, pg. 2536
EUROFINS ACMAA LABORATORIA B.V.—See Eurofins Scientific S.E.; *Int'l*, pg. 2536
EUROFINS ADME BIOANALYSES SAS—See Eurofins Scientific S.E.; *Int'l*, pg. 2542
EUROFINS ADVANTAR LABORATORIES, INC.—See Eurofins Scientific S.E.; *Int'l*, pg. 2536
EUROFINS ADVINUS AGROSCIENCES SERVICES INDIA PRIVATE LIMITED—See Eurofins Scientific S.E.; *Int'l*, pg. 2536
EUROFINS ADVINUS BIOPHARMA SERVICES INDIA PVT LTD—See Eurofins Scientific S.E.; *Int'l*, pg. 2536
EUROFINS ADVINUS DISCOVERY SERVICES PRIVATE LIMITED—See Eurofins Scientific S.E.; *Int'l*, pg. 2536
EUROFINS AGRARANALYTIK DEUTSCHLAND GMBH—See Eurofins Scientific S.E.; *Int'l*, pg. 2536
EUROFINS AGROAMBIENTAL SA—See Eurofins Scientific S.E.; *Int'l*, pg. 2536
EUROFINS AGRO-ANALYSES S.A.S.—See Eurofins Scientific S.E.; *Int'l*, pg. 2536
EUROFINS AGROSCIENCE SERVICES AUSTRIA GMBH—See Eurofins Scientific S.E.; *Int'l*, pg. 2536
EUROFINS AGROSCIENCE SERVICES CHEM GMBH—See Eurofins Scientific S.E.; *Int'l*, pg. 2536

EUROFINS AGROSCIENCE SERVICES CHEM SAS—See Eurofins Scientific S.E.; *Int'l*, pg. 2536
EUROFINS AGROSCIENCE SERVICES CHILE S.A—See Eurofins Scientific S.E.; *Int'l*, pg. 2536
EUROFINS AGROSCIENCE SERVICES EAG LABORATORIES GMBH—See Eurofins Scientific S.E.; *Int'l*, pg. 2536
EUROFINS AGROSCIENCE SERVICES ECOCHEM GMBH—See Eurofins Scientific S.E.; *Int'l*, pg. 2536
EUROFINS AGROSCIENCE SERVICES ECOTOX GMBH—See Eurofins Scientific S.E.; *Int'l*, pg. 2536
EUROFINS AGROSCIENCE SERVICES FRANCE SAS—See Eurofins Scientific S.E.; *Int'l*, pg. 2542
EUROFINS AGROSCIENCE SERVICES GMBH—See Eurofins Scientific S.E.; *Int'l*, pg. 2536
EUROFINS AGROSCIENCE SERVICES INC.—See Eurofins Scientific S.E.; *Int'l*, pg. 2548
EUROFINS AGROSCIENCE SERVICES ITALY S.R.L.—See Eurofins Scientific S.E.; *Int'l*, pg. 2536
EUROFINS AGROSCIENCE SERVICES KFT—See Eurofins Scientific S.E.; *Int'l*, pg. 2537
EUROFINS AGROSCIENCE SERVICES LTD—See Eurofins Scientific S.E.; *Int'l*, pg. 2537
EUROFINS AGROSCIENCE SERVICES LTD.—See Eurofins Scientific S.E.; *Int'l*, pg. 2536
EUROFINS AGROSCIENCE SERVICES MAROC SARL—See Eurofins Scientific S.E.; *Int'l*, pg. 2537
EUROFINS AGROSCIENCE SERVICES NZ LIMITED—See Eurofins Scientific S.E.; *Int'l*, pg. 2537
EUROFINS AGROSCIENCE SERVICES REGULATORY FRANCE SAS—See Eurofins Scientific S.E.; *Int'l*, pg. 2537
EUROFINS AGROSCIENCE SERVICES REGULATORY GERMANY GMBH—See Eurofins Scientific S.E.; *Int'l*, pg. 2537
EUROFINS AGROSCIENCE SERVICES REGULATORY SPAIN SL—See Eurofins Scientific S.E.; *Int'l*, pg. 2537
EUROFINS AGROSCIENCE SERVICES S.A.S.—See Eurofins Scientific S.E.; *Int'l*, pg. 2537
EUROFINS AGROSCIENCE SERVICES SEEDS FRANCE SAS—See Eurofins Scientific S.E.; *Int'l*, pg. 2537
EUROFINS AGROSCIENCE SERVICES SL—See Eurofins Scientific S.E.; *Int'l*, pg. 2537
EUROFINS AGROSCIENCE SERVICES SP. Z.O.O.—See Eurofins Scientific S.E.; *Int'l*, pg. 2536
EUROFINS AGROSCIENCE SERVICES SRL—See Eurofins Scientific S.E.; *Int'l*, pg. 2537
EUROFINS AGROSCIENCE SERVICES THAILAND CO. LTD.—See Eurofins Scientific S.E.; *Int'l*, pg. 2537
EUROFINS AGROSCIENCES SERVICES SAS—See Eurofins Scientific S.E.; *Int'l*, pg. 2542
EUROFINS AGROSCIENCES SERVICES SRL—See Eurofins Scientific S.E.; *Int'l*, pg. 2537
EUROFINS AGROSCIENCE TESTING NZ LIMITED—See Eurofins Scientific S.E.; *Int'l*, pg. 2537
EUROFINS AGROSCIENCE TESTING PTY LTD—See Eurofins Scientific S.E.; *Int'l*, pg. 2537
EUROFINS AGRO TESTING BELGIUM NV—See Eurofins Scientific S.E.; *Int'l*, pg. 2536
EUROFINS AGRO TESTING DENMARK A/S—See Eurofins Scientific S.E.; *Int'l*, pg. 2536
EUROFINS AGRO TESTING NORWAY AS—See Eurofins Scientific S.E.; *Int'l*, pg. 2536
EUROFINS AGRO TESTING SWEDEN AB—See Eurofins Scientific S.E.; *Int'l*, pg. 2536
EUROFINS AGRO TESTING UK LIMITED—See Eurofins Scientific S.E.; *Int'l*, pg. 2536
EUROFINS AGRO TESTING WAGENINGEN BV—See Eurofins Scientific S.E.; *Int'l*, pg. 2536
EUROFINS AHMA OY—See Eurofins Scientific S.E.; *Int'l*, pg. 2537
EUROFINS AIR A L'EMISSION FRANCE SAS—See Eurofins Scientific S.E.; *Int'l*, pg. 2542
EUROFINS AIR MONITORING BELGIUM N.V.—See Eurofins Scientific S.E.; *Int'l*, pg. 2537
EUROFINS AIR TOXICS, LLC—See Eurofins Scientific S.E.; *Int'l*, pg. 2548
EUROFINS ALBA SCIENCE LIMITED—See Eurofins Scientific S.E.; *Int'l*, pg. 2537
EUROFINS AMATSI ANALYTICS SAS—See Eurofins Scientific S.E.; *Int'l*, pg. 2537
EUROFINS AMATSIAQUITAINE S.A.S.—See Eurofins Scientific S.E.; *Int'l*, pg. 2537
EUROFINS AMATSIGROUP NV—See Eurofins Scientific S.E.; *Int'l*, pg. 2537
EUROFINS AMATSIGROUP S.A.S.—See Eurofins Scientific S.E.; *Int'l*, pg. 2537
EUROFINS AMS LABORATORIES PTY. LTD.—See Eurofins Scientific S.E.; *Int'l*, pg. 2550
EUROFINS ANALISIS AGRO, S.A.—See Eurofins Scientific S.E.; *Int'l*, pg. 2537
EUROFINS ANALISIS ALIMENTARIO NORDESTE SL—See Eurofins Scientific S.E.; *Int'l*, pg. 2537
EUROFINS ANALISIS ALIMENTARIO SL—See Eurofins Scientific S.E.; *Int'l*, pg. 2537
EUROFINS ANALISIS CLINICOS CANARIAS, SL—See Eurofins Scientific S.E.; *Int'l*, pg. 2537

EUROFINS ANALYSES DES MATERIAUX ET COMBUSTIBLES FRANCE SAS—See Eurofins Scientific S.E.; *Int'l*, pg. 2537
EUROFINS ANALYSES NUTRITIONNELLES FRANCE S.A.S.—See Eurofins Scientific S.E.; *Int'l*, pg. 2537
EUROFINS ANALYSES POUR LE BATIMENT ILE DE FRANCE—See Eurofins Scientific S.E.; *Int'l*, pg. 2542
EUROFINS ANALYSES POUR LE BATIMENT NORD-OUEST CEBAT S.A.S.—See Eurofins Scientific S.E.; *Int'l*, pg. 2537
EUROFINS ANALYSES POUR LE BATIMENT NORD SAS—See Eurofins Scientific S.E.; *Int'l*, pg. 2537
EUROFINS ANALYSES POUR LE BATIMENT OUEST SAS—See Eurofins Scientific S.E.; *Int'l*, pg. 2537
EUROFINS ANALYSES POUR LE BATIMENT SUD EST SAS—See Eurofins Scientific S.E.; *Int'l*, pg. 2537
EUROFINS ANALYSES POUR LE BATIMENT SUD-OUEST SAS—See Eurofins Scientific S.E.; *Int'l*, pg. 2537
EUROFINS ANALYSES POUR LE BATIMENT SUD SAS—See Eurofins Scientific S.E.; *Int'l*, pg. 2537
EUROFINS ANALYSES POUR L'ENVIRONNEMENT FRANCE SAS—See Eurofins Scientific S.E.; *Int'l*, pg. 2542
EUROFINS ANALYTICAL LABORATORIES, INC.—See Eurofins Scientific S.E.; *Int'l*, pg. 2537
EUROFINS ANALYTICAL SERVICES HUNGARY KFT.—See Eurofins Scientific S.E.; *Int'l*, pg. 2537
EUROFINS ANALYTICAL SERVICES INDIA PVT LTD—See Eurofins Scientific S.E.; *Int'l*, pg. 2537
EUROFINS ANALYTICAL TESTING CENTER INC.—See Eurofins Scientific S.E.; *Int'l*, pg. 2548
EUROFINS ANALYTICO FOOD BV—See Eurofins Scientific S.E.; *Int'l*, pg. 2537
EUROFINS ANALYTICO—See Eurofins Scientific S.E.; *Int'l*, pg. 2537
EUROFINS ANALYTICS FRANCE SAS—See Eurofins Scientific S.E.; *Int'l*, pg. 2542
EUROFINS ANALYTICS LLC—See Eurofins Scientific S.E.; *Int'l*, pg. 2537
EUROFINS ANALYTICS & SERVICES AUSTRIA GMBH—See Eurofins Scientific S.E.; *Int'l*, pg. 2537
EUROFINS ANALYTIK GMBH—See Eurofins Scientific S.E.; *Int'l*, pg. 2537
EUROFINS ANIMAL HEALTH AUSTRALIA PTY LTD — See Eurofins Scientific S.E.; *Int'l*, pg. 2537
EUROFINS APAL PTY. LTD.—See Eurofins Scientific S.E.; *Int'l*, pg. 2537
EUROFINS AQUATIC ECOTOXICOLOGY GMBH—See Eurofins Scientific S.E.; *Int'l*, pg. 2537
EUROFINS ASBESTOS TESTING BELGIUM NV—See Eurofins Scientific S.E.; *Int'l*, pg. 2537
EUROFINS ASBESTOS TESTING EUROPE SAS—See Eurofins Scientific S.E.; *Int'l*, pg. 2537
EUROFINS ASCAL BATIMENT NORD SAS—See Eurofins Scientific S.E.; *Int'l*, pg. 2542
EUROFINS ASCAL BATIMENT SUD EST SAS—See Eurofins Scientific S.E.; *Int'l*, pg. 2542
EUROFINS ASCAL ENVIRONNEMENT SAS—See Eurofins Scientific S.E.; *Int'l*, pg. 2542
EUROFINS A/S—See Eurofins Scientific S.E.; *Int'l*, pg. 2536
EUROFINS ASSURANCE CHINA CO., LTD.—See Eurofins Scientific S.E.; *Int'l*, pg. 2538
EUROFINS ASSURANCE INDIA PVT LTD.—See Eurofins Scientific S.E.; *Int'l*, pg. 2538
EUROFINS ASSURANCE MYANMAR LTD.—See Eurofins Scientific S.E.; *Int'l*, pg. 2538
EUROFINS ASSURANCE TURKEY KALITE VE DENETIM HIZMETLERI LIMITED SIRKETI—See Eurofins Scientific S.E.; *Int'l*, pg. 2538
EUROFINS ATS SAS—See Eurofins Scientific S.E.; *Int'l*, pg. 2542
EUROFINS AVD. MOSS—See Eurofins Scientific S.E.; *Int'l*, pg. 2550
EUROFINS BACTERIOLOGISCH ADVIESBURO BV—See Eurofins Scientific S.E.; *Int'l*, pg. 2538
EUROFINS BACTIMM BV—See Eurofins Scientific S.E.; *Int'l*, pg. 2538
EUROFINS BACTUP SAS—See Eurofins Scientific S.E.; *Int'l*, pg. 2538
EUROFINS BAY OF PLENTY LIMITED—See Eurofins Scientific S.E.; *Int'l*, pg. 2538
EUROFINS BEACON DISCOVERY, INC.—See Eurofins Scientific S.E.; *Int'l*, pg. 2538
EUROFINS BECEWA NV—See Eurofins Scientific S.E.; *Int'l*, pg. 2538
EUROFINS BELGIUM NV—See Eurofins Scientific S.E.; *Int'l*, pg. 2538
EUROFINS BEL/NOVAMANN S.R.O.—See Eurofins Scientific S.E.; *Int'l*, pg. 2538
EUROFINS BESTLAB OY—See Eurofins Scientific S.E.; *Int'l*, pg. 2550
EUROFINS BIODIAGNOSTICS, INC.—See Eurofins Scientific S.E.; *Int'l*, pg. 2548
EUROFINS BIOFFICE SELAS—See Eurofins Scientific S.E.; *Int'l*, pg. 2538
EUROFINS BIOFUEL & ENERGY TESTING SWEDEN AB—See Eurofins Scientific S.E.; *Int'l*, pg. 2538
EUROFINS BIOLAB SRL—See Eurofins Scientific S.E.; *Int'l*, pg. 2548
EUROFINS BIOLOGIE MEDICALE ILE DE FRANCE SAS—See Eurofins Scientific S.E.; *Int'l*, pg. 2538
EUROFINS BIOLOGIE MOLECULAIRE FRANCE SAS—See Eurofins Scientific S.E.; *Int'l*, pg. 2538
EUROFINS BIOMI KFT.—See Eurofins Scientific S.E.; *Int'l*, pg. 2538
EUROFINS BIOMNIS IRELAND LIMITED—See Eurofins Scientific S.E.; *Int'l*, pg. 2538
EUROFINS BIOMNIS SELAS—See Eurofins Scientific S.E.; *Int'l*, pg. 2538
EUROFINS BIOMNIS UK LIMITED—See Eurofins Scientific S.E.; *Int'l*, pg. 2538
EUROFINS BIOPHARMA PRODUCT TESTING COLUMBIA, INC.—See Eurofins Scientific S.E.; *Int'l*, pg. 2538
EUROFINS BIOPHARMA PRODUCT TESTING CZECH REPUBLIC S.R.O.—See Eurofins Scientific S.E.; *Int'l*, pg. 2538
EUROFINS BIOPHARMA PRODUCT TESTING DENMARK A/S—See Eurofins Scientific S.E.; *Int'l*, pg. 2538
EUROFINS BIOPHARMA PRODUCT TESTING ENCO, INC.—See Eurofins Scientific S.E.; *Int'l*, pg. 2538
EUROFINS BIOPHARMA PRODUCT TESTING HAMBURG GMBH—See Eurofins Scientific S.E.; *Int'l*, pg. 2538
EUROFINS BIOPHARMA PRODUCT TESTING HUNGARY KFT.—See Eurofins Scientific S.E.; *Int'l*, pg. 2538
EUROFINS BIOPHARMA PRODUCT TESTING INDIA PRIVATE LIMITED—See Eurofins Scientific S.E.; *Int'l*, pg. 2538
EUROFINS BIOPHARMA PRODUCT TESTING MUNICH GMBH—See Eurofins Scientific S.E.; *Int'l*, pg. 2538
EUROFINS BIOPHARMA PRODUCT TESTING NZ LIMITED—See Eurofins Scientific S.E.; *Int'l*, pg. 2538
EUROFINS BIOPHARMA PRODUCT TESTING SPAIN SLU—See Eurofins Scientific S.E.; *Int'l*, pg. 2538
EUROFINS BIOPHARMA PRODUCT TESTING SWEDEN AB—See Eurofins Scientific S.E.; *Int'l*, pg. 2538
EUROFINS BIOPHARMA PRODUCT TESTING SWITZERLAND AG—See Eurofins Scientific S.E.; *Int'l*, pg. 2538
EUROFINS BIOPHARMA PRODUCT TESTING UK LIMITED—See Eurofins Scientific S.E.; *Int'l*, pg. 2538
EUROFINS BIOSCIENCES CERVAC CONSULTING—See Eurofins Scientific S.E.; *Int'l*, pg. 2542
EUROFINS BIOSCIENCES SAS—See Eurofins Scientific S.E.; *Int'l*, pg. 2542
EUROFINS BIOSKIN GMBH—See Eurofins Scientific S.E.; *Int'l*, pg. 2538
EUROFINS BIOTALDE, S.L.U.—See Eurofins Scientific S.E.; *Int'l*, pg. 2538
EUROFINS BIOTESTING SERVICES NORD GMBH—See Eurofins Scientific S.E.; *Int'l*, pg. 2538
EUROFINS BIOTESTING SERVICES OST GMBH—See Eurofins Scientific S.E.; *Int'l*, pg. 2538
EUROFINS BLC LEATHER TECHNOLOGY CENTRE LIMITED—See Eurofins Scientific S.E.; *Int'l*, pg. 2538
EUROFINS BUREAU DE WIT B.V.—See Eurofins Scientific S.E.; *Int'l*, pg. 2538
EUROFINS CALIXAR S.A.S.—See Eurofins Scientific S.E.; *Int'l*, pg. 2539
EUROFINS CALSCIENCE, LLC—See Eurofins Scientific S.E.; *Int'l*, pg. 2548
EUROFINS CAVENDISH, S.L.U.—See Eurofins Scientific S.E.; *Int'l*, pg. 2539
EUROFINS CBM69 SELAS—See Eurofins Scientific S.E.; *Int'l*, pg. 2538
EUROFINS CDMO ALPHORA, INC.—See Eurofins Scientific S.E.; *Int'l*, pg. 2538
EUROFINS CEBAT SAS—See Eurofins Scientific S.E.; *Int'l*, pg. 2538
EUROFINS CEF SELAS—See Eurofins Scientific S.E.; *Int'l*, pg. 2538
EUROFINS CEI, INC.—See Eurofins Scientific S.E.; *Int'l*, pg. 2548
EUROFINS CELLTX, INC.—See Eurofins Scientific S.E.; *Int'l*, pg. 2539
EUROFINS CENTRAL ANALYTICAL LABORATORIES INC.—See Eurofins Scientific S.E.; *Int'l*, pg. 2548
EUROFINS CENTRAL LABORATORY CHINA CO., LTD.—See Eurofins Scientific S.E.; *Int'l*, pg. 2539
EUROFINS CENTRAL LABORATORY LLC—See Eurofins Scientific S.E.; *Int'l*, pg. 2539
EUROFINS CENTRAL LABORATORY PTE. LTD.—See Eurofins Scientific S.E.; *Int'l*, pg. 2539
EUROFINS CENTRAL LABORATORY—See Eurofins Scientific S.E.; *Int'l*, pg. 2539
EUROFINS CENTRO ANALITICO MIGUEZ MUINOS, S.L.U.—See Eurofins Scientific S.E.; *Int'l*, pg. 2539
EUROFINS CEREP SA—See Eurofins Scientific S.E.; *Int'l*, pg. 2542
EUROFINS CERTIFICATION SARL—See Eurofins Scientific S.E.; *Int'l*, pg. 2542
EUROFINS CERVAC SUD SAS—See Eurofins Scientific S.E.; *Int'l*, pg. 2542
EUROFINS CHEMICAL CONTROL SRL—See Eurofins Scientific S.E.; *Int'l*, pg. 2548
EUROFINS CHEMTEST LIMITED—See Eurofins Scientific S.E.; *Int'l*, pg. 2539
EUROFINS CHIMIE ALIMENTAIRE ROUEN S.A.S.—See Eurofins Scientific S.E.; *Int'l*, pg. 2539
EUROFINS CIDESAL, S.L.U.—See Eurofins Scientific S.E.; *Int'l*, pg. 2539
EUROFINS CIMERA ESTUDIOS APLICADOS, S.L.U.—See Eurofins Scientific S.E.; *Int'l*, pg. 2539
EUROFINS CLF SPECIALISED NUTRITION TESTING SERVICES GMBH—See Eurofins Scientific S.E.; *Int'l*, pg. 2538
EUROFINS CLINICAL DIAGNOSTICS BANGALORE PRIVATE LIMITED—See Eurofins Scientific S.E.; *Int'l*, pg. 2539
EUROFINS CLINICAL DIAGNOSTICS KORTRIJK N.V.—See Eurofins Scientific S.E.; *Int'l*, pg. 2539
EUROFINS CLINICAL DIAGNOSTICS PTE. LTD.—See Eurofins Scientific S.E.; *Int'l*, pg. 2539
EUROFINS CLINICAL DIAGNOSTICS UK LIMITED—See Eurofins Scientific S.E.; *Int'l*, pg. 2539
EUROFINS CLINICAL GENETICS INDIA PVT LTD—See Eurofins Scientific S.E.; *Int'l*, pg. 2539
EUROFINS CLINICAL GENETICS KK—See Eurofins Scientific S.E.; *Int'l*, pg. 2539
EUROFINS CLINICAL GENETICS UK LIMITED—See Eurofins Scientific S.E.; *Int'l*, pg. 2539
EUROFINS CLINICAL TESTING SWEDEN AB—See Eurofins Scientific S.E.; *Int'l*, pg. 2539
EUROFINS C MARK BV—See Eurofins Scientific S.E.; *Int'l*, pg. 2538
EUROFINS CONSULT GMBH—See Eurofins Scientific S.E.; *Int'l*, pg. 2539
EUROFINS CONSULTING AGROALIMENTAIRE SAS—See Eurofins Scientific S.E.; *Int'l*, pg. 2539
EUROFINS CONSULTING ITALIA SRL—See Eurofins Scientific S.E.; *Int'l*, pg. 2548
EUROFINS CONSUMER PRODUCT TESTING GMBH—See Eurofins Scientific S.E.; *Int'l*, pg. 2547
EUROFINS CONSUMER PRODUCT TESTING (GUANGZHOU) CO., LTD.—See Eurofins Scientific S.E.; *Int'l*, pg. 2539
EUROFINS CONSUMER PRODUCT TESTING IBLSC US, INC.—See Eurofins Scientific S.E.; *Int'l*, pg. 2539
EUROFINS CONSUMER PRODUCT TESTING VIETNAM CO. LTD.—See Eurofins Scientific S.E.; *Int'l*, pg. 2539
EUROFINS CONTROL AMBIENTAL Y ECOGESTOR, S.L.U.—See Eurofins Scientific S.E.; *Int'l*, pg. 2539
EUROFINS CONVET, S.L.U.—See Eurofins Scientific S.E.; *Int'l*, pg. 2539
EUROFINS COSMETIC & PERSONAL CARE ITALY SRL—See Eurofins Scientific S.E.; *Int'l*, pg. 2539
EUROFINS COSMETICS & PERSONAL CARE ITALY S.R.L.—See Eurofins Scientific S.E.; *Int'l*, pg. 2539
EUROFINS COSMETICS & PERSONAL CARE TESTING CANADA, INC.—See Eurofins Scientific S.E.; *Int'l*, pg. 2539
EUROFINS COUNTY PATHOLOGY LIMITED—See Eurofins Scientific S.E.; *Int'l*, pg. 2539
EUROFINS CRA CO., LTD.—See Eurofins Scientific S.E.; *Int'l*, pg. 2538
EUROFINS CRL COSMETICS, INC.—See Eurofins Scientific S.E.; *Int'l*, pg. 2538
EUROFINS CRL INC.—See Eurofins Scientific S.E.; *Int'l*, pg. 2538
EUROFINS CROATIAKONTROLA D.O.O.—See Eurofins Scientific S.E.; *Int'l*, pg. 2539
EUROFINS CTC GMBH—See Eurofins Scientific S.E.; *Int'l*, pg. 2541
EUROFINS CYBER SECURITY NETHERLANDS HOLDING BV—See Eurofins Scientific S.E.; *Int'l*, pg. 2539
EUROFINS DANMARK A/S—See Eurofins Scientific S.E.; *Int'l*, pg. 2539
EUROFINS DE BREDELAAR B.V.—See Eurofins Scientific S.E.; *Int'l*, pg. 2539
EUROFINS DERMATEST PTY LTD—See Eurofins Scientific S.E.; *Int'l*, pg. 2539
EUROFINS DERMA TRONNIER GMBH—See Eurofins Scientific S.E.; *Int'l*, pg. 2539
EUROFINS DERMSCAN POLAND SP. Z O.O.—See Eurofins Scientific S.E.; *Int'l*, pg. 2539
EUROFINS DERMSCAN TUNISIE S.A.R.L.—See Eurofins Scientific S.E.; *Int'l*, pg. 2539
EUROFINS DEUTSCHES INSTITUT FUR LEBENSMITTELUNTERSUCHUNG GMBH—See Eurofins Scientific S.E.; *Int'l*, pg. 2548
EUROFINS DIATHERIX LABORATORIES, LLC—See Eurofins Scientific S.E.; *Int'l*, pg. 2539
EUROFINS DIGITAL MEDIA SERVICES, LLC—See Eurofins Scientific S.E.; *Int'l*, pg. 2539
EUROFINS DIGITAL PRODUCT TESTING UK LIMITED—See Eurofins Scientific S.E.; *Int'l*, pg. 2539
EUROFINS DIGITAL TESTING BELGIUM NV—See Eurofins Scientific S.E.; *Int'l*, pg. 2540
EUROFINS DIGITAL TESTING SWEDEN AB—See Eurofins Scientific S.E.; *Int'l*, pg. 2539
EUROFINS DIGITAL TESTING UK HOLDING LIMITED—See Eurofins Scientific S.E.; *Int'l*, pg. 2539
EUROFINS DISCOVERX CORPORATION, INC.—See Eurofins Scientific S.E.; *Int'l*, pg. 2540
EUROFINS DISPOSABLE LAB S.A.S.—See Eurofins Scientific S.E.; *Int'l*, pg. 2540

EUROFINS DISPOSITIFS AU CONTACT DE L'EAU FRANCE SAS—See Eurofins Scientific S.E.; *Int'l*, pg. 2540
EUROFINS DO BRASIL ANALISE DE ALIMENTOS LTDA—See Eurofins Scientific S.E.; *Int'l*, pg. 2550
EUROFINS DONOR & PRODUCT TESTING, INC.—See Eurofins Scientific S.E.; *Int'l*, pg. 2540
EUROFINS DQCI—See Eurofins Scientific S.E.; *Int'l*, pg. 2548
EUROFINS DR. SPECHT EXPRESS GMBH—See Eurofins Scientific S.E.; *Int'l*, pg. 2540
EUROFINS DR. SPECHT EXPRESS TESTING & INSPECTION GMBH—See Eurofins Scientific S.E.; *Int'l*, pg. 2540
EUROFINS DR. SPECHT INTERNATIONAL GMBH—See Eurofins Scientific S.E.; *Int'l*, pg. 2540
EUROFINS DR. SPECHT LABORATORIEN GMBH—See Eurofins Scientific S.E.; *Int'l*, pg. 2548
EUROFINS DSG FORENSICS SAS—See Eurofins Scientific S.E.; *Int'l*, pg. 2539
EUROFINS EAC CORPORATION—See Eurofins Scientific S.E.; *Int'l*, pg. 2540
EUROFINS EAG AGROSCIENCE, LLC—See Eurofins Scientific S.E.; *Int'l*, pg. 2540
EUROFINS EAG EASTON—See Eurofins Scientific S.E.; *Int'l*, pg. 2549
EUROFINS EAG HERCULES—See Eurofins Scientific S.E.; *Int'l*, pg. 2549
EUROFINS EAG MATERIALS SCIENCE CHINA LTD.—See Eurofins Scientific S.E.; *Int'l*, pg. 2540
EUROFINS EAG MATERIALS SCIENCE NETHERLANDS B.V.—See Eurofins Scientific S.E.; *Int'l*, pg. 2540
EUROFINS EAG MATERIALS SCIENCE SINGAPORE, PTE. LTD.—See Eurofins Scientific S.E.; *Int'l*, pg. 2540
EUROFINS EAG MATERIALS SCIENCE TAIWAN, LTD.—See Eurofins Scientific S.E.; *Int'l*, pg. 2540
EUROFINS EAG MATERIALS SCIENCE TOKYO CORPORATION KK—See Eurofins Scientific S.E.; *Int'l*, pg. 2540
EUROFINS EAG PRINCETON—See Eurofins Scientific S.E.; *Int'l*, pg. 2549
EUROFINS EAG SANTA CLARA—See Eurofins Scientific S.E.; *Int'l*, pg. 2549
EUROFINS EAG SHANGHAI—See Eurofins Scientific S.E.; *Int'l*, pg. 2549
EUROFINS EAG SINGAPORE—See Eurofins Scientific S.E.; *Int'l*, pg. 2549
EUROFINS EAG ST LOUIS—See Eurofins Scientific S.E.; *Int'l*, pg. 2549
EUROFINS EAG SUNNYVALE—See Eurofins Scientific S.E.; *Int'l*, pg. 2549
EUROFINS EAG TAIWAN—See Eurofins Scientific S.E.; *Int'l*, pg. 2549
EUROFINS EAG TOKYO—See Eurofins Scientific S.E.; *Int'l*, pg. 2549
EUROFINS EAG TOULOUSE—See Eurofins Scientific S.E.; *Int'l*, pg. 2549
EUROFINS EARTH CONSUL KK—See Eurofins Scientific S.E.; *Int'l*, pg. 2540
EUROFINS EASTERN VENTURES BV—See Eurofins Scientific S.E.; *Int'l*, pg. 2540
EUROFINS EATON ANALYTICAL, LLC—See Eurofins Scientific S.E.; *Int'l*, pg. 2548
EUROFINS EAUX RESIDUAIRES SAS—See Eurofins Scientific S.E.; *Int'l*, pg. 2542
EUROFINS ECCA BTX B.V.—See Eurofins Scientific S.E.; *Int'l*, pg. 2540
EUROFINS ECCA N.V.—See Eurofins Scientific S.E.; *Int'l*, pg. 2540
EUROFINS ECOSUR SA—See Eurofins Scientific S.E.; *Int'l*, pg. 2540
EUROFINS ECOTOXICOLOGIE FRANCE S.A.S.—See Eurofins Scientific S.E.; *Int'l*, pg. 2540
EUROFINS E&E CML LIMITED—See Eurofins Scientific S.E.; *Int'l*, pg. 2540
EUROFINS E&E ETC LIMITED—See Eurofins Scientific S.E.; *Int'l*, pg. 2540
EUROFINS E&E HURSLEY LIMITED—See Eurofins Scientific S.E.; *Int'l*, pg. 2540
EUROFINS E&E TAIWAN, LTD.—See Eurofins Scientific S.E.; *Int'l*, pg. 2540
EUROFINS EICHROM RADIOACTIVITE SAS—See Eurofins Scientific S.E.; *Int'l*, pg. 2540
EUROFINS ELECTRICAL & ELECTRONICS FRANCE S.A.S.—See Eurofins Scientific S.E.; *Int'l*, pg. 2540
EUROFINS ELECTRICAL & ELECTRONIC UK LIMITED—See Eurofins Scientific S.E.; *Int'l*, pg. 2540
EUROFINS ELECTRICAL TESTING SERVICE (SHENZHEN) CO., LTD.—See Eurofins Scientific S.E.; *Int'l*, pg. 2540
EUROFINS ELECTRIC & ELECTRONIC PRODUCT TESTING AG—See Eurofins Scientific S.E.; *Int'l*, pg. 2540
EUROFINS ELECTRIC & ELECTRONICS FINLAND OY—See Eurofins Scientific S.E.; *Int'l*, pg. 2540
EUROFINS ELS LIMITED—See Eurofins Scientific S.E.; *Int'l*, pg. 2540
EUROFINS ENVIRON-LAB S.R.L.—See Eurofins Scientific S.E.; *Int'l*, pg. 2540

EUROFINS ENVIRONMENTAL SERVICES LTD—See Eurofins Scientific S.E.; *Int'l*, pg. 2544
EUROFINS ENVIRONMENT II DE GMBH—See Eurofins Scientific S.E.; *Int'l*, pg. 2544
EUROFINS ENVIRONMENT TESTING AUSTRALIA PTY LTD—See Eurofins Scientific S.E.; *Int'l*, pg. 2540
EUROFINS ENVIRONMENT TESTING ESTONIA OU—See Eurofins Scientific S.E.; *Int'l*, pg. 2540
EUROFINS ENVIRONMENT TESTING FINLAND OY—See Eurofins Scientific S.E.; *Int'l*, pg. 2540
EUROFINS ENVIRONMENT TESTING IRELAND LIMITED—See Eurofins Scientific S.E.; *Int'l*, pg. 2540
EUROFINS ENVIRONMENT TESTING ITALY SRL—See Eurofins Scientific S.E.; *Int'l*, pg. 2548
EUROFINS ENVIRONMENT TESTING LUX HOLDING SARL—See Eurofins Scientific S.E.; *Int'l*, pg. 2544
EUROFINS ENVIRONMENT TESTING NETHERLANDS HOLDING BV—See Eurofins Scientific S.E.; *Int'l*, pg. 2544
EUROFINS ENVIRONMENT TESTING NORTHEAST, LLC—See Eurofins Scientific S.E.; *Int'l*, pg. 2540
EUROFINS ENVIRONMENT TESTING NORTHWEST, LLC—See Eurofins Scientific S.E.; *Int'l*, pg. 2540
EUROFINS ENVIRONMENT TESTING NORWAY AS—See Eurofins Scientific S.E.; *Int'l*, pg. 2540
EUROFINS ENVIRONMENT TESTING NZ LIMITED—See Eurofins Scientific S.E.; *Int'l*, pg. 2540
EUROFINS ENVIRONMENT TESTING PHILADELPHIA, LLC—See Eurofins Scientific S.E.; *Int'l*, pg. 2540
EUROFINS ENVIRONMENT TESTING SOUTH CENTRAL, LLC—See Eurofins Scientific S.E.; *Int'l*, pg. 2540
EUROFINS ENVIRONMENT TESTING SOUTHEAST, LLC—See Eurofins Scientific S.E.; *Int'l*, pg. 2540
EUROFINS ENVIRONMENT TESTING SWEDEN AB—See Eurofins Scientific S.E.; *Int'l*, pg. 2541
EUROFINS ENVIRONMENT TESTING SWEDEN HOLDING AB—See Eurofins Scientific S.E.; *Int'l*, pg. 2541
EUROFINS ENVIRONNEMENT FORMATION ET CONSEIL S.A.S.—See Eurofins Scientific S.E.; *Int'l*, pg. 2541
EUROFINS ENVIRONNEMENT LOGISTIQUE FRANCE SAS—See Eurofins Scientific S.E.; *Int'l*, pg. 2541
EUROFINS ENVIRONNEMENT & SANTE SAS—See Eurofins Scientific S.E.; *Int'l*, pg. 2542
EUROFINS ENVIRONNEMENT SAS—See Eurofins Scientific S.E.; *Int'l*, pg. 2542
EUROFINS ENVIRO-WORKS, INC.—See Eurofins Scientific S.E.; *Int'l*, pg. 2540
EUROFINS EPK BUILT ENVIRONMENT TESTING, LLC—See Eurofins Scientific S.E.; *Int'l*, pg. 2540
EUROFINS EURACETA N.V.—See Eurofins Scientific S.E.; *Int'l*, pg. 2541
EUROFINS EVIC PRODUCT TESTING FRANCE SAS—See Eurofins Scientific S.E.; *Int'l*, pg. 2541
EUROFINS EVIC PRODUCT TESTING ROMANIA SRL—See Eurofins Scientific S.E.; *Int'l*, pg. 2541
EUROFINS EXPERTISE MICROBIOLOGIQUE FRANCE SAS—See Eurofins Scientific S.E.; *Int'l*, pg. 2541
EUROFINS EXPERTISES ENVIRONNEMENTALES SAS—See Eurofins Scientific S.E.; *Int'l*, pg. 2541
EUROFINS EXPERT SERVICES OY—See Eurofins Scientific S.E.; *Int'l*, pg. 2541
EUROFINS FINTELMANN UND MEYER GMP GMBH—See Eurofins Scientific S.E.; *Int'l*, pg. 2541
EUROFINS FOOD & AGRO TESTING SWEDEN AB—See Eurofins Scientific S.E.; *Int'l*, pg. 2541
EUROFINS FOOD ANALYTICA KFT.—See Eurofins Scientific S.E.; *Int'l*, pg. 2541
EUROFINS FOOD ASSURANCE CERTIFICATION US, LLC—See Eurofins Scientific S.E.; *Int'l*, pg. 2541
EUROFINS FOOD ASSURANCE ITALIA SRL—See Eurofins Scientific S.E.; *Int'l*, pg. 2541
EUROFINS FOOD ASSURANCE US, LLC—See Eurofins Scientific S.E.; *Int'l*, pg. 2541
EUROFINS FOOD BARCELONA, S.L.U.—See Eurofins Scientific S.E.; *Int'l*, pg. 2541
EUROFINS FOOD CHEMISTRY TESTING DES MOINES, INC.—See Eurofins Scientific S.E.; *Int'l*, pg. 2541
EUROFINS FOOD CHEMISTRY TESTING MADISON, INC.—See Eurofins Scientific S.E.; *Int'l*, pg. 2541
EUROFINS FOOD CONTROL SERVICES GMBH—See Eurofins Scientific S.E.; *Int'l*, pg. 2541
EUROFINS FOOD DENMARK HOLDING A/S—See Eurofins Scientific S.E.; *Int'l*, pg. 2541
EUROFINS FOOD & FEED TESTING LEIPZIG GMBH—See Eurofins Scientific S.E.; *Int'l*, pg. 2541
EUROFINS FOOD & FEED TESTING NORWAY AS—See Eurofins Scientific S.E.; *Int'l*, pg. 2541
EUROFINS FOOD & FEED TESTING SWEDEN AB—See Eurofins Scientific S.E.; *Int'l*, pg. 2541
EUROFINS FOOD GMBH—See Eurofins Scientific S.E.; *Int'l*, pg. 2541
EUROFINS FOOD INTEGRITY CONTROL SERVICES GMBH—See Eurofins Scientific S.E.; *Int'l*, pg. 2541
EUROFINS FOOD INTEGRITY TESTING UK LIMITED—See Eurofins Scientific S.E.; *Int'l*, pg. 2541
EUROFINS FOOD NETHERLANDS BV—See Eurofins Scientific S.E.; *Int'l*, pg. 2541

EUROFINS FOOD & PRODUCT TESTING JAPAN KK—See Eurofins Scientific S.E.; *Int'l*, pg. 2541
EUROFINS FOOD SAFETY SOLUTIONS BV—See Eurofins Scientific S.E.; *Int'l*, pg. 2541
EUROFINS FOOD SAFETY SOLUTIONS LIMITED—See Eurofins Scientific S.E.; *Int'l*, pg. 2541
EUROFINS FOOD TESTING BELGIUM NV—See Eurofins Scientific S.E.; *Int'l*, pg. 2541
EUROFINS FOOD TESTING IRELAND LIMITED—See Eurofins Scientific S.E.; *Int'l*, pg. 2547
EUROFINS FOOD TESTING JAPAN KK LTD.—See Eurofins Scientific S.E.; *Int'l*, pg. 2541
EUROFINS FOOD TESTING LISBOA, UNIPESSOAL, LTDA.—See Eurofins Scientific S.E.; *Int'l*, pg. 2541
EUROFINS FOOD TESTING NETHERLANDS HOLDING BV—See Eurofins Scientific S.E.; *Int'l*, pg. 2541
EUROFINS FOOD TESTING ROTTERDAM B.V.—See Eurofins Scientific S.E.; *Int'l*, pg. 2541
EUROFINS FOOD TESTING SERVICE (DALIAN) CO., LTD.—See Eurofins Scientific S.E.; *Int'l*, pg. 2541
EUROFINS FOOD TESTING SINGAPORE PTE. LTD.—See Eurofins Scientific S.E.; *Int'l*, pg. 2541
EUROFINS FOOD TESTING SLOVAKIA S.R.O.—See Eurofins Scientific S.E.; *Int'l*, pg. 2541
EUROFINS FOOD TESTING SRL—See Eurofins Scientific S.E.; *Int'l*, pg. 2541
EUROFINS FOOD TESTING SUD GMBH—See Eurofins Scientific S.E.; *Int'l*, pg. 2541
EUROFINS FOOD TESTING TAIWAN, LTD.—See Eurofins Scientific S.E.; *Int'l*, pg. 2541
EUROFINS FOOD TESTING THAILAND CO. LTD.—See Eurofins Scientific S.E.; *Int'l*, pg. 2541
EUROFINS FOOD TESTING UK LIMITED—See Eurofins Scientific S.E.; *Int'l*, pg. 2542
EUROFINS FOOD US HOLDINGS I BV—See Eurofins Scientific S.E.; *Int'l*, pg. 2542
EUROFINS FOOD US HOLDINGS II BV—See Eurofins Scientific S.E.; *Int'l*, pg. 2542
EUROFINS FORENSICS BELGIUM - BRUGGE—See Eurofins Scientific S.E.; *Int'l*, pg. 2542
EUROFINS FORENSIC SERVICES LIMITED—See Eurofins Scientific S.E.; *Int'l*, pg. 2542
EUROFINS FQL LTD.—See Eurofins Scientific S.E.; *Int'l*, pg. 2541
EUROFINS FRANCE HOLDING SAS—See Eurofins Scientific S.E.; *Int'l*, pg. 2542
EUROFINS-GAB GMBH—See Eurofins Scientific S.E.; *Int'l*, pg. 2550
EUROFINS GALYS SAS—See Eurofins Scientific S.E.; *Int'l*, pg. 2543
EUROFINS GELRE B.V.—See Eurofins Scientific S.E.; *Int'l*, pg. 2543
EUROFINS GENESCAN GMBH—See Eurofins Scientific S.E.; *Int'l*, pg. 2543
EUROFINS GENESCAN TECHNOLOGIES GMBH—See Eurofins Scientific S.E.; *Int'l*, pg. 2543
EUROFINS GENESCAN USA INC.—See Eurofins Scientific S.E.; *Int'l*, pg. 2548
EUROFINS GENETECH KK—See Eurofins Scientific S.E.; *Int'l*, pg. 2543
EUROFINS GENOMA GROUP SRL—See Eurofins Scientific S.E.; *Int'l*, pg. 2543
EUROFINS GENOME VALLEY HYDERABAD RESOURCES PRIVATE LIMITED—See Eurofins Scientific S.E.; *Int'l*, pg. 2543
EUROFINS GENOMICS AUSTRIA GMBH—See Eurofins Scientific S.E.; *Int'l*, pg. 2543
EUROFINS GENOMICS BLUE HERON LLC—See Eurofins Scientific S.E.; *Int'l*, pg. 2543
EUROFINS GENOMICS ENGINEERING, LLC—See Eurofins Scientific S.E.; *Int'l*, pg. 2543
EUROFINS GENOMICS EUROPE GENOTYPING A/S—See Eurofins Scientific S.E.; *Int'l*, pg. 2543
EUROFINS GENOMICS EUROPE PHARMA & DIAGNOSTICS PRODUCTS & SERVICES SANGER/PCR GMBH—See Eurofins Scientific S.E.; *Int'l*, pg. 2543
EUROFINS GENOMICS EUROPE SEQUENCING GMBH—See Eurofins Scientific S.E.; *Int'l*, pg. 2543
EUROFINS GENOMICS FRANCE S.A.S.—See Eurofins Scientific S.E.; *Int'l*, pg. 2543
EUROFINS GENOMICS GERMANY GMBH—See Eurofins Scientific S.E.; *Int'l*, pg. 2543
EUROFINS GENOMICS INC.—See Eurofins Scientific S.E.; *Int'l*, pg. 2539
EUROFINS GENOMICS INDIA PVT LTD—See Eurofins Scientific S.E.; *Int'l*, pg. 2543
EUROFINS GENOMICS KK—See Eurofins Scientific S.E.; *Int'l*, pg. 2543
EUROFINS GENOMICS SAS—See Eurofins Scientific S.E.; *Int'l*, pg. 2542
EUROFINS GENOMICS SRL—See Eurofins Scientific S.E.; *Int'l*, pg. 2543
EUROFINS GENOMICS SWEDEN AB—See Eurofins Scientific S.E.; *Int'l*, pg. 2543
EUROFINS GENOMICS UK LIMITED—See Eurofins Scientific S.E.; *Int'l*, pg. 2543
EUROFINS GFA GMBH—See Eurofins Scientific S.E.; *Int'l*, pg. 2543

COMPANY NAME INDEX

EUROFINS GFA LAB SERVICE GMBH—See Eurofins Scientific S.E.; *Int'l*, pg. 2548
EUROFINS GLOBAL CENTRAL LABORATORY—See Eurofins Scientific S.E.; *Int'l*, pg. 2543
EUROFINS GLOBAL CONTROL GMBH—See Eurofins Scientific S.E.; *Int'l*, pg. 2541
EUROFINS GSC LUX SARL—See Eurofins Scientific S.E.; *Int'l*, pg. 2544
EUROFINS GYNAE-SCREEN LIMITED—See Eurofins Scientific S.E.; *Int'l*, pg. 2543
EUROFINS HONG KONG LTD.—See Eurofins Scientific S.E.; *Int'l*, pg. 2543
EUROFINS HT-ANALYTIK GMBH—See Eurofins Scientific S.E.; *Int'l*, pg. 2543
EUROFINS HUMAN FACTORS MD, LLC—See Eurofins Scientific S.E.; *Int'l*, pg. 2544
EUROFINS HYDROBIOLOGIE FRANCE S.A.S.—See Eurofins Scientific S.E.; *Int'l*, pg. 2544
EUROFINS HYDROLOGIE CENTRE EST SAS—See Eurofins Scientific S.E.; *Int'l*, pg. 2544
EUROFINS HYDROLOGIE EST SAS—See Eurofins Scientific S.E.; *Int'l*, pg. 2544
EUROFINS HYDROLOGIE FRANCE SAS—See Eurofins Scientific S.E.; *Int'l*, pg. 2542
EUROFINS HYDROLOGIE ILE DE FRANCE SAS—See Eurofins Scientific S.E.; *Int'l*, pg. 2544
EUROFINS HYDROLOGIE NORD SAS—See Eurofins Scientific S.E.; *Int'l*, pg. 2544
EUROFINS HYDROLOGIE NORMANDIE SAS—See Eurofins Scientific S.E.; *Int'l*, pg. 2544
EUROFINS HYDROLOGIE OUEST SAS—See Eurofins Scientific S.E.; *Int'l*, pg. 2544
EUROFINS HYDROLOGIE SUD OUEST SAS—See Eurofins Scientific S.E.; *Int'l*, pg. 2544
EUROFINS HYDROLOGIE SUD SAS—See Eurofins Scientific S.E.; *Int'l*, pg. 2544
EUROFINS HYGIENE ALIMENTAIRE ILE-DE-FRANCE SAS—See Eurofins Scientific S.E.; *Int'l*, pg. 2544
EUROFINS HYGIENE ALIMENTAIRE NORD-EST SAS—See Eurofins Scientific S.E.; *Int'l*, pg. 2544
EUROFINS HYGIENE ALIMENTAIRE NORD-OUEST SAS—See Eurofins Scientific S.E.; *Int'l*, pg. 2544
EUROFINS HYGIENE ALIMENTAIRE SAS—See Eurofins Scientific S.E.; *Int'l*, pg. 2544
EUROFINS HYGIENE ALIMENTAIRE SUD-OUEST SAS—See Eurofins Scientific S.E.; *Int'l*, pg. 2544
EUROFINS HYGIENE DES LIEUX DE TRAVAIL SAS—See Eurofins Scientific S.E.; *Int'l*, pg. 2542
EUROFINS HYGIENE DU BATIMENT PARIS SAS—See Eurofins Scientific S.E.; *Int'l*, pg. 2542
EUROFINS HYGIENE HOSPITALIERE NORD S.A.S.—See Eurofins Scientific S.E.; *Int'l*, pg. 2544
EUROFINS HYGIENE HOSPITALIERE OUEST S.A.S.—See Eurofins Scientific S.E.; *Int'l*, pg. 2544
EUROFINS HYGIENE HOSPITALIERE SUD SAS—See Eurofins Scientific S.E.; *Int'l*, pg. 2544
EUROFINS HYGIENE INSTITUT BERG GMBH—See Eurofins Scientific S.E.; *Int'l*, pg. 2544
EUROFINS IDMYK SAS—See Eurofins Scientific S.E.; *Int'l*, pg. 2544
EUROFINS IESPM S.A.S.—See Eurofins Scientific S.E.; *Int'l*, pg. 2544
EUROFINS INDUSTRIAL TESTING LUX SARL—See Eurofins Scientific S.E.; *Int'l*, pg. 2544
EUROFINS INFORMATION SYSTEMS GMBH—See Eurofins Scientific S.E.; *Int'l*, pg. 2548
EUROFINS INLAB GMBH—See Eurofins Scientific S.E.; *Int'l*, pg. 2544
EUROFINS INPAC MEDIZINTECHNIK GMBH—See Eurofins Scientific S.E.; *Int'l*, pg. 2544
EUROFINS INSTITUT DR. APPELT HILTER GMBH—See Eurofins Scientific S.E.; *Int'l*, pg. 2544
EUROFINS INSTITUT DR. APPELT LEIPZIG GMBH—See Eurofins Scientific S.E.; *Int'l*, pg. 2544
EUROFINS INSTITUT DR. ROTHE GMBH—See Eurofins Scientific S.E.; *Int'l*, pg. 2544
EUROFINS INSTITUT JAGER GMBH—See Eurofins Scientific S.E.; *Int'l*, pg. 2544
EUROFINS INSTITUT NEHRING GMBH—See Eurofins Scientific S.E.; *Int'l*, pg. 2544
EUROFINS INTERLAB SELAS S.A.S—See Eurofins Scientific S.E.; *Int'l*, pg. 2544
EUROFINS INTERNATIONAL HOLDINGS LUX SARL—See Eurofins Scientific S.E.; *Int'l*, pg. 2544
EUROFINS IPL ENVIRONNEMENT SAS—See Eurofins Scientific S.E.; *Int'l*, pg. 2542
EUROFINS IPL EST SAS—See Eurofins Scientific S.E.; *Int'l*, pg. 2542
EUROFINS IPL ILE DE FRANCE SAS—See Eurofins Scientific S.E.; *Int'l*, pg. 2542
EUROFINS IPL SUD SAS—See Eurofins Scientific S.E.; *Int'l*, pg. 2542
EUROFINS IT-INFRASTRUCTURE GMBH—See Eurofins Scientific S.E.; *Int'l*, pg. 2548
EUROFINS IT INFRASTRUCTURE GSC S.A.—See Eurofins Scientific S.E.; *Int'l*, pg. 2544
EUROFINS IT SOLUTIONS INDIA PVT LTD—See Eurofins Scientific S.E.; *Int'l*, pg. 2544

EUROFINS I VERWALTUNGSGESELLSCHAFT GMBH—See Eurofins Scientific S.E.; *Int'l*, pg. 2544
EUROFINS IZMIR GIDA ANALIZ LABORATUVARLARI LIMITED SIRKETI—See Eurofins Scientific S.E.; *Int'l*, pg. 2544
EUROFINS J3 RESOURCES, INC.—See Eurofins Scientific S.E.; *Int'l*, pg. 2544
EUROFINS JAPAN ANALYTICAL CHEMISTRY CONSULTANTS CO., LTD.—See Eurofins Scientific S.E.; *Int'l*, pg. 2544
EUROFINS JAPAN KK—See Eurofins Scientific S.E.; *Int'l*, pg. 2544
EUROFINS KCTL CO., LTD.—See Eurofins Scientific S.E.; *Int'l*, pg. 2544
EUROFINS KOREA ANALYTIC SERVICE CO., LTD.—See Eurofins Scientific S.E.; *Int'l*, pg. 2544
EUROFINS KVI-PLUSZ KORNYEZETVEDELMI VIZSGALO IRODA KFT.—See Eurofins Scientific S.E.; *Int'l*, pg. 2544
EUROFINS LABAZUR BRETAGNE SELAS—See Eurofins Scientific S.E.; *Int'l*, pg. 2545
EUROFINS LABAZUR PROVENCE SELAS—See Eurofins Scientific S.E.; *Int'l*, pg. 2545
EUROFINS LABAZUR RHONE-ALPES SELAS—See Eurofins Scientific S.E.; *Int'l*, pg. 2545
EUROFINS LAB ENVIRONMENT TESTING PORTUGAL, UNIPESSOAL LDA.—See Eurofins Scientific S.E.; *Int'l*, pg. 2545
EUROFINS LABORATOIRE CENTRE SAS—See Eurofins Scientific S.E.; *Int'l*, pg. 2542
EUROFINS LABORATOIRE CONTAMINANTS SUD SAS—See Eurofins Scientific S.E.; *Int'l*, pg. 2545
EUROFINS LABORATOIRE DE BROMATOLOGIE OUEST ET BRETAGNE SAS—See Eurofins Scientific S.E.; *Int'l*, pg. 2545
EUROFINS LABORATOIRE DE MICROBIOLOGIE EST SAS—See Eurofins Scientific S.E.; *Int'l*, pg. 2542
EUROFINS LABORATOIRE DE MICROBIOLOGIE SUD SAS—See Eurofins Scientific S.E.; *Int'l*, pg. 2545
EUROFINS LABORATOIRE DE PATHOLOGIE VEGETALE SAS—See Eurofins Scientific S.E.; *Int'l*, pg. 2542
EUROFINS LABORATOIRE DERMSCAN SAS—See Eurofins Scientific S.E.; *Int'l*, pg. 2545
EUROFINS LABORATOIRE MICROBIOLOGIE RHONE-ALPES S.A.S.—See Eurofins Scientific S.E.; *Int'l*, pg. 2545
EUROFINS LABORATOIRE NORD SAS—See Eurofins Scientific S.E.; *Int'l*, pg. 2542
EUROFINS LABORATOIRES DE MICROBIOLOGIE OUEST SAS—See Eurofins Scientific S.E.; *Int'l*, pg. 2542
EUROFINS LABORATORIES LTD.—See Eurofins Scientific S.E.; *Int'l*, pg. 2545
EUROFINS LABORATORIO ALFALAB INTERNACIONAL, SL—See Eurofins Scientific S.E.; *Int'l*, pg. 2545
EUROFINS LABORATORIO ANGEL MENDEZ, SL—See Eurofins Scientific S.E.; *Int'l*, pg. 2545
EUROFINS LABORATORIO BERNAD-MUNOZ, SL—See Eurofins Scientific S.E.; *Int'l*, pg. 2545
EUROFINS LABORATORIO CALBO, SL—See Eurofins Scientific S.E.; *Int'l*, pg. 2545
EUROFINS LABORATORIO CLINICO SANITARIO, SL—See Eurofins Scientific S.E.; *Int'l*, pg. 2545
EUROFINS LABORATORIO DE CASTILLA Y LEON, SL—See Eurofins Scientific S.E.; *Int'l*, pg. 2545
EUROFINS LABORATORIO DRES. CERMENO, SL—See Eurofins Scientific S.E.; *Int'l*, pg. 2545
EUROFINS LABORATORIO DR. VALENZUELA, SL—See Eurofins Scientific S.E.; *Int'l*, pg. 2545
EUROFINS LABORATORIO MEDICANTABRIA SL—See Eurofins Scientific S.E.; *Int'l*, pg. 2545
EUROFINS LABORATORIO PILAR LARRAZ, SL—See Eurofins Scientific S.E.; *Int'l*, pg. 2545
EUROFINS LABORATORIO PREFASI SL—See Eurofins Scientific S.E.; *Int'l*, pg. 2545
EUROFINS LABORATORIO RECIO, SL—See Eurofins Scientific S.E.; *Int'l*, pg. 2545
EUROFINS LABORATORIO SARRO SL—See Eurofins Scientific S.E.; *Int'l*, pg. 2545
EUROFINS LABORATORIO SURLAB, SL—See Eurofins Scientific S.E.; *Int'l*, pg. 2545
EUROFINS LABORATORIO VIRTUDES SL—See Eurofins Scientific S.E.; *Int'l*, pg. 2545
EUROFINS LABORSERVICES GMBH—See Eurofins Scientific S.E.; *Int'l*, pg. 2545
EUROFINS LABO VAN POUCKE BVBA—See Eurofins Scientific S.E.; *Int'l*, pg. 2545
EUROFINS LAB SOLUTION SRL—See Eurofins Scientific S.E.; *Int'l*, pg. 2545
EUROFINS LABTARNA LIETUVA UAB—See Eurofins Scientific S.E.; *Int'l*, pg. 2545
EUROFINS LABTIUM OY—See Eurofins Scientific S.E.; *Int'l*, pg. 2545
EUROFINS LAB ZEEUWS-VLAANDEREN (LZV) BV—See Eurofins Scientific S.E.; *Int'l*, pg. 2545
EUROFINS LAMM S.R.L.—See Eurofins Scientific S.E.; *Int'l*, pg. 2545
EUROFINS LANAGRAM SAS—See Eurofins Scientific S.E.; *Int'l*, pg. 2545

EUROFINS LANCASTER LABORATORIES ENVIRONMENT TESTING, LLC—See Eurofins Scientific S.E.; *Int'l*, pg. 2545
EUROFINS LANCASTER LABORATORIES, INC. - PORTAGE—See Eurofins Scientific S.E.; *Int'l*, pg. 2548
EUROFINS LANCASTER LABORATORIES, INC.—See Eurofins Scientific S.E.; *Int'l*, pg. 2548
EUROFINS LARA SA—See Eurofins Scientific S.E.; *Int'l*, pg. 2542
EUROFINS LCDI SAS—See Eurofins Scientific S.E.; *Int'l*, pg. 2544
EUROFINS LCPL BV—See Eurofins Scientific S.E.; *Int'l*, pg. 2545
EUROFINS LEA SAS—See Eurofins Scientific S.E.; *Int'l*, pg. 2545
EUROFINS LEBENSMITTELANALYTIK OSTERREICH GMBH—See Eurofins Scientific S.E.; *Int'l*, pg. 2545
EUROFINS LEM SAS—See Eurofins Scientific S.E.; *Int'l*, pg. 2543
EUROFINS LGS MEGALAB ANALISIS VETERINARIOS SLU—See Eurofins Scientific S.E.; *Int'l*, pg. 2545
EUROFINS LIFECODEXX GMBH—See Eurofins Scientific S.E.; *Int'l*, pg. 2545
EUROFINS LIMED LTD.—See Eurofins Scientific S.E.; *Int'l*, pg. 2545
EUROFINS MARKETING RESEARCH SAS—See Eurofins Scientific S.E.; *Int'l*, pg. 2543
EUROFINS MAS CONTROL SLU—See Eurofins Scientific S.E.; *Int'l*, pg. 2545
EUROFINS MASER B.V.—See Eurofins Scientific S.E.; *Int'l*, pg. 2545
EUROFINS MATERIALS SCIENCE NETHERLANDS BV—See Eurofins Scientific S.E.; *Int'l*, pg. 2546
EUROFINS MECHEM PTE. LTD.—See Eurofins Scientific S.E.; *Int'l*, pg. 2546
EUROFINS MEDIGENOMIX FORENSIK GMBH—See Eurofins Scientific S.E.; *Int'l*, pg. 2546
EUROFINS MEDIGENOMIX GMBH—See Eurofins Scientific S.E.; *Int'l*, pg. 2546
EUROFINS MEDINET BV—See Eurofins Scientific S.E.; *Int'l*, pg. 2546
EUROFINS MEDINET INC.—See Eurofins Scientific S.E.; *Int'l*, pg. 2548
EUROFINS MEDINET PTE. LTD.—See Eurofins Scientific S.E.; *Int'l*, pg. 2546
EUROFINS MEDINET SAS—See Eurofins Scientific S.E.; *Int'l*, pg. 2543
EUROFINS MEDISCAN LABORATORIES SDN. BHD.—See Eurofins Scientific S.E.; *Int'l*, pg. 2546
EUROFINS MEDISCHE MICROBIOLOGIE B.V.—See Eurofins Scientific S.E.; *Int'l*, pg. 2546
EUROFINS MEGALAB SA—See Eurofins Scientific S.E.; *Int'l*, pg. 2546
EUROFINS METODOS SERVICIOS AGRICOLAS, S.L.U.—See Eurofins Scientific S.E.; *Int'l*, pg. 2546
EUROFINS MGS LABORATORIES LIMITED—See Eurofins Scientific S.E.; *Int'l*, pg. 2546
EUROFINS MICROBIOLOGIE DES EAUX OUEST SAS—See Eurofins Scientific S.E.; *Int'l*, pg. 2546
EUROFINS MICROBIOLOGY LABORATORIES INC.—See Eurofins Scientific S.E.; *Int'l*, pg. 2546
EUROFINS MICROSCAN S.A.—See Eurofins Scientific S.E.; *Int'l*, pg. 2546
EUROFINS MIKRO KEMI AB—See Eurofins Scientific S.E.; *Int'l*, pg. 2546
EUROFINS MILJO A/S—See Eurofins Scientific S.E.; *Int'l*, pg. 2546
EUROFINS MILJO (GALTEN)—See Eurofins Scientific S.E.; *Int'l*, pg. 2546
EUROFINS MILJO LUFT A/S—See Eurofins Scientific S.E.; *Int'l*, pg. 2546
EUROFINS MILK TESTING DENMARK A/S—See Eurofins Scientific S.E.; *Int'l*, pg. 2546
EUROFINS MILK TESTING SWEDEN AB—See Eurofins Scientific S.E.; *Int'l*, pg. 2546
EUROFINS MINERAG KFT.—See Eurofins Scientific S.E.; *Int'l*, pg. 2546
EUROFINS MITOX BV—See Eurofins Scientific S.E.; *Int'l*, pg. 2546
EUROFINS MITOX FOPSE S.A.R.L.—See Eurofins Scientific S.E.; *Int'l*, pg. 2546
EUROFINS MODERN TESTING SERVICES BANGLADESH LIMITED—See Eurofins Scientific S.E.; *Int'l*, pg. 2546
EUROFINS MODERN TESTING SERVICE TAIWAN, LTD.—See Eurofins Scientific S.E.; *Int'l*, pg. 2546
EUROFINS MODULO UNO SPA—See Eurofins Scientific S.E.; *Int'l*, pg. 2548
EUROFINS MTS CONSUMER PRODUCT TESTING CAMBODIA LTD.—See Eurofins Scientific S.E.; *Int'l*, pg. 2545
EUROFINS MTS CONSUMER PRODUCT TESTING GERMANY GMBH—See Eurofins Scientific S.E.; *Int'l*, pg. 2545
EUROFINS MTS CONSUMER PRODUCT TESTING (HONG KONG) CO., LTD.—See Eurofins Scientific S.E.; *Int'l*, pg. 2545

EURO-FINANCE LTD.

CORPORATE AFFILIATIONS

EUROFINS MTS CONSUMER PRODUCT TESTING (SHANGHAI) CO., LTD.—See Eurofins Scientific S.E.; *Int'l*, pg. 2545
EUROFINS MTS CONSUMER PRODUCT TESTING UK LIMITED—See Eurofins Scientific S.E.; *Int'l*, pg. 2545
EUROFINS MUNUERA, S.L.U.—See Eurofins Scientific S.E.; *Int'l*, pg. 2546
EUROFINS MWG BIOTECH FRANCE S.A.—See Eurofins Scientific S.E.; *Int'l*, pg. 2543
EUROFINS MWG GMBH—See Eurofins Scientific S.E.; *Int'l*, pg. 2551
EUROFINS MWG OPERON INC.—See Eurofins Scientific S.E.; *Int'l*, pg. 2548
EUROFINS MWG SYNTHESIS GMBH—See Eurofins Scientific S.E.; *Int'l*, pg. 2551
EUROFINS NAB LABS OY—See Eurofins Scientific S.E.; *Int'l*, pg. 2546
EUROFINS NANOLAB TECHNOLOGIES, INC.—See Eurofins Scientific S.E.; *Int'l*, pg. 2546
EUROFINS NBLSC ENVIRONMENT TESTING SPAIN, S.L.U.—See Eurofins Scientific S.E.; *Int'l*, pg. 2546
EUROFINS NDSC FOOD FRANCE SAS—See Eurofins Scientific S.E.; *Int'l*, pg. 2543
EUROFINS NDSC FOOD TESTING GERMANY GMBH—See Eurofins Scientific S.E.; *Int'l*, pg. 2546
EUROFINS NDSC UMWELTANALYTIK GMBH—See Eurofins Scientific S.E.; *Int'l*, pg. 2546
EUROFINS NDSM LIMITED—See Eurofins Scientific S.E.; *Int'l*, pg. 2546
EUROFINS NM LABORATORY SDN BHD—See Eurofins Scientific S.E.; *Int'l*, pg. 2546
EUROFINS NORSK MATANALYSE AS—See Eurofins Scientific S.E.; *Int'l*, pg. 2546
EUROFINS NORSK MILJOANALYSE AS—See Eurofins Scientific S.E.; *Int'l*, pg. 2546
EUROFINS NORTH MALAYA LABORATORY SDN BHD—See Eurofins Scientific S.E.; *Int'l*, pg. 2546
EUROFINS NSC DENMARK A/S—See Eurofins Scientific S.E.; *Int'l*, pg. 2546
EUROFINS NSC DEVELOPPEMENT FRANCE SAS—See Eurofins Scientific S.E.; *Int'l*, pg. 2543
EUROFINS NSC FINANCE GERMANY GMBH—See Eurofins Scientific S.E.; *Int'l*, pg. 2546
EUROFINS NSC NETHERLANDS BV—See Eurofins Scientific S.E.; *Int'l*, pg. 2546
EUROFINS NSC UK & IRELAND LTD—See Eurofins Scientific S.E.; *Int'l*, pg. 2546
EUROFINS NTD, INC.—See Eurofins Scientific S.E.; *Int'l*, pg. 2548
EUROFINS OBIKS POLSKA SP. Z.O.O.—See Eurofins Scientific S.E.; *Int'l*, pg. 2546
EUROFINS - OFI LEBENSMITTELANALYTIK GMBH—See Eurofins Scientific S.E.; *Int'l*, pg. 2536
EUROFINS OKOLABOR KFT.—See Eurofins Scientific S.E.; *Int'l*, pg. 2546
EUROFINS OKOMETRIC GMBH—See Eurofins Scientific S.E.; *Int'l*, pg. 2546
EUROFINS OMEGAM BV—See Eurofins Scientific S.E.; *Int'l*, pg. 2546
EUROFINS OPTIMED LYON SAS—See Eurofins Scientific S.E.; *Int'l*, pg. 2543
EUROFINS OPTIMED SAS—See Eurofins Scientific S.E.; *Int'l*, pg. 2543
EUROFINS PANLABS DISCOVERY SERVICES TAIWAN, LTD.—See Eurofins Scientific S.E.; *Int'l*, pg. 2546
EUROFINS PANLABS, INC.—See Eurofins Scientific S.E.; *Int'l*, pg. 2542
EUROFINS PATHOLOGIE SELAS—See Eurofins Scientific S.E.; *Int'l*, pg. 2547
EUROFINS PEGASUSLAB AB—See Eurofins Scientific S.E.; *Int'l*, pg. 2547
EUROFINS PHARMA BIOANALYTICS SERVICES US, INC.—See Eurofins Scientific S.E.; *Int'l*, pg. 2547
EUROFINS PHARMA CONTROL SAS—See Eurofins Scientific S.E.; *Int'l*, pg. 2543
EUROFINS PHARMA QUALITY CONTROL DENMARK A/S—See Eurofins Scientific S.E.; *Int'l*, pg. 2547
EUROFINS PHARMA QUALITY CONTROL SAS—See Eurofins Scientific S.E.; *Int'l*, pg. 2543
EUROFINS PHARMA SERVICES INDIA PVT LTD—See Eurofins Scientific S.E.; *Int'l*, pg. 2547
EUROFINS PHARMA US HOLDINGS BV—See Eurofins Scientific S.E.; *Int'l*, pg. 2547
EUROFINS PHAST DEVELOPMENT GMBH & CO. KG—See Eurofins Scientific S.E.; *Int'l*, pg. 2546
EUROFINS PHYLIAE S.A.S.—See Eurofins Scientific S.E.; *Int'l*, pg. 2547
EUROFINS PIVETTI SRL—See Eurofins Scientific S.E.; *Int'l*, pg. 2547
EUROFINS POLSKA SP. Z.O.O.—See Eurofins Scientific S.E.; *Int'l*, pg. 2547
EUROFINS PRECISION TEM, LLC—See Eurofins Scientific S.E.; *Int'l*, pg. 2547
EUROFINS PRELEVEMENT POUR LE BATIMENT EST SAS—See Eurofins Scientific S.E.; *Int'l*, pg. 2547
EUROFINS PRELEVEMENT POUR LE BATIMENT FRANCE SAS—See Eurofins Scientific S.E.; *Int'l*, pg. 2550

EUROFINS PRELEVEMENT POUR LE BATIMENT ILE-DE-FRANCE SAS—See Eurofins Scientific S.E.; *Int'l*, pg. 2547
EUROFINS PRELEVEMENT POUR LE BATIMENT NORD SAS—See Eurofins Scientific S.E.; *Int'l*, pg. 2550
EUROFINS PRELEVEMENT POUR LE BATIMENT OUEST SAS—See Eurofins Scientific S.E.; *Int'l*, pg. 2550
EUROFINS PRELEVEMENT POUR LE BATIMENT SUD-EST SAS—See Eurofins Scientific S.E.; *Int'l*, pg. 2550
EUROFINS PRELEVEMENT POUR LE BATIMENT SUD-OUEST SAS—See Eurofins Scientific S.E.; *Int'l*, pg. 2547
EUROFINS PRODUCT SAFETY LABS INC.—See Eurofins Scientific S.E.; *Int'l*, pg. 2547
EUROFINS PRODUCT SERVICE GMBH—See Eurofins Scientific S.E.; *Int'l*, pg. 2547
EUROFINS PRODUCT SERVICE (THAILAND) CO., LTD—See Eurofins Scientific S.E.; *Int'l*, pg. 2547
EUROFINS PRODUCT TESTING, COSMETICS & PERSONAL CARE SPAIN, S.L.U.—See Eurofins Scientific S.E.; *Int'l*, pg. 2547
EUROFINS PRODUCT TESTING DENMARK A/S—See Eurofins Scientific S.E.; *Int'l*, pg. 2547
EUROFINS PRODUCT TESTING INDIA PVT LTD—See Eurofins Scientific S.E.; *Int'l*, pg. 2547
EUROFINS PRODUCT TESTING ITALY SRL—See Eurofins Scientific S.E.; *Int'l*, pg. 2547
EUROFINS PRODUCT TESTING JAPAN KK—See Eurofins Scientific S.E.; *Int'l*, pg. 2547
EUROFINS PRODUCT TESTING SERVICE (SHANGHAI) CO., LTD—See Eurofins Scientific S.E.; *Int'l*, pg. 2547
EUROFINS PRODUCT TESTING SERVICES LTD—See Eurofins Scientific S.E.; *Int'l*, pg. 2547
EUROFINS PRODUCT TESTING US INC.—See Eurofins Scientific S.E.; *Int'l*, pg. 2547
EUROFINS PRODUCT TESTING VERWALTUNGS GMBH—See Eurofins Scientific S.E.; *Int'l*, pg. 2547
EUROFINS PROFESSIONAL SCIENTIFIC SERVICES BELGIUM NV—See Eurofins Scientific S.E.; *Int'l*, pg. 2547
EUROFINS PROMICRO PTY LTD.—See Eurofins Scientific S.E.; *Int'l*, pg. 2547
EUROFINS PROXY LABORATORIES BV—See Eurofins Scientific S.E.; *Int'l*, pg. 2546
EUROFINS Q-BIOANALYTIC GMBH—See Eurofins Scientific S.E.; *Int'l*, pg. 2547
EUROFINS QKEN KK—See Eurofins Scientific S.E.; *Int'l*, pg. 2547
EUROFINS QTA INC.—See Eurofins Scientific S.E.; *Int'l*, pg. 2547
EUROFINS QUALITECH AG—See Eurofins Scientific S.E.; *Int'l*, pg. 2547
EUROFINS QUIMICO ONUBENSE, S.L.U.—See Eurofins Scientific S.E.; *Int'l*, pg. 2547
EUROFINS RADONLAB AS—See Eurofins Scientific S.E.; *Int'l*, pg. 2547
EUROFINS RADON TESTING SWEDEN AB—See Eurofins Scientific S.E.; *Int'l*, pg. 2547
EUROFINS REGULATORY AG—See Eurofins Scientific S.E.; *Int'l*, pg. 2547
EUROFINS REGULATORY & CONSULTANCY SERVICES ITALY S.R.L.—See Eurofins Scientific S.E.; *Int'l*, pg. 2547
EUROFINS RESERVOIRS ENVIRONMENTAL, INC.—See Eurofins Scientific S.E.; *Int'l*, pg. 2547
EUROFINS SAC KY HAI DANG COMPANY LTD.—See Eurofins Scientific S.E.; *Int'l*, pg. 2547
EUROFINS SALUX B.V.—See Eurofins Scientific S.E.; *Int'l*, pg. 2547
EUROFINS SAM SENSORY & MARKETING ITALY SRL—See Eurofins Scientific S.E.; *Int'l*, pg. 2547
EUROFINS SANITAS INSPECTIONS BV—See Eurofins Scientific S.E.; *Int'l*, pg. 2547
EUROFINS SAUDI AJAL LABORATORIES LTD.—See Eurofins Scientific S.E.; *Int'l*, pg. 2547
EUROFINS SCIENTIFIC AGROGENE SARL—See Eurofins Scientific S.E.; *Int'l*, pg. 2543
EUROFINS SCIENTIFIC AG—See Eurofins Scientific S.E.; *Int'l*, pg. 2547
EUROFINS SCIENTIFIC ANALYTICS SAS—See Eurofins Scientific S.E.; *Int'l*, pg. 2543
EUROFINS SCIENTIFIC BIOSCIENCES SAS—See Eurofins Scientific S.E.; *Int'l*, pg. 2543
EUROFINS SCIENTIFIC BV—See Eurofins Scientific S.E.; *Int'l*, pg. 2547
EUROFINS SCIENTIFIC CZ S.R.O.—See Eurofins Scientific S.E.; *Int'l*, pg. 2548
EUROFINS SCIENTIFIC FINLAND OY—See Eurofins Scientific S.E.; *Int'l*, pg. 2548
EUROFINS SCIENTIFIC GMBH—See Eurofins Scientific S.E.; *Int'l*, pg. 2548
EUROFINS SCIENTIFIC, INC.—See Eurofins Scientific S.E.; *Int'l*, pg. 2548
EUROFINS SCIENTIFIC (IRELAND) LIMITED—See Eurofins Scientific S.E.; *Int'l*, pg. 2547
EUROFINS SCIENTIFIC ITALIA SRL—See Eurofins Scientific S.E.; *Int'l*, pg. 2548

EUROFINS SCIENTIFIC JAPAN K.K.—See Eurofins Scientific S.E.; *Int'l*, pg. 2548
EUROFINS SCIENTIFIC SERVICES S.A.—See Eurofins Scientific S.E.; *Int'l*, pg. 2548
EUROFINS SCIENTIFIC S.E.; *Int'l*, pg. 2535
EUROFINS SCIENTIFIC TEST CENTER SAS—See Eurofins Scientific S.E.; *Int'l*, pg. 2543
EUROFINS SCITEC S.A.—See Eurofins Scientific S.E.; *Int'l*, pg. 2548
EUROFINS SELCIA LIMITED—See Eurofins Scientific S.E.; *Int'l*, pg. 2548
EUROFINS SENSORY CONSUMER & PRODUCT RESEARCH (SHANGHAI), LTD.—See Eurofins Scientific S.E.; *Int'l*, pg. 2548
EUROFINS SEPO SP. Z O.O.—See Eurofins Scientific S.E.; *Int'l*, pg. 2547
EUROFINS SF ANALYTICAL LABORATORIES, INC.—See Eurofins Scientific S.E.; *Int'l*, pg. 2548
EUROFINS SICA AGRIQ SL—See Eurofins Scientific S.E.; *Int'l*, pg. 2548
EUROFINS SISTHEMA S.R.L.—See Eurofins Scientific S.E.; *Int'l*, pg. 2548
EUROFINS SOFIA GMBH—See Eurofins Scientific S.E.; *Int'l*, pg. 2547
EUROFINS SPECTRUM ANALYTICAL, LLC—See Eurofins Scientific S.E.; *Int'l*, pg. 2548
EUROFINS SPINNOVATION ANALYTICAL BV—See Eurofins Scientific S.E.; *Int'l*, pg. 2548
EUROFINS STEINS LABORATORIUM A/S—See Eurofins Scientific S.E.; *Int'l*, pg. 2541
EUROFINS STEINS LABORATORIUM SP. Z.O.O.—See Eurofins Scientific S.E.; *Int'l*, pg. 2540
EUROFINS SUMMIT TSIANDE ENVIRONMENTAL CO., LTD.—See Eurofins Scientific S.E.; *Int'l*, pg. 2548
EUROFINS TAIYO TECHNO RESEARCH KK—See Eurofins Scientific S.E.; *Int'l*, pg. 2549
EUROFINS TECHNOLOGIES AUSTRALIA PTY LTD—See Eurofins Scientific S.E.; *Int'l*, pg. 2549
EUROFINS TECHNOLOGY SERVICE (GUANGZHOU) CO., LTD.—See Eurofins Scientific S.E.; *Int'l*, pg. 2549
EUROFINS TECHNOLOGY SERVICE (QINGDAO) CO., LTD.—See Eurofins Scientific S.E.; *Int'l*, pg. 2549
EUROFINS TECHNOLOGY SERVICES (SUZHOU) CO., LTD—See Eurofins Scientific S.E.; *Int'l*, pg. 2549
EUROFINS TECHNOLOGY SERVICE (SUZHOU) LTD.—See Eurofins Scientific S.E.; *Int'l*, pg. 2549
EUROFINS TEST CENTER SAS—See Eurofins Scientific S.E.; *Int'l*, pg. 2543
EUROFINS TESTING A/S—See Eurofins Scientific S.E.; *Int'l*, pg. 2549
EUROFINS TESTING CHILE S.A.—See Eurofins Scientific S.E.; *Int'l*, pg. 2549
EUROFINS TESTING INSPECTION CERTIFICATION (CHENGDU) CO., LTD.—See Eurofins Scientific S.E.; *Int'l*, pg. 2549
EUROFINS TESTING INSPECTION CERTIFICATION (XIAMEN) CO., LTD.—See Eurofins Scientific S.E.; *Int'l*, pg. 2549
EUROFINS TESTING TECHNOLOGY (SHENZHEN) CO., LTD—See Eurofins Scientific S.E.; *Int'l*, pg. 2549
EUROFINS TESTIRANJA IN RAZISKAVE OKOLJA SLOVENIJA D.O.O.—See Eurofins Scientific S.E.; *Int'l*, pg. 2550
EUROFINS TESTOIL, INC.—See Eurofins Scientific S.E.; *Int'l*, pg. 2549
EUROFINS TEXTILE TESTING SPAIN SL—See Eurofins Scientific S.E.; *Int'l*, pg. 2549
EUROFINS TRIALCAMP, S.L.U.—See Eurofins Scientific S.E.; *Int'l*, pg. 2549
EUROFINS TSING HUA ENVIRONMENT TESTING CO., LTD.—See Eurofins Scientific S.E.; *Int'l*, pg. 2549
EUROFINS TUKETICI URUNLERI TEST HIZMETLERI A.S.—See Eurofins Scientific S.E.; *Int'l*, pg. 2549
EUROFINS TURKEY ANALIZ HIZMETLERI LIMITED SIRKETI—See Eurofins Scientific S.E.; *Int'l*, pg. 2549
EUROFINS UMWELT OST GMBH—See Eurofins Scientific S.E.; *Int'l*, pg. 2549
EUROFINS UMWELT WEST GMBH—See Eurofins Scientific S.E.; *Int'l*, pg. 2537
EUROFINS VBM LABORATORIET A/S—See Eurofins Scientific S.E.; *Int'l*, pg. 2549
EUROFINS VETCONTROL KFT.—See Eurofins Scientific S.E.; *Int'l*, pg. 2549
EUROFINS VILJAVUUSPALVELU OY—See Eurofins Scientific S.E.; *Int'l*, pg. 2549
EUROFINS VILLAPHARMA RESEARCH SL—See Eurofins Scientific S.E.; *Int'l*, pg. 2549
EUROFINS VIRACOR BIOPHARMA SERVICES, INC.—See Eurofins Scientific S.E.; *Int'l*, pg. 2549
EUROFINS VIRACOR, INC.—See Eurofins Scientific S.E.; *Int'l*, pg. 2549
EUROFINS VRL, INC.—See Eurofins Scientific S.E.; *Int'l*, pg. 2549
EUROFINS WATER TESTING SWEDEN AB—See Eurofins Scientific S.E.; *Int'l*, pg. 2550
EUROFINS WATER&WASTE GMBH—See Eurofins Scientific S.E.; *Int'l*, pg. 2550
EUROFINS WEJ CONTAMINANTS GMBH—See Eurofins Scientific S.E.; *Int'l*, pg. 2549

EUROFINS WFC ANALYTICS B.V.—See Eurofins Scientific S.E.; *Int'l*, pg. 2549
EUROFINS WFC-FOOD SAFETY B.V.—See Eurofins Scientific S.E.; *Int'l*, pg. 2549
EUROFINS WKS LABSERVICE GMBH—See Eurofins Scientific S.E.; *Int'l*, pg. 2549
EUROFINS WOOSOL CO., LTD.—See Eurofins Scientific S.E.; *Int'l*, pg. 2550
EUROFINS YORK LIMITED—See Eurofins Scientific S.E.; *Int'l*, pg. 2550
EUROFIX; *U.S. Private*, pg. 1433
EUROFLACO COMPIEGNE SARL; *Int'l*, pg. 2552
EUROFLEX TRANSMISSIONS (INDIA) PRIVATE LTD.—See Zurn Elkay Water Solutions Corporation; *U.S. Public*, pg. 2412
EUROFLOAT SAS—See Compagnie de Saint-Gobain SA; *Int'l*, pg. 1736
EUROFLON TEKNISKA PRODUKTER AB—See Indutrade AB; *Int'l*, pg. 3678
EUROFLORIST SVERIGE AB—See Litorina Capital Management AB; *Int'l*, pg. 4527
EUROFLUID HYDRAULIC S.R.L.—See Interpump Group S.p.A.; *Int'l*, pg. 3755
EUROFOAM BOHEMIA S.R.O.—See Greiner Holding AG; *Int'l*, pg. 3078
EUROFOAM DEUTSCHLAND GMBH SCHAUMSTOFFE—See Greiner Holding AG; *Int'l*, pg. 3078
EUROFOAM GDANSK SP. Z O.O.—See Greiner Holding AG; *Int'l*, pg. 3078
EUROFOAM G.E.I.E.—See Greiner Holding AG; *Int'l*, pg. 3078
EUROFOAM GMBH—See Greiner Holding AG; *Int'l*, pg. 3078
EUROFOAM HUNGARY KFT—See Greiner Holding AG; *Int'l*, pg. 3078
EUROFOAM POLSKA SP. Z O.O.—See Greiner Holding AG; *Int'l*, pg. 3078
EUROFOAM POZNAN SP. Z O.O.—See Greiner Holding AG; *Int'l*, pg. 3078
EUROFOAM S.R.L.—See Greiner Holding AG; *Int'l*, pg. 3078
EUROFOGA S.L.—See Foga System International AB; *Int'l*, pg. 2720
EUROFOIL LUXEMBOURG S.A.—See American Industrial Acquisition Corporation; *U.S. Private*, pg. 237
EUROFORUM BV—See Informa plc; *Int'l*, pg. 3691
EUROFORUM DEUTSCHLAND (HOLDING) GMBH—See Informa plc; *Int'l*, pg. 3691
EUROFRAGANCE, LLC—See Eurofragance SLU; *Int'l*, pg. 2552
EUROFRAGANCE SLU; *Int'l*, pg. 2552
EURO FRIGO A.D.; *Int'l*, pg. 2531
EUROFRIGO B.V.—See Nichirei Corporation; *Int'l*, pg. 5270
EUROFRIGO VENLO B.V.—See Nichirei Corporation; *Int'l*, pg. 5270
EURO GARAGES LTD.—See TDR Capital LLP; *Int'l*, pg. 7494
EURO GARAGE SOLUTIONS LTD—See LKQ Corporation; *U.S. Public*, pg. 1334
EURO GARANTIE AG—See Allianz SE; *Int'l*, pg. 353
EUROGAS INTERNATIONAL INC.; *Int'l*, pg. 2552
EUROGAZ-GDYNIA SP. Z O.O.—See Linde plc; *Int'l*, pg. 4504
EUROGENE AI SERVICES IRL LTD—See Livestock Improvement Corporation Limited; *Int'l*, pg. 4531
EUROGERM ANDINA—See Eurogerm SA; *Int'l*, pg. 2552
EUROGERM BRASIL PRODUTOS ALIMENTICIOS LIMITADA—See Eurogerm SA; *Int'l*, pg. 2552
EUROGERM IBERIA, S.L.U.—See Eurogerm SA; *Int'l*, pg. 2552
EUROGERM MAROC—See Eurogerm SA; *Int'l*, pg. 2552
EUROGERM MEXICO SA DE CV—See Eurogerm SA; *Int'l*, pg. 2552
EUROGERM SA; *Int'l*, pg. 2552
EUROGERM SENEGAL—See Eurogerm SA; *Int'l*, pg. 2552
EUROGERM SOUTH AFRICA (PTY) LTD.—See Eurogerm SA; *Int'l*, pg. 2552
EURO GLOBE HOLDINGS LTD.—See MAPFRE S.A.; *Int'l*, pg. 4685
EUROGRAFICA SYSTEMPLANUNGS-GMBH—See Allianz SE; *Int'l*, pg. 352
EUROGREEN AUSTRIA GMBH—See BayWa AG; *Int'l*, pg. 917
EUROGREEN CZ S.R.O.,—See BayWa AG; *Int'l*, pg. 917
EUROGREEN GMBH—See BayWa AG; *Int'l*, pg. 917
EUROGREEN ITALIA S.R.L.—See BayWa AG; *Int'l*, pg. 917
EUROGRID GMBH—See Elia Group SA; *Int'l*, pg. 2360
EUROGRID INTERNATIONAL CVBA/SCRL—See Elia Group SA; *Int'l*, pg. 2360
EUROGROUP DEUTSCHLAND GMBH—See Coop-Gruppe Genossenschaft; *Int'l*, pg. 1790
EUROGROUP LAMINATIONS S.P.A.; *Int'l*, pg. 2552
EUROGROUP SA—See Coop-Gruppe Genossenschaft; *Int'l*, pg. 1790

EUROGUARD INSURANCE COMPANY PCC LIMITED—See Alexander Forbes Group Holdings Limited; *Int'l*, pg. 307
EUROHAUS LLC; *Int'l*, pg. 2552
EUROHEALTH SYSTEMS FZ LLC—See Aster DM Healthcare Ltd.; *Int'l*, pg. 654
EUROHERC OSIGURANJE D.D.; *Int'l*, pg. 2552
EUROHOLD BULGARIA AD; *Int'l*, pg. 2552
EURO HOLDINGS BERHAD; *Int'l*, pg. 2531
EUROHYPO EUROPAISCHE HYPOTHEKENBANK S.A. DUBLIN BRANCH—See Commerzbank AG; *Int'l*, pg. 1718
EUROHYPO EUROPAISCHE HYPOTHEKENBANK S.A.—See Commerzbank AG; *Int'l*, pg. 1718
EUROIL LIMITED—See Bowleven plc; *Int'l*, pg. 1124
EUROIMMUN DIAGNOSTICS ESPANA, S.L.U.—See Revvity, Inc.; *U.S. Public*, pg. 1794
EUROIMMUN FRANCE SAS—See Revvity, Inc.; *U.S. Public*, pg. 1794
EUROIMMUN ITALIA DIAGNOSTICA MEDICA S.R.L.—See Revvity, Inc.; *U.S. Public*, pg. 1794
EUROIMMUN JAPAN CO. LTD.—See Revvity, Inc.; *U.S. Public*, pg. 1794
EUROIMMUN MEDICAL DIAGNOSTICS CANADA INC.—See Revvity, Inc.; *U.S. Public*, pg. 1794
EUROIMMUN MEDICAL DIAGNOSTICS (CHINA) CO., LTD—See Revvity, Inc.; *U.S. Public*, pg. 1794
EUROIMMUN MEDICAL LABORATORY DIAGNOSTICS SOUTH AFRICA (PTY) LTD.—See Revvity, Inc.; *U.S. Public*, pg. 1794
EUROIMMUN POLSKA SPOLKA Z O.O.—See Revvity, Inc.; *U.S. Public*, pg. 1794
EUROIMMUN PORTUGAL UNIPESSOAL LDA.—See Revvity, Inc.; *U.S. Public*, pg. 1794
EUROIMMUN SCHWEIZ AG—See Revvity, Inc.; *U.S. Public*, pg. 1794
EUROIMMUN (SOUTH EAST ASIA) PTE LTD—See Revvity, Inc.; *U.S. Public*, pg. 1794
EUROIMMUN TURKEY TIBBI LABORATUAR TESHISLERI A.S.—See Revvity, Inc.; *U.S. Public*, pg. 1794
EUROIMMUN UK LTD.—See Revvity, Inc.; *U.S. Public*, pg. 1794
EUROIMMUN US INC.—See Revvity, Inc.; *U.S. Public*, pg. 1794
EUROIMPIANTI ELECTRONIC S.P.A.—See Argo Finanziaria S.p.A.; *Int'l*, pg. 562
EURO INDIA FRESH FOODS LTD.; *Int'l*, pg. 2531
EURO INGATLAN CENTER KFT.—See BayernLB Holding AG; *Int'l*, pg. 913
EUROINS GEORGIA AD—See Eurohold Bulgaria AD; *Int'l*, pg. 2553
EUROINS INSURANCE AD SKOPJE—See Eurohold Bulgaria AD; *Int'l*, pg. 2553
EUROINS INSURANCE GROUP AD—See Eurohold Bulgaria AD; *Int'l*, pg. 2553
EUROINS INSURANCE PLC; *Int'l*, pg. 2553
EUROINSTRUMENTS CIA. LTDA.—See Endress+Hauser (International) Holding AG; *Int'l*, pg. 2408
EURO-JUICE G.M.B.H. IMPORT AND VERTRIEB—See PepsiCo, Inc.; *U.S. Public*, pg. 1668
EUROKAI GMBH & CO. KGAA; *Int'l*, pg. 2553
EURO KAPITAL YATIRIM ORTAKLIGI A.S.; *Int'l*, pg. 2531
EUROKAT SA—See Intracom Holdings S.A.; *Int'l*, pg. 3767
EUROKERA GUANGZHOU CO., LTD.—See Corning Incorporated; *U.S. Public*, pg. 579
EUROKERA NORTH AMERICA, INC.—See Compagnie de Saint-Gobain SA; *Int'l*, pg. 1730
EUROKERA NORTH AMERICA, INC.—See Corning Incorporated; *U.S. Public*, pg. 579
EUROKERA S.N.C.—See Corning Incorporated; *U.S. Public*, pg. 579
EUROKERA (THAILAND) LIMITED—See Corning Incorporated; *U.S. Public*, pg. 579
EUROKERN GIESSEREITECHNIK GMBH—See Huettenes-Albertus Chemische Werke GmbH; *Int'l*, pg. 3522
EUROKLIMAT SP. Z O.O.—See CEZ, a.s.; *Int'l*, pg. 1427
EUROKONSTRUKCJE SP. Z O.O.—See Huta Pokoj S.A.; *Int'l*, pg. 3540
EUROKONTOR S.R.O.—See BERGER Holding GmbH; *Int'l*, pg. 979
EUROLAB S.R.L.—See Sesa S.p.A.; *Int'l*, pg. 6728
EUROLAITE OY—See Addtech AB; *Int'l*, pg. 133
EUROLAND CORPORATE SA; *Int'l*, pg. 2553
EUROLAND FINANCE SA; *Int'l*, pg. 2553
EUROLEASE AMUN IMMOBILIEN LEASING GESELLSCHAFT M.B.H.—See UniCredit S.p.A.; *Int'l*, pg. 8037
EUROLEASE ANUBIS IMMOBILIEN LEASING GESELLSCHAFT M.B.H.—See UniCredit S.p.A.; *Int'l*, pg. 8037
EURO LEASE AUTO AD—See Eurohold Bulgaria AD; *Int'l*, pg. 2553
EUROLEASE GROUP EAD—See Eurohold Bulgaria AD; *Int'l*, pg. 2553
EUROLEASE ISIS IMMOBILIEN LEASING GESELLSCHAFT M.B.H.—See UniCredit S.p.A.; *Int'l*, pg. 8037
EUROLEASE RAMSES IMMOBILIEN LEASING GESELLSCHAFT M.B.H.—See UniCredit S.p.A.; *Int'l*, pg. 8037
EUROLEDER FASHION LIMITED; *Int'l*, pg. 2553

EUROLIFE ERB GENERAL INSURANCE S.A.—See Fairfax Financial Holdings Limited; *Int'l*, pg. 2606
EUROLIFE ERB GENERAL INSURANCE S.A.—See Ontario Municipal Employees Retirement System; *Int'l*, pg. 5584
EUROLIFE ERB INSURANCE GROUP HOLDINGS S.A.—See Fairfax Financial Holdings Limited; *Int'l*, pg. 2606
EUROLIFE ERB INSURANCE GROUP HOLDINGS S.A.—See Ontario Municipal Employees Retirement System; *Int'l*, pg. 5584
EUROLIFE LTD—See Bank of Cyprus Holdings Public Limited Company; *Int'l*, pg. 842
EUROLINER SAS—See VINCI S.A.; *Int'l*, pg. 8218
EUROLINERS—See Burelle S.A.; *Int'l*, pg. 1223
EUROLINES (UK) LIMITED—See Mobico Group PLC; *Int'l*, pg. 5009
EUROLLS CARBIDE S.R.L.—See EUROLLS S.p.A.; *Int'l*, pg. 2553
EUROLLS DE MEXICO S. DE R.L. DE C.V.—See EUROLLS S.p.A.; *Int'l*, pg. 2553
EUROLLS DO BRASIL LTDA—See EUROLLS S.p.A.; *Int'l*, pg. 2553
EUROLLS MACHINERY (SHANGHAI) CO. LTD.—See EUROLLS S.p.A.; *Int'l*, pg. 2553
EUROLLS S.P.A.; *Int'l*, pg. 2553
EUROLOG CANOLA SOCIMI, S.A.U.; *Int'l*, pg. 2553
EUROLOGISTIK-UMWELTSERVICE GMBH—See Veolia Environnement S.A.; *Int'l*, pg. 8153
EUROLOT SA—See LOT Polish Airlines S.A.; *Int'l*, pg. 4558
EUROLUX (PTY) LTD—See ARB HOLDINGS LIMITED; *Int'l*, pg. 536
EUROMAC SISTEMAS DE CONFECCION, S.A.—See CF Italia srl; *Int'l*, pg. 1429
EUROMAINT AB—See Construcciones y Auxiliar de Ferrocarriles S.A.; *Int'l*, pg. 1777
EUROMAINT GRUPPEN AB—See Construcciones y Auxiliar de Ferrocarriles S.A.; *Int'l*, pg. 1777
EUROMAINT RAIL AB—See Construcciones y Auxiliar de Ferrocarriles S.A.; *Int'l*, pg. 1777
EUROMAL GRUPA STOCZNI GDYNIA SP. Z O.O.—See Stocznia Gdynia S.A.; *Int'l*, pg. 7220
EURO MANGANESE, INC.; *Int'l*, pg. 2553
EURO MARINE CARRIER B.V.—See Mitsui O.S.K. Lines, Ltd.; *Int'l*, pg. 4989
EUROMARKET DESIGNS, INC.—See Otto GmbH & Co. KG; *Int'l*, pg. 5662
EUROMARK GMBH—See VINCI S.A.; *Int'l*, pg. 8218
EUROMARK ROADMARKING—See VINCI S.A.; *Int'l*, pg. 8220
EUROMASKIN AB—See J2L Holding AB; *Int'l*, pg. 3859
EUROMASTER AB—See Compagnie Generale des Etablissements Michelin SCA; *Int'l*, pg. 1742
EUROMASTER AUTOMOCION Y SERVICIOS, S.A.—See Compagnie Generale des Etablissements Michelin SCA; *Int'l*, pg. 1742
EUROMASTER BANDENSERVICE B.V.—See Compagnie Generale des Etablissements Michelin SCA; *Int'l*, pg. 1742
EUROMASTER CESKA REPUBLIKA S.R.O.—See Compagnie Generale des Etablissements Michelin SCA; *Int'l*, pg. 1742
EUROMASTER DANMARK A/S—See Compagnie Generale des Etablissements Michelin SCA; *Int'l*, pg. 1742
EUROMASTER FRANCE S.N.C—See Compagnie Generale des Etablissements Michelin SCA; *Int'l*, pg. 1742
EUROMASTER GMBH—See Compagnie Generale des Etablissements Michelin SCA; *Int'l*, pg. 1742
EUROMASTER ITALIA S.R.L.—See Compagnie Generale des Etablissements Michelin SCA; *Int'l*, pg. 1742
EUROMASTER LASTIK VE SERVIS LIMITED SIRKETI—See Compagnie Generale des Etablissements Michelin SCA; *Int'l*, pg. 1742
EUROMASTER POLSKA SP. Z.O.O.—See Compagnie Generale des Etablissements Michelin SCA; *Int'l*, pg. 1742
EUROMASTER REIFENSERVICE GMBH—See Compagnie Generale des Etablissements Michelin SCA; *Int'l*, pg. 1742
EUROMASTER (SUISSE) S.A.—See Compagnie Generale des Etablissements Michelin SCA; *Int'l*, pg. 1742
EUROMASTER TYRE & SERVICES ROMANIA S.A.—See Compagnie Generale des Etablissements Michelin SCA; *Int'l*, pg. 1742
EUROMAX RESOURCES LTD.; *Int'l*, pg. 2553
EUROMECCANICA S.P.A.—See Chien Wei Precise Technology Co., Ltd.; *Int'l*, pg. 1477
EURO M.E.C. GMBH—See China Machinery Engineering Corporation; *Int'l*, pg. 1516
EURO MECHANICAL & ELECTRICAL CONTRACTORS LTD.; *Int'l*, pg. 2531
EURO MEDIA GROUP SA—See PAI Partners S.A.S.; *Int'l*, pg. 5700
EUROMEDIA—See Vivendi SE; *Int'l*, pg. 8269
EUROMEDICA EXECUTIVE SEARCH GMBH—See Barclays PLC; *Int'l*, pg. 862
EUROMEDICA INTERNATIONAL LTD.—See Barclays PLC; *Int'l*, pg. 862

EURO MECHANICAL & ELECTRICAL CONTRACTORS LTD. CORPORATE AFFILIATIONS

EUROMEDICA LTD.—See Barclays PLC; *Int'l*, pg. 862
EUROMEDICA PALAIOU FALIROU S.A.—See AXON Holdings S.A.; *Int'l*, pg. 770
EUROMEDICA SARL—See Barclays PLC; *Int'l*, pg. 862
EUROMEDICA SA; *Int'l*, pg. 2554
EUROMED, INC.—See Mativ Holdings, Inc.; *U.S. Public*, pg. 1396
EUROMEDIS GROUPE SA; *Int'l*, pg. 2554
EURO MEDITECH CO., LTD.—See Ship Healthcare Holdings, Inc.; *Int'l*, pg. 6852
THE EURO-MEDITERRANEAN GUARANTEE NETWORK S.L.—See Jordan Loan Guarantee Corporation; *Int'l*, pg. 3999
EURO-MED LABORATORIES PHIL., INC.; *Int'l*, pg. 2531
EUROMED S.A.—See Dermapharm Holding SE; *Int'l*, pg. 2043
EUROMED SWISS AG—See AddLife AB; *Int'l*, pg. 129
EURO MENKUL KIYMET YATIRIM ORTAKLIGI AS; *Int'l*, pg. 2531
EURO MERCHANDISE (INDIA) LIMITED—See Euro Ceramics Ltd; *Int'l*, pg. 2531
EUROMETAAL HOLDING N.V.—See Rheinmetall AG; *Int'l*, pg. 6321
EUROMETAAL N.V.—See Rheinmetall AG; *Int'l*, pg. 6321
EURO METALL KFT.—See DIHAG Holding GmbH; *Int'l*, pg. 2124
EUROMEX N.V.—See Baloise Holding AG; *Int'l*, pg. 811
EUROMEZZANINE CONSEIL SAS; *Int'l*, pg. 2554
EURO-M FLEXIBLE PACKAGING SA; *Int'l*, pg. 2531
EURO MGA PRODUCT SRL—See SELENA FM S.A.; *Int'l*, pg. 6700
EUROMISI HIGH TECH, JIAXING CO., LTD.—See Euro-Group Laminations S.p.A.; *Int'l*, pg. 2552
EURO-MIT STAAL B.V.—See Mitsui & Co., Ltd.; *Int'l*, pg. 4973
EUROMOBILIARE ALTERNATIVE INVESTMENT SGR SPA—See Credito Emiliano S.p.A.; *Int'l*, pg. 1836
EUROMOBILIARE ASSET MANAGEMENT SGR SPA—See Credito Emiliano S.p.A.; *Int'l*, pg. 1836
EUROMOBILIARE FIDUCIARIA SPA—See Credito Emiliano S.p.A.; *Int'l*, pg. 1836
EUROMOBIL SDN BHD—See DRB-HICOM Berhad; *Int'l*, pg. 2201
EUROMOL B.V.—See Mitsui O.S.K. Lines, Ltd.; *Int'l*, pg. 4989
EUROMOLD GMBH—See Nexans S.A.; *Int'l*, pg. 5241
EUROMOLD NV—See Nexans S.A.; *Int'l*, pg. 5240
EUROMONEY TRAINING, INC.—See Astorg Partners S.A.S.; *Int'l*, pg. 656
EUROMONEY TRAINING, INC.—See Epiris Managers LLP; *Int'l*, pg. 2460
EUROMOTORS INC.; *U.S. Private*, pg. 1433
EURO MULTIVISION LTD.; *Int'l*, pg. 2554
EURONAV HONG KONG LTD—See Euronav NV; *Int'l*, pg. 2554
EURONAV LTD.—See Euronav NV; *Int'l*, pg. 2554
EURONAV LUXEMBOURG SA—See Euronav NV; *Int'l*, pg. 2554
EURONAV MI II INC.—See Euronav NV; *Int'l*, pg. 2554
EURONAV NV; *Int'l*, pg. 2554
EURONAV SAS—See Euronav NV; *Int'l*, pg. 2554
EURONAV SHIP MANAGEMENT (HELLAS) LTD—See Euronav NV; *Int'l*, pg. 2554
EURONAV SHIP MANAGEMENT SAS—See Euronav NV; *Int'l*, pg. 2554
EURONAV SINGAPORE PTE. LTD.—See Euronav NV; *Int'l*, pg. 2554
EURONAV (UK) AGENCIES LTD.—See Euronav NV; *Int'l*, pg. 2554
EURONAVY - TINTAS MARITIMAS E INDUSTRIAIS S.A.—See The Sherwin-Williams Company; *U.S. Public*, pg. 2127
EURONA WIRELESS TELECOM, *Int'l*, pg. 2554
EURONET BANKTECHNIKAI SZOLGALTATO KFT.—See Euronet Worldwide, Inc.; *U.S. Public*, pg. 797
EURONET CARD SERVICES, S.A.—See Euronet Worldwide, Inc.; *U.S. Public*, pg. 797
EURONET MIDDLE EAST W.L.L.—See Euronet Worldwide, Inc.; *U.S. Public*, pg. 797
EURONET POLSKA SPOLKA Z O.O.—See Euronet Worldwide, Inc.; *U.S. Public*, pg. 798
EURONET POLSKA SP. Z.O.O.—See Euronet Worldwide, Inc.; *U.S. Public*, pg. 798
EURONET SERVICES D.O.O.—See Euronet Worldwide, Inc.; *U.S. Public*, pg. 798
EURONET SERVICES GMBH—See Euronet Worldwide, Inc.; *U.S. Public*, pg. 798
EURONET SERVICES KFT.—See Euronet Worldwide, Inc.; *U.S. Public*, pg. 798
EURONET SERVICES SAS—See Euronet Worldwide, Inc.; *U.S. Public*, pg. 798
EURONET SERVICES—See Euronet Worldwide, Inc.; *U.S. Public*, pg. 798
EURONET SERVICES, SPOL. S.R.O.—See Euronet Worldwide, Inc.; *U.S. Public*, pg. 798
EURONET SERVICES SRL—See Euronet Worldwide, Inc.; *U.S. Public*, pg. 798
EURONET TELERECARGA, S.L.—See Euronet Worldwide, Inc.; *U.S. Public*, pg. 798

EURONET UKRAINE LLC—See Euronet Worldwide, Inc.; *U.S. Public*, pg. 798
EURONET USA INC.—See Euronet Worldwide, Inc.; *U.S. Public*, pg. 798
EURONET WORLDWIDE GREECE—See Euronet Worldwide, Inc.; *U.S. Public*, pg. 798
EURONET WORLDWIDE, INC.; *U.S. Public*, pg. 797
EURONEXT AMSTERDAM N.V.—See Euronext N.V.; *Int'l*, pg. 2554
EURONEXT BRUSSELS N.V./S.A.—See Euronext N.V.; *Int'l*, pg. 2554
EURONEXT LISBON - SOCIEDAD GESTORA DE MERCADOS REGULAMENTADOS, S.A.—See Euronext N.V.; *Int'l*, pg. 2554
EURONEXT LONDON LIMITED—See Euronext N.V.; *Int'l*, pg. 2554
EURONEXT N.V.; *Int'l*, pg. 2554
EURONEXT PARIS S.A.—See Euronext N.V.; *Int'l*, pg. 2554
EURONICS AB—See EURONICS International BV; *Int'l*, pg. 2555
EURONICS AUSTRIA REG. GENOSSENSCHAFT M.B.H.—See EURONICS International BV; *Int'l*, pg. 2555
EURONICS BALTIC OU—See EURONICS International BV; *Int'l*, pg. 2555
EURONICS BELGIUM CVBA—See EURONICS International BV; *Int'l*, pg. 2555
EURONICS CR A.S.—See EURONICS International BV; *Int'l*, pg. 2555
EURONICS DEUTSCHLAND EG—See EURONICS International BV; *Int'l*, pg. 2555
EURONICS ESPANA—See EURONICS International BV; *Int'l*, pg. 2555
EURONICS FRANCE—See EURONICS International BV; *Int'l*, pg. 2555
EURONICS INTERNATIONAL BV; *Int'l*, pg. 2554
EURONICS IRELAND—See EURONICS International BV; *Int'l*, pg. 2555
EURONICS ITALIA S.P.A.—See EURONICS International BV; *Int'l*, pg. 2555
EURONICS KFT.—See EURONICS International BV; *Int'l*, pg. 2555
EURONICS LATVIA SIA—See EURONICS International BV; *Int'l*, pg. 2555
EURONICS NORGE AS—See EURONICS International BV; *Int'l*, pg. 2555
EURONICS PORTUGAL—See EURONICS International BV; *Int'l*, pg. 2555
EURONICS SCHWEIZ AG—See EURONICS International BV; *Int'l*, pg. 2555
EURONICS SK A.S.—See EURONICS International BV; *Int'l*, pg. 2555
EURO NIPPON KAYAKU GMBH—See Nippon Kayaku Co., Ltd.; *Int'l*, pg. 5320
EURONIT FACHADAS Y CUBIERTAS S.L.—See Etex SA/NV; *Int'l*, pg. 2522
EURO NORDIC LOGISTICS B.V.—See China National Chemical Corporation; *Int'l*, pg. 1527
EURONOVA S.R.L.—See Otto GmbH & Co. KG; *Int'l*, pg. 5662
EUROPA APOTHEEK SERVICE VENLO B.V.—See Europa Apotheek Venlo BV; *Int'l*, pg. 2555
EUROPA APOTHEEK VENLO BV; *Int'l*, pg. 2555
EUROPA CAPITAL PARTNERS LIMITED—See Mitsubishi Estate Co., Ltd.; *Int'l*, pg. 4947
EUROPAC CARTONNERIE DE ROUEN SAS—See Papeles y Cartones de Europa SA; *Int'l*, pg. 5733
EURO PACIFIC CAPITAL, INC.; *U.S. Private*, pg. 1433
EUROPACIFIC METALS INC.; *Int'l*, pg. 2555
EUROPACIFICO ALIMENTOS DEL MAR SL—See Friosur Pesquera SA; *Int'l*, pg. 2793
EURO PACKAGING EUROPE—See Europackaging Ltd.; *Int'l*, pg. 2555
EUROPACKAGING LTD. - EURO PACKAGING LUXURY DIVISION—See Europackaging Ltd.; *Int'l*, pg. 2555
EUROPACKAGING LTD.; *Int'l*, pg. 2555
EUROPACORP; *Int'l*, pg. 2555
EUROPAEISKE REJSEFORSIKRING A/S—See Munchener Ruckversicherungs AG; *Int'l*, pg. 5088
EUROPA EYEWEAR—See Blue Point Capital Partners, LLC; *U.S. Private*, pg. 590
EUROPA FACILITY MANAGEMENT LTD.—See UniCredit S.p.A.; *Int'l*, pg. 8034
EUROPA-GAN BIZTOSITO—See Groupama SA; *Int'l*, pg. 3090
EUROPAGES BENELUX SPRL—See Paragon Partners GmbH; *Int'l*, pg. 5737
EUROPAGES S.A.—See Paragon Partners GmbH; *Int'l*, pg. 5737
EUROPA GROWTH COMPANY; *Int'l*, pg. 2555
EUROPA INVESTIMENTI S.P.A.—See Arrow Global Group PLC; *Int'l*, pg. 579
EUROPAISCHE FERNHOCHSCHULE HAMBURG GMBH—See Ernst Klett AG; *Int'l*, pg. 2495
EUROPAISCHE REISEVERSICHERUNG AG—See Munchener Ruckversicherungs AG; *Int'l*, pg. 5088
EUROPAISCHE REISEVERSICHERUNGS AG—See Assicurazioni Generali S.p.A.; *Int'l*, pg. 645

EUROPAISCHE REISEVERSICHERUNGS AG—See Helvetia Holding AG; *Int'l*, pg. 3339
EUROPAI UTAZASI BIZTOSITO RT.—See Assicurazioni Generali S.p.A.; *Int'l*, pg. 645
EUROPALACES SARL—See Pathe SA; *Int'l*, pg. 5756
EUROPA METALS LIMITED; *Int'l*, pg. 2555
EUROPA MULTIPURPOSE TERMINALS S.P.A.—See Abu Dhabi Investment Company; *Int'l*, pg. 72
EURO PANELS OVERSEAS NV—See Etex SA/NV; *Int'l*, pg. 2522
EUROPA OIL & GAS (HOLDINGS) PLC; *Int'l*, pg. 2555
EUROPA OIL & GAS LIMITED—See Europa Oil & Gas (Holdings) plc; *Int'l*, pg. 2555
EUROPAPIER ADRIA D.O.O.—See Heinzel Holding GmbH; *Int'l*, pg. 3325
EUROPAPIER ALPE D.O.O.—See Heinzel Holding GmbH; *Int'l*, pg. 3325
EUROPAPIER BOHEMIA SPOL. S R.O.—See Heinzel Holding GmbH; *Int'l*, pg. 3325
EUROPAPIER BUDAPEST KFT.—See Heinzel Holding GmbH; *Int'l*, pg. 3325
EUROPAPIER BULGARIA EOOD—See Heinzel Holding GmbH; *Int'l*, pg. 3325
EUROPAPIER CIS OOO—See Heinzel Holding GmbH; *Int'l*, pg. 3325
EUROPAPIER DUNAV D.O.O.—See Heinzel Holding GmbH; *Int'l*, pg. 3325
EUROPAPIER HERCEGTISAK D.O.O.—See Heinzel Holding GmbH; *Int'l*, pg. 3325
EUROPAPIER-IMPAP SP. Z O.O.—See Heinzel Holding GmbH; *Int'l*, pg. 3325
EUROPAPIER INTERNATIONAL AG—See Heinzel Holding GmbH; *Int'l*, pg. 3325
EUROPAPIER POLSKA SP.Z.O.O.—See Heinzel Holding GmbH; *Int'l*, pg. 3325
EUROPAPIER ROMANIA SRL—See Heinzel Holding GmbH; *Int'l*, pg. 3325
EUROPAPIER SLOVENSKO, S.R.O.—See Heinzel Holding GmbH; *Int'l*, pg. 3325
EUROPAPIER SRBIJA D.O.O.—See Heinzel Holding GmbH; *Int'l*, pg. 3325
EURO PARKING COLLECTION, PLC—See Verra Mobility Corporation; *U.S. Public*, pg. 2286
EUROPART HOLDING GMBH—See Alpha Associes Conseil SAS; *Int'l*, pg. 366
EUROPART I SVERIGE AB—See Alpha Associes Conseil SAS; *Int'l*, pg. 366
EUROPA SERVICE CAR LTD.—See Sixt SE; *Int'l*, pg. 6968
EUROPA SPORTS PRODUCTS, INC.; *U.S. Private*, pg. 1433
EUROP ASSISTANCE MALAYSIA SDN. BHD.—See Assicurazioni Generali S.p.A.; *Int'l*, pg. 644
EUROP ASSISTANCE (THAILAND) COMPANY LIMITED—See Assicurazioni Generali S.p.A.; *Int'l*, pg. 644
EUROP ASSISTANCE VAI S.P.A.—See Assicurazioni Generali S.p.A.; *Int'l*, pg. 644
EUROPASSUR SARL—See CVC Capital Partners SICAV-FIS S.A.; *Int'l*, pg. 1882
EUROPASTRY, S.A.; *Int'l*, pg. 2555
EUROPA WORKSPACE SOLUTIONS LIMITED—See EQT AB; *Int'l*, pg. 2468
EURO PAYMENT GROUP GMBH—See Gauselmann AG; *Int'l*, pg. 2890
EUROPCAR AUTOVERMIETUNG GMBH—See Porsche Automobil Holding SE; *Int'l*, pg. 5928
EUROPCAR FRANCE S.A.—See Porsche Automobil Holding SE; *Int'l*, pg. 5928
EUROPCAR HOLDING S.A.S.—See Porsche Automobil Holding SE; *Int'l*, pg. 5928
EUROPCAR IB, S.A.—See Porsche Automobil Holding SE; *Int'l*, pg. 5928
EUROPCAR INTERNATIONAL S.A. & CO. OHG—See Porsche Automobil Holding SE; *Int'l*, pg. 5928
EUROPCAR INTERNATIONAL S.A.—See Porsche Automobil Holding SE; *Int'l*, pg. 5928
EUROPCAR ITALIA S.P.A.—See Porsche Automobil Holding SE; *Int'l*, pg. 5928
EUROPCAR MOBILITY GROUP SA—See Porsche Automobil Holding SE; *Int'l*, pg. 5928
EUROPCAR S.A.—See Porsche Automobil Holding SE; *Int'l*, pg. 5929
EUROPCAR SOUTH AFRICA—See Dubai World Corporation; *Int'l*, pg. 2221
EUROPCAR UK LIMITED—See Porsche Automobil Holding SE; *Int'l*, pg. 5929
EUROP CONCEPT—See Hiolle Industries S.A.; *Int'l*, pg. 3401
EUROPE 1 IMMOBILIER—See Vivendi SE; *Int'l*, pg. 8274
EUROPE 1 TELECOMPAGNIE—See Vivendi SE; *Int'l*, pg. 8274
EUROPE 2 ENTREPRISES—See Vivendi SE; *Int'l*, pg. 8274
EUROPEA DE TITULIZACION, S.A. S.G.F.T.—See Banco Bilbao Vizcaya Argentaria, S.A.; *Int'l*, pg. 817
EUROPEA MICROFUSIONI AEROSPAZIALI S.P.A.—See Rolls-Royce Holdings plc; *Int'l*, pg. 6391

914

COMPANY NAME INDEX

EUROPEAN AERONAUTIC DEFENSE AND SPACE CO.—See Airbus SE; *Int'l*, pg. 247
EUROPEAN AMERICAN ASSOCIATION; *U.S. Private*, pg. 1434
EUROPEAN AUTOMOBILE CO.—See Stellantis N.V.; *Int'l*, pg. 7201
EUROPEAN AUTO SERVICE LTD.; *U.S. Private*, pg. 1434
EUROPEAN BANK FOR FINANCIAL SERVICES GMBH—See Caisse de Depot et Placement du Quebec; *Int'l*, pg. 1254
EUROPEAN BANK FOR FINANCIAL SERVICES GMBH—See Generation Investment Management LLP; *Int'l*, pg. 2920
EUROPEAN BANK FOR RECONSTRUCTION & DEVELOPMENT; *Int'l*, pg. 2555
EUROPEAN BATH, KITCHEN, TILE & STONE—See Blackfriars Corp.; *U.S. Private*, pg. 575
EUROPEAN BULK SERVICES (E.B.S.) B.V.—See H.E.S. Beheer N.V.; *Int'l*, pg. 3195
EUROPEAN CANNABIS CORPORATION LIMITED; *Int'l*, pg. 2555
EUROPEAN CARBON FIBER GMBH—See Solvay S.A.; *Int'l*, pg. 7078
EUROPEAN CATERING SERVICES INC.—See Air France-KLM S.A.; *Int'l*, pg. 237
EUROPEAN CENTRAL BANK; *Int'l*, pg. 2555
EUROPEAN CENTRAL COUNTERPARTY N.V.—See Cboe Global Markets, Inc.; *U.S. Public*, pg. 459
EUROPEAN COLOUR (PIGMENTS) LIMITED—See European Colour Plc; *Int'l*, pg. 2556
EUROPEAN COLOUR PLC; *Int'l*, pg. 2556
EUROPEAN COMMODITY CLEARING AG—See Deutsche Borse AG; *Int'l*, pg. 2064
EUROPEAN COMMODITY CLEARING LUXEMBOURG S.A R.L—See Deutsche Borse AG; *Int'l*, pg. 2064
EUROPEAN CONTRACT LOGISTICS - CZECH REPUBLIC SPOL.S.R.O.—See OBB-Holding AG; *Int'l*, pg. 5509
EUROPEAN CONTRACT LOGISTICS D.O.O.—See OBB-Holding AG; *Int'l*, pg. 5509
EUROPEAN DEPOSITARY BANK SA—See Apex Fund Services Holdings Ltd.; *Int'l*, pg. 510
EUROPEAN DIRECTORIES S.A.; *Int'l*, pg. 2556
EUROPEAN DRINKS S.A.; *Int'l*, pg. 2556
EUROPEAN ELECTRIC METALS INC; *Int'l*, pg. 2556
EUROPEAN ENERGY EXCHANGE AG—See Deutsche Borse AG; *Int'l*, pg. 2064
EUROPEAN ENERGY LIMITED; *Int'l*, pg. 2556
EUROPEAN ENERGY METALS CORP.; *Int'l*, pg. 2556
THE EUROPEAN EQUITY FUND, INC.; *U.S. Public*, pg. 2073
EUROPEAN EXCELLENT TEXTILE COMPONENTS CO. LTD.—See Rieter Holding Ltd.; *Int'l*, pg. 6338
EUROPEAN FERRO METALS LTD.; *Int'l*, pg. 2556
EUROPEAN FINANCE ASSOCIATES S.A.—See ELLAKTOR S.A.; *Int'l*, pg. 2365
EUROPEAN FINANCE REINSURANCE COMPANY LTD.—See Swiss Re Ltd.; *Int'l*, pg. 7371
EUROPEAN FINE WINES LTD.; *Int'l*, pg. 2556
EUROPEAN FOOD—See European Drinks S.A.; *Int'l*, pg. 2556
EUROPEAN GOLD REFINERIES HOLDING SA—See Newmont Corporation; *U.S. Public*, pg. 1516
EUROPEAN HEALTHCARE ACQUISITION & GROWTH COMPANY B.V.; *Int'l*, pg. 2556
EUROPEAN HOUSE OF BEDS AB—See Herkules Capital AS; *Int'l*, pg. 3362
EUROPEAN IMPORTS, LTD.—See Sysco Corporation; *U.S. Public*, pg. 1973
EUROPEAN INSTITUTE OF SCIENCE AB; *Int'l*, pg. 2556
EUROPEAN INSTITUTE OF THE MEDITERRANEAN S.L.—See Jordan Loan Guarantee Corporation; *Int'l*, pg. 3998
EUROPEAN INSURANCE & REINSURANCE BROKERS LTD.—See Vienna Insurance Group AG Wiener Versicherung Gruppe; *Int'l*, pg. 8194
EUROPEAN INTERNATIONAL REINSURANCE COMPANY LTD.—See Swiss Re Ltd.; *Int'l*, pg. 7371
EUROPEAN INVESTMENT BANK; *Int'l*, pg. 2556
EUROPEAN INVESTMENT FUND—See European Investment Bank; *Int'l*, pg. 2556
EUROPEAN INVESTOR RELATIONS SA; *Int'l*, pg. 2556
EUROPEAN LITHIUM LIMITED; *Int'l*, pg. 2556
EUROPEAN MANAGEMENT AND MARINE CORPORATION LIMITED—See Usha Martin Limited; *Int'l*, pg. 8096
EUROPEAN MASTER BATCH NV—See Sioen Industries NV; *Int'l*, pg. 6960
EUROPEAN MEDICAL CONTRACT MANUFACTURING B.V.—See aap Implantate AG; *Int'l*, pg. 36
EUROPEAN MERCHANT SERVICES B.V.—See Fiserv, Inc.; *U.S. Public*, pg. 850
THE EUROPEAN METADATA GROUP; *Int'l*, pg. 7640
EUROPEAN METAL RECYCLING BV—See European Metal Recycling Limited; *Int'l*, pg. 2556
EUROPEAN METAL RECYCLING GMBH—See European Metal Recycling Limited; *Int'l*, pg. 2556
EUROPEAN METAL RECYCLING GMBH—See European Metal Recycling Limited; *Int'l*, pg. 2556

EUROPEAN METAL RECYCLING LIMITED; *Int'l*, pg. 2556
EUROPEAN METALS CORP.; *Int'l*, pg. 2557
EUROPEAN METALS HOLDINGS LIMITED; *Int'l*, pg. 2557
EUROPEAN METALS UK LIMITED—See European Metals Holdings Limited; *Int'l*, pg. 2557
EUROPEAN MOTORCARS; *U.S. Private*, pg. 1434
EUROPEAN MOTOR HOLDINGS LTD.—See Inchcape plc; *Int'l*, pg. 3647
EUROPEAN NEWS EXCHANGE—See Bertelsmann SE & Co. KGaA; *Int'l*, pg. 994
EUROPEAN OFFICE SYSTEMS B.V.—See ECO Supplies Europe AB; *Int'l*, pg. 2292
EUROPEAN OFFICE SYSTEMS GMBH—See ECO Supplies Europe AB; *Int'l*, pg. 2292
EUROPEAN OFFICE SYSTEMS S.A.R.L—See ECO Supplies Europe AB; *Int'l*, pg. 2292
EUROPEAN OPPORTUNITIES TRUST PLC—See Jupiter Fund Management plc; *Int'l*, pg. 4029
EUROPEAN OWENS CORNING FIBERGLAS SPRL—See Owens Corning; *U.S. Public*, pg. 1626
EUROPEAN PNEUMATIC COMPONENT OVERHAUL & REPAIR B.V.—See Koninklijke Luchtvaart Maatschappij N.V.; *Int'l*, pg. 4267
EUROPEAN PNEUMATIC COMPONENT OVERHAUL & REPAIR (EPCOR) BV—See Air France-KLM S.A.; *Int'l*, pg. 237
EUROPEAN PORTWELL TECHNOLOGY B.V.—See Posiflex Technology Inc.; *Int'l*, pg. 5938
EUROPEAN PRECIOUS METAL TRADING GMBH—See StoneX Group Inc.; *U.S. Public*, pg. 1951
EUROPEAN PROPERTY INVESTMENT CORPORATION LIMITED—See Alrov Properties & Lodgings Ltd.; *Int'l*, pg. 377
EUROPEAN PUMP SERVICES B.V.—See ITT Inc.; *U.S. Public*, pg. 1177
EUROPEAN RAIL SOFTWARE APPLICATIONS (ERSA)—See Vision Capital, LLP; *Int'l*, pg. 8251
EUROPEAN REAL ESTATE INVESTMENT TRUST LIMITED; *Int'l*, pg. 2557
EUROPEAN REINSURANCE CORPORATION OF AMERICA—See Swiss Re Ltd.; *Int'l*, pg. 7371
EUROPEAN RELIANCE GENERAL INSURANCE S.A.; *Int'l*, pg. 2557
EUROPEAN RESIDENTIAL REIT; *Int'l*, pg. 2557
EUROPEAN ROAD STARS ACADEMY (ERSA) SPRL—See DEKRA e.V.; *Int'l*, pg. 2009
EUROPEAN RUBBER JOURNAL—See Crain Communications, Inc.; *U.S. Private*, pg. 1083
EUROPEAN SALT COMPANY—See K+S Aktiengesellschaft; *Int'l*, pg. 4039
EUROPEAN SATELLITE LINK GMBH; *Int'l*, pg. 2557
EUROPEAN SEAFOOD INVESTMENT PORTUGAL S.A.—See Thai Union Group Public Company Limited; *Int'l*, pg. 7596
THE EUROPEAN SMALLER COMPANIES TRUST PLC; *Int'l*, pg. 7641
EUROPEAN SPACE PROPULSION LIMITED—See L3Harris Technologies, Inc.; *U.S. Public*, pg. 1279
EUROPEAN SPRINGS & PRESSINGS LTD.—See Beijer Alma AB; *Int'l*, pg. 943
EUROPEAN SPRINGS & PRESSINGS LTD—See Beijer Alma AB; *Int'l*, pg. 943
EUROPEAN STUDY TOURS LIMITED—See Cox & Kings Limited; *Int'l*, pg. 1822
EUROPEAN SUPPORT LIMITED—See Amdocs Limited; *Int'l*, pg. 419
EUROPEAN SUSTAINABLE GROWTH ACQUISITION CORP.; *U.S. Public*, pg. 799
EUROPEAN TRAILER SYSTEMS S.R.O.—See VBG Group AB; *Int'l*, pg. 8138
EUROPEAN WAX CENTER INC.; *U.S. Public*, pg. 799
EUROPEAN WHOLESALE SECURITIES MARKET LIMITED—See Euronext N.V.; *Int'l*, pg. 2554
EUROPE ARAB BANK PLC—See Arab Bank plc; *Int'l*, pg. 529
EUROPE AUDIOVISUEL—See Vivendi SE; *Int'l*, pg. 8274
EUROPEBET LLC—See Betsson AB; *Int'l*, pg. 1003
EUROPE CHEMI-CON (DEUTSCHLAND) GMBH—See Nippon Chemi-Con Corporation; *Int'l*, pg. 5312
EUROPE CONTAINERS TERMINALS B.V.—See CK Hutchison Holdings Limited; *Int'l*, pg. 1637
EUROPE CORPORATION—See Hyundai Glovis Co., Ltd.; *Int'l*, pg. 3556
EUROPEENNE DE COUVERTURE AUTOMATIQUES,. S.A.R.L.—See Fluidra SA; *Int'l*, pg. 2714
EUROPEENNE DE LA MER SAS—See Thai Union Group Public Company Limited; *Int'l*, pg. 7596
EUROPEENNE DE PLATS CUISINES—See LDC SA; *Int'l*, pg. 4431
EUROPEENNE DE PRODUITS DE BEAUTE S.A.S.—See MacAndrews & Forbes Incorporated; *U.S. Private*, pg. 2533
EUROPEENNE DE PROTECTION JURIDIQUE S.A.—See Assicurazioni Generali S.p.A.; *Int'l*, pg. 644
EUROPEENNE DE TRAVAUX FERROVIAIRES S.A.—See VINCI S.A.; *Int'l*, pg. 8219

EUROPE ENVIRONMENT S.A.—See Europlasma SA; *Int'l*, pg. 2557
EUROPEISKA FORSOKRINGSAKTIEBOLAGET—See Munchener Ruckversicherungs AG; *Int'l*, pg. 5088
EUROPEJSKIE CENTRUM ODSZKODOWAN S.A.; pg. 2557
EUROPE ONLINE TRADE EAD; *Int'l*, pg. 2555
EUROPE POST APS—See Unifiedpost Group SA; *Int'l*, pg. 8043
EUROPERFIL S.A.—See ArcelorMittal S.A.; *Int'l*, pg. 544
EURO PERFORMANCE CARS, INC.; *U.S. Private*, pg. 1433
EUROPERFORMANCE SIX TELEKURS—See SIX Group AG; *Int'l*, pg. 6966
EUROPERFORMANCE—See SIX Group AG; *Int'l*, pg. 6967
EUROPE SANYOU ELECTRIC APPLIANCE CO., LTD.—See Sanyou Corporation Limited; *Int'l*, pg. 6565
EUROPEST ENVIRONMENTAL SERVICES LIMITED—See Rollins, Inc.; *U.S. Public*, pg. 1809
EUROPE TIANYING BVBA—See China Tianying Inc.; *Int'l*, pg. 1559
EUROPEUM BUSINESS CENTER S.R.O.—See Vienna Insurance Group AG Wiener Versicherung Gruppe; *Int'l*, pg. 8194
EUROPE VISION SYSTEMS S.R.O.—See GeoVision Inc.; *Int'l*, pg. 2942
EUROPHARM HOLDINGS S.A.—See Sarkis Group International SAL; *Int'l*, pg. 6578
EURO-PHYSICAL ACOUSTICS S.A.—See Mistras Group, Inc.; *U.S. Public*, pg. 1451
EUROPICKLING NV—See Commercial Metals Company; *U.S. Public*, pg. 546
EUROPIGMENTS S.L.—See LANXESS AG; *Int'l*, pg. 4414
EUROPILE PALTEKNIK AB—See VINCI S.A.; *Int'l*, pg. 8231
EUROPIPE 1. VERWALTUNGSGESELLSCHAFT MBH—See Salzgitter AG; *Int'l*, pg. 6496
EUROPIPE FRANCE S.A.—See Salzgitter AG; *Int'l*, pg. 6496
EUROPLAKAT BULGARIA OOD—See APG/SGA SA; *Int'l*, pg. 513
EUROPLAKAT D.O.O.—See APG/SGA SA; *Int'l*, pg. 513
EUROPLAKAT KFT—See APG/SGA SA; *Int'l*, pg. 513
EUROPLAKAT YUGOSLAVIA D.O.O.—See APG/SGA SA; *Int'l*, pg. 513
EUROPLASMA GMBH—See LFB S.A.; *Int'l*, pg. 4472
EUROPLASMA NV—See Gimv NV; *Int'l*, pg. 2976
EUROPLASMA SA; *Int'l*, pg. 2557
EUROPLASMA SRO—See LFB S.A.; *Int'l*, pg. 4472
EUROPLAY CAPITAL ADVISORS, LLC; *U.S. Private*, pg. 1434
EUROP MAINTENANCE—See Hiolle Industries S.A.; *Int'l*, pg. 3401
EUROPOLES GMBH & CO. KG—See VTC Partners GmbH; *Int'l*, pg. 8316
EUROPOLIS AG—See Starwood Capital Group Global I, LLC; *U.S. Private*, pg. 3789
EUROPOOL ITALIA S.R.L.—See The Carlyle Group Inc.; *U.S. Public*, pg. 2057
EUROPORTE FRANCE SAS—See Getlink SE; *Int'l*, pg. 2953
EUROPORTE PROXIMIT SAS—See Getlink SE; *Int'l*, pg. 2952
EUROPORTE—See Getlink SE; *Int'l*, pg. 2952
EUROPOWER CR S.R.O.—See Park-Ohio Holdings Corp.; *U.S. Public*, pg. 1638
EUROPRAXIS ATLANTE S.L.—See Indra Sistemas, S.A.; *Int'l*, pg. 3660
EUROPRAXIS CONSULTING S.R.L.—See Indra Sistemas, S.A.; *Int'l*, pg. 3660
EUROPRINT, INC.; *U.S. Private*, pg. 1434
EUROPRINT (PROMOTIONS) LIMITED—See International Game Technology PLC; *Int'l*, pg. 3749
EUROPRIS ASA; *Int'l*, pg. 2557
EURO-PRO CORPORATION; *Int'l*, pg. 2532
EUROPROCUREMENT AG—See REWE-Zentral-Aktiengesellschaft; *Int'l*, pg. 6315
EUROPROFIL AB—See IAI Holding A/S; *Int'l*, pg. 3568
EUROPROFIL NORGE AS—See IAI Holding A/S; *Int'l*, pg. 3568
EURO-PRO GESELLSCHAFT FUR DATA PROCESSING MBH—See Allianz SE; *Int'l*, pg. 352
EUROPROJECT LLC; *Int'l*, pg. 2557
EUROPROJECT OOD—See Tinexta S.p.A.; *Int'l*, pg. 7753
EUROPROPULSION SA—See Safran S.A.; *Int'l*, pg. 6473
EUROPTEC GMBH—See Glas Trosch Holding AG; *Int'l*, pg. 2988
EUROPTICS LIMITED—See The Furukawa Electric Co., Ltd.; *Int'l*, pg. 7644
EUROPTRONIC ELECTRONIC (SHENZHEN) CO., LTD.—See Europtronic Group Ltd.; *Int'l*, pg. 2557
EUROPTRONIC GREEN ENERGY PTE. LTD.—See Europtronic Group Ltd.; *Int'l*, pg. 2557
EUROPTRONIC GROUP LTD.; *Int'l*, pg. 2557
EUROPTRONIC (HK) COMPANY LIMITED—See Europtronic Group Ltd.; *Int'l*, pg. 2557
EUROPTRONIC INVESTMENT PTE. LTD.—See Europtronic Group Ltd.; *Int'l*, pg. 2557

EUROPTRONIC GROUP LTD.

EUROPTRONIC (SINGAPORE) PTE. LTD.—See Europtronic Group Ltd.; *Int'l*, pg. 2557
EUROPTRONIC (SUZHOU) CO., LTD.—See Nantong Jianghai Capacitor Co., Ltd.; *Int'l*, pg. 5145
EUROPTRONIC (TAIWAN) IND. CORP.—See Europtronic Group Ltd.; *Int'l*, pg. 2557
EUROP USINAGE—See Hiolle Industries S.A.; *Int'l*, pg. 3401
EUROQUALITY S.A.S.—See Tinexta S.p.A.; *Int'l*, pg. 7753
EUROQUARZ GMBH—See L. Possehl & Co. mbH; *Int'l*, pg. 4382
EUROQUARZ GMBH; *Int'l*, pg. 2558
EURO REGISTRATIE COLLECTIEF B.V.—See Walgreens Boots Alliance, Inc.; *U.S. Public*, pg. 2322
EURORESINS BENELUX B.V.—See Koninklijke DSM N.V.; *Int'l*, pg. 4266
EURORESINS INTERNATIONAL GMBH—See Cathay Investments Limited; *Int'l*, pg. 1360
EURORESINS SCANDINAVIA OY—See Cathay Investments Limited; *Int'l*, pg. 1360
EURORESINS UK LTD.—See Cathay Investments Limited; *Int'l*, pg. 1360
EURO RESSOURCES S.A.—See IAMGOLD Corporation; *Int'l*, pg. 3568
EURO RESSURS AS—See Bilfinger SE; *Int'l*, pg. 1028
EURO-RITE CABINETS LTD.—See Ebenisterie St-Urbain Ltee; *Int'l*, pg. 2285
EURORUBBER S.P.A.—See Certech SpA; *Int'l*, pg. 1423
EURO RUSZTOWANIA GRUPA STOCZNI GDYNIA SP. Z O.O.—See Stocznia Gdynia S.A.; *Int'l*, pg. 7220
EURO RX ARZNEIMITTEL GMBH—See Arzneiwerk AG VIDA; *Int'l*, pg. 589
EUROSAM—See Airbus SE; *Int'l*, pg. 247
EUROSAM—See BAE Systems plc; *Int'l*, pg. 798
EUROSAM—See Leonardo S.p.A.; *Int'l*, pg. 4460
EUROSAM—See Thales S.A.; *Int'l*, pg. 7598
EUROSCREEN S.A.; *Int'l*, pg. 2558
EUROSEAS LTD.; *Int'l*, pg. 2558
EUROSERVE GUVENLIK A.S.—See Compass Group PLC; *Int'l*, pg. 1752
EUROSERVICE MERANO S.R.L.—See KONE Oyj; *Int'l*, pg. 4247
EUROSERVICES BAYER GMBH—See Bayer Aktiengesellschaft; *Int'l*, pg. 907
EUROSERVICES BAYER S.L.—See Bayer Aktiengesellschaft; *Int'l*, pg. 908
EUROSERVIZI PER I NOTAI S.R.L.—See Gruppo Mutui-Online S.p.A.; *Int'l*, pg. 3141
EUROSERWIS SP. Z O.O.—See Huta Pokoj S.A.; *Int'l*, pg. 3540
EUROSHELL DEUTSCHLAND GMBH & CO. KG—See Shell plc; *Int'l*, pg. 6800
EURO-SHELTER SA—See GIAT Industries S.A.; *Int'l*, pg. 2962
EUROSIBENERGO PLC—See En+ Group Ltd.; *Int'l*, pg. 2395
EUROSIC S.A.—See Gecina S.A.; *Int'l*, pg. 2909
EUROSIGNS (UK) LTD.—See VINCI S.A.; *Int'l*, pg. 8220
EUROSITE POWER INC.—See Tecogen Inc.; *U.S. Public*, pg. 1989
EUROSITES AS—See Cox & Kings Limited; *Int'l*, pg. 1822
EUROSITES BV—See Cox & Kings Limited; *Int'l*, pg. 1822
EURO SKLEP S.A.—See Emperia Holding S.A; *Int'l*, pg. 2385
EUROSKYPARK GMBH—See RWE AG; *Int'l*, pg. 6434
EUROSLOT TOOLS S.R.L.—See EuroGroup Laminations S.p.A.; *Int'l*, pg. 2552
EUROSOFTWARE S.R.O—See Fujitsu Limited; *Int'l*, pg. 2837
EURO SOLUTIONS GROUP INC.; *U.S. Private*, pg. 1433
EUROSOND GMBH—See BERGER Holding GmbH; *Int'l*, pg. 979
EUROSOS ASSISTANCE, S.A.—See MAPFRE S.A.; *Int'l*, pg. 4684
EUROSOV PETROLEUM HOLDINGS (CYPRUS) LIMITED—See PJSC Gazprom; *Int'l*, pg. 5879
EURO SPACE INDUSTRIES (M) SDN BHD—See Eurospan Holdings Berhad; *Int'l*, pg. 2531
EUROSPAN FURNITURE SDN. BHD.—See Eurospan Holdings Berhad; *Int'l*, pg. 2558
EUROSPAN HOLDINGS BERHAD; *Int'l*, pg. 2558
EUROSPICE TECHNOLOGIES AND ADDITIVES—See VAN HEES GmbH; *Int'l*, pg. 8126
EUROSPORT DANMARK APS—See Warner Bros. Discovery, Inc.; *U.S. Public*, pg. 2326
EUROSPORT EVENTS LTD.—See Warner Bros. Discovery, Inc.; *U.S. Public*, pg. 2326
EUROSPORT FINLAND OY—See Warner Bros. Discovery, Inc.; *U.S. Public*, pg. 2327
EUROSPORT FRANCE SA—See Warner Bros. Discovery, Inc.; *U.S. Public*, pg. 2327
EUROSPORT INTERNATIONAL SA—See Warner Bros. Discovery, Inc.; *U.S. Public*, pg. 2326
EUROSPORT ITALIA SPA—See Warner Bros. Discovery, Inc.; *U.S. Public*, pg. 2327
EUROSPORT MEDIA GMBH—See Warner Bros. Discovery, Inc.; *U.S. Public*, pg. 2327
EUROSPORT MEDIA—See Warner Bros. Discovery, Inc.; *U.S. Public*, pg. 2327

EUROSPORT NORGE AS—See Warner Bros. Discovery, Inc.; *U.S. Public*, pg. 2327
EUROSPORT POLSKA SP. Z O.O.—See Warner Bros. Discovery, Inc.; *U.S. Public*, pg. 2327
EUROSPORT SAS—See Warner Bros. Discovery, Inc.; *U.S. Public*, pg. 2327
EUROSPORTS GLOBAL LIMITED; *Int'l*, pg. 2558
EUROSPORT TELEVISION AB—See Warner Bros. Discovery, Inc.; *U.S. Public*, pg. 2327
EUROSPORT TELEVISION BV—See Warner Bros. Discovery, Inc.; *U.S. Public*, pg. 2327
EUROSPORT TELEVISION SA—See Warner Bros. Discovery, Inc.; *U.S. Public*, pg. 2327
EUROSPORT TV LTD.—See Warner Bros. Discovery, Inc.; *U.S. Public*, pg. 2327
EURO-SPRINTERS SA/NV—See bpost NV/SA; *Int'l*, pg. 1133
EUROSTAF - EUROPE STRATEGIE ANALYSE FINANCIERE SAS—See LVMH Moet Hennessy Louis Vuitton SE; *Int'l*, pg. 4592
EUROSTAFF FINANCE GMBH—See Cordant Group PLC; *Int'l*, pg. 1796
EUROSTAFF GROUP GMBH—See Cordant Group PLC; *Int'l*, pg. 1796
EUROSTANDARD BANKA AD; *Int'l*, pg. 2558
EUROSTAR INTERNATIONAL LTD; *Int'l*, pg. 2558
EURO STEEL DANMARK A/S; *Int'l*, pg. 2531
EUROSTEEL (PORTUGAL) COMERCIO INTERNACIONAL LDA—See Stemcor Holdings Limited; *Int'l*, pg. 7205
EURO STYL S.A—See Dom Development S.A.; *Int'l*, pg. 2159
EURO SUN MINING INC.; *Int'l*, pg. 2531
EUROSYN DEVELOPPEMENT SAS—See Assystem S.A.; *Int'l*, pg. 651
EUROTAINER SA—See Ermewa Interservices Sarl; *Int'l*, pg. 2494
EUROTAPE MEDIA SERVICES GMBH—See Kurierverlags GmbH & Co. KG; *Int'l*, pg. 4339
EUROTEC B.V.—See ConvaTec Group PLC; *Int'l*, pg. 1786
EUROTEC DENTAL GMBH—See Fagron NV; *Int'l*, pg. 2603
EUROTEC GMBH—See ConvaTec Group PLC; *Int'l*, pg. 1786
EUROTECH AB—See Sdiptech AB; *Int'l*, pg. 6658
EUROTECH CYLINDERS PRIVATE LIMITED—See Nitin Fire Protection Industries Ltd; *Int'l*, pg. 5381
EURO TECH (FAR EAST) LTD.—See Euro Tech Holdings Company Limited; *Int'l*, pg. 2531
EUROTECH FRANCE S.A.S.—See Eurotech S.p.A.; *Int'l*, pg. 2558
EURO TECH HOLDINGS COMPANY LIMITED; *Int'l*, pg. 2531
EUROTECH INC.—See Eurotech S.p.A.; *Int'l*, pg. 2558
EUROTECH INC.—See Eurotech S.p.A.; *Int'l*, pg. 2558
EUROTECH LTD.—See Eurotech S.p.A.; *Int'l*, pg. 2558
EUROTECH SIRE SYSTEM AB—See Sdiptech AB; *Int'l*, pg. 6658
EUROTECH S.P.A.; *Int'l*, pg. 2558
EUROTEC LTD.—See Carel Industries S.p.A.; *Int'l*, pg. 1324
EUROTECNICA S.A.—See L'Air Liquide S.A.; *Int'l*, pg. 4375
EUROTEC SRL—See Illinois Tool Works Inc.; *U.S. Public*, pg. 1103
EUROTEKNA S.R.L.—See I.M.A. Industria Macchine Automatiche S.p.A.; *Int'l*, pg. 3565
EUROTEL; *Int'l*, pg. 2558
EUROTEM DEMIRYOLU ARACLARI SAN. VE TIC A.S.—See Hyundai Motor Company; *Int'l*, pg. 3559
EURO-TERMINAL AS—See Caiano AS; *Int'l*, pg. 1252
EURO TERMINAL SP. Z O O—See Caiano AS; *Int'l*, pg. 1252
EUROTERRA BULGARIA AD; *Int'l*, pg. 2558
EUROTERRA S.A.—See Piraeus Financial Holdings S.A.; *Int'l*, pg. 5873
EUROTEX INDUSTRIES & EXPORTS LIMITED; *Int'l*, pg. 2558
EUROTEX INTERNATIONAL LIMITED—See Tex Holdings Plc; *Int'l*, pg. 7582
EUROTHERM AB—See Schneider Electric SE; *Int'l*, pg. 6627
EUROTHERM AUTOMATION SAS—See Schneider Electric SE; *Int'l*, pg. 6627
EUROTHERM BV—See Schneider Electric SE; *Int'l*, pg. 6627
EUROTHERM INC.—See Schneider Electric SE; *Int'l*, pg. 6627
EUROTHERM INDIA PRIVATE LIMITED—See Schneider Electric SE; *Int'l*, pg. 6627
EUROTHERM KOREA CO., LTD.—See Schneider Electric SE; *Int'l*, pg. 6627
EUROTHERM LIMITED—See Schneider Electric SE; *Int'l*, pg. 6627
EUROTHERM LTDA—See Schneider Electric SE; *Int'l*, pg. 6623

CORPORATE AFFILIATIONS

EUROTHERM LTD.—See Schneider Electric SE; *Int'l*, pg. 6627
EUROTHERM SRL—See Schneider Electric SE; *Int'l*, pg. 6627
EURO TIMBER SPOL S.R.O.—See Stora Enso Oyj; *Int'l*, pg. 7225
EUROTIN INC.; *Int'l*, pg. 2558
EUROTOLL SAS—See ACS, Actividades de Construccion y Servicios, S.A.; *Int'l*, pg. 112
EUROTOTVS LTDA.—See TOTVS S.A.; *Int'l*, pg. 7846
EUROTRADE1 D.O.O.—See BHG Group AB; *Int'l*, pg. 1014
EUROTRADE1 SIA—See BHG Group AB; *Int'l*, pg. 1014
EUROTRADIA INTERNATIONAL—See Groupe Industriel Marcel Dassault S.A.; *Int'l*, pg. 3105
EURO-TRAMCO B.V.—See Ag Growth International Inc.; *Int'l*, pg. 198
EUROTRANCIATURA MEXICO S.A. DE C.V.—See EuroGroup Laminations S.p.A.; *Int'l*, pg. 2552
EUROTRANCIATURA S.P.A.—See EuroGroup Laminations S.p.A.; *Int'l*, pg. 2552
EUROTRANCIATURA TUNISIE S.A.R.L.—See EuroGroup Laminations S.p.A.; *Int'l*, pg. 2552
EUROTRED (NZ) LTD.—See Bridgestone Corporation; *Int'l*, pg. 1159
EURO TREND YATIRIM ORTAKLIGI AS; *Int'l*, pg. 2531
EURO-TRESORERIE S.A.—See Intesa Sanpaolo S.p.A.; *Int'l*, pg. 3765
EUROTRIAS S.R.L.—See Tulikivi Corporation; *Int'l*, pg. 7969
EUROTRONICS SISTEMAS DE SEGURIDAD S.A.U.—See Emerson Electric Co.; *U.S. Public*, pg. 749
EURO TRUCK & BUS (MALAYSIA) SDN BHD—See DRB-HICOM Berhad; *Int'l*, pg. 2201
EUROTUNNEL DEVELOPMENTS LIMITED—See Getlink SE; *Int'l*, pg. 2953
EUROTUNNEL DEVELOPMENTS S.A.—See Getlink SE; *Int'l*, pg. 2953
EUROTUNNELPLUS LIMITED—See Getlink SE; *Int'l*, pg. 2953
EUROTUNNEL SERVICES GIE—See Getlink SE; *Int'l*, pg. 2953
EUROTUNNEL SERVICES LIMITED—See Getlink SE; *Int'l*, pg. 2953
EUROVENDING S.R.L.—See IVS Group S.A.; *Int'l*, pg. 3848
EUROVESTECH PLC; *Int'l*, pg. 2558
EUROVIA ALPES SAS—See VINCI S.A.; *Int'l*, pg. 8218
EUROVIA ALSACE-LORRAINE SAS—See VINCI S.A.; *Int'l*, pg. 8218
EUROVIA AQUITAINE SAS—See VINCI S.A.; *Int'l*, pg. 8219
EUROVIA ATLANTIQUE SAS—See VINCI S.A.; *Int'l*, pg. 8218
EUROVIA BASSE-NORMANDIE S.A.S.—See VINCI S.A.; *Int'l*, pg. 8219
EUROVIA BAZALTY SA—See VINCI S.A.; *Int'l*, pg. 8218
EUROVIA BELGIUM SA—See VINCI S.A.; *Int'l*, pg. 8219
EUROVIA BETON GMBH—See VINCI S.A.; *Int'l*, pg. 8219
EUROVIA BETON S.A.S.—See VINCI S.A.; *Int'l*, pg. 8219
EUROVIA BOURGOGNE FC SAS—See VINCI S.A.; *Int'l*, pg. 8218
EUROVIA BOURGOGNE S.N.C.—See VINCI S.A.; *Int'l*, pg. 8219
EUROVIA BRETAGNE SAS—See VINCI S.A.; *Int'l*, pg. 8219
EUROVIA BRITISH COLUMBIA INC.—See VINCI S.A.; *Int'l*, pg. 8218
EUROVIA CENTRE LOIRE S.A.S.—See VINCI S.A.; *Int'l*, pg. 8219
EUROVIA CHAMPAGNE ARDENNE—See VINCI S.A.; *Int'l*, pg. 8219
EUROVIA CHAMPAGNE ARDENNES SAS—See VINCI S.A.; *Int'l*, pg. 8218
EUROVIA CONCRETE TECHNOLOGIES GMBH—See VINCI S.A.; *Int'l*, pg. 8218
EUROVIA CS, A.S.—See VINCI S.A.; *Int'l*, pg. 8219
EUROVIA DALA SAS—See VINCI S.A.; *Int'l*, pg. 8218
EUROVIA ETANCHEITE—See VINCI S.A.; *Int'l*, pg. 8218
EUROVIA GESTEIN GMBH—See VINCI S.A.; *Int'l*, pg. 8218
EUROVIA GIRONDE SAS—See VINCI S.A.; *Int'l*, pg. 8218
EUROVIA GMBH—See VINCI S.A.; *Int'l*, pg. 8219
EUROVIA GRANDS TRAVAUX SAS—See VINCI S.A.; *Int'l*, pg. 8218
EUROVIA HAUTE NORMANDIE SAS—See VINCI S.A.; *Int'l*, pg. 8218
EUROVIA ILE-DE-FRANCE S.A.S.—See VINCI S.A.; *Int'l*, pg. 8219
EUROVIA INDUSTRIE GMBH—See VINCI S.A.; *Int'l*, pg. 8219
EUROVIA INFRA GMBH—See VINCI S.A.; *Int'l*, pg. 8218
EUROVIA INFRASTRUCTURE LIMITED—See VINCI S.A.; *Int'l*, pg. 8219
EUROVIA JAKUBCOVICE, SRO.—See VINCI S.A.; *Int'l*, pg. 8219
EUROVIA KAMENOLOMY A.S.—See VINCI S.A.; *Int'l*, pg. 8218

COMPANY NAME INDEX

EUROVIA KAMENOLOMY, AS—See VINCI S.A.; *Int'l*, pg. 8219
EUROVIA KRUSZYWA SP. Z O.O.—See VINCI S.A.; *Int'l*, pg. 8218
EUROVIA LANGUEDOC-ROUSSILLON SAS—See VINCI S.A.; *Int'l*, pg. 8218
EUROVIA LIETUVA UAB—See VINCI S.A.; *Int'l*, pg. 8220
EUROVIA LORRAINE S.A.R.L.—See VINCI S.A.; *Int'l*, pg. 8220
EUROVIA LYON SAS—See VINCI S.A.; *Int'l*, pg. 8218
EUROVIA MANAGEMENT ESPANA SA—See VINCI S.A.; *Int'l*, pg. 8218
EUROVIA MANAGEMENT SNC—See VINCI S.A.; *Int'l*, pg. 8220
EUROVIA MIDI-PYRENEES SAS—See VINCI S.A.; *Int'l*, pg. 8220
EUROVIA PAS-DE-CALAIS—See VINCI S.A.; *Int'l*, pg. 8220
EUROVIA PICARDIE SAS—See VINCI S.A.; *Int'l*, pg. 8218
EUROVIA POITOU CHARENTES LIMOUSIN POITIERS—See VINCI S.A.; *Int'l*, pg. 8220
EUROVIA QUEBEC GRANDS PROJETS INC.—See VINCI S.A.; *Int'l*, pg. 8218
EUROVIA SA—See VINCI S.A.; *Int'l*, pg. 8218
EUROVIA SERVICES GMBH—See VINCI S.A.; *Int'l*, pg. 8219
EUROVIA SILBA, A.S.—See VINCI S.A.; *Int'l*, pg. 8219
EUROVIA SK, A.S. - MICHALOVCE PLANT—See VINCI S.A.; *Int'l*, pg. 8217
EUROVIA STONE CZ, S.R.O.—See VINCI S.A.; *Int'l*, pg. 8219
EUROVIA STR SAS—See VINCI S.A.; *Int'l*, pg. 8220
EUROVIA TEERBAU GMBH—See VINCI S.A.; *Int'l*, pg. 8219
EUROVIA VERKEHRSBAU UNION GMBH-LEIPZIG—See VINCI S.A.; *Int'l*, pg. 8219
EUROVIA VERKEHRSBAU UNION GMBH-MAGDEBURG—See VINCI S.A.; *Int'l*, pg. 8219
EUROVIA VERKEHRSBAU UNION GMBH-NEUBRANDENBURG—See VINCI S.A.; *Int'l*, pg. 8219
EUROVIA VERKEHRSBAU UNION GMBH—See VINCI S.A.; *Int'l*, pg. 8219
EUROVIDEO BILDPROGRAMM GMBH—See Bavaria Film GmbH; *Int'l*, pg. 800
EUROVIDEO BILDPROGRAMM GMBH—See Telepool GmbH; *Int'l*, pg. 7541
EUROVINIL S.P.A.—See ONEX Corporation; *Int'l*, pg. 5580
EUROVITA ASSICURAZIONI S.P.A—See Cinven Limited; *Int'l*, pg. 1612
EUROVITA HOLDING S.P.A.—See Cinven Limited; *Int'l*, pg. 1612
EUROVITA S.P.A.—See Cinven Limited; *Int'l*, pg. 1612
EUROVITI S.R.L.; *Int'l*, pg. 2559
EUROWAG D.O.O.—See W.A.G Payment Solutions Plc; *Int'l*, pg. 8321
EURO WASTE A.S.—See Mondi plc; *Int'l*, pg. 5026
EUROWEB ROMANIA, S.A.—See Mid Europa Partners LLP; *Int'l*, pg. 4882
EUROWHEEL BVBA—See Compagnie Generale des Etablissements Michelin SCA; *Int'l*, pg. 1742
EUROWINDOW., JSC—See Bunka Shutter Co., Ltd.; *Int'l*, pg. 1216
EUROWINGS GMBH—See Deutsche Lufthansa AG; *Int'l*, pg. 2066
EUROWRAP A/S—See Accent Equity Partners AB; *Int'l*, pg. 81
EUROWRAP LTD—See Accent Equity Partners AB; *Int'l*, pg. 81
EURO YATIRIM HOLDING AS; *Int'l*, pg. 2531
EUROZET SP. Z.O.O.; *Int'l*, pg. 2559
EUROZ HARTLEYS GROUP LIMITED; *Int'l*, pg. 2559
EUROZONE BRANDS LIMITED—See Colan Totte.Co., Ltd.; *Int'l*, pg. 1697
EURPAC SERVICE CO; *U.S. Private*, pg. 1434
EURPAC SERVICE INCORPORATED; *U.S. Private*, pg. 1434
EURUS BLOWER, INC.—See Shandong Zhangqiu Blower Co., Ltd.; *Int'l*, pg. 6760
EURUS ENERGY HOLDINGS CORPORATION—See Toyota Tsusho Corporation; *Int'l*, pg. 7877
EURYDICE PARTNERS SAS—See Synergie SA; *Int'l*, pg. 7383
EURYZA REIS GMBH—See Ebro Foods S.A.; *Int'l*, pg. 2286
EUSA PHARMA (UK) LIMITED—See Essex Woodlands Management, Inc.; *U.S. Private*, pg. 1428
EUSA PHARMA (US) LLC—See Essex Woodlands Management, Inc.; *U.S. Private*, pg. 1428
EUS COMMUNICATION INC.; *U.S. Private*, pg. 1434
EUSKALTEL SA; *Int'l*, pg. 2559
EUSTIS MORTGAGE CORP.; *U.S. Private*, pg. 1434
EUSTON FILMS LIMITED—See Bertelsmann SE & Co. KGaA; *Int'l*, pg. 992
EUSU HOLDINGS CO., LTD.; *Int'l*, pg. 2559
EUSU LOGISTICS CO., LTD.—See Eusu Holdings Co., Ltd.; *Int'l*, pg. 2559
EUSU LOGISTICS (HONG KONG) CO., LTD.—See Eusu Holdings Co., Ltd.; *Int'l*, pg. 2559

EUSU LOGISTICS JAPAN CO., LTD.—See Eusu Holdings Co., Ltd.; *Int'l*, pg. 2559
EUSU LOGISTICS LLC—See Eusu Holdings Co., Ltd.; *Int'l*, pg. 2559
EUSU LOGISTICS (M) SDN. BHD.—See Eusu Holdings Co., Ltd.; *Int'l*, pg. 2559
EUSU LOGISTICS (SHANGHAI) CO., LTD.—See Eusu Holdings Co., Ltd.; *Int'l*, pg. 2559
EUSU LOGISTICS (SHENZHEN) CO., LTD.—See Eusu Holdings Co., Ltd.; *Int'l*, pg. 2559
EUSU LOGISTICS SINGAPORE PTE. LTD.—See Eusu Holdings Co., Ltd.; *Int'l*, pg. 2559
EUSU LOGISTICS SPAIN S.A.—See Eusu Holdings Co., Ltd.; *Int'l*, pg. 2559
EUSU LOGISTICS SPAIN SA—See Financiere de L'Odet; *Int'l*, pg. 2667
EUSU LOGISTICS THAILAND CO., LTD.—See Eusu Holdings Co., Ltd.; *Int'l*, pg. 2559
EU SUPPLY PLC—See Mercell Holding AS; *Int'l*, pg. 4829
EUTAW CONSTRUCTION COMPANY INC.; *U.S. Private*, pg. 1434
EUTAWVILLE IGA—See W. Lee Flowers & Company Inc.; *U.S. Private*, pg. 4418
EU TAXFREE DEUTSCHLAND GMBH—See Eurazeo SE; *Int'l*, pg. 2528
EUTECH INSTRUMENTS PTE LTD.—See Thermo Fisher Scientific Inc.; *U.S. Public*, pg. 2146
EUTECH INSTRUMENTS PTE LTD.—See Thermo Fisher Scientific Inc.; *U.S. Public*, pg. 2146
EUTECTIC CANADA INC.—See MEC Holding GmbH; *Int'l*, pg. 4764
EUTECTIC CORPORATION—See MEC Holding GmbH; *Int'l*, pg. 4764
EUTECTIC DO BRASIL LTDA—See Enovis Corporation; *U.S. Public*, pg. 772
EUTECTIC KOREA LTD.—See MEC Holding GmbH; *Int'l*, pg. 4764
EUTECTIC MEXICO, S.A. DE C.V.—See MEC Holding GmbH; *Int'l*, pg. 4764
EUTECTIC USA—See MEC Holding GmbH; *Int'l*, pg. 4764
EUTEK SYSTEMS, INC.—See CRH plc; *Int'l*, pg. 1846
EUTELSAT AMERICA CORP.—See Eutelsat Communications SA; *Int'l*, pg. 2559
EUTELSAT ASIA PTE. LTD.—See Eutelsat Communications SA; *Int'l*, pg. 2559
EUTELSAT COMMUNICATIONS FINANCE S.A.S.—See Eutelsat Communications SA; *Int'l*, pg. 2559
EUTELSAT COMMUNICATIONS SA; *Int'l*, pg. 2559
EUTELSAT DO BRASIL PARTICIPATOES LTDA.—See Eutelsat Communications SA; *Int'l*, pg. 2560
EUTELSAT DO BRASIL SA—See Eutelsat Communications SA; *Int'l*, pg. 2559
EUTELSAT GMBH—See Eutelsat Communications SA; *Int'l*, pg. 2559
EUTELSAT LATIN AMERICA S.A.—See Eutelsat Communications SA; *Int'l*, pg. 2559
EUTELSAT MADEIRA LDA.—See Eutelsat Communications SA; *Int'l*, pg. 2559
EUTELSAT NETWORKS LLC—See Eutelsat Communications SA; *Int'l*, pg. 2559
EUTELSAT POLSKA S.P.Z.O.—See Eutelsat Communications SA; *Int'l*, pg. 2559
EUTELSAT S.A.—See Eutelsat Communications SA; *Int'l*, pg. 2559
EUTELSAT SERVICES UND BETEILIGUNGEN GMBH—See Eutelsat Communications SA; *Int'l*, pg. 2559
EUTELSAT UK LTD.—See Eutelsat Communications SA; *Int'l*, pg. 2559
EUTELSAT VAS S.A.S.—See Eutelsat Communications SA; *Int'l*, pg. 2559
EUTHYMICS BIOSCIENCE, INC.; *U.S. Private*, pg. 1434
EUTILEX CO., LTD.; *Int'l*, pg. 2560
EUTIMA BVBA—See Ontex Group N.V.; *Int'l*, pg. 5591
EUTOMATION & SCANSYS SA/NV—See Manders Industries B.V.; *Int'l*, pg. 4668
EUTROPE SAS—See LVMH Moet Hennessy Louis Vuitton SE; *Int'l*, pg. 4591
EUTROVISION SYSTEMS, INC.—See Keda Communications Ltd; *Int'l*, pg. 4114
EUVIPHARM PHARMACEUTICALS JOINT STOCK COMPANY—See JW Holdings Corporation; *Int'l*, pg. 4035
EUV RESIST MANUFACTURING & QUALIFICATION CENTER N.V.—See JSR Corp.; *Int'l*, pg. 4013
EUWAX AG; *Int'l*, pg. 2560
EU YAN SANG (HONG KONG) LIMITED—See Eu Yan Sang International Ltd.; *Int'l*, pg. 2525
EU YAN SANG INTEGRATIVE HEALTH PTE. LTD.—See Eu Yan Sang International Ltd.; *Int'l*, pg. 2525
EU YAN SANG INTERNATIONAL LTD.; *Int'l*, pg. 2525
EU YAN SANG MARKETING PTE LTD—See Eu Yan Sang International Ltd.; *Int'l*, pg. 2525
EU YAN SANG (SINGAPORE) PTE LTD—See Eu Yan Sang International Ltd.; *Int'l*, pg. 2525
EV3 CANADA INC.—See Medtronic plc; *Int'l*, pg. 4787
EV3, INC.—See Medtronic plc; *Int'l*, pg. 4787
EV3 MEDICAL DEVICES (BEIJING) COMPANY, LTD.—See Medtronic plc; *Int'l*, pg. 4790

EVANSHARDY & YOUNG, INC.

EV8 TECHNOLOGIES LIMITED; *Int'l*, pg. 2560
EVA AIRWAYS CORPORATION—See Evergreen Marine Corporation (Taiwan) Ltd.; *Int'l*, pg. 2566
EVAC E.U.R.L.—See Bridgepoint Group Plc; *Int'l*, pg. 1153
EVAC GERMANY GMBH—See Bridgepoint Group Plc; *Int'l*, pg. 1153
EVAC GMBH—See Safran SA; *Int'l*, pg. 6473
EVAC NORTH AMERICA INC.—See Bridgepoint Group Plc; *Int'l*, pg. 1153
EVAC NORWAY AS—See Bridgepoint Group Plc; *Int'l*, pg. 1153
EVACO SA—See The Swatch Group Ltd.; *Int'l*, pg. 7691
EVAC OY—See Bridgepoint Group Plc; *Int'l*, pg. 1153
EV ACQUISITION INC.—See Darling Ingredients Inc.; *U.S. Public*, pg. 634
EVAC VACUUM SYSTEMS (SHANGHAI) CO., LTD.—See Bridgepoint Group Plc; *Int'l*, pg. 1153
EVADIX LABELS S.R.L.—See Amcor plc; *Int'l*, pg. 418
EVADIX SA; *Int'l*, pg. 2560
EVA-DRY; *U.S. Private*, pg. 1434
EV ADVANCED MATERIAL CO., LTD.; *Int'l*, pg. 2560
EVAG EMDER VERKEHRS UND AUTOMOTIVE GESELLSCHAFT MBH—See Deutsche Bahn AG; *Int'l*, pg. 2051
E.V.A. GMBH—See Hochland SE; *Int'l*, pg. 3437
EVAGRACE PHARMA PRIVATE LIMITED—See Medico Intercontinental Limited; *Int'l*, pg. 4776
EVAL EUROPE N.V.—See Kuraray Co., Ltd.; *Int'l*, pg. 4337
EVALON TEXTILE CO., LTD.—See Triocean Industrial Corporation Co., Ltd.; *Int'l*, pg. 7925
EVALON TEXTILE (THAILAND) CO., LTD.—See Triocean Industrial Corporation Co., Ltd.; *Int'l*, pg. 7925
EVALUA INTERNATIONAL LTD. OY—See Terveystalo PLC; *Int'l*, pg. 7571
EVALUA NEDERLAND B.V.—See Terveystalo PLC; *Int'l*, pg. 7571
EVALUATOR GROUP, INC.—See Futurum, LLC; *U.S. Private*, pg. 1627
EVALUE VENTURES AG; *Int'l*, pg. 2560
EVALVE, INC.—See Abbott Laboratories; *U.S. Public*, pg. 19
EVALYTICA, LLC—See Veradigm Inc.; *U.S. Public*, pg. 2280
EVANA AUTOMATION SPECIALISTS—See Phillips Service Industries, Inc. (PSI); *U.S. Private*, pg. 3171
EVANCIA SAS; *Int'l*, pg. 2560
EVANDER GROUP LIMITED—See PAI Partners S.A.S.; *Int'l*, pg. 5702
EVANGELICAL CHILDREN'S HOME; *U.S. Private*, pg. 1434
EVANGELICAL HOMES OF MICHIGAN; *U.S. Private*, pg. 1434
EVANGELICAL LUTHERAN CHURCH IN AMERICA; *U.S. Private*, pg. 1434
THE EVANGELICAL LUTHERAN GOOD SAMARITAN FOUNDATION—See Sanford Health; *U.S. Private*, pg. 3545
THE EVANGELINE BANK & TRUST CO.; *U.S. Private*, pg. 4027
EVANS ADHESIVE CORPORATION—See Arsenal Capital Management LP; *U.S. Private*, pg. 339
THE EVANS AGENCY, LLC—See Arthur J. Gallagher & Co.; *U.S. Public*, pg. 207
EVANS ANALYTICAL GROUP, INC.—See Eurofins Scientific S.E.; *Int'l*, pg. 2549
EVANS & ASSOCIATES ENTERPRISES; *U.S. Private*, pg. 1434
EVANS BANCORP, INC.; *U.S. Public*, pg. 799
EVANS BANK, N.A.—See Evans Bancorp, Inc.; *U.S. Public*, pg. 799
EVANS BROTHERS INC.; *U.S. Private*, pg. 1434
EVANS CAPACITOR COMPANY—See Arcline Investment Management LP; *U.S. Private*, pg. 313
EVANS CONCRETE LLC; *U.S. Private*, pg. 1434
EVANS CONSOLES, INC.—See Carl Marks & Co., Inc.; *U.S. Private*, pg. 762
EVANS CONSTRUCTION COMPANY—See CRH plc; *Int'l*, pg. 1847
EVANS DEDICATED SYSTEMS, INC.; *U.S. Private*, pg. 1435
EVANS DELIVERY COMPANY, INC.—See Calera Capital Management, Inc.; *U.S. Private*, pg. 717
EVANS ELECTRIC LTD.; *Int'l*, pg. 2560
EVANS ENTERPRISES, INC.; *U.S. Private*, pg. 1435
EVANS ENVIRONMENTAL & GEOLOGICAL SCIENCE AND MANAGEMENT INC.; *U.S. Private*, pg. 1435
EVANS FOOD GROUP LTD.—See Wind Point Advisors LLC; *U.S. Private*, pg. 4534
EVANS FRUIT COMPANY; *U.S. Private*, pg. 1435
EVANS GRADING CO.; *U.S. Private*, pg. 1435
EVANS GRAIN & ELEVATOR CO. INC.; *U.S. Private*, pg. 1435
EVANS HALSHAW (CARDIFF) LIMITED—See Pinewood Technologies Group PLC; *Int'l*, pg. 5869
EVANS HALSHAW MOTORS LIMITED—See Pinewood Technologies Group PLC; *Int'l*, pg. 5869
EVANSHARDY & YOUNG, INC.; *U.S. Private*, pg. 1435
EVANS HOLDINGS LTD.—See Active Private Equity Advisory LLP; *Int'l*, pg. 120

EVANS HOTELS CORPORATION; *U.S. Private*, pg. 1435
EVANS INCORPORATED; *U.S. Private*, pg. 1435
EVANS LANDSCAPING INC.; *U.S. Private*, pg. 1435
EVANS MACTAVISH AGRICRAFT INC.; *U.S. Private*, pg. 1435
EVANS MACTAVISH AGRICRAFT—See Evans MacTavish Agricraft Inc.; *U.S. Private*, pg. 1435
EVANS MANUFACTURING INC.; *U.S. Private*, pg. 1435
EVANS MEATS, INCORPORATED; *U.S. Private*, pg. 1435
EVANS MEDICAL PLC; *Int'l*, pg. 2560
EVANS NATIONAL FINANCIAL SERVICES, LLC—See Evans Bancorp, Inc.; *U.S. Public*, pg. 799
EVANS NATIONAL HOLDING CORP.—See Evans Bancorp, Inc.; *U.S. Public*, pg. 799
EVANS & PARTNERS PTY. LIMITED—See E&P Financial Group Limited; *Int'l*, pg. 2247
EVANS PROPERTIES INC.; *U.S. Private*, pg. 1435
EVANS RULE COMPANY, INC.—See MiddleGround Management, LP; *U.S. Private*, pg. 2713
EVANS SERVICE COMPANY INC.; *U.S. Private*, pg. 1435
THE EVANS-SHERRATT CO.; *U.S. Private*, pg. 4027
EVANS & SONS CONSTRUCTION; *U.S. Private*, pg. 1434
EVANS SURGERY CENTER—See HCA Healthcare, Inc.; *U.S. Public*, pg. 996
EVANS & SUTHERLAND COMPUTER CORPORATION - DIGITAL THEATER DIVISION—See Elevate Entertainment, Inc.; *U.S. Private*, pg. 1358
EVANS & SUTHERLAND COMPUTER CORPORATION - SIMULATION DIVISION—See Elevate Entertainment, Inc.; *U.S. Private*, pg. 1358
EVANS & SUTHERLAND COMPUTER CORPORATION—See Elevate Entertainment, Inc.; *U.S. Private*, pg. 1358
EVANS TIRE & SERVICE CENTERS, INC.; *U.S. Private*, pg. 1435
EVANSTON CARBON FIBER, LLC—See Mitsubishi Chemical Group Corporation; *Int'l*, pg. 4933
EVANSTON CLINIC CORP.—See Quorum Health Corporation; *U.S. Private*, pg. 3329
THE EVANSTON GROUP, LLC—See Stone Point Capital LLC; *U.S. Private*, pg. 3823
EVANSTON HOSPITAL CORPORATION—See Quorum Health Corporation; *U.S. Private*, pg. 3329
EVANSTON HOSPITAL—See NorthShore University HealthSystem; *U.S. Private*, pg. 2957
EVANSTON INSURANCE COMPANY—See Markel Group Inc.; *U.S. Public*, pg. 1368
EVANSTON PARTNERS, LLC; *U.S. Private*, pg. 1435
EVANSTON SUBARU IN SKOKIE; *U.S. Private*, pg. 1435
EVANSVILLE COURIER COMPANY, INC.—See Gannett Co., Inc.; *U.S. Public*, pg. 898
EVANSVILLE TEACHERS FEDERAL CREDIT UNION; *U.S. Private*, pg. 1435
EVANSVILLE TREATMENT CENTER, LLC—See Acadia Healthcare Company, Inc.; *U.S. Public*, pg. 28
EVANTAGE TECHNOLOGIES, INC.—See Kellton Tech Solutions Ltd.; *Int'l*, pg. 4121
EVANTA VENTURES, INC.—See Gartner, Inc.; *U.S. Public*, pg. 906
EVAN THOMAS GLOBAL LLC; *U.S. Private*, pg. 1434
EVANTIC—See Edgewater Capital Partners, L.P.; *U.S. Private*, pg. 1334
EVAPORATED METAL FILMS CORPORATION—See Dynasil Corporation of America; *U.S. Private*, pg. 1299
EVA PRECISION INDUSTRIAL HOLDINGS LIMITED; *Int'l*, pg. 2560
EVA PRECISION INDUSTRIAL (SUZHOU) LIMITED—See EVA Precision Industrial Holdings Limited; *Int'l*, pg. 2560
EVAR AIR-CONDITIONING & ENGINEERING PTE LTD—See Nippon Air conditioning Services Co., Ltd.; *Int'l*, pg. 5310
EVA-SOCIEDADE DE INVESTIMENTOS MOBILIAROS E IMOBILIARIOS, LDA.—See Jeronimo Martins SGPS SA; *Int'l*, pg. 3931
EVASTEM CO., LTD.—See MEDIPOST Co., Ltd.; *Int'l*, pg. 4780
EVATEC AG; *Int'l*, pg. 2560
EVATEC EUROPE GMBH—See Evatec AG; *Int'l*, pg. 2561
EVATEC ITALIA S.R.L—See Evatec AG; *Int'l*, pg. 2561
EVATEC (LIECHTENSTEIN) AG—See Evatec AG; *Int'l*, pg. 2560
EVATEC NA INC.—See Evatec AG; *Int'l*, pg. 2561
EVATEC PROCESS SYSTEMS B.V.—See Evatec AG; *Int'l*, pg. 2561
EVA- THE BASEL LIFE SCIENCES START-UP AGENCY—See Basellandschaftliche Kantonalbank; *Int'l*, pg. 871
EVATHERM AG; *Int'l*, pg. 2561
EVATHERM GMBH—See EVATHERM AG; *Int'l*, pg. 2561
EVATHERM KFT.—See EVATHERM AG; *Int'l*, pg. 2561
EVAXION BIOTECH A/S; *Int'l*, pg. 2561
EVB-EVOLUTION BUREAU—See Omnicom Group Inc.; *U.S. Public*, pg. 1583
EVC DRESDEN-WILSCHDORF GMBH & CO. KG—See L'Air Liquide S.A.; *Int'l*, pg. 4370
EV CHARGE PARTNER SWEDEN AB—See Garo AB; *Int'l*, pg. 2885
EV CHARGING USA, INC.; *U.S. Private*, pg. 1434

EVCI CAREER COLLEGES HOLDING CORP.; *U.S. Private*, pg. 1435
EVCILER KIMYA MADENCILIK VE DEGERLI METALLER SAN.TIC A.S.—See Elemental Holding S.A.; *Int'l*, pg. 2358
EVCON INDUSTRIES, INC.—See Johnson Controls International plc; *Int'l*, pg. 3985
EVCO PLASTICS INC.; *U.S. Private*, pg. 1436
EVCO WHOLESALE FOODS; *U.S. Private*, pg. 1436
EVD BERHAD; *Int'l*, pg. 2561
EV DIGITAL INVEST AG; *Int'l*, pg. 2560
EV DYNAMICS (HOLDINGS) LIMITED; *Int'l*, pg. 2560
EVE & CO INCORPORATED; *Int'l*, pg. 2561
EVEDEN AUSTRALIA PTY LTD—See Wacoal Holdings Corp.; *Int'l*, pg. 8325
EVEDEN CANADA LTD.—See Wacoal Holdings Corp.; *Int'l*, pg. 8325
EVEDEN ISRAEL LIMITED—See Wacoal Holdings Corp.; *Int'l*, pg. 8325
EVEDEN LTD.—See Wacoal Holdings Corp.; *Int'l*, pg. 8325
EVE DESIGN AUTOMATION PVT. LTD.—See Synopsys, Inc.; *U.S. Public*, pg. 1970
EVED, LLC; *U.S. Private*, pg. 1436
EVE ENERGY CO., LTD. - JINGMEN FACTORY—See EVE Energy Co., Ltd.; *Int'l*, pg. 2561
EVE ENERGY CO., LTD.; *Int'l*, pg. 2561
EVE ENERGY CO., LTD. - XIKENG FACTORY—See EVE Energy Co., Ltd.; *Int'l*, pg. 2561
EVE ENERGY CO., LTD. - ZHONGKAI FACTORY—See EVE Energy Co., Ltd.; *Int'l*, pg. 2561
EVE ENERGY NORTH AMERICA CORPORATION—See EVE Energy Co., Ltd.; *Int'l*, pg. 2561
EVE GERMANY GMBH—See EVE Energy Co., Ltd.; *Int'l*, pg. 2561
EVE HEALTH GROUP LIMITED; *Int'l*, pg. 2561
EVE HOLDING, INC.; *U.S. Public*, pg. 799
EVE HOLDINGS INC.—See Japan Tobacco Inc.; *Int'l*, pg. 3907
EVE HYPERPOWER BATTERIES INC.—See EVE Energy Co., Ltd.; *Int'l*, pg. 2561
EVE INNOVATION ENERGY CO., LTD.—See EVE Energy Co., Ltd.; *Int'l*, pg. 2561
EVELAND'S INC.; *U.S. Private*, pg. 1436
EVELO BIOSCIENCES, INC.; *U.S. Public*, pg. 799
EVELYN & ARTHUR INC.; *U.S. Private*, pg. 1436
EVELYN PAGE RETIREMENT VILLAGE LIMITED—See Ryman Healthcare Ltd.; *Int'l*, pg. 6439
EVE MOBILITY ACQUISITION CORP.; *U.S. Public*, pg. 799
EVEN CONSTRUTORA E INCORPORADORA S.A.; *Int'l*, pg. 2561
E&V ENERGY CORPORATION; *U.S. Private*, pg. 1301
EVENFLO CANADA—See Goodbaby International Holdings Limited; *Int'l*, pg. 3039
EVENFLO COMPANY, INC.—See Goodbaby International Holdings Limited; *Int'l*, pg. 3039
EVENFLO MEXICO S.A. DE C.V.—See Goodbaby International Holdings Limited; *Int'l*, pg. 3039
THE EVENING CALL PUBLISHING COMPANY—See R.I.S.N. Operations Inc.; *U.S. Private*, pg. 3337
EVENING POST DIGITAL—See Evening Post Publishing Co.; *U.S. Private*, pg. 1436
EVENING POST PUBLISHING CO.; *U.S. Private*, pg. 1436
EVENING STANDARD LTD.; *Int'l*, pg. 2562
THE EVENING SUN—See Gannett Co., Inc.; *U.S. Public*, pg. 900
EVENKO—See Club de hockey Canadien, Inc.; *Int'l*, pg. 1664
EVEN SP 18/10 EMPREENDIMENTOS IMOBILIARIOS LTDA.—See Even Construtora e Incorporadora S.A.; *Int'l*, pg. 2562
EVEN - SP 35/10 EMPREENDIMENTOS IMOBILIAROS LTDA.—See Even Construtora e Incorporadora S.A.; *Int'l*, pg. 2561
EVEN - SP 47/10 EMPREENDIMENTOS IMOBILIARIOS LTDA.—See Even Construtora e Incorporadora S.A.; *Int'l*, pg. 2561
EVEN - SP 59/11 EMPREENDIMENTOS IMOBILIARIOS LTDA.—See Even Construtora e Incorporadora S.A.; *Int'l*, pg. 2561
EVENTA ENTERTAINMENT GROUP LTD.; *Int'l*, pg. 2562
THE EVENT AGENCY; *U.S. Private*, pg. 4027
EVENT AUDIO VISUAL GROUP, INC.—See Ushio, Inc.; *Int'l*, pg. 8097
EVENTBRITE, INC.; *U.S. Public*, pg. 799
EVENT CINEMAS LIMITED—See Event Hospitality & Entertainment Limited; *Int'l*, pg. 2562
EVENT & CONVENTION HOUSE, INC.—See Kintetsu Group Holdings Co.,Ltd.; *Int'l*, pg. 4183
EVENTDECK—See Myers Industries, Inc.; *U.S. Public*, pg. 1488
EVENT ELITE PRODUCTION AND PROMOTION LIMITED—See ManpowerGroup Inc.; *U.S. Public*, pg. 1357
EVENTEQ, LLC; *U.S. Private*, pg. 1437
EVENT EQUIPMENT LEASING, LLC—See National Association for Stock Car Auto Racing, Inc.; *U.S. Private*, pg. 2845

EVENTERPRISE GMBH—See Vivendi SE; *Int'l*, pg. 8276
EVENTFUL LIMITED—See Aeorema Communications Plc; *Int'l*, pg. 179
EVENT HOSPITALITY & ENTERTAINMENT LIMITED; *Int'l*, pg. 2562
EVENTIDE SENIOR LIVING COMMUNITIES; *U.S. Private*, pg. 1437
EVENTIKO INC.; *Int'l*, pg. 2562
EVENTIM BG O.O.D.—See CTS Eventim AG & Co. KGAA; *Int'l*, pg. 1872
EVENTIM D.O.O.—See CTS Eventim AG & Co. KGAA; *Int'l*, pg. 1873
EVENTIM MARKETING UND SPONSORING GMBH—See CTS Eventim AG & Co. KGAA; *Int'l*, pg. 1872
EVENTIM NORGE AS—See CTS Eventim AG & Co. KGAA; *Int'l*, pg. 1872
EVENTIM POPKURS HAMBURG GEMEINNUTZIGE GMBH—See CTS Eventim AG & Co. KGAA; *Int'l*, pg. 1872
EVENTIMPRESENTS GMBH & CO. KG—See CTS Eventim AG & Co. KGAA; *Int'l*, pg. 1874
EVENTIM RU S.R.L.—See CTS Eventim AG & Co. KGAA; *Int'l*, pg. 1873
EVENTIM SI D.O.O.—See CTS Eventim AG & Co. KGAA; *Int'l*, pg. 1872
EVENTIM SK, S.R.O.—See CTS Eventim AG & Co. KGAA; *Int'l*, pg. 1872
EVENTIM SPORTS CONSULTING GMBH—See CTS Eventim AG & Co. KGAA; *Int'l*, pg. 1872
EVENTIM SP. Z O.O.—See CTS Eventim AG & Co. KGAA; *Int'l*, pg. 1872
EVENTIM SVERIGE AB—See CTS Eventim AG & Co. KGAA; *Int'l*, pg. 1872
EVENTIM UK LIMITED—See CTS Eventim AG & Co. KGAA; *Int'l*, pg. 1872
EVENTINVENTORY.COM, INC.—See Live Nation Entertainment, Inc.; *U.S. Public*, pg. 1328
EVENT IT AG—See Deutsche Messe AG; *Int'l*, pg. 2071
EVENT MANAGEMENT SERVICES, INC.; *U.S. Private*, pg. 1436
EVENT MARKETING SERVICE GMBH; *Int'l*, pg. 2562
EVENT NETWORK, INC.; *U.S. Private*, pg. 1436
EVENTPRO STRATEGIES, INC.; *U.S. Private*, pg. 1437
EVENTPRO STRATEGIES, LLC; *U.S. Private*, pg. 1437
EVENT SALES INC.; *U.S. Private*, pg. 1437
EVENTS BY SUPERIOR—See Superior Products Distributors Inc.; *U.S. Private*, pg. 3880
EVENTS CLUB OY—See Live Nation Entertainment, Inc.; *U.S. Public*, pg. 1330
EVENTS.COM, INC.; *U.S. Private*, pg. 1437
THE EVENTS COMPANY—See Fertitta Entertainment, Inc.; *U.S. Private*, pg. 1499
EVENTS INTERNATIONAL LIMITED—See TUI AG; *Int'l*, pg. 7964
EVENTS INTERNATIONAL (SPORTS TRAVEL) LIMITED—See TUI AG; *Int'l*, pg. 7964
EVENT SOLUTIONS LLC; *U.S. Private*, pg. 1437
EVENTS SOCIAL MARKETING AND PRODUCTIONS AFRIKA (PTY) LTD—See African Equity Empowerment Investmts Limited; *Int'l*, pg. 191
EVENT STAGING DIVISION—See KVL Audio Visual Services; *U.S. Private*, pg. 2359
THE EVENT SUPPORT COMPANY BV—See Live Nation Entertainment, Inc.; *U.S. Public*, pg. 1331
EVENT SUPPORT CORPORATION—See National Association for Stock Car Auto Racing, Inc.; *U.S. Private*, pg. 2845
EVENT TECHNOLOGY, LLC; *U.S. Private*, pg. 1437
EVENTURE CAPITAL PARTNERS II, LLC—See Otto GmbH & Co. KG; *Int'l*, pg. 5663
E.VENTURES MANAGEMENTGESELLSCHAFT MBH—See Otto GmbH & Co. KG; *Int'l*, pg. 5663
EVENTWORKS INC.; *U.S. Private*, pg. 1437
EVEO INC.—See ALPHAEON Corporation; *U.S. Private*, pg. 200
EVE PARC (FALMOUTH) MANAGEMENT COMPANY LIMITED—See Persimmon plc; *Int'l*, pg. 5815
EVE PARK (FALMOUTH) MANAGEMENT COMPANY LIMITED—See Persimmon plc; *Int'l*, pg. 5815
EVER.AG CORPORATION—See Dairy, LLC; *U.S. Private*, pg. 1146
EVERARC HOLDINGS LIMITED; *Int'l*, pg. 2563
EVERARD (GUERNSEY) LIMITED—See James Fisher & Sons Public Limited Company; *Int'l*, pg. 3875
EVERARDS BREWERY LTD; *Int'l*, pg. 2563
EVERBANK WEALTH MANAGEMENT, INC.—See Teachers Insurance Association - College Retirement Fund; *U.S. Private*, pg. 3948
EVERBERG CAPITAL, LLC; *U.S. Private*, pg. 1437
EVERBEST PRINTING (GUANGZHOU) CO. LTD—See Thai Beverage Public Company Limited; *Int'l*, pg. 7590
EVERBEST PRINTING HOLDINGS LIMITED—See Thai Beverage Public Company Limited; *Int'l*, pg. 7590
EVERBEST PRINTING INVESTMENT LIMITED—See Thai Beverage Public Company Limited; *Int'l*, pg. 7589
EVER BRASIL INDUSTRIA E COMERCIO LTDA—See Esseco Group SRL; *Int'l*, pg. 2509
EVERBRIDGE ASIA PTE. LTD.—See Thoma Bravo, L.P.; *U.S. Private*, pg. 4147

COMPANY NAME INDEX

EVERBRIDGE EUROPE LIMITED—See Thoma Bravo, L.P.; *U.S. Private*, pg. 4147
EVERBRIDGE FINLAND OY—See Thoma Bravo, L.P.; *U.S. Private*, pg. 4147
EVERBRIDGE FRANCE SAS—See Thoma Bravo, L.P.; *U.S. Private*, pg. 4147
EVERBRIDGE, INC.—See Thoma Bravo, L.P.; *U.S. Private*, pg. 4147
EVERBRIDGE NORWAY AS—See Thoma Bravo, L.P.; *U.S. Private*, pg. 4147
EVERBRIGHT GRAND CHINA ASSETS LIMITED; *Int'l*, pg. 2563
EVERBRIGHT JIABAO CO., LTD.; *Int'l*, pg. 2563
EVERBRIGHT PGIM FUND MANAGEMENT CO., LTD.—See Prudential Financial, Inc.; *U.S. Public*, pg. 1731
EVERBRIGHT PRAMERICA FUND MANAGEMENT CO., LTD.—See Prudential Financial, Inc.; *U.S. Public*, pg. 1732
EVERBRIGHT SECURITIES CO., LTD.—See China Everbright Group Limited; *Int'l*, pg. 1501
EVERBRIGHT SECURITIES DIGITAL FINANCE (HK) LIMITED—See Allied Group Limited; *Int'l*, pg. 357
EVERBRITE ELECTRONICS, INC—See Everbrite, LLC; *U.S. Private*, pg. 1437
EVERBRITE LACROSSE—See Everbrite, LLC; *U.S. Private*, pg. 1437
EVERBRITE, LLC; *U.S. Private*, pg. 1437
EVERBRITE TECHNOLOGY CO., LTD.; *Int'l*, pg. 2563
EVERBUILD BUILDING PRODUCTS LIMITED—See Sika AG; *Int'l*, pg. 6914
THE EVERCARE COMPANY—See Ultimate Evercare Holdings, LLC; *U.S. Private*, pg. 4277
EVERCEL, INC.; *U.S. Private*, pg. 1437
EVERCHARGE, INC.—See SK Inc.; *Int'l*, pg. 6971
EVERCHINA INT'L HOLDINGS COMPANY LIMITED; *Int'l*, pg. 2563
EVER-CLEAR ENVIRONMENTAL ENG CORP.; *Int'l*, pg. 2563
EVERCOMMERCE INC.; *U.S. Public*, pg. 799
EVERCOMPOUNDS S.P.A.—See Caterpillar, Inc.; *U.S. Public*, pg. 452
EVERCORE ADVISORS L.L.C.—See Evercore, Inc.; *U.S. Public*, pg. 800
EVERCORE ADVISORY (MIDDLE EAST) LIMITED—See Evercore, Inc.; *U.S. Public*, pg. 800
EVERCORE ASIA LIMITED—See Evercore, Inc.; *U.S. Public*, pg. 800
EVERCORE ASIA (SINGAPORE) PTE. LTD.—See Evercore, Inc.; *U.S. Public*, pg. 800
EVERCORE CAPITAL PARTNERS—See Evercore, Inc.; *U.S. Public*, pg. 800
EVERCORE CASA DE BOLSA, S.A. DE C.V.—See Evercore, Inc.; *U.S. Public*, pg. 800
EVERCORE CONSULTING (BEIJING) CO. LTD.—See Evercore, Inc.; *U.S. Public*, pg. 800
EVERCORE GMBH—See Evercore, Inc.; *U.S. Public*, pg. 800
EVERCORE GROUP LLC—See Evercore, Inc.; *U.S. Public*, pg. 800
EVERCORE GROUP SERVICES LIMITED—See Evercore, Inc.; *U.S. Public*, pg. 800
EVERCORE, INC.; *U.S. Public*, pg. 799
EVERCORE ISI INTERNATIONAL LIMITED—See Evercore, Inc.; *U.S. Public*, pg. 800
EVERCORE (JAPAN) LTD.—See Evercore, Inc.; *U.S. Public*, pg. 800
EVERCORE PARTNERS CANADA LTD.—See Evercore, Inc.; *U.S. Public*, pg. 800
EVERCORE PARTNERS INTERNATIONAL L.L.P—See Evercore, Inc.; *U.S. Public*, pg. 800
EVERCORE PARTNERS LIMITED—See Evercore, Inc.; *U.S. Public*, pg. 800
EVERCORE PARTNERS MEXICO, S. DE R.L.—See Evercore, Inc.; *U.S. Public*, pg. 800
EVERCORE PARTNERS SERVICES EAST L.L.C.—See Evercore, Inc.; *U.S. Public*, pg. 800
EVERCORE TRUST COMPANY, N.A.—See Evercore, Inc.; *U.S. Public*, pg. 800
EVERCORE TRUST COMPANY OF DELAWARE—See Evercore, Inc.; *U.S. Public*, pg. 800
EVERCORE WEALTH MANAGEMENT L.L.C.—See Evercore, Inc.; *U.S. Public*, pg. 800
EVER CREATE PROFITS LIMITED—See HNA International Investment Holdings Limited; *Int'l*, pg. 3433
EVERCRISP SNACK PRODUCTOS DE CHILE S.A.—See PepsiCo, Inc.; *U.S. Public*, pg. 1668
EVERDIGM AMERICA INC.—See Hyundai Everdigm Corp; *Int'l*, pg. 3556
EVERDIGM HEAVY EQUIPMENT & MACHINERY TRADING LLC—See Hyundai Everdigm Corp; *Int'l*, pg. 3556
EVERDIGM MONGOLIA LLC—See Hyundai Everdigm Corp; *Int'l*, pg. 3556
EVERDISPLAY OPTRONICS SHANGHAI CO., LTD.; *Int'l*, pg. 2563
EVEREADY BATTERY COMPANY, INC.—See Energizer Holdings, Inc.; *U.S. Public*, pg. 761
EVEREADY DE MEXICO S.A. DE C.V.—See Energizer Holdings, Inc.; *U.S. Public*, pg. 761

EVEREADY EAST AFRICA PLC; *Int'l*, pg. 2563
EVEREADY ECUADOR C.A.—See Energizer Holdings, Inc.; *U.S. Public*, pg. 761
EVEREADY INDUSTRIES INDIA LTD; *Int'l*, pg. 2563
EVEREL—See Mohawk Industries, Inc.; *U.S. Public*, pg. 1457
EVERENCE; *U.S. Private*, pg. 1437
EVEREN LIMITED—See Energy Transfer LP; *U.S. Public*, pg. 764
EVEREN SPECIALTY LTD.—See Energy Transfer LP; *U.S. Public*, pg. 764
EVEREST ADVISORS (UK), LTD.—See Everest Group, Ltd.; *Int'l*, pg. 2564
EVEREST BANK LIMITED; *Int'l*, pg. 2563
EVEREST BRAND SOLUTIONS PVT. LTD.—See WPP plc; *Int'l*, pg. 8491
EVEREST CONSOLIDATOR ACQUISITION CORPORATION; *U.S. Public*, pg. 800
EVEREST CONSULTANTS INC.; *U.S. Private*, pg. 1437
EVEREST CONSULTING GROUP LP; *U.S. Private*, pg. 1437
EVEREST CONSULTING GROUP; *U.S. Private*, pg. 1437
EVEREST DENALI INSURANCE COMPANY—See Everest Group, Ltd.; *Int'l*, pg. 2564
EVEREST EQUIPMENT CO.—See Alamo Group Inc.; *U.S. Public*, pg. 71
EVEREST ESCROW, INC.—See Escrow Options Group Inc.; *U.S. Private*, pg. 1425
EVEREST FINANCIAL GROUP LIMITED; *Int'l*, pg. 2563
EVEREST GLOBAL SERVICES, INC.—See Everest Group, Ltd.; *Int'l*, pg. 2564
EVEREST GROUP, LTD.; *Int'l*, pg. 2564
EVEREST HOLDINGS & INVESTMENTS S.A.—See Marfin Investment Group Holdings S.A.; *Int'l*, pg. 4692
EVEREST INDEMNITY INSURANCE COMPANY—See Everest Group, Ltd.; *Int'l*, pg. 2564
EVEREST INDUSTRIES LTD; *Int'l*, pg. 2564
EVEREST INGENIERIA SRL—See Endress+Hauser (International) Holding AG; *Int'l*, pg. 2408
EVEREST INSURANCE COMPANY LTD.—See Himalayan Everest Insurance Limited; *Int'l*, pg. 3396
EVEREST INSURANCE COMPANY OF CANADA—See Everest Group, Ltd.; *Int'l*, pg. 2564
EVEREST INSURANCE (IRELAND), DAC—See Everest Group, Ltd.; *Int'l*, pg. 2564
EVEREST INSURANCE (IRELAND), DESIGNATED ACTIVITY COMPANY—See Everest Group, Ltd.; *Int'l*, pg. 2564
EVEREST KANTO CYLINDER LIMITED; *Int'l*, pg. 2564
EVEREST NATIONAL INSURANCE COMPANY—See Everest Group, Ltd.; *Int'l*, pg. 2564
EVEREST NATIONAL—See Everest Group, Ltd.; *Int'l*, pg. 2564
EVEREST ORGANICS LIMITED MEDAK FACTORY—See Everest Organics Limited; *Int'l*, pg. 2564
EVEREST ORGANICS LIMITED; *Int'l*, pg. 2564
EVEREST REINSURANCE (BERMUDA), LTD.—See Everest Group, Ltd.; *Int'l*, pg. 2564
EVEREST REINSURANCE COMPANY - ESCRITORIO DE REPRESENTA CAO NO BRASIL LTDA.—See Everest Group, Ltd.; *Int'l*, pg. 2564
EVEREST REINSURANCE COMPANY (IRELAND), LIMITED—See Everest Group, Ltd.; *Int'l*, pg. 2564
EVEREST REINSURANCE COMPANY—See Everest Group, Ltd.; *Int'l*, pg. 2564
EVEREST REINSURANCE COMPANY—See Everest Group, Ltd.; *Int'l*, pg. 2564
EVEREST REINSURANCE HOLDINGS, INC.—See Everest Group, Ltd.; *Int'l*, pg. 2564
EVEREST SECURITY INSURANCE COMPANY—See Everest Group, Ltd.; *Int'l*, pg. 2564
EVEREST SOFTWARE INC.—See ESW Capital, LLC; *U.S. Private*, pg. 1430
EVEREST SPECIALTY UNDERWRITERS, LLC—See Everest Group, Ltd.; *Int'l*, pg. 2564
EVEREST TEXTILE CO., LTD. - SHANGHAI FACTORY—See Everest Textile Co., Ltd.; *Int'l*, pg. 2565
EVEREST TEXTILE CO., LTD.; *Int'l*, pg. 2564
EVEREST TEXTILE CO., LTD. - THAILAND FACTORY—See Everest Textile Co., Ltd.; *Int'l*, pg. 2565
EVEREST TEXTILE (HK) CO. LTD.—See Everest Textile Co., Ltd.; *Int'l*, pg. 2565
EVEREST TEXTILE (SHANGHAI), LTD.—See Everest Textile Co., Ltd.; *Int'l*, pg. 2565
EVEREST TEXTILE USA, LLC—See Everest Textile Co., Ltd.; *Int'l*, pg. 2565
EVERETT BUICK PONTIAC GMC; *U.S. Private*, pg. 1438
EVERETT CASH MUTUAL INSURANCE CO.; *U.S. Private*, pg. 1438
EVERETT CHARLES TECHNOLOGIES LLC—See Cohu, Inc.; *U.S. Public*, pg. 530
EVERETT CHARLES TEST FIXTURE DIVISION—See Cohu, Inc.; *U.S. Public*, pg. 530
EVERETT CHEVROLET INC.; *U.S. Private*, pg. 1438
EVERETT DYKE'S GRASSING CO., INC.; *U.S. Private*, pg. 1438
EVERETT FINANCIAL, INC.; *U.S. Private*, pg. 1438

EVERGREEN FIBREBOARD BERHAD

EVERETT FOODLINER INC.; *U.S. Private*, pg. 1438
EVERETT HOLDING COMPANY; *U.S. Private*, pg. 1438
EVERETT J. PRESCOTT INC.; *U.S. Private*, pg. 1438
EVERETT LABORATORIES, INC.—See Insud Pharma, S.L.; *Int'l*, pg. 3725
EVERETT LOGISTICS, LLC—See Roadrunner Transportation Systems, Inc.; *U.S. Public*, pg. 1802
EVERETT MSO, INC.—See DaVita Inc.; *U.S. Public*, pg. 638
EVERETT SHIPYARD, INC.—See Stellex Capital Management LP; *U.S. Private*, pg. 3800
EVERETT SHIPYARD, INC.—See The Carlyle Group Inc.; *U.S. Public*, pg. 2056
EVERFAST INC.; *U.S. Private*, pg. 1438
EVER FAST LIMITED—See Sun Hung Kai Properties Limited; *Int'l*, pg. 7304
EVERFAST RECHARGEABLES LIMITED—See Eveready Industries India Ltd; *Int'l*, pg. 2563
EVERFI, INC.; *U.S. Private*, pg. 1438
EVERFLOW EASTERN PARTNERS L.P.; *U.S. Private*, pg. 1438
EVERFOCUS ELECTRONICS AG—See EverFocus Electronics Co., Ltd.; *Int'l*, pg. 2565
EVERFOCUS ELECTRONICS (BEIJING) CO., LTD.—See EverFocus Electronics Co., Ltd.; *Int'l*, pg. 2565
EVERFOCUS ELECTRONICS CO., LTD.; *Int'l*, pg. 2565
EVERFOCUS ELECTRONICS CORP.—See EverFocus Electronics Co., Ltd.; *Int'l*, pg. 2565
EVERFOCUS ELECTRONICS (INDIA) PRIVATE LTD.—See EverFocus Electronics Co., Ltd.; *Int'l*, pg. 2565
EVERFOCUS JAPAN CORP.—See EverFocus Electronics Co., Ltd.; *Int'l*, pg. 2565
EVERFRESH AB—See Dole plc; *Int'l*, pg. 2158
EVERFRESH BEVERAGES INC.—See National Beverage Corp.; *U.S. Public*, pg. 1494
EVERFUEL A/S; *Int'l*, pg. 2565
EVERGEN—See Montagu Private Equity LLP; *Int'l*, pg. 5036
EVERGENT INVESTMENTS SA; *Int'l*, pg. 2565
EVERGLADES BEVERAGE CORP.—See Sunburst Hospitality Corporation; *U.S. Private*, pg. 3865
EVERGLADES DIALYSIS, LLC—See DaVita Inc.; *U.S. Public*, pg. 638
EVERGLADES DIRECT INC—See Taylor Corporation; *U.S. Private*, pg. 3938
EVERGLADES TECHNOLOGIES; *U.S. Private*, pg. 1438
EVER-GLORY INTERNATIONAL GROUP INC.; *Int'l*, pg. 2563
EVER GLORY LOGISTICS PTE. LTD.; *Int'l*, pg. 2562
EVERGOLD CORP.; *Int'l*, pg. 2565
EVER-GOTESCO RESOURCES & HOLDINGS, INC.; *Int'l*, pg. 2563
EVERGRAIN GERMANY GMBH & CO. KG—See BayWa AG; *Int'l*, pg. 917
EVERGRANDE PROPERTY SERVICES GROUP LIMITED; *Int'l*, pg. 2565
EVERGREEB SHIPPING AGENCY (CHILE) SPA.—See Evergreen Marine Corporation (Taiwan) Ltd.; *Int'l*, pg. 2566
EVERGREEB SHIPPING AGENCY (MEXICO) S.A. DE C.V.—See Evergreen Marine Corporation (Taiwan) Ltd.; *Int'l*, pg. 2566
EVERGREEN ADHESIVE & CHEMICALS SDN. BHD.—See Evergreen Fibreboard Berhad; *Int'l*, pg. 2565
EVERGREEN ADVISORS, LLC; *U.S. Private*, pg. 1438
EVERGREEN AGENCY (SOUTH AFRICA) (PTY) LTD.—See Evergreen Marine Corporation (Taiwan) Ltd.; *Int'l*, pg. 2566
EVERGREEN-AGRA, INC.; *U.S. Public*, pg. 800
EVERGREEN ALLIANCE GOLF LTD—See Arcis Equity Partners LLC; *U.S. Private*, pg. 312
EVERGREEN AVIATION TECHNOLOGIES CORP.—See Evergreen Marine Corporation (Taiwan) Ltd.; *Int'l*, pg. 2566
EVERGREEN BAMBOO INTERNATIONAL LIMITED; *Int'l*, pg. 2565
EVERGREEN CAPITAL L.P.; *U.S. Private*, pg. 1438
EVERGREEN COAST CAPITAL CORP.—See Elliott Management Corporation; *U.S. Private*, pg. 1366
EVERGREEN CORPORATION; *Int'l*, pg. 2565
EVERGREEN CREDIT UNION; *U.S. Private*, pg. 1439
EVERGREEN DEVCO INC.; *U.S. Private*, pg. 1439
EVERGREEN DISPOSAL, INC.—See Waste Connections, Inc.; *Int'l*, pg. 8353
EVERGREENE ARCHITECTURAL ARTS, INC.; *U.S. Private*, pg. 1440
EVERGREEN ENERGY INC.; *U.S. Private*, pg. 1439
EVERGREEN ENTERPRISES, INC.; *U.S. Private*, pg. 1439
EVERGREEN ENTERTAINMENT CORPORATION—See Maverick Gold LLC; *U.S. Private*, pg. 2616
EVERGREEN ESCROW, INC.—See Del Toro Loan Servicing, Inc.; *U.S. Private*, pg. 1193
EVERGREEN FEDERAL SAVINGS & LOAN ASSOCIATION; *U.S. Private*, pg. 1439
EVERGREEN FIBREBOARD BERHAD; *Int'l*, pg. 2565

EVERGREEN FIBREBOARD BERHAD

EVERGREEN FIBREBOARD (JB) SDN. BHD.—See Evergreen Fibreboard Berhad; *Int'l*, pg. 2565
EVERGREEN FIBREBOARD (NILAI) SDN. BHD.—See Evergreen Fibreboard Berhad; *Int'l*, pg. 2565
EVERGREEN FIRE ALARMS, LLC; *U.S. Private*, pg. 1439
EVERGREEN FORD; *U.S. Private*, pg. 1439
EVERGREEN FS INC.; *U.S. Private*, pg. 1439
EVERGREEN GAMING CORPORATION—See Maverick Gold LLC; *U.S. Private*, pg. 2616
EVERGREEN GARDEN CARE AUSTRALIA PTY LTD.—See Exponent Private Equity LLP; *Int'l*, pg. 2590
EVERGREEN GARDEN CARE BELGIUM BVBA—See Exponent Private Equity LLP; *Int'l*, pg. 2590
EVERGREEN GARDEN CARE DEUTSCHLAND GMBH—See Exponent Private Equity LLP; *Int'l*, pg. 2590
EVERGREEN GARDEN CARE FRANCE SAS—See Exponent Private Equity LLP; *Int'l*, pg. 2590
EVERGREEN GARDEN CARE POLAND SP. Z O.O.—See Exponent Private Equity LLP; *Int'l*, pg. 2590
EVERGREEN GARDEN CARE (UK) LTD.—See Exponent Private Equity LLP; *Int'l*, pg. 2590
EVERGREEN GARDEN CENTER, LLC—See GrowLife, Inc.; *U.S. Public*, pg. 972
THE EVERGREEN GROUP, INC.—See Gryphon Investors, LLC; *U.S. Private*, pg. 1798
THE EVERGREEN GROUP VENTURES, LLC; *U.S. Private*, pg. 4027
EVERGREEN HEAVY INDUSTRIAL CORP (M) BERHAD—See Evergreen Marine Corporation (Taiwan) Ltd.; *Int'l*, pg. 2566
EVERGREEN HELICOPTERS INC.—See Erickson Incorporated; *U.S. Private*, pg. 1419
EVERGREEN HOLDINGS INC.; *U.S. Private*, pg. 1439
EVERGREEN IMPLEMENT CO.; *U.S. Private*, pg. 1439
EVERGREEN IMPLEMENT INC.; *U.S. Private*, pg. 1439
EVERGREEN INDUSTRIES INC.; *U.S. Private*, pg. 1439
EVERGREEN INTERNATIONAL HOLDINGS LIMITED; *Int'l*, pg. 2565
EVERGREEN INTERNATIONAL LOGISTICS (HK) LTD.—See Evergreen International Storage & Transport Corp.; *Int'l*, pg. 2565
EVERGREEN INTERNATIONAL LOGISTICS (KOREA) CO., LTD.—See Evergreen International Storage & Transport Corp.; *Int'l*, pg. 2566
EVERGREEN INTERNATIONAL NZ, LLC—See Evergreen Capital L.P.; *U.S. Private*, pg. 1438
EVERGREEN INTERNATIONAL STORAGE & TRANSPORT CORP.; *Int'l*, pg. 2565
EVERGREEN LABS, INC.; *U.S. Private*, pg. 1439
EVERGREEN LIFE SERVICES; *U.S. Private*, pg. 1439
EVERGREEN LITHIUM LIMITED; *Int'l*, pg. 2566
EVERGREEN LIVING INNOVATIONS, INC.; *U.S. Private*, pg. 1439
EVERGREEN LOGISTICS (INDIA) PRIVATE LTD.—See Evergreen International Storage & Transport Corp.; *Int'l*, pg. 2566
EVERGREEN LOGISTICS MALAYSIA SDN. BHD.—See Evergreen International Storage & Transport Corp.; *Int'l*, pg. 2566
EVERGREEN LOGISTICS PHILIPPINES CORP.—See Evergreen International Storage & Transport Corp.; *Int'l*, pg. 2566
EVERGREEN LOGISTICS VIETNAM CO., LTD.—See Evergreen International Storage & Transport Corp.; *Int'l*, pg. 2566
EVERGREEN LUMBER INC.—See Bain Capital, LP; *U.S. Private*, pg. 450
EVERGREEN MACHINE TOOLS PTE. LTD.—See Quaser Machine Tools, Inc.; *Int'l*, pg. 6156
EVERGREEN MARINE CORP. (MALAYSIA) SDN. BHD.—See Evergreen Marine Corporation (Taiwan) Ltd.; *Int'l*, pg. 2566
EVERGREEN MARINE CORPORATION (TAIWAN) LTD.; *Int'l*, pg. 2566
EVERGREEN MARINE (HONG KONG) LIMITED—See Evergreen Marine Corporation (Taiwan) Ltd.; *Int'l*, pg. 2566
EVERGREEN MEDICAL SERVICES, INC; *U.S. Private*, pg. 1439
EVER GREEN MOBILITY RENT S.R.L.—See Sesa S.p.A.; *Int'l*, pg. 6728
EVERGREEN MONEYSOURCE MORTGAGE CO.; *U.S. Private*, pg. 1439
EVERGREEN NATIONAL INDEMNITY CO.—See ProAlliance Corporation; *U.S. Private*, pg. 3271
EVERGREEN OAK ELECTRIC SUPPLY & SALES CO. INC.; *U.S. Private*, pg. 1439
EVERGREEN OIL COMPANY INC.; *U.S. Private*, pg. 1439
EVERGREEN PACIFIC MORTGAGE; *U.S. Private*, pg. 1440
EVERGREEN PACIFIC PARTNERS MANAGEMENT CO., INC.; *U.S. Private*, pg. 1440
EVERGREEN PACKAGING - ATHENS—See Rank Group Ltd.; *Int'l*, pg. 6208
EVERGREEN PACKAGING - CEDAR RAPIDS—See Rank Group Ltd.; *Int'l*, pg. 6208
EVERGREEN PACKAGING - CLINTON—See Rank Group Ltd.; *Int'l*, pg. 6208
EVERGREEN PACKAGING, INC.—See Rank Group Ltd.; *Int'l*, pg. 6208
EVERGREEN PACKAGING - OLMSTED FALLS—See Rank Group Ltd.; *Int'l*, pg. 6208
EVERGREEN PACKAGING - PLANT CITY—See Rank Group Ltd.; *Int'l*, pg. 6208
EVERGREEN PACKAGING - RALEIGH—See Rank Group Ltd.; *Int'l*, pg. 6208
EVERGREEN PACKAGING—See Rank Group Ltd.; *Int'l*, pg. 6208
EVERGREEN PACKAGING - TURLOCK—See Rank Group Ltd.; pg. 6208
EVERGREEN PFLEGE- UND BETREUUNGSZENTRUM BERGNEUSTADT GMBH—See Clariane SE; *Int'l*, pg. 1642
EVERGREEN PFLEGE- UND BETREUUNGSZENTRUM BUTZBACH GMBH—See Clariane SE; *Int'l*, pg. 1642
EVERGREEN PFLEGE- UND BETREUUNGSZENTRUM LANDSCHEID GMBH—See Clariane SE; *Int'l*, pg. 1642
EVERGREEN PFLEGE- UND BETREUUNGSZENTRUM PADERBORN GMBH—See Clariane SE; *Int'l*, pg. 1642
EVERGREEN PFLEGE- UND BETREUUNGSZENTRUM RECKLINGHAUSEN GMBH—See Clariane SE; *Int'l*, pg. 1642
EVERGREEN PFLEGE- UND BETREUUNGSZENTRUM SAARBURG GMBH—See Clariane SE; *Int'l*, pg. 1642
EVERGREEN PFLEGEZENTRUM AM ALTEN POSTSTADION GMBH—See Clariane SE; *Int'l*, pg. 1642
EVERGREEN PRINTING COMPANY; *U.S. Private*, pg. 1440
EVERGREEN PRODUCTS GROUP LIMITED; *Int'l*, pg. 2567
EVERGREEN RECREATIONAL VEHICLES, LLC; *U.S. Private*, pg. 1440
EVERGREEN RECYCLING AND DISPOSAL FACILITY, INC.—See Waste Management, Inc.; *U.S. Public*, pg. 2331
EVERGREEN REMEDIATION SERVICES, LLC—See Energy Transfer LP; *U.S. Public*, pg. 764
EVERGREEN RV CENTER, INC.; *U.S. Private*, pg. 1440
EVERGREEN SC, LLC; *U.S. Private*, pg. 1440
EVERGREEN SECURITY, INC.—See Bay Alarm Company Inc.; *U.S. Private*, pg. 491
EVERGREEN SERVICES GROUP LLC—See Alpine Investors; *U.S. Private*, pg. 201
EVERGREEN SHIPPING AGENCY (AUSTRALIA) PTY. LTD.—See Evergreen Marine Corporation (Taiwan) Ltd.; *Int'l*, pg. 2566
EVERGREEN SHIPPING AGENCY (COLOMBIA) S.A.S.—See Evergreen Marine Corporation (Taiwan) Ltd.; *Int'l*, pg. 2566
EVERGREEN SHIPPING AGENCY (DEUTSCHLAND) GMBH—See Evergreen Marine Corporation (Taiwan) Ltd.; *Int'l*, pg. 2566
EVERGREEN SHIPPING AGENCY FRANCE S.A.—See Evergreen Marine Corporation (Taiwan) Ltd.; *Int'l*, pg. 2566
EVERGREEN SHIPPING AGENCY (INDIA) PVT. LTD.—See Evergreen Marine Corporation (Taiwan) Ltd.; *Int'l*, pg. 2566
EVERGREEN SHIPPING AGENCY (IRELAND) LTD.—See Evergreen Marine Corporation (Taiwan) Ltd.; *Int'l*, pg. 2566
EVERGREEN SHIPPING AGENCY (ITALY) S.P.A.—See Evergreen Marine Corporation (Taiwan) Ltd.; *Int'l*, pg. 2566
EVERGREEN SHIPPING AGENCY (KOREA) CORPORATION—See Evergreen Marine Corporation (Taiwan) Ltd.; *Int'l*, pg. 2566
EVERGREEN SHIPPING AGENCY LANKA (PVT) LTD.—See Hemas Holdings PLC; *Int'l*, pg. 3340
EVERGREEN SHIPPING AGENCY (NETHERLANDS) B.V.—See Evergreen Marine Corporation (Taiwan) Ltd.; *Int'l*, pg. 2566
EVERGREEN SHIPPING AGENCY (PERU) S.A.C.—See Evergreen Marine Corporation (Taiwan) Ltd.; *Int'l*, pg. 2566
EVERGREEN SHIPPING AGENCY PHILIPPINES CORPORATION—See Evergreen Marine Corporation (Taiwan) Ltd.; *Int'l*, pg. 2566
EVERGREEN SHIPPING AGENCY (POLAND) SP. ZO.O—See Evergreen Marine Corporation (Taiwan) Ltd.; *Int'l*, pg. 2566
EVERGREEN SHIPPING AGENCY (RUSSIA) LTD.—See Evergreen Marine Corporation (Taiwan) Ltd.; *Int'l*, pg. 2566
EVERGREEN SHIPPING AGENCY (SINGAPORE) PTE. LTD.—See Evergreen Marine Corporation (Taiwan) Ltd.; *Int'l*, pg. 2566
EVERGREEN SHIPPING AGENCY (THAILAND) CO., LTD.—See Evergreen Marine Corporation (Taiwan) Ltd.; *Int'l*, pg. 2566
EVERGREEN SHIPPING AGENCY (UK) LIMITED—See Evergreen Marine Corporation (Taiwan) Ltd.; *Int'l*, pg. 2566
EVERGREEN SHIPPING AGENCY (VIETNAM) CORP.—See Evergreen Marine Corporation (Taiwan) Ltd.; *Int'l*, pg. 2566

CORPORATE AFFILIATIONS

EVERGREEN SHIPPING SERVICE (CAMBODIA) CO., LTD.—See Evergreen Marine Corporation (Taiwan) Ltd.; *Int'l*, pg. 2566
EVERGREEN SHIPPING (SPAIN) S.L.—See Evergreen Marine Corporation (Taiwan) Ltd.; *Int'l*, pg. 2566
EVERGREEN; *U.S. Private*, pg. 1438
EVERGREEN SUSTAINABLE ENTERPRISES, INC.; *U.S. Public*, pg. 800
EVERGREEN SWEETENERS, INC.; *U.S. Private*, pg. 1440
EVERGREEN SYSTEMS, INC.—See Sunstone Partners Management LLC; *U.S. Private*, pg. 3873
EVERGREEN TANK SOLUTIONS, INC.—See WillScot Mobile Mini Holdings Corp.; *U.S. Public*, pg. 2372
EVERGREEN TRANSPORT, LLC; *U.S. Private*, pg. 1440
EVERGREEN UTILITY CONTRACTORS, INC.—See Tetra Tech, Inc.; *U.S. Public*, pg. 2023
EVER-GROW ADVANCED MATERIALS SDN. BHD.—See Ni Hsin Group Berhad; *Int'l*, pg. 5259
EVERGY, INC.; *U.S. Public*, pg. 800
EVERGY KANSAS CENTRAL, INC.—See Evergy, Inc.; *U.S. Public*, pg. 800
EVERGY METRO, INC.—See Evergy, Inc.; *U.S. Public*, pg. 801
EVERGY SERVICES, INC.—See Evergy, Inc.; *U.S. Public*, pg. 801
EVER HARVEST GROUP HOLDINGS LIMITED; *Int'l*, pg. 2562
EVER HARVEST INTERNATIONAL GROUP INC.; *Int'l*, pg. 2562
EVERIENCE GMBH—See Neurones S.A.; *Int'l*, pg. 5219
E-VERIFILE.COM, INC.; *U.S. Private*, pg. 1303
EVERI HOLDINGS INC.; *U.S. Public*, pg. 801
EVERINSURANCE, INC.—See Teachers Insurance Association - College Retirement Fund; *U.S. Private*, pg. 3948
EVERINTEC GMBH—See Esseco Group SRL; *Int'l*, pg. 2509
EVERIS ITALIA, S.P.A.—See Nippon Telegraph & Telephone Corporation; *Int'l*, pg. 5343
EVERITE BUILDING PRODUCTS PTY LTD—See Group Five Limited; *Int'l*, pg. 3089
EVERITE MACHINE PRODUCTS CO.—See Arcline Investment Management LP; *U.S. Private*, pg. 313
EVERJOY HEALTH GROUP CO., LTD.; *Int'l*, pg. 2567
EVERKEY GLOBAL FUND, L.P.—See Wells Fargo & Company; *U.S. Public*, pg. 2343
EVERLANCE CO., LTD.; *Int'l*, pg. 2567
EVERLAND PUBLIC COMPANY LIMITED; *Int'l*, pg. 2567
EVERLAST ACCESS TECHNOLOGIES SDN. BHD.—See PMB Technology Berhad; *Int'l*, pg. 5899
EVERLAST ALUMINIUM (M) SDN. BHD.—See PMB Technology Berhad; *Int'l*, pg. 5899
EVERLAST CLIMBING INDUSTRIES, INC.—See Court Square Capital Partners, L.P.; *U.S. Private*, pg. 1069
EVERLASTING VALVE CO.—See Armstrong International, Inc.; *U.S. Private*, pg. 332
EVERLAST WORLDWIDE, INC.—See Frasers Group plc; *Int'l*, pg. 2765
EVERLEND MORTGAGE COMPANY—See Security National Financial Corporation; *U.S. Public*, pg. 1856
EVERLIGHT AMERICAS, INC.—See Everlight Electronics Co., Ltd.; *Int'l*, pg. 2567
EVERLIGHT CANADA, INC.—See Everlight Electronics Co., Ltd.; *Int'l*, pg. 2567
EVERLIGHT CHEMICAL INDUSTRIAL CO.; *Int'l*, pg. 2567
EVERLIGHT CHEMICAL INDUSTRIAL CO. - TAOYUAN 1ST PLANT—See Everlight Chemical Industrial Co.; *Int'l*, pg. 2567
EVERLIGHT CHEMICAL INDUSTRIAL CO. - TAOYUAN 2ND PLANT—See Everlight Chemical Industrial Co.; *Int'l*, pg. 2567
EVERLIGHT CHEMICAL INDUSTRIAL CO. - TAOYUAN 3RD PLANT—See Everlight Chemical Industrial Co.; *Int'l*, pg. 2567
EVERLIGHT CHEMICAL INDUSTRIAL CO. - TAOYUAN 4TH PLANT—See Everlight Chemical Industrial Co.; *Int'l*, pg. 2567
EVERLIGHT CHEMICALS (VIETNAM) COMPANY LIMITED—See Everlight Chemical Industrial Co.; *Int'l*, pg. 2567
EVERLIGHT ELECTRONICS CO., LTD.; *Int'l*, pg. 2567
EVERLIGHT ELECTRONICS (EUROPE) GMBH—See Everlight Electronics Co.; *Int'l*, pg. 2567
EVERLIGHT ELECTRONICS (SUZHOU) LTD.—See Everlight Electronics Co., Ltd.; *Int'l*, pg. 2567
EVERLIGHT EUROPE B.V.—See Everlight Chemical Industrial Co.; *Int'l*, pg. 2567
EVERLIGHT HONG KONG LIMITED—See Everlight Chemical Industrial Co.; *Int'l*, pg. 2567
EVERLIGHT INTELLIGENCE TECHNOLOGY CO., LTD.—See Everlight Electronics Co., Ltd.; *Int'l*, pg. 2567
EVERLIGHT JAPAN CORPORATION—See Everlight Electronics Co., Ltd.; *Int'l*, pg. 2567
EVERLIGHT OPTOELECTRONICS (M) SDN BHD—See Everlight Electronics Co., Ltd.; *Int'l*, pg. 2567
EVERLIGHT PTE. LTD.—See Everlight Chemical Industrial Co.; *Int'l*, pg. 2567

EVERLIGHT (SUZHOU) ADVANCED CHEMICALS LTD.—See Everlight Chemical Industrial Co.; *Int'l*, pg. 2567
EVERLIGHT USA, INC.—See Everlight Chemical Industrial Co.; *Int'l*, pg. 2567
EVERLON FINANCIALS LTD.; *Int'l*, pg. 2568
EVER-LONG SECURITIES COMPANY LIMITED—See Styland Holdings Limited; *Int'l*, pg. 7246
EVER LOTUS ENTERPRISE CO., LTD.; *Int'l*, pg. 2562
EVERLTH CO., LTD.—See Medipal Holdings Corporation; *Int'l*, pg. 4779
EVER LUMIN INCORPORATION—See Contrel Technology Co., Ltd.; *Int'l*, pg. 1785
EVERLY BANCORPORATION; *U.S. Private*, pg. 1440
EVERLYWELL, INC.; *U.S. Private*, pg. 1440
EVERMASTER GROUP BERHAD; *Int'l*, pg. 2568
THE EVERMEDIA GROUP, INC.; *U.S. Public*, pg. 2073
EVERMIX CONCRETE SDN. BHD.—See ES Ceramics Technology Bhd; *Int'l*, pg. 2500
EVERMORE CHEMICAL INDUSTRY CO., LTD.; *Int'l*, pg. 2568
EVERNORTH BEHAVIORAL HEALTH, INC.—See The Cigna Group; *U.S. Public*, pg. 2061
EVERNORTH BEHAVIORAL HEALTH OF CALIFORNIA, INC.—See The Cigna Group; *U.S. Public*, pg. 2061
EVERNORTH HEALTH, INC.—See The Cigna Group; *U.S. Public*, pg. 2061
EVERNOTE CORPORATION; *U.S. Private*, pg. 1440
EVERNUTRITION, INC.—See Trident Brands Incorporated; *U.S. Public*, pg. 2189
EVEROONN EDUCATION LIMITED; *Int'l*, pg. 2568
EVERON TECHNOLOGY SERVICES, LLC—See The Allstate Corporation; *U.S. Public*, pg. 2033
EVERPIA JOINT STOCK COMPANY - DONG NAI FACTORY—See Everpia Joint Stock Company; *Int'l*, pg. 2568
EVERPIA JOINT STOCK COMPANY - HANOI FACTORY—See Everpia Joint Stock Company; *Int'l*, pg. 2568
EVERPIA JOINT STOCK COMPANY; *Int'l*, pg. 2568
EVERPIA KOREA JSC—See Everpia Joint Stock Company; *Int'l*, pg. 2568
EVERPOWER WIND HOLDINGS INC—See Terra Firma Capital Partners Ltd.; *Int'l*, pg. 7566
EVER PROGRESSING SYSTEM PTE. LTD.—See EPS Holdings, Inc.; *Int'l*, pg. 2465
EVERPROSPER FOOD INDUSTRIES SDN. BHD.—See Thong Guan Industries Berhad; *Int'l*, pg. 7717
EVERPURE INC.—See Pentair plc; *Int'l*, pg. 5790
EVERPURE JAPAN INC.—See Pentair plc; *Int'l*, pg. 5790
EVERQUOTE, INC.; *U.S. Public*, pg. 801
EVER REACH GROUP (HOLDINGS) COMPANY LIMITED; *Int'l*, pg. 2562
EVER READY LIMITED—See Energizer Holdings, Inc.; *U.S. Public*, pg. 761
EVERRIS GMBH—See Israel Corporation Ltd.; *Int'l*, pg. 3822
EVERRIS INTERNATIONAL B.V.—See Israel Corporation Ltd.; *Int'l*, pg. 3822
EVERSAFE EXTINGUISHER PTE LTD—See Mitsubishi Chemical Group Corporation; *Int'l*, pg. 4936
EVERSAFE EXTINGUISHER SDN BHD—See Mitsubishi Chemical Group Corporation; *Int'l*, pg. 4936
EVERSAFE RUBBER BERHAD; *Int'l*, pg. 2568
EVERSAFE RUBBER WORKS SDN BHD—See Eversafe Rubber Berhad; *Int'l*, pg. 2568
EVERSAFE SYSTEM SDN. BHD.—See Mitsubishi Chemical Group Corporation; *Int'l*, pg. 4936
EVERSANA LIFE SCIENCE SERVICES, LLC—See JLL Partners, LLC; *U.S. Private*, pg. 2212
EVERSANA LIFE SCIENCE SERVICES, LLC—See Water Street Healthcare Partners, LLC; *U.S. Private*, pg. 4452
EVERSANA—See Water Street Healthcare Partners, LLC; *U.S. Private*, pg. 4452
EVERS AS—See QuattroR SGR S.p.A.; *Int'l*, pg. 6157
EVERS & CO. REAL ESTATE, INC.—See The Long & Foster Companies, Inc.; *U.S. Private*, pg. 4072
EVERSEAL GASKET, INC.; *U.S. Private*, pg. 1440
EVERSENDAI CONSTRUCTION PVT. LTD.—See Eversendai Corporation Berhad; *Int'l*, pg. 2568
EVERSENDAI CONSTRUCTIONS (M) SDN BHD—See Eversendai Corporation Berhad; *Int'l*, pg. 2568
EVERSENDAI CONSTRUCTION (S) PTE. LTD.—See Eversendai Corporation Berhad; *Int'l*, pg. 2568
EVERSENDAI CORPORATION BERHAD; *Int'l*, pg. 2568
EVERSENDAI ENGINEERING FZE—See Eversendai Corporation Berhad; *Int'l*, pg. 2568
EVERSENDAI ENGINEERING LLC—See Eversendai Corporation Berhad; *Int'l*, pg. 2568
EVERSENDAI ENGINEERING QATAR WLL—See Eversendai Corporation Berhad; *Int'l*, pg. 2568
EVERSENDAI ENGINEERING SAUDI LLC—See Eversendai Corporation Berhad; *Int'l*, pg. 2568
EVERSENDAI OFFSHORE RMC FZE—See Eversendai Corporation Berhad; *Int'l*, pg. 2568
EVERSENDAI OFFSHORE SDN BHD—See Eversendai Corporation Berhad; *Int'l*, pg. 2568
EVERSENDAI S-CON ENGINEERING CO. LTD. - SANAMCHAIKHED FACTORY—See Eversendai Corporation Berhad; *Int'l*, pg. 2568
EVERSENDAI S-CON ENGINEERING CO. LTD.—See Eversendai Corporation Berhad; *Int'l*, pg. 2568
EVERSET SA; *Int'l*, pg. 2568
EVERSHARP LTD—See Amalgamated Regional Trading (ART) Holdings Ltd.; *Int'l*, pg. 409
EVERSHEDS ATTORNEYS LTD.—See Eversheds LLP; *Int'l*, pg. 2568
EVERSHEDS LLP; *Int'l*, pg. 2568
EVERSHEDS SUTHERLAND (US) LLP—See Eversheds LLP; *Int'l*, pg. 2568
EVERS HEILIG, INC.; *U.S. Private*, pg. 1440
EVERS HEILIG, INC. - WAUKESHA—See Evers Heilig, Inc.; *U.S. Private*, pg. 1440
EVERSHINE GROUP HOLDINGS LIMITED; *Int'l*, pg. 2568
EVERSHOLT UK RAILS LIMITED—See CK Hutchison Holdings Limited; *Int'l*, pg. 1637
EVERSHORE FINANCIAL GROUP, INC.; *U.S. Private*, pg. 1440
EVERSHORE FINANCIAL GROUP, INC.—See Evershore Financial Group, Inc.; *U.S. Private*, pg. 1440
EVERSIDE HEALTH GROUP, INC.; *U.S. Public*, pg. 801
EVERSIDE HEALTH, LLC—See New Enterprise Associates, LLC; *U.S. Private*, pg. 2895
EVERSOURCE ENERGY; *U.S. Public*, pg. 801
EVERSOURCEENERGY—See Eversource Energy; *U.S. Public*, pg. 801
EVER SOURCE SCIENCE & TECHNOLOGY DEVELOPMENT GROUP CO., LIMITED—See CHYY Development Group Limited; *Int'l*, pg. 1600
EVERSPIN TECHNOLOGIES, INC; *U.S. Public*, pg. 802
EVERSPRING INDUSTRY CO., LTD.; *Int'l*, pg. 2569
EVERSPRING TECH USA, INC.—See Everspring Industry Co., Ltd.; *Int'l*, pg. 2569
EVER S.R.L.—See Esseco Group SRL; *Int'l*, pg. 2509
EVERSTAFF; *U.S. Private*, pg. 1440
EVERSTONE CAPITAL ADVISORS PVT. LTD.; *Int'l*, pg. 2569
EVERSTONE CAPITAL ASIA PTE. LTD.—See Everstone Capital Advisors Pvt. Ltd.; *Int'l*, pg. 2569
EVERSTONE CAPITAL LIMITED—See Everstone Capital Advisors Pvt. Ltd.; *Int'l*, pg. 2569
EVERSUN FOOTWEAR CO., LTD.—See Fulgent Sun International (Holding) Co., Ltd.; *Int'l*, pg. 2842
EVER SUPREME BIO TECHNOLOGY CO., LTD.; *Int'l*, pg. 2562
EVERSYS DIGITRONICS AG—See De'Longhi S.p.A.; *Int'l*, pg. 1997
EVERSYS S.A.—See De'Longhi S.p.A.; *Int'l*, pg. 1997
EVERTASTE OY—See Deutsche Lufthansa AG; *Int'l*, pg. 2066
EVERTEC BRASIL SOLUTIONS INFORMATICA LTDA.—See EVERTEC, Inc.; *U.S. Public*, pg. 802
EVERTEC CHILE SPA—See EVERTEC, Inc.; *U.S. Public*, pg. 802
EVERTEC COLOMBIA, SAS—See EVERTEC, Inc.; *U.S. Public*, pg. 802
EVERTEC COSTA RICA, S.A.—See EVERTEC, Inc.; *U.S. Public*, pg. 802
EVERTEC DOMINICANA, SAS—See EVERTEC, Inc.; *U.S. Public*, pg. 802
EVERTEC GROUP, LLC—See EVERTEC, Inc.; *U.S. Public*, pg. 802
EVERTEC GUATEMALA, S.A.—See EVERTEC, Inc.; *U.S. Public*, pg. 802
EVERTECHNO CO., LTD.; *Int'l*, pg. 2569
EVERTEC, INC.; *U.S. Public*, pg. 802
EVERTEC MEXICO SERVICIOS DE PROCESAMIENTO, S.A. DE C.V.—See EVERTEC, Inc.; *U.S. Public*, pg. 802
EVERTEC PANAMA, S.A.—See EVERTEC, Inc.; *U.S. Public*, pg. 802
EVERTEX FABRINOLOGY LIMITED; *Int'l*, pg. 2569
EVERTHOUGHT EDUCATION PTY. LTD.—See AWN Holdings Limited; *Int'l*, pg. 753
EVERTON MATTRESS FACTORY, INC.—See Restonic Mattress Corporation; *U.S. Private*, pg. 3409
EVERTON RESOURCES INC.; *Int'l*, pg. 2569
EVERTOP WIRE CABLE CORPORATION - CHUNGLI PLANT—See Evertop Wire Cable Corporation; *Int'l*, pg. 2569
EVERTOP WIRE CABLE CORPORATION; *Int'l*, pg. 2569
EVERTRADE (PTY) LTD.; *Int'l*, pg. 2569
EVER TRADE S.R.O.—See Esseco Group SRL; *Int'l*, pg. 2509
EVERTREE INSURANCE SERVICES, LLC—See Integrum Holdings LP; *Int'l*, pg. 3732
EVERTZ MICROSYSTEMS LIMITED; *Int'l*, pg. 2569
EVERTZ MICROSYSTEMS LTD.—See Evertz Microsystems Limited; *Int'l*, pg. 2569
EVERTZ UK LIMITED—See Evertz Microsystems Limited; *Int'l*, pg. 2569
EVERUN EUROPE GMBH—See Zhejiang Xinchai Co., Ltd.; *Int'l*, pg. 8666
EVERVISION ELECTRONICS CO., LTD.—See Everlight Electronics Co., Ltd.; *Int'l*, pg. 2567
EVERWARM LIMITED—See Cap10 Partners LLP; *Int'l*, pg. 1301
EVERWATCH CAPITAL; *U.S. Private*, pg. 1440
EVERWATCH CORP.—See Booz Allen Hamilton Holding Corporation; *U.S. Public*, pg. 369
EVERWEALTH PAPER INDUSTRIES (SHANGHAI) CO., LTD.—See Nippon Paper Industries Co., Ltd.; *Int'l*, pg. 5326
EVERWINER ENTERPRISE CO., LTD.—See WPG Holdings Limited; *Int'l*, pg. 8461
EVERYACTION, INC.—See Insight Venture Management, LLC; *U.S. Private*, pg. 2090
EVERYBODY LOVES LANGUAGES CORP.; *Int'l*, pg. 2569
EVERYBOT, INC.; *Int'l*, pg. 2569
EVERY CO., LTD.—See NCS&A Co., Ltd.; *Int'l*, pg. 5181
EVERYDAYFAMILY, INC.; *U.S. Private*, pg. 1441
EVERYDAY GREEN LLC—See Steven Winter Associates, Inc.; *U.S. Private*, pg. 3809
EVERYDAY HEALTH, INC.—See Ziff Davis, Inc.; *U.S. Public*, pg. 2404
EVERYDAY HERO LTD.—See Blackbaud, Inc.; *U.S. Public*, pg. 341
EVERYDAY HERO PTY. LTD.—See Blackbaud, Inc.; *U.S. Public*, pg. 341
EVERYDAY LIVING (GUANGZHOU) TRADING LIMITED—See Steve Leung Design Group Ltd.; *Int'l*, pg. 7213
EVERYDAY NETWORK CO., LTD.; *Int'l*, pg. 2569
EVERYDAY PEOPLE FINANCIAL CORP.; *Int'l*, pg. 2570
EVERYD.COM, INC.—See H2O Retailing Corp.; *Int'l*, pg. 3200
EVERYD MC, INC.—See McDonald's Corporation; *U.S. Public*, pg. 1406
EVERYMAN MEDIA GROUP PLC; *Int'l*, pg. 2570
EVERYMAN OY—See Wulff-Group Plc; *Int'l*, pg. 8502
EVERYMATRIX LTD.; *Int'l*, pg. 2570
EVERYMUNDO LLC—See PROS Holdings, Inc.; *U.S. Public*, pg. 1728
EVERYPAY AS—See LHV Group; *Int'l*, pg. 4479
EVERY'S CO., LTD.—See System Location Co., Ltd.; *Int'l*, pg. 7390
EVERYSPORT.NET, INC.; *U.S. Private*, pg. 1441
EVERYTHING2GO COM, LLC; *U.S. Private*, pg. 1441
EVERYTHING BLOCKCHAIN, INC.; *U.S. Public*, pg. 802
EVERYTHING ENERGY LLC—See NHG Energy, Inc.; *U.S. Public*, pg. 1550
EVERYTHING FRESH LTD.; *Int'l*, pg. 2570
EVERYTHING ICE, INC.; *U.S. Private*, pg. 1441
EVERYTHING LEGAL LTD.—See ARAG SE; *Int'l*, pg. 534
EVERYTHING WINE INC.—See The Jim Pattison Group; *Int'l*, pg. 7660
EVERYTICKET.COM; *U.S. Private*, pg. 1441
EVERYWARE GLOBAL, INC.; *U.S. Private*, pg. 1441
EVESHAM MUNICIPAL UTILITIES AUTHORITY; *U.S. Private*, pg. 1441
EVESHAM VETS4PETS LIMITED—See Pets at Home Group Plc; *Int'l*, pg. 5833
EVE SLEEP PLC; *Int'l*, pg. 2561
EVE SLEEP SASU—See Eve Sleep PLC; *Int'l*, pg. 2561
EVESONS FUELS LTD—See NWF Group Plc; *Int'l*, pg. 5499
EVEST CORPORATION—See Hitachi, Ltd.; *Int'l*, pg. 3424
EVESTMENT ALLIANCE AUSTRALIA PTY LTD—See Nasdaq, Inc.; *U.S. Public*, pg. 1492
EVESTMENT ALLIANCE, LLC—See Nasdaq, Inc.; *U.S. Public*, pg. 1492
EVESTMENT, INC—See Nasdaq, Inc.; *U.S. Public*, pg. 1492
EVEXIA LIFECARE LIMITED; *Int'l*, pg. 2570
EVGEN PHARMA PLC; *Int'l*, pg. 2570
EVGO INC.; *U.S. Public*, pg. 802
EVGO RECARGO, LLC—See EVgo Inc.; *U.S. Public*, pg. 802
EVGO SERVICES LLC—See LS Power Development, LLC; *U.S. Private*, pg. 2508
EVIAB GRUPPEN AB—See Storskogen Group AB; *Int'l*, pg. 7227
EVIALIS FRANCE—See Archer-Daniels-Midland Company; *U.S. Public*, pg. 185
EVIALIS GALICIA S.A.—See Archer-Daniels-Midland Company; *U.S. Public*, pg. 185
EVIANA HEALTH CORPORATION, INC.; *Int'l*, pg. 2570
EVIATION AIRCRAFT LTD.; *Int'l*, pg. 2570
EVI AUDIO GMBH—See Robert Bosch GmbH; *Int'l*, pg. 6360
EVICORE HEALTHCARE MSI, LLC—See The Cigna Group; *U.S. Public*, pg. 2062
EVIDENT, LLC—See TruBridge, Inc.; *U.S. Public*, pg. 2198
EVIDENT SOFTWARE, INC.; *U.S. Private*, pg. 1441
EVIDENT THERMOELECTRICS; *U.S. Private*, pg. 1441
EVIDERA, INC.—See Thermo Fisher Scientific Inc.; *U.S. Public*, pg. 2150
EVIDERA LTD.—See Thermo Fisher Scientific Inc.; *U.S. Public*, pg. 2146
EVIDERA MARKET ACCESS LIMITED—See Thermo Fisher Scientific Inc.; *U.S. Public*, pg. 2150
EVIDIAN-BULL JAPAN KK—See Atos SE; *Int'l*, pg. 692
EVIDIAN SA—See Atos SE; *Int'l*, pg. 692

EVIDENT THERMOELECTRICS

EVIDIAN SYSTEMS INC.—See Atos SE; *Int'l*, pg. 692
EVIDON, INC.—See CrownPeak Technology, Inc.; *U.S. Private*, pg. 1113
EVI EDUCATION ASIA LIMITED—See Legend Upstar Holdings Limited; *Int'l*, pg. 4444
EVIEW 360; *U.S. Private*, pg. 1441
EVIEW 360—See Eview 360; *U.S. Private*, pg. 1441
EVIGILANT SECURITY; *U.S. Private*, pg. 1441
EVI INDUSTRIES, INC.; *U.S. Public*, pg. 803
EVIIVO LTD.; *Int'l*, pg. 2570
EVIL EMPIRE DESIGNS, INC.; *U.S. Public*, pg. 803
EVIMBEC LTD.—See Roche Ltd., Consulting Group; *Int'l*, pg. 6376
EVIMERIA EMR AB—See Carasent ASA; *Int'l*, pg. 1319
EVINCE TEXTILES LTD.; *Int'l*, pg. 2570
EVINS COMMUNICATIONS, LTD.; *U.S. Private*, pg. 1441
EVINS PERSONNEL CONSULTANTS, INC.; *U.S. Private*, pg. 1442
EVIO, INC.; *U.S. Public*, pg. 803
EVION GROUP NL; *Int'l*, pg. 2570
EVIP GMBH—See RWE AG; *Int'l*, pg. 6434
E.VIRONMENT, LLC—See Charterhouse Capital Partners LLP; *Int'l*, pg. 1455
EVI SERVICES LIMITED—See Legend Upstar Holdings Limited; *Int'l*, pg. 4444
EVISO S.P.A.; *Int'l*, pg. 2570
EVITBE AB—See Addnode Group AB; *Int'l*, pg. 130
EVIVA-LEBORK SP.Z O.O.—See The AES Corporation; *U.S. Public*, pg. 2031
EVIVE HEALTH, LLC; *U.S. Private*, pg. 1442
EVI WEATHERFORD, INC.—See Weatherford International plc; *U.S. Public*, pg. 2339
EVIXAR INC.; *Int'l*, pg. 2570
EVLI AWARDS MANAGEMENT OY—See Evli Pankki Oyj; *Int'l*, pg. 2570
EVLI PANKKI OYJ; *Int'l*, pg. 2570
EVLITE ELECTRONICS CO., LTD.—See Everlight Electronics Co., Ltd.; *Int'l*, pg. 2567
EV LOGISTICS LTD. - AMBIENT FACILITY—See Deutsche Post AG; *Int'l*, pg. 2080
EV LOGISTICS LTD. - PERISHABLES FACILITY—See Deutsche Post AG; *Int'l*, pg. 2080
EV MARTIN CORPORATION; *U.S. Private*, pg. 1434
EVMO, INC.; *U.S. Public*, pg. 803
EVN AG; *Int'l*, pg. 2570
EVN BULGARIA ELEKTRORAZPREDELENIE AD—See EVN AG; *Int'l*, pg. 2570
EVN BULGARIA ELEKTROSNABDIAVANE AD—See EVN AG; *Int'l*, pg. 2571
EVN BULGARIA TOPLOFIKATSIA EAD—See EVN AG; *Int'l*, pg. 2571
EVN BUSINESS SERVICE GMBH—See EVN AG; *Int'l*, pg. 2571
EVN CROATIA PLIN D.O.O.—See EVN AG; *Int'l*, pg. 2571
EVN ENERGIEVERTRIEB GMBH & CO KG—See EVN AG; *Int'l*, pg. 2571
EVN FINANZSERVICE GMBH—See EVN AG; *Int'l*, pg. 2571
EVN GEOINFO GMBH—See EVN AG; *Int'l*, pg. 2571
EV NICKEL INC.; *Int'l*, pg. 2560
EVN KRAFTWERKS- UND BETEILIGUNGSGESELLSCHAFT MBH—See EVN AG; *Int'l*, pg. 2571
EVN MACEDONIA AD—See EVN AG; *Int'l*, pg. 2571
EVN MACEDONIA ELEKTRANI DOOEL—See EVN AG; *Int'l*, pg. 2571
EVN MACEDONIA ELEKTROSNABDUVANJE DOOEL—See EVN AG; *Int'l*, pg. 2571
EVN NATURKRAFT BETEILIGUNGS- UND BETRIEBS-GMBH—See EVN AG; *Int'l*, pg. 2571
EVN NATURKRAFT ERZEUGUNGSGESELLSCHAFT M.B.H.—See EVN AG; *Int'l*, pg. 2571
EVN NETZ GMBH—See EVN AG; *Int'l*, pg. 2571
EVN PROJEKTMANAGEMENT GMBH—See EVN AG; *Int'l*, pg. 2571
EVN TRADING D.O.O. BEOGRAD—See EVN AG; *Int'l*, pg. 2571
EVN TRADING SOUTH EAST EUROPE EAD—See EVN AG; *Int'l*, pg. 2571
EVN UMWELT BETEILIGUNGS UND SERVICE GMBH—See EVN AG; *Int'l*, pg. 2571
EVN UMWELT FINANZ- UND SERVICE-GMBH—See EVN AG; *Int'l*, pg. 2571
EVN UMWELTHOLDING UND BETRIEBS-GMBH—See EVN AG; *Int'l*, pg. 2571
EVN WARME GMBH—See EVN AG; *Int'l*, pg. 2571
EVN WASSER GMBH—See EVN AG; *Int'l*, pg. 2571
EVO ACQUISITION CORP.; *U.S. Public*, pg. 803
EVOAIR HOLDINGS INC; *Int'l*, pg. 2572
EVO AMERICA, LLC—See The Middleby Corporation; *U.S. Public*, pg. 2113
EVO BANCO S.A.—See Bankinter, S.A.; *Int'l*, pg. 850
EVOBUS AUSTRIA GMBH—See Mercedes-Benz Group AG; *Int'l*, pg. 4820
EVOBUS BELGIUM N.V.—See Mercedes-Benz Group AG; *Int'l*, pg. 4824
EVOBUS DANMARK A/S—See Mercedes-Benz Group AG; *Int'l*, pg. 4824
EVOBUS FRANCE SAS—See Mercedes-Benz Group AG; *Int'l*, pg. 4824

EVOBUS IBERICA, S. A.—See Mercedes-Benz Group AG; *Int'l*, pg. 4824
EVO BUSINESS SUPPLIES LIMITED—See Endless LLP; *Int'l*, pg. 2403
EVOBUS ITALIA S.P.A.—See Mercedes-Benz Group AG; *Int'l*, pg. 4824
EVOBUS NEDERLAND B.V.—See Mercedes-Benz Group AG; *Int'l*, pg. 4824
EVOBUS POLSKA SP. Z O.O.—See Mercedes-Benz Group AG; *Int'l*, pg. 4824
EVOBUS PORTUGAL, S.A.—See Mercedes-Benz Group AG; *Int'l*, pg. 4820
EVOBUS REUNION S. A.—See Mercedes-Benz Group AG; *Int'l*, pg. 4824
EVOBUS (SCHWEIZ) AG—See Mercedes-Benz Group AG; *Int'l*, pg. 4824
EVOBUS SVERIGE AB—See Mercedes-Benz Group AG; *Int'l*, pg. 4820
EVOBUS (UK) LTD.—See Mercedes-Benz Group AG; *Int'l*, pg. 4824
EVOCATIVE, INC.; *U.S. Private*, pg. 1442
EVOC INTELLIGENT TECHNOLOGY COMPANY LIMITED; *Int'l*, pg. 2572
EVO CNG, LLC—See EVO Transportation & Energy Services, Inc.; *U.S. Public*, pg. 804
EVO ENTERTAINMENT GROUP, LLC; *U.S. Private*, pg. 1442
EVOFEM BIOSCIENCES, INC.; *U.S. Public*, pg. 804
EVOFEM, INC—See Evofem Biosciences, Inc.; *U.S. Public*, pg. 804
EVOGENE LTD.—See Compugen Ltd.; *Int'l*, pg. 1755
EVOGUARD GMBH—See Krones AG; *Int'l*, pg. 4305
EVOK ADVERTISING; *U.S. Private*, pg. 1442
EVOKE PHARMA, INC.; *U.S. Public*, pg. 804
EVOKE PLC; *Int'l*, pg. 2572
EVOKE RESEARCH & CONSULTING LLC; *U.S. Private*, pg. 1442
EVOLA MUSIC CENTER INC.; *U.S. Private*, pg. 1442
EVOLEM S.A.; *Int'l*, pg. 2572
EVOLENT HEALTH, INC.; *U.S. Public*, pg. 804
EVOLENT TECHNISCHE HANDEL B.V.—See Quaser Machine Tools, Inc.; *Int'l*, pg. 6156
EVOL FOODS; *U.S. Private*, pg. 1442
EVOLINE B.V.—See Schulte Elektrotechnik GmbH & Co KG; *Int'l*, pg. 6641
EVOLINE CHILE—See Schulte Elektrotechnik GmbH & Co KG; *Int'l*, pg. 6641
EVOLINE ESPANA—See Schulte Elektrotechnik GmbH & Co KG; *Int'l*, pg. 6641
EVOLINE IRELAND—See Schulte Elektrotechnik GmbH & Co KG; *Int'l*, pg. 6641
EVOLINE NORGE AS—See Schulte Elektrotechnik GmbH & Co KG; *Int'l*, pg. 6641
EVOLINE NZ LTD—See Schulte Elektrotechnik GmbH & Co KG; *Int'l*, pg. 6641
EVOLINK AD—See DHH SpA; *Int'l*, pg. 2099
EVOLIT CONSULTING GMBH—See DZ BANK AG Deutsche Zentral-Genossenschaftsbank; *Int'l*, pg. 2244
EVO LOGISTICS, LLC—See EVO Transportation & Energy Services, Inc.; *U.S. Public*, pg. 804
EVOLTEC AG—See Komax Holding AG; *Int'l*, pg. 4240
EVOLUCIA INC.; *U.S. Private*, pg. 1442
EVOLUCION INNOVATIONS, INC.; *U.S. Private*, pg. 1442
EVOLUE JAPAN CO., LTD.—See Mitsui Chemicals, Inc.; *Int'l*, pg. 4981
EVOLUON-PHILIPS COMPETENCE CENTRE—See Koninklijke Philips N.V.; *Int'l*, pg. 4269
EVOLUS, INC.—See ALPHAEON Corporation; *U.S. Private*, pg. 200
EVOLUSYS SA—See Bechtle AG; *Int'l*, pg. 938
EVOLUTE CONSOLIDATED HOLDINGS, INC.—See PipelineRx; *U.S. Private*, pg. 3189
EVOLUTION1, INC.—See WEX, Inc.; *U.S. Public*, pg. 2364
EVOLUTION AB; *Int'l*, pg. 2572
EVOLUTIONARY GENOMICS, INC.; *U.S. Public*, pg. 804
EVOLUTIONARY TECHNOLOGIES INTERNATIONAL, INC.—See ESW Capital, LLC; *U.S. Private*, pg. 1430
EVOLUTION BLOCKCHAIN GROUP INC.; *Int'l*, pg. 2572
EVOLUTION BUREAU; *U.S. Private*, pg. 1442
EVOLUTION CAPITAL INVESTMENTS LLC—See Evolution Capital Management LLC; *U.S. Private*, pg. 1442
EVOLUTION CAPITAL MANAGEMENT LLC; *U.S. Private*, pg. 1442
EVOLUTION CAPITAL PARTNERS, LLC; *U.S. Private*, pg. 1443
EVOLUTION CAPITAL (UK) LIMITED; *Int'l*, pg. 2572
EVOLUTION ENERGY MINERALS LIMITED; *Int'l*, pg. 2572
EVOLUTION FILM & TAPE, INC.—See Metro-Goldwyn-Mayer Inc.; *U.S. Private*, pg. 2687
EVOLUTION FINANCIAL TECHNOLOGIES, LLC; *U.S. Private*, pg. 1443
EVOLUTION GROUP SERVICES LIMITED—See Investec Limited; *Int'l*, pg. 3778
EVOLUTION HEALTHCARE MANAGEMENT PTY. LTD.—See Evolution Healthcare Pty. Ltd.; *Int'l*, pg. 2572
EVOLUTION HEALTHCARE PTY. LTD.; *Int'l*, pg. 2572

CORPORATE AFFILIATIONS

EVOLUTION HEALTH, LLC—See Amedisys, Inc.; *U.S. Public*, pg. 93
EVOLUTION HURSTVILLE PTY. LTD.—See Evolution Healthcare Pty. Ltd.; *Int'l*, pg. 2572
EVOLUTION JAPAN CO., LTD.—See Evolution Capital Management LLC; *U.S. Private*, pg. 1443
EVOLUTION LIGHTING CANADA—See Boyne Capital Management, LLC; *U.S. Private*, pg. 628
EVOLUTION LIGHTING LLC—See Boyne Capital Management, LLC; *U.S. Private*, pg. 628
EVOLUTION LIGHTING LLC-TUPELO—See Boyne Capital Management, LLC; *U.S. Private*, pg. 628
EVOLUTION MARKETS, LLC—See Xpansiv Data Systems Inc.; *U.S. Private*, pg. 4582
EVOLUTION MINING LIMITED; *Int'l*, pg. 2572
EVOLUTION PETROLEUM CORPORATION; *U.S. Public*, pg. 804
EVOLUTION ROAD, LLC—See Clayton, Dubilier & Rice, LLC; *U.S. Private*, pg. 924
EVOLUTION SORBENT PRODUCTS, LLC—See National Packaging Services Corporation; *U.S. Private*, pg. 2860
EVOLUTION TECHNOLOGY RESOURCES, INC.; *Int'l*, pg. 2572
EVOLUTION TECHNOLOGY SERVICES LIMITED—See Arthur J. Gallagher & Co.; *U.S. Public*, pg. 204
EVOLUTION WATTERSON SECURITIES LIMITED—See Investec Limited; *Int'l*, pg. 3778
EVOLUTION WEALTH NETWORK LIMITED—See Schroders plc; *Int'l*, pg. 6639
EVOLUT S.P.A.—See EFORT Intelligent Equipment Co., Ltd.; *Int'l*, pg. 2321
EVOLUT (WUHU) ROBOTICS CO., LTD.—See EFORT Intelligent Equipment Co., Ltd.; *Int'l*, pg. 2321
EVOLVA A/S—See Evolva Holding SA; *Int'l*, pg. 2572
EVOLVA BIOTECH PRIVATE LIMITED—See Evolva Holding SA; *Int'l*, pg. 2572
EVOLVA HOLDING SA; *Int'l*, pg. 2572
EVOLVA SA—See Lallemand, Inc.; *Int'l*, pg. 4399
EVOLVE ANALYTICS LIMITED—See Gentrack Group Limited; *Int'l*, pg. 2929
EVOLVE BANK & TRUST; *U.S. Private*, pg. 1443
EVOLVE CONSULTING GROUP INC.—See GTCR LLC; *U.S. Private*, pg. 1803
EVOLVE CYBER INSURANCE SERVICES LLC—See Brown & Brown, Inc.; *U.S. Public*, pg. 400
EVOLVED INDUSTRIES, INC.; *U.S. Private*, pg. 1444
EVOLVE DISCOVERY LLC—See Fronteo, Inc.; *Int'l*, pg. 2794
EVOLVE EDUCATION GROUP LIMITED; *Int'l*, pg. 2572
EVOLVE IT AUSTRALIA PTY. LTD.; *Int'l*, pg. 2573
EVOLVE LTD.—See Attard & Co. Ltd.; *Int'l*, pg. 696
EVOLVE MANUFACTURING TECHNOLOGIES; *U.S. Private*, pg. 1443
EVOLVE MEDIA, LLC; *U.S. Private*, pg. 1443
EVOLVENT TECHNOLOGIES INC.; *U.S. Private*, pg. 1444
EVOLVER, INC.—See Converged Security Solutions LLC; *U.S. Private*, pg. 1035
E-VOLVE SYSTEMS LLC—See The Graham Group, Inc.; *U.S. Private*, pg. 4036
EVOLVE TALENT AGENCY; *U.S. Private*, pg. 1444
EVOLVE TRANSITION INFRASTRUCTURE LP; *U.S. Public*, pg. 804
EVOLVE USA CHARGING CORPORATION—See JNS Holdings Corporation; *U.S. Public*, pg. 1190
EVOLVING GOLD CORP.; *Int'l*, pg. 2573
EVOLVING SYSTEMS LIMITED—See CCUR Holdings Inc.; *U.S. Public*, pg. 461
EVOLVING SYSTEMS LIMITED—See CCUR Holdings Inc.; *U.S. Public*, pg. 461
EVOLVING SYSTEMS NC, INC.—See CCUR Holdings Inc.; *U.S. Public*, pg. 461
EVOLVING SYSTEMS NETWORKS INDIA PVT. LTD.—See CCUR Holdings Inc.; *U.S. Public*, pg. 461
EVOLVI RAIL SYSTEMS LIMITED—See Capita plc; *Int'l*, pg. 1309
EVOLV SOLUTIONS, LLC; *U.S. Private*, pg. 1443
EVOLV TECHNOLOGIES HOLDINGS INC.; *U.S. Public*, pg. 804
EVOME MEDICAL TECHNOLOGIES INC.; *U.S. Public*, pg. 804
EVO MERCHANT SERVICES CANADA CO.—See Global Payments Inc.; *U.S. Public*, pg. 943
EVONIK ANTWERPEN N.V.—See RAG-Stiftung; *Int'l*, pg. 6178
EVONIK CORPORATION—See RAG-Stiftung; *Int'l*, pg. 6178
EVONIK CYRO LLC—See RAG-Stiftung; *Int'l*, pg. 6179
EVONIK DEGUSSA - BIRMINGHAM LABS—See RAG-Stiftung; *Int'l*, pg. 6178
EVONIK DEGUSSA CANADA INC.—See RAG-Stiftung; *Int'l*, pg. 6178
EVONIK DEGUSSA (CHINA) CO., LTD.—See RAG-Stiftung; *Int'l*, pg. 6178
EVONIK DEGUSSA CORP. - LOCKLAND—See RAG-Stiftung; *Int'l*, pg. 6178
EVONIK DEGUSSA CORP. - MOBILE—See RAG-Stiftung; *Int'l*, pg. 6178
EVONIK GOLDSCHMIDT CORPORATION—See RAG-Stiftung; *Int'l*, pg. 6179

COMPANY NAME INDEX

EVONIK GOLDSCHMIDT GMBH—See RAG-Stiftung; *Int'l*, pg. 6178
EVONIK IMMOBILIEN GMBH—See RAG-Stiftung; *Int'l*, pg. 6179
EVONIK INDUSTRIES AG - FEED ADDITIVES—See RAG-Stiftung; *Int'l*, pg. 6179
EVONIK INDUSTRIES AG - HANAU-WOLFGANG CATALYSTS PLANT—See RAG-Stiftung; *Int'l*, pg. 6179
EVONIK INDUSTRIES AG - KREFELD PLANT—See RAG-Stiftung; *Int'l*, pg. 6179
EVONIK INDUSTRIES AG - MARL COATINGS & ADDITIVES PLANT—See RAG-Stiftung; *Int'l*, pg. 6179
EVONIK INDUSTRIES AG—See RAG-Stiftung; *Int'l*, pg. 6178
EVONIK INDUSTRIES JAPAN CO., LTD. - OSAKA OFFICE—See RAG-Stiftung; *Int'l*, pg. 6179
EVONIK OXENO GMBH—See RAG-Stiftung; *Int'l*, pg. 6179
EVONIK ROHM GMBH—See RAG-Stiftung; *Int'l*, pg. 6179
EVONIK STOCKHAUSEN, LLC - GARYVILLE—See RAG-Stiftung; *Int'l*, pg. 6178
EVONIK STOCKHAUSEN, LLC—See RAG-Stiftung; *Int'l*, pg. 6178
EVONIK TAIWAN LTD.—See RAG-Stiftung; *Int'l*, pg. 6178
EVO PAYMENTS, INC.—See Global Payments Inc.; *U.S. Public*, pg. 943
EVO PAYMENTS INTERNATIONAL CORP.—See Global Payments Inc.; *U.S. Public*, pg. 943
EVO PAYMENTS INTERNATIONAL GMBH—See EVO Payments International, LLC; *U.S. Private*, pg. 1442
EVO PAYMENTS INTERNATIONAL, LLC - CANADA—See EVO Payments International, LLC; *U.S. Private*, pg. 1442
EVO PAYMENTS INTERNATIONAL, LLC; *U.S. Private*, pg. 1442
EVO PAYMENTS INTERNATIONAL, LLC - USA—See EVO Payments International, LLC; *U.S. Private*, pg. 1442
EVO PAYMENTS INTERNATIONAL SP. Z O.O.—See Global Payments Inc.; *U.S. Public*, pg. 943
EVO PAYMENTS UK LTD.—See Global Payments Inc.; *U.S. Public*, pg. 943
EVOQ REMEDIES LIMITED; *Int'l*, pg. 2573
EVOQUA WATER TECHNOLOGIES CANADA—See Xylem Inc.; *U.S. Public*, pg. 2004
EVOQUA WATER TECHNOLOGIES CORP.—See Xylem Inc.; *U.S. Public*, pg. 2393
EVOQUA WATER TECHNOLOGIES GMBH—See Xylem Inc.; *U.S. Public*, pg. 2394
EVOQUA WATER TECHNOLOGIES INDIA PRIVATE LIMITED—See Xylem Inc.; *U.S. Public*, pg. 2393
EVOQUA WATER TECHNOLOGIES LLC—See Xylem Inc.; *U.S. Public*, pg. 2393
EVOQUA WATER TECHNOLOGIES PTY. LTD.—See Xylem Inc.; *U.S. Public*, pg. 2394
EVOQUA WATER TECHNOLOGIES (SHANGHAI) CO., LTD.—See Xylem Inc.; *U.S. Public*, pg. 2393
EVOQUA WATER TECHNOLOGIES—See Xylem Inc.; *U.S. Public*, pg. 2394
EVOQUA WATER TECHNOLOGIES—See Xylem Inc.; *U.S. Public*, pg. 2394
EVOQUA WATER TECHNOLOGIES—See Xylem Inc.; *U.S. Public*, pg. 2394
EVOQUA WATER TECHNOLOGIES—See Xylem Inc.; *U.S. Public*, pg. 2393
EVOQUA WATER TECHNOLOGIES—See Xylem Inc.; *U.S. Public*, pg. 2394
EVOQUA WATER TECHNOLOGIES—See Xylem Inc.; *U.S. Public*, pg. 2394
EVOQUA WATER TECHNOLOGIES—See Xylem Inc.; *U.S. Public*, pg. 2394
EVOQUA WATER TECHNOLOGIES—See Xylem Inc.; *U.S. Public*, pg. 2394
EVOQUA WATER TECHNOLOGIES—See Xylem Inc.; *U.S. Public*, pg. 2393
EVOQUA WATER TECHNOLOGIES—See Xylem Inc.; *U.S. Public*, pg. 2393
EVOQUA WATER TECHNOLOGIES—See Xylem Inc.; *U.S. Public*, pg. 2394
EVOQUA WATER TECHNOLOGIES—See Xylem Inc.; *U.S. Public*, pg. 2394
EVOQUA WATER TECHNOLOGIES—See Xylem Inc.; *U.S. Public*, pg. 2393
EVOQUA WATER TECHNOLOGIES—See Xylem Inc.; *U.S. Public*, pg. 2394
EVORA IT SOLUTIONS GMBH—See Allgeier SE; *Int'l*, pg. 337
EVORA IT SOLUTIONS GROUP GMBH—See Allgeier SE; *Int'l*, pg. 337
EVORA IT SOLUTIONS PVT. LTD.—See Allgeier SE; *Int'l*, pg. 337
EVORA S.A.; *Int'l*, pg. 2573
EVOS HAMBURG GMBH—See Koninklijke Vopak N.V.; *Int'l*, pg. 4272
EVOSOFT GMBH—See Siemens Aktiengesellschaft; *Int'l*, pg. 6901
EVOSOFT HUNGARY SZAMITASTECHNIKAI KFT.—See Siemens Aktiengesellschaft; *Int'l*, pg. 6901
EVOTECH S.A.S.—See Durr AG; *Int'l*, pg. 2232

EVOTEC (INDIA) PRIVATE LTD.—See Evotec SE; *Int'l*, pg. 2573
EVOTEC SE; *Int'l*, pg. 2573
EVOTEC (UK) LTD.—See Evotec SE; *Int'l*, pg. 2573
EVOTEST INC.—See ViTrox Corporation Berhad; *Int'l*, pg. 8262
EVO TRANSPORTATION & ENERGY SERVICES, INC.; *U.S. Public*, pg. 803
EVO-TREND CORPORATION (MALAYSIA) SDN. BHD.—See YHI International Limited; *Int'l*, pg. 8580
EVOTRE SRL—See Sesa S.p.A.; *Int'l*, pg. 6728
EVOWOOD PTY. LIMITED—See Jacobs Capital (Pty) Ltd.; *Int'l*, pg. 3865
EVOXX TECHNOLOGIES GMBH—See Advanced Enzyme Technologies Limited; *Int'l*, pg. 159
EV PARKING SERVICE CO., LTD.; *Int'l*, pg. 2560
EV PRIVATE EQUITY; *Int'l*, pg. 2560
EV PRODUCTS INC.—See Kromek Group PLC; *Int'l*, pg. 4304
EVPU A.S.; *Int'l*, pg. 2573
EVPU CR S.R.O.—See EVPU a.s.; *Int'l*, pg. 2573
EVPU DEFENCE A.S.—See EVPU a.s.; *Int'l*, pg. 2573
EVRARD-STRANG CONSTRUCTION, INC.; *U.S. Private*, pg. 1444
EVRAZ GROUP S.A.—See Evraz plc; *Int'l*, pg. 2573
EVRAZ HIGHVELD STEEL & VANADIUM LIMITED—See Evraz plc; *Int'l*, pg. 2574
EVRAZ INC. NA CANADA - CAMROSE—See Evraz plc; *Int'l*, pg. 2574
EVRAZ INC. NA CANADA—See Evraz plc; *Int'l*, pg. 2574
EVRAZ INC. NA - PUEBLO—See Evraz plc; *Int'l*, pg. 2574
EVRAZ INC. NA—See Evraz plc; *Int'l*, pg. 2574
EVRAZ LLC—See Evraz plc; *Int'l*, pg. 2573
EVRAZ MARKET JSC—See Evraz plc; *Int'l*, pg. 2573
EVRAZ NIKOM A.S.—See Evraz plc; *Int'l*, pg. 2574
EVRAZ NORTH AMERICA LIMITED—See Evraz plc; *Int'l*, pg. 2574
EVRAZ NORTH AMERICA PLC—See Evraz plc; *Int'l*, pg. 2574
EVRAZ PALINI E BERTOLI S.R.L—See Evraz plc; *Int'l*, pg. 2574
EVRAZ PLC; *Int'l*, pg. 2573
EVRAZ STRATCOR, INC.—See US Vanadium LLC; *U.S. Private*, pg. 4320
EV RESOURCES LIMITED; *Int'l*, pg. 2560
EVRIHOLDER PRODUCTS LLC—See Kainos Capital, LLC; *U.S. Private*, pg. 2255
E.V. ROBERTS & ASSOCIATES, INC.—See Carl Marks & Co., Inc.; *U.S. Private*, pg. 763
EVROFARMA SA; *Int'l*, pg. 2574
EVROFINANCE MOSNARBANK OJSC; *Int'l*, pg. 2574
EVROPA 2, SPOL. S R.O.—See Czech Media Invest as; *Int'l*, pg. 1898
EVROPA AD; *Int'l*, pg. 2574
EVROPEYSKAYA ELEKTROTEKHNICA PJSC; *Int'l*, pg. 2574
EVROPROEKT OOO—See OAO Group of Companies PIK; *Int'l*, pg. 5506
EVROPSKA CESTOVNI POJISTOVNA A.S.—See Munchener Ruckversicherungs AG; *Int'l*, pg. 5088
EVROPSKY INVESTICNI HOLDING A.S.—See Warimpex Finanz- und Beteiligungs AG; *Int'l*, pg. 8345
EVRORADIATORS LLC—See Robert Bosch GmbH; *Int'l*, pg. 6361
EVRY ASA—See TietoEVRY Oyj; *Int'l*, pg. 7745
EVRY CARD SERVICES AS—See TietoEVRY Oyj; *Int'l*, pg. 7745
EVRY CARD SERVICES OY—See TietoEVRY Oyj; *Int'l*, pg. 7745
EVRY FINANCING AB—See TietoEVRY Oyj; *Int'l*, pg. 7745
EVRY FINLAND OY—See TietoEVRY Oyj; *Int'l*, pg. 7745
EVRY INDIA PRIVATE LIMITED—See TietoEVRY Oyj; *Int'l*, pg. 7745
EVSA, INC.—See Equitable Holdings, Inc.; *U.S. Public*, pg. 789
EVS BROADCAST EQUIPMENT IBERICA S.L.—See EVS Broadcast Equipment S.A.; *Int'l*, pg. 2574
EVS BROADCAST EQUIPMENT LTD.—See EVS Broadcast Equipment S.A.; *Int'l*, pg. 2574
EVS BROADCAST EQUIPMENT S.A.; *Int'l*, pg. 2574
EVS BROADCAST UK LTD.—See EVS Broadcast Equipment S.A.; *Int'l*, pg. 2574
EVS CANADA INC.—See EVS Broadcast Equipment S.A.; *Int'l*, pg. 2574
EVS DEUTSCHLAND GMBH—See EVS Broadcast Equipment S.A.; *Int'l*, pg. 2574
EVS FRANCE DEVELOPPEMENT S.A.R.L.—See EVS Broadcast Equipment S.A.; *Int'l*, pg. 2574
EVS FRANCE S.A.—See EVS Broadcast Equipment S.A.; *Int'l*, pg. 2574
EVS INC.—See EVS Broadcast Equipment S.A.; *Int'l*, pg. 2574
EVS ITALY S.R.L.—See EVS Broadcast Equipment S.A.; *Int'l*, pg. 2574
EVT NV—See VINCI S.A.; *Int'l*, pg. 8217
EVT TECHNOLOGY CO., LTD.—See Chroma ATE Inc.; *Int'l*, pg. 1588
EVU.IT GMBH—See adesso SE; *Int'l*, pg. 144

E.V. WILLIAMS, INC.—See The Branch Group, Inc.; *U.S. Private*, pg. 3999
EVY OF CALIFORNIA, INC.; *U.S. Private*, pg. 1444
EVZ LIMITED; *Int'l*, pg. 2574
EWAG AG—See United Grinding Group AG; *Int'l*, pg. 8067
EWA GOVERNMENT SYSTEMS, INC.—See Sagewind Capital LLC; *U.S. Private*, pg. 3528
EWA INFORMATION AND INFRASTRUCTURE TECHNOLOGIES, INC.—See Sagewind Capital LLC; *U.S. Private*, pg. 3528
EWALD AUTOMOTIVE GROUP, LLC; *U.S. Private*, pg. 1444
EWALD CHEVROLET BUICK, LLC—See Ewald Automotive Group, LLC; *U.S. Private*, pg. 1444
EWALD CHRYSLER JEEP DODGE, LLC—See Ewald Automotive Group, LLC; *U.S. Private*, pg. 1444
EWALD CHRYSLER, LLC—See Ewald Automotive Group, LLC; *U.S. Private*, pg. 1444
EWALD'S HARTFORD FORD-LINCOLN-MERCURY, LLC—See Ewald Automotive Group, LLC; *U.S. Private*, pg. 1444
EWALD'S VENUS FORD, LLC; *U.S. Private*, pg. 1444
E-WASTE SYSTEMS, INC.; *U.S. Private*, pg. 1303
EWA TECHNOLOGIES—See Sagewind Capital LLC; *U.S. Private*, pg. 3528
E.W. AUDET & SONS, INC.; *U.S. Private*, pg. 1307
EWB KORNYEZETVEDELMI KFT—See McNally Bharat Engineering Co. Ltd.; *Int'l*, pg. 4760
EWB SOLUTIONS LIMITED—See Judges Scientific plc; *Int'l*, pg. 4021
E.W. BULLOCK ASSOCIATES, INC.; *U.S. Private*, pg. 1307
EWC AVENTURA, LLC—See European Wax Center Inc.; *U.S. Public*, pg. 799
EWC-HH&B HOLDINGS, LLC—See EverWatch Capital; *U.S. Private*, pg. 1441
EWE AKTIENGESELLSCHAFT; *Int'l*, pg. 2575
EWE BIOGAS GMBH & CO. KG—See EWE Aktiengesellschaft; *Int'l*, pg. 2575
EWE DIREKT GMBH—See EWE Aktiengesellschaft; *Int'l*, pg. 2575
EWEEK—See Ziff Davis Enterprise, Inc.; *U.S. Private*, pg. 4604
EWE ENERGIA SP. Z O.O.—See EWE Aktiengesellschaft; *Int'l*, pg. 2575
EWE ENERJI AS—See EWE Aktiengesellschaft; *Int'l*, pg. 2575
EWE ERNEUERBARE ENERGIEN GMBH—See EWE Aktiengesellschaft; *Int'l*, pg. 2575
EWE GASSPEICHER GMBH—See EWE Aktiengesellschaft; *Int'l*, pg. 2575
EWE IMMOBILIEN GMBH—See EWE Aktiengesellschaft; *Int'l*, pg. 2575
EWEIN BERHAD; *Int'l*, pg. 2576
EWE KUCHEN GMBH—See Nobia AB; *Int'l*, pg. 5395
EWEL, INC.—See Sumitomo Corporation; *Int'l*, pg. 7268
EWELLNESS HEALTHCARE CORPORATION; *U.S. Public*, pg. 805
EWEMOVE SALES & LETTINGS LTD.—See The Property Franchise Group PLC; *Int'l*, pg. 7676
EWE NETZ GMBH—See EWE Aktiengesellschaft; *Int'l*, pg. 2575
EWE OFFSHORE SERVICE & SOLUTIONS GMBH—See EWE Aktiengesellschaft; *Int'l*, pg. 2575
EWE POLSKA SP. Z O.O.—See EWE Aktiengesellschaft; *Int'l*, pg. 2575
EWE TEL GMBH—See EWE Aktiengesellschaft; *Int'l*, pg. 2575
EWE TRADING GMBH—See EWE Aktiengesellschaft; *Int'l*, pg. 2575
EWE TURKEY HOLDING A.S.—See State Oil Co. of Azerbaijan Republic; *Int'l*, pg. 7184
EWE URBANISATION DIENSTLEISTUNGS GMBH—See EWE Aktiengesellschaft; *Int'l*, pg. 2575
EWE VERTRIEB GMBH—See EWE Aktiengesellschaft; *Int'l*, pg. 2575
EWE WASSER GMBH—See EWE Aktiengesellschaft; *Int'l*, pg. 2575
EW GROUP GMBH; *Int'l*, pg. 2575
EWG SLUPSK SP. Z.O.O; *Int'l*, pg. 2576
EW HOF ANTR. U. SYSTEME GMBH—See AdCapital AG; *Int'l*, pg. 126
E.W. HOWELL COMPANY, INC.—See Obayashi Corporation; *Int'l*, pg. 5509
E. WICKLEIN GMBH—See Decora S.A.; *Int'l*, pg. 2001
EWI CONSTRUCTION, LLC; *U.S. Private*, pg. 1444
EWI CORPORATION—See Bristol-Myers Squibb Company; *U.S. Public*, pg. 386
E WIE EINFACH STROM & GAS GMBH—See E.ON SE; *Int'l*, pg. 2252
E. WIENER BIKE PARTS GMBH—See Accell Group N.V.; *Int'l*, pg. 80
EWIFOAM E. WICKLEIN GMBH—See Decora S.A.; *Int'l*, pg. 2001
EWINGCOLE, INC.; *U.S. Private*, pg. 1444
EWING CONSTRUCTION CO., INC.; *U.S. Private*, pg. 1444
EWING IRRIGATION PRODUCTS INC.; *U.S. Private*, pg. 1444

EWING-LEAVITT INSURANCE AGENCY, INC.

CORPORATE AFFILIATIONS

EWING-LEAVITT INSURANCE AGENCY, INC.; *U.S. Private*, pg. 1444
EWING PUBLIC RELATIONS, S.R.O.; *Int'l*, pg. 2576
EWINWIN, INC.; *U.S. Private*, pg. 1444
EWI RE, INC.—See Arthur J. Gallagher & Co.; *U.S. Public*, pg. 203
E.W. JAMES & SONS INC.; *U.S. Private*, pg. 1307
EWJ MACAU COMPANY LIMITED—See Emperor Watch & Jewellery Limited; *Int'l*, pg. 2386
EWON COMFORTECH CO., LTD. - JEONGUP FACTORY—See Ewon Comfortech Co., Ltd.; *Int'l*, pg. 2576
EWON COMFORTECH CO., LTD. - JIANGYANG FACTORY—See Ewon Comfortech Co., Ltd.; *Int'l*, pg. 2576
EWON COMFORTECH CO., LTD.; *Int'l*, pg. 2576
EWON COMFORTECH CO., LTD. - TURKEY FACTORY—See Ewon Comfortech Co., Ltd.; *Int'l*, pg. 2576
E.WONG S.A.—See Cencosud S.A.; *Int'l*, pg. 1400
EWOOSOFT CO., LTD.—See Vatech Co., Ltd.; *Int'l*, pg. 8135
EWORK DANMARK APS—See eWork Group AB; *Int'l*, pg. 2576
EWORK GROUP AB; *Int'l*, pg. 2576
EWORK HEALTHCARE—See Workway, Inc.; *U.S. Private*, pg. 4564
EWORK NORDIC OY—See eWork Group AB; *Int'l*, pg. 2576
EWORK NORGE AS—See eWork Group AB; *Int'l*, pg. 2576
E-WORLD CO., LTD.; *Int'l*, pg. 2249
EWOS AS—See Cargill, Inc.; *U.S. Private*, pg. 759
EWOS CANADA LTD.—See Cargill, Inc.; *U.S. Private*, pg. 759
EWOS CHILE ALIMENTOS LTDA.—See Cargill, Inc.; *U.S. Private*, pg. 759
EWOS CHILE S.A.—See Cargill, Inc.; *U.S. Private*, pg. 759
EWOS INNOVATION AS—See Cargill, Inc.; *U.S. Private*, pg. 759
EWOS LIMITED—See Cargill, Inc.; *U.S. Private*, pg. 759
EWP RENEWABLE CORPORATION—See Korea Electric Power Corporation; *Int'l*, pg. 4283
EWR WEATHER RADAR SYSTEMS; *U.S. Private*, pg. 1444
THE E.W. SCRIPPS COMPANY; *U.S. Public*, pg. 2067
EWS (MANUFACTURING) LIMITED—See Hadley Industries PLC; *Int'l*, pg. 3205
E.W. TOMPKINS COMPANY INC.; *U.S. Private*, pg. 1307
E-W TRUCK & EQUIPMENT CO., INC.; *U.S. Private*, pg. 1303
EWV ENERGIE- UND WASSER-VERSORGUNG GMBH—See RWE AG; *Int'l*, pg. 6434
E.W. WYLIE CORPORATION—See Daseke, Inc.; *U.S. Private*, pg. 1161
EX2 SOLUTIONS, INC.—See Builder Homesite, Inc.; *U.S. Private*, pg. 681
EXAB UTVECKLINGS AB—See Wihlborgs Fastigheter AB; *Int'l*, pg. 8407
EXABYTERS BETRIEBSGES MBH—See Salzgitter AG; *Int'l*, pg. 6496
EXACQ TECHNOLOGIES, INC.—See Johnson Controls International plc; *Int'l*, pg. 3988
EXACTA AEROSPACE, INC.—See Berkshire Hathaway Inc.; *U.S. Public*, pg. 314
EXACTA CORP.; *U.S. Private*, pg. 1445
EXACTAL EUROPE LIMITED—See Schneider Electric SE; *Int'l*, pg. 6624
EXACTAL MALAYSIA SDN. BHD.—See Schneider Electric SE; *Int'l*, pg. 6624
EXACT ANALYTICAL SDN. BHD.—See Muhibbah Engineering (M) Bhd.; *Int'l*, pg. 5078
EXACTA PACKAGING DESIGNS, INC.; *U.S. Private*, pg. 1445
EXACT AUTOMATION SDN. BHD.—See Muhibbah Engineering (M) Bhd.; *Int'l*, pg. 5078
EXACT CARE PHARMACY, LLC; *U.S. Private*, pg. 1444
EXACT COLOR SYSTEMS, LLC; *U.S. Private*, pg. 1444
EXACT CO. LTD.—See GMM Grammy Public Company Limited; *Int'l*, pg. 3012
EXACT DATA CONSUMERBASE LLC—See Exact Data, LLC; *U.S. Private*, pg. 1445
EXACT DATA, LLC; *U.S. Private*, pg. 1445
EXACTEARTH LTD.—See Spire Global, Inc.; *U.S. Public*, pg. 1918
EXACTECH DEUTSCHLAND GMBH—See TPG Capital, L.P.; *U.S. Public*, pg. 2173
EXACTECH FRANCE SAS—See TPG Capital, L.P.; *U.S. Public*, pg. 2173
EXACTECH, INC.—See Marine Travelift, Inc.; *U.S. Private*, pg. 2575
EXACTECH, INC.—See TPG Capital, L.P.; *U.S. Public*, pg. 2173
EXACTECH INTERNATIONAL OPERATION AG—See TPG Capital, L.P.; *U.S. Public*, pg. 2173
EXACTECH (UK) LTD.—See TPG Capital, L.P.; *U.S. Public*, pg. 2173

EXACT EMEA B.V.—See KKR & Co. Inc.; *U.S. Public*, pg. 1250
EXACT ESPANA SL—See KKR & Co. Inc.; *U.S. Public*, pg. 1250
EXACT GROUP B.V.—See KKR & Co. Inc.; *U.S. Public*, pg. 1250
EXACT HOLDING N.V.—See KKR & Co. Inc.; *U.S. Public*, pg. 1250
EXACT, INC.—See Indigo South Capital, Inc.; *U.S. Private*, pg. 2063
EXACT INTERNATIONAL DEVELOPMENT B.V.—See KKR & Co. Inc.; *U.S. Public*, pg. 1250
EXACTITUDE, INC.—See Platinum Equity, LLC; *U.S. Private*, pg. 3208
EXACT MANUFACTURING SYSTEMS (UK) LTD—See KKR & Co. Inc.; *U.S. Public*, pg. 1250
EXACT NEDERLAND B.V.—See KKR & Co. Inc.; *U.S. Public*, pg. 1250
EXACT OIL & GAS SDN. BHD.—See Muhibbah Engineering (M) Bhd.; *Int'l*, pg. 5078
EXACT ONLINE B.V.—See KKR & Co. Inc.; *U.S. Public*, pg. 1250
EXACTPRO SYSTEMS LLC—See London Stock Exchange Group plc; *Int'l*, pg. 4547
EXACTRAK LIMITED—See Illinois Tool Works Inc.; *U.S. Public*, pg. 1103
EXACT SCIENCES CORPORATION; *U.S. Public*, pg. 805
EXACT SCIENCES DEUTSCHLAND GMBH—See Exact Sciences Corporation; *U.S. Public*, pg. 805
EXACT SCIENCES LABORATORIES LLC—See Exact Sciences Corporation; *U.S. Public*, pg. 805
EXACT SCIENCES UK, LTD.—See Exact Sciences Corporation; *U.S. Public*, pg. 805
EXACT SOFTWARE (ANTILLES) N.V.—See KKR & Co. Inc.; *U.S. Public*, pg. 1250
EXACT SOFTWARE ASIA SDN. BHD.—See KKR & Co. Inc.; *U.S. Public*, pg. 1250
EXACT SOFTWARE AUSTRALIA PTY LTD—See KKR & Co. Inc.; *U.S. Public*, pg. 1251
EXACT SOFTWARE BELGIUM N.V.—See KKR & Co. Inc.; *U.S. Public*, pg. 1250
EXACT SOFTWARE CZECH REPUBLIC, S.R.O.—See KKR & Co. Inc.; *U.S. Public*, pg. 1250
EXACT SOFTWARE DE MEXICO S.A. DE C.V.—See KKR & Co. Inc.; *U.S. Public*, pg. 1251
EXACT SOFTWARE FRANCE SARL—See KKR & Co. Inc.; *U.S. Public*, pg. 1250
EXACT SOFTWARE (INTERNATIONAL) N.V.—See KKR & Co. Inc.; *U.S. Public*, pg. 1251
EXACT SOFTWARE (MALAYSIA) SDN. BHD.—See KKR & Co. Inc.; *U.S. Public*, pg. 1250
EXACT SOFTWARE NEDERLAND B.V. - EINDHOVEN—See KKR & Co. Inc.; *U.S. Public*, pg. 1250
EXACT SOFTWARE NORTH AMERICA LLC—See KKR & Co. Inc.; *U.S. Public*, pg. 1251
EXACT SOFTWARE POLAND SP. Z O.O.—See KKR & Co. Inc.; *U.S. Public*, pg. 1250
EXACT SOFTWARE (SHANGHAI) CO., LTD.—See KKR & Co. Inc.; *U.S. Public*, pg. 1250
EXACT SOFTWARE SINGAPORE PTE LTD—See KKR & Co. Inc.; *U.S. Public*, pg. 1251
EXACT SOFTWARE (UK) LTD.—See KKR & Co. Inc.; *U.S. Public*, pg. 1250
EXACT SOUTHEAST ASIA SDN. BHD.—See KKR & Co. Inc.; *U.S. Public*, pg. 1250
EXACT STAFF, INC.; *U.S. Public*, pg. 1445
EXACT SYSTEMS CZECH REPUBLIC S.R.O.—See CVI Dom Maklerski sp. z o.o.; *Int'l*, pg. 1889
EXACT SYSTEMS GMBH—See CVI Dom Maklerski sp. z o.o.; *Int'l*, pg. 1889
EXACT SYSTEMS S.A.—See CVI Dom Maklerski sp. z o.o.; *Int'l*, pg. 1889
EXACT SYSTEMS SLOVAKIA S.R.O.—See CVI Dom Maklerski sp. z o.o.; *Int'l*, pg. 1889
EXACTTARGET A.B.—See Salesforce, Inc.; *U.S. Public*, pg. 1837
EXACTTARGET GMBH—See Salesforce, Inc.; *U.S. Public*, pg. 1837
EXACTTARGET, INC.—See Salesforce, Inc.; *U.S. Public*, pg. 1837
EXACTTARGET PTE. LTD.—See Salesforce, Inc.; *U.S. Public*, pg. 1837
EXACTTARGET S.A.S.—See Salesforce, Inc.; *U.S. Public*, pg. 1837
EXACTTARGET TECNOLOGIA, LTDA.—See Salesforce, Inc.; *U.S. Public*, pg. 1837
EXACT THERAPEUTICS AS; *Int'l*, pg. 2576
EXACTUS PHARMACY SOLUTIONS, INC.—See Centene Corporation; *U.S. Public*, pg. 471
EXADEL, INC.—See Sun Capital Partners, LLC; *U.S. Private*, pg. 3859
EX A.D.; *Int'l*, pg. 2576
EXA E&C INC. - KIMPO FACTORY—See EXA E&C Inc.; *Int'l*, pg. 2576
EXA E&C INC.; *Int'l*, pg. 2576
EXAGEN INC.; *U.S. Public*, pg. 805
EXAGROUP SAS—See Cimpress plc; *Int'l*, pg. 1609

EXAKTERA LLC—See Union Park Capital; *U.S. Private*, pg. 4284
EXAKTIME, INC.; *U.S. Private*, pg. 1445
EXAKT KIESAUFBEREITUNG-GESELLSCHAFT MIT BESCHRANKTER HAFTUNG & CO KOMMANDITGESELLSCHAFT—See Heidelberg Materials AG; *Int'l*, pg. 3310
EXALCO BULGARIA A.D.—See Biokarpet S.A.; *Int'l*, pg. 1038
EXALCO FINANCE PLC; *Int'l*, pg. 2577
EXALCO ROMANIA SRL—See Biokarpet S.A.; *Int'l*, pg. 1038
EXAL CORPORATION—See Ontario Teachers' Pension Plan; *Int'l*, pg. 5589
EXALCO S.A.—See Biokarpet S.A.; *Int'l*, pg. 1038
EXALEAD INC.—See Dassault Systemes S.A.; *Int'l*, pg. 1975
EXALEAD S.A.—See Dassault Systemes S.A.; *Int'l*, pg. 1975
EXALENZ BIOSCIENCE INC.—See Meridian Bioscience Inc.; *U.S. Public*, pg. 1424
EXALENZ BIOSCIENCE LTD.—See Meridian Bioscience Inc.; *U.S. Public*, pg. 1424
EXALT INTEGRATED TECHNOLOGIES; *U.S. Private*, pg. 1445
EXAMINATION MANAGEMENT SERVICES, INC. - NATIONAL SERVICE CENTER—See Beecken Petty O'Keefe & Company, LLC; *U.S. Private*, pg. 514
EXAMINATION MANAGEMENT SERVICES, INC.—See Beecken Petty O'Keefe & Company, LLC; *U.S. Private*, pg. 514
THE EXAMINER NEWSPAPER PTY LTD—See Rural Press Pty Limited; *Int'l*, pg. 6429
THE EXAMINER—See Gannett Co., Inc.; *U.S. Public*, pg. 904
EXAMOBILE SA; *Int'l*, pg. 2577
EXAMONE CANADA, INC.—See Quest Diagnostics, Inc.; *U.S. Public*, pg. 1755
EXAMSOFT WORLDWIDE, INC.—See Advance Publications, Inc.; *U.S. Private*, pg. 87
EXAMWORKS CLINICAL SOLUTIONS, LLC—See GIC Pte. Ltd.; *Int'l*, pg. 2964
EXAMWORKS CLINICAL SOLUTIONS, LLC—See Leonard Green & Partners, L.P.; *U.S. Private*, pg. 2425
EXAMWORKS GROUP, INC.—See GIC Pte. Ltd.; *Int'l*, pg. 2964
EXAMWORKS GROUP, INC.—See Leonard Green & Partners, L.P.; *U.S. Private*, pg. 2425
EXAMWORKS GROUP, INC.—See GIC Pte. Ltd.; *Int'l*, pg. 2964
EXAMWORKS GROUP, INC.—See Leonard Green & Partners, L.P.; *U.S. Private*, pg. 2425
EXAMWORKS GROUP, INC.—See GIC Pte. Ltd.; *Int'l*, pg. 2964
EXAMWORKS GROUP, INC.—See Leonard Green & Partners, L.P.; *U.S. Private*, pg. 2425
EXAN ENTERPRISES INC.—See Henry Schein, Inc.; *U.S. Public*, pg. 1025
EXAPROBE SAS—See Econocom Group SA; *Int'l*, pg. 2298
EXARI GROUP, INC.—See Thoma Bravo, L.P.; *U.S. Private*, pg. 4147
EXARING AG—See freenet AG; *Int'l*, pg. 2770
EXASERV, INC.; *U.S. Private*, pg. 1445
EXASOL AG; *Int'l*, pg. 2577
EXASOL SCHWEIZ AG—See Exasol AG; *Int'l*, pg. 2577
EXASOL UK LTD.—See Exasol AG; *Int'l*, pg. 2577
EXA-SYSTEM CO., LTD.—See WiseTech Global Limited; *Int'l*, pg. 8437
EXATECH SOLUTIONS, INC.—See Vistronix, Inc.; *U.S. Private*, pg. 4403
EXATEL S.A.; *Int'l*, pg. 2577
EXA THERMOMETRICS INDIA PRIVATE LIMITED—See Amphenol Corporation; *U.S. Public*, pg. 130
EXBO SERVICES INTERNATIONAL SA/NV—See bpost NV/SA; *Int'l*, pg. 1133
EXCALA GROUP; *Int'l*, pg. 2577
EXCALIBAR MINERALS LLC—See Cimbar Performance Minerals, Inc.; *U.S. Private*, pg. 897
EXCALIBUR EXHIBITS; *U.S. Private*, pg. 1445
EXCALIBUR FUTURES LIMITED—See GoFintech Innovation Limited; *Int'l*, pg. 3021
EXCALIBUR GLOBAL FINANCIAL GROUP LTD.—See Excalibur Global Financial Holdings Ltd.; *Int'l*, pg. 2577
EXCALIBUR GLOBAL FINANCIAL HOLDINGS LTD.; *Int'l*, pg. 2577
EXCALIBUR MANAGEMENT CONSULTING (SHANGHAI) CO., LTD.—See Fiskars Oyj Abp; *Int'l*, pg. 2694
EXCALIBUR PIZZA LLC; *U.S. Private*, pg. 1445
EXCALIBUR SECURITIES LIMITED—See GoFintech Innovation Limited; *Int'l*, pg. 3021
EXCALIBUR TECHNOLOGY CORP.; *U.S. Private*, pg. 1445
EXCALIBUR VEHICLE ACCESSORIES (PTY) LTD—See ARGENT INDUSTRIAL LIMITED; *Int'l*, pg. 560
EXCEED COMPANY LTD.; *Int'l*, pg. 2577
EXCEED CORPORATION; *U.S. Private*, pg. 1445
EXCEED WORLD, INC.; *Int'l*, pg. 2577

EXCEET CARD AG—See H2APEX Group SCA; *Int'l*, pg. 3199
EXCEET CARD AUSTRIA GMBH—See H2APEX Group SCA; *Int'l*, pg. 3200
EXCEET CARD GROUP AG—See H2APEX Group SCA; *Int'l*, pg. 3199
EXCEET GROUP AG—See H2APEX Group SCA; *Int'l*, pg. 3199
EXCEET SECURE SOLUTIONS GMBH—See EQT AB; *Int'l*, pg. 2481
EXCEL AGRICULTURE—See Great Western Corporation Pty. Ltd.; *Int'l*, pg. 3066
EXCEL AIRWAYS GROUP PLC—See Eimskipafelag Islands Hf.; *Int'l*, pg. 2332
EXCEL ARCADE PRIVATE LTD.—See Housing Development & Infrastructure Limited; *Int'l*, pg. 3491
EXCEL ASIAN TAIWAN CO., LTD.—See Kaga Electronics Co., Ltd.; *Int'l*, pg. 4048
EXCEL ASPHALT LIMITED—See Wai Kee Holdings Limited; *Int'l*, pg. 8331
EXCEL BILLION HOLDINGS LIMITED—See Kowloon Development Company Limited; *Int'l*, pg. 4295
EXCEL CELL ELECTRONIC ANHUI CO., LTD.—See Excel Cell Electronic Co., Ltd.; *Int'l*, pg. 2577
EXCEL CELL ELECTRONIC CO., LTD.; *Int'l*, pg. 2577
EXCEL CELL ELECTRONIC (SUZHOU) CO., LTD.—See Excel Cell Electronic Co., Ltd.; *Int'l*, pg. 2577
EXCEL CELL ELECTRONIC (USA) CORP.—See Excel Cell Electronic Co., Ltd.; *Int'l*, pg. 2577
EXCEL CO., LTD.—See Kaga Electronics Co., Ltd.; *Int'l*, pg. 4048
EXCEL COMPANION CARE, INC.—See Centerbridge Partners, L.P.; *U.S. Private*, pg. 815
EXCEL COMPANION CARE, INC.—See The Vistria Group, LP; *U.S. Private*, pg. 4131
EXCEL CONCRETE LIMITED—See Wai Kee Holdings Limited; *Int'l*, pg. 8331
EXCEL CONCRETE PTY LTD—See Holcim Ltd.; *Int'l*, pg. 3446
EXCEL CONSULTING AND SOLUTIONS SDN. BHD.—See Yu Tak International Holdings Limited; *Int'l*, pg. 8607
EXCEL CORPORATION—See Cargill, Inc.; *U.S. Private*, pg. 750
EXCEL CORPORATION; *U.S. Public*, pg. 805
EXCEL CROP CARE LIMITED—See Sumitomo Chemical Company, Limited; *Int'l*, pg. 7266
EXCELDA MANUFACTURING COMPANY; *U.S. Private*, pg. 1445
EXCEL DE MEXICO S DE R.L. DE C.V.—See BizLink Holding Inc.; *Int'l*, pg. 1053
EXCEL DEVELOPMENT BANK LTD.; *Int'l*, pg. 2577
EXCELDOR COOPERATIVE AVICOLE - SAINT-ANSELME PLANT—See Exceldor Cooperative Avicole; *Int'l*, pg. 2577
EXCELDOR COOPERATIVE AVICOLE - SAINT-DAMASE PLANT—See Exceldor Cooperative Avicole; *Int'l*, pg. 2577
EXCELDOR COOPERATIVE AVICOLE; *Int'l*, pg. 2577
EXCEL ELECTRONICS (HONG KONG) LTD.—See Kaga Electronics Co., Ltd.; *Int'l*, pg. 4048
EXCEL ELECTRONICS (HUI ZHOU) LTD.—See Kaga Electronics Co., Ltd.; *Int'l*, pg. 4048
EXCEL ELECTRONICS TRADING (SHENZHEN) LTD.—See Kaga Electronics Co., Ltd.; *Int'l*, pg. 4048
EXCEL ELECTRONICS TRADING (THAILAND) CO., LTD.—See Kaga Electronics Co., Ltd.; *Int'l*, pg. 4048
EXCELENCIA EN TRANSPORTE DE PERSONAL, S.A.P.I. DE C.V.—See Grupo Traxion, S. A. B. de C. V.; *Int'l*, pg. 3138
EXCEL ENGINEERING, INCORPORATED—See Excel Group, Inc.; *U.S. Private*, pg. 1445
EXCEL FABRICATION & CONSTRUCTION, INC.—See Excel Group, Inc.; *U.S. Private*, pg. 1445
EXCELFIN ACQUISITION CORP.; *U.S. Public*, pg. 805
EXCELFORCE MSC BERHAD; *Int'l*, pg. 2578
EXCEL FOR FINANCIAL INVESTMENT COMPANY LTD.—See Bank of Jordan PLC; *Int'l*, pg. 845
EXCEL FOUNDRY & MACHINE INC.—See FLSmidth & Co. A/S; *Int'l*, pg. 2712
EXCEL FUNDS MANAGEMENT, INC.—See Sun Life Financial Inc.; *Int'l*, pg. 7305
EXCEL GLOBAL IT SERVICES (HANGZHOU) LIMITED—See Yu Tak International Holdings Limited; *Int'l*, pg. 8607
EXCEL GROUP, INC.; *U.S. Private*, pg. 1445
EXCELHIGH INC.; *U.S. Private*, pg. 1445
EXCEL HOMES GROUP, LLC—See Innovative Building Systems LLC; *U.S. Private*, pg. 2082
EXCEL HOMES LP—See Apex Limited Partnership; *Int'l*, pg. 511
EXCELIAN LIMITED—See DXC Technology Company; *U.S. Public*, pg. 696
EXCELIAN LUXOFT FINANCIAL SERVICES (SWITZERLAND) AG—See DXC Technology Company; *U.S. Public*, pg. 696
EXCEL INDUSTRIAL ELECTRONICS, INC.—See Regal Rexnord Corporation; *U.S. Public*, pg. 1772

EXCEL INDUSTRIES, INC.—See Stanley Black & Decker, Inc.; *U.S. Public*, pg. 1932
EXCEL INDUSTRIES LIMITED; *Int'l*, pg. 2577
EXCELINK TECHNOLOGY PTE LIMITED—See Yu Tak International Holdings Limited; *Int'l*, pg. 8607
EXCEL INTERNATIONAL TRADING (SHANGHAI) CO., LTD.—See Kaga Electronics Co., Ltd.; *Int'l*, pg. 4048
EXCELITAS CANADA, INC.—See AEA Investors LP; *U.S. Private*, pg. 113
EXCELITAS NOBLELIGHT GMBH—See AEA Investors LP; *U.S. Private*, pg. 113
EXCELITAS NOBLELIGHT LIMITED—See AEA Investors LP; *U.S. Private*, pg. 113
EXCELITAS TECHNOLOGIES CORP.—See AEA Investors LP; *U.S. Private*, pg. 113
EXCELITAS TECHNOLOGIES GMBH & CO. KG—See AEA Investors LP; *U.S. Private*, pg. 113
EXCELITAS TECHNOLOGIES PHILIPPINES, INC.—See AEA Investors LP; *U.S. Private*, pg. 113
EXCELITAS TECHNOLOGIES SHENZHEN CO., LTD.—See AEA Investors LP; *U.S. Private*, pg. 113
EXCELITAS TECHNOLOGIES SINGAPORE PTE. LTD.—See AEA Investors LP; *U.S. Private*, pg. 113
EXCELITY AUSTRALIA PTY LTD—See Dayforce, Inc.; *U.S. Public*, pg. 645
EXCELITY HCM SOLUTIONS SDN. BHD.—See Dayforce, Inc.; *U.S. Public*, pg. 645
EXCELITY PHILIPPINES, INC.—See Dayforce, Inc.; *U.S. Public*, pg. 645
EXCELLA CONSULTING; *U.S. Private*, pg. 1445
EXCELL AGENT SERVICES LLC; *U.S. Private*, pg. 1445
EXCELLA GMBH—See Fareva SA; *Int'l*, pg. 2618
EXCELLA HOME HEALTH AGENCY, LLC—See Encompass Health Corporation; *U.S. Public*, pg. 756
EXCEL LASER TECHNOLOGY PVT. LTD.—See Novanta Inc.; *U.S. Public*, pg. 1548
EXCEL LEASING & SALES COMPANY—See The Kretsinger Group, Inc.; *U.S. Private*, pg. 4066
EXCELLED SHEEPSKIN & LEATHER COAT CORPORATION; *U.S. Private*, pg. 1445
EXCELLED SHEEPSKIN & LEATHER COAT CORPORATION—See Excelled Sheepskin & Leather Coat Corporation; *U.S. Private*, pg. 1445
EXCELLED SHEEPSKIN & LEATHER COAT CORPORATION—See Excelled Sheepskin & Leather Coat Corporation; *U.S. Private*, pg. 1445
EXCELLENCE COMMERCIAL PROPERTY & FACILITIES MANAGEMENT GROUP LIMITED; *Int'l*, pg. 2578
EXCELLENCE DATA RESEARCH PVT. LTD—See Informa plc; *Int'l*, pg. 3692
EXCELLENCE ENGINEERING, LLC—See Bowman Consulting Group Ltd.; *U.S. Public*, pg. 376
EXCELLENCE IN MOTIVATION, INC.—See Aimia Inc.; *Int'l*, pg. 233
EXCELLENCE IN STONE, INC.—See Walker & Zanger, Inc.; *U.S. Private*, pg. 4428
EXCELLENCE INVESTMENTS LTD.—See Delek Group Ltd.; *Int'l*, pg. 2011
THE EXCELLENCE LIFE INSURANCE COMPANY—See iA Financial Corporation Inc.; *Int'l*, pg. 3568
EXCELLENCE REAL ESTATE GROUP LIMITED; *Int'l*, pg. 2578
EXCELLENCE SA; *Int'l*, pg. 2578
EXCELLENT COFFEE CO. INC.; *U.S. Private*, pg. 1446
EXCELLENT PACKAGING & SUPPLY; *U.S. Private*, pg. 1446
EXCELLENT RETAIL BRANDS B.V.; *Int'l*, pg. 2578
EXCELLENT SUCCESS INVESTMENT LIMITED—See Roma (meta) Group Limited; *Int'l*, pg. 6394
EXCELLERANT, INC.; *Int'l*, pg. 2578
EXCELLERATE HOLDINGS LTD.; *Int'l*, pg. 2578
EXCELLERE CAPITAL MANAGEMENT LLC; *U.S. Private*, pg. 1446
EXCELLERX, INC.—See Consonance Capital Partners LLC; *U.S. Private*, pg. 1023
EX-CELL HOME FASHIONS INC.; *U.S. Private*, pg. 1444
EXCELLIANCE MOS CORP.; *Int'l*, pg. 2578
EXCELLIGENCE LEARNING CORPORATION—See Brentwood Associates; *U.S. Private*, pg. 645
EXCELLINE FOOD PRODUCTS, LLC; *U.S. Private*, pg. 1446
EXCELLION SERVICOS BIOMEDICOS S.A.—See UnitedHealth Group Incorporated; *U.S. Public*, pg. 2240
EXCELLIUM SERVICES BELGIUM, S.A.—See Sonaecom SGPS SA; *Int'l*, pg. 7088
EXCELLIUM SERVICES, S.A.—See Sonaecom SGPS SA; *Int'l*, pg. 7088
EXCELLON RESOURCES INC.; *Int'l*, pg. 2578
EXCELLUS HEALTH PLAN, INC.—See The Lifetime Healthcare Companies; *U.S. Private*, pg. 4070
EXCELLUS TECHNOLOGIES, INC.—See J.H. Whitney & Co., LLC; *U.S. Private*, pg. 2166
EXCEL MARITIME CARRIERS LTD.; *Int'l*, pg. 2577
EXCEL MASTER LIMITED—See Creative Master Bermuda Ltd.; *Int'l*, pg. 1833
EXCEL MICRO, LLC—See Ziff Davis, Inc.; *U.S. Public*, pg. 2403

EXCEL MIDSTREAM SOLUTIONS, INCORPORATED—See Excel Group, Inc.; *U.S. Private*, pg. 1445
EXCELON CO., LTD.—See Pylon Public Company Limited; *Int'l*, pg. 6127
EXCELPOINT INTERNATIONAL TRADING (SHANGHAI) CO., LTD.—See WT Microelectronics Co., Ltd.; *Int'l*, pg. 8498
EXCELPOINT INTERNATIONAL TRADING (SHENZHEN) CO., LTD.—See WT Microelectronics Co., Ltd.; *Int'l*, pg. 8498
EXCELPOINT SYSTEMS (H.K.) LIMITED—See WT Microelectronics Co., Ltd.; *Int'l*, pg. 8498
EXCELPOINT SYSTEMS (INDIA) PRIVATE LIMITED—See WT Microelectronics Co., Ltd.; *Int'l*, pg. 8498
EXCELPOINT SYSTEMS (PTE) LTD—See WT Microelectronics Co., Ltd.; *Int'l*, pg. 8498
EXCELPOINT SYSTEMS SDN. BHD.—See WT Microelectronics Co., Ltd.; *Int'l*, pg. 8498
EXCELPOINT SYSTEMS (USA) INC.—See WT Microelectronics Co., Ltd.; *Int'l*, pg. 8498
EXCELPOINT TECHNOLOGY LTD—See WT Microelectronics Co., Ltd.; *Int'l*, pg. 8498
EXCEL REALTY N INFRA LTD.; *Int'l*, pg. 2577
EXCEL ROOFING SERVICES LIMITED—See Brickability Group plc; *Int'l*, pg. 1151
EXCELSA ACQUISITION CORP.; *U.S. Private*, pg. 1446
EXCEL S.A.—See YALCO - SOCRATES D. CONSTANTINOU & SON S.A.; *Int'l*, pg. 8547
EXCEL SCIENTIFIC, INC.—See Vance Street Capital LLC; *U.S. Private*, pg. 4342
EXCEL SEARCH GROUP, LLC—See Profectus, LLC; *U.S. Private*, pg. 3274
EXCEL SHANON CORPORATION—See Tokuyama Corporation; *Int'l*, pg. 7787
EXCELSIA INVESTMENT ADVISORS—See Bennett Thrasher; *U.S. Private*, pg. 527
EXCEL SINGAPORE PTE. LTD.—See Kaga Electronics Co., Ltd.; *Int'l*, pg. 4048
EXCELSIOR ALIMENTOS S.A.—See JBS S.A.; *Int'l*, pg. 3918
EXCELSIOR BIOPHARMA, INC.; *Int'l*, pg. 2578
EXCELSIOR CAPITAL ASIA (HK) LIMITED; *Int'l*, pg. 2578
EXCELSIOR CAPITAL KOREA LIMITED—See Excelsior Capital Asia (HK) Limited; *Int'l*, pg. 2578
EXCELSIOR CAPITAL LTD.; *Int'l*, pg. 2578
EXCELSIOR DEFENSE, INC.; *U.S. Private*, pg. 1446
EXCELSIOR DIECASTING PTY LIMITED—See Traffic Technologies Ltd.; *Int'l*, pg. 7889
EXCELSIOR EDUCATION MANAGEMENT SDN BHD—See Chip Eng Seng Corporation Ltd.; *Int'l*, pg. 1572
EXCELSIOR ELECTRIC MEMBERSHIP CORPORATION; *U.S. Private*, pg. 1446
EXCELSIOR ENVELOPPEN BV—See Bong AB; *Int'l*, pg. 1107
EXCELSIOR HOTEL BEOGRAD; *Int'l*, pg. 2579
EXCELSIOR HOTEL (BMG) PTY LTD—See Woolworths Group Limited; *Int'l*, pg. 8451
EXCELSIOR INTEGRATED, LLC—See Excelsior Printing Company; *U.S. Private*, pg. 1446
EXCELSIOR MANUFACTURING & SUPPLY CORP.—See Carrier Global Corporation; *U.S. Public*, pg. 444
EXCELSIOR MANUFACTURING & SUPPLY CORP.—See Watsco, Inc.; *U.S. Public*, pg. 2336
EXCELSIOR MEDICAL CO., LTD.; *Int'l*, pg. 2579
EXCELSIOR MEDICAL CORPORATION—See ICU Medical, Inc.; *U.S. Public*, pg. 1087
EXCELSIOR METALS, INC.—See Ryerson Holding Corporation; *U.S. Public*, pg. 1829
EXCELSIOR MINING CORP.; *Int'l*, pg. 2579
EXCELSIOR PRINTING COMPANY - OATMEAL STUDIOS DIVISION—See Excelsior Printing Company; *U.S. Private*, pg. 1446
EXCELSIOR PRINTING COMPANY; *U.S. Private*, pg. 1446
EXCELSIOR SOLUTIONS, LLC—See The Lockton Companies, LLC; *U.S. Private*, pg. 4071
EXCELSIOR UNITED DEVELOPMENT COMPANIES LIMITED; *Int'l*, pg. 2579
EXCEL SOFTWARE (SHENZHEN) CO., LTD.—See Yu Tak International Holdings Limited; *Int'l*, pg. 8607
EXCEL SOLUTION TECHNOLOGY LIMITED—See Yu Tak International Holdings Limited; *Int'l*, pg. 8607
EXCEL STAFFING COMPANIES; *U.S. Private*, pg. 1445
EXCELSYS TECHNOLOGIES LTD.—See Advanced Energy Industries, Inc.; *U.S. Public*, pg. 47
EXCELSYS TECHNOLOGIES; *U.S. Private*, pg. 1446
EXCEL SYSTEM (BEIJING) LIMITED; *Int'l*, pg. 2577
EXCEL TECH CORP.—See ArchiMed SAS; *Int'l*, pg. 548
EXCEL TECH, INC.—See Arrow Electronics, Inc.; *U.S. Public*, pg. 195
EXCEL TECH LTD.—See ArchiMed SAS; *Int'l*, pg. 548
EXCEL TECHNOLOGY, INC.—See Novanta Inc.; *U.S. Public*, pg. 1548
EXCEL TECHNOLOGY INTERNATIONAL (HONG KONG) LIMITED—See Yu Tak International Holdings Limited; *Int'l*, pg. 8607

EXCEL SYSTEM (BEIJING) LIMITED

EXCEL TECHNOLOGY (SHANGHAI) CO., LTD.—See Yu Tak International Holdings Limited; *Int'l*, pg. 8607
EXCEL TELECOMMUNICATIONS—See Blue Casa Communications, Inc.; *U.S. Private*, pg. 586
EXCEL TELECOMMUNICATIONS—See Garrison Investment Group LP; *U.S. Private*, pg. 1646
EXCEL TRANSPORTATION INC.; *Int'l*, pg. 2577
EXCEL TRUST, L.P.—See Blackstone Inc.; *U.S. Public*, pg. 350
EXCELVIEW LASER EYE CENTRE SDN BHD—See Focus Point Holdings Berhad; *Int'l*, pg. 2719
EXCENTA OY—See OP Financial Group; *Int'l*, pg. 5595
EXCENT CORPORATION—See Roper Technologies, Inc.; *U.S. Public*, pg. 1811
EXCENTRICGREY—See WPP plc; *Int'l*, pg. 8472
EXCENTUL TECHNOLOGY SERVICES, INC.—See The Chickasaw Nation; *U.S. Private*, pg. 4008
EXCENTUS CORP.—See TA Associates, Inc.; *U.S. Private*, pg. 3917
EXCEPTIONAL CHILDREN'S FOUNDATION; *U.S. Private*, pg. 1446
EXCEPTIONAL INNOVATION BV; *Int'l*, pg. 2579
EXCEPTIONAL RISK ADVISORS, LLC; *U.S. Private*, pg. 1446
EXCEPTIONAL SOFTWARE STRATEGIES, INC.—See Godspeed Capital Management LP; *U.S. Private*, pg. 1725
EXCERPTA MEDICA MEDICAL COMMUNICATIONS BV—See Omnicom Group Inc.; *U.S. Public*, pg. 1583
EXCESS REINSURANCE UNDERWRITERS, INC.—See Aon plc; *Int'l*, pg. 496
EXCET, INC.; *U.S. Private*, pg. 1446
EXCHANGE BANK OF MISSOURI—See Northern Missouri Bancshares, Inc.; *U.S. Private*, pg. 2953
EXCHANGE BANK OF NORTHEAST MISSOURI—See Lincoln County Bancorp., Inc.; *U.S. Private*, pg. 2457
EXCHANGE BANKSHARES, INC.; *U.S. Private*, pg. 1446
EXCHANGE BANK; *U.S. Public*, pg. 805
EXCHANGE BANK & TRUST; *U.S. Private*, pg. 1446
EXCHANGE ENTERPRISES LIMITED—See Gannett Co., Inc.; *U.S. Public*, pg. 897
EXCHANGE INCOME CORPORATION; *Int'l*, pg. 2579
EXCHANGER INDUSTRIES LTD—See Nova Capital Management Limited; *Int'l*, pg. 5450
EXCHANGE SERVICES L.L.C.—See Zions Bancorporation, National Association; *U.S. Public*, pg. 2408
EXCHANGE UNDERWRITERS, INCORPORATED—See World Insurance Associates LLC; *U.S. Private*, pg. 4565
EXCHEQUER ENTERPRISE SOFTWARE (NEW ZEALAND) LIMITED—See HgCapital Trust plc; *Int'l*, pg. 3376
EXCHEQUER SOFTWARE LTD—See HgCapital Trust plc; *Int'l*, pg. 3376
EXCIDOR AB—See Lagercrantz Group AB; *Int'l*, pg. 4394
EXCITE HOLDINGS CO., LTD.; *Int'l*, pg. 2579
EXCITE JAPAN CO., LTD.—See XTech Co., Ltd.; *Int'l*, pg. 8539
EXCITEPCR, CORPORATION—See PositiveID Corporation; *U.S. Private*, pg. 3233
EXCITE TECHNOLOGY SERVICES LIMITED; *Int'l*, pg. 2579
EXCITON TECHNOLOGY; *Int'l*, pg. 2580
EXCIVITY, INC.—See Arlington Capital Partners LLC; *U.S. Private*, pg. 327
EXCLAMATION INVESTMENTS CORP.; *Int'l*, pg. 2580
EXCLUSIVE CONCEPTS, INC; *U.S. Private*, pg. 1446
EXCLUSIVE CONTRACT SERVICES LIMITED; *Int'l*, pg. 2580
EXCLUSIVE GROUP SASU; *Int'l*, pg. 2580
EXCLUSIVE MARK (M) SDN. BHD.—See Citra Nusa Holdings Berhad; *Int'l*, pg. 1626
EXCLUSIVE NETWORKS ASIA PTE. LTD.—See Permira Advisers LLP; *Int'l*, pg. 5804
EXCLUSIVE NETWORKS AUSTRIA GMBH—See Permira Advisers LLP; *Int'l*, pg. 5804
EXCLUSIVE NETWORKS BH D.O.O.—See Permira Advisers LLP; *Int'l*, pg. 5804
EXCLUSIVE NETWORKS BILISIM A.S.—See Permira Advisers LLP; *Int'l*, pg. 5804
EXCLUSIVE NETWORKS DENMARK A/S—See Permira Advisers LLP; *Int'l*, pg. 5804
EXCLUSIVE NETWORKS DEUTSCHLAND GMBH—See Permira Advisers LLP; *Int'l*, pg. 5804
EXCLUSIVE NETWORKS FINLAND OY—See Permira Advisers LLP; *Int'l*, pg. 5804
EXCLUSIVE NETWORKS IRELAND LTD.—See Permira Advisers LLP; *Int'l*, pg. 5804
EXCLUSIVE NETWORKS MALAYSIA SDN. BHD.—See Permira Advisers LLP; *Int'l*, pg. 5804
EXCLUSIVE NETWORKS PH, INC.—See Permira Advisers LLP; *Int'l*, pg. 5804
EXCLUSIVE NETWORKS POLAND S.A.—See Permira Advisers LLP; *Int'l*, pg. 5804
EXCLUSIVE NETWORKS SA—See Permira Advisers LLP; *Int'l*, pg. 5804
EXCLUSIVE NETWORKS SINGAPORE PTE. LTD.—See Permira Advisers LLP; *Int'l*, pg. 5804

EXCLUSIVE NETWORKS SWITZERLAND AG—See Permira Advisers LLP; *Int'l*, pg. 5804
EXCLUSIVE NETWORKS TECHNOLOGY ROMANIA S.R.L.—See Permira Advisers LLP; *Int'l*, pg. 5804
EXCLUSIVE NETWORKS VIETNAM CO., LTD.—See Permira Advisers LLP; *Int'l*, pg. 5804
EXCLUSIVE RESORTS, LLC—See Revolution, LLC; *U.S. Private*, pg. 3417
EXCLUSIVE TYRE DISTRIBUTORS PTY LTD—See National Tyre & Wheel Limited; *Int'l*, pg. 5164
EXCLUSIVE TYRES DISTRIBUTORS PTY. LTD.—See National Tyre & Wheel Limited; *Int'l*, pg. 5164
EXCO AUTOMOTIVE SOLUTIONS L.P.—See Exco Technologies Limited; *Int'l*, pg. 2580
EXCO ENGINEERING—See Exco Technologies Limited; *Int'l*, pg. 2580
EXCO EXTRUSION DIES, INC.—See Exco Technologies Limited; *Int'l*, pg. 2580
EXCO HOLDING MLP, INC.—See EXCO Resources, Inc.; *U.S. Public*, pg. 805
EXCOLERE ACQUISITION CORP.; *U.S. Private*, pg. 1447
EXCO RESOURCES, INC.; *U.S. Public*, pg. 805
EXCO RESOURCES LIMITED—See Washington H. Soul Pattinson & Company Limited; *Int'l*, pg. 8351
EXCO RESOURCES-RAVENSWOOD—See EXCO Resources, Inc.; *U.S. Public*, pg. 805
EXCOR GMBH—See Northern Technologies International Corporation; *U.S. Public*, pg. 1537
EXCOR IBERICA—See Northern Technologies International Corporation; *U.S. Public*, pg. 1537
EXCOR SP. Z.O.O.—See Northern Technologies International Corporation; *U.S. Public*, pg. 1537
EXCO TECHNOLOGIES LIMITED; *Int'l*, pg. 2580
EXCO TOOLING SOLUTIONS—See Exco Technologies Limited; *Int'l*, pg. 2580
EXEBLOCK TECHNOLOGY CORP.; *Int'l*, pg. 2580
EXEC AIR MONTANA, INC.—See Leading Edge Aviation, Inc.; *U.S. Private*, pg. 2406
EXECHEALTH INC.—See WELL Health Technologies Corp.; *Int'l*, pg. 8372
EXECUFLORA PROPRIETARY LIMITED—See The Bidvest Group Limited; *Int'l*, pg. 7624
EXECUJET CHARTER SERVICE, INC.; *U.S. Private*, pg. 1447
EXECUPAY, INC.—See Vensure Employer Services, Inc.; *U.S. Private*, pg. 4357
EXECUPHARM, INC.—See Pamplona Capital Management LLP; *Int'l*, pg. 5712
EXECUS SPA; *Int'l*, pg. 2580
EXECUTECH UTAH, LLC; *U.S. Private*, pg. 1447
EXECUTIVE AFFILIATES INC.; *U.S. Private*, pg. 1447
EXECUTIVE AIR TAXI CORP; *U.S. Private*, pg. 1447
EXECUTIVE AVIATION INC.—See Baton Rouge Jet Center LLC; *U.S. Private*, pg. 487
EXECUTIVE BUSINESS CENTERS; *U.S. Private*, pg. 1447
EXECUTIVE BUSINESS SERVICES, INC.—See Roper Technologies, Inc.; *U.S. Public*, pg. 1811
EXECUTIVE CABINETRY, LLC; *U.S. Private*, pg. 1447
EXECUTIVE CAPITAL CORP.; *U.S. Private*, pg. 1447
EXECUTIVE CAR LEASING CO.; *U.S. Private*, pg. 1447
EXECUTIVE CATERERS INC.; *U.S. Private*, pg. 1447
EXECUTIVE COACH BUILDERS INC.; *U.S. Private*, pg. 1447
EXECUTIVE COFFEE SERVICE INC; *U.S. Private*, pg. 1447
EXECUTIVE COMMUNICATIONS, INC.; *U.S. Private*, pg. 1447
EXECUTIVE COURIER, INC.—See Storage & Transportation Co., Inc.; *U.S. Private*, pg. 3831
EXECUTIVE DIRECTION INC.; *U.S. Private*, pg. 1447
EXECUTIVE DODGE, INC.; *U.S. Private*, pg. 1447
EXECUTIVE EXPRESS, INC.; *U.S. Private*, pg. 1447
EXECUTIVE FLIGHT CENTRE FUEL SERVICES LTD.; *Int'l*, pg. 2580
EXECUTIVE HEALTH MANAGEMENT BV—See Air France-KLM S.A.; *Int'l*, pg. 237
EXECUTIVE HEALTH RESOURCES, INC.—See UnitedHealth Group Incorporated; *U.S. Public*, pg. 2240
EXECUTIVE IMAGE SOLUTIONS INC.; *U.S. Private*, pg. 1447
EXECUTIVE INFORMATION SYSTEMS, LLC; *U.S. Private*, pg. 1447
EXECUTIVE JEEP NISSAN; *U.S. Private*, pg. 1447
EXECUTIVE LEASE S.A.—See SFAKIANAKIS S.A.; *Int'l*, pg. 6738
EXECUTIVE MANAGEMENT ASSOCIATES, INC.; *U.S. Private*, pg. 1447
EXECUTIVE MANAGEMENT SERVICES INC.; *U.S. Private*, pg. 1447
EXECUTIVE MONETARY MANAGEMENT, LLC—See Genstar Capital, LLC; *U.S. Private*, pg. 1676
EXECUTIVE MOTOR GROUP LIMITED—See Pinewood Technologies Group PLC; *Int'l*, pg. 5869
EXECUTIVE NATIONAL BANK; *U.S. Public*, pg. 1448
EXECUTIVE NETWORK PARTNERING CORPORATION; *U.S. Public*, pg. 806
EXECUTIVE PERILS INSURANCE SERVICES; *U.S. Private*, pg. 1448

CORPORATE AFFILIATIONS

EXECUTIVE PERSONAL COMPUTERS INC.—See Tokyo Century Corporation; *Int'l*, pg. 7789
EXECUTIVE PLACEMENTS, LLC; *U.S. Private*, pg. 1448
EXECUTIVE PROTECTION SYSTEMS LLC; *U.S. Private*, pg. 1448
EXECUTIVE RELOCATION CORPORATION—See Madison Dearborn Partners, LLC; *U.S. Private*, pg. 2542
EXECUTIVE REPORTING SERVICE; *U.S. Private*, pg. 1448
EXECUTIVE RISK INDEMNITY INC.—See Chubb Limited; *Int'l*, pg. 1591
EXECUTIVE RISK SPECIALTY INSURANCE COMPANY—See Chubb Limited; *Int'l*, pg. 1591
EXECUTIVE SEARCH DIVISION—See Cook Associates, Inc.; *U.S. Private*, pg. 1037
EXECUTIVE SERVICES, INC.; *U.S. Private*, pg. 1448
EXECUTIVE SURGERY CENTER, LLC—See UnitedHealth Group Incorporated; *U.S. Public*, pg. 2240
EXECUTIVE TECHNOLOGIES, INC.—See Wells Fargo & Company; *U.S. Public*, pg. 2344
EXECUTIVE TRAVEL ASSOCIATES LLC—See Global Business Travel Group, Inc.; *U.S. Public*, pg. 941
EXECUTIVE TRAVEL, INC.—See BCD Holdings N.V.; *Int'l*, pg. 926
EXECUTONE TELECOMMUNICATIONS, LLC; *U.S. Private*, pg. 1448
EXECUTOR TRUSTEE AUSTRALIA LIMITED—See Insignia Financial Ltd.; *Int'l*, pg. 3719
EXEDY AMERICA CORPORATION—See Exedy Corporation; *Int'l*, pg. 2581
EXEDY AUSTRALIA PTY. LTD.—See Exedy Corporation; *Int'l*, pg. 2581
EXEDY BEIJING CO., LTD.—See Exedy Corporation; *Int'l*, pg. 2581
EXEDY CASTING CO., LTD.—See Exedy Corporation; *Int'l*, pg. 2580
EXEDY CHONGQING CO., LTD.—See Exedy Corporation; *Int'l*, pg. 2581
EXEDY CLUTCH EUROPE LTD.—See Exedy Corporation; *Int'l*, pg. 2581
EXEDY CLUTCH INDIA PVT. LTD.—See Exedy Corporation; *Int'l*, pg. 2581
EXEDY CORPORATION - KAWAGOE PLANT—See Exedy Corporation; *Int'l*, pg. 2581
EXEDY CORPORATION; *Int'l*, pg. 2580
EXEDY CORPORATION - UENO DIVISION—See Exedy Corporation; *Int'l*, pg. 2581
EXEDY-DYNAX AMERICA CORPORATION—See Exedy Corporation; *Int'l*, pg. 2581
EXEDY DYNAX EUROPE LTD.—See Exedy Corporation; *Int'l*, pg. 2581
EXEDY DYNAX MEXICO, S.A. DE C.V.—See Exedy Corporation; *Int'l*, pg. 2581
EXEDY DYNAX SHANGHAI CO., LTD.—See Exedy Corporation; *Int'l*, pg. 2581
EXEDY ELECTRIC FACILITIES CO., LTD.—See Exedy Corporation; *Int'l*, pg. 2581
EXEDY ENGINEERING ASIA CO., LTD.—See Exedy Corporation; *Int'l*, pg. 2581
EXEDY FRICTION MATERIAL CO.,LTD.—See Exedy Corporation; *Int'l*, pg. 2581
EXEDY FUKUSHIMA CO., LTD.—See Exedy Corporation; *Int'l*, pg. 2581
EXEDY GLOBALPARTS CORPORATION—See Exedy Corporation; *Int'l*, pg. 2581
EXEDY GUANGZHOU CO., LTD.—See Exedy Corporation; *Int'l*, pg. 2581
EXEDY HIROSHIMA CO., LTD.—See Exedy Corporation; *Int'l*, pg. 2580
EXEDY HOLDINGS OF AMERICA CORPORATION—See Exedy Corporation; *Int'l*, pg. 2581
EXEDY INDIA LTD.—See Exedy Corporation; *Int'l*, pg. 2581
EXEDY KYOTO CO., LTD.—See Exedy Corporation; *Int'l*, pg. 2580
EXEDY LATIN AMERICA S.A.—See Exedy Corporation; *Int'l*, pg. 2581
EXEDY LOGISTICS CO., LTD.—See Exedy Corporation; *Int'l*, pg. 2580
EXEDY (MALAYSIA) SDN.BHD.—See Exedy Corporation; *Int'l*, pg. 2580
EXEDY MEXICO AFTERMARKET SALES, S.A. DE C.V.—See Exedy Corporation; *Int'l*, pg. 2581
EXEDY MIDDLE EAST FZCO—See Exedy Corporation; *Int'l*, pg. 2581
EXEDY NARA CO., LTD.—See Exedy Corporation; *Int'l*, pg. 2581
EXEDY NEW ZEALAND LTD.—See Exedy Corporation; *Int'l*, pg. 2580
EXEDY POIPET CO., LTD.—See Exedy Corporation; *Int'l*, pg. 2581
EXEDY PRECISION CO., LTD.—See Exedy Corporation; *Int'l*, pg. 2580
EXEDY SB HYOGO CO., LTD.—See Exedy Corporation; *Int'l*, pg. 2581
EXEDY (SHANGHAI) CO., LTD.—See Exedy Corporation; *Int'l*, pg. 2580
EXEDY SINGAPORE PTE. LTD.—See Exedy Corporation; *Int'l*, pg. 2581

COMPANY NAME INDEX

EXEDY SUN CO., LTD.—See Exedy Corporation; *Int'l*, pg. 2580
EXEDY (THAILAND) CO., LTD.—See Exedy Corporation; *Int'l*, pg. 2580
EXEDY TRADING CO., LTD.—See Exedy Corporation; *Int'l*, pg. 2580
EXEDY VIETNAM CO.,LTD—See Exedy Corporation; *Int'l*, pg. 2581
EXEECO LTD—See Rotork Plc; *Int'l*, pg. 6405
EXEED PTE LTD—See VSTECS Holdings Limited; *Int'l*, pg. 8315
EXEGY, INC.—See Marlin Equity Partners, LLC; *U.S. Private*, pg. 2584
EXELAN PHARMACEUTICALS, INC.—See Cipla Ltd.; *Int'l*, pg. 1617
EXELA TECHNOLOGIES BV—See Exela Technologies, Inc.; *U.S. Public*, pg. 806
EXELA TECHNOLOGIES GMBH—See Exela Technologies, Inc.; *U.S. Public*, pg. 806
EXELA TECHNOLOGIES IBERCIA S.A.—See Exela Technologies, Inc.; *U.S. Public*, pg. 806
EXELA TECHNOLOGIES, INC.; *U.S. Public*, pg. 806
EXELA TECHNOLOGIES LIMITED—See Exela Technologies, Inc.; *U.S. Public*, pg. 806
EXELA TECHNOLOGIES S.A.—See Exela Technologies, Inc.; *U.S. Public*, pg. 806
EXELA TECHNOLOGIES S.P. Z O.O.—See Exela Technologies, Inc.; *U.S. Public*, pg. 806
EXELATE, INC.—See Brookfield Corporation; *Int'l*, pg. 1181
EXELATE, INC.—See Elliott Management Corporation; *U.S. Private*, pg. 1373
EXEL AUTOMOCION S.A. DE C.V.—See Deutsche Post AG; *Int'l*, pg. 2080
EXEL CANADA LTD.—See Deutsche Post AG; *Int'l*, pg. 2080
EXELCO INC.; *U.S. Private*, pg. 1448
EXEL COMPOSITES (AUSTRALIA) PTY LTD—See Exel Composites Oyj; *Int'l*, pg. 2581
EXEL COMPOSITES GMBH—See Exel Composites Oyj; *Int'l*, pg. 2581
EXEL COMPOSITES N.V.—See Exel Composites Oyj; *Int'l*, pg. 2581
EXEL COMPOSITES OYJ; *Int'l*, pg. 2581
EXEL COMPOSITES UK LTD.—See Exel Composites Oyj; *Int'l*, pg. 2581
EXEL DISTRIBUTION (THAILAND) LTD.—See Deutsche Post AG; *Int'l*, pg. 2080
EXELEAD INC.—See Merck KGaA; *Int'l*, pg. 4831
EXELED HOLDINGS, INC.; *U.S. Private*, pg. 1448
EXELERATE CAPITAL CORP.; *Int'l*, pg. 2583
EXEL FINISHING PVT LTD—See Exel Industries SA; *Int'l*, pg. 2582
EXELGEN DISCOVERY; *Int'l*, pg. 2583
EXEL GLOBAL LOGISTICS DO BRASIL S.A.—See Deutsche Post AG; *Int'l*, pg. 2080
EXEL GMBH—See Exel Composites Oyj; *Int'l*, pg. 2581
EXEL GROUP HOLDINGS (NEDERLAND) B.V.—See Deutsche Post AG; *Int'l*, pg. 2080
EXEL GSA SAS—See Exel Industries SA; *Int'l*, pg. 2582
EXEL INDUSTRIAL CANADA INC.—See Exel Industries SA; *Int'l*, pg. 2582
EXEL INDUSTRIAL E.P.E. LDTA—See Exel Industries SA; *Int'l*, pg. 2582
EXEL INDUSTRIAL E.P.E., S.A.—See Exel Industries SA; *Int'l*, pg. 2582
EXEL INDUSTRIES SA; *Int'l*, pg. 2582
EXEL INTERNATIONAL HOLDINGS (NETHERLANDS 1) B.V.—See Deutsche Post AG; *Int'l*, pg. 2080
EXEL INTERNATIONAL HOLDINGS (NETHERLANDS 2) B.V.—See Deutsche Post AG; *Int'l*, pg. 2080
EXEL INVESTMENTS INC.—See Deutsche Post AG; *Int'l*, pg. 2080
EXELIS C4I PTY LTD—See L3Harris Technologies, Inc.; *U.S. Public*, pg. 1279
EXELIS SERVICES A/S—See V2X, Inc.; *U.S. Public*, pg. 2270
EXELIS VIS KK—See L3Harris Technologies, Inc.; *U.S. Public*, pg. 1280
EXELIS VISUAL INFORMATION SOLUTIONS B.V.—See L3Harris Technologies, Inc.; *U.S. Public*, pg. 1280
EXELIS VISUAL INFORMATION SOLUTIONS FRANCE SARL—See L3Harris Technologies, Inc.; *U.S. Public*, pg. 1280
EXELIS VISUAL INFORMATION SOLUTIONS GMBH—See L3Harris Technologies, Inc.; *U.S. Public*, pg. 1280
EXELIS VISUAL INFORMATION SOLUTIONS, INC.—See L3Harris Technologies, Inc.; *U.S. Public*, pg. 1280
EXELIS VISUAL INFORMATION SOLUTIONS SRL—See L3Harris Technologies, Inc.; *U.S. Public*, pg. 1280
EXELIS VISUAL INFORMATION SOLUTIONS UK LIMITED—See L3Harris Technologies, Inc.; *U.S. Public*, pg. 1280
EXELIXIS, INC.; *U.S. Public*, pg. 806
EXELIXIS INVESTMENTS PUBLIC LIMITED; *Int'l*, pg. 2583
EXEL LACKIER- UND BESCHICHTUNGSSYSTEME GMBH—See Exel Industries SA; *Int'l*, pg. 2582

EXEL NORTH AMERICA INC.—See Exel Industries SA; *Int'l*, pg. 2582
EXELON CORPORATION; *U.S. Public*, pg. 806
EXELON ENERGY DELIVERY COMPANY, LLC—See Exelon Corporation; *U.S. Public*, pg. 806
EXELON NUCLEAR PARTNERS, LLC—See Constellation Energy Corporation; *U.S. Public*, pg. 572
EXELON POWERLABS, LLC—See Constellation Energy Corporation; *U.S. Public*, pg. 572
EXELON TRANSMISSION COMPANY, LLC—See Exelon Corporation; *U.S. Public*, pg. 807
EXEL S.A. DE C.V.—See Exel Industries SA; *Int'l*, pg. 2582
EXEL SPORTS NA—See Exel Composites Oyj; *Int'l*, pg. 2581
EXEL SPORTS SWEDEN AB—See Exel Composites Oyj; *Int'l*, pg. 2582
EXEL SUPPLY CHAIN SERVICES DE MEXICO, S.A. DE C.V.—See Deutsche Post AG; *Int'l*, pg. 2080
EXEL SUPPLY CHAIN SERVICES (SOUTH AFRICA) (PTY) LTD.—See Deutsche Post AG; *Int'l*, pg. 2080
EXEL SUPPLY CHAIN SOLUTIONS LTD.—See Deutsche Post AG; *Int'l*, pg. 2080
EXELTIS AUSTRIA—See Insud Pharma, S.L.; *Int'l*, pg. 3725
EXELTIS GERMANY GMBH—See Insud Pharma, S.L.; *Int'l*, pg. 3725
EXELTIS PROJECT, INC.—See Insud Pharma, S.L.; *Int'l*, pg. 3725
EXELTIS SINGAPORE—See Insud Pharma, S.L.; *Int'l*, pg. 3725
EXEL USA INC.—See Exel Composites Oyj; *Int'l*, pg. 2582
EXEM CHINA CO., LTD.—See EXEM Co., Ltd.; *Int'l*, pg. 2583
EXEM CO., LTD.; *Int'l*, pg. 2583
EXEM JAPAN CO., LTD.—See EXEM Co., Ltd.; *Int'l*, pg. 2583
EXEMPLAR GENETICS, LLC—See Precigen, Inc.; *U.S. Public*, pg. 1713
EXEMPLIS LLC; *U.S. Private*, pg. 1448
EXEM USA, INC.—See EXEM Co., Ltd.; *Int'l*, pg. 2583
EXENCIAL WEALTH ADVISORS, LLC; *U.S. Private*, pg. 1448
EXENT CORP.; *Int'l*, pg. 2583
EXEO ASIA CO., LTD.—See EXEO Group Inc.; *Int'l*, pg. 2583
EXEO DIGITAL SOLUTIONS, INC.—See EXEO Group Inc.; *Int'l*, pg. 2583
EXEO ENTERTAINMENT, INC.; *U.S. Public*, pg. 807
EXEO GROUP INC.; *Int'l*, pg. 2583
EXEO SANKO CORP.—See EXEO Group Inc.; *Int'l*, pg. 2583
EXEO TECH CORPORATION—See EXEO Group Inc.; *Int'l*, pg. 2583
EXERA MYANMAR LIMITED—See Asia Strategic Holdings Limited; *Int'l*, pg. 615
EXERGEN CORPORATION; *U.S. Private*, pg. 1448
EXERGY21 CO., LTD.; *Int'l*, pg. 2584
EXERGY FUEL CELLS S.R.L.—See Amasten Fastighets AB; *Int'l*, pg. 412
EXERION PRECISION TECHNOLOGY HOLDING B.V.; *Int'l*, pg. 2584
EXERION PRECISION TECHNOLOGY OLOMOUC, S.R.O.—See Exerion Precision Technology Holding B.V.; *Int'l*, pg. 2584
EXERION PRECISION TECHNOLOGY ULFT NL B.V.—See Exerion Precision Technology Holding B.V.; *Int'l*, pg. 2584
EXERTIS ARC TELECOM LIMITED—See DCC plc; *Int'l*, pg. 1990
EXERTIS CAPTECH AB—See DCC plc; *Int'l*, pg. 1990
EXERTIS FRANCE SAS—See DCC plc; *Int'l*, pg. 1990
EXERTIS HAMMER LIMITED—See DCC plc; *Int'l*, pg. 1990
EXERTIS IRELAND LIMITED—See DCC plc; *Int'l*, pg. 1990
EXERTIS SUPPLY CHAIN SERVICES LIMITED—See DCC plc; *Int'l*, pg. 1990
EXERTIS (UK) LIMITED—See DCC plc; *Int'l*, pg. 1990
EXERTIS (UK) LTD—See DCC plc; *Int'l*, pg. 1990
EXERTIS (UK) LTD.—See DCC plc; *Int'l*, pg. 1990
EXETARE PARTNERSHIP, L.L.P.—See Christensen Farms Midwest, LLC; *U.S. Private*, pg. 890
EXETER DEHYDRATOR INC.—See Sunshine Raisin Corporation; *U.S. Private*, pg. 3872
EXETER ENERGY LIMITED PARTNERSHIP—See CMS Energy Corporation; *U.S. Public*, pg. 518
EXETER FINANCE LLC—See Blackstone Inc.; *U.S. Public*, pg. 353
EXETER HEALTH RESOURCES, INC.—See Beth Israel Lahey Health Inc; *U.S. Private*, pg. 545
EXETER MEDICAL LIMITED—See Ramsay Health Care Limited; *Int'l*, pg. 6199
EXETER PRODUCE & STORAGE CO. LIMITED; *Int'l*, pg. 2584
EXETER TRUST COMPANY—See Callodine Acquisition Corporation; *U.S. Public*, pg. 424
EXEVO INDIA PRIVATE LTD.—See Moody's Corporation; *U.S. Public*, pg. 1467

EXIDE INDUSTRIES LIMITED

EXFIN AG—See DekaBank; *Int'l*, pg. 2005
EXFO AMERICA INC.—See EXFO Inc.; *Int'l*, pg. 2584
EXFO ASIA PACIFIC PTE LTD.—See EXFO Inc.; *Int'l*, pg. 2584
EXFO ASIA PACIFIC PTE. LTD.—See EXFO Inc.; *Int'l*, pg. 2584
EXFO ASIA PACIFIC PTE. LTD.—See EXFO Inc.; *Int'l*, pg. 2584
EXFO ELECTRO-OPTICAL ENGINEERING INDIA PRIVATE LTD.—See EXFO Inc.; *Int'l*, pg. 2584
EXFO EUROPE LTD.—See EXFO Inc.; *Int'l*, pg. 2584
EXFO FINLAND OY—See EXFO Inc.; *Int'l*, pg. 2584
EXFO INC.; *Int'l*, pg. 2584
EXFO INDIA—See EXFO Inc.; *Int'l*, pg. 2584
EXFO JAPAN—See EXFO Inc.; *Int'l*, pg. 2584
EXFO NAVTEL PRODUCT GROUP—See EXFO Inc.; *Int'l*, pg. 2584
EXFO SERVICE ASSURANCE INC.—See EXFO Inc.; *Int'l*, pg. 2584
EXFO TELECOM EQUIPMENT (SHENZHEN) CO. LTD.—See EXFO Inc.; *Int'l*, pg. 2584
EXGEN RESOURCES INC.; *Int'l*, pg. 2584
EXGEO CA—See CGG; *Int'l*, pg. 1432
EXG, INC.—See Viad Corp.; *U.S. Public*, pg. 2290
EX. GRADE CO., LTD.—See Nagase & Co., Ltd.; *Int'l*, pg. 5128
EXHALE ENTERPRISES III, INC.—See Hyatt Hotels Corporation; *U.S. Public*, pg. 1077
EXHALE ENTERPRISES II, LLC—See Hyatt Hotels Corporation; *U.S. Public*, pg. 1077
EXHALE ENTERPRISES IV, LLC—See Hyatt Hotels Corporation; *U.S. Public*, pg. 1077
EXHALE ENTERPRISES, LLC—See Hyatt Hotels Corporation; *U.S. Public*, pg. 1077
EXHALE ENTERPRISES VIII, INC.—See Hyatt Hotels Corporation; *U.S. Public*, pg. 1077
EXHALE ENTERPRISES V, LLC—See Hyatt Hotels Corporation; *U.S. Public*, pg. 1077
EXHALE ENTERPRISES XIV, LLC—See Hyatt Hotels Corporation; *U.S. Public*, pg. 1077
EXHALE ENTERPRISES XIX, LLC—See Hyatt Hotels Corporation; *U.S. Public*, pg. 1077
EXHALE ENTERPRISES XVIII, LLC—See Hyatt Hotels Corporation; *U.S. Public*, pg. 1077
EXHALE ENTERPRISES XVI, LLC—See Hyatt Hotels Corporation; *U.S. Public*, pg. 1077
EXHALE ENTERPRISES XXI, LLC—See Hyatt Hotels Corporation; *U.S. Public*, pg. 1077
EXHALE ENTERPRISES XXIV, LLC—See Hyatt Hotels Corporation; *U.S. Public*, pg. 1077
EXHALE ENTERPRISES XX, LLC—See Hyatt Hotels Corporation; *U.S. Public*, pg. 1077
EXHALE ENTERPRISES XXVIII, LLC—See Hyatt Hotels Corporation; *U.S. Public*, pg. 1077
EXHALE ENTERPRISES XXVI, LLC—See Hyatt Hotels Corporation; *U.S. Public*, pg. 1077
EXHALE ENTERPRISES XXXII, LLC—See Hyatt Hotels Corporation; *U.S. Public*, pg. 1077
EXHALE ENTERPRISES XXXI, LLC—See Hyatt Hotels Corporation; *U.S. Public*, pg. 1077
EXHAUSTO AB—See Aldes Aeraulique SAS; *Int'l*, pg. 304
EXHAUSTO A/S—See Aldes Aeraulique SAS; *Int'l*, pg. 304
EXHAUSTO GMBH—See Aldes Aeraulique SAS; *Int'l*, pg. 304
EXHEDRA SOLUTIONS, INC.; *U.S. Private*, pg. 1448
EXH GP LP LLC—See Archrock, Inc.; *U.S. Public*, pg. 186
EXHIBIT EDGE INC.—See Star Exhibits & Environments, Inc.; *U.S. Private*, pg. 3784
EXHIBITION CONSULTANTS LTD.—See Angus Montgomery Ltd.; *Int'l*, pg. 463
EXHIBITIONS AND TRADE FAIRS PTY LIMITED—See Freeman Decorating Co.; *U.S. Private*, pg. 1605
EXHIBITOR SOURCE BY SKYLINE; *U.S. Private*, pg. 1448
EXHIBITS INC PTE LTD—See Singapore Press Holdings Ltd.; *Int'l*, pg. 6942
EXHIBITS INC PTE LTD—See Temasek Holdings (Private) Limited; *Int'l*, pg. 7547
EXHIBIT SURVEYS, INC.—See Freeman Decorating Co.; *U.S. Private*, pg. 1605
EXHIBITS USA, INC.; *U.S. Private*, pg. 1448
EXHIBIT SYSTEMS, INC.; *U.S. Private*, pg. 1448
EXHIBIT WORKS INC.; *U.S. Private*, pg. 1448
EXHICON EVENTS MEDIA SOLUTIONS LTD.; *Int'l*, pg. 2584
EXH MLP LP LLC—See Archrock, Inc.; *U.S. Public*, pg. 186
EXICOM TELE-SYSTEMS LIMITED; *Int'l*, pg. 2584
EXICON CO., LTD.; *Int'l*, pg. 2584
EXICURE, INC.; *U.S. Public*, pg. 807
EXIDA.COM LLC; *U.S. Private*, pg. 1448
EXIDE HOLDING NETHERLANDS B.V.—See Exide Technologies, LLC; *U.S. Private*, pg. 1448
EXIDE INDUSTRIES LIMITED; *Int'l*, pg. 2584
EXIDE LIFE INSURANCE COMPANY LIMITED—See EXIDE INDUSTRIES LIMITED; *Int'l*, pg. 2585
EXIDE PAKISTAN LIMITED—See Vertiv Holdings Co; *U.S. Public*, pg. 2289

EXIDE SINGAPORE PTE LIMITED—See Exide Technologies, LLC; *U.S. Private*, pg. 1448
EXIDE SLOVAKIA S.R.O.—See Exide Technologies, LLC; *U.S. Private*, pg. 1448
EXIDE TECHNOLOGIES AB—See Exide Technologies, LLC; *U.S. Private*, pg. 1449
EXIDE TECHNOLOGIES AS—See Exide Technologies, LLC; *U.S. Private*, pg. 1449
EXIDE TECHNOLOGIES GMBH—See Exide Technologies, LLC; *U.S. Private*, pg. 1448
EXIDE TECHNOLOGIES, LLC; *U.S. Private*, pg. 1448
EXIDE TECHNOLOGIES OY—See Exide Technologies, LLC; *U.S. Private*, pg. 1449
EXIDE TECHNOLOGIES RECYCLING S.L.—See Exide Technologies, LLC; *U.S. Private*, pg. 1449
EXIDE TECHNOLOGIES SAS—See Exide Technologies, LLC; *U.S. Private*, pg. 1449
EXIDE TECHNOLOGIES (SHANGHAI) COMPANY LIMITED—See Exide Technologies, LLC; *U.S. Private*, pg. 1449
EXIDOR LIMITED—See ASSA ABLOY AB; *Int'l*, pg. 636
EXIGEN INC.; *U.S. Private*, pg. 1449
EXIGENT HOLDCO LLC—See Huron Capital Partners LLC; *U.S. Private*, pg. 2012
EXIGENT TECHNOLOGIES, LLC; *U.S. Private*, pg. 1449
EXIGER LLC; *U.S. Private*, pg. 1449
EXILE TECHNOLOGIES CORPORATION—See GEOSPACE TECHNOLOGIES CORPORATION; *U.S. Public*, pg. 934
EXILE TECHNOLOGIES LIMITED—See GEOSPACE TECHNOLOGIES CORPORATION; *U.S. Public*, pg. 934
EXILIGHT OY—See Lagercrantz Group AB; *Int'l*, pg. 4394
EXILLON ENERGY PLC; *Int'l*, pg. 2585
EXIM A.S.—See Hitay Investment Holdings A.S.; *Int'l*, pg. 3425
EXIMBANK KAZAKHSTAN JSC; *Int'l*, pg. 2585
EXIMBANK OF RUSSIA—See VEB.RF; *Int'l*, pg. 8143
EXIM EXCHANGE COMPANY (CANADA) LTD.—See Export Import Bank of Bangladesh Limited; *Int'l*, pg. 2590
EXIM EXCHANGE COMPANY (UK) LIMITED—See Export Import Bank of Bangladesh Limited; *Int'l*, pg. 2590
EXIM FINANCE (HONG KONG) LIMITED—See Export Import Bank of Bangladesh Limited; *Int'l*, pg. 2590
EXIM ISLAMI INVESTMENT LTD.—See Export Import Bank of Bangladesh Limited; *Int'l*, pg. 2590
EXIMO AGRO-MARKETING AG; *Int'l*, pg. 2585
EXIMO MEDICAL, LTD.—See AngioDynamics, Inc.; *U.S. Public*, pg. 137
EXIMO PROJECT SP. Z O.O.—See OPONEO.PL S.A.; *Int'l*, pg. 5600
EXINDA INC.—See GFI Software S.A.; *Int'l*, pg. 2957
EXINI DIAGNOSTICS AB—See Avista Capital Partners, L.P.; *U.S. Private*, pg. 408
EXIQON A/S—See QIAGEN N.V.; *Int'l*, pg. 6139
EXIR PHARMACEUTICAL COMPANY; *Int'l*, pg. 2585
EXISS ALUMINUM TRAILERS INC.; *U.S. Private*, pg. 1449
EXISS ALUMINUM TRAILERS, INC—See Corporate Partners LLC; *U.S. Private*, pg. 1055
EXITCERTIFIED CORP.—See Avnet, Inc.; *U.S. Public*, pg. 253
EXIT CERTIFIED LTD.—See Avnet, Inc.; *U.S. Public*, pg. 253
EXIT; *U.S. Private*, pg. 1449
EXIUM PARTNERS, LLC; *U.S. Private*, pg. 1449
EXKLUSIV KARTENVERLAG GMBH—See HAL Trust N.V.; *Int'l*, pg. 3224
EX-LABO CO., LTD.—See extreme Co., Ltd.; *Int'l*, pg. 2592
EXLAIR (NZ) LIMITED—See Atlas Copco AB; *Int'l*, pg. 682
EXLAR CORP.—See Curtiss-Wright Corporation; *U.S. Public*, pg. 612
EX-LAX, INC.—See Novartis AG; *Int'l*, pg. 5458
EXLER & COMPANY, INC.—See Horovitz, Rudoy & Roteman, LLC; *U.S. Private*, pg. 1984
EX LIBRIS AG—See The Federation of Migros Cooperatives; *Int'l*, pg. 7642
EX LIBRIS ASIA PTE LTD.—See Clarivate PLC; *Int'l*, pg. 1650
EX LIBRIS (AUSTRALIA) PTY LTD—See Clarivate PLC; *Int'l*, pg. 1649
EX LIBRIS ITALY S.R.L.—See Clarivate PLC; *Int'l*, pg. 1650
EX LIBRIS LTD.—See Clarivate PLC; *Int'l*, pg. 1649
EX LIBRIS (UK) LIMITED—See Clarivate PLC; *Int'l*, pg. 1649
EX LIBRIS (USA) INC.—See Clarivate PLC; *Int'l*, pg. 1649
EXLINE INC.; *U.S. Private*, pg. 1449
EXLITES HOLDINGS INTERNATIONAL, INC.; *U.S. Public*, pg. 807
EXLON EXTRUSION INC—See Odyssey Investment Partners, LLC; *U.S. Private*, pg. 2995
EXLSERVICE COLOMBIA, S.A.S.—See ExlService Holdings, Inc.; *U.S. Public*, pg. 807
EXLSERVICE.COM, INC.—See ExlService Holdings, Inc.; *U.S. Public*, pg. 807
EXLSERVICE.COM (INDIA) PRIVATE LIMITED—See ExlService Holdings, Inc.; *U.S. Public*, pg. 807

EXLSERVICE CZECH REPUBLIC S.R.O.—See ExlService Holdings, Inc.; *U.S. Public*, pg. 807
EXLSERVICE HOLDINGS, INC.; *U.S. Public*, pg. 807
EXLSERVICE PHILIPPINES, INC.—See ExlService Holdings, Inc.; *U.S. Public*, pg. 807
EXLSERVICE ROMANIA PRIVATE LIMITED S.R.L.—See ExlService Holdings, Inc.; *U.S. Public*, pg. 807
EXLSERVICE TECHNOLOGY SOLUTIONS, LLC—See ExlService Holdings, Inc.; *U.S. Public*, pg. 807
EXMAC AUTOMATION LIMITED—See L3Harris Technologies, Inc.; *U.S. Public*, pg. 1281
EXMAR ENERGY PARTNERS LP—See Exmar N.V.; *Int'l*, pg. 2585
EXMAR HONG KONG LTD.—See Exmar N.V.; *Int'l*, pg. 2585
EXMARK MANUFACTURING COMPANY INCORPORATED—See The Toro Company; *U.S. Public*, pg. 2135
EXMAR LUX SA—See Exmar N.V.; *Int'l*, pg. 2585
EXMAR MARINE N.V.—See Exmar N.V.; *Int'l*, pg. 2585
EXMAR N.V.; *Int'l*, pg. 2585
EXMAR OFFSHORE COMPANY—See Exmar N.V.; *Int'l*, pg. 2585
EXMAR OFFSHORE SERVICES SA—See Exmar N.V.; *Int'l*, pg. 2585
EXMAR SHIPMANAGEMENT INDIA, PVT. LTD.—See Exmar N.V.; *Int'l*, pg. 2585
EXMAR SHIPMANAGEMENT N.V.—See Exmar N.V.; *Int'l*, pg. 2585
EXMAR SHIPPING N.V.—See Exmar N.V.; *Int'l*, pg. 2585
EXMAR SHIPPING USA INC.—See Exmar N.V.; *Int'l*, pg. 2585
EXMAR SINGAPORE PTE. LTD.—See Exmar N.V.; *Int'l*, pg. 2585
EXMAR (UK) SHIPPING COMPANY LTD.—See Exmar N.V.; *Int'l*, pg. 2585
EXMAR YACHTING NV—See Exmar N.V.; *Int'l*, pg. 2585
EXMCEUTICALS INC.; *Int'l*, pg. 2585
EXM MANUFACTURING LTD.; *Int'l*, pg. 2585
EXMO, INC.—See Live Nation Entertainment, Inc.; *U.S. Public*, pg. 1328
EXMORE BENELUX BVBA—See Komax Holding AG; *Int'l*, pg. 4240
EXMOTION CO., LTD.; *Int'l*, pg. 2586
EXMOVERE HOLDINGS, INC.; *U.S. Private*, pg. 1449
EXNOS CO., LTD.—See Optex Group Co., Ltd.; *Int'l*, pg. 5601
EXOCOBIO INC.; *Int'l*, pg. 2586
EXODUS LIMITED COMPANY—See Lumax International Corp., Ltd.; *Int'l*, pg. 4577
EXODUS TRAVELS LIMITED—See TUI AG; *Int'l*, pg. 7964
EXODYNE INC.; *U.S. Private*, pg. 1449
EXO ENTERPRISES LIMITED—See Cafe de Coral Holdings Limited; *Int'l*, pg. 1250
EX OFFICIO, LLC—See Newell Brands Inc.; *U.S. Public*, pg. 1514
EXOIL LIMITED; *Int'l*, pg. 2586
EXO ITALIA, S.R.L.—See Crocs, Inc.; *U.S. Public*, pg. 595
EXOLVO GMBH—See Munchener Ruckversicherungs AG; *Int'l*, pg. 5088
EXOMA ENERGY LIMITED; *Int'l*, pg. 2586
EXONE AMERICAS LLC—See Desktop Metal, Inc.; *U.S. Public*, pg. 656
THE EXONE COMPANY—See Desktop Metal, Inc.; *U.S. Public*, pg. 656
EXONE GMBH—See Desktop Metal, Inc.; *U.S. Public*, pg. 656
EXONE ITALY S.R.L—See Desktop Metal, Inc.; *U.S. Public*, pg. 656
EXONE KK—See Desktop Metal, Inc.; *U.S. Public*, pg. 656
EXONE PROPERTY GMBH—See Desktop Metal, Inc.; *U.S. Public*, pg. 656
EXONE SWEDEN AB—See Desktop Metal, Inc.; *U.S. Public*, pg. 656
EXONY INC.—See eGain Corporation; *U.S. Public*, pg. 721
EXONY LTD.—See eGain Corporation; *U.S. Public*, pg. 721
EXOPHARM LTD.; *Int'l*, pg. 2586
EXOR CORPORATION—See Bentley Systems, Inc.; *U.S. Public*, pg. 297
EXOR N.V.—See Giovanni Agnelli B.V.; *Int'l*, pg. 2978
EXOSOME DIAGNOSTICS, INC.—See Bio-Techne Corporation; *U.S. Public*, pg. 334
EXOSOME SCIENCES, INC.—See Aethlon Medical, Inc.; *U.S. Public*, pg. 53
EXOSTAR LLC—See Arlington Capital Partners LLC; *U.S. Private*, pg. 327
EXOSTRATEGIES, INC.—See Ensco Inc.; *U.S. Private*, pg. 1402
EXOTIC AUTOMATION & SUPPLY, INC.; *U.S. Private*, pg. 1449
EXOTIC FOOD PUBLIC COMPANY LIMITED; *Int'l*, pg. 2586
EXOTIC METALS FORMING COMPANY LLC.; *U.S. Private*, pg. 1449
EXOTIFLORS LIMITED—See ENL Limited; *Int'l*, pg. 2441
EXO U INC.; *Int'l*, pg. 2586

EXOVA GROUP LIMITED—See Temasek Holdings (Private) Limited; *Int'l*, pg. 7547
EXOVA INC.—See Temasek Holdings (Private) Limited; *Int'l*, pg. 7547
EXPACARE LIMITED—See Marsh & McLennan Companies, Inc.; *U.S. Public*, pg. 1376
EXPANCEL INC.—See Akzo Nobel N.V.; *Int'l*, pg. 274
EXPANDA IMMOBILIEN LEASING GESELLSCHAFT M.B.H.—See UniCredit S.p.A.; *Int'l*, pg. 8037
EXPAND BV—See Randstad N.V.; *Int'l*, pg. 6201
EXPANDED LIMITED—See Laing O'Rourke Plc; *Int'l*, pg. 4396
THE EXPANDED METAL COMPANY LIMITED—See Gibraltar Industries, Inc.; *U.S. Public*, pg. 936
EXPANDED PILING LIMITED—See Laing O'Rourke Plc; *Int'l*, pg. 4396
EXPAND ENERGY CORPORATION; *U.S. Public*, pg. 808
EXPANDER ADVISORS SP. Z O.O.—See Aviva plc; *Int'l*, pg. 746
EXPAND FAST HOLDINGS (SINGAPORE) PTE. LIMITED—See Essel Corporate Resources Pvt. Ltd.; *Int'l*, pg. 2510
EXPAND, LLC—See DYN365, Inc.; *U.S. Private*, pg. 1297
EXPANKO, INC.—See RPM International Inc.; *U.S. Public*, pg. 1818
EXPANSCIENCE BELGIUM—See Laboratoires Expanscience; *Int'l*, pg. 4390
EXPANSCIENCE BRAZIL—See Laboratoires Expanscience; *Int'l*, pg. 4390
EXPANSCIENCE FRANCE—See Laboratoires Expanscience; *Int'l*, pg. 4390
EXPANSCIENCE ITALY—See Laboratoires Expanscience; *Int'l*, pg. 4390
EXPANSCIENCE MEXICO—See Laboratoires Expanscience; *Int'l*, pg. 4390
EXPANSCIENCE PORTUGAL—See Laboratoires Expanscience; *Int'l*, pg. 4390
EXPANSCIENCE SPAIN—See Laboratoires Expanscience; *Int'l*, pg. 4390
EXPANSCIENCE SWITZERLAND—See Laboratoires Expanscience; *Int'l*, pg. 4390
EXPANSCIENCE USA—See Laboratoires Expanscience; *Int'l*, pg. 4390
EXPANSIA S.A.S.—See Eurazeo SE; *Int'l*, pg. 2530
EXPANSION CAPITAL GROUP, LLC; *U.S. Private*, pg. 1449
EXPANSION STRATEGIES INC.; *U.S. Private*, pg. 1449
EXPATICORE SERVICES LLC—See Clune Technology Group; *Int'l*, pg. 1664
EXP AUSTRALIA PTY. LTD.—See eXp World Holdings, Inc.; *U.S. Public*, pg. 808
EXPECT A STAR SERVICES PTY LTD—See PeopleIn Limited; *Int'l*, pg. 5794
EXPECT DISTRIBUTION; *Int'l*, pg. 2586
EXPECTING PRODUCTIONS, LLC—See Stagwell, Inc.; *U.S. Public*, pg. 1926
EXPECTRA GESTION—See Randstad N.V.; *Int'l*, pg. 6202
EXPECTRA S.A.S.—See Randstad N.V.; *Int'l*, pg. 6201
EXPECTRA TECHNOLOGY S.A.—See Randstad N.V.; *Int'l*, pg. 6202
EXPEDIA FRANCE S.A.S.—See Expedia Group, Inc.; *U.S. Public*, pg. 809
EXPEDIA GROUP, INC.; *U.S. Public*, pg. 809
EXPEDIA LODGING PARTNER SERVICES SARL—See Expedia Group, Inc.; *U.S. Public*, pg. 809
EXPEDIA.NL B.V.—See Expedia Group, Inc.; *U.S. Public*, pg. 809
EXPEDIA ONLINE TRAVEL SERVICES INDIA PRIVATE LIMITED—See Expedia Group, Inc.; *U.S. Public*, pg. 809
EXPEDIA PARTNER SERVICES GROUP SARL—See Expedia Group, Inc.; *U.S. Public*, pg. 809
EXPEDIA SPAIN, S.L.—See Expedia Group, Inc.; *U.S. Public*, pg. 809
EXPEDIA SWEDEN AB—See Expedia Group, Inc.; *U.S. Public*, pg. 809
EXPEDIA US, INC.—See Expedia Group, Inc.; *U.S. Public*, pg. 809
EXPEDIEN, INC.; *U.S. Private*, pg. 1449
EXPEDIENT RESOURCES SDN BHD—See IJM Corporation Berhad; *Int'l*, pg. 3608
EXPEDIT AB—See Wanzl Metallwarenfabrik GmbH; *Int'l*, pg. 8343
EXPEDIT A/S—See Wanzl Metallwarenfabrik GmbH; *Int'l*, pg. 8343
EXPEDITED FREIGHT SYSTEMS, LLC—See Roadrunner Transportation Systems, Inc.; *U.S. Public*, pg. 1802
EXPEDITED LOGISTICS & FREIGHT SERVICES, LTD.—See Janel Corporation; *U.S. Public*, pg. 1187
EXPEDITED SOLUTIONS, INC.—See ArcBest Corporation; *U.S. Public*, pg. 180
EXPEDITE HEADHUNTERS—See Randstad N.V.; *Int'l*, pg. 6201
THE EXPEDITER, LLC—See Brookfield Corporation; *Int'l*, pg. 1176
EXPEDIT FINLAND OY—See Wanzl Metallwarenfabrik GmbH; *Int'l*, pg. 8343
EXPEDITION CAPITAL PARTNERS LLC; *U.S. Private*, pg. 1449

COMPANY NAME INDEX

EXPEDIT NORGE A/S—See Wanzl Metallwarenfabrik GmbH; *Int'l*, pg. 8343
EXPEDITORS (BANGLADESH), LTD.—See Expeditors International of Washington, Inc.; *U.S. Public*, pg. 810
EXPEDITORS CAMBODIA LTD.—See Expeditors International of Washington, Inc.; *U.S. Public*, pg. 810
EXPEDITORS CANADA, INC.—See Expeditors International of Washington, Inc.; *U.S. Public*, pg. 810
EXPEDITORS CARGO INSURANCE BROKERS B.V.—See Expeditors International of Washington, Inc.; *U.S. Public*, pg. 810
EXPEDITORS CHILE TRANSPORTES INTERNACIONALES LIMITADA—See Expeditors International of Washington, Inc.; *U.S. Public*, pg. 810
EXPEDITORS DE COLOMBIA LTDA.—See Expeditors International of Washington, Inc.; *U.S. Public*, pg. 812
EXPEDITORS DENMARK APS—See Expeditors International of Washington, Inc.; *U.S. Public*, pg. 810
EXPEDITORS DOMINICANA SAS—See Expeditors International of Washington, Inc.; *U.S. Public*, pg. 810
EXPEDITORS EGYPT S.A.E.—See Expeditors International of Washington, Inc.; *U.S. Public*, pg. 810
EXPEDITORS FINLAND OY—See Expeditors International of Washington, Inc.; *U.S. Public*, pg. 810
EXPEDITORS GUATEMALA S.A.—See Expeditors International of Washington, Inc.; *U.S. Public*, pg. 810
EXPEDITORS HONG KONG LIMITED—See Expeditors International of Washington, Inc.; *U.S. Public*, pg. 810
EXPEDITORS INTERNATIONAL BAHRAIN (SPC)—See Expeditors International of Washington, Inc.; *U.S. Public*, pg. 811
EXPEDITORS INTERNATIONAL B.V.—See Expeditors International of Washington, Inc.; *U.S. Public*, pg. 811
EXPEDITORS INTERNATIONAL CARGO CO. LTD.—See Expeditors International of Washington, Inc.; *U.S. Public*, pg. 811
EXPEDITORS INTERNATIONAL CR S.R.O.—See Expeditors International of Washington, Inc.; *U.S. Public*, pg. 811
EXPEDITORS INTERNATIONAL DE MEXICO, S.A. DE C.V.—See Expeditors International of Washington, Inc.; *U.S. Public*, pg. 811
EXPEDITORS INTERNATIONAL DE URUGUAY S.A.—See Expeditors International of Washington, Inc.; *U.S. Public*, pg. 811
EXPEDITORS INTERNATIONAL DO BRASIL LTDA.—See Expeditors International of Washington, Inc.; *U.S. Public*, pg. 811
EXPEDITORS INTERNATIONAL E.I. (SWITZERLAND) SAGL—See Expeditors International of Washington, Inc.; *U.S. Public*, pg. 811
EXPEDITORS INTERNATIONAL ESPANA, S.A.—See Expeditors International of Washington, Inc.; *U.S. Public*, pg. 811
EXPEDITORS INTERNATIONAL FORWARDING AND CLEARING (ABU DHABI) LLC—See Expeditors International of Washington, Inc.; *U.S. Public*, pg. 811
EXPEDITORS INTERNATIONAL FORWARDING AND CLEARING, LLC—See Expeditors International of Washington, Inc.; *U.S. Public*, pg. 811
EXPEDITORS INTERNATIONAL FRANCE, SAS—See Expeditors International of Washington, Inc.; *U.S. Public*, pg. 811
EXPEDITORS INTERNATIONAL GMBH—See Expeditors International of Washington, Inc.; *U.S. Public*, pg. 811
EXPEDITORS INTERNATIONAL HELLAS A.E.—See Expeditors International of Washington, Inc.; *U.S. Public*, pg. 811
EXPEDITORS INTERNATIONAL (HELLAS) S.A.—See Expeditors International of Washington, Inc.; *U.S. Public*, pg. 810
EXPEDITORS INTERNATIONAL HUNGARY KFT.—See Expeditors International of Washington, Inc.; *U.S. Public*, pg. 811
EXPEDITORS INTERNATIONAL (INDIA) PVT. LTD.—See Expeditors International of Washington, Inc.; *U.S. Public*, pg. 810
EXPEDITORS INTERNATIONAL ITALIA S.R.L.—See Expeditors International of Washington, Inc.; *U.S. Public*, pg. 811
EXPEDITORS INTERNATIONAL-JORDAN—See Expeditors International of Washington, Inc.; *U.S. Public*, pg. 811
EXPEDITORS INTERNATIONAL (KUWAIT) W.L.L.—See Expeditors International of Washington, Inc.; *U.S. Public*, pg. 810
EXPEDITORS INTERNATIONAL - LEBANON (S.A.L.)—See Expeditors International of Washington, Inc.; *U.S. Public*, pg. 811
EXPEDITORS INTERNATIONAL NORWAY AS—See Expeditors International of Washington, Inc.; *U.S. Public*, pg. 811
EXPEDITORS INTERNATIONAL N.V.—See Expeditors International of Washington, Inc.; *U.S. Public*, pg. 811
EXPEDITORS INTERNATIONAL (NZ) LTD.—See Expeditors International of Washington, Inc.; *U.S. Public*, pg. 810
EXPEDITORS INTERNATIONAL OCEAN, INC.—See Expeditors International of Washington, Inc.; *U.S. Public*, pg. 811
EXPEDITORS INTERNATIONAL OF WASHINGTON, INC.; *U.S. Public*, pg. 810
EXPEDITORS INTERNATIONAL PTY. LIMITED—See Expeditors International of Washington, Inc.; *U.S. Public*, pg. 811
EXPEDITORS INTERNATIONAL (PUERTO RICO) INC.—See Expeditors International of Washington, Inc.; *U.S. Public*, pg. 811
EXPEDITORS INTERNATIONAL ROMANIA S.R.L.—See Expeditors International of Washington, Inc.; *U.S. Public*, pg. 811
EXPEDITORS INTERNATIONAL SA (PROPRIETARY) LIMITED—See Expeditors International of Washington, Inc.; *U.S. Public*, pg. 811
EXPEDITORS INTERNATIONAL SVERIGE AB—See Expeditors International of Washington, Inc.; *U.S. Public*, pg. 811
EXPEDITORS INTERNATIONAL (SWITZERLAND) SAGL—See Expeditors International of Washington, Inc.; *U.S. Public*, pg. 811
EXPEDITORS INTERNATIONAL TASIMACILIK VE TICARET AS—See Expeditors International of Washington, Inc.; *U.S. Public*, pg. 811
EXPEDITORS INTERNATIONAL TRADING (SHANGHAI) CO., LTD—See Expeditors International of Washington, Inc.; *U.S. Public*, pg. 811
EXPEDITORS INTERNATIONAL (UK) LTD.—See Expeditors International of Washington, Inc.; *U.S. Public*, pg. 811
EXPEDITORS IRELAND LIMITED—See Expeditors International of Washington, Inc.; *U.S. Public*, pg. 811
EXPEDITORS JAPAN KK—See Expeditors International of Washington, Inc.; *U.S. Public*, pg. 811
EXPEDITORS KOREA LTD.—See Expeditors International of Washington, Inc.; *U.S. Public*, pg. 811
EXPEDITORS LITHUANIA, UAB—See Expeditors International of Washington, Inc.; *U.S. Public*, pg. 811
EXPEDITORS LLC—See Expeditors International of Washington, Inc.; *U.S. Public*, pg. 811
EXPEDITORS (MALAYSIA) SDN. BHD.—See Expeditors International of Washington, Inc.; *U.S. Public*, pg. 810
EXPEDITORS MAR Y TIERRA S.A.—See Expeditors International of Washington, Inc.; *U.S. Public*, pg. 811
EXPEDITORS PANAMA LOGISTICS SERVICES, INC.—See Expeditors International of Washington, Inc.; *U.S. Public*, pg. 811
EXPEDITORS PERU S.A.C.—See Expeditors International of Washington, Inc.; *U.S. Public*, pg. 811
EXPEDITORS PHILIPPINES, INC.—See Expeditors International of Washington, Inc.; *U.S. Public*, pg. 811
EXPEDITORS POLSKA SP. Z O. O.—See Expeditors International of Washington, Inc.; *U.S. Public*, pg. 811
EXPEDITORS (PORTUGAL) TRANSITARIOS INTERNACIONAIS LDA.—See Expeditors International of Washington, Inc.; *U.S. Public*, pg. 811
EXPEDITORS QATAR LLC—See Expeditors International of Washington, Inc.; *U.S. Public*, pg. 811
EXPEDITORS (SINGAPORE) PRIVATE LIMITED—See Expeditors International of Washington, Inc.; *U.S. Public*, pg. 810
EXPEDITORS SPEDITIONSGES.M.B.H.—See Expeditors International of Washington, Inc.; *U.S. Public*, pg. 811
EXPEDITORS SPEDITIONS GMBH—See Expeditors International of Washington, Inc.; *U.S. Public*, pg. 811
EXPEDITORS TAIWAN CO., LTD.—See Expeditors International of Washington, Inc.; *U.S. Public*, pg. 812
EXPEDITORS (THAILAND) LTD.—See Expeditors International of Washington, Inc.; *U.S. Public*, pg. 810
EXPEDITORS VIETNAM COMPANY LIMITED—See Expeditors International of Washington, Inc.; *U.S. Public*, pg. 812
EXPENSEWATCH, INC.—See Nexonia, Inc.; *Int'l*, pg. 5245
EXPENSE WIRE LLC—See Paychex, Inc.; *U.S. Public*, pg. 1655
EXPENSIFY, INC.; *U.S. Public*, pg. 812
EXPERCASH GMBH—See Mastercard Incorporated; *U.S. Public*, pg. 1394
EXPERIAN ASIA-PACIFIC HOLDINGS PTE. LTD.—See Experian plc; *Int'l*, pg. 2586
EXPERIAN A/S—See Experian plc; *Int'l*, pg. 2587
EXPERIAN AS—See Experian plc; *Int'l*, pg. 2586
EXPERIAN AUSTRALIA CREDIT SERVICES PTY LTD—See Experian plc; *Int'l*, pg. 2586
EXPERIAN AUSTRALIA PTY. LTD.—See Experian plc; *Int'l*, pg. 2587
EXPERIAN AUSTRALIA PTY. LTD. - SYDNEY OFFICE—See Experian plc; *Int'l*, pg. 2587
EXPERIAN BACKGROUND DATA, INC.—See Experian plc; *Int'l*, pg. 2586
EXPERIAN BILGI HIZMETLERI LIMITED SIRKETI—See Experian plc; *Int'l*, pg. 2586
EXPERIAN BULGARIA EAD—See Experian plc; *Int'l*, pg. 2586
EXPERIAN BUREAU DE CREDITO, S.A.—See Experian plc; *Int'l*, pg. 2586

EXPERIMENTAL AIRCRAFT ASSOCIATION

EXPERIAN CREDIT INFORMATION COMPANY OF INDIA PRIVATE LIMITED—See Experian plc; *Int'l*, pg. 2586
EXPERIAN CREDIT SERVICE (BEIJING) COMPANY LIMITED—See Experian plc; *Int'l*, pg. 2586
EXPERIAN DATA QUALITY UK—See Experian plc; *Int'l*, pg. 2586
EXPERIAN DATA SERVICES S.R.L.—See Experian plc; *Int'l*, pg. 2587
EXPERIAN DECISION ANALYTICS—See Experian plc; *Int'l*, pg. 2586
EXPERIAN DECISION ANALYTICS—See Experian plc; *Int'l*, pg. 2586
EXPERIAN DEUTSCHLAND HOLDING GMBH—See Experian plc; *Int'l*, pg. 2586
EXPERIAN ESPANA S.L.U.—See Experian plc; *Int'l*, pg. 2586
EXPERIAN FINANCE HOLDINGS LIMITED—See Experian plc; *Int'l*, pg. 2587
EXPERIAN FRANCE—See Experian plc; *Int'l*, pg. 2587
EXPERIAN GMBH—See Experian plc; *Int'l*, pg. 2587
EXPERIAN HEALTHCARE—See Experian plc; *Int'l*, pg. 2587
EXPERIAN HOLDINGS IRELAND LIMITED—See Experian plc; *Int'l*, pg. 2587
EXPERIAN HONG KONG LTD.—See Experian plc; *Int'l*, pg. 2587
EXPERIAN INFORMATION SERVICES (MALAYSIA) SDN. BHD.—See Experian plc; *Int'l*, pg. 2587
EXPERIAN INFORMATION SOLUTIONS, INC. - CHICAGO—See Experian plc; *Int'l*, pg. 2587
EXPERIAN INFORMATION SOLUTIONS, INC.—See Experian plc; *Int'l*, pg. 2587
EXPERIAN INVESTMENT HOLDINGS LIMITED—See Experian plc; *Int'l*, pg. 2587
EXPERIAN IRELAND LTD.—See Experian plc; *Int'l*, pg. 2587
EXPERIAN ITALIA S.P.A.—See Experian plc; *Int'l*, pg. 2587
EXPERIAN JAPAN CO., LTD.—See Experian plc; *Int'l*, pg. 2587
EXPERIAN LTD.—See Experian plc; *Int'l*, pg. 2587
EXPERIAN (MALAYSIA) SDN. BHD.—See Experian plc; *Int'l*, pg. 2586
EXPERIAN MICRO ANALYTICS SAM—See Experian plc; *Int'l*, pg. 2587
EXPERIAN NEDERLAND B.V.—See Experian plc; *Int'l*, pg. 2587
EXPERIAN NEW ZEALAND LIMITED—See Experian plc; *Int'l*, pg. 2587
EXPERIAN OSTERREICH GMBH—See Experian plc; *Int'l*, pg. 2587
EXPERIAN PERU S.A.C—See Experian plc; *Int'l*, pg. 2587
EXPERIAN PLC; *Int'l*, pg. 2586
EXPERIAN POLSKA SPOLKA Z OGRANICZONA ODPOWIEDZIALNOSCIA—See Experian plc; *Int'l*, pg. 2587
EXPERIAN-SCOREX S.R.L. ITALIA—See Experian plc; *Int'l*, pg. 2587
EXPERIAN SCOREX US, LLC—See Experian plc; *Int'l*, pg. 2587
EXPERIAN SERVICES CHILE S.A.—See Experian plc; *Int'l*, pg. 2587
EXPERIAN SERVICES COSTA RICA, S.A.—See Experian plc; *Int'l*, pg. 2587
EXPERIAN SERVICES INDIA PRIVATE LIMITED—See Experian plc; *Int'l*, pg. 2588
EXPERIAN SIMMONS—See Symphony Technology Group, LLC; *U.S. Private*, pg. 3900
EXPERIAN SINGAPORE PTE. LTD.—See Experian plc; *Int'l*, pg. 2587
EXPERIAN SOUTH AFRICA—See Experian plc; *Int'l*, pg. 2587
EXPERIAN STRATEGIC SOLUTIONS SA—See Experian plc; *Int'l*, pg. 2588
EXPERIAN TALLYMAN—See Experian plc; *Int'l*, pg. 2587
EXPERIAN TECNOLOGIA BRASIL LTDA—See Experian plc; *Int'l*, pg. 2588
EXPERIAN (THAILAND) CO., LTD.—See Experian plc; *Int'l*, pg. 2586
EXPERIENCE CO LIMITED; *Int'l*, pg. 2588
EXPERIENCED OFFICE SOLUTIONS LLC—See Alpine Investors; *U.S. Private*, pg. 201
EXPERIENCE WORKS, INC.; *U.S. Private*, pg. 1449
EXPERIEN INSURANCE SERVICES PTY. LTD.—See AUB Group Limited; *Int'l*, pg. 698
EXPERIENT—See The Riverside Company; *U.S. Private*, pg. 4108
EXPERIMENTAL AIRCRAFT ASSOCIATION; *U.S. Private*, pg. 1449
EXPERI-METAL INC.—See HMK Enterprises, Inc.; *U.S. Private*, pg. 1955
EXPERION BIOTECHNOLOGIES INC.—See The Valens Company Inc.; *Int'l*, pg. 7698
EXPERIOR GROUP LTD.—See QualiTest Group; *U.S. Private*, pg. 3317
EXPERIOR S.L.—See NEUCA S.A.; *Int'l*, pg. 5218
EXPERIS AB—See ManpowerGroup Inc.; *U.S. Public*, pg. 1357

EXPERIS AG—See ManpowerGroup Inc.; *U.S. Public*, pg. 1357
EXPERIS AS—See ManpowerGroup Inc.; *U.S. Public*, pg. 1357
EXPERIS A/S—See ManpowerGroup Inc.; *U.S. Public*, pg. 1357
EXPERIS BELGIUM SA—See ManpowerGroup Inc.; *U.S. Public*, pg. 1357
EXPERIS CIBER B.V.—See ManpowerGroup Inc.; *U.S. Public*, pg. 1357
EXPERIS CYBER LTD.—See ManpowerGroup Inc.; *U.S. Public*, pg. 1357
EXPERIS EXECUTIVE CO. LTD.—See ManpowerGroup Inc.; *U.S. Public*, pg. 1357
EXPERIS EXECUTIVE FRANCE SAS—See ManpowerGroup Inc.; *U.S. Public*, pg. 1358
EXPERIS EXECUTIVE FRANCE—See ManpowerGroup Inc.; *U.S. Public*, pg. 1358
EXPERIS EXECUTIVE LYON SAS—See ManpowerGroup Inc.; *U.S. Public*, pg. 1358
EXPERIS GMBH—See ManpowerGroup Inc.; *U.S. Public*, pg. 1358
EXPERIS GMBH—See ManpowerGroup Inc.; *U.S. Public*, pg. 1358
EXPERIS IT PRIVATE LIMITED—See ManpowerGroup Inc.; *U.S. Public*, pg. 1358
EXPERIS LIMITED—See ManpowerGroup Inc.; *U.S. Public*, pg. 1358
EXPERIS LIMITED—See ManpowerGroup Inc.; *U.S. Public*, pg. 1358
EXPERIS MANPOWERGROUP, S.L.—See ManpowerGroup Inc.; *U.S. Public*, pg. 1358
EXPERIS (M) SDN BHD—See ManpowerGroup Inc.; *U.S. Public*, pg. 1357
EXPERIS NEDERLAND B.V.—See ManpowerGroup Inc.; *U.S. Public*, pg. 1358
EXPERIS SOFTWARE—See ManpowerGroup Inc.; *U.S. Public*, pg. 1358
EXPERIS S.R.L.—See ManpowerGroup Inc.; *U.S. Public*, pg. 1358
EXPERIS TECHNOLOGY FUTURES CO. LTD.—See ManpowerGroup Inc.; *U.S. Public*, pg. 1358
EXPERITEC INC.; *U.S. Private*, pg. 1450
EXPERITY, INC.—See Warburg Pincus LLC; *U.S. Private*, pg. 4438
EXPERLOGIX INC.—See Featheringill Capital, LLC; *U.S. Private*, pg. 1486
EXPERTA ART S.A.—See Gregorio, Numo y Noel Werthein S.A.; *Int'l*, pg. 3078
EXPERT.AI S.P.A.; *Int'l*, pg. 2588
EXPERT ALLIANCE SYSTEMS & CONSULTANCY (HK) COMPANY LIMITED—See Qisda Corporation; *Int'l*, pg. 6146
EXPERT COMPUTER INTERNATIONAL; *U.S. Private*, pg. 1450
EXPERT CONSTRUCTION INC.; *U.S. Private*, pg. 1450
EXPERTEAM S.A./N.V.—See DXC Technology Company; *U.S. Public*, pg. 695
EXPERT & FINANCE S.A.—See Assicurazioni Generali S.p.A.; *Int'l*, pg. 645
EXPERTICITY, INC.; *U.S. Private*, pg. 1450
EXPERT INSULATION OF MINNESOTA, LLC—See Installed Building Products, Inc.; *U.S. Public*, pg. 1132
EXPERT LOGISTICS LTD.—See AO World PLC; *Int'l*, pg. 487
EXPERT OFFICE CO., LTD.—See Tokyo Tatemono Co. Ltd.; *Int'l*, pg. 7796
EXPERTOX INC—See Cytogen Co., Ltd; *Int'l*, pg. 1897
EXPERT PEST CONTROL, INC.—See Rollins, Inc.; *U.S. Public*, pg. 1810
EXPERT SEMICONDUCTOR TECH; *U.S. Private*, pg. 1450
THE EXPERTS, INC.; *U.S. Private*, pg. 4027
EXPERT SYSTEMS HOLDINGS LIMITED; *Int'l*, pg. 2588
EXPERT SYSTEMS (MACAU) LIMITED—See Expert Systems Holdings Limited; *Int'l*, pg. 2588
EXPERT SYSTEM USA INC.—See Expert.ai S.p.A.; *Int'l*, pg. 2588
EXPERT WIRELESS SOLUTIONS, INC.; *U.S. Private*, pg. 1450
EXPERT WIRELESS SOLUTIONS, INC.—See eXpert Wireless Solutions, Inc.; *U.S. Private*, pg. 1450
EXP FEDERAL INC.—See exp Global Inc.; *Int'l*, pg. 2586
EXP GLOBAL INC.; *Int'l*, pg. 2586
EXP GLOBAL INDIA—See eXp World Holdings, Inc.; *U.S. Public*, pg. 808
EXPICIENT INC.—See Publicis Groupe S.A.; *Int'l*, pg. 6099
EXPI-DOOR SYSTEMS INC.—See Bay Industries Inc.; *U.S. Private*, pg. 493
EXPION360 INC.; *U.S. Public*, pg. 812
EXPLAY, INC.—See Gree Inc.; *Int'l*, pg. 3069
EXPLEO ENGINEERING UK LTD—See Assystem S.A.; *Int'l*, pg. 651
EXPLEO GERMANY GMBH - MUNICH—See Assystem S.A.; *Int'l*, pg. 650
EXPLEO GERMANY HOLDING GMBH—See Assystem S.A.; *Int'l*, pg. 650

EXPLEO GROUP LIMITED—See Assystem S.A.; *Int'l*, pg. 650
EXPLEO NETHERLANDS BV—See Assystem S.A.; *Int'l*, pg. 650
EXPLEO NORDIC AB—See Assystem S.A.; *Int'l*, pg. 650
EXPLEO SOLUTIONS LIMITED—See Assystem S.A.; *Int'l*, pg. 650
EXPLEO TECHNOLOGY IRELAND LIMITED—See Assystem S.A.; *Int'l*, pg. 650
EXPLICIT FINANCE LIMITED; *Int'l*, pg. 2588
EXPL. MIJ. GRAND HOTEL KRASNAPOLSKY, B.V.—See Minor International PCL; *Int'l*, pg. 4911
EXPL. MIJ. HOTEL DOELEN, B.V.—See Minor International PCL; *Int'l*, pg. 4911
EXPLOITATIEMAATSCHAPPIJ INTRAPROGRES B.V.—See China International Marine Containers (Group) Co., Ltd.; *Int'l*, pg. 1511
EXPLOITATIEMIJ. TROPENHOTEL, B.V.—See Minor International PCL; *Int'l*, pg. 4911
EXPLOITS DISCOVERY CORP.; *Int'l*, pg. 2588
EXPLORA BIOLABS, INC.—See Charles River Laboratories International, Inc.; *U.S. Public*, pg. 480
EXPLORACIONES MINERAS S.A.—See Sociedad Quimica y Minera de Chile S.A.; *Int'l*, pg. 7032
EXPLORANCE, INC.; *Int'l*, pg. 2588
EXPLORATION & DEVELOPMENT RESEARCH INSTITUTE—See CPC Corporation; *Int'l*, pg. 1823
EXPLORATION DRILLING CORPORATION—See TVI Pacific Inc.; *Int'l*, pg. 7988
EXPLORATION INSURANCE GROUP, LLC—See Galiot Insurance Services, Inc.; *U.S. Private*, pg. 1638
EXPLORATION INVESTMENT RESOURCES II AS—See CGG; *Int'l*, pg. 1431
EXPLORATION & PRODUCTION BUSINESS DIVISION—See CPC Corporation; *Int'l*, pg. 1823
EXPLORATION SURVEYS, INC.—See Wilks Brothers LLC; *U.S. Private*, pg. 4521
EXPLORATION VESSEL RESOURCES AS—See CGG; *Int'l*, pg. 1431
EXPLORE COMMUNICATIONS; *U.S. Private*, pg. 1450
EXPLORE CONSULTING; *U.S. Private*, pg. 1450
EXPLORE INFORMATION SERVICES, LLC—See Vista Equity Partners, LLC; *U.S. Private*, pg. 4400
EXPLORE LIVING PLC—See Laing O'Rourke Plc; *Int'l*, pg. 4396
EXPLORER INC.—See PALTEK CORPORATION; *Int'l*, pg. 5710
EXPLORER PIPELINE COMPANY; *U.S. Private*, pg. 1450
EXPLORER RV INSURANCE AGENCY, INC.—See American Financial Group, Inc.; *U.S. Public*, pg. 103
EXPLORER S.R.L.—See Mohawk Industries, Inc.; *U.S. Public*, pg. 1457
EXPLORER VAN COMPANY; *U.S. Private*, pg. 1450
EXPLORE WORLDWIDE LIMITED—See Cox & Kings Limited; *Int'l*, pg. 1822
EXPLOREX RESOURCES INC.; *Int'l*, pg. 2588
EXPLORICA CANADA INC.—See Eurazeo SE; *Int'l*, pg. 2530
EXPLORICA, INC.—See Eurazeo SE; *Int'l*, pg. 2529
EXPLORING.COM, INC.; *U.S. Private*, pg. 1450
EXPLORNATION ENERGY, INC.; *U.S. Private*, pg. 1450
EXPLORNATION MANAGEMENT LLC—See ExplorNation Energy, Inc.; *U.S. Private*, pg. 1450
EXPLOSIVE CO., LTD.; *Int'l*, pg. 2588
EXPLOSIVOS DE MEXICO S.A. DE C.V.—See Orica Limited; *Int'l*, pg. 5619
EXPLOSIVOS MEXICANOS S.A. DE C.V.—See Orica Limited; *Int'l*, pg. 5619
EXPLOTACION COMERCIAL DE INTERCAMBIADORES, S.A.—See ACS, Actividades de Construccion y Servicios, S.A.; *Int'l*, pg. 112
EXPLOTACIONES HOTELERAS CONDOR, S.L.—See Minor International PCL; *Int'l*, pg. 4911
EXPLOTACION PESQUERA DE LA PATAGONIA S.A.—See Pesquera Veraz S.A.; *Int'l*, pg. 5823
EXPOBANK CZ A.S.—See Expobank LLC; *Int'l*, pg. 2589
EXPOBANK LLC; *Int'l*, pg. 2589
EXPOBOIS—See Compagnie de Saint-Gobain SA; *Int'l*, pg. 1723
EXPO BUSINESS PARK S.R.L.—See Immofinanz AG; *Int'l*, pg. 3628
EXPO-CARGO LTD.—See Lamprecht Transport AG; *Int'l*, pg. 4402
EXPO-CONSULT & SERVICES SPOL. S.R.O.—See Messe Munchen GmbH; *Int'l*, pg. 4841
EXPOCRETE CONCRETE PRODUCTS LTD.—See CRH plc; *Int'l*, pg. 1846
EXPO EXPERTS, LLC—See Professional Diversity Network, Inc.; *U.S. Public*, pg. 1724
EXPO FREIGHT (SHANGHAI) LIMITED—See Expolanka Holdings PLC; *Int'l*, pg. 2589
EXPO GAS CONTAINERS LTD.; *Int'l*, pg. 2589
THE EXPO GROUP, INC.—See New State Capital Partners LLC; *U.S. Private*, pg. 2907
EXPO INDUSTRIES, INC.; *U.S. Private*, pg. 1450
EXPOLANKA FREIGHT (PRIVATE) LIMITED—See Expolanka Holdings PLC; *Int'l*, pg. 2589
EXPOLANKA HOLDINGS PLC; *Int'l*, pg. 2589
EXPO LOGIC; *U.S. Private*, pg. 1450

EXPO MAZURY S.A.—See Mirbud S.A.; *Int'l*, pg. 4918
EXPOMOBILIA MCH GLOBAL SHANGHAI LTD.—See MCH Group AG; *Int'l*, pg. 4758
EXPONENT ENVIRONMENTAL GROUP—See Exponent, Inc.; *U.S. Public*, pg. 812
EXPONENT FAILURE ANALYSIS ASSOCIATES—See Exponent, Inc.; *U.S. Public*, pg. 812
EXPONENT GMBH—See Exponent, Inc.; *U.S. Public*, pg. 812
EXPONENTIAL-E LIMITED; *Int'l*, pg. 2590
EXPONENTIAL INTERACTIVE, INC.; *U.S. Private*, pg. 1450
EXPONENTIAL INVESTMENTS CO., LTD.—See ESTsoft Corp; *Int'l*, pg. 2519
EXPONENTIAL POWER, INC.—See High Road Capital Partners, LLC; *U.S. Private*, pg. 1936
EXPONENTIAL PROPERTY CONSTRUCTION, LLC; *U.S. Private*, pg. 1450
EXPONENT, INC.- ALEXANDRIA, VIRGINIA—See Exponent, Inc.; *U.S. Public*, pg. 812
EXPONENT, INC.-BOSTON AREA—See Exponent, Inc.; *U.S. Public*, pg. 812
EXPONENT, INC.-CHICAGO—See Exponent, Inc.; *U.S. Public*, pg. 812
EXPONENT, INC.-DENVER AREA—See Exponent, Inc.; *U.S. Public*, pg. 812
EXPONENT, INC.-DETROIT AREA—See Exponent, Inc.; *U.S. Public*, pg. 812
EXPONENT, INC.-LOS ANGELES—See Exponent, Inc.; *U.S. Public*, pg. 812
EXPONENT, INC - MENLO PARK—See Exponent, Inc.; *U.S. Public*, pg. 812
EXPONENT, INC.-NEW YORK—See Exponent, Inc.; *U.S. Public*, pg. 812
EXPONENT, INC., PHILADELPHIA—See Exponent, Inc.; *U.S. Public*, pg. 812
EXPONENT, INC.-PHOENIX—See Exponent, Inc.; *U.S. Public*, pg. 812
EXPONENT. INC.—See Exponent, Inc.; *U.S. Public*, pg. 812
EXPONENT INC—See Exponent, Inc.; *U.S. Public*, pg. 812
EXPONENT, INC.; *U.S. Public*, pg. 812
EXPONENT INTERNATIONAL LTD.—See Exponent, Inc.; *U.S. Public*, pg. 812
EXPONENT LIMITED—See Exponent, Inc.; *U.S. Public*, pg. 812
EXPONENT PRIVATE EQUITY LLP; *Int'l*, pg. 2589
EXPONENT SCIENCE AND TECHNOLOGY CONSULTING (SHANGHAI) CO., LTD.—See Exponent, Inc.; *U.S. Public*, pg. 812
EXPONENT—See Exponent, Inc.; *U.S. Public*, pg. 812
EXPONENT—See Stagwell, Inc.; *U.S. Public*, pg. 1926
EXPO PARTES S.A. DE C.V.—See NOV, Inc.; *U.S. Public*, pg. 1544
EXPORTADORA ATLANTIC S.A—See Ecom Agroindustrial Corporation Ltd.; *Int'l*, pg. 2296
EXPORTADORA Y SERVICIOS EL PARQUE S.P.A.—See Dole plc; *Int'l*, pg. 2158
EXPORT CREDIT INSURANCE & GUARANTEE (PTY) LTD—See Botswana Development Corporation Limited; *Int'l*, pg. 1118
EXPORT DEVELOPMENT BANK OF EGYPT; *Int'l*, pg. 2590
EXPORT DEVELOPMENT BANK; *Int'l*, pg. 2590
EXPORT DEVELOPMENT CANADA; *Int'l*, pg. 2590
EXPORT DEVELOPMENT CORPORATION—See Export Development Canada; *Int'l*, pg. 2590
EXPORT IMPORT BANK OF BANGLADESH LIMITED; *Int'l*, pg. 2590
THE EXPORT-IMPORT BANK OF KOREA - NEW YORK—See The Export-Import Bank of Korea; *Int'l*, pg. 7641
THE EXPORT-IMPORT BANK OF KOREA; *Int'l*, pg. 7641
THE EXPORT-IMPORT BANK OF KOREA—See The Export-Import Bank of Korea; *Int'l*, pg. 7641
EXPORT-IMPORT BANK OF THE UNITED STATES; *U.S. Private*, pg. 1450
EXPORT INSPECTION COUNCIL PRIVATE LIMITED—See Ecobank Transnational Incorporated; *Int'l*, pg. 2294
EXPORT INVESTMENT CO. LTD.; *Int'l*, pg. 2590
EXPORT OIL FIELD SUPPLY COMPANY INTERNATIONAL; *U.S. Private*, pg. 1450
EXPORT PACKAGING CO. INC.; *U.S. Private*, pg. 1450
EXPORT PACKERS COMPANY LIMITED; *Int'l*, pg. 2590
EXPORTS OF WASHINGTON INCORPORATED; *U.S. Private*, pg. 1451
EXPORT TRADING GROUP PTE LTD.; *Int'l*, pg. 2590
EXPORT WAMGROUP LLC—See WAMGROUP S.p.A.; *Int'l*, pg. 8339
EXPOS2 INC.; *U.S. Private*, pg. 1451
EXPOSERVICE APS—See Messe Munchen GmbH; *Int'l*, pg. 4841
EXPO SERVICES, A ROGERS COMPANY LLC—See The Rogers Company; *U.S. Private*, pg. 4112
EXPOSOFT SOLUTIONS INC.; *Int'l*, pg. 2590
EXPOSURES ONLINE—See Crosby Rock LLC; *U.S. Private*, pg. 1104

COMPANY NAME INDEX

EXP REALTY ASSOCIATES, LLC—See eXp World Holdings, Inc.; *U.S. Public*, pg. 808
EXP REALTY OF CANADA, INC.—See eXp World Holdings, Inc.; *U.S. Public*, pg. 808
EXPRES2ION BIOTECHNOLOGIES; *Int'l*, pg. 2590
EXPRES MEDIA S.R.O.—See Emmis Communications Corporation; *U.S. Public*, pg. 753
EXPRES NET A.S.—See Emmis Communications Corporation; *U.S. Public*, pg. 753
EXPRESOIL, DISTRIBUIDORA DE GASOLEOS SL—See Mubadala Investment Company PJSC; *Int'l*, pg. 5074
EXPRESS 2000, INC.—See CrossCountry Freight Solutions, Inc.; *U.S. Private*, pg. 1106
EXPRESS A BUTTON, INC.; *U.S. Private*, pg. 1451
EXPRESS AIR FREIGHT UNLIMITED, INC.; *U.S. Private*, pg. 1451
EXPRESS AIR SERVICES (NAMIBIA) (PTY) LIMITED—See The Bidvest Group Limited; *Int'l*, pg. 7624
EXPRESSBANK OJSC; *Int'l*, pg. 2590
EXPRESS CHECK ADVANCE LLC; *U.S. Private*, pg. 1451
EXPRESS CHECK ADVANCE OF SOUTH CAROLINA, LLC—See QC Holdings, Inc.; *U.S. Public*, pg. 1742
EXPRESSCO DIRECT LIMITED—See Tandem Group PLC; *Int'l*, pg. 7456
EXPRESS COURIER INTERNATIONAL, INC.—See Diligent Delivery Systems; *U.S. Private*, pg. 1231
EXPRESS COURIERS LTD—See New Zealand Post Limited; *Int'l*, pg. 5232
EXPRESS CREDIT AUTO, INC.; *U.S. Private*, pg. 1451
EXPRESS CUSTOMS CLEARANCE (USA), INC.—See A-Sonic Aerospace Limited; *Int'l*, pg. 21
EXPRESS CUSTOM TRAILERS MFG. INC.; *Int'l*, pg. 2590
EXPRESS DATA HOLDINGS PTY LTD—See Dicker Data Limited; *Int'l*, pg. 2111
EXPRESS DIAGNOSTICS INT'L, INC.—See W.H.P.M., Inc.; *U.S. Private*, pg. 4420
EXPRESS DIGITAL GRAPHICS, INC.—See Photoreflect, LLC; *U.S. Private*, pg. 3174
EXPRESS EMPLOYMENT PROFESSIONALS, INC.; *U.S. Private*, pg. 1451
EXPRESS EMPLOYMENT PROFESSIONALS; *U.S. Private*, pg. 1451
EXPRESS FASHION OPERATIONS, LLC—See WHP Global; *U.S. Private*, pg. 4515
EXPRESS FREIGHTERS AUSTRALIA PTY LIMITED—See Qantas Airways Limited; *Int'l*, pg. 6132
EXPRESS, INC.—See WHP Global; *U.S. Private*, pg. 4515
EXPRESS INDUSTRIAL & WELDING SUPPLIES LIMITED—See Linde plc; *Int'l*, pg. 4504
EXPRESS-INTERFRACHT BULGARIA SPEDITIONSGESELLSCHAFT EOOD—See OBB-Holding AG; *Int'l*, pg. 5510
EXPRESS-INTERFRACHT CROATIA D.O.O.—See OBB-Holding AG; *Int'l*, pg. 5509
EXPRESS-INTERFRACHT HUNGARIA KFT.—See OBB-Holding AG; *Int'l*, pg. 5510
EXPRESS-INTERFRACHT POLSKA SP. Z.O.O.—See OBB-Holding AG; *Int'l*, pg. 5509
EXPRESS-INTERFRACHT ROMANIA S.R.L.—See OBB-Holding AG; *Int'l*, pg. 5510
EXPRESSION NETWORKS, LLC; *U.S. Private*, pg. 1451
EXPRESSIONS CHIROPRACTIC & REHAB, P.A.—See Eco Innovation Group, Inc.; *U.S. Public*, pg. 712
EXPRESSIONS PARFUMEES S.A.S.—See Givaudan S.A.; *Int'l*, pg. 2980
EXPRESSIONS UNLIMITED, INC.—See Designer Greetings Inc.; *U.S. Private*, pg. 1214
EXPRESSION SYSTEMS, LLC—See Golden Gate Capital Management II, LLC; *U.S. Public*, pg. 1730
EXPRESSJET AIRLINES INC.; *U.S. Private*, pg. 1451
EXPRESSJET AIRLINES, INC.—See ExpressJet Airlines Inc.; *U.S. Private*, pg. 1451
EXPRESSJET SERVICES, LLC—See ExpressJet Airlines Inc.; *U.S. Private*, pg. 1451
EXPRESS KCS INC.; *U.S. Private*, pg. 1451
EXPRESS KITCHENS; *U.S. Private*, pg. 1451
EXPRESS LAINE CONVENIENCE STORES INC.; *U.S. Private*, pg. 1451
EXPRESS LANE INC.; *U.S. Private*, pg. 1451
EXPRESS LEASING INC.; *U.S. Private*, pg. 1451
EXPRESS MARKETS, INC.—See Eli Lilly & Company; *U.S. Public*, pg. 733
EXPRESS MICROBIOLOGY LIMITED—See Eurofins Scientific S.E.; *Int'l*, pg. 2550
EXPRESS MITTE HOLDING GMBH & CO. KG—See REWE-Zentral-Aktiengesellschaft; *Int'l*, pg. 6315
EXPRESS NETWORK CO., LTD.—See Yamato Holdings Co., Ltd.; *Int'l*, pg. 8554
EXPRESS NEWSPAPERS—See Reach PLC; *Int'l*, pg. 6231
EXPRESS NORD-WEST HOLDING GMBH & CO. KG—See REWE-Zentral-Aktiengesellschaft; *Int'l*, pg. 6315
EXPRESS OIL CHANGE LLC—See Golden Gate Capital Management II, LLC; *U.S. Public*, pg. 1731
EXPRESS ONE D.O.O.—See Osterreichische Post AG; *Int'l*, pg. 5653

EXPRESS ONE HUNGARY KFT.—See Osterreichische Post AG; *Int'l*, pg. 5653
EXPRESS PIPELINE LTD.—See Enbridge Inc.; *Int'l*, pg. 2397
EXPRESS PIPE & SUPPLY CO. INC.; *U.S. Private*, pg. 1451
EXPRESSPOINT TECHNOLOGY SERVICES, INC.; *U.S. Private*, pg. 1452
EXPRESS POLSKA SP. Z O.O.—See OBB-Holding AG; *Int'l*, pg. 5510
EXPRESS POSTAL OPTIONS INTERNATIONAL LLC—See Chatham Asset Management, LLC; *U.S. Private*, pg. 863
EXPRESS REINFORCEMENTS LTD.—See Celsa Group; *Int'l*, pg. 1395
EXPRESS SCRIPTS ADMINISTRATORS, LLC—See The Cigna Group; *U.S. Public*, pg. 2061
EXPRESS SCRIPTS CANADA CO.—See The Cigna Group; *U.S. Public*, pg. 2061
EXPRESS SCRIPTS HOLDING COMPANY—See The Cigna Group; *U.S. Public*, pg. 2061
EXPRESS SCRIPTS, INC.—See The Cigna Group; *U.S. Public*, pg. 2061
EXPRESS SCRIPTS—See The Cigna Group; *U.S. Public*, pg. 2061
EXPRESS S.R.L.—See IVS Group S.A.; *Int'l*, pg. 3848
EXPRESS TIMES—See Advance Publications, Inc.; *U.S. Private*, pg. 86
EXPRESS TIRE AUTO SERVICE CENTERS; *U.S. Private*, pg. 1451
EXPRESS TOPCO LLC—See WHP Global; *U.S. Private*, pg. 4515
EXPRESS TRANSPORT SA; *Int'l*, pg. 2590
EXPRESSWAY DODGE INC.; *U.S. Private*, pg. 1452
EXPRESSWAY MOTORS LTD; *Int'l*, pg. 2590
EXPRIMM IT—See Bouygues S.A.; *Int'l*, pg. 1123
EXPRIVIA PROJECTS S.R.L.—See Exprivia SpA; *Int'l*, pg. 2591
EXPRIVIA SPA; *Int'l*, pg. 2590
EXPRO GROUP AUSTRALIA PTY LTD—See Newgate Private Equity LLP; *Int'l*, pg. 5234
EXPRO GROUP HOLDINGS N.V.; *Int'l*, pg. 2591
EXPRO GROUP MALAYSIA SDN. BHD.—See Newgate Private Equity LLP; *Int'l*, pg. 5234
EXPRO INTERNATIONAL B.V.—See Newgate Private Equity LLP; *Int'l*, pg. 5234
EXPRO INTERNATIONAL GROUP LTD.—See Newgate Private Equity LLP; *Int'l*, pg. 5234
EXPRO NORWAY A/S—See Newgate Private Equity LLP; *Int'l*, pg. 5234
EXP U.S. SERVICES INC.—See exp Global Inc.; *Int'l*, pg. 2586
EXP WORLD HOLDINGS, INC.; *U.S. Public*, pg. 808
EXP WORLD UK LIMITED—See eXp World Holdings, Inc.; *U.S. Public*, pg. 808
EXQUISITA TORTILLAS INC.; *U.S. Private*, pg. 1452
EXQUISITE KNITTERS (GUANGZHOU) LIMITED—See Yangtzekiang Garment Limited; *Int'l*, pg. 8561
EXQUISITE PROPERTY LIMITED—See Mainland Headwear Holdings Ltd.; *Int'l*, pg. 4651
EXQUISITE TIMEPIECES, INC.; *U.S. Private*, pg. 1452
EXRO TECHNOLOGIES, INC.; *Int'l*, pg. 2591
EXSA EXPORT SANAYI MAMULLERI SATIS VE ARASTIRMA A.S.—See Haci Omer Sabanci Holding A.S.; *Int'l*, pg. 3204
EXSA S.A.—See Orica Limited; *Int'l*, pg. 5619
EXSCIENTIA PLC; *Int'l*, pg. 2591
EXSCRIBE, INC.—See Modernizing Medicine, Inc.; *U.S. Private*, pg. 2763
EXSEL PUMPS LIMITED—See Turner & Co. (Glasgow) Limited; *Int'l*, pg. 7978
EXSIF WORLDWIDE, INC.—See Berkshire Hathaway Inc.; *U.S. Public*, pg. 311
EXSITEC HOLDING AB; *Int'l*, pg. 2591
EXSULAR FINANCIAL GROUP INC.; *Int'l*, pg. 2591
EXTAND—See SNCF; *Int'l*, pg. 7026
EXTANG CORPORATION—See Kinderhook Industries, LLC; *U.S. Private*, pg. 2307
EXTANT COMPONENTS GROUP HOLDINGS, INC.—See TransDigm Group Incorporated; *U.S. Public*, pg. 2182
EXTECH INDUSTRIES INC.; *U.S. Private*, pg. 1452
EX-TECH PLASTICS, INC.—See Good Natured Products Inc.; *U.S. Public*, pg. 3038
EXTE - EXTRUDERTECHNIK GMBH; *Int'l*, pg. 2591
EXTEND COMUNICACIONES-WEBER SHANDWICK—See The Interpublic Group of Companies, Inc.; *U.S. Public*, pg. 2104
EXTENDED FAMILY, LLC—See HouseWorks, LLC; *U.S. Private*, pg. 1992
EXTENDED HOME LIVING SERVICES, INC.—See Rockwood Equity Partners, LLC; *U.S. Private*, pg. 3468
EXTENDED STAY AMERICA, INC.—See Blackstone Inc.; *U.S. Public*, pg. 350
EXTENDED STAY AMERICA, INC.—See Starwood Capital Group Global I, LLC; *U.S. Public*, pg. 3789
EXTENDED STAY HOTELS LLC—See Centerbridge Partners, L.P.; *U.S. Private*, pg. 814
EXTEND HEALTH, INC.—See Willis Towers Watson Public Limited Company; *Int'l*, pg. 8414

EXTERNETWORKS, INC.

EXTENDICARE (CANADA), INC.—See Extendicare Inc.; *Int'l*, pg. 2591
EXTENDICARE HEALTH SERVICES INC.—See Extendicare Inc.; *Int'l*, pg. 2591
EXTENDICARE, INC.—See Extendicare Inc.; *Int'l*, pg. 2591
EXTENDICARE INC.; *Int'l*, pg. 2591
EXTEND INSURANCE SERVICES - ILLINOIS—See Willis Towers Watson Public Limited Company; *Int'l*, pg. 8414
EXTEND INSURANCE SERVICES, LLC—See Willis Towers Watson Public Limited Company; *Int'l*, pg. 8414
EXTENET SYSTEMS, INC.—See Stonepeak Partners L.P.; *U.S. Private*, pg. 3829
EXTENSA DEVELOPMENT SA—See Ackermans & van Haaren NV; *Int'l*, pg. 105
EXTENSA GROUP SA—See Ackermans & van Haaren NV; *Int'l*, pg. 105
EXTENSA ISTANBUL—See Ackermans & van Haaren NV; *Int'l*, pg. 105
EXTENSA LAND II SA—See Ackermans & van Haaren NV; *Int'l*, pg. 106
EXTENSA NV—See Ackermans & van Haaren NV; *Int'l*, pg. 105
EXTENSA ROMANIA S.R.L—See Ackermans & van Haaren NV; *Int'l*, pg. 105
EXTENSA SLOVAKIA S.R.O.—See Ackermans & van Haaren NV; *Int'l*, pg. 106
EXTENSIA PTY. LTD.—See Hills Limited; *Int'l*, pg. 3393
EXTENSIONENGINE LLC; *U.S. Private*, pg. 1452
EXTENSIONENGINE—See ExtensionEngine LLC; *U.S. Private*, pg. 1452
EXTENSIVE TRADING COMPANY LIMITED—See FSE Services Group Limited; *Int'l*, pg. 2798
EXTENSYS, INC.; *U.S. Private*, pg. 1452
EXTERA IMPORTACAO E EXPORTACAO LTDA.—See Medartis Holding AG; *Int'l*, pg. 4768
EXTER B.V.; *Int'l*, pg. 2591
EXTERION MEDIA (IRELAND) LIMITED—See Platinum Equity, LLC; *U.S. Private*, pg. 3203
EXTERION MEDIA (NETHERLANDS) B.V.—See Platinum Equity, LLC; *U.S. Private*, pg. 3203
EXTERION MEDIA—See Platinum Equity, LLC; *U.S. Private*, pg. 3203
EXTERION MEDIA SPAIN, S.A.—See Platinum Equity, LLC; *U.S. Private*, pg. 3203
EXTERIOR DESIGNS, LLC—See UFP Industries, Inc.; *U.S. Public*, pg. 2219
EXTERIOR DIAGNOSTIC SERVICES, INC.—See Valcourt Building Services LLC; *U.S. Private*, pg. 4330
EXTERIOR WOOD INC.—See Avarga Limited; *Int'l*, pg. 737
EXTERNA HANDELS- UND BETEILIGUNGSGESELLSCHAFT MBH—See Freudenberg SE; *Int'l*, pg. 2785
EXTERNET TELECOMMUNICATIONS SERVICE PROVIDER PUBLIC CO.; *Int'l*, pg. 2591
EXTERNETWORKS, INC.; *U.S. Private*, pg. 1452
EXTERRAN ARGENTINA S.R.L.—See Enerflex Ltd.; *Int'l*, pg. 2418
EXTERRAN BAHRAIN S.P.C.—See Enerflex Ltd.; *Int'l*, pg. 2418
EXTERRAN BOLIVIA LTDA.—See Enerflex Ltd.; *Int'l*, pg. 2418
EXTERRAN BRASIL LTDA.—See Enerflex Ltd.; *Int'l*, pg. 2419
EXTERRAN CORPORATION—See Enerflex Ltd.; *Int'l*, pg. 2418
EXTERRAN EASTERN HEMISPHERE FZE—See Enerflex Ltd.; *Int'l*, pg. 2418
EXTERRAN ENERGY CORP.—See Archrock, Inc.; *U.S. Public*, pg. 186
EXTERRAN ENERGY DE MEXICO, S.A. DE C.V.—See Enerflex Ltd.; *Int'l*, pg. 2419
EXTERRAN ENERGY MALAYSIA SDN. BHD.—See Enerflex Ltd.; *Int'l*, pg. 2419
EXTERRANENERGY SOLUTIONS ECUADOR CIA. LTDA.—See Enerflex Ltd.; *Int'l*, pg. 2419
EXTERRAN ENERGY SOLUTIONS, L.P. - HOUSTON (BRITTMOORE) PLANT—See Enerflex Ltd.; *Int'l*, pg. 2419
EXTERRAN ENERGY SOLUTIONS, L.P. - HOUSTON (ROSSLYN) PLANT—See Enerflex Ltd.; *Int'l*, pg. 2419
EXTERRAN ENERGY SOLUTIONS, L.P.—See Enerflex Ltd.; *Int'l*, pg. 2418
EXTERRAN GENERAL HOLDINGS LLC—See Enerflex Ltd.; *Int'l*, pg. 2419
EXTERRAN GP LLC—See Archrock, Inc.; *U.S. Public*, pg. 186
EXTERRAN HL LLC—See Archrock, Inc.; *U.S. Public*, pg. 186
EXTERRAN HOLDING COMPANY NL B.V.—See Enerflex Ltd.; *Int'l*, pg. 2419
EXTERRAN INTERNATIONAL SA—See Enerflex Ltd.; *Int'l*, pg. 2419
EXTERRAN OFFSHORE PTE. LTD.—See Enerflex Ltd.; *Int'l*, pg. 2419
EXTERRAN PERU SELVA S.R.L.—See Enerflex Ltd.; *Int'l*, pg. 2419
EXTERRAN SERVICOS DE OLEO E GAS LTDA.—See Enerflex Ltd.; *Int'l*, pg. 2419

EXTERRAN (SINGAPORE) PTE. LTD.—See Enerflex Ltd.; *Int'l*, pg. 2418
EXTERRAN—See Enerflex Ltd.; *Int'l*, pg. 2418
EXTERRAN—See Enerflex Ltd.; *Int'l*, pg. 2418
EXTERRAN—See Enerflex Ltd.; *Int'l*, pg. 2419
EXTERRAN—See Enerflex Ltd.; *Int'l*, pg. 2419
EXTERRAN—See Enerflex Ltd.; *Int'l*, pg. 2419
EXTERRAN—See Enerflex Ltd.; *Int'l*, pg. 2419
EXTERRAN—See Enerflex Ltd.; *Int'l*, pg. 2419
EXTERRAN WATER SOLUTIONS ULC—See Enerflex Ltd.; *Int'l*, pg. 2419
EXTER-REAL INGATLANFORGALMAZASI KORLATOLT FELELOSSEGU TARSASAG—See BayernLB Holding AG; *Int'l*, pg. 913
EXTERRO, INC.—See Leeds Equity Partners, LLC; *U.S. Private*, pg. 2414
EXTEX ENGINEERED PRODUCTS, INC.—See Arcline Investment Management LP; *U.S. Private*, pg. 314
EXTIA—See Alten S.A.; *Int'l*, pg. 390
EXTOL COMMERCIAL LIMITED; *Int'l*, pg. 2592
EXTOL CORPORATION SDN BHD.—See AppAsia Berhad; *Int'l*, pg. 519
EXTOLE INC.; *U.S. Private*, pg. 1452
EXTOL INTERNATIONAL INC.—See CLEO Communications, Inc.; *U.S. Private*, pg. 940
EXTON RANCH, LLC—See Omega Flex, Inc.; *U.S. Public*, pg. 1571
EXTOR GMBH—See Delticom AG; *Int'l*, pg. 2021
EXTRACO BANKS—See Extraco Corporation; *U.S. Private*, pg. 1452
EXTRACO CORPORATION; *U.S. Private*, pg. 1452
EXTRACO MORTGAGE CORP.—See Extraco Corporation; *U.S. Private*, pg. 1452
EXTRACORP AKTIENGESELLSCHAFT—See DaVita Inc.; *U.S. Public*, pg. 638
EXTRACTABLE, INC.; *U.S. Private*, pg. 1452
EXTRACT-ECOTERRE SA.—See VINCI S.A.; *Int'l*, pg. 8220
EXTRACTED OIL & DERIVATIVES CO.; *U.S. Public*, pg. 813
EXTRACT GROUP LIMITED; *Int'l*, pg. 2592
EXTRACTION OIL & GAS, INC.—See Civitas Resources, Inc.; *U.S. Public*, pg. 507
EXTRACTION (PAKISTAN) LIMITED; *Int'l*, pg. 2592
EXTRACT TECHNOLOGY LIMITED—See WABASH NATIONAL CORPORATION; *U.S. Public*, pg. 2320
EXTRADEV, INC.—See DSS, Inc.; *U.S. Public*, pg. 689
EXTRADOM.PL SP. Z O.O.—See Wirtualna Polska Holding S.A.; *Int'l*, pg. 8434
EXTRA GAMES ENTERTAINMENT GMBH—See Novomatic AG; *Int'l*, pg. 5467
EXTRA INNINGS FRANCHISE COMPANY; *U.S. Private*, pg. 1452
EXTRAKARE LLC; *U.S. Private*, pg. 1452
EXTRAMED LIMITED—See Alcidion Group Limited; *Int'l*, pg. 301
EXTRA MILE TRANSPORTATION LLC; *U.S. Private*, pg. 1452
EXTRA SPACE STORAGE, INC.; *U.S. Public*, pg. 812
EXTRA SPACE STORAGE LP—See Extra Space Storage, Inc.; *U.S. Public*, pg. 813
EXTRA SPORTS WEAR INC.; *U.S. Private*, pg. 1452
EXTRA UK LTD.—See Storskogen Group AB; *Int'l*, pg. 7227
EXTRAWELL ENTERPRISES LIMITED—See Extrawell Pharmaceutical Holdings Ltd.; *Int'l*, pg. 2592
EXTRAWELL PHARMACEUTICAL (HK) LIMITED—See Extrawell Pharmaceutical Holdings Ltd.; *Int'l*, pg. 2592
EXTRAWELL PHARMACEUTICAL HOLDINGS LTD.; *Int'l*, pg. 2592
EXTREAK, INC.—See Sumitomo Corporation; *Int'l*, pg. 7270
EXTREMADURA MINING S.L.—See Infinity Lithium Corporation Limited; *Int'l*, pg. 3688
EXTREME ADHESIVES, LLC—See H.B. Fuller Company; *U.S. Public*, pg. 977
EXTREME BIODIESEL, INC.; *U.S. Public*, pg. 813
EXTREME CO., LTD.; *Int'l*, pg. 2592
EXTREME ENGINEERING, INC.—See LCI Industries; *U.S. Public*, pg. 1295
EXTREME ENGINEERING SOLUTIONS, INC.; *U.S. Private*, pg. 1452
EXTREME HOLDINGS, INC.; *U.S. Private*, pg. 1452
EXTREME LIFESTYLE CENTRE (PTY) LIMITED—See Super Group Limited; *Int'l*, pg. 7334
EXTREME LIVE GAMING LIMITED—See Pragmatic Play Ltd.; *Int'l*, pg. 5953
EXTREME NETWORKS AUSTRALIA PTE. LTD.—See Extreme Networks, Inc.; *U.S. Public*, pg. 813
EXTREME NETWORKS B.V.—See Extreme Networks, Inc.; *U.S. Public*, pg. 813
EXTREME NETWORKS CANADA, INC.—See Extreme Networks, Inc.; *U.S. Public*, pg. 813
EXTREME NETWORKS CHINA LTD.—See Extreme Networks, Inc.; *U.S. Public*, pg. 813
EXTREME NETWORKS GMBH—See Extreme Networks, Inc.; *U.S. Public*, pg. 813
EXTREME NETWORKS HONG KONG LTD.—See Extreme Networks, Inc.; *U.S. Public*, pg. 813
EXTREME NETWORKS, INC.; *U.S. Public*, pg. 813
EXTREME NETWORKS JAPAN, K.K.—See Extreme Networks, Inc.; *U.S. Public*, pg. 813
EXTREME NETWORKS MEXICO, SA DE CV—See Extreme Networks, Inc.; *U.S. Public*, pg. 813
EXTREME NETWORKS NETHERLANDS BV—See Extreme Networks, Inc.; *U.S. Public*, pg. 813
EXTREME NETWORKS SARL—See Extreme Networks, Inc.; *U.S. Public*, pg. 813
EXTREME NETWORKS SPAIN, SL—See Extreme Networks, Inc.; *U.S. Public*, pg. 813
EXTREME NETWORKS TECHNOLOGY CO. (BEIJING) LTD.—See Extreme Networks, Inc.; *U.S. Public*, pg. 813
EXTREME NETWORKS UK LIMITED—See Extreme Networks, Inc.; *U.S. Public*, pg. 813
EXTREME PLASTICS PLUS, LLC—See Blue Wolf Capital Partners LLC; *U.S. Private*, pg. 594
EXTREME PUMP SOLUTIONS—See Divergent Energy Services Corp.; *Int'l*, pg. 2137
EXTREME REACH, INC.; *U.S. Private*, pg. 1452
EXTREME STEEL, INC; *U.S. Private*, pg. 1452
EXTREME TECHNOLOGIES, LLC—See Drilling Tools International Corp.; *U.S. Public*, pg. 688
EXTREMETECH—See Ziff Davis, Inc.; *U.S. Public*, pg. 2404
EXTREME VIETNAM CO., LTD.—See extreme Co., Ltd.; *Int'l*, pg. 2592
EXTRON LOGISTICS, LLC; *U.S. Private*, pg. 1452
EXTRUDED METALS, INC.—See Mueller Industries, Inc.; *U.S. Public*, pg. 1484
EXTRUDE HONE KK—See Kennametal Inc.; *U.S. Public*, pg. 1221
EXTRUDE HONE LLC—See Kennametal Inc.; *U.S. Public*, pg. 1221
EXTRUSION DIES INDUSTRIES, LLC—See Nordson Corporation; *U.S. Public*, pg. 1532
EXTRUSIONS INC.; *U.S. Private*, pg. 1453
EXUBRIO GROUP LLC; *U.S. Private*, pg. 1453
EXUDE BENEFITS GROUP, INC.; *U.S. Private*, pg. 1453
EXUMA TECHNOLOGIES, INC.—See Valsef Group; *Int'l*, pg. 8122
EXUSIA INC.—See Globant S.A.; *Int'l*, pg. 3005
EXUS S.A.—See Piraeus Financial Holdings S.A.; *Int'l*, pg. 5873
EXVENT AS—See Zehnder Group AG; *Int'l*, pg. 8630
EXWORKS CAPITAL, LLC—See Capitol Financial Strategies, LLC; *U.S. Private*, pg. 743
EXWORKS CAPITAL, LLC—See RedRidge Finance Group, LLC; *U.S. Private*, pg. 3379
EXWORKS CAPITAL, LLC - WASHINGTON, D.C. OFFICE—See Capitol Financial Strategies, LLC; *U.S. Private*, pg. 744
EXWORKS CAPITAL, LLC - WASHINGTON, D.C. OFFICE—See RedRidge Finance Group, LLC; *U.S. Private*, pg. 3379
EXXACT EXPRESS INC.; *U.S. Private*, pg. 1453
EXXARO BASE METALS AND INDUSTRIAL MINERALS HOLDINGS (PTY) LIMITED—See Exxaro Resources Ltd.; *Int'l*, pg. 2592
EXXARO BASE METALS (PTY) LIMITED—See Exxaro Resources Ltd.; *Int'l*, pg. 2592
EXXARO COAL (PTY) LIMITED—See Exxaro Resources Ltd.; *Int'l*, pg. 2592
EXXARO HOLDINGS SANDS (PTY) LIMITED—See Exxaro Resources Ltd.; *Int'l*, pg. 2592
EXXARO INSURANCE COMPANY LIMITED—See Exxaro Resources Ltd.; *Int'l*, pg. 2592
EXXARO INTERNATIONAL COAL TRADING BV—See Exxaro Resources Ltd.; *Int'l*, pg. 2592
EXXARO INTERNATIONAL TRADING BV—See Exxaro Resources Ltd.; *Int'l*, pg. 2592
EXXARO RESOURCES LTD.; *Int'l*, pg. 2592
EXXARO TILES LIMITED; *Int'l*, pg. 2592
EXXCOM LIMITED—See Enghouse Systems Limited; *Int'l*, pg. 2427
EXXE GROUP, INC.; *U.S. Public*, pg. 813
EXXELIA SAS—See HEICO Corporation; *U.S. Public*, pg. 1019
EXXELLIN GMBH; *Int'l*, pg. 2592
EXXEL OUTDOORS, INC.; *U.S. Private*, pg. 1453
EXXEL PACIFIC, INC.; *U.S. Private*, pg. 1453
EXX INC.; *U.S. Private*, pg. 1453
EXXON AZERBAIJAN LIMITED—See Exxon Mobil Corporation; *U.S. Public*, pg. 814
EXXON INTERNATIONAL FINANCE COMPANY—See Exxon Mobil Corporation; *U.S. Public*, pg. 814
EXXONMOBIL AIRCRAFT OPERATIONS—See Exxon Mobil Corporation; *U.S. Public*, pg. 814
EXXONMOBIL ASIA PACIFIC PTE LTD.—See Exxon Mobil Corporation; *U.S. Public*, pg. 814
EXXONMOBIL AUSTRALIA PTY LTD.—See Exxon Mobil Corporation; *U.S. Public*, pg. 814
EXXONMOBIL CANADA LTD.—See Exxon Mobil Corporation; *U.S. Public*, pg. 814
EXXONMOBIL CANADA PROPERTIES—See Exxon Mobil Corporation; *U.S. Public*, pg. 814
EXXONMOBIL CENTRAL EUROPE HOLDING GMBH—See Exxon Mobil Corporation; *U.S. Public*, pg. 814
EXXONMOBIL CHEMICAL COMPANY - FILM DIV.—See Exxon Mobil Corporation; *U.S. Public*, pg. 814
EXXONMOBIL CHEMICAL COMPANY INC.—See Exxon Mobil Corporation; *U.S. Public*, pg. 814
EXXONMOBIL CHEMICAL COMPANY INC.—See Exxon Mobil Corporation; *U.S. Public*, pg. 814
EXXONMOBIL CHEMICAL COMPANY INC.—See Exxon Mobil Corporation; *U.S. Public*, pg. 814
EXXONMOBIL CHEMICAL COMPANY INC.—See Exxon Mobil Corporation; *U.S. Public*, pg. 814
EXXONMOBIL CHEMICAL COMPANY - MONT BELVIEU PLASTICS PLANT—See Exxon Mobil Corporation; *U.S. Public*, pg. 814
EXXONMOBIL CHEMICAL COMPANY—See Exxon Mobil Corporation; *U.S. Public*, pg. 814
EXXONMOBIL CHEMICAL COMPANY—See Exxon Mobil Corporation; *U.S. Public*, pg. 814
EXXONMOBIL CHEMICAL FILMS CANADA, LTD.—See Exxon Mobil Corporation; *U.S. Public*, pg. 814
EXXONMOBIL CHEMICAL HOLLAND B.V.—See Exxon Mobil Corporation; *U.S. Public*, pg. 814
EXXONMOBIL CHEMICAL LIMITED—See Exxon Mobil Corporation; *U.S. Public*, pg. 814
EXXONMOBIL CHEMICAL OPERATIONS PRIVATE LIMITED—See Exxon Mobil Corporation; *U.S. Public*, pg. 814
EXXONMOBIL (CHINA) INVESTMENT CO., LTD.—See Exxon Mobil Corporation; *U.S. Public*, pg. 814
EXXONMOBIL COAL AND MINERALS COMPANY—See Exxon Mobil Corporation; *U.S. Public*, pg. 815
EXXON MOBIL CORP. - DOWNSTREAM OPERATIONS—See Exxon Mobil Corporation; *U.S. Public*, pg. 814
EXXONMOBIL CORPORATION—See Exxon Mobil Corporation; *U.S. Public*, pg. 815
EXXONMOBIL CORPORATION—See Exxon Mobil Corporation; *U.S. Public*, pg. 815
EXXONMOBIL CORPORATION—See Exxon Mobil Corporation; *U.S. Public*, pg. 815
EXXONMOBIL CORPORATION—See Exxon Mobil Corporation; *U.S. Public*, pg. 815
EXXONMOBIL CORPORATION—See Exxon Mobil Corporation; *U.S. Public*, pg. 815
EXXONMOBIL CORPORATION—See Exxon Mobil Corporation; *U.S. Public*, pg. 815
EXXONMOBIL CORPORATION—See Exxon Mobil Corporation; *U.S. Public*, pg. 815
EXXONMOBIL CORPORATION—See Exxon Mobil Corporation; *U.S. Public*, pg. 815
EXXONMOBIL CORPORATION—See Exxon Mobil Corporation; *U.S. Public*, pg. 815
EXXONMOBIL CORPORATION—See Exxon Mobil Corporation; *U.S. Public*, pg. 815
EXXONMOBIL CORPORATION—See Exxon Mobil Corporation; *U.S. Public*, pg. 815
EXXONMOBIL CORPORATION—See Exxon Mobil Corporation; *U.S. Public*, pg. 815
EXXONMOBIL CORPORATION—See Exxon Mobil Corporation; *U.S. Public*, pg. 815
EXXONMOBIL CORPORATION—See Exxon Mobil Corporation; *U.S. Public*, pg. 815
EXXONMOBIL CORPORATION—See Exxon Mobil Corporation; *U.S. Public*, pg. 815
EXXONMOBIL CORPORATION—See Exxon Mobil Corporation; *U.S. Public*, pg. 815
EXXON MOBIL CORPORATION; *U.S. Public*, pg. 813
EXXONMOBIL EGYPT (S.A.E.)—See Exxon Mobil Corporation; *U.S. Public*, pg. 815
EXXONMOBIL EXPLORATION AND PRODUCTION NORWAY AS—See Exxon Mobil Corporation; *U.S. Public*, pg. 815
EXXON MOBIL EXPLORATION & PRODUCTION MALAYSIA INC.—See Exxon Mobil Corporation; *U.S. Public*, pg. 814
EXXONMOBIL EXPLORATION & PRODUCTION MALAYSIA INC.—See Exxon Mobil Corporation; *U.S. Public*, pg. 815
EXXONMOBIL EXPLORATION—See Exxon Mobil Corporation; *U.S. Public*, pg. 815
EXXONMOBIL FINANCE COMPANY LIMITED—See Exxon Mobil Corporation; *U.S. Public*, pg. 815
EXXONMOBIL FINLAND OY A.B.—See Exxon Mobil Corporation; *U.S. Public*, pg. 815
EXXONMOBIL FUELS & MARKETING—See Exxon Mobil Corporation; *U.S. Public*, pg. 815
EXXONMOBIL GAS MARKETING DEUTSCHLAND GMBH—See Exxon Mobil Corporation; *U.S. Public*, pg. 815
EXXONMOBIL GAS MARKETING EUROPE LIMITED—See Exxon Mobil Corporation; *U.S. Public*, pg. 815
EXXONMOBIL GLOBAL SERVICES COMPANY—See Exxon Mobil Corporation; *U.S. Public*, pg. 815
EXXON MOBIL GLOBAL SERVICES—See Exxon Mobil Corporation; *U.S. Public*, pg. 814

COMPANY NAME INDEX

EXXONMOBIL HONG KONG LIMITED—See Exxon Mobil Corporation; *U.S. Public*, pg. 815
EXXONMOBIL INTERNATIONAL HOLDINGS INC.—See Exxon Mobil Corporation; *U.S. Public*, pg. 815
EXXONMOBIL INTERNATIONAL LIMITED—See Exxon Mobil Corporation; *U.S. Public*, pg. 815
EXXONMOBIL ITALIANA GAS S.R.L.—See Exxon Mobil Corporation; *U.S. Public*, pg. 815
EXXONMOBIL LUBRICANTS & PETROLEUM SPECIALTIES—See Exxon Mobil Corporation; *U.S. Public*, pg. 815
EXXONMOBIL MARINE LIMITED—See Exxon Mobil Corporation; *U.S. Public*, pg. 815
EXXONMOBIL MEXICO S.A. DE C.V.—See Exxon Mobil Corporation; *U.S. Public*, pg. 815
EXXONMOBIL OIL CORPORATION RESEARCH AND ENGINEERING—See Exxon Mobil Corporation; *U.S. Public*, pg. 815
EXXONMOBIL OIL CORPORATION—See Exxon Mobil Corporation; *U.S. Public*, pg. 815
EXXONMOBIL OIL CORPORATION—See Exxon Mobil Corporation; *U.S. Public*, pg. 815
EXXONMOBIL OIL CORPORATION—See Exxon Mobil Corporation; *U.S. Public*, pg. 815
EXXONMOBIL OIL CORPORATION—See Exxon Mobil Corporation; *U.S. Public*, pg. 815
EXXONMOBIL OIL CORPORATION—See Exxon Mobil Corporation; *U.S. Public*, pg. 815
EXXONMOBIL OIL CORPORATION—See Exxon Mobil Corporation; *U.S. Public*, pg. 815
EXXONMOBIL OIL CORPORATION—See Exxon Mobil Corporation; *U.S. Public*, pg. 815
EXXONMOBIL OIL CORPORATION—See Exxon Mobil Corporation; *U.S. Public*, pg. 815
EXXONMOBIL OIL INDONESIA, INC.—See Exxon Mobil Corporation; *U.S. Public*, pg. 815
EXXONMOBIL PENSIONS-VERWALTUNGSGESELLSCHAFT MBH—See Exxon Mobil Corporation; *U.S. Public*, pg. 816
EXXONMOBIL PETROLEUM & CHEMICAL BVBA—See Exxon Mobil Corporation; *U.S. Public*, pg. 816
EXXON MOBIL PETROLEUM CHEMICAL—See Exxon Mobil Corporation; *U.S. Public*, pg. 814
EXXONMOBIL PIPELINE COMPANY LLC—See Exxon Mobil Corporation; *U.S. Public*, pg. 816
EXXONMOBIL PIPELINE COMPANY—See Exxon Mobil Corporation; *U.S. Public*, pg. 816
EXXONMOBIL PIPELINE COMPANY—See Exxon Mobil Corporation; *U.S. Public*, pg. 816
EXXONMOBIL PIPELINE COMPANY—See Exxon Mobil Corporation; *U.S. Public*, pg. 816
EXXONMOBIL PIPELINE COMPANY—See Exxon Mobil Corporation; *U.S. Public*, pg. 816
EXXONMOBIL PIPELINE COMPANY—See Exxon Mobil Corporation; *U.S. Public*, pg. 816
EXXONMOBIL PIPELINE COMPANY—See Exxon Mobil Corporation; *U.S. Public*, pg. 816
EXXONMOBIL PIPELINE COMPANY—See Exxon Mobil Corporation; *U.S. Public*, pg. 816
EXXONMOBIL PIPELINE COMPANY—See Exxon Mobil Corporation; *U.S. Public*, pg. 816
EXXONMOBIL PNG LIMITED—See Exxon Mobil Corporation; *U.S. Public*, pg. 816
EXXONMOBIL PRODUCING NETHERLANDS B.V.—See Exxon Mobil Corporation; *U.S. Public*, pg. 816
EXXONMOBIL REFINING & SUPPLY COMPANY—See Exxon Mobil Corporation; *U.S. Public*, pg. 816
EXXONMOBIL REFINING & SUPPLY—See Exxon Mobil Corporation; *U.S. Public*, pg. 816
EXXONMOBIL RESEARCH & ENGINEERING—See Exxon Mobil Corporation; *U.S. Public*, pg. 816
EXXONMOBIL RESEARCH & ENGINEERING—See Exxon Mobil Corporation; *U.S. Public*, pg. 816
EXXONMOBIL SALES & SUPPLY LLC—See Exxon Mobil Corporation; *U.S. Public*, pg. 816
EXXONMOBIL UK LIMITED—See Exxon Mobil Corporation; *U.S. Public*, pg. 816
EXXON NEFTEGAS LIMITED—See Exxon Mobil Corporation; *U.S. Public*, pg. 814
EXYTE CENTRAL EUROPE GMBH—See John Brown Voest GmbH; *Int'l*, pg. 3978
EXYTE GMBH—See M+W Group GmbH; *Int'l*, pg. 4613
EXZAC, INC.—See Asseco Poland S.A.; *Int'l*, pg. 642
EXZEO SOFTWARE PRIVATE LIMITED—See HCI Group, Inc.; *U.S. Public*, pg. 1014
EXZEO USA, INC.—See HCI Group, Inc.; *U.S. Public*, pg. 1014
EXZONE PLASTICS MANUFACTURERS SDN. BHD.—See Luster Industries Bhd.; *Int'l*, pg. 4587
EYAL OPTICAL IND. LTD.—See EssilorLuxottica SA; *Int'l*, pg. 2516
EYBL AUSTRIA GMBH—See Prevent DEV GmbH; *Int'l*, pg. 5967
EYBL DEVELOPMENT GMBH—See Prevent DEV GmbH; *Int'l*, pg. 5967
EYBL HUNGARIA TEXTILIPARI KFT.—See Prevent DEV GmbH; *Int'l*, pg. 5967
EYBL SLOVAKIA S.R.O.—See Prevent DEV GmbH; *Int'l*, pg. 5967
EYBL TRIER GMBH & CO. KG—See Prevent DEV GmbH; *Int'l*, pg. 5967
EYBL VERWALTUNGS GMBH—See Prevent DEV GmbH; *Int'l*, pg. 5967
EYBNA TECHNOLOGIES LTD.—See Seach Medical Group Ltd.; *Int'l*, pg. 6661
EYEBOBS, LLC—See Blue Point Capital Partners, LLC; *U.S. Private*, pg. 590
EYEBRIGHT MEDICAL TECHNOLOGY BEIJING CO., LTD.; *Int'l*, pg. 2592
EYE CARE ASSOCIATES; *U.S. Private*, pg. 1453
EYECARE CONSULTANTS SURGERY CENTER, LLC—See KKR & Co. Inc.; *U.S. Public*, pg. 1245
EYE CARE EXPRESS LAB INC.—See EssilorLuxottica SA; *Int'l*, pg. 2513
EYECARE PARTNERS LIMITED; *Int'l*, pg. 2592
EYECITY.COM, INC.; *U.S. Public*, pg. 817
EYECOM INC.—See Telalaska Inc.; *U.S. Private*, pg. 3959
EYECONCEPT LIMITED—See Arts Optical International Holdings Ltd; *Int'l*, pg. 586
EYECONIC, INC.—See Vision Service Plan; *U.S. Private*, pg. 4391
EYECON MARKETING GROUP; *U.S. Private*, pg. 1453
EYE DESIGNS, LLC—See Vision Service Plan; *U.S. Private*, pg. 4391
EYEEGO, LLC; *U.S. Private*, pg. 1453
EYEFI INC.—See Ricoh Company, Ltd.; *Int'l*, pg. 6336
EYEFINITY, INC.—See Vision Service Plan; *U.S. Private*, pg. 4391
EYEGATE PHARMA S.A.S.—See Kiora Pharmaceuticals, Inc.; *U.S. Public*, pg. 1235
EYEGENE INC.; *Int'l*, pg. 2593
EYEGLASS SERVICE INDUSTRIES; *U.S. Private*, pg. 1453
EYEGLASS WORLD—See KKR & Co. Inc.; *U.S. Public*, pg. 1261
EYE GRAPHICS CO., LTD.—See IWASAKI ELECTRIC Co., Ltd.; *Int'l*, pg. 3849
EYE GRAPHIC SDN. BHD.—See Texchem Resources Bhd.; *Int'l*, pg. 7583
EYE HEALTH AMERICA—See Independence Capital Partners, LLC; *U.S. Private*, pg. 2056
EYEKARE KILITCH LTD.—See Kilitch Drugs (India) Ltd.; *Int'l*, pg. 4162
EYELEVEL DISTRIBUTION SERVICES—See HH Global Group Limited; *Int'l*, pg. 3378
EYELEVEL, INC.—See HH Global Group Limited; *Int'l*, pg. 3378
EYELEVEL RETAIL SOLUTIONS CONSULTORIA LTDA—See HH Global Group Limited; *Int'l*, pg. 3378
EYELEVEL SOLUTIONS LTD.—See HH Global Group Limited; *Int'l*, pg. 3378
EYELEVEL S.R.O.—See HH Global Group Limited; *Int'l*, pg. 3378
EYE LIGHTING ASIA PACIFIC PTE. LTD.—See IWASAKI ELECTRIC Co., Ltd.; *Int'l*, pg. 3849
EYE LIGHTING AUSTRALIA PTY. LTD.—See IWASAKI ELECTRIC Co., Ltd.; *Int'l*, pg. 3849
EYE LIGHTING EUROPE LTD.—See IWASAKI ELECTRIC Co., Ltd.; *Int'l*, pg. 3849
EYE LIGHTING (HONG KONG) LTD.—See IWASAKI ELECTRIC Co., Ltd.; *Int'l*, pg. 3849
EYE LIGHTING INTERNATIONAL OF NORTH AMERICA, INC.—See IWASAKI ELECTRIC Co., Ltd.; *Int'l*, pg. 3849
EYE LIGHTING NEW ZEALAND LTD.—See IWASAKI ELECTRIC Co., Ltd.; *Int'l*, pg. 3849
EYELLO CZ K.S.—See EnBW Energie Baden-Wurttemberg AG; *Int'l*, pg. 2401
EYELOCK LLC—See VOXX International Corporation; *U.S. Public*, pg. 2311
EYELOGIC SYSTEMS INC.; *Int'l*, pg. 2593
EYE LOVE LLC; *U.S. Private*, pg. 1453
EYE-MART EXPRESS LTD.; *U.S. Private*, pg. 1453
EYEMAXX REAL ESTATE AG; *Int'l*, pg. 2593
EYENOVIA, INC.; *U.S. Public*, pg. 817
EYEON SOFTWARE, INC.—See Blackmagic Design Pty. Ltd.; *Int'l*, pg. 1061
EYEPOINT PHARMACEUTICALS, INC.; *U.S. Public*, pg. 817
EYEPOINT PHARMACEUTICALS US, INC.—See EyePoint Pharmaceuticals, Inc.; *U.S. Public*, pg. 817
EYEQ OPTOMETRISTS PTY. LTD.—See EYECARE PARTNERS LIMITED; *Int'l*, pg. 2592
EYEQUBE STUDIOS PVT. LTD.—See Eros International Plc; *Int'l*, pg. 2497
THE EYES CO., LTD—See CMO Public Company Limited; *Int'l*, pg. 1671
EYE-SHARE AS—See TietoEVRY Oyj; *Int'l*, pg. 7745
EYES ON THE GO, INC.; *U.S. Private*, pg. 1453
EYE SPECIALIST OF MID FLORIDA P.A.; *U.S. Private*, pg. 1453
EYE SURGEONS; *U.S. Private*, pg. 1453
EYE SURGERY CENTER, LLC—See KKR & Co. Inc.; *U.S. Public*, pg. 1245

E-Z MART STORES, INC.

EYE SURGERY CENTER OF NASHVILLE, LLC—See Tenet Healthcare Corporation; *U.S. Public*, pg. 2010
EYE SURGERY CENTER OF WESTERN OHIO, LLC—See KKR & Co. Inc.; *U.S. Public*, pg. 1245
EYESVISION CORP.; *Int'l*, pg. 2593
EYE TECH CARE—See BNP Paribas SA; *Int'l*, pg. 1089
EYETECH INC.—See Bausch Health Companies Inc.; *Int'l*, pg. 898
EYETIQUE LLC—See Riata Capital Group LLC; *U.S. Private*, pg. 3424
EYEVERIFY INC.—See Zhejiang Ant Small & Micro Financial Services Group Co., Ltd.; *Int'l*, pg. 8648
EYEVIEW, INC.; *U.S. Private*, pg. 1453
EYEWEAR DESIGNS, LTD.; *U.S. Private*, pg. 1453
EYKON WALL SOURCES INC.; *U.S. Private*, pg. 1454
EYNON PONTIAC BUICK INC.; *U.S. Private*, pg. 1454
EYP ARCHITECTURE & ENGINEERING, P.C.—See EYP, Inc.; *U.S. Private*, pg. 1454
EYP, INC.; *U.S. Private*, pg. 1454
EYP MISSION CRITICAL FACILITIES, INC.—See Hewlett Packard Enterprise Company; *U.S. Public*, pg. 1031
EYP REALTY, LLC—See Brookfield Corporation; *Int'l*, pg. 1186
EYRIR INVEST HF.; *Int'l*, pg. 2593
EYRISE B.V.—See Merck KGaA; *Int'l*, pg. 4833
EYS KANGHONG HERBAL PTE LTD—See Eu Yan Sang International Ltd.; *Int'l*, pg. 2525
E-Z-8 MOTEL INC.; *U.S. Private*, pg. 1303
EZAGOO LIMITED; *Int'l*, pg. 2593
EZAKI GLICO CO., LTD.; *Int'l*, pg. 2593
EZAKI GLICO USA CORPORATION—See Ezaki Glico Co., Ltd.; *Int'l*, pg. 2593
EZANGA.COM, INC.; *U.S. Private*, pg. 1454
EZBIOME, INC.—See CJ Corporation; *Int'l*, pg. 1633
EZCARETECH CO., LTD.; *Int'l*, pg. 2593
EZCARETECH JAPAN CO., LTD.—See ezCaretech Co., Ltd.; *Int'l*, pg. 2593
EZ CLONE ENTERPRISES INC.—See GrowLife, Inc.; *U.S. Public*, pg. 972
EZCONN CORPORATION; *Int'l*, pg. 2593
EZCONN CZECH A.S.—See Ezconn Corporation; *Int'l*, pg. 2593
EZCORP, INC.; *U.S. Public*, pg. 817
EZDAN HOLDING GROUP COMPANY (Q.S.C.); *Int'l*, pg. 2593
EZEE FIBER TEXAS LLC—See I Squared Capital Advisors (US) LLC; *U.S. Private*, pg. 2025
EZEFLOW, INC.—See Allied Fitting LP; *U.S. Private*, pg. 186
EZEL BAUUNTERNEHMUNG SINDELFINGEN GMBH—See STRABAG SE; *Int'l*, pg. 7230
EZ ELECTRIC; *U.S. Private*, pg. 1454
EZENIA! INC.; *U.S. Public*, pg. 818
EZEN TECH CO., LTD.; *Int'l*, pg. 2594
EZENTIS CHILE, S.A.—See Grupo Ezentis S.A.; *Int'l*, pg. 3129
EZE SOFTWARE GROUP, LLC—See SS&C Technologies Holdings, Inc.; *U.S. Public*, pg. 1923
EZETOP LTD.; *Int'l*, pg. 2594
EZFILL HOLDINGS INC.; *U.S. Public*, pg. 818
EZ-FLO INTERNATIONAL INC.—See Reliance Worldwide Corporation Limited; *Int'l*, pg. 6264
EZFLY INTERNATIONAL TRAVEL AGENT CO., LTD.; *Int'l*, pg. 2594
EZFOREX.COM, INC.—See Currency Exchange International, Corp.; *U.S. Public*, pg. 611
EZ FUEL & TANK SOLUTIONS; *U.S. Private*, pg. 1454
E-Z-GO CANADA LIMITED—See Textron Inc.; *U.S. Public*, pg. 2028
EZGO TECHNOLOGIES LTD.; *Int'l*, pg. 2594
E-Z-GO TEXTRON—See Textron Inc.; *U.S. Public*, pg. 2028
EZ GROUT CORPORATION, INC.; *U.S. Private*, pg. 1454
EZ HK, LTD.—See Global Payments Inc.; *U.S. Public*, pg. 943
EZH-SEON B.V.—See E.ON SE; *Int'l*, pg. 2257
EZIBUY LTD.—See Alceon Group Pty Ltd.; *Int'l*, pg. 300
EZIDEBIT PTY LTD.—See Global Payments Inc.; *U.S. Public*, pg. 943
EZI GMBH; *Int'l*, pg. 2594
EZI MANAGEMENT PTY LTD.—See Global Payments Inc.; *U.S. Public*, pg. 943
EZION HOLDINGS LIMITED; *Int'l*, pg. 2594
EZ-LINK PTE LTD CO.—See Land Transport Authority of Singapore; *Int'l*, pg. 4404
EZLINKS GOLF LLC—See Comcast Corporation; *U.S. Public*, pg. 539
EZ LOADER ADJUSTABLE SALES CORPORATION, INC.—See EZ Loader Boat Trailers, Inc.; *U.S. Private*, pg. 1454
EZ LOADER BOAT TRAILERS, INC.; *U.S. Private*, pg. 1454
EZ LOADER CUSTOM BOAT TRAILERS, INC.—See EZ Loader Boat Trailers, Inc.; *U.S. Private*, pg. 1454
EZLO, INC.; *U.S. Private*, pg. 1454
E-Z LOK—See TCI Precision Metals, Inc.; *U.S. Private*, pg. 3942
E-Z MART STORES, INC.; *U.S. Private*, pg. 1303

E-Z MART STORES, INC.

EZMONEY ALABAMA, INC.—See EZCORP, Inc.; *U.S. Public*, pg. 817
EZMONEY IDAHO, INC.—See EZCORP, Inc.; *U.S. Public*, pg. 817
EZMONEY SOUTH DAKOTA, INC.—See EZCORP, Inc.; *U.S. Public*, pg. 817
EZ-NERGY SAS—See Energy One Limited; *Int'l*, pg. 2423
EZONEONLINE.IN—See Future Corporate Resources Limited; *Int'l*, pg. 2853
EZ ONLINE OKLAHOMA, LLC—See EZCORP, Inc.; *U.S. Public*, pg. 817
EZOOM INFORMATION, INC.—See Marketech International Corp.; *Int'l*, pg. 4696
EZOSE SCIENCES, INC.—See Shionogi & Co., Ltd.; *Int'l*, pg. 6851
EZPAWN HOLDINGS, INC.—See EZCORP, Inc.; *U.S. Public*, pg. 817
EZPAWN INDIANA, INC.—See EZCORP, Inc.; *U.S. Public*, pg. 817
EZPAWN MANAGEMENT MEXICO, SRL DE CV (LTD., INC.)—See EZCORP, Inc.; *U.S. Public*, pg. 817
EZPAWN NEVADA, INC.—See EZCORP, Inc.; *U.S. Public*, pg. 817
EZ PAY PAYMENT CENTERS INC.; *U.S. Private*, pg. 1454
EZRA HOLDINGS LTD.; *Int'l*, pg. 2594
EZRAIDER CO.; *U.S. Public*, pg. 818
EZ RAIDER, LLC—See EZRaider Co.; *U.S. Public*, pg. 818
EZRAS CHOILIM HEALTH CENTER INC.; *U.S. Private*, pg. 1454
E-Z RENT-A-CAR GROUP HOLDING LLC—See The Catalyst Capital Group Inc.; *Int'l*, pg. 7630
EZSHIELD, INC.—See The Wicks Group of Companies, LLC; *U.S. Private*, pg. 4135
EZSTORAGE CORP. OF MARYLAND—See Public Storage; *U.S. Public*, pg. 1736
EZ SYSTEMS AS; *Int'l*, pg. 2593
EZ SYSTEMS CHINA—See eZ Systems AS; *Int'l*, pg. 2593
EZ SYSTEMS FRANCE—See eZ Systems AS; *Int'l*, pg. 2593
EZ SYSTEMS GERMANY—See eZ Systems AS; *Int'l*, pg. 2593
EZ SYSTEMS ITALY—See eZ Systems AS; *Int'l*, pg. 2593
EZ SYSTEMS JAPAN—See eZ Systems AS; *Int'l*, pg. 2593
EZ SYSTEMS NORDICS—See eZ Systems AS; *Int'l*, pg. 2593
EZ SYSTEMS POLSKA SP. Z O.O.—See eZ Systems AS; *Int'l*, pg. 2593
EZ SYSTEMS SPAIN—See eZ Systems AS; *Int'l*, pg. 2593
EZ SYSTEMS US INC.—See eZ Systems AS; *Int'l*, pg. 2593
EZTD INC.; *Int'l*, pg. 2594
EZTEC EMPREENDIMENTOS E PARTICIPACOES S.A.; *Int'l*, pg. 2594
EZUCE, INC.—See Thompson Street Capital Manager LLC; *U.S. Private*, pg. 4160
EZV GESELLSCHAFT FUR ZAHLUNGSSYSTEME MBH—See REWE-Zentral-Aktiengesellschaft; *Int'l*, pg. 6315
EZVIZ EUROPE B.V.—See Hangzhou Hikvision Digital Technology Co., Ltd.; *Int'l*, pg. 3247
EZY NET PTE LTD.; *Int'l*, pg. 2594
EZYSTRUT NEW SOUTH WALES—See Korvest Ltd.; *Int'l*, pg. 4289
EZYSTRUT QUEENSLAND—See Korvest Ltd.; *Int'l*, pg. 4289
EZYSTRUT SOUTH AUSTRALIA—See Korvest Ltd.; *Int'l*, pg. 4289
EZYSTRUT VICTORIA—See Korvest Ltd.; *Int'l*, pg. 4289
EZZELL TRUCKING INC.; *U.S. Private*, pg. 1454
EZZ FLAT STEEL COMPANY—See Ezz Steel Co. S.A.E.; *Int'l*, pg. 2594
EZZIES WHOLESALE INC.; *U.S. Private*, pg. 1454
EZZI VISION PTY LTD; *Int'l*, pg. 2594
EZZ LIFE SCIENCE HOLDINGS LIMITED; *Int'l*, pg. 2594
EZZ STEEL CO. S.A.E.; *Int'l*, pg. 2594

F

F12..NET, INC.; *Int'l*, pg. 2597
F1 COMPUTER SOLUTIONS, INC.; *U.S. Private*, pg. 1457
F24 AG—See HgCapital Trust plc; *Int'l*, pg. 3376
F24 CZECH REPUBLIC S.R.O.—See HgCapital Trust plc; *Int'l*, pg. 3376
F24 FRANCE SARL—See HgCapital Trust plc; *Int'l*, pg. 3376
F24 SERVICIOS DE COMUNICACION, S.L.U.—See HgCapital Trust plc; *Int'l*, pg. 3376
F24 UNITED STATES, INC.—See HgCapital Trust plc; *Int'l*, pg. 3376
F2 CHEMICALS LIMITED—See Resonac Holdings Corporation; *Int'l*, pg. 6298
F2I - FONDI ITALIANI PER LE INFRASTRUTTURE SGR S.P.A.; *Int'l*, pg. 2597
F2 STRATEGY, INC.—See Renovus Capital Partners; *U.S. Private*, pg. 3399
F3 TECHNOLOGY PARTNERS LLC—See Fulcrum IT Partners; *Int'l*, pg. 2841
F3 URANIUM CORP.; *Int'l*, pg. 2598
F45 TRAINING HOLDINGS INC.; *U.S. Private*, pg. 1457

F5 FINISHES, INC.; *U.S. Private*, pg. 1458
F5, INC.; *U.S. Public*, pg. 818
F5 NETWORKS AUSTRALIA PTY. LIMITED—See F5, Inc.; *U.S. Public*, pg. 819
F5 NETWORKS BENELUX B.V.—See F5, Inc.; *U.S. Public*, pg. 819
F5 NETWORKS CHINA—See F5, Inc.; *U.S. Public*, pg. 819
F5 NETWORKS COLOMBIA S.A.S.—See F5, Inc.; *U.S. Public*, pg. 819
F5 NETWORKS GMBH—See F5, Inc.; *U.S. Public*, pg. 819
F5 NETWORKS HONG KONG LIMITED—See F5, Inc.; *U.S. Public*, pg. 819
F5 NETWORKS IBERIA SL—See F5, Inc.; *U.S. Public*, pg. 819
F5 NETWORKS, INC. - LOWELL—See F5, Inc.; *U.S. Public*, pg. 819
F5 NETWORKS (ISRAEL) LTD.—See F5, Inc.; *U.S. Public*, pg. 819
F5 NETWORKS JAPAN K.K.—See F5, Inc.; *U.S. Public*, pg. 819
F5 NETWORKS KOREA LTD.—See F5, Inc.; *U.S. Public*, pg. 819
F5 NETWORKS LIMITED—See F5, Inc.; *U.S. Public*, pg. 819
F5 NETWORKS LLC—See F5, Inc.; *U.S. Public*, pg. 819
F5 NETWORKS NEW ZEALAND LTD.—See F5, Inc.; *U.S. Public*, pg. 819
F5 NETWORKS POLAND SP Z.O.O—See F5, Inc.; *U.S. Public*, pg. 819
F5 NETWORKS SARL—See F5, Inc.; *U.S. Public*, pg. 819
F5 NETWORKS SINGAPORE PTE LTD.—See F5, Inc.; *U.S. Public*, pg. 819
F8 ENTERPRISES (HOLDINGS) GROUP LIMITED; *Int'l*, pg. 2598
FAAB FABRICAUTO—See 3M Company; *U.S. Public*, pg. 6
FAAC, INCORPORATED—See Greenbriar Equity Group, L.P.; *U.S. Private*, pg. 1775
FAA CONCORD H, INC.—See Sonic Automotive, Inc.; *U.S. Public*, pg. 1902
FAA CREDIT UNION; *U.S. Private*, pg. 1458
FA. ANTON SCHLECKER; *Int'l*, pg. 2598
FAA POWAY H, INC.—See Sonic Automotive, Inc.; *U.S. Public*, pg. 1902
FAA SERRAMONTE H, INC.—See Sonic Automotive, Inc.; *U.S. Public*, pg. 1902
FABA AUTOGLAS TECHNIK GMBH—See Compagnie de Saint-Gobain SA; *Int'l*, pg. 1723
THE F.A. BARTLETT TREE EXPERT COMPANY; *U.S. Private*, pg. 4027
FABASOFT AG; *Int'l*, pg. 2598
FABASOFT AUSTRIA GMBH—See Fabasoft AG; *Int'l*, pg. 2598
FABASOFT DEUTSCHLAND GMBH—See Fabasoft AG; *Int'l*, pg. 2598
FABA VERMIETUNGSGESELLSCHAFT MBH—See Commerzbank AG; *Int'l*, pg. 1717
FABBIT PHILIPPINES INC.—See Apaman Co., Ltd.; *Int'l*, pg. 500
FABBRICA D'ARMI PIETRO BERETTA S.P.A.; *Int'l*, pg. 2598
FABBRICA ITALIANA ACCUMULATORI MOTOCARRI MONTECCHIO IBERICA S.A.—See Fiamm S.p.A.; *Int'l*, pg. 2650
FABBRI—See Sonepar S.A.; *Int'l*, pg. 7093
FABCO-AIR, INC.; *U.S. Private*, pg. 1458
FABCO AUTOMOTIVE CORPORATION—See Stone River Capital Partners, LLC; *U.S. Private*, pg. 3826
FABCO AUTOMOTIVE CORPORATION—See Wynnchurch Capital, L.P.; *U.S. Private*, pg. 4577
FABCO ENTERPRISES INC.; *U.S. Private*, pg. 1458
FABCON KYUSHU CORPORATION—See Hanwa Co., Ltd.; *Int'l*, pg. 3262
FABCON PRECAST LLC—See Solace Capital Partners, LLC; *U.S. Private*, pg. 3706
FABCOR 2001, INC.—See MasTec, Inc.; *U.S. Public*, pg. 1393
FABCOR TARGETCO LTD.—See MasTec, Inc.; *U.S. Public*, pg. 1393
FABCOS INVESTMENT HOLDING COMPANY (PROPRIETARY) LIMITED—See Hosken Consolidated Investments Limited; *Int'l*, pg. 3485
FABCO—See Fabick CAT; *U.S. Private*, pg. 1458
FABCOT PTY LTD—See Woolworths Group Limited; *Int'l*, pg. 8451
FABEGE AB; *Int'l*, pg. 2598
FABENCO, INC.—See Akoya Capital LLC; *U.S. Private*, pg. 146
FABENCO, INC.—See Gemini Investors LLC; *U.S. Private*, pg. 1658
FABENCO, INC.—See TMW Enterprises Inc.; *U.S. Private*, pg. 4180
FABER BROS. BROADLOOM CO.; *U.S. Private*, pg. 1458
FABER-CASTELL AG; *Int'l*, pg. 2598
FABER-CASTELL - CHILE S.A.—See Faber-Castell AG; *Int'l*, pg. 2599

CORPORATE AFFILIATIONS

FABER-CASTELL VERTRIEB GMBH—See Faber-Castell AG; *Int'l*, pg. 2599
FABER, COE & GREGG, INC.; *U.S. Private*, pg. 1458
FABER DEVELOPMENT HOLDINGS SDN BHD—See Khazanah Nasional Berhad; *Int'l*, pg. 4153
FABER ENTERPRISES, INC.; *U.S. Private*, pg. 1458
FABERGE (UK) LIMITED—See Gemfields Group Limited; *Int'l*, pg. 2916
FABER GRANDVIEW DEVELOPMENT (SABAH) SDN BHD—See Khazanah Nasional Berhad; *Int'l*, pg. 4153
FABER HEIGHTS MANAGEMENT SDN BHD—See Khazanah Nasional Berhad; *Int'l*, pg. 4153
FABER INTERNATIONAL BV—See The Glen Dimplex Group; *Int'l*, pg. 7649
FABER KOMPLEKS SDN. BHD.—See Hotel Royal Limited; *Int'l*, pg. 3489
FABER L.L.C.—See Khazanah Nasional Berhad; *Int'l*, pg. 4153
FABER SINDOORI MANAGEMENT SERVICES PRIVATE LIMITED—See Khazanah Nasional Berhad; *Int'l*, pg. 4153
FABER UNION SDN BHD—See Khazanah Nasional Berhad; *Int'l*, pg. 4153
FAB-FORM INDUSTRIES (1986) LTD.—See Fab-Form Industries Ltd.; *Int'l*, pg. 2598
FAB-FORM INDUSTRIES LTD.; *Int'l*, pg. 2598
FAB FOURS, INC.; *U.S. Private*, pg. 1458
FABIANO BROS INC.; *U.S. Private*, pg. 1458
FABIANO COMMUNICATIONS, INC.; *U.S. Private*, pg. 1458
FABI BOLSAS INDUSTRIALES S.A.—See Empresas CMPC S.A.; *Int'l*, pg. 2390
FABICK CAT; *U.S. Private*, pg. 1458
FABICK CAT - SPRINGFIELD—See Fabick CAT; *U.S. Private*, pg. 1458
FABICK CAT - WISCONSIN—See Fabick CAT; *U.S. Private*, pg. 1458
FABIG-PETERS MEDIZINTECHNIK GMBH & CO. KG—See L'Air Liquide S.A.; *Int'l*, pg. 4374
FAB, INC.—See PCH International Ltd.; *Int'l*, pg. 5768
FAB INDUSTRIES CORP.; *U.S. Private*, pg. 1458
FABINO LIFE SCIENCES LIMITED; *Int'l*, pg. 2599
FABIO PERINI GERMANY GMBH—See Korber AG; *Int'l*, pg. 4281
FABIO PERINI JAPAN CO., LTD.—See Korber AG; *Int'l*, pg. 4281
FABIO PERINI LTDA.—See Korber AG; *Int'l*, pg. 4281
FABIO PERINI NORTH AMERICA, INC.—See Korber AG; *Int'l*, pg. 4281
FABIO PERINI PACKAGING S.P.A.—See Korber AG; *Int'l*, pg. 4281
FABIO PERINI (SHANGHAI) CO., LTD.—See Korber AG; *Int'l*, pg. 4281
FABIO PERINI S.P.A.—See Korber AG; *Int'l*, pg. 4281
FABLAB S.R.L.—See CompuGroup Medical SE & Co. KGaA; *Int'l*, pg. 1756
FABLED COPPER CORP.; *Int'l*, pg. 2599
FAB-LITE BUILDING SOLUTIONS LIMITED—See Michelmersh Brick Holdings PLC; *Int'l*, pg. 4875
FAB-LITE FACADES LIMITED—See Michelmersh Brick Holdings PLC; *Int'l*, pg. 4875
FABMATICS GMBH; *Int'l*, pg. 2599
FABMATICS GMBH—See Fabmatics GmbH; *Int'l*, pg. 2599
FABO KERESKEDELMI ES SZOLGALTATO KFT.—See AUMA Riester GmbH & Co. KG; *Int'l*, pg. 705
FABORY CENTRES BELGIUM N.V.—See W.W. Grainger, Inc.; *U.S. Public*, pg. 2319
FABORY CZ HOLDING S.R.O.—See W.W. Grainger, Inc.; *U.S. Public*, pg. 2319
FABORY FRANCE S.A.—See W.W. Grainger, Inc.; *U.S. Public*, pg. 2319
FABORY KOTOELEM KERESKEDELMI KFT—See W.W. Grainger, Inc.; *U.S. Public*, pg. 2319
FABORY MASTERS IN FASTENERS GROUP B.V.—See W.W. Grainger, Inc.; *U.S. Public*, pg. 2320
FABORY NEDERLAND B.V.—See W.W. Grainger, Inc.; *U.S. Public*, pg. 2319
FABORY POLAND SP. Z.O.O.—See W.W. Grainger, Inc.; *U.S. Public*, pg. 2319
FABORY PORTUGAL LDA.—See W.W. Grainger, Inc.; *U.S. Public*, pg. 2319
FABORY SHANGHAI CO. LTD.—See W.W. Grainger, Inc.; *U.S. Public*, pg. 2319
FABORY SLOVAKIA SRO—See W.W. Grainger, Inc.; *U.S. Public*, pg. 2319
FABORY SRL—See W.W. Grainger, Inc.; *U.S. Public*, pg. 2319
FABORY UK LTD.—See W.W. Grainger, Inc.; *U.S. Public*, pg. 2319
FAB PRIVATE BANK (SUISSE) SA—See First Abu Dhabi Bank P.J.S.C.; *Int'l*, pg. 2681
FAB PROPERTIES—See First Abu Dhabi Bank P.J.S.C.; *Int'l*, pg. 2681
FABRAL, INC.—See Flack Steel LLC; *U.S. Private*, pg. 1538
FABRE CONSTRUCTION—See VINCI S.A.; *Int'l*, pg. 8220
FABREEKA INTERNATIONAL HOLDINGS, INC.—See Triton Advisers Limited; *Int'l*, pg. 7934

COMPANY NAME INDEX

FABREEKA INTERNATIONAL, INC.—See Triton Advisers Limited; *Int'l*, pg. 7934
FABRE ENGINEERING, INC.—See Bowman Consulting Group Ltd.; *U.S. Public*, pg. 376
FABREL AG; *Int'l*, pg. 2599
FABREL LOTOS AG—See Fabrel AG; *Int'l*, pg. 2599
FABRESINES—See Compagnie de Saint-Gobain SA; *Int'l*, pg. 1723
FABRICA BRASILEIRA DE FREIOS S.A.—See Haldex AB; *Int'l*, pg. 3228
FABRICACION DE MAQUINAS S.A. DE C.V.—See Vitro, S.A.B. de C.V.; *Int'l*, pg. 8262
FABRICA DE BLOQUES MASSO INC.—See Masso Enterprises; *U.S. Private*, pg. 2607
FABRICA DE GALLETAS LA MODERNA, S.A. DE C.V.—See Grupo La Moderna, S.A.B. de C.V.; *Int'l*, pg. 3131
FABRICA DE MATRITE SRL—See S.C. GRUPUL INDUSTRIAL ELECTROCONTACT S.A.; *Int'l*, pg. 6451
FABRICA DE PINTURAS UNIVERSALES, S.A. DE C.V.—See PPG Industries, Inc.; *U.S. Public*, pg. 1707
FABRICA DE SCULE RASNOV SA; *Int'l*, pg. 2599
FABRICA DE TECIDOS CARLOS RENAUX S.A.; *Int'l*, pg. 2599
FABRICA ELECTROTECNICA JOSA, S.A.—See Siemens Aktiengesellschaft; *Int'l*, pg. 6886
FABRICA INTERNATIONAL, INC.—See The Dixie Group, Inc.; *U.S. Public*, pg. 2067
FABRICA ITAUTEC-JUNDIAI—See Itausa - Investimentos Itau S.A.; *Int'l*, pg. 3831
FABRICA PERUANA ETERNIT S.A.—See Etex SA/NV; *Int'l*, pg. 2522
FABRICAS AGRUPADAS DE MUNECAS DE ONIL, S.A.—See Giochi Preziosi S.p.A.; *Int'l*, pg. 2977
FABRICAS MONTERREY, S.A. DE C.V.—See Crown Holdings, Inc.; *U.S. Public*, pg. 598
FABRICATED COMPONENTS CORPORATION; *U.S. Private*, pg. 1458
FABRICATED GLASS SPECIALTIES; *U.S. Private*, pg. 1458
FABRICATED METALS LLC; *U.S. Private*, pg. 1458
FABRICATED PIPE, INC.; *U.S. Private*, pg. 1458
FABRICATED PRODUCTS, INC.—See The Renco Group Inc.; *U.S. Private*, pg. 4104
FABRICATED STEEL PRODUCTS, INC.; *U.S. Private*, pg. 1458
FABRICATING SPECIALISTS, LLC—See Mayville Engineering Company, Inc.; *U.S. Public*, pg. 1403
FABRICATION & CONSTRUCTION SERVICES, LP; *U.S. Private*, pg. 1459
FABRICATIONS MECANIQUES DE L'ATLANTIQUE SA—See General Electric Company; *U.S. Public*, pg. 918
FABRICATIONS MECANIQUES DE L'ATLANTIQUE SA—See Safran SA; *Int'l*, pg. 6473
FABRICATORS SUPPLY COMPANY; *U.S. Private*, pg. 1459
FABRIC COM, INC.—See Amazon.com, Inc.; *U.S. Public*, pg. 90
FABRIC DEVELOPMENT INC.—See Haci Omer Sabanci Holding A.S.; *Int'l*, pg. 3204
FABRIC HOUSE PTE. LTD.—See Stamford Land Corporation Ltd.; *Int'l*, pg. 7165
FABRICLEAN SUPPLY, INC.; *U.S. Private*, pg. 1459
FABRICO CENTRAL—See Audax Group, Limited Partnership; *U.S. Private*, pg. 387
FABRICO, INC.—See Enpro Inc.; *U.S. Public*, pg. 775
FABRICOM OFFSHORE SERVICES LTD.—See ENGIE SA; *Int'l*, pg. 2429
FABRICOM OIL, GAS & POWER LIMITED—See ENGIE SA; *Int'l*, pg. 2429
FABRICON PRODUCTS INC.; *U.S. Private*, pg. 1459
FABRIC RESOURCES INTERNATIONAL LTD.; *U.S. Private*, pg. 1458
FABRIC RETAIL GLBL AB—See H&M Hennes & Mauritz AB; *Int'l*, pg. 3192
FABRIC SALES A/S—See H&M Hennes & Mauritz AB; *Int'l*, pg. 3192
FABRIC SALES NORWAY AS—See H&M Hennes & Mauritz AB; *Int'l*, pg. 3192
FABRICUT INC.; *U.S. Private*, pg. 1459
FABRIC WORLDWIDE—See WPP plc; *Int'l*, pg. 8469
THE FABRI-FORM COMPANY—See Kruger Brown Holdings, LLC; *U.S. Private*, pg. 2353
FABRIKA BAKARNIH CEVI A.D.; *Int'l*, pg. 2599
FABRIKA CEMENTA LUKAVAC D.D.; *Int'l*, pg. 2599
FABRIKA DUHANA SARAJEVO D.D.—See CID Adriatic Investments GmbH; *Int'l*, pg. 1603
FABRIKA HLEBA I MLEKA A.D.; *Int'l*, pg. 2599
FABRIKA KARPOS AD—See Gradezen Institut Makedonija; *Int'l*, pg. 3049
FABRIKA KOZE LAUS A.D.; *Int'l*, pg. 2599
FABRI-KAL CORPORATION—See Pactiv Evergreen Inc.; *U.S. Public*, pg. 1633
FABRIKA MAZIVA FAM A.D. KRUSEVAC; *Int'l*, pg. 2599
FABRIKA OPRUGA CACAK A.D.; *Int'l*, pg. 2599
FABRIKA PLASTIKOW POMERANIA - SP Z O.O.—See Plastiques du Val de Loire S.A.; *Int'l*, pg. 5892
FABRIKA STOCNE HRANE JABUKA A.D.; *Int'l*, pg. 2600

FABRIK ENTERTAINMENT, LLC—See ProSiebenSat.1 Media SE; *Int'l*, pg. 6000
FABRIK INDUSTRIES INC.; *U.S. Private*, pg. 1459
FABRINET—See H&Q Asia Pacific, Ltd.; *U.S. Private*, pg. 1823
FABRIQUE DE FOURNITURES DE BONNETAGE FFB SAS—See The Swatch Group Ltd.; *Int'l*, pg. 7691
FABRI-QUILT, INC.; *U.S. Private*, pg. 1458
FABRISTEEL PRIVATE LIMITED—See The Manitowoc Company, Inc.; *U.S. Public*, pg. 2111
FABRISTEEL PRODUCTS—See Whitesell Corporation; *U.S. Private*, pg. 4512
FABRI-TECH INC.—See Hader Industries Inc.; *U.S. Private*, pg. 1839
FABRITEC-OVERTOOM GMBH—See Manutan International SA; *Int'l*, pg. 4679
FABRIZI TRUCKING & PAVING CO.; *U.S. Private*, pg. 1459
FABRYCA OSI NAPEDOWYCH S.A.—See FLY Srl; *Int'l*, pg. 2715
FABRY INDUSTRIES SARANAC WORLD OF GLOVES; *U.S. Private*, pg. 1459
FABRYKA FARB I LAKIEROW SNIEZKA S.A.; *Int'l*, pg. 2600
FABRYKA LOZYSK TOCZNYCH - KRASNIK S.A.—See Xiangyang Automobile Bearing Co., Ltd.; *Int'l*, pg. 8527
FABRYKA PARAFIN NAFTOWAX SP. Z O.O.—See Orlen S.A.; *Int'l*, pg. 5641
FABRYKA PLASTIKOW GLIWICE - SP Z.O.O.—See Plastiques du Val de Loire S.A.; *Int'l*, pg. 5892
FABRYKA SILNIKOW ELEKTRYCZNYCH TAMEL SA—See Wolong Holding Group Co., Ltd.; *Int'l*, pg. 8443
FABRYKA WAGONOW GNIEWCZYNA SA; *Int'l*, pg. 2600
FABRYKI MEBLI FORTE S.A.; *Int'l*, pg. 2600
FABRYKI SPRZETU I NARZEDZI GORNICZYCH GRUPA KAPITALOWA FASING S.A.; *Int'l*, pg. 2600
FABRYO CORPORATION SRL—See Akzo Nobel N.V.; *Int'l*, pg. 274
FABSOL, LLC—See Prophet Equity L.P.; *U.S. Private*, pg. 3286
FABSPEED UK LIMITED—See Michelmersh Brick Holdings PLC; *Int'l*, pg. 4875
FAB TECH INC.; *U.S. Private*, pg. 1458
FABTECH INC.—See Diodes Incorporated; *U.S. Public*, pg. 667
FABTECH S.A. PTY. LTD.—See E&A Limited; *Int'l*, pg. 2247
FABULA LIMITED—See PJSC Gazprom; *Int'l*, pg. 5879
FABULOUS.COM PTY LIMITED—See Enero Group Limited; *Int'l*, pg. 2423
FABULOUS RANGE SDN. BHD.—See Lum Chang Holdings Limited; *Int'l*, pg. 4577
FAB UNIVERSAL CORP.; *U.S. Private*, pg. 1458
FACADEMASTER PTE LTD.—See Compact Metal Industries Ltd.; *Int'l*, pg. 1721
FACB INDUSTRIES INCORPORATED BERHAD; *Int'l*, pg. 2600
FACC AG; *Int'l*, pg. 2600
FACCHIANO, MICHAEL CONTRACTING INC.; *U.S. Private*, pg. 1459
FACCHINA CONSTRUCTION CO., INC.—See Empresas ICA S.A.B. de C.V.; *Int'l*, pg. 2390
FACCHINA GLOBAL SERVICES LLC; *U.S. Private*, pg. 1459
FACEDRIVE, INC.; *Int'l*, pg. 2600
FACEKEY CORPORATION; *U.S. Public*, pg. 819
FACEMIRE FOODS INC.; *U.S. Private*, pg. 1459
FACEO FM SAS—See VINCI S.A.; *Int'l*, pg. 8220
FACEPHI APAC, LTD.—See Facephi Biometria SA; *Int'l*, pg. 2600
FACEPHI BIOMETRIA SA; *Int'l*, pg. 2600
FACES MAGAZINE INC.; *U.S. Private*, pg. 1459
FACETIME STRATEGY; *U.S. Private*, pg. 1459
FACETIME STRATEGY—See FaceTime Strategy; *U.S. Private*, pg. 1459
FACETIME STRATEGY—See FaceTime Strategy; *U.S. Private*, pg. 1459
FACETS FINE JEWELRY, LLC—See Pohlad Companies; *U.S. Private*, pg. 3220
FACETS INTERIORS (PTY) LIMITED—See Basil Read Holdings Limited; *Int'l*, pg. 887
FACETS MULTI-MEDIA, INC.; *U.S. Private*, pg. 1459
FACET TECHNOLOGIES, LLC—See Tower Three Partners, LLC; *U.S. Private*, pg. 4194
FACHKLINIK RHEIN/RUHR FUR HERZ/KREISLAUF- UND BEWEGUNGSSYSTEM GMBH & CO. KG—See Asklepios Kliniken GmbH & Co. KGaA; *Int'l*, pg. 623
FACHKLINIKUM WIESEN GMBH—See Asklepios Kliniken GmbH & Co. KGaA; *Int'l*, pg. 623
FACHKLINIK ZWIESELBERG GMBH—See Asklepios Kliniken GmbH & Co. KGaA; *Int'l*, pg. 623
FACHKRANKENHAUS FUR PSYCHIATRIE UND NEUROLOGIE HILDBURGHAUSEN GMBH—See Fresenius SE & Co. KGaA; *Int'l*, pg. 2778
FACIL CORPORATE BVBA; *Int'l*, pg. 2600
FACILEASING EQUIPMENT, S.A. DE C.V.—See Banco Bilbao Vizcaya Argentaria, S.A.; *Int'l*, pg. 817

FACTORY BUILDER STORES INC.

FACILEASING S.A. DE C.V.—See Banco Bilbao Vizcaya Argentaria, S.A.; *Int'l*, pg. 817
FACIL EUROPE BVBA—See Facil Corporate BVBA; *Int'l*, pg. 2600
FACILISGROUP LLP—See The Pebble Group Plc; *Int'l*, pg. 7673
FACILITA BERLIN GMBH—See Deutsche Wohnen SE; *Int'l*, pg. 2085
FACILITATE DIGITAL HOLDINGS LIMITED—See Adslot Ltd.; *Int'l*, pg. 154
FACILITECH, INC.; *U.S. Private*, pg. 1459
FACILITEC, INC.; *U.S. Private*, pg. 1459
FACILITIES BY ADF PLC; *Int'l*, pg. 2600
FACILITIES CONNECTION, INC.; *U.S. Private*, pg. 1459
THE FACILITIES GROUP NATIONAL LLC—See Greenbriar Equity Group, L.P.; *U.S. Private*, pg. 1776
THE FACILITIES GROUP NATIONAL LLC—See Revolent Capital Solutions; *U.S. Private*, pg. 3416
FACILITIES RESOURCE GROUP INC.; *U.S. Private*, pg. 1459
FACILITY ASSOCIATES RECRUITMENT LIMITED—See Jones Lang LaSalle Incorporated; *U.S. Public*, pg. 1201
FACILITY CONCEPTS INC.; *U.S. Private*, pg. 1459
FACILITY GATEWAY CORPORATION; *U.S. Private*, pg. 1459
FACILITY INTERIORS INC.; *U.S. Private*, pg. 1459
FACILITY MATRIX GROUP INC.; *U.S. Private*, pg. 1460
FACILITY MERCHANDISING, INC.; *U.S. Private*, pg. 1460
FACILITYONE TECHNOLOGIES, LLC—See RainMaker Capital, LLC; *U.S. Private*, pg. 3348
FACILITY SERVICES INC.—See DJ International Incorporated; *U.S. Private*, pg. 1246
FACILITY SOLUTIONS GROUP, INC.; *U.S. Private*, pg. 1460
FACILITYSOURCE, LLC—See CBRE Group, Inc.; *U.S. Public*, pg. 460
FACILITY SUPPORT SERVICES, LLC—See Gold Belt Incorporated; *U.S. Private*, pg. 1727
FACIL NORTH AMERICA, INC.—See Facil Corporate BVBA; *Int'l*, pg. 2600
FACKELMANN HOUSEWARES PTY. LTD.—See Leifheit AG; *Int'l*, pg. 4446
FACOM BELGIE BVBA—See Stanley Black & Decker, Inc.; *U.S. Public*, pg. 1932
FACOM S.A.—See Stanley Black & Decker, Inc.; *U.S. Public*, pg. 1932
FACOM UK LTD.—See Stanley Black & Decker, Inc.; *U.S. Public*, pg. 1932
FACOR ALLOYS LIMITED; *Int'l*, pg. 2601
FAC PROPERTYS LLC; *U.S. Private*, pg. 1459
FACT CORPORATION; *Int'l*, pg. 2601
FACT DENMARK A / S—See Deutsche Post AG; *Int'l*, pg. 2080
FACT ENTERPRISE LIMITED; *Int'l*, pg. 2601
FACT, INC.; *Int'l*, pg. 2601
FACT INFORMATIONSSYSTEME UND CONSULTING AG—See Silver Lake Group, LLC; *U.S. Private*, pg. 3658
FACTION MEDIA; *U.S. Private*, pg. 1460
FACTLINES AS—See Arendals Fossekompani ASA; *Int'l*, pg. 559
FACTOR 3 MEDIA—See Masterminds; *U.S. Private*, pg. 2608
FACTOR 89 PARTNERS, LLC; *U.S. Private*, pg. 1460
FACTORAJE BANCOMER—See Banco Bilbao Vizcaya Argentaria, S.A.; *Int'l*, pg. 818
FACTORBANK AKTIENGESELLSCHAFT—See UniCredit S.p.A.; *Int'l*, pg. 8040
FACTOR FORMS LTD; *Int'l*, pg. 2601
FACTOR GAS LIQUIDS INC.; *Int'l*, pg. 2601
FACTORIA Y MANUFACTURA S.A. DE C.V.—See ManpowerGroup Inc.; *U.S. Public*, pg. 1358
FACT-O-RIG—See Dietswell S.A.; *Int'l*, pg. 2117
FACTORING CESKE SPORITELNY A.S.—See Erste Group Bank AG; *Int'l*, pg. 2498
FACTORING KB, A.S.—See Societe Generale S.A.; *Int'l*, pg. 7040
FACTORING.PLUS.GMBH—See flatexDEGIRO AG; *Int'l*, pg. 2698
FACTORIT S.P.A.—See Banca Popolare di Sondrio S.p.A.; *Int'l*, pg. 816
FACTOR MOKA, S.L.U.—See Vocento, S.A.; *Int'l*, pg. 8284
FACTORS AG—See UBS Group AG; *Int'l*, pg. 8007
FACTOR SALES, INC.; *U.S. Private*, pg. 1460
FACTOR—See W.R. Hess Company; *U.S. Private*, pg. 4422
FACTORS SOUTHWEST, LLC—See Oxford Bank Corporation; *U.S. Public*, pg. 1628
FACTOR SYSTEMS, INC.—See EQT AB; *Int'l*, pg. 2472
FACTORTRUST, INC.—See TransUnion; *U.S. Public*, pg. 2184
FACTORY 360; *U.S. Private*, pg. 1460
FACTORY BUILDER STORES INC.; *U.S. Private*, pg. 1460
FACTORY CARD OUTLET OF AMERICA LTD.—See Thomas H. Lee Partners, L.P.; *U.S. Private*, pg. 4156
FACTORY CARD & PARTY OUTLET CORP.—See Thomas H. Lee Partners, L.P.; *U.S. Private*, pg. 4156

FACTORY BUILDER STORES INC.

FACTORY CLEANING EQUIPMENT, INC.—See Incline MGMT Corp.; *U.S. Private*, pg. 2053
FACTORY CONNECTION, LLC; *U.S. Private*, pg. 1460
FACTORY CRO BV; *Int'l*, pg. 2601
FACTORY DESIGN LABS, INC.; *U.S. Private*, pg. 1460
FACTORY DIRECT APPLIANCE INC.; *U.S. Private*, pg. 1460
FACTORY DIRECT INC.—See Mathis Bros. Furniture Co. Inc.; *U.S. Private*, pg. 2611
FACTORY MUTUAL INSURANCE COMPANY - CANADA—See Factory Mutual Insurance Company; *U.S. Private*, pg. 1461
FACTORY MUTUAL INSURANCE COMPANY - CANADA—See Factory Mutual Insurance Company; *U.S. Private*, pg. 1461
FACTORY MUTUAL INSURANCE COMPANY; *U.S. Private*, pg. 1460
FACTORY OUTLET AIRPORT S.A.—See Folli Follie S.A.; *Int'l*, pg. 2721
FACTORY OUTLET S.A.—See Folli Follie S.A.; *Int'l*, pg. 2721
FACTORY STORE S.P.A.—See Giorgio Armani S.p.A.; *Int'l*, pg. 2978
FACTS & COMPARISONS—See Wolters Kluwer n.v.; *Int'l*, pg. 8444
FACTS EDUCATION SOLUTIONS, LLC—See Nelnet, Inc.; *U.S. Public*, pg. 1504
FACTSET BENELUX B.V.—See FactSet Research Systems Inc.; *U.S. Public*, pg. 819
FACTSET DATA SYSTEMS, INC.—See FactSet Research Systems Inc.; *U.S. Public*, pg. 819
FACTSET DIGITAL SOLUTIONS AG—See FactSet Research Systems Inc.; *U.S. Public*, pg. 819
FACTSET DIGITAL SOLUTIONS, LLC—See FactSet Research Systems Inc.; *U.S. Public*, pg. 819
FACTSET EUROPE LIMITED—See FactSet Research Systems Inc.; *U.S. Public*, pg. 819
FACTSET FRANCE S.A.R.L.—See FactSet Research Systems Inc.; *U.S. Public*, pg. 819
FACTSET FRANCE SAS—See FactSet Research Systems Inc.; *U.S. Public*, pg. 819
FACTSET GMBH—See FactSet Research Systems Inc.; *U.S. Public*, pg. 819
FACTSET HONG KONG LIMITED—See FactSet Research Systems Inc.; *U.S. Public*, pg. 819
FACTSET ITALIA S.R.L.—See FactSet Research Systems Inc.; *U.S. Public*, pg. 819
FACTSET JCF S.A.S.—See FactSet Research Systems Inc.; *U.S. Public*, pg. 819
FACTSET PACIFIC, INC.—See FactSet Research Systems Inc.; *U.S. Public*, pg. 820
FACTSET PACIFIC, INC.—See FactSet Research Systems Inc.; *U.S. Public*, pg. 819
FACTSET PHILIPPINES, INC.—See FactSet Research Systems Inc.; *U.S. Public*, pg. 819
FACTSET RESEARCH LIMITED—See FactSet Research Systems Inc.; *U.S. Public*, pg. 820
FACTSET RESEARCH SYSTEMS INC. - CONTENT COLLECTION—See FactSet Research Systems Inc.; *U.S. Public*, pg. 820
FACTSET RESEARCH SYSTEMS INC.; *U.S. Public*, pg. 819
FACTSET SINGAPORE PTE LTD—See FactSet Research Systems Inc.; *U.S. Public*, pg. 820
FACTSET SWITZERLAND AG—See FactSet Research Systems Inc.; *U.S. Public*, pg. 820
FACTSET SYSTEMS INDIA PRIVATE LIMITED—See FactSet Research Systems Inc.; *U.S. Public*, pg. 820
FACTSET UK LIMITED—See FactSet Research Systems Inc.; *U.S. Public*, pg. 820
FACTS & FICTION GMBH—See WPP plc; *Int'l*, pg. 8483
FACTS MANAGEMENT AUS PTY. LTD.—See Nelnet, Inc.; *U.S. Public*, pg. 1504
FACTUAL INC.—See Foursquare Labs, Inc.; *U.S. Private*, pg. 1583
FACTUM INVENIO—See Bain Capital, LP; *U.S. Private*, pg. 447
FACT UNTERNEHMENSBERATUNG GMBH—See Silver Lake Group, LLC; *U.S. Private*, pg. 3658
FACT UNTERNEHMENSBERATUNG SCHWEIZ AG—See Silver Lake Group, LLC; *U.S. Private*, pg. 3658
FACULTATIVE RESOURCES, INC.—See W.R. Berkley Corporation; *U.S. Public*, pg. 2318
FACULTY OF 1000 LTD.—See Sciencenow Limited; *Int'l*, pg. 6647
FACULTY PRODUCTIONS, LLC—See Live Nation Entertainment, Inc.; *U.S. Public*, pg. 1328
FAD A.D. GORNJI MILANOVAC; *Int'l*, pg. 2601
F&A DAIRY PRODUCTS INC.—See Saputo Inc.; *Int'l*, pg. 6575
FADAP A.D.; *Int'l*, pg. 2601
FADAPHARMA DEL ECUADOR S.A.—See Abbott Laboratories; *U.S. Public*, pg. 19
F.A. DAVIS PUBLISHING COMPANY; *U.S. Private*, pg. 1455
FADE GIDA YATIRIM SANAYI TICARET A.S.; *Int'l*, pg. 2601
FADO PUBS INC.; *U.S. Private*, pg. 1461

FAEDRELANDSVENNEN AS—See Schibsted ASA; *Int'l*, pg. 6616
FAEDRELANDSVENNEN DISTRIBUSJON AS—See Schibsted ASA; *Int'l*, pg. 6617
FAEGRE DRINKER BIDDLE & REATH LLP; *U.S. Private*, pg. 1461
FAEQUIP CORPORATION—See Zicom Group Limited; *Int'l*, pg. 8681
FAERCH A/S—See Advent International Corporation; *U.S. Private*, pg. 101
FAERCH FRANCE SAS—See Advent International Corporation; *U.S. Private*, pg. 101
FAERCH ITALY S.R.L.—See Italmobiliare S.p.A.; *Int'l*, pg. 3829
FAERCH PLAST BUNOL S.L.U.—See Advent International Corporation; *U.S. Private*, pg. 101
FAES FARMA DEL ECUADOR SA—See FAES Farma, S.A.; *Int'l*, pg. 2601
FAES FARMA, S.A.; *Int'l*, pg. 2601
FAE TECHNOLOGY S.P.A.; *Int'l*, pg. 2601
FAE THAI COMPANY LIMITED—See Zicom Group Limited; *Int'l*, pg. 8681
FAF INTERNATIONAL SIGORTA ARACILIK HIZMETIERI ANONIM SIRKETI—See First American Financial Corporation; *U.S. Public*, pg. 835
FAFNIR GMBH—See Vontier Corporation; *U.S. Public*, pg. 2308
F&A FOOD SALES CO. INC.; *U.S. Private*, pg. 1454
FAG AEROSPACE INC.—See INA-Holding Schaeffler GmbH & Co. KG; *Int'l*, pg. 3640
FAG AEROSPACE (SINGAPORE) PTE. LTD.—See INA-Holding Schaeffler GmbH & Co. KG; *Int'l*, pg. 3640
FAGAL SRL—See Nestle S.A.; *Int'l*, pg. 5202
THE FAGAN COMPANY—See EMCOR Group, Inc.; *U.S. Public*, pg. 739
FAGAN MOTORS LTD.—See The Colonial Motor Company Limited; *Int'l*, pg. 7634
FAG BEARINGS LLC—See INA-Holding Schaeffler GmbH & Co. KG; *Int'l*, pg. 3640
FAGE DAIRY INDUSTRY S.A.; *Int'l*, pg. 2601
FAGE ITALIA S.R.L.—See Fage Dairy Industry S.A.; *Int'l*, pg. 2601
FAGEN INC.; *U.S. Private*, pg. 1461
FA GEOTECH EQUIPMENT SDN BHD—See Zicom Group Limited; *Int'l*, pg. 8681
FAGER COMPANY; *U.S. Private*, pg. 1461
FAGERDALA (CHENGDU) PACKAGING CO., LTD.—See Sealed Air Corporation; *U.S. Public*, pg. 1853
FAGERDALA (CHONGQING) PACKAGING CO., LTD.—See Sealed Air Corporation; *U.S. Public*, pg. 1853
FAGERDALA (HUIYANG) PACKAGING CO., LTD.—See Sealed Air Corporation; *U.S. Public*, pg. 1853
FAGERDALA (LEAMCHABUNG) LTD.—See Sealed Air Corporation; *U.S. Public*, pg. 1853
FAGERDALA MALAYSIA SDN. BHD.—See Sealed Air Corporation; *U.S. Public*, pg. 1853
FAGERDALA MEXICO S.A. DE C.V.—See Sealed Air Corporation; *U.S. Public*, pg. 1853
FAGERDALA PACKAGING INC.—See Sealed Air Corporation; *U.S. Public*, pg. 1853
FAGERDALA (SHANGHAI) FOAMS CO. LTD.—See Sealed Air Corporation; *U.S. Public*, pg. 1853
FAGERDALA (SHANGHAI) POLYMER CO. LTD.—See Sealed Air Corporation; *U.S. Public*, pg. 1853
FAGERDALA SINGAPORE PTE. LTD.—See Sealed Air Corporation; *U.S. Public*, pg. 1853
FAGERDALA (SUZHOU) PACKAGING CO., LTD.—See Sealed Air Corporation; *U.S. Public*, pg. 1853
FAGERDALA (THAILAND) LTD.—See Sealed Air Corporation; *U.S. Public*, pg. 1853
FAGERDALA WORLD FOAMS AB; *Int'l*, pg. 2601
FAGERDALA (XIAMEN) PACKAGING CO. LTD.—See Sealed Air Corporation; *U.S. Public*, pg. 1853
FAGERHULT AS—See Fagerhult Group AB; *Int'l*, pg. 2602
FAGERHULT BELYSNING AS—See Fagerhult Group AB; *Int'l*, pg. 2602
FAGERHULT BV—See Fagerhult Group AB; *Int'l*, pg. 2602
FAGERHULT FRANCE—See Fagerhult Group AB; *Int'l*, pg. 2602
FAGERHULT GROUP AB; *Int'l*, pg. 2601
FAGERHULT LIGHTING LTD—See Fagerhult Group AB; *Int'l*, pg. 2602
FAGERHULT LIGHTING LTD—See Fagerhult Group AB; *Int'l*, pg. 2602
FAGERHULT LIGHTING SYSTEM (SUZHOU) CO. LTD.—See Fagerhult Group AB; *Int'l*, pg. 2602
FAGERHULT (NZ) LTD—See Fagerhult Group AB; *Int'l*, pg. 2602
FAGERHULT OU—See Fagerhult Group AB; *Int'l*, pg. 2602
FAGERHULT OY—See Fagerhult Group AB; *Int'l*, pg. 2602
FAGERHULT RETAIL AB—See Fagerhult Group AB; *Int'l*, pg. 2602
FAGERHULTS BELYSNING AB—See Fagerhult Group AB; *Int'l*, pg. 2602
FAGERHULTS BELYSNING SVERIGE AB—See Fagerhult Group AB; *Int'l*, pg. 2602
FAGERHULT S.L.—See Fagerhult Group AB; *Int'l*, pg. 2602

FAGERHULT SPB—See Fagerhult Group AB; *Int'l*, pg. 2602
FAGERHULT SP.Z.O.O—See Fagerhult Group AB; *Int'l*, pg. 2602
FAGERHULT S.R.O—See Fagerhult Group AB; *Int'l*, pg. 2602
FAGER-MCGEE COMMERCIAL CONSTRUCTION INC.; *U.S. Private*, pg. 1461
FAGERSTA STAINLESS AB—See Outokumpu Oyj; *Int'l*, pg. 5668
FAGE USA DAIRY INDUSTRY, INC.—See Fage Dairy Industry S.A.; *Int'l*, pg. 2601
FAGE USA HOLDINGS, INC.—See Fage Dairy Industry S.A.; *Int'l*, pg. 2601
FAGGS GEELONG PTY. LTD.—See Metcash Limited; *Int'l*, pg. 4852
FAG INDUSTRIAL SERVICES GMBH—See INA-Holding Schaeffler GmbH & Co. KG; *Int'l*, pg. 3639
FAGKAUP EHF.—See Endress+Hauser (International) Holding AG; *Int'l*, pg. 2408
FAG MAGYARORSZAG IPARI KFT.—See INA-Holding Schaeffler GmbH & Co. KG; *Int'l*, pg. 3640
FAGOR AUTOMATION (ASIA) LTD.—See Mondragon Corporation; *Int'l*, pg. 5029
FAGOR AUTOMATION CORP.—See Mondragon Corporation; *Int'l*, pg. 5029
FAGOR AUTOMATION DO BRAZIL COM.IMP.EXP. LTDA.—See Mondragon Corporation; *Int'l*, pg. 5029
FAGOR AUTOMATION FRANCE S.A.R.L.—See Mondragon Corporation; *Int'l*, pg. 5029
FAGOR AUTOMATION GMBH—See Mondragon Corporation; *Int'l*, pg. 5029
FAGOR AUTOMATION KOREA, LTD.—See Mondragon Corporation; *Int'l*, pg. 5029
FAGOR AUTOMATION LTDA.—See Mondragon Corporation; *Int'l*, pg. 5029
FAGOR AUTOMATION (M) SDN.BHD.—See Mondragon Corporation; *Int'l*, pg. 5029
FAGOR AUTOMATION RUS.—See Mondragon Corporation; *Int'l*, pg. 5029
FAGOR AUTOMATION (S) PTE. LTD.—See Mondragon Corporation; *Int'l*, pg. 5029
FAGOR AUTOMATION TAIWAN CO. LTD.—See Mondragon Corporation; *Int'l*, pg. 5029
FAGOR AUTOMATION UK LTD.—See Mondragon Corporation; *Int'l*, pg. 5029
FAGORBRANDT SAS—See Elco Limited; *Int'l*, pg. 2345
FAGORBRANDT SAS—See Mondragon Corporation; *Int'l*, pg. 5029
FAGOR CONTROL SYSTEMS PVT. LTD.—See Mondragon Corporation; *Int'l*, pg. 5029
FAGOR EDERLAN, S. COOP.—See Mondragon Corporation; *Int'l*, pg. 5029
FAGOR ELECTRODOMESTICOS—See Mondragon Corporation; *Int'l*, pg. 5029
FAGOR ELECTRONICA, S.COOP.—See Mondragon Corporation; *Int'l*, pg. 5029
FAGOR ITALIA S.R.L.—See Mondragon Corporation; *Int'l*, pg. 5029
FAG ROLLER BEARINGS PRIVATE LTD.—See INA-Holding Schaeffler GmbH & Co. KG; *Int'l*, pg. 3640
FAGRON A.S.—See Fagron NV; *Int'l*, pg. 2603
FAGRON BV—See Fagron NV; *Int'l*, pg. 2603
FAGRON CANADA INC.—See Fagron NV; *Int'l*, pg. 2603
FAGRON CARE SP. Z.O.O.—See Fagron NV; *Int'l*, pg. 2603
FAGRON COLOMBIA SAS—See Fagron NV; *Int'l*, pg. 2603
FAGRON GMBH & CO KG—See Fagron NV; *Int'l*, pg. 2603
FAGRON GROUP BV—See Fagron NV; *Int'l*, pg. 2603
FAGRON HRVATSKA D.O.O.—See Fagron NV; *Int'l*, pg. 2603
FAGRON IBERICA SAU—See Fagron NV; *Int'l*, pg. 2603
FAGRON, INC.—See Fagron NV; *Int'l*, pg. 2603
FAGRON NORDIC A/S—See Fagron NV; *Int'l*, pg. 2603
FAGRON NV; *Int'l*, pg. 2602
FAGRON SAS—See Fagron NV; *Int'l*, pg. 2603
FAGRON SERVICES BVBA—See Fagron NV; *Int'l*, pg. 2603
FAGRON SH LTD.—See Fagron NV; *Int'l*, pg. 2603
FAGRON SOUTH AFRICA LTD.—See Fagron NV; *Int'l*, pg. 2603
FAGRON SP. Z O.O—See Fagron NV; *Int'l*, pg. 2603
FAGRON UK LTD—See Fagron NV; *Int'l*, pg. 2603
FAHEY BANKING COMPANY; *U.S. Public*, pg. 820
FAHLGREN ADVERTISING—See Peopletomysite.com, LLC; *U.S. Private*, pg. 3143
FAHLGREN GRIP DIGITAL—See Peopletomysite.com, LLC; *U.S. Private*, pg. 3143
FAHLGREN, INC. - CINCINNATI—See Peopletomysite.com, LLC; *U.S. Private*, pg. 3143
FAHLGREN, INC. - DAYTON—See Peopletomysite.com, LLC; *U.S. Private*, pg. 3143
FAHLGREN, INC. - FORT LAUDERDALE—See Peopletomysite.com, LLC; *U.S. Private*, pg. 3143
FAHLGREN, INC. - PARKERSBURG—See Peopletomysite.com, LLC; *U.S. Private*, pg. 3143

COMPANY NAME INDEX

FAHLGREN, INC.—See Peopletomysite.com, LLC; *U.S. Private*, pg. 3143
FAHLGREN, INC. - TOLEDO—See Peopletomysite.com, LLC; *U.S. Private*, pg. 3143
FAHLGREN MORTINE PUBLIC RELATIONS—See Peopletomysite.com, LLC; *U.S. Private*, pg. 3143
FAH MAI HOLDINGS GROUP INC.; *U.S. Private*, pg. 1461
FAH MAI HOLDINGS, INC.; *Int'l*, pg. 2604
FAHNESTOCK PLUMBING, HVAC & ELECTRIC; *U.S. Private*, pg. 1461
FAHRENHEIT 212—See Capgemini SE; *Int'l*, pg. 1306
FAHRENHEIT IT, INC.—See Global Employment Holdings, Inc.; *U.S. Private*, pg. 1713
FAHRENHEIT—See Electricite de France S.A.; *Int'l*, pg. 2351
FAHRLEITUNGSBAU GMBH—See STRABAG SE; *Int'l*, pg. 7230
FAHRNER ASPHALT SEALERS, L.L.C.; *U.S. Private*, pg. 1461
FAHRNEY-KEEDY HOME & VILLAGE; *U.S. Private*, pg. 1461
FAHRZEUGTEILE SERVICE-ZENTRUM MELLENDORF GMBH—See Porsche Automobil Holding SE; *Int'l*, pg. 5929
FAI ALLIANZ LTD.—See Allianz SE; *Int'l*, pg. 353
FAI AUTOMOTIVE PLC—See Motus Holdings Limited; *Int'l*, pg. 5056
FAI CAPITAL MANAGEMENT INC.; *U.S. Private*, pg. 1461
FAI DO BRASIL CRIACAO ANIMAL LTDA—See Benchmark Holdings Plc; *Int'l*, pg. 970
FAI ELECTRONICS—See Future Electronics Inc.; *Int'l*, pg. 2854
FAIFEY INVEST SOCIMI, S.A.; *Int'l*, pg. 2604
FAIL TELECOMMUNICATIONS CORP.; *U.S. Private*, pg. 1461
FAIR AMERICAN INSURANCE & REINSURANCE COMPANY—See Berkshire Hathaway Inc.; *U.S. Public*, pg. 299
FAIR AMERICAN SELECT INSURANCE COMPANY—See Berkshire Hathaway Inc.; *U.S. Public*, pg. 299
FAIRANCE GMBH—See Munchener Ruckversicherungs AG; *Int'l*, pg. 5088
FAIRBAIRN PRIVATE BANK (JERSEY) LIMITED—See Nedbank Group Limited; *Int'l*, pg. 5187
FAIRBAIRN TRUST COMPANY LIMITED—See Nedbank Group Limited; *Int'l*, pg. 5187
FAIRBANK EQUIPMENT, INC.—See Great Range Capital, LLC; *U.S. Private*, pg. 1767
FAIRBANKS DAILY NEWS-MINER INC.; *U.S. Private*, pg. 1462
FAIRBANKS ENVIRONMENTAL LIMITED—See Dover Corporation; *U.S. Public*, pg. 681
FAIRBANKS GOLD MINING, INC—See Kinross Gold Corporation; *Int'l*, pg. 4182
FAIRBANKS MATERIALS, INC.—See MDU Resources Group, Inc.; *U.S. Public*, pg. 1410
FAIRBANKS MORSE, LLC—See Arcline Investment Management LP; *U.S. Private*, pg. 313
FAIRBANKS SCALES INC.; *U.S. Private*, pg. 1462
FAIRBANKS SYMPHONY ASSOCIATION; *U.S. Private*, pg. 1462
FAIRBORN CEMENT COMPANY LLC—See Eagle Materials Inc.; *U.S. Public*, pg. 702
FAIRBORN USA, INC.; *U.S. Private*, pg. 1462
FAIRBRIDGE PARTNERS LLC; *U.S. Private*, pg. 1462
FAIRBROTHER & COMPANY LLC; *U.S. Private*, pg. 1462
FAIRBURN READY-MIX, INC.; *U.S. Private*, pg. 1462
FAIRCAP GMBH; *Int'l*, pg. 2605
FAIR CHANCE PROPERTIES PTE LTD—See Second Chance Properties Ltd.; *Int'l*, pg. 6672
FAIRCHECK SCHADENSERVICE GMBH—See Helvetia Holding AG; *Int'l*, pg. 3340
FAIR CHEM INDUSTRIES PTE LTD—See GKE Corporation Limited; *Int'l*, pg. 2983
FAIRCHEM ORGANICS LIMITED; *Int'l*, pg. 2605
FAIRCHILD CAPITAL PARTNERS, LLC; *U.S. Private*, pg. 1462
FAIRCHILD DO BRASIL, LTDA.—See Rotork Plc; *Int'l*, pg. 6406
FAIRCHILD EQUIPMENT, INC.; *U.S. Private*, pg. 1462
FAIRCHILD INDIA PRIVATE LIMITED—See Rotork Plc; *Int'l*, pg. 6406
FAIRCHILD INDUSTRIAL PRODUCTS COMPANY—See Rotork Plc; *Int'l*, pg. 6406
FAIRCHILD INDUSTRIAL PRODUCTS (SICHUAN) COMPANY LIMITED—See Rotork Plc; *Int'l*, pg. 6406
FAIRCHILD INTERNATIONAL—See Envela Corporation; *U.S. Public*, pg. 780
FAIRCOM BRAZIL, INC.—See FairCom Corporation; *U.S. Private*, pg. 1462
FAIRCOM CORPORATION; *U.S. Private*, pg. 1462
FAIRCOM EUROPE S.R.L.—See FairCom Corporation; *U.S. Private*, pg. 1462
FAIRCOURT GOLD INCOME CORP.; *Int'l*, pg. 2605
FAIRCOURT SPLIT TRUST; *Int'l*, pg. 2605
FAIR DEAL CORPORATION PHARMACEUTICAL SA (PTY.) LIMITED—See FDC Ltd; *Int'l*, pg. 2629

FAIRDINKUM CONSULTING, LLC; *U.S. Private*, pg. 1462
FAIR EAGLE SECURITIES COMPANY LIMITED—See Chinese Estates Holdings Limited; *Int'l*, pg. 1569
FAIREY CHEVROLET CADILLAC; *U.S. Private*, pg. 1462
FAIRFAX BRASIL SEGUROS CORPORATIVOS S.A.—See Fairfax Financial Holdings Limited; *Int'l*, pg. 2606
FAIRFAX BUSINESS MEDIA—See Nine Entertainment Co. Holdings Limited; *Int'l*, pg. 5298
FAIRFAX CORPORATION PTY LIMITED—See Nine Entertainment Co. Holdings Limited; *Int'l*, pg. 5298
FAIRFAX COUNTY WATER AUTHORITY INC.; *U.S. Private*, pg. 1462
FAIRFAX DATA SYSTEMS, INC.; *U.S. Private*, pg. 1462
FAIRFAX DIGITAL AUSTRALIA & NEW ZEALAND PTY LTD—See Nine Entertainment Co. Holdings Limited; *Int'l*, pg. 5298
FAIRFAX DIGITAL LIMITED—See Nine Entertainment Co. Holdings Limited; *Int'l*, pg. 5298
FAIRFAX FINANCIAL HOLDINGS LIMITED; *Int'l*, pg. 2605
FAIRFAX HOLDING COMPANY INC.; *U.S. Private*, pg. 1463
FAIRFAX IMPORTS INC.; *U.S. Private*, pg. 1463
FAIRFAX INDIA HOLDINGS CORPORATION—See Fairfax Financial Holdings Limited; *Int'l*, pg. 2606
FAIRFAX MATERIALS INC.—See Fairfax Holding Company Inc.; *U.S. Private*, pg. 1463
FAIRFAX MEADOW EUROPE LIMITED—See Argent Group Europe Limited; *Int'l*, pg. 560
FAIRFAX MEDIA GROUP FINANCE PTY LIMITED—See Nine Entertainment Co. Holdings Limited; *Int'l*, pg. 5298
FAIRFAX MEDIA LIMITED—See Nine Entertainment Co. Holdings Limited; *Int'l*, pg. 5298
FAIRFAX MEDIA MANAGEMENT PTY LIMITED—See Nine Entertainment Co. Holdings Limited; *Int'l*, pg. 5298
FAIRFAX MEDIA PUBLICATIONS PTY LIMITED—See Nine Entertainment Co. Holdings Limited; *Int'l*, pg. 5298
FAIRFAX MEDIA (UK) LIMITED—See Nine Entertainment Co. Holdings Limited; *Int'l*, pg. 5298
FAIRFAX MEMORIAL FUNERAL HOME, LLC—See Carriage Services, Inc.; *U.S. Public*, pg. 439
FAIRFAX NEWS NETWORK PTY LIMITED—See Nine Entertainment Co. Holdings Limited; *Int'l*, pg. 5298
FAIRFAX NEW ZEALAND LIMITED—See Nine Entertainment Co. Holdings Limited; *Int'l*, pg. 5298
FAIRFAX REGIONAL PRINTERS PTY LIMITED—See Nine Entertainment Co. Holdings Limited; *Int'l*, pg. 5298
FAIRFAX SQUARE PARKING LLC—See Vornado Realty Trust; *U.S. Public*, pg. 2310
FAIRFAX SURGICAL CENTER, L.P.—See HCA Healthcare, Inc.; *U.S. Public*, pg. 996
FAIRFAX SURGICAL CENTER—See HCA Healthcare, Inc.; *U.S. Public*, pg. 996
FAIRFIELD ATLAS LTD.—See OC Oerlikon Corporation AG; *Int'l*, pg. 5514
FAIRFIELD AUTO GROUP INC.; *U.S. Private*, pg. 1463
FAIRFIELD BANCSHARES INC.; *U.S. Private*, pg. 1463
FAIRFIELD CHAIR COMPANY; *U.S. Private*, pg. 1463
FAIRFIELD CHEMICAL CARRIERS, INC—See Mitsui O.S.K. Lines, Ltd.; *Int'l*, pg. 4989
FAIRFIELD COUNTY BANK CORP.—See Fairfield County Bank, MHC; *U.S. Private*, pg. 1463
FAIRFIELD COUNTY BANK, MHC; *U.S. Private*, pg. 1463
FAIRFIELD COUNTY BANK—See Fairfield County Bank, MHC; *U.S. Private*, pg. 1463
FAIRFIELD COUNTY WEEKLY—See Tribune Publishing Company; *U.S. Private*, pg. 4228
FAIRFIELD DIALYSIS, LLC—See DaVita Inc.; *U.S. Public*, pg. 638
FAIRFIELD ELECTRIC COOPERATIVE; *U.S. Private*, pg. 1463
FAIRFIELD FEDERAL SAVINGS & LOAN ASSOCIATION; *U.S. Private*, pg. 1463
FAIRFIELD FMC, LLC—See Marriott International, Inc.; *U.S. Public*, pg. 1370
FAIRFIELD GLADE COMMUNITY CLUB; *U.S. Private*, pg. 1463
FAIRFIELD GOURMET FOOD CORP.; *U.S. Private*, pg. 1463
FAIRFIELD GROUP—See Franklin Resources, Inc.; *U.S. Public*, pg. 882
FAIRFIELD INDUSTRIES INC.—See Fairfield Maxwell Ltd.; *U.S. Private*, pg. 1463
FAIRFIELD LINE INC.; *U.S. Private*, pg. 1463
FAIRFIELD MANUFACTURING COMPANY, INC.—See OC Oerlikon Corporation AG; *Int'l*, pg. 5514
FAIRFIELD MAXWELL LTD.; *U.S. Private*, pg. 1463
FAIRFIELD MEDICAL CENTER; *U.S. Private*, pg. 1463
FAIRFIELD NATIONAL BANK—See Park National Corporation; *U.S. Public*, pg. 1638
FAIRFIELD NATIONAL BANK—See Fairfield Bancshares Inc.; *U.S. Private*, pg. 1463
FAIRFIELD PROCESSING CORP.; *U.S. Private*, pg. 1463
FAIRFIELD PROPERTIES L.P.; *U.S. Private*, pg. 1463
FAIRFIELD RESIDENTIAL COMPANY LLC—See Brookfield Corporation; *Int'l*, pg. 1187
FAIRFIELD SOLUTIONS LIMITED—See Addtech AB; *Int'l*, pg. 133
FAIRFIELD SOUTHERN COMPANY, INC.—See United States Steel Corporation; *U.S. Public*, pg. 2236

FAIR OAKS INCOME LIMITED

FAIRFIELD TECHNOLOGIES INC.; *U.S. Private*, pg. 1463
FAIRFIELD TRADING COMPANY LTD.—See Addtech AB; *Int'l*, pg. 133
FAIRFIELD WILLIAMSBURG—See Travel & Leisure Co.; *U.S. Public*, pg. 2185
FAIRFIRST INSURANCE LIMITED—See Fairfax Financial Holdings Limited; *Int'l*, pg. 2606
FAIRFORM MANUFACTURING COMPANY LIMITED—See Zhongzheng International Company Limited; *Int'l*, pg. 8677
FAIR FRIEND ENTERPRISE CO., LTD.—See Fair Friend Group; *Int'l*, pg. 2604
FAIR FRIEND ENTERPRISE GROUP—See Fair Friend Group; *Int'l*, pg. 2604
FAIR FRIEND GROUP; *Int'l*, pg. 2604
FAIRGREEN CAPITAL L.P.; *U.S. Private*, pg. 1464
FAIRGROUND HOLDINGS (PTY) LTD—See Botswana Development Corporation Limited; *Int'l*, pg. 1118
FAIR GROUNDS CORPORATION—See Churchill Downs, Inc.; *U.S. Public*, pg. 493
FAIRHAVEN CAPITAL MANAGEMENT, LLC; *U.S. Private*, pg. 1464
FAIRHAVEN CHRISTIAN RETIREMENT CENTER; *U.S. Private*, pg. 1464
FAIR HAVEN COMMUNITY HEALTH CENTER; *U.S. Private*, pg. 1462
FAIR HEALTH, INC.; *U.S. Private*, pg. 1462
FAIR ISAAC ADEPTRA, INC.—See Fair Isaac Corporation; *U.S. Public*, pg. 820
FAIR ISAAC ASIA PACIFIC CORP.—See Fair Isaac Corporation; *U.S. Public*, pg. 820
FAIR ISAAC (AUSTRALIA) PTY LTD—See Fair Isaac Corporation; *U.S. Public*, pg. 820
FAIR ISAAC CHILE SOFTWARE & SERVICES LTDA.—See Fair Isaac Corporation; *U.S. Public*, pg. 820
FAIR ISAAC CORPORATION; *U.S. Public*, pg. 820
FAIR ISAAC DEUTSCHLAND GMBH—See Fair Isaac Corporation; *U.S. Public*, pg. 820
FAIR, ISAAC DO BRASIL LTDA.—See Fair Isaac Corporation; *U.S. Public*, pg. 820
FAIR ISAAC GERMANY GMBH—See Fair Isaac Corporation; *U.S. Public*, pg. 820
FAIR ISAAC INFORMATION TECHNOLOGY (BEIJING) CO., LTD.—See Fair Isaac Corporation; *U.S. Public*, pg. 820
FAIR ISAAC INTERNATIONAL LIMITED—See Fair Isaac Corporation; *U.S. Public*, pg. 820
FAIR ISAAC SERVICES LIMITED—See Fair Isaac Corporation; *U.S. Public*, pg. 820
FAIR ISAAC SOUTH AFRICA (PTY) LTD.—See Fair Isaac Corporation; *U.S. Public*, pg. 820
FAIR ISAAC UK GROUP LIMITED—See Fair Isaac Corporation; *U.S. Public*, pg. 820
FAIR ISAAC UK INTERNATIONAL HOLDINGS LTD.—See Fair Isaac Corporation; *U.S. Public*, pg. 820
FAIRLAND MARKET INC.; *U.S. Private*, pg. 1464
FAIR LAND TITLE COMPANY, INC.—See Hovnanian Enterprises, Inc.; *U.S. Public*, pg. 1056
FAIRLANE FINANCIAL CORPORATION; *U.S. Private*, pg. 1464
FAIRLANE FORD SALES INC.; *U.S. Private*, pg. 1464
FAIRLANES BOWL, INC.—See Great Lakes Realty Corp.; *U.S. Private*, pg. 1765
FAIRLY PAINLESS ADVERTISING; *U.S. Private*, pg. 1464
THE FAIR MANUFACTURING CO. LTD.—See Spectrum Brands Holdings, Inc.; *U.S. Public*, pg. 1917
FAIRMED HEALTHCARE GMBH—See Strides Pharma Science Limited; *Int'l*, pg. 7240
FAIRMILE GOLDTECH INC.; *Int'l*, pg. 2609
FAIRMONT FOODS OF MINNESOTA INC.; *U.S. Private*, pg. 1464
FAIRMONT HOMES, INC.—See Cavco Industries, Inc.; *U.S. Public*, pg. 455
FAIRMONT HOTELS & RESORTS INC.—See Accor S.A.; *Int'l*, pg. 91
FAIRMONT PRESS, INC.; *U.S. Private*, pg. 1464
FAIRMONT RAFFLES HOTELS INTERNATIONAL INC.—See Accor S.A.; *Int'l*, pg. 91
FAIRMONT SIGN COMPANY; *U.S. Private*, pg. 1464
THE FAIRMONT SONOMA MISSION INN & SPA—See Accor S.A.; *Int'l*, pg. 91
FAIRMONT SPECIALTY—See Fairfax Financial Holdings Limited; *Int'l*, pg. 2606
FAIRMOUNT AUTOMATION, INC.—See Enovis Corporation; *U.S. Public*, pg. 772
FAIRMOUNT PENSION TRUSTEE LIMITED—See KBL European Private Bankers S.A.; *Int'l*, pg. 4107
FAIRMOUNT SANTROL HOLDINGS INC.—See Covia Holdings Corporation; *U.S. Private*, pg. 1072
FAIRMOUNT SANTROL INC.—See Covia Holdings Corporation; *U.S. Private*, pg. 1072
FAIRN & SWANSON INC.; *U.S. Private*, pg. 1464
FAIR OAKS FARMS INC.; *U.S. Private*, pg. 1462
FAIR OAKS INCOME LIMITED; *Int'l*, pg. 2605
FAIR PAY MANAGEMENT AB—See Intrum AB; *Int'l*, pg. 3770
FAIRPAY SOLUTIONS, INC.—See Stone Point Capital LLC; *U.S. Private*, pg. 3823

FAIRPLACE CONSULTING PLC—See Randstad N.V.; *Int'l*, pg. 6204
FAIRPLAY CORPORATION—See Trans-Lux Corporation; *U.S. Public*, pg. 2179
FAIRPLAY INC.; *U.S. Private*, pg. 1464
FAIRPLAY PROPERTIES REIT; *Int'l*, pg. 2609
FAIRPLAY SCHLEPPDAMPFSCHIFFS-REEDEREI RICHARD BORCHARD GMBH; *Int'l*, pg. 2609
FAIRPLAY; *U.S. Private*, pg. 1464
FAIRPLAY TOWAGE B.V.—See Fairplay Schleppdampfschiffs-Reederei Richard Borchard GmbH; *Int'l*, pg. 2609
FAIRPLAY TOWAGE POLSKA SP. Z.O.O. SP.K.—See Fairplay Schleppdampfschiffs-Reederei Richard Borchard GmbH; *Int'l*, pg. 2609
FAIRPOINT CARRIER SERVICES, INC.—See Consolidated Communications Holdings, Inc.; *U.S. Public*, pg. 570
FAIRPOINT GROUP PLC; *Int'l*, pg. 2609
FAIRPOINT PLASTIC INDUSTRIES SDN. BHD.—See Versatile Creative Berhad; *Int'l*, pg. 8174
FAIRRINGTON TRANSPORTATION CORP.—See Atlas Holdings, LLC; *U.S. Private*, pg. 377
FAIR-RITE PRODUCTS CORP.; *U.S. Private*, pg. 1462
FAIRSKF (TAIWAN) CO., LTD.—See SKF AB; *Int'l*, pg. 6981
FAIRSKQ (TAIWAN) CO., LTD.—See Fair Friend Group; *Int'l*, pg. 2604
FAIRS LIMITED—See Temenos AG; *Int'l*, pg. 7554
FAIRS & MORE, INC.—See Messe Munchen GmbH; *Int'l*, pg. 4841
FAIRSTAR HEAVY TRANSPORT N.V.—See HAL Trust N.V.; *Int'l*, pg. 3226
FAIRSTAR MARITIME SERVICES BV—See HAL Trust N.V.; *Int'l*, pg. 3226
FAIRSTAR RESOURCES LTD.; *Int'l*, pg. 2609
FAIRSTONE FINANCIAL INC.—See Centerbridge Partners, L.P.; *U.S. Private*, pg. 814
FAIRTEC SAS—See Veolia Environnement S.A.; *Int'l*, pg. 8154
FAIR TIME INTERNATIONAL LIMITED—See New Universe Environmental Group Limited; *Int'l*, pg. 5228
FAIRTRANS INTERNATIONAL LTD.—See Pico Far East Holdings Limited; *Int'l*, pg. 5860
FAIR VALUE REIT-AG—See DEMIRE Deutsche Mittelstand Real Estate AG; *Int'l*, pg. 2025
FAIRVALUE SUPERMARKET INC.; *U.S. Private*, pg. 1464
FAIRVEST LIMITED; *Int'l*, pg. 2609
FAIRVEST PROPERTY HOLDINGS LIMITED; *Int'l*, pg. 2609
FAIRVIEW ADVERTISING; *U.S. Private*, pg. 1464
FAIRVIEW CAPITAL PARTNERS, INC.; *U.S. Private*, pg. 1464
FAIRVIEW CARE CENTER OF BETHLEHEM PIKE—See Formation Capital, LLC; *U.S. Private*, pg. 1570
FAIRVIEW CARE CENTER OF PAPER MILL ROAD—See Formation Capital, LLC; *U.S. Private*, pg. 1570
FAIRVIEW COVE AUTO LTD.; *Int'l*, pg. 2609
FAIRVIEW HEALTH SERVICES; *U.S. Private*, pg. 1464
FAIRVIEW INSURANCE AGENCY ASSOCIATES INC; *U.S. Private*, pg. 1464
FAIRVIEW MILLS INC.; *U.S. Private*, pg. 1464
FAIRVIEW MILLWORK INCORPORATED; *U.S. Private*, pg. 1465
FAIRVIEW PARK HOSPITAL—See HCA Healthcare, Inc.; *U.S. Public*, pg. 996
FAIRVIEW PROPERTIES, INC.—See Future plc; *Int'l*, pg. 2857
FAIRWARNING LLC—See Thoma Bravo, L.P.; *U.S. Private*, pg. 4148
FAIRWARNING SARL—See Thoma Bravo, L.P.; *U.S. Private*, pg. 4148
FAIRWAY AUTO BODY REPAIR—See Fairway Ford, Inc.; *U.S. Private*, pg. 1465
FAIRWAY FORD HENDERSON, INC.; *U.S. Private*, pg. 1465
FAIRWAY FORD, INC.; *U.S. Private*, pg. 1465
FAIRWAY FORD OF AUGUSTA, INC.; *U.S. Private*, pg. 1465
FAIRWAY FORD SALES LTD.; *Int'l*, pg. 2609
FAIRWAY GREEN INC.—See CenterOak Partners LLC; *U.S. Private*, pg. 816
FAIRWAY GROUP HOLDINGS CORP.—See Sterling Investment Partners, L.P.; *U.S. Private*, pg. 3805
FAIRWAY INDEPENDENT MORTGAGE CORPORATION; *U.S. Private*, pg. 1465
FAIRWAY INJECTION MOLDS, INC.—See BlackBern Partners LLC; *U.S. Private*, pg. 573
FAIRWAY INJECTION MOLDS, INC.—See Lee Equity Partners LLC; *U.S. Private*, pg. 2413
FAIRWAY INVESTMENTS, LLC; *U.S. Private*, pg. 1465
FAIRWAY LAWNS, LLC; *U.S. Private*, pg. 1465
FAIRWAY MARKET, INC.—See Sterling Investment Partners, L.P.; *U.S. Private*, pg. 3805
FAIRWAY MARKETING GROUP—See U.S. Bancorp; *U.S. Public*, pg. 2212
FAIRWAY MOTORS INC.; *U.S. Private*, pg. 1465
FAIRWAY OUTDOOR ADVERTISING, LLC - ATHENS—See GTCR LLC; *U.S. Private*, pg. 1805

FAIRWAY OUTDOOR ADVERTISING, LLC - CHATTANOOGA—See GTCR LLC; *U.S. Private*, pg. 1805
FAIRWAY OUTDOOR ADVERTISING, LLC - DUNCAN—See GTCR LLC; *U.S. Private*, pg. 1805
FAIRWAY OUTDOOR ADVERTISING, LLC - GREENSBORO—See GTCR LLC; *U.S. Private*, pg. 1805
FAIRWAY OUTDOOR ADVERTISING, LLC - PRESTONSBURG—See GTCR LLC; *U.S. Private*, pg. 1805
FAIRWAY OUTDOOR ADVERTISING, LLC - RALEIGH—See GTCR LLC; *U.S. Private*, pg. 1805
FAIRWAY OUTDOOR ADVERTISING, LLC - ROCHESTER—See GTCR LLC; *U.S. Private*, pg. 1805
FAIRWAY OUTDOOR ADVERTISING, LLC—See GTCR LLC; *U.S. Private*, pg. 1805
FAIRWAY OUTDOOR ADVERTISING, LLC - VALDOSTA—See GTCR LLC; *U.S. Private*, pg. 1805
FAIRWAY PAYMENTS, LLC—See i3 Verticals, Inc.; *U.S. Public*, pg. 1081
FAIRWAY PRODUCTS—See Acme Mills Co. Inc.; *U.S. Private*, pg. 61
FAIRWAY SALVAGE INC.—See Sims Limited; *U.S. Public*, pg. 1883
FAIRWAYS BEVERAGE CORP.—See Sunburst Hospitality Corporation; *U.S. Private*, pg. 3865
FAIRWAYS INC.—See Sunburst Hospitality Corporation; *U.S. Private*, pg. 3865
FAIRWAYS INSURANCE SERVICES, INC.—See World Insurance Associates LLC; *U.S. Private*, pg. 4566
THE FAIRWAYS PARTNERSHIP LIMITED—See Co-operative Group Limited; *Int'l*, pg. 1679
THE FAIRWAYS RESORTS OF PALM AIRE—See Travel & Leisure Co.; *U.S. Public*, pg. 2186
FAIRWAY STORES INC.; *U.S. Private*, pg. 1465
FAIRWAY SUPPLY INC.; *U.S. Private*, pg. 1465
FAIRWAY TECHNOLOGIES, INC.—See Accenture plc; *Int'l*, pg. 87
FAIRWIND GMBH—See JAB Holding Company S.a.r.l.; *Int'l*, pg. 3862
FAIRWINDS CREDIT UNION; *U.S. Private*, pg. 1465
FAIRWINDS INTERNATIONAL; *U.S. Private*, pg. 1465
FAIRWINDS PARTNERS, LLC; *U.S. Private*, pg. 1465
FAIR WINDS PRESS INC—See The Quarto Group, Inc.; *Int'l*, pg. 7677
FAIRWOOD FAST FOOD LIMITED—See Fairwood Holdings Limited; *Int'l*, pg. 2609
FAIRWOOD HOLDINGS LIMITED; *Int'l*, pg. 2609
FAIRY FOREST CO., LTD.—See Fantasista Co., Ltd.; *Int'l*, pg. 2613
FAIRY HUB GENERAL TRADING COMPANY-W.L.L.—See Privatization Holding Company K.S.C.C.; *Int'l*, pg. 5984
FAISAL ISLAMIC BANK OF EGYPT; *Int'l*, pg. 2609
FAISAL SPINNING MILLS LIMITED; *Int'l*, pg. 2609
FAISON & ASSOCIATES LLC; *U.S. Private*, pg. 1465
FAISON OFFICE PRODUCTS, INC.—See Sycamore Partners Management, LP; *U.S. Private*, pg. 3897
FAISS FOLEY WARREN; *U.S. Private*, pg. 1465
FAIST CHEMTEC GMBH—See Sika AG; *Int'l*, pg. 6914
FAITAL S.P.A.—See Alps Alpine Co., Ltd.; *Int'l*, pg. 376
FAITEC CORPORATION—See DTS Corporation; *Int'l*, pg. 2217
FAITHBRIDGE GROUP LLC; *U.S. Private*, pg. 1466
FAITH DIRECT INC.; *U.S. Private*, pg. 1465
FAITHFUL+GOULD INC.—See AtkinsRealis Group Inc.; *Int'l*, pg. 673
FAITH, INC.; *Int'l*, pg. 2609
FAITH & LEARNING INTERNATIONAL; *U.S. Private*, pg. 1465
FAITHNETWORK CO., LTD.; *Int'l*, pg. 2609
FAITH PROSTHETIC-ORTHOTIC SERVICES, INC.—See Patient Square Capital, L.P.; *U.S. Private*, pg. 3107
FAITH REGIONAL HEALTH SERVICES; *U.S. Private*, pg. 1465
FAITH ROOT RECRUITMENT VIETNAM JOINT STOCK COMPANY—See Bain Capital, LP; *U.S. Private*, pg. 434
FAITHTEK LIMITED—See GigaLane Co., Ltd.; *Int'l*, pg. 2971
FAITHWAY FEED CO. INC.; *U.S. Private*, pg. 1466
FAITH WONDERWORKS, INC.—See Faith, Inc.; *Int'l*, pg. 2609
FAIVELEY RAILWAY TRADING CO., LTD.—See Westinghouse Air Brake Technologies Corporation; *U.S. Public*, pg. 2357
FAIVELEY TRANSPORT AMIENS S.A.S.—See Westinghouse Air Brake Technologies Corporation; *U.S. Public*, pg. 2357
FAIVELEY TRANSPORT AUSTRALIA LTD.—See Westinghouse Air Brake Technologies Corporation; *U.S. Public*, pg. 2357
FAIVELEY TRANSPORT BIRKENHEAD LTD.—See Westinghouse Air Brake Technologies Corporation; *U.S. Public*, pg. 2357
FAIVELEY TRANSPORT CZECH A.S—See Westinghouse Air Brake Technologies Corporation; *U.S. Public*, pg. 2357

FAIVELEY TRANSPORT DO BRASIL LTDA.—See Westinghouse Air Brake Technologies Corporation; *U.S. Public*, pg. 2358
FAIVELEY TRANSPORT FAR EAST LTD—See Westinghouse Air Brake Technologies Corporation; *U.S. Public*, pg. 2357
FAIVELEY TRANSPORT HOLDING GMBH & CO KG—See Westinghouse Air Brake Technologies Corporation; *U.S. Public*, pg. 2357
FAIVELEY TRANSPORT IBERICA SA—See Westinghouse Air Brake Technologies Corporation; *U.S. Public*, pg. 2357
FAIVELEY TRANSPORT ITALIA S.P.A.—See Westinghouse Air Brake Technologies Corporation; *U.S. Public*, pg. 2357
FAIVELEY TRANSPORT KOREA LTD.—See Westinghouse Air Brake Technologies Corporation; *U.S. Public*, pg. 2357
FAIVELEY TRANSPORT LEIPZIG GMBH & CO KG—See Westinghouse Air Brake Technologies Corporation; *U.S. Public*, pg. 2357
FAIVELEY TRANSPORT METRO TECHNOLOGY TAIWAN LTD.—See Westinghouse Air Brake Technologies Corporation; *U.S. Public*, pg. 2357
FAIVELEY TRANSPORT NORDIC AB—See Westinghouse Air Brake Technologies Corporation; *U.S. Public*, pg. 2357
FAIVELEY TRANSPORT NOWE GMBH—See Westinghouse Air Brake Technologies Corporation; *U.S. Public*, pg. 2357
FAIVELEY TRANSPORT N.S.F—See Westinghouse Air Brake Technologies Corporation; *U.S. Public*, pg. 2357
FAIVELEY TRANSPORT PLZEN S.R.O.—See Westinghouse Air Brake Technologies Corporation; *U.S. Public*, pg. 2357
FAIVELEY TRANSPORT RAIL TECHNOLOGIES INDIA LIMITED—See Westinghouse Air Brake Technologies Corporation; *U.S. Public*, pg. 2357
FAIVELEY TRANSPORT S.A.—See Westinghouse Air Brake Technologies Corporation; *U.S. Public*, pg. 2357
FAIVELEY TRANSPORT TAMWORTH LTD—See Westinghouse Air Brake Technologies Corporation; *U.S. Public*, pg. 2358
FAIVELEY TRANSPORT TOURS—See Westinghouse Air Brake Technologies Corporation; *U.S. Public*, pg. 2358
FAIVELEY TRANSPORT WITTEN GMBH—See Westinghouse Air Brake Technologies Corporation; *U.S. Public*, pg. 2357
FAJARBARU BUILDER GROUP BHD.; *Int'l*, pg. 2610
FAJARBARU BUILDER SDN. BHD.—See Fajarbaru Builder Group Bhd.; *Int'l*, pg. 2610
FAJR AL-GULF INSURANCE & REINSURANCE COMPANY—See Fairfax Financial Holdings Limited; *Int'l*, pg. 2607
FAKE LOVE LLC—See The New York Times Company; *U.S. Public*, pg. 2116
FAKHROO INTERNATIONAL TRADING AGENCIES CO.—See Einhell Germany AG; *Int'l*, pg. 2333
FAKOM AD; *Int'l*, pg. 2610
FAKTA A/S—See FDB Group; *Int'l*, pg. 2628
FAKTOR 3 AG; *Int'l*, pg. 2610
FAKTORTEL PTY LTD—See Over the Wire Holdings Limited; *Int'l*, pg. 5671
FAKTUM OY—See A-Lehdet Oy; *Int'l*, pg. 20
FALABELLA S.A.; *Int'l*, pg. 2610
FALA GMBH—See Compagnie des Levures Lesaffre SA; *Int'l*, pg. 1738
FALANX CYBER SECURITY LTD; *Int'l*, pg. 2610
FALBYGDENS OST AB—See Arla Foods amba; *Int'l*, pg. 573
FALCAN CHAAL PETROLEUM, LTD—See Candax Energy Inc.; *Int'l*, pg. 1289
FALCI S.R.L.—See Calvi Holding S.r.l.; *Int'l*, pg. 1266
FALCK ACCIAI-CNS SPA—See Falck S.p.A.; *Int'l*, pg. 2610
FALCK AKTIV ARBETSMEDICIN AB—See Lundbeckfonden; *Int'l*, pg. 4580
FALCK A/S—See Lundbeckfonden; *Int'l*, pg. 4580
FALCK AUTOABI OU—See Lundbeckfonden; *Int'l*, pg. 4580
FALCK AVD B.V.—See Lundbeckfonden; *Int'l*, pg. 4580
FALCK CASPIAN SAFE LLC—See Lundbeckfonden; *Int'l*, pg. 4583
FALCK CHILE S.A.—See Lundbeckfonden; *Int'l*, pg. 4580
FALCK DESIGN AB—See James Halstead PLC; *Int'l*, pg. 3877
FALCK EMERGENCY A.S.—See Lundbeckfonden; *Int'l*, pg. 4580
FALCK EMERGENCY SERVICES UK LTD.—See Lundbeckfonden; *Int'l*, pg. 4580
FALCK FIRE & SAFETY DO BRASIL S.A.—See Lundbeckfonden; *Int'l*, pg. 4580
FALCK FIRE SERVICES DE GMBH—See Lundbeckfonden; *Int'l*, pg. 4580
FALCK FIRE SERVICES NL B.V.—See Lundbeckfonden; *Int'l*, pg. 4580
FALCK GLOBAL ASSISTANCE AB—See Lundbeckfonden; *Int'l*, pg. 4580

COMPANY NAME INDEX

FALCK GLOBAL ASSISTANCE LLC—See Lundbeckfonden; *Int'l*, pg. 4580
FALCK GLOBAL ASSISTANCE NORWAY AS—See Lundbeckfonden; *Int'l*, pg. 4580
FALCK HEALTHCARE AB—See Lundbeckfonden; *Int'l*, pg. 4580
FALCK HJAELPEMIDLER A/S—See Lundbeckfonden; *Int'l*, pg. 4580
FALCK HOLDING B.V.—See Lundbeckfonden; *Int'l*, pg. 4580
FALCK INDIA LIMITED—See Lundbeckfonden; *Int'l*, pg. 4580
FALCK KAZAKHSTAN LLP—See Lundbeckfonden; *Int'l*, pg. 4581
FALCK NORTHERN CALIFORNIA CORP.—See Lundbeckfonden; *Int'l*, pg. 4580
FALCK NORTHWEST CORP.—See Lundbeckfonden; *Int'l*, pg. 4580
FALCK NUTEC AS—See Lundbeckfonden; *Int'l*, pg. 4580
FALCK NUTEC BRASIL TREINAMENTOS EM SEGURANCA MARITIMA LTDA—See Lundbeckfonden; *Int'l*, pg. 4580
FALCK NUTEC B.V.—See Lundbeckfonden; *Int'l*, pg. 4580
FALCK NUTEC (THAILAND) LTD—See Lundbeckfonden; *Int'l*, pg. 4580
FALCK NUTEC VIETNAM LIMITED—See Lundbeckfonden; *Int'l*, pg. 4580
FALCK OY—See Lundbeckfonden; *Int'l*, pg. 4580
FALCK PHARMA S.R.O.—See Lundbeckfonden; *Int'l*, pg. 4580
FALCK PRIME ATLANTIC LIMITED—See Lundbeckfonden; *Int'l*, pg. 4583
FALCK PTY LTD.—See Lundbeckfonden; *Int'l*, pg. 4580
FALCK RENEWABLES S.P.A.—See Falck S.p.A.; *Int'l*, pg. 2610
FALCK SAFETY SERVICES A/S—See Polaris Management A/S; *Int'l*, pg. 5908
FALCK SAFETY SERVICES BELGIUM BVBA—See Lundbeckfonden; *Int'l*, pg. 4583
FALCK SAFETY SERVICES CANADA LTD.—See Lundbeckfonden; *Int'l*, pg. 4583
FALCK SAFETY SERVICES DE MEXICO, S.A.P.I. DE C.V.—See Polaris Management A/S; *Int'l*, pg. 5908
FALCK SAFETY SERVICES HOLDING A/S—See Polaris Management A/S; *Int'l*, pg. 5908
FALCK SCI, S.A.—See Lundbeckfonden; *Int'l*, pg. 4580
FALCK SK A.S.—See Lundbeckfonden; *Int'l*, pg. 4580
FALCK S.P.A.; *Int'l*, pg. 2610
FALCK SVERIGE HOLDING AB—See Lundbeckfonden; *Int'l*, pg. 4580
FALCK UK LIMITED—See Lundbeckfonden; *Int'l*, pg. 4580
FALCK USA, INC.—See Lundbeckfonden; *Int'l*, pg. 4580
FALCK VL SERVICIOS SANITARIOS, S.L.—See Lundbeckfonden; *Int'l*, pg. 4580
FALCK ZACHRANNA A.S.—See Lundbeckfonden; *Int'l*, pg. 4580
FALCO BIOSYSTEMS LTD.—See FALCO Holdings Co., Ltd.; *Int'l*, pg. 2610
FALCO HOLDINGS CO., LTD.; *Int'l*, pg. 2610
FALCO LIME COMPANY—See HBM Holdings Company; *U.S. Private*, pg. 1887
FALCON ACQUISITION CORP.; *U.S. Private*, pg. 1466
FALCON AFFILIATES, LLC; *U.S. Private*, pg. 1466
FALCON AIR EXPRESS INC.; *U.S. Private*, pg. 1466
FALCON AIR SERVICES & TRANSPORT CO. LLC—See Oman Holdings International Company SAOG; *Int'l*, pg. 5560
FALCON ASPHALT REPAIR EQUIPMENT; *U.S. Private*, pg. 1466
FALCON-BELMONT—See Whippoorwill Associates, Inc.; *U.S. Private*, pg. 4507
FALCONBRIDGE DOMINICANA S.A.—See Glencore plc; *Int'l*, pg. 2990
FALCON COFFEES LIMITED—See Westrock Coffee Company; *U.S. Private*, pg. 2361
FALCON COMMUNICATIONS INC.; *U.S. Private*, pg. 1466
FALCON CONSULTING GROUP, LLC—See Avaap Inc.; *U.S. Private*, pg. 403
FALCON CONTAINERS; *U.S. Private*, pg. 1466
FALCON CONTRACTING CO., INC.; *U.S. Private*, pg. 1466
FALCON DE JUAREZ, S.A. DE C.V.—See Whippoorwill Associates, Inc.; *U.S. Private*, pg. 4506
FALCON ENERGY GROUP LIMITED; *Int'l*, pg. 2610
FALCONET PTY LTD—See Eagers Automotive Limited; *Int'l*, pg. 2263
FALCON EXECUTIVE AVIATION, INC.; *U.S. Private*, pg. 1466
FALCON FOODSERVICE EQUIPMENT—See Ali Holding S.r.l; *Int'l*, pg. 322
FALCON FOUNDRY COMPANY; *U.S. Private*, pg. 1466
FALCON GOLD CORP.; *Int'l*, pg. 2611
THE FALCON GROUP PLC—See Quilter plc; *Int'l*, pg. 6163
FALCONHEAD CAPITAL, LLC; *U.S. Private*, pg. 1467
FALCON HOLDINGS, LLC; *U.S. Private*, pg. 1466
FALCON INSURANCE COMPANY (HONG KONG) LIMITED—See Fairfax Financial Holdings Limited; *Int'l*, pg. 2606
FALCON INSURANCE COMPANY SAOC—See Al Yousef Group; *Int'l*, pg. 283
FALCON INTERNATIONAL BANK; *U.S. Private*, pg. 1466
FALCON INVESTMENT ADVISORS, LLC - NEW YORK OFFICE—See ONEX Corporation; *Int'l*, pg. 5578
FALCON INVESTMENT ADVISORS, LLC—See ONEX Corporation; *Int'l*, pg. 5578
FALCON LAKES, LTD—See American Realty Investors, Inc.; *U.S. Public*, pg. 108
FALCON LEASING, LLC—See Falcon National Bank; *U.S. Private*, pg. 1466
FALCON LEVEN N.V.—See ASR Nederland N.V.; *Int'l*, pg. 632
FALCON-LEWISVILLE—See Whippoorwill Associates, Inc.; *U.S. Private*, pg. 4507
FALCON MACHINE TOOLS CO. LTD.; *Int'l*, pg. 2611
FALCON METALS LIMITED; *Int'l*, pg. 2611
FALCON NATIONAL BANK; *U.S. Private*, pg. 1466
FALCON OIL & GAS LTD.—See Condor Petroleum Inc.; *Int'l*, pg. 1766
FALCON OIL & GAS LTD.; *Int'l*, pg. 2611
FALCON PACKAGING, INC.; *U.S. Private*, pg. 1466
FALCON PHARMACEUTICALS, LTD.—See Novartis AG; *Int'l*, pg. 5458
FALCON PLASTICS INC.; *U.S. Private*, pg. 1466
FALCON POWER CO., LTD.; *Int'l*, pg. 2611
FALCON PRIVATE BANK LTD.—See Mubadala Investment Company PJSC; *Int'l*, pg. 5074
FALCON PRIVATE WEALTH LTD.—See Dolfin Group Ltd.; *Int'l*, pg. 2158
FALCON'S BEYOND GLOBAL, INC.; *U.S. Public*, pg. 820
FALCON SEABOARD HOLDINGS LP; *U.S. Private*, pg. 1466
FALCON SEABOARD OIL & GAS COMPANY—See Falcon Seaboard Holdings LP; *U.S. Private*, pg. 1466
FALCON SOCIAL APS; *Int'l*, pg. 2611
FALCON-SOFTWARE COMPANY, INC.; *Int'l*, pg. 2611
FALCON STAMPING INC.; *U.S. Private*, pg. 1466
FALCON STEEL CO.; *U.S. Private*, pg. 1466
FALCON STEEL INC.; *U.S. Private*, pg. 1467
FALCONSTOR ASIA PACIFIC—See FalconStor Software, Inc.; *U.S. Public*, pg. 821
FALCONSTOR CHINA—See FalconStor Software, Inc.; *U.S. Public*, pg. 821
FALCONSTOR FRANCE—See FalconStor Software, Inc.; *U.S. Public*, pg. 821
FALCONSTOR JAPAN—See FalconStor Software, Inc.; *U.S. Public*, pg. 821
FALCONSTOR SOFTWARE, INC.; *U.S. Public*, pg. 821
FALCONSTOR SOFTWARE (KOREA), INC.—See FalconStor Software, Inc.; *U.S. Public*, pg. 821
FALCONTECH CO., LTD.—See Yinbang Clad Material Co., Ltd.; *Int'l*, pg. 8583
FALCON TECHNOLOGIES AND SERVICES, INC.—See CARBO Ceramics Inc.; *U.S. Private*, pg. 748
FALCON TECHNOLOGIES, INC.; *U.S. Public*, pg. 820
FALCON TRAINING CENTRE—See Groupe Industriel Marcel Dassault S.A.; *Int'l*, pg. 3105
FALCON TRANSPORT CO.; *U.S. Private*, pg. 1467
FALCO PELLAMI SPA—See Kering S.A.; *Int'l*, pg. 4134
FALCO PHARMACIES, LTD.—See FALCO Holdings Co., Ltd.; *Int'l*, pg. 2610
FALCO RESOURCES LTD.; *Int'l*, pg. 2610
FALCO-SOPRON BUTOR KFT.; *Int'l*, pg. 2610
FALDIS SA—See Carrefour SA; *Int'l*, pg. 1345
FAL ENERGY CO., LTD.—See FAL Group of Companies; *Int'l*, pg. 2610
FALFURRIAS CAPITAL PARTNERS, LP; *U.S. Private*, pg. 1467
FAL GROUP OF COMPANIES; *Int'l*, pg. 2610
FALK BUILDING SYSTEMS BV; *Int'l*, pg. 2611
FALKEN OFFICE PRODUCTS GMBH—See Pelikan International Corporation Berhad; *Int'l*, pg. 5782
FALKENROTH UMFORMTECHNIK GMBH—See Mutares SE & Co. KGaA; *Int'l*, pg. 5104
FALKENSTEIN NEBENWERTE AG—See SPARTA AG; *Int'l*, pg. 7127
FALKEN TIRE CORPORATION—See Sumitomo Rubber Industries, Ltd.; *Int'l*, pg. 7299
FALKEN TYRE EUROPE GMBH—See Sumitomo Rubber Industries, Ltd.; *Int'l*, pg. 7299
FALKEN TYRE INDIA PRIVATE LIMITED—See Sumitomo Rubber Industries, Ltd.; *Int'l*, pg. 7299
FALK INDUSTRIES INC.; *U.S. Private*, pg. 1467
FALK INTEGRATED TECHNOLOGIES; *U.S. Private*, pg. 1467
THE FALKIRK MINING CO.—See NACCO Industries, Inc.; *U.S. Public*, pg. 1490
THE FALKLAND ISLANDS COMPANY LIMITED—See FIH group plc; *Int'l*, pg. 2661
FALKLAND ISLANDS RADIO SERVICE; *Int'l*, pg. 2611
FALKLAND ISLANDS SHIPPING LIMITED—See FIH group plc; *Int'l*, pg. 2661
THE FALK SERVICE CORPORATION—See Zurn Elkay Water Solutions Corporation; *U.S. Public*, pg. 2414
FALL ADVERTISING; *U.S. Private*, pg. 1467

FAM GRUPA KAPITALOWA S.A.

FALLBROOK HOSPITAL CORPORATION—See Community Health Systems, Inc.; *U.S. Public*, pg. 553
FALLBROOK PUBLIC UTILITY DISTRICT; *U.S. Private*, pg. 1467
FALLBROOK TECHNOLOGIES INC.; *U.S. Private*, pg. 1467
FALLEK CHEMICAL JAPAN KK—See ICC Industries, Inc.; *U.S. Private*, pg. 2029
FALLEK CHEMICAL S.A.—See ICC Industries, Inc.; *U.S. Private*, pg. 2029
FALLER, DAVIS & ASSOCIATES, INC.; *U.S. Private*, pg. 1468
FALL MACHINE COMPANY, LLC.—See White Wolf Capital LLC; *U.S. Private*, pg. 4510
FALLMANS KOTT AB—See Martin Olsson Handels AB; *Int'l*, pg. 4704
FALLON HEALTH; *U.S. Private*, pg. 1468
FALLON LONDON—See Publicis Groupe S.A.; *Int'l*, pg. 6099
FALLON LUMINOUS PRODUCTS CORPORATION; *U.S. Private*, pg. 1468
FALLON MEDICA LLC; *U.S. Private*, pg. 1468
FALLON TOKYO—See Publicis Groupe S.A.; *Int'l*, pg. 6099
FALLON VISUAL PRODUCTS CORP.—See Fallon Luminous Products Corporation; *U.S. Private*, pg. 1468
FALLON WORLDWIDE—See Publicis Groupe S.A.; *Int'l*, pg. 6099
FALLOW (BENTON) RESIDENTS MANAGEMENT COMPANY LIMITED—See Persimmon plc; *Int'l*, pg. 5815
FALL RIVER FIVE CENTS SAVINGS BANK; *U.S. Private*, pg. 1467
THE FALL RIVER GROUP, INC.; *U.S. Private*, pg. 4027
FALL RIVER HEALTH SYSTEM; *U.S. Private*, pg. 1467
FALL RIVER KIDNEY CENTER, LLC—See Nautic Partners, LLC; *U.S. Private*, pg. 2870
FALL RIVER NEWS CO. INC.; *U.S. Private*, pg. 1467
FALL RIVER RURAL ELECTRIC COOPERATIVE, INC.; *U.S. Private*, pg. 1467
THE FALLS AGENCY; *U.S. Private*, pg. 4027
FALLS CHURCH BOWL INC.—See Bowlero Corp; *U.S. Public*, pg. 376
FALLS CITY BREWING COMPANY—See Neace Ventures; *U.S. Private*, pg. 2877
FALLS CITY MACHINE TECHNOLOGY—See PMC Capital Partners, LLC; *U.S. Private*, pg. 3218
FALLS COMMUNICATIONS, INC; *U.S. Private*, pg. 1468
FALLS COMMUNITY HOSPITAL & CLINIC; *U.S. Private*, pg. 1468
FALLS FABRICATING, INC.—See Spell Capital Partners, LLC; *U.S. Private*, pg. 3754
FALLS HEATING & COOLING, INC.—See User Friendly Home Services, LLC; *U.S. Private*, pg. 4322
FALLS SIDING, INC.; *U.S. Private*, pg. 1468
FALLS WATER CO., INC.—See Northwest Natural Holding Company; *U.S. Public*, pg. 1542
FALLSWAY EQUIPMENT CO., INC.; *U.S. Private*, pg. 1468
FALLUJAH FOR CONSTRUCTION MATERIALS CO.; *Int'l*, pg. 2611
FALMAC LIMITED; *Int'l*, pg. 2611
FALMAC MACHINERY (TIANJIN) LTD.—See Falmac Limited; *Int'l*, pg. 2611
FALMAC TEXTILE (TIANJIN) LTD.—See Falmac Limited; *Int'l*, pg. 2611
FALMOUTH TOYOTA, INC.; *U.S. Private*, pg. 1468
FAL SHIPPING CO., LTD.—See FAL Group of Companies; *Int'l*, pg. 2610
FALT COMMUNICATIONS AB—See Telia Company AB; *Int'l*, pg. 7543
FALTEC CO., LTD.—See TPR Co., Ltd.; *Int'l*, pg. 7883
FALTEC EUROPE LIMITED—See TPR Co., Ltd.; *Int'l*, pg. 7883
FALTMAN & MALMEN AB—See The Interpublic Group of Companies, Inc.; *U.S. Public*, pg. 2093
FALTON INVESTMENT LIMITED—See China Automobile New Retail (Holdings) Limited; *Int'l*, pg. 1484
FALVEY LINEN SUPPLY INC.; *U.S. Private*, pg. 1468
FALVEY'S MOTORS, INC.; *U.S. Private*, pg. 1468
FAM AB; *Int'l*, pg. 2611
FAMA PR, INC.; *U.S. Private*, pg. 1468
FAMAR FUEGUINA, S.A.—See Mirgor S.A.C.I.F.I.A.; *Int'l*, pg. 4919
FAMC CORPORATION; *U.S. Private*, pg. 1468
FAMECCANICA DATA S.P.A.—See Angelini ACRAF S.p.A.; *Int'l*, pg. 460
FAMECCANICA DATA S.P.A.—See The Procter & Gamble Company; *U.S. Public*, pg. 2120
FAMECCANICA MACHINERY (SHANGHAI) CO., LTD.—See The Procter & Gamble Company; *U.S. Public*, pg. 2120
FAMECCANICA NORTH AMERICA, INC.—See The Procter & Gamble Company; *U.S. Public*, pg. 2120
FAMEGLOW HOLDINGS LTD.; *Int'l*, pg. 2611
FAME PRODUCTIONS, INC.; *U.S. Public*, pg. 821
FAMEX COMERCIO ATACADISTA DE GAS CARBONICO LTDA.—See Linde plc; *Int'l*, pg. 4508
FAM GRUPA KAPITALOWA S.A.; *Int'l*, pg. 2611
FAMICORD SUISSE S.A.—See VITA 34 AG; *Int'l*, pg. 8257

FAM GRUPA KAPITALOWA S.A.
CORPORATE AFFILIATIONS

FAMIGLIA - DEBARTOLO, LLC—See DeBartolo Holdings, LLC; *U.S. Private*, pg. 1186
FAMILIAR, INC.—See Axon Enterprise, Inc.; *U.S. Public*, pg. 256
FAMILIES FIRST FUNERAL HOME & TRIBUTE CENTRE, INC.—See Service Corporation International; *U.S. Public*, pg. 1869
FAMILIES FORWARD PHILADELPHIA; *U.S. Private*, pg. 1468
FAMILIES MAGAZINES, INC.—See Northern Virginia Media Services; *U.S. Private*, pg. 2955
FAMILJEHEMSBANKEN AB—See Byggfakta Group Nordic HoldCo AB; *Int'l*, pg. 1234
FAMILY ADVERTISING; *Int'l*, pg. 2612
FAMILY ADVOCACY SERVICES, LLC—See Centerbridge Partners, L.P.; *U.S. Private*, pg. 813
FAMILY ALLERGY & ASTHMA; *U.S. Private*, pg. 1468
FAMILY BAKERY SDN. BHD.; *Int'l*, pg. 2612
FAMILY BENEFIT LIFE INSURANCE COMPANY—See FIRST TRINITY FINANCIAL CORPORATION; *U.S. Private*, pg. 1530
FAMILY BOOK CO., LTD.—See GEO Holdings Corporation; *Int'l*, pg. 2932
FAMILY BRANDS INTERNATIONAL LLC—See Cherokee Distributing Company, Inc.; *U.S. Private*, pg. 873
THE FAMILY BUSINESS INSTITUTE LLC—See The Travelers Companies, Inc.; *U.S. Public*, pg. 2136
FAMILY CARE AT ARBOR WALK, LLC—See HCA Healthcare, Inc.; *U.S. Public*, pg. 996
FAMILYCARE HEALTH PLANS, INC.; *U.S. Private*, pg. 1471
FAMILY CARE HOSPITALS LTD.; *Int'l*, pg. 2612
FAMILY CARE OF E. JACKSON COUNTY, LLC—See HCA Healthcare, Inc.; *U.S. Public*, pg. 996
FAMILY CARE PARTNERS, LLC—See HCA Healthcare, Inc.; *U.S. Public*, pg. 996
FAMILY CARE S.R.L.—See Openjobmetis S.p.A.; *Int'l*, pg. 5599
FAMILY CENTER OF HARRISONVILLE INC.; *U.S. Private*, pg. 1468
FAMILY CENTERS, INC.; *U.S. Private*, pg. 1469
FAMILY CENTRAL INC.; *U.S. Private*, pg. 1469
THE FAMILY CHANNEL, INC.—See DHX Media Ltd.; *Int'l*, pg. 2101
FAMILY CHEVROLET CADILLAC; *U.S. Private*, pg. 1469
FAMILY & CHILDREN'S ASSOCIATION; *U.S. Private*, pg. 1468
FAMILY & CHILDREN'S CENTER; *U.S. Private*, pg. 1468
FAMILY & CHILDRENS SERVICES; *U.S. Private*, pg. 1468
FAMILY CHRISTIAN STORES INC.; *U.S. Private*, pg. 1469
FAMILY CHRISTMAS SAVINGS CLUB LIMITED—See PayPoint plc; *Int'l*, pg. 5763
FAMILY CHRYSLER DODGE JEEP RAM; *U.S. Private*, pg. 1469
THE FAMILY CLINIC @ TOWNER PTE. LTD.—See Medinex Limited; *Int'l*, pg. 4778
FAMILY & COMMUNITY SERVICES, INC.; *U.S. Private*, pg. 1468
THE FAMILY CONSERVANCY; *U.S. Private*, pg. 4027
FAMILY CORPORATION INC.—See ITOCHU Corporation; *Int'l*, pg. 3836
FAMILY DAIRIES USA; *U.S. Private*, pg. 1469
FAMILY DOLLAR, INC.—See Dollar Tree, Inc.; *U.S. Public*, pg. 672
FAMILY DOLLAR STORES, INC.—See Dollar Tree, Inc.; *U.S. Public*, pg. 672
FAMILY EMPOWERMENT COUNCIL, INC.; *U.S. Private*, pg. 1469
FAMILY ER + URGENT CARE; *U.S. Private*, pg. 1469
FAMILY FEDERATION FOR WORLD PEACE & UNIFICATION; *U.S. Private*, pg. 1469
FAMILY FIRST HOSPICE INC.—See Dorilton Capital Advisors LLC; *U.S. Private*, pg. 1263
FAMILY FOCUS, INC.; *U.S. Private*, pg. 1470
FAMILY FOODS OF GATESVILLE; *U.S. Private*, pg. 1470
FAMILY FORD INC.; *U.S. Private*, pg. 1470
FAMILY FORD LINCOLN; *U.S. Private*, pg. 1470
FAMILY FORD OF EINFIELD; *U.S. Private*, pg. 1470
FAMILY FURNITURE CENTERS INC.; *U.S. Private*, pg. 1470
FAMILY GLOVE (TAIWAN) CO., LTD.—See S.T. CORPORATION; *Int'l*, pg. 6457
FAMILY GLOVE (THAILAND) CO., LTD.—See S.T. CORPORATION; *Int'l*, pg. 6457
FAMILY GLOVE (VIETNAM) CO., LTD.—See S.T. CORPORATION; *Int'l*, pg. 6457
FAMILY GUIDANCE CENTERS, INC.; *U.S. Private*, pg. 1470
FAMILY HEALTH CARE SERVICES—See UnitedHealth Group Incorporated; *U.S. Public*, pg. 2252
FAMILY HEALTHCARE; *U.S. Private*, pg. 1470
FAMILY HEALTH CENTER INC.; *U.S. Private*, pg. 1470
FAMILY HEALTH CENTERS, INC.; *U.S. Private*, pg. 1470
FAMILY HEALTH CENTERS OF SOUTHWEST FLORIDA INC.; *U.S. Private*, pg. 1470
FAMILY HEALTH CENTER; *U.S. Private*, pg. 1470

FAMILY HEALTH & HOUSING FOUNDATION INC.; *U.S. Private*, pg. 1470
FAMILY HEALTH MEDICAL GROUP OF OVERLAND PARK, LLC—See HCA Healthcare, Inc.; *U.S. Public*, pg. 996
FAMILY HEALTH MEDICAL GROUP OF OVERLAND PARK, LLC—See HCA Healthcare, Inc.; *U.S. Public*, pg. 996
FAMILY HEALTH RENTAL CO., LTD.—See JCR Pharmaceuticals Co., Ltd.; *Int'l*, pg. 3923
FAMILY HEALTH SERVICES CORPORATION; *U.S. Private*, pg. 1470
FAMILY HEALTH SPECIALISTS OF LEE'S SUMMIT, LLC—See HCA Healthcare, Inc.; *U.S. Public*, pg. 996
FAMILY HERITAGE LIFE INSURANCE COMPANY OF AMERICA—See Globe Life Inc.; *U.S. Public*, pg. 946
FAMILY HOME HEALTH CARE, INC.—See Amedisys, Inc.; *U.S. Public*, pg. 94
FAMILY HOME HEALTH SERVICES, INC.; *U.S. Private*, pg. 1470
FAMILY HOME HEALTH SERVICES LLC; *U.S. Private*, pg. 1470
FAMILY HOME HOSPICE, INC.—See UnitedHealth Group Incorporated; *U.S. Public*, pg. 2252
FAMILY, INC.; *Int'l*, pg. 2612
FAMILY INNS OF AMERICA, INC.; *U.S. Private*, pg. 1470
FAMILY INSURANCE SOLUTIONS INC.—See The Economical Insurance Group; *Int'l*, pg. 7637
FAMILY LEAGUE OF BALTIMORE CITY, INC.; *U.S. Private*, pg. 1470
FAMILY LEGACY MISSIONS INTERNATIONAL; *U.S. Private*, pg. 1471
FAMILY LIFE INSURANCE CO—See The Manhattan Insurance Group; *U.S. Private*, pg. 4074
FAMILYLINKS; *U.S. Private*, pg. 1471
FAMILY MANAGEMENT CORPORATION; *U.S. Private*, pg. 1471
FAMILY MARKETS LLC; *U.S. Private*, pg. 1471
FAMILYMART CO., LTD.—See ITOCHU Corporation; *Int'l*, pg. 3836
FAMILYMART CO., LTD.—See ITOCHU Corporation; *Int'l*, pg. 3836
FAMILY MEDICAL SUPPLY LLC—See Invacare Corporation; *U.S. Private*, pg. 2130
FAMILY MEDICINE ASSOCIATES OF EDMOND, LLC—See HCA Healthcare, Inc.; *U.S. Public*, pg. 996
FAMILY MEDICINE OF BLACKSBURG, LLC—See HCA Healthcare, Inc.; *U.S. Public*, pg. 996
FAMILY MEDICINE OF TERRE HAUTE, LLC—See HCA Healthcare, Inc.; *U.S. Public*, pg. 996
FAMILY MEMORIALS INC.; *Int'l*, pg. 2612
FAMILY MORTGAGE INC; *U.S. Private*, pg. 1471
FAMILY MOTORS GROUP; *U.S. Private*, pg. 1471
FAMILYNET JAPAN CORPORATION—See Tokyo Electric Power Company Holdings, Incorporated; *Int'l*, pg. 7790
FAMILY NURSE CARE, LLC—See Centene Corporation; *U.S. Public*, pg. 468
FAMILY OFFICE DER FRANKFURTER BANKGESELLSCHAFT AG—See Helaba Landesbank Hessen-Thuringen; *Int'l*, pg. 3327
FAMILYPARK GMBH INC.—See Compagnie des Alpes S.A.; *Int'l*, pg. 1738
FAMILY PHYSICIANS GROUP, INC.—See Humana, Inc.; *U.S. Public*, pg. 1069
FAMILY PHYSICIANS OF WINTER PARK, INC.—See Humana, Inc.; *U.S. Public*, pg. 1069
FAMILY PRESERVATION SERVICES, INC.—See ATAR Capital, LLC; *U.S. Private*, pg. 364
FAMILY PRESERVATION SERVICES OF NORTH CAROLINA, INC.—See ATAR Capital, LLC; *U.S. Private*, pg. 364
FAMILY PRESERVATION SERVICES OF WASHINGTON, D.C., INC.—See ATAR Capital, LLC; *U.S. Private*, pg. 364
FAMILY RESEARCH COUNCIL; *U.S. Private*, pg. 1471
FAMILY RESIDENCES AND ESSENTIAL ENTERPRISES INC.; *U.S. Private*, pg. 1471
FAMILY RESTAURANTS INC.; *U.S. Private*, pg. 1471
FAMILY ROOM ENTERTAINMENT CORPORATION; *U.S. Public*, pg. 821
FAMILY RV GROUP—See Redwood Capital Investments, LLC; *U.S. Private*, pg. 3380
FAMILY SAVINGS CREDIT UNION; *U.S. Private*, pg. 1471
FAMILY SECURITY CREDIT UNION; *U.S. Private*, pg. 1471
FAMILY SERVICE ASSOCIATION; *U.S. Private*, pg. 1471
FAMILY SERVICE OF RHODE ISLAND, INC.; *U.S. Private*, pg. 1471
FAMILY SERVICES OF WESTCHESTER; *U.S. Private*, pg. 1471
FAMILY SPORTS CONCEPTS, INC.; *U.S. Private*, pg. 1471
FAMILY STATIONS INC.; *U.S. Private*, pg. 1471
FAMILYTEX (BD) LIMITED; *Int'l*, pg. 2612
FAMILY TREE PRODUCE; *U.S. Private*, pg. 1471
FAMILY VIDEO MOVIE CLUB INC.—See Highland Ventures, Ltd.; *U.S. Private*, pg. 1939
FAMILY WEALTH ALLIANCE, LLC—See The Charles Schwab Corporation; *U.S. Public*, pg. 2058

FAMILY ZONE CYBER SAFETY LIMITED; *Int'l*, pg. 2612
FAMIMA.COM CO., LTD.—See ITOCHU Corporation; *Int'l*, pg. 3836
FAMIMA CORPORATION—See ITOCHU Corporation; *Int'l*, pg. 3836
FAMINGO PTE LTD.—See Gold Peak Technology Group Limited; *Int'l*, pg. 3025
FAMIS GMBH—See E.ON SE; *Int'l*, pg. 2257
FAMOS D.D.; *Int'l*, pg. 2612
FAMOS GRADNJA D.D.; *Int'l*, pg. 2612
FAMOS SA; *Int'l*, pg. 2612
FAMOSTAR EMERGENCY LIGHTING B.V.—See F.W. Thorpe plc; *Int'l*, pg. 2597
FAMOUS AMOS CHOCOLATE CHIP COOKIE CO., LLC—See Ferrero International S.A.; *Int'l*, pg. 2641
FAMOUS-AMOS RESTAURANTS INC.; *U.S. Private*, pg. 1472
FAMOUS ARTIST SCHOOL—See Cortina Learning International, Inc.; *U.S. Private*, pg. 1061
FAMOUS BRANDS CHEESE COMPANY (PTY) LTD.—See Famous Brands Limited; *Int'l*, pg. 2612
FAMOUS BRANDS COFFEE COMPANY (PTY) LTD.—See Famous Brands Limited; *Int'l*, pg. 2612
FAMOUS BRANDS INTERNATIONAL; *U.S. Private*, pg. 1471
FAMOUS BRANDS LIMITED; *Int'l*, pg. 2612
FAMOUS DAVE'S RIBS-U, INC.—See MTY Food Group Inc.; *Int'l*, pg. 5073
FAMOUS DISTRIBUTION INC.—See Famous Enterprises Inc.; *U.S. Private*, pg. 1471
FAMOUS ENTERPRISES INC.; *U.S. Private*, pg. 1471
FAMOUS FLAVOURS B.V.—See Compass Group PLC; *Int'l*, pg. 1752
FAMOUS FOOTWEAR—See Caleres, Inc.; *U.S. Public*, pg. 422
FAMOUS HOLDINGS PTE. LTD.—See Singapore Post Limited; *Int'l*, pg. 6941
FAMOUS HORSE INC.; *U.S. Private*, pg. 1472
FAMOUS INDUSTRIES INC.—See Famous Enterprises Inc.; *U.S. Private*, pg. 1471
FAMOUS MARKS, INC.; *U.S. Private*, pg. 1472
FAMOUS PACIFIC SHIPPING (NZ) LIMITED—See Singapore Post Limited; *Int'l*, pg. 6941
FAMOUS PACIFIC SHIPPING (WA) PTY. LTD.—See Singapore Post Limited; *Int'l*, pg. 6941
FAMOUS PAWN, INC.—See FirstCash Holdings, Inc.; *U.S. Public*, pg. 849
FAMOUS PLAYERS INVESTMENTS B.V.—See National Amusements, Inc.; *U.S. Private*, pg. 2841
FAMOUS RAMONA WATER, INC.; *U.S. Private*, pg. 1472
FAMOUS SUPPLY CO—See Famous Enterprises Inc.; *U.S. Private*, pg. 1471
FAMOUS TATE ELECTRIC CO., INC.; *U.S. Private*, pg. 1472
FAMOUS TOASTERY OF CONCORD, LLC; *U.S. Private*, pg. 1472
FAMOUS WRITERS SCHOOL—See Cortina Learning International, Inc.; *U.S. Private*, pg. 1061
FANAD PETTIGO TEORANTA—See Mowi ASA; *Int'l*, pg. 5059
FANALMATIC GESELLSCHAFT FUR UMWELTTECHNIK UND INDUSTRIEAUTOMATION MBH—See NORD Holding Unternehmensbeteiligungsgesellschaft mbH; *Int'l*, pg. 5416
FANA NARZEDZIA SP.Z.O.O.—See Cantoni Motor S.A.; *Int'l*, pg. 1299
FANAPOSTEN AS—See Schibsted ASA; *Int'l*, pg. 6617
FANATICS, INC.—See Kynetic LLC; *U.S. Private*, pg. 2360
FANATICS SPORTS AND PARTY TOURS PTY LIMITED—See TUI AG; *Int'l*, pg. 7964
FANATICS SPORTS & PARTY TOURS UK LIMITED—See TUI AG; *Int'l*, pg. 7964
FANAUTIC CLUB, S.L.—See Brunswick Corporation; *U.S. Public*, pg. 408
FAN BLADE ASSOCIATES, INC.—See Safran SA; *Int'l*, pg. 6473
FANCAMP EXPLORATION LTD.; *Int'l*, pg. 2612
FANCHEM, LTD.—See PVS Chemicals, Inc.; *U.S. Private*, pg. 3308
FANCHER CHAIR CO. INC.—See Fancher Industries Inc.; *U.S. Private*, pg. 1472
FANCHER INDUSTRIES INC.; *U.S. Private*, pg. 1472
FANCHEST, INC.; *U.S. Private*, pg. 1472
FANCL ASIA PTE LTD.—See Kirin Holdings Company, Limited; *Int'l*, pg. 4187
FANCL B&H CO., LTD.—See Kirin Holdings Company, Limited; *Int'l*, pg. 4187
FANCL CORPORATION—See Kirin Holdings Company, Limited; *Int'l*, pg. 4187
FANCL HOME LIFE CO., LTD.—See Kirin Holdings Company, Limited; *Int'l*, pg. 4187
FANCL INSURANCE SERVICE CORP.—See Kirin Holdings Company, Limited; *Int'l*, pg. 4187
FANCL INTERNATIONAL, INC.—See Kirin Holdings Company, Limited; *Int'l*, pg. 4187
FANCL SMILE CO., LTD.—See Kirin Holdings Company, Limited; *Int'l*, pg. 4187
FANCL TAIWAN CO., LTD.—See Kirin Holdings Company, Limited; *Int'l*, pg. 4187

COMPANY NAME INDEX

FANCL (THAILAND) CO., LTD.—See Kirin Holdings Company, Limited; *Int'l*, pg. 4187
FANCOM B.V.—See Berkshire Hathaway Inc.; *U.S. Public*, pg. 303
FANCOM E.U.R.L.—See Berkshire Hathaway Inc.; *U.S. Public*, pg. 304
FANCORT INDUSTRIES, INC.; *U.S. Private*, pg. 1472
FANCY ASSET COMPANY LIMITED—See Fancy Wood Industries Public Company Limited; *Int'l*, pg. 2613
FANCY CHAP, INC.—See WPEngine, Inc.; *U.S. Private*, pg. 4571
FANCY CHEER LIMITED—See Water Oasis Group Limited; *Int'l*, pg. 8356
FANCY FOODS INC.; *U.S. Private*, pg. 1472
FANCY PUBLICATIONS INC.; *U.S. Private*, pg. 1472
FANCY WOOD INDUSTRIES PUBLIC COMPANY LIMITED; *Int'l*, pg. 2613
FANCY WOOD INDUSTRIES PUBLIC COMPANY LIMITED - SURATTHANI FACTORY—See Fancy Wood Industries Public Company Limited; *Int'l*, pg. 2613
FANDANGO HOLDINGS PLC; *Int'l*, pg. 2613
FANDANGO, LLC—See Comcast Corporation; *U.S. Public*, pg. 540
FANDA SCIENTIFIC FZ-LLC—See HORIBA Ltd; *Int'l*, pg. 3475
F AND F CONCESSIONS, INC.—See Live Nation Entertainment, Inc.; *U.S. Public*, pg. 1328
FANDIFI TECHNOLOGY CORP.; *Int'l*, pg. 2613
FANDOTECH, LLC—See Cooperative Systems, LLC; *U.S. Private*, pg. 1043
FANDSTAN ELECTRIC GROUP LTD.—See Westinghouse Air Brake Technologies Corporation; *U.S. Public*, pg. 2358
FANDSTAN ELECTRIC, INC.—See Westinghouse Air Brake Technologies Corporation; *U.S. Public*, pg. 2358
FANDSTAN ELECTRIC LTD.—See Westinghouse Air Brake Technologies Corporation; *U.S. Public*, pg. 2358
FANDSTAN ELECTRIC SYSTEMS, LTD.—See Westinghouse Air Brake Technologies Corporation; *U.S. Public*, pg. 2358
FANDUEL INC.—See Flutter Entertainment plc; *Int'l*, pg. 2715
FANELLI HAAG KILGER PLLC—See Seyfarth Shaw; *U.S. Private*, pg. 3620
FANELLO INDUSTRIES, INC.—See Ryerson Holding Corporation; *U.S. Public*, pg. 1829
FANEUIL, INC.—See Skyview Capital, LLC; *U.S. Private*, pg. 3686
FANE VALLEY CO-OPERATIVE SOCIETY LTD.; *Int'l*, pg. 2613
FANG BROTHERS KNITTING LTD.; *Int'l*, pg. 2613
FANG CLOTHING INC.; *U.S. Private*, pg. 1472
FANGDA CARBON NEW MATERIAL CO., LTD.; *Int'l*, pg. 2613
FANGDA SPECIAL STEEL TECHNOLOGY CO., LTD.; *Int'l*, pg. 2613
FANGDD NETWORK GROUP LTD.; *Int'l*, pg. 2613
FANG HOLDINGS LTD.; *Int'l*, pg. 2613
FANHUA INC.; *Int'l*, pg. 2613
FA NIIGATA CO., LTD.—See Robert Bosch GmbH; *Int'l*, pg. 6361
F.A. NIIGATA CO., LTD.—See Robert Bosch GmbH; *Int'l*, pg. 6361
FAN LING MACHINE & MECHANICAL CENTRE—See Nishimatsu Construction Co., Ltd.; *Int'l*, pg. 5365
FANLOGIC INTERACTIVE INC.; *Int'l*, pg. 2613
FAN MILK LIMITED; *Int'l*, pg. 2612
FANNIE MAY CONFECTIONS BRANDS, INC.—See Ferrero International S.A.; *Int'l*, pg. 2640
FANNIN BANK; *U.S. Private*, pg. 1472
FANNIN INDUSTRIES INCORPORATED; *U.S. Private*, pg. 1472
FANNIN LIMITED—See DCC plc; *Int'l*, pg. 1990
FANNIN SURGICARE—See HCA Healthcare, Inc.; *U.S. Public*, pg. 996
FANNIN SURGICARE—See HCA Healthcare, Inc.; *U.S. Public*, pg. 996
FANNIN (UK) LIMITED—See ICU Medical, Inc.; *U.S. Public*, pg. 1087
FANNON PETROLEUM SERVICES INC.; *U.S. Private*, pg. 1472
FANSEDGE INCORPORATED—See Kynetic LLC; *U.S. Private*, pg. 2360
FANSFRENZY CORP.; *U.S. Public*, pg. 821
FANSIDE INC.—See FreeBit Co., Ltd.; *Int'l*, pg. 2769
FANSTEEL, INC.; *U.S. Private*, pg. 1472
FANSUNITE ENTERTAINMENT, INC.; *Int'l*, pg. 2613
FANTAGE.COM INC.—See Nexon Co., Ltd.; *Int'l*, pg. 5245
FANTAGIO CORP.; *Int'l*, pg. 2613
FANTAGRAPHICS BOOKS, INC.; *U.S. Private*, pg. 1472
FANTASEA WORLD INVESTMENTS (PTE) LTD—See John Keells Holdings PLC; *Int'l*, pg. 3978
FANTAS EYES INC.; *U.S. Private*, pg. 1472
FANTASIA ACCESSORIES LTD.; *U.S. Private*, pg. 1472
FANTASIA HOLDINGS GROUP CO., LIMITED; *Int'l*, pg. 2613
FANTASISTA CO., LTD.; *Int'l*, pg. 2613
FANTASMA GAMES AB—See EveryMatrix Ltd.; *Int'l*, pg. 2570

FANTAS TECHNOLOGY, INC.—See Vector Inc.; *Int'l*, pg. 8144
THE FANTASTIC COMPANY AG; *Int'l*, pg. 7641
FANTASTIC FURNITURE (LICENSING) PTY LTD—See Steinhoff International Holdings N.V.; *Int'l*, pg. 7194
FANTASTIC FURNITURE LIMITED—See Steinhoff International Holdings N.V.; *Int'l*, pg. 7194
FANTASTIC FURNITURE PTY LIMITED—See Steinhoff International Holdings N.V.; *Int'l*, pg. 7194
FANTASTIC HOLDINGS LIMITED—See Steinhoff International Holdings N.V.; *Int'l*, pg. 7194
FANTASTIC SAMS INTERNATIONAL CORPORATION—See Eurazeo SE; *Int'l*, pg. 2528
FANTASY ACES DAILY FANTASY SPORTS CORP.; *U.S. Public*, pg. 821
FANTASY FLIGHT GAMES; *U.S. Private*, pg. 1472
FANTASY SPORTS SHARK, LLC—See Bally's Corporation; *U.S. Public*, pg. 268
FANTECH INC.—See Systemair AB; *Int'l*, pg. 7391
FANTECH LTD.—See Systemair AB; *Int'l*, pg. 7391
FANTECH SYSTEMAIR MFG INC.—See Systemair AB; *Int'l*, pg. 7391
FANTEX, INC.; *U.S. Private*, pg. 1473
FANTINI & GORGA LLC; *U.S. Private*, pg. 1473
FANTOM DRIVES—See BNL Technologies Inc.; *U.S. Private*, pg. 602
FANT'S FOODLAND; *U.S. Private*, pg. 1472
FANUC ADRIA D.O.O.—See FANUC Corporation; *Int'l*, pg. 2614
FANUC AMERICA CORPORATION - MIDWEST—See FANUC Corporation; *Int'l*, pg. 2614
FANUC AMERICA CORPORATION—See FANUC Corporation; *Int'l*, pg. 2614
FANUC AUTOMATION ISRAEL LTD.—See FANUC Corporation; *Int'l*, pg. 2614
FANUC AUTOMATION ROMANIA S.R.L.—See FANUC Corporation; *Int'l*, pg. 2614
FANUC BENELUX BV—See FANUC Corporation; *Int'l*, pg. 2614
FANUC BULGARIA CORPORATION—See FANUC Corporation; *Int'l*, pg. 2614
FANUC CORPORATION; *Int'l*, pg. 2614
FANUC CZECH S.R.O.—See FANUC Corporation; *Int'l*, pg. 2614
FANUC EUROPE CORPORATION, S.A.—See FANUC Corporation; *Int'l*, pg. 2614
FANUC EUROPE GMBH—See FANUC Corporation; *Int'l*, pg. 2614
FANUC FA BULGARIA LTD.—See FANUC Corporation; *Int'l*, pg. 2614
FANUC FA DEUTSCHLAND GMBH—See FANUC Corporation; *Int'l*, pg. 2614
FANUC FA FRANCE S.A.S.—See FANUC Corporation; *Int'l*, pg. 2614
FANUC FA HUNGARY KFT—See FANUC Corporation; *Int'l*, pg. 2614
FANUC FA IBERIA S.A.U.—See FANUC Corporation; *Int'l*, pg. 2614
FANUC FA ITALIA S.R.L.—See FANUC Corporation; *Int'l*, pg. 2614
FANUC FA NORDIC AB—See FANUC Corporation; *Int'l*, pg. 2614
FANUC FA SATIS VE SERVIS TICARET LTD.—See FANUC Corporation; *Int'l*, pg. 2614
FANUC FA SWITZERLAND GMBH—See FANUC Corporation; *Int'l*, pg. 2614
FANUC FA UK LIMITED—See FANUC Corporation; *Int'l*, pg. 2614
FANUC FRANCE S.A.—See FANUC Corporation; *Int'l*, pg. 2614
FANUC GERMANY SERVICE GMBH—See FANUC Corporation; *Int'l*, pg. 2614
FANUC IBERIA S.L.U.—See FANUC Corporation; *Int'l*, pg. 2614
FANUC INDIA PRIVATE LIMITED—See FANUC Corporation; *Int'l*, pg. 2615
FANUC KOREA SERVICE CORPORATION—See FANUC Corporation; *Int'l*, pg. 2614
FANUC LLC—See FANUC Corporation; *Int'l*, pg. 2614
FANUC MECHATRONICS (MALAYSIA) SDN. BHD.—See FANUC Corporation; *Int'l*, pg. 2615
FANUC MEXICO S.A. DE C.V.—See FANUC Corporation; *Int'l*, pg. 2614
FANUC NORDIC AB—See FANUC Corporation; *Int'l*, pg. 2614
FANUC OCEANIA PTY. LIMITED—See FANUC Corporation; *Int'l*, pg. 2615
FANUC OSTERREICH GMBH—See FANUC Corporation; *Int'l*, pg. 2614
FANUC PHILIPPINES CORPORATION—See FANUC Corporation; *Int'l*, pg. 2615
FANUC POLSKA SP. Z O.O.—See FANUC Corporation; *Int'l*, pg. 2614
FANUC ROBOMACHINE EUROPE GMBH—See FANUC Corporation; *Int'l*, pg. 2614
FANUC ROBOMACHINE (SHENZHEN) LTD.—See FANUC Corporation; *Int'l*, pg. 2615
FANUC ROBOTICS EUROPE S.A.—See FANUC Corporation; *Int'l*, pg. 2614

FARBEST-TALLMAN FOODS CORP.

FANUC SERBIA D.O.O.—See FANUC Corporation; *Int'l*, pg. 2614
FANUC SINGAPORE PTE. LTD.—See FANUC Corporation; *Int'l*, pg. 2615
FANUC SLOVAKIA S.R.O.—See FANUC Corporation; *Int'l*, pg. 2614
FANUC SOUTH AFRICA PTY. LIMITED—See FANUC Corporation; *Int'l*, pg. 2615
FANUC SOUTH AMERICA EQUIPAMENTOS DE AUTOMACAO E SERVICOS LTDA.—See FANUC Corporation; *Int'l*, pg. 2614
FANUC TAIWAN LIMITED—See FANUC Corporation; *Int'l*, pg. 2615
FANUC THAI LIMITED—See FANUC Corporation; *Int'l*, pg. 2614
FANUC TURKEY ENDUSTRIYEL OTOMASYON TIC. LTD. STI.—See FANUC Corporation; *Int'l*, pg. 2614
FANUC TURKEY LTD.—See FANUC Corporation; *Int'l*, pg. 2615
FANUC U.K. LIMITED—See FANUC Corporation; *Int'l*, pg. 2615
FANUC UKRAINE LLC—See FANUC Corporation; *Int'l*, pg. 2614
FANUC VIETNAM LIMITED—See FANUC Corporation; *Int'l*, pg. 2614
FAO BULGARIA EOOD—See Amadeus IT Group, S.A.; *Int'l*, pg. 407
FAO GROUP GMBH—See Amadeus IT Group, S.A.; *Int'l*, pg. 407
FAO OFFICE GMBH—See ManpowerGroup Inc.; *U.S. Public*, pg. 1358
FAPCO INC.; *U.S. Private*, pg. 1473
FA PH. NEDERMAN GMBH—See Nederman Holding AB; *Int'l*, pg. 5189
FAP - KORPORACIJA A.D.; *Int'l*, pg. 2615
FAP PAFAL S.A.—See Apator S.A.; *Int'l*, pg. 501
FAPROGI S.N.C.—See L'Oreal S.A.; *Int'l*, pg. 4378
F.A.P'S INC.—See Stellex Capital Management LP; *U.S. Private*, pg. 3800
FAPS INC.; *U.S. Private*, pg. 1473
FARABI PHARMACEUTICAL.CO; *Int'l*, pg. 2617
FARADAY COPPER CORP.; *Int'l*, pg. 2617
FARADAY ENGINEERING COMPANY LIMITED—See SMC Corporation; *Int'l*, pg. 7003
FARADAY FUTURE INTELLIGENT ELECTRIC INC.; *U.S. Public*, pg. 821
FARADAY HOLDINGS LIMITED—See Berkshire Hathaway Inc.; *U.S. Public*, pg. 301
FARADAY REINSURANCE COMPANY LTD.—See Berkshire Hathaway Inc.; *U.S. Public*, pg. 301
FARADAY RESEARCH LLP—See StoneX Group Inc.; *U.S. Public*, pg. 1952
FARADAY TECHNOLOGY CHINA CORPORATION—See Faraday Technology Corporation; *Int'l*, pg. 2618
FARADAY TECHNOLOGY CORPORATION—See Faraday Technology Corporation; *Int'l*, pg. 2618
FARADAY TECHNOLOGY CORPORATION—See Faraday Technology Corporation; *Int'l*, pg. 2618
FARADAY TECHNOLOGY CORPORATION; *Int'l*, pg. 2617
FARADAY TECHNOLOGY, INC.—See Physical Sciences Inc.; *U.S. Private*, pg. 3175
FARADAY TECHNOLOGY JAPAN CORPORATION—See Faraday Technology Corporation; *Int'l*, pg. 2618
FARADAY TECHNOLOGY VIETNAM COMPANY LIMITED—See Faraday Technology Corporation; *Int'l*, pg. 2618
FARADAY UNDERWRITING LIMITED—See Berkshire Hathaway Inc.; *U.S. Public*, pg. 301
FAR AD; *Int'l*, pg. 2615
FARADYNE MOTORS LLC—See Pentair plc; *Int'l*, pg. 5789
FARADYNE MOTORS LLC—See Xylem Inc.; *U.S. Public*, pg. 2394
FARAGO+PARTNERS; *U.S. Private*, pg. 1473
FARALLON CAPITAL MANAGEMENT, L.L.C.; *U.S. Private*, pg. 1473
FARALLON CONSULTING, LLC; *U.S. Private*, pg. 1473
FARAN SUGAR MILLS LTD - SINDH MILL—See Faran Sugar Mills Ltd; *Int'l*, pg. 2618
FARAN SUGAR MILLS LTD; *Int'l*, pg. 2618
THE FARASH CORPORATION; *U.S. Private*, pg. 4027
FARASIS ENERGY (GANZHOU) CO., LTD.; *Int'l*, pg. 2618
FARATRONIC (HONG KONG) COMPANY LIMITED—See Xiamen Faratronic Co., Ltd.; *Int'l*, pg. 8524
FARAWAY LAND, LLC—See INSPIRATO INCORPORATED; *U.S. Public*, pg. 1131
FARBANCA S.P.A.; *Int'l*, pg. 2618
FAR BANK ENTERPRISES, INC.—See Joshua Green Corporation; *U.S. Private*, pg. 2237
FARBCHEMIE BRAUN KG; *Int'l*, pg. 2618
FARBER & SCHMID AG—See Indutrade AB; *Int'l*, pg. 3678
FARBER & SCHMID GMBH—See Indutrade AB; *Int'l*, pg. 3678
FARBEST FOODS, INC.; *U.S. Private*, pg. 1473
FARBEST INDUSTRIES LTD.—See Citizen Watch Co., Ltd.; *Int'l*, pg. 1625
FARBEST-TALLMAN FOODS CORP.; *U.S. Private*, pg. 1473

FARBEST-TALLMAN FOODS CORP.

CORPORATE AFFILIATIONS

FARCENT ENTERPRICE CO., LTD. - GUANYIN FACTORY—See Farcent Enterprice Co., Ltd.; *Int'l*, pg. 2618
FARCENT ENTERPRICE CO., LTD.; *Int'l*, pg. 2618
FAR CITY MINING LIMITED; *Int'l*, pg. 2615
FARCO PLASTICS SUPPLY INC.; *U.S. Private*, pg. 1473
FAR EAST ALUMINIUM WORKS CANADA CORPORATION—See China State Construction International Holdings Limited; *Int'l*, pg. 1554
FAR EAST ALUMINIUM WORKS COMPANY LIMITED—See China State Construction International Holdings Limited; *Int'l*, pg. 1554
FAR EAST ALUMINIUM WORKS (SINGAPORE) PTE. LTD.—See China State Construction International Holdings Limited; *Int'l*, pg. 1554
FAR EAST ALUMINUM WORKS (U.S.) CORPORATION—See China State Construction International Holdings Limited; *Int'l*, pg. 1554
FAR EAST CABLE CO., LTD.—See Far East Smarter Energy Co., Ltd.; *Int'l*, pg. 2617
FAR EAST CONSORTIUM HOLDINGS (AUSTRALIA) PTY LIMITED—See Far East Consortium International Limited; *Int'l*, pg. 2615
FAR EAST CONSORTIUM INTERNATIONAL LIMITED; *Int'l*, pg. 2615
FAR EAST CONSORTIUM LIMITED—See Far East Consortium International Limited; *Int'l*, pg. 2615
FAR EAST DDB—See Omnicom Group Inc.; *U.S. Public*, pg. 1581
FAR EAST DELIMA PLANTATIONS SDN BHD—See Far East Holdings Berhad; *Int'l*, pg. 2616
FAR EAST DEVELOPMENT B.V.—See Enka Insaat ve Sanayi A.S.; *Int'l*, pg. 2440
FAR EAST (EAG) LIMITED—See Eagle Nice (International) Holdings Ltd.; *Int'l*, pg. 2266
FAR EAST ENGINEERING SERVICES LIMITED—See FSE Services Group Limited; *Int'l*, pg. 2798
FAR EAST ENTERPRISES (JOHOR BAHRU) SDN BHD—See Far East Group Limited; *Int'l*, pg. 2616
FAR EAST ENTERPRISES (KUALA LUMPUR) SDN BHD—See Far East Group Limited; *Int'l*, pg. 2616
FAR EAST ENTERPRISES (PENANG) SD BHD—See Far East Group Limited; *Int'l*, pg. 2616
FAR EASTERN AI MAI CO., LTD.—See The Far Eastern Group; *Int'l*, pg. 7641
FAR EASTERN APPAREL CO., LTD.—See The Far Eastern Group; *Int'l*, pg. 7641
FAR EASTERN APPAREL (SUZHOU) CO., LTD.—See The Far Eastern Group; *Int'l*, pg. 7641
FAR EASTERN APPAREL (VIETNAM) LTD.—See The Far Eastern Group; *Int'l*, pg. 7641
FAR EASTERN ASSET MANAGEMENT CO., LTD.—See The Far Eastern Group; *Int'l*, pg. 7641
FAR EASTERN BANK OJSC; *Int'l*, pg. 2617
FAR EASTERN BIG CITY SHOPPING MALLS CO., LTD.—See The Far Eastern Group; *Int'l*, pg. 7641
FAR EASTERN CITY SUPER LTD.—See The Far Eastern Group; *Int'l*, pg. 7641
FAR EASTERN DEPARTMENT STORES LTD.—See The Far Eastern Group; *Int'l*, pg. 7641
FAR EASTERN DYEING & FINISHING (SUZHOU) LTD.—See The Far Eastern Group; *Int'l*, pg. 7641
FAR EASTERN ELECTRONIC TOLL COLLECTION CO., LTD.—See The Far Eastern Group; *Int'l*, pg. 7641
FAR EASTERN FIBERTECH CO., LTD.—See The Far Eastern Group; *Int'l*, pg. 7641
THE FAR EASTERN GROUP; *Int'l*, pg. 7641
FAR EASTERN INDUSTRIES (SHANGHAI) LTD.—See The Far Eastern Group; *Int'l*, pg. 7641
FAR EASTERN INDUSTRIES (WUXI) CO., LTD.—See The Far Eastern Group; *Int'l*, pg. 7641
FAR EASTERN INTERNATIONAL BANK—See The Far Eastern Group; *Int'l*, pg. 7641
FAR EASTERN INTERNATIONAL LEASING CORPORATION—See The Far Eastern Group; *Int'l*, pg. 7641
FAR EASTERN INTERNATIONAL SECURITIES CO., LTD.—See The Far Eastern Group; *Int'l*, pg. 7641
FAR EASTERN ISHIZUKA GREEN PET CORPORATION—See Ishizuka Glass Co., Ltd.; *Int'l*, pg. 3818
FAR EASTERN NEW CENTURY CORPORATION—See The Far Eastern Group; *Int'l*, pg. 7641
FAR EASTERN RESOURCE DEVELOPMENT LTD., COPORATION—See The Far Eastern Group; *Int'l*, pg. 7642
FAR EASTERN SHIPPING COMPANY OJSC; *Int'l*, pg. 2617
FAR EASTERN UNIVERSITY INC.; *Int'l*, pg. 2617
FAR EAST FACADE, INC.—See China State Construction International Holdings Limited; *Int'l*, pg. 1554
FAREAST FINANCE & INVESTMENT LIMITED; *Int'l*, pg. 2618
FAR EAST GROUP LIMITED; *Int'l*, pg. 2616
FAR EAST HOLDINGS BERHAD; *Int'l*, pg. 2616
FAR EAST HOLDINGS INTERNATIONAL LIMITED; *Int'l*, pg. 2616
FAR EAST HORIZON LIMITED—See Sinochem Corporation; *Int'l*, pg. 6949

FAR EAST HOSPITALITY TRUST—See Far East Organization Pte. Ltd.; *Int'l*, pg. 2616
FAR EAST HOTELS AND ENTERTAINMENT LIMITED; *Int'l*, pg. 2616
FAR EAST INTERGERATION TECHNOLOGY CO., LTD.—See Far East Smarter Energy Co., Ltd.; *Int'l*, pg. 2617
FAREAST ISLAMI LIFE INSURANCE CO. LTD.; *Int'l*, pg. 2618
FAREAST ISLAMI SECURITIES LIMITED—See Fareast Islami Life Insurance Co. Ltd.; *Int'l*, pg. 2618
FAR EAST KNITTING & DYEING INDUSTRIES LTD.; *Int'l*, pg. 2616
FAR EAST MAJU ENGINEERING WORKS SDN BHD—See Far East Group Limited; *Int'l*, pg. 2616
FAR EAST MATERIAL TRADING CENTER CO., LTD.—See Far East Smarter Energy Co., Ltd.; *Int'l*, pg. 2617
FAR EASTONE TELECOMMUNICATIONS CO. LTD.—See The Far Eastern Group; *Int'l*, pg. 7641
FAR EAST ORCHARD LIMITED; *Int'l*, pg. 2616
FAR EAST ORGANIZATION PTE. LTD.; *Int'l*, pg. 2616
FAR EAST PUBLICATIONS LTD—See Thai Beverage Public Company Limited; *Int'l*, pg. 7590
FAR EAST REFRIGERATION (KUCHING) SDN BHD—See Far East Group Limited; *Int'l*, pg. 2616
FAR EAST REFRIGERATION LIMITED—See Far East Group Limited; *Int'l*, pg. 2616
FAR EAST REFRIGERATION (M) SDN. BHD.—See Far East Group Limited; *Int'l*, pg. 2616
FAR EAST SMARTER ENERGY CO., LTD.; *Int'l*, pg. 2617
FAR EAST TECHNICAL SERVICES (MACAO) LIMITED—See FSE Services Group Limited; *Int'l*, pg. 2798
FAR EAST VAULT LIMITED—See Far East Consortium International Limited; *Int'l*, pg. 2615
FAR EAST WIND POWER CORP.; *Int'l*, pg. 2617
FARECO—See FAYAT SAS; *Int'l*, pg. 2625
FARELOGIX INC.—See Vista Equity Partners, LLC; *U.S. Private*, pg. 4394
FAREVA HOLDING SA—See Fareva SA; *Int'l*, pg. 2618
FAREVA ITUPEVA—See Fareva SA; *Int'l*, pg. 2618
FAREVA LOUVEIRA—See Fareva SA; *Int'l*, pg. 2618
FAREVA RICHMOND INC.—See Fareva SA; *Int'l*, pg. 2618
FAREVA SA; *Int'l*, pg. 2618
FAREWAY STORES, INC.; *U.S. Private*, pg. 1473
FARFALLI; *Int'l*, pg. 2618
FARFETCH LIMITED—See Coupang, Inc.; *Int'l*, pg. 1819
FARFETCH LIMITED—See Greenoaks Capital Partners LLC; *U.S. Private*, pg. 1779
FARFETCH PORTUGAL - UNIPESSOAL, LDA—See Coupang, Inc.; *Int'l*, pg. 1819
FARFETCH PORTUGAL - UNIPESSOAL, LDA—See Greenoaks Capital Partners LLC; *U.S. Private*, pg. 1779
FARGLORY F T Z INVESTMENT HOLDING CO., LTD.; *Int'l*, pg. 2618
FAR GLORY HOTEL CO., LTD.; *Int'l*, pg. 2617
FARGLORY LAND DEVELOPMENT CO., LTD.; *Int'l*, pg. 2618
FARGO ASSEMBLY COMPANY—See Cerberus Capital Management, L.P.; *U.S. Private*, pg. 838
FARGO ASSEMBLY OF EUROPE LTD—See Cerberus Capital Management, L.P.; *U.S. Private*, pg. 838
FARGO ASSEMBLY OF MISSISSIPPI, LLC—See Cerberus Capital Management, L.P.; *U.S. Private*, pg. 838
FARGO ASSEMBLY OF PA, INC.—See Cerberus Capital Management, L.P.; *U.S. Private*, pg. 838
FARGO AUTOMATION, INC.—See Korber AG; *Int'l*, pg. 4280
FARGO GLASS & PAINT COMPANY; *U.S. Private*, pg. 1473
FARGO MFG. COMPANY, INC.—See Hubbell Incorporated; *U.S. Public*, pg. 1066
FARGO-MOORHEAD SYMPHONY; *U.S. Private*, pg. 1473
FARGO TANK & STEEL CO.—See TrueNorth Steel Inc.; *U.S. Private*, pg. 4249
FARGO TELECOM ASIA LIMITED—See Link-Asia International MedTech Group Limited; *Int'l*, pg. 4514
FARGO TELECOM HOLDINGS LIMITED—See Link-Asia International MedTech Group Limited; *Int'l*, pg. 4514
FARGO TELECOM TECHNOLOGIES PVT. LTD.—See Link-Asia International MedTech Group Limited; *Int'l*, pg. 4514
FARGO TRUSS SYSTEMS INC.; *U.S. Private*, pg. 1473
FARHEAP SOLUTIONS, INC.; *U.S. Private*, pg. 1473
FARIA BEEDE INSTRUMENTS, INC.; *U.S. Private*, pg. 1474
FARIA BEEDE INSTRUMENTS, INC.; *U.S. Private*, pg. 1474
FARIA CORPORATION; *U.S. Private*, pg. 1474
FARIBAULT FOODS INC.; *U.S. Private*, pg. 1474
FARIBAULT FOODS, INC.—See Faribault Foods Inc.; *U.S. Private*, pg. 1474
FARIBAULT MILLS, INC.; *U.S. Private*, pg. 1474
FARINA PRESSE S.R.L.—See ANDRITZ AG; *Int'l*, pg. 455
FARINGOSI HINGES S.R.L.—See Sabaf S.p.A.; *Int'l*, pg. 6462
FARIS MACHINERY COMPANY; *U.S. Private*, pg. 1474

FARISSIA BTP EURL—See Haulotte Group SA; *Int'l*, pg. 3285
FARITEC HOLDINGS LIMITED; *Int'l*, pg. 2618
FARLIE, TURNER & CO., LLC; *U.S. Private*, pg. 1474
FARLIM GROUP (MALAYSIA) BHD; *Int'l*, pg. 2618
FAR LIMITED; *Int'l*, pg. 2617
FARMA3TEC S.R.L.—See CompuGroup Medical SE & Co. KGaA; *Int'l*, pg. 1756
FARMABIOS SPA—See Groupe Bruxelles Lambert SA; *Int'l*, pg. 3099
FARMABIOS SPA—See Parcom Capital Management B.V.; *Int'l*, pg. 5739
FARMABIOT SA DE CV—See Intas Pharmaceuticals Ltd.; *Int'l*, pg. 3728
FARMACEUTICA MONT BLANC, S.L.—See Abbott Laboratories; *U.S. Public*, pg. 19
FARMACEUTICA REMEDIA S.A.; *Int'l*, pg. 2619
FARMACEUTICI FORMENTI S.P.A.—See Grunenthal GmbH; *Int'l*, pg. 3114
FARMACIA PLUS D.O.O.—See ATLANTIC GRUPA d.d.; *Int'l*, pg. 675
FARMACIAS AHUMADA S.A.—See Walgreens Boots Alliance, Inc.; *U.S. Public*, pg. 2322
FARMACIAS BENAVIDES SAB DE CV—See Walgreens Boots Alliance, Inc.; *U.S. Public*, pg. 2323
FARMACOLOGIA EM AQUICULTURA VETERINARIA LTDA.—See Abbott Laboratories; *U.S. Public*, pg. 19
FARMACOLOGIA EN AQUACULTURA VETERINARIA FAV ECUADOR S.A.—See Abbott Laboratories; *U.S. Public*, pg. 19
FARMACOLOGIA EN AQUACULTURA VETERINARIA FAV S.A.—See Abbott Laboratories; *U.S. Public*, pg. 19
FARMACOL S.A.; *Int'l*, pg. 2619
FARMACOOP A.D.; *Int'l*, pg. 2619
FARMACOSMO S.P.A.; *Int'l*, pg. 2619
FARMAFORCE LIMITED; *Int'l*, pg. 2619
FARMAGES SOFTWARE, S.L.—See CompuGroup Medical SE & Co. KGaA; *Int'l*, pg. 1757
FARMAK JSC; *Int'l*, pg. 2619
FARMALAB INDUSTRIAS QUIIMICAS E FARMACEUTICAS LTDA—See Chiesi Farmaceutici SpA; *Int'l*, pg. 1478
FARMANDSTREDET ANS—See BNP Paribas SA; *Int'l*, pg. 1091
FARMANDSTREDET EIENDOM AS—See BNP Paribas SA; *Int'l*, pg. 1091
FARMANOVA SAGLIK HIZMETLERI LTD.—See Novartis AG; *Int'l*, pg. 5457
FARMASIX-PRODUTOS FARMACEUTICOS, LDA—See Merck & Co., Inc.; *U.S. Public*, pg. 1416
FARMAVITA D.O.O.—See Podravka d.d.; *Int'l*, pg. 5902
FARMAX INDIA LIMITED; *Int'l*, pg. 2619
FARMBIOTEC CO., LTD.—See LG Chem Ltd.; *Int'l*, pg. 4473
FARM BOY INC.; *Int'l*, pg. 2619
FARM BUREAU BANK FSB—See FB Bancorp; *U.S. Private*, pg. 1484
FARM BUREAU BUILDING, INC.—See Arkansas Farm Bureau Federation; *U.S. Private*, pg. 325
FARM BUREAU CASUALTY INSURANCE CO.—See Arkansas Farm Bureau Federation; *U.S. Private*, pg. 325
FARM BUREAU FINANCE COMPANY INC.—See Farm Bureau Mutual Insurance Company of Idaho, Inc.; *U.S. Private*, pg. 1474
FARM BUREAU INSURANCE AGENCY OF COLORADO, INC.—See Colorado Farm Bureau Mutual Insurance Co.; *U.S. Private*, pg. 973
FARM BUREAU LIFE INSURANCE COMPANY OF MISSOURI, INC.—See Missouri Farm Bureau; *U.S. Private*, pg. 2749
FARM BUREAU LIFE INSURANCE COMPANY—See Iowa Farm Bureau Federation; *U.S. Private*, pg. 2134
FARM BUREAU MUTUAL INSURANCE COMPANY OF IDAHO, INC.; *U.S. Private*, pg. 1474
FARM BUREAU MUTUAL INSURANCE COMPANY OF MICHIGAN INC.; *U.S. Private*, pg. 1474
FARM BUREAU MUTUAL INSURANCE CO, OF ARKANSAS—See Arkansas Farm Bureau Federation; *U.S. Private*, pg. 326
FARM BUREAU MUTUAL INSURANCE CO.—See Iowa Farm Bureau Federation; *U.S. Private*, pg. 2134
FARM BUREAU TOWN & COUNTRY INSURANCE CO. OF MISSOURI—See Missouri Farm Bureau; *U.S. Private*, pg. 2749
FARM BUSINESS CONSULTANTS INC.; *Int'l*, pg. 2619
FARMCARE LIMITED—See Co-operative Group Limited; *Int'l*, pg. 1679
FARMCERES CO., LTD.—See LG Chem Ltd.; *Int'l*, pg. 4473
FARMCHEM CORPORATION; *U.S. Private*, pg. 1475
FARM CHEMICALS INC.; *U.S. Private*, pg. 1474
FARM CHOICE CO., LTD.—See Nissui Corporation; *Int'l*, pg. 5377
FARM CITY ELEVATOR INC.; *U.S. Private*, pg. 1474
FARM COUNTRY CO-OP; *U.S. Private*, pg. 1474
FARM CREDIT BANK OF TEXAS—See Federal Farm Credit Banks Funding Corporation; *U.S. Private*, pg. 1487
FARM CREDIT CANADA; *Int'l*, pg. 2619

COMPANY NAME INDEX

FARM CREDIT EAST; *U.S. Private,* pg. 1474
FARM CREDIT LEASING SERVICES CORPORATION—See Federal Farm Credit Banks Funding Corporation; *U.S. Private,* pg. 1487
FARM CREDIT MID-AMERICA; *U.S. Private,* pg. 1474
FARM CREDIT OF CENTRAL FLORIDA ACA; *U.S. Private,* pg. 1474
FARM CREDIT OF FLORIDA; *U.S. Private,* pg. 1474
FARM CREDIT OF NORTH FLORIDA ACA; *U.S. Private,* pg. 1474
FARM CREDIT OF NORTHWEST FLORIDA ACA; *U.S. Private,* pg. 1475
FARM CREDIT OF WESTERN NEW YORK ACA INC.; *U.S. Private,* pg. 1475
FARM CREDIT SERVICE OF CENTRAL ARKANSAS INC.; *U.S. Private,* pg. 1475
FARM CREDIT SERVICES MANDAN; *U.S. Private,* pg. 1475
FARM CREDIT SERVICES MISSOURI; *U.S. Private,* pg. 1475
FARM CREDIT SERVICES OF AMERICA PCA/FLCA; *U.S. Private,* pg. 1475
FARM CREDIT SERVICES OF NORTH DAKOTA; *U.S. Private,* pg. 1475
FARM CREDIT SERVICES SOUTHWEST; *U.S. Private,* pg. 1475
FARM DESIGN, INC.—See Flex Ltd.; *Int'l,* pg. 2703
FARMEC NUOVA S.R.L.—See L'Air Liquide S.A.; *Int'l,* pg. 4375
FARM EQUIPMENT COMPANY; *U.S. Private,* pg. 1475
FARMER AUTOMATIC GMBH & CO. KG—See AGCO Corporation; *U.S. Public,* pg. 58
FARMER BOY AGRICULTURAL SYSTEMS INC.; *U.S. Private,* pg. 1475
FARMER BROS. CO.—See Farmer Brothers Co.; *U.S. Public,* pg. 821
FARMER BROTHERS CO.; *U.S. Public,* pg. 821
FARMER BUSINESS DEVELOPMENTS PLC; *Int'l,* pg. 2619
FARMER BUSINESS SYSTEMS—See Alliance Office Systems; *U.S. Private,* pg. 183
FARMER CONSTRUCTION LTD.; *Int'l,* pg. 2619
FARMER MAC II LLC—See Federal Agricultural Mortgage Corporation; *U.S. Public,* pg. 825
FARMERS' AERIAL APPLICATORS INC.—See Farmer's Supply Cooperative Inc.; *U.S. Private,* pg. 1475
FARMERS ALLIANCE MUTUAL INSURANCE CO., INC.; *U.S. Private,* pg. 1476
FARMERS ALLIANCE—See CHS INC.; *U.S. Public,* pg. 492
FARMERS AND MERCHANTS BANCSHARES, INC.; *U.S. Public,* pg. 822
FARMERS AND MERCHANTS BANK—See Country Bank Shares, Inc.; *U.S. Private,* pg. 1066
FARMERS AND MERCHANTS BANK—See Farmers and Merchants Bancshares, Inc.; *U.S. Public,* pg. 822
FARMERS AUTOMOBILE INSURANCE ASSOCIATION; *U.S. Private,* pg. 1476
FARMERS BANCORP INC.; *U.S. Public,* pg. 822
FARMERS BANCORPORATION, INC.; *U.S. Private,* pg. 1476
FARMERS BANCSHARES INC.; *U.S. Private,* pg. 1476
FARMERS BANK AND TRUST; *U.S. Private,* pg. 1476
THE FARMERS BANK OF APPOMATTOX; *U.S. Public,* pg. 2073
FARMERS BANK OF NORTHERN MISSOURI—See Northern Missouri Bancshares, Inc.; *U.S. Private,* pg. 2953
FARMERS BANKSHARES, INC.—See Towne Bank; *U.S. Public,* pg. 2165
FARMERS BANK—See Farmers Bancorporation, Inc.; *U.S. Private,* pg. 1476
THE FARMERS BANK—See First Farmers Bancshares Inc.; *U.S. Private,* pg. 1517
FARMERS BANK—See Park National Corporation; *U.S. Public,* pg. 1638
THE FARMERS BANK—See Putnam-Greene Financial Corporation; *U.S. Private,* pg. 3307
FARMERS BANK—See Towne Bank; *U.S. Public,* pg. 2166
FARMERS BANK & TRUST COMPANY—See Magnolia Banking Corporation; *U.S. Private,* pg. 2548
FARMERS BANK & TRUST; *U.S. Private,* pg. 1476
FARMERS BOY LIMITED—See Clayton, Dubilier & Rice, LLC; *U.S. Private,* pg. 930
FARMERS CHOICE FOOD BRANDS—See Promotion In Motion, Inc.; *U.S. Private,* pg. 3283
FARMER'S CHOICE LTD—See Aga Khan Development Network; *Int'l,* pg. 199
FARMERS COMMERCIAL BANK; *Int'l,* pg. 2619
FARMERS COOP ASSOCIATION; *U.S. Private,* pg. 1476
FARMERS CO-OP ELEVATOR CO. HUDSONVILLE; *U.S. Private,* pg. 1476
FARMERS COOP ELEVATOR OTTOSEN; *U.S. Private,* pg. 1476
FARMERS COOPERATIVE ASSOCIATION INC.; *U.S. Private,* pg. 1477
FARMERS COOPERATIVE ASSOCIATION OF RAVENNA; *U.S. Private,* pg. 1477

FARMERS COOPERATIVE ASSOCIATION; *U.S. Private,* pg. 1476
FARMERS COOPERATIVE ASSOCIATION; *U.S. Private,* pg. 1476
FARMERS COOPERATIVE ASSOCIATION; *U.S. Private,* pg. 1477
FARMERS COOPERATIVE ASSOCIATION; *U.S. Private,* pg. 1476
FARMERS COOPERATIVE CO. INC.; *U.S. Private,* pg. 1477
FARMERS COOPERATIVE COMPANY; *U.S. Private,* pg. 1477
FARMERS COOPERATIVE COMPANY; *U.S. Private,* pg. 1477
FARMERS COOPERATIVE COMPRESS INC.; *U.S. Private,* pg. 1477
FARMERS COOPERATIVE CO.; *U.S. Private,* pg. 1477
FARMERS COOPERATIVE CO.; *U.S. Private,* pg. 1477
FARMERS COOPERATIVE CO.; *U.S. Private,* pg. 1477
FARMERS COOPERATIVE ELEVATOR COMPANY; *U.S. Private,* pg. 1477
FARMERS COOPERATIVE ELEVATOR COMPANY; *U.S. Private,* pg. 1477
FARMERS COOPERATIVE ELEVATOR COMPANY; *U.S. Private,* pg. 1477
FARMERS COOPERATIVE ELEVATOR CO.; *U.S. Private,* pg. 1477
FARMERS COOPERATIVE ELEVATOR CO.; *U.S. Private,* pg. 1477
FARMERS COOPERATIVE ELEVATOR CO.; *U.S. Private,* pg. 1477
FARMERS COOPERATIVE ELEVATOR OF SISSETON & NEW EFFINGTON; *U.S. Private,* pg. 1477
FARMERS COOPERATIVE EQUITY CO.; *U.S. Private,* pg. 1477
FARMERS COOPERATIVE GRAIN ASSOCIATION; *U.S. Private,* pg. 1477
FARMERS COOPERATIVE, INC.; *U.S. Private,* pg. 1477
FARMERS COOPERATIVE INC.; *U.S. Private,* pg. 1477
FARMERS CO-OPERATIVE OIL CO.; *U.S. Private,* pg. 1476
FARMERS COOPERATIVE SOCIETY; *U.S. Private,* pg. 1477
FARMERS COOPERATIVE; *U.S. Private,* pg. 1476
FARMERS COOPERATIVE—See Farmers Cooperative; *U.S. Private,* pg. 1476
FARMERS COOPERATIVE; *U.S. Private,* pg. 1476
THE FARMERS COOP GRAIN ASSOCIATION; *U.S. Private,* pg. 4027
FARMERS CO-OP INC; *U.S. Private,* pg. 1476
FARMERS COOP MILL & ELEVATOR ASSOCIATION; *U.S. Private,* pg. 1476
FARMERS CO-OP OF HANSKA INC.; *U.S. Private,* pg. 1476
FARMERS CO-OP SUPPLY & SHIPPING ASSOCIATION; *U.S. Private,* pg. 1476
FARMERS COPPER & INDUSTRIAL SUPPLY—See Four Winds Investment Corp.; *U.S. Private,* pg. 1583
FARMERS CROP INSURANCE ALLIANCE, INC.—See American Financial Group, Inc.; *U.S. Public,* pg. 103
FARMERS DEPOSIT BANK OF MIDDLEBURG, INC.—See John R. Turner Holding Company; *U.S. Private,* pg. 2224
FARMERS ELECTRIC COOPERATIVE CORPORATION; *U.S. Private,* pg. 1477
FARMERS' ELECTRIC COOPERATIVE INC. OF NEW MEXICO; *U.S. Private,* pg. 1480
FARMERS ELECTRIC CO-OPERATIVE; *U.S. Private,* pg. 1477
FARMERS ELEVATOR COMPANY OF MANTENO; *U.S. Private,* pg. 1478
FARMERS ELEVATOR COMPANY; *U.S. Private,* pg. 1478
FARMERS ELEVATOR CO-OP; *U.S. Private,* pg. 1477
FARMERS ELEVATOR CO.—See CHS INC.; *U.S. Public,* pg. 492
FARMERS ELEVATOR GRAIN & SUPPLY; *U.S. Private,* pg. 1478
FARMERS ELEVATOR OF LAKEFIELD; *U.S. Private,* pg. 1478
FARMERS EQUIPMENT COMPANY; *U.S. Private,* pg. 1478
FARMERS FEED & GRAIN COMPANY; *U.S. Private,* pg. 1478
FARMERS FEED MILL INC.; *U.S. Private,* pg. 1478
FARMERS FOODS CHASE CITY INCORPORATED; *U.S. Private,* pg. 1478
FARMERS GRAIN & COAL CO. INC.; *U.S. Private,* pg. 1478
FARMERS GRAIN COMPANY; *U.S. Private,* pg. 1478
FARMERS GRAIN OF LATHAM INC.; *U.S. Private,* pg. 1478
FARMERS GRAIN TERMINAL INC.; *U.S. Private,* pg. 1478
FARMERS GROUP, INC.—See Zurich Insurance Group Limited; *Int'l,* pg. 8698
FARMERS INC.; *U.S. Private,* pg. 1478
FARMERS INDUSTRIES LIMITED—See GEA Group Aktiengesellschaft; *Int'l,* pg. 2897

FARMERS STATE BANK

FARMERS INSURANCE EXCHANGE—See Zurich Insurance Group Limited; *Int'l,* pg. 8698
FARMERS INSURANCE HAWAII—See Zurich Insurance Group Limited; *Int'l,* pg. 8698
FARMERS INSURANCE OF COLUMBUS INC.—See Zurich Insurance Group Limited; *Int'l,* pg. 8698
FARMERS INVESTMENT COMPANY, INC.—See Bale of Kentucky, Inc.; *U.S. Private,* pg. 459
FARMERS MARINE COPPER WORKS—See Four Winds Investment Corp.; *U.S. Private,* pg. 1583
FARMERS MARKETING ASSOCIATION OF HOUSTON TEXAS, INC.—See MLB Capital Partners, LLC; *U.S. Private,* pg. 2754
FARMERS & MERCHANTS BANCORP, INC.; *U.S. Public,* pg. 821
FARMERS & MERCHANTS BANCORP; *U.S. Public,* pg. 821
FARMERS MERCHANTS BANK LONG BEACH; *U.S. Public,* pg. 822
FARMERS & MERCHANTS BANK OF CENTRAL CALIFORNIA—See Farmers & Merchants Bancorp; *U.S. Public,* pg. 821
FARMERS-MERCHANTS BANK OF ILLINOIS—See Merchants Bancorp; *U.S. Public,* pg. 1415
FARMERS & MERCHANTS BANK OF SOUTH CAROLINA—See FMB of S.C. Bancshares, Incorporated; *U.S. Private,* pg. 1554
THE FARMERS & MERCHANTS BANKSHARES, INC.; *U.S. Private,* pg. 4027
FARMERS & MERCHANTS BANK; *U.S. Private,* pg. 1475
FARMERS & MERCHANTS BANK—See F&M Bank Corp.; *U.S. Public,* pg. 818
FARMERS & MERCHANTS BANK—See Putnam-Greene Financial Corporation; *U.S. Private,* pg. 3307
THE FARMERS & MERCHANTS BANK—See The Farmers & Merchants Bankshares, Inc.; *U.S. Private,* pg. 4027
FARMERS MERCHANTS COOP OIL CO.; *U.S. Private,* pg. 1478
FARMERS & MERCHANTS FINANCIAL SERVICES—See F&M Bank Corp.; *U.S. Public,* pg. 818
FARMERS & MERCHANTS INVESTMENT INC.; *U.S. Private,* pg. 1475
THE FARMERS & MERCHANTS MUTUAL TELEPHONE CO. OF WAYLAND, IOWA—See Kalona Cooperative Telephone Company; *U.S. Private,* pg. 2258
FARMERS & MERCHANTS STATE BANK—See Farmers & Merchants Bancorp, Inc.; *U.S. Public,* pg. 822
FARMERS & MERCHANTS TRUST CHAMBERSBURG—See Franklin Financial Services Corporation; *U.S. Public,* pg. 879
FARMERS MILL & ELEVATOR CO.; *U.S. Private,* pg. 1478
THE FARMERS' MUSEUM, INC.; *U.S. Private,* pg. 4027
FARMERS MUTUAL FIRE INSURANCE; *U.S. Private,* pg. 1478
FARMERS MUTUAL HAIL INSURANCE COMPANY OF IOWA; *U.S. Private,* pg. 1478
FARMERS MUTUAL INSURANCE COMPANY OF NEBRASKA INC.; *U.S. Private,* pg. 1478
FARMERS MUTUAL PROTECTIVE ASSOCIATION TEXAS; *U.S. Private,* pg. 1478
FARMERS NATIONAL BANC CORP.; *U.S. Public,* pg. 822
THE FARMERS NATIONAL BANK OF CANFIELD—See Farmers National Banc Corp.; *U.S. Public,* pg. 822
THE FARMERS NATIONAL BANK OF DANVILLE—See Boyle Bancorp Inc.; *U.S. Public,* pg. 378
THE FARMERS NATIONAL BANK OF EMLENTON—See Farmers National Banc Corp.; *U.S. Public,* pg. 822
FARMERS NATIONAL COMPANY; *U.S. Private,* pg. 1478
FARMERS NATIONAL INSURANCE LLC—See Farmers National Banc Corp.; *U.S. Public,* pg. 822
FARMERS NEW WORLD LIFE INSURANCE CO.—See Zurich Insurance Group Limited; *Int'l,* pg. 8698
FARMERS PRIDE, INC.—See Jamaica Broilers Group Limited; *Int'l,* pg. 3874
FARMERS PRODUCE EXCHANGE; *U.S. Private,* pg. 1478
FARMERS RANCHERS COOP ASSOC.; *U.S. Private,* pg. 1478
FARMERS REINSURANCE COMPANY—See Zurich Insurance Group Limited; *Int'l,* pg. 8697
FARMERS RICE COOPERATIVE; *U.S. Private,* pg. 1478
FARMERS RURAL ELECTRIC COOP CORP.; *U.S. Private,* pg. 1479
FARMERS SAVINGS BANK INC.; *U.S. Private,* pg. 1479
FARMERS SEAFOOD CO. INC.; *U.S. Private,* pg. 1479
FARMERS STATE BANK OF BRUSH—See First Pioneer Bank Corp.; *U.S. Private,* pg. 1524
FARMERS STATE BANK OF WATKINS—See Neisen Bancshares, Inc.; *U.S. Private,* pg. 2882
FARMERS STATE BANK; *U.S. Private,* pg. 1479
FARMERS STATE BANK—See F.S. Bancorp; *U.S. Private,* pg. 1457
FARMERS STATE BANK—See FSC Bancshares, Inc.; *U.S. Private,* pg. 1618
FARMERS STATE BANK—See Groesbeck Bancshares, Inc.; *U.S. Private,* pg. 1791

943

FARMERS STATE BANK

CORPORATE AFFILIATIONS

FARMERS STATE BANK—See Neighbor Insurance Services; *U.S. Private*, pg. 2881
FARMERS STATE BANK—See Farmers Bancshares Inc.; *U.S. Private*, pg. 1476
FARMERS SUPPLY ASSOCIATION; *U.S. Private*, pg. 1479
FARMER'S SUPPLY COOPERATIVE INC.; *U.S. Private*, pg. 1475
FARMERS SUPPLY SALES INC.; *U.S. Private*, pg. 1479
FARMERS TELECOMMUNICATIONS COOPERATIVE, INC.; *U.S. Private*, pg. 1479
FARMERS TELEPHONE CO. INC.; *U.S. Private*, pg. 1479
THE FARMERS TELEPHONE COMPANY, LLC—See Telephone & Data Systems, Inc.; *U.S. Public*, pg. 1998
FARMERS TELEPHONE COOPERATIVE; *U.S. Private*, pg. 1479
FARMERS TRUST COMPANY—See Farmers National Banc Corp.; *U.S. Public*, pg. 822
FARMERS TRUST & SAVINGS BANK—See FTS Financial, Inc.; *U.S. Private*, pg. 1619
FARMERS TRUST & SAVINGS BANK—See Koss-Winn Bancshares, Inc.; *U.S. Private*, pg. 2344
FARMERS TRUST & SAVINGS BANK—See Easter Enterprises, Inc.; *U.S. Private*, pg. 1319
FARMERS TRUST & SAVINGS BANK—See J. Carl H. Bancorporation; *U.S. Private*, pg. 2155
FARMERS UNION COOPERATIVE ASSOCIATION; *U.S. Private*, pg. 1479
FARMERS UNION COOPERATIVE; *U.S. Private*, pg. 1479
FARMERS UNION COOP; *U.S. Private*, pg. 1479
FARMERS UNION COOP SUPPLY COMPANY; *U.S. Private*, pg. 1479
FARMERS UNION HOSPITAL ASSOCIATION; *U.S. Private*, pg. 1479
FARMERS UNION MARKETING & PROCESSING ASSOCIATION; *U.S. Private*, pg. 1479
FARMERS UNION MUTUAL INSURANCE CO.; *U.S. Private*, pg. 1479
FARMERS UNION OIL BISMARCK/MANDAN; *U.S. Private*, pg. 1479
FARMERS UNION OIL COMPANY OF KENMARE; *U.S. Private*, pg. 1479
FARMERS UNION OIL COMPANY; *U.S. Private*, pg. 1479
FARMERS UNION OIL CO.; *U.S. Private*, pg. 1479
FARMERS UNION OIL MOHALL/SHERWOOD; *U.S. Private*, pg. 1479
FARMERS UNION OIL MOORHEAD; *U.S. Private*, pg. 1479
FARMERS UNION OIL OF SOUTHERN VALLEY; *U.S. Private*, pg. 1479
FARMERS WAREHOUSE—See A.L. Gilbert Company; *U.S. Private*, pg. 27
FARMERS WEST; *U.S. Private*, pg. 1480
FARMERS WORLD LIMITED—See Saudi Arabian Mining Company - Ma'aden; *Int'l*, pg. 7406
FARMFACTS GMBH—See BayWa AG; *Int'l*, pg. 917
FARMFACTS HUNGARY KFT—See BayWa AG; *Int'l*, pg. 917
FARM FAMILY CASUALTY INSURANCE COMPANY—See Brookfield Corporation; *Int'l*, pg. 1174
FARM FAMILY LIFE INSURANCE COMPANY—See Brookfield Corporation; *Int'l*, pg. 1174
FARM & FLEET OF DE KALB INC.; *U.S. Private*, pg. 1474
FARMFOODS LTD; *Int'l*, pg. 2619
FARM FRESH BERHAD; *Int'l*, pg. 2619
FARM FRESH FOODS, INC.—See Post Holdings, Inc.; *U.S. Public*, pg. 1703
FARMGIRL FLOWERS INC.; *U.S. Private*, pg. 1480
THE FARM GROUP—See WPP plc; *Int'l*, pg. 8466
FARMHANNONG AMERICA, INC.—See LG Chem Ltd.; *Int'l*, pg. 4473
FARMHANNONG CO., LTD.—See LG Chem Ltd.; *Int'l*, pg. 4473
FARMHANNONG (THAILAND) LTD.—See LG Chem Ltd.; *Int'l*, pg. 4473
FARM & HOME OIL COMPANY—See Industry Super Holdings Pty. Ltd.; *Int'l*, pg. 3676
FARMHOUSE FARE LIMITED—See The Hain Celestial Group, Inc.; *U.S. Public*, pg. 2086
FARMHOUSE, INC.; *U.S. Public*, pg. 822
FARMINDUSTRIA S.A.—See Abbott Laboratories; *U.S. Public*, pg. 19
FARMINGTON BANCORP, INC.; *U.S. Private*, pg. 1480
FARMINGTON COUNTRY CLUB; *U.S. Private*, pg. 1480
FARMINGTON HILLS AUTOMOTIVE, LLC—See Suburban Motors Company, LLC; *U.S. Private*, pg. 3848
FARMINGTON HILLS HOLDING COMPANY; *U.S. Private*, pg. 1480
THE FARMINGTON RIVER POWER COMPANY—See Stanley Black & Decker, Inc.; *U.S. Public*, pg. 1936
FARMINGTONS HOLDING GMBH; *Int'l*, pg. 2619
FARMIN ROTHROCK & PARROTT, INC.—See Stone Point Capital LLC; *U.S. Private*, pg. 3819
FARMINVESTE SGPS S.A.; *Int'l*, pg. 2620
FARM JOURNAL; *U.S. Private*, pg. 1475
FARM KING SUPPLY INC.; *U.S. Private*, pg. 1475
FARMLAND A.D.; *Int'l*, pg. 2620

FARMLAND CENTRAL BAKERY (S) PTE LTD.—See QAF Limited; *Int'l*, pg. 6131
FARMLAND CO-OP, INC.; *U.S. Private*, pg. 1480
FARMLAND DAIRIES LLC—See Grupo LALA S.A. de C.V.; *Int'l*, pg. 3131
FARMLAND PARTNERS INC.; *U.S. Public*, pg. 822
FARMLAND PARTNERS OPERATING PARTNERSHIP, L.P.—See Farmland Partners Inc.; *U.S. Public*, pg. 822
FARM LANDS OF AFRICA, INC; *Int'l*, pg. 2619
FARMMI, INC.; *Int'l*, pg. 2620
FARM-OP, INC.—See Lipman & Lipman, Inc.; *U.S. Private*, pg. 2465
FARMOVS PAREXEL (PROPRIETARY) LIMITED—See Pamplona Capital Management LLP; *Int'l*, pg. 5712
FARM PRIDE FOODS LTD.; *Int'l*, pg. 2619
FARM PUMP AND IRRIGATION CO.; *U.S. Private*, pg. 1475
FARM & RANCH AUTO SALES, INC.; *U.S. Private*, pg. 1474
FARM'S BEST FOOD INDUSTRIES SDN. BHD.—See Cab Cakaran Corporation Berhad; *Int'l*, pg. 1245
FARMS.COM LTD.; *Int'l*, pg. 2620
FARMS.COM RISK MANAGEMENT INC.—See Farms.com Ltd.; *Int'l*, pg. 2620
FARMSCO.; *Int'l*, pg. 2620
FARMSECURE HOLDINGS (PTY) LTD.; *Int'l*, pg. 2620
FARM SERVICE COMPANY; *U.S. Private*, pg. 1475
FARM SERVICE COOPERATIVE INC.; *U.S. Private*, pg. 1475
FARM SERVICE INCORPORATED; *U.S. Private*, pg. 1475
FARM-SERWIS SP. Z O.O.—See CEPD N.V.; *Int'l*, pg. 1420
FARM STAND FOODS; *U.S. Private*, pg. 1475
FARM STORES; *U.S. Private*, pg. 1475
FARMSTORY CO., LTD.; *Int'l*, pg. 2620
FARMTEC RESEARCH CO, LTD.—See YungShin Global Holding Corporation; *Int'l*, pg. 8614
FARMTRAC TRACTORS EUROPE SPOLKA Z O.O.—See Escorts Kubota Limited; *Int'l*, pg. 2502
FARMWAY CO-OP INC. - BELOIT FERTILIZER PLANT—See Farmway Co-Op Inc.; *U.S. Private*, pg. 1480
FARMWAY CO-OP INC. - NORKAN PLANT—See Farmway Co-Op Inc.; *U.S. Private*, pg. 1480
FARMWAY CO-OP INC.; *U.S. Private*, pg. 1480
FARMWAY; *U.S. Private*, pg. 1480
FARMWEB LIMITED—See Direct Line Insurance Group plc; *Int'l*, pg. 2129
FARNACIAS BENAVIDES S.A.B. DE C.V.—See Walgreens Boots Alliance, Inc.; *U.S. Public*, pg. 2322
FARNAM COMPANIES, INC.—See Central Garden & Pet Company; *U.S. Public*, pg. 473
FARNBOROUGH AIRPORT LIMITED—See TAG Aviation S.A.; *Int'l*, pg. 7406
FARNBOROUGH BUSINESS PARK LIMITED—See SEGRO plc; *Int'l*, pg. 6683
FARNBOROUGH LIMITED—See Global Business Travel Group, Inc.; *U.S. Public*, pg. 941
FARNCOMBE FRANCE SARL—See Blackstreet Capital Holdings LLC; *U.S. Private*, pg. 577
FARNELL AG—See Avnet, Inc.; *U.S. Public*, pg. 253
FARNELL (BELGIUM) NV—See Avnet, Inc.; *U.S. Public*, pg. 253
FARNELL COMPONENTS AB—See Avnet, Inc.; *U.S. Public*, pg. 253
FARNELL COMPONENTS (IRELAND) LIMITED—See Avnet, Inc.; *U.S. Public*, pg. 253
FARNELL COMPONENTS SL—See Avnet, Inc.; *U.S. Public*, pg. 253
FARNELL DANMARK AS—See Avnet, Inc.; *U.S. Public*, pg. 253
FARNELL ELECTRONIC COMPONENTS LIMITED—See Avnet, Inc.; *U.S. Public*, pg. 253
FARNELL (FRANCE) SAS—See Avnet, Inc.; *U.S. Public*, pg. 253
FARNELL GMBH—See Avnet, Inc.; *U.S. Public*, pg. 254
FARNELL ITALIA SRL—See Avnet, Inc.; *U.S. Public*, pg. 254
FARNELL (NETHERLANDS) BV—See Avnet, Inc.; *U.S. Public*, pg. 253
FARNER-BOCKEN CO.—See Core-Mark Holding Co. Inc.; *U.S. Public*, pg. 576
FARNER CONSULTING AG—See Omnicom Group Inc.; *U.S. Public*, pg. 1590
FARNER PORTER NOVELLI—See Omnicom Group Inc.; *U.S. Public*, pg. 1590
FARNER TEUBER COMMUNICATION—See Omnicom Group Inc.; *U.S. Public*, pg. 1590
FARNHAM & PFILE CONSTRUCTION, INC.; *U.S. Private*, pg. 1480
FAR NIENTE WINERY—See GI Manager L.P.; *U.S. Private*, pg. 1692
FAR NORTHERN COORDINATING COUNCIL ON DEVELOPMENTAL DISABILITIES, INC.; *U.S. Private*, pg. 1473
FARNSWORTH DEVELOPMENT COMPANIES; *U.S. Private*, pg. 1480

FARNSWORTH REALTY AND MANAGEMENT CO.—See Farnsworth Development Companies; *U.S. Private*, pg. 1480
FARNSWORTH WHOLESALE COMPANY; *U.S. Private*, pg. 1480
FARO BENELUX B.V.—See FARO Technologies, Inc.; *U.S. Public*, pg. 823
FARO DEUTSCHLAND HOLDING GMBH—See FARO Technologies, Inc.; *U.S. Public*, pg. 823
FAROE PETROLEUM NORGE AS—See DNO North Sea Plc; *Int'l*, pg. 2148
FAROE PETROLEUM (UK) LIMITED—See DNO North Sea Plc; *Int'l*, pg. 2148
FARO EUROPE GMBH & CO. KG—See FARO Technologies, Inc.; *U.S. Public*, pg. 823
FARO INTERNATIONAL, INC.—See AuBEX Corporation; *Int'l*, pg. 698
FARO INTERNATIONAL (SHANGHAI) CO., LTD—See FARO Technologies, Inc.; *U.S. Public*, pg. 823
FAROL ASSET MANAGEMENT LP; *U.S. Private*, pg. 1480
FARON PHARMACEUTICALS; *Int'l*, pg. 2620
FARO RECRUITMENT (CHINA) CO., LTD.—See Bain Capital, LP; *U.S. Private*, pg. 434
FARO RECRUITMENT (HONG KONG) CO., LIMITED—See Bain Capital, LP; *U.S. Private*, pg. 434
FARO RECRUITMENT (SINGAPORE) PTE. LTD.—See Bain Capital, LP; *U.S. Private*, pg. 434
FARO SHANGHAI CO, LTD—See FARO Technologies, Inc.; *U.S. Public*, pg. 823
FARO SINGAPORE PTE. LTD.—See FARO Technologies, Inc.; *U.S. Public*, pg. 823
FARO SPAIN S.L.U.—See FARO Technologies, Inc.; *U.S. Public*, pg. 823
FAROSSON PTE. LTD.—See Yinson Holdings Berhad; *Int'l*, pg. 8585
FARO TECHNOLOGIES DO BRASIL LTDA—See FARO Technologies, Inc.; *U.S. Public*, pg. 823
FARO TECHNOLOGIES, INC. - LASER DIVISION—See FARO Technologies, Inc.; *U.S. Public*, pg. 823
FARO TECHNOLOGIES, INC.; *U.S. Public*, pg. 823
FARO TECHNOLOGIES UK LTD.—See FARO Technologies, Inc.; *U.S. Public*, pg. 823
FARO TECHNOLOGY POLSKA SP. Z O.O.—See FARO Technologies, Inc.; *U.S. Public*, pg. 823
FARO TECH POLSKA—See FARO Technologies, Inc.; *U.S. Public*, pg. 823
FAROUDJA INC.—See STMicroelectronics N.V.; *Int'l*, pg. 7218
FARO UK—See FARO Technologies, Inc.; *U.S. Public*, pg. 823
FAR PEAK ACQUISITION CORPORATION; *U.S. Public*, pg. 821
FAR POINT ACQUISITION CORPORATION; *U.S. Public*, pg. 821
FARRAGUT DIALYSIS, LLC—See DaVita Inc.; *U.S. Public*, pg. 638
FARRAND CONTROLS DIVISION—See Ruhle Companies, Inc.; *U.S. Private*, pg. 3503
FARRAR CORPORATION; *U.S. Private*, pg. 1480
FARRAR & FARRAR; *U.S. Private*, pg. 1480
FARRAR, STRAUS & GIROUX, INC.—See Verlagsgruppe Georg von Holtzbrinck GmbH; *Int'l*, pg. 8170
FARRATECH, INC.; *U.S. Private*, pg. 1480
FAR REACH TECHNOLOGIES CORPORATION; *U.S. Private*, pg. 1473
FARREL CORPORATION; *U.S. Private*, pg. 1480
FARRELL & ASSOCIATES INSURANCE SERVICES—See The Carlyle Group Inc.; *U.S. Public*, pg. 2054
FARRELL-CALHOUN INC.; *U.S. Private*, pg. 1481
FARRELL DISTRIBUTING CORP.; *U.S. Private*, pg. 1480
FARRELL EQUIPMENT & SUPPLY CO., INC.; *U.S. Private*, pg. 1481
FARRELL FORWARDING CO. INC.; *U.S. Private*, pg. 1481
FARRELL INSURANCE ASSOCIATES, INC.—See Union Bay Risk Advisors LLC; *U.S. Public*, pg. 4284
FARREL LTD.—See Farrel Corporation; *U.S. Private*, pg. 1480
FARREY'S WHOLESALE HARDWARE CO., INC.; *U.S. Private*, pg. 1481
FARRIS BOBANGO PLC—See Phelps Dunbar LLP; *U.S. Private*, pg. 3167
FARRIS FASHIONS INC.; *U.S. Private*, pg. 1481
FARRIS FUNERAL SERVICE, INC.—See Birch Hill Equity Partners Management Inc.; *Int'l*, pg. 1046
FARRIS FUNERAL SERVICE, INC.—See Homesteaders Life Co. Inc.; *U.S. Private*, pg. 1974
FARRISH OF FAIRFAX INC.; *U.S. Private*, pg. 1481
FARR VINTNERS LTD; *Int'l*, pg. 2620
FARR VINTNERS LTD.—See Farr Vintners Ltd; *Int'l*, pg. 2620
FARS CEMENT COMPANY; *Int'l*, pg. 2620
FARS CHEMICAL INDUSTRIES COMPANY; *Int'l*, pg. 2620
FAR SHIPPING LANKA (PVT) LTD.—See Hemas Holdings PLC; *Int'l*, pg. 3340
FARSIGHT BIOSCIENCE LIMITED; *Int'l*, pg. 2620
FAR SIGHTED MEDIA INC.; *U.S. Private*, pg. 1473

FARSIGHT SECURITY SERVICES, LTD.—See Optex Group Co., Ltd.; *Int'l*, pg. 5601
FARS & KHUZESTAN CEMENT CO.; *Int'l*, pg. 2620
FARSNOV CEMENT CO.—See Fars & Khuzestan Cement Co.; *Int'l*, pg. 2620
FARSONS BEVERAGE IMPORTS COMPANY LIMITED—See Simonds Farsons Cisk plc; *Int'l*, pg. 6932
FARSONSDIRECT—See Simonds Farsons Cisk plc; *Int'l*, pg. 6932
FARSONS (SALES & MARKETING) LIMITED—See Simonds Farsons Cisk plc; *Int'l*, pg. 6932
FAR SOUTHEAST GOLD RESOURCES, INC.—See Lepanto Consolidated Mining Company; *Int'l*, pg. 4466
FARSTAD SHIPPING ASA—See Solstad Offshore ASA; *Int'l*, pg. 7075
FARSTAD SHIPPING (INDIAN PACIFIC) PTY. LTD.—See Solstad Offshore ASA; *Int'l*, pg. 7075
FARSTAD SHIPPING LTD.—See Solstad Offshore ASA; *Int'l*, pg. 7075
FARSTAD SHIPPING SINGAPORE PTE LTD—See Solstad Offshore ASA; *Int'l*, pg. 7075
FARSTARCAP INVESTMENT CORP.; *Int'l*, pg. 2620
FARSUND ALUMINIUM CASTING AS—See Porsche Automobil Holding SE; *Int'l*, pg. 5928
FARUKI PULP MILLS LIMITED - GUJRAT MILL—See JDW Sugar Mills Ltd.; *Int'l*, pg. 3925
FARUKI PULP MILLS LIMITED—See JDW Sugar Mills Ltd.; *Int'l*, pg. 3925
FARUQUE (PVT) LTD—See Cherat Cement Company Limited; *Int'l*, pg. 1471
FARU, S.L.U.—See Bunzl plc; *Int'l*, pg. 1218
FARUTEX SP.Z.O.O.—See The Bidvest Group Limited; *Int'l*, pg. 7624
FARWEST CORROSION CONTROL CO.; *U.S. Private*, pg. 1481
FAR WEST FIBERS INC.; *U.S. Private*, pg. 1473
FARWEST FREIGHT SYSTEMS INC.; *U.S. Private*, pg. 1481
FAR WEST PLYWOOD COMPANY—See Hardwoods Distribution Inc.; *Int'l*, pg. 3273
FAR WEST RICE; *U.S. Private*, pg. 1473
FARWEST STEEL CORPORATION; *U.S. Private*, pg. 1481
FARYLROBIN FOOTWEAR; *U.S. Private*, pg. 1481
FASAL—See Techint S.p.A.; *Int'l*, pg. 7505
FASANA GMBH—See Mutares SE & Co. KGaA; *Int'l*, pg. 5106
FASBEE INC.—See BEENOS Inc.; *Int'l*, pg. 939
F.A.S.B., INC.—See Stewart Information Services Corporation; *U.S. Public*, pg. 1947
FAS CAPITAL MANAGEMENT LTD.—See FAS Finance & Investment Limited; *Int'l*, pg. 2620
FASCO AUSTRALIA PTY. LTD.—See Regal Rexnord Corporation; *U.S. Public*, pg. 1773
FASCO MOTORS THAILAND LTD.—See Regal Rexnord Corporation; *U.S. Public*, pg. 1773
FASCOR, INC.—See Dunes Point Capital, LLC; *U.S. Private*, pg. 1288
F.A. SENING GMBH—See TechnipFMC plc; *Int'l*, pg. 7507
FA SERVICE CORPORATION—See TRUMPF SE + Co. KG; *Int'l*, pg. 7942
FAS FINANCE & INVESTMENT LIMITED; *Int'l*, pg. 2620
FASFORD TECHNOLOGY CO., LTD.—See Fuji Corporation; *Int'l*, pg. 2809
FASHINVEST, LTD.—See Penske Media Corporation; *U.S. Private*, pg. 3139
FASHION AVENUE KNITS, INC.; *U.S. Private*, pg. 1481
FASHION B AIR S.A.; *Int'l*, pg. 2620
FASHION BED GROUP—See Leggett & Platt, Incorporated; *U.S. Public*, pg. 1302
FASHION BOX GREECE S.A.—See Fashion Box S.p.A.; *Int'l*, pg. 2621
FASHION BOX S.P.A.; *Int'l*, pg. 2620
FASHION CARPETS INC.; *U.S. Private*, pg. 1481
FASHION-CO-LAB. CO., LTD.—See World Co., Ltd.; *Int'l*, pg. 8456
FASHIONCRAFT FLOORS INC.; *U.S. Private*, pg. 1481
FASHION DYNAMICS SINGAPORE PTE LTD.—See FJ Benjamin Holdings Ltd.; *Int'l*, pg. 2697
FASHION FAIR COSMETICS, LLC—See Johnson Publishing Company, Inc.; *U.S. Private*, pg. 2228
FASHION GLASS & MIRROR INC.; *U.S. Private*, pg. 1481
FASHION GPS, INC.—See Augure SA; *Int'l*, pg. 703
FASHION MAGAZINE—See St. Joseph Communications Inc.; *Int'l*, pg. 7159
FASHION NET INC.—See Nippon Steel Corporation; *Int'l*, pg. 5337
FASHIONOLOGY GROUP LLC—See Hilco Trading, LLC; *U.S. Private*, pg. 1943
FASHIONOLOGY GROUP LLC—See Tengram Capital Partners, Limited Partnership; *U.S. Private*, pg. 3967
FASHION OUTLETS OF CHICAGO LLC—See The Macerich Company; *U.S. Public*, pg. 2109
FASHIONPARTNER GROUP SAS—See Holding Financiere Dimotrans SA; *Int'l*, pg. 3450
FASHIONPHILE; *U.S. Private*, pg. 1481
FASHION SHOP OF KENTUCKY INC.; *U.S. Private*, pg. 1481

FASHION SHOW MALL—See Brookfield Corporation; *Int'l*, pg. 1185
FASHION SQUARE MALL CMBS, LLC—See CBL & Associates Properties, Inc.; *U.S. Public*, pg. 458
FASHIONTECH INC.; *U.S. Private*, pg. 1481
FASHION TO FIGURE, LLC—See RTW Retailwinds, Inc.; *U.S. Public*, pg. 1820
FASHION TV HOLDING LTD.; *Int'l*, pg. 2621
FASHION WAY SDN. BHD.—See Travelite Holdings Ltd.; *Int'l*, pg. 7907
FASHION WORLD INC.; *U.S. Private*, pg. 1481
FASHOFF UK LTD—See Aeffe SpA; *Int'l*, pg. 173
FASHY GMBH; *Int'l*, pg. 2621
FASIG-TIPTON CO. INC.; *U.S. Private*, pg. 1481
FASIG-TIPTON KENTUCKY, INC.—See Fasig-Tipton Co. Inc.; *U.S. Private*, pg. 1481
FASIL A.D.; *Int'l*, pg. 2621
FAS INC.—See Techwing Inc.; *Int'l*, pg. 7514
FAS-LINK CO., LTD.—See Hanwa Co., Ltd.; *Int'l*, pg. 3262
FASMA A.D.; *Int'l*, pg. 2621
FASO COTON SA—See Aga Khan Development Network; *Int'l*, pg. 199
FASONE & PARTNERS; *U.S. Private*, pg. 1481
FASOO CO.,LTD.; *Int'l*, pg. 2621
FASOO USA INC.—See FASOO Co.,Ltd.; *Int'l*, pg. 2621
FASOPLAST S.A.—See Aga Khan Development Network; *Int'l*, pg. 199
FASSCO CATERING SERVICES L.L.C.—See Temasek Holdings (Private) Limited; *Int'l*, pg. 7547
FASSE CO., LTD.—See Screen Holdings Co., Ltd.; *Int'l*, pg. 6655
FASSFORWARD CONSULTING GROUP; *U.S. Private*, pg. 1481
FASSI GRU S.P.A.—See Investindustrial Advisors Ltd.; *Int'l*, pg. 3779
FASSIO EGG FARMS, INC.—See Cal-Maine Foods, Inc.; *U.S. Public*, pg. 421
FASSON ROLL NORTH AMERICA - FORT WAYNE—See Avery Dennison Corporation; *U.S. Public*, pg. 244
FASSON ROLL NORTH AMERICA - PEACHTREE—See Avery Dennison Corporation; *U.S. Public*, pg. 244
FAST ACQUISITION CORP.; *U.S. Public*, pg. 823
FASTAFF—See Clarion Capital Partners, LLC; *U.S. Private*, pg. 911
FAST-AID PRODUCTS LIMITED; *Int'l*, pg. 2622
FAST APPROACH INC.—See Planet Green Holdings Corp.; *U.S. Public*, pg. 1697
FAST A/R FUNDING—See Republic Business Credit, LLC; *U.S. Private*, pg. 3401
FAST ASSETS SDN. BHD.—See Fast Energy Holdings Berhad; *Int'l*, pg. 2621
FASTATOR AB; *Int'l*, pg. 2622
FASTBOOKING S.A.—See Accor S.A.; *Int'l*, pg. 91
FASTBUCKS HOLDING CORPORATION; *U.S. Private*, pg. 1482
FASTCASE INC.—See Oakley Capital Limited; *Int'l*, pg. 5504
FAST CASUALWEAR AG; *Int'l*, pg. 2621
FAST COMPANY MAGAZINE—See Mansueto Ventures LLC; *U.S. Private*, pg. 2566
FASTCO (SHANGHAI) TRADING CO., LTD.—See Fastenal Company; *U.S. Public*, pg. 823
FASTCRED ADMINISTRACAO E SERVICOS LTDA.—See WEX, Inc.; *U.S. Public*, pg. 2364
FASTCUT TOOL CORPORATION—See Talbot Holdings Inc.; *U.S. Private*, pg. 3925
FASTDOMAIN INC.—See Clearlake Capital Group, L.P.; *U.S. Private*, pg. 934
FASTDOMAIN INC.—See Siris Capital Group, LLC; *U.S. Private*, pg. 3673
FASTECH & SOLUTIONS CO., LTD.—See World Co., Ltd.; *Int'l*, pg. 8456
FASTEC IMAGING CORP.—See SFW Capital Partners LLC; *U.S. Private*, pg. 3622
FASTEC INDUSTRIAL—See WESCO International, Inc.; *U.S. Public*, pg. 2351
FASTEEL INDUSTRIES LTD; *Int'l*, pg. 2622
FAST EJENDOM DANMARK A/S; *Int'l*, pg. 2621
FASTEK PRODUCTS INC.—See Quanex Building Products Corp.; *U.S. Public*, pg. 1749
FASTEMS AB—See Helvar Merca Oy AB; *Int'l*, pg. 3339
FASTEMS K.K.—See Helvar Merca Oy AB; *Int'l*, pg. 3339
FASTEMS LLC—See Helvar Merca Oy AB; *Int'l*, pg. 3339
FASTEMS OY AB—See Helvar Merca Oy AB; *Int'l*, pg. 3339
FASTEMS S.R.L.—See Helvar Merca Oy AB; *Int'l*, pg. 3339
FASTEMS SYSTEMS GMBH—See Helvar Merca Oy AB; *Int'l*, pg. 3339
FASTENAL BRASIL IMPORTACAO, EXPORTACAO E DISTRIBUICAO LTDA.—See Fastenal Company; *U.S. Public*, pg. 823
FASTENAL CANADA, LTD.—See Fastenal Company; *U.S. Public*, pg. 823
FASTENAL COLOMBIA S.A.S.—See Fastenal Company; *U.S. Public*, pg. 823
FASTENAL COMPANY PURCHASING—See Fastenal Company; *U.S. Public*, pg. 823
FASTENAL COMPANY; *U.S. Public*, pg. 823

FASTENAL EUROPE AB—See Fastenal Company; *U.S. Public*, pg. 823
FASTENAL EUROPE GMBH—See Fastenal Company; *U.S. Public*, pg. 824
FASTENAL EUROPE, KFT.—See Fastenal Company; *U.S. Public*, pg. 824
FASTENAL EUROPE, LTD.—See Fastenal Company; *U.S. Public*, pg. 824
FASTENAL EUROPE RO S.R.L.—See Fastenal Company; *U.S. Public*, pg. 824
FASTENAL EUROPE S.R.L.—See Fastenal Company; *U.S. Public*, pg. 824
FASTENAL EUROPE, S.R.O.—See Fastenal Company; *U.S. Public*, pg. 824
FASTENAL MALAYSIA SDN BHD—See Fastenal Company; *U.S. Public*, pg. 824
FASTENAL MEXICO SERVICES S. DE R.L. DE C.V.—See Fastenal Company; *U.S. Public*, pg. 824
FASTENAL PANAMA S.A.—See Fastenal Company; *U.S. Public*, pg. 824
FASTENAL SERVICES S. DE R.L. DE C.V.—See Fastenal Company; *U.S. Public*, pg. 824
FASTENAL (SHANGHAI) INTERNATIONAL TRADING CO. LTD.—See Fastenal Company; *U.S. Public*, pg. 823
FASTENAL SINGAPORE P.T.E. LTD.—See Fastenal Company; *U.S. Public*, pg. 824
FASTENAL (THAILAND) LTD.—See Fastenal Company; *U.S. Public*, pg. 823
FASTENAL (TIANJIN) INTERNATIONAL TRADING CO. LTD.—See Fastenal Company; *U.S. Public*, pg. 823
FASTENER DISTRIBUTION HOLDINGS LLC—See Audax Group, Limited Partnership; *U.S. Public*, pg. 387
FAST ENERGY HOLDINGS BERHAD; *Int'l*, pg. 2621
FAST ENERGY SDN. BHD.—See Fast Energy Holdings Berhad; *Int'l*, pg. 2621
FASTENER HOLDINGS, INC.—See KYOCERA Corporation; *Int'l*, pg. 4355
FASTENER INDUSTRIES INC.; *U.S. Private*, pg. 1482
FASTENER INNOVATION TECHNOLOGY, INC.—See Inflexion Private Equity Partners LLP; *Int'l*, pg. 3688
FASTENER JAMHER TAIWAN INC.—See Stanley Black & Decker, Inc.; *U.S. Public*, pg. 1932
FASTENERS INC.; *U.S. Private*, pg. 1482
FASTENER TECHNOLOGY CORP.—See Inflexion Private Equity Partners LLP; *Int'l*, pg. 3688
FASTENER TOOL & SUPPLY INC.; *U.S. Private*, pg. 1482
FASTENING & BUILDING SYSTEMS LIMITED—See Agostini's Limited; *Int'l*, pg. 213
FASTENING SOLUTION INC; *U.S. Private*, pg. 1482
FAST ENTERPRISES, LLC; *U.S. Private*, pg. 1481
FASTEQ LIMITED—See Platinum Equity, LLC; *U.S. Private*, pg. 3210
FAST EQUIPAMENTOS E SERVICOS LDA.—See Endress+Hauser (International) Holding AG; *Int'l*, pg. 2408
FASTER DO BRASIL LTDA.—See Helios Technologies, Inc.; *U.S. Public*, pg. 1023
FASTER ENTERPRISES LTD; *Int'l*, pg. 2622
FASTER GERMANY GMBH—See Helios Technologies, Inc.; *U.S. Public*, pg. 1023
FASTER HYDRAULICS PVT. LTD.—See Helios Technologies, Inc.; *U.S. Public*, pg. 1023
FASTER HYDRAULICS SHANGHAI CO. LTD.—See Helios Technologies, Inc.; *U.S. Public*, pg. 1023
FASTER INC.—See Helios Technologies, Inc.; *U.S. Public*, pg. 1023
FASTER S.P.A.—See Helios Technologies, Inc.; *U.S. Public*, pg. 1023
FASTEST, LLC—See Monster Beverage Corporation; *U.S. Public*, pg. 1465
FASTEXPERT, INC.; *U.S. Private*, pg. 1482
FASTFETCH CORP.—See ABCO Systems LLC; *U.S. Private*, pg. 36
FAST FINANCE 24 HOLDING AG; *Int'l*, pg. 2621
FAST FINANCE S.A.; *Int'l*, pg. 2621
FAST FITNESS JAPAN, INC.; *Int'l*, pg. 2621
FAST & FLUID MANAGEMENT AUSTRALIA PTY. LTD.—See IDEX Corp; *U.S. Public*, pg. 1090
FAST & FLUID MANAGEMENT AUSTRALIA—See IDEX Corp; *U.S. Public*, pg. 1090
FAST & FLUID MANAGEMENT B.V.—See IDEX Corp; *U.S. Public*, pg. 1090
FAST & FLUID MANAGEMENT EAST EUROPE SP. Z.O.O.—See IDEX Corp; *U.S. Public*, pg. 1090
FAST & FLUID MANAGEMENT IBERICA—See IDEX Corp; *U.S. Public*, pg. 1090
FAST & FLUID MANAGEMENT NETHERLANDS—See IDEX Corp; *U.S. Public*, pg. 1090
FAST & FLUID MANAGEMENT SRL—See IDEX Corp; *U.S. Public*, pg. 1090
FAST & FLUID MANAGEMENT S.R.L.—See IDEX Corp; *U.S. Public*, pg. 1090
FAST FOOD ENTERPRISES; *U.S. Private*, pg. 1482
FAST FOOD SUDAMERICANA, S. A.—See Alsea, S.A.B. de C.V.; *Int'l*, pg. 379
FASTFORMS INC.; *Int'l*, pg. 2622
FASTFRATE HOLDINGS INC. - CALGARY DIVISION—See Fenway Partners, LLC; *U.S. Private*, pg. 1496

FASTFORMS INC.

FASTFRATE HOLDINGS INC. - MONTREAL DIVISION—See Fenway Partners, LLC; *U.S. Private*, pg. 1496
FASTFRATE HOLDINGS INC.—See Fenway Partners, LLC; *U.S. Private*, pg. 1495
FASTFRATE HOLDINGS INC. - TORONTO DIVISION—See Fenway Partners, LLC; *U.S. Private*, pg. 1496
FASTFRATE HOLDINGS INC. - VANCOUVER DIVISION—See Fenway Partners, LLC; *U.S. Private*, pg. 1496
FAST FUSION LLC; *U.S. Private*, pg. 1482
FAST HARVEST LIMITED—See Ruixin International Holdings Limited; *Int'l*, pg. 6427
FAST HEAT INC.; *U.S. Private*, pg. 1482
FASTHOSTS INTERNET LTD.—See United Internet AG; *Int'l*, pg. 8069
FASTIGHETS AB ALLUM—See BNP Paribas SA; *Int'l*, pg. 1091
FASTIGHETS AB BALDER; *Int'l*, pg. 2622
FASTIGHETS AB BORLANGE KOPCENTRUM—See BNP Paribas SA; *Int'l*, pg. 1091
FASTIGHETS AB BRIGGEN—See Castellum AB; *Int'l*, pg. 1356
FASTIGHETS AB BROSTADEN—See Castellum AB; *Int'l*, pg. 1356
FASTIGHETS AB CENTRUMINVEST—See BNP Paribas SA; *Int'l*, pg. 1091
FASTIGHETS AB CENTRUM VASTERORT—See BNP Paribas SA; *Int'l*, pg. 1091
FASTIGHETS AB CORALLEN—See Castellum AB; *Int'l*, pg. 1356
FASTIGHETS AB EKUDDEN—See Peab AB; *Int'l*, pg. 5771
FASTIGHETS AB KLADESHANDLAREN—See Lone Star Funds; *U.S. Private*, pg. 2485
FASTIGHETS AB MARIEBERG CENTRUM—See BNP Paribas SA; *Int'l*, pg. 1091
FASTIGHETS AB OSTERBOTTEN—See Atrium Ljungberg AB; *Int'l*, pg. 694
FASTIGHETS AB OVERBY KOPCENTRUM—See BNP Paribas SA; *Int'l*, pg. 1091
FASTIGHETS AB OXIGENIUM—See Wihlborgs Fastigheter AB; *Int'l*, pg. 8407
FASTIGHETS AB SOLLENTUNA CENTRUM—See BNP Paribas SA; *Int'l*, pg. 1091
FASTIGHETS AB—See Saab AB; *Int'l*, pg. 6459
FASTIGHETS AB TORNET—See Fabege AB; *Int'l*, pg. 2598
FASTIGHETS AB TRIANON; *Int'l*, pg. 2622
FASTIGHETSFORVALTNINGS- BOLAGET GASELLEN 2 HB—See Peab AB; *Int'l*, pg. 5771
FASTIGHETS L E LUNDBERG AB—See L. E. Lundbergforetagen AB; *Int'l*, pg. 4381
FAST INTERNATIONAL CO.; *Int'l*, pg. 2621
FASTJET PLC—See Lonrho Limited; *Int'l*, pg. 4552
FASTJOBS SDN. BHD.—See Singapore Press Holdings Ltd.; *Int'l*, pg. 6942
FAST LANE ACQUISITION, INC.; *U.S. Private*, pg. 1482
FAST LANE CLOTHING COMPANY, INC.; *U.S. Private*, pg. 1482
FASTLANE; *U.S. Private*, pg. 1482
FAST LASER GROUP LTD.—See Yokogawa Electric Corporation; *Int'l*, pg. 8592
FASTLIGN LLC—See Searchlight Capital Partners, L.P.; *U.S. Private*, pg. 3590
FAST LINE HLDG, INC.; *Int'l*, pg. 2621
FASTLINE PUBLICATIONS INC.; *U.S. Private*, pg. 1482
FASTLY, INC.; *U.S. Public*, pg. 824
FASTMARKETS LIMITED—See Astorg Partners S.A.S.; *Int'l*, pg. 656
FASTMED URGENT CARE—See ABRY Partners LLC; *U.S. Private*, pg. 41
FASTMETRICS LLC—See Paxio Inc.; *U.S. Private*, pg. 3115
FASTNED B.V.; *Int'l*, pg. 2622
FASTNED DEUTSCHLAND GMBH & CO KG—See Fastned B.V.; *Int'l*, pg. 2622
FASTNED UK LTD.—See Fastned B.V.; *Int'l*, pg. 2622
FASTORQ, LLC—See Superior Energy Services, Inc.; *U.S. Private*, pg. 3877
FAST PACE MEDICAL CLINIC, PLLC—See Revelstoke Capital Partners LLC; *U.S. Private*, pg. 3413
FASTPARTNER AB; *Int'l*, pg. 2622
FASTPENCIL, INC.; *U.S. Private*, pg. 1482
FAST PETROLEUM, INC.; *U.S. Private*, pg. 1482
FAST PLASTIC PARTS LLC—See COMSovereign Holding Corp.; *U.S. Public*, pg. 562
FAST POINT FOOD STORES INC.; *U.S. Private*, pg. 1482
FAST PRO INC.—See Fast Undercar Inc.; *U.S. Private*, pg. 1482
FASTRACK COMPLETE CAR CARE; *U.S. Private*, pg. 1482
FASTRAC MARKETS LLC; *U.S. Private*, pg. 1482
FASTRAK RETAIL (UK) LIMITED—See Pollard Banknote Limited; *Int'l*, pg. 5910
FAST RETAILING CO., LTD.; *Int'l*, pg. 2621
FAST RETAILING USA, INC.—See Fast Retailing Co., Ltd.; *Int'l*, pg. 2621

FASTRON CO.; *U.S. Private*, pg. 1483
FAST RSQ B.V.—See Palfinger AG; *Int'l*, pg. 5708
FASTSIGNS INTERNATIONAL, INC.—See Freeman Spogli & Co. Incorporated; *U.S. Private*, pg. 1606
FASTSIGNS INTERNATIONAL, INC.—See LightBay Management, LLC; *U.S. Private*, pg. 2452
FAST SOLAR SDN. BHD.—See Fast Energy Holdings Berhad; *Int'l*, pg. 2621
FAST—See Microsoft Corporation; *U.S. Public*, pg. 1439
FAST-SPEC, INC.—See Summit Industries, Inc.; *U.S. Private*, pg. 3854
FAST SPEED NETWORK PTE. LTD.—See PT Indointernet Tbk; *Int'l*, pg. 6045
FAST SP. Z.O.O.—See ROCKWOOL A/S; *Int'l*, pg. 6380
FAST SWITCH, LTD.; *U.S. Private*, pg. 1482
FAST TECHNOLOGY SDN. BHD.—See Fast Energy Holdings Berhad; *Int'l*, pg. 2621
FAST TELECOMMUNICATION COMPANY—See Ooredoo Q.S.C.; *Int'l*, pg. 5594
FAST TRACK COMPUTER SOLUTIONS, INC.; *U.S. Private*, pg. 1482
FAST TRACK DIAGNOSTICS LTD.—See Siemens Aktiengesellschaft; *Int'l*, pg. 6887
FAST TRACK DIAGNOSTICS LUXEMBOURG S.A R.L.—See Siemens Aktiengesellschaft; *Int'l*, pg. 6887
FAST TRACK MANAGEMENT SERVICES (LONDON) LIMITED—See Empresaria Group Plc; *Int'l*, pg. 2388
FAST TRACK MANAGEMENT SERVICES (MIDLANDS) LIMITED—See Empresaria Group Plc; *Int'l*, pg. 2389
FAST TRACK SAILING LIMITED—See Wasserman Media Group, LLC; *U.S. Private*, pg. 4450
FASTTRACK S.A.—See AUTOHELLAS S.A.; *Int'l*, pg. 727
FASTTRAC TRANSPORTATION, INC.; *U.S. Private*, pg. 1483
FAST TRUCKING SERVICE LTD .; *Int'l*, pg. 2621
FAST UNDERCAR INC.; *U.S. Private*, pg. 1482
FASTVUE INC.; *U.S. Private*, pg. 1482
FASTVVIEWER GMBH—See Atos SE; *Int'l*, pg. 692
FASTWEB S.P.A.—See Swisscom AG; *Int'l*, pg. 7373
FAST WHITE CAT S.A.—See Digitree Group S.A.; *Int'l*, pg. 2124
FASTWIRE PTE. LTD.; *Int'l*, pg. 2622
FASVER SAS—See Illinois Tool Works Inc.; *U.S. Public*, pg. 1103
FASVER TECHNOLOGY, INC.—See Illinois Tool Works Inc.; *U.S. Public*, pg. 1103
FASZOLD SERVICE COMPANY—See Heartland Home Services, Inc.; *U.S. Private*, pg. 1900
FATA ASSICURAZIONI DANNI S.P.A.—See Societa Cattolica di Assicurazione-Societa Cooperativa; *Int'l*, pg. 7033
FATA AUTOMATION LIMITED—See CIEM S.p.A.; *Int'l*, pg. 1605
FATA GULF CO WLL—See Danieli & C. Officine Meccaniche S.p.A.; *Int'l*, pg. 1963
FATA LOGISTIC SYSTEMS SPA—See Leonardo S.p.A.; *Int'l*, pg. 4458
FATA SPA—See Danieli & C. Officine Meccaniche S.p.A.; *Int'l*, pg. 1963
FATBEAM LLC—See SDC Capital Partners, LLC; *U.S. Private*, pg. 3581
FAT BRANDS INC.—See Fog Cutter Capital Group Inc.; *U.S. Private*, pg. 1556
FATBURGER CORPORATION—See Fog Cutter Capital Group Inc.; *U.S. Private*, pg. 1557
FATBURGER NORTH AMERICA, INC.—See Fog Cutter Capital Group Inc.; *U.S. Private*, pg. 1557
FATCO HOLDINGS, LLC—See First American Financial Corporation; *U.S. Public*, pg. 835
FATEC CO.,LTD.—See Kumagai Gumi Co., Ltd.; *Int'l*, pg. 4329
FATEC CO.,LTD.—See Kumagai Gumi Co., Ltd.; *Int'l*, pg. 4329
FATEH INDUSTRIES LIMITED; *Int'l*, pg. 2622
FATEH SPORTS WEAR LIMITED; *Int'l*, pg. 2622
FATEH TEXTILE MILLS LIMITED; *Int'l*, pg. 2622
FATENT CO. DOO LAKTASI—See BayWa AG; *Int'l*, pg. 917
FATER PORTUGAL UNIPESSOAL LDA—See The Procter & Gamble Company; *U.S. Public*, pg. 2120
FATER S.P.A.—See Angelini ACRAF S.p.A.; *Int'l*, pg. 460
FATER S.P.A.—See The Procter & Gamble Company; *U.S. Public*, pg. 2120
FATES A.D.; *Int'l*, pg. 2622
FATE S.A.I.C.I.; *Int'l*, pg. 2622
FATE THERAPEUTICS, INC.; *U.S. Public*, pg. 824
FATEX A.D.; *Int'l*, pg. 2622
FATFISH GROUP LTD.; *Int'l*, pg. 2623
FATHER BILL'S & MAINSPRING; *U.S. Private*, pg. 1483
FATHERFORD VIEW (OKEHAMPTON) MANAGEMENT COMPANY LIMITED—See Persimmon plc; *Int'l*, pg. 5815
FATHERS AND SONS INC.; *U.S. Private*, pg. 1483
THE FATHER'S TABLE, LLC.; *U.S. Private*, pg. 4028
FATHER TIME, INC.; *U.S. Private*, pg. 1483
FATH MANAGEMENT COMPANY; *U.S. Private*, pg. 1483
FATHOM COMMUNICATIONS—See Omnicom Group Inc.; *U.S. Public*, pg. 1583

CORPORATE AFFILIATIONS

FATHOM COMMUNICATIONS—See Omnicom Group Inc.; *U.S. Public*, pg. 1583
FATHOM DIGITAL MANUFACTURING CORPORATION—See CORE Industrial Partners, LLC; *U.S. Private*, pg. 1048
FATHOM HOLDINGS INC.; *U.S. Public*, pg. 824
FATHOM, LLC; *U.S. Private*, pg. 1483
FATHOM NICKEL INC.; *Int'l*, pg. 2623
FATIGUE TECHNOLOGY INC.—See Berkshire Hathaway Inc.; *U.S. Public*, pg. 315
FATIMA FERTILIZER COMPANY LIMITED; *Int'l*, pg. 2623
FATIMA HOLDING LIMITED—See Reliance Weaving Mills Limited; *Int'l*, pg. 6264
FAT MEDIA LTD.; *Int'l*, pg. 2622
FATO PROFESSIONAL S.P.A.—See Cartiera Lucchese S.p.A.; *Int'l*, pg. 1348
FAT PATTY'S—See ARC Group, Inc.; *U.S. Public*, pg. 179
FATPIPE NETWORKS INC.; *U.S. Private*, pg. 1483
FAT PROJECTS ACQUISITION CORP.; *Int'l*, pg. 2622
FAT PROPHETS GLOBAL CONTRARIAN FUND LTD.; *Int'l*, pg. 2622
FAT PROPHETS GLOBAL PROPERTY FUND; *Int'l*, pg. 2622
FATRA, A.S.—See Agrofert Holding, a.s.; *Int'l*, pg. 219
FATRASTYLING INC.—See Autobacs Seven Co., Ltd.; *Int'l*, pg. 726
FAT S.A.—See Haco N.V.; *Int'l*, pg. 3204
FATTAL HOLDINGS (1998) LTD.; *Int'l*, pg. 2623
FATTAL HOTELS LTD.—See Fattal Holdings (1998) Ltd.; *Int'l*, pg. 2623
FATTORIE OSELLA S.P.A.—See Mondelez International, Inc.; *U.S. Public*, pg. 1461
FATTY CHEMICAL (MALAYSIA) SDN. BHD.—See Kao Corporation; *Int'l*, pg. 4073
FATUM GENERAL INSURANCE NV—See Guardian Holdings Limited; *Int'l*, pg. 3171
FATUM LIFE NV—See Guardian Holdings Limited; *Int'l*, pg. 3171
FAUBEL & CO. NACHFOLGER GMBH—See CCL Industries Inc.; *Int'l*, pg. 1369
FAUBEL PHARMA SERVICES CORP.—See CCL Industries Inc.; *Int'l*, pg. 1369
THE FAUCET-QUEENS, INC.—See Incline MGMT Corp.; *U.S. Private*, pg. 2054
FAUCHIER PARTNERS CORPORATION—See BNP Paribas SA; *Int'l*, pg. 1087
FAUJI AKBAR PORTIA MARINE TERMINALS LIMITED—See Akbar Group; *Int'l*, pg. 261
FAUJI AKBAR PORTIA MARINE TERMINALS LIMITED—See Fauji Foundation; *Int'l*, pg. 2623
FAUJI CEMENT COMPANY LIMITED—See Fauji Foundation; *Int'l*, pg. 2623
FAUJI CEREALS—See Fauji Foundation; *Int'l*, pg. 2623
FAUJI FERTILIZER BIN QASIM LIMITED—See Fauji Foundation; *Int'l*, pg. 2623
FAUJI FERTILIZER COMPANY LIMITED - PLANT I (GOTH MACHHI)—See Fauji Foundation; *Int'l*, pg. 2623
FAUJI FERTILIZER COMPANY LIMITED—See Fauji Foundation; *Int'l*, pg. 2623
FAUJI FOODS LIMITED; *Int'l*, pg. 2623
FAUJI FOUNDATION; *Int'l*, pg. 2623
FAUJI KABIRWALA POWER COMPANY LIMITED—See Fauji Foundation; *Int'l*, pg. 2623
FAUJI OIL TERMINAL & DISTRIBUTION COMPANY LIMITED—See Fauji Foundation; *Int'l*, pg. 2623
FAUJI OIL TERMINAL & DISTRIBUTION COMPANY LIMITED—See Infraavest Limited; *Int'l*, pg. 3697
FAULCONER CONSTRUCTION CO. INC.; *U.S. Private*, pg. 1483
FAULHABER BENELUX B.V.—See Dr. Fritz Faulhaber GmbH & Co. KG; *Int'l*, pg. 2191
FAULHABER DRIVE SYSTEM TECHNOLOGY (TAICANG) CO., LTD.—See Dr. Fritz Faulhaber GmbH & Co. KG; *Int'l*, pg. 2191
FAULHABER FRANCE SAS—See Dr. Fritz Faulhaber GmbH & Co. KG; *Int'l*, pg. 2191
FAULHABER SINGAPORE PTE LTD—See Dr. Fritz Faulhaber GmbH & Co. KG; *Int'l*, pg. 2191
FAULK & FOSTER REAL ESTATE; *U.S. Private*, pg. 1483
FAULK & MEEK GENERAL CONTRACTORS, LLC.; *U.S. Private*, pg. 1483
FAULKNER BUICK, GMC TRUCK INC.; *U.S. Private*, pg. 1483
FAULKNER CADILLAC INC.; *U.S. Private*, pg. 1483
FAULKNER CHEVROLET INC.; *U.S. Private*, pg. 1483
FAULKNER CIOCCA FORD OF SOUDERTON; *U.S. Private*, pg. 1483
FAULKNER & FLYNN, INC.—See Marsh & McLennan Companies, Inc.; *U.S. Public*, pg. 1375
FAULKNER FORD MERCURY INC.; *U.S. Private*, pg. 1483
FAULKNER HARRISBURG INC.; *U.S. Private*, pg. 1483
FAULKNER/HAYNES & ASSOCIATES, INC.; *U.S. Private*, pg. 1483
FAULKNER HOSPITAL INC.—See Partners HealthCare System, Inc.; *U.S. Private*, pg. 3102
FAULKNER INFORMATION SERVICES—See Information Today Inc.; *U.S. Private*, pg. 2073

FAULKNERUSA; *U.S. Private*, pg. 1483
FAULTLESS LAUNDRY COMPANY; *U.S. Private*, pg. 1483
   FAULTLESS RECOVERY SERVICES PTY. LTD.—See Butn Limited; *Int'l*, pg. 1229
   FAULTLESS STARCH/BON AMI COMPANY - GARDEN WEASEL DIVISION—See Faultless Starch/Bon Ami Company; *U.S. Private*, pg. 1484
FAULTLESS STARCH/BON AMI COMPANY; *U.S. Private*, pg. 1483
FAULTLINE BREWING CO. INC.; *U.S. Private*, pg. 1484
FAULU MICROFINANCE BANK LIMITED—See Old Mutual Limited; *Int'l*, pg. 5552
FAUN UMWELTTECHNIK GMBH & CO. KG—See KIRCHHOFF Gruppe; *Int'l*, pg. 4185
FAUN VIATEC GMBH—See KIRCHHOFF Gruppe; *Int'l*, pg. 4185
FAUN ZOELLER (UK) LIMITED—See KIRCHHOFF Gruppe; *Int'l*, pg. 4185
FAUQUIER BANKSHARES, INC.—See Virginia National Bankshares Corporation; *U.S. Public*, pg. 2299
FAUQUIER LONG-TERM CARE, LLC—See Apollo Global Management, Inc.; *U.S. Public*, pg. 155
FAUQUIER MEDICAL CENTER, LLC—See Apollo Global Management, Inc.; *U.S. Public*, pg. 155
FAURECIA ABGASTECHNIK GMBH—See FORVIA SE; *Int'l*, pg. 2746
FAURECIA ASIENTOS PARA AUTOMOVIL ESPANA, S.A.—See FORVIA SE; *Int'l*, pg. 2746
FAURECIA - ASSENTOS DE AUTOMOVEL, LIMITADA—See FORVIA SE; *Int'l*, pg. 2746
FAURECIA AST LUXEMBOURG S.A.—See FORVIA SE; *Int'l*, pg. 2746
FAURECIA AUTOMOTIVE ESPANA, S.L.—See FORVIA SE; *Int'l*, pg. 2746
FAURECIA AUTOMOTIVE ESPANIA—See FORVIA SE; *Int'l*, pg. 2746
FAURECIA AUTOMOTIVE ESPANIA—See FORVIA SE; *Int'l*, pg. 2746
FAURECIA AUTOMOTIVE ESPANIA—See FORVIA SE; *Int'l*, pg. 2746
FAURECIA AUTOMOTIVE EXTERIORS ESPANA, S.A.—See FORVIA SE; *Int'l*, pg. 2746
FAURECIA AUTOMOTIVE GMBH—See FORVIA SE; *Int'l*, pg. 2746
FAURECIA AUTOMOTIVE INDUSTRIE—See FORVIA SE; *Int'l*, pg. 2746
FAURECIA AUTOMOTIVE INDUSTRIE—See FORVIA SE; *Int'l*, pg. 2746
FAURECIA AUTOMOTIVE INDUSTRIE—See FORVIA SE; *Int'l*, pg. 2746
FAURECIA AUTOMOTIVE SEATING B.V.—See FORVIA SE; *Int'l*, pg. 2746
FAURECIA AUTOMOTIVE SEATING, INC—See FORVIA SE; *Int'l*, pg. 2747
FAURECIA AUTOSITZE GMBH—See FORVIA SE; *Int'l*, pg. 2746
FAURECIA BLOC AVANT—See FORVIA SE; *Int'l*, pg. 2746
FAURECIA (CHANGCHUN) AUTOMOTIVE SYSTEMS CO., LTD—See FORVIA SE; *Int'l*, pg. 2745
FAURECIA EMISSIONS CONTROL TECHNOLOGIES, (CHONGQING) CO., LTD—See FORVIA SE; *Int'l*, pg. 2746
FAURECIA EMISSIONS CONTROL TECHNOLOGIES, CORDOBA SA—See FORVIA SE; *Int'l*, pg. 2746
FAURECIA EMISSIONS CONTROL TECHNOLOGIES DEVELOPMENT (SHANGHAI) COMPANY LTD—See FORVIA SE; *Int'l*, pg. 2746
FAURECIA EMISSIONS CONTROL TECHNOLOGIES, FINNENTROP GMBH—See FORVIA SE; *Int'l*, pg. 2746
FAURECIA EMISSIONS CONTROL TECHNOLOGIES, GERMANY GMBH—See FORVIA SE; *Int'l*, pg. 2746
FAURECIA EMISSIONS CONTROL TECHNOLOGIES, MLADA BOLESLAV, S.R.O—See FORVIA SE; *Int'l*, pg. 2746
FAURECIA EMISSIONS CONTROL TECHNOLOGIES, NETHERLANDS B.V.—See FORVIA SE; *Int'l*, pg. 2746
FAURECIA EMISSIONS CONTROL TECHNOLOGIES, NOVAFERRA GMBH—See FORVIA SE; *Int'l*, pg. 2746
FAURECIA EMISSIONS CONTROL TECHNOLOGIES, PAMPELONA, S.L.—See FORVIA SE; *Int'l*, pg. 2746
FAURECIA EMISSIONS CONTROL TECHNOLOGIES, (SHANGHAI) CO., LTD.—See FORVIA SE; *Int'l*, pg. 2746
FAURECIA EMISSIONS CONTROL TECHNOLOGIES—See FORVIA SE; *Int'l*, pg. 2747
FAURECIA EMISSIONS CONTROL TECHNOLOGIES SPARTANBURG, INC.—See FORVIA SE; *Int'l*, pg. 2747
FAURECIA EMISSIONS CONTROL TECHNOLOGIES USA LLC—See FORVIA SE; *Int'l*, pg. 2747
FAURECIA EXHAUST MEXICANA, S.A. DE C.V.—See FORVIA SE; *Int'l*, pg. 2746
FAURECIA EXHAUST SYSTEMS, INC.—See FORVIA SE; *Int'l*, pg. 2746
FAURECIA EXHAUST SYSTEMS SOUTH AFRICA LTD—See FORVIA SE; *Int'l*, pg. 2746
FAURECIA FOTELE SAMOCHODOWE SP. ZO.O—See FORVIA SE; *Int'l*, pg. 2746

FAURECIA GROJEC R&D CENTER SP. ZO.O—See FORVIA SE; *Int'l*, pg. 2746
FAURECIA (GUANGZHOU) AUTOMOTIVE SYSTEMS CO., LTD—See FORVIA SE; *Int'l*, pg. 2745
FAURECIA INDUSTRIE N.V.—See FORVIA SE; *Int'l*, pg. 2746
FAURECIA INDUSTRIE—See FORVIA SE; *Int'l*, pg. 2746
FAURECIA INDUSTRIES S.A.S.—See FORVIA SE; *Int'l*, pg. 2746
FAURECIA INNENRAUM SYSTEME GMBH—See FORVIA SE; *Int'l*, pg. 2746
FAURECIA INTERIEUR INDUSTRIE—See FORVIA SE; *Int'l*, pg. 2746
FAURECIA INTERIEUR INDUSTRIE—See FORVIA SE; *Int'l*, pg. 2746
FAURECIA INTERIEUR INDUSTRIE—See FORVIA SE; *Int'l*, pg. 2746
FAURECIA INTERIEUR INDUSTRIE—See FORVIA SE; *Int'l*, pg. 2746
FAURECIA INTERIOR SYSTEMS BOHEMIA S.R.O.—See FORVIA SE; *Int'l*, pg. 2746
FAURECIA INTERIOR SYSTEMS ESPANA, S.A.—See FORVIA SE; *Int'l*, pg. 2746
FAURECIA INTERIOR SYSTEMS SALC ESPANA, S.L.—See FORVIA SE; *Int'l*, pg. 2747
FAURECIA INTERIOR SYSTEMS—See FORVIA SE; *Int'l*, pg. 2746
FAURECIA INTERIOR SYSTEMS—See FORVIA SE; *Int'l*, pg. 2747
FAURECIA INTERIOR SYSTEMS SOUTH AFRICA (PTY) LTD—See FORVIA SE; *Int'l*, pg. 2747
FAURECIA INTERIOR SYSTEMS THAILAND CO., LTD.—See FORVIA SE; *Int'l*, pg. 2747
FAURECIA JAPAN K.K.—See FORVIA SE; *Int'l*, pg. 2747
FAURECIA KUNSTSTOFFE AUTOMOBILSYSTEME GMBH—See FORVIA SE; *Int'l*, pg. 2747
FAURECIA NETHERLANDS HOLDING B.V.—See FORVIA SE; *Int'l*, pg. 2747
FAURECIA-NHK KYUSHU CO., LTD.—See NHK Spring Co., Ltd.; *Int'l*, pg. 5257
FAURECIA PORTUGAL—See FORVIA SE; *Int'l*, pg. 2747
FAURECIA (QINGDAO) EXHAUST SYSTEMS CO, LTD—See FORVIA SE; *Int'l*, pg. 2745
FAURECIA (SHANGHAI) AUTOMOTIVE SYSTEMS CO., LTD—See FORVIA SE; *Int'l*, pg. 2745
FAURECIA (SHANGHAI) MANAGEMENT COMPANY, LTD—See FORVIA SE; *Int'l*, pg. 2745
FAURECIA - SISTEMAS DE ESCAPE PORTUGAL, LDA—See FORVIA SE; *Int'l*, pg. 2746
FAURECIA SYSTEMES D'ECHAPPEMENT—See FORVIA SE; *Int'l*, pg. 2747
FAURECIA USA HOLDINGS, INC.—See FORVIA SE; *Int'l*, pg. 2747
FAURECIA (WUHAN) AUTOMOTIVE SEATING CO., LTD—See FORVIA SE; *Int'l*, pg. 2745
FAURECIA (WUHU) EXHAUST SYSTEMS CO, LTD—See FORVIA SE; *Int'l*, pg. 2746
FAURECIA (WUXI) SEATING COMPONENTS CO., LTD—See FORVIA SE; *Int'l*, pg. 2746
FAURE HERMAN METER, INC.—See BNP Paribas SA; *Int'l*, pg. 1083
FAURE HERMAN SAS—See BNP Paribas SA; *Int'l*, pg. 1083
FAURE QEI S.A.—See Groupe Gorge S.A.; *Int'l*, pg. 3103
FAUSER OIL COMPANY INCORPORATED; *U.S. Private*, pg. 1484
FAUST DISTRIBUTING CO., INC.; *U.S. Private*, pg. 1484
FAVELLE FAVCO BERHAD—See Muhibbah Engineering (M) Bhd.; *Int'l*, pg. 5078
FAVELLE FAVCO CRANES (M) SDN. BHD.—See Muhibbah Engineering (M) Bhd.; *Int'l*, pg. 5078
FAVELLE FAVCO CRANES PTE. LTD.—See Muhibbah Engineering (M) Bhd.; *Int'l*, pg. 5078
FAVELLE FAVCO CRANES PTY. LTD.—See Muhibbah Engineering (M) Bhd.; *Int'l*, pg. 5078
FAVELLE FAVCO CRANES (USA) INC.—See Muhibbah Engineering (M) Bhd.; *Int'l*, pg. 5078
FAVELLE FAVCO EQUIPMENT SERVICES SDN. BHD.—See Muhibbah Engineering (M) Bhd.; *Int'l*, pg. 5078
FAVELLE FAVCO MACHINERY & EQUIPMENT L.L.C.—See Muhibbah Engineering (M) Bhd.; *Int'l*, pg. 5078
FAVI ENTERTAINMENT; *U.S. Private*, pg. 1484
FAVINI S.R.L.—See Orlando Management AG; *Int'l*, pg. 5640
FAVITE INC.- RFID DIVISION—See FAVITE Inc.; *Int'l*, pg. 2623
FAVITE INC.; *Int'l*, pg. 2623
FAVO REALTY, INC.; *U.S. Private*, pg. 1484
FAVORINA CO., LTD.—See 4Cs Holdings Co., Ltd.; *Int'l*, pg. 11
FAVORITE FOODS, INC.; *U.S. Private*, pg. 1484
FAVORITE HEALTHCARE STAFFING, INC.; *U.S. Private*, pg. 1484
FAVORITE PRODUCTS COMPANY LTD.—See Oil-Dri Corporation of America; *U.S. Public*, pg. 1566
FAVORIT HOLD AD; *Int'l*, pg. 2623

FAVOR WOODPANEL (THAILAND) CO., LTD.—See Dominant Enterprise Berhad; *Int'l*, pg. 2161
FAVOURITE DESIGN SDN BHD—See Lii Hen Industries Bhd.; *Int'l*, pg. 4497
FAVRE SARL—See BBG Baugerate GmbH; *Int'l*, pg. 920
THE FAWCETT GROUP, INC.—See The Baldwin Insurance Group, Inc.; *U.S. Public*, pg. 2036
FAWCETT MARINE SUPPLIES LLC; *U.S. Private*, pg. 1484
FAWCETT MEMORIAL HOSPITAL, INC.—See HCA Healthcare, Inc.; *U.S. Public*, pg. 996
FAWCETT MEMORIAL HOSPITAL—See HCA Healthcare, Inc.; *U.S. Public*, pg. 996
FAWCETTS GARAGE (NEWBURY) LIMITED; *Int'l*, pg. 2623
FAW-EASTERN EUROPE LLC—See China FAW Group Corporation; *Int'l*, pg. 1502
FAWER AUTOMOTIVE PARTS LIMITED COMPANY; *Int'l*, pg. 2623
FAWER LIAONING AUTOMOTIVE SPRING COMPANY LIMITED—See FAWER Automotive Parts Limited Company; *Int'l*, pg. 2624
F.A. WILHELM CONSTRUCTION CO., INC.; *U.S. Private*, pg. 1455
FAW JIEFANG GROUP CO., LTD.—See China FAW Group Corporation; *Int'l*, pg. 1502
FAWLEY BRYANT ARCHITECTS, INC.; *U.S. Private*, pg. 1484
FAWN CREEK COURT SALES LTD.—See Crown Communities, LLC; *U.S. Private*, pg. 1110
FAWN DE MEXICO—See National Molding Corporation; *U.S. Private*, pg. 2859
FAWN ENGINEERING CORP.—See The Wittern Group; *U.S. Private*, pg. 4138
FAWN INDUSTRIES, INC.; *U.S. Private*, pg. 1484
FAWN VENDING SYSTEMS, INC.—See The Wittern Group; *U.S. Private*, pg. 4138
FAWORIT-AUTO COMPANY—See China FAW Group Corporation; *Int'l*, pg. 1502
FAW VEHICLE MANUFACTURERS SA (PTY) LTD—See China FAW Group Corporation; *Int'l*, pg. 1502
FAW-VOLKSWAGEN AUTOMOTIVE CO., LTD.—See China FAW Group Corporation; *Int'l*, pg. 1502
FAW-VOLKSWAGEN AUTOMOTIVE CO., LTD.—See Porsche Automobil Holding SE; *Int'l*, pg. 5929
FAXE BRYGGERI A/S—See Royal Unibrew A/S; *Int'l*, pg. 6414
FAXE KALK A/S—See Lhoist S.A.; *Int'l*, pg. 4478
FAXITRON BIOPTICS, LLC—See Hologic, Inc.; *U.S. Public*, pg. 1044
FAX LITE CO., LTD.—See Advanced Info Service Plc; *Int'l*, pg. 160
FAXONGILLIS HOMES INC.; *U.S. Private*, pg. 1484
FAXXON LEGAL INFORMATION SERVICES, INC.—See First American Financial Corporation; *U.S. Public*, pg. 836
FAYAT BATIMENT SAS—See FAYAT SAS; *Int'l*, pg. 2625
FAYAT BOMAG POLSKA SP. Z O.O.—See FAYAT SAS; *Int'l*, pg. 2624
FAYAT BOMAG RUS LLC—See FAYAT SAS; *Int'l*, pg. 2625
FAYAT CONSTRUCTION ACHATS INVESTISSEMENTS—See FAYAT SAS; *Int'l*, pg. 2625
FAYAT MIDDLE EAST FZE—See FAYAT SAS; *Int'l*, pg. 2625
FAYAT RO SRL—See FAYAT SAS; *Int'l*, pg. 2625
FAYAT SAS; *Int'l*, pg. 2624
FAYAT SYSTEME D'INFORMATION—See FAYAT SAS; *Int'l*, pg. 2625
FAYAT TP—See FAYAT SAS; *Int'l*, pg. 2625
FAYE BUSINESS SYSTEMS GROUP INC.; *U.S. Private*, pg. 1484
FAYE CLACK COMMUNICATIONS INC.; *Int'l*, pg. 2626
FAYEKING TECHNOLOGY LIMITED—See Perfect Optronics Ltd; *Int'l*, pg. 5799
FAYENCERIES DE SARREGUEMINES DIGOIN VITRY-LE-FRANCOIS SA; *Int'l*, pg. 2626
FAYETTE MEDICAL CENTER HOMECARE, LLC—See UnitedHealth Group Incorporated; *U.S. Public*, pg. 2245
FAYETTE MEMORIAL HOSPITAL ASSOCIATION INC; *U.S. Private*, pg. 1484
FAYETTEVILLE ARKANSAS HOSPITAL COMPANY, LLC—See Community Health Systems, Inc.; *U.S. Public*, pg. 553
FAYETTEVILLE ELECTRIC SYSTEM, INC.; *U.S. Private*, pg. 1484
FAYETTEVILLE EXPRESS PIPELINE, LLC—See Energy Transfer LP; *U.S. Public*, pg. 763
FAYETTEVILLE PUBLISHING CO.—See Gannett Co., Inc.; *U.S. Public*, pg. 902
FAYEZ SAROFIM & CO.; *U.S. Private*, pg. 1484
FAYGO BEVERAGES, INC.—See National Beverage Corp.; *U.S. Public*, pg. 1494
FAY INDUSTRIES, INC.—See Ryerson Holding Corporation; *U.S. Public*, pg. 1829
FAYOLLE CANADA INC.—See Fayolle et Fils; *Int'l*, pg. 2626
FAYOLLE ET FILS; *Int'l*, pg. 2626

FAYOLLE ET FILS

FAYREWOOD LTD.—See Letchworth Investments Ltd.; *Int'l*, pg. 4469
FAYSAL BANK LIMITED—See Dar Al-Maal Al-Islami Trust; *Int'l*, pg. 1971
FAYSER S.R.L.—See TE Connectivity Ltd.; *Int'l*, pg. 7494
FAY, SPOFFORD & THORNDIKE, INC.; *U.S. Private*, pg. 1484
FAZ 93.6 BERLIN—See Frankfurter Allgemeine Zeitung GmbH; *Int'l*, pg. 2761
FAZAL CLOTH MILLS LIMITED; *Int'l*, pg. 2626
FAZE HOLDINGS INC.—See GameSquare Holdings, Inc.; *Int'l*, pg. 2877
FAZER BAGERI AB—See Oy Karl Fazer Ab; *Int'l*, pg. 5677
FAZER BAKERIES B.V.—See Oy Karl Fazer Ab; *Int'l*, pg. 5677
FAZER EESTI AS—See Oy Karl Fazer Ab; *Int'l*, pg. 5677
FAZER FOOD OU—See Oy Karl Fazer Ab; *Int'l*, pg. 5677
FAZER FOOD SERVICES AB—See Compass Group PLC; *Int'l*, pg. 1752
FAZER FOOD SERVICES A/S—See Compass Group PLC; *Int'l*, pg. 1752
FAZER FOOD SERVICES AS—See Compass Group PLC; *Int'l*, pg. 1752
FAZER FOOD SERVICES OY—See Compass Group PLC; *Int'l*, pg. 1752
FAZER KONFEKTYR AB—See Oy Karl Fazer Ab; *Int'l*, pg. 5677
FAZER LEIPOMOT OY—See Oy Karl Fazer Ab; *Int'l*, pg. 5677
FAZERLES AD-SILISTRA; *Int'l*, pg. 2627
FAZER MAKEISET OY—See Oy Karl Fazer Ab; *Int'l*, pg. 5677
FAZE THREE AUTOFAB LIMITED—See AUNDE Achter & Ebels GmbH; *Int'l*, pg. 705
FAZE THREE AUTOFAB LIMITED—See Faze Three Limited; *Int'l*, pg. 2627
FAZE THREE LIMITED; *Int'l*, pg. 2627
FAZE THREE LIMITED - WORKS II—See Faze Three Limited; *Int'l*, pg. 2627
FAZOLI'S SYSTEM MANAGEMENT, LLC—See Sentinel Capital Partners, L.L.C.; *U.S. Private*, pg. 3609
FAZ RESTAURANT INC.; *U.S. Private*, pg. 1484
FAZZI ASSOCIATES, INC.—See Leonard Green & Partners, L.P.; *U.S. Private*, pg. 2430
FAZZI ASSOCIATES, INC.—See TPG Capital, L.P.; *U.S. Public*, pg. 2177
FBA II, INC.; *U.S. Private*, pg. 1485
FB BANCORP; *U.S. Private*, pg. 1484
FB CAPITAL PARTNERS, L.P.; *U.S. Private*, pg. 1485
FBC BANK LIMITED—See FBC Holdings Limited; *Int'l*, pg. 2627
FBC BUILDING SOCIETY—See FBC Holdings Limited; *Int'l*, pg. 2627
FBC FINANCE CO.—See Farmer Brothers Co.; *U.S. Public*, pg. 821
FB CHAIN LIMITED—See Addtech AB; *Int'l*, pg. 133
FBC HOLDINGS LIMITED; *Int'l*, pg. 2627
FBC INSURANCE COMPANY (PRIVATE) LIMITED—See FBC Holdings Limited; *Int'l*, pg. 2627
FBC MORTGAGE, LLC; *U.S. Private*, pg. 1485
FBC REINSURANCE LIMITED—See FBC Holdings Limited; *Int'l*, pg. 2627
FBC SECURITIES (PRIVATE) LIMITED—See FBC Holdings Limited; *Int'l*, pg. 2627
FBD HOLDINGS PLC; *Int'l*, pg. 2627
FBD HOTELS (IRELAND) LIMITED—See Farmer Business Developments plc; *Int'l*, pg. 2619
FBD INSURANCE BROKERS LIMITED—See Marsh & McLennan Companies, Inc.; *U.S. Public*, pg. 1376
FBD INSURANCE PLC—See FBD Holdings plc; *Int'l*, pg. 2627
FB DISTRO, INC.—See Mahwah Bergen Retail Group, Inc.; *U.S. Private*, pg. 2550
FBD LIFE & PENSIONS LIMITED—See FBD Holdings plc; *Int'l*, pg. 2627
FBD PROPERTY & LEISURE LIMITED—See Farmer Business Developments plc; *Int'l*, pg. 2619
FBEC WORLDWIDE, INC.; *U.S. Public*, pg. 824
F. BENDER LIMITED—See DOpla S.p.A.; *Int'l*, pg. 2174
F. BENDER LIMITED—See FLO S.p.A.; *Int'l*, pg. 2707
FBF FRISCHBETON AG—See Vicat S.A.; *Int'l*, pg. 8185
FB FINANCIAL CORPORATION; *U.S. Public*, pg. 824
FB FIRE TECHNOLOGIES LTD.—See Ilustrato Pictures International Inc.; *Int'l*, pg. 3616
FB FOOD SERVICE (2017) CO., LTD.—See Sojitz Corporation; *Int'l*, pg. 7061
FB GENERATION SERVICES B.V.—See Fortum Oyj; *Int'l*, pg. 2740
FBG GROUP PTY LTD.—See Madison Dearborn Partners, LLC; *U.S. Private*, pg. 2540
FB GROUP ENTERPRISES MANAGEMENT COMPANY LIMITED—See Future Bright Holdings Limited; *Int'l*, pg. 2852
F&B GROUP; *Int'l*, pg. 2595
FBG SERVICE CORPORATION; *U.S. Private*, pg. 1485
FB HELISERVICES LIMITED—See Advent International Corporation; *U.S. Private*, pg. 99
FBH INC SARL—See Pearson plc; *Int'l*, pg. 5775

FBHS (AUST) PTY LIMITED—See Fletcher Building Limited; *Int'l*, pg. 2699
FBI BUILDINGS, INC.; *U.S. Private*, pg. 1485
FB INDUSTRIES INC.—See Atlas Energy Solutions Inc.; *U.S. Public*, pg. 224
THE FB INSURANCE COMPANY INC.—See Kentucky Farm Bureau Mutual Insurance Company Inc.; *U.S. Private*, pg. 2288
FB INTERNATIONAL, INC.—See Italian Exhibition Group SpA; *Int'l*, pg. 3828
F.B. JOHNSTON GRAPHICS—See Fred B. Johnston Company, Inc.; *U.S. Private*, pg. 1600
FB KEDJOR AB—See Addtech AB; *Int'l*, pg. 133
FB KETJUTEKNIIKKA OY—See Addtech AB; *Int'l*, pg. 133
FB KETTEN GMBH—See Addtech AB; *Int'l*, pg. 133
FB KETTEN HANDELS GMBH—See Addtech AB; *Int'l*, pg. 133
FB KJEDER AS—See Addtech AB; *Int'l*, pg. 133
FBL FINANCIAL GROUP, INC.—See Iowa Farm Bureau Federation; *U.S. Private*, pg. 2134
FBL LEASING SERVICES, INC.—See Iowa Farm Bureau Federation; *U.S. Private*, pg. 2134
FBL MARKETING SERVICES, L.L.C.—See Iowa Farm Bureau Federation; *U.S. Private*, pg. 2134
FBMC BENEFITS MANAGEMENT, INC.; *U.S. Private*, pg. 1485
FBM CO., LTD.—See MUSASHI CO., LTD.; *Int'l*, pg. 5101
F&B MFG. LLC—See Thunderbird LLC; *U.S. Private*, pg. 4166
FBM HUDSON ITALIANA SPA—See KNM Group Berhad; *Int'l*, pg. 4209
FBM-KNM FZCO—See KNM Group Berhad; *Int'l*, pg. 4209
FBN BANK (UK) LTD—See FBN Holdings PLC; *Int'l*, pg. 2627
FBN CAPITAL LTD.—See FBN Holdings PLC; *Int'l*, pg. 2627
FBN HOLDINGS PLC; *Int'l*, pg. 2627
FBN INSURANCE BROKERS LIMITED—See FBN Holdings PLC; *Int'l*, pg. 2627
FBN (MERCHANT BANKERS) LIMITED—See FBN Holdings PLC; *Int'l*, pg. 2627
FBN MORTGAGES LTD.—See FBN Holdings PLC; *Int'l*, pg. 2627
F & B NUTRITION SDN. BHD.—See Can-One Berhad; *Int'l*, pg. 1276
FBO LAND (SETAPAK) SDN. BHD.—See Meta Bright Group Berhad; *Int'l*, pg. 4843
FBR FUND ADVISERS, LLC—See B. Riley Financial, Inc.; *U.S. Public*, pg. 260
FBSCIENCES HOLDINGS, INC.—See Sumitomo Chemical Company, Limited; *Int'l*, pg. 7266
FBSCIENCES INC.—See Sumitomo Chemical Company, Limited; *Int'l*, pg. 7266
FBS CO., LTD.—See Daiwa House Industry Co., Ltd.; *Int'l*, pg. 1946
FBS COMMUNICATIONS, L.P.—See Black Box Limited; *Int'l*, pg. 1058
FBSERWIS DOLNY SLASK SP. Z O.O.—See Ferrovial S.A.; *Int'l*, pg. 2644
FBSERWIS KAMIENSK SP. Z O.O.—See Ferrovial S.A.; *Int'l*, pg. 2644
FBSERWIS KARPATIA SP. Z O.O.—See Ferrovial S.A.; *Int'l*, pg. 2644
FBSERWIS ODBIOR SP. Z O.O.—See Ferrovial S.A.; *Int'l*, pg. 2644
FBSERWIS SA—See Ferrovial S.A.; *Int'l*, pg. 2644
FBSERWIS WROCLAW SP. Z O.O.—See Ferrovial S.A.; *Int'l*, pg. 2644
FBS FIRST COAST INC.; *U.S. Private*, pg. 1485
FBS GLOBAL LIMITED; *Int'l*, pg. 2627
FB SOLUTION SAS—See Holding Le Duff SA; *Int'l*, pg. 3450
FBS REAL ESTATE S.P.A.—See Banca IFIS S.p.A.; *Int'l*, pg. 815
FBV CONSTRUCTION JSC; *Int'l*, pg. 2627
F.B. WASHBURN CANDY CORP.; *U.S. Private*, pg. 1455
F.B. WRIGHT CO.; *U.S. Private*, pg. 1455
FCA AUSTRALIA PTY. LTD.—See Stellantis N.V.; *Int'l*, pg. 7197
FCA AUSTRIA GMBH—See Stellantis N.V.; *Int'l*, pg. 7198
FCA BELGIUM SA—See Stellantis N.V.; *Int'l*, pg. 7198
FCAB INGENIERIA Y SERVICIOS LIMITADA—See Antofagasta plc; *Int'l*, pg. 484
FCA COOP; *U.S. Private*, pg. 1485
FCA DENMARK A/S—See Stellantis N.V.; *Int'l*, pg. 7198
FCA FOUNDATION—See Stellantis N.V.; *Int'l*, pg. 7200
FCA GERMANY AG—See Stellantis N.V.; *Int'l*, pg. 7198
FCA, LLC—See Delos Capital, LLC; *U.S. Private*, pg. 1198
FCA MEXICO, S.A. DE C.V.—See Stellantis N.V.; *Int'l*, pg. 7197
FCA NEDERLAND B.V.—See Stellantis N.V.; *Int'l*, pg. 7200
FCA NETHERLANDS B.V.—See Stellantis N.V.; *Int'l*, pg. 7198
F&C ASSET MANAGERS LIMITED—See Bank of Montreal; *Int'l*, pg. 847
FCA SWITZERLAND SA—See Stellantis N.V.; *Int'l*, pg. 7198
FCA US LLC—See Stellantis N.V.; *Int'l*, pg. 7198

CORPORATE AFFILIATIONS

FCB AFRICA—See The Interpublic Group of Companies, Inc.; *U.S. Public*, pg. 2093
FCBANK, A DIVISION OF CNB BANK—See CNB Financial Corporation; *U.S. Public*, pg. 519
FCB AUSTRALIA PTY LTD—See The Interpublic Group of Companies, Inc.; *U.S. Public*, pg. 2093
FC BAYERN TOURS GMBH—See Global Business Travel Group, Inc.; *U.S. Public*, pg. 940
FCB CHICAGO—See The Interpublic Group of Companies, Inc.; *U.S. Public*, pg. 2093
FCB CREA PUBLICIDAD—See The Interpublic Group of Companies, Inc.; *U.S. Public*, pg. 2093
FCB DOS PUNTOS CREA—See The Interpublic Group of Companies, Inc.; *U.S. Public*, pg. 2093
FCB FINANCIAL CORP.; *U.S. Private*, pg. 1485
FCB-HARLOW BUTLER PTY LIMITED—See CME Group, Inc.; *U.S. Public*, pg. 516
FCB HEALTH—See The Interpublic Group of Companies, Inc.; *U.S. Public*, pg. 2093
FCB INTERNATIONAL LEASING CO., LTD.—See First Financial Holding Co., Ltd.; *Int'l*, pg. 2683
FCB KUALA LUMPUR—See The Interpublic Group of Companies, Inc.; *U.S. Public*, pg. 2093
FCB LEASING CO., LTD—See First Financial Holding Co., Ltd.; *Int'l*, pg. 2683
FCB MANILA—See The Interpublic Group of Companies, Inc.; *U.S. Public*, pg. 2093
FCBULKA ADVERTISING—See The Interpublic Group of Companies, Inc.; *U.S. Public*, pg. 2093
FCB WORLDWIDE, INC.—See The Interpublic Group of Companies, Inc.; *U.S. Public*, pg. 2092
F.C.C. (ADAMS), LLC—See F.C.C. Co., Ltd.; *Int'l*, pg. 2596
FCC AMBITO, S.A.—See Fomento de Construcciones y Contratas, S.A.; *Int'l*, pg. 2722
FCC BEC S.R.O.—See Fomento de Construcciones y Contratas, S.A.; *Int'l*, pg. 2722
FCC BRATISLAVA S.R.O.—See Fomento de Construcciones y Contratas, S.A.; *Int'l*, pg. 2722
FCC BULGARIA E.O.O.D.—See Fomento de Construcciones y Contratas, S.A.; *Int'l*, pg. 2722
FCC CESKA REPUBLIKA S.R.O.—See Fomento de Construcciones y Contratas, S.A.; *Int'l*, pg. 2722
FCC CESKE BUDEJOVICE S.R.O.—See Fomento de Construcciones y Contratas, S.A.; *Int'l*, pg. 2722
FCCC, INC.; *U.S. Public*, pg. 824
F.C.C. CO., LTD.; *Int'l*, pg. 2596
FCC CONSTRUCCION CHILE, SPA—See Fomento de Construcciones y Contratas, S.A.; *Int'l*, pg. 2722
FCC CONSTRUCCION COSTA RICA, S.A.—See Fomento de Construcciones y Contratas, S.A.; *Int'l*, pg. 2722
FCC CONSTRUCCION PERU, S.A.C.—See Fomento de Construcciones y Contratas, S.A.; *Int'l*, pg. 2722
FCC CONSTRUCTION INC.—See Fomento de Construcciones y Contratas, S.A.; *Int'l*, pg. 2722
FCC CONSTRUCTION IRELAND DAC—See Fomento de Construcciones y Contratas, S.A.; *Int'l*, pg. 2722
FCC CONSTRUGOES DO BRASIL LTDA.—See Fomento de Construcciones y Contratas, S.A.; *Int'l*, pg. 2722
FCC CORPORATION—See Bilfinger SE; *Int'l*, pg. 1028
FCC DACICE S.R.O.—See Fomento de Construcciones y Contratas, S.A.; *Int'l*, pg. 2722
FCC DO BRASIL LTDA.—See F.C.C. Co., Ltd.; *Int'l*, pg. 2596
FCC EKO D.O.O.—See Fomento de Construcciones y Contratas, S.A.; *Int'l*, pg. 2722
FCC EKO POLSKA SP. Z O.O.—See Fomento de Construcciones y Contratas, S.A.; *Int'l*, pg. 2722
FCC EKO-RADOMSKO SP. Z.O.O.—See Fomento de Construcciones y Contratas, S.A.; *Int'l*, pg. 2722
FCC ENVIRONMENT (LINCOLNSHIRE) LTD.—See Fomento de Construcciones y Contratas, S.A.; *Int'l*, pg. 2722
FCC ENVIRONMENT PORTUGAL, S.A.—See Fomento de Construcciones y Contratas, S.A.; *Int'l*, pg. 2723
FCC ENVIRONMENT ROMANIA S.R.L.—See Fomento de Construcciones y Contratas, S.A.; *Int'l*, pg. 2723
FCC ENVIRONMENT (UK) LIMITED—See Fomento de Construcciones y Contratas, S.A.; *Int'l*, pg. 2722
FCC FREISTADT ABFALL SERVICE GMBH—See Fomento de Construcciones y Contratas, S.A.; *Int'l*, pg. 2723
FCC HALBENRAIN ABFALL SERVICE GMBH & CO. NFG KG—See Fomento de Construcciones y Contratas, S.A.; *Int'l*, pg. 2723
FCC HP S.R.O.—See Fomento de Construcciones y Contratas, S.A.; *Int'l*, pg. 2723
FCCI INSURANCE GROUP INC.—See FCCI Mutual Insurance Holding Company; *U.S. Private*, pg. 1485
F&C (CI) LIMITED—See Bank of Montreal; *Int'l*, pg. 847
FCCI MUTUAL INSURANCE HOLDING COMPANY; *U.S. Private*, pg. 1485
FCC (INDIANA), INC.—See F.C.C. Co., Ltd.; *Int'l*, pg. 2596
FCC INMOBILIEN HOLDING GMBH—See Fomento de Construcciones y Contratas, S.A.; *Int'l*, pg. 2723
FCC LIBEREC S.R.O.—See Fomento de Construcciones y Contratas, S.A.; *Int'l*, pg. 2723
FCC LUBLIENEC SP. Z.O.O.—See Fomento de Construcciones y Contratas, S.A.; *Int'l*, pg. 2723

COMPANY NAME INDEX

FCC MAGYARORSZAG KFT—See Fomento de Construcciones y Contratas, S.A.; *Int'l*, pg. 2723
FCC MOSTVIERTEL ABFALL SERVICE GMBH—See Fomento de Construcciones y Contratas, S.A.; *Int'l*, pg. 2723
FCC NERATOVICE S.R.O.—See Fomento de Construcciones y Contratas, S.A.; *Int'l*, pg. 2723
FCC NEUNKIRCHEN ABFALL SERVICE GMBH—See Fomento de Construcciones y Contratas, S.A.; *Int'l*, pg. 2723
FCC (NORTH AMERICA), INC.—See F.C.C. Co., Ltd.; *Int'l*, pg. 2596
F.C.C. (NORTH CAROLINA), LLC—See F.C.C. Co., Ltd.; *Int'l*, pg. 2596
FC CONSTRUCTION SERVICES; *U.S. Private*, pg. 1485
FCC RECYCLING (UK) LIMITED—See Fomento de Construcciones y Contratas, S.A.; *Int'l*, pg. 2723
FCC REGIOS AS—See Fomento de Construcciones y Contratas, S.A.; *Int'l*, pg. 2723
FC CRESTONE LLC; *U.S. Private*, pg. 1485
FCC SLOVENSKO S.R.O.—See Fomento de Construcciones y Contratas, S.A.; *Int'l*, pg. 2723
FCC (TAIWAN) CO., LTD.—See F.C.C. Co., Ltd.; *Int'l*, pg. 2596
F.C.C. (TAIWAN) CO., LTD.—See F.C.C. Co., Ltd.; *Int'l*, pg. 2596
FCC TARNOBRZEG.SP. Z.O.O.—See Fomento de Construcciones y Contratas, S.A.; *Int'l*, pg. 2723
FCC TEXTIL2USE GMBH—See Fomento de Construcciones y Contratas, S.A.; *Int'l*, pg. 2723
F.C.C. (THAILAND) CO.,LTD.—See F.C.C. Co., Ltd.; *Int'l*, pg. 2596
FCC TRNAVA S.R.O.—See Fomento de Construcciones y Contratas, S.A.; *Int'l*, pg. 2723
FCC UHY S.R.O.—See Fomento de Construcciones y Contratas, S.A.; *Int'l*, pg. 2723
FCC UNANOV S.R.O.—See Fomento de Construcciones y Contratas, S.A.; *Int'l*, pg. 2723
FCC VENTURES—See Farm Credit Canada; *Int'l*, pg. 2619
FCC VRBAK D.O.O.—See Fomento de Construcciones y Contratas, S.A.; *Int'l*, pg. 2723
FCC WASTE SERVICES (UK) LIMITED—See Fomento de Construcciones y Contratas, S.A.; *Int'l*, pg. 2723
FCC ZARCICE S.R.O.—See Fomento de Construcciones y Contratas, S.A.; *Int'l*, pg. 2723
FCC ZABOVRESKY S.R.O.—See Fomento de Construcciones y Contratas, S.A.; *Int'l*, pg. 2723
FCC ZISTERDORF ABFALL SERVICE GMBH—See Fomento de Construcciones y Contratas, S.A.; *Int'l*, pg. 2723
FCC ZOHOR.S.R.O.—See Fomento de Construcciones y Contratas, S.A.; *Int'l*, pg. 2723
FCD ENTERPRISES, INC.—See Kottke Trucking, Inc.; *U.S. Private*, pg. 2345
FCE BANK PLC - AUSTRIA—See Ford Motor Company; *U.S. Public*, pg. 865
FCE BANK PLC—See Ford Motor Company; *U.S. Public*, pg. 865
FCE BANK PLC - SPAIN—See Ford Motor Company; *U.S. Public*, pg. 865
F&C EMERGING MARKETS LIMITED—See Bank of Montreal; *Int'l*, pg. 847
FCER MANAGEMENT LLC—See Adeptus Health Inc.; *U.S. Private*, pg. 78
FCF CO., LTD.; *Int'l*, pg. 2627
F.C. (FLYING CARGO) INTERNATIONAL TRANSPORTATION LTD.—See Deutsche Post AG; *Int'l*, pg. 2080
FCF MINERALS CORPORATION—See Metals Exploration PLC; *Int'l*, pg. 4849
FCF PARTNERS, LP; *U.S. Private*, pg. 1485
FCFS CO, INC.—See FirstCash Holdings, Inc.; *U.S. Public*, pg. 849
FCFS MO, INC.—See FirstCash Holdings, Inc.; *U.S. Public*, pg. 849
FCFS SC, INC.—See FirstCash Holdings, Inc.; *U.S. Public*, pg. 849
FCG, INC.; *U.S. Public*, pg. 824
FCG RESEARCH INSTITUTE, INC.—See Fuji Media Holdings, Inc.; *Int'l*, pg. 2813
F&C GROUP (HOLDINGS) LIMITED—See Bank of Montreal; *Int'l*, pg. 847
F&C GROUP MANAGEMENT LIMITED—See Bank of Montreal; *Int'l*, pg. 847
FCH ENTERPRISES INC.; *U.S. Private*, pg. 1485
F. CHRISTIANA & CO.—See US Foods Holding Corp.; *U.S. Public*, pg. 2266
FCIA MANAGEMENT COMPANY INC.—See American Financial Group, Inc.; *U.S. Public*, pg. 103
FCI COMPOSITE INSULATOR LTD.—See Benji Invest Kft.; *Int'l*, pg. 974
FCI CONNECTOR MALAYSIA SDN. BHD.—See Amphenol Corporation; *U.S. Public*, pg. 127
FCI CONNECTORS HONG KONG LTD.—See Amphenol Corporation; *U.S. Public*, pg. 127
FCI CONNECTORS KOREA LTD.—See Amphenol Corporation; *U.S. Public*, pg. 127
FCI CONNECTORS MALAYSIA SDN. BHD.—See Amphenol Corporation; *U.S. Public*, pg. 130

FCI CONNECTORS SHANGHAI CO. LTD.—See Amphenol Corporation; *U.S. Public*, pg. 127
FCI CONNECTORS SWEDEN AB—See Amphenol Corporation; *U.S. Public*, pg. 127
FCI CONSTRUCTORS INC.; *U.S. Private*, pg. 1486
FCI DEUTSCHLAND GMBH—See Amphenol Corporation; *U.S. Public*, pg. 127
FCI ELECTRONICS HUNGARY KFT—See Amphenol Corporation; *U.S. Public*, pg. 127
FCI FEDERAL, INC.—See Amentum Services, Inc.; *U.S. Private*, pg. 219
FCI JAPAN K. K.—See Amphenol Corporation; *U.S. Public*, pg. 127
F.C. INDUSTRIES INC.; *U.S. Private*, pg. 1455
FC INVESTMENT ADVISERS CO., LTD.—See Fund Creation Group Co., Ltd.; *Int'l*, pg. 2845
F&C INVESTMENT TRUST PLC; *Int'l*, pg. 2595
FCI OEN CONNECTORS LTD—See Amphenol Corporation; *U.S. Public*, pg. 127
FCI OPHTHALMICS INC.—See Carl-Zeiss-Stiftung; *Int'l*, pg. 1336
FCI TAIWAN LTD—See Amphenol Corporation; *U.S. Public*, pg. 127
FCI USA LLC - AUTOMOTIVE—See Amphenol Corporation; *U.S. Public*, pg. 127
FCI USA LLC—See Amphenol Corporation; *U.S. Public*, pg. 127
F.C. KERBECK & SONS; *U.S. Private*, pg. 1456
FCL BUILDERS INC.; *U.S. Private*, pg. 1486
FCL CENTREPOINT PTE LTD—See Frasers Property Limited; *Int'l*, pg. 2766
FCL ENTERPRISES LTD.—See Federated Co-operatives Limited; *Int'l*, pg. 2630
F.C.L. GRAPHICS; *U.S. Private*, pg. 1456
FCL PROPERTY INVESTMENTS PTE LTD—See Frasers Property Limited; *Int'l*, pg. 2766
FC LTD.—See PZ Cussons Plc; *Int'l*, pg. 6128
FCL VENTURES LTD.—See Federated Co-operatives Limited; *Int'l*, pg. 2630
F&C MANAGEMENT LIMITED—See Bank of Montreal; *Int'l*, pg. 847
FCM BANNOCKBURN; *U.S. Private*, pg. 1486
FCMB ASSET MANAGEMENT LIMITED—See FCMB Group Plc; *Int'l*, pg. 2628
FCMB BANK (UK) LIMITED—See FCMB Group Plc; *Int'l*, pg. 2628
FCMB CAPITAL MARKETS LIMITED—See FCMB Group Plc; *Int'l*, pg. 2628
FCMB GROUP PLC; *Int'l*, pg. 2627
FCMB MICROFINANCE BANK LIMITED—See FCMB Group Plc; *Int'l*, pg. 2628
FCMB PENSIONS LIMITED—See FCMB Group Plc; *Int'l*, pg. 2628
FCMB TRUSTEES LIMITED—See FCMB Group Plc; *Int'l*, pg. 2628
FCM CO., LTD.—See Aspirant Group, Inc.; *Int'l*, pg. 630
FC MEADOWBROOK LLC—See Sun Communities, Inc.; *U.S. Public*, pg. 1961
THE FCM GROUP, INC.; *U.S. Private*, pg. 4028
FCM TRAVEL SOLUTIONS (INDIA) PRIVATE LIMITED—See Flight Centre Travel Group Limited; *Int'l*, pg. 2706
FCM TRAVEL SOLUTIONS (L.L.C)—See Flight Centre Travel Group Limited; *Int'l*, pg. 2706
FCM TRAVEL SOLUTIONS SINGAPORE PTE. LTD.—See Flight Centre Travel Group Limited; *Int'l*, pg. 2706
FCM TRAVEL SOLUTIONS USA—See Flight Centre Travel Group Limited; *Int'l*, pg. 2706
FCN BANK; *U.S. Private*, pg. 1486
F&C NETHERLANDS B.V.—See Bank of Montreal; *Int'l*, pg. 847
FCNH, INC.—See Catterton Management Company, LLC; *U.S. Private*, pg. 794
FCN PITESTI—See S.N. Nuclearelectrica S.A.; *Int'l*, pg. 6456
FC PACKAGING (HARBIN) LIMITED—See CPMC Holdings Limited; *Int'l*, pg. 1826
FC PEBBLE CREEK LLC—See Sun Communities, Inc.; *U.S. Public*, pg. 1961
FCP GROTON LLC; *U.S. Private*, pg. 1486
F.C. PORTOMULTIMEDIA - EDICOES MULTIMEDIA, S.A.—See Futebol Clube do Porto; *Int'l*, pg. 2852
F&C PORTUGAL GESTAO DE PATRIMONIOS S.A.—See Bank of Montreal; *Int'l*, pg. 847
FC PRO, LLC—See Flotek Industries, Inc.; *U.S. Public*, pg. 853
F&C PROPERTY LIMITED—See Bank of Montreal; *Int'l*, pg. 847
F&C REIT CORPORATE FINANCE LIMITED—See Bank of Montreal; *Int'l*, pg. 847
FCR IMMOBILIEN AG; *Int'l*, pg. 2628
FCR, LLC—See Republic Services, Inc.; *U.S. Public*, pg. 1786
FCR VIETNAM PTE LTD—See Orange S.A.; *Int'l*, pg. 5608
FCS FINANCIAL; *U.S. Private*, pg. 1486
FCS SOFTWARE SOLUTIONS LTD; *Int'l*, pg. 2628
FCSTONE CANADA ULC—See StoneX Group Inc.; *U.S. Public*, pg. 1952

FDL CORPORATION

FCSTONE DO BRASIL LTDA.—See StoneX Group Inc.; *U.S. Public*, pg. 1952
FCSTONE GROUP, INC.—See StoneX Group Inc.; *U.S. Public*, pg. 1951
FCSTONE MERCHANT SERVICES, LLC—See StoneX Group Inc.; *U.S. Public*, pg. 1952
FCSTONE TRADING, LLC—See StoneX Group Inc.; *U.S. Public*, pg. 1952
FC TECHNIK AG—See RHI Magnesita N.V.; *Int'l*, pg. 6325
FCTI, INC.—See Seven Bank Ltd.; *Int'l*, pg. 6731
FC TRIDENT, LLC—See Welltower Inc.; *U.S. Public*, pg. 2348
FC USA INC.—See Flight Centre Travel Group Limited; *Int'l*, pg. 2706
FC VIETNAM CORPORATION—See Fujicopian Co., Ltd.; *Int'l*, pg. 2820
FCW HOLDINGS BERHAD; *Int'l*, pg. 2628
FCX OIL & GAS INC.—See Freeport-McMoRan Inc.; *U.S. Public*, pg. 884
FCX PERFORMANCE, INC.—See Applied Industrial Technologies, Inc.; *U.S. Public*, pg. 171
FD2S; *U.S. Private*, pg. 1486
FD ADVISORY, LTD.—See Hokkoku Financial Holdings, Inc.; *Int'l*, pg. 3443
FDA SDN. BHD.—See GLOMAC Berhad; *Int'l*, pg. 3008
FDB GROUP; *Int'l*, pg. 2628
FDC INTERNATIONAL HOTELS CORPORATION; *Int'l*, pg. 2628
FDC INTERNATIONAL LIMITED—See FDC Ltd; *Int'l*, pg. 2628
FDC LTD; *Int'l*, pg. 2628
FDC MANAGEMENT INC.; *U.S. Private*, pg. 1486
F.D.C. PRODUCTS INC.—See Yondashi Holdings Inc.; *Int'l*, pg. 8596
FDCTECH, INC.; *U.S. Public*, pg. 825
FDC UTILITIES, INC.—See Filinvest Development Corporation; *Int'l*, pg. 2663
FDC VITAMINS, INC.—See B. Riley Financial, Inc.; *U.S. Public*, pg. 261
FDC VITAMINS, INC.—See Irradiant Partners, LP; *U.S. Private*, pg. 2141
FDG ASSOCIATES LP; *U.S. Private*, pg. 1486
FDG ELECTRIC VEHICLES LIMITED; *Int'l*, pg. 2629
FDG KINETIC LIMITED—See FDG Electric Vehicles Limited; *Int'l*, pg. 2629
FD GROUP SRL—See Mittel S.p.A.; *Int'l*, pg. 4994
F.D. HAYES ELECTRIC COMPANY; *U.S. Private*, pg. 1456
F&D HUEBNER LLC; *U.S. Private*, pg. 1454
FDI PLANNING CONSULTANTS, INC.—See Kitchell Corporation; *U.S. Private*, pg. 2316
FDK AMERICA INC.—See Fujitsu Limited; *Int'l*, pg. 2832
FDK CORPORATION - KOSAI PLANT—See Fujitsu Limited; *Int'l*, pg. 2832
FDK CORPORATION - SANYO PLANT—See Fujitsu Limited; *Int'l*, pg. 2832
FDK CORPORATION—See Fujitsu Limited; *Int'l*, pg. 2832
FDK ECOTEC CO., LTD. - GIFU WORKS—See Fujitsu Limited; *Int'l*, pg. 2832
FDK ECOTEC CO., LTD.—See Fujitsu Limited; *Int'l*, pg. 2832
FDK ELECTRONICS GMBH—See Fujitsu Limited; *Int'l*, pg. 2832
FDK ENERGY CO., LTD.—See Fujitsu Limited; *Int'l*, pg. 2832
FDK ENGINEERING CO., LTD.—See Fujitsu Limited; *Int'l*, pg. 2832
FDK HONG KONG LTD.—See Fujitsu Limited; *Int'l*, pg. 2832
FDK KOREA LTD.—See Fujitsu Limited; *Int'l*, pg. 2832
FDK LANKA (PVT) LTD.—See Fujitsu Limited; *Int'l*, pg. 2832
FDK LIFETEC CORPORATION—See Fujitsu Limited; *Int'l*, pg. 2832
FDK SINGAPORE PTE. LTD.—See Fujitsu Limited; *Int'l*, pg. 2832
FDK TAIWAN LTD.—See Fujitsu Limited; *Int'l*, pg. 2832
FDK TATUNG (THAILAND) CO., LTD.—See Tatung Company; *Int'l*, pg. 7475
FDK TOTTORI CO., LTD.—See Fujitsu Limited; *Int'l*, pg. 2832
FDK TWICELL CO.,LTD.—See Fujitsu Limited; *Int'l*, pg. 2832
THE F.D. LAWRENCE ELECTRIC COMPANY; *U.S. Private*, pg. 4027
FDL CHINA—See Highlander Partners, LP.; *U.S. Private*, pg. 1939
FDL CORPORATION; *U.S. Private*, pg. 1486
FDLNET.CZ, S.R.O.—See CEZ, a.s.; *Int'l*, pg. 1427
FDM ASTRA IRELAND LIMITED—See FDM Group (Holdings) plc; *Int'l*, pg. 2629
FDM GMBH—See Piovan SpA; *Int'l*, pg. 5872
FDM GROUP AUSTRALIA PTY LTD.—See FDM Group (Holdings) plc; *Int'l*, pg. 2629
FDM GROUP CANADA INC.—See FDM Group (Holdings) plc; *Int'l*, pg. 2629
FDM GROUP GMBH—See Inflexion Private Equity Partners LLP; *Int'l*, pg. 3689

FDM GROUP HK LIMITED—See FDM Group (Holdings) plc; *Int'l*, pg. 2629
FDM GROUP (HOLDINGS) PLC; *Int'l*, pg. 2629
FDM GROUP INC.—See Inflexion Private Equity Partners LLP; *Int'l*, pg. 3689
FDM GROUP LTD.—See Inflexion Private Equity Partners LLP; *Int'l*, pg. 3689
FDM GROUP NV—See FDM Group (Holdings) plc; *Int'l*, pg. 2629
FDM GROUP SA—See Inflexion Private Equity Partners LLP; *Int'l*, pg. 3689
FDM SINGAPORE CONSULTING PTE LIMITED—See FDM Group (Holdings) plc; *Int'l*, pg. 2629
FDM SOFTWARE LTD.—See TA Associates, Inc.; *U.S. Private*, pg. 3914
FDM SOUTH AFRICA (PTY) LIMITED—See FDM Group (Holdings) plc; *Int'l*, pg. 2629
FDM SWITZERLAND GMBH—See FDM Group (Holdings) plc; *Int'l*, pg. 2629
FDM TECHNOLOGY (SHANGHAI) CO. LIMITED—See FDM Group (Holdings) plc; *Int'l*, pg. 2629
THE F. DOHMEN COMPANY—See Cardinal Health, Inc.; *U.S. Public*, pg. 434
FDS BANK—See Macy's, Inc.; *U.S. Public*, pg. 1353
F&D SCENE CHANGES LTD.; *Int'l*, pg. 2595
FDS GROUP SA—See Bridgepoint Group Plc; *Int'l*, pg. 1154
FD SIMS LTD—See IRCE S.p.A.; *Int'l*, pg. 3806
FDS INFORMAL FOODS LIMITED—See Raisio PLC; *Int'l*, pg. 6190
FDS MANUFACTURING COMPANY INCORPORATED; *U.S. Private*, pg. 1486
F.D. STERRITT LUMBER CO.; *U.S. Private*, pg. 1456
FD TECHNOLOGIES PLC; *Int'l*, pg. 2628
FDT FLACHDACH TECHNOLOGIE GMBH & CO. KG—See Holcim Ltd.; *Int'l*, pg. 3446
FDT FLACHDACH TECHNOLOGIE S.A./N.V.—See Mutares SE & Co. KGaA; *Int'l*, pg. 5104
FDT FRANCE S. A.S.—See Mutares SE & Co. KGaA; *Int'l*, pg. 5104
F.D. THOMAS INC.—See Arctic Slope Regional Corporation; *U.S. Private*, pg. 316
FDX ADVISORS INC.—See Actua Corporation; *U.S. Private*, pg. 71
FEAG INTERNATIONAL FREIGHT FORWARDERS LTD.—See Lamprecht Transport AG; *Int'l*, pg. 4402
F&E AIRCRAFT MAINTENANCE; *U.S. Private*, pg. 1454
FEA PLANTATIONS LIMITED—See Forest Enterprises Australia Limited; *Int'l*, pg. 2732
FEA PROCESS & TECHNOLOGICAL PLANTS S.R.L.—See Piovan SpA; *Int'l*, pg. 5872
FEARING INTERNATIONAL (STOCK AIDS) LIMITED—See Tru-Test Group; *Int'l*, pg. 7940
FEARLESS FILMS, INC.; *Int'l*, pg. 2629
FEARLESS MEDIA, LLC—See Infinite Realty; *U.S. Private*, pg. 2071
FEARNLEYS SHIPBROKING PRIVATE LIMITED—See Thoresen Thai Agencies Public Company Limited; *Int'l*, pg. 7718
FEARNLEYS (THAILAND) LTD.—See Thoresen Thai Agencies Public Company Limited; *Int'l*, pg. 7718
FEATHERINGILL CAPITAL, LLC; *U.S. Private*, pg. 1486
FEATHERLAND EGG FARMS, INC.—See Cal-Maine Foods, Inc.; *U.S. Public*, pg. 421
FEATHERLITE BUILDING PRODUCTS—See Berkshire Hathaway Inc.; *U.S. Public*, pg. 298
FEATHERLITE, INC.—See Corporate Partners LLC; *U.S. Private*, pg. 1055
FEATHERLITE INDUSTRIES LTD.—See Cuprum S.A. de C.V.; *Int'l*, pg. 1878
FEATHER PUBLISHING CO., INC.; *U.S. Private*, pg. 1486
FEATHER RIVER BULLETIN—See Feather Publishing Co., Inc.; *U.S. Private*, pg. 1486
FEATHER RIVER DISPOSAL, INC.—See Waste Management, Inc.; *U.S. Public*, pg. 2331
FEATURE FILMS FOR FAMILIES INC.; *U.S. Private*, pg. 1486
FEATURE INTEGRATION TECHNOLOGY, INC.; *Int'l*, pg. 2629
FE-AUTO CO., LTD.—See Kyokuto Kaihatsu Kogyo Co. Ltd.; *Int'l*, pg. 4363
FEBACS CO., LTD.—See Screen Holdings Co., Ltd.; *Int'l*, pg. 6655
FE BATTERY METALS CORP.; *Int'l*, pg. 2629
FEB D.D. SARAJEVO; *Int'l*, pg. 2629
FE & B ENGINEERING (M) SDN. BHD.—See Far East Group Limited; *Int'l*, pg. 2616
FEBER ASSOCIATES LIMITED—See The Mauritius Union Assurance Company Limited; *Int'l*, pg. 7666
FEBEX S.A.—See Arkema S.A.; *Int'l*, pg. 571
F.E. BORDING A/S; *Int'l*, pg. 2596
FEC CABLES (MALAYSIA) SDN. BHD.—See Permodalan Nasional Berhad; *Int'l*, pg. 5809
FEC CHAIN CORPORATION—See Chuo Spring Co., Ltd.; *Int'l*, pg. 1599
FEC CORPORATION—See SHOWA SHINKU CO., LTD.; *Int'l*, pg. 6862
THE FECHHEIMER BROTHERS COMPANY—See Berkshire Hathaway Inc.; *U.S. Public*, pg. 316

FECHTEL BEVERAGE & SALES INC.; *U.S. Private*, pg. 1486
FECO AJAX INC.—See Park-Ohio Holdings Corp.; *U.S. Public*, pg. 1639
FECON CORPORATION; *Int'l*, pg. 2629
FECON MINING JOINT STOCK COMPANY—See ASIA PILE HOLDINGS CORPORATION; *Int'l*, pg. 614
FEC RESOURCES INC.—See Philex Mining Corporation; *Int'l*, pg. 5844
FECT CO., LTD.—See Soulbrain Holdings Co., Ltd.; *Int'l*, pg. 7114
FECTO CEMENT LIMITED—See Fecto Group of Companies; *Int'l*, pg. 2629
FECTO GROUP OF COMPANIES; *Int'l*, pg. 2629
FECTO ORIENT (PVT.) LTD.—See Fecto Group of Companies; *Int'l*, pg. 2629
FECTO SUGAR MILLS LTD.—See Fecto Group of Companies; *Int'l*, pg. 2629
FEDCAP PARTNERS, LLC; *U.S. Private*, pg. 1486
FEDCAP REHABILITATION SERVICES, INC.; *U.S. Private*, pg. 1486
FEDCHEM LLC—See Federal Process Corporation; *U.S. Private*, pg. 1489
FEDCO ELECTRONICS, INC.; *U.S. Private*, pg. 1486
FEDDERS ELECTRIC AND ENGINEERING LIMITED; *Int'l*, pg. 2629
FEDDERS THAI COMPANY LIMITED—See Thiensurat Public Company Limited; *Int'l*, pg. 7709
FEDEA S.A.—See Corteva, Inc.; *U.S. Public*, pg. 582
THE FEDELI GROUP, INC.; *U.S. Private*, pg. 4028
FEDERACION DE ASC PECUARIAS PR; *U.S. Private*, pg. 1487
FEDERAL AGRICULTURAL MORTGAGE CORPORATION; *U.S. Public*, pg. 825
FEDERAL ASSIST—See MAPFRE S.A.; *Int'l*, pg. 4684
FEDERAL AUTOCAT RECYCLING, LLC—See Metalico Inc.; *U.S. Private*, pg. 2681
FEDERAL AUTO HOLDINGS BERHAD—See MBM Resources Berhad; *Int'l*, pg. 4754
FEDERAL BATTERIES QLD PTY LTD—See Bapcor Limited; *Int'l*, pg. 857
FEDERAL BROACH & MACHINE COMPANY—See Mitsubishi Heavy Industries, Ltd.; *Int'l*, pg. 4956
FEDERAL BUILDING SERVICES, INC.; *U.S. Private*, pg. 1487
FEDERAL BUSINESS PRODUCTS, INC.; *U.S. Private*, pg. 1487
FEDERAL CAPITAL PARTNERS; *U.S. Private*, pg. 1487
THE FEDERAL CAPITAL PRESS OF AUSTRALIA PTY LIMITED—See Nine Entertainment Co. Holdings Limited; *Int'l*, pg. 5299
FEDERAL CAPITAL PTE LTD—See Federal International (2000) Ltd; *Int'l*, pg. 2630
FEDERAL CARTRIDGE COMPANY—See Vista Outdoor Inc.; *U.S. Public*, pg. 2305
FEDERAL CASTERS CORPORATION; *U.S. Private*, pg. 1487
FEDERAL COACH COMPANY—See J.B. Poindexter & Co., Inc.; *U.S. Private*, pg. 2158
FEDERAL COACH, LLC—See J.B. Poindexter & Co., Inc.; *U.S. Private*, pg. 2158
FEDERAL COMPRESS & WAREHOUSE COMPANY, INC.; *U.S. Private*, pg. 1487
FEDERALCONFERENCE.COM; *U.S. Private*, pg. 1487
FEDERAL CONTRACTING GROUP—See M.A. Mortenson Company; *U.S. Private*, pg. 2527
FEDERAL CONTRACTING INC; *U.S. Private*, pg. 1487
FEDERAL CORPORATION; *Int'l*, pg. 2630
FEDERAL DEPOSIT INSURANCE CORPORATION; *U.S. Private*, pg. 1487
FEDERAL DISTRIBUTORS, INC.; *U.S. Private*, pg. 1487
FEDERAL ENERGI PTE LTD—See Federal International (2000) Ltd; *Int'l*, pg. 2630
FEDERAL ENVIRONMENTAL & ENERGY PTE. LTD.—See Federal International (2000) Ltd; *Int'l*, pg. 2630
FEDERAL EXPRESS ASIA PACIFIC—See FedEx Corporation; *U.S. Public*, pg. 828
FEDERAL EXPRESS CANADA CORPORATION—See FedEx Corporation; *U.S. Public*, pg. 828
FEDERAL EXPRESS CANADA LTD.—See FedEx Corporation; *U.S. Public*, pg. 828
FEDERAL EXPRESS CORPORATION—See FedEx Corporation; *U.S. Public*, pg. 828
FEDERAL EXPRESS EUROPE, INC.—See FedEx Corporation; *U.S. Public*, pg. 828
FEDERAL EXPRESS EUROPE, MIDDLE EAST & AFRICA—See FedEx Corporation; *U.S. Public*, pg. 828
FEDERAL EXPRESS INTERNATIONAL, INC.—See FedEx Corporation; *U.S. Public*, pg. 828
FEDERAL EXPRESS JAPAN G.K.—See FedEx Corporation; *U.S. Public*, pg. 828
FEDERAL EXPRESS KOREA LLC—See FedEx Corporation; *U.S. Public*, pg. 828
FEDERAL EXPRESS LATIN AMERICA-CARIBBEAN—See FedEx Corporation; *U.S. Public*, pg. 828
FEDERAL EXPRESS PACIFIC, INC.—See FedEx Corporation; *U.S. Public*, pg. 828

FEDERAL FABRICS-FIBERS INC.—See Charlesbank Capital Partners, LLC; *U.S. Private*, pg. 855
FEDERAL FARM CREDIT BANKS FUNDING CORPORATION; *U.S. Private*, pg. 1487
FEDERAL FIRE ENGINEERING PTE LTD—See Federal International (2000) Ltd; *Int'l*, pg. 2630
FEDERAL FLOOD CERTIFICATION LLC—See MetLife, Inc.; *U.S. Public*, pg. 1430
FEDERAL FOAM TECHNOLOGIES, INC. - COKATO DIVISION—See Federal International Inc.; *U.S. Private*, pg. 1489
FEDERAL FOAM TECHNOLOGIES INC.—See Federal International Inc.; *U.S. Private*, pg. 1489
FEDERAL FRUIT & PRODUCE CO., INC.; *U.S. Private*, pg. 1488
FEDERAL FURNITURE (1982) SDN BHD—See Federal International Holdings Berhad; *Int'l*, pg. 2630
FEDERAL FURNITURE INDUSTRIES SDN BHD—See Federal International Holdings Berhad; *Int'l*, pg. 2630
FEDERAL FURNITURE LIFESTYLE SDN BHD—See Federal International Holdings Berhad; *Int'l*, pg. 2630
FEDERAL FURNITURE (M) SDN BHD—See Federal International Holdings Berhad; *Int'l*, pg. 2630
FEDERAL HARDWARE ENGINEERING CO PTE LTD—See Federal International (2000) Ltd; *Int'l*, pg. 2630
FEDERAL HEATH SIGN COMPANY, LLC—See Marsh Global Holdings Ltd; *Int'l*, pg. 4701
FEDERAL HEATH SIGN CO.—See Marsh Global Holdings Ltd; *Int'l*, pg. 4701
FEDERAL HOME LOAN BANK OF ATLANTA; *U.S. Private*, pg. 1488
FEDERAL HOME LOAN BANK OF BOSTON; *U.S. Private*, pg. 1488
FEDERAL HOME LOAN BANK OF CHICAGO; *U.S. Private*, pg. 1488
FEDERAL HOME LOAN BANK OF CINCINNATI; *U.S. Private*, pg. 1488
FEDERAL HOME LOAN BANK OF DALLAS; *U.S. Private*, pg. 1488
FEDERAL HOME LOAN BANK OF DES MOINES; *U.S. Private*, pg. 1488
FEDERAL HOME LOAN BANK OF INDIANAPOLIS; *U.S. Private*, pg. 1488
FEDERAL HOME LOAN BANK OF NEW YORK; *U.S. Private*, pg. 1488
FEDERAL HOME LOAN BANK OF PITTSBURGH; *U.S. Private*, pg. 1488
FEDERAL HOME LOAN BANK OF SAN FRANCISCO; *U.S. Private*, pg. 1488
FEDERAL HOME LOAN BANK OF TOPEKA; *U.S. Private*, pg. 1488
FEDERAL HOME LOAN MORTGAGE CORPORATION; *U.S. Public*, pg. 825
FEDERAL HOSE MANUFACTURING INC.—See The Crawford Group Inc.; *U.S. Private*, pg. 4016
FEDERAL IESE ENVIRONMENTAL TECHNOLOGY (SHANGHAI) CO., LTD.—See Federal International (2000) Ltd; *Int'l*, pg. 2630
FEDERAL INDUSTRIES—See Standex International; *U.S. Public*, pg. 1930
FEDERAL INSURANCE COMPANY LIMITED; *Int'l*, pg. 2630
FEDERAL INSURANCE COMPANY—See Chubb Limited; *Int'l*, pg. 1591
FEDERAL INTERNATIONAL (2000) LTD; *Int'l*, pg. 2630
FEDERAL INTERNATIONAL HOLDINGS BERHAD; *Int'l*, pg. 2630
FEDERAL INTERNATIONAL INC.; *U.S. Private*, pg. 1489
FEDERAL INTERNATIONAL (SHANGHAI) CO., LTD.—See Federal International (2000) Ltd; *Int'l*, pg. 2630
THE FEDERALIST SOCIETY FOR LAW & PUBLIC POLICY STUDIES; *U.S. Private*, pg. 4028
FEDERAL LAND BANK ASSOCIATION YOSEMITE; *U.S. Private*, pg. 1489
FEDERAL LAND, INC.—See GT Capital Holdings, Inc.; *Int'l*, pg. 3150
FEDERAL LIFE GROUP, INC.; *U.S. Public*, pg. 825
FEDERAL LIFE INSURANCE COMPANY; *U.S. Private*, pg. 1489
FEDERAL MARINE TRANSMISSIONS, INC.; *U.S. Private*, pg. 1489
FEDERAL MARKET CO. INC.; *U.S. Private*, pg. 1489
THE FEDERAL METAL COMPANY—See Oakwood Industries Inc.; *U.S. Private*, pg. 2985
FEDERAL METAL PRINTING FACTORY SDN. BHD.—See Can-One Berhad; *Int'l*, pg. 1276
FEDERAL MFG. CO.—See Leonard Green & Partners, L.P.; *U.S. Private*, pg. 2427
FEDERAL-MOGUL ACQUISITION COMPANY LIMITED—See Apollo Global Management, Inc.; *U.S. Public*, pg. 162
FEDERAL-MOGUL AFTERMARKET ESPANA, SA—See Apollo Global Management, Inc.; *U.S. Public*, pg. 160
FEDERAL-MOGUL AFTERMARKET GMBH—See Apollo Global Management, Inc.; *U.S. Public*, pg. 160
FEDERAL-MOGUL AFTERMARKET UK LIMITED—See Apollo Global Management, Inc.; *U.S. Public*, pg. 162

FEDERAL-MOGUL ANAND SEALINGS INDIA LIMITED—See Apollo Global Management, Inc.; *U.S. Public*, pg. 160
FEDERAL MOGUL ARGENTINA SA.—See Apollo Global Management, Inc.; *U.S. Public*, pg. 160
FEDERAL-MOGUL ASIA INVESTMENTS LIMITED—See Apollo Global Management, Inc.; *U.S. Public*, pg. 160
FEDERAL-MOGUL AUTOMOTIVE PTY LTD.—See Apollo Global Management, Inc.; *U.S. Public*, pg. 160
FEDERAL-MOGUL AUTOMOTIVE—See Apollo Global Management, Inc.; *U.S. Public*, pg. 160
FEDERAL-MOGUL BEARINGS INDIA LIMITED—See Apollo Global Management, Inc.; *U.S. Public*, pg. 160
FEDERAL-MOGUL BRADFORD LIMITED—See Apollo Global Management, Inc.; *U.S. Public*, pg. 162
FEDERAL-MOGUL BURSCHEID BETEILIGUNGS GMBH—See Apollo Global Management, Inc.; *U.S. Public*, pg. 160
FEDERAL-MOGUL BURSCHEID GMBH—See Apollo Global Management, Inc.; *U.S. Public*, pg. 160
FEDERAL-MOGUL CANADA LIMITED—See Apollo Global Management, Inc.; *U.S. Public*, pg. 160
FEDERAL-MOGUL CHASSIS LLC—See Apollo Global Management, Inc.; *U.S. Public*, pg. 160
FEDERAL-MOGUL (CHINA) CO., LTD.—See Apollo Global Management, Inc.; *U.S. Public*, pg. 160
FEDERAL-MOGUL CONTROLLED POWER LIMITED—See Apollo Global Management, Inc.; *U.S. Public*, pg. 160
FEDERAL-MOGUL CORP. - FRANKFORT—See Apollo Global Management, Inc.; *U.S. Public*, pg. 161
FEDERAL-MOGUL CORP. - SKOKIE—See Apollo Global Management, Inc.; *U.S. Public*, pg. 161
FEDERAL-MOGUL CORP. - SUMMERTON—See Apollo Global Management, Inc.; *U.S. Public*, pg. 161
FEDERAL-MOGUL DE MEXICO S.A. DE C.V.—See Apollo Global Management, Inc.; *U.S. Public*, pg. 162
FEDERAL-MOGUL DEVA GMBH—See Apollo Global Management, Inc.; *U.S. Public*, pg. 160
FEDERAL-MOGUL DONGSUH (QINGDAO) PISTONS CO., LTD.—See Apollo Global Management, Inc.; *U.S. Public*, pg. 160
FEDERAL-MOGUL DUTCH HOLDINGS INC.—See Apollo Global Management, Inc.; *U.S. Public*, pg. 160
FEDERAL-MOGUL EMEA DISTRIBUTION SERVICES, BVBA—See Apollo Global Management, Inc.; *U.S. Public*, pg. 160
FEDERAL-MOGUL ENGINEERING LIMITED—See Apollo Global Management, Inc.; *U.S. Public*, pg. 162
FEDERAL-MOGUL FINANCIAL SERVICES SAS—See Apollo Global Management, Inc.; *U.S. Public*, pg. 160
FEDERAL-MOGUL FRICTION PRODUCTS A.S.—See Apollo Global Management, Inc.; *U.S. Public*, pg. 161
FEDERAL-MOGUL FRICTION PRODUCTS BARCELONA S.L.—See Apollo Global Management, Inc.; *U.S. Public*, pg. 161
FEDERAL-MOGUL FRICTION PRODUCTS INTERNATIONAL GMBH—See Apollo Global Management, Inc.; *U.S. Public*, pg. 161
FEDERAL-MOGUL FRICTION PRODUCTS LIMITED—See Apollo Global Management, Inc.; *U.S. Public*, pg. 162
FEDERAL-MOGUL FRICTION PRODUCTS SA—See Apollo Global Management, Inc.; *U.S. Public*, pg. 161
FEDERAL-MOGUL FRICTION PRODUCTS—See Apollo Global Management, Inc.; *U.S. Public*, pg. 161
FEDERAL-MOGUL FRICTION PRODUCTS—See Apollo Global Management, Inc.; *U.S. Public*, pg. 161
FEDERAL-MOGUL FRICTION PRODUCTS—See Apollo Global Management, Inc.; *U.S. Public*, pg. 161
FEDERAL-MOGUL FRICTION PRODUCTS (THAILAND) LTD—See Apollo Global Management, Inc.; *U.S. Public*, pg. 161
FEDERAL-MOGUL FRIEDBERG GMBH—See Apollo Global Management, Inc.; *U.S. Public*, pg. 161
FEDERAL-MOGUL GLOBAL AFTERMARKET EMEA, BVBA—See Apollo Global Management, Inc.; *U.S. Public*, pg. 161
FEDERAL-MOGUL GLOBAL INC.—See Apollo Global Management, Inc.; *U.S. Public*, pg. 161
FEDERAL-MOGUL GMBH—See Apollo Global Management, Inc.; *U.S. Public*, pg. 161
FEDERAL-MOGUL GOETZE (INDIA) LTD—See Apollo Global Management, Inc.; *U.S. Public*, pg. 161
FEDERAL-MOGUL GORZYCE SA—See Apollo Global Management, Inc.; *U.S. Public*, pg. 161
FEDERAL-MOGUL HOLDINGS DEUTSCHLAND GMBH—See Apollo Global Management, Inc.; *U.S. Public*, pg. 161
FEDERAL-MOGUL HOLDINGS LLC—See Apollo Global Management, Inc.; *U.S. Public*, pg. 160
FEDERAL-MOGUL HUNGARY KFT.—See Apollo Global Management, Inc.; *U.S. Public*, pg. 161
FEDERAL-MOGUL INDUSTRIA DE AUTOPECAS LTDA.—See Apollo Global Management, Inc.; *U.S. Public*, pg. 161
FEDERAL-MOGUL ITALY S.R.L.—See Apollo Global Management, Inc.; *U.S. Public*, pg. 161
FEDERAL-MOGUL IZMIT PISTON VE PIM URETIM TESISLERI A.S.—See Apollo Global Management, Inc.; *U.S. Public*, pg. 162
FEDERAL MOGUL JAPAN K.K.—See Apollo Global Management, Inc.; *U.S. Public*, pg. 162
FEDERAL-MOGUL LIMITED—See Apollo Global Management, Inc.; *U.S. Public*, pg. 162
FEDERAL-MOGUL LLC—See Apollo Global Management, Inc.; *U.S. Public*, pg. 161
FEDERAL-MOGUL MOTORPARTS MINORITY HOLDING B.V.—See Apollo Global Management, Inc.; *U.S. Public*, pg. 161
FEDERAL-MOGUL MOTORPARTS (SINGAPORE) PTE. LTD.—See Apollo Global Management, Inc.; *U.S. Public*, pg. 161
FEDERAL-MOGUL OPERATIONS FRANCE SAS—See Apollo Global Management, Inc.; *U.S. Public*, pg. 161
FEDERAL-MOGUL OPERATIONS ITALY S.R.L.—See Apollo Global Management, Inc.; *U.S. Public*, pg. 161
FEDERAL-MOGUL PISTON RINGS, INC.—See Apollo Global Management, Inc.; *U.S. Public*, pg. 161
FEDERAL-MOGUL POWERTRAIN ITALY S.R.L—See Apollo Global Management, Inc.; *U.S. Public*, pg. 161
FEDERAL-MOGUL POWERTRAIN, LLC—See Apollo Global Management, Inc.; *U.S. Public*, pg. 161
FEDERAL-MOGUL POWERTRAIN, LLC—See Apollo Global Management, Inc.; *U.S. Public*, pg. 161
FEDERAL MOGUL POWERTRAIN OTOMOTIV ANONIM SIRKETI—See Apollo Global Management, Inc.; *U.S. Public*, pg. 160
FEDERAL-MOGUL POWERTRAIN SOLUTIONS INDIA PRIVATE LIMITED—See Apollo Global Management, Inc.; *U.S. Public*, pg. 161
FEDERAL-MOGUL POWERTRAIN SYSTEMS SA (PTY) LTD—See Apollo Global Management, Inc.; *U.S. Public*, pg. 161
FEDERAL-MOGUL PTY. LTD.—See Apollo Global Management, Inc.; *U.S. Public*, pg. 161
FEDERAL-MOGUL SA DE CV—See Apollo Global Management, Inc.; *U.S. Public*, pg. 161
FEDERAL-MOGUL S.A.—See Apollo Global Management, Inc.; *U.S. Public*, pg. 161
FEDERAL-MOGUL SAS—See Apollo Global Management, Inc.; *U.S. Public*, pg. 161
FEDERAL-MOGUL SEALING SYSTEMS GMBH—See Apollo Global Management, Inc.; *U.S. Public*, pg. 161
FEDERAL-MOGUL SEALING SYSTEMS—See Apollo Global Management, Inc.; *U.S. Public*, pg. 161
FEDERAL-MOGUL SHANGHAI BEARING CO., LTD.—See Apollo Global Management, Inc.; *U.S. Public*, pg. 162
FEDERAL-MOGUL SINTERTECH, SAS—See Apollo Global Management, Inc.; *U.S. Public*, pg. 162
FEDERAL-MOGUL SOROCABA-HOLDING LTDA—See Apollo Global Management, Inc.; *U.S. Public*, pg. 162
FEDERAL-MOGUL TECHNICAL CENTER, LLC—See Apollo Global Management, Inc.; *U.S. Public*, pg. 162
FEDERAL-MOGUL TECHNOLOGY LIMITED—See Apollo Global Management, Inc.; *U.S. Public*, pg. 162
FEDERAL-MOGUL TP EUROPE GMBH & CO. KG—See TPR Co., Ltd.; *Int'l*, pg. 7883
FEDERAL-MOGUL TP LINER EUROPE OTOMOTIV LTD. STI.—See TPR Co., Ltd.; *Int'l*, pg. 7883
FEDERAL-MOGUL TP LINERS EUROPE OTOMOTIV LTD. STI.—See TPR Co., Ltd.; *Int'l*, pg. 7883
FEDERAL-MOGUL TP LINERS, INC.—See TPR Co., Ltd.; *Int'l*, pg. 7884
FEDERAL-MOGUL TP PISTON RINGS GMBH—See Apollo Global Management, Inc.; *U.S. Public*, pg. 161
FEDERAL-MOGUL UK HOLDING LTD.—See Apollo Global Management, Inc.; *U.S. Public*, pg. 162
FEDERAL-MOGUL UK HOLDINGS INC.—See Apollo Global Management, Inc.; *U.S. Public*, pg. 162
FEDERAL-MOGUL VALVETRAIN GMBH—See Apollo Global Management, Inc.; *U.S. Public*, pg. 161
FEDERAL-MOGUL VALVE TRAIN INTERNATIONAL LLC—See Apollo Global Management, Inc.; *U.S. Public*, pg. 162
FEDERAL-MOGUL VALVETRAIN LA SOURCE SAS—See Apollo Global Management, Inc.; *U.S. Public*, pg. 162
FEDERAL-MOGUL VALVETRAIN SCHIRMECK SAS—See Apollo Global Management, Inc.; *U.S. Public*, pg. 162
FEDERAL-MOGUL WIESBADEN GMBH—See Apollo Global Management, Inc.; *U.S. Public*, pg. 162
FEDERAL-MOGUL WORLD TRADE (ASIA) LIMITED—See Apollo Global Management, Inc.; *U.S. Public*, pg. 162
FEDERAL-MOGUL WORLD WIDE, INC.—See Apollo Global Management, Inc.; *U.S. Public*, pg. 162
FEDERAL NATIONAL MORTGAGE ASSOCIATION; *U.S. Public*, pg. 825
FEDERAL NEWS SERVICES—See The Economist Group Limited; *Int'l*, pg. 7637
FEDERAL OFFSHORE SERVICES PTE LTD—See Federal International (2000) Ltd; *Int'l*, pg. 2630
FEDERAL PACKAGES SDN. BHD.—See Muda Holdings Berhad; *Int'l*, pg. 5076
FEDERAL PETROLEUM CO., INC.—See Ferrellgas Partners, L.P.; *U.S. Public*, pg. 829
FEDERAL POWER SDN. BHD.—See Permodalan Nasional Berhad; *Int'l*, pg. 5809
FEDERAL PRETZEL BAKING COMPANY, LLC—See J&J Snack Foods Corporation; *U.S. Public*, pg. 1179
FEDERAL PRISON INDUSTRIES INC.; *U.S. Private*, pg. 1489
FEDERAL PROCESS CORPORATION; *U.S. Private*, pg. 1489
FEDERAL PUMP CORP.—See Bain Capital, LP; *U.S. Private*, pg. 432
FEDERAL REALTY INVESTMENT TRUST; *U.S. Public*, pg. 825
FEDERAL RESERVE BANK KANSAS CITY; *U.S. Private*, pg. 1489
FEDERAL RESERVE BANK OF ATLANTA; *U.S. Private*, pg. 1489
FEDERAL RESERVE BANK OF BOSTON; *U.S. Private*, pg. 1490
FEDERAL RESERVE BANK OF CHICAGO; *U.S. Private*, pg. 1490
FEDERAL RESERVE BANK OF CLEVELAND; *U.S. Private*, pg. 1490
FEDERAL RESERVE BANK OF DALLAS, HOUSTON BRANCH—See Federal Reserve Bank of Dallas; *U.S. Private*, pg. 1490
FEDERAL RESERVE BANK OF DALLAS; *U.S. Private*, pg. 1490
FEDERAL RESERVE BANK OF MINNEAPOLIS; *U.S. Private*, pg. 1490
FEDERAL RESERVE BANK OF NEW YORK; *U.S. Private*, pg. 1490
FEDERAL RESERVE BANK OF PHILADELPHIA; *U.S. Private*, pg. 1491
FEDERAL RESERVE BANK OF RICHMOND; *U.S. Private*, pg. 1491
FEDERAL RESERVE BANK OF ST. LOUIS; *U.S. Private*, pg. 1491
FEDERAL RESERVE BANK-SAN ANTONIO—See Federal Reserve Bank of Dallas; *U.S. Private*, pg. 1490
FEDERAL RESERVE—See Federal Reserve Bank of Dallas; *U.S. Private*, pg. 1490
FEDERAL RESOURCES SERVICES PTE LTD—See Federal International (2000) Ltd; *Int'l*, pg. 2630
FEDERAL RESOURCES SUPPLY COMPANY—See KLH Capital L.P.; *U.S. Private*, pg. 2319
FEDERAL SCREW WORKS-BIG RAPIDS DIV.—See Federal Screw Works; *U.S. Public*, pg. 826
FEDERAL SCREW WORKS ROMULUS DIVISION—See Federal Screw Works; *U.S. Public*, pg. 826
FEDERAL SCREW WORKS; *U.S. Public*, pg. 826
FEDERAL SIGNAL CORPORATION; *U.S. Public*, pg. 826
FEDERAL SIGNAL CREDIT CORPORATION—See Federal Signal Corporation; *U.S. Public*, pg. 826
FEDERAL SIGNAL ENVIRONMENTAL SOLUTIONS GROUP—See Federal Signal Corporation; *U.S. Public*, pg. 826
FEDERAL SIGNAL SAFETY & SECURITY SYSTEMS GROUP—See Federal Signal Corporation; *U.S. Public*, pg. 826
FEDERAL SIGNAL VAMA, S.A.—See Federal Signal Corporation; *U.S. Public*, pg. 826
FEDERAL SOLUTIONS GROUP LLC—See Vornado Realty Trust; *U.S. Public*, pg. 2309
FEDERAL STAFFING RESOURCES, LLC; *U.S. Private*, pg. 1491
FEDERAL STEEL SUPPLY INC.—See Vergani & Associates, LLC; *U.S. Private*, pg. 4359
FEDERAL STREET ACQUISITION CORP.—See Thomas H. Lee Partners, L.P.; *U.S. Private*, pg. 4156
FEDERAL STREET ADVISORS, INC.—See Lovell Minnick Partners LLC; *U.S. Private*, pg. 2503
FEDERAL TIRE (JIANGXI) CO., LTD.—See Federal Corporation; *Int'l*, pg. 2630
FEDERAL TRANSPORT, INC.—See Greif Inc.; *U.S. Public*, pg. 966
FEDERAL WAREHOUSE COMPANY; *U.S. Private*, pg. 1491
FEDERAL WHITE CEMENT, LTD.; *Int'l*, pg. 2630
FEDERAL WINE & LIQUOR COMPANY INC.—See Fedway Associates Inc.; *U.S. Private*, pg. 1492
FEDERATED AGENCIES LIMITED—See The Co-operators Group Limited; *Int'l*, pg. 7634
FEDERATED CO-OPERATIVES LIMITED - CALGARY FEED PLANT—See Federated Co-operatives Limited; *Int'l*, pg. 2631
FEDERATED CO-OPERATIVES LIMITED - EDMONTON FEED PLANT—See Federated Co-operatives Limited; *Int'l*, pg. 2631
FEDERATED CO-OPERATIVES LIMITED - MOOSOMIN FEED PLANT—See Federated Co-operatives Limited; *Int'l*, pg. 2631
FEDERATED CO-OPERATIVES LIMITED - SASKATOON FEED PLANT—See Federated Co-operatives Limited; *Int'l*, pg. 2631
FEDERATED CO-OPERATIVES LIMITED; *Int'l*, pg. 2630
FEDERATED EQUITY MANAGEMENT COMPANY OF PENNSYLVANIA—See Federated Hermes, Inc.; *U.S. Public*, pg. 827
THE FEDERATED GROUP, INC.; *U.S. Private*, pg. 4028
FEDERATED HEALTHCARE SUPPLY HOLDINGS, INC.; *U.S. Private*, pg. 1491

FEDERATED HEALTHCARE SUPPLY HOLDINGS, INC. CORPORATE AFFILIATIONS

FEDERATED HEALTHCARE SUPPLY, INC.—See Federated Healthcare Supply Holdings, Inc.; *U.S. Private*, pg. 1491
FEDERATED HERMES, INC.; *U.S. Public*, pg. 827
FEDERATED HERMES LIMITED—See Federated Hermes, Inc.; *U.S. Public*, pg. 827
FEDERATED HERMES PREMIER MUNICIPAL INCOME FUND; *U.S. Public*, pg. 827
FEDERATED HERMES (UK) LLP—See Federated Hermes, Inc.; *U.S. Public*, pg. 827
FEDERATED INSURANCE COMPANY OF CANADA—See Fairfax Financial Holdings Limited; *Int'l*, pg. 2607
FEDERATED INTERACTIVE LLC—See Federated Media Inc.; *U.S. Private*, pg. 1491
FEDERATED IT, INC.; *U.S. Private*, pg. 1491
FEDERATED LINEN & UNIFORM SERVICES; *U.S. Private*, pg. 1491
FEDERATED MDTA LLC—See Federated Hermes, Inc.; *U.S. Public*, pg. 827
FEDERATED MEDIA INC.; *U.S. Private*, pg. 1491
FEDERATED MUTUAL INSURANCE COMPANY; *U.S. Private*, pg. 1492
FEDERATED NATIONAL INSURANCE COMPANY—See FedNat Holding Company; *U.S. Public*, pg. 828
FEDERATED PAYMENT CANADA CORPORATION—See Global Payments Inc.; *U.S. Public*, pg. 943
FEDERATED PAYMENT SYSTEMS LLC—See Global Payments Inc.; *U.S. Public*, pg. 943
FEDERATED PUBLICATIONS, INC.—See Gannett Co., Inc.; *U.S. Public*, pg. 897
FEDERATED SECURITIES CORP.—See Federated Hermes, Inc.; *U.S. Public*, pg. 827
FEDERATION ASSET MANAGEMENT PTY. LTD.; *Int'l*, pg. 2631
FEDERATION INTERNATIONALE DE FOOTBALL ASSOCIATION; *Int'l*, pg. 2631
FEDERATION NATIONALE DES BANQUES POPULAIRES—See Groupe BPCE; *Int'l*, pg. 3094
FEDERATION NATIONALE DES CAISSES D'EPARGNE—See Groupe BPCE; *Int'l*, pg. 3097
FEDERATION OF AMERICAN SOCIETIES FOR EXPERIMENTAL BIOLOGY; *U.S. Private*, pg. 1492
THE FEDERATION OF MALAYSIAN MANUFACTURERS; *Int'l*, pg. 7642
THE FEDERATION OF MIGROS COOPERATIVES—See The Federation of Migros Cooperatives; *Int'l*, pg. 7643
THE FEDERATION OF MIGROS COOPERATIVES; *Int'l*, pg. 7642
FEDERATION OF ORGANIZATIONS; *U.S. Private*, pg. 1492
FEDERATION OF RESPONSIBLE CITIZENS, INC.; *U.S. Private*, pg. 1492
FEDERATION OF STATE BOARDS OF PHYSICAL THERAPY; *U.S. Private*, pg. 1492
FEDERATION SAHANALA VANILLE—See Archer-Daniels-Midland Company; *U.S. Public*, pg. 185
FEDERMAN, LALLY & REMIS LLC—See CBIZ, Inc.; *U.S. Public*, pg. 457
FEDERMANN ENTERPRISES, LTD.; *Int'l*, pg. 2631
FEDER'S SUBARU; *U.S. Private*, pg. 1487
FEDEX BRASIL LOGISTICA E TRANSPORTE S.A.—See FedEx Corporation; *U.S. Public*, pg. 827
FEDEX CORPORATE SERVICES, INC.—See FedEx Corporation; *U.S. Public*, pg. 827
FEDEX CORPORATION; *U.S. Public*, pg. 827
FEDEX CROSS BORDER—See FedEx Corporation; *U.S. Public*, pg. 827
FEDEX CROSS BORDER TECHNOLOGIES, INC.—See FedEx Corporation; *U.S. Public*, pg. 827
FEDEX CUSTOM CRITICAL, INC.—See FedEx Corporation; *U.S. Public*, pg. 827
FEDEX CUSTOMER INFORMATION SERVICES, INC.—See FedEx Corporation; *U.S. Public*, pg. 827
FEDEX EXPRESS GERMANY GMBH—See FedEx Corporation; *U.S. Public*, pg. 827
FEDEX EXPRESS GREECE SINGLE MEMBER L.L.C.—See FedEx Corporation; *U.S. Public*, pg. 827
FEDEX EXPRESS SVERIGE AB—See FedEx Corporation; *U.S. Public*, pg. 827
FEDEX EXPRESS TRANSPORTATION & SUPPLY CHAIN SERVICES (INDIA) PVT. LTD.—See FedEx Corporation; *U.S. Public*, pg. 827
FEDEX FREIGHT CANADA CORP.—See FedEx Corporation; *U.S. Public*, pg. 827
FEDEX FREIGHT CORPORATION—See FedEx Corporation; *U.S. Public*, pg. 827
FEDEX FREIGHT, INC.—See FedEx Corporation; *U.S. Public*, pg. 828
FEDEX GROUND PACKAGE SYSTEM, INC.—See FedEx Corporation; *U.S. Public*, pg. 828
FEDEX KINKO'S CANADA LIMITED—See FedEx Corporation; *U.S. Public*, pg. 827
FEDEX OFFICE & PRINT SERVICES, INC.—See FedEx Corporation; *U.S. Public*, pg. 827
FEDEX SMARTPOST, INC.—See FedEx Corporation; *U.S. Public*, pg. 828
FEDEX SUPPLY CHAIN DISTRIBUTION SYSTEM, INC.—See FedEx Corporation; *U.S. Public*, pg. 828

FEDEX SUPPLYCHAIN SYSTEMS, INC.—See FedEx Corporation; *U.S. Public*, pg. 828
FEDEX TRADE NETWORKS, INC.—See FedEx Corporation; *U.S. Public*, pg. 828
FEDEX TRADE NETWORKS—See FedEx Corporation; *U.S. Public*, pg. 828
FEDEX TRADE NETWORKS TRADE SERVICES, INC.—See FedEx Corporation; *U.S. Public*, pg. 828
FEDEX TRADE NETWORKS TRANSPORT & BROKERAGE (CANADA), INC—See FedEx Corporation; *U.S. Public*, pg. 828
FEDEX TRADE NETWORKS TRANSPORT & BROKERAGE (HONG KONG) LIMITED—See FedEx Corporation; *U.S. Public*, pg. 828
FEDEX TRADE NETWORKS TRANSPORT & BROKERAGE, INC.—See FedEx Corporation; *U.S. Public*, pg. 828
FEDEX UK LIMITED—See FedEx Corporation; *U.S. Public*, pg. 828
FEDIMMO S.A.—See Befimmo SCA; *Int'l*, pg. 940
FEDMET INTERNATIONAL CORPORATION—See Russel Metals Inc.; *Int'l*, pg. 6430
FEDMET TUBULARS—See Russel Metals Inc.; *Int'l*, pg. 6430
FEDMINE LLC—See Endicott Group Equity Partners, L.P.; *U.S. Private*, pg. 1391
FEDMINE LLC—See Thompson Street Capital Manager LLC; *U.S. Private*, pg. 4161
FEDNAT HOLDING COMPANY; *U.S. Public*, pg. 828
FEDNAT UNDERWRITERS, INC.—See FedNat Holding Company; *U.S. Public*, pg. 828
FEDNAV ASIA LTD.—See Fednav Limited; *Int'l*, pg. 2631
FEDNAV (BELGIUM) N.V.—See Fednav Limited; *Int'l*, pg. 2631
FEDNAV BRASIL AGENCIA MARITIMA LTDA—See Fednav Limited; *Int'l*, pg. 2631
FEDNAV EUROPE LIMITED—See Fednav Limited; *Int'l*, pg. 2631
FEDNAV (HAMBURG) GMBH—See Fednav Limited; *Int'l*, pg. 2631
FEDNAV INTERNATIONAL LTD.—See Fednav Limited; *Int'l*, pg. 2631
FEDNAV LIMITED; *Int'l*, pg. 2631
FEDNAV SINGAPORE PTE. LTD.—See Fednav Limited; *Int'l*, pg. 2631
FEDON AMERICA, INC—See EssilorLuxottica SA; *Int'l*, pg. 2515
FEDON FAR EAST LIMITED—See EssilorLuxottica SA; *Int'l*, pg. 2515
FEDRIGONI SPA; *Int'l*, pg. 2631
FEDRUS INTERNATIONAL NV; *Int'l*, pg. 2631
FEDSTORE CORPORATION; *U.S. Private*, pg. 1492
FEDTECH SERVICES, INC.; *U.S. Private*, pg. 1492
FEDVAR CORP.; *U.S. Private*, pg. 1492
FEDWAY ASSOCIATES INC.; *U.S. Private*, pg. 1492
FEECE OIL COMPANY; *U.S. Private*, pg. 1492
FEECO INTERNATIONAL INC.; *U.S. Private*, pg. 1492
F.E.E. CO., LTD.—See Kyokuto Kaihatsu Kogyo Co. Ltd.; *Int'l*, pg. 4363
FEECORP CORPORATION; *U.S. Private*, pg. 1492
FEED ADDITION CO., LTD.—See Thai Beverage Public Company Limited; *Int'l*, pg. 7589
FEED AMERICA FIRST; *U.S. Private*, pg. 1492
FEEDBACK EDUCATION, INC.—See Aurelius Equity Opportunities SE & Co. KGaA; *Int'l*, pg. 709
FEEDBACK/HILL & KNOWLTON—See WPP plc; *Int'l*, pg. 8477
FEEDBACK INSTRUMENTS LIMITED—See Aurelius Equity Opportunities SE & Co. KGaA; *Int'l*, pg. 709
FEEDBACK MEDICAL LIMITED—See Feedback plc; *Int'l*, pg. 2632
FEEDBACK PLC; *Int'l*, pg. 2631
FEED DYNAMIX GMBH—See Equistone Partners Europe Limited; *Int'l*, pg. 2487
FEEDERLINK B.V.—See Irish Continental Group plc; *Int'l*, pg. 3809
FEEDER SHIPPING AGENCY CO., LTD.—See Regional Container Lines Public Company Limited; *Int'l*, pg. 6254
FEEDERS SUPPLY COMPANY INC.—See Houchens Industries, Inc.; *U.S. Private*, pg. 1990
FEEDEX NUTRITION—See Agricola Group Ltd; *Int'l*, pg. 216
FEEDFORCE GROUP, INC.; *Int'l*, pg. 2632
FEEDHENRY (IRELAND) LIMITED—See International Business Machines Corporation; *U.S. Public*, pg. 1150
FEEDHENRY LLC—See International Business Machines Corporation; *U.S. Public*, pg. 1150
FEEDHENRY LTD.—See International Business Machines Corporation; *U.S. Public*, pg. 1150
FEED INGREDIENT TRADING CORP.; *U.S. Private*, pg. 1492
FEEDING SOUTH FLORIDA; *U.S. Private*, pg. 1492
FEEDMAX CORP.—See Paterson GlobalFoods Inc.; *Int'l*, pg. 5756
FEED ONE CO., LTD.; *Int'l*, pg. 2631
FEED PRODUCTS SOUTH INC.; *U.S. Private*, pg. 1492
FEEDR LIMITED—See Compass Group PLC; *Int'l*, pg. 1752

FEEDSTUFFS PROCESSING CO. INC.; *U.S. Private*, pg. 1493
FEED THE CHILDREN, INC.; *U.S. Private*, pg. 1492
FEEI CHERNG DEVELOP TECHNOLOGY CO., LTD.; *Int'l*, pg. 2632
FEE INVESTMENT MANAGEMENT & CONSULTANCY (SHANGHAI) CO., LTD.—See Federal International (2000) Ltd; *Int'l*, pg. 2630
FEELER HARDWARE INDUSTRIAL CORPORATION—See Fair Friend Group; *Int'l*, pg. 2604
FEELGOOD SVENSKA AB; *Int'l*, pg. 2632
FEELGOODZ, LLC; *U.S. Private*, pg. 1493
FEELUX CO., LTD.; *Int'l*, pg. 2632
FEELUX LIGHTING CO., LTD.—See FEELUX Co., Ltd.; *Int'l*, pg. 2632
FEELUX LIGHTING, INC.—See FEELUX Co., Ltd.; *Int'l*, pg. 2632
FEENEY BROTHERS EXCAVATION LLC; *U.S. Private*, pg. 1493
FEENSTRA ISOLATIE B.V.—See Vattenfall AB; *Int'l*, pg. 8136
FEENSTRA N.V.—See Vattenfall AB; *Int'l*, pg. 8136
FEENSTRA VERWARMING B.V.—See Vattenfall AB; *Int'l*, pg. 8136
FEERUM S.A.; *Int'l*, pg. 2632
FEGA POLAND SP. Z O.O.—See Wurth Verwaltungsgesellschaft mbH; *Int'l*, pg. 8504
FEGA & SCHMITT ELEKTROGROSSHANDEL GMBH—See Wurth Verwaltungsgesellschaft mbH; *Int'l*, pg. 8504
F.E.G. DE QUERETARO S.A. DE C.V—See F-Tech Inc.; *Int'l*, pg. 2595
FE-GROUP INVEST ZRT.—See MOL Magyar Olaj- es Gazipari Nyrt.; *Int'l*, pg. 5019
FEHA LASERTEC HALLE GMBH; *Int'l*, pg. 2632
F.E. HALE MANUFACTURING COMPANY; *U.S. Private*, pg. 1456
FEHBERGER STAHLBAU GMBH—See PORR AG; *Int'l*, pg. 5922
FEHR BROS INDUSTRIES INC.; *U.S. Private*, pg. 1493
FEHRMAN TOOL & DIE INC.—See The Velocity Group, Inc.; *U.S. Private*, pg. 4130
FEI ASIA PACIFIC CO., LTD—See Thermo Fisher Scientific Inc.; *U.S. Public*, pg. 2146
FEI AUSTRALIA PTY LTD.—See Thermo Fisher Scientific Inc.; *U.S. Public*, pg. 2147
FEIBRA GMBH—See Osterreichische Post AG; *Int'l*, pg. 5653
FEIBRA MAGYARORSZAG KFT—See Osterreichische Post AG; *Int'l*, pg. 5653
FEI COMMUNICATIONS, INC.—See Frequency Electronics, Inc.; *U.S. Public*, pg. 885
FEI COMPANY JAPAN LTD.—See Thermo Fisher Scientific Inc.; *U.S. Public*, pg. 2146
FEI COMPANY OF USA (S.E.A.) PTE. LTD.—See Thermo Fisher Scientific Inc.; *U.S. Public*, pg. 2146
FEI COMPANY—See Thermo Fisher Scientific Inc.; *U.S. Public*, pg. 2146
FEI CPD B.V.—See Thermo Fisher Scientific Inc.; *U.S. Public*, pg. 2146
FEI CZECH REPUBLIC S.R.O.—See Thermo Fisher Scientific Inc.; *U.S. Public*, pg. 2146
FEI DEUTSCHLAND GMBH—See Thermo Fisher Scientific Inc.; *U.S. Public*, pg. 2146
FEIDONG GOTION NEW MATERIAL CO., LTD.—See Gotion High-tech Co., Ltd.; *Int'l*, pg. 3044
FEI EFA, INC.—See Thermo Fisher Scientific Inc.; *U.S. Public*, pg. 2146
FEI-ELCOM TECH, INC.—See Frequency Electronics, Inc.; *U.S. Public*, pg. 885
FEI ELECTRON OPTICS INTERNATIONAL B.V.—See Thermo Fisher Scientific Inc.; *U.S. Public*, pg. 2147
FEI FOODS LTD—See Marbour SAS; *Int'l*, pg. 4688
FEI FRANCE SAS—See Thermo Fisher Scientific Inc.; *U.S. Public*, pg. 2147
FEI FREMONT—See Thermo Fisher Scientific Inc.; *U.S. Public*, pg. 2147
FEIGE INTELLIGENT TECHNOLOGY CO., LTD.—See Great Wall Motor Company Limited; *Int'l*, pg. 3066
FEIGHNER INSURANCE INC.; *U.S. Private*, pg. 1493
FEI GLOBAL HOLDINGS C.V.—See Thermo Fisher Scientific Inc.; *U.S. Public*, pg. 2147
FEI GOVERNMENT SYSTEMS, INC.—See Frequency Electronics, Inc.; *U.S. Public*, pg. 885
FEI GROUP—See CCA Global Partners, Inc.; *U.S. Private*, pg. 799
FEIHE INTERNATIONAL, INC.; *Int'l*, pg. 2632
FEI HOUSTON, INC.—See Thermo Fisher Scientific Inc.; *U.S. Public*, pg. 2147
FEI, INC; *U.S. Private*, pg. 1493
FEI ITALIA S.R.L.—See Thermo Fisher Scientific Inc.; *U.S. Public*, pg. 2147
FEI KOREA LTD.—See Thermo Fisher Scientific Inc.; *U.S. Public*, pg. 2147
FEILONG AUTO COMPONENTS CO., LTD.; *Int'l*, pg. 2632
FEIMA LTD—See Orange S.A.; *Int'l*, pg. 5608
FE (INDIA) LIMITED; *Int'l*, pg. 2629

COMPANY NAME INDEX

FEINIU E-COMMERCE HONG KONG LIMITED—See Alibaba Group Holding Limited; *Int'l*, pg. 326
FEINKOST DITTMANN REICHOLD FEINKOST GMBH; *Int'l*, pg. 2632
FEINMECHANIK MICHAEL DECKEL GMBH & CO. KG.; *Int'l*, pg. 2632
FEI NORWAY HOLDING AS—See Thermo Fisher Scientific Inc.; *U.S. Public*, pg. 2147
FEINSTEIN KEAN HEALTHCARE—See WPP plc; *Int'l*, pg. 8483
FEINSTEIN KEAN HEALTHCARE—See WPP plc; *Int'l*, pg. 8484
FEINTECHNIK GMBH—See ADKM, Inc.; *U.S. Private*, pg. 80
FEINTOOL AUTOMOTIVE SYSTEM PARTS (TIANJIN) CO., LTD.—See Artemis Holding AG; *Int'l*, pg. 582
FEINTOOL BEIJING SWISSTEC—See Artemis Holding AG; *Int'l*, pg. 582
FEINTOOL CINCINNATI, INC.—See Artemis Holding AG; *Int'l*, pg. 582
FEINTOOL EQUIPMENT CORP.—See Artemis Holding AG; *Int'l*, pg. 582
FEINTOOL FRANCE S.A.R.L.—See Artemis Holding AG; *Int'l*, pg. 582
FEINTOOL INTERNATIONAL HOLDING AG—See Artemis Holding AG; *Int'l*, pg. 582
FEINTOOL INTERNATIONAL MANAGEMENT LTD.—See Artemis Holding AG; *Int'l*, pg. 582
FEINTOOL ITALIA S.R.L.—See Artemis Holding AG; *Int'l*, pg. 582
FEINTOOL JAPAN CO., LTD.—See Artemis Holding AG; *Int'l*, pg. 582
FEINTOOL PARTS & COMPONENTS LTD.—See Artemis Holding AG; *Int'l*, pg. 582
FEINTOOL RESEARCH & DEVELOPMENT AG—See Artemis Holding AG; *Int'l*, pg. 582
FEINTOOL SYSTEM PARTS AG—See Artemis Holding AG; *Int'l*, pg. 582
FEINTOOL SYSTEM PARTS ETTLINGEN GMBH—See Artemis Holding AG; *Int'l*, pg. 582
FEINTOOL SYSTEM PARTS JENA GMBH—See Artemis Holding AG; *Int'l*, pg. 582
FEINTOOL TECHNOLOGY AG—See Certina Holding AG; *Int'l*, pg. 1423
FEINTOOL TEILE & KOMPONENTEN AG—See Artemis Holding AG; *Int'l*, pg. 582
FEINTOOL TENNESSEE, INC.—See Artemis Holding AG; *Int'l*, pg. 582
FEINTUCH COMMUNICATIONS, INC.—See Roher Public Relations; *U.S. Private*, pg. 3473
FE INVESTMENT CO., LTD.—See Kyokuto Securities Co., Ltd.; *Int'l*, pg. 4363
FE INVESTMENTS LIMITED; *Int'l*, pg. 2629
FEIRA NOVA-HIPERMERCADOS, S.A.—See Jeronimo Martins SGPS SA; *Int'l*, pg. 3931
FEI SANTA BARBARA—See Thermo Fisher Scientific Inc.; *U.S. Public*, pg. 2147
FEI SAS—See Thermo Fisher Scientific Inc.; *U.S. Public*, pg. 2147
FEI SHALE L.P.—See Repsol, S.A.; *Int'l*, pg. 6293
FEISHANG ANTHRACITE RESOURCES LIMITED; *Int'l*, pg. 2632
FEISHANG MINING HOLDING LIMITED—See China Natural Resources, Inc.; *Int'l*, pg. 1534
FEI TECHNOLOGY DE MEXICO S.A. DE C.V.—See Thermo Fisher Scientific Inc.; *U.S. Public*, pg. 2147
FEITIAN TECHNOLOGIES CO., LTD.; *Int'l*, pg. 2632
FEITIAN TECHNOLOGIES US,INC.—See Feitian Technologies Co., Ltd.; *Int'l*, pg. 2632
FEIT MANAGEMENT COMPANY; *U.S. Private*, pg. 1493
FEI TRONDHEIM AS—See Thermo Fisher Scientific Inc.; *U.S. Public*, pg. 2147
FEI UK LTD.—See Thermo Fisher Scientific Inc.; *U.S. Public*, pg. 2147
FEIYANG INTERNATIONAL HOLDINGS GROUP LIMITED; *Int'l*, pg. 2632
FEIYU TECHNOLOGY INTERNATIONAL COMPANY LTD.; *Int'l*, pg. 2632
FEI-ZYFER, INC.—See Frequency Electronics, Inc.; *U.S. Public*, pg. 885
FEIZY IMPORT & EXPORT COMPANY INC.; *U.S. Private*, pg. 1493
FE JONES (BUILDERS) LIMITED—See Emerson Developments (Holdings) Limited; *Int'l*, pg. 2379
FEK COMPANY LTD.—See Komax Holding AG; *Int'l*, pg. 4240
FEKKAI BRANDS, LLC—See LUXE Brands, Inc.; *U.S. Private*, pg. 2518
FEKKAI BRANDS, LLC—See SA Designer Parfums Ltd.; *Int'l*, pg. 6458
FELDA GLOBAL VENTURES PERLIS SDN BHD—See FGV Holdings Bhd; *Int'l*, pg. 2649
FELDA HOLDINGS BHD.—See FGV Holdings Bhd; *Int'l*, pg. 2649
FELDA PROPERTIES SDN. BHD.—See FGV Holdings Bhd; *Int'l*, pg. 2649
FELDA TRAVEL SDN. BHD.—See FGV Holdings Bhd; *Int'l*, pg. 2649
FELD ENTERTAINMENT, INC.; *U.S. Private*, pg. 1493

FELDER COMMUNICATIONS GROUP; *U.S. Private*, pg. 1493
FELDER GMBH; *Int'l*, pg. 2632
FELDERS CONSTRUCTION, LLC; *U.S. Private*, pg. 1493
FELDMANN IMPORTS MERCEDES-BENZ; *U.S. Private*, pg. 1493
FELDMAN WOOD PRODUCTS CO. INC.; *U.S. Private*, pg. 1493
FELDMEIER EQUIPMENT, INC.; *U.S. Private*, pg. 1493
FELD MOTOR SPORTS, INC.—See Feld Entertainment, Inc.; *U.S. Private*, pg. 1493
FELDMUEHLE GMBH—See Kairos Industries AG; *Int'l*, pg. 4052
FELDSCHLOSSCHEN BEVERAGES HOLDING LTD.—See Carlsberg A/S; *Int'l*, pg. 1340
FELDSCHLOSSCHEN BEVERAGES LTD.—See Carlsberg A/S; *Int'l*, pg. 1340
FELDSCHLOSSCHEN GETRANKE HOLDING AG—See Carlsberg A/S; *Int'l*, pg. 1340
FELGTEKNIKK NORGE AS—See Bilia AB; *Int'l*, pg. 1029
FELGUERA CALDERERIA PESADA, S.A.U.—See Duro Felguera, S.A.; *Int'l*, pg. 2228
FELGUERA GRUAS INDIA PRIVATE LIMITED—See Duro Felguera, S.A.; *Int'l*, pg. 2228
FELGUERA-IHI S.A.—See Duro Felguera, S.A.; *Int'l*, pg. 2229
FELGUERA-IHI S.A.—See IHI Corporation; *Int'l*, pg. 3604
FELGUERA RAIL, S.A.U.—See Duro Felguera, S.A.; *Int'l*, pg. 2229
FELICA NETWORKS, INC—See Sony Group Corporation; *Int'l*, pg. 7102
FELICA POCKET MARKETING INC.—See AEON Co., Ltd.; *Int'l*, pg. 177
FELICIANA BANK & TRUST COMPANY; *U.S. Public*, pg. 829
FELICIANA HOME HEALTH—See UnitedHealth Group Incorporated; *U.S. Public*, pg. 2245
FELICIANA HOME HEALTH SOUTH—See UnitedHealth Group Incorporated; *U.S. Public*, pg. 2245
FELICIANA PHYSICAL THERAPY SERVICES, LLC—See UnitedHealth Group Incorporated; *U.S. Public*, pg. 2245
FELICITY SCIENTIFIC CO., LTD.—See FEV GmbH; *Int'l*, pg. 2648
FELISON ASSURADEUREN B.V.—See ASR Nederland N.V.; *Int'l*, pg. 632
FELISSIMO CORPORATION; *Int'l*, pg. 2632
FELIX ABBA LAHDEN TEHDAS—See Orkla ASA; *Int'l*, pg. 5637
FELIX AUSTRIA GMBH—See Orkla ASA; *Int'l*, pg. 5637
FELIX CHEVROLET-CADILLAC; *U.S. Private*, pg. 1493
FELIX CONSTRUCTIONS SA—See FAYAT SAS; *Int'l*, pg. 2625
FELIX GLOBAL CORP.; *Int'l*, pg. 2632
FELIX GMBH & CO. KG—See Intersnack Group GmbH & Co. KG; *Int'l*, pg. 3760
FELIX GOLD LIMITED; *Int'l*, pg. 2633
FELIX GROUP HOLDINGS LIMITED; *Int'l*, pg. 2633
FELIX HOLTKEN GMBH—See Asterion Industrial Partners SGEIC SA; *Int'l*, pg. 654
FELIX INDUSTRIES LIMITED; *Int'l*, pg. 2633
FELIX KOCH OFFENBACH COULEUR UND KARAMEL GMBH; *Int'l*, pg. 2633
FELIX MEDIA SOLUTIONS, INC.; *U.S. Private*, pg. 1493
FELIX SCHOELLER HOLDING GMBH & CO. KG; *Int'l*, pg. 2633
FELIX SCHOELLER JR SHANGHAI—See Felix Schoeller Holding GmbH & Co. KG; *Int'l*, pg. 2633
FELIX SCHOELLER NORTH AMERICA—See Felix Schoeller Holding GmbH & Co. KG; *Int'l*, pg. 2633
FELIX SCHOELLER SUPPLY CHAIN TECHNOLOGIES GMBH & CO. KG—See Felix Schoeller Holding GmbH & Co. KG; *Int'l*, pg. 2633
FELIX SCHUH DAMMTECHNIK GMBH—See VINCI S.A.; *Int'l*, pg. 8238
FELKER BROTHERS CORPORATION - GLASGOW MANUFACTURING FACILITY—See Felker Brothers Corporation; *U.S. Private*, pg. 1493
FELKER BROTHERS CORPORATION - MARSHFIELD MANUFACTURING FACILITY—See Felker Brothers Corporation; *U.S. Private*, pg. 1493
FELKER BROTHERS CORPORATION; *U.S. Private*, pg. 1493
FELLAZO CORP.; *Int'l*, pg. 2633
FELLAZO INC.; *Int'l*, pg. 2633
FE LLC CAMOZZI AUTOMATION—See Camozzi Group; *Int'l*, pg. 1274
FELLER AG—See Schneider Electric SE; *Int'l*, pg. 6627
FELLERS, INC.; *U.S. Private*, pg. 1494
FELLESKJOPET AGRI SA; *Int'l*, pg. 2633
FELLFAB CORPORATION—See FELLFAB Limited; *Int'l*, pg. 2633
FELLFAB LIMITED; *Int'l*, pg. 2633
FELLING TRAILERS, INC.; *U.S. Private*, pg. 1494
FELLO AB—See Telia Company AB; *Int'l*, pg. 7543
FELLON-MCCORD & ASSOCIATES, LLC—See Trane Technologies Plc; *Int'l*, pg. 7891
FELLOWES (AUSTRALIA) PTY LTD—See Fellowes, Inc.; *U.S. Private*, pg. 1494

FEMCO HOLDINGS, LLC

FELLOWES BENELUX B.V.—See Fellowes, Inc.; *U.S. Private*, pg. 1494
FELLOWES CANADA LTD.—See Fellowes, Inc.; *U.S. Private*, pg. 1494
FELLOWES GERMANY GMBH—See Fellowes, Inc.; *U.S. Private*, pg. 1494
FELLOWES HI-Q MALAYSIA SDN BHD.—See Fellowes, Inc.; *U.S. Private*, pg. 1494
FELLOWES HI-Q SINGAPORE PTE LTD.—See Fellowes, Inc.; *U.S. Private*, pg. 1494
FELLOWES IBERICA S.L.—See Fellowes, Inc.; *U.S. Private*, pg. 1494
FELLOWES, INC.; *U.S. Private*, pg. 1494
FELLOWES JAPAN K.K.—See Fellowes, Inc.; *U.S. Private*, pg. 1494
FELLOWES LEONARDI S.P.A—See Fellowes, Inc.; *U.S. Private*, pg. 1494
FELLOWES RU LTD—See Fellowes, Inc.; *U.S. Private*, pg. 1494
FELLOWES UNITED KINGDOM LTD.—See Fellowes, Inc.; *U.S. Private*, pg. 1494
FELLOW FINANCE PLC—See Evli Pankki Oyj; *Int'l*, pg. 2570
FELLOW HEALTH PARTNERS, INC.; *U.S. Private*, pg. 1494
FELLOWSHIP FOUNDATION; *U.S. Private*, pg. 1494
THE FELLOWSHIP HOUSE—See Centerstone of America, Inc.; *U.S. Private*, pg. 817
FELLOWSHIP SENIOR LIVING; *U.S. Private*, pg. 1494
FELLS POINT WHOLESALE MEATS, INC.—See The Chefs' Warehouse, Inc.; *U.S. Public*, pg. 2059
FELMLEY-DICKERSON CO.; *U.S. Private*, pg. 1494
FELO-WERKZEUGFABRIK HOLLAND-LETZ GMBH—See Wurth Verwaltungsgesellschaft mbH; *Int'l*, pg. 8504
FELS BAKU LTD.—See Sembcorp Industries Ltd.; *Int'l*, pg. 6703
FELS HOLDING GMBH—See SigmaRoc Plc; *Int'l*, pg. 6909
FELSINEA FACTOR S.P.A.—See Societa Esercizi Commerciali Industriali; *Int'l*, pg. 7034
FELS OFFSHORE PTE LTD—See Sembcorp Industries Ltd.; *Int'l*, pg. 6703
FELS PROPERTY HOLDINGS PTE LTD—See Keppel Corporation Limited; *Int'l*, pg. 4130
FELSTED PRODUCTS LLC—See Orscheln Group; *U.S. Private*, pg. 3045
FELS VERTRIEBS UND SERVICE GMBH & CO. KG.—See SigmaRoc Plc; *Int'l*, pg. 6909
FELS-WERKE GMBH—See SigmaRoc Plc; *Int'l*, pg. 6909
FELT AUTO PARTS COMPANY—See National Auto Parts Warehouse, LLC; *U.S. Private*, pg. 2847
THE FELTERS GROUP; *U.S. Private*, pg. 4028
FELTERS OF SC, LLC—See The Felters Group; *U.S. Private*, pg. 4028
FELTEX AUTOMOTIVE (PTY) LTD. - FELTEX FOAM—See Steinhoff International Holdings N.V.; *Int'l*, pg. 7194
FELTEX AUTOMOTIVE (PTY) LTD.—See Steinhoff International Holdings N.V.; *Int'l*, pg. 7194
FELTEX AUTOMOTIVE TRIM LTD—See Steinhoff International Holdings N.V.; *Int'l*, pg. 7194
FELTEX CARPETS LTD.—See Mohawk Industries, Inc.; *U.S. Public*, pg. 1457
FELTEX CARPETS PTY. LTD.—See Mohawk Industries, Inc.; *U.S. Public*, pg. 1457
FELTEX FEHRER (PTY) LTD.—See Steinhoff International Holdings N.V.; *Int'l*, pg. 7194
FELTEX HOLDINGS (PTY) LTD. - UNITED FRAM FOOTWEAR—See Bolton Footwear (Pty) Ltd.; *Int'l*, pg. 1103
FELTEX HOLDINGS (PTY) LTD. - WAYNE PLASTICS—See Bolton Footwear (Pty) Ltd.; *Int'l*, pg. 1103
FELTON INC.; *U.S. Private*, pg. 1494
FELT PRODUCTS MANUFACTURING CO.—See Apollo Global Management, Inc.; *U.S. Public*, pg. 162
FELT PRODUCTS MFG. CO.—See Icahn Enterprises L.P.; *U.S. Public*, pg. 1084
FELT RACING, LLC—See Pierer Konzerngesellschaft mbH; *Int'l*, pg. 5862
FELUWA PUMPEN GMBH—See ARCA Regler GmbH; *Int'l*, pg. 540
FE-MA ENTERPRISES INC.; *U.S. Private*, pg. 1486
FE MAGNET WIRE (MALAYSIA) SDN. BHD.—See The Furukawa Electric Co., Ltd.; *Int'l*, pg. 7644
THE FEMALE HEALTH COMPANY LIMITED—See Veru Inc.; *U.S. Public*, pg. 2290
THE FEMALE HEALTH COMPANY (M) SDN BHD—See Veru Inc.; *U.S. Public*, pg. 2289
THE FEMALE HEALTH COMPANY (UK) PLC.—See Veru Inc.; *U.S. Public*, pg. 2290
FEMA S.R.L.—See Chart Industries, Inc.; *U.S. Public*, pg. 481
FEMASYS INC.; *U.S. Public*, pg. 829
FEMCARE AUSTRALIA LTD.—See Utah Medical Products, Inc.; *U.S. Public*, pg. 2267
FEMCARE GROUP LIMITED—See Utah Medical Products, Inc.; *U.S. Public*, pg. 2267
FEMCO HOLDINGS, LLC; *U.S. Private*, pg. 1494

FEMCO HOLDINGS, LLC

CORPORATE AFFILIATIONS

FEMCO MACHINE COMPANY—See Saugatuck Capital Company; *U.S. Private*, pg. 3554
FEM ELECTRIC ASSOCIATION, INC.; *U.S. Private*, pg. 1494
FEMI RINALDI S.P.A.—See Sonepar S.A.; *Int'l*, pg. 7092
F.E. MORAN SECURITY SOLUTIONS, LLC—See Securitas AB; *Int'l*, pg. 6675
F.E. MORAN—See Armon Inc.; *U.S. Private*, pg. 331
FEMPHARM PTY LTD—See Acrux Limited; *Int'l*, pg. 109
FEMPRO INC.—See First Quality Enterprises, Inc.; *U.S. Private*, pg. 1524
FEMSA COMERCIO, S.A. DE C.V.—See Fomento Economico Mexicano, S.A.B. de C.V.; *Int'l*, pg. 2724
FEMTEC HEALTH, INC.; *U.S. Private*, pg. 1494
FEM TECHNOLOGY CO., LTD.—See Korea Alcohol Industrial Co., Ltd.; *Int'l*, pg. 4282
FEMTOBIOMED INC.; *Int'l*, pg. 2633
FEMTO ENGINEERING S.R.L.—See LCI Industries; *U.S. Public*, pg. 1295
FEMTO GREEN HYDROGEN LIMITED—See Indo Thai Securities Ltd; *Int'l*, pg. 3657
FEMTO TECHNOLOGIES INC.; *Int'l*, pg. 2633
F.E. MYERS COMPANY—See Pentair plc; *Int'l*, pg. 5790
FENALU GESTAO DE INVESTIMENTOS E PARTICIPACOES SA; *Int'l*, pg. 2633
FENBI LTD.; *Int'l*, pg. 2633
FENBO HOLDINGS LIMITED; *Int'l*, pg. 2633
THE FENCE STORE; *U.S. Private*, pg. 4028
FENCE SUPPLY, INC.—See The Sterling Group, L.P.; *U.S. Private*, pg. 4123
FENCEWORKS INC.—See Gemspring Capital Management, LLC; *U.S. Private*, pg. 1658
FENCHURCH INSURANCE RISK MANAGEMENT LIMITED—See PSC Insurance Group Limited; *Int'l*, pg. 6016
FENCING AND GATES—See ARGENT INDUSTRIAL LIMITED; *Int'l*, pg. 560
FENDERCARE AUSTRALIA PTY LTD—See James Fisher & Sons Public Limited Company; *Int'l*, pg. 3875
FENDER CARE MARINE (ASIA PACIFIC) PTE LTD—See James Fisher & Sons Public Limited Company; *Int'l*, pg. 3875
FENDERCARE MARINE GHANA LIMITED—See James Fisher & Sons Public Limited Company; *Int'l*, pg. 3876
FENDERCARE MARINE LIMITED—See James Fisher & Sons Public Limited Company; *Int'l*, pg. 3875
FENDER CARE MARINE PRODUCTS (ASIA PACIFIC) PTE. LIMITED—See James Fisher & Sons Public Limited Company; *Int'l*, pg. 3875
FENDERCARE MARINE SOLUTIONS LTD—See James Fisher & Sons Public Limited Company; *Int'l*, pg. 3875
FENDERCARE NAVAL SOLUTIONS LTD—See James Fisher & Sons Public Limited Company; *Int'l*, pg. 3875
FENDER MUSICAL INSTRUMENTS CORPORATION—See TPG Capital, L.P.; *U.S. Public*, pg. 2173
FENDERS N'MORE, LLC—See Brookfield Corporation; *Int'l*, pg. 1176
FENDI ADELE S.R.L—See LVMH Moet Hennessy Louis Vuitton SE; *Int'l*, pg. 4592
FENDI DIS TICARET LSI—See LVMH Moet Hennessy Louis Vuitton SE; *Int'l*, pg. 4592
FENDI FRANCE SAS—See LVMH Moet Hennessy Louis Vuitton SE; *Int'l*, pg. 4601
FENDI GERMANY GMBH—See LVMH Moet Hennessy Louis Vuitton SE; *Int'l*, pg. 4601
FENDIGO S.A.—See SeQuent Scientific Limited; *Int'l*, pg. 6719
FENDI NORTH AMERICA INC—See LVMH Moet Hennessy Louis Vuitton SE; *Int'l*, pg. 4601
FENDI SILK SA—See LVMH Moet Hennessy Louis Vuitton SE; *Int'l*, pg. 4592
FENDI (SINGAPORE) PTE LTD—See LVMH Moet Hennessy Louis Vuitton SE; *Int'l*, pg. 4592
FENDI SRL—See LVMH Moet Hennessy Louis Vuitton SE; *Int'l*, pg. 4600
FENDI TAIWAN LTD—See LVMH Moet Hennessy Louis Vuitton SE; *Int'l*, pg. 4592
FENDRICH INDUSTRIES INC.; *U.S. Private*, pg. 1494
FENDT BUILDERS SUPPLY INC.; *U.S. Private*, pg. 1494
FENDX TECHNOLOGIES, INC.; *Int'l*, pg. 2633
FENERBAHCE FUTBOL ANONIM SIRKETI; *Int'l*, pg. 2633
FENES S.A.—See Cantoni Motor S.A.; *Int'l*, pg. 1299
FENG'AI (GUANGZHOU) AUTOMOTIVE SEAT PARTS CO., LTD.—See Toyota Boshoku Corporation; *Int'l*, pg. 7863
FENGATE CAPITAL MANAGEMENT LTD.; *Int'l*, pg. 2634
FENGCHENG SG AXLE SHAFT LLC—See Liaoning SG Automotive Group Co., Ltd.; *Int'l*, pg. 4483
FENG CHING METAL CORP.; *Int'l*, pg. 2633
FENG CHUAN TOOLING COMPANY LIMITED—See InnoTek Limited; *Int'l*, pg. 3710
FENG CHUAN TOOLING (DONGGUAN) CO. LTD.—See InnoTek Limited; *Int'l*, pg. 3710
FENGDA COMPANY LIMITED—See Atlantic China Welding Consumables, Inc.; *Int'l*, pg. 674
FENG HSIN STEEL CO., LTD.; *Int'l*, pg. 2634

FENGHUA ADVANCED TECHNOLOGY (HK) LTD—See Guangdong Fenghua Advanced Technology (Holding) Co., Ltd.; *Int'l*, pg. 3154
FENGQIFENG PRINTING TECHNOLOGY (SHANGHAI) CO., LTD.—See Longlide Intelligent Technology Co., Ltd.; *Int'l*, pg. 4551
FENGRAIN LTD.; *Int'l*, pg. 2634
FENG TAY ENTERPRISES CO., LTD.; *Int'l*, pg. 2634
FENGXIN GANFENG LITHIUM CO., LTD.—See Jiangxi Ganfeng Lithium Co., Ltd.; *Int'l*, pg. 3959
FENGXING CO., LTD.; *Int'l*, pg. 2634
FENHAMS LTD.—See Environ Group (Investments) plc; *Int'l*, pg. 2454
FENICE S.P.A.—See Electricite de France S.A.; *Int'l*, pg. 2351
FENICS FX, LLC—See BGC Group, Inc.; *U.S. Public*, pg. 328
FENICS MARKETS XCHANGE, LLC—See BGC Group, Inc.; *U.S. Public*, pg. 328
FENIE BROSSETTE; *Int'l*, pg. 2634
FENIKS D.O.O.—See Nova Ljubljanska banka d.d.; *Int'l*, pg. 5451
FENIKSS SLOTS SRL—See Novomatic AG; *Int'l*, pg. 5467
FENIX CONSTRUCTORS INC.; *U.S. Private*, pg. 1495
FENIX DIRECTO COMPANIA DE SEGUROS Y REASEGUROS S.A.—See Allianz SE; *Int'l*, pg. 343
FENIX ENTERTAINMENT S.P.A.; *Int'l*, pg. 2634
FENIX GOLD LIMITADA—See Rio2 Limited; *Int'l*, pg. 6348
FENIX INDUSTRIA DE ELETRONICOS LTDA.—See Hon Hai Precision Industry Co., Ltd.; *Int'l*, pg. 3456
FENIX MANUFACTURING SOLUTIONS, LLC; *U.S. Private*, pg. 1495
FENIX OUTDOOR AB—See Fenix Outdoor International AG; *Int'l*, pg. 2634
FENIX OUTDOOR AUSTRIA ITALY GMBH—See Fenix Outdoor International AG; *Int'l*, pg. 2634
FENIX OUTDOOR DANMARK APS—See Fenix Outdoor International AG; *Int'l*, pg. 2634
FENIX OUTDOOR FINLAND OY—See Fenix Outdoor International AG; *Int'l*, pg. 2634
FENIX OUTDOOR INTERNATIONAL AG; *Int'l*, pg. 2634
FENIX OUTDOOR LOGISTICS B.V.—See Fenix Outdoor International AG; *Int'l*, pg. 2634
FENIX OUTDOOR LOGISTICS GMBH—See Fenix Outdoor International AG; *Int'l*, pg. 2634
FENIX OUTDOOR NORGE A/S—See Fenix Outdoor International AG; *Int'l*, pg. 2634
FENIX OUTDOOR S.R.O—See Fenix Outdoor International AG; *Int'l*, pg. 2634
FENIX PARENT LLC—See Stellex Capital Management LP; *U.S. Private*, pg. 3800
FENIX RESOURCES LIMITED; *Int'l*, pg. 2634
FENIX SOLUTIONS OY—See Elisa Corporation; *Int'l*, pg. 2361
FENMAN LIMITED—See Merit Group PLC; *Int'l*, pg. 4836
FENNEC PHARMACEUTICALS, INC.; *U.S. Public*, pg. 829
FENNEMORE CRAIG, P.C.; *U.S. Private*, pg. 1495
FENNER CONVEYOR BELTING PRIVATE LIMITED—See Compagnie Generale des Etablissements Michelin SCA; *Int'l*, pg. 1744
FENNER CONVEYOR BELTING (SOUTH AFRICA) (PTY) LIMITED—See Compagnie Generale des Etablissements Michelin SCA; *Int'l*, pg. 1744
FENNER DUNLOP AMERICAS, LLC—See Compagnie Generale des Etablissements Michelin SCA; *Int'l*, pg. 1744
FENNER DUNLOP (ATLANTA), INC.—See Compagnie Generale des Etablissements Michelin SCA; *Int'l*, pg. 1744
FENNER DUNLOP AUSTRALIA PTY. LTD.—See Compagnie Generale des Etablissements Michelin SCA; *Int'l*, pg. 1744
FENNER DUNLOP (BRACEBRIDGE) INC.—See Compagnie Generale des Etablissements Michelin SCA; *Int'l*, pg. 1744
FENNER DUNLOP BV—See Compagnie Generale des Etablissements Michelin SCA; *Int'l*, pg. 1745
FENNER DUNLOP CHILE SPA—See Compagnie Generale des Etablissements Michelin SCA; *Int'l*, pg. 1742
FENNER DUNLOP CONVEYOR SERVICES, LLC—See Compagnie Generale des Etablissements Michelin SCA; *Int'l*, pg. 1744
FENNER DUNLOP CONVEYOR SYSTEMS & SERVICES, LLC.—See Compagnie Generale des Etablissements Michelin SCA; *Int'l*, pg. 1744
FENNER DUNLOP ITALIA S.R.L.—See Compagnie Generale des Etablissements Michelin SCA; *Int'l*, pg. 1742
FENNER DUNLOP LIMITED—See Compagnie Generale des Etablissements Michelin SCA; *Int'l*, pg. 1744
FENNER DUNLOP MAROC SARL—See Compagnie Generale des Etablissements Michelin SCA; *Int'l*, pg. 1742
FENNER DUNLOP (PORT CLINTON), INC.—See Compagnie Generale des Etablissements Michelin SCA; *Int'l*, pg. 1744
FENNER DUNLOP SARL—See Compagnie Generale des Etablissements Michelin SCA; *Int'l*, pg. 1742
FENNER DUNLOP S.L.—See Compagnie Generale des Etablissements Michelin SCA; *Int'l*, pg. 1742

FENNER DUNLOP (TOLEDO), LLC—See Compagnie Generale des Etablissements Michelin SCA; *Int'l*, pg. 1744
FENNER DUNLOP WHYALLA PTD. LTD.—See Compagnie Generale des Etablissements Michelin SCA; *Int'l*, pg. 1745
FENNER GROUP HOLDINGS LIMITED—See Compagnie Generale des Etablissements Michelin SCA; *Int'l*, pg. 1744
FENNER, INC.—See Compagnie Generale des Etablissements Michelin SCA; *Int'l*, pg. 1745
FENNIA GROUP; *Int'l*, pg. 2634
FENNICK/MCCREDIE ARCHITECTURE LTD.; *U.S. Private*, pg. 1495
FENNOPRO-CONSULTING OY—See Sweco AB; *Int'l*, pg. 7363
FENNOSTEEL OY—See Purso Group Oy; *Int'l*, pg. 6123
FENOPLAST LIMITED; *Int'l*, pg. 2634
FENPLAST; *Int'l*, pg. 2634
FENSTER-WEBSHOP.DE GMBH—See VKR Holding A/S; *Int'l*, pg. 8281
FENTELL CORPORATION; *U.S. Private*, pg. 1495
THE FENTON ART GLASS COMPANY; *U.S. Private*, pg. 4028
THE FENTON GROUP; *U.S. Private*, pg. 4028
FENTON RIGGING & CONTRACTING, INC.; *U.S. Private*, pg. 1495
FENTON'S OFFICE SOLUTIONS, INC.—See Pacific Office Automation, Inc.; *U.S. Private*, pg. 3069
FENTRESS ARCHITECTS; *U.S. Private*, pg. 1495
FENTSCH PACKAGING SOLUTIONS GMBH—See Janoschka GmbH; *Int'l*, pg. 3880
FENTURA FINANCIAL, INC.; *U.S. Public*, pg. 829
FENWAL CONTROLS OF JAPAN, LTD.; *Int'l*, pg. 2634
FENWAL, INC.—See Fresenius SE & Co. KGaA; *Int'l*, pg. 2777
FENWAY HEALTH; *U.S. Private*, pg. 1495
FENWAY PARTNERS, LLC; *U.S. Private*, pg. 1495
FENWAY SPORTS GROUP HOLDINGS, LLC; *U.S. Private*, pg. 1496
FENWICK IBERICA S.A.—See Fuji Corporation; *Int'l*, pg. 2809
FENWICK LEASE—See Societe Generale S.A.; *Int'l*, pg. 7039
FENWICK-LINDE HYDRAULICS—See KKR & Co. Inc.; *U.S. Public*, pg. 1255
FENWICK-LINDE HYDRAULICS—See The Goldman Sachs Group, Inc.; *U.S. Public*, pg. 2079
FENWICK-LINDE S.A.R.L.—See KKR & Co. Inc.; *U.S. Public*, pg. 1254
FENWICK-LINDE S.A.R.L.—See The Goldman Sachs Group, Inc.; *U.S. Public*, pg. 2079
FENWICK LTD.; *Int'l*, pg. 2635
FENWICK LTD.—See Fenwick Ltd.; *Int'l*, pg. 2635
FENWICK & WEST LLP; *U.S. Private*, pg. 1496
FE-ONE CO., LTD.—See Kyokuto Kaihatsu Kogyo Co. Ltd.; *Int'l*, pg. 4363
FEPA TEKSTIL SANAYI VE PAZARLAMA A.S.; *Int'l*, pg. 2635
FEPER SA; *Int'l*, pg. 2635
FEP FAHRZEUGELEKTRIK PIRNA GMBH—See Amphenol Corporation; *U.S. Public*, pg. 130
FERADYNE OUTDOORS LLC—See TruArc Partners, L.P.; *U.S. Private*, pg. 4245
FERAG AG—See WRH Walter Reist Holding AG; *Int'l*, pg. 8494
FERAG AMERICAS LLC—See WRH Walter Reist Holding AG; *Int'l*, pg. 8494
FERAL BREWING COMPANY PTY LTD—See COCA-COLA EUROPACIFIC PARTNERS PLC; *Int'l*, pg. 1684
FERALCO AB—See Mellby Gard Holding AB; *Int'l*, pg. 4811
FERALCO—See Blackstone Inc.; *U.S. Public*, pg. 348
FERALLOY CHARLESTON DIVISION—See Reliance Steel & Aluminum Co.; *U.S. Public*, pg. 1780
FERALLOY CORPORATION—See Reliance Steel & Aluminum Co.; *U.S. Public*, pg. 1780
FERALLOY INDIANA CORP.—See Reliance Steel & Aluminum Co.; *U.S. Public*, pg. 1780
FERALLOY MIDWEST (PORTAGE) DIVISION—See Reliance Steel & Aluminum Co.; *U.S. Public*, pg. 1780
FERALLOY OHIO CORP.—See Reliance Steel & Aluminum Co.; *U.S. Public*, pg. 1780
FERALLOY OREGON CORP.—See Reliance Steel & Aluminum Co.; *U.S. Public*, pg. 1780
FERALLOY PROCESSING COMPANY—See Reliance Steel & Aluminum Co.; *U.S. Public*, pg. 1780
FERALLOY PROCESSING COMPANY—See United States Steel Corporation; *U.S. Public*, pg. 2236
FERALLOY SOUTHERN DIVISION—See Reliance Steel & Aluminum Co.; *U.S. Public*, pg. 1780
FERALLOY ST. LOUIS DIVISION—See Reliance Steel & Aluminum Co.; *U.S. Public*, pg. 1780
FERALLOY WESTERN DIVISION—See Reliance Steel & Aluminum Co.; *U.S. Public*, pg. 1780
FERA SCIENCE LIMITED—See Bridgepoint Group Plc; *Int'l*, pg. 1155
FERATEL DEVELOPMENT CENTER EOOD—See Feratel Media Technologies AG; *Int'l*, pg. 2635

COMPANY NAME INDEX

FERATEL ESPANA SL—See Feratel Media Technologies AG; *Int'l*, pg. 2635
FERATEL MEDIA TECHNOLOGIES AG; *Int'l*, pg. 2635
FERATEL MEDIA TECHNOLOGIES B.V.—See Feratel Media Technologies AG; *Int'l*, pg. 2635
FERATEL MEDIA TECHNOLOGIES GMBH—See Feratel Media Technologies AG; *Int'l*, pg. 2635
FERATEL SCHWEIZ AG—See Feratel Media Technologies AG; *Int'l*, pg. 2635
FERAUD SARL; *Int'l*, pg. 2635
FERAVINO D.O.O.—See Nexe Grupa d.d.; *Int'l*, pg. 5243
FERAX CAPITAL AG; *Int'l*, pg. 2635
FERCABLE S.L.—See Prysmian S.p.A.; *Int'l*, pg. 6012
FERCHE MILLWORK, INC.; *U.S. Private*, pg. 1496
FERCOM EOLICA, S.L.—See AUDAX RENOVABLES, S.A.; *Int'l*, pg. 700
FERCO MOTORS, CORP.; *U.S. Private*, pg. 1496
FERD AS; *Int'l*, pg. 2635
FERD CORP.; *Int'l*, pg. 2637
FERD EIENDOM—See Ferd AS; *Int'l*, pg. 2636
FERDIGBETONG AS—See Peab AB; *Int'l*, pg. 5771
FERDINAND BUILDING DEVELOPMENT CORPORATION; *U.S. Private*, pg. 1496
FERDINAND GROSS CZECH, S.R.O.—See Ferdinand Gross GmbH & Co. KG; *Int'l*, pg. 2637
FERDINAND GROSS GMBH & CO. KG; *Int'l*, pg. 2637
FERDINAND GROSS HUNGARY KFT.—See Ferdinand Gross GmbH & Co. KG; *Int'l*, pg. 2637
FERDINAND GROSS POLSKA SP Z O.O.—See Ferdinand Gross GmbH & Co. KG; *Int'l*, pg. 2637
FERDINAND GROSS ROMANIA S.R.L.—See Ferdinand Gross GmbH & Co. KG; *Int'l*, pg. 2637
FERDINAND KREUTZER SABAMUHLE GMBH; *Int'l*, pg. 2637
FERDINAND LUSCH GMBH & CO. KG; *Int'l*, pg. 2637
FERDINAND PORSCHE FERNFH—See Ernst Klett AG; *Int'l*, pg. 2495
FERD INVESTMENT GROUP—See Ferd AS; *Int'l*, pg. 2636
FERD INVEST—See Ferd AS; *Int'l*, pg. 2636
FERD PRIVATE EQUITY—See Ferd AS; *Int'l*, pg. 2636
FERD SEAFOODS—See Ferd AS; *Int'l*, pg. 2636
FEREBEE ASPHALT CORPORATION—See Construction Partners, Inc.; *U.S. Public*, pg. 572
FEREBEE CORPORATION—See Construction Partners, Inc.; *U.S. Public*, pg. 572
FERENCIK LIBANOFF BRANDT BUSTAMANTE & GOLDSTEIN, P.A.—See Hinckley, Allen & Snyder LLP; *U.S. Private*, pg. 1948
FERFINA S.P.A.; *Int'l*, pg. 2637
FERGIN SVERIGE AB—See Indutrade AB; *Int'l*, pg. 3678
FERGO AISA, S.A.; *Int'l*, pg. 2637
FERGUSON BROS INC; *U.S. Private*, pg. 1496
FERGUSON BUICK GMC; *U.S. Private*, pg. 1496
FERGUSON CONSTRUCTION COMPANY INC.; *U.S. Private*, pg. 1496
FERGUSON CONSTRUCTION; *U.S. Private*, pg. 1496
FERGUSON CONSULTING INC.—See Stone Point Capital LLC; *U.S. Private*, pg. 3823
FERGUSON CONTAINERS, INC.—See Vinco Ventures, Inc.; *U.S. Public*, pg. 2298
FERGUSON COPELAND LLC—See Eighteen Seventy Corporation; *U.S. Private*, pg. 1347
FERGUSON ELECTRIC COMPANY INC.; *U.S. Private*, pg. 1496
FERGUSON ELECTRIC CONSTRUCTION CO., INC.—See Ferguson Electric Holdings Corp.; *U.S. Private*, pg. 1497
FERGUSON ELECTRIC HOLDINGS CORP.; *U.S. Private*, pg. 1496
FERGUSON ELECTRIC SERVICE CO., INC.—See Ferguson Electric Holdings Corp.; *U.S. Private*, pg. 1497
FERGUSON ENTERPRISES INC; *U.S. Private*, pg. 1497
FERGUSON ENTERPRISES, INC.—See Ferguson plc; *Int'l*, pg. 2637
FERGUSON ENTERPRISES, INC.—See Ferguson plc; *Int'l*, pg. 2637
FERGUSON ENTERPRISES, INC.—See Ferguson plc; *Int'l*, pg. 2637
FERGUSON ENTERPRISES, INC.—See Ferguson plc; *Int'l*, pg. 2637
FERGUSON ENTERPRISES, LLC—See Ferguson plc; *Int'l*, pg. 2637
FERGUSON ENTERPRISES MIDWEST, INC.—See Ferguson plc; *Int'l*, pg. 2637
FERGUSON ENTERPRISES—See Ferguson plc; *Int'l*, pg. 2637
FERGUSON FIRE & FABRICATION, INC.—See Ferguson plc; *Int'l*, pg. 2637
FERGUSON GROUP AUSTRALIA PTY LTD—See First Reserve Management, L.P.; *U.S. Private*, pg. 1526
FERGUSON GROUP LTD—See First Reserve Management, L.P.; *U.S. Private*, pg. 1526
FERGUSON GROUP SINGAPORE PTE LTD—See First Reserve Management, L.P.; *U.S. Private*, pg. 1526
FERGUSON HEATING & COOLING—See Ferguson plc; *Int'l*, pg. 2637
FERGUSON LYON CONKLIN & COMPANY INC.—See Ferguson plc; *Int'l*, pg. 2638

FERGUSON MANUFACTURING & EQUIPMENT COMPANY, INC.; *U.S. Private*, pg. 1497
FERGUSON MIDDLE EAST FZE—See First Reserve Management, L.P.; *U.S. Private*, pg. 1526
FERGUSON NORGE AS—See First Reserve Management, L.P.; *U.S. Private*, pg. 1526
FERGUSON PERFORATING COMPANY—See Reliance Steel & Aluminum Co.; *U.S. Public*, pg. 1780
FERGUSON PLC; *Int'l*, pg. 2637
FERGUSON PONTIAC-GMC INC.; *U.S. Private*, pg. 1497
FERGUSON PRODUCTION, INC.—See Ardian SAS; *Int'l*, pg. 554
FERGUSON SUPPLY & BOX MANUFACTURING CO; *U.S. Private*, pg. 1497
FERGUSON SUPPLY CO.; *U.S. Private*, pg. 1497
FERGUSON VALVES & AUTOMATION CO.—See Ferguson plc; *Int'l*, pg. 2638
FERGUSON WATERWORKS—See Ferguson plc; *Int'l*, pg. 2638
FERGUSON WATERWORKS—See Ferguson plc; *Int'l*, pg. 2638
FERGUSON WATERWORKS—See Ferguson plc; *Int'l*, pg. 2638
FERGUSON WIND FARM PTY. LTD.—See BayWa AG; *Int'l*, pg. 917
FERIA BEBE S.L.—See RCS MediaGroup S.p.A.; *Int'l*, pg. 6229
FERIA DE OSORNO S.A.; *Int'l*, pg. 2638
FERIAS Y EXPOSICIONES S.A.—See Grupo Clarin S.A.; *Int'l*, pg. 3125
FERIES S.R.L.—See HomeToGo SE; *Int'l*, pg. 3456
FERIFOS SA—See Ermewa Interservices Sarl; *Int'l*, pg. 2494
FERING D.D.; *Int'l*, pg. 2638
FERI TRUST (LUXEMBOURG) S.A.—See MLP SE; *Int'l*, pg. 5004
FERLAND INDUSTRIES INC.; *U.S. Private*, pg. 1497
FERLAT ACCIAI S.P.A.—See Acciaierie Valbruna S.p.A.; *Int'l*, pg. 89
FERMACA S.A. DE C.V.—See Partners Group Holding AG; *Int'l*, pg. 5749
FERMA CORP.; *U.S. Private*, pg. 1497
FERMAN AUTOMOTIVE MANAGEMENT SERVICES, INC.; *U.S. Private*, pg. 1497
FERMAN CHEVROLET—See Ferman Automotive Management Services, Inc.; *U.S. Private*, pg. 1497
FERMAN MOTOR CAR CO., INC.—See Ferman Automotive Management Services, Inc.; *U.S. Private*, pg. 1497
FERMAT CZ. S.R.O.—See FERMAT Group, a.s.; *Int'l*, pg. 2638
FERMAT GROUP, A.S.; *Int'l*, pg. 2638
FERMATIC FRESNAIS S.A.S.—See dormakaba Holding AG; *Int'l*, pg. 2177
FERMAT MACHINERY PVT. LTD.—See FERMAT Group, a.s.; *Int'l*, pg. 2638
FERMATOR NORDIC AB—See Tecnolama S.A.; *Int'l*, pg. 7516
FERMAT PRIVATE LTD.—See Moody's Corporation; *U.S. Public*, pg. 1467
FERME DES LOGES SARL—See Holding Le Duff SA; *Int'l*, pg. 3450
FERMENTA BIOTECH LIMITED; *Int'l*, pg. 2639
FERMENTALG SA; *Int'l*, pg. 2639
FERMENTA USA LLC—See Fermenta Biotech Limited; *Int'l*, pg. 2639
FERMETURES GROOM S.A.S.—See dormakaba Holding AG; *Int'l*, pg. 2177
FERMICAISE SA DE CV—See Enel S.p.A.; *Int'l*, pg. 2414
FERMION OY—See Orion Corporation; *Int'l*, pg. 5631
FERMOB SA; *Int'l*, pg. 2639
FERNAKADEMIE FUR ERWACHSENENBILDUNG GMBH—See Ernst Klett AG; *Int'l*, pg. 2495
FERNANDES CO., LTD.; *Int'l*, pg. 2639
FERNANDEZ ENTERTAINMENT; *U.S. Private*, pg. 1497
FERNANDEZ HOLDINGS, INC.; *U.S. Private*, pg. 1497
FERNAND HAZAN EDITEUR S A—See Vivendi SE; *Int'l*, pg. 8272
FERNAU LIMITED—See Moog Inc.; *U.S. Public*, pg. 1470
FERNBANK MUSEUM OF NATURAL HISTORY; *U.S. Private*, pg. 1497
FERNBROOK HOMES; *Int'l*, pg. 2639
FERNCO INCORPORATED; *U.S. Private*, pg. 1497
FERNDALE COLLISION, LLC—See Lithia Motors, Inc.; *U.S. Public*, pg. 1322
FERNDALE DIRECT SDN BHD—See Jiankun International Berhad; *Int'l*, pg. 3961
FERNDALE ELECTRIC COMPANY INC.; *U.S. Private*, pg. 1497
FERNDALE LABORATORIES INC.; *U.S. Private*, pg. 1497
FERNDALE READY MIX & GRAVEL; *U.S. Private*, pg. 1497
FERN EXPOSITION SERVICES LLC—See MSouth Equity Partners, LLC; *U.S. Private*, pg. 2808
FERNGAS NETZGESELLSCHAFT MBH—See Commonwealth Bank of Australia; *Int'l*, pg. 1720
FERNGAS NORDBAYERN GMBH—See E.ON SE; *Int'l*, pg. 2255
FERNHEIZWERK NEUKOLLN AG—See Vattenfall AB; *Int'l*, pg. 8137

FERNHILL BEVERAGE, INC.—See V Group Inc.; *U.S. Private*, pg. 4327
FERNHILL CORP.; *U.S. Public*, pg. 829
FERN-HOWARD LIMITED—See Matrix Holdings Limited; *Int'l*, pg. 4729
FERNIE CONTRACTORS LTD.—See Vertex Resource Group Ltd.; *Int'l*, pg. 8174
FERNLEA FLOWERS LTD.; *Int'l*, pg. 2639
FERNLEA NURSERY INC.—See Fernlea Flowers Ltd.; *Int'l*, pg. 2639
FERNO-WASHINGTON INC.; *U.S. Private*, pg. 1497
FERNOX LIMITED—See Element Solutions Inc.; *U.S. Public*, pg. 726
FERNRIDGE CONSULTING (PROPRIETARY) LIMITED—See Capital Eye Investments Limited; *Int'l*, pg. 1310
FERNWARMEVERSORGUNG HERNE GMBH—See E.ON SE; *Int'l*, pg. 2253
FERNWAY LIMITED—See Searchlight Capital Partners, L.P.; *U.S. Private*, pg. 3589
FEROELEKTRO D.D.; *Int'l*, pg. 2639
FEROLETO STEEL COMPANY, INC.—See Toyota Tsusho Corporation; *Int'l*, pg. 7879
FEROLIE CORPORATION; *U.S. Private*, pg. 1497
FEROLITO, VULTAGGIO & SONS; *U.S. Private*, pg. 1498
FERONIA INCORPORATED SERVICES LIMITED—See Feronia Inc.; *Int'l*, pg. 2639
FERONIA INC.; *Int'l*, pg. 2639
FERO STRATA SYSTEMS PTY. LTD.—See Sandvik AB; *Int'l*, pg. 6529
FERO WASTE & RECYCLING INC.—See Municipal Enterprises Limited; *Int'l*, pg. 5093
FEROZE1888 MILLS LIMITED—See 1888 Mills, LLC; *U.S. Private*, pg. 3
FEROZSONS LABORATORIES LIMITED; *Int'l*, pg. 2639
FER-PAL CONSTRUCTION LTD.—See Blue Wolf Capital Partners LLC; *U.S. Private*, pg. 594
FER-PAL CONSTRUCTION USA LLC.—See Ferpal Infrastructure Ltd.; *Int'l*, pg. 2639
FERPAL INFRASTRUCTURE LTD.; *Int'l*, pg. 2639
FERRAGAMO INC.—See Salvatore Ferragamo SpA; *Int'l*, pg. 6495
FERRAGAMO MEXICO S. DE R.L. DE C.V.—See Salvatore Ferragamo SpA; *Int'l*, pg. 6495
FERRAGAMO USA INC.—See Salvatore Ferragamo SpA; *Int'l*, pg. 6495
FERRAGON CORPORATION; *U.S. Private*, pg. 1498
FERRALCA, S.A.—See Alfonso Gallardo S.A.; *Int'l*, pg. 316
FERRAMENTA 2000 SPA—See Descours & Cabaud SA; *Int'l*, pg. 2044
FERRAN SERVICES & CONTRACTING; *U.S. Private*, pg. 1498
FERRANTI TECHNOLOGIES LIMITED—See Elbit Systems Limited; *Int'l*, pg. 2345
FERRARA ASCENSORI S.R.L.—See KONE Oyj; *Int'l*, pg. 4247
FERRARA BROS. BUILDING MATERIALS CORP.; *U.S. Private*, pg. 1498
THE FERRARA CANDY COMPANY—See Ferrero International S.A.; *Int'l*, pg. 2640
FERRARA FIRE APPARATUS INC.—See AIP, LLC; *U.S. Private*, pg. 135
FERRARA WINERY; *U.S. Private*, pg. 1498
FERRAR-CARANO VINEYARDS WINERY; *U.S. Private*, pg. 1498
FERRARELLE S.P.A.; *Int'l*, pg. 2639
FERRARELLE USA—See Ferrarelle S.p.A.; *Int'l*, pg. 2639
FERRARI FINANCIAL SERVICES S.P.A.—See Ferrari N.V.; *Int'l*, pg. 2639
FERRARI JAPAN KK—See Ferrari N.V.; *Int'l*, pg. 2639
FERRARI MANAGEMENT CONSULTING (SHANGHAI) CO., LTD.—See Ferrari N.V.; *Int'l*, pg. 2639
FERRARI NORTH AMERICA, INC.—See Ferrari N.V.; *Int'l*, pg. 2639
FERRARI NORTH EUROPE LIMITED—See Ferrari N.V.; *Int'l*, pg. 2639
FERRARI N.V.; *Int'l*, pg. 2639
FERRARI PARTNERS LP; *U.S. Private*, pg. 1498
FERRARI S.A.; *Int'l*, pg. 2639
FERRARI SOUTH WEST EUROPE S.A.R.L.—See Ferrari N.V.; *Int'l*, pg. 2639
FERRARI S.P.A.—See Ferrari N.V.; *Int'l*, pg. 2639
FERRARIS PISTON SERVICE LTD.—See Blackstone Inc.; *U.S. Public*, pg. 360
FERRARO FOODS INC.—See Kelso & Company, L.P.; *U.S. Private*, pg. 2278
FERRATUM AUSTRALIA PTY LTD—See Multitude SE; *Int'l*, pg. 5084
FERRATUM BANK PLC—See Multitude SE; *Int'l*, pg. 5084
FERRATUM CANADA INC.—See Multitude SE; *Int'l*, pg. 5084
FERRATUM SWEDEN AB—See Multitude SE; *Int'l*, pg. 5084
FERRATUM UK LTD.—See Multitude SE; *Int'l*, pg. 5084
FERREIRA CONSTRUCTION COMPANY, INC.; *U.S. Private*, pg. 1498
FERREIRA GOMES ENERGIA S.A.—See Alupar Investimento S.A.; *Int'l*, pg. 401

FERRELL BUILDER'S SUPPLY LTD.

CORPORATE AFFILIATIONS

FERRELL BUILDER'S SUPPLY LTD.; *Int'l*, pg. 2640
FERRELLGAS FINANCE CORP.—See Ferrellgas Partners, L.P.; *U.S. Public*, pg. 829
FERRELLGAS, INC. - BOSSIER CITY—See Ferrellgas Partners, L.P.; *U.S. Public*, pg. 829
FERRELLGAS, INC. - HILLSBORO—See Ferrellgas Partners, L.P.; *U.S. Public*, pg. 829
FERRELLGAS, INC. - HOUSTON—See Ferrellgas Partners, L.P.; *U.S. Public*, pg. 829
FERRELLGAS, INC. - ROOSEVELT PROPANE TERMINAL—See Ferrellgas Partners, L.P.; *U.S. Public*, pg. 829
FERRELLGAS, L.P.—See Ferrellgas Partners, L.P.; *U.S. Public*, pg. 829
FERRELLGAS PARTNERS FINANCE CORP.—See Ferrellgas Partners, L.P.; *U.S. Public*, pg. 829
FERRELLGAS PARTNERS, L.P.; *U.S. Public*, pg. 829
FERRELL NORTH AMERICA—See Ferrellgas Partners, L.P.; *U.S. Public*, pg. 829
FERRELS CARD SHOP INC.; *U.S. Private*, pg. 1498
FERRENGI HOUSEHOLD PRODUCTS (PTY) LTD—See Excellerate Holdings Ltd.; *Int'l*, pg. 2578
FERRER ESPANA, S.A.—See Grupo Ferrer Internacional, S.A.; *Int'l*, pg. 3129
FERRER FREEMAN & COMPANY, LLC; *U.S. Private*, pg. 1498
FERRERI SEARCH LLC; *U.S. Private*, pg. 1498
FERRERO ARDENNES S.A.—See Ferrero International S.A.; *Int'l*, pg. 2640
FERRERO ARGENTINA S.A. - PASTORA PLANT—See Ferrero International S.A.; *Int'l*, pg. 2640
FERRERO ARGENTINA S.A.—See Ferrero International S.A.; *Int'l*, pg. 2640
FERRERO ASIA LIMITED—See Ferrero International S.A.; *Int'l*, pg. 2640
FERRERO ASIA LTD (SINGAPORE)—See Ferrero International S.A.; *Int'l*, pg. 2640
FERRERO ASIA LTD—See Ferrero International S.A.; *Int'l*, pg. 2640
FERRERO B.V.—See Ferrero International S.A.; *Int'l*, pg. 2640
FERRERO CANADA LTD.—See Ferrero International S.A.; *Int'l*, pg. 2640
FERRERO CESKA S.R.O.—See Ferrero International S.A.; *Int'l*, pg. 2640
FERRERO DEL ECUADOR S.A—See Ferrero International S.A.; *Int'l*, pg. 2640
FERRERO DE MEXICO S.A. DE C.V. E—See Ferrero International S.A.; *Int'l*, pg. 2640
FERRERO DEUTSCHLAND G.M.B.H—See Ferrero International S.A.; *Int'l*, pg. 2640
FERRERO DO BRASIL INDUSTRIA DOCEIRA E ALIMENTAR LTDA—See Ferrero International S.A.; *Int'l*, pg. 2641
FERRERO D.O.O.—See Ferrero International S.A.; *Int'l*, pg. 2640
FERRERO FRANCE S.A.—See Ferrero International S.A.; *Int'l*, pg. 2640
FERRERO FSC LUXEMBOURG S.A.—See Ferrero International S.A.; *Int'l*, pg. 2640
FERRERO IBERICA S.A.—See Ferrero International S.A.; *Int'l*, pg. 2640
FERRERO INDIA PRIVATE LIMITED—See Ferrero International S.A.; *Int'l*, pg. 2640
FERRERO INTERNATIONAL S.A.; *Int'l*, pg. 2640
FERRERO IRELAND LIMITED—See Ferrero International S.A.; *Int'l*, pg. 2640
FERRERO ITHEMBA RSA (PTY) LTD—See Ferrero International S.A.; *Int'l*, pg. 2640
FERRERO JAPAN LTD—See Ferrero International S.A.; *Int'l*, pg. 2640
FERRERO LADM—See Ferrero International S.A.; *Int'l*, pg. 2640
FERRERO LANKA (PVT) LTD—See Ferrero International S.A.; *Int'l*, pg. 2640
FERRERO MAGYARORSZAG KFT.—See Ferrero International S.A.; *Int'l*, pg. 2640
FERRERO OSTERREICH HANDELS G. M.B.H.—See Ferrero International S.A.; *Int'l*, pg. 2640
FERRERO POLSKA SP. Z.O.O.—See Ferrero International S.A.; *Int'l*, pg. 2640
FERRERO PUBBLIREGIA S.R.L.—See Ferrero International S.A.; *Int'l*, pg. 2640
FERRERO ROMANIA S.R.L.—See Ferrero International S.A.; *Int'l*, pg. 2640
FERRERO RUSSIA CJSC—See Ferrero International S.A.; *Int'l*, pg. 2640
FERRERO SCANDINAVIA A/B—See Ferrero International S.A.; *Int'l*, pg. 2640
FERRERO SCHWEIZ A.G.—See Ferrero International S.A.; *Int'l*, pg. 2640
FERRERO S.P.A. - ANGELO DEI LOMBARDI FACTORY—See Ferrero International S.A.; *Int'l*, pg. 2640
FERRERO S.P.A. - BALVANO FACTORY—See Ferrero International S.A.; *Int'l*, pg. 2640
FERRERO S.P.A GREECE SINGLE-PARTNER LIMITED LIABILITY COMPANY—See Ferrero International S.A.; *Int'l*, pg. 2640

FERRERO S.P.A. - POZZUOLO MARTESANA FACTORY—See Ferrero International S.A.; *Int'l*, pg. 2640
FERRERO S.P.A.—See Ferrero International S.A.; *Int'l*, pg. 2640
FERRERO TRADING DUBAI—See Ferrero International S.A.; *Int'l*, pg. 2640
FERRERO TRADING (SHANGHAI) COMPANY, LTD—See Ferrero International S.A.; *Int'l*, pg. 2640
FERRERO TURKIYE CIKOLATA VE TARIM URUNLERI SANAYI VE DIS TICARET A.S.—See Ferrero International S.A.; *Int'l*, pg. 2640
FERRERO UK LTD.—See Ferrero International S.A.; *Int'l*, pg. 2641
FERRERO UKRAINE LLC—See Ferrero International S.A.; *Int'l*, pg. 2641
FERRERO U.S.A., INC.—See Ferrero International S.A.; *Int'l*, pg. 2641
FERRER USA—See Publicidad Ferrer y Asociados, S.A. de C.V.; *Int'l*, pg. 6097
FERRETERIA TESORO DEL EBANISTA; *U.S. Private*, pg. 1498
FERRETTI S.P.A.—See Shandong Heavy Industry Group Co., Ltd.; *Int'l*, pg. 6753
FERREXPO AG—See Ferrexpo plc; *Int'l*, pg. 2641
FERREXPO BELANOVO MINING LLC—See Ferrexpo plc; *Int'l*, pg. 2641
FERREXPO MIDDLE EAST FZE—See Ferrexpo plc; *Int'l*, pg. 2641
FERREXPO PLC; *Int'l*, pg. 2641
FERREXPO SINGAPORE PTE. LTD.—See Ferrexpo plc; *Int'l*, pg. 2641
FERRING AG—See Ferring Holding SA; *Int'l*, pg. 2641
FERRING ARZNEIMITTEL GESMBH—See Ferring Holding SA; *Int'l*, pg. 2641
FERRING ARZNEIMITTEL GMBH—See Ferring Holding SA; *Int'l*, pg. 2641
FERRING BV—See Ferring Holding SA; *Int'l*, pg. 2642
FERRING CONTROLLED THERAPEUTICS LTD—See Ferring Holding SA; *Int'l*, pg. 2641
FERRING GALENISCHES LABOR AG—See Ferring Holding SA; *Int'l*, pg. 2641
FERRING GMBH—See Ferring Holding SA; *Int'l*, pg. 2641
FERRING HELLAS PHARMACEUTICALS E.P.E.—See Ferring Holding SA; *Int'l*, pg. 2641
FERRING HOLDING SA; *Int'l*, pg. 2641
FERRING HUNGARY PHARMACEUTICAL TRADING CO LTD—See Ferring Holding SA; *Int'l*, pg. 2641
FERRING ILAC SANAYI VE TICARET LTD STI—See Ferring Holding SA; *Int'l*, pg. 2641
FERRING INC.—See Ferring Holding SA; *Int'l*, pg. 2641
FERRING INTERNATIONAL CENTER SA—See Ferring Holding SA; *Int'l*, pg. 2642
FERRING INTERNATIONAL PHARMASCIENCE CENTER U.S. INC.—See Ferring Holding SA; *Int'l*, pg. 2642
FERRING INTERNATIONAL PHARMA-SCIENCE CENTRE (CHINA) CO. LTD.—See Ferring Holding SA; *Int'l*, pg. 2641
FERRING (IRELAND) LTD.—See Ferring Holding SA; *Int'l*, pg. 2641
FERRING LAAKKEET OY—See Ferring Holding SA; *Int'l*, pg. 2641
FERRING LAEGEMIDLER A/S—See Ferring Holding SA; *Int'l*, pg. 2641
FERRING LAKEMEDEL AB—See Ferring Holding SA; *Int'l*, pg. 2641
FERRING LECIVA AS—See Ferring Holding SA; *Int'l*, pg. 2641
FERRING LEGEMIDLER AS—See Ferring Holding SA; *Int'l*, pg. 2641
FERRING NV—See Ferring Holding SA; *Int'l*, pg. 2641
FERRING PHARMACEUTICAL (CHINA) COMPANY LIMITED—See Ferring Holding SA; *Int'l*, pg. 2642
FERRING PHARMACEUTICALS (ASIA) CO. LTD.—See Ferring Holding SA; *Int'l*, pg. 2641
FERRING PHARMACEUTICALS CO. LTD.—See Ferring Holding SA; *Int'l*, pg. 2641
FERRING PHARMACEUTICALS KOREA CO., LTD.—See Ferring Holding SA; *Int'l*, pg. 2641
FERRING PHARMACEUTICALS LLC—See Ferring Holding SA; *Int'l*, pg. 2641
FERRING PHARMACEUTICALS LTD.—See Ferring Holding SA; *Int'l*, pg. 2641
FERRING PHARMACEUTICALS POLAND SP. Z O.O.—See Ferring Holding SA; *Int'l*, pg. 2642
FERRING PHARMACEUTICALS PTE LTD.—See Ferring Holding SA; *Int'l*, pg. 2642
FERRING PHARMACEUTICALS PTY LTD—See Ferring Holding SA; *Int'l*, pg. 2642
FERRING PHARMACEUTICALS PVT LTD—See Ferring Holding SA; *Int'l*, pg. 2642
FERRING PHARMACEUTICALS ROMANIA S.R.L.—See Ferring Holding SA; *Int'l*, pg. 2642
FERRING PHARMACEUTICALS SA—See Ferring Holding SA; *Int'l*, pg. 2642
FERRING PORTUGUESA PRODUTOS FARMACEUTICOS SOCIEDADE UNIPESSOAL, LDA.—See Ferring Holding SA; *Int'l*, pg. 2642

FERRING PRODUCTOS FARMACEUTICOS SPA—See Ferring Holding SA; *Int'l*, pg. 2642
FERRING PTY LTD—See Ferring Holding SA; *Int'l*, pg. 2642
FERRING RESEARCH INSTITUTE INC.—See Ferring Holding SA; *Int'l*, pg. 2642
FERRING SA DE CV—See Ferring Holding SA; *Int'l*, pg. 2642
FERRING S.A.S.—See Ferring Holding SA; *Int'l*, pg. 2642
FERRING SAU—See Ferring Holding SA; *Int'l*, pg. 2642
FERRING SDN BHD—See Ferring Holding SA; *Int'l*, pg. 2642
FERRING SLOVAKIA S.R.O.—See Ferring Holding SA; *Int'l*, pg. 2642
FERRING SPA—See Ferring Holding SA; *Int'l*, pg. 2642
FERRING THERAPEUTICS PRIVATE LTD.—See Ferring Holding SA; *Int'l*, pg. 2642
FERRINI USA INC.; *U.S. Private*, pg. 1498
FERRIOT, INC.; *U.S. Private*, pg. 1498
FERRI SUPERMARKETS INC.; *U.S. Private*, pg. 1498
FERRITE DOMEN COMPANY—See Russian Technologies State Corporation; *Int'l*, pg. 6432
FERRITE INTERNATIONAL COMPANY; *U.S. Private*, pg. 1498
FERRO-ALLOY RESOURCES LIMITED; *Int'l*, pg. 2642
FERRO ALLOYS CORPORATION LTD. - CHARGE CHROME PLANT—See Vedanta Resources Ltd; *Int'l*, pg. 8146
FERRO ALLOYS CORPORATION LTD.—See Vedanta Resources Ltd; *Int'l*, pg. 8146
FERROAMP ELEKTRONIK AB; *Int'l*, pg. 2642
FERRO ARGENTINA, S.A.—See American Securities LLC; *U.S. Private*, pg. 251
FERROATLANTICA, S.A.U.—See Sixth Street Partners LLC; *U.S. Private*, pg. 3677
FERRO (BELGIUM) SPRL—See American Securities LLC; *U.S. Private*, pg. 251
FERROBETON BETON-ES VASBETONELEM GYARTO ZRT—See CRH plc; *Int'l*, pg. 1844
FERROBETON CONCRETE AND REINFORCED CONCRETE PRODUCER PUBLIC LIMITED COMPANY—See CRH plc; *Int'l*, pg. 1844
FERROBETON DUNAUJVAROSI BETON- ES VASBETONELEM-GYARTO ZRT—See CRH plc; *Int'l*, pg. 1844
FERROBETON ROMANIA—See CRH plc; *Int'l*, pg. 1844
FERROBETON SLOVAKIA, S.R.O.—See CRH plc; *Int'l*, pg. 1844
FERROBOTICS COMPLIANT ROBOT TECHNOLOGY GMBH—See Berndorf AG; *Int'l*, pg. 987
FERRO B.V.—See American Securities LLC; *U.S. Private*, pg. 251
FERROCARRIL ANTOFAGASTA A BOLIVIA SA—See Antofagasta plc; *Int'l*, pg. 484
FERROCARRIL DEL PACIFICO S.A.—See Sigdo Koppers S.A.; *Int'l*, pg. 6907
FERROCARRILES CHIAPAS-MAYAB, S.A. DE C.V.—See Brookfield Infrastructure Partners L.P.; *Int'l*, pg. 1191
FERROCARRILES CHIAPAS-MAYAB, S.A. DE C.V.—See GIC Pte. Ltd.; *Int'l*, pg. 2965
FERROCARRIL MEXICANO, S.A. DE C.V.—See Grupo Mexico, S.A.B. de C.V.; *Int'l*, pg. 3132
FERROCART S.R.L.—See ACEA S.p.A.; *Int'l*, pg. 95
FERRO COLOMBIA PIGMENTOS S.A.S.—See American Securities LLC; *U.S. Private*, pg. 251
FERRO COLORES SA DE CV—See American Securities LLC; *U.S. Private*, pg. 251
FERROCONTROL STEUERUNGSSYSTEME GMBH & CO. KG—See Eckelmann AG; *Int'l*, pg. 2290
FERRO CORPORATION (AUSTRALIA) PTY. LTD.—See American Securities LLC; *U.S. Private*, pg. 251
FERRO CORPORATION - COLOR DIVISION—See American Securities LLC; *U.S. Private*, pg. 251
FERRO CORPORATION - EDISON SPECIALTY PLASTICS PLANT—See American Securities LLC; *U.S. Private*, pg. 251
FERRO CORPORATION - INDUSTRIAL COATINGS DIVISION—See American Securities LLC; *U.S. Private*, pg. 251
FERRO CORPORATION - PERFORMANCE COLORS & GLASS DIVISION—See American Securities LLC; *U.S. Private*, pg. 251
FERRO CORPORATION - PERFORMANCE COLORS & GLASS, ORRVILLE PLANT—See American Securities LLC; *U.S. Private*, pg. 251
FERRO CORPORATION—See American Securities LLC; *U.S. Private*, pg. 251
FERRO CORPORATION - SPECIALTY COLOR DIVISION—See American Securities LLC; *U.S. Private*, pg. 251
FERRO COULEURS FRANCE SA—See American Securities LLC; *U.S. Private*, pg. 251
FERRO EGYPT FOR GLAZE (S.A.E.)—See American Securities LLC; *U.S. Private*, pg. 251
FERRO ELECTRONIC MATERIALS INC. - PENN YAN—See American Securities LLC; *U.S. Private*, pg. 251
FERRO ELECTRONIC MATERIALS INC.—See American Securities LLC; *U.S. Private*, pg. 251

COMPANY NAME INDEX

FERRO ENAMEL DO BRASIL INDUSTRIA E COMERCIO LTDA.—See American Securities LLC; *U.S. Private*, pg. 252
FERRO ENAMEL DO BRASIL LTDA.—See American Securities LLC; *U.S. Private*, pg. 251
FERRO ENAMEL ESPANOLA, S.A.—See American Securities LLC; *U.S. Private*, pg. 252
FERRO FAR EAST COMPANY SDN, BHD—See American Securities LLC; *U.S. Private*, pg. 252
FERRO FAR EAST LTD.—See American Securities LLC; *U.S. Private*, pg. 252
FERRO FRANCE S.A.R.L.—See American Securities LLC; *U.S. Private*, pg. 251
FERROGLOBE PLC—See Grupo Villar Mir, S.A.U.; *Int'l*, pg. 3138
FERRO GMBH—See American Securities LLC; *U.S. Private*, pg. 252
FERRO GMBH—See American Securities LLC; *U.S. Private*, pg. 252
FERRO (GREAT BRITAIN) LTD—See American Securities LLC; *U.S. Private*, pg. 251
FERRO HOLDING GMBH—See American Securities LLC; *U.S. Private*, pg. 252
FERRO (HOLLAND) B.V.—See American Securities LLC; *U.S. Private*, pg. 251
FERRO INDIA PRIVATE LIMITED—See American Securities LLC; *U.S. Private*, pg. 251
FERRO INDUSTRIAL PRODUCTS (PTY) LIMITED—See Tiso Blackstar Group SE; *Int'l*, pg. 7759
FERRO INDUSTRIAS QUIMICAS (PORTUGAL) LDA—See American Securities LLC; *U.S. Private*, pg. 251
FERRO JAPAN K.K.—See American Securities LLC; *U.S. Private*, pg. 252
FERRO KAPLAMA MALZEMELERI LIMITED SIRKETI—See American Securities LLC; *U.S. Private*, pg. 252
FERROKIN BIOSCIENCES, INC.—See Takeda Pharmaceutical Company Limited; *Int'l*, pg. 7438
FERROKNEPPER BUDERUS S.A.—See Robert Bosch GmbH; *Int'l*, pg. 6361
FERROLUX METALS CO. LLC—See Ferragon Corporation; *U.S. Private*, pg. 1498
FERROLUX METALS CO. LLC—See Mitsui & Co., Ltd.; *Int'l*, pg. 4975
FERROMATIK MILACRON GMBH—See Hillenbrand, Inc.; *U.S. Public*, pg. 1037
FERROMATIK MILACRON INDIA LTD.—See Hillenbrand, Inc.; *U.S. Public*, pg. 1037
FERROMETAL BALTIC OU—See Wurth Verwaltungsgesellschaft mbH; *Int'l*, pg. 8504
FERRO METAL & CHEMICAL CORPORATION LTD.—See Phibro Animal Health Corporation; *U.S. Public*, pg. 1685
FERROMETALLI SAFEM S.P.A.—See ArcelorMittal S.A.; *Int'l*, pg. 545
FERROMETAL OY—See Wurth Verwaltungsgesellschaft mbH; *Int'l*, pg. 8513
FERRO MEXICANA, S.A. DE C.V.—See American Securities LLC; *U.S. Private*, pg. 252
FERROMONTANE DISTRIBUTION S.A.—See TELEFONIKA Kable Sp. z o.o. S.K.A.; *Int'l*, pg. 7528
FERRONORDIC AB; *Int'l*, pg. 2642
FERRONORDIC GMBH—See Ferronordic AB; *Int'l*, pg. 2642
FERRONORDIC KAZAKHSTAN LLP—See Ferronordic AB; *Int'l*, pg. 2642
FERRONORDIC MACHINES LLC—See Ferronordic AB; *Int'l*, pg. 2642
FERRONOUX HOLDINGS, INC.—See Megawide Construction Corporation; *Int'l*, pg. 4794
FERRO PERFORMANCE PIGMENTS BELGIUM NV—See American Securities LLC; *U.S. Private*, pg. 252
FERRO PERFORMANCE PIGMENTS FRANCE SAS—See American Securities LLC; *U.S. Private*, pg. 251
FERRO PERFORMANCE PIGMENTS ROMANIA SRL—See American Securities LLC; *U.S. Private*, pg. 252
FERRO PERFORMANCE PIGMENTS (SHANGHAI) CO., LTD.—See American Securities LLC; *U.S. Private*, pg. 252
FERRO PERFORMANCE PIGMENTS SPAIN S.L.—See American Securities LLC; *U.S. Private*, pg. 252
FERRO PFANSTIEHL LABORATORIES, INC.—See American Securities LLC; *U.S. Private*, pg. 252
FERROSAN A/S—See Altor Equity Partners AB; *Int'l*, pg. 394
FERROSAN A/S—See Pfizer Inc.; *U.S. Public*, pg. 1679
FERROSAN DO BRASIL LTDA.—See Altor Equity Partners AB; *Int'l*, pg. 394
FERROSAN INTERNATIONAL A/S—See Altor Equity Partners AB; *Int'l*, pg. 394
FERROSAN NORGE AS—See Altor Equity Partners AB; *Int'l*, pg. 394
FERROSAN POLAND SP. Z.O.O.—See Altor Equity Partners AB; *Int'l*, pg. 394
FERROSAN S.R.L—See Altor Equity Partners AB; *Int'l*, pg. 394

FERRO S.A.; *Int'l*, pg. 2642
FERRO SCRAP NIGAM LIMITED—See MSTC Ltd.; *Int'l*, pg. 5069
FERROSER—See Ferrovial S.A.; *Int'l*, pg. 2644
FERRO SPAIN SA—See American Securities LLC; *U.S. Private*, pg. 252
FERRO SPECIALTY MATERIALS, LLC—See American Securities LLC; *U.S. Private*, pg. 251
FERROSTAAL AUSTRALIA PTY LTD—See MPC Munchmeyer Petersen & Co. GmbH; *Int'l*, pg. 5061
FERROSTAAL CHRISTOF ROMANIA SRL—See Christof Holding AG; *Int'l*, pg. 1587
FERROSTAAL CHRISTOF ROMANIA SRL—See MPC Munchmeyer Petersen & Co. GmbH; *Int'l*, pg. 5061
FERROSTAAL DO BRASIL COMERCIO E INDUSTRIA LTDA.—See MPC Munchmeyer Petersen & Co. GmbH; *Int'l*, pg. 5061
FERROSTAAL EQUIPMENT SOLUTIONS NORTH AMERICA, INC.—See MPC Munchmeyer Petersen & Co. GmbH; *Int'l*, pg. 5061
FERROSTAAL GMBH—See MPC Munchmeyer Petersen & Co. GmbH; *Int'l*, pg. 5060
FERROSTAAL INCORPORATED—See MPC Munchmeyer Petersen & Co. GmbH; *Int'l*, pg. 5061
FERROSTAAL MAINTENANCE EISENHUTTENSTADT GMBH—See Pirson Montage SA; *Int'l*, pg. 5875
FERROSTAAL MEXICO, S.A. DE C.V.—See MPC Munchmeyer Petersen & Co. GmbH; *Int'l*, pg. 5061
FERROSTAAL PHILIPPINES INC.—See MPC Munchmeyer Petersen & Co. GmbH; *Int'l*, pg. 5061
FERROSTAAL PIPING SUPPLY GMBH—See MPC Munchmeyer Petersen & Co. GmbH; *Int'l*, pg. 5061
FERROSTAAL PROCUREMENT SERVICES NV—See MPC Munchmeyer Petersen & Co. GmbH; *Int'l*, pg. 5061
FERROSTAAL SINGAPORE PTE. LTD.—See MPC Munchmeyer Petersen & Co. GmbH; *Int'l*, pg. 5061
FERROSUR, SA DE CV—See Grupo Mexico, S.A.B. de C.V.; *Int'l*, pg. 3132
FERRO (SUZHOU) PERFORMANCE MATERIALS CO., LTD.—See American Securities LLC; *U.S. Private*, pg. 251
FERRO TAIWAN LTD—See American Securities LLC; *U.S. Private*, pg. 252
FERROTEC ALION CORPORATION—See Ferrotec Holdings Corporation; *Int'l*, pg. 2643
FERROTEC AMC MALAYSIA SDN. BHD.—See Ferrotec Holdings Corporation; *Int'l*, pg. 2643
FERROTEC (AN HUI) TECHNOLOGY DEVELOPMENT CO., LTD.; *Int'l*, pg. 2642
FERROTEC CERAMICS CORPORATION—See Ferrotec Holdings Corporation; *Int'l*, pg. 2643
FERROTEC CORPORATION SINGAPORE PTE LTD—See Ferrotec Holdings Corporation; *Int'l*, pg. 2643
FERROTEC GMBH—See Ferrotec Holdings Corporation; *Int'l*, pg. 2643
FERROTEC HOLDINGS CORPORATION; *Int'l*, pg. 2642
FERROTEC KOREA CORPORATION—See Ferrotec Holdings Corporation; *Int'l*, pg. 2643
FERROTEC MATERIAL TECHNOLOGIES CORPORATION—See Ferrotec Holdings Corporation; *Int'l*, pg. 2643
FERROTEC-NORD CORPORATION—See Ferrotec Holdings Corporation; *Int'l*, pg. 2643
FERROTEC POWER SEMICONDUCTOR GMBH—See Ferrotec Holdings Corporation; *Int'l*, pg. 2643
FERROTEC POWER SEMICONDUCTOR (JAPAN) CORP.—See Ferrotec Holdings Corporation; *Int'l*, pg. 2643
FERROTEC SEMICONDUCTOR MATERIAL CORPORATION—See Ferrotec Holdings Corporation; *Int'l*, pg. 2643
FERROTEC SILICON CORPORATION—See Ferrotec Holdings Corporation; *Int'l*, pg. 2643
FERROTEC S.R.L.—See Ferrotec Holdings Corporation; *Int'l*, pg. 2643
FERROTEC TAIWAN CO., LTD.—See Ferrotec Holdings Corporation; *Int'l*, pg. 2643
FERROTEC (USA) CORPORATION—See Ferrotec Holdings Corporation; *Int'l*, pg. 2643
FERRO (THAILAND) CO. LTD.—See American Securities LLC; *U.S. Private*, pg. 251
FERROTRADE SAS—See Derichebourg S.A.; *Int'l*, pg. 2041
FERRO TURKEY KAPLAMA CAM VE RENK COZUMLERI SANAYI VE TICARET LIMITED SIRKETI—See American Securities LLC; *U.S. Private*, pg. 252
FERROUS85" CO.—See Ferragon Corporation; *U.S. Private*, pg. 1498
FERROUSOUTH—See Ferragon Corporation; *U.S. Private*, pg. 1498
FERROUS PROCESSING & TRADING CO. - FPT FT LAUDERDALE/SUNRISE RECYCLING FACILITY—See Soave Enterprises, LLC; *U.S. Private*, pg. 3702
FERROUS PROCESSING & TRADING CO. - FPT WYOMING AVE. FACILITY—See Soave Enterprises, LLC; *U.S. Private*, pg. 3702

FERROUS PROCESSING & TRADING CO.—See Soave Enterprises, LLC; *U.S. Private*, pg. 3702
FERROVIA CENTRO-ATLANTICA S.A.; *Int'l*, pg. 2643
FERROVIAL AEROPUERTOS S.A.—See Ferrovial S.A.; *Int'l*, pg. 2644
FERROVIAL AGROMAN US CORP.—See Ferrovial S.A.; *Int'l*, pg. 2644
FERROVIAL CONSTRUCCION, S.A.—See Ferrovial S.A.; *Int'l*, pg. 2644
FERROVIAL CONSTRUCTION CANADA INC.—See Ferrovial S.A.; *Int'l*, pg. 2644
FERROVIAL CONSTRUCTION—See Ferrovial S.A.; pg. 2644
FERROVIAL CONSTRUCTION TEXAS, LLC—See Ferrovial S.A.; *Int'l*, pg. 2644
FERROVIAL CORPORACION, S.A.—See Ferrovial S.A.; *Int'l*, pg. 2644
FERROVIAL S.A.; *Int'l*, pg. 2644
FERROVIAL SERVICES US, INC.—See Apollo Global Management, Inc.; *U.S. Public*, pg. 166
FERROVIAL SERVICIOS AMBIENTALES S.A.—See Apollo Global Management, Inc.; *U.S. Public*, pg. 166
FERROVIAL SERVICIOS CHILE SPA—See Ferrovial S.A.; *Int'l*, pg. 2644
FERROVIAL SERVICIOS S.A.—See Ferrovial S.A.; *Int'l*, pg. 2644
FERROVIAL SERVICOS, S.A.—See Ferrovial S.A.; *Int'l*, pg. 2644
FERROVIE DELLO STATO ITALIANE S.P.A.; *Int'l*, pg. 2645
FERROXCUBE INTERNATIONAL HOLDING B.V.—See Yageo Corporation; *Int'l*, pg. 8545
FERROXCUBE USA INC.—See Yageo Corporation; *Int'l*, pg. 8545
FERRUFORM AB—See Porsche Automobil Holding SE; *Int'l*, pg. 5930
FERRUM S.A.; *Int'l*, pg. 2645
FERRYADS.COM—See Communication Associates; *U.S. Private*, pg. 988
THE FERRY CAP & SET SCREW COMPANY—See Dubai Holding LLC; *Int'l*, pg. 2218
FERRYGAS, S.A.—See Mitsubishi Chemical Group Corporation; *Int'l*, pg. 4937
FERRY INDUSTRIES INC.; *U.S. Private*, pg. 1498
FERRY-MORSE SEED COMPANY—See Jiffy International AS; *Int'l*, pg. 3962
FERRY SUNFLOWER LIMITED—See Mitsui O.S.K. Lines, Ltd.; *Int'l*, pg. 4989
FERRY SUNFLOWER, LTD.—See Mitsui O.S.K. Lines, Ltd.; *Int'l*, pg. 4989
FERSERVIZI S.P.A.—See Ferrovie dello Stato Italiane S.p.A.; *Int'l*, pg. 2645
FERSON TECHNOLOGIES, INC.—See OSI Systems, Inc.; *U.S. Public*, pg. 1621
FERSPED A.D.; *Int'l*, pg. 2646
FERS—See Vivendi SE; *Int'l*, pg. 8276
FERTAGRA DEUTSCHLAND GMBH—See Agrofert Holding, a.s.; *Int'l*, pg. 219
FERTEK, INC.; *Int'l*, pg. 2646
FERTIGAMA, S.L.; *Int'l*, pg. 2646
FERTIGBETON (FBU) GMBH—See Heidelberg Materials AG; *Int'l*, pg. 3310
FERTIG CABINET COMPANY INC.; *U.S. Private*, pg. 1498
FERTIGENT BVBA—See Koncernas Achemos Grupe; *Int'l*, pg. 4246
FERTIGLOBE PLC—See Abu Dhabi National Oil Company; *Int'l*, pg. 73
FERTIL D.O.O.—See Victoria Group a.d.; *Int'l*, pg. 8188
THE FERTILISERS AND CHEMICALS TRAVANCORE LIMITED; *Int'l*, pg. 7643
FERTILIVITA S.R.L.—See A2A S.p.A.; *Int'l*, pg. 29
FERTILIZANTES MITSUI S.A. INDUSTRIA E COMERCIO—See Mitsui & Co., Ltd.; *Int'l*, pg. 4973
FERTILIZANTES NATURALES S.A.—See Sociedad Quimica y Minera de Chile S.A.; *Int'l*, pg. 7032
FERTILIZANTES TOCANTINS LTDA—See Kovdorskiy GOK JSC; *Int'l*, pg. 4293
FERTILIZER COMPANY OF ARIZONA; *U.S. Private*, pg. 1499
FERTILIZER DEALER SUPPLY INC.; *U.S. Private*, pg. 1499
FERTILIZER EQUIPMENT INC.; *U.S. Private*, pg. 1499
FERTI-LOME DISTRIBUTORS INC.—See Voluntary Purchasing Groups, Inc.; *U.S. Private*, pg. 4411
FERTIMPORT S.A.—See Bunge Limited; *U.S. Public*, pg. 411
FERTIMPORT S.A.—See Bunge Limited; *U.S. Public*, pg. 412
FERTIN PHARMA A/S—See Philip Morris International Inc.; *U.S. Public*, pg. 1685
FERTITTA ENTERTAINMENT, INC.; *U.S. Private*, pg. 1499
FERTITTA ENTERTAINMENT, LLC—See Red Rock Resorts, Inc.; *U.S. Public*, pg. 1769
FERTOZ LTD.; *Int'l*, pg. 2646
FERTRADE D.O.O.—See Fersped A.D.; *Int'l*, pg. 2646
FER TUZOLTOSAG ES SZOLGALTATO KFT.—See MOL Magyar Olaj- es Gazipari Nyrt.; *Int'l*, pg. 5020

FERTOZ LTD.

CORPORATE AFFILIATIONS

FERUS INC. - DAWSON CREEK N2 PLANT—See Ferus Inc.; *Int'l*, pg. 2646
FERUS INC. - JOFFRE N2 PLANT—See Ferus Inc.; *Int'l*, pg. 2646
FERUS INC.; *Int'l*, pg. 2646
FERUS INC. - UTAH CO2 PLANT—See Ferus Inc.; *Int'l*, pg. 2646
FERVENT INDUSTRIAL DEVELOPMENT (SUZHOU) CO., LTD.—See Vibrant Group Limited; *Int'l*, pg. 8184
FERVENT SYNERGIES LIMITED; *Int'l*, pg. 2646
FERVI SPA; *Int'l*, pg. 2646
FESCO AGENCIES N.A. INC.—See Far Eastern Shipping Company OJSC; *Int'l*, pg. 2617
FESCO GROUP CO., LTD.; *Int'l*, pg. 2646
FESCO LINES MANAGEMENT LTD.—See Far Eastern Shipping Company OJSC; *Int'l*, pg. 2617
FESCO LOGISTIC LLC—See Far Eastern Shipping Company OJSC; *Int'l*, pg. 2617
FESCOPACK SP.ZO.O—See FLEXOPACK S.A.; *Int'l*, pg. 2705
FESCO SYSTEMS LLC; *U.S. Private*, pg. 1499
FES EQUIPMENT SERVICES SDN. BHD.—See Muhibbah Engineering (M) Bhd.; *Int'l*, pg. 5078
FES INDUSTRIES PTE LTD—See Food Empire Holdings Limited; *Int'l*, pg. 2727
FES INDUSTRIES SDN BHD—See Food Empire Holdings Limited; *Int'l*, pg. 2727
FESLER AUTO MALL; *U.S. Private*, pg. 1499
FESSENDEN CO-OP ASSOCIATION INC.; *U.S. Private*, pg. 1499
FESSENDEN HALL INCORPORATED; *U.S. Private*, pg. 1499
THE FESSLER AGENCY INC.; *U.S. Private*, pg. 4028
FESTA HOLDING PLC; *Int'l*, pg. 2646
FESTARIA HOLDINGS CO., LTD.; *Int'l*, pg. 2646
FESTI HF; *Int'l*, pg. 2646
FESTIVAL FUNPARKS LLC; *U.S. Private*, pg. 1499
FESTIVAL HALL VENUE MANAGEMENT PTY. LTD.—See Live Nation Entertainment, Inc.; *U.S. Public*, pg. 1328
FESTIVAL ICE CREAM CORP.; *U.S. Private*, pg. 1499
FESTIVAL PARK (EASTON) RESIDENTS MANAGEMENT COMPANY LIMITED—See Persimmon plc; *Int'l*, pg. 5815
FESTIVALS LIMBURG B.V.—See Live Nation Entertainment, Inc.; *U.S. Public*, pg. 1328
FESTIVA RESORTS LLC; *U.S. Private*, pg. 1499
FESTIVE FOODS, LLC.; *U.S. Private*, pg. 1499
FESTO AB—See Festo AG & Co. KG; *Int'l*, pg. 2646
FESTO AG & CO. KG; *Int'l*, pg. 2646
FESTO AG—See Festo AG & Co. KG; *Int'l*, pg. 2647
FESTO AS—See Festo AG & Co. KG; *Int'l*, pg. 2647
FESTO A/S—See Festo AG & Co. KG; *Int'l*, pg. 2646
FESTO - AUTOMACAO, UNIPESSOAL, LDA.—See Festo AG & Co. KG; *Int'l*, pg. 2646
FESTO AUTOMATION LTD.—See Festo AG & Co. KG; *Int'l*, pg. 2647
FESTO BELGIUM N.V./S.A.—See Festo AG & Co. KG; *Int'l*, pg. 2647
FESTO BRASIL LTDA.—See Festo AG & Co. KG; *Int'l*, pg. 2647
FESTO BULGARIA EOOD—See Festo AG & Co. KG; *Int'l*, pg. 2647
FESTO B.V.—See Festo AG & Co. KG; *Int'l*, pg. 2647
FESTO C.A.—See Festo AG & Co. KG; *Int'l*, pg. 2647
FESTO CHILE SA—See Festo AG & Co. KG; *Int'l*, pg. 2647
FESTO (CHINA) LTD.—See Festo AG & Co. KG; *Int'l*, pg. 2646
FESTO CO., LTD.—See Festo AG & Co. KG; *Int'l*, pg. 2647
FESTO CONTROLS PVT. LTD.—See Festo AG & Co. KG; *Int'l*, pg. 2647
FESTO CORPORATION—See Festo AG & Co. KG; *Int'l*, pg. 2647
FESTO DIDACTIC INC.—See Festo AG & Co. KG; *Int'l*, pg. 2647
FESTO DIDACTIC LTD.—See Festo AG & Co. KG; *Int'l*, pg. 2647
FESTO D.O.O. LJUBLJANA—See Festo AG & Co. KG; *Int'l*, pg. 2648
FESTO D.O.O.—See Festo AG & Co. KG; *Int'l*, pg. 2648
FESTO E.U.R.L.—See Festo AG & Co. KG; *Int'l*, pg. 2647
FESTO GMBH—See Festo AG & Co. KG; *Int'l*, pg. 2647
FESTO INC.—See Festo AG & Co. KG; *Int'l*, pg. 2647
FESTO INC.—See Festo AG & Co. KG; *Int'l*, pg. 2647
FESTO ISRAEL LTD—See Festo AG & Co. KG; *Int'l*, pg. 2647
FESTO KFT.—See Festo AG & Co. KG; *Int'l*, pg. 2647
FESTO K.K.—See Festo AG & Co. KG; *Int'l*, pg. 2647
FESTO KOREA CO. LTD.—See Festo AG & Co. KG; *Int'l*, pg. 2647
FESTO LIMITED—See Festo AG & Co. KG; *Int'l*, pg. 2647
FESTO LIMITED—See Festo AG & Co. KG; *Int'l*, pg. 2647
FESTO LIMITED—See Festo AG & Co. KG; *Int'l*, pg. 2647
FESTO LIMITED—See Festo AG & Co. KG; *Int'l*, pg. 2647
FESTO LTDA.—See Festo AG & Co. KG; *Int'l*, pg. 2647
FESTO LTD.—See Festo AG & Co. KG; *Int'l*, pg. 2647
FESTO LTD.—See Festo AG & Co. KG; *Int'l*, pg. 2647

FESTO OY AB EESTI FILIAAL—See Festo AG & Co. KG; *Int'l*, pg. 2647
FESTO OY—See Festo AG & Co. KG; *Int'l*, pg. 2647
FESTO PNEUMATIC S.A.—See Festo AG & Co. KG; *Int'l*, pg. 2647
FESTO PNEUMATIC S.A.—See Festo AG & Co. KG; *Int'l*, pg. 2647
FESTO PNEUMATIC S.K.—See Festo AG & Co. KG; *Int'l*, pg. 2647
FESTO PTE. LTD.—See Festo AG & Co. KG; *Int'l*, pg. 2647
FESTO (PTY.) LTD.—See Festo AG & Co. KG; *Int'l*, pg. 2646
FESTO PTY. LTD.—See Festo AG & Co. KG; *Int'l*, pg. 2647
FESTO SAN. VE TIC A.S.—See Festo AG & Co. KG; *Int'l*, pg. 2648
FESTO S.A.—See Festo AG & Co. KG; *Int'l*, pg. 2648
FESTO SDN. BHD.—See Festo AG & Co. KG; *Int'l*, pg. 2648
FESTO S.I.A.—See Festo AG & Co. KG; *Int'l*, pg. 2648
FESTO S.P.A.—See Festo AG & Co. KG; *Int'l*, pg. 2648
FESTO SPOL. S.R.O.—See Festo AG & Co. KG; *Int'l*, pg. 2648
FESTO SPOL. S.R.O.—See Festo AG & Co. KG; *Int'l*, pg. 2648
FESTO SP.Z.O.O.—See Festo AG & Co. KG; *Int'l*, pg. 2648
FESTO S.R.L.—See Festo AG & Co. KG; *Int'l*, pg. 2648
FESTO S.R.L.—See Festo AG & Co. KG; *Int'l*, pg. 2648
FESTO, S.R.O.—See Festo AG & Co. KG; *Int'l*, pg. 2648
FESTO U.A.B.—See Festo AG & Co. KG; *Int'l*, pg. 2648
FES (VIETNAM) CO. LTD.—See Food Empire Holdings Limited; *Int'l*, pg. 2727
FE TAEWOONG LLC—See Taewoong Logistics Co., Ltd.; *Int'l*, pg. 7405
FETCHING COMMUNICATIONS—See French/West/Vaughan, LLC; *U.S. Private*, pg. 1609
FETCH INSURANCE SERVICES, LLC—See Warburg Pincus LLC; *U.S. Private*, pg. 4438
FETCH LOGISTICS, INC.; *U.S. Private*, pg. 1499
FETCHS ENTERPRISES INC.; *U.S. Private*, pg. 1500
FETCO HOME DECOR INC.; *U.S. Private*, pg. 1500
F. E. TECH CO., LTD.—See Kyokuto Kaihatsu Kogyo Co. Ltd.; *Int'l*, pg. 4363
FET HOLDINGS LLC—See Forum Energy Technologies, Inc.; *U.S. Public*, pg. 873
FETIM B.V.; *Int'l*, pg. 2648
FETTER PRINTING COMPANY; *U.S. Private*, pg. 1500
FETZER VINEYARDS—See Vina Concha y Toro S.A.; *Int'l*, pg. 8209
FEU ALABANG, INC.—See Far Eastern University Inc.; *Int'l*, pg. 2617
FEUER IM STEIN GMBH & CO KG—See Tulikivi Corporation; *Int'l*, pg. 7969
FEUERLOESCHGERAETE GMBH NEURUPPIN—See Johnson Controls International plc; *Int'l*, pg. 3987
FEUERSCHUTZ HOLLMANN G.M.B.H.—See London Security PLC; *Int'l*, pg. 4547
FEUERSTRATER GMBH—See AGRAVIS Raiffeisen AG; *Int'l*, pg. 215
FEUMAS GMBH—See GAF Materials Corporation; *U.S. Private*, pg. 1633
FEUTRES DEPLAND S.A.S.—See Gascogne SA; *Int'l*, pg. 2887
FEUTZ CONTRACTORS, INC.; *U.S. Private*, pg. 1500
FEV AMERICA LATINA LTDA.—See FEV GmbH; *Int'l*, pg. 2648
FEV CHINA CO., LTD.—See FEV GmbH; *Int'l*, pg. 2648
FE VELCOM—See America Movil, S.A.B. de C.V.; *Int'l*, pg. 421
F. E. VENTURE SDN. BHD.—See Leong Hup International Berhad; *Int'l*, pg. 4461
FEVERTREE DRINKS PLC; *Int'l*, pg. 2648
FEVERTREE LIMITED—See Fevertree Drinks plc; *Int'l*, pg. 2648
FEVERTREE USA INC.—See Fevertree Drinks plc; *Int'l*, pg. 2648
FEV EUROPE GMBH—See E.ON SE; *Int'l*, pg. 2257
FEV FRANCE S.A.S.—See FEV GmbH; *Int'l*, pg. 2648
FEV GMBH; *Int'l*, pg. 2648
FEV IBERIA SL—See FEV GmbH; *Int'l*, pg. 2648
FEV, INC.—See FEV GmbH; *Int'l*, pg. 2648
FEV INDIA PRIVATE LIMITED—See FEV GmbH; *Int'l*, pg. 2648
FEV INDIA PVT. LTD.—See FEV GmbH; *Int'l*, pg. 2648
FEV ITALIA S.R.L.—See FEV GmbH; *Int'l*, pg. 2648
FEV JAPAN CO., LTD.—See FEV GmbH; *Int'l*, pg. 2648
FEV KOREA LTD.—See FEV GmbH; *Int'l*, pg. 2648
FEV NORTH AMERICA, INC.; *U.S. Private*, pg. 1500
FEV POLSKA SP. Z O.O.—See FEV GmbH; *Int'l*, pg. 2648
FEV SVERIGE AB—See FEV GmbH; *Int'l*, pg. 2648
FEV TR OTOMOTIV VE ENERJI ARASTIRMA VE MUHENDISLIK LTD. STI.—See FEV GmbH; *Int'l*, pg. 2648
FEV UK LTD.—See FEV GmbH; *Int'l*, pg. 2648
FE WUERTHBEL—See Wurth Verwaltungsgesellschaft mbH; *Int'l*, pg. 8504

FEXCO ASSET FINANCE—See FEXCO Holdings; *Int'l*, pg. 2649
FEXCO BUSINESS CONSULTING (SHANGHAI) LTD.—See FEXCO Holdings; *Int'l*, pg. 2649
FEXCO DCC SOLUTIONS FZ-LLC—See FEXCO Holdings; *Int'l*, pg. 2649
FEXCO FINANCIAL SERVICES—See FEXCO Holdings; *Int'l*, pg. 2649
FEXCO HOLDINGS; *Int'l*, pg. 2649
FEXCO LTD—See FEXCO Holdings; *Int'l*, pg. 2649
FEXCOM GMBH—See Philion SE; *Int'l*, pg. 5845
FEXCO PACIFIC NEW ZEALAND—See FEXCO Holdings; *Int'l*, pg. 2649
FEX L.P.—See Repsol, S.A.; *Int'l*, pg. 6293
FEYEN ZYLSTRA ELECTRIC INC.; *U.S. Private*, pg. 1500
FEY INDUSTRIES, INC.; *U.S. Private*, pg. 1500
FEY LAMELLENRINGE GMBH & CO. KG; *Int'l*, pg. 2649
FEY LAMELOVE KROUZKY PRODEJE S.R.O.—See Fey Lamellenringe GmbH & Co. KG; *Int'l*, pg. 2649
FEZELL ENTERPRISES II INC.—See Fezell Enterprises Inc.; *U.S. Private*, pg. 1500
FEZELL ENTERPRISES INC.; *U.S. Private*, pg. 1500
FFASTFILL AUSTRALIA PTY. LTD.—See ION Investment Group Ltd.; *Int'l*, pg. 3794
FFASTFILL LIMITED—See ION Investment Group Ltd.; *Int'l*, pg. 3794
FFASTFILL POST-TRADE PROCESSING LIMITED—See ION Investment Group Ltd.; *Int'l*, pg. 3794
FFBW, INC.; *U.S. Public*, pg. 829
FFC LIMITED PARTNERSHIP; *U.S. Private*, pg. 1500
FFC MANAGEMENT, INC.—See Fulton Financial Corporation; *U.S. Public*, pg. 892
F&F CO., LTD.—See Fuji Oil Holdings Inc.; *Int'l*, pg. 2815
FFC SERVICES INC.—See Linden Street Capital Corp.; *U.S. Private*, pg. 2460
FFD FINANCIAL CORPORATION; *U.S. Public*, pg. 830
FFDM-TIVOLY SA—See Tivoly S.A.; *Int'l*, pg. 7762
FFE INVEST A/S—See FLSmidth & Co. A/S; *Int'l*, pg. 2710
FFE LIMITED—See Halma plc; *Int'l*, pg. 3231
FFE TRANSPORTATION SERVICES, INC.—See Frozen Food Express Industries, Inc.; *U.S. Private*, pg. 1617
FFF ENTERPRISES INC.; *U.S. Private*, pg. 1500
FFG ASIA-PACIFIC LTD.—See Fair Friend Group; *Int'l*, pg. 2604
FFG BUSINESS CONSULTING CO., LTD.—See Fukuoka Financial Group, Inc.; *Int'l*, pg. 2840
FFG CARD CO., LTD.—See Fukuoka Financial Group, Inc.; *Int'l*, pg. 2840
FFG EUROPE MACHINERY (BEIJING) CO., LTD.—See Fair Friend Group; *Int'l*, pg. 2604
FFG EUROPE S.P.A.—See Fair Friend Group; *Int'l*, pg. 2604
FFG FINANZCHECK FINANZPORTALE GMBH—See Scout24 SE; *Int'l*, pg. 6653
FFG INSURANCE SERVICE CO., LTD.—See Fukuoka Financial Group, Inc.; *Int'l*, pg. 2840
FFG LEASE CO., LTD.—See Tokyo Century Corporation; *Int'l*, pg. 7789
FFG RUSSIA (RUSSIA) AUTOMATION SOLUTIONS—See Fair Friend Group; *Int'l*, pg. 2604
FFG SECURITIES CO., LTD.—See Fukuoka Financial Group, Inc.; *Int'l*, pg. 2840
FFGS TECHNO SERVICE CO., LTD.—See FUJIFILM Holdings Corporation; *Int'l*, pg. 2821
FFG WERKE GMBH—See Fair Friend Group; *Int'l*, pg. 2604
F&F HOLDINGS CO., LTD.; *Int'l*, pg. 2595
FFI CONTRACTING SERVICES; *U.S. Private*, pg. 1500
FFI HOLDINGS, INC.—See Simple Management Group, Inc.; *U.S. Private*, pg. 3666
FFI HOLDINGS LIMITED; *Int'l*, pg. 2649
FFJMP SDN. BHD.—See Fuji Furukawa Engineering & Construction Co., Ltd.; *Int'l*, pg. 2813
FFLIC CYFYNGEDIG—See Boomerang Plus plc; *Int'l*, pg. 1110
FFLO - INSIDE AUTO PARTS, INC.—See Free Flow, Inc.; *U.S. Public*, pg. 884
FFL PARTNERS, LLC; *U.S. Private*, pg. 1500
FFM BERHAD—See Kuok Brothers Sdn. Bhd.; *Int'l*, pg. 4334
FFM FARMS SDN BHD—See Kuok Brothers Sdn. Bhd.; *Int'l*, pg. 4334
FFM FEEDMILLS (SARAWAK) SDN BHD—See Kuok Brothers Sdn. Bhd.; *Int'l*, pg. 4334
FFM GRAINS & MILLS SDN. BHD.—See Kuok Brothers Sdn. Bhd.; *Int'l*, pg. 4334
FFM MARKETING SDN BHD—See Kuok Brothers Sdn. Bhd.; *Int'l*, pg. 4334
FFM PULAU INDAH SDN BHD—See Kuok Brothers Sdn. Bhd.; *Int'l*, pg. 4334
FFM (SABAH) SDN BHD—See Kuok Brothers Sdn. Bhd.; *Int'l*, pg. 4334
FFN HOLDING AG—See Fielmann Group AG; *Int'l*, pg. 2649
F.F. PHILLIPS INC.; *U.S. Private*, pg. 1456
FFP SA; *Int'l*, pg. 2649
FFRI SECURITY, INC.; *Int'l*, pg. 2649
FFSOL CO., LTD.—See SOLXYZ Co., Ltd.; *Int'l*, pg. 7083

COMPANY NAME INDEX

FF SOUCY WB L.P.—See Black Diamond Capital Holdings, LLC; *U.S. Private*, pg. 570
F&F S.R.L.—See Seri Industrial SpA; *Int'l*, pg. 6722
FF SYSTEMS INC.; *U.S. Private*, pg. 1500
FFT ESPANA TECNOLOGIAS DE AUTOMOCION S.A.—See Fosun International Limited; *Int'l*, pg. 2750
FFT GMBH & CO. KGAA—See Fosun International Limited; *Int'l*, pg. 2750
FFT INDIA PVT. LTD.—See Ava Risk Group Limited; *Int'l*, pg. 733
FFT MEXICO S.A. DE C.V.—See Fosun International Limited; *Int'l*, pg. 2750
FF TOHO INC—See TBS Holdings, Inc.; *Int'l*, pg. 7481
FFT PRODUCTION SYSTEMS, INC.—See Fosun International Limited; *Int'l*, pg. 2751
FFT PRODUCTION SYSTEMS (SHANGHAI) CO., LTD.—See Fosun International Limited; *Int'l*, pg. 2750
FFT PRODUCTION SYSTEMS S.R.L.—See Fosun International Limited; *Int'l*, pg. 2751
FFT PRODUKTIONSSYSTEME GMBH & CO. KG—See Fosun International Limited; *Int'l*, pg. 2750
FFVA MUTUAL INSURANCE CO.; *U.S. Private*, pg. 1500
FFV ORDNANCE AB—See Saab AB; *Int'l*, pg. 6459
FFW CORPORATION; *U.S. Public*, pg. 830
FFW—See ICTA AB; *Int'l*, pg. 3587
FFW—See ICTA AB; *Int'l*, pg. 3587
FGA INVESTIMENTI S.P.A.—See Stellantis N.V.; *Int'l*, pg. 7198
F&G ANNUITIES & LIFE, INC.—See Fidelity National Financial, Inc.; *U.S. Public*, pg. 831
FGA NORTH AMERICA INC.—See Figeac-Aero SA; *Int'l*, pg. 2660
FGA OFFICINE AUTOMOBILISTICHE GRUGLIASCO S.P.A.—See Stellantis N.V.; *Int'l*, pg. 7198
FGA RUSSIA S.R.L.—See Stellantis N.V.; *Int'l*, pg. 7198
FGA S.R.L.—See Interpump Group S.p.A.; *Int'l*, pg. 3755
F. GAVINA & SONS, INC.; *U.S. Private*, pg. 1455
F&G (BOTSWANA) (PTY) LIMITED—See Huabao International Holdings Limited; *Int'l*, pg. 3510
FG BUKIDNON POWER CORPORATION - BUKIDNON PLANT—See First Gen Corporation; *Int'l*, pg. 2684
F.G. EUROPE S.A.; *Int'l*, pg. 2596
FG FITNESS & MEDIA GROUP, INC.; *U.S. Public*, pg. 830
FG GROUP HOLDINGS INC —See Kingsway Financial Services Inc.; *U.S. Public*, pg. 1234
FG HAGGERTY COMPANY, INC.; *U.S. Private*, pg. 1501
FGH BANK N.V.—See Cooperatieve Centrale Raiffeisen-Boerenleenbank B.A.; *Int'l*, pg. 1791
FGIC UK LIMITED—See Financial Guaranty Insurance Company; *U.S. Private*, pg. 1507
FGI GROUP INC.; *U.S. Private*, pg. 1501
FGI INDUSTRIES LTD.; *U.S. Public*, pg. 830
F G INGENIERIE ET PROMOTION IMMOBILIERE—See BNP Paribas SA; *Int'l*, pg. 1091
FGINOX S.A.S.—See Thermador Groupe; *Int'l*, pg. 7707
FGI OPERATING COMPANY, LLC—See Cerberus Capital Management, L.P.; *U.S. Private*, pg. 838
F.G.J CO., LTD.—See H2O Retailing Corp.; *Int'l*, pg. 3200
FGL AIRCRAFT IRELAND LIMITED—See Fuyo General Lease Co., Ltd.; *Int'l*, pg. 2859
FGL GROUP BUSINESS SERVICE CO., LTD.—See Fuyo General Lease Co., Ltd.; *Int'l*, pg. 2859
FGL GROUP MANAGEMENT SERVICE CO., LTD.—See Fuyo General Lease Co., Ltd.; *Int'l*, pg. 2859
FGL HANDELSGESELLSCHAFT MBH—See AGRAVIS Raiffeisen AG; *Int'l*, pg. 215
FGL HOLDINGS—See Fidelity National Financial, Inc.; *U.S. Public*, pg. 831
FGL SPORTS LTD.—See Canadian Tire Corporation Limited; *Int'l*, pg. 1286
F&G MECHANICAL CORPORATION—See EMCOR Group, Inc.; *U.S. Public*, pg. 738
FGP INTERNATIONAL, INC.; *U.S. Private*, pg. 1501
FGP LTD.; *Int'l*, pg. 2649
FGR HANNA LIMITADA—See Lovell Minnick Partners LLC; *U.S. Private*, pg. 2502
F.G.S. CO., LTD.—See Funai Electric Co., Ltd.; *Int'l*, pg. 2844
FGSZ FOLDGAZSZALLITO ZRT - GELLENHAZA NATURAL GAS TRANSMISSION PLANT—See MOL Magyar Olaj- es Gazipari Nyrt.; *Int'l*, pg. 5020
FGSZ FOLDGAZSZALLITO ZRT - KECSKEMET NATURAL GAS TRANSMISSION PLANT—See MOL Magyar Olaj- es Gazipari Nyrt.; *Int'l*, pg. 5020
FGSZ FOLDGAZSZALLITO ZRT.—See MOL Magyar Olaj-es Gazipari Nyrt.; *Int'l*, pg. 5020
FGSZ FOLDGAZSZALLITO ZRT - VECSES NATURAL GAS TRANSMISSION PLANT—See MOL Magyar Olaj-es Gazipari Nyrt.; *Int'l*, pg. 5020
FGV AGRI SERVICES SDN. BHD.—See FGV Holdings Bhd; *Int'l*, pg. 2649
FGV AGRO FRESH TECHNOLOGY SDN. BHD.—See FGV Holdings Bhd; *Int'l*, pg. 2649
FGV DAIRY FARM SDN. BHD.—See FGV Holdings Bhd; *Int'l*, pg. 2649
FGV HOLDINGS BHD; *Int'l*, pg. 2649
FGV JOHOR BULKERS SDN. BHD.—See FGV Holdings Bhd; *Int'l*, pg. 2649

FGV JOHORE BULKERS SDN. BHD.—See FGV Holdings Bhd; *Int'l*, pg. 2649
FGV PRODATA SYSTEMS SDN. BHD.—See FGV Holdings Bhd; *Int'l*, pg. 2649
FGV SECURITY SERVICES SDN. BHD.—See FGV Holdings Bhd; *Int'l*, pg. 2649
FGV TRANSPORT SERVICES SDN. BHD.—See FGV Holdings Bhd; *Int'l*, pg. 2649
FGV USA PROPERTIES, INC—See FGV Holdings Bhd; *Int'l*, pg. 2649
FGX CANADA CORP—See EssilorLuxottica SA; *Int'l*, pg. 2514
FGX CANADA-FOSTERGRANT—See EssilorLuxottica SA; *Int'l*, pg. 2514
FGX DIRECT LLC—See EssilorLuxottica SA; *Int'l*, pg. 2514
FGX EUROPE, LTD.—See EssilorLuxottica SA; *Int'l*, pg. 2514
FGX INTERNATIONAL, INC.—See EssilorLuxottica SA; *Int'l*, pg. 2514
FGX INTERNATIONAL LIMITED CHINA—See EssilorLuxottica SA; *Int'l*, pg. 2514
FHB LIFE ANNUITY LTD.—See FHB Mortgage Bank Public Limited Company; *Int'l*, pg. 2650
FHB MANAGEMENT SDN. BHD.—See Fiamma Holdings Berhad; *Int'l*, pg. 2650
FHB MORTGAGE BANK PUBLIC LIMITED COMPANY; *Int'l*, pg. 2650
F.H. BONN COMPANY; *U.S. Private*, pg. 1456
FHB PROPERTIES, INC.—See BNP Paribas SA; *Int'l*, pg. 1088
FHB REAL ESTATE LEASING LTD.—See FHB Mortgage Bank Public Limited Company; *Int'l*, pg. 2650
FHB REAL ESTATE LTD.—See FHB Mortgage Bank Public Limited Company; *Int'l*, pg. 2650
FHB SERVICES LTD—See FHB Mortgage Bank Public Limited Company; *Int'l*, pg. 2650
FH CAPITAL LIMITED—See Finance House P.J.S.C.; *Int'l*, pg. 2664
FHC CONTRACTING, INC.; *U.S. Private*, pg. 1501
FH CENTER, INC.—See BNP Paribas SA; *Int'l*, pg. 1088
F.H. CHASE, INC.; *U.S. Private*, pg. 1456
FHC HEALTH SYSTEMS INC.; *U.S. Private*, pg. 1501
FHC HOLDING COMPANY; *U.S. Private*, pg. 1501
FHCHS OF PUERTO RICO, INC.—See Universal Health Services, Inc.; *U.S. Public*, pg. 2257
FHC MARKETING; *U.S. Private*, pg. 1501
FH COMPANIES, INC.; *U.S. Private*, pg. 1501
FH CONSTRUCTION OF MARION, LLC—See CenterPoint Energy, Inc.; *U.S. Public*, pg. 472
F&H CONSTRUCTION; *U.S. Private*, pg. 1454
F-HEALTH ACCELERATORS PRIVATE LIMITED—See Vaidya Sane Ayurved Laboratories Ltd.; *Int'l*, pg. 8108
F&H ELECTRICAL CONTRACTORS, INC.; *U.S. Private*, pg. 1454
FHE USA LLC - SAN ANTONIO—See J Fitzgibbons LLC; *U.S. Private*, pg. 2153
FHE USA LLC—See J Fitzgibbons LLC; *U.S. Private*, pg. 2153
FHF BERGBAUTECHNIK GMBH & CO. KG—See Eaton Corporation plc; *Int'l*, pg. 2281
FHF FUNKE+HUSTER FERNSIG GMBH—See Eaton Corporation plc; *Int'l*, pg. 2281
F&H FOOD EQUIPMENT CO; *U.S. Private*, pg. 1454
F.H.G. CORPORATION—See H.I.G. Capital, LLC; *U.S. Private*, pg. 1829
FHI 360; *U.S. Private*, pg. 1501
FHI (NINGBO) CO., LTD.—See Formosa Plastics Corporation; *Int'l*, pg. 2735
FHL DISTRIBUTION CENTRE PTY LTD—See Steinhoff International Holdings N.V.; *Int'l*, pg. 7194
FHL I. KIRIAKIDIS MARBLE - GRANITE SA; *Int'l*, pg. 2650
FHL LEASE HOLDING COMPANY INC.—See BNP Paribas SA; *Int'l*, pg. 1088
FHL PROPERTIES PTE LIMITED—See Fijian Holdings Limited; *Int'l*, pg. 2662
FHM INSURANCE COMPANY—See LUBA Mutual Holding Company; *U.S. Private*, pg. 2510
FHN FINANCIAL MAIN STREET ADVISORS, LLC—See First Horizon Corporation; *U.S. Public*, pg. 844
F. HOFFMANN-LA ROCHE AG—See Roche Holding AG; *Int'l*, pg. 6373
F.H. PAPENMEIER GMBH & CO. KG; *Int'l*, pg. 2596
F.H. PASCHEN, S.N. NIELSEN, INC.; *U.S. Private*, pg. 1456
FHP DI R. FREUDENBERG S.A.S.—See Freudenberg SE; *Int'l*, pg. 2785
FHP EXPORT GMBH—See Freudenberg SE; *Int'l*, pg. 2785
FHP - FREZITE HIGH PERFORMANCE, UNIPESSOAL, LDA.—See Sandvik AB; *Int'l*, pg. 6529
FHP HELLAS S.A.—See Freudenberg SE; *Int'l*, pg. 2785
FHP HOLDING GMBH—See Freudenberg SE; *Int'l*, pg. 2785
FHP MANUFACTURING COMPANY—See Robert Bosch GmbH; *Int'l*, pg. 6367
F&H PORTER NOVELLI—See Omnicom Group Inc.; *U.S. Public*, pg. 1590

FHP VILEDA S.A.—See Freudenberg SE; *Int'l*, pg. 2785
FHP VILEDA S.C.S.—See Freudenberg SE; *Int'l*, pg. 2785
FHP VILEDA SP. Z.O.O.—See Freudenberg SE; *Int'l*, pg. 2785
FHR ANLAGENBAU GMBH—See centrotherm photovoltaics AG; *Int'l*, pg. 1415
FHR PROPYLENE LLC—See Koch Industries, Inc.; *U.S. Private*, pg. 2327
F.H. STOLTZE LAND & LUMBER COMPANY; *U.S. Private*, pg. 1456
F&H SUPPLY CO. INC.; *U.S. Private*, pg. 1455
FHV BBDO—See Omnicom Group Inc.; *U.S. Public*, pg. 1575
FI360, INC.—See Broadridge Financial Solutions, Inc.; *U.S. Public*, pg. 391
FIACAO TEC SAO JOSE S.A.; *Int'l*, pg. 2650
FIAC S.P.A.—See Atlas Copco AB; *Int'l*, pg. 682
FIAMMA HOLDINGS BERHAD; *Int'l*, pg. 2650
FIAMMA PROPERTIES SDN BHD—See Fiamma Holdings Berhad; *Int'l*, pg. 2650
FIAMM ASIA PACIFIC PTE LTD.—See Fiamm S.p.A.; *Int'l*, pg. 2650
FIAMMA TRADING SDN. BHD.—See Fiamma Holdings Berhad; *Int'l*, pg. 2650
FIAMM AUTOMOTIVE CZECH A.S.—See Fiamm S.p.A.; *Int'l*, pg. 2650
FIAMM AUTOTECH CO., LTD—See Fiamm S.p.A.; *Int'l*, pg. 2650
FIAMM ENERGY LLC—See Fiamm S.p.A.; *Int'l*, pg. 2650
FIAMM ENERGY TECHNOLOGY (FRANCE) S.A.R.L.—See Fiamm S.p.A.; *Int'l*, pg. 2650
FIAMM ENERGY TECHNOLOGY S.P.A.—See Fiamm S.p.A.; *Int'l*, pg. 2650
FIAMM ENERGY TECHNOLOGY (USA) LLC—See Fiamm S.p.A.; *Int'l*, pg. 2650
FIAMM ENERGY TECHNOLOGY (WUHAN) CO., LTD.—See Fiamm S.p.A.; *Int'l*, pg. 2650
FIAMM FRANCE SARL—See Fiamm S.p.A.; *Int'l*, pg. 2650
FIAMM-GS S.P.A.—See Fiamm S.p.A.; *Int'l*, pg. 2650
FIAMM-GS S.P.A.—See GS Yuasa Corporation; *Int'l*, pg. 3143
FIAMM LATIN AMERICA LTDA.—See Fiamm S.p.A.; *Int'l*, pg. 2650
FIAMM MALAYSIA SDN. BHD.—See Fiamm S.p.A.; *Int'l*, pg. 2650
FIAMM SLOVAKIA S.R.O.—See Fiamm S.p.A.; *Int'l*, pg. 2650
FIAMM SONICK S.A.—See Fiamm S.p.A.; *Int'l*, pg. 2650
FIAMM S.P.A. - AVEZZANO PLANT—See Fiamm S.p.A.; *Int'l*, pg. 2650
FIAMM S.P.A.; *Int'l*, pg. 2650
FIAMM TECHNOLOGIES INC.—See Fiamm S.p.A.; *Int'l*, pg. 2650
FIAMM UK LIMITED—See Fiamm S.p.A.; *Int'l*, pg. 2650
FIAT ARGENTINA S.A.—See Stellantis N.V.; *Int'l*, pg. 7197
FIAT AUTO ARGENTINA S.A—See Stellantis N.V.; *Int'l*, pg. 7198
FIAT AUTO ESPANA MARKETING INSTITUTO AGRUPACION DE INTERES ECONOMICO—See Stellantis N.V.; *Int'l*, pg. 7198
FIAT AUTO IRELAND LTD.—See Stellantis N.V.; *Int'l*, pg. 7198
FIAT AUTOMOBILES SERVICE CO. LTD.—See Stellantis N.V.; *Int'l*, pg. 7198
FIAT AUTOMOBILES S.P.A.—See Stellantis N.V.; *Int'l*, pg. 7198
FIAT AUTO POLAND S.A.—See Stellantis N.V.; *Int'l*, pg. 7198
FIAT AUTO PORTUGUESA SA—See Stellantis N.V.; *Int'l*, pg. 7198
FIAT AUTO S.A. DE AHORRO PARA FINES DETERMINADOS—See Stellantis N.V.; *Int'l*, pg. 7198
FIAT AUTO VAR S.R.L.—See Stellantis N.V.; *Int'l*, pg. 7198
FIAT CHRYSLER AUTOMOBILES UK LTD.—See Stellantis N.V.; *Int'l*, pg. 7198
FIAT CHRYSLER FINANCE NORTH AMERICA, INC.—See Stellantis N.V.; *Int'l*, pg. 7197
FIATC MUTUA DE SEGUROS Y DE REASEGUROS APF; *Int'l*, pg. 2651
FIAT CR SPOL. S R.O.—See Stellantis N.V.; *Int'l*, pg. 7198
FIAT DO BRASIL SA—See Stellantis N.V.; *Int'l*, pg. 7200
FIAT FINANCAS BRASIL LTDA—See Stellantis N.V.; *Int'l*, pg. 7197
FIAT FINANCE AND TRADE LTD S.A.—See Stellantis N.V.; *Int'l*, pg. 7197
FIAT FINANCE ET SERVICES S.A.—See Stellantis N.V.; *Int'l*, pg. 7197
FIAT FINANCE S.P.A.—See Stellantis N.V.; *Int'l*, pg. 7197
FIAT FRANCE SA—See Stellantis N.V.; *Int'l*, pg. 7198
FIAT GESTIONE PARTECIPAZIONI S.P.A.—See Stellantis N.V.; *Int'l*, pg. 7197
FIAT GMBH—See Stellantis N.V.; *Int'l*, pg. 7197
FIAT GROUP AUTOMOBILES HELLAS S.A.—See Stellantis N.V.; *Int'l*, pg. 7198
FIAT GROUP AUTOMOBILES IRELAND LTD.—See Stellantis N.V.; *Int'l*, pg. 7198
FIAT GROUP AUTOMOBILES JAPAN K.K.—See Stellantis N.V.; *Int'l*, pg. 7198

FIAT GROUP AUTOMOBILES MAROC S.A.—See Stellantis N.V.; *Int'l*, pg. 7198
FIAT GROUP AUTOMOBILES SOUTH AFRICA (PROPRIETARY) LTD—See Stellantis N.V.; *Int'l*, pg. 7198
FIAT GROUP AUTOMOBILES SPAIN S.A.—See Stellantis N.V.; *Int'l*, pg. 7198
FIAT GROUP AUTOMOBILES S.P.A.—See Stellantis N.V.; *Int'l*, pg. 7197
FIAT GROUP AUTOMOBILES SWEDEN AB—See Stellantis N.V.; *Int'l*, pg. 7198
FIAT GROUP MARKETING & CORPORATE COMMUNICATION S.P.A.—See Stellantis N.V.; *Int'l*, pg. 7198
FIAT GROUP PURCHASING FRANCE S.A.R.L.—See Stellantis N.V.; *Int'l*, pg. 7197
FIAT GROUP PURCHASING POLAND SP. Z O.O.—See Stellantis N.V.; *Int'l*, pg. 7197
FIAT GROUP PURCHASING S.R.L.—See Stellantis N.V.; *Int'l*, pg. 7197
FIAT IBERICA S.A.—See Stellantis N.V.; *Int'l*, pg. 7197
FIAT INCORPORATED; *U.S. Private*, pg. 1501
FIAT INDUSTRIAL FINANCE NORTH AMERICA, INC.—See CNH Industrial N.V.; *Int'l*, pg. 1675
FIAT INDUSTRIAL FINANCE S.P.A.—See CNH Industrial N.V.; *Int'l*, pg. 1675
FIAT INDUSTRIAL S.P.A.—See CNH Industrial N.V.; *Int'l*, pg. 1675
FIAT INFORMATION TECHNOLOGY, EXCELLENCE AND METHODS S.P.A.—See Stellantis N.V.; *Int'l*, pg. 7197
FIAT MAGYARORSZAG KFT—See Stellantis N.V.; *Int'l*, pg. 7198
FIAT NETHERLANDS HOLDING B.V.—See Stellantis N.V.; *Int'l*, pg. 7198
FIAT NORTH AMERICA LLC—See Stellantis N.V.; *Int'l*, pg. 7198
FIAT PARTECIPAZIONI S.P.A.—See Stellantis N.V.; *Int'l*, pg. 7200
FIAT POWERTRAIN TECHNOLOGIES S.P.A.—See Stellantis N.V.; *Int'l*, pg. 7200
FIAT PROFESSIONAL S.P.A.—See Stellantis N.V.; *Int'l*, pg. 7200
FIAT REVI S.C.R.L.—See Stellantis N.V.; *Int'l*, pg. 7200
FIAT SERVICES POLSKA SP. Z O.O.—See Stellantis N.V.; *Int'l*, pg. 7197
FIAT SERVICES S.P.A.—See Stellantis N.V.; *Int'l*, pg. 7196
FIAT U.S.A., INC.—See Stellantis N.V.; *Int'l*, pg. 7200
FIAV L. MAZZACCHERA S.P.A.—See Calvi Holding S.r.l.; *Int'l*, pg. 1266
FIBA AIR HAVA TASIMACILIK VE HIZMETLERI A.S.—See Fiba Holding A.S.; *Int'l*, pg. 2651
FIBABANKA A.S.; *Int'l*, pg. 2651
FIBA EMEKLILIK VE HAYAT A.S.—See Fiba Holding A.S.; *Int'l*, pg. 2651
FIBA FAKTORING A.S.—See Fiba Holding A.S.; *Int'l*, pg. 2651
FIBA HOLDING A.S.; *Int'l*, pg. 2651
FIBAM COMPANHIA INDUSTRIAL; *Int'l*, pg. 2651
FIBANC PENSIONES S.G.F.P. S.A.—See Banca Mediolanum S.p.A.; *Int'l*, pg. 815
FIBANC SA—See Banca Mediolanum S.p.A.; *Int'l*, pg. 815
FIBA PORTFOY YONETIMI A.S.—See Fiba Holding A.S.; *Int'l*, pg. 2651
FIBA TECHNOLOGIES INC.; *U.S. Private*, pg. 1501
FIBEMI NV; *Int'l*, pg. 2651
FIBERAIL SDN. BHD.—See Telekom Malaysia Berhad; *Int'l*, pg. 7537
FIBERCLASS INSULATION, LLC—See Installed Building Products, Inc.; *U.S. Public*, pg. 1132
FIBERCOMPOSITE COMPANY, INC.—See Smiths Group plc; *Int'l*, pg. 7012
FIBER COMPOSITES, LLC; *U.S. Private*, pg. 1501
FIBERCON INTERNATIONAL INC.; *U.S. Private*, pg. 1501
FIBERCORE, LTD.—See Bridgepoint Group Plc; *Int'l*, pg. 1155
FIBERCORE MACHINERY JENA GMBH—See LEONI AG; *Int'l*, pg. 4464
FIBERDATA AB—See Transtema Group AB; *Int'l*, pg. 7906
FIBERDYNE LABS INC.; *U.S. Private*, pg. 1502
FIBER ENERGY PRODUCTS AR LLC—See EagleTree Capital, LP; *U.S. Private*, pg. 1311
FIBERESIN INDUSTRIES, INC.; *U.S. Private*, pg. 1502
FIBER FIX, LLC; *U.S. Private*, pg. 1501
FIBER FUELS INC.; *U.S. Private*, pg. 1501
FIBERGEL TECHNOLOGIES, INC.—See Agritech Worlwide, Inc.; *U.S. Private*, pg. 129
FIBERGLASS COLOMBIA S.A.—See Compagnie de Saint-Gobain SA; *Int'l*, pg. 1723
FIBER GLASS HAWAII INC.; *U.S. Private*, pg. 1501
FIBER GLASS INDUSTRIES INC.; *U.S. Private*, pg. 1501
FIBER GLASS SYSTEMS HOLDINGS, LLC—See NOV, Inc.; *U.S. Public*, pg. 1544
FIBER GLASS SYSTEMS L.P.—See NOV, Inc.; *U.S. Public*, pg. 1544
FIBERGLASS SYSTEMS—See NOV, Inc.; *U.S. Public*, pg. 1544
FIBERGLASS TECHNOLOGY INDUSTRIES—See Celstar Group Inc.; *U.S. Private*, pg. 808
FIBERGRATE COMPOSITE STRUCTURES, INC.—See RPM International Inc.; *U.S. Public*, pg. 1818

FIBERGRATE COMPOSITE STRUCTURES LIMITED—See RPM International Inc.; *U.S. Public*, pg. 1818
FIBERGUIDE INDUSTRIES INC.—See Koch Industries, Inc.; *U.S. Private*, pg. 2333
FIBERHOME TECHNOLOGIES GROUP; *Int'l*, pg. 2652
FIBER INNOVATION TECHNOLOGY INC.—See CHA Technologies Inc.; *U.S. Private*, pg. 845
FIBER INTERMEDIATE PRODUCTS COMPANY; *Int'l*, pg. 2652
FIBERKOM APS—See Bravida Holding AB; *Int'l*, pg. 1142
FIBERLABS INC.; *Int'l*, pg. 2652
FIBERLAY INC; *U.S. Private*, pg. 1502
FIBERLINE COMPOSITES A/S—See Gurit Holding AG; *Int'l*, pg. 3187
FIBER-LINE INTERNATIONAL B.V.—See Avient Corporation; *U.S. Public*, pg. 247
FIBER-LINE, LLC—See Avient Corporation; *U.S. Public*, pg. 247
FIBERLINKS TEXTILES INC.; *Int'l*, pg. 2652
FIBERLOCK TECHNOLOGIES, INC.—See Audax Group, Limited Partnership; *U.S. Private*, pg. 388
FIBERMARK INC.—See American Securities LLC; *U.S. Private*, pg. 248
FIBERMARK NORTH AMERICA, INC.—See American Securities LLC; *U.S. Private*, pg. 248
FIBERMARK—See American Securities LLC; *U.S. Private*, pg. 248
FIBER MATERIALS, INC.—See Edgewater Capital Partners, L.P.; *U.S. Private*, pg. 1334
FIBERNET CORP; *U.S. Private*, pg. 1502
FIBER NETWORK SOLUTIONS, INC.—See QualTek Services Inc.; *U.S. Public*, pg. 1748
FIBER OPTIC SENSING SOLUTIONS PRIVATE LIMITED—See TVS Srichakra Ltd; *Int'l*, pg. 7989
FIBEROPTICS TECHNOLOGY INC.; *U.S. Private*, pg. 1502
FIBERPACHS S.A.—See senata GmbH; *Int'l*, pg. 6707
FIBERPIPE, INC.—See Tonaquint Data Centers, Inc.; *U.S. Private*, pg. 4184
FIBERPLEX TECHNOLOGIES, LLC—See Patton Electronics Co.; *U.S. Private*, pg. 3111
FIBER PRO INC.—See Celstar Group Inc.; *U.S. Private*, pg. 808
FIBER REACH PTE. LTD.—See Ntegrator International Ltd; *Int'l*, pg. 5481
FIBER ROADS, LLC—See EchoStar Corporation; *U.S. Public*, pg. 711
FIBER SENSYS INC.—See Optex Group Co., Ltd.; *Int'l*, pg. 5601
FIBERS, INC.—See Pioneer Industries, Inc.; *U.S. Private*, pg. 2669
THE FIBERSMITH COMPANY; *U.S. Private*, pg. 4028
FIBERSOFT LIMITED—See Hines Global REIT, Inc.; *U.S. Private*, pg. 1949
FIBERSPAR AUSTRALIA PTY. LTD.—See NOV, Inc.; *U.S. Public*, pg. 1544
FIBERSPAR CORPORATION—See NOV, Inc.; *U.S. Public*, pg. 1544
FIBERSPAR LINEPIPE CANADA LTD.—See NOV, Inc.; *U.S. Public*, pg. 1544
FIBERSYSTEM AB—See Addtech AB; *Int'l*, pg. 133
FIBER SYSTEMS INTERNATIONAL, INC.—See Amphenol Corporation; *U.S. Public*, pg. 128
FIBERTECH CO., LTD.—See Fujikura Ltd.; *Int'l*, pg. 2827
FIBER-TECH INDUSTRIES, INC.—See Celstar Group Inc.; *U.S. Private*, pg. 808
FIBER TECHNOLOGIES, INC.—See Dycom Industries, Inc.; *U.S. Public*, pg. 699
FIBER TECHNOLOGIES SOLUTIONS, LLC—See Dycom Industries, Inc.; *U.S. Public*, pg. 698
FIBERTEK INSULATION LLC—See Owens Corning; *U.S. Public*, pg. 1626
FIBERTEL, LLC—See Quanta Services, Inc.; *U.S. Public*, pg. 1751
FIBERTEX, A.S.—See Aktieselskabet Schouw & Co.; *Int'l*, pg. 264
FIBERTEX ELEPHANT ESPANA, S.L.—See Aktieselskabet Schouw & Co.; *Int'l*, pg. 265
FIBERTEX FRANCE S.A.R.L.—See Aktieselskabet Schouw & Co.; *Int'l*, pg. 265
FIBERTEX NAOTECIDOS LTDA.—See Aktieselskabet Schouw & Co.; *Int'l*, pg. 265
FIBERTEX NONWOVENS A/S—See Aktieselskabet Schouw & Co.; *Int'l*, pg. 265
FIBERTEX NONWOVENS S.A.—See Aktieselskabet Schouw & Co.; *Int'l*, pg. 265
FIBERTEX NONWOVENS TEKSTIL SANAYI VE IHRACAT A.S.—See Aktieselskabet Schouw & Co.; *Int'l*, pg. 265
FIBERTEX PERSONAL CARE AG—See Aktieselskabet Schouw & Co.; *Int'l*, pg. 266
FIBERTEX PERSONAL CARE A/S—See Aktieselskabet Schouw & Co.; *Int'l*, pg. 265
FIBERTEX PERSONAL CARE CORPORATION—See Aktieselskabet Schouw & Co.; *Int'l*, pg. 265
FIBERTEX PERSONAL CARE SDN BHD—See Aktieselskabet Schouw & Co.; *Int'l*, pg. 266
FIBERTEX SOUTH AFRICA LTD.—See Aktieselskabet Schouw & Co.; *Int'l*, pg. 266

FIBERVISIONS A/S—See Indorama Ventures Public Company Limited; *Int'l*, pg. 3658
FIBERVISIONS CORPORATION—See Indorama Ventures Public Company Limited; *Int'l*, pg. 3658
FIBERVISIONS MANUFACTURING COMPANY—See Indorama Ventures Public Company Limited; *Int'l*, pg. 3658
FIBERVISIONS PRODUCTS, INC.—See Indorama Ventures Public Company Limited; *Int'l*, pg. 3658
FIBERWARE EQUIPAMENTOS E SERVICOS PARA INDUSTRIA LTDA—See Lupatech S.A.; *Int'l*, pg. 4585
FIBERWAVE CORP.; *U.S. Private*, pg. 1502
FIBERWEB GEOSYNTHETICS LTD—See Berry Global Group, Inc; *U.S. Public*, pg. 321
FIBERWEB (INDIA) LTD.; *Int'l*, pg. 2652
FIBERWEB ITALIA SPA—See Berry Global Group, Inc; *U.S. Public*, pg. 322
FIBER & YARN PRODUCTS INC.; *U.S. Private*, pg. 1501
FIBI HOLDINGS LTD.; *Int'l*, pg. 2652
FIBOCOM WIRELESS, INC.; *Int'l*, pg. 2652
FIBON AUSTRALIA PTY LTD—See Fibon Berhad; *Int'l*, pg. 2652
FIBON BERHAD; *Int'l*, pg. 2652
FIBON CAPITAL SDN. BHD.—See Fibon Berhad; *Int'l*, pg. 2652
FIBON ELECTRIC (M) SDN. BHD.—See Fibon Berhad; *Int'l*, pg. 2652
FIBON UK LIMITED—See Fibon Berhad; *Int'l*, pg. 2652
FIBOPE PORTUGUESA-FILMES BIORIENTADOS, S.A.—See Clearlake Capital Group, L.P.; *U.S. Private*, pg. 935
FIBO-TRESPA AS—See FSN Capital Partners AS; *Int'l*, pg. 2799
FIBRA DANHOS; *Int'l*, pg. 2652
FIBRA HD SERVICIOS SC; *Int'l*, pg. 2652
FIBRAHOTEL; *Int'l*, pg. 2653
FIBRA INGENIERIA Y CONSTRUCCION S.A.—See NOV, Inc.; *U.S. Public*, pg. 1544
FIBRA INN; *Int'l*, pg. 2652
FIBRA MACQUARIE; *Int'l*, pg. 2652
FIBRANT B.V.—See Highsun Holding Group Co., Ltd.; *Int'l*, pg. 3388
FIBRANT HOLDING B.V.—See Highsun Holding Group Co., Ltd.; *Int'l*, pg. 3388
FIBRANT, LLC—See Highsun Holding Group Co., Ltd.; *Int'l*, pg. 3388
FIBRA PROLOGIS; *Int'l*, pg. 2652
FIBRAS FIVENGLASS SA—See Compagnie de Saint-Gobain SA; *Int'l*, pg. 1723
FIBRA SHOP PORTAFOLIOS INMOBILIARIOS SAPI DE CV; *Int'l*, pg. 2653
FIBRA-SONICS (NY) INC.—See Bioventus Inc.; *U.S. Public*, pg. 339
FIBRA UNO ADMINISTRACION SA DE CV; *Int'l*, pg. 2653
FIBREBOND CORPORATION; *U.S. Private*, pg. 1502
THE FIBRE-CEMENT PRODUCTS (LAMPANG) CO., LTD.—See The Siam Cement Public Company Limited; *Int'l*, pg. 7684
FIBRECHEM TECHNOLOGIES LIMITED; *Int'l*, pg. 2653
FIBRECOMM NETWORK (M) SDN. BHD.—See Telekom Malaysia Berhad; *Int'l*, pg. 7537
FIBRE-CROWN MANUFACTURING, INC.; *Int'l*, pg. 2653
FIBRED-MARYLAND, INC.—See Arsenal Capital Management LP; *U.S. Private*, pg. 338
FIBRE EXCELLENCE SAINT-GAUDENS SAS—See PT Sinar Mas Group; *Int'l*, pg. 6074
FIBRE EXCELLENCE TARASCON SAS—See PT Sinar Mas Group; *Int'l*, pg. 6074
FIBRE FEDERAL CREDIT UNION; *U.S. Private*, pg. 1502
FIBRE FOAM (BOMBAY) PVT. LIMITED—See Ruia Group; *Int'l*, pg. 6426
FIBREGEN PLC; *Int'l*, pg. 2653
FIBREGRID LIMITED—See RPM International Inc.; *U.S. Public*, pg. 1817
FIBREK RECYCLING U.S. INC.—See PT Sinar Mas Group; *Int'l*, pg. 6073
FIBRELITE AUSTRALIA—See Fibrelite Composites Limited.; *Int'l*, pg. 2653
FIBRELITE COMPOSITES LIMITED.; *Int'l*, pg. 2653
FIBRENEST LIMITED—See Persimmon plc; *Int'l*, pg. 5815
FIBRES INTERNATIONAL, INC.; *U.S. Private*, pg. 1502
FIBRES INTERNATIONAL, INC.—See Fibres International, Inc.; *U.S. Private*, pg. 1502
FIBRESOURCES CORP.; *Int'l*, pg. 2653
FIBRE STAR (M) SDN.BHD.—See HHRG Berhad; *Int'l*, pg. 3379
FIBREWORKS CORPORATION; *U.S. Private*, pg. 1502
FIBRIA CELULOSE S.A.—See Suzano Holding S.A.; *Int'l*, pg. 7348
FIBRIA CELULOSE USA INC.—See Suzano Holding S.A.; *Int'l*, pg. 7348
FIBRIA INNOVATIONS LTD.—See Suzano Holding S.A.; *Int'l*, pg. 7348
FIBRIX LLC—See Branford Castle, Inc.; *U.S. Private*, pg. 639
FIBROBIOLOGICS, INC.; *U.S. Public*, pg. 830
FIBROCELL SCIENCE, INC.—See Castle Creek Pharmaceuticals Holdings, Inc.; *U.S. Public*, pg. 447

COMPANY NAME INDEX

FIBROCEMENTOS PUDAHUEL S.A.—See Etex SA/NV; *Int'l*, pg. 2522
FIBRO CHEM LLC.—See Polyventive LLC; *U.S. Private*, pg. 3226
FIBRO CORPORATION—See Genstar Capital, LLC; *U.S. Private*, pg. 1678
FIBROGEN, INC.; *U.S. Public*, pg. 830
FIBROLAN LTD.; *Int'l*, pg. 2653
FIBROLITH DAMMSTOFFE GMBH—See Etex SA/NV; *Int'l*, pg. 2522
FIBROTECH THERAPEUTICS PTY LTD—See Takeda Pharmaceutical Company Limited; *Int'l*, pg. 7437
FIBRWRAP CONSTRUCTION, INC.; *U.S. Private*, pg. 1502
FIBRWRAP CONSTRUCTION (M) SDN BHD—See New Mountain Capital, LLC; *U.S. Private*, pg. 2899
FIBRWRAP CONSTRUCTION PTE LTD—See New Mountain Capital, LLC; *U.S. Private*, pg. 2899
FIBRWRAP CONSTRUCTION SERVICES, INC.—See New Mountain Capital, LLC; *U.S. Private*, pg. 2899
FIBRWRAP CONSTRUCTION SERVICES LTD.—See New Mountain Capital, LLC; *U.S. Private*, pg. 2899
FIB S.P.A.—See Seri Industrial SpA; *Int'l*, pg. 6722
FIC AMERICA CORP.—See Futaba Industrial Co., Ltd.; *Int'l*, pg. 2851
FICANEX TECHNOLOGY INC.—See Prodigy Ventures, Inc.; *Int'l*, pg. 5988
FIC GLOBAL, INC; *Int'l*, pg. 2653
FICHA, INC.; *Int'l*, pg. 2653
FICHET SECURITY SOLUTIONS BELGIUM SA/NV—See OpenGate Capital Management, LLC; *U.S. Private*, pg. 3030
FICHET SECURITY SOLUTIONS FRANCE SAS—See OpenGate Capital Management, LLC; *U.S. Private*, pg. 3030
FICHET SECURITY SOLUTIONS—See OpenGate Capital Management, LLC; *U.S. Private*, pg. 3030
FICHOT HYGIENE SAS—See Bunzl plc; *Int'l*, pg. 1218
FICHOU SAS; *Int'l*, pg. 2653
FIC KITCHEN TECHNOLOGY SDN. BHD.—See MSM International Limited; *Int'l*, pg. 5068
FICKLER OIL COMPANY INC.; *U.S. Private*, pg. 1502
FICKLING & COMPANY INCORPORATED; *U.S. Private*, pg. 1502
FIC MEDICAL S A R L —See Recordati S.p.A.; *Int'l*, pg. 6239
FICO ASIA SDN. BHD.—See BE Semiconductor Industries N.V.; *Int'l*, pg. 931
FICO B.V.—See BE Semiconductor Industries N.V.; *Int'l*, pg. 931
FICODIS INC.; *Int'l*, pg. 2653
FICO INTERNATIONAL B.V.—See BE Semiconductor Industries N.V.; *Int'l*, pg. 931
FICON OY—See Sdiptech AB; *Int'l*, pg. 6658
FI CONSULTING; *U.S. Private*, pg. 1501
FICONT INDUSTRY BEIJING CO., LTD.; *Int'l*, pg. 2653
FICO PAN-UNITED CONCRETE JOINT STOCK COMPANY—See Pan-United Corporation Ltd.; *Int'l*, pg. 5716
FICO TOOLING LESHAN COMPANY LTD.—See BE Semiconductor Industries N.V.; *Int'l*, pg. 931
FICTION FACTORY LTD.—See Vitruvian Partners LLP; *Int'l*, pg. 8263
FIC USA INC.—See VINCI S.A.; *Int'l*, pg. 8221
FIDANTE PARTNERS EUROPE LIMITED—See Challenger Limited; *Int'l*, pg. 1438
FIDEA HOLDINGS CO. LTD.; *Int'l*, pg. 2653
FIDEA NV—See Baloise Holding AG; *Int'l*, pg. 811
FIDECO AG—See Metro AG; *Int'l*, pg. 4857
FIDEICOMISO DE CREDITO BANCO GENERAL COSTA RICA; *Int'l*, pg. 2654
FIDEICOMISO ENA NORTE; *Int'l*, pg. 2654
FIDEICOMISO ENA SUR; *Int'l*, pg. 2654
FIDELIA ASSISTANCE SA—See Covea Groupe S.A.S.; *Int'l*, pg. 1820
FIDELIDADE - COMPANHIA DE SEGUROS SA—See Fosun International Limited; *Int'l*, pg. 2751
FIDELIO CRUISE SOFTWARE GMBH—See Oracle Corporation; *U.S. Public*, pg. 1612
FIDELIO INDIA PRIVATE LTD.—See Oracle Corporation; *U.S. Public*, pg. 1612
FIDELIS ASSET MANAGEMENT, LLC—See Roofstock, Inc.; *U.S. Private*, pg. 3479
FIDELIS CAPITAL LLC; *U.S. Private*, pg. 1502
FIDELIS CYBERSECURITY SOLUTIONS, INC.—See Fonds de Solidarite des Travailleurs du Quebec; *Int'l*, pg. 2725
FIDELIS GROUP LLC—See Emerson Electric Co.; *U.S. Public*, pg. 741
FIDELIS INSURANCE HOLDINGS LIMITED; *Int'l*, pg. 2654
FIDELITAS INDUSTRIEHOLDING GMBH; *Int'l*, pg. 2654
FIDELITONE, INC.; *U.S. Private*, pg. 1502
FIDELITY ADT (PTY) LTD—See Fidelity Security Group (Pty) Ltd.; *Int'l*, pg. 2654
THE FIDELITY AND DEPOSIT COMPANY OF MARYLAND—See Zurich Insurance Group Limited; *Int'l*, pg. 8699
FIDELITY ASIAN VALUES PLC; *Int'l*, pg. 2654

FIDELITY ASSURANCE, INC.; *U.S. Private*, pg. 1502
THE FIDELITY BANK INC.; *U.S. Private*, pg. 4028
FIDELITY BANK OF FLORIDA, N.A.; *U.S. Private*, pg. 1502
FIDELITY BANK PLC.; *Int'l*, pg. 2654
FIDELITY BANK—See Fidelity Financial Corporation; *U.S. Private*, pg. 1503
FIDELITY BROKERAGE SERVICES LLC—See FMR LLC; *U.S. Private*, pg. 1555
FIDELITY CABLE VISION INC.—See Cable One, Inc.; *U.S. Public*, pg. 416
FIDELITY CHARITABLE GIFT FUND; *U.S. Private*, pg. 1502
FIDELITY COMMUNICATIONS CO.—See Cable One, Inc.; *U.S. Public*, pg. 416
FIDELITY CO-OPERATIVE BANK—See Mutual Bancorp; *U.S. Private*, pg. 2819
FIDELITY D & D BANCORP, INC.; *U.S. Public*, pg. 830
THE FIDELITY DEPOSIT & DISCOUNT BANK—See Fidelity D & D Bancorp, Inc.; *U.S. Public*, pg. 830
FIDELITY DEVELOPMENT, INC.—See Fidelity Financial Corporation; *U.S. Private*, pg. 1503
FIDELITY EMERGING MARKETS LIMITED; *Int'l*, pg. 2654
FIDELITY EMPLOYER SERVICES COMPANY LLC—See FMR LLC; *U.S. Private*, pg. 1555
FIDELITY ENGINEERING CORP. - ASHBURN—See Fidelity Engineering LLC; *U.S. Private*, pg. 1502
FIDELITY ENGINEERING LLC; *U.S. Private*, pg. 1502
FIDELITY EUROPEAN TRUST PLC; *Int'l*, pg. 2654
FIDELITY EXPRESS MONEY ORDER COMPANY—See GSC Enterprises, Inc.; *U.S. Private*, pg. 1800
FIDELITY FEDERAL BANCORP; *U.S. Public*, pg. 830
FIDELITY FINANCIAL CORPORATION; *U.S. Private*, pg. 1502
FIDELITY FOUNDATION; *U.S. Private*, pg. 1503
FIDELITY GUARANTY AND ACCEPTANCE CORP.—See Lennar Corporation; *U.S. Public*, pg. 1306
FIDELITY & GUARANTY LIFE INSURANCE COMPANY—See Fidelity National Financial, Inc.; *U.S. Public*, pg. 831
FIDELITY HOLDING CORP.—See Clean Vision Corporation; *U.S. Public*, pg. 510
FIDELITY HOMESTEAD SAVINGS BANK; *U.S. Private*, pg. 1503
FIDELITY INDUSTRIES INC.; *U.S. Private*, pg. 1503
FIDELITY INFORMATION SERVICES GMBH—See Fidelity National Infor; *U.S. Public*, pg. 832
FIDELITY INFORMATION SERVICES KORDOBA GMBH—See Fidelity National Infor; *U.S. Public*, pg. 832
FIDELITY INSURANCE AGENCY, INC.—See Fidelity Financial Corporation; *U.S. Private*, pg. 1503
THE FIDELITY INVESTMENT COMPANY—See Fidelity Financial Corporation; *U.S. Private*, pg. 1503
FIDELITY INVESTMENTS CANADA LTD.—See FMR LLC; *U.S. Private*, pg. 1555
FIDELITY INVESTMENTS INSTITUTIONAL SERVICES COMPANY—See FMR LLC; *U.S. Private*, pg. 1555
FIDELITY INVESTMENTS JAPAN LIMITED—See FMR LLC; *U.S. Private*, pg. 1555
FIDELITY INVESTMENTS LIFE INSURANCE COMPANY—See FMR LLC; *U.S. Private*, pg. 1555
FIDELITY INVESTMENTS MANAGEMENT (H.K.) LIMITED—See FMR LLC; *U.S. Private*, pg. 1555
FIDELITY JAPAN TRUST PLC; *Int'l*, pg. 2654
FIDELITY LIFE ASSET MANAGEMENT COMPANY (PRIVATE) LIMITED—See Fidelity Life Assurance Limited; *Int'l*, pg. 2654
FIDELITY LIFE ASSURANCE LIMITED; *Int'l*, pg. 2654
FIDELITY LIFE ASSURANCE OF ZIMBABWE LIMITED—See Zimre Holdings Limited; *Int'l*, pg. 8684
FIDELITY LIFE FINANCIAL SERVICES (PRIVATE) LIMITED—See Fidelity Life Assurance Limited; *Int'l*, pg. 2654
FIDELITY MANAGEMENT CORPORATION—See Fidelity Financial Corporation; *U.S. Private*, pg. 1503
FIDELITY MINERALS CORP.; *Int'l*, pg. 2654
FIDELITY MOTORS LTD.—See Goddard Enterprises Limited; *Int'l*, pg. 3018
FIDELITY MUTUAL HOLDING COMPANY—See Mutual Bancorp; *U.S. Private*, pg. 2819
FIDELITY NATIONAL CREDIT SERVICES LTD.—See American CyberSystems, Inc.; *U.S. Private*, pg. 230
FIDELITY NATIONAL FINANCIAL, INC.; *U.S. Public*, pg. 830
FIDELITY NATIONAL INFORMATION SERVICES, INC. - HERNDON—See Fidelity National Infor; *U.S. Public*, pg. 832
FIDELITY NATIONAL INFORMATION SERVICES, INC. - NORCROSS—See Fidelity National Infor; *U.S. Public*, pg. 832
FIDELITY NATIONAL INFORMATION SERVICES, INC. - ORLANDO—See Fidelity National Infor; *U.S. Public*, pg. 832
FIDELITY NATIONAL INFORMATION SERVICES, INC.; *U.S. Public*, pg. 831
FIDELITY NATIONAL INSURANCE COMPANY—See Fidelity National Financial, Inc.; *U.S. Public*, pg. 831

FIDELITY NATIONAL TITLE GROUP, INC.—See Fidelity National Financial, Inc.; *U.S. Public*, pg. 831
FIDELITY NATIONAL TITLE INSURANCE COMPANY OF NEW YORK—See Fidelity National Financial, Inc.; *U.S. Public*, pg. 831
FIDELITY PAPER & SUPPLY CORP.; *U.S. Private*, pg. 1503
FIDELITY PERSONAL TRUST COMPANY, FSB—See FMR LLC; *U.S. Private*, pg. 1555
FIDELITY PRIVATE CREDIT COMPANY LLC; *U.S. Private*, pg. 1503
FIDELITY PROCESSADORA S.A.—See Fidelity National Infor; *U.S. Public*, pg. 833
FIDELITY ROOF COMPANY—See HCI Equity Management, L.P.; *U.S. Private*, pg. 1889
FIDELITY SECURITY GROUP (PTY) LTD.; *Int'l*, pg. 2654
FIDELITY SECURITY LIFE INSURANCE COMPANY; *U.S. Private*, pg. 1503
FIDELITY SECURITY SERVICES (PTY) LTD.—See Fidelity Security Group (Pty) Ltd.; *Int'l*, pg. 2654
FIDELITY SPECIAL VALUES PLC; *Int'l*, pg. 2654
FIDELITY SYSTEMS PLUS INC.—See Cable One, Inc.; *U.S. Public*, pg. 416
FIDELITY TECHNOLOGIES CORP.; *U.S. Private*, pg. 1503
FIDELITY TITLE INSURANCE CORPORATION—See Fidelity National Financial, Inc.; *U.S. Public*, pg. 831
FIDELITY VOICE AND DATA; *U.S. Private*, pg. 1503
FIDELITY WARRANTY SERVICES, INC.—See JM Family Enterprises Inc.; *U.S. Private*, pg. 2214
FIDELIUM GMBH; *Int'l*, pg. 2654
FIDELIX CO., LTD.; *Int'l*, pg. 2654
FIDELTA D.O.O.—See Selvita S.A.; *Int'l*, pg. 6701
FIDENTA OY—See Nordea Bank Abp; *Int'l*, pg. 5417
FIDES HOLDING B.V.—See H2 Equity Partners B.V.; *Int'l*, pg. 3199
FIDESSA FINANCIAL CORPRATION—See ION Investment Group Ltd.; *Int'l*, pg. 3793
FIDESSA GROUP HOLDINGS LTD.—See ION Investment Group Ltd.; *Int'l*, pg. 3793
FIDESSA INVESTMENTS LTD—See ION Investment Group Ltd.; *Int'l*, pg. 3793
FIDESSA LATENTZERO LIMITED—See ION Investment Group Ltd.; *Int'l*, pg. 3794
FIDESSA LTD—See ION Investment Group Ltd.; *Int'l*, pg. 3794
FIDESSA PLC—See ION Investment Group Ltd.; *Int'l*, pg. 3794
FIDESSA SAS—See ION Investment Group Ltd.; *Int'l*, pg. 3794
FIDESSA SOFTWARE CORPORATION—See ION Investment Group Ltd.; *Int'l*, pg. 3794
FIDESSA SOFTWARE LIMITED—See ION Investment Group Ltd.; *Int'l*, pg. 3794
FIDESSA WLL—See ION Investment Group Ltd.; *Int'l*, pg. 3794
FIDES SERVIZI S.C.A R.L.—See Garofalo Health Care SpA; *Int'l*, pg. 2886
FIDES TREASURY SERVICES LTD.—See UBS Group AG; *Int'l*, pg. 8007
FIDEURAM ASSET MANAGEMENT UK LTD.—See Intesa Sanpaolo S.p.A.; *Int'l*, pg. 3765
FIDEURAM BANK LUXEMBOURG S.A.—See Intesa Sanpaolo S.p.A.; *Int'l*, pg. 3765
FIDEURAM - INTESA SANPAOLO PRIVATE BANKING S.P.A.—See Intesa Sanpaolo S.p.A.; *Int'l*, pg. 3765
FIDIA CO.—See FIDIA S.p.A.; *Int'l*, pg. 2654
FIDIA CO.—See FIDIA S.p.A.; *Int'l*, pg. 2654
FIDIA DO BRASIL COMERCIO DE EQUIPAMENTOS LTDA.—See FIDIA S.p.A.; *Int'l*, pg. 2655
FIDIA DO BRASIL LTDA.—See FIDIA S.p.A.; *Int'l*, pg. 2654
FIDIA FARMACEUTICI SPA—See P&R Holding; *Int'l*, pg. 5681
FIDIA GMBH—See FIDIA S.p.A.; *Int'l*, pg. 2654
FIDIA IBERICA S.A.—See FIDIA S.p.A.; *Int'l*, pg. 2655
FIDIA MACHINERY & ELECTRONICS CO. LTD.—See FIDIA S.p.A.; *Int'l*, pg. 2655
FIDIA S.A.R.L.—See FIDIA S.p.A.; *Int'l*, pg. 2655
FIDIA S.P.A.; *Int'l*, pg. 2654
FIDIFARM D.O.O.—See ATLANTIC GRUPA d.d.; *Int'l*, pg. 675
FIDION S.R.L—See Orlandi S.p.A.; *Int'l*, pg. 5639
FIDITALIA S.P.A.—See Societe Generale S.A.; *Int'l*, pg. 7039
FIDITOUR JOINT STOCK COMPANY; *Int'l*, pg. 2655
FIDMASH—See NOV, Inc.; *U.S. Public*, pg. 1544
FIDOR BANK AG—See Groupe BPCE; *Int'l*, pg. 3097
FIDSON HEALTHCARE PLC; *Int'l*, pg. 2655
FIDUCIAL EXPERTISE S.A.—See Fiducial; *Int'l*, pg. 2655
FIDUCIAL, INC.—See Fiducial; *Int'l*, pg. 2655
FIDUCIAL, INC.—See Fiducial; *Int'l*, pg. 2655
FIDUCIAL OFFICE SOLUTIONS SA; *Int'l*, pg. 2655
FIDUCIAL REAL ESTATE SA; *Int'l*, pg. 2655
FIDUCIAL SA—See Fiducial; *Int'l*, pg. 2655
FIDUCIAL; *Int'l*, pg. 2655
FIDUCIAN BUSINESS SERVICES PTY. LTD.—See Fiducian Group Limited; *Int'l*, pg. 2655
FIDUCIAN FINANCIAL SERVICES PTY. LTD.—See Fiducian Group Limited; *Int'l*, pg. 2655

FIDUCIAN GROUP LIMITED

FIDUCIAN GROUP LIMITED; *Int'l*, pg. 2655
FIDUCIAN PORTFOLIO SERVICES LIMITED—See Fiducian Group Limited; *Int'l*, pg. 2655
FIDUCIARY CAPITAL MANAGEMENT, INC.—See Public Financial Management, Inc.; *U.S. Private*, pg. 3299
FIDUCIARY COMPANY INCORPORATED; *U.S. Private*, pg. 1503
FIDUCIARY EXCHANGE, LLC—See Bain Capital, LP; *U.S. Private*, pg. 439
FIDUCIARY FINANCIAL SERVICES WEALTH MANAGEMENT—See B. Riley Financial, Inc.; *U.S. Public*, pg. 260
FIDUCIARY INTERNATIONAL, INC.—See Franklin Resources, Inc.; *U.S. Public*, pg. 880
FIDUCIARY INVESTMENT ADVISORS LLC—See Aon plc; *Int'l*, pg. 495
FIDUCIARY INVESTMENT MANAGEMENT INTERNATIONAL, INC.—See Franklin Resources, Inc.; *U.S. Public*, pg. 880
FIDUCIARY MANAGEMENT ASSOCIATES, LLC; *U.S. Private*, pg. 1503
FIDUCIARY TRUST CO. INC.—See Fiduciary Company Incorporated; *U.S. Private*, pg. 1503
FIDUCIARY TRUST COMPANY INTERNATIONAL—See Franklin Resources, Inc.; *U.S. Public*, pg. 880
FIDUCIARY TRUST COMPANY OF CANADA—See Franklin Resources, Inc.; *U.S. Public*, pg. 880
FIDUCIARY TRUST CO. OF NEW HAMPSHIRE—See Macquarie Group Limited; *Int'l*, pg. 4625
FIDUCIARY TRUST INTERNATIONAL LIMITED—See Franklin Resources, Inc.; *U.S. Public*, pg. 880
FIDUCIARY TRUST INTERNATIONAL OF CALIFORNIA—See Franklin Resources, Inc.; *U.S. Public*, pg. 880
FIDUCIARY TRUST INTERNATIONAL OF DELAWARE—See Franklin Resources, Inc.; *U.S. Public*, pg. 880
FIDUCIARY TRUST INTERNATIONAL OF THE SOUTH—See Franklin Resources, Inc.; *U.S. Public*, pg. 880
FIDUCIARY TRUST (INTERNATIONAL) SARL—See Franklin Resources, Inc.; *U.S. Public*, pg. 880
FIDUS INVESTMENT CORPORATION; *U.S. Public*, pg. 833
FIDUS MEZZANINE CAPITAL II, L.P.—See Fidus Investment Corporation; *U.S. Public*, pg. 833
FIEBIG & SCHILLINGS GMBH; *Int'l*, pg. 2655
FIEBIG+TEAM GMBH; *Int'l*, pg. 2655
FIEDLER GROUP; *U.S. Private*, pg. 1503
FIEDLER & LUNDGREN AB—See British American Tobacco plc; *Int'l*, pg. 1167
FIELDAIR HOLDINGS LIMITED—See Freightways Group Limited; *Int'l*, pg. 2771
FIELDALE FARMS CORPORATION; *U.S. Private*, pg. 1504
FIELD ASSET SERVICES, INC—See Assurant, Inc.; *U.S. Public*, pg. 215
FIELD AVIATION COMPANY INC.—See Hunting Plc; *Int'l*, pg. 3536
FIELDBROOK FOODS CORPORATION—See Wells Enterprises, Inc.; *U.S. Private*, pg. 4476
FIELDBROOK VALLEY WINERY INC.; *U.S. Private*, pg. 1504
FIELD CONTAINER QUERETARO (USA), L.L.C.—See Graphic Packaging Holding Company; *U.S. Public*, pg. 958
FIELD CONTROLS LLC—See The Heico Companies, L.L.C.; *U.S. Private*, pg. 4050
FIELDDATA.IO GMBH—See BAUER Aktiengesellschaft; *Int'l*, pg. 893
FIELD DAY INC.; *Int'l*, pg. 2655
FIELDERS AUSTRALIA PTY. LTD.—See BlueScope Steel Limited; *Int'l*, pg. 1073
FIELDERS MANUFACTURING PTY. LTD.—See BlueScope Steel Limited; *Int'l*, pg. 1073
FIELDFISHER RYSER—See Field Fisher Waterhouse LLP; *Int'l*, pg. 2655
FIELD FISHER WATERHOUSE LLP; *Int'l*, pg. 2655
FIELDFLEX BENELUX—See Ardian SAS; *Int'l*, pg. 555
FIELDFLEX EUROPE SAS—See Ardian SAS; *Int'l*, pg. 555
FIELDFRESH FOODS PVT. LTD.—See Bharti Enterprises Limited; *Int'l*, pg. 1013
FIELDFRESH FOODS PVT. LTD.—See Nutri-Asia Inc.; *Int'l*, pg. 5491
FIELDGLASS, INC.—See SAP SE; *Int'l*, pg. 6567
FIELDHOME; *U.S. Private*, pg. 1504
FIELD HOTEL ASSOCIATES; *U.S. Private*, pg. 1503
FIELD INDUSTRIES LLC; *U.S. Private*, pg. 1503
FIELDING CHEMICAL TECHNOLOGIES INC.—See BC Partners LLP; *Int'l*, pg. 923
FIELD INTELLIGENCE INC.—See Network Innovations Inc.; *Int'l*, pg. 5217
FIELD LINING SYSTEMS, INC.; *U.S. Private*, pg. 1504
FIELD LOGIC, INC.—See TruArc Partners, L.P.; *U.S. Private*, pg. 4245
THE FIELD MUSEUM; *U.S. Private*, pg. 4028
FIELD NATION, LLC; *U.S. Private*, pg. 1504
FIELDONE CORPORATION—See ACMOS INC.; *Int'l*, pg. 107

FIELD PAPER CO. INC.; *U.S. Private*, pg. 1504
FIELDPOINT PRIVATE BANK & TRUST; *U.S. Private*, pg. 1504
FIELD PROS DIRECT LLC; *U.S. Private*, pg. 1504
FIELDQUIP PTY LTD.—See Alamo Group Inc.; *U.S. Public*, pg. 71
THE FIELD ROAST GRAIN MEAT CO.—See Maple Leaf Foods, Inc.; *Int'l*, pg. 4686
FIELDS BMW OF DAYTONA; *U.S. Private*, pg. 1504
FIELDS BMW; *U.S. Private*, pg. 1504
FIELDS EQUIPMENT CO. INC.; *U.S. Private*, pg. 1504
FIELD SERVICE DEUTSCHLAND FSD GMBH—See freenet AG; *Int'l*, pg. 2770
FIELD SERVICES, INC.—See The Shaw Group Inc.; *U.S. Private*, pg. 4117
FIELDS IMPORTS INC.—See M.E. Fields Inc.; *U.S. Private*, pg. 2528
FIELDS, INC.; *U.S. Private*, pg. 1504
FIELDS JEEP, INC.—See M.E. Fields Inc.; *U.S. Private*, pg. 2528
FIELDS OF LAKE COUNTY INC.—See M.E. Fields Inc.; *U.S. Private*, pg. 2528
FIELD SOLUTIONS HOLDINGS LIMITED; *Int'l*, pg. 2655
FIELDSTON CLOTHES INC.—See S. Rothschild & Co., Inc.; *U.S. Private*, pg. 3515
FIELDSTONE LANDSCAPE SERVICES LLC; *U.S. Private*, pg. 1504
FIELD STONE WINERY & VINEYARD, INC.—See Jackson Family Wines, Inc.; *U.S. Private*, pg. 2176
FIELD & STREAM MAGAZINE—See Bonnier AB; *Int'l*, pg. 1108
FIELD SYSTEMS DESIGNS HOLDINGS PLC; *Int'l*, pg. 2655
FIELDTECH AVIONICS & INSTRUMENTS, INC.; *U.S. Private*, pg. 1504
FIELDTURF AUSTRALIA PTY LTD.—See Tarkett S.A.; *Int'l*, pg. 7462
FIELDTURF, INC.—See Tarkett S.A.; *Int'l*, pg. 7463
FIELD UNDERWRITERS AGENCY, INC.—See Aon plc; *Int'l*, pg. 496
FIELDVIEW SOLUTIONS, INC.—See Nlyte Software Americas Limited; *U.S. Private*, pg. 2931
FIELDWARE, LLC; *U.S. Private*, pg. 1504
FIELDWAY GROUP LIMITED; *Int'l*, pg. 2655
FIELDWISE, LLC—See Lindsay Corporation; *U.S. Public*, pg. 1319
FIELDWOOD ENERGY LLC; *U.S. Public*, pg. 833
FIELDWORK BREWING COMPANY; *U.S. Private*, pg. 1504
FIELEX S.A.—See Einhell Germany AG; *Int'l*, pg. 2333
FIELMANN AG & CO. AM HAUPTMARKT OHG—See Fielmann Group AG; *Int'l*, pg. 2658
FIELMANN AG & CO. AM KUGELBRUNNEN KG—See Fielmann Group AG; *Int'l*, pg. 2658
FIELMANN AG & CO. AM MARKT OHG—See Fielmann Group AG; *Int'l*, pg. 2658
FIELMANN AG & CO. BAD CANNSTATT OHG—See Fielmann Group AG; *Int'l*, pg. 2656
FIELMANN AG & CO. BARBAROSSAPLATZ OHG—See Fielmann Group AG; *Int'l*, pg. 2656
FIELMANN AG & CO. BARMEN OHG—See Fielmann Group AG; *Int'l*, pg. 2656
FIELMANN AG & CO. BERGEDORF OHG—See Fielmann Group AG; *Int'l*, pg. 2656
FIELMANN AG & CO. BERLIN-HELLERSDORF OHG—See Fielmann Group AG; *Int'l*, pg. 2656
FIELMANN AG & CO. BILLSTEDT KG—See Fielmann Group AG; *Int'l*, pg. 2656
FIELMANN AG & CO. BONN-BAD GODESBERG OHG—See Fielmann Group AG; *Int'l*, pg. 2656
FIELMANN AG & CO. BORNHEIM KG—See Fielmann Group AG; *Int'l*, pg. 2656
FIELMANN AG & CO. BRACKWEDE KG—See Fielmann Group AG; *Int'l*, pg. 2656
FIELMANN AG & CO. BRAMFELD KG—See Fielmann Group AG; *Int'l*, pg. 2656
FIELMANN AG & CO. BUER OHG—See Fielmann Group AG; *Int'l*, pg. 2656
FIELMANN AG & CO. CHORWEILER KG—See Fielmann Group AG; *Int'l*, pg. 2656
FIELMANN AG & CO. CITY-ARKADEN KG—See Fielmann Group AG; *Int'l*, pg. 2656
FIELMANN AG & CO. CITY GALERIE OHG—See Fielmann Group AG; *Int'l*, pg. 2656
FIELMANN AG & CO. DERENDORF OHG—See Fielmann Group AG; *Int'l*, pg. 2656
FIELMANN AG & CO. DRESDEN ALTSTADT OHG—See Fielmann Group AG; *Int'l*, pg. 2656
FIELMANN AG & CO. DRESDEN NEUSTADT OHG—See Fielmann Group AG; *Int'l*, pg. 2656
FIELMANN AG & CO. EBERTPLATZ KG—See Fielmann Group AG; *Int'l*, pg. 2656
FIELMANN AG & CO. EIMSBUTTEL OHG—See Fielmann Group AG; *Int'l*, pg. 2656
FIELMANN AG & CO. EKZ HAMBURGER STRABE KG—See Fielmann Group AG; *Int'l*, pg. 2656
FIELMANN AG & CO. EKZ HAMBURGER STRASSE KG—See Fielmann Group AG; *Int'l*, pg. 2656

CORPORATE AFFILIATIONS

FIELMANN AG & CO. EKZ MILANEO OHG—See Fielmann Group AG; *Int'l*, pg. 2656
FIELMANN AG & CO. EKZ WESTPARK OHG—See Fielmann Group AG; *Int'l*, pg. 2656
FIELMANN AG & CO. ELBERFELD OHG—See Fielmann Group AG; *Int'l*, pg. 2656
FIELMANN AG & CO. EPPENDORF KG—See Fielmann Group AG; *Int'l*, pg. 2656
FIELMANN AG & CO. ERNST-AUGUST-GALERIE KG—See Fielmann Group AG; *Int'l*, pg. 2656
FIELMANN AG & CO. ESSEN-RUTTENSCHEID OHG—See Fielmann Group AG; *Int'l*, pg. 2656
FIELMANN AG & CO. ESSEN-STEELE OHG—See Fielmann Group AG; *Int'l*, pg. 2656
FIELMANN AG & CO. FORUM MITTELRHEIN OHG—See Fielmann Group AG; *Int'l*, pg. 2656
FIELMANN AG & CO. FRIEDRICHSHAGEN OHG—See Fielmann Group AG; *Int'l*, pg. 2656
FIELMANN AG & CO. FRIEDRICHSHAIN OHG—See Fielmann Group AG; *Int'l*, pg. 2656
FIELMANN AG & CO. FRIEDRICHSTRASSE OHG—See Fielmann Group AG; *Int'l*, pg. 2656
FIELMANN AG & CO. GESUNDBRUNNEN-CENTER KG—See Fielmann Group AG; *Int'l*, pg. 2656
FIELMANN AG & CO. GLACIS-GALERIE OHG—See Fielmann Group AG; *Int'l*, pg. 2656
FIELMANN AG & CO. GROPIUS PASSAGEN OHG—See Fielmann Group AG; *Int'l*, pg. 2656
FIELMANN AG & CO. HAIDHAUSEN OHG—See Fielmann Group AG; *Int'l*, pg. 2656
FIELMANN AG & CO. HAMBORN KG—See Fielmann Group AG; *Int'l*, pg. 2656
FIELMANN AG & CO. HARBURG SAND OHG—See Fielmann Group AG; *Int'l*, pg. 2656
FIELMANN AG & CO. HESSEN-CENTER OHG—See Fielmann Group AG; *Int'l*, pg. 2656
FIELMANN AG & CO. HILTRUP OHG—See Fielmann Group AG; *Int'l*, pg. 2656
FIELMANN AG & CO. HOCHST OHG—See Fielmann Group AG; *Int'l*, pg. 2656
FIELMANN AG & CO. IM ALEXA KG—See Fielmann Group AG; *Int'l*, pg. 2658
FIELMANN AG & CO. IM ALSTERTALEINKAUFSZENTRUM OHG—See Fielmann Group AG; *Int'l*, pg. 2658
FIELMANN AG & CO. IM CENTRUM OHG—See Fielmann Group AG; *Int'l*, pg. 2658
FIELMANN AG & CO. IM DONAU-EINKAUFSZENTRUM KG—See Fielmann Group AG; *Int'l*, pg. 2658
FIELMANN AG & CO. IM ELBEEINKAUFSZENTRUM OHG—See Fielmann Group AG; *Int'l*, pg. 2658
FIELMANN AG & CO. JAHNPLATZ KG—See Fielmann Group AG; *Int'l*, pg. 2656
FIELMANN AG & CO. KAUFPARK KG—See Fielmann Group AG; *Int'l*, pg. 2657
FIELMANN AG & CO. KG—See Fielmann Group AG; *Int'l*, pg. 2656
FIELMANN AG & CO. KLOSTERSTRASSE OHG—See Fielmann Group AG; *Int'l*, pg. 2657
FIELMANN AG & CO. KONTAKTLINSEN-SERVICE KG—See Fielmann Group AG; *Int'l*, pg. 2657
FIELMANN AG & CO. KREUZBERG KG—See Fielmann Group AG; *Int'l*, pg. 2657
FIELMANN AG & CO. LEIPZIGER STRASSE OHG—See Fielmann Group AG; *Int'l*, pg. 2657
FIELMANN AG & CO. LEOPOLDSTRASSE OHG—See Fielmann Group AG; *Int'l*, pg. 2657
FIELMANN AG & CO. LINDEN-CENTER KG—See Fielmann Group AG; *Int'l*, pg. 2657
FIELMANN AG & CO. LISTER MEILE OHG—See Fielmann Group AG; *Int'l*, pg. 2657
FIELMANN AG & CO. MARKISCHES ZENTRUM KGB—See Fielmann Group AG; *Int'l*, pg. 2657
FIELMANN AG & CO. MARZAHN OHG—See Fielmann Group AG; *Int'l*, pg. 2657
FIELMANN AG & CO. MOABIT KG—See Fielmann Group AG; *Int'l*, pg. 2657
FIELMANN AG & CO. NEUKOLLN KG—See Fielmann Group AG; *Int'l*, pg. 2657
FIELMANN AG & CO. NEUMARKT KG—See Fielmann Group AG; *Int'l*, pg. 2657
FIELMANN AG & CO. NORDSTADT OHG—See Fielmann Group AG; *Int'l*, pg. 2657
FIELMANN AG & CO. NURNBERG-LANGWASSER OHG—See Fielmann Group AG; *Int'l*, pg. 2657
FIELMANN AG & CO. NURNBERG LORENZ OHG—See Fielmann Group AG; *Int'l*, pg. 2657
FIELMANN AG & CO. NURNBERG-SUD KG—See Fielmann Group AG; *Int'l*, pg. 2657
FIELMANN AG & CO. OBERHAUSEN OHG—See Fielmann Group AG; *Int'l*, pg. 2657
FIELMANN AG & CO. OBERKASSEL OHG—See Fielmann Group AG; *Int'l*, pg. 2657
FIELMANN AG & CO. OBERNSTRASSE OHG—See Fielmann Group AG; *Int'l*, pg. 2657
FIELMANN AG & CO. OCHSENZOLL OHG—See Fielmann Group AG; *Int'l*, pg. 2657
FIELMANN AG & CO. OHG AN DER ROTHENBURG—See Fielmann Group AG; *Int'l*, pg. 2658

COMPANY NAME INDEX

FIELMANN AG & CO. OHG BREMEN-NEUSTADT—See Fielmann Group AG; *Int'l*, pg. 2658
FIELMANN AG & CO. OHG CITY-GALERIE—See Fielmann Group AG; *Int'l*, pg. 2658
FIELMANN AG & CO. OHG KALK—See Fielmann Group AG; *Int'l*, pg. 2658
FIELMANN AG & CO. OHG KAVALIERSTRASSE—See Fielmann Group AG; *Int'l*, pg. 2658
FIELMANN AG & CO. OHG LUDWIGSPLATZ—See Fielmann Group AG; *Int'l*, pg. 2658
FIELMANN AG & CO. OHG MUNCHEN OEZ—See Fielmann Group AG; *Int'l*, pg. 2658
FIELMANN AG & CO. OHG MUNCHEN PEP—See Fielmann Group AG; *Int'l*, pg. 2658
FIELMANN AG & CO. OHG NIENDORF—See Fielmann Group AG; *Int'l*, pg. 2658
FIELMANN AG & CO. OHG SCHNELSEN—See Fielmann Group AG; *Int'l*, pg. 2658
FIELMANN AG & CO. OHG SENDLING—See Fielmann Group AG; *Int'l*, pg. 2658
FIELMANN AG & CO. OHG—See Fielmann Group AG; *Int'l*, pg. 2657
FIELMANN AG & CO. OHG STERKRADE—See Fielmann Group AG; *Int'l*, pg. 2657
FIELMANN AG & CO. OHG WELLINGDORF—See Fielmann Group AG; *Int'l*, pg. 2658
FIELMANN AG & CO. OTHMARSCHEN OHG—See Fielmann Group AG; *Int'l*, pg. 2657
FIELMANN AG & CO. OTTENSEN OHG—See Fielmann Group AG; *Int'l*, pg. 2657
FIELMANN AG & CO. PANKOW OHG—See Fielmann Group AG; *Int'l*, pg. 2657
FIELMANN AG & CO. PASING OHG—See Fielmann Group AG; *Int'l*, pg. 2657
FIELMANN AG & CO. PAUNSDORF-CENTER OHG—See Fielmann Group AG; *Int'l*, pg. 2657
FIELMANN AG & CO. PFERDEMARKT OHG—See Fielmann Group AG; *Int'l*, pg. 2657
FIELMANN AG & CO. PRENZLAUER BERG OHG—See Fielmann Group AG; *Int'l*, pg. 2657
FIELMANN AG & CO. RAHLSTEDT OHG—See Fielmann Group AG; *Int'l*, pg. 2657
FIELMANN AG & CO. RATHAUS OHG—See Fielmann Group AG; *Int'l*, pg. 2657
FIELMANN AG & CO. RETHELSTRASSE OHG—See Fielmann Group AG; *Int'l*, pg. 2657
FIELMANN AG & CO. RHEIN-GALERIE KG—See Fielmann Group AG; *Int'l*, pg. 2657
FIELMANN AG & CO. RHEINRUHRZENTRUM OHG—See Fielmann Group AG; *Int'l*, pg. 2657
FIELMANN AG & CO. RHEYDT OHG—See Fielmann Group AG; *Int'l*, pg. 2657
FIELMANN AG & CO. RIEM ARCADEN KG—See Fielmann Group AG; *Int'l*, pg. 2657
FIELMANN AG & CO. ROLAND-CENTER KG—See Fielmann Group AG; *Int'l*, pg. 2657
FIELMANN AG & CO. ROSSMARKT OHG—See Fielmann Group AG; *Int'l*, pg. 2657
FIELMANN AG & CO. SCHILDERGASSE OHG—See Fielmann Group AG; *Int'l*, pg. 2657
FIELMANN AG & CO. SCHLOSS-ARKADEN KG—See Fielmann Group AG; *Int'l*, pg. 2657
FIELMANN AG & CO. SCHONEWEIDE OHG—See Fielmann Group AG; *Int'l*, pg. 2657
FIELMANN AG & CO. SCHWARZER BAR OHG—See Fielmann Group AG; *Int'l*, pg. 2657
FIELMANN AG & CO. SCHWENNINGEN KG—See Fielmann Group AG; *Int'l*, pg. 2657
FIELMANN AG & CO. SPANDAU OHG—See Fielmann Group AG; *Int'l*, pg. 2657
FIELMANN AG & CO. STEGLITZ OHG—See Fielmann Group AG; *Int'l*, pg. 2657
FIELMANN AG & CO. STERN CENTER OHG—See Fielmann Group AG; *Int'l*, pg. 2657
FIELMANN AG & CO. SUDENBURG OHG—See Fielmann Group AG; *Int'l*, pg. 2657
FIELMANN AG & CO. TAL KG—See Fielmann Group AG; *Int'l*, pg. 2657
FIELMANN AG & CO. TEMPELHOF OHG—See Fielmann Group AG; *Int'l*, pg. 2657
FIELMANN AG & CO. THURINGEN-PARK OHG—See Fielmann Group AG; *Int'l*, pg. 2657
FIELMANN AG & CO. TREPTOW KG—See Fielmann Group AG; *Int'l*, pg. 2658
FIELMANN AG & CO. VEGESACK OHG—See Fielmann Group AG; *Int'l*, pg. 2658
FIELMANN AG & CO. VENLOER STRASSE OHG—See Fielmann Group AG; *Int'l*, pg. 2658
FIELMANN AG & CO. VITA-CENTER KG—See Fielmann Group AG; *Int'l*, pg. 2658
FIELMANN AG & CO. VOLKSDORF OHG—See Fielmann Group AG; *Int'l*, pg. 2658
FIELMANN AG & CO. WANDSBEK OHG—See Fielmann Group AG; *Int'l*, pg. 2658
FIELMANN AG & CO. WATTENSCHEID KG—See Fielmann Group AG; *Int'l*, pg. 2658
FIELMANN AG & CO. WEISSENSEE KG—See Fielmann Group AG; *Int'l*, pg. 2658

FIELMANN AG & CO. WESERPARK OHG—See Fielmann Group AG; *Int'l*, pg. 2658
FIELMANN AG & CO. WESTEND KG—See Fielmann Group AG; *Int'l*, pg. 2658
FIELMANN AG & CO. WESTLICHE KAISERSTRASSE KG—See Fielmann Group AG; *Int'l*, pg. 2658
FIELMANN AG & CO. WILMERSDORF KG—See Fielmann Group AG; *Int'l*, pg. 2658
FIELMANN AG & CO. ZENTRUM KG—See Fielmann Group AG; *Int'l*, pg. 2658
FIELMANN AG - VAREL—See Fielmann Group AG; *Int'l*, pg. 2658
FIELMANN AKADEMIE SCHLOSS PLON, GEMEINNUTZIGE BILDUNGSSTATTE DER AUGENOPTIK GMBH—See Fielmann Group AG; *Int'l*, pg. 2658
FIELMANN AUGENOPTIK AG & CO. HALLE-NEUSTADT OHG—See Fielmann Group AG; *Int'l*, pg. 2658
FIELMANN AUGENOPTIK AG & CO. OHG—See Fielmann Group AG; *Int'l*, pg. 2658
FIELMANN AUGENOPTIK AG—See Fielmann Group AG; *Int'l*, pg. 2658
FIELMANN AUGENOPTIK IM CENTRUM AG & CO. OHG—See Fielmann Group AG; *Int'l*, pg. 2658
FIELMANN B.V.—See Fielmann Group AG; *Int'l*, pg. 2658
FIELMANN FARMSEN FIELMANN GMBH & CO. KG—See Fielmann Group AG; *Int'l*, pg. 2659
FIELMANN FINANZSERVICE GMBH—See Fielmann Group AG; *Int'l*, pg. 2658
FIELMANN GMBH—See Fielmann Group AG; *Int'l*, pg. 2658
FIELMANN GROUP AG; *Int'l*, pg. 2655
FIELMANN HOLDING B.V.—See Fielmann Group AG; *Int'l*, pg. 2658
FIELMANN MODEBRILLEN RATHENOW AG & CO. KG—See Fielmann Group AG; *Int'l*, pg. 2658
FIELMANN-OPTIC FIELMANN GMBH & CO. KG—See Fielmann Group AG; *Int'l*, pg. 2658
FIELMANN SCHLOSS PLON HOTEL- UND CATERING GMBH—See Fielmann Group AG; *Int'l*, pg. 2658
FIELMANN SCHWEIZ AG—See Fielmann Group AG; *Int'l*, pg. 2658
FIELMANN VENTURES GMBH—See Fielmann Group AG; *Int'l*, pg. 2658
FIEM INDUSTRIES LTD.; *Int'l*, pg. 2659
FIERA CAPITAL (ASIA) HONG KONG LIMITED—See Fiera Capital Corporation; *Int'l*, pg. 2659
FIERA CAPITAL CORPORATION; *Int'l*, pg. 2659
FIERA CAPITAL (GERMANY) GMBH—See Fiera Capital Corporation; *Int'l*, pg. 2659
FIERA CAPITAL INC.—See Fiera Capital Corporation; *Int'l*, pg. 2659
FIERA CAPITAL (IOM) LIMITED—See Fiera Capital Corporation; *Int'l*, pg. 2659
FIERA CAPITAL (UK) LIMITED—See Fiera Capital Corporation; *Int'l*, pg. 2659
FIERA FOODS COMPANY; *Int'l*, pg. 2660
FIERA INFRASTRUCTURE INC.—See Fiera Capital Corporation; *Int'l*, pg. 2659
FIERA MILANO CONGRESSI SPA—See Fiera Milano SpA; *Int'l*, pg. 2660
FIERA MILANO EXHIBITIONS AFRICA PTY. LTD.—See Fiera Milano SpA; *Int'l*, pg. 2660
FIERA MILANO SPA; *Int'l*, pg. 2660
FIERA PROPERTIES LIMITED—See Fiera Capital Corporation; *Int'l*, pg. 2659
FIERATEX S.A.; *Int'l*, pg. 2660
FIERA YMG CAPITAL INC.; *Int'l*, pg. 2660
FIERCE INC.; *U.S. Private*, pg. 1504
FIERO FLUID POWER INC.—See Hartfiel Automation; *U.S. Private*, pg. 1873
FIERTE CORPORATION—See Avant Corporation; *Int'l*, pg. 735
FIESTA AUTO INSURANCE CENTER; *U.S. Private*, pg. 1504
FIESTA CANNING CO., INC.; *U.S. Private*, pg. 1505
FIESTA FORD LINCOLN MERCURY; *U.S. Private*, pg. 1505
FIESTA INN INC.—See Rushlake Hotels USA Inc.; *U.S. Private*, pg. 3505
FIESTA MART, LLC—See Grupo Comercial Chedraui S.A.B. de C.V.; *Int'l*, pg. 3125
FIESTA MEXICANA MARKET LTD. PARTNER; *U.S. Private*, pg. 1505
FIESTA REAL ESTATE AS—See Kesko Corporation; *Int'l*, pg. 4141
FIESTA RESTAURANT GROUP, INC.—See Garnett Station Partners, LLC; *U.S. Private*, pg. 1645
FIESTA SALONS, INC.—See Regis Corporation; *U.S. Public*, pg. 1777
FIESTA TEXAS, INC.—See Six Flags Entertainment Corp.; *U.S. Public*, pg. 1890
FIFA TICKETING AG—See Federation Internationale de Football Association; *Int'l*, pg. 2631
FIFA TRANSFER MATCHING SYSTEM GMBH—See Federation Internationale de Football Association; *Int'l*, pg. 2631
FIFE JOINERY MANUFACTURING LIMITED—See VKR Holding A/S; *Int'l*, pg. 8282
FIFIELD LAND CO.; *U.S. Private*, pg. 1505

FIFO WIRELESS; *U.S. Private*, pg. 1505
FIFTH AVENUE AUTO HAUS LTD.; *Int'l*, pg. 2660
FIFTH AVENUE HEALTHCARE CENTER—See Apollo Global Management, Inc.; *U.S. Public*, pg. 156
FIFTH AVENUE LUMBER CO., INC.—See Strait & Lamp Lumber Co. Inc.; *U.S. Private*, pg. 3833
FIFTH DISTRICT SAVINGS BANK; *U.S. Private*, pg. 1505
FIFTH ELEMENT RESOURCES LIMITED; *Int'l*, pg. 2660
FIFTH GEAR, INC.-MISSOURI—See Speed Commerce, Inc.; *U.S. Public*, pg. 1917
FIFTH GEAR, INC.-PENNSYLVANIA—See Speed Commerce, Inc.; *U.S. Public*, pg. 1917
FIFTH GEAR, INC.—See Speed Commerce, Inc.; *U.S. Public*, pg. 1917
FIFTH GEAR LLC; *U.S. Private*, pg. 1505
FIFTH GROUP RESTAURANTS; *U.S. Private*, pg. 1505
FIFTHPLAY N.V.—See Niko Group N.V.; *Int'l*, pg. 5291
FIFTH RING INC.—See Fifth Ring Ltd; *Int'l*, pg. 2660
FIFTH RING LLC—See Fifth Ring Ltd; *Int'l*, pg. 2660
FIFTH RING LTD; *Int'l*, pg. 2660
FIFTH STREET ASSET MANAGEMENT INC.; *U.S. Private*, pg. 1505
FIFTH STREET CAPITAL LLC; *U.S. Private*, pg. 1505
FIFTH STREET MANAGEMENT COMPANY, LLC—See Kim King Associates, LLC; *U.S. Private*, pg. 2305
FIFTH STREET MANAGEMENT LLC—See Fifth Street Capital LLC; *U.S. Private*, pg. 1505
FIFTH THIRD BANCORP; *U.S. Public*, pg. 833
FIFTH THIRD BANK, NATIONAL ASSOCIATION—See Fifth Third Bancorp; *U.S. Public*, pg. 833
FIFTH THIRD SECURITIES, INC.—See Fifth Third Bancorp; *U.S. Public*, pg. 833
FIFTH WHEEL TRUCK STOPS; *Int'l*, pg. 2660
FIFTY FIFTY ANTWERPEN B.V.—See Live Nation Entertainment, Inc.; *U.S. Public*, pg. 1328
FIGARO CLASSIFIEDS S.A.—See Groupe Industriel Marcel Dassault S.A.; *Int'l*, pg. 3105
FIGARO COFFEE GROUP INCORPORATED; *Int'l*, pg. 2660
FIGARO ENGINEERING INC.—See New Cosmos Electric Co., Ltd.; *Int'l*, pg. 5222
FIGARO USA, INC.—See New Cosmos Electric Co., Ltd.; *Int'l*, pg. 5222
FIGEAC AERO AUXERRE SASU—See Figeac-Aero SA; *Int'l*, pg. 2660
FIGEAC AERO NORTH AMERICA, INC—See Figeac-Aero SA; *Int'l*, pg. 2660
FIGEAC-AERO SA; *Int'l*, pg. 2660
FIGENE CAPITAL SA; *Int'l*, pg. 2661
FIGENE ENERGIA SP. Z O.O.—See Figene Capital SA; *Int'l*, pg. 2661
FIGESBAL—See Sumitomo Metal Mining Co., Ltd.; *Int'l*, pg. 7291
FIGI'S BUSINESS SERVICES, INC.—See Mason Companies, Inc.; *U.S. Private*, pg. 2602
FIGI'S, INC.—See Mason Companies, Inc.; *U.S. Private*, pg. 2602
FIG LEAF SOFTWARE INC; *U.S. Private*, pg. 1505
FIGLEAVES GLOBAL TRADING LIMITED—See N Brown Group plc; *Int'l*, pg. 5115
FIGO CO., LTD.—See United Arrows Ltd.; *Int'l*, pg. 8064
FIG PARTNERS LLC—See The Penn Mutual Life Insurance Company; *U.S. Private*, pg. 4092
FIGR CANNABIS INC.—See Pyxus International, Inc.; *U.S. Public*, pg. 1740
FIGS, INC.; *U.S. Public*, pg. 834
FIGTREE COMPANY, LLC—See Fifth Third Bancorp; *U.S. Public*, pg. 833
FIGTREE CREATIVE SERVICES LTD.—See Prophet Brand Strategy, Inc.; *U.S. Private*, pg. 3285
FIGTREE CREATIVE SERVICES-WANCHAI—See Prophet Brand Strategy, Inc.; *U.S. Private*, pg. 3285
FIGTREE HOLDINGS LIMITED; *Int'l*, pg. 2661
FIGTREE PROJECTS (SHANGHAI) CO., LTD.—See Figtree Holdings Limited; *Int'l*, pg. 2661
FI HEALTH INSURANCE AD—See First Investment Bank AD; *Int'l*, pg. 2685
FIH ERHVERVSBANK A/S; *Int'l*, pg. 2661
FIH GROUP PLC; *Int'l*, pg. 2661
FIH MEXICO INDUSTRY S.A. DE C.V.—See Hon Hai Precision Industry Co., Ltd.; *Int'l*, pg. 3456
FIH MOBILE LIMITED—See Hon Hai Precision Industry Co., Ltd.; *Int'l*, pg. 3457
FIHUMIN-GESELLSCHAFT M.B.H.; *Int'l*, pg. 2661
FIJACIONES NORMA S.A.U.—See NORMA Group SE; *Int'l*, pg. 5430
FIJIAN HOLDINGS LIMITED; *Int'l*, pg. 2661
FIJICARE INSURANCE LIMITED; *Int'l*, pg. 2662
FIJI DIRECTORIES LIMITED—See Fiji National Provident Fund; *Int'l*, pg. 2661
THE FIJI GAS CO LTD.—See Origin Energy Ltd.; *Int'l*, pg. 5630
FIJI INTERNATIONAL TELECOMMUNICATIONS LIMITED—See Fiji National Provident Fund; *Int'l*, pg. 2661
FIJI NATIONAL PROVIDENT FUND; *Int'l*, pg. 2661
FIJI PORTS TERMINAL LTD.—See Aitken Spence PLC; *Int'l*, pg. 254

FIJI TELEVISION LIMITED—See Fijian Holdings Limited; *Int'l*, pg. 2662
FIJI WATER COMPANY LLC—See The Wonderful Company LLC; *U.S. Private*, pg. 4138
FIJNMECHANISCHE INDUSTRIE VENRAY B.V.—See Aalberts N.V.; *Int'l*, pg. 34
FIKE CANADA, INC.—See Fike Corporation; *U.S. Private*, pg. 1505
FIKE CHEVROLET COMPANY; *U.S. Private*, pg. 1505
FIKE CORPORATION; *U.S. Private*, pg. 1505
FIKE EUROPE—See Fike Corporation; *U.S. Private*, pg. 1505
FIKE JAPAN CORPORATION—See Fike Corporation; *U.S. Private*, pg. 1505
FIKES CHEVROLET BUICK INCORPORATED; *U.S. Private*, pg. 1505
FIKES TRUCK LINE INC.; *U.S. Private*, pg. 1505
FIKES WHOLESALE INC.—See Casey's General Stores, Inc.; *U.S. Public*, pg. 446
FIKSU, INC.—See Clickdealer Asia Pte Ltd.; *Int'l*, pg. 1658
FILA ARGENTINA S.A.—See FILA Holdings Corporation; *Int'l*, pg. 2662
FILA ART PRODUCTS AG—See F.I.L.A. - Fabbrica Italiana Lapis ed Affini S.p.A.; *Int'l*, pg. 2597
FILA CANADA, INC.—See FILA Holdings Corporation; *Int'l*, pg. 2662
F.I.L.A. CHILE LTDA—See F.I.L.A. - Fabbrica Italiana Lapis ed Affini S.p.A.; *Int'l*, pg. 2596
FILAE SA—See MyHeritage Ltd; *Int'l*, pg. 5112
FILA EUROPE S.P.A.—See FILA Holdings Corporation; *Int'l*, pg. 2662
F.I.L.A. - FABBRICA ITALIANA LAPIS ED AFFINI S.P.A.; *Int'l*, pg. 2596
FILA FRANCE S.A.—See FILA Holdings Corporation; *Int'l*, pg. 2662
FILA HELLAS S.A.—See F.I.L.A. - Fabbrica Italiana Lapis ed Affini S.p.A.; *Int'l*, pg. 2597
F.I.L.A. HISPANIA S.L.—See F.I.L.A. - Fabbrica Italiana Lapis ed Affini S.p.A.; *Int'l*, pg. 2597
FILA HOLDINGS CORPORATION; *Int'l*, pg. 2662
FILA IBERIA S. L.—See F.I.L.A. - Fabbrica Italiana Lapis ed Affini S.p.A.; *Int'l*, pg. 2597
FILALYRA GB LTD.—See F.I.L.A. - Fabbrica Italiana Lapis ed Affini S.p.A.; *Int'l*, pg. 2596
FILAMAT COMPOSITES INC.—See Zurn Elkay Water Solutions Corporation; *U.S. Public*, pg. 2412
FILAMENT HEALTH CORP.; *Int'l*, pg. 2662
FILA POLSKA SP. Z O.O.—See F.I.L.A. - Fabbrica Italiana Lapis ed Affini S.p.A.; *Int'l*, pg. 2597
FILA SA PTY. LTD.—See F.I.L.A. - Fabbrica Italiana Lapis ed Affini S.p.A.; *Int'l*, pg. 2597
FILA SPORT (HONG KONG) LIMITED—See FILA Holdings Corporation; *Int'l*, pg. 2662
FILA SPORT TAIWAN LTD.—See FILA Holdings Corporation; *Int'l*, pg. 2662
FILA STATIONARY AND OFFICE EQUIPMENT INDUSTRY LTD. CO.—See F.I.L.A. - Fabbrica Italiana Lapis ed Affini S.p.A.; *Int'l*, pg. 2597
FILATEX FASHIONS LIMITED; *Int'l*, pg. 2662
FILATEX INDIA LTD.; *Int'l*, pg. 2662
FILATURA TOLLEGNO 1900 S.R.L.—See Indorama Ventures Public Company Limited; *Int'l*, pg. 3658
FILATURE DE LIN FILIN S.A.—See Marzotto S.p.A.; *Int'l*, pg. 4718
FILATURES ET CORDERIES STE. GERMAINE—See Universal Cooperatives, Inc.; *U.S. Private*, pg. 4304
FILA UK LIMITED—See FILA Holdings Corporation; *Int'l*, pg. 2662
FILA USA, INC.—See FILA Holdings Corporation; *Int'l*, pg. 2662
FILAVIE S.A.S—See Groupe Grimaud La Corbiere SA; *Int'l*, pg. 3103
FILCO, INC.; *U.S. Private*, pg. 1505
FILCON AMERICA, INC.—See Nippon Filcon Co., Ltd.; *Int'l*, pg. 5317
FILCON ELECTRONIC GMBH—See Diploma PLC; *Int'l*, pg. 2128
FILCON EUROPE SARL—See Nippon Filcon Co., Ltd.; *Int'l*, pg. 5317
FILCON FABRICS & TECHNOLOGY CO., LTD.—See Nippon Filcon Co., Ltd.; *Int'l*, pg. 5317
FILCONN, INC.—See PEI-Genesis Inc.; *U.S. Private*, pg. 3130
FILCORE CO., LTD.—See KITZ CORPORATION; *Int'l*, pg. 4196
FILEC-LECTRIC SARL—See Amphenol Corporation; *U.S. Public*, pg. 130
FILE KEEPERS, LLC—See Raleigh Enterprises; *U.S. Private*, pg. 3349
FILEMAKER, INC.—See Apple Inc.; *U.S. Public*, pg. 169
FILEMAKER JAPAN INC.—See Apple Inc.; *U.S. Public*, pg. 169
FILENE'S BASEMENT, INC.—See Trinity Place Holdings, Inc.; *U.S. Public*, pg. 2194
FILIAGGI HOLDING COMPANY INC.; *U.S. Private*, pg. 1505
FILIALA DE INMAGAZINARE GAZE NATURALE DEPOGAZ PLOIESTI S.R.L.—See S.N.G.N. Romgaz S.A.; *Int'l*, pg. 6457

FILIAL AF LEM EUROPE GMBH—See LEM Holding SA; *Int'l*, pg. 4447
FILIALES ASYTEL S.P.A.—See Econocom Group SA; *Int'l*, pg. 2298
FILING SERVICES CANADA INC.—See Issuer Direct Corporation; *U.S. Public*, pg. 1175
FILINVEST ALABANG INC.—See Filinvest Development Corporation; *Int'l*, pg. 2663
FILINVEST DEVELOPMENT CORPORATION; *Int'l*, pg. 2662
FILINVEST LAND INC.—See Filinvest Development Corporation; *Int'l*, pg. 2663
FILINVEST SUPERMALL INC.—See Filinvest Development Corporation; *Int'l*, pg. 2663
FILIOS, INC.—See IAC Inc.; *U.S. Public*, pg. 1082
FILIPINO FUND, INC.; *Int'l*, pg. 2663
FILIPPA K AB; *Int'l*, pg. 2663
FILISTER ENTERPRISES; *U.S. Private*, pg. 1505
FILLAUER COMPANIES, INC.—See Patient Square Capital, L.P.; *U.S. Private*, pg. 3107
FILLAUER EUROPE AB—See Patient Square Capital, L.P.; *U.S. Private*, pg. 3107
FILLAUER LLC—See Patient Square Capital, L.P.; *U.S. Private*, pg. 3107
FILL CARE CO., LTD.—See Sumitomo Forestry Co., Ltd.; *Int'l*, pg. 7285
FIL LIMITED—See FMR LLC; *U.S. Private*, pg. 1555
FILLING & PACKING MATERIALS MANUFACTURING COMPANY; *Int'l*, pg. 2663
FILLMORE CAPITAL PARTNERS, LLC; *U.S. Private*, pg. 1506
FILL-MORE SEEDS INC.—See Seaboard Corporation; *U.S. Public*, pg. 1850
FILLTECH CORPORATION—See Toenec Corporation; *Int'l*, pg. 7774
FIL (LUXEMBOURG) S.A., SVERIGE FILIAL—See FMR LLC; *U.S. Private*, pg. 1555
FILMCO INDUSTRIES INC.—See Thermwell Products Co., Inc.; *U.S. Private*, pg. 4143
FILMCUTTER ADVANCED MATERIAL S.R.L.—See Jolywood Suzhou Sunwatt Co., Ltd.; *Int'l*, pg. 3997
THE FILM DEPARTMENT HOLDINGS, INC.; *U.S. Private*, pg. 4028
FILMEC CO., LTD.—See Asahi Intecc Co., Ltd.; *Int'l*, pg. 594
FILMECC USA, INC.—See Asahi Intecc Co., Ltd.; *Int'l*, pg. 594
FILMET COLOR LABORATORIES INC.; *U.S. Private*, pg. 1506
FILMETRICS, INC.—See KLA Corporation; *U.S. Public*, pg. 1267
FILM EXPO GROUP LLC—See Shamrock Capital Advisors, LLC; *U.S. Private*, pg. 3624
FILMFAX, INC.; *U.S. Private*, pg. 1506
FILMLANCE INTERNATIONAL AB—See LOV Group Invest SAS; *Int'l*, pg. 4565
FILMOLUX BENELUX B.V.—See Blue Cap AG; *Int'l*, pg. 1067
FILMOLUX CO., LTD.—See Blue Cap AG; *Int'l*, pg. 1067
FILMOLUX DEUTSCHLAND GMBH—See Blue Cap AG; *Int'l*, pg. 1067
FILMOLUX ITALIA S.R.L.—See Blue Cap AG; *Int'l*, pg. 1067
FILMOLUX SARL—See Blue Cap AG; *Int'l*, pg. 1067
FILMOLUX SWISS AG—See Blue Cap AG; *Int'l*, pg. 1067
FILMON.COM PLC; *Int'l*, pg. 2663
FILMON NETWORKS USA—See FilmOn.com Plc; *Int'l*, pg. 2663
FILM PAYROLL SERVICES INC.—See Oberman Tivoli Miller Pickert; *U.S. Private*, pg. 2987
FILM ROMAN, LLC—See Lions Gate Entertainment Corp.; *Int'l*, pg. 4521
FILMS AT 59; *Int'l*, pg. 2663
FILM SCORE MONTHLY; *U.S. Private*, pg. 1506
FILMS FOR THE HUMANITIES & SCIENCES, INC.—See Veronis Suhler Stevenson Partners LLC; *U.S. Private*, pg. 4368
FILM SOCIETY OF LINCOLN CENTER, INC.; *U.S. Private*, pg. 1506
FILMS PARAMOUNT S.A.—See National Amusements, Inc.; *U.S. Private*, pg. 2842
FILMTEC CORPORATION—See DuPont de Nemours, Inc.; *U.S. Public*, pg. 693
FILMTECH CORP.—See Alpha Industries, Inc.; *U.S. Private*, pg. 197
FILMTOOLS; *U.S. Private*, pg. 1506
FILMTRACK INC.; *U.S. Private*, pg. 1506
FILMWEB AS—See Egmont Fonden; *Int'l*, pg. 2325
FILO CORP.; *Int'l*, pg. 2663
FILOMARKET S.R.L.—See Cefla S.C.; *Int'l*, pg. 1390
FILORGA AMERICAS INC.—See Colgate-Palmolive Company; *U.S. Public*, pg. 532
FILORGA PORTUGAL, UNIPESSOAL, LDA.—See Colgate-Palmolive Company; *U.S. Public*, pg. 532
FILOTIPO, LDA—See 2G Energy AG; *Int'l*, pg. 5
FILOZOO SRL—See Archer-Daniels-Midland Company; *U.S. Public*, pg. 185
FILPASSION SA—See Dainichiseika Color & Chemicals Mfg. Co., Ltd.; *Int'l*, pg. 1939

FILSYN CORPORATION; *Int'l*, pg. 2663
FILTA ENVIRONMENTAL CANADA LIMITED—See Franchise Brands plc; *Int'l*, pg. 2760
FILTA EUROPE B.V.—See Franchise Brands plc; *Int'l*, pg. 2760
FILTAFRY DEUTSCHLAND GMBH—See Franchise Brands plc; *Int'l*, pg. 2760
FILTA GROUP HOLDINGS PLC—See Franchise Brands plc; *Int'l*, pg. 2760
THE FILTA GROUP INCORPORATED—See Franchise Brands plc; *Int'l*, pg. 2760
THE FILTA GROUP LIMITED—See Franchise Brands plc; *Int'l*, pg. 2760
FILTECH FRANCE S.A.R.L.—See Zehnder Group AG; *Int'l*, pg. 8630
FILTECH NEDERLAND B.V.—See Zehnder Group AG; *Int'l*, pg. 8630
FILTECH SWISS S.A.—See Zehnder Group AG; *Int'l*, pg. 8630
FILTER ADVERTISING LLC—See Splendor Design Group, Inc.; *U.S. Private*, pg. 3759
FILTER & COATING TECHNOLOGY, INC.—See Genstar Capital, LLC; *U.S. Private*, pg. 1678
FILTEREN CO., LTD.—See Sojitz Corporation; *Int'l*, pg. 7061
FILTER LLC—See 24 Seven, LLC; *U.S. Private*, pg. 6
FILTERMECH PLANT SALES LIMITED—See CorpAcq Holdings Limited; *Int'l*, pg. 1802
FILTERMIST ASIA PTE. LTD.—See Absolent Air Care Group AB; *Int'l*, pg. 70
FILTERMIST GMBH—See Absolent Air Care Group AB; *Int'l*, pg. 70
FILTERMIST SHANGHAI LTD.—See Absolent Air Care Group AB; *Int'l*, pg. 70
FILTERMIST SYSTEMS LTD.—See Absolent Air Care Group AB; *Int'l*, pg. 70
FILTER QUEEN INC.—See HMI Industries Inc.; *U.S. Private*, pg. 1955
FILTER SALES & SERVICE INC.; *U.S. Private*, pg. 1506
FILTER SENSING TECHNOLOGIES, INC.—See CTS Corporation; *U.S. Public*, pg. 603
FILTERTEK B.V.—See Illinois Tool Works Inc.; *U.S. Public*, pg. 1103
FILTERTEK DE MEXICO, S.A. DE C.V.—See Illinois Tool Works Inc.; *U.S. Public*, pg. 1103
FILTERTEK DO BRASIL INDUSTRIA E COMERCIO LTDA.—See Illinois Tool Works Inc.; *U.S. Public*, pg. 1103
FILTERTEK DO BRAZIL INDUSTRIA E COMMERCIO LTDA.—See Illinois Tool Works Inc.; *U.S. Public*, pg. 1103
FILTERTEK INC.—See Illinois Tool Works Inc.; *U.S. Public*, pg. 1103
FILTERTEKNIK A/S—See Indutrade AB; *Int'l*, pg. 3678
FILTERTEKNIK SVERIGE AB—See Indutrade AB; *Int'l*, pg. 3678
FILTERTEK, S.A.—See Illinois Tool Works Inc.; *U.S. Public*, pg. 1103
FILTER VISION PUBLIC COMPANY LIMITED; *Int'l*, pg. 2663
FILTISAC SA; *Int'l*, pg. 2663
FILTON INDUSTRIES SDN. BHD.—See PT Selamat Sempurna Tbk; *Int'l*, pg. 6071
FILTRA CONSULTANTS & ENGINEERS LTD.; *Int'l*, pg. 2663
FILTRAFINE CORPORATION—See Bright Sheland International Co., Ltd.; *Int'l*, pg. 1162
FILTRAFINE JAPAN INC.—See Bright Sheland International Co., Ltd.; *Int'l*, pg. 1162
FILTRAFINE PTE. LTD.—See Bright Sheland International Co., Ltd.; *Int'l*, pg. 1162
FILTRAN LLC—See Madison Industries Holdings LLC; *U.S. Private*, pg. 2543
FILTRA-SYSTEMS COMPANY—See The Chickasaw Nation; *U.S. Private*, pg. 4008
FILTRATION & CONTROL SYSTEMS PTE LTD.—See Amiad Water Systems Ltd.; *Int'l*, pg. 427
FILTRATION GROUP CORPORATION—See Madison Industries Holdings LLC; *U.S. Private*, pg. 2543
FILTRATION LAB INC.; *Int'l*, pg. 2663
FILTRATION LTD.—See Indutrade AB; *Int'l*, pg. 3678
FILTRAUTO DO BRASIL LTDA.—See Compagnia Finanziaria de Benedetti S.p.A.; *Int'l*, pg. 1722
FILTRAUTO S.A.—See Compagnia Finanziaria de Benedetti S.p.A.; *Int'l*, pg. 1722
FILTRAUTO SLOVENIJA—See Compagnia Finanziaria de Benedetti S.p.A.; *Int'l*, pg. 1722
FILTREXX INTERNATIONAL, LLC—See Mativ Holdings, Inc.; *U.S. Public*, pg. 1396
FILTRIX B.V.—See Pentair plc; *Int'l*, pg. 5789
FILTRONA SPECIAL FIBER PRODUCTS NINGBO CO., LTD.—See Essentra plc; *Int'l*, pg. 2511
FILTRON ENGINEERS LIMITED; *Int'l*, pg. 2663
FILTRONIC AB—See Danaher Corporation; *U.S. Public*, pg. 626
FILTRONIC BROADBAND LTD.—See Filtronic plc; *Int'l*, pg. 2663
FILTRONIC PLC; *Int'l*, pg. 2663

COMPANY NAME INDEX

FILTRONIC (SUZHOU) TELECOMMUNICATION PRODUCTS CO. LTD.—See Filtronic plc; *Int'l*, pg. 2663
FILTRONIC WIRELESS LTD.—See Filtronic plc; *Int'l*, pg. 2663
FILTRONIC WIRELESS LTD.—See Filtronic plc; *Int'l*, pg. 2663
FILTROS BALDWIN DE MEXICO S.A. DE C.V.—See Parker Hannifin Corporation; *U.S. Public*, pg. 1641
FILTROS PARTMO S.A.S.—See Donaldson Company, Inc.; *U.S. Public*, pg. 676
FILTROX AG—See CRS Holding AG; *Int'l*, pg. 1859
FILWEL CO., LTD.—See Air Water Inc.; *Int'l*, pg. 240
FILZFELT INC.—See MillerKnoll, Inc.; *U.S. Public*, pg. 1447
FIMA BULKING SERVICES BERHAD—See Kumpulan Fima Berhad; *Int'l*, pg. 4331
FIMA CORPORATION BERHAD; *Int'l*, pg. 2663
FIMACO SDN. BHD.—See Fiamma Holdings Berhad; *Int'l*, pg. 2650
FIMAC SOLUTIONS LLC—See BancAdvice, LLC; *U.S. Private*, pg. 464
FIMA GLOBAL INVEST D.O.O; *Int'l*, pg. 2664
FIMA GREATALL TURBO MACHINERY CO., LTD—See Schaeff Maschinen GmbH & Co. KG; *Int'l*, pg. 6615
FIMA INDIA PVT LTD.—See Schaeff Maschinen GmbH & Co. KG; *Int'l*, pg. 6615
FIMA INSTANCO SDN. BHD.—See Kumpulan Fima Berhad; *Int'l*, pg. 4331
FIMALAC S.A.; *Int'l*, pg. 2664
FIMA MASCHINENBAU GMBH—See Schaeff Maschinen GmbH & Co. KG; *Int'l*, pg. 6615
FIMAPIERRE—See BNP Paribas SA; *Int'l*, pg. 1091
FIMARO INVEST SA; *Int'l*, pg. 2664
FIMAS GMBH—See TAMBURI INVESTMENT PARTNERS S.p.A; *Int'l*, pg. 7450
FIMA TECHNOLOGY SDN. BHD.—See Fima Corporation Berhad; *Int'l*, pg. 2663
FIMA/VG DISTRIBUICAO DE PRODUTOS ALIMENTARES, LDA.—See Jeronimo Martins SGPS SA; *Int'l*, pg. 3931
FIMA/VG DISTRIBUICAO DE PRODUTOS ALIMENTARES, LDA.—See Unilever PLC; *Int'l*, pg. 8044
FIMBAG FINANZMARKTBETEILIGUNG AKTIENGESELLSCHAFT DES BUNDES—See Osterreichische Beteiligungs AG; *Int'l*, pg. 5653
FIM BANK GROUP LTD.—See Kuwait Projects Company (Holding) K.S.C.P.; *Int'l*, pg. 4346
FIMBANK P.L.C.; *Int'l*, pg. 2664
FIMBEL DOOR COMPANY—See ASSA ABLOY AB; *Int'l*, pg. 634
FIM BUSINESS SOLUTIONS LIMITED—See FIMBank p.l.c.; *Int'l*, pg. 2664
FIMEC TECHNOLOGIES—See Materials Technologies; *Int'l*, pg. 4727
FI-MED MANAGEMENT, INC.; *U.S. Private*, pg. 1501
FIME—See Elica S.p.A.; *Int'l*, pg. 2361
FIME S.R.L.—See Wurth Verwaltungsgesellschaft mbH; *Int'l*, pg. 8504
FIMESTIC EXPANSION SA—See BNP Paribas SA; *Int'l*, pg. 1091
FIMI ALI S.P.A.—See Ali Holding S.r.l; *Int'l*, pg. 321
FIM INOX SAS—See ERG S.p.A.; *Int'l*, pg. 2491
FIMI S.R.L.—See Barco N.V.; *Int'l*, pg. 864
FIMOPART GROUP; *Int'l*, pg. 2664
FIM OYJ—See Swedbank AB; *Int'l*, pg. 7364
FIM PROPERTY INVESTMENT LIMITED—See FIMBank p.l.c.; *Int'l*, pg. 2664
FINA ANTWERP OLEFINS—See TotalEnergies SE; *Int'l*, pg. 7842
FINACCEL PTE LTD.; *Int'l*, pg. 2664
FINACCESS CAPITAL, S.A. DE C.V.—See Grupo Finaccess S.A.P.I. de C.V.; *Int'l*, pg. 3129
FINACITY CORPORATION—See White Oak Global Advisors, LLC; *U.S. Private*, pg. 4509
FINACOR & ASSOCIES S.A.—See Viel & Compagnie SA; *Int'l*, pg. 8192
FINACOR DEUTSCHLAND GMBH—See Viel & Compagnie SA; *Int'l*, pg. 8192
FINACOR DEUTSCHLAND GMBH—See Viel & Compagnie SA; *Int'l*, pg. 8192
FINADIS S.A.—See Otto GmbH & Co. KG; *Int'l*, pg. 5663
FINA ENERJI HOLDING A.S.—See Fiba Holding A.S.; *Int'l*, pg. 2651
FINA FINANCE & TRADING CO., LTD.—See Chailease Holding Company Limited; *Int'l*, pg. 1437
FINAGAZ—See UGI Corporation; *U.S. Public*, pg. 2222
FIN-AG INC.—See CHS INC.; *U.S. Public*, pg. 492
FINAGRA GROUP LIMITED—See Stone Point Capital LLC; *U.S. Private*, pg. 3821
FINAL DRAFT, INC.—See EQT AB; *Int'l*, pg. 2473
FINALE DESSERTERIE & BAKERY; *U.S. Private*, pg. 1506
FINALI CORPORATION—See Concentrix Corporation; *U.S. Public*, pg. 565
FINAL MILE LOGISTICS, INC.—See Mercury Air Group Inc.; *U.S. Private*, pg. 2670
FINALP ZRT.—See DDM Holding AG; *Int'l*, pg. 1993
THE FINALS—See Swimwear Anywhere, Inc.; *U.S. Private*, pg. 3893

FINALYSIS CREDIT & GUARANTEE CO. LTD.; *Int'l*, pg. 2664
FINAM INVESTMENT COMPANY JSC; *Int'l*, pg. 2664
FINANCE 2000 S.A.—See Viel & Compagnie SA; *Int'l*, pg. 8192
FINANCE 500, INC.—See Stifel Financial Corp.; *U.S. Public*, pg. 1949
FINANCE ACCOUNTANCY MOHASSABA SA—See Arab Bank plc; *Int'l*, pg. 529
FINANCE ALL SOLUTIONS CO., LTD.—See SBI Holdings, Inc.; *Int'l*, pg. 6604
FINANCE AND COMMERCE, INC.—See The Dolan Company; *U.S. Private*, pg. 4022
FINANCE CARE SP. Z O.O.—See Work Service S.A.; *Int'l*, pg. 8455
THE FINANCE COMPANY PLC - BUSINESS LEASING DIVISION—See The Finance Company PLC; *Int'l*, pg. 7643
THE FINANCE COMPANY PLC - CORPORATE FINANCE & TREASURY DIVISION—See The Finance Company PLC; *Int'l*, pg. 7643
THE FINANCE COMPANY PLC - FIXED DEPOSITS DIVISION—See The Finance Company PLC; *Int'l*, pg. 7643
THE FINANCE COMPANY PLC - MARKETING DIVISION—See The Finance Company PLC; *Int'l*, pg. 7643
THE FINANCE COMPANY PLC; *Int'l*, pg. 7643
FINANCE EXPRESS, LLC—See Vista Equity Partners, LLC; *U.S. Private*, pg. 4400
FINANCE FACTORS, LIMITED1952; *U.S. Private*, pg. 1506
FINANCE HOUSE P.J.S.C.; *Int'l*, pg. 2664
FINANCE INSURANCE LTD.—See Finance Factors, Limited1952; *U.S. Private*, pg. 1506
FINANCEIRA ALFA S.A.—See Banco Alfa De Investimento SA; *Int'l*, pg. 816
FINANCELIFE LEBENSVERSICHERUNG AG—See UNIQA Insurance Group AG; *Int'l*, pg. 8057
FINANCE OF AMERICA COMPANIES INC.; *U.S. Public*, pg. 834
FINANCE REALTY COMPANY LTD.—See Finance Factors, Limited1952; *U.S. Private*, pg. 1506
THE FINANCE STORE; *U.S. Private*, pg. 4028
FINANCE TV PTY LTD—See Sequoia Financial Group Limited; *Int'l*, pg. 6719
FINANCEWARE, LLC—See NewSpring Capital LLC; *U.S. Private*, pg. 2917
FINANCIA CREDIT, S.A.; *Int'l*, pg. 2664
FINANCIAL 15 SPLIT CORP.—See Quadravest Capital Management Inc.; *Int'l*, pg. 6149
FINANCIAL ACCOUNTING FOUNDATION; *U.S. Private*, pg. 1506
FINANCIAL ADVANTAGE INC.; *U.S. Private*, pg. 1506
FINANCIAL ARTS INC.—See Inszone Insurance Services, LLC; *U.S. Private*, pg. 2096
FINANCIAL ASSURANCE JAPAN, INC.—See Prudential Financial, Inc.; *U.S. Public*, pg. 1731
FINANCIAL ASSURANCE LIFE INSURANCE COMPANY—See Financial Holding Corp.; *U.S. Private*, pg. 1507
FINANCIAL BRAIN SYSTEMS INC.—See Business Brain Showa-Ota Inc.; *Int'l*, pg. 1228
FINANCIAL BROKERAGE GROUP—See EFG Holding; *Int'l*, pg. 2319
FINANCIAL CENTER CREDIT UNION; *U.S. Private*, pg. 1506
FINANCIAL COMPANY REAL-INVEST.KZ JSC; *Int'l*, pg. 2665
FINANCIAL CONCEPTS, INC.—See Aon plc; *Int'l*, pg. 496
FINANCIAL CONCEPTS OF THE TWIN CITIES, INC.—See Aon plc; *Int'l*, pg. 496
FINANCIAL CONSULTANTS OF AMERICA, INC.—See Arthur J. Gallagher & Co.; *U.S. Public*, pg. 204
FINANCIAL CONSULTING & TRADING INTERNATIONAL, INC.—See Seven Bank Ltd.; *Int'l*, pg. 6731
FINANCIAL CONTROL SYSTEMS, INC.—See STP Investment Services; *U.S. Private*, pg. 3832
THE FINANCIAL CORPORATION COMPANY SAOG; *Int'l*, pg. 7643
FINANCIAL CORPORATION OF LOUISIANA; *U.S. Private*, pg. 1506
FINANCIAL COUNSELORS INC.—See UBS Group AG; *Int'l*, pg. 8008
FINANCIAL DESIGN ASSOCIATES—See Massachusetts Mutual Life Insurance Company; *U.S. Private*, pg. 2605
FINANCIAL DESIGNS LTD.; *U.S. Private*, pg. 1507
FINANCIAL DIGITAL SOLUTIONS, LTD.—See Nomura Research Institute, Ltd.; *Int'l*, pg. 5413
FINANCIAL DYNAMICS IRELAND LTD.—See FTI Consulting, Inc.; *U.S. Public*, pg. 890
FINANCIAL & ENERGY EXCHANGE LIMITED; *Int'l*, pg. 2665
FINANCIAL ENGINEERING ASSOCIATES, INC.—See ION Investment Group Ltd.; *Int'l*, pg. 3794
FINANCIAL ENGINES ADVISORS L.L.C.—See Hellman & Friedman LLC; *U.S. Private*, pg. 1908
FINANCIAL FEDCORP, INC.; *U.S. Private*, pg. 1507

FINANCIAL SERVICES CORP.

FINANCIAL FEDERAL BANK—See Financial FedCorp, Inc.; *U.S. Private*, pg. 1507
FINANCIALFORCE.COM INC.—See UNIT4 N.V.; *Int'l*, pg. 8062
FINANCIAL FREEDOM ACQUISITION LLC—See First Citizens BancShares, Inc.; *U.S. Public*, pg. 841
FINANCIAL GRAVITY COMPANIES, INC.; *U.S. Public*, pg. 834
FINANCIAL GROUP FUTURE PJSC; *Int'l*, pg. 2665
FINANCIAL GUARANTY INSURANCE COMPANY; *U.S. Private*, pg. 1507
FINANCIAL GUARD, LLC—See Franklin Resources, Inc.; *U.S. Public*, pg. 882
FINANCIAL HOLDING CORP.; *U.S. Private*, pg. 1507
FINANCIAL INDEX AUSTRALIA PTY LTD.; *Int'l*, pg. 2665
FINANCIAL INDUSTRY REGULATORY AUTHORITY, INC.; *U.S. Private*, pg. 1507
FINANCIAL INFORMATION TECHNOLOGIES, INC.; *U.S. Private*, pg. 1507
FINANCIAL INNOVATIONS CENTER INC; *U.S. Private*, pg. 1507
FINANCIAL INSTITUTIONS, INC.; *U.S. Public*, pg. 834
FINANCIAL INVESTMENTS CORPORATION; *U.S. Private*, pg. 1507
FINANCIAL INVESTMENTS INC; *U.S. Private*, pg. 1508
FINANCIAL JAPAN, CO., LTD.—See SBI Shinsei Bank, Limited; *Int'l*, pg. 6606
FINANCIAL LINK CO., LTD.—See Sumitomo Mitsui Financial Group, Inc.; *Int'l*, pg. 7293
FINANCIAL MANAGEMENT SOLUTIONS, INC.—See Hellman & Friedman LLC; *U.S. Private*, pg. 1910
FINANCIAL MARKETS, INC.; *U.S. Private*, pg. 1508
FINANCIAL MODELS COMPANY LTD.—See SS&C Technologies Holdings, Inc.; *U.S. Public*, pg. 1923
FINANCIAL MORTGAGE GROUP LTD.; *U.S. Private*, pg. 1508
FINANCIAL NAVIGATOR, INC.—See Asset Vantage Systems Pvt. Ltd.; *Int'l*, pg. 642
FINANCIAL OBJECTS INC.—See Temenos AG; *Int'l*, pg. 7555
FINANCIAL OBJECTS INTERNATIONAL LIMITED—See Temenos AG; *Int'l*, pg. 7555
FINANCIAL OBJECTS LIMITED—See Temenos AG; *Int'l*, pg. 7555
FINANCIAL OBJECTS (UK) LIMITED—See Temenos AG; *Int'l*, pg. 7555
FINANCIAL & OFFICE SYSTEMS, INC.—See Smart Source of Georgia, LLC; *U.S. Private*, pg. 3691
FINANCIALOGIC, INC.; *U.S. Private*, pg. 1508
FINANCIAL ONE CREDIT UNION—See Magnifi Financial Credit Union; *U.S. Private*, pg. 2548
FINANCIAL PACIFIC INSURANCE COMPANY—See United Fire Group, Inc.; *U.S. Public*, pg. 2230
FINANCIAL PACIFIC LEASING, INC.—See Columbia Banking System, Inc.; *U.S. Public*, pg. 534
FINANCIAL PACIFIC LEASING, INC.—See Columbia Banking System, Inc.; *U.S. Public*, pg. 534
FINANCIAL PARTNERS CREDIT UNION; *U.S. Private*, pg. 1508
FINANCIAL PARTNERS GROUP CO., LTD.; *Int'l*, pg. 2665
FINANCIAL PLANNING ASSOCIATION; *U.S. Private*, pg. 1508
FINANCIAL PLUS CREDIT UNION; *U.S. Private*, pg. 1508
FINANCIAL PROCESSING SYSTEMS CORPORATION—See Orange Coast Title Company Inc.; *U.S. Private*, pg. 3037
FINANCIAL PROFESSIONAL RISK SOLUTIONS, INC.—See Aon plc; *Int'l*, pg. 494
FINANCIAL RECOVERY SERVICES, INC.; *U.S. Private*, pg. 1508
FINANCIAL RECOVERY TECHNOLOGIES LLC—See The Cross Country Group, LLC; *U.S. Private*, pg. 4017
FINANCIAL RESEARCH ASSOCIATES, LLC—See Wilmington plc; *Int'l*, pg. 8422
FINANCIAL RESOURCE MANAGEMENT GROUP, INC.—See Caisse de Depot et Placement du Quebec; *Int'l*, pg. 1256
FINANCIAL RESOURCE MANAGEMENT GROUP, INC.—See KKR & Co. Inc.; *U.S. Public*, pg. 1265
FINANCIAL RISK SOLUTIONS, INC.—See DOXA Insurance Holdings LLC; *U.S. Private*, pg. 1270
FINANCIAL SECURITY ASSOCIATES, INC.—See Simplicity Financial Marketing Holdings Inc.; *U.S. Private*, pg. 3667
FINANCIAL.SERVICE.PLUS GMBH—See flatexDEGIRO AG; *Int'l*, pg. 2698
FINANCIAL SERVICES ADVICE AND SUPPORT LIMITED—See Quilter plc; *Int'l*, pg. 6162
FINANCIAL SERVICES COMPANY SAOG; *Int'l*, pg. 2665
FINANCIAL SERVICES CORP.; *U.S. Private*, pg. 1508
FINANCIAL SERVICES ROUNDTABLE—See Bank Policy Institute; *U.S. Private*, pg. 467
FINANCIAL SOLUTIONS AG SERVICE & VERMITTLUNG—See Swiss Life Holding; *Int'l*, pg. 7368
FINANCIAL STABILITY INSTITUTE—See Bank for International Settlements; *Int'l*, pg. 838

FINANCIAL STATEMENT SERVICES

FINANCIAL STATEMENT SERVICES; *U.S. Private*, pg. 1508
FINANCIAL STRATEGIES ACQUISITION CORP.; *U.S. Public*, pg. 834
FINANCIAL STREET HOLDING CO., LTD.; *Int'l*, pg. 2665
FINANCIAL STREET PROPERTY COMPANY LIMITED; *Int'l*, pg. 2665
FINANCIAL SUPERMARKETS, INC.—See Market Contractors Ltd.; *U.S. Private*, pg. 2579
FINANCIAL TECHNOLOGY VENTURES MANAGEMENT CO. LLC; *U.S. Private*, pg. 1508
FINANCIAL TELEMARKETING SERVICES LTD.—See BNP Paribas SA; *Int'l*, pg. 1091
THE FINANCIAL TIMES GROUP LTD.—See Nikkei Inc.; *Int'l*, pg. 5290
THE FINANCIAL TIMES LTD.—See Nikkei Inc.; *Int'l*, pg. 5290
FINANCIAL WEST INVESTMENT GROUP INC.; *U.S. Private*, pg. 1508
FINANCIAL WISDOM LIMITED—See Commonwealth Bank of Australia; *Int'l*, pg. 1720
FINANCIARA SA—See Erste Group Bank AG; *Int'l*, pg. 2498
FINANCIERA AYUDAMOS S.A. DE C.V., SOFOMER—See Banco Bilbao Vizcaya Argentaria, S.A.; *Int'l*, pg. 817
FINANCIERA CONFIANZA S.A.A.; *Int'l*, pg. 2665
FINANCIERA EFECTIVA SA; *Int'l*, pg. 2665
FINANCIERA EL CORTE INGLES E.F.C., S.A.—See Banco Santander, *Int'l*, pg. 827
FINANCIERA FAMILIAR, S.A.; *Int'l*, pg. 2665
FINANCIERA FINACREDIT, S.A.—See Grupo Aliado S.A.; *Int'l*, pg. 3119
FINANCIERA FORTALEZA, S.A DE C.V.—See Bayport Management Limited; *Int'l*, pg. 915
FINANCIERA IBEROAMERICANA, S.A.—See Banco de Sabadell, S.A.; *Int'l*, pg. 821
FINANCIERA INDEPENDENCIA, S.A.B. DE C.V., SOFOM, E.N.R.; *Int'l*, pg. 2665
FINANCIERA QAPAQ S.A.; *Int'l*, pg. 2665
FINANCIERE BNP PARIBAS SAS—See BNP Paribas SA; *Int'l*, pg. 1091
FINANCIERE DE L'ODET; *Int'l*, pg. 2665
FINANCIERE DESSANGE SASU—See Eurazeo SE; *Int'l*, pg. 2528
FINANCIERE DE TUBIZE SA; *Int'l*, pg. 2668
FINANCIERE DU PATRIMOINE SAS—See Swiss Life Holding; *Int'l*, pg. 7368
FINANCIERE EIFFARIE—See Eiffage S.A.; *Int'l*, pg. 2331
FINANCIERE EIFFARIE—See Macquarie Group Limited; *Int'l*, pg. 4626
FINANCIERE FAURECIA—See FORVIA SE; *Int'l*, pg. 2747
FINANCIERE HOCHE BAINS-LES-BAINS SA; *Int'l*, pg. 2668
FINANCIERE IMMOBILIERE ETANG BERRE MEDIT SA; *Int'l*, pg. 2668
FINANCIERE LR SARL; *Int'l*, pg. 2668
FINANCIERE MARJOS SA; *Int'l*, pg. 2668
FINANCIERE MONCEY SA; *Int'l*, pg. 2668
FINANCIERE OFIC—See Astorg Partners S.A.S.; *Int'l*, pg. 656
FINANCIERE PARIS HAUSSMANN—See BNP Paribas SA; *Int'l*, pg. 1091
FINANCIERE PERGOLESE—See Stellantis N.V.; *Int'l*, pg. 7201
FINANCIERE PINAULT SCA; *Int'l*, pg. 2668
FINANCIERE QUICK S.A.S.; *Int'l*, pg. 2669
FINANCIERE SNOP DUNOIS SA; *Int'l*, pg. 2669
FINANCIERE SYZ & CO SA; *Int'l*, pg. 2669
FINANCO LIMITED—See Raymond James Financial, Inc.; *U.S. Public*, pg. 1764
FINANCO, LLC—See Raymond James Financial, Inc.; *U.S. Public*, pg. 1764
FINANGLIA FERRIES LIMITED—See Grimaldi Group SpA; *Int'l*, pg. 3085
FINANSA CREDIT LTD.—See FNS HOLDINGS PUBLIC COMPANY LIMITED; *Int'l*, pg. 2718
FINANSA FUND MANAGEMENT LIMITED—See FNS HOLDINGS PUBLIC COMPANY LIMITED; *Int'l*, pg. 2718
FINANSA SECURITIES LTD.—See FNS HOLDINGS PUBLIC COMPANY LIMITED; *Int'l*, pg. 2718
FINANSE AGENT TRANSFEROWY SP. Z O.O.—See PKO Bank Polski SA; *Int'l*, pg. 5887
FINANS FINANSAL KIRALAMA A.S.—See Qatar National Bank S.A.Q.; *Int'l*, pg. 6135
FINANSIA SYRUS SECURITIES PUBLIC COMPANY LIMITED; *Int'l*, pg. 2669
FINANSINOS S/A - CREDITO FINANCIAMENTO E INVESTIMENTO; *Int'l*, pg. 2669
FINANS LEASING A.S.—See National Bank of Greece S.A.; *Int'l*, pg. 5153
FINANS NORD A/S—See Spar Nord Bank A/S; *Int'l*, pg. 7125
FINANS PORTFOY YONETIMI A.S.—See Qatar National Bank S.A.Q.; *Int'l*, pg. 6135
FINANS YATIRIM MENKUL DEGERLER A.S.—See Qatar National Bank S.A.Q.; *Int'l*, pg. 6135
FINANTEC CO., LTD.; *Int'l*, pg. 2669
FINANZAS E INVERSIONES VALENCIANAS S.A.; *Int'l*, pg. 2669

FINANZA.TECH S.P.A. SB; *Int'l*, pg. 2669
FINANZAUTO, S.A.—See Barloworld Ltd.; *Int'l*, pg. 866
FINANZCHECKPRO GMBH—See Scout24 SE; *Int'l*, pg. 6654
FINANZIA AUTORENTING, S.A.—See Banco Bilbao Vizcaya Argentaria, S.A.; *Int'l*, pg. 817
FINANZ UND WIRTSCHAFT AG—See TX Group AG; *Int'l*, pg. 7991
FINARBIT SA—See Viel & Compagnie SA; *Int'l*, pg. 8192
FINARTE SPA; *Int'l*, pg. 2669
FINASTRA GROUP HOLDINGS LIMITED—See Vista Equity Partners, LLC; *U.S. Private*, pg. 4397
FINASUCRE HOLDINGS (AUSTRALIA) PTY LTD—See Finasucre S.A.; *Int'l*, pg. 2670
FINASUCRE INVESTMENTS (AUSTRALIA) PTY LTD—See Finasucre S.A.; *Int'l*, pg. 2670
FINASUCRE S.A.; *Int'l*, pg. 2669
FINATEM BETEILIGUNGSGESELLSCHAFT—See Groupe BPCE; *Int'l*, pg. 3095
FINATIS SA; *Int'l*, pg. 2670
FINAXIS NV—See Ackermans & van Haaren NV; *Int'l*, pg. 106
FINAXO ENVIRONNEMENT SA; *Int'l*, pg. 2670
FINAXYS—See Neurones S.A.; *Int'l*, pg. 5219
FINBANK SA—See Access Corporation; *Int'l*, pg. 89
FINBAR GROUP LIMITED; *Int'l*, pg. 2670
FINBAR TO RENT PTY. LTD.—See Finbar Group Limited; *Int'l*, pg. 2670
FINBERG ARASTIRMA GELISTIRME DANISMANLIK YATIRIM HIZMETLERI A.S.—See Fibabanka A.S.; *Int'l*, pg. 2651
FINBOND GROUP INTERNATIONAL LIMITED—See Finbond Group Limited; *Int'l*, pg. 2670
FINBOND GROUP LIMITED; *Int'l*, pg. 2670
FINBOND GROUP NORTH AMERICA, LLC—See Finbond Group Limited; *Int'l*, pg. 2670
FINCA LA CELIA S.A.—See L'Arche Green N.V.; *Int'l*, pg. 4377
FINCA LA CELIA S.A.—See Quinenco S.A.; *Int'l*, pg. 6164
FINCA MUSEUM S.L.—See Baron de Ley, S.A.; *Int'l*, pg. 867
FINCANNA CAPITAL CORP.; *Int'l*, pg. 2670
FINCANTIERI INFRASTRUCTURE OPERE MARITTIME S.P.A.—See Cassa Depositi e Prestiti S.p.A.; *Int'l*, pg. 1355
FINCANTIERI INFRASTRUCTURE S.P.A.—See Fincantieri S.p.A.; *Int'l*, pg. 2671
FINCANTIERI INFRASTRUCTURE S.P.A.—See Fincantieri S.p.A.; *Int'l*, pg. 2671
FINCANTIERI INFRASTRUTTURE SOCIALI S.P.A.—See Fincantieri S.p.A.; *Int'l*, pg. 2671
FINCANTIERI MARINE GROUP HOLDINGS INC.—See Fincantieri S.p.A.; *Int'l*, pg. 2671
FINCANTIERI MARINE GROUP, LLC—See Fincantieri S.p.A.; *Int'l*, pg. 2671
FINCANTIERI MARINE REPAIR LLC—See Fincantieri S.p.A.; *Int'l*, pg. 2671
FINCANTIERI MARINE SYSTEMS LLC—See Fincantieri S.p.A.; *Int'l*, pg. 2671
FINCANTIERI MARINE SYSTEMS NORTH AMERICA INC.—See Fincantieri S.p.A.; *Int'l*, pg. 2671
FINCANTIERI OIL & GAS S.P.A—See Fincantieri S.p.A.; *Int'l*, pg. 2671
FINCANTIERI (SHANGHAI) TRADING CO. LTD.—See Fincantieri S.p.A.; *Int'l*, pg. 2671
FINCANTIERI S.P.A.; *Int'l*, pg. 2671
FINCAS ANZIZU SL; *Int'l*, pg. 2672
FINCERA INC.; *Int'l*, pg. 2672
FINCHAIN CAPITAL PARTNERS AG; *Int'l*, pg. 2672
FINCH CAPITAL PARTNERS B.V; *Int'l*, pg. 2672
FINCHEY CORPORATION OF CA; *U.S. Private*, pg. 1508
FINCHOICE PTY LIMITED—See News Corporation; *U.S. Public*, pg. 1521
FINCH PAPER LLC—See Atlas Holdings, LLC; *U.S. Private*, pg. 376
FINCH THERAPEUTICS GROUP, INC.; *U.S. Public*, pg. 834
FINCH TRANSPORTATION, LLC; *U.S. Private*, pg. 1508
FINCH TURF EQUIPMENT INCORPORATED; *U.S. Private*, pg. 1508
FINCK CIGAR CO.; *U.S. Private*, pg. 1508
FINCLEAR PTY. LTD.—See Ariadne Australia Limited; *Int'l*, pg. 563
FINCONNECT (AUSTRALIA) PTY. LTD.—See Count Limited; *Int'l*, pg. 1817
FINCON REPLY GMBH—See Reply S.p.A.; *Int'l*, pg. 6291
FINCOR HOLDINGS, INC.—See Coverys; *U.S. Private*, pg. 1072
FINCORP INVESTMENT LIMITED—See The Mauritius Commercial Bank Ltd.; *Int'l*, pg. 7665
FINCRAFT CAPITAL JSC; *Int'l*, pg. 2672
FINCRAFT GROUP LLP; *Int'l*, pg. 2672
FINCRAFT INVESTMENT HOUSE JSC; *Int'l*, pg. 2672
FINCRAFT RESOURCES JSC; *Int'l*, pg. 2672
FIND A BABYSITTER PTY LIMITED—See Nine Entertainment Co. Holdings Limited; *Int'l*, pg. 5298
FINDASENSE ESPANA, S.L.—See Majorel Group Luxembourg S.A.; *Int'l*, pg. 4655

CORPORATE AFFILIATIONS

FINDEL EDUCATION LIMITED—See Endless LLP; *Int'l*, pg. 2403
FINDELTACO OY—See DistIT AB; *Int'l*, pg. 2136
FINDER ENERGY HOLDINGS LIMITED; *Int'l*, pg. 2672
FINDER POMPE S.P.A.—See Dover Corporation; *U.S. Public*, pg. 681
FINDER POMPES—See Dover Corporation; *U.S. Public*, pg. 681
FINDERS RESOURCES LIMITED; *Int'l*, pg. 2672
FINDEV INC.; *Int'l*, pg. 2672
FINDEXA FORLAG AS—See Eniro Group AB; *Int'l*, pg. 2439
FINDEX.COM, INC.; *U.S. Public*, pg. 834
FINDEX INC.; *Int'l*, pg. 2672
FINDINGS INC.—See Berkshire Hathaway Inc.; *U.S. Public*, pg. 316
FINDLAW—See Thomson Reuters Corporation; *Int'l*, pg. 7715
FINDLAY AUTOMOTIVE INC.; *U.S. Private*, pg. 1508
FINDLAY IMPLEMENT CO.; *U.S. Private*, pg. 1508
FINDLAY LINCOLN; *U.S. Private*, pg. 1508
FINDLAY PRODUCTS CORP.—See Midway Products Group, Inc.; *U.S. Private*, pg. 2719
FINDLAY SURGERY CENTER, LTD.—See Blanchard Valley Health System; *U.S. Private*, pg. 579
FINDLAY TOYOTA GROUP; *U.S. Private*, pg. 1508
FINDLAY VOLKSWAGEN; *U.S. Private*, pg. 1508
FINDLY, LLC—See Symphony Technology Group, LLC; *U.S. Private*, pg. 3900
FINDLY TALENT - ATLANTA—See Symphony Technology Group, LLC; *U.S. Private*, pg. 3900
FINDLY TALENT - HOUSTON—See Symphony Technology Group, LLC; *U.S. Private*, pg. 3900
FINDLY TALENT, LLC—See Symphony Technology Group, LLC; *U.S. Private*, pg. 3900
FINDLY TALENT - NEW JERSEY—See Symphony Technology Group, LLC; *U.S. Private*, pg. 3900
FINDLY TALENT - ORLANDO—See Symphony Technology Group, LLC; *U.S. Private*, pg. 3900
FINDLY TALENT - WASHINGTON, DC—See Symphony Technology Group, LLC; *U.S. Private*, pg. 3900
FINDMYCOMPANY.COM LLC; *U.S. Private*, pg. 1509
FINDMYPAST LIMITED—See D.C. Thomson & Co. Ltd.; *Int'l*, pg. 1900
FINDOLOGY INTERACTIVE MEDIA—See Enero Group Limited; *Int'l*, pg. 2424
FINDOMESTIC BANCA S.P.A—See BNP Paribas SA; *Int'l*, pg. 1090
FINDOS INVESTOR GMBH; *Int'l*, pg. 2672
FINDREWNO SP. Z O.O.—See Honkarakenne Oyj; *Int'l*, pg. 3471
FINDTAPE.COM LLC; *U.S. Private*, pg. 1509
FINDUS DANMARK A/S—See Nomad Foods Limited; *Int'l*, pg. 5408
FINDUS DENMARK A/S—See Nomad Foods Limited; *Int'l*, pg. 5408
FINDUS ESPANA S.L.U.—See Nomad Foods Limited; *Int'l*, pg. 5408
FINDUS FINLAND OY—See Nomad Foods Limited; *Int'l*, pg. 5408
FINDUS FRANCE S.A.S.—See Nomad Foods Limited; *Int'l*, pg. 5408
FINDUS GROUP LIMITED—See Lion Capital LLP; *Int'l*, pg. 4517
FINDUS NORGE AS—See Nomad Foods Limited; *Int'l*, pg. 5408
FINDUS SVERIGE AB—See Nomad Foods Limited; *Int'l*, pg. 5408
FINDUS SWITZERLAND AG—See Nomad Foods Limited; *Int'l*, pg. 5408
FINE ART GRAPHICS—See Visy Industries Holdings Pty. Ltd.; *Int'l*, pg. 8255
FINE ART GRAPHICS—See Visy Industries Holdings Pty. Ltd.; *Int'l*, pg. 8255
FINE ART GRAPHICS—See Visy Industries Holdings Pty. Ltd.; *Int'l*, pg. 8255
FINE ART GRAPHICS—See Visy Industries Holdings Pty. Ltd.; *Int'l*, pg. 8256
FINE ART GRAPHICS—See Visy Industries Holdings Pty. Ltd.; *Int'l*, pg. 8256
FINE ARTS ENTERPRISES, INC.; *U.S. Private*, pg. 1509
FINE ARTS MUSEUMS OF SAN FRANCISCO; *U.S. Private*, pg. 1509
FINE BESTEEL CO., LTD.; *Int'l*, pg. 2673
FINE BLANKING & TOOL CO.; *Int'l*, pg. 2673
FINEBRAND DIVISION—See National Corset Supply House; *U.S. Private*, pg. 2852
FINE BRIGHT TECHNOLOGY LIMITED—See Walsin Technology Corporation; *Int'l*, pg. 8335
FINECARE INC.—See MatsukiyoCocokara & Co.; *Int'l*, pg. 4730
FINE CHEMICAL LOGISITICS CHINA COMPANY LIMITED—See KKR & Co. Inc.; *U.S. Public*, pg. 1258
FINE CHEMICAL LOGISTICS HONG KONG CO., LTD.—See KKR & Co. Inc.; *U.S. Public*, pg. 1258
FINE CHEMICALS CORPORATION (PTY) LTD—See Aspen Pharmacare Holdings Limited; *Int'l*, pg. 629
FINECOBANK S.P.A.—See UniCredit S.p.A.; *Int'l*, pg. 8041

COMPANY NAME INDEX

FINECO LEASING S.P.A.—See UniCredit S.p.A.; *Int'l*, pg. 8034
FINE COMPONENTS (THAILAND) CO., LTD.—See Ingress Corporation Berhad; *Int'l*, pg. 3702
FINE CONTRACT RESEARCH LIMITED—See Lianhe Chemical Technology Co., Ltd.; *Int'l*, pg. 4482
FINE CREDIT CO., LTD.—See Yamato Holdings Co., Ltd.; *Int'l*, pg. 8554
FINE CRYSTAL CO., LTD.—See The Japan Steel Works, Ltd.; *Int'l*, pg. 7658
FINE CRYSTAL (H.K.) CO., LTD.—See The Japan Steel Works, Ltd.; *Int'l*, pg. 7658
FINE CRYSTAL IWAKI CO., LTD.—See The Japan Steel Works, Ltd.; *Int'l*, pg. 7658
FINE CRYSTAL PRECISION (S.Z.) CO., LTD.—See The Japan Steel Works, Ltd.; *Int'l*, pg. 7658
FINE DECOR WALLCOVERINGS LIMITED—See Brewster Wallpaper Corp.; *U.S. Private*, pg. 647
FINE DESIGNS STORE; *U.S. Private*, pg. 1509
FINEDIGITAL INC.; *Int'l*, pg. 2674
FINEDNC. CO., LTD.; *Int'l*, pg. 2674
FINE DNC CO., LTD.—See Finetechnix Co., Ltd.; *Int'l*, pg. 2674
FINE ENTERTAINMENT CO.; *U.S. Private*, pg. 1509
FINE ENVIRONMENTAL SERVICES LIMITED—See Lianhe Chemical Technology Co., Ltd.; *Int'l*, pg. 4482
FINE ENVIRONMENT TECHNOLOGIES CO., LTD.—See Ocean Plastics Co., Ltd.; *Int'l*, pg. 5516
FINE FOODS INC.; *Int'l*, pg. 2673
FINE FOODS & PHARMACEUTICALS N.T.M. S.P.A.; *Int'l*, pg. 2673
FINE IMPRESSIONS, INC.—See Taylor Corporation; *U.S. Private*, pg. 3938
FINE INDUSTRIES LIMITED—See Lianhe Chemical Technology Co., Ltd.; *Int'l*, pg. 4482
FINELAND LIVING SERVICES GROUP LIMITED; *Int'l*, pg. 2674
FINE LIGHT, INC.; *U.S. Private*, pg. 1509
FINE LIGHT, INC.—See Fine Light, Inc.; *U.S. Private*, pg. 1509
FINE-LINE CIRCUITS LIMITED; *Int'l*, pg. 2673
FINE LINE GRAPHICS CORP.; *U.S. Private*, pg. 1509
FINELINE INDUSTRIES INC.; *U.S. Private*, pg. 1509
FINELINE MEDIA FINANCE LIMITED—See Rothschild & Co SCA; *Int'l*, pg. 0402
FINELINENS.COM; *U.S. Private*, pg. 1509
FINELINE PROTOTYPING, INC.—See Proto Labs, Inc.; *U.S. Public*, pg. 1729
FINELINE SERVICES LIMITED—See Dialog Group Berhad; *Int'l*, pg. 2104
FINELINE TECHNOLOGIES, INC.—See Summit Partners, L.P.; *U.S. Private*, pg. 3855
FINELITE INC.; *U.S. Private*, pg. 1509
FINELLI CONSULTING ENGINEERS, INC.—See Finelli Consulting Engineers, Inc.; *U.S. Private*, pg. 1509
FINELLI CONSULTING ENGINEERS, INC.; *U.S. Private*, pg. 1509
FINEMAN PR—See Off Madison Ave, LLC; *U.S. Private*, pg. 3000
FINEMARK HOLDINGS, INC.; *U.S. Public*, pg. 834
FINEMARK NATIONAL BANK & TRUST—See FineMark Holdings, Inc.; *U.S. Public*, pg. 834
FINEMAT APPLIED MATERIALS CO., LTD.; *Int'l*, pg. 2674
FINE METAL TECHNOLOGIES PUBLIC COMPANY LIMITED; *Int'l*, pg. 2673
FINEMOST LIMITED—See Invesco Ltd.; *U.S. Public*, pg. 1161
FINE ORGANICS CORPORATION; *U.S. Private*, pg. 1509
FINE ORGANICS INDUSTRIES LTD.; *Int'l*, pg. 2673
FINE ORGANICS LIMITED—See Lianhe Chemical Technology Co., Ltd.; *Int'l*, pg. 4482
FINEOS CORP. LTD.; *Int'l*, pg. 2674
FINEOTEX CHEMICAL LTD.; *Int'l*, pg. 2674
FINEOUT ENTERPRISES INC.; *U.S. Private*, pg. 1509
FINE PAPER TAKEO (M) SDN. BHD.—See Japan Pulp and Paper Company Limited; *Int'l*, pg. 3903
FINEPART SWEDEN AB; *Int'l*, pg. 2674
FINE PROMOTIONS, INC.; *U.S. Private*, pg. 1509
FINER FOODS INC.; *U.S. Private*, pg. 1509
FINERGY DEVELOPMENT, LLC; *U.S. Private*, pg. 1509
FINERGY SOLUTIONS PTY. LTD.—See Arthur J. Gallagher & Co.; *U.S. Public*, pg. 204
FINERS STEPHENS INNOCENT LLP; *Int'l*, pg. 2674
FINE SEMITECH CORP.; *Int'l*, pg. 2673
FINE SHEER INDUSTRIES INC.; *U.S. Private*, pg. 1509
FINE SHEETMETAL TECHNOLOGIES PTE. LTD.—See FSM Holdings Limited; *Int'l*, pg. 2798
FINESIL TECHNOLOGY INC.—See RITEK CORPORATION; *Int'l*, pg. 6351
FINE SINTER CO., LTD. - KASUGAI PLANT—See Fine Sinter Co., Ltd.; *Int'l*, pg. 2673
FINE SINTER CO., LTD. - KAWAGOE PLANT—See Fine Sinter Co., Ltd.; *Int'l*, pg. 2673
FINE SINTER CO., LTD. - SHIGA PLANT—See Fine Sinter Co., Ltd.; *Int'l*, pg. 2673
FINE SINTER CO., LTD.; *Int'l*, pg. 2673
FINE SINTER CO., LTD. - TAMAGAWA PLANT—See Fine Sinter Co., Ltd.; *Int'l*, pg. 2673

FINE SINTER CO., LTD. - YAMASHINA PLANT—See Fine Sinter Co., Ltd.; *Int'l*, pg. 2673
FINE SINTER SANSHIN CO., LTD.—See Fine Sinter Co., Ltd.; *Int'l*, pg. 2673
FINE SINTER TOHOKU CO., LTD.—See Fine Sinter Co., Ltd.; *Int'l*, pg. 2673
FINE SOUNDS ASIA LIMITED—See Fine Sounds S.p.A.; *Int'l*, pg. 2673
FINE SOUNDS S.P.A.; *Int'l*, pg. 2673
FINESSE HOME LIVING; *Int'l*, pg. 2674
FINESSE MEDICAL LTD.—See Avery Dennison Corporation; *U.S. Public*, pg. 244
FINESSE SOLUTIONS, INC.—See Thermo Fisher Scientific Inc.; *U.S. Public*, pg. 2147
FINE STATIONERY, INC.—See Regent, L.P.; *U.S. Private*, pg. 3388
FINE SURFACE TECHNOLOGY CO., LTD.—See ULVAC, Inc.; *Int'l*, pg. 8020
FINETECHNIX CO., LTD.; *Int'l*, pg. 2674
FINETEK CO., LTD; *Int'l*, pg. 2674
FINETEX ENE, INC. - HWASUNG PLANT—See Finetex EnE, Inc.; *Int'l*, pg. 2674
FINETEX ENE, INC. - ROSARIO PLANT—See Finetex EnE, Inc.; *Int'l*, pg. 2674
FINETEX ENE, INC.; *Int'l*, pg. 2674
FINET GROUP LIMITED; *Int'l*, pg. 2674
FINET HOLDINGS LIMITED—See Finet Group Limited; *Int'l*, pg. 2674
FINET SECURITIES LIMITED—See Finet Group Limited; *Int'l*, pg. 2674
FINE TUBES LIMITED—See Superior Group, Inc.; *U.S. Private*, pg. 3878
FINEX CAPITAL MANAGEMENT LLP; *Int'l*, pg. 2674
FINEX CO., LTD.—See SK-Electronics Co., Ltd.; *Int'l*, pg. 6976
FINEXIA FINANCIAL GROUP LTD.; *Int'l*, pg. 2674
FINEX KREDIT OJSC; *Int'l*, pg. 2674
FINEX OY—See Johnson Matthey PLC; *Int'l*, pg. 3991
FINEX SICAV SIF S.A. - PRIVATE EQUITY VII—See Elemental Holding S.A.; *Int'l*, pg. 2358
FINEXT VAGYONKEZELO NYILVANOSAN MUKODO RESZVENYTARSASAG; *Int'l*, pg. 2674
FINFROCK; *U.S. Private*, pg. 1509
FINGEN S.P.A.; *Int'l*, pg. 2674
FINGER COMPANIES INC.; *U.S. Private*, pg. 1509
FINGER FOOD STUDIOS INC.—See Unity Software Inc.; *U.S. Public*, pg. 2254
FINGER FURNITURE COMPANY, INC.; *U.S. Private*, pg. 1509
FINGER INC.; *Int'l*, pg. 2675
FINGER LAKES AMBULANCE EMS INC.—See G.W. Lisk Company, Inc.; *U.S. Private*, pg. 1631
FINGER LAKES BUSINESS SERVICES; *U.S. Private*, pg. 1509
FINGER LAKES CHEMICALS INC.; *U.S. Private*, pg. 1509
FINGER LAKES CONSTRUCTION COMPANY; *U.S. Private*, pg. 1510
FINGER LAKES INSTRUMENTATION, LLC—See IDEX Corp; *U.S. Public*, pg. 1090
FINGER LAKES RACING ASSOCIATION INC.—See Delaware North Companies, Inc.; *U.S. Private*, pg. 1194
FINGER LAKES TIMES—See Community Media Group; *U.S. Private*, pg. 995
FINGERLE LUMBER CO.; *U.S. Private*, pg. 1510
FINGERMOTION, INC.; *U.S. Public*, pg. 834
FINGERPAINT MARKETING, INC.—See Knox Lane LP; *U.S. Private*, pg. 2324
FINGERPAINT MEDICAL COMMUNICATIONS—See Knox Lane LP; *U.S. Private*, pg. 2324
FINGERPRINT CARDS AB; *Int'l*, pg. 2675
FINGERPRINT SOLUTIONS, LLC—See General Atlantic Service Company, L.P.; *U.S. Private*, pg. 1663
FINGERPRINT SOLUTIONS, LLC—See Stone Point Capital LLC; *U.S. Private*, pg. 3825
FINGERTANGO, INC.; *Int'l*, pg. 2675
THE FINIAL COMPANY—See Rowley Company, LLC; *U.S. Private*, pg. 3490
FINIBANCO ANGOLA, S.A.—See Access Corporation; *Int'l*, pg. 89
FINICITY CORPORATION—See Mastercard Incorporated; *U.S. Public*, pg. 1394
FINIMETAL SASU—See Rettig Group Ltd.; *Int'l*, pg. 6310
FININVEST S.P.A.; *Int'l*, pg. 2675
FINISAR AUSTRALIA PTY. LTD.—See Coherent Corp.; *U.S. Public*, pg. 528
FINISAR CORP. - FREMONT—See Coherent Corp.; *U.S. Public*, pg. 528
FINISAR CORP. - HORSHAM—See Coherent Corp.; *U.S. Public*, pg. 528
FINISAR CORPORATION—See Coherent Corp.; *U.S. Public*, pg. 528
FINISAR ISRAEL LTD.—See Coherent Corp.; *U.S. Public*, pg. 528
FINISAR MALAYSIA SDN. BHD.—See Coherent Corp.; *U.S. Public*, pg. 528
FINISAR SHANGHAI INC.—See Coherent Corp.; *U.S. Public*, pg. 528

FINLOGIC S.P.A.

FINISHING ASSOCIATES, INC.—See Sintokogio Ltd.; *Int'l*, pg. 6958
FINISHING BRANDS GERMANY GMBH—See Graco, Inc.; *U.S. Public*, pg. 953
FINISHING BRANDS HOLDINGS INC.—See Carlisle Companies Incorporated; *U.S. Public*, pg. 436
FINISHING BRANDS - INTERNATIONAL—See Carlisle Companies Incorporated; *U.S. Public*, pg. 436
FINISHING BRANDS (SHANGHAI) CO., LTD.—See Graco, Inc.; *U.S. Public*, pg. 953
THE FINISH LINE, INC.—See Pentland Group Limited; *Int'l*, pg. 5792
FINISHLINE INDUSTRIES INC. OF GEORGIA—See John S. Frey Enterprises; *U.S. Private*, pg. 2224
FINISH LINE INDUSTRIES—See John S. Frey Enterprises; *U.S. Private*, pg. 2224
FINISH LINE PRODUCTS, INC.—See Compagnie de Saint-Gobain SA; *Int'l*, pg. 1730
THE FINISH LINE PUERTO RICO, INC.—See Pentland Group Limited; *Int'l*, pg. 5792
FINISHLINE TECHNOLOGIES, INC.—See Spray Equipment & Service Center, Inc.; *U.S. Private*, pg. 3762
FINISHMASTER, INC.—See LKQ Corporation; *U.S. Public*, pg. 1336
FINISH THOMPSON, INC.; *U.S. Private*, pg. 1510
FINISTERRA AS—See Indutrade AB; *Int'l*, pg. 3678
FINISTERRE CAPITAL LLP—See Principal Financial Group, Inc.; *U.S. Public*, pg. 1720
FINITALIA S.P.A.—See BPER BANCA S.p.A; *Int'l*, pg. 1132
FINITE CARBON CORPORATION—See BP plc; *Int'l*, pg. 1131
FINITEC SRL—See PAI Partners S.A.S.; *Int'l*, pg. 5701
THE FINIT GROUP LLC; *U.S. Private*, pg. 4028
FINITI GROUP, LLC—See Insight Venture Management, LLC; *U.S. Private*, pg. 2089
FINITI GROUP, LLC—See Stone Point Capital LLC; *U.S. Private*, pg. 3822
FINIX TECHNOLOGY PTE. LTD.—See Rokko Holdings Ltd.; *Int'l*, pg. 6388
FINJAN HOLDINGS, INC.—See SoftBank Group Corp.; *Int'l*, pg. 7053
FINKBINER EQUIPMENT CO. INC.—See American State Equipment Co. Inc.; *U.S. Private*, pg. 255
FINKENHOLL STAHL SERVICE CENTER GMBH—See Jacquet Metal Service SA; *Int'l*, pg. 3866
FINKLE TRANSPORT, INC.—See EVO Transportation & Energy Services, Inc.; *U.S. Public*, pg. 804
FINKOVA OY—See Indutrade AB; *Int'l*, pg. 3678
FINK'S JEWELERS INC.; *U.S. Private*, pg. 1510
FINLANDIA CHEESE CO., INC.—See Valio Ltd.; *Int'l*, pg. 8116
FINLANDIA VODKA WORLDWIDE LTD.—See Coca-Cola HBC AG; *Int'l*, pg. 1686
FINLAND TRAVEL BUREAU LTD.—See Finnair Plc; *Int'l*, pg. 2675
FINLAR FINE FOODS (PTY) LTD.—See Libstar Holdings Ltd.; *Int'l*, pg. 4487
FINLAY AIRLINE (AGENCIES) LTD—See John Swire & Sons Limited; *Int'l*, pg. 3979
FINLAY BEVERAGES LIMITED—See John Swire & Sons Limited; *Int'l*, pg. 3979
FINLAY COLD STORAGE (PVT) LIMITED—See Bay Grove Capital LLC; *U.S. Private*, pg. 492
FINLAY FLOWERS BV—See John Swire & Sons Limited; *Int'l*, pg. 3979
FINLAY HULL LIMITED—See John Swire & Sons Limited; *Int'l*, pg. 3980
FINLAY MANAGEMENT, INC.; *U.S. Private*, pg. 1510
FINLAY MINERALS LTD.; *Int'l*, pg. 2675
FINLAY PROPERTIES (PVT) LTD—See John Swire & Sons Limited; *Int'l*, pg. 3980
FINLAYS COLOMBO LIMITED—See John Swire & Sons Limited; *Int'l*, pg. 3980
FINLAYS HORTICULTURE HOLDINGS LTD.—See John Swire & Sons Limited; *Int'l*, pg. 3980
FINLAYS HORTICULTURE KENYA LTD.—See John Swire & Sons Limited; *Int'l*, pg. 3980
FINLAYS HORTICULTURE SOUTH AFRICA LTD—See John Swire & Sons Limited; *Int'l*, pg. 3980
FINLAYSON BANCSHARES, INC.; *U.S. Private*, pg. 1510
FINLAYSON TIMBER & HARDWARE PTY. LTD.—See Metcash Limited; *Int'l*, pg. 4852
FINLAY TEA SOLUTIONS (US) INC—See John Swire & Sons Limited; *Int'l*, pg. 3980
FINLAY TEAS (PVT) LTD—See John Swire & Sons Limited; *Int'l*, pg. 3980
FINLAY VIETNAM COMPANY LIMITED—See John Swire & Sons Limited; *Int'l*, pg. 3980
FINLEY-BUTTES LIMITED PARTNERSHIP—See Waste Connections, Inc.; *Int'l*, pg. 8353
FINLEY FARMERS GRAIN & ELEVATOR COMPANY; *U.S. Private*, pg. 1510
FINLEY FIRE EQUIPMENT CO.; *U.S. Private*, pg. 1510
FINLEY INDUSTRIES INC.; *U.S. Private*, pg. 1510
FINLEY TRI-STATES HEALTH GROUP, INC.—See UnityPoint Health; *U.S. Private*, pg. 4303
FINLOGIC S.P.A.; *Int'l*, pg. 2675
FINLOGIK INC.—See Canaccord Genuity Group Inc.; *Int'l*, pg. 1277

FINMAC LUMBER LTD.

FINMAC LUMBER LTD.; *Int'l*, pg. 2675
FIN-MARK S.R.L.—See Providence Equity Partners L.L.C.; *U.S. Private*, pg. 3292
FIN-MARK S.R.L.—See Searchlight Capital Partners, L.P.; *U.S. Private*, pg. 3587
FINMATICA S.P.A.; *Int'l*, pg. 2675
FINMECCANICA GROUP REAL ESTATE SPA—See Leonardo S.p.A.; *Int'l*, pg. 4458
FINMECCANICA GROUP SERVICES S.P.A.—See Leonardo S.p.A.; *Int'l*, pg. 4458
FINMECCANICA NORTH AMERICA INC.—See Leonardo S.p.A.; *Int'l*, pg. 4458
FINMECCANICA UK LIMITED—See Leonardo S.p.A.; *Int'l*, pg. 4459
FIN MILE LOGISTICS LIMITED; *Int'l*, pg. 2664
FINNAIR AIRCRAFT FINANCE OY—See Finnair Plc; *Int'l*, pg. 2676
FINNAIR BUSINESS SERVICES OU—See Finnair Plc; *Int'l*, pg. 2675
FINNAIR CARGO OY—See Finnair Plc; *Int'l*, pg. 2676
FINNAIR CARGO TERMINAL OPERATIONS OY—See Finnair Plc; *Int'l*, pg. 2676
FINNAIR CATERING OY—See Deutsche Lufthansa AG; *Int'l*, pg. 2067
FINNAIR FACILITIES MANAGEMENT OY—See Finnair Plc; *Int'l*, pg. 2676
FINNAIR FLIGHT ACADEMY OY—See Finnair Plc; *Int'l*, pg. 2676
FINNAIR OYJ-NEW YORK—See Finnair Plc; *Int'l*, pg. 2676
FINNAIR OYJ—See Finnair Plc; *Int'l*, pg. 2675
FINNAIR PLC; *Int'l*, pg. 2675
FINNAIR TECHNICAL SERVICES OY—See Finnair Plc; *Int'l*, pg. 2676
FINNAIR TRAVEL SERVICES OY—See Finnair Plc; *Int'l*, pg. 2676
FINN ALL SEASONS—See Finn Corporation; *U.S. Private*, pg. 1510
FINNAT FIDUCIARIA SPA—See Banca Finnat Euramerica S.p.A.; *Int'l*, pg. 814
FINNAT INVESTMENTS SPA—See Banca Finnat Euramerica S.p.A.; *Int'l*, pg. 814
FINNAT SERVIZI ASSICURATIVI S.R.L.—See Banca Finnat Euramerica S.p.A.; *Int'l*, pg. 814
FINNCHAIN OY—See Addtech AB; *Int'l*, pg. 133
FINNCHEM USA, INC. - AUGUSTA SODIUM CHLORATE PLANT—See Kemira Oyj; *Int'l*, pg. 4123
FINNCHEM USA INC.—See Kemira Oyj; *Int'l*, pg. 4123
FINN CORPORATION; *U.S. Private*, pg. 1510
FINNEGAN, HENDERSON, FARABOW, GARRETT & DUNNER, L.L.P.; *U.S. Private*, pg. 1510
FINNEY COUNTY LANDFILL, INC.—See Waste Connections, Inc.; *Int'l*, pg. 8353
FINNFEEDS FINLAND OY-NAANTALI—See DuPont de Nemours, Inc.; *U.S. Public*, pg. 693
FINNFEEDS FINLAND OY—See DuPont de Nemours, Inc.; *U.S. Public*, pg. 693
FINNFEEDS OY—See DuPont de Nemours, Inc.; *U.S. Public*, pg. 693
FINNING ARGENTINA S.A.—See Finning International Inc.; *Int'l*, pg. 2676
FINNING BOLIVIA S.A.—See Finning International Inc.; *Int'l*, pg. 2676
FINNING CANADA INC.—See Finning International Inc.; *Int'l*, pg. 2676
FINNING CHILE S.A.—See Finning International Inc.; *Int'l*, pg. 2676
FINNING INTERNATIONAL INC.; *Int'l*, pg. 2676
FINNING (IRELAND) LIMITED—See Finning International Inc.; *Int'l*, pg. 2676
FINNING SOLUCIONES MINERAS S.A.—See Finning International Inc.; *Int'l*, pg. 2676
FINNING (UK) LTD.—See Finning International Inc.; *Int'l*, pg. 2676
FINNING URUGUAY S.A.—See Finning International Inc.; *Int'l*, pg. 2676
FINNISH CHEMICALS OY—See Kemira Oyj; *Int'l*, pg. 4123
FINNISH LED-SIGNS OY—See Revenio Group Oyj; *Int'l*, pg. 6312
FINNKINO OY—See Ratos AB; *Int'l*, pg. 6218
FINNKUMU OY—See Harju Elekter AS; *Int'l*, pg. 3277
FINN-LEY VAKUUM, S.R.O.—See Atlas Copco AB; *Int'l*, pg. 683
FINNLIFT MATERIAALIKASITTELY OY—See Amplex AB; *Int'l*, pg. 434
FINNLINES BELGIUM N.V.—See Grimaldi Group SpA; *Int'l*, pg. 3085
FINNLINES DANMARK A/S—See Grimaldi Group SpA; *Int'l*, pg. 3085
FINNLINES DEUTSCHLAND GMBH—See Grimaldi Group SpA; *Int'l*, pg. 3085
FINNLINES OYJ—See Grimaldi Group SpA; *Int'l*, pg. 3085
FINNLINES POLSKA SP.Z.O.O—See Grimaldi Group SpA; *Int'l*, pg. 3085
FINNLINES UK LIMITED—See Grimaldi Group SpA; *Int'l*, pg. 3085
FINNLINK AB—See Grimaldi Group SpA; *Int'l*, pg. 3085

FINNMAP CONSULTING ENGINEERS (INDIA) PVT. LTD.—See Sweco AB; *Int'l*, pg. 7363
FINNMAP CONSULTING OY—See Sweco AB; *Int'l*, pg. 7363
FINNMARK HAVFISKE AS—See Austevoll Seafood ASA; *Int'l*, pg. 717
FINNMIRROR OY; *Int'l*, pg. 2676
FINN.NO AS—See Schibsted ASA; *Int'l*, pg. 6616
FINNOVA AG—See msg group GmbH; *Int'l*, pg. 5067
FINNOVATE ACQUISITION CORP.; *U.S. Public*, pg. 834
FINN PARTNERS, INC.; *U.S. Private*, pg. 1510
FINN PARTNERS, INC.—See Ruder Finn Group, Inc.; *U.S. Private*, pg. 3501
FINN POWER ENERGY CORP; *U.S. Private*, pg. 1510
FINN-POWER ITALIA SRL—See Prima Industrie SpA; *Int'l*, pg. 5974
FINN-POWER OY—See Prima Industrie SpA; *Int'l*, pg. 5974
FINN-POWER OY—See Prima Industrie SpA; *Int'l*, pg. 5974
FINNSEMENTTI OY—See CRH plc; *Int'l*, pg. 1844
FINNSTEVE OY—See Grimaldi Group SpA; *Int'l*, pg. 3085
FINNSUGAR LTD.—See Nordzucker AG; *Int'l*, pg. 5426
FINNVEDEN METAL STRUCTURES AB—See Shiloh Industries, Inc.; *U.S. Private*, pg. 3636
FINN WELLNESS KFT.—See Honkarakenne Oyj; *Int'l*, pg. 3471
FINNWEST N.V.—See Grimaldi Group SpA; *Int'l*, pg. 3085
FINOCOM AG—See Cisco Systems, Inc.; *U.S. Public*, pg. 497
FINO HOTELS CO., LTD.—See Polaris Holdings Co., Ltd.; *Int'l*, pg. 5907
FINOLEX CABLES LTD.—See Finolex Group; *Int'l*, pg. 2676
FINOLEX GROUP; *Int'l*, pg. 2676
FINOLEX INDUSTRIES LTD.—See Finolex Group; *Int'l*, pg. 2676
FINO PAYMENTS BANK LIMITED; *Int'l*, pg. 2676
FINOR LEASING D.O.O.—See Intesa Sanpaolo S.p.A.; *Int'l*, pg. 3765
FINOTEK CO., LTD.; *Int'l*, pg. 2676
FINOVO AG—See Helvetia Holding AG; *Int'l*, pg. 3339
FINOW ROHRSYSTEME GMBH—See Alpiq Holding AG; *Int'l*, pg. 372
FIN.PART S.P.A.; *Int'l*, pg. 2664
FIN POSILLIPO S.P.A.—See Petrone Group S.r.l.; *Int'l*, pg. 5831
FINPROJECT S.P.A.; *Int'l*, pg. 2676
FINPROM INSURANCE S.R.L.—See Gruppo MutuiOnline S.p.A.; *Int'l*, pg. 3141
FINPROM S.R.L.—See Gruppo MutuiOnline S.p.A.; *Int'l*, pg. 3141
FINRA DISPUTE RESOLUTION, INC.—See Financial Industry Regulatory Authority, Inc.; *U.S. Private*, pg. 1507
FINRA REGULATION—See Financial Industry Regulatory Authority, Inc.; *U.S. Private*, pg. 1507
FIN RESOURCES LIMITED; *Int'l*, pg. 2664
FINROCK GROWTH PARTNERS, LLC; *U.S. Private*, pg. 1511
FINSBURY FOOD GROUP, PLC—See DBAY Advisors Limited; *Int'l*, pg. 1986
FINSBURY PROPERTIES N.V.—See Retail Estates N.V.; *Int'l*, pg. 6305
FINSCIENCE S.R.L.—See Datrix S.p.A.; *Int'l*, pg. 1982
FINSERV ACQUISITION CORP.; *U.S. Public*, pg. 835
FINSETA PLC; *Int'l*, pg. 2676
FINS, FURS, FEATHERS, INC.; *U.S. Private*, pg. 1511
FINSHORE MANAGEMENT SERVICES LTD.; *Int'l*, pg. 2676
FINSINA S.P.A.—See Argo Finanziaria S.p.A.; *Int'l*, pg. 561
FINSKA STENINDUSTRI AB—See R.E.D. Graniti S.p.A.; *Int'l*, pg. 6170
FINSOFT FINANCIAL INVESTMENT HOLDINGS LIMITED; *Int'l*, pg. 2677
FINSOURCE CREDIT (M) SDN. BHD.—See Sunzen Biotech Berhad; *Int'l*, pg. 7333
FINSPIRE INC.—See Japan Investment Adviser Co., Ltd.; *Int'l*, pg. 3898
FINSURA HOLDINGS PTY. LTD.—See AUB Group Limited; *Int'l*, pg. 698
FINSURE FINANCE & INSURANCE PTY LTD—See BNK Banking Corporation Limited; *Int'l*, pg. 1079
FINTAN PARTNERS, LLC—See BGC Group, Inc.; *U.S. Public*, pg. 328
FINTAXI, SEC; *Int'l*, pg. 2677
FINTEC GLOBAL BERHAD; *Int'l*, pg. 2677
FINTECH ASIA LTD.; *Int'l*, pg. 2677
FINTECH ASSET MANAGEMENT INCORPORATED—See FinTech Global Incorporated; *Int'l*, pg. 2677
FINTECH CHAIN LIMITED; *Int'l*, pg. 2677
FINTECH ECOSYSTEM DEVELOPMENT CORP.; *U.S. Public*, pg. 835
FINTECH EVOLUTION ACQUISITION GROUP; *U.S. Public*, pg. 835
FINTECH GLOBAL INCORPORATED; *Int'l*, pg. 2677
FINTECH SCION LIMITED; *Int'l*, pg. 2677
FINTECH SELECT LTD.; *Int'l*, pg. 2677
FINTECNA S.P.A.—See Cassa Depositi e Prestiti S.p.A.; *Int'l*, pg. 1355

CORPORATE AFFILIATIONS

FINTEK FINANSAL TEKNOLOJI HIZMETLERI A.S.—See Turkiye Cumhuriyeti Ziraat Bankasi A.S.; *Int'l*, pg. 7975
FINTEL ENERGIA GROUP S.P.A.; *Int'l*, pg. 2677
FINTEL ENERGIA A.D—See Fintel Energia Group S.p.A.; *Int'l*, pg. 2677
FINTELLIGENCE PTY. LTD.—See Australia Finance Group Ltd; *Int'l*, pg. 720
FINTEL PLC; *Int'l*, pg. 2677
FINTERTECH CO. LTD.—See Daiwa Securities Group Inc.; *Int'l*, pg. 1949
FINTUBE, LLC—See Heartwood Partners, LLC; *U.S. Private*, pg. 1901
FINUM.PRIVATE FINANCE AG—See JDC Group AG; *Int'l*, pg. 3925
FINVIS BUSINESS SERVICES GMBH—See AGRAVIS Raiffeisen AG; *Int'l*, pg. 215
FINVOLUTION GROUP; *Int'l*, pg. 2677
FINWARD BANCORP; *U.S. Public*, pg. 835
FIN-WEST GROUP; *U.S. Private*, pg. 1506
FINWISE BANCORP; *U.S. Public*, pg. 850
FINWOOD PAPERS (PTY.) LTD.—See KPP Group Holdings Co., Ltd.; *Int'l*, pg. 4298
FINXACT LLC—See Fiserv, Inc.; *U.S. Public*, pg. 850
FINZSOFT SOLUTIONS LIMITED; *Int'l*, pg. 2677
FIO AUTOMOTIVE CANADA CORP.—See Futaba Industrial Co., Ltd.; *Int'l*, pg. 2851
FIOCCHI PRYM S.P.A.—See William Prym GmbH & Co. KG; *Int'l*, pg. 8413
FIONDELLA, MILONE & LASARACINA LLP; *U.S. Private*, pg. 1511
FIORANI & C. S.P.A—See Cremonini S.p.A.; *Int'l*, pg. 1838
FIORE ASCENSORI S.A.S.—See KONE Oyj; *Int'l*, pg. 4247
FIORE ASSOCIATES, INC.; *U.S. Private*, pg. 1511
FIORE BUICK GMC; *U.S. Private*, pg. 1511
THE FIORE COMPANIES; *U.S. Private*, pg. 4028
FIORE EXPLORATION LTD.; *Int'l*, pg. 2677
FIORE GOLD LTD.; *Int'l*, pg. 2678
FIORE MOTORS INC.; *U.S. Private*, pg. 1511
FIORE STONE, INC.; *U.S. Private*, pg. 1511
FIOR FAMILIE GMBH; *Int'l*, pg. 2678
FIORINO SHIPPING S.R.L.—See Savino Del Bene S.p.A.; *Int'l*, pg. 6600
FIOULMARKET.FR SAS—See TotalEnergies SE; *Int'l*, pg. 7836
FIPAS INC.—See Honyaku Center Inc.; *Int'l*, pg. 3472
FIP CONSTRUCTION INC.—See The FIP Corporation; *U.S. Private*, pg. 4029
THE FIP CORPORATION; *U.S. Private*, pg. 4028
FIPLASTO SA; *Int'l*, pg. 2678
FIPOFIX GMBH—See Kapsch-Group Beteiligungs GmbH; *Int'l*, pg. 4077
FIP PORTUGAL, UNIPESSOAL, LDA.—See Frontier IP Group plc; *Int'l*, pg. 2795
FIPP S.A.; *Int'l*, pg. 2678
F.I.P. PTY LTD.—See Westinghouse Air Brake Technologies Corporation; *U.S. Public*, pg. 2357
FIPROMER SASU—See Groupe BPCE; *Int'l*, pg. 3098
FIRAMUNICH, S.L.—See Messe Munchen GmbH; *Int'l*, pg. 4841
FIRAN TECHNOLOGY GROUP CORPORATION; *Int'l*, pg. 2678
FIRA PHOTONICS CO. LTD.—See KBIO COMPANY Inc.; *Int'l*, pg. 4107
FIRATEL SDN. BHD.—See OCK Group Berhad; *Int'l*, pg. 5520
FIRCOSOFT BRASIL CONSULTORIA E SERVICOS DE INFORMATICA LTDA—See RELX plc; *Int'l*, pg. 6266
FIRCOSOFT INDIA PRIVATE LIMITED—See RELX plc; *Int'l*, pg. 6266
FIRCOSOFT SAS—See RELX plc; *Int'l*, pg. 6266
FIRCROFT AUSTRALIA PTY LTD—See AEA Investors LP; *U.S. Private*, pg. 115
FIRCROFT CANADA INC—See AEA Investors LP; *U.S. Private*, pg. 115
FIRCROFT ENGINEERING SERVICES LTD.—See AEA Investors LP; *U.S. Private*, pg. 114
FIRCROFT INC—See AEA Investors LP; *U.S. Private*, pg. 115
FIRCROFT NORGE AS—See AEA Investors LP; *U.S. Private*, pg. 115
FIRCROFT PTE LTD—See AEA Investors LP; *U.S. Private*, pg. 115
FIRCROFT QATAR LLC—See AEA Investors LP; *U.S. Private*, pg. 115
FIRCROFT RUSSIA, LLC.—See AEA Investors LP; *U.S. Private*, pg. 115
FIRCROFT TANJUNG SDN BHD—See T7 Global Berhad; *Int'l*, pg. 7398
FIRCROFT THAILAND LIMITED—See AEA Investors LP; *U.S. Private*, pg. 115
FIRCROFT (VIETNAM) COMPANY LTD—See AEA Investors LP; *U.S. Private*, pg. 115
FIRE ADVERTAINMENT—See Omnicom Group Inc.; *U.S. Public*, pg. 1581
FIRE ALARM CONTROL SYSTEMS, INC.—See The Carlyle Group Inc.; *U.S. Public*, pg. 2053
FIRE ALARM FABRICATION SERVICES LIMITED—See Marlowe Plc; *Int'l*, pg. 4698

COMPANY NAME INDEX

FIRE ALARM SERVICES, INC.—See Pye-Barker Fire & Safety, LLC; *U.S. Private*, pg. 3309
FIRE AND LIFE SAFETY AMERICA, INC.—See Blue Point Capital Partners, LLC; *U.S. Private*, pg. 590
FIRE AND SECURITY HARDWARE PTY LIMITED—See Allegion Public Limited Company; *Int'l*, pg. 335
FIREANGEL SAFETY TECHNOLOGY GROUP PLC; *Int'l*, pg. 2678
FIREANGEL SAFETY TECHNOLOGY LIMITED—See Fire-Angel Safety Technology Group Plc; *Int'l*, pg. 2678
FIREARMS SIMULATION SYSTEMS INC.—See Advanced Interactive Systems; *U.S. Private*, pg. 90
FIREBIRD BULK CARRIERS, INC.—See Adams Resources & Energy, Inc.; *U.S. Public*, pg. 38
FIREBIRD MANAGEMENT LLC; *U.S. Private*, pg. 1511
FIREBIRD METALS LIMITED; *Int'l*, pg. 2678
FIREBRAND ART LTD—See Swan Mill Paper Company Ltd.; *Int'l*, pg. 7360
FIREBREAK FIRE SECURITIES LIMITED—See London Security PLC; *Int'l*, pg. 4547
FIREBRICK PHARMA LIMITED; *Int'l*, pg. 2678
FIREBUS SYSTEMS, INC.—See China Automation Group Limited; *Int'l*, pg. 1483
FIRECLICK, INC.—See Siris Capital Group, LLC; *U.S. Private*, pg. 3672
FIRECOM, INC.—See Wind Point Advisors LLC; *U.S. Private*, pg. 4535
FIRECREST CLINICAL LTD.—See ICON plc; *Int'l*, pg. 3584
FIREDART ENGINEERING UNDERWRITING MANAGERS (PTY.) LTD.—See Talanx AG; *Int'l*, pg. 7443
FIRED EARTH LIMITED—See The Middleby Corporation; *U.S. Public*, pg. 2114
FIRE-DEX, LLC; *U.S. Private*, pg. 1511
FIRE EATER A/S; *Int'l*, pg. 2678
FIRE EATER HUNGARIA KFT.—See Fire Eater A/S; *Int'l*, pg. 2678
FIRE EATER NORGE AS—See Fire Eater A/S; *Int'l*, pg. 2678
FIRE EATER POLAND SP. Z OO—See Fire Eater A/S; *Int'l*, pg. 2678
FIRE EATER SPAIN—See Fire Eater A/S; *Int'l*, pg. 2678
FIRE EATER SPOL. S.R.O.—See Fire Eater A/S; *Int'l*, pg. 2678
FIRE EQUIPMENT DE MEXICO, S.A. DE C.V.—See Johnson Controls International plc; *Int'l*, pg. 3987
FIREFIGHTERS BOOKSTORE, INC.—See L.N. Curtis & Sons; *U.S. Private*, pg. 2366
FIRE FIGHTING ENTERPRISES LIMITED—See Halma plc; *Int'l*, pg. 3231
FIREFINCH LIMITED; *Int'l*, pg. 2679
FIRE & FLAVOR GRILLING CO.; *U.S. Private*, pg. 1511
FIRE & FLOWER HOLDINGS CORP.; *Int'l*, pg. 2678
FIREFLY BOOKS; *Int'l*, pg. 2679
FIREFLY COMPUTERS, LLC—See Rotunda Capital Partners LLC; *U.S. Private*, pg. 3488
FIREFLY ENERGY, INC.; *U.S. Private*, pg. 1511
FIREFLY E-VENTURES LIMITED—See HT Media Limited; *Int'l*, pg. 3508
FIREFLY IT SERVICES INC.—See CloudScale365, Inc.; *U.S. Private*, pg. 947
FIREFLY LIGHTING DESIGN LTD.—See Firefly Point of View Ltd.; *Int'l*, pg. 2679
FIREFLY POINT OF VIEW LTD.; *Int'l*, pg. 2679
FIREFLY RESOURCES LIMITED—See Gascoyne Resources Limited; *Int'l*, pg. 2888
FIREFLY TECHNOLOGIES; *U.S. Private*, pg. 1511
FIREFOX GOLD CORP.; *Int'l*, pg. 2679
FIREGUARD, INC.; *U.S. Private*, pg. 1511
FIREGUARD LLC—See Align Capital Partners, LLC; *U.S. Private*, pg. 167
FIREHOST INC.; *U.S. Private*, pg. 1511
FIREHOUSE BREWING COMPANY, INC.; *U.S. Private*, pg. 1511
FIREHOUSE, INC.; *U.S. Private*, pg. 1511
FIREHOUSE RESTAURANT GROUP, INC.—See Restaurant Brands International Inc.; *Int'l*, pg. 6304
FIRE INSPECTOR COMPANY LIMITED—See Firetrade Engineering PCL; *Int'l*, pg. 2679
FIRE INSURANCE EXCHANGE—See Zurich Insurance Group Limited; *Int'l*, pg. 8698
FIRE KING SECURITY GROUP; *U.S. Private*, pg. 1511
FIRE KING SECURITY PRODUCTS, LLC—See Pfingsten Partners, LLC; *U.S. Private*, pg. 3164
FIRELAKE CAPITAL MANAGEMENT, LLC; *U.S. Private*, pg. 1512
FIRELANDS ELECTRIC COOPERATIVE, INC.; *U.S. Private*, pg. 1512
FIRE & LIFE SAFETY AMERICA, INC.—See Blue Point Capital Partners, LLC; *U.S. Private*, pg. 590
FIRELIGHT CAPITAL PARTNERS LLC; *U.S. Private*, pg. 1512
FIRELINE CORPORATION; *U.S. Private*, pg. 1512
FIRELINE, INC.; *U.S. Private*, pg. 1512
FIRELINE SPRINKLER CORPORATION; *U.S. Private*, pg. 1512
FIREMAN CAPITAL PARTNERS LLC; *U.S. Private*, pg. 1512

FIREMAN FUND SPECIALTIES—See Allianz SE; *Int'l*, pg. 347
FIREMANS CONTRACTORS, INC.; *U.S. Public*, pg. 835
FIREMAN'S FUND FINANCIAL SERVICES, LLC—See Allianz SE; *Int'l*, pg. 347
FIREMAN'S FUND INDEMNITY CORPORATION—See Allianz SE; *Int'l*, pg. 347
FIREMAN'S FUND INSURANCE COMPANY OF LOUISIANA, CORP.—See Allianz SE; *Int'l*, pg. 347
FIREMAN'S FUND INSURANCE COMPANY—See Allianz SE; *Int'l*, pg. 347
FIREMAN'S FUND INSURANCE COMPANY—See Allianz SE; *Int'l*, pg. 347
FIREMAN'S FUND INSURANCE CO. OF GEORGIA—See Allianz SE; *Int'l*, pg. 347
FIREMAN'S FUND INSURANCE CO. OF HAWAII, INC.—See Allianz SE; *Int'l*, pg. 347
FIREMAN'S FUND INSURANCE CO. OF NEW JERSEY—See Allianz SE; *Int'l*, pg. 347
FIREMAN'S FUND INSURANCE CO. OF TEXAS—See Allianz SE; *Int'l*, pg. 347
FIREMAN'S FUND MCGEE UNDERWRITERS—See Allianz SE; *Int'l*, pg. 347
FIREMON LLC—See Insight Venture Management, LLC; *U.S. Private*, pg. 2090
FIRENTIS AG—See Indutrade AB; *Int'l*, pg. 3678
FIREPLACE PRODUCTS AUSTRALIA PTY. LTD.—See NIBE Industrier AB; *Int'l*, pg. 5260
FIREPLACE PRODUCTS U.S., INC.—See NIBE Industrier AB; *Int'l*, pg. 5260
FIREPOWER TECHNOLOGY, INC.—See Japan Industrial Partners, Inc.; *Int'l*, pg. 3891
FIRE PROTECTION ENGINEERING AS—See HitecVision AS; *Int'l*, pg. 3426
FIRE PROTECTION SERVICES CORP.; *U.S. Private*, pg. 1511
FIRE & RAIN, LLC—See 2e Creative, Inc.; *U.S. Private*, pg. 6
FIRE RESCUE SAFETY AUSTRALIA PTY LTD.—See Bunzl plc; *Int'l*, pg. 1218
FIRERING STRATEGIC MINERALS PLC; *Int'l*, pg. 2679
FIRE RIVER GOLD CORP.; *Int'l*, pg. 2678
FIRE ROCK HOLDINGS LIMITED; *Int'l*, pg. 2678
FIRE SERVICE COLLEGE LIMITED—See Capita plc; *Int'l*, pg. 1309
FIRESIDE BANK—See Kemper Corporation; *U.S. Public*, pg. 1220
FIRESIDE HEARTH & HOME; *U.S. Private*, pg. 1512
FIRESIDE OFFICE PRODUCTS INC.; *U.S. Private*, pg. 1512
FIRE SOLUTIONS, INC.—See Compliance Science, Inc.; *U.S. Private*, pg. 1001
FIRESPRING; *U.S. Private*, pg. 1512
FIRE SPRINKLER SYSTEMS INC.; *U.S. Private*, pg. 1511
THE FIRESTATION 23 INC.—See Acreage Holdings, Inc.; *U.S. Public*, pg. 36
FIRESTEED CORPORATION—See Vintage Wine Estates, Inc.; *U.S. Public*, pg. 2298
FIRESTONE AGRICULTURAL-DES MOINES—See Cox Enterprises, Inc.; *U.S. Private*, pg. 1075
FIRESTONE BUILDING PRODUCTS-BEECH GROVE—See Bridgestone Corporation; *Int'l*, pg. 1156
FIRESTONE BUILDING PRODUCTS COMPANY, LLC - BRISTOL MANUFACTURING FACILITY—See Bridgestone Corporation; *Int'l*, pg. 1157
FIRESTONE BUILDING PRODUCTS COMPANY, LLC - CORSICANA MANUFACTURING FACILITY—See Bridgestone Corporation; *Int'l*, pg. 1157
FIRESTONE BUILDING PRODUCTS COMPANY, LLC - DEFOREST MANUFACTURING FACILITY—See Bridgestone Corporation; *Int'l*, pg. 1157
FIRESTONE BUILDING PRODUCTS COMPANY, LLC - FLORENCE MANUFACTURING FACILITY—See Bridgestone Corporation; *Int'l*, pg. 1157
FIRESTONE BUILDING PRODUCTS COMPANY, LLC - INDIANAPOLIS MANUFACTURING FACILITY—See Bridgestone Corporation; *Int'l*, pg. 1157
FIRESTONE BUILDING PRODUCTS COMPANY, LLC - JACKSONVILLE MANUFACTURING FACILITY—See Bridgestone Corporation; *Int'l*, pg. 1157
FIRESTONE BUILDING PRODUCTS COMPANY, LLC - PRESCOTT MANUFACTURING FACILITY—See Bridgestone Corporation; *Int'l*, pg. 1157
FIRESTONE BUILDING PRODUCTS COMPANY, LLC - SALT LAKE CITY MANUFACTURING FACILITY—See Bridgestone Corporation; *Int'l*, pg. 1157
FIRESTONE BUILDING PRODUCTS COMPANY, LLC—See Bridgestone Corporation; *Int'l*, pg. 1157
FIRESTONE BUILDING PRODUCTS COMPANY, LLC - TUSCUMBIA MANUFACTURING FACILITY—See Bridgestone Corporation; *Int'l*, pg. 1157
FIRESTONE BUILDING PRODUCTS COMPANY, LLC - WELLFORD MANUFACTURING FACILITY—See Bridgestone Corporation; *Int'l*, pg. 1157
FIRESTONE BUILDING PRODUCTS COMPANY, LLC - YOUNGWOOD MANUFACTURING FACILITY—See Bridgestone Corporation; *Int'l*, pg. 1157
FIRESTONE BUILDING PRODUCTS DIVISION—See Bridgestone Corporation; *Int'l*, pg. 1156

FIRESTONE BUILDING PRODUCTS-KINGSTREE—See Bridgestone Corporation; *Int'l*, pg. 1156
FIRESTONE BUILDING PRODUCTS-PRESCOTT—See Bridgestone Corporation; *Int'l*, pg. 1156
FIRESTONE COUNTRY CLUB—See Apollo Global Management, LLC; *U.S. Public*, pg. 149
FIRESTONE DIAMONDS PLC; *Int'l*, pg. 2679
FIRESTONE DIVERSIFIED PRODUCTS, LLC—See Bridgestone Corporation; *Int'l*, pg. 1157
FIRESTONE ENERGY SOLUTIONS—See Bridgestone Corporation; *Int'l*, pg. 1157
FIRESTONE FIBERS & TEXTILES COMPANY, LLC - GASTONIA MANUFACTURING FACILITY—See Bridgestone Corporation; *Int'l*, pg. 1156
FIRESTONE FIBERS & TEXTILES DIVISION—See Bridgestone Corporation; *Int'l*, pg. 1156
FIRESTONE FIBERS & TEXTILES-KINGS MOUNTAIN—See Bridgestone Corporation; *Int'l*, pg. 1156
FIRESTONE FINANCIAL, LLC—See Berkshire Hills Bancorp, Inc.; *U.S. Public*, pg. 320
FIRESTONE GENFLEX ROOFING SYSTEMS, LLC—See Bridgestone Corporation; *Int'l*, pg. 1157
FIRESTONE INDUSTRIAL PRODUCTS COMPANY-DYERSBURG—See Bridgestone Corporation; *Int'l*, pg. 1156
FIRESTONE INDUSTRIAL PRODUCTS DE COSTA RICA, S.A.—See Bridgestone Corporation; *Int'l*, pg. 1156
FIRESTONE INDUSTRIAL PRODUCTS DIVISION—See Bridgestone Corporation; *Int'l*, pg. 1156
FIRESTONE INDUSTRIAL PRODUCTS, LLC - ARNHEM MANUFACTURING FACILITY—See Bridgestone Corporation; *Int'l*, pg. 1156
FIRESTONE INDUSTRIAL PRODUCTS POLAND SP. Z O.O.—See Bridgestone Corporation; *Int'l*, pg. 1156
FIRESTONE INDUSTRIAL PRODUCTS-WILLIAMSBURG—See Bridgestone Corporation; *Int'l*, pg. 1156
FIRESTONE METAL PRODUCTS COMPANY, LLC - ANOKA MANUFACTURING FACILITY—See Bridgestone Corporation; *Int'l*, pg. 1159
FIRESTONE METAL PRODUCTS COMPANY, LLC - COLLEGE PARK MANUFACTURING FACILITY—See Bridgestone Corporation; *Int'l*, pg. 1160
FIRESTONE METAL PRODUCTS COMPANY, LLC - JACKSON MANUFACTURING FACILITY—See Bridgestone Corporation; *Int'l*, pg. 1160
FIRESTONE METAL PRODUCTS COMPANY, LLC - LAS VEGAS MANUFACTURING FACILITY—See Bridgestone Corporation; *Int'l*, pg. 1160
FIRESTONE METAL PRODUCTS COMPANY, LLC—See Bridgestone Corporation; *Int'l*, pg. 1159
FIRESTONE METAL PRODUCTS COMPANY, LLC - WARREN MANUFACTURING FACILITY—See Bridgestone Corporation; *Int'l*, pg. 1160
FIRESTONE NATURAL RUBBER COMPANY, LLC—See Bridgestone Corporation; *Int'l*, pg. 1157
FIRESTONE POLYMERS, LLC - LAKE CHARLES PLANT—See Bridgestone Corporation; *Int'l*, pg. 1157
FIRESTONE POLYMERS, LLC - ORANGE PLANT—See Bridgestone Corporation; *Int'l*, pg. 1157
FIRESTONE POLYMERS, LLC—See Bridgestone Corporation; *Int'l*, pg. 1157
FIRESTONE PRODUTOS INDUSTRIAIS AV.—See Bridgestone Corporation; *Int'l*, pg. 1156
FIRESTONE SYNTHETIC RUBBER & LATEX-ORANGE—See Bridgestone Corporation; *Int'l*, pg. 1156
FIRESTONE TEXTILES-WOODSTOCK—See Bridgestone Corporation; *Int'l*, pg. 1156
FIRESTONE TUBE DIVISION—See Cox Enterprises, Inc.; *U.S. Private*, pg. 1075
FIRESTONE VENTURES INC.; *Int'l*, pg. 2679
FIRESTONE VINEYARD—See Foley Family Wines Holdings Inc; *U.S. Private*, pg. 1558
FIRESTONE WALKER, LLC—See Fibemi NV; *Int'l*, pg. 2652
FIRESTORM SOLUTIONS, LLC—See Rekor Systems, Inc.; *U.S. Public*, pg. 1778
FIRESTREAM WORLDWIDE, INC.; *U.S. Private*, pg. 1512
FIRE SUPPORT (SSFR) HOLDINGS LTD.—See Bilfinger SE; *Int'l*, pg. 1028
FIRE SYSTEMS PROFESSIONALS, LLC—See The Riverside Company; *U.S. Private*, pg. 4108
FIRE SYSTEMS WEST INC.; *U.S. Private*, pg. 1511
FIRETAIL RESOURCES LIMITED; *Int'l*, pg. 2679
FIRE TESTING TECHNOLOGY LIMITED—See Judges Scientific plc; *Int'l*, pg. 4021
FIRETRACE AEROSPACE, LLC—See Halma plc; *Int'l*, pg. 3231
FIRETRACE USA, LLC—See Halma plc; *Int'l*, pg. 3231
FIRETRADE ENGINEERING PCL; *Int'l*, pg. 2679
FIRETREE, LTD.; *U.S. Private*, pg. 1512
FIRETROL, LLC—See Schneider Electric SE; *Int'l*, pg. 6633
FIRETROL PROTECTION SYSTEMS, INC.—See Intermediate Capital Group plc; *Int'l*, pg. 3742
FIRETROL PROTECTION SYSTEMS, INC.—See Kirkbi A/S; *Int'l*, pg. 4190

FIRE UNDERWRITERS ASSOCIATION—See Zurich Insurance Group Limited; *Int'l*, pg. 8698
FIREWATCH CONTRACTING OF FLORIDA LLC; *U.S. Private*, pg. 1512
FIREWEED ZINC LTD.; *Int'l*, pg. 2679
FIREX S.R.L.—See The Middleby Corporation; *U.S. Public*, pg. 2113
FIREYE, INC.—See Carrier Global Corporation; *U.S. Public*, pg. 440
FIRICH ENTERPRISES CO., LTD.; *Int'l*, pg. 2679
FIRICH KOREA CO., LTD.—See Firich Enterprises Co., Ltd.; *Int'l*, pg. 2679
FIRICH USA INC.—See Firich Enterprises Co., Ltd.; *Int'l*, pg. 2679
FIRING S.R.L.—See Manutencoop Societa Cooperativa; *Int'l*, pg. 4680
FIRION INVESTMENTS SL—See China Tianying Inc.; *Int'l*, pg. 1559
FIRKINS CHRYSLER JEEP DODGE RAM; *U.S. Private*, pg. 1512
FIRMA AMBU, S.L.—See Ambu A/S; *Int'l*, pg. 416
THE FIRM ADVISORS, LLC; *U.S. Private*, pg. 4029
FIRMA HOLDINGS CORP.; *U.S. Public*, pg. 835
FIRM CAPITAL APARTMENT REAL ESTATE INVESTMENT TRUST; *Int'l*, pg. 2679
FIRM CAPITAL MORTGAGE INVESTMENT CORPORATION; *Int'l*, pg. 2679
FIRM CAPITAL PROPERTY TRUST; *Int'l*, pg. 2679
FIRMCO LTD.; *Int'l*, pg. 2679
FIRMDECISIONS ASJP GERMANY GMBH—See Ebiquity plc; *Int'l*, pg. 2285
FIRMENICH AROMATICS (CHINA) CO. LTD.—See Firmenich International SA; *Int'l*, pg. 2680
FIRMENICH AROMATICS (INDIA) PVT LTD.—See Firmenich International SA; *Int'l*, pg. 2680
FIRMENICH AROMATICS PRODUCTION (INDIA) PVT. LTD.—See Firmenich International SA; *Int'l*, pg. 2680
FIRMENICH AROMATICS (SHANGHAI) CO.—See Firmenich International SA; *Int'l*, pg. 2680
FIRMENICH AROMATICS (ZHANGJIAGANG) CO., LTD.—See Firmenich International SA; *Int'l*, pg. 2680
FIRMENICH ASIA PTE. LTD.—See Firmenich International SA; *Int'l*, pg. 2680
FIRMENICH BELGIUM S.A.—See Firmenich International SA; *Int'l*, pg. 2680
FIRMENICH BJORGE BIOMARIN AS—See Firmenich International SA; *Int'l*, pg. 2680
FIRMENICH & CIA. LTDA—See Firmenich International SA; *Int'l*, pg. 2680
FIRMENICH & CIE. S.A.S.—See Firmenich International SA; *Int'l*, pg. 2680
FIRMENICH CO LTD—See Firmenich International SA; *Int'l*, pg. 2680
FIRMENICH DE MEXICO S.A. DE C.V.—See Firmenich International SA; *Int'l*, pg. 2680
FIRMENICH DENMARK APS—See Firmenich International SA; *Int'l*, pg. 2680
FIRMENICH DIS TIC. LTD. STI—See Firmenich International SA; *Int'l*, pg. 2680
FIRMENICH FZ-LLC—See Firmenich International SA; *Int'l*, pg. 2680
FIRMENICH GES.M.B.H.—See Firmenich International SA; *Int'l*, pg. 2680
FIRMENICH GMBH—See Firmenich International SA; *Int'l*, pg. 2680
FIRMENICH GRASSE SAS—See Firmenich International SA; *Int'l*, pg. 2680
FIRMENICH INCORPORATED—See Firmenich International SA; *Int'l*, pg. 2680
FIRMENICH INTERNATIONAL FINE FRAGRANCE CENTER—See Firmenich International SA; *Int'l*, pg. 2680
FIRMENICH INTERNATIONAL SA; *Int'l*, pg. 2679
FIRMENICH LIMITED—See Firmenich International SA; *Int'l*, pg. 2680
FIRMENICH LLC—See Firmenich International SA; *Int'l*, pg. 2680
FIRMENICH LLC—See Firmenich International SA; *Int'l*, pg. 2680
FIRMENICH (PHILIPPINES), INC.—See Firmenich International SA; *Int'l*, pg. 2680
FIRMENICH PRODUCTIONS S.A.S.—See Firmenich International SA; *Int'l*, pg. 2680
FIRMENICH (PTY.) LTD.—See Firmenich International SA; *Int'l*, pg. 2680
FIRMENICH S.A.I.C. Y F.—See Firmenich International SA; *Int'l*, pg. 2680
FIRMENICH S.A.—See Firmenich International SA; *Int'l*, pg. 2680
FIRMENICH S.A.—See Firmenich International SA; *Int'l*, pg. 2680
FIRMENICH SA—See Koninklijke DSM N.V.; *Int'l*, pg. 4266
FIRMENICH—See Firmenich International SA; *Int'l*, pg. 2680
FIRMENICH—See Firmenich International SA; *Int'l*, pg. 2680
FIRMENICH S.P.A.—See Firmenich International SA; *Int'l*, pg. 2680

FIRMENICH SP.Z O.O—See Firmenich International SA; *Int'l*, pg. 2680
FIRMENICH (THAILAND) LTD.—See Firmenich International SA; *Int'l*, pg. 2680
FIRMENICH UK LTD.—See Firmenich International SA; *Int'l*, pg. 2680
FIRMENICH UK LTD.—See Firmenich International SA; *Int'l*, pg. 2680
FIRMENICH VIETNAM LLC—See Firmenich International SA; *Int'l*, pg. 2680
FIRMENICH WELLINGBOROUGH (UK) LTD—See Firmenich International SA; *Int'l*, pg. 2680
FIRMES Y HORMIGONES SANI S.L.—See Camargo Correa S.A.; *Int'l*, pg. 1268
FIRM II, LLC—See Fidelity National Infor; *U.S. Public*, pg. 832
FIRM, INC.—See Genstar Capital, LLC; *U.S. Private*, pg. 1674
FIRM INDUSTRIE SARL—See PAI Partners S.A.S.; *Int'l*, pg. 5699
FIRM TRANSGARANT LLC—See Far Eastern Shipping Company OJSC; *Int'l*, pg. 2617
FIRMUS ENERGY LTD—See iCON Infrastructure LLP; *Int'l*, pg. 3583
FIROS S.A.—See SIF Muntenia S.A.; *Int'l*, pg. 6905
FIROUZA ENGINEERING COMPANY; *Int'l*, pg. 2681
FIRST2PROTECT LIMITED—See LSL Property Services plc; *Int'l*, pg. 4570
FIRST ABACUS FINANCIAL HOLDINGS CORPORATION; *Int'l*, pg. 2681
FIRST ABERDEEN LIMITED—See FirstGroup plc; *Int'l*, pg. 2688
FIRST ABU DHABI BANK MISR S.A.E—See First Abu Dhabi Bank P.J.S.C.; *Int'l*, pg. 2681
FIRST ABU DHABI BANK P.J.S.C.; *Int'l*, pg. 2681
FIRST ABU DHABI BANK USA N.V.—See First Abu Dhabi Bank P.J.S.C.; *Int'l*, pg. 2681
FIRST ACCEPTANCE CORPORATION; *U.S. Public*, pg. 835
FIRST ACCEPTANCE INSURANCE COMPANY, INC.—See First Acceptance Corporation; *U.S. Public*, pg. 835
FIRST ACCEPTANCE SERVICES, INC.—See First Acceptance Corporation; *U.S. Public*, pg. 835
FIRST ACT INC.—See Berkshire Hathaway Inc.; *U.S. Public*, pg. 298
FIRST ADVANTAGE AUSTRALASIA PTY. LTD.—See Silver Lake Group, LLC; *U.S. Private*, pg. 3654
FIRST ADVANTAGE BANCORP—See United Community Banks, Inc.; *U.S. Public*, pg. 2230
FIRST ADVANTAGE BANK—See United Community Banks, Inc.; *U.S. Public*, pg. 2230
FIRST ADVANTAGE CANADA INC.—See Silver Lake Group, LLC; *U.S. Private*, pg. 3654
FIRST ADVANTAGE CORPORATION—See Silver Lake Group, LLC; *U.S. Private*, pg. 3654
FIRST ADVANTAGE ENTERPRISE SCREENING CORPORATION—See Silver Lake Group, LLC; *U.S. Private*, pg. 3654
FIRST ADVANTAGE EUROPE LTD.—See Silver Lake Group, LLC; *U.S. Private*, pg. 3654
FIRST ADVANTAGE INVESTIGATIVE SERVICES—See Silver Lake Group, LLC; *U.S. Private*, pg. 3654
FIRST ADVANTAGE JAPAN K.K.—See Silver Lake Group, LLC; *U.S. Private*, pg. 3654
FIRST ADVANTAGE OCCUPATIONAL HEALTH SERVICES CORP.—See Silver Lake Group, LLC; *U.S. Private*, pg. 3654
FIRST ADVANTAGE PTE. LTD.—See Silver Lake Group, LLC; *U.S. Private*, pg. 3654
FIRST ADVANTAGE PVT. LTD.—See Silver Lake Group, LLC; *U.S. Private*, pg. 3654
FIRST ADVANTAGE RECRUITING SOLUTIONS—See Silver Lake Group, LLC; *U.S. Private*, pg. 3654
FIRST ADVANTAGE TAX CONSULTING SERVICES, LLC—See Silver Lake Group, LLC; *U.S. Private*, pg. 3655
FIRST ADVANTAGE TITLE, LLC—See Anywhere Real Estate Inc.; *U.S. Public*, pg. 142
FIRST ADVISORY GROUP LIMITED; *Int'l*, pg. 2681
FIRST AFFIRMATIVE FINANCIAL NETWORK LLC—See FOLIOfn, Inc.; *U.S. Private*, pg. 1559
FIRST AID ONLY INC.—See Acme United Corporation; *U.S. Public*, pg. 35
FIRST ALARM SECURITY & PATROL, INC.; *U.S. Private*, pg. 1512
FIRST ALARM—See First Alarm Security & Patrol, Inc.; *U.S. Private*, pg. 1512
FIRST ALERT (CANADA) INC.—See Newell Brands Inc.; *U.S. Public*, pg. 1514
FIRST ALERT, INC.—See Resideo Technologies, Inc.; *U.S. Public*, pg. 1789
FIRST ALLIED ADVISORY SERVICES, INC.—See RCAP Holdings, LLC; *U.S. Private*, pg. 3361
FIRST ALLIED SECURITIES, INC.—See RCAP Holdings, LLC; *U.S. Private*, pg. 3361
FIRST AL NOOR MODARABA; *Int'l*, pg. 2681
FIRST ALUMINIUM NIGERIA PLC; *Int'l*, pg. 2681

FIRST-AMERICA BANK—See Stark Bank Group Ltd.; *U.S. Private*, pg. 3786
FIRST AMERICAN ABSTRACT COMPANY—See First American Financial Corporation; *U.S. Public*, pg. 836
FIRST AMERICAN BANCSHARES, INC.; *U.S. Private*, pg. 1512
FIRST AMERICAN BANK CORPORATION; *U.S. Private*, pg. 1512
FIRST AMERICAN BANK—See First American Bank Corporation; *U.S. Private*, pg. 1513
FIRST AMERICAN BANK—See First Artesia Bancshares, Inc.; *U.S. Private*, pg. 1513
FIRST AMERICAN BANK & TRUST CO.; *U.S. Private*, pg. 1512
FIRST AMERICAN BANK & TRUST—See One American Corp.; *U.S. Private*, pg. 3020
FIRST AMERICAN COMMERCIAL BANCORP, INC.—See Royal Bank of Canada; *Int'l*, pg. 6409
FIRST AMERICAN COMMUNICATIONS ENTERPRISE INC.; *U.S. Private*, pg. 1513
FIRST AMERICAN DATA TREE LLC—See First American Financial Corporation; *U.S. Public*, pg. 836
FIRST AMERICAN EXCHANGE COMPANY, LLC—See First American Financial Corporation; *U.S. Public*, pg. 836
FIRST AMERICAN FINANCE CORPORATION—See The Marcus Corporation; *U.S. Public*, pg. 2112
FIRST AMERICAN FINANCIAL CORPORATION; *U.S. Public*, pg. 835
FIRST AMERICAN HOME BUYERS PROTECTION CORPORATION—See First American Financial Corporation; *U.S. Public*, pg. 836
FIRST AMERICAN (INDIA) PRIVATE LIMITED—See First American Financial Corporation; *U.S. Public*, pg. 836
FIRST AMERICAN LENDERS ADVANTAGE—See First American Financial Corporation; *U.S. Public*, pg. 836
FIRST AMERICAN MORTGAGE SOLUTIONS, LLC—See First American Financial Corporation; *U.S. Public*, pg. 836
FIRST AMERICAN NATIONAL BANK—See First American Bancshares, Inc.; *U.S. Private*, pg. 1512
FIRST AMERICAN NATIONAL DEFAULT TITLE SERVICES—See First American Financial Corporation; *U.S. Public*, pg. 836
FIRST AMERICAN PAYMENT SYSTEMS, L.P.—See Deluxe Corporation; *U.S. Public*, pg. 653
FIRST AMERICAN PROFESSIONAL REAL ESTATE SERVICES, INC—See First American Financial Corporation; *U.S. Public*, pg. 836
FIRST AMERICAN PROPERTY & CASUALTY INSURANCE COMPANY—See First American Financial Corporation; *U.S. Public*, pg. 836
FIRST AMERICAN PROPERTY & CASUALTY, INSURANCE—See First American Financial Corporation; *U.S. Public*, pg. 836
FIRST AMERICAN SCIENTIFIC CORP.; *Int'l*, pg. 2681
FIRST AMERICAN SERVICES CORPORATION—See Arch Capital Group Ltd.; *Int'l*, pg. 546
FIRST AMERICAN SHOSHONE TITLE—See First American Financial Corporation; *U.S. Public*, pg. 836
FIRST AMERICAN SMS, LLC—See First American Financial Corporation; *U.S. Public*, pg. 836
FIRST AMERICAN SPECIALTY INSURANCE COMPANY—See First American Financial Corporation; *U.S. Public*, pg. 836
FIRST AMERICAN STOCK TRANSFER, INC.—See Pacific Equity Partners Pty. Limited; *Int'l*, pg. 5689
FIRST AMERICAN TITLE & ABSTRACT CO.—See First American Financial Corporation; *U.S. Public*, pg. 836
FIRST AMERICAN TITLE COMPANY INC.—See First American Financial Corporation; *U.S. Public*, pg. 836
FIRST AMERICAN TITLE COMPANY-NATIONAL VACATION OWNERSHIP—See First American Financial Corporation; *U.S. Public*, pg. 836
FIRST AMERICAN TITLE COMPANY OF BELLINGHAM—See First American Financial Corporation; *U.S. Public*, pg. 836
FIRST AMERICAN TITLE COMPANY OF HOT SPRINGS COUNTY—See First American Financial Corporation; *U.S. Public*, pg. 836
FIRST AMERICAN TITLE COMPANY OF IDAHO, INC.—See First American Financial Corporation; *U.S. Public*, pg. 836
FIRST AMERICAN TITLE COMPANY OF LARAMIE COUNTY—See First American Financial Corporation; *U.S. Public*, pg. 836
FIRST AMERICAN TITLE COMPANY OF NEVADA (RENO)—See First American Financial Corporation; *U.S. Public*, pg. 836
FIRST AMERICAN TITLE COMPANY OF NEVADA—See First American Financial Corporation; *U.S. Public*, pg. 836
FIRST AMERICAN TITLE COMPANY OF OREGON—See First American Financial Corporation; *U.S. Public*, pg. 836
FIRST AMERICAN TITLE COMPANY OF OREGON—See First American Financial Corporation; *U.S. Public*, pg. 836

COMPANY NAME INDEX

FIRST BANK

FIRST AMERICAN TITLE COMPANY—See First American Financial Corporation; *U.S. Public*, pg. 836

FIRST AMERICAN TITLE CO. OF SPOKANE-ESCROW OPERS—See First American Financial Corporation; *U.S. Public*, pg. 836

FIRST AMERICAN TITLE INSURANCE AGENCY OF PINAL—See First American Financial Corporation; *U.S. Public*, pg. 836

FIRST AMERICAN TITLE INSURANCE COMPANY LENDERS ADVANTAGE—See First American Financial Corporation; *U.S. Public*, pg. 837

FIRST AMERICAN TITLE INSURANCE COMPANY OF AUSTRALIA PTY LIMITED—See First American Financial Corporation; *U.S. Public*, pg. 838

FIRST AMERICAN TITLE INSURANCE COMPANY OF LOUISIANA—See First American Financial Corporation; *U.S. Public*, pg. 838

FIRST AMERICAN TITLE INSURANCE COMPANY OF NEW YORK—See First American Financial Corporation; *U.S. Public*, pg. 837

FIRST AMERICAN TITLE INSURANCE COMPANY OF TEXAS—See First American Financial Corporation; *U.S. Public*, pg. 837

FIRST AMERICAN TITLE INSURANCE COMPANY OF THE CARIBBEAN & LATIN AMERICA—See First American Financial Corporation; *U.S. Public*, pg. 837

FIRST AMERICAN TITLE INSURANCE COMPANY—See First American Financial Corporation; *U.S. Public*, pg. 836

FIRST AMERICAN TITLE INSURANCE COMPANY—See First American Financial Corporation; *U.S. Public*, pg. 836

FIRST AMERICAN TITLE INSURANCE COMPANY—See First American Financial Corporation; *U.S. Public*, pg. 836

FIRST AMERICAN TITLE INSURANCE COMPANY—See First American Financial Corporation; *U.S. Public*, pg. 836

FIRST AMERICAN TITLE INSURANCE COMPANY—See First American Financial Corporation; *U.S. Public*, pg. 837

FIRST AMERICAN TITLE INSURANCE COMPANY—See First American Financial Corporation; *U.S. Public*, pg. 837

FIRST AMERICAN TITLE INSURANCE COMPANY—See First American Financial Corporation; *U.S. Public*, pg. 837

FIRST AMERICAN TITLE INSURANCE COMPANY—See First American Financial Corporation; *U.S. Public*, pg. 837

FIRST AMERICAN TITLE INSURANCE COMPANY—See First American Financial Corporation; *U.S. Public*, pg. 837

FIRST AMERICAN TITLE INSURANCE COMPANY—See First American Financial Corporation; *U.S. Public*, pg. 837

FIRST AMERICAN TITLE INSURANCE COMPANY—See First American Financial Corporation; *U.S. Public*, pg. 837

FIRST AMERICAN TITLE INSURANCE COMPANY—See First American Financial Corporation; *U.S. Public*, pg. 836

FIRST AMERICAN TITLE INSURANCE COMPANY—See First American Financial Corporation; *U.S. Public*, pg. 837

FIRST AMERICAN TITLE INSURANCE COMPANY—See First American Financial Corporation; *U.S. Public*, pg. 837

FIRST AMERICAN TITLE INSURANCE COMPANY—See First American Financial Corporation; *U.S. Public*, pg. 837

FIRST AMERICAN TITLE INSURANCE COMPANY—See First American Financial Corporation; *U.S. Public*, pg. 837

FIRST AMERICAN TITLE INSURANCE COMPANY - WYOMING—See First American Financial Corporation; *U.S. Public*, pg. 837

FIRST AMERICAN TITLE INSURANCE DE MEXICO, S.A. DE C.V.—See First American Financial Corporation; *U.S. Public*, pg. 838

FIRST AMERICAN TITLE—See First American Financial Corporation; *U.S. Public*, pg. 836

FIRST AMERICAN TITLE & TRUST COMPANY—See First American Financial Corporation; *U.S. Public*, pg. 836

FIRST AMERICAN TRUSTEE SERVICING SOLUTIONS, LLC—See First American Financial Corporation; *U.S. Public*, pg. 838

FIRST AMERICAN TRUST, F.S.B.—See First American Financial Corporation; *U.S. Public*, pg. 837

FIRST AMERICAN URANIUM INC.; *Int'l*, pg. 2681

FIRST AMERICAN VACATION OWNERSHIP SERVICES, INC.—See First American Financial Corporation; *U.S. Public*, pg. 838

FIRST AMERICAN VEHICLE TITLE INSURANCE—See First American Financial Corporation; *U.S. Public*, pg. 837

FIRST AMERICA RESOURCES CORPORATION; *U.S. Public*, pg. 835

FIRST AMERITAS LIFE INSURANCE CORP. OF NEW YORK—See Ameritas Mutual Holding Company; *U.S. Private*, pg. 261

THE FIRST, A NATIONAL BANKING ASSOCIATION—See The First Bancshares, Inc.; *U.S. Public*, pg. 2073

FIRST AND LAST HOTEL (BMG) PTY LTD—See Woolworths Group Limited; *Int'l*, pg. 8451

FIRST AND TEN INC.—See CSI Holdings Inc.; *U.S. Private*, pg. 1117

FIRST ANGULLA TRUST COMPANY LIMITED; *Int'l*, pg. 2682

FIRST ANNAPOLIS CONSULTING, INC.—See Accenture plc; *Int'l*, pg. 86

FIRST ANTLERS BANCORPORATION, INC.; *U.S. Private*, pg. 1513

FIRST ARKANSAS BANCSHARES, INC.; *U.S. Private*, pg. 1513

FIRST ARKANSAS BANK & TRUST—See First Arkansas Bancshares, Inc.; *U.S. Private*, pg. 1513

FIRST ARKANSAS MORTGAGE CO.—See First Arkansas Bancshares, Inc.; *U.S. Private*, pg. 1513

FIRSTAR PRECISION CORP.—See Empowered Ventures, Inc.; *U.S. Private*, pg. 1387

FIRST ARTESIA BANCSHARES, INC.; *U.S. Private*, pg. 1513

THE FIRST ARTIST COMPANY LTD.; *Int'l*, pg. 7643

FIRSTAR TRADE SERVICES CORPORATION—See U.S. Bancorp; *U.S. Public*, pg. 2212

FIRST ASIA HOLDINGS LIMITED; *Int'l*, pg. 2682

FIRST ASIA PROPERTIES (M) SDNBHD—See First Asia Holdings Limited; *Int'l*, pg. 2682

FIRST ASSET INVESTMENT MANAGEMENT INC.; *Int'l*, pg. 2682

FIRST ASSIST INC; *U.S. Private*, pg. 1513

FIRST ASSOCIATES LLC—See Equity CommonWealth; *U.S. Public*, pg. 790

FIRST ATLANTIC CAPITAL LTD.; *U.S. Private*, pg. 1513

FIRST ATLANTIC NICKEL CORP; *Int'l*, pg. 2682

FIRST ATLANTIC TITLE INSURANCE CORP.—See Stone Point Capital LLC; *U.S. Private*, pg. 3821

FIRST AU LIMITED; *Int'l*, pg. 2682

FIRST AVIATION SERVICES INC.—See First Equity Group, Inc.; *U.S. Private*, pg. 1517

FIRST BAKING CO., LTD.; *Int'l*, pg. 2682

FIRST BALFOUR, INC.—See Lopez, Inc.; *Int'l*, pg. 4556

FIRSTBANC OF ALABAMA, INC.; *U.S. Private*, pg. 1531

THE FIRST BANCORP, INC.; *U.S. Public*, pg. 2073

FIRST BANCORP OF INDIANA, INC.; *U.S. Public*, pg. 839

FIRST BANCORPORATION INC.; *U.S. Private*, pg. 1513

FIRST BANCORP; *U.S. Public*, pg. 838

FIRST BANCORP; *U.S. Public*, pg. 839

FIRST BANCSHARES CORPORATION; *U.S. Private*, pg. 1513

FIRST BANCSHARES INC OF COLD SPRING—See Granite Bank; *U.S. Private*, pg. 1755

FIRST BANCSHARES, INC.; *U.S. Private*, pg. 1513

FIRST BANCSHARES INC.; *U.S. Private*, pg. 1513

THE FIRST BANCSHARES, INC.; *U.S. Public*, pg. 2073

FIRST BANCSHARES, INC.; *U.S. Public*, pg. 839

FIRST BANCSHARES, INC.; *U.S. Public*, pg. 839

FIRST BANK AND TRUST—See First BankCorp Inc.; *U.S. Private*, pg. 1514

FIRSTBANK AT WADSWORTH/COLE MINE, INC.—See Firstbank Holding Company of Colorado, Inc.; *U.S. Private*, pg. 1531

FIRST BANKCORP INC.; *U.S. Private*, pg. 1514

FIRST BANK CORP.; *U.S. Private*, pg. 1514

FIRSTBANK DATA CORPORATION—See Firstbank Holding Company of Colorado, Inc.; *U.S. Private*, pg. 1531

FIRST BANK ELK RIVER—See First National Financial Services, Inc.; *U.S. Private*, pg. 1523

FIRST BANKERS TRUST COMPANY—See First Bankers Trustshares, Inc.; *U.S. Public*, pg. 840

FIRST BANKERS TRUSTSHARES INC.; *U.S. Public*, pg. 840

FIRST BANK FINANCIAL CENTRE—See Oconomowoc Bancshares, Inc.; *U.S. Public*, pg. 1563

FIRSTBANK FLORIDA—See First BanCorp; *U.S. Public*, pg. 839

FIRSTBANK, HAMPDEN & YOSEMITE—See Firstbank Holding Company of Colorado, Inc.; *U.S. Private*, pg. 1531

FIRSTBANK HOLDING COMPANY OF COLORADO, INC.; *U.S. Private*, pg. 1531

FIRSTBANK INSURANCE AGENCY, INC.—See First Bancorp; *U.S. Public*, pg. 839

FIRST BANK INSURANCE SERVICES, INC.—See First Bancorp; *U.S. Public*, pg. 839

FIRSTBANK NORTH—See Firstbank Holding Company of Colorado, Inc.; *U.S. Private*, pg. 1531

FIRST BANK OF ALABAMA—See FirstBanc of Alabama, Inc.; *U.S. Private*, pg. 1531

FIRST BANK OF ARAPAHOE COUNTY—See Firstbank Holding Company of Colorado, Inc.; *U.S. Private*, pg. 1531

FIRSTBANK OF ARVADA, INC.—See Firstbank Holding Company of Colorado, Inc.; *U.S. Private*, pg. 1531

FIRSTBANK OF AURORA, INC.—See Firstbank Holding Company of Colorado, Inc.; *U.S. Private*, pg. 1531

FIRSTBANK OF AVON, INC.—See Firstbank Holding Company of Colorado, Inc.; *U.S. Private*, pg. 1531

FIRST BANK OF BERNE—See First Berne Financial Corporation; *U.S. Private*, pg. 1514

FIRSTBANK OF BOULDER, INC.—See Firstbank Holding Company of Colorado, Inc.; *U.S. Private*, pg. 1531

FIRST BANK OF CHANDLER—See BancFirst Corporation; *U.S. Public*, pg. 269

FIRST BANK OF CHERRY CREEK—See Firstbank Holding Company of Colorado, Inc.; *U.S. Private*, pg. 1531

FIRST BANK OF COASTAL GEORGIA—See Putnam-Greene Financial Corporation; *U.S. Private*, pg. 3307

FIRSTBANK OF COLORADO, INC.—See Firstbank Holding Company of Colorado, Inc.; *U.S. Private*, pg. 1531

FIRSTBANK OF DOUGLAS COUNTY—See Firstbank Holding Company of Colorado, Inc.; *U.S. Private*, pg. 1531

FIRSTBANK OF ERIE, INC.—See Firstbank Holding Company of Colorado, Inc.; *U.S. Private*, pg. 1531

FIRST BANK OF HIGHLAND PARK; *U.S. Public*, pg. 1514

FIRST BANK OF JASPER—See Synovus Financial Corp.; *U.S. Public*, pg. 1971

FIRST BANK OF JASPER—See Synovus Financial Corp.; *U.S. Public*, pg. 1972

FIRSTBANK OF LAKEWOOD, INC.—See Firstbank Holding Company of Colorado, Inc.; *U.S. Private*, pg. 1531

FIRST BANK OF LINDEN—See First Linden Bancshares, Inc.; *U.S. Private*, pg. 1520

FIRST BANK OF LITTLETON, INC.—See Firstbank Holding Company of Colorado, Inc.; *U.S. Private*, pg. 1531

FIRSTBANK OF LONGMONT, INC.—See Firstbank Holding Company of Colorado, Inc.; *U.S. Private*, pg. 1531

FIRST BANK OF MONTANA—See Glacier Bancorp, Inc.; *U.S. Public*, pg. 938

FIRSTBANK OF NORTHERN COLORADO, INC.—See Firstbank Holding Company of Colorado, Inc.; *U.S. Private*, pg. 1531

FIRST BANK OF OHIO; *U.S. Public*, pg. 840

FIRST BANK OF OWASSO; *U.S. Private*, pg. 1514

FIRSTBANK OF SOUTH JEFFCO, INC.—See Firstbank Holding Company of Colorado, Inc.; *U.S. Private*, pg. 1531

FIRSTBANK OF SUMMIT COUNTY—See Firstbank Holding Company of Colorado, Inc.; *U.S. Private*, pg. 1531

FIRSTBANK OF TECH CENTER, INC.—See Firstbank Holding Company of Colorado, Inc.; *U.S. Private*, pg. 1531

THE FIRST BANK OF TOYAMA, LTD.; *Int'l*, pg. 7643

FIRSTBANK OF VAIL, INC.—See Firstbank Holding Company of Colorado, Inc.; *U.S. Private*, pg. 1531

FIRSTBANK OF WHEAT RIDGE, INC.—See Firstbank Holding Company of Colorado, Inc.; *U.S. Private*, pg. 1531

FIRST BANK OF WYOMING—See Glacier Bancorp, Inc.; *U.S. Public*, pg. 938

FIRSTBANK OVERSEAS CORP.—See First BanCorp; *U.S. Public*, pg. 839

FIRSTBANK PUERTO RICO—See First BanCorp; *U.S. Public*, pg. 839

FIRSTBANK, REPUBLIC PLAZA BRANCH—See Firstbank Holding Company of Colorado, Inc.; *U.S. Private*, pg. 1531

FIRST BANK RICHMOND—See First Mutual of Richmond, Inc.; *U.S. Private*, pg. 1521

FIRST BANKS, INC.; *U.S. Private*, pg. 1514

FIRST BANK CORP.; *U.S. Public*, pg. 839

FIRSTBANK—See First Antlers Bancorporation, Inc.; *U.S. Private*, pg. 1513

FIRST BANK—See First National Corporation; *U.S. Public*, pg. 846

FIRST BANK—See First Southwest Corporation; *U.S. Private*, pg. 1528

FIRST BANK—See Peoples Independent Bancshares, Inc.; *U.S. Private*, pg. 3142

FIRST BANK—See Pioneer Bankcorp, Inc.; *U.S. Public*, pg. 1692

FIRST BANK—See First Bancorp; *U.S. Public*, pg. 839
FIRST BANK—See First Banks, Inc.; *U.S. Private*, pg. 1514
FIRSTBANK SOUTHWEST—See FirstPerryton Bancorp, Inc.; *U.S. Private*, pg. 1532
FIRST BANK & TRUST COMPANY OF ILLINOIS INC.—See Northwest Bancorporation of Illinois, Inc.; *U.S. Private*, pg. 2959
FIRST BANK & TRUST COMPANY—See BancFirst Corporation; *U.S. Public*, pg. 269
FIRST BANK & TRUST COMPANY—See FNBT Bancshares, Perry, OK, Inc.; *U.S. Private*, pg. 1555
FIRST BANK & TRUST COMPANY—See Midwest Banco Corporation; *U.S. Private*, pg. 2720
FIRST BANK & TRUST CO.; *U.S. Private*, pg. 1513
FIRST BANK & TRUST EAST TEXAS; *U.S. Private*, pg. 1513
FIRST BANK & TRUST—See Firstrust Corporation; *U.S. Private*, pg. 1532
FIRST BANK & TRUST—See Heartland Financial USA, Inc.; *U.S. Public*, pg. 1018
FIRST BANK, UPPER MICHIGAN—See First Bancshares Corporation; *U.S. Private*, pg. 1513
FIRST BAUXITE CORPORATION—See RCF Management LLC; *U.S. Private*, pg. 3362
FIRST BEELINE BUSES LIMITED—See FirstGroup plc; *Int'l*, pg. 2688
FIRST BELLS BANKSHARES, INC.; *U.S. Private*, pg. 1514
FIRST BERNE FINANCIAL CORPORATION; *U.S. Private*, pg. 1514
FIRSTBEST SYSTEMS, INC.—See Guidewire Software, Inc.; *U.S. Public*, pg. 974
FIRST BOOK; *U.S. Private*, pg. 1514
FIRST BRAIN CO., LTD.—See Takebishi Corporation; *Int'l*, pg. 7436
FIRST BRANDS GROUP, LLC—See Crowne Group LLC; *U.S. Private*, pg. 1112
FIRST BRECKENRIDGE BANCSHARES; *U.S. Private*, pg. 1514
FIRST BRISTOL LIMITED—See FirstGroup plc; *Int'l*, pg. 2688
FIRST BROKEN ARROW CORPORATION; *U.S. Private*, pg. 1514
FIRST BROKERS REAL ESTATE—See Da-Ly Realty & Insurance Inc.; *U.S. Private*, pg. 1143
FIRST BROKERS SECURITIES LLC—See CME Group, Inc.; *U.S. Public*, pg. 517
FIRST BROTHERS ASSET MANAGEMENT CO., LTD.—See First Brothers Co., Ltd.; *Int'l*, pg. 2682
FIRST BROTHERS CAPITAL CO., LTD.—See First Brothers Co., Ltd.; *Int'l*, pg. 2682
FIRST BROTHERS CO., LTD.; *Int'l*, pg. 2682
FIRST BROTHERS DEVELOPMENT CO., LTD.—See First Brothers Co., Ltd.; *Int'l*, pg. 2682
FIRSTBUS CANADA—See FirstGroup plc; *Int'l*, pg. 2689
FIRST BUSEY CORPORATION; *U.S. Public*, pg. 840
FIRST BUSINESS BANCORP CO.; *U.S. Private*, pg. 1515
FIRST BUSINESS BANK-MILWAUKEE—See First Business Financial Services, Inc.; *U.S. Public*, pg. 840
FIRST BUSINESS BANK—See First Business Financial Services, Inc.; *U.S. Public*, pg. 840
FIRST BUSINESS CAPITAL CORP.—See First Business Financial Services, Inc.; *U.S. Public*, pg. 840
FIRST BUSINESS FINANCIAL SERVICES, INC.; *U.S. Public*, pg. 840
FIRST BUSINESS LEASING LLC—See First Business Financial Services, Inc.; *U.S. Public*, pg. 840
FIRST BUSINESS POST KFT.—See Unifiedpost Group SA; *Int'l*, pg. 8043
FIRST CAGAYAN CONVERGE DATA CENTER, INC.—See Leisure & Resorts World Corporation; *Int'l*, pg. 4447
FIRST CAGAYAN LEISURE & RESORTS CORPORATION—See Leisure & Resorts World Corporation; *Int'l*, pg. 4447
FIRST CALIFORNIA ESCROW CORPORATION—See Anywhere Real Estate Inc.; *U.S. Public*, pg. 142
FIRST CALL TEMPORARY SERVICES; *U.S. Private*, pg. 1515
FIRST CALL TRADING CORPORATION; *U.S. Private*, pg. 1515
FIRST CANADIAN MANAGEMENT CORPORATION; *Int'l*, pg. 2682
FIRST CANADIAN TITLE INSURANCE COMPANY LTD.—See First American Financial Corporation; *U.S. Public*, pg. 837
FIRST CAPITAL-AWIS LLC—See Brown & Brown, Inc.; *U.S. Public*, pg. 397
FIRST CAPITAL BANCSHARES INC; *U.S. Public*, pg. 841
FIRST CAPITAL BANK LIMITED—See FMBcapital Holdings plc; *Int'l*, pg. 2717
FIRST CAPITAL BANK PLC—See FMBcapital Holdings plc; *Int'l*, pg. 2717
FIRST CAPITAL CHINA CORPORATION; *Int'l*, pg. 2682
FIRST CAPITAL CONNECT LIMITED—See FirstGroup plc; *Int'l*, pg. 2689
FIRST CAPITAL EQUITIES LIMITED—See First Capital Securities Corporation Limited; *Int'l*, pg. 2682
FIRST CAPITAL HOLDINGS PLC; *Int'l*, pg. 2682

FIRST CAPITAL, INC.; *U.S. Public*, pg. 841
FIRST CAPITAL INTERNATIONAL FINANCE LIMITED—See China First Capital Group Limited; *Int'l*, pg. 1503
FIRST CAPITAL MANAGEMENT INC.—See First Financial Holding Co., Ltd.; *Int'l*, pg. 2683
FIRST CAPITAL NORTH LIMITED—See FirstGroup plc; *Int'l*, pg. 2689
FIRST CAPITAL PARTNERS, LLC—See Coherent Corp.; *U.S. Public*, pg. 528
FIRST CAPITAL PTE. LTD.—See Rich Capital Holdings Limited; *Int'l*, pg. 6329
FIRST CAPITAL REAL ESTATE TRUST INCORPORATED; *U.S. Private*, pg. 1515
FIRST CAPITAL REIT—See G City Ltd.; *Int'l*, pg. 2861
FIRST CAPITAL SECURITIES CO., LTD.; *Int'l*, pg. 2682
FIRST CAPITAL SECURITIES CORPORATION LIMITED; *Int'l*, pg. 2682
FIRST CAPITAL SECURITIES LIMITED—See China First Capital Group Limited; *Int'l*, pg. 1503
FIRST CAPITAL S.P.A.; *Int'l*, pg. 2682
FIRSTCARBON SOLUTIONS CORPORATION—See The ADEC Group; *U.S. Public*, pg. 3981
FIRST CARE MEDICAL SERVICES; *U.S. Private*, pg. 1515
FIRST CAROLINA FINANCIAL SERVICES, INC.; *U.S. Private*, pg. 1515
FIRST CAROLINA STATE BANK—See First Carolina Financial Services, Inc.; *U.S. Private*, pg. 1515
FIRSTCASH HOLDINGS, INC.; *U.S. Public*, pg. 848
THE FIRST CATHOLIC SLOVAK LADIES ASSOCIATION; *U.S. Private*, pg. 4029
FIRST CATHOLIC SLOVAK UNION US; *U.S. Private*, pg. 1515
FIRSTCAUTION SA; *Int'l*, pg. 2688
FIRST CECILIAN BANCORP, INC.; *U.S. Private*, pg. 1515
FIRST CENTENNIAL MORTGAGE CORPORATION—See McCarthy Group, LLC; *U.S. Private*, pg. 2626
FIRST CENTRAL BANK—See Central Bancompany, Inc.; *U.S. Public*, pg. 472
FIRST CENTURY BANCORP; *U.S. Private*, pg. 1515
FIRST CENTURY BANK, NATIONAL ASSOCIATION—See First Century Bancorp; *U.S. Private*, pg. 1515
FIRST CENTURY BANK; *U.S. Private*, pg. 1515
FIRST CHAIR HOUSING TRUSTEE LLC—See Vail Resorts, Inc.; *U.S. Public*, pg. 2271
FIRST CHATHAM BANK—See FCB Financial Corp.; *U.S. Private*, pg. 1485
FIRST CHECK DIAGNOSTICS, LLC—See Abbott Laboratories; *U.S. Public*, pg. 19
FIRST CHEMICAL CORP.—See The Chemours Company; *U.S. Public*, pg. 2059
FIRST CHEMICAL TEXAS, L.P.—See The Chemours Company; *U.S. Public*, pg. 2059
FIRST CHINA PHARMACEUTICAL GROUP, INC.; *Int'l*, pg. 2682
FIRST CHOICE BANCORP—See Enterprise Financial Services Corp; *U.S. Public*, pg. 778
FIRST CHOICE BANK—See Enterprise Financial Services Corp; *U.S. Public*, pg. 778
FIRST CHOICE CARE PTY LTD—See PeopleIn Limited; *Int'l*, pg. 5794
FIRST CHOICE CHILDREN'S HOMECARE, LP—See Encompass Health Corporation; *U.S. Public*, pg. 756
FIRST CHOICE COMMUNITY HEALTHCARE, INC.; *U.S. Private*, pg. 1515
FIRST CHOICE ER, LLC—See Adeptus Health Inc.; *U.S. Private*, pg. 78
FIRST CHOICE ESTATES PLC—See The Cardiff Property plc; *Int'l*, pg. 7630
FIRST CHOICE FACILITIES LIMITED—See Johnson Controls International plc; *Int'l*, pg. 3985
FIRST CHOICE HAIRCUTTERS, LTD—See Regis Corporation; *U.S. Public*, pg. 1777
FIRST CHOICE HEALTHCARE SOLUTIONS, INC.; *U.S. Public*, pg. 841
FIRST CHOICE HEALTH PLAN OF MISSISSIPPI, LLC—See Community Health Systems, Inc.; *U.S. Public*, pg. 553
FIRST CHOICE HOLIDAYS & FLIGHTS LIMITED—See TUI AG; *Int'l*, pg. 7968
FIRST CHOICE HOLIDAYS LIMITED—See TUI AG; *Int'l*, pg. 7964
FIRST-CHOICE HOME CARE, INC.; *U.S. Private*, pg. 1531
FIRST CHOICE HOME HEALTH—See The Pennant Group, Inc.; *U.S. Public*, pg. 2118
FIRST CHOICE HOME MEDICAL EQUIPMENT, LLC—See AdaptHealth Corp.; *U.S. Public*, pg. 88
FIRST CHOICE INGREDIENTS, INC.—See Koninklijke DSM N.V.; *Int'l*, pg. 4266
FIRST CHOICE LEISURE LIMITED—See TUI AG; *Int'l*, pg. 7964
FIRST CHOICE LOAN SERVICES INC.—See Crosscountry Mortgage, LLC; *U.S. Private*, pg. 1106
FIRST CHOICE LOGISTICS INC.—See Wind Point Advisors LLC; *U.S. Private*, pg. 4535
FIRST CHOICE LYON SAS—See TUI AG; *Int'l*, pg. 7964
FIRST CHOICE PACKAGING INC.; *U.S. Private*, pg. 1515

FIRST CHOICE POWER, L.P.—See NRG Energy, Inc.; *U.S. Public*, pg. 1549
FIRST CHOICE PRODUCTS INC.; *Int'l*, pg. 2683
FIRST CHOICE PROPERTIES CORP.—See Sunburst Hospitality Corporation; *U.S. Private*, pg. 3865
FIRST CHOICE PROPERTIES, INC.; *U.S. Private*, pg. 1515
FIRST CHOICE PURCHASING LIMITED—See Aramark; *U.S. Public*, pg. 178
FIRST CHOICE RETAIL (MANAGEMENT SERVICES) LIMITED—See TUI AG; *Int'l*, pg. 7968
FIRST CHOICE SEAFOOD, INC.; *U.S. Private*, pg. 1515
FIRST CHOICE TOUR OPERATIONS LIMITED—See TUI AG; *Int'l*, pg. 7964
FIRST CITIZENS BANCSHARES, INC.; *U.S. Public*, pg. 841
FIRST CITIZENS BANCSHARES, INC.; *U.S. Public*, pg. 841
FIRST CITIZENS BANK—See First Citizens Financial Corp.; *U.S. Private*, pg. 1515
FIRST-CITIZENS BANK & TRUST COMPANY—See First Citizens BancShares, Inc.; *U.S. Public*, pg. 842
FIRST CITIZENS CAPITAL LLC—See Civista Bancshares, Inc.; *U.S. Public*, pg. 507
FIRST CITIZENS COMMUNITY BANK—See Citizens Financial Services, Inc.; *U.S. Public*, pg. 506
FIRST CITIZENS FINANCIAL CORP.; *U.S. Private*, pg. 1515
FIRST CITIZENS INVESTMENTS, INC.—See Civista Bancshares, Inc.; *U.S. Public*, pg. 507
FIRST CITIZENS INVESTOR SERVICES, INC.—See First Citizens BancShares, Inc.; *U.S. Public*, pg. 842
THE FIRST CITIZENS NATIONAL BANK; *U.S. Private*, pg. 4029
FIRST-CITIZENS NATIONAL BANK—See First Citizens Bancshares, Inc.; *U.S. Public*, pg. 841
FIRST CITRUS BANCORPORATION, INC.; *U.S. Private*, pg. 1515
FIRST CITRUS BANK—See First Citrus Bancorporation, Inc.; *U.S. Private*, pg. 1515
FIRST CITY ADVERTISING—See Omnicom Group Inc.; *U.S. Public*, pg. 1575
FIRST CITY CARE (LONDON) PLC—See Johnson Controls International plc; *Int'l*, pg. 3987
FIRST CITY CREDIT UNION; *U.S. Private*, pg. 1515
FIRSTCITY FINANCIAL CORPORATION—See Varde Partners, Inc.; *U.S. Private*, pg. 4346
FIRST CITY MONUMENT BANK LIMITED—See FCMB Group Plc; *Int'l*, pg. 2628
FIRST CLASS EDUCATORS (FCE)—See Pasch Consulting Group, LLC; *U.S. Private*, pg. 3103
FIRSTCLASS FOODS-TROJAN, INC.—See US Foods Holding Corp.; *U.S. Public*, pg. 2266
FIRST CLASS, INC.; *U.S. Private*, pg. 1516
FIRST CLASS METALS PLC; *Int'l*, pg. 2683
FIRST CLASS & MORE FZE—See Asmallworld AG; *Int'l*, pg. 627
FIRST CLASS & MORE INTERNATIONAL AG—See Asmallworld AG; *Int'l*, pg. 627
FIRST CLASS MOVING SYSTEMS, INC.; *U.S. Private*, pg. 1515
FIRST CLASS PACKAGING, INC.—See Larson Packaging Company, LLC; *U.S. Private*, pg. 2394
FIRST CLASS SERVICE, INC.—See Fox Corporation; *U.S. Public*, pg. 875
FIRST CLASS SERVICES INC.; *U.S. Private*, pg. 1515
FIRST COAST AUCTION & REALTY, INC.; *U.S. Private*, pg. 1516
FIRST COAST LOGISTICS SERVICES; *U.S. Private*, pg. 1516
FIRST COAST NEWS—See TEGNA Inc.; *U.S. Public*, pg. 1990
FIRST COAST RAILROAD INC.—See Brookfield Infrastructure Partners L.P.; *Int'l*, pg. 1191
FIRST COAST RAILROAD INC.—See GIC Pte. Ltd.; *Int'l*, pg. 2965
FIRST COAST SERVICE OPTIONS INC.—See GuideWell Mutual Holding Corporation; *U.S. Private*, pg. 1813
FIRST COAST SUPPLY INC.; *U.S. Private*, pg. 1516
FIRST COAST WORKFORCE DEVELOPMENT, INC.; *U.S. Private*, pg. 1516
FIRST COLLINSVILLE BANK INC.; *U.S. Private*, pg. 1516
FIRST COLOMBIA GOLD CORP.; *U.S. Private*, pg. 1516
FIRST COLONIAL INSURANCE COMPANY—See The Allstate Corporation; *U.S. Public*, pg. 2033
FIRST COLONY COFFEE & TEA COMPANY; *U.S. Private*, pg. 1516
FIRST COLONY COMMUNITY ASSOCIATION; *U.S. Private*, pg. 1516
FIRST CO., LTD.—See Valor Holdings Co., Ltd.; *Int'l*, pg. 8122
FIRSTCOME ELECTRONICS LTD.—See Citizen Watch Co., Ltd.; *Int'l*, pg. 1625
FIRST COMMERCE BANK; *U.S. Public*, pg. 842
FIRST COMMERCE CREDIT UNION; *U.S. Private*, pg. 1516
FIRST COMMERCIAL BANK LTD.—See First Financial Holding Co., Ltd.; *Int'l*, pg. 2683

COMPANY NAME INDEX

FIRST COMMERCIAL BANK (U.S.A.)—See First Financial Holding Co., Ltd.; *Int'l*, pg. 2683
FIRST COMMONWEALTH BANK—See First Commonwealth Financial Corporation; *U.S. Public*, pg. 842
FIRST COMMONWEALTH FINANCIAL CORPORATION; *U.S. Public*, pg. 842
FIRST COMMUNICATIONS LLC—See North Central Equity LLC; *U.S. Private*, pg. 2943
FIRST COMMUNITY BANCORP, INC.—See Eagle Bancorp Montana, Inc.; *U.S. Public*, pg. 701
FIRST COMMUNITY BANCSHARES, INC.; *U.S. Private*, pg. 1516
FIRST COMMUNITY BANCSHARES, INC.; *U.S. Private*, pg. 1516
FIRST COMMUNITY BANKSHARES, INC.; *U.S. Public*, pg. 842
FIRST COMMUNITY BANK—See First Community Bancshares, Inc.; *U.S. Private*, pg. 1516
FIRST COMMUNITY BANK—See First Community Bankshares, Inc.; *U.S. Public*, pg. 842
FIRST COMMUNITY BANK—See First Community Corporation; *U.S. Public*, pg. 843
FIRST COMMUNITY CORPORATION; *U.S. Public*, pg. 842
FIRST COMMUNITY FINANCIAL CORPORATION; *U.S. Public*, pg. 843
FIRST COMMUNITY INSURANCE SERVICES, INC.—See First Community Bancshares, Inc.; *U.S. Public*, pg. 842
FIRST COMMUNITY WEALTH MANAGEMENT, INC.—See First Community Bankshares, Inc.; *U.S. Public*, pg. 842
FIRSTCOMP UNDERWRITERS GROUP, INC.—See Markel Group Inc.; *U.S. Public*, pg. 1368
FIRST CONSTRUCTION GROUP; *U.S. Private*, pg. 1516
FIRST CONVENIENCE BANK—See First Community Bancshares, Inc.; *U.S. Private*, pg. 1516
FIRST COOPERATIVE ASSOCIATION; *U.S. Private*, pg. 1516
FIRST COPPER TECHNOLOGY CO., LTD.; *Int'l*, pg. 2683
FIRST CORPORATE SEDANS INC.—See Elite Limousine Plus, Inc.; *U.S. Private*, pg. 1361
FIRST-CORPORATION INC.; *Int'l*, pg. 2688
FIRST COUNTY BANK; *U.S. Private*, pg. 1516
FIRST CREDIT AND INVESTMENT BANK LIMITED—See State Bank of Pakistan; *Int'l*, pg. 7182
FIRST CREDIT BANK; *U.S. Private*, pg. 1516
FIRST CREDIT FINANCE GROUP LIMITED; *Int'l*, pg. 2683
FIRST CREDIT UNION; *U.S. Private*, pg. 1516
THE FIRST CUSTODIAN FUND (INDIA) LTD.; *Int'l*, pg. 7643
FIRST DAKOTA ENTERPRISES INCORPORATED; *U.S. Private*, pg. 1516
FIRST DAKOTA FINANCIAL CORP.; *U.S. Private*, pg. 1516
FIRST DAKOTA NATIONAL BANK—See First Dakota Financial Corp.; *U.S. Private*, pg. 1516
FIRST DATA AUSTRIA GMBH—See Fiserv, Inc.; *U.S. Public*, pg. 850
FIRST DATABANK EUROPE LTD.—See The Hearst Corporation; *U.S. Private*, pg. 4045
FIRST DATABANK, INC.—See The Hearst Corporation; *U.S. Private*, pg. 4044
FIRST DATABANK—See The Hearst Corporation; *U.S. Private*, pg. 4045
FIRST DATA CANADA LTD.—See Fiserv, Inc.; *U.S. Public*, pg. 850
FIRST DATA COMMERCIAL SERVICES HOLDINGS, INC.—See Fiserv, Inc.; *U.S. Public*, pg. 850
FIRST DATA CORPORATION AUSTRALIA (HOLDINGS) PTY LIMITED—See Fiserv, Inc.; *U.S. Public*, pg. 850
FIRST DATA CORPORATION—See Fiserv, Inc.; *U.S. Public*, pg. 850
FIRST DATA CORPORATION; *U.S. Private*, pg. 1517
FIRST DATA DEUTSCHLAND GMBH—See Fiserv, Inc.; *U.S. Public*, pg. 850
FIRST DATA EUROPE LIMITED—See Fiserv, Inc.; *U.S. Public*, pg. 850
FIRST DATA GOVERNMENT SOLUTIONS, INC.—See Fiserv, Inc.; *U.S. Public*, pg. 850
FIRST DATA MAGYARORSZAG KFT.—See Fiserv, Inc.; *U.S. Public*, pg. 851
FIRST DATA MERCHANT SERVICES CORPORATION—See Fiserv, Inc.; *U.S. Public*, pg. 850
FIRST DATA MERCHANT SERVICES CORPORATION—See Fiserv, Inc.; *U.S. Public*, pg. 850
FIRST DATA MERCHANT SERVICES CORPORATION—See Fiserv, Inc.; *U.S. Public*, pg. 850
FIRST DATA MERCHANT SERVICES MEXICO, S. DE R.L. DE C.V.—See Fiserv, Inc.; *U.S. Public*, pg. 850
FIRST DATA MERCHANT SOLUTIONS AUSTRALIA PTY. LTD.—See Fiserv, Inc.; *U.S. Public*, pg. 850
FIRST DATA POLSKA S.A.—See Fiserv, Inc.; *U.S. Public*, pg. 851
FIRST DATA RESOURCES AUSTRALIA LIMITED—See Fiserv, Inc.; *U.S. Public*, pg. 850
FIRST DATA RESOURCES INC.—See Fiserv, Inc.; *U.S. Public*, pg. 851
FIRST DATA RESOURCES—See Fiserv, Inc.; *U.S. Public*, pg. 851

FIRST DAWOOD PROPERTIES LIMITED; *Int'l*, pg. 2683
FIRST-DDSG LOGISTICS HOLDING GMBH—See Ferrexpo plc; *Int'l*, pg. 2641
FIRST DEALER RESOURCES, INC.—See iA Financial Corporation Inc.; *U.S. Public*, pg. 3568
FIRST DENTAL HEALTH; *U.S. Private*, pg. 1517
FIRST DERIVATIVES CANADA INC.—See FD Technologies PLC; *Int'l*, pg. 2628
FIRST DERIVATIVES (HONG KONG) LIMITED—See FD Technologies PLC; *Int'l*, pg. 2628
FIRST DERIVATIVES (IRELAND) LIMITED—See FD Technologies PLC; *Int'l*, pg. 2628
FIRST DERIVATIVES JAPAN CO. LIMITED—See FD Technologies PLC; *Int'l*, pg. 2628
FIRST DERIVATIVES PTE LIMITED—See FD Technologies PLC; *Int'l*, pg. 2628
FIRST DERIVATIVES PTY LIMITED—See FD Technologies PLC; *Int'l*, pg. 2628
FIRST DEVON & CORNWALL LIMITED—See FirstGroup plc; *Int'l*, pg. 2689
FIRST DISTRICT ASSOCIATION; *U.S. Private*, pg. 1517
FIRST DUBAI FOR REAL ESTATE DEVELOPMENT COMPANY K.S.C.C.—See Al-Mazaya Holding Company K.S.C.P.; *Int'l*, pg. 287
FIRST DUBAI REAL ESTATE DEVELOPMENT COMPANY K.S.C.—See Al-Mazaya Holding Company K.S.C.P.; *Int'l*, pg. 287
FIRST EAGLE ALTERNATIVE CAPITAL BDC, INC.—See Crescent Capital BDC, Inc.; *U.S. Public*, pg. 593
FIRST EAGLE HOLDINGS, INC.—See Blackstone Inc.; *U.S. Public*, pg. 353
FIRST EAGLE HOLDINGS, INC.—See Corsair Capital, LLC; *U.S. Private*, pg. 1059
FIRST EAGLE INVESTMENT MANAGEMENT, LLC—See Blackstone Inc.; *U.S. Public*, pg. 353
FIRST EAGLE INVESTMENT MANAGEMENT, LLC—See Corsair Capital, LLC; *U.S. Private*, pg. 1059
FIRST EAGLE MANAGEMENT CORP.; *U.S. Private*, pg. 1517
FIRST EAGLE PRIVATE CREDIT, LLC—See Blackstone Inc.; *U.S. Public*, pg. 353
FIRST EAGLE PRIVATE CREDIT, LLC—See Corsair Capital, LLC; *U.S. Private*, pg. 1059
FIRST EASTERN COUNTIES BUSES LIMITED—See FirstGroup plc; *Int'l*, pg. 2689
FIRSTEC CO., LTD.; *Int'l*, pg. 2688
FIRSTECH, INC.—See First Busey Corporation; *U.S. Public*, pg. 840
FIRSTECH SOLUTIONS CO. LTD.—See Thai Reinsurance Public Co., Ltd.; *Int'l*, pg. 7595
FIRST EDGE SOLUTIONS, INC.; *U.S. Private*, pg. 1517
FIRST EFFORT INVESTMENTS LTD.; *Int'l*, pg. 2683
FIRST EFINANCE LIMITED—See First Shanghai Investments Limited; *Int'l*, pg. 2687
FIRST EIE SA; *Int'l*, pg. 2683
FIRST ELECTRIC COOPERATIVE CORP.; *U.S. Private*, pg. 1517
FIRST ELITE CAPITAL MODARABA; *Int'l*, pg. 2683
FIRST EMPIRE SECURITIES INC.; *U.S. Private*, pg. 1517
FIRST ENERGY CORPORATION—See Parker Holding Company, Inc.; *U.S. Private*, pg. 3097
FIRSTENERGY CORP.; *U.S. Public*, pg. 849
FIRSTENERGY FOUNDATION—See FirstEnergy Corp.; *U.S. Public*, pg. 849
FIRSTENERGY NUCLEAR OPERATING CO.—See FirstEnergy Corp.; *U.S. Public*, pg. 849
FIRSTENERGY SERVICE COMPANY—See FirstEnergy Corp.; *U.S. Public*, pg. 849
FIRSTENERGY SOLUTIONS CORP.—See FirstEnergy Corp.; *U.S. Public*, pg. 849
FIRST ENGINEERING CO., LTD.—See Hibino Corporation; *Int'l*, pg. 3383
FIRST ENGINEERING (GUANGZHOU) CO., LTD.—See Sunningdale Tech Ltd; *Int'l*, pg. 7318
FIRST ENGINEERING LIMITED—See Sunningdale Tech Ltd; *Int'l*, pg. 7318
FIRST ENGINEERING PLASTICS INDIA PRIVATE LIMITED—See Sunningdale Tech Ltd; *Int'l*, pg. 7318
FIRST ENGINEERING PLASTICS (MALAYSIA) SDN BHD—See Sunningdale Tech Ltd; *Int'l*, pg. 7318
FIRST ENGINEERING (SHANGHAI) CO., LTD.—See Sunningdale Tech Ltd; *Int'l*, pg. 7318
FIRST ENGINEERING (SUZHOU) CO., LTD.—See Sunningdale Tech Ltd; *Int'l*, pg. 7318
FIRST ENGLISH EDUCATION INSTITUTES LIMITED—See Aptech Limited; *Int'l*, pg. 523
FIRST ENTERPRISE BANK INC.; *U.S. Private*, pg. 1517
FIRST ENTERTAINMENT GMBH—See Bavaria Film GmbH; *Int'l*, pg. 899
FIRST EQUIPMENT CO.; *U.S. Private*, pg. 1517
FIRST EQUITY CARD CORPORATION—See Vervent Inc.; *U.S. Private*, pg. 4371
FIRST EQUITY DEVELOPMENT INCORPORATED—See First Equity Group, Inc.; *U.S. Private*, pg. 1517
FIRST EQUITY GROUP, INC.; *U.S. Private*, pg. 1517
FIRST EQUITY MORTGAGE BANKERS, INC.; *U.S. Private*, pg. 1517
FIRSTEXPRESS; *U.S. Private*, pg. 1531

FIRST FACILITIES CHALLENGED CO., LTD.—See Mitsui Fudosan Co., Ltd.; *Int'l*, pg. 4986
FIRST FACILITIES CHIBA CO., LTD.—See Mitsui Fudosan Co., Ltd.; *Int'l*, pg. 4986
FIRST FACILITIES CO., LTD.—See Mitsui Fudosan Co., Ltd.; *Int'l*, pg. 4986
FIRST FACILITIES GUNMA CO., LTD.—See Mitsui Fudosan Co., Ltd.; *Int'l*, pg. 4986
FIRST FACILITIES WEST CO., LTD.—See Mitsui Fudosan Co., Ltd.; *Int'l*, pg. 4986
FIRST FAMILY ENTERPRISE CO., LTD.—See Want Want China Holdings Ltd.; *Int'l*, pg. 8342
FIRST FAMILY INSURANCE, LLC—See UnitedHealth Group Incorporated; *U.S. Public*, pg. 2240
FIRST FARMERS AND MERCHANTS CORPORATION; *U.S. Public*, pg. 843
FIRST FARMERS BANCSHARES INC.; *U.S. Private*, pg. 1517
THE FIRST & FARMERS BANK—See Full Service Insurance Agency, Inc.; *U.S. Private*, pg. 1621
FIRST FARMERS BANK & TRUST COMPANY—See First Farmers Financial Corporation; *U.S. Private*, pg. 1517
FIRST FARMERS FINANCIAL CORPORATION; *U.S. Private*, pg. 1517
FIRST FARMERS & MERCHANTS BANK—See First Farmers and Merchants Corporation; *U.S. Public*, pg. 843
FIRST FARMERS & MERCHANTS NATIONAL BANK—See 215 Holding Co.; *U.S. Private*, pg. 5
FIRST FARMERS & MERCHANTS NATIONAL BANK—See 215 Holding Co.; *U.S. Private*, pg. 5
FIRST FARMERS & MERCHANTS NATIONAL BANK—See 215 Holding Co.; *U.S. Private*, pg. 5
FIRST FARMERS & MERCHANTS STATE BANK OF GRAND MEADOW—See 215 Holding Co.; *U.S. Private*, pg. 5
FIRST FARMERS & MERCHANTS STATE BANK—See 215 Holding Co.; *U.S. Private*, pg. 5
FIRST & FARMERS NATIONAL BANK, INC.—See Albany Bancorp, Inc.; *U.S. Private*, pg. 151
FIRSTFARMS AGRA M. S.R.O.—See FirstFarms A/S; *Int'l*, pg. 2688
FIRSTFARMS A/S; *Int'l*, pg. 2688
FIRSTFARMS SLOVAKIET APS—See FirstFarms A/S; *Int'l*, pg. 2688
FIRSTFED BANCORP, INC.; *U.S. Private*, pg. 1532
FIRST FEDERAL BANCORP, INC.; *U.S. Private*, pg. 1517
FIRST FEDERAL BANK, A FSB—See Southeastern Financial Inc.; *U.S. Private*, pg. 3728
FIRST FEDERAL BANK OF KANSAS CITY; *U.S. Private*, pg. 1517
FIRST FEDERAL BANK OF LOUISIANA; *U.S. Private*, pg. 1518
FIRST FEDERAL BANK OF OHIO; *U.S. Private*, pg. 1518
FIRST FEDERAL BANK OF THE MIDWEST—See Premier Financial Corp.; *U.S. Public*, pg. 1715
FIRST FEDERAL BANK—See First Federal Bancorp, Inc.; *U.S. Private*, pg. 1517
FIRST FEDERAL BANK—See Southeastern Bancorp, Inc.; *U.S. Private*, pg. 3727
FIRST FEDERAL COMMUNITY BANK, N.A.—See FFD Financial Corporation; *U.S. Public*, pg. 830
FIRST FEDERAL COMMUNITY BANK OF BUCYRUS—See Community Investors Bancorp, Inc.; *U.S. Public*, pg. 558
FIRST FEDERAL COMMUNITY BANK; *U.S. Private*, pg. 1518
FIRST FEDERAL FINANCE CORPORATION—See First BanCorp; *U.S. Public*, pg. 839
FIRST FEDERAL MHC; *U.S. Private*, pg. 1518
FIRST FEDERAL SAVINGS BANK OF CHAMPAIGN-URBANA—See Great American Bancorp, Inc.; *U.S. Public*, pg. 961
FIRST FEDERAL SAVINGS BANK OF FRANKFORT—See First Federal MHC; *U.S. Private*, pg. 1518
FIRST FEDERAL SAVINGS BANK; *U.S. Private*, pg. 1518
FIRST FEDERAL SAVINGS BANK; *U.S. Private*, pg. 1518
FIRST FEDERAL SAVINGS BANK; *U.S. Private*, pg. 1518
FIRST FEDERAL SAVINGS BANK—See First Bancorp of Indiana, Inc.; *U.S. Public*, pg. 839
FIRST FEDERAL SAVINGS BANK—See Northeast Indiana Bancorp, Inc.; *U.S. Public*, pg. 1537
FIRST FEDERAL SAVINGS BANK TWIN FALLS; *U.S. Private*, pg. 1518
FIRST FEDERAL SAVINGS & LOAN ASSOCIATION OF GREENE COUNTY; *U.S. Private*, pg. 1518
FIRST FEDERAL SAVINGS & LOAN ASSOCIATION OF LAKEWOOD; *U.S. Private*, pg. 1518
FIRST FEDERAL SAVINGS & LOAN ASSOCIATION OF LORAIN; *U.S. Private*, pg. 1518
FIRST FEDERAL SAVINGS & LOAN ASSOCIATION OF PASCAGOULA-MOSS POINT; *U.S. Private*, pg. 1518
FIRST FEDERAL SAVINGS & LOAN ASSOCIATION OF PORT ANGELES—See First Northwest Bancorp; *U.S. Public*, pg. 846
FIRST FEDERAL SAVINGS & LOAN ASSOCIATION—See First Federal MHC; *U.S. Private*, pg. 1518
FIRST FEDERAL SAVINGS & LOAN; *U.S. Private*, pg. 1518

FIRST FIDELITY BANCORP, INC.

FIRST FIDELITY BANCORP, INC.; *U.S. Private*, pg. 1518
FIRST FIDELITY BANK—See First Fidelity Bancorp, Inc.; *U.S. Private*, pg. 1519
FIRST FIDELITY LEASING MODARABA; *Int'l*, pg. 2683
FIRST FINANCE COMPANY Q.S.C.—See The International Bank of Qatar (Q.S.C); *Int'l*, pg. 7656
FIRST FINANCE CO.; *Int'l*, pg. 2683
FIRST FINANCE LIMITED; *Int'l*, pg. 2683
FIRST FINANCE PLC—See Phillip Capital Pte. Ltd.; *Int'l*, pg. 5846
FIRST FINANCIAL ASSETS MANAGEMENT CO., LTD.—See First Financial Holding Co., Ltd.; *Int'l*, pg. 2683
FIRST FINANCIAL BANC CORPORATION; *U.S. Private*, pg. 1519
FIRST FINANCIAL BANCORP SERVICE CORPORATION—See First Financial Bancorp.; *U.S. Public*, pg. 843
FIRST FINANCIAL BANCORP.; *U.S. Public*, pg. 843
FIRST FINANCIAL BANK, N.A.—See First Financial Bankshares, Inc.; *U.S. Public*, pg. 843
FIRST FINANCIAL BANK, N.A.—See First Financial Corporation; *U.S. Public*, pg. 843
FIRST FINANCIAL BANKSHARES, INC.; *U.S. Public*, pg. 843
FIRST FINANCIAL BANK—See FirstFed Bancorp, Inc.; *U.S. Private*, pg. 1532
FIRST FINANCIAL BANK—See First Financial Banc Corporation; *U.S. Private*, pg. 1519
FIRST FINANCIAL BANK—See First Financial Bancorp.; *U.S. Public*, pg. 843
FIRST FINANCIAL CORPORATE SERVICES, INC.—See JA Mitsui Leasing, Ltd.; *Int'l*, pg. 3859
FIRST FINANCIAL CORPORATION; *U.S. Public*, pg. 843
FIRST FINANCIAL CREDIT UNION; *U.S. Private*, pg. 1519
FIRST FINANCIAL CREDIT UNION; *U.S. Private*, pg. 1519
FIRST FINANCIAL DIVERSIFIED CORPORATION—See First Financial Northwest, Inc.; *U.S. Public*, pg. 844
FIRST FINANCIAL EMPLOYEE LEASING, INC.; *U.S. Private*, pg. 1519
FIRST FINANCIAL EQUIPMENT FINANCE, LLC—See First Financial Bancorp.; *U.S. Public*, pg. 843
FIRST FINANCIAL GROUP OF AMERICA—See American Fidelity Corporation; *U.S. Private*, pg. 233
FIRST FINANCIAL HOLDING CO., LTD.; *Int'l*, pg. 2683
FIRST FINANCIAL HOLDINGS INC.; *U.S. Private*, pg. 1519
FIRST FINANCIAL INSURANCE AGENCY, INC.—See First Financial Bankshares, Inc.; *U.S. Public*, pg. 843
FIRST FINANCIAL INSURANCE INDIANA—See First Financial Bancorp.; *U.S. Public*, pg. 843
FIRST FINANCIAL LEASING (CHENGDU) LTD.—See First Financial Holding Co., Ltd.; *Int'l*, pg. 2683
FIRST FINANCIAL MANAGEMENT CONSULTING CO., LTD.—See First Financial Holding Co., Ltd.; *Int'l*, pg. 2683
FIRST FINANCIAL NORTHWEST BANK—See First Financial Northwest, Inc.; *U.S. Public*, pg. 844
FIRST FINANCIAL NORTHWEST, INC.; *U.S. Public*, pg. 843
FIRST FINANCIAL OF TENNESSEE; *U.S. Private*, pg. 1519
FIRST FINANCIAL PREFERRED CAPITAL, INC.—See First Financial Bancorp.; *U.S. Public*, pg. 843
FIRST FINANCIAL RESOURCES INC.; *U.S. Private*, pg. 1519
FIRST FINANCIAL RESOURCES LTD.—See Aon plc; *Int'l*, pg. 496
FIRST FINANCIAL SERVICES, INC.; *U.S. Private*, pg. 1519
FIRST FINANCIAL TRUST, N.A.—See The Savings Bank; *U.S. Private*, pg. 4114
FIRST FITNESS INTERNATIONAL; *U.S. Private*, pg. 1519
FIRST FLEET CONCERTS, LLC—See Live Nation Entertainment, Inc.; *U.S. Public*, pg. 1328
FIRSTFLEET INC.; *U.S. Private*, pg. 1532
FIRST FLORIDA BUILDING CORP.; *U.S. Private*, pg. 1519
FIRST FLORIDA CREDIT UNION; *U.S. Private*, pg. 1519
FIRST FLORIDA INSURANCE NETWORK; *U.S. Private*, pg. 1519
FIRST FOOD DISTRIBUTORS (PTY) LIMITED—See The Bidvest Group Limited; *Int'l*, pg. 7624
FIRST FOOD SERVICES L.L.C.—See The Olayan Group; *Int'l*, pg. 7672
FIRST FOODS GROUP, INC.; *U.S. Public*, pg. 844
FIRST FORTUNE INTERNATIONAL COMPANY LIMITED; *Int'l*, pg. 2683
FIRST FOUNDATION ADVISORS—See First Foundation Inc.; *U.S. Public*, pg. 844
FIRST FOUNDATION BANK—See First Foundation Inc.; *U.S. Public*, pg. 844
FIRST FOUNDATION INC.; *U.S. Public*, pg. 844
FIRST FRANCHISE CAPITAL CORPORATION—See First Financial Bancorp.; *U.S. Public*, pg. 843
FIRST FUNDS LTD.—See FBN Holdings PLC; *Int'l*, pg. 2627

FIRST GAS POWER CORPORATION - BATANGAS PLANT—See First Gen Corporation; *Int'l*, pg. 2684
FIRST GEN CORPORATION; *Int'l*, pg. 2683
FIRST GENERAL BANK; *U.S. Public*, pg. 844
FIRST GENERATION; *U.S. Private*, pg. 1519
FIRST GENERATION—See First Generation; *U.S. Private*, pg. 1519
FIRST GENERATION—See First Generation; *U.S. Private*, pg. 1519
FIRST GEN HYDRO POWER CORPORATION - PANTABANGAN PLANT—See First Gen Corporation; *Int'l*, pg. 2684
FIRST GILMER BANKSHARES, INC.; *U.S. Private*, pg. 1519
FIRST GLASGOW (NO. 1) LIMITED—See FirstGroup plc; *Int'l*, pg. 2689
FIRST GLASGOW (NO. 2) LIMITED—See FirstGroup plc; *Int'l*, pg. 2689
FIRST GLOBAL BANK LTD—See GraceKennedy Limited; *Int'l*, pg. 3048
FIRST GLOBAL DATA LIMITED; *Int'l*, pg. 2684
FIRST GLOBAL FINANCIAL & INSURANCE SERVICES INC.—See Aon plc; *Int'l*, pg. 496
FIRST GLOBAL FINANCIAL SERVICES LTD.—See GraceKennedy Limited; *Int'l*, pg. 3048
FIRST GLOBAL HOLDINGS LIMITED—See GraceKennedy Limited; *Int'l*, pg. 3048
FIRST GLOBAL INSURANCE BROKERS LIMITED—See GraceKennedy Limited; *Int'l*, pg. 3048
FIRST GLOBAL TRINIDAD & TOBAGO LIMITED—See GraceKennedy Limited; *Int'l*, pg. 3048
FIRST GRAPHENE LIMITED; *Int'l*, pg. 2684
FIRST GRAPHENE (UK) LTD.—See First Graphene Limited; *Int'l*, pg. 2684
FIRST GREATER WESTERN LIMITED—See FirstGroup plc; *Int'l*, pg. 2689
FIRST GREENWICH FINANCIAL, INC.; *U.S. Public*, pg. 844
FIRST GROESBECK HOLDING COMPANY; *U.S. Private*, pg. 1519
FIRSTGROUP AMERICA INC.—See FirstGroup plc; *Int'l*, pg. 2689
FIRSTGROUP PLC; *Int'l*, pg. 2688
FIRST GROWTH HOLDINGS LTD.; *Int'l*, pg. 2684
FIRST GUARANTY BANCSHARES, INC.; *U.S. Public*, pg. 844
FIRST GUARANTY BANK—See First Guaranty Bancshares, Inc.; *U.S. Public*, pg. 844
FIRST GUARANTY INSURANCE, CO.—See Security National Financial Corporation; *U.S. Public*, pg. 1856
FIRST GUARANTY MORTGAGE CORP.; *U.S. Private*, pg. 1519
FIRST HABIB MODARABA—See Habib Bank AG Zurich; *Int'l*, pg. 3202
FIRSTHAND CAPITAL MANAGEMENT, INC.; *U.S. Private*, pg. 1532
FIRSTHAND TECHNOLOGY VALUE FUND, INC.—See Firsthand Capital Management, Inc.; *U.S. Private*, pg. 1532
FIRST HARRISON BANK—See First Capital, Inc.; *U.S. Public*, pg. 841
FIRST HARTFORD CORPORATION; *U.S. Public*, pg. 844
FIRST HAWAIIAN BANK—See BNP Paribas SA; *Int'l*, pg. 1088
FIRST HAWAIIAN CAPITAL 1—See BNP Paribas SA; *Int'l*, pg. 1088
FIRST HAWAIIAN, INC.—See BNP Paribas SA; *Int'l*, pg. 1087
FIRST HAWAIIAN LEASING, INC.—See BNP Paribas SA; *Int'l*, pg. 1088
FIRST HEALTH GROUP CORP.—See CVS Health Corporation; *U.S. Public*, pg. 615
FIRSTHEALTH MOORE REGIONAL HOSPITAL—See FirstHealth of the Carolinas, Inc.; *U.S. Private*, pg. 1532
FIRSTHEALTH OF THE CAROLINAS, INC.; *U.S. Private*, pg. 1532
FIRST HEALTH SYSTEM INCORPORATED—See Universal Health Services, Inc.; *U.S. Public*, pg. 2257
FIRST HEARTLAND CAPITAL JSC; *Int'l*, pg. 2684
FIRST HEARTLAND JUSAN BANK JSC—See First Heartland Capital JSC; *Int'l*, pg. 2684
FIRST HEARTLAND JUSAN INVEST JSC; *Int'l*, pg. 2684
FIRST HEARTLAND SECURITIES JSC—See First Heartland Capital JSC; *Int'l*, pg. 2684
FIRST HELIUM INC.; *Int'l*, pg. 2684
FIRST HELP FINANCIAL, LLC; *U.S. Private*, pg. 1519
FIRST HERITAGE CREDIT LLC—See CURO Group Holdings Corp.; *U.S. Public*, pg. 611
FIRST HIGH-SCHOOL EDUCATION GROUP CO., LTD.; *Int'l*, pg. 2684
FIRST HI-TEC ENTERPRISE CO., LTD.; *Int'l*, pg. 2684
FIRST HOME BANK—See First Bancshares, Inc.; *U.S. Public*, pg. 839
FIRST HOME BUILDERS OF FLORIDA; *U.S. Private*, pg. 1520
FIRST HONG KONG TITLE LTD.—See First American Financial Corporation; *U.S. Public*, pg. 837
FIRST HORIZON CORPORATION; *U.S. Public*, pg. 844

CORPORATE AFFILIATIONS

FIRST HOSPITALITY GROUP, INC.; *U.S. Private*, pg. 1520
FIRST HOSPITAL PANAMERICANO, INC.—See Universal Health Services, Inc.; *U.S. Public*, pg. 2257
FIRST HOTEL COMPANY LTD.; *Int'l*, pg. 2684
FIRST HOTELS AB; *Int'l*, pg. 2684
FIRST HOUSING DEVELOPMENT CORPORATION OF FLORIDA; *U.S. Private*, pg. 1520
FIRST HYDRO FINANCE PLC—See ENGIE SA; *Int'l*, pg. 2432
FIRST HYDROGEN CORP.; *Int'l*, pg. 2684
FIRST HYDRO HOLDINGS COMPANY—See ENGIE SA; *Int'l*, pg. 2429
FIRST IC BANK; *U.S. Public*, pg. 845
FIRST IDAHO RESOURCES INC.; *Int'l*, pg. 2684
FIRST ILLINOIS BANCORP, INC.; *U.S. Private*, pg. 1520
FIRST ILLINOIS BANK—See First Illinois Bancorp, Inc.; *U.S. Private*, pg. 1520
FIRST IMAGE MARKETING, INC.—See PetMed Express, Inc.; *U.S. Public*, pg. 1678
FIRSTIME DESIGN LIMITED; *U.S. Public*, pg. 849
FIRST IMPRESSION INTERACTIVE, LLC; *U.S. Private*, pg. 1520
FIRST INDEPENDENCE BANK—See First Independence Corporation; *U.S. Private*, pg. 1520
FIRST INDEPENDENCE CORPORATION; *U.S. Private*, pg. 1520
FIRST INDEPENDENT BANK—See Finlayson Bancshares, Inc.; *U.S. Private*, pg. 1510
FIRST INDEPENDENT BANK—See Western Alliance Bancorporation; *U.S. Public*, pg. 2354
FIRST INDUSTRIAL FINANCING PARTNERSHIP, L.P.—See First Industrial Realty Trust, Inc.; *U.S. Public*, pg. 845
FIRST INDUSTRIAL L.P.—See First Industrial Realty Trust, Inc.; *U.S. Public*, pg. 845
FIRST INDUSTRIAL REALTY TRUST, INC.; *U.S. Public*, pg. 845
FIRST INDUSTRIAL SCIENCE & TECHNOLOGY SCHOOL INC.—See Lopez, Inc.; *Int'l*, pg. 4557
FIRST INDUSTRIES CORPORATION—See Velocity Vehicle Group; *U.S. Private*, pg. 4354
FIRST INFRASTRUCTURE CAPITAL ADVISORS, LLC—See Quanta Services, Inc.; *U.S. Public*, pg. 1751
THE FIRST INSURANCE CO., LTD.; *Int'l*, pg. 7643
FIRST INSURANCE COMPANY OF HAWAII, LTD.—See Tokio Marine Holdings, Inc.; *Int'l*, pg. 7782
FIRST INSURANCE CO.; *Int'l*, pg. 2684
FIRST INSURANCE FUNDING CORP.—See Wintrust Financial Corporation; *U.S. Public*, pg. 2375
FIRST INSURANCE FUNDING OF CANADA, INC.—See Wintrust Financial Corporation; *U.S. Public*, pg. 2375
FIRST INSURANCE GROUP OF THE MIDWEST, INC.—See Kelso & Company, L.P.; *U.S. Private*, pg. 2279
FIRST INSURANCE NETWORK INC.—See Align Financial Group, LLC; *U.S. Private*, pg. 168
FIRST INSURANCE NETWORK INC.—See Excellere Capital Management LLC; *U.S. Private*, pg. 1446
FIRST INSURANCE PARTNERS LLC; *U.S. Private*, pg. 1520
FIRST INTERNATIONAL BANK OF ISRAEL LTD.—See FIBI Holdings Ltd.; *Int'l*, pg. 2652
FIRST INTERNATIONAL COMPANY, INC.—See VIA Technologies, Inc.; *Int'l*, pg. 8183
FIRST INTERNATIONAL COMPUTER, INC.; *Int'l*, pg. 2684
FIRST INTERNATIONAL COMPUTER, INC—See FIC Global, INC; *Int'l*, pg. 2653
THE FIRST INTERNATIONAL & CO.-UNDERWRITING AND INVESTMENT LTD.—See FIBI Holdings Ltd.; *Int'l*, pg. 2652
FIRST INTERNET BANCORP; *U.S. Public*, pg. 845
FIRST INTERNET BANK OF INDIANA—See First Internet Bancorp; *U.S. Public*, pg. 845
FIRST INTERSTATE BANCSYSTEM, INC.; *U.S. Public*, pg. 845
FIRST INTERSTATE BANK—See First Interstate BancSystem, Inc.; *U.S. Public*, pg. 845
FIRST INVESTEC MODARABA; *Int'l*, pg. 2684
FIRST INVESTMENT BANK AD; *Int'l*, pg. 2684
FIRST INVESTMENT BANK ALBANIA SH.A—See First Investment Bank AD; *Int'l*, pg. 2685
FIRST INVESTMENT COMPANY K.S.C.C.; *Int'l*, pg. 2685
FIRST INVESTORS FINANCIAL SERVICES GROUP, INC.—See Gallatin Point Capital LLC; *U.S. Private*, pg. 1639
FIRSTINVISION GESMBH; *Int'l*, pg. 2689
FIRST IPSWICH BANK—See Brookline Bancorp, Inc.; *U.S. Public*, pg. 396
FIRST ISRAEL MEZZANINE INVESTORS LTD.; *Int'l*, pg. 2685
FIRST ISRAEL TURNAROUND ENTERPRISE; *Int'l*, pg. 2685
FIRST JAPAN TIRE SERVICES COMPANY LIMITED—See Bridgestone Corporation; *Int'l*, pg. 1160
FIRST JERSEY TITLE SERVICES, INC.—See Columbia Financial, Inc.; *U.S. Public*, pg. 534

COMPANY NAME INDEX

FIRST JORDAN INVESTMENT COMPANY PLC; *Int'l*, pg. 2685
FIRST JUKEN CO., LTD.; *Int'l*, pg. 2685
FIRST KANSAS BANCSHARES, INC.; *U.S. Private*, pg. 1520
FIRST KENTUCKY BANK, INC.; *U.S. Private*, pg. 1520
FIRST KEYES BANCSHARES, INC.; *U.S. Private*, pg. 1520
FIRST KEYSTONE COMMUNITY BANK—See FIRST KEYSTONE CORPORATION; *U.S. Public*, pg. 845
FIRST KEYSTONE CORPORATION; *U.S. Public*, pg. 845
FIRST KITCHEN LTD—See The Wendy's Company; *U.S. Public*, pg. 2141
FIRST-KNOX NATIONAL BANK—See Park National Corporation; *U.S. Public*, pg. 1638
FIRST KONTACT LLC—See Advantage Communications, Inc.; *Int'l*, pg. 164
FIRST LEADS, LLC—See RE/MAX Holdings, Inc.; *U.S. Public*, pg. 1768
FIRST LENDERS MORTGAGE CORP.; *U.S. Private*, pg. 1520
FIRST LEVEL ENTERTAINMENT GROUP, INC.; *U.S. Private*, pg. 1520
FIRST LEVEL TECHNOLOGY LLC—See NCR Voyix Corporation; *U.S. Public*, pg. 1502
FIRST LEXINGTON CORP.; *U.S. Private*, pg. 1520
FIRST LIBERTY CAPITAL CORPORATION; *U.S. Private*, pg. 1520
FIRST LIFE ASSURANCE COMPANY LTD.—See Achmea B.V.; *Int'l*, pg. 103
FIRST LIFE INSURANCE CO., LTD.—See First Financial Holding Co., Ltd.; *Int'l*, pg. 2683
FIRST LIGHT ADMINISTRATION SERVICES (PTY) LTD.—See Grant Thornton South Africa (Pty) Ltd.; *Int'l*, pg. 3059
FIRST LIGHT BANCORP—See Indiana Members Credit Union; *U.S. Private*, pg. 2062
FIRSTLIGHT FIBER, INC.—See Antin Infrastructure Partners SAS; *Int'l*, pg. 483
FIRSTLIGHT HYDRO GENERATING COMPANY—See Public Sector Pension Investment Board; *Int'l*, pg. 6096
FIRSTLIGHT MEDIA LTD—See Highview Capital, LLC; *U.S. Private*, pg. 1942
FIRSTLIGHT POWER RESOURCES, INC.—See Public Sector Pension Investment Board; *Int'l*, pg. 6006
FIRST LINDEN BANCSHARES, INC.; *U.S. Private*, pg. 1520
FIRST LINE INSURANCE SERVICES, INC.—See Virtus LLC; *U.S. Private*, pg. 4389
FIRSTLINE NATIONAL INSURANCE COMPANY—See The Harford Mutual Insurance Company Inc.; *U.S. Private*, pg. 4043
FIRSTLINE SECURITY SYSTEMS, INC.—See Ares Management Corporation; *U.S. Public*, pg. 189
FIRST LINE TECHNOLOGY, LLC; *U.S. Private*, pg. 1520
FIRSTLINE TRANSPORTATION SECURITY, INC.—See SMS Holdings Corporation; *U.S. Private*, pg. 3699
FIRSTLINK INVESTMENTS CORPORATION LIMITED; *Int'l*, pg. 2689
FIRST LITHIUM MINERALS CORP.; *Int'l*, pg. 2685
FIRST LIVING ASSISTANCE CO., LTD.—See Nomura Real Estate Holdings, Inc; *Int'l*, pg. 5412
FIRSTLOGIC INC.; *Int'l*, pg. 2689
FIRST LOOK HOLDINGS, LLC—See Nu Image, Inc.; *U.S. Private*, pg. 2971
FIRST LOOK STUDIOS, INC.—See Nu Image, Inc.; *U.S. Private*, pg. 2971
FIRSTMAC HOLDINGS LTD.; *Int'l*, pg. 2689
FIRST MADISON BANK & TRUST—See United Community Banks, Inc.; *U.S. Public*, pg. 2230
FIRST MAJESTIC SILVER CORP.; *Int'l*, pg. 2685
FIRST MANCHESTER LIMITED—See FirstGroup plc; *Int'l*, pg. 2689
FIRST MANHATTAN CONSULTING GROUP, LLC—See Deluxe Corporation; *U.S. Public*, pg. 653
FIRST MANHATTAN CO.; *U.S. Private*, pg. 1521
FIRST MANISTIQUE AGENCY, INC.—See Mackinac Financial Corporation; *U.S. Private*, pg. 1352
FIRST MANUFACTURING COMPANY; *U.S. Private*, pg. 1521
FIRSTMARK AEROSPACE CORPORATION—See Hicks Holdings, LLC; *U.S. Private*, pg. 1934
FIRSTMARK AEROSPACE CORPORATION—See The Riverside Company; *U.S. Private*, pg. 4108
FIRSTMARK AEROSPACE CORPORATION—See Weinberg Capital Group, Inc.; *U.S. Private*, pg. 4471
FIRSTMARK CORP.—See Hicks Holdings, LLC; *U.S. Private*, pg. 1934
FIRSTMARK CORP.—See The Riverside Company; *U.S. Private*, pg. 4108
FIRSTMARK CORP.—See Weinberg Capital Group, Inc.; *U.S. Private*, pg. 4471
FIRSTMARK CREDIT UNION; *U.S. Private*, pg. 1532
FIRST MARKET RESEARCH CORP.; *U.S. Private*, pg. 1521
FIRSTMARK HORIZON ACQUISITION CORP.; *U.S. Public*, pg. 849
FIRST MEDIA GROUP INC.; *U.S. Private*, pg. 1521
FIRST MEDIA SERVICES, LLC; *U.S. Private*, pg. 1521

THE FIRST MERCANTILE TRUST COMPANY—See Mid Atlantic Capital Group, Inc.; *U.S. Private*, pg. 2705
FIRST MERCHANTS BANK—See First Merchants Corporation; *U.S. Public*, pg. 845
FIRST MERCHANTS CORPORATION; *U.S. Public*, pg. 845
FIRST MERCURY FINANCIAL CORPORATION—See Fairfax Financial Holdings Limited; *Int'l*, pg. 2606
FIRST MERCURY INSURANCE COMPANY—See Fairfax Financial Holdings Limited; *Int'l*, pg. 2606
FIRSTMERIT EQUIPMENT FINANCE, INC.—See Huntington Bancshares Incorporated; *U.S. Public*, pg. 1071
FIRSTMERIT MORTGAGE CORPORATION—See Huntington Bancshares Incorporated; *U.S. Public*, pg. 1071
FIRST METRO ASSET MANAGEMENT, INC.—See First Metro Investment Corporation; *Int'l*, pg. 2685
FIRST METRO INVESTMENT CORPORATION; *Int'l*, pg. 2685
FIRST METRO SECURITIES BROKERAGE CORPORATION—See Metropolitan Bank & Trust Company; *Int'l*, pg. 4864
FIRST MIAMI BANCORP, INC.—See United Community Banks, Inc.; *U.S. Public*, pg. 2230
FIRST MIAMI BANCSHARES, INC.; *U.S. Private*, pg. 1521
FIRST MICROFINANCE LAGHUBITTA BITTIYA SANSTHA LTD.; *Int'l*, pg. 2685
FIRST MID BANCSHARES, INC.; *U.S. Public*, pg. 845
FIRST MID BANK & TRUST, N.A.—See First Mid Bancshares, Inc.; *U.S. Public*, pg. 846
FIRST MID INSURANCE GROUP, INC.—See First Mid Bancshares, Inc.; *U.S. Public*, pg. 846
FIRST MIDLAND RED BUSES LIMITED—See FirstGroup plc; *Int'l*, pg. 2689
FIRST MIDWEST ACQUISITION CORP.; *U.S. Private*, pg. 1521
FIRST MIDWEST BANCORP, INC.—See Old National Bancorp; *U.S. Public*, pg. 1566
FIRST MIDWEST BANK OF POPLAR BLUFF; *U.S. Private*, pg. 1521
FIRST MIDWEST BANK—See Old National Bancorp; *U.S. Public*, pg. 1567
FIRST MIDWEST EQUIPMENT FINANCE CO.—See Old National Bancorp; *U.S. Public*, pg. 1567
FIRST MIDWEST TRUST CO.—See Old National Bancorp; *U.S. Public*, pg. 1567
FIRST MINING GOLD CORP.; *Int'l*, pg. 2685
FIRST MINNESOTA BANK—See McLeod Bancshares, Inc.; *U.S. Private*, pg. 2641
FIRST MODE IPP LIMITED—See Anglo American PLC; *Int'l*, pg. 462
FIRST MUTUAL HOLDINGS LIMITED; *Int'l*, pg. 2685
FIRST MUTUAL OF RICHMOND, INC.; *U.S. Private*, pg. 1521
FIRST MUTUAL PROPERTIES LIMITED; *Int'l*, pg. 2686
FIRST NAMES CORPORATE SERVICES LIMITED—See AnaCap Financial Partners LLP; *Int'l*, pg. 445
FIRST NAMES (CYPRUS) LIMITED—See AnaCap Financial Partners LLP; *Int'l*, pg. 445
FIRST NAMES (ISLE OF MAN) LIMITED—See AnaCap Financial Partners LLP; *Int'l*, pg. 445
FIRST NAMES (JERSEY) LIMITED—See AnaCap Financial Partners LLP; *Int'l*, pg. 445
THE FIRST, N.A.—See The First Bancorp, Inc.; *U.S. Public*, pg. 2073
FIRST NATIONAL ALARMCAP LP/PREMIERE SOCIETE EN COMMANDITE NATIONALE ALARMCAP—See Stanley Black & Decker, Inc.; *U.S. Public*, pg. 1932
FIRST NATIONAL ASSET MANAGEMENT INC.—See First National Financial Corporation; *Int'l*, pg. 2686
FIRST NATIONAL BANCORP, INC.; *U.S. Private*, pg. 1521
FIRST NATIONAL BANK ALASKA; *U.S. Public*, pg. 846
FIRST NATIONAL BANK, ALBANY/BRECKENRIDGE; *U.S. Private*, pg. 1523
FIRST NATIONAL BANK, AMES, IOWA—See Ames National Corporation; *U.S. Public*, pg. 115
FIRST NATIONAL BANK & CO.; *U.S. Private*, pg. 1522
FIRST NATIONAL BANKERS BANKSHARES, INC.; *U.S. Private*, pg. 1523
FIRST NATIONAL BANKER'S BANK—See First National Bankers Bankshares, Inc.; *U.S. Private*, pg. 1523
FIRST NATIONAL BANK FREMONT—See First National of Nebraska, Inc.; *U.S. Private*, pg. 1523
FIRST NATIONAL BANK IN ALAMOGORDO; *U.S. Private*, pg. 1522
THE FIRST NATIONAL BANK IN CRESTON—See Northwest Financial Corp.; *U.S. Private*, pg. 2960
FIRST NATIONAL BANK IN FAIRFIELD—See MidWestOne Financial Group, Inc.; *U.S. Public*, pg. 1446
FIRST NATIONAL BANK IN HOWELL—See FNBH Bancorp, Inc.; *U.S. Private*, pg. 1555
FIRST NATIONAL BANK IN NEW BREMEN; *U.S. Private*, pg. 1522
FIRST NATIONAL BANK IN OKEENE—See Grace Investment Company, Inc.; *U.S. Private*, pg. 1749
FIRST NATIONAL BANK IN OLNEY; *U.S. Private*, pg. 1522

FIRST NATIONAL BANK IN STAUNTON; *U.S. Private*, pg. 1522
THE FIRST NATIONAL BANK IN TREMONT; *U.S. Private*, pg. 4029
FIRST NATIONAL BANK MUSCATINE—See MidWestOne Financial Group, Inc.; *U.S. Public*, pg. 1446
FIRST NATIONAL BANK OF ABSECON—See Absecon Bancorp; *U.S. Public*, pg. 27
FIRST NATIONAL BANK OF ALTAVISTA—See Pinnacle Bankshares Corp.; *U.S. Public*, pg. 1691
FIRST NATIONAL BANK OF AMERICA INC.; *U.S. Private*, pg. 1522
FIRST NATIONAL BANK OF ARENZVILLE; *U.S. Private*, pg. 1522
FIRST NATIONAL BANK OF BASTROP; *U.S. Private*, pg. 1522
THE FIRST NATIONAL BANK OF BELLS/SAVOY—See First Bells Bankshares, Inc.; *U.S. Private*, pg. 1514
FIRST NATIONAL BANK OF BEMIDJI; *U.S. Private*, pg. 1522
FIRST NATIONAL BANK OF BOTSWANA—See FirstRand Limited; *Int'l*, pg. 2690
THE FIRST NATIONAL BANK OF CENTRAL TEXAS; *U.S. Private*, pg. 4029
FIRST NATIONAL BANK OF DECATUR COUNTY—See Bainbridge Bancshares, Inc.; *U.S. Private*, pg. 453
FIRST NATIONAL BANK OF DRYDEN; *U.S. Private*, pg. 1522
FIRST NATIONAL BANK OF ELMER—See Elmer Bancorp, Inc.; *U.S. Public*, pg. 735
THE FIRST NATIONAL BANK OF EMORY—See Emory Bancshares, Inc.; *U.S. Private*, pg. 1383
THE FIRST NATIONAL BANK OF FORT SMITH—See First Bank Corp.; *U.S. Private*, pg. 1514
FIRST NATIONAL BANK OF GILMER—See First Gilmer Bankshares, Inc.; *U.S. Private*, pg. 1519
FIRST NATIONAL BANK OF GRANBURY; *U.S. Private*, pg. 1522
FIRST NATIONAL BANK OF GROTON; *U.S. Public*, pg. 846
FIRST NATIONAL BANK OF HOLCOMB—See American State Bancshares, Inc.; *U.S. Private*, pg. 255
THE FIRST NATIONAL BANK OF HOOKER—See Hooker National Bancshares, Inc.; *U.S. Public*, pg. 1978
THE FIRST NATIONAL BANK OF HUGO—See First Liberty Capital Corporation; *U.S. Private*, pg. 1520
FIRST NATIONAL BANK OF HUNTSVILLE; *U.S. Private*, pg. 1522
THE FIRST NATIONAL BANK OF HUTCHINSON—See First Kansas Bancshares, Inc.; *U.S. Private*, pg. 1520
FIRST NATIONAL BANK OF ILLINOIS—See Wintrust Financial Corporation; *U.S. Public*, pg. 2375
FIRST NATIONAL BANK OF JASPER—See East Texas Bancshares, Inc.; *U.S. Private*, pg. 1318
THE FIRST NATIONAL BANK OF KEMP—See FNBK Holdings, Inc.; *U.S. Private*, pg. 1555
FIRST NATIONAL BANK OF LAYTON—See Glacier Bancorp, Inc.; *U.S. Public*, pg. 938
THE FIRST NATIONAL BANK OF LONG ISLAND—See The First of Long Island Corporation; *U.S. Public*, pg. 2074
FIRST NATIONAL BANK OF LOUISIANA—See Financial Corporation of Louisiana; *U.S. Private*, pg. 1506
FIRST NATIONAL BANK OF MIFFLINTOWN—See First Community Financial Corporation; *U.S. Public*, pg. 843
FIRST NATIONAL BANK OF MONTEREY; *U.S. Private*, pg. 1522
FIRST NATIONAL BANK OF OMAHA—See First National of Nebraska, Inc.; *U.S. Private*, pg. 1523
FIRST NATIONAL BANK OF ONEIDA; *U.S. Private*, pg. 1522
FIRST NATIONAL BANK OF OXFORD; *U.S. Private*, pg. 1522
FIRST NATIONAL BANK OF PALMERTON; *U.S. Private*, pg. 1523
FIRST NATIONAL BANK OF PASCO—See Florida Bancshares, Inc.; *U.S. Private*, pg. 1547
FIRST NATIONAL BANK OF PENNSYLVANIA—See F.N.B. Corporation; *U.S. Public*, pg. 818
FIRST NATIONAL BANK OF PONTOTOC; *U.S. Private*, pg. 1523
FIRST NATIONAL BANK OF PULASKI—See First Pulaski National Corporation; *U.S. Private*, pg. 1524
FIRST NATIONAL BANK OF RIVER FALLS; *U.S. Private*, pg. 1523
FIRST NATIONAL BANK OF ROGERS—See First Bank Corp.; *U.S. Private*, pg. 1514
FIRST NATIONAL BANK OF SCOTIA; *U.S. Private*, pg. 1523
FIRST NATIONAL BANK OF SHARP COUNTY; *U.S. Private*, pg. 1523
THE FIRST NATIONAL BANK OF SONORA—See First Sonora; *U.S. Private*, pg. 1528
THE FIRST NATIONAL BANK OF SOUTH MIAMI—See United Community Banks, Inc.; *U.S. Public*, pg. 2230
THE FIRST NATIONAL BANK OF TAHOKA—See Tahoka First Bancorp Inc.; *U.S. Private*, pg. 3923
FIRST NATIONAL BANK OF THE GULF COAST—See TGR Financial Inc.; *U.S. Private*, pg. 3979

FIRST NATIONAL BANK OF SHARP COUNTY   CORPORATE AFFILIATIONS

THE FIRST NATIONAL BANK OF TRENTON—See Captex Bancshares, Inc.; *U.S. Private*, pg. 746
THE FIRST NATIONAL BANK OF WYNNE—See First National Corporation of Wynne; *U.S. Private*, pg. 1523
FIRST NATIONAL BANK OF ZAMBIA LIMITED—See FirstRand Limited; *Int'l*, pg. 2690
FIRST NATIONAL BANK; *U.S. Private*, pg. 1521
FIRST NATIONAL BANK; *U.S. Private*, pg. 1522
FIRST NATIONAL BANK; *U.S. Private*, pg. 1522
FIRST NATIONAL BANK; *U.S. Private*, pg. 1522
FIRST NATIONAL BANK—See First Bancshares, Inc.; *U.S. Public*, pg. 839
FIRST NATIONAL BANK—See First Groesbeck Holding Company; *U.S. Private*, pg. 1519
FIRST NATIONAL BANK—See First Paragould Bankshares, Inc.; *U.S. Private*, pg. 1524
FIRST NATIONAL BANK—See FirstRand Limited; *Int'l*, pg. 2690
THE FIRST NATIONAL BANK—See MGB Bancshares, Inc.; *U.S. Private*, pg. 2694
FIRST NATIONAL BANK—See Sooner Southwest Bankshares, Inc.; *U.S. Private*, pg. 3715
FIRST NATIONAL BANK—See Spearman Bancshares, Inc.; *U.S. Private*, pg. 3748
FIRST NATIONAL BANK SOUTH DAKOTA—See First National of Nebraska, Inc.; *U.S. Private*, pg. 1523
FIRST NATIONAL BANK TEXAS—See First Community Bancshares, Inc.; *U.S. Private*, pg. 1516
FIRST NATIONAL BANK & TRUST COMPANY OF ARDMORE—See First National Corporation of Ardmore, Inc.; *U.S. Private*, pg. 1523
THE FIRST NATIONAL BANK & TRUST COMPANY OF BROKEN ARROW—See First Broken Arrow Corporation; *U.S. Private*, pg. 1514
THE FIRST NATIONAL BANK & TRUST COMPANY OF IRON MOUNTAIN—See FNB Bancshares Inc.; *U.S. Private*, pg. 1555
FIRST NATIONAL BANK & TRUST COMPANY OF MCALESTER—See First National Bank & Co.; *U.S. Private*, pg. 1522
THE FIRST NATIONAL BANK & TRUST COMPANY OF MIAMI—See First Miami Bancshares, Inc.; *U.S. Private*, pg. 1521
THE FIRST NATIONAL BANK & TRUST COMPANY OF OKMULGEE—See First Okmulgee Corporation; *U.S. Private*, pg. 1524
THE FIRST NATIONAL BANK & TRUST COMPANY—See Centre 1 Bancorp, Inc.; *U.S. Private*, pg. 827
FIRST NATIONAL BANK & TRUST CO OF NEWTOWN—See FNB Bancorp, Inc.; *U.S. Private*, pg. 1555
FIRST NATIONAL BANK & TRUST CO.; *U.S. Private*, pg. 1522
FIRST NATIONAL BANK WATERLOO—See First Waterloo Bancshares, Inc.; *U.S. Private*, pg. 1530
FIRST NATIONAL BATTERY COMPANY (PTY) LTD.—See Metair Investments Limited; *Int'l*, pg. 4844
FIRST NATIONAL BATTERY INDUSTRIAL (PTY) LTD.—See Metair Investments Limited; *Int'l*, pg. 4844
FIRST NATIONAL CORPORATION OF ARDMORE, INC.; *U.S. Private*, pg. 1523
FIRST NATIONAL CORPORATION OF WYNNE; *U.S. Private*, pg. 1523
FIRST NATIONAL CORPORATION; *U.S. Public*, pg. 846
FIRST NATIONAL ENERGY CORPORATION; *Int'l*, pg. 2686
FIRST NATIONAL EQUITIES LIMITED; *Int'l*, pg. 2686
FIRST NATIONAL FINANCIAL CORPORATION; *Int'l*, pg. 2686
FIRST NATIONAL FINANCIAL SERVICES, INC.; *U.S. Private*, pg. 1523
FIRST NATIONAL HOUSING TRUST LIMITED—See Henry Boot PLC; *Int'l*, pg. 3355
FIRST NATIONAL INSURANCE AGENCY, LLC—See F.N.B. Corporation; *U.S. Public*, pg. 818
FIRST NATIONAL INVESTMENT BANKING—See First National of Nebraska, Inc.; *U.S. Private*, pg. 1524
FIRST NATIONAL LIFE INSURANCE COMPANY OF THE USA, INC.—See Nelnet, Inc.; *U.S. Public*, pg. 1504
FIRST NATIONAL MORTGAGE INVESTMENT FUND; *Int'l*, pg. 2686
FIRST NATIONAL OF NEBRASKA, INC.; *U.S. Private*, pg. 1523
FIRST NATIONAL TRADING CO. INC.; *U.S. Private*, pg. 1524
FIRST NATIONAL TRUST COMPANY—See F.N.B. Corporation; *U.S. Public*, pg. 818
FIRST NATIONAL TRUSTEE COMPANY LIMITED—See Epiris Managers LLP; *Int'l*, pg. 2461
FIRST NATION GROUP LLC; *U.S. Private*, pg. 1521
FIRST NATIONS BANK OF CANADA; *Int'l*, pg. 2686
FIRST NATIONWIDE TITLE AGENCY LLC—See Stone Point Capital LLC; *U.S. Private*, pg. 3821
FIRST NATIONWIDE TITLE AGENCY OF TEXAS, LLC—See Stone Point Capital LLC; *U.S. Private*, pg. 3821
FIRST NEBRASKA BANK; *U.S. Private*, pg. 1524
FIRST NEODESHA BANK—See Southeast Bancshares, Inc.; *U.S. Private*, pg. 3725

FIRST NEW YORK SECURITIES LLC; *U.S. Private*, pg. 1524
FIRST NILES FINANCIAL, INC.; *U.S. Public*, pg. 846
FIRST NONPROFIT COMPANIES, INC.—See Stone Point Capital LLC; *U.S. Private*, pg. 3821
FIRST NONPROFIT INSURANCE COMPANY—See Stone Point Capital LLC; *U.S. Private*, pg. 3821
FIRST NORTHERN BANK OF DIXON—See First Northern Community Bancorp; *U.S. Public*, pg. 846
FIRST NORTHERN COMMUNITY BANCORP; *U.S. Public*, pg. 846
FIRST NORTHERN CREDIT UNION; *U.S. Private*, pg. 1524
FIRST NORTHWEST BANCORP; *U.S. Public*, pg. 846
FIRST NZ CAPITAL LIMITED; *Int'l*, pg. 2686
FIRSTOBJECT TECHNOLOGIES LTD.; *Int'l*, pg. 2689
FIRST OCEANIC PROPERTY MANAGEMENT, INC—See Alliance Global Group, Inc.; *Int'l*, pg. 339
THE FIRST OF LONG ISLAND CORPORATION; *U.S. Public*, pg. 2074
THE FIRST OF LONG ISLAND REIT, INC.—See The First of Long Island Corporation; *U.S. Public*, pg. 2074
FIRST OHIO HOME FINANCE, INC; *U.S. Private*, pg. 1524
FIRST OHIO TITLE INSURANCE AGENCY, LTD.—See Stewart Information Services Corporation; *U.S. Public*, pg. 1947
FIRST OKMULGEE CORPORATION; *U.S. Private*, pg. 1524
FIRST OLSEN AS—See Fred. Olsen & Co.; *Int'l*, pg. 2768
FIRST OMNI SDN. BHD.—See TT International Limited; *Int'l*, pg. 7960
FIRSTONSITE RESTORATION LTD.—See FirstService Corporation; *Int'l*, pg. 2691
FIRST OPTION BANK—See The Osawatomie Agency Inc.; *U.S. Private*, pg. 4089
FIRST ORIENTAL CYCLOTRON LIMITED—See Town Health International Medical Group Limited; *Int'l*, pg. 7851
FIRST PACIFIC ADVISORS, LLC; *U.S. Private*, pg. 1524
FIRST PACIFIC COMPANY LIMITED; *Int'l*, pg. 2686
FIRST PACIFIC LEADERSHIP ACADEMY—See Manila Electric Company; *Int'l*, pg. 4671
FIRST PALMETTO FINANCIAL CORP.; *U.S. Private*, pg. 1524
FIRST PARAGOULD BANKSHARES, INC.; *U.S. Private*, pg. 1524
FIRST PARAMOUNT MODARABA; *Int'l*, pg. 2686
FIRST PARK (PTY) LTD.—See Excellerate Holdings Ltd.; *Int'l*, pg. 2578
FIRST PENINSULA CREDIT SDN BHD—See Chin Hin Group Berhad; *Int'l*, pg. 1480
FIRST PENN-PACIFIC LIFE INSURANCE COMPANY—See Lincoln National Corporation; *U.S. Public*, pg. 1319
FIRST PENSION CUSTODIAN LTD.—See FBN Holdings PLC; *Int'l*, pg. 2627
FIRST PEOPLES BANKSHARES, INC.; *U.S. Private*, pg. 1524
FIRST PEOPLES BANK—See First Peoples Bankshares, Inc.; *U.S. Private*, pg. 1524
FIRST & PEOPLES BANK & TRUST CO.; *U.S. Private*, pg. 1512
FIRSTPERRYTON BANCORP, INC.; *U.S. Private*, pg. 1532
FIRST PERSON, INC.—See Aon plc; *Int'l*, pg. 496
FIRST PERSON LTD.; *Int'l*, pg. 2686
FIRST PET LIFE, INC.; *U.S. Public*, pg. 846
FIRST PHILIPPINE ELECTRIC CORPORATION—See Lopez, Inc.; *Int'l*, pg. 4557
FIRST PHILIPPINE HOLDINGS CORPORATION—See Lopez, Inc.; *Int'l*, pg. 4556
FIRST PHILIPPINE INDUSTRIAL PARK, INC.—See Lopez, Inc.; *Int'l*, pg. 4557
FIRST PIEDMONT FEDERAL SAVINGS & LOAN ASSOCIATION OF GAFFNEY; *U.S. Private*, pg. 1524
FIRST PIONEER BANK CORP.; *U.S. Private*, pg. 1524
FIRST PIONEER NATIONAL BANK—See First Pioneer Bank Corp.; *U.S. Private*, pg. 1524
FIRST PLACE FOODS, LLC.—See Swander Pace Capital, LLC; *U.S. Private*, pg. 3890
FIRST PLAZA INC.—See CV Industries Inc.; *U.S. Private*, pg. 1132
FIRSTPLUS FINANCIAL GROUP PLC—See Barclays PLC; *Int'l*, pg. 860
FIRST PLUS, INC.—See Iida Group Holdings Co., Ltd.; *Int'l*, pg. 3607
FIRSTPORT LIMITED—See Equistone Partners Europe Limited; *Int'l*, pg. 2486
FIRST POTTERIES LIMITED—See FirstGroup plc; *Int'l*, pg. 2689
FIRST PREMIER BANK—See United National Corporation; *U.S. Private*, pg. 4295
FIRSTPRO, INC.—See Staffing 360 Solutions, Inc.; *U.S. Public*, pg. 1925
FIRST PROPERTY AND CASUALTY INSURANCE AGENCY CO., LTD.—See First Financial Holding Co., Ltd.; *Int'l*, pg. 2683

FIRST PROPERTY ASSET MANAGEMENT LTD.—See First Property Group Plc; *Int'l*, pg. 2686
FIRST PROPERTY ASSET MANAGEMENT ROMANIA SRL—See First Property Group Plc; *Int'l*, pg. 2686
FIRST PROPERTY GROUP PLC; *Int'l*, pg. 2686
FIRST PROPERTY POLAND SP. Z O.O.—See First Property Group Plc; *Int'l*, pg. 2686
FIRST PRUDENTIAL MODARABA; *Int'l*, pg. 2686
FIRST PULASKI NATIONAL CORPORATION; *U.S. Private*, pg. 1524
FIRST PUNJAB MODARABA; *Int'l*, pg. 2686
FIRST QUADRANT, L.P.—See Affiliated Managers Group, Inc.; *U.S. Public*, pg. 54
FIRST QUALITY ENTERPRISES, INC.; *U.S. Private*, pg. 1524
FIRST QUALITY FIBERS, LLC—See First Quality Enterprises, Inc.; *U.S. Private*, pg. 1524
FIRST QUALITY PRODUCTS, INC.—See First Quality Enterprises, Inc.; *U.S. Private*, pg. 1524
FIRST QUANTUM MINERALS (AUSTRALIA) PTY LIMITED—See First Quantum Minerals Ltd.; *Int'l*, pg. 2687
FIRST QUANTUM MINERALS LTD.; *Int'l*, pg. 2687
FIRST QUANTUM (UK) LTD.—See First Quantum Minerals Ltd.; *Int'l*, pg. 2687
FIRSTRADE SECURITIES, INC.; *U.S. Private*, pg. 1532
FIRSTRAIN, INC.—See ESW Capital, LLC; *U.S. Private*, pg. 1430
FIRSTRAND BANK HOLDINGS LIMITED—See FirstRand Limited; *Int'l*, pg. 2690
FIRSTRAND BANK LIMITED - INDIA—See FirstRand Limited; *Int'l*, pg. 2690
FIRSTRAND BANK LIMITED—See FirstRand Limited; *Int'l*, pg. 2690
FIRSTRAND EMA HOLDINGS LIMITED—See FirstRand Limited; *Int'l*, pg. 2690
FIRSTRAND FINANCE COMPANY LIMITED—See FirstRand Limited; *Int'l*, pg. 2690
FIRSTRAND LIMITED; *Int'l*, pg. 2689
FIRSTRAND NAMIBIA LTD.—See FirstRand Limited; *Int'l*, pg. 2690
FIRST RATE ENTERPRISES LIMITED—See Bank of Ireland Group plc; *Int'l*, pg. 844
FIRST RATE EXCHANGE SERVICES LIMITED—See Bank of Ireland Group plc; *Int'l*, pg. 844
FIRST RATE, INC.; *U.S. Private*, pg. 1524
FIRST RATE STAFFING CORPORATION; *U.S. Private*, pg. 1524
FIRST REAL ESTATE INVESTMENT TRUST NEW JERSEY CO.; *U.S. Public*, pg. 847
FIRST REAL ESTATE INVESTMENT TRUST; *Int'l*, pg. 2687
FIRST REALTY/GMAC REAL ESTATE—See Berkshire Hathaway Inc.; *U.S. Public*, pg. 306
FIRST RECOVERY GROUP, LLC—See New Mountain Capital, LLC; *U.S. Private*, pg. 2902
FIRST REGISTRARS NIGERIA LIMITED—See FBN Holdings PLC; *Int'l*, pg. 2627
FIRST REHABILITATION LIFE INSURANCE CO. OF AMERICA INC.—See ShelterPoint Group, Inc.; *U.S. Private*, pg. 3632
FIRST REISEBURO—See TUI AG; *Int'l*, pg. 7967
FIRST RELIANCE BANCSHARES, INC.; *U.S. Public*, pg. 847
FIRST RELIANCE BANK—See First Reliance BancShares, Inc.; *U.S. Public*, pg. 847
FIRST RELIANCE STANDARD LIFE INSURANCE COMPANY—See Tokio Marine Holdings, Inc.; *Int'l*, pg. 7782
FIRST RENT A CAR AB—See AB Volvo; *Int'l*, pg. 42
FIRST REPUBLIC BANK—See JPMorgan Chase & Co.; *U.S. Public*, pg. 1206
THE FIRST REPUBLIC BUILDING CORP.—See The First Republic Corporation of America; *U.S. Public*, pg. 2074
THE FIRST REPUBLIC CORPORATION OF AMERICA; *U.S. Public*, pg. 2074
FIRST REPUBLIC CORP., REAL ESTATE DIV.—See The First Republic Corporation of America; *U.S. Public*, pg. 2074
FIRST REPUBLIC INVESTMENT MANAGEMENT, INC.—See JPMorgan Chase & Co.; *U.S. Public*, pg. 1207
FIRST REPUBLIC PREFERRED CAPITAL CORPORATION—See JPMorgan Chase & Co.; *U.S. Public*, pg. 1207
FIRST REPUBLIC SECURITIES COMPANY, LLC—See JPMorgan Chase & Co.; *U.S. Public*, pg. 1207
FIRST REPUBLIC TRUST COMPANY—See JPMorgan Chase & Co.; *U.S. Public*, pg. 1207
FIRST REPUBLIC WEALTH ADVISORS, LLC—See JPMorgan Chase & Co.; *U.S. Public*, pg. 1207
FIRST RESEARCH, INC.—See Cannae Holdings, Inc.; *U.S. Public*, pg. 429
FIRST RESEARCH, INC.—See CC Capital Partners, LLC; *U.S. Private*, pg. 798
FIRST RESEARCH, INC.—See Intercontinental Exchange, Inc.; *U.S. Public*, pg. 1142
FIRST RESERVE INTERNATIONAL LIMITED—See First Reserve Management, L.P.; *U.S. Private*, pg. 1525

COMPANY NAME INDEX

FIRST RESERVE MANAGEMENT, L.P. - HOUSTON—See First Reserve Management, L.P.; *U.S. Private*, pg. 1525
FIRST RESERVE MANAGEMENT, L.P.; *U.S. Private*, pg. 1525
FIRST RESERVE SUSTAINABLE GROWTH CORP.; *U.S. Public*, pg. 847
FIRST RESIDENTIAL MORTGAGE SERVICES CORP.; *U.S. Private*, pg. 1527
FIRST RESOURCE BANK; *U.S. Private*, pg. 1527
FIRST RESOURCE BANK—See Ameri Financial Group, Inc.; *U.S. Private*, pg. 220
FIRST RESOURCES LIMITED; *Int'l*, pg. 2687
FIRST RESPONSE FINANCE LTD.—See ITOCHU Corporation; *Int'l*, pg. 3836
FIRST ROBINSON FINANCIAL CORPORATION; *U.S. Public*, pg. 847
FIRST ROBINSON SAVINGS BANK N.A.—See First Robinson Financial Corporation; *U.S. Public*, pg. 847
FIRST RUSHMORE BANCORPORATION, INC.; *U.S. Private*, pg. 1527
FIRSTRUST BANK; *U.S. Private*, pg. 1532
FIRSTRUST CORPORATION; *U.S. Private*, pg. 1532
FIRST SAVINGS BANK FSB—See First Savings Bank; *U.S. Private*, pg. 1527
FIRST SAVINGS BANK OF HEGEWISCH; *U.S. Private*, pg. 1527
FIRST SAVINGS BANK PERKASIE; *U.S. Private*, pg. 1527
FIRST SAVINGS BANK—See First Savings Financial Group, Inc.; *U.S. Public*, pg. 847
FIRST SAVINGS BANK; *U.S. Private*, pg. 1527
FIRST SAVINGS FINANCIAL GROUP, INC.; *U.S. Public*, pg. 847
FIRST SAVINGS INVESTMENTS, INC.—See First Savings Financial Group, Inc.; *U.S. Public*, pg. 847
FIRST SAVINGS MORTGAGE CORP.; *U.S. Private*, pg. 1527
FIRST SCOTLAND EAST LIMITED—See FirstGroup plc; *Int'l*, pg. 2689
FIRST SCOTRAIL LIMITED—See FirstGroup plc; *Int'l*, pg. 2689
FIRST SEACOAST BANCORP, INC.; *U.S. Public*, pg. 847
FIRST SEACOAST BANK—See First Seacoast Bancorp, Inc.; *U.S. Public*, pg. 847
FIRST SECURITIES BROKERAGE COMPANY K.S.C—See Kuwait Projects Company (Holding) K.S.C.P.; *Int'l*, pg. 4346
FIRST SECURITIES INC.—See First Financial Holding Co., Ltd.; *Int'l*, pg. 2683
FIRST SECURITIES INVESTMENT TRUST CO., LTD—See First Financial Holding Co., Ltd.; *Int'l*, pg. 2683
FIRST SECURITY BANCORP, INC.—See Wirtz Corporation; *U.S. Private*, pg. 4547
FIRST SECURITY BANCORP; *U.S. Private*, pg. 1527
FIRST SECURITY BANK - CANBY—See First Sleepy Eye Bancorporation, Inc.; *U.S. Private*, pg. 1527
FIRST SECURITY BANK OF HELENA—See Ascent Bancorp; *U.S. Private*, pg. 348
FIRST SECURITY BANK OF MISSOULA—See Glacier Bancorp, Inc.; *U.S. Public*, pg. 938
FIRST SECURITY BANKSHARES INC.; *U.S. Private*, pg. 1527
FIRST SECURITY BANK - SLEEPY EYE—See First Sleepy Eye Bancorporation, Inc.; *U.S. Private*, pg. 1527
FIRST SECURITY BANK—See First Security Bancorp; *U.S. Private*, pg. 1527
FIRST SECURITY BANK—See Glacier Bancorp, Inc.; *U.S. Public*, pg. 938
FIRST SECURITY CAPITAL I—See Wells Fargo & Company; *U.S. Public*, pg. 2343
FIRST SECURITY COMPANY, INC.—See ABRY Partners, LLC; *U.S. Private*, pg. 42
FIRST SECURITY (GUARDS) LTD.—See Interserve Plc; *Int'l*, pg. 3759
FIRST SECURITY ISLAMI BANK LIMITED; *Int'l*, pg. 2687
FIRST SECURITY ISLAMI CAPITAL & INVESTMENT LIMITED—See First Security Islami Bank Limited; *Int'l*, pg. 2687
FIRST SECURITY SERVICES—See First Alarm Security & Patrol, Inc.; *U.S. Private*, pg. 1512
FIRST SECURITY TRUST & SAVINGS BANK—See Wirtz Corporation; *U.S. Private*, pg. 4547
FIRST SEED FARMS INC.; *U.S. Private*, pg. 1527
FIRST SENSOR AG—See TE Connectivity Ltd.; *Int'l*, pg. 7496
FIRST SENSOR CORP.—See TE Connectivity Ltd.; *Int'l*, pg. 7496
FIRST SENSOR FRANCE S.A.S.—See TE Connectivity Ltd.; *Int'l*, pg. 7496
FIRST SENSOR INC.—See TE Connectivity Ltd.; *Int'l*, pg. 7496
FIRST SENSOR LEWICKI GMBH—See TE Connectivity Ltd.; *Int'l*, pg. 7496
FIRST SENSOR MICROELECTRONIC PACKAGING GMBH—See TE Connectivity Ltd.; *Int'l*, pg. 7496
FIRST SENSOR MOBILITY GMBH—See TE Connectivity Ltd.; *Int'l*, pg. 7496

FIRST SENSOR TECHNICS LTD.—See TE Connectivity Ltd.; *Int'l*, pg. 7496
FIRST SENTIER INVESTORS (AUSTRALIA) IM LTD.—See Mitsubishi UFJ Financial Group, Inc.; *Int'l*, pg. 4971
FIRST SENTIER INVESTORS (HONG KONG) LIMITED—See KKR & Co. Inc.; *U.S. Public*, pg. 1243
FIRST SENTIER INVESTORS (SINGAPORE)—See KKR & Co. Inc.; *U.S. Public*, pg. 1243
FIRST SENTIER INVESTORS (UK) FUNDS LIMITED—See KKR & Co. Inc.; *U.S. Public*, pg. 1243
FIRST SERVE HOSPITALITY GROUP; *U.S. Private*, pg. 1527
FIRSTSERVER, INC.—See SoftBank Group Corp.; *Int'l*, pg. 7052
FIRST SERVICE CAROLINA, INC.—See Pineland Telephone Cooperative, Inc.; *U.S. Private*, pg. 3183
FIRSTSERVICE CORPORATION; *Int'l*, pg. 2690
FIRST SERVICE CREDIT UNION; *U.S. Private*, pg. 1527
FIRST SERVICE INSURANCE AGENTS & BROKERS, INC.—See GTCR LLC; *U.S. Private*, pg. 1803
FIRST SERVICE NETWORKS, INC.; *U.S. Private*, pg. 1527
FIRST SERVICE REALTY INC.; *U.S. Private*, pg. 1527
FIRSTSERVICE RESIDENTIAL FLORIDA, INC.—See FirstService Corporation; *Int'l*, pg. 2691
FIRSTSERVICE RESIDENTIAL, INC.—See FirstService Corporation; *Int'l*, pg. 2691
FIRSTSERVICE RESIDENTIAL, NEVADA, LLC—See FirstService Corporation; *Int'l*, pg. 2691
FIRST SHANGHAI CAPITAL LIMITED—See First Shanghai Investments Limited; *Int'l*, pg. 2687
FIRST SHANGHAI DIRECT INVESTMENTS LIMITED—See First Shanghai Investments Limited; *Int'l*, pg. 2687
FIRST SHANGHAI FINANCE LIMITED—See First Shanghai Investments Limited; *Int'l*, pg. 2687
FIRST SHANGHAI FINANCIAL HOLDING LIMITED—See First Shanghai Investments Limited; *Int'l*, pg. 2687
FIRST SHANGHAI FUTURES LIMITED—See First Shanghai Investments Limited; *Int'l*, pg. 2687
FIRST SHANGHAI INVESTMENTS LIMITED; *Int'l*, pg. 2687
FIRST SHANGHAI MANAGEMENT SERVICES LIMITED—See First Shanghai Investments Limited; *Int'l*, pg. 2687
FIRST SHANGHAI NOMINEES LIMITED—See First Shanghai Investments Limited; *Int'l*, pg. 2687
FIRST SHANGHAI PROPERTIES LIMITED—See First Shanghai Investments Limited; *Int'l*, pg. 2687
FIRST SHANGHAI SECURITIES LIMITED—See First Shanghai Investments Limited; *Int'l*, pg. 2687
FIRST SHIP LEASE TRUST; *Int'l*, pg. 2688
FIRST SHORE FEDERAL SAVINGS & LOAN ASSOCIATION; *U.S. Private*, pg. 1527
FIRSTSIGHT VISION SERVICES, INC.—See National Vision Holdings, Inc.; *U.S. Public*, pg. 1498
FIRST SLEEPY EYE BANCORPORATION, INC.; *U.S. Private*, pg. 1527
FIRST SOLAR ASSET MANAGEMENT, LLC—See First Solar, Inc.; *U.S. Public*, pg. 847
FIRST SOLAR (AUSTRALIA) PTY LTD—See First Solar, Inc.; *U.S. Public*, pg. 847
FIRST SOLAR ELECTRICO (CHILE) SPA—See First Solar, Inc.; *U.S. Public*, pg. 847
FIRST SOLAR GMBH—See First Solar, Inc.; *U.S. Public*, pg. 847
FIRST SOLAR, INC.; *U.S. Public*, pg. 847
FIRST SOLAR JAPAN GK—See First Solar, Inc.; *U.S. Public*, pg. 847
FIRST SOLAR MALAYSIA SDN. BHD.—See First Solar, Inc.; *U.S. Public*, pg. 847
FIRST SOLAR POWER INDIA PVT LTD—See First Solar, Inc.; *U.S. Public*, pg. 847
FIRST SOMERSET & AVON LIMITED—See FirstGroup plc; *Int'l*, pg. 2689
FIRST SONORA BANCSHARES, INC.; *U.S. Private*, pg. 1527
FIRST SOUND BANK; *U.S. Public*, pg. 847
FIRSTSOURCE ADVANTAGE LLC—See Firstsource Solutions Limited; *Int'l*, pg. 2691
FIRSTSOURCE ADVANTAGE LLC—See Firstsource Solutions Limited; *Int'l*, pg. 2691
FIRST SOURCE ELECTRONICS, LLC—See Woodson Equity LLC; *U.S. Private*, pg. 4560
FIRSTSOURCEHR, INC.; *U.S. Private*, pg. 1532
FIRSTSOURCE LABORATORY SOLUTIONS, INC.—See Laboratory Corporation of America Holdings; *U.S. Public*, pg. 1287
FIRST SOURCE, LLC—See Slate Capital Group LLC; *U.S. Private*, pg. 3687
FIRST SOURCE, LLC - TENNESSEE—See Slate Capital Group LLC; *U.S. Private*, pg. 3687
FIRSTSOURCE SOLUTIONS LIMITED; *Int'l*, pg. 2691
FIRST SOUTHERN BANCORP, INC.; *U.S. Private*, pg. 1528
FIRST SOUTHERN BANK—See Midwest Community Bancshares, Inc.; *U.S. Private*, pg. 2720

FIRST STERLING CORPORATION

FIRST SOUTHERN NATIONAL BANK—See First Southern Bancorp, Inc.; *U.S. Private*, pg. 1528
FIRST SOUTH FARM CREDIT; *U.S. Private*, pg. 1528
FIRST SOUTH FINANCIAL CREDIT UNION; *U.S. Private*, pg. 1528
FIRST SOUTHWEST CORPORATION; *U.S. Private*, pg. 1528
FIRST SOUTHWEST LEASING COMPANY—See Hilltop Holdings Inc.; *U.S. Public*, pg. 1038
FIRST SOUTH YORKSHIRE LIMITED—See FirstGroup plc; *Int'l*, pg. 2689
FIRST SPONSOR GROUP LIMITED; *Int'l*, pg. 2688
FIRST STAGE CORPORATION; *Int'l*, pg. 2688
FIRST STATE BANCORP, INC.; *U.S. Private*, pg. 1528
FIRST STATE BANCORPORATION, INC.; *U.S. Private*, pg. 1528
FIRST STATE BANCSHARES INC.; *U.S. Private*, pg. 1528
FIRST STATE BANCSHARES INC.; *U.S. Private*, pg. 1528
FIRST STATE BANCSHARES, INC.; *U.S. Private*, pg. 1528
FIRST STATE BANK AND TRUST CO.—See Synovus Financial Corp.; *U.S. Public*, pg. 1971
FIRST STATE BANK AND TRUST CO.—See Synovus Financial Corp.; *U.S. Public*, pg. 1972
FIRST STATE BANK INC.; *U.S. Private*, pg. 1528
THE FIRST STATE BANK, KIOWA, KANSAS—See Grace Investment Company, Inc.; *U.S. Private*, pg. 1749
FIRST STATE BANK NEBRASKA—See First State Holding Co.; *U.S. Private*, pg. 1529
FIRST STATE BANK OF BLOOMINGTON - HEYWORTH—See First State Bank of Bloomington; *U.S. Private*, pg. 1528
FIRST STATE BANK OF BLOOMINGTON; *U.S. Private*, pg. 1528
FIRST STATE BANK OF EAST DETROIT INC.—See First State Financial Corp.; *U.S. Private*, pg. 1529
FIRST STATE BANK OF LIVINGSTON—See East Texas Bancshares, Inc.; *U.S. Private*, pg. 1318
THE FIRST STATE BANK OF SHELBY—See Prairie Bancshares Corporation; *U.S. Private*, pg. 3242
FIRST STATE BANK OF THE FLORIDA KEYS; *U.S. Private*, pg. 1528
FIRST STATE BANK OF UVALDE; *U.S. Private*, pg. 1528
FIRST STATE BANK OF WARREN—See Bradley Bancshares, Inc.; *U.S. Private*, pg. 632
FIRST STATE BANK—See First State Bancshares Inc.; *U.S. Private*, pg. 1528
FIRST STATE BANK—See First State Bancshares, Inc.; *U.S. Private*, pg. 1528
FIRST STATE BANK—See Full Service Insurance Agency, Inc.; *U.S. Private*, pg. 1621
FIRST STATE BANK—See Glacier Bancorp, Inc.; *U.S. Public*, pg. 939
FIRST STATE BANK—See Nebraska Bankshares, Inc.; *U.S. Private*, pg. 2878
FIRST STATE BANK—See Nebraska Bankshares, Inc.; *U.S. Private*, pg. 2878
FIRST STATE BANK—See Tri-County Financial Group, Inc.; *U.S. Public*, pg. 2189
FIRST STATE BANK—See Van Diest Family, LLC; *U.S. Private*, pg. 4339
FIRST STATE BANK SOUTHWEST—See First Rushmore Bancorporation, Inc.; *U.S. Private*, pg. 1527
FIRST STATE BANK & TRUST COMPANY, INC.—See First State Bancorp, Inc.; *U.S. Private*, pg. 1528
FIRST STATE CHEVROLET, INC.; *U.S. Private*, pg. 1529
FIRST STATE CINDA FUND MANAGEMENT CO., LTD.—See China Cinda Asset Management Co., Ltd.; *Int'l*, pg. 1488
FIRST STATE COMMUNITY BANK—See First State Bancshares Inc.; *U.S. Private*, pg. 1528
FIRST STATE COMPUTING PTY LTD.—See BT Group plc; *Int'l*, pg. 1203
FIRST STATE CORP.; *U.S. Private*, pg. 1529
FIRST STATE FINANCIAL CORP.; *U.S. Private*, pg. 1529
FIRST STATE HOLDING CO.; *U.S. Private*, pg. 1529
FIRST STEAMSHIP CO., LTD.; *Int'l*, pg. 2688
FIRST STEAMSHIP S.A.—See First Steamship Co., Ltd.; *Int'l*, pg. 2688
FIRST STEP, INC.; *U.S. Private*, pg. 1529
FIRST STEP INDEPENDENT LIVING PROGRAM, INC.—See Centerbridge Partners, L.P.; *U.S. Private*, pg. 813
FIRST STEPS CHILDRENS NURSERY LIMITED—See Mid Counties Co-operative; *Int'l*, pg. 4882
FIRST STERLING CORPORATION; *U.S. Private*, pg. 1529
FIRSTSTREET FOR BOOMERS AND BEYOND, INC.—See Peloton Equity LLC; *U.S. Private*, pg. 3131
THE FIRST STRING HEALTHCARE, INC.—See AMN Healthcare Services, Inc.; *U.S. Public*, pg. 125
FIRST STUDENT CANADA—See FirstGroup plc; *Int'l*, pg. 2689
FIRST STUDENT INC.—See FirstGroup plc; *Int'l*, pg. 2689
FIRST STUDENT—See FirstGroup plc; *Int'l*, pg. 2689
FIRST STUDENT—See FirstGroup plc; *Int'l*, pg. 2689
FIRST SUMIDEN CIRCUITS, INC.—See Sumitomo Electric Industries, Ltd.; *Int'l*, pg. 7277

FIRSTSUN CAPITAL BANCORP

FIRSTSUN CAPITAL BANCORP; *U.S. Public*, pg. 849
FIRST SUN MANAGEMENT CORPORATION; *U.S. Private*, pg. 1529
FIRST SUPPLY GROUP INC.—See First Supply LLC; *U.S. Private*, pg. 1529
FIRST SUPPLY LLC - EAU CLAIRE—See First Supply LLC; *U.S. Private*, pg. 1529
FIRST SUPPLY LLC; *U.S. Private*, pg. 1529
FIRST SUPPLY MILWAUKEE INC.—See First Supply LLC; *U.S. Private*, pg. 1529
FIRST SUPPLY—See First Supply LLC; *U.S. Private*, pg. 1529
FIRST SURGICAL PARTNERS INC.; *U.S. Private*, pg. 1529
FIRST SYMETRA NATIONAL LIFE INSURANCE COMPANY OF NEW YORK—See Sumitomo Life Insurance Company; *Int'l*, pg. 7291
FIRST TAISEC SECURITIES INC.—See First Financial Holding Co., Ltd.; *Int'l*, pg. 2683
FIRST TAKAFUL INSURANCE COMPANY K.S.C.C.; *Int'l*, pg. 2688
FIRST TEAM FORD, LTD—See AutoNation, Inc.; *U.S. Public*, pg. 235
FIRST TEAM FORD, LTD.—See AutoNation, Inc.; *U.S. Public*, pg. 235
FIRST TEAM FORD OF MANATEE, LTD.—See AutoNation, Inc.; *U.S. Public*, pg. 235
FIRST TEAM HONDA—See Tallahassee Automotive, LLC; *U.S. Private*, pg. 3926
FIRST TEAM NISSAN OF CHRISTIANBURG—See Tallahassee Automotive, LLC; *U.S. Private*, pg. 3927
FIRST TEAM REAL ESTATE-ORANGE COUNTY INC. - FIRST TEAM COMMERCIAL DIVISION—See First Team Real Estate-Orange County Inc.; *U.S. Private*, pg. 1529
FIRST TEAM REAL ESTATE-ORANGE COUNTY INC.; *U.S. Private*, pg. 1529
FIRST TEAM TOYOTA—See Tallahassee Automotive, LLC; *U.S. Private*, pg. 3927
FIRST TECHNOLOGY (BEIJING) LTD.—See Fuji Corporation; *Int'l*, pg. 2809
FIRST TECHNOLOGY CAPITAL, INC.; *U.S. Private*, pg. 1529
FIRST TECHNOLOGY CHINA LTD.—See Fuji Corporation; *Int'l*, pg. 2809
FIRST TECHNOLOGY SHANGHAI LTD.—See Fuji Corporation; *Int'l*, pg. 2809
FIRST TEK, INC.; *U.S. Private*, pg. 1529
FIRST TELLURIUM CORP.; *Int'l*, pg. 2688
FIRST TENNESSEE BANK, N.A.—See First Horizon Corporation; *U.S. Public*, pg. 844
FIRST TENNESSEE BROKERAGE, INC.—See First Horizon Corporation; *U.S. Public*, pg. 844
FIRST TENNESSEE HUMAN RESOURCE AGENCY; *U.S. Private*, pg. 1529
FIRST TEXAS BANCORP, INC.; *U.S. Private*, pg. 1529
FIRST TEXAS BANK—See First Texas Bancorp, Inc.; *U.S. Private*, pg. 1530
FIRST TEXAS HOMES INC.; *U.S. Private*, pg. 1530
FIRST TEXAS HOSPITAL CARROLLTON LLC—See Adeptus Health Inc.; *U.S. Private*, pg. 78
FIRST TIN PLC; *Int'l*, pg. 2688
FIRST TITLE ABSTRACT & SERVICES, LLC; *U.S. Private*, pg. 1530
FIRST TITLE CEE (BIZTOSITASKOZVETITO KORLATOLT FELELOSSEGU TARSASAG)—See First American Financial Corporation; *U.S. Public*, pg. 838
FIRST TITLE INSURANCE PLC—See First American Financial Corporation; *U.S. Public*, pg. 838
FIRST TITLE PLC—See First American Financial Corporation; *U.S. Public*, pg. 837
FIRST TITLE REAL ESTATE GUARANTY CO., LTD.—See First American Financial Corporation; *U.S. Public*, pg. 838
FIRST TRACTOR COMPANY LIMITED; *Int'l*, pg. 2688
FIRST TRANSIT, INC.—See EQT AB; *Int'l*, pg. 2475
FIRST TRANSPENNINE EXPRESS LIMITED—See FirstGroup plc; *Int'l*, pg. 2689
FIRST TRAVEL GMBH—See TUI AG; *Int'l*, pg. 7964
FIRST TRAVEL SOLUTIONS LIMITED—See FirstGroup plc; *Int'l*, pg. 2689
FIRST TREET MANUFACTURING MODARABA—See Treet Corporation Limited; *Int'l*, pg. 7910
FIRST TRENTON INDEMNITY CO.—See The Travelers Companies, Inc.; *U.S. Public*, pg. 2136
FIRST TRINITY FINANCIAL CORPORATION; *U.S. Private*, pg. 1530
FIRST TRUST ABERDEEN EMERGING OPPORTUNITY FUND; *U.S. Public*, pg. 848
FIRST TRUST/ABRDN GLOBAL OPPORTUNITY INCOME FUND; *U.S. Public*, pg. 848
FIRST TRUST ADVISORS L.P.—See First Trust Portfolios L.P.; *U.S. Private*, pg. 1530
FIRST TRUST ENERGY INCOME & GROWTH FUND; *U.S. Public*, pg. 848
FIRST TRUST ENERGY INFRASTRUCTURE FUND—See First Trust Portfolios L.P.; *U.S. Private*, pg. 1530
FIRST TRUST ENHANCED EQUITY INCOME FUND; *U.S. Public*, pg. 848
FIRST TRUST HIGH INCOME LONG/SHORT FUND; *U.S. Public*, pg. 848
FIRST TRUST INTER DUR PREF& INCOME FUND; *U.S. Public*, pg. 848
FIRST TRUST MLP AND ENERGY INCOME FUND—See First Trust Portfolios L.P.; *U.S. Private*, pg. 1530
FIRST TRUST NEW OPPORTUNITIES MLP & ENERGY FUND; *U.S. Public*, pg. 848
FIRST TRUST OF MIDAMERICA—See Lolyn Financial Corporation; *U.S. Private*, pg. 2483
FIRST TRUST PORTFOLIOS L.P.; *U.S. Private*, pg. 1530
FIRST TRUST SENIOR FLOATING RATE 2022 TARGET TERM FUND; *U.S. Public*, pg. 848
FIRST TRUST SENIOR FLOATING RATE INCOME FUND II; *U.S. Public*, pg. 848
FIRST TRUST SPECIALTY FINANCE & FINANCIAL OPPORTUNITIES FUND; *U.S. Public*, pg. 848
FIRST UNDERWRITING LTD.—See White Mountains Insurance Group, Ltd.; *U.S. Public*, pg. 2369
FIRST UNION CAPITAL II—See Wells Fargo & Company; *U.S. Public*, pg. 2343
FIRST UNION DIRECT—See UnionBank of the Philippines; *Int'l*, pg. 8054
FIRST UNION FINANCIAL CORP.; *U.S. Private*, pg. 1530
FIRST UNION PLANS—See UnionBank of the Philippines; *Int'l*, pg. 8054
FIRST UNITED BANK & TRUST COMPANY—See Durant Bancorp, Inc.; *U.S. Private*, pg. 1292
FIRST UNITED BANK & TRUST—See First United Corporation; *U.S. Public*, pg. 848
FIRST UNITED CORPORATION; *U.S. Public*, pg. 848
FIRST UNITED DOOR TECHNOLOGIES, LLC—See CapitalWorks, LLC; *U.S. Private*, pg. 742
FIRST US BANCSHARES, INC.; *U.S. Public*, pg. 848
FIRST US BANK—See First US Bancshares, Inc.; *U.S. Public*, pg. 848
FIRST VANDALIA CORP.; *U.S. Private*, pg. 1530
FIRST VEHICLE SERVICES—See FirstGroup plc; *Int'l*, pg. 2689
FIRST VENTURE CAPITAL CO., LTD.—See First Financial Holding Co., Ltd.; *Int'l*, pg. 2683
FIRST VOLUNTEER BANK—See First Volunteer Corporation; *U.S. Private*, pg. 1530
FIRST VOLUNTEER CORPORATION; *U.S. Private*, pg. 1530
FIRST WASHINGTON REALTY INC.; *U.S. Private*, pg. 1530
FIRST WATCH RESTAURANT GROUP, INC.; *U.S. Public*, pg. 848
FIRST WATCH RESTAURANTS, INC.—See Advent International Corporation; *U.S. Private*, pg. 101
FIRST WATERLOO BANCSHARES, INC.; *U.S. Private*, pg. 1530
FIRST WAVE MARINE INC.; *U.S. Private*, pg. 1530
FIRST WESTERN BANCSHARES INC.; *U.S. Private*, pg. 1530
FIRST WESTERN BANK & TRUST; *U.S. Private*, pg. 1530
FIRST WESTERN FINANCIAL, INC.; *U.S. Public*, pg. 848
FIRST WESTERN TITLE COMPANY—See Colonial Savings, F.A.; *U.S. Private*, pg. 972
FIRST WESTERN TRUST BANK—See First Western Financial, Inc.; *U.S. Public*, pg. 848
FIRST WEST YORKSHIRE LIMITED—See FirstGroup plc; *Int'l*, pg. 2689
FIRST WINNER INDUSTRIES LIMITED; *Int'l*, pg. 2688
FIRST WINNER LIFESTYLE LTD.—See First Winner Industries Limited; *Int'l*, pg. 2688
FIRST WINTHROP CORPORATION—See Winthrop Financial Associates LP; *U.S. Private*, pg. 4545
FIRST WOOD CO., LTD.—See Iida Group Holdings Co., Ltd.; *Int'l*, pg. 3607
FIRST WORLD IMPORTS, INC.; *U.S. Private*, pg. 1531
FIRST WORLDSEC SECURITIES LIMITED—See First Financial Holding Co., Ltd.; *Int'l*, pg. 2683
FIRST WORLD TRADER (PTY) LIMITED—See Purple Group Limited; *Int'l*, pg. 6122
THE FIRST YEARS INC.—See Tomy Company, Ltd.; *Int'l*, pg. 7805
FIRST YORK BAN CORP.; *U.S. Private*, pg. 1531
FIRTH ROSS MARTIN ASSOCIATES LTD—See Randstad N.V.; *Int'l*, pg. 6201
FISA ANDINA S.A.S.—See Archer-Daniels-Midland Company; *U.S. Public*, pg. 185
FIS APPLICATION SERVICE PROVIDING UND IT-OUTSOURCING GMBH—See FIS Informationssysteme und Consulting GmbH; *Int'l*, pg. 2691
FIS BROKERAGE & SECURITIES SERVICES LLC—See Fidelity National Infor; *U.S. Public*, pg. 832
FIS BUSINESS SYSTEMS LLC—See Fidelity National Infor; *U.S. Public*, pg. 832
FISCALNOTE HOLDINGS, INC.; *U.S. Public*, pg. 850
FISCALSOFT CORP.—See Black Mountain Software, LLC; *U.S. Private*, pg. 572
FIS CARD PROCESSING SERVICES (CHILE) S.A.—See Fidelity National Infor; *U.S. Public*, pg. 832
FISCHBACH & DOUGHERTY, INC.; *U.S. Private*, pg. 1532
FISCHBEIN DEUTSCHLAND GMBH—See Warburg Pincus LLC; *U.S. Private*, pg. 4437

CORPORATE AFFILIATIONS

FISCHBEIN PACKAGING (S) PTE LTD.—See Warburg Pincus LLC; *U.S. Private*, pg. 4437
FISCHBEIN S.A.—See Warburg Pincus LLC; *U.S. Private*, pg. 4437
FISCHBEIN-SAXON, LTD.—See Warburg Pincus LLC; *U.S. Private*, pg. 4437
FISCHER AG PRAZISIONSSPINDELN; *Int'l*, pg. 2692
FISCHER AMERICA INC.—See fischerwerke GmbH & Co. KG; *Int'l*, pg. 2692
FISCHERAPPELT AG; *Int'l*, pg. 2692
FISCHER ARGENTINA S.A.—See fischerwerke GmbH & Co. KG; *Int'l*, pg. 2692
FISCHER A/S—See fischerwerke GmbH & Co. KG; *Int'l*, pg. 2692
FISCHER AUSTRIA GMBH—See Dortmunder Gussasphalt GmbH & Co. KG; *Int'l*, pg. 2180
FISCHER AUTOMOTIVE SYSTEMS GMBH & CO. KG—See fischerwerke GmbH & Co. KG; *Int'l*, pg. 2692
FISCHER BENELUX B.V.—See fischerwerke GmbH & Co. KG; *Int'l*, pg. 2692
FISCHER BRASIL INDUSTRIA E COMERCIO LTDA.—See fischerwerke GmbH & Co. KG; *Int'l*, pg. 2692
FISCHER CHEMIC LIMITED; *Int'l*, pg. 2692
FISCHER CHEVROLET & NISSAN; *U.S. Private*, pg. 1532
FISCHER COBEMABEL SNC—See fischerwerke GmbH & Co. KG; *Int'l*, pg. 2692
FISCHER CONSULTING GMBH—See fischerwerke GmbH & Co. KG; *Int'l*, pg. 2692
FISCHER ENGINEERING PTE. LTD.—See KS Energy Limited; *Int'l*, pg. 4310
FISCHER FALA—See Hakuhodo DY Holdings Incorporated; *Int'l*, pg. 3220
FISCHER FINLAND OY—See fischerwerke GmbH & Co. KG; *Int'l*, pg. 2692
FISCHER FIXINGS LLC—See fischerwerke GmbH & Co. KG; *Int'l*, pg. 2692
FISCHER FIXINGS UK LTD.—See fischerwerke GmbH & Co. KG; *Int'l*, pg. 2692
FISCHER, FRANCIS, TREES & WATTS, INC.—See BNP Paribas SA; *Int'l*, pg. 1082
FISCHER & FUNKE GESELLSCHAFT FUR PERSONALDIENSTLEISTUNGEN MBH—See BayernLB Holding AG; *Int'l*, pg. 914
FISCHER FZE—See fischerwerke GmbH & Co. KG; *Int'l*, pg. 2692
FISCHER HEIGHTS GIANT EAGLE; *U.S. Private*, pg. 1532
FISCHER HELLAS EMPORIKI EPE—See fischerwerke GmbH & Co. KG; *Int'l*, pg. 2692
FISCHER HUNGARIA BT.—See fischerwerke GmbH & Co. KG; *Int'l*, pg. 2692
FISCHER IBERICA S.A.U.—See fischerwerke GmbH & Co. KG; *Int'l*, pg. 2692
FISCHER INNOVATIVE SOLUTIONS CO. LTD.—See fischerwerke GmbH & Co. KG; *Int'l*, pg. 2692
FISCHER INTERNATIONAL S.R.O.—See fischerwerke GmbH & Co. KG; *Int'l*, pg. 2692
FISCHER INTERNATIONAL S.R.O.—See fischerwerke GmbH & Co. KG; *Int'l*, pg. 2692
FISCHER INTERNATIONAL SYSTEMS CORPORATION; *U.S. Private*, pg. 1532
FISCHER ITALIA S.R.L—See fischerwerke GmbH & Co. KG; *Int'l*, pg. 2692
FISCHER JAPAN K.K.—See fischerwerke GmbH & Co. KG; *Int'l*, pg. 2692
FISCHER KOREA CO., LTD—See fischerwerke GmbH & Co. KG; *Int'l*, pg. 2692
FISCHER LUMBER CO. INC.; *U.S. Private*, pg. 1533
FISCHER MEDTECH PTE LTD.—See Platinum Equity, LLC; *U.S. Private*, pg. 3207
FISCHER METAL SANAYI VE TICARET LTD STI—See fischerwerke GmbH & Co. KG; *Int'l*, pg. 2692
FISCHER NEW SARL—See Exel Industries SA; *Int'l*, pg. 2582
FISCHER NORGE AS—See fischerwerke GmbH & Co. KG; *Int'l*, pg. 2692
FISCHERPOLSKA SP.Z O.O—See fischerwerke GmbH & Co. KG; *Int'l*, pg. 2692
FISCHER PRECISE USA, INC.—See Fischer AG Prazisionsspindeln; *Int'l*, pg. 2692
FISCHER PROFIL GMBH—See Tata Sons Limited; *Int'l*, pg. 7472
FISCHER PUMP & VALVE COMPANY—See Tencarva Machinery Company, LLC; *U.S. Private*, pg. 3965
FISCHER S. A. S.—See fischerwerke GmbH & Co. KG; *Int'l*, pg. 2692
FISCHER SISTEMAS DE FIJACION, S.A. DE C.V.—See fischerwerke GmbH & Co. KG; *Int'l*, pg. 2692
FISCHER S.K. S.R.O.—See fischerwerke GmbH & Co. KG; *Int'l*, pg. 2692
FISCHER SOLUTION (SUZHOU) CO., LTD.—See Platinum Equity, LLC; *U.S. Private*, pg. 3207
FISCHER SVERIGE AB—See fischerwerke GmbH & Co. KG; *Int'l*, pg. 2692
FISCHER SYSTEMS ASIA PTE. LTD.—See fischerwerke GmbH & Co. KG; *Int'l*, pg. 2692
FISCHER (TAICANG) FIXINGS CO. LTD.—See fischerwerke GmbH & Co. KG; *Int'l*, pg. 2692

COMPANY NAME INDEX

FISCHER-TECH MALAYSIA—See Platinum Equity, LLC; U.S. Private, pg. 3207
FISCHERTECHNIK GMBH—See fischerwerke GmbH & Co. KG; Int'l, pg. 2692
FISCHER TECHNOLOGY PTE LTD.—See Platinum Equity, LLC; U.S. Private, pg. 3207
FISCHER TECH (SUZHOU) CO., LTD.—See Platinum Equity, LLC; U.S. Private, pg. 3207
FISCHER-TECH THAILAND—See Platinum Equity, LLC; U.S. Private, pg. 3207
FISCHER TOOL & DIE CORP.—See Schaufler Tooling GmbH & Co. KG; Int'l, pg. 6615
FISCHERWERKE GMBH & CO. KG; Int'l, pg. 2692
FISCHERWERKE PORTUGAL, LDA.—See fischerwerke GmbH & Co. KG; Int'l, pg. 2692
FISCHER & WIESER SPECIALTY FOODS, INC.; U.S. Private, pg. 1532
FISCHMARKT HAMBURG-ALTONA GESELLSCHAFT MIT BESCHRANKTER HAFTUNG—See Hamburger Hafen und Logistik AG; Int'l, pg. 3236
FISCO LTD—See Emerson Electric Co.; U.S. Public, pg. 749
FISCO TOOLS LTD—See Investment AB Latour; Int'l, pg. 3781
FIS DATA SYSTEMS INC.—See Fidelity National Infor; U.S. Public, pg. 832
FISEN CORP.; U.S. Private, pg. 1533
FIS ENERGY SOLUTIONS LIMITED—See Fidelity National Infor; U.S. Public, pg. 832
F&I SENTINEL, LLC; U.S. Private, pg. 1455
FISERV ASPAC PTE. LTD.—See Fiserv, Inc.; U.S. Public, pg. 851
FISERV AUTOMOTIVE SOLUTIONS, INC.—See Fiserv, Inc.; U.S. Public, pg. 851
FISERV CLEARING, INC.—See Fiserv, Inc.; U.S. Public, pg. 851
FISERV (EUROPE) LTD.—See Fiserv, Inc.; U.S. Public, pg. 851
FISERV, INC.; U.S. Public, pg. 850
FISERV LEMANS, INC.—See Fiserv, Inc.; U.S. Public, pg. 851
FISERV POLSKA SP. Z.O.O.—See Fiserv, Inc.; U.S. Public, pg. 851
FISERV SOLUTIONS, LLC—See Fiserv, Inc.; U.S. Public, pg. 851
FIS FINANCIAL SYSTEMS (FRANCE) SAS—See Fidelity National Infor; U.S. Public, pg. 832
FIS FINANCIAL SYSTEMS LLC—See Fidelity National Infor; U.S. Public, pg. 832
FIS GLOBAL TRADING (IBERICA) S.L. UNIPERSONAL—See Fidelity National Infor; U.S. Public, pg. 832
FISH4 LIMITED—See Reach PLC; Int'l, pg. 6231
FISHAWACK LTD.—See Lloyds Banking Group plc; Int'l, pg. 4537
FISHBACK FINANCIAL CORPORATION; U.S. Private, pg. 1533
FISHBELT FEEDS INC.; U.S. Private, pg. 1533
FISHBOWL INVENTORY; U.S. Private, pg. 1533
FISHBOWL MARKETING; U.S. Private, pg. 1533
FISHBURN HEDGES; Int'l, pg. 2692
FISH CONSTRUCTION COMPANY; U.S. Private, pg. 1533
FISH CONSULTING, LLC—See Greens Farms Capital LLC; U.S. Private, pg. 1779
FISH CONSULTING, LLC—See Landon Capital Partners, LLC; U.S. Private, pg. 2386
THE FISHEL COMPANY INC.; U.S. Private, pg. 4029
FISHER & ASSOCIATES, LLC; U.S. Private, pg. 1533
FISHER AUCTION COMPANY, INC.; U.S. Private, pg. 1534
FISHER AUTO PARTS INC.; U.S. Private, pg. 1534
FISHER-BARTON INCORPORATED; U.S. Private, pg. 1535
FISHER BIOSERVICES INC.—See Thermo Fisher Scientific Inc.; U.S. Public, pg. 2147
FISHER BROWN BOTTRELL INSURANCE, INC. - PENSACOLA OFFICE—See Marsh & McLennan Companies, Inc.; U.S. Public, pg. 1380
FISHER BROWN BOTTRELL INSURANCE, INC.—See Marsh & McLennan Companies, Inc.; U.S. Public, pg. 1380
FISHER CHEVROLET INC.; U.S. Private, pg. 1534
FISHER CLINICAL SERVICES GMBH—See Thermo Fisher Scientific Inc.; U.S. Public, pg. 2147
FISHER CLINICAL SERVICES INC.—See Thermo Fisher Scientific Inc.; U.S. Public, pg. 2147
FISHER CLINICAL SERVICES PTE LTD.—See Thermo Fisher Scientific Inc.; U.S. Public, pg. 2147
FISHER & COMPANY INCORPORATED; U.S. Private, pg. 1533
FISHER CONTROLS INTERNATIONAL—See Emerson Electric Co.; U.S. Public, pg. 748
FISHER DEVELOPMENT INC.; U.S. Private, pg. 1534
FISHER ENGINEERING LTD—See Severfield Plc; Int'l, pg. 6734
FISHER ENTERPRISES, LLC; U.S. Private, pg. 1534
FISHER FOODS MARKETING INC.; U.S. Private, pg. 1534
FISHER GRAHAM LIMITED; Int'l, pg. 2693

FISHER HERBST & KEMBLE, PC—See Whitley Penn LLP; U.S. Private, pg. 4513
FISHER HYDRAULICS, INC.—See Ligon Industries LLC; U.S. Private, pg. 2455
FISHERIES SUPPLY COMPANY; U.S. Private, pg. 1535
FISHER INDUSTRIES; U.S. Private, pg. 1534
FISHER INTERNATIONAL, INC.—See Battery Ventures, L.P.; U.S. Private, pg. 489
FISHER ISLAND CLUB, INC.; U.S. Private, pg. 1534
FISHER-KLOSTERMAN INC.—See CECO Environmental Corp.; U.S. Public, pg. 463
FISHER, LLC—See Douglas Dynamics, Inc.; U.S. Public, pg. 677
FISHER & LUDLOW—See Nucor Corporation; U.S. Public, pg. 1553
FISHER & LUDLOW—See Nucor Corporation; U.S. Public, pg. 1553
FISHER & LUDLOW—See Nucor Corporation; U.S. Public, pg. 1553
FISHER LYNCH CAPITAL, LLC - EAST COAST OFFICE—See Fisher Lynch Capital, LLC; U.S. Private, pg. 1534
FISHER LYNCH CAPITAL, LLC; U.S. Private, pg. 1534
FISHERMANS MARINE SUPPLY INC.; U.S. Private, pg. 1535
FISHERMAN'S MARKET INTERNATIONAL INC.; Int'l, pg. 2693
FISHERMAN'S WHARF MARINA HERVEY BAY PTY LTD—See Orascom Construction PLC; Int'l, pg. 5612
FISHER MANUFACTURING COMPANY; U.S. Private, pg. 1534
FISHERMEN'S COMMUNITY HOSPITAL, INC.—See Baptist Health South Florida, Inc.; U.S. Private, pg. 471
FISHER MEXICO, S. DE R.L. DE C.V.—See Thermo Fisher Scientific Inc.; U.S. Public, pg. 2147
FISHER & PAYKEL APPLIANCES CANADA, INC.—See Haier Smart Home Co., Ltd.; Int'l, pg. 3210
FISHER & PAYKEL APPLIANCES HOLDINGS LTD.—See Haier Smart Home Co., Ltd.; Int'l, pg. 3210
FISHER & PAYKEL APPLIANCES ITALY S.P.A.—See Haier Smart Home Co., Ltd.; Int'l, pg. 3210
FISHER & PAYKEL APPLIANCES LIMITED—See Haier Smart Home Co., Ltd.; Int'l, pg. 3210
FISHER & PAYKFI APPLIANCES (THAILAND) CO., LTD.—See Haier Smart Home Co., Ltd.; Int'l, pg. 3210
FISHER & PAYKEL CUSTOMER SERVICES PTY LIMITED—See Haier Smart Home Co., Ltd.; Int'l, pg. 3210
FISHER & PAYKEL DO BRASIL LTDA—See Fisher & Paykel Healthcare Corporation Limited; Int'l, pg. 2693
FISHER & PAYKEL FINANCE LIMITED—See Humm Group Limited; Int'l, pg. 3531
FISHER & PAYKEL FINANCIAL SERVICES LIMITED—See Haier Smart Home Co., Ltd.; Int'l, pg. 3210
FISHER & PAYKEL HEALTHCARE AB—See Fisher & Paykel Healthcare Corporation Limited; Int'l, pg. 2693
FISHER & PAYKEL HEALTHCARE ASIA LIMITED—See Fisher & Paykel Healthcare Corporation Limited; Int'l, pg. 2693
FISHER & PAYKEL HEALTHCARE CORPORATION LIMITED; Int'l, pg. 2692
FISHER & PAYKEL HEALTHCARE GMBH & CO. KG—See Fisher & Paykel Healthcare Corporation Limited; Int'l, pg. 2693
FISHER & PAYKEL HEALTHCARE (GUANGZHOU) LIMITED—See Fisher & Paykel Healthcare Corporation Limited; Int'l, pg. 2692
FISHER & PAYKEL HEALTHCARE INC.—See Fisher & Paykel Healthcare Corporation Limited; Int'l, pg. 2693
FISHER & PAYKEL HEALTHCARE INDIA PRIVATE LIMITED—See Fisher & Paykel Healthcare Corporation Limited; Int'l, pg. 2693
FISHER & PAYKEL HEALTHCARE K.K.—See Fisher & Paykel Healthcare Corporation Limited; Int'l, pg. 2693
FISHER & PAYKEL HEALTHCARE LIMITED—See Fisher & Paykel Healthcare Corporation Limited; Int'l, pg. 2693
FISHER & PAYKEL HEALTHCARE LIMITED—See Fisher & Paykel Healthcare Corporation Limited; Int'l, pg. 2693
FISHER & PAYKEL HEALTHCARE LIMITED—See Fisher & Paykel Healthcare Corporation Limited; Int'l, pg. 2693
FISHER & PAYKEL HEALTHCARE LIMITED—See Fisher & Paykel Healthcare Corporation Limited; Int'l, pg. 2693
FISHER & PAYKEL HEALTHCARE PROPERTIES LIMITED—See Fisher & Paykel Healthcare Corporation Limited; Int'l, pg. 2693
FISHER & PAYKEL HEALTHCARE PTY. LIMITED—See Fisher & Paykel Healthcare Corporation Limited; Int'l, pg. 2693
FISHER & PAYKEL HEALTHCARE S.A. DE C.V.—See Fisher & Paykel Healthcare Corporation Limited; Int'l, pg. 2693
FISHER & PAYKEL HEALTHCARE SAS—See Fisher & Paykel Healthcare Corporation Limited; Int'l, pg. 2693
FISHER & PAYKEL HOLDINGS GMBH—See Fisher & Paykel Healthcare Corporation Limited; Int'l, pg. 2693
FISHER & PAYKEL MANUFACTURING PTY LIMITED—See Haier Smart Home Co., Ltd.; Int'l, pg. 3210

FISH & GAME FRONTIERS, INC.

FISHER & PAYKEL PRODUCTION MACHINERY LIMITED—See Haier Smart Home Co., Ltd.; Int'l, pg. 3210
FISHER PAYKEL SAGLIK URUNLERI TICARET LIMITED SIRKETI—See Fisher & Paykel Healthcare Corporation Limited; Int'l, pg. 2693
FISHER & PAYKEL (SINGAPORE) PTE LIMITED—See Haier Smart Home Co., Ltd.; Int'l, pg. 3210
FISHER & PHILLIPS LLP; U.S. Private, pg. 1533
FISHER PIERCE OUTDOOR LIGHTING CONTROLS—See Electro Switch Corporation; U.S. Private, pg. 1354
FISHER-PRICE, INC.—See Mattel, Inc.; U.S. Public, pg. 1398
FISHER PRINTING INC.; U.S. Private, pg. 1534
FISHER PROPERTY GROUP, INC.; U.S. Private, pg. 1534
FISHER RESEARCH LABORATORY, INC.—See Cohu, Inc.; U.S. Public, pg. 530
FISHER RESOURCES PTY LIMITED—See Unico Silver Limited; U.S. Public, pg. 8033
FISHER ROSEMOUNT TEMPERATURE B.V.—See Emerson Electric Co.; U.S. Public, pg. 745
FISHER SAND & GRAVEL CO. INC.—See Fisher Industries; U.S. Private, pg. 1534
FISHERS BAKERY & SANDWICH CO., INC.; U.S. Private, pg. 1535
FISHER SCIENTIFIC AG—See Thermo Fisher Scientific Inc.; U.S. Public, pg. 2145
FISHER SCIENTIFIC A/S—See Thermo Fisher Scientific Inc.; U.S. Public, pg. 2147
FISHER SCIENTIFIC (AUSTRIA) GMBH—See Thermo Fisher Scientific Inc.; U.S. Public, pg. 2147
FISHER SCIENTIFIC BIOTECH LINE A/S—See Thermo Fisher Scientific Inc.; U.S. Public, pg. 2147
FISHER SCIENTIFIC COMPANY, LLC—See Thermo Fisher Scientific Inc.; U.S. Public, pg. 2148
FISHER SCIENTIFIC COMPANY—See Thermo Fisher Scientific Inc.; U.S. Public, pg. 2148
FISHER SCIENTIFIC D.O.O.—See Thermo Fisher Scientific Inc.; U.S. Public, pg. 2148
FISHER SCIENTIFIC GMBH—See Thermo Fisher Scientific Inc.; U.S. Public, pg. 2148
FISHER SCIENTIFIC GTF AB—See Thermo Fisher Scientific Inc.; U.S. Public, pg. 2148
FISHER SCIENTIFIC HOLDING U.K., LIMITED—See Thermo Fisher Scientific Inc.; U.S. Public, pg. 2148
FISHER SCIENTIFIC (HONG KONG) LIMITED—See Thermo Fisher Scientific Inc.; U.S. Public, pg. 2147
FISHER SCIENTIFIC IRELAND LIMITED—See Thermo Fisher Scientific Inc.; U.S. Public, pg. 2148
FISHER SCIENTIFIC JAPAN, LTD.—See Thermo Fisher Scientific Inc.; U.S. Public, pg. 2148
FISHER SCIENTIFIC KOREA LTD—See Thermo Fisher Scientific Inc.; U.S. Public, pg. 2148
FISHER SCIENTIFIC (M) SDN BHD—See Thermo Fisher Scientific Inc.; U.S. Public, pg. 2147
FISHER SCIENTIFIC NORWAY AS—See Thermo Fisher Scientific Inc.; U.S. Public, pg. 2148
FISHER SCIENTIFIC OF THE NETHERLANDS B.V.—See Thermo Fisher Scientific Inc.; U.S. Public, pg. 2148
FISHER SCIENTIFIC OY—See Thermo Fisher Scientific Inc.; U.S. Public, pg. 2148
FISHER SCIENTIFIC PTE. LTD.—See Thermo Fisher Scientific Inc.; U.S. Public, pg. 2148
FISHER SCIENTIFIC RESEARCH/FISHER SAFETY—See Thermo Fisher Scientific Inc.; U.S. Public, pg. 2148
FISHER SCIENTIFIC S.A.S.—See Thermo Fisher Scientific Inc.; U.S. Public, pg. 2148
FISHER SCIENTIFIC S.L.—See Thermo Fisher Scientific Inc.; U.S. Public, pg. 2148
FISHER SCIENTIFIC, SPOL. S.R.O—See Thermo Fisher Scientific Inc.; U.S. Public, pg. 2148
FISHER SCIENTIFIC SPRL—See Thermo Fisher Scientific Inc.; U.S. Public, pg. 2154
FISHER SCIENTIFIC SPRL—See Thermo Fisher Scientific Inc.; U.S. Public, pg. 2148
FISHER SCIENTIFIC UK LTD.—See Thermo Fisher Scientific Inc.; U.S. Public, pg. 2148
FISHER SCIENTIFIC, UNIPESSOAL, LDA.—See Thermo Fisher Scientific Inc.; U.S. Public, pg. 2148
FISHER'S DOCUMENT SYSTEMS, INC.; U.S. Private, pg. 1534
FISHER SKYLIGHTS, INC.—See Epwin Group Plc; Int'l, pg. 2466
FISHERS SERVICES LTD.—See K-Bro Linen Inc.; Int'l, pg. 4042
FISHERS STORES CONSOLIDATED PTY. LTD.; Int'l, pg. 2693
FISHER STORES INC.; U.S. Private, pg. 1534
FISHER TANK COMPANY; U.S. Private, pg. 1534
FISHERTECH—See Partners Group Holding AG; Int'l, pg. 5749
FISHER-TITUS MEDICAL CENTER; U.S. Private, pg. 1535
FISHER UNITECH LLC—See Court Square Capital Partners, L.P.; U.S. Private, pg. 1069
FISH FURNITURE SHOP INC.; U.S. Private, pg. 1533
FISH & GAME FRONTIERS, INC.; U.S. Private, pg. 1533

FISH & GAME FRONTIERS, INC.   CORPORATE AFFILIATIONS

THE FISHING HOLDINGS, LLC—See The Great American Outdoors Group LLC; *U.S. Private*, pg. 4038
FISHING WORLD, INC.—See Globeride, Inc.; *Int'l*, pg. 3007
FISHKIND & ASSOCIATES, INC.—See Public Financial Management, Inc.; *U.S. Private*, pg. 3299
FISHKING PROCESSORS, INC.—See Nissui Corporation; *Int'l*, pg. 5378
FISHMAN & ASSOCIATES, INC.; *U.S. Private*, pg. 1535
FISHMAN CENTER FOR TOTAL EYE CARE—See Blue Sea Capital Management LLC; *U.S. Private*, pg. 592
FISHMAN CENTER FOR TOTAL EYE CARE—See Ophthalmic Consultants of Long Island; *U.S. Private*, pg. 3032
FISHMAN PUBLIC RELATIONS; *U.S. Private*, pg. 1535
FISHMAN SUPPLY INC.; *U.S. Private*, pg. 1535
FISHMAN & TOBIN, INC.; *U.S. Private*, pg. 1535
FISH MARKETING; *U.S. Private*, pg. 1533
FISH POOL ASA—See Euronext N.V.; *Int'l*, pg. 2554
FISH & RICHARDSON PC; *U.S. Private*, pg. 1533
FISH & STILL EQUIPMENT CO. INC.; *U.S. Private*, pg. 1533
FISH VET GROUP LIMITED—See Zoetis, Inc.; *U.S. Public*, pg. 2409
FISH VET GROUP NORGE AS—See Zoetis, Inc.; *U.S. Public*, pg. 2409
FISH WINDOW CLEANING SERVICES INC.; *U.S. Private*, pg. 1533
FISIA ITALIMPIANTI S.P.A.—See Salini Costruttori S.p.A.; *Int'l*, pg. 6493
FIS INC.—See Nissha Co., Ltd.; *Int'l*, pg. 5371
FIS INFORMATIONSSYSTEME UND CONSULTING GMBH; *Int'l*, pg. 2691
FIS INFORMATION SYSTEMS INC.—See FIS Informationssysteme und Consulting GmbH; *Int'l*, pg. 2692
FIS INFORMATION SYSTEMS UK LIMITED—See FIS Informationssysteme und Consulting GmbH; *Int'l*, pg. 2692
FIS INVESTMENT SYSTEMS LLC—See Fidelity National Infor; *U.S. Public*, pg. 832
FISIOBIOS S.R.L.—See Bios S.p.A.; *Int'l*, pg. 1041
FISION CORP; *U.S. Public*, pg. 851
FISIOPHARMA S.R.L.—See BIOTON S.A.; *Int'l*, pg. 1043
FISKARHEDENVILLAN AB; *Int'l*, pg. 2693
FISKARS AMERICAS HOLDING OY AB—See Fiskars Oyj Abp; *Int'l*, pg. 2693
FISKARS AUSTRALIA PTY. LIMITED—See Fiskars Oyj Abp; *Int'l*, pg. 2693
FISKARS BENELUX B.V.—See Fiskars Oyj Abp; *Int'l*, pg. 2694
FISKARS BRANDS GERMANY GMBH—See Fiskars Oyj Abp; *Int'l*, pg. 2693
FISKARS BRANDS HUNGARY LTD.—See Fiskars Oyj Abp; *Int'l*, pg. 2693
FISKARS BRANDS, INC. - GERBER GEAR—See Fiskars Oyj Abp; *Int'l*, pg. 2693
FISKARS BRANDS, INC. - NELSON—See Fiskars Oyj Abp; *Int'l*, pg. 2693
FISKARS BRANDS, INC.—See Fiskars Oyj Abp; *Int'l*, pg. 2693
FISKARS BRANDS ITALY S.R.L.—See Fiskars Oyj Abp; *Int'l*, pg. 2693
FISKARS BRANDS OY AB—See Fiskars Oyj Abp; *Int'l*, pg. 2693
FISKARS BRANDS PTY. LTD.—See Fiskars Oyj Abp; *Int'l*, pg. 2693
FISKARS CANADA INC.—See Fiskars Oyj Abp; *Int'l*, pg. 2693
FISKARS COMMERCIAL (SHANGHAI) CO., LTD.—See Fiskars Oyj Abp; *Int'l*, pg. 2694
FISKARS CONSUMER GOODS (SHANGHAI) CO., LTD.—See Fiskars Oyj Abp; *Int'l*, pg. 2694
FISKARS DANMARK A/S—See Fiskars Oyj Abp; *Int'l*, pg. 2694
FISKARS DENMARK A/S—See Fiskars Oyj Abp; *Int'l*, pg. 2694
FISKARS ESTONIA AS—See Fiskars Oyj Abp; *Int'l*, pg. 2694
FISKARS EUROPE HOLDING OY AB—See Fiskars Oyj Abp; *Int'l*, pg. 2694
FISKARS FINLAND OY AB—See Fiskars Oyj Abp; *Int'l*, pg. 2694
FISKARS FRANCE S.A.R.L.—See Fiskars Oyj Abp; *Int'l*, pg. 2694
FISKARS GARDEN & OUTDOOR LIVING—See Fiskars Oyj Abp; *Int'l*, pg. 2693
FISKARS GERMANY GMBH—See Elho BV; *Int'l*, pg. 2360
FISKARS HONG KONG LTD.—See Fiskars Oyj Abp; *Int'l*, pg. 2694
FISKARS ITALY S.R.L.—See Fiskars Oyj Abp; *Int'l*, pg. 2694
FISKARS LIVING US, LLC—See Fiskars Oyj Abp; *Int'l*, pg. 2694
FISKARS NORGE A/S—See Fiskars Oyj Abp; *Int'l*, pg. 2694
FISKARS NORWAY AS—See Fiskars Oyj Abp; *Int'l*, pg. 2694
FISKARS OUTDOOR LEISURE PRODUCTS—See Fiskars Oyj Abp; *Int'l*, pg. 2693

FISKARS OYJ ABP - ARABIA PORCELAIN FACTORY—See Fiskars Oyj Abp; *Int'l*, pg. 2694
FISKARS OYJ ABP - IITTALA GLASS FACTORY—See Fiskars Oyj Abp; *Int'l*, pg. 2694
FISKARS OYJ ABP - NUUTAJARVI GLASS FACTORY—See Fiskars Oyj Abp; *Int'l*, pg. 2694
FISKARS OYJ ABP; *Int'l*, pg. 2693
FISKARS POLAND LTD.—See Fiskars Oyj Abp; *Int'l*, pg. 2694
FISKARS POLAND SP. Z.O.O.—See Fiskars Oyj Abp; *Int'l*, pg. 2694
FISKARS POLSKA SP. Z O.O.—See Fiskars Oyj Abp; *Int'l*, pg. 2694
FISKARS POLSKA SP. Z.O.O.—See Fiskars Oyj Abp; *Int'l*, pg. 2694
FISKARS REAL ESTATE—See Fiskars Oyj Abp; *Int'l*, pg. 2694
FISKARS SERVICES OY AB—See Fiskars Oyj Abp; *Int'l*, pg. 2694
FISKARS SPAIN S.L.—See Fiskars Oyj Abp; *Int'l*, pg. 2694
FISKARS SWEDEN AB—See Fiskars Oyj Abp; *Int'l*, pg. 2694
FISKARS (THAILAND) CO., LIMITED—See Fiskars Oyj Abp; *Int'l*, pg. 2693
FISKARS UK LIMITED—See Fiskars Oyj Abp; *Int'l*, pg. 2694
FISKE ASSOCIATES—See Investor AB; *Int'l*, pg. 3786
FISKE BROTHERS REFINING COMPANY; *U.S. Private*, pg. 1535
FISKE BROTHERS REFINING COMPANY - TOLEDO DIVISION—See Fiske Brothers Refining Company; *U.S. Private*, pg. 1535
FISKEBY BOARD AB—See Fiskeby International Holding AB; *Int'l*, pg. 2695
FISKEBY INTERNATIONAL HOLDING AB; *Int'l*, pg. 2695
FISK ELECTRIC COMPANY INC.—See Tutor Perini Corporation; *U.S. Public*, pg. 2206
FISKER INC.—See Fisker Inc.; *U.S. Public*, pg. 851
FISKER INC.; *U.S. Public*, pg. 851
FISO TECHNOLOGIES, INC.—See Nova Ventures Group Corp.; *U.S. Private*, pg. 2966
FIS PAYMENTS (UK) LIMITED—See Fidelity National Infor; *U.S. Public*, pg. 832
FISSION URANIUM CORP.; *Int'l*, pg. 2695
FIS-SST SP. Z O.O.—See Q_PERIOR AG; *Int'l*, pg. 6131
FIS SYSTEME GMBH—See Fidelity National Infor; *U.S. Public*, pg. 832
FIS TECHNOLOGY SERVICES (POLAND) SP. Z.O.O.—See Fidelity National Infor; *U.S. Public*, pg. 832
FIS TECHNOLOGY SERVICES SINGAPORE PTE. LTD.—See Fidelity National Infor; *U.S. Public*, pg. 832
FISTER DISTRIBUTION INC.—See Fister Incorporated; *U.S. Private*, pg. 1535
FISTER INCORPORATED; *U.S. Private*, pg. 1535
FISTER MOVING & STORAGE—See Fister Incorporated; *U.S. Private*, pg. 1535
FIS VIETNAM LLC—See Fidelity National Infor; *U.S. Public*, pg. 832
FIS WEALTH MANAGEMENT SERVICES, INC.—See Fidelity National Infor; *U.S. Public*, pg. 832
FIS WORKFLOW SOLUTIONS LLC—See Fidelity National Infor; *U.S. Public*, pg. 832
FIT AFTER FIFTY, INC.; *U.S. Private*, pg. 1535
FITAIHI HOLDING GROUP; *Int'l*, pg. 2695
FIT AMERICA INC.; *U.S. Private*, pg. 1535
FITAS VERWALTUNG GMBH & CO. REGIUM-OBJEKTE KG—See E.ON SE; *Int'l*, pg. 2257
FITAS VERWALTUNG GMBH & CO. VERMIETUNGS-KG—See E.ON SE; *Int'l*, pg. 2257
FIT-BIOCEUTICALS LIMITED—See Blackmores Limited; *Int'l*, pg. 1061
FIT BIOTECH OY; *Int'l*, pg. 2695
FITBIT, INC.—See Alphabet Inc.; *U.S. Public*, pg. 83
FIT BOXX HOLDINGS LIMITED; *Int'l*, pg. 2695
FITCH DESIGN PVT. LTD.—See WPP plc; *Int'l*, pg. 8463
FITCH DUBAI—See WPP plc; *Int'l*, pg. 8463
FITCH GROUP, INC.—See The Hearst Corporation; *U.S. Private*, pg. 4044
FITCH INC. - PHOENIX—See WPP plc; *Int'l*, pg. 8463
FITCH INC. - SEATTLE—See WPP plc; *Int'l*, pg. 8463
FITCH INC.—See WPP plc; *Int'l*, pg. 8463
FITCH LONDON—See WPP plc; *Int'l*, pg. 8463
FITCH: QATAR LIMITED—See WPP plc; *Int'l*, pg. 8463
FITCH RATINGS, INC. - CHICAGO—See The Hearst Corporation; *U.S. Private*, pg. 4044
FITCH RATINGS, INC. - SAN FRANCISCO—See The Hearst Corporation; *U.S. Private*, pg. 4044
FITCH RATINGS, INC.—See The Hearst Corporation; *U.S. Private*, pg. 4044
FITCH SOLUTIONS, INC.—See The Hearst Corporation; *U.S. Private*, pg. 4044
FITCH WORLDWIDE LIMITED—See WPP plc; *Int'l*, pg. 8463
FITCO BV—See Aksa Akrilik Kimya Sanayii A.S.; *Int'l*, pg. 264
FIT CO., LTD.; *Int'l*, pg. 2695
FIT.COM CO., LTD.—See Daiwa Computer Co., Ltd.; *Int'l*, pg. 1944

FITCORP PRIVATE FITNESS CENTERS—See Town Sports International Holdings, Inc.; *U.S. Private*, pg. 4197
FITCO SA—See Viohalco SA/NV; *Int'l*, pg. 8243
FITE BUILDING COMPANY; *U.S. Private*, pg. 1535
FITEC CORP.—See The Furukawa Electric Co., Ltd.; *Int'l*, pg. 7644
FITEK, LLC; *U.S. Private*, pg. 1535
FITELL CORPORATION; *Int'l*, pg. 2695
FITEL NOMINEES LIMITED—See WH Ireland Group PLC; *Int'l*, pg. 8396
FITESA FILM PRODUCTS LLC—See Tredegar Corporation; *U.S. Public*, pg. 2187
FITESA GERMANY GMBH—See Evora S.A.; *Int'l*, pg. 2573
FITESA ITALIA SRL—See Evora S.A.; *Int'l*, pg. 2573
FITESA MEXICO—See Evora S.A.; *Int'l*, pg. 2573
FITESA PERU S.A.C.—See Evora S.A.; *Int'l*, pg. 2573
FITESA SA—See Evora S.A.; *Int'l*, pg. 2573
FITESA SIMPSONVILLE, INC.—See Evora S.A.; *Int'l*, pg. 2573
FITESA SWEDEN AB—See Evora S.A.; *Int'l*, pg. 2573
FITESA WASHOUGAL, INC.—See Evora S.A.; *Int'l*, pg. 2573
FIT FABRIC SP. Z O.O.—See Benefit Systems SA; *Int'l*, pg. 972
F.I.T. FAHRZEUG INGENIEURTECHNIK GMBH—See Etteplan Oyj; *Int'l*, pg. 2525
FIT FOR FUN VERLAG GMBH—See Hubert Burda Media Holding Kommanditgesellschaft; *Int'l*, pg. 3520
FITGENES AUSTRALIA PTY LTD.; *Int'l*, pg. 2695
FIT HOLDING CO., LTD.—See Cheng Eui Precision Industry Co., Ltd.; *Int'l*, pg. 1465
FIT INSTITUTO DE TECNOLOGIA DA AMAZONIA—See Flex Ltd.; *Int'l*, pg. 2702
FIT INVERSION EN TALENTO, S.A.U.—See Nippon Telegraph & Telephone Corporation; *Int'l*, pg. 5343
F.I.T. INVESTMENT JSC; *Int'l*, pg. 2597
FITIPOWER INTEGRATED TECHNOLOGY, INC.; *Int'l*, pg. 2695
FIT KIT, INC.—See AutoNation, Inc.; *U.S. Public*, pg. 235
FIT KIT, INC.—See AutoNation, Inc.; *U.S. Public*, pg. 235
FITLIFE BRANDS, INC.; *U.S. Public*, pg. 851
FITLIFE FOODS; *U.S. Private*, pg. 1535
FIT MY FEET ORTHOTIC LAB & SHOES, INC.; *U.S. Private*, pg. 1535
FITNESS AND LIFESTYLE MANAGEMENT HEALTH CLUBS PTY. LTD.—See Quadrant Private Equity Pty. Ltd.; *Int'l*, pg. 6149
FITNESS ANYWHERE LLC; *U.S. Private*, pg. 1536
FITNESS CONNECTION—See Roark Capital Group Inc.; *U.S. Private*, pg. 3455
FITNESS CONSULTING GROUP; *U.S. Private*, pg. 1536
FITNESS CUBED INC.; *U.S. Private*, pg. 1536
FITNESS GALLERY INC.; *U.S. Private*, pg. 1536
FITNESS INSURANCE, LLC—See Brown & Brown, Inc.; *U.S. Public*, pg. 400
FITNESS INTERNATIONAL, LLC—See CIVC Partners LLC; *U.S. Private*, pg. 907
FITNESS INTERNATIONAL, LLC—See Madison Dearborn Partners, LLC; *U.S. Private*, pg. 2541
FITNESS INTERNATIONAL, LLC—See The Seidler Company, LLC; *U.S. Private*, pg. 4116
FITNESS MAGAZINE—See Meredith Corporation; *U.S. Public*, pg. 1422
FITNESS MARKET NORDIC AB—See Orkla ASA; *Int'l*, pg. 5637
FITNESS ONBOARD; *U.S. Private*, pg. 1536
FITNESS PLUS EQUIPMENT SERVICES INC.; *U.S. Private*, pg. 1536
FITNESS TOGETHER; *U.S. Private*, pg. 1536
FITNESS WORLD A/S—See Leonard Green & Partners, L.P.; *U.S. Private*, pg. 2428
FIT/NHNH, INC.; *U.S. Private*, pg. 1535
FITOUTETRIS SA—See Jones Lang LaSalle Incorporated; *U.S. Public*, pg. 1201
FITRACO N.V.—See KBC Group NV; *Int'l*, pg. 4106
FITRASYON ARITIM SISTEMLERI SANAYIVE TICARET FTS—See Amiad Water Systems Ltd.; *Int'l*, pg. 427
FITRUUMS PTE LTD—See Webjet Limited; *Int'l*, pg. 8366
FIT SERVICE S.P.A.—See Carrier Global Corporation; *U.S. Public*, pg. 443
FITTERS DIVERSIFIED BERHAD; *Int'l*, pg. 2695
FITTERS (IPOH) SDN BHD—See FITTERS Diversified Berhad; *Int'l*, pg. 2695
FITTERS MARKETING SDN BHD—See FITTERS Diversified Berhad; *Int'l*, pg. 2695
FITTERS (SARAWAK) SDN BHD—See FITTERS Diversified Berhad; *Int'l*, pg. 2695
FITTERS SDN BHD—See FITTERS Diversified Berhad; *Int'l*, pg. 2695
FITTERS (S) PTE LTD.—See FITTERS Diversified Berhad; *Int'l*, pg. 2695
FITTINGS GMBH FORMSTUCKE + ANLAGEN—See HCS Beteiligungsgesellschaft mbH; *Int'l*, pg. 3299
FITTINGS, INC.—See Bridgestone Corporation; *Int'l*, pg. 1156
THE FITTING SOURCE, INC.—See Hydraulics International, Inc.; *U.S. Private*, pg. 2017

FITTIO INC.—See Cross Marketing Group Inc.; *Int'l*, pg. 1856
FIT TRACKING SOLUTIONS—See Alcea Technologies Inc.; *Int'l*, pg. 300
FIT TURF, INC.—See Senske Lawn & Tree Care, Inc.; *U.S. Private*, pg. 3608
FITVIA GMBH—See Dermapharm Holding SE; *Int'l*, pg. 2043
FITWEISER HOLDINGS, INC.; *U.S. Private*, pg. 1536
FITWEL TOOLS & FORGINGS PRIVATE LIMITED—See Sansera Engineering Limited; *Int'l*, pg. 6555
FITWORKS HOLDING LLC; *U.S. Private*, pg. 1536
FITZ CHEM LLC—See Nagase & Co., Ltd.; *Int'l*, pg. 5127
FITZ DESIGN; *U.S. Private*, pg. 1536
FITZ & FLOYD, INC.—See Lifetime Brands, Inc.; *U.S. Public*, pg. 1313
FITZGERALD AUTO MALLS; *U.S. Private*, pg. 1536
FITZGERALD BROTHERS BEVERAGES; *U.S. Private*, pg. 1536
FITZGERALD+CO—See The Interpublic Group of Companies, Inc.; *U.S. Public*, pg. 2097
FITZGERALD EQUIPMENT COMPANY INCORPORATED; *U.S. Private*, pg. 1536
FITZGERALD & MASTROIANNI, INC.; *U.S. Private*, pg. 1536
THE FITZGERALD THEATER COMPANY INC.—See American Public Media Group; *U.S. Private*, pg. 245
FITZGIBBONS AGENCY LLC—See Pathfinder Bancorp, Inc.; *U.S. Public*, pg. 1651
FITZINN PTY LTD—See Wesfarmers Limited; *Int'l*, pg. 8381
FITZMARK, INC.—See Calera Capital Management, Inc.; *U.S. Private*, pg. 717
FITZMARTIN INC.; *U.S. Private*, pg. 1536
FITZPATRICK AUTO CENTER INC.; *U.S. Private*, pg. 1536
FITZPATRICK CELLA HARPER & SCINTO—See Venable LLP; *U.S. Private*, pg. 4355
FITZPATRICK COMPANIES INC.; *U.S. Private*, pg. 1536
THE FITZPATRICK COMPANY EUROPE N.V.—See IDEX Corp; *U.S. Public*, pg. 1092
THE FITZPATRICK COMPANY—See IDEX Corp; *U.S. Public*, pg. 1092
FITZPATRICK ENGINEERING GROUP, PLLC—See Structura, Inc.; *U.S. Private*, pg. 3841
FITZPATRICK & HUNT, PAGANO, AUBERT, LLP; *U.S. Private*, pg. 1536
FITZPATRICK MANUFACTURING CO.; *U.S. Private*, pg. 1537
FITZPATRICK'S GMC TRUCKS, INC.; *U.S. Private*, pg. 1537
FITZPATRICK & WELLER, INC.; *U.S. Private*, pg. 1536
FITZROY OPERATIONS PTY LTD—See National Veterinary Care Ltd; *Int'l*, pg. 5164
FITZROY RIVER CORPORATION LTD; *Int'l*, pg. 2695
FITZ, VOGT & ASSOCIATES, LTD.—See Charterhouse Capital Partners LLP; *Int'l*, pg. 1455
FIUDI S.R.L.—See OSG Corporation Co., Ltd.; *Int'l*, pg. 5649
FIVE9, INC.; *U.S. Public*, pg. 852
FIVE9, INC. UK LIMITED—See Five9, Inc.; *U.S. Public*, pg. 852
FIVE9 PHILIPPINES INC.—See Five9, Inc.; *U.S. Public*, pg. 852
FIVE9.RU—See Five9, Inc.; *U.S. Public*, pg. 852
FIVEABLE, INC.; *U.S. Private*, pg. 1538
FIVE ACRES - THE BOYS' AND GIRLS' AID SOCIETY OF LOS ANGELES COUNTY; *U.S. Private*, pg. 1537
FIVE AREA TELEPHONE COOP INC.; *U.S. Private*, pg. 1537
FIVE ARROWS CAPITAL PARTNERS—See Rothschild & Co SCA; *Int'l*, pg. 6403
FIVE ARROWS INC.; *U.S. Private*, pg. 1537
FIVE ARROWS MANAGERS SAS—See Rothschild & Co SCA; *Int'l*, pg. 6403
FIVE BELOW, INC.; *U.S. Public*, pg. 852
FIV E. BIANCHI S.P.A.—See Grimaldi Industri AB; *Int'l*, pg. 3086
FIVE BRIDGES ADVISORS LLC—See Radian Group, Inc.; *U.S. Public*, pg. 1759
FIVE BROKERS CAPITAL JSC; *Int'l*, pg. 2696
FIVE BY FIVE; *Int'l*, pg. 2696
FIVE CORE EXIM LIMITED; *Int'l*, pg. 2696
FIVE COUNTY CREDIT UNION; *U.S. Private*, pg. 1537
FIVE CROWNS CAPITAL, LLC; *U.S. Private*, pg. 1537
FIVE ELEVEN INC.—See Premier Ventures, Inc.; *U.S. Private*, pg. 3251
FIVE ELMS CAPITAL MANAGEMENT LLC; *U.S. Private*, pg. 1537
FIVE FOX MANAGEMENT CO., LTD.—See Fuyo General Lease Co., Ltd.; *Int'l*, pg. 2859
FIVE GUYS ENTERPRISES, LLC; *U.S. Private*, pg. 1537
FIVE INSURANCE BROKERS LIMITED—See Brown & Brown, Inc.; *U.S. Public*, pg. 400
FIVE LAKES AUTOMATION, LLC—See Jenoptik AG; *Int'l*, pg. 3928
FIVE MILE CAPITAL PARTNERS LLC; *U.S. Private*, pg. 1537

FIVE NINES TECHNOLOGY GROUP; *U.S. Private*, pg. 1537
FIVE-O MARKETING SERVICES INC.; *U.S. Private*, pg. 1538
FIVE POINT CAPITAL, INC.; *U.S. Private*, pg. 1537
FIVE POINT ENERGY LLC; *U.S. Private*, pg. 1537
FIVE POINT HOLDINGS, LLC; *U.S. Public*, pg. 852
FIVE POINT OPERATING COMPANY, LP—See Five Point Holdings, LLC; *U.S. Public*, pg. 852
FIVE POINTS BENEFITS SOLUTIONS, LLC—See Arthur J. Gallagher & Co.; *U.S. Public*, pg. 204
FIVE POINTS TECHNOLOGY GROUP, INC.; *U.S. Private*, pg. 1537
FIVE POINTS TITLE CO.—See The Deltona Corporation; *U.S. Private*, pg. 4020
FIVE PRIME THERAPEUTICS, INC.—See Amgen Inc.; *U.S. Public*, pg. 123
FIVE RIVERS CATTLE FEEDING, LLC—See Pinnacle Asset Management, L.P.; *U.S. Private*, pg. 3184
FIVE RIVERS MEDICAL CENTER INC; *U.S. Private*, pg. 1537
FIVE RIVERS THERAPY SERVICES, LIMITED PARTNERSHIP—See U.S. Physical Therapy, Inc.; *U.S. Public*, pg. 2214
FIVERR INTERNATIONAL LTD.; *Int'l*, pg. 2696
FIVES DMS—See FIVES, Societe Anonyme; *Int'l*, pg. 2696
FIVES FLETCHER LIMITED—See FIVES, Societe Anonyme; *Int'l*, pg. 2696
FIVES MACHINING SYSTEMS, INC. - FOND DU LAC—See FIVES, Societe Anonyme; *Int'l*, pg. 2696
FIVES MACHINING SYSTEMS, INC. - GLOBAL SERVICES, CHATSWORTH—See FIVES, Societe Anonyme; *Int'l*, pg. 2696
FIVES MACHINING SYSTEMS, INC. - HEBRON—See FIVES, Societe Anonyme; *Int'l*, pg. 2696
FIVES MACHINING SYSTEMS, INC.—See FIVES, Societe Anonyme; *Int'l*, pg. 2696
FIVES NORTH AMERICAN COMBUSTION, INC.—See FIVES, Societe Anonyme; *Int'l*, pg. 2696
FIVES, SOCIETE ANONYME; *Int'l*, pg. 2696
FIVE STAR AIRPORT ALLIANCE, INC.; *U.S. Private*, pg. 1537
FIVE STAR ASPENWOOD LLC—See AlerisLife Inc.; *U.S. Private*, pg. 160
FIVE STAR BANCORP; *U.S. Public*, pg. 852
FIVE STAR BANK—See Financial Institutions, Inc.; *U.S. Public*, pg. 834
FIVE STAR BEEF LTD.—See Itoham Yonekyu Holdings Inc.; *Int'l*, pg. 3842
FIVE-STAR BUSINESS FINANCE LIMITED; *Int'l*, pg. 2696
FIVE STAR CARY HEARTFIELDS LLC—See AlerisLife Inc.; *U.S. Private*, pg. 160
FIVE STAR COOPERATIVE; *U.S. Private*, pg. 1538
FIVE STAR CORAL OAKS LLC—See AlerisLife Inc.; *U.S. Private*, pg. 160
FIVE STAR CREDIT UNION; *U.S. Private*, pg. 1537
FIVE STAR CUSTOM FOODS, LTD.—See Cargill, Inc.; *U.S. Private*, pg. 759
FIVE STAR DESERT HARBOR LLC—See AlerisLife Inc.; *U.S. Private*, pg. 160
FIVE STAR DEVELOPMENT, INC.; *U.S. Private*, pg. 1537
FIVE STAR DIALYSIS, LLC—See DaVita Inc.; *U.S. Public*, pg. 638
FIVE STAR DISTRIBUTORS INC.—See Performance Food Group Company; *U.S. Public*, pg. 1674
FIVE STAR DODGE INC.; *U.S. Private*, pg. 1537
FIVE STAR EASTON HEARTFIELDS LLC—See AlerisLife Inc.; *U.S. Private*, pg. 161
FIVE STAR ELECTRIC CORP.—See WDF/Five Star Holding Corporation; *U.S. Private*, pg. 4462
FIVE STAR ELECTRIC MOTORS; *U.S. Private*, pg. 1537
FIVE STAR ELLICOTT CITY LLC—See AlerisLife Inc.; *U.S. Private*, pg. 161
FIVE STAR EQUIPMENT INC.; *U.S. Private*, pg. 1538
FIVE STAR FOOD SERVICE - CHATTANOOGA—See Freeman Spogli & Co. Incorporated; *U.S. Private*, pg. 1606
FIVE STAR FOOD SERVICE - COOKEVILLE—See Freeman Spogli & Co. Incorporated; *U.S. Private*, pg. 1606
FIVE STAR FOOD SERVICE INC.—See Freeman Spogli & Co. Incorporated; *U.S. Private*, pg. 1606
FIVE STAR FOOD SERVICE - KNOXVILLE—See Freeman Spogli & Co. Incorporated; *U.S. Private*, pg. 1606
FIVE STAR FOOD SERVICE - LAGRANGE—See Freeman Spogli & Co. Incorporated; *U.S. Private*, pg. 1606
FIVE STAR FOOD SERVICE - MARTINSVILLE—See Freeman Spogli & Co. Incorporated; *U.S. Private*, pg. 1606
FIVE STAR FOOD SERVICE - NASHVILLE—See Freeman Spogli & Co. Incorporated; *U.S. Private*, pg. 1606
FIVE STAR FORD; *U.S. Private*, pg. 1538
FIVE STAR FOULK MANOR NORTH LLC—See AlerisLife Inc.; *U.S. Private*, pg. 161
FIVE STAR FRAGRANCE COMPANY, INC.—See Perfumania Holdings, Inc.; *U.S. Private*, pg. 3150
FIVE STAR FREDERICK HEARTFIELDS LLC—See AlerisLife Inc.; *U.S. Private*, pg. 161
FIVE STAR HOME HEALTH, INC.—See AlerisLife Inc.; *U.S. Private*, pg. 161

FIVE STAR INSURANCE, INC.—See AlerisLife Inc.; *U.S. Private*, pg. 161
FIVE STAR INTERNATIONAL LLC; *U.S. Private*, pg. 1538
FIVE STAR KNIGHTSBRIDGE LLC—See AlerisLife Inc.; *U.S. Private*, pg. 161
FIVE STAR LINCOLN HEIGHTS LLC—See AlerisLife Inc.; *U.S. Private*, pg. 161
FIVE STAR MEMORIAL WOODS LLC—See AlerisLife Inc.; *U.S. Private*, pg. 161
FIVE STAR MONTEBELLO LLC—See AlerisLife Inc.; *U.S. Private*, pg. 161
FIVE STAR MORNINGSIDE BELLGRADE LLC—See AlerisLife Inc.; *U.S. Private*, pg. 161
FIVE STAR MORNINGSIDE CHARLOTTESVILLE LLC—See AlerisLife Inc.; *U.S. Private*, pg. 161
FIVE STAR MOTORS; *U.S. Private*, pg. 1538
FIVE STAR NEWPORT NEWS LLC—See AlerisLife Inc.; *U.S. Private*, pg. 161
FIVE STAR NORTHSHORE LLC—See AlerisLife Inc.; *U.S. Private*, pg. 161
FIVE STAR OF COLORADO INC.; *U.S. Private*, pg. 1538
FIVE STAR OF KNOX INC.; *U.S. Private*, pg. 1538
FIVE STAR OVERLAND PARK LLC—See AlerisLife Inc.; *U.S. Private*, pg. 161
FIVE STAR PARKING; *U.S. Private*, pg. 1538
FIVE STAR QUALITY CARE-CA, LLC—See AlerisLife Inc.; *U.S. Private*, pg. 161
FIVE STAR QUALITY CARE-GA, LLC—See AlerisLife Inc.; *U.S. Private*, pg. 161
FIVE STAR QUALITY CARE-GHV, LLC—See AlerisLife Inc.; *U.S. Private*, pg. 161
FIVE STAR QUALITY CARE-IA, INC.—See AlerisLife Inc.; *U.S. Private*, pg. 161
FIVE STAR QUALITY CARE-IL, LLC—See AlerisLife Inc.; *U.S. Private*, pg. 161
FIVE STAR QUALITY CARE-IN, LLC—See AlerisLife Inc.; *U.S. Private*, pg. 161
FIVE STAR QUALITY CARE-KS, LLC—See AlerisLife Inc.; *U.S. Private*, pg. 161
FIVE STAR QUALITY CARE-MS, LLC—See AlerisLife Inc.; *U.S. Private*, pg. 161
FIVE STAR QUALITY CARE-NJ, LLC—See AlerisLife Inc.; *U.S. Private*, pg. 161
FIVE STAR QUALITY CARE-SAVANNAH, LLC—See AlerisLife Inc.; *U.S. Private*, pg. 161
FIVE STAR QUALITY CARE-WY, LLC—See AlerisLife Inc.; *U.S. Private*, pg. 161
FIVE STAR REHABILITATION AND WELLNESS SERVICES, LLC—See AlerisLife Inc.; *U.S. Private*, pg. 161
FIVE STAR REMINGTON CLUB LLC—See AlerisLife Inc.; *U.S. Private*, pg. 161
FIVE STAR RESTAURANT LLC; *U.S. Private*, pg. 1538
FIVE STAR RIO LAS PALMAS LLC—See AlerisLife Inc.; *U.S. Private*, pg. 161
FIVE STAR SEVERNA PARK LLC—See AlerisLife Inc.; *U.S. Private*, pg. 161
FIVE STARS LOYALTY, INC.—See SumUp Payments Limited; *Int'l*, pg. 7303
FIVE STAR SPECIAL STEEL EUROPE S.R.L—See Tiangong International Company Limited; *Int'l*, pg. 7738
FIVE STAR SPECIALTY PROGRAMS—See Truist Financial Corporation; *U.S. Public*, pg. 2200
FIVE STAR TUCSON FORUM LLC—See AlerisLife Inc.; *U.S. Private*, pg. 161
FIVE TEN EUROPE NV/SA—See adidas AG; *Int'l*, pg. 146
FIVE X TRADECOM LIMITED; *Int'l*, pg. 2696
FIXATION MARKETING; *U.S. Private*, pg. 1538
FIXATION UK LTD.—See Aurelius Equity Opportunities SE & Co. KGaA; *Int'l*, pg. 708
FIX AUTO CANADA, INC.; *Int'l*, pg. 2696
FIXEDSPRING LIMITED—See GSK plc; *Int'l*, pg. 3145
FIXINOX SA; *Int'l*, pg. 2696
FIXIT AG; *Int'l*, pg. 2696
FIXNETIX LTD.—See DXC Technology Company; *U.S. Public*, pg. 695
FIX PRICE GROUP PLC; *Int'l*, pg. 2696
FIXSTARS CORPORATION; *Int'l*, pg. 2696
FIXSTARS SOLUTIONS INC.—See Fixstars Corporation; *Int'l*, pg. 2696
THE FIXTURE COMPANY—See Dewhurst Group plc; *Int'l*, pg. 2091
FIXTURE FINDERS (DE) LLC—See Hilco Trading, LLC; *U.S. Private*, pg. 1943
FIXTURES FURNITURE—See JSJ Corporation; *U.S. Private*, pg. 2241
FIYTA PRECISION TECHNOLOGY CO., LTD.; *Int'l*, pg. 2696
FIZZANO BROTHERS CONCRETE PRODUCTS; *U.S. Private*, pg. 1538
FIZZIOLOGY LLC—See Kohlberg & Company, LLC; *U.S. Private*, pg. 2338
FJA CHRISTIANSEN ROOFING CO., INC.—See Altas Partners LP; *Int'l*, pg. 386
FJALLINVEST AB—See SkiStar AB; *Int'l*, pg. 6990
FJALLMEDIA AB—See SkiStar AB; *Int'l*, pg. 6990
FJALLRAVEN GMBH—See Fenix Outdoor International AG; *Int'l*, pg. 2634
FJALLRAVEN INTERNATIONAL AB—See Fenix Outdoor International AG; *Int'l*, pg. 2634

FJALLRAVEN USA LLC—See Fenix Outdoor International AG; *Int'l*, pg. 2634
FJARDE AP-FONDEN; *Int'l*, pg. 2697
FJARSKIPTI HF.; *Int'l*, pg. 2697
F.J. ASCHWANDEN AG—See CRH plc; *Int'l*, pg. 1844
FJA-US, INC.—See msg group GmbH; *Int'l*, pg. 5067
FJA-US, INC.—See msg group GmbH; *Int'l*, pg. 5068
F J BENJAMIN CONCEPTS PTE LTD—See FJ Benjamin Holdings Ltd.; *Int'l*, pg. 2697
FJ BENJAMIN FASHIONS (HK) LTD.—See FJ Benjamin Holdings Ltd.; *Int'l*, pg. 2697
FJ BENJAMIN FASHIONS (SINGAPORE) PTE. LTD.—See FJ Benjamin Holdings Ltd.; *Int'l*, pg. 2697
F J BENJAMIN FASHIONS (U.S.) INC—See FJ Benjamin Holdings Ltd.; *Int'l*, pg. 2697
FJ BENJAMIN HOLDINGS LTD.; *Int'l*, pg. 2697
F J BENJAMIN LIFESTYLE SDN. BHD—See FJ Benjamin Holdings Ltd.; *Int'l*, pg. 2697
F J BENJAMIN LUXURY TIMEPIECES SDN. BHD—See FJ Benjamin Holdings Ltd.; *Int'l*, pg. 2697
F J BENJAMIN (M) SDN. BHD.—See FJ Benjamin Holdings Ltd.; *Int'l*, pg. 2697
F J BENJAMIN (SINGAPORE) PTE LTD—See FJ Benjamin Holdings Ltd.; *Int'l*, pg. 2697
FJ BENJAMIN SINGAPORE PTE. LTD.—See FJ Benjamin Holdings Ltd.; *Int'l*, pg. 2697
F J BENJAMIN (TAIWAN) LTD—See FJ Benjamin Holdings Ltd.; *Int'l*, pg. 2697
FJ BENJAMIN TRADING HK LTD—See FJ Benjamin Holdings Ltd.; *Int'l*, pg. 2697
F. J. B. INVESTMENT PTE LTD—See FJ Benjamin Holdings Ltd.; *Int'l*, pg. 2697
FJ CAPITAL MANAGEMENT; *U.S. Private*, pg. 1538
FJC & ASSOCIATES, INC.—See Stone Point Capital LLC; *U.S. Private*, pg. 3819
FJ COMMUNITY CO., LTD.—See FJ Next Holdings Co., Ltd.; *Int'l*, pg. 2697
FJC SECURITY SERVICES, INC.—See Allied Universal Manager LLC; *U.S. Private*, pg. 190
FJELLSPRENGER AS—See Nordisk Bergteknik AB; *Int'l*, pg. 5424
F.J. ELSNER TRADING GESELLSCHAFT MBH—See Scully Royalty Ltd.; *Int'l*, pg. 6656
FJERBY AS—See AF Gruppen ASA; *Int'l*, pg. 184
FJ FOODSERVICE, LLC—See Hormel Foods Corporation; *U.S. Public*, pg. 1054
F.J. KROB & CO., INC.; *U.S. Private*, pg. 1456
FJ MANAGEMENT, INC.; *U.S. Private*, pg. 1538
FJ NEXT HOLDINGS CO., LTD.; *Int'l*, pg. 2697
F. J. O'HARA & SONS INC.; *U.S. Private*, pg. 1455
FJORD1 ASA—See Havila Holding AS; *Int'l*, pg. 3287
FJORD1 ASA—See Vision Ridge Partners, LLC; *U.S. Private*, pg. 4391
FJORDKRAFT AS—See Statkraft AS; *Int'l*, pg. 7185
FJORDLAND AS—See TINE SA; *Int'l*, pg. 7753
FJORDLAND EXPLORATION INC.; *Int'l*, pg. 2697
FJORD MARIN TURKEY AS—See Selonda Aquaculture SA; *Int'l*, pg. 6701
FJORD OY—See Accenture plc; *Int'l*, pg. 87
FJORDS DIALYSIS, LLC—See DaVita Inc.; *U.S. Public*, pg. 638
FJORDS PROCESSING AUSTRALIA PTY LTD—See NOV, Inc.; *U.S. Public*, pg. 1544
FJORDS PROCESSING LIMITED—See NOV, Inc.; *U.S. Public*, pg. 1544
F & J PRINCE HOLDINGS CORPORATION; *Int'l*, pg. 2594
F.J. SCIAME CONSTRUCTION CO. INC.; *U.S. Private*, pg. 1456
FJ TRANSCOSMOS HUMAN RESOURCE PROFESSIONALS LIMITED—See Transcosmos Inc.; *Int'l*, pg. 7898
FJW CONSTRUCTION, LLC—See Broaddus & Associates, Inc.; *U.S. Private*, pg. 659
FKA GSI US, INC.—See Harvard Bioscience, Inc.; *U.S. Public*, pg. 987
FKAUBI, INC.—See Harvard Bioscience, Inc.; *U.S. Public*, pg. 987
F K GAILEY—See UGI Corporation; *U.S. Public*, pg. 2222
FKG OIL COMPANY—See Moto, Inc.; *U.S. Private*, pg. 2796
FKI LIMITED—See Melrose Industries PLC; *Int'l*, pg. 4812
F.K.K. KYOKUTO KOGEN CONCRETE SHINKO CO. LTD—See VINCI S.A.; *Int'l*, pg. 8231
FKL AD TEMERIN; *Int'l*, pg. 2697
FKM—See The Company of Others; *U.S. Private*, pg. 4013
F. KORBEL BROS. INC.; *U.S. Private*, pg. 1455
FKP AREA ONE GMBH—See CTS Eventim AG & Co. KGAA; *Int'l*, pg. 1873
FKP COMMERCIAL DEVELOPMENTS PTY. LTD.—See Brookfield Corporation; *Int'l*, pg. 1186
FKP FUNDS MANAGEMENT LIMITED—See Brookfield Corporation; *Int'l*, pg. 1186
FKP LIMITED—See Brookfield Corporation; *Int'l*, pg. 1185
FKP POLAND SP. Z O.O.—See CTS Eventim AG & Co. KGAA; *Int'l*, pg. 1873
FKP REAL ESTATE PTY. LTD.—See Brookfield Corporation; *Int'l*, pg. 1186
FKP RESIDENTIAL DEVELOPMENTS PTY. LTD.—See Brookfield Corporation; *Int'l*, pg. 1186

FKP SCORPIO BELGIUM B.V.—See CTS Eventim AG & Co. KGAA; *Int'l*, pg. 1873
FKP SCORPIO ENTERTAINMENT LTD.—See CTS Eventim AG & Co. KGAA; *Int'l*, pg. 1873
FKP SCORPIO KONZERTPRODUKTIONEN GMBH—See CTS Eventim AG & Co. KGAA; *Int'l*, pg. 1873
FKP SCORPIO NORGE AS—See CTS Eventim AG & Co. KGAA; *Int'l*, pg. 1873
FKP SCORPIO POLAND SP. Z O.O—See CTS Eventim AG & Co. KGAA; *Int'l*, pg. 1873
FKP SCORPIO SVERIGE AB—See CTS Eventim AG & Co. KGAA; *Int'l*, pg. 1873
FKP SHOW CREATIONS GMBH—See CTS Eventim AG & Co. KGAA; *Int'l*, pg. 1873
FKQ ADVERTISING + MARKETING INC.; *U.S. Private*, pg. 1538
FK SYSTEMBAU BETEILIGUNGS-GMBH—See STRABAG SE; *Int'l*, pg. 7230
F.K. SYSTEMBAU GMBH—See STRABAG SE; *Int'l*, pg. 7230
FLABEG DEUTSCHLAND GMBH—See CORDET Capital Partners LLP; *Int'l*, pg. 1796
FLABEG HOLDING GMBH—See CORDET Capital Partners LLP; *Int'l*, pg. 1796
FLABEG TECHNICAL GLASS CORP.—See CORDET Capital Partners LLP; *Int'l*, pg. 1796
FLACHGLAS TORGAU GMBH—See Compagnie de Saint-Gobain SA; *Int'l*, pg. 1723
FLACKS HOMES LLC; *U.S. Private*, pg. 1538
FLACK STEEL LLC; *U.S. Private*, pg. 1538
FLAD ARCHITECTS; *U.S. Private*, pg. 1539
FLAGA GAZ MAGYARORSZAG KFT.—See UGI Corporation; *U.S. Public*, pg. 2222
FLAGA GMBH—See UGI Corporation; *U.S. Public*, pg. 2222
FLAGA GPL ROMANIA S.R.L.—See UGI Corporation; *U.S. Public*, pg. 2222
FLAGA NG GMBH—See UGI Corporation; *U.S. Public*, pg. 2222
FLAGA SPOL S.R.O.—See UGI Corporation; *U.S. Public*, pg. 2222
FLAGA S.R.O.—See UGI Corporation; *U.S. Public*, pg. 2222
FLAGA SUISSE GMBH—See UGI Corporation; *U.S. Public*, pg. 2222
FLAGGER FORCE; *U.S. Private*, pg. 1539
FLAGG INC.—See Clayton, Dubilier & Rice, LLC; *U.S. Private*, pg. 930
FLAGG RV CENTER; *U.S. Private*, pg. 1539
FLAGHOUSE INC.; *U.S. Private*, pg. 1539
FLAG INTERMEDIATE HOLDINGS CORPORATION—See Reliance Steel & Aluminum Co.; *U.S. Public*, pg. 1780
FLAGLER BANCSHARES CORPORATION; *U.S. Private*, pg. 1539
FLAGLER BANK—See Dort Financial Credit Union; *U.S. Private*, pg. 1264
FLAGLERCE HOLDINGS, LLC—See Alta Equipment Group Inc.; *U.S. Public*, pg. 86
FLAGLER DEVELOPMENT COMPANY, LLC—See SoftBank Group Corp.; *Int'l*, pg. 7053
FLAGLER DEVELOPMENT GROUP LLC—See SoftBank Group Corp.; *Int'l*, pg. 7053
FLAGLER DIALYSIS, LLC—See DaVita Inc.; *U.S. Public*, pg. 638
FLAGLER SYSTEM INC.; *U.S. Private*, pg. 1539
FLAG PUBLICATION, INC; *U.S. Private*, pg. 1539
FLAGSHIP ATLANTA DAIRY LLC—See Southeast Milk, Inc.; *U.S. Private*, pg. 3726
FLAGSHIP AUTO CENTER; *U.S. Private*, pg. 1539
FLAGSHIP BANK MINNESOTA—See Flagship Financial Group, Inc.; *U.S. Private*, pg. 1539
FLAGSHIP BANK—See West Florida Bank Corporation; *U.S. Private*, pg. 4485
FLAGSHIP BIOSCIENCES, INC.; *U.S. Private*, pg. 1539
FLAGSHIP CITY INSURANCE COMPANY—See Erie Indemnity Company; *U.S. Public*, pg. 792
FLAGSHIP CO., LTD.—See Capcom Co., Ltd.; *Int'l*, pg. 1302
FLAGSHIP CONSTRUCTION CO., LLC—See National Construction Enterprises Inc.; *U.S. Private*, pg. 2851
FLAG SHIP CORPORATION; *U.S. Private*, pg. 1539
FLAGSHIP CREDIT ACCEPTANCE LLC—See Flagship Credit Corporation; *U.S. Private*, pg. 1539
FLAGSHIP CREDIT CORPORATION; *U.S. Private*, pg. 1539
FLAGSHIP FACILITY SERVICES, INC.; *U.S. Private*, pg. 1539
FLAGSHIP FINANCIAL GROUP, INC.; *U.S. Private*, pg. 1539
FLAGSHIP FOOD GROUP, LLC; *U.S. Private*, pg. 1539
FLAGSHIP GLOBAL CORPORATION; *Int'l*, pg. 2697
THE FLAGSHIP GROUP, LTD.—See Brown & Brown, Inc.; *U.S. Public*, pg. 402
FLAGSHIP INVESTMENTS LIMITED; *Int'l*, pg. 2697
FLAGSHIP RESORT DEVELOPMENT; *U.S. Private*, pg. 1539
FLAGSHIP STORE BOLOGNA 1 S.R.L.—See TIM S.p.A.; *Int'l*, pg. 7749

FLAGSHIP STORE CATANIA 1 S.R.L.—See TIM S.p.A.; *Int'l*, pg. 7749
FLAGSHIP STORE MILANO 2 S.R.L.—See TIM S.p.A.; *Int'l*, pg. 7749
FLAGSHIP STORE MODENA 1 S.R.L.—See TIM S.p.A.; *Int'l*, pg. 7749
FLAGSHIPSTORE ROMA 1 S.R.L.—See TIM S.p.A.; *Int'l*, pg. 7749
FLAGSHIPSTORE ROMA 2 S.R.L.—See TIM S.p.A.; *Int'l*, pg. 7749
FLAGSHIPSTORE TARANTO 1 S.R.L.—See TIM S.p.A.; *Int'l*, pg. 7749
FLAGSHIPSTORE TORINO 1 S.R.L.—See TIM S.p.A.; *Int'l*, pg. 7749
FLAGSHIP TRADING CORP.; *U.S. Private*, pg. 1539
FLAGSHIP VENTURES; *U.S. Private*, pg. 1539
FLAGSTAFF MALL SPE LLC—See The Macerich Company; *U.S. Public*, pg. 2110
FLAGSTAFF PUBLISHING CO.—See Lee Enterprises, Incorporated; *U.S. Public*, pg. 1299
FLAGSTAR BANCORP, INC.—See New York Community Bancorp, Inc.; *U.S. Public*, pg. 1512
FLAGSTAR BANK, FSB—See New York Community Bancorp, Inc.; *U.S. Public*, pg. 1512
FLAGSTAR COMMERCIAL CORPORATION—See New York Community Bancorp, Inc.; *U.S. Public*, pg. 1513
FLAGSTAR INVESTMENT GROUP, INC.—See New York Community Bancorp, Inc.; *U.S. Public*, pg. 1513
FLAGSTONE APARTMENT PROPERTY, LLC—See Wells Fargo & Company; *U.S. Public*, pg. 2343
FLAGSTONE FOODS INC.—See Atlas Holdings, LLC; *U.S. Private*, pg. 376
FLAGS UNLIMITED; *Int'l*, pg. 2697
FLAHERTY & CRUMRINE PREFERRED & INCOME SECURITIES FUND, INC.; *U.S. Public*, pg. 852
FLAIRIS SDN BHD—See ShawKwei & Partners Ltd.; *Int'l*, pg. 6792
FLAIRJET LIMITED—See Directional Capital LLC; *U.S. Private*, pg. 1236
FLAKEBOARD COMPANY LIMITED—See AntarChile S.A.; *Int'l*, pg. 481
FLAKK HOLDING AS; *Int'l*, pg. 2697
FLAKK INTERNATIONAL AS—See Flakk Holding AS; *Int'l*, pg. 2698
FLAKTGROUP BALTICS UAB—See Triton Advisers Limited; *Int'l*, pg. 7930
FLAKTGROUP DEUTSCHLAND GMBH—See Triton Advisers Limited; *Int'l*, pg. 7930
FLAKTGROUP HOLDING GMBH—See Triton Advisers Limited; *Int'l*, pg. 7930
FLAKTGROUP INDIA PRIVATE LIMITED—See Triton Advisers Limited; *Int'l*, pg. 7930
FLAKTGROUP ITALY SPA—See Triton Advisers Limited; *Int'l*, pg. 7930
FLAKTGROUP LATVIJA SIA—See Triton Advisers Limited; *Int'l*, pg. 7931
FLAKTGROUP POLAND SP. Z O.O.—See Triton Advisers Limited; *Int'l*, pg. 7930
FLAKTGROUP SINGAPORE PTE. LTD.—See Triton Advisers Limited; *Int'l*, pg. 7930
FLAKTGROUP SWEDEN AB—See Triton Advisers Limited; *Int'l*, pg. 7931
FLAKTGROUP SWITZERLAND AG—See Triton Advisers Limited; *Int'l*, pg. 7930
FLAKTGROUP WURZEN GMBH—See Triton Advisers Limited; *Int'l*, pg. 7930
FLAKT OU—See Triton Advisers Limited; *Int'l*, pg. 7930
FLAKT WOODS AS—See Triton Advisers Limited; *Int'l*, pg. 7930
FLAKT WOODS GMBH—See Triton Advisers Limited; *Int'l*, pg. 7930
FLAKT WOODS (IRELAND) LTD—See Triton Advisers Limited; *Int'l*, pg. 7930
FLAKT WOODS (L.L.C.)—See Triton Advisers Limited; *Int'l*, pg. 7930
FLAKT WOODS LTD.—See Triton Advisers Limited; *Int'l*, pg. 7930
FLAKT WOODS OY—See Triton Advisers Limited; *Int'l*, pg. 7930
FLAKT WOODS SAS—See Triton Advisers Limited; *Int'l*, pg. 7930
FLAMBEAU EUROPLAST, LTD.—See Nordic Group of Companies, Ltd.; *U.S. Private*, pg. 2936
FLAMBEAU, INC. - ARTBIN DIVISION—See Nordic Group of Companies, Ltd.; *U.S. Private*, pg. 2937
FLAMBEAU, INC. - FLAMBEAU BLOW MOLDING FACILITY—See Nordic Group of Companies, Ltd.; *U.S. Private*, pg. 2937
FLAMBEAU, INC. - FLAMBEAU COLUMBUS FACILITY—See Nordic Group of Companies, Ltd.; *U.S. Private*, pg. 2937
FLAMBEAU, INC. - FLAMBEAU FLUID SYSTEMS DIVISION—See Nordic Group of Companies, Ltd.; *U.S. Private*, pg. 2937
FLAMBEAU, INC. - FLAMBEAU HARDWARE PRODUCTS DIVISION—See Nordic Group of Companies, Ltd.; *U.S. Private*, pg. 2937

COMPANY NAME INDEX

FLAMBEAU, INC. - FLAMBEAU INJECTION MOLDING FACILITY—See Nordic Group of Companies, Ltd.; *U.S. Private*, pg. 2937
FLAMBEAU, INC. - FLAMBEAU MADISON FACILITY—See Nordic Group of Companies, Ltd.; *U.S. Private*, pg. 2937
FLAMBEAU, INC. - FLAMBEAU MIDDLEFIELD FACILITY—See Nordic Group of Companies, Ltd.; *U.S. Private*, pg. 2937
FLAMBEAU, INC. - FLAMBEAU OUTDOORS DIVISION—See Nordic Group of Companies, Ltd.; *U.S. Private*, pg. 2937
FLAMBEAU, INC. - FLAMBEAU PHOENIX FACILITY—See Nordic Group of Companies, Ltd.; *U.S. Private*, pg. 2937
FLAMBEAU, INC. - FLAMBEAU SHARON CENTER FACILITY—See Nordic Group of Companies, Ltd.; *U.S. Private*, pg. 2937
FLAMBEAU, INC. - FLAMBEAU WELDON FACILITY—See Nordic Group of Companies, Ltd.; *U.S. Private*, pg. 2937
FLAMBEAU, INC. - PLASTICOS FLAMBEAU FACILITY—See Nordic Group of Companies, Ltd.; *U.S. Private*, pg. 2937
FLAMBEAU, INC.—See Nordic Group of Companies, Ltd.; *U.S. Private*, pg. 2936
FLAMBEAU INC.—See Nordic Group of Companies, Ltd.; *U.S. Private*, pg. 2936
FLAMBEAU PLASTICS CO.—See Nordic Group of Companies, Ltd.; *U.S. Private*, pg. 2936
FLAMBEAU PRODUCTS-COLUMBUS—See Nordic Group of Companies, Ltd.; *U.S. Private*, pg. 2937
FLAMBEAU RIVER PAPERS LLC; *U.S. Private*, pg. 1540
FLAMBEAU SOUTHEAST CO.—See Nordic Group of Companies, Ltd.; *U.S. Private*, pg. 2937
FLAMBEAU TECHNOLOGIES—See Nordic Group of Companies, Ltd.; *U.S. Private*, pg. 2937
FLAMBORO DOWNS LIMITED—See Great Canadian Gaming Corporation; *Int'l*, pg. 3063
FLAMCO AG—See Aalberts N.V.; *Int'l*, pg. 34
FLAMCO B.V.—See Aalberts N.V.; *Int'l*, pg. 34
FLAMCO FLEXCON B.V.—See Aalberts N.V.; *Int'l*, pg. 34
FLAMCO FLEXCON LTD.—See Aalberts N.V.; *Int'l*, pg. 34
FLAMCO GMBH—See Aalberts N.V.; *Int'l*, pg. 34
FLAMCO IMZ B.V.—See Aalberts N.V.; *Int'l*, pg. 34
FLAMCO KFT.—See Aalberts N.V.; *Int'l*, pg. 34
FLAMCO LIMITED—See Aalberts N.V.; *Int'l*, pg. 34
FLAMCO S.A.R.L.—See Aalberts N.V.; *Int'l*, pg. 34
FLAMCO STAG GMBH—See Aalberts N.V.; *Int'l*, pg. 34
FLAME ENTERPRISES INCORPORATED; *U.S. Private*, pg. 1540
FLAMEFAST FIRE SYSTEMS LIMITED—See Marlowe Plc; *Int'l*, pg. 4698
FLAMEFIGHTER CORPORATION—See South Park Corporation; *U.S. Private*, pg. 3723
FLAME FURNACE CO.; *U.S. Private*, pg. 1540
FLAME GUARD B.V.—See AFG Group Nijmegen B.V.; *Int'l*, pg. 188
FLAME HEARTS CO., LTD.—See Digital Hearts Holdings Co., Ltd.; *Int'l*, pg. 2122
FLAMEL TECHNOLOGIES INC.—See AVADEL PHARMACEUTICALS PLC; *Int'l*, pg. 734
THE FLAMEMASTER CORPORATION—See Socomore S.A.; *Int'l*, pg. 7044
FLAME PROPANE—See UGI Corporation; *U.S. Public*, pg. 2222
FLAME SEAL PRODUCTS, INC.; *U.S. Public*, pg. 852
FLAME TREE GROUP HOLDINGS LTD.; *Int'l*, pg. 2698
FLAMEX, INC.—See Intermediate Capital Group plc; *Int'l*, pg. 3742
FLAMEX, INC.—See Kirkbi A/S; *Int'l*, pg. 4190
FLAMINGO ANESTHESIA ASSOCIATES, INC.—See KKR & Co. Inc.; *U.S. Public*, pg. 1245
FLAMINGO LAS VEGAS OPERATING COMPANY, LLC—See Caesars Entertainment, Inc.; *U.S. Public*, pg. 420
FLAMINGO LINE EL SALVADOR S.A. DE C.V.—See Allcargo Logistics Limited; *Int'l*, pg. 334
FLAMINGO LTD.—See Africa Israel Investments Ltd.; *Int'l*, pg. 190
FLAMINGO MANAGEMENT SDN. BHD.—See MPHB Capital Berhad; *Int'l*, pg. 5062
FLAMINGO OIL COMPANY; *U.S. Private*, pg. 1540
FLAMINGO PARK KIDNEY CENTER, INC.—See DaVita Inc.; *U.S. Public*, pg. 638
FLAMINGO PRODUCTS, INC.—See Erving Industries, Inc.; *U.S. Private*, pg. 1424
FLAMINGO—See Omnicom Group Inc.; *U.S. Public*, pg. 1583
FLAMINGO SURGERY CENTER—See HCA Healthcare, Inc.; *U.S. Public*, pg. 996
FLAMINGO THERAPEUTICS BV; *Int'l*, pg. 2698
FLAMINGO VENTURES PTY. LTD.—See Odessa Minerals Limited; *Int'l*, pg. 5525
FLAMMARION S.A.—See Madrigall SA; *Int'l*, pg. 4635
FLAMURA SA; *Int'l*, pg. 2698
FLANAGAN BROTHERS, INC.—See Hanwha Group; *Int'l*, pg. 3264
FLANAGAN FOODSERVICE, INC.; *Int'l*, pg. 2698

FLANDERS ELECTRIC MOTOR SERVICE INC.; *U.S. Private*, pg. 1540
FLANDERS INDUSTRIES, INC., *U.S. Private*, pg. 1540
FLANDRAU DIALYSIS, LLC—See DaVita Inc.; *U.S. Public*, pg. 638
F. LANG U. K. MENHOFER BAUGESELLSCHAFT M.B.H. & CO. KG—See STRABAG SE; *Int'l*, pg. 7230
FLANIGAN'S ENTERPRISES, INC. OF GEORGIA—See Flanigan's Enterprises, Inc.; *U.S. Public*, pg. 852
FLANIGAN'S ENTERPRISES, INC.—See Flanigan's Enterprises, Inc.; *U.S. Public*, pg. 852
FLANIGAN'S ENTERPRISES, INC.—See Flanigan's Enterprises, Inc.; *U.S. Public*, pg. 852
FLANIGAN'S ENTERPRISES, INC.—See Flanigan's Enterprises, Inc.; *U.S. Public*, pg. 852
FLANIGAN'S ENTERPRISES, INC.—See Flanigan's Enterprises, Inc.; *U.S. Public*, pg. 852
FLANIGAN'S ENTERPRISES, INC.; *U.S. Public*, pg. 852
FLANIGAN'S ENTERPRISES, INC.—See Flanigan's Enterprises, Inc.; *U.S. Public*, pg. 852
FLANIGAN'S ENTERPRISES, INC.—See Flanigan's Enterprises, Inc.; *U.S. Public*, pg. 852
FLANIGAN'S ENTERPRISES, INC. - SURFSIDE—See Flanigan's Enterprises, Inc.; *U.S. Public*, pg. 852
FLANIGAN'S RESTAURANTS—See Flanigan's Enterprises, Inc.; *U.S. Public*, pg. 852
FLANNER & BUCHANAN, INC.; *U.S. Private*, pg. 1540
FLANNERS AUDIO & VIDEO INC.; *U.S. Private*, pg. 1540
FLANNERY PHYSICAL THERAPY, LIMITED PARTNERSHIP.—See U.S. Physical Therapy, Inc.; *U.S. Public*, pg. 2214
FLAN TERRASSEMENT SAS—See VINCI S.A.; *Int'l*, pg. 8221
FLAP KONGRE TOPLANTI HIZMETLERI OTOMOTIV VE TURIZM A.S.; *Int'l*, pg. 2698
FLARE CONSTRUCTION, LLC—See Quanta Services, Inc.; *U.S. Public*, pg. 1751
FLARE INDUSTRIES, LLC—See Turnbridge Capital, LLC; *U.S. Private*, pg. 4260
FLAROS S.A.; *Int'l*, pg. 2698
FLASH AB—See Mellby Gard Holding AB; *Int'l*, pg. 4811
FLASHAPP INC.; *Int'l*, pg. 2698
FLASHBANC, LLC—See Independence Capital Partners, LLC; *U.S. Private*, pg. 2056
FLASHCO MANUFACTURING, INC.; *U.S. Private*, pg. 1540
FLASHES PUBLISHERS—See Gannett Co., Inc.; *U.S. Public*, pg. 901
FLASH EXTERMINATING, INC.; *U.S. Private*, pg. 1540
FLASHFUNDERS, INC.; *U.S. Private*, pg. 1540
FLASH, INC.; *U.S. Private*, pg. 1540
FLASH LOGISTICS SERVICES INC.; *U.S. Private*, pg. 1540
FLASH MARKETS INC.; *U.S. Private*, pg. 1540
FLASH NETWORKS INC.—See Constellation Software Inc.; *Int'l*, pg. 1775
FLASH NETWORKS LTD.—See Constellation Software Inc.; *Int'l*, pg. 1775
FLASH NETWORKS SINGAPORE PTE LTD—See Constellation Software Inc.; *Int'l*, pg. 1775
FLASHPARKING, INC.; *U.S. Private*, pg. 1540
FLASHTALKING, INC.—See Simplicity Marketing Ltd.; *Int'l*, pg. 6934
FLASH TECHNOLOGY, LLC—See SPX Technologies, Inc.; *U.S. Public*, pg. 1921
FLASHZERO CORP.; *U.S. Public*, pg. 852
FLASKAMP AG; *Int'l*, pg. 2698
FLASPOHLER RESEARCH GROUP, INC; *U.S. Private*, pg. 1540
FLASR, INC.; *Int'l*, pg. 2698
FLASTER CORP.; *U.S. Private*, pg. 1540
FLAT AUDIO TECHNOLOGIES, LLC; *U.S. Private*, pg. 1540
FLAT BRANCH HOME LOANS; *U.S. Private*, pg. 1541
FLATEK, INC.—See Sigurd Microelectronics Corp.; *Int'l*, pg. 6913
FLAT ENTERPRISES INC.; *U.S. Private*, pg. 1541
FLATEX BANK AG—See flatexDEGIRO AG; *Int'l*, pg. 2698
FLATEXDEGIRO AG; *Int'l*, pg. 2698
FLATFISH LTD.—See Nissui Corporation; *Int'l*, pg. 5377
FLAT GLASS GROUP CO., LTD.; *Int'l*, pg. 2698
FLAT GLASS INDUSTRIES LIMITED—See MHG Glass Pty Ltd; *Int'l*, pg. 4872
FLATHEAD ELECTRIC COOPERATIVE, INC.; *U.S. Private*, pg. 1541
FLATIRON CONSTRUCTION CORP. - HEAVY CIVIL DIVISION—See ACS, Actividades de Construccion y Servicios, S.A.; *Int'l*, pg. 113
FLATIRON CONSTRUCTION CORP.—See ACS, Actividades de Construccion y Servicios, S.A.; *Int'l*, pg. 113
FLATIRON PROPERTY HOLDING, LLC—See The Macerich Company; *U.S. Public*, pg. 2110
FLATIRONS SOLUTIONS, INC.—See InfoTrust Group, Inc.; *U.S. Private*, pg. 2074
FLATIRONS SURGERY CENTER, LLC—See Tenet Healthcare Corporation; *U.S. Public*, pg. 2010
THE FLATLEY COMPANY; *U.S. Private*, pg. 4029
THE FLAT MANAGERS LIMITED—See The Skipton Building Society; *Int'l*, pg. 7687
FLAT RATE MOVING NEW YORK; *U.S. Private*, pg. 1541
FLAT ROCK CAPITAL CORP.; *U.S. Private*, pg. 1541

FLATS AT PALISADES LLC—See UDR, Inc.; *U.S. Public*, pg. 2218
FLATWORK TECHNOLOGIES LLC; *U.S. Private*, pg. 1541
FLATWORLD ACQUISITION CORP.; *Int'l*, pg. 2698
FLAUREA CHEMICALS S.A.—See Aurea, S.A.; *Int'l*, pg. 707
FLAVELLE SAWMILL COMPANY LTD.—See Mill & Timber Products Ltd; *Int'l*, pg. 4895
FLAVINE NORTH AMERICA, INC.; *U.S. Private*, pg. 1541
FLAVOR BURST CO. LLP—See The Middleby Corporation; *U.S. Public*, pg. 2113
FLAVOR & FRAGRANCE SPECIALTIES; *U.S. Private*, pg. 1541
FLAVOR INFUSION INTERNATIONAL, S.A.—See Archer-Daniels-Midland Company; *U.S. Public*, pg. 185
FLAVOR INGREDIENT HOLDINGS, LLC—See T. Hasegawa Co. Ltd.; *Int'l*, pg. 7396
FLAVOR INN CORPORATION SDN BHD—See Croda International plc; *Int'l*, pg. 1853
FLAVORITE FOODS LIMITED; *Int'l*, pg. 2698
FLAVORPILL PRODUCTIONS LLC—See BDG Media, Inc.; *U.S. Private*, pg. 500
FLAVOR PRODUCERS, LLC—See Glanbia Co-Operative Society Limited; *Int'l*, pg. 2987
FLAVORS15, LLC; *U.S. Private*, pg. 1541
FLAVORS AND ESSENCES UK LIMITED—See International Flavors & Fragrances Inc.; *U.S. Public*, pg. 1151
FLAVORS DIRECT LTD—See Symrise AG; *Int'l*, pg. 7380
FLAVOURS, INC.—See Excellere Capital Management LLC; *U.S. Private*, pg. 1446
FLAVUS BETEILIGUNGEN AG; *Int'l*, pg. 2698
FLAX ARTIST'S MATERIALS; *U.S. Private*, pg. 1541
FLAX DESIGNS; *U.S. Private*, pg. 1541
FLAYCO PRODUCTS, INC.; *U.S. Private*, pg. 1541
FLC GROUP JOINT STOCK COMPANY; *Int'l*, pg. 2698
F.L. CRANE & SONS, INC.; *U.S. Private*, pg. 1456
F.L. CRANE & SONS, INC.; *U.S. Private*, pg. 1456
THE FLEA MARKET, INC.; *U.S. Public*, pg. 4029
FLECO INDUSTRIES, LLC—See CORE Industrial Partners, LLC; *U.S. Private*, pg. 1048
FLECTION FRANCE SAS—See Arrow Electronics, Inc.; *U.S. Public*, pg. 199
FLECTION GERMANY GMBH—See Arrow Electronics, Inc.; *U.S. Public*, pg. 199
FLECTION UNITED KINGDOM LTD.—See Arrow Electronics, Inc.; *U.S. Public*, pg. 199
THE FLECTO COMPANY, INC.—See RPM International Inc.; *U.S. Public*, pg. 1817
FLEEKDRIVE CO., LTD.—See SOLXYZ Co., Ltd.; *Int'l*, pg. 7083
FLEENOR SECURITY SYSTEMS, INC.; *U.S. Private*, pg. 1541
FLEENOR; *U.S. Private*, pg. 1541
FLEET ACQUISITIONS LLC; *U.S. Private*, pg. 1541
FLEET ADVANTAGE, LLC; *U.S. Private*, pg. 1541
FLEETAFRICA (PTY) LIMITED—See Super Group Limited; *Int'l*, pg. 7334
FLEET ASSISTANCE LIMITED—See Arthur J. Gallagher & Co.; *U.S. Public*, pg. 204
FLEET CANADA INC.; *Int'l*, pg. 2698
FLEET CARD FUELS INC.; *U.S. Private*, pg. 1541
FLEET CAR LEASE INC.; *U.S. Private*, pg. 1541
FLEETCO INC.; *U.S. Private*, pg. 1542
FLEETCOMPANY GMBH—See Porsche Automobil Holding SE; *Int'l*, pg. 5931
FLEETCOMPANY GMBH—See TUV SUD AG; *Int'l*, pg. 7984
FLEETCOR CZECH REPUBLIC SRO—See Corpay, Inc.; *U.S. Public*, pg. 579
FLEETCOR DEUTSCHLAND GMBH—See Corpay, Inc.; *U.S. Public*, pg. 579
FLEETCOR EUROPE LIMITED—See Corpay, Inc.; *U.S. Public*, pg. 579
FLEETCOR FUEL CARDS (EUROPE) LIMITED—See Corpay, Inc.; *U.S. Public*, pg. 580
FLEETCOR POLAND SPOEKA Z OGRANICZONA ODPOWIEDZIALNOSCIA—See Corpay, Inc.; *U.S. Public*, pg. 580
FLEETCOR SLOVAKIA S.R.O.—See Corpay, Inc.; *U.S. Public*, pg. 580
FLEETCROSS HOLDINGS, INC.—See The Hearst Corporation; *U.S. Private*, pg. 4045
FLEET ENGINEERS, INC.; *U.S. Private*, pg. 1541
FLEET EQUIPMENT LLC.—See Stonepeak Partners L.P.; *U.S. Private*, pg. 3829
FLEET FEET, INC.; *U.S. Private*, pg. 1541
FLEET FEET SPORTS, LLC—See Investors Management Corporation; *U.S. Public*, pg. 2132
FLEET FINANCIAL LIMITED—See Lookers plc; *Int'l*, pg. 4555
FLEETGISTICS HOLDINGS, INC.—See Harbour Group Industries, Inc.; *U.S. Private*, pg. 1860
FLEETGUARD FILTERS PVT. LTD.—See Cummins Inc.; *U.S. Public*, pg. 606
FLEET LABORATORIES INC.—See DDD Ltd.; *Int'l*, pg. 1993
FLEET LABORATORIES—See Prestige Consumer Healthcare Inc.; *U.S. Public*, pg. 1716

FLEET LEASE DISPOSAL INC.

CORPORATE AFFILIATIONS

FLEET LEASE DISPOSAL INC.; *U.S. Private*, pg. 1541
FLEET LEASE INC.—See Boerner Truck Center; *U.S. Private*, pg. 609
FLEETLINE PRODUCTS—See Berkshire Hathaway Inc.; *U.S. Public*, pg. 310
FLEET LOGISTICS AUSTRIA GMBH—See TUV SUD AG; *Int'l*, pg. 7984
FLEET LOGISTICS FINLAND OY—See TUV SUD AG; *Int'l*, pg. 7984
FLEET LOGISTICS FRANCE S.A.S—See TUV SUD AG; *Int'l*, pg. 7984
FLEET LOGISTICS HUNGARY KFT—See TUV SUD AG; *Int'l*, pg. 7984
FLEET LOGISTICS INTERNATIONAL NV—See TUV SUD AG; *Int'l*, pg. 7984
FLEET LOGISTICS ITALIA S.R.L.—See TUV SUD AG; *Int'l*, pg. 7984
FLEET LOGISTICS NETHERLANDS B.V.—See TUV SUD AG; *Int'l*, pg. 7984
FLEET LOGISTICS NORDIC AB—See TUV SUD AG; *Int'l*, pg. 7984
FLEET LOGISTICS POLAND SP. Z O.O.—See TUV SUD AG; *Int'l*, pg. 7984
FLEET LOGISTICS PORTUGAL UNIPESSOAL LDA—See TUV SUD AG; *Int'l*, pg. 7984
FLEET LOGISTICS ROMANIA—See TUV SUD AG; *Int'l*, pg. 7984
FLEET LOGISTICS RUSSIA—See TUV SUD AG; *Int'l*, pg. 7984
FLEET LOGISTICS SPAIN S.A.U.—See TUV SUD AG; *Int'l*, pg. 7984
FLEET LOGISTICS UK LIMITED—See TUV SUD AG; *Int'l*, pg. 7984
FLEET MAINTANCE—See VSE Corporation; *U.S. Public*, pg. 2313
FLEET MANAGEMENT SOLUTIONS, INC.—See Vector Capital Management, L.P.; *U.S. Private*, pg. 4353
FLEETMASTER EXPRESS INC.; *U.S. Private*, pg. 1542
FLEET MORRIS PETROLEUM INC.; *U.S. Private*, pg. 1542
FLEET MOVERS, INC.—See Daseke, Inc; *U.S. Private*, pg. 1161
FLEETNET AMERICA, INC.—See Cox Enterprises, Inc.; *U.S. Private*, pg. 1076
FLEET NETWORK PTY LIMITED—See Consolidated Operations Group Limited; *Int'l*, pg. 1771
FLEETONE FACTORING, LLC—See WEX, Inc.; *U.S. Public*, pg. 2364
FLEETONE, LLC—See WEX, Inc.; *U.S. Public*, pg. 2364
FLEETPARTNERS GROUP LIMITED; *Int'l*, pg. 2698
FLEET PARTNERS PTY. LTD.—See FleetPartners Group Limited; *Int'l*, pg. 2699
FLEET PARTS & SERVICE, INC.—See Boyne Capital Management, LLC; *U.S. Private*, pg. 629
FLEETPRIDE, INC.—See American Securities LLC; *U.S. Private*, pg. 248
FLEETPRIDE - NORTHEAST—See American Securities LLC; *U.S. Private*, pg. 248
FLEETPRIDE - SOUTHEAST—See American Securities LLC; *U.S. Private*, pg. 248
FLEETPRIDE - WESTERN/CENTRAL—See American Securities LLC; *U.S. Private*, pg. 248
FLEETPRO RIVER LTD.; *Int'l*, pg. 2699
FLEET RISK MANAGEMENT, INC.—See GTCR LLC; *U.S. Private*, pg. 1803
FLEET SALES LLC—See FJ Management, Inc.; *U.S. Private*, pg. 1538
FLEET STREET LTD.; *U.S. Private*, pg. 1542
FLEET TEAM, INC.; *U.S. Private*, pg. 1542
FLEET TECHNIQUE LIMITED—See ZIGUP plc; *Int'l*, pg. 8682
FLEET TIRE INCORPORATED; *U.S. Private*, pg. 1542
FLEET TRUCK SALES, INC.—See Werner Enterprises, Inc.; *U.S. Public*, pg. 2349
FLEETWASH, INC.—See ACON Investments, LLC; *U.S. Private*, pg. 62
FLEETWING CORPORATION; *U.S. Private*, pg. 1542
FLEETWOOD BANK; *U.S. Public*, pg. 852
FLEETWOOD-FIBRE PACKAGING & GRAPHICS, INC.; *U.S. Private*, pg. 1542
FLEETWOODGOLDCOWYARD AMBEC, INC.—See Barry-Wehmiller Companies, Inc.; *U.S. Private*, pg. 481
FLEETWOODGOLDCOWYARD—See Barry-Wehmiller Companies, Inc.; *U.S. Private*, pg. 481
FLEETWOODGOLDCOWYARD—See Barry-Wehmiller Companies, Inc.; *U.S. Private*, pg. 481
FLEETWOOD HOMES - DOUGLAS—See Cavco Industries, Inc.; *U.S. Public*, pg. 455
FLEETWOOD HOMES, INC.—See Cavco Industries, Inc.; *U.S. Public*, pg. 455
FLEETWOOD HOMES, INC.—See Cavco Industries, Inc.; *U.S. Public*, pg. 455
FLEETWOOD HOMES OF OREGON, INC.- WOODBURN/NORTH—See Cavco Industries, Inc.; *U.S. Public*, pg. 455
FLEETWOOD HOMES OF TEXAS, INC.- WACO/GHOLSON RD.—See Cavco Industries, Inc.; *U.S. Public*, pg. 455

FLEETWOOD HOMES OF VIRGINIA, INC.—See Cavco Industries, Inc.; *U.S. Public*, pg. 455
FLEETWOOD HOMES - WACO, TX—See Cavco Industries, Inc.; *U.S. Public*, pg. 455
FLEETWOOD LIMITED; *Int'l*, pg. 2699
FLEETWOOD METAL INDUSTRIES, INC.—See Cleveland-Cliffs, Inc.; *U.S. Public*, pg. 514
FLEETWOOD PTY LTD—See Fleetwood Limited; *Int'l*, pg. 2699
FLEETWOOD-SIGNODE—See Crown Holdings, Inc.; *U.S. Public*, pg. 599
FLEETWOOD TRANSPORTATION SERVICES INC.; *U.S. Private*, pg. 1542
FLEETWORTHY SOLUTIONS, INC.—See Bestpass, Inc.; *U.S. Private*, pg. 544
FLEGELS HOME FURNISHINGS; *U.S. Private*, pg. 1542
FLEGLER INVESTMENT COMPANY; *U.S. Private*, pg. 1542
FLEIMA-PLASTIC GMBH—See Masterflex SE; *Int'l*, pg. 4725
FLEISCHER-JACOBS & ASSOCIATES INC.—See Aon plc; *Int'l*, pg. 496
FLEISCHHACKER GMBH & CO. KG; *Int'l*, pg. 2699
FLEISCHMAN & GARCIA ARCHITECTS & PLANNERS, AIA—See BDG Architects LLP; *U.S. Private*, pg. 500
FLEISCHMANN SPEZIALSTAHL-HANDEL GMBH—See Jacquet Metal Service SA; *Int'l*, pg. 3867
FLEISCHMANN'S VINEGAR COMPANY, INC.—See Kerry Group plc; *Int'l*, pg. 4138
FLEISCHMANN'S YEAST—See The Garfield Weston Foundation; *Int'l*, pg. 7648
FLEISCH- UND WURSTWAREN TRADING GMBH—See Raiffeisenlandesbank Oberosterreich Aktiengesellschaft; *Int'l*, pg. 6188
FLEISHMAN-HILLARD AUSTRALIA PTY. LTD.—See Omnicom Group Inc.; *U.S. Public*, pg. 1583
FLEISHMAN-HILLARD BEIJING—See Omnicom Group Inc.; *U.S. Public*, pg. 1583
FLEISHMAN-HILLARD B.V.—See Omnicom Group Inc.; *U.S. Public*, pg. 1583
FLEISHMAN-HILLARD CANADA INC. - CALGARY—See Omnicom Group Inc.; *U.S. Public*, pg. 1584
FLEISHMAN-HILLARD CANADA INC. - OTTAWA—See Omnicom Group Inc.; *U.S. Public*, pg. 1584
FLEISHMAN-HILLARD CANADA INC. - TORONTO—See Omnicom Group Inc.; *U.S. Public*, pg. 1584
FLEISHMAN-HILLARD CANADA INC. - VANCOUVER—See Omnicom Group Inc.; *U.S. Public*, pg. 1584
FLEISHMAN-HILLARD CZECH REPUBLIC—See Omnicom Group Inc.; *U.S. Public*, pg. 1583
FLEISHMAN-HILLARD FRANCE—See Omnicom Group Inc.; *U.S. Public*, pg. 1583
FLEISHMAN-HILLARD GERMANY GMBH - BERLIN—See Omnicom Group Inc.; *U.S. Public*, pg. 1583
FLEISHMAN-HILLARD GERMANY GMBH - MUNICH—See Omnicom Group Inc.; *U.S. Public*, pg. 1583
FLEISHMAN-HILLARD GERMANY GMBH—See Omnicom Group Inc.; *U.S. Public*, pg. 1583
FLEISHMAN-HILLARD GROUP LTD. - EDINBURGH—See Omnicom Group Inc.; *U.S. Public*, pg. 1583
FLEISHMAN-HILLARD GROUP LTD.—See Omnicom Group Inc.; *U.S. Public*, pg. 1583
FLEISHMAN-HILLARD GUANGZHOU—See Omnicom Group Inc.; *U.S. Public*, pg. 1583
FLEISHMANHILLARD HIGHROAD—See Omnicom Group Inc.; *U.S. Public*, pg. 1584
FLEISHMAN-HILLARD HONG KONG LTD.—See Omnicom Group Inc.; *U.S. Public*, pg. 1583
FLEISHMAN-HILLARD INC. - BOSTON—See Omnicom Group Inc.; *U.S. Public*, pg. 1584
FLEISHMAN-HILLARD INC. - IRVINE—See Omnicom Group Inc.; *U.S. Public*, pg. 1584
FLEISHMAN-HILLARD INC. - PUERTO RICO—See Omnicom Group Inc.; *U.S. Public*, pg. 1584
FLEISHMAN-HILLARD INC.—See Omnicom Group Inc.; *U.S. Public*, pg. 1583
FLEISHMAN-HILLARD INC.—See Omnicom Group Inc.; *U.S. Public*, pg. 1583
FLEISHMAN-HILLARD INC.—See Omnicom Group Inc.; *U.S. Public*, pg. 1583
FLEISHMAN-HILLARD INC.—See Omnicom Group Inc.; *U.S. Public*, pg. 1583
FLEISHMAN-HILLARD INC.—See Omnicom Group Inc.; *U.S. Public*, pg. 1583
FLEISHMAN-HILLARD INC.—See Omnicom Group Inc.; *U.S. Public*, pg. 1584
FLEISHMAN-HILLARD INC.—See Omnicom Group Inc.; *U.S. Public*, pg. 1584
FLEISHMAN-HILLARD INC.—See Omnicom Group Inc.; *U.S. Public*, pg. 1584
FLEISHMAN-HILLARD INC.—See Omnicom Group Inc.; *U.S. Public*, pg. 1584
FLEISHMAN-HILLARD INC.—See Omnicom Group Inc.; *U.S. Public*, pg. 1584

FLEISHMAN-HILLARD INC.—See Omnicom Group Inc.; *U.S. Public*, pg. 1584
FLEISHMAN-HILLARD INC.—See Omnicom Group Inc.; *U.S. Public*, pg. 1584
FLEISHMAN-HILLARD INC.—See Omnicom Group Inc.; *U.S. Public*, pg. 1584
FLEISHMAN-HILLARD INC.—See Omnicom Group Inc.; *U.S. Public*, pg. 1584
FLEISHMAN-HILLARD INC.—See Omnicom Group Inc.; *U.S. Public*, pg. 1584
FLEISHMAN-HILLARD INC.—See Omnicom Group Inc.; *U.S. Public*, pg. 1584
FLEISHMAN-HILLARD ITALIA S.R.L.—See Omnicom Group Inc.; *U.S. Public*, pg. 1584
FLEISHMAN-HILLARD JAPAN KK—See Omnicom Group Inc.; *U.S. Public*, pg. 1584
FLEISHMAN-HILLARD KOREA—See Omnicom Group Inc.; *U.S. Public*, pg. 1584
FLEISHMAN-HILLARD LIMITED—See Omnicom Group Inc.; *U.S. Public*, pg. 1584
FLEISHMAN-HILLARD MANILA—See Omnicom Group Inc.; *U.S. Public*, pg. 1584
FLEISHMAN-HILLARD MEXICO, S.A. DE C.V.—See Omnicom Group Inc.; *U.S. Public*, pg. 1584
FLEISHMAN-HILLARD POLSKA SP. Z O.O.—See Omnicom Group Inc.; *U.S. Public*, pg. 1584
FLEISHMAN-HILLARD PTE. LTD.—See Omnicom Group Inc.; *U.S. Public*, pg. 1584
FLEISHMAN-HILLARD SA/NV—See Omnicom Group Inc.; *U.S. Public*, pg. 1584
FLEISHMANHILLARD—See Omnicom Group Inc.; *U.S. Public*, pg. 1583
FLEISHMAN-HILLARD SOUTH AFRICA (PTY) LTD.—See Omnicom Group Inc.; *U.S. Public*, pg. 1584
FLEISHMAN-HILLARD SPAIN, S.A.—See Omnicom Group Inc.; *U.S. Public*, pg. 1584
FLEMING BROTHERS OIL COMPANY INC; *U.S. Private*, pg. 1542
FLEMING CHICKS LIMITED—See Maple Lodge Farms Ltd.; *Int'l*, pg. 4686
FLEMING DOOR PRODUCTS LTD—See ASSA ABLOY AB; *Int'l*, pg. 637
FLEMING FEED & GRAIN INC.; *U.S. Private*, pg. 1542
FLEMING MEDICAL CENTER, LLC—See Apollo Global Management, Inc.; *U.S. Public*, pg. 155
FLEMING PHARMACEUTICALS; *U.S. Private*, pg. 1542
FLEMING'S OF BALTIMORE, LLC—See Bloomin' Brands, Inc.; *U.S. Public*, pg. 363
FLEMING'S PRIME STEAKHOUSE & WINE BAR—See Bloomin' Brands, Inc.; *U.S. Public*, pg. 363
FLEMINGTON AUDI PORSCHE VOLKSWAGEN; *U.S. Private*, pg. 1542
FLEMINGTON FIELDS PTY. LTD.—See Singapore Post Limited; *Int'l*, pg. 6941
FLEMINGTON INSTRUMENT CO. INC.; *U.S. Private*, pg. 1542
FLEMING & VAN METRE; *U.S. Private*, pg. 1542
FLEMISH CO., LTD.—See euglena Co., Ltd.; *Int'l*, pg. 2526
FLENDER CORPORATION—See The Carlyle Group Inc.; *U.S. Public*, pg. 2046
FLENDER DE MEXICO, S.A. DE C.V.—See The Carlyle Group Inc.; *U.S. Public*, pg. 2047
FLENDER GES.M.B.H.—See The Carlyle Group Inc.; *U.S. Public*, pg. 2046
FLENDER GMBH—See The Carlyle Group Inc.; *U.S. Public*, pg. 2046
FLENDER GRAFFENSTADEN S.A.—See The Carlyle Group Inc.; *U.S. Public*, pg. 2047
FLENDER IBERICA S.A.—See The Carlyle Group Inc.; *U.S. Public*, pg. 2047
FLENDER LIMITED—See Siemens Aktiengesellschaft; *Int'l*, pg. 6887
FLENDER LIMITED—See The Carlyle Group Inc.; *U.S. Public*, pg. 2047
FLENDER POWER TRANSMISSION (PTY.) LTD.—See The Carlyle Group Inc.; *U.S. Public*, pg. 2047
FLENDER (PTY) LTD.—See Siemens Aktiengesellschaft; *Int'l*, pg. 6887
FLENDER S.P.A.—See Siemens Aktiengesellschaft; *Int'l*, pg. 6887
FL ENTERTAINMENT N.V.; *Int'l*, pg. 2697
FLEQS B.V.—See Paragon Group Limited; *Int'l*, pg. 5737
FLERIE AB; *Int'l*, pg. 2699
THE FLESH COMPANY—See Ennis, Inc.; *U.S. Public*, pg. 769
FLETCHER ALLEN HEALTH CARE, INC.; *U.S. Private*, pg. 1542
FLETCHER ALUMINIUM—See Fletcher Building Limited; *Int'l*, pg. 2700
FLETCHER BUILDING AUSTRALIA—See Fletcher Building Limited; *Int'l*, pg. 2700
FLETCHER BUILDING HOLDINGS LIMITED—See Fletcher Building Limited; *Int'l*, pg. 2700
FLETCHER BUILDING LIMITED; *Int'l*, pg. 2699
FLETCHER BUILDING NETHERLANDS B.V.—See Fletcher Building Limited; *Int'l*, pg. 2700
FLETCHER BUILDING NOMINEES LIMITED—See Fletcher Building Limited; *Int'l*, pg. 2700

COMPANY NAME INDEX

FLETCHER BUILDING PRODUCTS LIMITED—See Fletcher Building Limited; *Int'l*, pg. 2700
FLETCHER CONCRETE AND INFRASTRUCTURE LIMITED—See Fletcher Building Limited; *Int'l*, pg. 2700
FLETCHER CONSTRUCTION AUSTRALIA PTY LIMITED—See Fletcher Building Limited; *Int'l*, pg. 2700
FLETCHER CONSTRUCTION BUILDINGS LIMITED—See Fletcher Building Limited; *Int'l*, pg. 2700
FLETCHER CONSTRUCTION COMPANY (FIJI) LIMITED—See Fletcher Building Limited; *Int'l*, pg. 2700
THE FLETCHER CONSTRUCTION COMPANY LIMITED—See Fletcher Building Limited; *Int'l*, pg. 2701
FLETCHER CONSTRUCTION (SOLOMON ISLANDS) LIMITED—See Fletcher Building Limited; *Int'l*, pg. 2700
FLETCHER DISTRIBUTION LIMITED—See Fletcher Building Limited; *Int'l*, pg. 2701
FLETCHER HEIGHTS STORAGE SOLUTIONS, L.L.C.—See National Storage Affiliates Trust; *U.S. Public*, pg. 1498
FLETCHER INDUSTRIES INC.; *U.S. Private*, pg. 1542
FLETCHER INDUSTRIES-INTERNATIONAL, INC.; *U.S. Private*, pg. 1542
FLETCHER INSULATION PTY. LIMITED—See Fletcher Building Limited; *Int'l*, pg. 2700
FLETCHER JONES MANAGEMENT GROUP, INC.; *U.S. Private*, pg. 1542
FLETCHER KING PLC; *Int'l*, pg. 2701
FLETCHER KING SERVICES LIMITED—See Fletcher King Plc; *Int'l*, pg. 2701
FLETCHER MCNEILL & PARTNERS LIMITED—See Baqus Group Limited; *Int'l*, pg. 857
FLETCHER MOROBE CONSTRUCTION PTY LIMITED—See Fletcher Building Limited; *Int'l*, pg. 2700
FLETCHER MUSIC CENTERS INC.; *U.S. Private*, pg. 1542
FLETCHER OIL CO. INC.—See Floco Unlimited Inc.; *U.S. Private*, pg. 1546
FLETCHER PACIFIC STEEL (FIJI) LIMITED—See Fletcher Building Limited; *Int'l*, pg. 2700
FLETCHER-REINHARDT COMPANY; *U.S. Private*, pg. 1543
FLETCHER RESIDENTIAL LIMITED—See Fletcher Building Limited; *Int'l*, pg. 2700
FLETCHERS BAKERIES LIMITED—See DBAY Advisors Limited; *Int'l*, pg. 1986
FLETCHER STEEL LIMITED—See Fletcher Building Limited; *Int'l*, pg. 2700
FLETCHER'S TIRE AND AUTO SERVICE; *U.S. Private*, pg. 1543
FLETCHER VAN GILDER LLP; *U.S. Private*, pg. 1543
FLETCHER WOOD PANELS (AUSTRALIA) PTY LIMITED—See Fletcher Building Limited; *Int'l*, pg. 2700
FLETCH'S INC.; *U.S. Private*, pg. 1542
FLEURESSE GMBH—See Dierig Holding AG; *Int'l*, pg. 2115
FLEURY MICHON LOGISTIQUE—See Fleury Michon SA; *Int'l*, pg. 2701
FLEURY MICHON SA; *Int'l*, pg. 2701
FLEURY S.A.; *Int'l*, pg. 2701
FLEWWELLING INSURANCE BROKERS LIMITED; *Int'l*, pg. 2701
FLEX ACADEMY D.O.O.—See NIBE Industrier AB; *Int'l*, pg. 5260
FLEXACOM AUTOMATION SYSTEM SDN. BHD.—See MSM International Limited; *Int'l*, pg. 5069
FLEXALIGHTING NORTH AMERICA LTD.—See Dexelance S.p.A.; *Int'l*, pg. 2092
FLEXALIGHTING S.R.L.—See Dexelance S.p.A.; *Int'l*, pg. 2092
FLEX-A-LITE CONSOLIDATED INC.; *U.S. Private*, pg. 1543
FLEX AMERICAS S.A. DE C.V.—See Uflex Ltd; *Int'l*, pg. 8015
FLEXAN, LLC—See New Mountain Capital, LLC; *U.S. Private*, pg. 2902
FLEXASEAL ENGINEERED SEALS AND SYSTEMS, LLC; *U.S. Private*, pg. 1543
FLEX-A-SEAL, INC.—See Flexaseal Engineered Seals and Systems, LLC; *U.S. Private*, pg. 1543
FLEXBAR MACHINE CORP.; *U.S. Private*, pg. 1543
FLEXBARRIER PRODUCTS, LLC—See ShoreView Industries, LLC; *U.S. Private*, pg. 3642
FLEXCITE SA—See Regie Autonome des Transports Parisiens; *Int'l*, pg. 6253
FLEXCO (AUST) PTY. LTD—See Flexible Steel Lacing Company; *U.S. Private*, pg. 1544
FLEXCO CONVEYING EQUIPMENT TRADING (SHANGHAI) CO., LTD.—See Flexible Steel Lacing Company; *U.S. Private*, pg. 1544
FLEXCO CORPORATION—See Roppe Corporation; *U.S. Private*, pg. 3480
FLEX CONCEPTS INC.—See Entegris, Inc.; *U.S. Public*, pg. 777
FLEXCON CORPORATION; *U.S. Private*, pg. 1543
FLEXCON GLENROTHES LTD—See FLEXcon Corporation; *U.S. Private*, pg. 1543
FLEXCON INDUSTRIES, INC.; *U.S. Private*, pg. 1543
FLEXCO PTE LTD—See Flexible Steel Lacing Company; *U.S. Private*, pg. 1544

FLEXDEAL SIMFE S.A.; *Int'l*, pg. 2704
FLEX-E-CARD LIMITED—See EML Payments Limited; *Int'l*, pg. 2383
FLEXENERGY GREEN SOLUTIONS, INC.; *U.S. Public*, pg. 852
FLEXENTIAL COLORADO CORP.—See GI Manager L.P.; *U.S. Private*, pg. 1693
FLEX EQUIPOS DE DESCANSO SA; *Int'l*, pg. 2701
FLEXERA SOFTWARE LLC—See Ontario Teachers' Pension Plan; *Int'l*, pg. 5589
FLEXERA SOFTWARE LLC—See TA Associates, Inc.; *U.S. Private*, pg. 3915
FLEXERA SOFTWARE LTD.—See Ontario Teachers' Pension Plan; *Int'l*, pg. 5589
FLEXERA SOFTWARE LTD.—See TA Associates, Inc.; *U.S. Private*, pg. 3915
FLEXERGIS SP. Z O.O.—See Ergis S.A.; *Int'l*, pg. 2491
FLEXFAB EUROPE LTD.—See Flexfab Horizons International, LLC; *U.S. Private*, pg. 1544
FLEXFAB HORIZONS INTERNATIONAL, LLC; *U.S. Private*, pg. 1544
FLEXFAB LLC—See Flexfab Horizons International, LLC; *U.S. Private*, pg. 1544
FLEXFAB SOUTH AMERICA LTDA.—See Flexfab Horizons International, LLC; *U.S. Private*, pg. 1544
FLEX FILMS EUROPA KORLATOLT FELELOSSEGU TARSASAG—See Uflex Ltd; *Int'l*, pg. 8015
FLEX FILMS EUROPA SP. Z O.O.—See Uflex Ltd; *Int'l*, pg. 8015
FLEX FILMS RUS LLC—See Uflex Ltd; *Int'l*, pg. 8015
FLEX FILMS (USA) INC.—See Uflex Ltd; *Int'l*, pg. 8015
FLEXFIN, LLC—See PhenixFIN Corp.; *U.S. Public*, pg. 1684
FLEXFIT HOSE LLC—See Audax Group, Limited Partnership; *U.S. Private*, pg. 388
FLEXFIT, LLC; *U.S. Private*, pg. 1544
FLEX FLEET RENTAL LLC—See Kaizen Automotive Group; *Int'l*, pg. 4053
FLEX FOODS LTD.—See Uflex Ltd; *Int'l*, pg. 8015
FLEXFRONT B.V.—See Mitsubishi UFJ Financial Group, Inc.; *Int'l*, pg. 4971
FLEXFUNDS ETP LLC; *U.S. Private*, pg. 1544
FLEXHEAD INDUSTRIES, INC.—See Tailwind Capital Group, LLC; *U.S. Private*, pg. 3923
FLEX HR, INC.; *U.S. Private*, pg. 1543
FLEXIBILITY & CO., LLC; *U.S. Private*, pg. 1544
FLEXIBLE BENEFIT ADMINISTRATORS INC.; *U.S. Private*, pg. 1544
FLEXIBLE BENEFITS SYSTEM INC.—See Genstar Capital, LLC; *U.S. Private*, pg. 1674
FLEXIBLE BUSINESS SYSTEMS; *U.S. Private*, pg. 1544
FLEXIBLE DUCTING, LIMITED—See Smiths Group plc; *Int'l*, pg. 7009
FLEXIBLE FERTIGUNGSTECHNIK GMBH—See ATON GmbH; *Int'l*, pg. 689
FLEXIBLE INDUSTRIAL PACKAGES CO. SAOC; *Int'l*, pg. 2704
FLEXIBLE METAL HOSE & RUBBER PRODUCTS; *U.S. Private*, pg. 1544
FLEXIBLE PACKAGES CONVERTORS (PROPRIETARY) LIMITED—See Packages Ltd.; *Int'l*, pg. 5693
FLEXIBLE PACKAGING & CO. INC.; *U.S. Private*, pg. 1544
FLEXIBLE PACKAGING HOLDING B.V.; *Int'l*, pg. 2704
FLEXIBLE PLAN INVESTMENTS LTD.; *U.S. Private*, pg. 1544
FLEXIBLE SOLUTIONS INTERNATIONAL, INC.; *Int'l*, pg. 2704
FLEXIBLE SOLUTIONS, LTD.—See Flexible Solutions International, Inc.; *Int'l*, pg. 2704
FLEXIBLE STAFFING OF GEORGIA, INC.; *U.S. Private*, pg. 1544
FLEXIBLE STEEL LACING COMPANY; *U.S. Private*, pg. 1544
FLEXIBLE TECHNOLOGIES INC.—See Smiths Group plc; *Int'l*, pg. 7012
FLEXIBRAS VITORIA—See TechnipFMC plc; *Int'l*, pg. 7507
FLEXICARE (GROUP) LIMITED; *Int'l*, pg. 2704
FLEXICARE MEDICAL LTD.—See Flexicare (Group) Limited; *Int'l*, pg. 2704
FLEXI-CELL (UK) LTD.—See HEXPOL AB; *Int'l*, pg. 3371
FLEXICON INC.; *U.S. Private*, pg. 1544
FLEXICORE OF TEXAS, L.P.; *U.S. Private*, pg. 1544
FLEXIDER S.P.A.—See Anamet Inc.; *U.S. Private*, pg. 272
FLEXI FORCE B.V.—See ASSA ABLOY AB; *Int'l*, pg. 639
FLEXIFORCE HUNGARY KFT.—See ASSA ABLOY AB; *Int'l*, pg. 639
FLEXI FORCE IBERICA, S.L.—See ASSA ABLOY AB; *Int'l*, pg. 639
FLEXI FORCE ITALIA S.R.L.—See ASSA ABLOY AB; *Int'l*, pg. 639
FLEXI FORCE POLAND SP. Z.O.O.—See ASSA ABLOY AB; *Int'l*, pg. 639
FLEXI FRANCE—See TechnipFMC plc; *Int'l*, pg. 7508
FLEXIGLASS CHALLENGE PTY LTD—See Eastern Polymer Group Public Company Limited; *Int'l*, pg. 2273
FLEXIGROUP (NEW ZEALAND) LIMITED—See Humm Group Limited; *Int'l*, pg. 3531

FLEXIUM INTERCONNECT, INC.

FLEXIGROUP (NZ) LTD—See Humm Group Limited; *Int'l*, pg. 3531
FLEXIHIRE PTY LIMITED—See Linde plc; *Int'l*, pg. 4504
FLEXIINTERNATIONAL SOFTWARE, INC.; *U.S. Public*, pg. 853
FLEXIM AMERICAS CORPORATION—See Emerson Electric Co.; *U.S. Public*, pg. 749
FLEXIM AUSTRALIA PTY. LTD.—See Emerson Electric Co.; *U.S. Public*, pg. 749
FLEXIM FLEXIBLE INDUSTRIEMESSTECHNICK GMBH—See Emerson Electric Co.; *U.S. Public*, pg. 749
FLEXIM FLOW INDIA PVT. LTD.—See Emerson Electric Co.; *U.S. Public*, pg. 749
FLEXIM FRANCE S.A.S.—See Emerson Electric Co.; *U.S. Public*, pg. 749
FLEXIM INSTRUMENTS ASIA PTE. LTD.—See Emerson Electric Co.; *U.S. Public*, pg. 749
FLEXIM INSTRUMENTS BENELUX B.V.—See Emerson Electric Co.; *U.S. Public*, pg. 749
FLEXIM INSTRUMENTS UK LTD.—See Emerson Electric Co.; *U.S. Public*, pg. 749
FLEXIM JAPAN LTD.—See Emerson Electric Co.; *U.S. Public*, pg. 749
FLEXIM S.A.—See Emerson Electric Co.; *U.S. Public*, pg. 749
FLEXION THERAPEUTICS, INC.—See Pacira BioSciences, Inc.; *U.S. Public*, pg. 5632
FLEXIRENT CAPITAL (NEW ZEALAND) LTD.—See Humm Group Limited; *Int'l*, pg. 3531
FLEXIRENT CAPITAL PTY. LTD.—See Humm Group Limited; *Int'l*, pg. 3531
FLEXIRENT HOLDINGS PTY LIMITED—See Humm Group Limited; *Int'l*, pg. 3531
FLEXIRENT IRELAND LIMITED—See Humm Group Limited; *Int'l*, pg. 3531
FLEXIRENT SPV NO 2 PTY LIMITED—See Humm Group Limited; *Int'l*, pg. 3531
FLEXIRENT SPV NO 4 PTY LIMITED—See Humm Group Limited; *Int'l*, pg. 3531
FLEXIROAM LIMITED; *Int'l*, pg. 2705
THE FLEXITALLIC GROUP, INC.—See Bridgepoint Group Plc; *Int'l*, pg. 1154
FLEXITALLIC LP—See Bridgepoint Group Plc; *Int'l*, pg. 1154
FLEXITALLIC LTD.—See Bridgepoint Group Plc; *Int'l*, pg. 1154
FLEXIT AUSTRALIA PTY LTD—See Imdex Limited; *Int'l*, pg. 3623
FLEXITECH SDN BHD—See Top Glove Corporation Bhd.; *Int'l*, pg. 7812
FLEXITEL TELEFONSERVICE GMBH—See Munchener Ruckversicherungs AG; *Int'l*, pg. 5088
FLEXITRON AB—See OEM International AB; *Int'l*, pg. 5528
FLEXITUFF TECHNOLOGY INTERNATIONAL LIMITED—See Flexituff Ventures International Limited; *Int'l*, pg. 2705
FLEXITUFF VENTURES INTERNATIONAL LIMITED; *Int'l*, pg. 2705
FLEXIUM INTERCONNECT AMERICA, LLC—See Flexium Interconnect, Inc.; *Int'l*, pg. 2705
FLEXIUM INTERCONNECT, INC - KUNSHAN PLANT—See Flexium Interconnect, Inc.; *Int'l*, pg. 2705
FLEXIUM INTERCONNECT, INC.; *Int'l*, pg. 2705
FLEXI-VAN LEASING, INC.—See Murdock Holdings, LLC; *U.S. Private*, pg. 2814
FLEXJET, LLC—See Directional Capital LLC; *U.S. Private*, pg. 1236
FLEX-KLEEN—See CECO Environmental Corp.; *U.S. Public*, pg. 464
FLEX LIGHTING SOLUTIONS, INC.—See Flex Ltd.; *Int'l*, pg. 2702
FLEXLINK AB—See Coesia S.p.A.; *Int'l*, pg. 1689
FLEXLINK AUTOMATION SDN BHD—See Coesia S.p.A.; *Int'l*, pg. 1689
FLEXLINK AUTOMATION (SHANGHAI) CO. LTD.—See Coesia S.p.A.; *Int'l*, pg. 1689
FLEXLINK SYSTEMS B.V.—See Coesia S.p.A.; *Int'l*, pg. 1689
FLEXLINK SYSTEMS CANADA, INC.—See Coesia S.p.A.; *Int'l*, pg. 1689
FLEXLINK SYSTEMS ESPANA, SL—See Coesia S.p.A.; *Int'l*, pg. 1689
FLEXLINK SYSTEMS GMBH—See Coesia S.p.A.; *Int'l*, pg. 1689
FLEXLINK SYSTEMS, INC.—See Coesia S.p.A.; *Int'l*, pg. 1689
FLEXLINK SYSTEMS INDIA PVT. LTD.—See Coesia S.p.A.; *Int'l*, pg. 1689
FLEXLINK SYSTEMS KFT.—See Coesia S.p.A.; *Int'l*, pg. 1689
FLEXLINK SYSTEMS LTDA—See Coesia S.p.A.; *Int'l*, pg. 1689
FLEXLINK SYSTEMS LTD—See Coesia S.p.A.; *Int'l*, pg. 1689
FLEXLINK SYSTEMS N.V.—See Coesia S.p.A.; *Int'l*, pg. 1689

FLEXIUM INTERCONNECT, INC.

CORPORATE AFFILIATIONS

FLEXLINK SYSTEMS POLSKA SP. Z O.O.—See Coesia S.p.A.; *Int'l*, pg. 1689
FLEXLINK SYSTEMS PTE LTD—See Coesia S.p.A.; *Int'l*, pg. 1689
FLEXLINK SYSTEMS PTY LTD—See Coesia S.p.A.; *Int'l*, pg. 1689
FLEXLINK SYSTEMS SAS—See Coesia S.p.A.; *Int'l*, pg. 1689
FLEXLINK SYSTEMS—See Coesia S.p.A.; *Int'l*, pg. 1689
FLEXLINK SYSTEMS—See Coesia S.p.A.; *Int'l*, pg. 1689
FLEXLINK SYSTEMS—See Coesia S.p.A.; *Int'l*, pg. 1689
FLEXLINK SYSTEMS S.P.A.—See Coesia S.p.A.; *Int'l*, pg. 1689
FLEXLINK SYSTEMS S.R.O.—See Coesia S.p.A.; *Int'l*, pg. 1689
FLEX LNG LTD.; *Int'l*, pg. 2701
FLEXLOL PACKAGING (I) LIMITED—See TVS Logistics Services Ltd.; *Int'l*, pg. 7989
FLEX LTD.; *Int'l*, pg. 2701
FLEXMAG INDUSTRIES INC.—See Compass Diversified Holdings; *U.S. Public*, pg. 560
FLEXMASTER USA, INC.—See Masterflex SE; *Int'l*, pg. 4725
FLEXMEDICAL DISPOSABLES—See Flex Ltd.; *Int'l*, pg. 2703
FLEXMEDICAL DISPOSABLES—See Flex Ltd.; *Int'l*, pg. 2703
FLEXMEDICAL DISPOSABLES—See Flex Ltd.; *Int'l*, pg. 2703
FLEXMEDICAL SLOVAKIA S.R.O.—See Flex Ltd.; *Int'l*, pg. 2702
FLEX MIDDLE EAST FZE—See Uflex Ltd; *Int'l*, pg. 8015
FLEXMINDER, INC.—See The Jellyvision Lab, Inc.; *U.S. Private*, pg. 4058
FLEXMODUS SDN. BHD.—See KVC Industrial Supplies Sdn. Bhd.; *Int'l*, pg. 4349
FLEX-N-GATE CANADA COMPANY—See Flex-N-Gate Corporation; *U.S. Private*, pg. 1543
FLEX-N-GATE CORPORATION; *U.S. Private*, pg. 1543
FLEX-O-FILM PLASTIC DIV.—See Flex-O-Glass, Inc.; *U.S. Private*, pg. 1543
FLEX-O-GLASS, INC.; *U.S. Private*, pg. 1543
FLEXOGRAPHIC PACKAGING CO.—See The Graham Group, Inc.; *U.S. Private*, pg. 4036
FLEXO-GRAPHICS, LLC—See AEA Investors LP; *U.S. Private*, pg. 114
FLEXO IMPRESSIONS—See Taylor Corporation; *U.S. Private*, pg. 3938
FLEX-O-LATORS, INCORPORATED—See Leggett & Platt, Incorporated; *U.S. Public*, pg. 1302
FLEXON INDUSTRIES INC.; *U.S. Private*, pg. 1544
FLEXOPACK DENMARK APS—See FLEXOPACK S.A.; *Int'l*, pg. 2705
FLEXOPACK PLASTICS S.A.—See FLEXOPACK S.A.; *Int'l*, pg. 2705
FLEXOPACK POLSKA SP. Z O.O.—See FLEXOPACK S.A.; *Int'l*, pg. 2705
FLEXOPACK PTY LTD—See FLEXOPACK S.A.; *Int'l*, pg. 2705
FLEXOPACK S.A.; *Int'l*, pg. 2705
FLEXO PRODUCTS LIMITED; *Int'l*, pg. 2705
FLEXOS FRANCE—See FleXos S.A.; *Int'l*, pg. 2705
FLEXOS S.A.; *Int'l*, pg. 2705
FLEXO TRANSPARENT, LLC—See First Atlantic Capital Ltd.; *U.S. Private*, pg. 1513
FLEXO UNIVERSAL SA DE CV—See Yunhong Green CTI Ltd.; *U.S. Public*, pg. 2400
FLEX-PAC, INC.; *U.S. Private*, pg. 1543
FLEX-PAC; *U.S. Private*, pg. 1543
FLEXPAK CORPORATION—See Kohlberg & Company, LLC; *U.S. Private*, pg. 2338
FLEX-PAK PACKAGING PRODUCTS, INC.—See Jacsten Holdings, LLC; *U.S. Private*, pg. 2181
FLEX P. FILMS (EGYPT) S.A.E.—See Uflex Ltd; *Int'l*, pg. 8015
FLEXPIPE SYSTEMS INC.—See ShawCor Ltd.; *Int'l*, pg. 6791
FLEXPOINT SENSOR SYSTEMS, INC.; *U.S. Public*, pg. 853
FLEXPORT INC.; *U.S. Private*, pg. 1544
FLEXPOSURE B.V.—See TKH Group N.V.; *Int'l*, pg. 7764
FLEX-POWER INC.; *U.S. Private*, pg. 1543
FLEXPOWER INDIA PRIVATE LIMITED—See Flex Ltd.; *Int'l*, pg. 2702
FLEXPRINT, LLC—See Oval Partners; *U.S. Private*, pg. 3052
THE FLEXPRO GROUP, LLC—See Beecken Petty O'Keefe & Company, LLC; *U.S. Private*, pg. 514
FLEXQUBE AB; *Int'l*, pg. 2705
FLEXQUBE EUROPE AB—See FlexQube AB; *Int'l*, pg. 2705
FLEXQUBE GMBH—See FlexQube AB; *Int'l*, pg. 2705
FLEXQUBE INC.—See FlexQube AB; *Int'l*, pg. 2705
FLEX RESORTS & REAL ESTATE COMPANY K.S.C.; *Int'l*, pg. 2704
FLEX-R LIMITED—See SIG plc; *Int'l*, pg. 6906
FLEXSCHLAUCH PRODUKTIONS GMBH—See Smiths Group plc; *Int'l*, pg. 7009

FLEXSERVICE SOLUTIONS BV—See ManpowerGroup Inc.; *U.S. Public*, pg. 1358
FLEXSHOPPER, INC.; *U.S. Public*, pg. 853
FLEXSITE DIAGNOSTICS, INC.—See Geonostics, Inc.; *U.S. Private*, pg. 1681
FLEXSOL PACKAGING CORP. - NORTH CAROLINA FACILITY—See Alpha Industries, Inc.; *U.S. Private*, pg. 197
FLEXSOL PACKAGING CORP.—See Alpha Industries, Inc.; *U.S. Private*, pg. 197
FLEXSOL PACKAGING CORP. - TENNESSEE FACILITY—See Alpha Industries, Inc.; *U.S. Private*, pg. 197
FLEXSOURCE LIMITED—See Bain Capital, LP; *U.S. Private*, pg. 433
FLEXSTAR TECHNOLOGY INC.—See Neosem Inc.; *Int'l*, pg. 5198
FLEXSTEEL COMMERCIAL SEATING DIVISION—See Flexsteel Industries, Inc.; *U.S. Public*, pg. 853
FLEXSTEEL DUBLIN DIVISION—See Flexsteel Industries, Inc.; *U.S. Public*, pg. 853
FLEXSTEEL DUBUQUE DIVISION—See Flexsteel Industries, Inc.; *U.S. Public*, pg. 853
FLEXSTEEL INDUSTRIES, INC.; *U.S. Public*, pg. 853
FLEXSTEEL LANCASTER DIVISION—See Flexsteel Industries, Inc.; *U.S. Public*, pg. 853
FLEXSTEEL METAL DIVISION—See Flexsteel Industries, Inc.; *U.S. Public*, pg. 853
FLEXSTEEL NEW PARIS DIVISION—See Flexsteel Industries, Inc.; *U.S. Public*, pg. 853
FLEXSTEEL RIVERSIDE DIVISION—See Flexsteel Industries, Inc.; *U.S. Public*, pg. 853
FLEXSTONE PARTNERS LLC—See Groupe BPCE; *Int'l*, pg. 3098
FLEXSTONE PARTNERS SAS—See Groupe BPCE; *Int'l*, pg. 3098
FLEX SUPPORT GROUP, INC.—See Key Family of Companies; *U.S. Private*, pg. 2293
FLEXSYS AMERICA CO.—See Eastman Chemical Company; *U.S. Public*, pg. 705
FLEXSYS AMERICA L.P.—See Eastman Chemical Company; *U.S. Public*, pg. 706
FLEXSYS CHEMICALS (M) SDN BHD—See Eastman Chemical Company; *U.S. Public*, pg. 706
FLEXSYS SA/NV—See Eastman Chemical Company; *U.S. Public*, pg. 705
FLEXSYS—See Eastman Chemical Company; *U.S. Public*, pg. 705
FLEXSYS VERKAUF GMBH—See Eastman Chemical Company; *U.S. Public*, pg. 706
FLEX-TEAM INC.—See Lingo Staffing, Inc.; *U.S. Private*, pg. 2461
FLEXTECH, INC.—See emids Technologies Pvt. Ltd. Corp.; *Int'l*, pg. 2380
FLEX TECHNOLOGIES INC. - POLYFLEX DIVISION—See Flex Technologies Inc.; *U.S. Private*, pg. 1543
FLEX TECHNOLOGIES INC.; *U.S. Private*, pg. 1543
FLEXTECH S.R.L.—See Ginegar Plastic Products Ltd.; *Int'l*, pg. 2976
FLEX-TEC INC.—See Cerberus Capital Management, L.P.; *U.S. Private*, pg. 838
FLEXTEK A/S—See J2L Holding AB; *Int'l*, pg. 3859
FLEX-TEK GROUP (US) LLC—See Smiths Group plc; *Int'l*, pg. 7009
FLEXTOR INC.—See CECO Environmental Corp.; *U.S. Public*, pg. 463
FLEXTRA LAB KFT.—See Bruker Corporation; *U.S. Public*, pg. 406
FLEXTRON GLOBAL SERVICES—See Flex Ltd.; *Int'l*, pg. 2703
FLEXTRONICS AMERICA, LLC—See Flex Ltd.; *Int'l*, pg. 2703
FLEXTRONICS AUSTRALIA PTY LTD—See Flex Ltd.; *Int'l*, pg. 2702
FLEXTRONICS AUTOMOTIVE INC—See Flex Ltd.; *Int'l*, pg. 2702
FLEXTRONICS AUTOMOTIVE USA, INC.—See Flex Ltd.; *Int'l*, pg. 2702
FLEXTRONICS BRASIL LTDA.—See Flex Ltd.; *Int'l*, pg. 2703
FLEXTRONICS CANADA DESIGN SERVICES, INC.—See Flex Ltd.; *Int'l*, pg. 2702
FLEXTRONICS COMPUTING (SUZHOU) CO., LTD.—See Flex Ltd.; *Int'l*, pg. 2702
FLEXTRONICS DESIGN KOREA LTD.—See Flex Ltd.; *Int'l*, pg. 2702
FLEXTRONICS DESIGN SRL—See Flex Ltd.; *Int'l*, pg. 2702
FLEXTRONICS DESIGN, S.R.O.—See Flex Ltd.; *Int'l*, pg. 2702
FLEXTRONICS DIGITAL DESIGN JAPAN, LTD.—See Flex Ltd.; *Int'l*, pg. 2703
FLEXTRONICS ELECTRONICS (MAURITIUS) LIMITED—See Flex Ltd.; *Int'l*, pg. 2702
FLEXTRONICS ELECTRONICS TECHNOLOGY (SUZHOU) CO., LTD.—See Flex Ltd.; *Int'l*, pg. 2702
FLEXTRONICS EMS CANADA INC.—See Flex Ltd.; *Int'l*, pg. 2702

FLEXTRONICS ENCLOSURES (HONG KONG) LTD.—See Flex Ltd.; *Int'l*, pg. 2702
FLEXTRONICS ENCLOSURE (ZHUHAI) CO., LTD.—See Flex Ltd.; *Int'l*, pg. 2702
FLEXTRONICS GERMANY HOLDING GMBH—See Flex Ltd.; *Int'l*, pg. 2702
FLEXTRONICS GLOBAL ENCLOSURES (SINGAPORE) PTE. LTD.—See Flex Ltd.; *Int'l*, pg. 2702
FLEXTRONICS GLOBAL SERVICES CANADA INC.—See Flex Ltd.; *Int'l*, pg. 2702
FLEXTRONICS GLOBAL SERVICES (MANCHESTER) LIMITED—See Flex Ltd.; *Int'l*, pg. 2702
FLEXTRONICS GROUP SWEDEN AB—See Flex Ltd.; *Int'l*, pg. 2702
FLEXTRONICS HOLDING GMBH—See Flex Ltd.; *Int'l*, pg. 2702
FLEXTRONICS HOLDINGS MEXICO, S.A. DE C.V.—See Flex Ltd.; *Int'l*, pg. 2702
FLEXTRONICS INTERNATIONAL AB—See Flex Ltd.; *Int'l*, pg. 2702
FLEXTRONICS INTERNATIONAL CORK B.V.—See Flex Ltd.; *Int'l*, pg. 2702
FLEXTRONICS INTERNATIONAL DENMARK A/S—See Flex Ltd.; *Int'l*, pg. 2702
FLEXTRONICS INTERNATIONAL GMBH—See Flex Ltd.; *Int'l*, pg. 2702
FLEXTRONICS INTERNATIONAL JAPAN CO., LTD.—See Flex Ltd.; *Int'l*, pg. 2702
FLEXTRONICS INTERNATIONAL KFT—See Flex Ltd.; *Int'l*, pg. 2702
FLEXTRONICS INTERNATIONAL KFT—See Flex Ltd.; *Int'l*, pg. 2702
FLEXTRONICS INTERNATIONAL KFT—See Flex Ltd.; *Int'l*, pg. 2702
FLEXTRONICS INTERNATIONAL KFT—See Flex Ltd.; *Int'l*, pg. 2702
FLEXTRONICS INTERNATIONAL LTD. - ASIA PACIFIC REGIONAL HEADQUARTERS—See Flex Ltd.; *Int'l*, pg. 2702
FLEXTRONICS INTERNATIONAL PA, INC.—See Flex Ltd.; *Int'l*, pg. 2703
FLEXTRONICS INTERNATIONAL POLAND SP Z.O.O.—See Flex Ltd.; *Int'l*, pg. 2703
FLEXTRONICS INTERNATIONAL—See Flex Ltd.; *Int'l*, pg. 2702
FLEXTRONICS INTERNATIONAL—See Flex Ltd.; *Int'l*, pg. 2702
FLEXTRONICS INTERNATIONAL—See Flex Ltd.; *Int'l*, pg. 2702
FLEXTRONICS INTERNATIONAL SWEDEN AB—See Flex Ltd.; *Int'l*, pg. 2703
FLEXTRONICS INTERNATIONAL TAIWAN LTD.—See Flex Ltd.; *Int'l*, pg. 2703
FLEXTRONICS INTERNATIONAL TECHNOLOGIA LTDA.—See Flex Ltd.; *Int'l*, pg. 2703
FLEXTRONICS INTERNATIONAL (UK) LTD—See Flex Ltd.; *Int'l*, pg. 2702
FLEXTRONICS INTERNATIONAL USA INC. - AUSTIN—See Flex Ltd.; *Int'l*, pg. 2703
FLEXTRONICS INTERNATIONAL USA, INC.—See Flex Ltd.; *Int'l*, pg. 2703
FLEXTRONICS INTERNATIONAL USA INC.—See Flex Ltd.; *Int'l*, pg. 2703
FLEXTRONICS INTERNATIONAL USA INC.—See Flex Ltd.; *Int'l*, pg. 2703
FLEXTRONICS INTERNATIONAL USA INC.—See Flex Ltd.; *Int'l*, pg. 2703
FLEXTRONICS (ISRAEL) LTD—See Flex Ltd.; *Int'l*, pg. 2702
FLEXTRONICS ITALY S.P.A—See Flex Ltd.; *Int'l*, pg. 2703
FLEXTRONICS JAPAN K.K.—See Flex Ltd.; *Int'l*, pg. 2703
FLEXTRONICS LAVAL S.N.C.—See Flex Ltd.; *Int'l*, pg. 2703
FLEXTRONICS LOGISTICS B.V.—See Flex Ltd.; *Int'l*, pg. 2703
FLEXTRONICS LOGISTICS POLAND SP. Z.O.O.—See Flex Ltd.; *Int'l*, pg. 2703
FLEXTRONICS (MALAYSIA) SDN. BHD.—See Flex Ltd.; *Int'l*, pg. 2702
FLEXTRONICS MANUFACTURING (H.K.) LTD.—See Flex Ltd.; *Int'l*, pg. 2703
FLEXTRONICS MANUFACTURING JUAREZ, S.A. DE C.V.—See Flex Ltd.; *Int'l*, pg. 2703
FLEXTRONICS MANUFACTURING MEXICO, S.A. DE C.V.—See Flex Ltd.; *Int'l*, pg. 2703
FLEXTRONICS MANUFACTURING MEXICO, S.A. DE C.V.—See Flex Ltd.; *Int'l*, pg. 2703
FLEXTRONICS MANUFACTURING (PENANG) SDN. BHD.—See Flex Ltd.; *Int'l*, pg. 2703
FLEXTRONICS MANUFACTURING (SINGAPORE) PTE. LTD.—See Flex Ltd.; *Int'l*, pg. 2703
FLEXTRONICS MANUFACTURING (ZHUHAI) CO., LTD.—See Flex Ltd.; *Int'l*, pg. 2703
FLEXTRONICS (NANJING) TECHNOLOGY CO., LTD.—See Flex Ltd.; *Int'l*, pg. 2703
FLEXTRONICS NETWORK SERVICES SWEDEN AB—See Flex Ltd.; *Int'l*, pg. 2703
FLEXTRONICS ODM NETHERLANDS NV—See Flex Ltd.; *Int'l*, pg. 2703

COMPANY NAME INDEX

FLEXTRONICS PLASTICS, S.A. DE C.V.—See Flex Ltd.; *Int'l*, pg. 2704
FLEXTRONICS PLASTICS (ZHUHAI) CO., LTD—See Flex Ltd.; *Int'l*, pg. 2704
FLEXTRONICS PLASTIC TECHNOLOGY (SHENZHEN) LTD.—See Flex Ltd.; *Int'l*, pg. 2704
FLEXTRONICS ROMANIA SRL—See Flex Ltd.; *Int'l*, pg. 2704
FLEXTRONICS SALES & MARKETING NORTH ASIA (L) LTD.—See Flex Ltd.; *Int'l*, pg. 2704
FLEXTRONICS SEMICONDUCTOR, INC.—See Flex Ltd.; *Int'l*, pg. 2703
FLEXTRONICS SERVICIOS GUADALAJARA, S.A. DE C.V.—See Flex Ltd.; *Int'l*, pg. 2704
FLEXTRONICS (SHANGHAI) CO., LTD.—See Flex Ltd.; *Int'l*, pg. 2702
FLEXTRONICS SPECIAL BUSINESS SOLUTIONS—See Flex Ltd.; *Int'l*, pg. 2704
FLEXTRONICS S.R.L—See Flex Ltd.; *Int'l*, pg. 2704
FLEXTRONICS SYSTEMS TEXAS LTD.—See Flex Ltd.; *Int'l*, pg. 2703
FLEXTRONICS TECHNOLOGIES (INDIA) PVT LTD.—See Flex Ltd.; *Int'l*, pg. 2704
FLEXTRONICS TECHNOLOGIES MEXICO, S.DE R.L. DE C.V.—See Flex Ltd.; *Int'l*, pg. 2704
FLEXTRONICS TECHNOLOGY (PENANG) SDN. BHD.—See Flex Ltd.; *Int'l*, pg. 2704
FLEXTRONICS TECHNOLOGY SDN BHD—See Flex Ltd.; *Int'l*, pg. 2704
FLEXTRONICS TECHNOLOGY (SHANGHAI) CO., LTD.—See Flex Ltd.; *Int'l*, pg. 2704
FLEXTRONICS TECHNOLOGY (SHENZHEN) CO., LTD.—See Flex Ltd.; *Int'l*, pg. 2704
FLEXTRONICS TECHNOLOGY (SHENZHEN) CO., LTD.—See Flex Ltd.; *Int'l*, pg. 2704
FLEXTRUS AB—See CVC Capital Partners SICAV-FIS S.A.; *Int'l*, pg. 1881
FLEXUS ELECTRONIC INC.—See Amphenol Corporation; *U.S. Public*, pg. 130
FLEXWARE INNOVATION, INC.—See Hitachi, Ltd.; *Int'l*, pg. 3412
FLEXWORK PROPERTIES LTD.; *Int'l*, pg. 2705
FLEXXRAY LLC—See Tilia Holdings LLC; *U.S. Private*, pg. 4170
FLEXXRAY LLC—See Warburg Pincus LLC; *U.S. Private*, pg. 4438
FLICK FUSION LLC; *U.S. Private*, pg. 1544
FLICK'S IGA LTD.; *U.S. Private*, pg. 1544
FLI ENERGY LIMITED—See FLI International Limited; *Int'l*, pg. 2705
FLI FRANCE SAS—See FLI International Limited; *Int'l*, pg. 2705
FLIGG HOLDING COMPANY; *U.S. Private*, pg. 1545
FLIGHT CENTRE TECHNOLOGY PTY. LTD.—See Flight Centre Travel Group Limited; *Int'l*, pg. 2706
FLIGHT CENTRE TRAVEL GROUP LIMITED; *Int'l*, pg. 2705
FLIGHT CENTRE (UK) LIMITED—See Flight Centre Travel Group Limited; *Int'l*, pg. 2706
FLIGHT CENTRE USA HOLDING CORP.—See Flight Centre Travel Group Limited; *Int'l*, pg. 2706
FLIGHT DATA SERVICES LIMITED—See L3Harris Technologies, Inc.; *U.S. Public*, pg. 1279
FLIGHT DELAY SERVICES LIMITED—See Deutsche Bahn AG; *Int'l*, pg. 2051
FLIGHT DIRECTOR INC.; *U.S. Private*, pg. 1545
FLIGHT ENVIRONMENTS INC.; *U.S. Private*, pg. 1545
FLIGHT EXPRESS INCORPORATED—See H.I.G. Capital, LLC; *U.S. Private*, pg. 1827
FLIGHT LANDATA, INC.—See Jacobs Engineering Group, Inc.; *U.S. Public*, pg. 1186
FLIGHTLINE DATA SERVICES, INC.—See Sabre Corporation; *U.S. Public*, pg. 1833
FLIGHTLINK INTERNATIONAL LIMITED—See ComfortDelGro Corporation Limited; *Int'l*, pg. 1712
FLIGHT OPTIONS LLC—See Directional Capital LLC; *U.S. Private*, pg. 1236
FLIGHT OPTIONS LLC—See Resilience Capital Partners, LLC; *U.S. Private*, pg. 3405
FLIGHT RAJA MIDDLEEAST FZ LLC—See Ebix Inc.; *U.S. Public*, pg. 710
FLIGHT RAJA TRAVELS PHILIPPINES—See Ebix Inc.; *U.S. Public*, pg. 710
FLIGHT REFUELLING LIMITED—See Advent International Corporation; *U.S. Private*, pg. 99
FLIGHTSAFETY INTERNATIONAL COURSEWARE SUPPORT—See Berkshire Hathaway Inc.; *U.S. Public*, pg. 305
FLIGHTSAFETY INTERNATIONAL, INC.—See Berkshire Hathaway Inc.; *U.S. Public*, pg. 304
FLIGHTSAFETY INTERNATIONAL SIMULATION SYSTEMS—See Berkshire Hathaway Inc.; *U.S. Public*, pg. 305
FLIGHTSAFETY INTERNATIONAL—See Berkshire Hathaway Inc.; *U.S. Public*, pg. 305
FLIGHTSAFETY SERVICES CORPORATION—See Berkshire Hathaway Inc.; *U.S. Public*, pg. 305
FLIGHTS HALLMARK LIMITED—See Rotala Group Limited; *Int'l*, pg. 6402

FLIGHT SIMULATION COMPANY B.V.—See CAE Inc.; *Int'l*, pg. 1249
FLIGHT SOLUTIONS CO., LTD.; *Int'l*, pg. 2706
FLIGHTSTAR AIRCRAFT SERVICES, LLC—See MRO Holdings LP; *U.S. Private*, pg. 2805
FLIGHTSTATS, INC.—See RELX plc; *Int'l*, pg. 6266
FLIGHT SYSTEMS DETROIT—See Flight Systems, Inc.; *U.S. Private*, pg. 1545
FLIGHT SYSTEMS, INC.; *U.S. Private*, pg. 1545
FLIGHTVIEW, INC.—See Vitruvian Partners LLP; *Int'l*, pg. 8263
FLIGHTWAYS OF LONG ISLAND, INC.—See Macquarie Group Limited; *Int'l*, pg. 4627
FLI INTERNATIONAL LIMITED; *Int'l*, pg. 2705
FLIK INTERNATIONAL—See Compass Group PLC; *Int'l*, pg. 1751
FLIMP MEDIA INC.; *U.S. Private*, pg. 1545
FLINCKHEUVEL BV—See Compass Group PLC; *Int'l*, pg. 1752
FLINDERS EXPLORATION LIMITED; *Int'l*, pg. 2706
FLINDERS MINES LIMITED; *Int'l*, pg. 2706
FLINDERS PORTS PTY LTD; *Int'l*, pg. 2706
F&L INDUSTRIAL SOLUTIONS, INC.—See Genuine Parts Company; *U.S. Public*, pg. 933
FLINN SCIENTIFIC, INC.; *U.S. Private*, pg. 1545
FLINTBROOK LIMITED—See Platinum Equity, LLC; *U.S. Private*, pg. 3210
FLINT CO. INC.; *U.S. Private*, pg. 1545
FLINT CO., LTD.—See F.C.C. Co., Ltd.; *Int'l*, pg. 2596
FLINT COMMUNICATIONS, INC. & ADFARM; *U.S. Private*, pg. 1545
FLINT CORP.; *Int'l*, pg. 2706
FLINT DISTRIBUTION LIMITED—See Avnet, Inc.; *U.S. Public*, pg. 253
FLINTEC FRANCE—See Indutrade AB; *Int'l*, pg. 3678
FLINTEC GMBH—See Indutrade AB; *Int'l*, pg. 3678
FLINTEC GROUP AB—See Indutrade AB; *Int'l*, pg. 3678
FLINTEC INC.—See Indutrade AB; *Int'l*, pg. 3678
FLINTEC ITALY—See Indutrade AB; *Int'l*, pg. 3678
FLINTEC UK LTD—See Indutrade AB; *Int'l*, pg. 3678
FLINT ELECTRIC MEMBERSHIP CORPORATION; *U.S. Private*, pg. 1545
FLINT ENERGY CONSTRUCTION SERVICES INC.; *U.S. Private*, pg. 1545
FLINT ENERGY SERVICES INC.—See AECOM; *U.S. Public*, pg. 51
FLINT EQUIPMENT CO. - ATLANTA—See Flint Equipment Holdings, Inc.; *U.S. Private*, pg. 1545
FLINT EQUIPMENT CO.—See Flint Equipment Holdings, Inc.; *U.S. Private*, pg. 1545
FLINT EQUIPMENT CO. - WEST COLUMBIA—See Flint Equipment Holdings, Inc.; *U.S. Private*, pg. 1545
FLINT EQUIPMENT HOLDINGS, INC.; *U.S. Private*, pg. 1545
FLINT GROUP GMBH—See Koch Industries, Inc.; *U.S. Private*, pg. 2327
FLINT GROUP GMBH—See The Goldman Sachs Group, Inc.; *U.S. Public*, pg. 2076
FLINT GROUP, INC.—See Koch Industries, Inc.; *U.S. Private*, pg. 2327
FLINT GROUP, INC.—See The Goldman Sachs Group, Inc.; *U.S. Public*, pg. 2076
FLINT GROUP SA—See Koch Industries, Inc.; *U.S. Private*, pg. 2327
FLINT GROUP SA—See The Goldman Sachs Group, Inc.; *U.S. Public*, pg. 2076
FLINT HILLS MUSIC, INC.—See Ernie Williamson, Inc.; *U.S. Private*, pg. 1422
FLINT HILLS RESOURCES CANADA, LP—See Koch Industries, Inc.; *U.S. Private*, pg. 2327
FLINT HILLS RESOURCES CHEMICAL INTERMEDIATES, LLC—See Koch Industries, Inc.; *U.S. Private*, pg. 2327
FLINT HILLS RESOURCES, LLC—See Koch Industries, Inc.; *U.S. Private*, pg. 2327
FLINT HILLS RESOURCES, LP—See Koch Industries, Inc.; *U.S. Private*, pg. 2327
FLINT HILLS RURAL ELECTRIC COOP; *U.S. Private*, pg. 1545
FLINT HYDROSTATICS, INC.—See Clearlake Capital Group, L.P.; *U.S. Public*, pg. 933
FLINT INDUSTRIES, INC.; *U.S. Private*, pg. 1545
FLINT INTERACTIVE—See Flint Communications, Inc. & Adfarm; *U.S. Private*, pg. 1545
FLINT INT'L SERVICES, INC.; *Int'l*, pg. 2706
FLINT PACKAGING, INC.—See Landaal Packaging Systems; *U.S. Private*, pg. 2384
FLINT POWER SYSTEMS—See Flint Equipment Holdings, Inc.; *U.S. Private*, pg. 1545
FLINT RIVER MILLS, INC.; *U.S. Private*, pg. 1545
FLINT RIVER SERVICES INC.—See Bay Grove Capital LLC; *U.S. Private*, pg. 492
FLINT SPECIAL SERVICES, INC.—See Universal Logistics Holdings, Inc.; *U.S. Public*, pg. 2261
FLINTSTONE MANAGEMENT SERVICES LIMITED—See OspreyFrank plc; *Int'l*, pg. 5652
FLINTSTONE TECHNOLOGY LIMITED—See NV Bekaert SA; *Int'l*, pg. 5496
FLINT TRADING, INC.—See Brazos Private Equity Partners, LLC; *U.S. Private*, pg. 642

FLOFORM COUNTERTOPS

FLINT & WALLING INC.—See Zoeller Co.; *U.S. Private*, pg. 4607
FLINT WARM AIR SUPPLY CO. (FWA); *U.S. Private*, pg. 1545
FLIPCHIP INTERNATIONAL, LLC—See Tianshui Huatian Technology Co., Ltd.; *Int'l*, pg. 7741
FLIP FILE (PTY) LTD.—See Caxton and CTP Publishers and Printers Ltd.; *Int'l*, pg. 1363
FLIP FLOP SHOPS; *U.S. Private*, pg. 1545
FLIPKART INTERNET PRIVATE LIMITED—See Walmart Inc.; *U.S. Public*, pg. 2325
FLIPKEY, INC.—See TripAdvisor, Inc.; *U.S. Public*, pg. 2195
FLIPPIN, BRUCE & PORTER, INC.—See Cantor Fitzgerald, L.P.; *U.S. Private*, pg. 736
FLIPPO CONSTRUCTION CO. INC.; *U.S. Private*, pg. 1546
FLIPSIDE GROUP—See The Interpublic Group of Companies, Inc.; *U.S. Public*, pg. 2104
FLIPSIDE, INC.; *U.S. Private*, pg. 1546
FLIR COMMERCIAL SYSTEMS, INC.—See Teledyne Technologies Incorporated; *U.S. Public*, pg. 1993
FLIR GOVERNMENT SYSTEMS, INC.—See Teledyne Technologies Incorporated; *U.S. Public*, pg. 1993
FLIRI & CONRAD ELECTRO, ZNL DER ELECTRA BUIN S.A.—See Burkhalter Holding AG; *Int'l*, pg. 1225
FLIR INTEGRATED IMAGING SOLUTIONS—See Teledyne Technologies Incorporated; *U.S. Public*, pg. 1993
FLIR OUTDOOR & TACTICAL SYSTEMS—See Teledyne Technologies Incorporated; *U.S. Public*, pg. 1993
FLIR SYSTEMS AB—See Teledyne Technologies Incorporated; *U.S. Public*, pg. 1993
FLIR SYSTEMS COMPANY LTD.—See Teledyne Technologies Incorporated; *U.S. Public*, pg. 1992
FLIR SYSTEMS CV—See Teledyne Technologies Incorporated; *U.S. Public*, pg. 1993
FLIR SYSTEMS HOLDING AB—See Teledyne Technologies Incorporated; *U.S. Public*, pg. 1993
FLIR SYSTEMS LTD.—See Teledyne Technologies Incorporated; *U.S. Public*, pg. 1993
FLIR UNMANNED AERIAL SYSTEMS AS—See Teledyne Technologies Incorporated; *U.S. Public*, pg. 1992
FLITEBOARD EUROPE B.V.—See Brunswick Corporation; *U.S. Public*, pg. 408
FLITEBOARD PTY LIMITED—See Brunswick Corporation; *U.S. Public*, pg. 408
FLITECH S.R.L.—See WAMGROUP S.p.A.; *Int'l*, pg. 8337
FLITE HOCKEY; *Int'l*, pg. 2706
FLITETEC LTD—See ALA SpA; *Int'l*, pg. 289
FLITTO INC.; *Int'l*, pg. 2706
FLITWAYS TECHNOLOGY INC.; *U.S. Public*, pg. 853
FLIVA APS; *Int'l*, pg. 2706
FLI WATER LIMITED—See FLI International Limited; *Int'l*, pg. 2705
FLIWAY GROUP LIMITED—See Yang Kee Logistics Pte Ltd.; *Int'l*, pg. 8559
FLIWAY INTERNATIONAL LIMITED—See Yang Kee Logistics Pte Ltd.; *Int'l*, pg. 8559
FLIWAY TRANSPORT LIMITED—See Yang Kee Logistics Pte Ltd.; *Int'l*, pg. 8559
FLIXENTERTAINMENT LLC; *U.S. Private*, pg. 1546
FLIXMOBILITY GMBH; *Int'l*, pg. 2706
FLJ GROUP LIMITED; *Int'l*, pg. 2706
FLLC LEIPURIN—See Aspo Oyj; *Int'l*, pg. 631
FLLC TELKO—See Aspo Oyj; *Int'l*, pg. 631
F.LLI FRANCHINI S.R.L.—See Hera S.p.A.; *Int'l*, pg. 3356
FLM GRAPHICS CORPORATION; *U.S. Private*, pg. 1546
FLM HARVEST—See Land O'Lakes, Inc.; *U.S. Private*, pg. 2383
F.L. MOTHERAL CO. INC.; *U.S. Private*, pg. 1456
FLN FEUERLOSCHGERATE NEURUPPIN VERTRIEBSGMBH—See Johnson Controls International plc; *Int'l*, pg. 3987
FLOATEL INTERNATIONAL AB—See Floatel International Ltd.; *Int'l*, pg. 2707
FLOATEL INTERNATIONAL LTD.; *Int'l*, pg. 2707
FLOATOGRAPH TECHNOLOGIES, LLC; *U.S. Private*, pg. 1546
FLOBAL CORPORATION; *Int'l*, pg. 2707
FLOCAST AUSTRALIA PTY LTD—See Arrowcrest Group Pty. Ltd.; *Int'l*, pg. 580
FLOCO FOODS INC.—See W. Lee Flowers & Company Inc.; *U.S. Private*, pg. 4418
FLOCON TECHNOLOGIES OY—See Axolot Solutions Holding AB; *Int'l*, pg. 770
FLO CONTROL, INC.; *U.S. Private*, pg. 1546
FLOCOR INC.—See Groupe Deschenes Inc.; *Int'l*, pg. 3102
FLOCO UNLIMITED INC.; *U.S. Private*, pg. 1546
FLO DEUTSCHLAND GMBH—See FLO S.p.A.; *Int'l*, pg. 2707
FLODOR S.A.S.; *Int'l*, pg. 2707
FLODYNE INC.; *U.S. Private*, pg. 1546
FLOE INTERNATIONAL, INC.; *U.S. Private*, pg. 1546
FLOERGER NEDERLAND BV—See SNF SAS; *Int'l*, pg. 7027
FLOFORM COUNTERTOPS; *Int'l*, pg. 2707
FLOGAS IRELAND LIMITED—See DCC plc; *Int'l*, pg. 1990
FLOGAS NORGE AS—See DCC plc; *Int'l*, pg. 1990

FLOFORM COUNTERTOPS

FLOGAS SVERIGE AB—See DCC plc; *Int'l*, pg. 1990
FLOGAS UK LIMITED—See DCC plc; *Int'l*, pg. 1990
F-LOGISTIIKKA OY—See Atria Plc; *Int'l*, pg. 694
FLOGISTIX, LP—See White Deer Management LLC; *U.S. Private*, pg. 4508
FLO JAPON CO., LTD.—See Bain Capital, LP; *U.S. Private*, pg. 444
FLOKK AS—See Triton Advisers Limited; *Int'l*, pg. 7933
FLOKK HOLDING AS—See Triton Advisers Limited; *Int'l*, pg. 7933
FLO-LINE HYDRAULICS PTE LTD.; *Int'l*, pg. 2707
FLOLO CORPORATION; *U.S. Private*, pg. 1546
FLOMATIC CORPORATION—See Boshart Industries Inc.; *Int'l*, pg. 1116
FLOMATIK A/S—See Teleste Corporation; *Int'l*, pg. 7541
FLOMATIK NETWORK SERVICES LTD.—See Teleste Corporation; *Int'l*, pg. 7541
FLOMAX PRODUCTS, INC.—See Shale-Inland Holdings LLC; *U.S. Private*, pg. 3623
FLOMET LLC—See ARC Group Worldwide, Inc.; *U.S. Public*, pg. 179
FLOMIC GLOBAL LOGISTICS LTD.; *Int'l*, pg. 2707
FLOM INC.—See GL Sciences Inc.; *Int'l*, pg. 2986
FLONEX AG—See SNF SAS; *Int'l*, pg. 7027
FLOOD COMMUNICATIONS; *U.S. Private*, pg. 1546
FLOOIDCX CORP.; *Int'l*, pg. 2707
FLOORABLE, LLC—See Live Ventures Incorporated; *U.S. Public*, pg. 1332
FLOOR ASSOCIATES INCORPORATED; *U.S. Private*, pg. 1546
FLOORCON CORPORATION—See Central Concrete Corporation; *U.S. Private*, pg. 819
FLOOR COVERINGS INTERNATIONAL, LTD.—See First-Service Corporation; *Int'l*, pg. 2691
FLOOR COVERING WEEKLY—See The Hearst Corporation; *U.S. Private*, pg. 4048
FLOORCRAFT INC.; *U.S. Private*, pg. 1546
FLOOR DECOR CENTER INC; *U.S. Private*, pg. 1546
FLOOR & DECOR HOLDINGS, INC.; *U.S. Public*, pg. 853
FLOOR & DECOR OUTLETS OF AMERICA, INC.—See Floor & Decor Holdings, Inc.; *U.S. Public*, pg. 853
FLOORING AMERICA, INC.—See CCA Global Partners, Inc.; *U.S. Private*, pg. 799
FLOORING GALLERY LLC; *U.S. Private*, pg. 1546
FLOORING INDUSTRIES LTD.—See Mohawk Industries, Inc.; *U.S. Public*, pg. 1457
FLOORING LIQUIDATORS, INC.—See Live Ventures Incorporated; *U.S. Public*, pg. 1332
FLOORING SOLUTIONS INC.—See Lynx Equity Limited; *Int'l*, pg. 4606
FLOORING XL B.V.—See Mohawk Industries, Inc.; *U.S. Public*, pg. 1457
FLOOR KING INC.; *U.S. Private*, pg. 1546
FLOORSCAPE LIMITED—See Mohawk Industries, Inc.; *U.S. Public*, pg. 1457
FLOORSHOP.COM, INC.; *U.S. Private*, pg. 1546
FLOORS INC.—See The Sterling Group, L.P.; *U.S. Private*, pg. 4122
FLOORS MY HOME LIMITED; *Int'l*, pg. 2707
FLOORS-N-MORE, LLC—See ALJ Regional Holdings, Inc.; *U.S. Public*, pg. 78
FLOORWORX AFRICA (PTY) LIMITED—See Accentuate Limited; *Int'l*, pg. 82
FLORACHEM CORPORATION—See SK Capital Partners, LP; *U.S. Private*, pg. 3679
FLORA CORPORATION LIMITED; *Int'l*, pg. 2707
FLORACRAFT CORPORATION; *U.S. Private*, pg. 1546
FLORACRAFT OF PHILADELPHIA INC.—See Floracraft Corporation; *U.S. Private*, pg. 1546
FLORA DEVELOPMENT SDN BHD—See IOI Corporation Berhad; *Int'l*, pg. 3791
FLOR-AG CORPORATION—See Prudential Financial, Inc.; *U.S. Public*, pg. 1732
FLORAGENEX, INC.—See Sedia Biosciences Corporation; *U.S. Private*, pg. 3597
FLORAGO SA—See Floridienne SA; *Int'l*, pg. 2708
FLORA GROWTH CORP.; *Int'l*, pg. 2707
FLORA INC.—See Flora Manufacturing & Distributing Ltd.; *Int'l*, pg. 2707
FLORALIFE INC.—See Smithers-Oasis Company; *U.S. Private*, pg. 3697
FLORAL PLANT GROWERS LLC—See Sentinel Capital Partners, L.L.C.; *U.S. Private*, pg. 3609
FLORAL SUPPLY SYNDICATE; *U.S. Private*, pg. 1546
FLORA MANUFACTURING & DISTRIBUTING LTD.; *Int'l*, pg. 2707
FLORAMEDIA AUSTRIA GMBH—See HAL Trust N.V.; *Int'l*, pg. 3224
FLORAMEDIA BELGIUM N.V.—See HAL Trust N.V.; *Int'l*, pg. 3224
FLORAMEDIA DEUTSCHLAND KG—See HAL Trust N.V.; *Int'l*, pg. 3224
FLORAMEDIA ESPANA, S.A.U.—See HAL Trust N.V.; *Int'l*, pg. 3224
FLORAMEDIA FRANCE—See HAL Trust N.V.; *Int'l*, pg. 3224
FLORAMEDIA GROUP B.V.—See HAL Trust N.V.; *Int'l*, pg. 3224

FLORAMEDIA POLSKA SP.Z O.O.—See HAL Trust N.V.; *Int'l*, pg. 3224
FLORAMEDIA SCHWEIZ AG—See HAL Trust N.V.; *Int'l*, pg. 3224
FLORAMEDIA UK LTD—See HAL Trust N.V.; *Int'l*, pg. 3224
FLORAS DISTRIBUTORS INC.; *U.S. Private*, pg. 1546
FLORA TEXTILES LIMITED; *Int'l*, pg. 2707
FLOREANE MEDICAL IMPLANTS—See Medtronic plc; *Int'l*, pg. 4787
FLOREASCA BUSINESS PARK SRL—See NEPI Rockcastle N.V.; *Int'l*, pg. 5200
FLORENCE CEMENT COMPANY; *U.S. Private*, pg. 1546
FLORENCE CONCRETE PRODUCTS CO. INC; *U.S. Private*, pg. 1547
FLORENCE CORPORATION OF KANSAS—See Gibraltar Industries, Inc.; *U.S. Public*, pg. 936
FLORENCE CORPORATION—See Gibraltar Industries, Inc.; *U.S. Public*, pg. 936
FLORENCE CORPORATION; *U.S. Private*, pg. 1547
FLORENCE ELECTRIC LLC; *U.S. Private*, pg. 1547
FLORENCE HOSPITAL AT ANTHEM, LLC—See Gilbert Hospital LLC; *U.S. Private*, pg. 1699
FLORENCE INVESTECH LIMITED—See JK Tyre & Industries Ltd.; *Int'l*, pg. 3972
FLORENCE REALTY, LLC—See Ventas, Inc.; *U.S. Public*, pg. 2278
FLORENCE SAVINGS BANK INC.; *U.S. Private*, pg. 1547
FLORENCE & WHITE FORD DEALERSHIP; *U.S. Private*, pg. 1546
FLORENS ASSET MANAGEMENT COMPANY LIMITED—See China COSCO Shipping Corporation Limited; *Int'l*, pg. 1492
FLORENS ASSET MANAGEMENT (USA), LIMITED—See China COSCO Shipping Corporation Limited; *Int'l*, pg. 1492
FLORENTAISE SA; *Int'l*, pg. 2707
FLORES & ASSOCIATES, LLC—See CNO Financial Group, Inc.; *U.S. Public*, pg. 520
FLORESTAS RIO DOCE S.A.—See Vale S.A.; *Int'l*, pg. 8111
FLORESTONE PRODUCTS CO.; *U.S. Private*, pg. 1547
FLORET TRADELINK PRIVATE LIMITED—See Gravita India Limited; *Int'l*, pg. 3062
THE FLORHAM PARK ENDOSCOPY ASC, LLC—See KKR & Co. Inc.; *U.S. Public*, pg. 1247
FLORIAN KONIG—See Maschinenfabrik Berthold Hermle AG; *Int'l*, pg. 4720
FLORIDA AERO PRECISION INC.—See Meyer Tool Inc.; *U.S. Private*, pg. 2693
FLORIDA AGENCY NETWORK, LLC; *U.S. Private*, pg. 1547
THE FLORIDA AQUARIUM, INC.; *U.S. Private*, pg. 4029
FLORIDA ARF; *U.S. Private*, pg. 1547
FLORIDA BANCSHARES, INC.; *U.S. Private*, pg. 1547
THE FLORIDA BAR FOUNDATION, INC.; *U.S. Private*, pg. 4029
FLORIDA BEARINGS—See Littlejohn & Co., LLC; *U.S. Private*, pg. 2471
FLORIDA BEAUTY FLORA, INC.—See MOGUL ENERGY INTERNATIONAL, INC.; *U.S. Public*, pg. 1457
FLORIDA BULK SALES INC.; *U.S. Private*, pg. 1547
FLORIDA BUSINESS DEVELOPMENT CORPORATION; *U.S. Private*, pg. 1547
FLORIDA BUSINESS INTERIORS INC.—See Business Office Systems Inc.; *U.S. Private*, pg. 695
FLORIDA BUSINESS INTERIORS - TAMPA BAY—See Business Office Systems Inc.; *U.S. Private*, pg. 695
FLORIDA CANCER SPECIALISTS, P.L.; *U.S. Private*, pg. 1547
FLORIDA CANYON MINING, INC.—See Jipangu Inc.; *Int'l*, pg. 3971
FLORIDA CAPITAL PARTNERS, INC.; *U.S. Private*, pg. 1547
FLORIDA CENTRAL RAILROAD—See Pinsly Railroad Co. Inc.; *U.S. Private*, pg. 3186
FLORIDA CHEMICAL COMPANY, INC.—See Archer-Daniels-Midland Company; *U.S. Public*, pg. 185
FLORIDA CITIZENS BANK; *U.S. Private*, pg. 1547
FLORIDA CITRUS MUTUAL, INC.; *U.S. Private*, pg. 1547
FLORIDA COASTAL HOMES INC.—See The Goldfield Corporation; *U.S. Public*, pg. 2075
FLORIDA COCA-COLA BOTTLING COMPANY—See The Coca-Cola Company; *U.S. Public*, pg. 2064
FLORIDA COMBINED LIFE INSURANCE COMPANY INC.—See GuideWell Mutual Holding Corporation; *U.S. Private*, pg. 1813
FLORIDA COMMERCIAL LAUNDRY SYSTEMS, INC.; *U.S. Private*, pg. 1547
FLORIDA COOL INC.—See Leonard Green & Partners, L.P.; *U.S. Private*, pg. 2430
FLORIDA COUNTRY STORES INC.—See John R. McKenzie Jobber; *U.S. Private*, pg. 2223
FLORIDA CREDIT UNION; *U.S. Private*, pg. 1547
FLORIDA CROWN DEVELOPMENT CORP.; *U.S. Private*, pg. 1547
FLORIDA CRYSTALS CORPORATION; *U.S. Private*, pg. 1548

CORPORATE AFFILIATIONS

FLORIDA DESIGN CONSULTANTS, INC.; *U.S. Private*, pg. 1548
FLORIDA DETROIT DIESEL-ALLISON INC.—See Mercedes-Benz Group AG; *Int'l*, pg. 4823
FLORIDA DETROIT DIESEL-ALLISON—See Mercedes-Benz Group AG; *Int'l*, pg. 4823
FLORIDA DETROIT DIESEL-ALLISON—See Mercedes-Benz Group AG; *Int'l*, pg. 4823
FLORIDA DETROIT DIESEL-ALLISON—See Mercedes-Benz Group AG; *Int'l*, pg. 4823
FLORIDA DETROIT DIESEL-ALLISON—See Mercedes-Benz Group AG; *Int'l*, pg. 4823
FLORIDA DETROIT DIESEL-ALLISON—See Mercedes-Benz Group AG; *Int'l*, pg. 4823
FLORIDA DETROIT DIESEL-ALLISON—See Mercedes-Benz Group AG; *Int'l*, pg. 4823
FLORIDA DIALYSIS CENTER OF CELEBRATION, LLC—See Nautic Partners, LLC; *U.S. Private*, pg. 2870
FLORIDA DIALYSIS CENTER OF ORLANDO, LLC—See Nautic Partners, LLC; *U.S. Private*, pg. 2870
FLORIDA DIGITAL NETWORK INC.; *U.S. Private*, pg. 1548
FLORIDA DIRECTIONAL BORING EQUIPMENT & SUPPLIES, INC.—See Spivey Utility Construction Co. Inc.; *U.S. Private*, pg. 3759
FLORIDA DISTRIBUTING CO. LLC—See Reyes Holdings, LLC; *U.S. Private*, pg. 3418
FLORIDA EAST COAST INDUSTRIES, INC.—See SoftBank Group Corp.; *Int'l*, pg. 7053
FLORIDA EAST COAST RAILWAY, LLC—See Grupo Mexico, S.A.B. de C.V.; *Int'l*, pg. 3132
FLORIDA ENDOSCOPY AND SURGERY CENTER, LLC—See Community Health Systems, Inc.; *U.S. Public*, pg. 553
FLORIDA EVERBLADES; *U.S. Private*, pg. 1548
FLORIDA EXECUTIVE REALTY; *U.S. Private*, pg. 1548
FLORIDA EYE SPECIALISTS, P.A.; *U.S. Private*, pg. 1548
FLORIDA FAMILY INSURANCE COMPANY; *U.S. Private*, pg. 1548
FLORIDA FARM BUREAU CASUALTY INSURANCE COMPANY, MAIN OFFICE—See Southern Farm Bureau Casualty Insurance Company; *U.S. Private*, pg. 3731
FLORIDA FIRST CAPITAL FINANCE CORPORATION; *U.S. Private*, pg. 1548
FLORIDA FLOATS INC.—See Bellwether Financial Group, Inc.; *U.S. Private*, pg. 520
FLORIDA FOOD PRODUCTS, LLC—See Ardian SAS; *Int'l*, pg. 555
FLORIDA FOREST PRODUCTS, LLC—See Tibbetts Lumber Co., LLC; *U.S. Private*, pg. 4166
FLORIDA GIFT FRUIT SHIPPERS ASSOCIATION INC.; *U.S. Private*, pg. 1548
FLORIDA GRAPHIC SERVICES, INC.—See Monomoy Capital Partners LLC; *U.S. Private*, pg. 2772
FLORIDA GROUNDWATER SERVICES, INC.; *U.S. Private*, pg. 1548
FLORIDA GULF CONTRACTING, INC.; *U.S. Private*, pg. 1548
FLORIDA GULFSHORE CAPITAL LLC; *U.S. Private*, pg. 1548
FLORIDA GULF-TO-BAY ANESTHESIOLOGY ASSOCIATES, LLC—See Blackstone Inc.; *U.S. Public*, pg. 359
FLORIDA HARDWARE LLC; *U.S. Private*, pg. 1548
FLORIDA HEALTH CARE NEWS, INC.; *U.S. Private*, pg. 1548
FLORIDA HEALTH CARE PLAN, INC.—See GuideWell Mutual Holding Corporation; *U.S. Private*, pg. 1813
FLORIDA HEALTHY KIDS CORPORATION; *U.S. Private*, pg. 1548
FLORIDA HOME BUILDERS ASSOCIATION, INC.; *U.S. Private*, pg. 1549
FLORIDA HOME IMPROVEMENT ASSOCIATES INC.; *U.S. Private*, pg. 1549
FLORIDA HOME PARTNERSHIP, INC.; *U.S. Private*, pg. 1549
FLORIDA HOSPITAL CREDIT UNION—See Adventist Health System Sunbelt Healthcare Corporation; *U.S. Private*, pg. 109
FLORIDA HOSPITAL DADE CITY, INC.—See Adventist Health System Sunbelt Healthcare Corporation; *U.S. Private*, pg. 109
FLORIDA HOSPITAL FOUNDATION—See Adventist Health System Sunbelt Healthcare Corporation; *U.S. Private*, pg. 109
FLORIDA HOSPITAL HEALTHCARE SYSTEM, INC.—See Adventist Health System Sunbelt Healthcare Corporation; *U.S. Private*, pg. 109
FLORIDA HOSPITAL HEARTLAND MEDICAL CENTER—See Adventist Health System Sunbelt Healthcare Corporation; *U.S. Private*, pg. 109
FLORIDA HOSPITAL MEDICAL GROUP, INC.—See Adventist Health System Sunbelt Healthcare Corporation; *U.S. Private*, pg. 109
FLORIDA HOSPITAL MEDICINE SERVICES, LLC—See Blackstone Inc.; *U.S. Public*, pg. 359
FLORIDA HOSPITAL WATERMAN, INC.—See Adventist Health System Sunbelt Healthcare Corporation; *U.S. Private*, pg. 109
FLORIDA HOUSING FINANCE CORPORATION; *U.S. Private*, pg. 1549
FLORIDA ICE AND FARM CO. S.A.; *Int'l*, pg. 2707

COMPANY NAME INDEX

FLORIDA INDUSTRIAL PRODUCTS INC.; *U.S. Private,* pg. 1549
FLORIDA INSURANCE GUARANTY ASSOCIATION, INC.; *U.S. Private,* pg. 1549
FLORIDA INTRACOASTAL UNDERWRITERS, LIMITED COMPANY—See Brown & Brown, Inc.; *U.S. Public,* pg. 400
FLORIDA IRRIGATION SUPPLY INC.—See Leonard Green & Partners, L.P.; *U.S. Private,* pg. 2429
FLORIDA KEYS AQUEDUCT AUTHORITY; *U.S. Private,* pg. 1549
FLORIDA KEYS ELECTRIC COOPERATIVE ASSOCIATION, INC.; *U.S. Private,* pg. 1549
FLORIDA KEYS FOOD STORES, INC.—See John R. McKenzie Jobber, Inc.; *U.S. Private,* pg. 2223
FLORIDA KNIFE CO.; *U.S. Private,* pg. 1549
FLORIDA LANDSCAPE CONSULTANTS INC.; *U.S. Private,* pg. 1549
FLORIDA LANDSCAPE DOCTOR, INC.; *U.S. Private,* pg. 1549
FLORIDA LEMARK CORPORATION; *U.S. Private,* pg. 1549
FLORIDA LIFESTYLE HOMES OF FORT MYERS, INC.; *U.S. Private,* pg. 1549
FLORIDA LIFT SYSTEMS, INC.; *U.S. Private,* pg. 1549
FLORIDA LIVING NURSING CENTER; *U.S. Private,* pg. 1549
FLORIDA LIVING OPTIONS INC; *U.S. Private,* pg. 1549
FLORIDA MADE DOOR CO.—See Owens Corning; *U.S. Public,* pg. 1626
FLORIDA MARINE TANKS, INC.; *U.S. Private,* pg. 1549
FLORIDA MARLINS, L.P.; *U.S. Private,* pg. 1549
FLORIDA MEDICAL CLINIC P.A.; *U.S. Private,* pg. 1550
FLORIDA METAL PRODUCTS INC.; *U.S. Private,* pg. 1550
FLORIDA MICROELECTRONICS, LLC—See Francisco Partners Management, LP; *U.S. Private,* pg. 1589
FLORIDA MIDLAND RAILROAD—See Pinsly Railroad Co. Inc.; *U.S. Private,* pg. 3186
FLORIDA MISCELLANEOUS STRUCTURAL PRODUCTS—See TTI Holdings Inc.; *U.S. Private,* pg. 4254
FLORIDA MUNICIPAL POWER AGENCY; *U.S. Private,* pg. 1550
FLORIDA NORTHERN RAILROAD—See Pinsly Railroad Co. Inc.; *U.S. Private,* pg. 3186
FLORIDA ORGANIC AQUACULTURE, LLC; *U.S. Private,* pg. 1550
FLORIDA PAINTS & COATINGS LLC; *U.S. Private,* pg. 1550
FLORIDA PANTHERS HOCKEY CLUB, LTD.—See Sunrise Sports & Entertainment LLLP; *U.S. Private,* pg. 3870
FLORIDA PENINSULA INSURANCE COMPANY; *U.S. Private,* pg. 1550
FLORIDA PEST CONTROL & CHEMICAL CO.—See Rentokil Initial plc; *Int'l,* pg. 6287
FLORIDA PNEUMATIC MANUFACTURING CORPORATION—See ShoreView Industries, LLC; *U.S. Private,* pg. 3642
FLORIDA POWER & LIGHT COMPANY—See NextEra Energy, Inc.; *U.S. Public,* pg. 1526
FLORIDA POWER & LIGHT COMPANY—See NextEra Energy, Inc.; *U.S. Public,* pg. 1526
FLORIDA PREFERRED ADMINISTRATORS, INC.—See Fosun International Limited; *Int'l,* pg. 2752
FLORIDA PRESS ASSOCIATION INC; *U.S. Private,* pg. 1550
FLORIDA PRODUCTION ENGINEERING INC.—See Ernie Green Industries, Inc.; *U.S. Private,* pg. 1422
FLORIDA PROGRESS CORPORATION—See Duke Energy Corporation; *U.S. Public,* pg. 691
FLORIDA PUBLIC UTILITIES COMPANY—See Chesapeake Utilities Corporation; *U.S. Public,* pg. 485
FLORIDA RADIOLOGY IMAGING; *U.S. Private,* pg. 1550
FLORIDA RESTORATION OF TAMPA BAY LLC; *U.S. Private,* pg. 1550
FLORIDA ROCK & TANK LINES, INC.—See FRP Holdings, Inc.; *U.S. Public,* pg. 888
FLORIDA ROPE & SUPPLY, INC.—See ALP Industries, Inc.; *U.S. Private,* pg. 196
FLORIDA SEALING PRODUCTS—See Applied Industrial Technologies, Inc.; *U.S. Public,* pg. 171
FLORIDA SEAL & RUBBER, LLC—See Wyatt Seal Inc.; *U.S. Private,* pg. 4575
FLORIDA SILICA SAND CO. INC.; *U.S. Private,* pg. 1550
FLORIDA'S NATURAL GROWERS—See Citrus World, Inc.; *U.S. Private,* pg. 905
FLORIDA SOUTHERN ROOFING & SHEET METAL, INC.; *U.S. Private,* pg. 1550
FLORIDA SPRINGS SURGERY CENTER, LLC—See Tenet Healthcare Corporation; *U.S. Public,* pg. 2002
FLORIDA STATE ELKS ASSOCIATION, INC.; *U.S. Private,* pg. 1550
FLORIDA STATE SECURITY, INC.; *U.S. Private,* pg. 1550
FLORIDA SUGAR DISTRIBUTORS INC.—See Florida Crystals Corporation; *U.S. Private,* pg. 1548
FLORIDA SUN PUBLICATIONS, INC.—See Pearson plc; *Int'l,* pg. 5777

FLORIDA TEXAS RESTAURANT GROUP—See Pacesetter Capital Group; *U.S. Private,* pg. 3064
FLORIDA TILE INC.—See Panariagroup Industrie Ceramiche S.p.A.; *Int'l,* pg. 5717
FLORIDA TILE INDUSTRIES, INC.—See Panariagroup Industrie Ceramiche S.p.A.; *Int'l,* pg. 5717
THE FLORIDA TIMES-UNION—See Gannett Co., Inc.; *U.S. Public,* pg. 904
FLORIDA TOURISM INDUSTRY MARKETING CORPORATION; *U.S. Private,* pg. 1550
FLORIDA TRAILS, INC.; *U.S. Private,* pg. 1550
FLORIDA TRUCK GROUP; *U.S. Private,* pg. 1550
FLORIDA TRUE HEALTH INC.—See GuideWell Mutual Holding Corporation; *U.S. Private,* pg. 1813
FLORIDA TURBINE TECHNOLOGIES INC.—See Kratos Defense & Security Solutions, Inc.; *U.S. Public,* pg. 1276
FLORIDA UNITED METHODIST CHILDREN'S HOME; *U.S. Private,* pg. 1551
FLORIDA UTILITY TRAILERS INC.; *U.S. Private,* pg. 1551
THE FLORIDA VALUE FUND LLLP; *U.S. Private,* pg. 4029
FLORIDA VESSEL MANAGEMENT LLC—See Albert Ballin KG; *Int'l,* pg. 294
FLORIDA WEST COAST CRUISES, INC.; *U.S. Private,* pg. 1551
FLORIDA WEST COAST PUBLIC BROADCASTING, INC.; *U.S. Private,* pg. 1551
FLORIDA WORKERS' COMPENSATION INSURANCE GUARANTY ASSOCIATION, INC.; *U.S. Private,* pg. 1551
FLORIDIAN NATURAL GAS STORAGE COMPANY, LLC—See Targa Resources Corp.; *U.S. Public,* pg. 1981
FLORIDIAN PARTNERS, LLC; *U.S. Private,* pg. 1551
FLORIDIENNE SA; *Int'l,* pg. 2708
FLORIEN FITOATIVOS LTDA—See Fagron NV; *Int'l,* pg. 2603
FLORIKAN ESA LLC; *U.S. Private,* pg. 1551
FLORIM CERAMICHE S.p.A.; *Int'l,* pg. 2708
FLORIM USA, INC.—See Florim Ceramiche S.p.A.; *Int'l,* pg. 2708
FLORIN GMBH—See DZ BANK AG Deutsche Zentral-Genossenschaftsbank; *Int'l,* pg. 2244
FLORIN MINING INVESTMENT COMPANY LIMITED; *Int'l,* pg. 2708
FLORINT B.V.; *Int'l,* pg. 2708
FLORINVEST SA—See Floridienne SA; *Int'l,* pg. 2708
FLORI ROBERTS—See Color Me Beautiful, Inc.; *U.S. Private,* pg. 973
FLORIS OBDAM B.V.—See BAT S.p.A.; *Int'l,* pg. 889
FLORISSA PTE LTD—See PT Wintermar Offshore Marine Tbk; *Int'l,* pg. 6083
FLORIST DISTRIBUTING, INC.—See Hy-Vee, Inc.; *U.S. Private,* pg. 2016
FLORISTS SUPPLY LTD.; *Int'l,* pg. 2708
FLORISTS' TRANSWORLD DELIVERY, INC.—See Tenth Avenue Holdings LLC; *U.S. Private,* pg. 3968
FLORSHEIM, INC.—See Weyco Group, Inc.; *U.S. Public,* pg. 2365
FLORSHEIM SHOES EUROPE S.R.L.—See Weyco Group, Inc.; *U.S. Public,* pg. 2365
FLORSTAR SALES, INC.; *U.S. Private,* pg. 1551
FLORTINE—See Carrefour SA; *Int'l,* pg. 1345
FLORY INDUSTRIES, INC.; *U.S. Private,* pg. 1551
FLOSIT SAS—See SOL S.p.A.; *Int'l,* pg. 7067
FLO S.P.A.; *Int'l,* pg. 2706
FLO SYSTEMS, INC.—See Bain Capital, LP; *U.S. Private,* pg. 432
FLOTA PROYECTOS SINGULARES, S.A—See ACS, Actividades de Construccion y Servicios, S.A.; *Int'l,* pg. 111
FLOTEC CORPORATION; *U.S. Private,* pg. 1551
FLO-TEC, INC.; *U.S. Private,* pg. 1546
FLOTEK CHEMISTRY, LLC—See Flotek Industries, Inc.; *U.S. Public,* pg. 853
FLOTEK INDUSTRIES, INC.; *U.S. Public,* pg. 853
FLO-TORK INC.—See Moog Inc.; *U.S. Public,* pg. 1469
FLOTRON AG—See BKW AG; *Int'l,* pg. 1055
FLOTTENMANAGEMENT GMBH—See Erste Group Bank AG; *Int'l,* pg. 2498
FLOTURN INC.; *U.S. Private,* pg. 1551
FLOTURN PHOTORECEPTOR (KUNSHAN) CO., LTD.—See Floturn Inc.; *U.S. Private,* pg. 1551
FLOURISH INC.; *U.S. Private,* pg. 1551
FLOUR MILLS C. SARANTOPOULOS S.A.; *Int'l,* pg. 2708
FLOUR MILLS KEPENOS S.A.; *Int'l,* pg. 2708
FLOUR MILLS OF FIJI LIMITED; *Int'l,* pg. 2708
FLOUR MILLS OF GHANA LIMITED—See Seaboard Corporation; *U.S. Public,* pg. 1850
FLOUR MILLS OF NIGERIA PLC.; *Int'l,* pg. 2708
FLOURNOY CONSTRUCTION COMPANY—See Kajima Corporation; *Int'l,* pg. 4054
FLOURNOY DEVELOPMENT CO. LLC; *U.S. Private,* pg. 1551
FLOVAL EQUIPMENT LTD.; *Int'l,* pg. 2709
FLO VENDING—See FLO S.p.A.; *Int'l,* pg. 2707
FLOW AEROSPACE—See AIP, LLC; *U.S. Private,* pg. 133

FLOW AMERICA, LLC—See Lone Star Funds; *U.S. Private,* pg. 2485
FLOW ASIA CORPORATION—See AIP, LLC; *U.S. Private,* pg. 137
FLOWATER, INC.—See Bluewater AB; *Int'l,* pg. 1075
FLOW AUTOMOTIVE CENTER OF WINSTON-SALEM, LLC; *U.S. Private,* pg. 1551
FLOW BANGALORE WATERJET PVT. LTD.—See AIP, LLC; *U.S. Private,* pg. 137
FLOWBIRD SVERIGE AB—See Astorg Partners S.A.S.; *Int'l,* pg. 656
FLOW BMW; *U.S. Private,* pg. 1551
FLOW BUICK GMC OF WINSTON-SALEM; *U.S. Private,* pg. 1551
FLOW CAPITAL CORP.; *Int'l,* pg. 2709
FLOWCARDIA, INC.—See Becton, Dickinson & Company; *U.S. Public,* pg. 291
FLOWCHEM LLC—See Entegris, Inc.; *U.S. Public,* pg. 776
FLOW-CHEM TECHNOLOGIES, LLC—See Dorf-Ketal Chemicals India Pvt. Ltd.; *Int'l,* pg. 2176
FLOWCO LIMITED—See Rotork Plc; *Int'l,* pg. 6405
FLOW CONTROL HOLDING GMBH & CO. KG—See Pentair plc; *Int'l,* pg. 5789
FLOW CONTROL HOLDINGS, LLC—See Audax Group, Limited Partnership; *U.S. Private,* pg. 388
FLOW CONTROLS LTD.—See SMC Corporation; *Int'l,* pg. 7003
FLOW CONTROLS S.A. DE C.V.—See Emerson Electric Co.; *U.S. Public,* pg. 744
FLOWCRETE ASIA SDN. BHD.—See RPM International Inc.; *U.S. Public,* pg. 1818
FLOWCRETE AUSTRALIA PTY. LIMITED—See RPM International Inc.; *U.S. Public,* pg. 1818
FLOWCRETE FRANCE S.A.S.—See RPM International Inc.; *U.S. Public,* pg. 1819
FLOWCRETE GROUP LTD.—See RPM International Inc.; *U.S. Public,* pg. 1819
FLOWCRETE (HONG KONG) LTD—See RPM International Inc.; *U.S. Public,* pg. 1818
FLOWCRETE INDIA PRIVATE LIMITED—See RPM International Inc.; *U.S. Public,* pg. 1819
FLOWCRETE MIDDLE EAST FZCO—See RPM International Inc.; *U.S. Public,* pg. 1819
FLOWCRETE NORTH AMERICA INC.—See RPM International Inc.; *U.S. Public,* pg. 1819
FLOWCRETE NORWAY AS—See RPM International Inc.; *U.S. Public,* pg. 1819
FLOWCRETE POLSKA SP. Z .O.O.—See RPM International Inc.; *U.S. Public,* pg. 1819
FLOWCRETE SA (PTY) LTD—See RPM International Inc.; *U.S. Public,* pg. 1819
FLOWCRETE SWEDEN AB—See RPM International Inc.; *U.S. Public,* pg. 1819
FLOWCRETE UK LIMITED—See RPM International Inc.; *U.S. Public,* pg. 1819
FLOW DESIGN INC—See IMI plc; *Int'l,* pg. 3625
FLOW DRY TECHNOLOGY LTD—See Brittany Stamping, LLC; *U.S. Private,* pg. 657
FLOW EASTERN EUROPE, S.R.O.—See AIP, LLC; *U.S. Private,* pg. 137
FLOW ENERGY LIMITED—See FAR Limited; *Int'l,* pg. 2617
FLOWEN S.A.C—See HORIBA Ltd; *Int'l,* pg. 3475
FLOWERBUD.COM; *U.S. Private,* pg. 1552
FLOWER CITY PEST ELIMINATION—See Rollins, Inc.; *U.S. Public,* pg. 1810
FLOWER CITY PRINTING INC.; *U.S. Private,* pg. 1551
FLOWER FACTORY INC.; *U.S. Private,* pg. 1551
FLOWER KING ECO-ENGINEERING INC.; *Int'l,* pg. 2709
FLOWER ONE HOLDINGS INC.; *Int'l,* pg. 2709
FLOWERS BAKERIES BRANDS, LLC—See Flowers Foods, Inc.; *U.S. Public,* pg. 854
FLOWERS BAKERIES, LLC—See Flowers Foods, Inc.; *U.S. Public,* pg. 854
FLOWERS BAKERY OF CLEVELAND, LLC—See Flowers Foods, Inc.; *U.S. Public,* pg. 854
FLOWERS BAKERY OF CROSSVILLE, LLC—See Flowers Foods, Inc.; *U.S. Public,* pg. 854
FLOWERS BAKERY OF LONDON, LLC—See Flowers Foods, Inc.; *U.S. Public,* pg. 854
FLOWERS BAKERY OF MONTGOMERY, LLC—See Flowers Foods, Inc.; *U.S. Public,* pg. 854
FLOWERS BAKERY OF TEXARKANA, LLC—See Flowers Foods, Inc.; *U.S. Public,* pg. 854
FLOWERS BAKERY OF WINSTON-SALEM, LLC—See Flowers Foods, Inc.; *U.S. Public,* pg. 854
FLOWERS BAKING CO. OF BARDSTOWN, LLC.; *U.S. Private,* pg. 1552
FLOWERS BAKING CO. OF BATESVILLE, LLC—See Flowers Foods, Inc.; *U.S. Public,* pg. 854
FLOWERS BAKING CO. OF BATON ROUGE, LLC—See Flowers Foods, Inc.; *U.S. Public,* pg. 854
FLOWERS BAKING CO. OF BIRMINGHAM, LLC—See Flowers Foods, Inc.; *U.S. Public,* pg. 854
FLOWERS BAKING CO. OF BRADENTON, LLC—See Flowers Foods, Inc.; *U.S. Public,* pg. 854
FLOWERS BAKING CO. OF DENTON, LLC—See Flowers Foods, Inc.; *U.S. Public,* pg. 854

FLOWERS BAKING CO. OF BARDSTOWN, LLC. CORPORATE AFFILIATIONS

FLOWERS BAKING CO. OF DENVER, LLC—See Flowers Foods, Inc.; *U.S. Public*, pg. 854
FLOWERS BAKING CO. OF EL PASO, LLC—See Flowers Foods, Inc.; *U.S. Public*, pg. 854
FLOWERS BAKING CO. OF FLORIDA, LLC—See Flowers Foods, Inc.; *U.S. Public*, pg. 854
FLOWERS BAKING CO. OF HENDERSON, LLC—See Flowers Foods, Inc.; *U.S. Public*, pg. 854
FLOWERS BAKING CO. OF JACKSONVILLE, LLC—See Flowers Foods, Inc.; *U.S. Public*, pg. 854
FLOWERS BAKING CO. OF JAMESTOWN, LLC—See Flowers Foods, Inc.; *U.S. Public*, pg. 854
FLOWERS BAKING CO. OF KNOXVILLE, LLC—See Flowers Foods, Inc.; *U.S. Public*, pg. 854
FLOWERS BAKING CO. OF LAFAYETTE, LLC—See Flowers Foods, Inc.; *U.S. Public*, pg. 854
FLOWERS BAKING CO. OF MCDONOUGH, LLC—See Flowers Foods, Inc.; *U.S. Public*, pg. 854
FLOWERS BAKING CO. OF MEMPHIS, LLC—See Flowers Foods, Inc.; *U.S. Public*, pg. 854
FLOWERS BAKING CO. OF MODESTO, LLC—See Flowers Foods, Inc.; *U.S. Public*, pg. 854
FLOWERS BAKING CO. OF NEW ORLEANS, LLC—See Flowers Foods, Inc.; *U.S. Public*, pg. 854
FLOWERS BAKING CO. OF NEWTON, LLC—See Flowers Foods, Inc.; *U.S. Public*, pg. 854
FLOWERS BAKING CO. OF NORFOLK, LLC—See Flowers Foods, Inc.; *U.S. Public*, pg. 854
FLOWERS BAKING CO. OF OHIO, LLC—See Flowers Foods, Inc.; *U.S. Public*, pg. 854
FLOWERS BAKING CO. OF OPELIKA, LLC—See Flowers Foods, Inc.; *U.S. Public*, pg. 854
FLOWERS BAKING CO. OF ORLANDO, LLC—See Flowers Foods, Inc.; *U.S. Public*, pg. 854
FLOWERS BAKING CO. OF SAN ANTONIO, LLC—See Flowers Foods, Inc.; *U.S. Public*, pg. 854
FLOWERS BAKING CO. OF THOMASVILLE, LLC—See Flowers Foods, Inc.; *U.S. Public*, pg. 855
FLOWERS BAKING CO. OF TUCKER, LLC—See Flowers Foods, Inc.; *U.S. Public*, pg. 855
FLOWERS BAKING CO. OF TUSCALOOSA, LLC—See Flowers Foods, Inc.; *U.S. Public*, pg. 855
FLOWERS BAKING CO. OF TYLER, LLC—See Flowers Foods, Inc.; *U.S. Public*, pg. 855
FLOWERS BAKING CO. OF VILLA RICA, LLC—See Flowers Foods, Inc.; *U.S. Public*, pg. 855
FLOWERS FOODS, INC.; *U.S. Public*, pg. 853
FLOWERS FOODS SPECIALTY GROUP, LLC—See Flowers Foods, Inc.; *U.S. Public*, pg. 855
FLOWERS INSURANCE AGENCY, LLC—See Galiot Insurance Services, Inc.; *U.S. Private*, pg. 1638
FLOWERS SPECIALTY SNACK SALES, INC.—See Flowers Foods, Inc.; *U.S. Public*, pg. 855
FLOWER TRANSFER INC.—See Delaware Valley Wholesale Florist Inc.; *U.S. Private*, pg. 1196
FLOWERY GOLD MINES COMPANY OF NEVADA; *U.S. Public*, pg. 855
FLOW EUROPE GMBH—See AIP, LLC; *U.S. Private*, pg. 137
FLOWFACT GMBH—See Scout24 SE; *Int'l*, pg. 6654
FLOW FACT SCHWEIZ AG—See Scout24 SE; *Int'l*, pg. 6654
FLOWGROUP PLC; *Int'l*, pg. 2709
FLOWING CLOUD TECHNOLOGY LTD.; *Int'l*, pg. 2709
FLOW INSTRUMENTS & ENGINEERING GMBH—See Chart Industries, Inc.; *U.S. Public*, pg. 481
FLOW INTERNATIONAL CORPORATION—See AIP, LLC; *U.S. Private*, pg. 137
FLOW ITALIA S.R.L.—See AIP, LLC; *U.S. Private*, pg. 137
FLOW JAPAN CORPORATION - NAGOYA—See AIP, LLC; *U.S. Private*, pg. 137
FLOW JAPAN CORPORATION—See AIP, LLC; *U.S. Private*, pg. 137
FLOWJO LLC—See Becton, Dickinson & Company; *U.S. Public*, pg. 292
FLOWLAB & SERVICE CO., LTD.—See The Siam Cement Public Company Limited; *Int'l*, pg. 7683
FLOW LATINO AMERICANA INDUSTRIA E COMERCIO LTDA.—See AIP, LLC; *U.S. Private*, pg. 137
FLOW MANAGEMENT DEVICES, LLC—See IDEX Corp; *U.S. Public*, pg. 1090
FLOW MANAGEMENT TECHNOLOGIES, INC.; *U.S. Private*, pg. 1551
FLOWMASTER INC.; *U.S. Private*, pg. 1552
FLOW METALS CORP.; *Int'l*, pg. 2709
FLOWMETRICS, INC—See Hydraulics International, Inc.; *U.S. Private*, pg. 2017
FLOWMOLE—See Avon Lippiatt Hobbs (Contracting) Limited; *Int'l*, pg. 749
FLOW MOTORS, INC.; *U.S. Private*, pg. 1551
FLOWORKS INTERNATIONAL LLC—See Wynnchurch Capital, L.P.; *U.S. Private*, pg. 4577
FLOWPLAY, INC.—See PCI Gaming Authority; *U.S. Private*, pg. 3120
FLOW POLYMERS LLC—See The Jordan Company, L.P.; *U.S. Private*, pg. 4061
FLOW-QUIP INC—See Rotork Plc; *Int'l*, pg. 6406
THE FLOWR CORP.; *Int'l*, pg. 7643

FLOWRIC CO., LTD.—See Nippon Paper Industries Co., Ltd.; *Int'l*, pg. 5327
FLOWROUTE, LLC—See Thompson Street Capital Manager LLC; *U.S. Private*, pg. 4160
FLOWSERVE AHAUS GMBH—See Flowserve Corporation; *U.S. Public*, pg. 855
FLOWSERVE - AL MANSOORI SERVICES COMPANY LTD.—See Flowserve Corporation; *U.S. Public*, pg. 855
FLOWSERVE AUSTRALIA PTY. LTD.—See Flowserve Corporation; *U.S. Public*, pg. 855
FLOWSERVE (AUSTRIA) GMBH—See Flowserve Corporation; *U.S. Public*, pg. 855
FLOWSERVE (BELGIUM) BVBA—See Flowserve Corporation; *U.S. Public*, pg. 855
FLOWSERVE BELGIUM N.V.—See Flowserve Corporation; *U.S. Public*, pg. 855
FLOWSERVE B.V.—See Flowserve Corporation; *U.S. Public*, pg. 855
FLOWSERVE CANADA CORP.—See Flowserve Corporation; *U.S. Public*, pg. 855
FLOWSERVE CHILE S.A.—See Flowserve Corporation; *U.S. Public*, pg. 855
FLOWSERVE COLOMBIA, LTDA.—See Flowserve Corporation; *U.S. Public*, pg. 855
FLOWSERVE CORPORATION; *U.S. Public*, pg. 855
FLOWSERVE CORP.—See Flowserve Corporation; *U.S. Public*, pg. 856
FLOWSERVE CORP.—See Flowserve Corporation; *U.S. Public*, pg. 856
FLOWSERVE CORP.—See Flowserve Corporation; *U.S. Public*, pg. 855
FLOWSERVE CORP.—See Flowserve Corporation; *U.S. Public*, pg. 855
FLOWSERVE CORP.—See Flowserve Corporation; *U.S. Public*, pg. 856
FLOWSERVE CORP.—See Flowserve Corporation; *U.S. Public*, pg. 856
FLOWSERVE CORP.—See Flowserve Corporation; *U.S. Public*, pg. 855
FLOWSERVE CORP.—See Flowserve Corporation; *U.S. Public*, pg. 855
FLOWSERVE CORP.—See Flowserve Corporation; *U.S. Public*, pg. 855
FLOWSERVE DORTMUND GMBH & CO. KG—See Flowserve Corporation; *U.S. Public*, pg. 856
FLOWSERVE DORTMUND VERWALTUNGS GMBH—See Flowserve Corporation; *U.S. Public*, pg. 856
FLOWSERVE EMA HOLDINGS B.V.—See Flowserve Corporation; *U.S. Public*, pg. 855
FLOWSERVE ESSEN GMBH—See Flowserve Corporation; *U.S. Public*, pg. 856
FLOWSERVE FINLAND OY—See Flowserve Corporation; *U.S. Public*, pg. 855
FLOWSERVE FLOW CONTROL BENELUX BV—See Flowserve Corporation; *U.S. Public*, pg. 856
FLOWSERVE FLOW CONTROL GMBH—See Flowserve Corporation; *U.S. Public*, pg. 856
FLOWSERVE GB LIMITED—See Flowserve Corporation; *U.S. Public*, pg. 856
FLOWSERVE GMBH—See Flowserve Corporation; *U.S. Public*, pg. 856
FLOWSERVE HAMBURG GMBH—See Flowserve Corporation; *U.S. Public*, pg. 856
FLOWSERVE INDIA CONTROLS PVT. LTD.—See Flowserve Corporation; *U.S. Public*, pg. 856
FLOWSERVE INTERNATIONAL LIMITED—See Flowserve Corporation; *U.S. Public*, pg. 856
FLOWSERVE LIMITORQUE DIV.—See Flowserve Corporation; *U.S. Public*, pg. 856
FLOWSERVE LTDA.—See Flowserve Corporation; *U.S. Public*, pg. 856
FLOWSERVE LTD.—See Flowserve Corporation; *U.S. Public*, pg. 856
FLOWSERVE NIIGATA WORTHINGTON COMPANY LTD.—See Flowserve Corporation; *U.S. Public*, pg. 856
FLOWSERVE PMV USA INC.—See Flowserve Corporation; *U.S. Public*, pg. 856
FLOWSERVE POMPES S.A.S.—See Flowserve Corporation; *U.S. Public*, pg. 856
FLOWSERVE PTE. LTD.—See Flowserve Corporation; *U.S. Public*, pg. 856
FLOWSERVE PUMPS LIMITED—See Flowserve Corporation; *U.S. Public*, pg. 856
FLOWSERVE S.A. DE C.V.—See Flowserve Corporation; *U.S. Public*, pg. 856
FLOWSERVE SANMAR LTD.—See Flowserve Corporation; *U.S. Public*, pg. 856
FLOWSERVE SANMAR LTD.—See Sanmar Holdings Ltd.; *Int'l*, pg. 6546
FLOWSERVE S.A.—See Flowserve Corporation; *U.S. Public*, pg. 856
FLOWSERVE S.A.S.—See Flowserve Corporation; *U.S. Public*, pg. 856
FLOWSERVE S. DE R.L. DE C.V.—See Flowserve Corporation; *U.S. Public*, pg. 856
FLOWSERVE SIHI AUSTRIA GMBH—See Flowserve Corporation; *U.S. Public*, pg. 856
FLOWSERVE SIHI BULGARIA EOOD—See Flowserve Corporation; *U.S. Public*, pg. 856

FLOWSERVE SIHI CZ S.R.O.—See Flowserve Corporation; *U.S. Public*, pg. 855
FLOWSERVE SIHI (FRANCE) SAS—See Flowserve Corporation; *U.S. Public*, pg. 856
FLOWSERVE SIHI GERMANY GMBH—See Flowserve Corporation; *U.S. Public*, pg. 855
FLOWSERVE SIHI HUNGARY KFT—See Flowserve Corporation; *U.S. Public*, pg. 856
FLOWSERVE SIHI (ITALY) S.R.L.—See Flowserve Corporation; *U.S. Public*, pg. 855
FLOWSERVE SIHI (SCHWEIZ) GMBH—See Flowserve Corporation; *U.S. Public*, pg. 856
FLOWSERVE SIHI (SPAIN) S.L.—See Flowserve Corporation; *U.S. Public*, pg. 855
FLOWSERVE S.P.A.—See Flowserve Corporation; *U.S. Public*, pg. 856
FLOWSERVE S.R.L.—See Flowserve Corporation; *U.S. Public*, pg. 856
FLOWSERVE S.R.L.—See Flowserve Corporation; *U.S. Public*, pg. 856
FLOWSERVE SWEDEN AB—See Flowserve Corporation; *U.S. Public*, pg. 856
FLOWSERVE (THAILAND) LTD.—See Flowserve Corporation; *U.S. Public*, pg. 855
FLOWSERVE WOODBRIDGE DIVISION—See Flowserve Corporation; *U.S. Public*, pg. 855
FLOWSERVE WORTHINGTON S.R.L.—See Flowserve Corporation; *U.S. Public*, pg. 856
FLOW SERVICE PARTNERS—See LP First Capital; *U.S. Private*, pg. 2507
FLOW SERVICE PARTNERS—See The RLJ Companies, LLC; *U.S. Private*, pg. 4111
FLOWTECH FLUIDPOWER PLC; *Int'l*, pg. 2709
FLOW-TECH, INC.—See Cross Company; *U.S. Private*, pg. 1104
FLOWTECHNOLOGY BENELUX B.V.—See Flowtech Fluidpower plc; *Int'l*, pg. 2709
FLOWTEC INDUSTRIETECHNIK GMBH—See Indutrade AB; *Int'l*, pg. 3678
FLOW-TEK INDUSTRIA E COMERCIO DE VALVULAS LTDA—See Bray International, Inc.; *U.S. Private*, pg. 642
FLOW-TEKNIKK AS—See Addtech AB; *Int'l*, pg. 133
FLOW THRU SYSTEMS INC.—See Libra Industries, Incorporated; *U.S. Private*, pg. 2447
FLOWTITE ANDERCOL S.A.—See Saudi Arabian Amiantit Company; *Int'l*, pg. 6588
FLOWTITE TECHNOLOGY—See Saudi Arabian Amiantit Company; *Int'l*, pg. 6588
FLOW TRADERS ASIA PTE. LTD.—See Flow Traders NV; *Int'l*, pg. 2709
FLOW TRADERS HONG KONG LTD.—See Flow Traders NV; *Int'l*, pg. 2709
FLOW TRADERS NV; *Int'l*, pg. 2709
FLOW TRADERS TECHNOLOGIES SRL—See Flow Traders NV; *Int'l*, pg. 2709
FLOW TRADERS U.S. LLC—See Flow Traders NV; *Int'l*, pg. 2709
FLOWTREND INC.—See Audax Group, Limited Partnership; *U.S. Private*, pg. 388
FLOWTRONEX PSI, LLC—See Motor Controls, Inc.; *U.S. Private*, pg. 2797
FLOW-TRONIC S.A.—See Sophora Unternehmerkapital GmbH; *Int'l*, pg. 7109
FLOWTRON OUTDOOR PRODUCTS—See Armatron International, Inc.; *U.S. Private*, pg. 330
FLOW UK LIMITED—See AIP, LLC; *U.S. Private*, pg. 137
FLOW ULTRA HIGH PRESSURE WATERJET TECHNOLOGY (SHANGHAI) CO., LTD.—See AIP, LLC; *U.S. Private*, pg. 137
FLOYD & BEASLEY TRANSFER CO. INC.; *U.S. Private*, pg. 1552
FLOYD ENERGY INC.; *U.S. Private*, pg. 1552
FLOYD HOMECARE, LLC—See UnitedHealth Group Incorporated; *U.S. Public*, pg. 2245
FLOYD PCL; *Int'l*, pg. 2709
FLOYDS STORES INC.; *U.S. Private*, pg. 1552
FLOYD'S TRUCK CENTER, INC.; *U.S. Private*, pg. 1552
FLP HOLDINGS INC.; *U.S. Private*, pg. 1552
F.L. ROBERTS & CO., INC.; *U.S. Private*, pg. 1456
FL SELENIA LUXCO S.C.A.—See Vestar Capital Partners, LLC; *U.S. Private*, pg. 4371
FLS GLOBAL FINANCE A/S—See FLSmidth & Co. A/S; *Int'l*, pg. 2710
FLS JAPAN LTD.—See FLSmidth & Co. A/S; *Int'l*, pg. 2710
FLS MAROC S.A.—See FLSmidth & Co. A/S; *Int'l*, pg. 2710
FLSMIDTH ABON PTY. LTD.—See FLSmidth & Co. A/S; *Int'l*, pg. 2711
FLSMIDTH AIRTECH—See FLSmidth & Co. A/S; *Int'l*, pg. 2710
FLSMIDTH A/S (JORDAN) LTD.—See FLSmidth & Co. A/S; *Int'l*, pg. 2710
FLSMIDTH A/S—See FLSmidth & Co. A/S; *Int'l*, pg. 2710
FLSMIDTH (BEIJING) LTD.—See FLSmidth & Co. A/S; *Int'l*, pg. 2710
FLSMIDTH BOISE, INC.—See FLSmidth & Co. A/S; *Int'l*, pg. 2712

FLSMIDTH BUFFALO (PTY.) LTD.—See FLSmidth & Co. A/S; *Int'l*, pg. 2711
FLSMIDTH CAUCASUS LIMITED LIABILITY COMPANY—See FLSmidth & Co. A/S; *Int'l*, pg. 2710
FLSMIDTH & CO. A/S; *Int'l*, pg. 2710
FLSMIDTH CO., LTD.—See FLSmidth & Co. A/S; *Int'l*, pg. 2710
FLSMIDTH CONVEYOR ENGINEERING, INC.—See FLSmidth & Co. A/S; *Int'l*, pg. 2712
FLSMIDTH DORR-OLIVER EIMCO GMBH—See FLSmidth & Co. A/S; *Int'l*, pg. 2711
FLSMIDTH DORR-OLIVER EIMCO PTY LIMITED—See FLSmidth & Co. A/S; *Int'l*, pg. 2711
FLSMIDTH GMBH—See FLSmidth & Co. A/S; *Int'l*, pg. 2710
FLSMIDTH HAMBURG GMBH—See FLSmidth & Co. A/S; *Int'l*, pg. 2710
FLSMIDTH INC.—See FLSmidth & Co. A/S; *Int'l*, pg. 2710
FLSMIDTH INDUSTRIAL SOLUTIONS (CANADA) INC.—See FLSmidth & Co. A/S; *Int'l*, pg. 2710
FLSMIDTH INDUSTRIAL SOLUTIONS MAKINE SANAYI VE TICARET A.S.—See FLSmidth & Co. A/S; *Int'l*, pg. 2710
FLSMIDTH (JERSEY) LIMITED—See FLSmidth & Co. A/S; *Int'l*, pg. 2710
FLSMIDTH KREBS AFRICA (PTY.) LTD.—See FLSmidth & Co. A/S; *Int'l*, pg. 2711
FLSMIDTH KREBS AUSTRALIA PTY. LTD.—See FLSmidth & Co. A/S; *Int'l*, pg. 2711
FLSMIDTH KREBS (BEIJING) LTD.—See FLSmidth & Co. A/S; *Int'l*, pg. 2712
FLSMIDTH KREBS CHILE LIMITADA—See FLSmidth & Co. A/S; *Int'l*, pg. 2710
FLSMIDTH KREBS GMBH—See FLSmidth & Co. A/S; *Int'l*, pg. 2710
FLSMIDTH KREBS INC.—See FLSmidth & Co. A/S; *Int'l*, pg. 2712
FLSMIDTH LTDA.—See FLSmidth & Co. A/S; *Int'l*, pg. 2710
FLSMIDTH MAAG GEAR AG—See FLSmidth & Co. A/S; *Int'l*, pg. 2710
FLSMIDTH MAAG GEAR S.P.A.—See FLSmidth & Co. A/S; *Int'l*, pg. 2710
FLSMIDTH MAAG GEAR SP. Z O.O.—See FLSmidth & Co. A/S; *Int'l*, pg. 2710
FLSMIDTH MILANO S.R.L.—See FLSmidth & Co. A/S; *Int'l*, pg. 2710
FLSMIDTH MINERALS A/S—See FLSmidth & Co. A/S; *Int'l*, pg. 2710
FLSMIDTH MINERALS HOLDING APS—See FLSmidth & Co. A/S; *Int'l*, pg. 2711
FLSMIDTH MINERALS INC.—See FLSmidth & Co. A/S; *Int'l*, pg. 2712
FLSMIDTH MINERALS LTD.—See FLSmidth & Co. A/S; *Int'l*, pg. 2711
FLSMIDTH MONGOLIA—See FLSmidth & Co. A/S; *Int'l*, pg. 2710
FLSMIDTH MOZAMBIQUE LIMITADA—See FLSmidth & Co. A/S; *Int'l*, pg. 2711
FLSMIDTH PFISTER GMBH—See FLSmidth & Co. A/S; *Int'l*, pg. 2712
FLSMIDTH PFISTER, INC.—See FLSmidth & Co. A/S; *Int'l*, pg. 2712
FLSMIDTH PFISTER LTDA.—See FLSmidth & Co. A/S; *Int'l*, pg. 2712
FLSMIDTH PHILIPPINES, INC.—See FLSmidth & Co. A/S; *Int'l*, pg. 2711
FLSMIDTH PRIVATE LIMITED—See FLSmidth & Co. A/S; *Int'l*, pg. 2710
FLSMIDTH (PRIVATE) LTD.—See FLSmidth & Co. A/S; *Int'l*, pg. 2710
FLSMIDTH (PTY.) LTD.—See FLSmidth & Co. A/S; *Int'l*, pg. 2711
FLSMIDTH PTY. LTD.—See FLSmidth & Co. A/S; *Int'l*, pg. 2711
FLSMIDTH PTY. LTD.—See FLSmidth & Co. A/S; *Int'l*, pg. 2711
FLSMIDTH QINGDAO LTD.—See FLSmidth & Co. A/S; *Int'l*, pg. 2711
FLSMIDTH ROYMEC (PTY.) LTD.—See FLSmidth & Co. A/S; *Int'l*, pg. 2711
FLSMIDTH RUSLAND HOLDING A/S—See FLSmidth & Co. A/S; *Int'l*, pg. 2710
FLSMIDTH RUS OOO—See FLSmidth & Co. A/S; *Int'l*, pg. 2710
FLSMIDTH S.A.C.—See FLSmidth & Co. A/S; *Int'l*, pg. 2711
FLSMIDTH S.A. DE C.V.—See FLSmidth & Co. A/S; *Int'l*, pg. 2711
FLSMIDTH SALT LAKE CITY, INC.—See FLSmidth & Co. A/S; *Int'l*, pg. 2712
FLSMIDTH SARL—See FLSmidth & Co. A/S; *Int'l*, pg. 2710
FLSMIDTH S.A.—See FLSmidth & Co. A/S; *Int'l*, pg. 2710
FLSMIDTH S.A.—See FLSmidth & Co. A/S; *Int'l*, pg. 2711
FLSMIDTH S.A.—See FLSmidth & Co. A/S; *Int'l*, pg. 2711
FLSMIDTH SAS—See FLSmidth & Co. A/S; *Int'l*, pg. 2711
FLSMIDTH SHANGHAI LTD.—See FLSmidth & Co. A/S; *Int'l*, pg. 2711

FLSMIDTH SPOKANE, INC.—See FLSmidth & Co. A/S; *Int'l*, pg. 2711
FLSMIDTH SPOL. S.R.O.—See FLSmidth & Co. A/S; *Int'l*, pg. 2711
FLSMIDTH SP. Z.O.O.—See FLSmidth & Co. A/S; *Int'l*, pg. 2710
FLSMIDTH (THAILAND) CO., LTD.—See FLSmidth & Co. A/S; *Int'l*, pg. 2710
FLSMIDTH (UK) LIMITED—See FLSmidth & Co. A/S; *Int'l*, pg. 2710
FLSMIDTH USA INC.—See FLSmidth & Co. A/S; *Int'l*, pg. 2712
FLSMIDTH VENTOMATIC SPA—See FLSmidth & Co. A/S; *Int'l*, pg. 2710
FLSMIDTH WIESBADEN GMBH—See FLSmidth & Co. A/S; *Int'l*, pg. 2711
FLSMIDTH WUPPERTAL GMBH—See FLSmidth & Co. A/S; *Int'l*, pg. 2711
FLS PLAST A/S—See FLSmidth & Co. A/S; *Int'l*, pg. 2710
FLS REAL ESTATE A/S—See FLSmidth & Co. A/S; *Int'l*, pg. 2710
FLS TRANSPORTATION SERVICES, LTD—See ABRY Partners, LLC; *U.S. Private*, pg. 41
FLS US HOLDINGS, INC.—See FLSmidth & Co. A/S; *Int'l*, pg. 2710
FLTL, LOGISTICS PORTUGAL, UNIPESSOAL LDA.—See TUV SUD AG; *Int'l*, pg. 7984
FL TOKUYAMA CORPORATION—See Tokuyama Corporation; *Int'l*, pg. 7787
FLT PRIME INSURANCE CORPORATION—See Ayalaland Logistics Holdings Corp.; *Int'l*, pg. 774
FLUDICON GMBH—See General Motors Company; *U.S. Public*, pg. 926
FLUENCE CORPORATION LIMITED; *U.S. Public*, pg. 857
FLUENCE ENERGY, INC.; *U.S. Public*, pg. 857
FLUENT, INC.; *U.S. Public*, pg. 857
FLUENT, LLC—See Fluent, Inc.; *U.S. Public*, pg. 857
FLUENTSTREAM TECHNOLOGIES, LLC; *U.S. Private*, pg. 1552
FLUGGER DENMARK A/S—See Flugger Group A/S; *Int'l*, pg. 2712
FLUGGER GROUP A/S; *Int'l*, pg. 2712
FLUGGER ICELAND EHF.—See Flugger Group A/S; *Int'l*, pg. 2712
FLUGGER NORWAY AS—See Flugger Group A/S; *Int'l*, pg. 2712
FLUGGER POLAND SP. Z O.O.—See Flugger Group A/S; *Int'l*, pg. 2712
FLUGGER SWEDEN AB—See Flugger Group A/S; *Int'l*, pg. 2712
FLUGHAFEN DUSSELDORF GMBH—See Public Sector Pension Investment Board; *Int'l*, pg. 6095
FLUGHAFEN FRANKFURT-HAHN GMBH—See Hainan Traffic Administration Holding Co., Ltd.; *Int'l*, pg. 3213
FLUGHAFEN HAMBURG GMBH—See Public Sector Pension Investment Board; *Int'l*, pg. 6095
FLUGHAFEN PARKEN GMBH—See Flughafen Wien Aktiengesellschaft; *Int'l*, pg. 2712
FLUGHAFEN SAARBRUECKEN GMBH—See Fraport AG; *Int'l*, pg. 2764
FLUGHAFEN WIEN AKTIENGESELLSCHAFT; *Int'l*, pg. 2712
FLUGHAFEN WIEN IMMOBILIENVERWERTUNGSGESELLSCHAFT M.B.H—See Flughafen Wien Aktiengesellschaft; *Int'l*, pg. 2712
FLUGHAFEN ZURICH AG; *Int'l*, pg. 2713
FLUGPLATZ SCHWABISCH HALL GMBH—See Wurth Verwaltungsgesellschaft mbH; *Int'l*, pg. 8504
FLUGPLATZ WERNEUCHEN GMBH—See BERGER Holding GmbH; *Int'l*, pg. 979
FLUGZEUG-UNION SUD GMBH—See Airbus SE; *Int'l*, pg. 242
FLUICELL AB; *Int'l*, pg. 2713
FLUID AIR CONTROLS LLC—See The Stratford-Cambridge Group Co.; *U.S. Private*, pg. 4123
FLUIDA, S.A. DE C.V.—See Grupo Industrial Saltillo S.A. de C.V.; *Int'l*, pg. 3130
FLUIDATA LTD.; *Int'l*, pg. 2713
FLUID AUTOMATION SYSTEMS GMBH—See IMI plc; *Int'l*, pg. 3625
FLUID AUTOMATION SYSTEMS SA—See IMI plc; *Int'l*, pg. 3625
FLUID AUTOMATION SYSTEMS TECHNOLOGIES SA—See IMI plc; *Int'l*, pg. 3625
FLUID BRASIL SISTEMAS E TECNOLOGIA LTDA.—See Mann+Hummel GmbH; *Int'l*, pg. 4673
FLUID CONSERVATION SYSTEMS INC—See Halma plc; *Int'l*, pg. 3231
FLUID CONTROL DIVISION—See Parker Hannifin Corporation; *U.S. Public*, pg. 1644
FLUID CONTROLS LIMITED—See Indutrade AB; *Int'l*, pg. 3678
FLUIDDRIVE HOLDINGS PTY LTD—See AMA Group Limited; *Int'l*, pg. 403
FLUIDEDGE CONSULTING, INC.—See CitiusTech Inc.; *U.S. Private*, pg. 902
FLUID END SALES, INC.; *U.S. Private*, pg. 1552
FLUID ENERGY PROCESSING & EQUIPMENT CO.; *U.S. Private*, pg. 1552

FLUID EQUIPMENT DEVELOPMENT COMPANY LLC; *U.S. Private*, pg. 1552
FLUID FLOW PRODUCTS INC.; *U.S. Private*, pg. 1552
FLUIDICS, INC.—See EMCOR Group, Inc.; *U.S. Public*, pg. 737
FLUIDGM CANADA INC.—See Standard BioTools Inc.; *U.S. Public*, pg. 1928
FLUIDIGM EUROPE, B.V.—See Standard BioTools Inc.; *U.S. Public*, pg. 1928
FLUIDIGM FRANCE SARL—See Standard BioTools Inc.; *U.S. Public*, pg. 1928
FLUIDIGM GMBH—See Standard BioTools Inc.; *U.S. Public*, pg. 1928
FLUIDIGM SCIENCES INC.—See Standard BioTools Inc.; *U.S. Public*, pg. 1928
FLUIDIGM (SHANGHAI) INSTRUMENT TECHNOLOGY COMPANY LIMITED—See Standard BioTools Inc.; *U.S. Public*, pg. 1928
FLUID IMAGING TECHNOLOGIES, INC.—See Yokogawa Electric Corporation; *Int'l*, pg. 8592
FLUID, INC.—See Astound Commerce Corp.; *U.S. Private*, pg. 361
FLUID MANAGEMENT CANADA, INC.—See IDEX Corp; *U.S. Public*, pg. 1090
FLUID MANAGEMENT COMPANY, LLC; *U.S. Private*, pg. 1552
FLUID MANAGEMENT EUROPE B.V.—See IDEX Corp; *U.S. Public*, pg. 1090
FLUID MANAGEMENT FRANCE SARL—See IDEX Corp; *U.S. Public*, pg. 1090
FLUID MANAGEMENT, INC.—See IDEX Corp; *U.S. Public*, pg. 1090
FLUID MANAGEMENT—See IDEX Corp; *U.S. Public*, pg. 1090
FLUIDMASTER, INC.; *U.S. Private*, pg. 1552
FLUID MECHANICS, LLC—See Woodward, Inc.; *U.S. Public*, pg. 2378
FLUIDMESH NETWORKS LLC; *U.S. Private*, pg. 1552
FLUIDMESH NETWORKS S.R.L.—See Cisco Systems, Inc.; *U.S. Public*, pg. 499
FLUIDO DENMARK A/S—See Infosys Limited; *Int'l*, pg. 3695
FLUIDOIL LIMITED; *Int'l*, pg. 2713
FLUIDOIL LIMITED—See FluidOil Limited; *Int'l*, pg. 2713
FLUIDOMAT LTD.; *Int'l*, pg. 2713
FLUIDOMAT UK PRIVATE LIMITED—See Fluidomat Ltd.; *Int'l*, pg. 2713
FLUIDO NORWAY A/S—See Infosys Limited; *Int'l*, pg. 3695
FLUIDO OY—See Infosys Limited; *Int'l*, pg. 3695
FLUIDO SLOVAKIA S.R.O—See Infosys Limited; *Int'l*, pg. 3695
FLUIDO SWEDEN AB—See Infosys Limited; *Int'l*, pg. 3695
FLUIDPARTNER GMBH—See KSB SE & Co. KGaA; *Int'l*, pg. 4310
FLUIDPOINT, A.S.—See Convum Ltd.; *Int'l*, pg. 1788
FLUID POLYMERS—See KKR & Co. Inc.; *U.S. Public*, pg. 1243
FLUID POWER AUTOMATION LLC—See Airline Hydraulics Corporation; *U.S. Private*, pg. 141
FLUIDPOWER GROUP SERVICES UK LIMITED—See Flowtech Fluidpower plc; *Int'l*, pg. 2709
FLUID POWER, INC.—See O2 Aero Acquisitions LLC; *U.S. Private*, pg. 2981
FLUID POWER PRODUCTS INC.; *U.S. Private*, pg. 1552
FLUID POWER SALES, INC.—See Applied Industrial Technologies, Inc.; *U.S. Public*, pg. 171
FLUID PROCESS EQUIPMENT, INC.; *U.S. Private*, pg. 1552
FLUIDRA MAGYARORSZAG KFT—See Fluidra SA; *Int'l*, pg. 2714
FLUIDRA POLSKA SP.Z O.O.—See Fluidra SA; *Int'l*, pg. 2714
FLUIDRA SA; *Int'l*, pg. 2713
FLUIDRA SOUTH AFRICA (PTY) LTD.—See Fluidra SA; *Int'l*, pg. 2714
FLUID REGULATORS CORP.—See TransDigm Group Incorporated; *U.S. Public*, pg. 2181
FLUID ROUTING SOLUTIONS, LLC—See Park-Ohio Holdings Corp.; *U.S. Public*, pg. 1639
FLUID SERVICE CORPORATION—See TruArc Partners, L.P.; *U.S. Private*, pg. 4245
FLUID SYSTEM COMPONENTS INC.; *U.S. Private*, pg. 1552
FLUID SYSTEMS ENGINEERING, INC.—See Frontenac Company LLC; *U.S. Private*, pg. 1614
FLUID SYSTEMS HAWAII INC.—See Consolidated Supply Co.; *U.S. Private*, pg. 1022
FLUID TECHNOLOGIES, INC.—See Madison Industries Holdings LLC; *U.S. Private*, pg. 2543
FLUID UTVA A.D.; *Int'l*, pg. 2713
FLUIDX LTD—See Azenta, Inc.; *U.S. Public*, pg. 258
FLUITEC INTERNATIONAL CHINA—See Fluitec International LLC; *U.S. Private*, pg. 1552
FLUITEC INTERNATIONAL EUROPE—See Fluitec International LLC; *U.S. Private*, pg. 1552
FLUITEC INTERNATIONAL LLC; *U.S. Private*, pg. 1552
FLUITRONICS GMBH; *Int'l*, pg. 2714

FLUITRONICS GMBH

FLUITRON, INC.—See Ara Partners Group; *U.S. Private*, pg. 306
FLUKE AUSTRALIA PTY LTD—See Fortive Corporation; *U.S. Public*, pg. 870
FLUKE AUSTRIA GMBH—See Fortive Corporation; *U.S. Public*, pg. 870
FLUKE BIOMEDICAL—See Fortive Corporation; *U.S. Public*, pg. 870
FLUKE BIOMEDICAL—See Cardinal Health, Inc.; *U.S. Public*, pg. 434
FLUKE CORPORATION—See Fortive Corporation; *U.S. Public*, pg. 870
FLUKE DEUTSCHLAND GMBH—See Fortive Corporation; *U.S. Public*, pg. 870
FLUKE ELECTRONICS CANADA LP—See Fortive Corporation; *U.S. Public*, pg. 870
FLUKE ENGENHARIA LTDA.—See Buckthorn Partners LLP; *Int'l*, pg. 1210
FLUKE ENGENHARIA LTDA.—See OEP Capital Advisors, L.P.; *U.S. Private*, pg. 2997
FLUKE EUROPE B.V.—See Fortive Corporation; *U.S. Public*, pg. 870
FLUKE ITALIA S.R.L.—See Fortive Corporation; *U.S. Public*, pg. 870
FLUKE NEDERLAND B.V.—See Fortive Corporation; *U.S. Public*, pg. 870
FLUKE NETWORKS INC.—See Fortive Corporation; *U.S. Public*, pg. 870
FLUKE OPERATIONS B.V.—See Danaher Corporation; *U.S. Public*, pg. 627
FLUKE PRECISION MEASUREMENT LTD.—See Fortive Corporation; *U.S. Public*, pg. 870
FLUKE PROCESS INSTRUMENTS GMBH—See Fortive Corporation; *U.S. Public*, pg. 870
FLUKE PROCESS INSTRUMENTS JAPAN—See Fortive Corporation; *U.S. Public*, pg. 870
FLUKE PROCESS INSTRUMENTS—See Fortive Corporation; *U.S. Public*, pg. 870
FLUKE SOUTH EAST ASIA PTE. LTD.—See Fortive Corporation; *U.S. Public*, pg. 870
FLUKE (SWITZERLAND) GMBH—See Fortive Corporation; *U.S. Public*, pg. 870
FLUKE TRANSPORTATION GROUP; *Int'l*, pg. 2714
FLUMAR TRANSPORTES DE QUIMICOS E GASES LTDA—See Odfjell SE; *Int'l*, pg. 5525
FLUMROC AG—See ROCKWOOL A/S; *Int'l*, pg. 6380
FLUOGUIDE A/S; *Int'l*, pg. 2715
FLUOPTICS IMAGING INC.—See Getinge AB; *Int'l*, pg. 2949
FLUOPTICS S.A.S.—See Getinge AB; *Int'l*, pg. 2949
FLUOR ARABIA LIMITED—See Fluor Corporation; *U.S. Public*, pg. 858
FLUOR AUSTRALIA PTY. LTD.—See Fluor Corporation; *U.S. Public*, pg. 858
FLUOR BRASIL, LTDA.—See Fluor Corporation; *U.S. Public*, pg. 858
FLUOR BV—See Fluor Corporation; *U.S. Public*, pg. 858
FLUOR-B&W PORTSMOUTH LLC—See Fluor Corporation; *U.S. Public*, pg. 859
FLUOR-BWXT PORTSMOUTH LLC—See Fluor Corporation; *U.S. Public*, pg. 859
FLUOR CANADA LTD.—See Fluor Corporation; *U.S. Public*, pg. 858
FLUOR CANADA LTD—See Fluor Corporation; *U.S. Public*, pg. 858
FLUOR CARLSBAD, LLC—See Fluor Corporation; *U.S. Public*, pg. 858
FLUOR CHILE INGENIERIA Y CONSTRUCCION S.A.—See Fluor Corporation; *U.S. Public*, pg. 858
FLUOR CHILE S.A.—See Fluor Corporation; *U.S. Public*, pg. 858
FLUOR (CHINA) ENGINEERING & CONSTRUCTION LTD.—See Fluor Corporation; *U.S. Public*, pg. 858
FLUOR CONSTRUCTORS CANADA LTD—See Fluor Corporation; *U.S. Public*, pg. 858
FLUOR CONSTRUCTORS INTERNATIONAL, INC.—See Fluor Corporation; *U.S. Public*, pg. 858
FLUOR CONSULTANTS BV—See Fluor Corporation; *U.S. Public*, pg. 858
FLUOR CORPORATION; *U.S. Public*, pg. 857
FLUOR DANIEL BRASIL, LTDA.—See Fluor Corporation; *U.S. Public*, pg. 858
FLUOR DANIEL CARIBBEAN, INC—See Fluor Corporation; *U.S. Public*, pg. 858
FLUOR DANIEL CHILE, S.A.—See Fluor Corporation; *U.S. Public*, pg. 858
FLUOR DANIEL ENGINEERS & CONSTRUCTORS, INC—See Fluor Corporation; *U.S. Public*, pg. 858
FLUOR DANIEL, INC. - PHILIPPINES—See Fluor Corporation; *U.S. Public*, pg. 858
FLUOR DANIEL, INC.—See Fluor Corporation; *U.S. Public*, pg. 858
FLUOR DANIEL INDIA PRIVATE LIMITED—See Fluor Corporation; *U.S. Public*, pg. 858
FLUOR DANIEL (JAPAN), INC.—See Fluor Corporation; *U.S. Public*, pg. 858
FLUOR DANIEL PACIFIC, INC.—See Fluor Corporation; *U.S. Public*, pg. 858

FLUOR ENGENHARIA E PROJETOS S.A.—See Fluor Corporation; *U.S. Public*, pg. 858
FLUOR ENTERPRISES, INC.—See Fluor Corporation; *U.S. Public*, pg. 858
FLUORESCO SERVICES LLC—See Everbrite, LLC; *U.S. Private*, pg. 1437
FLUOR EUROPE BV—See Fluor Corporation; *U.S. Public*, pg. 858
FLUOR FEDERAL SERVICES INC.—See Fluor Corporation; *U.S. Public*, pg. 858
FLUOR FEDERAL SERVICES, LLC—See Fluor Corporation; *U.S. Public*, pg. 859
FLUOR FERNALD INC.—See Fluor Corporation; *U.S. Public*, pg. 859
FLUOR GLOBAL SERVICES AUSTRALIA PTY. LTD.—See Fluor Corporation; *U.S. Public*, pg. 858
FLUOR HANFORD, INC.—See Fluor Corporation; *U.S. Public*, pg. 859
FLUOR HEAVY CIVIL, LLC—See Fluor Corporation; *U.S. Public*, pg. 859
FLUOR IDAHO, LLC—See Fluor Corporation; *U.S. Public*, pg. 859
FLUOR INFRASTRUCTURE BV—See Fluor Corporation; *U.S. Public*, pg. 858
FLUOR IRELAND LIMITED—See Fluor Corporation; *U.S. Public*, pg. 859
FLUORITA DE MEXICO, S.A. DE C.V.—See Grupo Empresarial Kaluz S.A. de C.V.; *Int'l*, pg. 3127
FLUOR LIMITED—See Fluor Corporation; *U.S. Public*, pg. 859
FLUOR MAINTENANCE SERVICES, INC.—See Fluor Corporation; *U.S. Public*, pg. 859
FLUOROPHARMA MEDICAL, INC.; *U.S. Public*, pg. 860
FLUOR PLANT ENGINEERING, S.A.—See Fluor Corporation; *U.S. Public*, pg. 859
FLUOR PORTSMOUTH LLC—See Fluor Corporation; *U.S. Public*, pg. 858
FLUOR S.A.—See Fluor Corporation; *U.S. Public*, pg. 859
FLUOR-SKM IRON ORE JOINT VENTURE—See Fluor Corporation; *U.S. Public*, pg. 858
FLUOR SUPPLY CHAIN SOLUTIONS LLC—See Fluor Corporation; *U.S. Public*, pg. 859
FLUORTEK, INC.—See Nordson Corporation; *U.S. Public*, pg. 1533
FLURIDA GROUP, INC.; *U.S. Private*, pg. 1552
FLURO GELENKLAGER GMBH—See Brd. Klee A/S; *Int'l*, pg. 1143
FLUROTECH LTD.; *Int'l*, pg. 2715
FLUSHING FINANCIAL CORPORATION; *U.S. Public*, pg. 860
FLUSHING HOSPITAL MEDICAL CENTER; *U.S. Private*, pg. 1553
FLUSHING SAVINGS BANK INC.—See Flushing Financial Corporation; *U.S. Public*, pg. 860
FLUTEK, CO LTD.—See Kawasaki Heavy Industries, Ltd.; *Int'l*, pg. 4095
FLUTEK, LTD. - UIRYEONG PLANT—See Kawasaki Heavy Industries, Ltd.; *Int'l*, pg. 4095
FLUTTER ENTERTAINMENT PLC; *Int'l*, pg. 2715
FLUX A/S—See discoverIE Group plc; *Int'l*, pg. 2133
FLUXDATA INC.—See Halma plc; *Int'l*, pg. 3231
FLUX GROUP AS—See HitecVision AS; *Int'l*, pg. 3426
FLUX INTERNATIONAL LTD.—See discoverIE Group plc; *Int'l*, pg. 2133
FLUXION BIOSCIENCES INC.—See Cell Microsystems, Inc.; *U.S. Private*, pg. 807
FLUX POWER HOLDINGS, INC.; *U.S. Public*, pg. 860
FLUXSWISS SAGL—See Publigas; *Int'l*, pg. 6114
FLUXTEK INTERNATIONAL CORP.; *Int'l*, pg. 2715
FLUXX LABS, INC.—See ABS Capital Partners, L.P.; *U.S. Private*, pg. 44
FLUXX LIMITED—See Newton Europe Ltd; *Int'l*, pg. 5239
FLUXYS BELGIUM SA—See Publigas; *Int'l*, pg. 6114
FLUXYS LNG SA—See Publigas; *Int'l*, pg. 6114
FLUXYS SA—See Publigas; *Int'l*, pg. 6114
FLUXYS TENP GMBH—See Publigas; *Int'l*, pg. 6115
FL-VERTRIEBS- UND SERVICE GMBH—See UNIQA Insurance Group AG; *Int'l*, pg. 8057
FLY AWAY AIRPORT PARKING SERVICES LLC—See Parkit Enterprise Inc.; *Int'l*, pg. 5743
FLY AWAY AIRPORT PARKING SERVICES LLC—See Propark, Inc.; *U.S. Private*, pg. 3284
FLY BN LIMITED—See B-N Group Limited; *Int'l*, pg. 785
FLYCELL, INC.—See Softlab S.p.A.; *Int'l*, pg. 7055
FLY-E GROUP, INC.; *U.S. Public*, pg. 860
FLYER DEFENSE, LLC—See Marvin Engineering Company, Inc.; *U.S. Private*, pg. 2598
FLYERS ENERGY, LLC; *U.S. Private*, pg. 1553
FLYERS SKATE ZONE, L.P.—See Comcast Corporation; *U.S. Public*, pg. 538
FLYERTECH LIMITED—See Gama Aviation plc; *Int'l*, pg. 2876
FLYEXCLUSIVE, INC.; *U.S. Public*, pg. 861
FLYGSTADEN INTRESSENTER I SODERHAMN AB—See Peab AB; *Int'l*, pg. 5771
FLYGT NIPPON K.K—See Xylem Inc.; *U.S. Public*, pg. 2396
FLYHT AEROSPACE SOLUTIONS LTD.—See Firan Technology Group Corporation; *Int'l*, pg. 2678

CORPORATE AFFILIATIONS

FLYHT INC—See Firan Technology Group Corporation; *Int'l*, pg. 2678
FLYING A PETROLEUM LTD.; *Int'l*, pg. 2716
FLYING A; *U.S. Private*, pg. 1553
FLYING CEMENT COMPANY LIMITED; *Int'l*, pg. 2716
FLYING COLOURS CORPORATION - SINGAPORE FACILITY—See Directional Capital LLC; *U.S. Private*, pg. 1236
FLYING COLOURS CORPORATION—See Directional Capital LLC; *U.S. Private*, pg. 1236
FLYING EAGLE PU TECHNICAL CORP.; *Int'l*, pg. 2716
FLYING FINANCIAL SERVICE HOLDINGS LIMITED; *Int'l*, pg. 2716
FLYING FISH INC.—See Naigai Trans Line Ltd.; *Int'l*, pg. 5130
FLYING FOOD FARE, INC.—See Flying Food Group, LLC; *U.S. Private*, pg. 1553
FLYING FOOD GROUP, LLC; *U.S. Private*, pg. 1553
FLYING GARDEN CO., LTD.; *Int'l*, pg. 2716
FLYING J, INC-REAL ESTATE DIVISION—See FJ Management, Inc.; *U.S. Private*, pg. 1538
FLYING J INSURANCE—See FJ Management, Inc.; *U.S. Private*, pg. 1538
FLYING J TRANSPORTATION (FUEL DISTRIBUTION)—See FJ Management, Inc.; *U.S. Private*, pg. 1538
FLYING MONKEY CAPITAL CORP.; *Int'l*, pg. 2716
FLYING PAPER INDUSTRIES LTD.—See FLYING CEMENT COMPANY LIMITED; *Int'l*, pg. 2716
FLYING PIE PIZZARIA, INC.; *U.S. Private*, pg. 1553
FLYING POINT MEDIA, INC.; *U.S. Private*, pg. 1553
FLYING SPARK LTD.; *Int'l*, pg. 2716
FLYING STAR TRANSPORT LLC—See Davidson Oil Company Inc.; *U.S. Private*, pg. 1172
FLYING TANKERS, INC.—See Coulson Group of Companies; *Int'l*, pg. 1817
FLYING TECHNOLOGY CO., LTD.; *Int'l*, pg. 2716
FLYING W PLASTICS INC.; *U.S. Private*, pg. 1553
FLYJAC LOGISTICS PVT. LTD.—See KKR & Co. Inc.; *U.S. Public*, pg. 1258
FLYKE INTERNATIONAL HOLDINGS LTD.; *Int'l*, pg. 2716
FLY LEASING LIMITED—See The Carlyle Group Inc.; *U.S. Public*, pg. 2047
FLYLINE TELE SALES & SERVICES GMBH—See International Consolidated Airlines Group S.A.; *Int'l*, pg. 3745
FLYNN BROTHERS CONTRACTING INC. - ASPHALT MATERIAL PLANT—See Flynn Brothers Contracting Inc.; *U.S. Private*, pg. 1553
FLYNN BROTHERS CONTRACTING INC.; *U.S. Private*, pg. 1553
FLYNN CANADA LTD.; *Int'l*, pg. 2716
FLYNN ENTERPRISES, LLC; *U.S. Private*, pg. 1553
FLYNN & FRIENDS; *U.S. Private*, pg. 1553
FLYNN GOLD LIMITED; *Int'l*, pg. 2716
FLYNN & O'HARA UNIFORMS INC.; *U.S. Private*, pg. 1553
FLYNN & REYNOLDS AGENCY INC.; *U.S. Private*, pg. 1553
FLYNN'S TIRE & AUTO SERVICE; *U.S. Private*, pg. 1553
FLYNN TRUCKING LLC—See Flynn Brothers Contracting Inc.; *U.S. Private*, pg. 1553
FLYOVER CANADA, INC.—See Viad Corp.; *U.S. Public*, pg. 2290
FLYOVER CAPITAL PARTNERS, LLC—See Mariner Wealth Advisors, LLC; *U.S. Private*, pg. 2575
FLYPRIVATE; *U.S. Private*, pg. 1553
FLY SITZ SCHWEIZ—See Maus Freres S.A.; *Int'l*, pg. 4732
FLY SRL; *Int'l*, pg. 2715
FLYTECH ELECTRONIC (SHANGHAI) CO., LTD.—See Flytech Technology Co., Ltd.; *Int'l*, pg. 2716
FLYTECH TECHNOLOGY CO., LTD.; *Int'l*, pg. 2716
FLYTECH TECHNOLOGY CO., LTD. - TAIPEI FACTORY—See Flytech Technology Co., Ltd.; *Int'l*, pg. 2716
FLYTECH TECHNOLOGY HONG KONG LTD.—See Flytech Technology Co., Ltd.; *Int'l*, pg. 2716
FLYTECH TECHNOLOGY (U.S.A.) INC.—See Flytech Technology Co., Ltd.; *Int'l*, pg. 2716
FLYTECH TECHNOLOGY (U.S.A.) INC.—See Flytech Technology Co., Ltd.; *Int'l*, pg. 2716
FLY TIMBER CO. INC.; *U.S. Private*, pg. 1553
FLYTXT; *Int'l*, pg. 2716
FLY VICTOR LTD.; *Int'l*, pg. 2716
FLYWHEEL ADVANCED TECHNOLOGY, INC.; *U.S. Public*, pg. 861
FLYWIRE CORPORATION; *U.S. Public*, pg. 861
FMA ALLIANCE LTD.; *U.S. Private*, pg. 1553
FMA COMMUNICATIONS, INC.; *U.S. Private*, pg. 1553
FMA GEBAUDEMANAGEMENT GMBH—See PORR AG; *Int'l*, pg. 5922
FM APPROVALS, LLC—See Factory Mutual Insurance Company; *U.S. Private*, pg. 1460
F&M BANCORP; *U.S. Public*, pg. 818
F&M BANK CORP.; *U.S. Public*, pg. 818
F&M BANK; *U.S. Private*, pg. 1455
F&M BANK—See F&M Financial Corporation; *U.S. Private*, pg. 1455

COMPANY NAME INDEX

F&M BANK-SOUTH SIOUX CITY—See F&M Bank; *U.S. Private*, pg. 1455
F&M BANK & TRUST COMPANY; *U.S. Private*, pg. 1455
FMBCAPITAL HOLDINGS PLC; *Int'l*, pg. 2717
FMB OF S.C. BANCSHARES, INCORPORATED; *U.S. Private*, pg. 1553
F.M. BROWN'S SONS INC.; *U.S. Private*, pg. 1456
FMC-AGRO HUNGARY KFT.—See FMC Corporation; *U.S. Public*, pg. 862
FMC AGRO LTD.—See FMC Corporation; *U.S. Public*, pg. 861
FMC AGROQUIMICA DE MEXICO S.R.L. DE C.V.—See FMC Corporation; *U.S. Public*, pg. 861
FMC ASIA-PACIFIC, INC.—See FMC Corporation; *U.S. Public*, pg. 861
FMC AUSTRALASIA PTY LTD.—See FMC Corporation; *U.S. Public*, pg. 861
FMC BIOPOLYMER AS—See DuPont de Nemours, Inc.; *U.S. Public*, pg. 693
FMC CHEMICALS LIMITED—See FMC Corporation; *U.S. Public*, pg. 862
FMC CHEMICAL SPRL—See FMC Corporation; *U.S. Public*, pg. 862
FMC CHEMICALS (THAILAND) LTD—See FMC Corporation; *U.S. Public*, pg. 862
F. MCCLURE & SONS LTD.; *Int'l*, pg. 2595
FMC COLOMBIA S.A.—See Fresenius Medical Care AG; *Int'l*, pg. 2774
FMC CORP. - BANGLADESH OFFICE—See FMC Corporation; *U.S. Public*, pg. 862
FMC CORP. - HEALTH & NUTRITION—See DuPont de Nemours, Inc.; *U.S. Public*, pg. 693
FMC CORP. - INDUSTRIAL CHEMICALS GROUP—See FMC Corporation; *U.S. Public*, pg. 862
FMC CORP. - LITHIUM DIVISION, BESSEMER PLANT—See FMC Corporation; *U.S. Public*, pg. 862
FMC CORPORATION; *U.S. Public*, pg. 861
FMC CORP. - POLAND OFFICE—See FMC Corporation; *U.S. Public*, pg. 862
FMC CORP. - RESEARCH & TECHNOLOGY CENTER—See FMC Corporation; *U.S. Public*, pg. 862
FMC CORP. - SPECIALTY CHEMICALS GROUP, LITHIUM DIVISION—See FMC Corporation; *U.S. Public*, pg. 862
FMC DEL PERU S.A.—See Fresenius Medical Care AG; *Int'l*, pg. 2774
FMC DIALIZIS CENTER KFT.—See Fresenius Medical Care AG; *Int'l*, pg. 2774
FMC ESPANA, S.A.U.—See Fresenius Medical Care AG; *Int'l*, pg. 2774
FMC FLUID CONTROL—See TechnipFMC plc; *Int'l*, pg. 7507
FMC FORET S.A.—See FMC Corporation; *U.S. Public*, pg. 862
FMC FRANCE S.A.—See FMC Corporation; *U.S. Public*, pg. 862
FMCG BUSINESS PARTNER AB; *Int'l*, pg. 2717
FMC GLOBALSAT HOLDINGS, INC.; *U.S. Private*, pg. 1554
FMC HOLDINGS, INC.—See Fresenius Medical Care AG; *Int'l*, pg. 2774
FMC HONG KONG LTD.—See Fresenius Medical Care AG; *Int'l*, pg. 2774
FMC INC.; *U.S. Private*, pg. 1554
FMC INSIGHTS LIMITED—See Die Schweizerische Post AG; *Int'l*, pg. 2113
FMC ITALY SRL—See FMC Corporation; *U.S. Public*, pg. 862
FMC JAPAN K.K.—See Fresenius Medical Care AG; *Int'l*, pg. 2774
FMC (JIANGSU) CO. LTD.—See Fresenius Medical Care AG; *Int'l*, pg. 2774
FMC KONGSBERG HOLDING AS—See TechnipFMC plc; *Int'l*, pg. 7507
FMC KONGSBERG SERVICES LIMITED—See TechnipFMC plc; *Int'l*, pg. 7507
FMC KONGSBERG SUBSEA AS—See TechnipFMC plc; *Int'l*, pg. 7507
FMC KOREA LTD.—See FMC Corporation; *U.S. Public*, pg. 862
FMC LASKENTAPALVELUT OY—See Sweco AB; *Int'l*, pg. 7363
FMC LTDA.—See Fresenius Medical Care AG; *Int'l*, pg. 2774
FMC LTD.—See Fresenius Medical Care AG; *Int'l*, pg. 2774
FMC MAGYARORSZAG EGESZSEGUGYI KORLATOLT FELELOSSEGU TARSASAG—See Fresenius Medical Care AG; *Int'l*, pg. 2775
FMC NORWAY HOLDING AS—See FMC Corporation; *U.S. Public*, pg. 862
FMC OF CANADA LIMITED—See FMC Corporation; *U.S. Public*, pg. 862
F&M CO., LTD.; *Int'l*, pg. 2595
F&M CONSTRUCTION CO.; *U.S. Private*, pg. 1455
FMC PHILIPPINES INC.—See FMC Corporation; *U.S. Public*, pg. 861
FMC PORTUGAL, S.A.—See Fresenius Medical Care AG; *Int'l*, pg. 2774

FMC QUIMICA DO BRASIL LTDA—See FMC Corporation; *U.S. Public*, pg. 862
FMC RENALCARE CORP.—See Fresenius Medical Care AG; *Int'l*, pg. 2775
FMC ROMANIA S.R.L.—See Fresenius Medical Care AG; *Int'l*, pg. 2774
FMC (SCHWEIZ) AG—See Fresenius Medical Care AG; *Int'l*, pg. 2774
FMC (SHANGHAI) CO., LTD.—See Fresenius Medical Care AG; *Int'l*, pg. 2774
FMC SHANGHAI COMMERCIAL ENTERPRISE—See FMC Corporation; *U.S. Public*, pg. 862
FMC SMAD S.A.S.—See Fresenius Medical Care AG; *Int'l*, pg. 2775
FMC SPECIALTY ALKALI CORPORATION—See FMC Corporation; *U.S. Public*, pg. 862
FMC SPECIALTY CHEMICALS RESEARCH & TECHNOLOGY CENTER—See FMC Corporation; *U.S. Public*, pg. 862
FMC SUOMI OY—See Fresenius Medical Care AG; *Int'l*, pg. 2774
FMC (SUZHOU) CROP CARE CO., LTD—See FMC Corporation; *U.S. Public*, pg. 861
FMC TECHNOLOGIES AG—See TechnipFMC plc; *Int'l*, pg. 7507
FMC TECHNOLOGIES ALGERIA SARL—See TechnipFMC plc; *Int'l*, pg. 7507
FMC TECHNOLOGIES ARGENTINA S.R.L.—See TechnipFMC plc; *Int'l*, pg. 7507
FMC TECHNOLOGIES CAMEROON SARL—See TechnipFMC plc; *Int'l*, pg. 7507
FMC TECHNOLOGIES CANADA CO.—See TechnipFMC plc; *Int'l*, pg. 7507
FMC TECHNOLOGIES COMPANY LTD.—See TechnipFMC plc; *Int'l*, pg. 7507
FMC TECHNOLOGIES DE MEXICO S.A. DE C.V.—See TechnipFMC plc; *Int'l*, pg. 7507
FMC TECHNOLOGIES EGYPT LLC—See TechnipFMC plc; *Int'l*, pg. 7507
FMC TECHNOLOGIES GABON S.A.R.L.—See TechnipFMC plc; *Int'l*, pg. 7507
FMC TECHNOLOGIES, INC.—See TechnipFMC plc; *Int'l*, pg. 7507
FMC TECHNOLOGIES INDIA PRIVATE LIMITED—See TechnipFMC plc; *Int'l*, pg. 7507
FMC TECHNOLOGIES LTD.—See TechnipFMC plc; *Int'l*, pg. 7507
FMC TECHNOLOGIES MEASUREMENT SOLUTIONS, INC.—See TechnipFMC plc; *Int'l*, pg. 7507
FMC TECHNOLOGIES MEASUREMENT SOLUTIONS—See TechnipFMC plc; *Int'l*, pg. 7507
FMC TECHNOLOGIES OVERSEAS, S.A.S.—See TechnipFMC plc; *Int'l*, pg. 7507
FMC TECHNOLOGIES SA—See TechnipFMC plc; *Int'l*, pg. 7507
FMC TECHNOLOGIES SERVICE SARL—See TechnipFMC plc; *Int'l*, pg. 7507
FMC TECHNOLOGIES SERVICIOS CORPORATIVOS, S. DE R.L DE C.V.—See TechnipFMC plc; *Int'l*, pg. 7507
FMC TECHNOLOGIES SINGAPORE PTE. LTD.—See TechnipFMC plc; *Int'l*, pg. 7507
FMC TECHNOLOGIES SURFACE WELLHEAD—See TechnipFMC plc; *Int'l*, pg. 7507
FMC (U.K.) LTD.—See Fresenius Medical Care AG; *Int'l*, pg. 2774
FMC VIETNAM LLC—See Fresenius Medical Care AG; *Int'l*, pg. 2774
FMC WEST PTY. LTD.—See Silk Logistics Holdings Limited; *Int'l*, pg. 6921
FMC WYOMING CORPORATION—See FMC Corporation; *U.S. Public*, pg. 862
FM DO BRASIL SERVICOS DE PREVENCAO DE PERDAS LTDA—See Factory Mutual Insurance Company; *U.S. Private*, pg. 1461
F MEC INTERNATIONAL FINANCIAL SERVICES LTD.; *Int'l*, pg. 2594
FM ENGINEERING CONSULTING (SHANGHAI) CO. LTD—See Factory Mutual Insurance Company; *U.S. Private*, pg. 1460
FM ENGINEERING INTERNATIONAL LIMITED—See Factory Mutual Insurance Company; *U.S. Private*, pg. 1460
FM ENGINEERING INTERNATIONAL LTD—See Factory Mutual Insurance Company; *U.S. Private*, pg. 1460
FM ENGINEERING INTERNATIONAL LTD—See Factory Mutual Insurance Company; *U.S. Private*, pg. 1460
FM ENGINEERING INTERNATIONAL LTD—See Factory Mutual Insurance Company; *U.S. Private*, pg. 1460
FM ENGINEERING INTERNATION LTD—See Factory Mutual Insurance Company; *U.S. Private*, pg. 1460
F&M EXPRESSIONS UNLIMITED; *U.S. Private*, pg. 1455
FM FACILITY MAINTENANCE, LLC; *U.S. Private*, pg. 1553
F&M FINANCIAL CORPORATION; *U.S. Private*, pg. 1455
F&M FINANCIAL CORP.; *U.S. Private*, pg. 1455
THE FMG GROUP; *U.S. Private*, pg. 4029
FMG LEGAL LLP—See ZIGUP plc; *Int'l*, pg. 8682
FM GLOBAL CONSOLIDATION SERVICES PRIVATE LIMITED—See FM Global Logistics Holdings Berhad; *Int'l*, pg. 2717

FM GLOBAL DE MEXICO—See Factory Mutual Insurance Company; *U.S. Private*, pg. 1460
FM GLOBAL LOGISTICS HOLDINGS BERHAD; *Int'l*, pg. 2716
FM GLOBAL LOGISTICS (IPOH) SDN. BHD.—See FM Global Logistics Holdings Berhad; *Int'l*, pg. 2717
FM GLOBAL LOGISTICS (M) SDN. BHD.—See FM Global Logistics Holdings Berhad; *Int'l*, pg. 2717
FM GLOBAL LOGISTICS (M) SDN. BHD.—See FM Global Logistics Holdings Berhad; *Int'l*, pg. 2717
FM GLOBAL LOGISTICS PTY LTD.—See FM Global Logistics Holdings Berhad; *Int'l*, pg. 2717
FMG PRIMECARE, LLC—See Community Health Systems, Inc.; *U.S. Public*, pg. 553
FMG SUITE, LLC; *U.S. Private*, pg. 1554
FMH AEROSPACE CORP.—See AMETEK, Inc.; *U.S. Public*, pg. 120
FMHC CORP.—See Jacobs Engineering Group, Inc.; *U.S. Public*, pg. 1184
FMH CONVEYORS, LLC - JONESBORO OPERATIONS—See Warburg Pincus LLC; *U.S. Private*, pg. 4437
FMH CONVEYORS LLC—See Warburg Pincus LLC; *U.S. Private*, pg. 4437
FM-HELLMANN WORLDWIDE LOGISTICS SDN. BHD.—See FM Global Logistics Holdings Berhad; *Int'l*, pg. 2717
FMH HEALTH SERVICES, LLC—See HCA Healthcare, Inc.; *U.S. Public*, pg. 996
FMH MATERIAL HANDLING SOLUTIONS—See GNCO, Inc.; *U.S. Private*, pg. 1723
F.M. HOWELL & CO. INC.; *U.S. Private*, pg. 1456
FMI AUTOMOTIVE COMPONENTS LTD.—See Futaba Industrial Co., Ltd.; *Int'l*, pg. 2851
FMI CORPORATION; *U.S. Private*, pg. 1554
FMI EXPRESS CORP.; *U.S. Private*, pg. 1554
FMI HANSA MEDICAL PRODUCTS, LLC; *U.S. Private*, pg. 1554
FMI, INC.—See AE Industrial Partners, LP; *U.S. Private*, pg. 112
FMI INTERNATIONAL, LLC - CARTERET FACILITY—See Japan Post Holdings Co., Ltd.; *Int'l*, pg. 3902
FMI INTERNATIONAL, LLC - MIAMI FACILITY—See Japan Post Holdings Co., Ltd.; *Int'l*, pg. 3902
FMI INTERNATIONAL, LLC—See Japan Post Holdings Co., Ltd.; *Int'l*, pg. 3902
F & M, INC.; *U.S. Private*, pg. 1454
FM INDUSTRIES, INC.—See NGK Insulators, Ltd.; *Int'l*, pg. 5254
FM INSURANCE COMPANY LIMITED—See Factory Mutual Insurance Company; *U.S. Private*, pg. 1461
FM INSURANCE COMPANY LIMITED—See Factory Mutual Insurance Company; *U.S. Private*, pg. 1461
FM INSURANCE COMPANY LIMITED—See Factory Mutual Insurance Company; *U.S. Private*, pg. 1461
FM INSURANCE COMPANY LIMITED—See Factory Mutual Insurance Company; *U.S. Private*, pg. 1461
FM INSURANCE COMPANY LIMITED—See Factory Mutual Insurance Company; *U.S. Private*, pg. 1461
FM INSURANCE COMPANY LIMITED—See Factory Mutual Insurance Company; *U.S. Private*, pg. 1461
FM INSURANCE COMPANY LIMITED—See Factory Mutual Insurance Company; *U.S. Private*, pg. 1461
FM INSURANCE COMPANY LIMITED—See Factory Mutual Insurance Company; *U.S. Private*, pg. 1461
FM INSURANCE COMPANY LIMITED—See Factory Mutual Insurance Company; *U.S. Private*, pg. 1461
FM INSURANCE COMPANY LIMITED—See Factory Mutual Insurance Company; *U.S. Private*, pg. 1461
FM INTERNATIONAL, LLC—See Apollo Global Management, Inc.; *U.S. Public*, pg. 160
FM-INTERNATIONAL OY FINNMAP—See SECOM Co., Ltd.; *Int'l*, pg. 6671
FMI TRUCK SALES & SERVICE; *U.S. Private*, pg. 1554
FM KUCHEN GMBH—See Nobia AB; *Int'l*, pg. 5395
FM LEASINGPARTNER GMBH—See Commerzbank AG; *Int'l*, pg. 1718
F&M MAFCO INC.—See OEP Capital Advisors, L.P.; *U.S. Private*, pg. 2998
FM MATTSSON MORA GROUP AB; *Int'l*, pg. 2717
FM MATTSSON MORA GROUP BELGIE NV—See FM Mattsson Mora Group AB; *Int'l*, pg. 2717
FM MATTSSON MORA GROUP NEDERLAND BV—See FM Mattsson Mora Group AB; *Int'l*, pg. 2717
FM MATTSSON MORA GROUP NORGE AS—See FM Mattsson Mora Group AB; *Int'l*, pg. 2717
FMM FACHMEDIEN MOBIL AG—See TX Group AG; *Int'l*, pg. 7991
FMM SERVICES SDN BHD—See The Federation of Malaysian Manufacturers; *Int'l*, pg. 7642
FM MULTIMODAL SERVICES SDN. BHD.—See FM Global Logistics Holdings Berhad; *Int'l*, pg. 2717
FMMX S. DE R.L DE C.V.—See Graham Holdings Company; *U.S. Public*, pg. 954
FMO ANTILLEN N.V.—See Nederlandse Financierings-Maatschappij voor Ontwikkelingslanden N.V.; *Int'l*, pg. 5188
FM PBW BEARINGS PRIVATE LIMITED—See Apollo Global Management, Inc.; *U.S. Public*, pg. 160

FM MATTSSON MORA GROUP AB

FMP FORDERUNGSMANAGEMENT POTSDAM GMBH—See BayernLB Holding AG; *Int'l*, pg. 914
F M P GROUP AUSTRALIA PTY LTD—See Robert Bosch GmbH; *Int'l*, pg. 6362
FMP GROUP (THAILAND) LTD.—See Robert Bosch GmbH; *Int'l*, pg. 6361
FMP PLANNING AND FACILITY MANAGEMENT POLAND SP. Z O.O—See PORR AG; *Int'l*, pg. 5925
FMPP VERWALTUNGSGESELLSCHAFT MBH—See Hellman & Friedman LLC; *U.S. Private*, pg. 1907
FMP RESTAURANT MANAGEMENT, LLC—See Food Management Partners, Inc.; *U.S. Private*, pg. 1561
FM PRODUCTION SERVICES LLC—See Comcast Corporation; *U.S. Public*, pg. 538
FM PROJECTS LTD OY—See Sweco AB; *Int'l*, pg. 7363
FMRC, INC.—See Huntington Bancshares Incorporated; *U.S. Public*, pg. 1071
FM RETAIL SERVICES INC.—See The Kroger Co.; *U.S. Public*, pg. 2107
FMR LLC; *U.S. Private*, pg. 1554
FMR RESOURCES LIMITED; *Int'l*, pg. 2717
FMSBONDS, INC.; *U.S. Private*, pg. 1555
FMS ENTERPRISES MIGUN LTD.; *Int'l*, pg. 2717
FMS EQUIPMENT RENTAL INC.—See Mitsubishi Heavy Industries, Ltd.; *Int'l*, pg. 4956
FM SERVICES COMPANY—See Freeport-McMoRan Inc.; *U.S. Public*, pg. 884
FMS MACHINE TOOL DISTRIBUTORS; *U.S. Private*, pg. 1555
FM SOLUTION CORPORATION—See Okamura Corporation; *Int'l*, pg. 5545
FMS PURCHASING & SERVICES, INC.; *U.S. Private*, pg. 1555
FMS SA—See Manuloc Group; *Int'l*, pg. 4679
FMS SOLUTIONS HOLDINGS, LLC—See New Heritage Capital LLC; *U.S. Private*, pg. 2896
FM STRUCTURAL PLASTIC TECHNOLOGY INC.; *U.S. Private*, pg. 1553
FMS WERTMANAGEMENT AOR; *Int'l*, pg. 2717
FM SYLVAN, INC.—See Blue Point Capital Partners, LLC; *U.S. Private*, pg. 590
FM:SYSTEMS GROUP, LLC—See Johnson Controls International plc; *Int'l*, pg. 3985
FM SYSTEMS LLC—See Lobster Point Properties Ltd.; *Int'l*, pg. 4539
F.M. TARBELL CO. INC.—See Tarbell Financial Corporation; *U.S. Private*, pg. 3933
FMT COLCHESTER Z.O.O.—See The 600 Group PLC; *Int'l*, pg. 7609
FMT FREZITE METAL TOOLING GMBH—See Sandvik AB; *Int'l*, pg. 6529
F-M TRADEMARKS LTD.—See Apollo Global Management, Inc.; *U.S. Public*, pg. 162
FMT TOOLING SYSTEMS LIMITED—See Sandvik AB; *Int'l*, pg. 6529
FMT TOOLING SYSTEMS S. DE R.L. DE C.V.—See Sandvik AB; *Int'l*, pg. 6529
F. MURPF AG; *Int'l*, pg. 2595
FMW INDUSTRIEANLAGENBAU GMBH—See HANNOVER Finanz GmbH; *Int'l*, pg. 3257
FNAC BELGIUM—See Kering S.A.; *Int'l*, pg. 4134
FNAC BRESIL SARL—See Groupe Fnac S.A.; *Int'l*, pg. 3103
FNAC PERIPHERIE—See Kering S.A.; *Int'l*, pg. 4134
FNAC PORTUGAL - ACDLDMPT, LDA—See Kering S.A.; *Int'l*, pg. 4134
FNAC SA—See Groupe Fnac S.A.; *Int'l*, pg. 3103
FNAC SUISSE SA—See Groupe Fnac S.A.; *Int'l*, pg. 3103
FNA FINANCIAL INC.—See Manulife Financial Corporation; *Int'l*, pg. 4678
FNA GROUP, INC.; *U.S. Private*, pg. 1555
FN AMERICA, INC.—See Herstal, S.A.; *Int'l*, pg. 3364
FN AMERICA, LLC—See Herstal, S.A.; *Int'l*, pg. 3364
F/NAZCA SAATCHI & SAATCHI—See Publicis Groupe S.A.; *Int'l*, pg. 6107
F/NAZCA SAATCHI & SAATCHI—See Publicis Groupe S.A.; *Int'l*, pg. 6107
FNB BANCORP, INC.; *U.S. Private*, pg. 1555
FNB BANCSHARES INC.; *U.S. Private*, pg. 1555
FNB BANCSHARES OF CENTRAL ALABAMA, INC.—See BankFirst Capital Corporation; *U.S. Public*, pg. 274
FNB BANK, N.A.—See Fulton Financial Corporation; *U.S. Public*, pg. 892
FNBC BANK & TRUST—See F.N.B.C. of La Grange, Inc.; *U.S. Private*, pg. 1457
F.N.B.C. OF LA GRANGE, INC.; *U.S. Private*, pg. 1456
FNB COMMUNITY BANK—See First Midwest Acquisition Corp.; *U.S. Private*, pg. 1521
THE FNB COMMUNITY BANK—See First Vandalia Corp.; *U.S. Private*, pg. 1530
F.N.B. CORPORATION; *U.S. Public*, pg. 818
FNBH BANCORP, INC.; *U.S. Private*, pg. 1555
FNB, INC.; *U.S. Public*, pg. 862
FNBJ HOLDING CORP.—See Jeffersonville Bancorp; *U.S. Public*, pg. 1189
FNBK HOLDINGS, INC.; *U.S. Private*, pg. 1555
FNB LESOTHO LIMITED—See FirstRand Limited; *Int'l*, pg. 2689

FNB OF CENTRAL ALABAMA—See BankFirst Capital Corporation; *U.S. Public*, pg. 274
FNBT BANCSHARES, PERRY, OK, INC.; *U.S. Private*, pg. 1555
FNBT BANK—See Southern National Banks, Inc.; *U.S. Private*, pg. 3734
FNB ZAMBIA LIMITED—See FirstRand Limited; *Int'l*, pg. 2689
FNC ENTERTAINMENT CO., LTD.; *Int'l*, pg. 2717
FNC, INC.—See Insight Venture Management, LLC; *U.S. Private*, pg. 2089
FNC, INC.—See Stone Point Capital LLC; *U.S. Private*, pg. 3822
FNC KOLON BEIJING CORP.—See Kolon Industries, Inc.; *Int'l*, pg. 4233
FNC KOLON SHANGHAI CORP.—See Kolon Industries, Inc.; *Int'l*, pg. 4233
FNC KOLON USA CORP.—See Kolon Industries, Inc.; *Int'l*, pg. 4233
F@N COMMUNICATIONS, INC.; *Int'l*, pg. 2598
F&N CREAMERIES (S) PTE. LTD.—See Thai Beverage Public Company Limited; *Int'l*, pg. 7589
FNC S.A.—See Anheuser-Busch InBev SA/NV; *Int'l*, pg. 465
F.N.C. TEXTILES INC.—See Carolace Embroidery Co., Inc.; *U.S. Private*, pg. 767
F&N DAIRIES (THAILAND) LIMITED—See Thai Beverage Public Company Limited; *Int'l*, pg. 7590
FNDS3000 CORP.; *U.S. Public*, pg. 862
FN FACTORY OUTLET PCL; *Int'l*, pg. 2717
FNF CONSTRUCTION INC.—See J.H. Whitney & Co., LLC; *U.S. Private*, pg. 2166
F&N FOODS PTE LTD—See Thai Beverage Public Company Limited; *Int'l*, pg. 7589
FNG GROUP NV; *Int'l*, pg. 2718
FNGUIDE INC.; *Int'l*, pg. 2718
FN HERSTAL FAR EAST & AUSTRALASIA PTE. LTD.—See Herstal, S.A.; *Int'l*, pg. 3364
FN HERSTAL S.A.—See Herstal, S.A.; *Int'l*, pg. 3364
FNH UK LIMITED—See Herstal, S.A.; *Int'l*, pg. 3364
F&N INTERFLAVINE PTE LTD—See Thai Beverage Public Company Limited; *Int'l*, pg. 7589
F&N INVESTMENTS PTE LTD—See Thai Beverage Public Company Limited; *Int'l*, pg. 7589
FNL INSURANCE COMPANY, LTD—See Wells Fargo & Company; *U.S. Public*, pg. 2343
FNL INSURANCE COMPANY—See Wells Fargo & Company; *U.S. Public*, pg. 2343
FNL TECHNOLOGIES, INC.; *U.S. Private*, pg. 1555
FNM S.P.A.; *Int'l*, pg. 2718
FNOF PRECIOUS HONOUR LIMITED—See Forebright Capital Management Ltd.; *Int'l*, pg. 2731
FNP, INC.; *U.S. Private*, pg. 1556
F.N. SHEPPARD & CO.; *U.S. Private*, pg. 1456
FNS HOLDINGS PUBLIC COMPANY LIMITED; *Int'l*, pg. 2718
FNS, INC.; *U.S. Private*, pg. 1556
FNS POWER TECHNOLOGY INC.—See Shandong Sacred Sun Power Sources Company Limited; *Int'l*, pg. 6757
FNSS SAVUNMA SISTEMLERI A.S.—See Nurol Holding A.S.; *Int'l*, pg. 5490
FNS TECH CO.,LTD; *Int'l*, pg. 2718
FNSTEEL BV—See Jingye Group; *Int'l*, pg. 3968
FNTC AMERICA LIMITED—See Epiris Managers LLP; *Int'l*, pg. 2461
FNY SERVICE CORP.—See The First of Long Island Corporation; *U.S. Public*, pg. 2074
FNZ GROUP LTD.; *Int'l*, pg. 2718
FNZ HOLDINGS LTD—See Caisse de Depot et Placement du Quebec; *Int'l*, pg. 1254
FNZ HOLDINGS LTD—See Generation Investment Management LLP; *Int'l*, pg. 2920
FNZ (UK) LTD—See Caisse de Depot et Placement du Quebec; *Int'l*, pg. 1254
FNZ (UK) LTD—See Generation Investment Management LLP; *Int'l*, pg. 2920
FOAMALITE LTD.—See Schweiter Technologies AG; *Int'l*, pg. 6645
FOAM CONCEPTS INC.—See Compass Diversified Holdings; *U.S. Public*, pg. 559
FOAM CRAFT, INC.—See Future Foam, Inc.; *U.S. Private*, pg. 1626
FOAMCRAFT INC.; *U.S. Private*, pg. 1556
FOAM DESIGN INCORPORATED; *U.S. Private*, pg. 1556
FOAM FABRICATORS INC. - MOLDING PLANT—See Compass Diversified Holdings; *U.S. Public*, pg. 559
FOAM FABRICATORS QUERETARO, S. DE R.L. DE C.V.—See Compass Diversified Holdings; *U.S. Public*, pg. 560
FOAMGLAS (ITALIA) SRL—See Owens Corning; *U.S. Public*, pg. 1626
FOAMGLAS (NORDIC) AB—See Owens Corning; *U.S. Public*, pg. 1626
FOAMHAND LIMITED—See OSI Systems, Inc.; *U.S. Public*, pg. 1621
FOAM KASEI CO., LTD.—See The Furukawa Electric Co., Ltd.; *Int'l*, pg. 7644

CORPORATE AFFILIATIONS

FOAM MOLDERS AND SPECIALTIES; *U.S. Private*, pg. 1556
FOAMPRO MANUFACTURING, INC.; *U.S. Private*, pg. 1556
FOAM RUBBER PRODUCTS COMPANY; *U.S. Private*, pg. 1556
FOAMTASTIC PRODUCTS, INC.—See Berkshire Hathaway Inc.; *U.S. Public*, pg. 312
FOARM FOLLOWING FUNCTION, INC.—See M-C Industries Inc.; *U.S. Private*, pg. 2525
FOA & SON CORPORATION; *U.S. Private*, pg. 1556
FOBI AI INC.; *Int'l*, pg. 2718
FOBOHA (GERMANY) GMBH—See Barnes Group Inc.; *U.S. Public*, pg. 277
FOBOHA (SWITZERLAND) AG—See Adval Tech Holding AG; *Int'l*, pg. 155
FOBOHA (US) INC.—See Adval Tech Holding AG; *Int'l*, pg. 155
FOCAL AIMS LAND SDN. BHD.—See Eco World Development Group Berhad; *Int'l*, pg. 2293
FOCAL AIMS SDN. BHD.—See Eco World Development Group Berhad; *Int'l*, pg. 2293
FOCAL INVESTIGATION & SECURITY AGENCY PTE. LTD.—See Prosegur Compania de Seguridad S.A.; *Int'l*, pg. 5999
FOCAL POINT, LLC—See Legrand S.A.; *Int'l*, pg. 4445
THE FOCAL POINT, LLC—See Trinity Hunt Management, L.P.; *U.S. Private*, pg. 4234
FOCAL TECHNOLOGIES CORPORATION—See Moog Inc.; *U.S. Public*, pg. 1471
FOCALTECH SYSTEMS CO., LTD.; *Int'l*, pg. 2718
FOCAL THERAPEUTICS INC.—See Hologic, Inc.; *U.S. Public*, pg. 1044
FOCE INDIA LIMITED; *Int'l*, pg. 2718
FOCI FIBER OPTIC COMMUNICATIONS, INC.; *Int'l*, pg. 2718
THE FOCIS GROUP LLC—See The Reserves Network Inc.; *U.S. Private*, pg. 4105
FOCKE & CO. (GMBH & CO.) VERPACKUNGSMASCHINEN; *Int'l*, pg. 2718
FOCKE & CO. (INC.)—See Focke & Co. (GmbH & Co.) Verpackungsmaschinen; *Int'l*, pg. 2718
FOCKE & CO. (UK) LTD.—See Focke & Co. (GmbH & Co.) Verpackungsmaschinen; *Int'l*, pg. 2718
FOCKE DO BRASIL LTDA.—See Focke & Co. (GmbH & Co.) Verpackungsmaschinen; *Int'l*, pg. 2718
FOCKE (HONG KONG) LTD.—See Focke & Co. (GmbH & Co.) Verpackungsmaschinen; *Int'l*, pg. 2718
FOCKE (SINGAPORE) PTE LTD—See Focke & Co. (GmbH & Co.) Verpackungsmaschinen; *Int'l*, pg. 2718
FOCUM BELGIUM BVBA—See Arrow Global Group PLC; *Int'l*, pg. 579
FOCUM GROEP B.V.—See Arrow Global Group PLC; *Int'l*, pg. 579
FOCUS 4U LTD.; *Int'l*, pg. 2718
FOCUS BRANDS, INC.—See Roark Capital Group Inc.; *U.S. Private*, pg. 3454
FOCUS BUSINESS SOLUTION LTD.; *Int'l*, pg. 2719
FOCUS BUSINESS SOLUTIONS, INC.; *U.S. Private*, pg. 1556
FOCUS COMMERCIAL, INC.—See The Randall Group Inc.; *U.S. Private*, pg. 4102
FOCUS DIAGNOSTICS, INC.—See DiaSorin S.p.A.; *Int'l*, pg. 2106
FOCUS DIGITAL MEDIA LIMITED; *Int'l*, pg. 2719
FOCUS DIGITAL MEDIA—See Focus 4U Ltd.; *Int'l*, pg. 2718
FOCUS (DIY) GROUP LTD.; *Int'l*, pg. 2718
FOCUS DYNAMICS GROUP BERHAD; *Int'l*, pg. 2719
FOCUSED COMMUNICATIONS CO., LTD.—See Allison & Partners LLC; *U.S. Private*, pg. 192
FOCUSED IMAGE; *U.S. Private*, pg. 1556
FOCUSED MONEY SOLUTIONS INC.; *Int'l*, pg. 2720
FOCUSED PHOTONICS (HANGZHOU), INC.; *Int'l*, pg. 2720
FOCUS ENTERPRISES INC.; *U.S. Private*, pg. 1556
FOCUS FEATURES LLC - NEW YORK—See Comcast Corporation; *U.S. Public*, pg. 540
FOCUS FEATURES LLC—See Comcast Corporation; *U.S. Public*, pg. 540
FOCUS FGW—See Freedman, Gibson & White Inc.; *U.S. Private*, pg. 1603
FOCUS FINANCIAL PARTNERS INC.—See Clayton, Dubilier & Rice, LLC; *U.S. Private*, pg. 923
FOCUS FINANCIAL PARTNERS INC.—See Stone Point Capital LLC; *U.S. Private*, pg. 3824
FOCUS FINANCIAL PARTNERS, LLC—See Clayton, Dubilier & Rice, LLC; *U.S. Private*, pg. 923
FOCUS FINANCIAL PARTNERS, LLC—See Stone Point Capital LLC; *U.S. Private*, pg. 3824
FOCUS FOODSERVICE, LLC—See Sysco Corporation; *U.S. Public*, pg. 1973
FOCUS FORWARD LLC; *U.S. Private*, pg. 1556
FOCUS GRAPHITE INC.; *Int'l*, pg. 2719
FOCUS HAND SURGICENTER, LLC—See HCA Healthcare, Inc.; *U.S. Public*, pg. 996
FOCUS HOME INTERACTIVE SAS; *Int'l*, pg. 2719
FOCUS HOSPITALITY SERVICES, LLC—See Focus Enterprises Inc.; *U.S. Private*, pg. 1556

COMPANY NAME INDEX

FOCUS HOTMELT COMPANY LTD.; *Int'l*, pg. 2719
FOCUS H&S CO., LTD.; *Int'l*, pg. 2719
FOCUS IMPACT BH3 ACQUISITION COMPANY; *U.S. Public*, pg. 862
FOCUS IMPRESA SRL—See Intesa Sanpaolo S.p.A.; *Int'l*, pg. 3766
FOCUS IN CHINUCH INC.; *U.S. Private*, pg. 1556
FOCUS INDUSTRIAL RESOURCES LIMITED; *Int'l*, pg. 2719
FOCUS LEARNING CORPORATION—See The Brydon Group LLC; *U.S. Private*, pg. 4001
FOCUS LIGHTING CORP.—See Focus Lighting & Fixtures Limited; *Int'l*, pg. 2719
FOCUS LIGHTING & FIXTURES LIMITED; *Int'l*, pg. 2719
FOCUS LIGHTING & FIXTURES PTE. LTD.—See Focus Lighting & Fixtures Limited; *Int'l*, pg. 2719
FOCUS LIGHTINGS TECH CO., LTD.; *Int'l*, pg. 2719
FOCUSLIGHT SWITZERLAND SA—See Focuslight Technologies Inc.; *Int'l*, pg. 2720
FOCUSLIGHT TECHNOLOGIES INC.; *Int'l*, pg. 2720
FOCUS LUMBER BERHAD; *Int'l*, pg. 2719
FOCUS MAGAZIN VERLAG—See Hubert Burda Media Holding Kommanditgesellschaft; *Int'l*, pg. 3520
FOCUS MALL ZIELONA GORA SP. Z O.O.—See Aviva plc; *Int'l*, pg. 746
FOCUS MANAGEMENT GROUP USA, INC.; *U.S. Private*, pg. 1556
FOCUS MEDIA HOLDING LIMITED; *Int'l*, pg. 2719
FOCUS MEDIA INFORMATION TECHNOLOGY CO., LTD.—See Focus Media Holding Limited; *Int'l*, pg. 2719
FOCUS MEDIA TECHNOLOGY (SHANGHAI) CO., LTD.—See Focus Media Holding Limited; *Int'l*, pg. 2719
FOCUS MINERALS LIMITED; *Int'l*, pg. 2719
FOCUS OPERATIONS PTY LTD—See Focus Minerals Limited; *Int'l*, pg. 2719
FOCUS OPTICS PTY. LTD.—See EYECARE PARTNERS LIMITED; *Int'l*, pg. 2593
FOCUS OPTICS—See NMC Health PLC; *Int'l*, pg. 5392
FOCUS PACKAGING & SUPPLY CO.—See Bain Capital, LP; *U.S. Private*, pg. 440
FOCUS POINT HOLDINGS BERHAD; *Int'l*, pg. 2719
FOCUS POINT VISION CARE GROUP SDN. BHD.—See Focus Point Holdings Berhad; *Int'l*, pg. 2719
FOCUS PRODUCTS GROUP INTERNATIONAL, LLC—See Centre Lane Partners, LLC; *U.S. Private*, pg. 827
FOCUS PUBLISHING LTD—See Singapore Press Holdings Ltd.; *Int'l*, pg. 6942
FOCUS RECEIVABLES MANAGEMENT, LLC; *U.S. Private*, pg. 1556
FOCUSRITE AUDIO ENGINEERING LTD.—See Focusrite plc; *Int'l*, pg. 2720
FOCUSRITE NOVATION DEUTSCHLAND—See Focusrite plc; *Int'l*, pg. 2720
FOCUSRITE PLC; *Int'l*, pg. 2720
FOCUS RX INC.—See UnitedHealth Group Incorporated; *U.S. Public*, pg. 2247
FOCUS SEARCH PARTNERS LLC—See Olympus Partners; *U.S. Private*, pg. 3014
FOCUS SOLUTIONS GROUP LTD.—See abrdn PLC; *Int'l*, pg. 68
FOCUS—See VITEC Multimedia S.A.; *Int'l*, pg. 8259
FOCUS SUITES SOLUTIONS & SERVICES LIMITED; *Int'l*, pg. 2720
FOCUS SYSTEMS CORPORATION; *Int'l*, pg. 2720
FOCUS TECHNOLOGY CO., LTD.; *Int'l*, pg. 2720
FOCUS TECHNOLOGY GROUP, INC.—See Levine Leichtman Capital Partners, LLC; *U.S. Private*, pg. 2435
FOCUS TECHNOLOGY SOLUTIONS, INC.; *U.S. Private*, pg. 1556
FOCUS UNIVERSAL INC.; *U.S. Public*, pg. 862
FOCUS VENTURE PARTNERS, INC.; *U.S. Private*, pg. 1556
FOCUSVISION WORLDWIDE, INC.—See EQT AB; *Int'l*, pg. 2475
FODOR'S TRAVEL PUBLICATIONS, INC.—See Bertelsmann SE & Co. KGaA; *Int'l*, pg. 991
FOELFACH STONE LIMITED—See SigmaRoc Plc; *Int'l*, pg. 6909
FOELGNER, RONZ & STRAW, P.A.; *U.S. Private*, pg. 1556
FOGA BENELUX B.V.—See Foga System International AB; *Int'l*, pg. 2720
FOGA INTERIJERE D.O.O.—See Foga System International AB; *Int'l*, pg. 2720
FOGA POLEN SP. Z O.O.—See Foga System International AB; *Int'l*, pg. 2720
FOGA SYSTEM CORPORATION—See Foga System International AB; *Int'l*, pg. 2720
FOGA SYSTEM ETHIOPIA—See Foga System International AB; *Int'l*, pg. 2720
FOGA SYSTEM FRANCE S.A.R.L.—See Foga System International AB; *Int'l*, pg. 2720
FOGA SYSTEM GMBH—See Foga System International AB; *Int'l*, pg. 2720
FOGA SYSTEM INTERNATIONAL AB; *Int'l*, pg. 2720
FOGA SYSTEMS AUSTRALIA PTY LTD—See Foga System International AB; *Int'l*, pg. 2720

FOGA SYSTEM SCANDINAVIA AB—See Foga System International AB; *Int'l*, pg. 2721
FOGAZ ZRT.—See ENKSZ Elso Nemzeti Kozmuszolgaltato Zrt.; *Int'l*, pg. 2440
FOGCO SYSTEMS INC.—See Pinewell Capital LLC; *U.S. Private*, pg. 3184
FOG CUTTER CAPITAL GROUP INC.; *U.S. Private*, pg. 1556
FOGEL ANDERSON CONSTRUCTION; *U.S. Private*, pg. 1557
FOGEL LEVIN 2/OGILVYONE—See WPP plc; *Int'l*, pg. 8484
FOGELMAN PROPERTIES, LLC; *U.S. Private*, pg. 1557
FOGG FILLER CO.—See Leonard Green & Partners, L.P.; *U.S. Private*, pg. 2427
FOGGS ACE HARDWARE BUILDING SUPPLIES; *U.S. Private*, pg. 1557
FOGHORN BREWERY PTY. LTD.—See Mighty Craft Limited; *Int'l*, pg. 4890
FOGHORN THERAPEUTICS INC.; *U.S. Public*, pg. 862
FOGLES INC.; *U.S. Private*, pg. 1557
FOGO DE CHAO (HOLDINGS) INC.—See Thomas H. Lee Partners, L.P.; *U.S. Private*, pg. 4156
FOGO DE CHAO, INC.—See Rhone Group, LLC; *U.S. Private*, pg. 3423
FOGO HOSPITALITY, INC.; *U.S. Private*, pg. 1557
FOGS D.D. SARAJEVO; *Int'l*, pg. 2721
FOG SOFTWARE GROUP—See Constellation Software Inc.; *Int'l*, pg. 1772
FOKKER AEROSTRUCTURES B.V. - HOOGEVEEN—See GKN plc; *Int'l*, pg. 2983
FOKKER AIRCRAFT SERVICES B.V.—See GKN plc; *Int'l*, pg. 2983
FOKKER ELMO B.V.—See GKN plc; *Int'l*, pg. 2983
FOKKER ELMO (LANGFANG) ELECTRICAL SYSTEMS CO., LTD.—See Melrose Industries PLC; *Int'l*, pg. 4812
FOKKER ENGINEERING ROMANIA S.R.L.—See Melrose Industries PLC; *Int'l*, pg. 4812
FOKKER LANDING GEAR B.V.—See Melrose Industries PLC; *Int'l*, pg. 4812
FOKKER SERVICES ASIA PTE. LTD.—See Melrose Industries PLC; *Int'l*, pg. 4812
FOKKER SERVICES B.V.—See Melrose Industries PLC; *Int'l*, pg. 4812
FOKKER TECHNOLOGIES HOLDING B.V.—See GKN plc; *Int'l*, pg. 2983
FOKUS BANK ASA—See Danske Bank A/S; *Int'l*, pg. 1969
FOKUS MINING CORPORATION; *Int'l*, pg. 2721
FOLCARELLI SHEET METAL INC.; *U.S. Private*, pg. 1557
FOLCOMER EQUIPMENT CORPORATION; *U.S. Private*, pg. 1557
FOLCRA BEACH INDUSTRIAL COMPANY LLC—See Dubai Investments PJSC; *Int'l*, pg. 2219
FOLDCRAFT COMPANY; *U.S. Private*, pg. 1557
FOLDER FACTORY, INC.; *U.S. Private*, pg. 1558
FOLDING GUARD, INC.—See Troax Group AB; *Int'l*, pg. 7938
FOLEY-BELSAW COMPANY; *U.S. Private*, pg. 1558
FOLEY-BELSAW INSTITUTE—See Foley-Belsaw Company; *U.S. Private*, pg. 1558
FOLEY CUSTOM POOLS INC.; *U.S. Private*, pg. 1558
FOLEY EQUIPMENT COMPANY—See Dean Operations, Inc.; *U.S. Private*, pg. 1184
FOLEY EQUIPMENT COMPANY—See Foley Industries, Inc.; *U.S. Private*, pg. 1558
FOLEY FAMILY WINES HOLDINGS INC; *U.S. Private*, pg. 1558
FOLEY FAMILY WINES, INC.—See Foley Family Wines Holdings Inc; *U.S. Private*, pg. 1558
FOLEY GROUP, INC.—See Convergence Partners, Inc.; *U.S. Private*, pg. 1035
FOLEY HOAG LLP; *U.S. Private*, pg. 1558
FOLEY HOSPITAL CORPORATION—See Community Health Systems, Inc.; *U.S. Public*, pg. 553
FOLEY INCORPORATED; *U.S. Private*, pg. 1558
FOLEY INDUSTRIES, INC.; *U.S. Private*, pg. 1558
FOLEY INSPECTION SERVICES, ULC—See Cypress Environmental Partners, L.P.; *U.S. Public*, pg. 618
FOLEY & LARDNER LLP; *U.S. Private*, pg. 1558
FOLEY PRODUCTS COMPANY, LLC; *U.S. Private*, pg. 1558
FOLEY RV CENTER, LLC—See Camping World Holdings, Inc.; *U.S. Public*, pg. 427
FOLEYS INC.; *U.S. Private*, pg. 1558
FOLEY TIMBER & LAND COMPANY, LP; *U.S. Private*, pg. 1558
FOLEY TRASIMENE ACQUISITION CORP II—See Paysafe Limited; *Int'l*, pg. 5764
FOLEY-UNITED/NEARY DIVISION—See Foley-Belsaw Company; *U.S. Private*, pg. 1558
FOLEY WINES LIMITED—See Foley Family Wines Holdings Inc; *U.S. Private*, pg. 1558
THE FOLGER COFFEE COMPANY—See SYSU International, Inc.; *Int'l*, pg. 7394
FOLGER NOLAN FLEMING DOUGLAS CAPITAL MANAGEMENT, INC.—See Folger Nolan Fleming Douglas Incorporated; *U.S. Private*, pg. 1558
FOLGER NOLAN FLEMING DOUGLAS INCORPORATED; *U.S. Private*, pg. 1558

FOMO WORLDWIDE, INC.

THE FOLGERS COFFEE COMPANY—See The J.M. Smucker Company; *U.S. Public*, pg. 2107
FOLGER SUBARU OF CHARLOTTE; *U.S. Private*, pg. 1559
FOLIA INC.—See P. Kaufmann Inc.; *U.S. Private*, pg. 3060
FOLIA LEASING GESELLSCHAFT M.B.H.—See UniCredit S.p.A.; *Int'l*, pg. 8036
FOLIATEAM SASU; *Int'l*, pg. 2721
FOLICA, INC.; *U.S. Private*, pg. 1559
FOLIENCE, INC.; *U.S. Private*, pg. 1559
FOLIENPRINT-RAKO GMBH—See Triton Advisers Limited; *Int'l*, pg. 7929
FOLIO DYNAMICS INC.—See Bain Capital, LP; *U.S. Private*, pg. 439
FOLIOFN, INC.; *U.S. Private*, pg. 1559
FOLIO LONDON LTD.—See Vitruvian Partners LLP; *Int'l*, pg. 8263
FOLIO WINE COMPANY, LLC—See Compagnie Champenoise PH-CHPiper Heidsieck SAS; *Int'l*, pg. 1722
FOLIUM GROUP LTD; *Int'l*, pg. 2721
FOLKERSON COMMUNICATIONS, LTD.—See Renaissance Systems, Inc.; *U.S. Private*, pg. 3397
FOLKESTONE LIMITED—See Charter Hall Limited; *Int'l*, pg. 1454
FOLK OIL CO. INC.; *U.S. Private*, pg. 1559
FOLKSAM OMSESIDIG LIVFORSAKRING—See Folksam omsesidig sakforsakring; *Int'l*, pg. 2721
FOLKSAM OMSESIDIG SAKFORSAKRING; *Int'l*, pg. 2721
FOLKSAM SKADEFORSAKRING AB—See Fennia Group; *Int'l*, pg. 2634
FOLKS RESTAURANTS, LTD.; *U.S. Private*, pg. 1559
FOLKTUNE LIMITED—See Fountain Set (Holdings) Limited; *Int'l*, pg. 2754
FOLKUP DEVELOPMENT INC.; *Int'l*, pg. 2721
FOLLETT CORPORATION; *U.S. Private*, pg. 1559
FOLLETT HIGHER EDUCATION GROUP, INC.—See Follett Corporation; *U.S. Private*, pg. 1559
FOLLETT LLC—See The Middleby Corporation; *U.S. Public*, pg. 2113
FOLLETT OF CANADA INC.—See Follett Corporation; *U.S. Private*, pg. 1559
FOLLETT SCHOOL SOLUTIONS, INC.—See Francisco Partners Management, LP; *U.S. Private*, pg. 1589
FOLLETT SOFTWARE COMPANY—See Follett Corporation; *U.S. Private*, pg. 1559
FOLLI FOLLIE HONG KONG LTD.—See Folli Follie S.A.; *Int'l*, pg. 2721
FOLLI FOLLIE JAPAN, LTD.—See Folli Follie S.A.; *Int'l*, pg. 2721
FOLLI FOLLIE KOREA LTD.—See Folli Follie S.A.; *Int'l*, pg. 2721
FOLLI FOLLIE MALAYSIA LTD.—See Folli Follie S.A.; *Int'l*, pg. 2721
FOLLI FOLLIE POLAND SP. Z O.O.—See Folli Follie S.A.; *Int'l*, pg. 2721
FOLLI FOLLIE S.A.; *Int'l*, pg. 2721
FOLLI FOLLIE SINGAPORE LTD.—See Folli Follie S.A.; *Int'l*, pg. 2721
FOLLI FOLLIE SPAIN S.A.—See Folli Follie S.A.; *Int'l*, pg. 2721
FOLLI FOLLIE TAIWAN LTD.—See Folli Follie S.A.; *Int'l*, pg. 2721
FOLLI FOLLIE THAILAND LTD.—See Folli Follie S.A.; *Int'l*, pg. 2721
FOLLI FOLLIE UK LTD.—See Folli Follie S.A.; *Int'l*, pg. 2721
FOLLUM INDUSTRIPARK AS—See Norske Skog ASA; *Int'l*, pg. 5437
FOLMAR & ASSOCIATES LLP; *U.S. Private*, pg. 1559
FOLSOM BUICK GMC; *U.S. Private*, pg. 1559
FOLSOM CHEVROLET; *U.S. Private*, pg. 1559
FOLSOM CORPORATION; *U.S. Private*, pg. 1559
FOLSOM INVESTMENTS INC.; *U.S. Private*, pg. 1559
FOLSOM LAKE FORD; *U.S. Private*, pg. 1559
FOLSOM OUTPATIENT SURGERY CENTER, L.P.—See Tenet Healthcare Corporation; *U.S. Public*, pg. 2010
FOLTENE LABS S.P.A.—See Gerolymatos Group of Companies; *Int'l*, pg. 2943
FOMA NORGE AS—See Tennant Company; *U.S. Public*, pg. 2016
FOMEMA SDN. BHD.—See Khazanah Nasional Berhad; *Int'l*, pg. 4152
FOMENTO DE CONSTRUCCIONES Y CONTRATAS CANADA LTD.—See Fomento de Construcciones y Contratas, S.A.; *Int'l*, pg. 2723
FOMENTO DE CONSTRUCCIONES Y CONTRATAS, S.A.; *Int'l*, pg. 2723
FOMENTO ECONOMICO MEXICANO, S.A.B. DE C.V.; *Int'l*, pg. 2723
FOMENTO RESORTS & HOTELS LTD; *Int'l*, pg. 2724
FOMM CORPORATION—See Banpu Power PCL; *Int'l*, pg. 851
FOMO WORLDWIDE, INC.; *U.S. Public*, pg. 863
FON4U TELECOM GMBH—See 3U Holding AG; *Int'l*, pg. 10
FONA DENTAL S.R.O.—See DENTSPLY SIRONA Inc.; *U.S. Public*, pg. 655

FOMO WORLDWIDE, INC.   CORPORATE AFFILIATIONS

FONA INTERNATIONAL, LLC—See McCormick & Company, Incorporated; *U.S. Public*, pg. 1404
FONALITY, INC.; *U.S. Private*, pg. 1559
FON ANLEGG AS—See Storskogen Group AB; *Int'l*, pg. 7227
FONAR CORPORATION; *U.S. Public*, pg. 863
FONA S.R.L.—See DENTSPLY SIRONA Inc.; *U.S. Public*, pg. 655
FONCIERE 7 INVESTISSEMENT SA; *Int'l*, pg. 2724
FONCIERE ATLAND SA; *Int'l*, pg. 2724
FONCIERE DE PARIS SIIC—See Gecina S.A.; *Int'l*, pg. 2909
FONCIERE DES MURS SCA—See Covivio; *Int'l*, pg. 1821
FONCIERE EURIS—See Finatis SA; *Int'l*, pg. 2670
FONCIERE INEA SA; *Int'l*, pg. 2724
FONCIERE PARIS NORD SA; *Int'l*, pg. 2724
FONCIERE R-PARIS SCA; *Int'l*, pg. 2724
FONCIERE VINDI SA; *Int'l*, pg. 2724
FONCIERE VOLTA SA; *Int'l*, pg. 2724
FONDACTION, LE FONDS DE DEVELOPPEMENT DE LA CONFEDERATION DES SYNDICATS NATIONAUX POUR LA COOPERATION ET L'EMPLOI; *Int'l*, pg. 2724
FONDASOL SA—See BNP Paribas SA; *Int'l*, pg. 1083
FONDATION JEAN-LUC LAGARDERE—See Vivendi SE; *Int'l*, pg. 8271
FONDATIONS CAPITAL SA; *Int'l*, pg. 2725
FONDATIONS CAPITAL SERVICES FRANCE SA—See Fondations Capital SA; *Int'l*, pg. 2725
FONDATRAV SAS—See VINCI S.A.; *Int'l*, pg. 8221
FONDAZIONE CASSA DI RISPARMIO DI TORINO; *Int'l*, pg. 2725
FONDAZIONE ZOE S.R.L.—See Zambon Company S.p.A.; *Int'l*, pg. 8622
FONDERIE GIROUD INDUSTRIE SAS; *Int'l*, pg. 2725
FONDERIE MORA GAVARDO SPA—See Camozzi Group; *Int'l*, pg. 1274
FONDERIE SCHLUMBERGER SAS—See NSC Groupe SA; *Int'l*, pg. 5476
FONDERIES NICOLAS SAS—See CVC Capital Partners SICAV-FIS S.A.; *Int'l*, pg. 1887
FONDERIE VRIGNAUD SA—See Beneteau S.A; *Int'l*, pg. 972
FONDI ALLEANZA S.G.R.P.A.—See Assicurazioni Generali S.p.A.; *Int'l*, pg. 643
FONDIA OYJ; *Int'l*, pg. 2725
FONDINVEST CAPITAL; *Int'l*, pg. 2725
FONDI SLLOVENO- KOSOVAR I PENSIONEVE SH.A.—See Prva Group plc; *Int'l*, pg. 6010
FONDITEL ENTIDAD GESTORA DE FONDOS DE PENSIONES, S.A.—See Telefonica, S.A.; *Int'l*, pg. 7535
FONDO ACH, S.A. DE C.V. SOFOM, E.N.R—See EZCORP, Inc.; *U.S. Public*, pg. 818
FONDO DE VALORES INMOBILIARIOS S.A.C.A.; *Int'l*, pg. 2725
FONDO ITALIANO DI INVESTIMENTO SGR S.P.A.—See Cassa Depositi e Prestiti S.p.A.; *Int'l*, pg. 1355
FONDS DE CONSOLIDATION ET DE DEVELOPPEMENT DES ENTREPRISES; *Int'l*, pg. 2725
FONDSDEPOT BANK GMBH—See Caisse de Depot et Placement du Quebec; *Int'l*, pg. 1752
FONDSDEPOT BANK GMBH—See Generation Investment Management LLP; *Int'l*, pg. 2920
FONDS DE SOLIDARITE DES TRAVAILLEURS DU QUEBEC; *Int'l*, pg. 2725
FONDSENBEHEER NEDERLAND B.V.—See Cooperatieve Centrale Raiffeisen-Boerenleenbank B.A.; *Int'l*, pg. 1791
FONDSFINANCE GMBH—See Norddeutsche Landesbank Girozentrale; *Int'l*, pg. 5417
FONDSMAEGLERSELSKABET MAJ INVEST A/S—See Maj Invest Holding A/S; *Int'l*, pg. 4653
FONDSMANAGEMENT BERLIN GMBH—See Bilfinger SE; *Int'l*, pg. 1028
FONDSMANAGEMENT DUSSELDORF GMBH—See Bilfinger SE; *Int'l*, pg. 1028
FONDS MERCATOR—See Dexia SA; *Int'l*, pg. 2092
FONDS NATIONAL D'INVESTISSEMENT; *Int'l*, pg. 2725
FONDUL ROMAN DE GARANTARE A CREDITELOR PENTRU INTREPRINZATORII PRIVATI - IFN S.A.—See SIF Muntenia S.A.; *Int'l*, pg. 6905
FONE4 COMMUNICATIONS (INDIA) LIMITED; *Int'l*, pg. 2725
FONEBILL LLC—See Roadpost Inc.; *Int'l*, pg. 6358
FONET BILGI TEKNOLOJILERI AS; *Int'l*, pg. 2726
FONEX DATA SYSTEMS INC.; *Int'l*, pg. 2726
FONEX SAS—See FONEX Data Systems Inc.; *Int'l*, pg. 2726
FONFUN CORPORATION; *Int'l*, pg. 2726
FONG BROTHERS PRINTING INC.; *U.S. Private*, pg. 1559
FONG CHIEN CONSTRUCTION CO., LTD.; *Int'l*, pg. 2726
FONG CONSULT PTE. LTD.—See OYO Corporation; *Int'l*, pg. 5678
FONGEPAR—See CNP Assurances SA; *Int'l*, pg. 1678
FONGMA TEK(SUZHOU) CO., LTD.—See Taiwan Line Tek Electronic Co., Ltd.; *Int'l*, pg. 7422
FONG YUE CO., LTD.—See Toyoda Gosei Co., Ltd.; *Int'l*, pg. 7861

FONIAL GMBH—See EnBW Energie Baden-Wurttemberg AG; *Int'l*, pg. 2401
FONIX MOBILE PLC; *Int'l*, pg. 2726
FONON CORPORATION; *U.S. Private*, pg. 1559
FONON SP. Z O.O.—See WASKO S.A.; *Int'l*, pg. 8352
FONROCHE ENERGIE SAS—See Eurazeo SE; *Int'l*, pg. 2528
FON SE; *Int'l*, pg. 2724
FONTAINEBLEAU HOTEL; *U.S. Private*, pg. 1559
FONTAINEBLEAU VASTGOED BV—See Carpetright plc; *Int'l*, pg. 1343
FONTAINE & CO. GMBH—See Putsch GmbH & Co. KG; *Int'l*, pg. 6124
FONTAINE ENGINEERING UND MASCHINEN GMBH—See SMS Holding GmbH; *Int'l*, pg. 7015
FONTAINE EUROPE SAS—See Zurn Elkay Water Solutions Corporation; *U.S. Public*, pg. 2412
FONTAINE FIFTH WHEEL COMPANY—See Berkshire Hathaway Inc.; *U.S. Public*, pg. 310
FONTAINE INDUSTRIES LTD.—See Zurn Elkay Water Solutions Corporation; *U.S. Public*, pg. 2412
FONTAINE MODIFICATION COMPANY—See Berkshire Hathaway Inc.; *U.S. Public*, pg. 310
FONTAINE TRAILER COMPANY—See Berkshire Hathaway Inc.; *U.S. Public*, pg. 310
FONTAINE USA INC.—See Zurn Elkay Water Solutions Corporation; *U.S. Public*, pg. 2412
FONTANA AMERICA INC.—See Fontana Luigi S.p.A.; *Int'l*, pg. 2726
FONTANA FASTENERS DE MEXICO S.A. C.V.—See Fontana Luigi S.p.A.; *Int'l*, pg. 2726
FONTANA FASTENERS DEUTSCHLAND GMBH—See Fontana Luigi S.p.A.; *Int'l*, pg. 2726
FONTANA FASTENERS DO BRASIL INDUSTRIA E COMERCIO DE FIXADORES LTDA—See Fontana Luigi S.p.A.; *Int'l*, pg. 2726
FONTANA FASTENERS FRANCE S.A.S.—See Fontana Luigi S.p.A.; *Int'l*, pg. 2726
FONTANA FASTENERS INC.—See Fontana Luigi S.p.A.; *Int'l*, pg. 2726
FONTANA FASTENERS INDIA PRIVATE LTD—See Fontana Luigi S.p.A.; *Int'l*, pg. 2726
FONTANA FASTENERS ITALIA S.P.A.—See Fontana Luigi S.p.A.; *Int'l*, pg. 2726
FONTANA FASTENERS POLAND SP. Z.O.O.—See Fontana Luigi S.p.A.; *Int'l*, pg. 2726
FONTANA FASTENERS S.A.—See Fontana Luigi S.p.A.; *Int'l*, pg. 2726
FONTANA FASTENERS SRL—See Fontana Luigi S.p.A.; *Int'l*, pg. 2726
FONTANA FASTENERS UK LTD—See Fontana Luigi S.p.A.; *Int'l*, pg. 2726
FONTANA INTERNATIONAL GMBH—See Sioen Industries NV; *Int'l*, pg. 6960
FONTANA LUIGI S.P.A.; *Int'l*, pg. 2726
FONTANA SELF STORAGE TRS, LLC—See CubeSmart; *U.S. Public*, pg. 603
FONTANA UNION WATER COMPANY—See Cucamonga Valley Water District; *U.S. Private*, pg. 1120
FONTANA UNIVERSAL SELF STORAGE—See National Storage Affiliates Trust; *U.S. Public*, pg. 1498
FONTANA WATER COMPANY; *U.S. Private*, pg. 1560
FONTANA WOOD PRODUCTS INC.; *U.S. Private*, pg. 1560
FONTANESI AND KANN COMPANY; *U.S. Private*, pg. 1560
FONTANIE—See Eiffage S.A.; *Int'l*, pg. 2331
FONTARGEN GESELLSCHAFT MIT BESCHRANKTER HAFTUNG—See voestalpine AG; *Int'l*, pg. 8288
FONTEC SA—See VINCI S.A.; *Int'l*, pg. 8231
FONTEM VENTURES B.V.—See Imperial Brands PLC; *Int'l*, pg. 3633
FONTERELLI GMBH & CO KGAA; *Int'l*, pg. 2726
FONTERRA BRANDS INDONESIA, PT—See Fonterra Co-Operative Group Ltd.; *Int'l*, pg. 2726
FONTERRA BRANDS LANKA (PRIVATE) LIMITED—See Fonterra Co-Operative Group Ltd.; *Int'l*, pg. 2726
FONTERRA BRANDS (MALAYSIA) SDN BHD—See Fonterra Co-Operative Group Ltd.; *Int'l*, pg. 2726
FONTERRA BRANDS (MIDDLE EAST) LLC—See Fonterra Co-Operative Group Ltd.; *Int'l*, pg. 2726
FONTERRA BRANDS (NEW ZEALAND) LIMITED—See Fonterra Co-Operative Group Ltd.; *Int'l*, pg. 2726
FONTERRA BRANDS (TIP TOP) LIMITED—See Nestle S.A.; *Int'l*, pg. 5202
FONTERRA BRANDS (TIP TOP) LIMITED—See PAI Partners S.A.S.; *Int'l*, pg. 5702
FONTERRA CO-OPERATIVE GROUP LTD.; *Int'l*, pg. 2726
FONTERRA (JAPAN) LTD.—See Fonterra Co-Operative Group Ltd.; *Int'l*, pg. 2726
FONTERRA (USA) INC.—See Fonterra Co-Operative Group Ltd.; *Int'l*, pg. 2726
FONTEVA INC.—See GI Manager L.P.; *U.S. Private*, pg. 1694
FONTE VIVA KFT.—See MOL Magyar Olaj- es Gazipari Nyrt.; *Int'l*, pg. 5020
FONTIS INTERNATIONAL, INC.—See Iron Mountain Incorporated; *U.S. Public*, pg. 1172

FONTIS SOLUTIONS, INC.—See Deluxe Corporation; *U.S. Public*, pg. 652
FONTSHOP INTERNATIONAL, INC.—See HGGC, LLC; *U.S. Private*, pg. 1930
FONT VELLA SA—See Danone; *Int'l*, pg. 1968
FONUA LTD.; *Int'l*, pg. 2726
FONUM OY—See Elisa Corporation; *Int'l*, pg. 2361
FONVILLE MORISEY REALTY—See The Long & Foster Companies, Inc.; *U.S. Private*, pg. 4072
FON WIRELESS LTD.; *Int'l*, pg. 2724
FOOD 4 LESS OF SOUTHERN CALIFORNIA, INC.—See The Kroger Co.; *U.S. Public*, pg. 2108
FOOD AFFAIRS GMBH—See Compass Group PLC; *Int'l*, pg. 1752
FOOD ALLERGY RESEARCH & EDUCATION, INC.; *U.S. Private*, pg. 1560
FOOD & ALLIED SUPPORT SERVICES CORPORATION PTE. LTD.—See Temasek Holdings (Private) Limited; *Int'l*, pg. 7547
FOOD AND DRINKS PUBLIC COMPANY LIMITED; *Int'l*, pg. 2727
FOODANE A/S—See Danish Crown AmbA; *Int'l*, pg. 1965
FOODARAMA INC—See United Natural Foods, Inc.; *U.S. Public*, pg. 2231
FOOD AUTOMATION - SERVICE TECHNIQUES, INC.; *U.S. Private*, pg. 1560
FOODAWORLD MARKETING PTE LTD—See Food Empire Holdings Limited; *Int'l*, pg. 2727
FOOD BANK OF CONTRA COSTA AND SOLANO; *U.S. Private*, pg. 1560
THE FOOD BANK OF NORTHEAST GEORGIA; *U.S. Private*, pg. 4029
FOOD BANK OF SAN LUIS OBISPO COUNTY; *U.S. Private*, pg. 1560
FOODBANK OF SOUTHEASTERN VIRGINIA AND THE EASTERN SHORE; *U.S. Private*, pg. 1561
FOOD BANK OF THE ROCKIES; *U.S. Private*, pg. 1560
THE FOOD BANK OF WESTERN MASSACHUSETTS; *U.S. Private*, pg. 4029
FOODBUY LLC—See Compass Group PLC; *Int'l*, pg. 1751
FOODBUY PTY LTD—See Compass Group PLC; *Int'l*, pg. 1752
FOOD CHAIN (HOLDINGS) LIMITED—See Simonds Farsons Cisk plc; *Int'l*, pg. 6932
FOODCHAIN ID GROUP, INC.—See Berkshire Partners LLC; *U.S. Private*, pg. 534
FOODCHAIN ID TECHNICAL SERVICES, INC—See Berkshire Partners LLC; *U.S. Private*, pg. 534
FOOD CIRCUS SUPERMARKETS INC.; *U.S. Private*, pg. 1560
FOOD CITY DISTRIBUTION CENTER—See K-VA-T Food Stores, Inc.; *U.S. Private*, pg. 2251
FOODCLIQUE (CAPEVIEW) PTE. LTD.—See Kimly Limited; *Int'l*, pg. 4163
FOODCO HOLDING CO P.J.S.C; *Int'l*, pg. 2727
FOOD CONCEPTS INTERNATIONAL; *U.S. Private*, pg. 1560
FOODCORP (PTY) LTD.—See Remgro Limited; *Int'l*, pg. 6270
FOODCORP S.A.—See Austevoll Seafood ASA; *Int'l*, pg. 717
FOOD COUNTRY USA INC.; *U.S. Private*, pg. 1560
FOODCRAFT INC.—See Thornico A/S; *Int'l*, pg. 7719
FOOD EMPIRE HOLDINGS LIMITED; *Int'l*, pg. 2727
FOOD EQUIPMENT REPRESENTATIVES, INC.; *U.S. Private*, pg. 1560
FOOD EQUIPMENT SERVICES CO.—See Berkshire Partners LLC; *U.S. Private*, pg. 535
FOODEXO SP. Z O.O.—See Saudi Dairy & Foodstuff Co. Ltd.; *Int'l*, pg. 6593
FOOD EXPORT ASSOCIATION OF THE MIDWEST USA; *U.S. Private*, pg. 1560
FOOD EXPRESS INC.; *U.S. Private*, pg. 1560
FOODEX S.A.R.L.—See Takara Holdings, Inc.; *Int'l*, pg. 7432
FOODEX S.A.S.—See Takara Holdings, Inc.; *Int'l*, pg. 7432
FOODEX S.R.L.—See Takara Holdings, Inc.; *Int'l*, pg. 7432
FOODEX SUD S.A.R.L.—See Takara Holdings, Inc.; *Int'l*, pg. 7432
FOOD FAST CORPORATION; *U.S. Private*, pg. 1560
THE FOODFELLAS LTD.—See Charoen Pokphand Foods Public Company Limited; *Int'l*, pg. 1453
FOODFEST INTERNATIONAL 2000 INC.; *U.S. Public*, pg. 863
FOODFIRST GLOBAL RESTAURANTS, INC.—See GP Investments, Ltd.; *Int'l*, pg. 3045
FOOD FOR LANE COUNTY; *U.S. Private*, pg. 1560
FOOD FOR THE POOR, INC.; *U.S. Private*, pg. 1560
FOOD & GAS, INC.; *U.S. Private*, pg. 1560
FOOD GIANT SUPERMARKETS, INC.—See Houchens Industries, Inc.; *U.S. Private*, pg. 1990
THE FOOD GROUP (CHICAGO)—See WPP plc; *Int'l*, pg. 8483
THE FOOD GROUP, INC.—See WPP plc; *Int'l*, pg. 8483
THE FOOD GROUP (LOS ANGELES)—See WPP plc; *Int'l*, pg. 8483
THE FOOD GROUP (TAMPA)—See WPP plc; *Int'l*, pg. 8483
FOODGUYS; *U.S. Private*, pg. 1561

COMPANY NAME INDEX

FOODHALL—See Future Corporate Resources Limited; *Int'l*, pg. 2853
FOODHANDLER INC.—See Bunzl plc; *Int'l*, pg. 1218
FOODIES GROUP LIMITED—See Simplicity Holding Ltd.; *Int'l*, pg. 6934
FOOD INNOVATIONS, INC.—See Innovative Food Holdings, Inc.; *U.S. Public*, pg. 1126
FOODINVEST N.V.—See Colruyt Group N.V.; *Int'l*, pg. 1705
FOODIO CONCEPTS SP. Z O.O.—See Agora S.A.; *Int'l*, pg. 212
FOOD JUNCTION HOLDINGS LIMITED—See Lippo Limited; *Int'l*, pg. 4522
FOOD JUNCTION MANAGEMENT PTE LTD—See BreadTalk Group Pte Ltd.; *Int'l*, pg. 1143
FOOD KING INC.; *U.S. Private*, pg. 1560
FOOD KING, INC.; *U.S. Private*, pg. 1561
FOODLAND PROPERTIES PTY. LTD.—See Metcash Limited; *Int'l*, pg. 4852
FOODLANDS RESTAURANT—See NMC Health PLC; *Int'l*, pg. 5392
FOODLANDS RESTAURANT—See NMC Health PLC; *Int'l*, pg. 5392
FOODLAND SUPER MARKET LIMITED; *U.S. Private*, pg. 1562
FOODLAND WAREHOUSE FOODS INC.; *U.S. Private*, pg. 1562
FOOD & LIFE COMPANIES LTD.; *Int'l*, pg. 2727
FOODLINES B.V.B.A.—See Colruyt Group N.V.; *Int'l*, pg. 1705
FOODLINK CORPORATION—See Mitsubishi Corporation; *Int'l*, pg. 4938
FOOD LION, LLC—See Koninklijke Ahold Delhaize N.V.; *Int'l*, pg. 4260
FOODLOGIQ, LLC—See The Riverside Company; *U.S. Private*, pg. 4108
FOOD MANAGEMENT PARTNERS, INC.; *U.S. Private*, pg. 1561
FOOD MARKETING GROUP INC.—See Brothers Trading Co. Inc.; *U.S. Private*, pg. 665
FOOD MARKETING SERVICES, INC.; *U.S. Private*, pg. 1561
FOOD MARKETING SERVICES—See Louis F. Leeper Company; *U.S. Private*, pg. 2498
FOOD MARKET MANAGEMENT, INC.; *U.S. Private*, pg. 1561
FOOD MASTERS INC.; *U.S. Private*, pg. 1561
FOODMASTER SUPER MARKETS INC.; *U.S. Private*, pg. 1562
FOODMAVEN CORPORATION; *U.S. Private*, pg. 1562
FOODMIX MARKETING COMMUNICATIONS; *U.S. Private*, pg. 1562
FOOD & MORE GMBH—See UniCredit S.p.A.; *Int'l*, pg. 8038
FOODNAMOO INC.; *Int'l*, pg. 2727
FOOD NETWORK MAGAZINE—See The Hearst Corporation; *U.S. Private*, pg. 4046
FOOD-N-FUN, INC.; *U.S. Private*, pg. 1561
FOOD OPPORTUNITIES ORGANIZATION &. DISTRIBUTION INC.; *U.S. Private*, pg. 1561
FOODORA AB—See Delivery Hero SE; *Int'l*, pg. 2013
FOODORA NORWAY AS—See Delivery Hero SE; *Int'l*, pg. 2013
FOODPACK B.V.—See Clayton, Dubilier & Rice, LLC; *U.S. Private*, pg. 926
FOOD PANTRY LTD. INC.; *U.S. Private*, pg. 1561
FOOD PLANET, INC.; *Int'l*, pg. 2727
FOODPRINTS—See PAI Partners S.A.S.; *Int'l*, pg. 5700
FOODPRO; *U.S. Private*, pg. 1562
FOOD PROTECTION SERVICES, L.L.C.—See Ecolab Inc.; *U.S. Public*, pg. 714
FOOD REPUBLIC PTE LTD—See BreadTalk Group Pte Ltd.; *Int'l*, pg. 1143
FOOD REPUBLIC TAIWAN CO., LTD.—See BreadTalk Group Pte Ltd.; *Int'l*, pg. 1143
THE FOOD REVOLUTION GROUP; *Int'l*, pg. 7643
FOOD SAFETY EVALUATION & RESEARCH INSTITUTE CO., LTD.—See NH Foods Ltd.; *Int'l*, pg. 5256
FOODS BOTSWANA (PTY) LIMITED - BEVERAGES—See Sefalana Holdings Company Limited; *Int'l*, pg. 6679
FOODS BOTSWANA (PTY.) LIMITED - MILLING—See Sefalana Holdings Company Limited; *Int'l*, pg. 6679
FOODSCIENCE CORPORATION—See Wind Point Advisors LLC; *U.S. Private*, pg. 4534
FOOD SCIENCES CORPORATION; *U.S. Private*, pg. 1561
FOOD SERVICE INSURANCE MANAGERS; *U.S. Private*, pg. 1561
FOOD SERVICE OF TALLAHASSEE; *U.S. Private*, pg. 1561
FOOD SERVICE PROJECT, SL—See Alsea, S.A.B. de C.V.; *Int'l*, pg. 379
FOOD SERVICE REFRIGERATION INC.; *U.S. Private*, pg. 1561
FOOD SERVICES OF AMERICA, INC.—See US Foods Holding Corp.; *U.S. Public*, pg. 2266
FOOD SERVICE SYSTEMS INC.—See The VPS Companies Inc.; *U.S. Private*, pg. 4132

FOODSERVICE TECHNOLOGIES, INC.—See HCI Equity Management, L.P.; *U.S. Private*, pg. 1889
FOODSERV SOLUTIONS (PTY) LTD.—See Excellerate Holdings Ltd.; *Int'l*, pg. 2578
FOOD SHOULD TASTE GOOD, INC.; *U.S. Private*, pg. 1561
FOODS & INNS LTD.; *Int'l*, pg. 2727
FOODS NORTH LLC; *U.S. Private*, pg. 1562
FOOD SPECIALISTS INC.; *U.S. Private*, pg. 1561
FOODSTATE, INC.—See Otsuka Holdings Co., Ltd.; *Int'l*, pg. 5660
FOODSWING, INC.; *U.S. Private*, pg. 1562
FOOD SYSTEMS UNLIMITED, INC.; *U.S. Private*, pg. 1561
FOODTASTIC INC.; *Int'l*, pg. 2727
FOODTEAM INC.; *U.S. Private*, pg. 1562
FOODTECH PRODUCTS (THAILAND) CO., LTD.—See Lacto Japan Co., Ltd.; *Int'l*, pg. 4391
FOODTEC UK LTD—See Ornua Co-operative Limited; *Int'l*, pg. 5642
FOODTOWN, INC.; *U.S. Private*, pg. 1562
FOODTOWN SUPERMARKET INC.—See Foodtown, Inc.; *U.S. Private*, pg. 1562
FOOD TRAC LTD.—See Charoen Pokphand Foods Public Company Limited; *Int'l*, pg. 1452
FOOD WAREHOUSE CORPORATION; *U.S. Private*, pg. 1561
FOOD WARMING EQUIPMENT CO., INC.—See Hatco Corporation; *U.S. Private*, pg. 1879
FOOD & WATER WATCH; *U.S. Private*, pg. 1560
FOODWELL CORPORATION - DAEGU FACTORY 1—See Foodwell Corporation; *Int'l*, pg. 2728
FOODWELL CORPORATION - DAEGU FACTORY 2—See Foodwell Corporation; *Int'l*, pg. 2728
FOODWELL CORPORATION; *Int'l*, pg. 2728
FOOD & WINE—See Meredith Corporation; *U.S. Public*, pg. 1422
FOODWORKS RETAIL PTY LTD—See Australian United Retailers Limited; *Int'l*, pg. 722
FOODWORLD SUPERMARKETS PVT. LTD.—See Jardine Matheson Holdings Limited; *Int'l*, pg. 3909
FOOK CHEONG HO INTERNATIONAL LIMITED—See China Ever Grand Financial Leasing Group Co., Ltd.; *Int'l*, pg. 1501
FOOSUNG CO., LTD.; *Int'l*, pg. 2728
FOOSUNG HDS CO., LTD.—See Foosung Co., Ltd.; *Int'l*, pg. 2728
FOOSUNG INDUSTRIAL CO., LTD. - EUMSUNG FACTORY—See Foosung Co., Ltd.; *Int'l*, pg. 2728
FOOSUNG INDUSTRIAL CO., LTD.—See Foosung Co., Ltd.; *Int'l*, pg. 2728
FOOSUNG PRECISION IND. CO., LTD. - BEIJING FACTORY—See Foosung Co., Ltd.; *Int'l*, pg. 2728
FOOSUNG PRECISION IND. CO., LTD. - GAJAE-RI FACTORY—See Foosung Co., Ltd.; *Int'l*, pg. 2728
FOOSUNG PRECISION IND. CO., LTD. - MUNMAK FACTORY—See Foosung Co., Ltd.; *Int'l*, pg. 2728
FOOSUNG PRECISION IND. CO., LTD. - NINGBO FPI FACTORY—See Foosung Co., Ltd.; *Int'l*, pg. 2728
FOOSUNG PRECISION IND. CO., LTD. - SUZHOU FACTORY—See Foosung Co., Ltd.; *Int'l*, pg. 2728
FOOSUNG PRECISION INDUSTRY CO., LTD.—See Foosung Co., Ltd.; *Int'l*, pg. 2728
FOOSUNGTECH CO., LTD.—See Foosung Co., Ltd.; *Int'l*, pg. 2728
FOOTAGE FIRM, INC.—See Great Hill Partners, L.P.; *U.S. Private*, pg. 1763
FOOT & ANKLE ASSOCIATES OF SOUTHWEST VIRGINIA, P.C.—See NMS Capital Services, LLC; *U.S. Private*, pg. 2932
FOOTASYLUM PLC—See Aurelius Equity Opportunities SE & Co. KGaA; *Int'l*, pg. 708
FOOTBALL CLUB DES GIRONDINS DE BORDEAUX—See B. Riley Financial, Inc.; *U.S. Public*, pg. 261
FOOTBALL POOLS 1923 LIMITED—See OpCapita LLP; *Int'l*, pg. 5595
THE FOOTBALL POOLS LIMITED—See OpCapita LLP; *Int'l*, pg. 5595
THE FOOTBRIDGE COMPANIES; *U.S. Private*, pg. 4029
FOOTE PARTNERS LLC; *U.S. Private*, pg. 1562
FOOTHILL COMMUNITY HEALTH CENTER—See Bay Area Community Health; *U.S. Private*, pg. 491
FOOTHILL ENGINEERING & DEWATERING, INC.—See Crossplane Capital Management LP; *U.S. Private*, pg. 1107
FOOTHILL NURSING COMPANY PARTNERSHIP—See Apollo Global Management, Inc.; *U.S. Public*, pg. 156
FOOTHILL RIDGE APARTMENTS; *U.S. Private*, pg. 1562
FOOTHILLS ASSET MANAGEMENT LTD.—See Capital Insight Partners, LLC; *U.S. Private*, pg. 740
THE FOOTHILLS BANK—See Glacier Bancorp, Inc.; *U.S. Public*, pg. 939
FOOTHILLS CONSULTING GROUP, INC.—See Stone Point Capital LLC; *U.S. Private*, pg. 3823
FOOTHILLS EXPLORATION, INC.; *U.S. Public*, pg. 864
FOOTHILLS FARMERS COOPERATIVE; *U.S. Private*, pg. 1562

FOOTHILLS LAND CONSERVANCY; *U.S. Private*, pg. 1562
FOOTHILLS MALL, INC.—See CBL & Associates Properties, Inc.; *U.S. Public*, pg. 458
FOOTHILLS RURAL TELEPHONE COOPERATIVE CORPORATION INC.; *U.S. Private*, pg. 1562
FOOTHILLS SELF STORAGE—See TDG Inc.; *U.S. Private*, pg. 3944
FOOTHILLS TRADER INC.—See Alden Global Capital LLC; *U.S. Private*, pg. 156
FOOT LOCKER ARTIGOS DESPORTIVOS E DE TEMPOS LIVRES, LDA.—See Foot Locker, Inc.; *U.S. Public*, pg. 863
FOOT LOCKER AUSTRALIA, INC.—See Foot Locker, Inc.; *U.S. Public*, pg. 863
FOOT LOCKER AUSTRIA GMBH—See Foot Locker, Inc.; *U.S. Public*, pg. 863
FOOT LOCKER BELGIUM B.V.B.A.—See Foot Locker, Inc.; *U.S. Public*, pg. 863
FOOTLOCKER.COM, INC.—See Foot Locker, Inc.; *U.S. Public*, pg. 863
FOOT LOCKER DENMARK B.V.—See Foot Locker, Inc.; *U.S. Public*, pg. 863
FOOT LOCKER EUROPE B.V.—See Foot Locker, Inc.; *U.S. Public*, pg. 863
FOOT LOCKER EUROPE.COM B.V.—See Foot Locker, Inc.; *U.S. Public*, pg. 863
FOOT LOCKER FRANCE S.A.S.—See Foot Locker, Inc.; *U.S. Public*, pg. 863
FOOT LOCKER, INC.; *U.S. Public*, pg. 863
FOOT LOCKER ITALY S.R.L.—See Foot Locker, Inc.; *U.S. Public*, pg. 863
FOOT LOCKER NETHERLANDS B.V.—See Foot Locker, Inc.; *U.S. Public*, pg. 863
FOOT LOCKER RETAIL, INC.—See Foot Locker, Inc.; *U.S. Public*, pg. 863
FOOT LOCKER SPAIN S.L.—See Foot Locker, Inc.; *U.S. Public*, pg. 863
FOOT LOCKER SPECIALTY, INC.—See Foot Locker, Inc.; *U.S. Public*, pg. 863
FOOT LOCKER SWEDEN AKTIEBOLAG—See Foot Locker, Inc.; *U.S. Public*, pg. 863
FOOT LOCKER SWITZERLAND LLC—See Foot Locker, Inc.; *U.S. Public*, pg. 863
FOOT LOCKER U.K. LIMITED—See Foot Locker, Inc.; *U.S. Public*, pg. 863
FOOT PETALS, INC.—See Remington Products Company; *U.S. Private*, pg. 3396
FOOTPRINT RETAIL SERVICES; *U.S. Private*, pg. 1562
FOOTSTEPS—See Omnicom Group Inc.; *U.S. Public*, pg. 1585
FOOTWAY GROUP AB; *Int'l*, pg. 2728
FOOTWEAR NEWS—See Penske Media Corporation; *U.S. Private*, pg. 3139
FOOTWEAR SPECIALTIES INTERNATIONAL LLC—See Partners Group Holding AG; *Int'l*, pg. 5750
FOOTWEAR UNLIMITED INC.; *U.S. Private*, pg. 1562
FOOTWORK INTERNATIONAL, INC.—See WEDS CO., LTD.; *Int'l*, pg. 8367
FOPAC MASCHINENBAU GMBH—See Focke & Co. (GmbH & Co.) Verpackungsmaschinen; *Int'l*, pg. 2718
FOPE S.R.L.; *Int'l*, pg. 2728
FORACO ARGENTINA SA—See Foraco International S.A.; *Int'l*, pg. 2728
FORACO BURKINA FASO SA—See Foraco International S.A.; *Int'l*, pg. 2728
FORACO CANADA LTD.—See Foraco International S.A.; *Int'l*, pg. 2728
FORACO CHILE SA—See Foraco International S.A.; *Int'l*, pg. 2728
FORACO CI S.A.—See Foraco International S.A.; *Int'l*, pg. 2728
FORACO GHANA LTD.—See Foraco International S.A.; *Int'l*, pg. 2728
FORACO GUINEE SARL—See Foraco International S.A.; *Int'l*, pg. 2728
FORACO INTERNATIONAL S.A.; *Int'l*, pg. 2728
FORACO NIGER S.A.—See Foraco International S.A.; *Int'l*, pg. 2728
FORACO PACIFIQUE SASU—See Foraco International S.A.; *Int'l*, pg. 2728
FORACO SAHEL SARL—See Foraco International S.A.; *Int'l*, pg. 2728
FORACO SINGAPORE PTE. LTD.—See Foraco International S.A.; *Int'l*, pg. 2728
FORADEX SUD SRL—See S.C. FORADEX S.A.; *Int'l*, pg. 6451
FORAFRIC GLOBAL PLC; *Int'l*, pg. 2728
FORAGE GENETICS INTERNATIONAL, LLC—See Land O'Lakes, Inc.; *U.S. Private*, pg. 2383
FORAGE MAJOR KENNEBEC DRILLING LTD—See Major Drilling Group International Inc.; *Int'l*, pg. 4654
FORAGES CABO INC.—See Cabo Drilling Corp.; *Int'l*, pg. 1246
FORAJ SONDE CRAIOVA; *Int'l*, pg. 2728
FORAKER ELEVATOR—See The Mennel Milling Company; *U.S. Private*, pg. 4077
FORALITH EQUIPMENT AG.—See BAUER Aktiengesellschaft; *Int'l*, pg. 893

FORAM GROUP, INC.

CORPORATE AFFILIATIONS

FORAM GROUP, INC.; *U.S. Private*, pg. 1562
FORAN ENERGY GROUP CO., LTD.; *Int'l*, pg. 2728
FORANKRA AB—See Axel Johnson Gruppen AB; *Int'l*, pg. 764
FORANKRA ESPANA SL—See Axel Johnson Gruppen AB; *Int'l*, pg. 764
FORANKRA POL SP. Z O.O.—See Axel Johnson Gruppen AB; *Int'l*, pg. 764
FORAN MINING CORPORATION; *Int'l*, pg. 2728
FORAN SPICE COMPANY; *U.S. Private*, pg. 1562
FORASTIERE FAMILY FUNERAL SERVICES, INC.—See Carriage Services, Inc.; *U.S. Public*, pg. 439
FORBES AIR SERVICES (PVT) LTD.—See Hemas Holdings PLC; *Int'l*, pg. 3340
FORBES BUMI ARMADA LIMITED—See Shapoorji Pallonji & Co. Ltd.; *Int'l*, pg. 6788
FORBES CHINA—See Forbes Media LLC; *U.S. Private*, pg. 1563
FORBES COAL (PTY) LTD.—See Buffalo Coal Corp.; *Int'l*, pg. 1211
FORBES.COM LLC—See Forbes Media LLC; *U.S. Private*, pg. 1563
FORBES & COMPANY LTD.—See Shapoorji Pallonji & Co. Ltd.; *Int'l*, pg. 6788
FORBES & DAVIES (NZ) LIMITED—See MotorCycle Holdings Limited; *Int'l*, pg. 5054
FORBES ENERGY SERVICES LTD.; *U.S. Public*, pg. 864
FORBES HAMILTON MANAGEMENT COMPANY; *U.S. Private*, pg. 1562
FORBES-HEWLETT TRANSPORT INC.; *Int'l*, pg. 2729
FORBES INDIA—See Forbes Media LLC; *U.S. Private*, pg. 1563
FORBES INDUSTRIES ASIA PTE. LTD.—See Winsford II Corporation; *U.S. Private*, pg. 4543
FORBES INDUSTRIES, INC.—See Winsford II Corporation; *U.S. Private*, pg. 4543
FORBES INVESTORS ADVISORY INSTITUTE INC.—See Forbes Media LLC; *U.S. Private*, pg. 1563
FORBES ISRAEL—See Forbes Media LLC; *U.S. Private*, pg. 1563
FORBES MAGAZINE—See Forbes Media LLC; *U.S. Private*, pg. 1563
FORBES MEDIA LLC; *U.S. Private*, pg. 1563
FORBES MOTORS INCORPORATED; *Int'l*, pg. 2729
FORBES ROMANIA—See Forbes Media LLC; *U.S. Private*, pg. 1563
FORBES RUSSIA—See Forbes Media LLC; *U.S. Private*, pg. 1563
FORBES TECHNOSYS LIMITED—See Shapoorji Pallonji & Co. Ltd.; *Int'l*, pg. 6788
FORBES TRAVEL INTERNATIONAL LTD.; *Int'l*, pg. 2729
FORBES UKRAINE—See Forbes Media LLC; *U.S. Private*, pg. 1563
FORBIDDEN FOODS LIMITED; *Int'l*, pg. 2729
FORBION CAPITAL PARTNERS GERMANY GMBH—See Forbion Capital Partners Management Holding BV; *Int'l*, pg. 2729
FORBION CAPITAL PARTNERS MANAGEMENT HOLDING BV; *Int'l*, pg. 2729
FORBION EUROPEAN ACQUISITION CORP.; *U.S. Public*, pg. 864
FORBION GROUP HOLDING B.V.—See Affiliated Managers Group, Inc.; *U.S. Public*, pg. 54
FORBO AMERICA INC.—See Forbo Holding Ltd.; *Int'l*, pg. 2729
FORBO CONTEL HANDELSGES. M.B.H.—See Forbo Holding Ltd.; *Int'l*, pg. 2729
FORBO ERFURT GMBH—See Forbo Holding Ltd.; *Int'l*, pg. 2729
FORBO EUROCOL BV—See Forbo Holding Ltd.; *Int'l*, pg. 2729
FORBO FINANZ AG—See Forbo Holding Ltd.; *Int'l*, pg. 2729
FORBO FLOORCOVERINGS PTY. LTD.—See Forbo Holding Ltd.; *Int'l*, pg. 2729
FORBO FLOORING B.V.—See Forbo Holding Ltd.; *Int'l*, pg. 2729
FORBO FLOORING GMBH—See Forbo Holding Ltd.; *Int'l*, pg. 2729
FORBO FLOORING, INC.—See Forbo Holding Ltd.; *Int'l*, pg. 2729
FORBO FLOORING—See Forbo Holding Ltd.; *Int'l*, pg. 2730
FORBO FLOORING UK LTD.—See Forbo Holding Ltd.; *Int'l*, pg. 2729
FORBO FLOORING UK LTD.—See Forbo Holding Ltd.; *Int'l*, pg. 2729
FORBO FLOORING UK LTD.—See Forbo Holding Ltd.; *Int'l*, pg. 2729
FORBO FLORING OY AB—See Forbo Holding Ltd.; *Int'l*, pg. 2729
FORBO GIUBIASCO SA—See Forbo Holding Ltd.; *Int'l*, pg. 2729
FORBO HOLDING LTD.; *Int'l*, pg. 2729
FORBO INTERNATIONAL HONG KONG LTD.—See Forbo Holding Ltd.; *Int'l*, pg. 2729
FORBO INTERNATIONAL SA—See Forbo Holding Ltd.; *Int'l*, pg. 2729
FORBO IRELAND LTD.—See Forbo Holding Ltd.; *Int'l*, pg. 2729
FORBO LINOLEUM A/S—See Forbo Holding Ltd.; *Int'l*, pg. 2729
FORBO LINOLEUM A/S—See Forbo Holding Ltd.; *Int'l*, pg. 2729
FORBO LINOLEUM, INC.—See Forbo Holding Ltd.; *Int'l*, pg. 2729
FORBO LINOLEUM—See Forbo Holding Ltd.; *Int'l*, pg. 2729
FORBO LINOLIUM B.V.—See Forbo Holding Ltd.; *Int'l*, pg. 2730
FORBO MANAGEMENT SA—See Forbo Holding Ltd.; *Int'l*, pg. 2730
FORBO-NAIRN LTD.—See Forbo Holding Ltd.; *Int'l*, pg. 2730
FORBO-NOVILON B.V.—See Forbo Holding Ltd.; *Int'l*, pg. 2730
FORBO PADLOBURKOLATOK KFT.—See Forbo Holding Ltd.; *Int'l*, pg. 2730
FORBO PARQUET AB—See Forbo Holding Ltd.; *Int'l*, pg. 2730
FORBO PAVIMENTOS SA—See Forbo Holding Ltd.; *Int'l*, pg. 2730
FORBO RESILIENTI S.R.L.—See Forbo Holding Ltd.; *Int'l*, pg. 2730
FORBO SARLINO SA—See Forbo Holding Ltd.; *Int'l*, pg. 2730
FORBO SIEGLING AUSTRIA GMBH—See Forbo Holding Ltd.; *Int'l*, pg. 2730
FORBO SIEGLING CANADA CORP.—See Forbo Holding Ltd.; *Int'l*, pg. 2730
FORBO SIEGLING FRANCE S.A.S.—See Forbo Holding Ltd.; *Int'l*, pg. 2730
FORBO SIEGLING GMBH—See Forbo Holding Ltd.; *Int'l*, pg. 2730
FORBO SIEGLING IBERICA S.A.—See Forbo Holding Ltd.; *Int'l*, pg. 2730
FORBO SIEGLING JAPAN LIMITED—See Forbo Holding Ltd.; *Int'l*, pg. 2730
FORBO SIEGLING LLC—See Forbo Holding Ltd.; *Int'l*, pg. 2729
FORBO SIEGLING (SHENYANG) BELTING CO. LTD—See Forbo Holding Ltd.; *Int'l*, pg. 2730
FORBO SIEGLING (SHENYANG)—See Forbo Holding Ltd.; *Int'l*, pg. 2730
FORBO SIEGLING SVENSKA AB—See Forbo Holding Ltd.; *Int'l*, pg. 2730
FORBO SIEGLING (THAILAND) CO. LTD.—See Forbo Holding Ltd.; *Int'l*, pg. 2730
FORBO S.R.O.—See Forbo Holding Ltd.; *Int'l*, pg. 2730
FORBO TAPIJT B.V.—See Forbo Holding Ltd.; *Int'l*, pg. 2730
FORBO UK LTD.—See Forbo Holding Ltd.; *Int'l*, pg. 2730
FORBRUGER-KONTAKT A/S—See North Media A/S; *Int'l*, pg. 5440
FORCAS, INC.—See Uzabase, Inc.; *Int'l*, pg. 8103
FORCE 10 MANUFACTURING CORPORATION—See ENO S.A.S.; *Int'l*, pg. 2444
FORCE 3, INC.—See CDW Corporation; *U.S. Public*, pg. 462
FORCE AMERICA INC.; *U.S. Private*, pg. 1563
FORCE BY DESIGN, INC.; *U.S. Private*, pg. 1563
FORCE COMMODITIES LIMITED; *Int'l*, pg. 2730
FORCE COMMUNICATIONS, LLC—See Keystone Group, L.P.; *U.S. Private*, pg. 2299
FORCECON TECH. CO., LTD.; *Int'l*, pg. 2730
FORCE CONTROL INDUSTRIES, INC.; *U.S. Private*, pg. 1563
FORCE EQUIPMENT PTY LTD—See Emeco Holdings Limited; *Int'l*, pg. 2376
FORCEFIELD ENERGY INC.; *U.S. Private*, pg. 1563
FORCE FUEL PROPRIETARY LIMITED—See Labat Africa Ltd; *Int'l*, pg. 4389
FORCELEAD TECHNOLOGY CORP.—See Sitronix Technology Corporation; *Int'l*, pg. 6965
FORCE LEGAL PTY. LTD.—See Credit Clear Limited; *Int'l*, pg. 1835
FORCE MANAGEMENT, LLC—See GrowthPlay LLC; *U.S. Private*, pg. 1796
FORCE MARKETING LLC; *U.S. Private*, pg. 1563
FORCE MINERALS CORP.; *U.S. Private*, pg. 1563
FORCE MOS TECHNOLOGY CO., LTD.; *Int'l*, pg. 2730
FORCE MOTORS LIMITED; *Int'l*, pg. 2730
FORCEPOINT DEUTSCHLAND GMBH—See Francisco Partners Management, LP; *U.S. Private*, pg. 1590
FORCEPOINT FRANCE—See Francisco Partners Management, LP; *U.S. Private*, pg. 1590
FORCEPOINT INTERNATIONAL LIMITED—See Francisco Partners Management, LP; *U.S. Private*, pg. 1590
FORCEPOINT INTERNATIONAL TECHNOLOGY LIMITED—See Francisco Partners Management, LP; *U.S. Private*, pg. 1590
FORCEPOINT ITALY S.R.L.—See Francisco Partners Management, LP; *U.S. Private*, pg. 1590
FORCEPOINT JAPAN KK—See Francisco Partners Management, LP; *U.S. Private*, pg. 1590
FORCEPOINT LLC—See Francisco Partners Management, LP; *U.S. Private*, pg. 1589
FORCEPOINT S.C. PTY LTD—See Francisco Partners Management, LP; *U.S. Private*, pg. 1590
FORCEPOINT UK LIMITED—See Francisco Partners Management, LP; *U.S. Private*, pg. 1590
FORCE PROTECTION, INC.—See General Dynamics Corporation; *U.S. Public*, pg. 914
FORCE PROTECTION VIDEO EQUIPMENT CORP.; *U.S. Public*, pg. 864
FORCERA MATERIALS CO., LTD.—See Solar Applied Materials Technology Corporation; *Int'l*, pg. 7069
FORCE REALTY; *U.S. Private*, pg. 1563
FORCE SECURITY SOLUTIONS, LLC—See Konica Minolta, Inc.; *Int'l*, pg. 4258
FORCEWORKS LLC; *U.S. Private*, pg. 1563
FORCEX INC.—See L3Harris Technologies, Inc.; *U.S. Public*, pg. 1281
FORCHEMEX LTD.—See Roche Ltd., Consulting Group; *Int'l*, pg. 6376
FORCHEM SP. Z O.O.—See BRENNTAG SE; *Int'l*, pg. 1149
FORCHT BANCORP, INC.—See Forcht Group of Kentucky, Inc.; *U.S. Private*, pg. 1563
FORCHT BANK, N.A.—See Forcht Group of Kentucky, Inc.; *U.S. Private*, pg. 1564
FORCHT BROADCASTING, INC.—See Forcht Group of Kentucky, Inc.; *U.S. Private*, pg. 1564
FORCHT GROUP OF KENTUCKY, INC.; *U.S. Private*, pg. 1563
FORCIT SWEDEN AB—See Oy Forcit AB; *Int'l*, pg. 5677
FORCIVITY, INC.—See Quad-C Management, Inc.; *U.S. Private*, pg. 3315
FORCLUM ALSACE FRANCHE COMTE SAS—See Eiffage S.A.; *Int'l*, pg. 2330
FORCLUMECA ANTILLES GUYANE—See Eiffage S.A.; *Int'l*, pg. 2331
FORCLUM RESEAUX NORD S.A.S—See Eiffage S.A.; *Int'l*, pg. 2330
FORCLUM RHONE ALPES S.A.S—See Eiffage S.A.; *Int'l*, pg. 2330
FORCS CO., LTD.; *Int'l*, pg. 2730
FORD ALBERIC AUTO SALES; *U.S. Private*, pg. 1564
FORD AUDIO-VIDEO SYSTEMS INC.; *U.S. Private*, pg. 1564
FORD AUTO BODY, INC.; *U.S. Private*, pg. 1564
FORD AUTOMOTIVE FINANCE (CHINA) LIMITED—See Ford Motor Company; *U.S. Public*, pg. 865
FORD, BACON AND DAVIS, LLC—See S&B Engineers & Constructors, Ltd.; *U.S. Private*, pg. 3512
FORD BANK GMBH—See Ford Motor Company; *U.S. Public*, pg. 864
FORD BUSINESS MACHINES, INC.; *U.S. Private*, pg. 1564
FORD BUSINESS MACHINES—See Ford Business Machines, Inc.; *U.S. Private*, pg. 1564
FORD CAPITAL B.V.—See Ford Motor Company; *U.S. Public*, pg. 864
FORD COMMUNICATIONS, INC.—See Ford Motor Company; *U.S. Public*, pg. 864
FORD COMPONENT SALES, L.L.C.—See Ford Motor Company; *U.S. Public*, pg. 865
FORD CONSTRUCTION COMPANY INC.; *U.S. Private*, pg. 1564
FORD CONSTRUCTION COMPANY; *U.S. Private*, pg. 1564
FORD COUNTY FEED YARD INC.—See Ford Holding Company Inc.; *U.S. Private*, pg. 1564
FORD CREDIT A/S—See Ford Motor Company; *U.S. Public*, pg. 865
FORD CREDIT AUTO RECEIVABLES CORPORATION—See Ford Motor Company; *U.S. Public*, pg. 865
FORD CREDIT B.V.—See Ford Motor Company; *U.S. Public*, pg. 865
FORD CREDIT CANADA COMPANY—See Ford Motor Company; *U.S. Public*, pg. 866
FORD CREDIT CP AUTO RECEIVABLES LLC—See Ford Motor Company; *U.S. Public*, pg. 866
FORD CREDIT DE MEXICO S.A. DE C.V.—See Ford Motor Company; *U.S. Public*, pg. 866
FORD CREDIT INTERNATIONAL, INC.—See Ford Motor Company; *U.S. Public*, pg. 866
FORD CREDIT ITALIA SPA—See Ford Motor Company; *U.S. Public*, pg. 866
FORD CREDIT PORTUGAL—See Ford Motor Company; *U.S. Public*, pg. 866
FORD CREDIT S.A.—See Ford Motor Company; *U.S. Public*, pg. 866
FORD CREDIT SPA—See Ford Motor Company; *U.S. Public*, pg. 866
FORD DEUTSCHLAND HOLDING GMBH—See Ford Motor Company; *U.S. Public*, pg. 865
FORD DEVELOPMENT CORPORATION; *U.S. Private*, pg. 1564
FORDE JOHNSON OIL COMPANY; *U.S. Private*, pg. 1565
FORDE REEDEREI SEETOURISTIK IBERIA S.L.U.—See FRS GmbH & Co. KG; *Int'l*, pg. 2797
FORD ESPANA SA—See Ford Motor Company; *U.S. Public*, pg. 865

COMPANY NAME INDEX

FORD ESSEX ENGINE PLANT—See Ford Motor Company; *U.S. Public*, pg. 865
FORD FINANCIAL FUND II, L.P.; *U.S. Private*, pg. 1564
FORD FINANCIAL SERVICES, INC.; *U.S. Private*, pg. 1564
FORD FRANCE—See Ford Motor Company; *U.S. Public*, pg. 865
FORD-GELATT & ASSOCIATES, INC.; *U.S. Private*, pg. 1565
FORD GLORY (CAMBODIA) MANUFACTURING LTD.—See Ford Glory International Limited; *Int'l*, pg. 2731
FORD GLORY INTERNATIONAL LIMITED; *Int'l*, pg. 2731
FORD GROVES; *U.S. Private*, pg. 1564
FORD GUM & MACHINE COMPANY, INC.; *U.S. Private*, pg. 1564
FORDHAM AUTO SALES INC.; *U.S. Private*, pg. 1565
FORDHAM BUSINESS ADVISORS PTY. LTD.—See Perpetual Limited; *Int'l*, pg. 5812
FORDHAM & DOMINION BREWING CO.; *U.S. Private*, pg. 1565
FORD HOLDING COMPANY INC.; *U.S. Private*, pg. 1564
FORDIA GROUP INC.—See Epiroc AB; *Int'l*, pg. 2462
FORDIE ESTATES LIMITED—See Averon Park Limited; *Int'l*, pg. 739
FORD INDIA PRIVATE LIMITED—See Ford Motor Company; *U.S. Public*, pg. 865
FORD INTERNATIONAL CAPITAL CORPORATION—See Ford Motor Company; *U.S. Public*, pg. 865
FORD INVESTMENT PARTNERSHIP—See Ford Motor Company; *U.S. Public*, pg. 865
FORD ITALIA S.P.A.—See Ford Motor Company; *U.S. Public*, pg. 865
FORD LAND—See Ford Motor Company; *U.S. Public*, pg. 865
FORD LEASING SPA—See Ford Motor Company; *U.S. Public*, pg. 866
FORD LINCOLN OF BELLEVUE—See AutoNation, Inc.; *U.S. Public*, pg. 235
FORD LINCOLN OF FRANKLIN—See Alexander Automotive Group; *U.S. Private*, pg. 163
FORD LIO HO MOTOR CO., LTD.—See Ford Motor Company; *U.S. Public*, pg. 865
FORD LUSITANA—See Ford Motor Company; *U.S. Public*, pg. 865
THE FORD METER BOX COMPANY, INC.; *U.S. Private*, pg. 4029
FORD MODELS INC.; *U.S. Private*, pg. 1564
FORD MOTOR AUSTRIA—See Ford Motor Company; *U.S. Public*, pg. 865
FORD MOTOR BELGIUM N.V.—See Ford Motor Company; *U.S. Public*, pg. 865
FORD MOTOR CO. - LINCOLN DIVISION—See Ford Motor Company; *U.S. Public*, pg. 865
FORD MOTOR COMPANY AB—See Ford Motor Company; *U.S. Public*, pg. 865
FORD MOTOR COMPANY A/S—See Ford Motor Company; *U.S. Public*, pg. 865
FORD MOTOR COMPANY (AUSTRIA) GMBH—See Ford Motor Company; *U.S. Public*, pg. 865
FORD MOTOR COMPANY BRASIL LTDA.—See Ford Motor Company; *U.S. Public*, pg. 865
FORD MOTOR COMPANY LIMITED—See Ford Motor Company; *U.S. Public*, pg. 865
FORD MOTOR COMPANY OF AUSTRALIA LIMITED—See Ford Motor Company; *U.S. Public*, pg. 865
FORD MOTOR COMPANY OF CANADA, LIMITED—See Ford Motor Company; *U.S. Public*, pg. 865
FORD MOTOR COMPANY OF NEW ZEALAND LTD.—See Ford Motor Company; *U.S. Public*, pg. 865
FORD MOTOR COMPANY OF SOUTHERN AFRICA (PTY) LIMITED—See Ford Motor Company; *U.S. Public*, pg. 865
FORD MOTOR COMPANY; *U.S. Public*, pg. 864
FORD MOTOR COMPANY SWITZERLAND S.A.—See Ford Motor Company; *U.S. Public*, pg. 865
FORD MOTOR CREDIT COMPANY LLC—See Ford Motor Company; *U.S. Public*, pg. 865
FORD MOTOR JAPAN LTD.—See Ford Motor Company; *U.S. Public*, pg. 866
FORD MOTOR LAND DEVELOPMENT CORPORATION—See Ford Motor Company; *U.S. Public*, pg. 866
FORD MOTOR LAND SERVICES CORP.—See Ford Motor Company; *U.S. Public*, pg. 866
FORD MOTOR NORGE A/S—See Ford Motor Company; *U.S. Public*, pg. 865
FORD MOTOR SERVICE COMPANY—See Ford Motor Company; *U.S. Public*, pg. 866
FORD NEDERLAND B.V.—See Ford Motor Company; *U.S. Public*, pg. 866
FORD OF KIRKLAND, INC.—See AutoNation, Inc.; *U.S. Public*, pg. 235
FORD OF MONTEBELLO, INC.; *U.S. Private*, pg. 1564
FORD OF OCALA INC.; *U.S. Private*, pg. 1564
FORD OF TULSA LLC; *U.S. Private*, pg. 1565
FORD OTOMOTIV SANAYI A.S.—See Ford Motor Company; *U.S. Public*, pg. 866

FORD OTOMOTIV SANAYI A.S.—See Koc Holding A.S.; *Int'l*, pg. 4223
FORD PLASTIC & TRIM PRODUCTS INTERNATIONAL, INC.—See Ford Motor Company; *U.S. Public*, pg. 866
FORD RETAIL GROUP LIMITED—See Ford Motor Company; *U.S. Public*, pg. 866
FORD ROMANIA S.A.—See Ford Motor Company; *U.S. Public*, pg. 864
FORD SALES & SERVICE (THAILAND) CO., LTD.—See Ford Motor Company; *U.S. Public*, pg. 866
FORDS INC.; *U.S. Private*, pg. 1565
FORD & SLATER LEICESTER; *Int'l*, pg. 2731
FORD SMART MOBILITY LLC—See Ford Motor Company; *U.S. Public*, pg. 866
FORD'S PRODUCE CO., INC.; *U.S. Private*, pg. 1565
FORD STEEL CHILE INDUSTRIAL SA—See North Shore Supply Company Inc.; *U.S. Private*, pg. 2947
FORD STEEL COMPANY—See North Shore Supply Company Inc.; *U.S. Private*, pg. 2947
FORD TOOL STEELS, INC.—See Ryerson Holding Corporation; *U.S. Public*, pg. 1829
FORD TOWN OF ALBANY INC.; *U.S. Private*, pg. 1565
FORD VIETNAM LIMITED—See Ford Motor Company; *U.S. Public*, pg. 866
FORD-WERKE GMBH—See Ford Motor Company; *U.S. Public*, pg. 866
FORD WHOLESALE CO., INC. OF SAN BERNARDINO; *U.S. Private*, pg. 1565
FORD WHOLESALE CO., INC. OF SAN JOSE—See Beacon Roofing Supply, Inc.; *U.S. Private*, pg. 286
FORDYCE AND PRINCETON R.R. CO.—See Brookfield Infrastructure Partners L.P.; *Int'l*, pg. 1191
FORDYCE AND PRINCETON R.R. CO.—See GIC Pte. Ltd.; *Int'l*, pg. 2965
FORDYCE CONCRETE COMPANY, INC.—See CRH plc; *Int'l*, pg. 1843
FOREBRIGHT CAPITAL MANAGEMENT LTD.; *Int'l*, pg. 2731
FORECAST COMMUNICATIONS INC.—See Nippon Television Holdings Inc.; *Int'l*, pg. 5356
FORECASTER OF BOSTON INC.; *U.S. Private*, pg. 1565
FORECAST HORIZON INC.—See Antuit, Inc.; *U.S. Private*, pg. 289
FORECAST INTERNATIONAL INC.; *U.S. Private*, pg. 1565
FORECLOSURE VENTURE CAPITAL, INC.; *U.S. Private*, pg. 1565
FORECON OY—See Byggfakta Group Nordic HoldCo AB; *Int'l*, pg. 1234
FORECROSS CORPORATION; *U.S. Public*, pg. 867
FOREFLIGHT LLC—See The Boeing Company; *U.S. Public*, pg. 2041
FOREFRONT MEDICAL TECHNOLOGY (PTE) LTD—See Vicplas International Ltd; *Int'l*, pg. 8187
FOREFRONT (XIAMEN) MEDICAL DEVICES CO., LTD.—See Vicplas International Ltd; *Int'l*, pg. 8187
FORE GOLF SERVICES, LP; *U.S. Private*, pg. 1565
FOREGROUND SECURITY; *U.S. Private*, pg. 1565
THE FOREIGN CANDY COMPANY, INC.; *U.S. Private*, pg. 4029
FOREIGN CURRENCY DIRECT PLC; *Int'l*, pg. 2731
FOREIGNEXCHANGE TRANSLATIONS INC.—See Rheinische-Bergische Verlagsgesellschaft mbH; *Int'l*, pg. 6321
FOREIGN PARTS SPECIALISTS—See Auto-Wares, LLC; *U.S. Private*, pg. 398
FOREIGN TIRE SALES INC.; *U.S. Private*, pg. 1565
FOREIGN TRADE DEVELOPMENT & INVESTMENT CORPORATION; *Int'l*, pg. 2731
FOREIGN TRADE & ECONOMIC COOPERATION CO., LTD.—See Datong Coal Mine Group Co., Ltd.; *Int'l*, pg. 1982
FOREIGN TRADE FIRM KRAZ LLC—See AutoKrAZ Holding Co.; *Int'l*, pg. 727
FOREIGN TRADERS, INC.; *U.S. Private*, pg. 1565
FOREIGN TRADE STANDARDS - INTERTEK TESTING SERVICES HONG KONG LTD.—See Intertek Group plc; *Int'l*, pg. 3762
FORE!KIDS FOUNDATION; *U.S. Private*, pg. 1565
FORELAND FABRICTECH HOLDINGS LIMITED; *Int'l*, pg. 2731
FOREL SONEPAR S.P.A.—See Sonepar S.A.; *Int'l*, pg. 7092
FORE MACHINE COMPANY, INC.—See P4G Capital Management, LLC; *U.S. Private*, pg. 3062
FOREMAN CAPITAL B.V.; *Int'l*, pg. 2731
FOREMANS INC.; *U.S. Private*, pg. 1565
FOREMOST BLUE SEAL, LTD.—See Sapporo Holdings Limited; *Int'l*, pg. 6573
FOREMOST BUSINESS SYSTEMS, INC.—See NCR Voyix Corporation.; *U.S. Public*, pg. 1502
FOREMOST CLEAN ENERGY LTD.; *Int'l*, pg. 2731
FOREMOSTCO INC.; *U.S. Private*, pg. 1566
FOREMOST FARMS USA COOPERATIVE; *U.S. Private*, pg. 1565
FOREMOST GROUPS, INC.—See Foremost Groups, Inc.; *U.S. Private*, pg. 1565
FOREMOST GROUPS, INC.; *U.S. Private*, pg. 1565
FOREMOST INCOME FUND; *Int'l*, pg. 2731

FORESITE TECHNOLOGIES, INC

FOREMOST INDUSTRIES INC.; *U.S. Private*, pg. 1566
FOREMOST INDUSTRIES LP—See Foremost Income Fund; *Int'l*, pg. 2731
FOREMOST INSURANCE COMPANY—See Zurich Insurance Group Limited; *Int'l*, pg. 8698
FOREMOST INTERNATIONAL LTD.—See Foremost Groups, Inc.; *U.S. Private*, pg. 1566
FOREMOST MARITIME PTE., LTD.—See PT Samudera Indonesia Tbk; *Int'l*, pg. 6069
FOREMOST PIPELINE CONSTRUCTION—See Sunland Construction Inc.; *U.S. Private*, pg. 3868
FOREMOST PROPERTY & CASUALTY INSURANCE COMPANY—See Zurich Insurance Group Limited; *Int'l*, pg. 8698
FOREMOST SIGNATURE INSURANCE COMPANY—See Zurich Insurance Group Limited; *Int'l*, pg. 8698
FOREMOST UNIVERSAL LP—See Foremost Income Fund; *Int'l*, pg. 2731
FORENADE LIV GRUPPFORSAKRING AB—See Folksam omsesidig sakforsakring; *Int'l*, pg. 2721
FORENINGEN AP PENSION F.M.B.A.; *Int'l*, pg. 2731
FORENINGS SPARBANKEN AB—See Swedbank AB; *Int'l*, pg. 7364
FORENINGSSPARBANKEN FASTIGHETSBYRA AB—See Swedbank AB; *Int'l*, pg. 7364
FORENINGSSPARBANKEN FINANS AB—See Swedbank AB; *Int'l*, pg. 7364
FORENINGSSPARBANKEN OLAND AB—See Swedbank AB; *Int'l*, pg. 7364
FORENSIC EXPERTS S.R.L.—See Gruppo MutuiOnline S.p.A; *Int'l*, pg. 3141
FORENSIC FLUIDS LABORATORIES, INC.; *U.S. Private*, pg. 1566
FORENSIC LOGIC INC.—See SoundThinking, Inc.; *U.S. Public*, pg. 1910
FORENSIC RESOLUTIONS, INC.—See Kelso & Company, L.P.; *U.S. Private*, pg. 2278
FORENSICS CONSULTING SOLUTIONS, LLC; *U.S. Private*, pg. 1566
FORENSIC TECHNOLOGY AEC THAILAND LIMITED—See Advent International Corporation; *U.S. Private*, pg. 100
FORENSIC TECHNOLOGY (EUROPE) LIMITED—See Advent International Corporation; *U.S. Private*, pg. 100
FORENTA L.P.; *U.S. Private*, pg. 1566
FORE-PAR GROUP INC.; *U.S. Private*, pg. 1565
FORE RIVER TRANSPORTATION CORPORATION—See FGV Holdings Bhd; *Int'l*, pg. 2649
FORESCOUT TECHNOLOGIES, INC.—See Advent International Corporation; *U.S. Private*, pg. 101
FORESCOUT TECHNOLOGIES ISRAEL LTD.—See Advent International Corporation; *U.S. Private*, pg. 101
FORESEE PHARMACEUTICALS CO., LTD.; *Int'l*, pg. 2731
FORESEE RESULTS, INC.—See Verint Systems Inc.; *U.S. Public*, pg. 2281
FORES ENGINEERING SRL—See Rosetti Marino S.p.A.; *Int'l*, pg. 6400
FORESHORE LIMITED—See Bahrain Telecommunications Company BSC; *Int'l*, pg. 801
FORESIDE FINANCIAL GROUP LLC—See Genstar Capital, LLC; *U.S. Private*, pg. 1677
FORESIGHT BIOTHERAPEUTICS, INC—See Takeda Pharmaceutical Company Limited; *Int'l*, pg. 7438
FORESIGHT ENERGY LP; *U.S. Public*, pg. 867
FORESIGHT ENERGY SERVICES LLC—See Foresight Energy LP; *U.S. Public*, pg. 867
FORESIGHT ENTERPRISE VCT PLC; *Int'l*, pg. 2731
FORESIGHT FINANCIAL GROUP INC.; *U.S. Public*, pg. 867
FORESIGHT GROUP CI LIMITED—See Foresight VCT Plc; *Int'l*, pg. 2732
FORESIGHT GROUP HOLDINGS LIMITED; *Int'l*, pg. 2731
FORESIGHT GROUP IBERIA SL—See Foresight VCT Plc; *Int'l*, pg. 2732
FORESIGHT GROUP LLP; *Int'l*, pg. 2732
FORESIGHT RESEARCH CO., LTD.—See Hakuhodo DY Holdings Incorporated; *Int'l*, pg. 3220
FORESIGHT SOFTWARE, LLC; *U.S. Private*, pg. 1566
FORESIGHT SOLAR FUND LIMITED; *Int'l*, pg. 2732
FORESIGHT SOLAR & TECHNOLOGY VCT PLC; *Int'l*, pg. 2732
FORESIGHT SUSTAINABLE FORESTRY COMPANY PLC—See Averon Park Limited; *Int'l*, pg. 739
FORESIGHT SYSTEM CO., LTD.—See Computer Engineering & Consulting Ltd.; *Int'l*, pg. 1759
FORESIGHT TECHNO CO., LTD—See MARUBUN CORPORATION; *Int'l*, pg. 4710
FORESIGHT VCT PLC; *Int'l*, pg. 2732
FORESITE CAPITAL MANAGEMENT, LLC; *U.S. Private*, pg. 1566
FORESITE GROUP, INC.; *U.S. Private*, pg. 1566
FORESITE LIFE SCIENCES CORP.; *U.S. Private*, pg. 1566
FORESITE TECHNOLOGIES, INC; *U.S. Private*, pg. 1566
FOREST2MARKET, INC.—See Battery Ventures, L.P.; *U.S. Private*, pg. 489
FORESTACIONES OPERATIVAS DE MEXICO, S.A. DE C.V.—See Grupo Kuo, S.A.B. de C.V.; *Int'l*, pg. 3131

999

FOREST AGRI SERVICES LTD.

FOREST AGRI SERVICES LTD.; *Int'l*, pg. 2732
FORESTAL ANCHILE LTDA.—See Daio Paper Corporation; *Int'l*, pg. 1940
FORESTAL BOSQUES DEL PLATA S.A.—See Empresas CMPC S.A.; *Int'l*, pg. 2390
FORESTAL CHOLGUAN S.A.; *Int'l*, pg. 2732
FORESTAL, CONSTRUCTORA Y COMERCIAL DEL PACIFICO SUR S.A.; *Int'l*, pg. 2732
FORESTAL MININCO S.A.—See Empresas CMPC S.A.; *Int'l*, pg. 2390
FORESTAL ORIENTAL S.A.—See UPM-Kymmene Corporation; *Int'l*, pg. 8090
FORESTAL TORNAGALEONES S.A.—See GrupoNueva S.A.; *Int'l*, pg. 3139
FORESTAL Y AGRICOLA MONTEAGUILA S.A.—See Empresas CMPC S.A.; *Int'l*, pg. 2390
FORESTAR GROUP INC.; *U.S. Public*, pg. 867
FORESTAR PETROLEUM CORPORATION—See Forestar Group Inc.; *U.S. Public*, pg. 867
FORESTAR (USA) REAL ESTATE GROUP INC. - ATLANTA—See Forestar Group Inc.; *U.S. Public*, pg. 867
FORESTAR (USA) REAL ESTATE GROUP INC. - LUFKIN—See Forestar Group Inc.; *U.S. Public*, pg. 867
FORESTAR (USA) REAL ESTATE GROUP INC.—See Forestar Group Inc.; *U.S. Public*, pg. 867
THE FOREST AT DUKE, INC.; *U.S. Private*, pg. 4029
FOREST AUSTELL PRODUCTS INC.; *U.S. Private*, pg. 1566
FOREST CAPITAL INC.—See KDDI Corporation; *Int'l*, pg. 4111
FOREST CITY BAYSIDE CORPORATION—See Brookfield Corporation; *Int'l*, pg. 1187
FOREST CITY CAPITAL CORPORATION—See Brookfield Corporation; *Int'l*, pg. 1187
FOREST CITY COMMERCIAL GROUP—See Brookfield Corporation; *Int'l*, pg. 1187
FOREST CITY COMMERCIAL MANAGEMENT, INC.—See Brookfield Corporation; *Int'l*, pg. 1187
FOREST CITY EQUITY SERVICES, INC.—See Brookfield Corporation; *Int'l*, pg. 1187
FOREST CITY MYRTLE ASSOCIATES, LLC—See Brookfield Corporation; *Int'l*, pg. 1187
FOREST CITY PHYSICAL THERAPY, LIMITED PARTNERSHIP—See U.S. Physical Therapy, Inc.; *U.S. Public*, pg. 2214
FOREST CITY RATNER COMPANIES, LLC—See Brookfield Corporation; *Int'l*, pg. 1187
FOREST CITY REALTY TRUST, INC.—See Brookfield Corporation; *Int'l*, pg. 1187
FOREST CITY RENTAL PROPERTIES CORPORATION—See Brookfield Corporation; *Int'l*, pg. 1187
FOREST CITY RESIDENTIAL DEVELOPMENT INC.—See Brookfield Corporation; *Int'l*, pg. 1187
FOREST CITY RESIDENTIAL GROUP, INC.—See Brookfield Corporation; *Int'l*, pg. 1187
FOREST CITY RESIDENTIAL GROUP, LLC—See Brookfield Corporation; *Int'l*, pg. 1187
FOREST CITY RESIDENTIAL MANAGEMENT, INC.—See Brookfield Corporation; *Int'l*, pg. 1187
FOREST CITY STAPLETON LAND, INC.—See Brookfield Corporation; *Int'l*, pg. 1187
FOREST CITY TECHNOLOGIES INC.; *U.S. Private*, pg. 1566
FOREST CITY TRADING GROUP, LLC; *U.S. Private*, pg. 1566
FOREST CITY WASHINGTON, INC.—See Brookfield Corporation; *Int'l*, pg. 1187
FOREST COACH LINES PTY. LIMITED—See ComfortDelGro Corporation Limited; *Int'l*, pg. 1713
FOREST CO., LTD.—See EDION Corporation; *Int'l*, pg. 2310
FOREST CONSTRUCTION COMPANY INC.—See Penn Line Corp.; *U.S. Private*, pg. 3134
FOREST CONSTRUCTION COMPANY; *U.S. Private*, pg. 1566
FOREST CORP.; *U.S. Private*, pg. 1567
FOREST CREEK GOLF CLUB—See OnCourse Strategies; *U.S. Private*, pg. 3019
FOREST CREEK WF HOLDCO, LLC—See E.ON SE; *Int'l*, pg. 2257
THE FOREST ELECTRIC COMPANY—See Yageo Corporation; *Int'l*, pg. 8545
FOREST ELECTRIC CORP.—See EMCOR Group, Inc.; *U.S. Public*, pg. 736
FOREST ENTERPRISES AUSTRALIA LIMITED; *Int'l*, pg. 2732
FORESTER HOLDINGS (EUROPE) LIMITED—See The Independent Order of Foresters; *Int'l*, pg. 7654
FORESTERS EQUITY SERVICES, INC.—See The Independent Order of Foresters; *Int'l*, pg. 7654
FORESTERS FINANCIAL HOLDING COMPANY, INC.—See Golden Gate Capital Management II, LLC; *U.S. Private*, pg. 1731
FORESTERS FINANCIAL SERVICES, INC.—See Golden Gate Capital Management II, LLC; *U.S. Private*, pg. 1731

FORESTERS INVESTMENT MANAGEMENT COMPANY, INC.—See Golden Gate Capital Management II, LLC; *U.S. Private*, pg. 1731
FORESTERS INVESTOR SERVICES, INC.—See Golden Gate Capital Management II, LLC; *U.S. Private*, pg. 1731
FORESTERS LIFE INSURANCE & ANNUITY COMPANY—See Golden Gate Capital Management II, LLC; *U.S. Private*, pg. 1731
FORESTERS LIFE INSURANCE COMPANY—See Golden Gate Capital Management II, LLC; *U.S. Private*, pg. 1731
FOREST FORD, INC.; *U.S. Private*, pg. 1567
FOREST GROVE MINI STORAGE, LLC—See National Storage Affiliates Trust; *U.S. Public*, pg. 1498
FOREST HAVEN, INC.—See Mid-Atlantic Health Care, LLC; *U.S. Private*, pg. 2707
FOREST HILLS ELECTRICAL SUPPLY, INC.—See Turtle & Hughes, Inc.; *U.S. Private*, pg. 4262
FORESTIA AS—See Byggma ASA; *Int'l*, pg. 1235
FORESTIERE EQUATORIALE SA; *Int'l*, pg. 2732
FORESTIER SA—See Corep Lighting group; *Int'l*, pg. 1799
FOREST INDUSTRIES, INC.—See Saunders Brothers; *U.S. Private*, pg. 3554
FOREST INVESTMENTS, INC.; *U.S. Private*, pg. 1567
FOREST LABORATORIES IRELAND LIMITED—See AbbVie Inc.; *U.S. Public*, pg. 23
FOREST LAKE CHRYSLER DODGE JEEP & RAM; *U.S. Private*, pg. 1567
FOREST LAWN GARDENS, INC.—See Axar Capital Management L.P.; *U.S. Private*, pg. 411
FOREST LAWN MEMORIAL CHAPEL, INC.—See Axar Capital Management L.P.; *U.S. Private*, pg. 411
FOREST LAWN MEMORY GARDENS, INC.—See Axar Capital Management L.P.; *U.S. Private*, pg. 411
FOREST MALL, LLC—See Washington Prime Group Inc.; *U.S. Private*, pg. 4448
FOREST MANAGEMENT SERVICES (NZ) LIMITED—See Greenheart Group Limited; *Int'l*, pg. 3075
FOREST OIL CORP. - LOUISIANA OFFICE—See Osaka Gas Co., Ltd.; *Int'l*, pg. 5646
FOREST ONE CO., LTD.—See WOOD ONE Co., Ltd.; *Int'l*, pg. 8449
FORESTON TRENDS, INC.; *U.S. Private*, pg. 1567
FOREST PACKAGING GROUP CO., LTD.; *Int'l*, pg. 2732
FOREST PARK FOREVER; *U.S. Private*, pg. 1567
FOREST PLACE MANAGEMENT LIMITED—See Brookfield Corporation; *Int'l*, pg. 1186
FOREST PLYWOOD SALES INC.; *U.S. Private*, pg. 1567
FOREST PRODUCTS DISTRIBUTORS, INC.; *U.S. Private*, pg. 1567
FOREST PRODUCTS TERMINAL CORPORATION LTD. (FORTERM)—See Blue Wolf Capital Partners LLC; *U.S. Private*, pg. 594
FOREST REALTY MANAGEMENT INC.; *U.S. Private*, pg. 1567
FOREST RIVER BUS, LLC—See Berkshire Hathaway Inc.; *U.S. Public*, pg. 305
FOREST RIVER, INC.—See Berkshire Hathaway Inc.; *U.S. Public*, pg. 305
FOREST RIVER INC.—See Berkshire Hathaway Inc.; *U.S. Public*, pg. 305
FOREST ROAD SECURITIES, LLC; *U.S. Private*, pg. 1567
FORESTRY RESOURCES, INC.; *U.S. Private*, pg. 1567
FOREST SALES CORPORATION; *U.S. Private*, pg. 1567
FOREST S.P.A.—See Campostano Group S.p.A.; *Int'l*, pg. 1275
FOREST SUPPORT SERVICES PLC; *Int'l*, pg. 2732
FOREST TOSARA LTD.—See AbbVie Inc.; *U.S. Public*, pg. 23
FOREST TRAFFIC SERVICES LIMITED—See Forest Support Services Plc; *Int'l*, pg. 2732
FOREST VIEW (CALVERTON) MANAGEMENT COMPANY LIMITED—See Persimmon plc; *Int'l*, pg. 5815
FORESTVIEW NURSING, L.L.C.—See Apollo Global Management, Inc.; *U.S. Public*, pg. 156
FOREST VIEW PSYCHIATRIC HOSPITAL—See Universal Health Services, Inc.; *U.S. Public*, pg. 2260
FOREST WATER ENVIRONMENTAL ENGINEERING CO., LTD.; *Int'l*, pg. 2732
FORE SUPPLY CO.; *U.S. Private*, pg. 1565
FORETHOUGHT FINANCIAL GROUP, INC.—See KKR & Co. Inc.; *U.S. Public*, pg. 1251
FORETRAVEL INC.; *U.S. Private*, pg. 1567
FOREVA SOLUTION PTY. LTD.—See VINCI S.A.; *Int'l*, pg. 8221
FOREVER 21, INC.—See Brookfield Corporation; *Int'l*, pg. 1186
FOREVER 21, INC.—See Leonard Green & Partners, L.P.; *U.S. Private*, pg. 2424
FOREVER 21, INC.—See Simon Property Group, Inc.; *U.S. Public*, pg. 1881
FOREVER CHANGED INTERNATIONAL; *U.S. Private*, pg. 1567
FOREVER ENTERTAINMENT S.A.; *Int'l*, pg. 2732
FOREVERGREEN INTERNATIONAL, LLC—See ForeverGreen Worldwide Corporation; *U.S. Public*, pg. 867

FOREVERGREEN INTERNATIONAL TAIWAN LTD—See ForeverGreen Worldwide Corporation; *U.S. Public*, pg. 867
FOREVERGREEN KOREA—See ForeverGreen Worldwide Corporation; *U.S. Public*, pg. 867
FOREVERGREEN SINGAPORE—See ForeverGreen Worldwide Corporation; *U.S. Public*, pg. 867
FOREVERGREEN WORLDWIDE CORPORATION; *U.S. Public*, pg. 867
FOREVER HAMEENLINNA OY—See Pihlajalinna Oy; *Int'l*, pg. 5865
FOREVER HERTTONIEMI OY—See Pihlajalinna Oy; *Int'l*, pg. 5865
FOREVER HIEKKAHARJU OY—See Pihlajalinna Oy; *Int'l*, pg. 5865
FOREVER JARVENPAA OY—See Pihlajalinna Oy; *Int'l*, pg. 5865
FOREVER LAHTI OY—See Pihlajalinna Oy; *Int'l*, pg. 5865
FOREVERLIVING.COM LLC—See Forever Living Products International, Inc.; *U.S. Private*, pg. 1567
FOREVER LIVING PRODUCTS INTERNATIONAL, INC.; *U.S. Private*, pg. 1567
FOREVER MATINKYLA OY—See Pihlajalinna Oy; *Int'l*, pg. 5865
FOREVER MEDIA, INC. - FRANKLIN—See Forever Media, Inc.; *U.S. Private*, pg. 1567
FOREVER MEDIA, INC.; *U.S. Private*, pg. 1567
FOREVER RESORTS, LLC; *U.S. Private*, pg. 1567
FOREVER VARISTO OY—See Pihlajalinna Oy; *Int'l*, pg. 5865
FOREWAY TRANSPORTATION INC.—See En-Way Enterprises Inc.; *U.S. Private*, pg. 1389
FOREX CAPITAL MARKETS LIMITED—See Global Brokerage, Inc.; *U.S. Public*, pg. 940
FOREX CAPITAL MARKETS LLC—See Global Brokerage, Inc.; *U.S. Public*, pg. 940
FOREX TRADING LLC—See Global Brokerage, Inc.; *U.S. Public*, pg. 940
FOREZ BENNES; *Int'l*, pg. 2732
FOREZ PISCINES SA—See Piscines Desjoyaux SA; *Int'l*, pg. 5876
FORFARMERS BEELITZ GMBH—See ForFarmers Group B.V; *Int'l*, pg. 2732
FORFARMERS BELGIUM B.V.B.A.—See ForFarmers Group B.V; *Int'l*, pg. 2732
FORFARMERS BM GMBH—See ForFarmers Group B.V; *Int'l*, pg. 2732
FORFARMERS DML B.V.—See ForFarmers Group B.V; *Int'l*, pg. 2732
FORFARMERS GROUP B.V; *Int'l*, pg. 2732
FORFARMERS HAMBURG GMBH & CO. KG—See ForFarmers Group B.V; *Int'l*, pg. 2732
FORFARMERS HENDRIX B.V.—See ForFarmers Group B.V; *Int'l*, pg. 2732
FORFARMERS LANGFORDEN GMBH—See ForFarmers Group B.V; *Int'l*, pg. 2732
FORFARMERS THESING MISCHFUTTER GMBH & CO. KG—See ForFarmers Group B.V; *Int'l*, pg. 2732
FORFARMERS UK LTD.—See ForFarmers Group B.V; *Int'l*, pg. 2732
FORFEITURE SUPPORT ASSOCIATES LLC—See L3Harris Technologies, Inc.; *U.S. Public*, pg. 1281
FORGAME HOLDINGS LIMITED; *Int'l*, pg. 2733
FORGE3, LIMITED—See FMG Suite, LLC; *U.S. Private*, pg. 1554
FORGE CAPITAL PARTNERS LLC; *U.S. Private*, pg. 1567
FORGE COMPANY INC.; *U.S. Private*, pg. 1567
FORGED COMPONENTS, INC.—See L.E. Simmons & Associates, Inc.; *U.S. Private*, pg. 2365
FORGED PRODUCTS, INC.—See Reserve Group Management Company; *U.S. Private*, pg. 3404
FORGED SOLUTIONS GROUP, LTD—See Arlington Capital Partners LLC; *U.S. Private*, pg. 327
FORGE ENGINEERING, INC.—See Cobepa S.A.; *Int'l*, pg. 1683
FORGE GLOBAL HOLDINGS, INC.; *U.S. Public*, pg. 867
FORGE GLOBAL, INC.—See Forge Global Holdings, Inc.; *U.S. Public*, pg. 867
FORGE INDUSTRIES, INC.; *U.S. Private*, pg. 1568
FORGE INNOVATION DEVELOPMENT CORP.; *U.S. Public*, pg. 867
FORGELIGHT, LLC; *U.S. Private*, pg. 1568
FORGE MARKETING COMMUNICATIONS; *U.S. Private*, pg. 1568
FORGE MEDIA GROUP LIMITED; *Int'l*, pg. 2733
FORGEN, LLC; *U.S. Private*, pg. 1568
FORGEPRO INDIA PRIVATE LIMITED—See Daifuku Co., Ltd.; *Int'l*, pg. 1926
FORGEROCK, INC.—See Thoma Bravo, L.P.; *U.S. Private*, pg. 4148
FORGES DE NIAUX; *Int'l*, pg. 2733
FORGES DE ZEEBRUGGE—See Thales S.A.; *Int'l*, pg. 7601
FORGE SERVICES, INC.—See Forge Global Holdings, Inc.; *U.S. Public*, pg. 867
FORGE SPONSORSHIP CONSULTING, LLC; *U.S. Private*, pg. 1568
FORGE STAFFING INC.; *U.S. Private*, pg. 1568

COMPANY NAME INDEX

FORGES TARDIEU LTD; *Int'l*, pg. 2733
FORGES THERMAL S.A.—See Groupe Partouche S.A.; *Int'l*, pg. 3109
FORGE WORLDWIDE; *U.S. Private*, pg. 1568
FORGING EQUIPMENT SUB-CO.—See Taiyuan Heavy Industry Co., Ltd.; *Int'l*, pg. 7427
FORGINGS FLANGES & FITTINGS, LLC—See Sumitomo Corporation; *Int'l*, pg. 7273
FORGING SUB-CO.—See Taiyuan Heavy Industry Co., Ltd.; *Int'l*, pg. 7427
FORGIVEN BOTTLING GROUP, INC.; *U.S. Private*, pg. 1568
FORGO FASTENERS—See Valley Fastener Group LLC; *U.S. Private*, pg. 4333
FORGOTTEN HARVEST, INC.; *U.S. Private*, pg. 1568
FOR HEALTH OF ARIZONA, INC.—See UnitedHealth Group Incorporated; *U.S. Public*, pg. 2240
FORHOUSE CORPORATION - DA-YA FACTORY—See Darwin Precisions Corporation; *Int'l*, pg. 1973
FORHOUSE CORPORATION - MALAYSIAN FACTORY—See Darwin Precisions Corporation; *Int'l*, pg. 1973
FORHOUSE CORPORATION - XIAMEN FACTORY—See Darwin Precisions Corporation; *Int'l*, pg. 1973
FORIA INTERNATIONAL INC.; *U.S. Private*, pg. 1569
FORIAN INC.; *U.S. Public*, pg. 868
FORI AUTOMATION LLC—See Lincoln Electric Holdings, Inc.; *U.S. Public*, pg. 1317
FORIND AVIO ELETTRONICA S.P.A.; *Int'l*, pg. 2733
FORINO CO., L.P.; *U.S. Private*, pg. 1569
FORINO DEVELOPERS COMPANY; *U.S. Private*, pg. 1569
FORIS AG; *Int'l*, pg. 2733
FORIS CORPORATION—See Haseko Corporation; *Int'l*, pg. 3283
FORISE INTERNATIONAL LTD.; *Int'l*, pg. 2733
FORISH CONSTRUCTION COMPANY, INC.; *U.S. Private*, pg. 1569
FOR IT INC.—See FreeBit Co., Ltd.; *Int'l*, pg. 2769
FORJAS DE CELAYA, S.A. DE C.V.—See Cie Automotive S.A.; *Int'l*, pg. 1604
FORKARDT DEUTSCHLAND GMBH—See Privet Fund Management, LLC; *U.S. Private*, pg. 3269
FORKARDT FRANCE SAS—See Privet Fund Management, LLC; *U.S. Private*, pg. 3269
FORKARDT INC.—See Privet Fund Management, LLC; *U.S. Private*, pg. 3269
FORKARDT INDIA LLP—See Privet Fund Management, LLC; *U.S. Private*, pg. 3269
FORK-CO USA SALES LLC; *U.S. Private*, pg. 1569
FORKLIFT OF CAPE GIRARDEAU—See Forklift of St. Louis Inc.; *U.S. Private*, pg. 1569
FORKLIFT OF ST. LOUIS INC.; *U.S. Private*, pg. 1569
FORKLIFTS OF CENTRAL MISSOURI—See Forklift of St. Louis Inc.; *U.S. Private*, pg. 1569
FORKLIFTS OF MINNESOTA, INC. - FORKLIFTS OF WISCONSIN DIVISION—See Forklifts of Minnesota, Inc.; *U.S. Private*, pg. 1569
FORKLIFTS OF MINNESOTA, INC.; *U.S. Private*, pg. 1569
FORKLIFTS OF NORTH DAKOTA, INC.—See Forklifts of Minnesota, Inc.; *U.S. Private*, pg. 1569
FORKLIFTS OF QUINCY, INC.—See Forklift of St. Louis Inc.; *U.S. Private*, pg. 1569
FORKLIFT SYSTEMS INC.; *U.S. Private*, pg. 1569
FORKLIFT TRAINING SYSTEMS, INC—See Fleet Team, Inc.; *U.S. Private*, pg. 1542
FORLAGET ANDERSEN A/S—See Karnov Group AB; *Int'l*, pg. 4084
FORLAGET STRILEN AS—See Schibsted ASA; *Int'l*, pg. 6617
FORLAGSHUSET VIGMOSTAD & BJORKE AS; *Int'l*, pg. 2733
FORLAND PETROCHEMICAL TECHNOLOGY LLC—See Qingdao Huicheng Environmental Technology Group Co., Ltd.; *Int'l*, pg. 6143
FORLIFE CO., LTD.; *Int'l*, pg. 2733
FOR LIFE PRODUCTS, LLC—See Spectrum Brands Holdings, Inc.; *U.S. Public*, pg. 1915
FORLINK SOFTWARE CORPORATION, INC.; *Int'l*, pg. 2733
FORM700 PTY. LTD.; *Int'l*, pg. 2733
FORMACH ASIA SDN. BHD.—See Grand Venture Technology Limited; *Int'l*, pg. 3057
FORMACION, SELECCION Y CONSULTORIA, S.A.—See Prosegur Compania de Seguridad S.A.; *Int'l*, pg. 5999
FORMADEMOS RABAT—See Demos S.A.; *Int'l*, pg. 2026
FORM-A-FEED, INC.; *U.S. Private*, pg. 1569
FORMAGGIO CHEESE; *U.S. Private*, pg. 1569
FORMAIRA S.R.L.—See Iren S.p.A.; *Int'l*, pg. 3808
FORMAN BUILDING SYSTEMS LIMITED—See Fletcher Building Limited; *Int'l*, pg. 2700
FORMAN BUILDING SYSTEMS PTY LIMITED—See Fletcher Building Limited; *Int'l*, pg. 2700
FORMAN EQUIPMENT, INC.—See Forman Inc.; *U.S. Private*, pg. 1569
FORMAN GROUP LIMITED—See Fletcher Building Limited; *Int'l*, pg. 2700
FORMAN INC.; *U.S. Private*, pg. 1569

FORMAN INSULATION LIMITED—See Fletcher Building Limited; *Int'l*, pg. 2700
FORMAN MANUFACTURING LIMITED—See Fletcher Building Limited; *Int'l*, pg. 2700
FORMAN MILLS, INC.—See Cohesive Capital Partners; *U.S. Private*, pg. 963
FORMAN MILLS, INC.—See Goode Partners, LLC; *U.S. Private*, pg. 1739
FORMAPAC SDN BHD—See Wipro Limited; *Int'l*, pg. 8432
FORMAPHARM ENGINEERING GROUP D.O.O.; *Int'l*, pg. 2733
FORMAPHARM ENGINEERING GROUP—See FormaPharm Engineering Group d.o.o.; *Int'l*, pg. 2733
FORMART LUXEMBURG S.A R.L.—See Instone Real Estate Group SE; *Int'l*, pg. 3724
FORMA THERAPEUTICS HOLDINGS, INC.—See Novo Nordisk Fonden; *Int'l*, pg. 5463
FORMATION8 PARTNERS LLC; *U.S. Private*, pg. 1571
FORMATION ARCHITECTURAL DESIGN LIMITED—See Formation Group PLC; *Int'l*, pg. 2733
FORMATION ASSET MANAGEMENT LIMITED—See Formation Group PLC; *Int'l*, pg. 2733
FORMATION BRANDS, LLC—See Pacific Market International, LLC; *U.S. Private*, pg. 3068
FORMATION CAPITAL CORPORATION, U.S.—See Sunshine Silver Mines Corporation; *U.S. Private*, pg. 3872
FORMATION CAPITAL, LLC; *U.S. Private*, pg. 1569
FORMATION DESIGN & BUILD LIMITED—See Formation Group PLC; *Int'l*, pg. 2733
FORMATION GROUP PLC; *Int'l*, pg. 2733
FORMATION MINERALS, INC.; *U.S. Public*, pg. 868
FORMATION SAARLOR FSL EURL—See TUV NORD AG; *Int'l*, pg. 7980
FORMATION SPORTS CAPITAL LIMITED—See Formation Group PLC; *Int'l*, pg. 2734
FORMATION WEALTH SOLUTIONS LIMITED—See Formation Group PLC; *Int'l*, pg. 2734
FORMATIV HEALTH—See Northwell Health, Inc.; *U.S. Private*, pg. 2958
FORMATIV HEALTH—See Pamplona Capital Management LLP; *Int'l*, pg. 5711
FORMATURA INEZIONE POLIMERI SPA—See Aliaxis S.A./N.V.; *Int'l*, pg. 324
FORMAT WERK GMBH & CO. KG; *Int'l*, pg. 2733
FORMAX, INC.—See Henry Crown & Company; *U.S. Private*, pg. 1917
FORM BIO CO., LTD.; *Int'l*, pg. 2733
FORMCAP CORP.; *U.S. Public*, pg. 868
FORMECA OY—See Amitec Oy; *Int'l*, pg. 428
FORMED FIBER TECHNOLOGIES, INC.—See MPE Partners, LLC; *U.S. Private*, pg. 2803
FORMEL D GMBH—See 3i Group plc; *Int'l*, pg. 8
FORMENERG S.A.—See CNTEE TRANSELECTRICA SA; *Int'l*, pg. 1678
FORMETAL; *Int'l*, pg. 2734
FORMET CELIK KAPI SANAYI VE TICARET AS; *Int'l*, pg. 2734
FORMETCO, INC.; *U.S. Private*, pg. 1571
FORMEX FINANCIAL PRESS LIMITED—See Universe Entertainment and Culture Group Company Limited; *Int'l*, pg. 8082
FORMEX INDUSTRIES (PROPRIETARY) LIMITED—See E Media Holdings Limited; *Int'l*, pg. 2246
FORMEX PRESSINGS (PROPRIETARY) LIMITED—See E Media Holdings Limited; *Int'l*, pg. 2246
FORMEX WATCH S.A.; *Int'l*, pg. 2734
FORMEX WATCH USA—See Formex Watch S.A.; *Int'l*, pg. 2734
FORMFACTOR BEAVERTON, INC.—See FormFactor, Inc.; *U.S. Public*, pg. 868
FORMFACTOR EUROPE GMBH—See FormFactor, Inc.; *U.S. Public*, pg. 868
FORMFACTOR GMBH—See FormFactor, Inc.; *U.S. Public*, pg. 868
FORMFACTOR, INC.; *U.S. Public*, pg. 868
FORMFACTOR K.K.—See FormFactor, Inc.; *U.S. Public*, pg. 868
FORMFACTOR KOREA, INC.—See FormFactor, Inc.; *U.S. Public*, pg. 868
FORMFIRE, LLC—See Resurgens Technology Partners, LLC; *U.S. Private*, pg. 3410
FORMFLEX METAL INDUSTRIAL (CHANGSHU) CO., LTD.—See Taiwan Fu Hsing Industrial Co., Ltd.; *Int'l*, pg. 7420
FORMGLAS JAPAN LTD.—See Formglas Products Ltd.; *Int'l*, pg. 2734
FORMGLAS PRODUCTS LTD.; *Int'l*, pg. 2734
FORM@HOME—See Kering S.A.; *Int'l*, pg. 4134
FORMICA ASIA LTD.—See HAL Trust N.V.; *Int'l*, pg. 3223
FORMICA CANADA, INC.—See HAL Trust N.V.; *Int'l*, pg. 3223
FORMICA CAPITAL AB—See Formica Capital Holding AB; *Int'l*, pg. 2734
FORMICA CAPITAL HOLDING AB; *Int'l*, pg. 2734
FORMICA CORPORATION—See HAL Trust N.V.; *Int'l*, pg. 3223
FORMICA DE MEXICO SA DE CV—See HAL Trust N.V.; *Int'l*, pg. 3223

FORMICA FINANCE LIMITED—See HAL Trust N.V.; *Int'l*, pg. 3223
FORMICA HOLDCO UK LIMITED—See HAL Trust N.V.; *Int'l*, pg. 3223
FORMICA IKI OY—See HAL Trust N.V.; *Int'l*, pg. 3223
FORMICA LTD.—See HAL Trust N.V.; *Int'l*, pg. 3223
FORMICA NETHERLAND B.V.—See HAL Trust N.V.; *Int'l*, pg. 3223
FORMICA NORGE A/S—See HAL Trust N.V.; *Int'l*, pg. 3223
FORMICA S.A.—See HAL Trust N.V.; *Int'l*, pg. 3223
FORMICA S.A.S—See HAL Trust N.V.; *Int'l*, pg. 3223
FORMICA (SINGAPORE) PTE. LTD—See HAL Trust N.V.; *Int'l*, pg. 3223
FORMICA SKANDINAVIEN AB—See HAL Trust N.V.; *Int'l*, pg. 3223
FORMICA SOCIETE ANONYME—See HAL Trust N.V.; *Int'l*, pg. 3223
FORMICA SWITZERLAND AG—See HAL Trust N.V.; *Int'l*, pg. 3223
FORMICA TAIWAN—See HAL Trust N.V.; *Int'l*, pg. 3223
FORMICA (THAILAND) CO., LTD. - PHRAPRADAENG FACTORY—See HAL Trust N.V.; *Int'l*, pg. 3223
FORMICA (THAILAND) CO.—See HAL Trust N.V.; *Int'l*, pg. 3223
FORMICA VERTRIEBS GMBH—See HAL Trust N.V.; *Int'l*, pg. 3223
FORMIC MEDIA, INC.; *U.S. Private*, pg. 1571
FORMIDO B.V.—See KKR & Co. Inc.; *U.S. Public*, pg. 1261
FORMIGONS GIRONA S.A.—See CRH plc; *Int'l*, pg. 1844
FORMING CONCEPTS, INC.—See Brand Industrial Services, Inc.; *U.S. Private*, pg. 636
FORMIS HOLDINGS BERHAD—See Omesti Berhad; *Int'l*, pg. 5562
FORMIS MEDIA TEKNOLOGI SDN. BHD.—See Omesti Berhad; *Int'l*, pg. 5562
FORMIS NETWORK SERVICES SDN. BHD.—See Omesti Berhad; *Int'l*, pg. 5562
FORMIS SYSTEMS & TECHNOLOGY SDN. BHD.—See Omesti Berhad; *Int'l*, pg. 5562
FORMITAS—See Omnicom Group Inc.; *U.S. Public*, pg. 1575
FORMO MOTORS; *Int'l*, pg. 2734
FORMOPLAST PLC; *Int'l*, pg. 2734
FORMOSA ADVANCED TECHNOLOGIES CO., LTD.; *Int'l*, pg. 2734
FORMOSA ASAHI SPANDEX CO., LTD.—See Asahi Kasei Corporation; *Int'l*, pg. 596
FORMOSA ASAHI SPANDEX CO., LTD.—See Formosa Plastics Corporation; *Int'l*, pg. 2735
FORMOSA CHEMICALS & FIBRE CORPORATION—See Formosa Petrochemical Corporation; *Int'l*, pg. 2735
FORMOSA DAIKIN ADVANCED CHEMICALS CO., LTD. - KAOHSIUNG REN-WU PLANT—See Formosa Plastics Corporation; *Int'l*, pg. 2735
FORMOSA DAIKIN ADVANCED CHEMICALS CO., LTD.—See Formosa Plastics Corporation; *Int'l*, pg. 2735
FORMOSA ELECTRONIC INDUSTRIES INC.; *Int'l*, pg. 2734
FORMOSA EPITAXY INCORPORATION—See Ennostar Inc.; *Int'l*, pg. 2443
FORMOSA HA TINH STEEL CORPORATION—See China Steel Corporation; *Int'l*, pg. 1555
FORMOSA HEAVY INDUSTRIES CORP. - JEN-WU PLANT—See Formosa Plastics Corporation; *Int'l*, pg. 2735
FORMOSA HEAVY INDUSTRIES CORP. - MAI-LIAO PLANT—See Formosa Plastics Corporation; *Int'l*, pg. 2735
FORMOSA HEAVY INDUSTRIES CORP.—See Formosa Plastics Corporation; *Int'l*, pg. 2735
FORMOSA HYDROCARBONS COMPANY, INC.—See Formosa Plastics Corporation; *Int'l*, pg. 2735
FORMOSA IDEMITSU PETROCHEMICAL CORPORATION—See Idemitsu Kosan Co., Ltd.; *Int'l*, pg. 3590
FORMOSA INTERNATIONAL HOTELS CORP.; *Int'l*, pg. 2734
FORMOSA LABORATORIES, INC.; *Int'l*, pg. 2735
FORMOSAN RUBBER GROUP INC.; *Int'l*, pg. 2736
FORMOSAN RUBBER GROUP INC. - TAOYUAN PLANT—See Formosan Rubber Group Inc.; *Int'l*, pg. 2736
FORMOSAN UNION CHEMICAL CORP.; *Int'l*, pg. 2736
FORMOSA OIL (ASIA PACIFIC) CORPORATION—See Formosa Petrochemical Corporation; *Int'l*, pg. 2735
FORMOSA OILSEED PROCESSING CO., LTD.; *Int'l*, pg. 2735
FORMOSA OPTICAL TECHNOLOGY CO., LTD.; *Int'l*, pg. 2735
FORMOSA PETROCHEMICAL CORPORATION; *Int'l*, pg. 2735
FORMOSA PETROCHEMICAL TRANSPORTATION CORPORATION—See Formosa Plastics Corporation; *Int'l*, pg. 2735
FORMOSA PHARMACEUTICALS, INC.—See Formosa Laboratories, Inc.; *Int'l*, pg. 2735

FORMOSA PETROCHEMICAL CORPORATION

FORMOSA PLASMA DISPLAY CORPORATION—See Formosa Plastics Corporation; *Int'l*, pg. 2735
FORMOSA PLASTICS CORPORATION - CARBIDE DIVISION—See Formosa Plastics Corporation; *Int'l*, pg. 2735
FORMOSA PLASTICS CORPORATION - CHEMICALS DIVISION—See Formosa Plastics Corporation; *Int'l*, pg. 2735
FORMOSA PLASTICS CORPORATION, DELAWARE—See Formosa Plastics Corporation; *Int'l*, pg. 2735
FORMOSA PLASTICS CORPORATION - LINYUAN PLANT—See Formosa Plastics Corporation; *Int'l*, pg. 2735
FORMOSA PLASTICS CORPORATION, LOUISIANA—See Formosa Plastics Corporation; *Int'l*, pg. 2736
FORMOSA PLASTICS CORPORATION - PLASTICS DIVISION—See Formosa Plastics Corporation; *Int'l*, pg. 2735
FORMOSA PLASTICS CORPORATION - POLYOLEFIN DIVISION—See Formosa Plastics Corporation; *Int'l*, pg. 2735
FORMOSA PLASTICS CORPORATION - POLYPROPYLENE DIVISION—See Formosa Plastics Corporation; *Int'l*, pg. 2735
FORMOSA PLASTICS CORPORATION; *Int'l*, pg. 2735
FORMOSA PLASTICS CORPORATION - TAIRYLAN DIVISION—See Formosa Plastics Corporation; *Int'l*, pg. 2735
FORMOSA PLASTICS CORPORATION, TEXAS—See Formosa Plastics Corporation; *Int'l*, pg. 2736
FORMOSA PLASTICS CORPORATION, U.S.A.—See Formosa Plastics Corporation; *Int'l*, pg. 2735
FORMOSA PROSONIC INDUSTRIES BERHAD; *Int'l*, pg. 2736
FORMOSA PROSONIC JAPAN CO. LTD.—See Formosa Prosonic Industries Berhad; *Int'l*, pg. 2736
FORMOSA PROSONIC MANUFACTURING SDN. BHD.—See Formosa Prosonic Industries Berhad; *Int'l*, pg. 2736
FORMOSA PROSONIC TECHNICS SDN. BHD.—See Formosa Prosonic Industries Berhad; *Int'l*, pg. 2736
FORMOSA SUMCO TECHNOLOGY CORPORATION—See SUMCO Corporation; *Int'l*, pg. 7260
FORMOSA SUN ENERGY CORP.—See RITEK CORPORATION; *Int'l*, pg. 6351
FORMOSA TAFFETA (CHANGSHU) CO., LTD.—See FORMOSA TAFFETA CO., LTD.; *Int'l*, pg. 2736
FORMOSA TAFFETA CO., LTD.; *Int'l*, pg. 2736
FORMOSA TAFFETA CORP.—See Formosa Petrochemical Corporation; *Int'l*, pg. 2735
FORMOSA TAFFETA DONG NAI CO., LTD.—See FORMOSA TAFFETA CO., LTD.; *Int'l*, pg. 2736
FORMOSA TEXTILE CO., (PTY) LTD.—See Nien Hsing Textile Co., Ltd.; *Int'l*, pg. 5280
FORMOST GRAPHIC COMMUNICATIONS, INC.; *U.S. Private*, pg. 1571
FORMOUS CORP.; *Int'l*, pg. 2736
FORMOX AB—See PAI Partners S.A.S.; *Int'l*, pg. 5702
FORMPAVE LIMITED—See Heidelberg Materials AG; *Int'l*, pg. 3310
FORMPIPE INC.—See FormPipe Software AB; *Int'l*, pg. 2736
FORMPIPE SOFTWARE AB; *Int'l*, pg. 2736
FORMPIPE SOFTWARE COPENHAGEN A/S—See FormPipe Software AB; *Int'l*, pg. 2736
FORMSCAN LIMITED; *Int'l*, pg. 2736
FORMS DISTRIBUTION CORP.; *U.S. Private*, pg. 1572
FORM SERVICES INC.; *U.S. Private*, pg. 1569
FORMS MANUFACTURERS INC.—See Ennis, Inc.; *U.S. Public*, pg. 769
FORMS & SUPPLY, INC.; *U.S. Private*, pg. 1571
FORMS & SURFACES, INC.; *U.S. Private*, pg. 1572
FORMSTACK, LLC—See PSG Equity L.L.C.; *U.S. Private*, pg. 3297
FORMSTACK, LLC—See Silversmith Management, L.P.; *U.S. Private*, pg. 3663
FORM SYSTEMS, INC.—See Deluxe Corporation; *U.S. Public*, pg. 653
FORM TECH CONCRETE FORMS INC.—See Clayton, Dubilier & Rice, LLC; *U.S. Private*, pg. 930
FORMTECH ENTERPRISES, INC.; *U.S. Private*, pg. 1572
FORM TECHNOLOGIES, INC.—See Partners Group Holding AG; *Int'l*, pg. 5749
FORMTEK ASIA-PACIFIC—See Mestek, Inc.; *U.S. Public*, pg. 1426
FORMTEK, INC.—See Mestek, Inc.; *U.S. Public*, pg. 1426
FORMTEK, INC.—See Marsh & McLennan Companies, Inc.; *U.S. Public*, pg. 1386
FORMTEX PLASTICS CORP.—See Good Natured Products Inc.; *Int'l*, pg. 3038
FORMULA 1 FEEDS INC.; *U.S. Private*, pg. 1572
FORMULA1 PTY—See Accor S.A.; *Int'l*, pg. 91
FORMULA BREWING, LLC; *U.S. Private*, pg. 1572
FORMULA FORD; *Int'l*, pg. 2736
FORMULA HONDA; *Int'l*, pg. 2737
FORMULA ONE ADMINISTRATION LIMITED—See Liberty Media Corporation; *U.S. Public*, pg. 1311

FORMULA PHARMACEUTICALS, INC.—See Genexine Inc.; *Int'l*, pg. 2923
FORMULA PHARMACEUTICALS, INC.—See SCM Lifescience Co., Ltd.; *Int'l*, pg. 6649
FORMULA POWELL L.P.—See Mullen Group Ltd.; *Int'l*, pg. 5080
FORMULA; *U.S. Private*, pg. 1572
FORMULA SYSTEMS (1985) LTD.—See Asseco Poland S.A.; *Int'l*, pg. 642
FORMULATED SOLUTIONS, LLC; *U.S. Private*, pg. 1572
FORMULATE KAINOS LIMITED—See Kainos Group plc; *Int'l*, pg. 4051
FORMULA TELECOM LIMITED—See Formula Telecom Solutions Limited; *Int'l*, pg. 2737
FORMULA TELECOM SOLUTIONS LIMITED; *Int'l*, pg. 2737
FORMULATION TECHNOLOGIES, LLC—See Akela Pharma, Inc.; *U.S. Private*, pg. 144
FORMWELD FITTINGS—See Canerector Inc.; *Int'l*, pg. 1290
FORMWORK & SCAFFOLDING PTY LIMITED—See Anchorage Capital Partners Pty. Limited; *Int'l*, pg. 448
FORMYCON AG; *Int'l*, pg. 2737
FORNACA INC.; *U.S. Private*, pg. 1572
FORNAX INFORMATIKA D.O.O.—See Intracom Holdings S.A.; *Int'l*, pg. 3767
FORNAX INTEGRATOR—See Intracom Holdings S.A.; *Int'l*, pg. 3767
FORNAX ZRT—See Intracom Holdings S.A.; *Int'l*, pg. 3767
FORNAZOR INTERNATIONAL INC.; *U.S. Private*, pg. 1572
FORNEBU CONSULTING AS—See Devoteam SA; *Int'l*, pg. 2090
FORNEBU UTVIKLING ASA—See OBOS BBL; *Int'l*, pg. 5512
FORNET, INC.—See H.U. Group Holdings, Inc.; *Int'l*, pg. 3197
FORNETTI KFT—See ARYZTA AG; *Int'l*, pg. 588
FORNEY CORPORATION—See Graham Holdings Company; *U.S. Public*, pg. 954
FORNEY INDUSTRIES INC.; *U.S. Private*, pg. 1572
FORNEY MAQUILA, LLC—See Graham Holdings Company; *U.S. Public*, pg. 954
FORO-MAREE S.A.; *Int'l*, pg. 2737
FORO.MED. PRODUCTION S.R.L.—See PAUL HARTMANN AG; *Int'l*, pg. 5760
FORONEX N.V.—See Renewi plc; *Int'l*, pg. 6279
FOROYAR KOLVETNI P/F—See DNO North Sea Plc; *Int'l*, pg. 2148
FORQUER GROUP, INC.—See MCPc Inc.; *U.S. Private*, pg. 2644
FORRATEC ARGENTINA S.A.—See Corteva, Inc.; *U.S. Public*, pg. 582
FORRENT, LLC—See CoStar Group, Inc.; *U.S. Public*, pg. 586
FORRER STRATEGIC BUSINESS INTERIORS INC.; *U.S. Private*, pg. 1572
FORRER SUPPLY COMPANY INC.; *U.S. Private*, pg. 1572
FORRESTANIA RESOURCES LIMITED; *Int'l*, pg. 2737
FORREST & BLAKE; *U.S. Private*, pg. 1572
FORREST CITY ARKANSAS HOSPITAL COMPANY, LLC—See Quorum Health Corporation; *U.S. Private*, pg. 3329
FORREST CITY CLINIC COMPANY, LLC—See Quorum Health Corporation; *U.S. Private*, pg. 3329
FORRESTER GERMANY GMBH—See Forrester Research, Inc.; *U.S. Public*, pg. 868
FORRESTER LINCOLN-MERCURY INC.; *U.S. Private*, pg. 1572
FORRESTER MARKET ADVISORY (BEIJING) CO., LTD.—See Forrester Research, Inc.; *U.S. Public*, pg. 868
FORRESTER RESEARCH B.V.—See Forrester Research, Inc.; *U.S. Public*, pg. 868
FORRESTER RESEARCH GMBH & CO. KG—See Forrester Research, Inc.; *U.S. Public*, pg. 868
FORRESTER RESEARCH, INC.—See Forrester Research, Inc.; *U.S. Public*, pg. 868
FORRESTER RESEARCH, INC.; *U.S. Public*, pg. 868
FORRESTER RESEARCH INDIA PRIVATE LIMITED—See Forrester Research, Inc.; *U.S. Public*, pg. 868
FORRESTER RESEARCH LTD.—See Forrester Research, Inc.; *U.S. Public*, pg. 868
FORRESTER RESEARCH SAS—See Forrester Research, Inc.; *U.S. Public*, pg. 868
FORRESTER SINGAPORE PTE. LTD.—See Forrester Research, Inc.; *U.S. Public*, pg. 868
FORRESTER SWITZERLAND GMBH—See Forrester Research, Inc.; *U.S. Public*, pg. 869
FORREST MACHINING INC.—See DVSM LLC; *U.S. Private*, pg. 1295
FORREST PAINT CO.; *U.S. Private*, pg. 1572
FORREST SOLUTIONS GROUP; *U.S. Private*, pg. 1572
FORREST T. JONES & COMPANY, INC.; *U.S. Private*, pg. 1572
FORRISTALL ENTERPRISES, INC.; *U.S. Private*, pg. 1572

CORPORATE AFFILIATIONS

FORSAC MEXICO S.A. DE C.V.—See Empresas CMPC, S.A.; *Int'l*, pg. 2390
FORSAKRINGSAKTIEBOLEGET ASSURANSINVEST MF—See Enstar Group Limited; *Int'l*, pg. 2449
FORSALEBYOWNER.COM, LLC, INC.—See ROCKET Homes Real Estate LLC; *U.S. Private*, pg. 3466
FORSBERG CONSTRUCTION, INC.; *U.S. Private*, pg. 1573
FORSCHUNGSINSTITUT FUR MOLEKULARE PATHOLOGIE GESELLSCHAFT MBH—See C.H. Boehringer Sohn AG & Co. KG; *Int'l*, pg. 1242
FORSEE POWER SAS; *Int'l*, pg. 2737
FORSHAW INC.; *U.S. Private*, pg. 1573
FORSIDE CO., LTD.; *Int'l*, pg. 2737
FORSIKRINGSSELSKABET PRIVATSIKRING A/S—See Intact Financial Corporation; *Int'l*, pg. 3727
FORSIKRINGSSELSKABET PRIVATSIKRING A/S—See Tryg A/S; *Int'l*, pg. 7946
FORSMAN & BODENFORS AB—See Stagwell, Inc.; *U.S. Public*, pg. 1926
FORSMAN & BODENFORS FACTORY AB—See Stagwell, Inc.; *U.S. Public*, pg. 1926
FORSMAN & BODENFORS INHOUSE AB—See Stagwell, Inc.; *U.S. Public*, pg. 1926
FORSMAN & BODENFORS - TORONTO—See Stagwell, Inc.; *U.S. Public*, pg. 1926
FORSMARKS KRAFTGRUPP AB—See Vattenfall AB; *Int'l*, pg. 8136
FORS MARSH GROUP LLC; *U.S. Private*, pg. 1572
FORSSAN HAMEENTIE 3 KOY—See Citycon Oyj; *Int'l*, pg. 1629
FORSSA PRINT—See Alma Media Corporation; *Int'l*, pg. 362
FORSTA AP-FONDEN; *Int'l*, pg. 2737
FORSTA INC.—See Ares Management Corporation; *U.S. Public*, pg. 190
FORSTA INC.—See Leonard Green & Partners, L.P.; *U.S. Private*, pg. 2427
FORSTER GMBH—See BayWa AG; *Int'l*, pg. 918
FORSTER & HOWELL INCORPORATED; *U.S. Private*, pg. 1573
FORSTER PRIVATE HOSPITAL PTY. LTD.—See Luye Medical Group; *Int'l*, pg. 4589
FORSTER SWISS HOME AG; *Int'l*, pg. 2737
FORSTMANN LITTLE & CO.; *U.S. Private*, pg. 1573
FORSTVERWALTUNG BRANNENBURG GMBH & CO. OHG—See Henkel AG & Co. KGaA; *Int'l*, pg. 3348
FORSYS METALS CORP.; *Int'l*, pg. 2737
FORSYTH CAPITAL INVESTORS LLC; *U.S. Private*, pg. 1573
FORSYTHE LUBRICATION ASSOCIATES LIMITED; *Int'l*, pg. 2737
FORSYTHE MCARTHUR ASSOCIATES, INC.—See CDW Corporation; *U.S. Public*, pg. 463
FORSYTHE SOLUTIONS GROUP, INC.—See CDW Corporation; *U.S. Public*, pg. 463
FORSYTHE TECHNOLOGY CANADA, INC.—See CDW Corporation; *U.S. Public*, pg. 463
FORSYTHE TECHNOLOGY INC.—See CDW Corporation; *U.S. Public*, pg. 463
FORSYTH HOLDINGS, INC.; *Int'l*, pg. 2737
FORTACO GROUP OY—See CapMan PLC; *Int'l*, pg. 1315
FORTACO ZRT.; *Int'l*, pg. 2737
FORTA FINANCIAL GROUP, INC.—See Financial Gravity Companies, Inc.; *U.S. Public*, pg. 834
FORT ANN TRANSFER STATION, LLC—See Waste Connections, Inc.; *Int'l*, pg. 8353
FORT ASHFORD HOLDINGS, LLC; *U.S. Private*, pg. 1574
FORT BELKNAP ELECTRIC COOP; *U.S. Private*, pg. 1574
FORT BEND REGIONAL LANDFILL, LP—See BC Partners LLP; *Int'l*, pg. 924
FORT BEND SERVICES INC.; *U.S. Private*, pg. 1574
FORT BLISS WATER SERVICES COMPANY—See American States Water Company; *U.S. Public*, pg. 110
FORT BOISE PRODUCE; *U.S. Private*, pg. 1574
FORT BRAGG ADVOCATE-NEWS—See Alden Global Capital LLC; *U.S. Private*, pg. 156
FORT CITY CHRYSLER SALES LTD.; *Int'l*, pg. 2737
FORT COLLINS COLORADOAN—See Gannett Co., Inc.; *U.S. Public*, pg. 897
FORT DAVIS STATE BANK; *U.S. Private*, pg. 1574
FORT DEARBORN - BOWLING GREEN—See Advent International Corporation; *U.S. Private*, pg. 101
FORT DEARBORN COMPANY—See Advent International Corporation; *U.S. Private*, pg. 101
FORT DEARBORN - FORT WORTH—See Advent International Corporation; *U.S. Private*, pg. 101
FORT DODGE ASPHALT CO. (INC.)—See Moore Brothers Asphalt Inc.; *U.S. Private*, pg. 2779
FORT DODGE FOODS, INC.—See Hormel Foods Corporation; *U.S. Public*, pg. 1054
FORT DUNCAN MEDICAL CENTER, INC.—See Universal Health Services, Inc.; *U.S. Public*, pg. 2257
FORTEBANK JSC; *Int'l*, pg. 2737
FORTE BIOSCIENCES, INC.; *U.S. Public*, pg. 869
FORTE CAPITAL ADVISORS, LLC; *U.S. Private*, pg. 1575
FORTEC ELEKTRONIK AG; *Int'l*, pg. 2737

COMPANY NAME INDEX

FORTECH ELECTRONICS CO., LTD.—See Chaintech Technology Corp.; *Int'l*, pg. 1437
FORTECH PRODUCTS, INC.; *U.S. Private*, pg. 1575
FORTEC SWITZERLAND AG—See FORTEC Elektronik AG; *Int'l*, pg. 2738
FORTEC TECHNOLOGY UK LIMITED—See FORTEC Elektronik AG; *Int'l*, pg. 2738
FORTE DESIGN SYSTEMS, K.K.—See Cadence Design Systems, Inc.; *U.S. Public*, pg. 418
FORTE FURNITURE LTD.—See Fabryki Mebli Forte S.A.; *Int'l*, pg. 2600
FORTEGRA FINANCIAL CORPORATION—See Tiptree Inc.; *U.S. Public*, pg. 2159
THE FORTEGRA GROUP, INC.—See Tiptree Inc.; *U.S. Public*, pg. 2159
FORTE GROUP INC.—See The Point Group; *U.S. Private*, pg. 4097
FORTE IBERIA—See Fabryki Mebli Forte S.A.; *Int'l*, pg. 2600
FORTELEASING JSC—See ForteBank JSC; *Int'l*, pg. 2737
FORTE LUBRICANTS LIMITED—See Illinois Tool Works Inc.; *U.S. Public*, pg. 1103
FORTE MINERALS CORP.; *Int'l*, pg. 2737
FORTE MOBILIER SARL—See Fabryki Mebli Forte S.A.; *Int'l*, pg. 2600
FORTE NOORD-WEST-EUROPA B.V.—See Illinois Tool Works Inc.; *U.S. Public*, pg. 1103
FORTENOVA GROUP D.D.; *Int'l*, pg. 2738
FORTE PAYMENT SYSTEMS, INC.—See CSG Systems International, Inc.; *U.S. Public*, pg. 601
FORTEQ CZECH S.R.O.—See forteq Group; *Int'l*, pg. 2738
FORTEQ DERENDINGEN AG—See forteq Group; *Int'l*, pg. 2738
FORTEQ GROUP; *Int'l*, pg. 2738
FORTEQ ITALY S.P.A.—See forteq Group; *Int'l*, pg. 2738
FORTEQ NETHERLANDS BV—See forteq Group; *Int'l*, pg. 2738
FORTEQ NORTH AMERICA, INC.—See forteq Group; *Int'l*, pg. 2738
FORTEQ SUZHOU LTD.—See forteq Group; *Int'l*, pg. 2738
FORTEQ UK LTD.—See forteq Group; *Int'l*, pg. 2738
FORTE RESEARCH SYSTEMS, INC.; *U.S. Private*, pg. 1575
FORTERRA BUILDING PRODUCTS LIMITED—See Lone Star Global Acquisitions, LLC; *U.S. Private*, pg. 2487
FORTERRA, INC.—See The Quikrete Companies, LLC; *U.S. Private*, pg. 4101
FORTERRA PLC—See Lone Star Global Acquisitions, LLC; *U.S. Private*, pg. 2487
FORTERUS HEALTH CARE SERVICES, INC.—See AAC Holdings, Inc.; *U.S. Private*, pg. 30
FORTE RUS LTD.—See Fabryki Mebli Forte S.A.; *Int'l*, pg. 2600
FORTESCUE LTD.; *Int'l*, pg. 2738
FORTE SK GMBH—See Fabryki Mebli Forte S.A.; *Int'l*, pg. 2600
FORTE TRANSPORTATION LOGISTICS; *U.S. Private*, pg. 1575
FORTE UKRAINE, LTD.—See Fabryki Mebli Forte S.A.; *Int'l*, pg. 2600
FORTEX, INC.; *U.S. Public*, pg. 869
FORT FRANKLIN; *U.S. Private*, pg. 1574
FORT GARRY BREWING COMPANY LTD.—See Westcap Mgt. Ltd.; *Int'l*, pg. 8387
FORT GLOSTER INDUSTRIES LIMITED—See Gloster Limited; *Int'l*, pg. 3011
FORTH CORPORATION PUBLIC COMPANY LIMITED - FORTH FACTORY—See Forth Corporation Public Company Limited; *Int'l*, pg. 2738
FORTH CORPORATION PUBLIC COMPANY LIMITED; *Int'l*, pg. 2738
FORTH DIMENSION DISPLAYS—See Kopin Corporation; *U.S. Public*, pg. 1271
FOR THE BRIDE BY DEMETRIOS; *U.S. Private*, pg. 1562
FOR THE EARTH CORP.; *U.S. Public*, pg. 864
FORTH ESTUARY TOWAGE LIMITED—See Arcus Infrastructure Partners LLP; *Int'l*, pg. 552
FORT HILL CONSTRUCTION INC.; *U.S. Private*, pg. 1574
FORT HILL NATURAL GAS AUTHORITY INC.; *U.S. Private*, pg. 1574
FORTHINK CO., LTD.—See Abalance Corporation Ltd.; *Int'l*, pg. 48
FORT HOOD FAMILY HOUSING LP.; *U.S. Private*, pg. 1574
FORT HOOD NATIONAL BANK—See First Community Bancshares, Inc.; *U.S. Private*, pg. 1516
FORTH PORTS PLC—See Arcus Infrastructure Partners LLP; *Int'l*, pg. 552
FORTH PROPERTIES LIMITED—See Arcus Infrastructure Partners LLP; *Int'l*, pg. 552
FORTH PROPERTY DEVELOPMENTS LTD—See Arcus Infrastructure Partners LLP; *Int'l*, pg. 552
FORTH'S FOODS, INC.; *U.S. Private*, pg. 1575
FORTH SMART CAPITAL CO., LTD.—See Forth Smart Service Public Company Limited; *Int'l*, pg. 2738
FORTH SMART SERVICE PUBLIC COMPANY LIMITED; *Int'l*, pg. 2738

FORTH VALLEY ENGINEERING LIMITED—See NOV, Inc.; *U.S. Public*, pg. 1544
FORTHVIEW CARE HOME—See Balhousie Holdings Limited; *Int'l*, pg. 808
FORTH WINES LTD; *Int'l*, pg. 2738
FORTIANA HOLDINGS LTD; *Int'l*, pg. 2738
FORTICRETE LTD—See Ibstock plc; *Int'l*, pg. 3577
FORTIER INC.; *U.S. Private*, pg. 1576
FORTIFIBER BUILDING SYSTEMS GROUP—See Fortifiber Corporation; *U.S. Private*, pg. 1576
FORTIFIBER CORPORATION; *U.S. Private*, pg. 1576
FORTIFIED PROVIDER NETWORK, INC.—See UnitedHealth Group Incorporated; *U.S. Public*, pg. 2240
FORTIFY RESOURCES INC.; *Int'l*, pg. 2739
FORTIGENT HOLDINGS COMPANY, INC.—See LPL Financial Holdings Inc.; *U.S. Public*, pg. 1343
FORTIGENT, LLC—See LPL Financial Holdings Inc.; *U.S. Public*, pg. 1343
FORTILINE, LLC—See Reece Limited; *Int'l*, pg. 6249
FORTILINE WATERWORKS, INC.; *U.S. Private*, pg. 1576
FORT INC.; *U.S. Private*, pg. 1574
FORTINET AUSTRIA GMBH—See Fortinet, Inc.; *U.S. Public*, pg. 869
FORTINET BELGIUM BV—See Fortinet, Inc.; *U.S. Public*, pg. 869
FORTINET BV—See Fortinet, Inc.; *U.S. Public*, pg. 869
FORTINET DENMARK APS—See Fortinet, Inc.; *U.S. Public*, pg. 869
FORTINET FEDERAL, INC.—See Fortinet, Inc.; *U.S. Public*, pg. 869
FORTINET FINLAND OY—See Fortinet, Inc.; *U.S. Public*, pg. 869
FORTINET GMBH—See Fortinet, Inc.; *U.S. Public*, pg. 869
FORTINET, INC.; *U.S. Public*, pg. 869
FORTINET INFORMATION TECHNOLOGY (BEIJING) CO., LTD.—See Fortinet, Inc.; *U.S. Public*, pg. 869
FORTINET INFORMATION TECHNOLOGY (TIANJIN) CO., LTD.—See Fortinet, Inc.; *U.S. Public*, pg. 869
FORTINET JAPAN CO. LTD.—See Fortinet, Inc.; *U.S. Public*, pg. 869
FORTINET MALAYSIA SDN. BHD.—See Fortinet, Inc.; *U.S. Public*, pg. 869
FORTINET MEXICO, S. DE R.L. DE C.V.—See Fortinet, Inc.; *U.S. Public*, pg. 869
FORTINET S.A.R.L—See Fortinet, Inc.; *U.S. Public*, pg. 869
FORTINET SECURITY ISRAEL LTD.—See Fortinet, Inc.; *U.S. Public*, pg. 869
FORTINET SECURITY KOREA LTD.—See Fortinet, Inc.; *U.S. Public*, pg. 869
FORTINET SECURITY NETWORK (THAILAND) LTD.—See Fortinet, Inc.; *U.S. Public*, pg. 869
FORTINET SECURITY PHILIPPINES, INC.—See Fortinet, Inc.; *U.S. Public*, pg. 869
FORTINET SECURITY SPAIN S.L—See Fortinet, Inc.; *U.S. Public*, pg. 869
FORTINET SINGAPORE PRIVATE LIMITED—See Fortinet, Inc.; *U.S. Public*, pg. 869
FORTINET SWITZERLAND GMBH—See Fortinet, Inc.; *U.S. Public*, pg. 869
FORTINET TECHNOLOGIES (CANADA), INC.—See Fortinet, Inc.; *U.S. Public*, pg. 869
FORTINET TECHNOLOGIES INDIA PRIVATE LIMITED—See Fortinet, Inc.; *U.S. Public*, pg. 869
FORTINET TURKEY GUVENLIK SISTEMLERI LIMITED SIRKETI—See Fortinet, Inc.; *U.S. Public*, pg. 869
FORTINET (UK) LTD.—See Fortinet, Inc.; *U.S. Public*, pg. 869
FORTINO CAPITAL PARTNERS; *Int'l*, pg. 2739
FORTINOX S.A.—See ThyssenKrupp AG; *Int'l*, pg. 7730
FORTIS ADVISORS, LLC; *U.S. Private*, pg. 1576
FORTISALBERTA INC.—See Fortis Inc.; *Int'l*, pg. 2739
FORTIS BANK POLSKA S.A.—See BNP Paribas SA; *Int'l*, pg. 1084
FORTIS BANQUE S.A.—See BNP Paribas SA; *Int'l*, pg. 1084
FORTISBC ENERGY INC.—See Fortis Inc.; *Int'l*, pg. 2739
FORTISBC HOLDINGS INC.—See Fortis Inc.; *Int'l*, pg. 2739
FORTISBC INC.—See Fortis Inc.; *Int'l*, pg. 2739
FORTIS BELIZE LIMITED—See Fortis Inc.; *Int'l*, pg. 2739
FORTIS CAPITAL CORP.—See BNP Paribas SA; *Int'l*, pg. 1084
FORTIS COLLEGE—See JLL Partners, LLC; *U.S. Private*, pg. 2212
FORTIS COMMERCIAL FINANCE S.A.S.—See BNP Paribas SA; *Int'l*, pg. 1084
FORTIS COMMERCIAL FINANCE S.P.A.—See BNP Paribas SA; *Int'l*, pg. 1084
FORTIS COMMERCIAL FINANCE SP. Z O.O.—See BNP Paribas SA; *Int'l*, pg. 1084
FORTIS CONSTRUCTION, INC.; *U.S. Private*, pg. 1576
FORTIS ENERGY SERVICES, INC.; *U.S. Private*, pg. 1576
FORTIS FAKTORING A.S.—See BNP Paribas SA; *Int'l*, pg. 1093
FORTIS FINANCE BELGIUM S.C.R.L.—See BNP Paribas SA; *Int'l*, pg. 1084
FORTIS FIRE & SAFETY, INC.; *U.S. Private*, pg. 1576

FORTIS HAITONG INVESTMENT MANAGEMENT CO., LTD.—See BNP Paribas SA; *Int'l*, pg. 1082
FORTIS HEALTHCARE LIMITED; *Int'l*, pg. 2739
FORTIS INC.; *Int'l*, pg. 2739
FORTIS INVESTMENT MANAGEMENT CHILE SA—See BNP Paribas SA; *Int'l*, pg. 1084
FORTIS LA FEMME LIMITED—See Fortis Healthcare Limited; *Int'l*, pg. 2739
FORTIS LEASE CAR & TRUCK S.A.—See BNP Paribas SA; *Int'l*, pg. 1085
FORTIS LEASE GROUP SERVICES S.A.—See BNP Paribas SA; *Int'l*, pg. 1085
FORTIS LIFE SCIENCES; *U.S. Private*, pg. 1576
FORTIS LUX FINANCIAL, INC.—See Massachusetts Mutual Life Insurance Company; *U.S. Private*, pg. 2605
FORTIS MALAR HOSPITALS LIMITED—See Fortis Healthcare Limited; *Int'l*, pg. 2739
FORTIS MINERALS, LLC; *U.S. Private*, pg. 1576
FORTISONTARIO INC—See Fortis Inc.; *Int'l*, pg. 2739
FORTIS PAYMENT SYSTEMS LLC; *U.S. Private*, pg. 1576
FORTIS PLASTICS LLC—See Monomoy Capital Partners LLC; *U.S. Private*, pg. 2772
FORTIS PRIVATE BANKING - BRUSSELS—See BNP Paribas SA; *Int'l*, pg. 1084
FORTIS PRIVATE EQUITY BELGIUM NV—See BNP Paribas SA; *Int'l*, pg. 1084
FORTIS PRIVATE EQUITY EXPANSION BELGIUM NV—See BNP Paribas SA; *Int'l*, pg. 1084
FORTIS PRIVATE INVESTMENT MANAGEMENT LIMITED—See BNP Paribas SA; *Int'l*, pg. 1084
FORTIS PROPERTIES BRUNSWICK SQUARE LTD.—See Fortis Inc.; *Int'l*, pg. 2739
FORTIS PROPERTIES CORPORATION—See Fortis Inc.; *Int'l*, pg. 2739
FORTIS RIDERS; *U.S. Private*, pg. 1576
FORTISSIMO CAPITAL MANAGEMENT LTD.; *Int'l*, pg. 2740
FORTISSIMO CO., LTD.—See MetLife, Inc.; *U.S. Public*, pg. 1430
FORTISSIMO FILM SALES; *Int'l*, pg. 2740
FORTISSIMO FILM SALES—See Fortissimo Film Sales; *Int'l*, pg. 2740
FORTIS SOLUTIONS GROUP LLC—See Harvest Partners L.P.; *U.S. Private*, pg. 1876
FORTIS STAR SDN. BHD.—See Pan-United Corporation Ltd.; *Int'l*, pg. 5716
FORTISTAR LLC; *U.S. Private*, pg. 1576
FORTISTAR NORTH TONAWANDA, INC.—See Fortistar LLC; *U.S. Private*, pg. 1576
FORTISTAR SUSTAINABLE SOLUTIONS CORP.; *U.S. Public*, pg. 869
FORTISTCI LIMITED—See Fortis Inc.; *Int'l*, pg. 2739
FORTIS TUGS CORPORATION—See Chelsea Logistics and Infrastructure Holdings Corp.; *Int'l*, pg. 1460
FORTITECH INC.—See Koninklijke DSM N.V.; *Int'l*, pg. 4265
FORTITUDE GOLD CORPORATION; *U.S. Public*, pg. 869
FORTITUDE GROUP HOLDINGS, LLC—See T&D Holdings, Inc.; *Int'l*, pg. 7395
FORTITUDE GROUP HOLDINGS, LLC—See The Carlyle Group Inc.; *U.S. Public*, pg. 2047
FORTITUDE PRODUCTION SERVICES, LLC—See ProSiebenSat.1 Media SE; *Int'l*, pg. 6000
FORTIUSONE, INC.—See Environmental Systems Research Institute Inc.; *U.S. Private*, pg. 1409
FORTIVA AB—See Investment AB Latour; *Int'l*, pg. 3782
FORTIVA DANMARK A/S—See Investment AB Latour; *Int'l*, pg. 3782
FORTIVE CORPORATION; *U.S. Public*, pg. 870
FORT LAUDERDALE HOSPITAL, INC.—See Universal Health Services, Inc.; *U.S. Public*, pg. 2159
FORT LINCOLN CEMETERY, INC.—See Service Corporation International; *U.S. Public*, pg. 1871
FORT LOUDOUN ELECTRIC COOPERATIVE; *U.S. Private*, pg. 1574
FORTMAN INSURANCE AGENCY, INC.—See Reliance Global Group, Inc.; *U.S. Public*, pg. 1778
FORT MCDOWELL YAVAPAI MATERIALS; *U.S. Private*, pg. 1574
THE FORT MILLER COMPANY INC.—See The Fort Miller Group Inc.; *U.S. Private*, pg. 4030
THE FORT MILLER GROUP INC.; *U.S. Private*, pg. 4029
THE FORT MILLER SERVICE CORP.—See The Fort Miller Group Inc.; *U.S. Private*, pg. 4030
FORT MILL FORD, INC.—See Sonic Automotive, Inc.; *U.S. Public*, pg. 1902
FORT MILL TELEPHONE COMPANY—See Comporium Group; *U.S. Private*, pg. 1002
FORT MOJAVE TRIBAL COUNCIL; *U.S. Private*, pg. 1574
FORT MOKOTOW SP. Z O.O.—See PKO Bank Polski SA; *Int'l*, pg. 5887
THE FORT MORGAN TIMES—See Alden Global Capital LLC; *U.S. Private*, pg. 157
FORT MYERS KIDNEY CENTER, LLC—See Nautic Partners, LLC; *U.S. Private*, pg. 2870

FORT MOJAVE TRIBAL COUNCIL

FORT MYERS MIRACLE PROFESSIONAL BASEBALL—See Pohlad Companies; *U.S. Private*, pg. 3221
FORTNEY & WEYGANDT INC.; *U.S. Private*, pg. 1576
FORT NORFOLK RETIREMENT COMMUNITY INC.; *U.S. Private*, pg. 1574
FORTNOX AB; *Int'l*, pg. 2740
FORTNUM & MASON PLC—See The Garfield Weston Foundation; *Int'l*, pg. 7649
FORTON ENTERPRISES LIMITED—See Essity Aktiebolag; *Int'l*, pg. 2517
FORT PAYNE HOME CARE CORPORATION—See Community Health Systems, Inc.; *U.S. Public*, pg. 553
FORT PAYNE HOSPITAL CORPORATION—See Quorum Health Corporation; *U.S. Private*, pg. 3330
FORT PAYNE RHC CORP.—See Quorum Health Corporation; *U.S. Private*, pg. 3330
FORT PIERCE ORTHOPAEDICS, LLC—See HCA Healthcare, Inc.; *U.S. Public*, pg. 996
FORT PIERCE UTILITIES AUTHORITY; *U.S. Private*, pg. 1574
FORT PITT CAPITAL GROUP, INC.—See Clayton, Dubilier & Rice, LLC; *U.S. Private*, pg. 923
FORT PITT CAPITAL GROUP, INC.—See Stone Point Capital LLC; *U.S. Private*, pg. 3824
FORT PITT CONSOLIDATORS INC.; *U.S. Private*, pg. 1574
FORT PNEUS; *Int'l*, pg. 2737
FORT POINT ASSOCIATES, INC.—See Tetra Tech, Inc.; *U.S. Public*, pg. 2023
FORT POINT CAPITAL, LLC; *U.S. Private*, pg. 1574
FORTRAN COMMUNICATIONS, INC.—See Fortran Corporation; *U.S. Public*, pg. 872
FORTRAN CORPORATION; *U.S. Public*, pg. 872
FORT RANDALL TELEPHONE COMPANY—See Hanson Communications Inc.; *U.S. Private*, pg. 1856
FORTREA HOLDINGS INC.; *U.S. Public*, pg. 872
FORT RECOVERY INDUSTRIES INC.; *U.S. Private*, pg. 1574
FORTRESS BANK—See First State Bancorporation, Inc.; *U.S. Private*, pg. 1528
FORTRESS BIOTECH, INC.; *U.S. Public*, pg. 872
FORTRESS CAPITAL ACQUISITION CORP.; *U.S. Public*, pg. 872
THE FORTRESS CORPORATION; *U.S. Private*, pg. 4030
FORTRESS CREDIT CORP.—See SoftBank Group Corp.; *Int'l*, pg. 7053
FORTRESS DISTRIBUTION SDN. BHD.—See OCK Group Berhad; *Int'l*, pg. 5520
FORTRESS DOOR CONTROL PRODUCT (CHANGSHU) CO., LTD.—See Taiwan Fu Hsing Industrial Co., Ltd.; *Int'l*, pg. 7420
FORTRESS FINANCIAL SOLUTIONS PTY. LTD.—See Arthur J. Gallagher & Co.; *U.S. Public*, pg. 205
FORTRESS GERMANY ASSET MANAGEMENT GMBH—See SoftBank Group Corp.; *Int'l*, pg. 7053
FORTRESS GLOBAL ENTERPRISES INC.; *Int'l*, pg. 2740
FORTRESS INDUSTRIAL CO., LTD.—See Taiwan Fu Hsing Industrial Co., Ltd.; *Int'l*, pg. 7420
FORTRESS INTERLOCKS LIMITED—See Halma plc; *Int'l*, pg. 3231
FORTRESS INTERLOCKS PTY LIMITED—See Halma plc; *Int'l*, pg. 3231
FORTRESS INVESTMENT GROUP (AUSTRALIA) PTY. LTD.—See SoftBank Group Corp.; *Int'l*, pg. 7053
FORTRESS INVESTMENT GROUP LLC - DALLAS—See SoftBank Group Corp.; *Int'l*, pg. 7053
FORTRESS INVESTMENT GROUP LLC - MENLO PARK—See SoftBank Group Corp.; *Int'l*, pg. 7053
FORTRESS INVESTMENT GROUP LLC—See SoftBank Group Corp.; *Int'l*, pg. 7052
FORTRESS ITX LLC; *U.S. Public*, pg. 1576
FORTRESS MEDICAL SYSTEMS, INC.—See XClinical GmbH; *Int'l*, pg. 8520
FORTRESS MINERALS LIMITED; *Int'l*, pg. 2740
FORTRESS PARTNERS CAPITAL MANAGEMENT, LTD.; *U.S. Private*, pg. 1576
FORTRESS PARTNERS STRATEGIC CAPITAL ADVISORS—See Fortress Partners Capital Management, Ltd.; *U.S. Private*, pg. 1576
FORTRESS PTE. LTD.—See OCK Group Berhad; *Int'l*, pg. 5520
FORTRESS REIT LIMITED; *Int'l*, pg. 2740
THE FORTRESS RESORTS PLC; *Int'l*, pg. 7643
FORTRESS RESOURCES, LLC—See The Shyft Group, Inc.; *U.S. Public*, pg. 2130
FORTRESS SYSTEMS PTY LIMITED—See Halma plc; *Int'l*, pg. 3231
FORTRESS TECHNOLOGIES, INC.—See General Dynamics Corporation; *U.S. Public*, pg. 913
FORTRESS WOOD PRODUCTS INC.—See The Lester Group Inc.; *U.S. Private*, pg. 4069
FORT RILEY UTILITY SERVICES, INC.—See American States Water Company; *U.S. Public*, pg. 110
FORT ROHR MOTORS INC.; *U.S. Private*, pg. 1575
FORTRON/SOURCE CORP.; *U.S. Private*, pg. 1577
FORT SANDERS REGIONAL MEDICAL CENTER; *U.S. Private*, pg. 1575

FORT SECURITE S.A.—See EMKA-Beschlagteile GmbH & Co. KG; *Int'l*, pg. 2383
FORT SILL APACHE TRIBE OF OKLAHOMA; *U.S. Private*, pg. 1575
FORT SILL FEDERAL CREDIT UNION; *U.S. Private*, pg. 1575
FORT SMITH HMA, LLC—See Community Health Systems, Inc.; *U.S. Public*, pg. 553
FORT ST. JAMES NICKEL CORP.; *Int'l*, pg. 2737
FORTSTONE INTERNATIONAL (HONG KONG) LIMITED—See China Biotech Services Holdings Limited; *Int'l*, pg. 1487
FORT STREET REAL ESTATE CAPITAL PTY. LIMITED—See E&P Financial Group Limited; *Int'l*, pg. 2247
FORT TRANSFER CO.—See Ontario Municipal Employees Retirement System; *Int'l*, pg. 5584
FORTUM 1 AB—See Fortum Oyj; *Int'l*, pg. 2741
FORTUM AMCO AB—See Fortum Oyj; *Int'l*, pg. 2741
FORTUM BCS OY—See Fortum Oyj; *Int'l*, pg. 2740
FORTUM BYTOM SA—See Fortum Oyj; *Int'l*, pg. 2741
FORTUM CHARGE & DRIVE INDIA PRIVATE LIMITED—See Fortum Oyj; *Int'l*, pg. 2740
FORTUM CORPORATION—See Fortum Oyj; *Int'l*, pg. 2740
FORTUM DISTRIBUTION AB—See Folksam omsesidig sakforsakring; *Int'l*, pg. 2721
FORTUM DISTRIBUTION AB—See Ontario Municipal Employees Retirement System; *Int'l*, pg. 5583
FORTUM DISTRIBUTION AS—See Hafslund ASA; *Int'l*, pg. 3206
FORTUM EESTI AS—See Fortum Oyj; *Int'l*, pg. 2740
FORTUM ENERGY LLC—See Fortum Oyj; *Int'l*, pg. 2740
FORTUM FNW OY—See Fortum Oyj; *Int'l*, pg. 2741
FORTUM FORVALTNING AS—See Fortum Oyj; *Int'l*, pg. 2741
FORTUM FRANCE S.N.C—See Fortum Oyj; *Int'l*, pg. 2741
FORTUM GENERATION AB—See Fortum Oyj; *Int'l*, pg. 2741
FORTUM HEAT NAANTALI OY—See Fortum Oyj; *Int'l*, pg. 2741
FORTUM INDIA PRIVATE LIMITED—See Fortum Oyj; *Int'l*, pg. 2741
FORTUM INVEST LLC—See Fortum Oyj; *Int'l*, pg. 2741
FORTUM LATVIA SIA—See Fortum Oyj; *Int'l*, pg. 2741
FORTUM MARKETING & SALES POLSKA S.A.—See Fortum Oyj; *Int'l*, pg. 2741
FORTUM MARKETS AB—See Fortum Oyj; *Int'l*, pg. 2741
FORTUM MARKETS AS—See Fortum Oyj; *Int'l*, pg. 2741
FORTUM MARKETS OY—See Fortum Oyj; *Int'l*, pg. 2741
FORTUM MARKETS POLSKA S.A.—See Fortum Oyj; *Int'l*, pg. 2741
FORTUM METER LEASE SNC—See Fortum Oyj; *Int'l*, pg. 2741
FORTUM NETWORK WROCLAW SP. Z O.O.—See Fortum Oyj; *Int'l*, pg. 2741
FORTUM NORDIC AB—See Fortum Oyj; *Int'l*, pg. 2741
FORTUM NUCLEAR SERVICES OY—See Fortum Oyj; *Int'l*, pg. 2741
FORTUM O&M (UK) LTD—See Fortum Oyj; *Int'l*, pg. 2741
FORTUM OSLO VARME AS—See Fortum Oyj; *Int'l*, pg. 2741
FORTUM OYJ; *Int'l*, pg. 2740
FORTUM OY—See Fortum Oyj; *Int'l*, pg. 2741
FORTUM PETROLEUM A/S—See Fortum Oyj; *Int'l*, pg. 2741
FORTUM PLOCK SP. Z.O.O.—See Fortum Oyj; *Int'l*, pg. 2741
FORTUM POLSKA SP. Z.O.O.—See Fortum Oyj; *Int'l*, pg. 2741
FORTUM POWER AND HEAT OY—See Fortum Oyj; *Int'l*, pg. 2741
FORTUM POWER AND HEAT OY—See Fortum Oyj; *Int'l*, pg. 2741
FORTUM POWER AND HEAT POLSKA SP. Z.O.O—See Fortum Oyj; *Int'l*, pg. 2741
FORTUM POWER & HEAT AB—See Fortum Oyj; *Int'l*, pg. 2741
FORTUM PRODUKTIONSNAT AB—See Fortum Oyj; *Int'l*, pg. 2741
FORTUM SERVICE DEUTSCHLAND GMBH—See Fortum Oyj; *Int'l*, pg. 2741
FORTUM SERVICE OY—See Fortum Oyj; *Int'l*, pg. 2741
FORTUM SMALL HYDRO HOLDING OY—See Fortum Oyj; *Int'l*, pg. 2741
FORTUM SVERIGE AB—See Fortum Oyj; *Int'l*, pg. 2741
FORTUM SWEDEN AB—See Fortum Oyj; *Int'l*, pg. 2741
FORTUM WASTE SOLUTIONS NORWAY AS—See Fortum Oyj; *Int'l*, pg. 2741
FORTUM WASTE SOLUTIONS OY—See Fortum Oyj; *Int'l*, pg. 2741
FORTUM ZABRZE SA—See Fortum Oyj; *Int'l*, pg. 2741
FORTUNA ENTERTAINMENT GROUP N.V.—See Penta Investments Limited; *Int'l*, pg. 5788
FORTUNA EXPLORATION LLC—See Repsol, S.A.; *Int'l*, pg. 6293
FORTUNA HERSTELLUNG GMBH—See Medios AG; *Int'l*, pg. 4778

CORPORATE AFFILIATIONS

FORTUNA INVESTMENT AG—See Assicurazioni Generali S.p.A.; *Int'l*, pg. 644
FORTUNA LEBENS-VERSICHERUNGS AG VADUZ—See FWU AG; *Int'l*, pg. 2859
FORTUNA MINING CORP.; *Int'l*, pg. 2742
FORTUNA MOTORS, INC.; *U.S. Private*, pg. 1577
FORTUNA RECHTSSCHUTZ-VERSICHERUNG-GESELLSCHAFT AG—See Assicurazioni Generali S.p.A.; *Int'l*, pg. 644
FORTUNA SAZKOVA KANCELAR, A.S.; *Int'l*, pg. 2743
FORTUNA (US) L.P.—See Repsol, S.A.; *Int'l*, pg. 6293
FORTUNE ASIA GROUP LTD; *Int'l*, pg. 2743
FORTUNE BRANDS DOORS, INC.—See Fortune Brands Innovations, Inc.; *U.S. Public*, pg. 873
FORTUNE BRANDS INNOVATIONS, INC.; *U.S. Public*, pg. 872
FORTUNE BRANDS STORAGE & SECURITY LLC—See Fortune Brands Innovations, Inc.; *U.S. Public*, pg. 873
FORTUNEBUILDERS INC.; *U.S. Private*, pg. 1577
FORTUNE CAPITAL PARTNERS, INC.; *U.S. Private*, pg. 1577
FORTUNE CASUALS, LLC; *U.S. Private*, pg. 1577
FORTUNE COAL LIMITED—See Fortune Minerals Limited; *Int'l*, pg. 2743
FORTUNE COURIERS LTD.—See Orient Press Limited; *Int'l*, pg. 5622
FORTUNE ELECTRIC AMERICA INC.—See Fortune Electric Co., Ltd.; *Int'l*, pg. 2743
FORTUNE ELECTRIC CO., LTD. - NORTH AMERICAN DIVISION—See Fortune Electric Co., Ltd.; *Int'l*, pg. 2743
FORTUNE ELECTRIC CO., LTD. - POWER DIVISION—See Fortune Electric Co., Ltd.; *Int'l*, pg. 2743
FORTUNE ELECTRIC CO., LTD.; *Int'l*, pg. 2743
FORTUNE ELECTRIC CO., LTD. - SWITCHGEAR DIVISION—See Fortune Electric Co., Ltd.; *Int'l*, pg. 2743
FORTUNE ELECTRIC EXTRA HIGH VOLTAGE CO., LTD.—See Fortune Electric Co., Ltd.; *Int'l*, pg. 2743
FORTUNE ELECTRIC (WUHAN) LTD.—See Fortune Electric Co., Ltd.; *Int'l*, pg. 2743
FORTUNE ENERGY CORPORATION—See CTCI Corporation; *Int'l*, pg. 1870
FORTUNE EQUITY BROKERS (INDIA) LTD.—See The Investment Trust of India Limited; *Int'l*, pg. 7656
FORTUNE FINANCIAL INC.; *U.S. Private*, pg. 1577
FORTUNE FOOD MANUFACTURING PTE LTD—See PSC Corporation Ltd.; *Int'l*, pg. 6015
FORTUNE FOOD MARKETING PTE LTD—See PSC Corporation Ltd.; *Int'l*, pg. 6015
FORTUNE FOOTWEAR INC.; *U.S. Private*, pg. 1577
FORTUNE FOUNTAIN (BEIJING) HOLDING GROUP CO., LTD.; *Int'l*, pg. 2743
FORTUNE GRAPHITE INC.; *Int'l*, pg. 2743
FORTUNE (HK) SECURITIES LIMITED—See GoFintech Innovation Limited; *Int'l*, pg. 3021
FORTUNE HOMES OF TALLAHASSEE INC.; *U.S. Private*, pg. 1577
FORTUNE INDUSTRIES INC.—See Paychex, Inc.; *U.S. Public*, pg. 1655
FORTUNE INFORMATION SYSTEM INTERNATIONAL CO., LTD.—See Fortune Information Systems Corp.; *Int'l*, pg. 2743
FORTUNE INFORMATION SYSTEMS CORP.; *Int'l*, pg. 2743
FORTUNE INTERNATIONAL, INC.; *U.S. Private*, pg. 1577
FORTUNE INTERNATIONAL LIMITED; *Int'l*, pg. 2743
FORTUNE INTERNATIONAL, LLC—See Investcorp Holdings B.S.C.; *Int'l*, pg. 3776
FORTUNE INTERNATIONAL REALTY, INC.; *U.S. Private*, pg. 1577
FORTUNE JOY INTERNATIONAL ACQUISITION CORP.; *Int'l*, pg. 2743
FORTUNE LABORATORIES SDN BHD—See McBride plc; *Int'l*, pg. 4755
FORTUNE MANAGEMENT INC.; *Int'l*, pg. 2743
FORTUNE MARITIME INC.—See Sealift Holdings Inc.; *U.S. Private*, pg. 3585
FORTUNE MINERALS LIMITED; *Int'l*, pg. 2743
FORTUNE MINERALS NWT INC.—See Fortune Minerals Limited; *Int'l*, pg. 2743
FORTUNE NG FUNG FOOD (HEBEI) CO., LTD.; *Int'l*, pg. 2744
FORTUNE OIL LIMITED; *Int'l*, pg. 2744
FORTUNE ORIENTAL COMPANY LIMITED; *Int'l*, pg. 2744
FORTUNE PARK HOTELS LIMITED—See ITC Limited; *Int'l*, pg. 3831
FORTUNE PARTS INDUSTRY PUBLIC COMPANY LIMITED; *Int'l*, pg. 2744
FORTUNE PROMOSEVEN DUBAI—See The Interpublic Group of Companies, Inc.; *U.S. Public*, pg. 2098
FORTUNE PROMOSEVEN-HQ—See The Interpublic Group of Companies, Inc.; *U.S. Public*, pg. 2099
FORTUNE PROMOSEVEN-LEBANON—See The Interpublic Group of Companies, Inc.; *U.S. Public*, pg. 2100
FORTUNE PROMOSEVEN-QATAR—See The Interpublic Group of Companies, Inc.; *U.S. Public*, pg. 2100

FORTUNE PROMOSEVEN—See The Interpublic Group of Companies, Inc.; *U.S. Public*, pg. 2100
FORTUNE REAL ESTATE INVESTMENT TRUST; *Int'l*, pg. 2744
FORTUNE RISE ACQUISITION CORPORATION; *U.S. Public*, pg. 873
FORTUNE SECURITIES CORPORATION; *Int'l*, pg. 2744
FORTUNE SHOES LTD.; *Int'l*, pg. 2744
THE FORTUNE SOCIETY; *U.S. Private*, pg. 4030
FORTUNE SOFTWARE (BEIJING) CO., LTD—See China Finance Online Co. Limited; *Int'l*, pg. 1502
FORTUNE; *U.S. Private*, pg. 1577
FORTUNE STAR ENTERTAINMENT (HK) LIMITED—See The Walt Disney Company; *U.S. Public*, pg. 2140
FORTUNE STAR MEDIA LIMITED—See STAR CM Holdings Limited; *Int'l*, pg. 7173
FORTUNE SUN (CHINA) HOLDINGS LIMITED; *Int'l*, pg. 2744
FORTUNE TECHNOLOGY SYSTEM CORP.—See Fortune Information Systems Corp.; *Int'l*, pg. 2743
FORTUNET, INC.—See AMCON Distributing Company; *U.S. Public*, pg. 93
FORTUNE TRIUMPH SDN. BHD.—See Dayang Enterprise Holdings Berhad; *Int'l*, pg. 1985
FORTUNE VACATION TRAVEL LTD.; *Int'l*, pg. 2744
FORTUNE VALLEY TREASURES, INC.; *Int'l*, pg. 2744
FORTUNE VENTURE CAPITAL CORP.—See United Microelectronics Corporation; *Int'l*, pg. 8070
FORTUNE WEALTH MANAGEMENT LIMITED—See GoFintech Innovation Limited; *Int'l*, pg. 3022
FORTUNE WIRELESS, INC.—See Paychex, Inc.; *U.S. Public*, pg. 1655
FORT UNION GAS GATHERING, LLC—See Kinder Morgan, Inc.; *U.S. Public*, pg. 1233
FORTUS GROUP INC.; *U.S. Private*, pg. 1577
FORTUS SA; *Int'l*, pg. 2744
FORT VALLEY DIALYSIS CENTER, LLC—See Nautic Partners, LLC; *U.S. Private*, pg. 2870
FORT WALTON BEACH MEDICAL CENTER, INC.—See HCA Healthcare, Inc.; *U.S. Public*, pg. 996
FORT WASHINGTON INVESTMENT ADVISORS, INC.—See Western & Southern Financial Group, Inc.; *U.S. Private*, pg. 4490
FORT WAYNE METALS IRELAND LTD—See Fort Wayne Metals Research Products Corp.; *U.S. Private*, pg. 1575
FORT WAYNE METALS RESEARCH PRODUCTS CORP.; *U.S. Private*, pg. 1575
FORT WAYNE NEWSPAPERS, INC.—See The Nutting Company, Inc.; *U.S. Private*, pg. 4086
FORT WAYNE WIRE DIE INC.; *U.S. Private*, pg. 1575
FORT WORTH BOLT & TOOL CO.; *U.S. Private*, pg. 1575
FORT WORTH CARRIER CORPORATION; *U.S. Private*, pg. 1575
FORT WORTH COMMUNITY CREDIT UNION; *U.S. Private*, pg. 1575
FORT WORTH F & D HEAD COMPANY; *U.S. Private*, pg. 1575
FORT WORTH LUMBER COMPANY; *U.S. Private*, pg. 1575
FORT WORTH MUSEUM OF SCIENCE AND HISTORY; *U.S. Private*, pg. 1575
FORT WORTH ROOFING SUPPLY, LLC—See Beacon Roofing Supply, Inc.; *U.S. Public*, pg. 286
FORT WORTH SASH AND DOOR CO.—See Fort Worth Lumber Company; *U.S. Private*, pg. 1575
FORT WORTH STAR-TELEGRAM—See Chatham Asset Management, LLC; *U.S. Private*, pg. 866
FORT WORTH SURGICARE PARTNERS, LTD.—See Tenet Healthcare Corporation; *U.S. Public*, pg. 2010
FORT WORTH TRANSITIONAL CENTER, LLC—See Corecivic, Inc.; *U.S. Public*, pg. 577
FORT WORTH VEHICLE AUCTION—See Cox Enterprises, Inc.; *U.S. Private*, pg. 1076
FORT WORTH & WESTERN RAILROAD INC.—See Davoil Inc.; *U.S. Private*, pg. 1175
FORT WORTH ZOOLOGICAL ASSOCIATION INC.; *U.S. Private*, pg. 1575
FORTY FORT EYE ASSOCIATES; *U.S. Private*, pg. 1577
FORTY PILLARS MINING CORP.—See Origen Resources, Inc.; *Int'l*, pg. 5628
FORTY SEVEN, INC.—See Gilead Sciences, Inc.; *U.S. Public*, pg. 936
FORTYSEVEN PARK STREET LIMITED—See Marriott Vacations Worldwide Corporation; *U.S. Public*, pg. 1373
FORTYTWO METALS INC.—See Quebec Rare Earth Elements Corp; *Int'l*, pg. 6158
FORUCOM REIT; *Int'l*, pg. 2744
FORU HOLDINGS, INC.; *U.S. Public*, pg. 873
FORUM AM BAHNHOF QUICKBORN GMBH & CO. KG—See PORR AG; *Int'l*, pg. 5922
FORUM ARABIA LIMITED—See Forum Energy Technologies, Inc.; *U.S. Public*, pg. 873
THE FORUM AT THE WOODLANDS, INC.—See AlerisLife Inc.; *U.S. Private*, pg. 162
FORUM BIOSCIENCE HOLDINGS LTD.—See Bain Capital, LP; *U.S. Private*, pg. 443

FORUM BIOSCIENCE HOLDINGS LTD.—See Cinven Limited; *Int'l*, pg. 1613
FORUM B+V OIL TOOLS GMBH—See Forum Energy Technologies, Inc.; *U.S. Public*, pg. 873
FORUM CANADA ULC—See Forum Energy Technologies, Inc.; *U.S. Public*, pg. 873
FORUM CAPITAL MARKETS, LLC—See Wells Fargo & Company; *U.S. Public*, pg. 2343
FORUM COMMUNICATIONS COMPANY; *U.S. Private*, pg. 1577
THE FORUM CORPORATION—See Providence Equity Partners L.L.C.; *U.S. Private*, pg. 3293
FORUM ENERGY ASIA PACIFIC PTE. LTD.—See Forum Energy Technologies, Inc.; *U.S. Public*, pg. 873
FORUM ENERGY LIMITED—See Philex Mining Corporation; *Int'l*, pg. 5844
FORUM ENERGY METALS CORP.; *Int'l*, pg. 2744
FORUM ENERGY TECHNOLOGIES, INC. - FLOAT EQUIPMENT—See Forum Energy Technologies, Inc.; *U.S. Public*, pg. 873
FORUM ENERGY TECHNOLOGIES, INC.; *U.S. Public*, pg. 873
FORUM ENERGY TECHNOLOGY (SHANGHAI) CO., LTD—See Forum Energy Technologies, Inc.; *U.S. Public*, pg. 873
FORUM ENGINEERING, INC.; *Int'l*, pg. 2744
FORUM EQUITY PARTNERS—See Providence Equity Partners L.L.C.; *U.S. Private*, pg. 3293
FORUM EUROPE LTD.—See Providence Equity Partners L.L.C.; *U.S. Private*, pg. 3294
FORUM FILM CZECH S.R.O.—See Cineworld Group plc; *Int'l*, pg. 1610
FORUM FILM SLOVAKIA S.R.O.—See Cineworld Group plc; *Int'l*, pg. 1610
FORUM GDANSK PROPERTY SP. Z O.O.—See NEPI Rockcastle N.V.; *Int'l*, pg. 5200
FORUM GDANSK SP. Z O.O.—See NEPI Rockcastle N.V.; *Int'l*, pg. 5200
FORUM GLOBAL TUBING LLC—See Forum Energy Technologies, Inc.; *U.S. Public*, pg. 873
FORUM GUIDO MONZANI S.R.L.—See BPER BANCA S.p.A; *Int'l*, pg. 1132
FORUM IMMOBILIENGESELLSCHAFT MBH—See Commerzbank AG; *Int'l*, pg. 1718
FORUM, INC.—See AIP, LLC; *U.S. Private*, pg. 134
FORUM INDUSTRIES, INC.—See Blue Point Capital Partners, LLC; *U.S. Private*, pg. 590
FORUM MEDIA GROUP GMBH—See WEKA Holding GmbH & Co.KG; *Int'l*, pg. 8371
FORUM PACIFIC INC.; *Int'l*, pg. 2744
FORUM PERSONNEL INC.; *U.S. Private*, pg. 1577
FORUM - PLASMAN A.D.; *Int'l*, pg. 2744
FORUM PUBLISHING GROUP, INC.—See Tribune Publishing Company; *U.S. Private*, pg. 4228
FORUM SERVICIOS FINANCIEROS, S.A.—See The Bank of Nova Scotia; *Int'l*, pg. 7618
FORUM STEGLITZ 2 GMBH—See Hammerson plc; *Int'l*, pg. 3238
FORUM VALVE SOLUTIONS—See Forum Energy Technologies, Inc.; *U.S. Public*, pg. 873
FORUM WETZLAR KG—See Deutsche EuroShop AG; *Int'l*, pg. 2065
FORUS S.A.; *Int'l*, pg. 2744
FORU WORLDWIDE INC.; *Int'l*, pg. 2744
FORVAL CORPORATION; *Int'l*, pg. 2745
FORVAL REALSTRAIGHT INC.; *Int'l*, pg. 2745
FORVAL TELECOM, INC.—See Forval Corporation; *Int'l*, pg. 2745
FORVIA SE; *Int'l*, pg. 2745
FORWARD AIR CORPORATION; *U.S. Public*, pg. 874
FORWARD AIR, INC.—See Forward Air Corporation; *U.S. Public*, pg. 874
FORWARD BY ELYSE WALKER, LLC—See Revolve Group, Inc.; *U.S. Public*, pg. 1793
FORWARD CORPORATION; *U.S. Private*, pg. 1577
FORWARD DIMENSION CAPITAL 1 LLP—See Forward Internet Group Ltd.; *Int'l*, pg. 2747
FORWARD ENERGY GENERATION LTD.—See Dagang NeXchange Berhad; *Int'l*, pg. 1912
FORWARD FASHION INTERNATIONAL HOLDINGS COMPANY LIMITED; *Int'l*, pg. 2747
FORWARD GRAPHIC ENTERPRISE CO., LTD.; *Int'l*, pg. 2747
FORWARD HEALTH; *U.S. Private*, pg. 1578
FORWARD INDUSTRIES, INC.; *U.S. Public*, pg. 874
FORWARD INDUSTRIES (SWITZERLAND) GMBH—See Forward Industries, Inc.; *U.S. Public*, pg. 874
FORWARD INNOVATIONS GMBH—See Forward Industries, Inc.; *U.S. Public*, pg. 874
FORWARD INTERNET GROUP LTD.; *Int'l*, pg. 2747
FORWARD LODGING—See Forward Corporation; *U.S. Private*, pg. 1577
FORWARDLY, INC.; *U.S. Public*, pg. 874
FORWARD MEDIA INC.; *U.S. Private*, pg. 1578
FORWARD PARTNERS GROUP PLC—See Molten Ventures VCT plc; *Int'l*, pg. 5023
FORWARD PARTNERS MANAGEMENT COMPANY LIMITED—See Molten Ventures VCT plc; *Int'l*, pg. 5023

FORWARD PARTNERS VENTURE ADVANCE LTD.—See Molten Ventures VCT plc; *Int'l*, pg. 5023
FORWARD PHARMA A/S; *Int'l*, pg. 2747
FORWARD PHARMA USA, LLC—See Forward Pharma A/S; *Int'l*, pg. 2747
FORWARDPMX GROUP LLC—See Stagwell, Inc.; *U.S. Public*, pg. 1928
FORWARD SETTLEMENT SOLUTIONS, INC.—See Redfin Corporation; *U.S. Public*, pg. 1770
FORWARD SLOPE, INC.—See Trive Capital Inc.; *U.S. Private*, pg. 4239
FORWARD SOLUTIONS; *U.S. Private*, pg. 1578
FORWARD SYSTEM CO., LTD.—See Univentures Public Company Limited; *Int'l*, pg. 8077
FORWARD TECHNOLOGY, INC.—See Crest Group Inc.; *U.S. Private*, pg. 1096
FORWARD TRANSPORT—See Forward Corporation; *U.S. Private*, pg. 1577
FORWARD WATER TECHNOLOGIES CORP; *Int'l*, pg. 2747
FORWEST DE VENEZUELA SA—See Valaris Limited; *Int'l*, pg. 8110
FORYOU CORPORATION; *Int'l*, pg. 2747
FORYOU GENERAL ELECTRONICS CO., LTD.—See Foryou Corporation; *Int'l*, pg. 2747
FOR YOU INSURANCE SERVICES GMBH—See Robert Bosch GmbH; *Int'l*, pg. 6368
FORZA LIEN, INC.—See Patriot National, Inc.; *U.S. Private*, pg. 3110
FORZA LITHIUM CORP.; *Int'l*, pg. 2747
FORZA MIGLIOZZI, LLC; *U.S. Private*, pg. 1578
FORZA MOTORS KOREA CORPORATION—See Hyosung Corporation; *Int'l*, pg. 3550
FORZA PETROLEUM LIMITED; *Int'l*, pg. 2747
FORZA PETROLEUM SERVICES S.A.—See Forza Petroleum Limited; *Int'l*, pg. 2748
FORZA SILICON CORPORATION—See AMETEK, Inc.; *U.S. Public*, pg. 120
FORZA X1, INC.—See Twin Vee PowerCats Co.; *U.S. Public*, pg. 2207
FOSBEL, INC.—See Ares Management Corporation; *U.S. Public*, pg. 189
FOS CAPITAL LIMITED; *Int'l*, pg. 2748
THE FOSCHINI GROUP LIMITED; *Int'l*, pg. 7643
FOSCHINI RETAIL GROUP PROPRIETARY LIMITED—See The Foschini Group Limited; *Int'l*, pg. 7643
FOS CO., LTD.—See Bain Capital, LP; *U.S. Private*, pg. 434
FOSECO ESPANOLA SA—See Vesuvius plc; *Int'l*, pg. 8179
FOSECO FOUNDRY (CHINA) LIMITED—See Vesuvius plc; *Int'l*, pg. 8179
FOSECO GOLDEN GATE COMPANY LIMITED—See Vesuvius plc; *Int'l*, pg. 8179
FOSECO INDIA LIMITED; *Int'l*, pg. 2748
FOSECO INDUSTRIAL E COMERCIAL LTDA.—See Vesuvius plc; *Int'l*, pg. 8179
FOSECO INTERNATIONAL HOLDING (THAILAND) LIMITED—See Vesuvius plc; *Int'l*, pg. 8179
FOSECO INTERNATIONAL LIMITED—See Vesuvius plc; *Int'l*, pg. 8179
FOSECO JAPAN LTD.—See Vesuvius plc; *Int'l*, pg. 8179
FOSECO KOREA LIMITED—See Vesuvius plc; *Int'l*, pg. 8179
FOSECO METALLURGICAL INC.—See Vesuvius plc; *Int'l*, pg. 8180
FOSECO NEDERLAND BV—See Vesuvius plc; *Int'l*, pg. 8179
FOSECO PHILIPPINES INC.—See Vesuvius plc; *Int'l*, pg. 8179
FOSECO PORTUGAL PRODUTOS PARA FUNDICAO LDA.—See Vesuvius plc; *Int'l*, pg. 8179
FOSECO PTY. LIMITED—See Vesuvius plc; *Int'l*, pg. 8179
FOSECO SAS—See Vesuvius plc; *Int'l*, pg. 8179
FOSECO (THAILAND) LIMITED—See Vesuvius plc; *Int'l*, pg. 8178
FOSECO VIETNAM LIMITED—See Vesuvius plc; *Int'l*, pg. 8179
FOSFATOS DEL PACIFICO SA; *Int'l*, pg. 2748
FOS GREEN TECH SRL—See FOS S.p.A.; *Int'l*, pg. 2748
FOSHAN ADVCORP SCAFFOLD LIMITED—See Oldfields Holdings Limited; *Int'l*, pg. 5553
FOSHAN BRANCH OF O.R.G TECHNOLOGY CO., LTD.—See ORG Technology Co., Ltd.; *Int'l*, pg. 5617
FO-SHAN CITY SHANSHUI LIANMEI CHEMICAL CO., LTD.—See Headway Advanced Materials Inc.; *Int'l*, pg. 3302
FOSHAN CONTINENTAL CAN CO. LIMITED—See Crown Holdings, Inc.; *U.S. Public*, pg. 598
FOSHAN CROWN EASY-OPENING END CO. LIMITED—See Crown Holdings, Inc.; *U.S. Public*, pg. 598
FOSHAN DEZHONG PHARMACEUTICAL CO., LTD.—See China National Pharmaceutical Group Corporation; *Int'l*, pg. 1534
FOSHAN DINGBAOHANG AUTOMOBILE SALES SERVICES CO., LTD.—See China ZhengTong Auto Services Holdings Limited; *Int'l*, pg. 1566

FOSFATOS DEL PACIFICO SA

FOSHAN DLT TECHNOLOGY CO., LTD.—See Keda Industrial Group Co., Ltd.; *Int'l*, pg. 4114
FOSHAN EFTEC AUTOMOTIVE MATERIALS CO., LTD.—See EMS-Chemie Holding AG; *Int'l*, pg. 2393
FOSHAN ELECTRICAL & LIGHTING CO., LTD.; *Int'l*, pg. 2748
FOSHAN FORTUNA HOTEL COMPANY LIMITED—See Capital Estate Limited; *Int'l*, pg. 1310
FOSHAN FOSUN CHANCHENG HOSPITAL COMPANY LIMITED—See Shanghai Fosun Pharmaceutical (Group) Co., Ltd.; *Int'l*, pg. 6767
FOSHAN FUYI SWELL AUTO PARTS CO., LTD.—See Guangdong Hongtu Technology (Holdings) Co., Ltd.; *Int'l*, pg. 3156
FOSHAN GOLDEN MILKY WAY INTELLIGENT EQUIPMENT CO., LTD.; *Int'l*, pg. 2748
FOSHAN HAITIAN FLAVOURING & FOOD COMPANY LTD.; *Int'l*, pg. 2748
FOSHAN HEPWORTH PIPE COMPANY LTD.—See Bharti Enterprises Limited; *Int'l*, pg. 1012
FOSHAN HUAGUO OPTICAL CO., LTD.—See Kinko Optical Co., Ltd.; *Int'l*, pg. 4181
FOSHAN HUAXIN PACKAGING CO., LTD.; *Int'l*, pg. 2748
FOSHAN ICHIKOH VALEO AUTO LIGHTING SYSTEMS CO., LTD.—See Valeo S.A.; *Int'l*, pg. 8112
FOSHAN INDER ADHESIVE PRODUCT CO., LTD.—See Yem Chio Co., Ltd.; *Int'l*, pg. 8577
FOSHAN JINXI JINLAN COLD ROLLED SHEETS CO., LTD.—See China Oriental Group Company Limited; *Int'l*, pg. 1538
FOSHAN KURASHIKI TEXTILE MANUFACTURING CO., LTD.—See Kurabo Industries Ltd.; *Int'l*, pg. 4335
FOSHAN LEPUDA MOTOR CO., LTD.—See Ozner Water International Holding Limited; *Int'l*, pg. 5679
FO SHAN MANITOWOC FOODSERVICE CO.—See Ali Holding S.r.l; *Int'l*, pg. 322
FOSHAN MEIXIN LEXUS AUTO SALES & SERVICES CO., LTD.—See China MeiDong Auto Holdings Limited; *Int'l*, pg. 1519
FOSHAN MIDEA MATERIAL SUPPLY CO., LTD.—See Midea Group Co., Ltd.; *Int'l*, pg. 4884
FOSHAN MITSUI CHEMICALS & SKC POLYURETHANES CO., LTD.—See Mitsui Chemicals, Inc.; *Int'l*, pg. 4981
FOSHAN NANFANG-RITCO ENERGY CLEAN TECHNOLOGY CO., LTD.—See Nanfeng Ventilator Co., Ltd.-A; *Int'l*, pg. 5139
FOSHAN NANHAI PINGZHOU ELECTRONIC FACTORY CO., LTD.—See TDK Corporation; *Int'l*, pg. 7488
FOSHAN NATIONSTAR OPTOELECTRONICS CO., LTD. - LED LIGHTING DIVISION—See Foshan Nationstar Optoelectronics Co., Ltd.; *Int'l*, pg. 2748
FOSHAN NATIONSTAR OPTOELECTRONICS CO., LTD.; *Int'l*, pg. 2748
FOSHAN NORATEL ELECTRIC CO., LTD.—See discoverIE Group plc; *Int'l*, pg. 2133
FOSHAN PARKER SURFACE MODIFICATION CO., LTD.—See Nihon Parkerizing Co., Ltd.; *Int'l*, pg. 5286
FOSHAN PEGUFORM AUTOMOTIVE PLASTICS TECHNOLOGY CO., LTD.—See Samvardhana Motherson International Limited; *Int'l*, pg. 6516
FOSHAN SEAH PRECISION METAL CO., LTD.—See SeAH Holdings Corp.; *Int'l*, pg. 6664
FOSHAN SHUNCHING SUPERMOON TRADING CO., LTD.—See Sonepar S.A.; *Int'l*, pg. 7091
FOSHAN SHUNDE DISTRICT JINGYI WANXI COPPER INDUSTRY CO., LTD.—See Guangdong Jingyi Metal Co., Ltd.; *Int'l*, pg. 3157
FOSHAN SHUNDE YIFU VEHICLE SALES & SERVICE CO., LTD.—See Zhongsheng Group Holdings Limited; *Int'l*, pg. 8674
FOSHAN SHUNRAN SHV GAS CO., LTD.—See SHV Holdings N.V.; *Int'l*, pg. 6873
FOSHAN SIME DARBY ELCO POWER EQUIPMENT LIMITED—See Sime Darby Berhad; *Int'l*, pg. 6928
FOSHAN SOUTHERN PACKAGING CO.,LTD.—See Southern Packaging Group Limited; *Int'l*, pg. 7120
FOSHAN TOKAIRIKA AUTOMOTIVE PARTS CO., LTD.—See Tokai Rika Co., Ltd.; *Int'l*, pg. 7780
FOSHAN VANKE PROPERTY COMPANY LIMITED—See China Vanke Co., Ltd.; *Int'l*, pg. 1562
FOSHAN YOWANT TECHNOLOGY CO., LTD.; *Int'l*, pg. 2748
FOSHAN ZHONGFU CONTAINER CO., LTD—See Zhuhai Zhongfu Enterprise Co., Ltd.; *Int'l*, pg. 8679
FOSHAN ZHONGSHENG STAR AUTOMOBILE SALES & SERVICE CO., LTD.—See Zhongsheng Group Holdings Limited; *Int'l*, pg. 8674
FOSINA MARKETING GROUP—See Digital Media Solutions, Inc.; *U.S. Public*, pg. 663
FOSKOR (PTY) LIMITED—See Industrial Development Corporation of South Africa; *Int'l*, pg. 3672
FOSKOR ZIRCONIA (PTY) LTD—See The Murugappa Group, Ltd.; *Int'l*, pg. 7668
FOSMAX LNG SAS—See ENGIE SA; *Int'l*, pg. 2429
FOSRICH CO., LTD.; *Int'l*, pg. 2748
FOSS ANALYTICAL A/S—See Foss A/S; *Int'l*, pg. 2748
FOSS A/S; *Int'l*, pg. 2748
FOSS (BEIJING) SCIENCE, TECHNOLOGY & TRADING CO.—See Foss A/S; *Int'l*, pg. 2748
FOSS BELGIUM B.V.—See Foss A/S; *Int'l*, pg. 2748
FOSS BENELUX B.V.—See Foss A/S; *Int'l*, pg. 2748
FOSS DIALYSIS, LLC—See DaVita Inc.; *U.S. Public*, pg. 639
FOSSE MASTER ISSUER PLC; *Int'l*, pg. 2749
FOSS ESPANA S.A.—See Foss A/S; *Int'l*, pg. 2748
FOSS FIBEROPTISK SYSTEMSALG AS—See discoverIE Group plc; *Int'l*, pg. 2133
FOSS FIBRE OPTICS S.R.O—See discoverIE Group plc; *Int'l*, pg. 2133
FOSS FRANCE S.A.S.—See Foss A/S; *Int'l*, pg. 2748
FOSS GMBH—See Foss A/S; *Int'l*, pg. 2749
FOSSIL ACCESSORIES SOUTH AFRICA PTY LTD—See Fossil Group, Inc.; *U.S. Public*, pg. 874
FOSSIL (ASIA) HOLDINGS LTD. - TAIWAN OFFICE—See Fossil Group, Inc.; *U.S. Public*, pg. 874
FOSSIL (AUSTRALIA) PTY LTD.—See Fossil Group, Inc.; *U.S. Public*, pg. 874
FOSSIL (EAST) LIMITED—See Fossil Group, Inc.; *U.S. Public*, pg. 874
FOSSIL EUROPE B.V.—See Fossil Group, Inc.; *U.S. Public*, pg. 874
FOSSIL EUROPE GMBH—See Fossil Group, Inc.; *U.S. Public*, pg. 875
FOSSIL FRANCE SA—See Fossil Group, Inc.; *U.S. Public*, pg. 875
FOSSIL GROUP, INC.; *U.S. Public*, pg. 874
FOSSIL (HONG KONG) LTD—See Fossil Group, Inc.; *U.S. Public*, pg. 874
FOSSIL INDIA PRIVATE LTD.—See Fossil Group, Inc.; *U.S. Public*, pg. 874
FOSSIL ITALIA, S.R.L.—See Fossil Group, Inc.; *U.S. Public*, pg. 875
FOSSIL MEXICO, S.A. DE C.V.—See Fossil Group, Inc.; *U.S. Public*, pg. 875
FOSSIL PARTNERS, L.P.—See Fossil Group, Inc.; *U.S. Public*, pg. 875
FOSSIL SINGAPORE PTE. LTD.—See Fossil Group, Inc.; *U.S. Public*, pg. 874
FOSSIL SWEDEN AB—See Fossil Group, Inc.; *U.S. Public*, pg. 875
FOSSIL SWITZERLAND GMBH—See Fossil Group, Inc.; *U.S. Public*, pg. 875
FOSSIL TIME MALAYSIA SDN. BHD.—See Fossil Group, Inc.; *U.S. Public*, pg. 874
FOSSIL U.K. HOLDINGS LTD.—See Fossil Group, Inc.; *U.S. Public*, pg. 875
FOSSIL UK LTD.—See Fossil Group, Inc.; *U.S. Public*, pg. 875
FOSS INDIA PVT. LTD.—See Foss A/S; *Int'l*, pg. 2748
FOSS ITALIA S.P.A.—See Foss A/S; *Int'l*, pg. 2749
FOSS JAPAN LTD.—See Foss A/S; *Int'l*, pg. 2749
FOSS KOREA LTD.—See Foss A/S; *Int'l*, pg. 2749
FOSS MANUFACTURING COMPANY LLC; *U.S. Private*, pg. 1578
FOSS MANUFACTURING COMPANY LLC - THE KUNIN GROUP DIVISION—See Foss Manufacturing Company LLC; *U.S. Private*, pg. 1578
FOSS MARITIME CO.—See Saltchuk Resources Inc.; *U.S. Private*, pg. 3534
FOSS MARITIME CO.—See Saltchuk Resources Inc.; *U.S. Private*, pg. 3534
FOSS MOTORS, INC.; *U.S. Private*, pg. 1578
FOSS NORTH AMERICA, INC.—See Foss A/S; *Int'l*, pg. 2749
FOSS PACIFIC (NZ) LTD.—See Foss A/S; *Int'l*, pg. 2749
FOSS PACIFIC PTY. LTD.—See Foss A/S; *Int'l*, pg. 2749
FOS S.P.A.; *Int'l*, pg. 2748
FOSS UK LTD.—See Foss A/S; *Int'l*, pg. 2749
FOSTER AND PARTNERS (HONG KONG) LIMITED—See Foster + Partners Ltd.; *Int'l*, pg. 2749
FOSTER ASSOCIATES, INC.; *U.S. Private*, pg. 1578
FOSTER AUTO PARTS INC.; *U.S. Private*, pg. 1578
FOSTER BLUE WATER OIL, LLC; *U.S. Private*, pg. 1578
FOSTER BUSINESS SERVICE LTD.—See Foster Electric Co., Ltd.; *Int'l*, pg. 2749
FOSTER CARE TO SUCCESS; *U.S. Private*, pg. 1578
FOSTER CHEVROLET-CADILLAC, INC.; *U.S. Private*, pg. 1578
FOSTER CORPORATION; *U.S. Private*, pg. 1578
FOSTER & CRANFIELD LTD.—See Epiris Managers LLP; *Int'l*, pg. 2461
FOSTER DENOVO LIMITED; *Int'l*, pg. 2749
FOSTER DEVELOPMENT COMPANY; *U.S. Private*, pg. 1578
FOSTER DOLAN ENTERPRISES INC.; *U.S. Private*, pg. 1578
FOSTER ELECTRIC (BAC NINH) CO., LTD.—See Foster Electric Co., Ltd.; *Int'l*, pg. 2749
FOSTER ELECTRIC CO., (GUANGZHOU) LTD.—See Foster Electric Co., Ltd.; *Int'l*, pg. 2749
FOSTER ELECTRIC CO., (HEYUAN) LTD.—See Foster Electric Co., Ltd.; *Int'l*, pg. 2749
FOSTER ELECTRIC CO., (HONG KONG) LTD.—See Foster Electric Co., Ltd.; *Int'l*, pg. 2749
FOSTER ELECTRIC CO., LTD.; *Int'l*, pg. 2749
FOSTER ELECTRIC CO., (TAIWAN) LTD.—See Foster Electric Co., Ltd.; *Int'l*, pg. 2749

CORPORATE AFFILIATIONS

FOSTER ELECTRIC (DA NANG) CO., LTD.—See Foster Electric Co., Ltd.; *Int'l*, pg. 2749
FOSTER ELECTRIC (EUROPE) GMBH—See Foster Electric Co., Ltd.; *Int'l*, pg. 2749
FOSTER ELECTRIC IPO (THAILAND) LTD.—See Foster Electric Co., Ltd.; *Int'l*, pg. 2749
FOSTER ELECTRIC (NANNING) CO., LTD.—See Foster Electric Co., Ltd.; *Int'l*, pg. 2749
FOSTER ELECTRIC PENANG SDN. BHD.—See Foster Electric Co., Ltd.; *Int'l*, pg. 2749
FOSTER ELECTRIC (QUANG NGAI) CO., LTD.—See Foster Electric Co., Ltd.; *Int'l*, pg. 2749
FOSTER ELECTRIC (SINGAPORE) PTE. LTD.—See Foster Electric Co., Ltd.; *Int'l*, pg. 2749
FOSTER ELECTRIC (THAILAND) CO., LTD.—See Foster Electric Co., Ltd.; *Int'l*, pg. 2749
FOSTER ELECTRIC (THILAWA) CO., LTD.—See Foster Electric Co., Ltd.; *Int'l*, pg. 2749
FOSTER ELECTRIC (U.S.A.), INC.—See Foster Electric Co., Ltd.; *Int'l*, pg. 2749
FOSTER ELECTRIC (U.S.A.), INC.—See Foster Electric Co., Ltd.; *Int'l*, pg. 2749
FOSTER ELECTRIC (VIETNAM) CO., LTD.—See Foster Electric Co., Ltd.; *Int'l*, pg. 2749
FOSTER ELECTRIC (VIETNAM) CO., LTD. - VIETNAM FACTORY 2—See Foster Electric Co., Ltd.; *Int'l*, pg. 2749
FOSTER ELECTRONICS LIMITED—See Foster Electric Co., Ltd.; *Int'l*, pg. 2750
FOSTER FARMS LLC—See Atlas Holdings, LLC; *U.S. Private*, pg. 376
FOSTER FINANCIAL GROUP; *U.S. Private*, pg. 1578
FOSTER & FOSTER CONSULTING ACTUARIES INC.; *U.S. Private*, pg. 1578
FOSTER FUELS INC.; *U.S. Private*, pg. 1578
FOSTER GARVEY PC; *U.S. Private*, pg. 1578
FOSTER HOLDING GROUP INC.; *U.S. Private*, pg. 1578
FOSTERING SUPPORT GROUP LIMITED—See Sheikh Holdings Group (Investments) Limited; *Int'l*, pg. 6794
FOSTER INTERNATIONAL PACKAGING (PTY.) LTD.—See Close the Loop Limited; *Int'l*, pg. 1661
FOSTER LUMBER YARD INC. - FAIRFIELD—See Foster Lumber Yard Inc.; *U.S. Private*, pg. 1579
FOSTER LUMBER YARD INC.; *U.S. Private*, pg. 1579
FOSTER MARKETING COMMUNICATIONS; *U.S. Private*, pg. 1579
FOSTER MARKETING COMMUNICATIONS—See Foster Marketing Communications; *U.S. Private*, pg. 1579
FOSTER-MILLER, INC.—See QinetiQ Group plc; *Int'l*, pg. 6142
FOSTER + PARTNERS LTD.; *Int'l*, pg. 2749
FOSTER PRINTING SERVICE, INC.; *U.S. Private*, pg. 1579
FOSTER RAFFAN IPLAN PTY. LTD.—See Azimut Holding SpA; *Int'l*, pg. 779
FOSTER REFRIGERATOR FRANCE S.A.S.—See Illinois Tool Works Inc.; *U.S. Public*, pg. 1103
FOSTER REFRIGERATOR (U.K.)—See Illinois Tool Works Inc.; *U.S. Public*, pg. 1103
FOSTERS FREEZE, LLC; *U.S. Private*, pg. 1579
FOSTERS INC.; *U.S. Private*, pg. 1579
FOSTER SUPPLY INC.—See Core & Main, Inc.; *U.S. Public*, pg. 576
FOSTERVILLE GOLD MINE PTY. LTD.—See Agnico Eagle Mines Limited; *Int'l*, pg. 212
FOSTERVILLE SOUTH EXPLORATION LTD.; *Int'l*, pg. 2750
FOSTER WAYLAND INCORPORATED; *U.S. Private*, pg. 1579
FOSTER WHEELER AG—See John Wood Group PLC; *Int'l*, pg. 3982
FOSTER WHEELER ARABIA, LTD.—See John Wood Group PLC; *Int'l*, pg. 3983
FOSTER WHEELER ASIA PACIFIC PTE. LTD.—See John Wood Group PLC; *Int'l*, pg. 3983
FOSTER WHEELER BIMAS A.S.—See John Wood Group PLC; *Int'l*, pg. 3983
FOSTER WHEELER ENERGY MANAGEMENT (SHANGHAI) COMPANY LIMITED—See John Wood Group PLC; *Int'l*, pg. 3983
FOSTER WHEELER LLC—See John Wood Group PLC; *Int'l*, pg. 3982
FOSTER WHEELER OOO—See John Wood Group PLC; *Int'l*, pg. 3983
FOSTER WHEELER (PHILIPPINES) CORPORATION—See John Wood Group PLC; *Int'l*, pg. 3982
FOSTER WHEELER POWER GROUP ASIA LIMITED—See John Wood Group PLC; *Int'l*, pg. 3983
FOSTER WHEELER SOUTH AFRICA (PTY) LIMITED—See John Wood Group PLC; *Int'l*, pg. 3983
FOSTEX CO., LTD.—See Foster Electric Co., Ltd.; *Int'l*, pg. 2750
FOSTORIA INDUSTRIES, INC.—See TPI Corp.; *U.S. Private*, pg. 4200
FOSUN INTERNATIONAL LIMITED; *Int'l*, pg. 2750
FOSUN KITE BIOTECHNOLOGY CO., LTD.—See Shanghai Fosun Pharmaceutical (Group) Co., Ltd.; *Int'l*, pg. 6767

COMPANY NAME INDEX

FOSUN PHARMA KITE BIOTECHNOLOGY CO., LTD.—See Gilead Sciences, Inc.; *U.S. Public*, pg. 937
FOSUN TOURISM GROUP.—See Fosun International Limited; *Int'l*, pg. 2751
FOTAFLEX LTD.—See Forges Tardieu Ltd; *Int'l*, pg. 2733
FOTEX HOLDING SE; *Int'l*, pg. 2752
FOTEX NETHERLANDS B.V.—See Fotex Holding SE; *Int'l*, pg. 2752
FOTEXNET KFT.—See Fotex Holding SE; *Int'l*, pg. 2752
FOTHERGILL CRENETTE LTD—See Groupe Porcher Industries; *Int'l*, pg. 3109
FOTH PRODUCTION SOLUTIONS, LLC—See Foth & Van Dyke & Associates Inc.; *U.S. Private*, pg. 1579
FOTH & VAN DYKE & ASSOCIATES INC; *U.S. Private*, pg. 1579
FOTOCOLOR GMBH—See CEWE Stiftung & Co. KGaA; *Int'l*, pg. 1425
FOTO ELECTRIC SUPPLY CO., INC.; *U.S. Private*, pg. 1579
FOTO FANTASY, INC.—See Dai Nippon Printing Co., Ltd.; *Int'l*, pg. 1914
FOTOFIX SCHNELLPHOTOAUTOMATEN GMBH—See ME Group International plc; *Int'l*, pg. 4762
FOTOJOKER SP. Z O. O.—See CEWE Stiftung & Co. KGaA; *Int'l*, pg. 1425
FOTOKNUDSEN AS—See Cimpress plc; *Int'l*, pg. 1609
FOTOLIA LLC—See Adobe Inc.; *U.S. Public*, pg. 42
FOTOLOG, INC.—See AdUX SA; *Int'l*, pg. 155
FOTOMAX (F.E.) LTD.—See China-Hong Kong Photo Products Holdings Limited; *Int'l*, pg. 1568
FOTONATION CORPORATION—See Adeia Inc.; *U.S. Public*, pg. 41
FOTONATION LIMITED; *Int'l*, pg. 2753
FOTON TRUCK (THAILAND) CO., LTD.—See Tan Chong International Limited; *Int'l*, pg. 7453
FOTOTRONIC IMAGER DIVISION—See ME Group International plc; *Int'l*, pg. 4762
FOTO-VIDEO SAUTER GMBH & CO. KG—See Aurelius Equity Opportunities SE & Co. KGaA; *Int'l*, pg. 708
FOTO-WEAR INC.; *U.S. Private*, pg. 1579
FOTV MEDIA NETWORKS INC.; *U.S. Private*, pg. 1579
FOUAD ALGHANIM & SONS AUTOMOTIVE CO.—See Fouad Alghanim & Sons Group of Companies; *Int'l*, pg. 2753
FOUAD ALGHANIM & SONS GROUP OF COMPANIES; *Int'l*, pg. 2753
FOUAD & TOUFIC FADEL & CO.—See Stora Enso Oyj; *Int'l*, pg. 7224
FOUAD TRAVEL & CARGO AGENCY—See Abdulla Fouad Holding Co.; *Int'l*, pg. 59
FOUGERA PHARMACEUTICALS INC.—See Sandoz Group AG; *Int'l*, pg. 6527
FOUGEROLLE S.A.—See Eiffage S.A.; *Int'l*, pg. 2330
FOUGHT & COMPANY INC.; *U.S. Private*, pg. 1579
FOULGER-PRATT CONTRACTING LLC; *U.S. Private*, pg. 1579
FOUNDAMENTAL GMBH—See Heidelberg Materials AG; *Int'l*, pg. 3310
FOUNDATION 9 ENTERTAINMENT, INC.; *U.S. Private*, pg. 1579
FOUNDATION ALLIANCE PTE. LTD.—See VINCI S.A.; *Int'l*, pg. 8221
FOUNDATION ASSOCIATES ENGINEERING PTE LTD—See Zicom Group Limited; *Int'l*, pg. 8681
FOUNDATION AUTOMOTIVE CORP; *U.S. Private*, pg. 1579
FOUNDATION BARIATRIC HOSPITAL OF SAN ANTONIO, LLC—See Foundation Healthcare, Inc.; *U.S. Private*, pg. 1580
FOUNDATION BUILDING MATERIALS, INC.—See American Securities LLC; *U.S. Private*, pg. 248
FOUNDATION BUILDING MATERIALS, LLC—See American Securities LLC; *U.S. Private*, pg. 248
FOUNDATION CAPITAL, LLC; *U.S. Private*, pg. 1579
FOUNDATION CARE, LLC—See Centene Corporation; *U.S. Public*, pg. 469
FOUNDATION CENTER; *U.S. Private*, pg. 1579
FOUNDATION COMMUNITIES; *U.S. Private*, pg. 1579
FOUNDATION CONSTRUCTORS INC.; *U.S. Private*, pg. 1579
FOUNDATION ENTERPRISE SYSTEMS—See Siemens Aktiengesellschaft; *Int'l*, pg. 6889
FOUNDATION FINANCIAL HOLDINGS, INC.; *U.S. Private*, pg. 1579
FOUNDATION FOR EDUCATIONAL SERVICES; *U.S. Private*, pg. 1580
FOUNDATION FOR EMBRYONIC COMPETENCE; *U.S. Private*, pg. 1580
FOUNDATION FOR EXCELLENCE IN EDUCATION; *U.S. Private*, pg. 1580
FOUNDATION FOR FOOD & AGRICULTURE RESEARCH; *U.S. Private*, pg. 1580
FOUNDATION FOR JEWISH PHILANTHROPIES; *U.S. Private*, pg. 1580
FOUNDATION FOR NEWARK'S FUTURE; *U.S. Private*, pg. 1580
FOUNDATION FOR SURGICAL FELLOWSHIP; *U.S. Private*, pg. 1580

FOUNDATION FOR THE CAROLINAS; *U.S. Private*, pg. 1580
FOUNDATION FOR THE ELDERLY; *U.S. Private*, pg. 1580
FOUNDATION FOR THE GLOBAL COMPACT; *U.S. Private*, pg. 1580
FOUNDATION GAS—See Fauji Foundation; *Int'l*, pg. 2623
FOUNDATION GLOBAL EDUCATION LIMITED—See Bright Scholar Education Holdings Limited; *Int'l*, pg. 1161
FOUNDATION HEALTHCARE, INC.; *U.S. Private*, pg. 1580
FOUNDATION ICT SOLUTIONS B.V.—See UNIT4 N.V.; *Int'l*, pg. 8062
FOUNDATION INVESTMENT PARTNERS, LLC; *U.S. Private*, pg. 1580
FOUNDATION MEDICINE, INC.—See Roche Holding AG; *Int'l*, pg. 6373
FOUNDATION RESERVE INSURANCE CO.—See New Mexico Mutual Casualty Company; *U.S. Private*, pg. 2898
FOUNDATIONS ATLANTA, LLC—See Universal Health Services, Inc.; *U.S. Public*, pg. 2257
FOUNDATION SECURITIES (PVT) LIMITED—See Fauji Foundation; *Int'l*, pg. 2623
FOUNDATIONS FOR CHANGE INC.—See Numinus Wellness Inc.; *Int'l*, pg. 5489
FOUNDATION SOFTWARE, INC.—See Thoma Bravo, L.P.; *U.S. Private*, pg. 4148
THE FOUNDATION—See De Agostini S.p.A.; *Int'l*, pg. 1994
FOUNDATION SOURCE PHILANTHROPIC SERVICES INC.—See GTCR LLC; *U.S. Private*, pg. 1805
FOUNDATIONS RECOVERY NETWORK, LLC—See Universal Health Services, Inc.; *U.S. Public*, pg. 2257
FOUNDATIONS SAN DIEGO, LLC—See Universal Health Services, Inc.; *U.S. Public*, pg. 2257
FOUNDATION SURGICAL HOSPITAL MANAGEMENT, LLC—See Foundation Healthcare, Inc.; *U.S. Private*, pg. 1580
FOUNDATIONS VIRGINIA, LLC—See Universal Health Services, Inc.; *U.S. Public*, pg. 2257
FOUNDATION TECHNOLOGIES, INC.; *U.S. Private*, pg. 1580
FOUNDATION TITLE, LLC; *U.S. Private*, pg. 1580
FOUNDATIONTV, INC.—See Cineverse Corp.; *U.S. Public*, pg. 495
FOUND CONCRETE PTY. LTD.—See Seven Group Holdings Limited; *Int'l*, pg. 6733
FOUNDER HOLDINGS LIMITED; *Int'l*, pg. 2753
FOUNDER INTERNATIONAL (BEIJING) CO., LTD.—See Founder Technology Group Corp.; *Int'l*, pg. 2753
FOUNDER INTERNATIONAL (CHANGCHUN) CO., LTD.—See Founder Technology Group Corp.; *Int'l*, pg. 2753
FOUNDER INTERNATIONAL CO., LTD.—See Founder Technology Group Corp.; *Int'l*, pg. 2753
FOUNDER INTERNATIONAL (GUANGZHOU) CO., LTD.—See Founder Technology Group Corp.; *Int'l*, pg. 2753
FOUNDER INTERNATIONAL (JIANGSU) CO., LTD.—See Founder Technology Group Corp.; *Int'l*, pg. 2753
FOUNDER INTERNATIONAL (WUHAN) CO., LTD.—See Founder Technology Group Corp.; *Int'l*, pg. 2753
FOUNDERS 3 REAL ESTATE SERVICES; *U.S. Private*, pg. 1580
FOUNDERS BAY HOLDINGS; *U.S. Public*, pg. 875
FOUNDERS BREWING CO.; *U.S. Private*, pg. 1580
FOUNDER'S CONSULTANTS HOLDINGS, INC.; *Int'l*, pg. 2753
FOUNDER SECURITIES CO., LTD.; *Int'l*, pg. 2753
FOUNDERS ENTERTAINMENT, LLC—See Live Nation Entertainment, Inc.; *U.S. Public*, pg. 1328
FOUNDERS EQUITY, INC.; *U.S. Private*, pg. 1580
FOUNDERS FUND INC.; *U.S. Private*, pg. 1581
FOUNDERS INSURANCE CO.—See Nationwide Group; *U.S. Private*, pg. 2866
FOUNDERS OIL & GAS, LLC—See D.R. Horton, Inc.; *U.S. Public*, pg. 620
FOUNDER SPORT GROUP—See Platinum Equity, LLC; *U.S. Private*, pg. 3207
FOUNDERS RX LLC—See The Ensign Group, Inc.; *U.S. Public*, pg. 2071
FOUNDERS TITLE AGENCY, INC.—See Hovnanian Enterprises, Inc.; *U.S. Public*, pg. 1056
FOUNDER TECHNOLOGY GROUP CORP.; *Int'l*, pg. 2753
FOUNDING CONSTRUCTION DEVELOPMENT CO., LTD.; *Int'l*, pg. 2753
FOUNDPAC GROUP BERHAD; *Int'l*, pg. 2753
FOUNDRY COMMERCIAL LLC; *U.S. Private*, pg. 1581
FOUNDRY ENGINEERING CORPORATION SDN. BHD.—See Golsta Sdn. Bhd.; *Int'l*, pg. 3037
FOUNDRY FUEL PRODUCTS LTD.; *Int'l*, pg. 2754
FOUNDRY GROUP LLC; *U.S. Private*, pg. 1581
FOUNDRY HEALTH, LLC—See IQVIA Holdings Inc.; *U.S. Public*, pg. 1168
FOUNDRY MEADOWS (BEXHILL) RESIDENTS MANAGEMENT COMPANY LIMITED—See Persimmon plc; *Int'l*, pg. 5815

FOUNDRY SERVICE GMBH—See Park-Ohio Holdings Corp.; *U.S. Public*, pg. 1638
FOUNDRY SERVICE GMBH—See Park-Ohio Holdings Corp.; *U.S. Public*, pg. 1639
FOUNDRY SERVICE GMBH—See Park-Ohio Holdings Corp.; *U.S. Public*, pg. 1639
FOUNDRY SERVICE GMBH—See Park-Ohio Holdings Corp.; *U.S. Public*, pg. 1639
FOUNDRY SERVICE GMBH—See Park-Ohio Holdings Corp.; *U.S. Public*, pg. 1639
THE FOUNDRY VISIONMONGERS LIMITED—See Roper Technologies, Inc.; *U.S. Public*, pg. 1813
FOUNDSTONE; *U.S. Private*, pg. 1581
FOUNTAIN ASSET CORP.; *U.S. Private*, pg. 2754
FOUNTAIN CAN CORPORATION—See Daiwa Can Company; *Int'l*, pg. 1944
FOUNTAIN CAN CORPORATION TAINAN FACTORY—See Daiwa Can Company; *Int'l*, pg. 1944
FOUNTAIN CONSTRUCTION COMPANY, INC.; *U.S. Private*, pg. 1581
FOUNTAIN COUNTY NEIGHBOR INC.—See Community Media Group; *U.S. Private*, pg. 995
FOUNTAINE PAJOT SA; *Int'l*, pg. 2754
FOUNTAIN FINANCIAL, INC.—See Ameris Bancorp; *U.S. Public*, pg. 114
FOUNTAIN FROZEN LTD .; *Int'l*, pg. 2754
THE FOUNTAIN GROUP, LLC; *U.S. Private*, pg. 4030
FOUNTAINHEAD CAPITAL MANAGEMENT, LLC; *U.S. Private*, pg. 1581
FOUNTAINHEAD DEVELOPMENT INC.; *U.S. Private*, pg. 1581
FOUNTAINHEAD DEVELOPMENT, LLC; *U.S. Private*, pg. 1581
THE FOUNTAINHEAD GROUP, INC.; *U.S. Private*, pg. 4030
FOUNTAIN HOUSE, INC.; *U.S. Private*, pg. 1581
FOUNTAIN INTERTRADE CORPORATION—See Statkraft AS; *Int'l*, pg. 7184
FOUNTAIN JADE PTY. LTD.—See Woolworths Group Limited; *Int'l*, pg. 8452
FOUNTAIN LEASING LLC—See SmartFinancial, Inc.; *U.S. Public*, pg. 1895
FOUNTAIN PLATING CO., INC.—See British Columbia Investment Management Corp.; *Int'l*, pg. 1170
FOUNTAIN POWERBOATS, INC.—See American Marine Holdings, LLC; *U.S. Private*, pg. 240
FOUNTAIN ROCK MANAGEMENT CORPORATION; *U.S. Private*, pg. 1581
FOUNTAINS AMERICA INC.—See OCS Group Limited; *Int'l*, pg. 5521
FOUNTAIN S.A.; *Int'l*, pg. 2754
THE FOUNTAINS AT FRANKLIN—See The Fountains, Inc.; *U.S. Private*, pg. 4030
FOUNTAINS COUNTRY CLUB; *U.S. Private*, pg. 1581
FOUNTAIN SET (EUROPE) LIMITED—See Fountain Set (Holdings) Limited; *Int'l*, pg. 2754
FOUNTAIN SET (HOLDINGS) LIMITED; *Int'l*, pg. 2754
FOUNTAIN SET LIMITED—See Fountain Set (Holdings) Limited; *Int'l*, pg. 2754
FOUNTAINS FORESTRY INC.—See OCS Group Limited; *Int'l*, pg. 5521
THE FOUNTAINS, INC.; *U.S. Private*, pg. 4030
FOUNTAINS LAND INC.—See OCS Group Limited; *Int'l*, pg. 5521
FOUNTAIN SQUARE MANAGEMENT CO.—See Fifth Third Bancorp; *U.S. Public*, pg. 833
THE FOUNTAINS—See Rohm Services, Corp.; *U.S. Private*, pg. 3473
FOUNTAINS SPATIAL INC.—See OCS Group Limited; *Int'l*, pg. 5521
THE FOUNTAIN STUDIOS; *Int'l*, pg. 7644
FOUNTAIN TIRE CORP.; *Int'l*, pg. 2754
FOUNTAIN TRADING COMPANY—See REHAU Verwaltungszentrale AG; *Int'l*, pg. 6255
FOUNTAIN VALLEY REGIONAL HOSPITAL & MEDICAL CENTER, INC.—See UCI Health; *U.S. Private*, pg. 4274
FOUNTAIN VALLEY SURGERY CENTER, LLC—See Tenet Healthcare Corporation; *U.S. Public*, pg. 2005
FOUNTAINVEST PARTNERS (ASIA) LIMITED; *Int'l*, pg. 2754
FOURACE INDUSTRIES GROUP HOLDINGS LIMITED; *Int'l*, pg. 2755
FOURCAR BELGIUM SA—See Carrefour SA; *Int'l*, pg. 1344
FOURCAR BV—See Carrefour SA; *Int'l*, pg. 1345
FOUR CIRCLES RECOVERY CENTER, LLC—See Acadia Healthcare Company, Inc.; *U.S. Public*, pg. 28
FOUR COMMUNICATIONS GROUP PLC; *Int'l*, pg. 2754
FOUR COMMUNICATIONS PLC—See Four Communications Group plc; *Int'l*, pg. 2754
FOUR CORNERS BREWING CO.—See Constellation Brands, Inc.; *U.S. Public*, pg. 571
FOUR CORNERS BUSINESS JOURNAL—See Gannett Co., Inc.; *U.S. Public*, pg. 900
FOUR CORNERS COMMUNITY BANK; *U.S. Private*, pg. 1581
FOUR CORNERS INSURANCE SERVICES—See Topa Equities Ltd, Inc.; *U.S. Private*, pg. 4186
FOUR CORNERS MATERIALS—See CRH plc; *Int'l*, pg. 1847

FOUR CORNERS PROPERTY TRUST, INC.

FOUR CORNERS PROPERTY TRUST, INC.; *U.S. Public*, pg. 875
FOUR COUNTY ELECTRIC MEMBERSHIP CORPORATION; *U.S. Private*, pg. 1582
FOUR COUNTY ELECTRIC POWER ASSOCIATION; *U.S. Private*, pg. 1582
FOUR CROWN INC.; *U.S. Private*, pg. 1582
FOUR DIRECTIONS ECOMMERCE LIMITED—See Vongroup Ltd; *Int'l*, pg. 8304
FOUR FOODS GROUP HOLDINGS; *U.S. Private*, pg. 1582
FOUR HANDS, LLC; *U.S. Private*, pg. 1582
FOURJAY LLC; *U.S. Private*, pg. 1583
FOUR LANE AUTO SALES; *U.S. Private*, pg. 1582
FOURLANE FORD SALES LTD.; *Int'l*, pg. 2755
FOUR LEAF ACQUISITION CORPORATION; *U.S. Public*, pg. 875
FOUR LEAF TECHNOLOGIES A/S—See Arrow Electronics, Inc.; *U.S. Public*, pg. 199
FOUR LEAVES PTE.LTD—See Yamazaki Baking Co., Ltd.; *Int'l*, pg. 8556
FOURLIS HOLDINGS S.A.; *Int'l*, pg. 2755
FOURLIS TRADE AEBE—See FOURLIS HOLDINGS S.A.; *Int'l*, pg. 2755
FOUR MARKETING LTD.; *Int'l*, pg. 2755
FOUR M HOLDINGS LLC; *U.S. Private*, pg. 1582
FOURMILE WIND ENERGY, LLC—See Constellation Energy Corporation; *U.S. Public*, pg. 572
FOUR M PROPACK PVT. LTD.—See Shriji Polymers (India) Ltd.; *Int'l*, pg. 6866
FOURNIE GROSPAUD RESEAUX SAS—See VINCI S.A.; *Int'l*, pg. 8221
FOURNIE GROSPAUD SYNERYS—See VINCI S.A.; *Int'l*, pg. 8237
FOURNIE GROSPAUD TOULOUSE SAS—See VINCI S.A.; *Int'l*, pg. 8221
FOURNIER PHARMA GMBH—See Abbott Laboratories; *U.S. Public*, pg. 19
FOUR NINES GOLD INC/CA; *Int'l*, pg. 2755
FOURNY NV—See H.B. Fuller Company; *U.S. Public*, pg. 977
FOUR OAKS FAMILY & CHILDREN'S SERVICES; *U.S. Private*, pg. 1582
FOUR PAWS PRODUCTS, LTD.—See Central Garden & Pet Company; *U.S. Public*, pg. 473
FOUR PEAKS BREWING COMPANY, INC.—See Anheuser-Busch InBev SA/NV; *Int'l*, pg. 466
FOUR POINT PRODUCTS—See American Thermoplastic Company; *U.S. Private*, pg. 257
FOUR POINTS BY SHERATON PHILADELPHIA AIRPORT—See Marriott International, Inc.; *U.S. Public*, pg. 1372
FOUR POINTS BY SHERATON PORTLAND EAST—See Marriott International, Inc.; *U.S. Public*, pg. 1372
FOUR POINTS BY SHERATON—See Marriott International, Inc.; *U.S. Public*, pg. 1372
FOUR POINTS BY SHERATON SUITES TAMPA AIRPORT WESTSHORE—See Marriott International, Inc.; *U.S. Public*, pg. 1372
FOUR POINTS BY SHERATON WAKEFIELD BOSTON HOTEL & CONFERENCE CENTER—See Marriott International, Inc.; *U.S. Public*, pg. 1372
FOUR ROSES DISTILLERY, LLC—See Kirin Holdings Company, Limited; *Int'l*, pg. 4187
FOUR SALES, LTD.; *U.S. Private*, pg. 1582
FOUR SEAS CONFECTIONERY (SHENZHEN) CO., LTD.—See Four Seas Mercantile Holdings Limited; *Int'l*, pg. 2755
FOUR SEAS (HEBEI) FOOD COMPANY LIMITED—See Four Seas Mercantile Holdings Limited; *Int'l*, pg. 2755
FOUR SEAS MERCANTILE HOLDINGS LIMITED; *Int'l*, pg. 2755
FOUR SEASON EQUIPMENT; *U.S. Private*, pg. 1582
FOUR SEASONS - A DIVISION OF STANDARD MOTOR PRODUCTS, INC.—See Standard Motor Products, Inc.; *U.S. Public*, pg. 1929
FOUR SEASONS EDUCATION (CAYMAN) INC; *Int'l*, pg. 2755
FOUR SEASONS ELECTRICAL SERVICES; *U.S. Private*, pg. 1582
FOUR SEASONS FORD; *U.S. Private*, pg. 1582
FOUR SEASONS HARVEST LTD.—See Dole plc; *Int'l*, pg. 2158
FOUR SEASONS HEALTH CARE LIMITED—See Terra Firma Capital Partners Ltd.; *Int'l*, pg. 7566
FOUR SEASONS HOTEL ATLANTA—See Cascade Investment LLC; *U.S. Private*, pg. 779
FOUR SEASONS HOTEL AUSTIN—See Cascade Investment LLC; *U.S. Private*, pg. 779
FOUR SEASONS HOTEL BOSTON—See Cascade Investment LLC; *U.S. Private*, pg. 779
FOUR SEASONS HOTEL CHICAGO—See Cascade Investment LLC; *U.S. Private*, pg. 779
FOUR SEASONS HOTEL HOUSTON—See Cascade Investment LLC; *U.S. Private*, pg. 779
FOUR SEASONS HOTEL ISTANBUL—See Cascade Investment LLC; *U.S. Private*, pg. 779
FOUR SEASONS HOTEL LAS VEGAS—See Cascade Investment LLC; *U.S. Private*, pg. 779
FOUR SEASONS HOTEL LONDON—See Cascade Investment LLC; *U.S. Private*, pg. 779
FOUR SEASONS HOTEL LOS ANGELES AT BEVERLY HILLS—See Cascade Investment LLC; *U.S. Private*, pg. 779
FOUR SEASONS HOTEL MEXICO, D.F.—See Cascade Investment LLC; *U.S. Private*, pg. 779
FOUR SEASONS HOTEL MILANO—See Cascade Investment LLC; *U.S. Private*, pg. 779
FOUR SEASONS HOTEL NEW YORK—See Cascade Investment LLC; *U.S. Private*, pg. 779
FOUR SEASONS HOTEL PHILADELPHIA—See Cascade Investment LLC; *U.S. Private*, pg. 779
FOUR SEASONS HOTEL RITZ LISBON—See Cascade Investment LLC; *U.S. Private*, pg. 779
FOUR SEASONS HOTELS INC.—See Cascade Investment LLC; *U.S. Private*, pg. 779
FOUR SEASONS HOTEL SINGAPORE—See Cascade Investment LLC; *U.S. Private*, pg. 779
FOUR SEASONS HOTELS & RESORTS—See Cascade Investment LLC; *U.S. Private*, pg. 780
FOUR SEASONS HOTEL TORONTO—See Cascade Investment LLC; *U.S. Private*, pg. 780
FOUR SEASONS HOTEL VANCOUVER—See Cascade Investment LLC; *U.S. Private*, pg. 780
FOUR SEASONS HOTEL WASHINGTON, DC—See Cascade Investment LLC; *U.S. Private*, pg. 780
FOUR SEASONS INTERNATIONAL REALTY, LLC—See Peerage Realty Partners, Inc.; *Int'l*, pg. 5779
FOUR SEASONS PRODUCE, INC.; *U.S. Private*, pg. 1582
FOUR SEASONS PTY. LTD.—See Wiseway Logistics Pty. Ltd.; *Int'l*, pg. 8437
FOUR SEASONS RESORT AVIARA—See Cascade Investment LLC; *U.S. Private*, pg. 780
FOUR SEASONS RESORT BALI—See Cascade Investment LLC; *U.S. Private*, pg. 780
FOUR SEASONS RESORT & CLUB DALLAS—See Cascade Investment LLC; *U.S. Private*, pg. 780
FOUR SEASONS RESORT HUALALAI—See Cascade Investment LLC; *U.S. Private*, pg. 780
FOUR SEASONS RESORT MAUI—See Cascade Investment LLC; *U.S. Private*, pg. 780
FOUR SEASONS RESORT NEVIS—See Cascade Investment LLC; *U.S. Private*, pg. 780
FOUR SEASONS RESORT PALM BEACH—See Cascade Investment LLC; *U.S. Private*, pg. 780
FOUR SEASONS RESORT SANTA BARBARA—See Cascade Investment LLC; *U.S. Private*, pg. 780
FOUR SEASONS RESORT SCOTTSDALE AT TROON NORTH—See Braemar Hotels & Resorts, Inc.; *U.S. Public*, pg. 379
FOUR SEASONS SALES & SERVICE, INC.—See Houchens Industries, Inc.; *U.S. Private*, pg. 1990
FOUR SEASONS SUNROOM—See Epwin Group Plc; *Int'l*, pg. 2466
FOUR SEASONS TRIANGLE STOP; *U.S. Private*, pg. 1582
FOUR SEASONS WINES LTD.—See Grover Zampa Vineyards Limited; *Int'l*, pg. 3112
FOUR SEAS (SUZHOU) FOOD CO., LTD.—See Four Seas Mercantile Holdings Limited; *Int'l*, pg. 2755
FOURSHORE CAPITAL LLC; *U.S. Private*, pg. 1583
FOURSIGHT CAPITAL LLC—See SoftBank Group Corp.; *Int'l*, pg. 7053
FOUR SOFT USA INC.—See Francisco Partners Management, LP; *U.S. Private*, pg. 1589
FOURSOME FINER FOODS INC.; *U.S. Private*, pg. 1583
FOUR SPRINGS CAPITAL TRUST; *U.S. Private*, pg. 1582
FOURSQUARE LABS, INC.; *U.S. Private*, pg. 1583
FOUR STAR HOLDINGS, INC.; *U.S. Private*, pg. 1582
FOUR STAR SALON SERVICES INC.; *U.S. Private*, pg. 1582
FOUR STAR TRANSPORTATION CO.; *U.S. Private*, pg. 1582
FOURSTAR WEALTH ADVISORS LLC; *U.S. Private*, pg. 1583
FOUR-STATE HYGIENE, INC.—See Ecolab Inc.; *U.S. Public*, pg. 714
FOURTH APPLE CO., LTD.—See RS Public Company Limited; *Int'l*, pg. 6418
THE FOURTH CONSTRUCTION CORPORATION—See China National Chemical Engineering Co., Ltd.; *Int'l*, pg. 1531
FOURTH CRYSTAL PARK ASSOCIATES LIMITED PARTNERSHIP—See Vornado Realty Trust; *U.S. Public*, pg. 2310
FOURTH DIMENSION DISPLAY LTD.—See Kopin Corporation; *U.S. Public*, pg. 1271
FOURTH DIMENSION SOLUTIONS LIMITED; *Int'l*, pg. 2755
FOURTH GENERATION INFORMATION SYSTEMS LIMITED; *Int'l*, pg. 2755
FOURTH GROUP INC—See Byrne Dairy Inc.; *U.S. Private*, pg. 701
FOURTH LTD.—See Marlin Equity Partners, LLC; *U.S. Private*, pg. 2584
FOURTH POINT WEALTH; *U.S. Private*, pg. 1583
FOURTH TECHNOLOGIES INC.; *U.S. Private*, pg. 1583

CORPORATE AFFILIATIONS

FOURTH WALL EVENTS, INC.—See InteleTravel.com; *U.S. Private*, pg. 2104
FOUR TWENTY SEVEN, INC.—See Moody's Corporation; *U.S. Public*, pg. 1467
FOUR WAY DISTRIBUTORS LTD.; *Int'l*, pg. 2755
FOUR WINDS INTERACTIVE LLC; *U.S. Private*, pg. 1582
FOUR WINDS INVESTMENT CORP; *U.S. Private*, pg. 1583
FOUR WINDS TRUCK BROKERS, INC.; *U.S. Private*, pg. 1583
FOUR WINNS, LLC—See Beneteau S.A.; *Int'l*, pg. 973
FOUSHEE & ASSOCIATES CO., INC.; *U.S. Private*, pg. 1583
FOUTZ & BURSUM CONSTRUCTION CO.; *U.S. Private*, pg. 1583
FOVEA JEWELRY HOLDINGS LTD.; *U.S. Public*, pg. 875
FOV FABRICS AB; *Int'l*, pg. 2755
FOWLER BUICK-GMC INC.; *U.S. Private*, pg. 1583
FOWLER CONSTRUCTION & DEVELOPMENT, INC.; *U.S. Private*, pg. 1583
FOWLER CUSTOM HOMES; *U.S. Private*, pg. 1583
FOWLER ELEVATOR INC.; *U.S. Private*, pg. 1583
FOWLER-FLEMISTER CONCRETE INC.; *U.S. Private*, pg. 1583
FOWLER FOODS INC.; *U.S. Private*, pg. 1583
FOWLER GENERAL CONSTRUCTION, INC.; *U.S. Private*, pg. 1583
FOWLER HYUNDAI LTD.; *Int'l*, pg. 2756
FOWLER PRODUCTS COMPANY, LLC—See Leonard Green & Partners, L.P.; *U.S. Private*, pg. 2427
FOWLERS ASPHALTING PTY. LIMITED—See Downer EDI Limited; *Int'l*, pg. 2186
FOWLERS INC.; *U.S. Private*, pg. 1583
FOWLER WELCH-COOLCHAIN BV—See Jet2 PLC; *Int'l*, pg. 3933
FOWLER WELCH LIMITED—See Unternehmensgruppe Theo Muller S.e.c.s.; *Int'l*, pg. 8085
FOWNES BROTHERS & CO., INC.; *U.S. Private*, pg. 1583
FOX ASSET MANAGEMENT LLC—See Morgan Stanley; *U.S. Public*, pg. 1471
FOX ASSOCIATES INC.; *U.S. Private*, pg. 1584
FOX AUTOMOTIVE GROUP—See AutoNation, Inc.; *U.S. Public*, pg. 235
FOX BASEBALL HOLDINGS, INC.—See Fox Corporation; *U.S. Public*, pg. 875
FOXBORO (MALAYSIA) SDN. BHD.—See Schneider Electric SE; *Int'l*, pg. 6623
FOXBORO TERMINALS CO. INC.—See Distribution Services of America, Inc.; *U.S. Private*, pg. 1239
FOXBOROUGH LODGE LIMITED PARTNERSHIP—See UDR, Inc.; *U.S. Public*, pg. 2218
FOX BROADCASTING COMPANY, LLC—See Fox Corporation; *U.S. Public*, pg. 875
FOX BROS PIGGLY WIGGLY INC.; *U.S. Private*, pg. 1584
FOX BROTHERS COMPANY—See Beacon Roofing Supply, Inc.; *U.S. Public*, pg. 286
FOX BUICK GMC—See DP Fox Ventures, LLC; *U.S. Private*, pg. 1270
FOX BUS LINES INC.—See Mobico Group PLC; *Int'l*, pg. 5008
FOX CABLE NETWORK SERVICES, LLC—See Fox Corporation; *U.S. Public*, pg. 876
FOX CABLE NETWORKS, INC.—See Fox Corporation; *U.S. Public*, pg. 875
FOX CHEVROLET, LLC—See AutoNation, Inc.; *U.S. Public*, pg. 235
FOX CHRYSLER DODGE JEEP; *U.S. Private*, pg. 1584
FOX COMPANIES; *U.S. Private*, pg. 1584
FOXCONN BAJA CALIFORNIA S.A. DE C.V.—See Hon Hai Precision Industry Co., Ltd.; *Int'l*, pg. 3456
FOXCONN CORPORATION—See Hon Hai Precision Industry Co., Ltd.; *Int'l*, pg. 3457
FOXCONN CZ S.R.O.—See Hon Hai Precision Industry Co., Ltd.; *Int'l*, pg. 3456
FOXCONN INDUSTRIAL INTERNET CO., LTD.—See Hon Hai Precision Industry Co., Ltd.; *Int'l*, pg. 3456
FOXCONN INTERCONNECT TECHNOLOGY JAPAN CO., LTD.—See Hon Hai Precision Industry Co., Ltd.; *Int'l*, pg. 3456
FOXCONN INTERCONNECT TECHNOLOGY LIMITED—See Hon Hai Precision Industry Co., Ltd.; *Int'l*, pg. 3456
FOXCONN OY—See Hon Hai Precision Industry Co., Ltd.; *Int'l*, pg. 3457
FOXCONN SINGAPORE PTE. LTD.—See Hon Hai Precision Industry Co., Ltd.; *Int'l*, pg. 3457
FOXCONN SLOVAKIA, SPOL. S R.O.—See Hon Hai Precision Industry Co., Ltd.; *Int'l*, pg. 3456
FOXCONN TECHNOLOGY CO., LTD.—See Hon Hai Precision Industry Co., Ltd.; *Int'l*, pg. 3456
FOX CONTRACTORS CORP.; *U.S. Private*, pg. 1584
FOX CONVERTING INC.; *U.S. Private*, pg. 1584
FOX CORPORATION; *U.S. Public*, pg. 875
FOX CREEK RESERVE, L.L.C.—See Sun Communities, Inc.; *U.S. Public*, pg. 1961
FOX CRIME MEDYA HIZMETLERI ANONIM SIRKETI—See Fox Corporation; *U.S. Public*, pg. 876

COMPANY NAME INDEX

FOXDALE VILLAGE CORPORATION; *U.S. Private*, pg. 1585
FOX DRILLING INC.—See Paramount Resources Ltd.; *Int'l*, pg. 5738
FOX DRILLING LIMITED PARTNERSHIP—See Paramount Resources Ltd.; *Int'l*, pg. 5738
FOX ELECTRIC LTD.; *U.S. Private*, pg. 1584
FOX ELECTRONICS AS—See Addtech AB; *Int'l*, pg. 133
FOX ENTERTAINMENT GROUP, INC.—See The Walt Disney Company; *U.S. Public*, pg. 2140
FOX FACTORY GMBH—See Fox Factory Holding Corp.; *U.S. Public*, pg. 877
FOX FACTORY HOLDING CORP.; *U.S. Public*, pg. 877
FOX FASHION APPAREL (S) PTE LTD—See Wing Tai Holdings Limited; *Int'l*, pg. 8427
FOXFIELDS (STOKE-ON-TRENT) MANAGEMENT COMPANY LIMITED—See Persimmon plc; *Int'l*, pg. 5816
FOXFIRE PRINTING & PACKAGING; *U.S. Private*, pg. 1585
FOX FORD—See DP Fox Ventures, LLC; *U.S. Private*, pg. 1270
FOX GROUP CANADA LTD.—See Fox-Wizel Ltd.; *Int'l*, pg. 2756
FOX HEAD CANADA, INC.—See Vista Outdoor Inc.; *U.S. Public*, pg. 2305
FOX HEAD EUROPE, SL—See Vista Outdoor Inc.; *U.S. Public*, pg. 2305
FOX HEAD, INC.—See Vista Outdoor Inc.; *U.S. Public*, pg. 2305
FOX HILL VILLAGE PARTNERSHIP—See Apollo Global Management, Inc.; *U.S. Public*, pg. 156
FOX HOME CENTER INC.; *U.S. Private*, pg. 1584
FOX HYUNDAI—See DP Fox Ventures, LLC; *U.S. Private*, pg. 1270
FOXINSIGHTS GMBH—See EnBW Energie Baden-Wurttemberg AG; *Int'l*, pg. 2399
FOX INTERNATIONAL CHANNELS ASIA PACIFIC LIMITED—See Fox Corporation; *U.S. Public*, pg. 876
FOX INTERNATIONAL CHANNELS CHILE LTDA.—See Fox Corporation; *U.S. Public*, pg. 876
FOX INTERNATIONAL CHANNELS SWEDEN AB—See Fox Corporation; *U.S. Public*, pg. 876
FOX INTERNATIONAL LLC—See Fox Corporation; *U.S. Public*, pg. 876
FOX INTERNATIONAL LTD., INC.—See Video Display Corporation; *U.S. Public*, pg. 2296
FOX-IT B.V.—See NCC Group Plc; *Int'l*, pg. 5180
FOXIT SOFTWARE INC.; *U.S. Private*, pg. 1585
FOX & JAMES INC.; *U.S. Private*, pg. 1583
FOXLAND HARVESTORE INC.; *U.S. Private*, pg. 1585
FOX LATIN AMERICAN CHANNELS (CHILE) LIMITADA—See Fox Corporation; *U.S. Public*, pg. 875
FOXLINE LOGISTICS PTY LTD—See CTI Logistics Limited; *Int'l*, pg. 1871
FOXLINK AUTOMOTIVE TECHNOLOGY CO., LTD.—See Cheng Eui Precision Industry Co., Ltd.; *Int'l*, pg. 1465
FOXLINK AUTOMOTIVE TECHNOLOGY (KUNSHAN) CO., LTD.—See Cheng Eui Precision Industry Co., Ltd.; *Int'l*, pg. 1465
FOXLINK INTERNATIONAL INC—See Cheng Eui Precision Industry Co., Ltd.; *Int'l*, pg. 1465
FOX MARBLE HOLDINGS PLC; *Int'l*, pg. 2756
FOX METALS & ALLOYS, INC.—See Reliance Steel & Aluminum Co.; *U.S. Public*, pg. 1780
FOX MOTORS, LLC—See AutoNation, Inc.; *U.S. Public*, pg. 235
FOX MUSIC, INC.—See Fox Corporation; *U.S. Public*, pg. 876
FOX NET, INC.—See Fox Corporation; *U.S. Public*, pg. 876
FOX NETWORKS GROUP ASIA PACIFIC LIMITED—See Fox Corporation; *U.S. Public*, pg. 876
FOX NETWORKS GROUP, LLC—See Fox Corporation; *U.S. Public*, pg. 876
FOX NETWORKS GROUP NORWAY AS—See Fox Corporation; *U.S. Public*, pg. 876
FOX NETWORKS GROUP POLAND SP.ZO.O.—See Fox Corporation; *U.S. Public*, pg. 876
FOX NEWS NETWORK, LLC—See Fox Corporation; *U.S. Public*, pg. 876
FOXO TECHNOLOGIES INC.; *U.S. Public*, pg. 877
FOX PAINE & COMPANY, LLC—See Paine Schwartz Partners, LLC; *U.S. Public*, pg. 3075
FOX PERFORMING ARTS CHARITABLE FOUNDATION; *U.S. Private*, pg. 1584
FOX PEST CONTROL - ALBANY LLC—See Rollins, Inc.; *U.S. Public*, pg. 1809
FOX PEST CONTROL - LONG ISLAND, LLC—See Rollins, Inc.; *U.S. Public*, pg. 1809
FOX PEST CONTROL - LOUISIANA LLC—See Rollins, Inc.; *U.S. Public*, pg. 1809
FOX PEST CONTROL - MCALLEN TX, LLC—See Rollins, Inc.; *U.S. Public*, pg. 1809
FOX PEST CONTROL - ORLANDO WEST, LLC—See Rollins, Inc.; *U.S. Public*, pg. 1809
FOX PEST CONTROL - PITTSBURGH, LLC—See Rollins, Inc.; *U.S. Public*, pg. 1809
FOX PEST CONTROL - RHODE ISLAND, LLC—See Rollins, Inc.; *U.S. Public*, pg. 1809

FOX PEST CONTROL - VIRGINIA BEACH, LLC—See Rollins, Inc.; *U.S. Public*, pg. 1809
FOX PEST SERVICES, LLC—See Rollins, Inc.; *U.S. Public*, pg. 1809
FOX PETROLEUM INC.; *U.S. Private*, pg. 1584
FOX POOL CORPORATION—See Wexco Incorporated; *U.S. Private*, pg. 4502
FOX POWERSPORTS LLC; *U.S. Private*, pg. 1584
FOX PRINTING COMPANY, INC.—See Harman Press; *U.S. Private*, pg. 1866
FOX PRODUCTION SERVICES PTY LIMITED—See Fox Corporation; *U.S. Public*, pg. 876
FOX RACING U.S.A. INC.—See Vista Outdoor Inc.; *U.S. Public*, pg. 2305
FOX RENT A CAR, INC.—See Porsche Automobil Holding SE; *Int'l*, pg. 5929
FOX RESTAURANT CONCEPTS, LLC—See Cheesecake Factory Incorporated; *U.S. Public*, pg. 483
FOX RIDGE HOMES—See NVR Incorporated; *U.S. Public*, pg. 1558
FOX RIVER FOODS INC.—See Performance Food Group Company; *U.S. Public*, pg. 1876
FOX RIVER FOODS TRANSPORT INC.—See F.R.F. Systems Inc.; *U.S. Private*, pg. 1457
FOX RIVER RESOURCES CORPORATION; *Int'l*, pg. 2756
FOX RIVER WATER RECLAMATION DISTRICT; *U.S. Private*, pg. 1584
FOX ROTHSCHILD LLP - SAN FRANCISCO, CA-FRONT STREET—See Fox Rothschild LLP; *U.S. Public*, pg. 1584
FOX ROTHSCHILD LLP; *U.S. Public*, pg. 1584
FOX-ROWDEN-MCBRAYER INC.; *U.S. Private*, pg. 1585
FOX RUN APARTMENTS, LTD.—See Apartment Investment and Management Company; *U.S. Public*, pg. 144
FOX RUN CENTER FOR CHILDREN & ADOLESCENTS—See Universal Health Services, Inc.; *U.S. Public*, pg. 2257
FOX RUN CRAFTSMEN; *U.S. Private*, pg. 1584
FOX SALES; *U.S. Private*, pg. 1584
FOX'S BISCUITS LTD.—See Boparan Holdings Limited; *Int'l*, pg. 1111
FOX'S BISCUITS - PRESTON—See Boparan Holdings Limited; *Int'l*, pg. 1111
FOX'S BISCUITS - STAFFORDSHIRE—See Boparan Holdings Limited; *Int'l*, pg. 1111
FOX'S CONFECTIONERY LIMITED—See CapVest Limited; *Int'l*, pg. 1318
FOXSEMICON INTEGRATED TECHNOLOGY INC.—See Hon Hai Precision Industry Co., Ltd.; *Int'l*, pg. 3457
FOX SERVICE CO.; *U.S. Private*, pg. 1585
FOX SERVICES, INC.—See Fox Corporation; *U.S. Public*, pg. 876
FOX SPORTS AUSTRALIA PTY LIMITED—See News Corporation; *U.S. Public*, pg. 1519
FOX SPORTS DIGITAL MEDIA, INC.—See Fox Corporation; *U.S. Public*, pg. 876
FOX SPORTS NET, LLC—See Sinclair, Inc.; *U.S. Public*, pg. 1885
FOX SPORTS NET OHIO, LLC—See Fox Corporation; *U.S. Public*, pg. 876
FOX SPORTS RADIO 1350 AM—See iHeartMedia, Inc.; *U.S. Public*, pg. 1097
FOX STATIONS SALES, INC.—See Fox Corporation; *U.S. Public*, pg. 876
FOX STUDIO LOT LLC—See Fox Corporation; *U.S. Public*, pg. 876
FOX STUDIOS AUSTRALIA PTY LIMITED—See Fox Corporation; *U.S. Public*, pg. 876
FOXTEL AUSTRALIA PTY LIMITED—See News Corporation; *U.S. Public*, pg. 1519
FOXTEL CABLE TELEVISION PTY. LIMITED—See News Corporation; *U.S. Public*, pg. 1519
FOXTEL CABLE TELEVISION PTY. LIMITED—See Telstra Group Limited; *Int'l*, pg. 7545
FOXTELECOLOMBIA, S.A.—See Fox Corporation; *U.S. Public*, pg. 876
FOX TELEVISION STATIONS, LLC—See Fox Corporation; *U.S. Public*, pg. 876
FOXTEL MANAGEMENT PTY. LTD.—See News Corporation; *U.S. Public*, pg. 1519
FOXTEL MANAGEMENT PTY. LTD.—See Telstra Group Limited; *Int'l*, pg. 7545
FOX THERMAL INSTRUMENTS, INC.—See Harbour Group Industries, Inc.; *U.S. Private*, pg. 1860
FOX THREE PARTNERS LLC; *U.S. Private*, pg. 1585
FOX-TOURS REISEN GMBH—See TUI AG; *Int'l*, pg. 7964
FOX TOYOTA SCION, INC.; *U.S. Private*, pg. 1585
FOX TRANSPORT CO.; *U.S. Private*, pg. 1585
FOXTRONICS EMS; *U.S. Private*, pg. 1585
FOXTRON VEHICLE TECHNOLOGIES CO., LTD.—See Hon Hai Precision Industry Co., Ltd.; *Int'l*, pg. 3457
FOX VALLEY BUICK-GMC, INC.—See General Motors Company; *U.S. Public*, pg. 924
FOX VALLEY CONTAINERS, INC.—See Kelso & Company, L.P.; *U.S. Private*, pg. 2278
FOX VALLEY FIRE & SAFETY COMPANY, INC.; *U.S. Private*, pg. 1585

FP CORPORATION

FOX VALLEY METAL TECH, LLC—See Littlejohn & Co., LLC; *U.S. Public*, pg. 2470
FOX VALLEY STEEL & WIRE CO.; *U.S. Private*, pg. 1585
FOX VALLEY SYSTEMS, INC.; *U.S. Private*, pg. 1585
FOX VALLEY TOOL & DIE, INC.; *U.S. Private*, pg. 1585
FOX VALLEY TRUCK SERVICE INC.; *U.S. Private*, pg. 1585
FOXWAYNE ENTERPRISES ACQUISITION CORP.; *U.S. Public*, pg. 877
FOX WIRE LIMITED; *Int'l*, pg. 2756
FOX-WIZEL LTD.; *Int'l*, pg. 2756
FOXWOODS RESORT CASINO—See Mashantucket Pequot Gaming Enterprise Inc.; *U.S. Private*, pg. 2601
FOX WORLD TRAVEL; *U.S. Private*, pg. 1585
FOXWORTH-GALBRAITH LUMBER COMPANY; *U.S. Private*, pg. 1585
FOXWORTH-GALBRAITH LUMBER COMPANY—See Foxworth-Galbraith Lumber Company; *U.S. Private*, pg. 1585
FOXWORTH GALBRAITH TRUSS CO.—See Foxworth-Galbraith Lumber Company; *U.S. Private*, pg. 1585
FOXX LIFE SCIENCES, LLC; *U.S. Private*, pg. 1585
FOYER S.A.; *Int'l*, pg. 2756
FOY INSURANCE GROUP, INC.—See World Insurance Associates LLC; *U.S. Private*, pg. 4566
FOY-JOHNSTON INC.; *U.S. Public*, pg. 877
FOYLE BIO-ENERGY—See Foyle Food Group Ltd.; *Int'l*, pg. 2756
FOYLE FOOD GROUP LTD.; *Int'l*, pg. 2756
FOYLE INGREDIENTS—See Foyle Food Group Ltd.; *Int'l*, pg. 2756
FOYSTON GORDON & PAYNE INC.—See Affiliated Managers Group, Inc.; *U.S. Public*, pg. 54
FOYSTON, GORDON & PAYNE INC.—See Affiliated Managers Group, Inc.; *U.S. Public*, pg. 55
FP1 STRATEGIES LLC—See Omnicom Group Inc.; *U.S. Public*, pg. 1589
FP7 ABU DHABI—See The Interpublic Group of Companies, Inc.; *U.S. Public*, pg. 2099
FP7 MCCANN ALGERIA—See The Interpublic Group of Companies, Inc.; *U.S. Public*, pg. 2099
FP7 MCCANN-TUNISIA—See The Interpublic Group of Companies, Inc.; *U.S. Public*, pg. 2099
F&P AMERICA MFG., INC.—See F-Tech Inc.; *Int'l*, pg. 2595
FPA PATENT ATTORNEYS ASIA PTE LTD.—See Adamantem Capital Management Pty Limited; *Int'l*, pg. 124
FPA PATENT ATTORNEYS PTY LTD—See Adamantem Capital Management Pty Limited; *Int'l*, pg. 124
FP ASSET MANAGEMENT HOLDINGS LIMITED—See Bank of Montreal; *Int'l*, pg. 847
FPA TECHNOLOGY SERVICES INC.—See VC3, Inc.; *U.S. Private*, pg. 4349
FPB HOLDING GMBH & CO. KG—See Stora Enso Oyj; *Int'l*, pg. 7223
F.P. BOURGAULT INDUSTRIES LTD.; *Int'l*, pg. 2597
FP CANADIAN NEWSPAPERS LIMITED PARTNERSHIP—See FP Newspapers Inc.; *Int'l*, pg. 2757
FPCAP ELECTRONICS (SUZHOU) CO., LTD.—See NICHICON CORPORATION; *Int'l*, pg. 5267
FPC CORPORATION; *U.S. Public*, pg. 1586
FPC DISTRIBUTION, INC.—See Kelso & Company, L.P.; *U.S. Private*, pg. 2279
FPC DISTRIBUTION, INC.—See Warburg Pincus LLC; *U.S. Private*, pg. 4437
FPC HOLDINGS, INC.—See Kelso & Company, L.P.; *U.S. Private*, pg. 2279
FPC HOLDINGS, INC.—See Warburg Pincus LLC; *U.S. Private*, pg. 4437
FP CHUPA CORP.—See FP Corporation; *Int'l*, pg. 2756
FPC LTD.—See INA-Industrija Nafte, d.d.; *Int'l*, pg. 3642
FPCO AI PACK CO.—See FP Corporation; *Int'l*, pg. 2756
FPCO ALRIGHT CO. LTD.—See FP Corporation; *Int'l*, pg. 2756
FPCO CHUBU CO.—See FP Corporation; *Int'l*, pg. 2756
FPCO DIA FOODS CO., LTD.—See FP Corporation; *Int'l*, pg. 2756
FPCO ENGINEERING, LTD.—See FP Corporation; *Int'l*, pg. 2756
FPCO FUKUYAMA CO.—See FP Corporation; *Int'l*, pg. 2756
FPCO INTERNATIONAL PACKAGE CO., LTD.—See FP Corporation; *Int'l*, pg. 2756
FPCO ISHIDA CO., LTD.—See FP Corporation; *Int'l*, pg. 2756
FPCO KASAOKA CO.—See FP Corporation; *Int'l*, pg. 2756
FPCO MINOSHIMA CO.—See FP Corporation; *Int'l*, pg. 2756
FP CORPORATION - FUKUYAMA PLANT—See FP Corporation; *Int'l*, pg. 2756
FP CORPORATION - HOKKAIDO PLANT—See FP Corporation; *Int'l*, pg. 2756
FP CORPORATION; *Int'l*, pg. 2756
FPCO SAGA CO, LTD.—See FP Corporation; *Int'l*, pg. 2756
FPCO SHIMODATE, LTD.—See FP Corporation; *Int'l*, pg. 2756
FPCO UEDA CO.—See FP Corporation; *Int'l*, pg. 2756

FP CORPORATION

CORPORATE AFFILIATIONS

FPCO YAMAGATA, LTD.—See FP Corporation; *Int'l*, pg. 2756
FP DIGITAL BUSINESS SOLUTIONS GMBH—See Francotyp-Postalia Holding AG; *Int'l*, pg. 2761
FPE GLOBAL LIMITED—See NorthEdge Capital LLP; *Int'l*, pg. 5442
FPE LIMITED—See Diploma PLC; *Int'l*, pg. 2128
F&P ENTERPRISES INC.; *U.S. Private*, pg. 1455
FP FINANCE B.V.—See Francotyp-Postalia Holding AG; *Int'l*, pg. 2761
FP FUND MANAGERS LIMITED—See Bank of Montreal; *Int'l*, pg. 847
FPG AMENTUM LIMITED—See Financial Partners Group Co., Ltd; *Int'l*, pg. 2665
F&P GEORGIA MFG., INC.—See F-Tech Inc.; *Int'l*, pg. 2595
FPG INSURANCE CO., INC.—See The Zuellig Group Inc.; *Int'l*, pg. 7705
FPG INSURANCE (THAILAND) COMPANY LIMITED—See The Zuellig Group Inc.; *Int'l*, pg. 7705
FPG OLEOCHEMICALS SDN. BHD.—See The Procter & Gamble Company; *U.S. Public*, pg. 2120
FP GROUP LIMITED—See Howden Group Holdings Limited; *Int'l*, pg. 3493
F.P. HORAK COMPANY; *U.S. Private*, pg. 1457
FPI AUTO PARTS INDIA PRIVATE LIMITED—See Fortune Parts Industry Public Company Limited; *Int'l*, pg. 2744
FPIC INSURANCE GROUP, INC.—See The Doctors Company; *U.S. Private*, pg. 4021
F.P.I. FERRARA PROMOZIONE INDUSTRIALE SRL; *Int'l*, pg. 2597
FPI FIREPLACE PRODUCTS INTERNATIONAL LTD.—See NIBE Industrier AB; *Int'l*, pg. 5260
FPI MANAGEMENT, INC.; *U.S. Private*, pg. 1586
FP INOVOLABS GMBH—See Francotyp-Postalia Holding AG; *Int'l*, pg. 2761
FP INTERNATIONAL, INC.; *U.S. Private*, pg. 1585
FPK NAKATAKE CO., LTD.—See Nakatake Co., Ltd.; *Int'l*, pg. 5133
FPLUS, INC.—See ODK Solutions Company, Ltd.; *Int'l*, pg. 5526
FPM AGROMEHANIKA A.D.; *Int'l*, pg. 2757
FP MARINE RISKS (AUSTRALIA) PTY LIMITED—See Howden Group Holdings Limited; *Int'l*, pg. 3493
FP MARINE RISKS LIMITED—See Howden Group Holdings Limited; *Int'l*, pg. 3493
FPM DEUTSCHLAND GMBH—See SoftBank Group Corp.; *Int'l*, pg. 7052
F&P MFG. DE MEXICO, S.A. DE C.V.—See F-Tech Inc.; *Int'l*, pg. 2595
F&P MFG. INC.—See F-Tech Inc.; *Int'l*, pg. 2595
F. P. NATURAL INGREDIENTS S.A.S—See ARIAKE JAPAN Co., Ltd.; *Int'l*, pg. 564
FP NEOMONITOR GMBH—See Francotyp-Postalia Holding AG; *Int'l*, pg. 2761
FP NEWHAVEN TWO LIMITED—See Arcus Infrastructure Partners LLP; *Int'l*, pg. 552
FP NEWSPAPERS INC.; *Int'l*, pg. 2757
F.P.N.I. BELGIUM N.V.—See ARIAKE JAPAN Co., Ltd.; *Int'l*, pg. 564
FPO, LLC; *U.S. Private*, pg. 1586
FP PROPERTY RESTORATION OF NORTH FLORIDA, LLC; *U.S. Private*, pg. 1585
FP REINSURANCE BROKERS LIMITED—See Howden Group Holdings Limited; *Int'l*, pg. 3493
FPR PARTNERS LLC—See Fremont Group, LLC; *U.S. Private*, pg. 1608
FPS DISTRIBUTION LIMITED—See Blackstone Inc.; *U.S. Public*, pg. 360
FPS FOOD PROCESSING SYSTEMS B.V.; *Int'l*, pg. 2757
FPS FRANKFURT PASSENGER SERVICES GMBH—See Fraport AG; *Int'l*, pg. 2764
FPS GLOBAL LOGISTICS PTE. LTD.—See Singapore Post Limited; *Int'l*, pg. 6941
FPS INFRASTRUKTUR HOLDING GMBH—See PORR AG; *Int'l*, pg. 5922
FPS LOGISTICS (USA) INC.—See Singapore Post Limited; *Int'l*, pg. 6941
FP STENCIL SDN. BHD.—See FoundPac Group Berhad; *Int'l*, pg. 2754
FPT ASIA PACIFIC PTE. LTD.—See FPT Corporation; *Int'l*, pg. 2757
FPT AUSTRALASIA PTY., LTD.—See FPT Corporation; *Int'l*, pg. 2757
FPT CANADA CO., LTD.—See FPT Corporation; *Int'l*, pg. 2757
FPT CANTON, LLC—See Soave Enterprises, LLC; *U.S. Private*, pg. 3702
FPT CLEVELAND, LLC—See Soave Enterprises, LLC; *U.S. Private*, pg. 3702
FPT COMPANY FOR INFORMATION TECHNOLOGY WLL—See FPT Corporation; *Int'l*, pg. 2757
FPT CORPORATION; *Int'l*, pg. 2757
FPT DEUTSCHLAND GMBH—See FPT Corporation; *Int'l*, pg. 2757
FPT DIGITAL RETAIL JOINT STOCK COMPANY—See FPT Corporation; *Int'l*, pg. 2757
FPT EDUCATION COMPANY LIMITED—See FPT Corporation; *Int'l*, pg. 2757

FPT FLORIDA, LLC—See Cleveland-Cliffs, Inc.; *U.S. Public*, pg. 514
FPT FT. MYERS, LLC—See Soave Enterprises, LLC; *U.S. Private*, pg. 3702
FPT INDIA PRIVATE LIMITED—See FPT Corporation; *Int'l*, pg. 2757
FPT INDUSTRIAL ARGENTINA S.A.—See CNH Industrial N.V.; *Int'l*, pg. 1675
FPT INDUSTRIAL S.P.A.—See CNH Industrial N.V.; *Int'l*, pg. 1675
FPT INFORMATICS SERVICES COMPANY LIMITED—See FPT Corporation; *Int'l*, pg. 2757
FPT INFORMATION SYSTEM COMPANY LIMITED—See FPT Corporation; *Int'l*, pg. 2757
FPT JAPAN HOLDINGS CO., LTD.—See FPT Corporation; *Int'l*, pg. 2757
FPT MOTORENFORSCHUNG AG—See CNH Industrial N.V.; *Int'l*, pg. 1675
FPT ONLINE SERVICES JOINT STOCK COMPANY—See FPT Corporation; *Int'l*, pg. 2757
F.P.TOOLS CO., LTD.—See OSG Corporation; *Int'l*, pg. 5649
FPT OPERATING COMPANY, LLC—See Alvarez & Marsal, Inc.; *U.S. Private*, pg. 212
FPT PONTIAC DIVISION, LLC—See Soave Enterprises, LLC; *U.S. Private*, pg. 3702
FPT - POWERTRAIN TECHNOLOGIES FRANCE S.A.—See CNH Industrial N.V.; *Int'l*, pg. 1675
FP TRADING CO., LTD.—See FP Corporation; *Int'l*, pg. 2756
FPT SCHLAFER DIVISION, LLC—See Soave Enterprises, LLC; *U.S. Private*, pg. 3702
FPT SEMICONDUCTOR JOINT STOCK COMPANY—See FPT Corporation; *Int'l*, pg. 2757
FPT SERVICE CO., LTD—See FPT Corporation; *Int'l*, pg. 2757
FPT SLOVAKIA S.R.O.—See FPT Corporation; *Int'l*, pg. 2757
FPT SMART CLOUD COMPANY LIMITED—See FPT Corporation; *Int'l*, pg. 2757
FPT SOFTWARE CENTRAL REGION COMPANY LIMITED—See FPT Corporation; *Int'l*, pg. 2757
FPT SOFTWARE COMPANY LIMITED—See FPT Corporation; *Int'l*, pg. 2757
FPT SOFTWARE EUROPE S.A.R.L.—See FPT Corporation; *Int'l*, pg. 2757
FPT SOFTWARE HO CHI MINH COMPANY LIMITED—See FPT Corporation; *Int'l*, pg. 2757
FPT SOFTWARE HUE CO., LTD.—See FPT Corporation; *Int'l*, pg. 2757
FPT SOFTWARE JAPAN CO., LTD.—See FPT Corporation; *Int'l*, pg. 2758
FPT SOFTWARE KOREA CO., LTD.—See FPT Corporation; *Int'l*, pg. 2758
FPT SOFTWARE MALAYSIA SDN. BHD.—See FPT Corporation; *Int'l*, pg. 2758
FPT SOFTWARE PHILIPPINES CORP.—See FPT Corporation; *Int'l*, pg. 2758
FPT SOFTWARE SOLUTIONS ASIA PACIFIC PTE. LTD.—See FPT Corporation; *Int'l*, pg. 2758
FPT SOFTWARE UNITED KINGDOM LTD.—See FPT Corporation; *Int'l*, pg. 2758
FPT TAIWAN CO., LTD.—See FPT Corporation; *Int'l*, pg. 2758
FPT TECHNOLOGY DMCC—See FPT Corporation; *Int'l*, pg. 2758
FPT TELECOM JOINT STOCK COMPANY—See FPT Corporation; *Int'l*, pg. 2758
FPT UNIVERSITY CO. LTD.—See FPT Corporation; *Int'l*, pg. 2758
FPX, LLC; *U.S. Private*, pg. 1586
FPX NICKEL CORP.; *Int'l*, pg. 2758
FPZ DEUTSCHLAND DEN RUCKEN STARKEN GMBH—See Pfizer Inc.; *U.S. Public*, pg. 1679
FQM AUSTRALIA HOLDINGS PTY LTD—See First Quantum Minerals Ltd.; *Int'l*, pg. 2687
FQM AUSTRALIA NICKEL PTY LTD—See First Quantum Minerals Ltd.; *Int'l*, pg. 2687
FQML SCANDINAVIA INC.—See First Quantum Minerals Ltd.; *Int'l*, pg. 2687
FQUBED, INC.—See Searchlight Pharma, Inc.; *Int'l*, pg. 6666
FRACARESERVICES GMBH—See Fraport AG; *Int'l*, pg. 2764
FRACASSO HELLAS S.A.—See Intracom Holdings S.A.; *Int'l*, pg. 3767
FRACTA, INC.—See Kurita Water Industries Ltd.; *Int'l*, pg. 4340
FRACTAL ANALYTICS INC.; *U.S. Private*, pg. 1586
FRACTAL GAMING GROUP AB; *Int'l*, pg. 2758
FRAC TECHNOLOGY AS—See Nine Energy Service, Inc.; *U.S. Public*, pg. 1529
FRACTURECODE CORPORATION APS; *Int'l*, pg. 2758
FRADENA TRANSPORT—See Derichebourg S.A.; *Int'l*, pg. 2042
FRADIN BRETTON SAS—See VINCI S.A.; *Int'l*, pg. 8221
FRAENKEL COMPANY, INC.; *U.S. Private*, pg. 1586
FRAEN MACHINING CORPORATION; *U.S. Private*, pg. 1586

FRAER LEASING SPA—See Societe Generale S.A.; *Int'l*, pg. 7039
FRAGBITE GROUP AB; *Int'l*, pg. 2758
FRAGOL BETEILIGUNGS GMBH + CO.KG; *Int'l*, pg. 2758
FRAGOMEN, DEL REY, BERNSEN & LOEWY, LLP; *U.S. Private*, pg. 1586
FRAGRANCE GROUP LIMITED; *Int'l*, pg. 2758
FRAGRANCE HOTEL MANAGEMENT PTE LTD—See Fragrance Group Limited; *Int'l*, pg. 2758
FRAGRANCE LAND PTE LTD—See Fragrance Group Limited; *Int'l*, pg. 2758
FRAGRANCENET.COM, INC.; *U.S. Public*, pg. 877
FRAGRANCE OILS (INTERNATIONAL) LIMITED—See Givaudan S.A.; *Int'l*, pg. 2980
FRAGRANCE OILS LIMITED—See Givaudan S.A.; *Int'l*, pg. 2980
FRAGRANCE OUTLET INC.; *U.S. Private*, pg. 1586
FRAGRANCE PRODUCTION S.A.S.—See JAB Holding Company S.a.r.l.; *Int'l*, pg. 3861
FRAGRANCES EXCLUSIVE INC.—See Chanel S.A.; *Int'l*, pg. 1441
FRAGRANCEX.COM; *U.S. Private*, pg. 1586
FRAGRANT PROSPERITY HOLDINGS LIMITED; *Int'l*, pg. 2758
FRAGROUND FRAPORT GROUND SERVICES GMBH—See Cerberus Capital Management, L.P.; *U.S. Private*, pg. 840
FRAGWILHELM GMBH—See DZ BANK AG Deutsche Zentral-Genossenschaftsbank; *Int'l*, pg. 2245
FRAKO CAPACITORS & PLANT CONSTRUCTION GMBH—See AdCapital AG; *Int'l*, pg. 126
FRALEX THERAPEUTICS INC.—See Boston Scientific Corporation; *U.S. Public*, pg. 374
FRALIN AND WALDRON, INC.; *U.S. Private*, pg. 1586
F. RAMADA, ACOS E INDUSTRIAS, S.A.—See F. Ramada Investimentos, SGPS, S.A.; *Int'l*, pg. 2596
F. RAMADA INVESTIMENTOS, SGPS, S.A.; *Int'l*, pg. 2596
FRA-MA-PIZZ S.A.S.—See Domino's Pizza Enterprises Ltd.; *Int'l*, pg. 2162
FRAMAS LIGHTINGS LIMITED—See Signify N.V.; *Int'l*, pg. 6912
FRAMATEQ S.A.S.; *Int'l*, pg. 2759
FRAMATOME CANADA LTD.—See Electricite de France S.A.; *Int'l*, pg. 2351
FRAMATOME GMBH—See Electricite de France S.A.; *Int'l*, pg. 2351
FRAMATOME INC.—See Electricite de France S.A.; *Int'l*, pg. 2351
FRAMATOME SAS—See Electricite de France S.A.; *Int'l*, pg. 2351
FRAMATOME SPAIN SLU—See Electricite de France S.A.; *Int'l*, pg. 2351
FRAMECO AB—See Addtech AB; *Int'l*, pg. 133
FRAMED PICTURES ENTERPRISE INC.; *U.S. Private*, pg. 1586
FRAMEHAWK, INC.—See Elliott Management Corporation; *U.S. Private*, pg. 1367
FRAMEHAWK, INC.—See Vista Equity Partners, LLC; *U.S. Private*, pg. 4396
FRAME.IO, INC.—See Adobe Inc.; *U.S. Public*, pg. 42
FRAMERICA CORPORATION; *U.S. Private*, pg. 1586
FRAMES DATA INC.—See The Wicks Group of Companies, LLC; *U.S. Private*, pg. 4135
FRAME SERVICE INC.—See American Securities LLC; *U.S. Private*, pg. 248
FRAMES FOR AMERICA INC—See EssilorLuxottica SA; *Int'l*, pg. 2514
FRAMES HOLDING BV—See Plug Power Inc.; *U.S. Public*, pg. 1699
FRAMESI S.P.A.; *Int'l*, pg. 2759
FRAMESI USA, INC.—See Framesi S.p.A.; *Int'l*, pg. 2759
FRAMESTORE INC.—See Cultural Investment Holdings Co., Ltd.; *Int'l*, pg. 1877
FRAMESTORE LIMITED—See Cultural Investment Holdings Co., Ltd.; *Int'l*, pg. 1877
FRAMES UNLIMITED INC.—See Zimdar Enterprises; *U.S. Private*, pg. 4605
FRAME USA, INC.—See Craig Frames, Inc.; *U.S. Private*, pg. 1082
FRAMEWORK CAPITAL PARTNERS; *U.S. Private*, pg. 1586
FRAMEWORKS MANUFACTURING INC.—See ASSA ABLOY AB; *Int'l*, pg. 639
FRAMEWORX INC.—See Daiwa House Industry Co., Ltd.; *Int'l*, pg. 1946
FRAM GROUP, LLC - ROGERS FACILITY—See Rank Group Ltd.; *Int'l*, pg. 6208
FRAM GROUP, LLC—See Rank Group Ltd.; *Int'l*, pg. 6208
FRAMHERJI APS—See Samherji hf; *Int'l*, pg. 6505
FRAMING ART CENTRE—See Franchise Concepts, Inc.; *U.S. Private*, pg. 1587
THE FRAMINGHAM TAB—See Gannett Co., Inc.; *U.S. Public*, pg. 903
FRAMO AS—See Alfa Laval AB; *Int'l*, pg. 311
FRAMO DO BRASIL LTDA.—See Alfa Laval AB; *Int'l*, pg. 312
FRAMO FLATEY AS—See Alfa Laval AB; *Int'l*, pg. 311

COMPANY NAME INDEX

FRAMO FLATOY AS—See Alfa Laval AB; *Int'l*, pg. 312
FRAMO FUSA AS—See Alfa Laval AB; *Int'l*, pg. 311
FRAMO HOLSNEY AS—See Alfa Laval AB; *Int'l*, pg. 311
FRAMO HOLSNOY AS—See Alfa Laval AB; *Int'l*, pg. 312
FRAMO HOUSTON INC.—See Alfa Laval AB; *Int'l*, pg. 311
FRAMO KOREA LTD.—See Alfa Laval AB; *Int'l*, pg. 311
FRAMO NEDERLAND BV—See Alfa Laval AB; *Int'l*, pg. 311
FRAMO NIPPON KK—See Alfa Laval AB; *Int'l*, pg. 311
FRAMOS ELECTRONICS LTD.—See FRAMOS GmbH; *Int'l*, pg. 2759
FRAMO SERVICES AS—See Alfa Laval AB; *Int'l*, pg. 311
FRAMOS FRANCE SA—See FRAMOS GmbH; *Int'l*, pg. 2759
FRAMOS GMBH; *Int'l*, pg. 2759
FRAMO SHANGHAI LTD.—See Alfa Laval AB; *Int'l*, pg. 312
FRAMO SINGAPORE PTE. LTD.—See Alfa Laval AB; *Int'l*, pg. 312
FRAMOS ITALIA SRL—See FRAMOS GmbH; *Int'l*, pg. 2759
FRAMOS TECHNOLOGIES INC.—See FRAMOS GmbH; *Int'l*, pg. 2759
FRAMTIDSUTVECKLING I SVERIGE AB—See AcadeMedia AB; *Int'l*, pg. 76
FRANA & ASSOCIATES INC.; *U.S. Private*, pg. 1586
FRANBO LINES CORP.; *Int'l*, pg. 2759
FRANCAIS CO., LTD.—See Meiji Holdings Co., Ltd.; *Int'l*, pg. 4800
FRANCAISE DE GASTRONOMIE—See Floridienne SA; *Int'l*, pg. 2708
FRANCAISE DE MECANIQUE—See Renault S.A.; *Int'l*, pg. 6273
FRANCE AIR MANAGEMENT SA—See AIRVANCE GROUP; *Int'l*, pg. 250
FRANCEBED CO., LTD.—See FRANCE BED HOLDINGS CO. LTD.; *Int'l*, pg. 2759
FRANCE BED HOLDINGS CO. LTD.; *Int'l*, pg. 2759
FRANCE BED MEDICAL SERVICE CO., LTD.—See FRANCE BED HOLDINGS CO. LTD.; *Int'l*, pg. 2759
FRANCEBED SALES CO., LTD.—See FRANCE BED HOLDINGS CO. LTD.; *Int'l*, pg. 2759
FRANCE BILLET S.A.—See Groupe Fnac S.A.; *Int'l*, pg. 3103
FRANCE CHIRURGIE INSTRUMENTATION (F.C.I.) SAS—See Carl-Zeiss-Stiftung; *Int'l*, pg. 1336
FRANCE CREME S.A.S—See Zuivelcooperatie FrieslandCampina U.A.; *Int'l*, pg. 8693
FRANCE DISTRIBUTION SAS—See ARYZTA AG; *Int'l*, pg. 588
FRANCE EXPRESS 44-NANTES—See SNCF; *Int'l*, pg. 7025
FRANCE FILIERES PLASTIQUES S.A.S.—See Greiner Holding AG; *Int'l*, pg. 3078
THE FRANCE FOUNDATION—See SmithBucklin Corporation; *U.S. Private*, pg. 3697
FRANCE GALVA SA; *Int'l*, pg. 2759
FRANCE INOX SAS—See Jacquet Metal Service SA; *Int'l*, pg. 3866
FRANCE KOREA WINES & SPIRITS LTD.—See LVMH Moet Hennessy Louis Vuitton SE; *Int'l*, pg. 4599
FRANCE LOISIRS SAS—See Bertelsmann SE & Co. KGaA; *Int'l*, pg. 992
FRANCEL S.A.—See Emerson Electric Co.; *U.S. Public*, pg. 749
FRANCE MELASSES SA—See W&R Barnett Ltd.; *Int'l*, pg. 8320
FRANCE MINIATURE SAS—See Compagnie des Alpes S.A.; *Int'l*, pg. 1738
FRANCE OXYGENE SARL—See SOL S.p.A.; *Int'l*, pg. 7067
FRANCEPRONET S.A.S.—See Motork Plc; *Int'l*, pg. 5054
FRANCE QUICK S.A.S.—See Groupe Bertrand SARL; *Int'l*, pg. 3092
FRANCESCA'S COLLECTIONS, INC.—See TerraMar Capital LLC; *U.S. Private*, pg. 3971
FRANCESCA'S HOLDINGS CORPORATION—See TerraMar Capital LLC; *U.S. Private*, pg. 3971
FRANCESCHI ADVERTISING & PUBLIC RELATIONS, INC.; *U.S. Private*, pg. 1586
FRANCESCO PARISI GMBH - COLOGNE—See Francesco Parisi S.p.A.; *Int'l*, pg. 2759
FRANCESCO PARISI GMBH—See Francesco Parisi S.p.A.; *Int'l*, pg. 2759
FRANCESCO PARISI S.A.G.L.—See Francesco Parisi S.p.A.; *Int'l*, pg. 2759
FRANCESCO PARISI S.P.A. - FERNETTI—See Francesco Parisi S.p.A.; *Int'l*, pg. 2759
FRANCESCO PARISI S.P.A. - GENOA—See Francesco Parisi S.p.A.; *Int'l*, pg. 2759
FRANCESCO PARISI S.P.A. - GORIZIA—See Francesco Parisi S.p.A.; *Int'l*, pg. 2759
FRANCESCO PARISI S.P.A. - LIVORNO—See Francesco Parisi S.p.A.; *Int'l*, pg. 2759
FRANCESCO PARISI S.P.A. - MILANO—See Francesco Parisi S.p.A.; *Int'l*, pg. 2759
FRANCESCO PARISI S.P.A. - MONFALCONE—See Francesco Parisi S.p.A.; *Int'l*, pg. 2759

FRANCESCO PARISI S.P.A. - PONTEBBA—See Francesco Parisi S.p.A.; *Int'l*, pg. 2759
FRANCESCO PARISI S.P.A. - RONCHI DEI LEGIONARI—See Francesco Parisi S.p.A.; *Int'l*, pg. 2759
FRANCESCO PARISI S.P.A. - SEDICO—See Francesco Parisi S.p.A.; *Int'l*, pg. 2759
FRANCESCO PARISI S.P.A.; *Int'l*, pg. 2759
FRANCESCO PARISI S.P.A. - VENEZIA-MESTRE—See Francesco Parisi S.p.A.; *Int'l*, pg. 2759
FRANCE SECURITE SAS—See Bunzl plc; *Int'l*, pg. 1218
FRANCE SEMI, S.A.—See ACS, Actividades de Construccion y Servicios, S.A.; *Int'l*, pg. 112
FRANCES HODGKINS RETIREMENT VILLAGE LIMITED—See Ryman Healthcare Ltd.; *Int'l*, pg. 6439
FRANCES MAHON DEACONESS HOSPITAL; *U.S. Private*, pg. 1586
FRANCES MARY ACCESSORIES, INC.; *U.S. Private*, pg. 1586
FRANCESOIR GROUPE SA; *Int'l*, pg. 2759
FRANCE TELECOM BRUXELLES—See Orange S.A.; *Int'l*, pg. 5608
FRANCE TELECOM INDIA—See Orange S.A.; *Int'l*, pg. 5608
FRANCE TELECOM JAPAN CO., LTD.—See Orange S.A.; *Int'l*, pg. 5608
FRANCE TELECOM R&D BEIJING—See Orange S.A.; *Int'l*, pg. 5608
FRANCE TELECOM VIETNAM—See Orange S.A.; *Int'l*, pg. 5608
FRANCETEL—See Orange S.A.; *Int'l*, pg. 5608
FRANCE TOURISME IMMOBILIER SA; *Int'l*, pg. 2759
FRANCE WAGONS S.A.—See SNCF; *Int'l*, pg. 7025
FRANCHETTI S.P.A.; *Int'l*, pg. 2759
FRANCHI MANAGEMENT COMPANY; *U.S. Private*, pg. 1587
FRANCHINO MOLD & ENGINEERING CO.; *U.S. Private*, pg. 1587
FRANCHISE BANCORP CONSULTING LTD.—See Franchise Bancorp Inc.; *Int'l*, pg. 2760
FRANCHISE BANCORP INC.; *Int'l*, pg. 2760
FRANCHISE BRANDS PLC; *Int'l*, pg. 2760
FRANCHISE CONCEPTS, INC.; *U.S. Private*, pg. 1587
FRANCHISE CONCEPTS LIMITED; *Int'l*, pg. 2760
FRANCHISE DEVELOPMENT, L.P.; *U.S. Private*, pg. 1587
FRANCHISE ENTERTAINMENT GROUP PTY LTD.; *Int'l*, pg. 2760
FRANCHISE GROUP, INC.—See B. Riley Financial, Inc.; *U.S. Public*, pg. 261
FRANCHISE GROUP, INC.—See Irradiant Partners, LP; *U.S. Private*, pg. 2140
FRANCHISE OPERATIONS INC.; *U.S. Private*, pg. 1587
FRANCHISE PAYMENT SERVICES PTY. LTD.—See QuickFee Limited; *Int'l*, pg. 6162
FRANCHISE SERVICES, INC.—See KOA Holdings Inc.; *U.S. Private*, pg. 2325
FRANCHISE SERVICES OF NORTH AMERICA INC.; *U.S. Private*, pg. 1587
FRANCHISE SUPPORT & SERVICES SL—See Pearson plc; *Int'l*, pg. 5775
FRANCISCAN ALLIANCE, INC.; *U.S. Private*, pg. 1587
FRANCISCAN ESTATE WINERY—See Constellation Brands, Inc.; *U.S. Public*, pg. 570
FRANCISCAN HEALTH SYSTEM; *U.S. Private*, pg. 1587
FRANCISCAN HOSPITAL FOR CHILDREN; *U.S. Private*, pg. 1587
FRANCISCAN VINEYARDS, INC.—See Constellation Brands, Inc.; *U.S. Public*, pg. 571
FRANCISCO INDUSTRIES, INC.; *U.S. Public*, pg. 877
FRANCISCO OLLER, S.A.—See CORTICEIRA AMORIM, S.G.P.S., S.A.; *Int'l*, pg. 1807
FRANCISCO PARTNERS MANAGEMENT, LP; *U.S. Private*, pg. 1587
FRANCISCO TAVARES INC.; *U.S. Private*, pg. 1593
FRANCIS DAVID CORPORATION—See BharCap Partners, LLC; *U.S. Private*, pg. 549
FRANCIS DRILLING FLUIDS LTD.; *U.S. Private*, pg. 1587
FRANCIS EMORY FITCH, INCORPORATED—See The Hearst Corporation; *U.S. Private*, pg. 4044
FRANCIS FORD COPPOLA WINERY; *U.S. Private*, pg. 1587
FRANCIS LEFEBVRE FORMATION SAS—See Editions Lefebvre Sarrut SA; *Int'l*, pg. 2311
FRANCIS MANUFACTURING CO.; *U.S. Private*, pg. 1587
FRANCIS M. WALLEY INSURANCE AGENCY, INC.—See C&S Insurance Agency, Inc.; *U.S. Private*, pg. 704
FRANCIS O. DAY CO., INC.; *U.S. Private*, pg. 1587
FRANCIS-SCHULZE, CO.—See Wynnchurch Capital, L.P.; *U.S. Private*, pg. 4578
FRANCIS SCOTT KEY AUDI; *U.S. Private*, pg. 1587
FRANCIS W BIRKETT & SONS LIMITED—See Westley Group Limited; *Int'l*, pg. 8390
FRANCK & FILS SA—See LVMH Moet Hennessy Louis Vuitton SE; *Int'l*, pg. 4598
FRANCODEX SAS—See Virbac S.A.; *Int'l*, pg. 8246
FRANCOFA EURODIS S.A.S.—See Rexel, S.A.; *Int'l*, pg. 6316
FRANCOFIN BV—See Carrefour SA; *Int'l*, pg. 1345

FRANCOIS-CHARLES OBERTHUR FIDUCIAIRE S.A.; *Int'l*, pg. 2760
FRANCOIS FRERES MANAGEMENT—See Tonnellerie Francois Freres; *Int'l*, pg. 7810
FRANCOIS GOLAY SA—See The Swatch Group Ltd.; *Int'l*, pg. 7691
FRANCOIS MARINE SERVICES PTE LTD—See Sinwa Singapore Pte Ltd; *Int'l*, pg. 6959
FRANCOIS OIL COMPANY INC.; *U.S. Private*, pg. 1593
FRANCO MANUFACTURING CO. INC.; *U.S. Private*, pg. 1593
FRANCO-NEVADA AUSTRALIA PTY. LTD.—See Franco-Nevada Corporation; *Int'l*, pg. 2760
FRANCO-NEVADA (BARBADOS) CORPORATION—See Franco-Nevada Corporation; *Int'l*, pg. 2760
FRANCO-NEVADA CORPORATION; *Int'l*, pg. 2760
FRANCO-NEVADA U.S. CORPORATION—See Franco-Nevada Corporation; *Int'l*, pg. 2760
FRANCONIA INDUSTRIES, INC.—See Diehl Stiftung & Co. KG; *Int'l*, pg. 2115
FRANCONIA INTERNATIONAL INC.; *U.S. Private*, pg. 1593
FRANCONIA REAL ESTATE SERVICES, INC.—See Weichert Co.; *U.S. Private*, pg. 4470
FRANCOPIA S.A.R.L.—See Sanofi; *Int'l*, pg. 6547
FRANCO PUBLIC RELATIONS GROUP; *U.S. Private*, pg. 1593
FRANCORP, INC.; *U.S. Private*, pg. 1593
FRANCO'S ATHLETIC CLUB; *U.S. Private*, pg. 1593
FRANCO SIGNOR LLC—See Verisk Analytics, Inc.; *U.S. Public*, pg. 2282
FRANCO TOSI MECCANICA S.P.A.—See Gammon India Limited; *Int'l*, pg. 2879
FRANCOTYP POSTALIA CANADA INC.—See Francotyp-Postalia Holding AG; *Int'l*, pg. 2761
FRANCOTYP-POSTALIA FRANCE SAS—See Francotyp-Postalia Holding AG; *Int'l*, pg. 2761
FRANCOTYP-POSTALIA GMBH—See Francotyp-Postalia Holding AG; *Int'l*, pg. 2761
FRANCOTYP-POSTALIA GMBH—See Francotyp-Postalia Holding AG; *Int'l*, pg. 2761
FRANCOTYP-POSTALIA HOLDING AG; *Int'l*, pg. 2760
FRANCOTYP-POSTALIA, INC.—See Francotyp-Postalia Holding AG; *Int'l*, pg. 2761
FRANCOTYP-POSTALIA LTD.—See Francotyp-Postalia Holding AG; *Int'l*, pg. 2761
FRANCOTYP-POSTALIA NV—See Francotyp-Postalia Holding AG; *Int'l*, pg. 2761
FRANCOTYP-POSTALIA SVERIGE AB—See Francotyp-Postalia Holding AG; *Int'l*, pg. 2761
FRANCOUDI & STEPHANOU LTD.; *Int'l*, pg. 2761
FRANCO VAGO INTERNATIONAL, INC.—See Nippon Express Holdings, Inc.; *Int'l*, pg. 5315
FRANCO VAGO SPA—See Nippon Express Holdings, Inc.; *Int'l*, pg. 5315
FRANDISCO PROPERTY & CASUALTY INSURANCE—See 1st Franklin Financial Corporation; *U.S. Private*, pg. 4
FRANDON SEAFOODS INC.—See Premium Brands Holdings Corporation; *Int'l*, pg. 5963
FRANDSEN BANK & TRUST—See Frandsen Corporation; *U.S. Private*, pg. 1593
FRANDSEN CORPORATION; *U.S. Private*, pg. 1593
FRANDSEN FINANCIAL CORPORATION—See Frandsen Corporation; *U.S. Private*, pg. 1593
FRANFINANCE ITALY SPA—See Societe Generale S.A.; *Int'l*, pg. 7039
FRANFINANCE LOCATION—See Societe Generale S.A.; *Int'l*, pg. 7039
FRANFINANCE S.A.—See Societe Generale S.A.; *Int'l*, pg. 7039
FRANFINANCE SPAIN—See Societe Generale S.A.; *Int'l*, pg. 7039
FRANFINANCE UK LTD.—See Societe Generale S.A.; *Int'l*, pg. 7039
FRANGER GAS CO. INC.; *U.S. Private*, pg. 1593
FRANGI S.P.A; *Int'l*, pg. 2761
THE FRANGOS GROUP, LLC; *U.S. Private*, pg. 4030
THE FRAN HAASCH LAW GROUP; *U.S. Private*, pg. 4030
THE FRANK AGENCY, INC.; *U.S. Private*, pg. 4030
FRANK AMBROSE INC.; *U.S. Private*, pg. 1593
FRANK B. ROSS CO. INC.; *U.S. Private*, pg. 1593
FRANK BRUNCKHORST CO., LLC; *U.S. Private*, pg. 1593
FRANK BRYAN INC.; *U.S. Private*, pg. 1594
FRANK CALANDRA, INC.; *U.S. Private*, pg. 1594
FRANK C. ALEGRE TRUCKING INC.; *U.S. Private*, pg. 1594
FRANK CHERVAN INC.; *U.S. Private*, pg. 1594
FRANK COLUCCIO CONSTRUCTION CO.; *U.S. Private*, pg. 1594
FRANK CONSOLIDATED ENTERPRISES; *U.S. Private*, pg. 1594
FRANK CROSSLEY & SON LTD—See Artinova AB; *Int'l*, pg. 584
FRANKCRUM; *U.S. Private*, pg. 1596
FRANK CRYSTAL & CO. INC.—See Stone Point Capital LLC; *U.S. Private*, pg. 3819

FRANKCRUM

FRANK DIGITAL PTY LIMITED—See Jaywing PLC; *Int'l*, pg. 3916
FRANK DONIO, INC.; *U.S. Private*, pg. 1594
FRANKE AQUAROTTER GMBH—See Artemis Holding AG; *Int'l*, pg. 582
FRANKE CONSUMER PRODUCTS, INC.—See Artemis Holding AG; *Int'l*, pg. 582
FRANKE CONSUMER PRODUCTS, INC.—See Artemis Holding AG; *Int'l*, pg. 582
FRANK EDWARDS CO. INC.; *U.S. Private*, pg. 1594
FRANKE FOODSERVICE SYSTEMS AG—See Artemis Holding AG; *Int'l*, pg. 582
FRANKE FOODSERVICE SYSTEMS, INC.—See Artemis Holding AG; *Int'l*, pg. 582
FRANKE HOLDING AG—See Artemis Holding AG; *Int'l*, pg. 582
FRANKE INDUSTRIE AG—See Artemis Holding AG; *Int'l*, pg. 582
FRANKE KAFFEEMASCHINEN AG—See Artemis Holding AG; *Int'l*, pg. 582
FRANKE KINDRED CANADA LIMITED—See Artemis Holding AG; *Int'l*, pg. 582
FRANKE KUCHENTECHNIK AG—See Artemis Holding AG; *Int'l*, pg. 582
FRANKEL CADILLAC CO.; *U.S. Private*, pg. 1596
FRANKEL MANAGEMENT INC.; *U.S. Private*, pg. 1596
FRANKEL STAFFING PARTNERS; *U.S. Private*, pg. 1596
FRANKE MANAGEMENT AG—See Artemis Holding AG; *Int'l*, pg. 582
FRANK E. NEAL & CO., INC.—See Brown & Brown, Inc.; *U.S. Public*, pg. 400
FRANKEN GUSS GMBH & CO. KG—See ZF Friedrichshafen AG; *Int'l*, pg. 8644
FRANKENLUK AG—See Alpiq Holding AG; *Int'l*, pg. 372
FRANKENLUK ENERGIEANLAGENBAU GMBH—See VINCI S.A.; *Int'l*, pg. 8238
FRANKENMUTH BAVARIAN INN, INC.; *U.S. Private*, pg. 1596
FRANKENMUTH MUTUAL INSURANCE CO.; *U.S. Private*, pg. 1596
FRANKEN PLASTIKS GMBH—See Enpro Inc.; *U.S. Public*, pg. 775
FRANKENWALDKLINIK KRONACH GMBH—See Fresenius SE & Co. KGaA; *Int'l*, pg. 2778
FRANKE WATER SYSTEMS AG—See Artemis Holding AG; *Int'l*, pg. 582
FRANK FLETCHER AUTO GROUP, LLC—See Frank Fletcher Companies, Ltd.; *U.S. Private*, pg. 1594
FRANK FLETCHER COMPANIES, LTD.; *U.S. Private*, pg. 1594
FRANK FLETCHER HONDA BENTONVILLE—See Frank Fletcher Companies, Ltd.; *U.S. Private*, pg. 1594
FRANK FLETCHER KIA BENTONVILLE—See Frank Fletcher Companies, Ltd.; *U.S. Private*, pg. 1594
FRANK FLETCHER NISSAN—See Frank Fletcher Companies, Ltd.; *U.S. Private*, pg. 1594
FRANKFORD CANDY & CHOCOLATE CO.; *U.S. Private*, pg. 1596
FRANKFORT FIRST BANCORP, INC.—See First Federal MHC; *U.S. Private*, pg. 1518
FRANKFORT REGIONAL MEDICAL CENTER—See HCA Healthcare, Inc.; *U.S. Public*, pg. 996
FRANKFURTER ALLGEMEINE ZEITUNG GMBH; *Int'l*, pg. 2761
FRANKFURTER BANKGESELLSCHAFT (SCHWEIZ) AG—See Helaba Landesbank Hessen-Thuringen; *Int'l*, pg. 3327
FRANKFURTER BANKGESELLSCHAFT—See Frankfurter Sparkasse; *Int'l*, pg. 2761
FRANKFURTER BETEILIGUNGS-TREUHAND GMBH—See Deutsche Bank Aktiengesellschaft; *Int'l*, pg. 2062
FRANKFURTER KANALREINIGUNGSGESELLSCHAFT MBH—See Fraport AG; *Int'l*, pg. 2764
FRANKFURTER LEBENSVERSICHERUNG AG—See Fosun International Limited; *Int'l*, pg. 2751
FRANKFURTER SPARKASSE; *Int'l*, pg. 2761
FRANKFURTER VERMOGENS-TREUHAND GESELLSCHAFT MIT BESCHRANKTER HAFTUNG—See Deutsche Bank Aktiengesellschaft; *Int'l*, pg. 2061
FRANKFURT FAMILY OFFICE GMBH—See Deutsche Bank Aktiengesellschaft; *Int'l*, pg. 2062
FRANKFURT MARRIOTT HOTELMANAGEMENT GMBH—See Marriott International, Inc.; *U.S. Public*, pg. 1370
FRANKFURT RH OPERATING COMPANY GMBH—See Marriott International, Inc.; *U.S. Public*, pg. 1370
FRANKFURT - TRUST INVEST LUXEMBOURG AG—See ODDO BHF SCA; *Int'l*, pg. 5525
FRANKFURT-TRUST INVESTMENT-GESELLSCHAFT MBH—See ODDO BHF SCA; *Int'l*, pg. 5525
FRANK G. LOVE ENVELOPES INC.; *U.S. Private*, pg. 1594
FRANK G. SULLIVAN JR. INC.; *U.S. Private*, pg. 1594
FRANK H DALE LTD.; *Int'l*, pg. 2761
FRANK HENRY EQUIPMENT (1987) LTD.; *Int'l*, pg. 2761
FRANK HILL ASSOCIATES; *U.S. Private*, pg. 1594
FRANK H. REIS INC.; *U.S. Private*, pg. 1594
FRANK-HUNGARIA KFT.—See Gesco AG; *Int'l*, pg. 2945

FRANK HYUNDAI—See Fornaca Inc.; *U.S. Private*, pg. 1572
FRANKI AFRICA (PTY) LIMITED—See Esor Limited; *Int'l*, pg. 2504
FRANKIE & BENNYS S.L.—See Apollo Global Management, Inc.; *U.S. Public*, pg. 164
FRANKI FONDATION—See FAYAT SAS; *Int'l*, pg. 2625
FRANKI GRUNDBAU GMBH & CO. KG—See PORR AG; *Int'l*, pg. 5924
FRANK INVESTMENT INC.; *U.S. Private*, pg. 1594
FRANKI PACIFIC HOLDINGS PTY. LTD.—See Keller Group plc; *Int'l*, pg. 4119
FRANKIPILE AUSTRALIA PTY LTD - EASTERN DIVISION—See Keller Group plc; *Int'l*, pg. 4119
FRANKIPILE AUSTRALIA PTY LTD - NORTHERN DIVISION—See Keller Group plc; *Int'l*, pg. 4119
FRANKIPILE AUSTRALIA PTY LTD—See Keller Group plc; *Int'l*, pg. 4119
FRANKIPILE AUSTRALIA PTY LTD - SOUTHERN DIVISION—See Keller Group plc; *Int'l*, pg. 4119
FRANKIPILE GHANA LIMITED—See Keller Group plc; *Int'l*, pg. 4119
FRANKIPILE INTERNATIONAL PROJECTS LIMITED—See Esor Limited; *Int'l*, pg. 2504
FRANKIPILE MAURITIUS INTERNATIONAL LIMITED—See Esor Limited; *Int'l*, pg. 2504
FRANKIPILE MOCAMBIQUE LIMITADA—See Keller Group plc; *Int'l*, pg. 4119
FRANKI POLSKA SPOLKA Z OGRANICZONA ODPOWIEDZIALNOSCIA—See PORR AG; *Int'l*, pg. 5922
FRANK I. ROUNDS COMPANY; *U.S. Private*, pg. 1594
FRANK KASMIR & ASSOCIATES INC.; *U.S. Private*, pg. 1594
FRANK KEY GROUP LIMITED; *Int'l*, pg. 2761
FRANK KEY (NOTTINGHAM) LIMITED—See Frank Key Group Limited; *Int'l*, pg. 2761
FRANKLAND RIVER OLIVE COMPANY LIMITED—See Toscana (WA) Pty Ltd.; *Int'l*, pg. 7831
FRANK L. BEIER RADIO INC.; *U.S. Private*, pg. 1595
FRANK L. BLUM CONSTRUCTION COMPANY; *U.S. Private*, pg. 1595
FRANK LEMEKS TOW—See Gesco AG; *Int'l*, pg. 2945
FRANK LILL & SON INC.; *U.S. Private*, pg. 1595
FRANKLIN ADVISERS, INC.—See Franklin Resources, Inc.; *U.S. Public*, pg. 880
FRANKLIN ADVISORY SERVICES, LLC—See Franklin Resources, Inc.; *U.S. Public*, pg. 880
FRANKLIN ALTERNATIVE STRATEGIES ADVISERS, LLC—See Franklin Resources, Inc.; *U.S. Public*, pg. 880
FRANKLIN AMERICAN MORTGAGE COMPANY (FAMC)—See FAMC Corporation; *U.S. Private*, pg. 1468
FRANKLIN AMERICAN MORTGAGE COMPANY (FAMC)—See FAMC Corporation; *U.S. Private*, pg. 1468
FRANKLIN AMERICAN MORTGAGE CO.—See Citizens Financial Group, Inc.; *U.S. Public*, pg. 505
FRANKLIN & ANDREWS LIMITED—See Mott MacDonald Group Ltd.; *Int'l*, pg. 5055
FRANKLIN BAKING COMPANY, LLC—See Flowers Foods, Inc.; *U.S. Public*, pg. 855
FRANKLIN BANCORP INC.; *U.S. Private*, pg. 1596
FRANKLIN BANK & TRUST COMPANY—See Franklin Bancorp Inc.; *U.S. Private*, pg. 1596
FRANKLIN BOWLES GALLERIES; *U.S. Private*, pg. 1596
FRANKLIN BRAID MANUFACTURING CO.—See Wayne Industries Inc.; *U.S. Private*, pg. 4459
FRANKLIN BRONZE & ALLOY COMPANY, INVESTMENT CASTING DIVISION—See Franklin Bronze & Alloy Co.; *U.S. Private*, pg. 1596
FRANKLIN BRONZE & ALLOY CO., SAND CASTING DIVISION—See Franklin Bronze & Alloy Co.; *U.S. Private*, pg. 1596
FRANKLIN BRONZE & ALLOY CO.; *U.S. Private*, pg. 1596
FRANKLIN BSP CAPITAL CORPORATION; *U.S. Private*, pg. 1596
FRANKLIN BSP LENDING CORPORATION; *U.S. Public*, pg. 877
FRANKLIN BSP REALTY TRUST, INC.—See Franklin Resources, Inc.; *U.S. Public*, pg. 879
FRANKLIN BUILDING SUPPLY CO. INC.; *U.S. Private*, pg. 1596
FRANKLIN CAPITAL CORPORATION—See Franklin Resources, Inc.; *U.S. Public*, pg. 880
FRANKLIN CLINIC CORP.—See Community Health Systems, Inc.; *U.S. Public*, pg. 553
FRANKLIN COLLECTION SERVICE, INC.; *U.S. Private*, pg. 1596
FRANKLIN COMMUNICATIONS, INC.—See Saga Communications, Inc.; *U.S. Public*, pg. 1835
FRANKLIN CONTROL SYSTEMS, INC.—See Franklin Electric Co., Inc.; *U.S. Public*, pg. 878
FRANKLIN CORPORATION; *U.S. Private*, pg. 1596
FRANKLIN COUNTY PUD CO.; *U.S. Public*, pg. 1597
FRANKLIN COUNTY RESIDENTIAL SERVICES, INC.; *U.S. Private*, pg. 1597

CORPORATE AFFILIATIONS

FRANKLIN COVEY BRASIL LTDA.—See Franklin Covey Company; *U.S. Public*, pg. 877
FRANKLIN COVEY CANADA, LTD.—See Franklin Covey Company; *U.S. Public*, pg. 877
FRANKLIN COVEY CATALOG SALES INC.—See Franklin Covey Company; *U.S. Public*, pg. 877
FRANKLIN COVEY CLIENT SALES, INC.—See Franklin Covey Company; *U.S. Public*, pg. 877
FRANKLIN COVEY COMPANY; *U.S. Public*, pg. 877
FRANKLIN COVEY DE MEXICO, S. DE R.L. DE C.V.—See Franklin Covey Company; *U.S. Public*, pg. 878
FRANKLIN COVEY EUROPE, LTD.—See Franklin Covey Company; *U.S. Public*, pg. 877
FRANKLIN COVEY FRANCE SARL—See Franklin Covey Company; *U.S. Public*, pg. 877
FRANKLIN COVEY GERMANY—See Franklin Covey Company; *U.S. Public*, pg. 877
FRANKLIN COVEY JAPAN CO. LTD.—See Franklin Covey Company; *U.S. Public*, pg. 877
FRANKLIN COVEY MIDDLE EAST COMPANY LTD.—See Alkhaleej Training & Education Company; *Int'l*, pg. 331
FRANKLIN COVEY NETHERLANDS BV—See Franklin Covey Company; *U.S. Public*, pg. 877
FRANKLIN COVEY PRINTING, INC.—See Franklin Covey Company; *U.S. Public*, pg. 877
FRANKLIN COVEY PRODUCT SALES, INC.—See Franklin Covey Company; *U.S. Public*, pg. 877
FRANKLIN COVEY PROPRIETARY LIMITED—See Franklin Covey Company; *U.S. Public*, pg. 878
FRANKLIN COVEY (SHENZHEN) LTD.—See Franklin Covey Company; *U.S. Public*, pg. 877
FRANKLIN COVEY—See Franklin Covey Company; *U.S. Public*, pg. 877
FRANKLIN COVEY TRAVEL, INC.—See Franklin Covey Company; *U.S. Public*, pg. 878
FRANKLIN CREDIT MANAGEMENT CORPORATION; *U.S. Public*, pg. 878
FRANKLIN DEVELOPMENT CORP.—See Franklin Covey Company; *U.S. Public*, pg. 878
FRANKLIN DISPLAY GROUP, INC.; *U.S. Private*, pg. 1597
FRANKLIN-DODD COMMUNICATIONS LLC—See Nationwide Argosy Solutions, LLC; *U.S. Private*, pg. 2865
FRANKLIN ELECTRIC (BOTSWANA) PTY LTD—See Franklin Electric Co., Inc.; *U.S. Public*, pg. 878
FRANKLIN ELECTRIC CANADA, INC.—See Franklin Electric Co., Inc.; *U.S. Public*, pg. 878
FRANKLIN ELECTRIC CO., INC.; *U.S. Public*, pg. 878
FRANKLIN ELECTRIC COLOMBIA SAS—See Franklin Electric Co., Inc.; *U.S. Public*, pg. 878
FRANKLIN ELECTRIC EUROPA, GMBH—See Franklin Electric Co., Inc.; *U.S. Public*, pg. 878
FRANKLIN ELECTRIC GERMANY HOLDING GMBH—See Franklin Electric Co., Inc.; *U.S. Public*, pg. 878
FRANKLIN ELECTRIC HOLDING B.V.—See Franklin Electric Co., Inc.; *U.S. Public*, pg. 878
FRANKLIN ELECTRIC INDIA PRIVATE LTD.—See Franklin Electric Co., Inc.; *U.S. Public*, pg. 878
FRANKLIN ELECTRIC INDUSTRIA DE MOTOBQMBAS SA—See Franklin Electric Co., Inc.; *U.S. Public*, pg. 878
FRANKLIN ELECTRIC (SEA) PTY. LTD.—See Franklin Electric Co., Inc.; *U.S. Public*, pg. 878
FRANKLIN ELECTRIC (SOUTH AFRICA) PTY. LTD.—See Franklin Electric Co., Inc.; *U.S. Public*, pg. 878
FRANKLIN ELECTRIC SPOL S.R.O.—See Franklin Electric Co., Inc.; *U.S. Public*, pg. 878
FRANKLIN ELECTRIC (SUZHOU) CO., LTD.—See Franklin Electric Co., Inc.; *U.S. Public*, pg. 878
FRANKLIN ELECTRONIC PUBLISHERS (AUST) PTY. LTD.—See Franklin Electronic Publishers, Inc.; *U.S. Private*, pg. 1597
FRANKLIN ELECTRONIC PUBLISHERS DEUTSCHLAND GMBH—See Franklin Electronic Publishers, Inc.; *U.S. Private*, pg. 1597
FRANKLIN ELECTRONIC PUBLISHERS FRANCE—See Franklin Electronic Publishers, Inc.; *U.S. Private*, pg. 1597
FRANKLIN ELECTRONIC PUBLISHERS, INC.; *U.S. Private*, pg. 1597
FRANKLIN ELECTRONIC PUBLISHERS, LTD.—See Franklin Electronic Publishers, Inc.; *U.S. Private*, pg. 1597
FRANKLIN ENDOSCOPY CENTER, LLC—See Tenet Healthcare Corporation; *U.S. Public*, pg. 2010
FRANKLIN ENERGY SERVICES LLC—See ABRY Partners, LLC; *U.S. Private*, pg. 41
FRANKLIN EQUIPMENT LLC—See United Rentals, Inc.; *U.S. Public*, pg. 2235
FRANKLIN FINANCIAL NETWORK, INC.—See FB Financial Corporation; *U.S. Public*, pg. 824
FRANKLIN FINANCIAL SERVICES CORPORATION; *U.S. Public*, pg. 879
FRANKLIN FOODS, INC.—See Hochland SE; *Int'l*, pg. 3437
FRANKLIN FORD; *U.S. Private*, pg. 1597

COMPANY NAME INDEX

FRANKLIN FUELING SISTEMAS DE COMBUSTIVEIS LTDA—See Franklin Electric Co., Inc.; *U.S. Public*, pg. 878
FRANKLIN FUELING SYSTEMS AUSTRALIA PTY. LTD.—See Franklin Electric Co., Inc.; *U.S. Public*, pg. 878
FRANKLIN FUELING SYSTEMS FRANCE SARL—See Franklin Electric Co., Inc.; *U.S. Public*, pg. 878
FRANKLIN FUELING SYSTEMS—See Franklin Electric Co., Inc.; *U.S. Public*, pg. 878
FRANKLIN/GLENBURN HOME, INC.; *U.S. Private*, pg. 1598
THE FRANKLIN GROUP, INC.; *U.S. Private*, pg. 4030
FRANKLIN HILL ACQUISITION CORPORATION; *U.S. Private*, pg. 1597
FRANKLIN HOLWERDA COMPANY—See FHC Holding Company; *U.S. Private*, pg. 1501
FRANKLIN HOME CARE SERVICES, LLC—See Community Health Systems, Inc.; *U.S. Public*, pg. 553
FRANKLIN HOSPITAL CORPORATION—See Bon Secours Mercy Health, Inc.; *U.S. Private*, pg. 612
FRANKLIN INDUSTRIAL MINERALS—See Lhoist S.A.; *Int'l*, pg. 4478
FRANKLIN INDUSTRIES LIMITED; *Int'l*, pg. 2762
FRANKLIN INSURANCE COMPANY—See United Fire Group, Inc.; *U.S. Public*, pg. 2230
FRANKLIN INTERIORS INC.; *U.S. Private*, pg. 1597
FRANKLIN INTERNATIONAL INC.; *U.S. Private*, pg. 1597
FRANKLIN INVESTMENT ADVISORY SERVICES, LLC—See Franklin Resources, Inc.; *U.S. Public*, pg. 880
FRANKLIN-JEFFERSON STRATEGIES, LLC; *U.S. Private*, pg. 1598
FRANKLIN LEASING & FINANCE LIMITED; *Int'l*, pg. 2762
FRANKLIN L. HANEY COMPANY; *U.S. Private*, pg. 1597
FRANKLIN LIMITED DURATION INCOME TRUST; *U.S. Public*, pg. 879
FRANKLIN MACHINE PRODUCTS, INC.—See New Mountain Capital, LLC; *U.S. Private*, pg. 2901
FRANKLIN MADISON GROUP LLC—See Guggenheim Partners, LLC; *U.S. Private*, pg. 1811
FRANKLIN MILLS LLC—See Simon Property Group, Inc.; *U.S. Public*, pg. 1882
FRANKLIN MINING, INC.; *U.S. Private*, pg. 1597
THE FRANKLIN MINT, LLC—See Sequential Brands Group, Inc.; *U.S. Public*, pg. 1868
FRANKLIN MOUNTAIN ENERGY, LLC; *U.S. Private*, pg. 1597
FRANKLIN MUTUAL ADVISERS, LLC—See Franklin Resources, Inc.; *U.S. Public*, pg. 880
THE FRANKLIN MUTUAL INSURANCE COMPANY; *U.S. Private*, pg. 4030
FRANKLIN PARK ASSOCIATES, LLC; *U.S. Private*, pg. 1597
FRANKLIN PONTIAC BUICK GMC; *U.S. Private*, pg. 1597
FRANKLIN PRECISION INDUSTRY, INC.—See Aisan Industry Co., Ltd.; *Int'l*, pg. 250
FRANKLIN PRIMARY HEALTH CENTER, INC.; *U.S. Private*, pg. 1597
FRANKLIN PROPERTY & DEVELOPMENT GROUP LLC; *U.S. Private*, pg. 1597
FRANKLIN PUBLISHERS DE MEXICO—See Franklin Electronic Publishers, Inc.; *U.S. Private*, pg. 1597
FRANKLIN RESOURCES, INC.; *U.S. Public*, pg. 879
FRANKLIN SAVINGS BANK; *U.S. Private*, pg. 1597
FRANKLIN SAVINGS BANK; *U.S. Private*, pg. 1598
FRANKLINS HOLDINGS, LLC—See TEGNA Inc.; *U.S. Public*, pg. 1990
FRANKLIN SKILLED NURSING & REHABILITATION CENTER—See Apollo Global Management, Inc.; *U.S. Public*, pg. 156
FRANKLIN SPORTS, INC.; *U.S. Private*, pg. 1598
FRANKLIN SPORTS, INC. - UNIFORCE TACTICAL DIVISION—See Franklin Sports, Inc.; *U.S. Private*, pg. 1598
FRANKLIN SQUARE HOLDINGS, L.P.; *U.S. Private*, pg. 1598
FRANKLIN STREET ADVISORS, INC.—See Fifth Third Bancorp; *U.S. Public*, pg. 833
FRANKLIN STREET MARKETING; *U.S. Private*, pg. 1598
FRANKLIN STREET PARTNERS, INC.—See Fifth Third Bancorp; *U.S. Public*, pg. 833
FRANKLIN STREET PROPERTIES CORP.; *U.S. Public*, pg. 883
FRANKLIN STREET; *U.S. Private*, pg. 1598
FRANKLIN-STRICKLAND FUNERAL HOME, INC.—See Service Corporation International; *U.S. Public*, pg. 1869
FRANKLIN SURGICAL CENTER, LLC—See UnitedHealth Group Incorporated; *U.S. Public*, pg. 2240
FRANKLIN SYNERGY BANK—See FB Financial Corporation; *U.S. Public*, pg. 824
FRANKLIN TELEPHONE COMPANY INC.—See Telapex Inc.; *U.S. Private*, pg. 3959
FRANKLIN TEMPLETON ASSET MANAGEMENT (INDIA) PRIVATE LIMITED—See Franklin Resources, Inc.; *U.S. Public*, pg. 880

FRANKLIN TEMPLETON ASSET MANAGEMENT MEXICO, S.A. DE C.V.—See Franklin Resources, Inc.; *U.S. Public*, pg. 880
FRANKLIN TEMPLETON AUSTRIA GMBH—See Franklin Resources, Inc.; *U.S. Public*, pg. 880
FRANKLIN TEMPLETON BANK & TRUST, F.S.B.—See Franklin Resources, Inc.; *U.S. Public*, pg. 880
FRANKLIN TEMPLETON COMPANIES, LLC—See Franklin Resources, Inc.; *U.S. Public*, pg. 880
FRANKLIN/TEMPLETON DISTRIBUTORS, INC.—See Franklin Resources, Inc.; *U.S. Public*, pg. 881
FRANKLIN TEMPLETON FRANCE S.A.—See Franklin Resources, Inc.; *U.S. Public*, pg. 880
FRANKLIN TEMPLETON FUND MANAGEMENT LIMITED—See Franklin Resources, Inc.; *U.S. Public*, pg. 880
FRANKLIN TEMPLETON INSTITUTIONAL, LLC—See Franklin Resources, Inc.; *U.S. Public*, pg. 880
FRANKLIN TEMPLETON INTENATIONAL SERVICES S.A.—See Franklin Resources, Inc.; *U.S. Public*, pg. 880
FRANKLIN TEMPLETON INTERNATIONAL SERVICES S.A.R.L.—See Franklin Resources, Inc.; *U.S. Public*, pg. 880
FRANKLIN TEMPLETON INVESTIMENTOS (BRASIL) LTDA.—See Franklin Resources, Inc.; *U.S. Public*, pg. 880
FRANKLIN TEMPLETON INVESTMENT MANAGEMENT LIMITED—See Franklin Resources, Inc.; *U.S. Public*, pg. 880
FRANKLIN TEMPLETON INVESTMENTS (ASIA) LIMITED—See Franklin Resources, Inc.; *U.S. Public*, pg. 880
FRANKLIN TEMPLETON INVESTMENTS AUSTRALIA LIMITED—See Franklin Resources, Inc.; *U.S. Public*, pg. 880
FRANKLIN TEMPLETON INVESTMENTS CORP.—See Franklin Resources, Inc.; *U.S. Public*, pg. 880
FRANKLIN TEMPLETON INVESTMENT SERVICES GMBH—See Franklin Resources, Inc.; *U.S. Public*, pg. 880
FRANKLIN TEMPLETON INVESTMENTS JAPAN LIMITED—See Franklin Resources, Inc.; *U.S. Public*, pg. 880
FRANKLIN TEMPLETON INVESTMENTS (ME) LIMITED—See Franklin Resources, Inc.; *U.S. Public*, pg. 880
FRANKLIN TEMPLETON INVESTMENTS POLAND SP. Z O.O.—See Franklin Resources, Inc.; *U.S. Public*, pg. 881
FRANKLIN TEMPLETON INVESTMENTS SOUTH AFRICA (PTY) LTD—See Franklin Resources, Inc.; *U.S. Public*, pg. 881
FRANKLIN TEMPLETON INVESTMENT TRUST MANAGEMENT CO., LTD.—See Franklin Resources, Inc.; *U.S. Public*, pg. 880
FRANKLIN TEMPLETON INVESTOR SERVICES, LLC—See Franklin Resources, Inc.; *U.S. Public*, pg. 881
FRANKLIN TEMPLETON ITALIA SIM S.P.A.—See Franklin Resources, Inc.; *U.S. Public*, pg. 881
FRANKLIN TEMPLETON SWITZERLAND LTD.—See Franklin Resources, Inc.; *U.S. Public*, pg. 881
FRANKLIN/TEMPLETON TRAVEL, INC.—See Franklin Resources, Inc.; *U.S. Public*, pg. 881
FRANKLIN U.K.—See Franklin Electronic Publishers, Inc.; *U.S. Private*, pg. 1597
FRANKLIN WIRELESS CORPORATION; *U.S. Public*, pg. 883
FRANK LIQUOR COMPANY INCORPORATED; *U.S. Private*, pg. 1595
FRANKL & KIRCHNER GMBH & CO KG; *Int'l*, pg. 2761
FRANKLY INC.—See GameSquare Holdings, Inc.; *Int'l*, pg. 2878
FRANKLYN SCHOLAR PTY LTD.—See Graham Holdings Company; *U.S. Public*, pg. 954
FRANK MARTZ COACH COMPANY INC.; *U.S. Private*, pg. 1595
FRANK MAYBORN ENTERPRISES; *U.S. Private*, pg. 1595
FRANK MAYER & ASSOCIATES INC.; *U.S. Private*, pg. 1595
FRANK M. BOOTH DESIGN BUILD CO.—See Frank M. Booth Inc.; *U.S. Private*, pg. 1595
FRANK M. BOOTH INC.; *U.S. Private*, pg. 1595
FRANK MERCEDE & SONS INC.; *U.S. Private*, pg. 1595
FRANK MILLARD CO. INC.; *U.S. Private*, pg. 1595
FRANK MOTORS, INC.—See Fornaca Inc.; *U.S. Private*, pg. 1572
FRANK MYERS AUTO MAXX; *U.S. Private*, pg. 1595
FRANK N. MAGID ASSOCIATES, INC.; *U.S. Private*, pg. 1595
FRANK NOVAK & SONS, INC.; *U.S. Private*, pg. 1595
FRANKONIA HANDELS GMBH & CO. KG—See Otto GmbH & Co. KG; *Int'l*, pg. 5662
FRANKORT & KONING B.V.—See Dole plc; *Int'l*, pg. 2158
FRANKORT & KONING POLSKA SP. Z O.O.—See Dole plc; *Int'l*, pg. 2158

FRANK PAXTON LUMBER COMPANY; *U.S. Private*, pg. 1595
FRANK PR AUSTRALIA PTY LIMITED—See Enero Group Limited; *Int'l*, pg. 2424
FRANK PR LIMITED—See Enero Group Limited; *Int'l*, pg. 2424
FRANK PRODUCTIONS, INC.—See Live Nation Entertainment, Inc.; *U.S. Public*, pg. 1328
FRANK REPLY GMBH—See Reply S.p.A.; *Int'l*, pg. 6291
FRANK REWOLD & SON, INC.; *U.S. Private*, pg. 1595
FRANK RUSSELL COMPANY—See The Northwestern Mutual Life Insurance Company; *U.S. Private*, pg. 4085
FRANK'S CASING CREW & RENTAL TOOLS, INC.; *U.S. Private*, pg. 1596
FRANKS EIENDOM AS—See Expro Group Holdings N.V.; *Int'l*, pg. 2591
FRANKS FOREIGN CAR SERVICE INC.; *U.S. Private*, pg. 1598
FRANK SHIREY CADILLAC INC.; *U.S. Private*, pg. 1595
FRANK SHIREY CADILLAC, INC.; *U.S. Private*, pg. 1595
FRANK SHOOP, INC.; *U.S. Private*, pg. 1595
FRANK'S INTERNATIONAL AS—See Expro Group Holdings N.V.; *Int'l*, pg. 2591
FRANK'S INTERNATIONAL C.V.—See Expro Group Holdings N.V.; *Int'l*, pg. 2591
FRANK'S INTERNATIONAL, LLC—See Expro Group Holdings N.V.; *Int'l*, pg. 2591
FRANK'S SUPPLY COMPANY INC.; *U.S. Private*, pg. 1596
FRANK'S TONG SERVICE INC.—See Frank's Casing Crew & Rental Tools, Inc.; *U.S. Private*, pg. 1596
FRANK'S VACUUM TRUCK SERVICE, INC.—See EQT AB; *Int'l*, pg. 2482
FRANKS VENDING SERVICE, INC.—See Freeman Spogli & Co. Incorporated; *U.S. Private*, pg. 1606
FRANK TAYLOR LUMBER & DEVELOPMENT CO.; *U.S. Private*, pg. 1595
FRANK THEATRES, LLC; *U.S. Private*, pg. 1595
FRANK VITALE INSURANCE AGENCY—See Inszone Insurance Services, LLC; *U.S. Private*, pg. 2096
FRANK WALZ- UND SCHMIEDETECHNIK GMBH—See Gesco AG; *Int'l*, pg. 2945
FRANK W. CAWOOD & ASSOCIATES; *U.S. Private*, pg. 1595
FRANK W. DIVER INC.; *U.S. Private*, pg. 1595
FRANK WRIGHT LIMITED—See SHV Holdings N.V.; *Int'l*, pg. 6872
FRANK W. WHITCOMB CONSTRUCTION CORP.; *U.S. Private*, pg. 1596
FRANK W. WINNE & SON, INC.; *U.S. Private*, pg. 1596
FRANNET LLC; *U.S. Private*, pg. 1598
FRANPOS, INC.; *U.S. Private*, pg. 1598
FRANSABANK EL DJAZAIR SPA—See Fransabank SAL; *Int'l*, pg. 2762
FRANSABANK (FRANCE) SA—See Fransabank SAL; *Int'l*, pg. 2762
FRANSABANK OJSC—See Fransabank SAL; *Int'l*, pg. 2762
FRANSABANK SAL; *Int'l*, pg. 2762
FRANSABANK SAL—See Fransabank SAL; *Int'l*, pg. 2762
FRANSABANK SYRIA SA—See Fransabank SAL; *Int'l*, pg. 2762
FRANSA INVEST BANK SAL—See Fransabank SAL; *Int'l*, pg. 2762
FRANSHIP OFFSHORE LUX SA—See Exmar N.V.; *Int'l*, pg. 2585
FRAN'S WICKER AND RATTAN INC.; *U.S. Private*, pg. 1586
FRANTIC FILMS CORPORATION—See Kew Media Group Inc.; *Int'l*, pg. 4143
FRANTOUR GROUP—See Accor S.A.; *Int'l*, pg. 91
FRANTZ MANUFACTURING COMPANY INC.; *U.S. Private*, pg. 1598
FRANTZ MEDICAL GROUP; *U.S. Private*, pg. 1598
FRANX B.V.—See ABN AMRO Group N.V.; *Int'l*, pg. 65
FRANZ BOCKS NACHF. ING. EVA UND KARL SCHINDLER GESELLSCHAFT M.B.H. AND CO.NFG.KG—See PORR AG; *Int'l*, pg. 5922
FRANZELLA PRODUCE INC.; *U.S. Private*, pg. 1598
FRANZ FOODS INC.; *U.S. Private*, pg. 1598
FRANZ FUNKE ZERSPANUNGSTECHNIK GMBH & CO. KG—See Gesco AG; *Int'l*, pg. 2945
FRANZ GREINER GESELLSCHAFT M.B.H.—See PORR AG; *Int'l*, pg. 5922
FRANZ HANIEL & CIE. GMBH; *Int'l*, pg. 2762
FRANZIA/SANGER WINERY; *U.S. Private*, pg. 1599
FRANZISKA RACKER CENTERS; *U.S. Private*, pg. 1599
FRANZ JANITORIAL SERVICE & SUPPLY, INC.—See Bain Capital, LP; *U.S. Private*, pg. 440
FRANZ JONAS GMBH & CO. KG—See Umdasch Group AG; *Int'l*, pg. 8023
FRANZ KASSECKER GMBH—See Bilfinger SE; *Int'l*, pg. 1028
FRANZ LOHR GMBH—See Alpiq Holding AG; *Int'l*, pg. 372
FRANZ REINKEMEIER GMBH; *Int'l*, pg. 2763
FRANZ SUTER GMBH-PUMPEN UND SYSTEME; *Int'l*, pg. 2763
FRAPORT AG; *Int'l*, pg. 2763

FRAPORT AG

FRAPORT CARGO SERVICES GMBH—See Cerberus Capital Management, L.P.; *U.S. Private*, pg. 840
FRAPORT CLEVELAND INC.—See Fraport AG; *Int'l*, pg. 2764
FRAPORT IC ICTAS HAVALIMAN YER HIZMETLERI AS—See Fraport AG; *Int'l*, pg. 2764
FRAPORT IMMOBILIENSERVICE UND -ENTWICKLUNGS GMBH & CO. KG—See Fraport AG; *Int'l*, pg. 2764
FRAPORT MALTA BUSINESS SERVICES LTD.—See Fraport AG; *Int'l*, pg. 2764
FRAPORT OBJEKT MONCHHOF GMBH—See Fraport AG; *Int'l*, pg. 2764
FRAPORT PITTSBURGH INC.—See Fraport AG; *Int'l*, pg. 2764
FRAPORT REAL ESTATE 162 163 GMBH & CO. KG—See Fraport AG; *Int'l*, pg. 2764
FRAPORT REAL ESTATE VERWALTUNGS GMBH—See Fraport AG; *Int'l*, pg. 2764
FRAPORT SAUDI ARABIA LTD.—See Fraport AG; *Int'l*, pg. 2764
FRAPORT SECURITY SERVICES GMBH—See Fraport AG; *Int'l*, pg. 2764
FRAPORT SLOVENIJA D.O.O—See Fraport AG; *Int'l*, pg. 2764
FRAPORT TWIN STAR AIRPORT MANAGEMENT AD—See Fraport AG; *Int'l*, pg. 2764
FRAPPANT ALTONA GMBH—See Hypo Real Estate Holding AG; *Int'l*, pg. 3553
FRAPPA; *Int'l*, pg. 2764
FRASCA INTERNATIONAL INC.; *U.S. Private*, pg. 1599
FRASCHERI S.P.A.—See Centrale del Latte di Torino & C. S.p.A.; *Int'l*, pg. 1410
FRASCO, INC.; *U.S. Private*, pg. 1599
FRASCONA BUICK, INC.; *U.S. Private*, pg. 1599
FRASEC FRAPORT SECURITY SERVICES GMBH—See Fraport AG; *Int'l*, pg. 2764
FRASER ADVANCED INFORMATION SYSTEMS; *U.S. Private*, pg. 1599
FRASER ALEXANDER (PTY) LTD—See Royal Bafokeng Holdings (Pty) Limited; *Int'l*, pg. 6409
FRASER & CHALMERS SIYAKHA (PTY) LIMITED—See Aveng Limited; *Int'l*, pg. 738
FRASER COMMUNICATIONS; *U.S. Private*, pg. 1599
FRASER & COMPANY LIMITED; *Int'l*, pg. 2765
FRASER FORD SALES LTD.; *Int'l*, pg. 2765
FRASER INTERNATIONAL COLLEGE LTD.—See Navitas Limited; *Int'l*, pg. 5176
FRASER MACANDREW RYAN LIMITED—See Arthur J. Gallagher & Co; *U.S. Public*, pg. 203
FRASER MACKENZIE ACCELERATOR CORP.—See Forward Water Technologies Corp; *Int'l*, pg. 2747
FRASER MARINE & INDUSTRIAL—See Algoma Central Corporation; *Int'l*, pg. 318
FRASER & NEAVE HOLDINGS BHD—See Thai Beverage Public Company Limited; *Int'l*, pg. 7589
FRASER & NEAVE LIMITED—See Thai Beverage Public Company Limited; *Int'l*, pg. 7589
FRASER RESIDENCE ORCHARD PTE LTD—See Frasers Property Limited; *Int'l*, pg. 2766
FRASER RIVER PILE & DREDGE (GP) INC.; *Int'l*, pg. 2765
FRASERS CENTREPOINT PROPERTY MANAGEMENT SERVICES PTE LTD—See Frasers Property Limited; *Int'l*, pg. 2766
FRASERS CITY QUARTER PTY LIMITED—See Frasers Property Limited; *Int'l*, pg. 2766
FRASERS COMMERCIAL TRUST—See Frasers Property Limited; *Int'l*, pg. 2766
FRASERS GROUP PLC; *Int'l*, pg. 2765
FRASERS HOSPITALITY JAPAN KABUSHIKI KAISHA—See Frasers Property Limited; *Int'l*, pg. 2766
FRASERS HOSPITALITY MANAGEMENT PTE LTD—See Frasers Property Limited; *Int'l*, pg. 2766
FRASERS HOSPITALITY PTE. LTD.—See Frasers Property Limited; *Int'l*, pg. 2766
FRASERS HOSPITALITY TRUST—See Frasers Property Limited; *Int'l*, pg. 2766
FRASERS HOSPITALITY (UK) LIMITED—See Frasers Property Limited; *Int'l*, pg. 2766
FRASERS LOGISTICS & INDUSTRIAL TRUST—See Frasers Property Limited; *Int'l*, pg. 2766
FRASERS PROPERTY AHL LIMITED—See Frasers Property Limited; *Int'l*, pg. 2766
FRASERS PROPERTY (APG) PTY. LIMITED—See Frasers Property Limited; *Int'l*, pg. 2766
FRASERS PROPERTY AUSTRALIA PTY LIMITED—See Frasers Property Limited; *Int'l*, pg. 2766
FRASERS PROPERTY DEVELOPMENTS LTD—See Frasers Property Limited; *Int'l*, pg. 2766
FRASERS PROPERTY (EUROPE) HOLDINGS PTE LTD—See Frasers Property Limited; *Int'l*, pg. 2766
FRASERS PROPERTY INDUSTRIAL (THAILAND) COMPANY LIMITED—See Frasers Property Limited; *Int'l*, pg. 2766
FRASERS PROPERTY LIMITED; *Int'l*, pg. 2765
FRASERS PROPERTY MANAGEMENT AUSTRALIA PTY LIMITED—See Frasers Property Limited; *Int'l*, pg. 2766
FRASERS PROPERTY THAILAND INDUSTRIAL FREEHOLD & LEASEHOLD REIT; *Int'l*, pg. 2766

FRASERS PROPERTY (THAILAND) PUBLIC COMPANY LIMITED—See Frasers Property Limited; *Int'l*, pg. 2766
FRASERS PROPERTY (UK) LIMITED—See Frasers Property Limited; *Int'l*, pg. 2766
FRASERS TOWN HALL PTY LTD—See Frasers Property Limited; *Int'l*, pg. 2766
FRASER SUITES SEEF SPC—See Seef Properties B.S.C.; *Int'l*, pg. 6678
FRASER SUITE SYDNEY—See Frasers Property Limited; *Int'l*, pg. 2766
FRASER SURREY DOCKS LP—See Dubai World Corporation; *Int'l*, pg. 2221
FRASER YACHTS CALIFORNIA—See MarineMax, Inc.; *U.S. Public*, pg. 1366
FRASER YACHTS FLORIDA, INC.—See MarineMax, Inc.; *U.S. Public*, pg. 1366
FRASER YACHTS LIMITED—See MarineMax, Inc.; *U.S. Public*, pg. 1366
FRASER YACHTS MANAGEMENT & SERVICES LLC—See MarineMax, Inc.; *U.S. Public*, pg. 1366
FRASER YACHTS SPAIN SLU—See MarineMax, Inc.; *U.S. Public*, pg. 1366
FRASIER TIRE SERVICE INC.; *U.S. Private*, pg. 1599
FRAS-LE AFRICA AUTOMOTIVE (PTY) LTD.—See Fras-le S.A.; *Int'l*, pg. 2765
FRAS-LE ANDINA COMERCIO Y REPRESENTACIONES LTDA.—See Fras-le S.A.; *Int'l*, pg. 2765
FRAS-LE ARGENTINA S.A.—See Fras-le S.A.; *Int'l*, pg. 2765
FRAS-LE EUROPE HANDELSGESELLSCHAFT MBH—See Fras-le S.A.; *Int'l*, pg. 2765
FRAS-LE FRICTION MATERIALS (PINGHU) CO., LTD.—See Fras-le S.A.; *Int'l*, pg. 2765
FRAS-LE MEXICO, S. DE R.L. DE C.V.—See Fras-le S.A.; *Int'l*, pg. 2765
FRAS-LE MIDDLE EAST—See Fras-le S.A.; *Int'l*, pg. 2765
FRAS-LE NORTH AMERICA INC.—See Fras-le S.A.; *Int'l*, pg. 2765
FRAS-LE S.A. - ALABAMA FACILITY—See Fras-le S.A.; *Int'l*, pg. 2765
FRAS-LE S.A.; *Int'l*, pg. 2764
FRASSINETI S.R.L.—See Onward Holdings Co., Ltd.; *Int'l*, pg. 5592
FRATELLI DE CECCO DI FILIPPO FARA SAN MARTINO S.P.A.; *Int'l*, pg. 2766
FRATELLI GANCIA & C. S.P.A.—See CJSC Russian Standard Corporation; *Int'l*, pg. 1634
FRATELLO TRADE D.O.O.—See Fratello Trade JSC Banja Luka; *Int'l*, pg. 2767
FRATELLO TRADE JSC BANJA LUKA; *Int'l*, pg. 2767
FRATINO B.V—See TomTom N.V.; *Int'l*, pg. 7804
FRATTALONE COMPANIES, INC.; *U.S. Private*, pg. 1599
FRATTALONE'S HARDWARE; *U.S. Private*, pg. 1599
FRAUENTHAL AUTOMOTIVE ADMINISTRATION GMBH—See Frauenthal Holding AG; *Int'l*, pg. 2767
FRAUENTHAL AUTOMOTIVE AZAMBUJA, UNIPESSOAL, LDA.—See Frauenthal Holding AG; *Int'l*, pg. 2767
FRAUENTHAL AUTOMOTIVE COMPONENTS GMBH—See Frauenthal Holding AG; *Int'l*, pg. 2767
FRAUENTHAL AUTOMOTIVE ELTERLEIN GMBH—See Frauenthal Holding AG; *Int'l*, pg. 2767
FRAUENTHAL AUTOMOTIVE SAXONY GMBH—See Frauenthal Holding AG; *Int'l*, pg. 2767
FRAUENTHAL GNOTEC CHINA CO. LTD.—See Frauenthal Holding AG; *Int'l*, pg. 2767
FRAUENTHAL GNOTEC SLOVAKIA S.R.O.—See Frauenthal Holding AG; *Int'l*, pg. 2767
FRAUENTHAL HOLDING AG; *Int'l*, pg. 2767
FRAUENTHAL OST BETEILIGUNGS-GMBH—See Frauenthal Holding AG; *Int'l*, pg. 2767
FRAUENTHAL POWERTRAIN MANAGEMENT GMBH & CO. KG—See Frauenthal Holding AG; *Int'l*, pg. 2767
FRAUNHOFER AUSTRIA RESEARCH GMBH—See Fraunhofer-Gesellschaft zur Forderung der angewandten Forschung e.V.; *Int'l*, pg. 2767
FRAUNHOFER-GESELLSCHAFT ZUR FORDERUNG DER ANGEWANDTEN FORSCHUNG E.V.; *Int'l*, pg. 2767
FRAUNHOFER ITALIA RESEARCH KONSORTIALGESELLSCHAFT MBH—See Fraunhofer-Gesellschaft zur Forderung der angewandten Forschung e.V.; *Int'l*, pg. 2767
FRAUNHOFER UK RESEARCH LTD.—See Fraunhofer-Gesellschaft zur Forderung der angewandten Forschung e.V.; *Int'l*, pg. 2767
FRAUNHOFER USA, INC.—See Fraunhofer-Gesellschaft zur Forderung der angewandten Forschung e.V.; *Int'l*, pg. 2767
FR AVIATION LIMITED—See Advent International Corporation; *U.S. Private*, pg. 99
FRAWO FRANKFURTER WOHNUNGS- UND SIEDLUNGS-GESELLSCHAFT MBH—See Helaba Landesbank Hessen-Thuringen; *Int'l*, pg. 3327
THE FRAYMAN GROUP, INC.—See IntApp, Inc.; *U.S. Public*, pg. 1134
F. RAY MOORE OIL CO. INC.; *U.S. Private*, pg. 1455
FRAZEE INC.; *U.S. Private*, pg. 1599
FRAZEL GROUP SDN. BHD.; *Int'l*, pg. 2767
FRAZER FROST, PLC; *U.S. Private*, pg. 1599

CORPORATE AFFILIATIONS

FRAZER & JONES DIVISION—See The Eastern Company; *U.S. Public*, pg. 2069
FRAZER-NASH AUSTRALIA PTY. LTD.—See KBR, Inc.; *U.S. Public*, pg. 1215
FRAZER-NASH CONSULTANCY (AUSTRALIA) PTY LTD—See KBR, Inc.; *U.S. Public*, pg. 1215
FRAZER-NASH CONSULTANCY LTD.—See KBR, Inc.; *U.S. Public*, pg. 1215
FRAZIER & COMPANY, INC.; *U.S. Private*, pg. 1599
FRAZIER & DEETER, LLC; *U.S. Private*, pg. 1599
FRAZIER & DEETER, LLC - TAMPA OFFICE—See Frazier & Deeter, LLC; *U.S. Private*, pg. 1600
FRAZIER & FRAZIER INDUSTRIES; *U.S. Private*, pg. 1600
FRAZIER INDUSTRIAL COMPANY INC.; *U.S. Private*, pg. 1600
FRAZIER LIFESCIENCES ACQUISITION CORPORATION; *U.S. Public*, pg. 883
FRAZIER MANAGEMENT, LLC; *U.S. Private*, pg. 1600
FRCH DESIGN WORLDWIDE; *U.S. Private*, pg. 1600
FRC HOLDING CORP.; *U.S. Private*, pg. 1600
FRC SYSTEMS INTERNATIONAL—See Sulzer Ltd.; *Int'l*, pg. 7257
FRD (HONG KONG) CO., LTD.—See Shenzhen FRD Science & Technology Co., Ltd.; *Int'l*, pg. 6810
F.R. DRAKE COMPANY—See The Middleby Corporation; *U.S. Public*, pg. 2113
FREAKOUT HOLDINGS, INC.; *Int'l*, pg. 2767
FREAKOUT TAIWAN CO., LTD.—See FreakOut Holdings, Inc.; *Int'l*, pg. 2767
FREAKOUT (THAILAND) CO., LTD.—See FreakOut Holdings, Inc.; *Int'l*, pg. 2767
FREBERG ENVIRONMENTAL, INC.—See Willis Towers Watson Public Limited Company; *Int'l*, pg. 8417
FRECH ASIA PTE. LTD.—See Oskar Frech GmbH + Co. KG; *Int'l*, pg. 5651
FRECH DO BRASIL LTDA.—See Oskar Frech GmbH + Co. KG; *Int'l*, pg. 5651
FRECH ESPANA S.A.U—See Oskar Frech GmbH + Co. KG; *Int'l*, pg. 5651
FRECH FAR EAST LTD.—See Oskar Frech GmbH + Co. KG; *Int'l*, pg. 5651
FRECH INDIA MACHINERY PVT. LTD—See Oskar Frech GmbH + Co. KG; *Int'l*, pg. 5651
FRECH ITALIA S.R.L—See Oskar Frech GmbH + Co. KG; *Int'l*, pg. 5651
FRECH POLSKA SP. Z.O.O.—See Oskar Frech GmbH + Co. KG; *Int'l*, pg. 5651
FRECH (SHANGHAI) DIE CASTING MACHINE CO., LTD.—See Oskar Frech GmbH + Co. KG; *Int'l*, pg. 5651
FRECH TAIWAN LTD.—See Oskar Frech GmbH + Co. KG; *Int'l*, pg. 5651
FRECH TOOLS POLAND SP. Z.O.O.—See Oskar Frech GmbH + Co. KG; *Int'l*, pg. 5651
FRECH U.K. LTD.—See Oskar Frech GmbH + Co. KG; *Int'l*, pg. 5651
FRECH USA INC.—See Oskar Frech GmbH + Co. KG; *Int'l*, pg. 5651
FRECHVERLAG GMBH—See Bertelsmann SE & Co. KGaA; *Int'l*, pg. 992
FRECNSYS SAS—See Soitec S.A.; *Int'l*, pg. 7060
FRE COMPOSITES INC.—See Clayton, Dubilier & Rice, LLC; *U.S. Private*, pg. 920
FREDAG AG—See Orior AG; *Int'l*, pg. 5633
FREDA H. GORDON HOSPICE & PALLIATIVE CARE OF TIDEWATER—See UnitedHealth Group Incorporated; *U.S. Public*, pg. 2245
FRED ALGER & COMPANY INCORPORATED—See Alger Associates, Inc.; *U.S. Private*, pg. 166
FRED ALGER MANAGEMENT, INC.—See Alger Associates, Inc.; *U.S. Private*, pg. 166
FRED ALLEN ENTERPRISES INC.; *U.S. Private*, pg. 1600
FRED A. MORETON & COMPANY; *U.S. Private*, pg. 1600
FRED BEANS CHEVROLET, INCORPORATED; *U.S. Private*, pg. 1600
FRED BEANS FORD OF BOYERTOWN; *U.S. Private*, pg. 1600
FRED BEANS LINCOLN MERCURY; *U.S. Private*, pg. 1600
FRED BERGLUND & SONS INC.; *U.S. Private*, pg. 1600
FRED B. JOHNSTON COMPANY, INC.; *U.S. Private*, pg. 1600
FRED BORMAN ENTERPRISES, INC.; *U.S. Private*, pg. 1600
FRED CARL'S NEW SALEM SAAB; *U.S. Private*, pg. 1600
FRED C. CHURCH INC.; *U.S. Private*, pg. 1600
FRED C. HOLMES LUMBER COMPANY; *U.S. Private*, pg. 1600
FRED CHRISTEN & SONS COMPANY; *U.S. Private*, pg. 1600
FRED DANIEL & SONS, INC.—See Stone Point Capital LLC; *U.S. Private*, pg. 3819
FREDDIE MAC INC; *U.S. Public*, pg. 1601
FREDDY HOLDINGS PTY LTD.—See TPG Capital, L.P.; *U.S. Public*, pg. 2176

FREDDY'S FROZEN CUSTARD LLC—See Thompson Street Capital Manager LLC; *U.S. Private*, pg. 4161
FREDE, NORMAN CHEVROLET; *U.S. Private*, pg. 1601
FREDERATOR NETWORKS INC.—See Kartoon Studios, Inc.; *U.S. Public*, pg. 1214
FREDERIC COLLIOU—See Michael Weinig AG; *Int'l*, pg. 4874
FREDERIC FEKKAI DALLAS, LLC—See LUXE Brands, Inc.; *U.S. Private*, pg. 2518
FREDERIC FEKKAI DALLAS, LLC—See SA Designer Parfums Ltd.; *Int'l*, pg. 6458
FREDERIC FEKKAI GREENWICH, LLC—See LUXE Brands, Inc.; *U.S. Private*, pg. 2518
FREDERIC FEKKAI GREENWICH, LLC—See SA Designer Parfums Ltd.; *Int'l*, pg. 6458
FREDERIC FEKKAI (MARK NY), LLC—See LUXE Brands, Inc.; *U.S. Private*, pg. 2518
FREDERIC FEKKAI (MARK NY), LLC—See SA Designer Parfums Ltd.; *Int'l*, pg. 6458
FREDERIC FEKKAI NEW YORK, LLC—See LUXE Brands, Inc.; *U.S. Private*, pg. 2518
FREDERIC FEKKAI NEW YORK, LLC—See SA Designer Parfums Ltd.; *Int'l*, pg. 6458
FREDERICK CHEVROLET INC.; *U.S. Private*, pg. 1601
FREDERICK COOPER LLC; *U.S. Private*, pg. 1601
FREDERICK COUNTY BANCORP, INC.—See ACNB Corporation; *U.S. Public*, pg. 36
FREDERICK DERR & COMPANY INCORPORATED; *U.S. Private*, pg. 1602
FREDERICK FELL PUBLISHERS, INC.; *U.S. Private*, pg. 1602
FREDERICK GOLDMAN INC.; *U.S. Private*, pg. 1602
FREDERICK LIVING; *U.S. Private*, pg. 1602
FREDERICK MEISWINKEL, INC.; *U.S. Private*, pg. 1602
FREDERICK MEMORIAL HOSPITAL, INC.; *U.S. Private*, pg. 1602
FREDERICK MOTOR CO.; *U.S. Private*, pg. 1602
FREDERICK OUTBACK, INC.—See Bloomin' Brands, Inc.; *U.S. Public*, pg. 363
FREDERICK P CLARK ASSOCIATES, INC.—See Hardesty & Hanover, LLC; *U.S. Private*, pg. 1863
FREDERICK P. WINNER, LTD.; *U.S. Private*, pg. 1602
FREDERICKSBURG AUTO AUCTION—See Cox Enterprises, Inc.; *U.S. Private*, pg. 1076
FREDERICKSBURG FARMERS COOP; *U.S. Private*, pg. 1602
FREDERICKSBURG FUDGE CO.—See Fischer & Wieser Specialty Foods, Inc.; *U.S. Private*, pg. 1532
FREDERICKSBURG PHYSICAL THERAPY, LIMITED PARTNERSHIP—See U.S. Physical Therapy, Inc.; *U.S. Public*, pg. 2214
FREDERICKS FUEL & HEATING SERVICE; *U.S. Private*, pg. 1602
FREDERICKSON POWER, LP—See Capital Power Corporation; *Int'l*, pg. 1312
FREDERICK SUPERMARKET OF CARS; *U.S. Private*, pg. 1602
FREDERICK-THOMPSON CO.; *U.S. Private*, pg. 1602
FREDERICKTOWN CHEVROLET CO., INC.—See General Motors Company; *U.S. Public*, pg. 924
FREDERICK WARNE & CO. LTD.—See Pearson plc; *Int'l*, pg. 5775
FREDERICK WILDMAN & SONS LTD.—See Cantine Riunite & CIV S.C.Agr.; *Int'l*, pg. 1299
FREDERIC, LLC—See The Procter & Gamble Company; *U.S. Public*, pg. 2120
FREDERIC PRINTING COMPANY—See Chatham Asset Management, LLC; *U.S. Private*, pg. 862
FREDERIK CHRISTIANSEN FOOD A/S—See Orkla ASA; *Int'l*, pg. 5637
FREDERIQUE CONSTANT HOLDING S.A.—See Citizen Watch Co., Ltd.; *Int'l*, pg. 1625
FRED FINCH YOUTH CENTER; *U.S. Private*, pg. 1600
FRED FORD MARTIN INC.; *U.S. Private*, pg. 1601
FRED FREDERICKS CHRYSLER; *U.S. Private*, pg. 1601
FRED GARRISON OIL COMPANY; *U.S. Private*, pg. 1601
FRED GELLER ELECTRICAL, INC.; *U.S. Private*, pg. 1601
FRED GROENESTEGE CONSTRUCTION LIMITED; *Int'l*, pg. 2767
FRED HAAS COUNTRY, L.P.—See Haas & Haas, LLC; *U.S. Private*, pg. 1837
FRED HAAS MOTORS, LTD.—See Haas & Haas, LLC; *U.S. Private*, pg. 1837
FRED HAAS NISSAN, L.P.—See Haas & Haas, LLC; *U.S. Private*, pg. 1837
FREDHOPPER BV—See CrownPeak Technology, Inc.; *U.S. Private*, pg. 1113
THE FRED JONES COMPANIES INC.; *U.S. Private*, pg. 4030
FRED JONES ENTERPRISES, INC.; *U.S. Private*, pg. 1601
FRED JONES ENTERPRISES; *U.S. Private*, pg. 1601
FRED LAVERY COMPANY—See US Auto Group Limited; *U.S. Private*, pg. 4317
FRED LOYA INSURANCE AGENCY; *U.S. Private*, pg. 1601
FREDMAN BAG COMPANY—See LongueVue Capital, LLC; *U.S. Private*, pg. 2493

FREDMAN BROS. FURNITURE COMPANY INC.; *U.S. Private*, pg. 1602
FRED MARTIN NISSAN LLC.; *U.S. Private*, pg. 1601
FRED MARTIN SUPERSTORE; *U.S. Private*, pg. 1601
FRED MCGILVRAY INC.; *U.S. Private*, pg. 1601
FRED MEYER, INC.—See The Kroger Co.; *U.S. Public*, pg. 2107
FRED MEYER JEWELERS, INC.—See The Kroger Co.; *U.S. Public*, pg. 2107
FRED MEYER OF ALASKA—See The Kroger Co.; *U.S. Public*, pg. 2107
FRED MEYER STORES, INC.—See The Kroger Co.; *U.S. Public*, pg. 2107
FRED MEYER STORES, INC.—See The Kroger Co.; *U.S. Public*, pg. 2107
FRED M. STARLING, INC.; *U.S. Private*, pg. 1601
FRED MUELLER AUTOMOTIVE, INC.; *U.S. Private*, pg. 1601
FRED NACKARD WHOLESALE LIQUOR CO.; *U.S. Private*, pg. 1601
FRED OLIVIERI CONSTRUCTION CO.; *U.S. Private*, pg. 1601
FRED. OLSEN & CO.; *Int'l*, pg. 2767
FRED. OLSEN CRUISE LINES LTD.—See Fred. Olsen & Co.; *Int'l*, pg. 2768
FRED. OLSEN FLY OG LUFTMATERIELL AS—See Fred. Olsen & Co.; *Int'l*, pg. 2768
FRED. OLSEN FREIGHT LIMITED—See Braemar PLC; *Int'l*, pg. 1136
FRED. OLSEN MARINE SERVICES AS—See Fred. Olsen & Co.; *Int'l*, pg. 2768
FRED. OLSEN RENEWABLES AS—See Fred. Olsen & Co.; *Int'l*, pg. 2768
FRED. OLSEN RENEWABLES LTD.—See Fred. Olsen & Co.; *Int'l*, pg. 2768
FRED. OLSEN TRAVEL AS—See Fred. Olsen & Co.; *Int'l*, pg. 2768
FREDONIA MINING INC.; *Int'l*, pg. 2769
FRED PARIS SA—See LVMH Moet Hennessy Louis Vuitton SE; *Int'l*, pg. 4593
FRED PERRY LTD.—See Hit Union Company Ltd.; *Int'l*, pg. 3408
FREDRICK RAMOND INCORPORATED; *U.S. Private*, pg. 1602
FREDRIC'S CORPORATION; *U.S. Private*, pg. 1602
FREDRIKSONS VERKSTADS AB—See XANO Industri AB; *Int'l*, pg. 8519
FRED S.A.—See LVMH Moet Hennessy Louis Vuitton SE; *Int'l*, pg. 4593
FRED'S CAPITAL MANAGEMENT COMPANY, INC.—See Fred's Inc.; *U.S. Public*, pg. 883
FRED'S INC.; *U.S. Public*, pg. 883
FRED SMITH COMPANY; *U.S. Private*, pg. 1601
FRED SMITH CONSTRUCTION, INC.—See Construction Partners, Inc.; *U.S. Public*, pg. 572
FRED'S STORES OF TENNESSEE, INC—See Fred's Inc.; *U.S. Public*, pg. 883
FRED TAYLOR COMPANY INC.; *U.S. Private*, pg. 1601
FRED TEITELBAUM CONSTRUCTION CO. INC.; *U.S. Private*, pg. 1601
FREDUN PHARMACEUTICALS LTD.; *Int'l*, pg. 2769
FRED USINGER, INC.; *U.S. Private*, pg. 1601
FRED V. FOWLER COMPANY, INC.; *U.S. Private*, pg. 1601
THE FRED W. ALBRECHT GROCERY CO.; *U.S. Private*, pg. 4030
FRED WEBER, INC.; *U.S. Private*, pg. 1601
FRED WILLIAMS, INC.—See ENGIE SA; *Int'l*, pg. 2429
FREEBAIRN & COMPANY PUBLIC RELATIONS—See Freebairn & Co.; *U.S. Private*, pg. 1602
FREEBAIRN & CO.; *U.S. Private*, pg. 1602
FREEBEES B.V.—See BP plc; *Int'l*, pg. 1131
FREEBIRD SEMICONDUCTOR CORPORATION—See HEICO Corporation; *U.S. Public*, pg. 1021
FREEBIT CO., LTD.; *Int'l*, pg. 2769
FREEBORDERS, INC.—See Symbio, LLC; *U.S. Private*, pg. 3899
FREEBORN COUNTY CO-OP OIL CO.; *U.S. Private*, pg. 1602
FREEBORN LUMBER COMPANY—See Bain Capital, LP; *U.S. Private*, pg. 450
FREECAST, INC.; *U.S. Private*, pg. 1602
FREECHARGE PAYMENT TECHNOLOGIES PVT. LTD.—See Axis Bank Limited; *Int'l*, pg. 769
FREE-COL LABORATORIES—See Modern Industries Inc.; *U.S. Private*, pg. 2761
FREED ADVERTISING; *U.S. Private*, pg. 1602
FREEDMAN FOOD SERVICE, INC.—See Sysco Corporation; *U.S. Public*, pg. 1973
FREEDMAN FOOD SERVICE OF DALLAS, INC.—See Sysco Corporation; *U.S. Public*, pg. 1973
FREEDMAN FOOD SERVICE OF DENVER, INC.—See Sysco Corporation; *U.S. Public*, pg. 1973
FREEDMAN FOOD SERVICE OF SAN ANTONIO, LP—See Sysco Corporation; *U.S. Public*, pg. 1973
FREEDMAN, GIBSON & WHITE INC.; *U.S. Private*, pg. 1603
FREEDMAN OFFICE FURNITURE, LLC; *U.S. Private*, pg. 1603

FREEDMONT MORTGAGE CORP.—See radius financial group, inc.; *U.S. Private*, pg. 3344
FREED OF LONDON LTD.; *Int'l*, pg. 2769
FREED OF LONDON LTD.—See Onward Holdings Co., Ltd.; *Int'l*, pg. 5592
FREED OF LONDON LTD.—See Freed of London Ltd.; *Int'l*, pg. 2769
FREED OF LONDON U.S.—See Freed of London Ltd.; *Int'l*, pg. 2769
FREEDOM 1, LLC—See US 1 Industries, Inc.; *U.S. Private*, pg. 4317
FREEDOM 3 CAPITAL, LLC; *U.S. Private*, pg. 1603
FREEDOM ALLOYS, INC.—See IBC Advanced Alloys Corp.; *U.S. Public*, pg. 1083
FREEDOM BANK OF AMERICA; *U.S. Private*, pg. 1603
THE FREEDOM BANK OF VIRGINIA; *U.S. Public*, pg. 2074
FREEDOM BOAT CLUB LLC—See Brunswick Corporation; *U.S. Public*, pg. 407
FREEDOM CHEVROLET - SAN ANTONIO—See Group 1 Automotive, Inc.; *U.S. Public*, pg. 971
FREEDOM COMMUNICATION TECHNOLOGIES, INC.—See Astronics Corporation; *U.S. Public*, pg. 217
FREEDOM CONSULTING GROUP LLC; *U.S. Private*, pg. 1603
FREEDOM CREDIT UNION; *U.S. Private*, pg. 1603
FREEDOM DATA SYSTEMS INC.—See UnitedHealth Group Incorporated; *U.S. Public*, pg. 2248
FREEDOM DESIGNS, INC.—See Invacare Corporation; *U.S. Private*, pg. 2130
FREEDOM ELECTRONICS LLC—See SPP Management Services, LLC; *U.S. Private*, pg. 3762
FREEDOM ENERGY INC.; *Int'l*, pg. 2769
FREEDOM FINANCE JSC; *Int'l*, pg. 2769
FREEDOM FORD SALES LTD; *Int'l*, pg. 2769
FREEDOM FOREVER LLC; *U.S. Private*, pg. 1603
THE FREEDOM FORUM INC.; *U.S. Private*, pg. 4030
FREEDOM FUELS AUSTRALIA PTY. LTD.—See Idemitsu Kosan Co., Ltd.; *Int'l*, pg. 3590
FREEDOM GRAPHIC SYSTEMS INC.; *U.S. Private*, pg. 1603
FREEDOM GROUP LIMITED; *Int'l*, pg. 2769
THE FREEDOM GROUP OF COMPANIES LIMITED—See Grovepoint Capital LLP; *Int'l*, pg. 3112
THE FREEDOM GROUP OF COMPANIES LIMITED—See Rubicon Partners Limited; *Int'l*, pg. 6422
FREEDOM HEALTH INC.; *U.S. Private*, pg. 1603
FREEDOM HOLDING CORP.; *Int'l*, pg. 2769
FREEDOM HOLDINGS, INC.; *U.S. Public*, pg. 884
FREEDOM HOUSE, INC.; *U.S. Private*, pg. 1603
FREEDOM IMAGING SYSTEMS INC.—See Freedom Graphic Systems Inc.; *U.S. Private*, pg. 1603
FREEDOM INFORMATION SYSTEMS, INC.; *U.S. Private*, pg. 1603
FREEDOM INNOVATIONS, LLC—See Proteor SAS; *Int'l*, pg. 6004
FREEDOM INTERNATIONAL BROKERAGE COMPANY—See BGC Group, Inc.; *U.S. Public*, pg. 328
FREEDOM INTERNET GROUP, INC.; *U.S. Private*, pg. 1603
FREEDOM INVESTMENTS, INC.—See Oppenheimer Holdings Inc.; *U.S. Public*, pg. 1608
FREEDOM LEAF, INC.; *U.S. Public*, pg. 884
FREEDOM LEXINGTON; *U.S. Private*, pg. 1603
FREEDOM LIFE INSURANCE COMPANY—See UBS Group AG; *Int'l*, pg. 8006
FREEDOM MANAGEMENT; *U.S. Private*, pg. 1603
FREEDOM MARKETING LIMITED—See Red Ventures, LLC; *U.S. Private*, pg. 3376
FREEDOM MEDICAL, INC.—See Freeman Spogli & Co. Incorporated; *U.S. Private*, pg. 1606
FREEDOM METALS INC.; *U.S. Private*, pg. 1603
FREEDOM MOBILE INC.—See Rogers Communications Inc.; *Int'l*, pg. 6383
FREEDOM MORTGAGE CORPORATION; *U.S. Private*, pg. 1604
FREEDOM NATIONAL BANK—See Bristol County Savings Bank; *U.S. Private*, pg. 656
FREEDOM OF CREATION B.V.—See 3D Systems Corporation; *U.S. Public*, pg. 4
FREEDOM OIL COMPANY; *U.S. Private*, pg. 1604
FREEDOM + PARTNERS; *U.S. Private*, pg. 1603
FREEDOM PARTNERS; *U.S. Private*, pg. 1604
FREEDOM PLAZA LTD.; *U.S. Private*, pg. 1604
FREEDOM POWER SYSTEMS, INC.—See Vicor Corporation; *U.S. Public*, pg. 2296
FREEDOM RESOURCES HOLDINGS CORP.; *Int'l*, pg. 2769
FREEDOMROADS, LLC—See Camping World Holdings, Inc.; *U.S. Public*, pg. 428
FREEDOM SCIENTIFIC GMBH—See Freedom Scientific Inc.; *U.S. Private*, pg. 1604
FREEDOM SCIENTIFIC INC.; *U.S. Private*, pg. 1604
FREEDOM SOLUTIONS GROUP INC.—See ARG, Inc.; *U.S. Private*, pg. 319
FREEDOM SOLUTIONS GROUP, L.L.C.; *U.S. Private*, pg. 1604

FREEDOM SOLUTIONS GROUP, L.L.C.

FREEDOM SPORTSLINE LIMITED—See Foot Locker, Inc.; *U.S. Public*, pg. 863
FREEDOM STORES INC.; *U.S. Private*, pg. 1604
FREEDOM TECHNOLOGIES, INC.; *U.S. Private*, pg. 1604
FREEDOM TRUCK CENTERS INC.; *U.S. Private*, pg. 1604
FREEDOM TRUST SERVICES LIMITED—See Marsh & McLennan Companies, Inc.; *U.S. Public*, pg. 1375
FREEDOM VILLAGE OF BRADENTON, LLC—See Brookdale Senior Living Inc.; *U.S. Public*, pg. 394
FREEDOM VILLAGE OF HOLLAND MICHIGAN—See Brookdale Senior Living Inc.; *U.S. Public*, pg. 394
FREEDOM VILLAGE OF SUN CITY CENTER, LTD.—See Brookdale Senior Living Inc.; *U.S. Public*, pg. 394
FREEDOM WASTE SERVICE, LLC—See BC Partners LLP; *Int'l*, pg. 924
THE FREEDONIA GROUP, INC.—See MarketResearch.com; *U.S. Public*, pg. 2581
FREEDREAMS B.V.—See Hubert Burda Media Holding Kommanditgesellschaft; *Int'l*, pg. 3520
FREED'S BAKERY LLC—See Swander Pace Capital, LLC; *U.S. Private*, pg. 3890
FREED, TELLER & FREED'S; *U.S. Private*, pg. 1603
FREEE K.K.; *Int'l*, pg. 2769
FREE ENERGY S.R.L.—See A2A S.p.A.; *Int'l*, pg. 29
FREE ENTERPRISES INC.; *U.S. Private*, pg. 1602
FREEFLIGHT SYSTEMS, LTD.—See The Jordan Company, L.P.; *U.S. Private*, pg. 4059
FREE FLOW, INC.; *U.S. Public*, pg. 884
FREE FOR ALL, INC.; *U.S. Private*, pg. 1602
FREEFORM TV—See The Walt Disney Company; *U.S. Public*, pg. 2137
FREEGOLD VENTURES LIMITED; *Int'l*, pg. 2769
FREEHILL MINING LTD.; *Int'l*, pg. 2769
FREEHOLD CARTAGE INC.; *U.S. Private*, pg. 1604
FREEHOLD CHRYSLER JEEP; *U.S. Private*, pg. 1604
FREEHOLD FORD INC.; *U.S. Private*, pg. 1604
FREEHOLD PONTIAC BUICK GMC; *U.S. Private*, pg. 1604
FREEHOLD RACEWAY OFF TRACK LLC—See PENN Entertainment, Inc.; *U.S. Public*, pg. 1662
FREEHOLD RESOURCES LTD.—See Freehold Royalties Ltd.; *Int'l*, pg. 2770
FREEHOLD ROYALTIES LTD.; *Int'l*, pg. 2769
FREEHOLD SAVINGS BANK; *U.S. Private*, pg. 1604
FREEHOLD SUBARU-DODGE; *U.S. Private*, pg. 1604
FREEHOLD TOYOTA; *U.S. Private*, pg. 1604
FREE HOUSE WINE & SPIRITS LTD.—See Icon Fine Wine & Spirits Ltd.; *Int'l*, pg. 3583
FREEILL CORPORATION—See ORIX Corporation; *Int'l*, pg. 5634
FREEIT DATA SOLUTIONS, INC.; *U.S. Private*, pg. 1604
FREELANCE.COM SA; *Int'l*, pg. 2770
FREELANCER LTD.; *Int'l*, pg. 2770
FREELANCERS CONSUMER OPERATED & ORIENTED PROGRAM OF NEW JERSEY, INC.; *U.S. Private*, pg. 1605
THE FREE LANCE-STAR PUBLISHING CO; *U.S. Private*, pg. 4030
THE FREELANCE-STAR RADIO GROUPS—See The Free Lance-Star Publishing Co.; *U.S. Private*, pg. 4030
FREELANCE SURGICAL LTD.—See Vimian Group AB; *Int'l*, pg. 8208
FREELANCE TECHNICAL ASSOCIATES, INC.; *U.S. Private*, pg. 1604
FREELAND & KAUFFMAN, INC.—See LJA Engineering, Inc.; *U.S. Private*, pg. 2474
FREELAND MOORE, INC.; *U.S. Private*, pg. 1605
FREELAND S.R.L; *Int'l*, pg. 2770
FREELINE THERAPEUTICS HOLDINGS PLC—See Syncona Ltd.; *Int'l*, pg. 7382
FREELINE THERAPEUTICS LIMITED—See Syncona Ltd.; *Int'l*, pg. 7382
FREELIN-WADE—See Coilhose Pneumatics Inc.; *U.S. Private*, pg. 964
FREEMAN AUDIO VISUAL, INC.—See Freeman Decorating Co.; *U.S. Private*, pg. 1605
FREEMAN AUTOMOTIVE COMPANY LLC; *U.S. Private*, pg. 1605
FREEMAN & CO., LLC.—See Houlihan Lokey, Inc.; *U.S. Public*, pg. 1055
FREEMAN CORPORATION; *U.S. Private*, pg. 1605
FREEMAN DECORATING CO.; *U.S. Private*, pg. 1605
FREEMAN ENCLOSURE SYSTEMS, LLC—See IES Holdings, Inc.; *U.S. Public*, pg. 1094
FREEMAN EXHIBIT FABRICATION & GRAPHICS—See Freeman Decorating Co.; *U.S. Private*, pg. 1605
FREEMAN FEED SERVICE INC—See Framar Farmers Cooperative Inc.; *U.S. Private*, pg. 1608
FREEMAN, FREEMAN & SMILEY, LLP—See Saul Ewing Arnstein & Lehr LLP; *U.S. Private*, pg. 3554
FREEMAN GAS & ELECTRIC CO. INC.—See Superior Plus Corp.; *Int'l*, pg. 7338
FREEMAN GOLD CORP.; *Int'l*, pg. 2770
FREEMAN INSURANCE SERVICES LIMITED—See Arta TechFin Corporation Limited; *Int'l*, pg. 581
FREEMAN INVESTMENT HOLDINGS LIMITED—See Arta TechFin Corporation Limited; *Int'l*, pg. 581
FREEMAN MANAGEMENT CORP.—See Founders Equity, Inc.; *U.S. Private*, pg. 1581
FREEMAN MANUFACTURING & SUPPLY COMPANY; *U.S. Private*, pg. 1605
FREEMAN MARINE EQUIPMENT, INC.; *U.S. Private*, pg. 1605
FREEMAN MATHIS & GARY, LLP; *U.S. Private*, pg. 1605
FREEMAN METAL PRODUCTS INC.—See Matthews International Corporation; *U.S. Public*, pg. 1399
FREEMAN NEWSPAPERS LLC—See Conley Publishing Group Ltd.; *U.S. Private*, pg. 1014
FREEMAN OIL COMPANY INC.; *U.S. Private*, pg. 1605
FREEMAN PRODUCTS—See Trophy Holdings Inc.; *U.S. Private*, pg. 4242
FREEMAN PUBLIC RELATIONS; *U.S. Private*, pg. 1605
FREEMANS GRATTAN HOLDINGS (FGH)—See Otto GmbH & Co. KG; *Int'l*, pg. 5662
FREEMAN SPOGLI & CO. INCORPORATED; *U.S. Private*, pg. 1605
FREEMAN SPOGLI MANAGEMENT CO., LLC—See Freeman Spogli & Co. Incorporated; *U.S. Private*, pg. 1606
FREEMANXP—See Freeman Decorating Co.; *U.S. Private*, pg. 1605
FREEMARKET (SWITZERLAND) GMBH—See Freelancer Ltd.; *Int'l*, pg. 2770
FREEMS CORPORATION; *Int'l*, pg. 2770
FREENET AG; *Int'l*, pg. 2770
FREENET CITYLINE GMBH—See freenet AG; *Int'l*, pg. 2770
FREENET DATENKOMMUNIKATIONS GMBH—See freenet AG; *Int'l*, pg. 2770
FREENET DIGITAL GMBH—See Verve Group SE; *Int'l*, pg. 8176
FREENET DIREKT GMBH—See freenet AG; *Int'l*, pg. 2770
FREENET ENERGY GMBH—See freenet AG; *Int'l*, pg. 2770
FREENOTES HARMONY PARK, INC.—See Court Square Capital Partners, L.P.; *U.S. Private*, pg. 1069
FREEPEOPLE.COM LLC—See Urban Outfitters, Inc.; *U.S. Public*, pg. 2265
FREE PEOPLE—See Urban Outfitters, Inc.; *U.S. Public*, pg. 2265
FREEPOINT COMMODITIES LLC—See Stone Point Capital LLC; *U.S. Private*, pg. 3824
FREEPORT-MCMORAN INC. - BAGDAD—See Freeport-McMoRan Inc.; *U.S. Public*, pg. 884
FREEPORT-MCMORAN INC. - ELIZABETH—See Freeport-McMoRan Inc.; *U.S. Public*, pg. 884
FREEPORT-MCMORAN INC. - EL PASO—See Freeport-McMoRan Inc.; *U.S. Public*, pg. 884
FREEPORT-MCMORAN INC. - MORENCI—See Freeport-McMoRan Inc.; *U.S. Public*, pg. 884
FREEPORT-MCMORAN INC. - SAFFORD—See Freeport-McMoRan Inc.; *U.S. Public*, pg. 884
FREEPORT-MCMORAN INC. - SIERRITA—See Freeport-McMoRan Inc.; *U.S. Public*, pg. 884
FREEPORT-MCMORAN INC.; *U.S. Public*, pg. 884
FREEPORT-MCMORAN MORENCI INC.—See Freeport-McMoRan Inc.; *U.S. Public*, pg. 884
FREEPORT-MCMORAN OIL & GAS INC.—See Freeport-McMoRan Inc.; *U.S. Public*, pg. 884
FREEPORT MINERALS CORPORATION—See Freeport-McMoRan Inc.; *U.S. Public*, pg. 884
FREEPORT MINING, LLC—See Alpha Natural Resources, Inc.; *U.S. Private*, pg. 199
FREEPORT PRESS INC.; *U.S. Private*, pg. 1606
FREEPORT RESOURCES INC.; *U.S. Private*, pg. 2771
FREEPORT RETAIL LIMITED—See The Carlyle Group Inc.; *U.S. Public*, pg. 2047
FREEPORT TRANSPORT INDUSTRIES, INC.; *U.S. Private*, pg. 1607
FREEPORT WELDING & FABRICATION INC; *U.S. Private*, pg. 1607
THE FREE PRESS—See Gannett Co., Inc.; *U.S. Public*, pg. 906
THE FREE RANGER PTY. LIMITED—See Inghams Group Limited; *Int'l*, pg. 3702
FREE RUNNING BUILDINGS LTD.; *Int'l*, pg. 2769
FREE SAS—See Iliad S.A.; *Int'l*, pg. 3614
FREESCALE SEMICONDUCTOR HONG KONG LIMITED—See NXP Semiconductors N.V.; *Int'l*, pg. 5499
FREESCALE SEMICONDUCTOR, INC.—See NXP Semiconductors N.V.; *Int'l*, pg. 5499
FREESCALE SEMICONDUCTOR ISRAEL LTD.—See NXP Semiconductors N.V.; *Int'l*, pg. 5499
FREESCALE SEMICONDUCTOR MALAYSIA SDN. BHD.—See NXP Semiconductors N.V.; *Int'l*, pg. 5499
FREESEAS INC.; *Int'l*, pg. 2771
FREESE JOHNSON, LLC; *U.S. Private*, pg. 1607
FREESE & NICHOLS INC.; *U.S. Private*, pg. 1607
FREESEN INC.—See United Contractors Midwest, Inc.; *U.S. Private*, pg. 4290
FREE SERVICE TIRE COMPANY, INC.; *U.S. Private*, pg. 1602
FREESIA HOUSE CO., LTD.—See Freesia Macross Corporation; *Int'l*, pg. 2771
FREESIA MACROSS CORPORATION; *Int'l*, pg. 2771

CORPORATE AFFILIATIONS

FREESIA TRADING CO., LTD.—See Freesia Macross Corporation; *Int'l*, pg. 2771
FREESORT GMBH—See Francotyp-Postalia Holding AG; *Int'l*, pg. 2761
FREESTONE ACQUISITION CORP.; *U.S. Public*, pg. 884
FREESTONE COMPANIES; *U.S. Private*, pg. 1607
FREESTONE RESOURCES, INC.; *U.S. Private*, pg. 1607
FREESTYLE MARKETING, LLC—See Touchstone Merchandise Group, LLC; *U.S. Private*, pg. 4193
FREESTYLE TECHNOLOGY CO., LTD.—See X2M Connect Limited; *Int'l*, pg. 8518
FREESTYLE TECHNOLOGY JAPAN KK LTD.—See X2M Connect Limited; *Int'l*, pg. 8518
FREESTYLE TECHNOLOGY TAIWAN LIMITED—See X2M Connect Limited; *Int'l*, pg. 8518
FREE TECHNICS B.V.—See Pon Holdings B.V.; *Int'l*, pg. 5919
FREETECH ROAD RECYCLING TECHNOLOGY (HOLDINGS) LIMITED; *Int'l*, pg. 2771
FREETRAILER GROUP A/S; *Int'l*, pg. 2771
FREEUS, LLC; *U.S. Private*, pg. 1607
FREEVILLE (M) SDN. BHD.—See Haisan Resources Berhad; *Int'l*, pg. 3217
FREEWAY CORPORATION; *U.S. Private*, pg. 1607
FREEWAY FOODS INC.; *U.S. Private*, pg. 1607
FREEWAY FORD TRUCK SALES, INC.; *U.S. Private*, pg. 1607
FREEWAY INSURANCE SERVICES INC.—See Stone Point Capital LLC; *U.S. Private*, pg. 3819
FREEWAY MOTORS INC.; *U.S. Private*, pg. 1607
FREEWAY ROCKFORD—See Freeway Corporation; *U.S. Private*, pg. 1607
FREEWAY WASHER, LTD.—See Freeway Corporation; *U.S. Private*, pg. 1607
THE FREE WEEKLY—See Wehco Media, Inc.; *U.S. Private*, pg. 4470
FREEWHEEL MEDIA INC.—See Comcast Corporation; *U.S. Public*, pg. 538
FREEWILL SOLUTIONS COMPANY LIMITED—See Charoen Pokphand Group Co., Ltd.; *Int'l*, pg. 1453
FREEWON CHINA CO., LTD.; *Int'l*, pg. 2771
FREEWORLD PLASCON NAMIBIA (PTY) LIMITED—See Kansai Paint Co., Ltd.; *Int'l*, pg. 4072
FREEWORLD PLASCON ZAMBIA LIMITED—See Kansai Paint Co., Ltd.; *Int'l*, pg. 4072
FREEWORLD TRADING LTD.; *Int'l*, pg. 2771
FREEXMEDIA GMBH—See freenet AG; *Int'l*, pg. 2770
FREEZE FRAME, INC.—See Pomvom Ltd.; *Int'l*, pg. 5918
FREEZER QUEEN FOODS, INC.—See Home Market Foods Incorporated; *U.S. Private*, pg. 1971
FREEZE TAG, INC.; *U.S. Public*, pg. 884
FREIBERGER COMPOUND MATERIALS GMBH—See Federmann Enterprises, Ltd.; *Int'l*, pg. 2631
FREIBERGER COMPOUND MATERIALS TAIWAN LTD.—See Federmann Enterprises, Ltd.; *Int'l*, pg. 2631
FREIBERGER COMPOUND MATERIALS USA, INC.—See Federmann Enterprises, Ltd.; *Int'l*, pg. 2631
FREIBERGER FRANCE SARL—See Suddeutsche Zuckerruben-Verwertungs-Genossenschaft eG; *Int'l*, pg. 7252
FREIBERGER LEBENSMITTEL GMBH & CO.—See Suddeutsche Zuckerruben-Verwertungs-Genossenschaft eG; *Int'l*, pg. 7252
FREIBERGER POLSKA SP.Z.O.O.—See Suddeutsche Zuckerruben-Verwertungs-Genossenschaft eG; *Int'l*, pg. 7252
FREIBERGER UK LTD.—See Suddeutsche Zuckerruben-Verwertungs-Genossenschaft eG; *Int'l*, pg. 7252
FREIBERGER USA, INC.—See Suddeutsche Zuckerruben-Verwertungs-Genossenschaft eG; *Int'l*, pg. 7252
FREIBI REIPAS SIA—See Nokian Renkaat Oyj; *Int'l*, pg. 5407
FREIGHQUOTE.COM, INC.—See C.H. Robinson Worldwide, Inc.; *U.S. Public*, pg. 415
FREIGHT 4U LOGISTICS NV-SA—See bpost NV/SA; *Int'l*, pg. 1133
FREIGHT ALL KINDS INC.; *U.S. Private*, pg. 1607
FREIGHT-BASE CUSTOMS BROKERS INC.—See Freight-Base Services Inc.; *U.S. Private*, pg. 1607
FREIGHT-BASE SERVICES INC.; *U.S. Private*, pg. 1607
FREIGHTBULK (PTY) LIMITED—See The Bidvest Group Limited; *Int'l*, pg. 7624
FREIGHTCAR AMERICA, INC.; *U.S. Public*, pg. 885
FREIGHTCAR ROANOKE, LLC—See FreightCar America, Inc.; *U.S. Public*, pg. 885
FREIGHT CAR SERVICES, INC.—See FreightCar America, Inc.; *U.S. Public*, pg. 885
FREIGHTCENTER INC.; *U.S. Private*, pg. 1607
FREIGHT CONNECTIONS, INC.—See Transportation and Logistics Systems, Inc.; *U.S. Public*, pg. 2184
FREIGHT DISTRIBUTION MANAGEMENT SYSTEMS PTY LTD—See bpost NV/SA; *Int'l*, pg. 1133
FREIGHT FORCE, INC.—See Wind Point Advisors LLC; *U.S. Private*, pg. 4535
FREIGHT HANDLERS INC.; *U.S. Private*, pg. 1607
FREIGHTLINER AUSTRALIA PTY LTD—See Brookfield Infrastructure Partners L.P.; *Int'l*, pg. 1191

COMPANY NAME INDEX

FREIGHTLINER AUSTRALIA PTY LTD—See GIC Pte. Ltd.; *Int'l*, pg. 2966
FREIGHTLINER CUSTOM CHASSIS—See Mercedes-Benz Group AG; *Int'l*, pg. 4823
FREIGHTLINER DE GMBH—See Brookfield Infrastructure Partners L.P.; *Int'l*, pg. 1191
FREIGHTLINER DE GMBH—See GIC Pte. Ltd.; *Int'l*, pg. 2966
FREIGHTLINER GROUP LIMITED—See Brookfield Infrastructure Partners L.P.; *Int'l*, pg. 1191
FREIGHTLINER GROUP LIMITED—See GIC Pte. Ltd.; *Int'l*, pg. 2965
FREIGHTLINER HEAVY HAUL LIMITED—See Brookfield Infrastructure Partners L.P.; *Int'l*, pg. 1191
FREIGHTLINER HEAVY HAUL LIMITED—See GIC Pte. Ltd.; *Int'l*, pg. 2966
FREIGHTLINER LIMITED—See Brookfield Infrastructure Partners L.P.; *Int'l*, pg. 1191
FREIGHTLINER LIMITED—See GIC Pte. Ltd.; *Int'l*, pg. 2966
FREIGHTLINER LLC—See Mercedes-Benz Group AG; *Int'l*, pg. 4823
FREIGHTLINER LLC—See Mercedes-Benz Group AG; *Int'l*, pg. 4823
FREIGHTLINER LLC—See Mercedes-Benz Group AG; *Int'l*, pg. 4823
FREIGHTLINER LLC—See Mercedes-Benz Group AG; *Int'l*, pg. 4823
FREIGHTLINER LLC—See Mercedes-Benz Group AG; *Int'l*, pg. 4823
FREIGHTLINER LLC—See Mercedes-Benz Group AG; *Int'l*, pg. 4823
FREIGHTLINER LLC—See Mercedes-Benz Group AG; *Int'l*, pg. 4823
FREIGHTLINER MANITOBA LTD.; *Int'l*, pg. 2771
FREIGHTLINER OF AUSTIN; *U.S. Private*, pg. 1607
FREIGHTLINER OF CANADA, LTD.—See Mercedes-Benz Group AG; *Int'l*, pg. 4823
FREIGHTLINER OF DES MOINES; *U.S. Private*, pg. 1608
FREIGHTLINER OF GRAND RAPIDS, INC.—See Mercedes-Benz Group AG; *Int'l*, pg. 4823
FREIGHTLINER OF HARTFORD, INC.; *U.S. Private*, pg. 1608
FREIGHTLINER OF KELOWNA LTD.—See Velocity Vehicle Group; *U.S. Private*, pg. 4355
FREIGHTLINER OF MAINE INC.—See Mercedes-Benz Group AG; *Int'l*, pg. 4823
FREIGHTLINER OF NEW HAMPSHIRE - LEBANON—See Freightliner of New Hampshire; *U.S. Private*, pg. 1608
FREIGHTLINER OF NEW HAMPSHIRE; *U.S. Private*, pg. 1608
FREIGHTLINER OF RED DEER INC; *Int'l*, pg. 2771
FREIGHTLINER OF SOUTHERN ALABAMA—See Mercedes-Benz Group AG; *Int'l*, pg. 4823
FREIGHTLINER OF UTAH, LLC; *U.S. Private*, pg. 1608
FREIGHTLINER PL SP. Z O. O.—See Brookfield Infrastructure Partners L.P.; *Int'l*, pg. 1191
FREIGHTLINER PL SP. Z O. O.—See GIC Pte. Ltd.; *Int'l*, pg. 2966
FREIGHTLINER SCOTLAND LTD—See Brookfield Infrastructure Partners L.P.; *Int'l*, pg. 1191
FREIGHTLINER SCOTLAND LTD—See GIC Pte. Ltd.; *Int'l*, pg. 2966
FREIGHTLINER SERVICE CENTER—See Mercedes-Benz Group AG; *Int'l*, pg. 4823
FREIGHTLINER TRUCKING L.L.C.—See Mercedes-Benz Group AG; *Int'l*, pg. 4823
FREIGHT LINKS E-LOGISTICS TECHNOPARK PTE. LTD.—See Vibrant Group Limited; *Int'l*, pg. 8184
FREIGHT LINKS EXPRESS ARCHIVERS PTE. LTD.—See Vibrant Group Limited; *Int'l*, pg. 8184
FREIGHT LINKS EXPRESS LOGISTICPARK PTE. LTD.—See Vibrant Group Limited; *Int'l*, pg. 8184
FREIGHT LINKS EXPRESS (M) SDN. BHD.—See Vibrant Group Limited; *Int'l*, pg. 8184
FREIGHT LINKS EXPRESS (PG) SDN. BHD.—See Vibrant Group Limited; *Int'l*, pg. 8184
FREIGHT LINKS EXPRESS PTE. LTD.—See Vibrant Group Limited; *Int'l*, pg. 8184
FREIGHT LINKS LOGISTICS PTE. LTD.—See Vibrant Group Limited; *Int'l*, pg. 8184
FREIGHT LINKS M&S (H.K.) LTD.—See Vibrant Group Limited; *Int'l*, pg. 8184
FREIGHT LINKS PROPERTIES PTE. LTD.—See Vibrant Group Limited; *Int'l*, pg. 8184
FREIGHT MANAGEMENT HOLDINGS PTY. LTD.—See Singapore Post Limited; *Int'l*, pg. 6942
FREIGHT MANAGEMENT, INC; *U.S. Private*, pg. 1607
FREIGHT MANAGEMENT (PENANG) SDN. BHD.—See FM Global Logistics Holdings Berhad; *Int'l*, pg. 2717
FREIGHT MANAGEMENT PLUS—See The Jordan Company, L.P.; *U.S. Private*, pg. 4061
FREIGHT MANAGEMENT TEAM INC.; *U.S. Private*, pg. 1607
FREIGHTOS LIMITED; *Int'l*, pg. 2771
FREIGHTQUOTE.COM—See C.H. Robinson Worldwide, Inc.; *U.S. Public*, pg. 414
FREIGHT SALES INC.; *U.S. Private*, pg. 1607

FREIGHT SOLUTION PROVIDERS; *U.S. Private*, pg. 1607
FREIGHT TECHNOLOGIES, INC.; *U.S. Public*, pg. 885
FREIGHTVALUE INC.—See ArcBest Corporation; *U.S. Public*, pg. 180
FREIGHTVIEW, INC.—See C.H. Robinson Worldwide, Inc.; *U.S. Public*, pg. 415
FREIGHTWATCH INTERNATIONAL (USA), INC.—See Carrier Global Corporation; *U.S. Public*, pg. 442
FREIGHTWAYS GROUP LIMITED; *Int'l*, pg. 2771
FREIGHTWAYS INFORMATION SERVICES LIMITED—See Freightways Group Limited; *Int'l*, pg. 2771
FREIGHTWISE, INC.—See Berkshire Hathaway Inc.; *U.S. Public*, pg. 303
FREINRAIL SYSTEMES FERROVIAIRES S.A.—See Knorr-Bremse AG; *Int'l*, pg. 4211
FREIXENET S.A.—See Dr. August Oetker KG; *Int'l*, pg. 2190
FREIXENET SONOMA CAVES, INC.—See Dr. August Oetker KG; *Int'l*, pg. 2190
FREIXENET U.S.A.—See Dr. August Oetker KG; *Int'l*, pg. 2190
FREJA EID GROUP AB; *Int'l*, pg. 2772
FREKHAUG VINDUET AS—See Ratos AB; *Int'l*, pg. 6220
FRELII, INC.; *U.S. Public*, pg. 885
FREMANTLE COMMUNITY FINANCIAL SERVICES LIMITED—See Bendigo & Adelaide Bank Ltd.; *Int'l*, pg. 971
FREMANTLE FREIGHT & STORAGE PTY. LTD.—See Silk Logistics Holdings Limited; *Int'l*, pg. 6921
FREMANTLE INDIA TV PRODUCTIONS PVT LTD—See Bertelsmann SE & Co. KGaA; *Int'l*, pg. 994
FREMANTLE LICENSING GERMANY GMBH—See Bertelsmann SE & Co. KGaA; *Int'l*, pg. 994
FREMANTLEMEDIA ASIA PTE LTD—See Bertelsmann SE & Co. KGaA; *Int'l*, pg. 994
FREMANTLEMEDIA AUSTRALIA PTY LTD—See Bertelsmann SE & Co. KGaA; *Int'l*, pg. 994
FREMANTLEMEDIA BELGIUM NV—See Bertelsmann SE & Co. KGaA; *Int'l*, pg. 994
FREMANTLEMEDIA BRAZIL PRODUCAO DE TELEVISAO LTDA—See Bertelsmann SE & Co. KGaA; *Int'l*, pg. 994
FREMANTLEMEDIA FINLAND OY—See Bertelsmann SE & Co. KGaA; *Int'l*, pg. 994
FREMANTLEMEDIA FRANCE SAS—See Bertelsmann SE & Co. KGaA; *Int'l*, pg. 994
FREMANTLEMEDIA HRVATSKA D.O.O.—See Bertelsmann SE & Co. KGaA; *Int'l*, pg. 994
FREMANTLEMEDIA ITALIA SPA—See Bertelsmann SE & Co. KGaA; *Int'l*, pg. 994
FREMANTLEMEDIA LATIN AMERICA INC—See Bertelsmann SE & Co. KGaA; *Int'l*, pg. 994
FREMANTLEMEDIA LTD—See Bertelsmann SE & Co. KGaA; *Int'l*, pg. 994
FREMANTLEMEDIA MEXICO SA DE CV—See Bertelsmann SE & Co. KGaA; *Int'l*, pg. 994
FREMANTLEMEDIA NORGE AS—See Bertelsmann SE & Co. KGaA; *Int'l*, pg. 994
FREMANTLEMEDIA NORTH AMERICA INC.—See Bertelsmann SE & Co. KGaA; *Int'l*, pg. 994
FREMANTLEMEDIA POLSKA SP.ZO.O.—See Bertelsmann SE & Co. KGaA; *Int'l*, pg. 994
FREMANTLEMEDIA PORTUGAL SA—See Bertelsmann SE & Co. KGaA; *Int'l*, pg. 994
FREMANTLEMEDIA SVERIGE AB—See Bertelsmann SE & Co. KGaA; *Int'l*, pg. 994
FREMANTLE PRODUCTIONS ASIA PTE. LTD.—See Bertelsmann SE & Co. KGaA; *Int'l*, pg. 992
FREMANTLE PRODUCTIONS NORTH AMERICA INC—See Bertelsmann SE & Co. KGaA; *Int'l*, pg. 994
FREMANTLE PRODUCTIONS SA—See Bertelsmann SE & Co. KGaA; *Int'l*, pg. 994
FREMAR FARMERS COOPERATIVE INC.; *U.S. Private*, pg. 1608
FREMAX S.A.—See Randon S.A. Implementos e. Participacoes.; *Int'l*, pg. 6201
FREMDENVERKEHRS GMBH—See Raiffeisenverband Salzburg reg. Gen.m.b.H.; *Int'l*, pg. 6188
FREMMAN CAPITAL LIMITED; *Int'l*, pg. 2772
FREMONT ANALYTICAL INC.—See Morgan Stanley; *U.S. Public*, pg. 1474
FREMONT AREA COMMUNITY FOUNDATION; *U.S. Private*, pg. 1608
FREMONT AUTO CENTER INC.; *U.S. Private*, pg. 1608
FREMONT BANCORPORATION; *U.S. Private*, pg. 1608
FREMONT BANK—See Fremont Bancorporation; *U.S. Private*, pg. 1608
FREMONT BEVERAGES INC.; *U.S. Private*, pg. 1608
THE FREMONT COMPANY; *U.S. Private*, pg. 4030
FREMONT CONTRACT CARRIERS—See HMN Inc.; *U.S. Private*, pg. 1955
THE FREMONT CO.—See The Fremont Company; *U.S. Private*, pg. 4030
FREMONT GOLD LTD.; *Int'l*, pg. 2772
FREMONT GOLD MINING LLC—See Stratabound Minerals Corp.; *Int'l*, pg. 7235

FREMONT INVESTMENT ADVISORS—See Fremont Group, LLC; *U.S. Private*, pg. 1608
FREMONT MOTOR COMPANY; *U.S. Private*, pg. 1608
FREMONT PRIVATE HOLDINGS, LLC—See Fremont Group, LLC; *U.S. Private*, pg. 1608
FREMONT REALTY CAPITAL (NEW YORK)—See Fremont Group, LLC; *U.S. Private*, pg. 1608
FREMONT REALTY CAPITAL—See Fremont Group, LLC; *U.S. Private*, pg. 1608
FREMONT-RIDEOUT HEALTH GROUP; *U.S. Private*, pg. 1608
FRENCH AMERICAN BANKING CORP.—See BNP Paribas SA; *Int'l*, pg. 1088
FRENCH-AMERICAN FOUNDATION; *U.S. Private*, pg. 1609
FRENCH & BEAN—See Associated Grocers of New England, Inc.; *U.S. Private*, pg. 356
FRENCH/BLITZER/SCOTT LLC; *U.S. Private*, pg. 1609
FRENCH BROAD ELECTRIC MEMBERSHIP CORPORATION; *U.S. Private*, pg. 1608
THE FRENCH COMPANY LLC—See Wanzl Metallwarenfabrik GmbH; *Int'l*, pg. 8343
FRENCH CONNECTION GROUP, INC.—See French Connection Group plc; *Int'l*, pg. 2772
FRENCH CONNECTION GROUP PLC; *Int'l*, pg. 2772
FRENCH CONNECTION HOLDINGS, INC.—See French Connection Group plc; *Int'l*, pg. 2772
FRENCH CONNECTION LIMITED—See French Connection Group plc; *Int'l*, pg. 2772
FRENCH CONNECTION (LONDON) LIMITED—See French Connection Group plc; *Int'l*, pg. 2772
FRENCH-ELLISON TRUCK CENTER INC.; *U.S. Private*, pg. 1609
FRENCH GERLEMAN ELECTRIC CO., INC.; *U.S. Private*, pg. 1608
FRENCHIES CHEVROLET; *U.S. Private*, pg. 1609
FRENCHIES MODERN NAIL CARE—See The Riverside Company; *U.S. Private*, pg. 4108
FRENCHKISS PICTURES SAS—See Mediawan SA; *Int'l*, pg. 4774
FRENCHMAN'S RESERVE COUNTRY CLUB, INC.—See Toll Brothers, Inc.; *U.S. Public*, pg. 2161
FRENCHMAN VALLEY COOP.—See Frenchman Valley Farmers Coop. Inc.; *U.S. Private*, pg. 1609
FRENCHMAN VALLEY FARMERS COOP. INC.; *U.S. Private*, pg. 1609
FRENCH PAPER CO.—See Atlas Holdings, LLC; *U.S. Private*, pg. 376
FRENCH RESTAURANTS PRIVATE LIMITED—See Sapphire Foods India Ltd.; *Int'l*, pg. 6572
THE FRENCH'S FOOD COMPANY LLC—See McCormick & Company, Incorporated; *U.S. Public*, pg. 1404
FRENCH TRANSIT LTD.—See Juggernaut Management, LLC; *U.S. Private*, pg. 2242
FRENCH/WEST/VAUGHAN, LLC; *U.S. Private*, pg. 1609
FRENCH/WEST/VAUGHAN, LLC—See French/West/Vaughan, LLC; *U.S. Private*, pg. 1609
FRENCH/WEST/VAUGHAN, LLC—See French/West/Vaughan, LLC; *U.S. Private*, pg. 1609
FRENCKEN AMERICA INC.—See Frencken Group Limited; *Int'l*, pg. 2772
FRENCKEN ENGINEERING B.V.—See Frencken Group Limited; *Int'l*, pg. 2772
FRENCKEN EUROPE B.V.—See Frencken Group Limited; *Int'l*, pg. 2772
FRENCKEN GROUP LIMITED; *Int'l*, pg. 2772
FRENCKEN MECHATRONICS B.V.—See Frencken Group Limited; *Int'l*, pg. 2772
FRENCKEN MECHATRONICS (M) SDN BHD—See Frencken Group Limited; *Int'l*, pg. 2772
FRENCKEN TECHNICAL PROJECTS ASSEMBLY B.V.—See Frencken Group Limited; *Int'l*, pg. 2772
FRENDS AS—See Storskogen Group AB; *Int'l*, pg. 7227
FRENDY ENERGY S.P.A.; *Int'l*, pg. 2773
FRENKEL BENEFITS, LLC—See Keystone Group, L.P.; *U.S. Private*, pg. 2297
FRENKEL-CD LTD.—See Veridis Environment Ltd; *Int'l*, pg. 8168
FRENKEL & COMPANY - BOSTON—See Keystone Group, L.P.; *U.S. Private*, pg. 2297
FRENKEL & COMPANY - JERSEY CITY—See Keystone Group, L.P.; *U.S. Private*, pg. 2297
FRENKEL & COMPANY—See Keystone Group, L.P.; *U.S. Private*, pg. 2297
FRENKEL TOPPING GROUP PLC; *Int'l*, pg. 2773
FRENKEL TOPPING LIMITED—See Frenkel Topping Group plc; *Int'l*, pg. 2773
FRENOS HIDRAULICOS AUTOMOTRICES, S.A. DE C.V.—See Apollo Global Management, Inc.; *U.S. Public*, pg. 162
FRENOS Y CONJUNTOS S.A.—See Lingotes Especiales, S.A.; *Int'l*, pg. 4512
FRENOS Y MECANISMOS, S. DE R.L. DE C.V.—See ZF Friedrichshafen AG; *Int'l*, pg. 8645
FRENS SPECIALTY CHEMICALS & EQUIPMENT LTD.—See Momar, Inc.; *U.S. Private*, pg. 2768
FREO GROUP PTY LTD—See Berkshire Hathaway Inc.; *U.S. Public*, pg. 305
FREPART AB—See Amplex AB; *Int'l*, pg. 433

FREQUENCY ELECTRONICS, INC.

FREQUENCY ELECTRONICS, INC.; *U.S. Public*, pg. 885
FREQUENCY TELECOM; *Int'l*, pg. 2773
FREQUENCY THERAPEUTICS, INC.; *U.S. Public*, pg. 885
FREQUENTIS AG; *Int'l*, pg. 2773
FREQUENTIS DEUTSCHLAND GMBH—See Frequentis AG; *Int'l*, pg. 2773
FREQUENTIS ORTHOGON GMBH—See Frequentis AG; *Int'l*, pg. 2773
FREQUENTIS USA INC.—See Frequentis AG; *Int'l*, pg. 2773
FRERE-BOURGEOIS; *Int'l*, pg. 2773
FRESARD COMPOSANTS S.A.—See The Swatch Group Ltd.; *Int'l*, pg. 7691
FRESCA GROUP LIMITED; *Int'l*, pg. 2774
FRESCA SAS—See ARYZTA AG; *Int'l*, pg. 588
FRESCA'S MEXICAN GRILL, INC.—See American Restaurant Holdings, Inc.; *U.S. Private*, pg. 246
FRESCHE SOLUTIONS INC.—See American Pacific Group, LLC; *U.S. Private*, pg. 242
FRESCHI SERVICE EXPERTS—See Lennox International Inc.; *U.S. Public*, pg. 1307
FRESCO EME LIMITED—See Daikin Industries, Ltd.; *Int'l*, pg. 1935
FRESCO LLC—See National Bank for Foreign Economic Activity of the Republic of Uzbekistan; *Int'l*, pg. 5151
FRESCO LOGIC INC.—See Parade Technologies, Ltd.; *Int'l*, pg. 5734
FRESCO SHIPS' A&F S.R.L.—See Orsero S.p.A.; *Int'l*, pg. 5644
FRES-CO SYSTEM USA INCORPORATED; *U.S. Private*, pg. 1609
FRESCURA INVESTMENTS B.V.—See Immofinanz AG; *Int'l*, pg. 3628
FRESENIUS HEMOCARE DEUTSCHLAND GMBH—See Fresenius SE & Co. KGaA; *Int'l*, pg. 2777
FRESENIUS HEMOCARE ITALIA S.R.L.—See Fresenius SE & Co. KGaA; *Int'l*, pg. 2777
FRESENIUS HEMOCARE NETHERLANDS B.V.—See Fresenius SE & Co. KGaA; *Int'l*, pg. 2777
FRESENIUS KABI AB—See Fresenius SE & Co. KGaA; *Int'l*, pg. 2777
FRESENIUS KABI AG—See Fresenius SE & Co. KGaA; *Int'l*, pg. 2777
FRESENIUS KABI ARGENTINA SA—See Fresenius SE & Co. KGaA; *Int'l*, pg. 2777
FRESENIUS KABI ASIA-PACIFIC LIMITED—See Fresenius SE & Co. KGaA; *Int'l*, pg. 2777
FRESENIUS KABI AUSTRALIA PTY LIMITED—See Fresenius SE & Co. KGaA; *Int'l*, pg. 2778
FRESENIUS KABI AUSTRIA GMBH—See Fresenius SE & Co. KGaA; *Int'l*, pg. 2777
FRESENIUS KABI BIDIPHAR JSC—See Fresenius SE & Co. KGaA; *Int'l*, pg. 2778
FRESENIUS KABI BRASIL LTDA.—See Fresenius SE & Co. KGaA; *Int'l*, pg. 2778
FRESENIUS KABI BRAZIL LTDA.—See Fresenius SE & Co. KGaA; *Int'l*, pg. 2777
FRESENIUS KABI BULGARIA EOOD—See Fresenius SE & Co. KGaA; *Int'l*, pg. 2778
FRESENIUS KABI CANADA LTD.—See Fresenius SE & Co. KGaA; *Int'l*, pg. 2778
FRESENIUS KABI CHILE LTDA.—See Fresenius SE & Co. KGaA; *Int'l*, pg. 2778
FRESENIUS KABI (CHINA) CO., LTD.—See Fresenius SE & Co. KGaA; *Int'l*, pg. 2777
FRESENIUS KABI COLOMBIA S.A.S.—See Fresenius SE & Co. KGaA; *Int'l*, pg. 2778
FRESENIUS KABI COMPOUNDING LLC—See Fagron NV; *Int'l*, pg. 2603
FRESENIUS KABI DANMARK A/S—See Fresenius SE & Co. KGaA; *Int'l*, pg. 2778
FRESENIUS KABI DEUTSCHLAND GMBH—See Fresenius SE & Co. KGaA; *Int'l*, pg. 2777
FRESENIUS KABI D.O.O.—See Fresenius SE & Co. KGaA; *Int'l*, pg. 2778
FRESENIUS KABI ESPANA S.A.—See Fresenius SE & Co. KGaA; *Int'l*, pg. 2777
FRESENIUS KABI FRANCE S.A.S.—See Fresenius SE & Co. KGaA; *Int'l*, pg. 2777
FRESENIUS KABI HONG KONG LIMITED—See Fresenius SE & Co. KGaA; *Int'l*, pg. 2778
FRESENIUS KABI HUNGARY KFT.—See Fresenius SE & Co. KGaA; *Int'l*, pg. 2778
FRESENIUS KABI ILAC SAN. VE TIC. LTD. STI.—See Fresenius SE & Co. KGaA; *Int'l*, pg. 2778
FRESENIUS KABI INDIA PVT. LTD.—See Fresenius SE & Co. KGaA; *Int'l*, pg. 2778
FRESENIUS KABI ITALIA S.R.L.—See Fresenius SE & Co. KGaA; *Int'l*, pg. 2777
FRESENIUS KABI JAPAN K.K.—See Fresenius SE & Co. KGaA; *Int'l*, pg. 2778
FRESENIUS KABI KOREA LTD.—See Fresenius SE & Co. KGaA; *Int'l*, pg. 2777
FRESENIUS KABI LOGISTIK GMBH—See Fresenius SE & Co. KGaA; *Int'l*, pg. 2778
FRESENIUS KABI LTD.—See Fresenius SE & Co. KGaA; *Int'l*, pg. 2777
FRESENIUS KABI MALAYSIA SDN. BHD.—See Fresenius SE & Co. KGaA; *Int'l*, pg. 2778
FRESENIUS KABI MEDTECH SERVICES GMBH—See Fresenius SE & Co. KGaA; *Int'l*, pg. 2778
FRESENIUS KABI MEXICO S.A. DE C.V.—See Fresenius SE & Co. KGaA; *Int'l*, pg. 2777
FRESENIUS KABI NEDERLAND B.V.—See Fresenius SE & Co. KGaA; *Int'l*, pg. 2778
FRESENIUS KABI NEW ZEALAND LIMITED—See Fresenius SE & Co. KGaA; *Int'l*, pg. 2778
FRESENIUS KABI NORGE A.S.—See Fresenius SE & Co. KGaA; *Int'l*, pg. 2777
FRESENIUS KABI NORWAY AS—See Fresenius SE & Co. KGaA; *Int'l*, pg. 2778
FRESENIUS KABI NV/SA—See Fresenius SE & Co. KGaA; *Int'l*, pg. 2778
FRESENIUS KABI ONCOLOGY LIMITED—See Fresenius SE & Co. KGaA; *Int'l*, pg. 2777
FRESENIUS KABI PHARMA PORTUGAL, LDA.—See Fresenius SE & Co. KGaA; *Int'l*, pg. 2778
FRESENIUS KABI PHILIPPINES, INC.—See Fresenius SE & Co. KGaA; *Int'l*, pg. 2778
FRESENIUS KABI POLSKA SP Z.O.O.—See Fresenius SE & Co. KGaA; *Int'l*, pg. 2778
FRESENIUS KABI S.A.—See Fresenius SE & Co. KGaA; *Int'l*, pg. 2778
FRESENIUS KABI (SCHWEIZ) AG—See Fresenius SE & Co. KGaA; *Int'l*, pg. 2777
FRESENIUS KABI SCIENTIFIC OFFICE EGYPT, LDA.—See Fresenius SE & Co. KGaA; *Int'l*, pg. 2778
FRESENIUS KABI (SINGAPORE) PTE. LTD.—See Fresenius SE & Co. KGaA; *Int'l*, pg. 2777
FRESENIUS KABI SOUTH AFRICA (PTY) LTD.—See Fresenius SE & Co. KGaA; *Int'l*, pg. 2778
FRESENIUS KABI S.R.O.—See Fresenius SE & Co. KGaA; *Int'l*, pg. 2778
FRESENIUS KABI (THAILAND) LTD.—See Fresenius SE & Co. KGaA; *Int'l*, pg. 2777
FRESENIUS KABI USA, LLC—See Fresenius SE & Co. KGaA; *Int'l*, pg. 2778
FRESENIUS MEDICAL CARE AG; *Int'l*, pg. 2774
FRESENIUS MEDICAL CARE ARGENTINA S.A.—See Fresenius Medical Care AG; *Int'l*, pg. 2774
FRESENIUS MEDICAL CARE AUSTRALIA PTY LTD. - NEPHROCARE AUSTRALIA DIVISION—See Fresenius Medical Care AG; *Int'l*, pg. 2774
FRESENIUS MEDICAL CARE AUSTRALIA PTY LTD.—See Fresenius Medical Care AG; *Int'l*, pg. 2774
FRESENIUS MEDICAL CARE AUSTRIA GMBH—See Fresenius Medical Care AG; *Int'l*, pg. 2774
FRESENIUS MEDICAL CARE BELGIUM N.V.—See Fresenius Medical Care AG; *Int'l*, pg. 2775
FRESENIUS MEDICAL CARE BH D.O.O.—See Fresenius Medical Care AG; *Int'l*, pg. 2774
FRESENIUS MEDICAL CARE COLOMBIA S.A.—See Fresenius Medical Care AG; *Int'l*, pg. 2775
FRESENIUS MEDICAL CARE CR, S.R.O.—See Fresenius Medical Care AG; *Int'l*, pg. 2775
FRESENIUS MEDICAL CARE DANMARK A/S—See Fresenius Medical Care AG; *Int'l*, pg. 2775
FRESENIUS MEDICAL CARE DEL PERU S.A.—See Fresenius Medical Care AG; *Int'l*, pg. 2775
FRESENIUS MEDICAL CARE DEUTSCHLAND GMBH—See Fresenius Medical Care AG; *Int'l*, pg. 2775
FRESENIUS MEDICAL CARE DEUTSCHLAND GMBH—See Fresenius Medical Care AG; *Int'l*, pg. 2775
FRESENIUS MEDICAL CARE DE VENEZUELA C.A.—See Fresenius Medical Care AG; *Int'l*, pg. 2775
FRESENIUS MEDICAL CARE - DS, S.R.O.—See Fresenius Medical Care AG; *Int'l*, pg. 2775
FRESENIUS MEDICAL CARE GROUPE FRANCE S.A.S.—See Fresenius Medical Care AG; *Int'l*, pg. 2775
FRESENIUS MEDICAL CARE HONG KONG LIMITED—See Fresenius Medical Care AG; *Int'l*, pg. 2775
FRESENIUS MEDICAL CARE INDIA PRIVATE LIMITED—See Fresenius Medical Care AG; *Int'l*, pg. 2775
FRESENIUS MEDICAL CARE (IRELAND) LIMITED—See Fresenius Medical Care AG; *Int'l*, pg. 2774
FRESENIUS MEDICAL CARE ITALIA S.P.A.—See Fresenius Medical Care AG; *Int'l*, pg. 2775
FRESENIUS MEDICAL CARE KOREA LTD.—See Fresenius Medical Care AG; *Int'l*, pg. 2775
FRESENIUS MEDICAL CARE LEBANON S.A.R.L.—See Fresenius Medical Care AG; *Int'l*, pg. 2775
FRESENIUS MEDICAL CARE LTDA.—See Fresenius Medical Care AG; *Int'l*, pg. 2775
FRESENIUS MEDICAL CARE MALAYSIA SDN. BHD.—See Fresenius Medical Care AG; *Int'l*, pg. 2775
FRESENIUS MEDICAL CARE MAROC S.A.—See Fresenius Medical Care AG; *Int'l*, pg. 2775
FRESENIUS MEDICAL CARE MEXICO S.A.—See Fresenius Medical Care AG; *Int'l*, pg. 2775
FRESENIUS MEDICAL CARE NEDERLAND B.V.—See Fresenius Medical Care AG; *Int'l*, pg. 2775
FRESENIUS MEDICAL CARE NEPHROLOGICA DEUTSCHLAND GMBH—See CSL Limited; *Int'l*, pg. 1866
FRESENIUS MEDICAL CARE NORTH AMERICA—See Fresenius Medical Care AG; *Int'l*, pg. 2774
FRESENIUS MEDICAL CARE PHILIPPINES, INC.—See Fresenius Medical Care AG; *Int'l*, pg. 2775
FRESENIUS MEDICAL CARE POLSKA S.A.—See Fresenius Medical Care AG; *Int'l*, pg. 2775
FRESENIUS MEDICAL CARE RENAL SERVICES LTD—See Fresenius Medical Care AG; *Int'l*, pg. 2774
FRESENIUS MEDICAL CARE ROMANIA SRL—See Fresenius Medical Care AG; *Int'l*, pg. 2775
FRESENIUS MEDICAL CARE (SCHWEIZ) AG—See Fresenius Medical Care AG; *Int'l*, pg. 2774
FRESENIUS MEDICAL CARE (SHANGHAI) CO., LTD.—See Fresenius Medical Care AG; *Int'l*, pg. 2774
FRESENIUS MEDICAL CARE SINGAPORE PTE. LTD.—See Fresenius Medical Care AG; *Int'l*, pg. 2775
FRESENIUS MEDICAL CARE SLOVENIJA D.O.O.—See Fresenius Medical Care AG; *Int'l*, pg. 2775
FRESENIUS MEDICAL CARE SLOVENSKO, SPOL. S.R.O.—See Fresenius Medical Care AG; *Int'l*, pg. 2775
FRESENIUS MEDICAL CARE SOUTH AFRICA (PTY) LTD.—See Fresenius Medical Care AG; *Int'l*, pg. 2775
FRESENIUS MEDICAL CARE SVERIGE AB—See Fresenius Medical Care AG; *Int'l*, pg. 2775
FRESENIUS MEDICAL CARE TAIWAN CO., LTD.—See Fresenius Medical Care AG; *Int'l*, pg. 2775
FRESENIUS MEDICAL CARE (U.K.) LTD.—See Fresenius Medical Care AG; *Int'l*, pg. 2774
FRESENIUS MEDICAL CARE UKRAINE LLC—See Fresenius Medical Care AG; *Int'l*, pg. 2775
FRESENIUS MEDIKAL HIZMETLER A.S.—See Fresenius Medical Care AG; *Int'l*, pg. 2775
FRESENIUS NETCARE GMBH—See Fresenius SE & Co. KGaA; *Int'l*, pg. 2778
FRESENIUS SE & CO. KGAA; *Int'l*, pg. 2777
FRESENIUS VIAL S.A.S.—See Fresenius SE & Co. KGaA; *Int'l*, pg. 2778
FRESE & WOLFF WERBEAGENTUR GMBH; *Int'l*, pg. 2774
FRESH2 GROUP LTD.; *Int'l*, pg. 2781
FRESHADDRESS, LLC—See TowerData, Inc.; *U.S. Private*, pg. 4196
FRESH AIR ENERGY X, LLC—See Duke Energy Corporation; *U.S. Public*, pg. 691
FRESH ALTERNATIVES, LLC—See Boyne Capital Management, LLC; *U.S. Private*, pg. 628
FRESH AS A DAISY, INC.; *U.S. Private*, pg. 1609
FRESHBAKED PR LTD; *Int'l*, pg. 2781
FRESHBREW GROUP USA, L.P.; *U.S. Private*, pg. 1610
FRESHBREW VENDING—See FreshBrew Group USA, L.P.; *U.S. Private*, pg. 1610
FRESH CONSULTING LLC; *U.S. Private*, pg. 1609
FRESH CORNER RESTAURANTS KFT.—See MOL Magyar Olaj- es Gazipari Nyrt.; *Int'l*, pg. 5020
FRESH COSMETICS LTD—See LVMH Moet Hennessy Louis Vuitton SE; *Int'l*, pg. 4597
FRESH DEL MONTE PRODUCE INC.; *U.S. Public*, pg. 885
THE FRESH DIET INC.; *U.S. Private*, pg. 4031
FRESH DINER CORPORATION—See Toyo Suisan Kaisha, Ltd.; *Int'l*, pg. 7858
FRESH DIRECT LIMITED—See Lonrho Limited; *Int'l*, pg. 4552
FRESH DIRECT LIMITED—See Sysco Corporation; *U.S. Public*, pg. 1973
FRESHDIRECT, LLC—See Koninklijke Ahold Delhaize N.V.; *Int'l*, pg. 4260
FRESH DIRECT (UK) LIMITED—See Sysco Corporation; *U.S. Public*, pg. 1973
FRESH & EASY NEIGHBORHOOD MARKET INC—See The Yucaipa Companies LLC; *U.S. Private*, pg. 4140
FRESHEDGE, LLC—See Wind Point Advisors LLC; *U.S. Private*, pg. 4534
FRESH ENCOUNTER INC.; *U.S. Private*, pg. 1609
FRESH ENTERPRISES, LLC; *U.S. Private*, pg. 1609
FRESH EXPRESS DELIVERY HOLDINGS GROUP CO., LTD.; *Int'l*, pg. 2781
FRESH EXPRESS FOODS CORPORATION, INC.; *U.S. Private*, pg. 1609
FRESH EXPRESS INC. - CHICAGO—See Banco Safra S.A.; *Int'l*, pg. 824
FRESH EXPRESS INC. - CHICAGO—See Sucocitrico Cutrale Ltda.; *Int'l*, pg. 7251
FRESH EXPRESS INC. - GRAND PRAIRIE—See Banco Safra S.A.; *Int'l*, pg. 824
FRESH EXPRESS INC. - GRAND PRAIRIE—See Sucocitrico Cutrale Ltda.; *Int'l*, pg. 7251
FRESH EXPRESS INCORPORATED—See Banco Safra S.A.; *Int'l*, pg. 824
FRESH EXPRESS INCORPORATED—See Sucocitrico Cutrale Ltda.; *Int'l*, pg. 7251
FRESH FACTORY B.C. LIMITED; *U.S. Public*, pg. 886
FRESHFAYRE LIMITED—See Sysco Corporation; *U.S. Public*, pg. 1973
FRESH FITNESS AS—See SATS ASA; *Int'l*, pg. 6587

COMPANY NAME INDEX

FRESH FOOD SERVICE CO., LTD.—See Nisshin Seifun Group, Inc.; *Int'l*, pg. 5372
FRESH & HEALTHY ENTERPRISES LTD.—See Container Corporation of India Ltd.; *Int'l*, pg. 1779
FRESH HEMP FOODS LTD.—See Tilray Brands, Inc.; *Int'l*, pg. 7748
FRESH IDEAS INC.—See Costa Fruit & Produce Inc.; *U.S. Private*, pg. 1062
FRESH IDEAS MANAGEMENT, LLC—See Compass Group PLC; *Int'l*, pg. 1750
FRESHII, INC.—See Foodtastic Inc.; *Int'l*, pg. 2728
FRESH INC.; *U.S. Private*, pg. 1609
FRESH INSURANCE SERVICES GROUP LIMITED—See White Mountains Insurance Group, Ltd.; *U.S. Public*, pg. 2369
FRESH INTERACTIVE TECHNOLOGIES S.A—See Mirada Plc; *Int'l*, pg. 4916
FRESH ISLAND FISH CO. INC.; *U.S. Private*, pg. 1609
FRESH JUICE INDUSTRY (KUNSHAN) CO., LTD—See Sunjuice Holdings Co., Ltd.; *Int'l*, pg. 7317
FRESH JUICE INDUSTRY (TIANJIN) CO., LTD.—See Sunjuice Holdings Co., Ltd.; *Int'l*, pg. 7317
FRESHKO PRODUCE SERVICES, LLC—See C&S Wholesale Grocers, Inc.; *U.S. Private*, pg. 704
FRESHLOCAL SOLUTIONS INC.; *Int'l*, pg. 2781
FRESH LOGISTICS, LLC—See Campbell Soup Company; *U.S. Public*, pg. 427
FRESH LOGISTICS POLSKA SP. Z O.O.—See Raben Management Services Sp. z o.o.; *Int'l*, pg. 6171
FRESH MADE, INC.—See Lifeway Foods, Inc.; *U.S. Public*, pg. 1313
THE FRESH MARKET HOLDINGS, INC.; *U.S. Public*, pg. 2074
THE FRESH MARKET, INC.—See Apollo Global Management, Inc.; *U.S. Public*, pg. 164
FRESH MARK, INC—See Fresh Mark, Inc.; *U.S. Private*, pg. 1610
FRESH MARK, INC.; *U.S. Private*, pg. 1609
FRESHMARK (PTY) LTD—See Shoprite Holdings Limited; *Int'l*, pg. 6860
FRESHMAX AUSTRALIA PTY LTD—See Maui Capital Ltd.; *Int'l*, pg. 4731
FRESHMAX NEW ZEALAND LTD.—See BayWa AG; *Int'l*, pg. 918
FRESHMAX PTY LTD—See Maui Capital Ltd.; *Int'l*, pg. 4731
FRESH MEADOW COUNTRY CLUB; *U.S. Private*, pg. 1610
FRESHMEALS DEUTSCHLAND GMBH—See What's Cooking Group NV; *Int'l*, pg. 8396
FRESHMEALS IBERICA SL—See What's Cooking Group NV; *Int'l*, pg. 8396
FRESHMEALS NEDERLAND BV—See What's Cooking Group NV; *Int'l*, pg. 8396
FRESHMEALS NV—See What's Cooking Group NV; *Int'l*, pg. 8396
FRESH NETWORK SYSTEMS CO., LTD.—See Meiji Holdings Co., Ltd.; *Int'l*, pg. 4800
FRESH ORGANIC CHOICE B.V.—See Organto Foods Inc.; *Int'l*, pg. 5619
FRESH ORIGINS, LLC—See Sun Capital Partners, Inc.; *U.S. Private*, pg. 3859
FRESHPACK PRODUCE, INC.—See Creation Gardens, Inc.; *U.S. Private*, pg. 1087
FRESH-PAK CORP—See ZL Star Inc.; *U.S. Private*, pg. 4606
FRESHPET, INC.; *U.S. Public*, pg. 886
FRESHPOINT ARIZONA, INC.—See Sysco Corporation; *U.S. Public*, pg. 1974
FRESHPOINT ATLANTA, INC.—See Sysco Corporation; *U.S. Public*, pg. 1974
FRESHPOINT CALIFORNIA, INC.—See Sysco Corporation; *U.S. Public*, pg. 1974
FRESHPOINT CENTRAL CALIFORNIA, INC.—See Sysco Corporation; *U.S. Public*, pg. 1974
FRESHPOINT CENTRAL FLORIDA, INC.—See Sysco Corporation; *U.S. Public*, pg. 1974
FRESHPOINT CONNECTICUT, LLC—See Sysco Corporation; *U.S. Public*, pg. 1974
FRESHPOINT DALLAS, INC.—See Sysco Corporation; *U.S. Public*, pg. 1974
FRESHPOINT DENVER, INC.—See Sysco Corporation; *U.S. Public*, pg. 1974
FRESHPOINT IL PAESE, INC.—See Sysco Corporation; *U.S. Public*, pg. 1974
FRESHPOINT, INC.—See Sysco Corporation; *U.S. Public*, pg. 1974
FRESHPOINT NASHVILLE, INC.—See Sysco Corporation; *U.S. Public*, pg. 1974
FRESHPOINT NORTH FLORIDA, INC.—See Sysco Corporation; *U.S. Public*, pg. 1974
FRESHPOINT OKLAHOMA CITY, LLC—See Sysco Corporation; *U.S. Public*, pg. 1974
FRESHPOINT PUERTO RICO, LLC—See Sysco Corporation; *U.S. Public*, pg. 1974
FRESHPOINT SAN FRANCISCO, INC.—See Sysco Corporation; *U.S. Public*, pg. 1974
FRESHPOINT SOUTHERN CALIFORNIA, INC.—See Sysco Corporation; *U.S. Public*, pg. 1974
FRESHPOINT SOUTH FLORIDA, INC.—See Sysco Corporation; *U.S. Public*, pg. 1974
FRESHPOINT SOUTH TEXAS, LP—See Sysco Corporation; *U.S. Public*, pg. 1974
FRESHPOINT TOMATO, LLC—See Sysco Corporation; *U.S. Public*, pg. 1974
FRESHPOINT VANCOUVER, LTD.—See Sysco Corporation; *U.S. Public*, pg. 1974
FRESH PRODUCE SPORTSWEAR INC.; *U.S. Private*, pg. 1610
FRESH QUEST INC; *U.S. Private*, pg. 1610
FRESH & READY FOODS LLC—See Compass Group PLC; *Int'l*, pg. 1752
FRESH START BAKERIES INDUSTRIAL LTDA—See ARYZTA AG; *Int'l*, pg. 588
FRESHSTOR INC.—See Boveda Inc.; *U.S. Private*, pg. 625
FRESHTEX PRODUCE LLC—See GrubMarket, Inc.; *U.S. Private*, pg. 1797
FRESHTIME UK LIMITED—See Greencore Group plc; *Int'l*, pg. 3074
FRESH TRACKS THERAPEUTICS, INC.; *U.S. Public*, pg. 886
FRESHTROP FRUITS LTD. - PLANT - II—See Green AgRevolution Pvt Ltd.; *Int'l*, pg. 3069
FRESHTROP FRUITS LTD.—See Green AgRevolution Pvt Ltd.; *Int'l*, pg. 3069
FRESH VINE WINE, INC.; *U.S. Public*, pg. 886
FRESHWATER CONSUMER LIMITED—See Freshwater UK PLC; *Int'l*, pg. 2782
THE FRESHWATER GROUP, INC.—See The Fountains, Inc.; *U.S. Private*, pg. 4030
FRESHWATER HEALTHCARE LIMITED—See Freshwater UK PLC; *Int'l*, pg. 2782
FRESH WATER MIIKE CO., LTD.—See Electric Power Development Co., Ltd.; *Int'l*, pg. 2349
FRESHWATER SCOTLAND LIMITED—See Freshwater UK PLC; *Int'l*, pg. 2782
FRESHWATER SOUTHERN LIMITED—See Freshwater UK PLC; *Int'l*, pg. 2782
FRESHWATER TECHNOLOGY LIMITED—See Freshwater UK PLC; *Int'l*, pg. 2782
FRESHWATER TECHNOLOGY; *Int'l*, pg. 2781
FRESHWATER UK PLC; *Int'l*, pg. 2782
FRESHWAY FOODS, INC.—See US Foods Holding Corp.; *U.S. Public*, pg. 2266
FRESHWAYS LIMITED—See Kerry Group plc; *Int'l*, pg. 4138
FRESHWORKS AUSTRALIA PTY. LTD.—See Freshworks Inc.; *U.S. Public*, pg. 886
FRESHWORKS GMBH—See Freshworks Inc.; *U.S. Public*, pg. 886
FRESHWORKS INC.; *U.S. Public*, pg. 886
FRESHWORKS SAS—See Freshworks Inc.; *U.S. Public*, pg. 886
FRESHWORKS TECHNOLOGIES B.V.—See Freshworks Inc.; *U.S. Public*, pg. 886
FRESHWORKS TECHNOLOGIES PRIVATE LIMITED—See Freshworks Inc.; *U.S. Public*, pg. 886
FRESHWORKS TECHNOLOGIES UK LIMITED—See Freshworks Inc.; *U.S. Public*, pg. 886
FRESH ZONE LIMITED—See Woolworths Group Limited; *Int'l*, pg. 8452
FRESKA PRODUCE INTERNATIONAL, LLC; *U.S. Private*, pg. 1610
FRESNILLO PLC; *Int'l*, pg. 2782
FRESNO AUTO DEALERS AUCTION—See Cox Enterprises, Inc.; *U.S. Private*, pg. 1076
THE FRESNO BEE—See Chatham Asset Management, LLC; *U.S. Private*, pg. 867
FRESNO CA ENDOSCOPY ASC, L.P.—See KKR & Co. Inc.; *U.S. Public*, pg. 1245
FRESNO CA MULTI ASC, L.P.—See KKR & Co. Inc.; *U.S. Public*, pg. 1245
FRESNO CHAFFEE ZOO; *U.S. Private*, pg. 1610
FRESNO ECONOMIC OPPORTUNITIES COMMISSION; *U.S. Private*, pg. 1610
FRESNO FIRST BANK—See Communities First Financial Corporation; *U.S. Public*, pg. 549
FRESNO HERITAGE PARTNERS, A CALIFORNIA LIMITED PARTNERSHIP—See AlerisLife Inc.; *U.S. Private*, pg. 161
FRESNO-MADERA FARM CREDIT ASSOCIATION; *U.S. Private*, pg. 1610
FRESNO OXYGEN; *U.S. Private*, pg. 1610
FRESNO PLUMBING & HEATING INC.; *U.S. Private*, pg. 1610
FRESNO PRODUCE, INC.—See Alvarez & Marsal, Inc.; *U.S. Private*, pg. 213
FRESNO PRODUCE, INC.—See Highview Capital, LLC; *U.S. Private*, pg. 1942
FRESNO SHOWER DOOR, INC.—See Patrick Industries, Inc.; *U.S. Public*, pg. 1652
FRESNO TRUCK CENTER; *U.S. Private*, pg. 1610
FRESNO VALVES & CASTINGS INC.; *U.S. Private*, pg. 1610
FRESPAC GINGER (FIJI) LTD—See Health and Plant Protein Group Limited; *Int'l*, pg. 3303
FRETT BARRINGTON LTD.—See R&R Insurance Services, Inc.; *U.S. Private*, pg. 3333
THE FRETZ CORPORATION INC.; *U.S. Private*, pg. 4031
FREUD AMERICA INC.—See Robert Bosch GmbH; *Int'l*, pg. 6367
FREUD CANADA INC.—See Robert Bosch GmbH; *Int'l*, pg. 6367
FREUD COMMUNICATIONS—See Publicis Groupe S.A.; *Int'l*, pg. 6099
FREUDENBERG ANLAGEN-UND WERKZEUGTECHNIK KG—See Freudenberg SE; *Int'l*, pg. 2785
FREUDENBERG AUSTRIA GMBH—See Freudenberg SE; *Int'l*, pg. 2785
FREUDENBERG BETEILIGUNGSGESELLSCHAFT MBH—See Freudenberg SE; *Int'l*, pg. 2785
FREUDENBERG CHEMICAL SPECIALITIES SE & CO. KG—See Freudenberg SE; *Int'l*, pg. 2785
FREUDENBERG & CO. LTD. PARTNERSHIP—See Freudenberg SE; *Int'l*, pg. 2785
FREUDENBERG DICHTUNGS- UND SCHWINGUNGSTECHNIK GMBH & CO. KG—See Freudenberg SE; *Int'l*, pg. 2786
FREUDENBERGER AUTOGLAS GMBH—See Compagnie de Saint-Gobain SA; *Int'l*, pg. 1736
FREUDENBERG ESPANA S.A.—See Freudenberg SE; *Int'l*, pg. 2786
FREUDENBERG ESPANA S.A., TELAS SIN TEJER S.EN—See Freudenberg SE; *Int'l*, pg. 2786
FREUDENBERG EVOLON S.A.R.L.—See Freudenberg SE; *Int'l*, pg. 2786
FREUDENBERG EVOLON S.A.S.U.—See Freudenberg SE; *Int'l*, pg. 2786
FREUDENBERG FAR EASTERN SPUNWEB COMP. LTD.—See Freudenberg SE; *Int'l*, pg. 2786
FREUDENBERG FILTRATION TECHNOLOGIES (AUST) PTY. LTD.—See Freudenberg SE; *Int'l*, pg. 2786
FREUDENBERG FILTRATION TECHNOLOGIES FINLAND OY—See Freudenberg SE; *Int'l*, pg. 2786
FREUDENBERG FILTRATION TECHNOLOGIES INC.—See Freudenberg SE; *Int'l*, pg. 2786
FREUDENBERG FILTRATION TECHNOLOGIES INDIA PRIVATE LIMITED—See Freudenberg SE; *Int'l*, pg. 2786
FREUDENBERG FILTRATION TECHNOLOGIES LP—See Freudenberg SE; *Int'l*, pg. 2786
FREUDENBERG FILTRATION TECHNOLOGIES OOO—See Freudenberg SE; *Int'l*, pg. 2786
FREUDENBERG FILTRATION TECHNOLOGIES (PTY) LTD.—See Freudenberg SE; *Int'l*, pg. 2786
FREUDENBERG FILTRATION TECHNOLOGIES SAS—See Freudenberg SE; *Int'l*, pg. 2786
FREUDENBERG FILTRATION TECHNOLOGIES SE & CO. KG—See Freudenberg SE; *Int'l*, pg. 2786
FREUDENBERG FILTRATION TECHNOLOGIES SLOVENSKO, S.R.O.—See Freudenberg SE; *Int'l*, pg. 2786
FREUDENBERG FILTRATION TECHNOLOGIES UK LIMITED—See Freudenberg SE; *Int'l*, pg. 2786
FREUDENBERG GOSPODINJSKI PROIZVODI D.O.O.—See Freudenberg SE; *Int'l*, pg. 2786
FREUDENBERG GYGLI AG—See Freudenberg SE; *Int'l*, pg. 2786
FREUDENBERG HAZTARTASI CIKKEK KERESKEDELMI BT—See Freudenberg SE; *Int'l*, pg. 2786
FREUDENBERG HOME & CLEANING SOLUTIONS IBERICA, S.L.U.—See Freudenberg SE; *Int'l*, pg. 2786
FREUDENBERG HOME & CLEANING SOLUTIONS S.R.O.—See Freudenberg SE; *Int'l*, pg. 2786
FREUDENBERG HOUSEHOLD PRODUCTS AB—See Freudenberg SE; *Int'l*, pg. 2786
FREUDENBERG HOUSEHOLD PRODUCTS AS—See Freudenberg SE; *Int'l*, pg. 2786
FREUDENBERG HOUSEHOLD PRODUCTS B.V.—See Freudenberg SE; *Int'l*, pg. 2786
FREUDENBERG HOUSEHOLD PRODUCTS EVICI KULLANIM ARACLARI SANAYI VE TICARET A.S.—See Freudenberg SE; *Int'l*, pg. 2786
FREUDENBERG HOUSEHOLD PRODUCTS INC.—See Freudenberg SE; *Int'l*, pg. 2787
FREUDENBERG HOUSEHOLD PRODUCTS LP—See Freudenberg SE; *Int'l*, pg. 2787
FREUDENBERG HOUSEHOLD PRODUCTS LP—See Freudenberg SE; *Int'l*, pg. 2787
FREUDENBERG HOUSEHOLD PRODUCTS LP—See Freudenberg SE; *Int'l*, pg. 2787
FREUDENBERG HOUSEHOLD PRODUCTS LP—See Freudenberg SE; *Int'l*, pg. 2787
FREUDENBERG HOUSEHOLD PRODUCTS LTD.—See Freudenberg SE; *Int'l*, pg. 2787
FREUDENBERG HOUSEHOLD PRODUCTS OY AB—See Freudenberg SE; *Int'l*, pg. 2787
FREUDENBERG HOUSEHOLD PRODUCTS (SUZHOU) CO., LTD.—See Freudenberg SE; *Int'l*, pg. 2786
FREUDENBERG HOUSEHOLD PRODUCTS (TAIWAN) CO., LTD.—See Freudenberg SE; *Int'l*, pg. 2786
FREUDENBERG IBERICA S.A., S.EN C.—See Freudenberg SE; *Int'l*, pg. 2787
FREUDENBERG IBERICA S.A.—See Freudenberg SE; *Int'l*, pg. 2787

THE FRETZ CORPORATION INC.

FREUDENBERG IT LP—See Freudenberg SE; *Int'l*, pg. 2787
FREUDENBERG IT (SUZHOU) CO., LTD.—See Freudenberg SE; *Int'l*, pg. 2787
FREUDENBERG JOINTS ELASTOMERES SAS—See Freudenberg SE; *Int'l*, pg. 2787
FREUDENBERG MEDICAL EUROPE GMBH—See Freudenberg SE; *Int'l*, pg. 2787
FREUDENBERG MEDICAL SRL.—See Freudenberg SE; *Int'l*, pg. 2787
FREUDENBERG NAO-TECIDOS LTDA. & CIA.—See Freudenberg SE; *Int'l*, pg. 2787
FREUDENBERG NAO-TECIDOS LTDA. & CIA.—See Freudenberg SE; *Int'l*, pg. 2787
FREUDENBERG NH CO. LTD.—See Freudenberg SE; *Int'l*, pg. 2787
FREUDENBERG-NOK-COMPONENTES BRASIL LTDA.—See Freudenberg SE; *Int'l*, pg. 2789
FREUDENBERG-NOK-COMPONENTES BRASIL LTDA.—See NOK Corporation; *Int'l*, pg. 5401
FREUDENBERG-NOK DE MEXICO—See Freudenberg SE; *Int'l*, pg. 2789
FREUDENBERG-NOK DE MEXICO—See NOK Corporation; *Int'l*, pg. 5401
FREUDENBERG-NOK DE QUERETARO, S.A. DE C.V.—See Freudenberg SE; *Int'l*, pg. 2789
FREUDENBERG-NOK DE QUERETARO, S.A. DE C.V.—See NOK Corporation; *Int'l*, pg. 5401
FREUDENBERG-NOK GENERAL PARTNERSHIP—See Freudenberg SE; *Int'l*, pg. 2788
FREUDENBERG-NOK GENERAL PARTNERSHIP—See NOK Corporation; *Int'l*, pg. 5401
FREUDENBERG-NOK INC.—See Freudenberg SE; *Int'l*, pg. 2788
FREUDENBERG-NOK INC.—See NOK Corporation; *Int'l*, pg. 5401
FREUDENBERG NOK-RUBBER PRODUCTS—See Freudenberg SE; *Int'l*, pg. 2788
FREUDENBERG NOK-RUBBER PRODUCTS—See Freudenberg SE; *Int'l*, pg. 2788
FREUDENBERG NOK-RUBBER PRODUCTS—See NOK Corporation; *Int'l*, pg. 5401
FREUDENBERG NOK-RUBBER PRODUCTS—See NOK Corporation; *Int'l*, pg. 5401
FREUDENBERG NOK-SEALANT PRODUCTS—See Freudenberg SE; *Int'l*, pg. 2788
FREUDENBERG NOK-SEALANT PRODUCTS—See NOK Corporation; *Int'l*, pg. 5401
FREUDENBERG NOK—See Freudenberg SE; *Int'l*, pg. 2788
FREUDENBERG NOK—See NOK Corporation; *Int'l*, pg. 5401
FREUDENBERG NOK—See Freudenberg SE; *Int'l*, pg. 2788
FREUDENBERG NOK—See NOK Corporation; *Int'l*, pg. 5401
FREUDENBERG NOK—See Freudenberg SE; *Int'l*, pg. 2788
FREUDENBERG NOK—See NOK Corporation; *Int'l*, pg. 5401
FREUDENBERG NOK—See Freudenberg SE; *Int'l*, pg. 2788
FREUDENBERG NOK—See NOK Corporation; *Int'l*, pg. 5401
FREUDENBERG NOK—See Freudenberg SE; *Int'l*, pg. 2788
FREUDENBERG NOK—See NOK Corporation; *Int'l*, pg. 5401
FREUDENBERG NONWOVENS INDIA PVT. LTD.—See Freudenberg SE; *Int'l*, pg. 2787
FREUDENBERG NONWOVENS LIMITED PARTNERSHIP—See Freudenberg SE; *Int'l*, pg. 2787
FREUDENBERG NONWOVENS LP—See Freudenberg SE; *Int'l*, pg. 2787
FREUDENBERG NONWOVENS LP VILENE INTERLININGS—See Freudenberg SE; *Int'l*, pg. 2787
FREUDENBERG NONWOVENS (PTY.) LTD.—See Freudenberg SE; *Int'l*, pg. 2785
FREUDENBERG NONWOVENS ROMANIA S.R.L.—See Freudenberg SE; *Int'l*, pg. 2787
FREUDENBERG NONWOVENS TUFT DIVISION—See Freudenberg SE; *Int'l*, pg. 2787
FREUDENBERG NORTH AMERICA LIMITED PARTNERSHIP—See Freudenberg SE; *Int'l*, pg. 2787
FREUDENBERG OIL & GAS CANADA INC.—See Freudenberg SE; *Int'l*, pg. 2787
FREUDENBERG OIL & GAS, LLC—See Freudenberg SE; *Int'l*, pg. 2787
FREUDENBERG OIL & GAS PTE. LTD.—See Freudenberg SE; *Int'l*, pg. 2787
FREUDENBERG OIL & GAS TECHNOLOGIES AS—See Freudenberg SE; *Int'l*, pg. 2787
FREUDENBERG OIL & GAS TECHNOLOGIES LTD.—See Freudenberg SE; *Int'l*, pg. 2787

FREUDENBERG OIL & GAS TECHNOLOGIES SDN. BHD.—See Freudenberg SE; *Int'l*, pg. 2787
FREUDENBERG OIL & GAS UK LTD.—See Freudenberg SE; *Int'l*, pg. 2787
FREUDENBERG PERFORMANCE MATERIALS APPAREL SE & CO. KG—See Freudenberg SE; *Int'l*, pg. 2787
FREUDENBERG PERFORMANCE MATERIALS HOLDING SE & CO. KG—See Freudenberg SE; *Int'l*, pg. 2787
FREUDENBERG PERFORMANCE MATERIALS LOGISTICS SE & CO. KG—See Freudenberg SE; *Int'l*, pg. 2787
FREUDENBERG PERFORMANCE MATERIALS LP—See Freudenberg SE; *Int'l*, pg. 2787
FREUDENBERG POLITEX LTD.—See Freudenberg SE; *Int'l*, pg. 2787
FREUDENBERG POLITEX OOO—See Freudenberg SE; *Int'l*, pg. 2787
FREUDENBERG POLITEX SP. Z O.O.—See Freudenberg SE; *Int'l*, pg. 2787
FREUDENBERG POTREBY PRO DOMACNOST, K.S.—See Freudenberg SE; *Int'l*, pg. 2787
FREUDENBERG PRODUCTOS DEL HOGAR LTDA.—See Freudenberg SE; *Int'l*, pg. 2787
FREUDENBERG PRODUCTOS DEL HOGAR, S.A. DE C.V.—See Freudenberg SE; *Int'l*, pg. 2787
FREUDENBERG PTY. LTD.—See Freudenberg SE; *Int'l*, pg. 2787
FREUDENBERG REAL ESTATE GMBH—See Freudenberg SE; *Int'l*, pg. 2788
FREUDENBERG S.A.S.—See Freudenberg SE; *Int'l*, pg. 2788
FREUDENBERG SCHWAB VIBRATION CONTROL AG—See Freudenberg SE; *Int'l*, pg. 2788
FREUDENBERG SEALING TECHNOLOGIES AG—See Freudenberg SE; *Int'l*, pg. 2788
FREUDENBERG SEALING TECHNOLOGIES GMBH & CO. KG—See Freudenberg SE; *Int'l*, pg. 2788
FREUDENBERG SEALING TECHNOLOGIES S.A.S. DI EXTERNA ITALIA S.R.L.U.—See Freudenberg SE; *Int'l*, pg. 2788
FREUDENBERG SEALING TECHNOLOGIES SAS—See Freudenberg SE; *Int'l*, pg. 2788
FREUDENBERG SEALING TECHNOLOGIES, S.L.U.—See Freudenberg SE; *Int'l*, pg. 2788
FREUDENBERG SEALING TECHNOLOGIES—See Freudenberg SE; *Int'l*, pg. 2788
FREUDENBERG SE; *Int'l*, pg. 2782
FREUDENBERG SIMMERRINGE KFT.—See Freudenberg SE; *Int'l*, pg. 2788
FREUDENBERG SIMRIT AG—See Freudenberg SE; *Int'l*, pg. 2788
FREUDENBERG SIMRIT A/S—See Freudenberg SE; *Int'l*, pg. 2788
FREUDENBERG SIMRIT B.V.—See Freudenberg SE; *Int'l*, pg. 2788
FREUDENBERG SIMRIT KUFSTEIN GES.M.B.H. & CO. KG—See Freudenberg SE; *Int'l*, pg. 2788
FREUDENBERG SIMRIT POLSKA SP. Z O.O.—See Freudenberg SE; *Int'l*, pg. 2788
FREUDENBERG SIMRIT SAS—See Freudenberg SE; *Int'l*, pg. 2788
FREUDENBERG S.P.A.—See Freudenberg SE; *Int'l*, pg. 2788
FREUDENBERG SPUNWEB JAPAN COMPANY, LTD.—See Freudenberg SE; *Int'l*, pg. 2788
FREUDENBERG TECHNICAL PRODUCTS LP—See Freudenberg SE; *Int'l*, pg. 2788
FREUDENBERG TELAS SIN TEJER S.A. DE C.V.—See Freudenberg SE; *Int'l*, pg. 2788
FREUDENBERG TELAS SIN TEJER S.A.—See Freudenberg SE; *Int'l*, pg. 2788
FREUDENBERG TEXTILE TECHNOLOGIES, S.A.—See Freudenberg SE; *Int'l*, pg. 2788
FREUDENBERG UCHIYAMA EUROPE S.A.S.—See Freudenberg SE; *Int'l*, pg. 2788
FREUDENBERG VERSICHERUNGSVERMITTLUNGS-GMBH—See Freudenberg SE; *Int'l*, pg. 2788
FREUDENBERG VERTRIEB EINLAGESTOFFE KG—See Freudenberg SE; *Int'l*, pg. 2788
FREUDENBERG & VILENE FILTER (THAILAND) CO. LTD.—See Freudenberg SE; *Int'l*, pg. 2785
FREUDENBERG VILENE NONWOVENS TAIWAN COMPANY LTD.—See Freudenberg SE; *Int'l*, pg. 2788
FREUDENBERG VILENE SP. Z.O.O.—See Freudenberg SE; *Int'l*, pg. 2788
FREUDENBERG VILENE TELA SAN. VE TIC. A.S.—See Freudenberg SE; *Int'l*, pg. 2788
FREUD, INC.; *U.S. Private*, pg. 1610
FREUD INTERNATIONAL TRADING (SHANGHAI) CO., LTD.—See Robert Bosch GmbH; *Int'l*, pg. 6361
FREUD S.P.A.—See Robert Bosch GmbH; *Int'l*, pg. 6361
FREUND-CHINEWAY PHARMACEUTICAL TECHNOLOGY CENTER CO., LTD.—See Freund Corporation; *Int'l*, pg. 2791
FREUND & COMPANY INC.; *U.S. Private*, pg. 1610
FREUND CORPORATION; *Int'l*, pg. 2791
FREUND PHARMATEC, LTD.—See Freund Corporation; *Int'l*, pg. 2791

CORPORATE AFFILIATIONS

FREUND-TURBO CORPORATION—See Freund Corporation; *Int'l*, pg. 2791
FREUND-VECTOR CORPORATION—See Freund Corporation; *Int'l*, pg. 2791
FREVVO INC.—See LoneTree Capital LLC; *U.S. Private*, pg. 2490
FREYABADI (THAILAND) CO., LTD.—See Fuji Oil Holdings Inc.; *Int'l*, pg. 2815
FREY AG—See Doppelmayr Group; *Int'l*, pg. 2175
FREY & ASSOCIATES, LLC; *U.S. Private*, pg. 1610
FREYCAN MAJOR PROJECTS LTD.—See VINCI S.A.; *Int'l*, pg. 8221
FREY + GNEHM INGENIEURE AG—See BKW AG; *Int'l*, pg. 1055
FREY INVEST S.L.—See Frey S.A.; *Int'l*, pg. 2791
FREYR BATTERY SA; *Int'l*, pg. 2791
FREYROM SA—See VINCI S.A.; *Int'l*, pg. 8231
FREYSAS-FREYSSINET STRUCTURAL SYSTEMS INC.—See Yapi Merkezi Holding A.S.; *Int'l*, pg. 8566
FREY S.A.; *Int'l*, pg. 2791
FREY SCIENTIFIC, INC.—See School Specialty, Inc.; *U.S. Public*, pg. 1848
FREYSSIMA (MAROC) SARL—See VINCI S.A.; *Int'l*, pg. 8221
FREYSSINET ADRIA SPECIALNI INZENIRING D.O.O.—See VINCI S.A.; *Int'l*, pg. 8221
FREYSSINET ARABIAN SEA LLC—See VINCI S.A.; *Int'l*, pg. 8231
FREYSSINET AUSTRALIA—See VINCI S.A.; *Int'l*, pg. 8231
FREYSSINET BELGIUM N.V.—See VINCI S.A.; *Int'l*, pg. 8231
FREYSSINET BULGARIA EOOD—See VINCI S.A.; *Int'l*, pg. 8221
FREYSSINET CANADA LTEE—See VINCI S.A.; *Int'l*, pg. 8221
FREYSSINET CHILE SPA—See VINCI S.A.; *Int'l*, pg. 8221
FREYSSINET DE MEXICO S.A. DE C.V.—See VINCI S.A.; *Int'l*, pg. 8221
FREYSSINET DE MEXICO - TIERRA ARMADA S.A.—See VINCI S.A.; *Int'l*, pg. 8232
FREYSSINET EAST AFRICA (KENYA) LTD.—See VINCI S.A.; *Int'l*, pg. 8221
FREYSSINET FRANCE—See VINCI S.A.; *Int'l*, pg. 8231
FREYSSINET GULF LLC—See VINCI S.A.; *Int'l*, pg. 8232
FREYSSINET HONG KONG LTD—See VINCI S.A.; *Int'l*, pg. 8232
FREYSSINET INC.—See VINCI S.A.; *Int'l*, pg. 8232
FREYSSINET INTERNATIONAL & CIE SAS—See VINCI S.A.; *Int'l*, pg. 8221
FREYSSINET INTERNATIONAL & CIE—See VINCI S.A.; *Int'l*, pg. 8230
FREYSSINET INTERNATIONAL & CIE—See VINCI S.A.; *Int'l*, pg. 8232
FREYSSINET IRELAND—See VINCI S.A.; *Int'l*, pg. 8232
FREYSSINET JORDAN LLC—See VINCI S.A.; *Int'l*, pg. 8232
FREYSSINET KOREA CO. LTD.—See VINCI S.A.; *Int'l*, pg. 8232
FREYSSINET KUWAIT—See VINCI S.A.; *Int'l*, pg. 8232
FREYSSINET LTD—See VINCI S.A.; *Int'l*, pg. 8232
FREYSSINET LUXEMBOURG SA—See VINCI S.A.; *Int'l*, pg. 8221
FREYSSINET MACAU LTD.—See VINCI S.A.; *Int'l*, pg. 8221
FREYSSINET MENARD INDIA PVT LTD—See VINCI S.A.; *Int'l*, pg. 8232
FREYSSINET MENARD NORTHERN EMIRATES LLC—See VINCI S.A.; *Int'l*, pg. 8221
FREYSSINET MENARD QATAR WLL—See VINCI S.A.; *Int'l*, pg. 8232
FREYSSINET MENARD SAUDI ARABIA LTD.—See VINCI S.A.; *Int'l*, pg. 8221
FREYSSINET MIDDLE EAST LLC—See VINCI S.A.; *Int'l*, pg. 8221
FREYSSINET MYANMAR CO., LTD.—See VINCI S.A.; *Int'l*, pg. 8221
FREYSSINET NEDERLAND B.V.—See VINCI S.A.; *Int'l*, pg. 8232
FREYSSINET NEW ZEALAND LIMITED—See VINCI S.A.; *Int'l*, pg. 8221
FREYSSINET OOO—See VINCI S.A.; *Int'l*, pg. 8232
FREYSSINET POLSKA SP. Z.O.O.—See VINCI S.A.; *Int'l*, pg. 8232
FREYSSINET POSTEN (PTY) LTD—See VINCI S.A.; *Int'l*, pg. 8232
FREYSSINET PRODUCTS COMPANY ASIA PTE. LTD.—See VINCI S.A.; *Int'l*, pg. 8221
FREYSSINET PRODUCTS COMPANY—See VINCI S.A.; *Int'l*, pg. 8232
FREYSSINET PSC (M) SDN BHD—See VINCI S.A.; *Int'l*, pg. 8232
FREYSSINET SA—See VINCI S.A.; *Int'l*, pg. 8232
FREYSSINET SAS—See VINCI S.A.; *Int'l*, pg. 8232
FREYSSINET SUISSE SA—See VINCI S.A.; *Int'l*, pg. 8221
FREYSSINET TAIWAN ENGINEERING. CO, LTD—See VINCI S.A.; *Int'l*, pg. 8232
FREYSSINET TERRA ARMADA PORTUGAL LTDA.—See VINCI S.A.; *Int'l*, pg. 8221

COMPANY NAME INDEX

FREYSSINET - TERRA ARMADA S.A.—See VINCI S.A.; *Int'l*, pg. 8231
FREYSSINET THAILAND LTD.—See VINCI S.A.; *Int'l*, pg. 8232
FREYSSINET - TIERRA ARMADA CA—See VINCI S.A.; *Int'l*, pg. 8231
FREYSSINET TIERRA ARMADA CHILE S.A.—See VINCI S.A.; *Int'l*, pg. 8232
FREYSSINET TIERRA ARMADA COLOMBIA SAS—See VINCI S.A.; *Int'l*, pg. 8221
FREYSSINET TIERRA ARMADA DE PANAMA SA—See VINCI S.A.; *Int'l*, pg. 8221
FREYSSINET TIERRA ARMADA PERU S.A.C.—See VINCI S.A.; *Int'l*, pg. 8221
FREYSSINET - TIERRA ARMADA S.A.—See VINCI S.A.; *Int'l*, pg. 8231
FREYSSINET TUNISIE—See VINCI S.A.; *Int'l*, pg. 8232
FREYSSINET VIETNAM—See VINCI S.A.; *Int'l*, pg. 8232
FREZIGEST, SGPS S.A.—See Sandvik AB; *Int'l*, pg. 6529
FREZITE FERRAMENTAS DE CORTE LTDA.—See Sandvik AB; *Int'l*, pg. 6529
FREZITE - FERRAMENTAS DE CORTE S.A.—See Sandvik AB; *Int'l*, pg. 6529
FREZITE HERRAMIENTAS DE CORTE S.L.—See Sandvik AB; *Int'l*, pg. 6529
FREZITE S.R.O.—See Sandvik AB; *Int'l*, pg. 6529
FR FREIRAUM GASTRONOMIE GMBH—See DO & CO Aktiengesellschaft; *Int'l*, pg. 2152
F.R.F. SYSTEMS INC.; *U.S. Private*, pg. 1457
FRHAM SAFETY PRODUCTS INC.; *U.S. Private*, pg. 1610
FRHUG FESTIVAL GMBH & CO. KG—See Live Nation Entertainment, Inc.; *U.S. Public*, pg. 1328
FRIASKOG AB; *Int'l*, pg. 2791
FRIATEC AG-CERAMICS DIVISION—See Aliaxis S.A./N.V.; *Int'l*, pg. 324
FRIATEC AG—See Aliaxis S.A./N.V.; *Int'l*, pg. 324
FRIATEC AG-TECHNICAL PLASTICS DIVISION—See Aliaxis S.A./N.V.; *Int'l*, pg. 324
FRIATEC BUILDING SERVICES—See Aliaxis S.A./N.V.; *Int'l*, pg. 324
FRIATEC DPL—See Aliaxis S.A./N.V.; *Int'l*, pg. 324
FRIATEC SARL—See Aliaxis S.A./N.V.; *Int'l*, pg. 324
THE FRICK COLLECTION; *U.S. Private*, pg. 4031
FRICK SERVICES INC.; *U.S. Private*, pg. 1610
FRICO AB—See Systemair AB; *Int'l*, pg. 7391
FRICO A/S—See Systemair AB; *Int'l*, pg. 7391
FRICO AS—See Systemair AB; *Int'l*, pg. 7391
FRICO B.V.—See Systemair AB; *Int'l*, pg. 7391
FRICO GMBH—See Systemair AB; *Int'l*, pg. 7391
FRICOM RECYCLING—See Derichebourg S.A.; *Int'l*, pg. 2041
FRICOPAN GMBH—See ARYZTA AG; *Int'l*, pg. 589
FRICO SAS—See Systemair AB; *Int'l*, pg. 7391
FRIC-ROT S.A.I.C.—See Apollo Global Management, Inc.; *U.S. Public*, pg. 162
FRICTAPE NET OY—See Lagercrantz Group AB; *Int'l*, pg. 4394
FRICTIONLESS SOLUTIONS, INC.; *U.S. Private*, pg. 1610
FRICTION PRODUCTS CO.—See Lone Star Funds; *U.S. Private*, pg. 2485
FRIDAY OIL CO. INC.; *U.S. Private*, pg. 1610
FRIDAYS HOLDINGS, INC.—See Boulevard Holdings, Inc.; *Int'l*, pg. 1119
FRIDAY TV AB—See LOV Group Invest SAS; *Int'l*, pg. 4565
FRIDENSON AIR & OCEAN LTD.—See Fridenson Logistic Services Ltd.; *Int'l*, pg. 2791
FRIDENSON LOGISTIC SERVICES LTD.; *Int'l*, pg. 2791
FRIEDERICH-HYDROTECH S.A.R.L.—See Hydac International GmbH; *Int'l*, pg. 3544
FRIEDHELM LOH STIFTUNG & CO. KG; *Int'l*, pg. 2791
THE FRIEDKIN GROUP, INC.; *U.S. Private*, pg. 4031
FRIEDLAND 035 INVESTMENTS (PTY) LTD—See Lesaka Technologies, Inc.; *Int'l*, pg. 4468
FRIEDLAND PARTICIPATION ET GESTION S.A.—See BNP Paribas SA; *Int'l*, pg. 1091
FRIEDL BUSINESS INFORMATION LIMITED; *Int'l*, pg. 2792
FRIEDLER CONSTRUCTION COMPANY; *U.S. Private*, pg. 1610
FRIEDMAN CORPORATION—See Constellation Software Inc.; *Int'l*, pg. 1773
FRIEDMAN ELECTRIC, INDUSTRIAL AUTOMATION DIVISION—See Sonepar S.A.; *Int'l*, pg. 7093
FRIEDMAN ELECTRIC SUPPLY CO—See Sonepar S.A.; *Int'l*, pg. 7093
FRIEDMAN & FRIEDMAN—See Kelso & Company, L.P.; *U.S. Private*, pg. 2279
FRIEDMAN INDUSTRIES, INC.; *U.S. Public*, pg. 886
FRIEDMAN LLP; *U.S. Private*, pg. 1611
FRIEDMAN RECYCLING COMPANY; *U.S. Private*, pg. 1611
FRIEDMAN'S LTD.—See CEPS PLC; *Int'l*, pg. 1420
FRIEDMAN TELECOM—See Sonepar S.A.; *Int'l*, pg. 7093
FRIEDOMTECH LLC; *U.S. Private*, pg. 1611
FRIEDRICH AIR CONDITIONING CO.—See Paloma Industries Limited; *Int'l*, pg. 5709

FRIEDRICH BOYSEN GMBH & CO. KG; *Int'l*, pg. 2792
FRIEDRICH EISEN GMBH—See Bilfinger SE; *Int'l*, pg. 1028
FRIEDRICH GOHRINGER ELEKTROTECHNIK GMBH—See Amphenol Corporation; *U.S. Public*, pg. 130
FRIEDRICH + LOCHNER GMBH—See Nemetschek SE; *Int'l*, pg. 5194
FRIEDRICH MULLER OMNIBUSUNTERNEHMEN GMBH—See Deutsche Bahn AG; *Int'l*, pg. 2051
FRIEDRICHSBAU VARIETE BETRIEBS- UND VERWALTUNGS GMBH—See DEAG Deutsche Entertainment AG; *Int'l*, pg. 1998
FRIEDRICH VORWERK SE & CO. KG—See MBB SE; *Int'l*, pg. 4751
FRIEDRICH WILHELMS - HUETTE GMBH—See Georgsmarienhutte Holding GmbH; *Int'l*, pg. 2940
FRIED.V.NEUMAN GMBH—See CAG Holding GmbH; *Int'l*, pg. 1250
FRIEL LUMBER CO.; *U.S. Private*, pg. 1611
FRIEMANN & WOLF BATTERIETECHNIK GMBH—See TotalEnergies SE; *Int'l*, pg. 7837
FRIENDABLE, INC.; *U.S. Public*, pg. 886
FRIEND BANK—See SNB Holdings, Inc.; *U.S. Private*, pg. 3700
FRIEND FAMILY HEALTH CENTER, INC.; *U.S. Private*, pg. 1611
FRIENDFINDER NETWORKS INC.; *U.S. Private*, pg. 1611
FRIENDFINDER VENTURES, INC.—See FriendFinder Networks Inc.; *U.S. Private*, pg. 1611
FRIENDLY CHECK CASHING CORP.; *U.S. Private*, pg. 1611
FRIENDLY CHEVROLET CO. INC.; *U.S. Private*, pg. 1611
FRIENDLY CHEVROLET, INC.; *U.S. Private*, pg. 1611
FRIENDLY CHRYSLER JEEP; *U.S. Private*, pg. 1611
FRIENDLY CORPORATION; *Int'l*, pg. 2792
FRIENDLY ENERGY EXPLORATION; *U.S. Private*, pg. 1611
FRIENDLY FORD, INC.; *U.S. Private*, pg. 1611
FRIENDLY FOOD, INC.; *U.S. Private*, pg. 1611
FRIENDLY FUELS INC.; *U.S. Private*, pg. 1611
FRIENDLY HILLS BANK; *U.S. Public*, pg. 886
FRIENDLY ICE CREAM CORPORATION—See Sun Capital Partners, Inc.; *U.S. Private*, pg. 3859
FRIENDLY SERVICE STATION INC.; *U.S. Private*, pg. 1611
FRIENDLYS MANUFACTURING AND RETAIL, LLC—See Dean Foods Company; *U.S. Private*, pg. 1184
FRIENDLY STRANGER HOLDINGS CORP.—See Fire & Flower Holdings Corp.; *Int'l*, pg. 2678
FRIENDS BANK—See FAIRWINDS Credit Union; *U.S. Private*, pg. 1465
FRIENDS BEHAVIORAL HEALTH SYSTEM, L.P.—See Universal Health Services, Inc.; *U.S. Public*, pg. 2257
FRIENDS & BRGRS AB OY—See NoHo Partners Plc; *Int'l*, pg. 5400
FRIENDS CHILD CARE CENTER; *U.S. Private*, pg. 1611
FRIENDS FIRST HOLDINGS LTD.—See Achmea B.V.; *Int'l*, pg. 103
FRIENDS FIRST IRELAND—See Achmea B.V.; *Int'l*, pg. 103
FRIENDSHIP AUTOMOTIVE INC.; *U.S. Private*, pg. 1612
FRIENDSHIP COMMUNITY; *U.S. Private*, pg. 1612
FRIENDSHIP DAIRIES, LLC—See Saputo Inc.; *Int'l*, pg. 6575
FRIENDSHIP HAVEN, INC.; *U.S. Private*, pg. 1612
FRIENDSHIP HOUSE; *U.S. Private*, pg. 1612
FRIENDSHIP STATE BANK; *U.S. Private*, pg. 1612
FRIENDS HOMES INC.; *U.S. Private*, pg. 1611
FRIEND SKOLER & CO., INC.; *U.S. Private*, pg. 1611
FRIENDS LIFE CARE; *U.S. Private*, pg. 1611
FRIENDS LIFE GROUP LIMITED—See Aviva plc; *Int'l*, pg. 746
FRIENDS LIFE MANAGEMENT SERVICES LIMITED—See Aviva plc; *Int'l*, pg. 746
FRIENDS OF MOSDOT GOOR, INC; *U.S. Private*, pg. 1611
THE FRIENDS OF THE BRIGHAM & WOMEN'S HOSPITAL—See Partners HealthCare System, Inc.; *U.S. Private*, pg. 3102
FRIENDS OF YOUTH; *U.S. Private*, pg. 1611
FRIENDS & PARTNERS S.P.A.—See CTS Eventim AG & Co. KGAA; *Int'l*, pg. 1873
FRIENDS PROVIDENT INTERNATIONAL LIMITED—See Cinven Limited; *Int'l*, pg. 1611
FRIENDS RETIREMENT CONCEPTS, INC.—See LCS Holdings Inc.; *U.S. Private*, pg. 2404
FRIENDSWOOD DEVELOPMENT COMPANY, LLC—See Lennar Corporation; *U.S. Private*, pg. 1306
FRIENDTIMES, INC.; *Int'l*, pg. 2792
FRIEND TIRE COMPANY—See Southern Tire Mart, LLC; *U.S. Private*, pg. 3735
FRIENDWORKS GMBH—See Easy Software AG; *Int'l*, pg. 2276
FRIESLAND ARABIA LTD.—See Zuivelcooperatie FrieslandCampina U.A.; *Int'l*, pg. 8693
FRIESLAND BETON HEERENVEEN B.V.—See Buzzi SpA; *Int'l*, pg. 1230

FRIESLANDCAMPINA AMEA PTE LTD—See Zuivelcooperatie FrieslandCampina U.A.; *Int'l*, pg. 8693
FRIESLANDCAMPINA AUSTRIA GMBH—See Zuivelcooperatie FrieslandCampina U.A.; *Int'l*, pg. 8693
FRIESLANDCAMPINA BELGIUM N.V—See Zuivelcooperatie FrieslandCampina U.A.; *Int'l*, pg. 8693
FRIESLANDCAMPINA CANARIAS S.A.—See Zuivelcooperatie FrieslandCampina U.A.; *Int'l*, pg. 8693
FRIESLANDCAMPINA CHEESE & BUTTER B.V—See Zuivelcooperatie FrieslandCampina U.A.; *Int'l*, pg. 8693
FRIESLANDCAMPINA CHEESE FRANCE S.A.S.—See Zuivelcooperatie FrieslandCampina U.A.; *Int'l*, pg. 8693
FRIESLANDCAMPINA CHEESE GERMANY—See Zuivelcooperatie FrieslandCampina U.A.; *Int'l*, pg. 8693
FRIESLANDCAMPINA CONSUMER PRODUCTS EUROPE B.V.—See Zuivelcooperatie FrieslandCampina U.A.; *Int'l*, pg. 8693
FRIESLANDCAMPINA CONSUMER PRODUCTS INTERNATIONAL B.V.—See Zuivelcooperatie FrieslandCampina U.A.; *Int'l*, pg. 8693
FRIESLANDCAMPINA CREAMY CREATION B.V.—See Wagram Equity Partners BV; *Int'l*, pg. 8328
FRIESLANDCAMPINA CREAMY CREATION LLC—See Wagram Equity Partners BV; *Int'l*, pg. 8328
FRIESLANDCAMPINA DMV—See Zuivelcooperatie FrieslandCampina U.A.; *Int'l*, pg. 8694
FRIESLANDCAMPINA FRESH (THAILAND) CO., LTD—See Zuivelcooperatie FrieslandCampina U.A.; *Int'l*, pg. 8693
FRIESLANDCAMPINA GERMANY GMBH—See Zuivelcooperatie FrieslandCampina U.A.; *Int'l*, pg. 8693
FRIESLANDCAMPINA GHANA—See Zuivelcooperatie FrieslandCampina U.A.; *Int'l*, pg. 8693
FRIESLANDCAMPINA HELLAS S.A.—See Zuivelcooperatie FrieslandCampina U.A.; *Int'l*, pg. 8694
FRIESLANDCAMPINA (HONG KONG) LTD.—See Zuivelcooperatie FrieslandCampina U.A.; *Int'l*, pg. 8693
FRIESLANDCAMPINA HUNGARIA ZRT—See Zuivelcooperatie FrieslandCampina U.A.; *Int'l*, pg. 8693
FRIESLANDCAMPINA INDONESIA—See Zuivelcooperatie FrieslandCampina U.A.; *Int'l*, pg. 8693
FRIESLANDCAMPINA INGREDIENTS LATIN AMERICA LTDA—See Zuivelcooperatie FrieslandCampina U.A.; *Int'l*, pg. 8693
FRIESLANDCAMPINA INGREDIENTS NORTH AMERICA, INC.—See Zuivelcooperatie FrieslandCampina U.A.; *Int'l*, pg. 8693
FRIESLANDCAMPINA ITALY SRL—See Zuivelcooperatie FrieslandCampina U.A.; *Int'l*, pg. 8693
FRIESLANDCAMPINA KIEVIT GMBH—See Zuivelcooperatie FrieslandCampina U.A.; *Int'l*, pg. 8693
FRIESLANDCAMPINA MIDDLE EAST JLT—See Zuivelcooperatie FrieslandCampina U.A.; *Int'l*, pg. 8693
FRIESLANDCAMPINA NEDERLAND HOLDING B.V.—See Zuivelcooperatie FrieslandCampina U.A.; *Int'l*, pg. 8693
FRIESLANDCAMPINA NUTRIFEED B.V.—See Zuivelcooperatie FrieslandCampina U.A.; *Int'l*, pg. 8693
FRIESLANDCAMPINA PROFESSIONAL NV—See Zuivelcooperatie FrieslandCampina U.A.; *Int'l*, pg. 8693
FRIESLANDCAMPINA ROMANIA S.A.—See Zuivelcooperatie FrieslandCampina U.A.; *Int'l*, pg. 8693
FRIESLANDCAMPINA RUSSIA—See Zuivelcooperatie FrieslandCampina U.A.; *Int'l*, pg. 8693
FRIESLANDCAMPINA (SINGAPORE) PTE. LTD.—See Zuivelcooperatie FrieslandCampina U.A.; *Int'l*, pg. 8693
FRIESLANDCAMPINA SPAIN—See Zuivelcooperatie FrieslandCampina U.A.; *Int'l*, pg. 8693
FRIESLANDCAMPINA (THAILAND) PCL—See Zuivelcooperatie FrieslandCampina U.A.; *Int'l*, pg. 8693
FRIESLANDCAMPINA TRADING (SHANGHAI) CO. LTD.—See Zuivelcooperatie FrieslandCampina U.A.; *Int'l*, pg. 8693
FRIESLANDCAMPINA UK LTD.—See Zuivelcooperatie FrieslandCampina U.A.; *Int'l*, pg. 8694
FRIESLANDCAMPINA VIETNAM CO. LTD.—See Zuivelcooperatie FrieslandCampina U.A.; *Int'l*, pg. 8694
FRIESLANDCAMPINA WAMCO NIGERIA PLC.—See Zuivelcooperatie FrieslandCampina U.A.; *Int'l*, pg. 8694
FRIESLANDCAMPINA WERKNEMERS B.V.—See Zuivelcooperatie FrieslandCampina U.A.; *Int'l*, pg. 8694
FRIESS ASSOCIATES, LLC—See Affiliated Managers Group, Inc.; *U.S. Public*, pg. 55
FRIESS ASSOCIATES OF DELAWARE, LLC—See Affiliated Managers Group, Inc.; *U.S. Public*, pg. 55
FRIEZE ADVERTISING INC.; *U.S. Private*, pg. 1612
FRIEZE EVENTS INC.—See Silver Lake Group, LLC; *U.S. Private*, pg. 3654
FRIEZE EVENTS LIMITED—See Silver Lake Group, LLC; *U.S. Private*, pg. 3654
FRIGATE AS; *Int'l*, pg. 2792
FRIGATE LUXEMBOURG S.A.—See Frigate AS; *Int'l*, pg. 2792
FRIGATE PAY UAB—See Frigate AS; *Int'l*, pg. 2792
FRIGATE SA—See Frigate AS; *Int'l*, pg. 2792
FRIGHT-RAGS, INC.; *U.S. Private*, pg. 1612
FRIGINOX—See Ali Holding S.r.l; *Int'l*, pg. 321
FRIGOBLOCK GROSSKOPF GMBH—See Ingersoll Rand Inc.; *U.S. Public*, pg. 1120

FRIGOCEL—See Grupo Empresarial Kaluz S.A. de C.V.; *Int'l*, pg. 3127
FRIGOCONSULT S.L.—See Frigosped GmbH; *Int'l*, pg. 2792
FRIGOGLASS EAST AFRICA LTD.—See Frigoglass S.A.I.C.; *Int'l*, pg. 2792
FRIGOGLASS EURASIA LLC—See Frigoglass S.A.I.C.; *Int'l*, pg. 2792
FRIGOGLASS GMBH—See Frigoglass S.A.I.C.; *Int'l*, pg. 2792
FRIGOGLASS (GUANGZHOU) ICE COLD EQUIPMENT CO., LTD.—See Frigoglass S.A.I.C.; *Int'l*, pg. 2792
FRIGOGLASS INDIA PVT. LTD.—See Frigoglass S.A.I.C.; *Int'l*, pg. 2792
FRIGOGLASS NORDIC AS—See Frigoglass S.A.I.C.; *Int'l*, pg. 2792
FRIGOGLASS S.A.I.C.; *Int'l*, pg. 2792
FRIGOGLASS SOUTH AFRICA LTD.—See Frigoglass S.A.I.C.; *Int'l*, pg. 2792
FRIGOGLASS SP. Z O.O—See Frigoglass S.A.I.C.; *Int'l*, pg. 2792
FRIGOGLASS WEST AFRICA LIMITED—See Frigoglass S.A.I.C.; *Int'l*, pg. 2792
FRIGOLOGISTICS CONSULTING LIMITED—See Frigosped GmbH; *Int'l*, pg. 2792
FRIGO LOGISTICS SP. Z O.O.—See Nichirei Corporation; *Int'l*, pg. 5270
FRIGO-PAK GIDA MADDELERI SANAYI VE TICARET A.S., *Int'l*, pg. 2792
FRIGORIFERI MILANESI S.P.A.—See Bastogi S.p.A.; *Int'l*, pg. 888
FRIGORIFICO PATAGONIA S.A.—See Marfrig Global Foods S.A.; *Int'l*, pg. 4692
FRIGOSCANDIA AB—See Dachser GmbH & Co.; *Int'l*, pg. 1904
FRIGOSCANDIA AKERI AB—See Mutares SE & Co. KGaA; *Int'l*, pg. 5104
FRIGOSCANDIA B. V—See Mutares SE & Co. KGaA; *Int'l*, pg. 5104
FRIGOSCANDIA DENMARK A / S—See Mutares SE & Co. KGaA; *Int'l*, pg. 5104
FRIGOSCANDIA TRANSPORT AS—See Mutares SE & Co. KGaA; *Int'l*, pg. 5104
FRIGOSPED GMBH; *Int'l*, pg. 2792
FRIGO ST. JOHANN AG—See Coop-Gruppe Genossenschaft; *Int'l*, pg. 1789
FRIGOTECH AB—See Sdiptech AB; *Int'l*, pg. 6658
FRIGOTEHNICA S.A.—See Axxess Capital; *Int'l*, pg. 772
FRIGRITE REFRIGERATION PTY LTD—See Crayon Group AS; *Int'l*, pg. 1829
FRIHEDEN INVEST A/S; *Int'l*, pg. 2792
FRIKA WEAVE (PTY) LTD—See Godrej & Boyce Mfg. Co. Ltd.; *Int'l*, pg. 3020
FRI KOPENSKAP FORLAGS AB—See Mentor Online AB; *Int'l*, pg. 4818
FRILAND DEUTSCHLAND GMBH—See Danish Crown AmbA; *Int'l*, pg. 1965
FRILO SOFTWARE GMBH—See Herbalife Nutrition Ltd.; *Int'l*, pg. 3359
FRILUFTSLAND A/S—See Fenix Outdoor International AG; *Int'l*, pg. 2634
FRIMANN-BERNER AS—See Berner SE; *Int'l*, pg. 988
FRIMA VAFLER A/S—See Orkla ASA; *Int'l*, pg. 5638
FRIMECA SAS—See VINCI S.A.; *Int'l*, pg. 8221
FRIMEX INVESTMENT LLC—See Hayel Saeed Anam Group of Companies; *Int'l*, pg. 3290
FRIMO GROUP GMBH—See Deutsche Beteiligungs AG; *Int'l*, pg. 2062
FRIMO INC.—See Deutsche Beteiligungs AG; *Int'l*, pg. 2062
FRIMONT, S.P.A.—See Ali Holding S.r.l; *Int'l*, pg. 321
FRIMO S.A.M.—See Cremonini S.p.A.; *Int'l*, pg. 1838
FRINA MOUSSE FRANCE S.A.R.L.—See Bystronic AG; *Int'l*, pg. 1236
FRINGE81 CO., LTD.; *Int'l*, pg. 2793
FRINGE BENEFIT GROUP LP; *U.S. Private*, pg. 1612
FRINX S.R.O.—See Elisa Corporation; *Int'l*, pg. 2361
FRIONA AGRICULTURE CREDIT CORP.—See Friona Industries, LP; *U.S. Private*, pg. 1612
FRIONA FEED YARD—See Friona Industries, LP; *U.S. Private*, pg. 1612
FRIONA INDUSTRIES, LP; *U.S. Private*, pg. 1612
FRIO PIPE LINE COMPANY INC.—See George R. Brown Partnership; *U.S. Private*, pg. 1683
FRIO REGIONAL HOSPITAL; *U.S. Private*, pg. 1612
FRIOSUR PESQUERA SA; *Int'l*, pg. 2793
FRI RESINS HOLDING CO.—See Arsenal Capital Management LP; *U.S. Private*, pg. 339
FRISCHBETON AG—See Vicat S.A.; *Int'l*, pg. 8185
FRISCHBETON S.R.O.—See STRABAG SE; *Int'l*, pg. 7230
FRISCHBETON THUN AG—See Vicat S.A.; *Int'l*, pg. 8185
FRISCHEPARADIES KG—See Dr. August Oetker KG; *Int'l*, pg. 2190
FRISCHHERTZ ELECTRIC COMPANY, INC.; *U.S. Private*, pg. 1612
FRISCH INDIANA LLC—See NRD Capital Management, LLC; *U.S. Private*, pg. 2969

FRISCH KENTUCKY LLC—See NRD Capital Management, LLC; *U.S. Private*, pg. 2969
FRISCH OHIO LLC—See NRD Capital Management, LLC; *U.S. Private*, pg. 2969
FRISCH'S RESTAURANTS, INC.—See NRD Capital Management, LLC; *U.S. Private*, pg. 2969
FRISCO MEDICAL CENTER, L.L.P.—See Tenet Healthcare Corporation; *U.S. Public*, pg. 2010
FRISCO PHYSICAL THERAPY, LIMITED PARTNERSHIP—See U.S. Physical Therapy, Inc.; *U.S. Public*, pg. 2214
FRISIA ZOUT B.V.—See K+S Aktiengesellschaft; *Int'l*, pg. 4039
FRISK INT. N.V.—See Perfetti Van Melle Holding B.V.; *Int'l*, pg. 5800
FRISO BOUWGROEP B.V.; *Int'l*, pg. 2793
FRISQ AB—See Nosa Plugs AB; *Int'l*, pg. 5448
FRISSBETON KFT.—See STRABAG SE; *Int'l*, pg. 7230
FRISTADS AB—See Investment AB Latour; *Int'l*, pg. 3781
FRISTADS AS—See Investment AB Latour; *Int'l*, pg. 3781
FRISTADS B.V.—See Investment AB Latour; *Int'l*, pg. 3781
FRISTADS FINLAND OY—See Investment AB Latour; *Int'l*, pg. 3781
FRISTADS GMBH—See Investment AB Latour; *Int'l*, pg. 3781
FRISTAM B.V.—See FRISTAM Pumpen F. Stamp GmbH & Co. KG; *Int'l*, pg. 2793
FRISTAM IBERICA S.L.—See FRISTAM Pumpen F. Stamp GmbH & Co. KG; *Int'l*, pg. 2793
FRISTAM POLSKA SP.Z.O.O.—See FRISTAM Pumpen F. Stamp GmbH & Co. KG; *Int'l*, pg. 2793
FRISTAM PUMPEN F. STAMP GMBH & CO. KG; *Int'l*, pg. 2793
FRISTAM PUMPEN, OOO—See FRISTAM Pumpen F. Stamp GmbH & Co. KG; *Int'l*, pg. 2793
FRISTAM PUMPER A/S—See FRISTAM Pumpen F. Stamp GmbH & Co. KG; *Int'l*, pg. 2793
FRISTAM PUMPS (I) PVT LTD—See FRISTAM Pumpen F. Stamp GmbH & Co. KG; *Int'l*, pg. 2793
FRISTAM PUMPS JAPAN CO., LTD.—See FRISTAM Pumpen F. Stamp GmbH & Co. KG; *Int'l*, pg. 2793
FRISTAM PUMPS LTD.—See FRISTAM Pumpen F. Stamp GmbH & Co. KG; *Int'l*, pg. 2793
FRISTAM PUMPS SOUTH EAST ASIA PTE. LTD—See FRISTAM Pumpen F. Stamp GmbH & Co. KG; *Int'l*, pg. 2793
FRISTAM PUMPS (TAICANG) CO., LTD.—See FRISTAM Pumpen F. Stamp GmbH & Co. KG; *Int'l*, pg. 2793
FRISTAM PUMPS (UK) LIMITED PARTNERSHIP—See FRISTAM Pumpen F. Stamp GmbH & Co. KG; *Int'l*, pg. 2793
FRISTAM PUMPS USA, LIMITED PARTNERSHIP—See FRISTAM Pumpen F. Stamp GmbH & Co. KG; *Int'l*, pg. 2793
THE FRIST CENTER FOR THE VISUAL ARTS, INC.; *U.S. Private*, pg. 4031
FRIT CAR INC.—See Frit Incorporated; *U.S. Private*, pg. 1612
FRITCH INC.; *U.S. Private*, pg. 1612
FRIT COCOWALK OWNER, LLC—See Federal Realty Investment Trust; *U.S. Public*, pg. 825
FRITIDSRESOR AB—See TUI AG; *Int'l*, pg. 7964
FRITIDSRESOR HOLDING SPAIN S.A.U.—See TUI AG; *Int'l*, pg. 7964
FRIT INCORPORATED; *U.S. Private*, pg. 1612
FRIT INDUSTRIES INC.—See Frit Incorporated; *U.S. Private*, pg. 1612
FRITO-LAY-CHARLOTTE—See PepsiCo, Inc.; *U.S. Public*, pg. 1670
FRITO-LAY DE CHILE—See PepsiCo, Inc.; *U.S. Public*, pg. 1670
FRITO-LAY GIDA SANAYI VE TICARET A.S.—See PepsiCo, Inc.; *U.S. Public*, pg. 1670
FRITO-LAY, INC.—See PepsiCo, Inc.; *U.S. Public*, pg. 1670
FRITO-LAY NETHERLANDS HOLDING B.V.—See PepsiCo, Inc.; *U.S. Public*, pg. 1670
FRITO-LAY NORTH AMERICA, INC.—See PepsiCo, Inc.; *U.S. Public*, pg. 1670
FRITO-LAY POLAND SP.Z.O.O.—See PepsiCo, Inc.; *U.S. Public*, pg. 1668
FRITO LAY SP.Z.O.O.—See PepsiCo, Inc.; *U.S. Public*, pg. 1670
FRITO-LAY TRADING COMPANY (EUROPE) GMBH—See PepsiCo, Inc.; *U.S. Public*, pg. 1670
FRITO-LAY TRADING COMPANY (POLAND) GMBH—See PepsiCo, Inc.; *U.S. Public*, pg. 1668
FRIT SHOPS AT SUNSET PLACE, LLC—See Federal Realty Investment Trust; *U.S. Public*, pg. 825
FRIT SOLAR, INC.—See Federal Realty Investment Trust; *U.S. Public*, pg. 825
FRITZ BERGER GMBH; *Int'l*, pg. 2793
FRITZ CLINIC, LLC—See Webster Equity Partners, LLC; *U.S. Private*, pg. 4466
FRITZ COMPANY; *U.S. Private*, pg. 1612
FRITZ EGGER AG—See Fritz Egger GmbH & Co.; *Int'l*, pg. 2794

FRITZ EGGER GMBH & CO. - EGGER PANNEAUX & DECORS—See Fritz Egger GmbH & Co.; *Int'l*, pg. 2794
FRITZ EGGER GMBH & CO.; *Int'l*, pg. 2793
FRITZ EGGER GMBH HUNGARY—See Fritz Egger GmbH & Co.; *Int'l*, pg. 2794
FRITZ ENTERPRISES INC.; *U.S. Private*, pg. 1613
FRITZ ENTERPRISES; *U.S. Private*, pg. 1612
FRITZ INDUSTRIES INC.; *U.S. Private*, pg. 1613
FRITZ LANGE GMBH; *Int'l*, pg. 2794
FRITZ MASSONG GMBH; *Int'l*, pg. 2794
FRITZ NAUER AG—See Bystronic AG; *Int'l*, pg. 1236
FRITZ NOLS AG; *Int'l*, pg. 2794
FRITZ PLANUNG GMBH; *Int'l*, pg. 2794
FRITZ STEPHAN GMBH; *Int'l*, pg. 2794
FRITZ STUDER AG—See United Grinding Group AG; *Int'l*, pg. 8067
FRITZ WEGMANN ELEKTRISCHE ANLAGEN AG—See Burkhalter Holding AG; *Int'l*, pg. 1225
FRITZY TECH INC.; *Int'l*, pg. 2794
FRIULCHEM SPA; *Int'l*, pg. 2794
FRIULINOX ALI SPA—See Ali Holding S.r.l; *Int'l*, pg. 321
FRIWO AG—See VTC Partners GmbH; *Int'l*, pg. 8316
FRIWO GERATEBAU GMBH—See VTC Partners GmbH; *Int'l*, pg. 8316
FRIZ KASCHIERTECHNIK GMBH—See Durr AG; *Int'l*, pg. 2232
FRIZZELL CONSTRUCTION CO. INC.; *U.S. Private*, pg. 1613
FR. KAISER GMBH; *Int'l*, pg. 2758
FRLP, INC.—See Federal Realty Investment Trust; *U.S. Public*, pg. 825
FR. LURSSEN WERFT GMBH & CO. KG; *Int'l*, pg. 2758
FR MERCER MALL, LLC—See Federal Realty Investment Trust; *U.S. Public*, pg. 825
FRMO CORP.; *U.S. Public*, pg. 886
FRN, INC.—See Universal Health Services, Inc.; *U.S. Public*, pg. 2257
FRN NASHVILLE, LLC—See Universal Health Services, Inc.; *U.S. Public*, pg. 2257
FRN OUTPATIENT, LLC—See Universal Health Services, Inc.; *U.S. Public*, pg. 2257
FRN SAN FRANCISCO, LLC—See Universal Health Services, Inc.; *U.S. Public*, pg. 2257
FRNT FINANCIAL INC.; *Int'l*, pg. 2794
FROCH ENTERPRISE CO., LTD.; *Int'l*, pg. 2794
FROEBEL-KAN CO., LTD.—See TOPPAN Holdings Inc.; *Int'l*, pg. 7816
FROEDTERT MEMORIAL LUTHERAN HOSPITAL, INC.; *U.S. Private*, pg. 1613
FROEHLICH BAU AG; *Int'l*, pg. 2794
FROEHLING & ROBERTSON INC.; *U.S. Private*, pg. 1613
FROESE FORENSIC PARTNERS LTD.—See Delta Consulting Group, Inc.; *U.S. Private*, pg. 1199
FROESEL OIL COMPANY INC.—See Cross Oil Company Inc.; *U.S. Public*, pg. 1105
FROG AGV SYSTEMS B.V.—See Oceaneering International, Inc.; *U.S. Public*, pg. 1562
FROGCO AMPHIBIOUS EQUIPMENT, LLC—See Grey Mountain Partners, LLC; *U.S. Private*, pg. 1784
FROG DESIGN, INC.—See Capgemini SE; *Int'l*, pg. 1305
FROG DESIGN S.R.L.—See Flex Ltd.; *Int'l*, pg. 2704
FROGGER, LLC; *U.S. Private*, pg. 1613
FROG PRINCE (CHINA) DAILY CHEMICALS CO., LIMITED—See Prosperous Future Holdings Limited; *Int'l*, pg. 6002
FROG STREET PRESS, INC.—See Brentwood Associates; *U.S. Private*, pg. 646
THE FROG, SWITCH & MANUFACTURING COMPANY; *U.S. Private*, pg. 4031
FROHN GMBH—See Sintokogio Ltd.; *Int'l*, pg. 6958
FROID 14 SAS—See VINCI S.A.; *Int'l*, pg. 8221
FROID DES MASCAREIGNES LIMITED—See Ireland Blyth Limited; *Int'l*, pg. 3807
FROLAND & NOSS ELEKTRO AS—See Instalco AB; *Int'l*, pg. 3721
FROMAGERIE HENRI HUTIN S.A.R.L.—See Hochland SE; *Int'l*, pg. 3437
FROMAGERIES BEL S.A.—See Unibel SA; *Int'l*, pg. 8081
FROMEX, S.A. DE C.V.—See Emerson Electric Co.; *U.S. Public*, pg. 749
FROMM ELECTRIC SUPPLY CORPORATION; *U.S. Private*, pg. 1613
FROMMELT SAFETY—See Rite-Hite Holding Corporation; *U.S. Private*, pg. 3442
FROMM FAMILY PET FOODS, INC.; *U.S. Private*, pg. 1613
FROMM INTERNATIONAL, INC.—See Firelight Capital Partners LLC; *U.S. Private*, pg. 1512
FROM YOU FLOWERS LLC—See Tenth Avenue Holdings LLC; *U.S. Private*, pg. 3968
FRONEK ANCHOR DARLING ENTERPRISES, INC—See Piping Technology & Products Inc.; *U.S. Private*, pg. 3190
FRONERI LTD.—See Nestle S.A.; *Int'l*, pg. 5202
FRONERI LTD.—See PAI Partners S.A.S.; *Int'l*, pg. 5702
FRONK OIL CO. INC.; *U.S. Private*, pg. 1613
FRONTAGE HOLDINGS CORPORATION—See Hangzhou Tigermed Consulting Co., Ltd.; *Int'l*, pg. 3251

COMPANY NAME INDEX

FRONTAGE INC.; *Int'l*, pg. 2794
FRONTAGE LABORATORIES, INC.—See Hangzhou Tigermed Consulting Co., Ltd.; *Int'l*, pg. 3251
FRONTAGE LABORATORIES (SHANGHAI) CO., LTD.—See Hangzhou Tigermed Consulting Co., Ltd.; *Int'l*, pg. 3251
FRONT BARNETT ASSOCIATES LLC—See Mesirow Financial Holdings, Inc.; *U.S. Private*, pg. 2678
FRONT BURNER BRANDS, INC.; *U.S. Private*, pg. 1613
FRONTDOOR, INC.; *U.S. Public*, pg. 886
FRONTEC AB—See Acando AB; *Int'l*, pg. 78
FRONTEC AFFARSSYSTEM AB—See Acando AB; *Int'l*, pg. 78
FRONTEC BUSINESS INTEGRATION AB—See Acando AB; *Int'l*, pg. 78
FRONTEC BUSINESS SOLUTIONS AB—See Acando AB; *Int'l*, pg. 78
FRONTEC MULTIDESIGN AB—See Acando AB; *Int'l*, pg. 78
FRONTEK ELECTRONICS CO., LTD.—See WPG Holdings Limited; *Int'l*, pg. 8460
FRONTEK TECHNOLOGY CORPORATION, LTD.—See WPG Holdings Limited; *Int'l*, pg. 8460
FRONTENAC AMBULATORY SURGERY & SPINE CARE CENTER, L.P.—See Tenet Healthcare Corporation; *U.S. Public*, pg. 2010
FRONTENAC COMPANY LLC; *U.S. Private*, pg. 1613
FRONTENAC DIALYSIS, LLC—See DaVita Inc.; *U.S. Public*, pg. 639
FRONTEO, INC.; *Int'l*, pg. 2794
FRONTEO KOREA, INC.—See Fronteo, Inc.; *Int'l*, pg. 2794
FRONTERA COPPER CORPORATION—See Invecture Group, S.A. de C.V.; *Int'l*, pg. 3772
FRONTERA ENERGY CORPORATION S.L.—See San Leon Energy plc; *Int'l*, pg. 6521
FRONTERA ENERGY CORPORATION; *Int'l*, pg. 2794
FRONTERA GENERATION LP—See NRG Energy, Inc.; *U.S. Public*, pg. 1549
FRONTERA GROUP INC.; *U.S. Public*, pg. 887
FRONTERA RESOURCES CORP.; *U.S. Public*, pg. 887
FRONTER AS—See Pearson plc; *Int'l*, pg. 5775
FRONTER GMBH—See Pearson plc; *Int'l*, pg. 5775
FRONTER OY—See Pearson plc; *Int'l*, pg. 5775
FRONTEX INTERNATIONAL EAD—See AG Capital; *Int'l*, pg. 197
FRONT GATE HOLDINGS, LLC—See Live Nation Entertainment, Inc.; *U.S. Public*, pg. 1328
FRONTGRADE COLORADO SPRINGS LLC—See Veritas Capital Fund Management, LLC; *U.S. Private*, pg. 4362
FRONTICA ENGINEERING AS—See Akastor ASA; *Int'l*, pg. 260
FRONTIER ACQUISITION CORP.; *U.S. Public*, pg. 887
FRONTIER ADJUSTERS, INC.—See HGGC, LLC; *U.S. Private*, pg. 1929
FRONTIER ADJUSTERS OF AMERICA, INC.—See Merrymeeting, Inc.; *U.S. Private*, pg. 2677
FRONTIER AG, INC.; *U.S. Private*, pg. 1614
FRONTIER AIRLINES, INC.—See Indigo Partners LLC; *U.S. Private*, pg. 2063
FRONTIER ANALYTICAL LABORATORY—See Montrose Environmental Corp.; *U.S. Public*, pg. 2777
FRONTIER BANK—See Whitcorp Financial Company; *U.S. Private*, pg. 4507
FRONTIER BEHAVIORAL HEALTH; *U.S. Private*, pg. 1614
FRONTIER BIOTECHNOLOGIES, INC.; *Int'l*, pg. 2794
FRONTIER CAPITAL INC.—See Frontier Management Inc.; *Int'l*, pg. 2795
FRONTIER CAPITAL LIMITED; *Int'l*, pg. 2795
FRONTIER CAPITAL LLC; *U.S. Private*, pg. 1615
FRONTIER CAPITAL MANAGEMENT COMPANY, LLC—See Affiliated Managers Group, Inc.; *U.S. Public*, pg. 55
FRONTIER CAR GROUP INC.—See Prosus N.V.; *Int'l*, pg. 6003
FRONTIER CERAMICS LIMITED; *Int'l*, pg. 2795
FRONTIER CHRYSLER LTD; *Int'l*, pg. 2795
FRONTIER CLAIMS SERVICES, INC.—See Evans Bancorp, Inc.; *U.S. Public*, pg. 799
FRONTIER CO., LTD.—See Hikari Tsushin, Inc.; *Int'l*, pg. 3390
FRONTIER COMMUNICATIONS CORPORATE SERVICES INC.—See Frontier Communications Parent, Inc.; *U.S. Public*, pg. 887
FRONTIER COMMUNICATIONS CORPORATION; *U.S. Private*, pg. 1615
FRONTIER COMMUNICATIONS CORPORATION—See Frontier Communications Parent, Inc.; *U.S. Public*, pg. 887
FRONTIER COMMUNICATIONS OF BREEZEWOOD, LLC—See Frontier Communications Parent, Inc.; *U.S. Public*, pg. 887
FRONTIER COMMUNICATIONS OF DELAWARE, INC.—See Frontier Communications Parent, Inc.; *U.S. Public*, pg. 887
FRONTIER COMMUNICATIONS OF MICHIGAN, INC.—See Frontier Communications Parent, Inc.; *U.S. Public*, pg. 887

FRONTIER COMMUNICATIONS OF MINNESOTA, INC.—See Frontier Communications Parent, Inc.; *U.S. Public*, pg. 887
FRONTIER COMMUNICATIONS OF MISSISSIPPI LLC—See Frontier Communications Parent, Inc.; *U.S. Public*, pg. 887
FRONTIER COMMUNICATIONS OF MT. PULASKI, INC.—See Frontier Communications Parent, Inc.; *U.S. Public*, pg. 887
FRONTIER COMMUNICATIONS OF NEW YORK, INC.—See Frontier Communications Parent, Inc.; *U.S. Public*, pg. 887
FRONTIER COMMUNICATIONS OF PENNSYLVANIA, LLC—See Frontier Communications Parent, Inc.; *U.S. Public*, pg. 887
FRONTIER COMMUNICATIONS OF THORNTOWN LLC—See Frontier Communications Parent, Inc.; *U.S. Public*, pg. 887
FRONTIER COMMUNICATIONS OF WISCONSIN LLC—See Frontier Communications Parent, Inc.; *U.S. Public*, pg. 887
FRONTIER COMMUNICATIONS PARENT, INC.; *U.S. Public*, pg. 887
FRONTIER COMMUNICATIONS—See Frontier Communications Parent, Inc.; *U.S. Public*, pg. 887
FRONTIER COMMUNICATIONS—See Frontier Communications Parent, Inc.; *U.S. Public*, pg. 887
FRONTIER COMMUNITY BUILDERS; *U.S. Private*, pg. 1615
FRONTIER COMMUNITY SERVICES; *U.S. Private*, pg. 1615
FRONTIER COMMUNITY SERVICES; *U.S. Private*, pg. 1615
FRONTIER COMPUTER CORP. B.V.—See Frontier Computer Corp.; *U.S. Private*, pg. 1615
FRONTIER COMPUTER CORP.; *U.S. Private*, pg. 1615
FRONTIER COMPUTER CORP. UK LTD.—See Frontier Computer Corp.; *U.S. Private*, pg. 1615
FRONTIER COOPERATIVE COMPANY, INC.; *U.S. Private*, pg. 1615
FRONTIER DEVELOPMENTS INC.—See Frontier Developments plc; *Int'l*, pg. 2795
FRONTIER DEVELOPMENTS PLC; *Int'l*, pg. 2795
FRONTIER DIALYSIS, LLC—See DaVita Inc.; *U.S. Public*, pg. 639
FRONTIER DIAMONDS LTD.; *Int'l*, pg. 2795
FRONTIER DIGITAL MARKETING CO., LTD.—See Hakuhodo DY Holdings Incorporated; *Int'l*, pg. 3221
FRONTIER DIGITAL VENTURES LIMITED; *Int'l*, pg. 2795
FRONTIER DIRECT INC.—See Frontier International, Inc.; *Int'l*, pg. 2795
FRONTIER DODGE—See Autoplex Automotive LP; *U.S. Private*, pg. 401
FRONTIER DRILLING AS—See Noble Corporation plc; *Int'l*, pg. 5396
FRONTIER EL DORADO REFINERY COMPANY—See HF Sinclair Corporation; *U.S. Public*, pg. 1033
FRONTIER ENERGY LIMITED; *Int'l*, pg. 2795
FRONTIER ENTERPRISES, INC.; *U.S. Private*, pg. 1615
FRONTIER FASTENER INC.—See Great Lakes Fasteners, Inc.; *U.S. Private*, pg. 1764
FRONTIER FIRE PROTECTION INC.—See Highview Capital, LLC; *U.S. Private*, pg. 1942
FRONTIER FORD; *U.S. Private*, pg. 1615
FRONTIER FS COOPERATIVE; *U.S. Private*, pg. 1615
FRONTIER FS COOPERATIVE—See Frontier FS Cooperative; *U.S. Private*, pg. 1615
FRONTIER FUNDS; *U.S. Private*, pg. 1615
FRONTIER GROUP HOLDINGS, INC.; *U.S. Public*, pg. 887
FRONTIER HEALTH; *U.S. Private*, pg. 1615
FRONTIER HOSPICE—See The Riverside Company; *U.S. Private*, pg. 4107
FRONTIER INDUSTRIAL TECHNOLOGY—See Delta Industrial Services, Inc.; *U.S. Private*, pg. 1200
FRONTIER INDUSTRIES INC.; *U.S. Private*, pg. 1615
FRONTIER INTEGRATOR (SABAH) SDN. BHD.—See OCK Group Berhad; *Int'l*, pg. 5520
FRONTIER INTERNATIONAL, INC.; *Int'l*, pg. 2795
FRONTIER INTERNATIONAL TRUCKS; *U.S. Private*, pg. 1615
FRONTIER INVESTMENT CORP.; *U.S. Public*, pg. 888
FRONTIER IP GROUP PLC; *Int'l*, pg. 2795
FRONTIER-KEMPER CONSTRUCTORS, INC.—See Tutor Perini Corporation; *U.S. Public*, pg. 2206
FRONTIER-KEMPER CONSTRUCTORS, INC.—See ATON GmbH; *Int'l*, pg. 688
FRONTIER LABS, INC.—See Greencastle Resources Ltd.; *Int'l*, pg. 3073
FRONTIER LITHIUM INC.; *Int'l*, pg. 2795
FRONTIER LOGISTICS, LP; *U.S. Private*, pg. 1615
FRONTIER MANAGEMENT INC.; *Int'l*, pg. 2795
FRONTIER MANAGEMENT LLC; *U.S. Private*, pg. 1615
FRONTIER MANAGEMENT (SHANGHAI) INC.—See Frontier Management Inc.; *Int'l*, pg. 2795
FRONTIERMEDEX CANADA LIMITED—See UnitedHealth Group Incorporated; *U.S. Public*, pg. 2241
FRONTIER MEDEX GROUP LIMITED—See UnitedHealth Group Incorporated; *U.S. Public*, pg. 2241

FRONTIER MEDEX LIMITED—See UnitedHealth Group Incorporated; *U.S. Public*, pg. 2241
FRONTIER MEDICAL, INC.; *U.S. Private*, pg. 1615
FRONTIER MINING LTD.; *Int'l*, pg. 2795
FRONTIER NATURAL GAS COMPANY—See First Reserve Management, L.P.; *U.S. Private*, pg. 1525
FRONTIER NATURAL PRODUCTS CO-OP; *U.S. Private*, pg. 1615
FRONTIER NORTH INC.—See Frontier Communications Parent, Inc.; *U.S. Public*, pg. 887
FRONTIER OIL CORPORATION; *Int'l*, pg. 2795
FRONTIER PACKAGING, INC.—See Gen Cap America, Inc.; *U.S. Private*, pg. 1659
FRONTIER PARTNERS INC.—See Magellan Financial Group Limited; *Int'l*, pg. 4637
FRONTIER PHARMA LIMITED; *Int'l*, pg. 2795
FRONTIER PIPELINE LLC—See HF Sinclair Corporation; *U.S. Public*, pg. 1033
FRONTIER PRECISION INC.; *U.S. Private*, pg. 1615
FRONTIER RARE EARTHS LIMITED; *Int'l*, pg. 2795
FRONTIER REAL ESTATE INVESTMENT CORPORATION; *Int'l*, pg. 2795
FRONTIER REFINING, INC.—See HF Sinclair Corporation; *U.S. Public*, pg. 1033
FRONTIER ROOFING, INC—See EMP Management, LLC; *U.S. Private*, pg. 1384
FRONTIER SCIENCE & TECHNOLOGY RESEARCH FOUNDATION, INC.; *U.S. Private*, pg. 1615
FRONTIER SCIENTIFIC INC.—See Avista Capital Partners, L.P.; *U.S. Private*, pg. 409
FRONTIER SCIENTIFIC SERVICES, INC.—See Avista Capital Partners, L.P.; *U.S. Private*, pg. 409
FRONTIER SERVICE PARTNERS—See Apex Service Partners LLC; *U.S. Private*, pg. 293
FRONTIER SERVICES GROUP LIMITED; *Int'l*, pg. 2796
FRONTIER SILICON LIMITED—See Science Group plc; *Int'l*, pg. 6647
FRONTIER SMART TECHNOLOGIES GROUP LIMITED—See Science Group plc; *Int'l*, pg. 6647
FRONTIER SPINNING MILLS, INC.—See American Securities LLC; *U.S. Private*, pg. 249
FRONTIER SPRINGS LTD.; *Int'l*, pg. 2796
FRONTIER STEEL COMPANY—See Russel Metals Inc.; *Int'l*, pg. 6430
FRONTIER STRATEGY GROUP LLC—See Ducker FSG Holdings LLC; *U.S. Private*, pg. 1284
FRONTIER TECHNOLOGIES S.R.O.—See EnBW Energie Baden-Wurttemberg AG; *Int'l*, pg. 2399
FRONTIER TECHNOLOGY LLC; *U.S. Private*, pg. 1615
FRONTIER TEMPERATURE CONTROL—See Online Transport System, Inc.; *U.S. Private*, pg. 3027
FRONTIER TOOLING & DESIGN, INC.—See Andersen Corporation; *U.S. Private*, pg. 275
FRONTIER TRANSPORTATION INC.—See The Osterkamp Group; *U.S. Private*, pg. 4089
FRONTIER TRANSPORT CORPORATION—See Online Transport System, Inc.; *U.S. Private*, pg. 3027
FRONTIER TRANSPORT HOLDINGS LIMITED; *Int'l*, pg. 2796
FRONTIER TRUCK GEAR; *U.S. Private*, pg. 1616
FRONTIER WATER SYSTEMS, LLC—See Xylem Inc.; *U.S. Public*, pg. 2394
FRONTIER WEALTH ENTERPRISES, LLC; *U.S. Private*, pg. 1616
FRONTIER WEALTH MANAGEMENT, LLC—See The CapFinancial Group, LLC; *U.S. Private*, pg. 4004
FRONTIER WEST VIRGINIA INC.—See Frontier Communications Parent, Inc.; *U.S. Public*, pg. 887
FRONTIER WEST VIRGINIA INC.—See Frontier Communications Parent, Inc.; *U.S. Public*, pg. 887
FRONTIER WEST VIRGINIA INC.—See Frontier Communications Parent, Inc.; *U.S. Public*, pg. 887
FRONTIER WEST VIRGINIA INC.—See Frontier Communications Parent, Inc.; *U.S. Public*, pg. 887
FRONTKEN CORPORATION BERHAD; *Int'l*, pg. 2796
FRONTKEN (EAST MALAYSIA) SDN. BHD. - KUCHING PLANT—See Frontken Corporation Berhad; *Int'l*, pg. 2796
FRONTKEN (JOHOR) SDN. BHD.—See Frontken Corporation Berhad; *Int'l*, pg. 2796
FRONTKEN MALAYSIA SDN. BHD. - KULIM PLANT—See Frontken Corporation Berhad; *Int'l*, pg. 2796
FRONTKEN MALAYSIA SDN. BHD. - SHAH ALAM PLANT—See Frontken Corporation Berhad; *Int'l*, pg. 2796
FRONTKEN PHILIPPINES INC—See Frontken Corporation Berhad; *Int'l*, pg. 2796
FRONTKEN (SINGAPORE) PTE. LTD. - JURONG PLANT 1—See Frontken Corporation Berhad; *Int'l*, pg. 2796
FRONTKEN (SINGAPORE) PTE. LTD. - JURONG PLANT 2—See Frontken Corporation Berhad; *Int'l*, pg. 2796
FRONTKEN (SINGAPORE) PTE. LTD.—See Frontken Corporation Berhad; *Int'l*, pg. 2796
FRONTKEN (THAILAND) CO. LTD.—See Frontken Corporation Berhad; *Int'l*, pg. 2796
FRONTLINE ADVERTISING, INC.; *U.S. Private*, pg. 1616
FRONTLINE AG LLC; *U.S. Private*, pg. 1616
FRONTLINE AG SOLUTIONS - LEWISTOWN—See Frontline AG LLC; *U.S. Private*, pg. 1616

FRONTLINE AG LLC

FRONTLINE BLDG. PRODUCTS INC.—See Bay Industries Inc.; *U.S. Private*, pg. 493
FRONTLINE CARRIER SYSTEMS INC.; *Int'l*, pg. 2796
FRONTLINE COMMUNICATIONS—See Oshkosh Corporation; *U.S. Public*, pg. 1621
FRONTLINE CORPORATE SERVICES LIMITED—See Frontline plc; *Int'l*, pg. 2796
FRONTLINE FREIGHT, INC.; *U.S. Private*, pg. 1616
FRONTLINE GOLD CORPORATION; *Int'l*, pg. 2796
FRONTLINE HOSPITAL, LLC—See Universal Health Services, Inc.; *U.S. Public*, pg. 2257
FRONTLINE LIMITED—See Heinrich Bauer Verlag KG; *Int'l*, pg. 3324
FRONTLINE MANAGEMENT AS—See Frontline plc; *Int'l*, pg. 2796
FRONTLINE MANAGEMENT (BERMUDA) LTD.—See Frontline plc; *Int'l*, pg. 2796
FRONTLINE MANUFACTURING INC.—See Patrick Industries, Inc.; *U.S. Public*, pg. 1652
FRONTLINE MEDICAL COMMUNICATIONS INC.—See KKR & Co. Inc.; *U.S. Public*, pg. 1253
FRONTLINE PLC; *Int'l*, pg. 2796
FRONTLINE RECRUITMENT (PTY), LTD.—See Adcorp Holdings Limited; *Int'l*, pg. 127
FRONTLINE RESIDENTIAL TREATMENT CENTER, LLC—See Universal Health Services, Inc.; *U.S. Public*, pg. 2257
FRONTLINE SECURITIES LTD.; *Int'l*, pg. 2796
FRONTLINE SELLING, LLC; *U.S. Private*, pg. 1616
FRONTLINE SHIPPING SINGAPORE PTE LTD—See Frontline plc; *Int'l*, pg. 2796
FRONTLINE SYSTEMS AUSTRALIA PTY LTD—See Nippon Telegraph & Telephone Corporation; *Int'l*, pg. 5344
FRONTLINE TECHNOLOGIES GROUP LLC—See Roper Technologies, Inc.; *U.S. Public*, pg. 1811
FRONTLINE TEST EQUIPMENT, INC.—See Teledyne Technologies Incorporated; *U.S. Public*, pg. 1994
FRONTMATEC B.V.—See KKR & Co. Inc.; *U.S. Public*, pg. 1241
FRONTMATEC GROUP APS—See KKR & Co. Inc.; *U.S. Public*, pg. 1241
FRONTMATEC HYGIENE GMBH—See KKR & Co. Inc.; *U.S. Public*, pg. 1241
FRONTMATEC KOLDING A/S—See KKR & Co. Inc.; *U.S. Public*, pg. 1241
FRONTMATEC SKIVE A/S—See KKR & Co. Inc.; *U.S. Public*, pg. 1241
FRONTMATEC TANDSLET A/S—See KKR & Co. Inc.; *U.S. Public*, pg. 1241
FRONTONE GMBH—See Bridgepoint Group Plc; *Int'l*, pg. 1155
FRONTPOINT MANAGEMENT INC.—See Morgan Stanley; *U.S. Public*, pg. 1472
FRONTPOINT PARTNERS LLC; *U.S. Private*, pg. 1616
FRONT PORCH MARKETING LLC; *U.S. Private*, pg. 1613
FRONT RANGE INSURANCE GROUP, LLC—See GTCR LLC; *U.S. Private*, pg. 1803
FRONT RANGE PIPELINE, LLC—See CHS INC.; *U.S. Public*, pg. 492
FRONT RANGE ROOFING SYSTEMS, LLC—See FirstService Corporation; *Int'l*, pg. 2691
FRONT RANGE STONE, INC.—See Patrick Industries, Inc.; *U.S. Public*, pg. 1652
FRONT ROW MOTORSPORTS, INC.; *U.S. Private*, pg. 1613
FRONT RUNNER GMBH—See Dometic Group AB; *Int'l*, pg. 2160
FRONT SIGHT MANAGEMENT LLC—See Nevada PF LLC; *U.S. Private*, pg. 2891
FRONTSTREAM HOLDINGS LLC; *U.S. Private*, pg. 1616
FRONTSTREET FACILITY SOLUTIONS, INC.—See Charterhouse Group, Inc.; *U.S. Private*, pg. 859
FRONT STREET FINANCING LLC—See The Hanover Insurance Group, Inc.; *U.S. Public*, pg. 2087
FRONTSTREET MANAGEMENT GROUP LLC—See Charterhouse Group, Inc.; *U.S. Private*, pg. 859
FRONTWORX INFORMATIONSTECHNOLOGIE AG—See Landesbank Baden-Wurttemberg; *Int'l*, pg. 4405
FRONT YARD RESIDENTIAL CORPORATION—See Ares Management Corporation; *U.S. Public*, pg. 191
FRONT YARD RESIDENTIAL CORPORATION—See Pretium Partners, LLC; *U.S. Private*, pg. 3257
FROSCH INTERNATIONAL TRAVEL INC.; *U.S. Private*, pg. 1616
FROSETH AS—See Peab AB; *Int'l*, pg. 5771
FROSTA AG; *Int'l*, pg. 2796
FROSTA CR S.R.O.—See FRoSTA AG; *Int'l*, pg. 2797
FROSTA FOODSERVICE GMBH—See FRoSTA AG; *Int'l*, pg. 2797
FROSTA FRANCE S.A.R.L.—See FRoSTA AG; *Int'l*, pg. 2797
FROSTA HUNGARY KFT.—See FRoSTA AG; *Int'l*, pg. 2797
FROSTA ITALIA S.R.L.—See FRoSTA AG; *Int'l*, pg. 2797
FROSTA ROMANIA S.R.L.—See FRoSTA AG; *Int'l*, pg. 2797
FROSTA SP. Z O.O.—See FRoSTA AG; *Int'l*, pg. 2797
FROSTA TIEFKUHLKOST GMBH—See FRoSTA AG; *Int'l*, pg. 2797

FROSTA TIEFKUHLKOST GMBH U. L.—See FRoSTA AG; *Int'l*, pg. 2797
FROST BANK—See Cullen/Frost Bankers, Inc.; *U.S. Public*, pg. 604
FROST BROKERAGE SERVICES, INC.—See Cullen/Frost Bankers, Inc.; *U.S. Public*, pg. 604
FROST BROWN TODD LLC; *U.S. Private*, pg. 1616
FROST CONVERTING SYSTEMS, INC.—See Matthews International Corporation; *U.S. Public*, pg. 1399
FROST & CO. PLLC—See CliftonLarsonAllen LLP; *U.S. Private*, pg. 943
FROST ELECTRIC SUPPLY COMPANY INC.; *U.S. Private*, pg. 1616
FROST EUROPE, S.L.—See Frost Inc.; *U.S. Private*, pg. 1616
FROST HR CONSULTING—See Cullen/Frost Bankers, Inc.; *U.S. Public*, pg. 604
FROST INC.; *U.S. Private*, pg. 1616
FROSTKRONE TIEFKUHLKOST GMBH—See EMERAM Capital Partners GmbH; *Int'l*, pg. 2378
FROST LINKS, INC.—See Frost Inc.; *U.S. Private*, pg. 1616
FROST OIL CO; *U.S. Private*, pg. 1616
FROSTPROOF NEWS—See Independent Newspapers, Inc.; *U.S. Private*, pg. 2060
FROST SECURITIES, INC.—See Cullen/Frost Bankers, Inc.; *U.S. Public*, pg. 604
FROSTY ACRES BRANDS, INC.; *U.S. Private*, pg. 1617
FROSTY TREATS INC.; *U.S. Private*, pg. 1617
FROUDE HOFMANN, INC.—See HWH Investments Limited; *Int'l*, pg. 3543
FROUDE HOFMANN LTD.—See HWH Investments Limited; *Int'l*, pg. 3543
FROU FROU CEREALS LTD—See Alkis H. Hadjikyriacos (Frou Frou Biscuits) Public Ltd.; *Int'l*, pg. 331
FROU FROU INVESTMENTS LTD—See Alkis H. Hadjikyriacos (Frou Frou Biscuits) Public Ltd.; *Int'l*, pg. 331
FROVIN VINDUER OG DORE A/S—See Ratos AB; *Int'l*, pg. 6220
FROY ASA—See The Goldman Sachs Group, Inc.; *U.S. Public*, pg. 2081
FROZEN FISH INTERNATIONAL GMBH—See Nomad Foods Limited; *Int'l*, pg. 5408
FROZEN FOOD EXPRESS INDUSTRIES, INC.; *U.S. Private*, pg. 1617
FROZEN GOURMET INC.; *U.S. Private*, pg. 1617
FROZEN SPECIALTIES INC.—See Swander Pace Capital, LLC; *U.S. Private*, pg. 3890
FROZSUN INC.; *U.S. Private*, pg. 1617
FRP ADVISORY GROUP PLC; *Int'l*, pg. 2797
FRP DEVELOPMENT CORP.—See FRP Holdings, Inc.; *U.S. Public*, pg. 888
FRP HOLDINGS, INC.; *U.S. Public*, pg. 888
FRP PROLINING GMBH—See Per Aarsleff Holding A/S; *Int'l*, pg. 5795
FRP TRANSIT BUSINESS PARK—See FRP Holdings, Inc.; *U.S. Public*, pg. 888
FRR FAX ROLL—See Nippon Paper Industries Co., Ltd.; *Int'l*, pg. 5326
FR SAN ANTONIO CENTER, LLC—See Federal Realty Investment Trust; *U.S. Public*, pg. 825
FRS GMBH & CO. KG; *Int'l*, pg. 2797
FRS HELGOLINE GMBH & CO. KG—See FRS GmbH & Co. KG; *Int'l*, pg. 2797
FRS MECHANICAL CORP.; *U.S. Private*, pg. 1617
FRS OFFSHORE GMBH & CO. KG—See FRS GmbH & Co. KG; *Int'l*, pg. 2797
FRS SHIP MANAGEMENT LTD.—See FRS GmbH & Co. KG; *Int'l*, pg. 2797
FRS SOFTWARE; *U.S. Private*, pg. 1617
FRSTEAM, INC.—See MidOcean Partners, LLP; *U.S. Private*, pg. 2717
F-R TECNOLOGIAS DE FLUJO, S.A. DE C.V.—See Emerson Electric Co.; *U.S. Public*, pg. 749
FRTEK CO., LTD.; *Int'l*, pg. 2797
FRTEK JAPAN INC.—See FRTEK Co., Ltd.; *Int'l*, pg. 2797
FRT INTERNATIONAL INCORPORATED; *U.S. Private*, pg. 1617
FRU-CON MEXICO S.A. DE C.V.—See Bilfinger SE; *Int'l*, pg. 1026
FRUEHAUF MAHAJAK CO., LTD.—See Nippon Light Metal Holdings Company, Ltd.; *Int'l*, pg. 5323
FRUGAL FANNIE'S FASHION WAREHOUSE—See Retail Therapy LLC; *U.S. Private*, pg. 3411
F. RUGGIERO & SONS INC.; *U.S. Private*, pg. 1455
FRUISEC S.A.S.—See Savencia Fromage & Dairy; *Int'l*, pg. 6597
FRUITA CONSUMERS COOP ASSOCIATION; *U.S. Private*, pg. 1617
FRUITAGE INTERNATIONAL CO., LTD—See Enterex International Limited; *Int'l*, pg. 2451
FRUITAGE INTERNATIONAL CO., LTD.—See Enterex International Limited; *Int'l*, pg. 2451
FRUIT BASKET GARDENS INC.; *U.S. Private*, pg. 1617
FRUITCROWN PRODUCTS CORP.; *U.S. Private*, pg. 1617
FRUIT DYNAMICS LLC; *U.S. Private*, pg. 1617
FRUITE SAS—See Britvic plc; *Int'l*, pg. 1171

CORPORATE AFFILIATIONS

FRUIT FACTORY S.R.O.—See Scandal Media Group s.r.o.; *Int'l*, pg. 6611
FRUIT FORMULATIONS PRIVATE LIMITED; *Int'l*, pg. 2797
FRUIT GROWERS SUPPLY CO. - FGS ONTARIO CARTON PLANT—See Fruit Growers Supply Co.; *U.S. Private*, pg. 1617
FRUIT GROWERS SUPPLY CO.; *U.S. Private*, pg. 1617
THE FRUITGUYS; *U.S. Private*, pg. 4031
FRUITION.NET; *U.S. Private*, pg. 1617
FRUITION PARTNERS B.V.—See DXC Technology Company; *U.S. Public*, pg. 696
FRUITION PARTNERS CANADA LTD.—See DXC Technology Company; *U.S. Public*, pg. 696
FRUITION PARTNERS; *U.S. Private*, pg. 1617
FRUITION VENTURES LIMITED; *Int'l*, pg. 2797
FRUIT OF THE EARTH INC.; *U.S. Private*, pg. 1617
FRUIT OF THE LOOM, INC.—See Berkshire Hathaway Inc.; *U.S. Public*, pg. 305
FRUIT OF THE LOOM LIMITED—See Berkshire Hathaway Inc.; *U.S. Public*, pg. 305
FRUIT OF THE LOOM SPORTS & LICENSING—See Berkshire Hathaway Inc.; *U.S. Public*, pg. 305
FRUITPARTNER B.V.—See Dole plc; *Int'l*, pg. 2158
FRUITRIDGE VISTA WATER CO.—See American Water Works Company, Inc.; *U.S. Public*, pg. 112
FRUITSMART, INC.—See Universal Corporation; *U.S. Public*, pg. 2254
FRUKO MESRUBAT SANAYI, LTD. STI.—See PepsiCo, Inc.; *U.S. Public*, pg. 1668
FRUMHERJI HF.—See Islandsbanki hf.; *Int'l*, pg. 3820
FRUTAFRUTA, INC.; *Int'l*, pg. 2797
FRUTAROM BELGIUM N.V.—See International Flavors & Fragrances Inc.; *U.S. Public*, pg. 1151
FRUTAROM CHILE S.A.—See International Flavors & Fragrances Inc.; *U.S. Public*, pg. 1151
FRUTAROM ETOL D.O.O.—See International Flavors & Fragrances Inc.; *U.S. Public*, pg. 1152
FRUTAROM FRANCE S.A.R.L.—See International Flavors & Fragrances Inc.; *U.S. Public*, pg. 1151
FRUTAROM GERMANY GMBH—See International Flavors & Fragrances Inc.; *U.S. Public*, pg. 1151
FRUTAROM INDUSTRIES LTD.—See International Flavors & Fragrances Inc.; *U.S. Public*, pg. 1151
FRUTAROM PERU S.A.—See International Flavors & Fragrances Inc.; *U.S. Public*, pg. 1152
FRUTAROM PRODUCTION GMBH—See International Flavors & Fragrances Inc.; *U.S. Public*, pg. 1152
FRUTAROM RUSSIA LTD.—See International Flavors & Fragrances Inc.; *U.S. Public*, pg. 1152
FRUTAROM SAVORY SOLUTIONS AUSTRIA GMBH—See International Flavors & Fragrances Inc.; *U.S. Public*, pg. 1152
FRUTAROM SAVORY SOLUTIONS GERMANY GMBH—See International Flavors & Fragrances Inc.; *U.S. Public*, pg. 1152
FRUTAROM SOUTH AFRICA (PROPRIETARY) LIMITED—See International Flavors & Fragrances Inc.; *U.S. Public*, pg. 1152
FRUTAROM (SWITZERLAND) AG—See International Flavors & Fragrances Inc.; *U.S. Public*, pg. 1152
FRUTAROM (UK) LTD.—See International Flavors & Fragrances Inc.; *U.S. Public*, pg. 1151
FRUTAROM USA INC.—See International Flavors & Fragrances Inc.; *U.S. Public*, pg. 1152
FRUTAROM USA INC.—See International Flavors & Fragrances Inc.; *U.S. Public*, pg. 1152
FRUTAS FAUSTINO S.L.—See Dole plc; *Int'l*, pg. 2158
FRUTAS IRU S.A.—See Dole plc; *Int'l*, pg. 2158
FRUTH, INC.; *U.S. Private*, pg. 1617
FRUTICOLA VICONTO S.A.; *Int'l*, pg. 2797
FRUTTAGEL S.C.P.A.; *Int'l*, pg. 2797
FRUTTAGEL SCRL - LARINO PLANT—See Fruttagel S.C.p.A.; *Int'l*, pg. 2797
FRX INNOVATIONS INC.; *U.S. Public*, pg. 888
FRX POLYMERS INC.—See FRX Innovations Inc.; *U.S. Public*, pg. 888
FRY COMMUNICATIONS INC.; *U.S. Private*, pg. 1617
FRYE BUILDERS & ASSOCIATES, INC.; *U.S. Private*, pg. 1618
FRYECARE PHYSICIANS, L.L.C.—See Tenet Healthcare Corporation; *U.S. Public*, pg. 2003
FRYECARE VALDESE, L.L.C.—See Tenet Healthcare Corporation; *U.S. Public*, pg. 2003
FRYECARE WATAUGA, L.L.C.—See Tenet Healthcare Corporation; *U.S. Public*, pg. 2003
THE FRYE COMPANY—See Jimlar Corporation; *U.S. Private*, pg. 2210
FRYE EXTERMINATING CO—See Arrow Exterminators Inc.; *U.S. Private*, pg. 335
FRYE REGIONAL MEDICAL CENTER, INC.—See Apollo Global Management, Inc.; *U.S. Public*, pg. 155
FRYE ROOFING, INC. - BECKLEY—See Frye Roofing, Inc.; *U.S. Private*, pg. 1618
FRYE ROOFING, INC.; *U.S. Private*, pg. 1618
FRY KRISP COMPANY; *U.S. Private*, pg. 1618
FRYMAKORUMA AG—See Capvis AG; *Int'l*, pg. 1318
FRYMASTER, L.L.C.—See Ali Holding S.r.l; *Int'l*, pg. 322
FRY REGLET CORPORATION; *U.S. Private*, pg. 1618

COMPANY NAME INDEX

FRY'S ELECTRONICS, INC.; *U.S. Private*, pg. 1618
FRY'S FOOD AND DRUG STORES—See The Kroger Co.; *U.S. Public*, pg. 2108
FRY STEEL COMPANY—See Reliance Steel & Aluminum Co.; *U.S. Public*, pg. 1780
FRY-WAGNER SYSTEMS INC.; *U.S. Private*, pg. 1618
FSA CONSTRUCTION, LLC—See Fort Sill Apache Tribe of Oklahoma; *U.S. Private*, pg. 1575
FSA GROUP LIMITED; *Int'l*, pg. 2798
FSA INDUSTRIES, LLC—See Fort Sill Apache Tribe of Oklahoma; *U.S. Private*, pg. 1575
FSA NETWORK INC.—See Forward Air Corporation; *U.S. Public*, pg. 874
FSA TECHNOLOGY, LLC—See Fort Sill Apache Tribe of Oklahoma; *U.S. Private*, pg. 1575
FS BANCORP, INC.; *U.S. Public*, pg. 888
F.S. BANCORP; *U.S. Private*, pg. 1457
FS-BF GMBH & CO. KG—See INDUS Holding AG; *Int'l*, pg. 3663
FSB INSURANCE SERVICE LIMITED—See Markel Group Inc.; *U.S. Public*, pg. 1368
FSBM CTECH SDN. BHD.—See FSBM Holdings Berhad; *Int'l*, pg. 2798
FSBM HOLDINGS BERHAD; *Int'l*, pg. 2798
FSBM MES ELITE SDN. BHD.—See FSBM Holdings Berhad; *Int'l*, pg. 2798
FSBM NET MEDIA SDN. BHD.—See FSBM Holdings Berhad; *Int'l*, pg. 2798
FS BRANDS, INC.—See FirstService Corporation; *Int'l*, pg. 2691
FS BRANDS, INC.—See FirstService Corporation; *Int'l*, pg. 2691
FS CABLES LIMITED—See Diploma PLC; *Int'l*, pg. 2128
F S CAPITAL GROUP—See Franklin Resources, Inc.; *U.S. Public*, pg. 879
FSC BANCSHARES, INC.; *U.S. Private*, pg. 1618
FSC CORP.—See Bank of America Corporation; *U.S. Public*, pg. 272
FSC HOLDINGS, LLC—See AVADEL PHARMACEUTICALS PLC; *Int'l*, pg. 734
F. SCHUMACHER & CO.; *U.S. Private*, pg. 1455
FSC MARKETING COMMUNICATIONS; *U.S. Private*, pg. 1618
FS CREDIT REAL ESTATE INCOME TRUST, INC.; *U.S. Private*, pg. 1618
FSC SECURITIES CORPORATION—See Reverence Capital Partners LLC; *U.S. Private*, pg. 3414
FS DEPOT, INC.—See Federal Signal Corporation; *U.S. Public*, pg. 826
FS DEVELOPMENT INVESTMENT HOLDINGS; *Int'l*, pg. 2797
F&S DISTRIBUTING, LLC—See California Cartage Company LLC; *U.S. Private*, pg. 718
FSD PHARMA INC.; *Int'l*, pg. 2798
F.S.E CORPORATION—See Contrel Technology Co., Ltd.; *Int'l*, pg. 1785
F-SECURE AB—See WithSecure Corporation; *Int'l*, pg. 8438
F-SECURE BELGIE—See WithSecure Corporation; *Int'l*, pg. 8438
F-SECURE BV BA—See WithSecure Corporation; *Int'l*, pg. 8438
F-SECURE DANMARK A/S—See WithSecure Corporation; *Int'l*, pg. 8438
F-SECURE ESTORE GMBH—See WithSecure Corporation; *Int'l*, pg. 8439
F-SECURE GMBH—See WithSecure Corporation; *Int'l*, pg. 8438
F-SECURE INC.—See WithSecure Corporation; *Int'l*, pg. 8438
F-SECURE INDIA PVT LTD—See WithSecure Corporation; *Int'l*, pg. 8438
F-SECURE KK—See WithSecure Corporation; *Int'l*, pg. 8439
F-SECURE MALAYSIA (M) SDN BHD—See WithSecure Corporation; *Int'l*, pg. 8439
F-SECURE NORGE—See WithSecure Corporation; *Int'l*, pg. 8439
F-SECURE PTE LTD—See WithSecure Corporation; *Int'l*, pg. 8439
F-SECURE PTY LTD—See WithSecure Corporation; *Int'l*, pg. 8439
F-SECURE PVT LTD—See WithSecure Corporation; *Int'l*, pg. 8439
F-SECURE SARL—See WithSecure Corporation; *Int'l*, pg. 8439
F-SECURE SDC SAS—See WithSecure Corporation; *Int'l*, pg. 8439
F-SECURE SP.Z.O.O.—See WithSecure Corporation; *Int'l*, pg. 8439
F-SECURE (UK) LTD—See WithSecure Corporation; *Int'l*, pg. 8438
FSE FIRE SAFETY SYSTEMS LIMITED—See Marlowe Plc; *Int'l*, pg. 4698
FS ENERGY & POWER FUND—See Franklin Square Holdings, L.P.; *U.S. Private*, pg. 1598
FSE SERVICES GROUP LIMITED; *Int'l*, pg. 2798
FS FAHRZEUG-SERVICE GMBH & CO. KG—See TUV NORD AG; *Int'l*, pg. 7980

F&S FINANCE AND SERVICE LEASING GMBH—See Erste Group Bank AG; *Int'l*, pg. 2498
FSG FACILITY SOLUTIONS GROUP; *U.S. Private*, pg. 1618
FSG, INC.; *U.S. Private*, pg. 1618
FSHC, LLC—See Mahwah Bergen Retail Group, Inc.; *U.S. Private*, pg. 2550
FS HOLDING AD; *Int'l*, pg. 2797
FSI ENERGY GROUP INC.; *Int'l*, pg. 2798
FSI INTERNATIONAL SERVICES LTD.—See FSI Energy Group Inc.; *Int'l*, pg. 2798
FSII SWEDEN HOLDINGS AB—See Thermo Fisher Scientific Inc.; *U.S. Public*, pg. 2147
FSILON HOME BUILDING MATERIALS CO., LTD.; *Int'l*, pg. 2798
FSI/MFP INCORPORATED—See Swander Pace Capital, LLC; *U.S. Private*, pg. 3890
FS-KARTON GMBH—See Mayr-Melnhof Karton AG; *Int'l*, pg. 4745
FSK ELECTRONICS SA (PTY) LTD—See The Carlyle Group Inc.; *U.S. Public*, pg. 2045
FS KKR CAPITAL CORP.—See Franklin Square Holdings, L.P.; *U.S. Private*, pg. 1598
FSK LAND CORPORATION; *U.S. Private*, pg. 1618
FSK L&S CO., LTD.—See SK Innovation Co., Ltd.; *Int'l*, pg. 6973
FSK (THAILAND) CO., LTD.—See Foster Electric Co., Ltd.; *Int'l*, pg. 2749
FS LEISURE PARK TENANT TRUST—See AlerisLife Inc.; *U.S. Private*, pg. 160
FS LEXINGTON TENANT TRUST—See AlerisLife Inc.; *U.S. Private*, pg. 160
FSL FLUGPLATZ SPEYER/LUDWIGSHAFEN GMBH—See BASF SE; *Int'l*, pg. 883
F.S. LOPKE CONTRACTING INC.; *U.S. Private*, pg. 1457
F.S. MACKENZIE LIMITED—See Singapore Post Limited; *Int'l*, pg. 6941
FSMC, INC.—See Madison Dearborn Partners, LLC; *U.S. Private*, pg. 2542
FSM HOLDINGS LIMITED; *Int'l*, pg. 2798
FSN CAPITAL PARTNERS AS; *Int'l*, pg. 2798
FSN DOORS LIMITED—See Brickability Group plc; *Int'l*, pg. 1151
FSN E-COMMERCE VENTURES LIMITED; *Int'l*, pg. 2800
FSN, INC.—See Modern Office Methods Inc.; *U.S. Private*, pg. 2762
FSO ONSITE OUTSOURCING; *U.S. Private*, pg. 1618
FSO OUTSOURCING—See FSO Onsite Outsourcing; *U.S. Private*, pg. 1618
FSO OUTSOURCING—See FSO Onsite Outsourcing; *U.S. Private*, pg. 1618
FSP 1999 BROADWAY LLC—See Franklin Street Properties Corp.; *U.S. Public*, pg. 883
FSP 303 EAST WACKER DRIVE CORP.; *U.S. Private*, pg. 1618
FSP ELDRIDGE GREEN LIMITED PARTNERSHIP—See Franklin Street Properties Corp.; *U.S. Public*, pg. 883
FSP-FAHRZEUG-SICHERHEITSPRUFUNG GESCHAFTSFUHRUNGS-GMBH—See TUV Rheinland Berlin-Brandenburg Pfalz e.V.; *Int'l*, pg. 7981
FSP-FAHRZEUG-SICHERHEITSPRUFUNG LEITUNG UND SERVICE GMBH—See TUV Rheinland Berlin-Brandenburg Pfalz e.V.; *Int'l*, pg. 7982
FSP (GB) LTD.—See FSP Technology Inc.; *Int'l*, pg. 2800
FSPG HI-TECH CO., LTD.; *Int'l*, pg. 2800
FSP GREENWOOD PLAZA CORP.—See Franklin Street Properties Corp.; *U.S. Public*, pg. 883
FSP GROUP USA CORP.—See FSP Technology Inc.; *Int'l*, pg. 2800
FSP INVESTMENTS LLC—See Franklin Street Properties Corp.; *U.S. Public*, pg. 883
FSP NORTH AMERICA, INC.—See FSP Technology Inc.; *Int'l*, pg. 2800
FSPORT AB; *Int'l*, pg. 2800
FSP PARK TEN LIMITED PARTNERSHIP—See Franklin Street Properties Corp.; *U.S. Public*, pg. 883
FSP PROPERTY MANAGEMENT LLC—See Franklin Street Properties Corp.; *U.S. Public*, pg. 883
FSP PTE LTD.—See Fujitec Co., Ltd.; *Int'l*, pg. 2831
FS PRECISION TECH CO. LLC—See Brookfield Corporation; *Int'l*, pg. 1181
FSP TECHNOLOGY INC.; *Int'l*, pg. 2800
FSP TECHNOLOGY INC.—See FSP Technology Inc.; *Int'l*, pg. 2800
FSP TECHNOLOGY KOREA CO., LTD.—See FSP Technology Inc.; *Int'l*, pg. 2800
FSP TECHNOLOGY USA INC.—See FSP Technology Inc.; *Int'l*, pg. 2800
FSQC-AL, LLC—See AlerisLife Inc.; *U.S. Private*, pg. 160
FSS, INC.; *U.S. Private*, pg. 1618
FSS INC.—See Advanced Interactive Systems; *U.S. Private*, pg. 90
FS SISTEMI URBANI S.R.L.—See Ferrovie dello Stato Italiane S.p.A.; *Int'l*, pg. 2645
F.S. SPERRY CO. INC.; *U.S. Private*, pg. 1457
FSS STAFFING SOLUTIONS—See FSO Onsite Outsourcing; *U.S. Private*, pg. 1618
F-STAR THERAPEUTICS, INC.—See Sino Biopharmaceutical Limited; *Int'l*, pg. 6946

FST CANADA INC.—See Federal Signal Corporation; *U.S. Public*, pg. 826
FST ENGINEERS, INC.—See Fay, Spofford & Thorndike, Inc.; *U.S. Private*, pg. 1484
FST LOGISTICS INC.; *U.S. Private*, pg. 1618
F & S TOOL, INC.—See Berry Global Group, Inc; *U.S. Public*, pg. 322
FS TRUCKS GMBH—See AGRAVIS Raiffeisen AG; *Int'l*, pg. 215
F & S UNI CO. LTD.—See Ship Healthcare Holdings, Inc.; *Int'l*, pg. 6852
F&S UNI MANAGEMENT CO., LTD.—See Ship Healthcare Holdings, Inc.; *Int'l*, pg. 6852
F.S. VANHOOSE & COMPANY INC.; *U.S. Private*, pg. 1457
FSV PAYMENT SYSTEMS, INC.—See U.S. Bancorp; *U.S. Public*, pg. 2213
FSW COATINGS LIMITED; *Int'l*, pg. 2800
FSW SECURITY PRODUCTS LTD.; *Int'l*, pg. 2800
FTAC ATHENA ACQUISITION CORP.; *U.S. Public*, pg. 888
FTAC EMERALD ACQUISITION CORP.; *U.S. Public*, pg. 888
FTAC HERA ACQUISITION CORP.; *U.S. Public*, pg. 888
FTAC OLYMPUS ACQUISITION CORP.—See Payoneer Global Inc.; *U.S. Public*, pg. 1656
FTAC PARNASSUS ACQUISITION CORP.; *U.S. Public*, pg. 888
FTAC ZEUS ACQUISITION CORP.; *U.S. Public*, pg. 888
FTA FILM- UND THEATERAUSSTATTUNG GMBH—See Bavaria Film GmbH; *Int'l*, pg. 899
FTA FOOD SOLUTIONS PTY LTD; *Int'l*, pg. 2800
FTAI AVIATION LTD.—See SoftBank Group Corp.; *Int'l*, pg. 7053
FTAI INFRASTRUCTURE, INC.; *U.S. Public*, pg. 888
FTA RESEARCH AND CONSULTANT, LLC—See Nippon Telegraph & Telephone Corporation; *Int'l*, pg. 5350
FTB ADVISORS, INC.—See First Horizon Corporation; *U.S. Public*, pg. 844
FT BESTAS A.S.—See LISI S.A.; *Int'l*, pg. 4523
F&T BUCKLEY (HOLDINGS) LIMITED—See Grafton Group plc; *Int'l*, pg. 3050
F&T BUCKLEY LIMITED—See Grafton Group plc; *Int'l*, pg. 3050
FTC INVESTOR SERVICES INC.—See Franklin Resources, Inc.; *U.S. Public*, pg. 879
FTC SOLAR, INC.; *U.S. Public*, pg. 888
FTC—See Omnicom Group Inc.; *U.S. Public*, pg. 1590
FTD.COM INC.—See Tenth Avenue Holdings LLC; *U.S. Private*, pg. 3968
FTD COMPANIES, INC.; *U.S. Private*, pg. 1618
FTD GROUP, INC.—See Nexus Capital Management LP; *U.S. Private*, pg. 2922
FTD, INC.—See Tenth Avenue Holdings LLC; *U.S. Private*, pg. 3968
FTD INDIA PRIVATE LIMITED—See FTD Companies, Inc.; *U.S. Private*, pg. 1619
FTE AUTOMOTIVE CZECHIA S.R.O.—See Valeo S.A.; *Int'l*, pg. 8112
FTE AUTOMOTIVE GMBH—See Valeo S.A.; *Int'l*, pg. 8112
F-TECH AUTOMOTIVE COMPONENTS PVT. LTD.—See F-Tech Inc.; *Int'l*, pg. 2595
F-TECH INC. - KAMEYAMA PLANT—See F-Tech Inc.; *Int'l*, pg. 2595
F-TECH INC. - KAMEYAMA WADA PLANT—See F-Tech Inc.; *Int'l*, pg. 2595
F-TECH INC. - KUKI PLANT—See F-Tech Inc.; *Int'l*, pg. 2595
F-TECH INC.; *Int'l*, pg. 2595
F.TECH MFG. (THAILAND) LTD.—See F-Tech Inc.; *Int'l*, pg. 2595
F-TECH PHILIPPINES MFG., INC.—See F-Tech Inc.; *Int'l*, pg. 2595
F.TECH R&D (GUANGZHOU) INC.—See F-Tech Inc.; *Int'l*, pg. 2595
F.TECH R&D NORTH AMERICA INC—See F-Tech Inc.; *Int'l*, pg. 2595
F.TECH R&D PHILIPPINES INC—See F-Tech Inc.; *Int'l*, pg. 2595
F-TECH WUHAN INC.—See F-Tech Inc.; *Int'l*, pg. 2595
F-TECH ZHONGSHAN INC.—See F-Tech Inc.; *Int'l*, pg. 2595
FTE NETWORKS, INC.; *U.S. Public*, pg. 889
FTEN, INC.—See Nasdaq, Inc.; *U.S. Public*, pg. 1491
FTF KRAZ—See AutoKrAZ Holding Co.; *Int'l*, pg. 727
FTF PHARMA PRIVATE LIMITED—See Shilpa Medicare Ltd; *Int'l*, pg. 6831
FTG AEROSPACE INC.—See Firan Technology Group Corporation; *Int'l*, pg. 2678
FTG CIRCUITS - CHATSWORTH—See Firan Technology Group Corporation; *Int'l*, pg. 2678
FTG CIRCUITS FREDERICKSBURG INC.—See Firan Technology Group Corporation; *Int'l*, pg. 2678
FTG CIRCUITS - TORONTO—See Firan Technology Group Corporation; *Int'l*, pg. 2678
F.T.G CO.,LTD—See Toyo Tire Corporation; *Int'l*, pg. 7859
FTG CRANES—See Norsk Hydro ASA; *Int'l*, pg. 5432
FTGROUP CO LTD.; *Int'l*, pg. 2800

FTI CAPITAL ADVISORS, LLC—See FTI Consulting, Inc.; *U.S. Public*, pg. 890
FTI COMMERCIAL CONSULTING (SHANGHAI) CO. LTD.—See FTI Consulting, Inc.; *U.S. Public*, pg. 890
FTI CONSULTING (ASIA) LTD—See FTI Consulting, Inc.; *U.S. Public*, pg. 890
FTI CONSULTING BELGIUM SA—See FTI Consulting, Inc.; *U.S. Public*, pg. 890
FTI CONSULTING (CHINA) LTD.—See FTI Consulting, Inc.; *U.S. Public*, pg. 890
FTI CONSULTING COLOMBIA S.A.S.—See FTI Consulting, Inc.; *U.S. Public*, pg. 890
FTI CONSULTING DENMARK APS—See FTI Consulting, Inc.; *U.S. Public*, pg. 890
FTI CONSULTING - FD AUSTRALIA HOLDINGS PTY LTD—See FTI Consulting, Inc.; *U.S. Public*, pg. 890
FTI CONSULTING, INC.; *U.S. Public*, pg. 889
FTI CONSULTING PANAMA, SDAD. LTDA.—See FTI Consulting, Inc.; *U.S. Public*, pg. 890
FTI CONSULTING S.A.—See FTI Consulting, Inc.; *U.S. Public*, pg. 890
FTI CONSULTING SC GMBH—See FTI Consulting, Inc.; *U.S. Public*, pg. 890
FTI CONSULTING (SC) INC.—See FTI Consulting, Inc.; *U.S. Public*, pg. 890
FTI CONSULTING (SC) LTDA.—See FTI Consulting, Inc.; *U.S. Public*, pg. 890
FTI CONSULTING SERVICES LIMITED—See FTI Consulting, Inc.; *U.S. Public*, pg. 890
FTI CONSULTING (SINGAPORE) PTE. LTD.—See FTI Consulting, Inc.; *U.S. Public*, pg. 890
FTI CONSULTING SOLUTIONS LIMITED—See FTI Consulting, Inc.; *U.S. Public*, pg. 891
FTI CONSULTING SPAIN, S.R.L.—See FTI Consulting, Inc.; *U.S. Public*, pg. 891
FTI CONSULTING TECHNOLOGY (SYDNEY) PTY LTD—See FTI Consulting, Inc.; *U.S. Public*, pg. 891
FTI CONSULTORIA LTDA.—See FTI Consulting, Inc.; *U.S. Public*, pg. 891
FTI ENGINEERING NETWORK GMBH—See Eckelmann AG; *Int'l*, pg. 2290
FTI FLOW TECHNOLOGY, INC.—See Roper Technologies, Inc.; *U.S. Public*, pg. 1811
FTI FOODTECH INTERNATIONAL INC.; *Int'l*, pg. 2800
FTI GROUPS, INC.—See ArcBest Corporation; *U.S. Public*, pg. 180
FT KNOWLEDGE MANAGEMENT COMPANY LIMITED—See 63 moons technologies limited; *Int'l*, pg. 14
F&T KUNSHAN TECHNO CO., LTD.—See Sumitomo Electric Industries, Ltd.; *Int'l*, pg. 7285
FTL ASIA HOLDINGS LIMITED—See Kunwu Jiuding Investment Holdings Co., Ltd.; *Int'l*, pg. 4333
FT. LAUDERDALE NISSAN, INC.—See AutoNation, Inc.; *U.S. Public*, pg. 235
FTL CORPORATION; *U.S. Private*, pg. 1619
FTLIFE INSURANCE COMPANY LIMITED—See Chow Tai Fook Enterprises Limited; *Int'l*, pg. 1585
FTL LTD.—See IDEX Corp; *U.S. Public*, pg. 1090
FTL SEALS TECHNOLOGY LTD—See IDEX Corp; *U.S. Public*, pg. 1090
FTL VENTURES CORP.; *Int'l*, pg. 2800
FT MARINE—See Orange S.A.; *Int'l*, pg. 5608
FTM FREIZEIT- UND TRENDMARKETING GMBH & CO. KG—See Hubert Burda Media Holding Kommanditgesellschaft; *Int'l*, pg. 3520
F T MORRELL & COMPANY LIMITED—See RPM International Inc.; *U.S. Public*, pg. 1817
FT. MYERS TOYOTA INC.; *U.S. Private*, pg. 1618
FTN COCOA PROCESSORS PLC; *Int'l*, pg. 2800
FTN FINANCIAL CORPORATION—See First Horizon Corporation; *U.S. Public*, pg. 844
FTN FINANCIAL MAIN STREET ADVISORS, LLC—See First Horizon Corporation; *U.S. Public*, pg. 844
FTN FINANCIAL SECURITIES CORP.—See First Horizon Corporation; *U.S. Public*, pg. 844
FTNON ALMELO B.V.—See John Bean Technologies Corporation; *U.S. Public*, pg. 1191
FTNON DELFT B.V.—See John Bean Technologies Corporation; *U.S. Public*, pg. 1191
FTNON USA INC.—See John Bean Technologies Corporation; *U.S. Public*, pg. 1191
FT PRECISION INC.—See Tanaka Seimitsu Kogyo Co., Ltd.; *Int'l*, pg. 7456
FT PUBLICATIONS INC—See Pearson plc; *Int'l*, pg. 5777
FT R&D BEIJING LTD CO—See Orange S.A.; *Int'l*, pg. 5608
F.T. REYNOLDS COMPANY; *U.S. Private*, pg. 1457
FTS CO., LTD.—See Toyoda Gosei Co., Ltd.; *Int'l*, pg. 7861
FT SEARCH INC—See Pearson plc; *Int'l*, pg. 5777
FT SECURITIES LIMITED—See Royal Bank of Canada; *Int'l*, pg. 6410
FTSE INTERNATIONAL LIMITED—See London Stock Exchange Group plc; *Int'l*, pg. 4547
FTSE ITALY S.P.A.—See London Stock Exchange Group plc; *Int'l*, pg. 4547
FTS FINANCIAL, INC.; *U.S. Private*, pg. 1619

FTS FINANCIAL SERVICES OY—See Finnair Plc; *Int'l*, pg. 2675
F.T.S- FORMULA TELECOM SOLUTIONS BULGARIA—See Formula Telecom Solutions Limited; *Int'l*, pg. 2737
F.T.S. GLOBAL LIMITED—See Formula Telecom Solutions Limited; *Int'l*, pg. 2737
FTS INTERNATIONAL EXPRESS INC.; *U.S. Private*, pg. 1619
FTS INTERNATIONAL, INC.; *U.S. Private*, pg. 1619
FTS LEESONA, INCORPORATED; *U.S. Private*, pg. 1619
FT STUDIOS GMBH—See Bertelsmann SE & Co. KGaA; *Int'l*, pg. 992
FTS USA, LLC—See Littlejohn & Co., LLC; *U.S. Private*, pg. 2472
FTS USA, LLC—See New Mountain Capital, LLC; *U.S. Private*, pg. 2903
FT SYSTEM S.R.L.—See Antares Vision SpA; *Int'l*, pg. 482
FTT DEUTSCHLAND GMBH—See Kratos Defense & Security Solutions, Inc.; *U.S. Public*, pg. 1276
FT TECHNO EUROPE GMBH—See AISIN Corporation; *Int'l*, pg. 253
FT TECHNO INC.—See AISIN Corporation; *Int'l*, pg. 253
FT TECHNO OF AMERICA, LLC—See AISIN Corporation; *Int'l*, pg. 253
FTT LLC—See Acroud AB; *Int'l*, pg. 109
FTT MANUFACTURING, INC.—See Fairchild Capital Partners, LLC; *U.S. Private*, pg. 1462
FTU BETEILIGUNGSVERWALTUNG GMBH—See ZF Friedrichshafen AG; *Int'l*, pg. 8641
FTV MANAGEMENT COMPANY LP; *U.S. Private*, pg. 1619
FT. WALTON BEACH ANESTHESIA SERVICES, LLC—See HCA Healthcare, Inc.; *U.S. Public*, pg. 996
FT. WAYNE PLASTICS INC.; *U.S. Private*, pg. 1618
FT. WAYNE TV, LLC—See Entertainment Studios, Inc.; *U.S. Private*, pg. 1405
FT. WORTH PIPE SERVICES, LP—See Savage Services Corporation; *U.S. Private*, pg. 3555
FTX LOGISTICS LIMITED—See KBR, Inc.; *U.S. Public*, pg. 1215
FTZ AUTODELE & VAERKTOJ A/S—See MEKO AB; *Int'l*, pg. 4805
FTZ INDUSTRIES, INC.—See nVent Electric plc; *Int'l*, pg. 5498
FUAN PHARMACEUTICAL (GROUP) CO., LTD.; *Int'l*, pg. 2801
FU'AN QINGMEI ENERGY MATERIALS CO., LTD.—See GEM Co., Ltd.; *Int'l*, pg. 2914
FUBAI INDUSTRY (SHENZHEN) CO., LTD.—See Pan-International Industrial Corporation; *Int'l*, pg. 5715
FU BO INDUSTRIAL (SHENZHEN) CO., LTD.—See Zhen Ding Technology Holding Limited; *Int'l*, pg. 8669
FUBON ASSET MANAGEMENT CO., LTD.—See Fubon Financial Holding Co. Ltd.; *Int'l*, pg. 2801
FUBON BANK (HONG KONG) LIMITED—See Fubon Financial Holding Co. Ltd.; *Int'l*, pg. 2801
FUBON DIRECT MARKETING CONSULTING CO., LTD.—See Fubon Financial Holding Co. Ltd.; *Int'l*, pg. 2801
FUBON FINANCIAL HOLDING CO. LTD.; *Int'l*, pg. 2801
FUBON FUTURES CO., LTD—See Fubon Financial Holding Co. Ltd.; *Int'l*, pg. 2801
FUBON INSURANCE CO., LTD.—See Fubon Financial Holding Co. Ltd.; *Int'l*, pg. 2802
FUBON INSURANCE (VIETNAM) CO., LTD—See Fubon Financial Holding Co. Ltd.; *Int'l*, pg. 2802
FUBON LIFE ASSURANCE CO., LTD.—See Fubon Financial Holding Co. Ltd.; *Int'l*, pg. 2802
FUBON LIFE INSURANCE CO., LTD—See Fubon Financial Holding Co. Ltd.; *Int'l*, pg. 2802
FUBON LIFE INSURANCE COMPANY HONG KONG LIMITED—See Fubon Financial Holding Co. Ltd.; *Int'l*, pg. 2802
FUBON LIFE INSURANCE (HONG KONG) COMPANY LIMITED—See Fubon Financial Holding Co. Ltd.; *Int'l*, pg. 2802
FUBON MULTIMEDIA TECHNOLOGY CO., LTD.—See Fubon Financial Holding Co. Ltd.; *Int'l*, pg. 2802
FUBON SECURITIES CO., LTD.—See Fubon Financial Holding Co. Ltd.; *Int'l*, pg. 2802
FUBON SECURITIES USA LLC—See Fubon Financial Holding Co. Ltd.; *Int'l*, pg. 2802
FUBOTV INC.; *U.S. Public*, pg. 891
FU BURG INDUSTRIAL CO., LTD.; *Int'l*, pg. 2800
FUCCILLO AUTOMOTIVE GROUP INC.; *U.S. Private*, pg. 1619
FUCCILLO CHEVROLET PONTIAC BUICK; *U.S. Private*, pg. 1619
FUCCILLO CHRYSLER OF NELLISTON, INC.; *U.S. Private*, pg. 1619
FU-CHIAN TIRE CO., LTD.; *Int'l*, pg. 2801
FUCHI ELECTRONICS CO., LTD.—See Fujitsu Limited; *Int'l*, pg. 2832
FUCHS ARGENTINA S.A.—See FUCHS SE; *Int'l*, pg. 2802
FUCHS AUSTRALIA PTY. LTD.—See FUCHS SE; *Int'l*, pg. 2803

FUCHS AUSTRIA SCHMIERMITTEL GES. MBH—See FUCHS SE; *Int'l*, pg. 2802
FUCHS BELGIUM N.V.—See FUCHS SE; *Int'l*, pg. 2802
FUCHS BRASIL S.A.—See FUCHS SE; *Int'l*, pg. 2802
FUCHS CORPORATION—See FUCHS SE; *Int'l*, pg. 2802
FUCHS DO BRASIL S.A.—See FUCHS SE; *Int'l*, pg. 2802
FUCHS ELECTRONICS (PTY) LTD—See Reunert Limited; *Int'l*, pg. 6312
FUCHS ENPROTEC GMBH—See METAWATER Co., Ltd.; *Int'l*, pg. 4851
FUCHS EUROPE SCHMIERSTOFFE GMBH & CO. KG—See FUCHS SE; *Int'l*, pg. 2802
FUCHS EUROPE SCHMIERSTOFFE GMBH - EXPORT DIVISION—See FUCHS SE; *Int'l*, pg. 2802
FUCHS EUROPE SCHMIERSTOFFE GMBH - KIEL PLANT—See FUCHS SE; *Int'l*, pg. 2802
FUCHS FINANZSERVICE GMBH—See FUCHS SE; *Int'l*, pg. 2802
FUCHS-GEWURZE GMBH; *Int'l*, pg. 2804
FUCHS HELLAS S.A.—See FUCHS SE; *Int'l*, pg. 2802
FUCHS JAPAN LTD. - CHIBA FACTORY—See FUCHS SE; *Int'l*, pg. 2803
FUCHS JAPAN LTD. - IGA UENO FACTORY—See FUCHS SE; *Int'l*, pg. 2803
FUCHS JAPAN LTD.—See FUCHS SE; *Int'l*, pg. 2803
FUCHS LUBRICANTES S.A.—See FUCHS SE; *Int'l*, pg. 2802
FUCHS LUBRICANTES S.A.—See FUCHS SE; *Int'l*, pg. 2802
FUCHS LUBRICANTS - ASIA PACIFIC REGIONAL HEADQUARTERS—See FUCHS SE; *Int'l*, pg. 2803
FUCHS LUBRICANTS (AUSTRALASIA) PTY. LTD.—See FUCHS SE; *Int'l*, pg. 2803
FUCHS LUBRICANTS BENELUX N.V. / S.A.—See FUCHS SE; *Int'l*, pg. 2802
FUCHS LUBRICANTS CANADA LTD.—See FUCHS SE; *Int'l*, pg. 2803
FUCHS LUBRICANTS (CHINA) LTD.—See FUCHS SE; *Int'l*, pg. 2803
FUCHS LUBRICANTS CO. - FUCHS LUBRITECH USA DIVISION—See FUCHS SE; *Int'l*, pg. 2803
FUCHS LUBRICANTS CO. - MINING DIVISION—See FUCHS SE; *Int'l*, pg. 2803
FUCHS LUBRICANTS CO.—See FUCHS SE; *Int'l*, pg. 2803
FUCHS LUBRICANTS (HONG KONG) LTD.—See FUCHS SE; *Int'l*, pg. 2803
FUCHS LUBRICANTS (INDIA) PVT. LTD.—See FUCHS SE; *Int'l*, pg. 2803
FUCHS LUBRICANTS-KANSAS CITY DIVISION—See FUCHS SE; *Int'l*, pg. 2803
FUCHS LUBRICANTS (KOREA) LTD.—See FUCHS SE; *Int'l*, pg. 2803
FUCHS LUBRICANTS (KOREA) LTD. - ULSAN PLANT—See FUCHS SE; *Int'l*, pg. 2803
FUCHS LUBRICANTS PTE. LTD.—See FUCHS SE; *Int'l*, pg. 2803
FUCHS LUBRICANTS (S.A.) (PTY.) LTD.—See FUCHS SE; *Int'l*, pg. 2802
FUCHS LUBRICANTS TAIWAN CORP.—See FUCHS SE; *Int'l*, pg. 2803
FUCHS LUBRICANTS (THAILAND) CO., LTD.—See FUCHS SE; *Int'l*, pg. 2803
FUCHS LUBRICANTS (UK) PLC—See FUCHS SE; *Int'l*, pg. 2802
FUCHS LUBRICANTS (YINGKOU) LTD.—See FUCHS SE; *Int'l*, pg. 2803
FUCHS LUBRIFIANT FRANCE S.A.—See FUCHS SE; *Int'l*, pg. 2803
FUCHS LUBRIFICANTES, UNIP. LDA.—See FUCHS SE; *Int'l*, pg. 2803
FUCHS LUBRIFICANTI S.P.A.—See FUCHS SE; *Int'l*, pg. 2802
FUCHS LUBRITECH GMBH - DOHNA PLANT—See FUCHS SE; *Int'l*, pg. 2803
FUCHS LUBRITECH GMBH - FLT OBERFLACHENTECHNIK PLANT—See FUCHS SE; *Int'l*, pg. 2803
FUCHS LUBRITECH GMBH - MOLY-PAUL DIVISION—See FUCHS SE; *Int'l*, pg. 2803
FUCHS LUBRITECH GMBH—See FUCHS SE; *Int'l*, pg. 2803
FUCHS LUBRITECH S.A.S—See FUCHS SE; *Int'l*, pg. 2802
FUCHS LUBRITECH (UK) LTD.—See FUCHS SE; *Int'l*, pg. 2803
FUCHS MAK DOOEL—See FUCHS SE; *Int'l*, pg. 2802
FUCHS MAZIVA D.O.O.—See FUCHS SE; *Int'l*, pg. 2803
FUCHS MAZIVA LSL D.O.O—See FUCHS SE; *Int'l*, pg. 2802
FUCHS NORTH AMERICA—See FUCHS-Gewurze GmbH; *Int'l*, pg. 2804
FUCHS OIL CORPORATION (CZ) SPOL. S R.O.—See FUCHS SE; *Int'l*, pg. 2803
FUCHS OIL CORPORATION (PL) SP. Z O.O.—See FUCHS SE; *Int'l*, pg. 2803
FUCHS OIL CORP. (SK), SPOL. S RO—See FUCHS SE; *Int'l*, pg. 2802
FUCHS OIL FINLAND OY—See FUCHS SE; *Int'l*, pg. 2803

FUCHS OIL HUNGARIA KFT—See FUCHS SE; *Int'l*, pg. 2802
FUCHS OIL MIDDLE EAST LTD.—See FUCHS SE; *Int'l*, pg. 2803
FUCHS PETROLEUM S.A.R.L.—See FUCHS SE; *Int'l*, pg. 2802
FUCHS PETROLUB AG - CASSIDA DIVISION—See FUCHS SE; *Int'l*, pg. 2803
FUCHS PETROLUB AG - HEIN DE WINDT DIVISION—See FUCHS SE; *Int'l*, pg. 2803
FUCHS PETROLUB AG - PACIFIC DIVISION—See FUCHS SE; *Int'l*, pg. 2804
FUCHS PETROLUB AG—See FUCHS SE; *Int'l*, pg. 2803
FUCHS PETROLUBE (MALAYSIA) SDN. BHD.—See FUCHS SE; *Int'l*, pg. 2803
FUCHS SE; *Int'l*, pg. 2802
FUCHS SMORJMEDEL SVERIGE AB—See FUCHS SE; *Int'l*, pg. 2802
FUCHS WISURA GMBH—See FUCHS SE; *Int'l*, pg. 2804
FUCHUAN CO., LTD.—See Hon Hai Precision Industry Co., Ltd.; *Int'l*, pg. 3457
FU CHUN SHIN MACHINERY MANUFACTURE CO., LTD.; *Int'l*, pg. 2800
FUDA ALLOY MATERIALS CO., LTD.; *Int'l*, pg. 2804
FUDA FAUCET WORKS, INC.; *Int'l*, pg. 2804
FU DA INTERNATIONAL LTD; *U.S. Private*, pg. 1619
FUDAN MICROELECTRONICS (USA) INC.—See Shanghai Fudan Microelectronics Group Co., Ltd.; *Int'l*, pg. 6768
FU DA TRANSPORTATION CO., LTD.—See Asia Cement Corporation; *Int'l*, pg. 611
FUDDRUCKERS OF ANNAPOLIS, LLC—See Luby's, Inc.; *U.S. Public*, pg. 1345
FUDE + SERRAHN GMBH & CO. KG—See DMK Deutsches Milchkontor GmbH; *Int'l*, pg. 2146
FUDO CONSTRUCTION INC.—See Fudo Tetra Corporation; *Int'l*, pg. 2804
FUDO TETRA CORPORATION; *Int'l*, pg. 2804
FUDOW COMPANY LIMITED—See Mitsubishi Gas Chemical Company, Inc.; *Int'l*, pg. 4948
FUEGO ENTERPRISES, INC.; *U.S. Public*, pg. 891
FUEL AGENCY, INC.; *U.S. Private*, pg. 1619
THE FUELCARD COMPANY UK LTD.—See Corpay, Inc.; *U.S. Public*, pg. 580
FUEL CARD SERVICES LIMITED—See DCC plc; *Int'l*, pg. 1990
FUELCELL ENERGY, INC.- EASTERN REGION—See FuelCell Energy, Inc.; *U.S. Public*, pg. 891
FUELCELL ENERGY, INC.- MANUFACTURING—See FuelCell Energy, Inc.; *U.S. Public*, pg. 891
FUELCELL ENERGY, INC.; *U.S. Public*, pg. 891
FUEL CONTROLS INC.; *U.S. Private*, pg. 1619
FUEL DME PRODUCTION CO., LTD.—See Mitsubishi Gas Chemical Company, Inc.; *Int'l*, pg. 4948
FUEL DOCTOR HOLDINGS, INC.; *U.S. Public*, pg. 891
FUEL FEED PLAZA HOME CENTERS; *U.S. Private*, pg. 1619
FUELFIX PTY LTD—See Archer Capital Pty. Ltd.; *Int'l*, pg. 547
FUELFX, LLC; *U.S. Private*, pg. 1619
FUELING SYSTEMS CONTRACTORS, LLC—See Quanta Services, Inc.; *U.S. Public*, pg. 1751
FUEL INTERACTIVE; *U.S. Private*, pg. 1619
FUELL ENGINEERING B.V.—See Perrot Duval Holding S.A.; *Int'l*, pg. 5814
FUELLGRAF ELECTRIC CO.; *U.S. Private*, pg. 1619
FUELL SYSTEMBAU GMBH—See Perrot Duval Holding S.A.; *Int'l*, pg. 5814
FUEL MANAGEMENT SYSTEM—See Van Manen Petroleum Group; *U.S. Private*, pg. 4340
FUEL MANAGERS INC.; *U.S. Private*, pg. 1619
FUEL MAN INC.—See NW Holding Co.; *U.S. Private*, pg. 2975
FUEL PERFORMANCE SOLUTIONS, INC.; *U.S. Private*, pg. 1619
FUELPOSITIVE CORPORATION; *Int'l*, pg. 2804
FUEL PROOF LIMITED—See ARGENT INDUSTRIAL LIMITED; *Int'l*, pg. 560
FUEL SERVICE - DJ'S MART LLC—See Pops Mart Fuels, LLC; *U.S. Private*, pg. 3229
FUELS, INC.; *U.S. Private*, pg. 1619
FUEL SOUTH INC.—See Jones Company, Inc.; *U.S. Private*, pg. 2232
FUELS & SUPPLIES INC.; *U.S. Private*, pg. 1619
FUELSTREAM, INC.; *U.S. Public*, pg. 891
FUEL SYSTEMS SOLUTIONS, INC.—See Westport Fuel Systems Inc.; *Int'l*, pg. 8392
FUEL TALENT, LLC; *U.S. Private*, pg. 1619
FUEL TECH, INC.; *U.S. Public*, pg. 891
FUEL TECH SRL—See Fuel Tech, Inc.; *U.S. Public*, pg. 891
FUENGFUANANT CO., LTD.—See Thai Beverage Public Company Limited; *Int'l*, pg. 7590
FUER INTERNATIONAL, INC.; *Int'l*, pg. 2804
FUER MARKT UND ABSATZFORSCHUNG GMBH—See Wuestenrot & Wuerttembergische AG; *Int'l*, pg. 8499
FUERST DAY LAWSON INDIA PRIVATE LIMITED; *Int'l*, pg. 2804

FUERST DAY LAWSON LTD.—See Highlander Partners, LP.; *U.S. Private*, pg. 1939
FUESSLER GROUP INC.; *U.S. Private*, pg. 1619
FUETREK CO., LTD.—See AI Co., Ltd.; *Int'l*, pg. 226
FUFENG GROUP LIMITED; *Int'l*, pg. 2804
FUFENG (SINGAPORE) PTE. LTD—See Fufeng Group Limited; *Int'l*, pg. 2804
FUGAKU KOKI CO., LTD.—See NOK Corporation; *Int'l*, pg. 5401
FUGANG ELECTRIC (KUNSHAN) CO., LTD.—See Cheng Eui Precision Industry Co., Ltd.; *Int'l*, pg. 1465
FUGANG ELECTRIC (MAANSHAN) CO., LTD.—See Cheng Eui Precision Industry Co., Ltd.; *Int'l*, pg. 1465
FUGANG ELECTRIC (NAN CHANG) CO., LTD.—See Cheng Eui Precision Industry Co., Ltd.; *Int'l*, pg. 1465
FUGANG ELECTRIC (XUZHOU) CO., LTD.—See Cheng Eui Precision Industry Co., Ltd.; *Int'l*, pg. 1465
FUGANG ELECTRONIC (DONG GUAN) CO., LTD.—See Cheng Eui Precision Industry Co., Ltd.; *Int'l*, pg. 1465
FUGATO LEASING GESELLSCHAFT M.B.H.—See Uni-Credit S.p.A.; *Int'l*, pg. 8036
FUGAZY INTERNATIONAL CORPORATION; *U.S. Private*, pg. 1619
FUGAZY TRANSPORTATION INC—See Fugazy International Corporation; *U.S. Private*, pg. 1620
FUGAZY TRAVEL—See Fugazy International Corporation; *U.S. Private*, pg. 1620
FUGRO AERIAL MAPPING A/S—See Fugro N.V.; *Int'l*, pg. 2805
FUGRO AERIAL MAPPING B.V.—See Fugro N.V.; *Int'l*, pg. 2807
FUGRO AIRBORNE SURVEYS, CORP.—See Fugro N.V.; *Int'l*, pg. 2805
FUGRO ALBANIA SH.P.K.—See Fugro N.V.; *Int'l*, pg. 2805
FUGRO ALLUVIAL OFFSHORE LTD.—See Fugro N.V.; *Int'l*, pg. 2805
FUGRO APERIO LTD.—See Fugro N.V.; *Int'l*, pg. 2805
FUGRO AUSTRIA GMBH—See Fugro N.V.; *Int'l*, pg. 2805
FUGRO BELGIQUE/BELGIE S.A./N.V.—See Fugro N.V.; *Int'l*, pg. 2805
FUGRO BELGIUM SRL—See Fugro N.V.; *Int'l*, pg. 2805
FUGRO BKS LTD.—See Fugro N.V.; *Int'l*, pg. 2805
FUGRO BRASIL LEVANTAMENTOS LTDA.—See Fugro N.V.; *Int'l*, pg. 2805
FUGRO BRASIL LTDA.—See Fugro N.V.; *Int'l*, pg. 2805
FUGRO BTW LTD.—See Fugro N.V.; *Int'l*, pg. 2805
FUGRO CAMEROUN SA—See Fugro N.V.; *Int'l*, pg. 2805
FUGRO (CANADA), INC.—See Fugro N.V.; *Int'l*, pg. 2805
FUGRO CERTIFICATION SERVICES LTD.—See Fugro N.V.; *Int'l*, pg. 2805
FUGRO CHANCE, INC.—See Fugro N.V.; *Int'l*, pg. 2805
FUGRO CHILE S.A.—See Fugro N.V.; *Int'l*, pg. 2805
FUGRO C.I.S. B.V.—See Fugro N.V.; *Int'l*, pg. 2807
FUGRO CONSULTANTS, INC.—See Fugro N.V.; *Int'l*, pg. 2805
FUGRO CONSULTANTS, INC.—See Fugro N.V.; *Int'l*, pg. 2805
FUGRO CONSULT GMBH—See Fugro N.V.; *Int'l*, pg. 2805
FUGRO CONSULT KFT.—See Fugro N.V.; *Int'l*, pg. 2805
FUGRO EARTHDATA, INC. - AVIATION—See Fugro N.V.; *Int'l*, pg. 2805
FUGRO EARTHDATA, INC.—See Fugro N.V.; *Int'l*, pg. 2805
FUGRO ECO CONSULT GMBH—See Fugro N.V.; *Int'l*, pg. 2806
FUGRO-ELBOCON B.V.—See Fugro N.V.; *Int'l*, pg. 2807
FUGRO EMU LTD.—See Fugro N.V.; *Int'l*, pg. 2806
FUGRO FINANCE AG—See Fugro N.V.; *Int'l*, pg. 2806
FUGRO FRANCE S.A.S.—See Fugro N.V.; *Int'l*, pg. 2806
FUGRO GABON SARL—See Fugro N.V.; *Int'l*, pg. 2806
FUGRO GEOCONSULTING, INC.—See Fugro N.V.; *Int'l*, pg. 2805
FUGRO GEOCONSULTING LTD.—See Fugro N.V.; *Int'l*, pg. 2806
FUGRO GEODETIC AG—See Fugro N.V.; *Int'l*, pg. 2806
FUGRO GEODETIC LTD.—See Fugro N.V.; *Int'l*, pg. 2806
FUGRO GEOID S.A.S.—See Fugro N.V.; *Int'l*, pg. 2806
FUGRO GEOLAB NOR AS—See Fugro N.V.; *Int'l*, pg. 2806
FUGRO GEOSERVICES B.V.—See Fugro N.V.; *Int'l*, pg. 2807
FUGRO GEOSERVICES, INC.—See Fugro N.V.; *Int'l*, pg. 2805
FUGRO GEOSERVICES LIMITED—See Fugro N.V.; *Int'l*, pg. 2806
FUGRO GEOSERVICES LTD.—See Fugro N.V.; *Int'l*, pg. 2806
FUGRO-GEOS, INC.—See Fugro N.V.; *Int'l*, pg. 2805
FUGRO-GEOS LTD.—See Fugro N.V.; *Int'l*, pg. 2808
FUGRO-GEOS PTE LTD.—See Fugro N.V.; *Int'l*, pg. 2808
FUGRO GEOSURVEYS, INC.—See Fugro N.V.; *Int'l*, pg. 2805
FUGRO GEOTECHNICAL SERVICES LTD.—See Fugro N.V.; *Int'l*, pg. 2806
FUGRO GEOTECHNICS AS—See Fugro N.V.; *Int'l*, pg. 2806
FUGRO GEOTECHNICS VIETNAM LLC—See Fugro N.V.; *Int'l*, pg. 2806
FUGRO GEOTECHNIQUE; *Int'l*, pg. 2805

FUGRO GEOTECH (PVT) LTD.—See Fugro N.V.; *Int'l*, pg. 2806
FUGRO GERMANY LAND GMBH—See Fugro N.V.; *Int'l*, pg. 2806
FUGRO GERMANY MARINE GMBH—See Fugro N.V.; *Int'l*, pg. 2806
FUGRO GHANA LIMITED—See Fugro N.V.; *Int'l*, pg. 2806
FUGRO HOLDING BELGIUM N.V.—See Fugro N.V.; *Int'l*, pg. 2806
FUGRO HOLDING FRANCE S.A.S.—See Fugro N.V.; *Int'l*, pg. 2806
FUGRO HOLDINGS (HONG KONG) LTD.—See Fugro N.V.; *Int'l*, pg. 2806
FUGRO HOLDINGS (NZ) LTD.—See Fugro N.V.; *Int'l*, pg. 2806
FUGRO HOLDINGS (UK) LTD.—See Fugro N.V.; *Int'l*, pg. 2806
FUGRO HONG KONG, LTD.—See Fugro N.V.; *Int'l*, pg. 2806
FUGRO-IMPROV, INC.—See Fugro N.V.; *Int'l*, pg. 2805
FUGRO-IMPROV LTD.—See Fugro N.V.; *Int'l*, pg. 2808
FUGRO-INPARK B.V.—See Fugro N.V.; *Int'l*, pg. 2807
FUGRO IN SITU GEOTECNIA LTDA.—See Fugro N.V.; *Int'l*, pg. 2806
FUGRO INTERRA S.A.—See Fugro N.V.; *Int'l*, pg. 2806
FUGRO INTERSITE B.V.—See Fugro N.V.; *Int'l*, pg. 2807
FUGRO ITALY S.P.A.—See Fugro N.V.; *Int'l*, pg. 2806
FUGRO JACQUES GEOSURVEYS, INC.—See Fugro N.V.; *Int'l*, pg. 2806
FUGRO JAPAN CO., LTD.—See Fugro N.V.; *Int'l*, pg. 2806
FUGRO LADS CORPORATION PTY LTD.—See Fugro N.V.; *Int'l*, pg. 2806
FUGRO LOADTEST LTD.—See Fugro N.V.; *Int'l*, pg. 2806
FUGRO LTD.—See Fugro N.V.; *Int'l*, pg. 2806
FUGRO MALAYSIA LAND SDN BHD—See Fugro N.V.; *Int'l*, pg. 2806
FUGRO MALAYSIA—See Fugro N.V.; *Int'l*, pg. 2806
FUGRO-MAPS GMBH—See Fugro N.V.; *Int'l*, pg. 2808
FUGRO-MAPS S.A.R.L.—See Fugro N.V.; *Int'l*, pg. 2808
FUGRO-MAPS (UAE)—See Fugro N.V.; *Int'l*, pg. 2808
FUGRO MARINE SERVICES B.V.—See Fugro N.V.; *Int'l*, pg. 2807
FUGRO MAURITIUS LTD.—See Fugro N.V.; *Int'l*, pg. 2806
FUGRO MEXICO S.A. DE C.V.—See Fugro N.V.; *Int'l*, pg. 2806
FUGRO MIDDLE EAST B.V.—See Fugro N.V.; *Int'l*, pg. 2806
FUGRO MIDDLE EAST & PARTNERS LLC—See Fugro N.V.; *Int'l*, pg. 2806
FUGRO MOZAMBIQUE LDA.—See Fugro N.V.; *Int'l*, pg. 2806
FUGRO MULTI CLIENT SERVICES, INC.—See Fugro N.V.; *Int'l*, pg. 2805
FUGRO MULTI CLIENT SERVICES PTY LTD.—See Fugro N.V.; *Int'l*, pg. 2806
FUGRO NEDERLAND B.V.—See Fugro N.V.; *Int'l*, pg. 2806
FUGRO NETHERLANDS MARINE BV—See Fugro N.V.; *Int'l*, pg. 2807
FUGRO NEW ZEALAND LTD.—See Fugro N.V.; *Int'l*, pg. 2807
FUGRO NIGERIA LIMITED—See Fugro N.V.; *Int'l*, pg. 2807
FUGRO NIGERIA LTD.—See Fugro N.V.; *Int'l*, pg. 2807
FUGRO NL LAND B.V.—See Fugro N.V.; *Int'l*, pg. 2807
FUGRO NORWAY AS—See Fugro N.V.; *Int'l*, pg. 2807
FUGRO N.V.; *Int'l*, pg. 2805
FUGRO OCEANOR AS—See Fugro N.V.; *Int'l*, pg. 2807
FUGRO OCEANSISMICA S.P.A.—See Fugro N.V.; *Int'l*, pg. 2807
FUGRO OFFSHORE SURVEY (SHENZHEN) CO. LTD.—See Fugro N.V.; *Int'l*, pg. 2807
FUGRO OSAE GMBH—See Fugro N.V.; *Int'l*, pg. 2807
FUGRO PACIFICA QINHUANGDAO CO. LTD.—See Fugro N.V.; *Int'l*, pg. 2807
FUGRO PANAMA SA—See Fugro N.V.; *Int'l*, pg. 2807
FUGRO PELAGROS, INC—See Fugro N.V.; *Int'l*, pg. 2805
FUGRO PENINSULAR—See Fugro N.V.; *Int'l*, pg. 2806
FUGRO PERU S.A.—See Fugro N.V.; *Int'l*, pg. 2807
FUGRO PHILIPPINES INC.—See Fugro N.V.; *Int'l*, pg. 2807
FUGRO ROADWARE, INC.—See Fugro N.V.; *Int'l*, pg. 2805
FUGRO ROADWARE, INC.—See Fugro N.V.; *Int'l*, pg. 2807
FUGRO ROAMES PTY LTD—See Fugro N.V.; *Int'l*, pg. 2807
FUGRO RUE AS—See Fugro N.V.; *Int'l*, pg. 2807
FUGRO S.A.E.—See Fugro N.V.; *Int'l*, pg. 2807
FUGRO SATELLITE POSITIONING PTE. LTD.—See Fugro N.V.; *Int'l*, pg. 2807
FUGRO SEACORE (AUSTRALIA) PTY LTD.—See Fugro N.V.; *Int'l*, pg. 2807
FUGRO SEA LTD.—See Fugro N.V.; *Int'l*, pg. 2807
FUGRO SEASTAR AS—See Fugro N.V.; *Int'l*, pg. 2807
FUGRO SEASTAR MAURITIUS LTD.—See Fugro N.V.; *Int'l*, pg. 2807
FUGRO SIAL LTD.—See Fugro N.V.; *Int'l*, pg. 2807

FUGRO N.V.

FUGRO SINGAPORE LAND PTE LTD—See Fugro N.V.; *Int'l*, pg. 2807
FUGRO SINGAPORE MARINE PTE. LTD.—See Fugro N.V.; *Int'l*, pg. 2807
FUGRO SINGAPORE PTE LTD.—See Fugro N.V.; *Int'l*, pg. 2807
FUGRO SOUTH AMERICA GMBH—See Fugro N.V.; *Int'l*, pg. 2807
FUGRO SPATIAL SOLUTIONS PTY LTD—See Fugro N.V.; *Int'l*, pg. 2807
FUGRO SUBSEA SERVICES AUSTRALIA PTY LTD—See Fugro N.V.; *Int'l*, pg. 2807
FUGRO SUBSEA TECHNOLOGIES PTE LTD.—See Fugro N.V.; *Int'l*, pg. 2807
FUGRO SURVEY AFRICA (PTY) LTD.—See Fugro N.V.; *Int'l*, pg. 2808
FUGRO SURVEY AS—See Fugro N.V.; *Int'l*, pg. 2807
FUGRO SURVEY (BRUNEI) SDN BHD.—See Fugro N.V.; *Int'l*, pg. 2807
FUGRO SURVEY B.V.—See Fugro N.V.; *Int'l*, pg. 2807
FUGRO SURVEY CARIBBEAN N.V.—See Fugro N.V.; *Int'l*, pg. 2808
FUGRO SURVEY INTERNATIONAL LTD.—See Fugro N.V.; *Int'l*, pg. 2808
FUGRO SURVEY LTD.—See Fugro N.V.; *Int'l*, pg. 2808
FUGRO SURVEY LTD.—See Fugro N.V.; *Int'l*, pg. 2808
FUGRO SURVEY MEXICO S.A. DE C.V.—See Fugro N.V.; *Int'l*, pg. 2808
FUGRO SURVEY (MIDDLE EAST) LTD.—See Fugro N.V.; *Int'l*, pg. 2807
FUGRO SURVEY PTY LTD.—See Fugro N.V.; *Int'l*, pg. 2808
FUGRO TECHNICAL SERVICES (GUANGZHOU) LTD.—See Fugro N.V.; *Int'l*, pg. 2808
FUGRO TECHNICAL SERVICES LTD.—See Fugro N.V.; *Int'l*, pg. 2808
FUGRO TECHNICAL SERVICES (MACAU) LTD.—See Fugro N.V.; *Int'l*, pg. 2808
FUGRO TRINIDAD LTD.—See Fugro N.V.; *Int'l*, pg. 2808
FUGRO (USA), INC.—See Fugro N.V.; *Int'l*, pg. 2805
FUGRO VASTGOED B.V.—See Fugro N.V.; *Int'l*, pg. 2807
FUGRO WEINHOLD ENGINEERING GMBH—See Fugro N.V.; *Int'l*, pg. 2808
FUGRO WILLIAM LETTIS & ASSOCIATES, INC.—See Fugro N.V.; *Int'l*, pg. 2805
FUGUINIAO CO., LTD.; *Int'l*, pg. 2808
FU HAO MANUFACTURING (M) SDN BHD—See Fu Yu Corporation Limited; *Int'l*, pg. 2801
FUHRMAN, SMOLSKY & FUREY, INC.—See HBE LLP; *U.S. Private*, pg. 1887
FU HSING AMERICA, INC.—See Taiwan Fu Hsing Industrial Co., Ltd.; *Int'l*, pg. 7420
FUHUA WEAVING CO., LTD.—See Zhe Jiang Taihua New Material Co., Ltd.; *Int'l*, pg. 8648
FUJAIRAH BUILDING INDUSTRIES COMPANY P.S.C. - EMIRATES CERAMIC FACTORY—See Fujairah Building Industries Company P.S.C.; *Int'l*, pg. 2808
FUJAIRAH BUILDING INDUSTRIES COMPANY P.S.C. - FUJAIRAH MARBLE & TILES FACTORY—See Fujairah Building Industries Company P.S.C.; *Int'l*, pg. 2808
FUJAIRAH BUILDING INDUSTRIES COMPANY P.S.C. - FUJAIRAH ROCKWOOL FACTORY—See Fujairah Building Industries Company P.S.C.; *Int'l*, pg. 2808
FUJAIRAH BUILDING INDUSTRIES COMPANY P.S.C.; *Int'l*, pg. 2808
FUJAIRAH CEMENT INDUSTRIES COMPANY PSC; *Int'l*, pg. 2808
FUJAIRAH CEMENT INDUSTRIES PJSC FZ—See Fujairah Cement Industries Company PSC; *Int'l*, pg. 2808
FUJAIRAH NATIONAL QUARRY—See Fujairah Building Industries Company P.S.C.; *Int'l*, pg. 2808
FUJAIRAH REFINERY COMPANY LTD.—See Vitol Holding B.V.; *Int'l*, pg. 8260
FUJAIRAH TRADE CENTRE COMPANY; *Int'l*, pg. 2808
FUJAN RAHBARAN CO.—See Messe Munchen GmbH; *Int'l*, pg. 4841
FUJEIJ WIND POWER COMPANY—See Korea Electric Power Corporation; *Int'l*, pg. 4283
FUJI AEROSPACE CORPORATION—See Subaru Corporation; *Int'l*, pg. 7246
FUJI AEROSPACE TECHNOLOGY CO.,LTD.—See Subaru Corporation; *Int'l*, pg. 7246
FUJI AIRCRAFT MAINTENANCE CO.,LTD.—See Subaru Corporation; *Int'l*, pg. 7246
FUJI AIR TOOLS CO., LTD—See Atlas Copco AB; *Int'l*, pg. 679
FUJI AITAC CO., LTD.—See Robert Bosch GmbH; *Int'l*, pg. 6361
FUJI ALCONIX MEXICO S.A. DE C.V.—See Alconix Corporation; *Int'l*, pg. 302
FUJI AMENITY SERVICE CO., LTD.—See Fuji Corporation Limited; *Int'l*, pg. 2810
FUJI AMERICA CORPORATION—See Fuji Corporation; *Int'l*, pg. 2809
FUJIAN ACETRON NEW MATERIALS CO., LTD.; pg. 2817
FUJIAN ANJOY FOODS CO LTD; *Int'l*, pg. 2817
FUJIAN AONONG BIOLOGICAL TECHNOLOGY GROUP INCORPORATION LIMITED; *Int'l*, pg. 2817

FUJIAN APEX SOFTWARE CO., LTD.; *Int'l*, pg. 2817
FUJIAN BAITAI AUTOMOBILE SALES & SERVICES CO., LTD.—See China Yongda Automobiles Services Holdings Limited; *Int'l*, pg. 1564
FUJIAN BOSS SOFTWARE CORP.; *Int'l*, pg. 2817
FUJIAN CEMENT INC.; *Int'l*, pg. 2817
FUJIAN COSUNTER PHARMACEUTICAL CO., LTD.; *Int'l*, pg. 2817
FUJIAN DABOMB PROTEIN BIOTECH CORP.—See DaBomb Protein Corp.; *Int'l*, pg. 1903
FUJIAN DONGBAI (GROUP) CO., LTD.; *Int'l*, pg. 2817
FUJIAN DONGSHAN AOZISHAN WIND POWER DEVELOPMENT CO., LTD.—See China Guodian Corporation; *Int'l*, pg. 1506
FUJIAN ELECTRIC POWER COMPANY—See State Grid Corporation of China; *Int'l*, pg. 7182
FUJIAN EXPRESSWAY DEVELOPMENT CO., LTD.; *Int'l*, pg. 2817
FUJIAN FC PACKAGING LIMITED—See CPMC Holdings Limited; *Int'l*, pg. 1826
FUJIAN FORECAM OPTICS CO., LTD.; *Int'l*, pg. 2817
FUJIAN FORY CO., LTD.—See Fujian Furi Electronics Co., Ltd.; *Int'l*, pg. 2818
FUJIAN FOXIT SOFTWARE DEVELOPMENT JOINT STOCK CO., LTD.; *Int'l*, pg. 2817
FUJIAN FU'AN CQRC VILLAGE & TOWNSHIP BANK CO., LTD.—See Chongqing Rural Commercial Bank Co., Ltd.; *Int'l*, pg. 1580
FUJIAN FUJITSU COMMUNICATION SOFTWARE CO., LTD.—See Fujitsu Limited; *Int'l*, pg. 2835
FUJIAN FUNENG CO., LTD.; *Int'l*, pg. 2818
FUJIAN FURI ELECTRONICS CO., LTD.; *Int'l*, pg. 2818
FUJIAN FUXIN SPECIAL STEEL CO., LTD.—See Formosa Plastics Corporation; *Int'l*, pg. 2735
FUJIAN FYNEX GARMENT CO., LTD.—See Fujian Fynex Textile Science & Technology Co., Ltd.; *Int'l*, pg. 2818
FUJIAN FYNEX TEXTILE SCIENCE & TECHNOLOGY CO., LTD.; *Int'l*, pg. 2818
FUJIAN GOLDEN STRAIT PAWN CO., LTD.—See Xiamen ITG Group Corp., Ltd.; *Int'l*, pg. 8524
FUJIAN GREEN PINE CO., LTD.; *Int'l*, pg. 2818
FUJIAN HAIXIA ENVIRONMENTAL PROTECTION GROUP CO., LTD.; *Int'l*, pg. 2818
FUJIAN HENGAN HOLDING CO., LTD.—See Hengan International Group Co. Ltd.; *Int'l*, pg. 3345
FUJIAN HI-TECH AUTOMATION CONTROL SYSTEM CO., LTD.—See Shanghai Hi-Tech Control System Co., Ltd.; *Int'l*, pg. 6770
FUJIAN HOLDINGS LIMITED; *Int'l*, pg. 2818
FUJIAN HONGHUI FRUIT & VEGETABLE CO. LTD.—See Great-Sun Foods Co.,LTD.; *Int'l*, pg. 3066
FUJIAN IDEAL JEWELLERY INDUSTRIAL CO., LTD.; *Int'l*, pg. 2818
FUJIAN JING'AN OPTOELECTRONICS CO., LTD.—See San'an Optoelectronics Co., Ltd.; *Int'l*, pg. 6522
FUJIAN JING'AN SAN'AN OPTOELECTRONICS CO., LTD.—See San'an Optoelectronics Co., Ltd.; *Int'l*, pg. 6522
FUJIAN JINSEN FORESTRY CO., LTD.; *Int'l*, pg. 2818
FUJIAN JK WIRING SYSTEMS CO., LTD.—See Sumitomo Electric Industries, Ltd.; *Int'l*, pg. 7277
FUJIAN JUAN KUANG YAMING ELECTRIC LTD.—See Luma Investments, Ltd.; *Int'l*, pg. 4577
FUJIAN JUNPENG COMMUNICATION TECHNOLOGY CO., LTD.—See Jiangsu Yinhe Electronics Co., Ltd.; *Int'l*, pg. 3956
FUJIAN KEERUN CATERING ADMINISTRATION CORP., LTD.—See Xiamen ITG Group Corp., Ltd.; *Int'l*, pg. 8524
FUJIAN KEMEN PORT SUPPLY CHAIN MANAGEMENT CO., LTD.—See China Master Logistics Co., Ltd.; *Int'l*, pg. 1517
FUJIAN KERUI PHARMACEUTICAL CO., LTD.—See MicroPort Scientific Corporation; *Int'l*, pg. 4880
FUJIAN KHUAN HUA PRECISE MOLD., LTD.—See Syncmold Enterprise Corp.; *Int'l*, pg. 7382
FUJIAN KUNCAI MATERIAL TECHNOLOGY CO., LTD.; *Int'l*, pg. 2818
FUJIAN LANDI COMMERCIAL EQUIPMENT CO., LTD.—See Apollo Global Management, Inc.; *U.S. Public*, pg. 151
FUJIAN LAYA OUTDOOR PRODUCTS CO., LTD.—See Fulgent Sun International (Holding) Co., Ltd.; *Int'l*, pg. 2842
FUJIAN LONGKING CO., LTD.; *Int'l*, pg. 2818
FUJIAN LONGXI BEARING (GROUP) CORPORATION LIMITED; *Int'l*, pg. 2818
FUJIAN MINDONG ELECTRIC POWER CO., LTD.; *Int'l*, pg. 2818
FUJIAN MINFA ALUMINIUM CO., LTD.; *Int'l*, pg. 2818
FUJIAN MINHANG ELECTRONICS CO., LTD.; *Int'l*, pg. 2819
FUJIAN NANPING NANFU BATTERY CO., LTD.—See CDH China Management Company Limited; *Int'l*, pg. 1370
FUJIAN NANPING SUN CABLE CO., LTD.; *Int'l*, pg. 2819
FUJIAN NEBULA ELECTRONICS CO., LTD.; *Int'l*, pg. 2819

FUJIAN NEWCHOICE PIPE TECHNOLOGY CO., LTD.; *Int'l*, pg. 2819
FUJIAN NEWL & AUTO-ID TECH. CO., LTD.—See Newland Digital Technology Co., Ltd.; *Int'l*, pg. 5235
FUJIAN NUOQI CO., LTD.—See Aceso Life Science Group Limited; *Int'l*, pg. 102
FUJIAN OPCON ENERGY TECHNOLOGY CO., LTD.—See Fujian Snowman Co., Ltd.; *Int'l*, pg. 2819
FUJIAN PINGTAN CQRC VILLAGE & TOWNSHIP BANK CO., LTD.—See Chongqing Rural Commercial Bank Co., Ltd.; *Int'l*, pg. 1580
FUJIAN QINGSHAN PAPER INDUSTRY CO., LTD.; *Int'l*, pg. 2819
FUJIAN RAYNEN TECHNOLOGY CO., LTD.; *Int'l*, pg. 2819
FUJIAN RONGJI SOFTWARE CO., LTD.; *Int'l*, pg. 2819
FUJIAN SANMING DOUBLE-WHEEL CHEMICAL MACHINERY CO. LTD—See China National Chemical Corporation; *Int'l*, pg. 1527
FUJIAN SANMING GEARBOX CO., LTD.—See Fujian Longxi Bearing (Group) Corporation Limited; *Int'l*, pg. 2818
FUJIAN SANMING GEAR CASE CO., LTD.—See Fujian Longxi Bearing (Group) Corporation Limited; *Int'l*, pg. 2818
FUJIAN SANMU GROUP CO., LTD.; *Int'l*, pg. 2819
FUJIAN SANXIANG ADVANCED MATERIALS INSTITUTE CO., LTD.—See Sanxiang Advanced Materials Co., Ltd.; *Int'l*, pg. 6561
FUJIAN SBS ZIPPER SCIENCE & TECHNOLOGY CO., LTD.; *Int'l*, pg. 2819
FUJIAN SCAS AUTOMOBILE SALES SERVICES CO., LTD.—See China ZhengTong Auto Services Holdings Limited; *Int'l*, pg. 1566
FUJIAN SECOM SECURITY CO., LTD.—See SECOM Co., Ltd.; *Int'l*, pg. 6671
FUJIAN SEPTWOLVES INDUSTRY CO., LTD.; *Int'l*, pg. 2819
FUJIAN SHANSHAN TECHNOLOGY CO., LTD.—See Ningbo Shanshan Co., Ltd.; *Int'l*, pg. 5305
FUJIAN SHAXIAN CQRC VILLAGE & TOWNSHIP BANK CO., LTD.—See Chongqing Rural Commercial Bank Co., Ltd.; *Int'l*, pg. 1581
FUJIAN SHIPBUILDING INDUSTRY TRADING CO., LTD.—See Xiamen C&D Inc.; *Int'l*, pg. 8523
FUJIAN SHISHI CQRC VILLAGE & TOWNSHIP BANK CO., LTD.—See Chongqing Rural Commercial Bank Co., Ltd.; *Int'l*, pg. 1581
FUJIAN SNOWMAN CO., LTD.; *Int'l*, pg. 2819
FUJIAN SPICER DRIVETRAIN SYSTEM CO., LTD.—See Dana Incorporated; *U.S. Public*, pg. 623
FUJIAN STAR-NET COMMUNICATION CO.,LTD; *Int'l*, pg. 2819
FUJIAN START GROUP CO., LTD.; *Int'l*, pg. 2819
FUJIAN SUMPO FOODS HOLDINGS COMPANY LIMITED—See Charoen Pokphand Foods Public Company Limited; *Int'l*, pg. 1452
FUJIAN SUNNER DEVELOPMENT CO., LTD.; *Int'l*, pg. 2819
FUJIAN SUNSHINE FOOTWEAR CO., LTD.—See Fulgent Sun International (Holding) Co., Ltd.; *Int'l*, pg. 2842
FUJIAN SUPERTECH ADVANCED MATERIAL CO., LTD.; *Int'l*, pg. 2820
FUJIAN TEA IMPORT & EXPORT CO., LTD.—See COFCO Limited; *Int'l*, pg. 1692
FUJIAN TECO PRECISION CO., LTD.—See Teco Electric & Machinery Co., Ltd.; *Int'l*, pg. 7518
FUJIAN TENDERING CO., LTD.; *Int'l*, pg. 2820
FUJIAN TIANMA SCIENCE & TECHNOLOGY GROUP CO., LTD.; *Int'l*, pg. 2820
FUJIAN TON YI TINPLATE CO., LTD.—See Uni-President Enterprises Corporation; *Int'l*, pg. 8028
FUJIAN TOPY AUTOPARTS CO., LTD.—See Topy Industries, Ltd.; *Int'l*, pg. 7821
FUJIAN TORCH ELECTRON TECHNOLOGY CO., LTD.; *Int'l*, pg. 2820
FUJIAN TUNG KANG STEEL CO.—See Tung Ho Steel Enterprise Corporation; *Int'l*, pg. 7970
FUJIAN WANCHEN BIOTECHNOLOGY GROUP CO., LTD.; *Int'l*, pg. 2820
FUJIAN WIDE PLUS PRECISION INSTRUMENTS CO., LTD.—See China High Precision Automation Group Limited; *Int'l*, pg. 1508
FUJIAN XIANGDA CAMEL FEED CO., LTD—See Tangrenshen Group Co., Ltd.; *Int'l*, pg. 7458
FUJIAN XING GANG PORT SERVICE CO., LTD.—See Pingtan Marine Enterprise Ltd.; *Int'l*, pg. 5870
FUJIAN YANJING HUIQUAN BREWERY CO., LTD.; *Int'l*, pg. 2820
FUJIAN YONGAN FORESTRY (GROUP) CO., LTD.; *Int'l*, pg. 2820
FUJIAN YONGDA AUTOMOBILE SALES AND SERVICES CO., LTD.—See China Yongda Automobiles Services Holdings Limited; *Int'l*, pg. 1564
FUJIAN YONGFU POWER ENGINEERING CO., LTD.; *Int'l*, pg. 2820
FUJIAN YUANLI ACTIVE CARBON CO., LTD.; *Int'l*, pg. 2820

FUJIAN YUANXIANG NEW MATERIALS CO., LTD.; *Int'l,* pg. 2820
FUJIAN ZHANGPING KIMURA FORESTRY PRODUCTS CO., LTD.—See China Environmental Technology & Bioenergy Holdings Limited; *Int'l,* pg. 1500
FUJIAN ZHANGZHOU DEVELOPMENT CO., LTD.; *Int'l,* pg. 2820
FUJIAN ZHENYUN PLASTICS INDUSTRY CO., LTD.; *Int'l,* pg. 2820
FUJIAN ZHONGDE TECHNOLOGY CO., LTD.—See CHINA CLEAN ENERGY INC.; *Int'l,* pg. 1489
FUJIAN ZHONGSHE MACHINERY & EQUIPMENT IMP. & EXP. CO., LTD.—See China Machinery Engineering Corporation; *Int'l,* pg. 1516
FUJIAN ZIJIN MINING & METALLURGY TESTING TECHNOLOGY COMPANY LIMITED—See Zijin Mining Group Company Limited; *Int'l,* pg. 8683
FUJI ART, INC.—See Fuji Media Holdings, Inc.; *Int'l,* pg. 2813
FUJI ASTEC, INC.—See Fuji Seal International, Inc.; *Int'l,* pg. 2816
FUJI AUTOTECH AB—See JTEKT Corporation; *Int'l,* pg. 4017
FUJI AUTOTECH FRANCE S.A.S.—See JTEKT Corporation; *Int'l,* pg. 4017
FUJI AUTOTECH (THAILAND) CO.,LTD.—See JTEKT Corporation; *Int'l,* pg. 4017
FUJIBO HOLDINGS, INC.; *Int'l,* pg. 2820
FUJI BOLT MANUFACTURING CO., LTD. - SHIROI PLANT—See Okabe Co., Ltd.; *Int'l,* pg. 5544
FUJI BOLT MANUFACTURING CO., LTD.—See Okabe Co., Ltd.; *Int'l,* pg. 5544
FUJI BORING CO., LTD.—See Mitsubishi Gas Chemical Company, Inc.; *Int'l,* pg. 4948
FUJI CAC JOINT STOCK COMPANY—See Fuji Electric Co., Ltd.; *Int'l,* pg. 2811
FUJI CARBON MANUFACTURING CO.—See Alconix Corporation; *Int'l,* pg. 302
FUJI CAREER DESIGN INC.—See Fuji Media Holdings, Inc.; *Int'l,* pg. 2813
FUJI CAR MANUFACTURING CO., LTD.—See Takeei Corporation; *Int'l,* pg. 7440
FUJICCO CO., LTD.; *Int'l,* pg. 2820
FUJI CHEMICAL INDUSTRIES CO., LTD - GOHKAKIZAWA—See Fuji Chemical Industries Co., Ltd; *Int'l,* pg. 2809
FUJI CHEMICAL INDUSTRIES CO., LTD. - OSAKA—See Fuji Chemical Industries Co., Ltd; *Int'l,* pg. 2809
FUJI CHEMICAL INDUSTRIES CO., LTD; *Int'l,* pg. 2808
FUJI CHEMICAL INDUSTRIES CO., LTD. - TOKYO—See Fuji Chemical Industries Co., Ltd; *Int'l,* pg. 2809
FUJI CHEMICAL INDUSTRIES USA, INC.—See Fuji Chemical Industries Co., Ltd; *Int'l,* pg. 2809
FUJICHEMI CO., LTD.—See Fujibo Holdings, Inc.; *Int'l,* pg. 2820
FUJICHEMI KINKI CO., LTD.—See Fujikura Kasei Co., Ltd.; *Int'l,* pg. 2826
FUJICHEMI TOKYO CO., LTD.—See Fujikura Kasei Co., Ltd.; *Int'l,* pg. 2826
FUJICHEM SONNEBORN LTD. - CHESTERFIELD PLANT—See Fujikura Kasei Co., Ltd.; *Int'l,* pg. 2826
FUJICHEM SONNEBORN LTD.—See Fujikura Kasei Co., Ltd.; *Int'l,* pg. 2826
FUJICOLOR BENELUX B.V.—See FUJIFILM Holdings Corporation; *Int'l,* pg. 2822
FUJICOLOR CENTRAL EUROPE PHOTOFINISHING GMBH & CO. KG—See FUJIFILM Holdings Corporation; *Int'l,* pg. 2822
FUJICOLOR SVERIGE AB—See FUJIFILM Holdings Corporation; *Int'l,* pg. 2822
FUJI CO., LTD.; *Int'l,* pg. 2809
FUJI CONTACT CO., LTD.—See Menicon Co., Ltd.; *Int'l,* pg. 4816
FUJICOPIAN CO., LTD. - OKAYAMA PLANT—See Fujicopian Co., Ltd.; *Int'l,* pg. 2820
FUJICOPIAN CO., LTD.; *Int'l,* pg. 2820
FUJI COPIAN (H.K.) LTD.—See Fujicopian Co., Ltd.; *Int'l,* pg. 2820
FUJI CORP INTERNATIONAL HONG KONG LTD.—See The Japan Wool Textile Co., Ltd.; *Int'l,* pg. 7659
FUJI CORPORATION LIMITED; *Int'l,* pg. 2810
FUJI CORPORATION—See The Japan Wool Textile Co., Ltd.; *Int'l,* pg. 7659
FUJI CORPORATION; *Int'l,* pg. 2809
FUJI CREATIVE CORPORATION—See Fuji Media Holdings, Inc.; *Int'l,* pg. 2813
FUJI CRS, K. K.—See Sony Group Corporation; *Int'l,* pg. 7102
FUJI DAIICHI TRAFFIC CO., LTD.—See Daiichi Koutsu Sangyo Co., Ltd.; *Int'l,* pg. 1928
FUJI DIE CO., LTD. - HADANO 1 & 2 FACTORY—See Fuji Die Co., Ltd.; *Int'l,* pg. 2810
FUJI DIE CO., LTD. - KORIYAMA 2 FACTORY—See Fuji Die Co., Ltd.; *Int'l,* pg. 2810
FUJI DIE CO., LTD. - MOJI FACTORY—See Fuji Die Co., Ltd.; *Int'l,* pg. 2810
FUJI DIE CO., LTD. - NAGOYA FACTORY—See Fuji Die Co., Ltd.; *Int'l,* pg. 2810

FUJI DIE CO., LTD. - OSAKA FACTORY—See Fuji Die Co., Ltd.; *Int'l,* pg. 2810
FUJI DIE CO., LTD.; *Int'l,* pg. 2810
FUJI DIE TRADING (SHANGHAI) CO., LTD.—See Fuji Die Co., Ltd.; *Int'l,* pg. 2810
FUJI DO BRASIL MAQUINAS INDUSTRIAIS LTDA.—See Fuji Corporation; *Int'l,* pg. 2810
FUJIEDA AUTO LIGHTING CO., LTD.—See Koito Manufacturing Co., Ltd.; *Int'l,* pg. 4230
FUJI ELECTRIC (ASIA) CO., LTD.—See Fuji Electric Co., Ltd.; *Int'l,* pg. 2811
FUJI ELECTRIC ASIA PACIFIC PTE. LTD.—See Fuji Electric Co., Ltd.; *Int'l,* pg. 2811
FUJI ELECTRIC BRAZIL-EUIPAMENTOS DE ENERGIA LTDA. (FEB)—See Fuji Electric Co., Ltd.; *Int'l,* pg. 2811
FUJI ELECTRIC (CHANGSHU) CO., LTD.—See Fuji Electric Co., Ltd.; *Int'l,* pg. 2811
FUJI ELECTRIC (CHINA) CO., LTD.—See Fuji Electric Co., Ltd.; *Int'l,* pg. 2811
FUJI ELECTRIC CO., LTD.; *Int'l,* pg. 2810
FUJI ELECTRIC CONSUL NEOWATT PRIVATE LIMITED—See Fuji Electric Co., Ltd.; *Int'l,* pg. 2811
FUJI ELECTRIC CORP OF AMERICA—See Fuji Electric Co., Ltd.; *Int'l,* pg. 2811
FUJI ELECTRIC CORPORATION OF AMERICA—See Fuji Electric Co., Ltd.; *Int'l,* pg. 2811
FUJI ELECTRIC DALIAN CO., LTD.—See Fuji Electric Co., Ltd.; *Int'l,* pg. 2811
FUJI ELECTRIC DEVICE TECHNOLOGY AMERICA, INC.—See Fuji Electric Co., Ltd.; *Int'l,* pg. 2811
FUJI ELECTRIC EUROPE GMBH—See Fuji Electric Co., Ltd.; *Int'l,* pg. 2811
FUJI ELECTRIC FA (ASIA) CO., LTD.—See Fuji Electric Co., Ltd.; *Int'l,* pg. 2811
FUJI ELECTRIC FA COMPONENTS & SYSTEMS CO., LTD.—See Fuji Electric Co., Ltd.; *Int'l,* pg. 2811
FUJI ELECTRIC FA KOREA CO., LTD.—See Fuji Electric Co., Ltd.; *Int'l,* pg. 2811
FUJI ELECTRIC FA KOREA CO., LTD.—See Fuji Electric Co., Ltd.; *Int'l,* pg. 2811
FUJI ELECTRIC FA SERVICE CO., LTD.—See Fuji Electric Co., Ltd.; *Int'l,* pg. 2811
FUJI ELECTRIC FA TAIWAN CO., LTD.—See Fuji Electric Co., Ltd.; *Int'l,* pg. 2811
FUJI ELECTRIC FINANCE & ACCOUNTING SUPPORT CO., LTD.—See Fuji Electric Co., Ltd.; *Int'l,* pg. 2811
FUJI ELECTRIC FRANCE S.A.—See Fuji Electric Co., Ltd.; *Int'l,* pg. 2811
FUJI ELECTRIC F-TECH CO., LTD.—See Fuji Electric Co., Ltd.; *Int'l,* pg. 2811
FUJI ELECTRIC (HANGZHOU) SOFTWARE CO., LTD.—See Fuji Electric Co., Ltd.; *Int'l,* pg. 2811
FUJI ELECTRIC HONG KONG CO., LTD.—See Fuji Electric Co., Ltd.; *Int'l,* pg. 2811
FUJI ELECTRIC INDIA PVT. LTD.—See Fuji Electric Co., Ltd.; *Int'l,* pg. 2811
FUJI ELECTRIC INDUSTRIES SINGAPORE PRIVATE LTD.—See Fuji Electric Co., Ltd.; *Int'l,* pg. 2811
FUJI ELECTRIC INDUSTRY CO., LTD. - KUSATSU FACTORY—See FUJI ELECTRIC INDUSTRY CO., LTD.; *Int'l,* pg. 2813
FUJI ELECTRIC INDUSTRY CO., LTD. - SHIN-ASAHI FACTORY—See FUJI ELECTRIC INDUSTRY CO., LTD.; *Int'l,* pg. 2813
FUJI ELECTRIC INDUSTRY CO., LTD.; *Int'l,* pg. 2813
FUJI ELECTRIC IT CENTER CO., LTD.—See Fuji Electric Co., Ltd.; *Int'l,* pg. 2811
FUJI ELECTRIC IT SOLUTIONS CO., LTD.—See Fuji Electric Co., Ltd.; *Int'l,* pg. 2811
FUJI ELECTRIC KOREA CO., LTD.—See Fuji Electric Co., Ltd.; *Int'l,* pg. 2811
FUJI ELECTRIC (MALAYSIA) SDN. BHD.—See Fuji Electric Co., Ltd.; *Int'l,* pg. 2811
FUJI ELECTRIC MANUFACTURING (THAILAND) CO., LTD.—See Fuji Electric Co., Ltd.; *Int'l,* pg. 2811
FUJI ELECTRIC METER CO., LTD.—See Fuji Electric Co., Ltd.; *Int'l,* pg. 2811
FUJI ELECTRIC MOTOR (DALIAN) CO., LTD.—See Fuji Electric Co., Ltd.; *Int'l,* pg. 2811
FUJI ELECTRIC PHILIPPINES, INC.—See Fuji Electric Co., Ltd.; *Int'l,* pg. 2811
FUJI ELECTRIC POWER SEMICONDUCTOR CO., LTD.—See Fuji Electric Co., Ltd.; *Int'l,* pg. 2811
FUJI ELECTRIC RETAIL SEVICE CO., LTD.—See Fuji Electric Co., Ltd.; *Int'l,* pg. 2811
FUJI ELECTRIC SALES MALAYSIA SDN. BHD.—See Fuji Electric Co., Ltd.; *Int'l,* pg. 2812
FUJI ELECTRIC SALES PHILIPPINES, INC.—See Fuji Electric Co., Ltd.; *Int'l,* pg. 2812
FUJI ELECTRIC (SHANGHAI) CO., LTD.—See Fuji Electric Co., Ltd.; *Int'l,* pg. 2811
FUJI ELECTRIC (SHENZHEN) CO., LTD.—See Fuji Electric Co., Ltd.; *Int'l,* pg. 2811
FUJI ELECTRIC TAIWAN CO., LTD.—See Fuji Electric Co., Ltd.; *Int'l,* pg. 2812
FUJI ELECTRIC TECHNICA CO., LTD.—See Fuji Electric Co., Ltd.; *Int'l,* pg. 2812
FUJI ELECTRIC TSUGARU SEMICONDUCTOR CO., LTD.—See Fuji Electric Co., Ltd.; *Int'l,* pg. 2812

FUJI ELECTRIC VIETNAM CO., LTD.—See Fuji Electric Co., Ltd.; *Int'l,* pg. 2812
FUJI ELECTRIC (ZHUHAI) CO., LTD.—See Fuji Electric Co., Ltd.; *Int'l,* pg. 2811
FUJI ELECTRONICS CO., LTD.—See Macnica Holdings, Inc.; *Int'l,* pg. 4624
FUJI ELECTRONICS INDUSTRIES CO., LTD.—See Seikoh Giken Co., Ltd.; *Int'l,* pg. 6689
FUJI ENTERTAINMENT AMERICA, INC—See Fuji Media Holdings, Inc.; *Int'l,* pg. 2814
FUJI EUROPE AFRICA B.V.—See Fuji Oil Holdings Inc.; *Int'l,* pg. 2815
THE FUJI FACILITY SERVICE, INC.—See First Brothers Co., Ltd.; *Int'l,* pg. 2682
FUJI FESTEC CO., LTD.—See Fuji Electric Co., Ltd.; *Int'l,* pg. 2812
FUJIFILM ASIA PACIFIC PTE. LTD.—See FUJIFILM Holdings Corporation; *Int'l,* pg. 2821
FUJIFILM AUSTRALIA PTY. LTD.—See FUJIFILM Holdings Corporation; *Int'l,* pg. 2821
FUJIFILM BUSINESS EXPERT CORPORATION—See FUJIFILM Holdings Corporation; *Int'l,* pg. 2821
FUJIFILM BUSINESS INNOVATION CORPORATION—See FUJIFILM Holdings Corporation; *Int'l,* pg. 2825
FUJIFILM BUSINESS SUPPLY CO., LTD.—See FUJIFILM Holdings Corporation; *Int'l,* pg. 2821
FUJIFILM CANADA INC.—See FUJIFILM Holdings Corporation; *Int'l,* pg. 2821
FUJIFILM CANDA INC.-GRAPHIC SYSTEMS DIVISION—See FUJIFILM Holdings Corporation; *Int'l,* pg. 2821
FUJIFILM (CHINA) INVESTMENT CO., LTD.—See FUJIFILM Holdings Corporation; *Int'l,* pg. 2821
FUJIFILM COLOMBIA S.A.S—See FUJIFILM Holdings Corporation; *Int'l,* pg. 2821
FUJIFILM COMPUTER SYSTEM CO., LTD.—See FUJIFILM Holdings Corporation; *Int'l,* pg. 2821
FUJIFILM CORPORATION—See FUJIFILM Holdings Corporation; *Int'l,* pg. 2821
FUJIFILM CZ, S.R.O.—See FUJIFILM Holdings Corporation; *Int'l,* pg. 2821
FUJIFILM DENMARK A/S—See FUJIFILM Holdings Corporation; *Int'l,* pg. 2821
FUJIFILM DIMATIX, INC.—See FUJIFILM Holdings Corporation; *Int'l,* pg. 2822
FUJIFILM DIOSYNTH BIOTECHNOLOGIES DENMARK APS—See FUJIFILM Holdings Corporation; *Int'l,* pg. 2821
FUJIFILM DIOSYNTH BIOTECHNOLOGIES HOLDINGS DENMARK APS—See FUJIFILM Holdings Corporation; *Int'l,* pg. 2824
FUJIFILM DIOSYNTH BIOTECHNOLOGIES INC.—See FUJIFILM Holdings Corporation; *Int'l,* pg. 2822
FUJIFILM DIOSYNTH BIOTECHNOLOGIES TEXAS, LLC—See FUJIFILM Holdings Corporation; *Int'l,* pg. 2824
FUJIFILM DIOSYNTH BIOTECHNOLOGIES UK LIMITED—See FUJIFILM Holdings Corporation; *Int'l,* pg. 2821
FUJIFILM DISPLAY SOLUTIONS KOREA CO., LTD.—See FUJIFILM Holdings Corporation; *Int'l,* pg. 2824
FUJIFILM DIS TICARET A.S.—See FUJIFILM Holdings Corporation; *Int'l,* pg. 2821
FUJIFILM DO BRASIL LTDA.—See FUJIFILM Holdings Corporation; *Int'l,* pg. 2823
FUJIFILM ELECTRONIC IMAGING EUROPE GMBH—See FUJIFILM Holdings Corporation; *Int'l,* pg. 2821
FUJIFILM ELECTRONIC IMAGING KOREA CO., LTD.—See FUJIFILM Holdings Corporation; *Int'l,* pg. 2821
FUJIFILM ELECTRONIC IMAGING LIMITED—See Xaar PLC; *Int'l,* pg. 8518
FUJIFILM ELECTRONIC MATERIALS CO., LTD.—See FUJIFILM Holdings Corporation; *Int'l,* pg. 2824
FUJIFILM ELECTRONIC MATERIALS (EUROPE) N.V.—See FUJIFILM Holdings Corporation; *Int'l,* pg. 2821
FUJIFILM ELECTRONIC MATERIALS (EUROPE) S.R.L.—See FUJIFILM Holdings Corporation; *Int'l,* pg. 2822
FUJIFILM ELECTRONIC MATERIALS (HONG KONG) CO., LTD.—See FUJIFILM Holdings Corporation; *Int'l,* pg. 2824
FUJIFILM ELECTRONIC MATERIALS KOREA CO., LTD.—See FUJIFILM Holdings Corporation; *Int'l,* pg. 2824
FUJIFILM ELECTRONIC MATERIALS MANUFACTURING KOREA CO., LTD.—See FUJIFILM Holdings Corporation; *Int'l,* pg. 2824
FUJIFILM ELECTRONIC MATERIALS (SINGAPORE) PTE. LTD.—See FUJIFILM Holdings Corporation; *Int'l,* pg. 2824
FUJIFILM ELECTRONIC MATERIALS (SUZHOU) CO., LTD.—See FUJIFILM Holdings Corporation; *Int'l,* pg. 2824
FUJIFILM ELECTRONIC MATERIALS TAIWAN CO., LTD.—See FUJIFILM Holdings Corporation; *Int'l,* pg. 2824

FUJI ELECTRIC INDUSTRY CO., LTD.

CORPORATE AFFILIATIONS

FUJIFILM ELECTRONIC MATERIALS U.S.A., INC.—See FUJIFILM Holdings Corporation; *Int'l*, pg. 2822
FUJIFILM ELECTRONIC MATERIALS U.S.A. INC.—See FUJIFILM Holdings Corporation; *Int'l*, pg. 2822
FUJIFILM ENGINEERING CO., LTD.—See FUJIFILM Holdings Corporation; *Int'l*, pg. 2824
FUJIFILM ESPANA, S.A.—See FUJIFILM Holdings Corporation; *Int'l*, pg. 2821
FUJIFILM E-SYSTEMS, INC.—See FUJIFILM Holdings Corporation; *Int'l*, pg. 2823
FUJIFILM EUROPE BUSINESS SERVICE SP.ZO.O.—See FUJIFILM Holdings Corporation; *Int'l*, pg. 2824
FUJIFILM EUROPE B.V.—See FUJIFILM Holdings Corporation; *Int'l*, pg. 2821
FUJIFILM EUROPE GMBH—See FUJIFILM Holdings Corporation; *Int'l*, pg. 2821
FUJIFILM EUROPE N.V.—See FUJIFILM Holdings Corporation; *Int'l*, pg. 2821
FUJIFILM FILMED TIBBI CIHAZLAR PAZARLAMA VE TICARET A.S.—See FUJIFILM Holdings Corporation; *Int'l*, pg. 2822
FUJIFILM FINECHEMICALS CO., LTD. - HIRONO FACTORY—See FUJIFILM Holdings Corporation; *Int'l*, pg. 2824
FUJIFILM FINECHEMICALS CO., LTD.—See FUJIFILM Holdings Corporation; *Int'l*, pg. 2824
FUJIFILM FINECHEMICALS (WUXI) CO., LTD—See FUJIFILM Holdings Corporation; *Int'l*, pg. 2824
FUJIFILM FRANCE S.A.S.—See FUJIFILM Holdings Corporation; *Int'l*, pg. 2822
FUJIFILM GLOBAL GRAPHIC SYSTEMS CO., LTD.—See FUJIFILM Holdings Corporation; *Int'l*, pg. 2824
FUJIFILM GRAPHIC SYSTEMS CO., LTD.—See FUJIFILM Holdings Corporation; *Int'l*, pg. 2824
FUJIFILM HAWAII, INC.—See FUJIFILM Holdings Corporation; *Int'l*, pg. 2822
FUJIFILM HEALTHCARE AMERICAS CORPORATION—See FUJIFILM Holdings Corporation; *Int'l*, pg. 2822
FUJIFILM HEALTHCARE LABORATORY CO., LTD.—See FUJIFILM Holdings Corporation; *Int'l*, pg. 2824
FUJIFILM HOLDINGS AMERICA CORPORATION—See FUJIFILM Holdings Corporation; *Int'l*, pg. 2824
FUJIFILM HOLDINGS AUSTRALASIA PTY LTD—See FUJIFILM Holdings Corporation; *Int'l*, pg. 2824
FUJIFILM HOLDINGS CORPORATION; *Int'l*, pg. 2820
FUJIFILM HOLDINGS NZ LIMITED—See FUJIFILM Holdings Corporation; *Int'l*, pg. 2824
FUJIFILM HONG KONG LIMITED—See FUJIFILM Holdings Corporation; *Int'l*, pg. 2822
FUJIFILM HUNGARY LTD.—See FUJIFILM Holdings Corporation; *Int'l*, pg. 2822
FUJIFILM HUNT CHEMICALS EUROPE N.V.—See FUJIFILM Holdings Corporation; *Int'l*, pg. 2821
FUJIFILM HUNT CHEMICALS SINGAPORE PTE. LTD.—See FUJIFILM Holdings Corporation; *Int'l*, pg. 2822
FUJIFILM HUNT CHEMICALS SPECIALTY PRODUCTS CO.—See FUJIFILM Holdings Corporation; *Int'l*, pg. 2823
FUJIFILM HUNT CHEMICALS USA, INC.—See FUJIFILM Holdings Corporation; *Int'l*, pg. 2823
FUJIFILM HUNT DO BRASIL - PRODUCAO DE QUIMICOS LTDA—See FUJIFILM Holdings Corporation; *Int'l*, pg. 2823
FUJIFILM HUNT PHOTOGRAPHIC CHEMICALS INC.—See FUJIFILM Holdings Corporation; *Int'l*, pg. 2823
FUJIFILM HUNT SMART SURFACE, LLC—See FUJIFILM Holdings Corporation; *Int'l*, pg. 2823
FUJIFILM IMAGING COLORANTS INC.—See FUJIFILM Holdings Corporation; *Int'l*, pg. 2823
FUJIFILM IMAGING COLORANTS LIMITED—See FUJIFILM Holdings Corporation; *Int'l*, pg. 2822
FUJIFILM IMAGING GERMANY GMBH & CO. KG—See FUJIFILM Holdings Corporation; *Int'l*, pg. 2822
FUJIFILM IMAGING PRODUCTS & SOLUTIONS GMBH & CO. KG.—See FUJIFILM Holdings Corporation; *Int'l*, pg. 2824
FUJIFILM IMAGING PROTEC CO., LTD.—See FUJIFILM Holdings Corporation; *Int'l*, pg. 2824
FUJIFILM IMAGING SYSTEMS CO., LTD.—See FUJIFILM Holdings Corporation; *Int'l*, pg. 2824
FUJIFILM IMAGING SYSTEMS GMBH & CO. KG—See FUJIFILM Holdings Corporation; *Int'l*, pg. 2824
FUJIFILM IMAGING SYSTEMS (SUZHOU) CO., LTD.—See FUJIFILM Holdings Corporation; *Int'l*, pg. 2822
FUJIFILM INDIA PRIVATE LIMITED—See FUJIFILM Holdings Corporation; *Int'l*, pg. 2823
FUJIFILM IRELAND LTD.—See FUJIFILM Holdings Corporation; *Int'l*, pg. 2822
FUJIFILM IRVINE SCIENTIFIC, INC.—See FUJIFILM Holdings Corporation; *Int'l*, pg. 2824
FUJIFILM ITALIA S.P.A.—See FUJIFILM Holdings Corporation; *Int'l*, pg. 2822
FUJIFILM LOGISTICS CO., LTD.—See FUJIFILM Holdings Corporation; *Int'l*, pg. 2824
FUJIFILM LOGISTICS SOLUTION (CHINA) LIMITED—See FUJIFILM Holdings Corporation; *Int'l*, pg. 2824
FUJIFILM (MALAYSIA) SDN. BHD.—See FUJIFILM Holdings Corporation; *Int'l*, pg. 2821
FUJIFILM MANUFACTURING EUROPE B.V.—See FUJIFILM Holdings Corporation; *Int'l*, pg. 2821
FUJIFILM MANUFACTURING USA, INC.—See FUJIFILM Holdings Corporation; *Int'l*, pg. 2823
FUJIFILM MEDIA CREST CO., LTD.—See FUJIFILM Holdings Corporation; *Int'l*, pg. 2824
FUJIFILM MEDIA MANUFACTURING CO., LTD.—See FUJIFILM Holdings Corporation; *Int'l*, pg. 2824
FUJIFILM MEDICAL CO., LTD.—See FUJIFILM Holdings Corporation; *Int'l*, pg. 2824
FUJIFILM MEDICAL IT SOLUTIONS CO., LTD.—See FUJIFILM Holdings Corporation; *Int'l*, pg. 2824
FUJIFILM MEDICAL SOLUTIONS CO., LTD.—See FUJIFILM Holdings Corporation; *Int'l*, pg. 2824
FUJIFILM MEDICAL SYSTEMS BENELUX N.V.—See FUJIFILM Holdings Corporation; *Int'l*, pg. 2822
FUJIFILM MEDICAL SYSTEMS (CALIFORNIA), INC.—See FUJIFILM Holdings Corporation; *Int'l*, pg. 2822
FUJIFILM MEDICAL SYSTEMS FRANCE S.A.S.—See FUJIFILM Holdings Corporation; *Int'l*, pg. 2822
FUJIFILM MEDICAL SYSTEMS TAIWAN CO., LTD.—See FUJIFILM Holdings Corporation; *Int'l*, pg. 2824
FUJIFILM MEDICAL SYSTEMS USA, INC. - ENDOSCOPY DIV—See FUJIFILM Holdings Corporation; *Int'l*, pg. 2822
FUJIFILM MEDICAL TECHNICAL SERVICE (SHANGHAI) CO., LTD.—See FUJIFILM Holdings Corporation; *Int'l*, pg. 2824
FUJIFILM MICRODISKS USA, INC.—See FUJIFILM Holdings Corporation; *Int'l*, pg. 2823
FUJIFILM MIDDLE EAST FZE—See FUJIFILM Holdings Corporation; *Int'l*, pg. 2822
FUJIFILM MYANMAR LIMITED—See FUJIFILM Holdings Corporation; *Int'l*, pg. 2824
FUJIFILM NORDIC AB—See FUJIFILM Holdings Corporation; *Int'l*, pg. 2822
FUJIFILM NORTH AMERICA CORPORATION—See FUJIFILM Holdings Corporation; *Int'l*, pg. 2822
FUJIFILM (NZ) LIMITED—See FUJIFILM Holdings Corporation; *Int'l*, pg. 2821
FUJIFILM OPT-ELECTRONICS (TIANJIN) CO., LTD.—See FUJIFILM Holdings Corporation; *Int'l*, pg. 2824
FUJIFILM OPTICAL DEVICES EUROPE GMBH—See FUJIFILM Holdings Corporation; *Int'l*, pg. 2824
FUJIFILM OPTICS CO., LTD.—See FUJIFILM Holdings Corporation; *Int'l*, pg. 2824
FUJIFILM OPTICS PHILIPPINES INC.—See FUJIFILM Holdings Corporation; *Int'l*, pg. 2824
FUJIFILM OPTO MATERIALS CO., LTD.—See FUJIFILM Holdings Corporation; *Int'l*, pg. 2824
FUJIFILM PHARMA CO., LTD.—See FUJIFILM Holdings Corporation; *Int'l*, pg. 2824
FUJIFILM PHILIPPINES INC.—See FUJIFILM Holdings Corporation; *Int'l*, pg. 2821
FUJIFILM PHOTO MANUFACTURING CO., LTD.—See FUJIFILM Holdings Corporation; *Int'l*, pg. 2824
FUJIFILM PLANAR SOLUTIONS, LLC—See FUJIFILM Holdings Corporation; *Int'l*, pg. 2822
FUJIFILM POLSKA DISTRIBUTION SPOLKA ZO.O—See FUJIFILM Holdings Corporation; *Int'l*, pg. 2822
FUJIFILM PRESENTEC CO., LTD.—See FUJIFILM Holdings Corporation; *Int'l*, pg. 2824
FUJIFILM PRINTING PLATE (CHINA) CO., LTD.—See FUJIFILM Holdings Corporation; *Int'l*, pg. 2825
FUJIFILM RECORDING MEDIA GMBH—See FUJIFILM Holdings Corporation; *Int'l*, pg. 2822
FUJIFILM RECORDING MEDIA ITALIA S.R.L.—See FUJIFILM Holdings Corporation; *Int'l*, pg. 2822
FUJIFILM RI PHARMA CO., LTD.—See FUJIFILM Holdings Corporation; *Int'l*, pg. 2825
FUJIFILM RUS LLC—See FUJIFILM Holdings Corporation; *Int'l*, pg. 2825
FUJI FILM SERICOL AG—See FUJIFILM Holdings Corporation; *Int'l*, pg. 2823
FUJIFILM SERICOL BRASIL PRODUTOS PARA IMPRESSAO LTDA—See FUJIFILM Holdings Corporation; *Int'l*, pg. 2823
FUJIFILM SERICOL INDIA PRIVATE LIMITED—See FUJIFILM Holdings Corporation; *Int'l*, pg. 2823
FUJIFILM SERICOL NEDERLAND BV—See FUJIFILM Holdings Corporation; *Int'l*, pg. 2823
FUJIFILM SERICOL OVERSEAS HOLDINGS LIMITED—See FUJIFILM Holdings Corporation; *Int'l*, pg. 2823
FUJIFILM SERICOL POLSKA SP. Z O.O.—See FUJIFILM Holdings Corporation; *Int'l*, pg. 2823
FUJIFILM SERICOL UK LIMITED—See FUJIFILM Holdings Corporation; *Int'l*, pg. 2823
FUJIFILM SERICOL USA, INC.—See FUJIFILM Holdings Corporation; *Int'l*, pg. 2823
FUJIFILM SHIZUOKA CO., LTD.—See FUJIFILM Holdings Corporation; *Int'l*, pg. 2825
FUJIFILM (SINGAPORE) PTE. LTD.—See FUJIFILM Holdings Corporation; *Int'l*, pg. 2821
FUJIFILM SOFTWARE CO., LTD.—See FUJIFILM Holdings Corporation; *Int'l*, pg. 2825
FUJIFILM SONOSITE, INC.—See FUJIFILM Holdings Corporation; *Int'l*, pg. 2825
FUJIFILM SOUTH AFRICA (PTY) LTD.—See FUJIFILM Holdings Corporation; *Int'l*, pg. 2823
FUJIFILM SPECIALITY INK SYSTEMS LTD.—See FUJIFILM Holdings Corporation; *Int'l*, pg. 2823
FUJIFILM SVERIGE AB—See Axel Johnson Gruppen AB; *Int'l*, pg. 764
FUJIFILM SYSTEMS CORPORATION—See FUJIFILM Holdings Corporation; *Int'l*, pg. 2825
FUJIFILM TECHNO PRODUCTS CO., LTD.—See FUJIFILM Holdings Corporation; *Int'l*, pg. 2825
FUJIFILM TECHNO SERVICE CO., LTD.—See FUJIFILM Holdings Corporation; *Int'l*, pg. 2825
FUJIFILM TERAMEDICA, INC.—See FUJIFILM Holdings Corporation; *Int'l*, pg. 2823
FUJIFILM (THAILAND) LTD.—See FUJIFILM Holdings Corporation; *Int'l*, pg. 2821
FUJIFILM TOYAMA CHEMICAL CO., LTD.—See FUJIFILM Holdings Corporation; *Int'l*, pg. 2825
FUJIFILM UK LTD.—See FUJIFILM Holdings Corporation; *Int'l*, pg. 2823
FUJIFILM UKRAINE LLC—See FUJIFILM Holdings Corporation; *Int'l*, pg. 2823
FUJIFILM ULTRA PURE SOLUTIONS INC.—See FUJIFILM Holdings Corporation; *Int'l*, pg. 2822
FUJIFILM VET SYSTEMS CO., LTD.—See FUJIFILM Holdings Corporation; *Int'l*, pg. 2825
FUJIFILM VIETNAM CO., LTD.—See FUJIFILM Holdings Corporation; *Int'l*, pg. 2823
FUJIFILM WAKO PURE CHEMICAL CORPORATION—See FUJIFILM Holdings Corporation; *Int'l*, pg. 2823
FUJI FLAVOR CO., LTD. - ECOLOGY & PHEROMONE DIVISION—See Japan Tobacco Inc.; *Int'l*, pg. 3906
FUJI FLAVOR CO., LTD. - FLAVOR DIVISION—See Japan Tobacco Inc.; *Int'l*, pg. 3906
FUJI FLAVOR CO., LTD. - PLANNING & GENERAL ADMINISTRATION DIVISION—See Japan Tobacco Inc.; *Int'l*, pg. 3906
FUJI FLAVOR CO., LTD.,—See Japan Tobacco Inc.; *Int'l*, pg. 3905
FUJI FLAVOR CO., LTD. - TOBACCO FLAVOR DIVISION—See Japan Tobacco Inc.; *Int'l*, pg. 3906
FUJI FLEX, INC.—See Fuji Seal International, Inc.; *Int'l*, pg. 2816
FUJI FOOD PRODUCTS, INC.—See Meruelo Group LLC; *U.S. Private*, pg. 2677
FUJI FRESH FOODS CO., LTD.—See Fuji Oil Holdings Inc.; *Int'l*, pg. 2815
FUJI FURMANITE CO., LTD.—See Fuji Electric Co., Ltd.; *Int'l*, pg. 2812
FUJI FURUKAWA E&C (CAMBODIA) CO. LTD.—See Fuji Furukawa Engineering & Construction Co., Ltd.; *Int'l*, pg. 2813
FUJI FURUKAWA E&C (MALAYSIA) SDN. BHD.—See Fuji Furukawa Engineering & Construction Co., Ltd.; *Int'l*, pg. 2813
FUJI FURUKAWA E&C (MYANMAR) CO., LTD.—See Fuji Furukawa Engineering & Construction Co., Ltd.; *Int'l*, pg. 2813
FUJI FURUKAWA E&C (VIETNAM) CO., LTD.—See Fuji Furukawa Engineering & Construction Co., Ltd.; *Int'l*, pg. 2813
FUJI FURUKAWA ENGINEERING & CONSTRUCTION CO., LTD.; *Int'l*, pg. 2813
FUJI GEMCO PRIVATE LIMITED—See Fuji Electric Co., Ltd.; *Int'l*, pg. 2812
FUJI GLASS CO., LTD.; *Int'l*, pg. 2813
FUJI GLOBAL CHOCOLATE (M) SDN. BHD.—See Fuji Oil Holdings Inc.; *Int'l*, pg. 2815
FUJI-HAYA ELECTRIC CORP. OF THE PHILIPPINES—See Fuji Electric Co., Ltd.; *Int'l*, pg. 2812
FUJI HEAVY INDUSTRIES, LTD., AIRCRAFT DIV.—See Subaru Corporation; *Int'l*, pg. 7247
FUJI HEAVY INDUSTRIES, LTD. - AIR SPACE DIV.—See Subaru Corporation; *Int'l*, pg. 7247
FUJI HEAVY INDUSTRIES, LTD., AUTOMOBILE DIV.—See Subaru Corporation; *Int'l*, pg. 7247
FUJI HEAVY INDUSTRIES LTD., CHINA OFFICE—See Subaru Corporation; *Int'l*, pg. 7247
FUJI HEAVY INDUSTRIES, LTD., ENGINE & MACHINERY DIV.—See Subaru Corporation; *Int'l*, pg. 7247
FUJI HEAVY INDUSTRIES, LTD. - GUNMA MAIN PLANT—See Subaru Corporation; *Int'l*, pg. 7247
FUJI HEAVY INDUSTRIES, LTD. - GUNMA OIZUMI PLANT—See Subaru Corporation; *Int'l*, pg. 7247
FUJI HEAVY INDUSTRIES, LTD. - GUNMA YAJIMA PLANT—See Subaru Corporation; *Int'l*, pg. 7247
FUJI HEAVY INDUSTRIES, LTD. - HANDA PLANT—See Subaru Corporation; *Int'l*, pg. 7247
FUJI HEAVY INDUSTRIES, LTD. - HANDA WEST PLANT—See Subaru Corporation; *Int'l*, pg. 7247
FUJI HEAVY INDUSTRIES, LTD. INDUSTRIAL PRODUCTS—See Subaru Corporation; *Int'l*, pg. 7247

COMPANY NAME INDEX

FUJI HEAVY INDUSTRIES, LTD., MANUFACTURING DIV.—See Subaru Corporation; *Int'l*
FUJI HEAVY INDUSTRIES, LTD. - OMIYA SUBARU BUILDING FACILITY—See Subaru Corporation; *Int'l*, pg. 7247
FUJI HEAVY INDUSTRIES, LTD. - SAITAMA PLANT—See Subaru Corporation; *Int'l*, pg. 7247
FUJI HEAVY INDUSTRIES, LTD. - UTSUNOMIYA PLANT—See Subaru Corporation; *Int'l*, pg. 7247
FUJI HEAVY INDUSTRIES (SINGAPORE) PTE. LTD.—See Subaru Corporation; *Int'l*, pg. 7246
FUJI HEAVY INDUSTRIES U.S.A. INC.—See Subaru Corporation; *Int'l*, pg. 7247
FUJI HEAVY INDUSTRIES U.S.A. INC.—See Subaru Corporation; *Int'l*, pg. 7247
FUJI HOME CO., LTD.—See Mugen Estate Co., Ltd.; *Int'l*, pg. 5078
FUJI HONING INDUSTRIAL CO., LTD.—See Fair Friend Group; *Int'l*, pg. 2604
FUJI-HOSO SHIKI CO., LTD.—See Rengo Co., Ltd.; *Int'l*, pg. 6279
FUJI HOUREN CO., LTD.—See Subaru Corporation; *Int'l*, pg. 7247
FUJI HUNT ASIAN PACIFIC HOLDING PTY LTD—See FUJIFILM Holdings Corporation; *Int'l*, pg. 2825
FUJI HUNT IBERICA S.L.—See FUJIFILM Holdings Corporation; *Int'l*, pg. 2821
FUJI HUNT NORDIC AB—See FUJIFILM Holdings Corporation; *Int'l*, pg. 2821
FUJI HUNT PHOTOGRAPHIC CHEMICALS, N.V.—See FUJIFILM Holdings Corporation; *Int'l*, pg. 2822
FUJI INDIA CORPORATION PRIVATE LIMITED—See Fuji Corporation; *Int'l*, pg. 2809
FUJII SANGYO CORPORATION; *Int'l*, pg. 2826
FUJI IT CO., LTD.—See Fuji Electric Co., Ltd.; *Int'l*, pg. 2812
FUJI I-TEC CO., LTD.—See Taihei Dengyo Kaisha Ltd.; *Int'l*, pg. 7411
FUJII TSUSHIN INC.—See Fujii Sangyo Corporation; *Int'l*, pg. 2826
FUJI JIDOSHA KOGYO CO., LTD.—See Sato shoji Corporation; *Int'l*, pg. 6586
FUJI KAKO CO., LTD.—See JFE Holdings, Inc.; *Int'l*, pg. 3904
FUJIKENSETSU CORPORATION—See Toa Road Corporation; *Int'l*, pg. 7769
FUJI KIKO AUTOTECH TOKAI CO., LTD.—See JTEKT Corporation; *Int'l*, pg. 4017
FUJI KIKO CO., LTD - HONJO FACTORY—See JTEKT Corporation; *Int'l*, pg. 4017
FUJI KIKO CO., LTD.—See JTEKT Corporation; *Int'l*, pg. 4017
FUJI KIKO CO., LTD - WASHIZU FACTORY—See JTEKT Corporation; *Int'l*, pg. 4017
FUJI KIZAI CO., LTD.—See Okabe Co., Ltd.; *Int'l*, pg. 5544
FUJIKOH COMPANY., LIMITED; *Int'l*, pg. 2826
FUJIKON INDUSTRIAL HOLDINGS LTD; *Int'l*, pg. 2826
FUJIKON PACKING MATERIAL COMPANY LIMITED—See Fujikon Industrial Holdings Ltd; *Int'l*, pg. 2826
FUJIKOSHI ACCOUNTING CO., LTD.—See Nachi-Fujikoshi Corp.; *Int'l*, pg. 5121
FUJIKOSHI COM SERVICE CO., LTD.—See Nachi-Fujikoshi Corp.; *Int'l*, pg. 5121
FUJIKOSHI INFORMATION SYSTEMS CO., LTD.—See Nachi-Fujikoshi Corp.; *Int'l*, pg. 5121
FUJIKOSHI-NACHI (MALAYSIA) SDN. BHD.—See Nachi-Fujikoshi Corp.; *Int'l*, pg. 5121
FUJI KOYO CZECH S.R.O.—See JTEKT Corporation; *Int'l*, pg. 4017
FUJIKURA AMERICA, INC. - DDK CONNECTOR DIVISION—See Fujikura Ltd.; *Int'l*, pg. 2827
FUJIKURA AMERICA INC.—See Fujikura Ltd.; *Int'l*, pg. 2827
FUJIKURA ASIA LIMITED—See Fujikura Ltd.; *Int'l*, pg. 2827
FUJIKURA ASIA LTD. - DDK CONNECTOR DIVISION—See Fujikura Ltd.; *Int'l*, pg. 2827
FUJIKURA ASIA (MALAYSIA) SDN. BHD.—See Fujikura Ltd.; *Int'l*, pg. 2827
FUJIKURA AUTOMOTIVE AMERICA LLC.—See Fujikura Ltd.; *Int'l*, pg. 2827
FUJIKURA AUTOMOTIVE ASIA LTD.—See Fujikura Ltd.; *Int'l*, pg. 2827
FUJIKURA AUTOMOTIVE CZECH REPUBLIC, S.R.O.—See Fujikura Ltd.; *Int'l*, pg. 2827
FUJIKURA AUTOMOTIVE DO BRAZIL LTDA.—See Fujikura Ltd.; *Int'l*, pg. 2828
FUJIKURA AUTOMOTIVE EUROPE GMBH—See Fujikura Ltd.; *Int'l*, pg. 2827
FUJIKURA AUTOMOTIVE EUROPE S.A.U.—See Fujikura Ltd.; *Int'l*, pg. 2827
FUJIKURA AUTOMOTIVE GUANGZHOU CO., LTD.—See Fujikura Ltd.; *Int'l*, pg. 2827
FUJIKURA AUTOMOTIVE MEXICO PUEBLA, S.A. DE C.V.—See Fujikura Ltd.; *Int'l*, pg. 2828
FUJIKURA AUTOMOTIVE MEXICO QUERETARO, S.A. DE C.V.—See Fujikura Ltd.; *Int'l*, pg. 2828

FUJIKURA AUTOMOTIVE MEXICO SALAMANCA, S.A. DE C.V.—See Fujikura Ltd.; *Int'l*, pg. 2828
FUJIKURA AUTOMOTIVE MEXICO S. DE R.L. DE C.V.—See Fujikura Ltd.; *Int'l*, pg. 2828
FUJIKURA AUTOMOTIVE MLD S.R.L.—See Fujikura Ltd.; *Int'l*, pg. 2828
FUJIKURA AUTOMOTIVE MOROCCO KENITRA, S.A.S.—See Fujikura Ltd.; *Int'l*, pg. 2828
FUJIKURA AUTOMOTIVE MOROCCO TANGIER, S.A.S.—See Fujikura Ltd.; *Int'l*, pg. 2828
FUJIKURA AUTOMOTIVE PARAGUAY S.A.—See Fujikura Ltd.; *Int'l*, pg. 2828
FUJIKURA AUTOMOTIVE ROMANIA S.R.L.—See Fujikura Ltd.; *Int'l*, pg. 2828
FUJIKURA AUTOMOTIVE (THAILAND) LTD.—See Fujikura Ltd.; *Int'l*, pg. 2827
FUJIKURA AUTOMOTIVE UKRAINE LVIV, LLC—See Fujikura Ltd.; *Int'l*, pg. 2828
FUJIKURA AUTOMOTIVE VIETNAM LTD.—See Fujikura Ltd.; *Int'l*, pg. 2828
FUJIKURA CABOS PARA ENERGIA E TELECOMUNICACOES LTDA.—See Fujikura Ltd.; *Int'l*, pg. 2828
FUJIKURA (CHINA) CO., LTD.—See Fujikura Ltd.; *Int'l*, pg. 2827
FUJIKURA COMPONENTS LTD.—See Fujikura Ltd.; *Int'l*, pg. 2828
FUJIKURA COMPOSITE AMERICA, INC.—See Fujikura Composites Inc.; *Int'l*, pg. 2826
FUJIKURA COMPOSITE HAIPHONG, INC.—See Fujikura Composites Inc.; *Int'l*, pg. 2826
FUJIKURA COMPOSITE KOREA, LTD.—See Fujikura Composites Inc.; *Int'l*, pg. 2826
FUJIKURA COMPOSITES EUROPE B.V.—See Fujikura Composites Inc.; *Int'l*, pg. 2826
FUJIKURA COMPOSITES INC.; *Int'l*, pg. 2826
FUJIKURA DIA CABLE LTD.—See Fujikura Ltd.; *Int'l*, pg. 2828
FUJIKURA ELECTRONICS SHANGHAI LTD.—See Fujikura Ltd.; *Int'l*, pg. 2828
FUJIKURA ELECTRONICS (THAILAND) LTD. - AYUTTHAYA FACTORY 1—See Fujikura Ltd.; *Int'l*, pg. 2828
FUJIKURA ELECTRONICS (THAILAND) LTD. - LAMPHUN FACTORY 1—See Fujikura Ltd.; *Int'l*, pg. 2828
FUJIKURA ELECTRONICS (THAILAND) LTD. - NAVANAKORN FACTORY 2—See Fujikura Ltd.; *Int'l*, pg. 2828
FUJIKURA ELECTRONICS (THAILAND) LTD. - NAVANAKORN FACTORY 3—See Fujikura Ltd.; *Int'l*, pg. 2828
FUJIKURA ELECTRONICS (THAILAND) LTD. - PRACHINBURI FACTORY 1—See Fujikura Ltd.; *Int'l*, pg. 2828
FUJIKURA ELECTRONICS (THAILAND) LTD.—See Fujikura Ltd.; *Int'l*, pg. 2828
FUJIKURA ELECTRONICS VIETNAM LTD.—See Fujikura Ltd.; *Int'l*, pg. 2828
FUJIKURA EUROPE LTD. - DDK CONNECTOR DIVISION—See Fujikura Ltd.; *Int'l*, pg. 2828
FUJIKURA EUROPE LTD. - ELECTRONICS DIVISION—See Fujikura Ltd.; *Int'l*, pg. 2828
FUJIKURA EUROPE LTD. - FIBRE OPTICS DIVISION—See Fujikura Ltd.; *Int'l*, pg. 2828
FUJIKURA EUROPE LTD. - PLANT & INFRASTRUCTURE CABLES DIVISION—See Fujikura Ltd.; *Int'l*, pg. 2828
FUJIKURA EUROPE LTD.—See Fujikura Ltd.; *Int'l*, pg. 2828
FUJIKURA FEDERAL CABLES SDN BHD—See Fujikura Ltd.; *Int'l*, pg. 2828
FUJIKURA FIBER-HOME OPTO-ELECTRONICS MATERIAL TECHNOLOGY CO., LTD.—See Fujikura Ltd.; *Int'l*, pg. 2828
FUJIKURA FIBER OPTICS VIETNAM LTD.—See Fujikura Ltd.; *Int'l*, pg. 2828
FUJIKURA GRAPHICS, INC.—See Fujikura Composites Inc.; *Int'l*, pg. 2826
FUJIKURA HENGTONG AERIAL CABLE SYSTEM LTD.—See Fujikura Ltd.; *Int'l*, pg. 2828
FUJIKURA HIGH OPT CO., LTD.—See Fujikura Ltd.; *Int'l*, pg. 2828
FUJIKURA HONG KONG LIMITED—See Fujikura Ltd.; *Int'l*, pg. 2828
FUJIKURA HONG KONG LTD. - DDK CONNECTOR DIVISION—See Fujikura Ltd.; *Int'l*, pg. 2828
FUJIKURA KASEI COATING INDIA PRIVATE LTD.—See Fujikura Kasei Co., Ltd.; *Int'l*, pg. 2827
FUJIKURA KASEI COATING (TIANJIN) CO., LTD.—See Fujikura Kasei Co., Ltd.; *Int'l*, pg. 2827
FUJIKURA KASEI CO., LTD. - SANO PLANT 1—See Fujikura Kasei Co., Ltd.; *Int'l*, pg. 2826
FUJIKURA KASEI CO., LTD. - SANO PLANT 2—See Fujikura Kasei Co., Ltd.; *Int'l*, pg. 2826
FUJIKURA KASEI CO., LTD.; *Int'l*, pg. 2826
FUJIKURA KASEI (FOSHAN) COATING CO., LTD.—See Fujikura Kasei Co., Ltd.; *Int'l*, pg. 2826
FUJIKURA KASEI MALAYSIA SDN. BHD.—See Fujikura Kasei Co., Ltd.; *Int'l*, pg. 2827
FUJIKURA KASEI (THAILAND) CO., LTD.—See Fujikura Kasei Co., Ltd.; *Int'l*, pg. 2827
FUJIKURA KASEI VIETNAM CO., LTD.—See Fujikura Kasei Co., Ltd.; *Int'l*, pg. 2827
FUJIKURA KOREA AUTOMOTIVE LTD.—See Fujikura Ltd.; *Int'l*, pg. 2828

FUJIKURA LOGISTICS CO., LTD.—See Fujikura Ltd.; *Int'l*, pg. 2828
FUJIKURA LTD.; *Int'l*, pg. 2827
FUJIKURA LTD.—See Fujikura Ltd.; *Int'l*, pg. 2828
FUJIKURA (MALAYSIA) SDN. BHD.—See Fujikura Ltd.; *Int'l*, pg. 2827
FUJIKURA PRECISION LTD.—See Fujikura Ltd.; *Int'l*, pg. 2828
FUJIKURA RICHARD MANUFACTURING INC.—See Fujikura Ltd.; *Int'l*, pg. 2828
FUJIKURA SHANGHAI OPTICAL COMPONENTS CO., LTD.—See Fujikura Ltd.; *Int'l*, pg. 2828
FUJIKURA SHANGHAI TRADING CO., LTD.—See Fujikura Ltd.; *Int'l*, pg. 2829
FUJIKURA SHOJI CO., LTD.—See Fujikura Ltd.; *Int'l*, pg. 2829
FUJIKURA SOLUTIONS LTD.—See Fujikura Ltd.; *Int'l*, pg. 2829
FUJIKURA TECHNOLOGY EUROPE GMBH—See Fujikura Ltd.; *Int'l*, pg. 2829
FUJIKURA ZHUHAI CO., LTD.—See Fujikura Ltd.; *Int'l*, pg. 2829
FUJIKYU CORPORATION; *Int'l*, pg. 2829
FUJI KYUKO CO., LTD.; *Int'l*, pg. 2813
FUJI LABEL CO., LTD.—See DIC Corporation; *Int'l*, pg. 2109
FUJI LATEX CO., LTD.; *Int'l*, pg. 2813
FUJI LATEX SHANGHAI CO., LTD.—See Fuji Latex Co., Ltd.; *Int'l*, pg. 2813
FUJI LIFE SCIENCE PRODUCTS LIMITED—See China-Hong Kong Photo Products Holdings Limited; *Int'l*, pg. 1568
FUJI LIGHTING AND TECHNOLOGY, INC.—See Fuji Media Holdings, Inc.; *Int'l*, pg. 2813
FUJI LINEAR CORPORATION—See Fuji Corporation; *Int'l*, pg. 2809
FUJILLOY INDIA PRIVATE LIMITED—See Fuji Die Co., Ltd.; *Int'l*, pg. 2810
FUJILLOY MALAYSIA SDN. BHD.—See Fuji Die Co., Ltd.; *Int'l*, pg. 2810
FUJILLOY THAILAND CO., LTD.—See Fuji Die Co., Ltd.; *Int'l*, pg. 2810
FUJI LOGISTICS CO., LTD.—See Mitsubishi Logistics Corporation; *Int'l*, pg. 4962
FUJI LOGISTICS (DALIAN FTZ) CO. LTD.—See Mitsubishi Logistics Corporation; *Int'l*, pg. 4962
FUJI LOGISTICS EUROPE B.V.—See Mitsubishi Logistics Corporation; *Int'l*, pg. 4962
FUJI LOGISTICS (H.K.) CO., LIMITED—See Mitsubishi Logistics Corporation; *Int'l*, pg. 4962
FUJI LOGISTICS OPERATIONS CO, LTD—See Mitsubishi Logistics Corporation; *Int'l*, pg. 4962
FUJI LOGISTICS (SHENZHEN) CO., LTD—See Mitsubishi Logistics Corporation; *Int'l*, pg. 4962
FUJI LOGISTICS SUPPORT CO., LTD—See Mitsubishi Logistics Corporation; *Int'l*, pg. 4962
FUJI MACHINE AMERICA CORPORATION—See Fuji Corporation; *Int'l*, pg. 2809
FUJI MACHINE ASIA PTE. LTD.—See Sojitz Corporation; *Int'l*, pg. 7061
FUJI MACHINE CHINA CO.,LTD.—See Fuji Corporation; *Int'l*, pg. 2809
FUJI MACHINE MANUFACTURING (EUROPE) GMBH—See Fuji Corporation; *Int'l*, pg. 2810
FUJI MACHINE MFG. CO., LTD. - FUJIOKA PLANT—See Fuji Corporation; *Int'l*, pg. 2810
FUJI MACHINE MFG. CO., LTD. - OKAZAKI PLANT—See Fuji Corporation; *Int'l*, pg. 2810
FUJI MACHINE MFG. (SINGAPORE) PTE. LTD.—See Sojitz Corporation; *Int'l*, pg. 7061
FUJI MACHINERY CO., LTD.—See Subaru Corporation; *Int'l*, pg. 7247
FUJIMAE STEEL CO., LTD.—See Kawada Technologies Inc.; *Int'l*, pg. 4093
FUJIMAK (CAMBODIA) CO., LTD.—See Fujimak Corporation; *Int'l*, pg. 2829
FUJIMAK CORPORATION; *Int'l*, pg. 2829
FUJIMAK FOOD SERVICE EQUIPMENT SINGAPORE PTE., LTD.—See Fujimak Corporation; *Int'l*, pg. 2829
FUJIMAK GUAM CORPORATION—See Fujimak Corporation; *Int'l*, pg. 2829
FUJIMAK HONG KONG COMPANY LIMITED—See Fujimak Corporation; *Int'l*, pg. 2829
FUJIMAK PHILIPPINES CORPORATION—See Fujimak Corporation; *Int'l*, pg. 2829
FUJIMAK SHANGHAI CORPORATION—See Fujimak Corporation; *Int'l*, pg. 2829
FUJIMAK TAIWAN CORPORATION—See Fujimak Corporation; *Int'l*, pg. 2829
FUJIMAK (THAILAND) COMPANY LIMITED—See Fujimak Corporation; *Int'l*, pg. 2829
FUJIMATSU CO., LTD.—See Sojitz Corporation; *Int'l*, pg. 7065
FUJIM DIGITAL SDN. BHD.—See ARTRONIQ BERHAD; *Int'l*, pg. 585
FUJI MEDIA HOLDINGS, INC.; *Int'l*, pg. 2813
FUJI MEDIA TECHNOLOGY, INC.—See Fuji Media Holdings, Inc.; *Int'l*, pg. 2813

FUJI MEDIA HOLDINGS, INC.

CORPORATE AFFILIATIONS

FUJI MEDICAL INSTRUMENTS MFG. CO., LTD.—See Johnson Health Tech. Co., Ltd.; *Int'l*, pg. 3991
FUJIMIC, INC.—See Fuji Media Holdings, Inc.; *Int'l*, pg. 2814
FUJIMI CORPORATION—See Fujimi Incorporated; *Int'l*, pg. 2829
FUJI MICRO CO., LTD.—See Advanex Inc.; *Int'l*, pg. 163
FUJI MICRO ELECTRONICS CO., LTD.—See Advanex Inc.; *Int'l*, pg. 163
FUJIMI EUROPE GMBH—See Fujimi Incorporated; *Int'l*, pg. 2829
FUJIMI INCORPORATED; *Int'l*, pg. 2829
FUJIMI-MICRO TECHNOLOGY SDN. BHD—See Fujimi Incorporated; *Int'l*, pg. 2829
FUJIMINO ECOWELLS CORPORATION—See Hitachi Zosen Corporation; *Int'l*, pg. 3410
FUJIMI SHENZHEN TECHNOLOGY CO., LTD.—See Fujimi Incorporated; *Int'l*, pg. 2829
FUJIMORI SANGYO CO., LTD.—See ZACROS Corporation; *Int'l*, pg. 8619
FUJIMOTO FOODS INC.; *Int'l*, pg. 2829
FUJI N2TELLIGENCE GMBH—See Fuji Electric Co., Ltd.; *Int'l*, pg. 2812
FUJINAGA PHARM CO., LTD.—See Qol Holdings Co., Ltd.; *Int'l*, pg. 6147
FUJINE SANGYO CO., LTD.—See Alconix Corporation; *Int'l*, pg. 302
FUJI NIHON SEITO CO., LTD.—See Sojitz Corporation; *Int'l*, pg. 7061
FUJINO CLUB CO., LTD.—See Amada Holdings Co., Ltd.; *Int'l*, pg. 404
FUJINON AUSTRALIA PTY. LTD.—See FUJIFILM Holdings Corporation; *Int'l*, 2823
FUJINON (EUROPE) GMBH—See FUJIFILM Holdings Corporation; *Int'l*, pg. 2822
FUJI OFFICE & LIFE SERVICE, CO., LTD.—See Fuji Electric Co., Ltd.; *Int'l*, pg. 2812
FUJI OFFSET PLATES MANUFACTURING LTD; *Int'l*, pg. 2814
FUJIO FOOD GROUP INC.; *Int'l*, pg. 2829
FUJIO FOOD SYSTEM U.S.A. CO., LTD.—See Fujio Food Group Inc.; *Int'l*, pg. 2830
FUJI OIL ASIA PTE. LTD.—See Fuji Oil Holdings Inc.; *Int'l*, pg. 2815
FUJI OIL (CHINA) INVESTMENT CO., LTD.—See Fuji Oil Holdings Inc.; *Int'l*, pg. 2815
FUJI OIL CO., LTD. - CHIBA PLANT—See Fuji Oil Holdings Inc.; *Int'l*, pg. 2815
FUJI OIL CO., LTD. - ISHIKAWA PLANT—See Fuji Oil Holdings Inc.; *Int'l*, pg. 2815
FUJI OIL CO., LTD. - KANTO PLANT—See Fuji Oil Holdings Inc.; *Int'l*, pg. 2815
FUJI OIL CO., LTD. - KOBE PLANT—See Fuji Oil Holdings Inc.; *Int'l*, pg. 2815
FUJI OIL CO., LTD. - PROTEIN FOODS TSUKUBA PLANT—See Fuji Oil Holdings Inc.; *Int'l*, pg. 2815
FUJI OIL CO., LTD. - RINKU PLANT—See Fuji Oil Holdings Inc.; *Int'l*, pg. 2815
FUJI OIL CO., LTD. - SAKAI PLANT—See Fuji Oil Holdings Inc.; *Int'l*, pg. 2815
FUJI OIL COMPANY, LTD.; *Int'l*, pg. 2814
FUJI OIL EUROPE—See Fuji Oil Holdings Inc.; *Int'l*, pg. 2815
FUJI OIL GHANA LTD.—See Fuji Oil Holdings Inc.; *Int'l*, pg. 2815
FUJI OIL HOLDINGS INC.; *Int'l*, pg. 2815
FUJI OIL (SINGAPORE) PTE. LTD.—See Fuji Oil Holdings Inc.; *Int'l*, pg. 2815
FUJI OIL (THAILAND) CO., LTD.—See Fuji Oil Holdings Inc.; *Int'l*, pg. 2815
FUJI OIL (ZHANG JIA GANG) CO., LTD.—See Fuji Oil Holdings Inc.; *Int'l*, pg. 2815
FUJIOKA-CHUHATSU CO., LTD.—See Chuo Spring Co., Ltd.; *Int'l*, pg. 1599
FUJI OOZX INC.; *Int'l*, pg. 2816
FUJI OOZX MEXICO, S.A. DE C.V.—See Daido Steel Co., Ltd.; *Int'l*, pg. 1923
FUJIPACIFIC MUSIC INC—See Fuji Media Holdings, Inc.; *Int'l*, pg. 2814
FUJI PACKAGING SERVICES, INC—See Fuji Seal International, Inc.; *Int'l*, pg. 2816
FUJI PHARMA CO., LTD.; *Int'l*, pg. 2816
FUJI PHOTO PRODUCTS COMPANY, LIMITED—See China-Hong Kong Photo Products Holdings Limited; *Int'l*, pg. 1568
FUJIPREAM CORPORATION - HIMEJI FACTORY—See Fujipream Corporation; *Int'l*, pg. 2830
FUJIPREAM CORPORATION - PV FACTORY—See Fujipream Corporation; *Int'l*, pg. 2830
FUJIPREAM CORPORATION; *Int'l*, pg. 2830
FUJI PRESS CO., LTD.—See Alconix Corporation; *Int'l*, pg. 302
FUJI P.S CORPORATION; *Int'l*, pg. 2816
FUJI QUALITY HOUSE CO., LTD.—See Yuasa Trading Co., Ltd.; *Int'l*, pg. 8609
FUJIREBIO CHINA CO., LTD.—See H.U. Group Holdings, Inc.; *Int'l*, pg. 3196
FUJIREBIO DIAGNOSTICS AB—See H.U. Group Holdings, Inc.; *Int'l*, pg. 3196

FUJIREBIO DIAGNOSTICS INC.—See H.U. Group Holdings, Inc.; *Int'l*, pg. 3196
FUJIREBIO EUROPE N.V.—See H.U. Group Holdings, Inc.; *Int'l*, pg. 3196
FUJIREBIO FRANCE SARL—See H.U. Group Holdings, Inc.; *Int'l*, pg. 3196
FUJIREBIO GERMANY GMBH—See H.U. Group Holdings, Inc.; *Int'l*, pg. 3196
FUJIREBIO HOLDINGS, INC.—See H.U. Group Holdings, Inc.; *Int'l*, pg. 3196
FUJIREBIO IBERIA SL—See H.U. Group Holdings, Inc.; *Int'l*, pg. 3196
FUJIREBIO INC.—See H.U. Group Holdings, Inc.; *Int'l*, pg. 3196
FUJIREBIO ITALIA S.R.L.—See H.U. Group Holdings, Inc.; *Int'l*, pg. 3196
FUJIREBIO TAIWAN, INC.—See H.U. Group Holdings, Inc.; *Int'l*, pg. 3196
FUJIREBIO US, INC.—See H.U. Group Holdings, Inc.; *Int'l*, pg. 3196
FUJI ROTO GRAVURE SDN. BHD.—See Fuji Offset Plates Manufacturing Ltd; *Int'l*, pg. 2814
FUJI ROZAI CO., LTD.—See ARE Holdings, Inc.; *Int'l*, pg. 557
FUJISANKEI AGENCY CO., LTD.—See Fuji Media Holdings, Inc.; *Int'l*, pg. 2814
FUJISANKEI COMMUNICATIONS INTERNATIONAL, INC. - LONDON OFFICE—See Fuji Media Holdings, Inc.; *Int'l*, pg. 2814
FUJISANKEI COMMUNICATIONS INTERNATIONAL, INC. - LOS ANGELES—See Fuji Media Holdings, Inc.; *Int'l*, pg. 2814
FUJISANKEI COMMUNICATIONS INTERNATIONAL, INC.—See Fuji Media Holdings, Inc.; *Int'l*, pg. 2814
FUJISANKEI PERSONNEL INC.—See Fuji Media Holdings, Inc.; *Int'l*, pg. 2814
FUJISAN MAGAZINE SERVICE CO., LTD.—See Transcosmos Inc.; *Int'l*, pg. 7898
FUJISAN TECHNOLOGIES LIMITED—See Thacker & Company Limited; *Int'l*, pg. 7589
FUJISASH CO., LTD.; *Int'l*, pg. 2830
FUJI SATELLITE BROADCASTING, INC.—See Fuji Media Holdings, Inc.; *Int'l*, pg. 2813
FUJISAWA HIGH TRUST CO., LTD.—See Takuma Co., Ltd.; *Int'l*, pg. 7442
FUJISAWA SA—See Astellas Pharma Inc.; *Int'l*, pg. 652
FUJISAWA SYNTHELABO PHARMACEUTICALS CO., LTD.—See Astellas Pharma Inc.; *Int'l*, pg. 653
FUJISAWA SYNTHELABO PHARMACEUTICALS CO., LTD.—See Sanofi; *Int'l*, pg. 6547
FUJISAWA TAIWAN CO., LTD.—See Astellas Pharma Inc.; *Int'l*, pg. 653
FUJI SEAL ENGINEERING CO., LTD.—See Fuji Seal International, Inc.; *Int'l*, pg. 2816
FUJI SEAL EUROPE B.V.—See Fuji Seal International, Inc.; *Int'l*, pg. 2816
FUJI SEAL EUROPE LTD.—See Fuji Seal International, Inc.; *Int'l*, pg. 2816
FUJI SEAL EUROPE S.A.S.—See Fuji Seal International, Inc.; *Int'l*, pg. 2816
FUJI SEAL FRANCE S.A.S.—See Fuji Seal International, Inc.; *Int'l*, pg. 2816
FUJI SEAL IBERIA, S.L.U—See Fuji Seal International, Inc.; *Int'l*, pg. 2816
FUJI SEAL, INC.—See Fuji Seal International, Inc.; *Int'l*, pg. 2816
FUJI SEAL INDIA PVT LTD—See Fuji Seal International, Inc.; *Int'l*, pg. 2816
FUJI SEAL INTERNATIONAL, INC - NARA FACTORY—See Fuji Seal International, Inc.; *Int'l*, pg. 2816
FUJI SEAL INTERNATIONAL, INC.; *Int'l*, pg. 2816
FUJI SEAL PACKAGING DE MEXICO, S.A. DE C.V—See Fuji Seal International, Inc.; *Int'l*, pg. 2816
FUJI SEAL PACKAGING (THAILAND) CO., LTD.—See Fuji Seal International, Inc.; *Int'l*, pg. 2816
FUJI SEAL PERSONNEL SERVICES, S.A. DE C.V—See Fuji Seal International, Inc.; *Int'l*, pg. 2816
FUJI SEAL POLAND SP.Z.O.O.—See Fuji Seal International, Inc.; *Int'l*, pg. 2816
FUJI SEAL SOUTHEAST ASIA, INC.—See Fuji Seal International, Inc.; *Int'l*, pg. 2816
FUJI SEAL VIETNAM CO., LTD.—See Fuji Seal International, Inc.; *Int'l*, pg. 2816
FUJI SEAL WEST, INC.—See Fuji Seal International, Inc.; *Int'l*, pg. 2816
FUJI SEATS (MALAYSIA) SDN. BHD.—See APM Automotive Holdings Berhad; *Int'l*, pg. 516
FUJI SEIKI CO., LTD. - MATSUYAMA FACTORY—See Fuji Seiki Co., Ltd.; *Int'l*, pg. 2817
FUJI SEIKI CO., LTD.; *Int'l*, pg. 2817
FUJI SEIKO HONSHA CO., LTD—See Okamura Corporation; *Int'l*, pg. 5545
FUJI SEMEC INC.—See Fuji Electric Co., Ltd.; *Int'l*, pg. 2812
FUJI SENKO TRANSPORT CO., LTD.—See Senko Group Holdings Co., Ltd.; *Int'l*, pg. 6709
FUJISEY CO., LTD.—See ANA Holdings Inc.; *Int'l*, pg. 444

FUJI SHAFT CO., LTD.—See Fuji Die Co., Ltd.; *Int'l*, pg. 2810
FUJI SHOJI CO., LTD.—See Carlit Co., Ltd.; *Int'l*, pg. 1338
FUJISHOJI CO., LTD.; *Int'l*, pg. 2830
FUJI SMBE ELECTRIC PTE LTD—See Fuji Electric Co., Ltd.; *Int'l*, pg. 2812
FUJI SMBE INDUSTRIES PTE LTD—See Fuji Electric Co., Ltd.; *Int'l*, pg. 2812
FUJI SMBE PTE. LTD.—See Fuji Electric Co., Ltd.; *Int'l*, pg. 2812
FUJI SMBE SYSTEMS PTE LTD—See Fuji Electric Co., Ltd.; *Int'l*, pg. 2812
FUJI SMBE TECHNOLOGY PTE LTD—See Fuji Electric Co., Ltd.; *Int'l*, pg. 2812
FUJISOFT AMERICA INC.—See FUJISOFT INCORPORATED; *Int'l*, pg. 2830
FUJISOFT DIS CO., LTD.—See Nomura Research Institute, Ltd.; *Int'l*, pg. 5413
FUJISOFT INCORPORATED; *Int'l*, pg. 2830
FUJISOFT KIKAKU LTD.—See FUJISOFT INCORPORATED; *Int'l*, pg. 2830
FUJISOFT SERVICE BUREAU INCORPORATED—See FUJISOFT INCORPORATED; *Int'l*, pg. 2830
FUJISOFT SSS, INC.—See FUJISOFT INCORPORATED; *Int'l*, pg. 2830
FUJISOFT TISSUE ENGINEERING CO., LTD.—See FUJISOFT INCORPORATED; *Int'l*, pg. 2830
FUJISOKU CORPORATION - OVERSEAS SALES DIVISION—See Nidec Corporation; *Int'l*, pg. 5274
FUJISOKU CORPORATION - SYSTEM DIVISION—See Nidec Corporation; *Int'l*, pg. 5274
FUJI SUNNY FOODS CO., LTD.—See Fuji Oil Holdings Inc.; *Int'l*, pg. 2815
FUJITA AMERICAS, INC.—See Daiwa House Industry Co., Ltd.; *Int'l*, pg. 1946
FUJITA BUILDING MAINTENANCE INC.—See Daiwa House Industry Co., Ltd.; *Int'l*, pg. 1946
FUJITA (CHINA) CONSTRUCTION CO., LTD.—See Daiwa House Industry Co., Ltd.; *Int'l*, pg. 1946
FUJI TACK EAST, INC.—See Fuji Seal International, Inc.; *Int'l*, pg. 2816
FUJI TACK, INC.—See Fuji Seal International, Inc.; *Int'l*, pg. 2816
FUJITA CORPORATION CO., LTD.—See Zensho Holdings Co., Ltd.; *Int'l*, pg. 8634
FUJITA CORPORATION (M) SDN. BHD.—See Daiwa House Industry Co., Ltd.; *Int'l*, pg. 1946
FUJITA CORPORATION SINGAPORE PTE. LTD.—See Daiwa House Industry Co., Ltd.; *Int'l*, pg. 1946
FUJITA CORPORATION—See Daiwa House Industry Co., Ltd.; *Int'l*, pg. 1946
FUJITA CORPORATION (THAILAND) LTD.—See Daiwa House Industry Co., Ltd.; *Int'l*, pg. 1946
FUJITA CORPORATION VIETNAM CO., LTD.—See Daiwa House Industry Co., Ltd.; *Int'l*, pg. 1946
FUJITA DEVICE CO., LTD.—See FUJITA ENGINEERING Co., Ltd.; *Int'l*, pg. 2831
FUJITA ENGINEERING CO., LTD.; *Int'l*, pg. 2831
FUJITA ENGINEERING INDIA PVT. LTD.—See Daiwa House Industry Co., Ltd.; *Int'l*, pg. 1946
FUJITA INTEGRAL MEXICO S.A. DE C.V.—See Daiwa House Industry Co., Ltd.; *Int'l*, pg. 1946
FUJITA KANKO INC.; *Int'l*, pg. 2831
FUJITA PHILIPPINES CONSTRUCTION & DEVELOPMENT, INC.—See Daiwa House Industry Co., Ltd.; *Int'l*, pg. 1946
FUJITA PHILIPPINES INC.—See Daiwa House Industry Co., Ltd.; *Int'l*, pg. 1946
FUJITA RESEARCH (ENCINO OFFICE)—See Daiwa House Industry Co., Ltd.; *Int'l*, pg. 1946
FUJITA ROAD CONSTRUCTION CO., LTD.—See Daiwa House Industry Co., Ltd.; *Int'l*, pg. 1946
FUJITA SHOJI CO., LTD.—See Daiwa House Industry Co., Ltd.; *Int'l*, pg. 1946
FUJITA SOLUTION PARTNERS CO., LTD.—See FUJITA ENGINEERING Co., Ltd.; *Int'l*, pg. 2831
FUJITEC AMERICA INC—See Fujitec Co., Ltd.; *Int'l*, pg. 2831
FUJITEC ARGENTINA S.A.—See Fujitec Co., Ltd.; *Int'l*, pg. 2831
FUJITEC CANADA, INC.—See Fujitec Co., Ltd.; *Int'l*, pg. 2831
FUJITEC CO., LTD.; *Int'l*, pg. 2831
FUJITEC EGYPT CO., LTD.—See Fujitec Co., Ltd.; *Int'l*, pg. 2831
FUJITEC ELEVATOR CO. INC.—See Fujitec Co., Ltd.; *Int'l*, pg. 2831
FUJITEC (HK) COMPANY LIMITED—See Fujitec Co., Ltd.; *Int'l*, pg. 2831
FUJI TECHNICA & MIYAZU INC.—See Toyo Seikan Group Holdings, Ltd.; *Int'l*, pg. 7857
FUJI TECHNO SERVICE CO., LTD.—See Subaru Corporation; *Int'l*, pg. 7247
FUJI TECHNO SOLUTIONS CO., INC.; *Int'l*, pg. 2817
FUJITEC INC.—See Fujitec Co., Ltd.; *Int'l*, pg. 2831
FUJITEC INDIA PRIVATE LTD.—See Fujitec Co., Ltd.; *Int'l*, pg. 2831
FUJITEC KOREA CO., LTD.—See Fujitec Co., Ltd.; *Int'l*, pg. 2831

COMPANY NAME INDEX

FUJITEC LANKA (PRIVATE) LTD.—See Fujitec Co., Ltd.; *Int'l*, pg. 2831
FUJITEC (MALAYSIA) SDN BHD—See Fujitec Co., Ltd.; *Int'l*, pg. 2831
FUJITEC MYANMAR CO., LTD.—See Fujitec Co., Ltd.; *Int'l*, pg. 2831
FUJITEC PACIFIC, INC.—See Fujitec Co., Ltd.; *Int'l*, pg. 2831
FUJITEC SAUDI ARABIA CO., LTD.—See Fujitec Co., Ltd.; *Int'l*, pg. 2831
FUJITEC SHANGHAI SOURCING CENTER CO., LTD.—See Fujitec Co., Ltd.; *Int'l*, pg. 2831
FUJITEC SHANGHAI TECHNOLOGIES CO., LTD.—See Fujitec Co., Ltd.; *Int'l*, pg. 2831
FUJITEC SINGAPORE CORPORATION LIMITED—See Fujitec Co., Ltd.; *Int'l*, pg. 2831
FUJITEC TAIWAN CO. LTD.—See Fujitec Co., Ltd.; *Int'l*, pg. 2831
FUJITEC (THAILAND) CO., LTD.—See Fujitec Co., Ltd.; *Int'l*, pg. 2831
FUJITEC UK LTD.—See Fujitec Co., Ltd.; *Int'l*, pg. 2831
FUJITEC URUGUAY S.A.—See Fujitec Co., Ltd.; *Int'l*, pg. 2831
FUJITEC VENEZUELA C.A.—See Fujitec Co., Ltd.; *Int'l*, pg. 2831
FUJITEC VIETNAM CO., LTD.—See Fujitec Co., Ltd.; *Int'l*, pg. 2831
FUJI TELECOMS CO., LTD.—See Takebishi Corporation; *Int'l*, pg. 7436
FUJI TELEVISION BANGKOK BUREAU—See Fuji Media Holdings, Inc.; *Int'l*, pg. 2813
FUJI TELEVISION BEIJING BUREAU—See Fuji Media Holdings, Inc.; *Int'l*, pg. 2814
FUJI TELEVISION MOSCOW BUREAU/ FNN MOSCOW BUREAU—See Fuji Media Holdings, Inc.; *Int'l*, pg. 2814
FUJI TELEVISION NETWORK, INC.—See Fuji Media Holdings, Inc.; *Int'l*, pg. 2814
FUJITOMI SECURITIES CO., LTD.; *Int'l*, pg. 2831
FUJITRANS CORPORATION; *Int'l*, pg. 2832
FUJITRANS U.S.A., INC.—See Fujitrans Corporation; *Int'l*, pg. 2832
FUJITSU AMERICA, INC.—See Fujitsu Limited; *Int'l*, pg. 2030
FUJITSU AMERICA, INC.—See Fujitsu Limited; *Int'l*, pg. 2833
FUJITSU AMERICA, INC.—See Fujitsu Limited; *Int'l*, pg. 2833
FUJITSU ASIA PTE. LTD.—See Fujitsu Limited; *Int'l*, pg. 2833
FUJITSU A/S—See Fujitsu Limited; *Int'l*, pg. 2833
FUJITSU AUSTRALIA LTD.—See Fujitsu Limited; *Int'l*, pg. 2833
FUJITSU AUSTRALIA PTY. LTD.—See Fujitsu Limited; *Int'l*, pg. 2833
FUJITSU AUSTRALIA SOFTWARE TECHNOLOGY PTY., LTD.—See Fujitsu Limited; *Int'l*, pg. 2835
FUJITSU BROAD SOLUTION & CONSULTING INC.—See Fujitsu Limited; *Int'l*, pg. 2833
FUJITSU BUSINESS COMMUNICATION SYSTEMS, INC.-SALES & MARKETING—See Fujitsu Limited; *Int'l*, pg. 2833
FUJITSU CANADA, INC.—See Fujitsu Limited; *Int'l*, pg. 2834
FUJITSU CANADA LIMITED—See Fujitsu Limited; *Int'l*, pg. 2834
FUJITSU CARIBBEAN (BARBADOS) LIMITED—See Fujitsu Limited; *Int'l*, pg. 2834
FUJITSU CARIBBEAN (TRINIDAD) LIMITED—See Fujitsu Limited; *Int'l*, pg. 2834
FUJITSU (CHINA) CO., LTD.—See Fujitsu Limited; *Int'l*, pg. 2833
FUJITSU (CHINA) HOLDINGS CO., LTD.—See Fujitsu Limited; *Int'l*, pg. 2833
FUJITSU COMPONENT LIMITED; *Int'l*, pg. 2832
FUJITSU COMPONENT (MALAYSIA) SDN. BHD.—See FUJITSU COMPONENT LIMITED; *Int'l*, pg. 2832
FUJITSU COMPONENTS AMERICA, INC.—See Fujitsu Limited; *Int'l*, pg. 2833
FUJITSU COMPONENTS ASIA PTE, LTD.—See FUJITSU COMPONENT LIMITED; *Int'l*, pg. 2832
FUJITSU COMPONENTS (CHANGZHOU) CO., LTD.—See FUJITSU COMPONENT LIMITED; *Int'l*, pg. 2832
FUJITSU COMPONENTS EUROPE B.V.—See Fujitsu Limited; *Int'l*, pg. 2834
FUJITSU COMPONENTS HONG KONG CO., LIMITED—See Fujitsu Limited; *Int'l*, pg. 2834
FUJITSU COMPONENTS KOREA LIMITED—See FUJITSU COMPONENT LIMITED; *Int'l*, pg. 2832
FUJITSU COMPONENTS (MALAYSIA) SDN. BHD.—See Fujitsu Limited; *Int'l*, pg. 2834
FUJITSU COMPUTER PRODUCTS OF AMERICA, INC.—See Fujitsu Limited; *Int'l*, pg. 2833
FUJITSU COMPUTER PRODUCTS OF AMERICA - RESEARCH & DEVELOPMENT—See Fujitsu Limited; *Int'l*, pg. 2833
FUJITSU COMPUTER PRODUCTS OF VIETNAM, INC.—See Fujitsu Limited; *Int'l*, pg. 2834

FUJITSU COMPUTER SYSTEMS CORPORATION—See Fujitsu Limited; *Int'l*, pg. 2833
FUJITSU CONSEIL (CANADA) INC.—See Fujitsu Limited; *Int'l*, pg. 2834
FUJITSU CONSULTING INDIA PVT LTD.—See Fujitsu Limited; *Int'l*, pg. 2836
FUJITSU CONSULTING (LUXEMBOURG) S.A.—See Fujitsu Limited; *Int'l*, pg. 2836
FUJITSU CONSULTING S.A.—See Fujitsu Limited; *Int'l*, pg. 2834
FUJITSU CONSULTING—See Fujitsu Limited; *Int'l*, pg. 2833
FUJITSU CONSULTING—See Fujitsu Limited; *Int'l*, pg. 2833
FUJITSU CONSULTING—See Fujitsu Limited; *Int'l*, pg. 2833
FUJITSU CONSULTING—See Fujitsu Limited; *Int'l*, pg. 2834
FUJITSU CONSULTING—See Fujitsu Limited; *Int'l*, pg. 2833
FUJITSU CONSULTING—See Fujitsu Limited; *Int'l*, pg. 2833
FUJITSU DENSO INTERNATIONAL LIMITED—See Fujitsu Limited; *Int'l*, pg. 2834
FUJITSU DEUTSCHLAND GMBH—See Fujitsu Limited; *Int'l*, pg. 2834
FUJITSU DEVICES (DALIAN) ENGINEERING LIMITED—See Kaga Electronics Co., Ltd.; *Int'l*, pg. 4048
FUJITSU DEVICES INC.—See Kaga Electronics Co., Ltd.; *Int'l*, pg. 4048
FUJITSU DIE-TECH CORPORATION OF THE PHILIPPINE—See Fujitsu Limited; *Int'l*, pg. 2834
FUJITSU DMR CONSULTING—See Fujitsu Limited; *Int'l*, pg. 2834
FUJITSU DO BRASIL LTDA—See Fujitsu Limited; *Int'l*, pg. 2834
FUJITSU ELECTRONIC COMPONENTS (SHANGHAI) CO., LTD.—See FUJITSU COMPONENT LIMITED; *Int'l*, pg. 2832
FUJITSU ELECTRONICS AMERICA, INC.—See Kaga Electronics Co., Ltd.; *Int'l*, pg. 4048
FUJITSU ELECTRONICS (DALIAN) SOFTWARE LTD.—See Kaga Electronics Co., Ltd.; *Int'l*, pg. 4048
FUJITSU ELECTRONICS EUROPE GMBH—See Kaga Electronics Co., Ltd.; *Int'l*, pg. 4048
FUJITSU ELECTRONICS INC.—See Kaga Electronics Co., Ltd.; *Int'l*, pg. 4048
FUJITSU ELECTRONICS KOREA LTD.—See Kaga Electronics Co., Ltd.; *Int'l*, pg. 4048
FUJITSU ELECTRONICS PACIFIC ASIA LTD.—See Kaga Electronics Co., Ltd.; *Int'l*, pg. 4048
FUJITSU ELECTRONICS (SHANGHAI) CO., LTD.—See Kaga Electronics Co., Ltd.; *Int'l*, pg. 4048
FUJITSU EMEA PLC—See Fujitsu Limited; *Int'l*, pg. 2833
FUJITSU ENABLING SOFTWARE TECHNOLOGY GMBH—See Fujitsu Limited; *Int'l*, pg. 2834
FUJITSU ESPANA, S.A.—See Fujitsu Limited; *Int'l*, pg. 2836
FUJITSU EUROPE LIMITED—See Fujitsu Limited; *Int'l*, pg. 2834
FUJITSU FINLAND OY—See Fujitsu Limited; *Int'l*, pg. 2834
FUJITSU FIP CORPORATION—See Fujitsu Limited; *Int'l*, pg. 2834
FUJITSU FRONTECH CANADA INC.—See Fujitsu Limited; *Int'l*, pg. 2834
FUJITSU FRONTECH LIMITED - NIIGATA PLANT—See Fujitsu Limited; *Int'l*, pg. 2834
FUJITSU FRONTECH LTD.—See Fujitsu Limited; *Int'l*, pg. 2834
FUJITSU FRONTECH NORTH AMERICA INC.—See Fujitsu Limited; *Int'l*, pg. 2834
FUJITSU FRONTECH (SHANGHAI) LIMITED—See Fujitsu Limited; *Int'l*, pg. 2834
FUJITSU FRONTECH SYSTEMS LIMITED—See Fujitsu Limited; *Int'l*, pg. 2834
FUJITSU FSAS INC.—See Fujitsu Limited; *Int'l*, pg. 2834
FUJITSU GENERAL AMERICA, INC.—See Fujitsu Limited; *Int'l*, pg. 2833
FUJITSU GENERAL (AUSTRALIA) PTY. LIMITED; *Int'l*, pg. 2832
FUJITSU GENERAL LTD.—See Fujitsu Limited; *Int'l*, pg. 2834
FUJITSU HONG KONG LIMITED—See Fujitsu Limited; *Int'l*, pg. 2836
FUJITSU INDIA PVT. LTD.—See Fujitsu Limited; *Int'l*, pg. 2836
FUJITSU INTERCONNECT TECHNOLOGIES LIMITED—See Fujitsu Limited; *Int'l*, pg. 2833
FUJITSU (IRELAND) LIMITED—See Fujitsu Limited; *Int'l*, pg. 2833
FUJITSU ISOTEC LIMITED—See Fujitsu Limited; *Int'l*, pg. 2834
FUJITSU IT PRODUCTS LTD.—See Fujitsu Limited; *Int'l*, pg. 2834
FUJITSU KOREA LTD.—See Fujitsu Limited; *Int'l*, pg. 2835
FUJITSU LABORATORIES LTD.—See Fujitsu Limited; *Int'l*, pg. 2835

FUJITSU LABORATORIES OF AMERICA, INC.—See Fujitsu Limited; *Int'l*, pg. 2835
FUJITSU LABORATORIES OF EUROPE LTD.—See Fujitsu Limited; *Int'l*, pg. 2835
FUJITSU LEASING CO., LTD.—See Tokyo Century Corporation; *Int'l*, pg. 7789
FUJITSU LIMITED - AIZU WAKAMATSU PLANT—See Fujitsu Limited; *Int'l*, pg. 2835
FUJITSU LIMITED - MIE PLANT—See Fujitsu Limited; *Int'l*, pg. 2835
FUJITSU LIMITED - NASU PLANT—See Fujitsu Limited; *Int'l*, pg. 2835
FUJITSU LIMITED - NUMAZU PLANT—See Fujitsu Limited; *Int'l*, pg. 2835
FUJITSU LIMITED - OYAMA PLANT—See Fujitsu Limited; *Int'l*, pg. 2835
FUJITSU LIMITED; *Int'l*, pg. 2832
FUJITSU LIMITED—See Fujitsu Limited; *Int'l*, pg. 2833
FUJITSU LIMITED - SUZAKA PLANT—See Fujitsu Limited; *Int'l*, pg. 2835
FUJITSU (MALAYSIA) SDN. BHD.—See Fujitsu Limited; *Int'l*, pg. 2835
FUJITSU MANAGEMENT SERVICES OF AMERICA, INC.—See Fujitsu Limited; *Int'l*, pg. 2833
FUJITSU MARKETING AGENT LTD.—See Fujitsu Limited; *Int'l*, pg. 2835
FUJITSU MARKETING LIMITED—See Fujitsu Limited; *Int'l*, pg. 2835
FUJITSU MARKETING OFFICE SERVICES LTD.—See Fujitsu Limited; *Int'l*, pg. 2835
FUJITSU MICRODEVICES LTD.—See Fujitsu Limited; *Int'l*, pg. 2835
FUJITSU NETWORK COMMUNICATIONS INC.—See Fujitsu Limited; *Int'l*, pg. 2833
FUJITSU NETWORK COMMUNICATIONS - RICHARDSON PLANT—See Fujitsu Limited; *Int'l*, pg. 2833
FUJITSU NETWORK SOLUTIONS LTD.—See Fujitsu Limited; *Int'l*, pg. 2835
FUJITSU NEW ZEALAND LTD.—See Fujitsu Limited; *Int'l*, pg. 2836
FUJITSU OPTICAL COMPONENTS AMERICA, INC.—See Fujitsu Limited; *Int'l*, pg. 2835
FUJITSU PC ASIA PACIFIC LTD—See Fujitsu Limited; *Int'l*, pg. 2835
FUJITSU PC ASIA PACIFIC PTE. LTD.—See Fujitsu Limited; *Int'l*, pg. 2835
FUJITSU PC AUSTRALIA PTY LTD—See Fujitsu Limited; *Int'l*, pg. 2835
FUJITSU PERIPHERALS LIMITED—See Fujitsu Limited; *Int'l*, pg. 2835
FUJITSU PHILIPPINES, INC.—See Fujitsu Limited; *Int'l*, pg. 2835
FUJITSU QUALITY LABORATORY (SUZHOU) LTD.—See Fujitsu Limited; *Int'l*, pg. 2835
FUJITSU RESEARCH AND DEVELOPMENT CENTER CO., LTD.—See Fujitsu Limited; *Int'l*, pg. 2835
FUJITSU SEMICONDUCTOR AMERICA, INC—See Fujitsu Limited; *Int'l*, pg. 2835
FUJITSU SEMICONDUCTOR ASIA PTE. LTD.—See Fujitsu Limited; *Int'l*, pg. 2835
FUJITSU SEMICONDUCTOR EMBEDDED SOLUTIONS AUSTRIA GMBH—See Fujitsu Limited; *Int'l*, pg. 2835
FUJITSU SEMICONDUCTOR EUROPE GMBH—See Fujitsu Limited; *Int'l*, pg. 2835
FUJITSU SEMICONDUCTOR EUROPE GMBH—See Fujitsu Limited; *Int'l*, pg. 2835
FUJITSU SEMICONDUCTOR KOREA LIMITED—See Fujitsu Limited; *Int'l*, pg. 2835
FUJITSU SEMICONDUCTOR LIMITED—See Fujitsu Limited; *Int'l*, pg. 2835
FUJITSU SEMICONDUCTOR PACIFIC ASIA LIMITED—See Fujitsu Limited; *Int'l*, pg. 2835
FUJITSU SEMICONDUCTOR (SHANGHAI) CO., LTD.—See Fujitsu Limited; *Int'l*, pg. 2835
FUJITSU SEMICONDUCTOR WIRELESS PRODUCTS, INC.—See Intel Corporation; *U.S. Public*, pg. 1139
FUJITSU SERVICE A/S—See Fujitsu Limited; *Int'l*, pg. 2836
FUJITSU SERVICES AB—See Fujitsu Limited; *Int'l*, pg. 2836
FUJITSU SERVICES AB—See Fujitsu Limited; *Int'l*, pg. 2835
FUJITSU SERVICES GMBH—See Fujitsu Limited; *Int'l*, pg. 2836
FUJITSU SERVICES HOLDINGS PLC—See Fujitsu Limited; *Int'l*, pg. 2836
FUJITSU SERVICES LIMITED—See Fujitsu Limited; *Int'l*, pg. 2835
FUJITSU SERVICES LIMITED—See Fujitsu Limited; *Int'l*, pg. 2836
FUJITSU SERVICES LTD—See Fujitsu Limited; *Int'l*, pg. 2836
FUJITSU SERVICES—See Fujitsu Limited; *Int'l*, pg. 2836
FUJITSU SERVICES—See Fujitsu Limited; *Int'l*, pg. 2836
FUJITSU SERVICES SOUTH AFRICA—See Fujitsu Limited; *Int'l*, pg. 2836
FUJITSU SERVICES SP. Z.O.O.—See Fujitsu Limited; *Int'l*, pg. 2836

FUJITSU LIMITED · CORPORATE AFFILIATIONS

FUJITSU (SINGAPORE) PTE. LTD.—See Fujitsu Limited; *Int'l*, pg. 2833
FUJITSU SOFTWARE CORPORATION—See Fujitsu Limited; *Int'l*, pg. 2836
FUJITSU SOUTH CHINA LIMITED—See Fujitsu Limited; *Int'l*, pg. 2836
FUJITSU SOUTH CHINA TECHNOLOGY SERVICES LIMITED—See Fujitsu Limited; *Int'l*, pg. 2835
FUJITSU SYSTEMS BUSINESS (THAILAND) LTD.—See Fujitsu Limited; *Int'l*, pg. 2836
FUJITSU SYSTEMS EAST LIMITED—See Fujitsu Limited; *Int'l*, pg. 2836
FUJITSU SYSTEMS WEST LIMITED—See Fujitsu Limited; *Int'l*, pg. 2836
FUJITSU TAIWAN LIMITED—See Fujitsu Limited; *Int'l*, pg. 2836
FUJITSU TECHNOLOGIES SOLUTION INTERNATIONAL S.P.A.—See Fujitsu Limited; *Int'l*, pg. 2836
FUJITSU TECHNOLOGY & BUSINESS OF AMERICA, INC.—See Fujitsu Limited; *Int'l*, pg. 2836
FUJITSU TECHNOLOGY SOLUTIONS AB—See Fujitsu Limited; *Int'l*, pg. 2836
FUJITSU TECHNOLOGY SOLUTIONS A.E.—See Fujitsu Limited; *Int'l*, pg. 2836
FUJITSU TECHNOLOGY SOLUTIONS AG—See Fujitsu Limited; *Int'l*, pg. 2836
FUJITSU TECHNOLOGY SOLUTIONS AS—See Fujitsu Limited; *Int'l*, pg. 2836
FUJITSU TECHNOLOGY SOLUTIONS BILISIM LTD. STI.—See Fujitsu Limited; *Int'l*, pg. 2836
FUJITSU TECHNOLOGY SOLUTIONS B.V.—See Fujitsu Limited; *Int'l*, pg. 2836
FUJITSU TECHNOLOGY SOLUTIONS D.O.O.—See Fujitsu Limited; *Int'l*, pg. 2837
FUJITSU TECHNOLOGY SOLUTIONS FZ LLC—See Fujitsu Limited; *Int'l*, pg. 2836
FUJITSU TECHNOLOGY SOLUTIONS GESMBH—See Fujitsu Limited; *Int'l*, pg. 2836
FUJITSU TECHNOLOGY SOLUTIONS GESMBH—See Fujitsu Limited; *Int'l*, pg. 2836
FUJITSU TECHNOLOGY SOLUTIONS GMBH—See Fujitsu Limited; *Int'l*, pg. 2836
FUJITSU TECHNOLOGY SOLUTIONS GMBH—See Fujitsu Limited; *Int'l*, pg. 2836
FUJITSU TECHNOLOGY SOLUTIONS (HOLDING) B.V.—See Fujitsu Limited; *Int'l*, pg. 2836
FUJITSU TECHNOLOGY SOLUTIONS INTERNATIONAL AG—See Fujitsu Limited; *Int'l*, pg. 2837
FUJITSU TECHNOLOGY SOLUTIONS INTERNATIONAL N.V.—See Fujitsu Limited; *Int'l*, pg. 2837
FUJITSU TECHNOLOGY SOLUTIONS INTERNATIONAL SA—See Fujitsu Limited; *Int'l*, pg. 2837
FUJITSU TECHNOLOGY SOLUTIONS LDA—See Fujitsu Limited; *Int'l*, pg. 2836
FUJITSU TECHNOLOGY SOLUTIONS LTD.—See Fujitsu Limited; *Int'l*, pg. 2837
FUJITSU TECHNOLOGY SOLUTIONS (LUXEMBOURG) SA—See Fujitsu Limited; *Int'l*, pg. 2836
FUJITSU TECHNOLOGY SOLUTIONS NV—See Fujitsu Limited; *Int'l*, pg. 2837
FUJITSU TECHNOLOGY SOLUTIONS OOO—See Fujitsu Limited; *Int'l*, pg. 2837
FUJITSU TECHNOLOGY SOLUTIONS (PTY) LTD.—See Fujitsu Limited; *Int'l*, pg. 2836
FUJITSU TECHNOLOGY SOLUTIONS S.A.R.L.—See Fujitsu Limited; *Int'l*, pg. 2837
FUJITSU TECHNOLOGY SOLUTIONS S.A—See Fujitsu Limited; *Int'l*, pg. 2837
FUJITSU TECHNOLOGY SOLUTIONS SL—See Fujitsu Limited; *Int'l*, pg. 2837
FUJITSU TECHNOLOGY SOLUTIONS S.P.A.—See Fujitsu Limited; *Int'l*, pg. 2837
FUJITSU TECHNOLOGY SOLUTIONS SP. Z O.O.—See Fujitsu Limited; *Int'l*, pg. 2837
FUJITSU TECHNOLOGY SOLUTIONS S.R.O—See Fujitsu Limited; *Int'l*, pg. 2837
FUJITSU TELECOMMUNICATIONS EUROPE LIMITED—See Fujitsu Limited; *Int'l*, pg. 2837
FUJITSU TELECOMMUNICATIONS FRANCE SAS—See Fujitsu Limited; *Int'l*, pg. 2837
FUJITSU TELECOM NETWORKS LIMITED—See Fujitsu Limited; *Int'l*, pg. 2837
FUJITSU TELECOM SYSTEMS PHILIPPINES, INC.—See Fujitsu Limited; *Int'l*, pg. 2837
FUJITSU TELECOMUNICACOES PORTUGAL, S.A.—See Fujitsu Limited; *Int'l*, pg. 2837
FUJITSU TRANSACTION SOLUTIONS CANADA INC.—See Fujitsu Limited; *Int'l*, pg. 2837
FUJITSU UT CO., LTD.—See UT Group Co., Ltd.; *Int'l*, pg. 8100
FUJITSU VIETNAM LIMITED—See Fujitsu Limited; *Int'l*, pg. 2837
FUJITSU (XI'AN) SYSTEM ENGINEERING CO., LTD.—See Fujitsu Limited; *Int'l*, pg. 2833
FUJI TUSCO CO., LTD.—See Fuji Electric Co., Ltd.; *Int'l*, pg. 2812
FUJI VALVE (GUANGDONG) CORPORATION—See Daido Steel Co., Ltd.; *Int'l*, pg. 1923

FUJI VEGETABLE OIL INC. - PLANT—See Fuji Oil Holdings Inc.; *Int'l*, pg. 2815
FUJI VEGETABLE OIL INC.—See Fuji Oil Holdings Inc.; *Int'l*, pg. 2815
FUJIWA DENKI CO., LTD.—See Sintokogio Ltd.; *Int'l*, pg. 6958
FUJIWA DENKI CO., LTD. - TOYOKAWA FACTORY—See Sintokogio Ltd.; *Int'l*, pg. 6958
FUJIWARA SEIMEN CO., LTD.—See Mitsubishi Corporation; *Int'l*, pg. 4940
FUJI XEROX ASIA PACIFIC PTE LTD. - INDOCHINA OPERATIONS—See FUJIFILM Holdings Corporation; *Int'l*, pg. 2825
FUJI XEROX ASIA PACIFIC PTE LTD. - MALAYSIA—See FUJIFILM Holdings Corporation; *Int'l*, pg. 2825
FUJI XEROX ASIA PACIFIC PTE LTD.—See FUJIFILM Holdings Corporation; *Int'l*, pg. 2825
FUJI XEROX ASIA PACIFIC PTE. LTD.—See FUJIFILM Holdings Corporation; *Int'l*, pg. 2825
FUJI XEROX AUSTRALIA PTY. LTD.—See FUJIFILM Holdings Corporation; *Int'l*, pg. 2825
FUJI XEROX (CHINA) LIMITED—See FUJIFILM Holdings Corporation; *Int'l*, pg. 2825
FUJI XEROX DOCUMENT MANAGEMENT SOLUTIONS ASIA LIMITED—See FUJIFILM Holdings Corporation; *Int'l*, pg. 2825
FUJI XEROX DOCUMENT MANAGEMENT SOLUTIONS PTY LTD—See FUJIFILM Holdings Corporation; *Int'l*, pg. 2825
FUJI XEROX FAR EAST LIMITED—See FUJIFILM Holdings Corporation; *Int'l*, pg. 2825
FUJI XEROX (HONG KONG) LIMITED—See FUJIFILM Holdings Corporation; *Int'l*, pg. 2825
FUJI XEROX INTERFIELD CO., LTD.—See FUJIFILM Holdings Corporation; *Int'l*, pg. 2825
FUJI XEROX KOREA COMPANY LIMITED—See FUJIFILM Holdings Corporation; *Int'l*, pg. 2825
FUJI XEROX LEARNING INSTITUTE INC.—See FUJIFILM Holdings Corporation; *Int'l*, pg. 2826
FUJI XEROX MANUFACTURING CO., LTD.—See FUJIFILM Holdings Corporation; *Int'l*, pg. 2825
FUJI XEROX NEW ZEALAND LTD.—See FUJIFILM Holdings Corporation; *Int'l*, pg. 2825
FUJI XEROX OF SHANGHAI LIMITED—See Shang Gong Group Co., Ltd.; *Int'l*, pg. 6760
FUJI XEROX PHILIPPINES INC.—See FUJIFILM Holdings Corporation; *Int'l*, pg. 2825
FUJI XEROX SERVICE CREATIVE CO., LTD.—See FUJIFILM Holdings Corporation; *Int'l*, pg. 2825
FUJI XEROX SERVICE LINK CO., LTD.—See FUJIFILM Holdings Corporation; *Int'l*, pg. 2825
FUJI XEROX SINGAPORE PTE LTD.—See FUJIFILM Holdings Corporation; *Int'l*, pg. 2826
FUJI XEROX SYSTEM SERVICE CO., LTD.—See FUJIFILM Holdings Corporation; *Int'l*, pg. 2825
FUJI XEROX TAIWAN CORPORATION—See FUJIFILM Holdings Corporation; *Int'l*, pg. 2825
FUJIX INTERNATIONAL (HONG KONG) LTD.—See FUJIX Ltd.; *Int'l*, pg. 2838
FUJIX LTD.; *Int'l*, pg. 2838
FUJIX (SHANGHAI) THREAD LTD.—See FUJIX Ltd.; *Int'l*, pg. 2838
FUJIYA CO., LTD.; *Int'l*, pg. 2838
FUJIYA FOOD SERVICE CO., LTD.—See Fujiya Co., Ltd.; *Int'l*, pg. 2838
FUJIYA KOBE CO., LTD.—See Fujiya Co., Ltd.; *Int'l*, pg. 2838
FUJI YAKUHIN CO., LTD.; *Int'l*, pg. 2817
FUJIYA MILK PRODUCT CO., LTD.—See Fujiya Co., Ltd.; *Int'l*, pg. 2838
FUJIYA SANYO LTD.—See Fujiya Co., Ltd.; *Int'l*, pg. 2838
FUJIYA SHOJI CO., LTD.—See Pan Pacific International Holdings Corporation; *Int'l*, pg. 5715
FUJIYA SYSTEM CENTER CO., LTD.—See Fujiya Co., Ltd.; *Int'l*, pg. 2838
FUKAE POWTEC CORPORATION—See Kawasaki Heavy Industries, Ltd.; *Int'l*, pg. 4095
FUKOKU AMERICA, INC.—See Fukoku Co., Ltd.; *Int'l*, pg. 2838
FUKOKU CO., LTD. - AICHI PLANT—See Fukoku Co., Ltd.; *Int'l*, pg. 2838
FUKOKU CO., LTD. - GUNMA PLANT 2—See Fukoku Co., Ltd.; *Int'l*, pg. 2838
FUKOKU CO., LTD. - GUNMA PLANT—See Fukoku Co., Ltd.; *Int'l*, pg. 2838
FUKOKU CO., LTD. - NISHIO PLANT—See Fukoku Co., Ltd.; *Int'l*, pg. 2838
FUKOKU CO., LTD.; *Int'l*, pg. 2838
FUKOKU CZECH S.R.O.—See Fukoku Co., Ltd.; *Int'l*, pg. 2839
FUKOKU DENKO CO., LTD.—See DKK Co., Ltd.; *Int'l*, pg. 2139
FUKOKU INDIA PRIVATE LIMITED—See Fukoku Co., Ltd.; *Int'l*, pg. 2839
FUKOKU KOREA CO., LTD. - BORYEONG PLANT—See Fukoku Co., Ltd.; *Int'l*, pg. 2839
FUKOKU KOREA CO., LTD.—See Fukoku Co., Ltd.; *Int'l*, pg. 2839

FUKOKU LIFE INTERNATIONAL (AMERICA) INC.—See Fukoku Mutual Life Insurance Company; *Int'l*, pg. 2839
FUKOKU LIFE INTERNATIONAL (U.K.) LTD.—See Fukoku Mutual Life Insurance Company; *Int'l*, pg. 2839
FUKOKU MUTUAL LIFE INSURANCE COMPANY; *Int'l*, pg. 2839
FUKOKU (SHANGHAI) TRADING CO., LTD.—See Fukoku Co., Ltd.; *Int'l*, pg. 2838
FUKOKU VIETNAM CO., LTD.—See Fukoku Co., Ltd.; *Int'l*, pg. 2839
FUKUCHIYAMA GOLF CO., LTD.—See Daiei Kankyo Co., Ltd.; *Int'l*, pg. 1924
FUKUDA ASIA PACIFIC PTE. LTD.—See Fukuda Denshi Co., Ltd.; *Int'l*, pg. 2839
FUKUDA CO., LTD. - SHIZUOKA FACTORY—See Nagano Keiki Co., Ltd.; *Int'l*, pg. 5125
FUKUDA CO., LTD.—See Nagano Keiki Co., Ltd.; *Int'l*, pg. 5125
FUKUDA CO., LTD. - TOHOKU FACTORY—See Nagano Keiki Co., Ltd.; *Int'l*, pg. 5125
FUKUDA CORPORATION; *Int'l*, pg. 2839
FUKUDA DENSHI CO., LTD.; *Int'l*, pg. 2839
FUKUDA DENSHI UK LTD.—See Fukuda Denshi Co., Ltd.; *Int'l*, pg. 2839
FUKUDA DENSHI USA, INC.—See Fukuda Denshi Co., Ltd.; *Int'l*, pg. 2840
FUKUDA ENGINEERING CO., LTD.—See F-Tech Inc.; *Int'l*, pg. 2595
FUKUDASANSHO CO., LTD.—See Japan Pulp and Paper Company Limited; *Int'l*, pg. 3903
FUKUDA (THAILAND) CO., LTD.—See Nagano Keiki Co., Ltd.; *Int'l*, pg. 5125
FUKUDA USA, INC.—See Nagano Keiki Co., Ltd.; *Int'l*, pg. 5125
FUKUGAWA DAIICHI TRAFFIC LTD—See Daiichi Koutsu Sangyo Co., Ltd.; *Int'l*, pg. 1928
FUKUGIN BUSINESS OPERATION SERVICE CO., LTD.—See Fukuoka Financial Group, Inc.; *Int'l*, pg. 2840
FUKUGIN GUARANTEE CO., LTD.—See Fukuoka Financial Group, Inc.; *Int'l*, pg. 2840
FUKUGIN REAL ESTATE ASSESSMENT SERVICE CO., LTD.—See Fukuoka Financial Group, Inc.; *Int'l*, pg. 2840
THE FUKUI BANK, LTD.; *Int'l*, pg. 7644
FUKUIBELT. INDUSTRIES, LTD.—See Bando Chemical Industries, Ltd.; *Int'l*, pg. 830
FUKUI CABLETV CO., LTD.—See Mitani Corporation; *Int'l*, pg. 4924
FUKUI COMPUTER HOLDINGS INC.; *Int'l*, pg. 2840
FUKUI ENERGY CO., LTD.—See Mitani Corporation; *Int'l*, pg. 4924
FUKUI HINO MOTORS LTD.—See Toyota Motor Corporation; *Int'l*, pg. 7870
FUKUI MURATA MANUFACTURING CO., LTD.—See Murata Manufacturing Co., Ltd.; *Int'l*, pg. 5097
FUKUI SEISAKUSHO CO., LTD.—See Mitani Corporation; *Int'l*, pg. 4924
FUKUI SHIN-ETSU QUARTZ CO., LTD.—See Shin-Etsu Chemical Co. Ltd.; *Int'l*, pg. 6838
FUKUI TONAMI TRANSPORTATION CO., LTD.—See TONAMI HOLDINGS CO., LTD.; *Int'l*, pg. 7805
FUKUI YAMADA CHEMICAL CO., LTD.—See Nagase & Co., Ltd.; *Int'l*, pg. 5126
FUKUMUSUME SAKE BREWERY CO., LTD.—See Oenon Holdings Inc; *Int'l*, pg. 5529
FUKUOKA CHUO BANK LTD.; *Int'l*, pg. 2840
FUKUOKA COMPUTER SERVICE CO., LTD.—See Fukuoka Financial Group, Inc.; *Int'l*, pg. 2840
FUKUOKA CSK CORPORATION—See Sumitomo Corporation; *Int'l*, pg. 7270
FUKUOKA ENERGY SERVICE CO., INC.—See Kyushu Electric Power Co., Inc.; *Int'l*, pg. 4367
FUKUOKA FINANCIAL GROUP, INC.; *Int'l*, pg. 2840
FUKUOKA KASEI INDUSTRIES CO., LTD.—See Yaskawa Electric Corporation; *Int'l*, pg. 8569
FUKUOKA KASEI INDUSTRIES CO., LTD. - YUKUHASHI PLANT—See Yaskawa Electric Corporation; *Int'l*, pg. 8569
FUKUOKA KIKI CO., LTD.—See Nippon Tungsten Co., Ltd.; *Int'l*, pg. 5357
FUKUOKA KOGYO CO., LTD.—See Hanwa Co., Ltd.; *Int'l*, pg. 3262
FUKUOKA LOGISTIC SYSTEMS CORP.—See Japan Logistic Systems Corp.; *Int'l*, pg. 3898
FUKUOKA NISSHIN ELECTRONICS CO., LTD.—See Nippon Signal Co., Ltd.; *Int'l*, pg. 5333
FUKUOKA PACKING CO., LTD.—See Toyo Seikan Group Holdings, Ltd.; *Int'l*, pg. 7856
FUKUOKA REIT CORPORATION; *Int'l*, pg. 2840
FUKUOKA SENKO TRANSPORT CO., LTD.—See Senko Group Holdings Co., Ltd.; *Int'l*, pg. 6709
FUKUOKA SERVICING CO., LTD.—See Fukuoka Financial Group, Inc.; *Int'l*, pg. 2840
FUKUOKA SOFTBANK HAWKS CORP.—See SoftBank Group Corp.; *Int'l*, pg. 7051
FUKUOKA SOFTBANK HAWKS MARKETING CORP.—See SoftBank Group Corp.; *Int'l*, pg. 7051

COMPANY NAME INDEX

FUKUOKA SUBARU INC.—See SUBARU CO., LTD.; *Int'l*, pg. 7246
FUKUOKA TOSHIBA CORPORATION—See Japan Industrial Partners, Inc.; *Int'l*, pg. 3889
FUKUOKA WACOAL SEWING CORP.—See Wacoal Holdings Corp.; *Int'l*, pg. 8325
FUKURIKOSEI CLUB KYUSHU CO., LTD.—See Relo Group, Inc.; *Int'l*, pg. 6265
FUKURI KOUSEI CLUB CHUBU CO., LTD.—See Relo Group, Inc.; *Int'l*, pg. 6265
FUKURI KOUSEI CLUB CHUGOKU CO., LTD.—See Relo Group, Inc.; *Int'l*, pg. 6265
FUKUROI GAS CO., LTD.—See Shizuokagas Co., Ltd.; *Int'l*, pg. 6856
FUKURYO CO., LTD.—See AOYAMA TRADING Co. Ltd.; *Int'l*, pg. 498
FUKUSAN CO., LTD.—See NICHIMO CO. LTD.; *Int'l*, pg. 5269
FUKUSEI TECH CO., LTD.—See UBE Corporation; *Int'l*, pg. 8000
FUKUSEI VENDER SERVICE CO., LTD.—See UBE Corporation; *Int'l*, pg. 8000
THE FUKUSHIMA BANK LTD.; *Int'l*, pg. 7644
FUKUSHIMA CANON INC.—See Canon Inc.; *Int'l*, pg. 1297
FUKUSHIMA ELECTROLYTIC INDUSTRY CORP.—See Nippon Chemi-Con Corporation; *Int'l*, pg. 5312
FUKUSHIMA FOODS CO., LTD.—See Toyo Suisan Kaisha, Ltd.; *Int'l*, pg. 7858
FUKUSHIMA GALILEI CO. LTD.; *Int'l*, pg. 2840
FUKUSHIMA GALILEI (H.K.) CO., LTD.—See Fukushima Galilei Co. Ltd.; *Int'l*, pg. 2840
FUKUSHIMA GALILEI MALAYSIA SDN. BHD.—See Fukushima Galilei Co. Ltd.; *Int'l*, pg. 2840
FUKUSHIMA GALILEI MYANMAR CO. LTD.—See Fukushima Galilei Co. Ltd.; *Int'l*, pg. 2841
FUKUSHIMA GALILEI PHILIPPINE CORPORATION—See Fukushima Galilei Co. Ltd.; *Int'l*, pg. 2841
FUKUSHIMA GALILEI (SHANGHAI) CO., LTD.—See Fukushima Galilei Co. Ltd.; *Int'l*, pg. 2840
FUKUSHIMA GALILEI SINGAPORE PTE. LTD.—See Fukushima Galilei Co. Ltd.; *Int'l*, pg. 2841
FUKUSHIMA GALILEI TAIWAN CO., LTD.—See Fukushima Galilei Co. Ltd.; *Int'l*, pg. 2841
FUKUSHIMA GALILEI (THAILAND)CO., LTD.—See Fukushima Galilei Co. Ltd.; *Int'l*, pg. 2840
FUKUSHIMA GALILEI VIETNAM CO., LTD.—See Fukushima Galilei Co. Ltd.; *Int'l*, pg. 2841
FUKUSHIMA GAS POWER CO., LTD.—See Japan Petroleum Exploration Co. Ltd.; *Int'l*, pg. 3900
FUKUSHIMA GRAVURE CO., LTD.—See Gunze Limited; *Int'l*, pg. 3185
FUKUSHIMA HAKUHODO, INC.—See Hakuhodo DY Holdings Incorporated; *Int'l*, pg. 3221
FUKUSHIMA HINO MOTOR LTD.—See Toyota Motor Corporation; *Int'l*, pg. 7870
FUKUSHIMA INDUSTRIES CORPORATION - OKAYAMA FACTORY—See Fukushima Galilei Co. Ltd.; *Int'l*, pg. 2841
FUKUSHIMA INDUSTRIES CORPORATION - SHIGA FACTORY—See Fukushima Galilei Co. Ltd.; *Int'l*, pg. 2841
FUKUSHIMA INTERNATIONAL (CAMBODIA) CO., LTD.—See Fukushima Galilei Co. Ltd.; *Int'l*, pg. 2841
FUKUSHIMA INTERNATIONAL KOREA CORPORATION—See Fukushima Galilei Co. Ltd.; *Int'l*, pg. 2841
FUKUSHIMA KYOEI CO., LTD.—See Kyoei Sangyo Co., Ltd.; *Int'l*, pg. 4361
FUKUSHIMA, LTD.—See UBE Corporation; *Int'l*, pg. 8002
FUKUSHIMA MAZDA CO., LTD.—See Mazda Motor Corporation; *Int'l*, pg. 4748
FUKUSHIMA NITTO SHINKO CORPORATION—See Nitto Denko Corporation; *Int'l*, pg. 5384
FUKUSHIMA PLASTICS CO., LTD.—See Gunze Limited; *Int'l*, pg. 3185
FUKUSHIMA RUBBER CO.,LTD—See Toyo Tire Corporation; *Int'l*, pg. 7859
FUKUSHIMA SANKEN CO., LTD.—See Sanken Electric Co., Ltd.; *Int'l*, pg. 6540
FUKUSHIMA SHIBAURA ELECTRONICS CO., LTD.—See Shibaura Electronics Co., Ltd.; *Int'l*, pg. 6827
FUKUSHIMA SPORTS ENTERTAINMENT CO., LTD.—See Shikigaku Co., Ltd.; *Int'l*, pg. 6830
FUKUSHIMA STEEL WORK CO., LTD.—See Toyota Motor Corporation; *Int'l*, pg. 7870
FUKUSHIMA TAIYO YUDEN CO., LTD.—See Taiyo Yuden Company Ltd.; *Int'l*, pg. 7426
FUKUSIMA INTERNATIONAL (H.K.) CO., LIMITED—See Fukushima Galilei Co. Ltd.; *Int'l*, pg. 2841
FUKUSIMA INTERNATIONAL (SHANGHAI) CO., LTD—See Fukushima Galilei Co. Ltd.; *Int'l*, pg. 2841
FUKUSIMA INTERNATIONAL (SINGAPORE) PTE., LTD—See Fukushima Galilei Co. Ltd.; *Int'l*, pg. 2841
FUKUSKE CORPORATION—See Toyota Tsusho Corporation; *Int'l*, pg. 7877
FUKUTOKUCHO CO., LTD.—See Oenon Holdings Inc; *Int'l*, pg. 5529
FUKUTOME MEAT PACKERS LTD.; *Int'l*, pg. 2841

FUKUVI CHEMICAL INDUSTRY CO., LTD. - AWARA FACTORY—See Fukuvi Chemical Industry Co., Ltd.; *Int'l*, pg. 2841
FUKUVI CHEMICAL INDUSTRY CO., LTD. - MIKATA FACTORY—See Fukuvi Chemical Industry Co., Ltd.; *Int'l*, pg. 2841
FUKUVI CHEMICAL INDUSTRY CO., LTD. - OSAKA FACTORY—See Fukuvi Chemical Industry Co., Ltd.; *Int'l*, pg. 2841
FUKUVI CHEMICAL INDUSTRY CO., LTD. - SAKAI FACTORY—See Fukuvi Chemical Industry Co., Ltd.; *Int'l*, pg. 2841
FUKUVI CHEMICAL INDUSTRY CO., LTD.; *Int'l*, pg. 2841
FUKUVI HOUSING CO., LTD.—See Fukuvi Chemical Industry Co., Ltd.; *Int'l*, pg. 2841
FUKUVI (THAILAND) CO., LTD.—See Fukuvi Chemical Industry Co., Ltd.; *Int'l*, pg. 2841
FUKUVI USA, INC.—See Fukuvi Chemical Industry Co., Ltd.; *Int'l*, pg. 2841
FUKUVI VIETNAM CO., LTD.—See Fukuvi Chemical Industry Co., Ltd.; *Int'l*, pg. 2841
FUKUYAMA BUSINESS NETWORK CO., LTD.—See Founder's Consultants Holdings, Inc.; *Int'l*, pg. 2753
FUKUYAMA CONSULTANTS COMPANY LIMITED; *Int'l*, pg. 2841
FUKUYAMA MIZUHO UNYU CO., LTD.—See Taiheiyo Cement Corporation; *Int'l*, pg. 7411
FUKUYAMA MORI SHIGYO CO., LTD.—See Oji Holdings Corporation; *Int'l*, pg. 5537
FUKUYAMA PAPER CO., LTD.—See Marubeni Corporation; *Int'l*, pg. 4705
FUKUYAMA TRANSPORTING CO., LTD.—See Kintetsu Group Holdings Co.,Ltd.; *Int'l*, pg. 4183
FUKUZUMI CORPORATION—See Kitakei Co., Ltd.; *Int'l*, pg. 4195
FULCO, INC.; *U.S. Private*, pg. 1620
FULCRUM ANALYTICS, INC.; *U.S. Private*, pg. 1620
FULCRUM BIOENERGY, INC.; *U.S. Private*, pg. 1620
FULCRUM BIOMETRICS, LLC—See Fujitsu Limited; *Int'l*, pg. 2834
FULCRUM CAPITAL PARTNERS INC.; *Int'l*, pg. 2841
FULCRUM COMMERCIAL REAL ESTATE SERVICES LLC—See Newmark Group, Inc.; *U.S. Public*, pg. 1515
FULCRUM CONTAINER LLC—See N.E.W. Plastics Corp.; *U.S. Private*, pg. 2828
FULCRUM DIGITAL INC.; *U.S. Private*, pg. 1620
FULCRUM IT PARTNERS; *Int'l*, pg. 2841
FULCRUM IT SERVICES, LLC—See Huntington Ingalls Industries, Inc.; *U.S. Public*, pg. 1072
FULCRUM LLC—See Wind Point Advisors LLC; *U.S. Private*, pg. 4536
FULCRUM LOGIC, INC.; *U.S. Private*, pg. 1620
FULCRUM MICROSYSTEMS, INC.—See Intel Corporation; *U.S. Public*, pg. 1138
FULCRUM PARTNERS, LLC—See New Mountain Capital, LLC; *U.S. Private*, pg. 2901
FULCRUM RESEARCH GROUP, LLC; *U.S. Private*, pg. 1620
FULCRUM RETAIL HOLDINGS LLC—See Just Energy Group Inc.; *Int'l*, pg. 4031
FULCRUM TECHNOLOGIES INC.; *U.S. Private*, pg. 1620
FULCRUM THERAPEUTICS, INC.; *U.S. Public*, pg. 891
FULCRUM UTILITY SERVICES LIMITED; *Int'l*, pg. 2841
FULD & COMPANY, INC.; *U.S. Private*, pg. 1620
FULFILLMENT CORPORATION OF AMERICA—See Palladium Equity Partners, LLC; *U.S. Private*, pg. 3078
FULFILLMENT SPECIALISTS OF AMERICA—See The Van Hoof Companies; *U.S. Private*, pg. 4130
FULFILLMENT STRATEGIES INTERNATIONAL; *U.S. Private*, pg. 1620
FULFILLMENT WORKS, LLC—See Stord, Inc.; *U.S. Private*, pg. 3831
FULFILMENT PLUS GMBH—See Droege Group AG; *Int'l*, pg. 2205
FULFLO SPECIALTIES—See Ruthman Pump & Engineering Inc.; *U.S. Private*, pg. 3558
FULFORD CONSTRUCTION INC.; *U.S. Private*, pg. 1620
FULFORD (INDIA) LTD.—See Organon & Co.; *U.S. Public*, pg. 1616
FULGENT GENETICS, INC.; *U.S. Public*, pg. 892
FULGENT SUN FOOTWEAR CO., LTD.—See Fulgent Sun International (Holding) Co., Ltd.; *Int'l*, pg. 2842
FULGENT SUN INTERNATIONAL (HOLDING) CO., LTD.; *Int'l*, pg. 2841
FULGHUM FIBREFUELS, LTD.—See Rentech, Inc.; *U.S. Private*, pg. 3400
FULGHUM FIBRES CHILE S.A.—See Rentech, Inc.; *U.S. Private*, pg. 3400
FULGHUM FIBRES COLLINS, INC.—See Rentech, Inc.; *U.S. Private*, pg. 3400
FULGHUM MACINDOE & ASSOCIATES, INC.—See Littlejohn & Co., LLC; *U.S. Private*, pg. 2469
FULGOR S.A.—See CENERGY HOLDINGS SA; *Int'l*, pg. 1401
FULHAM & CO., INC.; *U.S. Private*, pg. 1620
FULHAM CORRECTIONAL CENTRE—See The GEO Group, Inc.; *U.S. Public*, pg. 2075
THE FULHAM SHORE PLC; *Int'l*, pg. 7644

FULIAN KNITTING CO., LTD—See Foreland Fabrictech Holdings Limited; *Int'l*, pg. 2731
FULING GLOBAL INC.; *Int'l*, pg. 2842
FULIN PLASTIC INDUSTRY (CAYMAN) HOLDING CO., LTD.; *Int'l*, pg. 2842
FULL ALLIANCE GROUP, INC.; *U.S. Public*, pg. 892
FULLBEAUTY BRANDS, INC.—See Charlesbank Capital Partners, LLC; *U.S. Private*, pg. 855
FULLBEAUTY BRANDS, INC.—See Webster Equity Partners, LLC; *U.S. Private*, pg. 4467
FULLBEAUTY BRANDS, L.P.—See Charlesbank Capital Partners, LLC; *U.S. Private*, pg. 855
FULLBEAUTY BRANDS, L.P.—See Webster Equity Partners, LLC; *U.S. Private*, pg. 4467
FULLBEAUTY.COM—See Charlesbank Capital Partners, LLC; *U.S. Private*, pg. 855
FULLBEAUTY.COM—See Webster Equity Partners, LLC; *U.S. Private*, pg. 4467
FULLBLOOM BAKING COMPANY; *U.S. Private*, pg. 1621
FULLCAST ADVANCE CO., LTD.—See Fullcast Holdings Co., Ltd.; *Int'l*, pg. 2842
FULLCAST FINANCE CO., LTD.—See Fullcast Holdings Co., Ltd.; *Int'l*, pg. 2842
FULLCAST HOLDINGS CO., LTD.; *Int'l*, pg. 2842
FULLCAST TECHNOLOGY CO., LTD.—See Fullcast Holdings Co., Ltd.; *Int'l*, pg. 2842
FULL CIRCLE AG; *U.S. Private*, pg. 1620
FULL CIRCLE BREWING CO., LTD.; *U.S. Private*, pg. 1620
FULL CIRCLE FIBER PARTNERS, INC.—See Guggenheim Partners, LLC; *U.S. Private*, pg. 1812
FULL CIRCLE HOME LLC; *U.S. Private*, pg. 1620
FULL CIRCLE RESTORATION & CONSTRUCTION SERVICES, INC.—See Cotton Holdings, Inc.; *U.S. Private*, pg. 1064
FULL COMPASS SYSTEMS CONTRACTORS LLC—See Full Compass Systems Ltd. Inc.; *U.S. Private*, pg. 1620
FULL COMPASS SYSTEMS LTD. INC.; *U.S. Private*, pg. 1620
FULLCONTACT, INC.; *U.S. Private*, pg. 1621
FULLEN DOCK & WAREHOUSE INC.; *U.S. Private*, pg. 1621
FULLER AUSTIN INC.—See Bird Construction Inc.; *Int'l*, pg. 1047
FULLER BOX COMPANY INC.; *U.S. Private*, pg. 1621
THE FULLER BRUSH COMPANY, INC.—See Victory Park Capital Advisors, LLC; *U.S. Private*, pg. 4379
FULLER COMMUNICATIONS INC.; *U.S. Private*, pg. 1621
FULLER COMPANY—See FLSmidth & Co. A/S; *Int'l*, pg. 2710
FULLER COSMETICS S.A. DE C.V.—See Tupperware Brands Corporation; *U.S. Public*, pg. 2204
FULLER FORD, INC.; *U.S. Private*, pg. 1621
FULLER INTERNATIONAL INC.—See FLSmidth & Co. A/S; *Int'l*, pg. 2712
FULLER MADISON LLC—See Vornado Realty Trust; *U.S. Public*, pg. 2310
FULLER MARKET BASKET INC.; *U.S. Private*, pg. 1621
FULLERS BAY OF ISLANDS LIMITED—See Tourism Holdings Limited; *Int'l*, pg. 7848
FULLER, SMITH & TURNER PLC; *Int'l*, pg. 2842
FULLER SUPPLY CO. INC.; *U.S. Private*, pg. 1621
FULLERTON DIALYSIS CENTER, LLC—See DaVita Inc.; *U.S. Public*, pg. 639
FULLERTON LUMBER COMPANY; *U.S. Private*, pg. 1621
FULLERTON TECHNOLOGY CO., LTD.; *Int'l*, pg. 2842
FULLERTON TOWERS HOLDINGS, LLC—See Wells Fargo & Company; *U.S. Public*, pg. 2343
FULLER WESTERN RUBBER LININGS LTD.—See Corrosion & Abrasion Solutions Ltd.; *Int'l*, pg. 1806
FULLFILLMENT SYSTEMS, INC.; *U.S. Private*, pg. 1621
FULL FORTUNE HOLDINGS PTE LTD—See China Food Company Plc; *Int'l*, pg. 1503
FULL GOSPEL BUSINESS MEN'S FELLOWSHIP INTERNATIONAL; *U.S. Private*, pg. 1620
FULLHOUSE INTERACTIVE; *U.S. Private*, pg. 1621
FULL HOUSE RESORTS, INC.; *U.S. Public*, pg. 892
FULLHOUSE—See Fullhouse Interactive; *U.S. Private*, pg. 1621
FULL IMAGE SDN. BHD.—See Digistar Corporation Berhad; *Int'l*, pg. 2120
FULLINGTON AUTO BUS COMPANY—See Regie Autonome des Transports Parisiens; *Int'l*, pg. 6253
FULL IN PARTNERS MANAGEMENT, LLC; *U.S. Private*, pg. 1620
FULL LAB AUTOMATION GMBH—See Perrot Duval Holding S.A.; *Int'l*, pg. 5814
FULL LIFE CARE; *U.S. Private*, pg. 1620
FULL LINE EXHAUST INC.; *U.S. Private*, pg. 1620
FULL LINE SUPPLY AFRICA (PTY) LIMITED—See RHI Magnesita N.V.; *Int'l*, pg. 6325
FULLMER CONSTRUCTION INC.; *U.S. Private*, pg. 1621
FULL METAL MINERALS LTD.; *Int'l*, pg. 2842
FULL MOON HOLDINGS LIMITED; *Int'l*, pg. 2842
FULL MOTION BEVERAGE, INC.; *U.S. Public*, pg. 892
FULLNET COMMUNICATIONS, INC; *U.S. Public*, pg. 892
FULL ON PRODUCTIONS, INC.; *U.S. Private*, pg. 1621
FULL-O-PEP APPLIANCES INCORPORATED; *U.S. Private*, pg. 1621

FULL-O-PEP APPLIANCES INCORPORATED

FULL-PAK PERU BULK CONTAINERS S.A.—See Ultramar Ltda.; *Int'l*, pg. 8018
FULL PERSPECTIVE VIDEO SERVICES INC.; *U.S. Private*, pg. 1621
FULL PRODUCTION OY—See Live Nation Entertainment, Inc.; *U.S. Public*, pg. 1328
FULL SAIL BREWING CO.; *U.S. Private*, pg. 1621
FULL SALE TELEPERFORMANCE SA—See Teleperformance SE; *Int'l*, pg. 7540
FULL SERVICE AUTO PARTS OF SAN ANTONIO; *U.S. Private*, pg. 1621
FULL SERVICE FACILITY SOLUTIONS—See M.A. Mortenson Company; *U.S. Private*, pg. 2527
FULL SERVICE INSURANCE AGENCY, INC.; *U.S. Private*, pg. 1621
FULL SERVICE INSURANCE, INC.—See Caisse de Depot et Placement du Quebec; *Int'l*, pg. 1256
FULL SERVICE INSURANCE, INC.—See KKR & Co. Inc.; *U.S. Public*, pg. 1265
FULL SERVICE TRAVEL INC.; *U.S. Private*, pg. 1621
FULLSHARE HOLDINGS LIMITED; *Int'l*, pg. 2842
FULLSIX GROUP—See Vivendi SE; *Int'l*, pg. 8266
FULLSIX S.P.A.; *Int'l*, pg. 2843
FULL SPECTRUM GROUP, LLC—See CBRE Group, Inc.; *U.S. Public*, pg. 460
FULL SPEED INC.—See FreeBit Co., Ltd.; *Int'l*, pg. 2769
FULLSTEAM AGENCY OY—See CTS Eventim AG & Co. KGAA; *Int'l*, pg. 1873
FULLSUN INTERNATIONAL HOLDINGS GROUP CO., LIMITED; *Int'l*, pg. 2843
FULL SYSTEMBAU GMBH—See Perrot Duval Holding S.A.; *Int'l*, pg. 5814
FULLTECH CO., LTD.; *Int'l*, pg. 2843
FULLTECH FIBER GLASS CORP.; *Int'l*, pg. 2843
FULL THROTTLE ENERGY COMPANY—See Monster Beverage Corporation; *U.S. Public*, pg. 1465
FULL THROTTLE INDOOR KART RACING INC.; *U.S. Private*, pg. 1621
FULL THROTTLE SALOON; *U.S. Private*, pg. 1621
FULL TRUCK ALLIANCE CO. LTD.; *Int'l*, pg. 2842
FULL WANG INTERNATIONAL DEVELOPMENT CO., LTD.; *Int'l*, pg. 2842
FULLWEALTH INTERNATIONAL GROUP HOLDINGS LIMITED; *Int'l*, pg. 2843
FULLWISE INTERNATIONAL LIMITED—See Max Sight Group Holdings Ltd.; *Int'l*, pg. 4735
FULLY ACCOUNTABLE, LLC; *U.S. Private*, pg. 1621
FULLY EQUIPPED LIMITED—See Amotiv Limited; *Int'l*, pg. 431
FULLY EUROPE BVBA—See MillerKnoll, Inc.; *U.S. Public*, pg. 1447
FULLY, LLC—See MillerKnoll, Inc.; *U.S. Public*, pg. 1447
FULLY MOTOR CO. LIMITED - CHINA FACTORY—See Johnson Electric Holdings Limited; *Int'l*, pg. 3990
FULLY MOTOR CO. LIMITED—See Johnson Electric Holdings Limited; *Int'l*, pg. 3990
FULMAR INSURANCE COMPANY LTD.—See Compagnie de Saint-Gobain SA; *Int'l*, pg. 1725
FULMER LOGISTICS SERVICES, INC.; *U.S. Private*, pg. 1621
FU LOGITEC CO., LTD.; *Int'l*, pg. 2801
FULONGMA GROUP CO., LTD.; *Int'l*, pg. 2843
FULTON BANK, N.A.—See Fulton Financial Corporation; *U.S. Public*, pg. 892
FULTON BANK OF NEW JERSEY—See Fulton Financial Corporation; *U.S. Public*, pg. 892
FULTON BELLOWS, LLC—See Smiths Group plc; *Int'l*, pg. 7012
FULTON COUNTY MEDICAL CENTER; *U.S. Private*, pg. 1621
FULTON COUNTY PROPERTIES LLC—See BlueScope Steel Limited; *Int'l*, pg. 1073
FULTON COUNTY RAILWAY, LLC—See The Broe Companies, Inc.; *U.S. Private*, pg. 4001
FULTON COUNTY RURAL ELECTRIC MEMBERSHIP CORPORATION; *U.S. Private*, pg. 1621
FULTON FINANCIAL ADVISORS—See Fulton Financial Corporation; *U.S. Public*, pg. 892
FULTON FINANCIAL CORPORATION; *U.S. Public*, pg. 892
FULTON HOGAN EGIS O&M PTY LTD.—See Groupe Egis S.A.; *Int'l*, pg. 3102
FULTON HOGAN LIMITED - ALLIED ASPHALT PLANT—See Fulton Hogan Limited; *Int'l*, pg. 2843
FULTON HOGAN LIMITED - BAY OF PLENTY PLANT—See Fulton Hogan Limited; *Int'l*, pg. 2843
FULTON HOGAN LIMITED - BURNHAM FACILITY—See Fulton Hogan Limited; *Int'l*, pg. 2843
FULTON HOGAN LIMITED - CANTERBURY BAGGING PLANT—See Fulton Hogan Limited; *Int'l*, pg. 2843
FULTON HOGAN LIMITED - MINERS ROAD ASPHALT PLANT—See Fulton Hogan Limited; *Int'l*, pg. 2843
FULTON HOGAN LIMITED - NELSON BITUMEN PLANT—See Fulton Hogan Limited; *Int'l*, pg. 2843
FULTON HOGAN LIMITED - NORTHLAND PLANT—See Fulton Hogan Limited; *Int'l*, pg. 2843
FULTON HOGAN LIMITED - PAPAKURA FACILITY—See Fulton Hogan Limited; *Int'l*, pg. 2843
FULTON HOGAN LIMITED - RENWICK PLANT—See Fulton Hogan Limited; *Int'l*, pg. 2843
FULTON HOGAN LIMITED; *Int'l*, pg. 2843
FULTON HOGAN LIMITED - SOUTHLAND PLANT—See Fulton Hogan Limited; *Int'l*, pg. 2843
FULTON HOGAN LIMITED - WARRNAMBOOL PLANT—See Fulton Hogan Limited; *Int'l*, pg. 2843
FULTON HOGAN LIMITED - WELLINGTON PLANT—See Fulton Hogan Limited; *Int'l*, pg. 2843
FULTON INDUSTRIES INC.; *U.S. Private*, pg. 1622
FULTON INSURANCE AGENCIES LTD.; *Int'l*, pg. 2843
FULTON OUTFITTERS, INC.; *U.S. Private*, pg. 1622
FULTON PRODUCTS INDUSTRIAL CO., LTD.—See Sanoh Industrial Co., Ltd.; *Int'l*, pg. 6552
FULTON PROVISION COMPANY—See Sysco Corporation; *U.S. Public*, pg. 1974
FULTON SAVINGS BANK INC.; *U.S. Private*, pg. 1622
FULTON SUPPLY COMPANY INC.; *U.S. Private*, pg. 1622
FULTON TECHNOLOGIES, INC.—See ADDvantage Technologies Group, Inc.; *U.S. Public*, pg. 40
FULTRA SAPI DE CV; *Int'l*, pg. 2843
FULUHASHI CORPORATION (THAILAND) LTD—See Fuluhashi EPO Corporation; *Int'l*, pg. 2844
FULUHASHI CORPORATION (VIETNAM) LTD.—See Fuluhashi EPO Corporation; *Int'l*, pg. 2844
FULUHASHI EPO CORPORATION; *Int'l*, pg. 2844
FULU HOLDINGS LIMITED; *Int'l*, pg. 2844
FULUM FOOD (INTERNATIONAL) LIMITED—See Fulum Group Holdings Limited; *Int'l*, pg. 2844
FULUM GROUP HOLDINGS LIMITED; *Int'l*, pg. 2844
FULWEALTH METAL FACTORY LIMITED—See Golik Holdings Limited; *Int'l*, pg. 3036
FUMAKILLA AMERICA, S.A. DE C.V.—See Fumakilla Limited; *Int'l*, pg. 2844
FUMAKILLA LIMITED; *Int'l*, pg. 2844
FUMAKILLA MALAYSIA BERHAD—See Fumakilla Limited; *Int'l*, pg. 2844
FUMAKILLA MALAYSIA BERHAD—See Texchem Resources Bhd.; *Int'l*, pg. 7583
FUMA-TECH GMBH—See BWT Aktiengesellschaft; *Int'l*, pg. 1233
FUMIGACIONES YOUNG S.A.S.—See Rentokil Initial plc; *Int'l*, pg. 6287
FU-MING TRANSPORTATION CO., LTD.—See Asia Cement Corporation; *Int'l*, pg. 611
FUMOA S.A.—See Aga Khan Development Network; *Int'l*, pg. 199
FUMOUZE DIAGNOSTICS—See Church & Dwight Co., Inc.; *U.S. Public*, pg. 493
FUNABASHI KIKO CO., LTD.—See Godo Steel, Ltd.; *Int'l*, pg. 3020
FUN-AGENT D.O.O.—See Kapsch-Group Beteiligungs GmbH; *Int'l*, pg. 4077
FUNA GMBH NACHRICHTENTECHNIK—See L3Harris Technologies, Inc.; *U.S. Public*, pg. 1281
FUNAI CONSULTING, INC.—See Funai Soken Holdings Incorporated; *Int'l*, pg. 2845
FUNAI CONSULTING SHANGHAI, INC.—See Funai Soken Holdings Incorporated; *Int'l*, pg. 2845
FUNAI CORPORATION, INC.—See Funai Electric Co., Ltd.; *Int'l*, pg. 2844
FUNAI DEUTSCHLAND—See Funai Electric Co., Ltd.; *Int'l*, pg. 2844
FUNAI ELECTRIC ADVANCED APPLIED TECHNOLOGY RESEARCH INSTITUTE INC.—See Funai Electric Co., Ltd.; *Int'l*, pg. 2844
FUNAI ELECTRIC CEBU, INC.—See Funai Electric Co., Ltd.; *Int'l*, pg. 2844
FUNAI ELECTRIC CO., LTD.; *Int'l*, pg. 2844
FUNAI ELECTRIC EUROPE SP. Z.O.O. - FRENCH BUSINESS UNIT—See Funai Electric Co., Ltd.; *Int'l*, pg. 2844
FUNAI ELECTRIC EUROPE SP. Z.O.O. - GERMAN BUSINESS UNIT—See Funai Electric Co., Ltd.; *Int'l*, pg. 2844
FUNAI ELECTRIC EUROPE SP. Z.O.O. - POLISH BUSINESS UNIT—See Funai Electric Co., Ltd.; *Int'l*, pg. 2844
FUNAI ELECTRIC EUROPE SP. Z.O.O.—See Funai Electric Co., Ltd.; *Int'l*, pg. 2844
FUNAI ELECTRIC (H.K.) LTD.—See Funai Electric Co., Ltd.; *Int'l*, pg. 2844
FUNAI ELECTRIC (MALASIYA) SDN. BHD.—See Funai Electric Co., Ltd.; *Int'l*, pg. 2844
FUNAI ELECTRIC PHILIPPINES INC.—See Funai Electric Co., Ltd.; *Int'l*, pg. 2844
FUNAI ELECTRIC R&D (SHENZHEN) CO., LTD.—See Funai Electric Co., Ltd.; *Int'l*, pg. 2844
FUNAI GENERAL SERVICE CO., LTD.—See Funai Electric Co., Ltd.; *Int'l*, pg. 2844
FUNAI LEXINGTON TECHNOLOGY CORPORATION—See Funai Electric Co., Ltd.; *Int'l*, pg. 2845
FUNA INTERNATIONAL B.V.—See L3Harris Technologies, Inc.; *U.S. Public*, pg. 1281
FUNA INTERNATIONAL OY—See L3Harris Technologies, Inc.; *U.S. Public*, pg. 1281
FUNA INTERNATIONAL SRL—See L3Harris Technologies, Inc.; *U.S. Public*, pg. 1281

CORPORATE AFFILIATIONS

FUNAI SERVICE CO., LTD.—See Funai Electric Co., Ltd.; *Int'l*, pg. 2845
FUNAI SERVICE CORPORATION—See Funai Electric Co., Ltd.; *Int'l*, pg. 2844
FUNAI SOKEN CORPORATE RELATIONS, INC.—See Funai Soken Holdings Incorporated; *Int'l*, pg. 2845
FUNAI SOKEN DIGITAL INC.—See Funai Soken Holdings Incorporated; *Int'l*, pg. 2845
FUNAI SOKEN HOLDINGS INCORPORATED; *Int'l*, pg. 2845
FUNAI SOKEN LOGISTICS, INC.—See Funai Soken Holdings Incorporated; *Int'l*, pg. 2845
FUNAI TECHO-SYSTEMS CO., LTD.—See Funai Electric Co., Ltd.; *Int'l*, pg. 2845
FUNAI (THAILAND) CO., LTD.—See Funai Electric Co., Ltd.; *Int'l*, pg. 2844
FUNAI TRADING CORP.—See Funai Electric Co., Ltd.; *Int'l*, pg. 2845
FUNAKOSHI CO., LTD.—See Sumitomo Electric Industries, Ltd.; *Int'l*, pg. 7285
FUN AND FUNCTION LLC; *U.S. Private*, pg. 1622
FUNAO MINING CO., LTD.—See Nittetsu Mining Co., Ltd.; *Int'l*, pg. 5383
FUN BEVERAGE INC.; *U.S. Private*, pg. 1622
FUNBOX COMPANY LIMITED—See Asphere Innovations Public Company Limited; *Int'l*, pg. 630
FUNBOX INDIA PRIVATE LIMITED—See Pureprofile Limited; *Int'l*, pg. 6122
FUN-BRANDS HQ CAROUSEL, LLC—See Tregaron Management, LLC; *U.S. Private*, pg. 4217
FUN-BRANDS OF TEMPE, LLC—See Tregaron Management, LLC; *U.S. Private*, pg. 4217
FUNC FOOD FINLAND OY—See Celsius Holdings, Inc.; *U.S. Public*, pg. 466
FUNC FOOD GROUP OYJ—See Celsius Holdings, Inc.; *U.S. Public*, pg. 466
FUNCOM INC—See Tencent Holdings Limited; *Int'l*, pg. 7558
FUNCOM OSLO AS—See Tencent Holdings Limited; *Int'l*, pg. 7558
FUNCOM SE—See Tencent Holdings Limited; *Int'l*, pg. 7558
FUN COUNTRY RV'S & MARINE, INC.; *U.S. Private*, pg. 1622
FUNCTIONAL PATHWAYS, LLC.; *U.S. Private*, pg. 1622
FUNCTION INTERNATIONAL PUBLIC COMPANY LIMITED; *Int'l*, pg. 2845
FUNDABLE LLC; *U.S. Private*, pg. 1622
FUNDACAO ODEBRECHT—See Novonor S.A.; *Int'l*, pg. 5470
FUNDACAO PORTUGAL TELECOM—See Altice Europe N.V.; *Int'l*, pg. 392
FUNDACION ABBVIE—See AbbVie Inc.; *U.S. Public*, pg. 24
FUNDACION AES GENER—See The AES Corporation; *U.S. Public*, pg. 2031
FUNDACION AON ESPANA—See Aon plc; *Int'l*, pg. 494
FUNDACION BANCARIA CAIXA D'ESTALVIS I PENSIONS DE BARCELONA, LA CAIXA; *Int'l*, pg. 2845
FUNDACION BANMEDICA—See UnitedHealth Group Incorporated; *U.S. Public*, pg. 2241
FUNDACION BIOGEN—See Biogen Inc.; *U.S. Public*, pg. 337
FUNDACION CHRYSLER DE MEXICO I.A.P.—See Stellantis N.V.; *Int'l*, pg. 7200
FUNDACION OCESA ENTRETENIMIENTO, A.C.—See Live Nation Entertainment, Inc.; *U.S. Public*, pg. 1328
FUNDACION PARA EL DESAROLLO DEL HOGAR PROPIO, INC; *U.S. Private*, pg. 1622
FUNDACION TRAXION, A. C.—See Grupo Traxion, S. A. B. de C. V.; *Int'l*, pg. 3138
FUNDACJA JSW SA—See Jastrzebska Spolka Weglowa S.A.; *Int'l*, pg. 3913
FUNDADMINISTRATION, INC.—See Apex Fund Services Holdings Ltd.; *Int'l*, pg. 510
FUNDAMENTA ERTEKLANC INGATLANKOZVETITO ES SZOLGALTATO KFT.—See DZ BANK AG Deutsche Zentral-Genossenschaftsbank; *Int'l*, pg. 2244
FUNDAMENTAL ACOUSTIC RESEARCH (FAR)—See EVS Broadcast Equipment S.A.; *Int'l*, pg. 2574
FUNDAMENTAL ADVISORS LP; *U.S. Private*, pg. 1622
FUNDAMENTA-LAKASKASSZA LAKAS-TAKAREKPENZTAR ZRT.—See DZ BANK AG Deutsche Zentral-Genossenschaftsbank; *Int'l*, pg. 2244
FUNDAMENTAL GLOBAL INC.—See Kingsway Financial Services Inc.; *U.S. Public*, pg. 1234
FUNDAMENTAL GLOBAL INVESTORS, LLC; *U.S. Private*, pg. 1623
FUNDAMENTAL LONG TERM CARE HOLDINGS; *U.S. Private*, pg. 1623
FUNDAMENTAL TRACKER INVESTMENT MANAGEMENT LIMITED—See Pollen Street Limited; *Int'l*, pg. 5910
FUNDAMENTA REAL ESTATE AG; *Int'l*, pg. 2845
FUNDAMENTERING AS—See AF Gruppen ASA; *Int'l*, pg. 184
FUNDAMENTUM ASSET MANAGEMENT S.A.—See BNP Paribas SA; *Int'l*, pg. 1091

COMPANY NAME INDEX

FUNDAMETAL—See Siderurgica Venezolana Sivensa S.A.; *Int'l*, pg. 6883
FUNDAMO (PTY) LTD.—See Visa, Inc.; *U.S. Public*, pg. 2301
FUNDASSIST LIMITED—See Broadridge Financial Solutions, Inc.; *U.S. Public*, pg. 391
FUNDCORE INSTITUTIONAL INCOME TRUST INC.; *U.S. Private*, pg. 1623
FUNDCORP, INC.; *U.S. Private*, pg. 1623
FUND CREATION GROUP CO., LTD.; *Int'l*, pg. 2845
FUNDELY CO., LTD.; *Int'l*, pg. 2845
FUNDERA INC.; *U.S. Private*, pg. 1623
FUNDERBURK'S PHARMACY, INC.; *U.S. Private*, pg. 1623
FUNDERSTONE SECURITIES LIMITED—See G-Resources Group Limited; *Int'l*, pg. 2862
FUND ESTATES REIT; *Int'l*, pg. 2845
FUND EVALUATION GROUP, LLC; *U.S. Private*, pg. 1622
FUNDEX INVESTMENTS INC.—See iA Financial Corporation Inc.; *Int'l*, pg. 3567
FUND FOR FINANCIAL SUPPORT OF AGRICULTURE JOINT-STOCK COMPANY—See KazAgro National Management Holding JSC; *Int'l*, pg. 4102
FUND FOR THE PUBLIC INTEREST, INC.; *U.S. Private*, pg. 1622
FUNDICION TALLERES S.A.—See Corporacion Nacional del Cobre de Chile; *Int'l*, pg. 1805
FUNDIMMO SAS—See Fonciere Atland SA; *Int'l*, pg. 2724
FUNDIMO, S.A.—See Caixa Geral de Depositos S.A.; *Int'l*, pg. 1260
FUNDING CIRCLE DEUTSCHLAND GMBH—See Funding Circle Holdings PLC; *Int'l*, pg. 2845
FUNDING CIRCLE ESPANA S.L.—See Funding Circle Holdings PLC; *Int'l*, pg. 2845
FUNDING CIRCLE HOLDINGS PLC; *Int'l*, pg. 2845
FUNDING CIRCLE NEDERLAND B.V.—See Funding Circle Holdings PLC; *Int'l*, pg. 2845
FUNDINGPARTNER AS—See Schibsted ASA; *Int'l*, pg. 6616
FUNDINGSHIELD LLC; *U.S. Private*, pg. 1623
FUNDLY INC.—See NonProfitEasy, Inc.; *U.S. Private*, pg. 2934
FUNDO ALUMINIUM AB—See Norsk Hydro ASA; *Int'l*, pg. 5432
FUNDOS GROUP LLC; *U.S. Private*, pg. 1623
FUNDQUEST ADVISOR SASU—See BNP Paribas SA; *Int'l*, pg. 1091
FUNDQUEST MM LTD.—See BNP Paribas SA; *Int'l*, pg. 1091
FUNDQUEST UK LTD.—See BNP Paribas SA; *Int'l*, pg. 1091
FUNDSXPRESS FINANCIAL NETWORK, INC.—See Fiserv, Inc.; *U.S. Public*, pg. 851
FUNDUSZ HIPOTECZNY DOM S.A.—See IPOPEMA Securities S.A.; *Int'l*, pg. 3797
FUNDVISER CAPITAL (INDIA) LTD.; *Int'l*, pg. 2845
FUNEA BROADBAND SERVICES B.V—See TKH Group N.V.; *Int'l*, pg. 7764
FUNEHIKI SEIMITSU CO., LTD.—See Citizen Watch Co., Ltd.; *Int'l*, pg. 1625
FUNENG ORIENTAL EQUIPMENT TECHNOLOGY CO., LTD.; *Int'l*, pg. 2846
FUNERAL DIRECTORS CAPITAL VENTURES INC.—See Directors Investment Group Inc.; *U.S. Private*, pg. 1236
FUNERAL DIRECTORS LIFE INSURANCE CO. INC.—See Directors Investment Group Inc.; *U.S. Private*, pg. 1236
FUNERAL PARTNERS LIMITED—See Montagu Private Equity LLP; *Int'l*, pg. 5036
FUNERAL SERVICES NORTHERN IRELAND LIMITED—See Co-operative Group Limited; *Int'l*, pg. 1679
FUNESPANA, S.A.—See MAPFRE S.A.; *Int'l*, pg. 4684
FUN FACTORY INC.—See Fernandez Entertainment; *U.S. Private*, pg. 1497
FUN FASHION KUWAIT CO. W.L.L.—See LVMH Moet Hennessy Louis Vuitton SE; *Int'l*, pg. 4593
FUN FASHION NAPOLI SRL—See LVMH Moet Hennessy Louis Vuitton SE; *Int'l*, pg. 4593
FUNFRAP-FUNDICAO PORTUGUESA S.A.—See Stellantis N.V.; *Int'l*, pg. 7203
FUNFTE SAB TREUHAND UND VERWALTUNG GMBH & CO. SUHL RIMBACHZENTRUM KG—See Deutsche Bank Aktiengesellschaft; *Int'l*, pg. 2061
FUNFZEHNTE BASF ERWERBSGESELLSCHAFT MBH—See BASF SE; *Int'l*, pg. 883
FUNFZEHNTE BASF FINANZBETEILIGUNGSGESELLSCHAFT MBH—See BASF SE; *Int'l*, pg. 883
FUNFZEHNTE BASF PROJEKTENTWICKLUNGSGESELLSCHAFT MBH—See BASF SE; *Int'l*, pg. 883
FUNG HOLDINGS (1937) LIMITED—See King Lun Holdings Limited; *Int'l*, pg. 4169
FUNG YIK SDN. BHD.—See Asas Dunia Berhad; *Int'l*, pg. 599
FUN HOUSE LEISURE LIMITED—See Inspired Entertainment, Inc.; *U.S. Public*, pg. 1131
FUN INTERNATIONAL LTD—See Toys R Us ANZ Limited; *Int'l*, pg. 7881
FUNITURE ROW LLC; *U.S. Private*, pg. 1623

FUNJET VACATIONS INC.—See Apple Leisure Group; *U.S. Private*, pg. 296
FUNKE MEDIEN NRW GMBH—See Westdeutsche Allgemeine verlagsgesellschaft; *Int'l*, pg. 8387
FUNKHAUS HALLE GMBH & CO. KG—See Bertelsmann SE & Co. KGaA; *Int'l*, pg. 994
FUNKIN LIMITED—See A.G. Barr plc; *Int'l*, pg. 23
FUNK/LEVIS & ASSOCIATES; *U.S. Private*, pg. 1623
FUNKO GAMES, LLC—See Funko Inc.; *U.S. Public*, pg. 893
FUNKO INC.; *U.S. Public*, pg. 892
FUNKSJONSUTSTYR AS—See AddLife AB; *Int'l*, pg. 129
FUNK UND TECHNIK GMBH—See Morgan Stanley; *U.S. Public*, pg. 1473
FUNKWERK AG—See Hormann Holding GmbH & Co. KG; *Int'l*, pg. 3479
FUNKWERK IOT GMBH—See Hormann Holding GmbH & Co. KG; *Int'l*, pg. 3479
FUNKWERK PLETTAC ELECTRONIC GMBH—See Hormann Holding GmbH & Co. KG; *Int'l*, pg. 3479
FUNKWERK SECURITY COMMUNICATIONS GMBH—See Hormann Holding GmbH & Co. KG; *Int'l*, pg. 3479
FUNKWERK TECHNOLOGIES GMBH—See Hormann Holding GmbH & Co. KG; *Int'l*, pg. 3480
FUNK WERK VIDEO SYSTEME GMBH—See Hormann Holding GmbH & Co. KG; *Int'l*, pg. 3479
FUNKY BUDDHA BREWERY LLC—See Constellation Brands, Inc.; *U.S. Public*, pg. 571
FUNMOBILITY, INC.; *U.S. Private*, pg. 1623
FUNNELBOX INC; *U.S. Private*, pg. 1623
FUNNYBONES FOODSERVICE LIMITED—See GraceKennedy Limited; *Int'l*, pg. 3048
FUNNY SOFTWARE LIMITED; *Int'l*, pg. 2846
FUNOTEC (DALIAN) CO., LTD.—See Furuno Electric Co., Ltd.; *Int'l*, pg. 2847
FUNPEP CO., LTD.; *Int'l*, pg. 2846
FUN RADIO—See Metropole Television SA; *Int'l*, pg. 4863
FUNRISE DISTRIBUTION COMPANY—See Matrix Holdings Limited; *Int'l*, pg. 4729
FUNRISE, INC.—See Matrix Holdings Limited; *Int'l*, pg. 4729
FUNRISE INTERNATIONAL LIMITED—See Matrix Holdings Limited; *Int'l*, pg. 4729
FUNSHINE CULTURE GROUP CO., LTD.; *Int'l*, pg. 2846
FUN SPOT OF FLORIDA, INC.; *U.S. Private*, pg. 1622
FUNTALK CHINA HOLDINGS LIMITED; *Int'l*, pg. 2846
FUNTASTIC INTERNATIONAL LIMITED—See Toys R Us ANZ Limited; *Int'l*, pg. 7881
FUNTEES—See Delta Apparel, Inc.; *U.S. Public*, pg. 652
FUN TO FUN INC.—See Hirayama Holdings Co., Ltd.; *Int'l*, pg. 3404
FUNTORO INC.—See Micro-Star International Co., Ltd.; *Int'l*, pg. 4878
FUNTOWN HONG KONG LIMITED—See GigaMedia Limited; *Int'l*, pg. 2971
FUN TOWN RV LP; *U.S. Private*, pg. 1622
FUN TOWN SPLASH TOWN USA; *U.S. Private*, pg. 1622
FUNWORLD SRL—See Kontron AG; *Int'l*, pg. 4276
FUQI INTERNATIONAL, INC.; *Int'l*, pg. 2846
FUQIN FINTECH LIMITED; *Int'l*, pg. 2846
FUQING NAN PAO RESINS CO., LTD—See Nan Pao Resins Chemical Co., Ltd.; *Int'l*, pg. 5138
FURA GEMS INC.; *Int'l*, pg. 2846
FURAMA LTD.; *Int'l*, pg. 2846
FURA SERVICES DMCC—See Fura Gems Inc.; *Int'l*, pg. 2846
FURBAY ELECTRIC SUPPLY CO.; *U.S. Private*, pg. 1623
FURBER ADVERTISING; *U.S. Private*, pg. 1623
FUR BREEDERS AGRICULTURAL COOPERATIVE; *U.S. Private*, pg. 1623
FUREASU CO., LTD.; *Int'l*, pg. 2846
FURE FINANCIAL CORP.—See Genstar Capital, LLC; *U.S. Private*, pg. 1677
FURE FINANCIAL CORP.—See Keystone Group, L.P.; *U.S. Private*, pg. 2298
FUREN GROUP PHARMACEUTICAL CO., LTD.; *Int'l*, pg. 2846
FUREY FILTER & PUMP INC.—See Genstar Capital, LLC; *U.S. Private*, pg. 1678
FURGONETAS DE ALQUILER SA—See ZIGUP plc; *Int'l*, pg. 8682
FURGO-SUHAIMI LTD.—See Fugro N.V.; *Int'l*, pg. 2806
FURINO & SONS INC.; *U.S. Private*, pg. 1623
FURLONG MILLS LIMITED—See Churchill China plc; *Int'l*, pg. 1600
FURMAN CO., INC.—See CBRE Group, Inc.; *U.S. Public*, pg. 460
FURMAN, FEINER ADVERTISING—See Furman Roth Advertising; *U.S. Private*, pg. 1624
FURMANITE AB—See Team, Inc.; *U.S. Public*, pg. 1987
FURMANITE AS—See Team, Inc.; *U.S. Public*, pg. 1987
FURMANITE A/S—See Team, Inc.; *U.S. Public*, pg. 1987
FURMANITE BV—See Team, Inc.; *U.S. Public*, pg. 1987
FURMANITE CANADA CORP—See Team, Inc; *U.S. Public*, pg. 1987
FURMANITE CORPORATION—See Team, Inc.; *U.S. Public*, pg. 1987

FURMANITE GMBH—See Team, Inc.; *U.S. Public*, pg. 1988
FURMANITE INTERNATIONAL LTD. - IPSCO—See Team, Inc.; *U.S. Public*, pg. 1987
FURMANITE (MALAYSIA) SDN. BHD.—See Team, Inc.; *U.S. Public*, pg. 1987
FURMANITE SAS—See Team, Inc.; *U.S. Public*, pg. 1987
FURMANITE SINGAPORE PTE LTD.—See Team, Inc.; *U.S. Public*, pg. 1987
FURMANITE WORLDWIDE, INC.—See Team, Inc.; *U.S. Public*, pg. 1987
FURMANO FOODS, INC.; *U.S. Private*, pg. 1624
FURMAN ROTH ADVERTISING; *U.S. Private*, pg. 1623
FURMAN'S, INC.; *U.S. Private*, pg. 1624
FURNACE AND TUBE SERVICE INC.; *U.S. Private*, pg. 1624
FURNACE CONSTRUCTION CREMATORS LIMITED—See Matthews International Corporation; *U.S. Public*, pg. 1399
FURNACE ENGINEERING PTY LTD—See ESPEC Corp.; *Int'l*, pg. 2505
FURNACE PARTS, LLC—See Advent International Corporation; *U.S. Private*, pg. 100
FURNACES NUCLEAR APPLICATIONS GRENOBLE S.A.—See AMG Critical Materials N.V.; *Int'l*, pg. 425
FURNAS CENTRAIS ELETRICAS S.A.—See Centrais Eletricas Brasileiras S.A.; *Int'l*, pg. 1403
FURNESS BUILDING SOCIETY; *Int'l*, pg. 2846
FURNESS WITHY (AUSTRALIA) PTY. LIMITED—See John Swire & Sons Limited; *Int'l*, pg. 3981
FURNESS WITHY (CHARTERING) LTD.—See John Swire & Sons Limited; *Int'l*, pg. 3981
FURNISHED QUARTERS LLC; *U.S. Private*, pg. 1624
FURNITECH COMPONENTS (VIETNAM) CO., LTD.—See PRG Holdings Berhad; *Int'l*, pg. 5968
FURNITURE1 D.O.O.—See BHG Group AB; *Int'l*, pg. 1014
FURNITURE1 KFT—See BHG Group AB; *Int'l*, pg. 1014
FURNITURE1 UAB—See BHG Group AB; *Int'l*, pg. 1014
FURNITURE CONSULTANTS LLC; *U.S. Private*, pg. 1624
FURNITURE DISTRIBUTORS INC.; *U.S. Private*, pg. 1624
FURNITURE ENTERPRISES OF ALASKA; *U.S. Private*, pg. 1624
FURNITURE FACTORY OUTLET, LLC—See B. Riley Financial, Inc.; *U.S. Public*, pg. 261
FURNITURE FACTORY OUTLET, LLC—See Irradiant Partners, LP; *U.S. Private*, pg. 2140
FURNITURE FAIR INC.; *U.S. Private*, pg. 1624
FURNITURE & FURNISHINGS PTE. LTD.—See TT International Limited; *Int'l*, pg. 7960
FURNITURELAND SOUTH, INC.; *U.S. Private*, pg. 1624
FURNITURE MARKETING GROUP INC.; *U.S. Private*, pg. 1624
FURNITURE MEDIC LIMITED PARTNERSHIP—See EMP Management, LLC; *U.S. Private*, pg. 1384
FURNITURE ON CONSIGNMENT INC.; *U.S. Private*, pg. 1624
FURNITURE OUTLETS USA; *U.S. Private*, pg. 1624
FURNITURE RENTAL ASSOCIATES; *U.S. Private*, pg. 1624
FURNITURE ROW; *U.S. Private*, pg. 1624
FURNITURE & THINGS INC.; *U.S. Private*, pg. 1624
FURNITURE VILLAGE LIMITED; *Int'l*, pg. 2846
FURNIWEB HOLDINGS LIMITED; *Int'l*, pg. 2846
FURNIWEB MANUFACTURING SDN. BHD.—See PRG Holdings Berhad; *Int'l*, pg. 5968
FURNIWEB MANUFACTURING (VIETNAM) CO., LTD.—See PRG Holdings Berhad; *Int'l*, pg. 5968
FURNIWEB SAFETY WEBBING SDN. BHD.—See PRG Holdings Berhad; *Int'l*, pg. 5968
FURNIWEB (VIETNAM) SHAREHOLDING COMPANY—See Furniweb Holdings Limited; *Int'l*, pg. 2846
FURNLITE, INC.; *U.S. Private*, pg. 1624
FURST CONSTRUCTION CO. INC.—See Furst Enterprises Inc.; *U.S. Private*, pg. 1624
FURSTENBERG INSTITUT GMBH—See Asklepios Kliniken GmbH & Co. KGaA; *Int'l*, pg. 623
FURST ENTERPRISES INC.; *U.S. Private*, pg. 1624
FURSTENWALDER AUS- UND WEITERBILDUNGSZENTRUM GMBH—See AcadeMedia AB; *Int'l*, pg. 76
FURST GROUP—See Management Partners, Inc.; *U.S. Private*, pg. 2560
FURSTLICH FURSTENBERGISCHE BRAUEREI GMBH & CO. KG—See L'Arche Green N.V.; *Int'l*, pg. 4376
FURSTLICH FURSTENBERGISCHE BRAUEREI GMBH & CO. KG—See Schorghuber Stiftung & Co. Holding KG; *Int'l*, pg. 6639
FURST-MCNESS COMPANY; *U.S. Private*, pg. 1624
FURST-MCNESS OF CANADA—See Furst-McNess Company; *U.S. Private*, pg. 1624
FURSTPERSON, INC.—See Rubicon Technology Partners, LLC; *U.S. Private*, pg. 3500
FURSTSTAFFING, INC.; *U.S. Private*, pg. 1624
FURSYS, INC.; *Int'l*, pg. 2846
FURTHER GLOBAL CAPITAL MANAGEMENT, L.P.; *U.S. Private*, pg. 1624
FURUBAYASHI SHIKO CO., LTD.; *Int'l*, pg. 2846

FURUKAWA AMERICA INC - HIRATSUKA WORKS MAGNET WIRE PLANT—See The Furukawa Electric Co., Ltd.; *Int'l*, pg. 7644
FURUKAWA AMERICA INC - MIE WORKS, MAGNET WIRE PLANT—See The Furukawa Electric Co., Ltd.; *Int'l*, pg. 7644
FURUKAWA AUTOMOTIVE PARTS (DONG GUAN) LTD.—See The Furukawa Electric Co., Ltd.; *Int'l*, pg. 7644
FURUKAWA AUTOMOTIVE PARTS (VIETNAM) INC.—See The Furukawa Electric Co., Ltd.; *Int'l*, pg. 7644
FURUKAWA AUTOMOTIVE SYSTEMS DESIGN PHILIPPINES, INC.—See The Furukawa Electric Co., Ltd.; *Int'l*, pg. 7644
FURUKAWA AUTOMOTIVE SYSTEMS INC.—See The Furukawa Electric Co., Ltd.; *Int'l*, pg. 7644
FURUKAWA AUTOMOTIVE SYSTEMS LIMA PHILIPPINES,INC.—See The Furukawa Electric Co., Ltd.; *Int'l*, pg. 7644
FURUKAWA AUTOMOTIVE SYSTEMS MANAGEMENT (SHANGHAI) CO., LTD.—See The Furukawa Electric Co., Ltd.; *Int'l*, pg. 7644
FURUKAWA AUTOMOTIVE SYSTEMS MEXICO S.A. DE C.V.—See The Furukawa Electric Co., Ltd.; *Int'l*, pg. 7644
FURUKAWA AUTOMOTIVE SYSTEMS VIETNAM INC.—See The Furukawa Electric Co., Ltd.; *Int'l*, pg. 7644
FURUKAWA AUTO PARTS (HK) LTD.—See The Furukawa Electric Co., Ltd.; *Int'l*, pg. 7644
FURUKAWA AUTO PARTS (HUIZHOU) CO. LTD.—See The Furukawa Electric Co., Ltd.; *Int'l*, pg. 7644
FURUKAWA AVC ELECTRONICS (SUZHOU) CO., LTD.—See Asia Vital Components Co., Ltd.; *Int'l*, pg. 616
THE FURUKAWA BATTERY CO., LTD.—See The Furukawa Electric Co., Ltd.; *Int'l*, pg. 7647
FURUKAWA CASTEC CO., LTD.—See Furukawa Co., Ltd.; *Int'l*, pg. 2847
FURUKAWA C&B CO., LTD.—See The Furukawa Electric Co., Ltd.; *Int'l*, pg. 7644
FURUKAWA CHEMICALS CO., LTD.—See Furukawa Co., Ltd.; *Int'l*, pg. 2847
FURUKAWA CIRCUIT FOIL CO., LTD.—See The Furukawa Electric Co., Ltd.; *Int'l*, pg. 7644
FURUKAWA CIRCUIT FOIL (HONG KONG) CO., LTD.—See The Furukawa Electric Co., Ltd.; *Int'l*, pg. 7644
FURUKAWA CIRCUIT FOIL TAIWAN CORPORATION—See The Furukawa Electric Co., Ltd.; *Int'l*, pg. 7645
FURUKAWA COLOMBIA, SAS—See The Furukawa Electric Co., Ltd.; *Int'l*, pg. 7645
FURUKAWA CO., LTD. - REAL ESTATE DIVISION—See Furukawa Co., Ltd.; *Int'l*, pg. 2847
FURUKAWA CO., LTD.; *Int'l*, pg. 2846
FURUKAWA COMMUNICATION & BROADCASTING CO. LTD.—See The Furukawa Electric Co., Ltd.; *Int'l*, pg. 7645
FURUKAWA DENSHI CO., LTD. - OPTICAL COMPONENTS PLANT—See Furukawa Co., Ltd.; *Int'l*, pg. 2847
FURUKAWA DENSHI CO., LTD. - SEMICONDUCTOR MATERIALS PLANT—See Furukawa Co., Ltd.; *Int'l*, pg. 2847
FURUKAWA DENSHI CO., LTD.—See Furukawa Co., Ltd.; *Int'l*, pg. 2847
FURUKAWA ELECOM CO., LTD.—See The Furukawa Electric Co., Ltd.; *Int'l*, pg. 7645
FURUKAWA ELECTRIC ADVANCED ENGINEERING CO., LTD.—See The Furukawa Electric Co., Ltd.; *Int'l*, pg. 7645
FURUKAWA ELECTRIC AUTOPARTS CENTRAL EUROPE, S.R.O.(FACE)—See The Furukawa Electric Co., Ltd.; *Int'l*, pg. 7645
FURUKAWA ELECTRIC AUTOPARTS(PHILIPPINES)INC.—See The Furukawa Electric Co., Ltd.; *Int'l*, pg. 7645
FURUKAWA ELECTRIC BUSINESS & LIFE SUPPORT INC.—See The Furukawa Electric Co., Ltd.; *Int'l*, pg. 7645
THE FURUKAWA ELECTRIC CO., LTD.; *Int'l*, pg. 7644
FURUKAWA ELECTRIC COMMUNICATIONS SOUTH-EAST ASIA LTD.—See The Furukawa Electric Co., Ltd.; *Int'l*, pg. 7645
FURUKAWA ELECTRIC COPPER FOIL TAIWAN CO., LTD.—See The Furukawa Electric Co., Ltd.; *Int'l*, pg. 7645
FURUKAWA ELECTRIC ECOTEC CO., LTD.—See The Furukawa Electric Co., Ltd.; *Int'l*, pg. 7645
FURUKAWA ELECTRIC ENGINEERING SINGAPORE PTE. LTD.—See The Furukawa Electric Co., Ltd.; *Int'l*, pg. 7645
FURUKAWA ELECTRIC EUROPE LIMITED—See The Furukawa Electric Co., Ltd.; *Int'l*, pg. 7645
FURUKAWA ELECTRIC EUROPE LTD.—See The Furukawa Electric Co., Ltd.; *Int'l*, pg. 7645
FURUKAWA ELECTRIC HONG KONG LTD.—See The Furukawa Electric Co., Ltd.; *Int'l*, pg. 7645
FURUKAWA ELECTRIC INDUSTRIAL CABLE CO., LTD.—See The Furukawa Electric Co., Ltd.; *Int'l*, pg. 7645
FURUKAWA ELECTRIC INSTITUTE OF TECHNOLOGY CO., LTD.—See The Furukawa Electric Co., Ltd.; *Int'l*, pg. 7645
FURUKAWA ELECTRIC LATAM S.A.—See The Furukawa Electric Co., Ltd.; *Int'l*, pg. 7645
FURUKAWA ELECTRIC LATAM SA—See The Furukawa Electric Co., Ltd.; *Int'l*, pg. 7645
FURUKAWA ELECTRIC POWER SYSTEMS CO., LTD.—See The Furukawa Electric Co., Ltd.; *Int'l*, pg. 7645
FURUKAWA ELECTRIC (SHENZHEN) CO., LTD.—See The Furukawa Electric Co., Ltd.; *Int'l*, pg. 7645
FURUKAWA ELECTRIC SINGAPORE PTE. LTD.—See The Furukawa Electric Co., Ltd.; *Int'l*, pg. 7645
FURUKAWA ELECTRIC TRADING SZ LTD.—See The Furukawa Electric Co., Ltd.; *Int'l*, pg. 7645
FURUKAWA ELECTRIC (XI'AN) OPTICAL COMMUNICATION CO., LTD.—See The Furukawa Electric Co., Ltd.; *Int'l*, pg. 7645
FURUKAWA FITEL OPTICAL DEVICE CO., LTD.—See The Furukawa Electric Co., Ltd.; *Int'l*, pg. 7645
FURUKAWA FITEL OPTICAL PRODUCTS (SHANGHAI) CO., LTD.—See The Furukawa Electric Co., Ltd.; *Int'l*, pg. 7645
FURUKAWA FITEL (THAILAND) CO., LTD.—See The Furukawa Electric Co., Ltd.; *Int'l*, pg. 7645
FURUKAWA INDUSTRIAL COLOMBIA, SAS—See The Furukawa Electric Co., Ltd.; *Int'l*, pg. 7645
FURUKAWA INDUSTRIAL LATAM S.A.—See The Furukawa Electric Co., Ltd.; *Int'l*, pg. 7645
FURUKAWA INDUSTRIAL MACHINERY SYSTEMS CO., LTD. - OYAMA UNIT—See Furukawa Co., Ltd.; *Int'l*, pg. 2847
FURUKAWA INDUSTRIAL MACHINERY SYSTEMS CO., LTD.—See Furukawa Co., Ltd.; *Int'l*, pg. 2847
FURUKAWA INDUSTRIAL MACHINERY SYSTEMS CO., LTD. - TOCHIGI UNIT—See Furukawa Co., Ltd.; *Int'l*, pg. 2847
FURUKAWA INDUSTRIAL OPTOELETRONICA LTDA.—See The Furukawa Electric Co., Ltd.; *Int'l*, pg. 7645
FURUKAWA INDUSTRIAL PLASTICS CO., LTD.—See The Furukawa Electric Co., Ltd.; *Int'l*, pg. 7645
FURUKAWA INDUSTRIAL S.A. PRODUTOS ELETRICOS—See The Furukawa Electric Co., Ltd.; *Int'l*, pg. 7645
FURUKAWA INDUSTRIAL S.A.—See The Furukawa Electric Co., Ltd.; *Int'l*, pg. 7645
FURUKAWA LOGISTICS CORP.—See The Furukawa Electric Co., Ltd.; *Int'l*, pg. 7645
FURUKAWA LOGISTICS (SHANGHAI) CO., LTD.—See SBS Holdings Inc.; pg. 6607
FURUKAWA MACHINERY ASIA SDN. BHD.—See Furukawa Co., Ltd.; *Int'l*, pg. 2847
FURUKAWA MAGNET WIRE CO., LTD.—See The Furukawa Electric Co., Ltd.; *Int'l*, pg. 7645
FURUKAWA MANAGEMENT SHANGHAI, LTD.—See The Furukawa Electric Co., Ltd.; *Int'l*, pg. 7645
FURUKAWA METALS & RESOURCES CO., LTD.—See Furukawa Co., Ltd.; *Int'l*, pg. 2847
FURUKAWA MEXICO, S.A.DE C.V.—See The Furukawa Electric Co., Ltd.; *Int'l*, pg. 7645
FURUKAWA MINDA ELECTRIC PRIVATE LIMITED—See The Furukawa Electric Co., Ltd.; *Int'l*, pg. 7645
FURUKAWA NDK CO., LTD.—See NIHON DEMPA KOGYO.Co Ltd.; *Int'l*, pg. 5283
FURUKAWA NETWORK SOLUTION CORPORATION—See The Furukawa Electric Co., Ltd.; *Int'l*, pg. 7645
FURUKAWA NEW LEAF CO., LTD.—See The Furukawa Electric Co., Ltd.; *Int'l*, pg. 7645
FURUKAWA NIKKO POWER GENERATION INC.—See The Furukawa Electric Co., Ltd.; *Int'l*, pg. 7645
FURUKAWA PRECISION ENGINEERING CO., LTD.—See The Furukawa Electric Co., Ltd.; *Int'l*, pg. 7645
FURUKAWA PRECISION THAILAND CO., LTD.—See The Furukawa Electric Co., Ltd.; *Int'l*, pg. 7645
FURUKAWA RESEARCH INC.—See The Furukawa Electric Co., Ltd.; *Int'l*, pg. 7646
FURUKAWA ROCK DRILL CO., LTD.—See Furukawa Co., Ltd.; *Int'l*, pg. 2847
FURUKAWA ROCK DRILL CO., LTD. - TAKASAKI FACTORY—See Furukawa Co., Ltd.; *Int'l*, pg. 2847
FURUKAWA ROCK DRILL CO., LTD. - YOSHII FACTORY—See Furukawa Co., Ltd.; *Int'l*, pg. 2847
FURUKAWA ROCK DRILL EUROPE B.V.—See Furukawa Co., Ltd.; *Int'l*, pg. 2847
FURUKAWA ROCK DRILL INDIA PVT. LTD.—See Furukawa Co., Ltd.; *Int'l*, pg. 2847
FURUKAWA ROCK DRILL KOREA CO., LTD.—See Furukawa Co., Ltd.; *Int'l*, pg. 2847
FURUKAWA ROCK DRILL LATIN AMERICA S.A.—See Furukawa Co., Ltd.; *Int'l*, pg. 2847
FURUKAWA ROCK DRILL (SHANGHAI) CO., LTD.—See Furukawa Co., Ltd.; *Int'l*, pg. 2847
FURUKAWA ROCK DRILL USA CO., LTD. - BREAKER DIVISION—See Furukawa Co., Ltd.; *Int'l*, pg. 2847
FURUKAWA ROCK DRILL USA, INC.—See Furukawa Co., Ltd.; *Int'l*, pg. 2847
FURUKAWA SANGYO KAISHA (H.K.) LTD.—See The Furukawa Electric Co., Ltd.; *Int'l*, pg. 7646
FURUKAWA SANGYO KAISHA (INDIA) PVT. LTD.—See The Furukawa Electric Co., Ltd.; *Int'l*, pg. 7646
FURUKAWA SANGYO KAISHA, LTD.—See The Furukawa Electric Co., Ltd.; *Int'l*, pg. 7646
FURUKAWA SANGYO KAISHA (MALAYSIA) SDN. BHD.—See The Furukawa Electric Co., Ltd.; *Int'l*, pg. 7646
FURUKAWA SANGYO KAISHA PHILIPPINES, INC.—See The Furukawa Electric Co., Ltd.; *Int'l*, pg. 7646
FURUKAWA SANGYO KAISHA (S.Z.) LTD.—See The Furukawa Electric Co., Ltd.; *Int'l*, pg. 7646
FURUKAWA SANGYO KOREA CO., LTD.—See The Furukawa Electric Co., Ltd.; *Int'l*, pg. 7646
FURUKAWA SANGYO NORTH AMERICA, INC.—See The Furukawa Electric Co., Ltd.; *Int'l*, pg. 7646
FURUKAWA SANGYO SHANGHAI CO., LTD.—See The Furukawa Electric Co., Ltd.; *Int'l*, pg. 7646
FURUKAWA SANGYO VIETNAM COMPANY LIMITED—See The Furukawa Electric Co., Ltd.; *Int'l*, pg. 7646
FURUKAWA SHANGHAI LTD.—See The Furukawa Electric Co., Ltd.; *Int'l*, pg. 7646
FURUKAWA TECHNO MATERIAL CO., LTD.—See The Furukawa Electric Co., Ltd.; *Int'l*, pg. 7646
FURUKAWA (THAILAND) CO., LTD.—See The Furukawa Electric Co., Ltd.; *Int'l*, pg. 7644
FURUKAWA UACJ MEMORY DISK CO., LTD.—See The Furukawa Electric Co., Ltd.; *Int'l*, pg. 7646
FURUKAWA UNIC CORPORATION - SAKURA UNIT—See Furukawa Co., Ltd.; *Int'l*, pg. 2847
FURUKAWA UNIC CORPORATION—See Furukawa Co., Ltd.; *Int'l*, pg. 2847
FURUKAWA UNIC (THAILAND) CO., LTD.—See Furukawa Co., Ltd.; *Int'l*, pg. 2847
FURUKAWA UNYU CO., LTD.—See Furukawa Co., Ltd.; *Int'l*, pg. 2847
FURUKAWA WIRING SYSTEMS MEXICO, S.A. DE C.V.—See The Furukawa Electric Co., Ltd.; *Int'l*, pg. 7646
FURUNO CHINA CO., LIMITED—See Furuno Electric Co., Ltd.; *Int'l*, pg. 2847
FURUNO CIRCUITECH CO., LTD.—See Furuno Electric Co., Ltd.; *Int'l*, pg. 2847
FURUNO (CYPRUS) LTD.—See Furuno Electric Co., Ltd.; *Int'l*, pg. 2847
FURUNO DANMARK A/S—See Furuno Electric Co., Ltd.; *Int'l*, pg. 2847
FURUNO DEUTSCHLAND GMBH—See Furuno Electric Co., Ltd.; *Int'l*, pg. 2847
FURUNO DONGGUAN CO., LTD.—See Furuno Electric Co., Ltd.; *Int'l*, pg. 2847
FURUNO ELECTRIC CO., LTD.; *Int'l*, pg. 2847
FURUNO ELECTRIC (MALAYSIA) SDN. BHD.—See Furuno Electric Co., Ltd.; *Int'l*, pg. 2847
FURUNO ESPANA SA—See Furuno Electric Co., Ltd.; *Int'l*, pg. 2847
FURUNO EUROPE BV—See Furuno Electric Co., Ltd.; *Int'l*, pg. 2848
FURUNO EURUS LLC—See Furuno Electric Co., Ltd.; *Int'l*, pg. 2848
FURUNO FINLAND OY—See Furuno Electric Co., Ltd.; *Int'l*, pg. 2848
FURUNO FRANCE S.A.S.—See Furuno Electric Co., Ltd.; *Int'l*, pg. 2848
FURUNO HELLAS S.A.—See Furuno Electric Co., Ltd.; *Int'l*, pg. 2848
FURUNO HONG KONG CO., LTD.—See Furuno Electric Co., Ltd.; *Int'l*, pg. 2848
FURUNO KANSAI HAMBAI CO., LTD.—See Furuno Electric Co., Ltd.; *Int'l*, pg. 2848
FURUNO KANSAI HANBAI CO., LTD.—See Furuno Electric Co., Ltd.; *Int'l*, pg. 2848
FURUNO KOREA CO., LTD.—See Furuno Electric Co., Ltd.; *Int'l*, pg. 2848
FURUNO KYUSHU HAMBAI CO., LTD.—See Furuno Electric Co., Ltd.; *Int'l*, pg. 2848
FURUNO LIFE BEST CO., LTD.—See Furuno Electric Co., Ltd.; *Int'l*, pg. 2848
FURUNO NORGE AS—See Furuno Electric Co., Ltd.; *Int'l*, pg. 2848
FURUNO PANAMA, S.A.—See Furuno Electric Co., Ltd.; *Int'l*, pg. 2848
FURUNO POLSKA SP. Z O.O.—See Furuno Electric Co., Ltd.; *Int'l*, pg. 2848
FURUNO SHANGHAI CO., LTD.—See Furuno Electric Co., Ltd.; *Int'l*, pg. 2848
FURUNO SINGAPORE PTE LTD—See Furuno Electric Co., Ltd.; *Int'l*, pg. 2848
FURUNO SOFTECH CO., LTD.—See Furuno Electric Co., Ltd.; *Int'l*, pg. 2848
FURUNO SOFTECH (DALIAN) CO , LTD.—See Furuno Electric Co., Ltd.; *Int'l*, pg. 2848

COMPANY NAME INDEX

FURUNO SVERIGE AB—See Furuno Electric Co., Ltd.; *Int'l*, pg. 2848
FURUNO SYSTEMS CO ,LTD.—See Furuno Electric Co., Ltd.; *Int'l*, pg. 2848
FURUNO (UK) LTD.—See Furuno Electric Co., Ltd.; *Int'l*, pg. 2847
FURUNO USA, INC.—See Furuno Electric Co., Ltd.; *Int'l*, pg. 2848
FURUSATO. CO., LTD.—See Haseko Corporation; *Int'l*, pg. 3283
FURUSATO INDUSTRIES, LTD.—See Maruka Furusato Corporation; *Int'l*, pg. 4714
FURUTEC ELECTRICAL SDN. BHD.—See Eita Resources Berhad; *Int'l*, pg. 2337
FURUYA ECO-FRONT TECHNOLOGY CO., LTD.—See Furuya Metal Co., Ltd.; *Int'l*, pg. 2848
FURUYA METAL AMERICAS INC—See Furuya Metal Co., Ltd.; *Int'l*, pg. 2848
FURUYA METAL CO., LTD. - CHITOSE PLANT—See Furuya Metal Co., Ltd.; *Int'l*, pg. 2848
FURUYA METAL CO., LTD.; *Int'l*, pg. 2848
FURUYA METAL CO., LTD. - TSUCHIURA PLANT—See Furuya Metal Co., Ltd.; *Int'l*, pg. 2848
FURUYA METAL CO., LTD. - TSUKUBA PLANT—See Furuya Metal Co., Ltd.; *Int'l*, pg. 2848
FURUYA METAL KOREA CO., LTD.—See Furuya Metal Co., Ltd.; *Int'l*, pg. 2848
FURY GOLD MINES LIMITED; *Int'l*, pg. 2848
FURY MOTORS INC.; *U.S. Private*, pg. 1625
FURYU CORPORATION; *Int'l*, pg. 2848
THE FUSCO CORPORATION; *U.S. Private*, pg. 4031
FUSCO PERSONNEL, INC.; *U.S. Private*, pg. 1625
FUSE3 SOLUTIONS LLC; *U.S. Private*, pg. 1625
FUSE8 DELETE—See Fuse 8 Group Ltd; *Int'l*, pg. 2848
FUSE 8 GROUP LTD; *Int'l*, pg. 2848
FUSE8 RUSSIA—See Fuse 8 Group Ltd; *Int'l*, pg. 2848
FUSEAU; *Int'l*, pg. 2849
FUSE BATTERY METALS INC.; *Int'l*, pg. 2848
FUSEBILL INC.; *Int'l*, pg. 2849
FUSEFX, INC.—See EagleTree Capital, LP; *U.S. Private*, pg. 1311
FUSE GROUP HOLDING INC.; *U.S. Public*, pg. 893
FUSE/IDEAS; *U.S. Private*, pg. 1625
FUSE LLC; *U.S. Private*, pg. 1625
FUSE MEDICAL, INC.; *U.S. Public*, pg. 893
FUSE NETWORKS LLC—See SiTV, Inc.; *U.S. Private*, pg. 3677
FUSEN PHARMACEUTICAL CO., LTD.; *Int'l*, pg. 2849
FUSE PROJECT, LLC—See Bluefocus Intelligent Communications Group Co., Ltd.; *Int'l*, pg. 1071
FUSHAN QINGQUAN BEVERAGE CO., LTD.—See Zhuhai Zhongfu Enterprise Co., Ltd.; *Int'l*, pg. 8679
FUSHAN TECHNOLOGY (VIETNAM) LIMITED LIABILITY COMPANY—See Hon Hai Precision Industry Co., Ltd.; *Int'l*, pg. 3457
FU SHEK FINANCIAL HOLDINGS LIMITED; *Int'l*, pg. 2801
FU SHENG INDUSTRIAL CO., LTD.—See Brookfield Corporation; *Int'l*, pg. 1181
FU SHENG INSURANCE AGENCY CO., LTD.—See Fubon Financial Holding Co. Ltd.; *Int'l*, pg. 2801
FU SHENG USA INC—See Brookfield Corporation; *Int'l*, pg. 1181
FUSHI COPPERWELD EUROPE—See Fushi Copperweld, Inc.; *Int'l*, pg. 2849
FUSHI COPPERWELD, INC.; *Int'l*, pg. 2849
FUSHI INTERNATIONAL (DALIAN) BIMETALLIC CABLE CO., LTD.—See Fushi Copperweld, Inc.; *Int'l*, pg. 2849
FUSHIKI KAIRIKU UNSO CO.,LTD.; *Int'l*, pg. 2849
FUSHIMAN SHOJI CO., LTD.—See Yuasa Trading Co., Ltd.; *Int'l*, pg. 8609
FU SHOU YUAN INTERNATIONAL GROUP LIMITED; *Int'l*, pg. 2801
FUSHUN CARBON CO., LTD.—See Fangda Carbon New Material Co., Ltd.; *Int'l*, pg. 2613
FUSHUN SPECIAL STEEL CO., LTD.; *Int'l*, pg. 2849
FUSHUN TAKAOKA SWITCHGEAR COMPANY LIMITED—See Takaoka Toko Co., Ltd.; *Int'l*, pg. 7431
FUSHUN YIKESI NEW MATERIAL CO., LTD.—See Mesnac Co., Ltd.; *Int'l*, pg. 4840
FUSIC CO., LTD.; *Int'l*, pg. 2849
FUSION92; *U.S. Private*, pg. 1626
FUSION ACADEMY & LEARNING CENTER; *U.S. Private*, pg. 1625
FUSION ANTIBODIES PLC; *Int'l*, pg. 2849
FUSIONAPPS, LLC; *U.S. Private*, pg. 1626
FUSIONARY MEDIA; *U.S. Private*, pg. 1626
FUSION B2B, INC.; *U.S. Private*, pg. 1626
FUSIONBOX, INC.; *U.S. Private*, pg. 1626
FUSION CONNECT, INC.; *U.S. Private*, pg. 1625
FUSION CONSULTING INC.; *U.S. Private*, pg. 1625
FUSION DATA CO., LTD.; *Int'l*, pg. 2849
FUSION DATA CO., LTD.; *Int'l*, pg. 2849
FUSIONEX CORP. SDN. BHD.—See Fusionex International Plc; *Int'l*, pg. 2849
FUSIONEX INTERNATIONAL PLC; *Int'l*, pg. 2849
FUSIONFARM—See The Gazette Company; *U.S. Private*, pg. 4032

FUSION FOODS & CATERING PRIVATE LIMITED—See Updater Services Limited; *Int'l*, pg. 8087
FUSION GEOPHYSICAL LLC—See Symphony Technology Group, LLC; *U.S. Private*, pg. 3901
FUSION GROUP HOLDINGS PTY LIMITED—See AVK Holding A/S; *Int'l*, pg. 747
FUSION GROUP LTD.—See AVK Holding A/S; *Int'l*, pg. 747
FUSION HEALTH TECHNOLOGIES CORPORATION; *U.S. Private*, pg. 1625
FUSION HEATING LIMITED—See SSE Plc; *Int'l*, pg. 7155
FUSION IMAGING, INC.—See Vomela Specialty Company; *U.S. Private*, pg. 4412
FUSION INTERACTIVE CORP.; *U.S. Public*, pg. 893
FUSION INTERNATIONAL DISTRIBUTION, INC.—See Test-Rite International Co., Ltd.; *Int'l*, pg. 7575
FUSION ITALIA S.R.L—See AVK Holding A/S; *Int'l*, pg. 747
FUSION LIGHTING LIMITED—See Luceco PLC; *Int'l*, pg. 4573
FUSION MARKETING—See Silver Lake Group, LLC; *U.S. Private*, pg. 3657
FUSION MARKETING—See William Morris Endeavor Entertainment, LLC; *U.S. Private*, pg. 4523
FUSION MEDIA LTD.; *Int'l*, pg. 2849
FUSION MICRO FINANCE LIMITED; *Int'l*, pg. 2849
FUSION OEM; *U.S. Private*, pg. 1625
FUSION OPTIX, INC.; *U.S. Private*, pg. 1625
FUSION PACKAGING I, LLC—See AptarGroup, Inc.; *U.S. Public*, pg. 174
FUSION PAPERBOARD - PAPER MILL—See OpenGate Capital Management, LLC; *U.S. Private*, pg. 3030
FUSION PAPERBOARD US, INC.—See OpenGate Capital Management, LLC; *U.S. Private*, pg. 3030
FUSION PHARMACEUTICALS INC.—See AstraZeneca PLC; *Int'l*, pg. 661
FUSION POLSKA SP. Z O.O.—See AVK Holding A/S; *Int'l*, pg. 747
FUSION PPT LLC; *U.S. Private*, pg. 1625
FUSION PUBLIC RELATIONS, INC.—See Fusion Public Relations; *U.S. Private*, pg. 1625
FUSION PUBLIC RELATIONS; *U.S. Private*, pg. 1625
FUSION RECRUITING LABS, INC.; *U.S. Private*, pg. 1625
FUSION RESOURCES PTY LTD—See Paladin Energy Ltd.; *Int'l*, pg. 5705
FUSION RETAIL BRANDS, PTY. LTD.; *Int'l*, pg. 2849
FUSION RISK MANAGEMENT, INC.—See Great Hill Partners, L.P.; *U.S. Private*, pg. 1763
FUSION ROMANIA SRL—See AVK Holding A/S; *Int'l*, pg. 747
FUSION SOLUTIONS, INC.; *U.S. Private*, pg. 1626
FUSIONSTORM, INC.—See Computacenter plc; *Int'l*, pg. 1758
FUSIONTECH, INC.; *Int'l*, pg. 2849
FUSION TRADE HK LIMITED—See Fusion Trade, Inc.; *U.S. Private*, pg. 1626
FUSION TRADE, INC.; *U.S. Private*, pg. 1626
FUSION TRANSPORT, LLC—See Hudson Hill Capital LLC; *U.S. Private*, pg. 2002
FUSIONWARE CORP.; *U.S. Private*, pg. 1626
FUSION WEALTH LIMITED—See Schroders plc; *Int'l*, pg. 6639
FUSIONWORKS, INC.; *U.S. Private*, pg. 1626
FUSION X MARINE, LLC—See US Lighting Group, Inc.; *U.S. Public*, pg. 2266
FUSITE, B.V.—See Emerson Electric Co.; *U.S. Public*, pg. 744
FUSITE JAPAN—See Emerson Electric Co.; *U.S. Public*, pg. 744
FUSITE USA—See Emerson Electric Co.; *U.S. Public*, pg. 744
FUSO CHEMICAL CO., LTD - JUSO FACTORY—See Fuso Chemical Co., Ltd.; *Int'l*, pg. 2850
FUSO CHEMICAL CO., LTD - KYOTO FIRST FACTORY—See Fuso Chemical Co., Ltd.; *Int'l*, pg. 2850
FUSO CHEMICAL CO.,LTD - KYOTO SECOND FACTORY—See Fuso Chemical Co., Ltd.; *Int'l*, pg. 2850
FUSO CHEMICAL CO., LTD - OSAKA FACTORY—See Fuso Chemical Co., Ltd.; *Int'l*, pg. 2850
FUSO CHEMICAL CO., LTD.; *Int'l*, pg. 2849
FUSO CORPORATION CO LTD—See Fuso Chemical Co., Ltd.; *Int'l*, pg. 2850
FUSO DENTSU CO., LTD.; *Int'l*, pg. 2850
FUSO PHARMACEUTICAL INDUSTRIES, LTD.; *Int'l*, pg. 2850
FUSOSHA PUBLISHING INC.—See Fuji Media Holdings, Inc.; *Int'l*, pg. 2814
FUSO TEIYAKU (QINGDAO) CO., LTD.—See Fuso Chemical Co., Ltd.; *Int'l*, pg. 2850
FUSS BRANDS CORP.; *U.S. Public*, pg. 893
FUSSENEGGER HOCHBAU UND HOLZINDUSTRIE GMBH—See STRABAG SE; *Int'l*, pg. 7230
FUSTELARKO BOREC BITOLA AD; *Int'l*, pg. 2850
FUSTIPLAST DO BRASIL LTDA—See Greif Inc.; *U.S. Public*, pg. 967
FUSZ, LOUIS NISSAN- MAZDA, INC.; *U.S. Private*, pg. 1626

FUTABA INDUSTRIAL CO., LTD.

FUTABA BUSINESS SYSTEM CO., LTD.—See Futaba Corporation; *Int'l*, pg. 2850
FUTABA CHANGZHOU ENGINEERING & MARKETING CO., LTD.—See Futaba Industrial Co., Ltd.; *Int'l*, pg. 2851
FUTABA CORPORATION - AKASHI MACHINERY & TOOLING FACTORY—See Futaba Corporation; *Int'l*, pg. 2850
FUTABA CORPORATION - CHONAN MACHINERY & TOOLING FACTORY II—See Futaba Corporation; *Int'l*, pg. 2850
FUTABA CORPORATION - CHONAN MACHINERY & TOOLING FACTORY—See Futaba Corporation; *Int'l*, pg. 2850
FUTABA CORPORATION - CHOSEI ELECTRONIC SYSTEMS FACTORY—See Futaba Corporation; *Int'l*, pg. 2850
FUTABA CORPORATION - CHOSEI ELECTRON TUBE FACTORY—See Futaba Corporation; *Int'l*, pg. 2850
FUTABA CORPORATION - CHOSEI MACHINERY & TOOLING FACTORY—See Futaba Corporation; *Int'l*, pg. 2850
FUTABA CORPORATION - CHOSEI VFD MODULE FACTORY—See Futaba Corporation; *Int'l*, pg. 2850
FUTABA CORPORATION - MOBARA ELECTRON TUBE FACTORY—See Futaba Corporation; *Int'l*, pg. 2850
FUTABA CORPORATION - MUTSUZAWA MACHINERY & TOOLING FACTORY—See Futaba Corporation; *Int'l*, pg. 2850
FUTABA CORPORATION OF AMERICA—See Futaba Corporation; *Int'l*, pg. 2850
FUTABA CORPORATION OF AMERICA—See Futaba Corporation; *Int'l*, pg. 2850
FUTABA CORPORATION OF HUIZHOU—See Futaba Corporation; *Int'l*, pg. 2850
FUTABA CORPORATION OF THE PHILIPPINES—See Futaba Corporation; *Int'l*, pg. 2850
FUTABA CORPORATION; *Int'l*, pg. 2850
FUTABA CZECH, S.R.O.—See Futaba Industrial Co., Ltd.; *Int'l*, pg. 2851
FUTABA DENSHI CORP. (S) PTE. LTD.—See Futaba Corporation; *Int'l*, pg. 2850
FUTABA ELECTRONICS (BEIJING) CO., LTD.—See Futaba Corporation; *Int'l*, pg. 2850
FUTABA ELECTRONICS COMPONENTS KOREA CO., LTD.—See Futaba Corporation; *Int'l*, pg. 2850
FUTABA (EUROPE) GMBH—See Futaba Corporation; *Int'l*, pg. 2850
FUTABA GENERAL CO., LTD.—See Futaba Industrial Co., Ltd.; *Int'l*, pg. 2851
FUTABA HIRAIZUMI CO., LTD.—See Futaba Industrial Co., Ltd.; *Int'l*, pg. 2851
FUTABA (HONG KONG) CORPORATION LTD.—See Futaba Corporation; *Int'l*, pg. 2850
FUTABA INDIANA OF AMERICA CORP.—See Futaba Industrial Co., Ltd.; *Int'l*, pg. 2851
FUTABA INDUSTRIAL CO., LTD. - CHIRYU PLANT—See Futaba Industrial Co., Ltd.; *Int'l*, pg. 2851
FUTABA INDUSTRIAL CO., LTD. - KOTA PLANT—See Futaba Industrial Co., Ltd.; *Int'l*, pg. 2851
FUTABA INDUSTRIAL CO., LTD. - MIDORI PLANT—See Futaba Industrial Co., Ltd.; *Int'l*, pg. 2851
FUTABA INDUSTRIAL CO., LTD. - MUTSUMI PLANT—See Futaba Industrial Co., Ltd.; *Int'l*, pg. 2851
FUTABA INDUSTRIAL CO., LTD.; *Int'l*, pg. 2851
FUTABA INDUSTRIAL CO., LTD. - TAHARA PLANT—See Futaba Industrial Co., Ltd.; *Int'l*, pg. 2851
FUTABA INDUSTRIAL CO., LTD. - TAKAHASHI PLANT—See Futaba Industrial Co., Ltd.; *Int'l*, pg. 2851
FUTABA INDUSTRIAL GUJARAT PRIVATE LIMITED—See Futaba Industrial Co., Ltd.; *Int'l*, pg. 2851
FUTABA INDUSTRIAL TEXAS CORP.—See Futaba Industrial Co., Ltd.; *Int'l*, pg. 2851
FUTABA INDUSTRIAL U.K. LTD.—See Futaba Industrial Co., Ltd.; *Int'l*, pg. 2851
FUTABA INTERNATIONAL TRADING (SHANGHAI) CO., LTD.—See Futaba Corporation; *Int'l*, pg. 2850
FUTABA JTW (THAILAND) LTD.—See Futaba Corporation; *Int'l*, pg. 2850
FUTABA KYUSYU CO., LTD. - MIYATA PLANT—See Futaba Industrial Co., Ltd.; *Int'l*, pg. 2851
FUTABA KYUSYU CO., LTD. - NOGATA PLANT—See Futaba Industrial Co., Ltd.; *Int'l*, pg. 2851
FUTABA KYUSYU CO., LTD.—See Futaba Industrial Co., Ltd.; *Int'l*, pg. 2851
FUTABA MANUFACTURING U.K. LTD.—See Futaba Industrial Co., Ltd.; *Int'l*, pg. 2851
FUTABA MOBILE DISPLAY CORPORATION—See Futaba Corporation; *Int'l*, pg. 2850
FUTABA NORTH AMERICA ENGINEERING & MARKETING CO.—See Futaba Industrial Co., Ltd.; *Int'l*, pg. 2851
FUTABA PRECISION CO., LTD.—See Futaba Corporation; *Int'l*, pg. 2850
FUTABA PRECISION DIE & MOLD MACHINERY (CHINA) CO., LTD.—See Futaba Corporation; *Int'l*, pg. 2850
FUTABA PRECISION MOULD (SHENZHEN) CORPORATION, LTD.—See Futaba Corporation; *Int'l*, pg. 2850

FUTABA INDUSTRIAL CO., LTD.

FUTABA SOKKI CO., LTD.—See Nagano Keiki Co., Ltd.; *Int'l*, pg. 5125
FUTABA SUMI CORP.—See Futaba Industrial Co., Ltd.; *Int'l*, pg. 2851
FUTABA TECHNOLOGY LTD.—See Futaba Industrial Co., Ltd.; *Int'l*, pg. 2851
FUTABA TENNECO U.K. LIMITED—See Apollo Global Management, Inc.; *U.S. Public*, pg. 162
FUTABA TENNECO U.K. LIMITED—See Futaba Corporation; *Int'l*, pg. 2850
FUTABA (TIANJIN) CO., LTD.—See Futaba Industrial Co., Ltd.; *Int'l*, pg. 2851
FUTABA (VIETNAM) CO., LTD.—See Futaba Corporation; *Int'l*, pg. 2850
FUTA B.V.—See National Amusements, Inc.; *U.S. Private*, pg. 2843
FUTAI USA INC.; *U.S. Private*, pg. 1626
FUTALIS GMBH—See CEWE Stiftung & Co. KGaA; *Int'l*, pg. 1425
FUTAVIS GMBH—See DEUTZ AG; *Int'l*, pg. 2086
FUTBOL CLUB BARCELONA MERCHANDISING, S.L.—See NIKE, Inc.; *U.S. Public*, pg. 1528
FUTEBOL CLUBE DO PORTO; *Int'l*, pg. 2852
FUTEK TRADING CO.LTD—See Solomon Technology Corporation; *Int'l*, pg. 7075
FUTONG GROUP CO., LTD. - CHENGDU PLANT—See Futong Group Co., Ltd.; *Int'l*, pg. 2852
FUTONG GROUP CO., LTD. - SHENZHEN PLANT—See Futong Group Co., Ltd.; *Int'l*, pg. 2852
FUTONG GROUP CO., LTD.; *Int'l*, pg. 2852
FUTONG GROUP CO., LTD. - TIANJIN PLANT—See Futong Group Co., Ltd.; *Int'l*, pg. 2852
FUTONG GROUP (HONG KONG) CO., LTD.—See Futong Group Co., Ltd.; *Int'l*, pg. 2852
FUTONG TECHNOLOGY DEVELOPMENT HOLDINGS LIMITED; *Int'l*, pg. 2852
THE FUTON SHOP; *U.S. Private*, pg. 4031
FUTO WINES—See Wilson Daniels Wholesale LLC; *U.S. Private*, pg. 4530
FUTRIX LIMITED—See CVS Health Corporation; *U.S. Public*, pg. 614
FUTRON CORPORATION; *U.S. Private*, pg. 1626
FUTRONIC GMBH—See Bucher Industries AG; *Int'l*, pg. 1209
FUTTERMAN, LANZA & PASCULLI, LLP; *U.S. Private*, pg. 1626
FUTU HOLDINGS LIMITED; *Int'l*, pg. 2852
FUTURA AGRARHANDEL GMBH—See AGRAVIS Raiffeisen AG; *Int'l*, pg. 215
FUTURA CONSORCIO INMOBILIARIO SA; *Int'l*, pg. 2852
FUTURA CORPORATION; *U.S. Private*, pg. 1626
THE FUTURA CORPORATION; *Int'l*, pg. 7647
FUTURA DDB D.O.O.—See Melamin d.d.; *Int'l*, pg. 4807
FUTURA DDB—See Omnicom Group Inc.; *U.S. Public*, pg. 1581
FUTURAGENE LTD.—See Suzano Holding S.A.; *Int'l*, pg. 7348
FUTURA INDUSTRIES CORPORATION—See Tredegar Corporation; *U.S. Public*, pg. 2187
FUTURA MEDICAL DEVELOPMENTS LIMITED—See Futura Medical plc; *Int'l*, pg. 2852
FUTURA MEDICAL PLC; *Int'l*, pg. 2852
FUTURAMIC TOOL & ENGINEERING COMPANY INC.; *U.S. Private*, pg. 1626
FUTURA POLYESTERS LTD.; *Int'l*, pg. 2852
FUTURA PR D.O.O.—See Melamin d.d.; *Int'l*, pg. 4807
FUTURAQUA MINERAL WATER PRODUCTION AND ASSET MANAGEMENT PUBLIC LIMITED COMPANY; *Int'l*, pg. 2852
FUTURA SERVICES; *U.S. Private*, pg. 1626
FUTURA S.R.L.—See Kering S.A.; *Int'l*, pg. 4134
FUTURE ACE E-COMMERCE SDN. BHD.—See CWG Holdings Berhad; *Int'l*, pg. 1890
FUTUREADVISOR, INC.—See BlackRock, Inc.; *U.S. Public*, pg. 345
FUTUREAGE INFRASTRUCTURE INDIA LIMITED—See Infrastructure Leasing & Financial Services Limited; *Int'l*, pg. 3698
FUTURE APPLIED COMPUTER TECHNOLOGY COMPANY—See Al Baraka Banking Group B.S.C.; *Int'l*, pg. 276
FUTURE ARAB INVESTMENT CO.; *Int'l*, pg. 2852
FUTURE ARCHITECT, INC.—See Future Corporation; *Int'l*, pg. 2853
FUTURE AVIATION, INC.—See HEICO Corporation; *U.S. Public*, pg. 1019
FUTURE BATTERY MINERALS LIMITED; *Int'l*, pg. 2852
FUTUREBRAND GIO ROSSI—See The Interpublic Group of Companies, Inc.; *U.S. Public*, pg. 2097
FUTUREBRANDS LTD.—See Future Corporate Resources Limited; *Int'l*, pg. 2853
FUTUREBRAND—See The Interpublic Group of Companies, Inc.; *U.S. Public*, pg. 2097
FUTUREBRAND—See The Interpublic Group of Companies, Inc.; *U.S. Public*, pg. 2097
FUTUREBRAND—See The Interpublic Group of Companies, Inc.; *U.S. Public*, pg. 2097
FUTUREBRAND—See The Interpublic Group of Companies, Inc.; *U.S. Public*, pg. 2097
FUTUREBRAND—See The Interpublic Group of Companies, Inc.; *U.S. Public*, pg. 2097
FUTUREBRAND—See The Interpublic Group of Companies, Inc.; *U.S. Public*, pg. 2097
FUTUREBRAND—See The Interpublic Group of Companies, Inc.; *U.S. Public*, pg. 2097
FUTUREBRAND—See The Interpublic Group of Companies, Inc.; *U.S. Public*, pg. 2097
FUTUREBRAND—See The Interpublic Group of Companies, Inc.; *U.S. Public*, pg. 2097
FUTUREBRAND—See The Interpublic Group of Companies, Inc.; *U.S. Public*, pg. 2097
FUTUREBRAND—See The Interpublic Group of Companies, Inc.; *U.S. Public*, pg. 2097
FUTUREBRAND—See The Interpublic Group of Companies, Inc.; *U.S. Public*, pg. 2097
FUTURE BRIGHT HOLDINGS LIMITED; *Int'l*, pg. 2852
FUTURE BRIGHT MINING HOLDINGS LIMITED; *Int'l*, pg. 2852
FUTURE CAPITAL HOLDING CORPORATION; *U.S. Private*, pg. 1626
FUTURECHEM CO LTD; *Int'l*, pg. 2857
FUTURE COM DISTRIBUTORS INC.—See ePlus Inc.; *U.S. Public*, pg. 784
FUTURE COM LTD.—See ePlus Inc.; *U.S. Public*, pg. 784
FUTURE COMMUNICATIONS CO. GLOBAL K.S.C.C.; *Int'l*, pg. 2853
FUTURE COMMUNICATIONS GUIDANCE INT.—See National Technology Group; *Int'l*, pg. 5164
FUTURE COMPUTING SOLUTIONS INC.; *U.S. Private*, pg. 1626
FUTURECOM SYSTEMS GROUP INC.—See Motorola Solutions, Inc.; *U.S. Public*, pg. 1477
FUTURE CONSUMER LIMITED—See Future Corporate Resources Limited; *Int'l*, pg. 2853
FUTURECORE CO LTD; *Int'l*, pg. 2858
FUTURE CORPORATE RESOURCES LIMITED; *Int'l*, pg. 2853
FUTURE CORPORATION PTE LTD—See Food Empire Holdings Limited; *Int'l*, pg. 2727
FUTURE CORPORATION; *Int'l*, pg. 2853
FUTURE DATA GROUP LIMITED; *Int'l*, pg. 2853
FUTUREDONTICS, INC.; *U.S. Private*, pg. 1627
THE FUTURE EDUCATION GROUP INC.; *Int'l*, pg. 7647
FUTURE ELECTRICAL CONTROL CO., LTD.—See Gunkul Engineering Co., Ltd.; *Int'l*, pg. 3183
FUTURE ELECTRONICS AB—See Future Electronics Inc.; *Int'l*, pg. 2854
FUTURE ELECTRONICS A/S—See Future Electronics Inc.; *Int'l*, pg. 2854
FUTURE ELECTRONICS AUSTRIA GMBH—See Future Electronics Inc.; *Int'l*, pg. 2854
FUTURE ELECTRONICS CORP., AUSTRALIA—See Future Electronics Inc.; *Int'l*, pg. 2854
FUTURE ELECTRONICS CORP., AUSTRALIA—See Future Electronics Inc.; *Int'l*, pg. 2854
FUTURE ELECTRONICS CORP., BELGIUM—See Future Electronics Inc.; *Int'l*, pg. 2854
FUTURE ELECTRONICS CORP., BRAZIL—See Future Electronics Inc.; *Int'l*, pg. 2854
FUTURE ELECTRONICS CORP., BULGARIA—See Future Electronics Inc.; *Int'l*, pg. 2854
FUTURE ELECTRONICS CORP., CANADA—See Future Electronics Inc.; *Int'l*, pg. 2854
FUTURE ELECTRONICS CORP., CANADA—See Future Electronics Inc.; *Int'l*, pg. 2854
FUTURE ELECTRONICS CORP., DENMARK—See Future Electronics Inc.; *Int'l*, pg. 2854
FUTURE ELECTRONICS CORP., ERFURT—See Future Electronics Inc.; *Int'l*, pg. 2854
FUTURE ELECTRONICS CORP., FINLAND—See Future Electronics Inc.; *Int'l*, pg. 2854
FUTURE ELECTRONICS CORP., FRANCE—See Future Electronics Inc.; *Int'l*, pg. 2854
FUTURE ELECTRONICS CORP., FRANCE—See Future Electronics Inc.; *Int'l*, pg. 2854
FUTURE ELECTRONICS CORP., FRANCE—See Future Electronics Inc.; *Int'l*, pg. 2854
FUTURE ELECTRONICS CORP., FRANCE—See Future Electronics Inc.; *Int'l*, pg. 2855
FUTURE ELECTRONICS CORP., GERMANY—See Future Electronics Inc.; *Int'l*, pg. 2855
FUTURE ELECTRONICS CORP., HUNGARY—See Future Electronics Inc.; *Int'l*, pg. 2855
FUTURE ELECTRONICS CORP., IRELAND—See Future Electronics Inc.; *Int'l*, pg. 2855
FUTURE ELECTRONICS CORP., ISRAEL—See Future Electronics Inc.; *Int'l*, pg. 2855
FUTURE ELECTRONICS CORP., ITALY—See Future Electronics Inc.; *Int'l*, pg. 2855
FUTURE ELECTRONICS CORP., ITALY—See Future Electronics Inc.; *Int'l*, pg. 2855
FUTURE ELECTRONICS CORP., JAPAN—See Future Electronics Inc.; *Int'l*, pg. 2855
FUTURE ELECTRONICS CORP., KOREA—See Future Electronics Inc.; *Int'l*, pg. 2855
FUTURE ELECTRONICS CORP., MALAYSIA—See Future Electronics Inc.; *Int'l*, pg. 2855
FUTURE ELECTRONICS CORP., MEXICO—See Future Electronics Inc.; *Int'l*, pg. 2855
FUTURE ELECTRONICS CORP., MEXICO—See Future Electronics Inc.; *Int'l*, pg. 2855
FUTURE ELECTRONICS CORP., NEW ZEALAND—See Future Electronics Inc.; *Int'l*, pg. 2855
FUTURE ELECTRONICS CORP., NORWAY—See Future Electronics Inc.; *Int'l*, pg. 2855
FUTURE ELECTRONICS CORP., NORWAY—See Future Electronics Inc.; *Int'l*, pg. 2855
FUTURE ELECTRONICS CORP., POLAND—See Future Electronics Inc.; *Int'l*, pg. 2855
FUTURE ELECTRONICS CORP., SCOTLAND—See Future Electronics Inc.; *Int'l*, pg. 2855
FUTURE ELECTRONICS CORP., SINGAPORE—See Future Electronics Inc.; *Int'l*, pg. 2855
FUTURE ELECTRONICS CORP.—See Future Electronics Inc.; *Int'l*, pg. 2854
FUTURE ELECTRONICS CORP.—See Future Electronics Inc.; *Int'l*, pg. 2854
FUTURE ELECTRONICS CORP.—See Future Electronics Inc.; *Int'l*, pg. 2854
FUTURE ELECTRONICS CORP.—See Future Electronics Inc.; *Int'l*, pg. 2854
FUTURE ELECTRONICS CORP.—See Future Electronics Inc.; *Int'l*, pg. 2854
FUTURE ELECTRONICS CORP.—See Future Electronics Inc.; *Int'l*, pg. 2854
FUTURE ELECTRONICS CORP.—See Future Electronics Inc.; *Int'l*, pg. 2854
FUTURE ELECTRONICS CORP.—See Future Electronics Inc.; *Int'l*, pg. 2854
FUTURE ELECTRONICS CORP.—See Future Electronics Inc.; *Int'l*, pg. 2854
FUTURE ELECTRONICS CORP.—See Future Electronics Inc.; *Int'l*, pg. 2854
FUTURE ELECTRONICS CORP.—See Future Electronics Inc.; *Int'l*, pg. 2854
FUTURE ELECTRONICS CORP.—See Future Electronics Inc.; *Int'l*, pg. 2854
FUTURE ELECTRONICS CORP.—See Future Electronics Inc.; *Int'l*, pg. 2854
FUTURE ELECTRONICS CORP.—See Future Electronics Inc.; *Int'l*, pg. 2854
FUTURE ELECTRONICS CORP., SPAIN—See Future Electronics Inc.; *Int'l*, pg. 2855
FUTURE ELECTRONICS CORP., SPAIN—See Future Electronics Inc.; *Int'l*, pg. 2855
FUTURE ELECTRONICS CORP., SWEDEN—See Future Electronics Inc.; *Int'l*, pg. 2855
FUTURE ELECTRONICS CORP., SWEDEN—See Future Electronics Inc.; *Int'l*, pg. 2855
FUTURE ELECTRONICS CORP., SWEDEN—See Future Electronics Inc.; *Int'l*, pg. 2855
FUTURE ELECTRONICS CORP., TAIWAN—See Future Electronics Inc.; *Int'l*, pg. 2855
FUTURE ELECTRONICS CORP., TAIWAN—See Future Electronics Inc.; *Int'l*, pg. 2855
FUTURE ELECTRONICS CORP., THAILAND—See Future Electronics Inc.; *Int'l*, pg. 2855
FUTURE ELECTRONICS CORP., THE NETHERLANDS—See Future Electronics Inc.; *Int'l*, pg. 2855
FUTURE ELECTRONICS CORP., TURKEY—See Future Electronics Inc.; *Int'l*, pg. 2855
FUTURE ELECTRONICS DEUTSCHLAND GMBH—See Future Electronics Inc.; *Int'l*, pg. 2855
FUTURE ELECTRONICS DEUTSCHLAND—See Future Electronics Inc.; *Int'l*, pg. 2855
FUTURE ELECTRONICS HONG KONG LIMITED—See Future Electronics Inc.; *Int'l*, pg. 2855
FUTURE ELECTRONICS INC. (DISTRIBUTION) PTE LTD.—See Future Electronics Inc.; *Int'l*, pg. 2855
FUTURE ELECTRONICS INC (DISTRIBUTION) PTE LTD.—See Future Electronics Inc.; *Int'l*, pg. 2855
FUTURE ELECTRONICS INC.; *Int'l*, pg. 2854
FUTURE ELECTRONICS INC.—See Future Electronics Inc.; *Int'l*, pg. 2855
FUTURE ELECTRONICS INC. (WAREHOUSE) PTE LTD—See Future Electronics Inc.; *Int'l*, pg. 2855
FUTURE ELECTRONICS KFT—See Future Electronics Inc.; *Int'l*, pg. 2855
FUTURE ELECTRONICS K.K.—See Future Electronics Inc.; *Int'l*, pg. 2855
FUTURE ELECTRONICS LTD.—See Future Electronics Inc.; *Int'l*, pg. 2855

COMPANY NAME INDEX

FUTURE ELECTRONICS LTD.—See Future Electronics Inc.; *Int'l*, pg. 2855
FUTURE ELECTRONICS MKTG SERVICES CO, LTD.—See STMicroelectronics N.V.; *Int'l*, pg. 7217
FUTURE ELECTRONICS OU—See Future Electronics Inc.; *Int'l*, pg. 2856
FUTURE ELECTRONICS SAS—See Future Electronics Inc.; *Int'l*, pg. 2856
FUTURE ELECTRONICS SERVICE MALAYSIA—See Future Electronics Inc.; *Int'l*, pg. 2855
FUTURE ELECTRONICS SERVICES SDN. BHD.—See STMicroelectronics N.V.; *Int'l*, pg. 7217
FUTURE ELECTRONICS (SHANGHAI) CO., LTD—See Future Electronics Inc.; *Int'l*, pg. 2854
FUTURE ELECTRONICS STUTTGART—See Future Electronics Inc.; *Int'l*, pg. 2856
FUTURE ENERGY CORPORATION CO., LTD.—See Gunkul Engineering Co., Ltd.; *Int'l*, pg. 3183
FUTURE ENERGY SOLUTIONS; *U.S. Private*, pg. 1626
FUTURE ENTERPRISES LIMITED—See Future Corporate Resources Limited; *Int'l*, pg. 2853
FUTURE ENTERPRISES PTE LTD—See Food Empire Holdings Limited; *Int'l*, pg. 2727
FUTURE FARM TECHNOLOGIES INC.; *Int'l*, pg. 2856
FUTURE FILM GROUP PLC; *Int'l*, pg. 2856
FUTURE FILMS LIMITED—See Future Film Group plc; *Int'l*, pg. 2856
FUTURE FILMS USA LLC—See Future Film Group plc; *Int'l*, pg. 2856
FUTURE FINANCIAL STRATEGY CORP.—See Future Corporation; *Int'l*, pg. 2853
FUTURE FINTECH GROUP INC.; *Int'l*, pg. 2856
FUTURE FIRST TECHNOLOGIES LTD.; *Int'l*, pg. 2856
FUTURE FOAM, INC. - COUNCIL BLUFFS POURING PLANT—See Future Foam, Inc.; *U.S. Private*, pg. 1627
FUTURE FOAM, INC. - DALLAS FABRICATION PLANT—See Future Foam, Inc.; *U.S. Private*, pg. 1627
FUTURE FOAM, INC. - DENVER FABRICATION PLANT—See Future Foam, Inc.; *U.S. Private*, pg. 1627
FUTURE FOAM, INC. - FULLERTON POURING PLANT—See Future Foam, Inc.; *U.S. Private*, pg. 1627
FUTURE FOAM, INC. - HIGH POINT POURING PLANT—See Future Foam, Inc.; *U.S. Private*, pg. 1627
FUTURE FOAM, INC. - KANSAS CITY FABRICATION PLANT—See Future Foam, Inc.; *U.S. Private*, pg. 1627
FUTURE FOAM, INC. - MIDDLETON FABRICATION PLANT—See Future Foam, Inc.; *U.S. Private*, pg. 1627
FUTURE FOAM, INC. - NEWTON POURING PLANT—See Future Foam, Inc.; *U.S. Private*, pg. 1627
FUTURE FOAM, INC. - OKLAHOMA CITY FABRICATION PLANT—See Future Foam, Inc.; *U.S. Private*, pg. 1627
FUTURE FOAM, INC. - OMAHA FABRICATION PLANT—See Future Foam, Inc.; *U.S. Private*, pg. 1627
FUTURE FOAM, INC.; *U.S. Private*, pg. 1626
FUTURE FOAM, INC. - SPRINGFIELD FABRICATION PLANT—See Future Foam, Inc.; *U.S. Private*, pg. 1627
FUTURE FOCUS INFOTECH PVT. LTD.—See en-japan Inc.; *Int'l*, pg. 2395
FUTURE FORCE PERSONNEL SERVICES; *U.S. Private*, pg. 1627
FUTURE FORD OF CONCORD, LLC.; *U.S. Private*, pg. 1627
FUTURE FORESTS FIJI LTD.; *Int'l*, pg. 2856
FUTURE FRANCE SA—See Future plc; *Int'l*, pg. 2857
FUTUREFUEL CHEMICAL COMPANY—See FutureFuel Corp.; *U.S. Public*, pg. 893
FUTUREFUEL CORP.; *U.S. Public*, pg. 893
FUTURE FUND INVESTMENT INC.; *U.S. Private*, pg. 1627
FUTURE GENERATION AUSTRALIA LIMITED; *Int'l*, pg. 2856
FUTURE GENERATION GLOBAL LIMITED; *Int'l*, pg. 2856
FUTURE GRAPHICS LLC; *U.S. Private*, pg. 1627
FUTUREGROWTH ASSET MANAGEMENT PTY. LTD.; *Int'l*, pg. 2858
FUTURE HEALTH ESG CORP.; *U.S. Public*, pg. 893
FUTURE INDUSTRIAL SERVICES LTD—See Ancala Partners LLP; *Int'l*, pg. 448
FUTURE INDUSTRIAL SERVICES LTD—See Fiera Capital Corporation; *Int'l*, pg. 2659
FUTURE INDUSTRIAL & WELDING SUPPLIES LTD.—See Linde plc; *Int'l*, pg. 4504
FUTURE INNOVATION GROUP, INC.; *Int'l*, pg. 2856
FUTURE INSPACE, INC.—See Future Corporation; *Int'l*, pg. 2853
FUTURE INTERNATIONAL GROUP CORP.; *Int'l*, pg. 2856
FUTURE KID ENTERTAINMENT AND REAL ESTATE CO. K.S.C.C.; *Int'l*, pg. 2856
FUTURE LABO CO., LTD.—See Pharma Foods International Co., Ltd.; *Int'l*, pg. 5840
FUTURELAND, CORP.; *U.S. Public*, pg. 893
FUTURE LEADERS OF AMERICA FOUNDATION, INC; *U.S. Private*, pg. 1627
FUTURE LEARNING AND DEVELOPMENT LIMITED—See Future Corporate Resources Limited; *Int'l*, pg. 2853
FUTURE LIFESTYLE FASHIONS LIMITED—See Future Corporate Resources Limited; *Int'l*, pg. 2853

FUTURE MANAGEMENT INVESTMENTS B.V.—See Future Pipe Industries Group Ltd.; *Int'l*, pg. 2857
FUTUREMARK CORPORATION—See Underwriters Laboratories Inc.; *U.S. Private*, pg. 4280
FUTURE MARKET NETWORKS LIMITED; *Int'l*, pg. 2856
FUTUREMARK OY—See Underwriters Laboratories Inc.; *U.S. Private*, pg. 4280
FUTUREMATRIX INTERVENTIONAL, INC.—See Brookhaven Medical, Inc.; *U.S. Private*, pg. 663
FUTURE MEDIA CONCEPTS, INC.; *U.S. Private*, pg. 1627
FUTURE MEDIA (INDIA) LIMITED—See Future Corporate Resources Limited; *Int'l*, pg. 2853
FUTURE MEDICINE CO., LTD; *Int'l*, pg. 2856
FUTURE METALS, INC.—See Berkshire Hathaway Inc.; *U.S. Public*, pg. 309
FUTURE METALS NL; *Int'l*, pg. 2856
FUTURE MOBILITY SOLUTIONS LTD.; *Int'l*, pg. 2857
FUTURE MOBILITY SOLUTIONS; *Int'l*, pg. 2856
FUTURENET GROUP, INC.; *U.S. Private*, pg. 1627
FUTURE NRG SDN BHD—See FITTERS Diversified Berhad; *Int'l*, pg. 2695
FUTUREN SA—See Electricite de France S.A.; *Int'l*, pg. 2350
FUTURE OKINAWA CO., LTD.—See Okinawa Financial Group, Inc.; *Int'l*, pg. 5550
FUTURE OPTICS FL INC—See EssilorLuxottica SA; *Int'l*, pg. 2514
FUTURE PACKAGING & MACHINERY CAPE (PTY) LTD.—See Transpaco Ltd.; *Int'l*, pg. 7904
FUTURE PACKAGING & MACHINERY (PTY) LTD.—See Transpaco Ltd.; *Int'l*, pg. 7904
FUTURE PIPE INDUSTRIES B.V.—See Future Pipe Industries Group Ltd.; *Int'l*, pg. 2857
FUTURE PIPE INDUSTRIES GROUP LTD.; *Int'l*, pg. 2857
FUTURE PIPE INDUSTRIES, INC.—See Future Pipe Industries Group Ltd.; *Int'l*, pg. 2857
FUTURE PIPE INDUSTRIES LIMITED—See Future Pipe Industries Group Ltd.; *Int'l*, pg. 2857
FUTURE PIPE INDUSTRIES L.L.C.—See Future Pipe Industries Group Ltd.; *Int'l*, pg. 2857
FUTURE PIPE INDUSTRIES L.L.C.—See Future Pipe Industries Group Ltd.; *Int'l*, pg. 2857
FUTURE PIPE INDUSTRIES (PVT) LTD.—See Future Pipe Industries Group Ltd.; *Int'l*, pg. 2857
FUTURE PIPE INDUSTRIES Q.C.J.S.C—See Future Pipe Industries Group Ltd.; *Int'l*, pg. 2857
FUTURE PIPE INDUSTRIES S.A.E.—See Future Pipe Industries Group Ltd.; *Int'l*, pg. 2857
FUTURE PIPE INDUSTRIES S.A.L.—See Future Pipe Industries Group Ltd.; *Int'l*, pg. 2857
FUTURE PIPE LIMITED—See Future Pipe Industries Group Ltd.; *Int'l*, pg. 2857
FUTURE PIPE SARL—See Future Pipe Industries Group Ltd.; *Int'l*, pg. 2857
FUTURE PLC; *Int'l*, pg. 2857
FUTURE PUBLISHING LTD. - LONDON OFFICE—See Future plc; *Int'l*, pg. 2857
FUTURE PUBLISHING LTD.—See Future plc; *Int'l*, pg. 2857
FUTURE RESEARCH, CORPORATION; *U.S. Private*, pg. 1627
FUTURE RETAIL LIMITED—See Future Corporate Resources Limited; *Int'l*, pg. 2853
FUTURES CAPITAL AD; *Int'l*, pg. 2858
THE FUTURES COMPANY—See Bain Capital, LP; *U.S. Private*, pg. 448
FUTURE SHERIDAN FORD SALES INC.; *U.S. Private*, pg. 1627
FUTURES HOME INC.; *U.S. Private*, pg. 1627
FUTURE SHOP LTD.—See Best Buy Co., Inc.; *U.S. Public*, pg. 326
FUTURES MAGAZINE GROUP—See Summit Business Media, LLC; *U.S. Private*, pg. 3853
FUTURESOFT, INC.; *U.S. Private*, pg. 1627
FUTURE STATE CONSULTING LLC—See Odyssey Investment Partners, LLC; *U.S. Private*, pg. 2996
FUTURE STATE—See Accenture plc; *Int'l*, pg. 87
FUTURESTEP (ESPANA), S.L.—See Korn Ferry; *U.S. Public*, pg. 1274
FUTURESTEP RECRUITMENT SERVICES PRIVATE LTD.—See Korn Ferry; *U.S. Public*, pg. 1274
FUTURESTEP (SHANGHAI) TALENT CONSULTING COMPANY LIMITED—See Korn Ferry; *U.S. Public*, pg. 1272
FUTURESTEP (UK) LIMITED—See Korn Ferry; *U.S. Public*, pg. 1274
FUTURESTREAM NETWORKS CO., LTD.; *Int'l*, pg. 2858
FUTURE SUPPLY CHAIN SOLUTIONS LTD.—See Future Corporate Resources Limited; *Int'l*, pg. 2853
FUTURES WITHOUT VIOLENCE; *U.S. Private*, pg. 1627
FUTURE SYNTHETICS PTE. LTD.—See KTL Global Limited; *Int'l*, pg. 4317
FUTURE TECH CONSULTANTS OF NEW YORK, INC.—See Cobepa S.A.; *Int'l*, pg. 1683
FUTURE TECH METALS, INC.—See Avem Partners, LLC; *U.S. Private*, pg. 405
FUTURETEL S.A.; *Int'l*, pg. 2858

FUTURE TRANSFER CO. INC.—See Apollo Global Management, Inc.; *U.S. Public*, pg. 165
FUTURE US, INC.—See Future plc; *Int'l*, pg. 2857
FUTURE VENTURE CAPITAL CO., LTD.; *Int'l*, pg. 2857
FUTURE WORLD HOLDINGS LIMITED; *Int'l*, pg. 2857
FUTUREWORLD TECHNOLOGIES, INC.—See Blackwatch International Corp.; *U.S. Private*, pg. 577
FUTUREX INDUSTRIES INC.; *U.S. Private*, pg. 1627
FUTURIS AUTOMOTIVE INTERIORS (AUSTRALIA) PTY. LTD.—See Clearlake Capital Group, L.P.; *U.S. Private*, pg. 934
FUTURIS AUTOMOTIVE INTERIORS TRADING (SHANGHAI) CO. LTD.—See Clearlake Capital Group, L.P.; *U.S. Private*, pg. 934
FUTURIS COMPANY; *U.S. Public*, pg. 893
FUTURIS PTY. LTD.—See Clearlake Capital Group, L.P.; *U.S. Private*, pg. 934
FUTURIS TECHNOLOGY SERVICES, INC.—See Futuris Company; *U.S. Public*, pg. 893
FUTURISTIC OFFSHORE SERVICES & CHEMICAL LIMITED; *Int'l*, pg. 2858
FUTURISTIC SECURITIES LIMITED; *Int'l*, pg. 2858
FUTURISTIC SOLUTIONS LIMITED; *Int'l*, pg. 2858
FUTURO HOUSES, LLC—See US Lighting Group, Inc.; *U.S. Public*, pg. 2266
FUTUROL INDUSTRIE; *Int'l*, pg. 2858
FUTURUM A.D.; *Int'l*, pg. 2858
FUTURUM BANK AG—See Bitcoin Group SE; *Int'l*, pg. 1049
FUTURUM, LLC.; *U.S. Private*, pg. 1627
FUTURUM MEDIA LIMITED—See Informa plc; *Int'l*, pg. 3691
FUTU SECURITIES INTERNATIONAL (HONG KONG) LIMITED—See Futu Holdings Limited; *Int'l*, pg. 2852
FUVA BRAIN LIMITED; *Int'l*, pg. 2858
FU-WANG CERAMIC LIMITED; *Int'l*, pg. 2801
FU WANG ELECTRIC MANUFACTURING COMPANY LIMITED—See Johnson Electric Holdings Limited; *Int'l*, pg. 3990
FU-WANG FOODS LTD.; *Int'l*, pg. 2801
FUWEI FILMS (SHANDONG) CO., LTD.—See Baijiayun Group Ltd; *Int'l*, pg. 802
FUXIN DARE AUTOMOTIVE PARTS CO., LTD.; *Int'l*, pg. 2858
FUXING CHINA GROUP LIMITED; *Int'l*, pg. 2858
FUXING GARMENTS CO., LTD.; *Int'l*, pg. 2858
FUXIN LIDA STEEL CASTING CO. LTD.—See L.K. Technology Holdings Limited; *Int'l*, pg. 4386
FUXIN SUMIRIN WOOD PRODUCTS CO., LTD.; *Int'l*, pg. 2858
FUXI SHANGHAI CORPORATION—See Fujimak Corporation; *Int'l*, pg. 2829
FUYAO AUTOMOTIVE NORTH AMERICA, INC.—See Fuyao Glass Industry Group Co., Ltd.; *Int'l*, pg. 2858
FUYAO EUROPE GMBH—See Fuyao Glass Industry Group Co., Ltd.; *Int'l*, pg. 2858
FUYAO GLASS AMERICA INC.—See Fuyao Glass Industry Group Co., Ltd.; *Int'l*, pg. 2858
FUYAO GLASS ILLINOIS, INC.—See Fuyao Glass Industry Group Co., Ltd.; *Int'l*, pg. 2858
FUYAO GLASS INDUSTRY GROUP CO., LTD.; *Int'l*, pg. 2858
FUYAO NORTH AMERICA INCORPORATED—See Fuyao Glass Industry Group Co., Ltd.; *Int'l*, pg. 2858
FU YIK COMPANY LIMITED—See Hang Lung Group Limited; *Int'l*, pg. 3245
FUYO AUTO LEASE CO., LTD.—See Fuyo General Lease Co., Ltd.; *Int'l*, pg. 2859
FUYO DAIICHI TRAFFIC CO., LTD.—See Daiichi Koutsu Sangyo Co., Ltd.; *Int'l*, pg. 1928
FUYO DISTRIBUTION CO., LTD.—See Ozu Corporation; *Int'l*, pg. 5679
FUYO GENERAL LEASE (ASIA) PTE. LTD.—See Fuyo General Lease Co., Ltd.; *Int'l*, pg. 2859
FUYO GENERAL LEASE CO., LTD.; *Int'l*, pg. 2858
FUYO GENERAL LEASE (HK) LIMITED—See Fuyo General Lease Co., Ltd.; *Int'l*, pg. 2859
FUYO GENERAL LEASE (USA) INC.—See Fuyo General Lease Co., Ltd.; *Int'l*, pg. 2859
FUYO KANKO CO., LTD.—See Marubeni Corporation; *Int'l*, pg. 4705
FUYO LEASE SALES CO., LTD.—See Fuyo General Lease Co., Ltd.; *Int'l*, pg. 2859
FUYO NETWORK SERVICE CO., LTD.—See Fuyo General Lease Co., Ltd.; *Int'l*, pg. 2859
FUYO PERLITE CO., LTD.—See Resonac Holdings Corporation; *Int'l*, pg. 6298
FUYO PERLITE CO., LTD. - SUWA PLANT—See Resonac Holdings Corporation; *Int'l*, pg. 6298
FU YU CORPORATION LIMITED; *Int'l*, pg. 2801
FU YU MOULDING & TOOLING (CHONGQING) CO., LTD.—See Fu Yu Corporation Limited; *Int'l*, pg. 2801
FU YU MOULDING & TOOLING (DONGGUAN) CO., LTD.—See Fu Yu Corporation Limited; *Int'l*, pg. 2801
FU YU MOULDING & TOOLING (SHANGHAI) CO., LTD.—See Fu Yu Corporation Limited; *Int'l*, pg. 2801
FU YU MOULDING & TOOLING (SUZHOU) CO, LTD.—See Fu Yu Corporation Limited; *Int'l*, pg. 2801

FU YU MOULDING & TOOLING (WUJIANG) CO., LTD—See Fu Yu Corporation Limited; *Int'l*, pg. 2801
FU YU MOULDING & TOOLING (ZHUHAI) CO., LTD.—See Fu Yu Corporation Limited; *Int'l*, pg. 2801
FUYUN JINSHAN MINING AND METALLURGY COMPANY LIMITED—See Zijin Mining Group Company Limited; *Int'l*, pg. 8683
FU YU PROPERTY CO., LTD.; *Int'l*, pg. 2801
FUZE, INC.—See 8x8, Inc.; *U.S. Public*, pg. 10
FUZETEC TECHNOLOGY CO., LTD.—See Ocean Plastics Co., Ltd.; *Int'l*, pg. 5516
FUZETEC TECHNOLOGY (SUZHOU) CO., LTD.—See Ocean Plastics Co., Ltd.; *Int'l*, pg. 5516
FUZHOU BOE OPTOELECTRONICS TECHNOLOGY CO., LTD.—See BOE Technology Group Co., Ltd.; *Int'l*, pg. 1099
FUZHOU DIGITAL CHINA COMPANY LIMITED—See Digital China Holdings Limited; *Int'l*, pg. 2121
FUZHOU DINGWO AUTOMOBILE SALES SERVICES CO., LTD.—See China ZhengTong Auto Services Holdings Limited; *Int'l*, pg. 1566
FUZHOU EURO MOTORS SALES & SERVICES CO., LTD.—See G.A. Holdings Limited; *Int'l*, pg. 2865
FUZHOU IBARA LIOHO MACHINERY CO.,LTD.—See Universal Cement Corporation; *Int'l*, pg. 8078
FUZHOU KING DUAN INDUSTRIAL CO., LTD.—See Universal Cement Corporation; *Int'l*, pg. 8078
FUZHOU KOITO TAYIH AUTOMOTIVE LAMP CO., LTD.—See Koito Manufacturing Co., Ltd.; *Int'l*, pg. 4230
FUZHOU LIOHO MACHINERY CO.,LTD.—See Universal Cement Corporation; *Int'l*, pg. 8078
FUZHOU PHOTOP OPTICS CO., LTD.—See Coherent Corp.; *U.S. Public*, pg. 528
FUZHOU ROCKCHIP ELECTRONICS CO., LTD.; *Int'l*, pg. 2859
FUZHOU SEMBCORP WATER CO LTD—See Sembcorp Industries Ltd.; *Int'l*, pg. 6702
FUZHOU SHINTAI AUTO PARTS CO., LTD.—See Minth Group Limited; *Int'l*, pg. 4914
FUZHOU SINGAMAS CONTAINER CO.—See Xiamen Xiangyu Co., Ltd.; *Int'l*, pg. 8526
FUZHOU SUMAVISION SMART CARDS CO., LTD.—See Sumavision Technologies Co., Ltd.; *Int'l*, pg. 7260
FUZHOU TIANLONG ELECTRONICS CO., LTD.—See Ningbo Tianlong Electronics Co., Ltd.; *Int'l*, pg. 5306
FUZHOU YONGDA AUTOMOBILE SALES AND SERVICES CO., LTD.—See China Yongda Automobiles Services Holdings Limited; *Int'l*, pg. 1564
FUZHOU ZHU WIRING SYSTEMS CO., LTD.—See Sumitomo Electric Industries, Ltd.; *Int'l*, pg. 7278
FUZZIBUNZ LLC; *U.S. Private*, pg. 1627
FUZZ PRODUCTIONS LLC—See Monstar Lab, Inc.; *Int'l*, pg. 5035
FUZZY LOGIX, LLC; *U.S. Private*, pg. 1627
F. VAN LANSCHOT BANKIERS NV—See Van Lanschot Kempen NV; *Int'l*, pg. 8126
F. VAN LANSCHOT BANKIERS (SCHWEIZ) AG—See Van Lanschot Kempen NV; *Int'l*, pg. 8126
F. VAN LANSCHOT MANAGEMENT BV—See Van Lanschot Kempen NV; *Int'l*, pg. 8126
F. VAN LANSCHOT PARTICIPATIES BV—See Van Lanschot Kempen NV; *Int'l*, pg. 8126
FVCBANKCORP, INC.; *U.S. Public*, pg. 893
FVCBANK—See FVCBankcorp, Inc.; *U.S. Public*, pg. 893
FVE EC LLC—See AlerisLife Inc.; *U.S. Private*, pg. 160
FVE SE HOME PLACE NEW BERN LLC—See AlerisLife Inc.; *U.S. Private*, pg. 160
FVLCRUM PARTNERS LLC; *U.S. Private*, pg. 1627
FVM STRATEGIC COMMUNICATIONS; *U.S. Private*, pg. 1628
FV PHARMA INTERNATIONAL CORP.; *Int'l*, pg. 2859
FV S.A.; *Int'l*, pg. 2859
FVTS ACQUISITION CO., INC.; *U.S. Private*, pg. 1628
FWA EQUIPMENT & MUD COMPANY, INC.—See ConocoPhillips; *U.S. Public*, pg. 569
F. WALTHER ELECTRIC CORP.—See Walther-Werke Ferdinand Walther GmbH; *Int'l*, pg. 8337
F. WALTHER SARL—See Walther-Werke Ferdinand Walther GmbH; *Int'l*, pg. 8337
F.W. BARNES FUNERAL SERVICES PTY LTD—See Propel Funeral Partners Limited; *Int'l*, pg. 5997
FWB KUNSTSTOFFTECHNIK GMBH—See Hella GmbH & Co, KGaA; *Int'l*, pg. 3331
F.W. BROKELMANN ALUMINIUMWERK GMBH + CO. KG—See Knauf Interfer SE; *Int'l*, pg. 4205
F.W. BRYCE, INC.; *U.S. Private*, pg. 1457
FWC—See Farnsworth Wholesale Company; *U.S. Private*, pg. 1480
F.W. DAVISON & COMPANY, INC.; *U.S. Private*, pg. 1457
FWD FUJI LIFE INSURANCE COMPANY, LIMITED—See Pacific Century Group Holdings Limited; *Int'l*, pg. 5686
FWD GROUP FINANCIAL SERVICES PTE. LTD.—See Pacific Century Group Holdings Limited; *Int'l*, pg. 5686
FWD GROUP HOLDINGS LIMITED—See Pacific Century Group Holdings Limited; *Int'l*, pg. 5686
FWD GROUP LIMITED—See Pacific Century Group Holdings Limited; *Int'l*, pg. 5686

FWD GROUP MANAGEMENT HOLDINGS LIMITED—See Pacific Century Group Holdings Limited; *Int'l*, pg. 5686
FWD SINGAPORE PTE. LTD.—See Pacific Century Group Holdings Limited; *Int'l*, pg. 5686
F&W FORESTRY SERVICES INC.; *U.S. Private*, pg. 1455
F.W. HEMPEL METALLURGICAL GMBH—See Campine N.V.; *Int'l*, pg. 1275
F.W. HONERKAMP, CO. INC.—See Hardwoods Distribution Inc.; *Int'l*, pg. 3273
FW IL-RIVERSIDE/RIVERS EDGE, LLC—See Regency Centers Corporation; *U.S. Public*, pg. 1774
FWINES CO., LTD.—See Suntory Holdings Limited; *Int'l*, pg. 7326
F.W. KIBLER MILLING INC.; *U.S. Private*, pg. 1457
F+W MEDIA, INC.—See Tinicum Enterprises, Inc.; *U.S. Private*, pg. 4174
FW MURPHY PRODUCTION CONTROLS LLC—See Dover Corporation; *U.S. Public*, pg. 679
F.W. NEUKIRCH (GMBH & CO.) KG; *Int'l*, pg. 2597
F. W. OWENS COMPANY, INC.; *U.S. Private*, pg. 1455
F&W PUBLICATIONS - BOOKS—See Tinicum Enterprises, Inc.; *U.S. Private*, pg. 4174
F.W. RICKARD SEEDS, INC.—See Altria Group, Inc.; *U.S. Public*, pg. 89
F.W. THORPE PLC; *Int'l*, pg. 2597
FWT HUNGARIA KFT.—See Raiffeisenlandesbank Oberosterreich Aktiengesellschaft; *Int'l*, pg. 6188
FWU AG; *Int'l*, pg. 2859
FWU PROVISIONS-FACTORING GMBH—See FWU AG; *Int'l*, pg. 2859
FWUSOW INDUSTRY CO., LTD. - SHA-LU FACTORY—See Fwusow Industry Co., Ltd.; *Int'l*, pg. 2859
FWUSOW INDUSTRY CO., LTD.; *Int'l*, pg. 2859
FWUSOW INDUSTRY CO., LTD. - TAICHUNG HARBOR FACTORY—See Fwusow Industry Co., Ltd.; *Int'l*, pg. 2859
F.W. VAN ZILE POPULAR TOURS INC.; *U.S. Private*, pg. 1457
F.W. WALTON ROOFING, INC.; *U.S. Private*, pg. 1457
F.W. WEBB COMPANY; *U.S. Private*, pg. 1457
F.W. WEBB COMPANY - VICTOR MANUFACTURING DIVISION—See F.W. Webb Company; *U.S. Private*, pg. 1457
F.W. WEBB COMPANY - WEBB BIO-PHARM DIVISION—See F.W. Webb Company; *U.S. Private*, pg. 1457
F.W. WEBB COMPANY - WEBB WATER SYSTEMS DIVISION—See F.W. Webb Company; *U.S. Private*, pg. 1457
FX ALLIANCE INC.—See Thomson Reuters Corporation; *Int'l*, pg. 7715
FX ALLIANCE, LLC—See Thomson Reuters Corporation; *Int'l*, pg. 7715
FXCM CHRYSLER PLYMOUTH INC.; *U.S. Private*, pg. 1628
FXCM AUSTRALIA LIMITED—See Global Brokerage, Inc.; *U.S. Public*, pg. 940
FXCM BULLION LIMITED—See Global Brokerage, Inc.; *U.S. Public*, pg. 940
FXCM HOLDINGS, LLC—See Global Brokerage, Inc.; *U.S. Public*, pg. 940
FXCM PRO LLC—See Global Brokerage, Inc.; *U.S. Public*, pg. 940
FX CONNECT, LLC—See State Street Corporation; *U.S. Public*, pg. 1940
FXDIRECTDEALER LLC—See Viel & Compagnie SA; *Int'l*, pg. 8192
FX GLOBAL INC.—See FUJIFILM Holdings Corporation; *Int'l*, pg. 2825
FX HOTELS GROUP, INC.; *Int'l*, pg. 2859
FXI HOLDINGS, INC.—See One Rock Capital Partners, LLC; *U.S. Private*, pg. 3022
FXI, INC.—See One Rock Capital Partners, LLC; *U.S. Private*, pg. 3022
THE F.X. MATT BREWING CO.; *U.S. Private*, pg. 4027
FX NETWORKS, LLC—See The Walt Disney Company; *U.S. Public*, pg. 2140
FXONLINE JAPAN CO., LTD.—See IG Group Holdings plc; *Int'l*, pg. 3601
FX PALO ALTO LABORATORY INC.—See FUJIFILM Holdings Corporation; *Int'l*, pg. 2825
FX PRIME BY GMO CORPORATION—See GMO Internet Group, Inc.; *Int'l*, pg. 3013
FXPRO FINANCIAL SERVICES LTD; *Int'l*, pg. 2859
F.X. WIENINGER GMBH & CO KG—See Lallemand, Inc.; *Int'l*, pg. 4399
FYBERCOM, LLC; *U.S. Private*, pg. 1628
FYBER GMBH—See Digital Turbine, Inc.; *U.S. Public*, pg. 664
FYBER N.V.—See Digital Turbine, Inc.; *U.S. Public*, pg. 664
FYBROC—See CECO Environmental Corp.; *U.S. Public*, pg. 464
FYFE ASIA PTE. LTD.—See New Mountain Capital, LLC; *U.S. Private*, pg. 2899
FYFE BORNEO SDN BHD—See New Mountain Capital, LLC; *U.S. Private*, pg. 2899
FYFE CO. LLC—See New Mountain Capital, LLC; *U.S. Private*, pg. 2899

FYFE (HONG KONG) LIMITED—See New Mountain Capital, LLC; *U.S. Private*, pg. 2899
FYFE JAPAN CO. LTD.—See New Mountain Capital, LLC; *U.S. Private*, pg. 2899
FYFFE BV—See Sumitomo Corporation; *Int'l*, pg. 7268
FYFFES BANANAS (SWORDS) LIMITED—See Sumitomo Corporation; *Int'l*, pg. 7268
FYFFES GROUP LIMITED—See Sumitomo Corporation; *Int'l*, pg. 7268
FYFFES INTERNATIONAL HOLDINGS LIMITED—See Sumitomo Corporation; *Int'l*, pg. 7268
FYFFES LIMITED—See Sumitomo Corporation; *Int'l*, pg. 7268
FYFFES NORTH AMERICA INC.—See Sumitomo Corporation; *Int'l*, pg. 7268
FYFFES TROPICAL (IRELAND) LIMITED—See Sumitomo Corporation; *Int'l*, pg. 7268
FY FINANCIAL (SHENZHEN) CO., LTD.; *Int'l*, pg. 2859
FYI RESOURCES LIMITED; *Int'l*, pg. 2860
FYI SYSTEMS, INC.; *U.S. Private*, pg. 1628
FYLDE FRESH & FABULOUS LTD.; *Int'l*, pg. 2860
FYNSKE BANK A/S; *Int'l*, pg. 2860
FYPON, LTD.; *U.S. Private*, pg. 1628
FYRNETICS (HONG KONG) LIMITED—See Carrier Global Corporation; *U.S. Public*, pg. 441
FYSAM AUTO DECORATIVE GMBH—See Fuyao Glass Industry Group Co., Ltd.; *Int'l*, pg. 2858
F+Z BAUGESELLSCHAFT MBH—See Bilfinger SE; *Int'l*, pg. 1024
FZ CORPORATION—See Rosemore Inc.; *U.S. Private*, pg. 3483

G

G1440 INC.—See Constellation Software Inc.; *Int'l*, pg. 1772
G1R MASS, LLC—See Group 1 Automotive, Inc.; *U.S. Public*, pg. 971
G1 THERAPEUTICS, INC.; *U.S. Private*, pg. 1632
G2 BUILDERS, LLC.; *U.S. Private*, pg. 1632
G2 CONSULTING GROUP, LLC; *U.S. Private*, pg. 1632
G2 DIRECT & DIGITAL—See WPP plc; *Int'l*, pg. 8463
G2 DIRECT INTERACTIVE KUALA LUMPUR—See WPP plc; *Int'l*, pg. 8463
G2 ENERGY CORP.; *Int'l*, pg. 2866
THE G2G3 GROUP LTD.—See Capita plc; *Int'l*, pg. 1309
G2 GOLDFIELDS INC.; *Int'l*, pg. 2866
G2, INC.; *U.S. Private*, pg. 1632
G2 INTERACTIVE—See WPP plc; *Int'l*, pg. 8470
G2 INTERACTIVE—See WPP plc; *Int'l*, pg. 8470
G-2 INTERNATIONAL—See Enviro Clean Services LLC; *U.S. Private*, pg. 1406
G2 ISTANBUL—See WPP plc; *Int'l*, pg. 8463
G2 KUALA LUMPUR—See WPP plc; *Int'l*, pg. 8463
G2METRIC LIMITED—See Searchlight Capital Partners, L.P.; *U.S. Private*, pg. 3588
G2METRIC—See Searchlight Capital Partners, L.P.; *U.S. Private*, pg. 3588
G2 MOSCOW—See WPP plc; *Int'l*, pg. 8463
G2POWER CO., LTD.; *Int'l*, pg. 2866
G2 STOCKHOLM—See WPP plc; *Int'l*, pg. 8463
G2 TOKYO—See WPP plc; *Int'l*, pg. 8463
G2 WEB SERVICES, INC.—See Stellex Capital Management LP; *U.S. Private*, pg. 3800
G3 CANADA LIMITED—See Bunge Limited; *U.S. Public*, pg. 412
G3 COMMS LTD.; *Int'l*, pg. 2866
G3 COMMUNICATIONS—See ONEX Corporation; *Int'l*, pg. 5579
G3 EXPLORATION LIMITED; *Int'l*, pg. 2866
G3 GLOBAL BERHAD; *Int'l*, pg. 2866
THE G3 GROUP; *U.S. Private*, pg. 4031
G3 VRM ACQUISITION CORP.; *U.S. Public*, pg. 894
G4 MEDIA, LLC—See Comcast Corporation; *U.S. Public*, pg. 539
G4S BEHEER BV—See Allied Universal Manager LLC; *U.S. Private*, pg. 188
G4S (BOTSWANA) LTD.—See Allied Universal Manager LLC; *U.S. Private*, pg. 188
G4S CASH SOLUTIONS (BELGIUM) SA/NV—See Allied Universal Manager LLC; *U.S. Private*, pg. 188
G4S CASH SOLUTIONS BV—See Allied Universal Manager LLC; *U.S. Private*, pg. 188
G4S CASH SOLUTIONS (IRELAND) LIMITED—See Allied Universal Manager LLC; *U.S. Private*, pg. 188
G4S CASH SOLUTIONS SRL—See Allied Universal Manager LLC; *U.S. Private*, pg. 188
G4S COMPLIANCE & NVESTIGATIONS (IRELAND) LIMITED—See Allied Universal Manager LLC; *U.S. Private*, pg. 188
G4S (DRC) S.A.R.L.—See Allied Universal Manager LLC; *U.S. Private*, pg. 188
G4S FIRE & SAFETY BV—See Allied Universal Manager LLC; *U.S. Private*, pg. 189
G4S (HELLAS), S.A.—See Allied Universal Manager LLC; *U.S. Private*, pg. 188
G4S HOLDINGS (HONG KONG) LTD.—See Allied Universal Manager LLC; *U.S. Private*, pg. 189

COMPANY NAME INDEX

G4S (HONG KONG - HOLDING) LTD.—See Allied Universal Manager LLC; *U.S. Private*, pg. 188
G4S INTERNATIONAL LOGISITICS (HONG KONG) LTD.—See Allied Universal Manager LLC; *U.S. Private*, pg. 189
G4S INTERNATIONAL LOGISTICS (GERMANY) GMBH—See Allied Universal Manager LLC; *U.S. Private*, pg. 189
G4S INTERNATIONAL LOGISTICS (USA), INC.—See Allied Universal Manager LLC; *U.S. Private*, pg. 189
G4S KENYA LIMITED—See Allied Universal Manager LLC; *U.S. Private*, pg. 189
G4S KESZPENZLOGISZTIKAI KFT—See Allied Universal Manager LLC; *U.S. Private*, pg. 189
G4S (MALI) SARL—See Allied Universal Manager LLC; *U.S. Private*, pg. 188
G4S PLC—See Allied Universal Manager LLC; *U.S. Private*, pg. 188
G4S RISK CONSULTING LTD.—See Allied Universal Manager LLC; *U.S. Private*, pg. 189
G4S RISK MANAGEMENT LIMITED—See Allied Universal Manager LLC; *U.S. Private*, pg. 189
G4S SECURE INTEGRATION LLC—See Allied Universal Manager LLC; *U.S. Private*, pg. 189
G4S SECURE SOLUTIONS AG—See Allied Universal Manager LLC; *U.S. Private*, pg. 189
G4S SECURE SOLUTIONS (CANADA) LIMITED—See Allied Universal Manager LLC; *U.S. Private*, pg. 189
G4S SECURE SOLUTIONS (CI) SA—See Allied Universal Manager LLC; *U.S. Private*, pg. 189
G4S SECURE SOLUTIONS (CYPRUS) LIMITED—See Allied Universal Manager LLC; *U.S. Private*, pg. 189
G4S SECURE SOLUTIONS D.O.O.—See Allied Universal Manager LLC; *U.S. Private*, pg. 189
G4S SECURE SOLUTIONS (EGYPT) LLC—See Allied Universal Manager LLC; *U.S. Private*, pg. 189
G4S SECURE SOLUTIONS FRANCE SAS—See Allied Universal Manager LLC; *U.S. Private*, pg. 189
G4S SECURE SOLUTIONS (GAMBIA) LTD.—See Allied Universal Manager LLC; *U.S. Private*, pg. 189
G4S SECURE SOLUTIONS JAPAN K.K.—See Allied Universal Manager LLC; *U.S. Private*, pg. 189
G4S SECURE SOLUTIONS (MACAU) LTD.—See Allied Universal Manager LLC; *U.S. Private*, pg. 189
G4S SECURE SOLUTIONS MOCAMBIQUE LIMITADA—See Allied Universal Manager LLC; *U.S. Private*, pg. 189
G4S SECURE SOLUTIONS NIGERIA LTD.—See Allied Universal Manager LLC; *U.S. Private*, pg. 189
G4S SECURE SOLUTIONS (SA) (PTY) LIMITED—See Allied Universal Manager LLC; *U.S. Private*, pg. 189
G4S SECURE SOLUTIONS (SINGAPORE) PTE. LTD.—See Allied Universal Manager LLC; *U.S. Private*, pg. 189
G4S SECURE SOLUTIONS (SL) LTD.—See Allied Universal Manager LLC; *U.S. Private*, pg. 189
G4S SECURE SOLUTIONS (TRINIDAD) LTD.—See Allied Universal Manager LLC; *U.S. Private*, pg. 189
G4S SECURE SOLUTIONS (UK) LIMITED—See Allied Universal Manager LLC; *U.S. Private*, pg. 189
G4S SECURE SOLUTIONS (URUGUAY) S.A.—See Allied Universal Manager LLC; *U.S. Private*, pg. 189
G4S SECURE SOLUTIONS (USA) INC.—See Allied Universal Manager LLC; *U.S. Private*, pg. 189
G4S SECURE SOLUTIONS ZAMBIA LTD.—See Allied Universal Manager LLC; *U.S. Private*, pg. 189
G4S SECURITY SERVICES AG—See Allied Universal Manager LLC; *U.S. Private*, pg. 190
G4S SECURITY SERVICES A/S—See Allied Universal Manager LLC; *U.S. Private*, pg. 190
G4S SECURITY SERVICES CANADA LTD.—See Allied Universal Manager LLC; *U.S. Private*, pg. 190
G4S SECURITY SERVICES (INDIA) PVT. LIMITED—See Allied Universal Manager LLC; *U.S. Private*, pg. 189
G4S SECURITY SERVICES (MAURITANIA) SA—See Allied Universal Manager LLC; *U.S. Private*, pg. 190
G4S SECURITY SERVICES NEPAL (P) LTD.—See Allied Universal Manager LLC; *U.S. Private*, pg. 190
G4S SECURITY SERVICES SA/NV—See Allied Universal Manager LLC; *U.S. Private*, pg. 190
G4S SECURITY SERVICES (THAILAND) LIMITED—See Allied Universal Manager LLC; *U.S. Private*, pg. 190
G4S SECURITY SOLUTIONS AB—See Allied Universal Manager LLC; *U.S. Private*, pg. 190
G4S SECURITY SOLUTIONS SARL—See Allied Universal Manager LLC; *U.S. Private*, pg. 190
G4S SECURITY SYSTEMS GMBH—See Allied Universal Manager LLC; *U.S. Private*, pg. 190
G4S SECURITY SYSTEMS LEBANON SAL—See Allied Universal Manager LLC; *U.S. Private*, pg. 190
G4S SOLUCIONES DE SEGURIDAD S.A.—See Allied Universal Manager LLC; *U.S. Private*, pg. 190
G4 STATION PTE LTD—See Sinjia Land Limited; *Int'l*, pg. 6945
G4S TECHNOLOGY LTD.—See Allied Universal Manager LLC; *U.S. Private*, pg. 190
G4S WACKENHUT (UK) LTD.—See Allied Universal Manager LLC; *U.S. Private*, pg. 189

G5 ENTERPRISES, INC.—See Quad-C Management, Inc.; *U.S. Private*, pg. 3315
G5 ENTERTAINMENT AB; *Int'l*, pg. 2866
G5 SEARCH MARKETING, INC.—See PeakEquity Partners; *U.S. Private*, pg. 3125
G6 HOSPITALITY LLC—See Blackstone Inc.; *U.S. Public*, pg. 353
G6 MATERIALS CORP.; *U.S. Public*, pg. 894
G-7 AGRI JAPAN CO., LTD.—See G-7 HOLDINGS Inc.; *Int'l*, pg. 2862
G-7 AUTO SERVICE CO., LTD.—See G-7 HOLDINGS Inc.; *Int'l*, pg. 2862
G-7 BIKE WORLD CO., LTD.—See G-7 HOLDINGS Inc.; *Int'l*, pg. 2862
G-7.CROWNTRADING CO., LTD.—See G-7 HOLDINGS Inc.; *Int'l*, pg. 2862
G-7 DEVELOPMENT CO., LTD.—See G-7 HOLDINGS Inc.; *Int'l*, pg. 2862
G7 ENTREPRISES; *Int'l*, pg. 2867
G-7 HOLDINGS INC.; *Int'l*, pg. 2862
G-7 INTERNATIONAL PTE. LTD.—See G-7 HOLDINGS Inc.; *Int'l*, pg. 2862
G7 JAPAN FOOD SERVICE CO., LTD.—See G-7 HOLDINGS Inc.; *Int'l*, pg. 2862
G-7 MEAT TERABAYASHI CO., LTD.—See G-7 HOLDINGS Inc.; *Int'l*, pg. 2862
G-7 MOTORS CO., LTD.—See G-7 HOLDINGS Inc.; *Int'l*, pg. 2862
G7 RETAIL MALAYSIA SDN. BHD.—See G-7 HOLDINGS Inc.; *Int'l*, pg. 2862
G-7 SUPER MART CO., LTD.—See G-7 HOLDINGS Inc.; *Int'l*, pg. 2862
G7 TAXI SERVICE—See G7 Entreprises; *Int'l*, pg. 2867
G8 CONSULTANTS PTY. LTD.—See SABINA CORPORATION LIMITED; *Int'l*, pg. 6462
G8 EDUCATION LTD.; *Int'l*, pg. 2867
G9 LANDSKAB, PARK & BYRUM A/S—See Lagercrantz Group AB; *Int'l*, pg. 4394
G9PHARMA CO. LTD; *Int'l*, pg. 2867
GAAP POINT-OF-SALE (PROPRIETARY) LIMITED—See Capital Eye Investments Limited; *Int'l*, pg. 1310
GAASIENERGIA AS—See Gasum Oy; *Int'l*, pg. 2888
GAAS LABS, LLC; *U.S. Private*, pg. 1632
GA AUSTRIA GMBH—See Alpiq Holding AG; *Int'l*, pg. 373
THE G A AVRIL CO.; *U.S. Private*, pg. 4031
GABA B.V.—See Colgate-Palmolive Company; *U.S. Public*, pg. 532
GABA CORPORATION—See Nova Holdings Co., Ltd.; *Int'l*, pg. 5450
GABA INTERNATIONAL AG—See Colgate-Palmolive Company; *U.S. Public*, pg. 532
GABAN CO., LTD.—See House Foods Group Inc.; *Int'l*, pg. 3490
GABAN SPICE MANUFACTURING (M) SDN. BHD.—See House Foods Group Inc.; *Int'l*, pg. 3490
GABATHER AB; *Int'l*, pg. 2867
GABAY PROPERTIES AND DEVELOPMENT LTD; *Int'l*, pg. 2867
GABBA LLC; *U.S. Private*, pg. 1632
THE GABBER; *U.S. Private*, pg. 4031
GABBERTS DESIGN STUDIO & FINE FURNISHINGS—See HOM Furniture, Inc.; *U.S. Private*, pg. 1969
GABBIT CORP.; *Int'l*, pg. 2867
GABELLI & COMPANY, INC.—See GAMCO Investors, Inc.; *U.S. Public*, pg. 895
GABELLI & COMPANY INVESTMENT ADVISERS, INC.—See GAMCO Investors, Inc.; *U.S. Public*, pg. 895
GABELLI DIVIDEND & INCOME TRUST; *U.S. Public*, pg. 894
THE GABELLI EQUITY TRUST INC.—See GAMCO Investors, Inc.; *U.S. Public*, pg. 895
GABELLI FUNDS, LLC—See GAMCO Investors, Inc.; *U.S. Public*, pg. 895
THE GABELLI GLOBAL SMALL & MID CAP VALUE TRUST; *U.S. Public*, pg. 2074
GABELLI GLOBAL UTILITY & INCOME TRUST—See GAMCO Investors, Inc.; *U.S. Public*, pg. 895
THE GABELLI GO ANYWHERE TRUST; *U.S. Public*, pg. 2074
GABELLI HEALTHCARE & WELLNESSRX TRUST; *U.S. Public*, pg. 894
GABELLI MULTIMEDIA TRUST, INC.; *U.S. Public*, pg. 894
GABELLI VALUE FOR ITALY SPA; *Int'l*, pg. 2867
GAB EMPACADORA INC.; *U.S. Private*, pg. 1632
GABETTI PROPERTY SOLUTIONS SPA; *Int'l*, pg. 2867
GABETTI S.P.A.—See Gabetti Property Solutions SpA; *Int'l*, pg. 2867
GAB EZEE ATM LP—See Morgan Stanley; *U.S. Public*, pg. 1474
GAB FRANCE SARL—See Eurofins Scientific S.E.; *Int'l*, pg. 2543
GABIA INC.; *Int'l*, pg. 2867
GAB INVESTMENT COMPANY, INC.—See German American Bancorp, Inc.; *U.S. Public*, pg. 934
G.A. BLANCO & SONS INC.; *U.S. Private*, pg. 1630
GABLER AS; *Int'l*, pg. 2867

GAC CONTRACTORS

GABLER ENGINEERING GMBH—See Hillenbrand, Inc.; *U.S. Public*, pg. 1036
GABLER MASCHINENBAU GMBH—See L. Possehl & Co. mbH; *Int'l*, pg. 4382
THE GABLES PUBLISHING COMPANY—See Chatham Asset Management, LLC; *U.S. Private*, pg. 867
GABLES RESIDENTIAL TRUST—See Franklin Resources, Inc.; *U.S. Public*, pg. 881
G.A. BLOCKER GRADING CONTRACTOR, INC.—See Curran Group, Inc.; *U.S. Private*, pg. 1125
GABON PORT MANAGEMENT S.A.—See Mitsui & Co., Ltd.; *Int'l*, pg. 4980
GABON TELECOM SA—See Emirates Telecommunications Group Compapny PJSC; *Int'l*, pg. 2382
GA BRAUN INC.; *U.S. Private*, pg. 1632
GABRIEL BROTHERS INC.—See Warburg Pincus LLC; *U.S. Private*, pg. 4438
GABRIEL DEGROOD BENDT LLC—See Evening Post Publishing Co.; *U.S. Private*, pg. 1436
GABRIEL EUROPE—See Cummins Inc.; *U.S. Public*, pg. 608
GABRIEL HOLDING A/S; *Int'l*, pg. 2867
GABRIEL INDIA LTD; *Int'l*, pg. 2867
GABRIELLA WHITE LLC; *U.S. Private*, pg. 1632
GABRIELLE SHAW COMMUNICATIONS; *Int'l*, pg. 2867
GABRIELLE—See FAYAT SAS; *Int'l*, pg. 2625
GABRIELLE STUDIO INC—See LVMH Moet Hennessy Louis Vuitton SE; *Int'l*, pg. 4601
GABRIELLI TRUCK SALES LTD.; *U.S. Private*, pg. 1632
GABRIEL NORTH AMERICA INC.—See Gabriel Holding A/S; *Int'l*, pg. 2867
GABRIEL PROPERTIES, LLC; *U.S. Private*, pg. 1632
GABRIEL RESOURCES LTD.; *Int'l*, pg. 2867
GABRIEL'S HOLDINGS LTD.; *U.S. Private*, pg. 1632
GABRIEL (TIANJIN) INTERNATIONAL TRADING CO. LTD.—See Gabriel Holding A/S; *Int'l*, pg. 2867
GABUNGAN AQRS BERHAD; *Int'l*, pg. 2867
GABUNGAN STRATEGIK SDN. BHD.—See Gabungan AQRS Berhad; *Int'l*, pg. 2868
GABY INC.; *Int'l*, pg. 2868
G A CARLSSON AB - GEA'S—See Atria Plc; *Int'l*, pg. 694
GAC AUTO GROUP, INC.; *U.S. Private*, pg. 1632
GAC BUNKER FUELS—See Gulf Agency Company Ltd.; *Int'l*, pg. 3178
GAC CARGO SYSTEMS (MALAYSIA) SDN. BHD—See Gulf Agency Company Ltd.; *Int'l*, pg. 3178
GA-CC COLUMBUS, INC.—See AutoNation, Inc.; *U.S. Public*, pg. 235
GAC CHANGFENG MOTOR CO., LTD.—See Guangzhou Automobile Industry Group Co., Ltd.; *Int'l*, pg. 3164
GAC CHEMICAL CORP—See GAC Chemical Corp.; *U.S. Private*, pg. 1633
GAC CHEMICAL CORP.; *U.S. Private*, pg. 1633
GAC CONTRACTORS; *U.S. Private*, pg. 1633
GAC CORPORATION - ANJO PLANT—See Denso Corporation; *Int'l*, pg. 2032
GAC CORPORATION—See Denso Corporation; *Int'l*, pg. 2032
GAC DENMARK A/S—See Gulf Agency Company Ltd.; *Int'l*, pg. 3178
GAC DEUTSCHLAND GMBH—See DENTSPLY SIRONA Inc.; *U.S. Public*, pg. 655
GA CDJR MOTORS, LLC—See AutoNation, Inc.; *U.S. Public*, pg. 235
GAC DO BRASIL LTDA—See Gulf Agency Company Ltd.; *Int'l*, pg. 3179
GACEM COMPANY LIMITED—See Heidelberg Materials AG; *Int'l*, pg. 3316
GAC ENERGY AND MARINE SERVICES LTD—See Gulf Agency Company Ltd.; *Int'l*, pg. 3178
GAC FORWARDING & SHIPPING (SHANGHAI) LTD—See Gulf Agency Company Ltd.; *Int'l*, pg. 3178
GAC FRANCHISING, LLC—See Fog Cutter Capital Group Inc.; *U.S. Private*, pg. 1557
GAC GHANA—See Gulf Agency Company Ltd.; *Int'l*, pg. 3178
GAC KAZAKHSTAN LLP—See Gulf Agency Company Ltd.; *Int'l*, pg. 3178
GACK SPIEL- UND FREIZEIT GMBH—See Nayax Ltd.; *Int'l*, pg. 3178
GAC LASER INTERNATIONAL LOGISTICS (PTY) LIMITED—See Gulf Agency Company Ltd.; *Int'l*, pg. 3178
GACL-NALCO ALKALIES & CHEMICALS PVT. LTD.—See Gujarat Alkalies & Chemicals Ltd; *Int'l*, pg. 3175
GAC LOGISTICS (UK) LTD—See Gulf Agency Company Ltd.; *Int'l*, pg. 3178
GAC MARINE L.L.C.—See Gulf Agency Company Ltd.; *Int'l*, pg. 3178
GAC MARINE LOGISTICS INC.—See Gulf Agency Company Ltd.; *Int'l*, pg. 3178
GAC MARINE—See Gulf Agency Company Ltd.; *Int'l*, pg. 3178
GAC NETHERLANDS LTD—See Gulf Agency Company Ltd.; *Int'l*, pg. 3178
GAC NORWAY AS—See Gulf Agency Company Ltd.; *Int'l*, pg. 3178
GAC-NURMINEN NAVIS OY—See Gulf Agency Company Ltd.; *Int'l*, pg. 3179

GAC CONTRACTORS

GA COLUMBUS IMPORTS, LLC—See AutoNation, Inc.; *U.S. Public*, pg. 235
GA COMMUNICATIONS INC.; *U.S. Private*, pg. 1632
GA COMMUNICATIONS—See GA Communications Inc.; *U.S. Private*, pg. 1632
GA COMMUNICATIONS—See GA Communications Inc.; *U.S. Private*, pg. 1632
GA COMMUNICATIONS—See GA Communications Inc.; *U.S. Private*, pg. 1632
GA-COM TELEKOMMUNIKATION UND TELEMATIK GMBH—See Alpiq Holding AG; *Int'l*, pg. 372
GACO WESTERN INC—See Bridgestone Corporation; *Int'l*, pg. 1157
GAC PHILIPPINES, INC—See Gulf Agency Company Ltd.; *Int'l*, pg. 3178
GAC (POLAND) SP. Z.O.O.—See Gulf Agency Company Ltd.; *Int'l*, pg. 3178
GAC SERVICES (JAPAN) LIMITED—See Gulf Agency Company Ltd.; *Int'l*, pg. 3178
GAC SHIPPING AND LOGISTICS LIMITED—See Gulf Agency Company Ltd.; *Int'l*, pg. 3178
GAC SHIPPING (INDIA) PVT. LTD.—See Gulf Agency Company Ltd.; *Int'l*, pg. 3178
GAC SHIPPING LIMITED—See Gulf Agency Company Ltd.; *Int'l*, pg. 3178
GAC SHIPPING NIGERIA LIMITED—See Albert Ballin KG; *Int'l*, pg. 294
GAC SHIPPING (S.A.) (PTY) LIMITED—See Gulf Agency Company Ltd.; *Int'l*, pg. 3178
GAC SHIPPING SA—See Gulf Agency Company Ltd.; *Int'l*, pg. 3178
GAC SHIPPING SERVICES (NIGERIA) LTD.—See Gulf Agency Company Ltd.; *Int'l*, pg. 3178
GAC SHIPPING (USA) INC.—See Gulf Agency Company Ltd.; *Int'l*, pg. 3179
GAC SUPPLY, LLC—See Fog Cutter Capital Group Inc.; *U.S. Private*, pg. 1557
GAC SWEDEN AB—See Gulf Agency Company Ltd.; *Int'l*, pg. 3179
GAC (TAIWAN) LTD.—See Gulf Agency Company Ltd.; *Int'l*, pg. 3178
GACTEL TURNKEY PROJECTS LIMITED—See Gammon India Limited; *Int'l*, pg. 2879
GAC THORESEN LOGISTICS LTD.—See Thoresen Thai Agencies Public Company Limited; *Int'l*, pg. 7718
GAC TRANSFER SERVICES S.A.—See Gulf Agency Company Ltd.; *Int'l*, pg. 3179
GAC USA—See Gulf Agency Company Ltd.; *Int'l*, pg. 3179
GADABOUT INC.; *U.S. Private*, pg. 1633
GADANG ENGINEERING (M) SDN BHD.—See Gadang Holdings Berhad; *Int'l*, pg. 2868
GADANG HOLDINGS BERHAD; *Int'l*, pg. 2868
GADBERRY GROUP, LLC—See RE/MAX Holdings, Inc.; *U.S. Public*, pg. 1768
GADDIE-SHAMROCK LLC; *U.S. Private*, pg. 1633
GADDIS CAPITAL CORPORATION; *U.S. Private*, pg. 1633
GAD EG; *Int'l*, pg. 2868
GADELLNET CONSULTING SERVICES, LLC; *U.S. Private*, pg. 1633
GAD ENVIRONMENTAL TECHNOLOGY CO., LTD.; *Int'l*, pg. 2868
GADGET ABC ENTERTAINMENT GROUP AG—See CTS Eventim AG & Co. KGAA; *Int'l*, pg. 1873
GADGET REPAIR SOLUTIONS LIMITED—See Stone Point Capital LLC; *U.S. Private*, pg. 3821
GADGITKIDS, LLC; *U.S. Private*, pg. 1633
GADIV GMBH—See adesso SE; *Int'l*, pg. 144
GADIV PETROCHEMICAL INDUSTRIES LTD.—See Israel Corporation Ltd.; *Int'l*, pg. 3823
GADIV PETROCHEMICAL INDUSTRIES LTD.—See Israel Petrochemical Enterprises Ltd; *Int'l*, pg. 3824
GADNIUM GROUP LLC; *U.S. Private*, pg. 1633
GADOON TEXTILE MILLS LIMITED; *Int'l*, pg. 2868
GADORA TOBACCO P.S.C.—See Pyxus International, Inc.; *U.S. Public*, pg. 1740
GADOT BIO-CHEM (EUROPE) B.V.—See Delek Group Ltd.; *Int'l*, pg. 2011
GADOT BIOCHEMICAL INDUSTRIES LTD.—See Delek Group Ltd.; *Int'l*, pg. 2011
GADSDEN GROWTH PROPERTIES, INC.—See Gadsden Properties, Inc.; *U.S. Public*, pg. 894
GADSDEN HOME CARE SERVICES, LLC—See Community Health Systems, Inc.; *U.S. Public*, pg. 553
GADSDEN PROPERTIES, INC.; *U.S. Public*, pg. 894
GADSDEN REGIONAL MEDICAL CENTER, LLC—See Community Health Systems, Inc.; *U.S. Public*, pg. 553
GADSDEN REGIONAL PRIMARY CARE, LLC—See Community Health Systems, Inc.; *U.S. Public*, pg. 553
GADSDEN SURGERY CENTER, LLC—See UnitedHealth Group Incorporated; *U.S. Public*, pg. 2241
GADSDEN SURGERY CENTER, LTD.—See UnitedHealth Group Incorporated; *U.S. Public*, pg. 2241
THE GADSDEN TIMES—See Gannett Co., Inc.; *U.S. Public*, pg. 905
GAD-TEK PROPRIETARY LTD—See Bowler Metcalf Limited; *Int'l*, pg. 1124
G ADVENTURES, INC.; *Int'l*, pg. 2861

GADYACHGAZ, PJSC—See Limited Liability Company "Group" Sodruzhestvo; *Int'l*, pg. 4499
GADZOOKS INC.; *U.S. Private*, pg. 1633
GAEART CO., LTD.—See Kumagai Gumi Co., Ltd.; *Int'l*, pg. 4329
GAEART TK CO., LTD.—See Kumagai Gumi Co., Ltd.; *Int'l*, pg. 4329
GAEASOFT; *Int'l*, pg. 2868
GAEDABAKSTUR EHF—See Orkla ASA; *Int'l*, pg. 5637
GAEDEKE HOLDINGS LTD.; *U.S. Private*, pg. 1633
THE GAEKWAR MILLS LIMITED; *Int'l*, pg. 7647
GA ENERGIEANLAGENBAU NORD GMBH—See VINCI S.A.; *Int'l*, pg. 8238
GA ENERGIEANLAGENBAU SUD GMBH—See VINCI S.A.; *Int'l*, pg. 8238
GA ENERGO TECHNIK S.R.O.—See Alpiq Holding AG; *Int'l*, pg. 373
GAENSEL ENERGY GROUP, INC.; *U.S. Public*, pg. 894
GAENSLEN VOELTER GMBH & CO. KG—See Gaenslen Voelter; *Int'l*, pg. 2868
GAENSLEN VOELTER; *Int'l*, pg. 2868
GAERNER GMBH—See Franz Haniel & Cie. GmbH; *Int'l*, pg. 2763
GAES COLOMBIA SAS—See Amplifon S.p.A.; *Int'l*, pg. 435
GAFCON INC.; *U.S. Private*, pg. 1634
G.A. & F.C. WAGMAN, INC.—See Wagman Companies, Inc.; *U.S. Private*, pg. 4426
GAF DECKING SYSTEMS LLC—See GAF Materials Corporation; *U.S. Private*, pg. 1633
GA FERAL AB—See Norsk Hydro ASA; *Int'l*, pg. 5432
GAFFNEY BUICK-GMC, INC.; *U.S. Private*, pg. 1634
GAFFNEY HMA, INC.—See Spartanburg Regional Health Services District, Inc.; *U.S. Private*, pg. 3747
GAFFNEY-KROESE SUPPLY CORP.; *U.S. Private*, pg. 1634
GAFFNEY-KROESE SUPPLY INDIA PRIVATE LIMITED—See Gaffney-Kroese Supply Corp.; *U.S. Private*, pg. 1634
GAFFNEY-KROESE SUPPLY PRIVATE LIMITED—See Gaffney-Kroese Supply Corp.; *U.S. Private*, pg. 1634
GAFFNEY-KROESE TRINIDAD LIMITED—See Gaffney-Kroese Supply Corp.; *U.S. Private*, pg. 1634
GAFFNEY-KROESE UK LTD—See Gaffney-Kroese Supply Corp.; *U.S. Private*, pg. 1634
GAFFOGLIO FAMILY METALCRAFTERS INC.; *U.S. Private*, pg. 1634
GAFFOS INC.; *U.S. Private*, pg. 1634
GAFISA S.A.; *Int'l*, pg. 2868
GAFISA VENDAS INTERMEDIACAO IMOBILIARIA LTDA.—See Gafisa S.A.; *Int'l*, pg. 2868
GAF MATERIALS CORPORATION; *U.S. Private*, pg. 1633
G.A. FOOD SERVICES OF PINELLAS COUNTY INC.; *U.S. Private*, pg. 1630
GAGA CORPORATION—See T.Y. Limited, Inc.; *Int'l*, pg. 7398
GAGAN GASES LTD.; *Int'l*, pg. 2868
GAGAN POLYCOT INDIA LIMITED; *Int'l*, pg. 2868
GAGASAN NADI CERGAS BHD; *Int'l*, pg. 2868
GAGE CHEVROLET INC.; *U.S. Private*, pg. 1634
GAGE CHRYSLER-PLYMOUTH-DODGE INC.; *U.S. Private*, pg. 1634
THE GAGE COMPANY; *U.S. Private*, pg. 4031
GAGE CORPORATION; *U.S. Private*, pg. 1634
GAGE DO BRASIL LTDA.—See Gage Corporation; *U.S. Private*, pg. 1634
GAGE GLOBAL SERVICES—See Gage Corporation; *U.S. Private*, pg. 1634
GAGE INDUSTRIES INC.; *U.S. Private*, pg. 1634
GAGEN MACDONALD, LLC—See APCO Worldwide; *U.S. Private*, pg. 291
GAGE PRODUCTS COMPANY DE MEXICO, S. DE R.L. DE C.V.—See Gage Corporation; *U.S. Private*, pg. 1634
GAGE PRODUCTS COMPANY—See Gage Corporation; *U.S. Private*, pg. 1634
GAGE'S FERTILIZER & GRAIN, INC.; *U.S. Private*, pg. 1634
GAGE; *U.S. Private*, pg. 1634
GAGE-WEST—See Gage; *U.S. Private*, pg. 1634
GAGFAH FACILITY MANAGEMENT GMBH—See Vonovia SE; *Int'l*, pg. 8305
GAGGENAU HAUSGERATE GMBH—See Robert Bosch GmbH; *Int'l*, pg. 6358
GAGGIA S.P.A.—See Koninklijke Philips N.V.; *Int'l*, pg. 4267
GAG IMMOBILIEN AG; *Int'l*, pg. 2868
GAG LUDWIGSHAFEN AM RHEIN AKTIENGESELL- SCHAFT; *Int'l*, pg. 2868
GAGMARS INC.; *U.S. Private*, pg. 1635
GAGNON INCORPORATED; *U.S. Private*, pg. 1635
GAGS & GAMES INC.—See Thomas H. Lee Partners, L.P.; *U.S. Private*, pg. 4156
GAH EUROPE GMBH—See Sdiptech AB; *Int'l*, pg. 6658
GA H IMPORTS, LLC—See AutoNation, Inc.; *U.S. Public*, pg. 235
GA HOCHSPANNUNG LEITUNGSBAU GMBH—See VINCI S.A.; *Int'l*, pg. 8238
GA HOLDING GMBH—See VINCI S.A.; *Int'l*, pg. 8238

CORPORATE AFFILIATIONS

G.A. HOLDINGS LIMITED; *Int'l*, pg. 2865
GAH PENSIONS GMBH—See Alpiq Holding AG; *Int'l*, pg. 372
GAHTANI INTERNATIONAL MARITIME AGENCY—See HAK Algahtani Group of Companies; *Int'l*, pg. 3219
GA HY IMPORTS, LLC—See AutoNation, Inc.; *U.S. Public*, pg. 235
GAIA CORPORATION CO., LTD.; *Int'l*, pg. 2868
GAIA GROW CORP.; *Int'l*, pg. 2868
GAIA HERBS INC.—See Givaudan S.A.; *Int'l*, pg. 2981
GAIA, INC.; *U.S. Public*, pg. 894
GAIAM AMERICAS, INC.—See Sequential Brands Group, Inc.; *U.S. Public*, pg. 1868
GAIAM PTY—See Sequential Brands Group, Inc.; *U.S. Public*, pg. 1868
GAIA SCIENCE SDN BHD; *Int'l*, pg. 2868
GAIA SECURITIZADORA S.A.; *Int'l*, pg. 2869
GAIA-WIND LTD.; *Int'l*, pg. 2869
GAIAX CO., LTD.; *Int'l*, pg. 2869
GAI BEACH HOTEL; *Int'l*, pg. 2868
GAI CONSTRUCTION MONITORING SERVICES, INC.—See Comvest Group Holdings LLC; *U.S. Private*, pg. 1007
GAI CONSULTANTS, INC.—See Comvest Group Holdings LLC; *U.S. Private*, pg. 1007
GAI CONSULTANTS INC.—See Comvest Group Holdings LLC; *U.S. Private*, pg. 1007
GAI CONSULTANTS INC.—See Comvest Group Holdings LLC; *U.S. Private*, pg. 1007
GAIKAI, INC.—See Sony Group Corporation; *Int'l*, pg. 7103
GAIL GAS LIMITED—See GAIL (India) Limited; *Int'l*, pg. 2869
GAIL GLOBAL SINGAPORE PTE. LTD.—See GAIL (India) Limited; *Int'l*, pg. 2869
GAIL GLOBAL (USA) INC.—See GAIL (India) Limited; *Int'l*, pg. 2869
GAIL (INDIA) LIMITED; *Int'l*, pg. 2869
GAILLAC AUTO; *Int'l*, pg. 2869
GAILLARD PERFORMANCE HALL FOUNDATION; *U.S. Private*, pg. 1635
GAIL'S HARLEY-DAVIDSON INC; *U.S. Private*, pg. 1635
GAINBASE INDUSTRIAL LIMITED - CHINA FACTORY—See Onpress PCB Limited; *Int'l*, pg. 5583
GAINBASE INDUSTRIAL LIMITED—See Onpress PCB Limited; *Int'l*, pg. 5583
GAIN CAPITAL-FOREX.COM U.K., LTD.—See StoneX Group Inc.; *U.S. Public*, pg. 1952
GAIN CAPITAL GROUP LLC—See StoneX Group Inc.; *U.S. Public*, pg. 1952
GAIN CAPITAL HOLDINGS, INC.—See StoneX Group Inc.; *U.S. Public*, pg. 1952
GAIN CAPITAL JAPAN CO., LTD.—See StoneX Group Inc.; *U.S. Public*, pg. 1952
GAIN CAPITAL SINGAPORE PTE. LTD.—See StoneX Group Inc.; *U.S. Public*, pg. 1952
GAIN CAPITAL UK LIMITED—See StoneX Group Inc.; *U.S. Public*, pg. 1952
GAIN CITIES LIMITED; *U.S. Private*, pg. 1635
GAINCLIENTS, INC.; *U.S. Public*, pg. 894
GA INDUSTRIES HOLDINGS, LLC—See Zurn Elkay Water Solutions Corporation; *U.S. Public*, pg. 2412
GA INDUSTRIES, INC.—See Zurn Elkay Water Solutions Corporation; *U.S. Public*, pg. 2413
GAINES MOTOR LINES INCORPORATED; *U.S. Private*, pg. 1635
GAINESVILLE ENDOSCOPY CENTER, LLC—See Tenet Healthcare Corporation; *U.S. Public*, pg. 2002
GAINESVILLE FAMILY PHYSICIANS—See HCA Healthcare, Inc.; *U.S. Public*, pg. 996
GAINESVILLE REGIONAL UTILITIES INC.; *U.S. Private*, pg. 1635
GAINESVILLE SUN PUBLISHING COMPANY—See Gannett Co., Inc.; *U.S. Public*, pg. 905
GAINEY RESOURCES LTD.; *Int'l*, pg. 2869
GAINLINE CAPITAL PARTNERS LP; *U.S. Private*, pg. 1635
GAIN PLUS HOLDINGS LIMITED; *Int'l*, pg. 2869
GAINSBOROUGH HARDWARE INDUSTRIES LIMITED—See GWA Group Limited; *Int'l*, pg. 3190
GAINSCO, INC.—See State Farm Mutual Automobile Insurance Company; *U.S. Private*, pg. 3792
GAINSCO SERVICE CORP.—See State Farm Mutual Automobile Insurance Company; *U.S. Private*, pg. 3792
GAINSIGHT, INC.—See Vista Equity Partners, LLC; *U.S. Private*, pg. 4397
GAINS INVESTMENT CORPORATION—See China Steel Corporation; *Int'l*, pg. 1555
GAIN THERAPEUTICS, INC.; *U.S. Public*, pg. 894
GAINTREND SDN. BHD.—See PLB Engineering Berhad; *Int'l*, pg. 5895
GAINVEST URUGUAY ASSET MANAGEMENT S.A.—See StoneX Group Inc.; *U.S. Public*, pg. 1952
GAINWELL SECURITIES CO. LTD.—See Mizuho Financial Group, Inc.; *Int'l*, pg. 4998
GAIOTTO AUTOMATION S.P.A.—See Sacmi Imola S.C.A.R.L.; *Int'l*, pg. 6463

COMPANY NAME INDEX

GAIRMEIDI CAOMHNAITHE DHUN NA NGALL TEORANTA LTD.—See Sioen Industries NV; *Int'l*, pg. 6960
GAITAME.COM CO., LTD.—See Viel & Compagnie SA; *Int'l*, pg. 8192
GAITHER MANAGEMENT GROUP; *U.S. Private*, pg. 1635
GAITHERSBURG FARMERS SUPPLY; *U.S. Private*, pg. 1635
GAI-TRONICS CORPORATION—See Hubbell Incorporated; *U.S. Public*, pg. 1066
GAI-TRONICS LIMITED—See Hubbell Incorporated; *U.S. Public*, pg. 1066
GAI-TRONICS S.R.L.—See Hubbell Incorporated; *U.S. Public*, pg. 1066
GAIZHOU CITY AOXIN Q & M STOMATOLOGY HOSPITAL CO., LTD.—See Aoxin Q & M Dental Group Limited; *Int'l*, pg. 498
GAJANAN SECURITIES SERVICES LIMITED; *Int'l*, pg. 2869
GAJRA BEVEL GEARS LIMITED; *Int'l*, pg. 2869
G.A. KIESEL GMBH; *Int'l*, pg. 2865
GAKKEN COCOFUMP NURSERY CO., LTD.—See Gakken Holdings Co., Ltd.; *Int'l*, pg. 2869
GAKKEN EDUCATIONAL CO., LTD.—See Gakken Holdings Co., Ltd.; *Int'l*, pg. 2869
GAKKEN EDUCATION MALAYSIA SDN. BHD.—See Gakken Holdings Co., Ltd.; *Int'l*, pg. 2869
GAKKEN HOLDINGS CO., LTD.; *Int'l*, pg. 2869
GAKKEN (HONG KONG) CO., LTD.—See Gakken Holdings Co., Ltd.; *Int'l*, pg. 2869
GAKKEN JUKU HOLDINGS CO., LTD.—See Gakken Holdings Co., Ltd.; *Int'l*, pg. 2869
GAKKEN MEDICAL SHUJUNSHA CO., LTD.—See Gakken Holdings Co., Ltd.; *Int'l*, pg. 2869
GAKKEN MEDICAL SUPPORT CO., LTD.—See Gakken Holdings Co., Ltd.; *Int'l*, pg. 2869
GAKKEN PLUS CO., LTD.—See Gakken Holdings Co., Ltd.; *Int'l*, pg. 2869
GAKKEN PRODUCTS SUPPORT CO., LTD.—See Gakken Holdings Co., Ltd.; *Int'l*, pg. 2869
GAKKEN SHUPPAN HOLDINGS CO., LTD.—See Gakken Holdings Co., Ltd.; *Int'l*, pg. 2869
GAKKEN SMILEHEART CO., LTD.—See Gakken Holdings Co., Ltd.; *Int'l*, pg. 2869
GAKKEN STA:FUL CO., LTD.—See Gakken Holdings Co., Ltd.; *Int'l*, pg. 2869
GAKKEN STUDY CO., LTD.—See Gakken Holdings Co., Ltd.; *Int'l*, pg. 2869
GAKKO TOSHO CO., LTD.—See TOPPAN Holdings Inc.; *Int'l*, pg. 7816
GAKKYUSHA CO., LTD.; *Int'l*, pg. 2870
GAKO DEUTSCHLAND GMBH—See Fagron NV; *Int'l*, pg. 2603
GAKUJO CO., LTD.; *Int'l*, pg. 2870
GALA CAPITAL PARTNERS, LLC; *U.S. Private*, pg. 1635
GALACTIC BIOQUIMICOS LTDA.—See Finasucre S.A.; *Int'l*, pg. 2670
GALACTIC INC—See Finasucre S.A.; *Int'l*, pg. 2670
GALACTICO CORPORATE SERVICES LIMITED; *Int'l*, pg. 2870
GALACTIC S.A.—See Finasucre S.A.; *Int'l*, pg. 2670
GALADA FINANCE LIMITED; *Int'l*, pg. 2870
GALADA POWER & TELECOMMUNICATION LTD.; *Int'l*, pg. 2870
GALADARI BROTHERS GROUP—See Investment Corporation of Dubai; *Int'l*, pg. 3785
GALADARI HOTELS (LANKA) PLC; *Int'l*, pg. 2870
GALADCO CO. INC.; *U.S. Private*, pg. 1636
GALA INCORPORATED; *Int'l*, pg. 2870
GALA INDUSTRIES ASIA LIMITED—See Dover Corporation; *U.S. Public*, pg. 681
GALA INDUSTRIES, INC.—See Dover Corporation; *U.S. Public*, pg. 681
GALA INTERACTIVE (GIBRALTAR) LIMITED—See Entain PLC; *Int'l*, pg. 2450
GALA KUNSTSTOFF- UND KAUTSCHUKMASCHINEN GMBH—See Dover Corporation; *U.S. Public*, pg. 681
GALA LAB CORP.—See GALA INCORPORATED; *Int'l*, pg. 2870
GALA LEISURE LTD.—See ITV plc; *Int'l*, pg. 3845
GALA-MIBRAG-SERVICE GMBH—See Energeticky a Prumyslovy Holding, a.s.; *Int'l*, pg. 2420
GALANE GOLD LTD.; *Int'l*, pg. 2870
GALAN LITHIUM LIMITED; *Int'l*, pg. 2870
GALANTAS GOLD CORPORATION; *Int'l*, pg. 2870
GALANTAS IRISH GOLD LIMITED—See Galantas Gold Corporation; *Int'l*, pg. 2870
GALANZ (NORTH AMERICA) INC.—See Guangdong Galanz Group Co., Ltd.; *Int'l*, pg. 3154
GALAPAGOS BIOPHARMA AUSTRIA GMBH—See Galapagos N.V.; *Int'l*, pg. 2870
GALAPAGOS BIOPHARMA NORWAY AS—See Galapagos N.V.; *Int'l*, pg. 2870
GALAPAGOS B.V.—See Galapagos N.V.; *Int'l*, pg. 2870
GALAPAGOS N.V.; *Int'l*, pg. 2870
GALAPAGOS SASU—See Galapagos N.V.; *Int'l*, pg. 2870
GALA PHARMACEUTICAL, INC.; *U.S. Private*, pg. 1636
GALAPROM A.D.; *Int'l*, pg. 2871

GALARDI GROUP, INC.; *U.S. Private*, pg. 1636
GALA S.P.A.; *Int'l*, pg. 2870
GALASSO TRUCKING, INC.; *U.S. Private*, pg. 1636
GALASYS GLOBAL (SUZHOU) CO. LTD.—See Beijing Shiji Information Technology Co., Ltd.; *Int'l*, pg. 956
GALATA INVESTMENT COMPANY AD; *Int'l*, pg. 2871
GALATA MADENCILIK SAN. VE TIC. LTD.—See Ariana Resources plc; *Int'l*, pg. 564
GALATA MINERAL MADENCILIK SAN. VE TIC. A.S.—See Ariana Resources plc; *Int'l*, pg. 564
GALATASARAY SPORTIF SINAI VETICARI YATIRIMLAR AS; *Int'l*, pg. 2871
GALATA WIND ENERJI A.S.; *Int'l*, pg. 2871
GALATEA AB—See Martin Olsson Handels AB; *Int'l*, pg. 4704
GALATEA LTD—See Sarine Technologies Ltd.; *Int'l*, pg. 6577
GALATEA SURGICAL, INC.—See Becton, Dickinson & Company; *U.S. Public*, pg. 292
GALA TECHNOLOGY HOLDING LIMITED; *Int'l*, pg. 2870
GALATIAN INC.; *U.S. Private*, pg. 1636
GALATI YACHT SALES; *U.S. Private*, pg. 1636
GALAVISION, INC.—See ForgeLight, LLC; *U.S. Private*, pg. 1568
GALAVISION, INC.—See Searchlight Capital Partners, L.P.; *U.S. Private*, pg. 3590
GALAXIA DEVICE CO., LTD.—See Hyosung Corporation; *Int'l*, pg. 3550
GALAXIA ELECTRONICS CO., LTD.—See Hyosung Corporation; *Int'l*, pg. 3550
GALAXIA MONEYTREE CO., LTD.; *Int'l*, pg. 2871
GALAXIA MONEYTREE CO. LTD.—See Hyosung ITX CO., LTD.; *Int'l*, pg. 3552
GALAXIA SM INC.; *Int'l*, pg. 2871
GALAXIDI MARINE FARM S.A.; *Int'l*, pg. 2871
GALAXIE CORPORATION; *U.S. Private*, pg. 1636
GALAX TREATMENT CENTER, INC.—See Acadia Healthcare Company, Inc.; *U.S. Public*, pg. 28
GALAXY AGRICO EXPORTS LIMITED; *Int'l*, pg. 2871
GALAXY BEARINGS LIMITED; *Int'l*, pg. 2871
GALAXY BIOMEDICAL INVESTMENT CO., LTD.; *Int'l*, pg. 2871
GALAXY BRANDS LLC—See Sequential Brands Group, Inc.; *U.S. Public*, pg. 1868
GALAXY CERTIFICATION SERVICES PRIVATE LIMITED—See EKI Energy Services Limited; *Int'l*, pg. 2338
GALAXY CLOUD KITCHENS LIMITED; *Int'l*, pg. 2871
GALAXY COMPOUND SEMICONDUCTORS, INC.—See IQE plc; *Int'l*, pg. 3803
GALAXY CONSOLIDATED FINANCE LIMITED; *Int'l*, pg. 2871
GALAXY DESSERTS; *U.S. Private*, pg. 1636
GALAXY DIGITAL HOLDINGS LTD.; *U.S. Public*, pg. 894
GALAXY ENTERPRISES INC.; *U.S. Private*, pg. 1636
GALAXY ENTERTAINMENT GROUP LIMITED; *Int'l*, pg. 2871
GALAXY ENTERTAINMENT INC.—See Cineplex Inc.; *Int'l*, pg. 1610
GALAXY FUTURES COMPANY LIMITED—See China Galaxy Securities Company Limited; *Int'l*, pg. 1503
GALAXY GAMING INC.; *U.S. Public*, pg. 894
GALAXY GLASS & ALUMINUM INC.; *U.S. Private*, pg. 1636
GALAXY HOTEL SYSTEMS LLC—See Marriott International, Inc.; *U.S. Public*, pg. 1371
GALAXY INSURANCE CONSULTANTS PTE LTD—See Steadfast Group Limited; *Int'l*, pg. 7187
GALAXY INTERNATIONAL INC.; *U.S. Private*, pg. 1636
GALAXY LITHIUM (CANADA) INC.—See Allkem Limited; *Int'l*, pg. 359
GALAXY LITHIUM (SAL DE VIDA) S.A.—See Allkem Limited; *Int'l*, pg. 359
GALAXY MACHINERY PVT. LTD.—See The Ugar Sugar Works Limited; *Int'l*, pg. 7697
GALAXY MANAGEMENT S.A.—See ITOCHU Corporation; *Int'l*, pg. 3836
GALAXY MARKETING SOLUTIONS LLC; *U.S. Private*, pg. 1636
GALAXY MARKETING; *U.S. Private*, pg. 1636
GALAXY MULTI RIDES; *U.S. Private*, pg. 1636
GALAXY NEXT GENERATION, INC.; *U.S. Public*, pg. 894
GALAXY NUTRITIONAL FOODS, INC.—See GreenSpace Brands Inc.; *Int'l*, pg. 3076
GALAXY PARTNERS LLC; *U.S. Private*, pg. 1636
GALAXY PAYROLL GROUP LIMITED; *Int'l*, pg. 2871
GALAXY RESOURCES LIMITED—See Allkem Limited; *Int'l*, pg. 359
GALAXY SEMICONDUCTOR CO., LTD.; *Int'l*, pg. 2871
GALAXY SHOWERS—See The Glen Dimplex Group; *Int'l*, pg. 7649
GALAXY SOFTWARE SOLUTIONS INC.; *U.S. Private*, pg. 1636
GALAXY SURFACTANTS LIMITED; *Int'l*, pg. 2871
GALAXY SURFACTANTS LTD-ASIA PACIFIC—See Galaxy Surfactants Limited; *Int'l*, pg. 2872
GALAXY TECHNOLOGIES CORP.; *U.S. Private*, pg. 1636
GALAXY TOYOTA; *U.S. Private*, pg. 1636

GALE FORCE SOFTWARE CORPORATION

GALAXY WINE COMPANY LLC—See Wilson Daniels Wholesale LLC; *U.S. Private*, pg. 4530
GALAZ, YAMAZAKI, RUIZ URQUIZA, S.C.; *Int'l*, pg. 2872
GALBANI FRANCE—See Danone; *Int'l*, pg. 1968
GALBANI—See Danone; *Int'l*, pg. 1968
GALBRAITH LABORATORIES, INC.—See Bureau Veritas S.A.; *Int'l*, pg. 1222
GAL CANADA ELEVATOR PRODUCTS CORP.—See Golden Gate Capital Management II, LLC; *U.S. Private*, pg. 1732
GALCO INDUSTRIAL ELECTRONICS, INC.—See Freeman Spogli & Co. Incorporated; *U.S. Private*, pg. 1606
GALDERMA ARGENTINA S.A.—See Nestle S.A.; *Int'l*, pg. 5202
GALDERMA AUSTRIA GMBH—See Nestle S.A.; *Int'l*, pg. 5203
GALDERMA BENELUX B.V.—See Nestle S.A.; *Int'l*, pg. 5203
GALDERMA BRASIL LTDA.—See Abu Dhabi Investment Authority; *Int'l*, pg. 71
GALDERMA BRASIL LTDA.—See EQT Corporation; *U.S. Public*, pg. 785
GALDERMA BRASIL LTDA.—See Public Sector Pension Investment Board; *Int'l*, pg. 6095
GALDERMA CANADA, INC.—See Abu Dhabi Investment Authority; *Int'l*, pg. 71
GALDERMA CANADA, INC.—See EQT Corporation; *U.S. Public*, pg. 785
GALDERMA CANADA, INC.—See Public Sector Pension Investment Board; *Int'l*, pg. 6096
GALDERMA CHILE LABORATORIOS LTDA.—See Nestle S.A.; *Int'l*, pg. 5203
GALDERMA DE COLOMBIA S.A.—See Nestle S.A.; *Int'l*, pg. 5203
GALDERMA HOLDING S.A.—See Abu Dhabi Investment Authority; *Int'l*, pg. 71
GALDERMA HOLDING S.A.—See EQT Corporation; *U.S. Public*, pg. 785
GALDERMA HOLDING S.A.—See Public Sector Pension Investment Board; *Int'l*, pg. 6095
GALDERMA HONG KONG LIMITED—See Nestle S.A.; *Int'l*, pg. 5203
GALDERMA INTERNATIONAL SAS—See Abu Dhabi Investment Authority; *Int'l*, pg. 71
GALDERMA INTERNATIONAL SAS—See EQT Corporation; *U.S. Public*, pg. 785
GALDERMA INTERNATIONAL SAS—See Public Sector Pension Investment Board; *Int'l*, pg. 6096
GALDERMA ITALIA S.P.A.—See Nestle S.A.; *Int'l*, pg. 5203
GALDERMA LABORATORIES, L.P.—See Abu Dhabi Investment Authority; *Int'l*, pg. 71
GALDERMA LABORATORIES, L.P.—See EQT Corporation; *U.S. Public*, pg. 785
GALDERMA LABORATORIES, L.P.—See Public Sector Pension Investment Board; *Int'l*, pg. 6096
GALDERMA LABORATORIES SOUTH AFRICA (PTY) LTD.—See Nestle S.A.; *Int'l*, pg. 5203
GALDERMA LABORATORIUM GMBH—See Abu Dhabi Investment Authority; *Int'l*, pg. 71
GALDERMA LABORATORIUM GMBH—See EQT Corporation; *U.S. Public*, pg. 785
GALDERMA LABORATORIUM GMBH—See Public Sector Pension Investment Board; *Int'l*, pg. 6096
GALDERMA MEXICO, S.A. DE C.V.—See Nestle S.A.; *Int'l*, pg. 5203
GALDERMA NORDIC AB—See Nestle S.A.; *Int'l*, pg. 5203
GALDERMA PHARMA S.A.—See Abu Dhabi Investment Authority; *Int'l*, pg. 71
GALDERMA PHARMA S.A.—See EQT Corporation; *U.S. Public*, pg. 785
GALDERMA PHARMA S.A.—See Public Sector Pension Investment Board; *Int'l*, pg. 6095
GALDERMA PRODUCTION CANADA INC.—See Abu Dhabi Investment Authority; *Int'l*, pg. 71
GALDERMA PRODUCTION CANADA INC.—See EQT Corporation; *U.S. Public*, pg. 785
GALDERMA PRODUCTION CANADA INC.—See Public Sector Pension Investment Board; *Int'l*, pg. 6096
GALDERMA SINGAPORE PRIVATE LTD.—See Nestle S.A.; *Int'l*, pg. 5203
GALDERMA (THAILAND) LTD.—See Nestle S.A.; *Int'l*, pg. 5202
GALDERMA TRADING (SHANGHAI) CO., LIMITED—See Nestle S.A.; *Int'l*, pg. 5203
GALDERMA (UK) LTD.—See Nestle S.A.; *Int'l*, pg. 5202
GALEANA AUTOMOTIVE GROUP; *U.S. Private*, pg. 1636
GALEANA CHRYSLER DODGE JEEP—See Galeana Automotive Group; *U.S. Private*, pg. 1636
GALE CREATIVE AGENCY PRIVATE LIMITED—See Stagwell, Inc.; *U.S. Public*, pg. 1926
GALECTIN THERAPEUTICS, INC.; *U.S. Public*, pg. 895
GALECTO, INC.; *Int'l*, pg. 2872
GALE FORCE HOLDINGS, LP; *U.S. Private*, pg. 1636
GALE FORCE SOFTWARE CORPORATION; *U.S. Private*, pg. 1636
GALE FORCE SPORTS & ENTERTAINMENT, LLC—See Gale Force Holdings, LP; *U.S. Private*, pg. 1636

GALE FORCE SOFTWARE CORPORATION

GALE GROUP INC.—See Apax Partners LLP; *Int'l*, pg. 503
GALE GROUP INC.—See Apollo Global Management, Inc.; *U.S. Public*, pg. 168
GALE GROUP INC.—See KKR & Co. Inc.; *U.S. Public*, pg. 1256
GALE GROUP INC.—See Searchlight Capital Partners, L.P.; *U.S. Private*, pg. 3587
GALEMED CORPORATION; *Int'l*, pg. 2872
GALENA ASSET MANAGEMENT LIMITED—See Trafigura Beheer B.V.; *Int'l*, pg. 7889
GALENA ASSET MANAGEMENT S.A.—See Trafigura Beheer B.V.; *Int'l*, pg. 7889
GALENA ASSOCIATES, LLC; *U.S. Private*, pg. 1637
GALENA MINING LIMITED; *Int'l*, pg. 2872
GALENFEHA, INC.; *U.S. Private*, pg. 1637
GALEN HEALTHCARE SOLUTIONS—See Rothschild & Co SCA; *Int'l*, pg. 6403
GALEN HEALTHCARE SOLUTIONS—See TA Associates, Inc.; *U.S. Private*, pg. 3918
GALEN HEALTH INSTITUTES, INC.—See HCA Healthcare, Inc.; *U.S. Public*, pg. 996
GALEN HOSPITAL ALASKA, INC.—See HCA Healthcare, Inc.; *U.S. Public*, pg. 996
GALENICA FINANCE LIMITED—See CSL Limited; *Int'l*, pg. 1866
GALENIKA-FITOFARMACIJA A.D.; *Int'l*, pg. 2872
GALEN LIMITED—See Almac Sciences Group Ltd.; *Int'l*, pg. 363
GALEN PARTNERS, L.P.; *U.S. Private*, pg. 1637
GALEN PHARMA IRELAND LIMITED—See Almac Sciences Group Ltd.; *Int'l*, pg. 363
GALENUS MANNHEIM GMBH—See Roche Holding AG; *Int'l*, pg. 6374
GALEO CONCEPT SA; *Int'l*, pg. 2872
GALE PACIFIC FZE—See Gale Pacific Limited; *Int'l*, pg. 2872
GALE PACIFIC INC.—See Gale Pacific Limited; *Int'l*, pg. 2872
GALE PACIFIC LIMITED; *Int'l*, pg. 2872
GALE PACIFIC (NZ) LIMITED—See Gale Pacific Limited; *Int'l*, pg. 2872
GALE PACIFIC SPECIAL TEXTILES (NINGBO) LIMITED—See Gale Pacific Limited; *Int'l*, pg. 2872
GALE PARTNERS INC.—See Stagwell, Inc.; *U.S. Public*, pg. 1926
GALE PARTNERS LLC—See Stagwell, Inc.; *U.S. Public*, pg. 1927
GALERA THERAPEUTICS, INC.; *U.S. Public*, pg. 895
GALERE SA—See Koninklijke BAM Groep N.V.; *Int'l*, pg. 4261
GALERIA KAUFHOF GMBH—See SIGNA Holding GmbH; *Int'l*, pg. 6909
GALERIE ALKOHOLI SP. Z.O.O.—See Marie Brizard Wine & Spirits S.A.; *Int'l*, pg. 4693
GALERIE LIPPE GMBH & CO. KG—See Helaba Landesbank Hessen-Thuringen; *Int'l*, pg. 3328
GALERIES LAFAYETTE SA; *Int'l*, pg. 2872
GALESBURG BROADCASTING CO.—See Pritchard Broadcasting Corp.; *U.S. Private*, pg. 3268
GALESBURG HOME CARE CORPORATION—See Community Health Systems, Inc.; *U.S. Public*, pg. 553
GALESBURG HOSPITAL CORPORATION—See Quorum Health Corporation; *U.S. Private*, pg. 3330
GALESBURG MANUFACTURING CO.; *U.S. Private*, pg. 1637
GALESBURG NISSAN; *U.S. Private*, pg. 1637
GALESI GROUP—See Galesi Group; *U.S. Private*, pg. 1637
GALESI GROUP; *U.S. Private*, pg. 1637
GALE SOUTH BEACH & REGENT HOTEL—See Menin Hotels, Inc.; *U.S. Private*, pg. 2666
GALE TECHNOLOGIES, INC.—See Dell Technologies Inc.; *U.S. Public*, pg. 650
GALE TOYOTA; *U.S. Private*, pg. 1636
GALEXIS AG—See CSL Limited; *Int'l*, pg. 1866
GALFAB, INC.—See Cargotec Corporation; *Int'l*, pg. 1326
GALFAR ENGINEERING & CONTRACTING SAOG; *Int'l*, pg. 2872
GALFAR ENGINEERING & CONTRACTING WLL—See Galfar Engineering & Contracting SAOG; *Int'l*, pg. 2872
GALFARM SP. Z.O.O.—See Fagron NV; *Int'l*, pg. 2603
GALFAR PEMBINAAN DAN PERUSAHAAN (B) SDN BHD—See Galfar Engineering & Contracting SAOG; *Int'l*, pg. 2872
GALFAR TRAINING INSTITUTE LLC—See Galfar Engineering & Contracting SAOG; *Int'l*, pg. 2872
GALGON INDUSTRIES INC.; *U.S. Private*, pg. 1637
GALHEIROS GERACAO DE ENERGIA ELETRICA S.A.—See ContourGlobal Limited; *Int'l*, pg. 1785
GALIANO GOLD INC.; *Int'l*, pg. 2872
GALICHIA HEART HOSPITAL—See HCA Healthcare, Inc.; *U.S. Public*, pg. 996
GALICIA ADMINISTRADORA DE FONDOS S.A.—See Grupo Financiero Galicia S.A.; *Int'l*, pg. 3129
GALICIA SECURITIES S.A.—See Grupo Financiero Galicia S.A.; *Int'l*, pg. 3129
GALILEE ENERGY LIMITED; *Int'l*, pg. 2873

GALILEE RESOURCES LIMITED—See Galilee Energy Limited; *Int'l*, pg. 2873
GALILEI BELGIUM—See Randstad N.V.; *Int'l*, pg. 6201
GALILEI (THAILAND) CO., LTD.—See Fukushima Galilei Co. Ltd.; *Int'l*, pg. 2841
GALILEO DEUTSCHLAND GMBH—See Elliott Management Corporation; *U.S. Private*, pg. 1373
GALILEO DEUTSCHLAND GMBH—See Siris Capital Group, LLC; *U.S. Private*, pg. 3674
GALILEO GLOBAL ADVISORS, LLC; *U.S. Private*, pg. 1637
GALILEO GLOBAL BRANDING GROUP INC.—See Bain Capital, LP; *U.S. Private*, pg. 439
GALILEO GLOBAL EDUCATION; *Int'l*, pg. 2873
GALILEO GLOBAL SECURITIES, LLC—See Galileo Global Advisors, LLC; *U.S. Private*, pg. 1637
GALILEO INTERNATIONAL, LLC—See Elliott Management Corporation; *U.S. Private*, pg. 1373
GALILEO INTERNATIONAL, LLC—See Siris Capital Group, LLC; *U.S. Private*, pg. 3674
GALILEO IRELAND LTD.—See Elliott Management Corporation; *U.S. Private*, pg. 1373
GALILEO IRELAND LTD.—See Siris Capital Group, LLC; *U.S. Private*, pg. 3674
GALILEO MINING LTD.; *Int'l*, pg. 2873
GALILEO RESOURCES PLC; *Int'l*, pg. 2873
GALILEO TECH LTD.; *Int'l*, pg. 2873
GALIL MEDICAL INC.—See Boston Scientific Corporation; *U.S. Public*, pg. 373
GALIMMO SA—See Carmila SA; *Int'l*, pg. 1342
GA LINDBERG AB—See Indutrade AB; *Int'l*, pg. 3678
G A LINDBERG CHEMTECH AB—See Indutrade AB; *Int'l*, pg. 3678
G A LINDBERG PROCESSTEKNIK AB—See Indutrade AB; *Int'l*, pg. 3678
G A LINDBERG SEALTECH AB—See Indutrade AB; *Int'l*, pg. 3678
GALION SA—See Berry Global Group, Inc; *U.S. Public*, pg. 322
GALIOT INSURANCE SERVICES, INC.; *U.S. Private*, pg. 1637
GALI SERVICE INDUSTRIES, INC.; *U.S. Private*, pg. 1637
GALITT SAS—See Sopra Steria Group S.A.; *Int'l*, pg. 7109
GALJADEN FASTIGHETER AB—See Bronsstadet AB; *Int'l*, pg. 1174
GALKIN AUTOMATED PRODUCTS CORP.—See Leggett & Platt, Incorporated; *U.S. Public*, pg. 1302
GALLADE CHEMICAL INC.; *U.S. Private*, pg. 1638
GALLA FOODS LTD.—See Amara Raja Energy & Mobility Limited; *Int'l*, pg. 411
GALLAGHER ASPHALT CORPORATION; *U.S. Private*, pg. 1638
GALLAGHER BASSETT CANADA, INC.—See Arthur J. Gallagher & Co.; *U.S. Public*, pg. 205
GALLAGHER BASSETT INTERNATIONAL LTD. (UK)—See Arthur J. Gallagher & Co.; *U.S. Public*, pg. 205
GALLAGHER BASSETT SERVICES, INC.—See Arthur J. Gallagher & Co.; *U.S. Public*, pg. 205
GALLAGHER BASSETT SERVICES PTY. LTD.—See Arthur J. Gallagher & Co.; *U.S. Public*, pg. 205
GALLAGHER BASSETT SERVICES PTY. LTD.—See Arthur J. Gallagher & Co.; *U.S. Public*, pg. 205
GALLAGHER BASSETT SERVICES WORKERS COMPENSATION VICTORIA PTY. LTD.—See Arthur J. Gallagher & Co.; *U.S. Public*, pg. 205
GALLAGHER BENEFIT SERVICES, INC.—See Arthur J. Gallagher & Co.; *U.S. Public*, pg. 205
GALLAGHER & BURK INC.; *U.S. Private*, pg. 1638
GALLAGHER COMMUNICATION—See Arthur J. Gallagher & Co.; *U.S. Public*, pg. 202
GALLAGHER CONSTRUCTION SERVICES—See Arthur J. Gallagher & Co.; *U.S. Public*, pg. 205
GALLAGHER ESTATE HOLDINGS LIMITED—See Hosken Consolidated Investments Limited; *Int'l*, pg. 3485
GALLAGHER FLUID SEALS INC.; *U.S. Private*, pg. 1638
GALLAGHER HEALTHCARE INSURANCE SERVICES, INC.—See Arthur J. Gallagher & Co.; *U.S. Public*, pg. 205
GALLAGHER & HENRY, INC.; *U.S. Private*, pg. 1638
GALLAGHER HOLDINGS LTD.; *Int'l*, pg. 2873
GALLAGHER INSURANCE BROKERS (ST. LUCIA) LIMITED—See Arthur J. Gallagher & Co.; *U.S. Public*, pg. 205
GALLAGHER INSURANCE BROKERS (ST. VINCENT) LIMITED—See Arthur J. Gallagher & Co.; *U.S. Public*, pg. 205
GALLAGHER-KAISER CORPORATION; *U.S. Private*, pg. 1638
GALLAGHER SECURITY CORP.; *Int'l*, pg. 2873
GALLAGHER TIRE INC.; *U.S. Private*, pg. 1638
GALLAHAN OIL COMPANY INC.; *U.S. Private*, pg. 1639
GALLAHER & ASSOCIATES, INC.; *U.S. Private*, pg. 1639
GALLAHER FRANCE EURL—See Japan Tobacco Inc.; *Int'l*, pg. 3906
GALLAHER SPAIN SA—See Japan Tobacco Inc.; *Int'l*, pg. 3906

CORPORATE AFFILIATIONS

GALLANT CAPITAL PARTNERS, LLC; *U.S. Private*, pg. 1639
GALLANT MICRO MACHINING CO., LTD.; *Int'l*, pg. 2873
GALLANT MICRO. MACHINING (SUZHOU) CO., LTD.—See Gallant Precision Machining Co., Ltd.; *Int'l*, pg. 2873
GALLANT PRECISION INDUSTRIES (SUZHOU) CO., LTD.—See Gallant Precision Machining Co., Ltd.; *Int'l*, pg. 2873
GALLANT PRECISION MACHINING CO., LTD.; *Int'l*, pg. 2873
GALLANT QUALITY SDN. BHD.—See Comfort Gloves Berhad; *Int'l*, pg. 1711
GALLANTT ISPAT LIMITED; *Int'l*, pg. 2874
GALLANT VENTURE LTD.; *Int'l*, pg. 2873
GALLARDO DANCE S.L.—See Onward Holdings Co., Ltd.; *Int'l*, pg. 5592
GALLATI AG—See Burkhalter Holding AG; *Int'l*, pg. 1225
GALLATIN POINT CAPITAL LLC; *U.S. Private*, pg. 1639
GALLATIN REDRYING & STORAGE CO.—See R.C. Owen Holding Company; *U.S. Private*, pg. 3335
GALLAY MEDICAL & SCIENTIFIC NZ PTY LTD—See Ecolab Inc.; *U.S. Public*, pg. 714
GALLAY MEDICAL & SCIENTIFIC PTY LTD—See Ecolab Inc.; *U.S. Public*, pg. 714
GALLBRAITH LIMITED—See Yue Xiu Enterprises (Holdings) Limited; *Int'l*, pg. 8610
GALLE FACE CAPITAL PARTNERS PLC—See Carson Cumberbatch PLC; *Int'l*, pg. 1347
GALLE FORT HOTEL (PVT) LTD.—See Lankem Ceylon PLC; *Int'l*, pg. 4412
GALLEGOS CORPORATION; *U.S. Private*, pg. 1639
GALLEGOS SANITATION, INC.; *U.S. Private*, pg. 1639
GALLEHER LLC—See Transom Capital Group, LLC; *U.S. Private*, pg. 4209
GALLEHER LUMBER CO.—See Boyne Capital Management, LLC; *U.S. Private*, pg. 629
GALLEON GOLD CORP.; *Int'l*, pg. 2874
GALLERY 63, INC.; *U.S. Private*, pg. 1639
GALLERY AUTOMOTIVE GROUP, LLC; *U.S. Private*, pg. 1639
GALLERY GOLD PTY LTD.—See Galane Gold Ltd.; *Int'l*, pg. 2870
GALLERY INDUSTRIES INC.; *U.S. Private*, pg. 1639
GALLERY MODEL HOMES, INC.; *U.S. Private*, pg. 1639
GALLERY OF HISTORY AUCTIONS, INC.—See GALLERY OF HISTORY, INC.; *U.S. Private*, pg. 1639
GALLERY OF HISTORY, INC.; *U.S. Private*, pg. 1639
GALLERY RARE LTD.—See Aucnet Inc.; *Int'l*, pg. 700
GALLERY RESOURCES LIMITED; *Int'l*, pg. 2874
GALLES CHEVROLET COMPANY; *U.S. Private*, pg. 1639
GALLES CHEVROLET; *U.S. Private*, pg. 1639
GALLEY REACH HOLDINGS LTD.—See SIPEF NV; *Int'l*, pg. 6961
GALL & GALL B.V.—See Koninklijke Ahold Delhaize N.V.; *Int'l*, pg. 4261
GALL & GALL B.V.—See Koninklijke Ahold Delhaize N.V.; *Int'l*, pg. 4261
GALL & GALL B.V.—See Koninklijke Ahold Delhaize N.V.; *Int'l*, pg. 4261
GALL & GALL B.V.—See Koninklijke Ahold Delhaize N.V.; *Int'l*, pg. 4261
GALLIARD CAPITAL MANAGEMENT, INC.—See Wells Fargo & Company; *U.S. Public*, pg. 2343
GALLIFORD HOMES LIMITED—See Persimmon plc; *Int'l*, pg. 5816
GALLIFORD TRY BUILDING 2014 LIMITED—See Galliford Try Holdings plc; *Int'l*, pg. 2874
GALLIFORD TRY CONSTRUCTION CENTRAL—See Galliford Try Holdings plc; *Int'l*, pg. 2874
GALLIFORD TRY CONSTRUCTION LIMITED—See Galliford Try Holdings plc; *Int'l*, pg. 2874
GALLIFORD TRY CONSTRUCTION SOUTH—See Galliford Try Holdings plc; *Int'l*, pg. 2874
GALLIFORD TRY EMPLOYMENT LIMITED—See Galliford Try Holdings plc; *Int'l*, pg. 2874
GALLIFORD TRY HOLDINGS PLC; *Int'l*, pg. 2874
GALLIFORD TRY INFRASTRUCTURE LIMITED—See Galliford Try Holdings plc; *Int'l*, pg. 2874
GALLIFORD TRY INVESTMENTS LIMITED—See Galliford Try Holdings plc; *Int'l*, pg. 2874
GALLIFORD TRY PARTNERSHIPS LIMITED—See Galliford Try Holdings plc; *Int'l*, pg. 2874
GALLIFORD TRY PLANT LIMITED—See Galliford Try Holdings plc; *Int'l*, pg. 2874
GALLIFORD TRY SERVICES LIMITED—See Galliford Try Holdings plc; *Int'l*, pg. 2874
GALLI GIOVANNI & C. S.R.L.—See El.En. S.p.A.; *Int'l*, pg. 2342
GALLIKER DAIRY COMPANY INC.; *U.S. Private*, pg. 1639
GALLINGER FORD LINCOLN; *Int'l*, pg. 2874
GALLIONS HOUSING ASSOCIATION LIMITED—See Peabody; *Int'l*, pg. 5773
GALLIOT ACQUISITION CORP.; *U.S. Private*, pg. 1639
GALLITO LTD.—See Absolent Air Care Group AB; *Int'l*, pg. 70
GALLO CORPORATION; *U.S. Private*, pg. 1639
GALLO EQUIPMENT CO.; *U.S. Private*, pg. 1639

COMPANY NAME INDEX

GALLO MECHANICAL CONTRACTORS—See Gallo Corporation; *U.S. Private,* pg. 1639
GALLO MOTOR CENTER CORP.; *U.S. Private,* pg. 1640
GALLOO HALLUIN—See Galloo n.v.; *Int'l,* pg. 2875
GALLO OIL (JERSEY) LTD.—See PT Bumi Resources Tbk; *Int'l,* pg. 6031
GALLOO N.V.; *Int'l,* pg. 2875
GALLOPING HILL SURGICAL CORPORATION—See Quadrant Management, Inc.; *U.S. Private,* pg. 3316
GALLOPS ENTERPRISE LIMITED; *Int'l,* pg. 2875
GALLO VIDRO, S.A.—See Vidrala S.A.; *Int'l,* pg. 8192
GALLOWAY FAMILY OF DEALERSHIPS; *U.S. Private,* pg. 1640
GALLOWAY GAZETTE LTD—See JPIMedia Holdings Limited; *Int'l,* pg. 4006
GALLOWAY RIDGE, INC.; *U.S. Private,* pg. 1640
GALLOWAY TIRE COMPANY INC.—See Farmers Cooperative Inc.; *U.S. Private,* pg. 1477
GALLO WINE SALES OF NJ INC.; *U.S. Private,* pg. 1640
GALLS, LLC—See Charlesbank Capital Partners, LLC; *U.S. Private,* pg. 855
GALL THOMSON ENVIRONMENTAL LIMITED—See Trelleborg AB; *Int'l,* pg. 7911
GALLUP CONSULTING—See The Gallup Organization; *U.S. Private,* pg. 4031
GALLUP LUMBER & SUPPLY; *U.S. Private,* pg. 1640
THE GALLUP ORGANIZATION-PRINCETON—See The Gallup Organization; *U.S. Private,* pg. 4031
THE GALLUP ORGANIZATION; *U.S. Private,* pg. 4031
GALLUS DRUCKMASCHINEN GMBH—See Heidelberger Druckmaschinen AG; *Int'l,* pg. 3321
GALLUS FERD. RUESCH AG—See Heidelberger Druckmaschinen AG; *Int'l,* pg. 3321
GAL MANUFACTURING CORPORATION—See Golden Gate Capital Management II, LLC; *U.S. Private,* pg. 1732
GALMED PHARMACEUTICALS LTD.; *Int'l,* pg. 2875
GALORE CREEK MINING CORPORATION—See Newmont Corporation; *U.S. Public,* pg. 1516
GALORE PARK PUBLISHING LTD.—See Vivendi SE; *Int'l,* pg. 8271
GALORE RESOURCES INC.; *Int'l,* pg. 2875
GALP ACORES - DISTRIB. E COMERCIALIZACAO DE OOMBUSTIVEIS E LUBRIFICANTES, S.A.—See Galp Energia SGPS, S.A.; *Int'l,* pg. 2875
GALP COMERCIALIZACAO PORTUGAL, LDA.—See Galp Energia SGPS, S.A.; *Int'l,* pg. 2875
GALP DISTRIBUICION OIL ESPANA, S.A.U.—See Galp Energia SGPS, S.A.; *Int'l,* pg. 2875
GALP ENERGIA ESPANA SAU—See Galp Energia SGPS, S.A.; *Int'l,* pg. 2875
GALP ENERGIA SGPS, S.A.; *Int'l,* pg. 2875
GALP GAMBIA, LIMITED—See Galp Energia SGPS, S.A.; *Int'l,* pg. 2875
GALPGESTE, LDA.—See Galp Energia SGPS, S.A.; *Int'l,* pg. 2875
GALPIN FORD INCORPORATED; *U.S. Private,* pg. 1640
GALPIN MOTORS, INC.; *U.S. Private,* pg. 1640
GALPRES A.D.; *Int'l,* pg. 2876
GALP SERVIEXPRESS - SERV. DE DISTRIB. E COMERCIALIZACAO DE PRODUTOS PETROLIFEROS, S.A.—See Galp Energia SGPS, S.A.; *Int'l,* pg. 2875
GALSON LABORATORIES, INC.—See SGS SA; *Int'l,* pg. 6744
GALSTONBURY SOUTHERN GAGE—See Alpha Q, Inc.; *U.S. Private,* pg. 199
GALT CHRYSLER DODGE LTD.; *Int'l,* pg. 2876
GALTECH CANADA INC.—See Interpump Group S.p.A.; *Int'l,* pg. 3755
GALTEC N.V.—See ArcelorMittal S.A.; *Int'l,* pg. 545
GAL-TEX HOTEL CORPORATION; *U.S. Private,* pg. 1635
GALT FOUNDATION; *U.S. Private,* pg. 1640
GALT MEDICAL CORP.—See Juniper Investment Company, LLC; *U.S. Private,* pg. 2244
GALT PETROLEUM, INC.; *U.S. Private,* pg. 1640
GALTRONICS CANADA CO., LTD.—See Baylin Technologies Inc.; *Int'l,* pg. 914
GALTRONICS CORPORATION LTD.—See Baylin Technologies Inc.; *Int'l,* pg. 914
GALTRONICS ELECTRONICS (WUXI) CO., LTD.—See Baylin Technologies Inc.; *Int'l,* pg. 914
GALTRONICS USA INC—See Baylin Technologies Inc.; *Int'l,* pg. 914
GALT & TAGGART—See JSC Bank of Georgia; *Int'l,* pg. 4008
GALVA 45 S.A.—See Nyrstar NV; *Int'l,* pg. 5501
GALVANEK & WAHL LLC; *U.S. Private,* pg. 1640
GALVANI BIOELECTRONICS LIMITED—See GSK plc; *Int'l,* pg. 3145
GALVANIC APPLIED SCIENCES INC.; *Int'l,* pg. 2876
GALVANIC APPLIED SCIENCES USA INC—See Galvanic Applied Sciences Inc.; *Int'l,* pg. 2876
GALVANIZE INC.—See Stride, Inc.; *U.S. Public,* pg. 1955
GALVANO DIVISION—See The Heico Companies, L.L.C.; *U.S. Private,* pg. 4050
GALVANO GROOTHANDEL BV—See Compagnie de Saint-Gobain SA; *Int'l,* pg. 1723
GALVANOTECHNIK BAUM GMBH; *Int'l,* pg. 2876

GALVANOTECHNISCHE OBERFLACHEN GMBH—See KAP Beteiligungs-AG; *Int'l,* pg. 4076
GALVAN RESEARCH & TRADING, LTD.—See StoneX Group Inc.; *U.S. Public,* pg. 1952
GALVATEX CORP.—See JFE Holdings, Inc.; *Int'l,* pg. 3934
GALVOSURGE DENTAL AG—See Straumann Holding AG; *Int'l,* pg. 7237
GALWAY METAL COMPANY LTD.—See Madison Dearborn Partners, LLC; *U.S. Private,* pg. 2541
GALWAY METALS INC.; *Int'l,* pg. 2876
GALY PROPERTY MANAGEMENT LIMITED—See Wah Ha Realty Company Limited; *Int'l,* pg. 8328
GALYPSO INTERNATIONAL; *U.S. Private,* pg. 1640
GAMA 29 SAS—See Bunzl plc; *Int'l,* pg. 1218
GAMA AVIATION LLC—See Wheels Up Experience Inc.; *U.S. Public,* pg. 2366
GAMA AVIATION PLC; *Int'l,* pg. 2876
GAMA AVIATION SA—See Gama Aviation plc; *Int'l,* pg. 2876
GAMA CONSULTORES ASSOCIADOS LTDA.—See Marsh & McLennan Companies, Inc.; *U.S. Public,* pg. 1375
GAMA EXPLORATIONS INC.; *Int'l,* pg. 2876
GAMA GASES ESPECIAIS LTDA.—See Linde plc; *Int'l,* pg. 4508
GA-MAGYARORSZAG KFT.—See Alpiq Holding AG; *Int'l,* pg. 373
GAMA HEALTHCARE AUSTRALIA PTY LTD.—See Hancock & Gore Ltd.; *Int'l,* pg. 3242
GAMAJET CLEANING SYSTEMS, INC.—See Alfa Laval AB; *Int'l,* pg. 309
GAMAKABEL PLC; *Int'l,* pg. 2876
GAMA MEDIA INTERNATIONAL (BVI) LTD.—See Media Prima Berhad; *Int'l,* pg. 4771
GAMA PARTICIPACOES S.A.; *Int'l,* pg. 2876
G-A MASONRY CORP.OF NEW YORK; *U.S. Private,* pg. 1630
GAMA SUPPORT SERVICES FZE—See Gama Aviation plc; *Int'l,* pg. 2876
G.A. MAVON & COMPANY—See Arthur J. Gallagher & Co.; *U.S. Public,* pg. 205
GAMBADO LIMITED—See Wates Group Limited; *Int'l,* pg. 8358
GAMBER-JOHNSON, LLC—See Main Street Capital Corporation; *U.S. Public,* pg. 1354
GAMBERO ROSSO S.P.A.; *Int'l,* pg. 2877
GAMBETTI KENOLOGIA SRL; *Int'l,* pg. 2877
GAMBIA TELECOMMUNICATIONS COMPANY LTD.; *Int'l,* pg. 2877
GAMBIT FINANCIAL SOLUTIONS SA—See BNP Paribas SA; *Int'l,* pg. 1091
GAMBIT HILL & KNOWLTON—See WPP plc; *Int'l,* pg. 8477
GAMBLES ONTARIO PRODUCE INC.—See Dole plc; *Int'l,* pg. 2158
GAMBLING.COM GROUP LIMITED; *Int'l,* pg. 2877
GAMBOAS BODY & FRAME INC.; *U.S. Private,* pg. 1640
THE GAMBONE GROUP; *U.S. Private,* pg. 4031
THE GAMBRINUS COMPANY; *U.S. Private,* pg. 4031
GAMBRO AB—See Baxter International Inc.; *U.S. Public,* pg. 281
GAMBRO A/S—See Baxter International Inc.; *U.S. Public,* pg. 281
GAMBRO BICART—See Baxter International Inc.; *U.S. Public,* pg. 282
GAMBRO CHINA LTD.—See Baxter International Inc.; *U.S. Public,* pg. 281
GAMBRO DASCO S.P.A.—See Baxter International Inc.; *U.S. Public,* pg. 281
GAMBRO DE MEXICO, S.A. DE C.V.—See Baxter International Inc.; *U.S. Public,* pg. 282
GAMBRO DIALISIS DE MEXICO, SA. DE R.L.—See Baxter International Inc.; *U.S. Public,* pg. 282
GAMBRO DIALYSATOREN GMBH—See Baxter International Inc.; *U.S. Public,* pg. 282
GAMBRO EXPORT—See Baxter International Inc.; *U.S. Public,* pg. 281
GAMBRO GMBH—See Baxter International Inc.; *U.S. Public,* pg. 281
GAMBRO HOLDING AB—See Baxter International Inc.; *U.S. Public,* pg. 282
GAMBRO/HOSPAL AUSTRIA GMBH—See Baxter International Inc.; *U.S. Public,* pg. 282
GAMBRO/HOSPAL GMBH—See Baxter International Inc.; *U.S. Public,* pg. 282
GAMBRO/HOSPAL INDUSTRIE S.A.—See Baxter International Inc.; *U.S. Public,* pg. 282
GAMBRO/HOSPAL LTD.—See Baxter International Inc.; *U.S. Public,* pg. 282
GAMBRO/HOSPAL SCHWEIZ AG—See Baxter International Inc.; *U.S. Public,* pg. 282
GAMBRO HOSPAL S.P.A.—See Baxter International Inc.; *U.S. Public,* pg. 281
GAMBRO INC.—See Baxter International Inc.; *U.S. Public,* pg. 281
GAMBRO INC.—See Baxter International Inc.; *U.S. Public,* pg. 281
GAMBRO INDUSTRIES SAS—See Baxter International Inc.; *U.S. Public,* pg. 282

GAMBRO KOREA LTD.—See Baxter International Inc.; *U.S. Public,* pg. 282
GAMBRO MEDICAL PRODUCTS (SHANGHAI) CO. LTD.—See Baxter International Inc.; *U.S. Public,* pg. 281
GAMBRO MEOPTA S.R.O.—See Baxter International Inc.; *U.S. Public,* pg. 282
GAMBRO NORGE NUF—See Baxter International Inc.; *U.S. Public,* pg. 282
GAMBRO POLAND SP. Z O.O.—See Baxter International Inc.; *U.S. Public,* pg. 282
GAMBRO PTY. LTD. (BRISBANE)—See Baxter International Inc.; *U.S. Public,* pg. 282
GAMBRO PTY. LTD. (SYDNEY)—See Baxter International Inc.; *U.S. Public,* pg. 282
GAMBRO RESEARCH—See Baxter International Inc.; *U.S. Public,* pg. 282
GAMBRO S.A.—See Baxter International Inc.; *U.S. Public,* pg. 282
GAMBRO S.A.S.—See Baxter International Inc.; *U.S. Public,* pg. 282
GAMBRO S.P.A.—See Baxter International Inc.; *U.S. Public,* pg. 281
GAMBRO S.P.A.—See Baxter International Inc.; *U.S. Public,* pg. 281
GAMBRO TAIWAN LTD.—See Baxter International Inc.; *U.S. Public,* pg. 282
GAMBRO UF SOLUTIONS, INC.—See Baxter International Inc.; *U.S. Public,* pg. 282
GAMCO ASSET MANAGEMENT INC.—See GAMCO Investors, Inc.; *U.S. Public,* pg. 895
GAMCO ASSET MANAGEMENT (UK) LIMITED—See GAMCO Investors, Inc.; *U.S. Public,* pg. 895
GAMCO INVESTORS, INC.; *U.S. Public,* pg. 895
GAMCO NATURAL RESOURCES, GOLD & INCOME TRUST—See GAMCO Investors, Inc.; *U.S. Public,* pg. 895
GAM CONSULTORIA ECONOMICA LTDA.—See Prudential Financial, Inc.; *U.S. Public,* pg. 1731
GAM (DEUTSCHLAND) AG—See GAM Holding AG; *Int'l,* pg. 2876
GAM DUBAI LTD.—See GAM Holding AG; *Int'l,* pg. 2876
GAME 7 ATHLETICS S.R.L.—See Hanesbrands Inc.; *U.S. Public,* pg. 983
THE GAME AGENCY LLC—See Fundos Group LLC; *U.S. Private,* pg. 1623
THE GAME AGENCY LLC—See Trinity Private Equity Group, LLC; *U.S. Private,* pg. 4235
GAMEBASE, INC.; *U.S. Private,* pg. 1640
GAMECARD-JOYCO HOLDINGS, INC.; *Int'l,* pg. 2877
GAME CHANGER HOLDINGS INC.—See Mitsui & Co., Ltd.; *Int'l,* pg. 4975
GAMECHANGER PRODUCTS LLC; *U.S. Private,* pg. 1640
GAME DIGITAL PLC—See Frasers Group plc; *Int'l,* pg. 2765
GAME DIGITAL PLC - SPAIN OFFICE—See Frasers Group plc; *Int'l,* pg. 2765
GAMEFLY, INC.; *U.S. Private,* pg. 1640
GAMEFORGE AG; *Int'l,* pg. 2877
GAMEHOST INC.; *Int'l,* pg. 2877
GAME HOUSE EUROPE B.V.—See RealNetworks, Inc.; *U.S. Private,* pg. 3369
GAMEHOUSE EUROPE B.V.—See RealNetworks, Inc.; *U.S. Private,* pg. 3369
GAME INGENIERIE S.A.S—See Eiffage S.A.; *Int'l,* pg. 2331
GAMEKO FABRICACION DE COMPONENTES, S.A.—See Cie Automotive S.A.; *Int'l,* pg. 1604
GAMELANCER MEDIA CORP.; *Int'l,* pg. 2877
GAMELOFT CO., LTD.—See Vivendi SE; *Int'l,* pg. 8266
GAMELOFT CORPORATION—See Vivendi SE; *Int'l,* pg. 8266
GAMELOFT IBERICA S.A.—See Vivendi SE; *Int'l,* pg. 8266
GAMELOFT, INC.—See Vivendi SE; *Int'l,* pg. 8266
GAMELOFT KK—See Vivendi SE; *Int'l,* pg. 8266
GAMELOFT SOFTWARE BEIJING LTD.—See Vivendi SE; *Int'l,* pg. 8266
GAMENET GROUP S.P.A.; *Int'l,* pg. 2877
GAMEON CO., LTD.—See NEOWIZ Holdings Corporation; *Int'l,* pg. 5198
GAMEONE HOLDINGS LTD.; *Int'l,* pg. 2877
GAME ONE SAS—See National Amusements, Inc.; *U.S. Private,* pg. 2841
GAME OUTLET EUROPE AB—See Nordic Games Holding AB; *Int'l,* pg. 5422
GAMEPLAN FINANCIAL MARKETING, LLC; *U.S. Private,* pg. 1640
GAME PLAN HOLDINGS, INC.; *U.S. Private,* pg. 1640
GAME RETAIL LIMITED; *Int'l,* pg. 2877
GAMER PAKISTAN INC.; *U.S. Public,* pg. 895
GAMESA BLADE TIANJIN CO LTD.—See Siemens Energy AG; *Int'l,* pg. 6902
GAMESA ELECTRIC, S.A.—See Siemens Energy AG; *Int'l,* pg. 6902
GAMESA ENERGIAKI HELLAS, A.E.—See Siemens Energy AG; *Int'l,* pg. 6902

GAMESA ENERGIA POLSKA SP. Z.O.O—See Siemens Energy AG; *Int'l*, pg. 6902
GAMESA ENERGIE FRANCE, E.U.R.L.—See Siemens Energy AG; *Int'l*, pg. 6902
GAMESA EOLICA BRASIL, LTD.—See Siemens Energy AG; *Int'l*, pg. 6902
GAMESA EOLICA FRANCE SARL—See Siemens Energy AG; *Int'l*, pg. 6902
GAMESA S. DE R.L. DE C.V.—See PepsiCo, Inc.; *U.S. Public*, pg. 1670
GAMESA USA, INC.—See PepsiCo, Inc.; *U.S. Public*, pg. 1670
GAMESA WIND, GMBH—See Siemens Energy AG; *Int'l*, pg. 6902
GAMESA WIND PA LLC—See Siemens Energy AG; *Int'l*, pg. 6902
GAMESA WIND SWEDEN AB—See Siemens Energy AG; *Int'l*, pg. 6902
GAMESA WIND US LLC—See Siemens Energy AG; *Int'l*, pg. 6902
GAME SERVICE S.R.L.—See Digital Bros SpA; *Int'l*, pg. 2120
GAMES & ESPORTS EXPERIENCE ACQUISITION CORP.; *U.S. Public*, pg. 895
GAME SHOW NETWORK, LLC—See Sony Group Corporation; *Int'l*, pg. 7105
GAMESIM, INC.—See Canada Pension Plan Investment Board; *Int'l*, pg. 1280
GAMESIM, INC.—See EQT AB; *Int'l*, pg. 2482
GAMESIM, INC.—See Temasek Holdings (Private) Limited; *Int'l*, pg. 7548
GAMESMAN LTD.—See TransDigm Group Incorporated; *U.S. Public*, pg. 2180
GAMES NETWORK LTD.—See Novomatic AG; *Int'l*, pg. 5467
GAMES OPERATORS S.A.; *Int'l*, pg. 2877
GAME SOURCE, INC.; *U.S. Private*, pg. 1640
GAMESQUARE ESPORTS INC.—See GameSquare Holdings, Inc.; *Int'l*, pg. 2878
GAMESQUARE HOLDINGS, INC.; *Int'l*, pg. 2877
GAMESTEC LEISURE LIMITED—See Novomatic AG; *Int'l*, pg. 5466
GAMESTOP CORP.; *U.S. Public*, pg. 895
GAMESTOP DEUTSCHLAND GMBH—See GameStop Corp.; *U.S. Public*, pg. 895
GAMESTOP GROUP LIMITED—See GameStop Corp.; *U.S. Public*, pg. 896
GAMESTOP IBERIA S.L.—See GameStop Corp.; *U.S. Public*, pg. 896
GAMESTOP, INC.—See GameStop Corp.; *U.S. Public*, pg. 896
GAMESTOP LTD.—See GameStop Corp.; *U.S. Public*, pg. 896
GAMESTOP NORWAY AS—See GameStop Corp.; *U.S. Public*, pg. 896
GAMESTOP SCHWEIZ GMBH—See GameStop Corp.; *U.S. Public*, pg. 896
GAMESTOP SWEDEN AB—See GameStop Corp.; *U.S. Public*, pg. 896
GAMESTOP UK LIMITED—See GameStop Corp.; *U.S. Public*, pg. 896
GAME STORES GROUP SWEDEN AB—See Game Retail Limited; *Int'l*, pg. 2877
GAMESVILLE, INC.—See Brightcom Group Ltd.; *Int'l*, pg. 1162
GAMES WORKSHOP DEUTSCHLAND GMBH—See Games Workshop Group PLC; *Int'l*, pg. 2877
GAMES WORKSHOP GOOD HOBBY (SHANGHAI) COMMERCIAL CO., LTD.—See Games Workshop Group PLC; *Int'l*, pg. 2877
GAMES WORKSHOP GROUP PLC; *Int'l*, pg. 2877
GAMES WORKSHOP ITALIA SRL—See Games Workshop Group PLC; *Int'l*, pg. 2877
GAMES WORKSHOP LIMITED—See Games Workshop Group PLC; *Int'l*, pg. 2877
GAMES WORKSHOP OZ PTY LIMITED—See Games Workshop Group PLC; *Int'l*, pg. 2877
GAMES WORKSHOP RETAIL INC.—See Games Workshop Group PLC; *Int'l*, pg. 2877
GAMES WORKSHOP SL—See Games Workshop Group PLC; *Int'l*, pg. 2877
GAMES WORKSHOP-SQUARE ONE—See Games Workshop Group PLC; *Int'l*, pg. 2877
GAMES WORKSHOP STOCKHOLM AB—See Games Workshop Group PLC; *Int'l*, pg. 2877
GAMESXP—See National Technology Group; *Int'l*, pg. 5164
GAMESYS GROUP PLC—See Bally's Corporation; *U.S. Public*, pg. 268
GAMET BEARINGS LTD—See The 600 Group PLC; *Int'l*, pg. 7609
GAMETIME LLC—See Court Square Capital Partners, L.P.; *U.S. Private*, pg. 1069
GAME TOPIA CO., LTD.—See Soft-World International Corporation; *Int'l*, pg. 7050
GAMEVIL USA, INC.—See Com2uS Holdings, Inc.; *Int'l*, pg. 1706
GAMEWITH, INC.; *Int'l*, pg. 2878

GAMEWOOD TECHNOLOGY GROUP, INC.; *U.S. Private*, pg. 1640
GAMEWRIGHT—See Ceaco Inc.; *U.S. Private*, pg. 804
GAMEX CB S.R.O.—See Viscofan SA; *Int'l*, pg. 8250
GAMEZEBO, INC.—See Flipside, Inc.; *U.S. Private*, pg. 1546
GAM FUND MANAGEMENT LTD.—See GAM Holding AG; *Int'l*, pg. 2876
GAM HOLDING AG; *Int'l*, pg. 2876
GAM HONG KONG LTD.—See GAM Holding AG; *Int'l*, pg. 2876
GAMIDA CELL LTD.—See Gamida for Life B.V.; *Int'l*, pg. 2878
GAMIDA FOR LIFE B.V.; *Int'l*, pg. 2878
GAMIDA LTD.—See Gamida for Life B.V.; *Int'l*, pg. 2878
GAMIDA SA—See Gamida for Life B.V.; *Int'l*, pg. 2878
GAMIDOR DIAGNOSTICS LTD.—See Gamida for Life B.V.; *Int'l*, pg. 2878
GAMIDOR TECHNICAL SERVICES LTD—See Gamida for Life B.V.; *Int'l*, pg. 2878
GAMIGO AG—See Verve Group SE; *Int'l*, pg. 8176
GAMIGO US INC.—See Verve Group SE; *Int'l*, pg. 8176
GAMING AND LEISURE PROPERTIES, INC.; *U.S. Public*, pg. 896
GAMING ENTERTAINMENT INTERNATIONAL, INC.; *U.S. Private*, pg. 1640
GAMING & HOSPITALITY ACQUISITION CORP.; *U.S. Public*, pg. 896
GAMING INNOVATION GROUP INC.; *U.S. Public*, pg. 896
GAMING LABORATORIES INTERNATIONAL LLC; *U.S. Private*, pg. 1640
GAMING PARTNERS INTERNATIONAL CORPORATION—See Angel Holdings Godo Kaisha; *Int'l*, pg. 459
GAMING PARTNERS INTERNATIONAL—See Angel Holdings Godo Kaisha; *Int'l*, pg. 459
GAMING REALMS PLC; *Int'l*, pg. 2878
GAMING SOLUTIONS INTERNATIONAL SAC—See INTRALOT S.A.; *Int'l*, pg. 3768
GAMING TECHNOLOGIES, INC.; *U.S. Public*, pg. 896
GAMING VC CORPORATION LIMITED—See Entain PLC; *Int'l*, pg. 2449
GAMING VENTURES OF LAS VEGAS, INC.—See Maverick Gold LLC; *U.S. Private*, pg. 2616
GAM INVESTMENT MANAGEMENT (SWITZERLAND) AG—See GAM Holding AG; *Int'l*, pg. 2876
GAM INVESTMENTS (AUSTRALIA) PTY LTD—See GAM Holding AG; *Int'l*, pg. 2876
GAM INVESTMENTS (SINGAPORE) PTE. LTD.—See GAM Holding AG; *Int'l*, pg. 2876
GAM (ITALIA) SGR S.P.A.—See GAM Holding AG; *Int'l*, pg. 2876
GAMIVO S.A.; *Int'l*, pg. 2878
GAM JAPAN LIMITED—See GAM Holding AG; *Int'l*, pg. 2876
GAMKO B.V.—See Illinois Tool Works Inc.; *U.S. Public*, pg. 1103
GAMKO REFRIGERATION EURL—See Illinois Tool Works Inc.; *U.S. Public*, pg. 1103
GAMKO REFRIGERATION U.K. LIMITED—See Illinois Tool Works Inc.; *U.S. Public*, pg. 1103
GAMLA HAREL RESIDENTIAL REAL-ESTATE LTD.; *Int'l*, pg. 2878
GAM LIMITED—See GAM Holding AG; *Int'l*, pg. 2876
GAM LONDON LTD.—See GAM Holding AG; *Int'l*, pg. 2876
GAM (LUXEMBOURG) S.A. - MADRID BRANCH—See GAM Holding AG; *Int'l*, pg. 2876
GAM (LUXEMBOURG) S.A.—See GAM Holding AG; *Int'l*, pg. 2876
GAMMA ARREDAMENTI INT.l INC.—See Dexelance S.p.A.; *Int'l*, pg. 2092
GAMMA ARREDAMENTI INT.l S.P.A.—See Dexelance S.p.A.; *Int'l*, pg. 2092
GAMMA BUSINESS COMMUNICATIONS LIMITED—See Gamma Communications PLC; *Int'l*, pg. 2878
GAMMA-CIVIC CONSTRUCTION LTD—See Gamma-Civic Ltd; *Int'l*, pg. 2878
GAMMA-CIVIC LTD; *Int'l*, pg. 2878
GAMMA COMMUNICATIONS BENELUX B.V.—See Gamma Communications PLC; *Int'l*, pg. 2878
GAMMA COMMUNICATIONS GERMANY GMBH—See Gamma Communications PLC; *Int'l*, pg. 2878
GAMMA COMMUNICATIONS GMBH—See Gamma Communications PLC; *Int'l*, pg. 2878
GAMMA COMMUNICATIONS PLC; *Int'l*, pg. 2878
GAMMA CONSTRUCTION COMPANY INC.; *U.S. Private*, pg. 1640
GAMMA CONSTRUCTION LTD—See Gamma-Civic Ltd; *Int'l*, pg. 2878
GAMMAFLUX INC.—See Barnes Group Inc.; *U.S. Public*, pg. 277
GAMMA FOUNDRIES LTD.—See Victaulic Company; *U.S. Private*, pg. 4377
GAMMA GRUNDSTUCKSVERWALTUNGSGESELLSCHAFT MBH—See Gilde Buy Out Partners B.V.; *Int'l*, pg. 2974

GAMMA GRUNDSTUCKSVERWALTUNGSGESELLSCHAFT MBH—See Parcom Capital Management B.V.; *Int'l*, pg. 5740
GAMMA HOLDING NEDERLAND N.V.—See Gilde Buy Out Partners B.V.; *Int'l*, pg. 2974
GAMMA HOLDING NEDERLAND N.V.—See Parcom Capital Management B.V.; *Int'l*, pg. 5740
GAMMA HOLDING N.V.—See Gilde Buy Out Partners B.V.; *Int'l*, pg. 2974
GAMMA HOLDING N.V.—See Parcom Capital Management B.V.; *Int'l*, pg. 5739
GAMMA INDUSTRIES INC.—See RED Holdings Group Inc.; *U.S. Private*, pg. 3374
GAMMA NETWORK SOLUTIONS LIMITED—See Gamma Communications PLC; *Int'l*, pg. 2878
GAMMA NU THETA INC.—See Hyulim Networks Co., Ltd.; *Int'l*, pg. 3555
GAMMA PROJECTS LTD.—See Enghouse Systems Limited; *Int'l*, pg. 2427
GAMMA SOLUTIONS S.A.—See G7 Entreprises; *Int'l*, pg. 2867
GAMMA SPORTS; *U.S. Private*, pg. 1640
GAMMA SURGERY CENTER, LLC—See Tenet Healthcare Corporation; *U.S. Public*, pg. 2010
GAMMATECH COMPUTER CORPORATION—See Twinhead International Corp.; *Int'l*, pg. 7990
GAMMA TELECOM LIMITED—See Gamma Communications PLC; *Int'l*, pg. 2878
GAMMAU CONSTRUCTION SDN. BHD.—See Gamuda Berhad; *Int'l*, pg. 2879
GAMMA USA, INC.—See RED Holdings Group Inc.; *U.S. Private*, pg. 3375
GAMMA WINDOWS AND WALLS INTERNATIONAL INC.—See China State Construction International Holdings Limited; *Int'l*, pg. 1554
GAMMERLER GMBH—See Blue Cap AG; *Int'l*, pg. 1067
GAMMETER OU—See Komax Holding AG; *Int'l*, pg. 4240
GAMMEX RMI GMBH—See Gammex RMI Inc.; *U.S. Private*, pg. 1641
GAMMEX RMI INC.; *U.S. Private*, pg. 1641
GAMMEX RMI LIMITED—See Gammex RMI Inc.; *U.S. Private*, pg. 1641
GAMMID GROUP PROPRIETARY LIMITED—See ARGENT INDUSTRIAL LIMITED; *Int'l*, pg. 560
GAMMID TRADING (PTY) LTD—See ARGENT INDUSTRIAL LIMITED; *Int'l*, pg. 560
GAMMON AND BILLIMORIA LLC—See Gammon India Limited; *Int'l*, pg. 2879
GAMMON CONSTRUCTION LTD.—See Balfour Beatty plc; *Int'l*, pg. 807
GAMMON CONSTRUCTION LTD.—See Jardine Matheson Holdings Limited; *Int'l*, pg. 3908
GAMMON EQUIPMENT COMPANY INC.; *U.S. Private*, pg. 1641
GAMMON HOLDINGS B.V.—See Gammon India Limited; *Int'l*, pg. 2879
GAMMON INDIA LIMITED; *Int'l*, pg. 2879
GAMMON INDIA LIMITED (T&D BUSINESS)—See Gammon India Limited; *Int'l*, pg. 2879
GAMMON INTERNATIONAL B.V.—See Gammon India Limited; *Int'l*, pg. 2879
GAMMON INTERNATIONAL, FZE—See Gammon India Limited; *Int'l*, pg. 2879
GAMMON PAKISTAN LIMITED; *Int'l*, pg. 2879
GAMM VERT SA—See Union InVivo - Union de Cooperatives Agricoles; *Int'l*, pg. 8053
GAMNED SAS—See Television Francaise 1 S.A.; *Int'l*, pg. 7542
GAMO OUTDOOR USA, INC.—See Bruckmann, Rosser, Sherrill & Co., LLC; *U.S. Private*, pg. 671
GAMORE CORPORATION SDN BHD—See IOI Corporation Berhad; *Int'l*, pg. 3791
GAMPAC EXPRESS, INC.—See US Foods Holding Corp.; *U.S. Public*, pg. 2266
GAMRAT S.A.—See Lentex S.A.; *Int'l*, pg. 4454
GAM (SCHWEIZ) AG—See GAM Holding AG; *Int'l*, pg. 2876
THE GAMS GROUP, INC.; *U.S. Private*, pg. 4032
GAM SHENG MACAO COMMERCIAL OFFSHORE LIMITED—See Wasion Holdings Limited; *Int'l*, pg. 8352
G.A.M. STEEL PTY, LTD.—See Commercial Metals Company; *U.S. Public*, pg. 546
SAMSUNG CORPORATION CO., LTD.; *Int'l*, pg. 2879
GAMUDA BERHAD; *Int'l*, pg. 2879
GAMUDA INDUSTRIAL BUILDING SYSTEM SDN. BHD.—See Gamuda Berhad; *Int'l*, pg. 2879
GAMUDA LAND (HCMC) JOINT STOCK COMPANY—See Gamuda Berhad; *Int'l*, pg. 2879
GAMUDA LAND SDN. BHD.—See Gamuda Berhad; *Int'l*, pg. 2879
GAMUDA LAND VIETNAM LIMITED LIABILITY COMPANY—See Gamuda Berhad; *Int'l*, pg. 2879
GAMUDA NAIM ENGINEERING & CONSTRUCTION (GNEC) SDN. BHD.—See Gamuda Berhad; *Int'l*, pg. 2879
GAMUDA TRADING SDN. BHD.—See Gamuda Berhad; *Int'l*, pg. 2879
GAMUDA WATER SDN. BHD.—See Gamuda Berhad; *Int'l*, pg. 2879

COMPANY NAME INDEX

GAM USA INC.—See GAM Holding AG; *Int'l*, pg. 2876
GAMUT CAPITAL MANAGEMENT, L.P.; *U.S. Private*, pg. 1641
GAMUT SUPPLY LLC—See W.W. Grainger, Inc.; *U.S. Public*, pg. 2319
GAMZIO MOBILE INC.; *U.S. Private*, pg. 1641
GANACHE GOURMET, INC.—See Tricor Pacific Founders Capital, Inc.; *Int'l*, pg. 7920
GANAHL LUMBER COMPANY; *U.S. Private*, pg. 1641
GANANOQUE MOTORS LTD; *Int'l*, pg. 2880
GANBARO SRL—See HORIBA Ltd; *Int'l*, pg. 3475
GAN CORPORATION; *U.S. Private*, pg. 1641
GANDA ANGGUN SDN BHD—See S P Setia Berhad; *Int'l*, pg. 6443
GANDAKI BIKASH BANK LIMITED; *Int'l*, pg. 2880
GANDALF SP. Z O.O.—See Penta Investments Limited; *Int'l*, pg. 5788
GANDARA MENTAL HEALTH CENTER, INC.; *U.S. Private*, pg. 1641
GANDER GOLD CORP.; *Int'l*, pg. 2880
GANDER, INC.; *U.S. Private*, pg. 1641
GANDER MOUNTAIN COMPANY; *U.S. Private*, pg. 1641
GANDHI SPECIAL TUBES LTD.; *Int'l*, pg. 2880
GANDY COMPANY; *U.S. Private*, pg. 1641
GANDY'S DAIRIES, LLC—See Dean Foods Company; *U.S. Private*, pg. 1183
GANEDEN BIOTECH, INC.—See Kerry Group plc; *Int'l*, pg. 4138
GANESHA ECOSPHERE LTD.; *Int'l*, pg. 2880
GANESHA ECOVERSE LTD.; *Int'l*, pg. 2880
GANESH BENZOPLAST LTD.; *Int'l*, pg. 2880
GANESH HOUSING CORPORATION LTD; *Int'l*, pg. 2880
GANESH INFRASTRUCTURE (INDIA) PVT LTD—See Ganesh Housing Corporation Ltd; *Int'l*, pg. 2880
GA NETZTECHNIK GMBH—See VINCI S.A.; *Int'l*, pg. 8238
GANFLEC ARCHITECTS & ENGINEERS, INC.—See OceanSound Partners, LP; *U.S. Private*, pg. 2991
GANGA FORGING LIMITED; *Int'l*, pg. 2880
GANGA PAPERS INDIA LIMITED; *Int'l*, pg. 2880
GANGA PHARMACEUTICALS LTD.; *Int'l*, pg. 2880
GANGDONG CO., LTD.—See Gangdong Industry Co., Ltd.; *Int'l*, pg. 2880
GANGDONG INDUSTRY CO., LTD.; *Int'l*, pg. 2880
GANGER ROLF ASA—See Fred. Olsen & Co.; *Int'l*, pg. 2768
GANGES SECURITIES LIMITED; *Int'l*, pg. 2880
GANGLOFF INDUSTRIES, INC.; *U.S. Private*, pg. 1641
GANGLONG CHINA PROPERTY GROUP LIMITED; *Int'l*, pg. 2880
GANGNAM KITCHEN PTE. LTD.—See E-Station Green Technology Group Co., Limited; *Int'l*, pg. 2249
GANGOTRI IRON & STEEL COMPANY LTD.; *Int'l*, pg. 2880
GANGOTRI TEXTILES LTD; *Int'l*, pg. 2881
GANGOTRI TEXTILES LTD - UNIT - III—See Gangotri Textiles Ltd; *Int'l*, pg. 2881
GANGOTRI TEXTILES LTD - UNIT - I—See Gangotri Textiles Ltd; *Int'l*, pg. 2881
GANGWON CO., LTD.; *Int'l*, pg. 2881
GAN ITALIA VITA S.P.A.—See Groupama SA; *Int'l*, pg. 3090
GAN KHERLEN JOINT STOCK COMPANY; *Int'l*, pg. 2880
GAN & LEE PHARMACEUTICALS CO., LTD.; *Int'l*, pg. 2879
GANLEY CHRYSLER JEEP DODGE RAM, INC.; *U.S. Private*, pg. 1641
GANLEY EAST INC.; *U.S. Private*, pg. 1641
GAN LIMITED; *U.S. Public*, pg. 896
GANLOT, INC.—See Posiflex Technology Inc.; *Int'l*, pg. 5938
GANNETT CO., INC.; *U.S. Public*, pg. 896
GANNETT DIRECT MARKETING SERVICES—See TEGNA Inc.; *U.S. Public*, pg. 1990
GANNETT FLEMING, INC. - BALTIMORE—See OceanSound Partners, LP; *U.S. Private*, pg. 2991
GANNETT FLEMING, INC. - GANCOM DIVISION—See OceanSound Partners, LP; *U.S. Private*, pg. 2991
GANNETT FLEMING, INC. - GEODECISIONS DIVISION—See OceanSound Partners, LP; *U.S. Private*, pg. 2991
GANNETT FLEMING, INC. - ROSEVILLE—See OceanSound Partners, LP; *U.S. Private*, pg. 2991
GANNETT FLEMING, INC.—See OceanSound Partners, LP; *U.S. Private*, pg. 2991
GANNETT FLEMING, INC. - TAMPA (CORPORATE LAKE DRIVE), FL—See OceanSound Partners, LP; *U.S. Private*, pg. 2991
GANNETT FLEMING PROJECT DEVELOPMENT CORP.—See OceanSound Partners, LP; *U.S. Private*, pg. 2991
GANNETT FLEMING TRANSIT & RAIL SYSTEMS—See OceanSound Partners, LP; *U.S. Private*, pg. 2991
GANNETT FLEMING VALUATION & RATE CONSULTANTS, LLC—See OceanSound Partners, LP; *U.S. Private*, pg. 2991
GANNETT HEALTHCARE GROUP—See Bertelsmann SE & Co. KGaA; *Int'l*, pg. 990
GANNETT MEDIA CORP.—See Gannett Co., Inc.; *U.S. Public*, pg. 896
GANNETT MISSOURI PUBLISHING, INC.—See Gannett Co., Inc.; *U.S. Public*, pg. 897
GANNETT PUBLISHING SERVICES, LLC—See Gannett Co., Inc.; *U.S. Public*, pg. 897
GANNETT SUPPLY CORPORATION—See Gannett Co., Inc.; *U.S. Public*, pg. 897
GANNETT VERMONT PUBLISHING, INC.—See Gannett Co., Inc.; *U.S. Public*, pg. 897
GANON PRODUCTS LIMITED; *Int'l*, pg. 2881
GAN OUTRE MER IARD—See Groupama SA; *Int'l*, pg. 3090
GAN PACIFIQUE—See Groupama SA; *Int'l*, pg. 3090
GAN PACIFIQUE—See Groupama SA; *Int'l*, pg. 3090
GAN PLC; *Int'l*, pg. 2880
GAN SHMUEL FOODS LTD.; *Int'l*, pg. 2880
GANS INK & SUPPLY COMPANY, INC.; *U.S. Private*, pg. 1641
GANSO CO., LTD.; *Int'l*, pg. 2881
GANSU AIRPORT GROUP CO., LTD.—See Hainan Traffic Administration Holding Co., Ltd.; *Int'l*, pg. 3213
GANSU CIMC HUAJUN VEHICLE CO., LTD.—See China International Marine Containers (Group) Co., Ltd.; *Int'l*, pg. 1511
GANSU DALI FOODS CO., LTD.—See Dali Foods Group Co. Ltd.; *Int'l*, pg. 1951
GANSU DUNHUANG SEED GROUP CO., LTD.; *Int'l*, pg. 2881
GANSU ELECTRIC POWER COMPANY—See State Grid Corporation of China; *Int'l*, pg. 7182
GANSU ENGINEERING CONSULTING GROUP CO., LTD.; *Int'l*, pg. 2881
GANSU GANGTAI HOLDING GROUP CO., LTD.; *Int'l*, pg. 2881
GANSU GOLDEN SOLAR CO., LTD; *Int'l*, pg. 2881
GANSU GOME LOGISTICS COMPANY LIMITED—See Gome Retail Holdings Limited; *Int'l*, pg. 3037
GANSU GUOFANG INDUSTRY & TRADE GROUP CO., LTD.; *Int'l*, pg. 2881
GANSU HONGTENG OIL & GAS EQUIPMENT MANUFACTURING CO., LTD.—See Honghua Group Ltd; *Int'l*, pg. 3470
GANSU HUANGTAI WINE-MARKETING INDUSTRY CO., LTD.; *Int'l*, pg. 2881
GANSU JINGYUAN COAL INDUSTRY & ELECTRICITY POWER CO., LTD.; *Int'l*, pg. 2881
GANSU JIU STEEL GROUP HONGXING IRON & STEEL CO., LTD.; *Int'l*, pg. 2881
GANSU JOY AGRICULTURAL TECHNOLOGY CO., LTD.; *Int'l*, pg. 2881
GANSU LONGSHENRONGFA PHRMCTCL IND CO LTD; *Int'l*, pg. 2881
GANSU MOGAO INDUSTRIAL DEVELOPMENT CO., LTD.; *Int'l*, pg. 2881
GANSU QILIANSHAN CEMENT GROUP CO., LTD; *Int'l*, pg. 2881
GANSU RONGHUA INDUSTRY GROUP CO., LTD.; *Int'l*, pg. 2881
GANSU SHANGFENG CEMENT CO LTD; *Int'l*, pg. 2881
GANSU YASHENG INDUSTRIAL (GROUP) CO., LTD.; *Int'l*, pg. 2882
GANSU YATE INVESTMENT GROUP CO., LTD.; *Int'l*, pg. 2882
GANT AB—See Gant Sweden; *Int'l*, pg. 2882
GANTAN BEAUTY INDUSTRY CO. LTD; *Int'l*, pg. 2882
GANTECH, INC.—See Sagewind Capital LLC; *U.S. Private*, pg. 3527
GANTER INTERIOR GMBH—See Mutares SE & Co. KGaA; *Int'l*, pg. 5104
GANTER ITALIA S. R. L.—See Mutares SE & Co. KGaA; *Int'l*, pg. 5105
GANT HOME AB—See Gant Sweden; *Int'l*, pg. 2882
GANTOIS SA; *Int'l*, pg. 2882
GANTRADE CORPORATION; *U.S. Private*, pg. 1641
GANTRADE EUROPE, LTD.—See Gantrade Corporation; *U.S. Private*, pg. 1641
GANTRAIL (MIDDLE EAST) LTD—See Gantry Railing Limited; *Int'l*, pg. 2882
GANTRY RAILING LIMITED; *Int'l*, pg. 2882
GANT SWEDEN; *Int'l*, pg. 2882
GANT SWEDEN—See Gant Sweden; *Int'l*, pg. 2882
GANT UK LTD—See Gant Sweden; *Int'l*, pg. 2882
GANT USA CORPORATION—See Gant Sweden; *Int'l*, pg. 2882
GANT USA CORPORATION; *U.S. Private*, pg. 1641
GANYUAN FOODS CO., LTD.; *Int'l*, pg. 2882
GANZ BIOFUELS SDN. BHD.—See Fintec Global Berhad; *Int'l*, pg. 2677
GANZHOU ACHTECK TOOL TECHNOLOGY CO., LTD.—See Chongyi Zhangyuan Tungsten Co., Ltd.; *Int'l*, pg. 1582
GANZHOU BAOZE AUTOMOBILE SALES SERVICES CO., LTD.—See China ZhengTong Auto Services Holdings Limited; *Int'l*, pg. 1566
GANZHOU CHENGUANG RARE EARTH NEW MATERIAL CO., LTD.—See Shenghe Resources Holding Co., Ltd.; *Int'l*, pg. 6801
GANZHOU DEPUT TECHNOLOGY CO., LTD.—See Wuhu Token Sciences Co., Ltd.; *Int'l*, pg. 8502
GANZHOU GANNAN TUNGSTEN CO., LTD.—See China Rare Earth Resources And Technology Co., Ltd.; *Int'l*, pg. 1545
GANZHOU JXTC SUMMIT AT&M NEW MATERIALS CO., LTD.—See Advanced Technology & Materials Co., Ltd.; *Int'l*, pg. 162
GANZHOU KINGSIGNAL CABLE TECHNOLOGY CO., LTD.—See Kingsignal Technology Co., Ltd.; *Int'l*, pg. 4175
GANZHOU KINGSIGNAL OPTICAL FIBER & CABLE CO., LTD.—See Kingsignal Technology Co., Ltd.; *Int'l*, pg. 4175
GANZHOU TENG YUAN COBALT NEW MATERIAL CO., LTD.; *Int'l*, pg. 2882
GANZHOU TONGXINGDA ELECTRONIC TECHNOLOGY CO., LTD.—See Shenzhen TXD Technology Co Ltd; *Int'l*, pg. 6823
GANZHOU YIHAO NEW MATERIALS CO., LTD.; *Int'l*, pg. 2882
GANZHOU ZHAORI RARE EARTH NEW MATERIALS CO., LTD.—See Resonac Holdings Corporation; *Int'l*, pg. 6298
GANZ METER COMPANY LTD.—See Itron, Inc.; *U.S. Public*, pg. 1175
GAOAN TFC PHOTOELECTRIC TECHNOLOGY CO., LTD.—See Suzhou TFC Optical Communication Co., Ltd.; *Int'l*, pg. 7352
GAONA AERO MATERIAL CO., LTD.; *Int'l*, pg. 2882
GAON CABLE CO., LTD. - GUNPO PLANT—See GAON Cable Co., Ltd.; *Int'l*, pg. 2882
GAON CABLE CO., LTD. - JEONJU PLANT—See GAON Cable Co., Ltd.; *Int'l*, pg. 2882
GAON CABLE CO., LTD.; *Int'l*, pg. 2882
GAON GROUP LTD; *Int'l*, pg. 2882
GAOTU TECHEDU INC.; *Int'l*, pg. 2882
G&A OUTSOURCING, INC.; *U.S. Private*, pg. 1628
GAOYAO ACEDIE CASTING TECHNOLOGY CO., LTD.—See Ace Technologies Corp.; *Int'l*, pg. 95
GAOYAO ACE MECHATRONIX CO., LTD.—See Ace Technologies Corp.; *Int'l*, pg. 95
GAOYAO G-ACE INDUSTRY CO., LTD.—See Ace Technologies Corp.; *Int'l*, pg. 95
GAOZHOU COILS ELECTRONIC CO. LTD.—See CEC International Holdings Limited; *Int'l*, pg. 1372
GAP AG—See CapMan PLC; *Int'l*, pg. 1315
GAP AG—See Osprey Capital LLC; *U.S. Private*, pg. 3048
G.A. PAPER INTERNATIONAL INC.; *Int'l*, pg. 2865
GAP CANADA, INC.—See The Gap, Inc.; *U.S. Public*, pg. 2074
GAP EXPERTEN AB—See Sdiptech AB; *Int'l*, pg. 6658
GAP FISH GMBH—See Cint Group AB; *Int'l*, pg. 1611
THE GAP, INC.; *U.S. Public*, pg. 2074
GAP INTELLIGENCE; *U.S. Private*, pg. 1641
GAP INTERNATIONAL SOURCING LIMITED—See The Gap, Inc.; *U.S. Public*, pg. 2074
GAP (ITALY) SRL.—See The Gap, Inc.; *U.S. Public*, pg. 2074
GAP PERSONNEL HOLDINGS LIMITED—See Open Up Group Inc; *Int'l*, pg. 5598
GAP PRUDENTIAL ALOCACAO DE RECURSOS LTDA.—See Prudential Financial, Inc.; *U.S. Public*, pg. 1731
GAP ROOFING INC.; *U.S. Private*, pg. 1642
GAP SOLUTIONS, INC.—See System One Holdings, LLC; *U.S. Private*, pg. 3906
THE GAP—See The Gap, Inc.; *U.S. Public*, pg. 2074
GAP (UK HOLDINGS) LIMITED—See The Gap, Inc.; *U.S. Public*, pg. 2074
GAPUMA CHINA—See Gapuma (UK) Limited; *Int'l*, pg. 2882
GAPUMA GHANA LIMITED—See Gapuma (UK) Limited; *Int'l*, pg. 2882
GAPUMA INDONESIA—See Gapuma (UK) Limited; *Int'l*, pg. 2883
GAPUMA NIGERIA LIMITED—See Gapuma (UK) Limited; *Int'l*, pg. 2883
GAPUMA ROMANIA—See Gapuma (UK) Limited; *Int'l*, pg. 2883
GAPUMA THAILAND—See Gapuma (UK) Limited; *Int'l*, pg. 2883
GAPUMA UGANDA LIMITED—See Gapuma (UK) Limited; *Int'l*, pg. 2883
GAPUMA (UK) LIMITED; *Int'l*, pg. 2882
G.A.P VASSILOPOULOS PUBLIC LIMITED; *Int'l*, pg. 2865
GAPWAVES AB; *Int'l*, pg. 2883
GARADOR LTD.—See Hormann KG Verkaufsgesellschaf; *Int'l*, pg. 3480
GARAGA INC.; *Int'l*, pg. 2883
GARAGE AUBREE; *Int'l*, pg. 2883
GARAGE AUTO DE L OUEST; *Int'l*, pg. 2883
GARAGE DOOR STORE—See APi Group Corporation; *Int'l*, pg. 626
GARAGE DU BOIS VERT; *Int'l*, pg. 2883
GARAGE HEINZLE; *Int'l*, pg. 2883
GARAGE ISLA VERDE, INC.; *U.S. Private*, pg. 1642
GARAGE LAMERAIN S.A.S; *Int'l*, pg. 2883

GARAGE MANAGEMENT CORPORATION CO
CORPORATE AFFILIATIONS

GARAGE MANAGEMENT CORPORATION CO; *U.S. Private*, pg. 1642
GARAGE MARCEL VILLENEUVE INC.; *Int'l*, pg. 2883
GARAGETEK INC.; *U.S. Private*, pg. 1642
GARAGE VURPILLOT; *Int'l*, pg. 2883
GARAJE ELOY GRANOLLERS S.A.—See Stellantis N.V.; *Int'l*, pg. 7201
GARAN, INCORPORATED—See Berkshire Hathaway Inc.; *U.S. Public*, pg. 305
GARAN MANUFACTURING CORP.—See Berkshire Hathaway Inc.; *U.S. Public*, pg. 305
GARANT GP—See Griffon Corporation; *U.S. Public*, pg. 969
GARANTIA INSURANCE COMPANY LTD.—See Taaleri Oyj; *Int'l*, pg. 7401
GARANTIBANK BBVA INTERNATIONAL N.V.—See Banco Bilbao Vizcaya Argentaria, S.A.; *Int'l*, pg. 818
GARANTIBANK INTERNATIONAL N.V.—See Turkiye Garanti Bankasi A.S.; *Int'l*, pg. 7975
GARANTIBANK MOSCOW—See Turkiye Garanti Bankasi A.S.; *Int'l*, pg. 7975
GARANTI BANK SA—See Banco Bilbao Vizcaya Argentaria, S.A.; *Int'l*, pg. 818
GARANTI BBVA AS—See Banco Bilbao Vizcaya Argentaria, S.A.; *Int'l*, pg. 817
GARANTI BBVA EMEKLILIK AS—See Banco Bilbao Vizcaya Argentaria, S.A.; *Int'l*, pg. 818
GARANTI BBVA FACTORING AS—See Banco Bilbao Vizcaya Argentaria, S.A.; *Int'l*, pg. 818
GARANTI BBVA FILO AS—See Banco Bilbao Vizcaya Argentaria, S.A.; *Int'l*, pg. 818
GARANTI BBVA FILO YONETIM HIZMETLERI A.S.—See Garanti Finansal Kiralama A.S.; *Int'l*, pg. 2883
GARANTI BBVA LEASING AS—See Banco Bilbao Vizcaya Argentaria, S.A.; *Int'l*, pg. 818
GARANTI BBVA PORTFOY AS—See Banco Bilbao Vizcaya Argentaria, S.A.; *Int'l*, pg. 818
GARANTI BBVA YATIRIM AS—See Banco Bilbao Vizcaya Argentaria, S.A.; *Int'l*, pg. 818
GARANTJE ASSISTANCE S.A.—See Swiss Life Holding; *Int'l*, pg. 7368
GARANTI FAKTORING A.S.—See Turkiye Garanti Bankasi A.S.; *Int'l*, pg. 7975
GARANTI FINANSAL KIRALAMA A.S.; *Int'l*, pg. 2883
GARANTI KONUT FINANSMAN DANISMANLIK HIZMETLERI A.S.—See Turkiye Garanti Bankasi A.S.; *Int'l*, pg. 7975
GARANTI KOZA CONSTRUCTION INDUSTRY AND COMMERCE CO. INC.—See Garanti Koza Insaat Sanayi ve Ticaret A.S.; *Int'l*, pg. 2883
GARANTI KOZA INSAAT SANAYI VE TICARET A.S.; *Int'l*, pg. 2883
GARANT-INVEST COMMERCIAL BANK JSC; *Int'l*, pg. 2883
GARANT INVEST HOLDING AD; *Int'l*, pg. 2883
GARANTI ODEME SISTEMLERI AS—See Banco Bilbao Vizcaya Argentaria, S.A.; *Int'l*, pg. 818
GARANTI PORTFOY YONETIMI AS—See Turkiye Garanti Bankasi A.S.; *Int'l*, pg. 7975
GARANTI YATIRIM MENKUL KIYMETLER AS—See Turkiye Garanti Bankasi A.S.; *Int'l*, pg. 7975
GARANTI YATIRIM ORTAKLIGI AS; *Int'l*, pg. 2883
GARANTIZAR S.G.R.—See Banco Macro S.A.; *Int'l*, pg. 823
GARANT MASCHINENHANDEL GMBH—See Windmoeller & Hoelscher KG; *Int'l*, pg. 8425
GARANT PRODUCTIONS GMBH—See SFS Group AG; *Int'l*, pg. 6738
GARANT-TIERNAHRUNG GESELLSCHAFT M.B.H—See BayWa AG; *Int'l*, pg. 918
GARANT TUREN-UND ZARGEN GMBH—See Arbonia AG; *Int'l*, pg. 538
GARAVENTA AG—See Doppelmayr Group; *Int'l*, pg. 2175
GARAVENTA ALGERIE SARL—See Doppelmayr Group; *Int'l*, pg. 2175
GARAVENTA (CANADA) LTD.—See Savaria Corporation; *Int'l*, pg. 6596
GARAVENTA SA—See Doppelmayr Group; *Int'l*, pg. 2175
GARAVENTA USA, INC.—See Savaria Corporation; *Int'l*, pg. 6596
THE GARBAGE COMPANY INC.—See BC Partners LLP; *Int'l*, pg. 924
GARBAGEMAN CO; *U.S. Private*, pg. 1642
GARBARY SP. Z O.O.—See Commerzbank AG; *Int'l*, pg. 1719
GARBER BROS INC.; *U.S. Private*, pg. 1642
GARBER BUICK COMPANY INC.—See Garber Management Group Inc.; *U.S. Private*, pg. 1642
GARBER BUICK GMC; *U.S. Private*, pg. 1642
GARBER CHEVROLET INC.—See Garber Management Group Inc.; *U.S. Private*, pg. 1642
GARBER ELECTRICAL CONTRACTORS INC.; *U.S. Private*, pg. 1642
GARBER FARMS; *U.S. Private*, pg. 1642
GARBER FORD MERCURY INC.—See Garber Management Group Inc.; *U.S. Private*, pg. 1642
GARBER & GOODMAN ADVERTISING, INC.; *U.S. Private*, pg. 1642

GARBER MANAGEMENT GROUP INC.; *U.S. Private*, pg. 1642
GARBER NISSAN INC.—See Garber Management Group Inc.; *U.S. Private*, pg. 1642
GARBER'S TRAVEL SERVICE, INC.—See Flight Centre Travel Group Limited; *Int'l*, pg. 2706
GARBI FINVEST LTD; *Int'l*, pg. 2883
GARBI LINEA 5 S.C.A.R.L.—See Salini Costruttori S.p.A.; *Int'l*, pg. 6493
GARBOLI S.P.A.—See Mipien S.p.A; *Int'l*, pg. 4915
GARBUIO S.P.A.; *Int'l*, pg. 2883
GARCIA & ASSOCIATES, INC.—See Goldberg Lindsay & Co., LLC; *U.S. Private*, pg. 1729
GARCIA FOODS, INC.—See Mission Consumer Capital; *U.S. Private*, pg. 2747
GARCIA IMPORTS INC.; *U.S. Private*, pg. 1642
GARCIA & ORTIZ, PA; *U.S. Private*, pg. 1642
GARCIA ROOFING & SHEET METAL; *U.S. Private*, pg. 1642
GARCOA INC.—See Vitamin Classics Inc.; *U.S. Private*, pg. 4405
GARCO BUILDING SYSTEMS, INC.—See Clayton, Dubilier & Rice, LLC; *U.S. Private*, pg. 920
GARCO CONSTRUCTION, INC.; *U.S. Private*, pg. 1642
GARCO, INC.—See EQT AB; *Int'l*, pg. 2474
GARCY PIEDMONT—See Leggett & Platt, Incorporated; *U.S. Public*, pg. 1302
GARCZYNSKI TRAPLOIR—See VINCI S.A.; *Int'l*, pg. 8237
GARDA CAPITAL GROUP; *Int'l*, pg. 2883
GARDA CAPITAL PARTNERS LP—See Affiliated Managers Group, Inc.; *U.S. Public*, pg. 55
GARDA CL ATLANTIC, INC.—See BC Partners LLP; *Int'l*, pg. 924
GARDA CL GREAT LAKES, INC.—See BC Partners LLP; *Int'l*, pg. 924
GARDA CL NORTHWEST, INC.—See BC Partners LLP; *Int'l*, pg. 924
GARDA CL WEST, INC.—See BC Partners LLP; *Int'l*, pg. 924
GARDALAND S.R.L.—See Merlin Entertainments plc; *Int'l*, pg. 4837
GARDANNE AUTOMOBILES; *Int'l*, pg. 2884
GARDA PROPERTY GROUP; *Int'l*, pg. 2884
GARDA SECURITY SCREENING INC.—See BC Partners LLP; *Int'l*, pg. 924
GARDASOFT VISION LIMITED—See Optex Group Co, Ltd.; *Int'l*, pg. 5602
GARDA WORLD SECURITY CORPORATION—See BC Partners LLP; *Int'l*, pg. 924
GARDEL FOOD EQUIPMENT & CUTLERY; *U.S. Private*, pg. 1642
GARDENA AG—See Husqvarna AB; *Int'l*, pg. 3538
GARDENA FRANCE S.A.R.L.—See Husqvarna AB; *Int'l*, pg. 3539
GARDENA MANUFACTURING GMBH—See Husqvarna AB; *Int'l*, pg. 3539
GARDENA NORDEN AB—See Husqvarna AB; *Int'l*, pg. 3539
GARDENA NORDEN AB—See Husqvarna AB; *Int'l*, pg. 3539
GARDENA OSTERREICH GMBH—See Husqvarna AB; *Int'l*, pg. 3539
GARDENA SPOL.S.R.O.—See Husqvarna AB; *Int'l*, pg. 3539
GARDENBURGER, LLC—See Kellanova; *U.S. Public*, pg. 1218
GARDEN CITY-CJD, LLC—See Lithia Motors, Inc.; *U.S. Public*, pg. 1322
THE GARDEN CITY COMPANY; *U.S. Public*, pg. 2074
THE GARDEN CITY CO-OP INC - DIGHTON—See The Garden City Co-Op Inc.; *U.S. Private*, pg. 4032
THE GARDEN CITY CO-OP INC.; *U.S. Private*, pg. 4032
GARDEN CITY GROUP COMMUNICATIONS; *U.S. Private*, pg. 1642
GARDEN CITY HOTEL INC.; *U.S. Private*, pg. 1643
GARDEN CITY PLUMBING & HEATING; *U.S. Private*, pg. 1643
GARDEN CITY TOWNHOMES, LLC—See AvalonBay Communities, Inc.; *U.S. Public*, pg. 240
GARDEN CITY WESTERN RAILWAY, INC.—See Pioneer Railcorp; *U.S. Public*, pg. 3188
GARDENDALE SURGICAL ASSOCIATES, LLC—See Tenet Healthcare Corporation; *U.S. Public*, pg. 2002
GARDEN DEVELOPMENT PTE. LTD.—See Keppel Corporation Limited; *Int'l*, pg. 4130
GARDENER'S SUPPLY COMPANY; *U.S. Private*, pg. 1643
GARDEN-FRESH FOODS INC.; *U.S. Private*, pg. 1643
GARDEN FRESH GOURMET, LLC—See Aliments Fontaine Sante, Inc.; *Int'l*, pg. 328
GARDEN FRESH RESTAURANT LLC—See Cerberus Capital Management, L.P.; *U.S. Private*, pg. 838
GARDEN & GUN—See Evening Post Publishing Co.; *U.S. Private*, pg. 1436
GARDEN HOTEL SHANGHAI; *Int'l*, pg. 2884
GARDENIA BAKERIES (EAST MALAYSIA) SDN. BHD.—See Kim Teck Cheong Consolidated Berhad; *Int'l*, pg. 4162

GARDENIA BAKERIES (KL) SDN BHD—See QAF Limited; *Int'l*, pg. 6131
GARDENIA BAKERIES (PHILIPPINES) INC.—See QAF Limited; *Int'l*, pg. 6132
GARDENIA FOODS PTE LTD.—See QAF Limited; *Int'l*, pg. 6132
GARDENIA-QUIMICA SA—See American Securities LLC; *U.S. Private*, pg. 252
GARDENIA SALES & DISTRIBUTION SDN BHD—See QAF Limited; *Int'l*, pg. 6132
GARDENMASTER—See PRO Group, Inc.; *U.S. Private*, pg. 3270
GARDEN MEDICAL CENTRE LIMITED—See Bamboos Health Care Holdings Limited; *Int'l*, pg. 813
GARDEN MUSEUM HIEI CO., LTD.—See Keihan Holdings Co., Ltd.; *Int'l*, pg. 4116
GARDEN NETWORK, LTD.—See Densan System Co., Ltd.; *Int'l*, pg. 2028
GARDEN OF E; *U.S. Private*, pg. 1643
GARDEN OF LIFE, INC.; *U.S. Private*, pg. 1643
GARDEN PARK COMMUNITY HOSPITAL LIMITED PARTNERSHIP—See HCA Healthcare, Inc.; *U.S. Public*, pg. 996
GARDEN PARK HOSPITALIST PROGRAM, LLC—See HCA Healthcare, Inc.; *U.S. Public*, pg. 996
GARDEN PARK MEDICAL CENTER—See HCA Healthcare, Inc.; *U.S. Public*, pg. 996
GARDEN PARK PHYSICIAN GROUP, INC.—See HCA Healthcare, Inc.; *U.S. Public*, pg. 996
THE GARDEN PRODUCTIONS LIMITED—See ITV plc; *Int'l*, pg. 3845
GARDEN PROTEIN INTERNATIONAL INC.—See Conagra Brands, Inc.; *U.S. Public*, pg. 564
GARDEN REACH SHIPBUILDERS & ENGINEERS LTD.; *Int'l*, pg. 2884
GARDEN RIDGE POTTERY; *U.S. Private*, pg. 1643
GARDEN ROUTE CASINO (PTY) LTD.—See Hosken Consolidated Investments Limited; *Int'l*, pg. 3485
GARDENS ALIVE!, INC.; *U.S. Private*, pg. 1643
GARDENS EFL IMAGING CENTER, LLC—See HCA Healthcare, Inc.; *U.S. Public*, pg. 996
GARDENSIDE LTD.—See BIG Camera Corporation PCL; *Int'l*, pg. 1021
GARDEN SILK MILLS PRIVATE LIMITED—See The Chatterjee Group; *U.S. Private*, pg. 4007
THE GARDENS OF BAGATELLE LTD.—See ENL Limited; *Int'l*, pg. 2442
THE GARDENS ON EL PASEO LLC—See Simon Property Group, Inc.; *U.S. Public*, pg. 1882
GARDENS PENSION TRUSTEES LIMITED—See 3i Group plc; *Int'l*, pg. 8
GARDEN SPOT VILLAGE; *U.S. Private*, pg. 1643
GARDENS REGIONAL HOSPITAL & MEDICAL CENTER; *U.S. Private*, pg. 1643
GARDEN STATE ENGINE & EQUIPMENT CO.; *U.S. Private*, pg. 1643
GARDEN STATE LIFE INSURANCE COMPANY—See Brookfield Corporation; *Int'l*, pg. 1174
GARDEN STATE RADIOLOGY NETWORK, LLC—See RadNet, Inc.; *U.S. Public*, pg. 1761
GARDEN STATE SECURITIES INC.; *U.S. Private*, pg. 1643
GARDEN STATE TILE DISTRIBUTORS; *U.S. Private*, pg. 1643
THE GARDENS THEATRE SDN. BHD.—See IGB Berhad; *Int'l*, pg. 3602
GARDEN STREET IRON & METAL; *U.S. Private*, pg. 1643
GARDEN SUPPLY HARDSCAPES—See Trilantic Capital Management L.P.; *U.S. Private*, pg. 4231
GARDEN VALLEY CORPORATION; *U.S. Private*, pg. 1643
GARDEN VALLEY TELEPHONE COMPANY; *U.S. Private*, pg. 1643
GARDENVISION, LLC—See Markel Group Inc.; *U.S. Public*, pg. 1368
THE GARDEN WHOLESALE, INC.; *U.S. Private*, pg. 4032
GARDEN-WISE DISTRIBUTORS INC.; *U.S. Private*, pg. 1643
GARDERE WYNNE SEWELL LLP—See Foley & Lardner LLP; *U.S. Private*, pg. 1558
GARDERMOEN PARK AS—See Olav Thon Eiendomsselskap ASA; *Int'l*, pg. 5552
GARDE SERVICES PTY. LIMITED—See MAAS Group Holdings Limited; *Int'l*, pg. 4618
GARDETTO'S BAKERY, INC.—See General Mills, Inc.; *U.S. Public*, pg. 921
GARDEWINE GROUP LIMITED PARTNERSHIP—See Mullen Group Ltd.; *Int'l*, pg. 5080
GARDIEN JAPAN CO., LTD.—See ESO Partners L.P.; *Int'l*, pg. 2504
GARDIEN PACIFIC LTD.—See ESO Partners L.P.; *Int'l*, pg. 2504
GARDIEN—See ESO Partners L.P.; *Int'l*, pg. 2504
GARDINER HEALTHCARE ACQUISITIONS CORP.; *U.S. Public*, pg. 906
GARDINERS HOME FURNISHING CENTER; *U.S. Private*, pg. 1643
GARDINIA HOME DECOR GMBH; *Int'l*, pg. 2884

COMPANY NAME INDEX

GARDLINE SHIPPING LIMITED—See HAL Trust N.V.; *Int'l*, pg. 3226
GARDNER ABRASIVES—See FIVES, Societe Anonyme; *Int'l*, pg. 2696
GARDNER AEROSPACE HOLDINGS LTD.—See Ligeance Aerospace Technology Co., Ltd.; *Int'l*, pg. 4496
GARDNER APOC—See Audax Group, Limited Partnership; *U.S. Private*, pg. 388
GARDNER AVIATION SPECIALIST, INC.—See GenNx360 Capital Partners, L.P.; *U.S. Private*, pg. 1672
GARDNER BENDER—See nVent Electric plc; *Int'l*, pg. 5498
GARDNER BUSINESS MEDIA INC.; *U.S. Private*, pg. 1643
GARDNER DENVER AUSTRIA GMBH—See Ingersoll Rand Inc.; *U.S. Public*, pg. 1118
GARDNER DENVER BELGIUM NV—See Ingersoll Rand Inc.; *U.S. Public*, pg. 1118
GARDNER DENVER CANADA CORP.—See Ingersoll Rand Inc.; *U.S. Public*, pg. 1118
GARDNER DENVER CZ + SK, S.R.O.—See Ingersoll Rand Inc.; *U.S. Public*, pg. 1118
GARDNER DENVER DENMARK A/S—See Ingersoll Rand Inc.; *U.S. Public*, pg. 1119
GARDNER DENVER DEUTSCHLAND GMBH—See Ingersoll Rand Inc.; *U.S. Public*, pg. 1119
GARDNER DENVER DRUM LTD.—See Ingersoll Rand Inc.; *U.S. Public*, pg. 1119
GARDNER DENVER ENGINEERED PRODUCTS INDIA PTE LTD.—See Ingersoll Rand Inc.; *U.S. Public*, pg. 1119
GARDNER DENVER FRANCE SAS—See Ingersoll Rand Inc.; *U.S. Public*, pg. 1119
GARDNER DENVER HONG KONG LTD.—See Ingersoll Rand Inc.; *U.S. Public*, pg. 1119
GARDNER DENVER IBERICA, SL—See Ingersoll Rand Inc.; *U.S. Public*, pg. 1119
GARDNER DENVER, INC.—See Ingersoll Rand Inc.; *U.S. Public*, pg. 1118
GARDNER DENVER INDUSTRIES AUSTRALIA PTY LTD.—See Ingersoll Rand Inc.; *U.S. Public*, pg. 1119
GARDNER DENVER INDUSTRIES SA—See Ingersoll Rand Inc.; *U.S. Public*, pg. 1119
GARDNER DENVER JAPAN LTD.—See Ingersoll Rand Inc.; *U.S. Public*, pg. 1119
GARDNER DENVER LTD.—See Ingersoll Rand Inc.; *U.S. Public*, pg. 1119
GARDNER DENVER MACHINERY (SHANGHAI) CO. LTD.—See Ingersoll Rand Inc.; *U.S. Public*, pg. 1119
GARDNER DENVER NASH AUSTRALIA—See Ingersoll Rand Inc.; *U.S. Public*, pg. 1119
GARDNER DENVER NASH BRASIL INDUSTRIA E COMERCIO DE BOMBAS LTDA.—See Ingersoll Rand Inc.; *U.S. Public*, pg. 1119
GARDNER DENVER NASH LLC—See Ingersoll Rand Inc.; *U.S. Public*, pg. 1119
GARDNER DENVER NASH SINGAPORE PTE LTD.—See Ingersoll Rand Inc.; *U.S. Public*, pg. 1119
GARDNER DENVER NEDERLAND BV—See Ingersoll Rand Inc.; *U.S. Public*, pg. 1119
GARDNER DENVER NEW ZEALAND LTD.—See Ingersoll Rand Inc.; *U.S. Public*, pg. 1119
GARDNER DENVER OBERDORFER PUMPS, INC.—See Ingersoll Rand Inc.; *U.S. Public*, pg. 1119
GARDNER DENVER PETROLEUM PUMPS, LLC—See Ingersoll Rand Inc.; *U.S. Public*, pg. 1118
GARDNER DENVER PTE. LTD.—See Ingersoll Rand Inc.; *U.S. Public*, pg. 1118
GARDNER DENVER - ROBUSCHI DIVISION—See Ingersoll Rand Inc.; *U.S. Public*, pg. 1119
GARDNER DENVER SLOVAKIA S.R.O.—See Ingersoll Rand Inc.; *U.S. Public*, pg. 1119
GARDNER DENVER SRL—See Ingersoll Rand Inc.; *U.S. Public*, pg. 1119
GARDNER DENVER TAIWAN LTD.—See Ingersoll Rand Inc.; *U.S. Public*, pg. 1119
GARDNER DENVER (THAILAND) CO., LTD.—See Ingersoll Rand Inc.; *U.S. Public*, pg. 1118
GARDNER DENVER THOMAS GMBH—See Ingersoll Rand Inc.; *U.S. Public*, pg. 1119
GARDNER DENVER THOMAS, INC.—See Ingersoll Rand Inc.; *U.S. Public*, pg. 1119
GARDNER DENVER THOMAS - MONROE—See Ingersoll Rand Inc.; *U.S. Public*, pg. 1119
GARDNER DENVER THOMAS PNEUMATIC SYSTEMS (WUXI) CO., LTD.—See Ingersoll Rand Inc.; *U.S. Public*, pg. 1119
GARDNER DENVER TRADING (SHANGHAI) CO. LTD.—See Ingersoll Rand Inc.; *U.S. Public*, pg. 1119
GARDNER DENVER WATER JETTING SYSTEMS, INC.—See Ingersoll Rand Inc.; *U.S. Public*, pg. 1119
GARDNER DISTRIBUTING CO.; *U.S. Private*, pg. 1643
GARDNER-GIBSON, INC.—See Audax Group, Limited Partnership; *U.S. Private*, pg. 388
GARDNER GLASS PRODUCTS INC.; *U.S. Private*, pg. 1643
GARDNER INC.; *U.S. Private*, pg. 1643
GARDNER MARSH GAS EQUIPMENT COMPANY, INC.; *U.S. Private*, pg. 1643

GARDNER NELSON & PARTNERS; *U.S. Private*, pg. 1644
GARDNER NEWS INC.; *U.S. Private*, pg. 1644
GARDNER OIL COMPANY INC.; *U.S. Private*, pg. 1644
GARDNER STANDARD LLC; *U.S. Private*, pg. 1644
GARDNER TELECOMMUNICATIONS, INC.; *U.S. Private*, pg. 1644
GARDNER TRUCKING, INC.—See CRST International, Inc.; *U.S. Private*, pg. 1113
GARDNER & WHITE CORPORATION; *U.S. Private*, pg. 1643
THE GARDNER ZEMKE COMPANY - MECHANICAL DIVISION—See The Gardner Zemke Company; *U.S. Private*, pg. 4032
THE GARDNER ZEMKE COMPANY; *U.S. Private*, pg. 4032
GARDOSERV (PVT) LIMITED—See Cambria Africa Plc; *Int'l*, pg. 1269
GARD ROGARD INC.; *U.S. Private*, pg. 1642
GARDRUM HOLDINGS LIMITED; *Int'l*, pg. 2884
GARDUNOS RESTAURANT; *U.S. Private*, pg. 1644
GARED HOLDINGS, LLC—See Gen Cap America, Inc.; *U.S. Private*, pg. 1660
GARED SPORTS—See Gen Cap America, Inc.; *U.S. Private*, pg. 1660
GARELICK FARMS, LLC—See Dean Foods Company; *U.S. Private*, pg. 1184
GARELICK FARMS, LLC—See Dean Foods Company; *U.S. Private*, pg. 1184
GARELICK MANUFACTURING CO.; *U.S. Private*, pg. 1644
GARELLI SA; *Int'l*, pg. 2884
GARENDON PARK RESIDENTS MANAGEMENT COMPANY LTD.—See Persimmon plc; *Int'l*, pg. 5816
GARENET CO., LTD.—See Yumeshin Holdings Co., Ltd.; *Int'l*, pg. 8613
GARENTA ULASIM COZUMLERI A.S.—See AG Anadolu Grubu Holding A.S.; *Int'l*, pg. 197
GARFF ENTERPRISES, INC.; *U.S. Private*, pg. 1644
GARFIELD BEACH CVS, L.L.C.—See CVS Health Corporation; *U.S. Public*, pg. 616
THE GARFIELD GROUP, INC.—See Aquiline Capital Partners LLC; *U.S. Private*, pg. 305
GARFIELD PARK HOSPITAL, LLC—See Universal Health Services, Inc.; *U.S. Public*, pg. 2257
THE GARFIELD WESTON FOUNDATION; *Int'l*, pg. 7647
GARG FURNACE LTD.; *Int'l*, pg. 2884
GARGI HUTTENES-ALBERTUS PVT. LTD.—See Huettenes-Albertus Chemische Werke GmbH; *Int'l*, pg. 3522
GARG INTERNATIONAL PRIVATE LIMITED—See Garg Furnace Ltd.; *Int'l*, pg. 2884
GARGIULO, INC.; *U.S. Private*, pg. 1644
GARIA INC.—See Platinum Equity, LLC; *U.S. Private*, pg. 3202
GARIBALDI RESOURCES CORP.; *Int'l*, pg. 2884
GARICH INC.; *U.S. Private*, pg. 1644
GARICK, LLC—See Hendricks Holding Company, Inc.; *U.S. Private*, pg. 1915
GARIC LIMITED—See Bibby Line Group Limited; *Int'l*, pg. 1018
GARIMA BIKAS BANK LIMITED; *Int'l*, pg. 2884
GARKALNES GRANTS SIA—See Heidelberg Materials AG; *Int'l*, pg. 3310
GARKANE ENERGY COOPERATIVE, INC.; *U.S. Private*, pg. 1644
GARLAND BEHAVIORAL HOSPITAL, INC.—See Universal Health Services, Inc.; *U.S. Public*, pg. 2257
GARLAND CANADA INC.—See Garland Industries Inc.; *U.S. Private*, pg. 1644
GARLAND C. NORRIS CO.—See S.P. Richards Company; *U.S. Private*, pg. 3518
GARLAND COMMERCIAL RANGES, LTD.—See Ali Holding S.r.l; *Int'l*, pg. 322
THE GARLAND COMPANY INC.—See Garland Industries Inc.; *U.S. Private*, pg. 1644
THE GARLAND COMPANY UK LIMITED—See Garland Industries Inc.; *U.S. Private*, pg. 1644
GARLAND INDUSTRIES INC.; *U.S. Private*, pg. 1644
GARLAND INSULATING COMPANY; *U.S. Private*, pg. 1644
GARLAND INSULATING, LTD.—See TopBuild Corp.; *U.S. Public*, pg. 2163
GARLAND SALES INC.; *U.S. Private*, pg. 1644
GARLAND'S, INC.; *U.S. Private*, pg. 1644
GARLAND SURGICARE PARTNERS, LTD.—See Tenet Healthcare Corporation; *U.S. Public*, pg. 2010
GARLAND WOODWORKS, INC.—See Prengler Products Corporation; *U.S. Private*, pg. 3252
GARLIK LIMITED—See Experian plc; *Int'l*, pg. 2588
GARLING CONSTRUCTION INC.; *U.S. Private*, pg. 1644
GARLINGHOUSE COMPANY; *U.S. Private*, pg. 1644
GARLOCK CHICAGO INC.—See Hines Corporation; *U.S. Private*, pg. 1949
GARLOCK DO BRASIL PRODUTOS INDUSTRIAIS LTDA.—See Enpro Inc.; *U.S. Public*, pg. 775
GARLOCK EAST EQUIPMENT CO—See Hines Corporation; *U.S. Private*, pg. 1949

GARNER ENVIRONMENTAL SERVICES

GARLOCK EQUIPMENT COMPANY—See Hines Corporation; *U.S. Private*, pg. 1949
GARLOCK GMBH—See Enpro Inc.; *U.S. Public*, pg. 775
GARLOCK (GREAT BRITAIN) LIMITED—See Enpro Inc.; *U.S. Public*, pg. 774
GARLOCK HYGIENIC TECHNOLOGIES, LLC—See Enpro Inc.; *U.S. Public*, pg. 775
GARLOCK INDIA PRIVATE LIMITED—See Enpro Inc.; *U.S. Public*, pg. 775
GARLOCK PIPELINE TECHNOLOGIES, INC.—See Enpro Inc.; *U.S. Public*, pg. 775
GARLOCK PIPELINE TECHNOLOGIES LIMITED—See Enpro Inc.; *U.S. Public*, pg. 775
GARLOCK PRINTING AND CONVERTING INC—See Seaman Paper Company of Massachusetts Inc.; *U.S. Private*, pg. 3585
GARLOCK SEALING TECHNOLOGIES (SHANGHAI) CO., LTD.—See Enpro Inc.; *U.S. Public*, pg. 775
GARLOCK SEALING TECHNOLOGIES—See Enpro Inc.; *U.S. Public*, pg. 775
GARLOCK SINGAPORE PTE. LTD.—See Enpro Inc.; *U.S. Public*, pg. 775
GARLOCK VALQUA JAPAN, INC.—See VALQUA, LTD.; *Int'l*, pg. 8122
GARLON POLYFAB INDUSTRIES LTD.; *Int'l*, pg. 2884
GARLYN O. SHELTON INC.; *U.S. Private*, pg. 1645
GARMAN CABINET & MILLWORK, INC.; *U.S. Private*, pg. 1645
GARMENDIA MACUS S.A.—See Air Products & Chemicals, Inc.; *U.S. Public*, pg. 66
GARMENT MANTRA LIFESTYLE LTD.; *Int'l*, pg. 2884
GARMEX SAIGON CORPORATION; *Int'l*, pg. 2884
GARMIN ARGENTINA SRL—See Garmin Ltd.; *Int'l*, pg. 2884
GARMIN (ASIA) CORPORATION—See Garmin Ltd.; *Int'l*, pg. 2885
GARMIN AT, INC.—See Garmin Ltd.; *Int'l*, pg. 2885
GARMIN AUSTRIA GMBH—See Garmin Ltd.; *Int'l*, pg. 2885
GARMIN AUSTRIA HOLDING GMBH—See Garmin Ltd.; *Int'l*, pg. 2885
GARMIN BELUX N.V./S.A—See Garmin Ltd.; *Int'l*, pg. 2885
GARMIN CHILE LDA—See Garmin Ltd.; *Int'l*, pg. 2884
GARMIN CHINA CO. LTD.—See Garmin Ltd.; *Int'l*, pg. 2884
GARMIN CORPORATION—See Garmin Ltd.; *Int'l*, pg. 2885
GARMIN CZECH S.R.O—See Garmin Ltd.; *Int'l*, pg. 2884
GARMIN DEUTSCHLAND BETEILIGUNGS GMBH & CO, KG—See Garmin Ltd.; *Int'l*, pg. 2885
GARMIN DEUTSCHLAND GMBH—See Garmin Ltd.; *Int'l*, pg. 2885
GARMIN (EUROPE) LTD.—See Garmin Ltd.; *Int'l*, pg. 2885
GARMIN FRANCE SAS—See Garmin Ltd.; *Int'l*, pg. 2885
GARMIN HRVATSKA D.O.O.—See Garmin Ltd.; *Int'l*, pg. 2884
GARMIN IBERIA S.A.—See Garmin Ltd.; *Int'l*, pg. 2884
GARMIN INDIA PRIVATE LTD.—See Garmin Ltd.; *Int'l*, pg. 2885
GARMIN INTERNATIONAL, INC.—See Garmin Ltd.; *Int'l*, pg. 2884
GARMIN ITALIA S.P.A.—See Garmin Ltd.; *Int'l*, pg. 2885
GARMIN LTD.; *Int'l*, pg. 2884
GARMIN NEW ZEALAND LTD.—See Garmin Ltd.; *Int'l*, pg. 2885
GARMIN NORDIC DENMARK A/S—See Garmin Ltd.; *Int'l*, pg. 2885
GARMIN NORDIC FINLAND OY—See Garmin Ltd.; *Int'l*, pg. 2885
GARMIN NORDIC NORWAY AS—See Garmin Ltd.; *Int'l*, pg. 2885
GARMIN NORDIC SWEDEN AB—See Garmin Ltd.; *Int'l*, pg. 2885
GARMIN NORGE AS—See Garmin Ltd.; *Int'l*, pg. 2885
GARMIN POLSKA SP. Z O.O.—See Garmin Ltd.; *Int'l*, pg. 2885
GARMIN PORTUGAL - EQUIPAMENTOS DE COMUNICACOES E DE NAVEGACAO LTDA.—See Garmin Ltd.; *Int'l*, pg. 2885
GARMIN SINGAPORE PTE. LTD.—See Garmin Ltd.; *Int'l*, pg. 2885
GARMIN SUOMI OY—See Garmin Ltd.; *Int'l*, pg. 2885
GARMIN SWEDEN AB—See Garmin Ltd.; *Int'l*, pg. 2885
GARMIN SWEDEN TECHNOLOGIES AB—See Garmin Ltd.; *Int'l*, pg. 2885
GARMIN SWITZERLAND GMBH—See Garmin Ltd.; *Int'l*, pg. 2885
GARMIN (THAILAND) LTD.—See Garmin Ltd.; *Int'l*, pg. 2884
GARMIN, TRGOVINA IN SERVIS, D.O.O.—See Garmin Ltd.; *Int'l*, pg. 2885
GARMIN USA, INC.—See Garmin Ltd.; *Int'l*, pg. 2885
GARMIN VIETNAM LTD.—See Garmin Ltd.; *Int'l*, pg. 2885
THE GARMON CORP.—See Swedencare AB; *Int'l*, pg. 7365
GARNER ENVIRONMENTAL SERVICES; *U.S. Private*, pg. 1645

GARNER ENVIRONMENTAL SERVICES

GARNER & GLOVER COMPANY—See Arthur J. Gallagher & Co.; *U.S. Public*, pg. 205
GARNER PRINTING COMPANY—See Chatham Asset Management, LLC; *U.S. Private*, pg. 862
GARNER REBUILT WATER PUMPS INCORPORATED; *U.S. Private*, pg. 1645
GARNER TRANSPORTATION GROUP, INC.; *U.S. Private*, pg. 1645
GARNET CONSTRUCTION LIMITED; *Int'l*, pg. 2885
GARNET ELECTRIC CO., INC.; *U.S. Private*, pg. 1645
GARNET HILL, INC.—See Qurate Retail, Inc.; *U.S. Public*, pg. 1758
GARNET INTERNATIONAL LIMITED; *Int'l*, pg. 2885
GARNETT & HELFRICH CAPITAL, LLC; *U.S. Private*, pg. 1645
GARNETT STATION PARTNERS, LLC; *U.S. Private*, pg. 1645
GARNEY COMPANIES, INC.—See Garney Holding Company, Inc.; *U.S. Private*, pg. 1645
GARNEY CONSTRUCTION COMPANY—See Garney Holding Company, Inc.; *U.S. Private*, pg. 1645
GARNEY HOLDING COMPANY, INC.; *U.S. Private*, pg. 1645
GARNIER BBDO—See Omnicom Group Inc.; *U.S. Public*, pg. 1575
GARO AB; *Int'l*, pg. 2885
GARO AS—See Garo AB; *Int'l*, pg. 2885
GARODIA CHEMICALS LIMITED; *Int'l*, pg. 2885
GAROFALO HEALTH CARE SPA; *Int'l*, pg. 2886
GARO POLSKA SP. Z O.O.—See Garo AB; *Int'l*, pg. 2885
GAROVAGLIO & ZORRAQUIN SA; *Int'l*, pg. 2886
GAR PAKISTAN (PVT.) LIMITED—See Golden Agri-Resources Ltd.; *Int'l*, pg. 3027
GARRAND & COMPANY; *U.S. Private*, pg. 1645
GARRATT-CALLAHAN COMPANY; *U.S. Private*, pg. 1645
GARRAWAYS LTD—See Primo Water Corporation; *U.S. Public*, pg. 1718
THE GARRETSON RESOLUTION GROUP, INC.—See Ontario Municipal Employees Retirement System; *Int'l*, pg. 5584
GARRETTCOM EUROPE LTD.—See Belden, Inc.; *U.S. Public*, pg. 294
GARRETTCOM INDIA PVT. LTD.—See Belden, Inc.; *U.S. Public*, pg. 294
GARRETT CONSTRUCTION COMPANY; *U.S. Private*, pg. 1645
GARRETT ENTERPRISES INC.; *U.S. Private*, pg. 1645
GARRETT MOTION INC.; *Int'l*, pg. 2886
GARRETT MOTION JAPAN INC.—See Garrett Motion Inc.; *Int'l*, pg. 2886
GARRETT PACKING CO.—See Smith Frozen Foods, Inc.; *U.S. Private*, pg. 3694
GARRETT PAPER, INC.—See Bain Capital, LP; *U.S. Private*, pg. 440
GARRETT REALTY SERVICES, INC.; *U.S. Private*, pg. 1645
GARRETT-STOTZ COMPANY, LLC—See Arthur J. Gallagher & Co.; *U.S. Public*, pg. 205
GARRIE PEST CONTROL, LLC—See Rentokil Initial plc; *Int'l*, pg. 6288
GARRINGTON GROUP OF COMPANIES INC.; *Int'l*, pg. 2886
GARRIS-EVANS LUMBER CO. INC.; *U.S. Private*, pg. 1645
GARRISON BREWER—See Champion Industries, Inc.; *U.S. Public*, pg. 478
GARRISON INVESTMENT GROUP LP; *U.S. Private*, pg. 1645
GARRITY ASPHALT RECLAIMING INC.; *U.S. Private*, pg. 1646
GARROTT BROTHERS CONTINUOUS MIX, INC.; *U.S. Private*, pg. 1646
GARROW OIL CORP.; *U.S. Private*, pg. 1646
GARRY GRIBBLE'S RUNNING SPORTS, LLC—See Pentland Group Limited; *Int'l*, pg. 5792
GARRY MERCER TRUCKING INC.; *Int'l*, pg. 2886
GARRY STRUTHERS ASSOCIATES, INC.; *U.S. Private*, pg. 1646
GARSITE PROGRESS LLC—See AFI Partners LLC; *U.S. Private*, pg. 123
THE GART COMPANIES, INC.; *U.S. Private*, pg. 4032
GARTEC LTD.—See Investment AB Latour; *Int'l*, pg. 3782
GARTENHILFE GES.M.B.H.—See Stender AG; *Int'l*, pg. 7207
GARTEN SERVICES, INC.; *U.S. Private*, pg. 1646
GARTNER AUSTRALASIA PTY. LTD.—See Gartner, Inc.; *U.S. Public*, pg. 906
GARTNER AUSTRALIA - BRISBANE—See Gartner, Inc.; *U.S. Public*, pg. 906
GARTNER AUSTRALIA - CANBERRA—See Gartner, Inc.; *U.S. Public*, pg. 907
GARTNER AUSTRALIA - MELBOURNE—See Gartner, Inc.; *U.S. Public*, pg. 907
GARTNER AUSTRIA GMBH—See Gartner, Inc.; *U.S. Public*, pg. 907
GARTNER BEIJING—See Gartner, Inc.; *U.S. Public*, pg. 907
GARTNER BELGIUM BVBA—See Gartner, Inc.; *U.S. Public*, pg. 907

GARTNER CANADA CO.—See Gartner, Inc.; *U.S. Public*, pg. 907
GARTNER CZECH REPUBLIC S.R.O.—See Gartner, Inc.; *U.S. Public*, pg. 907
GARTNER DANMARK APS—See Gartner, Inc.; *U.S. Public*, pg. 907
GARTNER ESPANA, S.L.—See Gartner, Inc.; *U.S. Public*, pg. 907
GARTNER EXTRUSION GMBH—See ALCO Hellas S.A.; *Int'l*, pg. 301
GARTNER FINLAND OY—See Gartner, Inc.; *U.S. Public*, pg. 907
GARTNER FRANCE S.A.R.L.—See Gartner, Inc.; *U.S. Public*, pg. 907
GARTNER HONG KONG, LIMITED—See Gartner, Inc.; *U.S. Public*, pg. 907
GARTNER, INC.; *U.S. Public*, pg. 906
GARTNER ISRAEL ADVISORY LTD.—See Gartner, Inc.; *U.S. Public*, pg. 907
GARTNER ITALIA, S.R.L.—See Gartner, Inc.; *U.S. Public*, pg. 907
GARTNER JAPAN LTD.—See Gartner, Inc.; *U.S. Public*, pg. 907
GARTNER NEDERLAND B.V.—See Gartner, Inc.; *U.S. Public*, pg. 907
GARTNER POLAND SP Z.O.O—See Gartner, Inc.; *U.S. Public*, pg. 907
GARTNER RESEARCH & ADVISORY KOREA CO., LTD.—See Gartner, Inc.; *U.S. Public*, pg. 907
GARTNER RUS LLC—See Gartner, Inc.; *U.S. Public*, pg. 907
GARTNER SAUDI ARABIA LTD—See Gartner, Inc.; *U.S. Public*, pg. 907
GARTNER STEEL AND GLASS GMBH—See Atlas Holdings, LLC; *U.S. Private*, pg. 377
GARTNER STUDIOS, INC.; *U.S. Private*, pg. 1646
GARTNER SVERIGE AB—See Gartner, Inc.; *U.S. Public*, pg. 907
GARTNER TURKEY TEKNOLOJI ARASTIRMA VE DANISMANLIK HIZMETLERI LIMITED SIRKETI—See Gartner, Inc.; *U.S. Public*, pg. 907
GARTNER U.K. LIMITED—See Gartner, Inc.; *U.S. Public*, pg. 907
GARTON TRACTOR INC.; *U.S. Private*, pg. 1646
GARTRAN, L.L.C.—See Waste Management, Inc.; *U.S. Public*, pg. 2331
GARUDA CAPITAL CORP.; *Int'l*, pg. 2886
GARUDAFOOD PUTRA PUTRI JAYA; *Int'l*, pg. 2886
GARUDA INDONESIA HOLIDAY FRANCE S.A.S—See PT Garuda Indonesia (Persero) Tbk; *Int'l*, pg. 6040
GARUDA INTERNATIONAL LIMITED—See Zhen Ding Technology Holding Limited; *Int'l*, pg. 8669
GARUDA PADANG RESTAURANT (SINGAPORE) PTE LTD—See Tung Lok Restaurants (2000) Ltd; *Int'l*, pg. 7971
GARUDA TECHNOLOGY CO., LTD.—See Zhen Ding Technology Holding Limited; *Int'l*, pg. 8669
GARVEY BUILDERS PROVIDERS LIMITED—See Grafton Group plc; *Int'l*, pg. 3050
GARVEY CORPORATION—See Columbus McKinnon Corporation; *U.S. Public*, pg. 536
GARVEY PRODUCTS INC.—See Taylor Corporation; *U.S. Private*, pg. 3938
GARVEY'S OFFICE PRODUCTS; *U.S. Private*, pg. 1646
GARVEY SPACECRAFT CORPORATION—See Vector Space Systems; *U.S. Private*, pg. 4353
GARVEY VOLKSWAGEN INC.; *U.S. Private*, pg. 1646
GARVIN CONSTRUCTION PRODUCTS, INC.—See Beacon Roofing Supply, Inc.; *U.S. Public*, pg. 286
GARVIN OIL COMPANY INC.; *U.S. Private*, pg. 1646
GARWARE HI-TECH FILMS LIMITED; *Int'l*, pg. 2886
GARWARE MARINE INDUSTRIES LTD.; *Int'l*, pg. 2886
GARWARE POLYESTER LTD. - CHIKALTHANA WORKS—See Garware Hi-Tech Films Limited; *Int'l*, pg. 2886
GARWARE POLYESTER LTD. - NASIK WORKS—See Garware Hi-Tech Films Limited; *Int'l*, pg. 2886
GARWARE POLYESTER LTD. - WALUJ WORKS—See Garware Hi-Tech Films Limited; *Int'l*, pg. 2886
GARWARE SYNTHETICS LIMITED; *Int'l*, pg. 2887
GARWARE TECHNICAL FIBRES LTD.; *Int'l*, pg. 2887
GARWICH BBDO (QUITO)—See Omnicom Group Inc.; *U.S. Public*, pg. 1575
GARWICH BBDO—See Omnicom Group Inc.; *U.S. Public*, pg. 1575
GARY A. DOSSICK & ASSOCIATES, INC.—See Callahan Financial Planning Company; *U.S. Private*, pg. 722
GARY AMOTH TRUCKING, INC.; *U.S. Private*, pg. 1646
GARY COMMUNITY INVESTMENT COMPANY; *U.S. Private*, pg. 1646
GARY D. NELSON ASSOCIATES, INC.; *U.S. Private*, pg. 1646
GARY G. OETGEN, INC.—See Fidelity National Financial, Inc.; *U.S. Public*, pg. 831
THE GARY GROUP; *U.S. Private*, pg. 4032
GARY-HOBART ROOFING & SUPPLY COMPANY—See Leonard Green & Partners, L.P.; *U.S. Private*, pg. 2429

CORPORATE AFFILIATIONS

GARY L. KAUFMAN FUNERAL HOME AT MEADOWRIDGE MEMORIAL PARK, INC.—See Service Corporation International; *U.S. Public*, pg. 1869
GARY MATHEWS MOTORS INC.; *U.S. Private*, pg. 1646
GARY MERLINO CONSTRUCTION CO., INC.; *U.S. Private*, pg. 1646
GARY METALS MANUFACTURING LLC; *U.S. Private*, pg. 1646
GARY RAILWAY COMPANY—See SoftBank Group Corp.; *Int'l*, pg. 7053
GARY'S & COMPANY NEWPORT BEACH; *U.S. Private*, pg. 1647
GARY'S U-PULL-IT, INC.—See Stellex Capital Management LP; *U.S. Private*, pg. 3800
GARY SURDYKE MOTORCYCLE INC.; *U.S. Private*, pg. 1646
GARY'S WINE & MARKETPLACE; *U.S. Private*, pg. 1647
GARY V. BURROWS INC.; *U.S. Private*, pg. 1646
GARY W. CURRY, INC.; *U.S. Private*, pg. 1646
GARY-WILLIAMS PRODUCTION CO.—See Gary Community Investment Company; *U.S. Private*, pg. 1646
GARY WOOD ASSOCIATES, INC.; *U.S. Private*, pg. 1647
GARY YAMAMOTO CUSTOM BAITS; *U.S. Private*, pg. 1647
GARY YEOMANS FORD INC.; *U.S. Private*, pg. 1647
GARZA CREATIVE GROUP; *U.S. Private*, pg. 1647
GAS2GRID LIMITED; *Int'l*, pg. 2887
GASAG AG—See ENGIE SA; *Int'l*, pg. 2429
GASAG AG—See E.ON SE; *Int'l*, pg. 2257
GASAG AG—See Vattenfall AB; *Int'l*, pg. 8137
GASAG CONTRACTING GMBH—See ENGIE SA; *Int'l*, pg. 2429
GASAG CONTRACTING GMBH—See E.ON SE; *Int'l*, pg. 2257
GASAG CONTRACTING GMBH—See Vattenfall AB; *Int'l*, pg. 8137
GASAG SOLUTION PLUS GMBH—See ENGIE SA; *Int'l*, pg. 2429
GASAG SOLUTION PLUS GMBH—See E.ON SE; *Int'l*, pg. 2257
GASAG SOLUTION PLUS GMBH—See Vattenfall AB; *Int'l*, pg. 8137
GASALARM A.D.; *Int'l*, pg. 2887
GAS & ALLOY SUPPLY COMPANY, INC.—See CI Capital Partners LLC; *U.S. Private*, pg. 895
GAS AND POWER CO., LTD—See Osaka Gas Co., Ltd.; *Int'l*, pg. 5645
GASAN ZAMMIT MOTORS CO., LTD.—See Honda Motor Co., Ltd.; *Int'l*, pg. 3460
GAS ARABIAN SERVICES CO.; *Int'l*, pg. 2887
GAS-ARC GROUP LIMITED—See Enovis Corporation; *U.S. Public*, pg. 773
GAS ATACAMA CHILE SA—See Enel S.p.A.; *Int'l*, pg. 2414
GASBARRE PRODUCTS INC., MCKEE CARBIDE TOOL DIVISION—See Gasbarre Products Inc.; *U.S. Private*, pg. 1648
GASBARRE PRODUCTS INC., SINTERITE FURNACE DIVISION—See Gasbarre Products Inc.; *U.S. Private*, pg. 1648
GASBARRE PRODUCTS INC.; *U.S. Private*, pg. 1648
GASBARRE PRODUCTS—See Gasbarre Products Inc.; *U.S. Private*, pg. 1648
GAS BETON CELKON A.D.; *Int'l*, pg. 2887
GASBOTTLING N.V.—See UGI Corporation; *U.S. Public*, pg. 2222
GASBOY INTERNATIONAL, INC.—See Danaher Corporation; *U.S. Public*, pg. 627
GASCADE GASTRANSPORT GMBH—See BASF SE; *Int'l*, pg. 883
GAS CALL SERVICES LIMITED; *Int'l*, pg. 2887
G.A.S. CAPITAL, INC.; *U.S. Private*, pg. 1630
GASCH PRINTING LLC; *U.S. Private*, pg. 1648
GASCO AFFILIATES, LLC—See CI Capital Partners LLC; *U.S. Private*, pg. 895
GASCO ENERGY, INC.; *U.S. Private*, pg. 1648
GASCO ENERGY SUPPLY, LLC—See Ferrellgas Partners, L.P.; *U.S. Public*, pg. 829
GASCOGNE BOIS ESCOURCE SAS—See Gascogne SA; *Int'l*, pg. 2887
GASCOGNE FLEXIBLE GERMANY GMBH—See Gascogne SA; *Int'l*, pg. 2887
GASCOGNE ITALIA SRL—See Gascogne SA; *Int'l*, pg. 2887
GASCOGNE LAMINATES SWITZERLAND SA—See UPM-Kymmene Corporation; *Int'l*, pg. 8091
GASCOGNE PACKAGING USA, INC.—See Gascogne SA; *Int'l*, pg. 2887
GASCOGNE PAPIER SAS—See Gascogne SA; *Int'l*, pg. 2887
GASCOGNE SACK AIGIS SA—See Gascogne SA; *Int'l*, pg. 2887
GASCOGNE SACK DEUTSCHLAND GMBH—See Gascogne SA; *Int'l*, pg. 2887
GASCOGNE SACS MIMIZAN SAS—See Gascogne SA; *Int'l*, pg. 2887
GASCOGNE SACS SAINT-HERBLAIN SAS—See Gascogne SA; *Int'l*, pg. 2888
GASCOGNE SA; *Int'l*, pg. 2887

COMPANY NAME INDEX

GASCOGNE SPAIN SL—See Gascogne SA; *Int'l*, pg. 2888
GASCOGNE UK LTD—See Gascogne SA; *Int'l*, pg. 2888
GASCOGNE USA, INC. - ORANGEVALE—See Gascogne SA; *Int'l*, pg. 2888
GASCOGNE USA INC—See Gascogne SA; *Int'l*, pg. 2888
THE GAS COMPANY LLC—See Macquarie Group Limited; *Int'l*, pg. 4628
GAS CONDITIONING OF MEXICO, S. DE R.L. DE C.V.—See Enerflex Ltd.; *Int'l*, pg. 2419
GAS CONNECT AUSTRIA GMBH—See Allianz SE; *Int'l*, pg. 344
GAS CONNECT AUSTRIA GMBH—See Eni S.p.A.; *Int'l*, pg. 2438
GAS CONNECT AUSTRIA GMBH—See OMV Aktiengesellschaft; *Int'l*, pg. 5567
GAS CONNECTION, LLC—See Suburban Propane Partners, L.P.; *U.S. Public*, pg. 1958
GAS CONTROL EQUIPMENT IBERICA S.L.—See Enovis Corporation; *U.S. Public*, pg. 772
GAS CONTROL EQUIPMENT S.A. DE C.V.—See Enovis Corporation; *U.S. Public*, pg. 773
GASCO PRODUCTION COMPANY—See Gasco Energy, Inc.; *U.S. Private*, pg. 1648
GASCOSAGE ELECTRIC COOPERATIVE; *U.S. Private*, pg. 1648
GASCOYNE RESOURCES LIMITED; *Int'l*, pg. 2888
GASDAL BYGNINGSINDUSTRI A/S—See VKR Holding A/S; *Int'l*, pg. 8281
GAS DEPOT OIL CO.; *U.S. Private*, pg. 1647
GAS DIRECT LIMITED—See Air Products & Chemicals, Inc.; *U.S. Public*, pg. 66
GAS DRIVE GLOBAL LP—See Enerflex Ltd.; *Int'l*, pg. 2419
GAS EQUIPMENT COMPANY, INC.; *U.S. Private*, pg. 1647
GAS EQUIPMENT COMPANY INC.—See Gas Equipment Company, Inc.; *U.S. Private*, pg. 1647
GASES & ARC SUPPLY, INC.—See CI Capital Partners LLC; *U.S. Private*, pg. 895
GASES DEL PACIFICO S.A.C.—See Grupo Aval Acciones y Valores S.A.; *Int'l*, pg. 3121
GASES INDUSTRIALES DE COLUMBIA S.A.—See Air Products & Chemicals, Inc.; *U.S. Public*, pg. 66
GASETERIA OIL CORP.; *U.S. Private*, pg. 1648
GAS-FIRED PRODUCTS, INC.; *U.S. Private*, pg. 1648
GAS-FIRED PRODUCTS (U.K.) LTD—See Gas-Fired Products, Inc.; *U.S. Private*, pg. 1648
GAS GALICIA SOCIEDAD PARA EL DESARROLLO DEL GAS, S.A.—See Naturgy Energy Group, S.A.; *Int'l*, pg. 5169
GASGRUVAN KALCIT AB—See Omya (Schweiz) AG; *Int'l*, pg. 5570
GASHO OF JAPAN INTERNATIONAL LTD.; *U.S. Private*, pg. 1648
GASHO OF JAPAN LONG ISLAND—See Gasho of Japan International Ltd.; *U.S. Private*, pg. 1648
G-ASIAPACIFIC SDN. BHD.—See K-One Technology Berhad; *Int'l*, pg. 4042
GAS INCORPORATED; *U.S. Private*, pg. 1647
GASIN - GASES INDUSTRIAIS, S.A.R.L.—See Air Products & Chemicals, Inc.; *U.S. Public*, pg. 66
GASIN II UNIPESSOAL LDA—See Air Products & Chemicals, Inc.; *U.S. Public*, pg. 66
GAS INNOVATIONS INC.; *U.S. Private*, pg. 1647
GASINSULAR - COMBUSTIVEIS DO ATLANTICO, S.A.—See Galp Energia SGPS, S.A.; *Int'l*, pg. 2875
GAS INVESTMENTS & SERVICES COMPANY LIMITED—See Shell plc; *Int'l*, pg. 6795
GASIQ AB—See Lagercrantz Group AB; *Int'l*, pg. 4394
GASKELL MACKAY CARPETS LIMITED—See Victoria Plc; *Int'l*, pg. 8188
GASKET (SUZHOU) VALVE COMPONENTS COMPANY, LIMITED—See TotalEnergies SE; *Int'l*, pg. 7836
GAS KING OIL CO. LTD.; *Int'l*, pg. 2887
GAS LAMP MEDIA; *U.S. Private*, pg. 1647
GASLAMP POPCORN COMPANY, LLC—See Rudolph Foods Company; *U.S. Private*, pg. 3502
GAS LAND PETROLEUM INC.; *U.S. Private*, pg. 1647
GAS LAND TRUCKING INC.—See Gas Land Petroleum Inc.; *U.S. Private*, pg. 1647
GASLIGHT PROMOTIONAL CONSULTING, INC.—See CE Competitive Edge LLC; *U.S. Private*, pg. 803
GAS LINK GLOBAL LIMITED—See Liquefied Natural Gas Limited; *Int'l*, pg. 4522
GASLINK NIGERIA LIMITED—See Oando PLC; *Int'l*, pg. 5505
GAS LIVING CHUBU CO., LTD.—See Sala Corporation; *Int'l*, pg. 6490
GAS LIVING HAMAMATSU HOKUBU CO., LTD.—See Sala Corporation; *Int'l*, pg. 6490
GAS LIVING HAMAMATSU SEIBU CO., LTD.—See Sala Corporation; *Int'l*, pg. 6490
GASLOG ASIA PTE. LTD.—See GasLog Ltd.; *Int'l*, pg. 2888
GAS LOGIC LTD—See Pearson plc; *Int'l*, pg. 5775
GASLOG LNG SERVICES LTD.—See GasLog Ltd.; *Int'l*, pg. 2888
GASLOG LTD.; *Int'l*, pg. 2888

GASLOG PARTNERS LP—See GasLog Ltd.; *Int'l*, pg. 2888
GAS MAINTENANCE AND TRAINING LIMITED—See Booth Securities Ltd.; *Int'l*, pg. 1111
GAS MALAYSIA BERHAD; *Int'l*, pg. 2887
GAS MALAYSIA VIRTUAL PIPELINE SDN. BHD.—See Gas Malaysia Berhad; *Int'l*, pg. 2887
GAS MANAGEMENT SERVICES LIMITED—See Publigas; *Int'l*, pg. 6115
GASMAR - TRANSPORTES MARITIMOS, LDA.—See Galp Energia SGPS, S.A.; *Int'l*, pg. 2875
GASMART USA INC.; *U.S. Private*, pg. 1648
GAS MEASUREMENT INSTRUMENTS LIMITED—See Teledyne Technologies Incorporated; *U.S. Public*, pg. 1992
GASMET TECHNOLOGIES (ASIA) LTD.—See Nederman Holding AB; *Int'l*, pg. 5189
GASMET TECHNOLOGIES GMBH—See Nederman Holding AB; *Int'l*, pg. 5189
GASMET TECHNOLOGIES INC.—See Nederman Holding AB; *Int'l*, pg. 5189
GASMET TECHNOLOGIES OY—See Nederman Holding AB; *Int'l*, pg. 5189
GASMET TECHNOLOGIES (UK) LTD.—See Nederman Holding AB; *Int'l*, pg. 5189
GAS MONKEY GARAGE; *U.S. Private*, pg. 1647
G&A SNACK DISTRIBUTING INC.—See Grande Foods California Corporation; *U.S. Private*, pg. 1753
GAS NATURAL ANDALUCIA S.A.—See Naturgy Energy Group, S.A.; *Int'l*, pg. 5169
GAS NATURAL CASTILLA LA-MANCHA, S.A.—See Naturgy Energy Group, S.A.; *Int'l*, pg. 5169
GAS NATURAL CASTILLA Y LEON, S.A.—See Naturgy Energy Group, S.A.; *Int'l*, pg. 5169
GAS NATURAL CEGAS, S.A.—See Naturgy Energy Group, S.A.; *Int'l*, pg. 5169
GAS NATURAL COMERCIALIZADORA, S.A.—See Naturgy Energy Group, S.A.; *Int'l*, pg. 5169
GAS NATURAL DE LIMA Y CALLAO S.A.—See Ashmore Group plc; *Int'l*, pg. 608
GAS NATURAL EUROPE, S.A.S.—See Naturgy Energy Group, S.A.; *Int'l*, pg. 5169
GAS NATURAL LA CORUNA, S.A.—See Naturgy Energy Group, S.A.; *Int'l*, pg. 5169
GAS NATURAL MEXICO, S.A. DE C.V.—See Naturgy Energy Group, S.A.; *Int'l*, pg. 5169
GAS NATURAL MURCIA SDG, S.A.—See Naturgy Energy Group, S.A.; *Int'l*, pg. 5169
GAS NATURAL REDES GLP, S.A.—See Naturgy Energy Group, S.A.; *Int'l*, pg. 5169
GAS NATURAL RIOJA, S.A.—See Naturgy Energy Group, S.A.; *Int'l*, pg. 5169
GAS NAVARRA, S.A.—See Naturgy Energy Group, S.A.; *Int'l*, pg. 5169
GAS NEA SA; *Int'l*, pg. 2887
GASNETZ HAMBURG GMBH; *Int'l*, pg. 2888
GASNOR AS—See Shell plc; *Int'l*, pg. 6795
GASNOR S.A.—See Naturgy Energy Group, S.A.; *Int'l*, pg. 5169
GASODUCTO ATACAMA ARGENTINA SA—See Enel S.p.A.; *Int'l*, pg. 2413
GASODUCTO DEL PACIFICO S.A.—See Naturgy Energy Group, S.A.; *Int'l*, pg. 5169
GASODUCTO GASANDES S.A.—See The AES Corporation; *U.S. Public*, pg. 2031
GASODUCTO NOR ANDINO ARGENTINA—See ENGIE SA; *Int'l*, pg. 2434
GASODUCTO NOR ANDINO CHILE S.A.—See ENGIE SA; *Int'l*, pg. 2434
GASODUCTOS Y REDES GISCA, S.A.—See ACS, Actividades de Construccion y Servicios, S.A.; *Int'l*, pg. 112
GASODUTO CAMPO MAIOR-LEIRIA_BRAGA—See REN - Redes Energeticas Nacionais SGPS, S.A.; *Int'l*, pg. 6272
GASOIL ENGINEERING A.S.—See PBG S.A.; *Int'l*, pg. 5765
GAS OIL LLC—See PJSC Gazprom; *Int'l*, pg. 5879
GASOL PLC; *Int'l*, pg. 2888
GASPAL CO LTD—See Daito Trust Construction Co., Ltd.; *Int'l*, pg. 1943
GASPAL KYUSHU CORPORATION—See Daito Trust Construction Co., Ltd.; *Int'l*, pg. 1943
GASPAR & ASOCIADOS—See The Interpublic Group of Companies, Inc.; *U.S. Public*, pg. 2104
GASPARILLA INN, INC.; *U.S. Private*, pg. 1648
GASPARILLA ISLAND CONSERVATION & IMPROVEMENT ASSOCIATION, INC.; *U.S. Private*, pg. 1648
GASPARI NUTRA LLC; *U.S. Private*, pg. 1648
GASPARI NUTRITION, INC.—See Gaspari Nutra LLC; *U.S. Private*, pg. 1648
GASPER ENGINEERING, INC—See Arsenal Capital Management LP; *U.S. Private*, pg. 338
GASPER JANIC ENERGA D.O.O.—See TCS TurControlSysteme AG; *Int'l*, pg. 7485
GAS PLUS INC.; *Int'l*, pg. 2887
GAS PLUS INTERNATIONAL B.V.—See Gas Plus S.p.A.; *Int'l*, pg. 2887
GAS PLUS S.P.A.; *Int'l*, pg. 2887

GAS PLUS VENDITE S.R.L.—See Gas Plus S.p.A.; *Int'l*, pg. 2887
GASPOL S.A.—See SHV Holdings N.V.; *Int'l*, pg. 6873
GASPOROX AB; *Int'l*, pg. 2888
GAS PRODUCTS LIMITED—See Massy Holdings Ltd.; *Int'l*, pg. 4723
GASPROJECT S.A.—See Air Products & Chemicals, Inc.; *U.S. Public*, pg. 66
GAS PURIFICATION ENGINEERING CORPORATION; *U.S. Private*, pg. 1647
GASQUE ADVERTISING, INC.; *U.S. Private*, pg. 1648
GASQUET ENTREPRISE—See VINCI S.A.; *Int'l*, pg. 8237
GAS RECOVERY SYSTEMS INC.; *U.S. Private*, pg. 1647
GASSCO AS; *Int'l*, pg. 2888
GASSEARCH DRILLING SERVICES CORPORATION—See Coterra Energy Inc.; *U.S. Public*, pg. 587
GASSECURE AS—See Draegerwerk AG & Co. KGaA; *Int'l*, pg. 2198
GASSER CHAIR COMPANY INC.; *U.S. Private*, pg. 1648
GASSER & SONS, INC.; *U.S. Private*, pg. 1648
GAS SERVICES NZ LTD.; *Int'l*, pg. 2887
GASSIER SAS—See AdVini S.A.; *Int'l*, pg. 168
GASSO PORTUGAL LDA—See Comercial Gasso SA; *Int'l*, pg. 1710
GAS STRATEGIES CONSULTING LTD.—See S&P Global Inc.; *U.S. Public*, pg. 1831
GAS STRATEGIES GROUP LTD—See S&P Global Inc.; *U.S. Public*, pg. 1831
GAS SUPPLY COMPANY THESSALONIKI - THESSALIA SA—See Eni S.p.A.; *Int'l*, pg. 2438
GAS SUPPLY RESOURCES LLC—See NGL Energy Partners LP; *U.S. Public*, pg. 1527
GAS SUR S.A.—See Naturgy Energy Group, S.A.; *Int'l*, pg. 5169
GASTAR CO., LTD.—See Rinnai Corporation; *Int'l*, pg. 6344
GASTAR EXPLORATION LLC—See Ares Management Corporation; *U.S. Public*, pg. 189
GAST ASIA, INC.—See IDEX Corp; *U.S. Public*, pg. 1090
GASTECH-ENERGI A/S—See Ariston Holding N.V.; *Int'l*, pg. 567
GAS TECHNOLOGY INSTITUTE; *U.S. Private*, pg. 1647
GAS TECHNOLOGY PRODUCTS LLC—See Merichem Company; *U.S. Private*, pg. 2672
GASTEC SERVICE INC.—See Sala Corporation; *Int'l*, pg. 6490
GASTEHAUS SCHLOB SAARECK BETREIBERGESELLSCHAFT MBH—See Villeroy & Boch AG; *Int'l*, pg. 8207
GASTEINER MINERALWASSER GMBH—See L'Arche Green N.V.; *Int'l*, pg. 4377
GASTEL DOO—See P.S. Telefonija a.d. Beograd; *Int'l*, pg. 5682
GASTERRA B.V.; *Int'l*, pg. 2888
GAST GROUP LTD.—See IDEX Corp; *U.S. Public*, pg. 1090
GASTITE SYSTEMS DEUTSCHLAND GMBH—See Smiths Group plc; *Int'l*, pg. 7009
GASTITE SYSTEMS LIMITED—See Smiths Group plc; *Int'l*, pg. 7009
GAST MANUFACTURING, INC.—See IDEX Corp; *U.S. Public*, pg. 1090
GAS TO LIQUID JSC; *Int'l*, pg. 2887
GASTON ADVERTISING; *U.S. Private*, pg. 1649
GASTON COUNTY DYEING MACHINE COMPANY; *U.S. Private*, pg. 1649
GASTON ELECTRICAL CO., LLC—See EMCOR Group, Inc.; *U.S. Public*, pg. 738
THE GASTON GAZETTE—See Gannett Co., Inc.; *U.S. Public*, pg. 906
GASTON GRAWEY; *Int'l*, pg. 2888
GASTONIA SHEET METAL; *U.S. Private*, pg. 1649
GASTON INVESTMENTS SP. Z O.O.—See CPD S.A.; *Int'l*, pg. 1824
GASTON SECURITY INC.—See Apollo Global Management, Inc.; *U.S. Public*, pg. 146
GASTON & SHEEHAN AUCTIONEERS, INC.; *U.S. Private*, pg. 1648
GASTON SYSTEMS, INC.—See Tubular Textile Machinery, Inc.; *U.S. Private*, pg. 4256
GAS TRANSMISSION NORTHWEST LLC—See TC Energy Corporation; *Int'l*, pg. 7482
GAS TRANSMISSION SYSTEMS, INC.—See Goldberg Lindsay & Co., LLC; *U.S. Private*, pg. 1729
GASTRANSPORT NORD GMBH—See EWE Aktiengesellschaft; *Int'l*, pg. 2575
GAS TRANSPORT SERVICES B.V.—See N.V. Nederlandse Gasunie; *Int'l*, pg. 5117
GASTROENTEROLOGY ASSOCIATES OF NORTHERN VIRGINIA, LLC—See Gastro Health, LLC; *U.S. Private*, pg. 1649
GASTROENTEROLOGY SPECIALISTS OF MIDDLE TENNESSEE, LLC—See HCA Healthcare, Inc.; *U.S. Public*, pg. 996
GASTRO HEALTH, LLC; *U.S. Private*, pg. 1649
GASTRONOMICA SANTA FE, S.A. DE C.V.—See Industry Super Holdings Pty. Ltd.; *Int'l*, pg. 3675
GASTRONOMIE- U. UNTERHALTUNGSELEKTRONIK BETRIEBS GMBH—See Novomatic AG; *Int'l*, pg. 5467

GASTRONOM SA

GASTRONOM SA; *Int'l*, pg. 2888
GASTRONOMY INC.; *U.S. Private*, pg. 1649
GASTRO PRIMO LIMITED—See Bakkavor Group plc; *Int'l*, pg. 806
GASTRO STAR AG—See Coop-Gruppe Genossenschaft; *Int'l*, pg. 1790
GAS TURBINE EFFICIENCY AB—See Gas Turbine Efficiency, LLC; *U.S. Private*, pg. 1647
GAS TURBINE EFFICIENCY, LLC; *U.S. Private*, pg. 1647
GASUM ENERGIAPALVELUT OY—See Gasum Oy; *Int'l*, pg. 2888
GASUM OY; *Int'l*, pg. 2888
GASUNIE BBL B.V.—See N.V. Nederlandse Gasunie; *Int'l*, pg. 5117
GASUNIE DEUTSCHLAND GMBH & CO. KG—See N.V. Nederlandse Gasunie; *Int'l*, pg. 5117
GASUNIE ENGINEERING B.V.—See N.V. Nederlandse Gasunie; *Int'l*, pg. 5117
GASUNIE INFRASTRUKTUR AG—See N.V. Nederlandse Gasunie; *Int'l*, pg. 5117
GASUNIE LNG HOLDING B.V.—See N.V. Nederlandse Gasunie; *Int'l*, pg. 5117
GASUNIE ZUIDWENDING B.V.—See N.V. Nederlandse Gasunie; *Int'l*, pg. 5117
GAS-UNION GMBH—See E.ON SE; *Int'l*, pg. 2255
GAS VALPO SPA—See Marubeni Corporation; *Int'l*, pg. 4705
GASVERSORGUNG GORLITZ GMBH—See Veolia Environnement S.A.; *Int'l*, pg. 8153
GASVERSORGUNG HUNXE GMBH—See Gelsenwasser AG; *Int'l*, pg. 2914
GASVERSORGUNG IM LANDKREIS GIFHORN GMBH—See E.ON SE; *Int'l*, pg. 2257
GASVERSORGUNG SUDDEUTSCHLAND GMBH—See EnBW Energie Baden-Wurttemberg AG; *Int'l*, pg. 2399
GASVERSORGUNG UNTERLAND GMBH—See EnBW Energie Baden-Wurttemberg AG; *Int'l*, pg. 2399
GAS/WILSON, L.P.—See G.A.S. Capital, Inc.; *U.S. Private*, pg. 1630
GAS Y ELECTRICIDAD GENERACION SAU—See Enel S.p.A.; *Int'l*, pg. 2414
GATACKO POLJE A.D.; *Int'l*, pg. 2888
GAT AIRLINE GROUND SUPPORT, INC.—See Atlantic Street Capital Management LLC; *U.S. Private*, pg. 374
GATAN, INC.—See AMETEK, Inc.; *U.S. Public*, pg. 120
GATAN, INC.—See AMETEK, Inc.; *U.S. Public*, pg. 120
GATAN U.K. LIMITED—See Roper Technologies, Inc.; *U.S. Public*, pg. 1811
GATEAU AB—See Oy Karl Fazer Ab; *Int'l*, pg. 5677
GATECHNOLOGIES CO., LTD.; *Int'l*, pg. 2888
GATE CITY BANK; *U.S. Private*, pg. 1649
GATE CITY BEVERAGE DISTRIBUTORS—See Reyes Holdings, LLC; *U.S. Private*, pg. 3418
GATE CITY LINCOLN MERCURY; *U.S. Private*, pg. 1649
GATE FRANCE SAS—See Johnson Electric Holdings Limited; *Int'l*, pg. 3990
GATE GOURMET AEROPORT DE BALE-MULHOUSE SAS—See RRJ Capital Ltd.; *Int'l*, pg. 6417
GATE GOURMET AMSTERDAM B.V.—See RRJ Capital Ltd.; *Int'l*, pg. 6417
GATE GOURMET ARGENTINA S.R.L.—See RRJ Capital Ltd.; *Int'l*, pg. 6417
GATE GOURMET CANADA INC.—See RRJ Capital Ltd.; *Int'l*, pg. 6417
GATE GOURMET COLOMBIA LTDA—See RRJ Capital Ltd.; *Int'l*, pg. 6417
GATE GOURMET DEL ECUADOR CIA LTDA.—See RRJ Capital Ltd.; *Int'l*, pg. 6417
GATE GOURMET DENMARK APS—See RRJ Capital Ltd.; *Int'l*, pg. 6417
GATE GOURMET GMBH DEUTSCHLAND—See RRJ Capital Ltd.; *Int'l*, pg. 6417
GATE GOURMET GMBH WEST—See RRJ Capital Ltd.; *Int'l*, pg. 6417
GATE GOURMET (HOLDINGS) PTY. LTD.—See RRJ Capital Ltd.; *Int'l*, pg. 6417
GATE GOURMET HOLDINGS UK LTD.—See RRJ Capital Ltd.; *Int'l*, pg. 6417
GATE GOURMET, INC.—See RRJ Capital Ltd.; *Int'l*, pg. 6417
GATE GOURMET IRELAND LTD—See RRJ Capital Ltd.; *Int'l*, pg. 6417
GATE GOURMET LONDON LTD.—See RRJ Capital Ltd.; *Int'l*, pg. 6417
GATE GOURMET NORTHERN EUROPE APS—See RRJ Capital Ltd.; *Int'l*, pg. 6417
GATE GOURMET NORWAY AS—See RRJ Capital Ltd.; *Int'l*, pg. 6417
GATE GOURMET PERU S.R.L.—See RRJ Capital Ltd.; *Int'l*, pg. 6417
GATE GOURMET SINGAPORE PTE LTD—See RRJ Capital Ltd.; *Int'l*, pg. 6417
GATE GOURMET SWEDEN AB—See RRJ Capital Ltd.; *Int'l*, pg. 6417
GATE GOURMET SWITZERLAND GMBH—See RRJ Capital Ltd.; *Int'l*, pg. 6417
GATEGROUP HOLDING AG—See RRJ Capital Ltd.; *Int'l*, pg. 6416

GATEHOUSE BANK PLC—See The Securities House K.S.C.C.; *Int'l*, pg. 7681
GATEHOUSE COMPANIES, INC.; *U.S. Private*, pg. 1649
GATEHOUSE CONSULTING LIMITED—See Arthur J. Gallagher & Co.; *U.S. Public*, pg. 205
GATEHOUSE LIVE, LLC—See Gannett Co., Inc.; *U.S. Public*, pg. 901
GATEHOUSE MEDIA, LLC—See Gannett Co., Inc.; *U.S. Public*, pg. 901
GATEHOUSE MEDIA NEW ENGLAND—See Gannett Co., Inc.; *U.S. Public*, pg. 901
GATEHOUSE MEDIA OHIO HOLDINGS II, INC.—See Gannett Co., Inc.; *U.S. Public*, pg. 903
GATE INFORMATIC AG—See Bechtle AG; *Int'l*, pg. 938
GATEKEEPER INTELLIGENT SECURITY UK LTD.—See OSI Systems, Inc.; *U.S. Public*, pg. 1621
GATEKEEPER SECURITY MIDDLE EAST FTZ—See OSI Systems, Inc.; *U.S. Public*, pg. 1621
GATEKEEPER SERVICES LIMITED—See Mastercard Incorporated; *U.S. Public*, pg. 1394
GATEKEEPER SYSTEMS CANADA, LTD.—See The Graham Group, Inc.; *U.S. Private*, pg. 4037
GATEKEEPER SYSTEMS (HK), LTD.—See The Graham Group, Inc.; *U.S. Private*, pg. 4036
GATEKEEPER SYSTEMS INC.; *Int'l*, pg. 2889
GATEKEEPER SYSTEMS, INC.—See The Graham Group, Inc.; *U.S. Private*, pg. 4036
GATEKEEPER SYSTEMS UK, LTD.—See The Graham Group, Inc.; *U.S. Private*, pg. 4037
GATEKEEPER USA, INC.; *U.S. Public*, pg. 907
GATELAB S.R.L.—See London Stock Exchange Group plc; *Int'l*, pg. 4548
GA TELESIS COMPOSITE REPAIR GROUP SOUTHEAST—See GA Telesis LLC; *U.S. Private*, pg. 1632
GA TELESIS LLC; *U.S. Private*, pg. 1632
GA TELESIS UK LTD.—See GA Telesis LLC; *U.S. Private*, pg. 1632
GATELEY (HOLDINGS) PLC; *Int'l*, pg. 2889
GATELY COMMUNICATION COMPANY—See Sentinel Capital Partners, L.L.C.; *U.S. Private*, pg. 3609
GATE MANOR APARTMENTS, LTD., A TENNESSEE LIMITED PARTNERSHIP—See Apartment Investment and Management Company; *U.S. Public*, pg. 144
GATE MARITIME PROPERTIES, INC.—See Gate Petroleum Company; *U.S. Private*, pg. 1649
GATE MARKETING—See Gate Petroleum Company; *U.S. Private*, pg. 1649
GATEMORE CAPITAL MANAGEMENT LLP; *Int'l*, pg. 2889
GATEONE, INC.; *U.S. Private*, pg. 1649
GATE PETROLEUM COMPANY; *U.S. Private*, pg. 1649
GATE PETROLEUM - DEVELOPMENT DIVISION—See Gate Petroleum Company; *U.S. Private*, pg. 1649
GATE PRECAST COMPANY - JACKSONVILLE—See Gate Petroleum Company; *U.S. Private*, pg. 1649
GATE PRECAST COMPANY—See Gate Petroleum Company; *U.S. Private*, pg. 1649
GATE PRECAST CO.—See Gate Petroleum Company; *U.S. Private*, pg. 1649
GATE PRECAST CO.—See Gate Petroleum Company; *U.S. Private*, pg. 1649
GATE PRECAST CO.—See Gate Petroleum Company; *U.S. Private*, pg. 1649
GATE PRECAST CO.—See Gate Petroleum Company; *U.S. Private*, pg. 1649
GATE PRECAST CO.—See Gate Petroleum Company; *U.S. Private*, pg. 1649
GATE RIVERPLACE COMPANY—See Gate Petroleum Company; *U.S. Private*, pg. 1649
GATESAIR, INC. - QUINCY—See The Gores Group, LLC; *U.S. Private*, pg. 4034
GATESAIR, INC.—See The Gores Group, LLC; *U.S. Private*, pg. 4034
GATES ARGENTINA S.A.—See Blackstone Inc.; *U.S. Public*, pg. 353
GATES AUSTRALIA PTY. LTD.—See Blackstone Inc.; *U.S. Public*, pg. 353
GATES AUTOMOTIVE CENTER; *U.S. Private*, pg. 1650
GATES BANKING & TRUST COMPANY—See Security BanCorp of Tennessee, Inc.; *U.S. Private*, pg. 3595
GATES CANADA INC.—See Blackstone Inc.; *U.S. Public*, pg. 353
GATES CORPORATION—See Blackstone Inc.; *U.S. Public*, pg. 353
GATES CORP—See Blackstone Inc.; *U.S. Public*, pg. 354
GATES CORP—See Blackstone Inc.; *U.S. Public*, pg. 353
GATES DE MEXICO S.A. DE C.V.—See Blackstone Inc.; *U.S. Public*, pg. 354
GATES DO BRASIL INDUSTRIA E COMERICO LIMITED—See Blackstone Inc.; *U.S. Public*, pg. 354
GATES EUROPE B.V.B.A—See Blackstone Inc.; *U.S. Public*, pg. 354
GATES FINANCING, LLC—See AvalonBay Communities, Inc.; *U.S. Public*, pg. 240
GATES GROUP CAPITAL PARTNERS, LLC; *U.S. Private*, pg. 1650

CORPORATE AFFILIATIONS

GATES HYDRAULICS LTD.—See Blackstone Inc.; *U.S. Public*, pg. 354
GATES INDUSTRIAL CORPORATION PLC—See Blackstone Inc.; *U.S. Public*, pg. 353
GATESMAN, INC. - CHICAGO—See Gatesman, Inc.; *U.S. Private*, pg. 1650
GATESMAN, INC.; *U.S. Private*, pg. 1650
GATESMAN, INC. - SPRINGFIELD—See Gatesman, Inc.; *U.S. Private*, pg. 1650
GATES PT SPAIN S.A.—See Blackstone Inc.; *U.S. Public*, pg. 354
GATE S.R.L.—See Johnson Electric Holdings Limited; *Int'l*, pg. 3990
GATES RUBBER CO. INC.—See Blackstone Inc.; *U.S. Public*, pg. 354
THE GATES RUBBER COMPANY—See Blackstone Inc.; *U.S. Public*, pg. 354
GATES & SONS INCORPORATED; *U.S. Private*, pg. 1649
GATES UNITTA ASIA COMPANY—See Nitta Corporation; *Int'l*, pg. 5382
GATETECH TECHNOLOGY INC.—See China Motor Corporation; *Int'l*, pg. 1525
GATE TERMINAL B.V.—See N.V. Nederlandse Gasunie; *Int'l*, pg. 5117
GATE TERMINAL MANAGEMENT B.V.—See N.V. Nederlandse Gasunie; *Int'l*, pg. 5117
GATE THREE HEALTHCARE LLC—See The Ensign Group, Inc.; *U.S. Public*, pg. 2071
GATEWAY AMBULANCE SERVICE LLC—See Interlock Industries, Inc.; *U.S. Private*, pg. 2111
GATEWAY ANALYTICAL LLC—See AptarGroup, Inc.; *U.S. Public*, pg. 174
GATEWAY BANK, F.S.B.—See RBB Bancorp; *U.S. Public*, pg. 1766
GATEWAY BOBCAT, LLC—See Brightstar Capital Partners, L.P.; *U.S. Private*, pg. 653
GATEWAY BUICK GMC; *U.S. Private*, pg. 1650
GATEWAY CASINOS & ENTERTAINMENT LIMITED—See The Catalyst Capital Group Inc.; *Int'l*, pg. 7630
GATEWAY CHEMICALS, LTD.—See Iron Path Capital, L.P.; *U.S. Private*, pg. 2139
GATEWAY COMPANY; *U.S. Private*, pg. 1650
GATEWAY CON FORMING SYSTEMS; *U.S. Private*, pg. 1650
GATEWAY CONSTRUCTION & ENGINEERING LTD.; *Int'l*, pg. 2889
GATEWAY DISTRIBUTORS INC.—See Fedway Associates Inc.; *U.S. Private*, pg. 1492
GATEWAY DISTRIPARKS LTD.; *Int'l*, pg. 2889
GATEWAY ECONOMIC DEVELOPMENT CORPORATION OF GREATER CLEVELAND; *U.S. Private*, pg. 1650
GATEWAY ENDOSCOPY CENTER, L.P.—See Tenet Healthcare Corporation; *U.S. Public*, pg. 2010
GATEWAY ENERGY COMPANY, LLC; *U.S. Private*, pg. 1650
GATEWAY ENERGY SERVICES CORPORATION—See NRG Energy, Inc.; *U.S. Public*, pg. 1549
GATEWAY ENTERPRISE COMPANY LIMITED—See Aspial Corporation Limited; *Int'l*, pg. 630
GATEWAY ENTERPRISE COMPANY LIMITED—See Fragrance Group Limited; *Int'l*, pg. 2758
GATEWAY EUROPE B.V.—See Acer Incorporated; *Int'l*, pg. 99
GATEWAY FOODS INC.; *U.S. Private*, pg. 1650
GATEWAY FS, INC.; *U.S. Private*, pg. 1650
GATEWAY GATHERING & MARKETING CO.—See Rosemore Inc.; *U.S. Private*, pg. 3483
GATEWAY GROUP ONE; *U.S. Private*, pg. 1650
GATEWAY GROUP ONE—See Gateway Group One; *U.S. Private*, pg. 1650
GATEWAY HEALTH ALLIANCE, INC.—See Apollo Global Management, Inc.; *U.S. Public*, pg. 155
GATEWAY HEALTHCARE, INC.—See The Ensign Group, Inc.; *U.S. Public*, pg. 2071
GATEWAY HEALTH PLAN, INC.—See Highmark Health; *U.S. Private*, pg. 1940
GATEWAY HEALTH SYSTEM—See Community Health Systems, Inc.; *U.S. Public*, pg. 552
GATEWAY HOME & GARDEN CENTER, LLC—See SiteOne Landscape Supply, Inc.; *U.S. Public*, pg. 1888
GATEWAY HOMES LTD; *U.S. Private*, pg. 1650
GATEWAY HONG KONG LTD—See Acer Incorporated; *Int'l*, pg. 99
GATEWAY, INC.—See Acer Incorporated; *Int'l*, pg. 99
GATEWAY INSTITUTIONAL TAX CREDIT FUND II, LTD—See Raymond James Financial, Inc.; *U.S. Public*, pg. 1764
GATEWAY INSURANCE COMPANY—See Buckle Agency LLC; *U.S. Private*, pg. 678
GATEWAY INSURANCE SERVICES, INC.—See TrueNorth Companies L.C.; *U.S. Private*, pg. 4249
GATEWAY INVESTMENT ADVISERS, L.P.—See Groupe BPCE; *Int'l*, pg. 3096
GATEWAY LIFESTYLE GROUP; *Int'l*, pg. 2889
GATEWAY LINCOLN-MERCURY INCORPORATED; *U.S. Private*, pg. 1650
GATEWAY-LONGVIEW, INC.; *U.S. Private*, pg. 1651
GATEWAY MANAGEMENT SERVICES LTD; *U.S. Private*, pg. 1650

GATEWAY MANUFACTURING LLC—See Acer Incorporated; *Int'l*, pg. 99
GATEWAY MINING LIMITED; *Int'l*, pg. 2889
GATEWAY MORTGAGE GROUP LLC; *U.S. Private*, pg. 1650
GATEWAY MOTORSPORTS PARK; *U.S. Private*, pg. 1650
GATEWAY PACKAGING COMPANY LLC—See The Pritzker Group - Chicago, LLC; *U.S. Private*, pg. 4099
GATEWAY PIPELINE COMPANY—See Gateway Energy Company, LLC; *U.S. Private*, pg. 1650
GATEWAY PLASTICS, INC.—See Silgan Holdings, Inc.; *U.S. Public*, pg. 1878
GATEWAY PRESS, INC.; *U.S. Private*, pg. 1650
GATEWAY PRINTING & OFFICE SUPPLY, INC.; *U.S. Private*, pg. 1651
GATEWAY RADIOLOGY CONSULTANTS, P.A.; *U.S. Private*, pg. 1651
GATEWAY RAIL FREIGHT LTD.—See Gateway Distriparks Ltd.; *Int'l*, pg. 2889
GATEWAY REAL ESTATE AG; *Int'l*, pg. 2889
GATEWAY REHABILITATION CENTER; *U.S. Private*, pg. 1651
GATEWAY SERVICES LIMITED—See Cotecna Inspection S.A.; *Int'l*, pg. 1816
GATEWAYS HOSPITAL AND MENTAL HEALTH CENTER; *U.S. Private*, pg. 1651
GATEWAYS INDUSTRIES; *U.S. Private*, pg. 1651
GATEWAYS INTERNATIONAL INC.—See The Pasha Group; *U.S. Private*, pg. 4091
GATEWAY STRATEGIC ACQUISITION CO.; *Int'l*, pg. 2889
GATEWAY SUPPLY COMPANY INC.; *U.S. Private*, pg. 1651
GATEWAY SURVEYING SERVICES LIMITED—See Simplybiz Group plc; *Int'l*, pg. 6934
GATEWAY TERMINALS INDIA PVT. LTD.—See A.P. Moller-Maersk A/S; *Int'l*, pg. 26
GATEWAY TERMINALS LLC—See Harvestone Group LLC; *U.S. Private*, pg. 1877
GATEWAY (TEXTILES) LIMITED—See Leggett & Platt, Incorporated; *U.S. Public*, pg. 1302
GATEWAY TICKETING SYSTEMS, INC.; *U.S. Private*, pg. 1651
GATEWAY TIRE OF ARKANSAS INC.; *U.S. Private*, pg. 1651
GATEWAY TRADE CENTER, INC.—See New Enterprise Stone & Lime Co., Inc.; *U.S. Private*, pg. 2895
GATEWAY TRANSFER STATION, INC.—See Waste Management, Inc.; *U.S. Public*, pg. 2331
GATEWAY TRANSPORT; *U.S. Private*, pg. 1651
GATEWAY US RETAIL, INC.—See Acer Incorporated; *Int'l*, pg. 99
GATEWAY WAREHOUSE INC.; *U.S. Private*, pg. 1651
GATEWORKS, CORP.; *U.S. Private*, pg. 1651
THE GATE WORLDWIDE CHANNEL ISLANDS—See The Gate Worldwide Limited; *Int'l*, pg. 7649
THE GATE WORLDWIDE EDINBURGH—See The Gate Worldwide Limited; *Int'l*, pg. 7649
THE GATE WORLDWIDE HONG KONG—See The Gate Worldwide Limited; *Int'l*, pg. 7649
THE GATE WORLDWIDE LIMITED; *Int'l*, pg. 7649
THE GATE WORLDWIDE NEW YORK—See The Gate Worldwide Limited; *Int'l*, pg. 7649
THE GATE WORLDWIDE SHANGHAI—See The Gate Worldwide Limited; *Int'l*, pg. 7649
THE GATE WORLDWIDE (S) PTE LIMITED—See The Gate Worldwide Limited; *Int'l*, pg. 7649
GAT - GESELLSCHAFT FUR ANTRIEBSTECHNIK MBH—See ZF Friedrichshafen AG; *Int'l*, pg. 8641
GATHERGATES ELEKTRIK SDN BHD—See NITTO KOGYO CORPORATION; *Int'l*, pg. 5387
GATHERGATES GROUP LTD—See NITTO KOGYO CORPORATION; *Int'l*, pg. 5387
GATHERGATES SWITCHGEAR (M) SDN BHD—See NITTO KOGYO CORPORATION; *Int'l*, pg. 5387
GATHERGATES SWITCHGEAR PTE LTD—See NITTO KOGYO CORPORATION; *Int'l*, pg. 5387
GATHERING PLACE BOOKS & COFFEE INC.—See Family Christian Stores Inc.; *U.S. Private*, pg. 1469
GATHERWELL LIMITED—See Jumbo Interactive Limited; *Int'l*, pg. 4026
GATHER WORKSPACES, LLC; *U.S. Private*, pg. 1651
GATHID LTD.; *Int'l*, pg. 2889
GATHR OUTDOORS—See Centre Partners Management LLC; *U.S. Private*, pg. 828
GATI ASIA PACIFIC PTE LTD.—See Gati Ltd.; *Int'l*, pg. 2889
GATIC PTY LIMITED—See Fletcher Building Limited; *Int'l*, pg. 2700
GATI HONG KONG LTD.—See Gati Ltd.; *Int'l*, pg. 2889
GATI LTD.; *Int'l*, pg. 2889
GATLIN CORPORATION—See Applied Industrial Technologies, Inc.; *U.S. Public*, pg. 171
GATLING EXPLORATION INC.—See MAG Silver Corp.; *Int'l*, pg. 4636
GATO INVESTMENTS LP—See Searchlight Capital Partners, L.P.; *U.S. Private*, pg. 3587
THE GATORADE COMPANY OF AUSTRALIA PTY LIMITED—See PepsiCo, Inc.; *U.S. Public*, pg. 1672

THE GATORADE COMPANY—See PepsiCo, Inc.; *U.S. Public*, pg. 1670
GATOR AIR CONDITIONING; *U.S. Private*, pg. 1651
GATOR CAPITAL MANAGEMENT LLC; *U.S. Private*, pg. 1651
GATOR CHRYSLER INC.; *U.S. Private*, pg. 1651
GATOR FORD TRUCK SALES INC.; *U.S. Private*, pg. 1651
GATOR FOURE INC.; *U.S. Private*, pg. 1651
GATOR GYPSUM INC.—See GMS Inc.; *U.S. Public*, pg. 948
GATOR OF FLORIDA INCORPORATED; *U.S. Private*, pg. 1651
GATOR VET INC.; *U.S. Private*, pg. 1651
GATOS SILVER CANADA CORPORATION—See Gatos Silver, Inc.; *U.S. Public*, pg. 907
GATOS SILVER, INC.; *U.S. Public*, pg. 907
GATRON INDUSTRIES LIMITED; *Int'l*, pg. 2889
GATR TECHNOLOGIES INC.—See Elliott Management Corporation; *U.S. Private*, pg. 1368
GATR TECHNOLOGIES INC.—See Veritas Capital Fund Management, LLC; *U.S. Private*, pg. 4362
GATSBY SPAS, INC.—See Investindustrial Advisors Ltd.; *Int'l*, pg. 3779
GATSKI COMMERCIAL REAL ESTATE SERVICES; *U.S. Private*, pg. 1651
GATSO AUSTRALIA PTY LTD.—See Sensys Gatso Group AB; *Int'l*, pg. 6714
GATSO DEUTSCHLAND GMBH—See Sensys Gatso Group AB; *Int'l*, pg. 6714
GATSOMETER BV—See Sensys Gatso Group AB; *Int'l*, pg. 6714
GATSTEEL INDUSTRIES INC.; *Int'l*, pg. 2889
GATTACA PLC; *Int'l*, pg. 2890
GATTACA PROJECTS LIMITED—See Gattaca plc; *Int'l*, pg. 2890
GATTACA SOLUTIONS LIMITED—See Gattaca plc; *Int'l*, pg. 2890
GATTON STAR PTY LTD—See ARN Media Limited; *Int'l*, pg. 576
GAT TRANSMISSION TECHNOLOGY (BEIJING) CO. LTD.—See ZF Friedrichshafen AG; *Int'l*, pg. 8641
GATT TECHNOLOGIES B.V.—See Johnson & Johnson; *U.S. Public*, pg. 1196
GATUNGURU TEA FACTORY COMPANY LIMITED—See Kenya Tea Development Agency Limited; *Int'l*, pg. 4129
GATWICK AIRPORT LTD.—See VINCI S.A.; *Int'l*, pg. 8230
GATWICK EXPRESS LTD—See Mobico Group PLC; *Int'l*, pg. 5008
GATX CORPORATION—See GATX Corporation; *U.S. Public*, pg. 907
GATX CORPORATION; *U.S. Public*, pg. 907
GATX GLOBAL FINANCE B.V.—See GATX Corporation; *U.S. Public*, pg. 907
GATX RAIL AUSTRIA GMBH—See GATX Corporation; *U.S. Public*, pg. 908
GATX RAIL CANADA—See GATX Corporation; *U.S. Public*, pg. 908
GATX RAIL GERMANY GMBH—See GATX Corporation; *U.S. Public*, pg. 908
GATX RAIL—See GATX Corporation; *U.S. Public*, pg. 908
GAUBERT OIL COMPANY INCORPORATED; *U.S. Private*, pg. 1651
GAUCHO GROUP HOLDINGS, INC.; *U.S. Public*, pg. 908
GAUDENZIA, INC.; *U.S. Private*, pg. 1652
GAUDE SAS—See VINCI S.A.; *Int'l*, pg. 8222
GAUDET ASSOCIATES, INC.—See NV5 Global, Inc.; *U.S. Public*, pg. 1557
GAUDFRIN; *Int'l*, pg. 2890
GAUDLITZ GMBH—See H&R KGaA; *Int'l*, pg. 3193
GAUDLITZ PRECISION S.R.O.—See H&R KGaA; *Int'l*, pg. 3193
GAUDLITZ PRECISION TECHNOLOGY (WUXI) CO., LTD.—See H&R KGaA; *Int'l*, pg. 3193
GAUDREAU GROUP INC.—See Caisse de Depot et Placement du Quebec; *Int'l*, pg. 1256
GAUDREAU GROUP INC.—See KKR & Co. Inc.; *U.S. Public*, pg. 1265
GAUDREAU, INC.—See EwingCole, Inc.; *U.S. Private*, pg. 1444
GAUDRE UAB—See Wurth Verwaltungsgesellschaft mbH; *Int'l*, pg. 8504
GAUGE CAPITAL LLC; *U.S. Private*, pg. 1652
GAUGER + ASSOCIATES; *U.S. Private*, pg. 1652
GAUL GMBH—See STRABAG SE; *Int'l*, pg. 7230
GAULT CHEVROLET CO. INC.; *U.S. Private*, pg. 1652
GAULTER RUSSELL NZ LIMITED—See Rubicor Group Limited; *Int'l*, pg. 6422
GAUMER COMPANY, INC.—See NIBE Industrier AB; *Int'l*, pg. 5260
GAUM, INC.—See Universal Technical Resource Services, Inc.; *U.S. Private*, pg. 4306
GAUMONT S.A.; *Int'l*, pg. 2890
GAUNTLET INSURANCE SERVICES LIMITED—See Brown & Brown, Inc.; *U.S. Public*, pg. 400
GAURIAU ENTREPRISE SAS—See VINCI S.A.; *Int'l*, pg. 8222
GAUSELMANN AG; *Int'l*, pg. 2890

GAUSELMANN GROSSHANDEL GMBH—See Gauselmann AG; *Int'l*, pg. 2890
GAUSH MEDITECH LTD.; *Int'l*, pg. 2891
GAUSSIN SA; *Int'l*, pg. 2891
GAUSS LABS INC.—See SK hynix Inc.; *Int'l*, pg. 6970
GAUTAM EXIM LIMITED; *Int'l*, pg. 2891
GAUTAM GEMS LIMITED; *Int'l*, pg. 2891
GAUTHIER MARKETING; *U.S. Private*, pg. 1652
GAUTHIER SAS—See VINCI S.A.; *Int'l*, pg. 8235
GAUTIER SPECIALTY METALS, LLC—See Reserve Group Management Company; *U.S. Private*, pg. 3404
GAUTIER STEEL, LTD.—See Reserve Group Management Company; *U.S. Private*, pg. 3404
GAUZY AG.—See Hamilton Global Opportunities Plc; *Int'l*, pg. 3238
GAVAN & BARKER, INC.—See Huitt-Zollars, Inc.; *U.S. Private*, pg. 2004
GAVAP SAS—See RUAG Holding AG; *Int'l*, pg. 6421
GAVEA INVESTIMENTOS LTDA.—See JPMorgan Chase & Co.; *U.S. Public*, pg. 1207
GAVECO AB—See Indutrade AB; *Int'l*, pg. 3679
GAVEKORTET.DK A/S—See Egmont Fonden; *Int'l*, pg. 2326
GAVEL INTERNATIONAL CORPORATION; *U.S. Private*, pg. 1652
GAVEN INDUSTRIES, INC.—See 3 Rivers Capital, LLC; *U.S. Private*, pg. 7
GAVIAL ENGINEERING & MANUFACTURING; *U.S. Private*, pg. 1652
GAVIAL ITC—See Gavial Engineering & Manufacturing; *U.S. Private*, pg. 1652
GAVILON AGRICULTURE INVESTMENT, INC.—See Marubeni Corporation; *Int'l*, pg. 4706
GAVILON AG SERVICE, LLC—See Marubeni Corporation; *Int'l*, pg. 4706
GAVILON FERTILIZER, LLC—See Marubeni Corporation; *Int'l*, pg. 4706
GAVILON GRAIN, LLC—See Marubeni Corporation; *Int'l*, pg. 4706
GAVILON, LLC—See NGL Energy Partners LP; *U.S. Public*, pg. 1527
GAVIOTA RE S.A.—See Repsol, S.A.; *Int'l*, pg. 6292
GAVIS PHARMACEUTICALS, LLC—See Lupin Limited; *Int'l*, pg. 4586
GAVITA AS—See The Scotts Miracle-Gro Company; *U.S. Public*, pg. 2126
GAVITA INTERNATIONAL B.V.—See The Scotts Miracle-Gro Company; *U.S. Public*, pg. 2126
GAVLE TOMOKU HUS AB—See Tomoku Co., Ltd.; *Int'l*, pg. 7801
GAV-YAM LANDS CORP. LTD—See IDB Development Corporation Ltd.; *Int'l*, pg. 3588
GAW CAPITAL ADVISORS LIMITED; *Int'l*, pg. 2891
GAW CAPITAL ADVISORS (SHANGHAI) CO., LTD.—See Gaw Capital Advisors Limited; *Int'l*, pg. 2891
GAW CAPITAL PARTNERS (USA), LLC—See Gaw Capital Advisors Limited; *Int'l*, pg. 2891
G.A. WEST & COMPANY INC.; *U.S. Private*, pg. 1630
G.A. WILLIAMS & SONS INC.; *U.S. Private*, pg. 1630
G.A. WINTZER AND SON COMPANY; *U.S. Private*, pg. 1630
GAWK, INCORPORATED; *U.S. Private*, pg. 1652
GAXOS.AI INC.; *U.S. Public*, pg. 908
GAYA CO. LTD.—See Systena Corporation; *Int'l*, pg. 7393
GAYATRI BIOORGANICS LTD.; *Int'l*, pg. 2891
GAYATRI HIGHWAYS LTD.; *Int'l*, pg. 2891
GAYATRI PROJECTS LTD; *Int'l*, pg. 2891
GAYATRI SUGARS LIMITED; *Int'l*, pg. 2891
GAY JOHNSON'S, INC.; *U.S. Private*, pg. 1652
GAYLA INDUSTRIES, INC.; *U.S. Private*, pg. 1652
GAY LEA FOODS CO-OPERATIVE LTD.; *Int'l*, pg. 2891
GAY LEE CORPORATION—See L Squared Capital Management LP; *U.S. Private*, pg. 2362
GAYLE MANUFACTURING CO. INC.; *U.S. Private*, pg. 1652
GAYLIN VIETNAM PTE LTD—See AMOS Group Limited; *Int'l*, pg. 430
GAYLORD CHEMICAL COMPANY LLC—See EagleTree Capital, LP; *U.S. Private*, pg. 1311
GAYLORD HOSPITAL; *U.S. Private*, pg. 1652
GAYLORD INTEREST, LLC; *U.S. Private*, pg. 1652
GAYLOR INC.; *U.S. Private*, pg. 1652
GAYLOR INC. - UTILITY DIVISION—See Gaylor Inc.; *U.S. Private*, pg. 1652
GAY-LUSSAC GESTION—See Raymond James Financial, Inc.; *U.S. Public*, pg. 1764
GAY MEN'S HEALTH CRISIS, INC.; *U.S. Private*, pg. 1652
GAYSHA LIMITED—See MBH Corporation Plc; *Int'l*, pg. 4752
GAY & SON MASONRY INC.; *U.S. Private*, pg. 1652
GAYTAN FOODS—See Wind Point Advisors LLC; *U.S. Private*, pg. 4534
GAZAL APPAREL PTY LIMITED—See PVH Corp.; *U.S. Public*, pg. 1739
GAZAL CLOTHING COMPANY PTY LIMITED—See PVH Corp.; *U.S. Public*, pg. 1739
GAZAL CORPORATION LIMITED—See PVH Corp.; *U.S. Public*, pg. 1739

GAZALKENT STONE LLC—See National Bank for Foreign Economic Activity of the Republic of Uzbekistan; *Int'l*, pg. 5151
GAZAL (NZ) LIMITED—See PVH Corp.; *U.S. Public*, pg. 1739
GAZAVTOMATIKA—See PJSC Gazprom; *Int'l*, pg. 5879
GAZCO LTD.—See NIBE Industrier AB; *Int'l*, pg. 5260
GAZ DE PARIS SAS—See DCC plc; *Int'l*, pg. 1990
GAZ DU CAMEROUN SARL—See Victoria Oil & Gas PLC; *Int'l*, pg. 8188
GAZDUIRE WEB S.R.L—See Cyber_Folks S.A.; *Int'l*, pg. 1892
GAZ ELECTRICITE DE GRENOBLE SE—See ENGIE SA; *Int'l*, pg. 2434
GAZELLE ASSET MANAGEMENT PTE LTD.; *Int'l*, pg. 2891
GAZELLE, INC.; *U.S. Private*, pg. 1652
GAZELLES INC.; *U.S. Private*, pg. 1652
GAZELLE TRANSPORTATION INC.; *U.S. Private*, pg. 1652
GAZETTE COMMUNICATIONS, INC.—See The Gazette Company; *U.S. Private*, pg. 4032
THE GAZETTE COMPANY; *U.S. Private*, pg. 4032
GAZETTE MEDIA CO LTD—See Reach PLC; *Int'l*, pg. 6231
GAZETTE NEWSPAPERS—See Alden Global Capital LLC; *U.S. Private*, pg. 156
THE GAZETTE—See The Anschutz Corporation; *U.S. Private*, pg. 3987
GAZEXPORT—See PJSC Gazprom; *Int'l*, pg. 5879
GAZ GROUP MANAGEMENT COMPANY LLC; *Int'l*, pg. 2891
GAZIFERE INC.—See Enbridge Inc.; *Int'l*, pg. 2397
GAZKON AO; *Int'l*, pg. 2891
GAZMASH—See PJSC Gazprom; *Int'l*, pg. 5879
GAZ MEDIA SP. Z O.O.—See Polskie Gornictwo Naftowe i Gazownictwo S.A.; *Int'l*, pg. 5912
GAZ METRO INC.—See Caisse de Depot et Placement du Quebec; *Int'l*, pg. 1255
GAZ METRO LIMITED PARTNERSHIP—See Caisse de Depot et Placement du Quebec; *Int'l*, pg. 1255
GAZ METRO PLUS INC.—See Caisse de Depot et Placement du Quebec; *Int'l*, pg. 1256
GAZNAT SA—See EnBW Energie Baden-Wurttemberg AG; *Int'l*, pg. 2398
GAZOMAT SARL; *Int'l*, pg. 2891
GAZOO ENERGY GROUP, INC.; *U.S. Private*, pg. 1653
GAZPROMAVIA—See PJSC Gazprom; *Int'l*, pg. 5879
GAZPROMBANK - ASSET MANAGEMENT CJSC; See Gazprombank JSC; *Int'l*, pg. 2892
GAZPROMBANK-INVEST LLC—See Gazprombank JSC; *Int'l*, pg. 2892
GAZPROMBANK JSC; *Int'l*, pg. 2891
GAZPROMBANK LEASING JSC—See Gazprombank JSC; *Int'l*, pg. 2892
GAZPROMBANK (SWITZERLAND) LTD.—See Gazprombank JSC; *Int'l*, pg. 2892
GAZPROM EP INTERNATIONAL B.V.—See PJSC Gazprom; *Int'l*, pg. 5879
GAZPROM GAZORASP ROSTOV AO; *Int'l*, pg. 2891
GAZPROM GEROSGAZ HOLDING B.V.—See PJSC Gazprom; *Int'l*, pg. 5879
GAZPROM GLOBAL LNG LTD.—See PJSC Gazprom; *Int'l*, pg. 5879
GAZPROM-MEDIA HOLDING JSC—See Gazprombank JSC; *Int'l*, pg. 2892
GAZPROM NEFT TRADING GMBH—See PJSC Gazprom; *Int'l*, pg. 5879
GAZPROM SCHWEIZ AG—See PJSC Gazprom; *Int'l*, pg. 5879
GAZPROM TRANSGAZ KAZAN LLC—See PJSC Gazprom; *Int'l*, pg. 5879
GAZPROM TRANSGAZ STAVROPOL—See PJSC Gazprom; *Int'l*, pg. 5879
GAZ-SERVIS AO; *Int'l*, pg. 2891
GAZ SP. Z O.O.—See Polskie Gornictwo Naftowe i Gazownictwo S.A.; *Int'l*, pg. 5912
GAZSTROIDETAL—See PJSC Gazprom; *Int'l*, pg. 5879
GAZ-SYSTEM S.A.—See PERN S.A.; *Int'l*, pg. 5809
GAZ-TEK PAO; *Int'l*, pg. 2891
GAZTRANSPORT ET TECHNIGAZ SA; *Int'l*, pg. 2892
GB 500 SATELLITE INC.; *U.S. Private*, pg. 1653
GB ACQUISITIONS, LLC—See Universal Health Services, Inc.; *U.S. Public*, pg. 2257
G. BAILEY COMPANY INC.; *U.S. Private*, pg. 1630
GBB POWER LTD.; *Int'l*, pg. 2893
GBB TK GMBH; *Int'l*, pg. 2893
GB CHEMICALS PTE LTD—See AP Oil International Ltd.; *Int'l*, pg. 499
GB COLLECTS, LLC; *U.S. Private*, pg. 1653
GBCORP BSC—See GFH Financial Group B.S.C.; *Int'l*, pg. 2956
GBCORP TOWER REAL ESTATE W.L.L.—See GFH Financial Group B.S.C.; *Int'l*, pg. 2956
GBC SCIENTIFIC EQUIPMENT DE MEXICO S.A. DE C.V.—See GBC Scientific Equipment Pty Ltd.; *Int'l*, pg. 2893
GBC SCIENTIFIC EQUIPMENT PTY LTD.; *Int'l*, pg. 2893

GBC SCIENTIFIC EQUIPMENT USA, LLC—See GBC Scientific Equipment Pty Ltd.; *Int'l*, pg. 2893
GBG (AUSTRALIA) PTY. LTD.—See GB Group plc; *Int'l*, pg. 2892
GBG INC. OF PENNSYLVANIA; *U.S. Private*, pg. 1653
GB GLOBAL LIMITED; *Int'l*, pg. 2892
GBG (MALAYSIA) SDN BHD—See GB Group plc; *Int'l*, pg. 2892
GB GMBH—See Goodbaby International Holdings Limited; *Int'l*, pg. 3039
G.B. GROUP CORPORATION; *Int'l*, pg. 2865
GB GROUP PLC; *Int'l*, pg. 2892
GB GROUP S.A.; *Int'l*, pg. 2892
GBG SOCKS, LLC—See Global Brands Group Holding Ltd; *Int'l*, pg. 2993
GBG VOGELSANGER STRASSE GMBH—See Munchener Ruckversicherungs AG; *Int'l*, pg. 5088
GBH BATHROOM PRODUCTS SDN. BHD.—See Paragon Globe Berhad; *Int'l*, pg. 5736
GBH COMMUNICATIONS INC.; *Int'l*, pg. 2893
GBI ARGENTINA—See Compagnie des Levures Lesaffre SA; *Int'l*, pg. 1738
GBI HOLDINGS PTY., LTD.; *Int'l*, pg. 2893
GB IMPEX (PVT.) LIMITED—See Doppelmayr Group; *Int'l*, pg. 2175
G.B. IMPORT SALES & SERVICE, LLC—See AutoNation, Inc.; *U.S. Public*, pg. 235
GB INTERNATIONAL, INC.—See PepsiCo, Inc.; *U.S. Public*, pg. 1668
GBI SALES PTY., LTD.—See GBI Holdings Pty., Ltd.; *Int'l*, pg. 2893
G-BITS NETWORK TECHNOLOGY (XIAMEN) CO., LTD.; *Int'l*, pg. 2862
GBJ, INC.—See TBL Group, Inc.; *U.S. Private*, pg. 3941
GBJOBS.COM LTD.—See Netel Technology (Holdings) Limited; *Int'l*, pg. 5214
GBK CORP.; *U.S. Private*, pg. 1653
GBK, HEYE WERBEAGENTUR GMBH—See Omnicom Group Inc.; *U.S. Public*, pg. 1581
GBK RESTAURANTS LIMITED—See Famous Brands Limited; *Int'l*, pg. 2612
G.B. KUARI SDN. BHD.—See Gamuda Berhad; *Int'l*, pg. 2879
GBL INDUSTRIES LIMITED; *Int'l*, pg. 2893
GBL SYSTEMS CORPORATION; *U.S. Private*, pg. 1653
GBLT CORP.; *Int'l*, pg. 2893
GB MANAGEMENT SYSTEMS, INC.; *U.S. Private*, pg. 1653
GBM GOLD LIMITED; *Int'l*, pg. 2893
G&B/MILLER ADVERTISING—See Miller Advertising Agency, Inc.; *U.S. Private*, pg. 2732
GBM PAKISTAN PVT. LTD.—See Gulf Business Machines EC; *Int'l*, pg. 3179
GBM RESOURCES LTD; *Int'l*, pg. 2893
GBN,LLC—See MetLife, Inc.; *U.S. Public*, pg. 1430
GBO FASTENING SYSTEMS AB—See Simpson Manufacturing Company, Inc.; *U.S. Public*, pg. 1882
GBO FASTENING SYSTEMS AB—See Simpson Manufacturing Company, Inc.; *U.S. Public*, pg. 1882
GBO FASTENING SYSTEMS AB—See Simpson Manufacturing Company, Inc.; *U.S. Public*, pg. 1882
GBO FASTENING SYSTEMS AB—See Simpson Manufacturing Company, Inc.; *U.S. Public*, pg. 1882
G&B OIL COMPANY INC.; *U.S. Private*, pg. 1628
G-BOX SA DE CV.—See Graphic Packaging Holding Company; *U.S. Public*, pg. 958
GB PARTNERSHIPS LIMITED; *Int'l*, pg. 2893
GB PLANGE PORTUGAL S.A.—See Wilh. Werhahn KG; *Int'l*, pg. 8410
GB PLANGE THE NETHERLANDS B.V.—See Wilh. Werhahn KG; *Int'l*, pg. 8410
GB POLO BUS MANUFACTURING COMPANY—See Ghabbour Auto S.A.E.; *Int'l*, pg. 2958
GB POLO BUS MANUFACTURING COMPANY—See Marcopolo S.A.; *Int'l*, pg. 4690
GB RAILFREIGHT LIMITED—See EQT AB; *Int'l*, pg. 2475
GBR GEMEINSCHAFTSKRAFTWERK WEST—See Asterion Industrial Partners SGEIC SA; *Int'l*, pg. 654
GBR HELICOPTERS PTY. LTD.—See Experience Co Limited; *Int'l*, pg. 2588
GB RICAMBI S.P.A.; *Int'l*, pg. 2893
G-BRIM INTERNATIONAL CORP.—See Zippy Technology Corp.; *Int'l*, pg. 8685
GBRITT P.R. & MARKETING; *U.S. Private*, pg. 1653
GBS ADMINISTRATORS, INC.—See Arthur J. Gallagher & Co.; *U.S. Public*, pg. 205
GBS ALLIANCE PTE LTD.—See Transition Evergreen; *Int'l*, pg. 7901
GBS BUILDING SUPPLY - US LBM, LLC—See Bain Capital, LP; *U.S. Private*, pg. 450
GB SCIENCES, INC.; *U.S. Public*, pg. 908
GBS CORP.; *U.S. Private*, pg. 1653
GBS EUROPA GMBH—See BULPROS Consulting AD; *Int'l*, pg. 1214
GBS INSURANCE AND FINANCIAL SERVICES, INC.—See Arthur J. Gallagher & Co.; *U.S. Public*, pg. 205
GBS LTD.—See Gil-Bar Industries, Inc.; *U.S. Private*, pg. 1698

G&B SPECIALTIES, INC.—See Westinghouse Air Brake Technologies Corporation; *U.S. Public*, pg. 2358
GBS RETIREMENT SERVICES, INC.—See Arthur J. Gallagher & Co.; *U.S. Public*, pg. 205
GBS SOLUTIONS NA LLC—See BULPROS Consulting AD; *Int'l*, pg. 1214
GBST HOLDINGS LIMITED - GBST FINANCIAL SERVICES DIVISION—See GBST Holdings Limited; *Int'l*, pg. 2893
GBST HOLDINGS LIMITED - GBST WEALTH MANAGEMENT DIVISION—See GBST Holdings Limited; *Int'l*, pg. 2893
GBST HOLDINGS LIMITED; *Int'l*, pg. 2893
GBT CR, S.R.O.—See Global Business Travel Group, Inc.; *U.S. Public*, pg. 941
GB TECH, INC.; *U.S. Private*, pg. 1653
GBT FINLAND OY—See Global Business Travel Group, Inc.; *U.S. Public*, pg. 941
GBT III B.V.—See Global Business Travel Group, Inc.; *U.S. Public*, pg. 940
G.B.T. INC.—See Giga-Byte Technology Co., Ltd.; *Int'l*, pg. 2971
GBT INDIA PRIVATE LIMITED—See Global Business Travel Group, Inc.; *U.S. Public*, pg. 941
GBT TECHNOLOGIES INC.; *U.S. Public*, pg. 908
G.B.T. TECHNOLOGY TRADING GMBH—See Giga-Byte Technology Co., Ltd.; *Int'l*, pg. 2971
GBT TRAVEL SERVICES UK LTD.—See Global Business Travel Group, Inc.; *U.S. Public*, pg. 941
GBU FINANCIAL LIFE; *U.S. Private*, pg. 1653
GBW RAILCAR SERVICES, LLC—See Kinder Morgan, Inc.; *U.S. Public*, pg. 1233
GBW RAILCAR SERVICES, LLC—See The Greenbrier Companies, Inc.; *U.S. Public*, pg. 2085
GBX LOGISTICS LTD.—See Albert Ballin KG; *Int'l*, pg. 294
GB YACHTS PTE. LTD.—See Grand Banks Yachts Limited; *Int'l*, pg. 3054
GCA CHEMICAL CORPORATION; *U.S. Private*, pg. 1653
GCA CHINA COMPANY, LIMITED—See Houlihan Lokey, Inc.; *U.S. Public*, pg. 1055
GCA CORPORATION—See Houlihan Lokey, Inc.; *U.S. Public*, pg. 1055
GC ADVANCED TECHNOLOGIES INC.—See GC Corporation; *Int'l*, pg. 2894
GC AESTHETICS PLC; *Int'l*, pg. 2893
GCA INDIA INVESTMENT ADVISERS PRIVATE LIMITED—See Houlihan Lokey, Inc.; *U.S. Public*, pg. 1055
GCA (MACAU) S.A.—See Everi Holdings Inc.; *U.S. Public*, pg. 801
GC AMERICA, INC.—See GC Corporation; *Int'l*, pg. 2894
GCAM, INC.—See GC Biopharma Corp.; *Int'l*, pg. 2893
G CAPITAL BERHAD; *Int'l*, pg. 2861
G CAPITAL PUBLIC COMPANY LIMITED; *Int'l*, pg. 2861
G. CAPPA PLC; *Int'l*, pg. 2864
GCA SAVIAN HOLDINGS CORPORATION—See Houlihan Lokey, Inc.; *U.S. Public*, pg. 1055
GCA SAVVIAN ADVISORS LLC—See Houlihan Lokey, Inc.; *U.S. Public*, pg. 1055
GCA SAVVIAN CAPITAL LLC—See Houlihan Lokey, Inc.; *U.S. Public*, pg. 1055
GCA SAVVIAN LLC—See Houlihan Lokey, Inc.; *U.S. Public*, pg. 1055
GCA SERVICES GROUP, INC.—See ABM Industries, Inc.; *U.S. Public*, pg. 26
GC ASIA DENTAL PTE. LTD.—See GC Corporation; *Int'l*, pg. 2894
GCA SINGAPORE PRIVATE LIMITED—See Houlihan Lokey, Inc.; *U.S. Public*, pg. 1055
G-CAST CONCRETE SDN BHD—See Chin Hin Group Berhad; *Int'l*, pg. 1480
G-CAST UHPC SDN BHD—See Chin Hin Group Berhad; *Int'l*, pg. 1480
GC AUSTRALASIA DENTAL PTY. LTD.—See GC Corporation; *Int'l*, pg. 2894
GC AUSTRIA GMBH—See GC Corporation; *Int'l*, pg. 2894
GCB BANK LIMITED; *Int'l*, pg. 2894
GCB COCOA SINGAPORE PTE. LTD.—See Guan Chong Berhad; *Int'l*, pg. 3152
GCB COCOA UK LIMITED—See Guan Chong Berhad; *Int'l*, pg. 3152
GCB FOODS SDN. BHD.—See Guan Chong Berhad; *Int'l*, pg. 3152
GC BIOPHARMA CORP.; *Int'l*, pg. 2893
GC BIOPHARMA USA, INC.—See GC Biopharma Corp.; *Int'l*, pg. 2893
GCB SPA.—See Sonatrach International Holding Corporation; *Int'l*, pg. 7089
GC BUILDERS INC; *U.S. Private*, pg. 1653
GCC ALLIANCE CONCRETE INC.—See GCC, S.A.B. de C.V.; *Int'l*, pg. 2894
GCC CONSUMO ESTABLECIMIENTO FINANCIERO DE CREDITO SA—See BNP Paribas SA; *Int'l*, pg. 1091
GCC DACOTAH INC.; *U.S. Private*, pg. 1653
GC CELL CORP.—See Green Cross WellBeing Corp.; *Int'l*, pg. 3070
GCC GLOBAL CAPITAL CORPORATION; *Int'l*, pg. 2894
GCCL CONSTRUCTION & REALITIES LTD.; *Int'l*, pg. 2895

COMPANY NAME INDEX

GC CONSTRUCTION HOLDINGS LTD.; *Int'l*, pg. 2894
GC CORPORATION; *Int'l*, pg. 2894
GCCP RESOURCES LIMITED; *Int'l*, pg. 2895
GC CREDIT-BAIL QUEBEC INC.—See Grenke AG; *Int'l*, pg. 3080
GCC, S.A.B. DE C.V.; *Int'l*, pg. 2894
GCC SAS; *Int'l*, pg. 2894
GCC SERVICING SYSTEMS, INC.—See Constellation Software Inc.; *Int'l*, pg. 1774
GC DENTAL (SUZHOU) CO., LTD.—See GC Corporation; *Int'l*, pg. 2894
GC DO BRASIL CONSULTORIA DE NEGOCIOS LTDA.—See Green Cross WellBeing Corp.; *Int'l*, pg. 3070
G.C. DUKE EQUIPMENT LTD; *Int'l*, pg. 2865
GCE GAS CONTROL EQUIPMENT CO., LTD.—See Enovis Corporation; *U.S. Public*, pg. 772
GCE GAS CONTROL EQUIPMENT, INC.—See Enovis Corporation; *U.S. Public*, pg. 772
GCE GMBH—See Enovis Corporation; *U.S. Public*, pg. 772
GCE GROUP AB—See Enovis Corporation; *U.S. Public*, pg. 772
GCE HUNGARIA KFT.—See Enovis Corporation; *U.S. Public*, pg. 772
GCE INDIA LTD.—See Enovis Corporation; *U.S. Public*, pg. 772
GCE INDUSTRIES, INC.—See Dubai Holding LLC; *Int'l*, pg. 2218
GCE LATIN AMERICA LTD.—See Enovis Corporation; *U.S. Public*, pg. 772
GCE MUJELLI S.P.A.—See Enovis Corporation; *U.S. Public*, pg. 772
GCE PORTUGAL UNIPESSOAL LDA—See Enovis Corporation; *U.S. Public*, pg. 772
GCE ROMANIA S.R.L.—See Enovis Corporation; *U.S. Public*, pg. 772
GCE S.A.S.—See Enovis Corporation; *U.S. Public*, pg. 772
GCE SOLUTIONS, GMBH—See IQVIA Holdings Inc.; *U.S. Public*, pg. 1168
GCE SP. Z O.O.—See Enovis Corporation; *U.S. Public*, pg. 772
GC&E SYSTEMS GROUP, INC.; *U.S. Private*, pg. 1653
GC EUROPE N.V.—See GC Corporation; *Int'l*, pg. 2894
GC FACTORING AAF SRL—See Grenke AG; *Int'l*, pg. 3080
GC FACTORING LIMITED—See Grenke AG; *Int'l*, pg. 3080
GC FINANCIAL SOLUTIONS LTD.—See Grenke AG; *Int'l*, pg. 3080
GCF, INC.; *U.S. Private*, pg. 1653
GC FIRE PROTECTION LIMITED—See London Security PLC; *Int'l*, pg. 4547
GC FRANCE S.A.S.—See GC Corporation; *Int'l*, pg. 2894
GCG ADVERTISING; *U.S. Private*, pg. 1653
GCG CONSTRUCTION INC.; *U.S. Private*, pg. 1653
GCG CONSTRUCTION, INC.; *U.S. Private*, pg. 1653
GC GENOME CORPORATION—See Green Cross WellBeing Corp.; *Int'l*, pg. 3070
GC GERMANY GMBH—See GC Corporation; *Int'l*, pg. 2894
GCG FINANCIAL, LLC—See Genstar Capital, LLC; *U.S. Private*, pg. 1674
GCG GROUND SERVICES (BARBADOS) LIMITED—See Goddard Enterprises Limited; *Int'l*, pg. 3019
GCG GROUND SERVICES, LLC—See Goddard Enterprises Limited; *Int'l*, pg. 3019
GCG GROUP—See Goddard Enterprises Limited; *Int'l*, pg. 3019
GC GLYCOL COMPANY LIMITED—See PTT Global Chemical Public Company Limited; *Int'l*, pg. 6091
GCG RISK MANAGEMENT, INC.—See Aon plc; *Int'l*, pg. 496
G.C. HAHN & CIE. S.A.R.L.—See Tate & Lyle PLC; *Int'l*, pg. 7473
G.C. HAHN & CO. LIMITED—See Tate & Lyle PLC; *Int'l*, pg. 7473
G.C. HAHN & CO. STABILISIERUNGSTECHNIK GMBH—See Tate & Lyle PLC; *Int'l*, pg. 7473
G.C. HAHN & CO. STABILIZACNI TECHNIKA S.R.O.—See Tate & Lyle PLC; *Int'l*, pg. 7473
G.C. HAHN & CO. TECHNIKA STABILIZOWANIA SP. Z.O.O.—See Tate & Lyle PLC; *Int'l*, pg. 7473
G.C. HAHN ESTABILIZANTES Y TECNOLOGIA PARA ALIMENTOS SL—See Tate & Lyle PLC; *Int'l*, pg. 7473
G.C. HANFORD MANUFACTURING COMPANY; *U.S. Private*, pg. 1630
GC HEALTH CARE CORPORATION—See GC Biopharma Corp.; *Int'l*, pg. 2893
GCH POLYMER MATERIAL (HONGKONG) CO. LIMITED—See GCH Technology Co., Ltd.; *Int'l*, pg. 2895
GCH RETAIL (MALAYSIA) SDN. BHD.—See Jardine Matheson Holdings Limited; *Int'l*, pg. 3909
GCH TECHNOLOGY CO., LTD.; *Int'l*, pg. 2895
GCI CABLE, INC.—See Liberty Broadband Corporation; *U.S. Public*, pg. 1310
GCI COMMUNICATION CORP.—See Liberty Broadband Corporation; *U.S. Public*, pg. 1310

GCI HEALTH—See WPP plc; *Int'l*, pg. 8469
GCI LIBERTY, INC.—See Liberty Broadband Corporation; *U.S. Public*, pg. 1310
GCI, LLC—See Liberty Broadband Corporation; *U.S. Public*, pg. 1310
GC INTERNATIONAL CORPORATION—See PTT Global Chemical Public Company Limited; *Int'l*, pg. 6091
GCI INVACFARM INC.—See Green Cross WellBeing Corp.; *Int'l*, pg. 3070
GCI OUTDOOR, INC.—See Centre Partners Management LLC; *U.S. Private*, pg. 828
GCI SYSTEMS; *U.S. Private*, pg. 1653
GC ITALIA S.R.L.—See GC Corporation; *Int'l*, pg. 2894
G CITY EUROPE LIMITED—See G City Ltd.; *Int'l*, pg. 2861
G CITY LTD.; *Int'l*, pg. 2861
GC JBP CORPORATION—See GC Biopharma Corp.; *Int'l*, pg. 2893
GCJ ENTERPRISES INC.; *U.S. Private*, pg. 1653
GC KOREA CO., LTD.—See GC Corporation; *Int'l*, pg. 2894
GC LABTECH, INC.—See GC Biopharma Corp.; *Int'l*, pg. 2893
G CLASSER CO., LTD.—See KING JIM CO., LTD.; *Int'l*, pg. 4169
GCL CAPACITA SA—See Eurofins Scientific S.E.; *Int'l*, pg. 2550
GC LEASE SINGAPORE PTE. LTD.—See Grenke AG; *Int'l*, pg. 3080
GC LEASING AZ LLC—See Grenke AG; *Int'l*, pg. 3080
GC LEASING D.O.O.—See Grenke AG; *Int'l*, pg. 3080
GC LEASING MELBOURNE PTY. LTD.—See Grenke AG; *Int'l*, pg. 3080
GC LEASING MIDDLE EAST FZCO—See Grenke AG; *Int'l*, pg. 3080
GC LEASING NORWAY AS—See Grenke AG; *Int'l*, pg. 3080
GC LEASING ONTARIO INC.—See Grenke AG; *Int'l*, pg. 3080
GC LEASING SYDNEY PTY. LTD.—See Grenke AG; *Int'l*, pg. 3080
GCL ENERGY TECHNOLOGY CO., LTD.; *Int'l*, pg. 2895
GCL NEW ENERGY HOLDINGS LIMITED—See Golden Concord Holdings Limited; *Int'l*, pg. 3028
GCL LOCACAO DE EQUIPAMENTOS LTDA.—See Grenke AG; *Int'l*, pg. 3080
GCL LOGISTICS SOLUTIONS COMPANY LIMITED—See PTT Global Chemical Public Company Limited; *Int'l*, pg. 6091
GCL SYSTEM INTEGRATION TECHNOLOGY CO., LTD.—See Golden Concord Holdings Limited; *Int'l*, pg. 3028
GCL TECHNOLOGY HOLDINGS LIMITED—See Golden Concord Holdings Limited; *Int'l*, pg. 3029
G-CLUSTER GLOBAL CORPORATION; *Int'l*, pg. 2862
GC MAINTENANCE & ENGINEERING COMPANY LIMITED—See PTT Global Chemical Public Company Limited; *Int'l*, pg. 6091
G&C MARKETING CO.; *U.S. Private*, pg. 1628
GC MARKETING SOLUTIONS COMPANY LIMITED—See PTT Global Chemical Public Company Limited; *Int'l*, pg. 6091
GC MARKETING SOLUTIONS MYANMAR CO., LTD.—See PTT Global Chemical Public Company Limited; *Int'l*, pg. 6091
GC MARKETING SOLUTIONS VIETNAM CO., LTD.—See PTT Global Chemical Public Company Limited; *Int'l*, pg. 6091
GCM CAPITAL ADVISORS LTD; *Int'l*, pg. 2895
GCMC INFORMATION TECHNOLOGY CO., LTD.—See CMC Corporation; *Int'l*, pg. 1669
GCM CO., LTD.—See Medley, Inc.; *Int'l*, pg. 4784
GCM COMMODITY & DERIVATIVES LTD.; *Int'l*, pg. 2895
GCM CONTRACTING SOLUTIONS, INC.; *U.S. Private*, pg. 1654
GC MEDIA TEAMWORK LIMITED—See SING TAO NEWS CORPORATION LIMITED; *Int'l*, pg. 6939
GCM GROSVENOR HOLDINGS (CANADA) ULC—See GCM Grosvenor Inc.; *U.S. Public*, pg. 908
GCM GROSVENOR INC.; *U.S. Public*, pg. 908
GCM HOLDING CORPORATION—See Avista Capital Partners, L.P.; *U.S. Private*, pg. 408
GCM INVESTMENTS HONG KONG LIMITED—See GCM Grosvenor Inc.; *U.S. Public*, pg. 908
GCM INVESTMENTS JAPAN K.K.—See GCM Grosvenor Inc.; *U.S. Public*, pg. 908
GCM INVESTMENTS UK LLP—See GCM Grosvenor Inc.; *U.S. Public*, pg. 908
GCM MEDICAL & OEM, INC.—See Avista Capital Partners, L.P.; *U.S. Private*, pg. 408
GC MOGAM, INC.—See Green Cross WellBeing Corp.; *Int'l*, pg. 3070
GCM PACKAGING (VIETNAM) CO., LTD.—See Great China Metal Ind. Co., Ltd.; *Int'l*, pg. 3064
GCM POLYMER TRADING DMCC—See PTT Global Chemical Public Company Limited; *Int'l*, pg. 6091
GC-M PTA COMPANY LIMITED—See PTT Global Chemical Public Company Limited; *Int'l*, pg. 6091
GCM RESOURCES PLC; *Int'l*, pg. 2895

GCM SECURITIES LIMITED—See Global Capital Markets Limited; *Int'l*, pg. 2994
GC NORDIC AB—See GC Corporation; *Int'l*, pg. 2894
G COMMERCE EUROPE SPA—See Kering S.A.; *Int'l*, pg. 4134
G.COMMUNICATION CO., LTD.—See Kobe Bussan Co., Ltd.; *Int'l*, pg. 4217
GCOM SOFTWARE LLC—See Sagewind Capital LLC; *U.S. Private*, pg. 3527
G. COOPER EQUIPMENT RENTALS LTD.—See SeaFort Capital, Inc.; *Int'l*, pg. 6662
GC PACKAGING, LLC—See Graphic Converting Inc.; *U.S. Private*, pg. 1757
G&C PALERMO SRL; *Int'l*, pg. 2862
G C PAN EUROPEAN CROSSING FRANCE; *Int'l*, pg. 2861
GCP APPLIED TECHNOLOGIES INC.—See Compagnie de Saint-Gobain SA; *Int'l*, pg. 1730
GC PARTNERS INC.; *U.S. Private*, pg. 1653
GCP ASSET BACKED INCOME FUND LTD.; *Int'l*, pg. 2895
GCP CAPITAL PARTNERS EUROPE LIMITED—See GCP Capital Partners Holdings LLC; *U.S. Private*, pg. 1654
GCP CAPITAL PARTNERS HOLDINGS LLC; *U.S. Private*, pg. 1654
GCP CAPITAL PARTNERS LLC—See GCP Capital Partners Holdings LLC; *U.S. Private*, pg. 1654
GCP HOSPITALITY MANAGEMENT LTD.—See Gaw Capital Advisors Limited; *Int'l*, pg. 2891
GCP INFRASTRUCTURE INVESTMENTS LIMITED; *Int'l*, pg. 2895
GCP LAMPLIGHTER, LLC—See Sun Communities, Inc.; *U.S. Public*, pg. 1961
GC POLYOLS COMPANY LIMITED—See PTT Global Chemical Public Company Limited; *Int'l*, pg. 6091
GC PRODUCTIONS INC.—See National Amusements, Inc.; *U.S. Private*, pg. 2843
GCP STUDENT LIVING PLC—See iQ Student Accommodation; *Int'l*, pg. 3803
GCP STUDENT LIVING PLC—See Scape Living Plc; *Int'l*, pg. 6613
GCP VENTURE PARTNERS LLC—See GCP Capital Partners Holdings LLC; *U.S. Private*, pg. 1654
GC RENT CHILE SPA—See Grenke AG; *Int'l*, pg. 3080
GCREST, INC.—See CyberAgent, Inc.; *Int'l*, pg. 1892
GC RIEBER AS; *Int'l*, pg. 2894
GC RIEBER SHIPPING ASA—See GC Rieber AS; *Int'l*, pg. 2894
GCR MONGOLIA LLC—See Murray & Roberts Holdings Ltd.; *Int'l*, pg. 5100
GCR TIRE CENTERS—See Bridgestone Corporation; *Int'l*, pg. 1157
GCSA AMBULATORY SURGERY CENTER, LLC—See Tenet Healthcare Corporation; *U.S. Public*, pg. 2005
GC SBIC V, L.P.—See Golub Capital, Inc.; *U.S. Private*, pg. 1736
GCS CAPITAL (HK) CO., LTD.; *Int'l*, pg. 2895
GC SERVICES LP; *U.S. Private*, pg. 1653
GCS GESELLSCHAFT FUR CLEANING SERVICE MBH & CO. AIRPORT FRANKFURT/ MAIN KG—See Fraport AG; *Int'l*, pg. 2764
GCS HIRE PTY. LTD.—See SRG Global Limited; *Int'l*, pg. 7149
GCS HOLDINGS, INC.; *Int'l*, pg. 2895
GCS MACHINERY PTE LTD.—See Nicolas Correa S.A.; *Int'l*, pg. 5273
GCS NORTHWEST PTY. LTD.—See SRG Global Limited; *Int'l*, pg. 7149
GC SPORTSWEAR OY—See New Wave Group AB; *Int'l*, pg. 5229
GCS RECRUITMENT SPECIALISTS INC.—See nGAGE Specialist Recruitment Limited; *Int'l*, pg. 5253
GCS RECRUITMENT SPECIALISTS LIMITED—See nGAGE Specialist Recruitment Limited; *Int'l*, pg. 5253
GCS SECURITY SCAFFOLDING PTY. LTD.—See SRG Global Limited; *Int'l*, pg. 7149
GCS SERVICE, INC.—See Ecolab Inc.; *U.S. Public*, pg. 714
GCS SERVICE, INC.—See Ecolab Inc.; *U.S. Public*, pg. 714
GCS TECHNOLOGIES, INC.; *U.S. Private*, pg. 1654
GC TAIWAN DENTAL CORP.—See GC Corporation; *Int'l*, pg. 2894
GC TECH COMPANY LIMITED—See Sungchang Enterprise Holdings Limited; *Int'l*, pg. 7314
GC TECH. EUROPE N.V.—See GC Corporation; *Int'l*, pg. 2894
GCTI TELECOMMUNICATIONS LABORATORIES AB—See Permira Advisers LLP; *Int'l*, pg. 5804
GCT RESEARCH, INC.—See GCT Semiconductor Holding, Inc.; *U.S. Public*, pg. 908
GCT SEMICONDUCTOR HOLDING, INC.; *U.S. Public*, pg. 908
GCT SEMICONDUCTOR, INC.—See GCT Semiconductor Holding, Inc.; *U.S. Public*, pg. 908
GCUBE INSURANCE SERVICES INC.—See Marsh & McLennan Companies, Inc.; *U.S. Public*, pg. 1375
GCUBE UNDERWRITING LIMITED—See Marsh & McLennan Companies, Inc.; *U.S. Public*, pg. 1375

GC UNITED KINGDOM LTD.—See GC Corporation; *Int'l*, pg. 2894
GCV SERVICES LIMITED; *Int'l*, pg. 2895
GCW/USS ENERGY, LLC—See United States Steel Corporation; *U.S. Public*, pg. 2236
GCX CORPORATION—See Audax Group, Limited Partnership; *U.S. Private*, pg. 388
GDA FUND PARTNER LIMITED—See Scottish Enterprise; *Int'l*, pg. 6652
GDA INTERNATIONAL LIMITED—See Scottish Enterprise; *Int'l*, pg. 6652
G&D AMERICA DO SUL INDUSTRIA E COMERCIO DE SMART CARDS SOCIEDADE ANONIMA—See Giesecke & Devrient GmbH; *Int'l*, pg. 2969
GDANSKIE ZAKLADY NAWOZOW FOSFOROWYCH FOSFORY SP. Z O.O.—See Kulczyk Investments S.A.; *Int'l*, pg. 4328
GD ARABIA LTD.—See General Dynamics Corporation; *U.S. Public*, pg. 913
GD ASSIST LTD.—See Green Delta Insurance Company Limited; *Int'l*, pg. 3070
G.D AUTOMATIC PACKAGING—See Coesia S.p.A.; *Int'l*, pg. 1689
G.D AUTOMATISCHE VERPACKUNGSMASCHINEN GMBH—See Coesia S.p.A.; *Int'l*, pg. 1689
G.D. BARRI & ASSOCIATES INC.; *U.S. Private*, pg. 1630
GDB GEOTECHNICS SDN. BHD.—See GDB Holdings Berhad; *Int'l*, pg. 2896
GDB HOLDINGS BERHAD; *Int'l*, pg. 2895
GDB INTERNATIONAL, INC.; *U.S. Private*, pg. 1654
GDC CONSTRUCTION INC.; *U.S. Private*, pg. 1654
GDC DIGITAL CINEMA NETWORK (BRASIL) LTD—See Huayi Brothers Media Corp.; *Int'l*, pg. 3515
GDC DIGITAL CINEMA NETWORK GG—See Huayi Brothers Media Corp.; *Int'l*, pg. 3515
GDC DIGITAL CINEMA NETWORK (MEXICO) S. DE R.L. DE C.V.—See Huayi Brothers Media Corp.; *Int'l*, pg. 3515
GDC DIGITAL CINEMA NETWORK (PERU), SAC—See Huayi Brothers Media Corp.; *Int'l*, pg. 3515
GDC DIGITAL CINEMA TECHNOLOGY EUROPE, SL—See Huayi Brothers Media Corp.; *Int'l*, pg. 3515
G.D CHINA AUTOMATIC MACHINERY LTD.—See Coesia S.p.A.; *Int'l*, pg. 1689
G.D CHINA LIMITED—See Coesia S.p.A.; *Int'l*, pg. 1690
G.D.C., INC.; *U.S. Private*, pg. 1630
G&D COMMUNICATIONS CORPORATION; *U.S. Private*, pg. 1628
GDC PROPERTIES, LLC; *U.S. Private*, pg. 1654
GDC TECHNOLOGY (BEIJING) LIMITED—See Huayi Brothers Media Corp.; *Int'l*, pg. 3516
GDC TECHNOLOGY INDIA PVT. LTD.—See Huayi Brothers Media Corp.; *Int'l*, pg. 3516
GDC TECHNOLOGY LIMITED—See Huayi Brothers Media Corp.; *Int'l*, pg. 3515
GDC TECHNOLOGY PTE LIMITED—See Huayi Brothers Media Corp.; *Int'l*, pg. 3516
GDC TECHNOLOGY (SHENZHEN) LIMITED—See Huayi Brothers Media Corp.; *Int'l*, pg. 3516
GDC TECHNOLOGY (USA) LLC—See Huayi Brothers Media Corp.; *Int'l*, pg. 3516
GD CULTURE GROUP LIMITED; *Int'l*, pg. 2895
G.D DO BRASIL—See Coesia S.p.A.; *Int'l*, pg. 1690
GDD POLET; *Int'l*, pg. 2896
GD EUROPEAN LAND SYSTEMS HOLDING GMBH—See General Dynamics Corporation; *U.S. Public*, pg. 913
GD EUROPEAN LAND SYSTEMS - STEYR GMBH—See General Dynamics Corporation; *U.S. Public*, pg. 913
GDEV INC.; *Int'l*, pg. 2896
GD EXPRESS SDN BHD.; *Int'l*, pg. 2895
GDF BRITAIN LTD.—See ENGIE SA; *Int'l*, pg. 2432
GDF GESELLSCHAFT FUR DENTALE FORSCHUNG UND INNOVATIONEN GMBH—See BayernLB Holding AG; *Int'l*, pg. 914
GDF, INC.—See New Rite Aid, LLC; *U.S. Private*, pg. 2905
GDF SUEZ BIOENERGIA SP. Z O.O.—See ENGIE SA; *Int'l*, pg. 2433
GDF SUEZ CC SCRL—See ENGIE SA; *Int'l*, pg. 2433
GDF SUEZ ENERGIA ESPANA SLU—See ENGIE SA; *Int'l*, pg. 2433
GDF SUEZ ENERGIA POLSKA SA—See ENGIE SA; *Int'l*, pg. 2433
GDF SUEZ ENERGIE SERVICES SA—See ENGIE SA; *Int'l*, pg. 2429
GDF SUEZ ENERGY ANDINO S.A.—See ENGIE SA; *Int'l*, pg. 2434
GDF SUEZ ENERGY ARGENTINA—See ENGIE SA; *Int'l*, pg. 2434
GDF SUEZ ENERGY ASIA—See ENGIE SA; *Int'l*, pg. 2433
GDF SUEZ ENERGY BRASIL—See ENGIE SA; *Int'l*, pg. 2434
GDF SUEZ ENERGY INTERNATIONAL—See ENGIE SA; *Int'l*, pg. 2431
GDF SUEZ ENERGY LATIN AMERICA—See ENGIE SA; *Int'l*, pg. 2433
GDF SUEZ ENERGY PERU—See ENGIE SA; *Int'l*, pg. 2434

GDF SUEZ ENERGY UK LIMITED—See ENGIE SA; *Int'l*, pg. 2432
GDF SUEZ ENERGY UK RETAIL—See ENGIE SA; *Int'l*, pg. 2433
GDF SUEZ E&P DEUTSCHLAND GMBH—See ENGIE SA; *Int'l*, pg. 2431
GDF SUEZ E&P NEDERLAND B.V.—See ENGIE SA; *Int'l*, pg. 2433
GDF SUEZ E&P NORGE AS—See ENGIE SA; *Int'l*, pg. 2433
GDF SUEZ E&P UK LTD—See ENGIE SA; *Int'l*, pg. 2433
GDF SUEZ GAS ENERGY SALES GMBH—See ENGIE SA; *Int'l*, pg. 2431
GDF SUEZ GAS NA HOLDINGS LLC—See ENGIE SA; *Int'l*, pg. 2433
GDF SUEZ GAS SUPPLY & SALES NEDERLAND BV—See ENGIE SA; *Int'l*, pg. 2434
GDF SUEZ GLOBAL GAS & LNG—See ENGIE SA; *Int'l*, pg. 2434
GDF SUEZ INFRASTRUCTURES—See ENGIE SA; *Int'l*, pg. 2434
GDF SUEZ SALES LTD—See ENGIE SA; *Int'l*, pg. 2432
GDF SUEZ SERVICES LIMITED—See ENGIE SA; *Int'l*, pg. 2432
GDF SUEZ SHOTTON LIMITED—See ENGIE SA; *Int'l*, pg. 2432
GDF SUEZ SOLUTIONS LIMITED—See ENGIE SA; *Int'l*, pg. 2432
GDF SUEZ TEESSIDE LTD—See ENGIE SA; *Int'l*, pg. 2432
GDF SUEZ TRADING SAS—See ENGIE SA; *Int'l*, pg. 2429
G.D GERMANY—See Coesia S.p.A.; *Int'l*, pg. 1690
GDG INFO ET GESTION INC.—See Alan Allman Associates SA; *Int'l*, pg. 290
GDH 559 COMPANY LIMITED—See GMM Grammy Public Company Limited; *Int'l*, pg. 3012
GD HANDELSYSTEME GMBH—See The Goodyear Tire & Rubber Company; *U.S. Public*, pg. 2083
GDH CONSULTING, INC.; *U.S. Private*, pg. 1654
G.D. HEIL INC.; *U.S. Private*, pg. 1630
GDH GUANGNAN (HOLDINGS) LIMITED—See GDH Limited; *Int'l*, pg. 2896
GDH GUANGNAN (HOLDINGS) LIMITED—See GDH Limited; *Int'l*, pg. 2896
GDH LIMITED; *Int'l*, pg. 2896
GDH REAL ESTATES (CHINA) CO. LIMITED—See GDH Limited; *Int'l*, pg. 2896
GDI INTEGRATED FACILITY SERVICES INC.; *Int'l*, pg. 2896
GDI INTEGRATED FACILITY SERVICES USA INC.—See GDI Integrated Facility Services Inc.; *Int'l*, pg. 2896
G.D. INDIA PVT. LTD.—See Coesia S.p.A.; *Int'l*, pg. 1690
GD INDONESIA—See Coesia S.p.A.; *Int'l*, pg. 1690
GD INDUSTRIAL PRODUCTS MALAYSIA SDN—See Ingersoll Rand Inc.; *U.S. Public*, pg. 1118
G & D INTEGRATED; *U.S. Private*, pg. 1628
GDI PROPERTY GROUP; *Int'l*, pg. 2896
GDI TECHNICAL SERVICES—See GDI Integrated Facility Services Inc.; *Int'l*, pg. 2896
G.D JAPAN—See Coesia S.p.A.; *Int'l*, pg. 1690
GDKN CORPORATION; *U.S. Private*, pg. 1654
GDL FUND; *U.S. Public*, pg. 908
GDL LEASING & FINANCE LIMITED; *Int'l*, pg. 2896
G&D LOMO, ZAO—See Giesecke & Devrient GmbH; *Int'l*, pg. 2969
GDL REAL ESTATE PTY. LTD.—See Nutrien Ltd.; *Int'l*, pg. 5492
GDM ADVISORY GROUP LTD.—See TA Associates, Inc.; *U.S. Private*, pg. 3919
GDMCOM GMBH—See EnBW Energie Baden-Wurttemberg AG; *Int'l*, pg. 2400
GDMI INC.; *U.S. Private*, pg. 1654
GDM SPA—See Coesia S.p.A.; *Int'l*, pg. 1690
GDO SPORTS, INC.—See Golf Digest Online Inc.; *Int'l*, pg. 3035
GDP COMPANIES, INC.—See One Rock Capital Partners, LLC; *U.S. Private*, pg. 3022
GDP GLOBAL DRINKS PARTNERSHIP GMBH—See Fevertree Drinks plc; *Int'l*, pg. 2649
GD POWER DEVELOPMENT CO., LTD.—See China Guodian Corporation; *Int'l*, pg. 1506
GDP SILVERCOTE INC.—See Pacific Avenue Capital Partners, LLC; *U.S. Private*, pg. 3065
GDP TECHNOLOGIES, INC.—See Xerox Holdings Corporation; *U.S. Public*, pg. 2387
GDP VENDOME; *Int'l*, pg. 2896
GDR COMERCIAL IMPRTACAO E EXPORTACAO LTDA.—See REHAU Verwaltungszentrale AG; *Int'l*, pg. 6255
GD RESEARCH CENTRE PRIVATE LIMITED—See GlobalData Plc; *Int'l*, pg. 3003
G.D RUSSIAN FEDERATION—See Coesia S.p.A.; *Int'l*, pg. 1690
GDS AUTOMOBILES; *Int'l*, pg. 2896
GDS CLEVELAND—See Republic Services, Inc.; *U.S. Public*, pg. 1786
GDS FOODS INCORPORATED—See Kelso & Company, L.P.; *U.S. Private*, pg. 2278

GDS GLOBAL LIMITED; *Int'l*, pg. 2896
GDS GMBH—See Technotrans AG; *Int'l*, pg. 7512
GDS HOLDINGS LIMITED; *Int'l*, pg. 2896
GDS INTERNATIONAL, LLC—See Premium Oilfield Technologies LLC; *U.S. Private*, pg. 3252
G.D SOUTH EAST ASIA—See Coesia S.p.A.; *Int'l*, pg. 1690
GD S.P.A.—See Coesia S.p.A.; *Int'l*, pg. 1689
GDS RISK SOLUTION CORREDURIA DE SEGUROS S.L.—See Aon plc; *Int'l*, pg. 494
GDS-SPRACHENWELT GMBH—See Technotrans AG; *Int'l*, pg. 7512
G.D.S. VALORIBOIS INC.—See Groupe De Scieries G.D.S. Inc.; *Int'l*, pg. 3101
GD-TIKVES AD; *Int'l*, pg. 2895
GD USA, INC.—See Coesia S.p.A.; *Int'l*, pg. 1690
G.D. VAN WAGENEN FINANCIAL SERVICES, INC.—See Bankers International Financial Corporation; *U.S. Private*, pg. 468
GD VERSICHERUNGSSERVICE GMBH—See The Goodyear Tire & Rubber Company; *U.S. Public*, pg. 2083
GDW CANADIAN DIVISION—See Graycliff Partners LP; *U.S. Private*, pg. 1760
GDW EUROPEAN DIVISION—See Graycliff Partners LP; *U.S. Private*, pg. 1760
GDW WESTERN DIVISION—See Graycliff Partners LP; *U.S. Private*, pg. 1760
GDYNIA AMERICA SHIPPING LINES (LONDON) LIMITED—See KBC Group NV; *Int'l*, pg. 4104
GEA AEROFREEZE SYSTEMS, INC.—See GEA Group Aktiengesellschaft; *Int'l*, pg. 2897
GEA ANDINA S.A.S.—See GEA Group Aktiengesellschaft; *Int'l*, pg. 2897
GEA ARABIA LTD.—See GEA Group Aktiengesellschaft; *Int'l*, pg. 2897
GEA ASEPTOMAG AG—See GEA Group Aktiengesellschaft; *Int'l*, pg. 2897
GEA AUSTRIA GMBH—See GEA Group Aktiengesellschaft; *Int'l*, pg. 2897
GEA AVAPAC LTD.—See GEA Group Aktiengesellschaft; *Int'l*, pg. 2897
GEA AWP GMBH—See GEA Group Aktiengesellschaft; *Int'l*, pg. 2897
GEA BALTICS UAB—See GEA Group Aktiengesellschaft; *Int'l*, pg. 2897
GEA BARR ROSIN, INC.—See GEA Group Aktiengesellschaft; *Int'l*, pg. 2897
GEA BARR ROSIN LTD.—See GEA Group Aktiengesellschaft; *Int'l*, pg. 2897
GEA BATIGNOLLES THERMAL TECHNOLOGIES (CHANGSHU) CO., LTD.—See Triton Advisers Limited; *Int'l*, pg. 7932
GEA BISCHOFF GMBH—See GEA Group Aktiengesellschaft; *Int'l*, pg. 2897
GEA BISCHOFF, INC.—See GEA Group Aktiengesellschaft; *Int'l*, pg. 2898
GEA BISCHOFF OY—See GEA Group Aktiengesellschaft; *Int'l*, pg. 2898
GEA BOCK ASIA PTE. LTD.—See NORD Holding Unternehmensbeteiligungsgesellschaft mbH; *Int'l*, pg. 5416
GEA BOCK COMPRESSORS (HANGZHOU) CO., LTD.—See NORD Holding Unternehmensbeteiligungsgesellschaft mbH; *Int'l*, pg. 5416
GEA BOCK CZECH S.R.O.—See NORD Holding Unternehmensbeteiligungsgesellschaft mbH; *Int'l*, pg. 5416
GEA BOCK GMBH—See NORD Holding Unternehmensbeteiligungsgesellschaft mbH; *Int'l*, pg. 5416
GEA BOCK GMBH—See NORD Holding Unternehmensbeteiligungsgesellschaft mbH; *Int'l*, pg. 5416
GEA BOCK MALAYSIA SDN. BHD.—See NORD Holding Unternehmensbeteiligungsgesellschaft mbH; *Int'l*, pg. 5416
GEA BREWERY SYSTEMS GMBH—See GEA Group Aktiengesellschaft; *Int'l*, pg. 2898
GEA CALDEMON, S.A.—See GEA Group Aktiengesellschaft; *Int'l*, pg. 2898
GEA CANADA INC.—See GEA Group Aktiengesellschaft; *Int'l*, pg. 2898
GEA CFS BAKEL B.V.—See GEA Group Aktiengesellschaft; *Int'l*, pg. 2898
GEA CFS BUHL GMBH—See GEA Group Aktiengesellschaft; *Int'l*, pg. 2898
GEA CFS FINANCE B.V.—See GEA Group Aktiengesellschaft; *Int'l*, pg. 2898
GEA CFS GROUP B.V.—See GEA Group Aktiengesellschaft; *Int'l*, pg. 2898
GEA CFS HOLDING B.V.—See GEA Group Aktiengesellschaft; *Int'l*, pg. 2898
GEA CFS HOLDING GMBH—See GEA Group Aktiengesellschaft; *Int'l*, pg. 2898
GEA CFS INTERNATIONAL B.V.—See GEA Group Aktiengesellschaft; *Int'l*, pg. 2898
GEA CFS REAL ESTATE GMBH—See GEA Group Aktiengesellschaft; *Int'l*, pg. 2898
GEA CFS UDEN B.V.—See GEA Group Aktiengesellschaft; *Int'l*, pg. 2898

GEA CFS WEERT B.V.—See GEA Group Aktiengesellschaft; *Int'l*, pg. 2898
GEA CONVENIENCE FOOD TECHNOLOGIES B.V.—See GEA Group Aktiengesellschaft; *Int'l*, pg. 2898
GEA CZECH REPUBLIC S.R.O.—See GEA Group Aktiengesellschaft; *Int'l*, pg. 2898
GEA DIESSEL GMBH—See GEA Group Aktiengesellschaft; *Int'l*, pg. 2898
GEA ECOFLEX CHINA CO., LTD.—See Triton Advisers Limited; *Int'l*, pg. 7931
GEA EEC BULGARIA EOOD—See GEA Group Aktiengesellschaft; *Int'l*, pg. 2898
GEA EEC SERBIA D.O.O.—See GEA Group Aktiengesellschaft; *Int'l*, pg. 2898
GEA EGI ENERGIAGAZDALKODASI ZRT.—See GEA Group Aktiengesellschaft; *Int'l*, pg. 2898
GEA ENGENHARIA DE PROCESSOS E SISTEMA INDUSTRIAIS DO BRASIL LTDA—See GEA Group Aktiengesellschaft; *Int'l*, pg. 2898
GEA ENGENHARIA DE PROCESSOS E SISTEMAS INDUSTRIAIS LTDA.—See GEA Group Aktiengesellschaft; *Int'l*, pg. 2898
GEA EQUIPAMENTOS E SOLUCOES LTDA.—See GEA Group Aktiengesellschaft; *Int'l*, pg. 2898
GEA FARM TECHNOLOGIES ACIER SAS—See GEA Group Aktiengesellschaft; *Int'l*, pg. 2898
GEA FARM TECHNOLOGIES ARGENTINA S.R.L.—See GEA Group Aktiengesellschaft; *Int'l*, pg. 2898
GEA FARM TECHNOLOGIES AUSTRALIA PTY. LTD.—See GEA Group Aktiengesellschaft; *Int'l*, pg. 2898
GEA FARM TECHNOLOGIES AUSTRIA GMBH—See GEA Group Aktiengesellschaft; *Int'l*, pg. 2898
GEA FARM TECHNOLOGIES BELGIUM N.V/S.A.—See GEA Group Aktiengesellschaft; *Int'l*, pg. 2898
GEA FARM TECHNOLOGIES BULGARIA EOOD—See GEA Group Aktiengesellschaft; *Int'l*, pg. 2898
GEA FARM TECHNOLOGIES CANADA INC.—See GEA Group Aktiengesellschaft; *Int'l*, pg. 2898
GEA FARM TECHNOLOGIES CZ, SPOL. S.R.O.—See GEA Group Aktiengesellschaft; *Int'l*, pg. 2898
GEA FARM TECHNOLOGIES DO BRASIL, INDUSTRIA E COMERCIO DE EQUIPAMENTOS AGRICOLAS E PECUARIOS LTDA.—See GEA Group Aktiengesellschaft; *Int'l*, pg. 2899
GEA FARM TECHNOLOGIES DO BRASIL LTDA.—See GEA Group Aktiengesellschaft; *Int'l*, pg. 2899
GEA FARM TECHNOLOGIES FRANCE SAS—See GEA Group Aktiengesellschaft; *Int'l*, pg. 2898
GEA FARM TECHNOLOGIES GMBH—See GEA Group Aktiengesellschaft; *Int'l*, pg. 2898
GEA FARM TECHNOLOGIES IBERICA S.L.—See GEA Group Aktiengesellschaft; *Int'l*, pg. 2898
GEA FARM TECHNOLOGIES INC.—See GEA Group Aktiengesellschaft; *Int'l*, pg. 2899
GEA FARM TECHNOLOGIES (IRELAND) LTD.—See GEA Group Aktiengesellschaft; *Int'l*, pg. 2898
GEA FARM TECHNOLOGIES JAPY SAS—See Mutares SE & Co. KGaA; *Int'l*, pg. 5104
GEA FARM TECHNOLOGIES MULLERUP A/S—See GEA Group Aktiengesellschaft; *Int'l*, pg. 2898
GEA FARM TECHNOLOGIES NEDERLAND B.V.—See GEA Group Aktiengesellschaft; *Int'l*, pg. 2898
GEA FARM TECHNOLOGIES NEW ZEALAND LIMITED—See GEA Group Aktiengesellschaft; *Int'l*, pg. 2899
GEA FARM TECHNOLOGIES ROMANIA S.R.L.—See GEA Group Aktiengesellschaft; *Int'l*, pg. 2899
GEA FARM TECHNOLOGIES SERBIA D.O.O.—See GEA Group Aktiengesellschaft; *Int'l*, pg. 2899
GEA FARM TECHNOLOGIES SLOVAKIA SPOL. S.R.O.—See GEA Group Aktiengesellschaft; *Int'l*, pg. 2899
GEA FARM TECHNOLOGIES SP. Z O.O.—See GEA Group Aktiengesellschaft; *Int'l*, pg. 2899
GEA FARM TECHNOLOGIES SUISSE AG—See GEA Group Aktiengesellschaft; *Int'l*, pg. 2899
GEA FARM TECHNOLOGIES TARIM EKIP. MAK. KIM. TEK. DAN. SAN. TIC. LTD. STI.—See GEA Group Aktiengesellschaft; *Int'l*, pg. 2899
GEA FARM TECHNOLOGIES (UK) LIMITED—See GEA Group Aktiengesellschaft; *Int'l*, pg. 2899
GEA FILTRATION INC.—See GEA Group Aktiengesellschaft; *Int'l*, pg. 2899
GEA FINANCE B.V.—See GEA Group Aktiengesellschaft; *Int'l*, pg. 2899
GEA FINLAND OY—See GEA Group Aktiengesellschaft; *Int'l*, pg. 2899
GEAFOND NUMERO DOS FUERTEVENTURA S.A.—See TUI AG; *Int'l*, pg. 7964
GEA FOOD SOLUTIONS CHILE COMERCIALIZADORA LTDA.—See GEA Group Aktiengesellschaft; *Int'l*, pg. 2899
GEA FOOD SOLUTIONS COMERCIALIZADORA LTDA.—See GEA Group Aktiengesellschaft; *Int'l*, pg. 2899
GEA FOOD SOLUTIONS DENMARK A/S—See GEA Group Aktiengesellschaft; *Int'l*, pg. 2899

GEA FOOD SOLUTIONS FRANCE S.A.S.—See GEA Group Aktiengesellschaft; *Int'l*, pg. 2899
GEA FOOD SOLUTIONS GMBH—See GEA Group Aktiengesellschaft; *Int'l*, pg. 2898
GEA FOOD SOLUTIONS NORTH AMERICA, INC.—See GEA Group Aktiengesellschaft; *Int'l*, pg. 2899
GEA FOOD SOLUTIONS UKRAINE LLC—See GEA Group Aktiengesellschaft; *Int'l*, pg. 2899
GEA FOOD SOLUTIONS WEERT B.V.—See GEA Group Aktiengesellschaft; *Int'l*, pg. 2899
GEA GENEGLACE S.A.S.—See GEA Group Aktiengesellschaft; *Int'l*, pg. 2899
GEA GRASSO PHILIPPINES, INC.—See GEA Group Aktiengesellschaft; *Int'l*, pg. 2902
GEA GRASSO SPOLKA Z O.O.—See GEA Group Aktiengesellschaft; *Int'l*, pg. 2902
GEA GRASSO S.R.O.—See GEA Group Aktiengesellschaft; *Int'l*, pg. 2902
GEA GRASSO (THAILAND) CO. LTD.—See GEA Group Aktiengesellschaft; *Int'l*, pg. 2902
GEA GRASSO TOV—See GEA Group Aktiengesellschaft; *Int'l*, pg. 2902
GEA GRASSO UAB—See GEA Group Aktiengesellschaft; *Int'l*, pg. 2902
GEA GRENCO AFRICA (PTY) LTD—See GEA Group Aktiengesellschaft; *Int'l*, pg. 2899
GEA GRENCO IRELAND LTD.—See GEA Group Aktiengesellschaft; *Int'l*, pg. 2899
GEA GRENCO LTD.—See GEA Group Aktiengesellschaft; *Int'l*, pg. 2899
GEA GROUP AKTIENGESELLSCHAFT; *Int'l*, pg. 2897
GEA GROUP HOLDING FRANCE SAS—See GEA Group Aktiengesellschaft; *Int'l*, pg. 2899
GEA GROUP HOLDING GMBH—See GEA Group Aktiengesellschaft; *Int'l*, pg. 2899
GEA GROUP HOLDINGS (UK) LIMITED—See GEA Group Aktiengesellschaft; *Int'l*, pg. 2899
GEA HOULE, INC.—See GEA Group Aktiengesellschaft; *Int'l*, pg. 2899
GEA HOVEX B.V.—See GEA Group Aktiengesellschaft; *Int'l*, pg. 2899
GEA INDUSTRIAL HEAT EXCHANGER SYSTEMS (CHINA) LTD.—See GEA Group Aktiengesellschaft; *Int'l*, pg. 2899
GE AIRCRAFT ENGINES UK—See General Electric Company; *U.S. Public*, pg. 918
GEA IRELAND LIMITED—See GEA Group Aktiengesellschaft; *Int'l*, pg. 2899
GEA ISISAN TESISAT INSAAT TAAHHUT TICARET VE SANAYI A.S.—See GEA Group Aktiengesellschaft; *Int'l*, pg. 2899
GEA IT SERVICES GMBH—See GEA Group Aktiengesellschaft; *Int'l*, pg. 2899
GEA KLIMATYZACJA SPOLKA Z O.O.—See GEA Group Aktiengesellschaft; *Int'l*, pg. 2899
GEA KOREA LTD.—See GEA Group Aktiengesellschaft; *Int'l*, pg. 2899
GE ALBANY US HOLDINGS LLC—See General Electric Company; *U.S. Public*, pg. 916
GEA LYOPHIL (BEIJING) CO. LTD.—See GEA Group Aktiengesellschaft; *Int'l*, pg. 2899
GEA LYOPHIL GMBH—See GEA Group Aktiengesellschaft; *Int'l*, pg. 2899
GEA MECHANICAL EQUIPMENT CANADA, INC.—See GEA Group Aktiengesellschaft; *Int'l*, pg. 2899
GEA MECHANICAL EQUIPMENT GMBH—See GEA Group Aktiengesellschaft; *Int'l*, pg. 2899
GEA MECHANICAL EQUIPMENT ITALIA S.P.A.—See GEA Group Aktiengesellschaft; *Int'l*, pg. 2901
GEA MECHANICAL EQUIPMENT UK LIMITED—See GEA Group Aktiengesellschaft; *Int'l*, pg. 2901
GEA MECHANICAL EQUIPMENT US, INC.—See GEA Group Aktiengesellschaft; *Int'l*, pg. 2901
GEA MESSO GMBH—See GEA Group Aktiengesellschaft; *Int'l*, pg. 2901
GEA MESSO PT—See GEA Group Aktiengesellschaft; *Int'l*, pg. 2901
GEA MIDDLE EAST FZE—See GEA Group Aktiengesellschaft; *Int'l*, pg. 2900
GEA MTS FLOWTEC AG—See GEA Group Aktiengesellschaft; *Int'l*, pg. 2901
GEA NEDERLAND B.V.—See GEA Group Aktiengesellschaft; *Int'l*, pg. 2901
GEA NIRO PT B.V.—See GEA Group Aktiengesellschaft; *Int'l*, pg. 2901
GEA NIRO SOAVI BRAZIL—See GEA Group Aktiengesellschaft; *Int'l*, pg. 2901
GEA NIRO SOAVI NORTH AMERICA INC—See GEA Group Aktiengesellschaft; *Int'l*, pg. 2903
GEA NIRO SOAVI S.P.A.—See GEA Group Aktiengesellschaft; *Int'l*, pg. 2901
GEA NIRO SOAVI U.K.—See GEA Group Aktiengesellschaft; *Int'l*, pg. 2901
GEA NORWAY AS—See GEA Group Aktiengesellschaft; *Int'l*, pg. 2901
GEA NU-CON LTD.—See GEA Group Aktiengesellschaft; *Int'l*, pg. 2901
GEA NU-CON MANUFACTURING LIMITED—See GEA Group Aktiengesellschaft; *Int'l*, pg. 2901

GEA NU-CON PTY. LTD.—See GEA Group Aktiengesellschaft; *Int'l*, pg. 2901
GEA PERUANA SAC—See GEA Group Aktiengesellschaft; *Int'l*, pg. 2901
GEA PHARMA SYSTEMS AG—See GEA Group Aktiengesellschaft; *Int'l*, pg. 2901
GEA PHARMA SYSTEMS (INDIA) PRIVATE LIMITED—See GEA Group Aktiengesellschaft; *Int'l*, pg. 2901
GEA PHARMA SYSTEMS LIMITED—See GEA Group Aktiengesellschaft; *Int'l*, pg. 2901
GEA PILIPINAS INC.—See GEA Group Aktiengesellschaft; *Int'l*, pg. 2901
GEA POLACEL COOLING TOWERS, LLC—See GEA Group Aktiengesellschaft; *Int'l*, pg. 2901
GEA POWER COOLING TECHNOLOGY (CHINA) LTD.—See Triton Advisers Limited; *Int'l*, pg. 7930
GEA PROCESS ENGINEERING A/S—See GEA Group Aktiengesellschaft; *Int'l*, pg. 2901
GEA PROCESS ENGINEERING CEE KFT.—See GEA Group Aktiengesellschaft; *Int'l*, pg. 2901
GEA PROCESS ENGINEERING CHILE S.A.—See GEA Group Aktiengesellschaft; *Int'l*, pg. 2901
GEA PROCESS ENGINEERING CHINA LIMITED—See GEA Group Aktiengesellschaft; *Int'l*, pg. 2901
GEA PROCESS ENGINEERING INC. - FOOD & DAIRY DIVISION—See GEA Group Aktiengesellschaft; *Int'l*, pg. 2901
GEA PROCESS ENGINEERING INC.—See GEA Group Aktiengesellschaft; *Int'l*, pg. 2901
GEA PROCESS ENGINEERING (INDIA) LIMITED—See GEA Group Aktiengesellschaft; *Int'l*, pg. 2901
GEA PROCESS ENGINEERING IRELAND LTD—See GEA Group Aktiengesellschaft; *Int'l*, pg. 2901
GEA PROCESS ENGINEERING JAPAN LTD.—See GEA Group Aktiengesellschaft; *Int'l*, pg. 2901
GEA PROCESS ENGINEERING LTD.—See GEA Group Aktiengesellschaft; *Int'l*, pg. 2901
GEA PROCESS ENGINEERING LTD.—See GEA Group Aktiengesellschaft; *Int'l*, pg. 2901
GEA PROCESS ENGINEERING NEDERLAND B.V.—See GEA Group Aktiengesellschaft; *Int'l*, pg. 2902
GEA PROCESS ENGINEERING N.V.—See GEA Group Aktiengesellschaft; *Int'l*, pg. 2901
GEA PROCESS ENGINEERING OOO—See GEA Group Aktiengesellschaft; *Int'l*, pg. 2901
GEA PROCESS ENGINEERING OY—See GEA Group Aktiengesellschaft; *Int'l*, pg. 2902
GEA PROCESS ENGINEERING (PTY) LTD.—See GEA Group Aktiengesellschaft; *Int'l*, pg. 2901
GEA PROCESS ENGINEERING PTY. LTD.—See GEA Group Aktiengesellschaft; *Int'l*, pg. 2902
GEA PROCESS ENGINEERING S.A. DE C.V.—See GEA Group Aktiengesellschaft; *Int'l*, pg. 2902
GEA PROCESS ENGINEERING S.A.—See GEA Group Aktiengesellschaft; *Int'l*, pg. 2902
GEA PROCESS ENGINEERING S.A.—See GEA Group Aktiengesellschaft; *Int'l*, pg. 2902
GEA PROCESS ENGINEERING S.A.S.—See GEA Group Aktiengesellschaft; *Int'l*, pg. 2902
GEA PROCESS ENGINEERING S.A.S.—See GEA Group Aktiengesellschaft; *Int'l*, pg. 2902
GEA PROCESS ENGINEERING (S.E.A.) PTE. LTD.—See GEA Group Aktiengesellschaft; *Int'l*, pg. 2901
GEA PROCESS ENGINEERING S.P.A.—See GEA Group Aktiengesellschaft; *Int'l*, pg. 2902
GEA PROCESS ENGINEERING SP. Z O.O.—See GEA Group Aktiengesellschaft; *Int'l*, pg. 2902
GEA PROCESS ENGINEERING S.R.O.—See GEA Group Aktiengesellschaft; *Int'l*, pg. 2902
GEA PROCESS ENGINEERING TAIWAN LTD.—See GEA Group Aktiengesellschaft; *Int'l*, pg. 2902
GEA PROCESS ENGINEERING Z O.O.—See GEA Group Aktiengesellschaft; *Int'l*, pg. 2902
GEA PROCESS MUHENDISLIK MAKINE INSAAT TAAHUT ITHALAT IHRACAT DANISMANLIK SANAYI VE TICARET LTD. STI.—See GEA Group Aktiengesellschaft; *Int'l*, pg. 2902
GEA PROCESS TECHNOLOGIES IRELAND LIMITED—See GEA Group Aktiengesellschaft; *Int'l*, pg. 2902
GEA PROCESS TECHNOLOGY NETHERLANDS B.V.—See GEA Group Aktiengesellschaft; *Int'l*, pg. 2902
GEA PROCOMAC S.P.A. - PACKAGING UNIT—See GEA Group Aktiengesellschaft; *Int'l*, pg. 2902
GEA PROCOMAC S.P.A.—See GEA Group Aktiengesellschaft; *Int'l*, pg. 2902
GEA PT FRANCE SAS—See GEA Group Aktiengesellschaft; *Int'l*, pg. 2901
GEAR4MUSIC (HOLDINGS) PLC; *Int'l*, pg. 2904
GEAR AID, INC.; *U.S. Private*, pg. 1654
GEAR ASSET MANAGEMENT LIMITED—See ETS Group Limited; *Int'l*, pg. 2524
GEARBOX DEL PRAT, S.A.—See Porsche Automobil Holding SE; *Int'l*, pg. 5929
GEARBOX EXPRESS, LLC; *U.S. Private*, pg. 1654

GEARCHIEF EISSMANN AUTOMOTIVE PARTS CO., LTD—See Eissmann Automotive Deutschland GmbH; *Int'l*, pg. 2336
GEARCO, INC.—See Hanesbrands Inc.; *U.S. Public*, pg. 983
GEAR COMPANY OF AMERICA, INC.; *U.S. Private*, pg. 1654
GEARCOR, INC.—See Incline MGMT Corp.; *U.S. Private*, pg. 2053
GEAR DESIGN SOLUTIONS, INC.—See ANSYS, Inc.; *U.S. Public*, pg. 139
GEA REAL ESTATE GMBH—See GEA Group Aktiengesellschaft; *Int'l*, pg. 2902
GEA REFRIGERATION AFRICA (PTY) LTD.—See GEA Group Aktiengesellschaft; *Int'l*, pg. 2902
GEA REFRIGERATION CANADA INC.—See GEA Group Aktiengesellschaft; *Int'l*, pg. 2902
GEA REFRIGERATION COMPONENTS (AUSTRALIA) PTY. LTD.—See GEA Group Aktiengesellschaft; *Int'l*, pg. 2902
GEA REFRIGERATION COMPONENTS (NORDIC) A/S—See GEA Group Aktiengesellschaft; *Int'l*, pg. 2902
GEA REFRIGERATION COMPONENTS (UK) LTD.—See GEA Group Aktiengesellschaft; *Int'l*, pg. 2902
GEA REFRIGERATION FRANCE SAS—See Ardian SAS; *Int'l*, pg. 556
GEA REFRIGERATION GERMANY GMBH—See GEA Group Aktiengesellschaft; *Int'l*, pg. 2902
GEA REFRIGERATION IBERICA S.A.—See GEA Group Aktiengesellschaft; *Int'l*, pg. 2902
GEA REFRIGERATION MALAYSIA SDN. BHD.—See GEA Group Aktiengesellschaft; *Int'l*, pg. 2902
GEA REFRIGERATION NETHERLANDS N.V.—See GEA Group Aktiengesellschaft; *Int'l*, pg. 2902
GEA REFRIGERATION NORTH AMERICA INC.—See GEA Group Aktiengesellschaft; *Int'l*, pg. 2902
GEA REFRIGERATION PHILIPPINES, INC.—See GEA Group Aktiengesellschaft; *Int'l*, pg. 2902
GEA REFRIGERATION ROMANIA S.R.L.—See GEA Group Aktiengesellschaft; *Int'l*, pg. 2902
GEA REFRIGERATION TECHNOLOGIES GMBH—See GEA Group Aktiengesellschaft; *Int'l*, pg. 2902
GEA REFRIGERATION TECHNOLOGIES INDIA PVT LTD.—See GEA Group Aktiengesellschaft; *Int'l*, pg. 2903
GEA REFRIGERATION TECHNOLOGIES IRELAND—See GEA Group Aktiengesellschaft; *Int'l*, pg. 2903
GEA REFRIGERATION TECHNOLOGIES—See GEA Group Aktiengesellschaft; *Int'l*, pg. 2902
GEA REFRIGERATION TECHNOLOGY CO., LTD.—See GEA Group Aktiengesellschaft; *Int'l*, pg. 2903
GEA REFRIGERATION TECHNOLOGY (SUZHOU) CO., LTD.—See GEA Group Aktiengesellschaft; *Int'l*, pg. 2903
GEA REFRIGERATION (THAILAND) CO. LTD.—See GEA Group Aktiengesellschaft; *Int'l*, pg. 2902
GEA REFRIGERATION UK LTD.—See GEA Group Aktiengesellschaft; *Int'l*, pg. 2903
GEA REFRIGERATION VIETNAM CO. LTD.—See GEA Group Aktiengesellschaft; *Int'l*, pg. 2903
GEAR ENERGY LTD.; *Int'l*, pg. 2904
GEARHART AUSTRALIA LIMITED—See SGS SA; *Int'l*, pg. 6742
GEARHART UNITED PTY LTD.—See SGS SA; *Int'l*, pg. 6743
GEAR HEAD CO., LTD.—See Bangkok Broadcasting & TV Co., Ltd.; *Int'l*, pg. 833
GEARHEAD ENGINES INC.—See LKQ Corporation; *U.S. Public*, pg. 1334
GEARHEAD OUTFITTERS, INC.; *U.S. Private*, pg. 1655
GEAR HEADQUARTERS INC.—See Headco Industries; *U.S. Private*, pg. 1891
GEARHEART COMMUNICATIONS COMPANY, INC.; *U.S. Private*, pg. 1655
GEARHOUSE ACTIS SAS—See Gravity Media Group Limited; *Int'l*, pg. 3062
GEARHOUSE BROADCAST LLC—See Gravity Media Group Limited; *Int'l*, pg. 3062
GEARHOUSE BROADCAST PTY LIMITED—See Gravity Media Group Limited; *Int'l*, pg. 3062
GEARING MOSS SUPPLIES (PTY) LTD—See enX Group Limited; *Int'l*, pg. 2456
GEAR MOTION GMBH—See KAP Beteiligungs-AG; *Int'l*, pg. 4076
GEARON HOFFMAN INC.; *U.S. Private*, pg. 1655
GEAR-O-RAMA SUPPLY LTD.; *Int'l*, pg. 2904
GEAR PRODUCTS INC.—See Dover Corporation; *U.S. Public*, pg. 679
GEAR SECURITIES INVESTMENT LIMITED—See ETS Group Limited; *Int'l*, pg. 2524
GEAR SHOP INC.—See ITV plc; *Int'l*, pg. 3845
GEARS & SPROCKETTS, INC.—See Headco Industries; *U.S. Private*, pg. 1891
GEARS & TRANSMISSION SUB-CO.—See Taiyuan Heavy Industry Co., Ltd.; *Int'l*, pg. 7427
GEAR-TEC GMBH—See KSB SE & Co. KGaA; *Int'l*, pg. 4313
GEARTEC, INC.—See United Stars Inc.; *U.S. Private*, pg. 4298

GE ARTESIA BANK—See General Electric Company; *U.S. Public*, pg. 920
GEARUP INVESTMENTS LIMITED—See Hysan Development Company Limited; *Int'l*, pg. 3554
GEAR WASH LLC—See Fire-Dex, LLC; *U.S. Private*, pg. 1511
THE GEARY COMPANY; *U.S. Private*, pg. 4032
GEARY LSF GROUP, INC. - SAN DIEGO—See Geary LSF Group, Inc.; *U.S. Private*, pg. 1655
GEARY LSF GROUP, INC.; *U.S. Private*, pg. 1655
GEARY PACIFIC CORPORATION; *U.S. Private*, pg. 1655
GEARY PACIFIC OF ARIZONA - FORT MOJAVE—See Geary Pacific Corporation; *U.S. Private*, pg. 1655
GEARY PACIFIC SUPPLY - SACRAMENTO—See Geary Pacific Corporation; *U.S. Private*, pg. 1655
GEA SAUDI ARABIA LLC—See Triton Advisers Limited; *Int'l*, pg. 7930
GEA SEGMENT MANAGEMENT HOLDING GMBH—See GEA Group Aktiengesellschaft; *Int'l*, pg. 2903
GEAS ENERGIEWACHT B.V.—See RWE AG; *Int'l*, pg. 6434
GEA (SHANGHAI) FARM TECHNOLOGIES COMPANY LTD.—See GEA Group Aktiengesellschaft; *Int'l*, pg. 2898
GEA SISTEMAS DE RESFRIAMENTO LTDA.—See GEA Group Aktiengesellschaft; *Int'l*, pg. 2903
GEA S.R.L.—See CogenInfra SpA; *Int'l*, pg. 1694
GEA SUISSE AG—See GEA Group Aktiengesellschaft; *Int'l*, pg. 2903
GEA SWEDEN AB—See GEA Group Aktiengesellschaft; *Int'l*, pg. 2903
GEA TDS GMBH—See GEA Group Aktiengesellschaft; *Int'l*, pg. 2903
GEA (THAILAND) CO., LTD.—See GEA Group Aktiengesellschaft; *Int'l*, pg. 2897
GEA TUCHENHAGEN CANADA, INC.—See GEA Group Aktiengesellschaft; *Int'l*, pg. 2900
GEA TUCHENHAGEN FRANCE SARL—See GEA Group Aktiengesellschaft; *Int'l*, pg. 2900
GEA TUCHENHAGEN GMBH—See GEA Group Aktiengesellschaft; *Int'l*, pg. 2899
GEA TUCHENHAGEN POLSKA SP. Z O.O.—See GEA Group Aktiengesellschaft; *Int'l*, pg. 2900
GEA TUCHENHAGEN US, LLC—See GEA Group Aktiengesellschaft; *Int'l*, pg. 2900
GEAUGA LAKE & WILDWATER KINGDOM—See Six Flags Entertainment Corporation; *U.S. Public*, pg. 1890
GEAUGA SAVINGS BANK INC.; *U.S. Private*, pg. 1655
GEA UNIVALVE E.U.R.L—See GEA Group Aktiengesellschaft; *Int'l*, pg. 2903
GE AVIATION CZECH S.R.O.—See General Electric Company; *U.S. Public*, pg. 918
GE AVIATION DISTRIBUTION JAPAN CO., LTD.—See General Electric Company; *U.S. Public*, pg. 918
GE AVIATION SERVICE OPERATION LLP—See General Electric Company; *U.S. Public*, pg. 918
GE AVIATION SYSTEMS GROUP LIMITED—See General Electric Company; *U.S. Public*, pg. 918
GE AVIATION SYSTEMS LIMITED—See General Electric Company; *U.S. Public*, pg. 918
GE AVIATION SYSTEMS LLC - BOHEMIA—See General Electric Company; *U.S. Public*, pg. 918
GE AVIATION SYSTEMS LLC - CLEARWATER—See General Electric Company; *U.S. Public*, pg. 918
GE AVIATION SYSTEMS LLC - GRAND RAPIDS—See General Electric Company; *U.S. Public*, pg. 918
GE AVIATION SYSTEMS LLC - POMPANO BEACH—See General Electric Company; *U.S. Public*, pg. 918
GE AVIATION SYSTEMS LLC—See General Electric Company; *U.S. Public*, pg. 918
GE AVIATION SYSTEMS LTD. - EASTLEIGH—See General Electric Company; *U.S. Public*, pg. 918
GE AVIATION SYSTEMS LTD. - SOUTHAMPTON—See General Electric Company; *U.S. Public*, pg. 918
GE AVIO S.R.L.—See General Electric Company; *U.S. Public*, pg. 919
GEA WEST AFRICA LTD.—See GEA Group Aktiengesellschaft; *Int'l*, pg. 2903
GEA WESTFALIA SEPARATING EQUIPMENT (TIANJIN) CO., LTD.—See GEA Group Aktiengesellschaft; *Int'l*, pg. 2900
GEA WESTFALIA SEPARATOR ARGENTINA S.A.—See GEA Group Aktiengesellschaft; *Int'l*, pg. 2900
GEA WESTFALIA SEPARATOR AUSTRALIA PTY. LTD.—See GEA Group Aktiengesellschaft; *Int'l*, pg. 2903
GEA WESTFALIA SEPARATOR AUSTRIA GMBH—See GEA Group Aktiengesellschaft; *Int'l*, pg. 2900
GEA WESTFALIA SEPARATOR BELGIUM N.V.—See GEA Group Aktiengesellschaft; *Int'l*, pg. 2900
GEA WESTFALIA SEPARATOR CANADA, INC.—See GEA Group Aktiengesellschaft; *Int'l*, pg. 2900
GEA WESTFALIA SEPARATOR CHILE S.A.—See GEA Group Aktiengesellschaft; *Int'l*, pg. 2900
GEA WESTFALIA SEPARATOR (CHINA) LTD.—See GEA Group Aktiengesellschaft; *Int'l*, pg. 2900
GEA WESTFALIA SEPARATOR CIS LTD.—See GEA Group Aktiengesellschaft; *Int'l*, pg. 2900

GEA WESTFALIA SEPARATOR CZ S.R.O.—See GEA Group Aktiengesellschaft; *Int'l*, pg. 2900
GEA WESTFALIA SEPARATOR DEUTSCHLAND GMBH—See GEA Group Aktiengesellschaft; *Int'l*, pg. 2900
GEA WESTFALIA SEPARATOR DK A/S—See GEA Group Aktiengesellschaft; *Int'l*, pg. 2900
GEA WESTFALIA SEPARATOR DO BRASIL INDUSTRIA DE CENTRIFUGAS LTDA.—See GEA Group Aktiengesellschaft; *Int'l*, pg. 2901
GEA WESTFALIA SEPARATOR FRANCE SAS—See GEA Group Aktiengesellschaft; *Int'l*, pg. 2900
GEA WESTFALIA SEPARATOR GROUP GMBH—See GEA Group Aktiengesellschaft; *Int'l*, pg. 2900
GEA WESTFALIA SEPARATOR HELLAS A.E.—See GEA Group Aktiengesellschaft; *Int'l*, pg. 2903
GEA WESTFALIA SEPARATOR HELLAS S.A.—See GEA Group Aktiengesellschaft; *Int'l*, pg. 2900
GEA WESTFALIA SEPARATOR HUNGARIA KFT.—See GEA Group Aktiengesellschaft; *Int'l*, pg. 2900
GEA WESTFALIA SEPARATOR IBERICA, S.A.—See GEA Group Aktiengesellschaft; *Int'l*, pg. 2900
GEA WESTFALIA SEPARATOR ICELAND EHF—See GEA Group Aktiengesellschaft; *Int'l*, pg. 2900
GEA WESTFALIA SEPARATOR IRELAND LTD.—See GEA Group Aktiengesellschaft; *Int'l*, pg. 2900
GEA WESTFALIA SEPARATOR ITALIA S.R.L.—See GEA Group Aktiengesellschaft; *Int'l*, pg. 2900
GEA WESTFALIA SEPARATOR JAPAN K.K.—See GEA Group Aktiengesellschaft; *Int'l*, pg. 2900
GEA WESTFALIA SEPARATOR KOREA LTD.—See GEA Group Aktiengesellschaft; *Int'l*, pg. 2900
GEA WESTFALIA SEPARATOR (MALAYSIA) SDN BHD—See GEA Group Aktiengesellschaft; *Int'l*, pg. 2900
GEA WESTFALIA SEPARATOR MEXICANA S.A. DE C.V.—See GEA Group Aktiengesellschaft; *Int'l*, pg. 2900
GEA WESTFALIA SEPARATOR NEDERLAND B.V.—See GEA Group Aktiengesellschaft; *Int'l*, pg. 2900
GEA WESTFALIA SEPARATOR NORWAY AS—See GEA Group Aktiengesellschaft; *Int'l*, pg. 2900
GEA WESTFALIA SEPARATOR NZ LTD.—See GEA Group Aktiengesellschaft; *Int'l*, pg. 2900
GEA WESTFALIA SEPARATOR PHILIPPINES INC.—See GEA Group Aktiengesellschaft; *Int'l*, pg. 2900
GEA WESTFALIA SEPARATOR POLSKA SP. Z O.O.—See GEA Group Aktiengesellschaft; *Int'l*, pg. 2900
GEA WESTFALIA SEPARATOR PRODUCTION FRANCE SAS—See Altifort France SAS; *Int'l*, pg. 393
GEA WESTFALIA SEPARATOR ROMANIA SRL—See GEA Group Aktiengesellschaft; *Int'l*, pg. 2900
GEA WESTFALIA SEPARATOR SANAYI VE TICARET LTD. STI.—See GEA Group Aktiengesellschaft; *Int'l*, pg. 2901
GEA WESTFALIA SEPARATOR (S.E.A.) PTE. LTD.—See GEA Group Aktiengesellschaft; *Int'l*, pg. 2900
GEA WESTFALIA SEPARATOR SOUTH AFRICA (PTY) LTD.—See GEA Group Aktiengesellschaft; *Int'l*, pg. 2901
GEA WESTFALIA SEPARATOR SWEDEN AB—See GEA Group Aktiengesellschaft; *Int'l*, pg. 2901
GEA WESTFALIA SEPARATOR (THAILAND) LTD.—See GEA Group Aktiengesellschaft; *Int'l*, pg. 2900
GEA WESTFALIA SEPARATOR (TIANJIN) CO., LTD.—See GEA Group Aktiengesellschaft; *Int'l*, pg. 2900
GEA WESTFALIASURGE ACIER SAS—See GEA Group Aktiengesellschaft; *Int'l*, pg. 2904
GEA WESTFALIASURGE CANADA COMPANY—See GEA Group Aktiengesellschaft; *Int'l*, pg. 2904
GEA WESTFALIASURGE CHILE S.A.—See GEA Group Aktiengesellschaft; *Int'l*, pg. 2904
GEA WESTFALIASURGE FRANCE SAS—See GEA Group Aktiengesellschaft; *Int'l*, pg. 2904
GEA WESTFALIASURGE MEXICANA S.A. DE C.V., I.L.—See GEA Group Aktiengesellschaft; *Int'l*, pg. 2904
GEA WESTFALIASURGE NEDERLAND B.V.—See GEA Group Aktiengesellschaft; *Int'l*, pg. 2904
GEA WESTFALIASURGE NORDIC A/S—See GEA Group Aktiengesellschaft; *Int'l*, pg. 2904
GEA WESTFALIASURGE UK LTD.—See GEA Group Aktiengesellschaft; *Int'l*, pg. 2904
GEA WESTFALIASURGE UKRAINE GMBH—See GEA Group Aktiengesellschaft; *Int'l*, pg. 2904
GEA WIEGAND GMBH—See GEA Group Aktiengesellschaft; *Int'l*, pg. 2903
GEA WIEGAND (SCHWEIZ) GMBH—See GEA Group Aktiengesellschaft; *Int'l*, pg. 2903
GEA WS SOUTHEAST, INC.—See GEA Group Aktiengesellschaft; *Int'l*, pg. 2900
GEBAUDELEASING GRUNDSTUCKSVERWALTUNGSGESELLSCHAFT M.B.H.—See UniCredit S.p.A.; *Int'l*, pg. 8036
GEBAUDE SERVICE GESELLSCHAFT UBERSEERING 35 MBH—See Munchener Ruckversicherungs AG; *Int'l*, pg. 5088
GEBBS HEALTHCARE SOLUTIONS INC.—See ChrysCapital Management Co.; *Int'l*, pg. 1588

GEBECO GESELLSCHAFT FUR INTERNATIONALE BE-GEGNUNG UND COOPERATION MBH & CO. KG—See TUI AG; *Int'l*, pg. 7964
GE BE PRIVATE LTD.—See GE HealthCare Technologies Inc.; *U.S. Public*, pg. 908
GEBERIT AB—See Geberit AG; *Int'l*, pg. 2904
GEBERIT AG; *Int'l*, pg. 2904
GEBERIT APPARATE AG—See Geberit AG; *Int'l*, pg. 2904
GEBERIT AS—See Geberit AG; *Int'l*, pg. 2904
GEBERIT A/S—See Geberit AG; *Int'l*, pg. 2904
GEBERIT BETEILIGUNGSVERWALTUNG GMBH—See Geberit AG; *Int'l*, pg. 2904
GEBERIT B.V.—See Geberit AG; *Int'l*, pg. 2904
GEBERIT CERAMICA S.P.A.—See Geberit AG; *Int'l*, pg. 2904
GEBERIT HOLDING AG—See Geberit AG; *Int'l*, pg. 2904
GEBERIT HUTER GMBH—See Geberit AG; *Int'l*, pg. 2904
GEBERIT INDIA MANUFACTURING PVT. LTD.—See Geberit AG; *Int'l*, pg. 2904
GEBERIT INTERNATIONAL AG—See Geberit AG; *Int'l*, pg. 2904
GEBERIT INTERNATIONAL B.V.—See Geberit AG; *Int'l*, pg. 2904
GEBERIT INTERNATIONAL SALES AG—See Geberit AG; *Int'l*, pg. 2904
GEBERIT ISRAEL LTD.—See Geberit AG; *Int'l*, pg. 2904
GEBERIT KFT—See Geberit AG; *Int'l*, pg. 2904
GEBERIT LICHTENSTEIN GMBH—See Geberit AG; *Int'l*, pg. 2904
GEBERIT LOGISTIK GMBH—See Geberit AG; *Int'l*, pg. 2904
GEBERIT MAPRESS GMBH—See Geberit AG; *Int'l*, pg. 2904
GEBERIT MARKETING E DISTRIBUZIONE SA—See Geberit AG; *Int'l*, pg. 2904
GEBERIT NIGERIA LTD.—See Geberit AG; *Int'l*, pg. 2904
GEBERIT N.V.—See Geberit AG; *Int'l*, pg. 2904
GEBERIT OY—See Geberit AG; *Int'l*, pg. 2905
GEBERIT OZORKOW SP. Z O.O.—See Geberit AG; *Int'l*, pg. 2905
GEBERIT PLUMBING TECHNOLOGY CO. LTD.—See Geberit AG; *Int'l*, pg. 2905
GEBERIT PLUMBING TECHNOLOGY INDIA PVT. LTD.—See Geberit AG; *Int'l*, pg. 2905
GEBERIT PRODAJA D.O.O.—See Geberit AG; *Int'l*, pg. 2905
GEBERIT PRODUCTION OY—See Geberit AG; *Int'l*, pg. 2905
GEBERIT PRODUKCJA SP. Z O.O.—See Geberit AG; *Int'l*, pg. 2905
GEBERIT PRODUKTIONS AG—See Geberit AG; *Int'l*, pg. 2905
GEBERIT PRODUKTIONS GMBH & CO. KG—See Geberit AG; *Int'l*, pg. 2905
GEBERIT PRODUKTIONS GMBH—See Geberit AG; *Int'l*, pg. 2905
GEBERIT PRODUZIONE S.P.A.—See Geberit AG; *Int'l*, pg. 2905
GEBERIT PROIZVODNJA D.O.O.—See Geberit AG; *Int'l*, pg. 2905
GEBERIT PTY LTD.—See Geberit AG; *Int'l*, pg. 2905
GEBERIT RLS BETEILIGUNGS GMBH—See Geberit AG; *Int'l*, pg. 2905
GEBERIT RUS LLC—See Geberit AG; *Int'l*, pg. 2905
GEBERIT SALES LTD.—See Geberit AG; *Int'l*, pg. 2905
GEBERIT SANITARNA TEHNIKA D.O.O.—See Geberit AG; *Int'l*, pg. 2905
GEBERIT S.A.U.—See Geberit AG; *Int'l*, pg. 2905
GEBERIT SERVICE OY—See Geberit AG; *Int'l*, pg. 2905
GEBERIT SERVICE SP. Z O.O.—See Geberit AG; *Int'l*, pg. 2905
GEBERIT SHANGHAI INVESTMENT ADMINISTRATION CO., LTD.—See Geberit AG; *Int'l*, pg. 2905
GEBERIT SHANGHAI TRADING CO. LTD.—See Geberit AG; *Int'l*, pg. 2905
GEBERIT SLOVENSKO S.R.O.—See Geberit AG; *Int'l*, pg. 2905
GEBERIT SOUTH EAST ASIA PTE. LTD.—See Geberit AG; *Int'l*, pg. 2905
GEBERIT SOUTHERN AFRICA (PTY.) LTD.—See Geberit AG; *Int'l*, pg. 2905
GEBERIT SPOL. S.R.O.—See Geberit AG; *Int'l*, pg. 2905
GEBERIT SP.Z.O.O.—See Geberit AG; *Int'l*, pg. 2905
GEBERIT TECHNIK AG—See Geberit AG; *Int'l*, pg. 2905
GEBERIT TECNOLOGIA SANITARIA S.A.—See Geberit AG; *Int'l*, pg. 2905
GEBERIT TESISAT SISTEMLERI TICARET LTD.—See Geberit AG; *Int'l*, pg. 2905
GEBERIT TRADING LLC—See Geberit AG; *Int'l*, pg. 2905
GEBERIT VERTRIEBS AG—See Geberit AG; *Int'l*, pg. 2905
GEBERIT VERTRIEBS AG & CO. KG—See Geberit AG; *Int'l*, pg. 2905
GEBERIT VERTRIEBS GMBH—See Geberit AG; *Int'l*, pg. 2905
GEBERIT VERWALTUNGS AG—See Geberit AG; *Int'l*, pg. 2905
GEBERIT VERWALTUNGS GMBH—See Geberit AG; *Int'l*, pg. 2905

GEBERIT WEILHEIM GMBH—See Geberit AG; *Int'l*, pg. 2905
GEBHARDT AUTOMOTIVE INC.; *U.S. Private*, pg. 1655
GEBO CERMEX CANADA INC.—See Tetra Laval International S.A.; *Int'l*, pg. 7576
GEBO CERMEX USA INC.—See Tetra Laval International S.A.; *Int'l*, pg. 7576
GEBO DISTRIBUTING CO., INC.; *U.S. Private*, pg. 1655
GEBRAUCHTGERATE-ZENTRUM DRESDEN GMBH & CO. KG—See Jungheinrich AG; *Int'l*, pg. 4027
GEBR. BODE GMBH & CO. KG—See The Carlyle Group Inc.; *U.S. Public*, pg. 2053
GEBR. GRUNEWALD GMBH & CO. KG; *Int'l*, pg. 2905
GEBR. HEINEMANN SE & CO. KG; *Int'l*, pg. 2905
GEBR. KEMPER GMBH & CO. KG; *Int'l*, pg. 2906
GEBR. KEMPER UK & IRELAND LTD.—See Gebr. Kemper GmbH & Co, KG; *Int'l*, pg. 2906
GEBR. KNAUF KG; *Int'l*, pg. 2906
GEBR. LENNARTZ GMBH & CO.KG; *Int'l*, pg. 2908
GEBR. MARKLIN & CIE. GMBH; *Int'l*, pg. 2909
GEBROEDERS CAPPELLE FRERES S.A.R.L.—See Cappelle Pignenes N.V.; *Int'l*, pg. 1315
GEBROEDERS KRAMER B.V.—See Sligro Food Group N.V.; *Int'l*, pg. 6997
GEBR. REINFURT GMBH & CO. KG—See Arcline Investment Management LP; *U.S. Private*, pg. 314
GEBR. SCHNITTGER GMBH—See RETHMANN AG & Co. KG; *Int'l*, pg. 6306
GEBRUDER DURRBECK KUNSTSTOFFE GMBH; *Int'l*, pg. 2909
GEBRUDER EBERHARD GMBH & CO. KG; *Int'l*, pg. 2909
GEBRUDER GAUSELMANN GMBH—See Gauselmann AG; *Int'l*, pg. 2890
GEBRUDER JOSEF UND MATTHAUS ZIEGLER GMBH—See Hawesko Holding AG; *Int'l*, pg. 3288
GEBRUDER LANG GMBH PAPIERFABRIK—See UPM-Kymmene Corporation; *Int'l*, pg. 8090
GEBRUDER WEISS GESELLSCHAFT M.B.H.; *Int'l*, pg. 2909
GEBRUDER WEISS, INC.—See Gebruder Weiss Gesellschaft m.b.H.; *Int'l*, pg. 2909
GEBR. VAN LEEUWEN HARMELEN B.V.—See Ronesans Holding A.S.; *Int'l*, pg. 6396
GEBR. WILLACH GMBH; *Int'l*, pg. 2909
GEBZE ELEKTRIK URETIM LIMITED SIRKETI—See Enka Insaat ve Sanayi A.S.; *Int'l*, pg. 2440
GEBZE GAZ AS—See SOL S.p.A.; *Int'l*, pg. 7067
GEBZE IZMIR OTOYOLU ISLETME A.S.—See Groupe Egis S.A.; *Int'l*, pg. 3102
GE CALEDONIAN LIMITED—See General Electric Company; *U.S. Public*, pg. 916
GECAMINES—See Vicat S.A.; *Int'l*, pg. 8185
GE CANADA—See General Electric Company; *U.S. Public*, pg. 919
GE CAPITAL AVIATION SERVICES LLC—See General Electric Company; *U.S. Public*, pg. 920
GE CAPITAL BANK LIMITED—See General Electric Company; *U.S. Public*, pg. 920
GE CAPITAL FINANCE AUSTRALASIA PTY. LTD.—See General Electric Company; *U.S. Public*, pg. 920
GE CAPITAL GLOBAL HOLDINGS, LLC—See General Electric Company; *U.S. Public*, pg. 916
GE CAPITAL REAL ESTATE—See General Electric Company; *U.S. Public*, pg. 920
GE CAPITAL TRANSPORTATION FINANCIAL SERVICES, LTD.—See General Electric Company; *U.S. Public*, pg. 920
GECASA—See Ente Vasco de la Energia; *Int'l*, pg. 2450
GECAS ASSET MANAGEMENT SERVICES—See General Electric Company; *U.S. Public*, pg. 920
GEC BRUNEI SDN. BHD.—See Telent Limited; *Int'l*, pg. 7539
GEC DURHAM INDUSTRIES, INC.—See Durham Co.; *U.S. Private*, pg. 1293
GECI ENGINEERING SERVICES SRL—See GECI International SA; *Int'l*, pg. 2909
GECI GMBH—See GECI International SA; *Int'l*, pg. 2909
GECI INGENIERIA S.L.—See GECI International SA; *Int'l*, pg. 2909
GECI INTERNATIONAL SA; *Int'l*, pg. 2909
GECI LTD—See GECI International SA; *Int'l*, pg. 2909
GECINA NOM; *Int'l*, pg. 2909
GECINA S.A.; *Int'l*, pg. 2909
GEC, INC.; *U.S. Private*, pg. 1655
GECI PORTUGAL—See GECI International SA; *Int'l*, pg. 2909
GECI SOUTH AFRICA PTY LTD—See GECI International SA; *Int'l*, pg. 2909
GECKO HOSPITALITY INC—See Triumph Higher Education Group, LLC; *U.S. Private*, pg. 4239
GECKOSYSTEMS INTL. CORP.; *U.S. Public*, pg. 909
GECKO TRADING LIMITED—See L. Possehl & Co. mbH; *Int'l*, pg. 4382
GECMA COMPONENTS ELECTRONIC GMBH—See Eaton Corporation plc; *Int'l*, pg. 2278
GECOSS CORPORATION—See JFE Holdings, Inc.; *Int'l*, pg. 3937
GECOS S.p.A.; *Int'l*, pg. 2909

GECOSS VIETNAM COMPANY LIMITED—See JFE Holdings, Inc.; *Int'l*, pg. 3937
G. E. CRANE N.Z. HOLDINGS LTD—See Fletcher Building Limited; *Int'l*, pg. 2700
GE CREDITLINE—See General Electric Company; *U.S. Public*, pg. 920
GEC SMART FURNITURE LTD.—See Global Education Communities Corp; *Int'l*, pg. 2995
GEDAS AG—See Deutsche Telekom AG; *Int'l*, pg. 2084
GEDAS ARGENTINA, S.A.—See Deutsche Telekom AG; *Int'l*, pg. 2084
GEDAS GAYRIMENKUL DEGERLEME A.S.—See T.C. Toplu Konut Idaresi Baskanligi; *Int'l*, pg. 7396
GEDAS MEXICO, S.A. DE C.V.—See Deutsche Telekom AG; *Int'l*, pg. 2084
GEDAS UNITED KINGDOM LTD.—See Deutsche Telekom AG; *Int'l*, pg. 2084
GEDEL SARL—See Carrefour SA; *Int'l*, pg. 1345
GEDEON RICHTER AUSTRALIA PTY. LTD.—See Gedeon Richter Plc.; *Int'l*, pg. 2909
GEDEON RICHTER AUSTRIA GMBH—See Gedeon Richter Plc.; *Int'l*, pg. 2909
GEDEON RICHTER BOLIVIA SRL—See Gedeon Richter Plc.; *Int'l*, pg. 2909
GEDEON RICHTER BULGARIA LTD.—See Gedeon Richter Plc.; *Int'l*, pg. 2909
GEDEON RICHTER CHILE SPA—See Gedeon Richter Plc.; *Int'l*, pg. 2909
GEDEON RICHTER COLOMBIA S.A.S.—See Gedeon Richter Plc.; *Int'l*, pg. 2910
GEDEON RICHTER CROATIA D.O.O.—See Gedeon Richter Plc.; *Int'l*, pg. 2910
GEDEONRICHTER ECUADOR S.A.—See Gedeon Richter Plc.; *Int'l*, pg. 2910
GEDEON RICHTER FRANCE S.A.R.L.—See Gedeon Richter Plc.; *Int'l*, pg. 2910
GEDEON RICHTER IBERICA S.A—See Gedeon Richter Plc.; *Int'l*, pg. 2910
GEDEON RICHTER ITALIA S.R.L—See Gedeon Richter Plc.; *Int'l*, pg. 2910
GEDEON RICHTER KZ LLP—See Chemical Works of Gedeon Richter Plc; *Int'l*, pg. 1462
GEDEON RICHTER MARKETING CR S.R.O.—See Gedeon Richter Plc.; *Int'l*, pg. 2910
GEDEON RICHTER MARKETING POLSKA SP. Z O.O.—See Gedeon Richter Plc.; *Int'l*, pg. 2910
GEDEON RICHTER PERU S.A.C.—See Gedeon Richter Plc.; *Int'l*, pg. 2910
GEDEON RICHTER PHARMA GMBH—See Gedeon Richter Plc.; *Int'l*, pg. 2910
GEDEON RICHTER PHARMA O.O.O.—See Gedeon Richter Plc.; *Int'l*, pg. 2910
GEDEON RICHTER PLC.; *Int'l*, pg. 2909
GEDEON RICHTER POLSKA SP. Z O.O—See Gedeon Richter Plc.; *Int'l*, pg. 2910
GEDEON RICHTER - RETEA FARMACEUTICA S.R.L—See Gedeon Richter Plc.; *Int'l*, pg. 2909
GEDEON RICHTER ROMANIA S.A—See Gedeon Richter Plc.; *Int'l*, pg. 2910
GEDEON RICHTER (SCHWEIZ) AG—See Gedeon Richter Plc.; *Int'l*, pg. 2909
GEDEON RICHTER SLOVAKIA S.R.O.—See Gedeon Richter Plc.; *Int'l*, pg. 2910
GEDEON RICHTER SLOVENIJA, D.O.O.—See Gedeon Richter Plc.; *Int'l*, pg. 2910
GEDEON RICHTER UA TOV—See Chemical Works of Gedeon Richter Plc; *Int'l*, pg. 1462
GEDEON RICHTER UA V.A.T—See Gedeon Richter Plc.; *Int'l*, pg. 2910
GEDEON RICHTER UK LTD—See Gedeon Richter Plc.; *Int'l*, pg. 2910
GEDEON RICHTER UKRFARM O.O.O—See Gedeon Richter Plc.; *Int'l*, pg. 2910
GEDEON RICHTER USA, INC—See Gedeon Richter Plc.; *Int'l*, pg. 2910
GEDEON RICHTER VIETNAM LTD.—See Chemical Works of Gedeon Richter Plc; *Int'l*, pg. 1462
GEDEVELOP AB—See Indutrade AB; *Int'l*, pg. 3679
GED GARTNER ELECTRONIC DESIGN GMBH—See ELMOS Semiconductor AG; *Int'l*, pg. 2368
GEDIA S.A.; *Int'l*, pg. 2910
GEDI GRUPPO EDITORIALE S.P.A.—See Giovanni Agnelli B.V.; *Int'l*, pg. 2978
GEDIK YATIRIM HOLDING AS; *Int'l*, pg. 2910
GEDIK YATIRIM MENKUL DEGERLER A.S.; *Int'l*, pg. 2910
GED INTEGRATED SOLUTIONS, INC.—See The Beekman Group, LLC; *U.S. Private*, pg. 3993
GEDIS GMBH—See Rohde & Schwarz GmbH & Co. KG; *Int'l*, pg. 6384
GE DISTRIBUTED POWER, INC.—See General Electric Company; *U.S. Public*, pg. 916
GEDIZ AMBALAJ SANAYI VE TICARET A.S.; *Int'l*, pg. 2910
GEDNEY FOODS COMPANY—See PMC Capital Partners, LLC; *U.S. Private*, pg. 3217
GE DRIVES & CONTROLS INC.—See General Electric Company; *U.S. Public*, pg. 919

GEDIZ AMBALAJ SANAYI VE TICARET A.S.

GE DRUCK HOLDINGS LIMITED—See General Electric Company; *U.S. Public*, pg. 916
GED TESTING SERVICE LLC—See Pearson plc; *Int'l*, pg. 5775
GEDY IBERICA, S.A.—See Gedy S.p.A.; *Int'l*, pg. 2910
GEDY S.P.A.; *Int'l*, pg. 2910
GEECEE VENTURES LIMITED; *Int'l*, pg. 2910
GEECEE VENTURES LTD. - CHEMICAL PLANT 2—See GeeCee Ventures Limited; *Int'l*, pg. 2911
GEECHS, INC.; *Int'l*, pg. 2911
GEECOMMS PTE. LTD.—See Wei Yuan Holdings Limited; *Int'l*, pg. 8369
GEE CONSULTANTS, INC.; *U.S. Private*, pg. 1655
GEEFCEE FINANCE LIMITED; *Int'l*, pg. 2911
GEE GROUP INC.; *U.S. Public*, pg. 909
GEEKAY WIRES LTD.; *Int'l*, pg. 2911
GEEKDOM; *U.S. Private*, pg. 1655
GEEKS2U PTY LIMITED—See Wesfarmers Limited; *Int'l*, pg. 8381
GEEKS ON CALL HOLDINGS, INC.; *U.S. Private*, pg. 1655
GEELMUYDEN-KIESE—See The Interpublic Group of Companies, Inc.; *U.S. Public*, pg. 2104
GEELMUYDEN-KIESE—See The Interpublic Group of Companies, Inc.; *U.S. Public*, pg. 2104
THE GEELONG ADVERTISER PTY. LIMITED—See News Corporation; *U.S. Public*, pg. 1521
GEELONG ADVERTISER—See News Corporation; *U.S. Public*, pg. 1520
GEE LTD.—See BMT Group Limited; *Int'l*, pg. 1078
GEELY AUTOMOBILE HOLDINGS LTD.—See Zhejiang Geely Holding Group Co., Ltd.; *Int'l*, pg. 8652
GEELY INTERNATIONAL CORPORATION—See Zhejiang Geely Holding Group Co., Ltd.; *Int'l*, pg. 8652
GEELY-MOTORS LLC—See Zhejiang Geely Holding Group Co., Ltd.; *Int'l*, pg. 8652
GE ENERGY EUROPE BV—See General Electric Company; *U.S. Public*, pg. 917
GE ENERGY FINANCIAL SERVICES—See General Electric Company; *U.S. Public*, pg. 920
GE ENERGY GERMANY—See General Electric Company; *U.S. Public*, pg. 919
GE ENERGY & INDUSTRIAL SERVICES, INC.—See General Electric Company; *U.S. Public*, pg. 919
GE ENERGY OILFIELD TECHNOLOGY, INC.—See General Electric Company; *U.S. Public*, pg. 920
GE ENERGY OILFIELD TECHNOLOGY—See General Electric Company; *U.S. Public*, pg. 920
GE ENERGY POWER CONVERSION GMBH—See General Electric Company; *U.S. Public*, pg. 916
GE ENERGY POWER CONVERSION UK HOLDINGS LIMITED—See General Electric Company; *U.S. Public*, pg. 916
GE ENERGY POWER CONVERSION USA INC.—See General Electric Company; *U.S. Public*, pg. 916
GE ENERGY PRODUCTS FRANCE SNC—See General Electric Company; *U.S. Public*, pg. 917
GE ENERGY - SAN JOSE—See General Electric Company; *U.S. Public*, pg. 917
GE ENERGY—See General Electric Company; *U.S. Public*, pg. 917
GE ENERGY—See General Electric Company; *U.S. Public*, pg. 917
GE ENERGY—See General Electric Company; *U.S. Public*, pg. 917
GE ENERGY—See General Electric Company; *U.S. Public*, pg. 917
GE ENERGY—See General Electric Company; *U.S. Public*, pg. 917
GE ENERGY—See General Electric Company; *U.S. Public*, pg. 917
GE ENERGY—See General Electric Company; *U.S. Public*, pg. 917
GE ENERGY SWITZERLAND GMBH—See General Electric Company; *U.S. Public*, pg. 916
GE ENERGY (USA), LLC—See General Electric Company; *U.S. Public*, pg. 919
GE ENGINE SERVICES DISTRIBUTION, LLC—See General Electric Company; *U.S. Public*, pg. 916
GE ENGINE SERVICES, INC.—See General Electric Company; *U.S. Public*, pg. 919
GE ENGINE SERVICES, LLC—See General Electric Company; *U.S. Public*, pg. 916
GEENIUS, INC.; *U.S. Private*, pg. 1655
GEE PEE AEROSPACE & DEFENCE PRIVATE LIMITED—See Mtar Technologies Limited; *Int'l*, pg. 5069
GEEPEE SHIPPING AGENCIES PVT., LTD.—See Precious Shipping Public Company Limited; *Int'l*, pg. 5956
GEEPEE SHIPPING AGENCIES PVT., LTD.—See Precious Shipping Public Company Limited; *Int'l*, pg. 5956
GEEPEE SHIPPING AGENCIES PVT., LTD.—See Precious Shipping Public Company Limited; *Int'l*, pg. 5956
GEERPRES INC.; *U.S. Private*, pg. 1655
GEERS HALLOKESZULEK KFT—See HAL Trust N.V.; *Int'l*, pg. 3223
GEER TANK TRUCKS INC.—See One Cypress Energy LLC; *U.S. Private*, pg. 3020

GEE SHENG MACHINERY & ENGINEERING PTE. LTD.—See Union Steel Holdings Limited; *Int'l*, pg. 8053
GEESINK B.V.—See Geesink Group B.V.; *Int'l*, pg. 2911
GEESINK GROUP B.V.; *Int'l*, pg. 2911
GEESINKNORBA AB—See Geesink Group B.V.; *Int'l*, pg. 2911
GEESINK NORBA LTD.—See Geesink Group B.V.; *Int'l*, pg. 2911
GEETA MONITORS PRIVATE LIMITED.—See Cerebra Integrated Technologies Ltd.; *Int'l*, pg. 1422
GEETANJALI CREDIT & CAPITAL LTD.; *Int'l*, pg. 2911
GE EVERGREEN ENGINE SERVICES CORPORATION—See General Electric Company; *U.S. Public*, pg. 917
GEEVERS AUTO PARTS B.V.—See s.a. D'Ieteren n.v.; *Int'l*, pg. 6448
GEEYA TECHNOLOGY CO., LTD.; *Int'l*, pg. 2911
GEFA BANK GMBH—See Societe Generale S.A.; *Int'l*, pg. 7039
GE FABBRI PHOENIX SP. Z .O.O. LTD.—See Eaglemoss Publications Ltd; *Int'l*, pg. 2266
GEF ACQUISITION CORPORATION; *U.S. Private*, pg. 1655
GEFA GESELLSCHAFT FUR ABSATZFINANZIERUNG MBH—See Societe Generale S.A.; *Int'l*, pg. 7039
GE-FAIRCHILD LLC—See General Electric Company; *U.S. Public*, pg. 918
GEFA LEASING GMBH—See Societe Generale S.A.; *Int'l*, pg. 7039
GEFA PROCESSTECHNIK GMBH—See Indutrade AB; *Int'l*, pg. 3678
GEFCO ARGENTINA S.A.—See JSC Russian Railways; *Int'l*, pg. 4011
GEFCO BALTIC SIA—See JSC Russian Railways; *Int'l*, pg. 4011
GEFCO BENELUX S.A.—See JSC Russian Railways; *Int'l*, pg. 4011
GEFCO BULGARIA LTD—See JSC Russian Railways; *Int'l*, pg. 4011
GEFCO CESKA REPUBLICA S.R.O.—See JSC Russian Railways; *Int'l*, pg. 4011
GEFCO DEUTSCHLAND GMBH—See JSC Russian Railways; *Int'l*, pg. 4011
GEFCO DO BRASIL LTDA—See JSC Russian Railways; *Int'l*, pg. 4011
GEFCO ESPANA S.A.—See JSC Russian Railways; *Int'l*, pg. 4011
GEFCO FORWARDING INTERNATIONAL B.V.—See JSC Russian Railways; *Int'l*, pg. 4011
GEFCO FORWARDING UK LTD—See JSC Russian Railways; *Int'l*, pg. 4011
GEFCO HONG KONG COMPANY LIMITED—See JSC Russian Railways; *Int'l*, pg. 4011
GEFCO, INC.—See Astec Industries, Inc.; *U.S. Public*, pg. 216
GEFCO ITALIA S.P.A.—See JSC Russian Railways; *Int'l*, pg. 4011
GEFCO MAGYARORSZAG KFT—See JSC Russian Railways; *Int'l*, pg. 4011
GEFCO MEXICO SA DE CV—See JSC Russian Railways; *Int'l*, pg. 4011
GEFCO MIDDLE EAST FZE—See JSC Russian Railways; *Int'l*, pg. 4011
GEFCO OSTERREICH GMBH—See JSC Russian Railways; *Int'l*, pg. 4011
GEFCO PARTICIPACOES LTDA—See JSC Russian Railways; *Int'l*, pg. 4011
GEFCO POLSKA SP. Z.O.O.—See JSC Russian Railways; *Int'l*, pg. 4011
GEFCO (PORTUGAL) TRANSITARIOS, LDA.—See JSC Russian Railways; *Int'l*, pg. 4011
GEFCO PREVOZNISTVO IN LOGISTICA D.O.O.—See JSC Russian Railways; *Int'l*, pg. 4011
GEFCO ROMANIA S.R.L.—See JSC Russian Railways; *Int'l*, pg. 4011
GEFCO RUSSIA—See JSC Russian Railways; *Int'l*, pg. 4011
GEFCO S.A.—See JSC Russian Railways; *Int'l*, pg. 4011
GEFCO SLOVAKIA S.R.O.—See JSC Russian Railways; *Int'l*, pg. 4011
GEFCO (SUISSE) SA—See JSC Russian Railways; *Int'l*, pg. 4011
GEFCO TASIMACILIK VE LOJISTIK ANONIM SIRKETI—See JSC Russian Railways; *Int'l*, pg. 4011
GEFCO TUNISIE SA—See JSC Russian Railways; *Int'l*, pg. 4011
GEFCO U.K. LTD.—See JSC Russian Railways; *Int'l*, pg. 4011
GEFCO UKRAINE LLC—See JSC Russian Railways; *Int'l*, pg. 4011
GEFEN BIOMED INVESTMENTS LTD.; *Int'l*, pg. 2911
GEFEN INTERNATIONAL A.I LTD.; *Int'l*, pg. 2911
GEFEN LANDA ACQUISITION CORP.; *Int'l*, pg. 2911
GEFEN TECHNOLOGIES A.I. LTD.—See Gefen International A.I Ltd.; *Int'l*, pg. 2911
GEFFEN RECORDS—See Universal Music Group N.V.; *Int'l*, pg. 8079
GEFFEN RESIDENCE & RENEWAL LTD; *Int'l*, pg. 2911

CORPORATE AFFILIATIONS

GEFINOR FINANCE S.A.—See Gefinor S.A.; *Int'l*, pg. 2911
GEFINOR FINANCE S.A.—See Gefinor S.A.; *Int'l*, pg. 2911
GEFINOR S.A.; *Int'l*, pg. 2911
GEFINOR U.S.A., INC.—See Gefinor S.A.; *Int'l*, pg. 2911
GEFION GROUP A/S; *Int'l*, pg. 2911
GEFIT DALIAN INDUSTRIAL TECHNOLOGY CO., LTD.—See GEFIT S.p.A.; *Int'l*, pg. 2912
GEFIT LIVERNOIS ENGINEERING, LLC—See GEFIT S.p.A.; *Int'l*, pg. 2911
GEFIT S.P.A. - GEFIT MOULDS & ASSEMBLY DIVISION—See GEFIT S.p.A.; *Int'l*, pg. 2911
GEFIT S.P.A.; *Int'l*, pg. 2911
GE FOODLAND, INC.; *U.S. Private*, pg. 1654
GEFRAN ASIA PTE. LTD.—See Gefran S.p.A.; *Int'l*, pg. 2912
GEFRAN BENELUX N.V.—See Gefran S.p.A.; *Int'l*, pg. 2912
GEFRAN BRASIL ELETROELETRONICA LTDA.—See Gefran S.p.A.; *Int'l*, pg. 2912
GEFRAN BRASIL ELETTROEL. LTDA.—See Gefran S.p.A.; *Int'l*, pg. 2912
GEFRAN DEUTSCHLAND GMBH—See Gefran S.p.A.; *Int'l*, pg. 2912
GEFRAN DRIVES & MOTION S.R.L.—See Gefran S.p.A.; *Int'l*, pg. 2912
GEFRAN FRANCE S.A.—See Gefran S.p.A.; *Int'l*, pg. 2912
GEFRAN, INC.—See Gefran S.p.A.; *Int'l*, pg. 2912
GEFRAN INDIA LTD.—See Gefran S.p.A.; *Int'l*, pg. 2912
GEFRAN SIEI DRIVES TECH. CO., LTD.—See Gefran S.p.A.; *Int'l*, pg. 2912
GEFRAN SIEI DRIVES TECHNOLOGY (SHANGHAI) CO.,LTD—See Gefran S.p.A.; *Int'l*, pg. 2912
GEFRAN SIEI ELECTRIC (SHANGHAI) PTE LTD—See Gefran S.p.A.; *Int'l*, pg. 2912
GEFRAN S.P.A.; *Int'l*, pg. 2912
GEFRAN SUISSE SA—See Gefran S.p.A.; *Int'l*, pg. 2912
GEFRAN UK LTD.—See Gefran S.p.A.; *Int'l*, pg. 2912
GEFTECH KFT.—See GEFIT S.p.A.; *Int'l*, pg. 2912
GEFYRA LITOURGIA S.A.—See VINCI S.A.; *Int'l*, pg. 8230
GEFYRA S.A.—See VINCI S.A.; *Int'l*, pg. 8230
GEG MANAGEMENT S.A.M.—See ITOCHU Corporation; *Int'l*, pg. 3836
GE GRID GMBH—See General Electric Company; *U.S. Public*, pg. 918
GE GRID SOLUTIONS LLC—See Alstom S.A.; *Int'l*, pg. 381
GE GRID SOLUTIONS LLC—See General Electric Company; *U.S. Public*, pg. 917
GE GRID SOLUTIONS PTE. LTD.—See General Electric Company; *U.S. Public*, pg. 918
GEHAN HOMES LTD.—See Sumitomo Forestry Co., Ltd.; *Int'l*, pg. 7285
GE HEALTHCARE AB—See GE HealthCare Technologies Inc.; *U.S. Public*, pg. 908
GE HEALTHCARE ALGERIE SARL—See GE HealthCare Technologies Inc.; *U.S. Public*, pg. 908
GE HEALTHCARE AS—See GE HealthCare Technologies Inc.; *U.S. Public*, pg. 909
GE HEALTHCARE BIO-SCIENCES AB—See GE HealthCare Technologies Inc.; *U.S. Public*, pg. 909
GE HEALTHCARE BIO-SCIENCES EUROPE GMBH—See GE HealthCare Technologies Inc.; *U.S. Public*, pg. 909
GE HEALTHCARE BIO-SCIENCES—See GE HealthCare Technologies Inc.; *U.S. Public*, pg. 909
GE HEALTHCARE BUCHLER GMBH & CO. KG—See GE HealthCare Technologies Inc.; *U.S. Public*, pg. 909
GE HEALTHCARE COTE D'IVOIRE SARL—See GE HealthCare Technologies Inc.; *U.S. Public*, pg. 909
GE HEALTHCARE DANMARK A/S—See GE HealthCare Technologies Inc.; *U.S. Public*, pg. 909
GE HEALTHCARE FINANCIAL SERVICES—See GE HealthCare Technologies Inc.; *U.S. Public*, pg. 909
GE HEALTHCARE FINLAND OY—See GE HealthCare Technologies Inc.; *U.S. Public*, pg. 909
GE HEALTHCARE GMBH—See GE HealthCare Technologies Inc.; *U.S. Public*, pg. 909
GE HEALTHCARE HANDELS GMBH—See GE HealthCare Technologies Inc.; *U.S. Public*, pg. 909
GE HEALTHCARE JAPAN CORPORATION—See GE HealthCare Technologies Inc.; *U.S. Public*, pg. 909
GE HEALTHCARE KENYA LIMITED—See GE HealthCare Technologies Inc.; *U.S. Public*, pg. 909
GE HEALTHCARE KOREA, INC.—See GE HealthCare Technologies Inc.; *U.S. Public*, pg. 908
GE HEALTHCARE LIMITED—See General Electric Company; *U.S. Public*, pg. 917
GE HEALTHCARE LIMITED—See GE HealthCare Technologies Inc.; *U.S. Public*, pg. 909
GE HEALTHCARE MAGYARORSZAG KFT.—See GE HealthCare Technologies Inc.; *U.S. Public*, pg. 909
GE HEALTHCARE PHARMA LIMITED—See GE HealthCare Technologies Inc.; *U.S. Public*, pg. 909
GE HEALTHCARE SVERIGE AB—See GE HealthCare Technologies Inc.; *U.S. Public*, pg. 909
GE HEALTHCARE TECHNOLOGIES INC.; *U.S. Public*, pg. 908

COMPANY NAME INDEX

GE HEALTHCARE TUNISIA SARL—See GE HealthCare Technologies Inc.; *U.S. Public*, pg. 909
G&E HERBAL BIOTECHNOLOGY CO., LTD.; *Int'l*, pg. 2862
GEHLENBERG APS—See Athena Investments A/S; *Int'l*, pg. 669
GEHL FOODS, LLC—See Wind Point Advisors LLC; *U.S. Private*, pg. 4534
GEHL POWER PRODUCTS, INC.—See Manitou BF S.A.; *Int'l*, pg. 4672
GE HONDA AERO ENGINES LLC—See Honda Motor Co., Ltd.; *Int'l*, pg. 3460
GEHR DEVELOPMENT—See The Gehr Group; *U.S. Private*, pg. 4032
THE GEHR GROUP; *U.S. Private*, pg. 4032
GEHRIG GROUP AG—See Metall Zug AG; *Int'l*, pg. 4847
GEHR INDUSTRIES INC.—See The Gehr Group; *U.S. Private*, pg. 4032
THE GEHRING GROUP, INC.—See Kelso & Company, L.P.; *U.S. Private*, pg. 2280
GEHRKI COMMERCIAL REAL ESTATE, LLC—See Colliers International Group Inc.; *Int'l*, pg. 1701
GEHRLICHER-IKHWEZI (PTY) LTD—See Gehrlicher Solar AG; *Int'l*, pg. 2912
GEHRLICHER SOLAR AG; *Int'l*, pg. 2912
GEHRLICHER SOLAR AMERICA CORP.—See M+W Group GmbH; *Int'l*, pg. 4613
GEHRLICHER SOLAR ESPANA S.L.—See Gehrlicher Solar AG; *Int'l*, pg. 2912
GEHRLICHER SOLAR FRANCE SAS—See Gehrlicher Solar AG; *Int'l*, pg. 2912
GEHRY TECHNOLOGIES MIDDLE EAST LLC—See Trimble, Inc.; *U.S. Public*, pg. 2190
GE HUNGARY CO. LTD.—See General Electric Company; *U.S. Public*, pg. 917
GE HUNGARY KFT.—See General Electric Company; *U.S. Public*, pg. 917
GE HYDRO FRANCE—See General Electric Company; *U.S. Public*, pg. 917
GEICO BRASIL LTDA.—See Taikisha Ltd.; *Int'l*, pg. 7413
GEICO CHOICE INSURANCE COMPANY—See Berkshire Hathaway Inc.; *U.S. Public*, pg. 305
GEICO CORPORATION—See Berkshire Hathaway Inc.; *U.S. Public*, pg. 305
GEICO GENERAL INSURANCE COMPANY—See Berkshire Hathaway Inc.; *U.S. Public*, pg. 305
GEICO INDEMNITY COMPANY—See Berkshire Hathaway Inc.; *U.S. Public*, pg. 305
GEI CONSULTANTS, INC.—See Global Infrastructure Solutions, Inc.; *U.S. Private*, pg. 1715
GEICO PAINTING SYSTEM (SUZHOU) CO., LTD.—See Taikisha Ltd.; *Int'l*, pg. 7413
GEICO PAINT SHOP INDIA PRIVATE LIMITED—See Taikisha Ltd.; *Int'l*, pg. 7413
GEICO RUSSIA LLC—See Taikisha Ltd.; *Int'l*, pg. 7413
G.E.I.E. A.I.G.L.E.—See Groupe Limagrain Holding SA; *Int'l*, pg. 3107
G.E.I.E. NICKERSON INTERNATIONAL RESEARCH—See Groupe Limagrain Holding SA; *Int'l*, pg. 3107
GEIGER AUTOMOTIVE DE MEXICO S. DE R.L. DE C.V.—See Sanoh Industrial Co., Ltd.; *Int'l*, pg. 6552
GEIGER AUTOMOTIVE GMBH—See Sanoh Industrial Co., Ltd.; *Int'l*, pg. 6552
GEIGER AUTOMOTIVE POLSKA SP. Z O.O.—See Sanoh Industrial Co., Ltd.; *Int'l*, pg. 6552
GEIGER BAUWERKSANIERUNG GMBH & CO. KG—See Wilhelm Geiger GmbH & Co. KG; *Int'l*, pg. 8411
GEIGER BETON GMBH & CO. KG—See Wilhelm Geiger GmbH & Co. KG; *Int'l*, pg. 8411
GEIGER BROTHERS; *U.S. Private*, pg. 1655
GEIGER COUNTER LIMITED; *Int'l*, pg. 2912
GEIGER EXCAVATING, INC.; *U.S. Private*, pg. 1656
GEIGER EXCAVATING, INC.—See Zemba Bros Inc; *U.S. Private*, pg. 4601
GEIGER FERTIGUNGSTECHNOLOGIE GMBH—See Zhejiang Tieliu Clutch Co., Ltd.; *Int'l*, pg. 8664
GEIGER INTERNATIONAL—See MillerKnoll, Inc.; *U.S. Public*, pg. 1447
GEIGER KANALTECHNIK GMBH & CO. KG—See Wilhelm Geiger GmbH & Co. KG; *Int'l*, pg. 8411
GEIGER PUMP & EQUIPMENT COMPANY—See AEA Investors LP; *U.S. Private*, pg. 113
GEIGER READY MIX COMPANY INCORPORATED; *U.S. Private*, pg. 1656
GEIGER UMWELT GMBH—See Wilhelm Geiger GmbH & Co. KG; *Int'l*, pg. 8411
GEI GLOBAL ENERGY CORP.; *U.S. Private*, pg. 1655
GEI-IMMO AG; *Int'l*, pg. 2912
GEI INDUSTRIAL SYSTEMS LTD.; *Int'l*, pg. 2912
GEILE/LEON MARKETING COMMUNICATIONS; *U.S. Private*, pg. 1656
GEINAN SHOKUHIN CO., LTD.—See Aohata Corporation; *Int'l*, pg. 487
GE INTELLIGENT PLATFORMS EMBEDDED SYSTEMS, INC.—See General Electric Company; *U.S. Public*, pg. 917
GE INTELLIGENT PLATFORMS, INC.—HUNTSVILLE—See Emerson Electric Co.; *U.S. Public*, pg. 749

GE INTELLIGENT PLATFORMS, INC.—See Emerson Electric Co.; *U.S. Public*, pg. 749
GE INVESTMENTS, INC.—See General Electric Company; *U.S. Public*, pg. 917
GEIRHOS-BETON GMBH—See BERGER Holding GmbH; *Int'l*, pg. 979
GEISEL HEATING, AIR CONDITIONING & PLUMBING, INC.—See Brookfield Corporation; *Int'l*, pg. 1188
GEISINGER - BLOOMSBURG HOSPITAL—See Geisinger Health System; *U.S. Private*, pg. 1656
GEISINGER HEALTH PLAN—See Geisinger Health System; *U.S. Private*, pg. 1656
GEISINGER HEALTHSOUTH REHABILITATION HOSPITAL—See Encompass Health Corporation; *U.S. Public*, pg. 756
GEISINGER HEALTHSOUTH REHABILITATION HOSPITAL—See Geisinger Health System; *U.S. Private*, pg. 1656
GEISINGER HEALTH SYSTEM; *U.S. Private*, pg. 1656
GEISMAR DO BRASIL MATERIAL FERROVIARIO LTDA—See Geismar S.A.; *Int'l*, pg. 2912
GEISMAR S.A. - COLMAR FACTORY—See Geismar S.A.; *Int'l*, pg. 2912
GEISMAR S.A.; *Int'l*, pg. 2912
GEISMAR SEA PTE LTD—See Geismar S.A.; *Int'l*, pg. 2912
GEISMAR (UK) LTD—See Geismar S.A.; *Int'l*, pg. 2912
GEISS, DESTIN & DUNN, INC.—See Perrigo Company plc; *Int'l*, pg. 5813
GEISSLER'S SUPERMARKET INCORPORATED; *U.S. Private*, pg. 1656
GEIST MANUFACTURING INC.—See PCE, Inc.; *U.S. Private*, pg. 3120
GEITH INC.—See HD Hyundai Infracore Co., Ltd.; *Int'l*, pg. 3300
GEITH INTERNATIONAL LTD—See HD Hyundai Infracore Co., Ltd.; *Int'l*, pg. 3300
GEITH INTERNATIONAL LTD.—See HD Hyundai Infracore Co., Ltd.; *Int'l*, pg. 3300
GE JENBACHER GMBH—See General Electric Company; *U.S. Public*, pg. 917
G.E. JOHNSON CONSTRUCTION COMPANY, INC.; *U.S. Private*, pg. 1630
GEKA GMBH—See Sulzer Ltd.; *Int'l*, pg. 7257
GEKAY SALES & SERVICE CO. INC.; *U.S. Private*, pg. 1656
GEKE S.A; *Int'l*, pg. 2913
GEKKO SAS—See Accenture plc; *Int'l*, pg. 87
GEK SERVICES S.A—See Gek Terna Societe Anonyme Holdings Real Estate Constructions; *Int'l*, pg. 2913
GEK TERNA SOCIETE ANONYME HOLDINGS REAL ESTATE CONSTRUCTIONS; *Int'l*, pg. 2913
GELAN DETECTIESYSTEMEN B.V.—See Mettler-Toledo International, Inc.; *U.S. Public*, pg. 1432
GELBER GROUP LLC; *U.S. Private*, pg. 1656
GELCAPS EXPORTADORA DE MEXICO, S.A. DE C.V.—See Perrigo Company plc; *Int'l*, pg. 5813
GELCO CORPORATION—See Element Fleet Management Corporation; *Int'l*, pg. 2358
GELCO LIFTS LTD.—See KONE Oyj; *Int'l*, pg. 4247
GELCO S.R.L.—See Perfetti Van Melle Holding B.V.; *Int'l*, pg. 5800
GEL-DEL TECHNOLOGIES INC.—See PetVivo Holdings, Inc.; *U.S. Public*, pg. 1679
GELDER & ASSOCIATES, INC.—See Construction Partners, Inc.; *U.S. Public*, pg. 572
GELD & GRUND IMMOBILIEN VERTRIEBS GMBH—See MONDURA Liegenschaften AG; *Int'l*, pg. 5031
GELECEK VARLIK YONETIMI A.S.; *Int'l*, pg. 2913
GELEC (HK) LTD.—See Shriro Pacific Ltd.; *Int'l*, pg. 6866
GELEC (MACAU) LIMITADA—See Shriro Pacific Ltd.; *Int'l*, pg. 6866
GELEC (UK) LTD—See Shriro Pacific Ltd.; *Int'l*, pg. 6866
GELEEN UTILITY LEIDINGEN BV—See Koninklijke DSM N.V.; *Int'l*, pg. 4266
GELESIS HOLDINGS, INC.; *U.S. Public*, pg. 910
GELESIS, INC.—See Gelesis Holdings, Inc.; *U.S. Public*, pg. 910
GELEST, INC.—See Mitsubishi Chemical Group Corporation; *Int'l*, pg. 4932
GELEST INTERMEDIATE HOLDINGS, INC.—See Mitsubishi Chemical Group Corporation; *Int'l*, pg. 4932
GELFAND RENNERT & FELDMAN LLP; *U.S. Private*, pg. 1656
GELF MANAGEMENT (LUX) SARL—See Goodman Limited; *Int'l*, pg. 3040
GELFORD GMBH—See MEDIQON Group AG; *Int'l*, pg. 4780
THE GEL GROUP, INC.; *U.S. Private*, pg. 4032
GEL GROUP PTY LIMITED—See Rubicor Group Limited; *Int'l*, pg. 6422
GELIA INDUSTRI AB—See Ahlsell AB; *Int'l*, pg. 223
GELIA-MEDIA, INC.; *U.S. Private*, pg. 1656
GELINS-KGK AB—See Indutrade AB; *Int'l*, pg. 3679
GELION PLC; *Int'l*, pg. 2913
GELITA AG; *Int'l*, pg. 2913
GELITA AG - SUPPLY PLANT—See Gelita AG; *Int'l*, pg. 2913

GEMADEPT CORPORATION

GELITA AUSTRALIA PTY. LTD.—See Gelita AG; *Int'l*, pg. 2913
GELITA CANGNAN GELATINE CO. LTD.—See Gelita AG; *Int'l*, pg. 2913
GELITA DO BRASIL LTDA.—See Gelita AG; *Int'l*, pg. 2913
GELITA FRANCE SARL—See Gelita AG; *Int'l*, pg. 2913
GELITA HEALTH GMBH—See Gelita AG; *Int'l*, pg. 2913
GELITA (LIAOYUAN) GELATINE CO. LTD.—See Gelita AG; *Int'l*, pg. 2913
GELITA MEXICO S. DE R.L. DE C.V.—See Gelita AG; *Int'l*, pg. 2913
GELITA NEDERLAND B.V.—See Gelita AG; *Int'l*, pg. 2913
GELITA NZ. LTD.—See Gelita AG; *Int'l*, pg. 2913
GELITA SHANGHAI CONSULTING CO. LTD.—See Gelita AG; *Int'l*, pg. 2913
GELITA (SHANGHAI) ENTERPRISE MANAGEMENT CO., LTD—See Gelita AG; *Int'l*, pg. 2913
GELITA SOUTH AFRICA PTY. LTD.—See Gelita AG; *Int'l*, pg. 2913
GELITA SWEDEN AB—See Gelita AG; *Int'l*, pg. 2913
GELITA UK LTD.—See Gelita AG; *Int'l*, pg. 2913
GELITA USA INC.—See Gelita AG; *Int'l*, pg. 2913
GELIT SRL—See Consilium SGR p.A.; *Int'l*, pg. 1770
GELIT SRL—See Progressio SGR S.p.A.; *Int'l*, pg. 5990
GELLER & COMPANY; *U.S. Private*, pg. 1656
GELLER & CO.; *U.S. Private*, pg. 1656
GELLER NESSIS D'ARCY—See Publicis Groupe S.A.; *Int'l*, pg. 6099
GELLERT GLOBAL GROUP; *U.S. Private*, pg. 1656
GELLMAN MANAGEMENT LLC—See Live Nation Entertainment, Inc.; *U.S. Public*, pg. 1328
GELMART INDUSTRIES INC.; *U.S. Private*, pg. 1657
GEL-PAK LLC; *U.S. Private*, pg. 1656
GELSENBERG VERWALTUNGS GMBH—See E.ON SE; *Int'l*, pg. 2257
GELSENWASSER AG; *Int'l*, pg. 2913
GELSENWASSER ENERGIENETZE GMBH—See Gelsenwasser AG; *Int'l*, pg. 2913
GELSENWASSER PROJEKTGESELLSCHAFT MBH—See Gelsenwasser AG; *Int'l*, pg. 2913
GELSIGHT, INC.; *U.S. Private*, pg. 1657
GELSON'S MARKETS—See TPG Capital, L.P.; *U.S. Public*, pg. 2168
GEL S.P.A.; *Int'l*, pg. 2913
GEL SPICE COMPANY INC.—See Temasek Holdings (Private) Limited; *Int'l*, pg. 7549
GELSTAT CORPORATION; *U.S. Public*, pg. 910
GELTECH SOLUTIONS, INC.; *U.S. Public*, pg. 910
GELTEQ LIMITED; *Int'l*, pg. 2914
GELTER-RINGSDORFF, S.A.—See SGL Carbon SE; *Int'l*, pg. 6741
GELUKSKOFFER SCHOLEN B.V.—See Sanoma Oyj; *Int'l*, pg. 6553
GELWIN TECHNOLOGY LTD—See Ledtech Electronics Corporation; *Int'l*, pg. 4439
GEMAC ENGINEERING MACHINERY CO., LTD.; *Int'l*, pg. 2915
GEMADEPT CORPORATION; *Int'l*, pg. 2915
GEMADEPT DUNG QUAT INTERNATIONAL PORT J.S.C.—See Gemadept Corporation; *Int'l*, pg. 2915
GEMADEPT HAI PHONG ONE MEMBER COMPANY LIMITED—See CJ Corporation; *Int'l*, pg. 1633
GEMADEPT LOGISTICS ONE MEMBER COMPANY LIMITED—See CJ Corporation; *Int'l*, pg. 1634
GEMADEPT (MALAYSIA) SDN. BHD.—See Gemadept Corporation; *Int'l*, pg. 2915
GEMA EUROPE S.R.L.—See Graco, Inc.; *U.S. Public*, pg. 953
GEMAIRE DISTRIBUTORS LLC—See Watsco, Inc.; *U.S. Public*, pg. 2336
GEMALTO AB—See Thales S.A.; *Int'l*, pg. 7599
GEMALTO ARGENTINA S.A—See Thales S.A.; *Int'l*, pg. 7599
GEMALTO B.V.—See Thales S.A.; *Int'l*, pg. 7599
GEMALTO CANADA INC.—See Thales S.A.; *Int'l*, pg. 7599
GEMALTO CARD INTERNATIONAL ESPANA S.A.—See Thales S.A.; *Int'l*, pg. 7599
GEMALTO CARDS LTD.—See Thales S.A.; *Int'l*, pg. 7599
GEMALTO COGENT, INC.—See Thales S.A.; *Int'l*, pg. 7599
GEMALTO COLOMBIA S.A.—See Thales S.A.; *Int'l*, pg. 7599
GEMALTO DANMARK A/S—See Thales S.A.; *Int'l*, pg. 7599
GEMALTO DE MEXICO S.A. DE C.V.—See Thales S.A.; *Int'l*, pg. 7600
GEMALTO DIGITAL SECURITY LTD—See Thales S.A.; *Int'l*, pg. 7599
GEMALTO DO BRAZIL CARTOES E TERMINAIS LTDA—See Thales S.A.; *Int'l*, pg. 7600
GEMALTO EBANKING—See Thales S.A.; *Int'l*, pg. 7600
GEMALTO GMBH—See Thales S.A.; *Int'l*, pg. 7599
GEMALTO HOLDING PTE LTD—See Thales S.A.; *Int'l*, pg. 7599
GEMALTO HUNGARY COMMERCIAL AND SERVICES LTD.—See Thales S.A.; *Int'l*, pg. 7599
GEMALTO INC.—See Thales S.A.; *Int'l*, pg. 7599
GEMALTO INDUSTRIAL S.A. DE C.V.—See Thales S.A.; *Int'l*, pg. 7599

GEMADEPT CORPORATION

GEMALTO INTERNATIONAL S.A.S.—See Thales S.A.; *Int'l*, pg. 7599
GEMALTO KART VE TERMINALLER LTD SIRKETI—See Thales S.A.; *Int'l*, pg. 7599
GEMALTO LLC—See Thales S.A.; *Int'l*, pg. 7599
GEMALTO MIDDLE EAST—See Thales S.A.; *Int'l*, pg. 7599
GEMALTO NORGE AS—See Thales S.A.; *Int'l*, pg. 7599
GEMALTO N.V.—See Thales S.A.; *Int'l*, pg. 7599
GEMALTO OY—See Thales S.A.; *Int'l*, pg. 7599
GEMALTO PARTICIPATIONS S.A.S.—See Thales S.A.; *Int'l*, pg. 7599
GEMALTO PHILIPPINES INC.—See Thales S.A.; *Int'l*, pg. 7599
GEMALTO PTE LTD.—See Thales S.A.; *Int'l*, pg. 7599
GEMALTO PTY LTD—See Thales S.A.; *Int'l*, pg. 7599
GEMALTO S.A.—See Thales S.A.; *Int'l*, pg. 7599
GEMALTO S.A.S.—See Thales S.A.; *Int'l*, pg. 7599
GEMALTO SDN BHD—See Thales S.A.; *Int'l*, pg. 7600
GEMALTO SOUTHERN AFRICA PTY. LTD.—See Thales S.A.; *Int'l*, pg. 7600
GEMALTO SPA—See Thales S.A.; *Int'l*, pg. 7600
GEMALTO SP S.A.—See Thales S.A.; *Int'l*, pg. 7600
GEMALTO SP. Z.O.O—See Thales S.A.; *Int'l*, pg. 7600
GEMALTO S.R.O.—See Thales S.A.; *Int'l*, pg. 7599
GEMALTO SVERIGE AB—See Thales S.A.; *Int'l*, pg. 7600
GEMALTO TAIWAN CO. LTD.—See Thales S.A.; *Int'l*, pg. 7600
GEMALTO TECHNOLOGIES ASIA LTD—See Thales S.A.; *Int'l*, pg. 7600
GEMALTO TERMINALS INDIA PRIVATE LTD—See Thales S.A.; *Int'l*, pg. 7600
GEMALTO TERMINALS LTD.—See Thales S.A.; *Int'l*, pg. 7600
GEMALTO (THAILAND) LTD—See Thales S.A.; *Int'l*, pg. 7599
GEMA MEXICO POWDER FINISHING, S. DE R.L. DE C.V.—See Graco, Inc.; *U.S. Public*, pg. 953
GEMA (SHANGHAI) CO., LTD.—See Graco, Inc.; *U.S. Public*, pg. 953
GEMA SWITZERLAND AG—See Graco, Inc.; *U.S. Public*, pg. 953
GEMATEK OOO—See B. Braun Melsungen AG; *Int'l*, pg. 787
GEMA USA INC.—See Graco, Inc.; *U.S. Public*, pg. 953
GEMBALLA GMBH—See GEMBALLA Holding SE; *Int'l*, pg. 2915
GEMBALLA HOLDING SE; *Int'l*, pg. 2915
GEMBU CO., LTD.—See DKS Co. Ltd.; *Int'l*, pg. 2140
GEMCHEM, INC.—See American Vanguard Corporation; *U.S. Public*, pg. 112
GEM (CHENZHOU) SOLID WASTE TREATMENT CO., LTD.—See GEM Co., Ltd.; *Int'l*, pg. 2914
THE GEM CITY ENGINEERING CO., INC.—See Capital-Works, LLC; *U.S. Private*, pg. 742
GEM CITY HOME CARE, LLC—See KKR & Co. Inc.; *U.S. Public*, pg. 1249
GEMCO CONSTRUCTION LTD.; *Int'l*, pg. 2915
GEMCO CONSTRUCTORS, LLC; *U.S. Private*, pg. 1657
GEMCO ENGINEERS B.V.; *Int'l*, pg. 2915
GEM CO., LTD.; *Int'l*, pg. 2914
GEMCO RAIL PTY. LTD.—See Engenco Limited; *Int'l*, pg. 2427
GEMCOR II, LLC—See AIP, LLC; *U.S. Private*, pg. 133
GEMCRAFT HOMES INC.; *U.S. Private*, pg. 1657
GEMDALE CORPORATION; *Int'l*, pg. 2915
GEMDALE DONGGUAN COMPANY—See Gemdale Corporation; *Int'l*, pg. 2915
GEMDALE PROPERTIES AND INVESTMENT CORPORATION LIMITED—See Gemdale Corporation; *Int'l*, pg. 2915
GEMDALE SHAOXING COMPANY—See Gemdale Corporation; *Int'l*, pg. 2915
GEMDALE USA CORPORATION—See Gemdale Corporation; *Int'l*, pg. 2915
GEM-DANDY, INC.; *U.S. Private*, pg. 1657
GEM DIAMONDS LIMITED; *Int'l*, pg. 2914
GEM DIAMONDS MARKETING SERVICES BVBA—See Gem Diamonds Limited; *Int'l*, pg. 2914
GEM DIAMOND TECHNICAL SERVICES (PROPRIETARY) LIMITED—See Gem Diamonds Limited; *Int'l*, pg. 2914
GEMEAZ CUSIN S.P.A.—See Charterhouse Capital Partners LLP; *Int'l*, pg. 1455
GEM ECOPRO NEW ENERGY MATERIALS CO., LTD.—See GEM Co., Ltd.; *Int'l*, pg. 2914
GE MEDICAL SYSTEMS GLOBAL TECHNOLOGY COMPANY, LLC—See GE HealthCare Technologies Inc.; *U.S. Public*, pg. 909
GE MEDICAL SYSTEMS, INC.—See GE HealthCare Technologies Inc.; *U.S. Public*, pg. 909
GE MEDICAL SYSTEMS INFORMATION TECHNOLOGIES, INC.—See GE HealthCare Technologies Inc.; *U.S. Public*, pg. 909
GE MEDICAL SYSTEMS LIMITED—See GE HealthCare Technologies Inc.; *U.S. Public*, pg. 909
GE MEDICAL SYSTEMS POLSKA SP. Z O.O.—See GE HealthCare Technologies Inc.; *U.S. Public*, pg. 909

GE MEDICAL SYSTEMS (SCHWEIZ) AG—See GE HealthCare Technologies Inc.; *U.S. Public*, pg. 909
GEMEENTE SINT-PIETERS-LEEUW; *Int'l*, pg. 2915
GEMEINNUTZIGE INDUSTRIE-WOHNUNGSAKTIENGESELL—See Vienna Insurance Group AG Wiener Versicherung Gruppe; *Int'l*, pg. 8194
GEMEINNUTZIGE MURZ-YBBS SIEDLUNGSANLAGEN-GMBH—See Vienna Insurance Group AG Wiener Versicherung Gruppe; *Int'l*, pg. 8194
GEMEINNUTZIGE SIEDLUNGSGESELLSCHAFT M.B.H.—See Lenzing Aktiengesellschaft; *Int'l*, pg. 4455
GEMEINNUTZIGE WOHNUNGSGESELLSCHAFT MBH HESSEN—See Helaba Landesbank Hessen-Thuringen; *Int'l*, pg. 3328
GEMEINSCHAFTSKERNKRAFTWERK GROHNDE GMBH—See E.ON SE; *Int'l*, pg. 2253
GEMEINSCHAFTSKERNKRAFTWERK GROHNDE MANAGEMENT GMBH—See E.ON SE; *Int'l*, pg. 2257
GEMEINSCHAFTSKERNKRAFTWERK ISAR 2 GMBH—See E.ON SE; *Int'l*, pg. 2257
GEMEINSCHAFTSKRAFTWERK BREMEN GMBH & CO. KG—See EWE Aktiengesellschaft; *Int'l*, pg. 2575
GEMEINSCHAFTSKRAFTWERK IRSCHING GMBH—See Fortum Oyj; *Int'l*, pg. 2742
GEMEINSCHAFTSKRAFTWERK KIEL GMBH—See E.ON SE; *Int'l*, pg. 2253
GEMEINSCHAFTSKRAFTWERK VELTHEIM GESELLSCHAFT MIT BESCHRANKTER HAFTUNG—See E.ON SE; *Int'l*, pg. 2258
GEM ENERGY LLC.—See The Rudolph/Libbe Companies; *U.S. Private*, pg. 4113
GEM EQUIPMENT OF OREGON INC.; *U.S. Private*, pg. 1657
GEMEY MAYBELLINE GARNIER S.N.C.—See L'Oreal S.A.; *Int'l*, pg. 4378
GEMEY PARIS-MAYBELLINE NEW YORK—See L'Oreal S.A.; *Int'l*, pg. 4378
GEMFIELDS GROUP LIMITED; *Int'l*, pg. 2916
GEMFIELDS LIMITED—See Gemfields Group Limited; *Int'l*, pg. 2916
GEMGAS S.R.L.—See Linde plc; *Int'l*, pg. 4508
GEMGROUP INC.—See Angel Holdings Godo Kaisha; *Int'l*, pg. 459
GEM GROUP INC.; *U.S. Private*, pg. 1657
GEMILANG INTERNATIONAL LIMITED; *Int'l*, pg. 2916
GEMINA LABORATORIES LTD.; *Int'l*, pg. 2916
GEMINA TERMIX PRODUCTION A/S—See Danfoss A/S; *Int'l*, pg. 1961
GEM INDUSTRIAL, INC.—See The Rudolph/Libbe Companies; *U.S. Private*, pg. 4113
GEM INDUSTRIES CORPORATION; *U.S. Private*, pg. 1657
GEM INDUSTRIES—See Gem Industries Corporation; *U.S. Private*, pg. 1657
GEMINI ALUMINUM CORPORATION; *U.S. Private*, pg. 1657
GEMINI AUTO INC.; *Int'l*, pg. 2916
GEMINI BIO-PRODUCTS, LLC—See BelHealth Investment Partners LLC; *U.S. Private*, pg. 517
GEMINI CAD SYSTEMS S.A.—See Lectra SA; *Int'l*, pg. 4437
GEMINI COMMUNICATION LTD.; *Int'l*, pg. 2916
GEMINI COMMUNICATIONS; *U.S. Private*, pg. 1657
GEMINI CORPORATION; *Int'l*, pg. 2916
GEMINI COSMETICS, INC.; *U.S. Private*, pg. 1657
GEMINI EDIBLES & FATS INDIA PRIVATE LIMITED—See Golden Agri-Resources Ltd.; *Int'l*, pg. 3027
GEMINI ENGI-FAB LIMITED; *Int'l*, pg. 2916
GEMINI ENGINEERED SOLUTIONS LP—See Gemini Corporation; *Int'l*, pg. 2916
GEMINI ENGINEERING LIMITED—See Gemini Corporation; *Int'l*, pg. 2916
GEMINI FIELD SOLUTIONS LP—See Gemini Corporation; *Int'l*, pg. 2916
GEMINI GROUP GLOBAL CORP.; *U.S. Public*, pg. 910
GEMINI GROUP, INC.; *U.S. Private*, pg. 1657
GEMINI GROUP SERVICE CORPORATION; *U.S. Private*, pg. 1657
GEMINI INCORPORATED; *U.S. Private*, pg. 1658
GEMINI INDUSTRIES INC.; *U.S. Private*, pg. 1658
GEMINI INSURANCE COMPANY—See W.R. Berkley Corporation; *U.S. Public*, pg. 2318
GEMINI INVESTMENT (HOLDING) LIMITED—See Sino-Ocean Group Holdings Limited; *Int'l*, pg. 6949
GEMINI INVESTORS, INC.; *U.S. Private*, pg. 1658
GEMINI LEGAL SUPPORT, INC.; *U.S. Private*, pg. 1658
GEMINI MANAGEMENT LTD.—See Avio Global, Inc.; *U.S. Private*, pg. 407
GEMINI MOTOR TRANSPORT, LP—See Love's Travel Stops & Country Stores, Inc.; *U.S. Private*, pg. 2501
GEMINI OPEN CLOUD COMPUTING, INC.—See Super Micro Computer, Inc.; *U.S. Public*, pg. 1966
GEMINI PLASTICS DE MEXICO S. DE R.L. DE C.V.—See Gemini Group, Inc.; *U.S. Private*, pg. 1658
GEMINI PLASTICS, INC.—See Gemini Group, Inc.; *U.S. Private*, pg. 1658
GEMINI SEA FOOD PLC; *Int'l*, pg. 2916
GEMINI SOUND PRODUCTS CORP.; *U.S. Private*, pg. 1658

CORPORATE AFFILIATIONS

GEMINI TRANSPORTATION UNDERWRITERS, LLC—See W.R. Berkley Corporation; *U.S. Public*, pg. 2317
GEMINI TRAZE RFID PVT. LTD.—See Gemini Communication Ltd.; *Int'l*, pg. 2916
GEMINI-TUR EXCURSOES PASSAGENS E TURISMO LTDA.—See Mercedes-Benz Group AG; *Int'l*, pg. 4824
GEMINI VALVE; *U.S. Private*, pg. 1658
GEMINYS S.L.—See Construcciones y Auxiliar de Ferrocarriles S.A.; *Int'l*, pg. 1777
GEMISYS FINANCIAL; *U.S. Private*, pg. 1658
GEM JEWELRY INC.; *U.S. Private*, pg. 1657
GEM (JIANGSU) COBALT INDUSTRY CO., LTD.—See GEM Co., Ltd.; *Int'l*, pg. 2914
GEMLINE FRAME CO. INC.; *U.S. Private*, pg. 1658
GEMMA PLANT OPERATIONS, LLC—See Argan, Inc.; *U.S. Public*, pg. 191
GEMMA POWER SYSTEMS, LLC—See Argan, Inc.; *U.S. Public*, pg. 191
GEMMA—See HITIM Group; *Int'l*, pg. 3426
GEM MATTHEWS INTERNATIONAL S.R.L.—See Matthews International Corporation; *U.S. Public*, pg. 1400
GEMMEL RX; *U.S. Private*, pg. 1658
GEM MINNEAPOLIS; *U.S. Private*, pg. 1657
GEMOSCAN CANADA, INC.; *Int'l*, pg. 2916
GE MOZAMBIQUE LIMITADA—See Westinghouse Air Brake Technologies Corporation; *U.S. Public*, pg. 2358
GEMPLER'S—See The Riverside Company; *U.S. Private*, pg. 4108
GEMPLUS B.V.—See Thales S.A.; *Int'l*, pg. 7600
GEMPLUS (TIANJIN) NEW TECHNOLOGIES CO. LTD—See Thales S.A.; *Int'l*, pg. 7600
GEMPORIA PARTNERSHIP LIMITED; *Int'l*, pg. 2916
GEM REFRIGERATOR COMPANY, INC.; *U.S. Private*, pg. 1657
GEMSA ENTERPRISES, LLC—See Marubeni Corporation; *Int'l*, pg. 4705
GEMSHARES PHYSICAL DIAMOND TRUST; *U.S. Private*, pg. 1658
GEM SHOPPING NETWORK, INC.—See Sun Capital Partners, Inc.; *U.S. Private*, pg. 3859
GEMS MARINE PTE. LTD.—See Koon Holdings Limited; *Int'l*, pg. 4278
GEM SOUTHEAST, INC.—See Gem Industries Corporation; *U.S. Private*, pg. 1657
GEM SPINNERS INDIA LIMITED; *Int'l*, pg. 2915
GEMSPRING CAPITAL MANAGEMENT, LLC; *U.S. Private*, pg. 1658
GEM S.R.L.; *Int'l*, pg. 2915
GEMS SENSORS INC.—See Fortive Corporation; *U.S. Public*, pg. 870
GEMS SERVICES S.A.—See Eli Lilly & Company; *U.S. Public*, pg. 733
GEMSTAR TECHNOLOGY (CHINA) CO. LIMITED—See Universal Electronics, Inc.; *U.S. Public*, pg. 2255
GEM STATE DISTRIBUTORS INCORPORATED; *U.S. Private*, pg. 1657
GEM STATE WATER COMPANY, LLC—See Northwest Natural Holding Company; *U.S. Public*, pg. 1542
GEMSTONE HOTELS & RESORTS, LLC—See Benchmark Hospitality International Inc.; *U.S. Private*, pg. 524
GEMSTONE INVESTMENTS LIMITED; *Int'l*, pg. 2916
GEM SUPPLY CHAIN MANAGEMENT (SHANGHAI) CO., LTD.—See GEM Co., Ltd.; *Int'l*, pg. 2914
GEMTECH OPTOELECTRONICS CORP.—See Cheng Loong Corp.; *Int'l*, pg. 1466
GEMTEK TECHNOLOGY CO., LTD.—See MiTAC International Corp.; *Int'l*, pg. 4923
GEM TERMINAL IND. CO., LTD.; *Int'l*, pg. 2915
GEM (TIANJIN) URBAN MINERALS RECYCLING INDUSTRY DEVELOPMENT CO., LTD.—See GEM Co., Ltd.; *Int'l*, pg. 2914
GEMTOP MANUFACTURING, INC.—See Brand FX Body Company; *U.S. Private*, pg. 635
GEMTRON DE MEXICO S.A. DE C.V.—See Carl-Zeiss-Stiftung; *Int'l*, pg. 1336
GE MULTILIN—See General Electric Company; *U.S. Public*, pg. 918
GEMVARA, INC.—See Berkshire Hathaway Inc.; *U.S. Public*, pg. 316
GEMVAX & KAEL CO., LTD.; *Int'l*, pg. 2916
GEM (WUHAN) NEW ENERGY VEHICLE SERVICE CO., LTD.—See GEM Co., Ltd.; *Int'l*, pg. 2914
GEM (WUHAN) URBAN MINERALS RECYCLING INDUSTRY PARK DEVELOPMENT CO., LTD.—See GEM Co., Ltd.; *Int'l*, pg. 2914
GEM (WUXI) ENERGY MATERIALS CO., LTD.—See GEM Co., Ltd.; *Int'l*, pg. 2914
GEMXX CORPORATION; *U.S. Public*, pg. 910
GEM-YEAR INDUSTRIAL CO., LTD.; *Int'l*, pg. 2915
GEMY PONTIVY; *Int'l*, pg. 2916
GEMZ CORP.; *U.S. Public*, pg. 910
GEN3 MARKETING LLC—See Comvest Group Holdings LLC; *U.S. Private*, pg. 1007
GENABILITY, INC.—See Enel S.p.A.; *Int'l*, pg. 2414
GENAE AMERICAS, INC.—See IQVIA Holdings Inc.; *U.S. Public*, pg. 1170
GENAE ASSOCIATES NV—See IQVIA Holdings Inc.; *U.S. Public*, pg. 1170

COMPANY NAME INDEX

GENAGRICOLA 1851 S.P.A.—See Assicurazioni Generali S.p.A.; *Int'l*, pg. 644
GENAGRICOLA S.P.A.—See Assicurazioni Generali S.p.A.; *Int'l*, pg. 644
GENALTA POWER INC.—See Enbridge Inc.; *Int'l*, pg. 2397
GENALYSIS LABORATORY SERVICES PTY LIMITED—See Intertek Group plc; *Int'l*, pg. 3762
GENARRAYTION INC.—See Nephros, Inc.; *U.S. Public*, pg. 1506
GENARTS, INC.—See Boris FX, Inc.; *U.S. Private*, pg. 618
GENASYS II SPAIN, S.A.U.—See Genasys, Inc.; *U.S. Public*, pg. 911
GENASYS, INC.; *U.S. Public*, pg. 911
GENAXIS GROUP SDN. BHD.—See Dagang NeXchange Berhad; *Int'l*, pg. 1912
GENBAND US LLC—See Ribbon Communications Inc.; *U.S. Public*, pg. 1797
GENBOOK, INC.—See Booksy Inc.; *U.S. Private*, pg. 616
GENBYTE TECHNOLOGY, INC.; *Int'l*, pg. 2916
GENCAN CAPITAL, INC.; *Int'l*, pg. 2917
GEN CAP AMERICA, INC.; *U.S. Private*, pg. 1659
GENCELL BIOSYSTEMS LTD.—See Becton, Dickinson & Company; *U.S. Public*, pg. 292
GENCELL LTD.; *Int'l*, pg. 2917
GENCHEM HOLDINGS LIMITED—See Clarkson PLC; *Int'l*, pg. 1651
GENC MAGAZALARI A.S.—See Fiba Holding A.S.; *Int'l*, pg. 2651
GENCO BULGARIA LTD—See FOURLIS HOLDINGS S.A.; *Int'l*, pg. 2755
GENCO DISTRIBUTION SYSTEM, INC.—See FedEx Corporation; *U.S. Public*, pg. 828
GENCO ENERGY SERVICES, INC.; *U.S. Private*, pg. 1660
GENCO FUTURES INC.—See Coffee America (USA) Corporation; *U.S. Private*, pg. 961
GENCO HOLDINGS LIMITED—See Genco Shipping & Trading Limited; *U.S. Public*, pg. 911
GENCO INC.; *U.S. Private*, pg. 1660
GENCO MARKETPLACE, INC.—See FedEx Corporation; *U.S. Public*, pg. 828
GENCOM TECHNOLOGIES LTD.—See Hills Limited; *Int'l*, pg. 3390
GENCONN BIOTECH CO., LTD.—See Hon Hai Precision Industry Co., Ltd.; *Int'l*, pg. 3457
GENCOR INDUSTRIES, INC.; *U.S. Public*, pg. 911
GENCORP INSURANCE GROUP INC.—See ABRY Partners, LLC; *U.S. Private*, pg. 43
GENCO SHIPPING A/S—See Genco Shipping & Trading Limited; *U.S. Public*, pg. 911
GENCO SHIPPING PTE. LIMITED—See Genco Shipping & Trading Limited; *U.S. Public*, pg. 911
GENCO SHIPPING & TRADING LIMITED; *U.S. Public*, pg. 911
GENCO TRADE SRL—See FOURLIS HOLDINGS S.A.; *Int'l*, pg. 2755
GENCURIX, INC.; *Int'l*, pg. 2917
GENDAI AGENCY INC.; *Int'l*, pg. 2917
GEN.DEL. SA—See Tod's S.p.A.; *Int'l*, pg. 7772
GENDEX DENTAL SYSTEMS—See Danaher Corporation; *U.S. Public*, pg. 627
GEN DIGITAL INC.; *U.S. Public*, pg. 910
GENDIS INC.; *Int'l*, pg. 2917
GENDIS REALTY, INC.—See Gendis Inc.; *Int'l*, pg. 2917
GENDRON FORD; *Int'l*, pg. 2917
GENDRON INC.—See GF Health Products, Inc.; *U.S. Private*, pg. 1689
GENE B. GLICK COMPANY, INC.; *U.S. Private*, pg. 1660
GENE BIO TECH CO., LTD.; *Int'l*, pg. 2917
GENE BIOTHERAPEUTICS INC.; *U.S. Public*, pg. 911
GENECA, LLC; *U.S. Private*, pg. 1660
GENECOS S.A.—See Viohalco SA/NV; *Int'l*, pg. 8243
GENEDATA AG—See Danaher Corporation; *U.S. Public*, pg. 627
GENEDESIGN, INC.—See Ajinomoto Company, Inc.; *Int'l*, pg. 257
GENEDIS SAS—See Carrefour SA; *Int'l*, pg. 1345
GENEDRIVE PLC; *Int'l*, pg. 2917
GENEDX HOLDINGS CORP.; *U.S. Public*, pg. 911
GENEDX, INC.—See GeneDx Holdings Corp.; *U.S. Public*, pg. 911
GENEED, INC.—See Microsoft Corporation; *U.S. Public*, pg. 1439
GENE EVANS FORD, LLC—See AutoNation, Inc.; *U.S. Public*, pg. 235
GENE EVANS FORD, LLC—See AutoNation, Inc.; *U.S. Public*, pg. 235
GENEFERM BIOTECHNOLOGY CO., LTD.; *Int'l*, pg. 2917
GENEFIC—See Dalrada Financial Corporation; *U.S. Public*, pg. 621
GENEFIM S.A.—See Societe Generale S.A.; *Int'l*, pg. 7039
GENEFRONTIER CORPORATION—See Kaneka Corporation; *Int'l*, pg. 4067
GENEGIS II—See Societe Generale S.A.; *Int'l*, pg. 7039
GENEGIS L SAS—See Societe Generale S.A.; *Int'l*, pg. 7039
GENE HARRIS PETROLEUM INC.; *U.S. Private*, pg. 1660

GENE HUGGINS IMPORTS INC.—See Pearson-Huggins Companies Inc.; *U.S. Private*, pg. 3126
GENEJET BIOTECH CO., LTD.—See BenQ Materials Corp.; *Int'l*, pg. 975
GENE JUAREZ SALONS LLC—See Transom Capital Group, LLC; *U.S. Private*, pg. 4209
GENE LATTA FORD INC.; *U.S. Private*, pg. 1660
GENE LATTA FORD, INC.; *U.S. Private*, pg. 1660
GENEL ENERGY PLC; *Int'l*, pg. 2917
GENEL ENERGY YONETIM HIZMETLERI ANONIM SIRKETI—See Genel Energy plc; *Int'l*, pg. 2917
GENEMATRIX INC.; *Int'l*, pg. 2917
GENEMED BIOTECHNOLOGIES, INC.—See Sakura Finetek Japan Co., Ltd.; *Int'l*, pg. 6489
GENENCOR INTERNATIONAL INC. - ROCHESTER—See DuPont de Nemours, Inc.; *U.S. Public*, pg. 692
GENENCOR INTERNATIONAL, INC.—See DuPont de Nemours, Inc.; *U.S. Public*, pg. 692
GENENCOR INTERNATIONAL OY - HANKO—See DuPont de Nemours, Inc.; *U.S. Public*, pg. 693
GENENCOR INTERNATIONAL OY—See DuPont de Nemours, Inc.; *U.S. Public*, pg. 692
GENENDER INTERNATIONAL INC.; *U.S. Private*, pg. 1660
GENENEWS CORPORATION—See StageZero Life Sciences, Ltd.; *Int'l*, pg. 7163
GENENTA SCIENCE S.P.A.; *Int'l*, pg. 2917
GENENTECH, INC.—See Roche Holding AG; *Int'l*, pg. 6373
GENEOHM SCIENCES CANADA INC.—See Becton, Dickinson & Company; *U.S. Public*, pg. 292
GENEQ CORPORATION—See Nippon Yusen Kabushiki Kaisha; *Int'l*, pg. 5357
GENEQUITY MORTGAGE, INC.—See Paragon Global Resources, Inc.; *U.S. Private*, pg. 3091
GENER8, LLC—See Sverica Capital Management LP; *U.S. Private*, pg. 3888
GENER8 MARITIME MANAGEMENT LLC—See Euronav NV; *Int'l*, pg. 2554
GENER8 MEDIA CORP.; *Int'l*, pg. 2917
GENERA AGRI CORP LIMITED; *Int'l*, pg. 2917
GENERA BIOSYSTEMS LIMITED; *Int'l*, pg. 2917
GENERAC BRASIL LTDA—See Generac Holdings Inc.; *U.S. Public*, pg. 912
GENERAC HOLDINGS INC.; *U.S. Public*, pg. 912
GENERACION ELECTRICA PENINSULAR S.A.—See Mubadala Investment Company PJSC; *Int'l*, pg. 5074
GENERAC MEXICO ADMINISTRACION, S.A. DE C.V.—See Generac Holdings Inc.; *U.S. Public*, pg. 912
GENERAC MOBILE PRODUCTS, LLC—See Generac Holdings Inc.; *U.S. Public*, pg. 912
GENERAC MOBILE PRODUCTS S.R.L—See Generac Holdings Inc.; *U.S. Public*, pg. 912
GENERAC MOBILE PRODUCTS UK LTD—See Generac Holdings Inc.; *U.S. Public*, pg. 912
GENERA CORPORATION—See TYC Brother Industrial Co., Ltd.; *Int'l*, pg. 7994
GENERAC POWER SYSTEMS, INC. - OSHKOSH PLANT—See Generac Holdings Inc.; *U.S. Public*, pg. 912
GENERAC POWER SYSTEMS, INC.—See Generac Holdings Inc.; *U.S. Public*, pg. 912
GENERAC SERVICES, INC.—See Generac Holdings Inc.; *U.S. Public*, pg. 912
GENERA D.D.—See EQT AB; *Int'l*, pg. 2474
GENERA D.O.O. SARAJEVO—See EQT AB; *Int'l*, pg. 2475
GENERADORA DE OCCIDENTE LTDA—See Enel S.p.A.; *Int'l*, pg. 2413
GENERA ENERGY, LLC—See Ara Partners Group; *U.S. Private*, pg. 306
GENERAL ACCESSORY MANUFACTURING COMPANY—See Masco Corporation; *U.S. Public*, pg. 1390
GENERAL AGGREGATE EQUIPMENT SALES ULC—See General Equipment & Supplies Inc.; *U.S. Private*, pg. 1664
GENERAL AIR SERVICE & SUPPLY CO.; *U.S. Private*, pg. 1660
GENERAL ALUMINIUM WORKS (M) SDN. BHD.—See W T K Holdings Berhad; *Int'l*, pg. 8320
GENERAL ALUMINUM FORGINGS, LLC—See SIFCO Industries, Inc.; *U.S. Public*, pg. 1877
GENERAL ALUMINUM MANUFACTURING COMPANY—See Park-Ohio Holdings Corp.; *U.S. Public*, pg. 1639
GENERAL ALUMINUM—See Park-Ohio Holdings Corp.; *U.S. Public*, pg. 1639
GENERAL AMERICAN INVESTORS, INC.; *U.S. Public*, pg. 913
GENERAL ASPHALT CO., INC.; *U.S. Private*, pg. 1660
GENERAL ASP INC.; *U.S. Private*, pg. 1660
GENERAL ATLANTIC L.P.—See General Atlantic Service Company, L.P.; *U.S. Private*, pg. 1661
GENERAL ATLANTIC SERVICE COMPANY, L.P.; *U.S. Private*, pg. 1660
GENERAL ATOMICS AERONAUTICAL SYSTEMS INC.—See General Atomics; *U.S. Private*, pg. 1663

GENERAL ATOMICS - CRYOTECH DEICING TECHNOLOGY DIVISION—See General Atomics; *U.S. Private*, pg. 1663
GENERAL ATOMICS ELECTRONIC SYSTEMS, INC.—See General Atomics; *U.S. Private*, pg. 1663
GENERAL ATOMICS—See General Atomics; *U.S. Private*, pg. 1663
GENERAL ATOMICS; *U.S. Private*, pg. 1663
GENERAL ATOMICS SYSTEMS INTEGRATION, LLC—See General Atomics; *U.S. Private*, pg. 1663
GENERAL AUTO ELECTRIC CORPORATION—See s.a. D'Ieteren n.v.; *Int'l*, pg. 6448
GENERAL AVIATION FLYING SERVICES, INC.—See BlackRock, Inc.; *U.S. Public*, pg. 346
GENERAL AVIATION FLYING SERVICES, INC.—See Blackstone Inc.; *U.S. Public*, pg. 358
GENERAL AVIATION FLYING SERVICES, INC.—See Cascade Investment LLC; *U.S. Private*, pg. 780
GENERAL AVIATION IMPORT EXPORT JSC—See Vietnam Airlines Corporation; *Int'l*, pg. 8197
GENERAL AVIATION MAINTENANCE & ENGINEERING CO., LTD—See Airbus SE; *Int'l*, pg. 243
GENERAL AVIATION SERVICES, L.L.C.—See G.A.S. Capital, Inc.; *U.S. Private*, pg. 1630
GENERAL AVIATION TECHNOLOGIES, L.P.—See G.A.S. Capital, Inc.; *U.S. Private*, pg. 1630
GENERAL BANDAGES, INC.; *U.S. Private*, pg. 1664
GENERAL BANK OF GREECE S.A.; *Int'l*, pg. 2917
GENERAL BEARING CORPORATION—See SKF AB; *Int'l*, pg. 6985
GENERAL BEARING INTERNATIONAL TRADING LTD.—See SKF AB; *Int'l*, pg. 6981
GENERAL BINDING LLC—See ACCO Brands Corporation; *U.S. Public*, pg. 33
GENERAL BIOLOGICALS CORPORATION; *Int'l*, pg. 2918
GENERAL BODY MANUFACTURING COMPANY—See J.B. Poindexter & Co., Inc.; *U.S. Private*, pg. 2159
GENERAL BOOKBINDING COMPANY—See The HF Group LLC; *U.S. Private*, pg. 4052
GENERAL BRANDS S.A.R.L.—See Holdal s.a.l.; *Int'l*, pg. 3449
GENERAL BROACH COMPANY—See Utica Enterprises, Inc.; *U.S. Private*, pg. 4325
GENERAL BUILDING MAINTENANCE, INC.; *U.S. Private*, pg. 1664
GENERAL BUSINESS SERVICES CO., LTD.—See JBCC Holdings Inc.; *Int'l*, pg. 3917
GENERAL CABLE AUTOMOTIVA BRASIL FABRICACAO DE CABOS ELETRICOS LTDA.—See Prysmian S.p.A.; *Int'l*, pg. 6011
GENERAL CABLE BRASIL INDUSTRIA E COMERCIO DE CONDUTORES ELETRICOS LTDA.—See Prysmian S.p.A.; *Int'l*, pg. 6011
GENERAL CABLE CELCAT, ENERGIA E TELECOMUNICACOES SA—See Prysmian S.p.A.; *Int'l*, pg. 6011
GENERAL CABLE (CHINA) COMPANY LIMITED—See Prysmian S.p.A.; *Int'l*, pg. 6011
GENERAL CABLE CONDEL, CABOS DE ENERGIA E TELECOMUNICACOES SA—See Prysmian S.p.A.; *Int'l*, pg. 6011
GENERAL CABLE CORP. - FRANKLIN PLANT—See Prysmian S.p.A.; *Int'l*, pg. 6011
GENERAL CABLE CORP. - JACKSON PLANT—See Prysmian S.p.A.; *Int'l*, pg. 6011
GENERAL CABLE CORPORATION—See Prysmian S.p.A.; *Int'l*, pg. 6010
GENERAL CABLE CORP. - WILLIMANTIC PLANT & TECH CENTER—See Prysmian S.p.A.; *Int'l*, pg. 6011
GENERAL CABLE DE MEXICO DEL NORTE, S.A. DE C.V.—See Prysmian S.p.A.; *Int'l*, pg. 6011
GENERAL CABLE EGYPT S.A.E.—See Emerging Investment Partners; *Int'l*, pg. 2379
GENERAL CABLE HOLDINGS (SPAIN) S.L.—See Prysmian S.p.A.; *Int'l*, pg. 6011
GENERAL CABLE ITALIA, SARL—See Prysmian S.p.A.; *Int'l*, pg. 6011
GENERAL CABLE (JIANGYIN) CO. LTD.—See Prysmian S.p.A.; *Int'l*, pg. 6011
GENERAL CABLE MAROC SARL—See Prysmian S.p.A.; *Int'l*, pg. 6011
GENERAL CABLE NORDIC A/S—See Prysmian S.p.A.; *Int'l*, pg. 6011
GENERAL CABLE NORGE A/S—See Prysmian S.p.A.; *Int'l*, pg. 6011
GENERAL CABLE OMAN, LLC—See Prysmian S.p.A.; *Int'l*, pg. 6011
GENERAL CABLE PERU S.A.C.—See Prysmian S.p.A.; *Int'l*, pg. 6011
GENERAL CABLE SERVICES EUROPE LIMITED—See Prysmian S.p.A.; *Int'l*, pg. 6011
GENERAL CASUALTY CO. OF ILLINOIS—See QBE Insurance Group Limited; *Int'l*, pg. 6137
GENERAL CASUALTY INSURANCE—See QBE Insurance Group Limited; *Int'l*, pg. 6137
GENERAL CASUALTY—See QBE Insurance Group Limited; *Int'l*, pg. 6137

GENERAL BUILDING MAINTENANCE, INC.

CORPORATE AFFILIATIONS

GENERAL CASUALTY (SOUTHERN GUARANTY) INSURANCE CO.—See QBE Insurance Group Limited; *Int'l*, pg. 6137

GENERAL CASUALTY (SOUTHERN GUARANTY) INSURANCE—See QBE Insurance Group Limited; *Int'l*, pg. 6137

GENERAL CATALYST PARTNERS; *U.S. Private*, pg. 1664

GENERAL CEILING & PARTITIONS, INC.—See Installed Building Products, Inc.; *U.S. Public*, pg. 1132

GENERAL CERAMICS LTD.; *Int'l*, pg. 2918

GENERAL CHEMICAL GROUP, INC.; *U.S. Public*, pg. 913

GENERAL CHEMICAL INDUSTRIAL PRODUCTS INC.—See Tata Sons Limited; *Int'l*, pg. 7469

GENERAL CHEMICAL PERFORMANCE PRODUCTS LLC—See American Securities LLC; *U.S. Private*, pg. 249

GENERAL CIGAR CO. INC.—See Skandinavisk Holding A/S; *Int'l*, pg. 6976

GENERAL CIGAR DOMINICANA S.A.—See Skandinavisk Holding A/S; *Int'l*, pg. 6976

GENERAL COATINGS CORPORATION; *U.S. Private*, pg. 1664

GENERAL COATINGS TECHNOLOGIES; *U.S. Private*, pg. 1664

GENERALCOLOGNE RE IBERICA CORRESDORES DE REASEGUROS, S.A.—See Berkshire Hathaway Inc.; *U.S. Public*, pg. 301

GENERALCOLOGNE RE—See Berkshire Hathaway Inc.; *U.S. Public*, pg. 301

GENERAL & COLOGNE RE (SUR) COMPANIA DE REASEGUROS S.A.—See Berkshire Hathaway Inc.; *U.S. Public*, pg. 301

GENERAL COLOR & CHEMICAL CO., INC.; *U.S. Private*, pg. 1664

GENERAL COMBUSTION CORPORATION—See Gencor Industries, Inc.; *U.S. Public*, pg. 911

GENERAL COMMERCIAL & INDUSTRIAL SA; *Int'l*, pg. 2918

GENERAL COMMERCIAL NORTHERN GREECE S.A.—See GENERAL COMMERCIAL & INDUSTRIAL SA; *Int'l*, pg. 2918

GENERAL COMMUNICATIONS—See Hills Limited; *Int'l*, pg. 3393

GENERAL COMPANY FOR CERAMIC & PORCELAIN PRODUCTS; *Int'l*, pg. 2918

GENERAL COMPANY FOR PAPER INDUSTRY (RAKTA)—See Chemical Industries Holding Company; *Int'l*, pg. 1462

GENERALCOM SA; *Int'l*, pg. 2920

GENERAL CONTRACTING COMPANY—See The Olayan Group; *Int'l*, pg. 7672

GENERAL CONTROL EQUIPMENT COMPANY; *U.S. Private*, pg. 1664

GENERAL CONVERTING, INC.—See CORE Industrial Partners, LLC; *U.S. Private*, pg. 1048

GENERAL CUBICLE—See Construction Specialties, Inc.; *U.S. Private*, pg. 1024

GENERAL DATACOMM INDUSTRIES, INC.; *U.S. Public*, pg. 913

GENERAL DE ALQUILER DE MAQUINARIA, S.A.; *Int'l*, pg. 2918

GENERAL DE MINERALES, S.A. DE C.V.—See Grupo Lamosa S.A. de C.V.; *Int'l*, pg. 3131

GENERAL DE PRODUCCIONES Y DISENO, S.A.—See Acciona, S.A.; *Int'l*, pg. 90

GENERAL DE SEGUROS, S. A.—See Banco General, S.A.; *Int'l*, pg. 822

GENERAL DE SERVICIOS ITV, S.A.—See SGS SA; *Int'l*, pg. 6742

GENERAL DEVICES CO. INC.; *U.S. Private*, pg. 1664

GENERAL DIE CASTERS INC.; *U.S. Private*, pg. 1664

GENERAL DISTRIBUTORS INC.; *U.S. Private*, pg. 1664

GENERAL DISTRIBUTORS LIMITED—See Woolworths Group Limited; *Int'l*, pg. 8452

GENERAL DOORS CORP.; *U.S. Private*, pg. 1664

GENERAL DYNAMICS AEROSPACE GROUP—See General Dynamics Corporation; *U.S. Public*, pg. 913

GENERAL DYNAMICS ARMAMENT & TECHNICAL PRODUCTS—See General Dynamics Corporation; *U.S. Public*, pg. 913

GENERAL DYNAMICS COMBAT SYSTEMS GROUP—See General Dynamics Corporation; *U.S. Public*, pg. 913

GENERAL DYNAMICS COMMERCIAL CYBER SERVICES, LLC—See General Dynamics Corporation; *U.S. Public*, pg. 914

GENERAL DYNAMICS CORP. - CONVAIR DIVISION—See General Dynamics Corporation; *U.S. Public*, pg. 914

GENERAL DYNAMICS CORPORATION; *U.S. Public*, pg. 913

GENERAL DYNAMICS EUROPEAN LAND SYSTEMS - AUSTRIA GMBH—See General Dynamics Corporation; *U.S. Public*, pg. 914

GENERAL DYNAMICS EUROPEAN LAND SYSTEMS - BRIDGE SYSTEMS GMBH—See General Dynamics Corporation; *U.S. Public*, pg. 914

GENERAL DYNAMICS EUROPEAN LAND SYSTEMS - CZECH S.R.O.—See General Dynamics Corporation; *U.S. Public*, pg. 914

GENERAL DYNAMICS EUROPEAN LAND SYSTEMS - DEUTSCHLAND GMBH—See General Dynamics Corporation; *U.S. Public*, pg. 914

GENERAL DYNAMICS EUROPEAN LAND SYSTEMS - FWW GMBH—See General Dynamics Corporation; *U.S. Public*, pg. 914

GENERAL DYNAMICS EUROPEAN LAND SYSTEMS GERMANY GMBH—See General Dynamics Corporation; *U.S. Public*, pg. 914

GENERAL DYNAMICS EUROPEAN LAND SYSTEMS GMBH—See General Dynamics Corporation; *U.S. Public*, pg. 914

GENERAL DYNAMICS EUROPEAN LAND SYSTEMS - MOWAG GMBH—See General Dynamics Corporation; *U.S. Public*, pg. 914

GENERAL DYNAMICS EUROPEAN LAND SYSTEMS - STEYR—See General Dynamics Corporation; *U.S. Public*, pg. 914

GENERAL DYNAMICS GLOBAL IMAGING TECHNOLOGIES, INC. - CULLMAN—See General Dynamics Corporation; *U.S. Public*, pg. 915

GENERAL DYNAMICS GLOBAL IMAGING TECHNOLOGIES, INC. - ROCHESTER HILLS—See General Dynamics Corporation; *U.S. Public*, pg. 915

GENERAL DYNAMICS GLOBAL IMAGING TECHNOLOGIES, INC. - SAN DIEGO—See General Dynamics Corporation; *U.S. Public*, pg. 915

GENERAL DYNAMICS GLOBAL IMAGING TECHNOLOGIES, INC.—See General Dynamics Corporation; *U.S. Public*, pg. 915

GENERAL DYNAMICS GOVERNMENT SYSTEMS CORPORATION—See General Dynamics Corporation; *U.S. Public*, pg. 914

GENERAL DYNAMICS INFORMATION SYSTEMS & TECHNOLOGY GROUP—See General Dynamics Corporation; *U.S. Public*, pg. 914

GENERAL DYNAMICS INFORMATION TECHNOLOGY CANADA, LIMITED—See General Dynamics Corporation; *U.S. Public*, pg. 915

GENERAL DYNAMICS INFORMATION TECHNOLOGY COMMERCIAL SOLUTIONS, LLC—See General Dynamics Corporation; *U.S. Public*, pg. 915

GENERAL DYNAMICS INFORMATION TECHNOLOGY, INC.—See General Dynamics Corporation; *U.S. Public*, pg. 914

GENERAL DYNAMICS INFORMATION TECHNOLOGY LIMITED—See General Dynamics Corporation; *U.S. Public*, pg. 915

GENERAL DYNAMICS INFORMATION TECHNOLOGY—See General Dynamics Corporation; *U.S. Public*, pg. 914

GENERAL DYNAMICS INFORMATION TECHNOLOGY—See General Dynamics Corporation; *U.S. Public*, pg. 914

GENERAL DYNAMICS INFORMATION TECHNOLOGY—See General Dynamics Corporation; *U.S. Public*, pg. 914

GENERAL DYNAMICS INFORMATION TECHNOLOGY—See General Dynamics Corporation; *U.S. Public*, pg. 914

GENERAL DYNAMICS INFORMATION TECHNOLOGY—See General Dynamics Corporation; *U.S. Public*, pg. 914

GENERAL DYNAMICS ITRONIX EUROPE LTD.—See General Dynamics Corporation; *U.S. Public*, pg. 915

GENERAL DYNAMICS LAND SYSTEMS - CANADA CORPORATION—See General Dynamics Corporation; *U.S. Public*, pg. 915

GENERAL DYNAMICS LAND SYSTEMS CUSTOMER SERVICE & SUPPORT COMPANY—See General Dynamics Corporation; *U.S. Public*, pg. 915

GENERAL DYNAMICS LAND SYSTEMS INC.—See General Dynamics Corporation; *U.S. Public*, pg. 914

GENERAL DYNAMICS MARINE SYSTEMS, INC.—See General Dynamics Corporation; *U.S. Public*, pg. 915

GENERAL DYNAMICS MISSION SYSTEMS ASIA-PACIFIC SDN. BHD.—See General Dynamics Corporation; *U.S. Public*, pg. 915

GENERAL DYNAMICS MISSION SYSTEMS - CANADA—See General Dynamics Corporation; *U.S. Public*, pg. 915

GENERAL DYNAMICS MISSION SYSTEMS, INC.—See General Dynamics Corporation; *U.S. Public*, pg. 914

GENERAL DYNAMICS MISSION SYSTEMS, INC.—See General Dynamics Corporation; *U.S. Public*, pg. 915

GENERAL DYNAMICS MISSION SYSTEMS, INC.—See General Dynamics Corporation; *U.S. Public*, pg. 915

GENERAL DYNAMICS MISSION SYSTEMS, INC.—See General Dynamics Corporation; *U.S. Public*, pg. 915

GENERAL DYNAMICS MISSION SYSTEMS - ITALY S.R.L.—See General Dynamics Corporation; *U.S. Public*, pg. 915

GENERAL DYNAMICS MISSION SYSTEMS, LLC—See General Dynamics Corporation; *U.S. Public*, pg. 915

GENERAL DYNAMICS ORDNANCE AND TACTICAL SYSTEMS-CANADA INC.—See General Dynamics Corporation; *U.S. Public*, pg. 914

GENERAL DYNAMICS ORDNANCE AND TACTICAL SYSTEMS - CANADA VALLEYFIELD INC.—See General Dynamics Corporation; *U.S. Public*, pg. 915

GENERAL DYNAMICS ORDNANCE AND TACTICAL SYSTEMS, INC.—See General Dynamics Corporation; *U.S. Public*, pg. 914

GENERAL DYNAMICS ORDNANCE AND TACTICAL SYSTEMS - MUNITION SERVICES—See General Dynamics Corporation; *U.S. Public*, pg. 914

GENERAL DYNAMICS ORDNANCE AND TACTICAL SYSTEMS - SIMUNITION OPERATIONS, INC.—See General Dynamics Corporation; *U.S. Public*, pg. 915

GENERAL DYNAMICS ORDNANCE & TACTICAL SYSTEMS—See General Dynamics Corporation; *U.S. Public*, pg. 914

GENERAL DYNAMICS OTS (DRI), INC.—See General Dynamics Corporation; *U.S. Public*, pg. 914

GENERAL DYNAMICS-OTS, INC.—See General Dynamics Corporation; *U.S. Public*, pg. 916

GENERAL DYNAMICS OTS (NICEVILLE), INC.—See General Dynamics Corporation; *U.S. Public*, pg. 915

GENERAL DYNAMICS OTS (PENNSYLVANIA), INC.—See General Dynamics Corporation; *U.S. Public*, pg. 915

GENERAL DYNAMICS OTS (VERSATRON), INC.—See General Dynamics Corporation; *U.S. Public*, pg. 914

GENERAL DYNAMICS PROPERTIES, INC.—See General Dynamics Corporation; *U.S. Public*, pg. 915

GENERAL DYNAMICS ROBOTIC SYSTEMS—See General Dynamics Corporation; *U.S. Public*, pg. 914

GENERAL DYNAMICS SATCOM TECHNOLOGIES ASIA PRIVATE LIMITED—See General Dynamics Corporation; *U.S. Public*, pg. 915

GENERAL DYNAMICS SATELLITE COMMUNICATION SERVICES, INC.—See General Dynamics Corporation; *U.S. Public*, pg. 915

GENERAL DYNAMICS SHARED RESOURCES, INC.—See General Dynamics Corporation; *U.S. Public*, pg. 915

GENERAL DYNAMICS UK LTD.—See General Dynamics Corporation; *U.S. Public*, pg. 915

GENERAL DYNAMICS UNITED KINGDOM LIMITED—See General Dynamics Corporation; *U.S. Public*, pg. 916

GENERAL DYNAMICS VERTEX RSI—See General Dynamics Corporation; *U.S. Public*, pg. 916

GENERAL DYNAMICS WORLDWIDE HOLDINGS, INC.—See General Dynamics Corporation; *U.S. Public*, pg. 915

GENERALE BISCUIT GLICO FRANCE S.A.—See Ezaki Glico Co., Ltd.; *Int'l*, pg. 2593

GENERALE BISCUIT SAS—See Mondelez International, Inc.; *U.S. Public*, pg. 1463

GENERAL ECOLOGY, INC.—See Loar Group, Inc.; *U.S. Private*, pg. 2477

GENERAL ELECTRIC AUSTRIA GMBH—See General Electric Company; *U.S. Public*, pg. 918

GENERAL ELECTRIC CANADA COMPANY—See General Electric Company; *U.S. Public*, pg. 918

GENERAL ELECTRIC CAPITAL CORPORATION—See General Electric Company; *U.S. Public*, pg. 920

GENERAL ELECTRIC CAPITAL SERVICES, INC.—See General Electric Company; *U.S. Public*, pg. 918

GENERAL ELECTRIC COMPANY POLSKA SP. Z O.O.—See General Electric Company; *U.S. Public*, pg. 920

GENERAL ELECTRIC COMPANY; *U.S. Public*, pg. 916

GENERAL ELECTRIC CREDIT UNION; *U.S. Private*, pg. 1664

GENERAL ELECTRIC DEUTSCHLAND HOLDING GMBH—See General Electric Company; *U.S. Public*, pg. 920

GENERAL ELECTRIC HEALTHCARE PORTUGAL, SOCIEDADE UNIPESSOAL, LDA.—See GE HealthCare Technologies Inc.; *U.S. Public*, pg. 909

GENERAL ELECTRIC (SWITZERLAND) GMBH—See General Electric Company; *U.S. Public*, pg. 918

GENERAL ELECTRONICS & INSTRUMENTATION CORPORATION PRIVATE LIMITED—See New Wave Holdings Ltd.; *Int'l*, pg. 5231

GENERAL ELEVATOR CO., LTD.; *Int'l*, pg. 2918

GENERAL ENERGY SOLUTIONS INC.—See United Renewable Energy Co., Ltd.; *Int'l*, pg. 8073

GENERAL ENERGY SOLUTIONS UK LIMITED—See United Renewable Energy Co., Ltd.; *Int'l*, pg. 8073

GENERAL ENGINEERING CORP—See TTI Holdings Inc.; *U.S. Private*, pg. 4254

GENERAL ENGINEERING MAURITIUS LIMITED—See General Engineering Public Company Limited; *Int'l*, pg. 2918

GENERAL ENGINEERING PUBLIC COMPANY LIMITED; *Int'l*, pg. 2918

GENERAL ENGINEERS LTD.—See Inter-Gamma Investment Company Ltd.; *Int'l*, pg. 3735

GENERAL ENGINE PRODUCTS LLC—See MacAndrews & Forbes Incorporated; *U.S. Private*, pg. 2532

GENERAL ENGINE PRODUCTS LLC—See The Renco Group Inc.; *U.S. Private*, pg. 4104

COMPANY NAME INDEX

GENERAL ENGINES COMPANY INC.; *U.S. Private*, pg. 1664
GENERAL ENTERPRISE VENTURES, INC.; *U.S. Public*, pg. 920
GENERAL ENVIRONMENTAL CONSERVATION PUBLIC COMPANY LIMITED - MAP TAPHUT WASTE TREATMENT FACILITY—See General Environmental Conservation Public Company Limited; *Int'l*, pg. 2918
GENERAL ENVIRONMENTAL CONSERVATION PUBLIC COMPANY LIMITED - SAMAEDUM WASTE TREATMENT FACILITY—See General Environmental Conservation Public Company Limited; *Int'l*, pg. 2918
GENERAL ENVIRONMENTAL CONSERVATION PUBLIC COMPANY LIMITED; *Int'l*, pg. 2918
GENERAL EQUIPMENT & SUPPLIES INC.; *U.S. Private*, pg. 1664
GENERAL EQUITIES INC.; *U.S. Private*, pg. 1664
GENERAL EXCAVATING COMPANY; *U.S. Private*, pg. 1665
GENERAL EXTRUSIONS INC.; *U.S. Private*, pg. 1665
GENERAL FABRICS COMPANY; *U.S. Private*, pg. 1665
GENERAL FASTENERS COMPANY INC.; *U.S. Private*, pg. 1665
GENERAL FILMS, INC.; *U.S. Private*, pg. 1665
GENERAL FILTERS, INC.; *U.S. Private*, pg. 1665
GENERAL FINANCE CORPORATION—See United Rentals, Inc.; *U.S. Public*, pg. 2235
GENERAL FINANCE & DEVELOPMENT, INC.; *U.S. Public*, pg. 920
GENERALFINANCE S.P.A.; *Int'l*, pg. 2920
GENERAL FINANCIAL SUPPLY, INC.—See Ennis, Inc.; *U.S. Public*, pg. 769
GENERAL FINANCIAL SUPPLY, INC. - VIRGINIA—See Ennis, Inc.; *U.S. Public*, pg. 769
GENERAL FLANGE & FORGE LLC—See Quadrant Management, Inc.; *U.S. Private*, pg. 3316
GENERAL FLOOR INDUSTRIES INC.; *U.S. Private*, pg. 1665
GENERAL FOAM PLASTICS CORP.; *U.S. Private*, pg. 1665
GENERAL FREIGHT INC—See Savino Del Bene S.p.A.; *Int'l*, pg. 6600
GENERAL GERMAN AGED PEOPLE'S HOME OF BALTIMORE; *U.S. Private*, pg. 1005
GENERAL GLASS CO., LTD.—See Saha Pathanapibul Public Company Limited; *Int'l*, pg. 6479
GENERAL GLASS INTERNATIONAL CORP.; *U.S. Private*, pg. 1665
GENERAL GMC TRUCK SALES & SERVICE, INC.—See SF Holding Corp.; *U.S. Private*, pg. 3621
GENERAL HEALTHCARE GROUP LTD; *Int'l*, pg. 2918
GENERAL HEALTHCARE RESOURCES, LLC—See Platform Partners LLC; *U.S. Private*, pg. 3200
GENERAL HEALTH SYSTEM FOUNDATION, INC.—See General Health System Inc.; *U.S. Private*, pg. 1665
GENERAL HEALTH SYSTEM INC.; *U.S. Private*, pg. 1665
GENERAL HEATING & AIR CONDITIONING INC.—See Hooper Corporation; *U.S. Private*, pg. 1978
GENERAL HELICOPTERS INTERNATIONAL, INC.—See G.A.S. Capital, Inc.; *U.S. Private*, pg. 1630
GENERAL HOMES CORP.—See Wells Fargo & Company; *U.S. Public*, pg. 2343
GENERAL HOSPITAL CAMPUS OF ST. JOSEPH HOSPITAL—See Saint Joseph Hospital; *U.S. Private*, pg. 3529
GENERAL HOSPITAL PRODUCTS PCL—See Bangkok Dusit Medical Services Public Company Limited; *Int'l*, pg. 834
GENERAL HOTEL MANAGEMENT LTD.; *Int'l*, pg. 2918
GENERAL HOUSING CORPORATION; *U.S. Private*, pg. 1665
GENERAL HOUSING INC.—See Strategic Investments & Holding Inc.; *U.S. Private*, pg. 3835
GENERALI AKADEMIE GMBH I.L.—See Assicurazioni Generali S.p.A.; *Int'l*, pg. 644
GENERALI ALAPKEZELO ZARTKORUEN MUKODO RESZVENYTARSASAG—See Assicurazioni Generali S.p.A.; *Int'l*, pg. 644
GENERALI ALLGEMEINE VERSICHERUNGEN AG—See Assicurazioni Generali S.p.A.; *Int'l*, pg. 644
GENERALI ARGENTINA S.A.—See Assicurazioni Generali S.p.A.; *Int'l*, pg. 644
GENERALI ASIA N.V.—See Assicurazioni Generali S.p.A.; *Int'l*, pg. 647
GENERALI ASIGURARI S.A.—See Assicurazioni Generali S.p.A.; *Int'l*, pg. 645
GENERALI ASSET MANAGEMENT S.P.A.—See Assicurazioni Generali S.p.A.; *Int'l*, pg. 644
GENERALI ASSURANCES GENERALES—See Assicurazioni Generali S.p.A.; *Int'l*, pg. 644
GENERALI BANK AG—See Assicurazioni Generali S.p.A.; *Int'l*, pg. 645
GENERALI BELGIUM S.A.—See Apollo Global Management, Inc.; *U.S. Public*, pg. 644
GENERALI BIZTOSITO—See PPF Group N.V.; *Int'l*, pg. 5950
GENERALI BRASIL SEGUROS S.A.—See Assicurazioni Generali S.p.A.; *Int'l*, pg. 644

GENERALI BULGARIA HOLDING AD—See Assicurazioni Generali S.p.A.; *Int'l*, pg. 644
GENERALI BUSINESS SOLUTIONS S.C.P.A.—See Assicurazioni Generali S.p.A.; *Int'l*, pg. 644
GENERALI CAPITAL FINANCE B.V.—See Assicurazioni Generali S.p.A.; *Int'l*, pg. 647
GENERALI CAR CARE S.R.O.—See Assicurazioni Generali S.p.A.; *Int'l*, pg. 646
GENERALI CEE HOLDING B.V.—See Assicurazioni Generali S.p.A.; *Int'l*, pg. 644
GENERALI CESKA POJISTOVNA A.S.—See Assicurazioni Generali S.p.A.; *Int'l*, pg. 644
GENERALI CONSULTING SOLUTIONS LLC—See Assicurazioni Generali S.p.A.; *Int'l*, pg. 644
GENERALI DEUTSCHLAND GESELLSCHAFT FUR BAV MBH—See Assicurazioni Generali S.p.A.; *Int'l*, pg. 644
GENERALI DEUTSCHLAND KRANKENVERSICHERUNG AG—See Assicurazioni Generali S.p.A.; *Int'l*, pg. 644
GENERALI DEUTSCHLAND LEBENSVERSICHERUNG AG—See Assicurazioni Generali S.p.A.; *Int'l*, pg. 644
GENERALI DEVELOPMENT SPOL SRO—See Assicurazioni Generali S.p.A.; *Int'l*, pg. 646
GENERALI DO BRASIL PARTIPACOES S.A.—See Assicurazioni Generali S.p.A.; *Int'l*, pg. 647
GENERALI ECUADOR COMPANIA DE SEGUROS S.A.—See Assicurazioni Generali S.p.A.; *Int'l*, pg. 644
GENERALI EMPLOYEE BENEFITS BRUXELLES—See Assicurazioni Generali S.p.A.; *Int'l*, pg. 644
GENERALI ENGAGEMENT SOLUTIONS GMBH—See Assicurazioni Generali S.p.A.; *Int'l*, pg. 644
GENERALI ESPANA, HOLDING DE ENTIDADES DE SEGUROS, S.A.—See Assicurazioni Generali S.p.A.; *Int'l*, pg. 644
GENERALI ESPANA, S.A. DE SEGUROS Y REASEGUROS—See Assicurazioni Generali S.p.A.; *Int'l*, pg. 644
GENERALI FINANCE B.V.—See Assicurazioni Generali S.p.A.; *Int'l*, pg. 647
GENERALI FINANCE SPOLKA Z OGRANICZONA ODPOWIEDZIALNOSCIA—See Assicurazioni Generali S.p.A.; *Int'l*, pg. 644
GENERALI FINANZSERVICE GMBH—See Assicurazioni Generali S.p.A.; *Int'l*, pg. 645
GENFRAI I FRANCE ASSURANCES S.A.—See Assicurazioni Generali S.p.A.; *Int'l*, pg. 644
GENERALI FRANCE HOLDING S.A.—See Assicurazioni Generali S.p.A.; *Int'l*, pg. 644
GENERALI FRANCE IMMOBILIER SAS—See Assicurazioni Generali S.p.A.; *Int'l*, pg. 645
GENERALI FRANCE S.A.—See Assicurazioni Generali S.p.A.; *Int'l*, pg. 645
GENERALI FUND MANAGEMENT S.A.—See Assicurazioni Generali S.p.A.; *Int'l*, pg. 643
GENERALI GERANCE S.A.—See Assicurazioni Generali S.p.A.; *Int'l*, pg. 645
GENERALI GROUP INSURANCE AG—See Assicurazioni Generali S.p.A.; *Int'l*, pg. 645
GENERALI HEALTH SOLUTIONS GMBH—See Assicurazioni Generali S.p.A.; *Int'l*, pg. 645
GENERALI HELLAS A.E.A.Z. PROPERTY & CASUALTY INSURANCE CO.—See Assicurazioni Generali S.p.A.; *Int'l*, pg. 645
GENERALI HELLAS INSURANCE COMPANY S.A.—See Assicurazioni Generali S.p.A.; *Int'l*, pg. 645
GENERALI HELLAS INSURANCE COMPANY S.A.—See Assicurazioni Generali S.p.A.; *Int'l*, pg. 645
GENERALI HOLDING VIENNA AG—See Assicurazioni Generali S.p.A.; *Int'l*, pg. 645
GENERALI IARD S.A.—See Assicurazioni Generali S.p.A.; *Int'l*, pg. 645
GENERALI IMMOBILIARE ITALIA SGR S.P.A.—See Assicurazioni Generali S.p.A.; *Int'l*, pg. 646
GENERALI IMMOBILIEN AG—See Assicurazioni Generali S.p.A.; *Int'l*, pg. 645
GENERALI INFORMATIQUE S.A.—See Assicurazioni Generali S.p.A.; *Int'l*, pg. 645
GENERALI-INGATLAN VAGYONKEZELO ES SZOLGALTATO KFT.—See Assicurazioni Generali S.p.A.; *Int'l*, pg. 647
GENERALI INSURANCE AD—See Assicurazioni Generali S.p.A.; *Int'l*, pg. 644
GENERALI INSURANCE AGENCY COMPANY LIMITED—See Assicurazioni Generali S.p.A.; *Int'l*, pg. 646
GENERALI INSURANCE (THAILAND) CO., LTD.—See Assicurazioni Generali S.p.A.; *Int'l*, pg. 646
GENERALI INTERNATIONAL LIMITED—See Utmost International Group Holdings Limited; *Int'l*, pg. 8101
GENERALI INVESTMENTS ASIA LIMITED—See Assicurazioni Generali S.p.A.; *Int'l*, pg. 646
GENERALI INVESTMENTS CEE, INVESTICNI SPOLECNOST, A.S.—See Assicurazioni Generali S.p.A.; *Int'l*, pg. 646
GENERALI INVESTMENTS, DRUZBA ZA UPRAVLJANJE, D.O.O.—See Assicurazioni Generali S.p.A.; *Int'l*, pg. 646
GENERALI INVESTMENTS EUROPE S.P.A.—See Assicurazioni Generali S.p.A.; *Int'l*, pg. 646

GENERAL INVESTMENT CO., LTD.

GENERALI INVESTMENTS PARTNERS S.P.A. SOCIETA DI GESTIONE RISPARMIO—See Assicurazioni Generali S.p.A.; *Int'l*, pg. 646
GENERALI INVESTMENTS SCHWEIZ AG—See Assicurazioni Generali S.p.A.; *Int'l*, pg. 644
GENERALI ITALIA S.P.A.—See Assicurazioni Generali S.p.A.; *Int'l*, pg. 646
GENERALI IT-SOLUTIONS GMBH—See Assicurazioni Generali S.p.A.; *Int'l*, pg. 645
GENERALI KENT B.V.—See Assicurazioni Generali S.p.A.; *Int'l*, pg. 647
GENERALI LEASING GMBH—See Assicurazioni Generali S.p.A.; *Int'l*, pg. 646
GENERALI LEBENSVERSICHERUNG AG—See Cinven Limited; *Int'l*, pg. 1616
GENERALI LEBENSVERSICHERUNG AG—See Talanx AG; *Int'l*, pg. 7445
GENERALI LIFE ASSURANCE PHILIPPINES, INC.—See Assicurazioni Generali S.p.A.; *Int'l*, pg. 647
GENERALI LIFE (HONG KONG) LIMITED—See Assicurazioni Generali S.p.A.; *Int'l*, pg. 647
GENERALI LUXEMBOURG S.A.—See Assicurazioni Generali S.p.A.; *Int'l*, pg. 645
GENERAL IMPLEMENT DISTRIBUTORS—See Arnold Machinery Company; *U.S. Private*, pg. 333
THE GENERAL INC.—See PAL GROUP Holdings Co., Ltd.; *Int'l*, pg. 5705
GENERAL INDEMNITY GROUP, LLC—See Boston Omaha Corporation; *U.S. Public*, pg. 372
GENERAL INDUSTRIES & PACKAGES COMPANY—See Hayel Saeed Anam Group of Companies; *Int'l*, pg. 3290
GENERAL INFORMATICS; *U.S. Private*, pg. 1665
GENERAL INNKEEPING ACCEPTANCE CORPORATION—See InterContinental Hotels Group PLC; *Int'l*, pg. 3737
GENERAL INSTRUMENT CORPORATION INDIA PRIVATE LIMITED—See CommScope Holding Company, Inc.; *U.S. Public*, pg. 548
GENERAL INSTRUMENT LLC—See CommScope Holding Company, Inc.; *U.S. Public*, pg. 548
GENERAL INSULATION CO. INC.; *U.S. Private*, pg. 1665
GENERAL INSURANCE COMPANY (SUDAN) LIMITED; *Int'l*, pg. 2918
GENERAL INSURANCE CORPORATION OF INDIA; *Int'l*, pg. 2918
GENERAL INSURANCE OF CYPRUS LTD—See Bank of Cyprus Holdings Public Limited Company; *Int'l*, pg. 842
GENERAL INTERFACE SOLUTION (GIS) HOLDING LTD.; *Int'l*, pg. 2918
GENERAL INVESTMENT CO., LTD.; *Int'l*, pg. 2919
GENERAL INVESTMENT S.R.L.—See NEPI Rockcastle N.V.; *Int'l*, pg. 5200
GENERALI OSIGURANJE D.D.—See Assicurazioni Generali S.p.A.; *Int'l*, pg. 646
GENERALI OSIGURANJE SRBIJA A.D.O.—See Assicurazioni Generali S.p.A.; *Int'l*, pg. 646
GENERALI PARTNER GMBH—See Cinven Limited; *Int'l*, pg. 1616
GENERALI PARTNER GMBH—See Talanx AG; *Int'l*, pg. 7445
GENERALI PATRIMOINE—See Assicurazioni Generali S.p.A.; *Int'l*, pg. 645
GENERALI PENSIONSFONDS AG—See Assicurazioni Generali S.p.A.; *Int'l*, pg. 646
GENERALI PENSIONSKASSE AG—See Assicurazioni Generali S.p.A.; *Int'l*, pg. 646
GENERALI PENSIONSMANAGEMENT GMBH—See Cinven Limited; *Int'l*, pg. 1616
GENERALI PENSIONSMANAGEMENT GMBH—See Talanx AG; *Int'l*, pg. 7445
GENERALI PENSIONS- UND SICHERUNGSMANAGEMENT GMBH—See Assicurazioni Generali S.p.A.; *Int'l*, pg. 646
GENERALI PENZIJNI FOND A.S.—See Assicurazioni Generali S.p.A.; *Int'l*, pg. 646
GENERALI PENZIJNI SPOLECNOST, A.S.—See Assicurazioni Generali S.p.A.; *Int'l*, pg. 647
GENERALI PERSONENVERSICHERUNGEN AG—See Assicurazioni Generali S.p.A.; *Int'l*, pg. 644
GENERALI POJISTOVNA A.S.—See Assicurazioni Generali S.p.A.; *Int'l*, pg. 646
GENERALI PORTFOLIO MANAGEMENT (CI) LIMITED—See Utmost International Group Holdings Limited; *Int'l*, pg. 8101
GENERALI POWSZECHNE TOWARZYSTWO EMERYTALNE S.A.—See Assicurazioni Generali S.p.A.; *Int'l*, pg. 646
GENERALI PPF HOLDING BV—See Assicurazioni Generali S.p.A.; *Int'l*, pg. 646
GENERALI PROPERTIES FUND I GMBH & CO. KG.—See Cinven Limited; *Int'l*, pg. 1616
GENERALI PROPERTIES FUND I GMBH & CO. KG—See Talanx AG; *Int'l*, pg. 7445
GENERALI PROPERTIES S.P.A.—See Assicurazioni Generali S.p.A.; *Int'l*, pg. 646
GENERALI PROVIDENCIA BIZTOSITO RT.—See Assicurazioni Generali S.p.A.; *Int'l*, pg. 646

GENERAL INVESTMENT CO., LTD.

CORPORATE AFFILIATIONS

GENERALI REAL ESTATE INVESTMENTS B.V.—See Apollo Global Management, Inc.; *U.S. Public*, pg. 147
GENERALI REAL ESTATE S.P.A.—See Assicurazioni Generali S.p.A.; *Int'l*, pg. 646
GENERALI REALTIES LTD—See Assicurazioni Generali S.p.A.; *Int'l*, pg. 646
GENERALI ROMANIA ASIGURARE REASIGURARE S.A.—See PPF Group N.V.; *Int'l*, pg. 5950
GENERALI RUCKVERSICHERUNG AG—See Assicurazioni Generali S.p.A.; *Int'l*, pg. 647
GENERALI SALES PROMOTION GMBH—See Assicurazioni Generali S.p.A.; *Int'l*, pg. 646
GENERALI SAXON LAND DEVELOPMENT COMPANY LIMITED—See Assicurazioni Generali S.p.A.; *Int'l*, pg. 647
GENERALI (SCHWEIZ) HOLDING AG—See Assicurazioni Generali S.p.A.; *Int'l*, pg. 644
GENERALI SEGUROS, S.A.—See Assicurazioni Generali S.p.A.; *Int'l*, pg. 647
GENERALI SICHERUNGSTREUHAND GMBH—See Assicurazioni Generali S.p.A.; *Int'l*, pg. 647
GENERALI SIGORTA A.S.—See Assicurazioni Generali S.p.A.; *Int'l*, pg. 647
GENERALI SLOVENSKO POIST'OVNA A.S.—See Assicurazioni Generali S.p.A.; *Int'l*, pg. 646
GENERALI SOCIETATE DE ADMINISTRARE A FONDURILOR DE PENSII PRIVATE S.A.—See Assicurazioni Generali S.p.A.; *Int'l*, pg. 647
GENERAL ISRAEL ORPHAN HOME FOR GIRLS JERUSALEM; *U.S. Private*, pg. 1665
GENERALI TELEFON- + AUFTRAGSSERVICE GMBH—See Assicurazioni Generali S.p.A.; *Int'l*, pg. 645
GENERALI TOWARZYSTWO UBEZPIEC.—See PPF Group N.V.; *Int'l*, pg. 5950
GENERALI TURKEY HOLDING B.V.—See Assicurazioni Generali S.p.A.; *Int'l*, pg. 647
GENERALI TVG VORSORGEMANAGEMENT GMBH—See Assicurazioni Generali S.p.A.; *Int'l*, pg. 646
GENERALI VELKY SPALICEK S.R.O.—See Assicurazioni Generali S.p.A.; *Int'l*, pg. 645
GENERALI VIE S.A.—See Assicurazioni Generali S.p.A.; *Int'l*, pg. 645
GENERALI VIETNAM LIFE INSURANCE LTD.—See Assicurazioni Generali S.p.A.; *Int'l*, pg. 647
GENERALI VIS INFORMATIK GMBH—See Assicurazioni Generali S.p.A.; *Int'l*, pg. 646
GENERALI WARRANTY SERVICES, LLC—See Assicurazioni Generali S.p.A.; *Int'l*, pg. 644
GENERALI WORLDWIDE INSURANCE COMPANY LIMITED—See Utmost International Group Holdings Limited; *Int'l*, pg. 8101
GENERALI ZAKRILA HEALTH INSURANCE AD—See Assicurazioni Generali S.p.A.; *Int'l*, pg. 644
GENERALI ZAKRILA MEDICAL & DENTAL CENTRE EOOD—See Assicurazioni Generali S.p.A.; *Int'l*, pg. 647
GENERALI ZAVAROVALNICA D.D.—See Assicurazioni Generali S.p.A.; *Int'l*, pg. 646
GENERALI ZYCIE TOWARZYSTWO UBEZPIECZEN S.A.—See Assicurazioni Generali S.p.A.; *Int'l*, pg. 647
GENERAL JOHN J PERSHING MEMORIAL HOSPITAL ASSOCIATION; *U.S. Private*, pg. 1665
GENERAL LABELS & LABELLING (JB) SDN. BHD.—See Komarkcorp Berhad; *Int'l*, pg. 4234
GENERAL LABELS & LABELLING PTE. LTD.—See Komarkcorp Berhad; *Int'l*, pg. 4234
GENERAL LABOR STAFFING SERVICES INC.; *U.S. Private*, pg. 1665
GENERAL LED, INC.—See The CapStreet Group LLC; *U.S. Private*, pg. 4004
GENERAL LIFE RE UK LIMITED—See Berkshire Hathaway Inc.; *U.S. Public*, pg. 301
GENERAL LIQUIDS CANADA—See Municipal Enterprises Limited; *Int'l*, pg. 5093
GENERAL LOGISTICS SYSTEMS AUSTRIA GMBH—See International Distributions Services plc; *Int'l*, pg. 3747
GENERAL LOGISTICS SYSTEMS B.V.—See International Distributions Services plc; *Int'l*, pg. 3747
GENERAL LOGISTICS SYSTEMS CZECH REPUBLIC S.R.O.—See International Distributions Services plc; *Int'l*, pg. 3747
GENERAL LOGISTICS SYSTEMS FINLAND OY—See International Distributions Services plc; *Int'l*, pg. 3747
GENERAL LOGISTICS SYSTEMS GERMANY GMBH & CO. OHG—See International Distributions Services plc; *Int'l*, pg. 3747
GENERAL LOGISTICS SYSTEMS IRELAND LIMITED—See International Distributions Services plc; *Int'l*, pg. 3747
GENERAL LOGISTICS SYSTEMS, LOGISTICNE STORITVE, D.O.O.—See International Distributions Services plc; *Int'l*, pg. 3748
GENERAL LOGISTICS SYSTEMS POLAND SPOLKA Z O.O.—See International Distributions Services plc; *Int'l*, pg. 3747
GENERAL LOGISTICS SYSTEMS PORTUGAL LDA.—See International Distributions Services plc; *Int'l*, pg. 3748

GENERAL LOGISTICS SYSTEMS US, INC.—See International Distributions Services plc; *Int'l*, pg. 3748
GENERAL MACHINE CORPORATION—See JEP Management, Inc.; *U.S. Private*, pg. 2201
GENERAL MACHINERY COMPANY INC.; *U.S. Private*, pg. 1665
GENERAL MAGNAPLATE CALIFORNIA—See General Magnaplate Corporation; *U.S. Private*, pg. 1665
GENERAL MAGNAPLATE CANADA LTD.—See General Magnaplate Corporation; *U.S. Private*, pg. 1666
GENERAL MAGNAPLATE CORPORATION; *U.S. Private*, pg. 1665
GENERAL MAGNAPLATE TEXAS—See General Magnaplate Corporation; *U.S. Private*, pg. 1666
GENERAL MARINE COMPANY LIMITED—See Asian Marine Services Public Company Limited; *Int'l*, pg. 618
GENERAL MARKETING SRL—See CEMBRE S.p.A.; *Int'l*, pg. 1396
GENERAL MATERIALS BIOCHEMISTRY FERTILIZER JOINT STOCK COMPANY; *Int'l*, pg. 2919
GENERAL, MECHANICAL & CIVIL CONTRACTORS LTD.; *Int'l*, pg. 2920
GENERAL MECHANICAL CONTRACTORS INC; *U.S. Private*, pg. 1666
GENERAL MEDICAL APPLICATIONS, INC.—See Modernizing Medicine, Inc.; *U.S. Private*, pg. 2763
GENERAL MEDICAL CLINICS LIMITED—See HCA Healthcare, Inc.; *U.S. Public*, pg. 996
GENERAL MEDICAL S.R.L.—See Mitsubishi Chemical Group Corporation; *Int'l*, pg. 4937
GENERAL MEDICALS W.L.L.—See International Agencies Company Ltd.; *Int'l*, pg. 3743
GENERAL METAL FINISHING LLC—See NN, Inc.; *U.S. Public*, pg. 1531
GENERAL METALS OF TACOMA, INC.—See Radius Recycling, Inc.; *U.S. Public*, pg. 1760
GENERAL MICROCIRCUITS, INC.—See East West Manufacturing, LLC; *U.S. Private*, pg. 1319
GENERAL MICROSYSTEMS, INC.; *U.S. Private*, pg. 1666
GENERAL MICROWAVE CORPORATION—See Kratos Defense & Security Solutions, Inc.; *U.S. Public*, pg. 1276
GENERAL MILLS ARGENTINA S.A.—See General Mills, Inc.; *U.S. Public*, pg. 921
GENERAL MILLS AUSTRALIA PTY. LTD.—See General Mills, Inc.; *U.S. Public*, pg. 922
GENERAL MILLS BAKERY & FOODSERVICE PTY LTD—See General Mills, Inc.; *U.S. Public*, pg. 922
GENERAL MILLS BRAZIL LTDA.—See General Mills, Inc.; *U.S. Public*, pg. 922
GENERAL MILLS CANADA CORP.—See General Mills, Inc.; *U.S. Public*, pg. 922
GENERAL MILLS CEREALS HOLDING (SOUTH AFRICA) PTY LIMITED—See General Mills, Inc.; *U.S. Public*, pg. 921
GENERAL MILLS, CONSUMER FOODS SALES DIVISION—See General Mills, Inc.; *U.S. Public*, pg. 922
GENERAL MILLS DE MEXICO, S. DE R.L. DE C.V.—See General Mills, Inc.; *U.S. Public*, pg. 921
GENERAL MILLS DE VENEZUELA, C.A.; *Int'l*, pg. 2919
GENERAL MILLS DIRECT MARKETING, INC.—See General Mills, Inc.; *U.S. Public*, pg. 921
GENERAL MILLS FOODS, INC.—See General Mills, Inc.; *U.S. Public*, pg. 921
GENERAL MILLS FRANCE (SAS)—See General Mills, Inc.; *U.S. Public*, pg. 922
GENERAL MILLS GMBH—See General Mills, Inc.; *U.S. Public*, pg. 922
GENERAL MILLS HELLAS S.A.—See General Mills, Inc.; *U.S. Public*, pg. 922
GENERAL MILLS HOLDING (AUSTRALIA) PTY LIMITED—See General Mills, Inc.; *U.S. Public*, pg. 921
GENERAL MILLS HOLDING ONE (GERMANY) GMBH—See General Mills, Inc.; *U.S. Public*, pg. 921
GENERAL MILLS HONG KONG LIMITED—See General Mills, Inc.; *U.S. Public*, pg. 922
GENERAL MILLS IBERICA, S.A.U.—See General Mills, Inc.; *U.S. Public*, pg. 922
GENERAL MILLS, INC.; *U.S. Public*, pg. 921
GENERAL MILLS INDIA PRIVATE LIMITED—See General Mills, Inc.; *U.S. Public*, pg. 922
GENERAL MILLS INTERNATIONAL BUSINESSES, INC.—See General Mills, Inc.; *U.S. Public*, pg. 921
GENERAL MILLS INTERNATIONAL SARL—See General Mills, Inc.; *U.S. Public*, pg. 921
GENERAL MILLS ISRAEL LTD.—See General Mills, Inc.; *U.S. Public*, pg. 922
GENERAL MILLS KOREA CO. LTD.—See General Mills, Inc.; *U.S. Public*, pg. 922
GENERAL MILLS MALAYSIA SDN. BHD.—See General Mills, Inc.; *U.S. Public*, pg. 921
GENERAL MILLS MANUFACTURING AUSTRALIA PTY LIMITED—See General Mills, Inc.; *U.S. Public*, pg. 921
GENERAL MILLS MARKETING, INC.—See General Mills, Inc.; *U.S. Public*, pg. 921
GENERAL MILLS MIDDLE EAST & NORTH AFRICA FZE—See General Mills, Inc.; *U.S. Public*, pg. 921

GENERAL MILLS NEW ZEALAND LIMITED—See General Mills, Inc.; *U.S. Public*, pg. 921
GENERAL MILLS OPERATIONS, INC.—See General Mills, Inc.; *U.S. Public*, pg. 922
GENERAL MILLS SALES SINGAPORE PTE. LTD.—See General Mills, Inc.; *U.S. Public*, pg. 921
GENERAL MILLS SAN ADRIAN, S.L. UNIPERSONAL—See General Mills, Inc.; *U.S. Public*, pg. 921
GENERAL MILLS SCANDINAVIA AB—See General Mills, Inc.; *U.S. Public*, pg. 921
GENERAL MILLS SINGAPORE PTE. LTD.—See General Mills, Inc.; *U.S. Public*, pg. 921
GENERAL MILLS—See General Mills, Inc.; *U.S. Public*, pg. 921
GENERAL MILLS—See General Mills, Inc.; *U.S. Public*, pg. 922
GENERAL MILLS—See General Mills, Inc.; *U.S. Public*, pg. 922
GENERAL MILLS—See General Mills, Inc.; *U.S. Public*, pg. 921
GENERAL MILLS—See General Mills, Inc.; *U.S. Public*, pg. 921
GENERAL MILLS SOUTH AFRICA (PTY) LTD.—See General Mills, Inc.; *U.S. Public*, pg. 922
GENERAL MILLS TAIWAN LIMITED—See General Mills, Inc.; *U.S. Public*, pg. 922
GENERAL MILLS UK LTD.—See General Mills, Inc.; *U.S. Public*, pg. 922
GENERAL MILLS - WELLSTON PLANT—See General Mills, Inc.; *U.S. Public*, pg. 922
GENERAL MINING; *Int'l*, pg. 2919
GENERAL MOLY, INC.; *U.S. Private*, pg. 1666
GENERAL MONITORS INC.—See MSA Safety Incorporated; *U.S. Public*, pg. 1481
GENERAL MONITORS IRELAND LIMITED—See MSA Safety Incorporated; *U.S. Public*, pg. 1481
GENERAL MOTORS ASIA PACIFIC HOLDINGS, LLC—See General Motors Company; *U.S. Public*, pg. 924
GENERAL MOTORS ASIA PACIFIC (PTE) LTD.—See General Motors Company; *U.S. Public*, pg. 924
GENERAL MOTORS ASSET MANAGEMENT CORPORATION—See General Motors Company; *U.S. Public*, pg. 924
GENERAL MOTORS AUSTRIA GMBH—See General Motors Company; *U.S. Public*, pg. 927
GENERAL MOTORS AUTOMOBILES PHILIPPINES, INC.—See General Motors Company; *U.S. Public*, pg. 924
GENERAL MOTORS BELGIUM N.V.—See General Motors Company; *U.S. Public*, pg. 927
GENERAL MOTORS BENELUX—See General Motors Company; *U.S. Public*, pg. 927
GENERAL MOTORS CANADA COMPONENTS DIV.—See General Motors Company; *U.S. Public*, pg. 925
GENERAL MOTORS CANADA ENGINE DIV.—See General Motors Company; *U.S. Public*, pg. 925
GENERAL MOTORS CANADA TRANSMISSION DIV.—See General Motors Company; *U.S. Public*, pg. 925
GENERAL MOTORS CHILE INDUSTRIA AUTOMOTRIZ LIMITADA—See General Motors Company; *U.S. Public*, pg. 924
GENERAL MOTORS CHILE S.A., INDUSTRIA AUTOMOTRIZ—See General Motors Company; *U.S. Public*, pg. 924
GENERAL MOTORS COLMOTORES, S.A.—See General Motors Company; *U.S. Public*, pg. 924
GENERAL MOTORS COMPANY; *U.S. Public*, pg. 923
GENERAL MOTORS CONTINENTAL—See General Motors Company; *U.S. Public*, pg. 927
GENERAL MOTORS DE ARGENTINA S.R.L.—See General Motors Company; *U.S. Public*, pg. 925
GENERAL MOTORS DEL ECUADOR S.A.—See General Motors Company; *U.S. Public*, pg. 924
GENERAL MOTORS DE MEXICO, S.A. DE C.V.—See General Motors Company; *U.S. Public*, pg. 925
GENERAL MOTORS DE PORTUGAL, SOCIEDADE ANONIMA—See General Motors Company; *U.S. Public*, pg. 927
GENERAL MOTORS DO BRASIL LTDA.—See General Motors Company; *U.S. Public*, pg. 925
GENERAL MOTORS EGYPT S.A.E.—See General Motors Company; *U.S. Public*, pg. 927
GENERAL MOTORS ESPANA S.L.—See General Motors Company; *U.S. Public*, pg. 927
GENERAL MOTORS EUROPE HOLDINGS, S.L.—See General Motors Company; *U.S. Public*, pg. 927
GENERAL MOTORS FINANCIAL COMPANY, INC.—See General Motors Company; *U.S. Public*, pg. 924
GENERAL MOTORS FINANCIAL OF CANADA LIMITED—See General Motors Company; *U.S. Public*, pg. 925
GENERAL MOTORS FINANCIAL SUISSE SA—See General Motors Company; *U.S. Public*, pg. 925
GENERAL MOTORS FINLAND OY—See General Motors Company; *U.S. Public*, pg. 927

COMPANY NAME INDEX

GENERAL MOTORS FRANCE AUTOMOBILES S.A.—See General Motors Company; *U.S. Public*, pg. 927
GENERAL MOTORS GLOBAL SERVICE OPERATIONS, INC.—See General Motors Company; *U.S. Public*, pg. 925
GENERAL MOTORS HELLAS S.A.—See General Motors Company; *U.S. Public*, pg. 927
GENERAL MOTORS HOLDINGS LLC—See General Motors Company; *U.S. Public*, pg. 925
GENERAL MOTORS INDIA PRIVATE LIMITED—See General Motors Company; *U.S. Public*, pg. 925
GENERAL MOTORS INTERNATIONAL HOLDINGS, INC.—See General Motors Company; *U.S. Public*, pg. 925
GENERAL MOTORS JAPAN LIMITED—See General Motors Company; *U.S. Public*, pg. 925
GENERAL MOTORS MANUFACTURING POLAND SP. Z O.O.—See General Motors Company; *U.S. Public*, pg. 927
GENERAL MOTORS NEDERLAND B.V.—See General Motors Company; *U.S. Public*, pg. 927
GENERAL MOTORS OF CANADA COMPANY—See General Motors Company; *U.S. Public*, pg. 925
GENERAL MOTORS OVERSEAS DISTRIBUTION LLC—See General Motors Company; *U.S. Public*, pg. 925
GENERAL MOTORS PERU S.A.—See General Motors Company; *U.S. Public*, pg. 925
GENERAL MOTORS POLAND SPOLKA, Z O. O.—See General Motors Company; *U.S. Public*, pg. 927
GENERAL MOTORS PORTUGAL LDA.—See General Motors Company; *U.S. Public*, pg. 927
GENERAL MOTORS POWERTRAIN - GERMANY GMBH—See General Motors Company; *U.S. Public*, pg. 927
GENERAL MOTORS POWERTRAIN (THAILAND) LIMITED—See General Motors Company; *U.S. Public*, pg. 925
GENERAL MOTORS R*WORKS—See The Interpublic Group of Companies, Inc.; *U.S. Public*, pg. 2093
GENERAL MOTORS (THAILAND) LIMITED—See General Motors Company; *U.S. Public*, pg. 924
GENERAL MOTORS TRKIYE LIMITED SIRKETI—See General Motors Company; *U.S. Public*, pg. 925
GENERAL NAVIGATION AND COMMERCE COMPANY (GENAVCO) L.L.C—See Juma Al Majid Group; *Int'l*, pg. 4025
GENERAL NICE DEVELOPMENT LIMITED; *Int'l*, pg. 2919
GENERAL NIPPON CONCRETE INDUSTRIES LIMITED—See General Engineering Public Company Limited; *Int'l*, pg. 2918
GENERAL NOLI S.L.—See Savino Del Bene S.p.A.; *Int'l*, pg. 6600
GENERAL NOLI SPEDIZIONI INTERNAZIONALI SPA—See Savino Del Bene S.p.A.; *Int'l*, pg. 6600
GENERAL NOVELTY LTD.; *U.S. Private*, pg. 1666
GENERAL NUTRITION CENTERS, INC.—See Ares Management Corporation; *U.S. Public*, pg. 189
GENERAL NUTRITION CENTERS, INC.—See Ontario Teachers' Pension Plan; *Int'l*, pg. 5589
GENERAL NUTRITION CENTRES COMPANY—See Ares Management Corporation; *U.S. Public*, pg. 189
GENERAL NUTRITION CENTRES COMPANY—See Ontario Teachers' Pension Plan; *Int'l*, pg. 5589
GENERAL NUTRITION INVESTMENT COMPANY—See Ares Management Corporation; *U.S. Public*, pg. 189
GENERAL NUTRITION INVESTMENT COMPANY—See Ontario Teachers' Pension Plan; *Int'l*, pg. 5589
GENERAL OCEANS AS; *Int'l*, pg. 2919
GENERAL OFFICE INTERIORS, INC.—See Officeworks, Inc.; *U.S. Private*, pg. 3002
GENERAL OPTICA S.A.—See De Rigo S.p.A.; *Int'l*, pg. 1997
GENERAL OYSTER, INC.; *Int'l*, pg. 2919
GENERAL PACKAGING CORPORATION; *U.S. Private*, pg. 1666
GENERAL PACKAGING PRODUCTS INC.; *U.S. Private*, pg. 1666
GENERAL PACKER AMERICA CORPORATION—See General Packer Co., Ltd.; *Int'l*, pg. 2919
GENERAL PACKER CHINA CO., LTD.—See General Packer Co., Ltd.; *Int'l*, pg. 2919
GENERAL PACKER CO., LTD.; *Int'l*, pg. 2919
GENERAL PARTS, INC.—See Advance Auto Parts, Inc.; *U.S. Public*, pg. 45
GENERAL PARTS INTERNATIONAL, INC.—See Advance Auto Parts, Inc.; *U.S. Public*, pg. 44
GENERAL PARTS, LLC—See Berkshire Partners LLC; *U.S. Private*, pg. 535
GENERAL PARTS OF MINNESOTA INC.; *U.S. Private*, pg. 1666
GENERAL PATTERN CO. INC.; *U.S. Private*, pg. 1666
GENERAL PAYMENT SYSTEMS, INC.; *U.S. Public*, pg. 929
GENERAL PENCIL COMPANY; *U.S. Private*, pg. 1666
GENERAL PENCIL CO.—See General Pencil Company; *U.S. Private*, pg. 1666
GENERAL PENSION PLANNING CORP.—See TWG Benefits, Inc.; *U.S. Private*, pg. 4264

GENERAL PERFUME & COSMETICS DISTRIBUTORS INC.; *U.S. Private*, pg. 1666
GENERAL PETROLEUM INCORPORATED; *U.S. Private*, pg. 1666
GENERAL PET SUPPLY, INC.—See Central Garden & Pet Company; *U.S. Public*, pg. 473
GENERAL PHOTONICS CORPORATION—See Luna Innovations Incorporated; *U.S. Public*, pg. 1348
GENERAL PHYSICS (UK) LTD.—See Learning Technologies Group plc; *Int'l*, pg. 4435
GENERAL PLASTIC INDUSTRIAL CO., LTD.; *Int'l*, pg. 2919
GENERAL PLASTICS & COMPOSITES LP; *U.S. Private*, pg. 1666
GENERAL PLASTICS GROUP, INC.—See PMC Capital Partners, LLC; *U.S. Private*, pg. 3217
GENERAL PLASTICS MANUFACTURING COMPANY; *U.S. Private*, pg. 1666
GENERAL PLUG & MANUFACTURING CO.; *U.S. Private*, pg. 1666
GENERAL PLUMBING SUPPLY COMPANY INC.; *U.S. Private*, pg. 1666
GENERAL PLUMBING SUPPLY; *U.S. Private*, pg. 1666
GENERALPLUS TECHNOLOGY (H.K.) CO., LIMITED.—See Generalplus Technology Inc.; *Int'l*, pg. 2920
GENERALPLUS TECHNOLOGY INC.; *Int'l*, pg. 2920
GENERALPLUS TECHNOLOGY (SHENZHEN) INC.—See Generalplus Technology Inc.; *Int'l*, pg. 2920
GENERAL POLYMERIC CORP.; *U.S. Private*, pg. 1666
GENERAL PRODUCE CO. LTD.; *U.S. Private*, pg. 1666
GENERAL PRODUCTS PARTNERS INC.; *U.S. Private*, pg. 1666
GENERAL PROPELLER COMPANY, INC.; *U.S. Private*, pg. 1666
GENERAL PUMP INC.—See Interpump Group S.p.A.; *Int'l*, pg. 3755
GENERAL PURPOSE STEEL INC.; *U.S. Private*, pg. 1667
GENERAL QUIMICA, S.A.—See Repsol, S.A.; *Int'l*, pg. 6293
GENERAL REAL ESTATE COMPANY S.P.C.—See Qatar General Insurance and Reinsurance Company S.A.Q.; *Int'l*, pg. 6133
GENERAL RE AUSTRALIA LTD.—See Berkshire Hathaway Inc.; *U.S. Public*, pg. 302
GENERAL RE BEIRUT S.A.L.—See Berkshire Hathaway Inc.; *U.S. Public*, pg. 301
GENERAL RE CORPORATION—See Berkshire Hathaway Inc.; *U.S. Public*, pg. 301
GENERAL REINSURANCE AFRICA LTD.—See Berkshire Hathaway Inc.; *U.S. Public*, pg. 301
GENERAL REINSURANCE AG—See Berkshire Hathaway Inc.; *U.S. Public*, pg. 301
GENERAL REINSURANCE AG—See Berkshire Hathaway Inc.; *U.S. Public*, pg. 306
GENERAL REINSURANCE AUSTRALIA LTD.—See Berkshire Hathaway Inc.; *U.S. Public*, pg. 302
GENERAL REINSURANCE AUSTRALIA LTD.—See Berkshire Hathaway Inc.; *U.S. Public*, pg. 302
GENERAL REINSURANCE CORPORATION—See Berkshire Hathaway Inc.; *U.S. Public*, pg. 301
GENERAL REINSURANCE CORPORATION—See Berkshire Hathaway Inc.; *U.S. Public*, pg. 302
GENERAL REINSURANCE CORPORATION—See Berkshire Hathaway Inc.; *U.S. Public*, pg. 302
GENERAL REINSURANCE CORPORATION—See Berkshire Hathaway Inc.; *U.S. Public*, pg. 302
GENERAL REINSURANCE CORPORATION—See Berkshire Hathaway Inc.; *U.S. Public*, pg. 302
GENERAL REINSURANCE CORPORATION—See Berkshire Hathaway Inc.; *U.S. Public*, pg. 302
GENERAL REINSURANCE CORPORATION—See Berkshire Hathaway Inc.; *U.S. Public*, pg. 302
GENERAL REINSURANCE CORPORATION—See Berkshire Hathaway Inc.; *U.S. Public*, pg. 302
GENERAL REINSURANCE CORPORATION—See Berkshire Hathaway Inc.; *U.S. Public*, pg. 302
GENERAL REINSURANCE CORPORATION—See Berkshire Hathaway Inc.; *U.S. Public*, pg. 302
GENERAL REINSURANCE CORPORATION—See Berkshire Hathaway Inc.; *U.S. Public*, pg. 302
GENERAL REINSURANCE CORPORATION—See Berkshire Hathaway Inc.; *U.S. Public*, pg. 302
GENERAL REINSURANCE LIFE AUSTRALIA LTD.—See Berkshire Hathaway Inc.; *U.S. Public*, pg. 302
GENERAL REINSURANCE SCANDINAVIA A/S—See Berkshire Hathaway Inc.; *U.S. Public*, pg. 301
GENERAL REINSURANCE UK LIMITED—See Berkshire Hathaway Inc.; *U.S. Public*, pg. 302
GENERAL RE LIFE CORPORATION—See Berkshire Hathaway Inc.; *U.S. Public*, pg. 306
GENERAL RE RIGA SIA—See Berkshire Hathaway Inc.; *U.S. Public*, pg. 301
GENERAL RESOURCE TECHNOLOGY, INC.—See Mapei SpA; *Int'l*, pg. 4682
GENERAL REVENUE CORPORATION—See SinglePoint Group International, Inc.; *Int'l*, pg. 6944

GENERAL TRANSPORT SA

GENERAL ROBOTIX, INC.—See Kawada Technologies Inc.; *Int'l*, pg. 4093
GENERAL RUBBER CO.—See Minnesota Flexible Corp.; *U.S. Private*, pg. 2743
GENERAL RUBBER PLASTICS OF LOUISVILLE; *U.S. Private*, pg. 1667
GENERAL RV CENTER INC.; *U.S. Private*, pg. 1667
GENERAL SALES COMPANY OF WEST CHESTER, INC.—See General Motors Company; *U.S. Public*, pg. 925
GENERAL SCIENTIFIC SAFETY EQUIPMENT CO.; *U.S. Private*, pg. 1667
GENERAL SECURITIES CORP.—See Assicurazioni Generali S.p.A.; *Int'l*, pg. 644
GENERAL SECURITY, INC.; *U.S. Private*, pg. 1667
GENERAL SECURITY SERVICES CORPORATION; *U.S. Private*, pg. 1667
GENERAL SEMICONDUCTOR (CHINA) CO., LTD.—See Vishay Intertechnology, Inc.; *U.S. Public*, pg. 2302
GENERAL SERVICES CORPORATION (GSC); *U.S. Private*, pg. 1667
GENERAL SERVICES, INC.—See AEON Co., Ltd.; *Int'l*, pg. 177
GENERAL SHALE BRICK, INC.—See Wienerberger AG; *Int'l*, pg. 8405
GENERAL SHALE BRICK INC.—See Wienerberger AG; *Int'l*, pg. 8405
GENERAL SHOPPING E OUTLETS DO BRASIL S.A.; *Int'l*, pg. 2919
GENERAL SOUTHWEST INSURANCE AGENCY, INC.—See Arthur J. Gallagher & Co.; *U.S. Public*, pg. 205
GENERAL SPORTS & ENTERTAINMENT, LLC; *U.S. Private*, pg. 1667
GENERAL SPORTSWEAR CO. INC.; *U.S. Private*, pg. 1667
GENERAL STAR INDEMNITY COMPANY—See Berkshire Hathaway Inc.; *U.S. Public*, pg. 301
GENERAL STAR NATIONAL INSURANCE COMPANY—See Berkshire Hathaway Inc.; *U.S. Public*, pg. 301
GENERAL STEAMSHIP AGENCIES; *U.S. Private*, pg. 1667
GENERAL STEEL DRUM LLC—See Myers Container, LLC; *U.S. Private*, pg. 2824
GENERAL STEEL HOLDINGS, INC.; *Int'l*, pg. 2920
GENERAL STEEL INC.; *U.S. Private*, pg. 1667
GENERAL STEEL & SUPPLY CO., INC.—See Fisher Industries; *U.S. Private*, pg. 1534
GENERAL STORAGE COMPANY PTE. LTD.—See Singapore Post Limited; *Int'l*, pg. 6942
GENERAL SULLIVAN CORP.—See General Sullivan Group Inc.; *U.S. Private*, pg. 1667
GENERAL SULLIVAN GROUP INC.; *U.S. Private*, pg. 1667
GENERAL SUPPLY COMPANY; *U.S. Private*, pg. 1667
GENERAL SURGEONS OF PASADENA, PLLC—See HCA Healthcare, Inc.; *U.S. Public*, pg. 996
GENERAL SURGERY OF JUPITER MEDICAL SPECIALISTS, LLC—See KKR & Co. Inc.; *U.S. Public*, pg. 1245
GENERAL TAKAFUL COMPANY S.P.C.—See Qatar General Insurance and Reinsurance Company S.A.Q.; *Int'l*, pg. 6133
GENERAL TANK CONTAINERS CO., LTD.—See Yongtaiyun Chemical Logistics Co., Ltd.; *Int'l*, pg. 8597
GENERAL TANK CONTAINERS (SHANGHAI) CO., LTD.—See Yongtaiyun Chemical Logistics Co., Ltd.; *Int'l*, pg. 8597
GENERAL TECHNOLOGY, INC.—See UCA Group Component Specialty Inc.; *U.S. Private*, pg. 4273
GENERAL TECHNOLOGY S.R.L.—See Interpump Group S.p.A.; *Int'l*, pg. 3755
GENERAL TELEVISION CORPORATION PTY. LIMITED—See Nine Entertainment Co. Holdings Limited; *Int'l*, pg. 5299
GENERAL TOOL COMPANY INC.; *U.S. Private*, pg. 1667
GENERAL TOOLS & INSTRUMENTS COMPANY LLC—See Worthington Industries, Inc.; *U.S. Public*, pg. 2382
GENERAL TOOL & SUPPLY CO. INC.—See Genuine Parts Company; *U.S. Public*, pg. 933
GENERAL TOURS WORLD TRAVELER, INC.; *U.S. Private*, pg. 1667
GENERAL TRADING & CHEMICALS CO.—See Chemical Industries Holding Company; *Int'l*, pg. 1462
GENERAL TRADING CO., INC.; *U.S. Private*, pg. 1667
GENERAL TRADING COMPANY—See The Olayan Group; *Int'l*, pg. 7672
GENERAL TRAILER PARTS LLC; *U.S. Private*, pg. 1667
GENERAL TRANSERVICE INC.—See Global Capital Corp.; *U.S. Private*, pg. 1712
GENERAL TRANSPORTATION, INC.; *U.S. Private*, pg. 1667
GENERAL TRANSPORTATION SERVICES; *U.S. Private*, pg. 1667
GENERAL TRANSPORT EQUIPMENT PTY. LTD.—See CIMC Vehicle (Group) Co., Ltd.; *Int'l*, pg. 1608
GENERAL TRANSPORT SA; *Int'l*, pg. 2920

1069

GENERAL TRUCK EQUIPMENT & TRAILER SALES

GENERAL TRUCK EQUIPMENT & TRAILER SALES; *U.S. Private*, pg. 1667
GENERAL TRUCK PARTS & EQUIPMENT CO.; *U.S. Private*, pg. 1667
GENERAL TRUCK SALES & SERVICE; *U.S. Private*, pg. 1667
GENERAL TYRE EAST AFRICA LTD.—See Continental Aktiengesellschaft; *Int'l*, pg. 1783
THE GENERAL TYRE & RUBBER COMPANY OF PAKISTAN LIMITED; *Int'l*, pg. 7649
GENERAL WAX CO. INC.; *U.S. Private*, pg. 1668
GENERAL WELDING WORKS INC.; *U.S. Private*, pg. 1668
GENERAL WHOLESALE COMPANY, INC.; *U.S. Private*, pg. 1668
GENERAL WHOLESALE COMPANY, INC.—See General Wholesale Company, Inc.; *U.S. Private*, pg. 1668
GENERAL WHOLESALE COMPANY—See General Wholesale Company, Inc.; *U.S. Private*, pg. 1668
GENERAL WHOLESALE DISTRIBUTORS; *U.S. Private*, pg. 1668
GENERAL WIRELESS OPERATIONS INC.—See Standard General LP; *U.S. Private*, pg. 3778
GENERAL WOODWORKING INC.; *U.S. Private*, pg. 1668
GENERAL WORK PRODUCTS, INC.—See Altamont Capital Partners; *U.S. Private*, pg. 204
GENERAL WORKS, LLC—See Altas Partners LP; *Int'l*, pg. 386
GENERA PHARMA D.O.O.—See EQT AB; *Int'l*, pg. 2474
GENERA SOLUTIONS LP—See The Jim Pattison Group; *Int'l*, pg. 7660
GENERA TECHNOLOGIES LIMITED—See Severn Trent Plc; *Int'l*, pg. 6735
GENERATE, INC.—See News Corporation; *U.S. Public*, pg. 1518
GENERATE LIFE SCIENCES, INC.—See The Cooper Companies, Inc.; *U.S. Public*, pg. 2066
GENERATION 3 CAPITAL, LLC; *U.S. Private*, pg. 1668
GENERATION AGGREGATES - ASH PRODUCTS—See RWE AG; *Int'l*, pg. 6435
GENERATIONAL CAPITAL, LLC—See Generational Equity Group, Inc.; *U.S. Private*, pg. 1668
GENERATIONAL EQUITY GROUP, INC.; *U.S. Private*, pg. 1668
GENERATIONAL EQUITY, LLC—See Generational Equity Group, Inc.; *U.S. Private*, pg. 1668
GENERATION ALPHA, INC.; *U.S. Public*, pg. 929
GENERATION BIO CO.; *U.S. Public*, pg. 929
GENERATION BRANDS LLC—See AEA Investors LP; *U.S. Private*, pg. 114
GENERATION CAPITAL LTD.; *Int'l*, pg. 2920
GENERATION DEVELOPMENT COMPANY, LLC—See Black Hills Corporation; *U.S. Public*, pg. 341
GENERATION DEVELOPMENT GROUP; *Int'l*, pg. 2920
GENERATIONE CONSULTING, LLC—See Lotus Innovations LLC; *U.S. Private*, pg. 2497
GENERATION GROWTH CAPITAL, INC.; *U.S. Private*, pg. 1668
GENERATION INCOME PROPERTIES, INC.; *U.S. Public*, pg. 929
GENERATION INVESTMENT MANAGEMENT LLP; *Int'l*, pg. 2920
GENERATION MINING LTD.—See Herkules S.A.; *Int'l*, pg. 3362
GENERATION NEXT FASHIONS LIMITED; *Int'l*, pg. 2920
GENERATION NEXT FRANCHISE BRANDS, INC.; *U.S. Private*, pg. 1668
GENERATION PARTNERS; *U.S. Private*, pg. 1668
GENERATION PASS CO., LTD.; *Int'l*, pg. 2920
GENERATIONS AGENCY, INC.—See Generations Bancorp NY, Inc.; *U.S. Public*, pg. 930
GENERATIONS BANCORP NY, INC.; *U.S. Public*, pg. 929
GENERATIONS BANK—See Generations Bancorp NY, Inc.; *U.S. Public*, pg. 930
GENERATIONS BEHAVIORAL HEALTH, LLC—See Acadia Healthcare Company, Inc.; *U.S. Public*, pg. 29
GENERATIONS FAMILY HEALTH CENTER, INC.; *U.S. Private*, pg. 1668
GENERATIONS GROUP OF COMPANIES INC.—See Genesis Land Development Corp.; *Int'l*, pg. 2921
GENERATIONS IN AVIATION, INC.—See Atlantic Street Capital Management LLC; *U.S. Private*, pg. 374
GENERATION UK LIMITED—See Altrad Investment Authority SAS; *Int'l*, pg. 398
GENERATION VIE S.A.—See Allianz SE; *Int'l*, pg. 353
GENERATION ZERO GROUP, INC.; *U.S. Private*, pg. 1668
GENERATIVE AI SOLUTIONS CORP.; *Int'l*, pg. 2920
GENERATOR & MOTOR SERVICES OF PENNSYLVANIA LLC—See Melrose Industries PLC; *Int'l*, pg. 4813
GENERATOR SOURCE, LLC—See Regent Square Capital, LLC; *U.S. Private*, pg. 3387
GENEREACH BIOTECHNOLOGY CORP.; *Int'l*, pg. 2920
GENEREX BIOTECHNOLOGY CORPORATION; *U.S. Public*, pg. 930
GENERFID S.P.A.—See Assicurazioni Generali S.p.A.; *Int'l*, pg. 643
GENERIC ENGINEERING CONSTRUCTION AND PROJECTS LIMITED; *Int'l*, pg. 2920

GENERIC GOLD CORP.; *Int'l*, pg. 2920
GENERIC HEALTH PTY LTD.—See Lupin Limited; *Int'l*, pg. 4586
GENERICS HOLDING GMBH—See Bayer Aktiengesellschaft; *Int'l*, pg. 905
GENERIC SOFTWARE CONSULTANTS LIMITED—See Triad Group plc; *Int'l*, pg. 7918
GENERIC VALUE PRODUCTS, INC.—See Sally Beauty Holdings, Inc.; *U.S. Public*, pg. 1838
GENERIS FARMACEUTICA, S.A.—See Aurobindo Pharma Ltd.; *Int'l*, pg. 713
GENERIS PHAR, UNIPESSOAL LD WOS—See Aurobindo Pharma Ltd.; *Int'l*, pg. 713
GENERIX GROUP FRANCE SA; *Int'l*, pg. 2921
GENERSOL, S.A.—See Ecoener, S.A.; *Int'l*, pg. 2295
GENERTECH PAKISTAN LIMITED; *Int'l*, pg. 2921
GENERTEC MEHECO TIBET ZHONGJIAN CO., LTD.—See China Meheco Group Co., Ltd.; *Int'l*, pg. 1519
GENERTEC UNIVERSAL MEDICAL GROUP COMPANY LIMITED; *Int'l*, pg. 2921
GENERTEL BIZTOSITO ZRT—See Assicurazioni Generali S.p.A.; *Int'l*, pg. 646
GENERTELLIFE S.P.A.—See Assicurazioni Generali S.p.A.; *Int'l*, pg. 647
GENERTEL SERVIZI ASSICURATIVI S.R.L.—See Assicurazioni Generali S.p.A.; *Int'l*, pg. 647
GENERTEL S.P.A.—See Assicurazioni Generali S.p.A.; *Int'l*, pg. 647
GENESAR INC.; *U.S. Private*, pg. 1668
THE GENE SCHICK COMPANY—See Viking Range, LLC; *U.S. Private*, pg. 4382
GENESCIENCE PHARMACEUTICALS CO., LTD.—See Changchun High & New Technology Industry (Group) Inc.; *Int'l*, pg. 1442
GENESCO BRANDS, LLC—See Genesco Inc.; *U.S. Public*, pg. 930
GENESCO INC.; *U.S. Public*, pg. 930
GENESCO MERGER COMPANY, INC.—See Genesco Inc.; *U.S. Public*, pg. 930
GENESEAS AQUACULTURA LTDA.; *Int'l*, pg. 2921
GENESEE A & B, INC.—See Genesee Group, Inc.; *U.S. Private*, pg. 1669
GENESEE BREWING COMPANY—See Florida Ice and Farm Co. S.A.; *Int'l*, pg. 2707
GENESEE CERAMIC TILE DISTRIBUTORS; *U.S. Private*, pg. 1669
GENESEE CUT STONE & MARBLE CO.; *U.S. Private*, pg. 1669
GENESEE GLOBAL GROUP, INC.—See Genesee Group, Inc.; *U.S. Private*, pg. 1669
GENESEE GROUP, INC.; *U.S. Private*, pg. 1669
GENESEEK, INC.—See Neogen Corporation; *U.S. Public*, pg. 1505
GENESEE PACKAGING INC.; *U.S. Private*, pg. 1669
GENESEE POWER STATION LIMITED PARTNERSHIP—See CMS Energy Corporation; *U.S. Public*, pg. 519
GENESEE STAMPING & FABRICATING, INC.—See Genesee Group, Inc.; *U.S. Private*, pg. 1669
GENESEE & WYOMING AUSTRALIA PTY LTD—See Brookfield Infrastructure Partners L.P.; *Int'l*, pg. 1191
GENESEE & WYOMING AUSTRALIA PTY LTD—See GIC Pte. Ltd.; *Int'l*, pg. 2966
GENESEE & WYOMING CANADA INC.—See Brookfield Infrastructure Partners L.P.; *Int'l*, pg. 1191
GENESEE & WYOMING CANADA INC.—See GIC Pte. Ltd.; *Int'l*, pg. 2966
GENESEE & WYOMING INC.—See Brookfield Infrastructure Partners L.P.; *Int'l*, pg. 1190
GENESEE & WYOMING INC.—See GIC Pte. Ltd.; *Int'l*, pg. 2965
GENESEE & WYOMING RAILROAD COMPANY—See Brookfield Infrastructure Partners L.P.; *Int'l*, pg. 1191
GENESEE & WYOMING RAILROAD COMPANY—See GIC Pte. Ltd.; *Int'l*, pg. 2966
GENESEE & WYOMING RAILROAD SERVICES, INC.—See Brookfield Infrastructure Partners L.P.; *Int'l*, pg. 1191
GENESEE & WYOMING RAILROAD SERVICES, INC.—See GIC Pte. Ltd.; *Int'l*, pg. 2966
GENESEM INC.; *Int'l*, pg. 2921
GENE SHEARS—See Groupe Limagrain Holding SA; *Int'l*, pg. 3107
GENESIS ABSTRACT, LLC—See Old Republic International Corporation; *U.S. Public*, pg. 1567
GENESIS ACQUISITION CORP.; *Int'l*, pg. 2921
GENESIS ALKALI WYOMING, LP—See Genesis Energy, L.P.; *U.S. Public*, pg. 930
GENESIS ALLOYS (NINGBO) LIMITED—See Lee Kee Holdings Limited; *Int'l*, pg. 4440
GENESIS ARCHITECTURE LLC—See Welsh Companies LLC; *U.S. Private*, pg. 4479
GENESIS ASC PARTNERS, LLC—See Tenet Healthcare Corporation; *U.S. Public*, pg. 2010
GENESIS ATC; *U.S. Private*, pg. 1669
GENESIS ATTACHMENTS, LLC—See Nippon Pneumatic Mfg. Co., Ltd.; *Int'l*, pg. 5329

CORPORATE AFFILIATIONS

GENESIS BIOTECHNOLOGY GROUP, LLC; *U.S. Private*, pg. 1669
GENESIS BUILDERS GROUP INC—See Genesis Land Development Corp.; *Int'l*, pg. 2921
GENESIS BURSON-MARSTELLER—See WPP plc; *Int'l*, pg. 8468
GENESIS BURSON-MARSTELLER—See WPP plc; *Int'l*, pg. 8468
GENESIS BURSON-MARSTELLER—See WPP plc; *Int'l*, pg. 8468
GENESIS CAPITAL REAL ESTATE ADVISORS, INC.—See Rithm Capital Corp.; *U.S. Public*, pg. 1800
GENESIS CAPITAL S.R.O.; *Int'l*, pg. 2921
GENESIS CAREGIVERS—See Genesis HealthCare System; *U.S. Private*, pg. 1669
GENESIS CARE PTY. LTD.—See China Resources (Holdings) Co., Ltd.; *Int'l*, pg. 1548
GENESIS CONSULTING PARTNERS, LLC; *U.S. Private*, pg. 1669
GENESIS CORP.; *U.S. Private*, pg. 1669
GENESIS DRUG DISCOVERY & DEVELOPMENT LLC—See Genesis Biotechnology Group, LLC; *U.S. Private*, pg. 1669
GENESIS ELDERCARE CENTERS - HARSTON, INC.—See Welltower Inc.; *U.S. Public*, pg. 2348
GENESIS ELDERCARE NATIONAL CENTERS, INC.—See Welltower Inc.; *U.S. Public*, pg. 2348
GENESIS ENERGIES CONSULTANTS LTD.—See Technip Energies N.V.; *Int'l*, pg. 7506
GENESIS ENERGY LIMITED; *Int'l*, pg. 2921
GENESIS ENERGY, L.P.; *U.S. Public*, pg. 930
GENESIS EUROPE GMBH & CO. KG—See Nippon Pneumatic Mfg. Co., Ltd.; *Int'l*, pg. 5329
GENESIS FINANCIAL HOLDINGS LIMITED; *Int'l*, pg. 2921
GENESIS FINANCIAL, INC.—See FDCTECH, INC.; *U.S. Public*, pg. 825
GENESIS FINANCIAL SOLUTIONS, INC.—See Castlelake, L.P.; *U.S. Private*, pg. 785
GENESIS FORWARDING GROUP LIMITED—See Japan Post Holdings Co., Ltd.; *Int'l*, pg. 3902
GENESIS GROUP INC; *U.S. Private*, pg. 1669
THE GENESIS GROUP; *U.S. Private*, pg. 4032
GENESIS GROWTH TECH ACQUISITION CORP.; *Int'l*, pg. 2921
GENESIS HC LLC—See Welltower Inc.; *U.S. Public*, pg. 2348
GENESIS HEALTHCARE CORPORATION—See Formation Capital, LLC; *U.S. Private*, pg. 1569
GENESIS HEALTHCARE CORPORATION - WESTERN DIVISION—See Formation Capital, LLC; *U.S. Private*, pg. 1570
GENESIS HEALTHCARE, INC.—See Formation Capital, LLC; *U.S. Private*, pg. 1569
GENESIS HEALTHCARE, LLC- SILVER LAKE CENTER—See Welltower Inc.; *U.S. Public*, pg. 2348
GENESIS HEALTHCARE LOPATCONG CENTER—See Formation Capital, LLC; *U.S. Private*, pg. 1570
GENESIS HEALTHCARE-PHILLIPSBURG CENTER—See Formation Capital, LLC; *U.S. Private*, pg. 1570
GENESIS HEALTHCARE SYSTEM; *U.S. Private*, pg. 1669
GENESIS HEALTH, INC.; *U.S. Private*, pg. 1669
GENESIS HEALTH VENTURES OF WILKES-BARRE, INC.—See Welltower Inc.; *U.S. Public*, pg. 2348
GENESIS IBRC INDIA LIMITED; *Int'l*, pg. 2921
GENESIS INDEMNITY INSURANCE COMPANY—See Berkshire Hathaway Inc.; *U.S. Public*, pg. 301
GENESIS INSURANCE BROKERS (KZN) PROPRIETARY LIMITED—See The Bidvest Group Limited; *Int'l*, pg. 7624
GENESIS INSURANCE COMPANY—See Berkshire Hathaway Inc.; *U.S. Public*, pg. 301
GENESIS INVEST AG; *Int'l*, pg. 2921
GENESIS INVESTMENT BANK LIMITED—See Genesis Financial Holdings Limited; *Int'l*, pg. 2921
GENESIS INVESTMENT MANAGEMENT, LLP—See Affiliated Managers Group, Inc.; *U.S. Public*, pg. 55
GENESIS-IT AB—See Stenvalls Tra AB; *Int'l*, pg. 7208
GENESIS LAND DEVELOPMENT CORP.; *Int'l*, pg. 2921
GENESIS LOGISTICS INC. - CHARLESTOWN FACILITY—See Deutsche Post AG; *Int'l*, pg. 2079
GENESIS LOGISTICS INC. - DAYTON FACILITY—See Deutsche Post AG; *Int'l*, pg. 2079
GENESIS LOGISTICS INC. - EAGAN FACILITY—See Deutsche Post AG; *Int'l*, pg. 2079
GENESIS LOGISTICS INC. - FOREST PARK FACILITY—See Deutsche Post AG; *Int'l*, pg. 2079
GENESIS LOGISTICS INC.—See Deutsche Post AG; *Int'l*, pg. 2079
GENESIS MAGNOLIA RIDGE—See Formation Capital, LLC; *U.S. Private*, pg. 1570
GENESIS METALS CORP.—See Northern Superior Resources Inc.; *Int'l*, pg. 5445
GENESIS MICROCHIP INC.—See STMicroelectronics N.V.; *Int'l*, pg. 7218
GENESIS MINERALS LIMITED; *Int'l*, pg. 2921
GENESIS NETWORKS ENTERPRISES, LLC; *U.S. Private*, pg. 1669

GENESIS OIL & GAS CONSULTANTS INC.—See TechnipFMC plc; *Int'l*, pg. 7508
GENESIS OIL & GAS CONSULTANTS LTD—See TechnipFMC plc; *Int'l*, pg. 7508
GENESIS OIL & GAS CONSULTANTS LTD.—See TechnipFMC plc; *Int'l*, pg. 7508
GENESIS OIL & GAS CONSULTANTS—See TechnipFMC plc; *Int'l*, pg. 7508
GENESIS OIL & GAS PTY. LTD.—See TechnipFMC plc; *Int'l*, pg. 7508
GENESIS PARK, LP; *U.S. Private*, pg. 1669
GENESIS PHOTONICS INC.; *Int'l*, pg. 2921
GENESIS PRODUCTS, INC.; *U.S. Private*, pg. 1670
GENESIS PUBLIC RELATIONS PVT LTD—See WPP plc; *Int'l*, pg. 8468
GENESIS PUBLIC RELATIONS PVT LTD—See WPP plc; *Int'l*, pg. 8468
GENESIS REHABILITATION HOSPITAL, INC.—See Genesis Health, Inc.; *U.S. Private*, pg. 1669
GENESIS RESEARCH & DEVELOPMENT CORPORATION LIMITED; *Int'l*, pg. 2921
GENESIS RESOURCES LTD.; *Int'l*, pg. 2922
GENESI S.R.L.—See PAUL HARTMANN AG; *Int'l*, pg. 5760
GENESIS SYSTEMS GROUP, LLC—See IPG Photonics Corporation; *U.S. Public*, pg. 1167
GENESIS SYSTEMS, INC.—See Wynnchurch Capital, L.P.; *U.S. Private*, pg. 4577
GENESIS TECHNOLOGIES, INC.; *U.S. Private*, pg. 1670
GENESIS TODAY INC.; *U.S. Private*, pg. 1670
GENESIS TRANSPORTATION INC.; *U.S. Private*, pg. 1670
GENESIS UNDERWRITING MANAGEMENT COMPANY—See Berkshire Hathaway Inc.; *U.S. Public*, pg. 301
GENESIS UNICORN CAPITAL CORP.; *U.S. Public*, pg. 930
GENESIS VII INC.; *U.S. Private*, pg. 1670
GENEST CONCRETE WORKS INC.; *U.S. Private*, pg. 1670
GENES TECH GROUP HOLDINGS COMPANY LIMITED; *Int'l*, pg. 2921
GENE STEVENS HONDA; *U.S. Private*, pg. 1660
GENES THRIFTWAY INC.—See Garrett Enterprises Inc.; *U.S. Private*, pg. 1645
GENE STIMSON'S OF ARKANSAS; *U.S. Private*, pg. 1660
GENESYS ENGINEERING, P.C.—See Willdan Group, Inc.; *U.S. Public*, pg. 2370
GENESYS ENTERPRISES INC.—See GI Engineering Solutions Limited; *Int'l*, pg. 2960
GENESYS INDUSTRIES INC.; *Int'l*, pg. 2922
GENESYS INTERNATIONAL CORPORATION LTD; *Int'l*, pg. 2922
GENESYS JAPAN CO., LTD.—See Permira Advisers LLP; *Int'l*, pg. 5804
GENESYS LABORATORIES AUSTRALASIA PTY. LTD.—See Permira Advisers LLP; *Int'l*, pg. 5804
GENESYS TELECOMMUNICATION LABORATORIES S.L.—See Permira Advisers LLP; *Int'l*, pg. 5804
GENESYS TELECOMMUNICATIONS LABORATORIES ASIA PTE. LTD.—See Permira Advisers LLP; *Int'l*, pg. 5805
GENESYS TELECOMMUNICATIONS LABORATORIES B.V.—See Permira Advisers LLP; *Int'l*, pg. 5804
GENESYS TELECOMMUNICATIONS LABORATORIES - EUROPE LIMITED—See Permira Advisers LLP; *Int'l*, pg. 5804
GENESYS TELECOMMUNICATIONS LABORATORIES GMBH—See Permira Advisers LLP; *Int'l*, pg. 5805
GENESYS TELECOMMUNICATIONS LABORATORIES, INC.—See Permira Advisers LLP; *Int'l*, pg. 5804
GENESYS TELECOMMUNICATIONS LABORATORIES S.R.L.—See Permira Advisers LLP; *Int'l*, pg. 5805
GENESYS TELECOMMUNICATIONS SAS—See Permira Advisers LLP; *Int'l*, pg. 5805
GENESYSTEM CO., LTD.; *Int'l*, pg. 2922
GENESYSWORKS; *U.S. Private*, pg. 1670
GENE TAYLOR'S SPORTSMEN SUPPLY, INC.; *U.S. Private*, pg. 1660
GENETEC ASIA PACIFIC PTE LTD—See Genetec Inc.; *Int'l*, pg. 2922
GENETEC CORPORATION; *Int'l*, pg. 2922
GENETEC INC.; *Int'l*, pg. 2922
GENETEC TECHNOLOGY BERHAD; *Int'l*, pg. 2922
GENETETHER THERAPEUTICS INC.; *Int'l*, pg. 2922
GENETHERA, INC.; *U.S. Public*, pg. 930
GENETIC ANALYSIS AS; *Int'l*, pg. 2922
GENETIC IMMUNITY, INC.—See Power of the Dream Ventures, Inc.; *Int'l*, pg. 5946
GENETIC LAB CO., LTD.—See Eurofins Scientific S.E.; *Int'l*, pg. 2550
GENETICS GENERATION ADVANCEMENT CORP.; *Int'l*, pg. 2922
GENETICS GENERATION ASIA SDN. BHD.—See Genetics Generation Advancement Corp.; *Int'l*, pg. 2922
GENETIC SIGNATURES LIMITED; *Int'l*, pg. 2922
GENETICS & IVF INSTITUTE, INC.—See Amulet Capital Partners, L.P.; *U.S. Private*, pg. 268

GENETIC TECHNOLOGIES CORPORATION PTY. LTD.—See Genetic Technologies Limited; *Int'l*, pg. 2922
GENETIC TECHNOLOGIES LIMITED; *Int'l*, pg. 2922
GENETIER SAS—See EssilorLuxottica SA; *Int'l*, pg. 2515
GENETIX CORP.—See Danaher Corporation; *U.S. Public*, pg. 627
GENETIX GMBH—See Danaher Corporation; *U.S. Public*, pg. 627
GENET PROPERTY GROUP, INC.; *U.S. Private*, pg. 1670
GENE-TRAK, INC.—See Abbott Laboratories; *U.S. Public*, pg. 20
GENETRON HOLDINGS LIMITED; *Int'l*, pg. 2922
GENETYPE CORPORATION INC.—See Genetic Technologies Limited; *Int'l*, pg. 2922
GENEURO SA; *Int'l*, pg. 2922
GENEVA CAPITAL LIMITED—See Geneva Finance Limited; *Int'l*, pg. 2922
GENEVA CAPITAL MANAGEMENT, LLC—See Janus Henderson Group plc; *Int'l*, pg. 3881
GENEVA CONSULTING GROUP, INC.—See TSR, Inc.; *U.S. Public*, pg. 2202
GENEVA CORPORATION; *U.S. Private*, pg. 1670
GENEVA FINANCE LIMITED; *Int'l*, pg. 2922
THE GENEVA FOUNDATION; *U.S. Private*, pg. 4032
GENEVA INTERNATIONAL CORPORATION; *U.S. Private*, pg. 1670
GENEVA MANAGEMENT INC.; *U.S. Private*, pg. 1670
GENEVA PIPE COMPANY—See Northwest Pipe Company; *U.S. Public*, pg. 1542
GENEVA ROCK PRODUCTS INC.—See Clyde Companies Inc.; *U.S. Private*, pg. 949
GENEVA SCIENTIFIC, INC.—See Argosy Capital Group, LLC; *U.S. Private*, pg. 321
GENEVA SUPPLY, INC.; *U.S. Private*, pg. 1670
GENEVA SURGICAL SUITES, LLC—See Tenet Healthcare Corporation; *U.S. Public*, pg. 2002
GENEVA WATCH GROUP; *U.S. Private*, pg. 1670
GENEVA WOODS PHARMACY, LLC—See CVS Health Corporation; *U.S. Public*, pg. 616
GENEVA WORLDWIDE, INC.; *U.S. Private*, pg. 1670
GENEVE BUTANE INC—See StealthGas Inc.; *Int'l*, pg. 7188
GENEVE CAPITAL GROUP INC.—See Geneve Holdings Corp.; *U.S. Private*, pg. 1670
GENEVE CORPORATION—See Geneve Holdings Corp.; *U.S. Private*, pg. 1670
GENEVE CREDIT & LEASING SA—See BNP Paribas SA; *Int'l*, pg. 1091
GENEVE HOLDINGS CORP.; *U.S. Private*, pg. 1670
GENEVOISE LIFE INSURANCE COMPANY LTD.—See Zurich Insurance Group Limited; *Int'l*, pg. 8697
GENEWEL CO., LTD.—See Dongsung Chemical Co., Ltd.; *Int'l*, pg. 2170
GENEWIZ FRANCE, LTD.—See Azenta, Inc.; *U.S. Public*, pg. 258
GENEWIZ GMBH—See Azenta, Inc.; *U.S. Public*, pg. 258
GENEWIZ (GUANGZHOU), LTD.—See Azenta, Inc.; *U.S. Public*, pg. 258
GENEWIZ, INC.—See Azenta, Inc.; *U.S. Public*, pg. 258
GENEWIZ JAPAN—See Azenta, Inc.; *U.S. Public*, pg. 258
GENEWIZ (SUZHOU), LTD.—See Azenta, Inc.; *U.S. Public*, pg. 258
GENEWIZ TIANJIN, LTD.—See Azenta, Inc.; *U.S. Public*, pg. 258
GENEW TECHNOLOGIES CO., LTD.; *Int'l*, pg. 2922
GENEX CANADA—See Cooperative Resources International Inc.; *U.S. Private*, pg. 1043
GENEX CO., LTD.—See Idemitsu Kosan Co., Ltd.; *Int'l*, pg. 3590
GENEX INC.—See Cooperative Resources International Inc.; *U.S. Private*, pg. 1043
GENEXINE INC. - NEW YORK BRANCH—See Genexine Inc.; *Int'l*, pg. 2923
GENEXINE INC.; *Int'l*, pg. 2923
GENEX INFOSYS LTD.—See China Baoan Group Co., Ltd.; *Int'l*, pg. 1485
GENEX POWER LIMITED; *Int'l*, pg. 2923
GENEX SERVICES, LLC—See Stone Point Capital LLC; *U.S. Private*, pg. 3823
GENEX SERVICES OF CANADA, INC.—See Stone Point Capital LLC; *U.S. Private*, pg. 3823
GENEXTRA S.P.A.; *Int'l*, pg. 2923
GENEXT STUDENTS PRIVATE LIMITED—See Navneet Education Ltd; *Int'l*, pg. 5177
GENEZEN LABORATORIES INC.—See Ampersand Management LLC; *U.S. Private*, pg. 265
GENEZONE INTERNATIONAL HEALTH MANAGEMENT LIMITED—See China Biotech Services Holdings Limited; *Int'l*, pg. 1487
GENFAR S.A.—See Sanofi; *Int'l*, pg. 6547
GENFIT CORPORATION—See Genfit S.A.; *Int'l*, pg. 2923
GENFIT S.A.; *Int'l*, pg. 2923
GENFLOW BIOSCIENCES PLC; *Int'l*, pg. 2923
GENFLOW BIOSCIENCES S.R.L.—See Genflow Biosciences Plc; *Int'l*, pg. 2923
GENFOOD CO., LTD.—See MSC Co., Ltd.; *Int'l*, pg. 5067
GENFOOT INC.; *Int'l*, pg. 2923
GENFOOT, INC.—See Genfoot Inc.; *Int'l*, pg. 2923

G.EN. GAZ ENERGIA SP. Z O.O.—See EnBW Energie Baden-Wurttemberg AG; *Int'l*, pg. 2400
GENGHIS GRILL; *U.S. Private*, pg. 1671
GENGRAS MOTOR CARS, INC.; *U.S. Private*, pg. 1671
GENHAM DIAMOND TOOLING, INC.—See L Squared Capital Management LP; *U.S. Private*, pg. 2361
GENHELIX S.A.—See Insud Pharma, S.L.; *Int'l*, pg. 3725
GENIALLOYD SPA—See Allianz SE; *Int'l*, pg. 350
GENIANS INC; *Int'l*, pg. 2923
GENIANT, LLC; *U.S. Private*, pg. 1671
GENIA PHOTONICS INC.; *Int'l*, pg. 2923
GENICA CORPORATION; *U.S. Private*, pg. 1671
GENICAD, S.R.O.—See Xometry, Inc.; *U.S. Public*, pg. 2391
GENIC CO., LTD. - NONSAN 1ST PLANT—See Genic Co., Ltd.; *Int'l*, pg. 2923
GENIC CO., LTD. - NONSAN 2ND PLANT—See Genic Co., Ltd.; *Int'l*, pg. 2923
GENIC CO., LTD.; *Int'l*, pg. 2923
GENIE AUSTRALIA PTY. LTD.—See Terex Corporation; *U.S. Public*, pg. 2019
GENIE BRASIL LTDA—See Terex Corporation; *U.S. Public*, pg. 2019
GENIE CIVIL INDUSTRIEL—See Eiffage S.A.; *Int'l*, pg. 2330
GENIEE, INC.; *Int'l*, pg. 2923
GENIE ELECTRONICS COMPANY; *U.S. Private*, pg. 1671
GENIE ENERGY LTD.; *U.S. Public*, pg. 930
GENIE FRANCE S.A.R.L.—See Terex Corporation; *U.S. Public*, pg. 2019
GENIE GATEWAY; *U.S. Private*, pg. 1671
GENIE GERMANY GMBH—See Terex Corporation; *U.S. Public*, pg. 2019
GENIE INDUSTRIES IBERICA, S.L.—See Terex Corporation; *U.S. Public*, pg. 2019
GENIE INDUSTRIES, INC.—See Terex Corporation; *U.S. Public*, pg. 2019
GENIE MANUFACTURING, INC.—See Terex Corporation; *U.S. Public*, pg. 2019
GENIE MUSIC CORPORATION—See KT Corporation; *Int'l*, pg. 4314
GENIE SCANDINAVIA AB—See Terex Corporation; *U.S. Public*, pg. 2019
GENIE UK LIMITED—See Terex Corporation; *U.S. Public*, pg. 2019
GENII CAPITAL SA—See Genii Capital SA; *Int'l*, pg. 2923
GENII CAPITAL SA; *Int'l*, pg. 2923
GENII CAPITAL UK LTD.—See Genii Capital SA; *Int'l*, pg. 2923
GENII, INC.—See STERIS plc; *Int'l*, pg. 7211
GENIKI INFORMATION S.A.—See Piraeus Financial Holdings S.A.; *Int'l*, pg. 5873
GENILEX INFORMATION TECHNOLOGY CO., LTD.—See RELX plc; *Int'l*, pg. 6267
GENIMOUS TECHNOLOGY CO., LTD.; *Int'l*, pg. 2923
GENINCODE PLC; *Int'l*, pg. 2923
GENINCODE U.S. INC.—See GENinCode Plc; *Int'l*, pg. 2924
GEN INDUSTRIAL, S.A. DE C.V.—See Promotora Ambiental S.A.B de C.V.; *Int'l*, pg. 5994
GENINUS INC.; *Int'l*, pg. 2924
GENISPHERE INC.—See Getinge AB; *Int'l*, pg. 2951
GENIS PRODUCTIONS, INC.; *U.S. Private*, pg. 1671
GENISYS CONTROLS, LLC; *U.S. Private*, pg. 1671
GENISYS CREDIT UNION; *U.S. Private*, pg. 1671
GENISYS GROUP INC.; *U.S. Private*, pg. 1671
GENISYS TECHNOLOGY LIMITED—See Temenos AG; *Int'l*, pg. 7554
GENIUS.COM, INCORPORATED; *U.S. Private*, pg. 1671
GENIUS.COM UK—See Genius.com, Incorporated; *U.S. Private*, pg. 1671
GENIUS-DMS GMBH—See Nippon Telegraph & Telephone Corporation; *Int'l*, pg. 5343
GENIUS ELECTRONIC OPTICAL CO., LTD.; *Int'l*, pg. 2924
GENIUS ELECTRONIC OPTICAL (SHENZHEN) CO., LTD.—See Genius Electronic Optical Co., Ltd.; *Int'l*, pg. 2924
GENIUS ELECTRONIC OPTICAL (XIAMEN) CO., LTD.—See Genius Electronic Optical Co., Ltd.; *Int'l*, pg. 2924
GENIUS FOODS LIMITED—See Xaver Fassin GmbH; *Int'l*, pg. 8520
GENIUS GROUP LIMITED; *Int'l*, pg. 2924
GENIUS JONES INC.; *U.S. Private*, pg. 1671
GENIUS METALS, INC; *Int'l*, pg. 2924
GENIUS SOLUTIONS ENGINEERING CORPORATION—See Standex International; *U.S. Public*, pg. 1930
GENIUS SYSTEMS LTD.; *Int'l*, pg. 2924
GENIUS TECHNOLOGY (SHENZHEN) CO., LTD.—See KYE Systems Corp.; *Int'l*, pg. 4355
GENIUS TERMINAL CO., LTD.—See Gem Terminal Ind. Co., Ltd.; *Int'l*, pg. 2915
GENIUS TERMINAL (HK) LTD.—See Gem Terminal Ind. Co., Ltd.; *Int'l*, pg. 2915
GENIUS TRAFFIC SYSTEM COMPANY LIMITED—See Forth Corporation Public Company Limited; *Int'l*, pg. 2738

GENIX PHARMACEUTICALS CORPORATION

GENIX PHARMACEUTICALS CORPORATION; *Int'l*, pg. 2924
GENKAI TECHNICAL ENGINEERING CO., LTD.—See Namura Shipbuilding Co., Ltd.; *Int'l*, pg. 5136
GENKI CO., LTD.—See Daikoku Denki Co., Ltd.; *Int'l*, pg. 1937
GENKI GLOBAL DINING CONCEPTS CORPORATION; *Int'l*, pg. 2924
GENKI SUSHI HONG KONG LIMITED—See Genki Global Dining Concepts Corporation; *Int'l*, pg. 2924
GENKI SUSHI USA INC.—See Genki Global Dining Concepts Corporation; *Int'l*, pg. 2924
GENKO ITALIA SRL; *Int'l*, pg. 2924
GENKY DRUGSTORES CO., LTD.; *Int'l*, pg. 2924
GENKYOTEX S.A.—See Asahi Kasei Corporation; *Int'l*, pg. 596
GENKY STORES, INC.; *Int'l*, pg. 2924
GENLABS; *U.S. Private*, pg. 1672
GENMAB A/S; *Int'l*, pg. 2924
GENMAB B.V.—See Genmab A/S; *Int'l*, pg. 2924
GENMAB HOLDING B.V.—See Genmab A/S; *Int'l*, pg. 2924
GENMAB, INC.—See Genmab A/S; *Int'l*, pg. 2924
GENMAB US, INC.—See Genmab A/S; *Int'l*, pg. 2924
GENMAO ELECTRONICS (SUZHOU) CO., LTD.—See Lien Chang Electronic Enterprise Co., Ltd.; *Int'l*, pg. 4492
GENMARK AUTOMATION GMBH—See Nidec Corporation; *Int'l*, pg. 5275
GENMARK AUTOMATION INC.—See Nidec Corporation; *Int'l*, pg. 5275
GENMARK DIAGNOSTICS EUROPE GMBH—See Roche Holding AG; *Int'l*, pg. 6376
GENMARK DIAGNOSTICS, INC.—See Roche Holding AG; *Int'l*, pg. 6376
GENMARK TAIWAN—See Nidec Corporation; *Int'l*, pg. 5275
GENMAR YAPI URUNLERI A.S.—See Gentas AS; *Int'l*, pg. 2928
GENMECH ENGINEERING (S) PTE. LTD.—See Embelton Limited; *Int'l*, pg. 2375
GEN MEDIA PARTNERS LLC; *U.S. Private*, pg. 1660
GENMINI LIMITED; *Int'l*, pg. 2924
GENMONT BIOTECH INCORPORATION; *Int'l*, pg. 2924
GENNARO AURICCHIO S.P.A.; *Int'l*, pg. 2924
GENNBIO INC.; *Int'l*, pg. 2925
GENNBIO, INC.; *Int'l*, pg. 2925
GENNEX LABORATORIES LTD.; *Int'l*, pg. 2925
GENNIUS, INC.—See Thoma Bravo, L.P.; *U.S. Private*, pg. 4150
GENNUM CORP. - OTTAWA DESIGN CENTER—See Semtech Corporation; *U.S. Public*, pg. 1864
GENNUM UK LIMITED—See Semtech Corporation; *U.S. Public*, pg. 1864
GENNX360 CAPITAL PARTNERS, L.P.; *U.S. Private*, pg. 1672
GENOA CONSTRUCTION SERVICES, INC.; *U.S. Private*, pg. 1672
GENOA HEALTHCARE, INC.—See UnitedHealth Group Incorporated; *U.S. Public*, pg. 2241
GENOA HEALTHCARE LLC; *U.S. Private*, pg. 1672
GENOA MOTORS INC.; *U.S. Private*, pg. 1673
GENOA TELEPSYCHIATRY, INC.—See UnitedHealth Group Incorporated; *U.S. Public*, pg. 2241
GENO BROKER GMBH—See DZ BANK AG Deutsche Zentral-Genossenschaftsbank; *Int'l*, pg. 2244
GENOCEA BIOSCIENCES, INC.; *U.S. Public*, pg. 931
GENOFOCUS, INC.; *Int'l*, pg. 2925
GENO-HAUS STUTTGART GMBH & CO. KG VERWALTUNGSGESELLSCHAFT—See DZ BANK AG Deutsche Zentral-Genossenschaftsbank; *Int'l*, pg. 2244
GENOHCO, INC.; *Int'l*, pg. 2925
GENOIL INC.; *U.S. Public*, pg. 931
GENOL GESELLSCHAFT M.B.H. & CO. KG—See BayWa AG; *Int'l*, pg. 919
GENOL GESELLSCHAFT MBH—See BayWa AG; *Int'l*, pg. 918
GENOLIER SWISS MEDICAL NETWORK SA—See AEVIS VICTORIA SA; *Int'l*, pg. 183
GENO LLC; *U.S. Private*, pg. 1672
GENOLUTION INC.; *Int'l*, pg. 2925
GENOLUX CO., LTD; *Int'l*, pg. 2925
GENOLYTIC DIAGNOSTIK GMBH—See Eurofins Scientific S.E.; *Int'l*, pg. 2550
GENOMAS INC.—See Rennova Health, Inc.; *U.S. Public*, pg. 1783
GENOMATICA, INC.; *U.S. Private*, pg. 1673
GENOMATIX, INC.—See Precigen, Inc.; *U.S. Public*, pg. 1713
GENOME & COMPANY; *Int'l*, pg. 2925
GENOME COMPILER CORPORATION—See Twist Bioscience Corporation; *U.S. Public*, pg. 2207
GENOME, INC.—See Apollo Global Management, Inc.; *U.S. Public*, pg. 167
GENOMEWEB, LLC—See Crain Communications, Inc.; *U.S. Private*, pg. 1084
GENOMICA, S.A.U.—See Zeltia, S.A.; *Int'l*, pg. 8631
GENOMIC HEALTH, INC.—See Exact Sciences Corporation; *U.S. Public*, pg. 805

GENOMIC HEALTH ITALIA S.R.L.—See Exact Sciences Corporation; *U.S. Public*, pg. 805
GENOMICS BIOSCI & TECH CO., LTD.; *Int'l*, pg. 2925
GENOMICTREE, INC.; *Int'l*, pg. 2925
GENOMIC VALLEY BIOTECH LIMITED; *Int'l*, pg. 2925
GENOMIC VISION SA; *Int'l*, pg. 2925
GENOMMA LAB INTERNATIONAL SAB DE CV; *Int'l*, pg. 2925
GENOMTEC SA; *Int'l*, pg. 2925
GENON AMERICAS GENERATION, LLC—See NRG Energy, Inc.; *U.S. Public*, pg. 1550
G ENONE ENERGY CO., LTD.; *Int'l*, pg. 2861
GENON ENERGY, INC.—See NRG Energy, Inc.; *U.S. Public*, pg. 1550
GENON LABORATORIES LIMITED—See Cinven Limited; *Int'l*, pg. 1614
GENON MID-ATLANTIC, LLC—See NRG Energy, Inc.; *U.S. Public*, pg. 1550
GENOPTIX, INC.—See NeoGenomics, Inc.; *U.S. Public*, pg. 1505
GENORAY AMERICA INC.—See Genoray Co., Ltd.; *Int'l*, pg. 2925
GENORAY CO., LTD.; *Int'l*, pg. 2925
GENORAY EU GMBH—See Genoray Co., Ltd.; *Int'l*, pg. 2925
GENORAY JAPAN, K.K.—See Genoray Co., Ltd.; *Int'l*, pg. 2925
GENOR BIOPHARMA CO., LTD.; *Int'l*, pg. 2925
GENOSKAN A/S—See Eurofins Scientific S.E.; *Int'l*, pg. 2550
GENOSPACE, LLC—See HCA Healthcare, Inc.; *U.S. Public*, pg. 997
GENOST CONSULTING GMBH—See CORESTATE Capital Holding SA; *Int'l*, pg. 1800
GENOTECH CORPORATION - GMP PLANT—See GenoTech Corporation; *Int'l*, pg. 2925
GENOTECH CORPORATION; *Int'l*, pg. 2925
GENOVA DIAGNOSTICS, INC.—See Levine Leichtman Capital Partners, LLC; *U.S. Private*, pg. 2436
GENOVA EAST EUROPE—See Genova Products, Inc.; *U.S. Private*, pg. 1673
GENOVA INC.; *Int'l*, pg. 2926
GENOVA-INDIANA, INC.—See Genova Products, Inc.; *U.S. Private*, pg. 1673
GENOVA-MINNESOTA, INC.—See Genova Products, Inc.; *U.S. Private*, pg. 1673
GENOVA-NEVADA—See Genova Products, Inc.; *U.S. Private*, pg. 1673
GENOVA & PARTNERS, INC.; *U.S. Private*, pg. 1673
GENOVA-PENNSYLVANIA, INC.—See Genova Products, Inc.; *U.S. Private*, pg. 1673
GENOVA PRODUCTS, INC. - GENOVA MINNESOTA FACTORY—See Genova Products, Inc.; *U.S. Private*, pg. 1673
GENOVA PRODUCTS, INC. - GENOVA NEVADA FACTORY—See Genova Products, Inc.; *U.S. Private*, pg. 1673
GENOVA PRODUCTS, INC. - RENSSELAER PLASTICS FACTORY—See Genova Products, Inc.; *U.S. Private*, pg. 1673
GENOVA PRODUCTS, INC.; *U.S. Private*, pg. 1673
GENOVA PROPERTY GROUP AB; *Int'l*, pg. 2926
GENOVASI MALAYSIA SDN. BHD.—See Ancom Nylex Berhad; *Int'l*, pg. 449
GENOVATE BIOTECHNOLOGY CO., LTD.; *Int'l*, pg. 2926
GENOVA WESTERN EUROPE—See Genova Products, Inc.; *U.S. Private*, pg. 1673
GENOVEL ORTHOPEDICS, INC.—See INNOVATE Corp.; *U.S. Public*, pg. 1126
GENOVIQUE SPECIALTIES WUHAN YOUJI CHEMICAL CO., LTD.—See Eastman Chemical Company; *U.S. Public*, pg. 705
GENOVIS AB; *Int'l*, pg. 2926
GENOVIS INC.—See Genovis AB; *Int'l*, pg. 2926
GENOVO, INC.—See Armata Pharmaceuticals, Inc.; *U.S. Public*, pg. 193
GENOWAY S.A.; *Int'l*, pg. 2926
GENOYER GROUP, INC.—See Groupe BPCE; *Int'l*, pg. 3095
GENOYER S.A.—See Groupe BPCE; *Int'l*, pg. 3095
GENPACT AUSTRALIA PTY LTD—See Genpact Limited; *Int'l*, pg. 2926
GENPACT CANADA SERVICES COMPANY—See Genpact Limited; *Int'l*, pg. 2926
GENPACT CONSULTING KK—See Genpact Limited; *Int'l*, pg. 2926
GENPACT (DALIAN) CO, LTD.—See Genpact Limited; *Int'l*, pg. 2926
GENPACT (DALIAN) INFORMATION & TECHNOLOGY SERVICE CO., LTD.—See Genpact Limited; *Int'l*, pg. 2926
GENPACT ENTERPRISE RISK CONSULTING LLP—See Genpact Limited; *Int'l*, pg. 2926
GENPACT (FOSHAN) INFORMATION & TECHNOLOGY SERVICE CO., LTD.—See Genpact Limited; *Int'l*, pg. 2926
GENPACT HUNGARY PROCESS SZOLGALTATO KFT.—See Genpact Limited; *Int'l*, pg. 2927
GENPACT INDIA—See Genpact Limited; *Int'l*, pg. 2926

GENPACT INTERNATIONAL, INC.—See Genpact Limited; *Int'l*, pg. 2926
GENPACT ISRAEL LTD.—See Genpact Limited; *Int'l*, pg. 2926
GENPACT KENYA LIMITED—See Genpact Limited; *Int'l*, pg. 2926
GENPACT LATVIA SIA—See Genpact Limited; *Int'l*, pg. 2926
GENPACT LIMITED; *Int'l*, pg. 2926
GENPACT LLC—See Genpact Limited; *Int'l*, pg. 2926
GENPACT NETHERLANDS B.V.—See Genpact Limited; *Int'l*, pg. 2927
GENPACT NL B.V.—See Genpact Limited; *Int'l*, pg. 2927
GENPACT OUTSOURCING SERVICES COSTA RICA, S.R.L.—See Genpact Limited; *Int'l*, pg. 2927
GENPACT PL SP. Z O.O.—See Genpact Limited; *Int'l*, pg. 2927
GENPACT (QINGDAO) INFORMATION & TECHNOLOGY SERVICE CO., LTD.—See Genpact Limited; *Int'l*, pg. 2926
GENPACT REGULATORY AFFAIRS UK LIMITED—See Genpact Limited; *Int'l*, pg. 2927
GENPACT RESOURCING SERVICES B.V.—See Genpact Limited; *Int'l*, pg. 2927
GENPACT ROMANIA SRL—See Genpact Limited; *Int'l*, pg. 2927
GENPACT SERVICES CZECH S.R.O.—See Genpact Limited; *Int'l*, pg. 2927
GENPACT SERVICES HUNGARY KFT—See Genpact Limited; *Int'l*, pg. 2927
GENPACT SERVICES LLC—See Genpact Limited; *Int'l*, pg. 2926
GENPACT SINGAPORE PTE. LTD.—See Genpact Limited; *Int'l*, pg. 2927
GENPACT SOUTH AFRICA (PROPRIETARY) LIMITED—See Genpact Limited; *Int'l*, pg. 2927
GENPACT (SUZHOU) INFORMATION & TECHNOLOGY SERVICE CO., LTD.—See Genpact Limited; *Int'l*, pg. 2926
GENPACT WB LLC—See Genpact Limited; *Int'l*, pg. 2927
GENPAK LLC—See First Atlantic Capital Ltd.; *U.S. Private*, pg. 1513
GENPAK LLC—See The Jim Pattison Group; *Int'l*, pg. 7660
GENPAK LP.—See The Jim Pattison Group; *Int'l*, pg. 7660
GENPAK—See First Atlantic Capital Ltd.; *U.S. Private*, pg. 1513
GENPHARMASEC LIMITED; *Int'l*, pg. 2927
GENPREX, INC.; *U.S. Public*, pg. 931
GEN-PROBE DENMARK APS—See Hologic, Inc.; *U.S. Public*, pg. 1044
GEN-PROBE INCORPORATED—See Hologic, Inc.; *U.S. Public*, pg. 1044
GEN-PROBE PRODESSE, INC.—See Hologic, Inc.; *U.S. Public*, pg. 1044
GEN-PROBE SWEDEN AB—See Hologic, Inc.; *U.S. Public*, pg. 1045
GENPRO TRANSPORTATION INC.; *U.S. Private*, pg. 1673
GENQUEST, INC.; *U.S. Private*, pg. 1673
GENR8 DIGITAL MEDIA PTY LTD.—See Ausmani Limited; *Int'l*, pg. 716
GENREC ENGINEERING (PTY) LTD.—See Southern Palace Group of Companies (Pty) Ltd.; *Int'l*, pg. 7120
GEN RE CORPORATION—See Berkshire Hathaway Inc.; *U.S. Public*, pg. 301
GEN RE INTERMEDIARIES CORPORATION—See Berkshire Hathaway Inc.; *U.S. Public*, pg. 301
GEN RE MEXICO, S.A—See Berkshire Hathaway Inc.; *U.S. Public*, pg. 301
GEN RE SECURITIES HOLDINGS LLC—See Berkshire Hathaway Inc.; *U.S. Public*, pg. 301
GEN RESTAURANT GROUP, INC.; *U.S. Public*, pg. 911
GENROBOTIC INNOVATIONS PRIVATE LIMITED; *Int'l*, pg. 2927
GENSCAPE, INC.—See Verisk Analytics, Inc.; *U.S. Public*, pg. 2282
GENSCAPE INTERNATIONAL, INC.—See Verisk Analytics, Inc.; *U.S. Public*, pg. 2282
GENSCO INC.; *U.S. Private*, pg. 1673
GENSCRIPT BIOTECH CORPORATION; *Int'l*, pg. 2927
GENSCRIPT JAPAN INC.—See GenScript Biotech Corporation; *Int'l*, pg. 2927
GENSCRIPT USA INCORPORATED—See GenScript Biotech Corporation; *Int'l*, pg. 2927
GENSENTA ILAC SANAYI VE TICARET ANONIM SIRKETI—See Amgen Inc.; *U.S. Public*, pg. 123
GENSERVE INC.—See GenNx360 Capital Partners, L.P.; *U.S. Private*, pg. 1672
GEN SERV, INC.; *U.S. Private*, pg. 1660
GENSIGHT BIOLOGICS S.A.; *Int'l*, pg. 2927
GENSINGER MOTORS INC.; *U.S. Private*, pg. 1673
GENSOL ENGINEERING LTD.; *Int'l*, pg. 2928
GENSOURCE POTASH CORPORATION; *Int'l*, pg. 2928
GEN-S POWER GROUP CO., LTD.; *Int'l*, pg. 2916
GENSPRING FAMILY OFFICES, L.L.C.—See Truist Financial Corporation; *U.S. Public*, pg. 2199
GENSTAR CAPITAL, LLC; *U.S. Private*, pg. 1673

COMPANY NAME INDEX

GENSTAR DEVELOPMENT COMPANY; *U.S. Private*, pg. 1679
GENSUN CASUAL LIVING; *U.S. Private*, pg. 1679
GENSUR LTDA—See Livestock Improvement Corporation Limited; *Int'l*, pg. 4531
GENSYM B.V.—See ESW Capital, LLC; *U.S. Private*, pg. 1430
GENSYM CORPORATION—See ESW Capital, LLC; *U.S. Private*, pg. 1430
GENTAS AS; *Int'l*, pg. 2928
GENTAS KIMYA SANAYI VE TICARET PAZARLAMA A.S.—See Gentas AS; *Int'l*, pg. 2928
GENTECH ASSOCIATES, INC.; *U.S. Private*, pg. 1679
GENTEC INC.—See Hensall District Co-operative, Inc.; *Int'l*, pg. 3355
GENTEC; *Int'l*, pg. 2928
GENTEK BUILDING PRODUCTS, INC.—See Hellman & Friedman LLC; *U.S. Private*, pg. 1907
GENTEK BUILDING PRODUCTS LTD.; *Int'l*, pg. 2928
GENTERA, S.A.B. DE C.V.; *Int'l*, pg. 2928
GENTEX CORPORATION; *U.S. Private*, pg. 1679
GENTEX CORPORATION; *U.S. Public*, pg. 931
GENTEX FRANCE, SAS—See Gentex Corporation; *U.S. Public*, pg. 931
GENTEX GMBH—See Gentex Corporation; *U.S. Public*, pg. 931
GENTEX HOLDINGS, INC.—See Gentex Corporation; *U.S. Public*, pg. 931
GENTEX MIRRORS LTD.—See Gentex Corporation; *U.S. Public*, pg. 931
GENTEX OPTICS, INC.—See EssilorLuxottica SA; *Int'l*, pg. 2514
GENTEX (SHANGHAI) ELECTRONIC TECHNOLOGY CO., INC.—See Gentex Corporation; *U.S. Public*, pg. 931
GENTEX—See Lower Colorado River Authority; *U.S. Private*, pg. 2505
GENTHERM ASIA PACIFIC INCORPORATED—See Gentherm Incorporated; *U.S. Public*, pg. 931
GENTHERM AUTOMOTIVE SYSTEMS (CHINA) LTD.—See Gentherm Incorporated; *U.S. Public*, pg. 931
GENTHERM DE MEXICO S.A. DE C.V—See Gentherm Incorporated; *U.S. Public*, pg. 932
GENTHERM ENTERPRISES GMBH—See Gentherm Incorporated; *U.S. Public*, pg. 931
GENTHERM EUROPE GMBH—See Gentherm Incorporated; *U.S. Public*, pg. 931
GENTHERM GLOBAL POWER TECHNOLOGIES—See Gentherm Incorporated; *U.S. Public*, pg. 931
GENTHERM GMBH—See Gentherm Incorporated; *U.S. Public*, pg. 931
GENTHERM HUNGARY KFT—See Gentherm Incorporated; *U.S. Public*, pg. 932
GENTHERM INCORPORATED; *U.S. Public*, pg. 931
GENTHERM JAPAN INC.—See Gentherm Incorporated; *U.S. Public*, pg. 932
GENTHERM KOREA INC.—See Gentherm Incorporated; *U.S. Public*, pg. 932
GENTHERM MEDICAL, LLC—See Gentherm Incorporated; *U.S. Public*, pg. 932
GENTHERM TECHNOLOGIES (SHANGHAI) CO. LTD.—See Gentherm Incorporated; *U.S. Public*, pg. 932
GENTHERM U.K. LTD.—See Gentherm Incorporated; *U.S. Public*, pg. 932
GENTIAN DIAGNOSTICS AS; *Int'l*, pg. 2928
GENTIAN USA INC.—See Gentian Diagnostics AS; *Int'l*, pg. 2928
GENTICS SOFTWARE GMBH—See APA-Austria Presse Agentur eG; *Int'l*, pg. 500
GENTILI MOSCONI S.P.A.; *Int'l*, pg. 2928
GENTING BERHAD; *Int'l*, pg. 2928
GENTING BIO-OIL SDN BHD—See Genting Berhad; *Int'l*, pg. 2928
GENTING HONG KONG LIMITED; *Int'l*, pg. 2929
GENTING INTERNATIONAL JAPAN CO. LTD—See Genting Berhad; *Int'l*, pg. 2928
GENTING INTERNATIONAL SDN BHD—See Genting Berhad; *Int'l*, pg. 2928
GENTING INTERNATIONAL (SINGAPORE) PTE LTD—See Genting Berhad; *Int'l*, pg. 2928
GENTING (LABUAN) LIMITED—See Genting Berhad; *Int'l*, pg. 2928
GENTING MALAYSIA BERHAD—See Genting Berhad; *Int'l*, pg. 2928
GENTING MANAGEMENT AND CONSULTANCY SERVICES SDN BHD—See Genting Berhad; *Int'l*, pg. 2928
GENTING OIL & GAS LIMITED—See Genting Berhad; *Int'l*, pg. 2928
GENTING OIL & GAS SDN BHD—See Genting Berhad; *Int'l*, pg. 2928
GENTING PLANTATIONS BERHAD—See Genting Berhad; *Int'l*, pg. 2928
GENTING PROPERTY SDN. BHD.—See Genting Berhad; *Int'l*, pg. 2929
GENTING SANYEN PAPERBOARD SDN BHD—See Genting Berhad; *Int'l*, pg. 2929
GENTING SANYEN POWER SDN BHD—See Genting Berhad; *Int'l*, pg. 2929
GENTING SINGAPORE LIMITED—See Genting Berhad; *Int'l*, pg. 2929
GENTING SINGAPORE PLC—See Genting Berhad; *Int'l*, pg. 2929
GENTIUM SPA—See Jazz Pharmaceuticals plc; *Int'l*, pg. 3916
GENTIUM S.R.L.—See Jazz Pharmaceuticals plc; *Int'l*, pg. 3916
GENTIVA HEALTH SERVICES, INC.—See Apollo Global Management, Inc.; *U.S. Public*, pg. 156
GENTIVA HOSPICE—See Apollo Global Management, Inc.; *U.S. Public*, pg. 156
GENTLEBROOK, INC.; *U.S. Private*, pg. 1679
GENTLE CO., LTD.—See TAKE AND GIVE. NEEDS Co. Ltd.; *Int'l*, pg. 7436
GENTLEFIT TRADING LIMITED—See Daphne International Holdings Limited; *Int'l*, pg. 1970
GENTLE GIANT MOVING CO. INC.; *U.S. Private*, pg. 1679
GENTLE GIANT STUDIOS, INC.—See 3D Systems Corporation; *U.S. Public*, pg. 4
GENTLEMENS EQUITY S.A.; *Int'l*, pg. 2929
GENTLE PATH PRESS—See International Institute for Trauma and Addiction Professionals; *U.S. Private*, pg. 2118
GENTNER INC.; *U.S. Private*, pg. 1679
GENTOFTE DYREKLINIK APS—See Vimian Group AB; *Int'l*, pg. 8208
GENTOO GROUP LTD.; *Int'l*, pg. 2929
GENTOR RESOURCES, INC.; *Int'l*, pg. 2929
GENTOR, S.A. DE C.V.; *Int'l*, pg. 2929
GENTRACK GROUP LIMITED; *Int'l*, pg. 2929
GENTRACK LIMITED; *Int'l*, pg. 2929
GENTRACK LTD.—See Gentrack Limited; *Int'l*, pg. 2929
GENTRACK PTY. LTD.—See Gentrack Limited; *Int'l*, pg. 2929
GENTRACK UK LIMITED—See Gentrack Group Limited; *Int'l*, pg. 2929
GENTRACO FEED JSC; *Int'l*, pg. 2929
GENTRY AIR INC.—See Palladin Consumer Retail Partners, LLC; *U.S. Private*, pg. 3077
GENTRY FINANCE CORPORATION; *U.S. Private*, pg. 1679
GENTRY HOMELOANS, LLC—See Central Pacific Financial Corporation; *U.S. Public*, pg. 473
GENTRY HOMES LTD; *U.S. Private*, pg. 1680
GENTRY INSURANCE AGENCY, INC.—See ABRY Partners, LLC; *U.S. Private*, pg. 43
GENTRY PACIFIC, LTD.; *U.S. Private*, pg. 1680
GENTS PLACE MEN'S FINE GROOM—See Massage Heights; *U.S. Private*, pg. 2606
GENT STORE BY BILIA VERSTRAETEN BVBA—See Bilia AB; *Int'l*, pg. 1029
GENTZLER ELECTRIC; *U.S. Private*, pg. 1680
GENUENT, LLC—See Willis Group LLC; *U.S. Private*, pg. 4528
GENUENT USA, LLC—See Willis Group LLC; *U.S. Private*, pg. 4528
GENUFOOD ENERGY ENZYMES CORP.; *U.S. Public*, pg. 932
GENUI GMBH; *Int'l*, pg. 2930
GENUINE AUTO PARTS OF FAIRBANKS—See Genuine Parts Company; *U.S. Public*, pg. 932
GENUINE BIO-FUEL, INC.; *U.S. Private*, pg. 1680
GENUINE CABLE GROUP LLC—See Audax Group, Limited Partnership; *U.S. Private*, pg. 390
THE GENUINE CANADIAN CORP—See Carter's, Inc.; *U.S. Public*, pg. 445
GENUINE C&C INC.—See WPG Holdings Limited; *Int'l*, pg. 8460
GENUINE INTERACTIVE, LLC—See The Interpublic Group of Companies, Inc.; *U.S. Public*, pg. 2096
GENUINE MOTORCARS, INC.; *U.S. Private*, pg. 1680
GENUINE PARTS COMPANY EASTERN DIVISION—See Genuine Parts Company; *U.S. Public*, pg. 932
GENUINE PARTS COMPANY MOUNTAIN & WESTERN DIVISION—See Genuine Parts Company; *U.S. Public*, pg. 932
GENUINE PARTS COMPANY; *U.S. Public*, pg. 932
GENUINE PARTS COMPANY - U.S. AUTOMOTIVE PARTS GROUP—See Genuine Parts Company; *U.S. Public*, pg. 932
GENUINE SOLUTIONS LIMITED; *Int'l*, pg. 2930
GENUINE ZEBRA TECHNOLOGIES TRADING (SHANGHAI) CO., LTD.—See Zebra Technologies Corporation; *U.S. Public*, pg. 2401
GENUIT GROUP PLC; *Int'l*, pg. 2930
GENU PATH LABS LIMITED—See Sastasundar Ventures Limited; *Int'l*, pg. 6584
GENUS ABS COLOMBIA SAS—See Genus Plc; *Int'l*, pg. 2930
GENUS APPARELS LTD.—See Kailash Group; *Int'l*, pg. 4051
GENUS AUSTRALIA PTY LTD—See Genus Plc; *Int'l*, pg. 2930
GENUS BREEDING INDIA PRIVATE LIMITED—See Genus Plc; *Int'l*, pg. 2930

GENZINK STEEL SUPPLY & WELDING CO.

GENUS BREEDING LTD—See Genus Plc; *Int'l*, pg. 2930
GENUS ELECTROTECH LTD.—See Kailash Group; *Int'l*, pg. 4051
GENUS INNOVATION LTD.—See Kailash Group; *Int'l*, pg. 4051
GENUS LIFE INSURANCE SERVICES PTY LTD.—See NobleOak Life Limited; *Int'l*, pg. 5398
GENUS PAPER & BOARDS LIMITED—See Kailash Group; *Int'l*, pg. 4051
GENUS PHARMACEUTICALS LTD.—See Bain Capital, LP; *U.S. Private*, pg. 443
GENUS PHARMACEUTICALS LTD.—See Cinven Limited; *Int'l*, pg. 1613
GENUS PLC; *Int'l*, pg. 2930
GENUSPLUS GROUP LTD.; *Int'l*, pg. 2931
GENUS POWER INFRASTRUCTURES LTD.; *Int'l*, pg. 2931
GENUS PRIME INFRA LIMITED—See Kailash Group; *Int'l*, pg. 4051
GENUS UKRAINE LLC—See Genus Plc; *Int'l*, pg. 2930
GENVEC, INC.—See Precigen, Inc.; *U.S. Public*, pg. 1713
GENVEX A/S—See NIBE Industrier AB; *Int'l*, pg. 5260
GENWORTH CONSULTING SERVICES (BEIJING) LIMITED—See Genworth Financial, Inc.; *U.S. Public*, pg. 933
GENWORTH FINANCIAL ADVISERS CORPORATION—See Genworth Financial, Inc.; *U.S. Public*, pg. 933
GENWORTH FINANCIAL CANADA—See Genworth Financial, Inc.; *U.S. Public*, pg. 933
GENWORTH FINANCIAL, INC.; *U.S. Public*, pg. 933
GENWORTH FINANCIAL INDIA PRIVATE LIMITED—See Genworth Financial, Inc.; *U.S. Public*, pg. 934
GENWORTH FINANCIAL TRUST COMPANY—See Genworth Financial, Inc.; *U.S. Public*, pg. 934
GENWORTH LIFE AND ANNUITY INSURANCE COMPANY—See Genworth Financial, Inc.; *U.S. Public*, pg. 934
GENWORTH MORTGAGE INSURANCE CORPORATION OF NORTH CAROLINA—See Genworth Financial, Inc.; *U.S. Public*, pg. 934
GENWORTH MORTGAGE SERVICES, LLC—See Genworth Financial, Inc.; *U.S. Public*, pg. 934
GENWORTH OPERACIONES COLOMBIA S.A.S.—See Genworth Financial, Inc.; *U.S. Public*, pg. 934
GENXMEX FOODS, INC.; *U.S. Private*, pg. 1680
GENX MOBILE, INC.—See Sierra Wireless, Inc.; *Int'l*, pg. 6904
GENZINK STEEL SUPPLY & WELDING CO.; *U.S. Private*, pg. 1680
GENZYME AUSTRALIA PTY. LTD—See Sanofi; *Int'l*, pg. 6547
GENZYME AUSTRIA GMBH—See Sanofi; *Int'l*, pg. 6547
GENZYME BELGIUM NV/SA—See Sanofi; *Int'l*, pg. 6547
GENZYME BIOPHARMACEUTICALS SOUTH AFRICA (PTY) LTD—See Sanofi; *Int'l*, pg. 6547
GENZYME BIOSURGERY—See Sanofi; *Int'l*, pg. 6547
GENZYME CHILE LTDA.—See Sanofi; *Int'l*, pg. 6547
GENZYME COLOMBIA S. A.—See Sanofi; *Int'l*, pg. 6547
GENZYME CORPORATION—See Sanofi; *Int'l*, pg. 6547
GENZYME CZECH S. R. O.—See Sanofi; *Int'l*, pg. 6547
GENZYME DE ARGENTINA S.A.—See Sanofi; *Int'l*, pg. 6548
GENZYME DENMARK A/S—See Sanofi; *Int'l*, pg. 6547
GENZYME DE PERU S.A.C—See Sanofi; *Int'l*, pg. 6548
GENZYME DO BRASIL LTDA.—See Sanofi; *Int'l*, pg. 6548
GENZYME EUROPE B.V.—See Sanofi; *Int'l*, pg. 6547
GENZYME FRANCE S.A.S.—See Sanofi; *Int'l*, pg. 6547
GENZYME HELLAS LLC—See Sanofi; *Int'l*, pg. 6548
GENZYME INDIA PVT. LTD.—See Sanofi; *Int'l*, pg. 6548
GENZYME IN GEEL B.V.B.A./S.P.R.L.—See Sanofi; *Int'l*, pg. 6548
GENZYME IRELAND LTD.—See Sanofi; *Int'l*, pg. 6548
GENZYME ISRAEL LTD.—See Sanofi; *Int'l*, pg. 6548
GENZYME ITALY S.A.S.—See Sanofi; *Int'l*, pg. 6548
GENZYME JAPAN K.K.—See Sanofi; *Int'l*, pg. 6548
GENZYME KOREA CO., LTD.—See Sanofi; *Int'l*, pg. 6548
GENZYME MALAYSIA SDN BHD—See Sanofi; *Int'l*, pg. 6548
GENZYME MEXICO S DE RL DE CV—See Sanofi; *Int'l*, pg. 6548
GENZYME MIDDLE EAST FZ LLC—See Sanofi; *Int'l*, pg. 6548
GENZYME ONCOLOGY, INC.—See Sanofi; *Int'l*, pg. 6548
GENZYME POLYCLONALS SAS—See Sanofi; *Int'l*, pg. 6548
GENZYME PORTUGAL S.A.—See Sanofi; *Int'l*, pg. 6548
GENZYME S.L.U.—See Sanofi; *Int'l*, pg. 6548
GENZYME TAIWAN LTD.—See Sanofi; *Int'l*, pg. 6548
GENZYME THERAPEUTICS LTD—See Sanofi; *Int'l*, pg. 6548
GENZYME TURKEY LTD—See Sanofi; *Int'l*, pg. 6548
GEOACOUSTICS ASIA PACIFIC PTE LTD.—See Kongsberg Gruppen ASA; *Int'l*, pg. 4255
GEOACOUSTICS LTD.—See Kongsberg Gruppen ASA; *Int'l*, pg. 4255
GEOACOUSTICS LTD—See Kongsberg Gruppen ASA; *Int'l*, pg. 4255

GEOALCALI SLU—See Highfield Resources Limited; *Int'l*, pg. 3387
GEO AMEY PECS, LTD.—See The GEO Group, Inc.; *U.S. Public*, pg. 2075
GEO AUSTRALIA MANAGEMENT SERVICES PTY, LTD.—See The GEO Group, Inc.; *U.S. Public*, pg. 2075
GEOBRA BRANDSTATTER GMBH & CO. KG; *Int'l*, pg. 2932
GEO BUSINESS SUPPORT CO., LTD.—See GEO Holdings Corporation; *Int'l*, pg. 2932
GEO. BYERS SONS HOLDING INC.; *U.S. Private*, pg. 1680
GEOCAPITOL ENGINEERING LLC—See Terracon Consultants, Inc.; *U.S. Private*, pg. 3971
GEO CARE, INC.—See The GEO Group, Inc.; *U.S. Public*, pg. 2075
GEO CARE OF SOUTH CAROLINA, INC.—See The GEO Group, Inc.; *U.S. Public*, pg. 2075
GEOCEAN PERU S.A.C.—See VINCI S.A.; *Int'l*, pg. 8217
GEOCEAN S.A.—See VINCI S.A.; *Int'l*, pg. 8217
GEOCEL CORPORATION; *U.S. Private*, pg. 1680
GEOCEL LIMITED—See The Sherwin-Williams Company; *U.S. Public*, pg. 2127
GEOCELL LLC—See Silk Road Group S.A.; *Int'l*, pg. 6921
GEOCENTER TOURISTIK MEDIENSERVICE GMBH; *Int'l*, pg. 2932
GEOCENT, LLC—See DFW Capital Partners; *U.S. Private*, pg. 1221
GEOCENT, LLC—See Enlightenment Capital LLC; *U.S. Private*, pg. 1400
GEOCHEM INTERNATIONAL CORP.; *U.S. Private*, pg. 1680
GEOCLIMA S.R.L.—See Zamil Industrial Investment Company; *Int'l*, pg. 8623
GEOCODE CO., LTD.; *Int'l*, pg. 2932
GEO COMPACTION DYNAMICS (PTY) LIMITED—See Esor Limited; *Int'l*, pg. 2504
GEOCOMPLEX AS; *Int'l*, pg. 2932
GEOCONCEPT CHINA LTD—See GeoConcept SA; *Int'l*, pg. 2932
GEOCONCEPT INDIA PRIVATE LIMITED—See GeoConcept SA; *Int'l*, pg. 2933
GEOCONCEPT INTERNATIONAL SOFTWARE (SUISSE) SA—See GeoConcept SA; *Int'l*, pg. 2932
GEOCONCEPT JAPAN KK—See GeoConcept SA; *Int'l*, pg. 2932
GEOCONCEPT SA; *Int'l*, pg. 2932
GEO CORRECTIONS AND DETENTION, LLC—See The GEO Group, Inc.; *U.S. Public*, pg. 2075
GEOCURVE LIMITED—See Nanosynth Group PLC; *Int'l*, pg. 5144
GEOCYCLE PTY. LTD.—See Heidelberg Materials AG; *Int'l*, pg. 3311
GEOCYCLE PTY. LTD.—See Holcim Ltd.; *Int'l*, pg. 3446
GEOCYCLE S.A.—See Holcim Ltd.; *Int'l*, pg. 3446
GEOD CORPORATION—See MFS Consulting Engineers & Surveyor Corporation; *U.S. Private*, pg. 2693
GEODESIC LIMITED; *Int'l*, pg. 2933
GEODESIGN, INC.—See NV5 Global, Inc.; *U.S. Public*, pg. 1557
GEODETICS INCORPORATED—See AEVEX Aerospace; *U.S. Private*, pg. 120
GEODIGITAL INTERNATIONAL CORP.—See GeoDigital International Inc.; *Int'l*, pg. 2933
GEODIGITAL INTERNATIONAL INC.; *Int'l*, pg. 2933
GEODIGITAL SOLUTIONS, INC.—See GeoDigital International Inc.; *Int'l*, pg. 2933
GEODIS BERNIS—See SNCF; *Int'l*, pg. 7025
GEODIS CALBERSON—See SNCF; *Int'l*, pg. 7025
GEODIS DUSOLIER CALBERSON—See SNCF; *Int'l*, pg. 7025
GEODIS GLOBAL SOLUTIONS USA, INC.—See SNCF; *Int'l*, pg. 7026
GEODIS LOGISTICS LLC—See SNCF; *Int'l*, pg. 7026
GEODIS LOGISTICS SAS—See SNCF; *Int'l*, pg. 7025
GEODIS SA—See SNCF; *Int'l*, pg. 7025
GEODIS USA, INC.—See SNCF; *Int'l*, pg. 7026
GEODIS WILSON BELGIUM NV—See SNCF; *Int'l*, pg. 7026
GEODIS WILSON CANADA LTD—See SNCF; *Int'l*, pg. 7026
GEODIS WILSON CHILE SA—See SNCF; *Int'l*, pg. 7026
GEODIS WILSON DENMARK A/S—See SNCF; *Int'l*, pg. 7026
GEODIS WILSON FINLAND OY—See SNCF; *Int'l*, pg. 7026
GEODIS WILSON GERMANY GMBH—See SNCF; *Int'l*, pg. 7026
GEODIS WILSON HONG KONG LTD—See SNCF; *Int'l*, pg. 7026
GEODIS WILSON INDUSTRIAL PROJECTS K.S.A.—See SNCF; *Int'l*, pg. 7026
GEODIS WILSON KOREA LTD.—See SNCF; *Int'l*, pg. 7026
GEODIS WILSON MALAYSIA SDN BHD—See SNCF; *Int'l*, pg. 7026
GEODIS WILSON NEW ZEALAND LTD.—See SNCF; *Int'l*, pg. 7026

GEODIS WILSON NORWAY AS—See SNCF; *Int'l*, pg. 7026
GEODIS WILSON SINGAPORE LTD.—See SNCF; *Int'l*, pg. 7026
GEODIS WILSON SWEDEN AB—See SNCF; *Int'l*, pg. 7026
GEODIS WILSON TAIWAN LTD.—See SNCF; *Int'l*, pg. 7026
GEODIS WILSON THAILAND LTD.—See SNCF; *Int'l*, pg. 7026
GEODIS WILSON UK LTD.—See SNCF; *Int'l*, pg. 7026
GEODRILL COTE D'IVOIRE SARL—See Geodrill Limited; *Int'l*, pg. 2933
GEO DRILLING FLUIDS INC.; *U.S. Private*, pg. 1680
GEODRILL LIMITED; *Int'l*, pg. 2933
GEODRILL LIMITED—See Geodrill Limited; *Int'l*, pg. 2933
GEODRILL ZAMBIA LIMITED—See Geodrill Limited; *Int'l*, pg. 2933
GEODYNAMICS, INC.—See Oil States International, Inc.; *U.S. Public*, pg. 1565
GEODYNAMICS (U.K.) LIMITED—See Oil States International, Inc.; *U.S. Public*, pg. 1565
GEOENERGIE SPA—See Radici Partecipazioni S.p.A.; *Int'l*, pg. 6175
GEOENERGIE TAUFKIRCHEN GMBH & CO. KG—See Daldrup & Sohne AG; *Int'l*, pg. 1950
GEO ENERGY RESOURCES LIMITED; *Int'l*, pg. 2931
GEO+ ENVIRONNEMENT SAS—See ABO-Group NV/SA; *Int'l*, pg. 66
GEOFER - PRODUCAO E COMERCIALIZACAO DE BENS E EQUIPAMENTOS, S.A.—See Camargo Correa S.A.; *Int'l*, pg. 1268
GEOFFREY HUGHES (EXPORT) PTY LIMITED—See Grove International Pty Limited; *Int'l*, pg. 3112
GEOFFREY, LLC—See WHP Global; *U.S. Private*, pg. 4515
GEOFIELDS, INC.—See Emerson Electric Co.; *U.S. Public*, pg. 749
GEOFIZYKA KRAKOW SP. Z.O.O.—See Polskie Gornictwo Naftowe i Gazownictwo S.A.; *Int'l*, pg. 5912
GEOFIZYKA TORUN SP. Z.O.O.—See Polskie Gornictwo Naftowe i Gazownictwo S.A.; *Int'l*, pg. 5912
GEOFON A.D.; *Int'l*, pg. 2933
GEOFORCE, INC.—See Independence Capital Partners, LLC; *U.S. Private*, pg. 2056
GEOFOR GABON SA—See Fugro N.V.; *Int'l*, pg. 2808
GEOFUNDACIONES S.A.S.—See VINCI S.A.; *Int'l*, pg. 8222
GEOGAS PTY. LTD.—See Runge ICT Group Pty Limited; *Int'l*, pg. 6427
GEOGRACE RESOURCES PHILIPPINES, INC.; *Int'l*, pg. 2933
GEO GRADEL CO.; *U.S. Private*, pg. 1680
GEOGRAPHIC INFORMATION SERVICES, INC.—See Bluestone Investment Partners, LLC; *U.S. Private*, pg. 598
GEO GRAPHICS, INC.; *U.S. Private*, pg. 1680
GEOGRAPHIC SOLUTIONS, INC.; *U.S. Private*, pg. 1680
GEOGREEN SAS—See VINCI S.A.; *Int'l*, pg. 8217
GEOGREEN SPA—See Radici Partecipazioni S.p.A.; *Int'l*, pg. 6175
THE GEO GROUP AUSTRALIA PTY, LTD.—See The GEO Group, Inc.; *U.S. Public*, pg. 2075
THE GEO GROUP, INC.; *U.S. Public*, pg. 2075
THE GEO GROUP LTD.—See The GEO Group, Inc.; *U.S. Public*, pg. 2075
THE GEO GROUP UK LTD—See The GEO Group, Inc.; *U.S. Public*, pg. 2075
GEO. GROWNEY MOTORS, INC.; *U.S. Private*, pg. 1680
GEO HOLDINGS CORPORATION; *Int'l*, pg. 2932
GEO HOSPITALS LLC—See Vienna Insurance Group AG Wiener Versicherung Gruppe; *Int'l*, pg. 8194
GE OIL & GAS, INC. - TWINSBURG—See General Electric Company; *U.S. Public*, pg. 919
GE OIL & GAS ROTOFLOW—See General Electric Company; *U.S. Public*, pg. 919
GE OIL & GAS U.K. LIMITED—See General Electric Company; *U.S. Public*, pg. 917
GEOINFORM KFT.—See MOL Magyar Olaj- es Gazipari Nyrt.; *Int'l*, pg. 5020
GEOINGENIERIA S.A.—See Centric Holding B.V.; *Int'l*, pg. 1412
GEO-JADE PETROLEUM CORPORATION; *Int'l*, pg. 2932
GEOJIT CREDITS PRIVATE LIMITED—See Geojit Financial Services Limited; *Int'l*, pg. 2933
GEOJIT FINANCIAL DISTRIBUTION PRIVATE LIMITED—See Geojit Financial Services Limited; *Int'l*, pg. 2933
GEOJIT FINANCIAL SERVICES LIMITED; *Int'l*, pg. 2933
GEOJIT TECHNOLOGIES PRIVATE LIMITED—See Geojit Financial Services Limited; *Int'l*, pg. 2933
GEO JS TECH GROUP CORP.; *U.S. Public*, pg. 934
GEOJUNXION B.V.—See GeoJunxion NV; *Int'l*, pg. 2933
GEOJUNXION NV; *Int'l*, pg. 2933
GEOKNOWLEDGE AS—See Schlumberger Limited; *U.S. Public*, pg. 1844
GEOKNOWLEDGE USA, INC.—See Schlumberger Limited; *U.S. Public*, pg. 1844

GEOLANG LIMITED—See Shearwater Group plc; *Int'l*, pg. 6792
GEOLGICA RESOURCE CORP.; *Int'l*, pg. 2933
GEO LINK NUSANTARA PTE LTD—See Federal International (2000) Ltd; *Int'l*, pg. 2630
GEOLOCATION TECHNOLOGY, INC.; *Int'l*, pg. 2933
GEO-LOGICAL INC.; *U.S. Private*, pg. 1680
GEOLOGICS CORP.; *U.S. Private*, pg. 1680
GEOLOGISTICS CORPORATION—See Agility; *Int'l*, pg. 210
GEOMAGIC GMBH—See 3D Systems Corporation; *U.S. Public*, pg. 4
GEOMAGIC, INC.—See 3D Systems Corporation; *U.S. Public*, pg. 4
GEOMAGIC (SHANGHAI) SOFTWARE CO., LTD.—See 3D Systems Corporation; *U.S. Public*, pg. 4
GEO-MARINE, INC.—See Kingswood Capital Management LLC; *U.S. Private*, pg. 2312
GEOMASINA A.D.; *Int'l*, pg. 2933
GEOMAT ANTILLES SAS—See VINCI S.A.; *Int'l*, pg. 8222
GEOMATEC CO., LTD. - AKO FACTORY—See GEOMATEC Co., Ltd.; *Int'l*, pg. 2933
GEOMATEC CO., LTD. - KANNARI FACTORY—See GEOMATEC Co., Ltd.; *Int'l*, pg. 2933
GEOMATEC CO., LTD.; *Int'l*, pg. 2933
GEOMATEC (WUXI) CO., LTD.; *Int'l*, pg. 2933
GEOMATICS DATA SOLUTIONS, LLC—See Woolpert Inc.; *U.S. Private*, pg. 4562
GEOMEDIA N.V.—See Omnicom Group Inc.; *U.S. Public*, pg. 1585
GEOMEGA RESOURCES INC.; *Int'l*, pg. 2933
GEOMERICS LIMITED—See SoftBank Group Corp.; *Int'l*, pg. 7051
GEOMETRICA, INC.; *U.S. Private*, pg. 1680
GEOMETRIC AMERICAS, INC. - SCOTTSDALE—See HCL Technologies Ltd.; *Int'l*, pg. 3298
GEOMETRIC AMERICAS, INC.—See HCL Technologies Ltd.; *Int'l*, pg. 3298
GEOMETRIC CHINA INC.—See HCL Technologies Ltd.; *Int'l*, pg. 3298
GEOMETRIC EUROPE GMBH—See HCL Technologies Ltd.; *Int'l*, pg. 3298
GEOMETRIC JAPAN K.K.—See HCL Technologies Ltd.; *Int'l*, pg. 3298
GEOMETRIC LIMITED—See HCL Technologies Ltd.; *Int'l*, pg. 3298
GEOMETRIC RESULTS HOLDINGS LIMITED—See Bain Capital, LP; *U.S. Private*, pg. 441
GEOMETRIC RESULTS, INC.—See Bain Capital, LP; *U.S. Private*, pg. 441
GEOMETRICS, INC.—See OYO Corporation; *Int'l*, pg. 5678
GEOMETRIC SRL—See HCL Technologies Ltd.; *Int'l*, pg. 3298
GEOMETRY GLOBAL - AMSTERDAM—See WPP plc; *Int'l*, pg. 8463
GEOMETRY GLOBAL - BEIJING—See WPP plc; *Int'l*, pg. 8463
GEOMETRY GLOBAL - BERLIN—See WPP plc; *Int'l*, pg. 8463
GEOMETRY GLOBAL - BOGOTA—See WPP plc; *Int'l*, pg. 8463
GEOMETRY GLOBAL - BRAZIL—See WPP plc; *Int'l*, pg. 8463
GEOMETRY GLOBAL - BUDAPEST—See WPP plc; *Int'l*, pg. 8463
GEOMETRY GLOBAL - BUENOS AIRES—See WPP plc; *Int'l*, pg. 8463
GEOMETRY GLOBAL - CAPE TOWN—See WPP plc; *Int'l*, pg. 8463
GEOMETRY GLOBAL - CARACAS—See WPP plc; *Int'l*, pg. 8463
GEOMETRY GLOBAL - COPENHAGEN—See WPP plc; *Int'l*, pg. 8463
GEOMETRY GLOBAL - DUBAI—See WPP plc; *Int'l*, pg. 8463
GEOMETRY GLOBAL - DUSSELDORF—See WPP plc; *Int'l*, pg. 8463
GEOMETRY GLOBAL - JAKARTA—See WPP plc; *Int'l*, pg. 8463
GEOMETRY GLOBAL - JOHANNESBURG—See WPP plc; *Int'l*, pg. 8463
GEOMETRY GLOBAL - KIEV—See WPP plc; *Int'l*, pg. 8463
GEOMETRY GLOBAL - LIMA—See WPP plc; *Int'l*, pg. 8463
GEOMETRY GLOBAL LIMITED—See WPP plc; *Int'l*, pg. 8463
GEOMETRY GLOBAL LLC—See WPP plc; *Int'l*, pg. 8463
GEOMETRY GLOBAL - MADRID—See WPP plc; *Int'l*, pg. 8463
GEOMETRY GLOBAL - MEXICO—See WPP plc; *Int'l*, pg. 8463
GEOMETRY GLOBAL - MILAN—See WPP plc; *Int'l*, pg. 8464
GEOMETRY GLOBAL - MUMBAI—See WPP plc; *Int'l*, pg. 8464
GEOMETRY GLOBAL - NEW ZEALAND—See WPP plc; *Int'l*, pg. 8464

COMPANY NAME INDEX

GEOMETRY GLOBAL - PARIS—See WPP plc; *Int'l*, pg. 8464
GEOMETRY GLOBAL - PRAGUE—See WPP plc; *Int'l*, pg. 8464
GEOMETRY GLOBAL - RIO DE JANEIRO—See WPP plc; *Int'l*, pg. 8463
GEOMETRY GLOBAL - SANTIAGO—See WPP plc; *Int'l*, pg. 8464
GEOMETRY GLOBAL - SEOUL—See WPP plc; *Int'l*, pg. 8464
GEOMETRY GLOBAL - SHANGHAI—See WPP plc; *Int'l*, pg. 8464
GEOMETRY GLOBAL - SINGAPORE—See WPP plc; *Int'l*, pg. 8464
GEOMETRY GLOBAL - TAIPEI—See WPP plc; *Int'l*, pg. 8464
GEOMETRY GLOBAL - TOKYO—See WPP plc; *Int'l*, pg. 8464
GEOMET S.R.O.—See CEZ, a.s.; *Int'l*, pg. 1428
GEOMET S.R.O—See European Metals Holdings Limited; *Int'l*, pg. 2557
GEOMET TECHNOLOGIES, LLC—See Kingswood Capital Management LLC; *U.S. Private*, pg. 2312
GEOMNI, INC.—See Verisk Analytics, Inc.; *U.S. Public*, pg. 2283
GEOMOG INC.—See Roche Ltd., Consulting Group; *Int'l*, pg. 6376
GEONERCO INC.; *U.S. Private*, pg. 1681
GEONETRIC, INC.; *U.S. Private*, pg. 1681
GEO NETWORKS CORPORATION—See GEO Holdings Corporation; *Int'l*, pg. 2932
GEONOR AS—See Lagercrantz Group AB; *Int'l*, pg. 4394
GEONOSTICS, INC.; *U.S. Private*, pg. 1681
GEOPACIFIC RESOURCES LIMITED; *Int'l*, pg. 2933
GEOPARK ARGENTINA LIMITED-BERMUDA—See GeoPark Limited; *Int'l*, pg. 2934
GEOPARK CHILE LIMITED-BERMUDA—See GeoPark Limited; *Int'l*, pg. 2934
GEOPARK LIMITED; *Int'l*, pg. 2934
GEO PAYMENT SERVICE CORPORATION—See GEO Holdings Corporation; *Int'l*, pg. 2932
GEOPETRO ALASKA LLC—See GeoPetro Resources Company; *U.S. Private*, pg. 1681
GEOPETRO RESOURCES COMPANY; *U.S. Private*, pg. 1681
GEOPHEX LTD.—See Geotech Ltd.; *Int'l*, pg. 2941
GEOPHY B.V.—See Walker & Dunlop, Inc.; *U.S. Public*, pg. 2324
GEOPHYSICAL ELECTRICAL SUPPLY, INC.; *U.S. Private*, pg. 1681
GEOPHYSICAL EXPLORATION TECHNOLOGY INC.—See Getech Group plc; *Int'l*, pg. 2947
GEOPHYSICAL SURVEYING CO., LTD.—See Japan Petroleum Exploration Co. Ltd.; *Int'l*, pg. 3900
GEOPHYSICAL SURVEY SYSTEMS, INC.—See OYO Corporation; *Int'l*, pg. 5678
GEOPIER FOUNDATION COMPANY—See Commercial Metals Company; *U.S. Public*, pg. 547
GEOPLAN NAMTECH INC.—See FinTech Global Incorporated; *Int'l*, pg. 2677
GEOPLIN D.O.O.—See Petrol, Slovenska energetska druzba, d.d.; *Int'l*, pg. 5827
GEOPOINT SURVEYING, INC.; *U.S. Private*, pg. 1681
GEOPOLIS SP. Z O.O.—See ComArch S.A.; *Int'l*, pg. 1707
GEOPOST SA—See La Poste S.A.; *Int'l*, pg. 4388
GEOPRIN S.A.—See Indra Sistemas, S.A.; *Int'l*, pg. 3661
GEOPROJECTS CANADA LIMITED—See RPS Group plc; *Int'l*, pg. 6415
GEOPROMINING LTD.; *Int'l*, pg. 2934
GEO PROPERTY GROUP LIMITED—See AVID Property Group; *Int'l*, pg. 743
GEOQUIP LIMITED—See CRH plc; *Int'l*, pg. 1844
GEORESULTS, INC.—See ShareTracker, LLC; *U.S. Private*, pg. 3626
GEORG D.O.O.—See OTP Bank Plc; *Int'l*, pg. 5657
GEORGE A. DICKEL & CO.—See Diageo plc; *Int'l*, pg. 2102
GEORGE A. GRANT, INC.; *U.S. Private*, pg. 1681
GEORGE BALLENTINE FORD INC.; *U.S. Private*, pg. 1681
GEORGE BANCO LIMITED—See Non-Standard Finance PLC; *Int'l*, pg. 5414
GEORGE B. HOLMAN & CO. INC.—See Xonex Inc.; *U.S. Private*, pg. 4582
GEORGE BRAZILLER, INC.; *U.S. Private*, pg. 1681
GEORGE B. WITTMER ASSOCIATES, INC.—See QSAM Biosciences, Inc.; *U.S. Public*, pg. 1744
GEORGE B. WOODCOCK & CO.; *U.S. Private*, pg. 1681
GEORGE C. BRANDT INC.; *U.S. Private*, pg. 1681
GEORGE CHEVROLET A CALIFORNIA CORPORATION; *U.S. Private*, pg. 1681
GEORGE C. HOPKINS CONSTRUCTION COMPANY, INC.; *U.S. Private*, pg. 1681
GEORGECO INC.; *U.S. Private*, pg. 1684
GEORGE COLEMAN MOTOR CO., INC.; *U.S. Private*, pg. 1681
GEORGE C. STAFFORD & SONS INC.; *U.S. Private*, pg. 1681

GEORGE DELALLO COMPANY, INC.; *U.S. Private*, pg. 1681
GEORGE E. BOOTH CO., INC.; *U.S. Private*, pg. 1681
GEORGE E. FERN COMPANY—See Budco Group, Inc.; *U.S. Private*, pg. 679
GEORGE E. MASKER, INC.; *U.S. Private*, pg. 1681
GEORGE E. WARREN CORPORATION; *U.S. Private*, pg. 1681
GEORGE F. BROCKE & SONS, INC.; *U.S. Private*, pg. 1681
GEORGE FISCHER IPS PTY LTD—See Georg Fischer AG; *Int'l*, pg. 2937
GEORGE FISCHER (M) SDN BHD—See Georg Fischer AG; *Int'l*, pg. 2937
GEORGE FISCHER SALES LTD—See Georg Fischer AG; *Int'l*, pg. 2937
GEORGE FISCHER SLOANE, INC.—See Georg Fischer AG; *Int'l*, pg. 2936
GEORGE F. KEMPF SUPPLY CO.; *U.S. Private*, pg. 1681
GEORGE FORREST INTERNATIONAL S.A.; *Int'l*, pg. 2938
GEORGE F. YOUNG, INC.; *U.S. Private*, pg. 1682
GEORGE GEE AUTOMOTIVE; *U.S. Private*, pg. 1682
GEORGE GLOVE CO., INC.; *U.S. Private*, pg. 1682
GEORGE GROUP INC; *U.S. Private*, pg. 1682
GEORGE G. SHARP INC.; *U.S. Private*, pg. 1682
GEORGE HARMS CONSTRUCTION COMPANY, INC.; *U.S. Private*, pg. 1682
GEORGE HARTE NISSAN INC.; *U.S. Private*, pg. 1682
GEORGE H. BLOUCH FUEL SERVICE; *U.S. Private*, pg. 1682
GEORGE H & IRENE L WALKER HOME FOR CHILDREN INCORPORATED; *U.S. Private*, pg. 1682
GEORGE INDUSTRIES, INC.—See Valmont Industries, Inc.; *U.S. Public*, pg. 2273
GEORGE INDUSTRIES LLC—See Behrman Brothers Management Corp.; *U.S. Private*, pg. 515
GEORGE I. REITZ & SONS INC.; *U.S. Private*, pg. 1682
GEORGE J. FOSTER CO. INC.; *U.S. Private*, pg. 1682
GEORGE J. HAYDEN INC.; *U.S. Private*, pg. 1682
GEORGE J. IGEL & COMPANY, INC.; *U.S. Private*, pg. 1682
GEORGE K. BAUM & COMPANY—See Stifel Financial Corp.; *U.S. Public*, pg. 1949
GEORGE K. BAUM HOLDINGS, INC.; *U.S. Private*, pg. 1682
GEORGE K. BAUM MERCHANT BANC—See George K. Baum Holdings, Inc.; *U.S. Private*, pg. 1682
GEORGE KENT (MALAYSIA) BERHAD; *Int'l*, pg. 2938
GEORGE KLEITZ + ASSOCIATES, INC., PUBLIC RELATIONS DIVISION; *U.S. Private*, pg. 1682
GEORGE KOCH SONS DE MEXICO S. DE R.L. DE C.V.—See Koch Enterprises, Inc.; *U.S. Private*, pg. 2326
GEORGE KOCH SONS EUROPE LTD.—See Koch Enterprises, Inc.; *U.S. Private*, pg. 2326
GEORGE KOCH SONS LLC—See Koch Enterprises, Inc.; *U.S. Private*, pg. 2326
GEORGE LAY SIGNS, INC.—See Miracle Signs, Inc.; *U.S. Private*, pg. 2745
GEORGE & LYNCH, INC.; *U.S. Private*, pg. 1681
GEORGE MASON MORTGAGE, LLC—See United Bankshares, Inc.; *U.S. Public*, pg. 2229
GEORGE M. TAYLOR & SON, INC.; *U.S. Private*, pg. 1682
GEORGE M. YOCUM, INCORPORATED; *U.S. Private*, pg. 1682
GEORGE NAHAS OLDSMOBILE INC.; *U.S. Private*, pg. 1682
GEORGE O. PASQUEL CO.; *U.S. Private*, pg. 1682
GEORGE PATTON ASSOCIATES, INC.—See Franz Haniel & Cie. GmbH; *Int'l*, pg. 2763
GEORGE P. BANE, INC.; *U.S. Private*, pg. 1682
GEORGE P. JOHNSON (AUSTRALIA) PTY., LTD.—See Project: Worldwide, Inc.; *U.S. Private*, pg. 3280
GEORGE P. JOHNSON BRASIL LTDA.—See Project: Worldwide, Inc.; *U.S. Private*, pg. 3281
GEORGE P. JOHNSON CO. - BOSTON—See Project: Worldwide, Inc.; *U.S. Private*, pg. 3281
GEORGE P. JOHNSON CO. - EMT DIVISION—See Project: Worldwide, Inc.; *U.S. Private*, pg. 3281
GEORGE P. JOHNSON CO. - G7 ENTERTAINMENT MARKETING—See Project: Worldwide, Inc.; *U.S. Private*, pg. 3281
GEORGE P. JOHNSON COMPANY - BELGIUM—See Project: Worldwide, Inc.; *U.S. Private*, pg. 3281
GEORGE P. JOHNSON CO. - SAN CARLOS—See Project: Worldwide, Inc.; *U.S. Private*, pg. 3281
GEORGE P. JOHNSON EVENT MARKETING CO. LTD.—See Project: Worldwide, Inc.; *U.S. Private*, pg. 3281
GEORGE P. JOHNSON EVENT MARKETING CO. LTD.—See Project: Worldwide, Inc.; *U.S. Private*, pg. 3281
GEORGE P. JOHNSON EVENT MARKETING PVT. LTD.—See Project: Worldwide, Inc.; *U.S. Private*, pg. 3281

GEORGE P. JOHNSON EVENT MARKETING PVT., LTD.—See Project: Worldwide, Inc.; *U.S. Private*, pg. 3281
GEORGE P. JOHNSON (FRANCE) SARL—See Project: Worldwide, Inc.; *U.S. Private*, pg. 3281
GEORGE P. JOHNSON GMBH—See Project: Worldwide, Inc.; *U.S. Private*, pg. 3281
GEORGE P. JOHNSON HONG KONG LTD.—See Project: Worldwide, Inc.; *U.S. Private*, pg. 3281
GEORGE P. JOHNSON (JAPAN) LTD.—See Project: Worldwide, Inc.; *U.S. Private*, pg. 3281
GEORGE P. JOHNSON (KOREA) LLC—See Project: Worldwide, Inc.; *U.S. Private*, pg. 3281
GEORGE P. JOHNSON (UK) LTD—See Project: Worldwide, Inc.; *U.S. Private*, pg. 3281
GEORGE P. REINTJES CO., INC.; *U.S. Private*, pg. 1682
GEORGE R. BROWN PARTNERSHIP; *U.S. Private*, pg. 1683
GEORGE RISK INDUSTRIES, INC.; *U.S. Public*, pg. 934
GEORGE SCHMITT & CO. INC.; *U.S. Private*, pg. 1683
GEORGE S. COYNE CHEMICAL CO. INC.; *U.S. Private*, pg. 1683
GEORGE'S FARMS INC.—See George's Inc.; *U.S. Private*, pg. 1683
GEORGE'S GAS CO. INC.—See George's Inc.; *U.S. Private*, pg. 1683
GEORGE'S INC. - CASSVILLE FEED MILL—See George's Inc.; *U.S. Private*, pg. 1683
GEORGE'S INC. - CASSVILLE PROCESSING PLANT—See George's Inc.; *U.S. Private*, pg. 1683
GEORGE'S INC. - EDINBURG PROCESSING PLANT—See George's Inc.; *U.S. Private*, pg. 1683
GEORGE'S INC. - HARRISONBURG FEED MILL—See George's Inc.; *U.S. Private*, pg. 1684
GEORGE'S INC. - HARRISONBURG PROCESSING PLANT—See George's Inc.; *U.S. Private*, pg. 1684
GEORGE'S INC. - MOUNT JACKSON FEED MILL—See George's Inc.; *U.S. Private*, pg. 1684
GEORGE'S INC.; *U.S. Private*, pg. 1683
GEORGE'S INC. - SPRINGDALE FEED MILL—See George's Inc.; *U.S. Private*, pg. 1684
GEORGE'S INC. - SPRINGDALE PLANT—See George's Inc.; *U.S. Private*, pg. 1684
GEORGE SOLLITT CONSTRUCTION; *U.S. Private*, pg. 1683
GEORGESON LLC—See Computershare Limited; *Int'l*, pg. 1760
GEORGESON SHAREHOLDER COMMUNICATIONS AUSTRALIA PTY. LTD.—See Computershare Limited; *Int'l*, pg. 1760
GEORGESON SHAREHOLDER SAS—See Computershare Limited; *Int'l*, pg. 1760
GEORGESON S.L.—See Computershare Limited; *Int'l*, pg. 1760
GEORGESON S.R.L.—See Computershare Limited; *Int'l*, pg. 1760
GEORGE'S PROCESSING INC.—See George's Inc.; *U.S. Private*, pg. 1684
GEORGES RENAULT S.A.—See Atlas Copco AB; *Int'l*, pg. 678
GEORGE STREET PHOTO & VIDEO, LLC; *U.S. Private*, pg. 1683
GEORGE SUTHERLIN NISSAN, LLC—See AutoNation, Inc.; *U.S. Public*, pg. 235
GEORGE T. HALL CO. INC.; *U.S. Private*, pg. 1683
GEORGE THIRD & SON PARTNERSHIP—See Dynamic Technologies Group Inc.; *Int'l*, pg. 2241
GEORGETOWN COMMUNICATIONS, INC.—See Evening Post Publishing Co.; *U.S. Private*, pg. 1436
GEORGETOWN COMMUNITY HOSPITAL, LLC—See Apollo Global Management, Inc.; *U.S. Public*, pg. 155
THE GEORGETOWN COMPANY, LLC; *U.S. Private*, pg. 4032
GEORGETOWN MANOR INC.; *U.S. Private*, pg. 1684
GEORGETOWN RETIREMENT RESIDENCE—See Holladay Corporation; *U.S. Private*, pg. 1963
GEORGETOWN WOODS SENIOR APARTMENTS, L.P.—See Apartment Investment and Management Company; *U.S. Public*, pg. 144
GEORGE T. SANDERS COMPANY; *U.S. Private*, pg. 1683
GEORGE T. SCHMIDT, INC.; *U.S. Private*, pg. 1683
GEORGETTE'S FASHIONS, INC.; *U.S. Private*, pg. 1684
GEORGE T. WILKINSON, INC.; *U.S. Private*, pg. 1683
GEORGE UHE COMPANY, INC.; *U.S. Private*, pg. 1683
GEORGE VETESNIK MOTORS INC.; *U.S. Private*, pg. 1683
GEORGE WASHINGTON CEMETERY COMPANY, LLC—See Service Corporation International; *U.S. Public*, pg. 1869
GEORGE WASHINGTON'S MOUNT VERNON; *U.S. Private*, pg. 1683
GEORGE W. AUCH COMPANY; *U.S. Private*, pg. 1683
GEORGE WEBER CHEVROLET COMPANY; *U.S. Private*, pg. 1683
GEORGE WEST MENTAL HEALTH FOUNDATION; *U.S. Private*, pg. 1683
GEORGE WESTON CONSUMER SERVICES—See George Weston Limited; *Int'l*, pg. 2939

GEORGE WEST MENTAL HEALTH FOUNDATION
CORPORATE AFFILIATIONS

GEORGE WESTON FOODS LIMITED—See The Garfield Weston Foundation; *Int'l*, pg. 7648
GEORGE WESTON FOODS (NZ) LIMITED—See The Garfield Weston Foundation; *Int'l*, pg. 7648
GEORGE WESTON LIMITED; *Int'l*, pg. 2938
GEORGE WILSON INDUSTRIES LIMITED; *Int'l*, pg. 2939
GEORGE W. LOWRY INC.; *U.S. Private*, pg. 1683
GEORGE W. PARK SEED COMPANY, INC.; *U.S. Private*, pg. 1683
GEORGE W. PRESCOTT PUBLISHING COMPANY, LLC—See Gannett Co., Inc.; *U.S. Public*, pg. 905
GEORGE W. WARDEN COMPANY INCORPORATED; *U.S. Private*, pg. 1683
GEORG FESSL GMBH.—See Swietelsky Baugesellschaft m.b.H.; *Int'l*, pg. 7367
GEORG FISCHER AB—See Georg Fischer AG; *Int'l*, pg. 2935
GEORG FISCHER AG; *Int'l*, pg. 2934
GEORG FISCHER A.S.—See Georg Fischer AG; *Int'l*, pg. 2935
GEORG FISCHER A/S—See Georg Fischer AG; *Int'l*, pg. 2935
GEORG FISCHER AUTOMOBILGUSS GMBH—See Georg Fischer AG; *Int'l*, pg. 2935
GEORG FISCHER AUTOMOBILGUSS GMBH—See Georg Fischer AG; *Int'l*, pg. 2935
GEORG FISCHER AUTOMOTIVE AG—See Georg Fischer AG; *Int'l*, pg. 2935
GEORG FISCHER AUTOMOTIVE (KUNSHAN) CO., LTD.—See Georg Fischer AG; *Int'l*, pg. 2935
GEORG FISCHER AUTOMOTIVE PRODUCTS INC.—See Georg Fischer AG; *Int'l*, pg. 2935
GEORG FISCHER AUTOMOTIVE (SUZHOU) CO LTD—See Georg Fischer AG; *Int'l*, pg. 2935
GEORG FISCHER CENTRAL PLASTICS CO.—See Georg Fischer AG; *Int'l*, pg. 2936
GEORG FISCHER CENTRAL PLASTICS SUDAMERICA SRL—See Georg Fischer AG; *Int'l*, pg. 2936
GEORG FISCHER CO LTD—See Georg Fischer AG; *Int'l*, pg. 2935
GEORG FISCHER DEKA GMBH—See Georg Fischer AG; *Int'l*, pg. 2935
GEORG FISCHER DRUCKGUSS GMBH & CO KG; *Int'l*, pg. 2938
GEORG FISCHER EISENGUSS GMBH—See Georg Fischer AG; *Int'l*, pg. 2935
GEORG FISCHER ENGINEERING AG—See Georg Fischer AG; *Int'l*, pg. 2935
GEORG FISCHER FAHRZEUGTECHNIK AG—See Georg Fischer AG; *Int'l*, pg. 2935
GEORG FISCHER FINANZ AG—See Georg Fischer AG; *Int'l*, pg. 2935
GEORG FISCHER FITTINGS GMBH—See Georg Fischer AG; *Int'l*, pg. 2935
GEORG FISCHER FLUORPOLYMER PRODUCTS GMBH—See Georg Fischer AG; *Int'l*, pg. 2935
GEORG FISCHER GESCHAFTSFUHRUNGS-GMBH—See Georg Fischer AG; *Int'l*, pg. 2935
GEORG FISCHER GIESSEREITECHNOLOGIE GMBH—See Georg Fischer AG; *Int'l*, pg. 2935
GEORG FISCHER GMBH & CO KG—See Georg Fischer AG; *Int'l*, pg. 2936
GEORG FISCHER GMBH & CO KG—See Georg Fischer AG; *Int'l*, pg. 2936
GEORG FISCHER GMBH—See Georg Fischer AG; *Int'l*, pg. 2935
GEORG FISCHER GMBH—See Georg Fischer AG; *Int'l*, pg. 2936
GEORG FISCHER (GREAT BRITAIN) LTD.—See Georg Fischer AG; *Int'l*, pg. 2935
GEORG FISCHER HARVEL LLC - BAKERSFIELD PLANT—See Georg Fischer AG; *Int'l*, pg. 2936
GEORG FISCHER HARVEL LLC—See Georg Fischer AG; *Int'l*, pg. 2936
GEORG FISCHER HOLDING (N.V.)—See Georg Fischer AG; *Int'l*, pg. 2936
GEORG FISCHER HOLDING SRL—See Georg Fischer AG; *Int'l*, pg. 2936
GEORG FISCHER IMMOBILIEN AG—See Georg Fischer AG; *Int'l*, pg. 2936
GEORG FISCHER JRG AG—See Georg Fischer AG; *Int'l*, pg. 2936
GEORG FISCHER KOKILLENGUSS GMBH—See Georg Fischer AG; *Int'l*, pg. 2936
GEORG FISCHER KOREA CO. LTD—See Georg Fischer AG; *Int'l*, pg. 2936
GEORG FISCHER KUNSTSTOFFARMATUREN AG—See Georg Fischer AG; *Int'l*, pg. 2936
GEORG FISCHER LIEGENSCHAFTEN AG—See Georg Fischer AG; *Int'l*, pg. 2936
GEORG FISCHER LLC—See Georg Fischer AG; *Int'l*, pg. 2936
GEORG FISCHER LTD.—See Georg Fischer AG; *Int'l*, pg. 2936
GEORG FISCHER LTD—See Georg Fischer AG; *Int'l*, pg. 2936
GEORG FISCHER NV-SA—See Georg Fischer AG; *Int'l*, pg. 2936

GEORG FISCHER N.V.—See Georg Fischer AG; *Int'l*, pg. 2936
GEORG FISCHER OMICRON SRL—See Georg Fischer AG; *Int'l*, pg. 2936
GEORG FISCHER PFCI SRL—See Georg Fischer AG; *Int'l*, pg. 2936
GEORG FISCHER PIPING SYSTEMS LTD.—See Georg Fischer AG; *Int'l*, pg. 2936
GEORG FISCHER PIPING SYSTEMS LTD—See Georg Fischer AG; *Int'l*, pg. 2936
GEORG FISCHER PIPING SYSTEMS LTD—See Georg Fischer AG; *Int'l*, pg. 2936
GEORG FISCHER PIPING SYSTEMS LTD—See Georg Fischer AG; *Int'l*, pg. 2936
GEORG FISCHER PIPING SYSTEMS PVT LTD—See Georg Fischer AG; *Int'l*, pg. 2936
GEORG FISCHER PIPING SYSTEMS (TRADING) LTD—See Georg Fischer AG; *Int'l*, pg. 2936
GEORG FISCHER PTE. LTD.—See Georg Fischer AG; *Int'l*, pg. 2936
GEORG FISCHER PTY. LTD.—See Georg Fischer AG; *Int'l*, pg. 2936
GEORG FISCHER PTY. LTD.—See Georg Fischer AG; *Int'l*, pg. 2936
GEORG FISCHER RISK MANAGEMENT AG—See Georg Fischer AG; *Int'l*, pg. 2936
GEORG FISCHER ROHRLEITUNGSSYSTEME AG—See Georg Fischer AG; *Int'l*, pg. 2937
GEORG FISCHER ROHRLEITUNGSSYSTEME (ELVETIA) S.A.—See Georg Fischer AG; *Int'l*, pg. 2936
GEORG FISCHER ROHRLEITUNGSSYSTEME (SCHWEIZ) AG—See Georg Fischer AG; *Int'l*, pg. 2936
GEORG FISCHER ROHRLEITUNGSSYSTEMS GMBH—See Georg Fischer AG; *Int'l*, pg. 2937
GEORG FISCHER SA DE CV—See Georg Fischer AG; *Int'l*, pg. 2937
GEORG FISCHER SALES LTD.—See Georg Fischer AG; *Int'l*, pg. 2937
GEORG FISCHER, S.A.—See Georg Fischer AG; *Int'l*, pg. 2937
GEORG FISCHER SAS—See Georg Fischer AG; *Int'l*, pg. 2937
GEORG FISCHER SIGNET LLC—See Georg Fischer AG; *Int'l*, pg. 2936
GEORG FISCHER SISTEMAS DE TUBULACOES LTDA—See Georg Fischer AG; *Int'l*, pg. 2937
GEORG FISCHER S.P.A.—See Georg Fischer AG; *Int'l*, pg. 2937
GEORG FISCHER S.P.A.—See Georg Fischer AG; *Int'l*, pg. 2937
GEORG FISCHER SP. Z.O.O.—See Georg Fischer AG; *Int'l*, pg. 2937
GEORG FISCHER TPA SRL—See Georg Fischer AG; *Int'l*, pg. 2937
GEORG FISCHER TRENTON LTD.—See Georg Fischer AG; *Int'l*, pg. 2937
GEORG FISCHER VERWALTUNGS GMBH—See Georg Fischer AG; *Int'l*, pg. 2937
GEORG FISCHER WAGA N.V.—See Georg Fischer AG; *Int'l*, pg. 2937
GEORG H. LUH FARBEN- UND CHEMIKALIEN GROSSHANDELSGES GMBH; *Int'l*, pg. 2938
GEORGIA/ATLANTIC CONTRACTORS, INC; *U.S. Private*, pg. 1685
GEORGIA AUTOMOTIVE GROUP, INC.—See General Motors Company; *U.S. Public*, pg. 925
GEORGIA BANKING COMPANY—See FJ Capital Management; *U.S. Private*, pg. 1538
GEORGIA BANKING COMPANY—See Independence Capital Partners, LLC; *U.S. Private*, pg. 2056
GEORGIA BIOMASS, LLC—See Enviva Inc.; *U.S. Public*, pg. 782
GEORGIA BOOT, LLC—See Rocky Brands, Inc.; *U.S. Public*, pg. 1807
GEORGIA CAPITAL PLC; *Int'l*, pg. 2939
GEORGIA CASH AMERICA, INC.—See FirstCash Holdings, Inc.; *U.S. Public*, pg. 849
GEORGIA CENTRAL RAILWAY, L.P.—See Brookfield Infrastructure Partners L.P.; *Int'l*, pg. 1191
GEORGIA CENTRAL RAILWAY, L.P.—See GIC Pte. Ltd.; *Int'l*, pg. 2966
GEORGIA COMPOSITES, LLC.—See Innovative Composites International, Inc.; *Int'l*, pg. 3712
GEORGIA CORRECTIONAL INDUSTRIES; *U.S. Private*, pg. 1684
GEORGIA CRATE & BASKET COMPANY; *U.S. Private*, pg. 1684
GEORGIA CROWN DISTRIBUTING CO.; *U.S. Private*, pg. 1684
GEORGIA DUPLICATING PRODUCTS, INC.—See Xerox Holdings Corporation; *U.S. Public*, pg. 2632
GEORGIA ELECTRIC MEMBERSHIP CORPORATION; *U.S. Private*, pg. 1684
GEORGIA ENDOSCOPY CENTER, LLC—See Tenet Healthcare Corporation; *U.S. Public*, pg. 2010
GEORGIA ENERGY COOPERATIVE; *U.S. Private*, pg. 1684
GEORGIA FARM BUREAU FEDERATION; *U.S. Private*, pg. 1684

GEORGIA FARM BUREAU MUTUAL INSURANCE CO.; *U.S. Private*, pg. 1684
GEORGIA FENCE WHOLESALE INC.; *U.S. Private*, pg. 1684
GEORGIA FIRE-RESCUE SUPPLY—See Ilustrato Pictures International Inc.; *Int'l*, pg. 3616
GEORGIA & FLORIDA RAILWAY, LLC—See The Broe Companies, Inc.; *U.S. Private*, pg. 4001
GEORGIA GOAL SCHOLARSHIP PROGRAM, INC.; *U.S. Private*, pg. 1684
GEORGIA HEALTHCARE GROUP PLC—See Georgia Capital PLC; *Int'l*, pg. 2939
GEORGIA HOMECARE OF HARRIS, LLC—See UnitedHealth Group Incorporated; *U.S. Public*, pg. 2245
GEORGIA HOME MEDICAL, INC.—See AdaptHealth Corp.; *U.S. Public*, pg. 38
GEORGIA INTERNATIONAL TRAVEL, INC.—See ABRY Partners, LLC; *U.S. Private*, pg. 41
GEORGIA KAOLIN TERMINALS, INC.—See Colonial Group, Inc.; *U.S. Private*, pg. 971
GEORGIA LAND EQUIPMENT LLC—See Tym Corporation; *Int'l*, pg. 7994
GEORGIA LEGAL SERVICES PROGRAM; *U.S. Private*, pg. 1684
GEORGIA LOGOS, L.L.C.—See Lamar Advertising Company; *U.S. Public*, pg. 1290
GEORGIA METAL COATINGS CO.—See NOF Corporation; *Int'l*, pg. 5399
GEORGIA MOTOR TRUCKS INC.; *U.S. Private*, pg. 1684
GEORGIA MUSEUMS, INC.; *U.S. Private*, pg. 1684
GEORGIAN AIRWAYS LTD.; *Int'l*, pg. 2939
GEORGIA NATURAL GAS COMPANY—See The Southern Company; *U.S. Public*, pg. 2131
GEORGIAN CHEVROLET BUICK GMC; *Int'l*, pg. 2939
GEORGIAN DOWNS LIMITED—See Great Canadian Gaming Corporation; *Int'l*, pg. 3063
THE GEORGIAN HOTEL—See BLVD Companies; *U.S. Private*, pg. 600
THE GEORGIAN HOTEL—See ESI Ventures LLC; *U.S. Private*, pg. 1426
THE GEORGIAN HOTEL—See Global Mutual Properties Limited; *Int'l*, pg. 2999
GEORGIAN INTERNATIONAL LIMITED; *Int'l*, pg. 2939
GEORGIAN LEASING COMPANY LTD.—See JSC Bank of Georgia; *Int'l*, pg. 4008
GEORGIA NORTH FOODS INC.; *U.S. Private*, pg. 1684
GEORGIA NORTHSIDE EAR, NOSE AND THROAT, L.L.C.—See Tenet Healthcare Corporation; *U.S. Public*, pg. 2002
GEORGIAN PARTNERS GROWTH LP; *Int'l*, pg. 2939
GEORGIAN STOCK EXCHANGE; *Int'l*, pg. 2939
GEORGIA NUT COMPANY; *U.S. Private*, pg. 1684
GEORGIAN WATER AND POWER, LLC—See Georgia Capital PLC; *Int'l*, pg. 2939
GEORGIA-PACIFIC CANADA, INC.—See Koch Industries, Inc.; *U.S. Private*, pg. 2328
GEORGIA-PACIFIC CONSUMER PRODUCTS LP—See Koch Industries, Inc.; *U.S. Private*, pg. 2328
GEORGIA-PACIFIC CONTAINERBOARD LLC—See Koch Industries, Inc.; *U.S. Private*, pg. 2328
GEORGIA-PACIFIC CORPORATION PRYOR—See Koch Industries, Inc.; *U.S. Private*, pg. 2328
GEORGIA-PACIFIC CORPORATION—See Koch Industries, Inc.; *U.S. Private*, pg. 2327
GEORGIA-PACIFIC CORPORATION—See Koch Industries, Inc.; *U.S. Private*, pg. 2327
GEORGIA-PACIFIC CORPORATION—See Koch Industries, Inc.; *U.S. Private*, pg. 2327
GEORGIA-PACIFIC CORPORATION—See Koch Industries, Inc.; *U.S. Private*, pg. 2327
GEORGIA-PACIFIC CORPORATION—See Koch Industries, Inc.; *U.S. Private*, pg. 2327
GEORGIA-PACIFIC CORPORATION—See Koch Industries, Inc.; *U.S. Private*, pg. 2329
GEORGIA-PACIFIC CORPORATION—See Koch Industries, Inc.; *U.S. Private*, pg. 2329
GEORGIA-PACIFIC CORPORATION—See Koch Industries, Inc.; *U.S. Private*, pg. 2328
GEORGIA-PACIFIC CORPORATION—See Koch Industries, Inc.; *U.S. Private*, pg. 2328
GEORGIA-PACIFIC CORPORATION—See Koch Industries, Inc.; *U.S. Private*, pg. 2328
GEORGIA-PACIFIC CORPORATION—See Koch Industries, Inc.; *U.S. Private*, pg. 2328
GEORGIA-PACIFIC CORPORATION—See Koch Industries, Inc.; *U.S. Private*, pg. 2328
GEORGIA-PACIFIC CORPORATION—See Koch Industries, Inc.; *U.S. Private*, pg. 2328
GEORGIA-PACIFIC CORPORATION—See Koch Industries, Inc.; *U.S. Private*, pg. 2328
GEORGIA-PACIFIC CORPORATION—See Koch Industries, Inc.; *U.S. Private*, pg. 2328
GEORGIA-PACIFIC CORPORATION—See Koch Industries, Inc.; *U.S. Private*, pg. 2328

COMPANY NAME INDEX

GEORGIA-PACIFIC CORPORATION—See Koch Industries, Inc.; *U.S. Private*, pg. 2328
GEORGIA-PACIFIC CORPORATION—See Koch Industries, Inc.; *U.S. Private*, pg. 2329
GEORGIA-PACIFIC CORRUGATED-MARTINSVILLE FACILITY—See Koch Industries, Inc.; *U.S. Private*, pg. 2328
GEORGIA-PACIFIC FAYETTE LUMBER PLANT—See Koch Industries, Inc.; *U.S. Private*, pg. 2328
GEORGIA-PACIFIC GREEN BAY OPERATIONS—See Koch Industries, Inc.; *U.S. Private*, pg. 2328
GEORGIA-PACIFIC GURDON WOOD PRODUCTS COMPLEX—See Koch Industries, Inc.; *U.S. Private*, pg. 2328
GEORGIA-PACIFIC GYPSUM LLC - LAS VEGAS TOUGHROCK PLANT—See Koch Industries, Inc.; *U.S. Private*, pg. 2328
GEORGIA-PACIFIC GYPSUM LLC—See Koch Industries, Inc.; *U.S. Private*, pg. 2328
GEORGIA-PACIFIC LLC—See Koch Industries, Inc.; *U.S. Private*, pg. 2327
GEORGIA-PACIFIC MONTICELLO PRE-FINISHED MDF PLANT—See Koch Industries, Inc.; *U.S. Private*, pg. 2328
GEORGIA-PACIFIC MUSKOGEE—See Koch Industries, Inc.; *U.S. Private*, pg. 2329
GEORGIA-PACIFIC ORIENTED STRAND BOARD PLANT—See Koch Industries, Inc.; *U.S. Private*, pg. 2328
GEORGIA-PACIFIC ORIENTED STRAND BOARD PLANT—See Koch Industries, Inc.; *U.S. Private*, pg. 2328
GEORGIA-PACIFIC PACKAGING - AUGUSTA—See Koch Industries, Inc.; *U.S. Private*, pg. 2328
GEORGIA-PACIFIC PACKAGING DIVISION—See Koch Industries, Inc.; *U.S. Private*, pg. 2328
GEORGIA-PACIFIC PALATKA PULP & PAPER OPERATIONS—See Koch Industries, Inc.; *U.S. Private*, pg. 2328
GEORGIA-PACIFIC PAPER DIVISION—See Koch Industries, Inc.; *U.S. Private*, pg. 2328
GEORGIA-PACIFIC PINE CHIP & SAW MILL—See Koch Industries, Inc.; *U.S. Private*, pg. 2328
GEORGIA PACIFIC PLYWOOD PLANT—See Koch Industries, Inc.; *U.S. Private*, pg. 2328
GEORGIA-PACIFIC PLYWOOD PLANT—See Koch Industries, Inc.; *U.S. Private*, pg. 2328
GEORGIA-PACIFIC PLYWOOD PLANT—See Koch Industries, Inc.; *U.S. Private*, pg. 2328
GEORGIA PACIFIC PULP & PAPER MILL—See Koch Industries, Inc.; *U.S. Private*, pg. 2327
GEORGIA-PACIFIC PULP & PAPER MILL—See Koch Industries, Inc.; *U.S. Private*, pg. 2328
GEORGIA-PACIFIC PULP & PAPER MILL—See Koch Industries, Inc.; *U.S. Private*, pg. 2328
GEORGIA-PACIFIC PULP & PAPER MILL—See Koch Industries, Inc.; *U.S. Private*, pg. 2328
GEORGIA-PACIFIC RESINS, INC.—See Koch Industries, Inc.; *U.S. Private*, pg. 2329
GEORGIA-PACIFIC RESINS, INC.—See Koch Industries, Inc.; *U.S. Private*, pg. 2329
GEORGIA-PACIFIC RESINS TAYLORSVILLE—See Koch Industries, Inc.; *U.S. Private*, pg. 2329
GEORGIA-PACIFIC RESINS VIENNA—See Koch Industries, Inc.; *U.S. Private*, pg. 2329
GEORGIA-PACIFIC SAW MILL—See Koch Industries, Inc.; *U.S. Private*, pg. 2328
GEORGIA-PACIFIC SOFTWOOD SAWMILL—See Koch Industries, Inc.; *U.S. Private*, pg. 2328
GEORGIA-PACIFIC WEST, INC.—See Koch Industries, Inc.; *U.S. Private*, pg. 2329
GEORGIA-PACIFIC WOOD PRODUCTS LLC—See Koch Industries, Inc.; *U.S. Private*, pg. 2329
GEORGIA PERFECT PACKERS—See HI-Boy Group Inc.; *U.S. Private*, pg. 1931
GEORGIA PHYSICAL THERAPY, INC.—See Select Medical Holdings Corporation; *U.S. Public*, pg. 1858
GEORGIA PIPE COMPANY—See Clayton, Dubilier & Rice, LLC; *U.S. Private*, pg. 919
GEORGIA POWER COMPANY—See The Southern Company; *U.S. Public*, pg. 2130
GEORGIA PUBLIC WEB—See OpenFiber Kentucky Co. LLC; *U.S. Private*, pg. 3030
GEORGIA SCAPES, INC.—See Centre Partners Management LLC; *U.S. Private*, pg. 829
GEORGIA SCAPES, INC.—See LP First Capital; *U.S. Private*, pg. 2507
GEORGIA'S OWN CREDIT UNION; *U.S. Private*, pg. 1685
GEORGIA SPINE SURGERY CENTER, LLC—See Tenet Healthcare Corporation; *U.S. Public*, pg. 2002
GEORGIA TELEVISION COMPANY—See Apollo Global Management, Inc.; *U.S. Public*, pg. 164
GEORGIA TRANSMISSION CORPORATION; *U.S. Private*, pg. 1684
GEORGIA UNITED CREDIT UNION; *U.S. Private*, pg. 1685
GEORGIA WASTE SYSTEMS, INC.—See Waste Management, Inc.; *U.S. Private*, pg. 2331

GEORGIA WOODLANDS RAILROAD—See The Broe Companies, Inc.; *U.S. Private*, pg. 4001
GEORGIA WORLD CONGRESS CENTER AUTHORITY; *U.S. Private*, pg. 1685
GEORGINO INDUSTRIAL SUPPLY; *U.S. Private*, pg. 1685
GEORGIOU GROUP PTY. LTD.; *Int'l*, pg. 2939
GEORG JENSEN ANTIQUES—See Investcorp Holdings B.S.C.; *Int'l*, pg. 3776
GEORG JENSEN A/S—See Investcorp Holdings B.S.C.; *Int'l*, pg. 3775
GEORG KESEL GMBH & CO. KG—See Gesco AG; *Int'l*, pg. 2945
GEORG PIENING GMBH & CO. KG—See AGRAVIS Raiffeisen AG; *Int'l*, pg. 215
GEORG PIENING HAUSTECHNIK UND ENERGIESERVICE GMBH—See AGRAVIS Raiffeisen AG; *Int'l*, pg. 215
GEORG SAHM GMBH & CO. KG—See Starlinger & Co. GmbH; *Int'l*, pg. 7178
GEORG SCHARDT KG; *Int'l*, pg. 2938
GEORGSMARIENHUTTE GMBH—See Georgsmarienhutte Holding GmbH; *Int'l*, pg. 2940
GEORGSMARIENHUTTE HOLDING GMBH; *Int'l*, pg. 2940
GEORG VON HOLTZBRINCK GMBH & CO. KG—See Verlagsgruppe Georg von Holtzbrinck GmbH; *Int'l*, pg. 8169
GEO. R. PIERCE INC.; *U.S. Private*, pg. 1680
GEOSCAPE CORPORATION—See Hazama Ando Corporation; *Int'l*, pg. 3294
GEO. SCHOFIELD CO. INC.—See Trilantic Capital Management L.P.; *U.S. Private*, pg. 4231
GEOSCIENCE ASSOCIATES AUSTRALIA PTY. LTD.—See UXA Resources Limited; *Int'l*, pg. 8102
GEOSCIENCE (BEIJING) LTD.—See CGG; *Int'l*, pg. 1432
GEOSEARCH SOUTH AFRICA (PROPRIETARY) LIMITED—See Unicorn Capital Partners Limited; *Int'l*, pg. 8033
GEO SEMICONDUCTOR INC.—See indie Semiconductor, Inc.; *U.S. Public*, pg. 1116
GEOSERVICES, LLC—See Suhail Bahwan Group (Holding) LLC; *Int'l*, pg. 7254
GEOSIDE S.P.A.—See Italgas S.p.A.; *Int'l*, pg. 3828
GEOSMART INTERNATIONAL PTE. LTD.—See OYO Corporation; *Int'l*, pg. 5678
GEOSOFT INC.—See Bentley Systems, Inc.; *U.S. Public*, pg. 297
GEOSOFT PTE LTD—See Tritech Group Limited; *Int'l*, pg. 7928
GEOSOL BETEILIGUNGSGESELLSCHAFT MBH—See Japan Asia Group Limited; *Int'l*, pg. 3885
GEOSOL ITALIA S.R.L.—See Japan Asia Group Limited; *Int'l*, pg. 3885
GEO-SOLUTIONS INC.; *U.S. Private*, pg. 1680
GEOSOLUTIONS, LLC—See Peak Rock Capital LLC; *U.S. Private*, pg. 3124
GEOSONDA BVBA—See ABO-Group NV/SA; *Int'l*, pg. 66
GEOSONDA ENVIRONMENT NV—See ABO-Group NV/SA; *Int'l*, pg. 66
GEOSONDA-FUNDIRANJE A.D.; *Int'l*, pg. 2941
GEOSONDA KONSOLIDACIJA A.D.; *Int'l*, pg. 2941
GEOSONDA NETHERLANDS BV—See ABO-Group NV/SA; *Int'l*, pg. 66
GEOSONIC FRANCE SAS—See ABO-Group NV/SA; *Int'l*, pg. 66
GEOSPACE ENGINEERING RESOURCES INTERNATIONAL, INC.—See GEOSPACE TECHNOLOGIES CORPORATION; *U.S. Public*, pg. 934
GEOSPACE TECHNOLOGIES CANADA, INC.—See GEOSPACE TECHNOLOGIES CORPORATION; *U.S. Public*, pg. 934
GEOSPACE TECHNOLOGIES CORPORATION; *U.S. Public*, pg. 934
GEO SPECIALTY CHEMICALS - BASTROP—See Arsenal Capital Management LP; *U.S. Private*, pg. 337
GEO SPECIALTY CHEMICALS - CEDARTOWN—See Arsenal Capital Management LP; *U.S. Private*, pg. 337
GEO SPECIALTY CHEMICALS, INC.—See Arsenal Capital Management LP; *U.S. Private*, pg. 337
GEOSPHERE CONSULTANTS, INC.—See GI Manager L.P.; *U.S. Private*, pg. 1691
GEOSPIZA, INC.—See Revvity, Inc.; *U.S. Public*, pg. 1794
GE.O.S. SARDEGNA S.R.L.—See IVS Group S.A.; *Int'l*, pg. 3848
GEOSTELLAR, INC.—See NRG Energy, Inc.; *U.S. Public*, pg. 1550
GEOST LLC—See ATL Partners, LLC; *U.S. Private*, pg. 369
GEOSTOCK ASIA PTE LTD.—See VINCI S.A.; *Int'l*, pg. 8218
GEOSTOCK SANDIA INC.—See VINCI S.A.; *Int'l*, pg. 8218
GEOSTRATA RESOURCES INC.; *Int'l*, pg. 2941
GEOSYNTEC CONSULTANTS, INC. - ACTON—See Geosyntec Consultants, Inc.; *U.S. Private*, pg. 1685
GEOSYNTEC CONSULTANTS, INC. - COLORADO—See Geosyntec Consultants, Inc.; *U.S. Private*, pg. 1685
GEOSYNTEC CONSULTANTS, INC.; *U.S. Private*, pg. 1685

GEO-SYNTHETICS, INC.; *U.S. Private*, pg. 1680
GEOSYS, INC.—See Japan Petroleum Exploration Co. Ltd.; *Int'l*, pg. 3900
GEOSYSTEMS GESELLSCHAFT FUR VERTRIEB UND INSTALLATION VON FERNERKUNDUNGS- UND GEOINFORMATIONSSYSTEMEN MBH—See OHB SE; *Int'l*, pg. 5532
GEO SYSTEM SOLUTIONS VIETNAM CO., LTD.—See GEO Holdings Corporation; *Int'l*, pg. 2932
GEOTAB, INC.; *Int'l*, pg. 2941
GEOTAG INC.; *U.S. Private*, pg. 1685
GEOTECH AVIATION LTD.—See Geotech Ltd.; *Int'l*, pg. 2941
GEOTECH ENVIRONMENTAL EQUIPMENT, INC.; *U.S. Private*, pg. 1685
GEOTECH HOLDINGS LTD.; *Int'l*, pg. 2941
GEOTECH INSTRUMENTS—See Geotech Environmental Equipment, Inc.; *U.S. Private*, pg. 1685
GEOTECH LTD.; *Int'l*, pg. 2941
GEOTECHNICAL INSTRUMENTS (HONG KONG) LTD.—See Fugro N.V.; *Int'l*, pg. 2808
GEOTECHNICAL INSTRUMENTS (U.K.) LIMITED—See Graco, Inc.; *U.S. Public*, pg. 953
GEO TECHNICAL LABORATORY CO., LTD.—See Zenrin Co., Ltd.; *Int'l*, pg. 8634
GEOTECHNICAL SERVICES LTD—See Taylor Smith Group; *Int'l*, pg. 7478
GEOTECHNOS CO., LTD.—See Dowa Holdings Co., Ltd.; *Int'l*, pg. 2184
GEO-TECH POLYMERS, LLC—See Wastren Advantage, Inc.; *U.S. Private*, pg. 4451
GEOTECH PTY LTD.—See Acciona, S.A.; *Int'l*, pg. 90
GEOTECH SEISMIC SERVICES PJSC; *Int'l*, pg. 2941
GEOTECNIA y CIMIENTOS, S.A.—See ACS, Actividades de Construccion y Servicios, S.A.; *Int'l*, pg. 112
GEOTEHNIKA-INZENJERING D.O.O.—See INSTITUT IGH d.d.; *Int'l*, pg. 3723
GEOTEK, INC.—See Granite Equity Partners LLC; *U.S. Private*, pg. 1755
GEOTEMPS INC.; *U.S. Private*, pg. 1685
GEOTESTING LIMITED—See WSP Global, Inc.; *Int'l*, pg. 8496
GEOTEXT TRANSLATIONS, INC.—See Geotext Translations, Inc.; *U.S. Private*, pg. 1685
GEOTEXT TRANSLATIONS, INC.; *U.S. Private*, pg. 1685
GEOTHERMAL EXPLORATION CO., INC.—See Barnwell Industries, Inc.; *U.S. Public*, pg. 278
GEOTHERMAL RESOURCES LIMITED—See Havilah Resources Limited; *Int'l*, pg. 3287
GEOTHERMIE NEURIED VERWALTUNGS GMBH—See Daldrup & Sohne AG; *Int'l*, pg. 1950
GEOTIK SP. Z O.O.—See Arcus S.A.; *Int'l*, pg. 553
GEOTRAC SYSTEMS INC.—See Trimble, Inc.; *U.S. Public*, pg. 2190
GEOTRAQ INC.—See ALT5 Sigma Corporation; *U.S. Public*, pg. 85
GEOTRIM OY—See Indutrade AB; *Int'l*, pg. 3679
GEOTRON CIA. LTDA.—See Aiphone Co., Ltd.; *Int'l*, pg. 235
GEOTRONICS SOUTHERN EUROPE S.L—See Trimble, Inc.; *U.S. Public*, pg. 2190
GEOVANTAGE, INC.—See Jacobs Engineering Group, Inc.; *U.S. Public*, pg. 1186
GEOVAULT PTY LIMITED—See Buru Energy Limited; *Int'l*, pg. 1227
GEOVAX LABS, INC.; *U.S. Public*, pg. 934
GEO V BULLEN & SON, INC.—See Kelso & Company, L.P.; *U.S. Private*, pg. 2279
GEOVERA HOLDINGS, INC.—See Edwards Capital, LLC; *U.S. Private*, pg. 1341
GEOVERA INSURANCE COMPANY INC.—See Edwards Capital, LLC; *U.S. Private*, pg. 1341
GEOVIC MINING CORP.; *U.S. Private*, pg. 1685
GEOVIEW, INC.—See Ambient Technologies, Inc.; *U.S. Private*, pg. 217
GEOVISION INC.; *Int'l*, pg. 2942
GEOVISION JAPAN INC.—See GeoVision Inc.; *Int'l*, pg. 2942
GEOVISION TECHNOLOGY (SHANGHAI) CO., LTD.—See GeoVision Inc.; *Int'l*, pg. 2942
GEOVISION VIETNAM SYSTEMS CO., LTD.—See GeoVision Inc.; *Int'l*, pg. 2942
GEOVIS TECHNOLOGY CO., LTD.; *Int'l*, pg. 2942
GEOVITA FUNTIONAL INGREDIENTS S.R.L.—See Ebro Foods S.A.; *Int'l*, pg. 2286
GEOVITA SP. Z O.O.—See Polskie Gornictwo Naftowe i Gazownictwo S.A.; *Int'l*, pg. 5912
GEOVITA S.R.L.—See Ebro Foods S.A.; *Int'l*, pg. 2286
GEOWAGGLE, LLC; *U.S. Private*, pg. 1685
GEO WEB SERVICE CO., LTD—See GEO Holdings Corporation; *Int'l*, pg. 2932
GEOX S.P.A.—See LIR S.r.l.; *Int'l*, pg. 4523
GE PACIFIC PTE. LTD.—See General Electric Company; *U.S. Public*, pg. 917
GE PACKAGED POWER, INC.—See General Electric Company; *U.S. Public*, pg. 917
GE PACKAGED POWER, L.P.—See General Electric Company; *U.S. Public*, pg. 917

GEOWAGGLE, LLC

CORPORATE AFFILIATIONS

GEPADI FLIESEN GMBH—See Sto SE & Co. KGaA; *Int'l*, pg. 7219
GEPADO - SOFTWARELOSUNGEN FUR GENETIK - GMBH—See NEXUS AG; *Int'l*, pg. 5250
GEPBER HUNGARIA KFT—See Group Thermote & Vanhalst; *Int'l*, pg. 3089
GEPCO, LTD.; *U.S. Private*, pg. 1685
GEPE-BIWEX AB—See Gepe Holding AG; *Int'l*, pg. 2942
GEPE-GEIMUPLAST GMBH—See Gepe Holding AG; *Int'l*, pg. 2942
GEPE HOLDING AG; *Int'l*, pg. 2942
GEP ENERGIES SA—See Global EcoPower SA; *Int'l*, pg. 2995
GEP - GESTAO DE PERITAGENS AUTOMOVEIS, S.A.—See Caixa Geral de Depositos S.A.; *Int'l*, pg. 1260
GEPIC ENERGY DEVELOPMENT CO., LTD.; *Int'l*, pg. 2942
GE POWER AG—See General Electric Company; *U.S. Public*, pg. 917
GE POWER CONVERSION FRANCE SAS—See General Electric Company; *U.S. Public*, pg. 917
GE POWER CONVERSION—See General Electric Company; *U.S. Public*, pg. 917
GE POWER CONVERSION UK LTD.—See General Electric Company; *U.S. Public*, pg. 917
GE POWER INDIA LIMITED; *Int'l*, pg. 2897
GE POWER NORWAY AS—See General Electric Company; *U.S. Public*, pg. 917
GE POWER—See General Electric Company; *U.S. Public*, pg. 917
GE POWER—See General Electric Company; *U.S. Public*, pg. 917
GE POWER S.R.O—See General Electric Company; *U.S. Public*, pg. 917
GE POWER SWEDEN AB—See General Electric Company; *U.S. Public*, pg. 917
GE POWER SWEDEN AB—See General Electric Company; *U.S. Public*, pg. 917
GE POWER SWEDEN AB—See General Electric Company; *U.S. Public*, pg. 917
GE POWER SYSTEMS GMBH—See General Electric Company; *U.S. Public*, pg. 917
GEPROM SOFTWARE ENGINEERING S.A. DE C.V.—See Telefonica, S.A.; *Int'l*, pg. 7535
GEPROM SOFTWARE ENGINEERING S.L.—See Telefonica, S.A.; *Int'l*, pg. 7535
GEPSA—See ENGIE SA; *Int'l*, pg. 2431
GER2I—See Eiffage S.A.; *Int'l*, pg. 2331
GERACE CONSTRUCTION COMPANY INC.; *U.S. Private*, pg. 1685
GERAER BATTERIE-DIENST GMBH; *Int'l*, pg. 2942
GERAK INTENSIF SDN. BHD.—See Transocean Holdings Bhd.; *Int'l*, pg. 7902
GERAL AUTOMATION SA—See Gerard Perrier Industrie S.A.; *Int'l*, pg. 2942
GERAL CONSTRUCTIONS ELECTRIQUES ET TRAVAUX INDUSTRIELS SAS—See Gerard Perrier Industrie S.A.; *Int'l*, pg. 2942
GERALD EVE FINANCIAL SERVICES LIMITED—See Alkido Pharma Inc.; *U.S. Public*, pg. 63
GERALD FINANCIAL GROUP INC—See Gerald Metals Inc.; *U.S. Private*, pg. 1686
GERALD GRAIN CENTER INC.; *U.S. Private*, pg. 1685
GERALD H. PHIPPS, INC.; *U.S. Private*, pg. 1685
GERALDINE NOMINEES PTY LTD—See Eagers Automotive Limited; *Int'l*, pg. 2263
GERALD JONES VOLKSWAGEN INC.; *U.S. Private*, pg. 1685
GERALD METALS INC.; *U.S. Private*, pg. 1686
GERALD METALS S.A.—See Gerald Metals Inc.; *U.S. Private*, pg. 1686
GERALD NISSAN OF NORTH AURORA; *U.S. Private*, pg. 1686
GERALDTON FUEL COMPANY PTY LTD—See Ampol Limited; *Int'l*, pg. 436
GERALD WOOD HOMES LIMITED—See Galliford Try Holdings plc; *Int'l*, pg. 2874
GERAMA; *Int'l*, pg. 2942
GERANT CO., LTD.—See Screen Holdings Co., Ltd.; *Int'l*, pg. 6655
GERARD B TRACY ASSOCIATES, INC.—See Kelso & Company; *U.S. Private*, pg. 2279
GERARD DANIEL WORLDWIDE, INC.—See Graycliff Partners LP; *U.S. Private*, pg. 1760
GERARD DANIEL WORLDWIDE—See Graycliff Partners LP; *U.S. Private*, pg. 1760
GERARD DESIGN; *U.S. Private*, pg. 1686
GERARDI CONSTRUCTION, INC.; *U.S. Private*, pg. 1686
GERARD KLUYSKENS COMPANY INC.; *U.S. Private*, pg. 1686
GERARD LIGHTING (NZ) LIMITED—See Bain Capital, LP; *U.S. Private*, pg. 439
GERARD LIGHTING (NZ) LIMITED—See Investec Limited; *Int'l*, pg. 3777
GERARD LIGHTING PTY LTD—See Bain Capital, LP; *U.S. Private*, pg. 439
GERARD LIGHTING PTY LTD—See Investec Limited; *Int'l*, pg. 3777

GERARD PERRIER INDUSTRIE S.A.; *Int'l*, pg. 2942
GERATHERM MEDICAL AG; *Int'l*, pg. 2942
GERATHERM RESPIRATORY GMBH—See Geratherm Medical AG; *Int'l*, pg. 2942
GERAWAN FARMING SERVICES, INC.—See Paine Schwartz Partners, LLC; *U.S. Private*, pg. 3076
GERBER AGRI INTERNATIONAL, LLC; *U.S. Private*, pg. 1686
GERBER CHILDRENSWEAR LLC - GREENVILLE OPERATIONS CENTER—See Gerber Childrenswear LLC; *U.S. Private*, pg. 1686
GERBER CHILDRENSWEAR LLC; *U.S. Private*, pg. 1686
GERBER CHILE S.A.—See Nestle S.A.; *Int'l*, pg. 5203
GERBER COLLISION & GLASS - DENVER—See Boyd Group Services Inc.; *Int'l*, pg. 1125
GERBER COLLISION & GLASS (KANSAS), INC.—See Boyd Group Services Inc.; *Int'l*, pg. 1125
GERBER GMBH & CO. KG—See Wuestenrot & Wuerttembergische AG; *Int'l*, pg. 8499
THE GERBER GROUP, INC.—See Boyd Group Services Inc.; *Int'l*, pg. 1124
GERBER LIFE INSURANCE COMPANY—See Western & Southern Financial Group, Inc.; *U.S. Private*, pg. 4490
GERBER PLUMBING FIXTURES CORPORATION; *U.S. Private*, pg. 1686
GERBER PRODUCTS COMPANY OF PUERTO RICO, INC.—See Nestle S.A.; *Int'l*, pg. 5208
GERBER PRODUCTS COMPANY—See Nestle S.A.; *Int'l*, pg. 5208
GERBER PRODUCTS COMPANY—See Nestle S.A.; *Int'l*, pg. 5208
GERBER PRODUCTS COMPANY—See Nestle S.A.; *Int'l*, pg. 5208
GERBER PRODUCTS DIVISION-BABY CARE—See Nestle S.A.; *Int'l*, pg. 5208
GERBER SCIENTIFIC, INC. - GERBER INNOVATIONS DIVISION—See Vector Capital Management, L.P.; *U.S. Private*, pg. 4351
GERBER SCIENTIFIC, INC. - GERBER SCIENTIFIC PRODUCTS GROUP—See Vector Capital Management, L.P.; *U.S. Private*, pg. 4350
GERBER SCIENTIFIC, INC. - GERBER TECHNOLOGY GROUP—See Vector Capital Management, L.P.; *U.S. Private*, pg. 4350
GERBER SCIENTIFIC INTERNATIONAL LDA.—See Vector Capital Management, L.P.; *U.S. Private*, pg. 4350
GERBER SCIENTIFIC LLC—See Vector Capital Management, L.P.; *U.S. Private*, pg. 4350
GERBER SCIENTIFIC (SHANGHAI) CO., LTD.—See Vector Capital Management, L.P.; *U.S. Private*, pg. 4350
GERBER & SONS INC.; *U.S. Private*, pg. 1686
GERBER TECHNOLOGY GMBH—See Vector Capital Management, L.P.; *U.S. Private*, pg. 4351
GERBER TECHNOLOGY LLC—See AIP, LLC; *U.S. Private*, pg. 134
GERBER TECHNOLOGY, LTD.—See Vector Capital Management, L.P.; *U.S. Private*, pg. 4351
GERBER TECHNOLOGY PTY. LTD.—See Vector Capital Management, L.P.; *U.S. Private*, pg. 4351
GERBER TECHNOLOGY SA DE CV—See Vector Capital Management, L.P.; *U.S. Private*, pg. 4351
GERBER TECHNOLOGY SARL—See Vector Capital Management, L.P.; *U.S. Private*, pg. 4351
GERBER TRADE FINANCE, INC.; *U.S. Private*, pg. 1686
GERBIG, SNELL/WEISHEIMER ADVERTISING, LLC - NEW YORK—See Elliott Management Corporation; *U.S. Private*, pg. 1366
GERBIG, SNELL/WEISHEIMER ADVERTISING, LLC - NEW YORK—See Patient Square Capital, L.P.; *U.S. Private*, pg. 3108
GERBIG, SNELL/WEISHEIMER ADVERTISING, LLC - NEW YORK—See Veritas Capital Fund Management, LLC; *U.S. Private*, pg. 4365
GERBIG, SNELL/WEISHEIMER ADVERTISING, LLC—See Elliott Management Corporation; *U.S. Private*, pg. 1366
GERBIG, SNELL/WEISHEIMER ADVERTISING, LLC—See Patient Square Capital, L.P.; *U.S. Private*, pg. 3108
GERBIG, SNELL/WEISHEIMER ADVERTISING, LLC—See Veritas Capital Fund Management, LLC; *U.S. Private*, pg. 4365
GERDAU ACOMINAS S.A.—See Metalurgica Gerdau S.A.; *Int'l*, pg. 4849
GERDAU ACOS ESPECIAIS S.A.—See Metalurgica Gerdau S.A.; *Int'l*, pg. 4849
GERDAU ACOS ESTICIAIS S.A.—See Metalurgica Gerdau S.A.; *Int'l*, pg. 4849
GERDAU ACOS LONGOS S.A.—See Metalurgica Gerdau S.A.; *Int'l*, pg. 4849
GERDAU AMERISTEEL CORPORATION—See Metalurgica Gerdau S.A.; *Int'l*, pg. 4849
GERDAU AMERISTEEL PERTH AMBOY INC.—See Metalurgica Gerdau S.A.; *Int'l*, pg. 4850
GERDAU CAMBRIDGE STEEL MILL—See Metalurgica Gerdau S.A.; *Int'l*, pg. 4850
GERDAU CARTERSVILLE STEEL MILL—See Metalurgica Gerdau S.A.; *Int'l*, pg. 4850
GERDAU CHARLOTTE STEEL MILL—See Metalurgica Gerdau S.A.; *Int'l*, pg. 4850

GERDAU CINCINNATI REINFORCING STEEL—See Metalurgica Gerdau S.A.; *Int'l*, pg. 4850
GERDAU COMERCIAL DE ACOS S.A.—See Metalurgica Gerdau S.A.; *Int'l*, pg. 4850
GERDAU FORESTRY—See Metalurgica Gerdau S.A.; *Int'l*, pg. 4849
GERDAU FORT SMITH MILL—See Metalurgica Gerdau S.A.; *Int'l*, pg. 4850
GERDAU GTL SPAIN S.L.—See Metalurgica Gerdau S.A.; *Int'l*, pg. 4850
GERDAU JOLIET STEEL MILL—See Metalurgica Gerdau S.A.; *Int'l*, pg. 4850
GERDAU KNOXVILLE STEEL MILL—See Commercial Metals Company; *U.S. Public*, pg. 546
GERDAU LAISA—See Metalurgica Gerdau S.A.; *Int'l*, pg. 4850
GERDAU LONG STEEL NORTH AMERICA—See Metalurgica Gerdau S.A.; *Int'l*, pg. 4849
GERDAU MACSTEEL INC.—See Metalurgica Gerdau S.A.; *Int'l*, pg. 4850
GERDAU MANITOBA STEEL MILL—See Metalurgica Gerdau S.A.; *Int'l*, pg. 4850
GERDAU MIDLOTHIAN STEEL MILL—See Metalurgica Gerdau S.A.; *Int'l*, pg. 4850
GERDAU MONROE MILL—See Metalurgica Gerdau S.A.; *Int'l*, pg. 4850
GERDAU MUNCIE REINFORCING & COATING—See Metalurgica Gerdau S.A.; *Int'l*, pg. 4850
GERDAU NASHVILLE REINFORCING STEEL—See Metalurgica Gerdau S.A.; *Int'l*, pg. 4850
GERDAU NEW ORLEANS REBAR EXPRESS—See Metalurgica Gerdau S.A.; *Int'l*, pg. 4850
GERDAU PERTH AMBOY RECYCLING DIVISION—See Metalurgica Gerdau S.A.; *Int'l*, pg. 4850
GERDAU RANCHO CUCAMONGA STEEL MILL—See Commercial Metals Company; *U.S. Public*, pg. 546
GERDAU REINFORCING STEEL WEST—See Metalurgica Gerdau S.A.; *Int'l*, pg. 4850
GERDAU SA (CHILE); *Int'l*, pg. 2942
GERDAU S.A.—See Metalurgica Gerdau S.A.; *Int'l*, pg. 4849
GERDAU SAYREVILLE STEEL MILL—See Commercial Metals Company; *U.S. Public*, pg. 546
GERDAU SPECIAL STEEL NORTH AMERICA NITRO STEEL - PLEASANT PRAIRIE FACILITY—See Metalurgica Gerdau S.A.; *Int'l*, pg. 4850
GERDAU SPECIAL STEEL NORTH AMERICA QUENCH & TEMPER PROCESSES- HUNTINGTON FACILITY—See Metalurgica Gerdau S.A.; *Int'l*, pg. 4850
GERDAU SPECIAL STEEL NORTH AMERICA—See Metalurgica Gerdau S.A.; *Int'l*, pg. 4850
GERDAU STEEL INC.—See Metalurgica Gerdau S.A.; *Int'l*, pg. 4850
GERDAU WHITBY STEEL MILL—See Metalurgica Gerdau S.A.; *Int'l*, pg. 4850
GERDMANS INREDNIGAR AB—See Franz Haniel & Cie. GmbH; *Int'l*, pg. 2763
GERDT FURNITURE & INTERIORS; *U.S. Private*, pg. 1686
GERELCO ELECTRICAL CONTRACTORS; *U.S. Private*, pg. 1686
GEREMARIE CORPORATION—See Patrick Industries, Inc.; *U.S. Public*, pg. 1652
GEREMIA POOLS; *U.S. Private*, pg. 1686
GEREP SAS—See Groupe Seche SAS; *Int'l*, pg. 3110
GERETT PRODUCTS—See Western Industries, Inc.; *U.S. Private*, pg. 4494
GERFLOR SA—See Cobepa S.A.; *Int'l*, pg. 1683
GERFLOR USA, INC.—See Cobepa S.A.; *Int'l*, pg. 1683
GERHARD HAAS KG; *Int'l*, pg. 2942
GERHARD PRAZISIONSPRESSTECHNIK GMBH—See Schunk GmbH; *Int'l*, pg. 6641
GERIATRIC MEDICAL & SURGICAL SUPPLY, INC.—See GMSS Holdings, LLC; *U.S. Private*, pg. 1723
GERIATRIC SERVICES, INC.; *U.S. Private*, pg. 1686
GERIATROS S.A.U.—See PAI Partners S.A.S.; *Int'l*, pg. 5700
GERICARE MEDICAL SUPPLY INC.; *U.S. Private*, pg. 1686
G.E. RICHARDS GRAPHIC SUPPLIES CO. INC.; *U.S. Private*, pg. 1631
GERIFONDS S.A.—See Banque Cantonale Vaudoise; *Int'l*, pg. 853
GERIS ENGENHARIA E SERVICOS LTDA.—See TUV Rheinland Berlin-Brandenburg Pfalz e.V.; *Int'l*, pg. 7982
GERITREX CORP.—See BelHealth Investment Partners LLC; *U.S. Private*, pg. 518
GERKEN MATERIALS INC.; *U.S. Private*, pg. 1686
GERKEN PAVING INC.—See Gerken Materials Inc.; *U.S. Private*, pg. 1686
GERKEN SAS—See Westinghouse Air Brake Technologies Corporation; *U.S. Public*, pg. 2358
GERLACH AG—See Deutsche Post AG; *Int'l*, pg. 2080
GERLACH & CO INTERNATIONALE EXPEDITEURS B.V.—See Deutsche Post AG; *Int'l*, pg. 2080
GERLACH & CO. NV—See Deutsche Post AG; *Int'l*, pg. 2080

COMPANY NAME INDEX

GERLACH CUSTOMS SERVICES EOOD—See Deutsche Post AG; *Int'l*, pg. 2080
GERLACH CUSTOMS SERVICES UK LIMITED—See Deutsche Post AG; *Int'l*, pg. 2080
GERLACH EUROPEAN CUSTOMS SERVICES, SPOL. S.R.O.—See Deutsche Post AG; *Int'l*, pg. 2080
GERLACH EUROPEAN SERVICES S.R.L.—See Deutsche Post AG; *Int'l*, pg. 2080
GERLACH SPOL S.R.O.—See Deutsche Post AG; *Int'l*, pg. 2080
GERLACH SWEDEN AB—See Deutsche Post AG; *Int'l*, pg. 2080
GERLACH ZOLLDIENSTE GMBH—See Deutsche Post AG; *Int'l*, pg. 2080
GERLER & SON, INC.—See Hardy Capital Corporation; *Int'l*, pg. 3273
GERLICHER GMBH—See RETHMANN AG & Co. KG; *Int'l*, pg. 6306
GERLI & CO., INC.; *U.S. Private*, pg. 1686
GERLING APPLIED ENGINEERING, INC.—See Harald Quandt Holding GmbH; *Int'l*, pg. 3270
GERLINGER STEEL & SUPPLY COMPANY, CO.; *U.S. Private*, pg. 1686
GERLOFF COMPANY INC.; *U.S. Private*, pg. 1686
GERMAIN ARMATURES; *Int'l*, pg. 2942
GERMAIN AUTOMOTIVE PARTNERSHIP, INC.—See Germain Motor Company; *U.S. Private*, pg. 1687
GERMAINE'S LUAU, INC.—See Zippy's, Inc.; *U.S. Private*, pg. 4606
GERMAINE—See Omnicom Group Inc.; *U.S. Public*, pg. 1575
GERMAIN FORD OF COLUMBUS, LLC—See Germain Motor Company; *U.S. Private*, pg. 1687
GERMAIN LEXUS OF DUBLIN—See Germain Motor Company; *U.S. Private*, pg. 1687
GERMAIN LEXUS OF EASTON—See Germain Motor Company; *U.S. Private*, pg. 1687
GERMAIN MOTOR COMPANY; *U.S. Private*, pg. 1686
GERMAIN NISSAN OF NEW ALBANY, INC.—See Germain Motor Company; *U.S. Private*, pg. 1687
GERMAIN OF NAPLES, INC.—See Germain Motor Company; *U.S. Private*, pg. 1687
GERMAIN ON TAMIAMI, LLC—See Germain Motor Company; *U.S. Private*, pg. 1687
GERMAN AMERICAN BANCORP, INC.; *U.S. Public*, pg. 934
GERMAN AMERICAN BANK—See German American Bancorp, Inc.; *U.S. Public*, pg. 934
GERMAN AMERICAN FINANCIAL ADVISORS & TRUST COMPANY—See German American Bancorp, Inc.; *U.S. Public*, pg. 934
GERMAN AMERICAN INSURANCE, INC.—See ABRY Partners, LLC; *U.S. Private*, pg. 43
GERMAN ASSET MANAGERS AG; *Int'l*, pg. 2942
GERMAN AUTO IMPORT NETWORK - VANCOUVER ISLAND; *Int'l*, pg. 2942
GERMAN AUTOMOBILES LIMITED—See G.A. Holdings Limited; *Int'l*, pg. 2865
GERMAN BRAUN MEDICAL CO., LTD.—See B. Braun Melsungen AG; *Int'l*, pg. 787
GERMAN BULK CHARTERING GMBH—See K+S Aktiengesellschaft; *Int'l*, pg. 4040
GERMAN BUSINESS PROTECTION GMBH—See KOTTER Gmbh & Co. KG; *Int'l*, pg. 4293
GERMAN CENTRE FOR INDUSTRY AND TRADE PTE. LTD.—See Landesbank Baden-Wurttemberg; *Int'l*, pg. 4405
GERMAN CENTRE FOR INDUSTRY AND TRADE SHANGHAI CO. LTD.—See BayernLB Holding AG; *Int'l*, pg. 914
GERMAN CENTRE FOR INDUSTRY & TRADE BEIJING CO., LTD.—See Landesbank Baden-Wurttemberg; *Int'l*, pg. 4405
GERMAN CENTRE FOR INDUSTRY & TRADE GMBH—See Landesbank Baden-Wurttemberg; *Int'l*, pg. 4405
GERMAN EDGE CLOUD GMBH & CO.KG—See Friedhelm Loh Stiftung & Co. KG; *Int'l*, pg. 2791
GERMANE SYSTEMS LC; *U.S. Private*, pg. 1687
GERMAN-GULF ENTERPRISES LTD.—See Hydac International GmbH; *Int'l*, pg. 3544
GERMAN HIGH STREET PROPERTIES A/S; *Int'l*, pg. 2943
GERMANIA FARM MUTUAL INSURANCE ASSOCIATION; *U.S. Private*, pg. 1687
GERMANISCHER LLOYD ARGENTINA S.A.—See DNV GL Group AS; *Int'l*, pg. 2149
GERMANISCHER LLOYD (AUSTRALIA) PTY. LTD.—See DNV GL Group AS; *Int'l*, pg. 2149
GERMANISCHER LLOYD AUSTRIA GMBH—See DNV GL Group AS; *Int'l*, pg. 2149
GERMANISCHER LLOYD BANGLADESH LTD.—See DNV GL Group AS; *Int'l*, pg. 2149
GERMANISCHER LLOYD BELGIUM N.V.—See DNV GL Group AS; *Int'l*, pg. 2149
GERMANISCHER LLOYD BULGARIA LTD.—See DNV GL Group AS; *Int'l*, pg. 2149
GERMANISCHER LLOYD CANADA LTD.—See DNV GL Group AS; *Int'l*, pg. 2149

GERMANISCHER LLOYD CERTIFICATION GMBH—See DNV GL Group AS; *Int'l*, pg. 2149
GERMANISCHER LLOYD CERTIFICATION SERVICES, S.L.—See DNV GL Group AS; *Int'l*, pg. 2149
GERMANISCHER LLOYD (CHILE) LTDA.—See DNV GL Group AS; *Int'l*, pg. 2149
GERMANISCHER LLOYD COLOMBIA LTDA.—See DNV GL Group AS; *Int'l*, pg. 2149
GERMANISCHER LLOYD COLOMBO PVT. LTD.—See DNV GL Group AS; *Int'l*, pg. 2149
GERMANISCHER LLOYD DE PANAMA, LTD.—See DNV GL Group AS; *Int'l*, pg. 2150
GERMANISCHER LLOYD DO BRASIL, LTDA.—See DNV GL Group AS; *Int'l*, pg. 2150
GERMANISCHER LLOYD ENGINEERING SERVICES EAST ASIA (ESEA)—See DNV GL Group AS; *Int'l*, pg. 2149
GERMANISCHER LLOYD ESPANA, S.L.—See DNV GL Group AS; *Int'l*, pg. 2149
GERMANISCHER LLOYD ESTONIA OU—See DNV GL Group AS; *Int'l*, pg. 2149
GERMANISCHER LLOYD FINLAND OY—See DNV GL Group AS; *Int'l*, pg. 2149
GERMANISCHER LLOYD FRANCE SARL—See DNV GL Group AS; *Int'l*, pg. 2149
GERMANISCHER LLOYD GLM SDN. BHD.—See DNV GL Group AS; *Int'l*, pg. 2149
GERMANISCHER LLOYD-HAVANA—See DNV GL Group AS; *Int'l*, pg. 2150
GERMANISCHER LLOYD HELLAS SURVEY E.P.E.—See DNV GL Group AS; *Int'l*, pg. 2149
GERMANISCHER LLOYD HONG KONG LTD.—See DNV GL Group AS; *Int'l*, pg. 2149
GERMANISCHER LLOYD HUNGARY KFT.—See DNV GL Group AS; *Int'l*, pg. 2149
GERMANISCHER LLOYD ICELAND LTD.—See DNV GL Group AS; *Int'l*, pg. 2149
GERMANISCHER LLOYD INDUSTRIAL SERVICES CO.,LTD.—See DNV GL Group AS; *Int'l*, pg. 2149
GERMANISCHER LLOYD INDUSTRIAL SERVICES DO BRASIL LTDA.—See DNV GL Group AS; *Int'l*, pg. 2150
GERMANISCHER LLOYD INDUSTRIAL SERVICES EGYPT LTD.—See DNV GL Group AS; *Int'l*, pg. 2149
GERMANISCHER LLOYD INDUSTRIAL SERVICES ITALIA S.R.L.—See DNV GL Group AS; *Int'l*, pg. 2150
GERMANISCHER LLOYD INDUSTRIE SERVICES RUSSLAND (LCC)—See DNV GL Group AS; *Int'l*, pg. 2150
GERMANISCHER LLOYD IRELAND LTD.—See DNV GL Group AS; *Int'l*, pg. 2150
GERMANISCHER LLOYD ISRAEL LTD.—See DNV GL Group AS; *Int'l*, pg. 2150
GERMANISCHER LLOYD (KAOHSIUNG) TAIWAN PTE LTD.—See DNV GL Group AS; *Int'l*, pg. 2149
GERMANISCHER LLOYD (KOREA) PTY LTD.—See DNV GL Group AS; *Int'l*, pg. 2149
GERMANISCHER LLOYD - LEBANON S.A.R.L.—See DNV GL Group AS; *Int'l*, pg. 2149
GERMANISCHER LLOYD (MALAYSIA) SDN. BHD.—See DNV GL Group AS; *Int'l*, pg. 2149
GERMANISCHER LLOYD MALTA LTD.—See DNV GL Group AS; *Int'l*, pg. 2150
GERMANISCHER LLOYD MOROCCO S.A.R.L.—See DNV GL Group AS; *Int'l*, pg. 2150
GERMANISCHER LLOYD NETHERLANDS B.V.—See DNV GL Group AS; *Int'l*, pg. 2150
GERMANISCHER LLOYD NEW ZEALAND LTD.—See DNV GL Group AS; *Int'l*, pg. 2150
GERMANISCHER LLOYD NORGE AS—See DNV GL Group AS; *Int'l*, pg. 2150
GERMANISCHER LLOYD OFFSHORE & INDUSTRIAL SERVICES KOREA LTD. CO.—See DNV GL Group AS; *Int'l*, pg. 2150
GERMANISCHER LLOYD PERU S.A.C.—See DNV GL Group AS; *Int'l*, pg. 2150
GERMANISCHER LLOYD PHILIPPINES, INC.—See DNV GL Group AS; *Int'l*, pg. 2150
GERMANISCHER LLOYD POLEN SP. Z O.O.—See DNV GL Group AS; *Int'l*, pg. 2150
GERMANISCHER LLOYD PORTUGAL INSPECCAO DE NAVIOS, LDA.—See DNV GL Group AS; *Int'l*, pg. 2150
GERMANISCHER LLOYD PRUFLABOR GMBH—See DNV GL Group AS; *Int'l*, pg. 2150
GERMANISCHER LLOYD ROMANIA S.R.L.—See DNV GL Group AS; *Int'l*, pg. 2150
GERMANISCHER LLOYD SANKT PETERSBURG GMBH—See DNV GL Group AS; *Int'l*, pg. 2150
GERMANISCHER LLOYD SHANGHAI CO.,LTD.—See DNV GL Group AS; *Int'l*, pg. 2150
GERMANISCHER LLOYD SINGAPORE PTE. LTD.—See DNV GL Group AS; *Int'l*, pg. 2150
GERMANISCHER LLOYD SLOVENIJA D.O.O.—See DNV GL Group AS; *Int'l*, pg. 2150
GERMANISCHER LLOYD SOUTH AFRICA (PTY) LTD.—See DNV GL Group AS; *Int'l*, pg. 2150
GERMANISCHER LLOYD SPLIT D.O.O.—See DNV GL Group AS; *Int'l*, pg. 2150
GERMANISCHER LLOYD TEKNIK HIZMETLER LTD. STI.—See DNV GL Group AS; *Int'l*, pg. 2150

GERMANISCHER LLOYD (THAILAND) CO., LTD.—See DNV GL Group AS; *Int'l*, pg. 2149
GERMANISCHER LLOYD UKRAINE—See DNV GL Group AS; *Int'l*, pg. 2150
GERMANISCHER LLOYD UNIVERSAL INDUSTRIAL SERVICES LTD.—See DNV GL Group AS; *Int'l*, pg. 2150
GERMANISCHER LLOYD (USA), INC.—See DNV GL Group AS; *Int'l*, pg. 2149
GERMANN ROAD LAND DEVELOPMENT, LLC—See Brookfield Corporation; *Int'l*, pg. 1174
GERMANOS S.A.—See Hellenic Telecommunications Organization S.A.; *Int'l*, pg. 3333
GERMANOS TELECOM ROMANIA S.A.—See Hellenic Telecommunications Organization S.A.; *Int'l*, pg. 3333
GERMANOS TELECOM S.A.—See Hellenic Telecommunications Organization S.A.; *Int'l*, pg. 3333
GERMANOW-SIMON CORPORATION; *U.S. Private*, pg. 1687
GERMAN REMEDIES LIMITED—See Zydus Lifesciences Limited; *Int'l*, pg. 8700
GERMAN STARTUPS GROUP GMBH & CO. KGAA; *Int'l*, pg. 2943
GERMANTOWN LIFE ENRICHMENT CENTER; *U.S. Private*, pg. 1687
GERMAN VALUES PROPERTY GROUP AG; *Int'l*, pg. 2943
GERMANWINGS GMBH—See Deutsche Lufthansa AG; *Int'l*, pg. 2066
GERMANY AEROTECH GMBH—See Aerotech Inc.; *U.S. Private*, pg. 119
GERMANY DINAS SEMICONDUCTOR LASER CO., LTD.—See Coherent Corp.; *U.S. Public*, pg. 527
GERMEFA B.V.—See Standard Investment Management B.V.; *Int'l*, pg. 7169
GERMFREE LABORATORIES INC.; *U.S. Private*, pg. 1687
GERMICOPA S.A.; *Int'l*, pg. 2943
GERNATT ASPHALT PRODUCTS INC.; *U.S. Private*, pg. 1687
GERNEP GMBH—See Krones AG; *Int'l*, pg. 4305
GEROLPHARM S.A.—See Gerolymatos Group of Companies; *Int'l*, pg. 2943
GEROLYMATOS GROUP OF COMPANIES; *Int'l*, pg. 2943
GEROLYMATOS INC—See Gerolymatos Group of Companies; *Int'l*, pg. 2943
GEROME MANUFACTURING COMPANY, INC.; *U.S. Private*, pg. 1687
GEROME TECHNOLOGIES, INC.—See Audax Group, Limited Partnership; *U.S. Private*, pg. 387
GEROM SA; *Int'l*, pg. 2943
GERON CORPORATION; *U.S. Public*, pg. 934
GERONIMO INNS LIMITED—See Young & Co.'s Brewery Plc; *Int'l*, pg. 8602
THE GERONTOLOGICAL SOCIETY OF AMERICA; *U.S. Private*, pg. 4032
GEROQUIP INC.; *Int'l*, pg. 2943
GEROTECH INC.; *U.S. Private*, pg. 1687
GEROVA FINANCIAL GROUP, LTD.; *Int'l*, pg. 2943
GERPANG HEALTHCARE GROUP; *Int'l*, pg. 2943
GERRARD FINANCIAL PLANNING LIMITED—See Barclays PLC; *Int'l*, pg. 862
GERRARD INVESTMENT MANAGEMENT LIMITED—See Barclays PLC; *Int'l*, pg. 862
GERRARD MANAGEMENT SERVICES LIMITED—See Barclays PLC; *Int'l*, pg. 862
GERRARD-OVALSTRAPPING—See Samuel, Son & Co., Limited; *Int'l*, pg. 6515
GERRARDS (COMERCIAL OFFSHORE DE MACAU) LTD—See Beijing Health (Holdings) Limited; *Int'l*, pg. 951
GERRESHEIMER AG; *Int'l*, pg. 2943
GERRESHEIMER BOLESLAWIEC S.A.—See Gerresheimer AG; *Int'l*, pg. 2943
GERRESHEIMER BUNDE GMBH—See Gerresheimer AG; *Int'l*, pg. 2943
GERRESHEIMER CHALON S.A.—See Gerresheimer AG; *Int'l*, pg. 2943
GERRESHEIMER DENMARK A/S—See Gerresheimer AG; *Int'l*, pg. 2943
GERRESHEIMER ESSEN GMBH—See Gerresheimer AG; *Int'l*, pg. 2943
GERRESHEIMER GLAS GMBH—See Gerresheimer AG; *Int'l*, pg. 2943
GERRESHEIMER GLASS INC. - CHICAGO HEIGHTS PLANT—See Gerresheimer AG; *Int'l*, pg. 2943
GERRESHEIMER GLASS INC. - FOREST GROVE PLANT—See Gerresheimer AG; *Int'l*, pg. 2943
GERRESHEIMER GLASS INC. - MILLVILLE PLANT—See Gerresheimer AG; *Int'l*, pg. 2943
GERRESHEIMER GLASS INC. - MORGANTON PLANT—See Gerresheimer AG; *Int'l*, pg. 2943
GERRESHEIMER GLASS INC.—See Gerresheimer AG; *Int'l*, pg. 2943
GERRESHEIMER HOLDINGS GMBH—See Gerresheimer AG; *Int'l*, pg. 2943
GERRESHEIMER HORSOVSKY TYN SPOL. S R O.—See Gerresheimer AG; *Int'l*, pg. 2943
GERRESHEIMER ITEM GMBH—See Gerresheimer AG; *Int'l*, pg. 2943

GERRESHEIMER AG

GERRESHEIMER LOHR GMBH—See Gerresheimer AG; *Int'l*, pg. 2943
GERRESHEIMER MEDICAL PLASTIC SYSTEMS DONGGUAN CO. LTD.—See Gerresheimer AG; *Int'l*, pg. 2943
GERRESHEIMER MOMIGNIES S.A.—See Gerresheimer AG; *Int'l*, pg. 2943
GERRESHEIMER MOULDED GLASS GMBH.—See Gerresheimer AG; *Int'l*, pg. 2943
GERRESHEIMER PEACHTREE CITY, INC.—See Gerresheimer AG; *Int'l*, pg. 2943
GERRESHEIMER PEACHTREE CITY (USA), L.P.—See Gerresheimer AG; *Int'l*, pg. 2944
GERRESHEIMER PHARMACEUTICAL PACKAGING MUMBAI PRIVATE LTD.—See Gerresheimer AG; *Int'l*, pg. 2944
GERRESHEIMER PLASTICOS SAO PAULO LTDA.—See Gerresheimer AG; *Int'l*, pg. 2944
GERRESHEIMER PLASTIC PACKAGING (CHANGZHOU) CO., LTD.—See Gerresheimer AG; *Int'l*, pg. 2944
GERRESHEIMER PLASTIC PACKAGING S.A.S.—See Gerresheimer AG; *Int'l*, pg. 2944
GERRESHEIMER QUERETARO S.A.—See Gerresheimer AG; *Int'l*, pg. 2944
GERRESHEIMER REGENSBURG GMBH - PFREIMD PLANT—See Gerresheimer AG; *Int'l*, pg. 2944
GERRESHEIMER REGENSBURG GMBH—See Gerresheimer AG; *Int'l*, pg. 2944
GERRESHEIMER RESPIMETRIX GMBH—See Gerresheimer AG; *Int'l*, pg. 2944
GERRESHEIMER SHUANGFENG PHARMACEUTICAL GLASS (DANYANG) CO. LTD. - NEW PLANT—See Gerresheimer AG; *Int'l*, pg. 2944
GERRESHEIMER SHUANGFENG PHARMACEUTICAL GLASS (DANYANG) CO. LTD.—See Gerresheimer AG; *Int'l*, pg. 2944
GERRESHEIMER SHUANGFENG PHARMACEUTICAL PACKAGING (ZHENJIANG) CO. LTD.—See Gerresheimer AG; *Int'l*, pg. 2944
GERRESHEIMER SINGAPORE PTE. LTD.—See Gerresheimer AG; *Int'l*, pg. 2944
GERRESHEIMER SISTEMAS PLASTICOS MEDICINAIS SAO PAULO LTDA.—See Gerresheimer AG; *Int'l*, pg. 2944
GERRESHEIMER TETTAU GMBH—See Gerresheimer AG; *Int'l*, pg. 2944
GERRESHEIMER VAERLOESE A/S—See Gerresheimer AG; *Int'l*, pg. 2944
GERRESHEIMER WERKZEUGBAU WACKERSDORF GMBH—See Gerresheimer AG; *Int'l*, pg. 2944
GERRESHEIMER WERKZEUG- UND AUTOMATISIERUNGSTECHNIK GMBH—See Gerresheimer AG; *Int'l*, pg. 2944
GERRESHEIMER WERTHEIM GMBH—See Gerresheimer AG; *Int'l*, pg. 2944
GERRESHEIMER WILDEN ASIA MEDICAL AND TECHNICAL PLASTIC SYSTEMS CO. LTD.—See Gerresheimer AG; *Int'l*, pg. 2944
GERRESHEIMER WILDEN CZECH SPOL. S R.O.—See Gerresheimer AG; *Int'l*, pg. 2944
GERRESHEIMER ZARAGOZA S.A.—See Gerresheimer AG; *Int'l*, pg. 2944
GERRETSEN BUILDING SUPPLY, CO.—See TAL Holdings LLC; *U.S. Private*, pg. 3925
GERRISH HONDA; *U.S. Private*, pg. 1687
GERRITY COMPANY INCORPORATED; *U.S. Private*, pg. 1687
GERRITY'S SUPERMARKETS INC.; *U.S. Private*, pg. 1687
GERRITY STONE INC.—See Gerrity Company Incorporated; *U.S. Private*, pg. 1687
GERRY RED INC.; *U.S. Private*, pg. 1687
GERRY'S TRUCK CENTRE LTD.; *Int'l*, pg. 2945
GERRY WEBER BELGIEN GMBH—See GERRY WEBER International AG; *Int'l*, pg. 2944
GERRY WEBER CANADA LTD.—See GERRY WEBER International AG; *Int'l*, pg. 2944
GERRY WEBER DENMARK APS—See GERRY WEBER International AG; *Int'l*, pg. 2944
GERRY WEBER FAR EAST LIMITED—See GERRY WEBER International AG; *Int'l*, pg. 2944
GERRY WEBER FASHION IBERICA S.L.—See GERRY WEBER International AG; *Int'l*, pg. 2944
GERRY WEBER FRANCE S.A.R.L.—See GERRY WEBER International AG; *Int'l*, pg. 2944
GERRY WEBER GMBH—See GERRY WEBER International AG; *Int'l*, pg. 2944
GERRY WEBER IBERICA S.L.U—See GERRY WEBER International AG; *Int'l*, pg. 2944
GERRY WEBER INTERNATIONAL AG; *Int'l*, pg. 2944
GERRY WEBER LIFE-STYLE FASHION GMBH—See GERRY WEBER International AG; *Int'l*, pg. 2944
GERRY WEBER MANAGEMENT & EVENT OHG—See GERRY WEBER International AG; *Int'l*, pg. 2944
GERRY WEBER NORGE AS—See GERRY WEBER International AG; *Int'l*, pg. 2944
GERRY WEBER OUTLET BVBA—See GERRY WEBER International AG; *Int'l*, pg. 2944
GERRY WEBER RETAIL GMBH—See GERRY WEBER International AG; *Int'l*, pg. 2944
GERRY WEBER SPORTPARK HOTEL GMBH & CO. KG—See GERRY WEBER International AG; *Int'l*, pg. 2944
GERRY WEBER SUPPORT S.R.L.—See GERRY WEBER International AG; *Int'l*, pg. 2945
GERRY WEBER UK LTD.—See GERRY WEBER International AG; *Int'l*, pg. 2945
GERRY WEBER WHOLESALE FASHION GMBH—See GERRY WEBER International AG; *Int'l*, pg. 2945
GERRY WOOD AUTOMOTIVE, LLC.; *U.S. Private*, pg. 1687
GERSAN ELEKTRIK TICARET VE SANAYI AS; *Int'l*, pg. 2945
GERS DISTRIBUTION; *Int'l*, pg. 2945
GERSH ACADEMY, INC.; *U.S. Private*, pg. 1688
GERSHMAN MORTGAGE CORPORATION; *U.S. Private*, pg. 1688
GERSHOW RECYCLING CORPORATION; *U.S. Private*, pg. 1688
THE GERSON COMPANY INC.; *U.S. Private*, pg. 4033
GERSON & GERSON, INC.; *U.S. Private*, pg. 1688
GERSON LEHRMAN GROUP, INC.; *U.S. Public*, pg. 934
GERSTAD BUILDERS INC.; *U.S. Private*, pg. 1688
GERSTEIN, FISHER & ASSOCIATES, INC.—See M&T Bank Corporation; *U.S. Public*, pg. 1851
GERSTENBERG SCHRODER BRASIL LTDA.—See SPX Technologies, Inc.; *U.S. Public*, pg. 1921
THE GERSTENSLAGER COMPANY—See Worthington Industries, Inc.; *U.S. Public*, pg. 2383
GERSTHOFER BACKBETRIEBE GMBH—See Serafin Unternehmensgruppe GmbH; *Int'l*, pg. 6720
GERTEN GREENHOUSES & GARDEN CENTER, INC.; *U.S. Private*, pg. 1688
GERTH MEDIEN GMBH—See SCM Stiftung Christliche Medien; *Int'l*, pg. 6649
GERTNER SERVICE GMBH—See Atlas Copco AB; *Int'l*, pg. 683
GERTRUDE DIALYSIS, LLC—See DaVita Inc.; *U.S. Public*, pg. 639
GERTRUDE HAWK CHOCOLATES, INC.; *U.S. Private*, pg. 1688
GERUSTBAU MUEHLHAN GMBH—See Brand Industrial Services, Inc.; *U.S. Private*, pg. 636
GERVAIS LINCOLN MERCURY INC.; *U.S. Private*, pg. 1688
GERVAS (B) SDN BHD—See Wipro Limited; *Int'l*, pg. 8432
GERVASONI S.P.A.—See Dexelance S.p.A.; *Int'l*, pg. 2092
GESA CREDIT UNION; *U.S. Private*, pg. 1688
GESA GAS SAU—See Enel S.p.A.; *Int'l*, pg. 2414
GESA GEMUSESAFT GMBH—See Orior AG; *Int'l*, pg. 5633
GES AUTOMATION TECHNOLOGY INC.—See Edwin L. Heim Company Inc.; *U.S. Private*, pg. 1342
GESCA, LTEE.—See Power Corporation of Canada; *Int'l*, pg. 5943
GES CANADA LIMITED—See Viad Corp.; *U.S. Public*, pg. 2291
GESCAN BC—See Sonepar S.A.; *Int'l*, pg. 7091
GESCAN ONTARIO—See Sonepar S.A.; *Int'l*, pg. 7091
GESCAN PRAIRIES—See Sonepar S.A.; *Int'l*, pg. 7091
GES.CAR. S.R.L.—See Cremonini S.p.A.; *Int'l*, pg. 1838
GESCO AG; *Int'l*, pg. 2945
GESCORO INC.—See Euronet Worldwide, Inc.; *U.S. Public*, pg. 798
GESD CAPITAL PARTNERS; *U.S. Private*, pg. 1688
GESELLSCHAFT FUR ARBEITSMEDIZIN UND UMWELTSCHUTZ MBH - AMUS—See INA-Holding Schaeffler GmbH & Co. KG; *Int'l*, pg. 3639
GESELLSCHAFT FUR BAUWESEN GMBH—See PORR AG; *Int'l*, pg. 5922
GESELLSCHAFT FUR DAS RECYCLING KONTAMINIERTER INDUSTRIEBRACHEN MBH—See L. Possehl & Co. mbH; *Int'l*, pg. 4382
GESELLSCHAFT FUR ENERGIE UND KLIMASCHUTZ SCHLESWIG- HOLSTEIN GMBH—See E.ON SE; *Int'l*, pg. 2258
GESELLSCHAFT FUR FLUGZIELDARSTELLUNG MBH—See Airbus SE; *Int'l*, pg. 242
GESELLSCHAFT FUR GRUNDSTUCKSVERMIETUNG UND FINANZIERUNGSVERMITTLUNG MBH—See R. STAHL AG; *Int'l*, pg. 6169
GESELLSCHAFT FUR KREDITSICHERUNG MBH—See Commerzbank AG; *Int'l*, pg. 1718
GESELLSCHAFT FUR MINERALOL-ANALYTIK UND QUALITATSMANAGEMENT MBH. + CO. KG—See Marquard & Bahls AG; *Int'l*, pg. 4699
GESELLSCHAFT FUR WOHNEN DATTELN MBH—See RAG-Stiftung; *Int'l*, pg. 6179
GESELLSCHAFT ZUR SCHAFFUNG VON WOHNUNGSEIGENTUM GESELLSCHAFT M.B.H.—See PORR AG; *Int'l*, pg. 5923
GES ENERJI A.S—See Global Yatirim Holding A.S.; *Int'l*, pg. 3002
GESENKSCHMIEDE SCHNEIDER GMBH—See Mutares SE & Co. KGaA; *Int'l*, pg. 5105
GES EXPOSITION SERVICES, INC.—See Viad Corp.; *U.S. Public*, pg. 2291

CORPORATE AFFILIATIONS

GES FIBANC S.G.I.I.C. S.A.—See Banca Mediolanum S.p.A.; *Int'l*, pg. 815
G.E.S. GAS EQUIPMENT SERVICE GMBH.—See Hoyer GmbH; *Int'l*, pg. 3498
GES GEOFIZIKAI SZOLGALTATO KFT.—See MOL Magyar Olaj- es Gazipari Nyrt.; *Int'l*, pg. 5020
GES GMBH & CO. KG—See Viad Corp.; *U.S. Public*, pg. 2291
GES GROUNDWATER & ENVIRONMENTAL SERVICES, INC.; *U.S. Private*, pg. 1688
GE-SHEN CORPORATION BERHAD; *Int'l*, pg. 2897
GE-SHEN PLASTIC (M) SDN. BHD.—See Ge-Shen Corporation Berhad; *Int'l*, pg. 2897
GE.S.IN. GESTIONE SERVIZI INTEGRATI - SOCIETA COOPERATIVA—See CAMST-Cooperativa Albergo Mensa Spettacolo e Turismo, Soc. Coop. a.r.l.; *Int'l*, pg. 1275
GES INTERNATIONAL LIMITED—See Venture Corporation Limited; *Int'l*, pg. 8151
GES INVESTMENT PTE. LTD.—See Venture Corporation Limited; *Int'l*, pg. 8151
GESIPA BLINDNIETTECHNIK GMBH—See SFS Group AG; *Int'l*, pg. 6738
GESIS GESELLSCHAFT FUR INFORMATIONSSYSTEME MBH—See Salzgitter AG; *Int'l*, pg. 6496
GES JAPAN CORPORATION—See United Renewable Energy Co., Ltd.; *Int'l*, pg. 8073
GES KFT.—See MOL Magyar Olaj- es Gazipari Nyrt.; *Int'l*, pg. 5020
GES LTD.; *Int'l*, pg. 2945
GES MANUFACTURING SERVICES (M) SDN BHD—See Venture Corporation Limited; *Int'l*, pg. 8151
GES MECHANICAL SERVICES, INC.—See Amco Group Inc.; *U.S. Private*, pg. 218
G.E.S. OBERHAUSEN GMBH—See Hoyer GmbH; *Int'l*, pg. 3498
GESPEVESA, S.A.—See El Corte Ingles, S.A.; *Int'l*, pg. 2340
GESPLAN S.A.—See TOTVS S.A.; *Int'l*, pg. 7846
GES (SINGAPORE) PTE. LTD.—See Venture Corporation Limited; *Int'l*, pg. 8151
GESSNER INDUSTRIES INC.; *U.S. Private*, pg. 1688
GESSNER/MILLER CORPORATION—See GHM Industries, Inc.; *U.S. Private*, pg. 1691
GESSNER PRODUCTS COMPANY, INC.—See New ThermoServ, Ltd.; *U.S. Private*, pg. 2907
GESTALT, LLC—See Accenture plc; *Int'l*, pg. 86
GESTAMP ABRERA, S.A.—See Acek Desarrollo y Gestion Industrial SL; *Int'l*, pg. 96
GESTAMP AGUAS CALIENTES, S.A. DE C.V.—See Acek Desarrollo y Gestion Industrial SL; *Int'l*, pg. 96
GESTAMP ALABAMA, INC.—See Acek Desarrollo y Gestion Industrial SL; *Int'l*, pg. 97
GESTAMP ARAGON, S.A.—See Acek Desarrollo y Gestion Industrial SL; *Int'l*, pg. 96
GESTAMP AUTOCOMPONENTS (DONGGUAN),CO. LTD.—See Acek Desarrollo y Gestion Industrial SL; *Int'l*, pg. 96
GESTAMP AUTOCOMPONENTS (SHENYANG), CO. LTD.—See Acek Desarrollo y Gestion Industrial SL; *Int'l*, pg. 96
GESTAMP AUTOMACION S.A.—See Acek Desarrollo y Gestion Industrial SL; *Int'l*, pg. 96
GESTAMP AUTOMOCION S.A. - GESTAMP BAIRES-ESCOBAR (I, II) PLANT—See Acek Desarrollo y Gestion Industrial SL; *Int'l*, pg. 96
GESTAMP AUTOMOCION S.A. - GESTAMP BEYCELIK (I, II) PLANT—See Acek Desarrollo y Gestion Industrial SL; *Int'l*, pg. 96
GESTAMP AUTOMOCION S.A. - GESTAMP GRAVATAI PLANT—See Acek Desarrollo y Gestion Industrial SL; *Int'l*, pg. 96
GESTAMP AUTOMOCION S.A. - GESTAMP GRIWE HAYNRODE PLANT—See Acek Desarrollo y Gestion Industrial SL; *Int'l*, pg. 96
GESTAMP AUTOMOCION S.A. - GESTAMP LLANELLI PLANT—See Acek Desarrollo y Gestion Industrial SL; *Int'l*, pg. 96
GESTAMP AUTOMOCION S.A. - GESTAMP NILUFER TURKEY PLANT—See Acek Desarrollo y Gestion Industrial SL; *Int'l*, pg. 96
GESTAMP AUTOMOCION S.A. - GESTAMP PARANA PLANT—See Acek Desarrollo y Gestion Industrial SL; *Int'l*, pg. 96
GESTAMP AUTOMOCION S.A. - GESTAMP SANTA ISABEL PLANT—See Acek Desarrollo y Gestion Industrial SL; *Int'l*, pg. 96
GESTAMP AUTOMOCION S.A. - GESTAMP SANTPEDOR PLANT—See Acek Desarrollo y Gestion Industrial SL; *Int'l*, pg. 96
GESTAMP AUTOMOCION S.A. - GESTAMP TAUBATE PLANT—See Acek Desarrollo y Gestion Industrial SL; *Int'l*, pg. 96
GESTAMP AUTOMOCION S.A. - GESTAMP WROCLAW PLANT—See Acek Desarrollo y Gestion Industrial SL; *Int'l*, pg. 96
GESTAMP AUTOMOCION S.A. - GMF OTOMOTIV PLANT—See Acek Desarrollo y Gestion Industrial SL; *Int'l*, pg. 96

COMPANY NAME INDEX

GESTAMP AUTOMOCION S.A. - LOIRE SAFE PLANT—See Acek Desarrollo y Gestion Industrial SL; *Int'l*, pg. 96
GESTAMP AUTOMOCION S.A. -SOFEDIT LE THEIL PLANT—See Acek Desarrollo y Gestion Industrial SL; *Int'l*, pg. 96
GESTAMP AUTOMOCION S.A. - SOFEDIT SERMAISES PLANT—See Acek Desarrollo y Gestion Industrial SL; *Int'l*, pg. 96
GESTAMP AUTOMOCION S.A. - SOFEDIT ST. ROMAIN PLANT—See Acek Desarrollo y Gestion Industrial SL; *Int'l*, pg. 96
GESTAMP AUTOMOTIVE CHENNAI PRIVATE LIMITED—See Acek Desarrollo y Gestion Industrial SL; *Int'l*, pg. 96
GESTAMP AUTOMOTIVE INDIA PRIVATE LTD.—See Acek Desarrollo y Gestion Industrial SL; *Int'l*, pg. 97
GESTAMP AVEIRO, S.A.—See Acek Desarrollo y Gestion Industrial SL; *Int'l*, pg. 97
GESTAMP BAIRES, S.A.—See Acek Desarrollo y Gestion Industrial SL; *Int'l*, pg. 97
GESTAMP BIZKAIA, S.A.—See Acek Desarrollo y Gestion Industrial SL; *Int'l*, pg. 97
GESTAMP CERVEIRA, LDA.—See Acek Desarrollo y Gestion Industrial SL; *Int'l*, pg. 97
GESTAMP CHATTANOOGA, LLC.—See Acek Desarrollo y Gestion Industrial SL; *Int'l*, pg. 97
GESTAMP CORDOBA, S.A.—See Acek Desarrollo y Gestion Industrial SL; *Int'l*, pg. 97
GESTAMP EDSCHA JAPAN CO., LTD.—See Acek Desarrollo y Gestion Industrial SL; *Int'l*, pg. 97
GESTAMP ESMAR, S.A.—See Acek Desarrollo y Gestion Industrial SL; *Int'l*, pg. 97
GESTAMP GALVANIZADOS, S.A.—See Acek Desarrollo y Gestion Industrial SL; *Int'l*, pg. 97
GESTAMP GRIWE WESTERBURG, GMBH—See Acek Desarrollo y Gestion Industrial SL; *Int'l*, pg. 97
GESTAMP HARDTECH, A.B.—See Acek Desarrollo y Gestion Industrial SL; *Int'l*, pg. 97
GESTAMP HUNGARIA, KFT—See Acek Desarrollo y Gestion Industrial SL; *Int'l*, pg. 97
GESTAMP INGENIERIA EUROPA SUR, S.L.—See Acek Desarrollo y Gestion Industrial SL; *Int'l*, pg. 97
GESTAMP KANTEK CO, LTD.—See Acek Desarrollo y Gestion Industrial SL; *Int'l*, pg. 97
GESTAMP LEVANTE, S.A.—See Acek Desarrollo y Gestion Industrial SL; *Int'l*, pg. 97
GESTAMP LINARES, S.A.—See Acek Desarrollo y Gestion Industrial SL; *Int'l*, pg. 97
GESTAMP LOUNY, S.R.O.—See Acek Desarrollo y Gestion Industrial SL; *Int'l*, pg. 97
GESTAMP MANUFACTURING AUTOCHASIS, S.L.—See Acek Desarrollo y Gestion Industrial SL; *Int'l*, pg. 97
GESTAMP MASON, LLC.—See Acek Desarrollo y Gestion Industrial SL; *Int'l*, pg. 97
GESTAMP METAL FORMING (CHONGQING) CO., LTD—See Acek Desarrollo y Gestion Industrial SL; *Int'l*, pg. 97
GESTAMP METAL FORMING (WUHAN), LTD.—See Acek Desarrollo y Gestion Industrial SL; *Int'l*, pg. 97
GESTAMP NAVARRA, S.A.—See Acek Desarrollo y Gestion Industrial SL; *Int'l*, pg. 97
GESTAMP NORTH AMERICA, INC.—See Acek Desarrollo y Gestion Industrial SL; *Int'l*, pg. 97
GESTAMP NORTH EUROPE SERVICES, S.L—See Acek Desarrollo y Gestion Industrial SL; *Int'l*, pg. 97
GESTAMP NOURY S.A.S.—See Acek Desarrollo y Gestion Industrial SL; *Int'l*, pg. 97
GESTAMP PALENCIA, S.A.—See Acek Desarrollo y Gestion Industrial SL; *Int'l*, pg. 97
GESTAMP POLSKA SP. Z.O.O.—See Acek Desarrollo y Gestion Industrial SL; *Int'l*, pg. 97
GESTAMP PORTUGAL LTDA.—See Corporacion Gestamp SL; *Int'l*, pg. 1804
GESTAMP PRISMA S.A.S—See Acek Desarrollo y Gestion Industrial SL; *Int'l*, pg. 97
GESTAMP PUEBLA, S.A. DE C.V.—See Acek Desarrollo y Gestion Industrial SL; *Int'l*, pg. 97
GESTAMP RENEWABLES—See Corporacion Gestamp SL; *Int'l*, pg. 1804
GESTAMP RONCHAMP, S.A.S.—See Acek Desarrollo y Gestion Industrial SL; *Int'l*, pg. 97
GESTAMP SEVERSTAL KALUGA, LLC.—See Acek Desarrollo y Gestion Industrial SL; *Int'l*, pg. 97
GESTAMP SEVERSTAL VSEVOLOZHSK LLC.—See Acek Desarrollo y Gestion Industrial SL; *Int'l*, pg. 97
GESTAMP SOLBLANK NAVARRA, S.L.U—See Acek Desarrollo y Gestion Industrial SL; *Int'l*, pg. 97
GESTAMP SOLBLANK, S.A.—See Acek Desarrollo y Gestion Industrial SL; *Int'l*, pg. 97
GESTAMP SOUTH CAROLINA, LLC.—See Acek Desarrollo y Gestion Industrial SL; *Int'l*, pg. 97
GESTAMP TALLENT, LTD.—See Acek Desarrollo y Gestion Industrial SL; *Int'l*, pg. 97
GESTAMP TOGLIATTI, LLC.—See Acek Desarrollo y Gestion Industrial SL; *Int'l*, pg. 97
GESTAMP TOLEDO, S.A.—See Acek Desarrollo y Gestion Industrial SL; *Int'l*, pg. 97
GESTAMP TOLUCA, S.A. DE C. V.—See Acek Desarrollo y Gestion Industrial SL; *Int'l*, pg. 97
GESTAMP TOOL HARDENING, S.L.—See Acek Desarrollo y Gestion Industrial SL; *Int'l*, pg. 97
GESTAMP UMFORMTECHNIK GMBH—See Acek Desarrollo y Gestion Industrial SL; *Int'l*, pg. 97
GESTAMP VENDAS NOVAS, LDA.—See Acek Desarrollo y Gestion Industrial SL; *Int'l*, pg. 97
GESTAMP VIGO, S.A.—See Acek Desarrollo y Gestion Industrial SL; *Int'l*, pg. 97
GESTAMP WASHINGTON, UK LTD.—See Acek Desarrollo y Gestion Industrial SL; *Int'l*, pg. 98
GESTAMP WEST VIRGINIA LLC.—See Acek Desarrollo y Gestion Industrial SL; *Int'l*, pg. 98
GESTAMP WIND—See Corporacion Gestamp SL; *Int'l*, pg. 1804
GE STEAM POWER S & E AFRICA PROPRIETARY LIMITED—See General Electric Company; *U.S. Public*, pg. 917
GESTETNER BANGLADESH LTD.—See Ricoh Company, Ltd.; *Int'l*, pg. 6333
GESTETNER (ISRAEL) LIMITED—See Ricoh Company, Ltd.; *Int'l*, pg. 6334
GESTETNER LIMITED (MALAWI)—See Ricoh Company, Ltd.; *Int'l*, pg. 6334
GESTETNER OF CEYLON PLC; *Int'l*, pg. 2946
GESTIGON GMBH—See Valeo S.A.; *Int'l*, pg. 8115
GESTIMMOBILI S.R.L.—See Vittoria Assicurazioni S.p.A.; *Int'l*, pg. 8264
GESTIN POLSKA SP. Z O.O.—See Stellantis N.V.; *Int'l*, pg. 7198
GESTIO D'ACTIUS TITULITZATS, S.G.F.T.H.—See Banco Bilbao Vizcaya Argentaria, S.A.; *Int'l*, pg. 817
GESTIO I SERVIES TRADE CENTER S.A.—See TAV Havalimanlari Holding A.S.; *Int'l*, pg. 7477
GESTION AMBIENAL CONSULTORES S.A.—See WSP Global, Inc.; *Int'l*, pg. 8496
GESTION AMBIENTAL CONSULTORES S.A.—See WSP Global, Inc.; *Int'l*, pg. 8496
GESTION AUDEM, INC.; *Int'l*, pg. 2946
GESTION CLAUDE ROBERT INC.; *Int'l*, pg. 2946
GESTION COMPARTIDA S.A.—See Grupo Clarin S.A.; *Int'l*, pg. 3125
GESTION DE PARTICIPES DE BIORRECICLAJE, S.A.—See GS Holdings Corp.; *Int'l*, pg. 3142
GESTION ET LOCATION HOLDING S.A.S.—See BNP Paribas SA; *Int'l*, pg. 1091
GESTION FORESTIERE DU SAINT-MAURICE INC.—See Investissement Quebec; *Int'l*, pg. 3780
GESTION FORESTIERE LACROIX INC.—See Investissement Quebec; *Int'l*, pg. 3780
GESTION HUNT INC.—See Synergie SA; *Int'l*, pg. 7383
GESTION MARTIN POITRAS INC; *Int'l*, pg. 2946
GESTION MODA SHOPPING S.A.—See MAPFRE S.A.; *Int'l*, pg. 4685
GESTION VIAL, S.A.—See Sacyr, S.A.; *Int'l*, pg. 6465
GESTION Y PROTECCION AMBIENTAL, S.L.—See ACS, Actividades de Construccion y Servicios, S.A.; *Int'l*, pg. 112
GESTIRETALHO-GESTAO E CONSULTADORIA PARA A DISTRIBUICAO A RETALHO, S.A.—See Jeronimo Martins SGPS SA; *Int'l*, pg. 3931
GESTMUSIC ENDEMOL S.A.—See LOV Group Invest SAS; *Int'l*, pg. 4564
GESTRA AG—See Spirax-Sarco Engineering plc; *Int'l*, pg. 7137
GESTRA ESPANLOA SA—See Spirax-Sarco Engineering plc; *Int'l*, pg. 7137
GESTRA POLONIA SP. Z.O.O—See Spirax-Sarco Engineering plc; *Int'l*, pg. 7137
GESTRA PORTUGAL, LDA.—See Spirax-Sarco Engineering plc; *Int'l*, pg. 7137
GESTRA SINGAPORE PTE. LTD.—See Spirax-Sarco Engineering plc; *Int'l*, pg. 7137
GESTRA UK LTD.—See Spirax-Sarco Engineering plc; *Int'l*, pg. 7137
GESTRA USA, INC.—See Spirax-Sarco Engineering plc; *Int'l*, pg. 7137
GEST S.P.A.—See Regie Autonome des Transports Parisiens; *Int'l*, pg. 6253
GESUNDHEITSWELT CHIEMGAU AG; *Int'l*, pg. 2946
GES US (NEW ENGLAND), INC.—See Venture Corporation Limited; *Int'l*, pg. 8151
GE SWEDEN HOLDINGS AB—See General Electric Company; *U.S. Public*, pg. 917
GETABEC PUBLIC COMPANY LIMITED; *Int'l*, pg. 2947
GETAC HOLDINGS CORPORATION—See MiTAC International Corp.; *Int'l*, pg. 4923
GETAC INC.—See MiTAC International Corp.; *Int'l*, pg. 4923
GETAC (UK) LTD.—See MiTAC International Corp.; *Int'l*, pg. 4923
GETALONG ENTERPRISE LIMITED; *Int'l*, pg. 2947
GETAROUND, INC.; *U.S. Public*, pg. 935
GET AS—See Telia Company AB; *Int'l*, pg. 7544
GET-A-TICKET B.V.—See CM.com N.V.; *Int'l*, pg. 1666
GETBACK SPOLKA AKCYJNA; *Int'l*, pg. 2947
GETBLEND INC.; *U.S. Private*, pg. 1688
GETBRIDGE LLC—See Learning Technologies Group plc; *Int'l*, pg. 4435
GETBUSY PLC; *Int'l*, pg. 2947
GETC ASIA PRIVATE LIMITED—See CNA Group Ltd.; *Int'l*, pg. 1673
GETCHELL GOLD CORP.; *Int'l*, pg. 2947
GE T&D INDIA LTD.—See General Electric Company; *U.S. Public*, pg. 917
GETEC ENERGIE AG—See BP plc; *Int'l*, pg. 1131
GETEC ENERGIE HOLDING GMBH; *Int'l*, pg. 2947
GETEC HEAT & POWER AG—See GETEC Energie Holding GmbH; *Int'l*, pg. 2947
GETECH GROUP PLC; *Int'l*, pg. 2947
GETEC NORTH AMERICA, INC.—See Keller Group plc; *Int'l*, pg. 4119
GET EDUCATED INTERNATIONAL PROPRIETARY LIMITED—See 2U, Inc.; *U.S. Public*, pg. 3
GETEIN BIOTECH, INC.; *Int'l*, pg. 2947
GETELEC GUADELOUPE SAS—See VINCI S.A.; *Int'l*, pg. 8222
GETELEC GUYANE SAS—See VINCI S.A.; *Int'l*, pg. 8222
GETELEC MARTINIQUE SAS—See VINCI S.A.; *Int'l*, pg. 8222
GETELEC SAS—See VINCI S.A.; *Int'l*, pg. 8222
GETELEC TP SASU—See VINCI S.A.; *Int'l*, pg. 8222
GET ELECTRONIQUE S.A.S.—See Airbus SE; *Int'l*, pg. 246
GETELMAN CORP.; *U.S. Private*, pg. 1688
GE-TE MEDIA AB; *Int'l*, pg. 2897
G.E.T. ENTERPRISES, LLC—See Olympus Partners; *U.S. Private*, pg. 3013
GETFEEDBACK, INC.—See Symphony Technology Group, LLC; *U.S. Private*, pg. 3901
GET FRESH PRODUCE LLC—See Wind Point Advisors LLC; *U.S. Private*, pg. 4534
GETGO CONSULTING GMBH—See CTS Eventim AG & Co. KGAA; *Int'l*, pg. 1874
GETHEALTHINSURANCE.COM AGENCY INC.—See UnitedHealth Group Incorporated; *U.S. Public*, pg. 2253
GETHMANN CONSTRUCTION COMPANY; *U.S. Private*, pg. 1688
GET HOLDINGS LIMITED; *Int'l*, pg. 2946
GETIAN GENERAL SERVICES LTD—See Charilaos Apostolides Public Ltd.; *Int'l*, pg. 1450
GETICA AB—See Gentian Diagnostics AS; *Int'l*, pg. 2928
GET IMAGING, INC.—See MIDCON Data Services LLC; *U.S. Private*, pg. 2710
GET INCORPORATED; *U.S. Private*, pg. 1688
GETINGE AB; *Int'l*, pg. 2947
GETINGE ARJO A/S—See Getinge AB; *Int'l*, pg. 2949
GETINGE ARJO HOLDING NETHERLANDS B.V.—See Getinge AB; *Int'l*, pg. 2949
GETINGE AUSTRALIA PTY LTD.—See Getinge AB; *Int'l*, pg. 2949
GETINGE B.V.—See Getinge AB; *Int'l*, pg. 2949
GETINGE CANADA LTD.—See Getinge AB; *Int'l*, pg. 2949
GETINGE CETREA A/S—See Getinge AB; *Int'l*, pg. 2949
GETINGE COLOMBIA SAS—See Getinge AB; *Int'l*, pg. 2949
GETINGE CZECH REPUBLIC, S.R.O.—See Getinge AB; *Int'l*, pg. 2949
GETINGE DANMARK A/S—See Getinge AB; *Int'l*, pg. 2949
GETINGE DEUTSCHLAND GMBH—See Getinge AB; *Int'l*, pg. 2949
GETINGE DISINFECTION AB—See Getinge AB; *Int'l*, pg. 2949
GETINGE DO BRASIL EQUIPAMENTOS MEDICOS LTDA.—See Getinge AB; *Int'l*, pg. 2951
GETINGE D.S.E. NV—See Getinge AB; *Int'l*, pg. 2949
GETINGE FINANCIAL SERVICES GMBH—See Getinge AB; *Int'l*, pg. 2949
GETINGE FINLAND OY—See Getinge AB; *Int'l*, pg. 2949
GETINGE FRANCE SAS—See Getinge AB; *Int'l*, pg. 2949
GETINGE GROUP HONG KONG LTD.—See Getinge AB; *Int'l*, pg. 2949
GETINGE GROUP LOGISTICS AMERICAS, LLC—See Getinge AB; *Int'l*, pg. 2949
GETINGE GROUP MIDDLE EAST FZ-LLC—See Getinge AB; *Int'l*, pg. 2949
GETINGE GROUP PORTUGAL UNIPESSOAL LDA.—See Getinge AB; *Int'l*, pg. 2949
GETINGE GROUP SOUTH EAST EUROPE D.O.O—See Getinge AB; *Int'l*, pg. 2949
GETINGE GROUP SPAIN SL—See Getinge AB; *Int'l*, pg. 2949
GETINGE GROUP TAIWAN CO., LTD.—See Getinge AB; *Int'l*, pg. 2949
GETINGE HEALTHCARE SAS—See Getinge AB; *Int'l*, pg. 2949
GETINGE HONG KONG COMPANY LTD.—See Getinge AB; *Int'l*, pg. 2950
GETINGE IBERICA S.L.—See Getinge AB; *Int'l*, pg. 2950
GETINGE IC PRODUCTION POLAND SP. Z O.O.—See Getinge AB; *Int'l*, pg. 2950
GETINGE INDIA PVT LTD.—See Getinge AB; *Int'l*, pg. 2950
GETINGE INFECTION CONTROL AB—See Getinge AB; *Int'l*, pg. 2950

GETINGE AB

GETINGE INTERNATIONAL AB—See Getinge AB; *Int'l*, pg. 2950
GETINGE INTERNATIONAL ASIA LTD.—See Getinge AB; *Int'l*, pg. 2950
GETINGE IRELAND LTD.—See Getinge AB; *Int'l*, pg. 2950
GETINGE ITALIA S.R.L.—See Getinge AB; *Int'l*, pg. 2950
GETINGE IT-SOLUTION APS—See Getinge AB; *Int'l*, pg. 2950
GETINGE IT SOLUTIONS GMBH—See Getinge AB; *Int'l*, pg. 2950
GETINGE IT SOLUTIONS LTD.—See Getinge AB; *Int'l*, pg. 2950
GETINGE JAPAN KK—See Getinge AB; *Int'l*, pg. 2950
GETINGE KOREA CO. LTD.—See Getinge AB; *Int'l*, pg. 2950
GETINGE LA CALHENE FRANCE SA—See Getinge AB; *Int'l*, pg. 2950
GETINGE-LA CALHENE USA INC—See Getinge AB; *Int'l*, pg. 2951
GETINGE LANCER SAS—See Getinge AB; *Int'l*, pg. 2950
GETINGE LETTING AB—See Getinge AB; *Int'l*, pg. 2950
GETINGE LIFE SCIENCE AMERICAS—See Getinge AB; *Int'l*, pg. 2950
GETINGE LIFE SCIENCES SAS—See Getinge AB; *Int'l*, pg. 2950
GETINGE LINAC TECHNOLOGIES SA—See Getinge AB; *Int'l*, pg. 2950
GETINGE-MAQUET GERMANY HOLDING GMBH—See Getinge AB; *Int'l*, pg. 2951
GETINGE MEDICAL INDIA PVT LTD.—See Getinge AB; *Int'l*, pg. 2950
GETINGE MEDICAL KOREA CO., LTD.—See Getinge AB; *Int'l*, pg. 2950
GETINGE MEDIKAL SISTEMLER SAN VE TIC A.S—See Getinge AB; *Int'l*, pg. 2950
GETINGE MIDDLE EAST & AFRICA—See Getinge AB; *Int'l*, pg. 2950
GETINGE NORGE AS—See Getinge AB; *Int'l*, pg. 2950
GETINGE ODELGA GMBH—See Getinge AB; *Int'l*, pg. 2950
GETINGE OSTERREICH GMBH—See Getinge AB; *Int'l*, pg. 2950
GETINGE POLAND SP. Z.O.O.—See Getinge AB; *Int'l*, pg. 2950
GETINGE POLSKA SP. Z O.O.—See Getinge AB; *Int'l*, pg. 2950
GETINGE PRODUCTION FRANCE SAS—See Getinge AB; *Int'l*, pg. 2950
GETINGE (SHANGHAI) TRADING CO. LTD.—See Getinge AB; *Int'l*, pg. 2949
GETINGE SHARED SERVICES SP. Z O.O—See Getinge AB; *Int'l*, pg. 2950
GETINGE SINGAPORE PTE. LTD.—See Getinge AB; *Int'l*, pg. 2950
GETINGE SKARHAMN AB—See Getinge AB; *Int'l*, pg. 2950
GETINGE SLOVAKIA S.R.O.—See Getinge AB; *Int'l*, pg. 2950
GETINGE SOURCING LLC—See Getinge AB; *Int'l*, pg. 2950
GETINGE SOUTH AFRICA (PTY) LTD.—See Getinge AB; *Int'l*, pg. 2950
GETINGE SOUTH EAST ASIA PTE. LTD.—See Getinge AB; *Int'l*, pg. 2950
GETINGE S.P.A.—See Getinge AB; *Int'l*, pg. 2950
GETINGE STERICOOL MEDIKAL ALETLER SAN. VE TIC. A.S—See Getinge AB; *Int'l*, pg. 2950
GETINGE STERILIZATION AB—See Getinge AB; *Int'l*, pg. 2950
GETINGE (SUZHOU) CO., LTD.—See Getinge AB; *Int'l*, pg. 2949
GETINGE SVERIGE AB—See Getinge AB; *Int'l*, pg. 2950
GETINGE TREASURY AB—See Getinge AB; *Int'l*, pg. 2950
GETINGE TREASURY IRELAND DAC—See Getinge AB; *Int'l*, pg. 2950
GETINGE UK LTD.—See Getinge AB; *Int'l*, pg. 2950
GETINGE USA, INC. - FLORIDA—See Getinge AB; *Int'l*, pg. 2951
GETINGE USA, INC.—See Getinge AB; *Int'l*, pg. 2951
GETINGE USA SALES, LLC—See Getinge AB; *Int'l*, pg. 2951
GETINGE VERTRIEB UND SERVICE GMBH—See Getinge AB; *Int'l*, pg. 2951
GETINGE VIETNAM COMPANY LTD.—See Getinge AB; *Int'l*, pg. 2951
GETIN HOLDING S.A.; *Int'l*, pg. 2947
GETIN NOBLE BANK S.A.; *Int'l*, pg. 2947
GET IN SHAPE FOR WOMEN, INC.; *U.S. Private*, pg. 1688
GETLINK SE; *Int'l*, pg. 2952
GETMAN CORPORATION; *U.S. Private*, pg. 1688
GETMAPPING PLC; *Int'l*, pg. 2953
GET MATCHES LLC; *U.S. Private*, pg. 1688
GET ME IN! LTD.—See Live Nation Entertainment, Inc.; *U.S. Public*, pg. 1331
GETMYHOMESVALUE.COM; *U.S. Private*, pg. 1688
GET NICE FINANCIAL GROUP LIMITED—See Get Nice Holdings Limited; *Int'l*, pg. 2946

GET NICE HOLDINGS LIMITED; *Int'l*, pg. 2946
GETO & DEMILLY INC.; *U.S. Private*, pg. 1688
GETON ENERGY SIA—See UAB Ignitis grupe; *Int'l*, pg. 7998
GETONTV GMBH—See Mountain Alliance AG; *Int'l*, pg. 5057
GETOP (THAILAND) CO., LTD.—See Xiamen C&D Inc.; *Int'l*, pg. 8523
GE TOSHIBA TURBINE COMPONENTS DE MEXICO S.R.L. DE C.V.—See Japan Industrial Partners, Inc.; *Int'l*, pg. 3889
GET PREPPED LLC—See Manhattan Review Inc.; *U.S. Private*, pg. 2563
GET PRICE PTY. LTD.; *Int'l*, pg. 2946
GETRAG ALL WHEEL DRIVE—See Zhejiang Geely Holding Group Co., Ltd.; *Int'l*, pg. 8653
GETRAG ASIA PACIFIC—See Magna International Inc.; *Int'l*, pg. 4639
GETRAG ASIA PACIFIC TRANSMISSION TECHNOLOGY (SHANGHAI) CO. LTD.—See Magna International Inc.; *Int'l*, pg. 4639
GETRAG B.V. & CO. KG - BAD WINDSHEIM PLANT—See Magna International Inc.; *Int'l*, pg. 4639
GETRAG B.V. & CO. KG - NEUENSTEIN PLANT—See Magna International Inc.; *Int'l*, pg. 4639
GETRAG B.V. & CO. KG - ROSENBERG PLANT—See Magna International Inc.; *Int'l*, pg. 4639
GETRAG FORD TRANSMISSIONS GMBH - BORDEAUX PLANT—See Ford Motor Company; *U.S. Public*, pg. 866
GETRAG FORD TRANSMISSIONS GMBH - BORDEAUX PLANT—See Magna International Inc.; *Int'l*, pg. 4639
GETRAG FORD TRANSMISSIONS GMBH - COLOGNE-MERKENICH—See Ford Motor Company; *U.S. Public*, pg. 866
GETRAG FORD TRANSMISSIONS GMBH - COLOGNE-MERKENICH—See Magna International Inc.; *Int'l*, pg. 4639
GETRAG FORD TRANSMISSIONS GMBH - HALEWOOD PLANT—See Ford Motor Company; *U.S. Public*, pg. 866
GETRAG FORD TRANSMISSIONS GMBH - HALEWOOD PLANT—See Magna International Inc.; *Int'l*, pg. 4639
GETRAG FORD TRANSMISSIONS GMBH—See Ford Motor Company; *U.S. Public*, pg. 866
GETRAG FORD TRANSMISSIONS GMBH—See Magna International Inc.; *Int'l*, pg. 4639
GETRAG FORD TRANSMISSIONS SLOVAKIA SRO—See Ford Motor Company; *U.S. Public*, pg. 866
GETRAG FORD TRANSMISSIONS SLOVAKIA SRO—See Magna International Inc.; *Int'l*, pg. 4639
GETRAG (JIANGXI) TRANSMISSION CO. LTD.—See Magna International Inc.; *Int'l*, pg. 4639
GETRAG SPA—See Magna International Inc.; *Int'l*, pg. 4639
GETRAG S.R.O.—See Magna International Inc.; *Int'l*, pg. 4640
GETRAG SYSTEMTECHNIK GMBH—See Magna International Inc.; *Int'l*, pg. 4639
GETRANKE HORNUNG GMBH—See Warsteiner Brauerei Haus Cramer KG; *Int'l*, pg. 8346
GETRANKE KRIETEMEYER GMBH—See Warsteiner Brauerei Haus Cramer KG; *Int'l*, pg. 8346
GE TRANSPORTATION RAIL—See General Electric Company; *U.S. Public*, pg. 920
GE TRANSPORTATION—See Westinghouse Air Brake Technologies Corporation; *U.S. Public*, pg. 2358
GETRIEBEBAU NORD AG—See Getriebebau NORD GmbH & Co. KG; *Int'l*, pg. 2953
GETRIEBEBAU NORD GMBH & CO. KG; *Int'l*, pg. 2953
GETRIEBEBAU NORD GMBH—See Getriebebau NORD GmbH & Co. KG; *Int'l*, pg. 2953
GETRONICS BELGIUM NV/SA; *Int'l*, pg. 2953
GETRONICS COLUMBIA LTDA—See OpenGate Capital Management, LLC; *U.S. Private*, pg. 3030
GETRONICS DEUTSCHLAND GMBH—See Aurelius Equity Opportunities SE & Co. KGaA; *Int'l*, pg. 708
GETRONICS GLOBAL SERVICES BV—See Aurelius Equity Opportunities SE & Co. KGaA; *Int'l*, pg. 708
GETRONICS HUNGARY KFT—See Aurelius Equity Opportunities SE & Co. KGaA; *Int'l*, pg. 708
GETRONICS MIDDLE EAST—See National Technology Group; *Int'l*, pg. 5164
GETRONICS (SCHWEIZ) AG—See Aurelius Equity Opportunities SE & Co. KGaA; *Int'l*, pg. 708
GETRONICS SOLUTIONS (S) PTE LTD—See Aurelius Equity Opportunities SE & Co. KGaA; *Int'l*, pg. 708
GETRONICS (UK) LIMITED—See Aurelius Equity Opportunities SE & Co. KGaA; *Int'l*, pg. 708
GETSAVVI HEALTH PROPRIETARY LIMITED—See Workforce Holdings Ltd.; *Int'l*, pg. 8455
GETSERVICE-FLUGHAFEN-SICHERHEITS- UND SERVICEDIENST GMBH—See Flughafen Wien Aktiengesellschaft; *Int'l*, pg. 2712
GETSMARTER ONLINE LIMITED—See 2U, Inc.; *U.S. Public*, pg. 3
GET SOLUTIONS, INC.; *U.S. Private*, pg. 1688
GET SPIFFY, INC.; *U.S. Private*, pg. 1688

CORPORATE AFFILIATIONS

GETSWIFT LIMITED—See GetSwift Technologies Limited; *U.S. Public*, pg. 935
GETSWIFT TECHNOLOGIES LIMITED; *U.S. Public*, pg. 935
GETTEL AUTOMOTIVE MANAGEMENT GROUP; *U.S. Private*, pg. 1689
GETTEL ENTERPRISE INC.; *U.S. Private*, pg. 1689
GETTEL FORD-MERCURY INC.; *U.S. Private*, pg. 1689
GETTER GROUP LTD.; *Int'l*, pg. 2953
G.E.T.T. GOLD INC.; *Int'l*, pg. 2865
GETTICKETS E SOLUTIONS INC.—See UOMO Media Inc.; *Int'l*, pg. 8086
GETTING PERSONAL LTD—See Sportswift Limited; *Int'l*, pg. 7143
GETTLE, INC.; *U.S. Private*, pg. 1689
GETTOP ACOUSTIC CO., LTD.; *Int'l*, pg. 2953
GETTRY MARCUS CPA, P.C. - NEW YORK CITY (EAST SIDE) OFFICE—See Citrin Cooperman & Company, LLP; *U.S. Private*, pg. 904
GETTRY MARCUS CPA, P.C. - NEW YORK CITY (WEST SIDE) OFFICE—See Citrin Cooperman & Company, LLP; *U.S. Private*, pg. 904
GETTRY MARCUS CPA, P.C.—See Citrin Cooperman & Company, LLP; *U.S. Private*, pg. 904
GETTY COPPER INC.; *Int'l*, pg. 2953
GETTY IMAGES FRANCE—See CC Capital Partners, LLC; *U.S. Private*, pg. 797
GETTY IMAGES HOLDINGS, INC.; *U.S. Public*, pg. 935
GETTY IMAGES, INC.—See CC Capital Partners, LLC; *U.S. Private*, pg. 797
GETTY IMAGES PTY. LTD.—See CC Capital Partners, LLC; *U.S. Private*, pg. 797
GETTY IMAGES (UK) LIMITED—See CC Capital Partners, LLC; *U.S. Private*, pg. 797
GETTY PETROLEUM MARKETING INC.—See PJSC Lukoil; *Int'l*, pg. 5882
GETTY PROPERTIES CORP.—See Getty Realty Corp.; *U.S. Public*, pg. 935
GETTY REALTY CORP.; *U.S. Public*, pg. 935
THE GETTYSBURG FOUNDATION; *U.S. Private*, pg. 4033
GETTY TERMINALS—See PJSC Lukoil; *Int'l*, pg. 5882
GETUPDATED SVERIGE AB—See Oniva Online Group Europe AB; *Int'l*, pg. 5581
GETUSROI LLC—See Softeon, Inc.; *U.S. Private*, pg. 3705
GETWELLNETWORK, INC.; *U.S. Private*, pg. 1689
GETWIRELESS, LLC; *U.S. Private*, pg. 1689
GET YOUR FEELZ ON; *U.S. Public*, pg. 935
GETZNER TEXTIL AG; *Int'l*, pg. 2954
GETZNER TEXTIL HANDEL GMBH—See Getzner Textil AG; *Int'l*, pg. 2954
GETZNER TEXTIL WEBEREI GMBH—See Getzner Textil AG; *Int'l*, pg. 2954
GETZS, INC.; *U.S. Private*, pg. 1689
GEUMHWA PSC CO., LTD.; *Int'l*, pg. 2954
GEUMJIN BIOTECH—See TONGYANG Group; *Int'l*, pg. 7809
GEUMSAN GINSENG HERB DEVELOPMENT AGENCY; *Int'l*, pg. 2954
GEUMVIT CORP.; *Int'l*, pg. 2954
GEVAS BRASIL LTDA.—See OPTIMA Packaging Group GmbH; *Int'l*, pg. 5603
GEVAS GMBH—See OPTIMA Packaging Group GmbH; *Int'l*, pg. 5603
GEVEA AB—See Addtech AB; *Int'l*, pg. 133
GEVEKE B.V.—See Nikkiso Co., Ltd.; *Int'l*, pg. 5291
GEVEKO MARKINGS DENMARK A/S—See Solix Group AB; *Int'l*, pg. 7073
GEVEKO MARKINGS FRANCE SARL.—See Solix Group AB; *Int'l*, pg. 7073
GEVEKO MARKINGS GERMANY GMBH—See Solix Group AB; *Int'l*, pg. 7073
GEVEKO MARKINGS ITALY SRL—See Solix Group AB; *Int'l*, pg. 7073
GEVEKO MARKINGS NETHERLANDS BV—See Solix Group AB; *Int'l*, pg. 7073
GEVEKO MARKINGS NORWAY A/S—See Solix Group AB; *Int'l*, pg. 7073
GEVEKO MARKINGS SWEDEN AB—See Solix Group AB; *Int'l*, pg. 7073
GEVEKO MARKINGS SWITZERLAND AG—See Solix Group AB; *Int'l*, pg. 7073
GEVELOT EXTRUSION—See Gevelot S.A.; *Int'l*, pg. 2954
GEVELOT S.A.; *Int'l*, pg. 2954
GE VERNOVA INC.; *U.S. Public*, pg. 909
GEV GMBH—See Advent International Corporation; *U.S. Private*, pg. 96
GEV GMBH—See Centerbridge Partners, L.P.; *U.S. Private*, pg. 812
GEV GRUNDSTUCKSGESELLSCHAFT HERZOGENAURACH MBH & CO. KG—See adidas AG; *Int'l*, pg. 146
GE VIETNAM LIMITED—See General Electric Company; *U.S. Public*, pg. 918
GE VINGMED ULTRASOUND A/S—See GE HealthCare Technologies Inc.; *U.S. Public*, pg. 909
GEVO, INC.; *U.S. Public*, pg. 935
G.E. WALKER, INC.; *U.S. Private*, pg. 1631
GEWEKE CO.; *U.S. Private*, pg. 1689

COMPANY NAME INDEX

GEWERBEGRUND AIRPORT GMBH & CO. HALLBERG-MOOS KG—See BayernLB Holding AG; *Int'l*, pg. 914
GEWERBEGRUND AIRPORT GMBH & CO. SCHWAIG KG—See BayernLB Holding AG; *Int'l*, pg. 914
GEWERBEPARK AM BORSIGTURM GMBH—See Salzgitter AG; *Int'l*, pg. 6496
GEWERBE PARK GUNZBURG GMBH—See VIB Vermogen AG; *Int'l*, pg. 8184
GEWERBESIEDLUNGS-GESELLSCHAFT GMBH—See CPI Property Group, S.A.; *Int'l*, pg. 1825
GEWERKSCHAFT DES KONSOLIDIERTEN STEINKOHLENBERGWERKS BREITENBACH GMBH—See BASF SE; *Int'l*, pg. 883
GEWETE GELDWECHSEL- UND SICHERHEITSTECHNIK GMBH—See Gauselmann AG; *Int'l*, pg. 2890
GEWISS CHILE LTDA—See Gewiss S.p.A.; *Int'l*, pg. 2955
GEWISS DEUTSCHLAND GMBH—See Gewiss S.p.A.; *Int'l*, pg. 2955
GEWISS ELEKTRIK TESISAT MALZEMELERI TICARET LTD.—See Gewiss S.p.A.; *Int'l*, pg. 2955
GEWISS FRANCE SA—See Gewiss S.p.A.; *Int'l*, pg. 2955
GEWISS GULF FZE—See Gewiss S.p.A.; *Int'l*, pg. 2955
GEWISS IBERICA SA—See Gewiss S.p.A.; *Int'l*, pg. 2955
GEWISS PORTUGAL LDA—See Gewiss S.p.A.; *Int'l*, pg. 2955
GEWISS ROMANIA SRL—See Gewiss S.p.A.; *Int'l*, pg. 2955
GEWISS S.P.A.—See Gewiss S.p.A.; *Int'l*, pg. 2955
GEWISS S.P.A.; *Int'l*, pg. 2955
GEWISS TRADING (SHANGHAI) CO., LTD.—See Gewiss S.p.A.; *Int'l*, pg. 2955
GEWISS UK LTD.—See Gewiss S.p.A.; *Int'l*, pg. 2955
GEWISTA WERBEGESELLSCHAFT.MBH—See JCDecaux S.A.; *Int'l*, pg. 3920
GEXA ENERGY, L.P.—See NextEra Energy, Inc.; *U.S. Public*, pg. 1526
GEXEED CO., LTD.; *Int'l*, pg. 2955
GEX MANAGEMENT, INC.; *U.S. Public*, pg. 935
GEXPRO—See Rexel, S.A.; *Int'l*, pg. 6316
GEYEN GROUP, INC.; *U.S. Private*, pg. 1689
GEYER PRINTING COMPANY, INC.—See Chatham Asset Management, LLC; *U.S. Private*, pg. 862
GEYERS MARKETS INC.; *U.S. Private*, pg. 1689
GEYSER BRANDS, INC.; *Int'l*, pg. 2955
GEYSER DIALYSIS, LLC—See DaVita Inc.; *U.S. Public*, pg. 639
GEYSER HPC, S.A.U.—See HPC AG; *Int'l*, pg. 3500
GEYSER PEAK WINERY—See Francis Ford Coppola Winery; *U.S. Private*, pg. 1587
GEYSERS INTERNATIONAL INC.—See Banco de Sabadell, S.A.; *Int'l*, pg. 821
GEZIRA TANNERY CO., LTD.—See POSCO Holdings Inc.; *Int'l*, pg. 5938
GEZON MOTORS, INC.; *U.S. Private*, pg. 1689
GFA-ANLAGENBAU GMBH—See SMS Holding GmbH; *Int'l*, pg. 7016
GFA CARAIBES SA—See Assicurazioni Generali S.p.A.; *Int'l*, pg. 645
GFA CESKA REP. S.R.O.—See VINCI S.A.; *Int'l*, pg. 8237
GFA CO., LTD.; *Int'l*, pg. 2955
GFA CORPORATION (THAILAND) CO., LTD.—See PTG Energy Public Company Limited; *Int'l*, pg. 6090
GF ACQUISITION CORP.; *U.S. Private*, pg. 1689
G-FACTORY CO., LTD.; *Int'l*, pg. 2862
GFA CORPORATION FUR ANLAGENBAU MBH—See VINCI S.A.; *Int'l*, pg. 8221
GF AGIECHARMILLES—See Georg Fischer AG; *Int'l*, pg. 2934
GFA GMBH—See Eurofins Scientific S.E.; *Int'l*, pg. 2550
GFA INCORPORATED; *U.S. Private*, pg. 1689
GFA INTERNATIONAL, INC.—See Universal Engineering Sciences, LLC; *U.S. Private*, pg. 4304
GFA PREMIER LIMITED—See London Security PLC; *Int'l*, pg. 4547
GF ASSET MANAGEMENT (HONG KONG) LIMITED—See GF Securities Co., Ltd.; *Int'l*, pg. 2955
GFBB PRUFTECHNIK GMBH & CO. KG—See Buzzi SpA; *Int'l*, pg. 1230
GFBIOCHEMICALS ITALY SPA; *Int'l*, pg. 2956
GFB S.R.L.—See Orsero S.p.A.; *Int'l*, pg. 5644
GF CANADA HOLDINGS COMPANY LIMITED—See GF Securities Co., Ltd.; *Int'l*, pg. 2955
GFC ANTRIEBSSYSTEME GMBH—See AUMA Riester GmbH & Co. KG; *Int'l*, pg. 705
GF CAPITAL (HONG KONG) LIMITED—See GF Securities Co., Ltd.; *Int'l*, pg. 2955
GF CAPITAL MANAGEMENT & ADVISORS, LLC; *U.S. Private*, pg. 1689
GF CAPITAL (THAILAND) CO., LTD.—See G-Factory Co., Ltd.; *Int'l*, pg. 2862
GFC CONSTRUCTION INC.; *U.S. Private*, pg. 1689
GFC CONSTRUCTION SA—See Bouygues S.A.; *Int'l*, pg. 1122
GFC GLOBAL FOUNDERS CAPITAL GMBH—See Rocket Internet SE; *Int'l*, pg. 6378
G.F.C. GREEN FIELDS CAPITAL LTD.; *Int'l*, pg. 2865
GFC, LTD.; *Int'l*, pg. 2956
GF COMMODITIES CO., LTD.—See GF Securities Co., Ltd.; *Int'l*, pg. 2955
GF CONTROLS GMBH—See Barnes Group Inc.; *U.S. Public*, pg. 277
GFDK GESELLSCHAFT FUR DIGITALE KAUFBERATUNG GMBH—See Team Internet Group plc; *Int'l*, pg. 7500
G F D; *Int'l*, pg. 2861
GFE FREMAT GMBH—See AMG Critical Materials N.V.; *Int'l*, pg. 426
GFE GESELLSCHAFT FUR ELEKTROMETALLURGIE MBH—See AMG Critical Materials N.V.; *Int'l*, pg. 426
GFE MATERIALS TECHNOLOGY, INC.—See AMG Critical Materials N.V.; *Int'l*, pg. 426
GFE METALLE UND MATERIALIEN GMBH—See AMG Critical Materials N.V.; *Int'l*, pg. 426
GFE-MIR ALLOYS AND MINERALS SA (PTY) LTD—See GFE-MIR Holdings AG; *Int'l*, pg. 2956
GFE-MIR BERLIN—See GFE-MIR Holdings AG; *Int'l*, pg. 2956
GFE-MIR GMBH—See GFE-MIR Holdings AG; *Int'l*, pg. 2956
GFE-MIR HOLDINGS AG; *Int'l*, pg. 2956
GFE-MIR POLAND SP—See GFE-MIR Holdings AG; *Int'l*, pg. 2956
GFE-MIR (SHANGHAI) LTD—See GFE-MIR Holdings AG; *Int'l*, pg. 2956
GF ENERGY B.V.—See Verdo A/S; *Int'l*, pg. 8168
GF FAKTOR ZRT.—See Grenke AG; *Int'l*, pg. 3080
GFF (ILE DE FRANCE)—See Caisse des Depots et Consignations; *Int'l*, pg. 1258
GF FINANCIAL MARKETS (U.K.) LTD.—See GF Securities Co., Ltd.; *Int'l*, pg. 2955
GFF INC.; *U.S. Private*, pg. 1690
GFF SA—See Beijer Ref AB; *Int'l*, pg. 944
GF FUND MANAGEMENT CO., LTD.—See GF Securities Co., Ltd.; *Int'l*, pg. 2955
GF FUTURES CO., LTD.—See GF Securities Co., Ltd.; *Int'l*, pg. 2955
GF FUTURES CO., LTD.—See GF Securities Co., Ltd.; *Int'l*, pg. 2955
GFG ALLIANCE LIMITED; *Int'l*, pg. 2956
GF GLOBAL CAPITAL LIMITED—See GF Securities Co., Ltd.; *Int'l*, pg. 2955
GFG RESOURCES INC.; *Int'l*, pg. 2956
GF HEALTH PRODUCTS, INC.; *U.S. Private*, pg. 1689
GFH FINANCIAL GROUP B.S.C.; *Int'l*, pg. 2956
GF HOLDINGS (HONG KONG) CORPORATION LIMITED—See GF Securities Co., Ltd.; *Int'l*, pg. 2955
GFH PARTNERS LTD—See GFH Financial Group B.S.C.; *Int'l*, pg. 2956
GFH UNDERWRITING AGENCY LTD.—See Kuehne + Nagel International AG; *Int'l*, pg. 4324
GFI ASIA PACIFIC PTY LTD—See GFI Software S.A.; *Int'l*, pg. 2957
GFI BELUX—See Mannai Corporation QPSC; *Int'l*, pg. 4674
GFI CONTROL SYSTEMS, INC.—See Westport Fuel Systems Inc.; *Int'l*, pg. 8392
GFI ENERGY VENTURES LLC—See Brookfield Corporation; *Int'l*, pg. 1181
GFI GROUP INC.—See BGC Group, Inc.; *U.S. Public*, pg. 328
GFI GROUP PTE. LTD.—See BGC Group, Inc.; *U.S. Public*, pg. 329
GFI GROUP SERVICES LUX LTD—See BGC Group, Inc.; *U.S. Public*, pg. 329
GFI INFORMATIQUE MAROC—See Mannai Corporation QPSC; *Int'l*, pg. 4674
GFI INTERNATIONAL SA—See Mannai Corporation QPSC; *Int'l*, pg. 4674
GFINITY PLC; *Int'l*, pg. 2957
GF INTERNATIONAL INVESTMENT MANAGEMENT LIMITED—See GF Securities Co., Ltd.; *Int'l*, pg. 2955
GF INVESTMENT MANAGEMENT (HONG KONG) COMPANY LIMITED—See GF Securities Co., Ltd.; *Int'l*, pg. 2955
GF INVESTMENTS (HONG KONG) COMPANY LIMITED—See GF Securities Co., Ltd.; *Int'l*, pg. 2955
GFI PORTUGAL—See Mannai Corporation QPSC; *Int'l*, pg. 4674
GFI SECURITIES LTD.—See BGC Group, Inc.; *U.S. Public*, pg. 329
GFI SOFTWARE S.A.; *Int'l*, pg. 2957
GFI SOFTWARE USA, INC.—See GFI Software S.A.; *Int'l*, pg. 2957
G-FIVE, INC.—See Xerox Holdings Corporation; *U.S. Public*, pg. 2389
GFK CUSTOM RESEARCH, LLC - MINNEAPOLIS—See Advent International Corporation; *U.S. Private*, pg. 105
GFK CUSTOM RESEARCH, LLC - PRINCETON—See Advent International Corporation; *U.S. Private*, pg. 105
GFK CUSTOM RESEARCH, LLC—See Advent International Corporation; *U.S. Private*, pg. 105
GFK MEDIAMARK RESEARCH & INTELLIGENCE, LLC—See Advent International Corporation; *U.S. Private*, pg. 105
GFK NOP LTD.—See Advent International Corporation; *U.S. Private*, pg. 105
GFK SE—See Advent International Corporation; *U.S. Private*, pg. 105
G. FLEISCHHAUER GMBH—See Opportunity Investment Management PLC; *Int'l*, pg. 5600
G. FLEISCHHAUER INGENIEUR-BURO BREMEN GMBH—See Opportunity Investment Management PLC; *Int'l*, pg. 5600
G. FLEISCHHAUER INGENIEUR-BURO GMBH & CO. KG—See Opportunity Investment Management PLC; *Int'l*, pg. 5600
GFL ENVIRONMENTAL INC. - LIQUID WASTE EAST DIVISION—See BC Partners LLP; *Int'l*, pg. 923
GFL ENVIRONMENTAL INC. - LIQUID WASTE WEST DIVISION—See BC Partners LLP; *Int'l*, pg. 923
GFL ENVIRONMENTAL INC. - MATERIAL RECYCLING FACILITY—See BC Partners LLP; *Int'l*, pg. 924
GFL ENVIRONMENTAL INC. - SAULT STE MARIE FACILITY—See BC Partners LLP; *Int'l*, pg. 924
GFL ENVIRONMENTAL INC. - SOLID WASTE TRANSFER DIVISION—See BC Partners LLP; *Int'l*, pg. 924
GFL ENVIRONMENTAL INC.—See BC Partners LLP; *Int'l*, pg. 923
GF LIGHTHOUSE CAPITAL MANAGEMENT COMPANY LIMITED—See GF Securities Co., Ltd.; *Int'l*, pg. 2955
GFL MINING SERVICES LIMITED—See Gold Fields Limited; *Int'l*, pg. 3024
G.F. LOGISTICA SRL—See Kering S.A.; *Int'l*, pg. 4134
GF MACHINING SOLUTIONS LTD.—See Georg Fischer AG; *Int'l*, pg. 2934
GF MACHINING SOLUTIONS SP. Z O.O.—See Georg Fischer AG; *Int'l*, pg. 2935
GF MANAGEMENT, INC.; *U.S. Private*, pg. 1689
GF MANAGEMENT, LLC—See GF Management, Inc.; *U.S. Private*, pg. 1689
GFM CORPORATION—See L.G. Balakrishnan & Bros. Ltd.; *Int'l*, pg. 4386
GFM RESOURCES LIMITED—See Grupo Ferrominero, S.A. de C.V.; *Int'l*, pg. 3129
GFM SERVICES BERHAD; *Int'l*, pg. 2957
GFOOT CO., LTD.; *Int'l*, pg. 2957
G-FORCE LOGISTICS SOLUTIONS SDN. BHD.—See Tiong Nam Logistics Holdings Berhad; *Int'l*, pg. 7755
GFORCE—See WPP plc; *Int'l*, pg. 8470
G FOX SWAZILAND PROPRIETARY LIMITED—See The Bidvest Group Limited; *Int'l*, pg. 7624
GFPT NICHIREI (THAILAND) CO.—See Nichirei Corporation; *Int'l*, pg. 5269
GFPT PUBLIC COMPANY LIMITED - GFPT PLANT—See GFPT Public Company Limited; *Int'l*, pg. 2957
GFPT PUBLIC COMPANY LIMITED; *Int'l*, pg. 2957
GFRC SHELTERS, INC.; *U.S. Private*, pg. 1690
GFR-GESELLSCHAFT FUR REGELUNGSTECHNIK UND ENERGIEEINSPARUNG MBH—See Robert Bosch GmbH; *Int'l*, pg. 6361
G. FRIED FLOORING AMERICA; *U.S. Private*, pg. 1630
G & F ROOF SUPPLY INC.—See Hendricks Holding Company, Inc.; *U.S. Private*, pg. 1914
GFS CANADA—See Castlelake, L.P.; *U.S. Private*, pg. 785
GFS CHEMICALS, INC.; *U.S. Private*, pg. 1690
GF SECURITIES (CANADA) CO., LTD.—See GF Securities Co., Ltd.; *Int'l*, pg. 2955
GF SECURITIES CO., LTD.; *Int'l*, pg. 2955
GF SECURITIES (HONG KONG) BROKERAGE LIMITED—See GF Securities Co., Ltd.; *Int'l*, pg. 2955
G.F. SERVICES SRL—See Kering S.A.; *Int'l*, pg. 4134
GFSI, INC.—See Hanesbrands Inc.; *U.S. Public*, pg. 983
GFS ONTARIO—See Gordon Food Service Inc.; *U.S. Private*, pg. 1743
GFT BRASIL CONSULTORIA INFORMATICA LTDA.—See GFT Technologies SE; *Int'l*, pg. 2957
GFT CANADA INC.—See GFT Technologies SE; *Int'l*, pg. 2957
GFT COSTA RICA S.A.—See GFT Technologies SE; *Int'l*, pg. 2957
GF-TEC GMBH.—See BAUER Aktiengesellschaft; *Int'l*, pg. 893
GFT FINANCIAL LIMITED—See GFT Technologies SE; *Int'l*, pg. 2957
GFT GLOBAL MARKETS ASIA PTE, LTD.—See StoneX Group Inc.; *U.S. Public*, pg. 1952
GFT IBERIA SOLUTIONS S.A.—See GFT Technologies SE; *Int'l*, pg. 2957
GFT INBOXX GMBH.—See GFT Technologies SE; *Int'l*, pg. 2957
GFT ITALIA S.R.L.—See GFT Technologies SE; *Int'l*, pg. 2957
GFT IT CONSULTING, S.L.U.—See GFT Technologies SE; *Int'l*, pg. 2957
GFT MEXICO S.A. DE C.V.—See GFT Technologies SE; *Int'l*, pg. 2957
GFT POLAND SP. Z O.O—See GFT Technologies SE; *Int'l*, pg. 2957
G. F. TRUSS, INC.; *U.S. Private*, pg. 1630
GFT SWITZERLAND AG—See GFT Technologies SE; *Int'l*, pg. 2957
GFT TECHNOLOGIES CANADA INC.—See GFT Technologies SE; *Int'l*, pg. 2957
GFT TECHNOLOGIES (SCHWEIZ) AG.—See GFT Technologies SE; *Int'l*, pg. 2957
GFT TECHNOLOGIES SE; *Int'l*, pg. 2957

GFT TECHNOLOGIES SE

GFT UK LIMITED—See GFT Technologies SE; *Int'l*, pg. 2957

GFT USA INC.—See GFT Technologies SE; *Int'l*, pg. 2957

GFTZ IWAKI ENGINEERING & TRADING CO., LTD.—See Iwaki Co., Ltd.; *Int'l*, pg. 3848

GFUN INDUSTRIAL CORP.—See Singtex Industrial Co., Ltd.; *Int'l*, pg. 6944

G.F. VAUGHAN TOBACCO CO. INC.; *U.S. Private*, pg. 1631

GFWA PTY LTD—See VINCI S.A.; *Int'l*, pg. 8232

GF WEALTH MANAGEMENT (HONG KONG) LIMITED—See GF Securities Co., Ltd.; *Int'l*, pg. 2955

GFX CORPORATION—See CME Group, Inc.; *U.S. Public*, pg. 516

GF XINDE INVESTMENT MANAGEMENT CO., LTD.—See GF Securities Co., Ltd.; *Int'l*, pg. 2955

GFX INTERNATIONAL INC.—See Keystone Group, L.P.; *U.S. Private*, pg. 2298

G&G ADVERTISING, INC.; *U.S. Private*, pg. 1628

G&G ADVERTISING; *U.S. Private*, pg. 1628

G&G ADVERTISING—See G&G Advertising, Inc.; *U.S. Private*, pg. 1628

G&G AGENCY LTD.—See Principal Financial Group, Inc.; *U.S. Public*, pg. 1721

G GAS LOGISTICS COMPANY LIMITED—See Takuni Group Public Company Limited; *Int'l*, pg. 7443

G. G. AUTOMOTIVE GEARS LIMITED; *Int'l*, pg. 2864

GGB AUSTRIA GMBH—See The Timken Company; *U.S. Public*, pg. 2132

GGB BEARING TECHNOLOGY (SUZHOU) CO., LTD.—See Enpro Inc.; *U.S. Public*, pg. 774

GGB BRASIL INDUSTRIA DE MANCAIS E COMPONENTES LTDA.—See The Timken Company; *U.S. Public*, pg. 2132

G&G BEVERAGES INC.—See Bergmann's Inc.; *U.S. Private*, pg. 531

GGB FRANCE E.U.R.L.—See Enpro Inc.; *U.S. Public*, pg. 774

G-G-B GEBAUDE- UND GRUNDBESITZ GMBH—See Commerzbank AG; *Int'l*, pg. 1718

GGB GMBH—See Hirsch Servo AG; *Int'l*, pg. 3405

GGB, INC.—See The Timken Company; *U.S. Public*, pg. 2132

G.G. DANDEKAR MACHINE WORKS LTD. - BHIWANDI PLANT—See G.G. Dandekar Properties Ltd.; *Int'l*, pg. 2865

G.G. DANDEKAR PROPERTIES LTD.; *Int'l*, pg. 2865

GGEC AMERICA, INC.—See GuoGuang Electric Company Limited; *Int'l*, pg. 3186

GGEC HONG KONG LTD.—See GuoGuang Electric Company Limited; *Int'l*, pg. 3186

G&G ELECTRIC & PLUMBING DISTRIBUTORS; *U.S. Private*, pg. 1628

G G ENGINEERING LIMITED; *Int'l*, pg. 2861

G&G FURNITURE IMPORTS PTY. LTD.—See Steinhoff International Holdings N.V.; *Int'l*, pg. 7194

GGG GESELLSCHAFT FUR GRUNDSTUCKS- UND GEBAUDENUTZUNG MBH—See E.ON SE; *Int'l*, pg. 2257

GGI GENEVA GROUP INTERNATIONAL AG; *Int'l*, pg. 2957

G&G INCORPORATED; *U.S. Private*, pg. 1628

GGI SOLUTIONS; *Int'l*, pg. 2957

GGI TECHNOLOGY LTD.—See Gunze Limited; *Int'l*, pg. 3185

GGK ZURICH WERBEAGENTUR AG; *Int'l*, pg. 2957

G & G LAWN CARE, INC.—See Senske Lawn & Tree Care, Inc.; *U.S. Private*, pg. 3608

GGL RESOURCES CORP.; *Int'l*, pg. 2957

G&G MANUFACTURING CO.; *U.S. Private*, pg. 1629

GG MANUFACTURING S.R.L.—See Graco, Inc.; *U.S. Public*, pg. 953

G.G. McGUIGGAN CORP.; *U.S. Private*, pg. 1631

GGMC PARKING, LLC; *U.S. Private*, pg. 1690

GGM GESELLSCHAFT FUR GEBAUDE MANAGEMENT MBH—See Helaba Landesbank Hessen-Thuringen; *Int'l*, pg. 3327

GGM PUEBLA, S.A. DE C.V.—See Acek Desarrollo y Gestion Industrial SL; *Int'l*, pg. 96

G&G OUTFITTERS, INC.; *U.S. Private*, pg. 1629

GGP-GATEWAY MALL L.L.C.—See Brookfield Corporation; *Int'l*, pg. 1185

GGP MEDIA GMBH—See Bertelsmann SE & Co. KGaA; *Int'l*, pg. 994

GGP SWEDEN AB; *Int'l*, pg. 2958

G.G. SCHMITT & SONS INC.—See Patrick Industries, Inc.; *U.S. Public*, pg. 1652

G&G SCIENCE CO., LTD.—See JSR Corp.; *Int'l*, pg. 4014

G&G STEEL; *U.S. Private*, pg. 1629

G&G TECHNICAL INC.; *U.S. Private*, pg. 1629

GGUMBI CO,. LTD.; *Int'l*, pg. 2958

GG UNIQUEFIBER AS—See The Hain Celestial Group, Inc.; *U.S. Public*, pg. 2086

GGW ITALIA SRL—See Kering S.A.; *Int'l*, pg. 4134

GGX GOLD CORP.; *Int'l*, pg. 2958

GHABBOUR AUTO S.A.E.; *Int'l*, pg. 2958

GHABBOUR CONTINENTAL TRADING CO. S.A.E.—See Ghabbour Auto S.A.E.; *Int'l*, pg. 2958

GHACEM LTD.—See Heidelberg Materials AG; *Int'l*, pg. 3315

GHA/DDB—See Omnicom Group Inc.; *U.S. Public*, pg. 1581

GHADEER MINERAL WATER CO. WLL—See Nestle S.A.; *Int'l*, pg. 5203

GHADIR INVESTMENT COMPANY; *Int'l*, pg. 2958

GHAFARI ASSOCIATES LLC—See Ghafari Associates, L.L.C.; *U.S. Private*, pg. 1690

GHAFARI ASSOCIATES, L.L.C.; *U.S. Private*, pg. 1690

G+H AKOESTIEK B.V.—See VINCI S.A.; *Int'l*, pg. 8238

THE GHANA AIRPORTS COMPANY LIMITED; *Int'l*, pg. 7649

GHANA COCOA BOARD - COCOA HEALTH AND EXTENSION DIVISION—See Ghana Cocoa Board; *Int'l*, pg. 2958

GHANA COCOA BOARD; *Int'l*, pg. 2958

GHANA COCOA MARKETING COMPANY (UK) LTD—See Ghana Cocoa Board; *Int'l*, pg. 2958

GHANA COMMUNITY NETWORK SERVICES LIMITED—See SGS SA; *Int'l*, pg. 6742

GHANADHARA INDUSTRIES LTD.—See Bibojee Services Private Limited; *Int'l*, pg. 1018

GHANA INTERBANK PAYMENT AND SETTLEMENT SYSTEMS LTD—See Bank of Ghana; *Int'l*, pg. 843

GHANA INTERNATIONAL BANK PLC—See Bank of Ghana; *Int'l*, pg. 843

GHANA STOCK EXCHANGE; *Int'l*, pg. 2958

GHANA TEXTILE PRINTING COMPANY LTD.—See General Atlantic Service Company, L.P.; *U.S. Private*, pg. 1661

GHANDHARA AUTOMOBILES LIMITED—See Bibojee Services Private Limited; *Int'l*, pg. 1018

GHANI AUTOMOBILE INDUSTRIES LIMITED; *Int'l*, pg. 2958

GHANI GLASS LIMITED - HATTAR PLANT—See Ghani Glass Limited; *Int'l*, pg. 2958

GHANI GLASS LIMITED - SHEIKHUPURA (FLOAT GLASS PLANT)—See Ghani Glass Limited; *Int'l*, pg. 2958

GHANI GLASS LIMITED; *Int'l*, pg. 2958

GHANI GLOBAL GLASS LIMITED—See Ghani Global Holdings Limited; *Int'l*, pg. 2958

GHANI GLOBAL HOLDINGS LIMITED; *Int'l*, pg. 2958

GHANI VALUE GLASS LIMITED; *Int'l*, pg. 2958

GHARDA CHEMICALS LIMITED - DOMBIVILI PLANT—See Gharda Chemicals Limited; *Int'l*, pg. 2958

GHARDA CHEMICALS LIMITED - LOTE PLANT—See Gharda Chemicals Limited; *Int'l*, pg. 2958

GHARDA CHEMICALS LIMITED - PANOLI PLANT—See Gharda Chemicals Limited; *Int'l*, pg. 2958

GHARDA CHEMICALS LIMITED; *Int'l*, pg. 2958

GHARIBWAL CEMENT LIMITED; *Int'l*, pg. 2959

GHARIBWAL CEMENT LTD. - FACTORY—See GHARIBWAL CEMENT LIMITED; *Int'l*, pg. 2959

GHAR INC.; *U.S. Private*, pg. 1690

GHA TECHNOLOGIES, INC.; *U.S. Private*, pg. 1690

GH AUTO PARTS INDUSTRIES INC—See H-One Co., Ltd.; *Int'l*, pg. 3194

GHAZI FABRICS INTERNATIONAL LIMITED; *Int'l*, pg. 2959

GHAZVIN SUGAR COMPANY; *Int'l*, pg. 2959

G.H. BASS & CO.—See G-III Apparel Group, Ltd.; *U.S. Public*, pg. 894

G+H BAUTEC UNTERSTUTZUNGSKASSE GMBH—See VINCI S.A.; *Int'l*, pg. 8221

G. H. BERLIN-WINDWARD—See Booth Waltz Enterprises, Inc.; *U.S. Private*, pg. 617

GHCL LIMITED; *Int'l*, pg. 2959

GHD E.ON BAYERN AG & CO. KG—See E.ON SE; *Int'l*, pg. 2257

GHD GROUP PTY LTD.; *Int'l*, pg. 2959

G&H DIVERSIFIED MANUFACTURING LP; *U.S. Private*, pg. 1629

GHD LIMITED—See GHD Group Pty Ltd.; *Int'l*, pg. 2959

GHD S.A.—See GHD Group Pty Ltd.; *Int'l*, pg. 2959

GH ELECTROTHERMIE, S.A.S.—See Park-Ohio Holdings Corp.; *U.S. Public*, pg. 1639

GHENCEA MEDICAL CENTER SA—See MedLife S.A.; *Int'l*, pg. 4785

GHENT CHEVROLET CADILLAC; *U.S. Private*, pg. 1690

GHENT MOTOR CO.; *U.S. Private*, pg. 1690

GHETTO FILM SCHOOL, INC.; *U.S. Private*, pg. 1690

G+H FASSADENTECHNIK GMBH—See VINCI S.A.; *Int'l*, pg. 8238

GHG ASSET MANAGEMENT LLC—See Icahn Enterprises L.P.; *U.S. Public*, pg. 1084

GHG COLOMBO PVT. LTD.—See Gulf Hotels Group B.S.C.; *Int'l*, pg. 3180

GHG FACILITAIR B.V.—See Groothandelsgebouwen N.V.; *Int'l*, pg. 3088

GHG GREYHEALTH GROUP LLC - KANSAS CITY—See WPP plc; *Int'l*, pg. 8470

GHG GREYHEALTH GROUP LLC—See WPP plc; *Int'l*, pg. 8470

GHG REDUCTION TECHNOLOGIES PRIVATE LIMITED—See EKI Energy Services Limited; *Int'l*, pg. 2338

GHGS COAL MINE METHANE, LLC—See The AES Corporation; *U.S. Public*, pg. 2031

CORPORATE AFFILIATIONS

GHI ASIA PACIFIC PTE. LTD.—See Quaker Chemical Corporation; *U.S. Public*, pg. 1745

GHI AUTOMOTIVE SERVICES INC.; *U.S. Private*, pg. 1690

GHI HOLDINGS INC.; *U.S. Private*, pg. 1690

GHILOTTI BROS INC.; *U.S. Private*, pg. 1690

GHILOTTI CONSTRUCTION COMPANY INC.; *U.S. Private*, pg. 1690

GH INDUCTION ATMOSPHERES, LLC—See Park-Ohio Holdings Corp.; *U.S. Public*, pg. 1639

GH INDUCTION DEUTSCHLAND GMBH—See Park-Ohio Holdings Corp.; *U.S. Public*, pg. 1639

GH INDUCTION EQUIPMENT SHANGHAI CO. LTD.—See Park-Ohio Holdings Corp.; *U.S. Public*, pg. 1639

GH INDUCTION INDIA PVT. LTD.—See Park-Ohio Holdings Corp.; *U.S. Public*, pg. 1639

G+H INDUSTRIE SERVICE GMBH—See VINCI S.A.; *Int'l*, pg. 8221

G+H INNENAUSBAU GMBH—See VINCI S.A.; *Int'l*, pg. 8239

G+H INSULATION INDIA PVT. LTD.—See VINCI S.A.; *Int'l*, pg. 8221

G. HINTEREGGER & SOHNE BAUGESELLSCHAFT M.B.H.—See PORR AG; *Int'l*, pg. 5922

GHIRARDELLI ALBERTO—See A.A.G. STUCCHI s.r.l.; *Int'l*, pg. 23

GHIRARDELLI CHOCOLATE COMPANY—See Chocoladefabriken Lindt & Sprungli AG; *Int'l*, pg. 1576

GHIROTTI & COMPANHIA—See Omnicom Group Inc.; *U.S. Public*, pg. 1581

GHISALBA S.P.A.; *Int'l*, pg. 2959

G+H ISOLIERUNG GMBH—See VINCI S.A.; *Int'l*, pg. 8238

GHK CAPITAL PARTNERS LP; *U.S. Private*, pg. 1690

GHK HOLDINGS LTD.—See ICF International, Inc.; *U.S. Public*, pg. 1086

G+H KUHLLAGER- UND INDUSTRIEBAU GMBH—See VINCI S.A.; *Int'l*, pg. 8221

GHL (BEIJING) CO. LTD.—See General Atlantic Service Company, L.P.; *U.S. Private*, pg. 1661

GHL (CHINA) CO. LTD.—See General Atlantic Service Company, L.P.; *U.S. Private*, pg. 1661

GHL GESELLSCHAFT FUR HAFEN- UND LAGEREIIMMOBILIEN-VERWALTUNG BLOCK D MBH—See Hamburger Hafen und Logistik AG; *Int'l*, pg. 3236

GH LII MANAGEMENT, LLC—See Anywhere Real Estate Inc.; *U.S. Public*, pg. 140

GHLSYS PHILIPPINES INC.—See General Atlantic Service Company, L.P.; *U.S. Private*, pg. 1661

GHL SYSTEMS BERHAD—See General Atlantic Service Company, L.P.; *U.S. Private*, pg. 1661

GHL (THAILAND) CO. LTD.—See General Atlantic Service Company, L.P.; *U.S. Private*, pg. 1661

GHL TRANSACT SDN. BHD.—See General Atlantic Service Company, L.P.; *U.S. Private*, pg. 1661

GHL ZWEITE GESELLSCHAFT FUR HAFEN- UND LAGEREIIMMOBILIEN-VERWALTUNG MBH—See Hamburger Hafen und Logistik AG; *Int'l*, pg. 3236

GHM CORP.; *U.S. Private*, pg. 1690

G+H METALLTECHNIK GMBH—See VINCI S.A.; *Int'l*, pg. 8221

GH METAL SOLUTIONS, INC.—See Reliance Steel & Aluminum Co.; *U.S. Public*, pg. 1780

GH MEXICANA, S.A. DE C.V.—See Park-Ohio Holdings Corp.; *U.S. Public*, pg. 1639

G.H.M. (GROUP) LIMITED; *Int'l*, pg. 2865

GHM INDUSTRIES, INC. - MILLER LIFTING PRODUCTS DIVSION—See GHM Industries, Inc.; *U.S. Private*, pg. 1691

GHM INDUSTRIES, INC.; *U.S. Private*, pg. 1691

GHM MESSTECHNIK GMBH; *Int'l*, pg. 2959

GHM MESSTECHNIK GMBH - STANDORT GREISINGER—See GHM Messtechnik GmbH; *Int'l*, pg. 2959

GHM MESSTECHNIK GMBH - STANDORT HONSBERG—See GHM Messtechnik GmbH; *Int'l*, pg. 2959

GHM MESSTECHNIK GMBH - STANDORT IMTRON—See GHM Messtechnik GmbH; *Int'l*, pg. 2959

GHM MESSTECHNIK GMBH - STANDORT MARTENS—See GHM Messtechnik GmbH; *Int'l*, pg. 2959

G+H MONTAGE BULGARIA GMBH—See VINCI S.A.; *Int'l*, pg. 8221

G+H MONTAGE N.V.—See VINCI S.A.; *Int'l*, pg. 8221

G.H. MUMM & CIE - STE VINICOLE DE CHAMPAGNE SUCCESSEUR—See Pernod Ricard S.A.; *Int'l*, pg. 5810

GHN AGRISPAN HOLDING COMPANY; *Int'l*, pg. 2959

GHN—See Everbrite, LLC; *U.S. Private*, pg. 1437

GH NV—See Mondragon Corporation; *Int'l*, pg. 5029

GHO CAPITAL PARTNERS LLP; *Int'l*, pg. 2959

GHO CRETEIL LE LAC SAS—See Eurazeo SE; *Int'l*, pg. 2528

GHO GRENOBLE NORD VOREPPE SAS—See Eurazeo SE; *Int'l*, pg. 2529

GHO REIMS PARC DES EXPOSITIONS SAS—See Eurazeo SE; *Int'l*, pg. 2529

COMPANY NAME INDEX

G&H ORTHODONTICS—See The Riverside Company; *U.S. Private*, pg. 4108
GHOST-BIKES GMBH; *Int'l*, pg. 2960
GHOST STORY GAMES, LLC—See Take-Two Interactive Software, Inc.; *U.S. Public*, pg. 1979
GHOST STUDIO LTD.; *Int'l*, pg. 2959
GHOTEL DEUTSCHLAND GMBH—See Art-Invest Real Estate Management GmbH & Co. KG; *Int'l*, pg. 580
GHOTEL GERMANY GMBH—See Art-Invest Real Estate Management GmbH & Co. KG; *Int'l*, pg. 580
GHOTEL GMBH—See Art-Invest Real Estate Management GmbH & Co. KG; *Int'l*, pg. 580
GHOTEL HOTEL UND BOARDINGHAUS DEUTSCHLAND GMBH—See Art-Invest Real Estate Management GmbH & Co. KG; *Int'l*, pg. 580
GHO VITRY SUR SEINE A86 BORDS DE SEINE SAS—See Eurazeo SE; *Int'l*, pg. 2529
GHP ASSET MANAGEMENT LIMITED—See GHP Group; *Int'l*, pg. 2960
GHP DIRECT RUS O.O.O.—See Osterreichische Post AG; *Int'l*, pg. 5653
GHP FAR EAST CO. LTD.—See Die Schweizerische Post AG; *Int'l*, pg. 2113
GHP GROUP - REAL ESTATE DIVISION—See GHP Group; *Int'l*, pg. 2960
GHP GROUP; *Int'l*, pg. 2960
GHP MEDIA, INC.; *U.S. Private*, pg. 1691
GHP NOETIC SCIENCE-PSYCHEDELIC PHARMA, INC.; *Int'l*, pg. 2960
GHP SPECIALTY CARE AB—See Apax Partners LLP; *Int'l*, pg. 502
GHR ACQUISITION, LLC—See Platform Partners LLC; *U.S. Private*, pg. 3200
G+H REINRAUMTECHNIK GMBH—See VINCI S.A.; *Int'l*, pg. 8221
GH RESEARCH PLC; *Int'l*, pg. 2958
G+H SCHALLSCHUTZ GMBH—See VINCI S.A.; *Int'l*, pg. 8238
GHS CLASSIC DRINKS LIMITED—See Sysco Corporation; *U.S. Public*, pg. 1974
GHS CORPORATION—See LIXIL Group Corporation; *Int'l*, pg. 4533
GHS CORP.; *U.S. Private*, pg. 1691
GHS INTERACTIVE SECURITY, LLC—See Arena Investors, LP, *U.S. Private*, pg. 318
GHSP, INC.—See JSJ Corporation; *U.S. Private*, pg. 2241
GHT CO., LTD.; *Int'l*, pg. 2960
GHT GESELLSCHAFT FUR PROJEKTMANAGEMENT HESSEN-THURINGEN MBH—See Helaba Landesbank Hessen-Thuringen; *Int'l*, pg. 3327
G&H TOWING CO. INC.; *U.S. Private*, pg. 1629
GH TRANSPORT LIMITED—See HAK Algahtani Group of Companies; *Int'l*, pg. 3219
G&H TRUCK LEASING INC.—See Astleford International Trucks, Inc.; *U.S. Private*, pg. 360
GHUSHINE FINTRRADE OCEAN LIMITED; *Int'l*, pg. 2960
GHW EUROCHEMICALS S.R.O.—See GHW International; *Int'l*, pg. 2960
GHW INTERNATIONAL; *Int'l*, pg. 2960
GHW USA LLC—See GHW International; *Int'l*, pg. 2960
GHW (VIETNAM) CHEMICALS LIMITED COMPANY—See GHW International; *Int'l*, pg. 2960
GHX HOLDINGS, LLC—See Clayton, Dubilier & Rice, LLC; *U.S. Private*, pg. 926
GHX INDUSTRIAL, LLC—See Clayton, Dubilier & Rice, LLC; *U.S. Private*, pg. 926
GHX UK LTD.—See Temasek Holdings (Private) Limited; *Int'l*, pg. 7547
GHY CULTURE & MEDIA HOLDING CO., LIMITED; *Int'l*, pg. 2960
GHY CULTURE & MEDIA (MALAYSIA) SDN. BHD.—See GHY Culture & Media Holding Co., Limited; *Int'l*, pg. 2960
GHZ COMPOSITE MATERIAL CORP.—See Long Young Electronic (Kunshan) Co., Ltd.; *Int'l*, pg. 4549
GIA-AIR HOLDINGS CORP.; *U.S. Private*, pg. 1694
GIA CAUCASIA LOGISTICS LTD.—See Endress+Hauser (International) Holding AG; *Int'l*, pg. 2408
GIACCI BROS. PTY LTD—See Qube Holdings Limited; *Int'l*, pg. 6158
GIACCI HOLDINGS PTY LTD—See Qube Holdings Limited; *Int'l*, pg. 6158
GIACOM (CLOUD) HOLDINGS LIMITED; *Int'l*, pg. 2961
GIACOM (CLOUD) LIMITED—See Giacom (Cloud) Holdings Limited; *Int'l*, pg. 2961
GIACT SYSTEMS, LLC—See London Stock Exchange Group plc; *Int'l*, pg. 4548
GIA ENTERPRISES; *U.S. Private*, pg. 1694
GIAI JACQUIS SAS; *Int'l*, pg. 2961
GIA LAI ELECTRICITY JOINT STOCK COMPANY; *Int'l*, pg. 2960
GIALAMAS COMPANY INCORPORATED; *U.S. Private*, pg. 1694
GIAMBRONE + PARTNERS; *U.S. Private*, pg. 1694
GIANFRANCO FERRE S.P.A.—See Paris Group International LLC; *Int'l*, pg. 5742
GIANFRANCO FERRE USA INC.—See Paris Group International LLC; *Int'l*, pg. 5742
GIAN LIFE CARE LIMITED; *Int'l*, pg. 2961

GIANNI VERSACE S.P.A—See Capri Holdings Limited; *Int'l*, pg. 1316
GIANT ACE SDN. BHD.—See Ace Hardware Corporation; *U.S. Private*, pg. 56
GIANT AUTOMOTIVE GROUP; *U.S. Private*, pg. 1694
GIANT AUTOS (1997) PTY LTD—See Eagers Automotive Limited; *Int'l*, pg. 2263
GIANT BELGIUM N.V.—See Giant Manufacturing Co., Ltd.; *Int'l*, pg. 2961
GIANT BENELUX B.V.—See Giant Manufacturing Co., Ltd.; *Int'l*, pg. 2961
GIANT BICYCLE CANADA, INC.—See Giant Manufacturing Co., Ltd.; *Int'l*, pg. 2961
GIANT BICYCLE CO. LTD.—See Giant Manufacturing Co., Ltd.; *Int'l*, pg. 2961
GIANT BICYCLE CO. PTY. LTD.—See Giant Manufacturing Co., Ltd.; *Int'l*, pg. 2961
GIANT BICYCLE DE MEXICO S DE R.L. DE C.V.—See Giant Manufacturing Co., Ltd.; *Int'l*, pg. 2961
GIANT BICYCLE INC.—See Giant Manufacturing Co., Ltd.; *Int'l*, pg. 2961
GIANT BIKE CO., LTD.—See Giant Manufacturing Co., Ltd.; *Int'l*, pg. 2961
GIANT BIKES IBERICA S.A.—See Giant Manufacturing Co., Ltd.; *Int'l*, pg. 2961
GIANT BIOGENE HOLDING CO., LTD.; *Int'l*, pg. 2961
GIANT CEMENT COMPANY—See Grupo Empresarial Kaluz S.A. de C.V.; *Int'l*, pg. 3127
GIANT CEMENT HOLDING, INC.—See Grupo Empresarial Kaluz S.A. de C.V.; *Int'l*, pg. 3127
GIANT CEMENT NC, INC.—See Grupo Empresarial Kaluz S.A. de C.V.; *Int'l*, pg. 3127
GIANT CHEVROLET COMPANY; *U.S. Private*, pg. 1694
GIANT (CHINA) CO. LTD.—See Giant Manufacturing Co., Ltd.; *Int'l*, pg. 2961
GIANTCODE CORPORATION PLC; *Int'l*, pg. 2962
GIANT COLOMBIA DISANDINA S.A.—See Giant Manufacturing Co., Ltd.; *Int'l*, pg. 2961
GIANT COMMUNICATIONS, INC.—See LICT Corporation; *U.S. Public*, pg. 1312
THE GIANT COMPANY LLC—See Koninklijke Ahold Delhaize N.V.; *Int'l*, pg. 4260
GIANT CREATIVE STRATEGY LLC—See Clayton, Dubilier & Rice, LLC; *U.S. Private*, pg. 924
GIANT DEUTSCHLAND GMBH—See Giant Manufacturing Co., Ltd.; *Int'l*, pg. 2961
GIANT DISCOUNT FOOD INC.; *U.S. Private*, pg. 1694
GIANT EAGLE AMERICAN SEAWAY FOODS—See Giant Eagle, Inc.; *U.S. Private*, pg. 1694
GIANT EAGLE, INC.; *U.S. Private*, pg. 1694
GIANT EAGLE—See Giant Eagle, Inc.; *U.S. Private*, pg. 1694
GIANTEC SEMICONDUCTOR INC.—See SummitView Capital Management Ltd.; *Int'l*, pg. 7302
GIANT ELECTRIC VEHICLE (KUNSHAN) CO., LTD.—See Giant Manufacturing Co., Ltd.; *Int'l*, pg. 2961
GIANT EUROPE B.V.—See Giant Manufacturing Co., Ltd.; *Int'l*, pg. 2961
GIANT EUROPE MANUFACTURING B.V.—See Giant Manufacturing Co., Ltd.; *Int'l*, pg. 2961
GIANT FACTORIES INC.—See A. O. Smith Corporation; *U.S. Public*, pg. 12
GIANT FLOOR & WALL COVERING CO., INC.; *U.S. Private*, pg. 1694
GIANT FRANCE S.A.R.L.—See Giant Manufacturing Co., Ltd.; *Int'l*, pg. 2961
GIANT GROUP LTD.; *U.S. Private*, pg. 1694
GIANT HOLLAND B.V.—See Giant Manufacturing Co., Ltd.; *Int'l*, pg. 2961
GIANT IDEAS; *U.S. Private*, pg. 1694
GIANT IMPACT, LLC—See LC Group LLC; *U.S. Private*, pg. 2403
GIANT INDUSTRIES, INC.; *U.S. Private*, pg. 1695
GIANT INLAND EMPIRE RV CENTER; *U.S. Private*, pg. 1695
GIANT INTERACTIVE GROUP INC.—See Giant Network Group Co., Ltd.; *Int'l*, pg. 2962
GIANT ITALIA S.R.L.—See Giant Manufacturing Co., Ltd.; *Int'l*, pg. 2961
GIANT KONE ELEVATOR CO., LTD.—See KONE Oyj; *Int'l*, pg. 4247
GIANT KOREA CO., LTD.—See Giant Manufacturing Co., Ltd.; *Int'l*, pg. 2961
GIANT LIGHT METAL TECHNOLOGY (MALAYSIA) SDN. BHD.—See Giant Manufacturing Co., Ltd.; *Int'l*, pg. 2961
GIANT MAGELLAN TELESCOPE ORGANIZATION; *U.S. Private*, pg. 1695
GIANT MANUFACTURING CO., LTD.; *Int'l*, pg. 2961
GIANT MANUFACTURING HUNGARY LTD.—See Giant Manufacturing Co., Ltd.; *Int'l*, pg. 2961
GIANT MEXICO S. DE R.L. DE C.V.—See Giant Manufacturing Co., Ltd.; *Int'l*, pg. 2961
GIANTMICROBES INC.; *U.S. Private*, pg. 1695
GIANTMICROBES UK LIMITED—See Giantmicrobes Inc.; *U.S. Private*, pg. 1695
GIANT NETWORK GROUP CO., LTD.; *Int'l*, pg. 2961
GIANT OAK CORPORATION; *U.S. Private*, pg. 1695

GIANT OF MARYLAND LLC—See Koninklijke Ahold Delhaize N.V.; *Int'l*, pg. 4260
GIANT OIL INC.; *U.S. Private*, pg. 1695
GIANT PARTNERS; *U.S. Private*, pg. 1695
GIANTPLUS TECHNOLOGY CO., LTD. - BADE PLANT—See TOPPAN Holdings Inc.; *Int'l*, pg. 7817
GIANTPLUS TECHNOLOGY CO., LTD. - HSINCHU PLANT—See TOPPAN Holdings Inc.; *Int'l*, pg. 7817
GIANTPLUS TECHNOLOGY CO., LTD.—See TOPPAN Holdings Inc.; *Int'l*, pg. 7817
GIANT POLSKA SP. Z.O.O.—See Giant Manufacturing Co., Ltd.; *Int'l*, pg. 2961
GIANT POLSKA SP. Z O.O. UL.—See Giant Manufacturing Co., Ltd.; *Int'l*, pg. 2961
GIANT RESOURCE RECOVERY COMPANY, INC.—See Grupo Empresarial Kaluz S.A. de C.V.; *Int'l*, pg. 3127
GIANT SALES COMPANY LTD.—See Giant Manufacturing Co., Ltd.; *Int'l*, pg. 2961
GIANT STAR TRADING CO., LTD.—See Evermore Chemical Industry Co., Ltd.; *Int'l*, pg. 2568
GIANTSTEP INC.; *Int'l*, pg. 2962
GIANT TIRE & SERVICE COMPANY LIMITED—See Bridgestone Corporation; *Int'l*, pg. 1160
GIANT TMC (B) SDN BHD—See Jardine Matheson Holdings Limited; *Int'l*, pg. 3909
GIANT UK LTD.—See Giant Manufacturing Co., Ltd.; *Int'l*, pg. 2961
GIANT VIETNAM MANUFACTURING COMPANY LIMITED—See Giant Manufacturing Co., Ltd.; *Int'l*, pg. 2961
GIAQUINTO ASSOCIATES INC.; *U.S. Private*, pg. 1695
GIA (SHANGHAI) MINING EQUIPMENT CO., LTD.—See Epiroc AB; *Int'l*, pg. 2462
GI ASSOCIATES OF LEWISVILLE, PLLC—See HCA Healthcare, Inc.; *U.S. Public*, pg. 996
GIAT INDUSTRIES S.A.; *Int'l*, pg. 2962
GIA TZOONG ENTERPRISE LTD.; *Int'l*, pg. 2960
GIBAUD PHARMA EURL—See Innothera SA; *Int'l*, pg. 3711
GIBAUD SAS—See Innothera SA; *Int'l*, pg. 3711
GIBAUD SUISSE SA—See Innothera SA; *Int'l*, pg. 3711
GIBB GROUP LTD.—See Clarkson PLC; *Int'l*, pg. 1651
GIBB GROUP (NETHERLANDS) B.V.—See Clarkson PLC; *Int'l*, pg. 1651
GIBBON PACKING, LLC—See Rosens Diversified, Inc.; *U.S. Private*, pg. 3484
GIBBONS P.C.; *U.S. Private*, pg. 1695
GIBB RIVER DIAMONDS LIMITED; *Int'l*, pg. 2962
GIBBS AND DANDY PLC—See Compagnie de Saint-Gobain SA; *Int'l*, pg. 1733
GIBBS CALIFORNIA WILD RICE; *U.S. Private*, pg. 1695
GIBBS & COX INC.—See Leidos Holdings, Inc.; *U.S. Public*, pg. 1304
GIBBS DIE CASTING CORP.—See Koch Enterprises, Inc.; *U.S. Private*, pg. 2326
GIBBS-HUNGARY DIE CASTING KFT.—See Koch Enterprises, Inc.; *U.S. Private*, pg. 2326
GIBBS INTERNATIONAL TRUCK CENTERS INCORPORATED; *U.S. Private*, pg. 1695
GIBBS & SOELL - CHICAGO—See Gibbs & Soell, Inc.; *U.S. Private*, pg. 1695
GIBBS & SOELL GMBH—See Gibbs & Soell, Inc.; *U.S. Private*, pg. 1695
GIBBS & SOELL, INC.; *U.S. Private*, pg. 1695
GIBBS & SOELL - RALEIGH—See Gibbs & Soell, Inc.; *U.S. Private*, pg. 1695
GIBBS WIRE & STEEL COMPANY, INC.; *U.S. Private*, pg. 1695
GIBBS WIRE & STEEL COMPANY OF CANADA LTD.—See Gibbs Wire & Steel Company, Inc.; *U.S. Private*, pg. 1695
GIBBS WIRE & STEEL CO.—See Gibbs Wire & Steel Company, Inc.; *U.S. Private*, pg. 1695
GIBBS WIRE & STEEL CO.—See Gibbs Wire & Steel Company, Inc.; *U.S. Private*, pg. 1695
GIBBS WIRE & STEEL CO.—See Gibbs Wire & Steel Company, Inc.; *U.S. Private*, pg. 1695
GIBBS WIRE & STEEL CO.—See Gibbs Wire & Steel Company, Inc.; *U.S. Private*, pg. 1695
GIBCA CRUSHING & QUARRY OPERATIONS CO. LTD.—See GIBCA Limited; *Int'l*, pg. 2962
GIBCA FURNITURE INDUSTRIES CO. LTD.—See GIBCA Limited; *Int'l*, pg. 2962
GIBCA LIMITED; *Int'l*, pg. 2962
GIBCA PETROLEUM SERVICES LLC—See GIBCA Limited; *Int'l*, pg. 2962
GIB CAPITAL GROUP, INC.; *Int'l*, pg. 2962
GIB CAPITAL—See Gulf International Bank B.S.C.; *Int'l*, pg. 3181
GIBELA RAIL TRANSPORT CONSORTIUM (PTY) LTD—See Alstom S.A.; *Int'l*, pg. 383
GIBMEDIA S.A.R.L.; *Int'l*, pg. 2963
GIB OIL LIMITED—See World Kinect Corporation; *U.S. Public*, pg. 2380
GIB OIL (UK) LIMITED—See World Kinect Corporation; *U.S. Public*, pg. 2380
GIBO PLAST A/S—See SP Group A/S; *Int'l*, pg. 7122
GIBO POLAND Z O.O.—See SP Group A/S; *Int'l*, pg. 7122

GIBMEDIA S.A.R.L.

CORPORATE AFFILIATIONS

GIBRALTAR BSN LIFE BERHAD—See Prudential Financial, Inc.; *U.S. Public*, pg. 1733
GIBRALTAR CABLE BARRIER SYSTEMS, LP—See Framework Capital Partners; *U.S. Private*, pg. 1586
GIBRALTAR CABLE BARRIER SYSTEMS, LP—See Tecum Capital Partners, LLC; *U.S. Private*, pg. 3957
GIBRALTAR CAPITAL AND ASSET MANAGEMENT, LLC.—See Toll Brothers, Inc.; *U.S. Public*, pg. 2161
GIBRALTAR CONSTRUCTION CO, INC.; *U.S. Private*, pg. 1695
GIBRALTAR CONSTRUCTION, CORP.; *U.S. Private*, pg. 1696
GIBRALTAR INDUSTRIES, INC.; *U.S. Public*, pg. 935
GIBRALTAR IT, LLC; *U.S. Private*, pg. 1696
THE GIBRALTAR LIFE INSURANCE COMPANY, LTD.—See Prudential Financial, Inc.; *U.S. Public*, pg. 1733
GIBRALTAR MINES LTD.—See Taseko Mines Limited; *Int'l*, pg. 7465
GIBRALTAR MORTGAGE SERVICES, LLC—See Blackstone Inc.; *U.S. Public*, pg. 359
GIBRALTAR PROPERTIES, INC.—See Prudential Financial, Inc.; *U.S. Public*, pg. 1731
GIBRALTAR REAL ESTATE CAPITAL LLC—See Toll Brothers, Inc.; *U.S. Public*, pg. 2161
GIBRALTAR STEEL CORPORATION OF NEW YORK—See Gibraltar Industries, Inc.; *U.S. Public*, pg. 936
GIBRALTAR TRADE CENTER INC.; *U.S. Private*, pg. 1696
GIBRALTAR US, INC.; *U.S. Private*, pg. 1696
GIBRALT CAPITAL CORPORATION; *Int'l*, pg. 2963
GIBSON ACOUSTIC—See Gibson Brands, Inc.; *U.S. Private*, pg. 1696
GIBSON (ASIA) LTD—See E.A. Gibson Shipbrokers Limited; *Int'l*, pg. 2250
GIBSON BENNESS INDUSTRIES PTY., LTD.—See GBI Holdings Pty., Ltd.; *Int'l*, pg. 2893
GIBSON BRANDS, INC.; *U.S. Private*, pg. 1696
GIBSON BROKERS PTE. LTD—See E.A. Gibson Shipbrokers Limited; *Int'l*, pg. 2250
GIBSON COUNTY COAL, LLC—See Alliance Holdings GP, L.P.; *U.S. Private*, pg. 183
GIBSON CUSTOM, ART & HISTORIC—See Gibson Brands, Inc.; *U.S. Private*, pg. 1696
GIBSON, DUNN & CRUTCHER LLP; *U.S. Private*, pg. 1697
GIBSON, DUNN & CRUTCHER; *U.S. Private*, pg. 1697
GIBSON ELECTRIC MEMBERSHIP CORP.; *U.S. Private*, pg. 1696
GIBSON ELECTRIC & TECHNOLOGY SOLUTIONS—See EMCOR Group, Inc.; *U.S. Public*, pg. 736
GIBSON ENERGY INC.; *Int'l*, pg. 2963
GIBSON ENERGY MARKETING, LLC—See Gibson Energy Inc.; *Int'l*, pg. 2963
GIBSON ENERGY ULC—See Gibson Energy Inc.; *Int'l*, pg. 2963
GIBSON ENGINEERING COMPANY, INC.—See Applied Industrial Technologies, Inc.; *U.S. Public*, pg. 171
GIBSON FARMERS COOPERATIVE—See Tennessee Farmers Cooperative; *U.S. Private*, pg. 3967
GIBSON GEAR—See Gibson Brands, Inc.; *U.S. Private*, pg. 1696
THE GIBSON GROUP INC.; *U.S. Private*, pg. 4033
GIBSON GUITAR CORP. - ENTERTAINMENT RELATIONS—See Gibson Brands, Inc.; *U.S. Private*, pg. 1696
GIBSON GUITAR CORP. - ENTERTAINMENT RELATIONS—See Gibson Brands, Inc.; *U.S. Private*, pg. 1696
GIBSON GUITAR CORP. - ENTERTAINMENT RELATIONS—See Gibson Brands, Inc.; *U.S. Private*, pg. 1696
GIBSON GUITAR CORP. - ENTERTAINMENT RELATIONS—See Gibson Brands, Inc.; *U.S. Private*, pg. 1696
GIBSON INSURANCE AGENCY INC.; *U.S. Private*, pg. 1696
GIBSON INTERNATIONAL—See Pacific Union International, Inc.; *U.S. Private*, pg. 3071
GIBSON-LEWIS, LLC—See National Construction Enterprises Inc.; *U.S. Private*, pg. 2851
GIBSON-LEWIS OF INDIANAPOLIS, LLC—See National Construction Enterprises Inc.; *U.S. Private*, pg. 2851
GIBSON MERCHANDISE GROUP INC.; *U.S. Private*, pg. 1696
GIBSON OIL CO.; *U.S. Private*, pg. 1696
GIBSON PROPANE—See UGI Corporation; *U.S. Public*, pg. 2221
GIBSON PROPERTIES INC.—See Gibson Merchandise Group Inc.; *U.S. Private*, pg. 1696
GIBSON TECHNICAL SERVICES, INC.—See Streeterville Capital LLC; *U.S. Private*, pg. 3838
GIBSON WINE COMPANY; *U.S. Private*, pg. 1696
GIBTELECOM—See Telekom Slovenije, d.d.; *Int'l*, pg. 7538
GIBUI HOLDING LTD.; *Int'l*, pg. 2963
GIBUNCO GROUP LIMITED; *Int'l*, pg. 2963

GIBUNCO MECHANICAL LTD—See Gibunco Group Limited; *Int'l*, pg. 2963
GIBUNCO SHIP AGENCY SL—See Gibunco Group Limited; *Int'l*, pg. 2963
GIBUS SPA; *Int'l*, pg. 2963
GIC ASSET MANAGEMENT PTE. LTD.—See GIC Pte. Ltd.; *Int'l*, pg. 2964
GICHNER HOLDINGS, INC.—See Kratos Defense & Security Solutions, Inc.; *U.S. Public*, pg. 1276
GICHNER SYSTEMS GROUP INC.—See Kratos Defense & Security Solutions, Inc.; *U.S. Public*, pg. 1276
GICHNER SYSTEMS INTERNATIONAL, INC.—See Kratos Defense & Security Solutions, Inc.; *U.S. Public*, pg. 1276
GIC HOUSING FINANCE LIMITED; *Int'l*, pg. 2963
GICIEL; *Int'l*, pg. 2968
GI CO., LTD.—See BCnC Co., Ltd.; *Int'l*, pg. 928
GICON PUMPS & EQUIPMENT, LLC; *U.S. Private*, pg. 1697
GICON PUMPS & EQUIPMENT, LTD.; *U.S. Private*, pg. 1697
GIC PTE. LTD.; *Int'l*, pg. 2963
GIC REAL ESTATE, INC.—See GIC Pte. Ltd.; *Int'l*, pg. 2964
GIC REAL ESTATE PTE. LTD.—See GIC Pte. Ltd.; *Int'l*, pg. 2964
GIC RE SOUTH AFRICA LTD.—See General Insurance Corporation Of India; *Int'l*, pg. 2918
GICSA-GOYMAR INGENIEROS CONSULTORES S.L.—See Indra Sistemas, S.A.; *Int'l*, pg. 3661
GIC SPECIAL INVESTMENTS PTE. LTD.—See GIC Pte. Ltd.; *Int'l*, pg. 2964
GIDA PAKETLEME VE SANAYI VE TICARET A.S.—See BIM Birlesik Magazalar A.S.; *Int'l*, pg. 1032
GIDASER GIDA DAGITIM SANAYI VE TICARET A.S.—See ESAS Holding A.S.; *Int'l*, pg. 2501
GIDDENS INDUSTRIES—See Arlington Capital Partners LLC; *U.S. Private*, pg. 327
GIDDY-UP GO TERMITE & PEST CONTROL, INC.—See TORCO Termite & Pest Control Company, LLC; *U.S. Private*, pg. 4188
GID GROUP INC.—See Wooridul Huebrain Ltd.; *Int'l*, pg. 8454
GID INVESTMENT ADVISOR LLC; *U.S. Private*, pg. 1697
GIDROAGREGAT JSC—See Russian Technologies State Corporation; *Int'l*, pg. 6432
GIDROAVTOMATIKA JSC—See Russian Technologies State Corporation; *Int'l*, pg. 6432
GI DYNAMICS, INC.; *U.S. Private*, pg. 1691
GIEAG IMMOBILIEN AG; *Int'l*, pg. 2968
GIE AXA—See AXA S.A.; *Int'l*, pg. 759
GIEBELER GMBH; *Int'l*, pg. 2968
GIEBEL KALTWALZWERK GMBH—See Knauf Interfer SE; *Int'l*, pg. 4205
GIE BNP PARIBAS CARDIF S.A.—See BNP Paribas SA; *Int'l*, pg. 1083
GIE ETEX PLASTICS GESTION—See Aliaxis S.A./N.V.; *Int'l*, pg. 324
G.I.E. GOODYEAR MIREVAL—See The Goodyear Tire & Rubber Company; *U.S. Public*, pg. 2083
GIELDA PAPIEROW WARTOSCIOWYCH W WARSZAWIE S.A.; *Int'l*, pg. 2968
GIELDA PRAW MAJATKOWYCH VINDEXUS S.A.; *Int'l*, pg. 2968
GI ENGINEERING SOLUTIONS LIMITED; *Int'l*, pg. 2960
GIE PSA TRESORERIE—See Stellantis N.V.; *Int'l*, pg. 7201
GIER OIL CO. INC.; *U.S. Private*, pg. 1697
GIERTSEN COMPANY; *U.S. Private*, pg. 1697
GIERTZ VINIMPORT AB—See Viva Wine Group AB; *Int'l*, pg. 8264
GIESECKE & DEVRIENT 3S AB—See Giesecke & Devrient GmbH; *Int'l*, pg. 2969
GIESECKE & DEVRIENT 3S GMBH—See Giesecke & Devrient GmbH; *Int'l*, pg. 2969
GIESECKE & DEVRIENT 3S OY—See Giesecke & Devrient GmbH; *Int'l*, pg. 2969
GIESECKE+DEVRIENT ADVANCE52 GMBH—See Giesecke & Devrient GmbH; *Int'l*, pg. 2970
GIESECKE & DEVRIENT AFRICA LTD.—See Giesecke & Devrient GmbH; *Int'l*, pg. 2969
GIESECKE & DEVRIENT AMERICA, INC.—See Giesecke & Devrient GmbH; *Int'l*, pg. 2969
GIESECKE & DEVRIENT AMERICA-PRINT INSPECTION DIVISION—See Giesecke & Devrient GmbH; *Int'l*, pg. 2969
GIESECKE & DEVRIENT ASIA PACIFIC BANKING SYSTEMS (SHANGHAI) CO. LTD.—See Giesecke & Devrient GmbH; *Int'l*, pg. 2969
GIESECKE & DEVRIENT ASIA PACIFIC (KOREA)—See Giesecke & Devrient GmbH; *Int'l*, pg. 2969
GIESECKE & DEVRIENT ASIA PACIFIC LTD—See Giesecke & Devrient GmbH; *Int'l*, pg. 2969
GIESECKE & DEVRIENT ASIA PTE. LTD.—See Giesecke & Devrient GmbH; *Int'l*, pg. 2969
GIESECKE & DEVRIENT AUSTRALASIA PTY. LTD.—See Giesecke & Devrient GmbH; *Int'l*, pg. 2969
GIESECKE & DEVRIENT BRASIL LTDA—See Giesecke & Devrient GmbH; *Int'l*, pg. 2969

GIESECKE & DEVRIENT (CHINA) INFORMATION TECHNOLOGIES CO., LTD.—See Giesecke & Devrient GmbH; *Int'l*, pg. 2969
GIESECKE & DEVRIENT EGYPT SERVICES LLC—See Giesecke & Devrient GmbH; *Int'l*, pg. 2969
GIESECKE & DEVRIENT FRANCE S.A.S.—See Giesecke & Devrient GmbH; *Int'l*, pg. 2969
GIESECKE & DEVRIENT FZE—See Giesecke & Devrient GmbH; *Int'l*, pg. 2969
GIESECKE & DEVRIENT GB LTD.—See Giesecke & Devrient GmbH; *Int'l*, pg. 2969
GIESECKE & DEVRIENT GMBH; *Int'l*, pg. 2969
GIESECKE & DEVRIENT INDIA PRIVATE LIMITED—See Giesecke & Devrient GmbH; *Int'l*, pg. 2969
GIESECKE & DEVRIENT ISTANBUL TICARET VE SERVIS LTD. SIRKETI—See Giesecke & Devrient GmbH; *Int'l*, pg. 2969
GIESECKE & DEVRIENT ITALIA, S.R.L.—See Giesecke & Devrient GmbH; *Int'l*, pg. 2969
GIESECKE & DEVRIENT KABUSHIKI KAISHA—See Giesecke & Devrient GmbH; *Int'l*, pg. 2969
GIESECKE & DEVRIENT MALAYSIA SDN BHD—See Giesecke & Devrient GmbH; *Int'l*, pg. 2969
GIESECKE & DEVRIENT MATSOUKIS, SECURITY PRINTING, S.A.—See Giesecke & Devrient GmbH; *Int'l*, pg. 2969
GIESECKE & DEVRIENT SLOVAKIA, S.R.O.—See Giesecke & Devrient GmbH; *Int'l*, pg. 2969
GIESECKE & DEVRIENT (SOUTHERN AFRICA) (PTY) LTD.—See Giesecke & Devrient GmbH; *Int'l*, pg. 2969
GIESECKE & DEVRIENT SYSTEMS CANADA, INC.—See Giesecke & Devrient GmbH; *Int'l*, pg. 2969
GIESECKE Y DEVRIENT CURRENCY TECHNOLOGY DE MEXICO, S.A. DE C.V.—See Giesecke & Devrient GmbH; *Int'l*, pg. 2969
GIESECKE Y DEVRIENT DE MEXICO S.A. DE C.V.—See Giesecke & Devrient GmbH; *Int'l*, pg. 2970
GIES HOLDING GMBH; *Int'l*, pg. 2969
GIES KERZEN GMBH—See Gies Holding GmbH; *Int'l*, pg. 2969
GIES NATURA HANDELSGESELLSCHAFT MBH—See Gies Holding GmbH; *Int'l*, pg. 2969
GIESSE GROUP HELLAS S.A.—See Quanex Building Products Corp.; *U.S. Public*, pg. 1749
GIESSE S.P.A.—See Quanex Building Products Corp.; *U.S. Public*, pg. 1749
GIETBURG HOLDING—See Nimbus B.V.; *Int'l*, pg. 5296
GIEVES LIMITED—See Trinity Limited; *Int'l*, pg. 7925
GIFA, INC.; *U.S. Public*, pg. 936
GIF ENTERPRISES, INC.—See Apex Companies, LLC; *U.S. Private*, pg. 292
GIFFARD GENIE CIVIL SAS—See VINCI S.A.; *Int'l*, pg. 8222
GIFFEN & KAMINSKI, LLC—See Perez & Morris LLC; *U.S. Private*, pg. 3147
GIFFORDS FAMOUS ICE CREAM; *U.S. Private*, pg. 1697
GIFFORD STREET WELLNESS CENTER, LLC—See Acadia Healthcare Company, Inc.; *U.S. Public*, pg. 29
GIF GEWERBE- UND INDUSTRIEPARK BAD FRIEDRICHSHALL GMBH—See Porsche Automobil Holding SE; *Int'l*, pg. 5926
GIFI SA; *Int'l*, pg. 2970
GIFLO ENGINEERING (PTY) LTD—See ARGENT INDUSTRIAL LIMITED; *Int'l*, pg. 560
GIFORE AGRICULTURAL SCIENCE & TECHNOLOGY SERVICE CO., LTD.; *Int'l*, pg. 2970
GIF SERVICES INC.; *U.S. Private*, pg. 1697
GIFTCARDRESCUE.COM, LLC; *U.S. Private*, pg. 1697
GIFTCERTIFICATES.COM CORPORATION—See Financial Technology Ventures Management Co. LLC; *U.S. Private*, pg. 1508
GIFTCO, INC.—See Qurate Retail, Inc.; *U.S. Public*, pg. 1757
GIFTCRAFT INC.—See Giftcraft Ltd.; *Int'l*, pg. 2970
GIFTCRAFT LTD.; *Int'l*, pg. 2970
GIFTEE, INC.; *Int'l*, pg. 2970
GIFTEE MEKONG COMPANY LTD.—See Giftee, Inc.; *Int'l*, pg. 2970
GIFT HOLDINGS INC.; *Int'l*, pg. 2970
GIFT INFINITE PUBLIC COMPANY LIMITED; *Int'l*, pg. 2970
GIFT OF HOPE ORGAN & TISSUE DONOR NETWORK; *U.S. Private*, pg. 1697
GIFT SAS; *Int'l*, pg. 2970
GIFTS BY DESIGN, INC.—See Superior Group Of Companies, Inc.; *U.S. Public*, pg. 1966
GIFTS SOFTWARE, INC.—See Fidelity National Infor; *U.S. Public*, pg. 833
GIFT UNIVERSE GROUP LIMITED; *Int'l*, pg. 2970
GIFT USA INC.—See GIFT Holdings Inc.; *Int'l*, pg. 2970
GIFU AICHI ELECTRIC CO., LTD.—See Aichi Electric Co., Ltd.; *Int'l*, pg. 229
GIFU BUS CO., LTD.—See Nagoya Railroad Co., Ltd.; *Int'l*, pg. 5129
GIFU-CHUHATSU CO., LTD.—See Chuo Spring Co., Ltd.; *Int'l*, pg. 1599
GIFU DS OPERATION LTD.—See LECIP Holdings Corporation; *Int'l*, pg. 4437

COMPANY NAME INDEX

GIFU HINO MOTOR CO., LTD.—See Seino Holdings Co., Ltd.; *Int'l*, pg. 6690
GIFU ISUZU CORPORATION—See Mitsubishi Corporation; *Int'l*, pg. 4938
GIFU LANDSCAPE ARCHITECT CO., LTD.; *Int'l*, pg. 2970
GIFU RECOMM CO., LTD.—See TOUMEI Co., Ltd.; *Int'l*, pg. 7847
GIFU TECHNICAL INSTITUTE—See Kawasaki Heavy Industries, Ltd.; *Int'l*, pg. 4095
GIFU TOKODEN CO., LTD.—See Imasen Electric Industrial Co., Ltd.; *Int'l*, pg. 3620
GIGABOARD POLSKA SP ZOO—See JCDecaux S.A.; *Int'l*, pg. 3920
GIGA-BYTE COMMUNICATION INC.—See Giga-Byte Technology Co., Ltd.; *Int'l*, pg. 2971
GIGA-BYTE TECHNOLOGY B.V.—See Giga-Byte Technology Co., Ltd.; *Int'l*, pg. 2971
GIGA-BYTE TECHNOLOGY CO., LTD. - GIGABYTE NANPING FACTORY—See Giga-Byte Technology Co., Ltd.; *Int'l*, pg. 2971
GIGA-BYTE TECHNOLOGY CO., LTD.; *Int'l*, pg. 2971
GIGABYTE TECHNOLOGY PTY. LTD.—See Giga-Byte Technology Co., Ltd.; *Int'l*, pg. 2971
GIGACLEAR PLC; *Int'l*, pg. 2971
GIGACLOUD TECHNOLOGY, INC.; *Int'l*, pg. 2971
GIGA CO., LTD.—See Core Corporation; *Int'l*, pg. 1797
GIGACOM AB—See Addtech AB; *Int'l*, pg. 133
GIGADEVICE SEMICONDUCTOR (BEIJING) INC - SANTA CLARA BRANCH—See GigaDevice Semiconductor (Beijing) Inc; *Int'l*, pg. 2971
GIGADEVICE SEMICONDUCTOR (BEIJING) INC; *Int'l*, pg. 2971
GIGADEVICE SEMICONDUCTOR EUROPE LTD—See GigaDevice Semiconductor (Beijing) Inc; *Int'l*, pg. 2971
GIGADEVICE SEMICONDUCTOR (HEFEI) INC.—See GigaDevice Semiconductor (Beijing) Inc; *Int'l*, pg. 2971
GIGA DIGITAL AG—See Stroer SE & Co. KGaA; *Int'l*, pg. 7242
GIGAFAST INC.; *U.S. Private*, pg. 1697
GIGA FIXXOO GMBH—See Stroer SE & Co. KGaA; *Int'l*, pg. 7242
GIGAFLOPS JAPAN INC.—See CYBIRD Holdings Co., Ltd.; *Int'l*, pg. 1894
GIGA GAS & ELECTRONIC MATERIALS COMPANY—See Central Glass Co., Ltd.; *Int'l*, pg. 1407
GIGA GMBH—See Delticom AG; *Int'l*, pg. 2021
GIGAHERTZ LLC; *U.S. Private*, pg. 1697
GIGALANE CO., LTD.; *Int'l*, pg. 2971
GIGAMEDIA LIMITED; *Int'l*, pg. 2971
GIGAMES NORTE S.L.—See Novomatic AG; *Int'l*, pg. 5467
GIGAMES S.L.—See Novomatic AG; *Int'l*, pg. 5467
GIGA METALS CORPORATION; *Int'l*, pg. 2971
GIGAMIC SARL—See Vivendi SE; *Int'l*, pg. 8271
GIGAMON INC.—See Elliott Management Corporation; *U.S. Private*, pg. 1368
GIGANT AB—See Nordstjernan AB; *Int'l*, pg. 5425
GIGANTE SALMON AS; *Int'l*, pg. 2972
GIGANTE VAZ PARTNERS ADVERTISING, INC.; *U.S. Private*, pg. 1697
GIGANTE VERDE S. DE R.L. DE C.V.—See General Mills, Inc.; *U.S. Public*, pg. 921
GIGANT TYOPISTEET OY—See Nordstjernan AB; *Int'l*, pg. 5425
GIGAPHOTON CHINA INC.—See Komatsu Ltd.; *Int'l*, pg. 4235
GIGAPHOTON EUROPE B.V.—See Komatsu Ltd.; *Int'l*, pg. 4235
GIGAPHOTON, INC.—See Komatsu Ltd.; *Int'l*, pg. 4235
GIGAPHOTON KOREA INC.—See Komatsu Ltd.; *Int'l*, pg. 4235
GIGAPHOTON TAIWAN INC.—See Komatsu Ltd.; *Int'l*, pg. 4235
GIGAPHOTON USA INC.—See Komatsu Ltd.; *Int'l*, pg. 4235
GIGA PRIZE CO., LTD.; *Int'l*, pg. 2971
GIGASET AG; *Int'l*, pg. 2972
GIGASET COMMUNICATIONS GMBH—See Gigaset AG; *Int'l*, pg. 2972
GIGASET ILETISIM CIHAZLARI A.S.—See Gigaset AG; *Int'l*, pg. 2972
GIGAS HOSTING S.A; *Int'l*, pg. 2972
GIGA SOLAR MATERIALS CORP.; *Int'l*, pg. 2971
GIGA SOLUTION TECH. CO., LTD.—See Ardentec Corporation; *Int'l*, pg. 554
GIGASTONE CORPORATION; *Int'l*, pg. 2972
GIGASTORAGE CORP.; *Int'l*, pg. 2972
GIGA TECH CO., LTD.—See FreeBit Co., Ltd.; *Int'l*, pg. 2769
GIGA-TRONICS INSTRUMENTS—See Ault Alliance, Inc.; *U.S. Public*, pg. 227
GIGAVAC, LLC—See Sensata Technologies Holding plc; *U.S. Public*, pg. 1865
GIGAVIS CO., LTD.; *Int'l*, pg. 2972
GIGAWATT GLOBAL RWANDA LTD.—See Scatec ASA; *Int'l*, pg. 6613
GIGAWATTS, LLC—See APPLIED DIGITAL CORPORATION; *U.S. Public*, pg. 170

GI GENERAL INSURANCE LIMITED—See IGI Holdings Limited; *Int'l*, pg. 3602
GIG GEFLUGELINTEGRATION GMBH—See AGRAVIS Raiffeisen AG; *Int'l*, pg. 215
GIGGLE BROADBAND LIMITED—See Digital 9 Infrastructure Plc; *Int'l*, pg. 2120
GIGGLE, INC.; *U.S. Private*, pg. 1697
GIGGLES N HUGS, INC.; *U.S. Private*, pg. 1697
GIG GULF—See AXA S.A.; *Int'l*, pg. 759
GIGIGO GROUP S.L.—See Econocom Group SA; *Int'l*, pg. 2298
GIGI'S CUPCAKES—See FundCorp, Inc.; *U.S. Private*, pg. 1623
GIG KARASEK GMBH—See Dr. Aichhorn GmbH; *Int'l*, pg. 2190
GIGLIO.COM S.P.A.; *Int'l*, pg. 2972
GIGLIO DISTRIBUTING COMPANY, INC.; *U.S. Private*, pg. 1698
GIGLIO GROUP S.P.A.; *Int'l*, pg. 2972
GIG OF MISSOURI INC.—See American International Group, Inc.; *U.S. Public*, pg. 106
GIGOPTIX-HELIX AG—See Renesas Electronics Corporation; *Int'l*, pg. 6276
GIGPEAK, INC.—See Renesas Electronics Corporation; *Int'l*, pg. 6276
GIGTECH B.V.—See Live Nation Entertainment, Inc.; *U.S. Public*, pg. 1328
GIG WORKS INC.; *Int'l*, pg. 2971
G&I HOMES, INC.—See Berkshire Hathaway Inc.; *U.S. Public*, pg. 304
GIIB HEALTHCARE PRODUCTS SDN. BHD.—See GIIB HOLDINGS BERHAD; *Int'l*, pg. 2972
GIIB HOLDINGS BERHAD; *Int'l*, pg. 2972
G-III APPAREL GROUP, LTD.; *U.S. Public*, pg. 893
G-III LEATHER FASHIONS, INC.—See G-III Apparel Group, Ltd.; *U.S. Public*, pg. 894
GI INDUSTRIES, INC.; *U.S. Private*, pg. 1691
G.I. INDUSTRIES—See Waste Management, Inc.; *U.S. Public*, pg. 2331
GI INNOVATION INC.; *Int'l*, pg. 2960
GIIR AMERICA INC.—See HS Ad Inc.; *Int'l*, pg. 3502
GIIR COMMUNICATIONS PVT. LTD.—See HS Ad Inc.; *Int'l*, pg. 3502
GIIR GERMANY GMBH—See HS Ad Inc.; *Int'l*, pg. 3502
GIIR GROUP LG—See HS Ad Inc.; *Int'l*, pg. 3502
GIJIMAAST AMERICAS INCORPORATED—See FirstRand Limited; *Int'l*, pg. 2690
GIJIMAAST AMERICAS INCORPORATED—See Hasso Plattner Ventures Africa (Pty) Ltd.; *Int'l*, pg. 3283
GIJIMAAST AMERICAS INCORPORATED—See Shalamuka Capital (Pty) Ltd.; *Int'l*, pg. 6750
GIJIMAAST ELECTRONIC AND SECURITY SYSTEMS (PTY) LIMITED—See Guma Group; *Int'l*, pg. 3183
GIJIMAAST HOLDINGS (PTY) LIMITED—See Guma Group; *Int'l*, pg. 3183
GIJIMAAST INFORMATION TECHNOLOGY SERVICES (PTY) LIMITED—See Guma Group; *Int'l*, pg. 3183
GIJIMAAST (PTY) LIMITED—See FirstRand Limited; *Int'l*, pg. 2690
GIJIMAAST (PTY) LIMITED—See Hasso Plattner Ventures Africa (Pty) Ltd.; *Int'l*, pg. 3284
GIJIMAAST (PTY) LIMITED—See Shalamuka Capital (Pty) Ltd.; *Int'l*, pg. 6750
GIJIMA GROUP LIMITED—See Guma Group; *Int'l*, pg. 3183
GIKEN AMERICA CORPORATION—See GIKEN Ltd.; *Int'l*, pg. 2972
GIKEN EUROPE B.V.—See GIKEN Ltd.; *Int'l*, pg. 2972
GIKEN HOLDINGS CO., LTD.; *Int'l*, pg. 2972
GIKEN KOGYO CO., LTD.; *Int'l*, pg. 2972
GIKEN LTD.; *Int'l*, pg. 2972
GIKEN LTD. - TOKYO FACTORY—See GIKEN Ltd.; *Int'l*, pg. 2972
GIKEN PRECISION ENGINEERING (S) PTE LTD—See GSS Energy Ltd.; *Int'l*, pg. 3150
GIKEN SAKATA (SINGAPORE) LIMITED; *Int'l*, pg. 2972
GIKEN SEISAKUSHO ASIA PTE., LTD.—See GIKEN Ltd.; *Int'l*, pg. 2972
GIKEN SEKO CO., LTD. - KANSAI FACTORY—See GIKEN Ltd.; *Int'l*, pg. 2972
GIKEN SEKO CO., LTD.—See GIKEN Ltd.; *Int'l*, pg. 2972
GIKEN TRASTEM CO., LTD.—See Optex Group Co., Ltd.; *Int'l*, pg. 5601
GIK OKO D.D.; *Int'l*, pg. 2972
GILADA FINANCE & INVESTMENTS LTD.; *Int'l*, pg. 2973
GILA, LLC—See Navient Corporation; *U.S. Public*, pg. 1500
GILARDI & CO , LLC—See Computershare Limited; *Int'l*, pg. 1760
GILAT COLOMBIA S.A. E.S.P.—See Gilat Satellite Networks Ltd.; *Int'l*, pg. 2973
GILAT DO BRAZIL LTDA.—See Gilat Satellite Networks Ltd.; *Int'l*, pg. 2973
GILAT SATELLITE NETWORK MDC—See Gilat Satellite Networks Ltd.; *Int'l*, pg. 2973
GILAT SATELLITE NETWORKS B.V.—See Gilat Satellite Networks Ltd.; *Int'l*, pg. 2973
GILAT SATELLITE NETWORKS (HOLLAND) B.V.—See Gilat Satellite Networks Ltd.; *Int'l*, pg. 2973

GILCHRIST HOSPICE CARE INC.

GILAT SATELLITE NETWORKS INDIA PRIVATE LTD.—See Gilat Satellite Networks Ltd.; *Int'l*, pg. 2973
GILAT SATELLITE NETWORKS LTD.; *Int'l*, pg. 2973
GILAT SATELLITE NETWORKS LTD.—See Gilat Satellite Networks Ltd.; *Int'l*, pg. 2973
GILAT SATELLITE NETWORKS (MEXICO) S.A. DE C.V.—See Gilat Satellite Networks Ltd.; *Int'l*, pg. 2973
GILAT SATELLITE NETWORKS (THAILAND) LTD.—See Gilat Satellite Networks Ltd.; *Int'l*, pg. 2973
GILAT TELECOM LTD.; *Int'l*, pg. 2973
GILAT TO HOME PERU S.A—See Gilat Satellite Networks Ltd.; *Int'l*, pg. 2973
GILBANE BUILDING COMPANY—See Gilbane, Inc.; *U.S. Private*, pg. 1698
GILBANE DEVELOPMENT COMPANY—See Gilbane, Inc.; *U.S. Private*, pg. 1698
GILBANE, INC.; *U.S. Private*, pg. 1698
GILBANE, INC.—See Gilbane, Inc.; *U.S. Private*, pg. 1698
GILBARCO ACIS KFT.—See Vontier Corporation; *U.S. Public*, pg. 2308
GILBARCO ACIS SRL—See Vontier Corporation; *U.S. Public*, pg. 2308
GILBARCO AUSTRALIA PTY LTD.—See Vontier Corporation; *U.S. Public*, pg. 2308
GILBARCO AUTOTANK AS—See Vontier Corporation; *U.S. Public*, pg. 2308
GILBARCO CHINA CO. LTD—See Vontier Corporation; *U.S. Public*, pg. 2308
GILBARCO GMBH & CO. KG—See Vontier Corporation; *U.S. Public*, pg. 2308
GILBARCO INC.—See Vontier Corporation; *U.S. Public*, pg. 2308
GILBARCO ITALIA S.R.L.—See Vontier Corporation; *U.S. Public*, pg. 2309
GILBARCO LATIN AMERICA ANDINA LTDA.—See Vontier Corporation; *U.S. Public*, pg. 2309
GILBARCO LATIN AMERICA SRL—See Vontier Corporation; *U.S. Public*, pg. 2309
GILBARCO QUEENSLAND PTY. LTD.—See Vontier Corporation; *U.S. Public*, pg. 2308
GILBARCO VEEDER-ROOT AB—See Vontier Corporation; *U.S. Public*, pg. 2309
GILBARCO VEEDER-ROOT ASIA PTE. LTD.—See Vontier Corporation; *U.S. Public*, pg. 2309
GILBARCO VEEDER-ROOT AS—See Vontier Corporation; *U.S. Public*, pg. 2309
GILBARCO VEEDER-ROOT ITALY—See Vontier Corporation; *U.S. Public*, pg. 2309
GILBARCO VEEDER-ROOT OU—See Vontier Corporation; *U.S. Public*, pg. 2309
GILBARCO VEEDER-ROOT SOLUCOES INDUSTRIA E COMERCIO LTDA.—See Vontier Corporation; *U.S. Public*, pg. 2309
GILBARCO VEEDER ROOT SPOLKA Z.O.O.—See Vontier Corporation; *U.S. Public*, pg. 2309
GILBARCO VEEDER ROOT S.R.L.—See Vontier Corporation; *U.S. Public*, pg. 2309
GILBARCO VEEDER-ROOT UK—See Vontier Corporation; *U.S. Public*, pg. 2309
GIL-BAR INDUSTRIES, INC.; *U.S. Private*, pg. 1698
GILBERT BODY SHOP, INC.—See AutoNation, Inc.; *U.S. Public*, pg. 235
GILBERT CHEVROLET INC.; *U.S. Private*, pg. 1698
GILBERT DISPLAY INC.; *U.S. Private*, pg. 1698
GILBERT GLOBAL EQUITY PARTNERS; *U.S. Private*, pg. 1698
GILBERT HARDWOOD CENTERS INC. OF TENNESSEE—See Gilbert Hardwoods Inc.; *U.S. Private*, pg. 1699
GILBERT HARDWOODS INC.; *U.S. Private*, pg. 1699
GILBERT HOSPITAL LLC; *U.S. Private*, pg. 1699
GILBERT H. WILD & SON, LLC; *U.S. Private*, pg. 1699
GILBERT & JONES CO., INC.—See Gemspring Capital Management, LLC; *U.S. Private*, pg. 1659
GILBERT LAW SUMMARIES—See Thomson Reuters Corporation; *Int'l*, pg. 7715
GILBERT MARTIN WOODWORKING COMPANY, INC.; *U.S. Private*, pg. 1699
GILBERT MECHANICAL CONTRACTORS, LLC—See Blackstone Inc.; *U.S. Public*, pg. 361
GILBERT MEDICAL CENTER LLC—See Adeptus Health Inc.; *U.S. Private*, pg. 78
GILBERTON COAL COMPANY—See Reading Anthracite Company; *U.S. Private*, pg. 3366
GILBERTON POWER COMPANY—See Reading Anthracite Company; *U.S. Private*, pg. 3366
THE GILBERTSON GROUP, INC.—See Argosy Capital Group, LLC; *U.S. Private*, pg. 321
GILBERT STEEL LIMITED; *Int'l*, pg. 2973
GILBEY'S OF IRELAND, LTD.—See C&C Group Plc; *Int'l*, pg. 1238
GILBOY FORD MERCURY INC.; *U.S. Private*, pg. 1699
GILBRETH PACKAGING SYSTEMS—See Genstar Capital, LLC; *U.S. Private*, pg. 1676
GILCHRIST ENTERPRISES; *U.S. Private*, pg. 1699
GILCHRIST HOSPICE CARE INC.; *U.S. Private*, pg. 1699
GILCHRIST & SOAMES HOLDINGS CORPORATION—See Sysco Corporation; *U.S. Public*, pg. 1974

GILCHRIST HOSPICE CARE INC.

GILCHRIST & SOAMES, INC.—See Sysco Corporation; *U.S. Public*, pg. 1976
GILCHRIST & SOAMES UK LIMITED—See Sysco Corporation; *U.S. Public*, pg. 1974
GILC INCORPORATED—See Granite Construction Incorporated; *U.S. Public*, pg. 957
GILCO LUMBER, INC.—See International Industries, Inc.; *U.S. Private*, pg. 2117
GILCREST ELECTRIC & SUPPLY CO.; *U.S. Private*, pg. 1699
GILCREST/JEWETT LUMBER COMPANY—See Bain Capital, LP; *U.S. Private*, pg. 450
GILDAN ACTIVEWEAR DISTRIBUTION INC.—See Gildan Activewear Inc.; *Int'l*, pg. 2973
GILDAN ACTIVEWEAR DOMINICAN REPUBLIC TEXTILE COMPANY INC.—See Gildan Activewear Inc.; *Int'l*, pg. 2973
GILDAN ACTIVEWEAR (EDEN) INC.—See Gildan Activewear Inc.; *Int'l*, pg. 2973
GILDAN ACTIVEWEAR INC.; *Int'l*, pg. 2973
GILDAN ACTIVEWEAR SRL—See Gildan Activewear Inc.; *Int'l*, pg. 2973
GILDAN ACTIVEWEAR (UK) LIMITED—See Gildan Activewear Inc.; *Int'l*, pg. 2973
GILDAN HONDURAS—See Gildan Activewear Inc.; *Int'l*, pg. 2973
GILDAN USA INC.—See Gildan Activewear Inc.; *Int'l*, pg. 2973
GILDE BRAUEREI AG; *Int'l*, pg. 2973
GILDE BUY OUT PARTNERS AG—See Gilde Buy Out Partners B.V.; *Int'l*, pg. 2974
GILDE BUY OUT PARTNERS BVBA—See Gilde Buy Out Partners B.V.; *Int'l*, pg. 2974
GILDE BUY OUT PARTNERS B.V.; *Int'l*, pg. 2974
GILDE EQUITY MANAGEMENT (GEM) BENELUX PARTNERS B.V.; *Int'l*, pg. 2975
GILDE HEALTHCARE PARTNERS B.V.; *Int'l*, pg. 2975
GILDE HEALTHCARE PARTNERS US—See Gilde Healthcare Partners B.V.; *Int'l*, pg. 2975
GILDE INVESTMENT MANAGEMENT B.V.; *Int'l*, pg. 2975
GILDEMEISTER BETEILIGUNGEN AG—See DMG MORI Co., Ltd.; *Int'l*, pg. 2144
GILDEMEISTER DREHMASCHINEN GMBH—See DMG MORI Co., Ltd.; *Int'l*, pg. 2144
GILDEMEISTER ITALIANA S.P.A.—See DMG MORI Co., Ltd.; *Int'l*, pg. 2144
THE GILDER LEHRMAN INSTITUTE OF AMERICAN HISTORY; *U.S. Private*, pg. 4033
GILDNER AUTO GROUP; *U.S. Private*, pg. 1699
GILEAD ALBERTA ULC—See Gilead Sciences, Inc.; *U.S. Public*, pg. 937
GILEAD COMMUNITY SERVICES, INC.; *U.S. Private*, pg. 1699
GILEAD CONNECTICUT, INC.—See Gilead Sciences, Inc.; *U.S. Public*, pg. 937
GILEAD SCIENCES BELGIUM BVBA/SPRL—See Gilead Sciences, Inc.; *U.S. Public*, pg. 937
GILEAD SCIENCES CANADA, INC.—See Gilead Sciences, Inc.; *U.S. Public*, pg. 937
GILEAD SCIENCES EUROPE LTD.—See Gilead Sciences, Inc.; *U.S. Public*, pg. 937
GILEAD SCIENCES FARMACEUTICA DO BRASIL LTDA—See Gilead Sciences, Inc.; *U.S. Public*, pg. 937
GILEAD SCIENCES FINLAND OY—See Gilead Sciences, Inc.; *U.S. Public*, pg. 937
GILEAD SCIENCES GES M.B.H.—See Gilead Sciences, Inc.; *U.S. Public*, pg. 937
GILEAD SCIENCES GMBH—See Gilead Sciences, Inc.; *U.S. Public*, pg. 937
GILEAD SCIENCES HELLAS .EPE.—See Gilead Sciences, Inc.; *U.S. Public*, pg. 937
GILEAD SCIENCES HONG KONG LIMITED—See Gilead Sciences, Inc.; *U.S. Public*, pg. 937
GILEAD SCIENCES, INC. - SEATTLE—See Gilead Sciences, Inc.; *U.S. Public*, pg. 937
GILEAD SCIENCES, INC.; *U.S. Public*, pg. 936
GILEAD SCIENCES INTERNATIONAL LTD.—See Gilead Sciences, Inc.; *U.S. Public*, pg. 937
GILEAD SCIENCES IRELAND UC—See Gilead Sciences, Inc.; *U.S. Public*, pg. 937
GILEAD SCIENCES ISRAEL LIMITED—See Gilead Sciences, Inc.; *U.S. Public*, pg. 937
GILEAD SCIENCES KK—See Gilead Sciences, Inc.; *U.S. Public*, pg. 937
GILEAD SCIENCES KOREA LIMITED—See Gilead Sciences, Inc.; *U.S. Public*, pg. 937
GILEAD SCIENCES, LDA.—See Gilead Sciences, Inc.; *U.S. Public*, pg. 937
GILEAD SCIENCES LLAC LTD—See Gilead Sciences, Inc.; *U.S. Public*, pg. 937
GILEAD SCIENCES LTD.—See Gilead Sciences, Inc.; *U.S. Public*, pg. 937
GILEAD SCIENCES LTD.—See Gilead Sciences, Inc.; *U.S. Public*, pg. 937
GILEAD SCIENCES MEXICO S. DE R.L. DE C.V.—See Gilead Sciences, Inc.; *U.S. Public*, pg. 937
GILEAD SCIENCES NETHERLANDS BV—See Gilead Sciences, Inc.; *U.S. Public*, pg. 937
GILEAD SCIENCES POLAND—See Gilead Sciences, Inc.; *U.S. Public*, pg. 937
GILEAD SCIENCES PTY LTD—See Gilead Sciences, Inc.; *U.S. Public*, pg. 937
GILEAD SCIENCES RUSSIA LLC—See Gilead Sciences, Inc.; *U.S. Public*, pg. 937
GILEAD SCIENCES SAS—See Gilead Sciences, Inc.; *U.S. Public*, pg. 937
GILEAD SCIENCES (SHANGHAI) CONSULTING CO., LTD.—See Gilead Sciences, Inc.; *U.S. Public*, pg. 937
GILEAD SCIENCES SINGAPORE PTE. LTD.—See Gilead Sciences, Inc.; *U.S. Public*, pg. 937
GILEAD SCIENCES SLOVAKIA S.R.O.—See Gilead Sciences, Inc.; *U.S. Public*, pg. 937
GILEAD SCIENCES, S.L.—See Gilead Sciences, Inc.; *U.S. Public*, pg. 937
GILEAD SCIENCES SOUTH AFRICA (PTY) LTD—See Gilead Sciences, Inc.; *U.S. Public*, pg. 937
GILEAD SCIENCES S.R.L—See Gilead Sciences, Inc.; *U.S. Public*, pg. 937
GILEAD SCIENCES S.R.O.—See Gilead Sciences, Inc.; *U.S. Public*, pg. 937
GILEAD SCIENCES SWEDEN AB—See Gilead Sciences, Inc.; *U.S. Public*, pg. 937
GILEAD SCIENCES SWITZERLAND SARL—See Gilead Sciences, Inc.; *U.S. Public*, pg. 937
GILEAD YM ULC—See Gilead Sciences, Inc.; *U.S. Public*, pg. 937
GILES AUTOMOTIVE GROUP, INC.; *U.S. Private*, pg. 1699
GILES CHEMICAL CORP.; *U.S. Private*, pg. 1699
GILES INSURANCE BROKERS LTD.—See Arthur J. Gallagher & Co.; *U.S. Public*, pg. 202
GILES & KENDALL INC.; *U.S. Private*, pg. 1699
GILES & RANSOME, INC. - ALLENTOWN FACILITY—See Giles & Ransome, Inc.; *U.S. Private*, pg. 1699
GILES & RANSOME, INC.; *U.S. Private*, pg. 1699
GILETTA S.P.A.—See Bucher Industries AG; *Int'l*, pg. 1208
GILEVE; *Int'l*, pg. 2975
GILFORD CORPORATION; *U.S. Private*, pg. 1699
GILFORD GRAPHICS INTERNATIONAL; *U.S. Private*, pg. 1699
GILFORD-JOHNSON FLOORING LLC; *U.S. Private*, pg. 1700
GILFORD SECURITIES INC.; *U.S. Private*, pg. 1700
GILGEN DOOR SYSTEMS AG—See Nabtesco Corporation; *Int'l*, pg. 5119
GILGEN DOOR SYSTEMS AUSTRIA GMBH—See Nabtesco Corporation; *Int'l*, pg. 5119
GILGEN DOOR SYSTEMS FRANCE S.A.S.—See Nabtesco Corporation; *Int'l*, pg. 5119
GILGEN DOOR SYSTEMS GERMANY GMBH—See Nabtesco Corporation; *Int'l*, pg. 5119
GILGEN DOOR SYSTEMS ITALY SR.L.—See Nabtesco Corporation; *Int'l*, pg. 5119
GILGEN DOOR SYSTEMS (SUZHOU) CO., LTD.—See Nabtesco Corporation; *Int'l*, pg. 5119
GILGEN DOOR SYSTEMS UK LIMITED—See Nabtesco Corporation; *Int'l*, pg. 5119
GILGEN DOOR SYSTEMS UK LTD.—See Nabtesco Corporation; *Int'l*, pg. 5119
GILGEN NABTESCO (HONG KONG) LIMITED—See Nabtesco Corporation; *Int'l*, pg. 5119
GIL GMBH—See Trimble, Inc.; *U.S. Public*, pg. 2190
GIL HAUGAN CONSTRUCTION, INC.; *U.S. Private*, pg. 1698
GIL HAUGAN CONSTRUCTION—See Gil Haugan Construction, Inc.; *U.S. Private*, pg. 1698
GI LI CO., LTD.—See Ju Teng International Holdings Limited; *Int'l*, pg. 4020
GI/LINDE ALGERIE—See Linde plc; *Int'l*, pg. 4504
GILINOX S.R.L.—See Scope Metals Group Ltd.; *Int'l*, pg. 6650
GIL INVESTMENTS LTD.; *Int'l*, pg. 2973
GILKEY WINDOW COMPANY INC.; *U.S. Private*, pg. 1700
GILKYO E&C CO., LTD.; *Int'l*, pg. 2975
GILLA INC.; *U.S. Public*, pg. 938
GILLAM-FEI, S.A.—See Frequency Electronics, Inc.; *U.S. Public*, pg. 885
GILLAND CHEVROLET-PONTIAC-GMC INC.; *U.S. Private*, pg. 1700
GILLANDERS ARBUTHNOT & CO., LTD.; *Int'l*, pg. 2975
GILLANDERS CONSTRUCTION INC.; *Int'l*, pg. 2976
GILL ATHLETICS, INC.—See Litania Sports Group, Inc.; *U.S. Private*, pg. 2467
GILL AUTOMOTIVE GROUP, INC.; *U.S. Private*, pg. 1700
GILLCO FINANCE COMPANY—See Gillman Companies; *U.S. Private*, pg. 1700
GILLCO PRODUCTS, INC.—See EQT AB; *Int'l*, pg. 2469
GILLEBAARD USA CORPORATION; *U.S. Private*, pg. 1700
GILLELAND CHEVROLET INC.; *U.S. Private*, pg. 1700
GILLESPIE DIESEL SERVICES (PTY) LIMITED—See Power Development Services (Pty) Limited; *Int'l*, pg. 5945
GILLESPIE, INC.—See The Interpublic Group of Companies, Inc.; *U.S. Public*, pg. 2093
GILLESPIE & POWERS INC.—See Gillespie Powers Refrigeration & Engineering; *U.S. Private*, pg. 1700
GILLESPIE POWERS REFRIGERATION & ENGINEERING; *U.S. Private*, pg. 1700
GILLETTE AESOP LTD.—See The Procter & Gamble Company; *U.S. Public*, pg. 2124
GILLETTE AUSTRALIA PTY. LTD.—See The Procter & Gamble Company; *U.S. Public*, pg. 2120
GILLETTE BETEILIGUNGS GMBH—See The Procter & Gamble Company; *U.S. Public*, pg. 2124
THE GILLETTE COMPANY—See The Procter & Gamble Company; *U.S. Public*, pg. 2124
GILLETTE DEL PERU S.C.—See The Procter & Gamble Company; *U.S. Public*, pg. 2124
GILLETTE DEL URUGUAY, S.A.—See The Procter & Gamble Company; *U.S. Public*, pg. 2120
GILLETTE DEUTSCHLAND GMBH & CO. OHG—See The Procter & Gamble Company; *U.S. Public*, pg. 2124
GILLETTE DOMINICANA, S.A.—See The Procter & Gamble Company; *U.S. Public*, pg. 2120
GILLETTE GRUPPE DEUTSCHLAND GMBH & CO.OHG—See The Procter & Gamble Company; *U.S. Public*, pg. 2124
GILLETTE HOLDING GMBH—See The Procter & Gamble Company; *U.S. Public*, pg. 2124
GILLETTE (HONG KONG) LIMITED—See The Procter & Gamble Company; *U.S. Public*, pg. 2124
GILLETTE INDIA LIMITED—See The Procter & Gamble Company; *U.S. Public*, pg. 2124
GILLETTE INDUSTRIES LIMITED—See The Procter & Gamble Company; *U.S. Public*, pg. 2124
GILLETTE INTERNATIONAL B.V.—See The Procter & Gamble Company; *U.S. Public*, pg. 2124
GILLETTE PAKISTAN LIMITED—See The Procter & Gamble Company; *U.S. Public*, pg. 2124
GILLETTE POLAND INTERNATIONAL SP. ZO.O.—See The Procter & Gamble Company; *U.S. Public*, pg. 2124
GILLETTE SAFETY RAZOR COMPANY—See The Procter & Gamble Company; *U.S. Public*, pg. 2124
GILLETTE—See The Procter & Gamble Company; *U.S. Public*, pg. 2124
GILLETTE UK LTD.—See The Procter & Gamble Company; *U.S. Public*, pg. 2124
GILLET TUBES TECHNOLOGIES S.A.S.—See Apollo Global Management, Inc.; *U.S. Public*, pg. 162
GILLFOR DISTRIBUTION INC.; *U.S. Private*, pg. 2976
GILLIAM BELL MOSER LLP; *U.S. Private*, pg. 1700
GILLIAM COBLE & MOSER LLP—See Gilliam Bell Moser LLP; *U.S. Private*, pg. 1700
GILLIAN GAMSY INTERNATIONAL—See The Interpublic Group of Companies, Inc.; *U.S. Public*, pg. 2105
GILLIE HYDE AUTO GROUP; *U.S. Private*, pg. 1700
GILLIES LUMBER INC.—See Alpa Lumber Inc; *Int'l*, pg. 366
GILLIGAN & FERNEMAN, LLC; *U.S. Private*, pg. 1700
GILLILAND GOLD YOUNG CONSULTING INC.—See Moody's Corporation; *U.S. Public*, pg. 1467
GILL INDUSTRIES, INC.—See PowerSphyr Inc.; *U.S. Private*, pg. 3240
GILL INDUSTRIES INC.; *U.S. Private*, pg. 1700
GILLINGHAM VETS4PETS LIMITED—See Pets at Home Group Plc; *Int'l*, pg. 5833
GILLIS, ELLIS & BAKER, INC.—See Arthur J. Gallagher & Co.; *U.S. Public*, pg. 205
GILLIS GILKERSON INC.; *U.S. Private*, pg. 1700
GILLIS QUARRIES LTD.; *Int'l*, pg. 2976
GILLISS & GILLISI INC.; *U.S. Private*, pg. 1700
GILLMAN CHRYSLER JEEP DODGE RAM—See Gillman Companies; *U.S. Private*, pg. 1700
GILLMAN COMPANIES; *U.S. Private*, pg. 1700
GILLMAN IMPORTS NORTH INC.—See Gillman Companies; *U.S. Private*, pg. 1700
GILLMAN NORTH INC.—See Gillman Companies; *U.S. Private*, pg. 1700
GILL NORTH AMERICA, LTD.—See POP Capital LLC; *U.S. Private*, pg. 3228
GILLONS INSURANCE BROKERS LTD.—See Westland Insurance Group Ltd.; *Int'l*, pg. 8390
GILL QUERETARO S DE RL DE CV—See Gill Industries Inc.; *U.S. Private*, pg. 1700
GILL-SIMPSON INCORPORATED; *U.S. Private*, pg. 1700
GILLY HICKS LLC—See Abercrombie & Fitch Co.; *U.S. Public*, pg. 25
GILMAN BUILDING PRODUCTS COMPANY; *U.S. Private*, pg. 1700
GILMAN CHEESE CORPORATION; *U.S. Private*, pg. 1701
GILMAN CIOCIA, INC.—See B. Riley Financial, Inc.; *U.S. Public*, pg. 261
GILMAN YACHT SALES, INC.; *U.S. Private*, pg. 1701
GILMAN YACHTS OF FORT LAUDERDALE, INC.—See Gilman Yacht Sales, Inc.; *U.S. Private*, pg. 1701
GIL-MAR MANUFACTURING CO.; *U.S. Private*, pg. 1698
GILMARTIN FUNERAL HOME AND CREMATION CO., INC.—See H.E. Turner & Co., Inc.; *U.S. Private*, pg. 1826
GILMEDICA, S.A.—See Biotronik GmbH & Co.; *Int'l*, pg. 1044

COMPANY NAME INDEX

GILMORE & ASSOCIATES, INC.—See Gilmore & Associates Inc.; *U.S. Private*, pg. 1701
GILMORE & ASSOCIATES INC.; *U.S. Private*, pg. 1701
GILMORE & QUINN INDUSTRIES INC.; *U.S. Private*, pg. 1701
GILO VENTURES, LLC; *U.S. Private*, pg. 1701
GILROY CHEVROLET CADILLAC INC.; *U.S. Private*, pg. 1701
GILROY DISPATCH—See Metro Publishing, Inc.; *U.S. Private*, pg. 2686
GILROY ENERGY CENTER, LLC—See Energy Capital Partners Management, LP; *U.S. Private*, pg. 1394
GILROY HONDA, INC.; *U.S. Private*, pg. 1701
GILSBAR INC.; *U.S. Private*, pg. 1701
GILSON COMPANY, INC.; *U.S. Private*, pg. 1701
GILSON ENGINEERING SALES, INC.; *U.S. Private*, pg. 1701
GILSON, INC.; *U.S. Private*, pg. 1701
GILSTER-MARY LEE CORPORATION; *U.S. Private*, pg. 1701
GILSTER-MARY LEE CORPORATION—See Gilster-Mary Lee Corporation; *U.S. Private*, pg. 1701
GILVIN-TERRILL INC.; *U.S. Private*, pg. 1701
GIMA INTERNATIONAL EXHIBITION GROUP GMBH & CO. KG—See Providence Equity Partners L.L.C.; *U.S. Private*, pg. 3292
GIMA INTERNATIONAL EXHIBITION GROUP GMBH & CO. KG—See Searchlight Capital Partners, L.P.; *U.S. Private*, pg. 3587
GIMAK ENERJI URETIM LTD.—See Parsan Makina Parcalari Sanayii AS; *Int'l*, pg. 5747
GI MANAGER L.P.; *U.S. Private*, pg. 1691
GIMA S.P.A.—See I.M.A. Industria Macchine Automatiche S.p.A.; *Int'l*, pg. 3565
GIMATIC AUTOMATION ENGINEERING (CHANGSHU) CO., LTD.—See Barnes Group Inc.; *U.S. Public*, pg. 277
GIMATIC AUTOMATION TECHNOLOGY (SHANGHAI) CO., LTD.—See Barnes Group Inc.; *U.S. Public*, pg. 277
GIMATIC BALKAN D.O.O. BEOGRAD - SAVSKI VENAC—See Barnes Group Inc.; *U.S. Public*, pg. 277
GIMATIC BULGARIA LTD.—See Barnes Group Inc.; *U.S. Public*, pg. 277
GIMATIC FRANCE S.A.R.L.—See Barnes Group Inc.; *U.S. Public*, pg. 277
GIMATIC IBERIA S.L.—See Barnes Group Inc.; *U.S. Public*, pg. 277
GIMATIC JAPAN LIMITED—See Barnes Group Inc.; *U.S. Public*, pg. 277
GIMATIC KOREA LIMITED—See Barnes Group Inc.; *U.S. Public*, pg. 277
GIMATIC NORDIC A.B.—See Barnes Group Inc.; *U.S. Public*, pg. 277
GIMATIC OTOMASYON TICARET ANONIM SIRKETI—See Barnes Group Inc.; *U.S. Public*, pg. 277
GIMATIC POLSKA SP. Z O.O—See Barnes Group Inc.; *U.S. Public*, pg. 277
GIMATIC SISTEMI INDUSTRIJSKA AVTOMATIZACIJA, D.O.O.—See Barnes Group Inc.; *U.S. Public*, pg. 277
GIMATIC S.R.L.—See Barnes Group Inc.; *U.S. Public*, pg. 277
GIMATIC UK LIMITED—See Barnes Group Inc.; *U.S. Public*, pg. 277
GIMATRADE S.R.L.—See Barnes Group Inc.; *U.S. Public*, pg. 277
GIMBERT SURGELES SARL; *Int'l*, pg. 2976
GIMDX, INC—See Improve Medical Instruments Co., Ltd; *Int'l*, pg. 3638
GIMEL TRADING CO., LTD.—See Tanaka Holdings Co., Ltd.; *Int'l*, pg. 7455
GIMEX TECHNISCHE KERAMIEK B.V.—See Indutrade AB; *Int'l*, pg. 3679
GIMFLOW SDN. BHD.—See Greenyield Berhad; *Int'l*, pg. 3078
GIMHAE TECHNO VALLEY CO., LTD.—See Hanwha Group; *Int'l*, pg. 3264
GIMIL OOO—See Silvano Fashion Group AS; *Int'l*, pg. 6922
GIMMAL GROUP, INC.; *U.S. Private*, pg. 1701
GIMMAL LLC—See Gimmal Group, Inc.; *U.S. Private*, pg. 1701
G IMMO SCI—See Groupe BPCE; *Int'l*, pg. 3098
GIMO UTBILDNINGSAKTIEBOLAG—See Sandvik AB; *Int'l*, pg. 6529
GIMPEX-GULF IMPORT EXPORT L.L.C.—See VIMPEX Handelsgesellschaft mbH; *Int'l*, pg. 8209
GIMSAN GEDIZ IPLIK VE MENSUCAT SANAYII AS; *Int'l*, pg. 2976
GIMV GERMANY HOLDING GMBH—See Gimv NV; *Int'l*, pg. 2976
GIMV NV; *Int'l*, pg. 2976
GINALFI FINANCE—See BGC Group, Inc.; *U.S. Public*, pg. 329
GINAR TECHNOLOGY CO., LTD.; *Int'l*, pg. 2976
GINBIS FOUR SEAS FOODS (SHANTOU) COMPANY LIMITED—See Four Seas Mercantile Holdings Limited; *Int'l*, pg. 2755
GIN-COR INDUSTRIES INC.; *Int'l*, pg. 2976

GINDALBIE METALS LTD—See Anshan Iron & Steel Group Corporation; *Int'l*, pg. 479
GINDRE COMPOSANT S.A.—See Umcor AG; *Int'l*, pg. 8021
GINDRE COPPER INC.—See Umcor AG; *Int'l*, pg. 8021
GINDRE DUCHAVANY S.A.—See Umcor AG; *Int'l*, pg. 8021
GINDRE TORNS S.L.—See Umcor AG; *Int'l*, pg. 8022
GINEBRA SAN MIGUEL, INC.—See Top Frontier Investment Holdings, Inc.; *Int'l*, pg. 7811
GINEGAR IBERICA S.L.—See Ginegar Plastic Products Ltd.; *Int'l*, pg. 2976
GINEGAR INDUSTRIA DE PLASTICOS LTDA.—See Ginegar Plastic Products Ltd.; *Int'l*, pg. 2976
GINEGAR PLASTIC INC.—See Ginegar Plastic Products Ltd.; *Int'l*, pg. 2976
GINEGAR PLASTIC PRODUCTS LTD.; *Int'l*, pg. 2976
GINEGAR SPECIALTY PLASTIC PRIVATE LIMITED—See Ginegar Plastic Products Ltd.; *Int'l*, pg. 2976
GINGA PETROLEUM (SINGAPORE) PTE LTD—See BGC Group, Inc.; *U.S. Public*, pg. 329
GINGER BAY SALON GROUP, LTD.; *U.S. Private*, pg. 1701
GINGER BEEF CHOICE LTD.—See Ginger Beef Corporation; *Int'l*, pg. 2976
GINGER BEEF CORPORATION; *Int'l*, pg. 2976
GINGER BEEF EXPRESS LTD.—See Ginger Beef Corporation; *Int'l*, pg. 2977
GINGERNUT CREATIVE LTD.—See The Mission Group Public Limited Company; *Int'l*, pg. 7667
GINGER TELEVISION PRODUCTIONS LIMITED—See STV Group plc; *Int'l*, pg. 7245
GINGERTOM RESOURCES PTY. LTD.—See Twenty Seven Co. Limited; *Int'l*, pg. 7990
GINGKO LTD.—See Aurelius Equity Opportunities SE & Co. KGaA; *Int'l*, pg. 709
GINIDA PTY. LIMITED—See Petsec Energy Ltd.; *Int'l*, pg. 5834
GIN INTERNATIONAL LTD.—See GINSMS Inc.; *Int'l*, pg. 2977
GINI SILK MILLS LIMITED; *Int'l*, pg. 2977
GINKGO BIOWORKS HOLDINGS, INC.; *U.S. Public*, pg. 938
GINKGO BIOWORKS, INC.—See Ginkgo Bioworks Holdings, Inc.; *U.S. Public*, pg. 938
GINKGO RESIDENTIAL TRUST INC.; *U.S. Private*, pg. 1701
GINKO INTERNATIONAL CO., LTD.; *Int'l*, pg. 2977
GINLONG TECHNOLOGIES CO., LTD.; *Int'l*, pg. 2977
GINN CHEVROLET; *U.S. Private*, pg. 1702
THE GINN GROUP, INC.; *U.S. Private*, pg. 4033
GINNI FILAMENTS LIMITED; *Int'l*, pg. 2977
GINO CO. S.P.A.—See Onward Holdings Co., Ltd.; *Int'l*, pg. 5592
GINO MORENA ENTERPRISES, LLC; *U.S. Private*, pg. 1702
GINOP SALES INC.; *U.S. Private*, pg. 1702
GINORI 1735 S.A.S.—See Kering S.A.; *Int'l*, pg. 4134
GINO ROSSI S.A.—See CCC S.A.; *Int'l*, pg. 1366
GINSANA SA—See Soho Flordis International Pty Ltd.; *Int'l*, pg. 7059
GINSBERG'S INSTITUTIONAL FOODS, INC.; *U.S. Private*, pg. 1702
GINSBURG DEVELOPMENT CORP.; *U.S. Private*, pg. 1702
GINSEY INDUSTRIES, INC.; *U.S. Private*, pg. 1702
GINSMS INC.; *Int'l*, pg. 2977
GINSTERS LIMITED—See Samworth Brothers Ltd.; *Int'l*, pg. 6519
GINTECH ENERGY CORPORATION; *Int'l*, pg. 2977
GINT SOFTWARE, INC.—See Bentley Systems, Inc.; *U.S. Public*, pg. 297
GINTZLER GRAPHICS, INC.—See Ares Management Corporation; *U.S. Public*, pg. 190
GINWA ENTERPRISE (GROUP) INC.; *Int'l*, pg. 2977
GINZA INDUSTRIES LTD.; *Int'l*, pg. 2977
GINZAMARKETS, INC.; *U.S. Private*, pg. 1702
GINZA RENOIR CO., LTD.; *Int'l*, pg. 2977
GINZA STEFANY COSMETICS CO., LTD.—See LG Corp.; *Int'l*, pg. 4476
GINZA YAMAGATAYA CO., LTD.; *Int'l*, pg. 2977
GINZA YOSHINOYA CO., LTD.; *Int'l*, pg. 2977
GIO AUTOMATION TECHNOLOGY CO., LTD.—See Hitachi, Ltd.; *Int'l*, pg. 3425
GIOCHI PREZIOSI S.P.A.; *Int'l*, pg. 2977
GIO GENERAL LIMITED—See Dai-ichi Life Holdings, Inc.; *Int'l*, pg. 1918
GIOIA SAILS INC.; *U.S. Private*, pg. 1702
GIO OPTOELECTRONICS CORP.—See Innolux Corporation; *Int'l*, pg. 3710
GIORDANO (AUSTRALIA) PTY. LIMITED—See Giordano International Limited; *Int'l*, pg. 2977
GIORDANO CONSTRUCTION CO., INC.; *U.S. Private*, pg. 1702
GIORDANO FASHIONS (INDIA) PRIVATE LIMITED—See Giordano International Limited; *Int'l*, pg. 2977
GIORDANO INTERNATIONAL LIMITED; *Int'l*, pg. 2977
GIORDANO LIMITED—See Giordano International Limited; *Int'l*, pg. 2977

GIRMATIC AG

GIORDANO MIDDLE EAST FZE—See Giordano International Limited; *Int'l*, pg. 2978
GIORDANO (M) SDN. BHD.—See Giordano International Limited; *Int'l*, pg. 2977
GIORDANO ORIGINALS (SINGAPORE) PRIVATE LTD—See Giordano International Limited; *Int'l*, pg. 2978
GIORDANO'S ENTERPRISES, INC.; *U.S. Private*, pg. 1702
GIORDANO (THAI) CO., LTD.—See Giordano International Limited; *Int'l*, pg. 2977
GIORDANO VINI S.P.A.—See Italian Wine Brands S.p.A.; *Int'l*, pg. 3828
GIORGI BROS; *U.S. Private*, pg. 1702
GIORGIO ARMANI CORPORATION—See Giorgio Armani S.p.A.; *Int'l*, pg. 2978
GIORGIO ARMANI DISTRIBUZIONE SRL—See Giorgio Armani S.p.A.; *Int'l*, pg. 2978
GIORGIO ARMANI FRANCE SARL—See Giorgio Armani S.p.A.; *Int'l*, pg. 2978
GIORGIO ARMANI RETAIL SRL—See Giorgio Armani S.p.A.; *Int'l*, pg. 2978
GIORGIO ARMANI S.P.A.; *Int'l*, pg. 2978
GIORGIO FEDON & FIGLI SPA—See EssilorLuxottica SA; *Int'l*, pg. 2515
GIORGIO FOODS INC; *U.S. Private*, pg. 1702
GIORGIO GORI (FRANCE) SAS—See Deutsche Post AG; *Int'l*, pg. 2080
GIORGIO GORI INTERNATIONAL FREIGHT FORWARDS (PTY) LTD.—See Deutsche Post AG; *Int'l*, pg. 2080
GIORGIO GORI S.R.L.—See Deutsche Post AG; *Int'l*, pg. 2080
GIORGIO GORI USA, INC.—See Deutsche Post AG; *Int'l*, pg. 2080
GIORGIO HEALTH & WELFARE PLAN; *U.S. Private*, pg. 1702
GIORGIO VISCONTI S.P.A.; *Int'l*, pg. 2978
GIORGI SAS—See VINCI S.A.; *Int'l*, pg. 8222
GIORNALE DI MERATE S.R.L.—See Netweek S.p.A.; *Int'l*, pg. 5217
GIOVANNI AGNELLI B.V.; *Int'l*, pg. 2978
GIOVANNI BOZZETTO (SHANGHAI) CHEMICAL TRADING CO., LTD.—See Aimia Inc.; *Int'l*, pg. 234
GIOVANNI BOZZETTO S.P.A.—See Aimia Inc.; *Int'l*, pg. 233
GIOVANNI FOOD COMPANY, INC.; *U.S. Private*, pg. 1702
GIOVENCO INDUSTRIES (AUST) PTY LIMITED—See Fluor Corporation; *U.S. Public*, pg. 858
GI PARTNERS U.K. LIMITED—See GI Manager L.P.; *U.S. Private*, pg. 1692
GIP DEVELOPMENT SARL—See Aurelius Equity Opportunities SE & Co. KGaA; *Int'l*, pg. 708
GI PHILIPPINES CORP.—See Wirecard AG; *Int'l*, pg. 8434
GIPPS AERO PTY LIMITED—See Mahindra & Mahindra Limited; *Int'l*, pg. 4645
GIPPSLAND ASPHALT PTY. LTD.—See Downer EDI Limited; *Int'l*, pg. 2186
GIPRONICKEL INSTITUTE, LTD.—See PJSC MMC Norilsk Nickel; *Int'l*, pg. 5882
GI PROPERTIES INC.; *U.S. Private*, pg. 1694
GIPROTRUBOPROVOD, JSC—See OAO AK Transneft; *Int'l*, pg. 5505
GI PROVISION LIMITED—See Global Invacom Group Limited; *Int'l*, pg. 2998
GIPS D.D.; *Int'l*, pg. 2979
GIP SP. Z O.O.—See LSI Software S.A; *Int'l*, pg. 4570
GI QUALITAS LIMITADA—See Tessi S.A.; *Int'l*, pg. 7574
GIRAL BETEILIGUNGSVERWALTUNGS GMBH & CO. KG—See PORR AG; *Int'l*, pg. 5923
GIRAL BETEILIGUNGSVERWALTUNGS GMBH—See PORR AG; *Int'l*, pg. 5923
GIRARD FORD; *U.S. Private*, pg. 1702
GIRARDIN BLUE BIRD COMPANY; *Int'l*, pg. 2979
GIRARD PARTNERS LTD.—See Univest Financial Corporation; *U.S. Public*, pg. 2263
GIRARD SECURITIES, INC.—See RCAP Holdings, LLC; *U.S. Private*, pg. 3361
GIRARD TRANSMISSIONS SAS—See Nidec Corporation; *Int'l*, pg. 5276
GIRARD WOOD PRODUCTS INC.; *U.S. Private*, pg. 1702
GIRASOLES DEL PLATA S.A.—See Adecoagro S.A.; *Int'l*, pg. 141
GIRAUD RESTAURANT SYSTEM CO., LTD—See Odakyu Electric Railway Co., Ltd.; *Int'l*, pg. 5523
GIRAUD—See Compagnie de Saint-Gobain SA; *Int'l*, pg. 1723
GIRAUDY VIACOM OUTDOOR S.A.—See National Amusements, Inc.; *U.S. Private*, pg. 2841
GIRDHARILAL SUGAR & ALLIED INDUSTRIES LIMITED; *Int'l*, pg. 2979
GIRIRAJ CIVIL DEVELOPERS LTD.; *Int'l*, pg. 2979
GIRISIM VARLIK YONETIMI A.S.—See Fiba Holding A.S.; *Int'l*, pg. 2651
GIRKIN DEVELOPMENT, LLC; *U.S. Private*, pg. 1702
GIRLINGS RETIREMENT RENTALS LIMITED—See Places for People Group Limited; *Int'l*, pg. 5888
GIRLS' LIFE, INC.—See Monarch Services, Inc.; *U.S. Public*, pg. 1460
GIRMATIC AG; *Int'l*, pg. 2979

GIRMES INTERNATIONAL GMBH

GIRMES INTERNATIONAL GMBH; *Int'l*, pg. 2979
GIROA SA—See Veolia Environnement S.A.; *Int'l*, pg. 8157
GIROD MAROC—See Signaux Girod S.A.; *Int'l*, pg. 6911
GIROD SEMNALIZARE RUTIERA RSL—See Signaux Girod S.A.; *Int'l*, pg. 6911
GIRO INC.; *Int'l*, pg. 2979
GIROMEX INC.—See Nexxar Group Inc.; *U.S. Private*, pg. 2922
GIRONDE HAUT DEBIT—See Orange S.A.; *Int'l*, pg. 5608
GIRONDINS HORIZONS SAS—See Metropole Television SA; *Int'l*, pg. 4863
GIRO SPORT DESIGN—See Vista Outdoor Inc.; *U.S. Public*, pg. 2305
GIROVENTILATION AB—See Lindab International AB; *Int'l*, pg. 4503
GIRPI S.A.—See Aliaxis S.A./N.V.; *Int'l*, pg. 324
GIRTMAN & ASSOCIATES—See Platinum Equity, LLC; *U.S. Private*, pg. 3208
GISAB GALLIVARE INDUSTRISERVICE AB—See Axel Johnson Gruppen AB; *Int'l*, pg. 763
GISA GMBH—See Nippon Telegraph & Telephone Corporation; *Int'l*, pg. 5343
GISBORNE HOLDINGS LTD.; *Int'l*, pg. 2979
GISH INTERNATIONAL CO., LTD.; *Int'l*, pg. 2979
GISH OIL CO; *U.S. Private*, pg. 1702
GIS HOKKAIDO CO., LTD.—See SECOM Co., Ltd.; *Int'l*, pg. 6671
GISH, SHERWOOD & FRIENDS, INC.; *U.S. Private*, pg. 1702
GIS KANTO CO., LTD.—See SECOM Co., Ltd.; *Int'l*, pg. 6671
GISLAVED FOLIE AB—See Surteco Group SE; *Int'l*, pg. 7345
GISLAVED GUMMI AB—See HEXPOL AB; *Int'l*, pg. 3371
GISLAVED GUMMI LANKA (PVT) LTD.—See HEXPOL AB; *Int'l*, pg. 3371
GISLAVED GUMMI (QINGDAO) CO., LTD.—See HEXPOL AB; *Int'l*, pg. 3371
GISMONDI 1754 S.P.A.; *Int'l*, pg. 2979
GIS PLANNING, INC.—See Nikkei Inc.; *Int'l*, pg. 5290
GIS SURVEYORS, INC.; *U.S. Private*, pg. 1702
GISTAR INNOVATION INC.—See FTGroup Co Ltd.; *Int'l*, pg. 2800
GIST-BROCADES BEHEER BV—See Koninklijke DSM N.V.; *Int'l*, pg. 4266
GIST COMMUNICATIONS, INC.; *U.S. Private*, pg. 1702
GIST & ERDMANN, INC.; *U.S. Private*, pg. 1702
GIST, INC.; *U.S. Private*, pg. 1703
GIST LIMITED—See Marks & Spencer Group plc; *Int'l*, pg. 4697
GIST NEDERLAND B.V.—See Marks & Spencer Group plc; *Int'l*, pg. 4697
GISTRANS CZECH REPUBLIC S.R.O.—See Linde plc; *Int'l*, pg. 4505
GIS WORKSHOP, LLC; *U.S. Private*, pg. 1702
GITA KASTURI SDN BHD—See S P Setia Berhad; *Int'l*, pg. 6443
GITAMBBDO—See Omnicom Group Inc.; *U.S. Public*, pg. 1575
GITAM PORTER NOVELLI—See Omnicom Group Inc.; *U.S. Public*, pg. 1590
GITA POWER & INFRASTRUCTURE PRIVATE LIMITED—See OPG Power Ventures plc; *Int'l*, pg. 5600
GITA RENEWABLE ENERGY LIMITED; *Int'l*, pg. 2979
GITA TECHNOLOGIES LTD.—See Verint Systems Inc.; *U.S. Public*, pg. 2281
GITEC CONSULT GMBH; *Int'l*, pg. 2979
GI TECH CO LTD.; *Int'l*, pg. 2960
GI TECHNOLOGY GROUP CO., LTD.; *Int'l*, pg. 2960
GI TECHNOLOGY PTE. LTD.—See Wirecard AG; *Int'l*, pg. 8434
GITENNES EXPLORATION INC.; *Int'l*, pg. 2979
GITHUB, INC.—See Microsoft Corporation; *U.S. Public*, pg. 1439
GITIESSE S.R.L.—See Eaton Corporation plc; *Int'l*, pg. 2281
GITI TIRE (CHINA) INVESTMENT CO., LTD.—See Giti Tire Pte. Ltd.; *Int'l*, pg. 2979
GITI TIRE CORPORATION—See Giti Tire Pte. Ltd.; *Int'l*, pg. 2979
GITI TIRE PTE. LTD.; *Int'l*, pg. 2979
GITI TIRE (USA) LTD.—See Giti Tire Pte. Ltd.; *Int'l*, pg. 2979
GITLAB INC.; *U.S. Public*, pg. 938
GIT-N-GO CONVENIENCE STORES; *U.S. Private*, pg. 1703
GITN SDN BERHAD—See Telekom Malaysia Berhad; *Int'l*, pg. 7537
GITTINGS PROTECTIVE SECURITY, INC.; *U.S. Private*, pg. 1703
GITZO SA—See Videndum plc; *Int'l*, pg. 8190
GIUFFRE BROS CRANES, INC.; *U.S. Private*, pg. 1703
GIUFFRE FRANCIS LEFEBVRE SPA—See Editions Lefebvre Sarrut SA; *Int'l*, pg. 2311
GIUFFRE; *U.S. Private*, pg. 1703
GIUFFRE VOLVO INC.; *U.S. Private*, pg. 1703

GIUGIARO DESIGN—See Porsche Automobil Holding SE; *Int'l*, pg. 5926
GIULIANI METALLI S.A.S.—See CRONIMET Holding GmbH; *Int'l*, pg. 1855
GIULIANI PARTNERS LLC; *U.S. Private*, pg. 1703
GIULIANO-PAGANO CORPORATION; *U.S. Private*, pg. 1703
GIULIANO'S DELICATESSEN & BAKERY; *U.S. Private*, pg. 1703
GIULIO EINAUDI EDITORE S.P.A.—See Fininvest S.p.A.; *Int'l*, pg. 2675
GIUMARRA VINEYARDS CORPORATION; *U.S. Private*, pg. 1703
GIUNTA BROTHERS INC.; *U.S. Private*, pg. 1703
GIURGIU NAV SA; *Int'l*, pg. 2979
GIUSTO SPECIALTY FOODS INC.; *U.S. Private*, pg. 1703
GIVAT SAVYON LTD.—See Africa Israel Investments Ltd.; *Int'l*, pg. 190
GIVAUDAN ARGENTINA S.A.—See Givaudan S.A.; *Int'l*, pg. 2980
GIVAUDAN ARGENTINA SA—See Givaudan S.A.; *Int'l*, pg. 2980
GIVAUDAN ARGENTINA SERVICIOS SA—See Givaudan S.A.; *Int'l*, pg. 2980
GIVAUDAN AROMA VE ESANS SANAYI VE TICARET LTD., STI.—See Givaudan S.A.; *Int'l*, pg. 2980
GIVAUDAN AUSTRALIA PTY. LTD.—See Givaudan S.A.; *Int'l*, pg. 2980
GIVAUDAN AUSTRALIA PTY LTD.—See Givaudan S.A.; *Int'l*, pg. 2980
GIVAUDAN AUSTRIA GMBH—See Givaudan S.A.; *Int'l*, pg. 2980
GIVAUDAN BUSINESS SOLUTIONS KFT—See Givaudan S.A.; *Int'l*, pg. 2980
GIVAUDAN CANADA, INC.—See Givaudan S.A.; *Int'l*, pg. 2980
GIVAUDAN CHILE LTDA—See Givaudan S.A.; *Int'l*, pg. 2980
GIVAUDAN COLOMBIA SA—See Givaudan S.A.; *Int'l*, pg. 2980
GIVAUDAN COLOMBIA SAS—See Givaudan S.A.; *Int'l*, pg. 2980
GIVAUDAN CR, S.R.O.—See Givaudan S.A.; *Int'l*, pg. 2980
GIVAUDAN DE MEXICO S.A. DE C.V.—See Givaudan S.A.; *Int'l*, pg. 2981
GIVAUDAN DE MEXICO SA DE CV—See Givaudan S.A.; *Int'l*, pg. 2981
GIVAUDAN DEUTSCHLAND GMBH—See Givaudan S.A.; *Int'l*, pg. 2980
GIVAUDAN DEUTSCHLAND GMBH—See Givaudan S.A.; *Int'l*, pg. 2980
GIVAUDAN DO BRASIL LTDA—See Givaudan S.A.; *Int'l*, pg. 2980
GIVAUDAN EGYPT FRAGRANCE LLC—See Givaudan S.A.; *Int'l*, pg. 2980
GIVAUDAN EGYPT SAE—See Givaudan S.A.; *Int'l*, pg. 2980
GIVAUDAN ERFTSTADT GMBH & CO. KG—See Givaudan S.A.; *Int'l*, pg. 2980
GIVAUDAN FLAVORS AND FRAGRANCES, INC.—See Givaudan S.A.; *Int'l*, pg. 2981
GIVAUDAN FLAVORS CORPORATION - ELGIN—See Givaudan S.A.; *Int'l*, pg. 2981
GIVAUDAN FLAVORS CORPORATION - ITASCA—See Givaudan S.A.; *Int'l*, pg. 2981
GIVAUDAN FLAVORS CORPORATION—See Givaudan S.A.; *Int'l*, pg. 2981
GIVAUDAN FLAVORS (NANTONG) LTD.—See Givaudan S.A.; *Int'l*, pg. 2980
GIVAUDAN FLAVORS (SHANGHAI) LTD.—See Givaudan S.A.; *Int'l*, pg. 2981
GIVAUDAN FLAVOURS & FRAGRANCES MALAYSIA SDN. BHD.—See Givaudan S.A.; *Int'l*, pg. 2980
GIVAUDAN FRAGRANCES CORPORATION—See Givaudan S.A.; *Int'l*, pg. 2981
GIVAUDAN FRAGRANCES (GUANGZHOU) CO. LTD.—See Givaudan S.A.; *Int'l*, pg. 2980
GIVAUDAN FRAGRANCES (SHANGHAI) LTD.—See Givaudan S.A.; *Int'l*, pg. 2980
GIVAUDAN FRANCE AROMES SAS—See Givaudan S.A.; *Int'l*, pg. 2980
GIVAUDAN FRANCE FRAGRANCES SAS—See Givaudan S.A.; *Int'l*, pg. 2980
GIVAUDAN FRANCE NATURALS S.A.S.—See Givaudan S.A.; *Int'l*, pg. 2980
GIVAUDAN GUATEMALA S.A.—See Givaudan S.A.; *Int'l*, pg. 2980
GIVAUDAN HOLDINGS UK LTD—See Givaudan S.A.; *Int'l*, pg. 2980
GIVAUDAN HONG KONG LTD.—See Givaudan S.A.; *Int'l*, pg. 2980
GIVAUDAN HUNGARY KFT—See Givaudan S.A.; *Int'l*, pg. 2980
GIVAUDAN IBERICA SA—See Givaudan S.A.; *Int'l*, pg. 2980
GIVAUDAN (INDIA) PVT. LTD.—See Givaudan S.A.; *Int'l*, pg. 2980

CORPORATE AFFILIATIONS

GIVAUDAN INTERNATIONAL SA—See Givaudan S.A.; *Int'l*, pg. 2980
GIVAUDAN ITALIA S.P.A.—See Givaudan S.A.; *Int'l*, pg. 2980
GIVAUDAN JAPAN K.K.—See Givaudan S.A.; *Int'l*, pg. 2980
GIVAUDAN JAPAN K.K. - YOKOHAMA—See Givaudan S.A.; *Int'l*, pg. 2980
GIVAUDAN KOREA LTD.—See Givaudan S.A.; *Int'l*, pg. 2980
GIVAUDAN-LAVIROTTE—See L'Air Liquide S.A.; *Int'l*, pg. 4374
GIVAUDAN MALAYSIA SDN. BHD.—See Givaudan S.A.; *Int'l*, pg. 2981
GIVAUDAN MIDDLE EAST & AFRICA FZE—See Givaudan S.A.; *Int'l*, pg. 2981
GIVAUDAN NEDERLAND BV—See Givaudan S.A.; *Int'l*, pg. 2981
GIVAUDAN NEDERLAND FINANCE BV—See Givaudan S.A.; *Int'l*, pg. 2981
GIVAUDAN NORTH EUROPE AB—See Givaudan S.A.; *Int'l*, pg. 2981
GIVAUDAN NZ LTD.—See Givaudan S.A.; *Int'l*, pg. 2981
GIVAUDAN PERU SAC—See Givaudan S.A.; *Int'l*, pg. 2981
GIVAUDAN POLSKA SP. Z.O.O.—See Givaudan S.A.; *Int'l*, pg. 2981
GIVAUDAN RUS LLC—See Givaudan S.A.; *Int'l*, pg. 2981
GIVAUDAN S.A.; *Int'l*, pg. 2979
GIVAUDAN SCANDINAVIA A/S—See Givaudan S.A.; *Int'l*, pg. 2981
GIVAUDAN SINGAPORE PTE LTD. PHILIPPINES—See Givaudan S.A.; *Int'l*, pg. 2981
GIVAUDAN SINGAPORE PTE LTD.—See Givaudan S.A.; *Int'l*, pg. 2981
GIVAUDAN SPECIALTY PRODUCTS (SHANGHAI) LTD—See Givaudan S.A.; *Int'l*, pg. 2981
GIVAUDAN SUISSE SA—See Givaudan S.A.; *Int'l*, pg. 2981
GIVAUDAN (THAILAND) LTD.—See Givaudan S.A.; *Int'l*, pg. 2980
GIVAUDAN TREASURY INTERNATIONAL B.V.—See Givaudan S.A.; *Int'l*, pg. 2981
GIVAUDAN UK LIMITED—See Givaudan S.A.; *Int'l*, pg. 2980
GIVAUDAN UK LIMITED - STAINES—See Givaudan S.A.; *Int'l*, pg. 2980
GIVAUDAN UK LIMITED - WIRRAL—See Givaudan S.A.; *Int'l*, pg. 2980
GIVAUDAN UK LTD—See Givaudan S.A.; *Int'l*, pg. 2980
GIVAUDAN UNITED STATES, INC.—See Givaudan S.A.; *Int'l*, pg. 2981
GIVAUDAN VENEZUELA SA—See Givaudan S.A.; *Int'l*, pg. 2981
GIVE2ASIA; *U.S. Private*, pg. 1703
GIVEANYTHING.COM, INC.—See The Riverside Company; *U.S. Private*, pg. 4108
GIVEGAB INC.—See Insight Venture Management, LLC; *U.S. Private*, pg. 2090
GIVE KIDS THE WORLD, INC.; *U.S. Private*, pg. 1703
GIVEMEPOWER CORP.; *Int'l*, pg. 2982
GIVENCHY CHINA COMPANY LIMITED—See LVMH Moet Hennessy Louis Vuitton SE; *Int'l*, pg. 4593
GIVENCHY CORP.—See LVMH Moet Hennessy Louis Vuitton SE; *Int'l*, pg. 4593
GIVENCHY JAPAN CO. LTD—See LVMH Moet Hennessy Louis Vuitton SE; *Int'l*, pg. 4593
GIVENCHY S.A.—See LVMH Moet Hennessy Louis Vuitton SE; *Int'l*, pg. 4593
GIVENCHY SHANGHAI COMMERCIAL AND TRADING CO LTD—See LVMH Moet Hennessy Louis Vuitton SE; *Int'l*, pg. 4593
GIVEN IMAGING (ASIA) COMPANY LIMITED—See Medtronic plc; *Int'l*, pg. 4789
GIVEN IMAGING DO BRAZIL LTDA.—See Medtronic plc; *Int'l*, pg. 4787
GIVEN IMAGING GMBH—See Medtronic plc; *Int'l*, pg. 4789
GIVEN IMAGING K.K.—See Medtronic plc; *Int'l*, pg. 4789
GIVEN IMAGING (LOS ANGELES) LLC—See Medtronic plc; *Int'l*, pg. 4787
GIVEN IMAGING LTD.—See Medtronic plc; *Int'l*, pg. 4789
GIVEN IMAGING PTY. LTD.—See Medtronic plc; *Int'l*, pg. 4789
GIVEN IMAGING VIETNAM CO., LTD.—See Medtronic plc; *Int'l*, pg. 4787
GI VENTURES; *Int'l*, pg. 2960
GIVE SOMETHING BACK LLC; *U.S. Private*, pg. 1703
GIVHAN DIALYSIS, LLC—See DaVita Inc.; *U.S. Public*, pg. 639
GIVING.COM LIMITED; *Int'l*, pg. 2982
GIVNFLOW COMPANY LIMITED—See Greenyield Berhad; *Int'l*, pg. 3078
GIVOT OLAM OIL EXPLORATION LIMITED PARTNERSHIP (1993); *Int'l*, pg. 2982
GIVRAUVAL ENROBES SAS—See VINCI S.A.; *Int'l*, pg. 8222
GIV-TECH, INC.—See Global Information, Inc.; *Int'l*, pg. 2997

COMPANY NAME INDEX

GIWARITE LTD.—See Etex SA/NV; *Int'l*, pg. 2522
GIX MARTECH INNOVATION; *Int'l*, pg. 2982
GIYANI METALS CORP.; *Int'l*, pg. 2982
GIZA GENERAL CONTRACTING & REAL ESTATE INVESTMENT; *Int'l*, pg. 2982
GIZA TECHNOLOGIES INC.; *U.S. Private*, pg. 1703
GIZEH DISPOFORM SP. Z O.O.—See GIZEH Verpackungen GmbH & Co. KG; *Int'l*, pg. 2982
GIZEH EMBALLAGES ANGERS SAS—See GIZEH Verpackungen GmbH & Co. KG; *Int'l*, pg. 2982
GIZEH PACKAGING NA INC.—See GIZEH Verpackungen GmbH & Co. KG; *Int'l*, pg. 2982
GIZEH VERPACKUNGEN GMBH & CO. KG; *Int'l*, pg. 2982
G JACQUEMMOZ ET FILS; *Int'l*, pg. 2861
GJ-BETEILIGUNGS GMBH—See Vonovia SE; *Int'l*, pg. 8305
G&J BROOKS ENTERPRISE, INC.; *U.S. Private*, pg. 1629
G. J. CHEMICAL CO. INC.; *U.S. Private*, pg. 1630
G+J ELECTRONIC MEDIA SALES GMBH—See Bertelsmann SE & Co. KGaA; *Int'l*, pg. 992
GJENSIDIGE BALTIC—See Gjensidige Forsikring ASA; *Int'l*, pg. 2982
GJENSIDIGE FORSIKRING ASA; *Int'l*, pg. 2982
GJERDE & BYHRING AS—See Bridgestone Corporation; *Int'l*, pg. 1160
GJERDEN FJELLSIKRING AS—See Nordisk Bergteknik AB; *Int'l*, pg. 5424
G+J ESPANA S.A.—See Bertelsmann SE & Co. KGaA; *Int'l*, pg. 992
G.J. HOPKINS, INC.—See The Branch Group, Inc.; *U.S. Private*, pg. 3999
G+J IMS BVBA—See Bertelsmann SE & Co. KGaA; *Int'l*, pg. 992
GJ INTERNATIONAL MEDIA SALES LTD.—See Bertelsmann SE & Co. KGaA; *Int'l*, pg. 992
G+J INTERNATIONAL SALES ITALY S.R.L.—See Bertelsmann SE & Co. KGaA; *Int'l*, pg. 992
G+J / KLAMBT STYLE-VERLAG GMBH & CO. KG—See Bertelsmann SE & Co. KGaA; *Int'l*, pg. 994
GJ LEASING COMPANY INC.—See Slay Industries Inc.; *U.S. Private*, pg. 3687
GJ&L INC.; *U.S. Private*, pg. 1703
G. JOANNOU CYCLE CO. INC.; *U.S. Private*, pg. 1630
GJOVIK CHEVROLET BUICK PONTIAC GMC, INC.; *U.S. Private*, pg. 1703
GJOVIK FORD-MERCURY, INC.; *U.S. Private*, pg. 1703
G&J PEPSI-COLA BOTTLERS INC.; *U.S. Private*, pg. 1629
G&J SEIBERLICH & CO., LLP; *U.S. Private*, pg. 1629
GJ STEEL PUBLIC COMPANY LIMITED; *Int'l*, pg. 2982
G.K. ASSEMBLY CO., LTD.—See Gunkul Engineering Co., Ltd.; *Int'l*, pg. 3183
GKB-BERGBAU GMBH—See Osterreichische Beteiligungs AG; *Int'l*, pg. 5653
GK BIO INTERNATIONAL SDN. BHD.—See All Cosmos Bio-Tech Holding Corporation; *Int'l*, pg. 332
GKB KLINIKBETRIEBE GMBH—See Asklepios Kliniken GmbH & Co. KGaA; *Int'l*, pg. 623
GKB OPHTHALMICS LTD.; *Int'l*, pg. 2983
G.K. CONSULTANTS LIMITED; *Int'l*, pg. 2865
GKD (BEIJING) IND. TECHNOLOGIES CO., LTD.—See GKD - Gebr. Kufferath AG; *Int'l*, pg. 2983
GKD BUISMET (PTY) LTD.—See GKD - Gebr. Kufferath AG; *Int'l*, pg. 2983
GKD - GEBR. KUFFERATH AG; *Int'l*, pg. 2983
GKD INDIA LTD.—See GKD - Gebr. Kufferath AG; *Int'l*, pg. 2983
GKD LATAM S.A.—See GKD - Gebr. Kufferath AG; *Int'l*, pg. 2983
GK DRIVE SYSTEMS (SUZHOU) CO., LTD.—See Dana Incorporated; *U.S. Public*, pg. 623
GKD (UK) LTD.—See GKD - Gebr. Kufferath AG; *Int'l*, pg. 2983
GKD-USA, INC.—See GKD - Gebr. Kufferath AG; *Int'l*, pg. 2983
GKE CORPORATION LIMITED; *Int'l*, pg. 2983
GKE EXPRESS LOGISTICS PTE LTD—See GKE Corporation Limited; *Int'l*, pg. 2983
GKE FREIGHT PTE LTD—See GKE Corporation Limited; *Int'l*, pg. 2983
GKE METAL LOGISTICS PTE. LTD.—See GKE Corporation Limited; *Int'l*, pg. 2983
GK ENTERPRISES, INC.; *U.S. Private*, pg. 1703
GKE PRIVATE LIMITED—See GKE Corporation Limited; *Int'l*, pg. 2983
GK EQUITIES SDN. BHD.—See George Kent (Malaysia) Berhad; *Int'l*, pg. 2938
GKE SERVICES PTE. LTD.—See GKE Corporation Limited; *Int'l*, pg. 2983
GKE (SHANGHAI) METAL LOGISTICS CO., LTD.—See GKE Corporation Limited; *Int'l*, pg. 2983
GKE WAREHOUSING & LOGISTICS PTE LTD—See GKE Corporation Limited; *Int'l*, pg. 2983
G.K. FOUR TWENTY SEVEN JAPAN—See Moody's Corporation; *U.S. Public*, pg. 1467

GKF VERMOGENSVERWALTUNGSGESELLSCHAFT MBH & CO. OBJEKT WIESBADEN-NORDENSTADT KG—See Metro AG; *Int'l*, pg. 4857
GKF VERMOGENSVERWALTUNGSGESELLSCHAFT MIT BESCHRANKTER HAFTUNG—See Metro AG; *Int'l*, pg. 4857
GKG ASIA PTE. LTD.—See GKG Precision Machine Co., Ltd.; *Int'l*, pg. 2983
G. K. GOH HOLDINGS LIMITED; *Int'l*, pg. 2864
GKG PRECISION MACHINE CO., LTD.; *Int'l*, pg. 2983
GK GRAPHIT KROPFMUHL GMBH—See AMG Critical Materials N.V.; *Int'l*, pg. 426
GKI ELECTRONIC ENCLOSURES—See Electromet Corporation; *U.S. Private*, pg. 1354
GKI INCORPORATED; *U.S. Private*, pg. 1704
GK INDUSTRIAL REFUSE SYSTEMS—See Bestige Holdings LLC; *U.S. Private*, pg. 544
GK INSURANCE BROKERS LIMITED—See GraceKennedy Limited; *Int'l*, pg. 3048
GKI-OFU INDUSTRIEOFENBAU GMBH—See ThyssenKrupp AG; *Int'l*, pg. 7724
GKK DIALOGGROUP GMBH—See WPP plc; *Int'l*, pg. 8463
GKK GUTACHTERZENTRALE GMBH—See DEKRA e.V.; *Int'l*, pg. 2009
GKKWORKS CONSTRUCTION SERVICES, INC; *U.S. Private*, pg. 1704
GKL VENTILATIE TECHNIEK B.V.—See Grafton Group plc; *Int'l*, pg. 3050
G&K MANAGEMENT COMPANY; *U.S. Private*, pg. 1629
G & K MANAGEMENT; *U.S. Private*, pg. 1628
GKMC CONSTRUCTION & CONSULTING INC.—See Maeda Corporation; *Int'l*, pg. 4635
GK MECHANICAL SYSTEMS LLC—See KKR & Co. Inc.; *U.S. Public*, pg. 1262
GKM HOLDINGS JOINT STOCK COMPANY; *Int'l*, pg. 2983
GKN AEROSPACE AEROSTRUCTURES NORTH AMERICA—See GKN plc; *Int'l*, pg. 2983
GKN AEROSPACE ALABAMA—See GKN plc; *Int'l*, pg. 2983
GKN AEROSPACE BANDY MACHINING INC—See GKN plc; *Int'l*, pg. 2984
GKN AEROSPACE CHEM-TRONICS, INC.—See GKN plc; *Int'l*, pg. 2984
GKN AEROSPACE CINCINNATI INC—See GKN plc; *Int'l*, pg. 2984
GKN AEROSPACE DEUTSCHLAND GMBH—See GKN plc; *Int'l*, pg. 2984
GKN AEROSPACE ENGINE PRODUCTS—See GKN plc; *Int'l*, pg. 2984
GKN AEROSPACE ENGINE SYSTEMS INDIA PRIVATE LIMITED—See Melrose Industries PLC; *Int'l*, pg. 4812
GKN AEROSPACE, INC.—See Melrose Industries PLC; *Int'l*, pg. 4813
GKN AEROSPACE - MONITOR, INC.—See GKN plc; *Int'l*, pg. 2983
GKN AEROSPACE MUNCIE INC—See GKN plc; *Int'l*, pg. 2984
GKN AEROSPACE NEW ENGLAND INC—See GKN plc; *Int'l*, pg. 2984
GKN AEROSPACE NORTH AMERICA INC—See GKN plc; *Int'l*, pg. 2984
GKN AEROSPACE NORWAY AS—See Melrose Industries PLC; *Int'l*, pg. 4812
GKN AEROSPACE PRECISION MACHINING, INC.—See Melrose Industries PLC; *Int'l*, pg. 4812
GKN AEROSPACE SERVICES LTD—See GKN plc; *Int'l*, pg. 2984
GKN AEROSPACE SERVICES STRUCTURES LLC—See Melrose Industries PLC; *Int'l*, pg. 4812
GKN AEROSPACE SWEDEN AB—See Melrose Industries PLC; *Int'l*, pg. 4812
GKN AEROSPACE TRANSPARENCY SYSTEMS INC—See GKN plc; *Int'l*, pg. 2984
GKN AEROSPACE TRANSPARENCY SYSTEMS (KINGS NORTON) LIMITED—See Melrose Industries PLC; *Int'l*, pg. 4812
GKN AEROSPACE TRANSPARENCY SYSTEMS (LUTON) LIMITED—See Melrose Industries PLC; *Int'l*, pg. 4813
GKN AEROSPACE TRANSPARENCY SYSTEMS (THAILAND) LIMITED—See Melrose Industries PLC; *Int'l*, pg. 4813
GKN AMERICA CORP—See GKN plc; *Int'l*, pg. 2984
GKN ARMSTRONG WHEELS INC.—See GKN plc; *Int'l*, pg. 2984
GKN AUTOMOTIVE BENGALURU PRIVATE LIMITED—See Melrose Industries PLC; *Int'l*, pg. 4813
GKN AUTOMOTIVE, INC - ALAMANCE FACILITY—See GKN plc; *Int'l*, pg. 2984
GKN AUTOMOTIVE LIMITED—See Melrose Industries PLC; *Int'l*, pg. 4813
GKN AUTOSTRUCTURES LTD.—See GKN plc; *Int'l*, pg. 2984
GKN AYRA SERVICIO SA—See GKN plc; *Int'l*, pg. 2984
GKN CEDU LIMITED—See GKN plc; *Int'l*, pg. 2984
GKN DANYANG INDUSTRIES COMPANY LTD—See GKN plc; *Int'l*, pg. 2984
GKN DO BRASIL LTDA.—See GKN plc; *Int'l*, pg. 2986

GKN PLC

GKN DRIVELINE ARNAGE—See GKN plc; *Int'l*, pg. 2984
GKN DRIVELINE BIRMINGHAM - ERDINGTON PLANT—See GKN plc; *Int'l*, pg. 2984
GKN DRIVELINE BOWLING GREEN INC—See GKN plc; *Int'l*, pg. 2984
GKN DRIVELINE BRUNECK AG—See GKN plc; *Int'l*, pg. 2984
GKN DRIVELINE CELAYA SA DE CV—See GKN plc; *Int'l*, pg. 2984
GKN DRIVELINE DEUTSCHLAND GMBH—See GKN plc; *Int'l*, pg. 2984
GKN DRIVELINE FIRENZE SPA—See GKN plc; *Int'l*, pg. 2984
GKN DRIVELINE INTERNATIONAL GMBH—See GKN plc; *Int'l*, pg. 2984
GKN DRIVELINE JAPAN LTD—See GKN plc; *Int'l*, pg. 2984
GKN DRIVELINE JTEKT MANUFACTURING LTD—See GKN plc; *Int'l*, pg. 2984
GKN DRIVELINE KIEL—See GKN plc; *Int'l*, pg. 2984
GKN DRIVELINE KOPING AB—See GKN plc; *Int'l*, pg. 2984
GKN DRIVELINE KOPING AB—See GKN plc; *Int'l*, pg. 2984
GKN DRIVELINE KOREA LTD—See GKN plc; *Int'l*, pg. 2984
GKN DRIVELINE LEGAZPI—See GKN plc; *Int'l*, pg. 2984
GKN DRIVELINE LOHMAR—See GKN plc; *Int'l*, pg. 2984
GKN DRIVELINE LTD.—See GKN plc; *Int'l*, pg. 2984
GKN DRIVELINE NEWTON LLC—See GKN plc; *Int'l*, pg. 2984
GKN DRIVELINE NORTH AMERICA INC.—See GKN plc; *Int'l*, pg. 2984
GKN DRIVELINE OFFENBACH—See GKN plc; *Int'l*, pg. 2984
GKN DRIVELINE POLSKA SP. Z O.O.—See GKN plc; *Int'l*, pg. 2985
GKN DRIVELINE SA—See GKN plc; *Int'l*, pg. 2984
GKN DRIVELINE SERVICE LTD—See GKN plc; *Int'l*, pg. 2984
GKN DRIVELINE SERVICE SCANDINAVIA AB—See GKN plc; *Int'l*, pg. 2984
GKN DRIVELINE SINGAPORE PTE LTD—See GKN plc; *Int'l*, pg. 2984
GKN DRIVELINE SLOVENIJA D.O.O.—See GKN plc; *Int'l*, pg. 2985
GKN DRIVELINE (THAILAND) LTD—See GKN plc; *Int'l*, pg. 2984
GKN DRIVELINE TORQUE TECHNOLOGY (SHANGHAI) CO LTD—See GKN plc; *Int'l*, pg. 2985
GKN DRIVELINE TRIER—See GKN plc; *Int'l*, pg. 2985
GKN DRIVELINE URUGUAY SA—See GKN plc; *Int'l*, pg. 2985
GKN DRIVELINE VIGO—See GKN plc; *Int'l*, pg. 2985
GKN DRIVELINE VILLAGRAN SA DE CV—See GKN plc; *Int'l*, pg. 2985
GKN DRIVELINE WALSALL LTD—See GKN plc; *Int'l*, pg. 2985
GKN DRIVELINE ZUMAIA—See GKN plc; *Int'l*, pg. 2985
GKN ESKISEHIR AUTOMOTIVE PRODUCTS MANUFACTURE AND SALES A.S.—See GKN plc; *Int'l*, pg. 2985
GKN FLORANGE SARL—See GKN plc; *Int'l*, pg. 2985
GKN FOKKER AEROSPACE—See GKN plc; *Int'l*, pg. 2983
GKN FREIGHT SERVICES LTD., EDGWARE—See GKN plc; *Int'l*, pg. 2985
GKN GELENKWELLENWERK KAISERSLAUTERN GMBH—See GKN plc; *Int'l*, pg. 2985
GKN GEPLASMETAL SA—See GKN plc; *Int'l*, pg. 2985
GKN GLENCO SA—See GKN plc; *Int'l*, pg. 2985
GKN HOLDINGS PLC—See GKN plc; *Int'l*, pg. 2985
GKN HYDROGEN CORP.—See Melrose Industries PLC; *Int'l*, pg. 4813
GKN INDUSTRIES LTD—See GKN plc; *Int'l*, pg. 2985
GKN LAND SYSTEMS LTD—See GKN plc; *Int'l*, pg. 2985
GKN NORTH AMERICA SERVICES INC.—See GKN plc; *Int'l*, pg. 2985
GKN OFFHIGHWAY SYSTEMS LTD.—See GKN plc; *Int'l*, pg. 2985
GKN PLC; *Int'l*, pg. 2983
GKN RIBEMONT SARL—See GKN plc; *Int'l*, pg. 2985
GKN ROCKFORD, INC.—See GKN plc; *Int'l*, pg. 2985
GKN SANKEY LTD.—See GKN plc; *Int'l*, pg. 2985
GKN SERVICE AUSTRIA GMBH—See GKN plc; *Int'l*, pg. 2985
GKN SERVICE BENELUX BV—See GKN plc; *Int'l*, pg. 2985
GKN SERVICE INTERNATIONAL GMBH—See GKN plc; *Int'l*, pg. 2985
GKN SHEEPBRIDGE STOKES LTD.—See GKN plc; *Int'l*, pg. 2985
GKN SINTER ISTANBUL METAL SANAYI VE TICARET ANONIM SIRKETI—See Melrose Industries PLC; *Int'l*, pg. 4813
GKN SINTER METALS CAPE TOWN (PTY) LTD—See GKN plc; *Int'l*, pg. 2985
GKN SINTER METALS COMPONENTS GMBH—See GKN plc; *Int'l*, pg. 2985
GKN SINTER METALS DE ARGENTINA S.A.—See Concentric AB; *Int'l*, pg. 1764

GKN PLC

GKN SINTER METALS ENGINEERING GMBH—See GKN plc; *Int'l*, pg. 2985
GKN SINTER METALS FILTERS GMBH—See GKN plc; *Int'l*, pg. 2985
GKN SINTER METALS GMBH BAD BRUCKENAU—See GKN plc; *Int'l*, pg. 2985
GKN SINTER METALS GMBH RADEVORMWALD GERMANY—See GKN plc; *Int'l*, pg. 2985
GKN SINTER METALS HOLDINGS LTD—See GKN plc; *Int'l*, pg. 2985
GKN SINTER METALS INC.—See GKN plc; *Int'l*, pg. 2985
GKN SINTER METALS LTDA—See GKN plc; *Int'l*, pg. 2985
GKN SINTER METALS LTD.—See GKN plc; *Int'l*, pg. 2985
GKN SINTER METALS PRIVATE LTD—See GKN plc; *Int'l*, pg. 2985
GKN SINTER METALS—See GKN plc; *Int'l*, pg. 2985
GKN SINTER METALS SPA—See GKN plc; *Int'l*, pg. 2985
GKN SINTER METALS ST THOMAS LTD—See GKN plc; *Int'l*, pg. 2985
GKN THOMPSON CHASSIS LTD—See GKN plc; *Int'l*, pg. 2985
GKN (UNITED KINGDOM) PLC—See GKN plc; *Int'l*, pg. 2983
GKN VISCODRIVE GMBH—See GKN plc; *Int'l*, pg. 2985
GKN WALTERSCHEID GETRIEBE GMBH—See GKN plc; *Int'l*, pg. 2985
GKN WALTERSCHEID GMBH—See OEP Capital Advisors, L.P.; *U.S. Private*, pg. 2999
GKN WALTERSCHEID INC.—See OEP Capital Advisors, L.P.; *U.S. Private*, pg. 2999
GKN WALTERSSCHEID AS—See GKN plc; *Int'l*, pg. 2986
GKN WESTLAND AEROSPACE INC—See GKN plc; *Int'l*, pg. 2986
GKN WHEELS (LIUZHOU) COMPANY LTD—See GKN plc; *Int'l*, pg. 2986
GKN WHEELS, LTD.—See GKN plc; *Int'l*, pg. 2986
GKN WHEELS NAGBOL A/S—See GKN plc; *Int'l*, pg. 2986
GKN ZHONGYUAN CYLINDER LINER COMPANY LIMITED—See Melrose Industries PLC; *Int'l*, pg. 4813
GK PACKAGING INC.; *U.S. Private*, pg. 1703
G.K.POWER PRODUCTS CO., LTD.—See Gunkul Engineering Co., Ltd.; *Int'l*, pg. 3183
G.K.P PRINTING & PACKAGING LTD.; *Int'l*, pg. 2866
G.K. REAL ESTATE (2564) CO., LTD.—See Gunkul Engineering Co., Ltd.; *Int'l*, pg. 3183
GK RESOURCES LTD.; *Int'l*, pg. 2982
G&K SERVICES CANADA, INC.—See Cintas Corporation; *U.S. Public*, pg. 496
G&K SERVICES, LLC - LAUREL—See Cintas Corporation; *U.S. Public*, pg. 496
G&K SERVICES, LLC—See Cintas Corporation; *U.S. Public*, pg. 496
G.K. SMART FARMING CO., LTD.—See Gunkul Engineering Co., Ltd.; *Int'l*, pg. 3183
GK SOFTWARE AFRICA (PTY) LTD.—See Fujitsu Limited; *Int'l*, pg. 2837
GK SOFTWARE SE—See Fujitsu Limited; *Int'l*, pg. 2837
GK SOFTWARE USA, INC.—See Fujitsu Limited; *Int'l*, pg. 2837
GK SPRINKLER SP.Z.O.O—See VINCI S.A.; *Int'l*, pg. 8222
G.K.S. SWIETELSKY KFT.—See Swietelsky Baugesellschaft m.b.H.; *Int'l*, pg. 7367
G-KT DO BRASIL LTDA.—See G-TEKT Corporation; *Int'l*, pg. 2863
GK TECHNOLOGIES, INC.—See Prysmian S.p.A.; *Int'l*, pg. 6011
GK TNS ENERGO PAO; *Int'l*, pg. 2982
GKV COMMUNICATIONS; *U.S. Private*, pg. 1704
GKW LIMITED - POWMEX STEELS DIVISION—See GKW Limited; *Int'l*, pg. 2986
GKW LIMITED; *Int'l*, pg. 2986
GKW (OVERSEAS TRADING) LIMITED—See GKW Limited; *Int'l*, pg. 2986
GLABARCO LEADER GROUP INC.—See Danaher Corporation; *U.S. Public*, pg. 627
GLABMAN FURNITURE INC.; *U.S. Private*, pg. 1704
G-LABS SAGL—See Guess? Inc.; *U.S. Public*, pg. 974
GLACELL SVERIGE AB—See Peab AB; *Int'l*, pg. 5771
GLACERIES DE SAINT-ROCH GERMANIA—See Compagnie de Saint-Gobain SA; *Int'l*, pg. 1723
GLACERIES DE SAINT-ROCH SA—See Compagnie de Saint-Gobain SA; *Int'l*, pg. 1723
GLACIAL PLAINS COOPERATIVE; *U.S. Private*, pg. 1704
GLACIAR PESQUERA S.A.—See Premium Brands Holdings Corporation; *Int'l*, pg. 5963
GLACIER BANCORP, INC.; *U.S. Public*, pg. 938
GLACIER BANK—See Glacier Bancorp, Inc.; *U.S. Public*, pg. 938
GLACIER BAY TECHNOLOGY; *U.S. Private*, pg. 1704
GLACIER DRILLING COMPANY—See ConocoPhillips; *U.S. Public*, pg. 569
GLACIER ENTERPRISES (PTY) LTD—See Cullinan Holdings Limited; *Int'l*, pg. 1877
GLACIER FINANCIAL HOLDINGS (PTY) LTD—See Sanlam Limited; *Int'l*, pg. 6545

GLACIER FINANCIAL SOLUTIONS (PTY) LTD—See Sanlam Limited; *Int'l*, pg. 6545
GLACIER HILLS SENIOR LIVING COMMUNITY; *U.S. Private*, pg. 1704
GLACIER INSURANCE OF LIBBY, INC.—See Hellman & Friedman LLC; *U.S. Private*, pg. 1908
GLACIER LAKE RESOURCES, INC.; *Int'l*, pg. 2987
GLACIER MANAGEMENT COMPANY LTD.—See Sanlam Limited; *Int'l*, pg. 6545
GLACIER MEDIA INC.; *Int'l*, pg. 2987
GLACIER PARK, INC.—See Viad Corp.; *U.S. Public*, pg. 2291
GLACIER PARK MARINE SERVICES INC.—See Gold Belt Incorporated; *U.S. Private*, pg. 1727
GLACIERPOINT ENTERPRISES, INC.—See Guggenheim Partners, LLC; *U.S. Private*, pg. 1812
GLACIER RESTAURANT GROUP LLC; *U.S. Private*, pg. 1704
GLACIER SALES INC.; *U.S. Private*, pg. 1704
GLACIER SERVICES, INC.—See Koniag Inc.; *U.S. Private*, pg. 2342
GLACIER VILLAGE SUPERMARKET; *U.S. Private*, pg. 1704
GLACIER WORLDWIDE, INC.; *U.S. Private*, pg. 1704
GLADEDALE HOLDINGS PLC; *Int'l*, pg. 2987
GLADES COUNTY DEMOCRAT—See Independent Newspapers, Inc.; *U.S. Private*, pg. 2060
GLADES ELECTRIC COOPERATIVE; *U.S. Private*, pg. 1704
GLADIATOR RESOURCES LIMITED; *Int'l*, pg. 2987
GLADIATOR TECHNOLOGY SERVICES, INC.—See Jack Henry & Associates, Inc.; *U.S. Public*, pg. 1182
GLADIEUX TRADING AND MARKETING CO. LP; *U.S. Private*, pg. 1704
GLADIFI; *U.S. Private*, pg. 1704
GLADLE ASSOCIATES, INC.—See Dairy Farmers of America, Inc.; *U.S. Private*, pg. 1145
GLAD MANUFACTURING CO.—See The Clorox Company; *U.S. Public*, pg. 2062
GLAD MANUFACTURING—See The Clorox Company; *U.S. Public*, pg. 2062
THE GLAD PRODUCTS COMPANY—See The Clorox Company; *U.S. Public*, pg. 2063
GLADRON CHEMICALS SDN. BHD.—See Ritamix Global Limited; *Int'l*, pg. 6351
GLADSON INTERACTIVE, LLC; *U.S. Private*, pg. 1705
GLADSTEIN, NEANDROSS & ASSOCIATES LLC—See TRC Companies, Inc.; *U.S. Private*, pg. 4215
GLADSTONE CAPITAL CORPORATION—See Gladstone Management Corporation; *U.S. Private*, pg. 1705
GLADSTONE COMMERCIAL CORPORATION—See Gladstone Management Corporation; *U.S. Private*, pg. 1705
GLADSTONE COMMERCIAL PARTNERS, LLC—See Gladstone Management Corporation; *U.S. Private*, pg. 1705
THE GLADSTONE COMPANIES, INC.; *U.S. Private*, pg. 4033
GLADSTONE INVESTMENT CORPORATION—See Gladstone Management Corporation; *U.S. Private*, pg. 1705
GLADSTONE LAND CORPORATION—See Gladstone Management Corporation; *U.S. Private*, pg. 1705
GLADSTONE MANAGEMENT CORPORATION; *U.S. Private*, pg. 1705
GLADSTONE MRM AUSTRALIA PTY LTD—See Gladstone PLC; *Int'l*, pg. 2987
GLADSTONE MRM LIMITED—See Gladstone PLC; *Int'l*, pg. 2987
GLADSTONE NEWSPAPER COMPANY PTY LTD—See ARN Media Limited; *Int'l*, pg. 576
GLADSTONE PACIFIC NICKEL LIMITED; *Int'l*, pg. 2987
GLADSTONE PLC; *Int'l*, pg. 2987
GLADSTONE PORTS CORPORATION LIMITED; *Int'l*, pg. 2987
GLADSTONE PRESSURE WELDERS PTY LTD—See Fluor Corporation; *U.S. Public*, pg. 859
THE GLADWIN COUNTY RECORD—See American Consolidated Media LP; *U.S. Private*, pg. 228
GLADWIN MACHINERY & SUPPLY CO; *U.S. Private*, pg. 1705
GLADWIN PAINT COMPANY AUSTIN, LTD.—See LKQ Corporation; *U.S. Public*, pg. 1336
GLAENZER-SEURRE NV/SA—See GKN plc; *Int'l*, pg. 2986
GLAJZ-THG PTE LTD—See The Hour Glass Limited; *Int'l*, pg. 7653
GL ALTESSE SAS—See Renaissance Industries SAS; *Int'l*, pg. 6272
GLAM MEDIA, INC.; *U.S. Private*, pg. 1706
GLAMORISE FOUNDATIONS, INC.; *U.S. Private*, pg. 1706
GLAMOUR—See Advance Publications, Inc.; *U.S. Private*, pg. 86
GLAMOUR TEXTILE MILLS LIMITED; *Int'l*, pg. 2987
GLAMOX AB—See Triton Advisers Limited; *Int'l*, pg. 7931
GLAMOX AQUA SIGNAL CORPORATION—See Triton Advisers Limited; *Int'l*, pg. 7931
GLAMOX AS—See Triton Advisers Limited; *Int'l*, pg. 7931
GLAMOX A/S—See Triton Advisers Limited; *Int'l*, pg. 7931

CORPORATE AFFILIATIONS

GLAMOX CANADA INC.—See Triton Advisers Limited; *Int'l*, pg. 7931
GLAMOX FAR EAST PTE LTD.—See Arendals Fossekompani ASA; *Int'l*, pg. 559
GLAMOX GMBH—See Triton Advisers Limited; *Int'l*, pg. 7931
GLAMOX IRELAND LTD.—See Triton Advisers Limited; *Int'l*, pg. 7931
GLAMOX LTD.—See Triton Advisers Limited; *Int'l*, pg. 7931
GLAMOX OY—See Triton Advisers Limited; *Int'l*, pg. 7931
GLAMOX (SUZHOU) LIGHTING CO. LTD—See Triton Advisers Limited; *Int'l*, pg. 7931
GLAN AGUA, LTD—See Mota-Engil SGPS, S.A.; *Int'l*, pg. 5052
GLANBIA AGRIBUSINESS—See Glanbia Co-Operative Society Limited; *Int'l*, pg. 2988
GLANBIA - BALLYRAGGET FACTORY—See Glanbia Co-Operative Society Limited; *Int'l*, pg. 2987
GLANBIA CHEESE—See Glanbia Co-Operative Society Limited; *Int'l*, pg. 2988
GLANBIA CONSUMER FOODS LIMITED—See Glanbia Co-Operative Society Limited; *Int'l*, pg. 2988
GLANBIA CONSUMER FOODS LTD. - IRELAND—See Glanbia Co-Operative Society Limited; *Int'l*, pg. 2988
GLANBIA CO-OPERATIVE SOCIETY LIMITED; *Int'l*, pg. 2987
GLANBIA FOOD INGREDIENTS—See Glanbia Co-Operative Society Limited; *Int'l*, pg. 2988
GLANBIA FOODS B.V.—See Glanbia Co-Operative Society Limited; *Int'l*, pg. 2988
GLANBIA FOODS INC.—See Glanbia Co-Operative Society Limited; *Int'l*, pg. 2988
GLANBIA INGREDIENTS, INC—See Glanbia Co-Operative Society Limited; *Int'l*, pg. 2988
GLANBIA INGREDIENTS IRELAND—See Glanbia Co-Operative Society Limited; *Int'l*, pg. 2988
GLANBIA INVESTMENTS (IRELAND) LIMITED—See Glanbia Co-Operative Society Limited; *Int'l*, pg. 2988
GLANBIA NUTRITIONALS DEUTSCHLAND GMBH—See Glanbia Co-Operative Society Limited; *Int'l*, pg. 2988
GLANBIA NUTRITIONALS (EUROPE) LIMITED—See Glanbia Co-Operative Society Limited; *Int'l*, pg. 2988
GLANBIA NUTRITIONALS (IRELAND) LIMITED—See Glanbia Co-Operative Society Limited; *Int'l*, pg. 2988
GLANBIA NUTRITIONALS (NA), INC.—See Glanbia Co-Operative Society Limited; *Int'l*, pg. 2988
GLANBIA NUTRITIONALS SINGAPORE PTE LIMITED—See Glanbia Co-Operative Society Limited; *Int'l*, pg. 2988
GLANBIA NUTRITIONALS (SUZHOU) COMPANY LIMITED—See Glanbia Co-Operative Society Limited; *Int'l*, pg. 2988
GLANBIA NUTRITIONALS (UK) LIMITED—See Glanbia Co-Operative Society Limited; *Int'l*, pg. 2988
GLANBIA PLC—See Glanbia Co-Operative Society Limited; *Int'l*, pg. 2987
GLANCE FINANCE LIMITED; *Int'l*, pg. 2988
GLANCE NETWORKS, INC.; *U.S. Private*, pg. 1706
GLAND PHARMA LIMITED—See Fosun International Limited; *Int'l*, pg. 2751
GLANTUS HOLDINGS PLC—See Accel Partners L.P.; *U.S. Private*, pg. 48
GLANTUS HOLDINGS PLC—See KKR & Co. Inc.; *U.S. Public*, pg. 1238
GLANTUS HOLDINGS PLC—See Long Path Partners, LP; *U.S. Private*, pg. 2491
GLANTUS LTD.; *Int'l*, pg. 2988
GLANUA UK LIMITED—See Biomass Heating Solutions Ltd.; *Int'l*, pg. 1039
GLANZSTOFF BOHEMIA S.R.O.—See Indorama Ventures Public Company Limited; *Int'l*, pg. 3658
GLANZSTOFF INDUSTRIES AG—See Indorama Ventures Public Company Limited; *Int'l*, pg. 3658
GLANZSTOFF INDUSTRIES (QINGDAO) CO., LTD.—See Indorama Ventures Public Company Limited; *Int'l*, pg. 3658
GLANZSTOFF LONGLAVILLE S.A.S.—See Indorama Ventures Public Company Limited; *Int'l*, pg. 3658
GLARNER KANTONALBANK; *Int'l*, pg. 2988
GLARUN TECHNOLOGY CO., LTD.; *Int'l*, pg. 2988
GLASBAU HAHN AMERICA LLC—See GLASBAU HAHN GmbH; *Int'l*, pg. 2988
GLASBAU HAHN GMBH; *Int'l*, pg. 2988
GLASBAU JAPAN CO. LTD.—See GLASBAU HAHN GmbH; *Int'l*, pg. 2988
GLAS-CRAFT, INC.—See Graco, Inc.; *U.S. Public*, pg. 953
GLASDRAAD BV—See TINC Comm. VA; *Int'l*, pg. 7753
GLASER ISB CAD PROGRAMMSYSTEME GMBH; *Int'l*, pg. 2988
GLASER-MILLER CO. INC.; *U.S. Private*, pg. 1706
GLASERNE MOLKEREI GMBH—See Mutares SE & Co. KGaA; *Int'l*, pg. 5105
GLASER'S COLLISION CENTER; *U.S. Private*, pg. 1706
GLASFABRIEK SAS VAN GENT B.V.—See Compagnie de Saint-Gobain SA; *Int'l*, pg. 1723
GLASFASER DIREKT GMBH—See MEDIQON Group AG; *Int'l*, pg. 4780
GLASFLOSS INDUSTRIES; *U.S. Private*, pg. 1706

GLASFORMS, INC.—See Avient Corporation; *U.S. Public*, pg. 247
GLASGOW AIRPORT LTD.—See Ferrovial S.A.; *Int'l*, pg. 2644
GLASGOW INC.; *U.S. Private*, pg. 1706
THE GLASGOW NUFFIELD HOSPITAL—See Nuffield Health; *Int'l*, pg. 5487
GLASGOW PRESTWICK AIRPORT LIMITED; *Int'l*, pg. 2989
GLASGOW SCIENCE CENTRE LIMITED—See Scottish Enterprise; *Int'l*, pg. 6652
GLASGOW SCIENCE CENTRE (TRADING) LIMITED—See Scottish Enterprise; *Int'l*, pg. 6652
GLASGOW STUDENT VILLAGES LIMITED—See Sanctuary Housing Association; *Int'l*, pg. 6523
GLASHUSET I SVERIGE AB—See Compagnie de Saint-Gobain SA; *Int'l*, pg. 1723
GLASHUTTER UHRENBETRIEB GMBH—See The Swatch Group Ltd; *Int'l*, pg. 7691
GLASMA AB—See New Wave Group AB; *Int'l*, pg. 5229
GLASMACHERVIERTEL GMBH & CO. KG—See ADLER Group SA; *Int'l*, pg. 150
GLASMEYER & CO. KG; *Int'l*, pg. 2989
GLAS PODRINJA A.D.; *Int'l*, pg. 2988
GLASRECYCLING NOORD-OOST NEDERLAND B.V.—See Renewi plc; *Int'l*, pg. 6278
GLASS AMERICA, INC.—See Boyd Group Services Inc.; *Int'l*, pg. 1125
THE GLASS BARON INC.; *U.S. Private*, pg. 4033
GLASSBOX LTD.; *Int'l*, pg. 2989
GLASSBOX US INC.—See Glassbox Ltd.; *Int'l*, pg. 2989
GLASSBRIDGE ASSET MANAGEMENT, LLC—See GlassBridge Enterprises, Inc.; *U.S. Public*, pg. 939
GLASSBRIDGE ENTERPRISES, INC.; *U.S. Public*, pg. 939
GLASSCOCK COMPANY INC.—See Summit Materials, Inc.; *U.S. Public*, pg. 1959
GLASS CONSTRUCTION; *U.S. Private*, pg. 1706
GLASSCRAFT DECORATIVE LIMITED—See CorpAcq Holdings Limited; *Int'l*, pg. 1802
GLASSDOOR, INC.—See Recruit Holdings Co., Ltd.; *Int'l*, pg. 6240
GLASS & DOOR INTERNATIONAL; *U.S. Private*, pg. 1706
GLASSEAL PRODUCTS—See AMETEK, Inc.; *U.S. Public*, pg. 116
GLASSEC VIDROS DE SEGURANCA LTD.—See Apogee Enterprises, Inc.; *U.S. Public*, pg. 145
GLASSEN CONSULTING & AUTOMATION, LLC—See T.J. Haggerty, Inc.; *U.S. Private*, pg. 3912
GLASS EQUIPMENT (INDIA) LTD—See Hindusthan National Glass & Industries Limited; *Int'l*, pg. 3400
GLASS FAB INC.; *U.S. Private*, pg. 1706
GLASSFORD MOTORS LIMITED; *Int'l*, pg. 2989
GLASS GARDENS INC.; *U.S. Private*, pg. 1706
GLASS HOUSE BRANDS INC.; *U.S. Public*, pg. 939
THE GLASSHOUSE L.L.C—See GIBCA Limited; *Int'l*, pg. 2963
GLASS HOUSES ACQUISITION CORP.; *U.S. Public*, pg. 939
GLASSHOUSE TECHNOLOGIES, INC.; *U.S. Private*, pg. 1706
GLASSHOUSE TECHNOLOGIES LTD.—See GLASSHOUSE TECHNOLOGIES, INC.; *U.S. Private*, pg. 1706
GLASSHOUSE TECHNOLOGIES (UK) LIMITED—See GLASSHOUSE TECHNOLOGIES, INC.; *U.S. Private*, pg. 1706
GLASS IDROMASSAGGIO SRL—See Masco Corporation; *U.S. Public*, pg. 1391
GLASSLAND DIALYSIS, LLC—See DaVita Inc.; *U.S. Public*, pg. 639
GLASS, LEWIS & CO., LLC—See Peloton Capital Management, Inc.; *Int'l*, pg. 5784
GLASS LEWIS EUROPE, LTD.—See Peloton Capital Management, Inc.; *Int'l*, pg. 5784
GLASS LLC—See Dubai Investments PJSC; *Int'l*, pg. 2219
GLASS MACHINING SERVICES LIMITED—See Recticel S.A.; *Int'l*, pg. 6241
GLASSMAN AUTOMOTIVE GROUP; *U.S. Private*, pg. 1706
GLASSMAN HIGH VOLTAGE, INC.—See XP Power Limited; *Int'l*, pg. 8537
GLASSMAN OLDSMOBILE INC.; *U.S. Private*, pg. 1707
GLASSMASTER CONTROLS COMPANY, INC.; *U.S. Private*, pg. 1707
GLASSMASTERS AUTOGLASS LTD—See The Wawanesa Mutual Insurance Company; *Int'l*, pg. 7699
GLASS MCCLURE; *U.S. Private*, pg. 1706
GLASSMERE FUEL SERVICE INC.; *U.S. Private*, pg. 1707
GLASS MOUNTAIN CAPITAL, LLC; *U.S. Private*, pg. 1706
GLASS MOUNTAIN HOLDING, LLC—See Energy Transfer LP; *U.S. Public*, pg. 764
GLASSOLUTIONS BV—See Aequita SE & Co. KGaA; *Int'l*, pg. 179
GLASS ONE TECHNOLOGY CORPORATION; *Int'l*, pg. 2989
GLASS ONE TECHNOLOGY TAIWAN CORPORATION—See Glass One Technology Corporation; *Int'l*, pg. 2989
GLASSON FERTILIZERS LIMITED—See Wynnstay Group Plc; *Int'l*, pg. 8517
GLASSON GRAIN LIMITED—See Wynnstay Group Plc; *Int'l*, pg. 8517
GLASSON GROUP (LANCASTER) LIMITED—See Wynnstay Group Plc; *Int'l*, pg. 8517
GLASSON SHIPPING SERVICES LIMITED—See Wynnstay Group Plc; *Int'l*, pg. 8517
GLASSONS LIMITED—See Hallenstein Glasson Holdings Limited; *Int'l*, pg. 3230
GLASS PRO INC.; *U.S. Private*, pg. 1706
GLASSPRO, INC.—See s.a. D'Ieteren n.v.; *Int'l*, pg. 6448
GLASSRATNER ADVISORY & CAPITAL GROUP, LLC—See B. Riley Financial, Inc.; *U.S. Public*, pg. 261
GLASS RECYCLERS INC.; *U.S. Private*, pg. 1706
GLASS REINFORCED CONCRETE UK LIMITED—See Laing O'Rourke Plc; *Int'l*, pg. 4396
GLASSROCK INSULATION COMPANY—See ASEC Company for Mining; *Int'l*, pg. 605
GLASS SRPSKI-TRGOVINA A.D.; *Int'l*, pg. 2988
GLASS & SASH INC.; *U.S. Private*, pg. 1706
GLASS & SILICE, S.A. DE C.V.—See Crown Holdings, Inc.; *U.S. Public*, pg. 598
GLASSTECH INC.; *U.S. Private*, pg. 1707
GLASSWELLS LTD; *Int'l*, pg. 2989
GLASSWERKS LA CO.; *U.S. Private*, pg. 1707
GLASTIC CORPORATION-BIRMINGHAM—See Rochling SE & Co. KG; *Int'l*, pg. 6377
GLASTIC CORPORATION—See Rochling SE & Co. KG; *Int'l*, pg. 6377
GLASTON AMERICA INC—See Glaston Oyj Abp; *Int'l*, pg. 2989
GLASTON EMERGING TECHNOLOGIES OY—See Glaston Oyj Abp; *Int'l*, pg. 2989
GLASTON ESTONIA OU—See Glaston Oyj Abp; *Int'l*, pg. 2989
GLASTON FINLAND OY—See Glaston Oyj Abp; *Int'l*, pg. 2989
GLASTON FRANCE S.A.S.U.—See Glaston Oyj Abp; *Int'l*, pg. 2989
GLASTON GERMANY GMBH—See Glaston Oyj Abp; *Int'l*, pg. 2989
GLASTON MANAGEMENT (SHANGHAI) CO. LTD—See Glaston Oyj Abp; *Int'l*, pg. 2989
GLASTON MEXICO, S.A. DE C.V.—See Glaston Oyj Abp; *Int'l*, pg. 2989
GLASTON MIDDLE EAST—See Glaston Oyj Abp; *Int'l*, pg. 2989
GLASTON NORTH AMERICA (USA), INC—See Glaston Oyj Abp; *Int'l*, pg. 2989
GLASTON OYJ ABP; *Int'l*, pg. 2989
GLASTON SERVICES LTD. OY—See Glaston Oyj Abp; *Int'l*, pg. 2989
GLASTON SHANGHAI CO., LTD.—See Glaston Oyj Abp; *Int'l*, pg. 2989
GLASTON SINGAPORE PTE. LTD.—See Glaston Oyj Abp; *Int'l*, pg. 2989
GLASTON SOUTH AMERICA LTDA.—See Glaston Oyj Abp; *Int'l*, pg. 2989
GLASTON SPAIN S.L.—See Glaston Oyj Abp; *Int'l*, pg. 2989
GLASTON SWITZERLAND AG—See Glaston Oyj Abp; *Int'l*, pg. 2989
GLASTON SWITZERLAND AG—See Glaston Oyj Abp; *Int'l*, pg. 2989
GLASTON TIANJIN CO. LTD.—See Glaston Oyj Abp; *Int'l*, pg. 2989
GLASTON UK LTD.—See Glaston Oyj Abp; *Int'l*, pg. 2989
GLASTRON, LLC—See Beneteau S.A.; *Int'l*, pg. 973
GLAS TROSCH AG HY-TECH-GLASS—See Glas Trosch Holding AG; *Int'l*, pg. 2988
GLAS TROSCH HOLDING AG; *Int'l*, pg. 2988
GLASVERARBEITUNGSGESELLSCHAFT DEGGENDORF MBH—See Arbonia AG; *Int'l*, pg. 538
GLASWEGIAN ENTERPRISES LTD; *Int'l*, pg. 2989
GLAS ZIEGLER GESMBH—See Compagnie de Saint-Gobain SA; *Int'l*, pg. 1723
GLATFELTER BROKERAGE SERVICE—See American International Group, Inc.; *U.S. Public*, pg. 106
GLATFELTER CAERPHILLY LTD.—See Glatfelter Corporation; *U.S. Public*, pg. 939
GLATFELTER CANADA, INC.—See Glatfelter Corporation; *U.S. Public*, pg. 939
GLATFELTER CLAIMS MANAGEMENT, INC.—See American International Group, Inc.; *U.S. Public*, pg. 106
GLATFELTER CORPORATION; *U.S. Public*, pg. 939
GLATFELTER COSTA RICA, S.R.L.—See Glatfelter Corporation; *U.S. Public*, pg. 939
GLATFELTER DRESDEN GMBH—See Glatfelter Corporation; *U.S. Public*, pg. 939
GLATFELTER FALKENHAGEN GMBH—See Glatfelter Corporation; *U.S. Public*, pg. 939
GLATFELTER FALKENHAGEN HOLDINGS GMBH—See Glatfelter Corporation; *U.S. Public*, pg. 939
GLATFELTER FRANCE SARL—See Glatfelter Corporation; *U.S. Public*, pg. 939
GLATFELTER GATINEAU, LTEE.—See Glatfelter Corporation; *U.S. Public*, pg. 939
GLATFELTER GERNSBACH GMBH—See Glatfelter Corporation; *U.S. Public*, pg. 939
GLATFELTER INSURANCE GROUP—See American International Group, Inc.; *U.S. Public*, pg. 106
GLATFELTER LYDNEY, LTD.—See Glatfelter Corporation; *U.S. Public*, pg. 939
GLATFELTER OBERSCHMITTEN GMBH—See Glatfelter Corporation; *U.S. Public*, pg. 939
THE GLATFELTER PULP WOOD COMPANY—See Glatfelter Corporation; *U.S. Public*, pg. 939
GLATFELTER SCAER SAS—See Glatfelter Corporation; *U.S. Public*, pg. 939
GLATFELTER STEINFURT GMBH—See Glatfelter Corporation; *U.S. Public*, pg. 939
GLATFELTER UNDERWRITING SERVICES, INC.—See American International Group, Inc.; *U.S. Public*, pg. 106
GLATT AIR TECHNIQUES, INC.; *U.S. Private*, pg. 1707
GLAUBER EQUIPMENT CORP.; *U.S. Private*, pg. 1707
GLAUKOS AUSTRALIA PTY LTD—See Glaukos Corporation; *U.S. Public*, pg. 940
GLAUKOS CANADA INC.—See Glaukos Corporation; *U.S. Public*, pg. 940
GLAUKOS CORPORATION; *U.S. Public*, pg. 939
GLAUKOS EUROPE GMBH—See Glaukos Corporation; *U.S. Public*, pg. 940
GLAUKOS GERMANY GMBH—See Glaukos Corporation; *U.S. Public*, pg. 940
GLAUKOS JAPAN GK—See Glaukos Corporation; *U.S. Public*, pg. 940
GLAUKOS PRODUTOS MEDICOS LTDA.—See Glaukos Corporation; *U.S. Public*, pg. 940
GLAUSER INTERNATIONAL MM; *Int'l*, pg. 2989
G&L AUTO SALES INC.; *U.S. Private*, pg. 1629
GLAVSKAZKA INTERNATIONAL LLC—See Unilever PLC; *Int'l*, pg. 8044
GLAXOCHEM PTE LTD—See GSK plc; *Int'l*, pg. 3148
GLAXO FINANCE BERMUDA LIMITED—See GSK plc; *Int'l*, pg. 3145
GLAXOSMITHKLINE AB—See GSK plc; *Int'l*, pg. 3146
GLAXOSMITHKLINE AG—See GSK plc; *Int'l*, pg. 3146
GLAXOSMITHKLINE ALGERIA SPA—See GSK plc; *Int'l*, pg. 3146
GLAXOSMITHKLINE ALGERIE S.P.A.—See GSK plc; *Int'l*, pg. 3146
GLAXOSMITHKLINE ARGENTINA SA—See GSK plc; *Int'l*, pg. 3146
GLAXOSMITHKLINE AS—See GSK plc; *Int'l*, pg. 3146
GLAXOSMITHKLINE AUSTRALIA PTY. LTD. - CONSUMER HEALTHCARE DIVISION—See GSK plc; *Int'l*, pg. 3146
GLAXOSMITHKLINE AUSTRALIA PTY LTD.—See GSK plc; *Int'l*, pg. 3146
GLAXOSMITHKLINE BANGLADESH LTD.—See Unilever PLC; *Int'l*, pg. 8044
GLAXOSMITHKLINE BIOLOGICALS BIOTECH S.A.—See GSK plc; *Int'l*, pg. 3146
GLAXOSMITHKLINE BIOLOGICALS KFT.—See GSK plc; *Int'l*, pg. 3146
GLAXOSMITHKLINE BIOLOGICALS MANUFACTURING S.A.—See GSK plc; *Int'l*, pg. 3146
GLAXOSMITHKLINE BIOLOGICALS S.A.—See GSK plc; *Int'l*, pg. 3146
GLAXOSMITHKLINE BIOLOGICALS S.A.S.—See GSK plc; *Int'l*, pg. 3146
GLAXOSMITHKLINE BIOLOGICALS (SHANGHAI) LTD—See GSK plc; *Int'l*, pg. 3146
GLAXOSMITHKLINE BRASIL LTDA.—See GSK plc; *Int'l*, pg. 3147
GLAXOSMITHKLINE B.V.—See GSK plc; *Int'l*, pg. 3146
GLAXOSMITHKLINE CAPITAL PLC—See GSK plc; *Int'l*, pg. 3147
GLAXOSMITHKLINE CHILE FARMACEUTICA LIMITADA—See GSK plc; *Int'l*, pg. 3147
GLAXOSMITHKLINE (CHINA) INVESTMENT CO. LTD—See GSK plc; *Int'l*, pg. 3146
GLAXOSMITHKLINE (CHINA) LIMITED—See GSK plc; *Int'l*, pg. 3146
GLAXOSMITHKLINE (CHINA) R&D CO., LTD.—See GSK plc; *Int'l*, pg. 3146
GLAXOSMITHKLINE COLOMBIA S.A.—See GSK plc; *Int'l*, pg. 3147
GLAXOSMITHKLINE CONSUMER HEALTHCARE AB—See GSK plc; *Int'l*, pg. 3147
GLAXOSMITHKLINE CONSUMER HEALTHCARE A/S—See GSK plc; *Int'l*, pg. 3147
GLAXOSMITHKLINE CONSUMER HEALTHCARE AUSTRALIA PTY LTD—See GSK plc; *Int'l*, pg. 3147
GLAXOSMITHKLINE CONSUMER HEALTHCARE B.V.—See GSK plc; *Int'l*, pg. 3147
GLAXOSMITHKLINE CONSUMER HEALTHCARE COLOMBIA SAS—See GSK plc; *Int'l*, pg. 3147
GLAXOSMITHKLINE CONSUMER HEALTHCARE CZECH REPUBLIC S.R.O.—See GSK plc; *Int'l*, pg. 3147
GLAXOSMITHKLINE CONSUMER HEALTHCARE FINLAND OY—See G&K plc; *Int'l*, pg. 3147
GLAXOSMITHKLINE CONSUMER HEALTHCARE GMBH & CO KG—See GSK plc; *Int'l*, pg. 3147

GLAXOSMITHKLINE CONSUMER HEALTHCARE (IRELAND) LIMITED—See GSK plc; *Int'l*, pg. 3147
GLAXOSMITHKLINE CONSUMER HEALTHCARE KOREA CO., LTD.—See GSK plc; *Int'l*, pg. 3147
GLAXOSMITHKLINE CONSUMER HEALTHCARE LTD.—See Unilever PLC; *Int'l*, pg. 8044
GLAXOSMITHKLINE CONSUMER HEALTHCARE PAKISTAN LIMITED—See GSK plc; *Int'l*, pg. 3147
GLAXOSMITHKLINE CONSUMER HEALTHCARE (PVT) LTD—See GSK plc; *Int'l*, pg. 3147
GLAXOSMITHKLINE CONSUMER HEALTHCARE S.A.—See GSK plc; *Int'l*, pg. 3147
GLAXOSMITHKLINE CONSUMER HEALTHCARE SDN. BHD.—See GSK plc; *Int'l*, pg. 3147
GLAXOSMITHKLINE CONSUMER HEALTHCARE SLOVAKIA S. R. O.—See GSK plc; *Int'l*, pg. 3147
GLAXOSMITHKLINE CONSUMER HEALTHCARE—See GSK plc; *Int'l*, pg. 3147
GLAXOSMITHKLINE CONSUMER HEALTHCARE S.P.A.—See GSK plc; *Int'l*, pg. 3147
GLAXOSMITHKLINE CONSUMER HEALTHCARE S.P.A.—See GSK plc; *Int'l*, pg. 3147
GLAXOSMITHKLINE CONSUMER HEALTHCARE SP.Z O.O.—See GSK plc; *Int'l*, pg. 3147
GLAXOSMITHKLINE CONSUMER HEALTHCARE (THAILAND) LIMITED—See GSK plc; *Int'l*, pg. 3147
GLAXOSMITHKLINE-CONSUMER HUNGARY LIMITED LIABILITY COMPANY—See GSK plc; *Int'l*, pg. 3149
GLAXOSMITHKLINE CONSUMER NIGERIA PLC—See GSK plc; *Int'l*, pg. 3147
GLAXOSMITHKLINE COSTA RICA S.A.—See GSK plc; *Int'l*, pg. 3147
GLAXOSMITHKLINE D.O.O.—See GSK plc; *Int'l*, pg. 3149
GLAXOSMITHKLINE D.O.O.—See GSK plc; *Int'l*, pg. 3149
GLAXOSMITHKLINE DUNGARVAN LTD.—See GSK plc; *Int'l*, pg. 3147
GLAXOSMITHKLINE ECUADOR S.A.—See GSK plc; *Int'l*, pg. 3147
GLAXOSMITHKLINE EESTI OU—See GSK plc; *Int'l*, pg. 3147
GLAXOSMITHKLINE EGYPT—See GSK plc; *Int'l*, pg. 3147
GLAXOSMITHKLINE EHF.—See GSK plc; *Int'l*, pg. 3147
GLAXOSMITHKLINE EL SALVADOR, S.A. DE C.V.—See GSK plc; *Int'l*, pg. 3147
GLAXOSMITHKLINE EOOD—See GSK plc; *Int'l*, pg. 3147
GLAXOSMITHKLINE - EVREUX PLANT—See GSK plc; *Int'l*, pg. 3149
GLAXOSMITHKLINE EXPORT LIMITED GHANA—See GSK plc; *Int'l*, pg. 3147
GLAXOSMITHKLINE EXPORT LTD.—See GSK plc; *Int'l*, pg. 3147
GLAXOSMITHKLINE FARMACEUTICA LTDA.—See GSK plc; *Int'l*, pg. 3147
GLAXOSMITHKLINE FINANCE PLC—See GSK plc; *Int'l*, pg. 3147
GLAXOSMITHKLINE GMBH & CO. KG—See GSK plc; *Int'l*, pg. 3147
GLAXOSMITHKLINE (GSK) S.R.L.—See GSK plc; *Int'l*, pg. 3146
GLAXOSMITHKLINE GUATEMALA S.A.—See GSK plc; *Int'l*, pg. 3147
GLAXOSMITHKLINE HEALTHCARE AO—See GSK plc; *Int'l*, pg. 3147
GLAXOSMITHKLINE HOLDINGS (AMERICAS) INC.—See GSK plc; *Int'l*, pg. 3147
GLAXOSMITHKLINE HOLDINGS LIMITED—See GSK plc; *Int'l*, pg. 3147
GLAXOSMITHKLINE HOLDINGS (ONE) LIMITED—See GSK plc; *Int'l*, pg. 3147
GLAXOSMITHKLINE HONDURAS S.A.—See GSK plc; *Int'l*, pg. 3147
GLAXOSMITHKLINE ILACLARI SANAYI VE TICARET A.S.—See GSK plc; *Int'l*, pg. 3148
GLAXOSMITHKLINE ILAC SANAYI VE TICARET AS—See GSK plc; *Int'l*, pg. 3148
GLAXO SMITH KLINE INC.—See Bora Pharmaceuticals Co., Ltd.; *Int'l*, pg. 1112
GLAXOSMITHKLINE INSURANCE LTD.—See GSK plc; *Int'l*, pg. 3148
GLAXOSMITHKLINE INTERNATIONAL (LUXEMBOURG) S.A.R.L—See GSK plc; *Int'l*, pg. 3148
GLAXOSMITHKLINE (IRELAND) LIMITED—See GSK plc; *Int'l*, pg. 3146
GLAXOSMITHKLINE ISRAEL—See GSK plc; *Int'l*, pg. 3148
GLAXOSMITHKLINE KFT.—See GSK plc; *Int'l*, pg. 3148
GLAXOSMITHKLINE K.K.—See GSK plc; *Int'l*, pg. 3148
GLAXOSMITHKLINE - KOREA—See GSK plc; *Int'l*, pg. 3146
GLAXOSMITHKLINE LIETUVA UAB—See GSK plc; *Int'l*, pg. 3148
GLAXOSMITHKLINE LIMITED—See GSK plc; *Int'l*, pg. 3148
GLAXOSMITHKLINE LIMITED—See GSK plc; *Int'l*, pg. 3149
GLAXOSMITHKLINE LTD.—See GSK plc; *Int'l*, pg. 3149
GLAXOSMITHKLINE (MALTA) LIMITED—See GSK plc; *Int'l*, pg. 3146

GLAXOSMITHKLINE (MANUFACTURING) LTD.—See Thermo Fisher Scientific Inc.; *U.S. Public*, pg. 2148
GLAXOSMITHKLINE MANUFACTURING S.P.A.—See GSK plc; *Int'l*, pg. 3148
GLAXOSMITHKLINE MAROC S.A.—See GSK plc; *Int'l*, pg. 3148
GLAXOSMITHKLINE MDR-BOSTON FACILITY—See GSK plc; *Int'l*, pg. 3148
GLAXOSMITHKLINE MEXICO S.A. DE C.V.—See GSK plc; *Int'l*, pg. 3148
GLAXOSMITHKLINE (NZ) LTD. CONSUMER HEALTH DIV.—See GSK plc; *Int'l*, pg. 3146
GLAXOSMITHKLINE (NZ) LTD.—See GSK plc; *Int'l*, pg. 3146
GLAXOSMITHKLINE ORAL CARE PLANT (IRELAND)—See GSK plc; *Int'l*, pg. 3148
GLAXOSMITHKLINE OTC INC.—See GSK plc; *Int'l*, pg. 3148
GLAXOSMITHKLINE OY—See GSK plc; *Int'l*, pg. 3148
GLAXOSMITHKLINE PAKISTAN LTD.—See GSK plc; *Int'l*, pg. 3148
GLAXOSMITHKLINE PERU S.A.—See GSK plc; *Int'l*, pg. 3148
GLAXOSMITHKLINE PHARMA A/S—See GSK plc; *Int'l*, pg. 3148
GLAXOSMITHKLINE PHARMACEUTICAL SDN. BHD.—See GSK plc; *Int'l*, pg. 3148
GLAXOSMITHKLINE PHARMACEUTICALS EUROPE B.V.—See GSK plc; *Int'l*, pg. 3148
GLAXOSMITHKLINE PHARMACEUTICALS LTD.—See GSK plc; *Int'l*, pg. 3148
GLAXOSMITHKLINE PHARMACEUTICALS LTD.—See GSK plc; *Int'l*, pg. 3148
GLAXOSMITHKLINE PHARMACEUTICALS S.A.—See GSK plc; *Int'l*, pg. 3148
GLAXOSMITHKLINE PHARMACEUTICALS S.A.—See GSK plc; *Int'l*, pg. 3148
GLAXOSMITHKLINE PHARMACEUTICALS (SUZHOU) LTD.—See Shanghai Fosun Pharmaceutical (Group) Co., Ltd.; *Int'l*, pg. 6767
GLAXOSMITHKLINE PHARMACEUTICALS UKRAINE LLC—See GSK plc; *Int'l*, pg. 3148
GLAXOSMITHKLINE PHARMA GMBH—See GSK plc; *Int'l*, pg. 3147
GLAXOSMITHKLINE PHARMA GMBH—See GSK plc; *Int'l*, pg. 3148
GLAXOSMITHKLINE PHILIPPINES, INC.—See GSK plc; *Int'l*, pg. 3148
GLAXOSMITHKLINE PRODUTOS FARMACEUTICOS LTDA.—See GSK plc; *Int'l*, pg. 3148
GLAXOSMITHKLINE (PROPRIETARY) LIMITED—See GSK plc; *Int'l*, pg. 3146
GLAXOSMITHKLINE PTE. LTD. - NEURAL PATHWAYS DISCOVERY PERFORMANCE UNIT—See GSK plc; *Int'l*, pg. 3148
GLAXOSMITHKLINE PTE. LTD.—See GSK plc; *Int'l*, pg. 3148
GLAXOSMITHKLINE PUERTO RICO—See GSK plc; *Int'l*, pg. 3148
GLAXOSMITHKLINE REPUBLICA DOMINICANA S.A.—See GSK plc; *Int'l*, pg. 3148
GLAXOSMITHKLINE RESEARCH & DEVELOPMENT LTD.—See GSK plc; *Int'l*, pg. 3148
GLAXOSMITHKLINE S.A.E.—See GSK plc; *Int'l*, pg. 3148
GLAXOSMITHKLINE SANTE GRAND PUBLIC—See GSK plc; *Int'l*, pg. 3149
GLAXOSMITHKLINE S.A.—See GSK plc; *Int'l*, pg. 3148
GLAXOSMITHKLINE S.A.—See GSK plc; *Int'l*, pg. 3148
GLAXOSMITHKLINE SAUDI ARABIA—See GSK plc; *Int'l*, pg. 3148
GLAXOSMITHKLINE SERVICES UNLIMITED—See GSK plc; *Int'l*, pg. 3149
GLAXOSMITHKLINE SINGLE MEMBER A.E.B.E.—See GSK plc; *Int'l*, pg. 3149
GLAXOSMITHKLINE SLOVAKIA S.R.Q.—See GSK plc; *Int'l*, pg. 3149
GLAXOSMITHKLINE—See Bora Pharmaceuticals Co., Ltd.; *Int'l*, pg. 1112
GLAXOSMITHKLINE—See GSK plc; *Int'l*, pg. 3145
GLAXOSMITHKLINE—See GSK plc; *Int'l*, pg. 3145
GLAXOSMITHKLINE—See GSK plc; *Int'l*, pg. 3145
GLAXOSMITHKLINE—See GSK plc; *Int'l*, pg. 3146
GLAXOSMITHKLINE—See GSK plc; *Int'l*, pg. 3146
GLAXOSMITHKLINE—See GSK plc; *Int'l*, pg. 3146
GLAXOSMITHKLINE—See GSK plc; *Int'l*, pg. 3146
GLAXOSMITHKLINE—See GSK plc; *Int'l*, pg. 3146
GLAXOSMITHKLINE—See GSK plc; *Int'l*, pg. 3146
GLAXOSMITHKLINE—See GSK plc; *Int'l*, pg. 3146
GLAXOSMITHKLINE—See GSK plc; *Int'l*, pg. 3146
GLAXOSMITHKLINE—See Bora Pharmaceuticals Co., Ltd.; *Int'l*, pg. 1112
GLAXOSMITHKLINE—See GSK plc; *Int'l*, pg. 3146
GLAXOSMITHKLINE—See GSK plc; *Int'l*, pg. 3146
GLAXOSMITHKLINE—See GSK plc; *Int'l*, pg. 3146
GLAXOSMITHKLINE—See GSK plc; *Int'l*, pg. 3146
GLAXOSMITHKLINE SOUTH AFRICA (PTY) LIMITED—See GSK plc; *Int'l*, pg. 3149

GLAXOSMITHKLINE S.P.A.—See GSK plc; *Int'l*, pg. 3148
GLAXOSMITHKLINE S.R.L.—See GSK plc; *Int'l*, pg. 3148
GLAXOSMITHKLINE SRO—See GSK plc; *Int'l*, pg. 3148
GLAXOSMITHKLINE (THAILAND) LIMITED—See GSK plc; *Int'l*, pg. 3146
GLAXOSMITHKLINE (TIANJIN) CO. LTD.—See GSK plc; *Int'l*, pg. 3146
GLAXOSMITHKLINE TRADING SERVICES LIMITED—See GSK plc; *Int'l*, pg. 3149
GLAXOSMITHKLINE TUNISIA S.A.R.L.—See GSK plc; *Int'l*, pg. 3149
GLAXOSMITHKLINE UK LIMITED—See GSK plc; *Int'l*, pg. 3149
GLAXOSMITHKLINE VENEZUELA C.A.—See GSK plc; *Int'l*, pg. 3149
GLAXO WELLCOME CEYLON LIMITED—See GSK plc; *Int'l*, pg. 3145
GLAXO WELLCOME INTERNATIONAL B.V.—See GSK plc; *Int'l*, pg. 3145
GLAXO WELLCOME INVESTMENTS B.V.—See GSK plc; *Int'l*, pg. 3145
GLAXO WELLCOME (KENYA) LIMITED—See GSK plc; *Int'l*, pg. 3145
GLAXO WELLCOME MANUFACTURING PTE LTD—See GSK plc; *Int'l*, pg. 3148
GLAXO WELLCOME S.A.—See GSK plc; *Int'l*, pg. 3145
GLAXO WELLCOME TAIWAN LIMITED—See GSK plc; *Int'l*, pg. 3145
GLAZER-KENNEDY INSIDER'S CIRCLE, LLC; *U.S. Private*, pg. 1708
GLAZER'S BEER AND BEVERAGE, LLC—See Glazer's Family of Companies; *U.S. Private*, pg. 1707
GLAZER'S DISTRIBUTORS OF ARKANSAS, INC.—See Glazer's Family of Companies; *U.S. Private*, pg. 1707
GLAZER'S DISTRIBUTORS OF INDIANA, LLC—See Glazer's Family of Companies; *U.S. Private*, pg. 1707
GLAZER'S DISTRIBUTORS OF IOWA, INC. - CEDAR RAPIDS—See Glazer's Family of Companies; *U.S. Private*, pg. 1707
GLAZER'S DISTRIBUTORS OF IOWA, INC.—See Glazer's Family of Companies; *U.S. Private*, pg. 1707
GLAZER'S DISTRIBUTORS OF MISSOURI, INC.—See Glazer's Family of Companies; *U.S. Private*, pg. 1707
GLAZER'S DISTRIBUTORS OF MISSOURI, INC. - SPRINGFIELD—See Glazer's Family of Companies; *U.S. Private*, pg. 1707
GLAZER'S DISTRIBUTORS OF TEXAS, INC. - DALLAS—See Glazer's Family of Companies; *U.S. Private*, pg. 1707
GLAZER'S DISTRIBUTORS OF TEXAS, INC. - PRESTIGE SALES DIVISION—See Glazer's Family of Companies; *U.S. Private*, pg. 1707
GLAZER'S DISTRIBUTORS OF TEXAS, INC. - SAN ANTONIO—See Glazer's Family of Companies; *U.S. Private*, pg. 1707
GLAZER'S DISTRIBUTORS OF TEXAS, INC.—See Glazer's Family of Companies; *U.S. Private*, pg. 1707
GLAZER'S FAMILY OF COMPANIES; *U.S. Private*, pg. 1707
GLAZIER FOODS COMPANY; *U.S. Private*, pg. 1708
G & L BEIJER A/S—See Beijer Ref AB; *Int'l*, pg. 944
G & L BEIJER FORVALTNING AB—See Beijer Ref AB; *Int'l*, pg. 944
GLB INSURANCE GROUP OF NEVADA—See Genstar Capital, LLC; *U.S. Private*, pg. 1674
G. & L. CLOTHING, INC.—See Boot Barn Holdings, Inc.; *U.S. Public*, pg. 368
GL DIRECT—See Great Lakes Integrated; *U.S. Private*, pg. 1764
GLEAM FABMAT LIMITED; *Int'l*, pg. 2990
THE GLEANER COMPANY (MEDIA) LIMITED—See Radio Jamaica Limited; *Int'l*, pg. 6176
THE GLEANER COMPANY (UK) LIMITED—See Radio Jamaica Limited; *Int'l*, pg. 6176
THE GLEANER COMPANY (USA) LIMITED—See Radio Jamaica Limited; *Int'l*, pg. 6176
GLEANER LIFE INSURANCE SOCIETY INC.; *U.S. Private*, pg. 1708
GLEASON CORPORATION - GLEASON K2 PLASTICS PLANT—See Gleason Corporation; *U.S. Private*, pg. 1708
GLEASON CORPORATION; *U.S. Private*, pg. 1708
GLEASON CORPORATION; *U.S. Private*, pg. 1708
GLEASON CUTTING TOOLS CORPORATION—See Gleason Corporation; *U.S. Private*, pg. 1708
GLEASON GEAR TECHNOLOGY (SUZHOU) CO., LTD.—See Gleason Corporation; *U.S. Private*, pg. 1708
GLEASON-HURTH MASCHINEN UND WERKZEUGE GMBH—See Gleason Corporation; *U.S. Private*, pg. 1708
GLEASON INDUSTRIAL PRODUCTS INC.—See Gleason Corporation; *U.S. Private*, pg. 1708
GLEASON INDUSTRIES, INC.; *U.S. Private*, pg. 1708
GLEASON METROLOGY SYSTEMS CORPORATION—See Gleason Corporation; *U.S. Private*, pg. 1708
GLEASON MILANO—See Gleason Corporation; *U.S. Private*, pg. 1708

COMPANY NAME INDEX

GLEASON - M&M PRECISION SYSTEMS CORPORATION—See Gleason Corporation; *U.S. Private*, pg. 1708
GLEASON-PFAUTER MACHINENFABRIK GMBH—See Gleason Corporation; *U.S. Private*, pg. 1708
GLEASON-PFAUTER MASCHINENFABRIK GMBH—See Gleason Corporation; *U.S. Private*, pg. 1708
GLEASON REEL CORPORATION—See Hubbell Incorporated; *U.S. Public*, pg. 1066
GLEASON WOODWORK, INC.; *U.S. Private*, pg. 1708
GLEASON WORKS (INDIA) PRIVATE LTD.—See Gleason Corporation; *U.S. Private*, pg. 1708
THE GLEASON WORKS—See Gleason Corporation; *U.S. Private*, pg. 1708
GLE ASSOCIATES, INC.; *U.S. Private*, pg. 1708
GLEBAR COMPANY, INC.—See Arcline Investment Management LP; *U.S. Private*, pg. 313
GLEESON DEVELOPMENTS LIMITED—See MJ Gleeson Plc; *Int'l*, pg. 5000
GLEESON HOMES LTD.—See MJ Gleeson Plc; *Int'l*, pg. 5000
GLEESON LAND LIMITED—See MJ Gleeson Plc; *Int'l*, pg. 5000
GLEESON REGENERATION LIMITED—See MJ Gleeson Plc; *Int'l*, pg. 5000
GLEIM THE JEWELER INC.; *U.S. Private*, pg. 1708
GLENAIR INC.; *U.S. Private*, pg. 1709
GLENAIR UK LTD.—See Glenair Inc.; *U.S. Private*, pg. 1709
GLENBARD ELECTRIC SUPPLY INC.—See Revere Electric Supply Company; *U.S. Private*, pg. 3414
GLENBRAE REST HOME & HOSPITAL LIMITED—See Arvida Group Limited; *Int'l*, pg. 587
GLENBROOK BUILDING SUPPLY, INC.—See Star Equity Holdings, Inc.; *U.S. Public*, pg. 1937
GLENBROOK COCA-COLA—See The Coca-Cola Company; *U.S. Public*, pg. 2065
GLENBROOK HOSPITAL—See NorthShore University HealthSystem; *U.S. Private*, pg. 2957
GLEN BUILDERS INC.; *U.S. Private*, pg. 1709
GLEN BURNIE BANCORP; *U.S. Public*, pg. 940
GLENCARE S.A.—See Industria de Diseno Textil, S.A.; *Int'l*, pg. 3665
GLENCAR UNDERWRITING MANAGERS, INC.—See Talanx AG; *Int'l*, pg. 7443
GLENCOE CAPITAL LLC; *U.S. Private*, pg. 1709
GLENCOE GROUP HOLDINGS LTD.—See RenaissanceRe Holdings Ltd.; *Int'l*, pg. 6273
GLENCOE/MCGRAW-HILL—See Platinum Equity, LLC; *U.S. Private*, pg. 3205
GLENCOE REGIONAL HEALTH SERVICES; *U.S. Private*, pg. 1709
GLENCORE RESOURCES LTD.; *Int'l*, pg. 2990
GLENCORE AUSTRALIA HOLDINGS PTY LTD—See Glencore plc; *Int'l*, pg. 2990
GLENCORE CANADA CORPORATION—See Glencore plc; *Int'l*, pg. 2990
GLENCORE CANADA FINANCIAL CORP.—See Glencore plc; *Int'l*, pg. 2990
GLENCORE COAL PTY. LTD.—See Glencore plc; *Int'l*, pg. 2990
GLENCORE COAL QUEENSLAND PTY. LIMITED—See Glencore plc; *Int'l*, pg. 2990
GLENCORE GRAIN B.V.—See Glencore plc; *Int'l*, pg. 2990
GLENCORE GRAIN PTY. LTD.—See Glencore plc; *Int'l*, pg. 2990
GLENCORE GROUP FUNDING LIMITED—See Glencore plc; *Int'l*, pg. 2990
GLENCORE INTERNATIONAL AG—See Glencore plc; *Int'l*, pg. 2990
GLENCORE NICKEL - SUDBURY—See Glencore plc; *Int'l*, pg. 2991
GLENCORE NIKKELVERK AS—See Glencore plc; *Int'l*, pg. 2991
GLENCORE PLC; *Int'l*, pg. 2990
GLENCORE QUEENSLAND LIMITED—See Glencore plc; *Int'l*, pg. 2991
GLENCORE RECYCLING INC.—See Glencore plc; *Int'l*, pg. 2990
GLENCORE RECYCLING LLC—See Glencore plc; *Int'l*, pg. 2990
GLENCORE (SCHWEIZ) AG—See Glencore plc; *Int'l*, pg. 2990
GLENCORE SERVICES UK LIMITED—See Glencore plc; *Int'l*, pg. 2990
GLENCORE TECHNOLOGY PTY. LTD.—See Glencore plc; *Int'l*, pg. 2991
GLEN COVE MANSION HOTEL & CONFERENCE CENTER—See Montclair Hotel Investors, Inc.; *U.S. Private*, pg. 2775
GLEN COVE PROPERTIES LTD. INC.; *U.S. Private*, pg. 1709
GLEN CRESTON LTD.—See Verder International B.V.; *Int'l*, pg. 8166
GLENCROFT; *U.S. Private*, pg. 1709
GLENDALE COUNTRYSIDE LIMITED—See Parkwood Holdings Limited; *Int'l*, pg. 5745
GLENDALE DODGE CHRYSLER JEEP; *U.S. Private*, pg. 1710
GLENDALE GOLF LIMITED—See Parkwood Holdings Limited; *Int'l*, pg. 5745
GLENDALE INFINITI—See Sage Holding Company; *U.S. Private*, pg. 3526
GLENDALE IRON & METAL CO.; *U.S. Private*, pg. 1710
GLENDALE MANAGED SERVICES LIMITED—See Parkwood Holdings Limited; *Int'l*, pg. 5745
GLENDALE MEMORIAL HOSPITAL & HEALTH CENTER—See Catholic Health Initiatives; *U.S. Private*, pg. 789
GLENDALE NISSAN/INFINITI, INC.—See Sage Holding Company; *U.S. Private*, pg. 3526
GLENDALE OPHTHALMOLOGY ASC, L.P.—See KKR & Co. Inc.; *U.S. Public*, pg. 1245
GLENDALE PLUMBING & FIRE SUPPLY, INC.; *U.S. Private*, pg. 1710
GLENDALE RECYCLING LIMITED—See Parkwood Holdings Limited; *Int'l*, pg. 5745
GLENDALE SALT DEVELOPMENT LLC—See K+S Aktiengesellschaft; *Int'l*, pg. 4040
GLENDENNING PTY LIMITED—See AMP Limited; *Int'l*, pg. 432
GLEN DIMPLEX AMERICAS COMPANY—See The Glen Dimplex Group; *Int'l*, pg. 7649
GLEN DIMPLEX AUSTRALIA PTY LTD—See The Glen Dimplex Group; *Int'l*, pg. 7649
GLEN DIMPLEX BENELUX B.V.—See The Glen Dimplex Group; *Int'l*, pg. 7649
GLEN DIMPLEX BENELUX B.V.—See The Glen Dimplex Group; *Int'l*, pg. 7649
GLEN DIMPLEX BOILERS—See The Glen Dimplex Group; *Int'l*, pg. 7649
GLEN DIMPLEX DEUTSCHLAND GMBH—See The Glen Dimplex Group; *Int'l*, pg. 7650
GLEN DIMPLEX ESPANA S.L.—See The Glen Dimplex Group; *Int'l*, pg. 7650
GLEN DIMPLEX EXPORTS LTD.—See The Glen Dimplex Group; *Int'l*, pg. 7650
GLEN DIMPLEX FRANCE—See The Glen Dimplex Group; *Int'l*, pg. 7650
THE GLEN DIMPLEX GROUP; *Int'l*, pg. 7649
GLEN DIMPLEX HOME APPLIANCES LTD.—See The Glen Dimplex Group; *Int'l*, pg. 7650
GLEN DIMPLEX HONG KONG LIMITED—See The Glen Dimplex Group; *Int'l*, pg. 7650
GLEN DIMPLEX IRELAND—See The Glen Dimplex Group; *Int'l*, pg. 7650
GLEN DIMPLEX ITALIA S.R.L.—See The Glen Dimplex Group; *Int'l*, pg. 7650
GLEN DIMPLEX NEW ZEALAND LTD.—See The Glen Dimplex Group; *Int'l*, pg. 7650
GLEN DIMPLEX NORDIC AS—See The Glen Dimplex Group; *Int'l*, pg. 7650
GLEN DIMPLEX NORTHERN IRELAND LIMITED—See The Glen Dimplex Group; *Int'l*, pg. 7650
GLEN DIMPLEX POLSKA SP. Z.O.O.—See The Glen Dimplex Group; *Int'l*, pg. 7650
GLEN DIMPLEX UK—See The Glen Dimplex Group; *Int'l*, pg. 7650
GLENDINNING MARINE PRODUCTS, INC.—See Orscheln Group; *U.S. Private*, pg. 3045
GLENDIVE COCA COLA BOTTLING CO INC.—See Coca-Cola Bottling Company High Country; *U.S. Private*, pg. 959
GLENDIVE MEDICAL CENTER; *U.S. Private*, pg. 1710
GLENDONTODD CAPITAL LLC; *U.S. Private*, pg. 1710
THE GLENDORA CA ENDOSCOPY ASC, L.P.—See KKR & Co. Inc.; *U.S. Public*, pg. 1247
GLENDORA HIGHLANDER—See Alden Global Capital LLC; *U.S. Private*, pg. 158
GLENDOWER CAPITAL LLP; *Int'l*, pg. 2991
GLEN EAGLE RESOURCES INC.; *Int'l*, pg. 2990
GLENEAGLES COUNTRY CLUB—See Apollo Global Management, Inc.; *U.S. Public*, pg. 149
GLENEAGLES GLOBAL HOSPITALS—See Khazanah Nasional Berhad; *Int'l*, pg. 4152
THE GLENEAGLES HOTEL—See Diageo plc; *Int'l*, pg. 2103
GLENEAGLES MEDICAL CENTRE LTD—See Khazanah Nasional Berhad; *Int'l*, pg. 4152
GLENEAGLES MEDICAL HOLDINGS LIMITED—See Khazanah Nasional Berhad; *Int'l*, pg. 4152
GLENEAGLES PHARMACY PTE LTD—See Khazanah Nasional Berhad; *Int'l*, pg. 4152
GLENEAGLES RADIOLOGY CONSULTANTS PTE LTD—See Khazanah Nasional Berhad; *Int'l*, pg. 4152
GLENEALY PLANTATIONS (MALAYA) BERHAD—See Samling Strategic Corporation Sdn. Bhd.; *Int'l*, pg. 6507
GLEN ECHO SURGERY CENTER, LLC—See Tenet Healthcare Corporation; *U.S. Public*, pg. 2002
GLEN ELECTRIC—See The Glen Dimplex Group; *Int'l*, pg. 7650
GLENELG FUNERALS PTY. LTD.—See Propel Funeral Partners Limited; *Int'l*, pg. 5997
GLEN ELLEN VILLAGE MARKET—See Nugget Market Inc.; *U.S. Private*, pg. 2972
GLEN ENDOSCOPY CENTER, LLC—See KKR & Co. Inc.; *U.S. Public*, pg. 1245
GLENFARNE GROUP, LLC; *U.S. Private*, pg. 1710
GLENFARNE MERGER CORP.; *U.S. Public*, pg. 940
GLENFERRIE PRIVATE HOSPITAL PTY LIMITED—See Ramsay Health Care Limited; *Int'l*, pg. 6199
GLENFIELD VALVES LIMITED—See AVK Holding A/S; *Int'l*, pg. 747
GLENGALA HOTEL (BMG) PTY LTD—See Woolworths Group Limited; *Int'l*, pg. 8451
GLEN-GERY CORPORATION—See Brickworks Limited; *Int'l*, pg. 1152
GLENGLASSAUGH DISTILLERY LTD.—See Brown-Forman Corporation; *U.S. Public*, pg. 403
GLENHILL ADVISORS, LLC; *U.S. Private*, pg. 1710
GLENHILL CAPITAL ADVISORS, LLC—See Glenhill Advisors, LLC; *U.S. Private*, pg. 1710
GLENHILL CAPITAL MANAGEMENT, LLC—See Glenhill Advisors, LLC; *U.S. Private*, pg. 1710
GLENIGAN LIMITED—See Informa plc; *Int'l*, pg. 3691
THE GLENLIVET DISTILLERS LTD—See Pernod Ricard S.A.; *Int'l*, pg. 5812
GLENMARIE PROPERTIES SDN. BHD.—See DRB-HICOM Berhad; *Int'l*, pg. 2201
GLENMARK ARZNEIMITTEL GMBH—See Glenmark Pharmaceuticals Limited; *Int'l*, pg. 2991
GLENMARK ASSOCIATES, INC.—See Welltower Inc.; *U.S. Public*, pg. 2348
GLENMARK FARMACEUTICA LTDA.—See Glenmark Pharmaceuticals Limited; *Int'l*, pg. 2991
GLENMARK GENERICS INC.—See Glenmark Pharmaceuticals Limited; *Int'l*, pg. 2991
GLENMARK GENERICS LIMITED—See Glenmark Pharmaceuticals Limited; *Int'l*, pg. 2991
GLENMARK GENERICS S.A.—See Glenmark Pharmaceuticals Limited; *Int'l*, pg. 2992
GLENMARK HOLDING S.A.—See Glenmark Pharmaceuticals Limited; *Int'l*, pg. 2992
GLENMARK LIFE SCIENCES LTD.—See NIRMA LIMITED; *Int'l*, pg. 5363
GLENMARK PHARMACEUTICALS B.V.—See Glenmark Pharmaceuticals Limited; *Int'l*, pg. 2992
GLENMARK PHARMACEUTICALS COLOMBIA LTDA.—See Glenmark Pharmaceuticals Limited; *Int'l*, pg. 2992
GLENMARK PHARMACEUTICALS ECUADOR S.A.—See Glenmark Pharmaceuticals Limited; *Int'l*, pg. 2992
GLENMARK PHARMACEUTICALS EUROPE LTD.—See Glenmark Pharmaceuticals Limited; *Int'l*, pg. 2992
GLENMARK PHARMACEUTICALS INC.—See Glenmark Pharmaceuticals Limited; *Int'l*, pg. 2992
GLENMARK PHARMACEUTICALS LIMITED; *Int'l*, pg. 2991
GLENMARK PHARMACEUTICALS MALAYSIA SDN. BHD.—See Glenmark Pharmaceuticals Limited; *Int'l*, pg. 2992
GLENMARK PHARMACEUTICALS NORDIC AB—See Glenmark Pharmaceuticals Limited; *Int'l*, pg. 2992
GLENMARK PHARMACEUTICALS S.A.—See Glenmark Pharmaceuticals Limited; *Int'l*, pg. 2992
GLENMARK PHARMACEUTICALS SK SRO—See Glenmark Pharmaceuticals Limited; *Int'l*, pg. 2992
GLENMARK PHARMACEUTICALS SOUTH AFRICA (PTY) LTD.—See Glenmark Pharmaceuticals Limited; *Int'l*, pg. 2992
GLENMARK PHARMACEUTICALS SP Z.O.O.—See Glenmark Pharmaceuticals Limited; *Int'l*, pg. 2992
GLENMARK PHARMACEUTICALS S.R.L.—See Glenmark Pharmaceuticals Limited; *Int'l*, pg. 2992
GLENMARK PHARMACEUTICALS S.R.O.—See Glenmark Pharmaceuticals Limited; *Int'l*, pg. 2992
GLENMARK PHILIPPINES INC.—See Glenmark Pharmaceuticals Limited; *Int'l*, pg. 2992
GLENMARK UKRAINE LLC—See Glenmark Pharmaceuticals Limited; *Int'l*, pg. 2992
GLENMEADOW, INC.; *U.S. Private*, pg. 1710
THE GLENMEDE TRUST COMPANY; *U.S. Private*, pg. 4033
GLENMOORE CAPITAL REIT; *Int'l*, pg. 2992
THE GLENMORANGIE COMPANY—See LVMH Moet Hennessy Louis Vuitton SE; *Int'l*, pg. 4600
GLENMORE DISTILLERIES CO; *U.S. Private*, pg. 1710
GLENMOUNT GLOBAL SOLUTIONS, INC.—See The Graham Group, Inc.; *U.S. Private*, pg. 4036
GLENN C BARBER & ASOC.; *U.S. Private*, pg. 1710
GLENN/DAVIS & ASSOCIATES, INC.—See GTCR LLC; *U.S. Public*, pg. 1803
GLENN DISTRIBUTOR INC.; *U.S. Private*, pg. 1710
GLENN E. THOMAS CHRYSLER DODGE JEEP; *U.S. Private*, pg. 1710
GLENN FUQUA, INC.; *U.S. Private*, pg. 1710
GLENN G GEIGER COMPANY INC—See LTC Global, Inc.; *U.S. Private*, pg. 2509
THE GLENN GROUP; *U.S. Private*, pg. 4033
GLENN HARRIS & ASSOCIATES, INC.—See Galiot Insurance Services, Inc.; *U.S. Private*, pg. 1638
GLENN H. JOHNSON CONSTRUCTION; *U.S. Private*, pg. 1710
GLENN JONES AUTO CENTER; *U.S. Private*, pg. 1710

1095

GLENN MACHINE WORKS, INC.

GLENN MACHINE WORKS, INC.; *U.S. Private*, pg. 1710
GLENN NISSAN INC.; *U.S. Private*, pg. 1710
GLENN O. HAWBAKER, INC.; *U.S. Private*, pg. 1710
GLENNON BITTAN INVESTMENTS; *U.S. Private*, pg. 1711
GLENNON SMALL COMPANIES LIMITED; *Int'l*, pg. 2992
GLENN POLK AUTOPLEX, INC.; *U.S. Private*, pg. 1710
GLENN RIEDER, INC.; *U.S. Private*, pg. 1711
GLENN ROBERTS TIRE & RECAPPING CO. INC.—See Appalachian Tire Products Inc.; *U.S. Private*, pg. 295
GLENN SALES COMPANY INC.; *U.S. Private*, pg. 1711
GLENN SPRINGS HOLDINGS, INC.—See Occidental Petroleum Corporation; *U.S. Public*, pg. 1561
GLENN THURMAN, INC.; *U.S. Private*, pg. 1711
GLENN & WRIGHT, INC.; *U.S. Private*, pg. 1710
GLEN OAK COUNTRY CLUB; *U.S. Private*, pg. 1709
GLEN OAK LUMBER & MILLING INC.; *U.S. Private*, pg. 1709
GLEN OAKS CLUB; *U.S. Private*, pg. 1709
GLENOAKS FARMS, INC.—See Lifeway Foods, Inc.; *U.S. Public*, pg. 1313
GLEN OAKS HOSPITAL—See Universal Health Services, Inc.; *U.S. Public*, pg. 2260
GLENOIT FABRICS HG CORP.—See Haixin Group Company Ltd.; *Int'l*, pg. 3218
GLENORA LUMBER & BUILDING SUPPLIES LTD.; *Int'l*, pg. 2992
GLENPOINTE ASSOCIATES II LLC; *U.S. Private*, pg. 1711
GLEN RAVEN CUSTOM FABRICS, LLC - ANDERSON PLANT—See Glen Raven, Inc.; *U.S. Private*, pg. 1709
GLEN RAVEN CUSTOM FABRICS, LLC - NORLINA PLANT—See Glen Raven, Inc.; *U.S. Private*, pg. 1709
GLEN RAVEN CUSTOM FABRICS, LLC - PLANT ONE—See Glen Raven, Inc.; *U.S. Private*, pg. 1709
GLEN RAVEN CUSTOM FABRICS, L.L.C.—See Glen Raven, Inc.; *U.S. Private*, pg. 1709
GLEN RAVEN FILAMENT FABRICS LLC—See Glen Raven, Inc.; *U.S. Private*, pg. 1709
GLEN RAVEN, INC.; *U.S. Private*, pg. 1709
GLEN RAVEN, INC.—See Glen Raven, Inc.; *U.S. Private*, pg. 1709
GLEN RAVEN, INC.—See Glen Raven, Inc.; *U.S. Private*, pg. 1709
GLEN RAVEN LOGISTICS, INC.—See Glen Raven, Inc.; *U.S. Private*, pg. 1709
GLEN RAVEN TECHNICAL FABRICS, LLC - PARK AVENUE FACILITY—See Glen Raven, Inc.; *U.S. Private*, pg. 1709
GLEN RAVEN TECHNICAL FABRICS, LLC—See Glen Raven, Inc.; *U.S. Private*, pg. 1709
THE GLEN RAVEN TECHNICAL FABRICS LLC—See Glen Raven, Inc.; *U.S. Private*, pg. 1709
GLEN RAVEN TRANSPORTATION INC.—See Glen Raven, Inc.; *U.S. Private*, pg. 1709
GLEN RESEARCH CORP.—See Maravai LifeSciences, Inc.; *U.S. Private*, pg. 2570
GLENRISE GROVE, L.L.C.—See Hovnanian Enterprises, Inc.; *U.S. Public*, pg. 1056
GLEN ROCK SAVINGS BANK; *U.S. Private*, pg. 1709
GLENRO INC.; *U.S. Private*, pg. 1711
GLENROTHES DISTILLERY CO LTD—See The Edrington Group; *Int'l*, pg. 7638
GLENROY CONSTRUCTION CO. INC.; *U.S. Private*, pg. 1711
GLENROYD HOUSE LIMITED—See Sheikh Holdings Group (Investments) Limited; *Int'l*, pg. 6794
GLENROY INC.; *U.S. Private*, pg. 1711
GLENRYE PROPERTIES SERVICES LIMITED—See Aramark; *U.S. Public*, pg. 177
GLENS CARE HOME BRECHIN—See Balhousie Holdings Limited; *Int'l*, pg. 808
GLENS FALLS INTERWEB INC.—See Valmet Oyj; *Int'l*, pg. 8118
GLENS FALLS NATIONAL BANK & TRUST COMPANY—See Arrow Financial Corporation; *U.S. Public*, pg. 200
GLENS FOOD CENTER INCORPORATED; *U.S. Private*, pg. 1711
THE GLEN SHOPPING CENTRE—See Hyprop Investments Limited; *Int'l*, pg. 3554
GLEN'S SANITARY LANDFILL, INC.—See Waste Management, Inc.; *U.S. Public*, pg. 2331
GLEN TAY TRANSPORTATION LP—See TFI International Inc.; *Int'l*, pg. 7585
GLENTEL INC.—See BCE Inc.; *Int'l*, pg. 927
GLENTRA CAPITAL P/S; *Int'l*, pg. 2992
GLENTURRET DISTILLERY—See The Edrington Group; *Int'l*, pg. 7638
GLENVEAGH PROPERTIES PLC; *Int'l*, pg. 2992
GLENVIEW STATE BANK—See Crane NXT, Co.; *U.S. Public*, pg. 591
GLENVILLE BANK HOLDING CO., INC.; *U.S. Public*, pg. 940
GLENVILLE ESTATE INVESTMENT PTE LTD—See Keppel Corporation Limited; *Int'l*, pg. 4130
GLENWAY DISTRIBUTION; *U.S. Private*, pg. 1711
GLENWAY MOTOR CAR CO., INC.; *U.S. Private*, pg. 1711

GLENWOOD FOODS, L.L.C.—See Braswell Milling Company; *U.S. Private*, pg. 640
GLENWOOD LLC; *U.S. Private*, pg. 1711
GLENWOOD PRIVATE EQUITY CO., LTD.; *Int'l*, pg. 2992
GLENWOOD PROPERTIES, INC.—See Fidelity Financial Corporation; *U.S. Private*, pg. 1503
GLENWOOD SPRINGS FORD, INC.; *U.S. Private*, pg. 1711
GLENWOOD SURGICAL CENTER, L.P.—See UnitedHealth Group Incorporated; *U.S. Public*, pg. 2241
GLESBY BUILDING MATERIALS CO.; *U.S. Private*, pg. 1711
GLESBY-MARKS LTD; *U.S. Private*, pg. 1711
GLESSDOX GMBH & CO. KG—See Wurth Verwaltungsgesellschaft mbH; *Int'l*, pg. 8504
GL EVENTS S.A.—See Societe Polygone S.A.; *Int'l*, pg. 7043
GL FOOD MARKET LTD.—See Goddard Enterprises Limited; *Int'l*, pg. 3019
GL GARRAD HASSAN DEUTSCHLAND GMBH—See DNV GL Group AS; *Int'l*, pg. 2149
GLG CORP LTD.; *Int'l*, pg. 2992
G.L.G. CORPORATION—See NHK Spring Co., Ltd.; *Int'l*, pg. 5257
GLG LIFE TECH CORPORATION; *Int'l*, pg. 2992
GL GMBH METALL- UND WERKSTATTTECHNIK; *Int'l*, pg. 2986
GLG NETZ GMBH—See E.ON SE; *Int'l*, pg. 2257
GLG PARTNERS, INC.—See MAN Group plc; *Int'l*, pg. 4664
GLG PARTNERS LP—See MAN Group plc; *Int'l*, pg. 4664
GL GROUP, INC.; *U.S. Private*, pg. 1704
GLH GMBH—See ThyssenKrupp AG; *Int'l*, pg. 7724
GLH HOTELS LIMITED—See Hong Leong Investment Holdings Pte. Ltd.; *Int'l*, pg. 3468
GLH HOTELS MANAGEMENT (UK) LIMITED—See Hong Leong Investment Holdings Pte. Ltd.; *Int'l*, pg. 3468
GL HOMES OF FLORIDA CORP.; *U.S. Private*, pg. 1704
GLICO ASIA PACIFIC PTE. LTD—See Ezaki Glico Co., Ltd.; *Int'l*, pg. 2593
GLICO CANADA CORPORATION—See Ezaki Glico Co., Ltd.; *Int'l*, pg. 2593
GLIDEFAST CONSULTING LLC—See ASGN Incorporated; *U.S. Public*, pg. 210
GLIDEROL INTERNATIONAL PTY LIMITED—See Reliance Doors Pty Ltd.; *Int'l*, pg. 6263
G LIFE GROUP, INC.—See LIXIL Group Corporation; *Int'l*, pg. 4533
THE GLIK COMPANY; *U.S. Private*, pg. 4033
GLIMCHER GROUP INCORPORATED; *U.S. Private*, pg. 1711
GLIMMER, INC.; *U.S. Private*, pg. 1711
THE GLIMPSE GROUP, INC.; *U.S. Public*, pg. 2075
GLINES & RHODES, INC.; *U.S. Private*, pg. 1711
GLINTT ANGOLA, LDA.—See Glintt - Global Intelligent Technologies, S.A.; *Int'l*, pg. 2992
GLINTT BRASIL, LTDA.—See Glintt - Global Intelligent Technologies, S.A.; *Int'l*, pg. 2992
GLINTT ESPANA, S.L.—See Glintt - Global Intelligent Technologies, S.A.; *Int'l*, pg. 2992
GLINTT - GLOBAL INTELLIGENT TECHNOLOGIES, S.A.; *Int'l*, pg. 2992
GLINTT POLSKA, SP. Z O.O.—See Glintt - Global Intelligent Technologies, S.A.; *Int'l*, pg. 2992
GLISSEN CHEMICAL CO. INC.; *U.S. Private*, pg. 1711
GLISTEN CONFECTIONERY—See Raisio PLC; *Int'l*, pg. 6190
GLISTEN LTD.—See Raisio PLC; *Int'l*, pg. 6190
GLISTEN SNACKS LIMITED—See Raisio PLC; *Int'l*, pg. 6190
GLITTEK GRANITES LTD.; *Int'l*, pg. 2992
GLK ENTERPRISES, INC.—See Francisco Partners Management, LP; *U.S. Private*, pg. 1588
GLK FOODS, LLC; *U.S. Private*, pg. 1711
GL LEASING BRITISH COLUMBIA INC.—See Grenke AG; *Int'l*, pg. 3080
GL LIMITED—See Hong Leong Investment Holdings Pte. Ltd.; *Int'l*, pg. 3468
GLL REAL ESTATE PARTNERS GMBH (GLL)—See Cinven Limited; *Int'l*, pg. 1616
GLL REAL ESTATE PARTNERS GMBH (GLL)—See Talanx AG; *Int'l*, pg. 7445
GL LUXEMBOURG GMBH—See DNV GL Group AS; *Int'l*, pg. 2149
GL MANAGEMENT, INC.—See Golden Leaf Holdings Ltd.; *Int'l*, pg. 3030
G.L. MEZZETTA INC.; *U.S. Private*, pg. 1631
GLM LANDSCAPE SUPPLY, LLC; *U.S. Private*, pg. 1711
G L MORRIS GENERAL BUILDING CONTRACTORS; *U.S. Private*, pg. 1628
GLM TRADING LTD.—See Health and Plant Protein Group Limited; *Int'l*, pg. 3303
G&L MUSIC SALES INC.—See BBE Sound Inc.; *U.S. Private*, pg. 498
GLN INC.; *U.S. Private*, pg. 1711
GLOBAC LIMITED—See Supply Network Limited; *Int'l*, pg. 7340
GLOBAIR HUNGARY KFT.—See Marriott International, Inc.; *U.S. Public*, pg. 1370

CORPORATE AFFILIATIONS

GLOBAL-5, INC.; *U.S. Private*, pg. 1719
GLOBAL ACCESS HEALTH NETWORK SARL—See Discovery Limited; *Int'l*, pg. 2134
GLOBAL ACCESS (PTY) LTD.; *Int'l*, pg. 2993
GLOBAL ACCESS UNLIMITED INC.; *U.S. Private*, pg. 1711
GLOBAL ACOUSTIC PARTNERS LLC—See Evolution Capital Management LLC; *U.S. Private*, pg. 1442
GLOBAL ACQUISITIONS CORPORATION; *U.S. Public*, pg. 940
GLOBAL ACTIVE LIMITED—See OSIM International Ltd.; *Int'l*, pg. 5650
GLOBAL ADRENALINE INC.—See The Walt Disney Company; *U.S. Public*, pg. 2140
GLOBAL ADVANCED METALS K. K.—See Global Advanced Metals Pty. Ltd.; *Int'l*, pg. 2993
GLOBAL ADVANCED METALS PTY. LTD.; *Int'l*, pg. 2993
GLOBAL ADVANCED METALS USA, INC. - GLOBAL ADVANCED METALS—See Global Advanced Metals Pty. Ltd.; *Int'l*, pg. 2993
GLOBAL ADVANCED METALS USA INC.—See Global Advanced Metals Pty. Ltd.; *Int'l*, pg. 2993
GLOBAL ADVANCE METALS TECHNOLOGY (S) PTE. LTD.—See Singapore Asahi Chemical & Solder Industries Pte. Ltd.; *Int'l*, pg. 6940
GLOBAL ADVERTISING STRATEGIES, INC.; *U.S. Private*, pg. 1711
GLOBAL AEROSPACE, INC.—See Global Aerospace Underwriting Managers Limited; *Int'l*, pg. 2993
GLOBAL AEROSPACE LOGISTICS LLC—See International Golden Group PJSC; *Int'l*, pg. 3749
GLOBAL AEROSPACE UNDERWRITING MANAGERS LIMITED; *Int'l*, pg. 2993
GLOBAL AG ASSOCIATES INC.; *U.S. Private*, pg. 1712
GLOBAL AG INSURANCE SERVICES, LLC—See Farmers Mutual Hail Insurance Company of Iowa; *U.S. Private*, pg. 1478
GLOBAL AI, INC.; *U.S. Public*, pg. 940
GLOBAL AIRCRAFT SERVICE, INC.; *U.S. Private*, pg. 1712
GLOBAL ALERTS LLC—See Quest Resource Holding Corporation; *U.S. Public*, pg. 1756
GLOBAL ALUMINIUM LTD.—See Vimetco N.V.; *Int'l*, pg. 8207
GLOBAL ANALYTICAL DEVELOPMENT LLC—See Abbott Laboratories; *U.S. Public*, pg. 19
GLOBAL ANIMAL MANAGEMENT, INC.—See Merck & Co., Inc.; *U.S. Public*, pg. 1416
GLOBAL ARCHITECTURAL METALS INC—See Allan Window Technologies Ltd.; *Int'l*, pg. 333
GLOBAL ARCHITECTURAL PANELS—See Weiss Sheet Metal Company; *U.S. Private*, pg. 4473
GLOBAL ARDOUR RECYCLING LIMITED—See Ardour World Limited; *Int'l*, pg. 557
GLOBAL ARDOUR RECYCLING LIMITED—See Global Metcorp Ltd; *Int'l*, pg. 2999
GLOBAL ARENA HOLDING, INC.; *U.S. Public*, pg. 940
GLOBAL ASCENT, INC.—See Team, Inc.; *U.S. Public*, pg. 1988
GLOBAL ASSET ADVISORS, LLC—See StoneX Group Inc.; *U.S. Public*, pg. 1952
GLOBAL ASSET MANAGEMENT LIMITED; *Int'l*, pg. 2993
GLOBAL ASSET PROTECTION SERVICES, LLC—See AXA S.A.; *Int'l*, pg. 760
GLOBAL ASSET SOLUTION COMPANY LIMITED—See Mitsubishi HC Capital Inc.; *Int'l*, pg. 4951
GLOBAL ASSISTANCE POLSKA SP.Z.O.O.—See Vienna Insurance Group AG Wiener Versicherung Gruppe; *Int'l*, pg. 8194
GLOBAL ASSISTANCE SERVICES S.R.O.—See Vienna Insurance Group AG Wiener Versicherung Gruppe; *Int'l*, pg. 8194
GLOBAL ASSISTANCE SLOVAKIA S.R.O.—See Vienna Insurance Group AG Wiener Versicherung Gruppe; *Int'l*, pg. 8194
GLOBAL ATLANTIC FINANCIAL GROUP LIMITED—See KKR & Co. Inc.; *U.S. Public*, pg. 1251
THE GLOBAL ATLANTIC FINANCIAL GROUP LLC—See KKR & Co. Inc.; *U.S. Public*, pg. 1264
GLOBAL ATOMIC CORPORATION; *Int'l*, pg. 2993
GLOBAL ATREO S.L.—See The AES Corporation; *U.S. Public*, pg. 2031
GLOBAL AUTOMOTIVE SYSTEMS LLC—See Patriarch Partners, LLC; *U.S. Private*, pg. 3109
GLOBAL AUTO PROCESSING SERVICES GEORGIA LLC—See Hyundai Glovis Co., Ltd.; *Int'l*, pg. 3557
GLOBAL AUTO PROCESSING SERVICES, LLC—See Hyundai Glovis Co., Ltd.; *Int'l*, pg. 3557
GLOBAL AUTO PROCESSING SERVICES—See Hyundai Glovis Co., Ltd.; *Int'l*, pg. 3557
GLOBAL AVIATION HOLDINGS, INC.—See MatlinPatterson Global Advisers LLC; *U.S. Private*, pg. 2611
GLOBAL AVIATION SERVICES, LLC—See The Carlyle Group Inc.; *U.S. Public*, pg. 2052
GLOBAL AXCESS CORP.; *U.S. Private*, pg. 1712
GLOBAL BAGGAGE PROTECTION SYSTEMS, INC.—See Safe Bag S.p.A.; *Int'l*, pg. 6469
GLOBAL BAKERIES—See Surge Private Equity LLC; *U.S. Private*, pg. 3884

COMPANY NAME INDEX

GLOBAL BANK CORPORATION; *Int'l*, pg. 2993
GLOBAL BANKERS INSURANCE GROUP, LLC—See Eli Global, LLC; *U.S. Private*, pg. 1359
GLOBAL BATTERY CO., LTD—See GS Yuasa Corporation; *Int'l*, pg. 3143
GLOBAL BATTERY METALS LTD.; *Int'l*, pg. 2993
GLOBAL BEAUTY IMAGE, INC.; *U.S. Private*, pg. 1712
GLOBAL BEER GEORGIA, LLC—See Bank of Georgia Group PLC; *Int'l*, pg. 843
GLOBAL BEHAVIORAL SOLUTIONS LLC; *U.S. Private*, pg. 1712
GLOBAL BIFS ACADEMY PVT. LTD.—See Global Education Limited; *Int'l*, pg. 2995
GLOBAL BIM INC.—See Kajima Corporation; *Int'l*, pg. 4054
GLOBAL BIO-CHEM TECHNOLOGY GROUP COMPANY LIMITED; *Int'l*, pg. 2993
GLOBAL BIOENERGIES SA; *Int'l*, pg. 2993
GLOBAL BLOCKCHAIN ACQUISITION CORP.; *U.S. Public*, pg. 940
GLOBALBLOCK DIGITAL ASSET TRADING LIMITED; *Int'l*, pg. 3003
GLOBAL BLOOD THERAPEUTICS, INC.—See Pfizer Inc.; *U.S. Public*, pg. 1679
GLOBAL BLUE GROUP HOLDING AG; *Int'l*, pg. 2993
GLOBAL BLUE S.A.—See Partners Group Holding AG; *Int'l*, pg. 5749
GLOBAL BLUE S.A.—See Silver Lake Group, LLC; *U.S. Private*, pg. 3657
GLOBAL BLUE (UK) LIMITED—See Partners Group Holding AG; *Int'l*, pg. 5749
GLOBAL BLUE (UK) LIMITED—See Silver Lake Group, LLC; *U.S. Private*, pg. 3657
GLOBAL BOOK PUBLISHING PTY LIMITED—See The Quarto Group, Inc.; *Int'l*, pg. 7677
GLOBAL BRANDS GROUP HOLDING LTD; *Int'l*, pg. 2993
GLOBAL BRANDS MANUFACTURE (DONGGUAN) LTD.—See Global Brands Manufacture Ltd.; *Int'l*, pg. 2993
GLOBAL BRANDS MANUFACTURE LTD - CHINA GUANGDONG HUANGJIAN PCBA PLANT—See Global Brands Manufacture Ltd.; *Int'l*, pg. 2993
GLOBAL BRANDS MANUFACTURE LTD.; *Int'l*, pg. 2993
GLOBAL BRASS AND COPPER HOLDINGS, INC.—See Wieland-Werke AG; *Int'l*, pg. 8402
GLOBAL BRASS & COPPER, INC.—See Wieland-Werke AG; *Int'l*, pg. 8402
GLOBALBRIDGE RESOURCES CORPORATION—See Globe Telecom, Inc.; *Int'l*, pg. 3006
GLOBAL BRIGADES, INC.; *U.S. Private*, pg. 1712
GLOBAL BROKERAGE, INC.; *U.S. Public*, pg. 940
GLOBAL BUILDING CO., LTD.—See Japan Airlines Co., Ltd.; *Int'l*, pg. 3881
GLOBAL BUSINESS CENTERS CORP.; *U.S. Private*, pg. 1712
GLOBAL BUSINESS COLLEGE OF AUSTRALIA PTY. LTD.—See Edvantage Group Holdings Limited; *Int'l*, pg. 2316
GLOBAL BUSINESS CONSULTING SERVICES, INC.; *U.S. Private*, pg. 1712
GLOBAL BUSINESS SOLUTIONS, INC.; *U.S. Private*, pg. 1712
GLOBAL BUSINESS SUPPORT SYSTEMS, INC.; *U.S. Private*, pg. 1712
GLOBAL BUSINESS TRAVEL ASSOCIATION; *U.S. Private*, pg. 1712
GLOBAL BUSINESS TRAVEL GROUP, INC.; *U.S. Public*, pg. 940
GLOBAL CAPITAL CORP.; *U.S. Private*, pg. 1712
GLOBAL CAPITAL LIMITED; *U.S. Private*, pg. 1712
GLOBAL CAPITAL MARKETS LIMITED; *Int'l*, pg. 2993
GLOBAL CAPITAL PARTNERS, INC.; *U.S. Public*, pg. 941
GLOBAL CARD SYSTEM, INC.—See GMO Internet Group, Inc.; *Int'l*, pg. 3014
GLOBAL CARE S.R.L.—See Gruppo MutuiOnline S.p.A; *Int'l*, pg. 3141
GLOBAL CARRIERS BHD; *Int'l*, pg. 2994
GLOBAL CASH CARD, INC.—See Automatic Data Processing, Inc.; *U.S. Public*, pg. 230
GLOBAL CASTINGS A/S—See VTC Partners GmbH; *Int'l*, pg. 8316
GLOBAL CASTINGS GULDSMEDSHYTTAN AB—See VTC Partners GmbH; *Int'l*, pg. 8316
GLOBAL CASTINGS MAGDEBURG GMBH—See VTC Partners GmbH; *Int'l*, pg. 8316
GLOBAL CASTINGS STADE GMBH—See VTC Partners GmbH; *Int'l*, pg. 8316
GLOBAL CASTINGS (TIANJIN) CO., LTD.—See VTC Partners GmbH; *Int'l*, pg. 8316
GLOBAL CASTINGS (XUZHOU) CO., LTD.—See VTC Partners GmbH; *Int'l*, pg. 8316
GLOBAL CATHODIC PROTECTION, INC.—See Hancom, Inc.; *Int'l*, pg. 3242
GLOBAL CELLULAR INC.; *U.S. Private*, pg. 1712
GLOBAL CENTER KFT.—See Ablon Group Limited; *Int'l*, pg. 63

GLOBAL CERAMIC MATERIALS LTD—See Darling Ingredients Inc.; *U.S. Public*, pg. 634
GLOBAL CHAMPIONS SPLIT CORP.; *Int'l*, pg. 2994
GLOBAL CHEM INTERNATIONAL INC.; *U.S. Private*, pg. 1712
GLOBAL CHINA CIRCULATION & DISTRIBUTION LIMITED—See SING TAO NEWS CORPORATION LIMITED; *Int'l*, pg. 6939
GLOBAL CITY HOLDINGS N.V.; *Int'l*, pg. 2994
GLOBAL CLEAN ENERGY HOLDINGS, INC.; *U.S. Public*, pg. 941
GLOBAL CLEAN ENERGY INC.; *U.S. Public*, pg. 941
GLOBAL CLEARING HOUSE SYSTEMS K.S.C.C.—See Agility; *Int'l*, pg. 210
GLOBAL CLIENT SOLUTIONS LLC—See Anywhere Real Estate Inc.; *U.S. Public*, pg. 141
GLOBAL CLOSURE SYSTEMS FRANCE 1 SAS—See Berry Global Group, Inc; *U.S. Public*, pg. 322
GLOBAL CLOTHING NETWORK INC.; *U.S. Private*, pg. 1712
GLOBAL COLLECT SERVICES USA, INC.—See Apollo Global Management, Inc.; *U.S. Public*, pg. 151
GLOBAL COLORS POLSKA SA—See Plastika Kritis S.A.; *Int'l*, pg. 5892
GLOBAL COMMERCE & INFORMATION, INC.; *U.S. Private*, pg. 1712
GLOBAL COMMUNICATION EXPERTS GMBH; *Int'l*, pg. 2994
GLOBAL COMMUNICATION NETWORKS INC.; *U.S. Private*, pg. 1712
GLOBAL COMMUNICATION PLANNING CO., LTD.; *Int'l*, pg. 2994
GLOBAL COMMUNICATION SEMICONDUCTORS, INC.—See GCS Holdings, Inc.; *Int'l*, pg. 2895
GLOBAL COMMUNICATIONS GROUP, INC.; *U.S. Private*, pg. 1712
GLOBAL COMMUNITY CO., LTD.—See Daiwa House Industry Co., Ltd.; *Int'l*, pg. 1946
GLOBAL COMPANIES LLC—See Global Partners LP; *U.S. Public*, pg. 942
GLOBAL COMPLIANCE APPLICATIONS CORP.; *Int'l*, pg. 2994
GLOBAL COMPONENTS INC.—See TCB-Arrow Ltd; *Int'l*, pg. 7482
GLOBAL COMPONENT TECHNOLOGIES CORPORATION—See Mitsubishi Heavy Industries, Ltd.; *Int'l*, pg. 4953
GLOBAL CONCEPTS ENTERPRISE; *U.S. Private*, pg. 1713
GLOBAL CONCERTS GMBH—See DEAG Deutsche Entertainment AG; *Int'l*, pg. 1998
GLOBAL CONCERTS TOURING GMBH—See DEAG Deutsche Entertainment AG; *Int'l*, pg. 1998
GLOBAL CONNECTION INC. OF AMERICA—See Milestone Partners Ltd.; *U.S. Private*, pg. 2728
GLOBAL CONNECTIONS PUBLIC COMPANY LIMITED; *Int'l*, pg. 2994
GLOBAL CONNECT, LLC—See TCN, Inc.; *U.S. Private*, pg. 3943
GLOBAL CONSORTIUM, INC.; *U.S. Public*, pg. 941
GLOBAL CONSTRUCTORS LLC.; *U.S. Private*, pg. 1713
GLOBAL CONSUMER ACQUISITION CORP.; *U.S. Private*, pg. 1713
GLOBAL CONTINUITY (SA) (PTY) LTD—See Metrofile Holdings Limited; *Int'l*, pg. 4862
GLOBAL CONVERGENCE, INC.; *U.S. Private*, pg. 1713
GLOBAL CONVERGENCE SOLUTIONS, INC.; *U.S. Private*, pg. 1713
GLOBAL COOLING, INC.—See Liberty Broadband Corporation; *U.S. Public*, pg. 1310
GLOBAL COPPER PRIVATE LIMITED—See Ram Ratna Wires Limited; *Int'l*, pg. 6196
GLOBAL CORD BLOOD CORPORATION; *Int'l*, pg. 2994
GLOBAL CORNERSTONE HOLDINGS LIMITED; *U.S. Private*, pg. 1713
GLOBAL COSMED GROUP S.A.—See Miele Cosmed Group S.A.; *Int'l*, pg. 4890
GLOBAL COSMETICS, INC.; *Int'l*, pg. 2994
GLOBAL CRANES PTY LTD—See Berkshire Hathaway Inc.; *U.S. Public*, pg. 306
GLOBAL CREDIT UNION; *U.S. Private*, pg. 1713
GLOBAL CROSSING AIRLINES GROUP INC.; *U.S. Public*, pg. 941
GLOBAL CROSSING AIRLINES, INC.—See Global Crossing Airlines Group Inc.; *U.S. Public*, pg. 941
GLOBAL CROSSING AIRLINES OPERATIONS LLC—See Global Crossing Airlines Group Inc.; *U.S. Public*, pg. 941
GLOBAL CURRENTS INVESTMENT MANAGEMENT, LLC—See Franklin Resources, Inc.; *U.S. Public*, pg. 881
GLOBAL DAILY FANTASY SPORTS, INC.; *Int'l*, pg. 2994
GLOBALDATA AUSTRALIA PTY LIMITED—See GlobalData Plc; *Int'l*, pg. 3003
GLOBAL DATA MANAGEMENT SYSTEMS, LLC; *U.S. Private*, pg. 1713
GLOBALDATA PLC; *Int'l*, pg. 3003
GLOBAL DATA POINT LTD.—See Sciencenow Limited; *Int'l*, pg. 6647

GLOBAL ENERGY METALS CORPORATION

GLOBAL DATA SERVICES OF INDIA LIMITED—See S&P Global Inc.; *U.S. Public*, pg. 1831
GLOBAL DATA SYSTEMS INC.; *U.S. Private*, pg. 1713
GLOBALDATA TRADING (SHANGHAI) CO., LIMITED—See GlobalData Plc; *Int'l*, pg. 3003
GLOBAL DATA VAULT, LLC; *U.S. Private*, pg. 1713
GLOBAL DEVELOPMENT KFT.—See Ablon Group Limited; *Int'l*, pg. 63
GLOBAL DEVELOPMENTS, INC.; *U.S. Public*, pg. 941
GLOBAL DIAGNOSTICS IRELAND LIMITED—See IK Investment Partners Limited; *Int'l*, pg. 3609
GLOBAL DIGITAL CREATIONS HOLDINGS LIMITED; *Int'l*, pg. 2994
GLOBAL DIGITAL SOLUTIONS, INC.; *U.S. Public*, pg. 942
GLOBAL DINING, INC. - MYOGADANI FACTORY—See Global Dining, Inc.; *Int'l*, pg. 2994
GLOBAL DINING, INC.; *Int'l*, pg. 2994
GLOBAL-DINING, INC.—See Global Dining, Inc.; *Int'l*, pg. 2994
GLOBAL DIRECTMAIL B.V.—See Global Industrial Company; *U.S. Public*, pg. 942
GLOBAL DISPLAY CO., LTD.; *Int'l*, pg. 2994
GLOBAL DISPOMEDIKA, PT; *Int'l*, pg. 2994
GLOBAL DIVERSIFIED INDUSTRIES, INC.; *U.S. Private*, pg. 1713
GLOBAL DIVERSIFIED INVESTMENT GRADE INCOME TRUST II; *Int'l*, pg. 2994
GLOBAL DIVIDEND GROWERS INCOME FUND; *Int'l*, pg. 2994
GLOBAL DIVING & SALVAGE, INC.; *U.S. Private*, pg. 1713
GLOBAL DOLPHIN DRILLING COMPANY LIMITED—See Transocean Ltd.; *Int'l*, pg. 7903
GLOBAL DOMAINS INTERNATIONAL, INC.; *U.S. Private*, pg. 1713
GLOBAL DOMINION ACCESS SA; *Int'l*, pg. 2995
GLOBAL DRAGON LIMITED; *Int'l*, pg. 2995
GLOBAL DRAW LIMITED—See Light & Wonder, Inc.; *U.S. Public*, pg. 1314
GLOBAL DRILLING SUPPLIERS INC.; *U.S. Private*, pg. 1713
GLOBAL E-BUSINESS SERVICES LIMITED—See Computer & Technologies Holdings Limited; *Int'l*, pg. 1758
GLOBAL ECO-CAN STOCK (THAILAND) CO., LTD.—See Toyo Seikan Group Holdings, Ltd.; *Int'l*, pg. 7856
GLOBAL ECO CHEMICALS MALAYSIA SDN. BHD.—See Lion Corporation; *Int'l*, pg. 4517
GLOBAL ECO CHEMICALS MALAYSIA SDN. BHD.—See Wilmar International Limited; *Int'l*, pg. 8420
GLOBAL ECO CHEMICALS SINGAPORE PTE. LTD.—See Lion Corporation; *Int'l*, pg. 4517
GLOBAL ECO CHEMICALS SINGAPORE PTE. LTD.—See Wilmar International Limited; *Int'l*, pg. 8420
GLOBAL ECOLOGY CORPORATION; *U.S. Public*, pg. 942
GLOBAL ECOMMERCE LIMITED—See Dagang NeXchange Berhad; *Int'l*, pg. 1912
GLOBAL ECONOMIC ADVANTAGE PVT LTD; *Int'l*, pg. 2995
GLOBAL ECONO TRADE (PVT) LIMITED—See Treet Corporation Limited; *Int'l*, pg. 7910
GLOBAL ECOPOWER SA; *Int'l*, pg. 2995
GLOBAL EDM SUPPLIES, INC.; *U.S. Private*, pg. 1713
GLOBAL EDUCATION ALLIANCE INC.—See Global Education Communities Corp; *Int'l*, pg. 2995
GLOBAL EDUCATION CITY HOLDINGS INC.—See Global Education Communities Corp; *Int'l*, pg. 2995
GLOBAL EDUCATION COMMUNITIES CORP; *Int'l*, pg. 2995
GLOBAL EDUCATION LIMITED; *Int'l*, pg. 2995
GLOBAL EDUCATION NETWORK—See Allen Holding Inc.; *U.S. Public*, pg. 179
GLOBAL EDUCATION & TECHNOLOGY GROUP LIMITED—See Puxin Limited; *Int'l*, pg. 6124
GLOBAL EDUHUB PTE. LTD.—See NetDragon Websoft Holdings Limited; *Int'l*, pg. 5213
GLOBAL ELECTRIC MOTORCARS LLC—See Polaris, Inc.; *U.S. Public*, pg. 1700
GLOBAL ELECTRONICS LLC—See Panasonic Holdings Corporation; *Int'l*, pg. 5717
GLOBALELECTROSERVICE, OJSC—See Summa Group; *Int'l*, pg. 7300
GLOBAL EMERGENCY RESOURCES, LLC—See Central Research, Inc.; *U.S. Private*, pg. 824
GLOBAL EMPLOYMENT HOLDINGS, INC.; *U.S. Private*, pg. 1713
GLOBAL EMPLOYMENT SERVICES, INC.—See Tyson Foods, Inc.; *U.S. Public*, pg. 2209
GLOBAL EMPLOYMENT SOLUTIONS, INC.—See ManpowerGroup Inc.; *U.S. Public*, pg. 1362
GLOBAL ENERGY (HOLDINGS) LTD.; *Int'l*, pg. 2995
GLOBAL ENERGY MARKETING II LLC—See Global Partners LP; *U.S. Public*, pg. 942
GLOBAL ENERGY MARKET SERVICES, LLC—See Trane Technologies Plc; *Int'l*, pg. 7891
GLOBAL ENERGY METALS CORPORATION; *Int'l*, pg. 2995

1097

GLOBAL ENERGY METALS CORPORATION

GLOBAL ENERGY SERVICES LIMITED—See Global Energy (Holdings) Ltd.; *Int'l*, pg. 2995
GLOBAL ENGINEERING SERVICE CO., LTD.—See Chugoku Marine Paints, Ltd.; *Int'l*, pg. 1595
GLOBAL ENGINEERING SOLUTIONS, INC.; *U.S. Private*, pg. 1713
GLOBALENGLISH CORPORATION—See THI Investments GmbH; *Int'l*, pg. 7709
GLOBAL-ENTECH CO., LTD.—See Chung-Hsin Electric & Machinery Manufacturing Corp.; *Int'l*, pg. 1597
GLOBAL ENTERTAINMENT HOLDINGS, INC.; *U.S. Public*, pg. 942
GLOBAL ENVIRONMENTAL ENERGY CORP.; *Int'l*, pg. 2995
GLOBAL ENVIRONMENTAL MANAGEMENT SERVICES, LLC; *Int'l*, pg. 2996
GLOBAL ENVIRONMENTAL SOLUTIONS LTD.—See Azrieli Group Ltd.; *Int'l*, pg. 781
GLOBAL-E ONLINE LTD.; *Int'l*, pg. 3003
GLOBAL EQUIPMENT COMPANY INC.—See Global Industrial Company; *U.S. Public*, pg. 942
GLOBAL EQUIPMENT SERVICES & MANUFACTURING VIETNAM COMPANY LIMITED—See Kimball Electronics, Inc.; *U.S. Public*, pg. 1228
GLOBAL EQUITY CAPITAL, LLC; *U.S. Private*, pg. 1713
GLOBAL EQUITY HIGH YIELD FUND B.V.—See Morgan Stanley; *U.S. Public*, pg. 1472
GLOBAL EQUITY PARTNERS BETEILIGUNGS-MANAGEMENT AG; *Int'l*, pg. 2996
GLOBALE RUECKVERSICHERUNGS-AG; *Int'l*, pg. 3004
GLOBALE RUECKVERSICHERUNGS-AG—See GLOBALE Rueckversicherungs-AG; *Int'l*, pg. 3004
GLOBALE RUECKVERSICHERUNGS-AG—See GLOBALE Rueckversicherungs-AG; *Int'l*, pg. 3004
GLOBAL ESCIENCE CORP; *U.S. Private*, pg. 1714
GLOBAL ESOLUTIONS (HK) LIMITED—See Novacon Technology Group Limited; *Int'l*, pg. 5454
GLOBAL-ESTATE RESORTS, INC.—See Alliance Global Group, Inc.; *Int'l*, pg. 339
GLOBAL E-TRADING SERVICES LIMITED—See Computer & Technologies Holdings Limited; *Int'l*, pg. 1758
GLOBAL EXCESS PARTNERS—See H.W. Kaufman Financial Group, Inc.; *U.S. Private*, pg. 1836
GLOBAL EXECUTIVE SOLUTIONS GROUP, LLC; *U.S. Private*, pg. 1714
GLOBAL EXPANDED METALS—See Omnimax Holdings, Inc.; *U.S. Private*, pg. 3017
GLOBALEXPENSE (CONSULTING) LIMITED—See SAP SE; *Int'l*, pg. 6567
GLOBAL EXPERIENCES, INC.—See American Institute for Foreign Study, Inc.; *U.S. Private*, pg. 238
GLOBAL EXPERIENCE SPECIALISTS (GES) EXHIBITION SERVICES LLC—See Viad Corp.; *U.S. Public*, pg. 2291
GLOBAL EXPERIENCE SPECIALISTS (GES) LIMITED—See Viad Corp.; *U.S. Public*, pg. 2291
GLOBAL EXPERIENCE SPECIALISTS, INC.—See Viad Corp.; *U.S. Public*, pg. 2291
GLOBAL EXPRESS (HK) LIMITED—See Allan International Holdings Limited; *Int'l*, pg. 332
GLOBAL FASHION GROUP S.A.—See Kinnevik AB; *Int'l*, pg. 4181
GLOBAL FERRONICKEL HOLDINGS, INC.; *Int'l*, pg. 2996
GLOBAL FERTIGATION SOLUTIONS, INC.—See Roto-Gro International Limited; *Int'l*, pg. 6405
GLOBAL FILE REGISTRY, INC.—See Brilliant Digital Entertainment, Inc.; *U.S. Private*, pg. 654
GLOBAL FINANCE SA; *Int'l*, pg. 2996
GLOBAL FINANCIAL & CREDIT, LLC—See Lovell Minnick Partners LLC; *U.S. Private*, pg. 2503
GLOBAL FINANCIAL INVESTMENTS HOLDING SAOG; *Int'l*, pg. 2996
GLOBAL FINANCIAL SERVICES LLC—See Lee Equity Partners LLC; *U.S. Private*, pg. 2412
GLOBAL FINISHING SOLUTIONS LLC—See Curran Group, Inc.; *U.S. Private*, pg. 1125
GLOBAL FLIGHT HANDLING SERVICES PRIVATE LIMITED—See Updater Services Limited; *Int'l*, pg. 8087
GLOBAL FLOW TECHNOLOGIES, INC.—See Forum Energy Technologies, Inc.; *U.S. Public*, pg. 874
GLOBALFLUENCY; *U.S. Private*, pg. 1719
GLOBALFLUENCY—See GlobalFluency; *U.S. Private*, pg. 1719
GLOBAL FOCUS GROUP; *U.S. Private*, pg. 1714
GLOBAL FOOD CREATORS CO., LTD.; *Int'l*, pg. 2996
GLOBAL FOREX TRADING—See StoneX Group Inc.; *U.S. Public*, pg. 1952
GLOBAL FORMAT GMBH & CO. KG—See BayernLB Holding AG; *Int'l*, pg. 914
GLOBAL FORTUNE INVESTMENT LIMITED; *Int'l*, pg. 2997
GLOBAL FORWARDING ENTERPRISES LIMITED LIABILITY COMPANY; *U.S. Private*, pg. 1714
GLOBALFOUNDRIES ENGINEERING PRIVATE LIMITED—See Mubadala Investment Company PJSC; *Int'l*, pg. 5075

GLOBALFOUNDRIES EUROPE LTD.—See Mubadala Investment Company PJSC; *Int'l*, pg. 5075
GLOBALFOUNDRIES EUROPE SALES & SUPPORT GMBH—See Mubadala Investment Company PJSC; *Int'l*, pg. 5075
GLOBALFOUNDRIES INC.—See Mubadala Investment Company PJSC; *Int'l*, pg. 5075
GLOBALFOUNDRIES JAPAN K.K.—See Mubadala Investment Company PJSC; *Int'l*, pg. 5075
GLOBALFOUNDRIES MANAGEMENT SERVICES LLC & CO. KG—See Mubadala Investment Company PJSC; *Int'l*, pg. 5075
GLOBALFOUNDRIES SINGAPORE PTE. LTD.—See Mubadala Investment Company PJSC; *Int'l*, pg. 5075
GLOBALFOUNDRIES TAIWAN LTD.—See Mubadala Investment Company PJSC; *Int'l*, pg. 5075
GLOBALFOUNDRIES TECHNOLOGIES LLC—See Mubadala Investment Company PJSC; *Int'l*, pg. 5075
GLOBALFOUNDRIES U.S. 2 LLC—See Mubadala Investment Company PJSC; *Int'l*, pg. 5075
GLOBALFOUNDRIES U.S. INC.—See Mubadala Investment Company PJSC; *Int'l*, pg. 5075
GLOBAL FRANCHISE GROUP, LLC—See Fog Cutter Capital Group Inc.; *U.S. Private*, pg. 1557
GLOBAL FREIGHT SOURCE—See Providence Equity Partners L.L.C.; *U.S. Private*, pg. 3292
GLOBAL FRESH SUPPLY CO., LTD.—See Zensho Holdings Co., Ltd.; *Int'l*, pg. 8634
THE GLOBAL FUND FOR WOMEN, INC.; *U.S. Private*, pg. 4033
GLOBAL FUND INVESTMENTS LLC; *U.S. Private*, pg. 1714
GLOBAL FUNDS MANAGEMENT S.A.—See Nomura Holdings, Inc.; *Int'l*, pg. 5409
GLOBAL FUTURES & FOREX, LTD.—See StoneX Group Inc.; *U.S. Public*, pg. 1952
GLOBAL GAMING RP, LLC—See Global Gaming Solutions, LLC; *U.S. Private*, pg. 1714
GLOBAL GAMING SOLUTIONS, LLC; *U.S. Private*, pg. 1714
GLOBAL GAS CORPORATION; *U.S. Public*, pg. 942
GLOBAL GATE PROPERTY CORP.; *U.S. Private*, pg. 1714
GLOBAL GEAR & MACHINING—See Innovative Manufacturing Solutions Corp.; *U.S. Private*, pg. 2082
GLOBAL GENERAL & REINSURANCE COMPANY LTD.—See GLOBALE Rueckversicherungs-AG; *Int'l*, pg. 3004
GLOBAL GENES; *U.S. Private*, pg. 1714
GLOBAL GEOPHYSICAL SERVICES, INC.; *U.S. Private*, pg. 1714
GLOBAL GEOPHYSICAL SERVICES, SP. Z.O.O.—See Global Geophysical Services, Inc.; *U.S. Private*, pg. 1714
GLOBAL GOLD CORPORATION; *U.S. Public*, pg. 942
GLOBAL GOLD, INC.—See Golden Touch Imports, Inc.; *U.S. Private*, pg. 1733
GLOBAL GRAIN AUSTRALIA PTY LIMITED—See Paterson GlobalFoods Inc.; *Int'l*, pg. 5756
GLOBAL GRAPHICS KK—See Hybrid Software Group PLC; *Int'l*, pg. 3544
GLOBAL GRAPHICS SOFTWARE INC.—See Hybrid Software Group PLC; *Int'l*, pg. 3544
GLOBAL GRAPHICS SOFTWARE (INDIA) PVT LTD—See Hybrid Software Group PLC; *Int'l*, pg. 3544
GLOBAL GRAPHICS SOFTWARE LTD—See Hybrid Software Group PLC; *Int'l*, pg. 3544
GLOBAL GREEN CHEMICALS PUBLIC COMPANY LIMITED; *Int'l*, pg. 2997
THE GLOBAL GREEN COMPANY LIMITED - HYDERABAD UNIT—See Avantha Group; *Int'l*, pg. 736
THE GLOBAL GREEN COMPANY LIMITED—See Avantha Group; *Int'l*, pg. 736
GLOBAL GREEN, INC.—See Nutritional Health Institute Laboratories, LLC; *U.S. Private*, pg. 2974
GLOBAL GREEN INTERNATIONAL NV—See Avantha Group; *Int'l*, pg. 736
GLOBAL GREEN INTERNATIONAL—See Avantha Group; *Int'l*, pg. 736
GLOBAL GREEN SOLUTIONS INC.; *Int'l*, pg. 2997
GLOBAL GREEN USA LTD.—See Avantha Group; *Int'l*, pg. 736
GLOBAL GROUND SUPPORT LLC—See Air T, Inc.; *U.S. Public*, pg. 67
GLOBAL GUARDIAN AIR AMBULANCE—See Global Guardian, LLC; *U.S. Private*, pg. 1714
GLOBAL GUARDIAN, LLC; *U.S. Private*, pg. 1714
GLOBAL HEALTHCARE & EDUCATION MANAGEMENT, INC.; *U.S. Public*, pg. 942
GLOBAL HEALTHCARE EXCHANGE, LLC—See Temasek Holdings (Private) Limited; *Int'l*, pg. 7547
GLOBAL HEALTH CLINICS LTD.; *Int'l*, pg. 2997
GLOBAL HEALTH LIMITED; *Int'l*, pg. 2997
GLOBAL HEALTH PARTNER SWE AB—See Apax Partners LLP; *Int'l*, pg. 502
GLOBAL HEALTH TECHNOLOGIES, INC.; *U.S. Private*, pg. 1714
GLOBAL HELIUM CORP.; *Int'l*, pg. 2997
GLOBAL HEMP GROUP INC.; *Int'l*, pg. 2997

CORPORATE AFFILIATIONS

GLOBAL HOLDINGS (BOTSWANA) (PTY) LIMITED—See CIC Holdings Limited; *Int'l*, pg. 1602
GLOBAL HOUSE (CAMBODIA) CO., LTD.—See Siam Global House Public Company Limited; *Int'l*, pg. 6875
GLOBAL HUNGER PROJECT; *U.S. Private*, pg. 1714
GLOBAL HUNTER CORPORATION; *Int'l*, pg. 2997
GLOBAL IDEAS DIRECT LLC—See Nippon Telegraph & Telephone Corporation; *Int'l*, pg. 5350
GLOBAL IMAGING HOLDINGS REALTY, LLC; *U.S. Private*, pg. 1714
GLOBAL IME BANK LIMITED; *Int'l*, pg. 2997
GLOBAL IME CAPITAL LTD.—See Global IME Bank Limited; *Int'l*, pg. 2997
GLOBAL IME LAGHUBITTA BITTIYA SANSTHA LTD.—See Global IME Bank Limited; *Int'l*, pg. 2997
GLOBAL IMPEX, INC.; *U.S. Private*, pg. 1714
GLOBAL INDEMNITY GROUP, INC.—See Paine Schwartz Partners, LLC; *U.S. Private*, pg. 3075
GLOBAL INDEMNITY GROUP, LLC—See Paine Schwartz Partners, LLC; *U.S. Private*, pg. 3075
GLOBAL INDEMNITY INSURANCE AGENCY, INC.; *U.S. Private*, pg. 1714
GLOBAL INDUSTRIAL CANADA INC.—See Global Industrial Company; *U.S. Public*, pg. 942
GLOBAL INDUSTRIAL COMPANY; *U.S. Public*, pg. 942
GLOBAL INDUSTRIAL COMPONENTS; *U.S. Private*, pg. 1714
GLOBAL INDUSTRIAL CORPORATION—See Dow Inc.; *U.S. Public*, pg. 685
GLOBAL INDUSTRIAL LTDA.—See Quarterhill Inc.; *Int'l*, pg. 6155
GLOBAL INDUSTRIAL SERVICES INC.—See Global Industrial Company; *U.S. Public*, pg. 942
GLOBAL INDUSTRIES INC.; *U.S. Private*, pg. 1714
GLOBAL INFORMATION, INC.; *Int'l*, pg. 2997
GLOBAL INFORMATION TECHNOLOGY CO., LTD.—See SYS Holdings Co., Ltd.; *Int'l*, pg. 7388
GLOBAL INFOTECH CO., LTD.; *Int'l*, pg. 2997
GLOBAL INFOTECH CORP.—See Intelliswift Software Inc.; *U.S. Private*, pg. 2106
GLOBAL INFRASTRUCTURE MANAGEMENT, LLC—See BlackRock, Inc.; *U.S. Public*, pg. 345
GLOBAL INFRASTRUCTURE SOLUTIONS, INC.; *U.S. Private*, pg. 1715
GLOBAL INFRATECH & FINANCE LIMITED; *Int'l*, pg. 2997
GLOBALINK INVESTMENT INC.; *U.S. Public*, pg. 946
GLOBAL INKJET SYSTEMS COMPANY—See Nano Dimension Ltd; *Int'l*, pg. 5143
GLOBALINK, LTD.; *Int'l*, pg. 3004
GLOBAL INNOVATIVE PLATFORMS INC.; *U.S. Public*, pg. 942
GLOBAL INSURANCE LIMITED; *Int'l*, pg. 2997
GLOBAL INTELLIGENCE ALLIANCE BENELUX B.V.—See M-Brain Oy; *Int'l*, pg. 4614
GLOBAL INTELLIGENCE ALLIANCE HONG KONG—See M-Brain Oy; *Int'l*, pg. 4614
GLOBAL INTELLISYSTEMS, LLC; *U.S. Private*, pg. 1715
GLOBAL INTERNATIONAL CREDIT GROUP LIMITED; *Int'l*, pg. 2997
GLOBAL INTERNATIONAL REINSURANCE COMPANY LTD.—See GLOBALE Rueckversicherungs-AG; *Int'l*, pg. 3004
GLOBAL INTERTRADE GROUP—See Hayel Saeed Anam Group of Companies; *Int'l*, pg. 3290
GLOBAL INVACOM GROUP LIMITED; *Int'l*, pg. 2998
GLOBAL INVACOM LIMITED—See Global Invacom Group Limited; *Int'l*, pg. 2998
GLOBAL INVACOM MANUFACTURING PTE LTD—See Global Invacom Group Limited; *Int'l*, pg. 2998
GLOBAL INVACOM MANUFACTURING (SHANGHAI) CO., LTD.—See Global Invacom Group Limited; *Int'l*, pg. 2998
GLOBAL INVACOM MANUFACTURING (UK) LIMITED—See Global Invacom Group Limited; *Int'l*, pg. 2998
GLOBAL INVACOM SDN. BHD.—See Global Invacom Group Limited; *Int'l*, pg. 2998
GLOBAL INVACOM WAVEGUIDE—See Global Invacom Group Limited; *Int'l*, pg. 2998
GLOBAL INVENTURES, INC.—See SmithBucklin Corporation; *U.S. Private*, pg. 3697
GLOBAL INVESTIGATIVE SERVICES, LLC—See Kinderhook Industries, LLC; *U.S. Private*, pg. 2307
GLOBAL INVESTMENT HOUSE K.S.C.C.—See Kuwait Projects Company (Holding) K.S.C.P.; *Int'l*, pg. 4347
GLOBAL INVESTMENT HOUSE SAUDI ARABIA—See Kuwait Projects Company (Holding) K.S.C.P.; *Int'l*, pg. 4347
GLOBAL INVESTMENT RECOVERY, INC.; *U.S. Private*, pg. 1715
GLOBAL INVESTMENTS CAPITAL CORP.; *Int'l*, pg. 2998
GLOBAL INVESTMENT SERVICES SA; *Int'l*, pg. 2998
GLOBAL INVESTMENTS LIMITED; *Int'l*, pg. 2998
GLOBAL INVESTMENT STRATEGY UK LIMITED—See Octagonal plc; *Int'l*, pg. 5521
GLOBAL IOT TECHNOLOGY VENTURES, INC.—See BROADBAND TOWER, INC.; *Int'l*, pg. 1172
GLOBALISE; *U.S. Private*, pg. 1719

COMPANY NAME INDEX

GLOBAL IT, INC.—See Brightcom Group Ltd.; *Int'l*, pg. 1162
GLOBALIVE COMMUNICATIONS INC.; *Int'l*, pg. 3004
GLOBALIVE TECHNOLOGY, INC.; *Int'l*, pg. 3004
GLOBALIZATION PARTNERS INTERNATIONAL; *U.S. Private*, pg. 1719
GLOBAL JUHAN CORPORATION; *Int'l*, pg. 2998
GLOBAL KEY INVESTMENT LIMITED; *Int'l*, pg. 2998
GLOBAL KIDS COMPANY CORP.; *Int'l*, pg. 2998
GLOBAL KNAFAIM LEASING LTD.—See Knafaim Holdings Limited; *Int'l*, pg. 4205
GLOBAL KNOWLEDGE TRAINING CENTER-VICTORIA—See MidOcean Partners, LLP; *U.S. Private*, pg. 2716
GLOBAL KNOWLEDGE TRAINING LLC—See MidOcean Partners, LLP; *U.S. Private*, pg. 2716
GLOBAL KOMITED SDN BHD—See Weststar Group; *Int'l*, pg. 8393
GLOBAL LABORATORY SERVICES, INC.—See Universal Corporation; *U.S. Public*, pg. 2254
GLOBAL LAND MASTERS CORPORATION LIMITED; *Int'l*, pg. 2998
GLOBAL LANGUAGE SOLUTIONS, LLC—See Welocalize, Inc.; *U.S. Private*, pg. 4479
GLOBAL LEADERS CORP.; *Int'l*, pg. 2998
GLOBAL LEISURE PARTNERS LLC—See Global Leisure Partners LLP; *Int'l*, pg. 2998
GLOBAL LEISURE PARTNERS LLP; *Int'l*, pg. 2998
GLOBAL LEISURE PRODUCTS SDN BHD—See Waterco Limited; *Int'l*, pg. 8356
GLOBAL LIFE REINSURANCE COMPANY OF AUSTRALIA PTY. LTD.—See GLOBALE Rueckversicherungs-AG; *Int'l*, pg. 3004
GLOBAL LIFE SCIENCES SOLUTIONS SINGAPORE PTE LTD—See Danaher Corporation; *U.S. Public*, pg. 627
GLOBAL LIFE SCIENCES SOLUTIONS USA LLC—See Danaher Corporation; *U.S. Public*, pg. 627
GLOBAL LIFE SCIENCES TECHNOLOGIES JAPAN KK—See Danaher Corporation; *U.S. Public*, pg. 627
GLOBAL LIGHTING TECHNOLOGIES INC.; *Int'l*, pg. 2998
GLOBAL LIGHTING TECHNOLOGIES, INC.—See Global Lighting Technologies Inc.; *Int'l*, pg. 2998
GLOBAL LIGHTS ACQUISITION CORP.; *Int'l*, pg. 2998
GLOBAL LI-ION GRAPHITE CORP.; *Int'l*, pg. 2998
GLOBAL LIMAN ISLETMELERI A.S—See Global Yatirim Holding A.S.; *Int'l*, pg. 3002
GLOBAL LINK COMMUNICATIONS HOLDINGS LIMITED—See Goldstream Investment Limited; *Int'l*, pg. 3034
GLOBAL LINK MANAGEMENT, INC.; *Int'l*, pg. 2998
GLOBAL-LINK MP EVENTS INTERNATIONAL INC.—See Pico Far East Holdings Limited; *Int'l*, pg. 5860
GLOBAL LINK PARTNERS INC.—See Global Link Management, Inc.; *Int'l*, pg. 2998
GLOBAL LINKS CORP.; *U.S. Public*, pg. 942
GLOBAL LITHIUM RESOURCES LIMITED; *Int'l*, pg. 2998
GLOBAL LNTELLIGENCE ALLIANCE ASIA-PACIFIC PTE. LTD.—See M-Brain Oy; *Int'l*, pg. 4614
GLOBAL LNTELLIGENCE ALLIANCE ESTRATEGIA E CONSULTORIA EM MARKETING LTDA—See M-Brain Oy; *Int'l*, pg. 4614
GLOBAL LNTELLIGENCE ALLIANCE GERMANY GMBH—See M-Brain Oy; *Int'l*, pg. 4614
GLOBAL LNTELLIGENCE ALLIANCE GREATER CHINA LTD—See M-Brain Oy; *Int'l*, pg. 4614
GLOBAL LNTELLIGENCE ALLIANCE GROUP OY—See M-Brain Oy; *Int'l*, pg. 4614
GLOBAL LNTELLIGENCE ALLIANCE NORTH AMERICA LNC.—See M-Brain Oy; *Int'l*, pg. 4614
GLOBAL LNTELLIGENCE ALLIANCE UK LTD.—See M-Brain Oy; *Int'l*, pg. 4614
GLOBAL LNTELLIGENCE ALLIANCE USA LNC.—See M-Brain Oy; *Int'l*, pg. 4614
GLOBAL LOAD CONTROL (PTY) LTD.—See Deutsche Lufthansa AG; *Int'l*, pg. 2066
GLOBAL LOCK SAFETY (INTERNATIONAL) GROUP CO., LTD.; *Int'l*, pg. 2999
GLOBALLOGIC INC.—See Hitachi, Ltd.; *Int'l*, pg. 3413
GLOBAL LOGISTIC PROPERTIES LIMITED; *Int'l*, pg. 2999
GLOBAL LOGISTICS INC.; *U.S. Private*, pg. 1716
GLOBAL LOGISTICS NEW JERSEY, LLC—See Hyundai Glovis Co., Ltd.; *Int'l*, pg. 3557
GLOBAL LOGISTICS PROPERTIES INC.—See Global Logistic Properties Limited; *Int'l*, pg. 2999
GLOBAL LOGISTICS SYSTEM EUROPE COMPANY FOR CARGO INFORMATION SERVICES GMBH—See Air France-KLM S.A.; *Int'l*, pg. 237
GLOBAL LOGISTICS SYSTEM EUROPE COMPANY FOR CARGO INFORMATION SERVICES GMBH—See Deutsche Lufthansa AG; *Int'l*, pg. 2066
GLOBAL LOGISTICS SYSTEM (HK) COMPANY LIMITED—See Cathay Pacific Airways Limited; *Int'l*, pg. 1360
GLOBAL LONGLIFE HOSPITAL & RESEARCH LIMITED; *Int'l*, pg. 2999
THE GLOBAL LTD.—See SBI Holdings, Inc.; *Int'l*, pg. 6606
GLOBAL MACRO TRUST; *U.S. Private*, pg. 1716

GLOBAL MAIL (AUSTRIA) GES. M.B.H.—See Deutsche Post AG; *Int'l*, pg. 2079
GLOBAL MAIL, INC.—See Deutsche Post AG; *Int'l*, pg. 2080
GLOBAL MANAGEMENT LTD.—See Rickmers Holding AG; *Int'l*, pg. 6332
GLOBAL MANAGEMENT SYSTEMS INC.—See Dinocrates Group LLC; *U.S. Private*, pg. 1233
GLOBAL MANAGEMENT TECHNOLOGIES CORPORATION—See Verint Systems Inc.; *U.S. Public*, pg. 2281
GLOBAL MANUFACTURING & ASSEMBLY; *U.S. Private*, pg. 1716
GLOBAL MARINE BROKERAGE, LLC—See MarineMax, Inc.; *U.S. Public*, pg. 1366
GLOBAL MARINE CABLE SYSTEMS PTE, LTD—See INNOVATE Corp.; *U.S. Public*, pg. 1126
GLOBAL MARINE HOLDINGS LIMITED—See J.F. Lehman & Company, Inc.; *U.S. Private*, pg. 2163
GLOBAL MARINE SEARCH, LTD—See INNOVATE Corp.; *U.S. Public*, pg. 1126
GLOBAL MARINE SYSTEMS (AMERICAS) INC.—See J.F. Lehman & Company, Inc.; *U.S. Private*, pg. 2163
GLOBAL MARINE SYSTEMS LIMITED—See J.F. Lehman & Company, Inc.; *U.S. Private*, pg. 2163
GLOBAL MARINE SYSTEMS OIL AND GAS, LTD—See INNOVATE Corp.; *U.S. Public*, pg. 1126
GLOBAL MARINE SYSTEMS PENSION TRUSTEE, LTD—See INNOVATE Corp.; *U.S. Public*, pg. 1126
GLOBAL MARINE TRAVEL LLC—See Ackermans & van Haaren NV; *Int'l*, pg. 106
GLOBAL MARINE TRAVEL LLC—See STAR Capital Partners Limited; *Int'l*, pg. 7173
GLOBAL MARINE & PORT SERVICES PTE LTD—See Yongnam Holdings Limited; *Int'l*, pg. 8597
GLOBAL MARITIME SERVICES LTD.—See Albert Ballin KG; *Int'l*, pg. 294
GLOBAL MARKET GROUP LIMITED; *Int'l*, pg. 2999
GLOBAL MARKET INSITE, INC.—See Bain Capital, LP; *U.S. Private*, pg. 448
GLOBAL MASTERMIND HOLDINGS LTD.; *Int'l*, pg. 2999
GLOBAL MASTERS FUND LIMITED; *Int'l*, pg. 2999
GLOBAL MATERIAL TECHNOLOGIES, INC.—See ASW Holding Corporation; *U.S. Private*, pg. 363
GLOBAL MECHANICAL, INC.; *U.S. Private*, pg. 1716
GLOBALMED GROUP, LLC.; *U.S. Private*, pg. 1719
GLOBALMEDIA GROUP LLC; *U.S. Private*, pg. 1719
GLOBAL MEDIA OUTREACH; *U.S. Private*, pg. 1716
GLOBAL MEDICAL REIT INC.; *U.S. Public*, pg. 942
GLOBAL MEDICAL RESPONSE, INC.—See KKR & Co. Inc.; *U.S. Public*, pg. 1251
GLOBAL MEDICAL SOLUTIONS, LTD.; *U.S. Private*, pg. 1716
GLOBAL MEDICAL STAFFING LIMITED, INC.—See Ares Management Corporation; *U.S. Public*, pg. 188
GLOBAL MEDICAL STAFFING LIMITED, INC.—See Leonard Green & Partners, L.P.; *U.S. Private*, pg. 2425
GLOBAL MEDICS LTD.—See Servoca Plc; *Int'l*, pg. 6726
GLOBAL MEDICS NZ LIMITED—See HFBG Holding B.V.; *Int'l*, pg. 3374
GLOBAL MEDICS PTY LIMITED—See HFBG Holding B.V.; *Int'l*, pg. 3374
GLOBAL MEMORY PROCUREMENT CORP.; *U.S. Private*, pg. 1716
GLOBAL MENKUL DEGERLER A.S—See Global Yatirim Holding A.S.; *Int'l*, pg. 3002
GLOBAL MERCHANT FUND CORP.; *U.S. Private*, pg. 1716
GLOBAL METALS PTY LTD—See Stemcor Holdings Limited; *Int'l*, pg. 7206
GLOBAL METCORP LTD; *Int'l*, pg. 2999
GLOBALM-GROUP PLC; *Int'l*, pg. 3004
GLOBAL MIAMI ACQUISITION COMPANY, LLC—See Digital Realty Trust, Inc.; *U.S. Public*, pg. 663
GLOBAL MIXED-MODE TECHNOLOGY INC.; *Int'l*, pg. 2999
GLOBAL MOFY METAVERSE LIMITED; *Int'l*, pg. 2999
GLOBAL MONTELLO GROUP CORPORATION—See Global Partners LP; *U.S. Public*, pg. 942
GLOBAL MOTION MEDIA, INC.—See TripAdvisor, Inc.; *U.S. Public*, pg. 2195
GLOBALMOTION MEDIA, INC.—See TripAdvisor, Inc.; *U.S. Public*, pg. 2195
GLOBAL MOTOR SPORT GROUP, INC.; *U.S. Private*, pg. 1716
GLOBAL-MSI PLC—See MS International plc; *Int'l*, pg. 5065
GLOBAL-MSI SP. Z O.O.—See MS International plc; *Int'l*, pg. 5065
GLOBAL MUTUAL PROPERTIES LIMITED; *Int'l*, pg. 2999
GLOBAL NET DISTRIB. (PTY) LTD.—See Teixeira Duarte SA; *Int'l*, pg. 7525
GLOBAL NET LEASE, INC.—See AR Global Investments, LLC; *U.S. Private*, pg. 306
GLOBAL NET SOLUTIONS LTD—See Intracom Holdings S.A.; *Int'l*, pg. 3768
GLOBAL NETWATCH, INC.—See The Strawhecker Group, LLC; *U.S. Private*, pg. 4123

GLOBAL NETWORKERS, INC.—See BCforward; *U.S. Private*, pg. 499
GLOBAL NETWORK OF GUARANTEE INSTITUTIONS B.V.—See Jordan Loan Guarantee Corporation; *Int'l*, pg. 3998
GLOBAL NETWORK SYSTEMS, INC.; *U.S. Private*, pg. 1716
GLOBAL NEURO-DIAGNOSTICS, LP—See ArchiMed SAS; *Int'l*, pg. 548
GLOBAL NEW MATERIAL INTERNATIONAL HOLDINGS LIMITED; *Int'l*, pg. 2999
GLOBAL NUCLEAR FUEL - JAPAN CO., LTD.—See General Electric Company; *U.S. Public*, pg. 920
GLOBAL OFFICE SOLUTIONS; *U.S. Private*, pg. 1716
GLOBAL OFFSHORE (MALAYSIA) SDN. BHD.—See Puncak Niaga Holdings Berhad; *Int'l*, pg. 6118
GLOBAL OFFSHORE SERVICES B.V.—See Global Offshore Services Ltd.; *Int'l*, pg. 2999
GLOBAL OFFSHORE SERVICES LTD.; *Int'l*, pg. 2999
GLOBALOGIX, INC.; *U.S. Private*, pg. 1719
GLOBAL OLED TECHNOLOGY LLC—See Idemitsu Kosan Co., Ltd.; *Int'l*, pg. 3590
GLOBAL OLED TECHNOLOGY LLC—See LG Corp.; *Int'l*, pg. 4475
GLOBAL ONE-PAK LIMITED—See Coral Products PLC; *Int'l*, pg. 1795
GLOBAL ONE REAL ESTATE INVESTMENT CORPORATION; *Int'l*, pg. 2999
GLOBAL OPERATIONS AND DEVELOPMENT; *U.S. Private*, pg. 1716
GLOBAL OPPORTUNITIES TRUST PLC; *Int'l*, pg. 2999
GLOBAL OPTICS LIMITED—See Global-Tech Advanced Innovations Inc.; *Int'l*, pg. 3003
GLOBAL ORDNANCE LLC; *U.S. Private*, pg. 1716
GLOBAL ORGANIC SPECIALTY SOURCE, INC.; *U.S. Private*, pg. 1716
GLOBAL ORIENTAL BERHAD; *Int'l*, pg. 2999
GLOBAL OUTREACH INTERNATIONAL, INC.; *U.S. Private*, pg. 1716
GLOBAL-PACIFIC MANUFACTURING SDN. BHD.—See Success Transformer Corporation Berhad; *Int'l*, pg. 7250
GLOBAL PACIFIC PRODUCE, INC.; *U.S. Private*, pg. 1716
GLOBAL PACKAGING SOLUTIONS, INC.; *U.S. Private*, pg. 1716
GLOBAL PALM RESOURCES HOLDINGS LIMITED; *Int'l*, pg. 3000
GLOBAL PARCEL DELIVERY (PVT) LTD.—See Aitken Spence PLC; *Int'l*, pg. 254
GLOBAL PARTNERS LP; *U.S. Public*, pg. 942
GLOBAL PARTS, INC.—See VSE Corporation; *U.S. Public*, pg. 2313
GLOBAL PARTS, S.R.L—See HD Hyundai Infracore Co., Ltd.; *Int'l*, pg. 3300
GLOBAL PAYMENTS ASIA-PACIFIC LANKA (PRIVATE) LIMITED—See Global Payments Inc.; *U.S. Public*, pg. 943
GLOBAL PAYMENTS ASIA PACIFIC LIMITED—See Global Payments Inc.; *U.S. Public*, pg. 943
GLOBAL PAYMENTS ASIA-PACIFIC PHILIPPINES INCORPORATED—See Global Payments Inc.; *U.S. Public*, pg. 943
GLOBAL PAYMENTS ASIA-PACIFIC (SINGAPORE) PRIVATE LIMITED—See Global Payments Inc.; *U.S. Public*, pg. 943
GLOBAL PAYMENTS CANADA INC.—See Global Payments Inc.; *U.S. Public*, pg. 943
GLOBAL PAYMENTS DIRECT, INC.—See Global Payments Inc.; *U.S. Public*, pg. 944
GLOBAL PAYMENT SERVICES W.L.L.—See BBK B.S.C.; *Int'l*, pg. 920
GLOBAL PAYMENTS EUROPE, S.R.O.—See Global Payments Inc.; *U.S. Public*, pg. 944
GLOBAL PAYMENTS GAMING SERVICES, INC.—See Global Payments Inc.; *U.S. Public*, pg. 944
GLOBAL PAYMENTS INC.; *U.S. Public*, pg. 943
GLOBAL PAYMENTS, INC.; *U.S. Public*, pg. 945
GLOBAL PAYMENTS LIMITED—See Global Payments Inc.; *U.S. Public*, pg. 944
GLOBAL PAYMENT SYSTEMS ASIA-PACIFIC (MALAYSIA) SDN. BHD.—See Global Payments Inc.; *U.S. Public*, pg. 943
GLOBAL PAYMENT TECHNOLOGIES (EUROPE) LIMITED—See Global Payment Technologies, Inc.; *U.S. Public*, pg. 943
GLOBAL PAYMENT TECHNOLOGIES, INC.; *U.S. Public*, pg. 942
GLOBAL PAYMENT TECHNOLOGIES PROPRIETARY LIMITED—See The Bidvest Group Limited; *Int'l*, pg. 7624
GLOBALPAYNET HOLDINGS INC.; *U.S. Private*, pg. 1719
GLOBAL PERFORMANCE; *U.S. Private*, pg. 1716
GLOBAL PERSONALS LTD.; *U.S. Private*, pg. 3000
GLOBAL PET FILMS INC.—See Garware Hi-Tech Films Limited; *Int'l*, pg. 2886
GLOBAL PET FOODS DISTRIBUTION LTD.—See Franchise Bancorp Inc.; *Int'l*, pg. 2760

GLOBAL PERSONALS LTD.

GLOBAL PET FOOD STORES INC.—See Franchise Bancorp Inc.; *Int'l*, pg. 2760
GLOBAL PETROLEUM ALBANIA SH.A—See HELLENiQ ENERGY Holdings S.A.; *Int'l*, pg. 3334
GLOBAL PETROLEUM LIMITED; *Int'l*, pg. 3000
GLOBALPHARMA COMPANY LLC—See Dubai Investments PJSC; *Int'l*, pg. 2219
GLOBAL PHARMATECH, INC.; *Int'l*, pg. 3000
GLOBAL PHILATELIC NETWORK; *Int'l*, pg. 3000
GLOBAL PHOTONIC ENERGY CORPORATION—See NanoFlex Power Corporation; *U.S. Public*, pg. 1490
GLOBAL PHYSICS SOLUTIONS, INC.—See Fortive Corporation; *U.S. Public*, pg. 871
GLOBAL PIELAGO, SOCIMI, S.A.; *Int'l*, pg. 3000
GLOBAL PIONEER ALUMINIUM INDUSTRIAL FZE—See Al Hamad Contracting Company LLC; *Int'l*, pg. 278
GLOBAL PMX CO., LTD.; *Int'l*, pg. 3000
GLOBAL POLE TRUSION GROUP CORP.; *U.S. Public*, pg. 945
GLOBAL POLYACETAL CO., LTD.—See Mitsubishi Gas Chemical Company, Inc.; *Int'l*, pg. 4948
GLOBALPOPS, INC.—See Ad-Base Group, Inc.; *U.S. Private*, pg. 72
GLOBALPORT 900 INC.; *Int'l*, pg. 3004
GLOBAL PORTFOY YONETIMI A.S—See Global Yatirim Holding A.S.; *Int'l*, pg. 3002
GLOBAL PORT SERVICES LIMITED—See Global Energy (Holdings) Ltd.; *Int'l*, pg. 2995
GLOBAL PORTS HOLDING PLC—See Global Yatirim Holding A.S.; *Int'l*, pg. 3002
GLOBAL PORTS INVESTMENTS PLC—See Delo Group; *Int'l*, pg. 2014
GLOBAL POSITIONING AUGMENTATION SERVICE CORPORATION—See Hitachi Zosen Corporation; *Int'l*, pg. 3410
GLOBAL POVERTY PROJECT, INC.; *U.S. Private*, pg. 1716
GLOBAL POWER GROUP, INC.; *U.S. Private*, pg. 1716
GLOBAL POWER SUPPLY, LLC; *U.S. Private*, pg. 1716
GLOBAL POWER SYNERGY PUBLIC COMPANY LIMITED—See PTT Public Company Limited; *Int'l*, pg. 6092
GLOBAL POWER TECHNOLOGY INC.—See METRAWATT International GmbH; *Int'l*, pg. 4856
GLOBAL PREMIUM FINANCE COMPANY—See Marsh & McLennan Companies, Inc.; *U.S. Public*, pg. 1375
GLOBAL PREMIUM HOTELS LIMITED; *Int'l*, pg. 3000
GLOBAL PRINTER SERVICES INC.; *U.S. Private*, pg. 1717
GLOBAL PROCESSING COMPANIES RUS, LIMITED LIABILITY COMPANY—See Corpay, Inc.; *U.S. Public*, pg. 580
GLOBAL PROCESS SYSTEMS LLC—See Al Jaber Group; *Int'l*, pg. 280
GLOBAL PROCESS SYSTEMS PTE LTD—See Al Jaber Group; *Int'l*, pg. 280
GLOBAL PROCESS SYSTEMS SDN BHD—See Al Jaber Group; *Int'l*, pg. 280
GLOBAL PROCUREMENT SOLUTIONS SHANGAI LTD.—See VINCI S.A.; *Int'l*, pg. 8222
GLOBAL PRODUCTS INC.; *U.S. Private*, pg. 1717
GLOBAL PROFESSIONAL MEDIA LIMITED—See Apax Partners LLP; *Int'l*, pg. 504
GLOBAL PROFIT TECHNOLOGIES, INC.; *U.S. Public*, pg. 945
GLOBAL PROJECT (SERVICES) LTD—See Blue Water Energy LLP; *Int'l*, pg. 1070
GLOBAL PROPERTY STRATEGIC ALLIANCE PTE. LTD.—See GPS Alliance Holdings Limited; *Int'l*, pg. 3047
GLOBAL PROTECTION CORP.—See Karex Berhad; *Int'l*, pg. 4081
GLOBAL PUBLIC SAFETY, LLC—See Rekor Systems, Inc.; *U.S. Public*, pg. 1778
GLOBAL PV SPECIALISTS; *U.S. Private*, pg. 1717
GLOBAL RADAR ACQUISITION LLC—See Audax Group, Limited Partnership; *U.S. Private*, pg. 387
GLOBAL RADIO GROUP LIMITED; *Int'l*, pg. 3000
GLOBAL REAL ESTATE GROUP; *Int'l*, pg. 3000
GLOBAL REAL ESTATE HOLDINGS, INC.; *U.S. Private*, pg. 1717
GLOBAL REALTY SERVICES GROUP LLC; *U.S. Private*, pg. 1717
GLOBAL RECRUITERS NETWORK, INC.; *U.S. Private*, pg. 1717
GLOBAL RECYCLING INC.; *U.S. Private*, pg. 1717
GLOBAL REDEMPTION INC.; *U.S. Private*, pg. 1717
GLOBAL REINSURANCE COMPANY—See GLOBALE Rueckversicherungs-AG; *Int'l*, pg. 3004
GLOBAL REINSURANCE COMPANY—See GLOBALE Rueckversicherungs-AG; *Int'l*, pg. 3004
GLOBAL RELIEF TECHNOLOGIES, LLC—See Persephone Capital Partners LLC; *U.S. Private*, pg. 3155
GLOBAL REMEDIES LTD.—See Strides Pharma Science Limited; *Int'l*, pg. 7240
GLOBAL RESALE LLC; *U.S. Private*, pg. 1717
GLOBAL RESOURCE MANAGEMENT INC.; *U.S. Private*, pg. 1717

GLOBAL RESOURCES INTERNATIONAL, INC.—See Winner Holding Limited; *Int'l*, pg. 8429
GLOBAL RESPONSE CORPORATION; *U.S. Private*, pg. 1717
GLOBAL RETIREMENT PARTNERS, LLC; *U.S. Private*, pg. 1717
GLOBAL RETREAT (MM2H) SDN. BHD.—See MKH Berhad; *Int'l*, pg. 5002
GLOBAL RISK CONSULTANTS (AUSTRALIA) PTY LTD—See TUV SUD AG; *Int'l*, pg. 7984
GLOBAL RISK CONSULTANTS CORP.—See TUV SUD AG; *Int'l*, pg. 7985
GLOBAL RISK CONSULTANTS LTD.—See TUV SUD AG; *Int'l*, pg. 7984
GLOBAL RISK CONSULTANTS (MALAYSIA) SDN. BHD.—See TUV SUD AG; *Int'l*, pg. 7984
GLOBAL RISK CONSULTANTS (SINGAPORE) PTE. LTD.—See TUV SUD AG; *Int'l*, pg. 7984
GLOBAL RISK SOLUTIONS, INC.; *U.S. Private*, pg. 1717
GLOBAL ROLLFORMING CORPORATION—See voestalpine AG; *Int'l*, pg. 8289
GLOBAL ROOFING SOLUTIONS (PTY) LTD.—See Tiso Blackstar Group SE; *Int'l*, pg. 7759
GLOBAL ROUNDTABLE CORPORATION; *U.S. Public*, pg. 945
GLOBAL ROYALTY CORP.—See Coeur Mining, Inc.; *U.S. Public*, pg. 522
GLOBAL SAE-A CO., LTD.; *Int'l*, pg. 3000
GLOBAL SAFETY SURVEILLANCE, INC.—See HCL Technologies Ltd.; *Int'l*, pg. 3299
GLOBALSANTAFE DRILLING COMPANY—See Transocean Ltd.; *Int'l*, pg. 7903
GLOBALSAT WORLDCOM CORP.; *Int'l*, pg. 3004
GLOBALSCAPE INC.—See HGGC, LLC; *U.S. Private*, pg. 1929
GLOBAL SCIENCE AND TECHNOLOGY LTD.—See Avantor, Inc.; *U.S. Public*, pg. 241
GLOBAL SCIENCES HOLDINGS, INC.—See CBD Global Sciences, Inc.; *U.S. Public*, pg. 455
GLOBAL SCIENCE & TECHNOLOGY INC.; *U.S. Private*, pg. 1717
GLOBAL SCS LTD—See Global Energy (Holdings) Ltd.; *Int'l*, pg. 2995
GLOBAL SEAFOOD, LTD.—See Zensho Holdings Co., Ltd.; *Int'l*, pg. 8634
GLOBAL SEAFOOD TECHNOLOGIES; *U.S. Private*, pg. 1717
GLOBAL SECURITIES HOUSE FOR ECONOMIC & FINANCIAL CONSULTANCY K.S.C.—See The Securities House K.S.C.C.; *Int'l*, pg. 7681
GLOBAL SECURITIES (USA), INC.—See Global Yatirim Holding A.S.; *Int'l*, pg. 3003
GLOBAL SECURITY AGENCY INC.; *U.S. Private*, pg. 1717
GLOBAL SECURITY EXPERTS INC.—See Business Brain Showa-Ota Inc.; *Int'l*, pg. 1228
GLOBAL SECURITY GLAZING LLC—See Grey Mountain Partners, LLC; *U.S. Private*, pg. 1784
GLOBAL SELF STORAGE, INC.; *U.S. Public*, pg. 945
GLOBALSERVE, INC.—See PC Connection, Inc.; *U.S. Public*, pg. 1658
GLOBAL SERVICE CENTER PUBLIC COMPANY LIMITED; *Int'l*, pg. 3000
GLOBAL SERVICES BULGARIA JSC—See Vienna Insurance Group AG Wiener Versicherung Gruppe; *Int'l*, pg. 8194
GLOBAL SERVICE SOLUTIONS, INC.; *U.S. Private*, pg. 1717
GLOBAL SERVICOS GEOFISICOS, LTDA.—See Global Geophysical Services, Inc.; *U.S. Private*, pg. 1714
GLOBAL SHIP LEASE, INC.; *Int'l*, pg. 3001
GLOBAL SHIP LEASE SERVICES LIMITED—See Global Ship Lease, Inc.; *Int'l*, pg. 3001
GLOBAL SIDE GMBH—See msg group GmbH; *Int'l*, pg. 5067
GLOBALSIGN CHINA CO., LTD—See GMO GlobalSign Holdings K.K.; *Int'l*, pg. 3013
GLOBALSIGN K.K.—See GMO Internet Group, Inc.; *Int'l*, pg. 3014
GLOBALSIGN NV—See GMO GlobalSign Holdings K.K.; *Int'l*, pg. 3013
GLOBAL SIGORTA Aracilik HIZMETLERI A.S—See Global Yatirim Holding A.S.; *Int'l*, pg. 3003
GLOBALSIM, INC.; *U.S. Private*, pg. 1719
THE GLOBAL SMALLER COMPANIES TRUST PLC; *Int'l*, pg. 7650
GLOBAL SMART CAPITAL CORP.; *Int'l*, pg. 3001
GLOBAL SMOOTHIE SUPPLY, INC.; *U.S. Private*, pg. 1717
GLOBAL SM TECH LIMITED; *Int'l*, pg. 3001
GLOBAL SOFT SA—See PROFILE SYSTEMS & SOFTWARE S.R.L.; *Int'l*, pg. 5989
GLOBAL SOFTWARE, LLC—See TA Associates, Inc.; *U.S. Private*, pg. 3915
GLOBAL SOLAR ENERGY DEUTSCHLAND GMBH—See Global Solar Energy, Inc.; *U.S. Private*, pg. 1717
GLOBAL SOLAR ENERGY, INC.; *U.S. Private*, pg. 1717
GLOBAL SOURCES LTD.—See Blackstone Inc.; *U.S. Public*, pg. 360

CORPORATE AFFILIATIONS

GLOBAL SOURCING COMPANY LLC—See MTN Group Limited; *Int'l*, pg. 5071
GLOBAL SOURCING GROUP, INC.; *U.S. Private*, pg. 1717
GLOBAL SOURCING INC.; *U.S. Private*, pg. 1717
GLOBALSPACE TECHNOLOGIES LIMITED; *Int'l*, pg. 3004
GLOBAL SPAC PARTNERS CO.—See Gorilla Technology Group Inc.; *Int'l*, pg. 3043
GLOBAL SPECIAL RISKS, LLC—See Ryan Specialty Holdings, Inc.; *U.S. Public*, pg. 1828
GLOBAL SPECIALTY CONTRACTORS; *U.S. Public*, pg. 1718
GLOBAL SPECIMEN SOLUTIONS INC—See Laboratory Corporation of America Holdings; *U.S. Public*, pg. 1287
GLOBAL STAINLESS SUPPLY, INC.—See Sumitomo Corporation; *Int'l*, pg. 7273
GLOBAL STANDARDS LLC—See Munchener Ruckversicherungs AG; *Int'l*, pg. 5088
GLOBAL STANDARD TECHNOLOGY CO., LTD.; *Int'l*, pg. 3001
GLOBAL STAR ACQUISITION INC.; *U.S. Public*, pg. 945
GLOBALSTAR ARGENTINA S.R.L.—See Globalstar, Inc.; *U.S. Public*, pg. 946
GLOBALSTAR CANADA SATELLITE CO.—See Globalstar, Inc.; *U.S. Public*, pg. 946
GLOBALSTAR EMEA LTD.; *Int'l*, pg. 3004
GLOBALSTAR, INC.; *U.S. Public*, pg. 946
GLOBALSTAR JAPAN, INC.—See Globalstar, Inc.; *U.S. Public*, pg. 946
GLOBALSTAR SLOVAKIA, S.R.O.—See Globalstar, Inc.; *U.S. Public*, pg. 946
GLOBAL STEEL HOLDINGS LTD.; *Int'l*, pg. 3001
GLOBAL STEEL PRODUCTS CORPORATION—See ITR Industries Inc.; *U.S. Private*, pg. 2150
GLOBAL STEEL WIRE, S.A.—See Celsa Group; *Int'l*, pg. 1395
GLOBAL STRATEGIC GROUP LIMITED; *Int'l*, pg. 3001
GLOBAL STRATEGIC MANAGEMENT INSTITUTE (GSMI); *U.S. Private*, pg. 1718
GLOBAL STRATEGIES, INCORPORATED; *U.S. Private*, pg. 1718
GLOBAL STRATEGIES—See Global Strategies, Incorporated; *U.S. Private*, pg. 1718
GLOBALSTREAMS, INC.; *U.S. Private*, pg. 1719
GLOBAL STUDIO; *U.S. Private*, pg. 1718
GLOBAL STYLE CO., LTD.; *Int'l*, pg. 3001
GLOBAL SUPPLY, A.S.—See HTC holding a.s.; *Int'l*, pg. 3508
GLOBAL SUPPLY CHAIN SOLUTIONS INC.; *U.S. Private*, pg. 1718
GLOBAL SUPPLY LLC; *U.S. Private*, pg. 1718
GLOBAL SUPPLY SOLUTIONS LLC; *U.S. Private*, pg. 1718
GLOBAL SURFACES FZE—See Global Surfaces Limited; *Int'l*, pg. 3001
GLOBAL SURFACES LIMITED; *Int'l*, pg. 3001
GLOBAL SURGICAL PARTNERS, INC.—See KKR & Co. Inc.; *U.S. Public*, pg. 1245
GLOBAL SWEETENERS HOLDINGS LIMITED; *Int'l*, pg. 3001
GLOBAL SWEETENERS TRADE DEVELOPMENT (DALIAN) CO., LTD.—See Global Sweeteners Holdings Limited; *Int'l*, pg. 3001
GLOBAL SYNERGY ACQUISITION CORP.; *U.S. Public*, pg. 945
GLOBAL SYNERGY BUYING GROUP S.A.—See ELGEKA S.A.; *Int'l*, pg. 2359
GLOBAL SYSTEMS DYNAMIC, INC.; *U.S. Public*, pg. 945
GLOBAL SYSTEMS TECHNOLOGIES, INC.—See Broadtree Partners, LLC; *U.S. Private*, pg. 659
GLOBAL TABLE SUPPLY CO., LTD.—See Zensho Holdings Co., Ltd.; *Int'l*, pg. 8634
GLOBAL TAX FREE CO., LTD.; *Int'l*, pg. 3001
GLOBAL TCC—See Global Energy (Holdings) Ltd.; *Int'l*, pg. 2995
GLOBALTEC FORMATION BERHAD; *Int'l*, pg. 3004
GLOBAL-TECH ADVANCED INNOVATIONS INC.; *Int'l*, pg. 3003
GLOBALTECH CORPORATION PTY LTD—See Boart Longyear Ltd.; *Int'l*, pg. 1095
GLOBALTECH CORPORATION; *U.S. Public*, pg. 946
GLOBAL TECH DESIGN PTE LTD.—See Atlas Holdings, LLC; *U.S. Private*, pg. 377
GLOBALTECH HOLDINGS, INC.; *U.S. Public*, pg. 946
GLOBAL TECH, INC.—See Tetra Tech, Inc.; *U.S. Public*, pg. 2023
GLOBAL TECH INDUSTRIES GROUP, INC.; *U.S. Public*, pg. 945
GLOBALTECH INDUSTRIES INC.; *U.S. Private*, pg. 1719
GLOBAL TECH LED LLC; *U.S. Private*, pg. 1718
GLOBAL TECHNICAL SERVICES, INC.; *U.S. Private*, pg. 1718
GLOBAL TECHNICAL SYSTEMS - GTS INFORMATION AND SENSOR SYSTEMS FACILITY—See Global Technical Systems; *U.S. Private*, pg. 1718
GLOBAL TECHNICAL SYSTEMS; *U.S. Private*, pg. 1718
GLOBAL TECHNOLOGIES, LTD.; *U.S. Public*, pg. 945

COMPANY NAME INDEX

GLOBAL TECHNOLOGY ASSOCIATES, LLC—See Kelly Services, Inc.; *U.S. Public*, pg. 1218
GLOBAL TECHNOLOGY ASSOCIATES, LTD.; *U.S. Private*, pg. 1718
GLOBAL TECHNOLOGY FINANCE, LLC—See Mitsubishi HC Capital Inc.; *Int'l*, pg. 4951
GLOBAL TECHNOLOGY GROUP PTY LTD—See Golden Matrix Group, Inc.; *U.S. Public*, pg. 950
GLOBAL TECHNOS LTD.—See Hota Industrial Mfg. Co., Ltd.; *Int'l*, pg. 3487
GLOBAL TECH SOLUTIONS, INC.; *U.S. Private*, pg. 1718
GLOBALTECH SYSTEMS ENGINEERING PTE. LTD.—See KS Energy Limited; *Int'l*, pg. 4309
GLOBAL TEK FABRICATION CO., LTD.; *Int'l*, pg. 3001
GLOBAL-TEK-MANUFACTURING LLC—See Crawford United Corporation; *U.S. Public*, pg. 592
GLOBAL TELECOM HOLDING S.A.E.—See VEON Ltd.; *Int'l*, pg. 8163
GLOBAL TELECOM LLC—See Panasonic Holdings Corporation; *Int'l*, pg. 5717
GLOBAL TELECOM & TECHNOLOGY AMERICAS, INC.—See GTT Communications, Inc.; *U.S. Private*, pg. 1808
GLOBAL TELECOM & UTILITIES INCOME FUND—See Harvest Portfolios Group Inc.; *Int'l*, pg. 3281
GLOBAL TELE SALES BRNO S.R.O.—See Deutsche Lufthansa AG; *Int'l*, pg. 2069
GLOBAL TELESALES OF CANADA, INC.—See Deutsche Lufthansa AG; *Int'l*, pg. 2069
GLOBAL TELE SALES PTY LIMITED—See Deutsche Lufthansa AG; *Int'l*, pg. 2069
GLOBAL TELE SALES (PTY) LTD.—See Deutsche Lufthansa AG; *Int'l*, pg. 2069
GLOBAL TELESAT COMMUNICATIONS LIMITED—See NextPlat Corp.; *U.S. Public*, pg. 1526
GLOBAL TELESOURCING, LLC; *U.S. Private*, pg. 1718
GLOBAL TEL LINK CORPORATION—See American Securities LLC; *U.S. Private*, pg. 249
GLOBAL TEL LINK CORPORATION - VALIDATION STATION—See American Securities LLC; *U.S. Private*, pg. 249
GLOBAL TERMINAL & CONTAINER SERVICES INC.—See China COSCO Shipping Corporation Limited; *Int'l*, pg. 1495
GLOBAL TESTING CORPORATION LIMITED; *Int'l*, pg. 3001
GLOBAL TEST SUPPLY, LLC; *U.S. Private*, pg. 1718
GLOBAL TEXTILE SERVICES LLC; *U.S. Private*, pg. 1718
GLOBAL TITANIUM INC.—See Palladium Equity Partners, LLC; *U.S. Private*, pg. 3078
GLOBAL TOKEN LIMITED; *Int'l*, pg. 3001
GLOBAL TOOLING SYSTEMS INC.—See AIP, LLC; *U.S. Private*, pg. 133
GLOBAL TOP E-COMMERCE CO., LTD.; *Int'l*, pg. 3002
GLOBAL TOWER, LLC—See American Tower Corporation; *U.S. Public*, pg. 111
GLOBAL TOWER SERVICES, LLC—See American Tower Corporation; *U.S. Public*, pg. 111
GLOBAL TOWER SITES I, LLC—See American Tower Corporation; *U.S. Public*, pg. 111
GLOBALTRACO INTERNATIONAL PTE. LTD.—See Tuan Sing Holdings Limited; *Int'l*, pg. 7962
GLOBAL TRADE ALLIANCE INC.—See LKQ Corporation; *U.S. Public*, pg. 1334
GLOBAL TRADE CENTRE S.A.; *Int'l*, pg. 3002
GLOBAL TRADING RESOURCES, INC.—See Janel Corporation; *U.S. Public*, pg. 1187
GLOBAL TRAFFIC NETWORK (UK) LIMITED—See GTCR LLC; *U.S. Private*, pg. 1805
GLOBAL TRAFFIC TECHNOLOGIES, LLC—See Miovision Technologies, Inc.; *Int'l*, pg. 4915
GLOBALTRANS INVESTMENT PLC; *Int'l*, pg. 3004
GLOBAL TRANSIT 2 LIMITED—See TIME dotCom Berhad; *Int'l*, pg. 7750
GLOBAL TRANSIT (HONG KONG) LIMITED—See TIME dotCom Berhad; *Int'l*, pg. 7750
GLOBAL TRANSPORTATION SERVICES, INC.—See The Jordan Company, L.P.; *U.S. Private*, pg. 4060
GLOBAL TRANSPORT & AUTOMOTIVE INSURANCE SOLUTIONS PTY LIMITED—See Allianz SE; *Int'l*, pg. 353
GLOBAL TRANSPORT LOGISTICS, INC.—See Hudson Hill Capital LLC; *U.S. Private*, pg. 2002
GLOBALTRANZ ENTERPRISES, INC.—See Providence Equity Partners L.L.C.; *U.S. Private*, pg. 3292
GLOBAL TRAVEL INTERNATIONAL, INC.; *U.S. Private*, pg. 1718
GLOBAL TRIM SALES INC.—See Crane NXT, Co.; *U.S. Public*, pg. 592
GLOBALTRUCK MANAGEMENT PJSC—See Monopoly, JSC; *Int'l*, pg. 5035
GLOBAL TRUST COMPANY, INC.—See Community Bank System, Inc.; *U.S. Public*, pg. 550
GLOBAL TRUST SAVINGS & LOANS LIMITED—See Industrial & General Insurance Plc; *Int'l*, pg. 3670
GLOBAL TS SDN. BHD.—See Global Carriers Bhd; *Int'l*, pg. 2994
GLOBAL TUBING, LLC—See Forum Energy Technologies, Inc.; *U.S. Public*, pg. 874

GLOBAL TUNGSTEN & POWDERS CORP.—See PLANSEE Holding AG; *Int'l*, pg. 5890
GLOBAL TUNGSTEN & POWDERS SPOL. S R.O.—See PLANSEE Holding AG; *Int'l*, pg. 5890
GLOBAL UAV TECHNOLOGIES LTD.; *Int'l*, pg. 3002
GLOBAL UIN INTELLIGENCE HOLDINGS LIMITED; *Int'l*, pg. 3002
GLOBAL UNICHIP CORP. EUROPE B.V.—See Global Unichip Corp.; *Int'l*, pg. 3002
GLOBAL UNICHIP CORP.; *Int'l*, pg. 3002
GLOBAL UNICHIP CORP.—See Global Unichip Corp.; *Int'l*, pg. 3002
GLOBAL UNICHIP CORP.—See Global Unichip Corp.; *Int'l*, pg. 3002
GLOBAL UNICHIP JAPAN CO., LTD.—See Global Unichip Corp.; *Int'l*, pg. 3002
GLOBAL UNICHIP (NANJING) LTD.—See Global Unichip Corp.; *Int'l*, pg. 3002
GLOBAL UNICHIP (SHANGHAI) COMPANY, LIMITED—See Global Unichip Corp.; *Int'l*, pg. 3002
GLOBAL UNICORN HOLDINGS, INC.; *U.S. Private*, pg. 1718
GLOBAL UPSIDE, INC.; *U.S. Private*, pg. 1718
GLOBAL USED TRUCK SALES, LLC; *U.S. Private*, pg. 1718
GLOBAL VALLEY NETWORKS—See J.H. Evans Inc.; *U.S. Private*, pg. 2165
GLOBAL VALUE FUND LIMITED; *Int'l*, pg. 3002
GLOBAL VECTRA HELICORP LTD.; *Int'l*, pg. 3002
GLOBALVIA INVERSIONES, S.A.U.; *Int'l*, pg. 3005
GLOBAL VIEW COMPANY LIMITED; *Int'l*, pg. 3002
GLOBALVIEW SOFTWARE, INC.—See Hellman & Friedman LLC; *U.S. Private*, pg. 1908
GLOBAL VIRTUAL DESIGN & CONSTRUCTION LIMITED—See Yau Lee Holdings Limited; *Int'l*, pg. 8571
GLOBAL VIRTUAL DESIGN & CONSTRUCTION SDN. BHD.—See Yau Lee Holdings Limited; *Int'l*, pg. 8571
GLOBAL VIRTUAL DESIGN & CONSTRUCTION (SINGAPORE) PTE. LTD.—See Yau Lee Holdings Limited; *Int'l*, pg. 8571
GLOBALWAFERS CO., LTD.—See Sino-American Silicon Products Inc.; *Int'l*, pg. 6948
GLOBALWAFERS JAPAN CO., LTD.—See Sino-American Silicon Products Inc.; *Int'l*, pg. 6948
GLOBAL WALL MALAYSIA SDN. BHD.—See Atlas Holdings, LLC; *U.S. Private*, pg. 377
GLOBALWARE SOLUTIONS INC.; *U.S. Private*, pg. 1719
GLOBAL WARE SOLUTIONS—See Globalware Solutions Inc.; *U.S. Private*, pg. 1719
GLOBALWARE SOLUTIONS—See Globalware Solutions Inc.; *U.S. Private*, pg. 1719
GLOBAL WARMING SOLUTIONS, INC.; *U.S. Public*, pg. 945
GLOBAL WARRANTY GROUP, LLC; *U.S. Private*, pg. 1718
GLOBAL WATER ASSET CORPORATION; *Int'l*, pg. 3002
GLOBAL WATER GROUP, INC.—See Eastern Water Resources Development & Management Public Company Limited; *Int'l*, pg. 2274
GLOBAL WATER MANAGEMENT, INC.—See Global Water Resources, Inc.; *U.S. Public*, pg. 945
GLOBAL WATER RESOURCES, INC.; *U.S. Public*, pg. 945
GLOBAL WATER TECHNOLOGIES, INC.; *U.S. Public*, pg. 945
GLOBAL WAVE TECHNOLOGIES PVT LIMITED—See MTI Wireless Edge Ltd.; *Int'l*, pg. 5070
GLOBALWAY, INC.; *Int'l*, pg. 3005
GLOBAL WEDGE, INC.; *U.S. Private*, pg. 1719
GLOBAL WELLNESS STRATEGIES INC.; *Int'l*, pg. 3002
GLOBAL WHOLEHEALTH PARTNERS CORPORATION; *U.S. Public*, pg. 945
GLOBALWIDE INTERNATIONAL PTE. LTD.—See Air Water Inc.; *Int'l*, pg. 240
GLOBALWIDE M&E PTE. LTD.—See Air Water Inc.; *Int'l*, pg. 240
GLOBAL WILDLIFE CONSERVATION; *U.S. Private*, pg. 1719
GLOBALWINE AG—See Hawesko Holding AG; *Int'l*, pg. 3288
GLOBAL WIRE LTD.—See First Israel Turnaround Enterprise; *Int'l*, pg. 2685
GLOBALWORKS; *U.S. Private*, pg. 1719
GLOBALWORTH POLAND—See Globalworth Real Estate Investments Limited; *Int'l*, pg. 3005
GLOBALWORTH REAL ESTATE INVESTMENTS LIMITED; *Int'l*, pg. 3005
GLOBAL X-RAY & TESTING CORP.—See Intertek Group plc; *Int'l*, pg. 3762
GLOBAL YATIRIM HOLDING A.S.; *Int'l*, pg. 3002
GLOBAL YP SDN BHD—See Rumah & Co. Pte. Ltd.; *Int'l*, pg. 6427
GLOBAL ZEUS INC.—See ZEUS CO., Ltd; *Int'l*, pg. 8640
GLOBANET CONSULTING SERVICES, INC.—See The Carlyle Group L.P.; *U.S. Public*, pg. 2056
GLOBANT S.A.; *Int'l*, pg. 3005
GLOBA SERVICE INC.—See Nidec Corporation; *Int'l*, pg. 5274

GLOBAVEND HOLDINGS LIMITED; *Int'l*, pg. 3005
GLOBE ADHESIVE TECHNOLOGY (ZHUHAI) CO., LTD.—See Globe Industries Corporation; *Int'l*, pg. 3006
GLOBEAT JAPAN INC.—See Fullcast Holdings Co., Ltd.; *Int'l*, pg. 2842
GLOBE-BAY AREA FORKLIFT—See The Pape Group, Inc.; *U.S. Private*, pg. 4090
GLOBE BUSINESS INTERIORS; *U.S. Private*, pg. 1719
GLOBE CAPITAL LIMITED; *Int'l*, pg. 3006
GLOBECARE TRADING (SHANGHAI) CO., LTD—See YungShin Global Holding Corporation; *Int'l*, pg. 8614
GLOBECAST AFRICA PTY. LTD.—See Orange S.A.; *Int'l*, pg. 5608
GLOBECAST AMERICA INC. - LOS ANGELES OPERATIONS CENTER—See Orange S.A.; *Int'l*, pg. 5608
GLOBECAST AMERICA INC. - MIAMI OPERATIONS CENTER—See Orange S.A.; *Int'l*, pg. 5608
GLOBECAST AMERICA INCORPORATED—See Orange S.A.; *Int'l*, pg. 5608
GLOBECAST ASIA PTE. LTD.—See Orange S.A.; *Int'l*, pg. 5608
GLOBECAST BRAZIL—See Orange S.A.; *Int'l*, pg. 5608
GLOBECAST FRANCE—See Orange S.A.; *Int'l*, pg. 5608
GLOBECAST HOLDING S.A.—See Orange S.A.; *Int'l*, pg. 5608
GLOBECAST HONG KONG LIMITED—See Orange S.A.; *Int'l*, pg. 5608
GLOBECAST INDIA PVT. LTD.—See Orange S.A.; *Int'l*, pg. 5608
GLOBECAST ITALIA S.R.L.—See Orange S.A.; *Int'l*, pg. 5608
GLOBECAST NEAR & MIDDLE EAST—See Orange S.A.; *Int'l*, pg. 5608
GLOBECAST REPORTAGES—See Orange S.A.; *Int'l*, pg. 5608
GLOBECAST UK LIMITED—See Orange S.A.; *Int'l*, pg. 5608
GLOBE CEMENT COMPANY LIMITED—See Siam City Cement Public Company Limited; *Int'l*, pg. 6874
GLOBECOMM ASIA PTE. LTD—See SpeedCast International Limited; *Int'l*, pg. 7132
GLOBE COMMERCIALS LIMITED; *Int'l*, pg. 3006
GLOBECOMM EUROPE BV—See SpeedCast International Limited; *Int'l*, pg. 7133
GLOBECOMM NETWORK SERVICES CORPORATION—See SpeedCast International Limited; *Int'l*, pg. 7133
GLOBECOMM SERVICES MARYLAND LLC—See SpeedCast International Limited; *Int'l*, pg. 7133
GLOBECOMM SYSTEMS INC.—See SpeedCast International Limited; *Int'l*, pg. 7132
GLOBECOMM SYSTEMS SA PROPRIETARY LTD—See SpeedCast International Limited; *Int'l*, pg. 7133
GLOBE COMMUNICATIONS, LLC—See Dycom Industries, Inc.; *U.S. Public*, pg. 698
GLOBE COMPOSITE SOLUTIONS, LLC—See ESCO Technologies, Inc.; *U.S. Public*, pg. 794
GLOBEDIRECT, LLC—See NE Media Group, Inc.; *U.S. Private*, pg. 2877
GLOBEE INC.; *Int'l*, pg. 3007
GLOBE ENERGY SERVICES, LLC—See Clearlake Capital Group, L.P.; *U.S. Private*, pg. 935
GLOBE EXPLORATION (Y.C.D.) LIMITED PARTNERSHIP; *Int'l*, pg. 3006
GLOBE EXPRESS SERVICES LTD.; *U.S. Private*, pg. 1719
GLOBE FOOD EQUIPMENT COMPANY—See The Middleby Corporation; *U.S. Public*, pg. 2114
GLOBE-GAZETTE—See Lee Enterprises, Incorporated; *U.S. Public*, pg. 1299
GLOBEIMMUNE, INC.—See NantWorks, LLC; *U.S. Private*, pg. 2833
GLOBE INDUSTRIES CORPORATION; *Int'l*, pg. 3006
GLOBE INTERNATIONAL CARRIERS LTD.; *Int'l*, pg. 3006
GLOBE INTERNATIONAL LIMITED; *Int'l*, pg. 3006
GLOBELEQ ADVISORS LIMITED—See General Atlantic Service Company, L.P.; *U.S. Private*, pg. 1661
GLOBELEQ GENERATION LIMITED—See General Atlantic Service Company, L.P.; *U.S. Private*, pg. 1661
GLOBELEQ INC.—See General Atlantic Service Company, L.P.; *U.S. Private*, pg. 1661
GLOBE LIFE & ACCIDENT INSURANCE COMPANY—See Globe Life Inc.; *U.S. Public*, pg. 946
GLOBE LIFE INC.; *U.S. Public*, pg. 946
GLOBE LIFE INSURANCE COMPANY OF NEW YORK—See Globe Life Inc.; *U.S. Public*, pg. 946
GLOBELINK-TRANS (TIANJIN) INTERNATIONAL FORWARDING CO., LTD.—See CWT International Limited; *Int'l*, pg. 1891
GLOBELTR ENERGY, INC.—See Clearlake Capital Group, L.P.; *U.S. Private*, pg. 934
THE GLOBE & MAIL INC.—See The Woodbridge Company Limited; *Int'l*, pg. 7701
GLOBE MANUFACTURING COMPANY, INC.—See MSA Safety Incorporated; *U.S. Public*, pg. 1481
GLOBE MECHANICAL, INC.; *U.S. Private*, pg. 1719
GLOBE METALLURGICAL, INC.—See Grupo Villar Mir, S.A.U.; *Int'l*, pg. 3138

1101

GLOBE METALS & MINING LIMITED; *Int'l*, pg. 3006
GLOBE MORTGAGE AMERICA, LLC; *U.S. Private*, pg. 1720
GLOBE MOTORS DE MEXICO, S.A. DE C.V.—See Allient Inc.; *U.S. Public*, pg. 80
GLOBE MOTORS, INC.—See Allient Inc.; *U.S. Public*, pg. 80
GLOBE MOTORS PORTUGAL LDA.—See Allient Inc.; *U.S. Public*, pg. 80
GLOBE MOTORS—See Allient Inc.; *U.S. Public*, pg. 80
GLOBENET INTERNATIONAL CORPORATION; *U.S. Private*, pg. 1720
GLOBENEWSWIRE, INC.—See Apollo Global Management, Inc.; *U.S. Public*, pg. 152
GLOBENEWSWIRE UK LIMITED—See Apollo Global Management, Inc.; *U.S. Public*, pg. 152
GLOBEOP FINANCIAL SERVICES (CAYMAN) LIMITED—See SS&C Technologies Holdings, Inc.; *U.S. Public*, pg. 1923
GLOBEOP FINANCIAL SERVICES (INDIA) PRIVATE LIMITED—See SS&C Technologies Holdings, Inc.; *U.S. Public*, pg. 1923
GLOBEOP FINANCIAL SERVICES LIMITED—See SS&C Technologies Holdings, Inc.; *U.S. Public*, pg. 1923
GLOBEOP FINANCIAL SERVICES LLC—See SS&C Technologies Holdings, Inc.; *U.S. Public*, pg. 1923
GLOBEOP FINANCIAL SERVICES TECHNOLOGIES (INDIA) PRIVATE LIMITED—See SS&C Technologies Holdings, Inc.; *U.S. Public*, pg. 1924
GLOBEOSS (BRUNEI) SDN. BHD.—See Captii Limited; *Int'l*, pg. 1317
GLOBEOSS PTE LTD—See Captii Limited; *Int'l*, pg. 1317
GLOBEOSS SDN BHD—See Captii Limited; *Int'l*, pg. 1317
THE GLOBE PEQUOT PRESS, INC.—See Shivers Trading & Operating Company; *U.S. Private*, pg. 3638
GLOBE PHOTOST, INC.; *U.S. Public*, pg. 946
GLOBERANGER CORPORATION—See Fujitsu Limited; *Int'l*, pg. 2836
GLOBERER, INC—See Enso Group; *Int'l*, pg. 2448
GLOBERIDE, INC.; *Int'l*, pg. 3007
GLOBESCAN CAPITAL INC.—See Brasada Capital Management LP; *U.S. Private*, pg. 640
GLOBE SCIENTIFIC, INC.—See L Squared Capital Management LP; *U.S. Private*, pg. 2362
GLOBESHERPA LLC—See Mercedes-Benz Group AG; *Int'l*, pg. 4829
GLOBE SPECIALTY METALS, INC.—See Grupo Villar Mir, S.A.U.; *Int'l*, pg. 3138
GLOBE SPECIALTY PRODUCTS, INC.—See NE Media Group, Inc.; *U.S. Private*, pg. 2877
GLOBES PUBLISHER ITONUT (1983) LTD—See Monitin Group; *Int'l*, pg. 5034
GLOBESTAR THERAPEUTICS CORPORATION; *U.S. Public*, pg. 946
GLOBE STORAGE & MOVING CO. INC.; *U.S. Private*, pg. 1720
GLOBETEC CONSTRUCTION, LLC—See MasTec, Inc.; *U.S. Public*, pg. 1393
GLOBE TECHNOLOGY GMBH—See REALTECH AG; *Int'l*, pg. 6234
GLOBE TELECOM, INC.; *Int'l*, pg. 3006
GLOBE TEXTILE MILLS (OE) LIMITED; *Int'l*, pg. 3006
GLOBE TEXTILES (INDIA) LTD.; *Int'l*, pg. 3006
GLOBE TRADE CENTRE S.A.; *Int'l*, pg. 3006
GLOBE TRAILER MANUFACTURING, INC.; *U.S. Private*, pg. 1720
GLOBE TRAILERS OF FLORIDA, INC.; *U.S. Private*, pg. 1720
GLOBETRONICS (KL) SDN. BHD.—See Globetronics Technology Bhd.; *Int'l*, pg. 3007
GLOBETRONICS MANUFACTURING SDN. BHD.—See Globetronics Technology Bhd.; *Int'l*, pg. 3007
GLOBETRONICS MEDICAL TECHNOLOGY SDN BHD—See Globetronics Technology Bhd.; *Int'l*, pg. 3007
GLOBETRONICS SDN. BHD.—See Globetronics Technology Bhd.; *Int'l*, pg. 3007
GLOBETRONICS TECHNOLOGY BHD.; *Int'l*, pg. 3007
GLOBE UNDERWRITING LIMITED—See BGC Group, Inc.; *U.S. Public*, pg. 329
GLOBE UNION INDUSTRIAL CORP.; *Int'l*, pg. 3007
GLOBE WIRELESS INC.—See ViaSat, Inc.; *U.S. Public*, pg. 2291
GLOBEX MINING ENTERPRISES INC.; *Int'l*, pg. 3007
GLOBIS ACQUISITION CORP.; *U.S. Public*, pg. 946
GLOBIS ASIA PACIFIC PTE. LTD.—See Globis Corporation; *Int'l*, pg. 3007
GLOBIS CAPITAL PARTNERS & CO.—See Globis Corporation; *Int'l*, pg. 3007
GLOBIS CHINA CO., LTD.—See Globis Corporation; *Int'l*, pg. 3007
GLOBIS CORPORATION; *Int'l*, pg. 3007
GLOBITTECH, INC.—See Sino-American Silicon Products Inc.; *Int'l*, pg. 6948
GLOBLEX HOLDING MANAGEMENT PUBLIC COMPANY LIMITED; *Int'l*, pg. 3007
GLOBLEX SECURITES CO., LTD.—See Globlex Holding Management Public Company Limited; *Int'l*, pg. 3007

GLOBOCAM ANJOU—See Mercedes-Benz Group AG; *Int'l*, pg. 4823
GLOBO FOODS LTD.; *Int'l*, pg. 3007
GLOBOFORCE GROUP PLC; *Int'l*, pg. 3007
GLOBOKAS PERU SA; *Int'l*, pg. 3008
GLOBON CO., LTD.; *Int'l*, pg. 3008
GLOBOPLASTT S.R.O.—See Illinois Tool Works Inc.; *U.S. Public*, pg. 1103
GLOBOS OSIGURANJE A.D.; *Int'l*, pg. 3008
GLOBOS QUALATEX DE PIONEER, S.A. DE C.V.—See Continental American Corporation; *U.S. Private*, pg. 1028
GLOBOTEK HOLDINGS INC.; *U.S. Private*, pg. 1720
GLOBRANDS GROUP LTD.; *Int'l*, pg. 3008
GLOBTEK, INC.; *U.S. Private*, pg. 1720
GLOBUS DEPARTMENT STORES—See The Federation of Migros Cooperatives; *Int'l*, pg. 7642
GLOBUS-GRUPPE—See The Federation of Migros Cooperatives; *Int'l*, pg. 7642
GLOBUS KONFEKCIJA D.D.; *Int'l*, pg. 3008
GLOBUS MARITIME LIMITED; *Int'l*, pg. 3008
GLOBUS MEDICAL AUSTRALIA PTY LIMITED—See Globus Medical, Inc.; *U.S. Public*, pg. 947
GLOBUS MEDICAL AUSTRIA GMBH—See Globus Medical, Inc.; *U.S. Public*, pg. 947
GLOBUS MEDICAL BRASIL LTDA.—See Globus Medical, Inc.; *U.S. Public*, pg. 947
GLOBUS MEDICAL BRAZIL LDTA.—See Globus Medical, Inc.; *U.S. Public*, pg. 947
GLOBUS MEDICAL, INC.; *U.S. Public*, pg. 946
GLOBUS MEDICAL ITALY S.R.L.—See Globus Medical, Inc.; *U.S. Public*, pg. 947
GLOBUS MEDICAL JAPAN, INC.—See Globus Medical, Inc.; *U.S. Public*, pg. 947
GLOBUS MEDICAL SOUTH AFRICA PTY LIMITED—See Globus Medical, Inc.; *U.S. Public*, pg. 947
GLOBUS MEDICAL SWEDEN AB—See Globus Medical, Inc.; *U.S. Public*, pg. 947
GLOBUS MEDICAL UK LIMITED—See Globus Medical, Inc.; *U.S. Public*, pg. 947
GLOBUS POWER GENERATION LIMITED; *Int'l*, pg. 3008
GLOBUS RELIEF; *U.S. Private*, pg. 1720
GLOBUS SPIRITS LTD; *Int'l*, pg. 3008
GLOBYS INC.; *U.S. Private*, pg. 1720
GLOCAL CO., LTD.—See Bain Capital, LP; *U.S. Private*, pg. 434
GLOCAL EDUCATION SERVICES LIMITED—See Bexcellent Group Holdings Limited; *Int'l*, pg. 1005
GLOCKNER CHEVROLET CO. INC.; *U.S. Private*, pg. 1720
GLOCKNER OIL COMPANY INC.—See Glockner Chevrolet Co. Inc.; *U.S. Private*, pg. 1720
GLOCKNER QUALITY LEASING—See Glockner Chevrolet Co. Inc.; *U.S. Private*, pg. 1720
GLOCZUS, INC.—See Fujitsu Limited; *Int'l*, pg. 2837
GLODINA (PTY) LTD.—See Steinhoff International Holdings N.V.; *Int'l*, pg. 7194
GLODON CO., LTD.; *Int'l*, pg. 3008
GLOHAB, INC.; *U.S. Private*, pg. 1720
GLOMAC ALLIANCE SDN. BHD.—See GLOMAC Berhad; *Int'l*, pg. 3008
GLOMAC BERHAD; *Int'l*, pg. 3008
GLOMAC BINA SDN. BHD.—See GLOMAC Berhad; *Int'l*, pg. 3008
GLOMAC CITY SDN. BHD.—See GLOMAC Berhad; *Int'l*, pg. 3008
GLOMAC RAWANG SDN. BHD.—See GLOMAC Berhad; *Int'l*, pg. 3008
GLOMAC SUTERA SDN. BHD.—See GLOMAC Berhad; *Int'l*, pg. 3008
GLOMATO TECHNOLOGIES SDN. BHD.—See Quaser Machine Tools, Inc.; *Int'l*, pg. 6156
GLOMED PHARMACEUTICAL COMPANY LIMITED—See Abbott Laboratories; *U.S. Public*, pg. 20
GLOME HOLDING, INC.; *Int'l*, pg. 3008
GLOME MANAGEMENT, INC.—See Glome Holding, Inc.; *Int'l*, pg. 3008
GLOMEX GMBH—See ProSiebenSat.1 Media SE; *Int'l*, pg. 6000
G.LOOMIS, INC.—See Shimano, Inc.; *Int'l*, pg. 6833
G-LOOMIS PRODUCTS, INC.—See Shimano, Inc.; *Int'l*, pg. 6833
GLORIA GMBH—See Carrier Global Corporation; *U.S. Public*, pg. 443
GLORIA JEAN'S, INC.—See Praise International North America; *U.S. Private*, pg. 3243
GLORIA LANCE INC.; *U.S. Private*, pg. 1720
GLORIA MATERIAL TECHNOLOGY CORP.; *Int'l*, pg. 3008
GLORIA NILSON, INC.; *U.S. Private*, pg. 1720
GLORI ENERGY INC.; *U.S. Public*, pg. 947
GLORIETA GEOSCIENCE, INC.—See GZA GeoEnvironmental Inc.; *U.S. Private*, pg. 1822
GLORIOUS PROPERTY HOLDINGS LTD.; *Int'l*, pg. 3008
GLORIOUS SUN ENTERPRISES LIMITED; *Int'l*, pg. 3009
GLORY AUSTRIA GMBH—See GLORY Ltd.; *Int'l*, pg. 3009
GLORY AZ SYSTEM CO., LTD.—See GLORY Ltd.; *Int'l*, pg. 3009

GLORY CURRENCY AUTOMATION INDIA PVT. LTD.—See GLORY Ltd.; *Int'l*, pg. 3009
GLORY DAYS GRILL; *U.S. Private*, pg. 1720
GLORY DENSHI KOGYO (SUZHOU) LTD.—See GLORY Ltd.; *Int'l*, pg. 3009
GLORY ENGINEERING LTD.—See GLORY Ltd.; *Int'l*, pg. 3009
GLORY F&C CO., LTD.—See GLORY Ltd.; *Int'l*, pg. 3009
GLORYFEEL GMBH—See Bayer Aktiengesellschaft; *Int'l*, pg. 908
GLORY FILMS LIMITED; *Int'l*, pg. 3009
GLORY FLAME HOLDINGS LIMITED; *Int'l*, pg. 3009
GLORY FRANCE—See GLORY Ltd.; *Int'l*, pg. 3009
GLORY FRIENDLY CO., LTD.—See GLORY Ltd.; *Int'l*, pg. 3009
GLORY GLOBAL SOLUTIONS ASIA PACIFIC—See GLORY Ltd.; *Int'l*, pg. 3010
GLORY GLOBAL SOLUTIONS (AUSTRALIA) PTY. LTD.—See GLORY Ltd.; *Int'l*, pg. 3009
GLORY GLOBAL SOLUTIONS (BELGIUM) N. V./S. A.—See GLORY Ltd.; *Int'l*, pg. 3009
GLORY GLOBAL SOLUTIONS (BRASIL) MAQUINAS E EQUIPAMENTOS LTDA.—See GLORY Ltd.; *Int'l*, pg. 3010
GLORY GLOBAL SOLUTIONS (CANADA) INC.—See GLORY Ltd.; *Int'l*, pg. 3010
GLORY GLOBAL SOLUTIONS (COLOMBIA) S.A.—See GLORY Ltd.; *Int'l*, pg. 3009
GLORY GLOBAL SOLUTIONS (FRANCE) S.A.S.—See GLORY Ltd.; *Int'l*, pg. 3010
GLORY GLOBAL SOLUTIONS (GERMANY) GMBH—See GLORY Ltd.; *Int'l*, pg. 3010
GLORY GLOBAL SOLUTIONS GMBH—See GLORY Ltd.; *Int'l*, pg. 3010
GLORY GLOBAL SOLUTIONS (HONG KONG) LTD.—See GLORY Ltd.; *Int'l*, pg. 3009
GLORY GLOBAL SOLUTIONS INC.—See GLORY Ltd.; *Int'l*, pg. 3010
GLORY GLOBAL SOLUTIONS (INTERNATIONAL) LTD.—See GLORY Ltd.; *Int'l*, pg. 3009
GLORY GLOBAL SOLUTIONS (IRELAND) LTD.—See GLORY Ltd.; *Int'l*, pg. 3010
GLORY GLOBAL SOLUTIONS LTD.—See GLORY Ltd.; *Int'l*, pg. 3010
GLORY GLOBAL SOLUTIONS (MALAYSIA) SDN. BHD.—See GLORY Ltd.; *Int'l*, pg. 3010
GLORY GLOBAL SOLUTIONS MEXICO, S.A. DE C.V.—See GLORY Ltd.; *Int'l*, pg. 3010
GLORY GLOBAL SOLUTIONS NAKIT OTOMASYON TEKNOLOJILERI LTD. STI.—See GLORY Ltd.; *Int'l*, pg. 3010
GLORY GLOBAL SOLUTIONS (NETHERLANDS) BV—See GLORY Ltd.; *Int'l*, pg. 3010
GLORY GLOBAL SOLUTIONS (NEW ZEALAND) LTD.—See GLORY Ltd.; *Int'l*, pg. 3010
GLORY GLOBAL SOLUTIONS (PORTUGAL) S. A.—See GLORY Ltd.; *Int'l*, pg. 3010
GLORY GLOBAL SOLUTIONS RUS, LLC—See GLORY Ltd.; *Int'l*, pg. 3010
GLORY GLOBAL SOLUTIONS (SHANGHAI) CO., LTD.—See GLORY Ltd.; *Int'l*, pg. 3010
GLORY GLOBAL SOLUTIONS (SINGAPORE) PTE. LTD.—See GLORY Ltd.; *Int'l*, pg. 3010
GLORY GLOBAL SOLUTIONS—See GLORY Ltd.; *Int'l*, pg. 3010
GLORY GLOBAL SOLUTIONS (SOUTH ASIA) PVT. LTD.—See GLORY Ltd.; *Int'l*, pg. 3010
GLORY GLOBAL SOLUTIONS (SPAIN) S.A.—See GLORY Ltd.; *Int'l*, pg. 3010
GLORY GLOBAL SOLUTIONS (SWITZERLAND) A. G.—See GLORY Ltd.; *Int'l*, pg. 3010
GLORY HEALTH INDUSTRY LIMITED; *Int'l*, pg. 3009
GLORY INTERNATIONAL TRADING (SHANGHAI) CO., LTD.—See GLORY Ltd.; *Int'l*, pg. 3010
GLORY IPO ASIA LTD.—See GLORY Ltd.; *Int'l*, pg. 3010
GLORY IPO CHINA LTD.—See GLORY Ltd.; *Int'l*, pg. 3009
GLORY IST CO., LTD.—See GLORY Ltd.; *Int'l*, pg. 3010
GLORY KIKI CO., LTD.—See GLORY Ltd.; *Int'l*, pg. 3010
GLORY LTD. - SAITAMA FACTORY—See GLORY Ltd.; *Int'l*, pg. 3009
GLORY LTD.; *Int'l*, pg. 3009
GLORY MARK ELECTRONIC LIMITED—See China United Venture Investment Limited; *Int'l*, pg. 1561
GLORY MECHATRONICS LTD.—See GLORY Ltd.; *Int'l*, pg. 3010
GLORY NASCA LTD.—See GLORY Ltd.; *Int'l*, pg. 3009
GLORY (PHILIPPINES) INC.—See GLORY Ltd.; *Int'l*, pg. 3009
GLORY PRODUCTS LTD.—See GLORY Ltd.; *Int'l*, pg. 3010
GLORY SCIENCE CO., LTD.—See Cheng Eui Precision Industry Co., Ltd.; *Int'l*, pg. 1465
GLORY SERVICE CO., LTD.—See GLORY Ltd.; *Int'l*, pg. 3010
GLORY SUN FINANCIAL GROUP LIMITED; *Int'l*, pg. 3010
GLORY SUN LAND GROUP LIMITED—See Glory Sun Financial Group Limited; *Int'l*, pg. 3011

COMPANY NAME INDEX

GLORY SYSTEM CREATE LTD.—See GLORY Ltd.; *Int'l*, pg. 3009
GLORY TECHNO 24 CO., LTD.—See GLORY Ltd.; *Int'l*, pg. 3010
GLORYTEK (YANCHENG) CO., LTD.—See Cheng Eui Precision Industry Co., Ltd.; *Int'l*, pg. 1465
GLORY USA, INC.—See GLORY Ltd.; *Int'l*, pg. 3010
GLORY VIEW TECHNOLOGY CO., LTD.; *Int'l*, pg. 3011
GLORYWIN ENTERTAINMENT GROUP, INC.; *U.S. Public*, pg. 947
GLOSEL CO., LTD.—See Macnica Holdings, Inc.; *Int'l*, pg. 4624
GLOSEL ELECTRONICS SINGAPORE PTE. LTD.—See Macnica Holdings, Inc.; *Int'l*, pg. 4624
GLOSEL HONG KONG LIMITED—See Macnica Holdings, Inc.; *Int'l*, pg. 4624
GLOSEL SHANGHAI TRADING CO., LTD.—See Macnica Holdings, Inc.; *Int'l*, pg. 4624
GLOSEL TAIWAN CO., LTD.—See Macnica Holdings, Inc.; *Int'l*, pg. 4624
GLOSS MIND APPAREL (HONG KONG) LIMITED—See Giordano International Limited; *Int'l*, pg. 2978
GLOSSOM, INC.—See Gree Inc.; *Int'l*, pg. 3069
GLOSTEN, INC.; *U.S. Private*, pg. 1720
GLOSTER LIMITED; *Int'l*, pg. 3011
GLOSTREAM, INC.; *U.S. Private*, pg. 1720
GLOSTREXT TECHNOLOGY SDN. BHD.—See Spectest Sdn. Bhd.; *Int'l*, pg. 7129
GLOSTREXT TECHNOLOGY (S) PTE. LTD.—See Spectest Sdn. Bhd.; *Int'l*, pg. 7129
GLOTECH ELECTRONICS (SUZHOU) CORP.—See Glotech Industrial Corp.; *Int'l*, pg. 3011
GLOTECH INDUSTRIAL CORP.; *Int'l*, pg. 3011
GLOTECH TECHNICAL MATERIALS CORP.—See Glotech Industrial Corp.; *Int'l*, pg. 3011
GLOTEL INC.—See The Gores Group, LLC; *U.S. Private*, pg. 4034
GLOTFELTY ENTERPRISES INC.; *U.S. Private*, pg. 1720
GLOVCONCEPT SDN. BHD.—See Luster Industries Bhd.; *Int'l*, pg. 4587
GLOVE ALLIANCES SDN. BHD.—See Nexgram Holdings Berhad; *Int'l*, pg. 5244
GLOVER FOODS, INC.; *U.S. Private*, pg. 1720
GLOVER MAINTENANCE; *U.S. Private*, pg. 1720
GLOVES INTERNATIONAL INC.; *U.S. Private*, pg. 1720
GLOVIA INTERNATIONAL, INC.—See Fujitsu Limited; *Int'l*, pg. 2833
GLOVIS ALABAMA, LLC—See Hyundai Glovis Co., Ltd.; *Int'l*, pg. 3557
GLOVIS AMERICA INC.—See Hyundai Glovis Co., Ltd.; *Int'l*, pg. 3556
GLOVIS AUSTRALIA PTY. LTD.—See Hyundai Glovis Co., Ltd.; *Int'l*, pg. 3556
GLOVIS BRAZIL LOGISTICA LTDA.—See Hyundai Glovis Co., Ltd.; *Int'l*, pg. 3556
GLOVIS CANADA INC.—See Hyundai Glovis Co., Ltd.; *Int'l*, pg. 3556
GLOVIS CHENNAI CORPORATION—See Hyundai Glovis Co., Ltd.; *Int'l*, pg. 3557
GLOVIS CZECH REPUBLIC S.R.O.—See Hyundai Glovis Co., Ltd.; *Int'l*, pg. 3556
GLOVIS EUROPE GMBH—See Hyundai Glovis Co., Ltd.; *Int'l*, pg. 3556
GLOVIS GEORGIA, LLC—See Hyundai Glovis Co., Ltd.; *Int'l*, pg. 3557
GLOVIS HOLDINGS MONGOL—See Hyundai Glovis Co., Ltd.; *Int'l*, pg. 3556
GLOVIS INDIA PVT. LTD.—See Hyundai Glovis Co., Ltd.; *Int'l*, pg. 3556
GLOVISION, INC.—See Kadokawa Corporation; *Int'l*, pg. 4047
GLOVIS RUSSIA, LLC—See Hyundai Glovis Co., Ltd.; *Int'l*, pg. 3557
GLOVIS SLOVAKIA S.R.O.—See Hyundai Glovis Co., Ltd.; *Int'l*, pg. 3557
GLOVIS TURKEY LOJISTIK TIC. SAN. VE TIC. LTD. STI.—See Hyundai Glovis Co., Ltd.; *Int'l*, pg. 3557
GLOVMASTER SDN. BHD.—See Luster Industries Bhd.; *Int'l*, pg. 4587
GLOWAC, HARRIS, MADISON INC.; *U.S. Private*, pg. 1721
GLOWAY BROADCAST SERVICES, S.L.—See Telefonica, S.A.; *Int'l*, pg. 7535
GLOW CO., LTD.—See PTT Public Company Limited; *Int'l*, pg. 6092
GLOW ENERGY PUBLIC COMPANY LIMITED—See PTT Public Company Limited; *Int'l*, pg. 6092
GLOW EVENTS, LLC—See Live Nation Entertainment, Inc.; *U.S. Public*, pg. 1329
GLOW GREEN LIMITED—See Telecom Plus Plc; *Int'l*, pg. 7530
GLOW INTERACTIVE, INC.; *U.S. Private*, pg. 1721
GLOW IPP COMPANY LIMITED—See PTT Public Company Limited; *Int'l*, pg. 6092
GLOW NETWORKS, INC.; *U.S. Private*, pg. 1721
GLOW NETWORKS PVT LTD—See Glow Networks, Inc.; *U.S. Private*, pg. 1721
GLOW SPP 1 CO., LTD. - DEMIN WATER PLANT—See B. Grimm Group; *Int'l*, pg. 788

GLOW SPP 1 COMPANY LIMITED—See B. Grimm Group; *Int'l*, pg. 788
GLOW SPP 3 CO., LTD.—See PTT Public Company Limited; *Int'l*, pg. 6092
GLOWTOUCH TECHNOLOGIES; *U.S. Private*, pg. 1721
GLOWWORM INC.; *U.S. Private*, pg. 1721
GLOXIS DEVELOPMENT LIMITED—See King's Flair International (Holdings) Ltd.; *Int'l*, pg. 4170
GLP BRASIL EMPREENDIMENTOS E PARTICIPACOES LTDA.—See Global Logistic Properties Limited; *Int'l*, pg. 2999
GLP CAPITAL, L.P.—See Gaming and Leisure Properties, Inc.; *U.S. Public*, pg. 896
GL PHARM TECH CORP; *Int'l*, pg. 2986
GLP INVESTMENT MANAGEMENT (CHINA) CO., LTD.—See Global Logistic Properties Limited; *Int'l*, pg. 2999
GLP INVESTMENT MANAGEMENT PTE. LTD.—See Global Logistic Properties Limited; *Int'l*, pg. 2999
GLP JAPAN ADVISORS INC.—See Global Logistic Properties Limited; *Int'l*, pg. 2999
GLP J-REIT; *Int'l*, pg. 3011
GL PLANT LIMITED—See MJ Gleeson Plc; *Int'l*, pg. 5000
GLP MEDICAL GMBH—See Sonic Healthcare Limited; *Int'l*, pg. 7097
GLP US MANAGEMENT LLC—See Global Logistic Properties Limited; *Int'l*, pg. 2999
G&L REALTY CORP.; *U.S. Private*, pg. 1629
GLR NETWORKS, LLC—See Promotora de Informaciones S.A.; *Int'l*, pg. 5995
G.L. SAYRE INCORPORATED; *U.S. Private*, pg. 1631
GLS BETEILIGUNGS GMBH—See International Distributions Services plc; *Int'l*, pg. 3747
GL SCIENCES B.V.—See GL Sciences Inc.; *Int'l*, pg. 2986
GL SCIENCES INC.; *Int'l*, pg. 2986
GL SCIENCES (SHANGHAI) LIMITED—See GL Sciences Inc.; *Int'l*, pg. 2986
GLS CORPORATION—See Avient Corporation; *U.S. Public*, pg. 247
G.L. SEAMAN & COMPANY-FORT WORTH—See G.L. Seaman & Company; *U.S. Private*, pg. 1631
G.L. SEAMAN & COMPANY; *U.S. Private*, pg. 1631
G&L SENIOR CARE PROPERTIES, LLC—See G&L Realty Corp.; *U.S. Private*, pg. 1629
GLS GENERAL LOGISTICS SYSTEMS HUNGARY KFT.—See International Distributions Services plc; *Int'l*, pg. 3747
GLS GENERAL LOGISTICS SYSTEMS ROMANIA SRL—See International Distributions Services plc; *Int'l*, pg. 3747
GLS GENERAL LOGISTICS SYSTEMS SLOVAKIA S.R.O.—See International Distributions Services plc; *Int'l*, pg. 3747
GLSG GERSTHOFER LOGISTIK- UND SPEDITIONSGESELLSCHAFT MBH; *Int'l*, pg. 3011
GLS HONG KONG LIMITED—See Avient Corporation; *U.S. Public*, pg. 247
GL. SKOVRIDERGAARD A/S—See Jyske Bank A/S; *Int'l*, pg. 4037
GLS LOGISTICS SYSTEMS CANADA LTD.—See International Distributions Services plc; *Int'l*, pg. 3747
GLS PHARMA LIMITED—See Aurobindo Pharma Ltd.; *Int'l*, pg. 713
GLS SUPPLY CHAIN EQUIPMENT PROPRIETARY LIMITED—See Super Group Limited; *Int'l*, pg. 7334
GL STATION NINGBO CO.,LTD.—See DNV GL Group AS; *Int'l*, pg. 2149
GLS THERMOPLASTIC ALLOYS SUZHOU CO., LTD.—See Avient Corporation; *U.S. Public*, pg. 247
GL TECH CO., LTD.; *Int'l*, pg. 2986
GLT INC.; *U.S. Private*, pg. 1721
GL TRADE S.A.—See Fidelity National Infor; *U.S. Public*, pg. 832
GLUCKAUF IMMOBILIEN GMBH (GIG)—See Salzgitter AG; *Int'l*, pg. 6496
GLUCKAUF LOGISTIK GMBH & CO.—See RUAG Holding AG; *Int'l*, pg. 6421
GLUCOSAN COMPANY; *Int'l*, pg. 3011
GLUCOSE HEALTH, INC.; *U.S. Public*, pg. 947
GLUCOTRACK, INC.; *Int'l*, pg. 3011
GLUD & MARSTRAND A/S—See AAC Capital Partners Holding B.V.; *Int'l*, pg. 31
GLUEFAST COMPANY, INC.; *U.S. Private*, pg. 1721
GLUEGENT, INC.—See SIOS Corp.; *Int'l*, pg. 6960
GLU EMEA-GLU MOBILE LTD.—See Electronic Arts Inc.; *U.S. Public*, pg. 724
G. LUFFT MESS- UND REGELTECHNIK GMBH—See Danaher Corporation; *U.S. Public*, pg. 627
GLU MOBILE INC.—See Electronic Arts Inc.; *U.S. Public*, pg. 724
GLU MOBILE TECHNOLOGY (BEIJING) CO. LTD.—See Electronic Arts Inc.; *U.S. Public*, pg. 724
GLUNZ & JENSEN HOLDING A/S; *Int'l*, pg. 3011
GLUNZ & JENSEN, INC.—See Glunz & Jensen Holding A/S; *Int'l*, pg. 3011
GLUNZ & JENSEN LTD.—See Glunz & Jensen Holding A/S; *Int'l*, pg. 3011
GLUNZ & JENSEN S.R.O.—See Glunz & Jensen Holding A/S; *Int'l*, pg. 3011

GLUSKIN SHEFF + ASSOCIATES INC.—See ONEX Corporation; *Int'l*, pg. 5578
G-L VENEER CO. INC.; *U.S. Private*, pg. 1630
GL&V INDIA PVT. LTD.—See GL&V Pulp & Paper; *Int'l*, pg. 2986
GL&V PULP & PAPER; *Int'l*, pg. 2986
GL&V RUSSIA—See GL&V Pulp & Paper; *Int'l*, pg. 2986
GL&V SWEDEN AB - STOCKHOLM—See GL&V Pulp & Paper; *Int'l*, pg. 2986
GL&V SWEDEN AB - TAMPERE—See GL&V Pulp & Paper; *Int'l*, pg. 2986
GL&V USA INC. - HUDSON FALLS—See GL&V Pulp & Paper; *Int'l*, pg. 2987
GL&V USA INC. - LENOX—See GL&V Pulp & Paper; *Int'l*, pg. 2987
GL&V USA INC. - NASHUA—See GL&V Pulp & Paper; *Int'l*, pg. 2987
G.L. WILSON BUILDING COMPANY; *U.S. Private*, pg. 1631
GLYCOMIMETICS, INC.; *U.S. Public*, pg. 947
GLYCONEX, INC.; *Int'l*, pg. 3011
GLY CONSTRUCTION INC.; *U.S. Private*, pg. 1721
GLYCOREX TRANSPLANTATION AB; *Int'l*, pg. 3011
GLYCOTEST, INC.—See NetScientific plc; *Int'l*, pg. 5215
GLYECO ACQUISITION CORP #7—See GlyEco, Inc.; *U.S. Private*, pg. 1721
GLYECO, INC.; *U.S. Private*, pg. 1721
GLYENCE CO., LTD.—See JSR Corp.; *Int'l*, pg. 4014
GLYN GMBH & CO. KG; *Int'l*, pg. 3011
GLYN HUNGARY KFT.—See GLYN GmbH & Co. KG; *Int'l*, pg. 3011
GLYN LTD.—See GLYN GmbH & Co. KG; *Int'l*, pg. 3011
GLYN LTD.—See GLYN GmbH & Co. KG; *Int'l*, pg. 3011
GLYNLYON, INC.—See Silver Lake Group, LLC; *U.S. Private*, pg. 3661
THE GLYNMILL INN INCORPORATED—See Stingray Group Inc.; *Int'l*, pg. 7216
GLYNNDEVINS ADVERTISING & MARKETING; *U.S. Private*, pg. 1721
GLYN POLAND—See GLYN GmbH & Co. KG; *Int'l*, pg. 3011
GLYN SCHWEDEN—See GLYN GmbH & Co. KG; *Int'l*, pg. 3011
GLYN SWITZERLAND—See GLYN GmbH & Co. KG; *Int'l*, pg. 3011
GLYNWED AB—See Aliaxis S.A./N.V.; *Int'l*, pg. 324
GLYNWED AG—See Aliaxis S.A./N.V.; *Int'l*, pg. 324
GLYNWED A/S—See Aliaxis S.A./N.V.; *Int'l*, pg. 324
GLYNWED B.V.—See Aliaxis S.A./N.V.; *Int'l*, pg. 324
GLYNWED N.V.—See Aliaxis S.A./N.V.; *Int'l*, pg. 324
GLYNWED PACIFIC HOLDINGS PTY LTD—See Aliaxis S.A./N.V.; *Int'l*, pg. 324
GLYNWED PIPE SYSTEMS (ASIA) PTE. LTD.—See Aliaxis S.A./N.V.; *Int'l*, pg. 324
GLYNWED PIPE SYSTEMS LTD.—See Aliaxis S.A./N.V.; *Int'l*, pg. 324
GLYNWED S.A.S.—See Aliaxis S.A./N.V.; *Int'l*, pg. 324
GLYNWED SRL—See Aliaxis S.A./N.V.; *Int'l*, pg. 324
GLYNWED S.R.O.—See Aliaxis S.A./N.V.; *Int'l*, pg. 324
GLYNWOOD CENTER, INC.; *U.S. Private*, pg. 1721
GM7 INC.—See Pasona Group Inc.; *Int'l*, pg. 5753
GMA ACCESSORIES/CAPELLI OF NEW YORK; *U.S. Private*, pg. 1721
GMAC ADMINISTRADORA DE CONSORCIOS LTDA.—See General Motors Company; *U.S. Public*, pg. 925
GMAC BANQUE S.A.—See General Motors Company; *U.S. Public*, pg. 925
GMAC DE VENEZUELA, C.A.—See General Motors Company; *U.S. Public*, pg. 925
GMAC ESPANA DE FINANCIACION, S.A. UNIPERSONAL—See General Motors Company; *U.S. Public*, pg. 925
G.M.A.C. FINANCIERA DE COLOMBIA S.A. COMPANIA DE FINANCIAMIENTO COMERCIAL—See General Motors Company; *U.S. Public*, pg. 925
GMAC - INSTITUICAO FINANCEIRA DE CREDITO, S.A.—See General Motors Company; *U.S. Public*, pg. 925
GMAC INTERNATIONAL HOLDINGS B.V.—See General Motors Company; *U.S. Public*, pg. 925
GMAC INTERNATIONAL INSURANCE SERVICES LIMITED—See Stone Point Capital LLC; *U.S. Private*, pg. 3821
GMAC ITALIA SPA—See General Motors Company; *U.S. Public*, pg. 925
GMAC NEDERLAND N.V.—See General Motors Company; *U.S. Public*, pg. 925
GMAC SERVICIOS S.A.S.—See General Motors Company; *U.S. Public*, pg. 925
GMAC UK PLC—See General Motors Company; *U.S. Public*, pg. 925
GMA GESELLSCHAFT FUR MARKT- UND ABSATZFORSCHUNG MBH—See Wuestenrot & Wuerttembergische AG; *Int'l*, pg. 8499
GMA HOLDING B.V.—See Mistras Group, Inc.; *U.S. Public*, pg. 1451
GMA HOLDINGS, INC.; *Int'l*, pg. 3012

GMA HOLDINGS, INC.

CORPORATE AFFILIATIONS

GMA-MADISON, INC.—See Welltower Inc.; *U.S. Public*, pg. 2348
GMA NETWORK, INC.; *Int'l*, pg. 3012
GMA NEW MEDIA, INC.—See GMA Holdings, Inc.; *Int'l*, pg. 3012
G-MARINE SERVICE CO., LTD.—See Hyundai Motor Company; *Int'l*, pg. 3558
G-MARK, INC.—See GSI Creos Corporation; *Int'l*, pg. 3144
G-MART BORNEO RETAIL SDN BHD—See Lay Hong Berhad; *Int'l*, pg. 4427
G.MATICA S.R.L.—See Novomatic AG; *Int'l*, pg. 5467
GM AUTOMOTIVE UK—See General Motors Company; *U.S. Public*, pg. 928
GMA WORLDWIDE (PHILIPPINES), INC.—See GMA Holdings, Inc.; *Int'l*, pg. 3012
GMB CORP.; *Int'l*, pg. 3012
GMB ENGINEERS & PLANNERS INC.—See Vanasse Hangen Brustlin, Inc.; *U.S. Private*, pg. 4342
GMB KOREA CORP.—See GMB Corp.; *Int'l*, pg. 3012
GMB NORTH AMERICA, INC.—See GMB Corp.; *Int'l*, pg. 3012
G.M.BREWERIES LIMITED; *Int'l*, pg. 2866
GM CAMI ASSEMBLY—See General Motors Company; *U.S. Public*, pg. 925
GM CAPITAL CORP.; *Int'l*, pg. 3011
GMC BERGEYS INC.—See Bergeys Inc.; *U.S. Private*, pg. 531
GMC+COMPANY; *U.S. Private*, pg. 1721
GMC HARDWOODS INC.; *U.S. Private*, pg. 1721
GMCI CORP.; *Int'l*, pg. 3012
GMC-I MESSTECHNIK GMBH—See METRAWATT International GmbH; *Int'l*, pg. 4856
GMC-INSTRUMENTS AUSTRIA GMBH—See METRAWATT International GmbH; *Int'l*, pg. 4856
GMC-INSTRUMENTS FRANCE SAS—See METRAWATT International GmbH; *Int'l*, pg. 4856
GMC-INSTRUMENTS ITALIA S.R.L.—See METRAWATT International GmbH; *Int'l*, pg. 4856
GMC-INSTRUMENTS NEDERLAND B.V.—See METRAWATT International GmbH; *Int'l*, pg. 4856
GMC-INSTRUMENTS SCHWEIZ AG—See METRAWATT International GmbH; *Int'l*, pg. 4856
GMC-INSTRUMENTS (TIANJIN) CO., LTD—See METRAWATT International GmbH; *Int'l*, pg. 4856
GMC-I PROSYS LTD.—See METRAWATT International GmbH; *Int'l*, pg. 4856
GMC-I SERVICE GMBH—See METRAWATT International GmbH; *Int'l*, pg. 4856
GMC, LLC—See TREES Corporation; *U.S. Public*, pg. 2188
GMC MERICI TECHNIKA S.R.O.—See METRAWATT International GmbH; *Int'l*, pg. 4856
GM COMPONENTS HOLDINGS, LLC—See General Motors Company; *U.S. Public*, pg. 924
GM CORRETORA DE SEGUROS LTDA.—See General Motors Company; *U.S. Public*, pg. 924
GMC POWERLINES (PTY) LTD—See ARB HOLDINGS LIMITED; *Int'l*, pg. 537
GMC PRODUKT AS—See James Fisher & Sons Public Limited Company; *Int'l*, pg. 3876
G.M. CRISALLI ASSOCIATES, INC.; *U.S. Private*, pg. 1631
GM CRUISE HOLDINGS LLC—See General Motors Company; *U.S. Public*, pg. 924
GM DAEWOO AUSTRALIA PTY. LIMITED—See General Motors Company; *U.S. Public*, pg. 924
GM DAEWOO AUTO & TECHNOLOGY CO.—See General Motors Company; *U.S. Public*, pg. 924
GM DAEWOO UK LIMITED—See General Motors Company; *U.S. Public*, pg. 924
GMDI LEASING CORP.; *U.S. Private*, pg. 1721
GME AEROSPACE INDUSTRIA DE MATERIAL COMPOSTO S.A.—See EFORT Intelligent Equipment Co., Ltd.; *Int'l*, pg. 2321
G MECHANICAL LTD.—See Pic Investment Group Inc.; *Int'l*, pg. 5859
GMED HEALTHCARE BVBA—See Johnson & Johnson; *U.S. Public*, pg. 1196
G MEDICAL DIAGNOSTIC SERVICES, INC.—See G Medical Innovations Holdings Ltd.; *Int'l*, pg. 2861
G MEDICAL INNOVATIONS HOLDINGS LTD.; *Int'l*, pg. 2861
GME GROUP HOLDINGS LIMITED; *Int'l*, pg. 3012
GMEINDER LOKOMOTIVENFABRIK GMBH I.I.—See Landesbank Baden-Wurttemberg; *Int'l*, pg. 4405
GMEINER GMBH—See Bucher Industries AG; *Int'l*, pg. 1208
GME INNOTAINMENT, INC.; *Int'l*, pg. 3012
G&M ELECTRICAL CONTRACTORS CO. INC.; *U.S. Private*, pg. 1629
GME MEDICAL SUPPLY, INC.—See AdaptHealth Corp.; *U.S. Public*, pg. 38
GM EQUIPEMENT S.A.S.—See Bunzl plc; *Int'l*, pg. 1218
G-MES HOLDINGS INC.; *Int'l*, pg. 2862
GMES LLC—See Incline MGMT Corp.; *U.S. Private*, pg. 2053
GMF ASSURANCES S.A.—See Covea Groupe S.A.S.; *Int'l*, pg. 1820

GMF CAPITAL LLC; *U.S. Private*, pg. 1721
GM FINANCE CO. HOLDINGS LLC—See General Motors Company; *U.S. Public*, pg. 924
GM FINANCIAL AB—See General Motors Company; *U.S. Public*, pg. 925
GM FINANCIAL GMBH—See General Motors Company; *U.S. Public*, pg. 925
GMF LEASING LLC—See General Motors Company; *U.S. Public*, pg. 924
GM FOODS CO., LTD.—See Zensho Holdings Co., Ltd.; *Int'l*, pg. 8634
GMFS LLC—See Waterfall Asset Management LLC; *U.S. Private*, pg. 4453
GMG/AXIS, INC.—See ION Geophysical Corporation; *U.S. Public*, pg. 1166
GMG GLOBAL LIMITED—See China Hainan Rubber Industry Group Co., Ltd.; *Int'l*, pg. 1506
GM GLOBAL PURCHASING AND SUPPLY CHAIN ROMANIA SRL—See General Motors Company; *U.S. Public*, pg. 927
GM GLOBAL TECHNOLOGY OPERATIONS LLC—See General Motors Company; *U.S. Public*, pg. 924
GMH AKADEMIE GMBH—See Georgsmarienhutte Holding GmbH; *Int'l*, pg. 2940
GMH ASSOCIATES INC.; *U.S. Private*, pg. 1722
GMH BLANKSTAHL GMBH—See Georgsmarienhutte Holding GmbH; *Int'l*, pg. 2940
GMH COMMUNITIES, LP—See Blackstone Inc.; *U.S. Public*, pg. 347
GMH EAST EUROPE GMBH—See Georgsmarienhutte Holding GmbH; *Int'l*, pg. 2940
GMH FRANCE S.A.R.L.—See Georgsmarienhutte Holding GmbH; *Int'l*, pg. 2940
GMH GROUP DO BRASIL—See Georgsmarienhutte Holding GmbH; *Int'l*, pg. 2940
GMH INDIA PVT. LTD.—See Georgsmarienhutte Holding GmbH; *Int'l*, pg. 2940
GMH INTERNATIONAL S.R.L.—See Georgsmarienhutte Holding GmbH; *Int'l*, pg. 2940
GMH INTERNATIONAL S.R.L.—See Georgsmarienhutte Holding GmbH; *Int'l*, pg. 2940
GM HOLDEN LTD.—See General Motors Company; *U.S. Public*, pg. 924
G & M HOLDINGS LIMITED; *Int'l*, pg. 2861
GMH PRUFTECHNIK GMBH—See Georgsmarienhutte Holding GmbH; *Int'l*, pg. 2940
GMH RECYCLING SAAR GMBH—See Georgsmarienhutte Holding GmbH; *Int'l*, pg. 2940
GMH RINGVERTRIEBS GMBH—See Georgsmarienhutte Holding GmbH; *Int'l*, pg. 2940
GMH SYSTEMS GMBH—See Georgsmarienhutte Holding GmbH; *Int'l*, pg. 2940
GMH UK LTD.—See Georgsmarienhutte Holding GmbH; *Int'l*, pg. 2940
GMI COMPANIES, INC.; *U.S. Private*, pg. 1722
GMI HOLDING, INC.; *U.S. Private*, pg. 1722
G MINING VENTURES CORP.; *Int'l*, pg. 2861
GMI; *U.S. Private*, pg. 1722
G.M.I. TECHNOLOGY INC.; *Int'l*, pg. 2866
GM LAAM HOLDINGS, LLC—See General Motors Company; *U.S. Public*, pg. 924
GML COATINGS, LLC—See Primoris Services Corporation; *U.S. Public*, pg. 1718
GM LEATHER S.P.A.; *Int'l*, pg. 3011
GMLV-GLOBAL MARKETING WITH A LOCAL VISION; *U.S. Private*, pg. 1722
GMMB INC. - SEATTLE—See Omnicom Group Inc.; *U.S. Public*, pg. 1585
GMMB INC—See Omnicom Group Inc.; *U.S. Public*, pg. 1584
GMM CAPITAL LLC; *U.S. Private*, pg. 1722
G.M. MCCROSSIN INC.; *U.S. Private*, pg. 1631
GM MEDICAL PTY LTD—See Paragon Care Limited; *Int'l*, pg. 5736
GMM FITNESS CLUB CO., LTD.—See GMM Grammy Public Company Limited; *Int'l*, pg. 3012
GMM GRAMMY PUBLIC COMPANY LIMITED; *Int'l*, pg. 3012
GMM MEDIA PLC—See GMM Grammy Public Company Limited; *Int'l*, pg. 3012
GMM MUSIC PUBLISHING INTERNATIONAL CO., LTD—See GMM Grammy Public Company Limited; *Int'l*, pg. 3013
GMM TAI HUB CO., LTD.—See GMM Grammy Public Company Limited; *Int'l*, pg. 3012
GM NAMEPLATE INC.—See The Goldman Sachs Group, Inc.; *U.S. Public*, pg. 2080
G.M. NORTHRUP CORPORATION; *U.S. Private*, pg. 1631
GMO AD MARKETING INC.—See GMO Internet Group, Inc.; *Int'l*, pg. 3013
GMO AD PARTNERS INC.—See GMO Internet Group, Inc.; *Int'l*, pg. 3013
GMO BEAUTY INC.—See GMO Internet Group, Inc.; *Int'l*, pg. 3013
GMO BRAND SECURITY INC.—See GMO Internet Group, Inc.; *Int'l*, pg. 3013
GMO BRIGHTS CONSULTING INC.—See GMO Internet Group, Inc.; *Int'l*, pg. 3013

GMO CARD SYSTEM, INC.—See GMO Internet Group, Inc.; *Int'l*, pg. 3013
GMO CARS K.K.—See GMO Internet Group, Inc.; *Int'l*, pg. 3013
GMO CLICK SECURITIES, INC.—See GMO Internet Group, Inc.; *Int'l*, pg. 3013
GMO COMMERCE, INC.—See GMO Internet Group, Inc.; *Int'l*, pg. 3013
GMO CONNECT INC.—See GMO Internet Group, Inc.; *Int'l*, pg. 3013
GMO CREATORS NETWORK, INC.—See GMO Internet Group, Inc.; *Int'l*, pg. 3013
GMO DATA, INC.—See GMO Internet Group, Inc.; *Int'l*, pg. 3013
GMO DIGIROCK, INC.—See GMO Internet Group, Inc.; *Int'l*, pg. 3013
GMO DIGITAL LAB K.K.—See GMO GlobalSign Holdings K.K.; *Int'l*, pg. 3013
GMO DREAM WAVE INC.—See GMO Internet Group, Inc.; *Int'l*, pg. 3013
GMO E-LAB MARKETING RESEARCH (SHANGHAI) CO., LTD.—See GMO Internet Group, Inc.; *Int'l*, pg. 3013
GMO ENGINE INC.—See GMO Internet Group, Inc.; *Int'l*, pg. 3013
GM OFFSHORE, INC.—See Tidewater Inc.; *U.S. Public*, pg. 2158
GMO FINANCIAL GATE, INC.—See GMO Internet Group, Inc.; *Int'l*, pg. 3013
GMO FINANCIAL HOLDINGS, INC.—See GMO Internet Group, Inc.; *Int'l*, pg. 3013
GMO GAMEPOT INC.—See GMO Internet Group, Inc.; *Int'l*, pg. 3013
GMO GLOBALSIGN CERTIFICATE SERVICES PRIVATE LIMITED—See GMO GlobalSign Holdings K.K.; *Int'l*, pg. 3013
GMO GLOBALSIGN CHINA CO., LTD.—See GMO Internet Group, Inc.; *Int'l*, pg. 3013
GMO GLOBALSIGN FZ-LLC—See GMO GlobalSign Holdings K.K.; *Int'l*, pg. 3013
GMO GLOBALSIGN HOLDINGS K.K.; *Int'l*, pg. 3013
GMO GLOBALSIGN, INC.—See GMO GlobalSign Holdings K.K.; *Int'l*, pg. 3013
GMO GLOBALSIGN, INC.—See GMO GlobalSign Holdings K.K.; *Int'l*, pg. 3013
GMO GLOBALSIGN K.K.—See GMO GlobalSign Holdings K.K.; *Int'l*, pg. 3013
GMO GLOBALSIGN LTD.—See GMO GlobalSign Holdings K.K.; *Int'l*, pg. 3013
GMO GLOBALSIGN PHILIPPINES CORP.—See GMO Internet Group, Inc.; *Int'l*, pg. 3013
GMO GLOBALSIGN PTE. LTD.—See GMO GlobalSign Holdings K.K.; *Int'l*, pg. 3013
GMO GLOBALSIGN RUSSIA LLC—See GMO GlobalSign Holdings K.K.; *Int'l*, pg. 3013
G&M OIL CO. INC.; *U.S. Private*, pg. 1629
G&M OIL COMPANY INC.; *U.S. Private*, pg. 1629
GMO INSIGHT INC.—See GMO Internet Group, Inc.; *Int'l*, pg. 3013
GMO INTERNET GROUP, INC.; *Int'l*, pg. 3013
GMO JAPAN MARKET INTELLIGENCE K.K.—See GMO Internet Group, Inc.; *Int'l*, pg. 3014
GMO KUMAPON INC.—See GMO Internet Group, Inc.; *Int'l*, pg. 3014
GMO MAKESHOP CO. LTD.—See GMO Internet Group, Inc.; *Int'l*, pg. 3014
GMO MEDIA, INC.—See GMO Internet Group, Inc.; *Int'l*, pg. 3014
GMO MEDICAL RESERVATIONS TECHNOLOGY CO., LTD.—See GMO Internet Group, Inc.; *Int'l*, pg. 3014
GMO MOBILE, INC.—See GMO Internet Group, Inc.; *Int'l*, pg. 3014
GMO NETSHOP SUPPORT, INC.—See GMO Internet Group, Inc.; *Int'l*, pg. 3014
GMO NIKKO INC.—See GMO Internet Group, Inc.; *Int'l*, pg. 3014
GMO OSHIETE AI, INC.—See GMO Internet Group, Inc.; *Int'l*, pg. 3014
GMO PAYMENT GATEWAY INC.—See GMO Internet Group, Inc.; *Int'l*, pg. 3014
GMO PEPABO, INC.—See GMO Internet Group, Inc.; *Int'l*, pg. 3014
GMO REGISTRY, INC.—See GMO Internet Group, Inc.; *Int'l*, pg. 3014
GMO RESEARCH & AI, INC.—See GMO Internet Group, Inc.; *Int'l*, pg. 3014
GMO RESEARCH PTE. LTD.—See GMO Internet Group, Inc.; *Int'l*, pg. 3014
GMO RESEARCH PVT. LTD.—See GMO Internet Group, Inc.; *Int'l*, pg. 3014
GMO RESEARCH SDN. BHD.—See GMO Internet Group, Inc.; *Int'l*, pg. 3014
GMO RETECH, INC.—See GMO Internet Group, Inc.; *Int'l*, pg. 3014
GMO RUNSYSTEM INC.—See GMO Internet Group, Inc.; *Int'l*, pg. 3014
GMO SOLUTION PARTNER, INC.—See GMO Internet Group, Inc.; *Int'l*, pg. 3014
GMO SYSTEM CONSULTING, INC.—See GMO Internet Group, Inc.; *Int'l*, pg. 3014

COMPANY NAME INDEX

GMO TECH, INC.—See GMO Internet Group, Inc.; *Int'l*, pg. 3014
GMO UNITEX INC.—See GMO Internet Group, Inc.; *Int'l*, pg. 3014
GMO VENTURE PARTNERS, INC.—See GMO Internet Group, Inc.; *Int'l*, pg. 3014
GMO-Z.COM ACE CO., LTD.—See GMO Internet Group, Inc.; *Int'l*, pg. 3014
GMO-Z.COM BRAND SECURITY VIETNAM CO., LTD.—See GMO Internet Group, Inc.; *Int'l*, pg. 3014
GMO-Z.COM BRIGHTS VIETNAM CO., LTD.—See GMO Internet Group, Inc.; *Int'l*, pg. 3014
GMO-Z COM NETDESIGN HOLDINGS CO., LTD.—See GMO Internet Group, Inc.; *Int'l*, pg. 3014
GMO-Z.COM RESEARCH PTE. LTD.—See GMO Internet Group, Inc.; *Int'l*, pg. 3014
GMO-Z.COM RESEARCH PVT. LTD.—See GMO Internet Group, Inc.; *Int'l*, pg. 3014
GMO Z COM RESEARCH SDN. BHD.—See GMO Internet Group, Inc.; *Int'l*, pg. 3014
GMO-Z.COM RUNSYSTEM JSC—See GMO Internet Group, Inc.; *Int'l*, pg. 3014
GMO-Z.COM USA INC.—See GMO Internet Group, Inc.; *Int'l*, pg. 3014
GMO-Z.COM VIETNAM LAB CENTER CO., LTD.—See GMO Internet Group, Inc.; *Int'l*, pg. 3014
GMPC; *U.S. Private*, pg. 1723
GM PETROLEUM DISTRIBUTORS INC.; *U.S. Private*, pg. 1721
GM PHILIPPINES, INC.—See General Motors Company; *U.S. Public*, pg. 924
GM PLACE INC.; *U.S. Private*, pg. 1721
GMP METAL PRODUCTS—See Wozniak Industries, Inc.; *U.S. Private*, pg. 4571
GM POLYPLAST LIMITED; *Int'l*, pg. 3012
GM POWERTRAIN GROUP—See General Motors Company; *U.S. Public*, pg. 924
GMP PROGRAPHICS GERMANY GMBH—See VT Co., Ltd.; *Int'l*, pg. 8315
GMP PROPERTY SOCIMI SA; *Int'l*, pg. 3014
GM PREFERRED FINANCE CO. HOLDINGS LLC—See General Motors Company; *U.S. Public*, pg. 924
GMP SECURITIES, LLC—See StoneX Group Inc.; *U.S. Public*, pg. 1952
GMP SECURITIES L.P.—See RF Capital Group Inc.; *Int'l*, pg. 6318
GMP TECHNICAL SOLUTIONS PRIVATE LIMITED—See Mitsubishi Heavy Industries, Ltd.; *Int'l*, pg. 4961
G&M PTE LTD.; *Int'l*, pg. 2862
GMR AERO TECHNIC LIMITED—See GMR Airports Infrastructure Limited; *Int'l*, pg. 3015
GMR AIRPORTS INFRASTRUCTURE LIMITED; *Int'l*, pg. 3015
GMR AVIATION PRIVATE LIMITED—See GMR Airports Infrastructure Limited; *Int'l*, pg. 3015
GMR ENTERTAINMENT—See Omnicom Group Inc.; *U.S. Public*, pg. 1593
THE GMR GROUP—See Omnicom Group Inc.; *U.S. Public*, pg. 1599
GMR LONDON—See Omnicom Group Inc.; *U.S. Public*, pg. 1593
GMR MARKETING LLC—See Omnicom Group Inc.; *U.S. Public*, pg. 1593
GMR MARKETING—See Omnicom Group Inc.; *U.S. Public*, pg. 1593
GMR MARKETING—See Omnicom Group Inc.; *U.S. Public*, pg. 1593
GMR MARKETING—See Omnicom Group Inc.; *U.S. Public*, pg. 1593
GMR MARKETING—See Omnicom Group Inc.; *U.S. Public*, pg. 1593
GMR MARKETING—See Omnicom Group Inc.; *U.S. Public*, pg. 1593
GMR MARKETING SPAIN—See Omnicom Group Inc.; *U.S. Public*, pg. 1593
G & M SALES OF EASTERN NC, INC.; *U.S. Private*, pg. 1628
GMS INC.; *U.S. Public*, pg. 947
GM SINGAPORE PTE. LIMITED—See General Motors Company; *U.S. Public*, pg. 924
GMS MINE REPAIR & MAINTENANCE; *U.S. Private*, pg. 1723
GMSS HOLDINGS, LLC; *U.S. Private*, pg. 1723
GMS STRATEGIC SOLUTIONS, INC.—See GMS Inc.; *U.S. Public*, pg. 948
GMST, LLC; *U.S. Private*, pg. 1723
GMT CAPITAL CORP.; *U.S. Private*, pg. 1723
GMT COMMUNICATIONS PARTNERS LLP; *Int'l*, pg. 3015
GMT CORPORATION; *U.S. Private*, pg. 1723
GM TECHNICAL CENTER KOREA, LTD.—See General Motors Company; *U.S. Public*, pg. 924
GMTEST CO., LTD.—See TSE Co., Ltd.; *Int'l*, pg. 7949
GMT GLOBAL REPUBLIC AVIATION LTD.—See Republic Financial Corporation; *U.S. Private*, pg. 3402
GMT GMBH—See National Industries Group Holding S.A.K.; *Int'l*, pg. 5159

GMT MEMBRANTECHNIK GMBH—See KNM Group Berhad; *Int'l*, pg. 4209
GMTM HOLDINGS PTE. LTD.—See VibroPower Corporation Limited; *Int'l*, pg. 8185
G&M TOWING & RECOVERY, LLC—See Total Recovery Group, LLC; *U.S. Private*, pg. 4191
GMT PRODUCTIONS S.A.S.—See Vivendi SE; *Int'l*, pg. 8275
GMT TABUR ELECTRICITE SA—See Sonepar S.A.; *Int'l*, pg. 7090
GM (UK) PENSION TRUSTEES LIMITED—See General Motors Company; *U.S. Public*, pg. 928
GMUL INVESTMENT COMPANY, LTD.; *Int'l*, pg. 3015
GMUNDNERBERG HOLDING GMBH—See Fresenius SE & Co. KGaA; *Int'l*, pg. 2778
GMV ESCHMANN INTERNATIONAL SAS—See voestalpine AG; *Int'l*, pg. 8289
GMV INNOVATING SOLUTIONS, S.L.—See Grupo Tecnologico e Industrial GMV, S.A.; *Int'l*, pg. 3135
GMV MINERALS INC.; *Int'l*, pg. 3015
GM VOICES, INC.—See GetBlend Inc.; *U.S. Private*, pg. 1688
G & M WAREHOUSING ENTERPRISES LIMITED—See Hadco Limited; *Int'l*, pg. 3205
GM WESTBERRY, LLC—See Greystar Real Estate Partners, LLC; *U.S. Private*, pg. 1785
GMX GMBH—See United Internet AG; *Int'l*, pg. 8069
GMX INC.; *U.S. Private*, pg. 1723
GMX INTERNET SERVICES GMBH—See United Internet AG; *Int'l*, pg. 8069
GMX RESOURCES INC.; *U.S. Private*, pg. 1723
GMX—See Garland Industries Inc.; *U.S. Private*, pg. 1644
GMZ ENERGY, INC.—See Evident Thermoelectrics; *U.S. Private*, pg. 1441
GMZ, INC.—See EQT AB; *Int'l*, pg. 2469
GNA AXLES LIMITED; *Int'l*, pg. 3016
GNARUS ADVISORS LLC—See Nathan Associates Inc.; *U.S. Private*, pg. 2838
GN AUDIO AUSTRALIA PTY. LTD.—See GN Store Nord A/S; *Int'l*, pg. 3015
GN AUDIO (CHINA) LTD.—See GN Store Nord A/S; *Int'l*, pg. 3015
GN AUDIO FRANCE SA—See GN Store Nord A/S; *Int'l*, pg. 3015
GN AUDIO HONG KONG LIMITED—See GN Store Nord A/S; *Int'l*, pg. 3015
GN AUDIO ITALY S.R.L.—See GN Store Nord A/S; *Int'l*, pg. 3015
GN AUDIO LOGISTIC (XIAMEN) LTD.—See GN Store Nord A/S; *Int'l*, pg. 3015
GN AUDIO (SHANGHAI) CO., LTD.—See GN Store Nord A/S; *Int'l*, pg. 3015
GN AUDIO SINGAPORE PTE. LTD.—See GN Store Nord A/S; *Int'l*, pg. 3015
GN AUDIO SPAIN, S.A.—See GN Store Nord A/S; *Int'l*, pg. 3015
GN AUDIO SWEDEN AB—See GN Store Nord A/S; *Int'l*, pg. 3015
GN AUDIO UK LTD.—See GN Store Nord A/S; *Int'l*, pg. 3015
GN AUDIO USA, INC.—See GN Store Nord A/S; *Int'l*, pg. 3015
GNB BANCORPORATION; *U.S. Private*, pg. 1723
GNB - COMPANHIA DE SEGUROS DE VIDA, S.A.—See Apax Partners LLP; *Int'l*, pg. 504
GNB CORPORATION—See Ellison Technologies Inc.; *U.S. Private*, pg. 1374
GNBS ECO CO.,LTD; *Int'l*, pg. 3016
GNCC CAPITAL, INC.; *U.S. Public*, pg. 949
GNC CORPORATION—See Ares Management Corporation; *U.S. Public*, pg. 189
GNC CORPORATION—See Ontario Teachers' Pension Plan; *Int'l*, pg. 5589
GNC ENERGY CO., LTD.; *Int'l*, pg. 3016
GNC HOLDINGS INC.—See Ares Management Corporation; *U.S. Public*, pg. 189
GNC HOLDINGS INC.—See Ontario Teachers' Pension Plan; *Int'l*, pg. 5589
GNC HONG KONG LIMITED—See Ares Management Corporation; *U.S. Public*, pg. 189
GNC HONG KONG LIMITED—See Ontario Teachers' Pension Plan; *Int'l*, pg. 5589
GNC MANUFACTURING, S.A—See Nicolas Correa S.A.; *Int'l*, pg. 5273
GNCO CO., LTD.; *Int'l*, pg. 3016
GNCO, INC.; *U.S. Private*, pg. 1723
GNC PARENT LLC—See Ares Management Corporation; *U.S. Public*, pg. 189
GNC PARENT LLC—See Ontario Teachers' Pension Plan; *Int'l*, pg. 5589
GN EJENDOMME A/S—See GN Store Nord A/S; *Int'l*, pg. 3015
G-NET CORPORATION—See Maruka Furusato Corporation; *Int'l*, pg. 4714
G-NEXT, INC.; *Int'l*, pg. 2862
GN HEARING A/S—See GN Store Nord A/S; *Int'l*, pg. 3015
GN HEARING AUSTRALIA PTY. LTD.—See GN Store Nord A/S; *Int'l*, pg. 3015

GNOSTECH, INC.

GN HEARING AUSTRIA GMBH—See GN Store Nord A/S; *Int'l*, pg. 3015
GN HEARING BENELUX B.V.—See GN Store Nord A/S; *Int'l*, pg. 3015
GN HEARING CARE CANADA LTD—See GN Store Nord A/S; *Int'l*, pg. 3015
GN HEARING CARE CORPORATION—See GN Store Nord A/S; *Int'l*, pg. 3015
GN HEARING CARE S.A.—See GN Store Nord A/S; *Int'l*, pg. 3015
GN HEARING CZECH REPUBLIC SPOL. S R.O.—See GN Store Nord A/S; *Int'l*, pg. 3015
GN HEARING FINLAND OY/AB—See GN Store Nord A/S; *Int'l*, pg. 3015
GN HEARING GMBH—See GN Store Nord A/S; *Int'l*, pg. 3016
GN HEARING INDIA PRIVATE LIMITED—See GN Store Nord A/S; *Int'l*, pg. 3015
GN HEARING JAPAN K.K.—See GN Store Nord A/S; *Int'l*, pg. 3015
GN HEARING KOREA CO., LTD.—See GN Store Nord A/S; *Int'l*, pg. 3015
GN HEARING (MALAYSIA) SDN. BHD.—See GN Store Nord A/S; *Int'l*, pg. 3015
GN HEARING NEW ZEALAND LIMITED—See GN Store Nord A/S; *Int'l*, pg. 3015
GN HEARING NORWAY AS—See GN Store Nord A/S; *Int'l*, pg. 3015
GN HEARING PTE. LTD.—See GN Store Nord A/S; *Int'l*, pg. 3015
GN HEARING SAS—See GN Store Nord A/S; *Int'l*, pg. 3015
GN HEARING SRL—See GN Store Nord A/S; *Int'l*, pg. 3016
GN HEARING SVERIGE AB—See GN Store Nord A/S; *Int'l*, pg. 3015
GN HEARING SWITZERLAND AG—See GN Store Nord A/S; *Int'l*, pg. 3015
GNI GROUP LTD.; *Int'l*, pg. 3017
G.N. JOHNSTON EQUIPMENT CO., LTD.—See Toyota Industries Corporation; *Int'l*, pg. 7869
G. N. JOHNSTON EQUIPMENT CO., LTD.—See Toyota Industries Corporation; *Int'l*, pg. 7869
GNL CHILE S.A.—See Enel S.p.A.; *Int'l*, pg. 2414
GNL ITALIA S.P.A.—See Eni S.p.A.; *Int'l*, pg. 2438
GNM AUSTRALIA PTY LIMITED—See The Scott Trust Limited; *Int'l*, pg. 7680
GN NETCOM AB—See GN Store Nord A/S; *Int'l*, pg. 3016
GN NETCOM A/S—See GN Store Nord A/S; *Int'l*, pg. 3016
GN NETCOM BENELUX B.V.—See GN Store Nord A/S; *Int'l*, pg. 3016
GN NETCOM GMBH—See GN Store Nord A/S; *Int'l*, pg. 3016
GN NETCOM (IBERICA) S.A.—See GN Store Nord A/S; *Int'l*, pg. 3016
GN NETCOM INC.—See GN Store Nord A/S; *Int'l*, pg. 3016
GN NETCOM (ITALIA) S.R.L—See GN Store Nord A/S; *Int'l*, pg. 3016
GN NETCOM (UK) LTD.—See GN Store Nord A/S; *Int'l*, pg. 3016
GNO INTERNATIONAL LLC; *U.S. Private*, pg. 1723
GNOMESTAR CRAFT INC.; *Int'l*, pg. 3017
GNOMI + DRAFTFCB—See The Interpublic Group of Companies, Inc.; *U.S. Public*, pg. 2093
GNOSCO AB—See Barco N.V.; *Int'l*, pg. 864
GNOSIS BIORESEARCH S.A.—See Societa Esercizi Commerciali Industriali; *Int'l*, pg. 7034
GNOSIS BIORESEARCH S.R.L.—See Societa Esercizi Commerciali Industriali; *Int'l*, pg. 7034
GNOSIS S.P.A.—See Societa Esercizi Commerciali Industriali; *Int'l*, pg. 7034
GNOSIS USA INC.—See Societa Esercizi Commerciali Industriali; *Int'l*, pg. 7034
GNOSJOPLAST AB—See Duroc AB; *Int'l*, pg. 2229
GNOSTECH, INC. - SAN DIEGO—See Gnostech, Inc.; *U.S. Private*, pg. 1723
GNOSTECH, INC.; *U.S. Private*, pg. 1723
GNPOWER KAUSWAGAN CO., LTD.—See Ayala Corporation; *Int'l*, pg. 774
GNPOWER MARIVELES ENERGY CENTER LTD. CO.—See Aboitiz Equity Ventures, Inc.; *Int'l*, pg. 66
GN RESEARCH FRANCE—See Teleperformance SE; *Int'l*, pg. 7540
GN RESEARCH GERMANY GMBH—See Teleperformance SE; *Int'l*, pg. 7540
GNRESEARCH ITALIA—See Teleperformance SE; *Int'l*, pg. 7541
GN RESOUND AB—See GN Store Nord A/S; *Int'l*, pg. 3016
GN RESOUND AG—See GN Store Nord A/S; *Int'l*, pg. 3016
GN RESOUND A/S—See GN Store Nord A/S; *Int'l*, pg. 3016
GN RESOUND CHINA LTD.—See GN Store Nord A/S; *Int'l*, pg. 3016
GN RESOUND CORPORATION—See GN Store Nord A/S; *Int'l*, pg. 3016

GNOSTECH, INC.

GN RESOUND DO BRAZIL LTDA.—See GN Store Nord A/S; *Int'l*, pg. 3016
GN RESOUND HEARING CARE EQU. (SHANGHAI)—See GN Store Nord A/S; *Int'l*, pg. 3016
GN RESOUND INDIA PRIVATE LIMITED—See GN Store Nord A/S; *Int'l*, pg. 3016
GN RESOUND ITALIA SRL—See GN Store Nord A/S; *Int'l*, pg. 3016
GN RESOUND LTD.—See GN Store Nord A/S; *Int'l*, pg. 3016
GN RESOUND NORGE AS—See GN Store Nord A/S; *Int'l*, pg. 3016
GN RESOUND PTY. LTD.—See GN Store Nord A/S; *Int'l*, pg. 3016
GN RESOUND S.A.S—See GN Store Nord A/S; *Int'l*, pg. 3016
GN RESOUND SINGAPORE PTE. LTD.—See GN Store Nord A/S; *Int'l*, pg. 3016
THE GNS GROUP, INC.; *U.S. Public*, pg. 2075
GN STORE NORD A/S; *Int'l*, pg. 3015
GN US HOLDINGS INC.; *U.S. Private*, pg. 1723
GNUTTI CARLO GERMANY GMBH—See Gnutti Carlo S.p.A.; *Int'l*, pg. 3017
GNUTTI CARLO INDIA LTD—See Gnutti Carlo S.p.A.; *Int'l*, pg. 3017
GNUTTI CARLO S.P.A.; *Int'l*, pg. 3017
GNUTTI CARLO SWEDEN AB KUNGSOR FACILITY—See Gnutti Carlo S.p.A.; *Int'l*, pg. 3017
GNUTTI CARLO SWEDEN AB—See Gnutti Carlo S.p.A.; *Int'l*, pg. 3017
GNUTTI CARLO UK LTD—See Gnutti Carlo S.p.A.; *Int'l*, pg. 3017
GNUTTI CARLO USA, INC.—See Gnutti Carlo S.p.A.; *Int'l*, pg. 3017
GNUTTI CARLO (WUXI) ENGINE COMPONENTS CO., LTD.—See Gnutti Carlo S.p.A.; *Int'l*, pg. 3017
GNUTTI LTD.—See Gnutti Carlo S.p.A.; *Int'l*, pg. 3017
GO2CALL.COM, INC.; *U.S. Private*, pg. 1724
GO2 COMMUNICATIONS, INC.—See Gemspring Capital Management, LLC; *U.S. Private*, pg. 1659
GO2TEL.COM, INC.—See INNOVATE Corp.; *U.S. Public*, pg. 1126
GO4YU D.O.O.—See Telekomunikacije Republike Srpske a.d.; *Int'l*, pg. 7538
GOA CARBON LTD.; *Int'l*, pg. 3017
GO ACQUISITION CORP.; *U.S. Public*, pg. 949
GO ADVERTISING PTY. LTD.—See WPP plc; *Int'l*, pg. 8484
GOA GLASS FIBRE LIMITED—See The Braj Binani Group; *Int'l*, pg. 7627
THE GO-AHEAD GROUP PLC—See GLOBALVIA Inversiones, S.A.U.; *Int'l*, pg. 3005
THE GO-AHEAD GROUP PLC—See Kinetic Group Services Pty Ltd.; *Int'l*, pg. 4167
GO-AHEAD LEASING LIMITED—See GLOBALVIA Inversiones, S.A.U.; *Int'l*, pg. 3005
GO-AHEAD LEASING LIMITED—See Kinetic Group Services Pty Ltd.; *Int'l*, pg. 4167
GO-AHEAD LONDON—See GLOBALVIA Inversiones, S.A.U.; *Int'l*, pg. 3005
GO-AHEAD LONDON—See Kinetic Group Services Pty Ltd.; *Int'l*, pg. 4167
GO-AHEAD TRANSPORT SERVICES (DUBLIN) LIMITED—See GLOBALVIA Inversiones, S.A.U.; *Int'l*, pg. 3005
GO-AHEAD TRANSPORT SERVICES (DUBLIN) LIMITED—See Kinetic Group Services Pty Ltd.; *Int'l*, pg. 4167
GOA INVEST S.A.—See Industria de Diseno Textil, S.A.; *Int'l*, pg. 3665
GOAL ACQUISITIONS CORP.; *U.S. Public*, pg. 949
GOALAND ENERGY CONSERVATION TECH USA LTD.—See Guangzhou Goaland Energy Conservation Tech Co.; *Int'l*, pg. 3165
GOAL.COM NORTH AMERICA, INC.—See Vista Equity Partners, LLC; *U.S. Public*, pg. 4401
GOAL FINANCIAL, LLC; *U.S. Private*, pg. 1724
GOAL GERMAN OPERATING AIRCRAFT LEASING GMBH—See Commerzbank AG; *Int'l*, pg. 1718
GOAL GERMAN OPERATING AIRCRAFT LEASING GMBH—See Deutsche Lufthansa AG; *Int'l*, pg. 2066
THE GOAL INC.—See Dentsu Group Inc.; *Int'l*, pg. 2039
GOALSETTER SYSTEMS, INC.—See Escalade, Incorporated; *U.S. Public*, pg. 793
GOALS SOCCER CENTRES PLC; *Int'l*, pg. 3018
GOAL VERWALTUNGSGESELLSCHAFT MBH & CO. PROJEKT NR. 5 KG I.L.—See Deutsche Lufthansa AG; *Int'l*, pg. 2066
GOAL ZERO LLC—See NRG Energy, Inc.; *U.S. Public*, pg. 1550
GOAR, ALLISON & ASSOCIATES, LLC—See Fluor Corporation; *U.S. Public*, pg. 859
GOAT EVEN EMPREENDIMENTOS IMOBILIARIOS LTDA.—See Even Construtora e Incorporadora S.A.; *Int'l*, pg. 2562
GOAT INDUSTRIES LTD.; *Int'l*, pg. 3018
GOAT MILK POWDER B.V.—See Emmi AG; *Int'l*, pg. 2384
THE GO AUTO GROUP; *Int'l*, pg. 7650
GO AUTO; *Int'l*, pg. 3017

GOBARTO SA; *Int'l*, pg. 3018
GOBBA VITRAGE—See Compagnie de Saint-Gobain SA; *Int'l*, pg. 1723
GOBI ACQUISITION CORP.; *Int'l*, pg. 3018
GOBI JOINT STOCK COMPANY; *Int'l*, pg. 3018
GOBI LIBRARY SOLTUIONS—See EBSCO Industries, Inc.; *U.S. Private*, pg. 1325
GOBINS INC.—See All Copy Products LLC; *U.S. Private*, pg. 170
GOBLIN FRANCE SARL—See Goblin India Ltd.; *Int'l*, pg. 3018
GOBLIN INDIA LTD.; *Int'l*, pg. 3018
GOBO DAIICHI TRAFFIC CO., LTD.—See Daiichi Koutsu Sangyo Co., Ltd.; *Int'l*, pg. 1928
GOBOOKINGS SYSTEMS PTY. LIMITED—See Visionflex Group Limited; *Int'l*, pg. 8253
GOBRANDGO, LLC; *U.S. Private*, pg. 1724
GOBRANDS, INC.; *U.S. Private*, pg. 1724
GOCARDLESS LTD.; *Int'l*, pg. 3018
GO CAR FINANCE 2 LTD.—See Solvar Limited; *Int'l*, pg. 7077
G.O. CARLSON, INC.; *U.S. Private*, pg. 1631
GO CARS AND TRUCKS—See AutoNation, Inc.; *U.S. Public*, pg. 235
GOC CO., LTD.; *Int'l*, pg. 3018
GOCL CORPORATION LIMITED—See Hinduja Group Ltd.; *Int'l*, pg. 3398
GOC LTD.; *U.S. Private*, pg. 1724
GOCO GROUP PLC—See Future plc; *Int'l*, pg. 2857
GO COMPANIES, LLC; *U.S. Private*, pg. 1723
GOCOMPARE.COM LIMITED—See Future plc; *Int'l*, pg. 2857
GO CONCEPTS, INC.—See VC3, Inc.; *U.S. Private*, pg. 4349
GOCONNECT LIMITED; *Int'l*, pg. 3018
GOCONVERGENCE; *U.S. Private*, pg. 1724
GOC (PAK) LIMITED; *Int'l*, pg. 3018
GODACO SEAFOOD JOINT STOCK COMPANY; *Int'l*, pg. 3018
GODADDY.COM, LLC—See KKR & Co. Inc.; *U.S. Public*, pg. 1252
GODADDY.COM, LLC—See Silver Lake Group, LLC; *U.S. Private*, pg. 3657
GODADDY.COM, LLC—See TCMI, Inc.; *U.S. Private*, pg. 3943
GODADDY, INC.—See KKR & Co. Inc.; *U.S. Public*, pg. 1252
GODADDY, INC.—See Silver Lake Group, LLC; *U.S. Private*, pg. 3657
GODADDY, INC.—See TCMI, Inc.; *U.S. Private*, pg. 3943
GOD A.D.; *Int'l*, pg. 3018
GODAVARI DRUGS LIMITED; *Int'l*, pg. 3018
GODAWARI ENERGY LIMITED—See Godawari Power & Ispat Ltd.; *Int'l*, pg. 3018
GODAWARI GREEN ENERGY LIMITED—See KKR & Co. Inc.; *U.S. Public*, pg. 1266
GODAWARI POWER & ISPAT LTD.; *Int'l*, pg. 3018
GOD BLESS THE USA, INCORPORATED—See Waste Connections, Inc.; *Int'l*, pg. 8353
GODBY HOME FURNISHINGS INC.; *U.S. Private*, pg. 1724
GODDARD CATERING GROUP (ANTIGUA) LIMITED—See Goddard Enterprises Limited; *Int'l*, pg. 3019
GODDARD CATERING GROUP BOGOTA LTDA.—See Goddard Enterprises Limited; *Int'l*, pg. 3019
GODDARD CATERING GROUP CARACAS S.A.—See Goddard Enterprises Limited; *Int'l*, pg. 3019
GODDARD CATERING GROUP CURACAO, N.V—See Goddard Enterprises Limited; *Int'l*, pg. 3019
GODDARD CATERING GROUP EL SALVADOR, S.A. DE C.V.—See Goddard Enterprises Limited; *Int'l*, pg. 3019
GODDARD CATERING GROUP (GUATEMALA) S.A.—See Goddard Enterprises Limited; *Int'l*, pg. 3019
GODDARD CATERING GROUP GUAYAQUIL S.A.—See Goddard Enterprises Limited; *Int'l*, pg. 3019
GODDARD CATERING GROUP INC.—See Goddard Enterprises Limited; *Int'l*, pg. 3019
GODDARD CATERING GROUP (JAMAICA) LTD.—See Goddard Enterprises Limited; *Int'l*, pg. 3019
GODDARD CATERING GROUP URUGUAY S.A.—See Goddard Enterprises Limited; *Int'l*, pg. 3019
GODDARD ENTERPRISES LIMITED; *Int'l*, pg. 3018
GODDARDS SHIPPING & TOURS LIMITED—See Goddard Enterprises Limited; *Int'l*, pg. 3019
GODDARD SYSTEMS, INC.—See Wind River Holdings, L.P.; *U.S. Private*, pg. 4536
GODECKE GMBH—See Pfizer Inc.; *U.S. Public*, pg. 1680
GODENGO, INC.; *U.S. Private*, pg. 1724
GODERICH-EXETER RAILWAY COMPANY LIMITED—See Brookfield Infrastructure Partners L.P.; *Int'l*, pg. 1191
GODERICH-EXETER RAILWAY COMPANY LIMITED—See GIC Pte. Ltd.; *Int'l*, pg. 2966
GODEX EUROPE GMBH—See Godex International Co. Ltd.; *Int'l*, pg. 3019
GODEX INTERNATIONAL AMERICA, LLC—See Godex International Co., Ltd.; *Int'l*, pg. 3019
GODEX INTERNATIONAL CO., LTD.; *Int'l*, pg. 3019

CORPORATE AFFILIATIONS

GODFATHER'S PIZZA, INC.; *U.S. Private*, pg. 1724
GODFREY ADVERTISING, INC.; *U.S. Private*, pg. 1724
GODFREY HIRST AUSTRALIA PTY. LTD.—See Mohawk Industries, Inc.; *U.S. Public*, pg. 1457
GODFREY HIRST NZ LTD.—See Mohawk Industries, Inc.; *U.S. Public*, pg. 1457
GODFREY HIRST (SINGAPORE) PTE. LTD.—See Mohawk Industries, Inc.; *U.S. Public*, pg. 1457
GODFREY & KAHN, S.C.; *U.S. Private*, pg. 1724
GODFREY PEMBROKE LIMITED—See National Australia Bank Limited; *Int'l*, pg. 5151
GODFREY PHILLIPS INDIA LTD.; *Int'l*, pg. 3019
GODFREY PHILLIPS MIDDLEEAST DMCC—See Godfrey Phillips India Ltd.; *Int'l*, pg. 3019
GODFREYS GROUP LIMITED; *Int'l*, pg. 3019
GODFREYS GROUP LIMITED—See Pacific Equity Partners Pty. Limited; *Int'l*, pg. 5688
GODFREYS GROUP LIMITED—See Unitas Capital Pte. Ltd.; *Int'l*, pg. 8063
GODHA CABCON & INSULATION LTD.; *Int'l*, pg. 3020
G/O DIGITAL MARKETING, LLC—See TEGNA Inc.; *U.S. Public*, pg. 1990
GODIGITAL MEDIA GROUP, LLC; *U.S. Private*, pg. 1724
GODINGER SILVER ART CO. LTD.; *U.S. Private*, pg. 1724
GODIN GUITARS; *Int'l*, pg. 3020
GODISH.COM; *U.S. Private*, pg. 1724
GODIVA BELGIUM BVBA—See Yildiz Holding AS; *Int'l*, pg. 8583
GODIVA CHOCOLATIER, INC.—See Yildiz Holding AS; *Int'l*, pg. 8583
GODIVA LTD.—See IDEX Corp.; *U.S. Public*, pg. 1090
GODIVA MORTGAGES LIMITED—See Coventry Building Society; *Int'l*, pg. 1821
GODIVA SAVINGS LIMITED—See Coventry Building Society; *Int'l*, pg. 1821
GODLAN, INC. - REGIONAL OFFICE—See Godlan, Inc.; *U.S. Private*, pg. 1724
GODLAN, INC.; *U.S. Private*, pg. 1724
GODLEY AUCTION COMPANY, INC.; *U.S. Private*, pg. 1724
GODO CERAMICS LTD.—See Godo Steel, Ltd.; *Int'l*, pg. 3020
GO DOG GO INC.—See Pet Stuff Illinois, LLC; *U.S. Private*, pg. 3156
GODO KAISHA SOURCEFIRE—See Cisco Systems, Inc.; *U.S. Public*, pg. 500
GODOLPHIN RESOURCES LIMITED; *Int'l*, pg. 3020
GODO MARINE INDUSTRY CO., LTD.—See Iino Kaiun Kaisha Ltd.; *Int'l*, pg. 3607
GODO SENPAKU KOGYO CO., LTD.—See Iino Kaiun Kaisha Ltd.; *Int'l*, pg. 3608
GODO SHUSEI CO., LTD.—See Oenon Holdings Inc; *Int'l*, pg. 5529
GODO SOLUTION INC.—See ShinMaywa Industries, Ltd.; *Int'l*, pg. 6846
GODO STEEL, LTD. - FUNABASHI WORKS—See Godo Steel, Ltd.; *Int'l*, pg. 3020
GODO STEEL, LTD. - HIMEJI WORKS—See Godo Steel, Ltd.; *Int'l*, pg. 3020
GODO STEEL, LTD. - OSAKA WORKS—See Godo Steel, Ltd.; *Int'l*, pg. 3020
GODO STEEL, LTD.; *Int'l*, pg. 3020
GODREJ AGROVET LTD.—See Godrej & Boyce Mfg. Co. Ltd.; *Int'l*, pg. 3020
GODREJ AMERICAS INC. USA—See Godrej & Boyce Mfg. Co. Ltd.; *Int'l*, pg. 3020
GODREJ & BOYCE MFG. CO. LTD.; *Int'l*, pg. 3020
GODREJ CONSUMER PRODUCTS LIMITED—See Godrej & Boyce Mfg. Co. Ltd.; *Int'l*, pg. 3020
GODREJ CONSUMER PRODUCTS (UK) LTD—See Jordan/Zalaznick Advisers, Inc.; *U.S. Private*, pg. 2235
GODREJ EFACEC AUTOMATION & ROBOTICS LTD.—See Efacec Capital, SGPS, S.A.; *Int'l*, pg. 2318
GODREJ EFACEC AUTOMATION & ROBOTICS LTD.—See Godrej & Boyce Mfg. Co. Ltd.; *Int'l*, pg. 3020
GODREJ GLOBAL MID EAST FZE—See Godrej & Boyce Mfg. Co. Ltd.; *Int'l*, pg. 3020
GODREJ HOUSEHOLD PRODUCTS LIMITED—See Godrej & Boyce Mfg. Co. Ltd.; *Int'l*, pg. 3021
GODREJ INDUSTRIES LTD—See Godrej & Boyce Mfg. Co. Ltd.; *Int'l*, pg. 3020
GODREJ INFOTECH LTD.—See Godrej & Boyce Mfg. Co. Ltd.; *Int'l*, pg. 3020
GODREJ (MALAYSIA) SDN. BHD.—See Godrej & Boyce Mfg. Co. Ltd.; *Int'l*, pg. 3020
GODREJ NIGERIA LTD.—See Godrej & Boyce Mfg. Co. Ltd.; *Int'l*, pg. 3021
GODREJ PROPERTIES LIMITED—See Godrej & Boyce Mfg. Co. Ltd.; *Int'l*, pg. 3021
GODREJ (SINGAPORE) PTE. LTD.—See Godrej & Boyce Mfg. Co. Ltd.; *Int'l*, pg. 3020
GODREJ TYSON FOODS LTD.—See Godrej & Boyce Mfg. Co. Ltd.; *Int'l*, pg. 3020
GODREJ (VIETNAM) CO. LTD.—See Godrej & Boyce Mfg. Co. Ltd.; *Int'l*, pg. 3020
GODSELL CONSTRUCTION CORP.; *U.S. Private*, pg. 1724

COMPANY NAME INDEX

GODSHALL QUALITY MEATS INC.; *U.S. Private*, pg. 1724
GODSIL CONSTRUCTION, INC.; *U.S. Private*, pg. 1725
GODSINLOSEN NORDIC AB; *Int'l*, pg. 3021
GODSPEED CAPITAL MANAGEMENT LP; *U.S. Private*, pg. 1725
GOD'S PIT CREW; *U.S. Private*, pg. 1724
GOD'S WORLD PUBLICATIONS INC.; *U.S. Private*, pg. 1724
GODWIN ADVERTISING AGENCY, INC.; *U.S. Private*, pg. 1725
THE GODWIN GROUP; *U.S. Private*, pg. 4033
GODWINGROUP—See Godwin Advertising Agency, Inc.; *U.S. Private*, pg. 1725
GODWIN HARDWARE, INC.; *U.S. Private*, pg. 1725
GODWIN MANUFACTURING COMPANY INC.—See The Godwin Group; *U.S. Private*, pg. 4033
GODWIN PLUMBING INC.—See Godwin Hardware, Inc.; *U.S. Private*, pg. 1725
GODWIN & REESE INSURANCE AGENCY, INC.; *U.S. Private*, pg. 1725
GODWIN-SBO L.P.—See Schoeller-Bleckmann Oilfield Equipment AG; *Int'l*, pg. 6637
GODWIN'S GATORLAND, INC.; *U.S. Private*, pg. 1725
GOEASY LTD.; *Int'l*, pg. 3021
GOEBEL FIXTURE CO.; *U.S. Private*, pg. 1725
GOEBEL GATHERING COMPANY, L.L.C.—See The Williams Companies, Inc.; *U.S. Public*, pg. 2142
GOECART; *U.S. Private*, pg. 1725
GO ELECTRIC INC.—See TotalEnergies SE; *Int'l*, pg. 7837
GO ELEMENT CO., LTD.; *Int'l*, pg. 3017
GOEL FOOD PRODUCTS LIMITED; *Int'l*, pg. 3021
GOELLNER, INC.; *U.S. Private*, pg. 1726
GO ENERGISTICS LLC; *U.S. Private*, pg. 1723
GOENERGY COMPANY LIMITED—See GOIL PLC; *Int'l*, pg. 3022
GO ENGINEER, INC.—See Court Square Capital Partners, L.P.; *U.S. Private*, pg. 1069
GOENKA BUSINESS & FINANCE LTD.; *Int'l*, pg. 3021
GOENKA DIAMOND AND JEWELS LIMITED; *Int'l*, pg. 3021
GO EPIC HEALTH, INC.—See Leone Asset Management, Inc.; *U.S. Public*, pg. 1308
GOERTEK ELECTRONICS,INC.—See GoerTek Inc.; *Int'l*, pg. 3021
GOERTEK INC.; *Int'l*, pg. 3021
GOERTEK KOREA TECHNOLOGY INC.—See GoerTek Inc.; *Int'l*, pg. 3021
GOERTEK ROBOTICS CO., LTD.—See GoerTek Inc.; *Int'l*, pg. 3021
GOERTEK SHINNEI TECHNOLOGY CO., LTD.—See GoerTek Inc.; *Int'l*, pg. 3021
GOERTEK TECHNOLOGY JAPAN CO., LTD.—See GoerTek Inc.; *Int'l*, pg. 3021
GOESSLING USA, INC.—See Dr. Ing. Gossling Maschinenfabrik GmbH; *Int'l*, pg. 2192
GOETECH LLC—See Becton, Dickinson & Company; *U.S. Public*, pg. 292
GOETTFERT (CHINA) LIMITED—See GOTTFERT Werkstoff-Prufmaschinen GmbH; *Int'l*, pg. 3044
GOETTFERT - DATAPHYSICS INSTRUMENTS INDIA PVT. LTD.—See GOTTFERT Werkstoff-Prufmaschinen GmbH; *Int'l*, pg. 3044
GOETTFERT INC.—See GOTTFERT Werkstoff-Prufmaschinen GmbH; *Int'l*, pg. 3044
GOETZE DENTAL; *U.S. Private*, pg. 1726
GOETZ ENERGY CORPORATION; *U.S. Private*, pg. 1726
GOEVA N.V.—See Umdasch Group AG; *Int'l*, pg. 8023
GOEX CORPORATION; *U.S. Private*, pg. 1726
GOEX INTERNATIONAL INC.—See Incitec Pivot Limited; *Int'l*, pg. 3648
GO FASHION INDIA LIMITED; *Int'l*, pg. 3017
GO FAST SPORTS & BEVERAGE CO.—See CBD Global Sciences, Inc.; *U.S. Public*, pg. 455
GOFBA, INC.; *U.S. Private*, pg. 1726
GOFEMININ.DE GMBH—See Television Francaise 1 S.A.; *Int'l*, pg. 7542
GOFEN & GLOSSBERG, LLC; *U.S. Private*, pg. 1726
GOFF CAPITAL, INC.; *U.S. Private*, pg. 1726
GOFF COMMUNICATIONS INC.; *U.S. Private*, pg. 1726
GOFF INC.; *U.S. Private*, pg. 1726
GOFF'S ENTERPRISES INC.; *U.S. Private*, pg. 1726
GOFINTECH INNOVATION LIMITED; *Int'l*, pg. 3021
GOFIVE CO., LTD.—See T.K.S. Technologies Public Company Limited; *Int'l*, pg. 7397
GO FLY A KITE—See JAKKS Pacific, Inc.; *U.S. Public*, pg. 1186
GOFORE PLC; *Int'l*, pg. 3022
GOGAS GOCH GMBH & CO. KG; *Int'l*, pg. 3022
GO GASTSTATTENBETRIEBS GMBH; *Int'l*, pg. 3017
GOGEBIC RANGE BANK—See West End Financial Corp.; *U.S. Private*, pg. 4485
GOGERTY STARK MARRIOTT; *U.S. Private*, pg. 1726
GOG FOUNDATION, INC.; *U.S. Private*, pg. 1726
THE GOG FOUNDATION, INC.; *U.S. Private*, pg. 4033
GOGIA CAPITAL SERVICES LIMITED; *Int'l*, pg. 3022
THE GOGIN AGENCY CO., LTD.—See The San-In Godo Bank, Ltd.; *Int'l*, pg. 7680

THE GOGIN BUSINESS SERVICES CO., LTD.—See The San-In Godo Bank, Ltd.; *Int'l*, pg. 7680
THE GOGIN CAPITAL CO., LTD.—See The San-In Godo Bank, Ltd.; *Int'l*, pg. 7680
THE GOGIN STAFF SERVICES CO., LTD.—See The San-In Godo Bank, Ltd.; *Int'l*, pg. 7680
GOGLANIAN BAKERIES INC.; *U.S. Private*, pg. 1726
GOGLIO S.P.A.; *Int'l*, pg. 3022
GOGO AIR INTERNATIONAL SARL—See Gogo Inc.; *U.S. Public*, pg. 949
GO-GO BABYZ, CORP.; *U.S. Private*, pg. 1723
GOGO BUSINESS AVIATION LLC—See Gogo Inc.; *U.S. Public*, pg. 949
GOGO ENERGY LIMITED—See GOGOX Holdings Limited; *Int'l*, pg. 3022
GOGO ENERGY SINGAPORE PTE. LTD.—See GOGOX Holdings Limited; *Int'l*, pg. 3022
GOGO INC.; *U.S. Public*, pg. 949
GOGOLD RESOURCES INC.; *Int'l*, pg. 3022
GOGO LLC—See Gogo Inc.; *U.S. Public*, pg. 949
GOGOLOOK CO., LTD.; *Int'l*, pg. 3022
GOGORO INC.; *Int'l*, pg. 3022
GOGOX HOLDINGS LIMITED; *Int'l*, pg. 3022
GO GREEN GLOBAL TECHNOLOGIES CORP.; *U.S. Public*, pg. 949
GOGREEN INVESTMENTS CORP.; *U.S. Public*, pg. 949
GO GREEN (OH) LLC—See W.P. Carey Inc.; *U.S. Public*, pg. 2315
GOH CLEAN ENERGY LLC—See Elixir Energy Limited; *Int'l*, pg. 2363
GOHEALTH, INC.; *U.S. Public*, pg. 949
GOHIGH NETWORKS CO., LTD.; *Int'l*, pg. 3022
GOH KWANG HENG PTE LTD—See Chasen Holdings Limited; *Int'l*, pg. 1457
GOHMANN ASPHALT & CONSTRUCTION INC.; *U.S. Private*, pg. 1726
GOHOME H.K. CO. LTD.—See News Corporation; *U.S. Public*, pg. 1519
GOIDINGER BAU GMBH—See PORR AG; *Int'l*, pg. 5923
G.O.I. ENERGY LIMITED; *Int'l*, pg. 2866
GOIJENS RECYCLING N.V.—See SigmaRoc Plc; *Int'l*, pg. 6909
GOIL PLC; *Int'l*, pg. 3022
GOINDUSTRY DOVEBID ASSET MANAGEMENT (H.K.) LTD.—See Liquidity Services, Inc.; *U.S. Public*, pg. 1320
GOINDUSTRY-DOVEBID (AUSTRALIA) PTY. LTD.—See Liquidity Services, Inc.; *U.S. Public*, pg. 1320
GOINDUSTRY-DOVEBID (HONG KONG) LTD—See Liquidity Services, Inc.; *U.S. Public*, pg. 1320
GOINDUSTRY-DOVEBID LIMITED—See Liquidity Services, Inc.; *U.S. Public*, pg. 1320
GOINDUSTRY-DOVEBID (MALAYSIA) SDN. BHD.—See Liquidity Services, Inc.; *U.S. Public*, pg. 1321
GOINDUSTRY-DOVEBID MEXICO SA DE CV—See Liquidity Services, Inc.; *U.S. Public*, pg. 1321
GOINDUSTRY-DOVEBID PHILIPPINES, INC.—See Liquidity Services, Inc.; *U.S. Public*, pg. 1321
GOINDUSTRY-DOVEBID (SHANGHAI) CO., LTD.—See Liquidity Services, Inc.; *U.S. Public*, pg. 1321
GOINDUSTRY DOVEBID (S) PTE. LTD—See Liquidity Services, Inc.; *U.S. Public*, pg. 1320
GOINGPUBLIC MEDIA AG; *Int'l*, pg. 3022
GOIN' POSTAL FRANCHISE CORPORATION; *U.S. Private*, pg. 1726
GO INSPIRE GROUP LIMITED—See Xerox Holdings Corporation; *U.S. Public*, pg. 2386
GO INTERNET S.P.A.; *Int'l*, pg. 3017
GOITI ITALIA SRL—See Mondragon Corporation; *Int'l*, pg. 5028
GOJO INDUSTRIES, INC.; *U.S. Private*, pg. 1726
GO JO INDUSTRIES, INC.; *U.S. Private*, pg. 1723
GOKAK TEXTILES LTD.; *Int'l*, pg. 3022
GOKALDAS EXPORTS LTD; *Int'l*, pg. 3022
GOKALS LABOREX GHANA—See Toyota Tsusho Corporation; *Int'l*, pg. 7876
GOKE MICROELECTRONICS CO., LTD.; *Int'l*, pg. 3022
GOKOH SHOJI CO., LTD.—See Sumitomo Electric Industries, Ltd.; *Int'l*, pg. 7278
GOKOH TRADING (SHANGHAI) CO., LTD.—See Sumitomo Electric Industries, Ltd.; *Int'l*, pg. 7278
GOKO KASEI INDUSTRIAL CO., LTD.—See Moriroku Holdings Company, Ltd.; *Int'l*, pg. 5047
GOKO TRADING CO., LTD.—See JSR Corp.; *Int'l*, pg. 4013
GOK REGLER- UND ARMATUREN- GESELLSCHAFT MBH & CO. KG; *Int'l*, pg. 3022
GOKUL AGRI INTERNATIONAL LTD.—See Gokul Refoils and Solvent Limited; *Int'l*, pg. 3022
GOKUL AGRO RESOURCES LTD.—See Gokul Refoils and Solvent Limited; *Int'l*, pg. 3023
GOKUL REFOILS AND SOLVENT LIMITED - GANDHIDHAM UNIT—See Gokul Refoils and Solvent Limited; *Int'l*, pg. 3023
GOKUL REFOILS AND SOLVENT LIMITED; *Int'l*, pg. 3022
GOKUL SOLUTIONS LIMITED; *Int'l*, pg. 3023
GOKURA CO., LTD.—See Japan Pulp and Paper Company Limited; *Int'l*, pg. 3903

GOLDBELT EMPIRES LIMITED

GOKURAKUYU HOLDINGS CO., LTD.; *Int'l*, pg. 3023
GOLAN MEAT INDUSTRY COMPANY—See MAS Economic Group; *Int'l*, pg. 4718
GOLAN PIPE SYSTEMS APS—See Golan Plastic Products Ltd.; *Int'l*, pg. 3023
GOLAN PLASTIC PRODUCTS LTD.; *Int'l*, pg. 3023
GOLAN TELECOM LTD.—See IDB Development Corporation Ltd.; *Int'l*, pg. 3588
GOLAR CAMEROON SASU—See Golar LNG Limited; *Int'l*, pg. 3023
GOLAR LNG LIMITED; *Int'l*, pg. 3023
GOLAR LNG PARTNERS LP—See New Fortress Energy Inc.; *U.S. Public*, pg. 1511
GOLAR MANAGEMENT LTD.—See Golar LNG Limited; *Int'l*, pg. 3023
GOLAR MANAGEMENT OSLO—See Golar LNG Limited; *Int'l*, pg. 3023
GOLAR MANAGEMENT (UK) LIMITED—See Golar LNG Limited; *Int'l*, pg. 3023
GOLAR VIKING MANAGEMENT D.O.O.—See Golar LNG Limited; *Int'l*, pg. 3023
GOLAY BUCHEL & CIE SA—See Norinvest Holding SA; *Int'l*, pg. 5428
GOLBON—See Oppenheimer Companies, Inc.; *U.S. Private*, pg. 3033
GOLCAP RESOURCES CORP.; *Int'l*, pg. 3023
GOLD 50 LIMITED; *Int'l*, pg. 3023
GOLD79 MINES LTD.; *Int'l*, pg. 3026
GOLD ACRE EMPREENDIMENTOS IMOBILIARIOS SPE LTDA.—See PDG Realty S.A. Empreendimentos e Participacoes; *Int'l*, pg. 5770
GOLDA GIDA IHTIYAC MADDELER SAN. AND TRADE INC.—See Bera Holding A.S.; *Int'l*, pg. 978
GOLD ALASKA EMPREENDIMENTOS IMOBILIARIOS SPE LTDA.—See PDG Realty S.A. Empreendimentos e Participacoes; *Int'l*, pg. 5770
GOLD AMAPA EMPREENDIMENTOS IMOBILIARIOS LTDA—See PDG Realty S.A. Empreendimentos e Participacoes; *Int'l*, pg. 5770
GOLD AND GEMSTONE MINING INC.; *U.S. Public*, pg. 949
GOLD APPLE (HK) INT'L TRADING CO. LIMITED—See Jinli Group Holdings Limited; *Int'l*, pg. 3969
GOLDARD WATER TECHNOLOGY CO., LTD.—See Goldcard Smart Group Co., Ltd.; *Int'l*, pg. 3027
GOLD AVIATION SERVICES, INC.; *U.S. Private*, pg. 1727
GOLDBACH AUDIENCE AUSTRIA GMBH—See TX Group AG; *Int'l*, pg. 7991
GOLDBACH AUDIENCE ROMANIA SRL—See TX Group AG; *Int'l*, pg. 7991
GOLDBACH AUDIENCE (SLOVENIA) D.O.O.—See TX Group AG; *Int'l*, pg. 7991
GOLDBACH AUDIENCE (SWITZERLAND) AG—See TX Group AG; *Int'l*, pg. 7991
GOLDBACH AUSTRIA GMBH—See TX Group AG; *Int'l*, pg. 7991
GOLDBACH GERMANY GMBH—See TX Group AG; *Int'l*, pg. 7991
GOLDBACH GROUP AG—See TX Group AG; *Int'l*, pg. 7991
GOLDBACH HOLDING (POLAND) SP.Z.O.O.—See TX Group AG; *Int'l*, pg. 7992
GOLDBACH INTERACTIVE (AUSTRIA) AG—See TX Group AG; *Int'l*, pg. 7992
GOLDBACH INTERACTIVE (GERMANY) AG—See TX Group AG; *Int'l*, pg. 7992
GOLDBACH INTERACTIVE POLAND SP. Z.O.O.—See TX Group AG; *Int'l*, pg. 7992
GOLDBACH INTERACTIVE (SWITZERLAND) AG—See TX Group AG; *Int'l*, pg. 7992
GOLDBACH MANAGEMENT AG—See TX Group AG; *Int'l*, pg. 7992
GOLDBACH MEDIA AUSTRIA GMBH—See TX Group AG; *Int'l*, pg. 7992
GOLDBACH MEDIA (SWITZERLAND) AG—See TX Group AG; *Int'l*, pg. 7992
GOLDBACH MOBILE AG—See TX Group AG; *Int'l*, pg. 7992
GOLDBACH NEO OOH AG—See TX Group AG; *Int'l*, pg. 7992
GOLDBANK MINING CORPORATION; *Int'l*, pg. 3026
GOLD BASIN RESOURCES CORPORATION; *Int'l*, pg. 3023
GOLDBELL CAR RENTAL PTE LTD—See Goldbell Corporation; *Int'l*, pg. 3027
GOLDBELL CORPORATION; *Int'l*, pg. 3026
GOLDBELL EQUIPMENT SDN BHD—See Goldbell Corporation; *Int'l*, pg. 3027
GOLDBELL EQUIPMENT (VIETNAM) CO., LTD—See Goldbell Corporation; *Int'l*, pg. 3027
GOLDBELL LEASING (DALIAN) CO., LTD—See Goldbell Corporation; *Int'l*, pg. 3027
GOLDBELL LEASING PTE LTD—See Goldbell Corporation; *Int'l*, pg. 3027
GOLDBELL LEASING (SHANGHAI) CO., LTD—See Goldbell Corporation; *Int'l*, pg. 3027
GOLDBELT EAGLE, LLC—See Gold Belt Incorporated; *U.S. Private*, pg. 1727
GOLDBELT EMPIRES LIMITED; *Int'l*, pg. 3027

GOLDBELT EMPIRES LIMITED

GOLDBELT FALCON, LLC—See Gold Belt Incorporated; *U.S. Private*, pg. 1727
GOLDBELT GLACIER HEALTH SERVICES, LLC—See Gold Belt Incorporated; *U.S. Private*, pg. 1727
GOLDBELT HAWK, LLC—See Gold Belt Incorporated; *U.S. Private*, pg. 1727
GOLD BELT INCORPORATED; *U.S. Private*, pg. 1727
GOLDBELT ORCA, LLC—See Gold Belt Incorporated; *U.S. Private*, pg. 1727
GOLDBELT RAVEN, LLC—See Gold Belt Incorporated; *U.S. Private*, pg. 1727
GOLDBELT SECURITY SERVICES, LLC—See Gold Belt Incorporated; *U.S. Private*, pg. 1727
GOLDBELT WOLF, LLC—See Gold Belt Incorporated; *U.S. Private*, pg. 1727
GOLDBERG AND SOLOVY FOODS, INC.—See Sysco Corporation; *U.S. Public*, pg. 1974
THE GOLDBERGER COMPANY, LLC; *U.S. Private*, pg. 4034
GOLDBERG LINDSAY & CO., LLC; *U.S. Private*, pg. 1728
GOLDBERG & OSBORNE; *U.S. Private*, pg. 1728
GOLDBERRY WEALTH GMBH—See Franklin Resources, Inc.; *U.S. Public*, pg. 881
GOLDBLOCK CAPITAL, INC.; *Int'l*, pg. 3027
GOLD BOND GROUP LTD.; *Int'l*, pg. 3023
GOLDBOND GROUP; *Int'l*, pg. 3027
GOLD BOND INC.; *U.S. Private*, pg. 1727
GOLD BRIDGE SHIPPING LTD.—See PT Berlian Laju Tanker Tbk; *Int'l*, pg. 6029
GOLD BULL RESOURCES CORP.; *Int'l*, pg. 3023
GOLD BULL RESOURCES CORP.; *Int'l*, pg. 3023
GOLD BY GOLD S.A.; *Int'l*, pg. 3023
GOLD CAP RESOURCES INC.; *Int'l*, pg. 3023
GOLDCARD SMART GROUP CO., LTD.; *Int'l*, pg. 3027
GOLD CIRCUIT ELECTRONICS - CHANGSHU PLANT—See Gold Circuit Electronics; *Int'l*, pg. 3024
GOLD CIRCUIT ELECTRONICS - CHUNG LI PLANT—See Gold Circuit Electronics; *Int'l*, pg. 3024
GOLD CIRCUIT ELECTRONICS; *Int'l*, pg. 3023
GOLDCLIFF RESOURCE CORPORATION; *Int'l*, pg. 3027
GOLD COAST ANIMAL REFERRAL & EMERGENCY PTY LTD.—See TPG Capital, L.P.; *U.S. Public*, pg. 2176
GOLD COAST BEVERAGE DISTRIBUTORS INC.; *U.S. Private*, pg. 1727
GOLD COAST BROADCASTING LLC—See Point Broadcasting Company; *U.S. Private*, pg. 3221
GOLD COAST EAGLE DISTRIBUTING L.P.; *U.S. Private*, pg. 1727
GOLD COAST HI-LIFT, INC.—See Skyworks LLC; *U.S. Private*, pg. 3686
GOLD COAST INGREDIENTS, INC.; *U.S. Private*, pg. 1727
GOLD COAST MILK PTY. LTD.—See Groupe Lactalis SA; *Int'l*, pg. 3106
THE GOLD COAST PRESS PTY LIMITED—See ARN Media Limited; *Int'l*, pg. 576
GOLD COAST PUBLICATIONS PTY. LIMITED—See News Corporation; *U.S. Public*, pg. 1520
GOLD COIN BIOTECHNOLOGIES SDN. BHD.—See Gold Coin Holdings Sdn Bhd; *Int'l*, pg. 3024
GOLDCO INC.—See Restaurant Brands International Inc.; *Int'l*, pg. 6304
GOLD COIN FEEDMILL (DONGGUAN) CO. LTD.—See Gold Coin Holdings Sdn Bhd; *Int'l*, pg. 3024
GOLD COIN FEEDMILL (DONG NAI) CO LTD—See Gold Coin Holdings Sdn Bhd; *Int'l*, pg. 3024
GOLD COIN FEEDMILL (KUNMING) CO. LTD.—See Gold Coin Holdings Sdn Bhd; *Int'l*, pg. 3024
GOLD COIN FEEDMILL (SABAH) SDN. BHD.—See Gold Coin Holdings Sdn Bhd; *Int'l*, pg. 3024
GOLD COIN FEED MILLS (LANKA) LIMITED—See Gold Coin Holdings Sdn Bhd; *Int'l*, pg. 3024
GOLD COIN FEEDMILLS MALAYSIA SDN BHD—See Aboitiz Equity Ventures, Inc.; *Int'l*, pg. 67
GOLD COIN FEEDMILLS MALAYSIA—See Aboitiz Equity Ventures, Inc.; *Int'l*, pg. 67
GOLD COIN FEEDMILLS (M) SDN BHD—See Aboitiz Equity Ventures, Inc.; *Int'l*, pg. 67
GOLD COIN FEEDMILLS SDN BHD—See Aboitiz Equity Ventures, Inc.; *Int'l*, pg. 67
GOLDCOIN HEALTH FOODS LIMITED; *Int'l*, pg. 3027
GOLD COIN HOLDINGS SDN BHD; *Int'l*, pg. 3024
GOLD COIN SERVICES SINGAPORE PTE. LTD.—See Aboitiz Equity Ventures, Inc.; *Int'l*, pg. 66
GOLD COIN SPECIALITIES (THAILAND) CO, LTD.—See Gold Coin Holdings Sdn Bhd; *Int'l*, pg. 3024
GOLD COIN (ZHANGZHOU) CO., LTD.—See Aboitiz Equity Ventures, Inc.; *Int'l*, pg. 66
GOLD COIN (ZHUHAI) CO., LTD.—See Aboitiz Equity Ventures, Inc.; *Int'l*, pg. 66
GOLDCORP INC.—See Newmont Corporation; *U.S. Public*, pg. 1516
GOLDCORP INC. - TORONTO OFFICE—See Newmont Corporation; *U.S. Public*, pg. 1516
THE GOLD CORPORATION; *U.S. Private*, pg. 4033
GOLDCORP S.A. DE C.V.—See Newmont Corporation; *U.S. Public*, pg. 1516
GOLD CRAFT JEWELRY CORP.; *U.S. Private*, pg. 1727

GOLD CREST CO., LTD.; *Int'l*, pg. 3024
GOLDCREST CORPORATION LIMITED; *Int'l*, pg. 3027
GOLD CROSS AMBULANCE SERVICES, INC.—See KKR & Co. Inc.; *U.S. Public*, pg. 1249
GOLDCROSS CYCLES PTY LTD—See Super Retail Group Limited; *Int'l*, pg. 7335
GOLD CROSS SERVICES INC.; *U.S. Private*, pg. 1727
GOLD CRUST BAKING COMPANY, INC.; *U.S. Private*, pg. 1727
GOLDCUP ELECTRIC APPARATUS CO., LTD.; *Int'l*, pg. 3027
GOLD CUP ELECTRIC HENGYANG CABLES CO., LTD.—See Goldcup Electric Apparatus Co., Ltd.; *Int'l*, pg. 3027
GOLD & DIAMOND SOURCE; *U.S. Private*, pg. 1726
GOLD DRAGON ENTERPRISES INC.; *Int'l*, pg. 3024
GOLD DYNAMICS CORP.; *U.S. Private*, pg. 1727
GOLD EAGLE COMPANY - INTERNATIONAL DIVISION—See Gold Eagle Company; *U.S. Private*, pg. 1728
GOLD EAGLE COMPANY - PRIVATE LABEL DIVISION—See Gold Eagle Company; *U.S. Private*, pg. 1728
GOLD EAGLE COMPANY; *U.S. Private*, pg. 1727
GOLD EAGLE COMPANY - THE GOLDEN TOUCH DIVISION—See Gold Eagle Company; *U.S. Private*, pg. 1728
GOLD EAGLE COMPANY - WHOLESALE/RETAIL DIVISION—See Gold Eagle Company; *U.S. Private*, pg. 1728
GOLD-EAGLE COOPERATIVE INC.; *U.S. Private*, pg. 1728
GOLDE AUBURN HILLS, LLC—See Cie Automotive S.A.; *Int'l*, pg. 1604
GOLDE CHANGCHUN CO., LTD.—See Cie Automotive S.A.; *Int'l*, pg. 1604
GOLDECK BERGBAHNEN GMBH—See STRABAG SE; *Int'l*, pg. 7230
GOLDE LOZORNO, SPOL, S.R.O.—See Cie Automotive S.A.; *Int'l*, pg. 1604
GOLDEN 1 CREDIT UNION; *U.S. Private*, pg. 1730
GOLDEN AGE EXPLORATION LTD.; *Int'l*, pg. 3027
GOLDEN AGE INC.; *U.S. Private*, pg. 1730
GOLDEN AGRI INTERNATIONAL (M) TRADING SDN. BHD.—See Golden Agri-Resources Ltd.; *Int'l*, pg. 3027
GOLDEN AGRI-RESOURCES COLOMBIA S.A.S.—See Golden Agri-Resources Ltd.; *Int'l*, pg. 3028
GOLDEN AGRI-RESOURCES IBERIA, S.L.—See Golden Agri-Resources Ltd.; *Int'l*, pg. 3028
GOLDEN AGRI RESOURCES (INDIA) PRIVATE LIMITED—See Golden Agri-Resources Ltd.; *Int'l*, pg. 3027
GOLDEN AGRI-RESOURCES LTD.; *Int'l*, pg. 3027
GOLDEN ALLY LIFETECH GROUP, INC.; *U.S. Public*, pg. 950
GOLDEN ALTOS CORPORATION—See Eico Inc.; *U.S. Private*, pg. 1346
GOLDEN APPLE (CHINA) CO., LTD.—See Jinli Group Holdings Limited; *Int'l*, pg. 3969
GOLDEN APPROACH SDN. BHD.—See PGF Capital Bhd; *Int'l*, pg. 5838
GOLDEN ARCH ENTERPRISES; *U.S. Private*, pg. 1730
GOLDEN ARCHES RESTAURANTS SDN. BHD.—See McDonald's Corporation; *U.S. Public*, pg. 1406
GOLDEN ARROW BUS SERVICES (PROPRIETARY) LIMITED—See Hosken Consolidated Investments Limited; *Int'l*, pg. 3485
GOLDEN ARROW MERGER CORP.; *U.S. Public*, pg. 950
GOLDEN ARROW RESOURCES CORPORATION - EXPLORATION SERVICES—See Golden Arrow Resources Corporation; *Int'l*, pg. 3028
GOLDEN ARROW RESOURCES CORPORATION; *Int'l*, pg. 3028
GOLDEN ASSOCIATED PORTUGAL LTD.—See WSP Global, Inc.; *Int'l*, pg. 8496
GOLDEN BALES CORPORATION; *Int'l*, pg. 3028
GOLDEN BAY REALTY (PRIVATE) LIMITED—See Hiap Hoe Limited; *Int'l*, pg. 3382
GOLDEN BEANS COFFEE JOINT STOCK COMPANY—See The Pan Group Joint Stock Company; *Int'l*, pg. 7673
GOLDEN BEAR GOLF CLUB AT INDIGO RUN—See Apollo Global Management, Inc.; *U.S. Public*, pg. 149
GOLDEN BEVERAGE COMPANY LLC; *U.S. Private*, pg. 1730
GOLDEN BIOTECHNOLOGY CORP.; *Int'l*, pg. 3028
GOLDEN BOY FOODS LTD.—See Post Holdings, Inc.; *U.S. Public*, pg. 1703
GOLDEN BOY NUT CORPORATION—See Post Holdings, Inc.; *U.S. Public*, pg. 1703
GOLDEN BOY PORTALES, LLC—See Post Holdings, Inc.; *U.S. Public*, pg. 1703
GOLDEN BRAND CLOTHING (CANADA) LTD.—See Tailored Brands, Inc.; *U.S. Public*, pg. 1979
GOLDENBRIDGE ACQUISITION LIMITED; *Int'l*, pg. 3028
GOLDEN BRIDGE ELECTECH INC.; *Int'l*, pg. 3028
GOLDENBRIDGE NO.2 SPECIAL PURPOSE ACQUISITION CO., LTD; *Int'l*, pg. 3032

CORPORATE AFFILIATIONS

GOLDENBRIDGE NO.4 SPECIAL PURPOSE ACQUISITION CO., LTD.; *Int'l*, pg. 3032
GOLDEN BRIDGE SHIPS LIMITED—See Seacon Shipping Group Holdings Limited; *Int'l*, pg. 6662
GOLDEN BRIDGE VIETNAM SECURITIES JOINT STOCK COMPANY; *Int'l*, pg. 3028
GOLDEN BRIGHT PLASTIC MANUFACTURING COMPANY LIMITED—See Highway Holdings Limited; *Int'l*, pg. 3389
GOLDEN CAPITAL INVESTMENT LIMITED—See Hysan Development Company Limited; *Int'l*, pg. 3554
GOLDEN CAPITAL MANAGEMENT, LLC—See Wells Fargo & Company; *U.S. Public*, pg. 2343
GOLDEN CARIBOO RESOURCES LTD.—See The Resource Group, Inc.; *Int'l*, pg. 7678
GOLDEN CARPETS LIMITED; *Int'l*, pg. 3028
GOLDEN CARRIERS INC.; *U.S. Private*, pg. 1730
GOLDEN CENTURY INTERNATIONAL HOLDINGS GROUP LIMITED; *Int'l*, pg. 3028
GOLDEN CHANCE GOLDSMITH PTE LTD—See Second Chance Properties Ltd.; *Int'l*, pg. 6672
GOLDEN CIGNET SDN BHD—See Mulpha International Bhd.; *Int'l*, pg. 5081
GOLDEN COAST COMPANY; *Int'l*, pg. 3028
GOLDEN COAST ENERGY CORP.; *Int'l*, pg. 3028
GOLDEN & COHEN LLC—See Aon plc; *Int'l*, pg. 496
GOLDEN CONCEPT DEVELOPMENT LIMITED—See Kingboard Holdings Limited; *Int'l*, pg. 4171
GOLDEN CONCORD HOLDINGS LIMITED; *Int'l*, pg. 3028
GOLDEN CORRAL CORPORATION—See Investors Management Corporation; *U.S. Private*, pg. 2132
GOLDEN COW DAIRIES LIMITED—See Kerry Group plc; *Int'l*, pg. 4138
GOLDEN CREST EDUCATION & SERVICES LIMITED; *Int'l*, pg. 3029
GOLDEN CROSS OPERATIONS PTY. LTD.—See Golden Cross Resources Limited; *Int'l*, pg. 3029
GOLDENCROSS PHARMA PVT. LTD.—See Cipla Ltd.; *Int'l*, pg. 1617
GOLDEN CROSS RESOURCES LIMITED; *Int'l*, pg. 3029
GOLDEN CROWN DEPOT; *U.S. Private*, pg. 1730
GOLDEN CUT POULTRY LTD.—See Maple Lodge Farms Ltd.; *Int'l*, pg. 4686
GOLDENDALE DIALYSIS, LLC—See DaVita Inc.; *U.S. Public*, pg. 639
GOLDEN DEEPS LIMITED; *Int'l*, pg. 3029
GOLDEN DENTAL PLANS, INC.—See DENCAP Dental Plans, Inc.; *U.S. Private*, pg. 1204
GOLDEN DEVELOPING SOLUTIONS, INC.; *U.S. Public*, pg. 950
THE GOLDEN DOOR HEALTH RETREAT - ELYSIA PTY LIMITED—See Lasseters International Holdings Limited; *Int'l*, pg. 4421
GOLDEN DOWA ECO-SYSTEM MYANMAR COMPANY LIMITED—See Dowa Holdings Co., Ltd.; *Int'l*, pg. 2184
GOLDEN EAGLE DISTRIBUTING CO.; *U.S. Private*, pg. 1730
GOLDEN EAGLE DISTRIBUTING—See Golden Eagle Distributing Co.; *U.S. Private*, pg. 1730
GOLDEN EAGLE DISTRIBUTORS, INC.; *U.S. Private*, pg. 1730
GOLDEN EAGLE EXPLORATION LLC USA—See Aleator Energy Limited; *Int'l*, pg. 305
GOLDEN EAGLE EXPRESS INC.; *U.S. Private*, pg. 1730
GOLDEN EAGLE EXTRUSIONS INC.; *U.S. Private*, pg. 1730
GOLDEN EAGLE INSURANCE CORP.—See Liberty Mutual Holding Company Inc.; *U.S. Private*, pg. 2445
GOLDEN EAGLE LOG HOMES, INC.; *U.S. Private*, pg. 1730
GOLDEN EAGLE RETAIL GROUP LIMITED; *Int'l*, pg. 3029
GOLDEN EAGLE ROOFING COMPANY—See Cherubim Interests, Inc.; *U.S. Public*, pg. 485
GOLDEN EAGLES LESSEE LLC—See Pebblebrook Hotel Trust; *U.S. Public*, pg. 1660
GOLDEN ENERGY AND RESOURCES LIMITED; *Int'l*, pg. 3029
GOLDEN ENERGY OFFSHORE SERVICES AS; *Int'l*, pg. 3029
GOLDEN ENTERPRISES INC.—See Utz Brands, Inc.; *U.S. Public*, pg. 2268
GOLDEN ENTERTAINMENT, INC.; *U.S. Public*, pg. 950
GOLDEN EQUIPMENT COMPANY—See Power Equipment Company; *U.S. Private*, pg. 3238
GOLDEN EQUITIES, INC.—See Graphic Packaging Holding Company; *U.S. Public*, pg. 958
GOLDEN EQUITY INVESTMENTS LLC; *U.S. Private*, pg. 1730
GOLDENEYE RESOURCES CORP.; *Int'l*, pg. 3033
GOLDEN FAITH GROUP HOLDINGS LIMITED; *Int'l*, pg. 3029
GOLDEN FALCON ACQUISITION CORP.; *U.S. Public*, pg. 950
GOLDEN FERTILIZER COMPANY LIMITED—See Flour Mills of Nigeria Plc; *Int'l*, pg. 2709
GOLDEN FLAKE SNACK FOODS, INC.—See Utz Brands, Inc.; *U.S. Public*, pg. 2268

COMPANY NAME INDEX

GOLDENFLASH ELECTRONICS CO., LTD.—See EDOM Technology Co., Ltd.; *Int'l*, pg. 2313
GOLDEN FOREST, S.A.; *Int'l*, pg. 3029
GOLDEN FRONTIER BERHAD; *Int'l*, pg. 3029
GOLDEN FRONTIER PACKAGING SDN. BHD.—See Golden Frontier Berhad; *Int'l*, pg. 3029
GOLDEN FURROW FERTILIZER - BLOOMFIELD—See Golden Furrow Fertilizer Inc.; *U.S. Private*, pg. 1730
GOLDEN FURROW FERTILIZER INC.; *U.S. Private*, pg. 1730
GOLDEN GAIT TRAILERS, LLC—See Redwood Capital Investments, LLC; *U.S. Private*, pg. 3380
GOLDEN GAMING, LLC—See Golden Entertainment, Inc.; *U.S. Public*, pg. 950
GOLDEN GATE BRIDGE HIGHWAY & TRANSPORTATION DISTRICT; *U.S. Private*, pg. 1730
GOLDEN GATE CAPITAL MANAGEMENT II, LLC; *U.S. Private*, pg. 1730
GOLDEN GATE HEALTHCARE CENTER—See Apollo Global Management, Inc.; *U.S. Public*, pg. 156
GOLDEN GATE NATIONAL PARKS CONSERVANCY; *U.S. Private*, pg. 1732
GOLDEN GATE PETROLEUM CO.; *U.S. Private*, pg. 1732
GOLDEN GATE REGIONAL CENTER INC.; *U.S. Private*, pg. 1732
GOLDEN GLOBAL CORP.; *U.S. Private*, pg. 1732
GOLDEN GOLIATH RESOURCES LTD.; *Int'l*, pg. 3029
GOLDEN GRAIL TECHNOLOGY CORP.; *U.S. Public*, pg. 950
GOLDEN GRAIN ENERGY, LLC; *U.S. Private*, pg. 1732
GOLDEN GRASS, INC.; *Int'l*, pg. 3029
GOLDEN GROWERS COOPERATIVE; *U.S. Public*, pg. 950
GOLDEN GUINEA BREWERIES PLC; *Int'l*, pg. 3029
GOLDEN HARP RESOURCES INC.; *Int'l*, pg. 3029
GOLDEN HARVEST ENTERTAINMENT (HOLDINGS) LTD.; *Int'l*, pg. 3029
GOLDEN HARVEST FOOD BANK; *U.S. Private*, pg. 1732
GOLDEN HARVEST, INC.—See XPV Water Partners; *Int'l*, pg. 8538
GOLDEN HARVEST (MACAO COMMERCIAL OFFSHORE) LIMITED—See Heng Tai Consumables Group Limited; *Int'l*, pg. 3345
GOLDEN HARVEST MIDDLE EAST FZC—See Aries Agro Limited; *Int'l*, pg. 564
GOLDEN HEAVEN GROUP HOLDINGS LTD.; *Int'l*, pg. 3029
GOLDEN HIGHWAY MEXICO, S. DE R.L. DE C.V.—See GHW International; *Int'l*, pg. 2960
GOLDEN HILL TOWER LTD.—See YKK Corporation; *Int'l*, pg. 8588
GOLDENHOME LIVING CO., LTD.; *Int'l*, pg. 3033
GOLDEN HOPE LATEX SDN. BHD.—See Sime Darby Berhad; *Int'l*, pg. 6929
GOLDEN HOTEL LIMITED PARTNERSHIP; *U.S. Private*, pg. 1732
GOLDEN HOUR DATA SYSTEMS, INC.—See Asahi Kasei Corporation; *Int'l*, pg. 597
GOLDEN HOUSE LTD.; *Int'l*, pg. 3029
GOLDEN I LIMITED—See Morgan Sindall Group Plc; *Int'l*, pg. 5044
GOLDEN INDUSTRIES INC.; *U.S. Private*, pg. 1732
GOLDEN ISLAND JERKY COMPANY, INC.—See Tyson Foods, Inc.; *U.S. Public*, pg. 2209
GOLDEN ISLES AVIATION—See Quantem FBO Group LLC; *U.S. Private*, pg. 3322
GOLDEN ISLES CUSTOM HOMES LLC; *U.S. Private*, pg. 1732
GOLDEN ISLES TERMINAL RAILROAD, INC.—See Brookfield Infrastructure Partners L.P.; *Int'l*, pg. 1191
GOLDEN ISLES TERMINAL RAILROAD, INC.—See GIC Pte. Ltd.; *Int'l*, pg. 2966
GOLDEN KEY GROUP, LLC; *U.S. Private*, pg. 1732
GOLDEN LADY S.P.A.; *Int'l*, pg. 3029
GOLDEN LAKE EXPLORATION, INC.; *Int'l*, pg. 3030
GOLDEN LAND BERHAD; *Int'l*, pg. 3030
GOLDEN LAND PROPERTY DEVELOPMENT PUBLIC COMPANY LIMITED—See Frasers Property Limited; *Int'l*, pg. 2766
GOLDEN LEAF HOLDINGS LTD.; *Int'l*, pg. 3030
GOLDEN LEGAND LEASING & FINANCE LTD.; *Int'l*, pg. 3030
GOLDEN LIGHTING COMPANY; *U.S. Private*, pg. 1732
GOLDEN LIME PUBLIC COMPANY LIMITED; *Int'l*, pg. 3030
GOLDEN LIVING—See Fillmore Capital Partners, LLC; *U.S. Private*, pg. 1506
GOLDEN LONG TENG DEVELOPMENT CO., LTD.; *Int'l*, pg. 3030
GOLDENMARC (PTY) LTD.—See Bounty Brands Pty Ltd.; *Int'l*, pg. 1119
GOLDEN MARDI GRAS CASINO—See Bally's Corporation; *U.S. Public*, pg. 268
GOLDEN MATRIX GROUP, INC.; *U.S. Public*, pg. 950
GOLDEN M CO. INC.; *U.S. Private*, pg. 1732
GOLDEN MEDIA; *U.S. Private*, pg. 1732
GOLDEN MEDITECH (BVI) COMPANY LIMITED—See Golden Meditech Holdings Limited; *Int'l*, pg. 3030

GOLDEN MEDITECH HERBAL TREATMENT (BVI) COMPANY LIMITED—See Golden Meditech Holdings Limited; *Int'l*, pg. 3030
GOLDEN MEDITECH HOLDINGS LIMITED; *Int'l*, pg. 3030
GOLDEN METROPOLIS INTERNATIONAL LIMITED; *Int'l*, pg. 3030
GOLDEN MILE RESOURCES LTD.; *Int'l*, pg. 3030
GOLDENMILES PETROTECH, INC.—See New Jcm Group CO., Ltd; *Int'l*, pg. 5226
GOLDEN MINERALS COMPANY; *U.S. Public*, pg. 950
GOLDEN MOOR INC.; *Int'l*, pg. 3030
GOLDEN MORGEN BVBA—See Clariane SE; *Int'l*, pg. 1642
GOLDEN MV HOLDINGS INC.; *Int'l*, pg. 3030
GOLDEN MYANMAR SEA COMPANY LTD.—See mDR Limited; *Int'l*, pg. 4762
GOLDEN NEO LIFE DIAMITE INTERNATIONAL; *U.S. Private*, pg. 1732
GOLDEN NOODLES NIGERIA LIMITED—See Flour Mills of Nigeria Plc.; *Int'l*, pg. 2709
GOLDEN NUGGET HOTEL & CASINO - ATLANTIC CITY—See Fertitta Entertainment, Inc.; *U.S. Private*, pg. 1499
GOLDEN NUGGET HOTEL & CASINO - LAS VEGAS—See Fertitta Entertainment, Inc.; *U.S. Private*, pg. 1499
GOLDEN NUGGET HOTEL & CASINO - LAUGHLIN—See Fertitta Entertainment, Inc.; *U.S. Private*, pg. 1499
GOLDEN NUGGET ONLINE GAMING, INC.—See DraftKings Inc.; *U.S. Public*, pg. 687
GOLDEN NUGGET ONLINE GAMING, LLC—See DraftKings Inc.; *U.S. Public*, pg. 687
GOLDEN NUT COMPANY (USA) INC.—See Post Holdings, Inc.; *U.S. Public*, pg. 1703
GOLDEN OCEAN GROUP LTD.; *Int'l*, pg. 3030
GOLDEN OCEAN MANAGEMENT ASIA PTE. LTD.—See Golden Ocean Group Ltd.; *Int'l*, pg. 3030
GOLDEN OCEAN MANAGEMENT AS—See Golden Ocean Group Ltd.; *Int'l*, pg. 3030
GOLDEN OCEAN SHIPPING CO PTE. LTD.—See Golden Ocean Group Ltd.; *Int'l*, pg. 3030
GOLDEN OFFICE TRAILERS INC.—See Pacific Mobile Structures Inc.; *U.S. Private*, pg. 3068
GOLDEN ORGANICS—See Innovative Food Holdings, Inc.; *U.S. Public*, pg. 1127
GOLDEN OUTLOOK, INC.—See UnitedHealth Group Incorporated; *U.S. Public*, pg. 2241
GOLDEN PACIFIC BANCORP, INC.; *U.S. Public*, pg. 950
GOLDEN PACIFIC BANK, N.A.—See Golden Pacific Bancorp, Inc.; *U.S. Public*, pg. 950
GOLDEN PACIFIC HOMES INC.; *U.S. Private*, pg. 1732
GOLDEN PAHRUMP NUGGET, LLC—See Golden Entertainment, Inc.; *U.S. Public*, pg. 950
GOLDEN PAHRUMP TOWN, LLC—See Golden Entertainment, Inc.; *U.S. Public*, pg. 950
GOLDEN PALM PETROLEUM SERVICES COMPANY W.L.L.—See Endress+Hauser (International) Holding AG; *Int'l*, pg. 2408
GOLDEN PARTNERS INC.—See Brentwood Associates; *U.S. Private*, pg. 646
GOLDEN PAVILION RESOURCES LTD.—See Independence Gold Corp.; *Int'l*, pg. 3650
GOLDEN PEANUT AND TREE NUT SA (PTY) LTD.—See Archer-Daniels-Midland Company; *U.S. Public*, pg. 185
GOLDEN PEANUT ARGENTINA S.A.—See Archer-Daniels-Midland Company; *U.S. Public*, pg. 185
GOLDEN PEANUT COMPANY, LLC—See Archer-Daniels-Midland Company; *U.S. Public*, pg. 185
GOLDEN PEANUT & TREE NUTS S.A.—See Archer-Daniels-Midland Company; *U.S. Public*, pg. 185
GOLDEN PET INDUSTRIES SDN BHD—See Spritzer Bhd.; *Int'l*, pg. 7145
GOLDEN PHAROS BERHAD; *Int'l*, pg. 3030
GOLDEN PHAROS DOORS SDN BHD—See Golden Pharos Berhad; *Int'l*, pg. 3030
GOLDEN PHAROS EUROPE LTD—See Golden Pharos Berhad; *Int'l*, pg. 3030
GOLDEN PHAROS GLASS SDN BHD—See Golden Pharos Berhad; *Int'l*, pg. 3030
GOLDEN PHEASANT FOODS LLC—See Swander Pace Capital, LLC; *U.S. Private*, pg. 3890
GOLDEN PHOENIX MINERALS, INC.; *U.S. Private*, pg. 1732
GOLDEN POGADA LLC—See Green Leader Holdings Group Limited; *Int'l*, pg. 3071
GOLDEN POINT GROUP PTY LTD—See Shen Yao Holdings Limited; *Int'l*, pg. 6800
GOLDEN POINT GROUP PTY LTD.—See Shen Yao Holdings Limited; *Int'l*, pg. 6800
GOLDEN PONDER HOLDINGS LIMITED; *Int'l*, pg. 3031
GOLDENPORT HOLDINGS INC.; *Int'l*, pg. 3033
GOLDEN POWER GROUP HOLDINGS LTD.; *Int'l*, pg. 3031
GOLDEN PREDATOR MINING CORP.—See Victoria Gold Corp.; *Int'l*, pg. 8188
GOLDEN PRODUCTS CORPORATION—See Nestle S.A.; *Int'l*, pg. 5209
GOLDEN PURSUIT RESOURCES LTD.; *Int'l*, pg. 3031
GOLDEN PYRAMIDS PLAZA; *Int'l*, pg. 3031

GOLDEN STATE FOODS CORP.

GOLDEN RAIN FOUNDATION; *U.S. Private*, pg. 1732
GOLDEN RESERVE, LLC; *U.S. Private*, pg. 1732
GOLDEN RESOURCES DEVELOPMENT INTERNATIONAL LIMITED; *Int'l*, pg. 3031
GOLDEN RESOURCES DEVELOPMENT LIMITED—See Golden Resources Development International Limited; *Int'l*, pg. 3031
GOLDEN RESOURCES RICE TRADING LIMITED—See Golden Resources Development International Limited; *Int'l*, pg. 3031
GOLDEN RICH SECURITIES LIMITED—See China Finance Investment Holdings Limited; *Int'l*, pg. 1502
GOLDEN RIDGE RESOURCES LTD.; *Int'l*, pg. 3031
GOLDEN RIDGE RICE MILLES, INC.—See RICEBRAN TECHNOLOGIES; *U.S. Public*, pg. 1797
GOLDEN RIM RESOURCES LTD; *Int'l*, pg. 3031
GOLDEN RIVER RESOURCES CORPORATION; *Int'l*, pg. 3031
GOLDEN ROAD MOTOR INN, INC.—See Monarch Casino & Resort, Inc.; *U.S. Public*, pg. 1460
GOLDEN ROCK GLOBAL PLC; *Int'l*, pg. 3031
GOLDEN ROD BROILERS INC.; *U.S. Private*, pg. 1732
GOLDEN ROUTE OPERATIONS LLC—See Golden Entertainment, Inc.; *U.S. Public*, pg. 950
GOLDEN ROYAL DEVELOPMENT, INC.; *U.S. Private*, pg. 1733
GOLDEN RULE FINANCIAL CORP.—See UnitedHealth Group Incorporated; *U.S. Public*, pg. 2251
GOLDEN RULE INSURANCE COMPANY INC.—See UnitedHealth Group Incorporated; *U.S. Public*, pg. 2251
GOLDEN SAINT AUSTRALIA LIMITED—See Golden Saint Resources Limited; *Int'l*, pg. 3031
GOLDEN SAINT RESOURCES LIMITED; *Int'l*, pg. 3031
GOLDEN SAND RIVER CALIFORNIA CORP.—See Beijing Century GSR Ventures Management Co., Ltd.; *Int'l*, pg. 947
GOLDEN SAND RIVER (HONG KONG) LIMITED—See Beijing Century GSR Ventures Management Co., Ltd.; *Int'l*, pg. 947
GOLDEN SANDS BEACH RESORT SDN BERHAD—See Shangri-La Asia Limited; *Int'l*, pg. 6783
GOLDEN SCREEN CINEMAS SDN. BHD.—See Kuok Brothers Sdn. Bhd.; *Int'l*, pg. 4334
GOLDEN SECRET VENTURES LTD; *Int'l*, pg. 3031
GOLDEN SECTOR AGRO-DEVELOPMENT LIMITED—See Heng Tai Consumables Group Limited; *Int'l*, pg. 3345
GOLDEN SECTOR LIMITED—See Heng Tai Consumables Group Limited; *Int'l*, pg. 3345
GOLDEN SHARE RESOURCES CORPORATION; *Int'l*, pg. 3031
GOLDEN SHIELD HOLDINGS (INDUSTRIAL) LTD.; *Int'l*, pg. 3031
GOLDEN SKY MINERALS CORP.; *Int'l*, pg. 3031
GOLDEN SOLAR NEW ENERGY TECHNOLOGY HOLDINGS LIMITED; *Int'l*, pg. 3031
GOLDEN SON LIMITED; *Int'l*, pg. 3032
GOLDEN SOURCE CORPORATION; *U.S. Private*, pg. 1733
GOLDEN SPIKE RESOURCES CORP.; *Int'l*, pg. 3032
GOLDEN STAR ACQUISITION CORP.; *U.S. Public*, pg. 951
GOLDEN STAR CORPORATION; *U.S. Private*, pg. 1733
GOLDEN STAR FACILITIES & SERVICES PRIVATE LIMITED—See Quess Corp Limited; *Int'l*, pg. 6160
GOLDEN STAR INC.; *U.S. Private*, pg. 1733
GOLDEN STAR RESOURCE CORP.; *U.S. Public*, pg. 951
GOLDEN STAR RESOURCES LTD.; *Int'l*, pg. 3032
GOLDEN STATE BANCORP; *U.S. Public*, pg. 951
GOLDEN STATE CELLULAR, INC.—See Verizon Communications Inc.; *U.S. Public*, pg. 2284
GOLDEN STATE ENGINEERING INC.; *U.S. Private*, pg. 1733
GOLDEN STATE ENVIRONMENTAL TEDAGUA CORPORATION, S.A.—See ACS, Actividades de Construccion y Servicios, S.A.; *Int'l*, pg. 112
GOLDEN STATE FARM CREDIT; *U.S. Private*, pg. 1733
GOLDEN STATE FIRE PROTECTION, INC.—See Fortis Fire & Safety, Inc.; *U.S. Private*, pg. 1576
GOLDEN STATE FOODS-CITY OF INDUSTRY DIVISION—See Golden State Foods Corp.; *U.S. Private*, pg. 1733
GOLDEN STATE FOODS CORP.; *U.S. Private*, pg. 1733
GOLDEN STATE FOODS-GEORGIA DIVISION—See Golden State Foods Corp.; *U.S. Private*, pg. 1733
GOLDEN STATE FOODS-HAWAII DIVISION—See Golden State Foods Corp.; *U.S. Private*, pg. 1733
GOLDEN STATE FOODS-NORTHWEST DIVISION—See Golden State Foods Corp.; *U.S. Private*, pg. 1733
GOLDEN STATE FOODS-OAK BROOK—See Golden State Foods Corp.; *U.S. Private*, pg. 1733
GOLDEN STATE FOODS-PHOENIX DIVISION—See Golden State Foods Corp.; *U.S. Private*, pg. 1733
GOLDEN STATE FOODS-ROCHESTER DIVISION—See Golden State Foods Corp.; *U.S. Private*, pg. 1733
GOLDEN STATE FOODS-SOUTH CAROLINA DIVISION—See Golden State Foods Corp.; *U.S. Private*, pg. 1733

GOLDEN STATE IRRIGATION SERVICES / CORPORATE AFFILIATIONS

GOLDEN STATE IRRIGATION SERVICES; *U.S. Private*, pg. 1733
GOLDEN STATE LUMBER INC.; *U.S. Private*, pg. 1733
GOLDEN STATE MEDICARE HEALTH PLAN; *U.S. Private*, pg. 1733
GOLDEN STATE METALS, INC.—See Sims Limited; *U.S. Public*, pg. 1883
GOLDEN STATE MINING LIMITED; *Int'l*, pg. 3032
GOLDEN STATE SERVICE INDUSTRIES, INC.—See Golden State Foods Corp.; *U.S. Private*, pg. 1733
GOLDEN STATE STORAGE ONE, LLC—See Ojai Oil Company; *U.S. Public*, pg. 1566
GOLDEN STATE WARRIORS, LLC; *U.S. Private*, pg. 1733
GOLDEN STATE WATER COMPANY—See American States Water Company; *U.S. Public*, pg. 110
GOLDENSTONE ACQUISITION LTD.; *U.S. Public*, pg. 951
GOLDEN SUGAR COMPANY LIMITED—See Flour Mills of Nigeria Plc.; *Int'l*, pg. 2709
GOLDEN SUN BEAR, LLC—See DaVita Inc.; *U.S. Public*, pg. 639
GOLDEN SUN HEALTH TECHNOLOGY GROUP LIMITED; *Int'l*, pg. 3032
GOLDEN SUN, INC.; *U.S. Private*, pg. 1733
GOLDEN SUPREME INTERNATIONAL TRADING (SHANGHAI) CO., LTD.—See Supreme Electronics Co., Ltd.; *Int'l*, pg. 7340
GOLDEN TADCO INTERNATIONAL CORPORATION; *U.S. Private*, pg. 1733
GOLDEN TAG MEXICO SA DE CV—See Golden Tag Resources Ltd.; *Int'l*, pg. 3032
GOLDEN TAG RESOURCES LTD.; *Int'l*, pg. 3032
GOLDENTECH COMPUTER TECHNOLOGY (SUZHOU) CO.,LTD.—See CAC Corporation; *Int'l*, pg. 1247
GOLDEN TECHNOLOGIES COMPANY, INC.—See Ingredion Incorporated; *U.S. Public*, pg. 1123
GOLDEN TELECOM LLC—See VEON Ltd.; *Int'l*, pg. 8164
GOLDEN TEXTILES & CLOTHES WOOL; *Int'l*, pg. 3032
GOLDEN THROAT HOLDINGS GROUP CO. LTD.; *Int'l*, pg. 3032
GOLDEN TIGER—See Ajinomoto Company, Inc.; *Int'l*, pg. 257
GOLDEN TIME NETWORK MARKETING LTD.; *U.S. Public*, pg. 951
GOLDEN TOBACCO LIMITED; *Int'l*, pg. 3032
GOLDEN TOKYU CONSTRUCTION CO., LTD—See Tokyu Construction Co., Ltd.; *Int'l*, pg. 7797
GOLDEN TOUCH IMPORTS, INC.; *U.S. Private*, pg. 1733
GOLDEN TOUCH TRANSPORTATION OF NEW YORK—See Caisse des Depots et Consignations; *Int'l*, pg. 1258
GOLDEN TOWN APPLE PRODUCTS—See Lassonde Industries, Inc.; *Int'l*, pg. 4421
GOLDENTREE ASSET MANAGEMENT LLC—See GoldenTree Asset Management LP; *U.S. Private*, pg. 1734
GOLDENTREE ASSET MANAGEMENT LP; *U.S. Private*, pg. 1734
GOLDENTREE ASSET MANAGEMENT SINGAPORE PTE. LTD.—See GoldenTree Asset Management LP; *U.S. Private*, pg. 1734
GOLDENTREE ASSET MANAGEMENT UK LLP—See GoldenTree Asset Management LP; *U.S. Private*, pg. 1734
GOLDEN TRIANGLE DAIRY QUEENS, INC.; *U.S. Private*, pg. 1734
GOLDEN TRIANGLE GENERATORS LIMITED—See I Squared Capital Advisors (US) LLC; *U.S. Private*, pg. 2021
GOLDEN TRIANGLE GENERATORS LIMITED—See TDR Capital LLP; *Int'l*, pg. 7490
GOLDEN TRIANGLE PHYSICIAN ALLIANCE—See Centene Corporation; *U.S. Public*, pg. 471
GOLDEN TRIANGLE RAILROAD, LLC—See Mitsubishi UFJ Financial Group, Inc.; *Int'l*, pg. 4971
GOLDEN TRIANGLE SURGICENTER, L.P.—See United-Health Group Incorporated; *U.S. Public*, pg. 2241
GOLDEN TRIANGLE VENTURES, INC.; *U.S. Public*, pg. 951
GOLDEN TULIP WARSAW CENTRE HOTEL—See Starwood Capital Group Global I, LLC; *U.S. Private*, pg. 3789
GOLDEN VALLEY BANK; *U.S. Public*, pg. 951
GOLDEN VALLEY DEVELOPMENT, INC.; *U.S. Public*, pg. 951
GOLDEN VALLEY ELECTRIC ASSOCIATION; *U.S. Private*, pg. 1734
GOLDEN VALLEY GRAPE JUICE & WINE; *U.S. Private*, pg. 1734
GOLDEN VALLEY MINES LTD.; *Int'l*, pg. 3032
GOLDEN VENTURES ACQUISITION CORP.; *Int'l*, pg. 3032
GOLDEN VENTURES LEASEHOLD REAL ESTATE INVESTMENT TRUST; *Int'l*, pg. 3032
GOLDEN VERTEX CORP.—See Northern Vertex Mining Corp.; *Int'l*, pg. 5445
GOLDEN VILLAGE MULTIPLEX PTE LIMITED—See Orange Sky Golden Harvest Entertainment (Holdings) Limited; *Int'l*, pg. 5611

GOLDEN VILLA HOMES INC.; *U.S. Private*, pg. 1734
GOLDENWAY, INC.; *Int'l*, pg. 3033
GOLDEN WEB LTD.; *Int'l*, pg. 3032
GOLDENWELL BIOTECH, INC.; *U.S. Public*, pg. 951
GOLDEN WEST DENTAL & VISION HEALTH PLANS, INC.—See Elevance Health, Inc.; *U.S. Public*, pg. 730
GOLDENWEST DIAMOND CORPORATION; *U.S. Private*, pg. 1734
GOLDEN WEST HEALTH PLAN, INC.—See Elevance Health, Inc.; *U.S. Public*, pg. 730
GOLDEN WEST IRRIGATION & EQUIPMENT LLC; *U.S. Private*, pg. 1734
GOLDENWEST LUBRICANTS, INC.; *U.S. Private*, pg. 1734
GOLDEN WEST NETWORK PTY LIMITED—See Seven West Media Limited; *Int'l*, pg. 6734
GOLDEN WEST NUTS INC.; *U.S. Private*, pg. 1734
GOLDEN WEST PACKAGING GROUP LLC—See Goldberg Lindsay & Co., LLC; *U.S. Private*, pg. 1729
GOLDEN WEST PIPE & SUPPLY CO.; *U.S. Private*, pg. 1734
GOLDEN WEST REFINING COMPANY—See Thrifty Oil Co.; *U.S. Private*, pg. 4165
GOLDEN WEST TELECOMMUNICATIONS; *U.S. Private*, pg. 1734
GOLDEN WHEAT MILLS COMPANY—See Arab Supply & Trading Co.; *Int'l*, pg. 532
GOLDEN WHEAT (NANJING) INTERNATIONAL TRADE CO., LTD.—See Anhui Jinhe Industrial Co., Ltd.; *Int'l*, pg. 468
GOLDEN WHEEL TIANDI HOLDINGS COMPANY LIMITED; *Int'l*, pg. 3032
GOLDEN WILL FASHIONS LIMITED; *Int'l*, pg. 3032
GOLDEN WINDOWS LIMITED; *Int'l*, pg. 3032
GOLDEO INC.; *U.S. Private*, pg. 1735
GOLDE ORADEA, SRL—See Cie Automotive S.A.; *Int'l*, pg. 1604
GOLDER ASSOCIATES AB—See WSP Global, Inc.; *Int'l*, pg. 8496
GOLDER ASSOCIATES AFRICA (PTY) LTD.—See WSP Global, Inc.; *Int'l*, pg. 8496
GOLDER ASSOCIATES ARGENTINA S.A.—See WSP Global, Inc.; *Int'l*, pg. 8496
GOLDER ASSOCIATES AS—See WSP Global, Inc.; *Int'l*, pg. 8496
GOLDER ASSOCIATES A/S—See WSP Global, Inc.; *Int'l*, pg. 8496
GOLDER ASSOCIATES BRASIL CONSULTORIA E PROJETOS LTDA.—See WSP Global, Inc.; *Int'l*, pg. 8496
GOLDER ASSOCIATES GMBH—See WSP Global, Inc.; *Int'l*, pg. 8496
GOLDER ASSOCIATES (HK) LIMITED—See WSP Global, Inc.; *Int'l*, pg. 8496
GOLDER ASSOCIATES, INC.—See WSP Global, Inc.; *Int'l*, pg. 8496
GOLDER ASSOCIATES IRELAND LIMITED—See WSP Global, Inc.; *Int'l*, pg. 8496
GOLDER ASSOCIATES LTD.—See WSP Global, Inc.; *Int'l*, pg. 8496
GOLDER ASSOCIATES (NZ) LIMITED—See WSP Global, Inc.; *Int'l*, pg. 8496
GOLDER ASSOCIATES OY—See WSP Global, Inc.; *Int'l*, pg. 8496
GOLDER ASSOCIATES (PHILIPPINES) INC.—See WSP Global, Inc.; *Int'l*, pg. 8496
GOLDER ASSOCIATES PTY LTD.—See WSP Global, Inc.; *Int'l*, pg. 8496
GOLDER ASSOCIATES SARL—See WSP Global, Inc.; *Int'l*, pg. 8496
GOLDER ASSOCIATES (SINGAPORE) PTE LTD.—See WSP Global, Inc.; *Int'l*, pg. 8496
GOLDER ASSOCIATES S.R.L.—See WSP Global, Inc.; *Int'l*, pg. 8496
GOLDER ASSOCIATES TURKEY LTD.—See WSP Global, Inc.; *Int'l*, pg. 8496
GOLDER ASSOCIATES (UK) LTD.—See WSP Global, Inc.; *Int'l*, pg. 8496
GOLDER PASTE TECHNOLOGY LTD.—See WSP Global, Inc.; *Int'l*, pg. 8496
GOLDE SHANDONG CO., LTD.—See Cie Automotive S.A.; *Int'l*, pg. 1604
GOLDE SHANGHAI CO., LTD.—See Cie Automotive S.A.; *Int'l*, pg. 1604
GOLDE TIANJIN CO., LTD.—See Cie Automotive S.A.; *Int'l*, pg. 1604
GOLDE WUHAN CO., LTD.—See Cie Automotive S.A.; *Int'l*, pg. 1604
GOLD EXPRESS, LLC; *U.S. Private*, pg. 1728
GOLDEX RESOURCES CORPORATION; *Int'l*, pg. 3033
GOLDFARB 12 EMPREENDIMENTO IMOBILIARIO LTDA.—See PDG Realty S.A. Empreendimentos e Participacoes; *Int'l*, pg. 5770
THE GOLDFARB CORPORATION; *Int'l*, pg. 7650
THE GOLDFIELD CORPORATION; *U.S. Public*, pg. 2075
GOLDFIELD PROPERTIES LIMITED; *Int'l*, pg. 3033
GOLD FIELDS AUSTRALIA PTY LTD—See Gold Fields Limited; *Int'l*, pg. 3024

GOLDFIELDS CASINO & ENTERTAINMENT CENTRE (PTY) LTD.—See Hosken Consolidated Investments Limited; *Int'l*, pg. 3485
GOLD FIELDS EXTERNAL TRAINING SERVICES (PTY) LIMITED—See Adcorp Holdings Limited; *Int'l*, pg. 127
GOLDFIELDS GAS TRANSMISSION PTY, LTD.—See APA Group; *Int'l*, pg. 500
GOLD FIELDS GHANA LIMITED—See Gold Fields Limited; *Int'l*, pg. 3024
GOLD FIELDS GROUP SERVICES LIMITED—See Gold Fields Limited; *Int'l*, pg. 3024
GOLDFIELDS INTERNATIONAL INC.; *U.S. Private*, pg. 1735
GOLD FIELDS LIMITED; *Int'l*, pg. 3024
GOLDFIELDS MINE MANAGEMENT PTY LTD—See Tattarang Pty. Ltd.; *Int'l*, pg. 7475
GOLD FIELDS NETHERLANDS SERVICES B.V.—See Gold Fields Limited; *Int'l*, pg. 3024
GOLD FIELDS OROGEN HOLDING (BVI) LIMITED—See Gold Fields Limited; *Int'l*, pg. 3024
GOLDFINE MANUFACTURERS PUBLIC COMPANY LIMITED; *Int'l*, pg. 3033
GOLDFINGER TECHNOLOGIES LLC—See NAURA Technology Group Co., Ltd.; *Int'l*, pg. 5172
GOLDFISH SWIM SCHOOL FRANCHISING LLC; *U.S. Private*, pg. 1735
GOLDFISH SWIM SCHOOL—See Goldfish Swim School Franchising LLC; *U.S. Private*, pg. 1735
GOLDFLARE EXPLORATION INC.; *Int'l*, pg. 3033
GOLD FLORA CORP.; *U.S. Public*, pg. 949
GOLD FROST LTD—See Willi-Food Investments Ltd.; *Int'l*, pg. 8412
GOLDGAS GMBH—See EnBW Energie Baden-Wurttemberg AG; *Int'l*, pg. 2400
GOLDGAS GMBH—See EnBW Energie Baden-Wurttemberg AG; *Int'l*, pg. 2400
GOLDGROUP MINING INC.; *Int'l*, pg. 3033
GOLDHAVEN RESOURCES CORP.; *Int'l*, pg. 3033
GOLDHEART BULLION PTE. LTD.—See Aspial Corporation Limited; *Int'l*, pg. 630
GOLD HILL HOTEL, INC.—See COMSTOCK INC.; *U.S. Public*, pg. 562
GOLD HILL RESOURCES, INC.; *U.S. Private*, pg. 1728
GOLDHILLS HOLDING LTD.; *Int'l*, pg. 3033
GOLD HORN INTERNATIONAL ENTERPRISES GROUP LIMITED; *Int'l*, pg. 3024
GOLD HORSE INTERNATIONAL, INC.; *Int'l*, pg. 3024
GOLD HYDROGEN LIMITED; *Int'l*, pg. 3024
GOLDIAM INTERNATIONAL LIMITED; *Int'l*, pg. 3033
GOLDIAM JEWELLERY LIMITED—See Goldiam International Limited; *Int'l*, pg. 3033
GOLDIAM USA, INC.—See Goldiam International Limited; *Int'l*, pg. 3033
GOLD IKRALIA EMPREEND. IMOB. SPE LTDA.—See PDG Realty S.A. Empreendimentos e Participacoes; *Int'l*, pg. 5770
GOLDIN ASSOCIATES, LLC—See CVC Capital Partners SICAV-FIS S.A.; *Int'l*, pg. 1888
GOLDIN FACTORING LIMITED—See Goldin Financial Holdings Limited; *Int'l*, pg. 3033
GOLDIN FINANCIAL HOLDINGS LIMITED; *Int'l*, pg. 3033
GOLDING CONTRACTORS PTY. LTD.—See NRW Holdings Limited; *Int'l*, pg. 5475
GOLDING FARMS FOODS, INC.; *U.S. Private*, pg. 1735
GOLDIN PROPERTIES HOLDINGS LIMITED; *Int'l*, pg. 3033
GOLDIS WATER SDN BHD—See IGB Berhad; *Int'l*, pg. 3601
GOLDKART JEWELS LIMITED; *Int'l*, pg. 3033
GOLDKEY CORPORATION; *U.S. Public*, pg. 951
GOLD KEY MEDIA—See Advance Publications, Inc.; *U.S. Private*, pg. 85
GOLD KEY MEDIA—See The Hearst Corporation; *U.S. Private*, pg. 4047
GOLD KEY/PHR, LLC; *U.S. Private*, pg. 1728
GOLDKEY PROCESSING, INC.—See HEXPOL AB; *Int'l*, pg. 3372
GOLD KOGYO LAGUNA PHILIPPINES, INC.—See Air Water Inc.; *Int'l*, pg. 240
GOLD LAKES CORP.; *U.S. Public*, pg. 949
GOLD LANDSCAPE, LLC—See Guggenheim Partners, LLC; *U.S. Private*, pg. 1811
GOLDLEAF PHARM, INC.—See Pyxus International, Inc.; *U.S. Public*, pg. 1740
GOLDLEAF TECHNOLOGIES, LLC—See Jack Henry & Associates, Inc.; *U.S. Public*, pg. 1182
GOLDLINE CONTROLS, INC.—See CCMP Capital Advisors, LP; *U.S. Private*, pg. 800
GOLDLINE CONTROLS, INC.—See MSD Capital, L.P.; *U.S. Private*, pg. 2807
GOLDLINE INC.—See A-Mark Precious Metals, Inc.; *U.S. Public*, pg. 10
GOLD LINE INC.—See Frank Martz Coach Company Inc.; *U.S. Private*, pg. 1595
GOLD LINE INTERNATIONAL FINVEST LIMITED; *Int'l*, pg. 3024
GOLD LINE RESOURCES LTD.—See Barsele Minerals Corp.; *Int'l*, pg. 870
GOLDLINK INSURANCE PLC.; *Int'l*, pg. 3033

COMPANY NAME INDEX

GOLDLINK THREAD LIMITED—See Fountain Set (Holdings) Limited; *Int'l*, pg. 2754
GOLDLION DISTRIBUTION (M) SDN. BHD.—See Goldlion Holdings Limited; *Int'l*, pg. 3033
GOLDLION ENTERPRISE (SINGAPORE) PTE LIMITED—See Goldlion Holdings Limited; *Int'l*, pg. 3033
GOLDLION HOLDINGS LIMITED; *Int'l*, pg. 3033
GOLD LION RESOURCES, INC.; *Int'l*, pg. 3024
GOLDLOK HOLDINGS (GUANGDONG) CO., LTD.; *Int'l*, pg. 3034
GOLDMAN & ASSOCIATES; *U.S. Private*, pg. 1735
GOLDMAN EQUIPMENT CO., LLC.; *U.S. Private*, pg. 1735
GOLDMAN PAPER COMPANY, INC.—See Bain Capital, LP; *U.S. Private*, pg. 440
GOLDMAN PROPERTIES; *U.S. Private*, pg. 1735
GOLDMAN & ROSEN, LTD.—See Day Ketterer Ltd.; *U.S. Private*, pg. 1176
GOLDMAN SACHS (ASIA) LLC—See The Goldman Sachs Group, Inc.; *U.S. Public*, pg. 2081
GOLDMAN SACHS ASSET MANAGEMENT CO., LTD.—See The Goldman Sachs Group, Inc.; *U.S. Public*, pg. 2081
GOLDMAN SACHS ASSET MANAGEMENT INTERNATIONAL—See The Goldman Sachs Group, Inc.; *U.S. Public*, pg. 2081
GOLDMAN SACHS ASSET MANAGEMENT, L.P.—See The Goldman Sachs Group, Inc.; *U.S. Public*, pg. 2081
GOLDMAN SACHS AUSTRALIA GROUP HOLDINGS PTY LTD—See The Goldman Sachs Group, Inc.; *U.S. Public*, pg. 2081
GOLDMAN SACHS AUSTRALIA PTY LTD—See The Goldman Sachs Group, Inc.; *U.S. Public*, pg. 2081
GOLDMAN SACHS BANK (EUROPE) PLC—See The Goldman Sachs Group, Inc.; *U.S. Public*, pg. 2081
GOLDMAN SACHS BANK EUROPE SE—See The Goldman Sachs Group, Inc.; *U.S. Public*, pg. 2081
GOLDMAN SACHS BANK USA—See The Goldman Sachs Group, Inc.; *U.S. Public*, pg. 2081
GOLDMAN SACHS BDC, INC.—See The Goldman Sachs Group, Inc.; *U.S. Public*, pg. 2081
GOLDMAN SACHS CANADA INC.—See The Goldman Sachs Group, Inc.; *U.S. Public*, pg. 2076
GOLDMAN SACHS CANADA INC.—See The Goldman Sachs Group, Inc.; *U.S. Public*, pg. 2076
GOLDMAN SACHS & CO. LLC—See The Goldman Sachs Group, Inc.; *U.S. Public*, pg. 2076
GOLDMAN, SACHS & CO.—See The Goldman Sachs Group, Inc.; *U.S. Public*, pg. 2081
GOLDMAN, SACHS & CO. WERTPAPIER GMBH—See The Goldman Sachs Group, Inc.; *U.S. Public*, pg. 2081
GOLDMAN SACHS DO BRASIL BANCO MULTIPLO S/A—See The Goldman Sachs Group, Inc.; *U.S. Public*, pg. 2076
GOLDMAN SACHS FOREIGN EXCHANGE (SINGAPORE) PTE—See The Goldman Sachs Group, Inc.; *U.S. Public*, pg. 2081
GOLDMAN SACHS GLOBAL COMMODITIES (CANADA) CORPORATION—See The Goldman Sachs Group, Inc.; *U.S. Public*, pg. 2081
GOLDMAN SACHS GROUP HOLDINGS (U.K.)—See The Goldman Sachs Group, Inc.; *U.S. Public*, pg. 2081
THE GOLDMAN SACHS GROUP, INC.; *U.S. Public*, pg. 2076
GOLDMAN SACHS INTERNATIONAL BANK—See The Goldman Sachs Group, Inc.; *U.S. Public*, pg. 2081
GOLDMAN SACHS INTERNATIONAL—See The Goldman Sachs Group, Inc.; *U.S. Public*, pg. 2081
GOLDMAN SACHS JAPAN CO., LTD.—See The Goldman Sachs Group, Inc.; *U.S. Public*, pg. 2081
GOLDMAN SACHS MERCHANT BANKING DIVISION—See The Goldman Sachs Group, Inc.; *U.S. Public*, pg. 2076
GOLDMAN SACHS MIDDLE MARKET LENDING CORP.—See The Goldman Sachs Group, Inc.; *U.S. Public*, pg. 2081
GOLDMAN SACHS MITSUI MARINE DERIVATIVE PRODUCTS, LP—See The Goldman Sachs Group, Inc.; *U.S. Public*, pg. 2081
GOLDMAN SACHS MLP & ENERGY RENAISSANCE FUND; *U.S. Public*, pg. 951
GOLDMAN SACHS PARIS INC. ET CIE—See The Goldman Sachs Group, Inc.; *U.S. Public*, pg. 2081
GOLDMAN SACHS PRIVATE CREDIT CORP.; *U.S. Private*, pg. 1735
GOLDMAN SACHS PRIVATE MIDDLE MARKET CREDIT LLC—See The Goldman Sachs Group, Inc.; *U.S. Public*, pg. 2081
GOLDMAN SACHS REALTY JAPAN LTD.—See The Goldman Sachs Group, Inc.; *U.S. Public*, pg. 2081
GOLDMAN SACHS REALTY MANAGEMENT EUROPE GMBH—See The Goldman Sachs Group, Inc.; *U.S. Public*, pg. 2081
GOLDMAN SACHS (SINGAPORE) PTE.—See The Goldman Sachs Group, Inc.; *U.S. Public*, pg. 2081
GOLDMAN SACHS URBAN INVESTMENT GROUP—See The Goldman Sachs Group, Inc.; *U.S. Public*, pg. 2081

GOLD MANTIS ART CO. LTD.—See Suzhou Gold Mantis Construction Decoration Co., Ltd.; *Int'l*, pg. 7349
GOLD MANTIS EXHIBITION DESIGN COMPANY—See Suzhou Gold Mantis Construction Decoration Co., Ltd.; *Int'l*, pg. 7349
GOLD MANTIS JOSTECHNOLOGIES INC.—See Suzhou Gold Mantis Construction Decoration Co., Ltd.; *Int'l*, pg. 7349
GOLD MANTIS RESIDENTIAL INTEGRATED DECORATION CO. LTD.—See Suzhou Gold Mantis Construction Decoration Co., Ltd.; *Int'l*, pg. 7349
GOLDMARK KFT—See Warimpex Finanz- und Beteiligungs AG; *Int'l*, pg. 8345
GOLD MEDAL HAIR PRODUCTS, INC.; *U.S. Private*, pg. 1728
GOLD MEDAL PLUMBING HEATING COOLING ELECTRIC, INC.—See New Mountain Capital, LLC; *U.S. Private*, pg. 2902
GOLD MEDAL PRODUCTS CO.; *U.S. Private*, pg. 1728
GOLD MEDAL SERVICE, LLC—See New Mountain Capital, LLC; *U.S. Private*, pg. 2902
GOLD MEDAL SERVICES, LLC—See Kinderhook Industries, LLC; *U.S. Private*, pg. 2307
GOLDMINING INC.; *Int'l*, pg. 3034
GOLD MOTORS, INC.; *U.S. Private*, pg. 1728
GOLD MOUNTAIN LIMITED; *Int'l*, pg. 3025
GOLD MOUNTAIN MINING CORP.; *Int'l*, pg. 3025
GOLD MOUNTAINS (H.K.) INTERNATIONAL MINING COMPANY LIMITED—See Zijin Mining Group Company Limited; *Int'l*, pg. 8683
GOLDNER ASSOCIATES, INC.; *U.S. Private*, pg. 1735
GOLDNER HAWN JOHNSON & MORRISON INC.; *U.S. Private*, pg. 1735
GOLD'N PLUMP FARMS, LLC—See JBS S.A.; *Int'l*, pg. 3919
GOLD'N PLUMP POULTRY, LLC—See JBS S.A.; *Int'l*, pg. 3919
GOLD OIL PERU S.A.C—See Sunda Energy Plc; *Int'l*, pg. 7311
GOLD ONE AFRICA LIMITED—See Baiyin Nonferrous Metal (Group) Co., Ltd.; *Int'l*, pg. 803
GOLD ONE AFRICA LIMITED—See Long March Capital Ltd.; *Int'l*, pg. 4549
GOLDON RESOURCES LTD.; *Int'l*, pg. 3034
GOLDPAC DATACARD SOLUTIONS CO. LTD.—See Thales S.A.; *Int'l*, pg. 7600
GOLDPAC GROUP LIMITED; *Int'l*, pg. 3034
GOLDPAC INTERNATIONAL (HOLDING) LIMITED—See Thales S.A.; *Int'l*, pg. 7600
GOLDPAC SECURE-CARD ZHUHAI LTD—See Thales S.A.; *Int'l*, pg. 7600
GOLD-PAK CO., LTD.—See Air Water Inc.; *Int'l*, pg. 240
GOLD PEAK INDUSTRIES (TAIWAN) LTD.—See Gold Peak Technology Group Limited; *Int'l*, pg. 3025
GOLD PEAK TECHNOLOGY GROUP LIMITED; *Int'l*, pg. 3025
GOLD PEG INTERNATIONAL PTY. LTD.—See Hochland SE; *Int'l*, pg. 3437
GOLDPLAT PLC; *Int'l*, pg. 3034
GOLDPLAT RECOVERY (PTY) LTD.—See Goldplat Plc; *Int'l*, pg. 3034
GOLD POINT ENERGY CORP.—See San Leon Energy plc; *Int'l*, pg. 6521
GOLD POINT LODGING AND REALTY, INC.; *U.S. Private*, pg. 1728
GOLDPOINT PARTNERS LLC—See New York Life Insurance Company; *U.S. Private*, pg. 2910
GOLD POLONIA EMPREENDIMENTOS IMOBILIARIOS SPE LTDA—See PDG Realty S.A. Empreendimentos e Participacoes; *Int'l*, pg. 5770
GOLD PORT CORPORATION; *Int'l*, pg. 3026
GOLD PORTUGAL EMPREENDIMENTOS IMOBILIARIOS SPE LTDA—See PDG Realty S.A. Empreendimentos e Participacoes; *Int'l*, pg. 5770
GOLD PRICE GROUP, INC.—See A-Mark Precious Metals, Inc.; *U.S. Public*, pg. 10
GOLDQUEST MINING CORP.; *Int'l*, pg. 3034
GOLD RAIN ENTERPRISES CORP.; *Int'l*, pg. 3026
GOLDREA RESOURCES CORP.; *Int'l*, pg. 3034
GOLD RED EMPREENDIMENTOS IMOBILIARIOS SPE LTDA—See PDG Realty S.A. Empreendimentos e Participacoes; *Int'l*, pg. 5770
GOLD REEF CITY THEME PARK—See Hosken Consolidated Investments Limited; *Int'l*, pg. 3485
GOLD RESERVE INC.; *U.S. Public*, pg. 949
GOLD RESOURCE CORPORATION; *U.S. Public*, pg. 949
GOLDRICH & KEST INDUSTRIES LLC—See G&K Management Company; *U.S. Private*, pg. 1629
GOLDRICH MINING COMPANY; *U.S. Public*, pg. 951
GOLD RIDGE EXPLORATION CORP.; *Int'l*, pg. 3026
GOLDRING GULF DISTRIBUTING COMPANY, LLC—See Gulf Distributing Holdings LLC; *U.S. Private*, pg. 1816
GOLDRIVER ORCHARDS, INC.; *U.S. Private*, pg. 1735
GOLD ROAD RESOURCES LIMITED; *Int'l*, pg. 3026
GOLD ROAST FOOD INDUSTRY (SINGAPORE) PTE LTD—See Investcorp Holdings B.S.C.; *Int'l*, pg. 3777
GOLD ROCK HOLDINGS INC.; *U.S. Public*, pg. 950
GOLDROOSTER AG; *Int'l*, pg. 3034
GOLD ROYALTY CORP.; *Int'l*, pg. 3026

GOLDSTONE HOSIERY CO. INC.

GOLD RUSH CARIBOO CORP.; *Int'l*, pg. 3026
GOLDRUSH INSURANCE SERVICES, INC.—See Prism Technologies Group, Inc.; *U.S. Public*, pg. 1722
GOLDSANDS DEVELOPMENT COMPANY; *Int'l*, pg. 3034
GOLD SAO PAULO EMPREENDIMENTOS IMOBILIARIOS SPE LTDA.—See PDG Realty S.A. Empreendimentos e Participacoes; *Int'l*, pg. 5770
GOLDSBORO MILLING COMPANY; *U.S. Private*, pg. 1735
GOLDSBOROUGH PTY LTD—See Octanex Ltd; *Int'l*, pg. 5522
GOLDSCHMIDT THERMIT GMBH—See Vermogensverwaltung Erben Dr. Karl Goldschmidt GmbH; *Int'l*, pg. 8173
GOLDSCHMITT TECHMOBIL GMBH—See Thor Industries, Inc.; *U.S. Public*, pg. 2156
GOLD&S CO., LTD.; *Int'l*, pg. 3026
GOLD SEAL AVON POLYMERS PRIVATE LIMITED—See AKWEL; *Int'l*, pg. 268
GOLDSEEK RESOURCES, INC.; *Int'l*, pg. 3034
GOLD'S GYM INTERNATIONAL, INC.—See TRT Holdings, Inc.; *U.S. Private*, pg. 4244
GOLDSHIELD FIBERGLASS, INC.—See AIP, LLC; *U.S. Private*, pg. 135
GOLD SHOPPING CENTRE HOLDINGS SDN. BHD.—See The Store Corporation Berhad; *Int'l*, pg. 7689
GOLDSHORE RESOURCES INC.; *Int'l*, pg. 3034
GOLD & SILVER BUYERS; *U.S. Private*, pg. 1727
GOLD & SILVER COIN SHOP, INC.; *U.S. Private*, pg. 1727
GOLDSOURCE MINES INC.—See Mako Mining Corp.; *Int'l*, pg. 4658
GOLD SPRINGS RESOURCE CORP.; *Int'l*, pg. 3026
GOLD'S PURE FOODS, LLC—See LSCG Management, Inc.; *U.S. Private*, pg. 2509
GOLD STANDARD BAKING, INC.—See 37 Baking Holdings, LLC; *U.S. Public*, pg. 8
GOLD STANDARD DIAGNOSIS FRANKFURT GMBH—See Eurofins Scientific S.E.; *Int'l*, pg. 2550
GOLD STANDARD DIAGNOSTICS CD KASSEL GMBH—See Eurofins Scientific S.E.; *Int'l*, pg. 2550
GOLD STANDARD DIAGNOSTICS CORP, INC.—See Eurofins Scientific S.E.; *Int'l*, pg. 2550
GOLD STANDARD DIAGNOSTICS FREIBURG GMBH—See Eurofins Scientific S.E.; *Int'l*, pg. 2550
GOLD STANDARD DIAGNOSTICS HORSHAM, INC.—See Eurofins Scientific S.E.; *Int'l*, pg. 2550
GOLD STANDARD DIAGNOSTICS KASSEL GMBH—See Eurofins Scientific S.E.; *Int'l*, pg. 2550
GOLD STANDARD DIAGNOSTICS SHANGHAI CO., LTD.—See Eurofins Scientific S.E.; *Int'l*, pg. 2550
GOLD STANDARD DIAGNOSTICS SINGAPORE PTE. LTD.—See Eurofins Scientific S.E.; *Int'l*, pg. 2550
GOLD STANDARD DIAGNOSTICS TRIESTE S.R.L.—See Eurofins Scientific S.E.; *Int'l*, pg. 2550
GOLD STANDARD ENTERPRISES INC.; *U.S. Private*, pg. 1728
GOLD STANDARD MINING COMPANY; *U.S. Private*, pg. 1728
GOLD STANDARD RESOURCES, INC.—See The Ensign Group, Inc.; *U.S. Public*, pg. 2071
GOLD STANDARD VENTURES CORP.—See Orla Mining Ltd.; *Int'l*, pg. 5639
GOLD STAR BRAZIL LIMITED—See Goodwin PLC; *Int'l*, pg. 3042
GOLD STAR CHILI INC.; *U.S. Private*, pg. 1728
GOLD STAR FOODS INC.—See Alvarez & Marsal, Inc.; *U.S. Private*, pg. 213
GOLD STAR FOODS INC.—See Highview Capital, LLC; *U.S. Private*, pg. 1942
GOLD STAR FS INC.; *U.S. Private*, pg. 1728
GOLD STAR INSULATION LP—See Installed Building Products, Inc.; *U.S. Public*, pg. 1132
GOLD STAR MORTGAGE FINANCIAL GROUP CORP.; *U.S. Private*, pg. 1728
GOLDSTAR NORTHAMERICAN MINING INC.; *U.S. Private*, pg. 1735
GOLD STAR POWDERS PRIVATE LIMITED—See Goodwin PLC; *Int'l*, pg. 3042
GOLD STAR POWDERS UK—See Goodwin PLC; *Int'l*, pg. 3042
GOLD STAR PRODUCTS; *U.S. Private*, pg. 1728
GOLD STAR TRANSPORTATION INC.; *U.S. Private*, pg. 1728
GOLD STAR TUTORING SERVICES, INC.; *U.S. Private*, pg. 1728
GOLDSTEIN ENTERPRISES INC.; *U.S. Private*, pg. 1735
GOLDSTEIN ESWOOD COMMERCIAL COOKING PTY LTD—See The Middleby Corporation; *U.S. Public*, pg. 2114
GOLDSTEIN MUNGER & ASSOCIATES—See Genstar Capital, LLC; *U.S. Private*, pg. 1677
GOLDSTEIN MUNGER & ASSOCIATES—See Keystone Group, L.P.; *U.S. Private*, pg. 2298
GOLDSTONE HOSIERY CO. INC.; *U.S. Private*, pg. 1735
GOLDSTONE INFRATECH LIMITED - UNIT I—See Olectra Greentech Ltd; *Int'l*, pg. 5553

GOLDSTONE INVESTMENT CO., LTD.—See CITIC Securities Co., Ltd.; *Int'l*, pg. 1622
GOLDSTONE INVESTMENT GROUP LIMITED; *Int'l*, pg. 3034
GOLDSTONE RESOURCES LTD.; *Int'l*, pg. 3034
GOLDSTREAM CAPITAL MANAGEMENT LIMITED—See Goldstream Investment Limited; *Int'l*, pg. 3034
GOLDSTREAM INVESTMENT LIMITED; *Int'l*, pg. 3034
GOLDSTREAM MINERALS INC.; *Int'l*, pg. 3034
GOLDSTRIKE RESOURCES LTD.; *Int'l*, pg. 3034
GOLDSUN BUILDING MATERIALS CO., LTD.; *Int'l*, pg. 3035
GOLDTECH ACCESS SDN. BHD.—See Pabrik Kertas Tjiwi Kimia Tbk; *Int'l*, pg. 5684
GOLDTEK TECHNOLOGY (SHENZHEN) CO., LTD.—See Ennoconn Corporation; *Int'l*, pg. 2443
GOLD TERRA RESOURCE CORP.; *Int'l*, pg. 3026
GOLD TIP, LLC—See Vista Outdoor Inc.; *U.S. Public*, pg. 2305
GOLD TORRENT, INC.; *U.S. Private*, pg. 1728
GOLD TREE RESOURCES LTD.; *Int'l*, pg. 3026
GOLD VALLEY PTY. LTD.; *Int'l*, pg. 3026
GOLDWAY EDUCATION GROUP LIMITED; *Int'l*, pg. 3035
GOLDWELL COSMETICS (CZ) S.R.O.—See Kao Corporation; *Int'l*, pg. 4073
GOLDWIN AMERICA, INC.—See Goldwin, Inc.; *Int'l*, pg. 3035
GOLDWIN CHINA,LTD.—See Goldwin, Inc.; *Int'l*, pg. 3035
GOLDWIN DEVELOPMENT INC.—See Goldwin, Inc.; *Int'l*, pg. 3035
GOLDWIN ENTERPRISE INC.—See Goldwin, Inc.; *Int'l*, pg. 3035
GOLDWIN EUROPE AG—See Goldwin, Inc.; *Int'l*, pg. 3035
GOLDWIN, INC.; *Int'l*, pg. 3035
GOLDWIN ITALIA SRL—See Goldwin, Inc.; *Int'l*, pg. 3035
GOLDWIN KOREA CORPORATION—See Goldwin, Inc.; *Int'l*, pg. 3035
GOLDWIN LOGITEM INC.—See Goldwin, Inc.; *Int'l*, pg. 3035
GOLDWIN SAI GON VIETNAM CO., LTD.—See Goldwin, Inc.; *Int'l*, pg. 3035
GOLDWIN TECHNICAL CENTER INC.—See Goldwin, Inc.; *Int'l*, pg. 3035
GOLDWIN TRADING INC.—See Goldwin, Inc.; *Int'l*, pg. 3035
GOLD WITHE EMPREENDIMENTOS IMOBILIARIOS SPE LTDA—See PDG Realty S.A. Empreendimentos e Participacoes; *Int'l*, pg. 5770
GOLD X MINING CORP.—See Gran Colombia Gold Corp.; *Int'l*, pg. 3053
GOLD-ZACK AG; *Int'l*, pg. 3026
GOLD-ZACK KURZWAREN GMBH—See William Prym GmbH & Co. KG; *Int'l*, pg. 8413
GOLECHHA GLOBAL FINANCE LTD.; *Int'l*, pg. 3035
GOLETA WATER DISTRICT; *U.S. Private*, pg. 1735
GOLETZ GMBH; *Int'l*, pg. 3035
GOLF AMBER BALTIC SP.Z.O.O.—See Warimpex Finanz- und Beteiligungs AG; *Int'l*, pg. 8345
GOLF APPAREL BRANDS, INC.; *U.S. Private*, pg. 1735
GOLF ARBORETUM, D.O.O.—See Zavarovalnica Triglav, d.d.; *Int'l*, pg. 8626
GOLFBALLS.COM, INC.; *U.S. Private*, pg. 1736
GOLFBOX A/S—See FirstRand Limited; *Int'l*, pg. 2690
GOLF CARD INTERNATIONAL, LLC—See Camping World Holdings, Inc.; *U.S. Public*, pg. 428
GOLF CART WORLD, INC.—See LPI, Inc.; *U.S. Private*, pg. 2507
THE GOLF CHANNEL, LLC—See Comcast Corporation; *U.S. Public*, pg. 539
THE GOLF CLUB AT DOVE MOUNTAIN—See Escalante Golf, Inc.; *U.S. Private*, pg. 1424
THE GOLF CLUB OF AMELIA ISLAND—See Concert Golf Partners, LLC; *U.S. Private*, pg. 1009
GOLF & CO. LTD.—See Access Industries, Inc.; *U.S. Private*, pg. 51
GOLF CORPORATION; *U.S. Private*, pg. 1735
GOLF COURSE MEDIA NETWORK; *U.S. Private*, pg. 1735
GOLF COURSE SUPERINTENDENTS ASSOCIATION OF AMERICA; *U.S. Private*, pg. 1736
GOLF DIGEST ONLINE INC.; *Int'l*, pg. 3035
GOLF DIGEST PUBLICATIONS—See Advance Publications, Inc.; *U.S. Private*, pg. 86
GOLF DISCOUNT OF ST. LOUIS INCORPORATED; *U.S. Private*, pg. 1736
GOLF DO CO., LTD.; *Int'l*, pg. 3035
GOLFERS WAREHOUSE INC.—See Worldwide Golf Enterprises, Inc.; *U.S. Private*, pg. 4569
GOLF ETC. OF AMERICA, INC.; *U.S. Private*, pg. 1736
GOLFETTO SANGATI S.R.L.—See GEA Group Aktiengesellschaft; *Int'l*, pg. 2903
GOLF GALAXY GOLFWORKS, INC.—See Dick's Sporting Goods, Inc.; *U.S. Public*, pg. 659
GOLF GALAXY, INC.—See Dick's Sporting Goods, Inc.; *U.S. Public*, pg. 659
GOLF GRAD OTOCEC, D. O. O.—See Krka, d.d., Novo Mesto; *Int'l*, pg. 4302

GOLF HOST SECURITIES, INC.—See Salamander Innisbrook, LLC; *U.S. Private*, pg. 3530
GOLF HOUSE DIREKTVERSAND GMBH; *Int'l*, pg. 3035
THE GOLF JOY CO., LTD.—See The Nisshin OilliO Group, Ltd.; *Int'l*, pg. 7671
GOLFLAND ENTERTAINMENT CENTERS; *U.S. Private*, pg. 1736
GOLF MAGAZINE—See Meredith Corporation; *U.S. Public*, pg. 1423
GOLF MART INC.; *U.S. Private*, pg. 1736
GOLF MILL FORD; *U.S. Private*, pg. 1736
GOLF PARTNER CO., LTD.—See XEBIO Holdings Co., Ltd.; *Int'l*, pg. 8520
GOLFPLATZ EGGEBERG GMBH & CO. ANLAGEN KG—See GERRY WEBER International AG; *Int'l*, pg. 2945
GOLF PORTO CARRAS S.A.—See Technical Olympic SA; *Int'l*, pg. 7506
GOLF & SKI WAREHOUSE INC.; *U.S. Private*, pg. 1736
GOLFTEC INTELLECTUAL PROPERTY, LLC—See Golf Digest Online Inc.; *Int'l*, pg. 3035
GOLF TOWN LIMITED—See Fairfax Financial Holdings Limited; *Int'l*, pg. 2606
GOLF- UND COUNTRY CLUB SEDDINER SEE IMMOBILIEN GMBH—See UniCredit S.p.A.; *Int'l*, pg. 8034
GOLFWALKER PTE LTD; *Int'l*, pg. 3035
THE GOLF WAREHOUSE, INC.—See Northern Tool & Equipment Company, Inc.; *U.S. Private*, pg. 2954
GOLF WORLD BUSINESS—See Advance Publications, Inc.; *U.S. Private*, pg. 86
GOLFZON CO., LTD.; *Int'l*, pg. 3035
GOLFZON NEWDIN HOLDINGS CO., LTD.; *Int'l*, pg. 3036
GOLGOHAR MINING & INDUSTRIAL CO.; *Int'l*, pg. 3036
GOLIAD DIALYSIS, LLC—See DaVita Inc.; *U.S. Public*, pg. 639
GOLIATH FILM & MEDIA HOLDINGS, INC.; *U.S. Public*, pg. 951
GOLIATH GAMES, LLC—See Goliath International Holding BV; *Int'l*, pg. 3036
GOLIATH INTERNATIONAL HOLDING BV; *Int'l*, pg. 3036
GOLIATH RESOURCES LIMITED; *Int'l*, pg. 3036
GOLICK MARTINS INC.; *U.S. Private*, pg. 1736
GO LIFE INTERNATIONAL LTD.; *Int'l*, pg. 3017
GOLIK CONCRETE (HK) LIMITED—See Golik Holdings Limited; *Int'l*, pg. 3036
GOLIK CONCRETE LIMITED—See Golik Holdings Limited; *Int'l*, pg. 3036
GOLIK GODOWN LIMITED—See Golik Holdings Limited; *Int'l*, pg. 3036
GOLIK HOLDINGS LIMITED; *Int'l*, pg. 3036
GOLIK METAL INDUSTRIAL COMPANY LIMITED—See Golik Holdings Limited; *Int'l*, pg. 3036
GOLIK METAL MANUFACTURING CO. LIMITED—See Golik Holdings Limited; *Int'l*, pg. 3036
GOLIK STEEL COMPANY LIMITED—See Golik Holdings Limited; *Int'l*, pg. 3036
GOLIK STEEL (HK) LIMITED—See Golik Holdings Limited; *Int'l*, pg. 3036
GOLIK WIRE ROPE HONG KONG LIMITED—See Golik Holdings Limited; *Int'l*, pg. 3036
GOLIN/HARRIS INTERNATIONAL, INC.—See The Interpublic Group of Companies, Inc.; *U.S. Public*, pg. 2093
GOLINHARRIS/PANACHE—See The Interpublic Group of Companies, Inc.; *U.S. Public*, pg. 2094
GOLINHARRIS—See The Interpublic Group of Companies, Inc.; *U.S. Public*, pg. 2094
GOLINHARRIS—See The Interpublic Group of Companies, Inc.; *U.S. Public*, pg. 2094
GOLINHARRIS—See The Interpublic Group of Companies, Inc.; *U.S. Public*, pg. 2094
GOLINHARRIS—See The Interpublic Group of Companies, Inc.; *U.S. Public*, pg. 2094
GOLINHARRIS—See The Interpublic Group of Companies, Inc.; *U.S. Public*, pg. 2094
GOLINHARRIS—See The Interpublic Group of Companies, Inc.; *U.S. Public*, pg. 2094
GOLINHARRIS—See The Interpublic Group of Companies, Inc.; *U.S. Public*, pg. 2094
GOLINHARRIS—See The Interpublic Group of Companies, Inc.; *U.S. Public*, pg. 2094
GOLINHARRIS—See The Interpublic Group of Companies, Inc.; *U.S. Public*, pg. 2094
GOLINHARRIS—See The Interpublic Group of Companies, Inc.; *U.S. Public*, pg. 2094
GOLINHARRIS—See The Interpublic Group of Companies, Inc.; *U.S. Public*, pg. 2094
GOLINHARRIS—See The Interpublic Group of Companies, Inc.; *U.S. Public*, pg. 2094
GOLINHARRIS—See The Interpublic Group of Companies, Inc.; *U.S. Public*, pg. 2094
GOLINHARRIS—See The Interpublic Group of Companies, Inc.; *U.S. Public*, pg. 2094

GOLINHARRIS—See The Interpublic Group of Companies, Inc.; *U.S. Public*, pg. 2094
GOLINHARRIS—See The Interpublic Group of Companies, Inc.; *U.S. Public*, pg. 2094
GOLINHARRIS—See The Interpublic Group of Companies, Inc.; *U.S. Public*, pg. 2094
GOLINHARRIS—See The Interpublic Group of Companies, Inc.; *U.S. Public*, pg. 2094
GOLINHARRIS—See The Interpublic Group of Companies, Inc.; *U.S. Public*, pg. 2094
GOLINK ONLINE CO., LTD.—See Plan B Media Public Company Limited; *Int'l*, pg. 5888
GOLIVE! MOBILE, LLC; *U.S. Private*, pg. 1736
GOLIVE YAZILIM HIZMETLERI A.S.—See Verusa Holding A.S.; *Int'l*, pg. 8175
GOLKONDA ALUMINIUM EXTRUSIONS LTD.; *Int'l*, pg. 3036
GOLKONDA ENGINEERING ENTERPRISES LIMITED; *Int'l*, pg. 3036
GOLKUNDA DIAMONDS & JEWELLERY LIMITED; *Int'l*, pg. 3036
GOLLEY SLATER CENTRAL—See Golley Slater Group Limited; *Int'l*, pg. 3036
GOLLEY SLATER GROUP LIMITED; *Int'l*, pg. 3036
GOLLEY SLATER LONDON—See Golley Slater Group Limited; *Int'l*, pg. 3036
GOLLEY SLATER RETAIL—See Golley Slater Group Limited; *Int'l*, pg. 3036
GOLLING PONTIAC GMC TRUCK INC.; *U.S. Private*, pg. 1736
GOL LINHAS AEREAS INTELIGENTES S.A.; *Int'l*, pg. 3023
GOLLUCKE & ROTHFOS GMBH—See ED&F Man Holdings Limited; *Int'l*, pg. 2303
GOLLUECKE & ROTHFOS GMBH—See ED&F Man Holdings Limited; *Int'l*, pg. 2303
GOLOG HOLDING S.A.; *Int'l*, pg. 3036
GOLOGIQ, INC.; *U.S. Public*, pg. 951
GOLO, INC.; *Int'l*, pg. 3036
GOLSTA SDN. BHD.; *Int'l*, pg. 3037
GOLTAS CIMENTO A.S.; *Int'l*, pg. 3037
GOL TRANSPORTES AEREOS—See Gol Linhas Aereas Inteligentes S.A.; *Int'l*, pg. 3023
GOLUB CAPITAL BDC, INC.—See Golub Capital, Inc.; *U.S. Private*, pg. 1736
GOLUB CAPITAL BDC REVOLVER FUNDING LLC—See Golub Capital, Inc.; *U.S. Private*, pg. 1736
GOLUB CAPITAL DIRECT LENDING UNLEVERED CORPORATION; *U.S. Private*, pg. 1736
GOLUB CAPITAL, INC.; *U.S. Private*, pg. 1736
GOLUB CORPORATION; *U.S. Private*, pg. 1736
GOLUB & CO; *U.S. Private*, pg. 1736
GOLUB REALTY SERVICES LLC—See Golub & Co; *U.S. Private*, pg. 1736
GOLUB SERVICE STATIONS, INC.—See Golub Corporation; *U.S. Private*, pg. 1736
GOLU KLIMAATBEHEERSING B.V.—See CENTROTEC SE; *Int'l*, pg. 1414
GOLVPOOLEN HELSINGBORG AB—See BHG Group AB; *Int'l*, pg. 1015
GOMAJI CORP LTD.; *Int'l*, pg. 3037
GOM AMERICAS INC.—See Carl-Zeiss-Stiftung; *Int'l*, pg. 1336
GOMAN BAKERIET AS—See Coop Norge SA; *Int'l*, pg. 1789
GO-MART, INC.; *U.S. Private*, pg. 1723
GOMAX ELECTRONICS, INC.; *Int'l*, pg. 3037
GO MEDIA, INC.—See Great Hill Partners, L.P.; *U.S. Private*, pg. 1763
GOMEDUS GMBH & CO. KG—See Munchener Ruckversicherungs AG; *Int'l*, pg. 5092
GOMEDUS PARTNERKLINIKEN GMBH—See Munchener Ruckversicherungs AG; *Int'l*, pg. 5092
GOMEEKI PTY LTD.; *Int'l*, pg. 3037
GOME FINANCE TECHNOLOGY CO., LTD.; *Int'l*, pg. 3037
GOMERDINGER & ASSOCIATES, LLC—See Aprio, LLP; *U.S. Private*, pg. 301
GOME RETAIL HOLDINGS LIMITED; *Int'l*, pg. 3037
GO METALS CORP; *Int'l*, pg. 3017
GOME TELECOM EQUIPMENT CO., LTD.; *Int'l*, pg. 3037
GOMEZ CONSTRUCTION COMPANY; *U.S. Private*, pg. 1737
GOMEZ CONSULTING CO., LTD.—See SBI Holdings, Inc.; *Int'l*, pg. 6605
GOMEZ FLOOR COVERING, INC.; *U.S. Private*, pg. 1737
GOM FRANCE SAS—See Carl-Zeiss-Stiftung; *Int'l*, pg. 1336
GOM GMBH—See Carl-Zeiss-Stiftung; *Int'l*, pg. 1336
GO MINI'S LLC; *U.S. Private*, pg. 1723
GOM ITALIA S.R.L.—See Carl-Zeiss-Stiftung; *Int'l*, pg. 1336
GOMITEX S.A.—See Rieter Holding Ltd.; *Int'l*, pg. 6338
GO MODULAR, INC.; *U.S. Private*, pg. 1723
GO MORTGAGE GROUP, LLC; *U.S. Private*, pg. 1723
GO MORTGAGE, LLC—See Go Companies, LLC; *U.S. Private*, pg. 1723
GO MOTOR RETAILING LIMITED—See General Motors Company; *U.S. Public*, pg. 928

COMPANY NAME INDEX

GOMSPACE GROUP AB; *Int'l*, pg. 3037
GOM UK LIMITED—See Carl-Zeiss-Stiftung; *Int'l*, pg. 1336
GONARMEX, S.A. DE C.V.—See Grupo Televisa, S.A.B.; *Int'l*, pg. 3136
G-ONE AUTO PARTS DE MEXICO, S.A. DE C.V.—See H-One Co., Ltd.; *Int'l*, pg. 3194
GONGCO FOODS; *U.S. Private*, pg. 1737
GONGIN PRECISION INDUSTRIAL CO., LTD.; *Int'l*, pg. 3037
GONGOS RESEARCH; *U.S. Private*, pg. 1737
GONG'S MARKET OF SANGER INC.; *U.S. Private*, pg. 1737
GONG VENTURES INC.—See Gong's Market of Sanger Inc.; *U.S. Private*, pg. 1737
GONNELLA BAKING COMPANY; *U.S. Private*, pg. 1737
GONNELLA FROZEN PRODUCTS—See Gonnella Baking Company; *U.S. Private*, pg. 1737
GO NORTH EAST LIMITED—See GLOBALVIA Inversiones, S.A.U.; *Int'l*, pg. 3005
GO NORTH EAST LIMITED—See Kinetic Group Services Pty Ltd.; *Int'l*, pg. 4167
GO NORTH WEST LIMITED—See GLOBALVIA Inversiones, S.A.U.; *Int'l*, pg. 3005
GO NORTH WEST LIMITED—See Kinetic Group Services Pty Ltd.; *Int'l*, pg. 4167
GONPACHI RESTAURANT LIMITED—See 1957 & Co. (Hospitality) Limited; *Int'l*, pg. 3
GONSALVES & SANTUCCI INC.; *U.S. Private*, pg. 1737
GONVARRI GALICIA, S.A.—See Corporacion Gestamp SL; *Int'l*, pg. 1804
GONVARRI STEEL SERVICES—See Corporacion Gestamp SL; *Int'l*, pg. 1804
GONVAUTO ASTURIAS, S.L.—See Corporacion Gestamp SL; *Int'l*, pg. 1804
GONVAUTO, S.A.—See Corporacion Gestamp SL; *Int'l*, pg. 1804
GONZALES CONSULTING SERVICES, INC.; *U.S. Private*, pg. 1737
GONZALES DIALYSIS CENTERS - SOUTHEAST, LP—See DaVita Inc.; *U.S. Public*, pg. 639
GONZALES LABOR SYSTEMS INC.; *U.S. Private*, pg. 1737
GONZALEZ DESIGN ENGINEERING COMPANY INC.; *U.S. Private*, pg. 1737
GONZALEZ LUNA, MORENO Y ARMIDA, S.C.—See DLA Piper Global; *Int'l*, pg. 2140
GONZALEZ MANUFACTURING TECHNOLOGIES; *U.S. Private*, pg. 1737
GONZALEZ PICO SYSTEMS INC.—See Gonzalez Design Engineering Company Inc.; *U.S. Private*, pg. 1737
GONZALEZ & TAPANES FOODS INC.—See GraceKennedy Limited; *Int'l*, pg. 3049
GONZMART FAMILY FOUNDATION—See Columbia Restaurant Group; *U.S. Private*, pg. 977
GOO CHEMICAL CO., LTD. - FUKUI FACTORY—See GOO Chemical Co., Ltd.; *Int'l*, pg. 3037
GOO CHEMICAL CO., LTD. - SHIGA FACTORY—See GOO Chemical Co., Ltd.; *Int'l*, pg. 3037
GOO CHEMICAL CO., LTD.; *Int'l*, pg. 3037
GOOCH & HOUSEGO (CALIFORNIA) LLC—See Gooch & Housego PLC; *Int'l*, pg. 3038
GOOCH & HOUSEGO (DEUTSCHLAND) GMBH—See Gooch & Housego PLC; *Int'l*, pg. 3038
GOOCH & HOUSEGO JAPAN KK—See Gooch & Housego PLC; *Int'l*, pg. 3038
GOOCH & HOUSEGO (OHIO) LLC—See Gooch & Housego PLC; *Int'l*, pg. 3038
GOOCH & HOUSEGO (PALO ALTO) LLC—See Gooch & Housego PLC; *Int'l*, pg. 3038
GOOCH & HOUSEGO PLC; *Int'l*, pg. 3037
GOOCH & HOUSEGO (TORQUAY) LIMITED—See Gooch & Housego PLC; *Int'l*, pg. 3038
GOOCH & HOUSEGO (UK) LIMITED—See Gooch & Housego PLC; *Int'l*, pg. 3038
GOOD2GO CORP.; *Int'l*, pg. 3039
GOOD360; *U.S. Private*, pg. 1738
GOOD ADVERTISING, INC.; *U.S. Private*, pg. 1737
GOODALE DIALYSIS, LLC—See DaVita Inc.; *U.S. Public*, pg. 639
GOODALL AND BOURNE PROPERTIES (PROPRIETARY) LIMITED—See CONDUIT CAPITAL LIMITED; *Int'l*, pg. 1766
GOODALL HOMES & COMMUNITIES—See Berkshire Hathaway Inc.; *U.S. Public*, pg. 304
GOODALL MFG. LLC; *U.S. Private*, pg. 1738
GOOD-ARK (H.K.) ELECTRONICS LTD.—See Suzhou Good-Ark Electronics Co., Ltd.; *Int'l*, pg. 7350
GOOD-ARK SEMICONDUCTOR USA CORP.—See Suzhou Good-Ark Electronics Co., Ltd.; *Int'l*, pg. 7350
GOODBABY CHINA COMMERCIAL CO., LTD—See Goodbaby International Holdings Limited; *Int'l*, pg. 3039
GOODBABY (HONG KONG) LIMITED—See Goodbaby International Holdings Limited; *Int'l*, pg. 3039
GOODBABY INTERNATIONAL HOLDINGS LIMITED; *Int'l*, pg. 3039
GOODBABY JAPAN CO., LTD.—See Goodbaby International Holdings Limited; *Int'l*, pg. 3039
GOODBEE AND ASSOCIATES, INC.; *U.S. Private*, pg. 1738

GOOD.BEE HOLDING GMBH—See Erste Group Bank AG; *Int'l*, pg. 2499
GOOD.BEE SERVICE RO SRL—See Erste Group Bank AG; *Int'l*, pg. 2499
GOODBERRY CREAMERY INC.; *U.S. Private*, pg. 1738
GOODBODY CORPORATE FINANCE—See FEXCO Holdings; *Int'l*, pg. 2649
GOODBODY STOCKBROKERS UC—See AIB Group plc; *Int'l*, pg. 228
GOOD BROTHERS FLOORING PLUS; *U.S. Private*, pg. 1737
GOODBULK LTD.; *Int'l*, pg. 3039
GOODBYE KANSAS GROUP AB; *Int'l*, pg. 3039
GOODBY, SILVERSTEIN & PARTNERS, INC. - NEW YORK—See Omnicom Group Inc.; *U.S. Public*, pg. 1585
GOODBY, SILVERSTEIN & PARTNERS, INC.—See Omnicom Group Inc.; *U.S. Public*, pg. 1585
GOODCEN CO., LTD.—See Itcen Co., Ltd.; *Int'l*, pg. 3832
GOOD CHANCE PROPERTIES PTE LTD—See Second Chance Properties Ltd.; *Int'l*, pg. 6672
THE GOOD CLINIC, LLC—See Mitesco, Inc.; *U.S. Public*, pg. 1452
THE GOOD COLLECTIVE PTY LTD—See BWX Limited; *Int'l*, pg. 1233
GOOD COM ASSET CO., LTD.; *Int'l*, pg. 3038
GOOD COM CO., LTD.—See Good Com Asset Co., Ltd.; *Int'l*, pg. 3038
GOOD COMMERCE ACQUISITION CORP.; *U.S. Private*, pg. 1737
GOOD COMPANIES; *U.S. Private*, pg. 1737
GOODCONCERT CO., LTD.—See CJ Corporation; *Int'l*, pg. 1634
GOODDATA CORPORATION; *U.S. Private*, pg. 1738
GOODDATA PTY LTD—See GoodData Corporation; *U.S. Private*, pg. 1739
GOODDAYS HOLDINGS, INC.; *Int'l*, pg. 3039
GOOD DRINKS AUSTRALIA LTD.; *Int'l*, pg. 3038
GOOD EARTH CANADA LIMITED—See Good Earth, Inc.; *U.S. Private*, pg. 1738
GOOD EARTH, INC.; *U.S. Private*, pg. 1737
GOOD EARTH RESTAURANTS OF MINNESOTA—See Parasole Restaurant Holdings, Inc.; *U.S. Private*, pg. 3093
GOOD EARTH RESTAURANTS OF MINNESOTA—See Parasole Restaurant Holdings, Inc.; *U.S. Private*, pg. 3093
GOODEARTH SHIPBUILDING PVT LIMITED—See Infrastructure Leasing & Financial Services Limited; *Int'l*, pg. 3698
GOOD EARTH TEAS, INC.—See Tata Sons Limited; *Int'l*, pg. 7470
GOOD EAT COMPANY INC.—See Nippon Telegraph & Telephone Corporation; *Int'l*, pg. 5343
GOOD EATS HOLDING COMPANY INC.—See Cracken, Harkey & Co., LLC; *U.S. Private*, pg. 1081
GOODE COMPANIES, INC.; *U.S. Private*, pg. 1739
GOODE-COOK INC.; *U.S. Private*, pg. 1739
GOOD ENERGY GROUP PLC; *Int'l*, pg. 3038
GOODE PARTNERS, LLC; *U.S. Private*, pg. 1739
GOODERSON LEISURE CORPORATION; *Int'l*, pg. 3039
GOODFELLOW BROS., INC.; *U.S. Private*, pg. 1739
GOOD FELLOW HEALTHCARE HOLDINGS LIMITED; *Int'l*, pg. 3038
GOODFELLOW INC. - MANCHESTER BRANCH—See Goodfellow Inc.; *Int'l*, pg. 3040
GOODFELLOW INC. - OLIVER LUMBER DIVISION—See Goodfellow Inc.; *Int'l*, pg. 3040
GOODFELLOW INC.; *Int'l*, pg. 3040
GOODFELLOW UK LTD—See Goodfellow Inc.; *Int'l*, pg. 3040
GOOD FINANCE SECURITIES CO LTD; *Int'l*, pg. 3038
GOOD FOOD HOLDINGS LLC; *U.S. Private*, pg. 1738
GOODFOOD MARKET CORP.; *Int'l*, pg. 3040
GOOD FOODS GROCERY, INC.—See The Autism Program of Virginia, Inc.; *U.S. Private*, pg. 3990
GOOD FORTUNES EAST, LLC—See Hilton Grand Vacations Inc.; *U.S. Public*, pg. 1039
GOOD FRIEND INTERNATIONAL HOLDINGS INC.; *Int'l*, pg. 3038
GOOD FUNDS SERVICES LIMITED—See KWOON CHUNG BUS HOLDINGS LIMITED; *Int'l*, pg. 4351
GOOD GAMING, INC.—See CMG Holdings Group, Inc.; *U.S. Public*, pg. 518
GOOD + GEEK, LLC—See Blackbaud, Inc.; *U.S. Public*, pg. 341
GOODGENE INC.—See Bit Computer Co., Ltd.; *Int'l*, pg. 1049
THE GOOD GUYS DISCOUNT WAREHOUSES (AUSTRALIA) PTY. LTD.—See JB HI-FI Limited; *Int'l*, pg. 3917
GOODGUYS TIRE CENTERS INC.; *U.S. Private*, pg. 1739
GOODHART NATIONAL GORMAN AGENCY, INC.; *U.S. Private*, pg. 1739
THE GOODHEART-WILLCOX CO., INC.; *U.S. Public*, pg. 2082
GOODHOPE ASIA HOLDINGS LTD—See Carson Cumberbatch PLC; *Int'l*, pg. 1347
GOOD HOPE PLC—See Carson Cumberbatch PLC; *Int'l*, pg. 1347

GOOD HOUSEKEEPING—See The Hearst Corporation; *U.S. Private*, pg. 4046
GOOD HOUSER CO., LTD.—See JUTEC Holdings Corporation; *Int'l*, pg. 4031
GOODHUE HAWKINS NAVY YARD, LLC; *U.S. Private*, pg. 1739
GOODIER COSMETICS, INC.—See RoundTable Healthcare Management, Inc.; *U.S. Private*, pg. 3489
GOODIES FROM GOODMAN, INC.; *U.S. Private*, pg. 1739
GOODIN COMPANY; *U.S. Private*, pg. 1739
GOODING CO., INC.—See Holden Industries, Inc.; *U.S. Private*, pg. 1962
GOODING & COMPANY, INC.; *U.S. Private*, pg. 1739
GOOD JOB CREATIONS (SINGAPORE) PTE. LTD.—See Will Group, Inc.; *Int'l*, pg. 8412
GOODLAND CAPITAL PTE. LTD.—See Goodland Group Limited; *Int'l*, pg. 3040
GOODLAND DEVELOPMENT PTE. LTD.—See Goodland Group Limited; *Int'l*, pg. 3040
GOODLAND GROUP CONSTRUCTION PTE. LTD.—See Goodland Group Limited; *Int'l*, pg. 3040
GOODLAND GROUP LIMITED; *Int'l*, pg. 3040
GOODLAND HOMES PTE. LTD.—See Goodland Group Limited; *Int'l*, pg. 3040
GOODLAND INVESTMENTS PTE. LTD.—See Goodland Group Limited; *Int'l*, pg. 3040
GOOD LIFE CHEMIST—See Aamal Company Q.S.C.; *Int'l*, pg. 36
GOOD LIFE COMPANIES LLC; *U.S. Private*, pg. 1738
GOOD LIFE COMPANY, INC.; *Int'l*, pg. 3038
GOOD LIFE SALA KANTO CO., LTD.—See Sala Corporation; *Int'l*, pg. 6490
GOOD LIIVE CO., LTD.—See Takashimaya Company, Limited; *Int'l*, pg. 7435
GOODLIVE ARTISTS GMBH & CO. KG—See Live Nation Entertainment, Inc.; *U.S. Public*, pg. 1329
GOODLIVE GMBH—See Live Nation Entertainment, Inc.; *U.S. Public*, pg. 1329
GOODLUCK CORPORATION CO., LTD.—See TAKE AND GIVE. NEEDS Co. Ltd.; *Int'l*, pg. 7436
GOODLUCK INDIA LIMITED; *Int'l*, pg. 3040
GOODLUCK INDUSTRIES LTD.; *Int'l*, pg. 3040
GOODMAID CHEMICAL CORPORATION SDN BHD—See CIMB Group Holdings Berhad; *Int'l*, pg. 1608
GOODMAID MARKETING SDN BHD—See CIMB Group Holdings Berhad; *Int'l*, pg. 1608
GOODMAN ASIA LIMITED—See Goodman Limited; *Int'l*, pg. 3040
GOODMAN BALL INC.—See C.E. Niehoff & Co.; *U.S. Private*, pg. 706
GOODMAN BELGIUM NV—See Goodman Limited; *Int'l*, pg. 3040
GOODMAN CO., LTD.—See Nipro Corporation; *Int'l*, pg. 5361
GOODMAN DISTRIBUTION—See Daikin Industries, Ltd.; *Int'l*, pg. 1935
GOODMAN DISTRIBUTION—See Daikin Industries, Ltd.; *Int'l*, pg. 1935
GOODMAN DISTRIBUTION—See Daikin Industries, Ltd.; *Int'l*, pg. 1935
GOODMAN DISTRIBUTION SOUTHEAST, INC.—See Daikin Industries, Ltd.; *Int'l*, pg. 1935
GOODMAN FACTORS, INC.—See Independent Bank; *U.S. Private*, pg. 2058
GOODMAN FAMILY OF BUILDERS; *U.S. Private*, pg. 1739
GOODMAN FIELDER LIMITED—See Wilmar International Limited; *Int'l*, pg. 8420
GOODMAN FIELDER NEW ZEALAND, LTD.—See Wilmar International Limited; *Int'l*, pg. 8420
GOODMAN FIELDER PTY. LTD.—See Wilmar International Limited; *Int'l*, pg. 8420
GOODMAN FOOD PRODUCTS INC.; *U.S. Private*, pg. 1739
GOODMAN FRANCE SARL—See Goodman Limited; *Int'l*, pg. 3040
GOODMAN GERMANY GMBH—See Goodman Limited; *Int'l*, pg. 3040
GOODMAN GLOBAL, INC.—See Daikin Industries, Ltd.; *Int'l*, pg. 1935
THE GOODMAN GROUP, INC.; *U.S. Private*, pg. 4034
THE GOODMAN GROUP UK—See The Goodman Group, Inc.; *U.S. Private*, pg. 4034
GOODMAN ITALY S.R.L.—See Goodman Limited; *Int'l*, pg. 3040
GOODMAN JAPAN FUNDS LIMITED—See Goodman Limited; *Int'l*, pg. 3040
GOODMAN JAPAN LIMITED—See Goodman Limited; *Int'l*, pg. 3040
GOODMAN LIMITED; *Int'l*, pg. 3040
GOODMAN LOGISTICS DEVELOPMENTS (UK) LTD—See Goodman Limited; *Int'l*, pg. 3040
GOODMAN MANAGEMENT CONSULTING (BEIJING) CO., LTD.—See Goodman Limited; *Int'l*, pg. 3040
GOODMAN MANAGEMENT CONSULTING (SHANGHAI) CO., LTD.—See Goodman Limited; *Int'l*, pg. 3040
GOODMAN MANAGEMENT HOLDINGS (LUX) SARL—See Goodman Limited; *Int'l*, pg. 3040

GOODMAN MANUFACTURING COMPANY, L.P.—See Daikin Industries, Ltd.; *Int'l*, pg. 1935
GOODMAN MEDICAL IRELAND LIMITED—See Nipro Corporation; *Int'l*, pg. 5361
GOODMAN MEDICAL SUPPLIES LIMITED—See Luyan (Fujian) Pharma Co., Ltd.; *Int'l*, pg. 4589
GOODMAN NETHERLANDS BV—See Goodman Limited; *Int'l*, pg. 3040
GOODMAN NETWORKS, INC.; *U.S. Private*, pg. 1739
GOODMAN OPERATOR (UK) LIMITED—See Goodman Limited; *Int'l*, pg. 3040
GOODMAN PLUS TRUST; *Int'l*, pg. 3041
GOODMAN PROPERTY SERVICES (NZ) LIMITED—See Goodman Limited; *Int'l*, pg. 3040
GOODMAN REAL ESTATE (SPAIN) S.L.—See Goodman Limited; *Int'l*, pg. 3041
GOODMANS, INC.; *U.S. Private*, pg. 1739
GOODMANS INTERIOR STRUCTURES—See Goodmans, Inc.; *U.S. Private*, pg. 1739
GOODMANS MATZOH PRODUCTS INC—See Joyce Food Products Inc.; *U.S. Private*, pg. 2239
GOODMANS OFFICE FURNITURE—See Goodmans, Inc.; *U.S. Private*, pg. 1739
GOODMANS OFFICE FURNITURE—See Goodmans, Inc.; *U.S. Private*, pg. 1740
THE GOODMAN THEATRE; *U.S. Private*, pg. 4034
GOODMAN TRUCK & TRACTOR COMPANY, INC.; *U.S. Private*, pg. 1739
GOODMAN UK LTD.—See Goodman Limited; *Int'l*, pg. 3041
GOODMAN VENEER & LUMBER COMPANY—See The Hoffmann Family of Companies; *U.S. Private*, pg. 4053
GOOD MEDS, INC.—See CRYOMASS TECHNOLOGIES INC.; *U.S. Public*, pg. 600
GOODMILLS DEUTSCHLAND GMBH—See Raiffeisen-Holding Niederosterreich-Wien reg. Gen.m.b.H.; *Int'l*, pg. 6185
GOODMILLS GROUP GMBH—See Raiffeisen-Holding Niederosterreich-Wien reg. Gen.m.b.H.; *Int'l*, pg. 6185
GOOD MORNING SECURITIES USA LIMITED—See Shinhan Financial Group Co., Ltd.; *Int'l*, pg. 6843
GOODMORNING SHINHAN SECURITIES CO., LTD.—See Shinhan Financial Group Co., Ltd.; *Int'l*, pg. 6843
GOODMORTGAGE.COM—See First Guaranty Mortgage Corp.; *U.S. Private*, pg. 1519
GOOD NATURED PRODUCTS INC.; *Int'l*, pg. 3038
GOOD NEIGHBOR PHARMACY—See Cencora, Inc.; *U.S. Public*, pg. 467
GOODNESS GREENESS; *U.S. Private*, pg. 1740
GOODNESS MFG.—See Trailer Park; *U.S. Private*, pg. 4203
GOOD NEWS PEST SOLUTIONS; *U.S. Private*, pg. 1738
GOOD NEWS PRODUCTIONS AG—See Ringier Holding AG; *Int'l*, pg. 6343
GOOD NEWS PUBLISHERS; *U.S. Private*, pg. 1738
GOODNIGHT BROTHERS PRODUCE CO., INC.; *U.S. Private*, pg. 1740
GOODNIGHT INTERNATIONAL, LLC; *U.S. Private*, pg. 1740
GOOD-NITE INN INC.; *U.S. Private*, pg. 1738
GOOD OIL CO. INC.; *U.S. Private*, pg. 1738
GOOD OLD DAYS FOODS, INC.; *U.S. Private*, pg. 1738
GOODPASTURE MOTOR COMPANY, INC.—See Thompson Distribution Company, Inc.; *U.S. Private*, pg. 4159
GOODPATCH, INC.; *Int'l*, pg. 3041
GOOD PEOPLE CO., LTD; *Int'l*, pg. 3038
GOOD RELATIONS LIMITED—See Providence Equity Partners L.L.C.; *U.S. Private*, pg. 3291
GOOD RESOURCES HOLDINGS LIMITED; *Int'l*, pg. 3038
GOODRICH AEROSPACE EUROPE GMBH—See RTX Corporation; *U.S. Public*, pg. 1821
GOODRICH AEROSTRUCTURES SERVICE CENTER - ASIA PTE. LTD.—See RTX Corporation; *U.S. Public*, pg. 1821
GOODRICH CONTROL SYSTEMS GMBH—See RTX Corporation; *U.S. Public*, pg. 1823
GOODRICH GLOBAL HOLDINGS PTE., LTD.—See Sangetsu Co., Ltd.; *Int'l*, pg. 6537
GOODRICH GLOBAL LIMITED—See Sangetsu Co., Ltd.; *Int'l*, pg. 6537
GOODRICH GLOBAL SDN. BHD.—See Sangetsu Co., Ltd.; *Int'l*, pg. 6537
GOODRICH LIGHTING SYSTEMS GMBH & CO. KG—See RTX Corporation; *U.S. Public*, pg. 1821
GOODRICH LUMBER CO.—See Kodiak Building Partners LLC; *U.S. Private*, pg. 2336
GOODRICH PETROLEUM CORPORATION—See EnCap Investments L.P.; *U.S. Private*, pg. 1390
GOODRICH QUALITY THEATERS INC.—See Goodrich Radio and Theaters Inc.; *U.S. Private*, pg. 1740
GOODRICH RADIO AND THEATERS INC.; *U.S. Private*, pg. 1740
GOODRICH RADIO MARKETING INC.—See Goodrich Radio and Theaters Inc.; *U.S. Private*, pg. 1740
GOODRICKE GROUP LIMITED—See Camellia Plc; *Int'l*, pg. 1271
GOODRINGTON CO., LTD.—See Citizen Watch Co., Ltd.; *Int'l*, pg. 1625
GOODRX HOLDINGS, INC.; *U.S. Public*, pg. 951

THE GOOD SAMARITAN HEALTH SERVICES FOUNDATION OF LEBANON, PENNSYLVANIA—See WellSpan Health; *U.S. Private*, pg. 4477
THE GOOD SAMARITAN HOME OF QUINCY; *U.S. Private*, pg. 4034
GOOD SAMARITAN HOSPITAL, LLC—See HCA Healthcare, Inc.; *U.S. Public*, pg. 997
GOOD SAMARITAN HOSPITAL, LOS ANGELES—See Presbyterian Intercommunity Hospital, Inc.; *U.S. Private*, pg. 3253
GOOD SAMARITAN HOSPITAL, L.P.—See HCA Healthcare, Inc.; *U.S. Public*, pg. 997
GOOD SAMARITAN HOSPITAL MEDICAL CENTER—See Catholic Health Services of Long Island; *U.S. Private*, pg. 791
GOOD SAMARITAN HOSPITAL—See Catholic Health Initiatives; *U.S. Private*, pg. 790
GOOD SAMARITAN MEDICAL CENTER, INC.—See Tenet Healthcare Corporation; *U.S. Public*, pg. 2008
GOOD SAMARITAN NURSING HOME, INC.—See Catholic Health Services of Long Island; *U.S. Private*, pg. 791
GOOD SAM ENTERPRISES, LLC—See Camping World Holdings, Inc.; *U.S. Public*, pg. 428
GOOD SAM MOB INVESTORS, LLC—See Ventas, Inc.; *U.S. Public*, pg. 2278
GOODS FURNITURE HOUSE INC.; *U.S. Private*, pg. 1740
GOOD SHEPHERD HEALTH CARE SYSTEM; *U.S. Private*, pg. 1738
GOOD SHEPHERD HOSPICE—See Catholic Health Services of Long Island; *U.S. Private*, pg. 791
GOOD SHEPHERD SERVICES; *U.S. Private*, pg. 1738
GOOD SKY RELAY (SHENZHEN) CO., LTD.—See Excel Cell Electronic Co., Ltd.; *Int'l*, pg. 2577
GOOD SOLUTIONS GROUP; *U.S. Private*, pg. 1738
GOODSON NORTH, LLC—See Penske Automotive Group, Inc.; *U.S. Public*, pg. 1665
GOODSONS SUPERMARKETS INC.; *U.S. Private*, pg. 1740
GOOD SOURCE SOLUTIONS, INC.—See Alvarez & Marsal, Inc.; *U.S. Private*, pg. 213
GOOD SOURCE SOLUTIONS, INC.—See Highview Capital, LLC; *U.S. Private*, pg. 1942
GOOD SOURCE SOLUTIONS—See Alvarez & Marsal, Inc.; *U.S. Private*, pg. 213
GOOD SOURCE SOLUTIONS—See Highview Capital, LLC; *U.S. Private*, pg. 1942
GOODSPEED CO., LTD.; *Int'l*, pg. 3041
GOOD SPIRITS HOSPITALITY LIMITED; *Int'l*, pg. 3039
GOOD SPORTSMAN MARKETING, LLC; *U.S. Private*, pg. 1738
GOOD START GENETICS, INC.—See Invitae Corporation; *U.S. Public*, pg. 1165
GOOD STEEL PARTNERS CO., LTD.; *Int'l*, pg. 3039
GOODSUITE; *U.S. Private*, pg. 1740
GOODTEC CO., LTD.—See Nipro Corporation; *Int'l*, pg. 5361
GOODTECH ASA; *Int'l*, pg. 3041
GOODTECH ENVIRONMENT AB—See Goodtech ASA; *Int'l*, pg. 3041
GOODTECH ENVIRONMENT SORUMSAND AS—See Goodtech ASA; *Int'l*, pg. 3041
GOODTECH GERMANY GMBH—See Goodtech ASA; *Int'l*, pg. 3041
GOODTECH GMBH—See Grant Thornton International Limited; *Int'l*, pg. 3059
GOODTECH MANAGEMENT LIMITED—See Wang On Group Ltd; *Int'l*, pg. 8341
GOODTECH PACKAGING SYSTEMS AS—See Goodtech ASA; *Int'l*, pg. 3041
GOODTECH PROCESS AB—See Goodtech ASA; *Int'l*, pg. 3041
GOODTECH PROJECTS & SERVICES AB—See Goodtech ASA; *Int'l*, pg. 3041
GOODTECH RECOVERY TECHNOLOGY AS—See Goodtech ASA; *Int'l*, pg. 3041
GOODTECH SOLUTIONS AB—See Goodtech ASA; *Int'l*, pg. 3041
GOODTECH SOLUTIONS AS—See Goodtech ASA; *Int'l*, pg. 3041
GOODTECH SOLUTIONS INDUSTRIAUTOMATION AB—See Goodtech ASA; *Int'l*, pg. 3041
GOODTECH SOLUTIONS KARLSTAD AB—See Goodtech ASA; *Int'l*, pg. 3041
GOODTECH SOLUTIONS MANUFACTURING AB—See BE Group AB; *Int'l*, pg. 3041
GOODTECH SOLUTIONS SAFFLE AB—See Goodtech ASA; *Int'l*, pg. 3041
GOOD TIME LIVING CO. LTD.—See Daiwa Securities Group Inc.; *Int'l*, pg. 1949
GOOD TIMES DRIVE-THRU, INC.—See Good Times Restaurants, Inc.; *U.S. Public*, pg. 951
GOOD TIMES RESTAURANTS, INC.; *U.S. Public*, pg. 951
GOOD TIMES—See Metro Publishing, Inc.; *U.S. Private*, pg. 2686
GOOD TIRE SERVICE INC.; *U.S. Private*, pg. 1738
GOOD TRANSPORT SERVICES, INC.; *U.S. Private*, pg. 1738
GOODUS, INC.—See SNet Systems Inc.; *Int'l*, pg. 7027

GOOD VIBRATIONS SHOES INC.; *U.S. Public*, pg. 951
GOODWAY EUROPE (SWEDEN) AB—See GIIB HOLDINGS BERHAD; *Int'l*, pg. 2972
GOODWAY GRAPHICS OF VA INC.; *U.S. Private*, pg. 1740
GOODWAY MACHINE CORP.; *Int'l*, pg. 3041
GOODWAY RUBBER INDUSTRIES SDN. BHD.—See GIIB HOLDINGS BERHAD; *Int'l*, pg. 2972
GOODWAY (SUZHOU) MACHINE CORP.—See GOODWAY MACHINE CORP.; *Int'l*, pg. 3041
GOODWAY TECHNOLOGIES CORPORATION; *U.S. Private*, pg. 1740
GOOD WAY TECHNOLOGY CO., LTD.; *Int'l*, pg. 3039
GOODWELL PROPERTY MANAGEMENT LIMITED—See CK Asset Holdings Limited; *Int'l*, pg. 1635
GOODWEST INDUSTRIES, INC.—See The Jordan Company, L.P.; *U.S. Private*, pg. 4062
GOOD WHEELS AUTOMOTIVE GROUP LLC; *U.S. Private*, pg. 1738
GOODWILL FINANCE LIMITED; *Int'l*, pg. 3041
GOODWILL HOSPITAL AND RESEARCH CENTRE LIMITED—See Ojjus Medicare Private Limited; *Int'l*, pg. 5539
GOODWILL INDUSTRIES INTERNATIONAL, INC.; *U.S. Private*, pg. 1740
GOODWILL INDUSTRIES-MANASOTA, INC.; *U.S. Private*, pg. 1740
GOODWILL INDUSTRIES OF CENTRAL INDIANA, INC.—See Goodwill Industries International, Inc.; *U.S. Private*, pg. 1740
GOODWILL INDUSTRIES OF KANAWHA VALLEY, INC.; *U.S. Private*, pg. 1740
GOODWILL INDUSTRIES OF THE VALLEYS, INC.—See Goodwill Industries International, Inc.; *U.S. Private*, pg. 1740
GOODWILL INDUSTRIES-SUNCOAST, INC.; *U.S. Private*, pg. 1740
GOOD WILL INSTRUMENT CO., LTD.; *Int'l*, pg. 3039
GOOD WILL INSTRUMENT EURO B.V.—See Good Will Instrument Co., Ltd.; *Int'l*, pg. 3039
GOOD WILL INSTRUMENT KOREA CO., LTD.—See Good Will Instrument Co., Ltd.; *Int'l*, pg. 3039
GOOD WILL INSTRUMENT (SEA) SDN. BHD.—See Good Will Instrument Co., Ltd.; *Int'l*, pg. 3039
GOODWILL KEYSTONE AREA, INC.—See Goodwill Industries International, Inc.; *U.S. Private*, pg. 1740
GOODWILL OF GREATER WASHINGTON; *U.S. Private*, pg. 1740
GOODWILL OF NORTH FLORIDA; *U.S. Private*, pg. 1741
GOOD WILL PUBLISHERS INC.; *U.S. Private*, pg. 1738
GOODWILL RETIREMENT COMMUNITY; *U.S. Private*, pg. 1741
GOODWIN AMMONIA COMPANY; *U.S. Private*, pg. 1741
GOODWIN INDUSTRIA E COMERCIO DE VALVULAS DE RETENCAO E BOMBAS SUBMERSAS LTDA.—See Goodwin PLC; *Int'l*, pg. 3041
GOODWIN INTERNATIONAL LTD.—See Goodwin PLC; *Int'l*, pg. 3041
GOODWIN KOREA LTD.—See Goodwin PLC; *Int'l*, pg. 3041
GOODWIN PLC; *Int'l*, pg. 3041
GOODWIN PROCTER LLP; *U.S. Private*, pg. 1741
GOODWIN REFRACTORY SERVICES HOLDINGS LIMITED—See Goodwin PLC; *Int'l*, pg. 3041
GOODWIN REFRACTORY SERVICES LIMITED—See Goodwin PLC; *Int'l*, pg. 3041
GOODWIN'S CHEVROLET COMPANY; *U.S. Private*, pg. 1741
GOODWIN (SHANXI) PUMP CO., LTD.—See Goodwin PLC; *Int'l*, pg. 3041
GOODWIN STEEL CASTINGS LTD.—See Goodwin PLC; *Int'l*, pg. 3042
GOOD WORKS ACQUISITION CORP.; *U.S. Public*, pg. 951
GOODWORKS FINANCIAL GROUP—See GTCR LLC; *U.S. Private*, pg. 1803
GOODYEAR AUSTRALIA PTY LIMITED—See The Goodyear Tire & Rubber Company; *U.S. Public*, pg. 2083
GOODYEAR BELGIUM N.V./SA—See The Goodyear Tire & Rubber Company; *U.S. Public*, pg. 2083
GOODYEAR CANADA INC.—See The Goodyear Tire & Rubber Company; *U.S. Public*, pg. 2083
GOODYEAR DE CHILE S.A.I.C.—See The Goodyear Tire & Rubber Company; *U.S. Public*, pg. 2082
GOODYEAR DE COLOMBIA S.A.—See The Goodyear Tire & Rubber Company; *U.S. Public*, pg. 2082
GOODYEAR DUNLOP SAVA TIRES D.O.O.—See The Goodyear Tire & Rubber Company; *U.S. Public*, pg. 2083
GOODYEAR DUNLOP TIRES AUSTRIA GMBH—See The Goodyear Tire & Rubber Company; *U.S. Public*, pg. 2083
GOODYEAR DUNLOP TIRES BALTIC OU—See The Goodyear Tire & Rubber Company; *U.S. Public*, pg. 2083
GOODYEAR DUNLOP TIRES BELGIUM N.V.—See The Goodyear Tire & Rubber Company; *U.S. Public*, pg. 2083

GOODYEAR DUNLOP TIRES CZECH S.R.O.—See The Goodyear Tire & Rubber Company; *U.S. Public*, pg. 2083
GOODYEAR DUNLOP TIRES DANMARK A/S—See The Goodyear Tire & Rubber Company; *U.S. Public*, pg. 2083
GOODYEAR DUNLOP TIRES ESPANA S.A.—See The Goodyear Tire & Rubber Company; *U.S. Public*, pg. 2083
GOODYEAR DUNLOP TIRES EUROPE B.V.—See The Goodyear Tire & Rubber Company; *U.S. Public*, pg. 2083
GOODYEAR DUNLOP TIRES FRANCE—See The Goodyear Tire & Rubber Company; *U.S. Public*, pg. 2083
GOODYEAR DUNLOP TIRES HELLAS S.A.I.C.—See The Goodyear Tire & Rubber Company; *U.S. Public*, pg. 2083
GOODYEAR DUNLOP TIRES IRELAND LTD—See The Goodyear Tire & Rubber Company; *U.S. Public*, pg. 2083
GOODYEAR DUNLOP TIRES ITALIA S.P.A.—See The Goodyear Tire & Rubber Company; *U.S. Public*, pg. 2083
GOODYEAR DUNLOP TIRES OPERATIONS ROMANIA S.R.L.—See The Goodyear Tire & Rubber Company; *U.S. Public*, pg. 2083
GOODYEAR DUNLOP TIRES OPERATIONS S.A.—See The Goodyear Tire & Rubber Company; *U.S. Public*, pg. 2083
GOODYEAR DUNLOP TIRES POLSKA SP Z.O.O.—See The Goodyear Tire & Rubber Company; *U.S. Public*, pg. 2083
GOODYEAR DUNLOP TIRES PORTUGAL UNIPESSOAL, LTDA—See The Goodyear Tire & Rubber Company; *U.S. Public*, pg. 2083
GOODYEAR DUNLOP TIRES ROMANIA S.R.L.—See The Goodyear Tire & Rubber Company; *U.S. Public*, pg. 2083
GOODYEAR DUNLOP TIRES SLOVAKIA S.R.O.—See The Goodyear Tire & Rubber Company; *U.S. Public*, pg. 2084
GOODYEAR DUNLOP TIRES SUISSE SA—See The Goodyear Tire & Rubber Company; *U.S. Public*, pg. 2084
GOODYEAR DUNLOP TIRES SVERIGE AB—See The Goodyear Tire & Rubber Company; *U.S. Public*, pg. 2084
GOODYEAR & DUNLOP TYRES (AUSTRALIA) PTY LTD—See The Goodyear Tire & Rubber Company; *U.S. Public*, pg. 2083
GOODYEAR & DUNLOP TYRES (NZ) LIMITED—See The Goodyear Tire & Rubber Company; *U.S. Public*, pg. 2083
GOODYEAR DUNLOP TYRES UK LTD.—See The Goodyear Tire & Rubber Company; *U.S. Public*, pg. 2084
GOODYEAR EARTHMOVER PTY LIMITED—See The Goodyear Tire & Rubber Company; *U.S. Public*, pg. 2083
GOODYEAR EUROPE B.V.—See The Goodyear Tire & Rubber Company; *U.S. Public*, pg. 2084
GOODYEAR EXPORT INC.—See The Goodyear Tire & Rubber Company; *U.S. Public*, pg. 2084
GOODYEAR FRANCE SAS—See The Goodyear Tire & Rubber Company; *U.S. Public*, pg. 2084
GOODYEAR GERMANY GMBH—See The Goodyear Tire & Rubber Company; *U.S. Public*, pg. 2084
GOODYEAR HELLAS S.A.I.C.—See The Goodyear Tire & Rubber Company; *U.S. Public*, pg. 2084
GOODYEAR HRVATSKA D.O.O.—See The Goodyear Tire & Rubber Company; *U.S. Public*, pg. 2084
GOODYEAR INDIA LTD.—See The Goodyear Tire & Rubber Company; *U.S. Public*, pg. 2084
GOODYEAR INTERNATIONAL CORPORATION—See The Goodyear Tire & Rubber Company; *U.S. Public*, pg. 2084
GOODYEAR JAPAN LTD.—See The Goodyear Tire & Rubber Company; *U.S. Public*, pg. 2084
GOOD YEAR LASTIKLERI TAS; *Int'l*, pg. 3039
GOODYEAR LASTIKLERI TURK ANONIM SIRKETI—See The Goodyear Tire & Rubber Company; *U.S. Public*, pg. 2084
GOODYEAR LUXEMBOURG TIRES SA—See The Goodyear Tire & Rubber Company; *U.S. Public*, pg. 2084
GOODYEAR MALAYSIA BHD—See The Goodyear Tire & Rubber Company; *U.S. Public*, pg. 2084
GOODYEAR MARKETING & SALES SDN. BHD.—See The Goodyear Tire & Rubber Company; *U.S. Public*, pg. 2084
GOODYEAR MIDDLE EAST FZE—See The Goodyear Tire & Rubber Company; *U.S. Public*, pg. 2084
GOODYEAR NEDERLAND BV—See The Goodyear Tire & Rubber Company; *U.S. Public*, pg. 2084
GOODYEAR ORIENT COMPANY PRIVATE LIMITED—See The Goodyear Tire & Rubber Company; *U.S. Public*, pg. 2084
GOODYEAR PHILIPPINES, INC.—See The Goodyear Tire & Rubber Company; *U.S. Public*, pg. 2084
GOODYEAR POLSKA SP. Z O.O.—See The Goodyear Tire & Rubber Company; *U.S. Public*, pg. 2084

GOODYEAR PORTUGAL UNIPESSOAL, LTDA—See The Goodyear Tire & Rubber Company; *U.S. Public*, pg. 2084
GOODYEAR S.A.—See The Goodyear Tire & Rubber Company; *U.S. Public*, pg. 2084
GOODYEAR SERVICIOS COMERCIALES S.A. DE C.V.—See The Goodyear Tire & Rubber Company; *U.S. Public*, pg. 2084
GOODYEAR SOUTH AFRICA (PTY) LTD—See The Goodyear Tire & Rubber Company; *U.S. Public*, pg. 2084
GOODYEAR SUISSE S.A.—See The Goodyear Tire & Rubber Company; *U.S. Public*, pg. 2084
GOODYEAR SVERIGE A.B.—See The Goodyear Tire & Rubber Company; *U.S. Public*, pg. 2084
GOODYEAR TAIWAN LIMITED—See The Goodyear Tire & Rubber Company; *U.S. Public*, pg. 2084
GOODYEAR THAILAND PUBLIC CO. LTD.—See The Goodyear Tire & Rubber Company; *U.S. Public*, pg. 2084
GOODYEAR TIRE MANAGEMENT COMPANY (SHANGHAI) LTD.—See The Goodyear Tire & Rubber Company; *U.S. Public*, pg. 2084
THE GOODYEAR TIRE & RUBBER COMPANY; *U.S. Public*, pg. 2082
GOODYEAR TYRE & RUBBER HOLDINGS (PTY) LTD—See The Goodyear Tire & Rubber Company; *U.S. Public*, pg. 2084
GOODYEAR TYRES IRELAND LTD.—See The Goodyear Tire & Rubber Company; *U.S. Public*, pg. 2084
GOODYEAR TYRES PTY LTD—See The Goodyear Tire & Rubber Company; *U.S. Public*, pg. 2083
GOODYEAR TYRES UK LIMITED—See The Goodyear Tire & Rubber Company; *U.S. Public*, pg. 2084
GOODYEAR UKRAINE—See The Goodyear Tire & Rubber Company; *U.S. Public*, pg. 2084
GOODY FILM (THAILAND) CO., LTD.—See Bangkok Broadcasting & TV Co., Ltd.; *Int'l*, pg. 833
GOODY POINT, INC.—See Faith, Inc.; *Int'l*, pg. 2609
GOODY PRODUCTS, INC.—See ACON Investments, LLC; *U.S. Private*, pg. 62
GOODY SCIENCE & TECHNOLOGY CO., LTD.; *Int'l*, pg. 3042
GOOGLE-ATLANTA—See Alphabet Inc.; *U.S. Public*, pg. 83
GOOGLE AUSTRALIA PTY, LTD.—See Alphabet Inc.; *U.S. Public*, pg. 83
GOOGLE-BOSTON—See Alphabet Inc.; *U.S. Public*, pg. 83
GOOGLE-CANADA—See Alphabet Inc.; *U.S. Public*, pg. 83
GOOGLE-CHICAGO—See Alphabet Inc.; *U.S. Public*, pg. 83
GOOGLE-DETROIT—See Alphabet Inc.; *U.S. Public*, pg. 83
GOOGLE FIBER INC.—See Alphabet Inc.; *U.S. Public*, pg. 83
GOOGLE FRANCE SARL—See Alphabet Inc.; *U.S. Public*, pg. 83
GOOGLE GERMANY GMBH—See Alphabet Inc.; *U.S. Public*, pg. 83
GOOGLE-GREATER CHINA—See Alphabet Inc.; *U.S. Public*, pg. 83
GOOGLE INDIA PVT LTD—See Alphabet Inc.; *U.S. Public*, pg. 83
GOOGLE INTERNATIONAL LLC—See Alphabet Inc.; *U.S. Public*, pg. 83
GOOGLE IRELAND HOLDINGS—See Alphabet Inc.; *U.S. Public*, pg. 83
GOOGLE IRELAND LIMITED—See Alphabet Inc.; *U.S. Public*, pg. 83
GOOGLE ITALY S.R.L.—See Alphabet Inc.; *U.S. Public*, pg. 83
GOOGLE JAPAN INC.—See Alphabet Inc.; *U.S. Public*, pg. 83
GOOGLE LLC—See Alphabet Inc.; *U.S. Public*, pg. 83
GOOGLE NETHERLANDS B.V.—See Alphabet Inc.; *U.S. Public*, pg. 83
GOOGLE-NEW YORK—See Alphabet Inc.; *U.S. Public*, pg. 83
GOOGLE-SEATTLE—See Alphabet Inc.; *U.S. Public*, pg. 83
GOOGLE SPAIN, S.L.—See Alphabet Inc.; *U.S. Public*, pg. 83
GOOGLE UK LIMITED—See Alphabet Inc.; *U.S. Public*, pg. 83
GOOI GLOBAL; *U.S. Public*, pg. 952
GOOLD HEALTH SYSTEMS—See McKesson Corporation; *U.S. Public*, pg. 1407
GOOOGREEN, INC.; *U.S. Public*, pg. 952
GOOROO VENTURES LIMITED; *Int'l*, pg. 3042
GOOSEBERRY PATCH—See The Rowman & Littlefield Publishing Group, Inc.; *U.S. Public*, pg. 4112
GOOSECROSS CELLARS, INC.—See Golden Equity Investments LLC; *U.S. Private*, pg. 1730
GOOSEHEAD INSURANCE, INC.; *U.S. Public*, pg. 952
GOOSENECK IMPLEMENT COMPANY; *U.S. Private*, pg. 1741
GO OUTDOORS LIMITED—See Pentland Group Limited; *Int'l*, pg. 5792

GOPA CONSULTANTS; *Int'l*, pg. 3042
GO-PAGE CORPORATION; *U.S. Public*, pg. 949
GOPAL IRON & STEELS CO. (GUJARAT) LIMITED; *Int'l*, pg. 3042
GOPAY VIETNAM PAYMENT SERVICES COMPANY LIMITED—See PT GoTo Gojek Tokopedia Tbk; *Int'l*, pg. 6041
GOPE EXPLORATION COMPANY (PROPRIETARY) LIMITED—See Gem Diamonds Limited; *Int'l*, pg. 2915
GOPENG BERHAD; *Int'l*, pg. 3042
GOPETRO TRANSPORT LLC—See Sunoco LP; *U.S. Public*, pg. 1965
GOPHARMA S.R.L.—See IMCD N.V.; *Int'l*, pg. 3621
GOPHER ASSET MANAGEMENT CO., LTD.—See Noah Holdings Limited; *Int'l*, pg. 5394
GOPHERCENTRAL.COM—See NextEra Media, LLC; *U.S. Private*, pg. 2921
GOPHER NEWS COMPANY; *U.S. Private*, pg. 1741
GOPHER RESOURCE LLC—See Energy Capital Partners Management, LP; *U.S. Private*, pg. 1394
GO PLAY LTD.—See KOMPAN A/S; *Int'l*, pg. 4243
GO P.L.C.—See Tunisie Telecom; *Int'l*, pg. 7972
GOPOINT SDN. BHD.—See W T K Holdings Berhad; *Int'l*, pg. 8320
GOPPERT FINANCIAL BANK—See Goppert Financial Corp.; *U.S. Private*, pg. 1741
GOPPERT FINANCIAL CORP.; *U.S. Private*, pg. 1741
GOPPERT STATE SERVICE BANK—See Goppert Financial Corp.; *U.S. Private*, pg. 1741
GOPPERT-TRINITY FAMILY CARE, LLC—See HCA Healthcare, Inc.; *U.S. Public*, pg. 997
GOPRO GMBH—See GoPro, Inc.; *U.S. Public*, pg. 952
GOPRO, INC.; *U.S. Public*, pg. 952
GOPROTO, INC.—See CORE Industrial Partners, LLC; *U.S. Private*, pg. 1048
GORA/MCGAHEY ARCHITECTS; *U.S. Private*, pg. 1741
GORAN CAPITAL INC.; *Int'l*, pg. 3042
GORANI INDUSTRIES LIMITED; *Int'l*, pg. 3042
GORANT CANDIES INC.; *U.S. Private*, pg. 1741
GOR APPLICAZIONI SPECIALI S.P.A.—See Solvay S.A.; *Int'l*, pg. 7078
GORAZDE PUTEVI D.D. GORAZDE; *Int'l*, pg. 3042
GORAZDZE BETON SP. Z O.O.—See Heidelberg Materials AG; *Int'l*, pg. 3310
GORAZDZE CEMENT S.A.—See Heidelberg Materials AG; *Int'l*, pg. 3310
GORAZDZE KRUSZYWA—See Heidelberg Materials AG; *Int'l*, pg. 3310
GOR DET SELV HTH ARHUS A/S—See Nobia AB; *Int'l*, pg. 5395
THE GORDIAN GROUP, INC.—See Fortive Corporation; *U.S. Public*, pg. 872
GORDIAN MEDICAL, INC.—See OEP Capital Advisors, L.P.; *U.S. Private*, pg. 2999
GORDIAN MEDICAL, INC.—See Silverfern Capital Management, LLC; *U.S. Private*, pg. 3663
GORDIE BOUCHER FORD OF KENOSHA, INC.—See The Boucher Group, Inc.; *U.S. Private*, pg. 3998
GORDIE BOUCHER FORD OF MENOMONEE FALLS, INC.—See The Boucher Group, Inc.; *U.S. Private*, pg. 3998
GORDMANS, INC.—See Sun Capital Partners, Inc.; *U.S. Private*, pg. 3859
GORDMANS STORES INC.—See Sun Capital Partners, Inc.; *U.S. Private*, pg. 3859
GORDON ALUMINUM INDUSTRIES, INC.; *U.S. Private*, pg. 1741
GORDON AUTO BODY PARTS CO., LTD. - PLANT 2—See Gordon Auto Body Parts Co., Ltd.; *Int'l*, pg. 3042
GORDON AUTO BODY PARTS CO., LTD.; *Int'l*, pg. 3042
GORDON B. ROBERTS AGENCY, LLC—See Community Bank System, Inc.; *U.S. Public*, pg. 550
GORDON BROTHERS ASSET ADVISORS, LLC—See Gordon Brothers Group, LLC; *U.S. Private*, pg. 1742
GORDON BROTHERS EUROPE—See Gordon Brothers Group, LLC; *U.S. Private*, pg. 1742
GORDON BROTHERS GROUP, LLC; *U.S. Private*, pg. 1741
GORDON BROTHERS INDUSTRIES PTY. LIMITED - BENDIGO FACTORY—See Gordon Brothers Industries Pty. Limited; *Int'l*, pg. 3042
GORDON BROTHERS INDUSTRIES PTY. LIMITED; *Int'l*, pg. 3042
GORDON BROTHERS INTERNATIONAL, LLC—See Gordon Brothers Group, LLC; *U.S. Private*, pg. 1742
GORDON BROTHERS RETAIL PARTNERS, LLC—See Gordon Brothers Group, LLC; *U.S. Private*, pg. 1742
GORDON BRUSH MFG CO, INC.; *U.S. Private*, pg. 1742
GORDON CHEVROLET CO.; *U.S. Private*, pg. 1742
GORDON CHEVROLET-GEO; *U.S. Private*, pg. 1742
GORDON COMPANIES INC.; *U.S. Private*, pg. 1742
GORDON CORPORATION—See PBI/Gordon Corporation; *U.S. Private*, pg. 3118
GORDON CREEK ENERGY INC.; *Int'l*, pg. 3042
GORDON-DARBY INC.; *U.S. Private*, pg. 1743
GORDON-DARBY SYSTEMS, INC.—See Searchlight Capital Partners, L.P.; *U.S. Private*, pg. 3590

GORDON DOCUMENT PRODUCTS INC.   CORPORATE AFFILIATIONS

GORDON DOCUMENT PRODUCTS INC.; *U.S. Private*, pg. 1743
GORDON ELECTRIC; *Int'l*, pg. 3042
GORDON FLESCH COMPANY, INC.; *U.S. Private*, pg. 1743
GORDON FOOD SERVICE - FLORIDA—See Gordon Food Service Inc.; *U.S. Private*, pg. 1743
GORDON FOOD SERVICE INC.—See Gordon Food Service Inc.; *U.S. Private*, pg. 1743
GORDON FOOD SERVICE INC.; *U.S. Private*, pg. 1743
GORDON FOOD SERVICE—See Gordon Food Service Inc.; *U.S. Private*, pg. 1743
GORDON FRANKS TRAINING LTD.—See Hexatronic Group AB; *Int'l*, pg. 3370
GORDON & GOTCH—See IVE Group Limited; *Int'l*, pg. 3847
GORDON HANRAHAN, INC.; *U.S. Private*, pg. 1743
GORDON HOLDINGS (NETHERLANDS) B.V.—See Barclays PLC; *Int'l*, pg. 862
GORDON LOW PRODUCTS LTD.—See Kingspan Group PLC; *Int'l*, pg. 4178
THE GORDON LUMBER COMPANY; *U.S. Private*, pg. 4034
GORDON PAPER COMPANY INCORPORATED; *U.S. Private*, pg. 1743
GORDON & REES LLP; *U.S. Private*, pg. 1741
GORDON RESEARCH CONFERENCES; *U.S. Private*, pg. 1743
GORDON SIGN CO.—See Lincolnshire Management, Inc.; *U.S. Private*, pg. 2459
GORDON STREET CORPORATION—See Martin Supply Company Inc.; *U.S. Private*, pg. 2596
GORDONS WALTHAM LIQUOR STORES INC.; *U.S. Private*, pg. 1743
GORD SCOTT NISSAN; *Int'l*, pg. 3042
GORDY'S, INC.; *U.S. Private*, pg. 1743
GORE INDUSTRIAL PRODUCTS TRADE (SHANGHAI) CO., LTD—See W.L. Gore & Associates, Inc.; *U.S. Private*, pg. 4421
GORE MUTUAL INSURANCE COMPANY; *Int'l*, pg. 3043
GORENJE APARATI ZA DOMACINSTVO D.O.O.—See Hisense Co., Ltd.; *Int'l*, pg. 3407
GORENJE AUSTRIA HANDELSGESELLCHAFT MBH—See Hisense Co., Ltd.; *Int'l*, pg. 3407
GORENJE BELUX S.A.R.L.—See Hisense Co., Ltd.; *Int'l*, pg. 3407
GORENJE BUDAPEST KFT—See Hisense Co., Ltd.; *Int'l*, pg. 3407
GORENJE, D.D.—See Hisense Co., Ltd.; *Int'l*, pg. 3407
GORENJE D.O.O.—See Hisense Co., Ltd.; *Int'l*, pg. 3407
GORENJE ESPANA S.L.—See Hisense Co., Ltd.; *Int'l*, pg. 3407
GORENJE FRANCE S.A.S.—See Hisense Co., Ltd.; *Int'l*, pg. 3407
GORENJE GTI D.O.O.—See Hisense Co., Ltd.; *Int'l*, pg. 3407
GORENJE GULF FZE—See Hisense Co., Ltd.; *Int'l*, pg. 3407
GORENJE ISTANBUL LTD.—See Hisense Co., Ltd.; *Int'l*, pg. 3407
GORENJE KAZAKHSTAN TOO—See Hisense Co., Ltd.; *Int'l*, pg. 3407
GORENJE KORTING ITALIA S.R.L.—See Hisense Co., Ltd.; *Int'l*, pg. 3407
GORENJE KUCHEN GMBH—See Hisense Co., Ltd.; *Int'l*, pg. 3407
GORENJE SKANDINAVIEN A/S—See Hisense Co., Ltd.; *Int'l*, pg. 3407
GORENJE SKOPJE D.O.O.—See Hisense Co., Ltd.; *Int'l*, pg. 3407
GORENJE SLOVAKIA S.R.O.—See Hisense Co., Ltd.; *Int'l*, pg. 3407
GORENJE TIKI D.O.O.—See Hisense Co., Ltd.; *Int'l*, pg. 3407
GORENJE TIKI D.O.O.—See Hisense Co., Ltd.; *Int'l*, pg. 3407
GORENJE ZAGREB D.O.O.—See Hisense Co., Ltd.; *Int'l*, pg. 3407
GORENJSKI TISK STORITVE D.O.O.; *Int'l*, pg. 3043
GO REPLY GMBH—See Reply S.p.A.; *Int'l*, pg. 6291
GO REPLY S.R.L.—See Reply S.p.A.; *Int'l*, pg. 6291
THE GORES GROUP, LLC - BOULDER BRANCH—See The Gores Group, LLC; *U.S. Private*, pg. 4035
THE GORES GROUP, LLC; *U.S. Private*, pg. 4034
THE GORES GROUP, LLC; *U.S. Private*, pg. 4035
GORES GUGGENHEIM, INC.; *U.S. Public*, pg. 952
GORES, INC.; *U.S. Private*, pg. 1743
GORES TECHNOLOGY PARTNERS, INC.; *U.S. Public*, pg. 952
GORE STREET ENERGY STORAGE FUND PLC; *Int'l*, pg. 3043
GORGE ROCK PRODUCTS, INC.—See Clyde Companies Inc.; *U.S. Private*, pg. 949
GORGES MOTOR COMPANY INC.; *U.S. Private*, pg. 1743
GORHAM BANCORP, MHC; *U.S. Private*, pg. 1743
GORHAM SAVINGS BANK—See Gorham Bancorp, MHC; *U.S. Private*, pg. 1743

GORI ARGENTINA S.A.—See Deutsche Post AG; *Int'l*, pg. 2080
GORI AUSTRALIA PTY LTD.—See Deutsche Post AG; *Int'l*, pg. 2080
GORI IBERIA S.L.—See Deutsche Post AG; *Int'l*, pg. 2080
GORI IBERIA TRANSITARIOS, LIMITADA—See Deutsche Post AG; *Int'l*, pg. 2080
GORILLA CAPITAL; *U.S. Private*, pg. 1743
GORILLA COMMERCE; *U.S. Private*, pg. 1743
GORILLA GLUE CO.; *U.S. Private*, pg. 1743
GORILLA GROUP LTD.—See Boomerang Plus plc; *Int'l*, pg. 1110
GORILLA, LLC—See WPP plc; *Int'l*, pg. 8479
GORILLA LOGIC, INC.; *U.S. Private*, pg. 1743
GORILLA NATION MEDIA, LLC; *U.S. Private*, pg. 1744
GORILLA STATIONERS LLC; *U.S. Private*, pg. 1744
GORILLA TECHNOLOGY GROUP INC.; *Int'l*, pg. 3043
GORISKE OPEKARNE D.D.; *Int'l*, pg. 3043
GORISPAC S.P.A—See Radici Partecipazioni S.p.A.; *Int'l*, pg. 6175
GORJI BISCUIT COMPANY; *Int'l*, pg. 3043
GORKA CEMENT SP. Z O.O.—See Mapei SpA; *Int'l*, pg. 4681
GORKANA—See Platinum Equity, LLC; *U.S. Private*, pg. 3201
GORKHA BREWERY LIMITED—See Carlsberg A/S; *Int'l*, pg. 1340
GORMAN BROTHERS INC.; *U.S. Private*, pg. 1744
GORMAN & COMPANY INC.; *U.S. Private*, pg. 1744
GORMAN CORY SHIPPING LIMITED—See Braemar PLC; *Int'l*, pg. 1135
GORMAN FOODS INC.; *U.S. Private*, pg. 1744
GORMAN HEALTH GROUP, LLC—See TPG Capital, L.P.; *U.S. Public*, pg. 2170
GORMAN LEARNING CENTER, INC.; *U.S. Private*, pg. 1744
GORMAN MILLING CO. INC.; *U.S. Private*, pg. 1744
GORMAN-RUPP BELGIUM SA—See The Gorman-Rupp Company; *U.S. Public*, pg. 2085
THE GORMAN-RUPP COMPANY; *U.S. Public*, pg. 2085
GORMAN-RUPP EUROPE B.V.—See The Gorman-Rupp Company; *U.S. Public*, pg. 2085
GORMAN-RUPP INDUSTRIES—See The Gorman-Rupp Company; *U.S. Public*, pg. 2085
THE GORMAN-RUPP INTERNATIONAL COMPANY—See The Gorman-Rupp Company; *U.S. Public*, pg. 2085
GORMAN-RUPP OF CANADA LIMITED—See The Gorman-Rupp Company; *U.S. Public*, pg. 2085
GORMAN-RUPP RENTAL SPRL—See The Gorman-Rupp Company; *U.S. Public*, pg. 2085
GORMAN'S FURNITURE INC.; *U.S. Private*, pg. 1744
GORM, INC.—See Kelso & Company, L.P.; *U.S. Private*, pg. 2279
GORM, INC.—See Warburg Pincus LLC; *U.S. Private*, pg. 4437
GORNO FORD; *U.S. Private*, pg. 1744
GORNOSLASKA SPOLKA GAZOWNICTWA SP. Z O.O.—See Polskie Gornictwo Naftowe i Gazownictwo S.A.; *Int'l*, pg. 5912
GORSUCH LTD.; *U.S. Private*, pg. 1744
THE GORTON GROUP—See Nissui Corporation; *Int'l*, pg. 5379
GORTON'S, INC.—See Nissui Corporation; *Int'l*, pg. 5378
GOSA FOM A.D.; *Int'l*, pg. 3043
GOSA MONTAZA A.D.; *Int'l*, pg. 3043
GOSECURE INC.; *U.S. Private*, pg. 1744
GOSFORD QUARRIES PTY. LTD.; *Int'l*, pg. 3043
GOSHEN COACH, INC.—See AIP, LLC; *U.S. Public*, pg. 135
GOSHEN COUNTY ABSTRACT & TITLE COMPANY—See First American Financial Corporation; *U.S. Public*, pg. 837
GOSHEN HEALTH SYSTEM; *U.S. Private*, pg. 1744
GOSHEN HOSPITAL & HEALTH CARE FOUNDATION INC.; *U.S. Private*, pg. 1744
GOSHEN MEDICAL CENTER, INC.; *U.S. Private*, pg. 1744
GOSH ENTERPRISES, INC.; *U.S. Private*, pg. 1744
GOSHI GIKEN CO., LTD.—See Honda Motor Co., Ltd.; *Int'l*, pg. 3464
GOSHI INDIA AUTO PARTS PRIVATE LTD.—See Honda Motor Co., Ltd.; *Int'l*, pg. 3464
GOSHI PHILIPPINES, INC.—See Honda Motor Co., Ltd.; *Int'l*, pg. 3464
GOSHI-THANGLONG AUTO-PARTS CO., LTD.—See Honda Motor Co., Ltd.; *Int'l*, pg. 3464
GOSIGER INC.; *U.S. Private*, pg. 1744
GO SMART DEVELOPMENT LIMITED—See InnoTek Limited; *Int'l*, pg. 3710
GOSNELL BUILDERS—See Pointe Group Ltd.; *U.S. Private*, pg. 3222
GOSOFT (THAILAND) COMPANY LIMITED—See C.P. All Public Company Limited; *Int'l*, pg. 1244
GO SOUTH COAST LIMITED—See GLOBALVIA Inversiones, S.A.U.; *Int'l*, pg. 3005
GO SOUTH COAST LIMITED—See Kinetic Group Services Pty Ltd.; *Int'l*, pg. 4167
GOSPELL DIGITAL TECHNOLOGY CO., LTD.; *Int'l*, pg. 3043

GOSPEL LIGHT PUBLICATIONS; *U.S. Private*, pg. 1744
GOSPORT FERRY LIMITED—See FIH group plc; *Int'l*, pg. 2661
GOSSAMER BIO, INC.; *U.S. Public*, pg. 952
GOSSAN RESOURCES LIMITED; *Int'l*, pg. 3043
GOSS DODGE, INC.; *U.S. Private*, pg. 1744
GOSS DODGE INC.; *U.S. Private*, pg. 1744
GOSSELIN EXPRESS; *Int'l*, pg. 3043
GOSSETT MOTOR CARS INC.; *U.S. Private*, pg. 1744
GOSS GRAPHIC SYSTEMS JAPAN CORPORATION - SAYAMA—See AIP, LLC; *U.S. Public*, pg. 134
GOSS INTERNATIONAL AMERICAS, LLC—See AIP, LLC; *U.S. Public*, pg. 134
GOSS INTERNATIONAL EUROPE UK LTD.—See AIP, LLC; *U.S. Public*, pg. 134
GOSS STEEL CO.—See Olympic Steel Inc.; *U.S. Public*, pg. 1570
GOSTA TORSSELL HOLDING AB; *Int'l*, pg. 3043
GOSTATS; *Int'l*, pg. 3043
GO STEEL FRYDEK MISTEK A.S.—See Stalprodukt S.A.; *Int'l*, pg. 7164
GOSTENA BETEILIGUNGSVERWALTUNGS GMBH—See PORR AG; *Int'l*, pg. 5923
GO STUDY AUSTRALIA PTY LIMITED—See iCollege Limited; *Int'l*, pg. 3582
GOSUNCN TECHNOLOGY GROUP CO., LTD.; *Int'l*, pg. 3043
GOSUN HOLDING CO., LTD.; *Int'l*, pg. 3043
GOTA ENERGI AB—See Fortum Oyj; *Int'l*, pg. 2741
GOTA LEJON LIVE AB—See Live Nation Entertainment, Inc.; *U.S. Public*, pg. 1329
GOTA MEDIA AB; *Int'l*, pg. 3043
GOTAPACK INTERNATIONAL AB—See Addtech AB; *Int'l*, pg. 133
GOTAVERKEN ARENDAL AB; *Int'l*, pg. 3043
GOTAVERKEN CITYVARVET AB—See Damen Shipyards Group; *Int'l*, pg. 1956
GOTAVERKEN MILJO AB—See Babcock & Wilcox Enterprises, Inc.; *U.S. Public*, pg. 263
GOTCHA MOBILITY, LLC—See Bolt Mobility Corp.; *U.S. Private*, pg. 1020
GOTEBORG ELECTRONIC DEFENCE SYSTEMS—See Saab AB; *Int'l*, pg. 6459
GOTEBORGS KEX AB—See Orkla ASA; *Int'l*, pg. 5637
GOTEBORGS STAL AB—See SSAB AB; *Int'l*, pg. 7153
GOTECH CO., LTD.—See Oenon Holdings Inc; *Int'l*, pg. 5529
GO-TECH ENERGY CO., LTD.—See Supreme Electronics Co., Ltd.; *Int'l*, pg. 7340
GOTEE RECORDS, INC.—See Zealot Networks, Inc.; *U.S. Private*, pg. 4599
GO TELECOM BV—See DCC plc; *Int'l*, pg. 1991
GOTEMBA GAS CO., LTD.—See Shizuokagas Co., Ltd.; *Int'l*, pg. 6856
GOTEMBA KOGEN BREWERY, CO., LTD.—See Itoham Yonekyu Holdings Inc.; *Int'l*, pg. 3843
GOTENBAOYAMA ENVIRONMENT TECHNOLOGY CO., LTD.—See Hitachi Zosen Corporation; *Int'l*, pg. 3410
GOTENEHUS GROUP AB; *Int'l*, pg. 3043
GOTENE KYLTRANSPORTER AB—See Mutares SE & Co. KGaA; *Int'l*, pg. 5105
GOTESCO LAND INC.; *Int'l*, pg. 3043
GOTETSU OSAKA BUTURYU CO., LTD.—See Godo Steel, Ltd.; *Int'l*, pg. 3020
GOTETSU SANGYO CO., LTD.—See Godo Steel, Ltd.; *Int'l*, pg. 3020
GOTEX S.A.—See Coats Group plc; *Int'l*, pg. 1682
GOT GERMAN OIL TOOLS GMBH—See NOV, Inc.; *U.S. Public*, pg. 1544
GOTHAM APARTMENTS, LIMITED PARTNERSHIP—See Apartment Investment and Management Company; *U.S. Public*, pg. 144
GOTHAM CIGARS, LLC; *U.S. Private*, pg. 1744
GOTHAM DIGITAL SCIENCE, LLC—See Aon plc; *Int'l*, pg. 493
GOTHAM IMAGE WORKS INC.—See Wiegers Capital Partners; *U.S. Private*, pg. 4516
GOTHAM INCORPORATED—See The Interpublic Group of Companies, Inc.; *U.S. Public*, pg. 2094
GOTHAM ORGANIZATION INC.; *U.S. Private*, pg. 1745
GOTHAM SECURITY, INC.—See Abacus Group LLC; *U.S. Private*, pg. 34
GOTHAM TECHNOLOGY GROUP, LLC; *U.S. Private*, pg. 1745
GOTHENBURG RO/RO TERMINAL AB—See DFDS A/S; *Int'l*, pg. 2095
GOTHIA A/S—See Bertelsmann SE & Co. KGaA; *Int'l*, pg. 996
GOTHIA AS—See Bertelsmann SE & Co. KGaA; *Int'l*, pg. 996
GOTHIA DEUTSCHLAND GMBH—See Bertelsmann SE & Co. KGaA; *Int'l*, pg. 996
GOTHIA FINANCIAL GROUP AB—See Bertelsmann SE & Co. KGaA; *Int'l*, pg. 996
GOTHIA OY—See Bertelsmann SE & Co. KGaA; *Int'l*, pg. 996
GOTHIC LANDSCAPE, INC.; *U.S. Private*, pg. 1745
GOTHIC LANDSCAPING INC.; *U.S. Private*, pg. 1745
GOTHI PLASCON INDIA LIMITED; *Int'l*, pg. 3043

COMPANY NAME INDEX

GOTION HIGH-TECH CO., LTD.; *Int'l*, pg. 3043
GOTLANDS ENERGI AB—See Vattenfall AB; *Int'l*, pg. 8136
GOTLANDS ENERGIVERK AB—See Vattenfall AB; *Int'l*, pg. 8136
GOTLANDS SNUS AB—See Philip Morris International Inc.; *U.S. Public*, pg. 1687
GOTLITAS UAB—See UAB Ignitis grupe; *Int'l*, pg. 7999
GOTOBILLING, INC.—See Fortis Payment Systems LLC; *U.S. Private*, pg. 1576
GOTOH PHILIPPINES CORP.—See Mitsubishi Materials Corporation; *Int'l*, pg. 4963
GOTO MFG CO., LTD.—See Mitsubishi Materials Corporation; *Int'l*, pg. 4963
GOTO NO TSUBAKI INC.—See MTG Co., Ltd.; *Int'l*, pg. 5070
GOTOP CO., LTD.—See Pasona Group Inc.; *Int'l*, pg. 5753
GOT-RACK.COM INC.; *U.S. Private*, pg. 1744
GOTRUCK PTE. LTD.—See Pan-United Corporation Ltd.; *Int'l*, pg. 5716
GOTSE DELCHEV TABAC AD; *Int'l*, pg. 3044
GOTT COMPANY INC.; *U.S. Private*, pg. 1745
GOTTEX MODELS LTD.—See Africa Israel Investments Ltd.; *Int'l*, pg. 190
GOTTFERT WERKSTOFF-PRUFMASCHINEN GMBH; *Int'l*, pg. 3044
GOTTHARD SCHETTLER KLINIK GMBH—See MK-Kliniken AG; *Int'l*, pg. 5001
GOTTHARDT INFORMATIONSSYSTEME GMBH—See CompuGroup Medical SE & Co. KGaA; *Int'l*, pg. 1756
GOTTLIEB PALUDAN ARCHITECTS A/S—See AFRY AB; *Int'l*, pg. 194
GOTTLIEB TESCH BAUUNTERNEHMEN GMBH; *Int'l*, pg. 3044
GOTTSCHALK FEUERSCHUTZANLAGEN GMBH—See VINCI S.A.; *Int'l*, pg. 8222
GOTTSUOBIN CO., LTD.—See Seven & i Holdings Co., Ltd.; *Int'l*, pg. 6730
GOTUWIRED, INC.; *U.S. Private*, pg. 1745
GOTWALS INC.; *U.S. Private*, pg. 1745
GOTZ-UDO HARTMANN GMBH + CO. KG—See Phoenix Mecano AG; *Int'l*, pg. 5852
GOUDEN GIDS B.V.—See Apax Partners LLP; *Int'l*, pg. 507
GOUDEN GIDS B.V.—See Cinven Limited; *Int'l*, pg. 1615
GOUGEON FOURNITURES S.A.S.; *Int'l*, pg. 3044
GOUGH INC.; *U.S. Private*, pg. 1745
GOULARD ENROBES SAS—See VINCI S.A.; *Int'l*, pg. 8222
GOULD & ASSOCIATES GLOBAL SERVICES, INC.; *U.S. Private*, pg. 1745
GOULD CHEVROLET; *U.S. Private*, pg. 1745
GOULD ELECTRONICS GMBH—See ENEOS Holdings, Inc.; *Int'l*, pg. 2416
GOULD EVANS AFFILIATES P.A.; *U.S. Private*, pg. 1745
GOULD EVANS ASSOCIATES LLC—See Gould Evans Affiliates P.A.; *U.S. Private*, pg. 1745
GOULD & GOODRICH LEATHER, INC.—See JLL Partners, LLC; *U.S. Private*, pg. 2213
GOULD HOLDINGS PTY. LTD.—See Vita Group Limited; *Int'l*, pg. 8257
GOULDING CHEMICALS LIMITED—See ARYZTA AG; *Int'l*, pg. 589
GOULD INTERNATIONAL PACKAGING—See Gould Paper Corporation; *U.S. Private*, pg. 1745
GOULD INTERNATIONAL UK LIMITED—See Japan Pulp and Paper Company Limited; *Int'l*, pg. 3903
GOULD INVESTORS, L.P.; *U.S. Public*, pg. 952
GOULD MIDWEST, INC.—See Stephen Gould Corporation; *U.S. Private*, pg. 3802
GOULD PAPER COMPANY OF MARYLAND LLC—See Gould Paper Corporation; *U.S. Private*, pg. 1745
GOULD PAPER CORP. - CHICAGO—See Gould Paper Corporation; *U.S. Private*, pg. 1745
GOULD PAPER CORP. - METRO—See Gould Paper Corporation; *U.S. Private*, pg. 1745
GOULD PAPER CORP. - MID ATLANTIC—See Gould Paper Corporation; *U.S. Private*, pg. 1745
GOULD PAPER CORPORATION; *U.S. Private*, pg. 1745
GOULD PAPER NORTH AMERICA—See Gould Paper Corporation; *U.S. Private*, pg. 1745
GOULD PAPER OF FLORIDA, INC.—See Stephen Gould Corporation; *U.S. Private*, pg. 3802
GOULD PAPER OF FLORIDA, INC.—See Stephen Gould Corporation; *U.S. Private*, pg. 3802
GOULD PAPIERS FRANCE SARLU—See Japan Pulp and Paper Company Limited; *Int'l*, pg. 3903
GOULD PUBLICATION PAPERS UK LIMITED—See Japan Pulp and Paper Company Limited; *Int'l*, pg. 3903
GOULD SOUTHERN—See Stephen Gould Corporation; *U.S. Private*, pg. 3802
GOULDS PUMPS CO. LTD.—See ITT Inc.; *U.S. Public*, pg. 1177
GOULDS PUMPS, INC. - HUNTINGTON—See ITT Inc.; *U.S. Public*, pg. 1177
GOULDS PUMPS, INC. - LOS ANGELES—See ITT Inc.; *U.S. Public*, pg. 1177

GOULDS PUMPS, INC. - MEMPHIS—See ITT Inc.; *U.S. Public*, pg. 1177
GOULDS PUMPS, INC.—See ITT Inc.; *U.S. Public*, pg. 1177
GOULDS PUMPS (NY), INC.—See ITT Inc.; *U.S. Public*, pg. 1177
GOULDS PUMPS (NY), INC.—See ITT Inc.; *U.S. Public*, pg. 1177
GOULDS PUMPS U.K. LTD.—See ITT Inc.; *U.S. Public*, pg. 1177
GOULDS WATER TECHNOLOGY - AUBURN—See Xylem Inc.; *U.S. Public*, pg. 2396
GOULDS WATER TECHNOLOGY - LUBBOCK—See Xylem Inc.; *U.S. Public*, pg. 2396
GOULDS WATER TECHNOLOGY PHILIPPINES, INC.—See Xylem Inc.; *U.S. Public*, pg. 2396
GOULDS WATER TECHNOLOGY - SENECA FALLS—See Xylem Inc.; *U.S. Public*, pg. 2395
GOULDS WATER TECHNOLOGY - SLATON—See Xylem Inc.; *U.S. Public*, pg. 2396
GOULD TECHNOLOGY LLC—See Gooch & Housego PLC; *Int'l*, pg. 3038
GOULSTON & STORRS PC; *U.S. Private*, pg. 1745
GOUPIL INDUSTRIE S.A.—See Polaris, Inc.; *U.S. Public*, pg. 1700
GOUR MEDICAL AG; *Int'l*, pg. 3044
GOURMET BAKER, INC.—See Swander Pace Capital, LLC; *U.S. Private*, pg. 3890
GOURMET BAKER, INC.—See The Bank of Nova Scotia; *Int'l*, pg. 7617
GOURMET BOUTIQUE; *U.S. Private*, pg. 1746
GOURMET BRANDS COMPANY INC.—See create restaurants holdings inc.; *Int'l*, pg. 1832
GOURMET BRYGGERIET APS—See Harboes Bryggeri A/S; *Int'l*, pg. 3271
GOURMET DELICA CO., LTD.—See Mitsubishi Corporation; *Int'l*, pg. 4938
GOURMET DINING, LLC—See Compass Group PLC; *Int'l*, pg. 1752
GOURMET EXPRESS LLC; *U.S. Private*, pg. 1746
GOURMET FOOD NEW ZEALAND LTD.—See Mondelez International, Inc.; *U.S. Public*, pg. 1461
GOURMET FOODS AUSTRALIA PTY LIMITED—See Retail Food Group Limited; *Int'l*, pg. 6305
GOURMET FOODS, LTD.—See The Marygold Companies, Inc.; *U.S. Public*, pg. 2112
GOURMET GARAGE; *U.S. Private*, pg. 1746
GOURMETGIFTBASKETS.COM; *U.S. Private*, pg. 1746
GOURMET INVESTMENTS PVT LTD—See Bharti Enterprises Limited; *Int'l*, pg. 1013
GOURMET KINEYA CO., LTD.; *Int'l*, pg. 3044
GOURMET MASTER CO. LTD.; *Int'l*, pg. 3044
GOURMET MENU-SERVICE GMBH & CO. KG—See Raiffeisenlandesbank Oberosterreich Aktiengesellschaft; *Int'l*, pg. 6187
GOURMET OCEAN PRODUCTS INC.; *Int'l*, pg. 3044
GOURMET PRIMO CO., LTD.—See Bangkok Airways Public Company Limited; *Int'l*, pg. 832
GOURMET SERVICE AB—See Atria Plc; *Int'l*, pg. 693
GOURMET SERVICES INC.; *U.S. Private*, pg. 1746
GOURMET VEG-PAQ, INC.; *U.S. Private*, pg. 1746
GOURMONDO FOOD GMBH—See Delticom AG; *Int'l*, pg. 2021
GOUVERNEUR BANCORP, INC.—See Cambray Mutual Holding Company; *U.S. Private*, pg. 726
GOUVERNEUR BV—See Thomas Fleurs SA; *Int'l*, pg. 7714
GOUVERNEUR SAVINGS & LOAN ASSOCIATION—See Cambray Mutual Holding Company; *U.S. Private*, pg. 726
GOUVIA MARINA S.A.—See Kiriacoulis Mediterranean Cruises Shipping S.A.; *Int'l*, pg. 4186
GOVANGUARD, LLC—See Abacus Group LLC; *U.S. Private*, pg. 33
GOVCO, LLC—See Citigroup Inc.; *U.S. Public*, pg. 504
GOVDESK LLC—See Viel & Compagnie SA; *Int'l*, pg. 8192
GOVDOCS, INC.; *U.S. Private*, pg. 1746
GOVERNALE CO., INC.—See Burnham Holdings, Inc.; *U.S. Public*, pg. 412
GOVERNANCE FOR OWNERS JAPAN KK—See Governance for Owners LLP; *Int'l*, pg. 3044
GOVERNANCE FOR OWNERS LLP; *Int'l*, pg. 3044
GOVERNANCE FOR OWNERS USA, INC.—See Governance for Owners LLP; *Int'l*, pg. 3044
GOVERNING MAGAZINE—See e.Republic, Inc.; *U.S. Private*, pg. 1307
GOVERNMENT ACCOUNTABILITY INSTITUTE; *U.S. Private*, pg. 1746
GOVERNMENT ACQUISITIONS, INC.; *U.S. Private*, pg. 1746
GOVERNMENTAL & EDUCATIONAL ASSISTANCE CORPORATION; *U.S. Private*, pg. 1746
GOVERNMENTAUCTIONS.ORG—See Cyweb Holdings Inc.; *U.S. Public*, pg. 1136
GOVERNMENT BOULEVARD MOTORS, INC.—See AutoNation, Inc.; *U.S. Public*, pg. 235
GOVERNMENT CAPITAL CORPORATION; *U.S. Private*, pg. 1746

GOYA FOODS, INC.

GOVERNMENT CAPITAL CORPORATION-SOUTHEASTERN REGION—See Government Capital Corporation; *U.S. Private*, pg. 1746
GOVERNMENT CAPITAL CORPORATION-SOUTH TEXAS—See Government Capital Corporation; *U.S. Private*, pg. 1746
GOVERNMENT CONTRACTING RESOURCES, INC.; *U.S. Private*, pg. 1746
GOVERNMENT CONTRACT SOLUTIONS, INC.; *U.S. Private*, pg. 1746
GOVERNMENT EMPLOYEES ASSOCIATION—See One80 Intermediaries LLC; *U.S. Private*, pg. 3024
GOVERNMENT EMPLOYEES HEALTH ASSOCIATION, INC.; *U.S. Private*, pg. 1746
GOVERNMENT EMPLOYEES INSURANCE COMPANY—See Berkshire Hathaway Inc.; *U.S. Public*, pg. 302
GOVERNMENT EXECUTIVE MEDIA GROUP LLC—See Growth Catalyst Partners, LLC; *U.S. Private*, pg. 1796
GOVERNMENT HEALTH SERVICES, L.L.C.—See Elevance Health, Inc.; *U.S. Public*, pg. 730
GOVERNMENT LIQUIDATION.COM, LLC—See Liquidity Services, Inc.; *U.S. Public*, pg. 1321
GOVERNMENT LOAN SOLUTIONS, INC.—See Live Oak Bancshares, Inc.; *U.S. Public*, pg. 1331
GOVERNMENT PERSONNEL MUTUAL LIFE INSURANCE COMPANY; *U.S. Private*, pg. 1746
GOVERNMENT REVENUE SOLUTIONS, LLC—See Guggenheim Partners, LLC; *U.S. Private*, pg. 1812
GOVERNMENT SERVICES UK—See Intertek Group plc; *Int'l*, pg. 3762
GOVERNMENT SOURCING SOLUTIONS; *U.S. Private*, pg. 1746
THE GOVERNOR AND COMPANY OF THE BANK OF IRELAND—See Bank of Ireland Group plc; *Int'l*, pg. 844
THE GOVERNOR S RETIREMENT RESORT PTY LTD—See Australian Unity Limited; *Int'l*, pg. 723
GOVERNOUR'S SQUARE OF COLUMBUS CO. L.P.—See UDR, Inc.; *U.S. Public*, pg. 2218
GOVERTIS ADVISORY SERVICES PERU S.A.C.—See Telefonica, S.A.; *Int'l*, pg. 7535
GOVERTIS ADVISORY SERVICES S.L.—See Telefonica, S.A.; *Int'l*, pg. 7535
GOVIA LIMITED—See GLOBALVIA Inversiones, S.A.U.; *Int'l*, pg. 3005
GOVIA LIMITED—See Kinetic Group Services Pty Ltd.; *Int'l*, pg. 4167
GOVIEX URANIUM INC.; *Int'l*, pg. 3044
GOVIND DEVELOPMENT, LLC.; *U.S. Private*, pg. 1746
GOVIND POY OXYGEN LTD.; *Int'l*, pg. 3044
GOVIND RUBBER LTD.; *Int'l*, pg. 3044
GOVISION, LP—See Atairos Group, Inc.; *U.S. Private*, pg. 363
GOVLOOP, INC.—See Vista Equity Partners, LLC; *U.S. Private*, pg. 4398
GO VOYAGES—See Accor S.A.; *Int'l*, pg. 91
GOVPLACE, INC.; *U.S. Private*, pg. 1746
GOWAII VACATION HOLDING S.L.; *Int'l*, pg. 3044
GOWAN COMPANY LLC; *U.S. Private*, pg. 1746
GOWANDA COMPONENTS GROUP—See The Jordan Company, L.P.; *U.S. Private*, pg. 4063
GOWANDA - GEC LLC—See The Jordan Company, L.P.; *U.S. Private*, pg. 4063
GOWAN, INC.—See EMCOR Group, Inc.; *U.S. Public*, pg. 737
GO WELSH; *U.S. Private*, pg. 1723
GOWER CORPORATION; *U.S. Private*, pg. 1747
GOWER FURNITURE LTD.—See Nobia AB; *Int'l*, pg. 5395
GOWER HOUSE LIMITED—See Brown & Brown, Inc.; *U.S. Public*, pg. 400
GOWEST GOLD LTD.; *Int'l*, pg. 3044
GOWILY LIMITED—See Hang Lung Group Limited; *Int'l*, pg. 3245
GOWING BROTHERS LIMITED; *Int'l*, pg. 3044
GOWIRELESS, INC.,; *U.S. Private*, pg. 1747
GOWIRELESS, INC.—See ABC Phones of North Carolina, Inc.; *U.S. Private*, pg. 36
GOWLING WLG (CANADA) LLP—See Gowling WLG International Limited; *Int'l*, pg. 3045
GOWLING WLG INTERNATIONAL LIMITED; *Int'l*, pg. 3045
GOWLING WLG (UK) LLP—See Gowling WLG International Limited; *Int'l*, pg. 3045
GOWRA LEASING & FINANCE LIMITED; *Int'l*, pg. 3045
GOWRI GOPAL HOSPITALS PRIVATE LTD.—See TGV Sraac Limited; *Int'l*, pg. 7588
GOWRINGS MOBILITY LTD.—See Newship Ltd; *Int'l*, pg. 5238
GOXUS INC.; *Int'l*, pg. 3045
GOYA EN ESPANA S.A.—See Goya Foods, Inc.; *U.S. Private*, pg. 1747
GOYA FOODS, INC.; *U.S. Private*, pg. 1747
GOYA FOODS INC.—See Goya Foods, Inc.; *U.S. Private*, pg. 1747
GOYA FOODS OF CALIFORNIA—See Goya Foods, Inc.; *U.S. Private*, pg. 1747
GOYA FOODS OF FLORIDA—See Goya Foods, Inc.; *U.S. Private*, pg. 1747

GOYA FOODS, INC.

GOYA FOODS OF FLORIDA—See Goya Foods, Inc.; *U.S. Private*, pg. 1747
GOYA FOODS OF GREAT LAKES NEW YORK—See Goya Foods, Inc.; *U.S. Private*, pg. 1747
GOYA FOODS OF ILLINOIS—See Goya Foods, Inc.; *U.S. Private*, pg. 1747
GOYA FOODS OF LONG ISLAND—See Goya Foods, Inc.; *U.S. Private*, pg. 1747
GOYA FOODS OF MADRID—See Goya Foods, Inc.; *U.S. Private*, pg. 1747
GOYA FOODS OF PUERTO RICO—See Goya Foods, Inc.; *U.S. Private*, pg. 1747
GOYA FOODS OF SOUTH JERSEY—See Goya Foods, Inc.; *U.S. Private*, pg. 1747
GOYA FOODS OF TEXAS—See Goya Foods, Inc.; *U.S. Private*, pg. 1747
GOYA FOODS OF THE DOMINICAN REPUBLIC, S.A.—See Goya Foods, Inc.; *U.S. Private*, pg. 1747
GOYAL ALUMINIUMS LIMITED; *Int'l*, pg. 3045
GOYAL ASSOCIATES LTD; *Int'l*, pg. 3045
GOYAL SALT LIMITED; *Int'l*, pg. 3045
GOYEN CONTROLS CO, PTY LIMITED—See Emerson Electric Co.; *U.S. Public*, pg. 751
GOYEN CONTROLS CO UK LIMITED—See Emerson Electric Co.; *U.S. Public*, pg. 751
GOYEN VALVE LLC—See Emerson Electric Co.; *U.S. Public*, pg. 751
GOYETTE MECHANICAL; *U.S. Private*, pg. 1747
GOYO ELECTRONICS CO., LTD.—See Nisshinbo Holdings Inc.; *Int'l*, pg. 5373
GOYO FOODS INDUSTRY CO., LTD.; *Int'l*, pg. 3045
GOYO INTEX CO., LTD.; *Int'l*, pg. 3045
GOYO KAIUN KAISHA, LTD.—See Isewan Terminal Service Co., Ltd.; *Int'l*, pg. 3816
GOZAISHO ROPEWAY CO., LTD.—See Mie Kotsu Group Holdings, Inc.; *Int'l*, pg. 4888
GOZDE GIRISIM SERMAYESI YATIRIM ORTAKLIGI A.S.; *Int'l*, pg. 3045
GOZDE GIYIM SAN. VE TIC. A.S.; *Int'l*, pg. 3045
GP 7. JUL A.D.; *Int'l*, pg. 3045
GP ACOUSTICS GMBH—See Gold Peak Technology Group Limited; *Int'l*, pg. 3025
GP ACOUSTICS (HK) LIMITED—See Gold Peak Technology Group Limited; *Int'l*, pg. 3025
GP ACOUSTICS INTERNATIONAL LIMITED—See Gold Peak Technology Group Limited; *Int'l*, pg. 3025
GP ACOUSTICS (MIDDLE EAST) DWC-LLC—See Gold Peak Technology Group Limited; *Int'l*, pg. 3025
GP ACOUSTICS (TAIWAN) LIMITED—See Gold Peak Technology Group Limited; *Int'l*, pg. 3025
GP ACOUSTICS (UK) LIMITED—See Gold Peak Technology Group Limited; *Int'l*, pg. 3025
G&P ACQUISITION CORP.; *U.S. Public*, pg. 893
GPA FLOWSYSTEM AB—See Indutrade AB; *Int'l*, pg. 3678
GPA FLOWSYSTEM AS—See Indutrade AB; *Int'l*, pg. 3678
GPA-IARD S.A.—See Assicurazioni Generali S.p.A.; *Int'l*, pg. 644
GPA PLAST AB—See Indutrade AB; *Int'l*, pg. 3679
GPA PLAST A/S—See Indutrade AB; *Int'l*, pg. 3678
GPA, SPECIALTY SUBSTRATE SOLUTIONS; *U.S. Private*, pg. 1747
GPA TECHNOLOGIES, INC.; *U.S. Private*, pg. 1747
GP AUTOBAT SDN. BHD.—See Joe Holding Berhad; *Int'l*, pg. 3977
GPB AFRICA (PTY) LTD—See Gazprombank JSC; *Int'l*, pg. 2892
GP BATTERIES (AMERICAS) INC.—See Gold Peak Technology Group Limited; *Int'l*, pg. 3025
GP BATTERIES (CHINA) LTD.—See Gold Peak Technology Group Limited; *Int'l*, pg. 3025
GP BATTERIES INTERNATIONAL LIMITED—See Gold Peak Technology Group Limited; *Int'l*, pg. 3025
GP BATTERIES (MALAYSIA) SDN. BHD—See Gold Peak Technology Group Limited; *Int'l*, pg. 3025
GP BATTERIES (SHENZHEN) CO., LTD.—See Gold Peak Technology Group Limited; *Int'l*, pg. 3025
GP BATTERIES (U.K.) LIMITED—See Gold Peak Technology Group Limited; *Int'l*, pg. 3025
GP BATTERIES (VIETNAM) LIMITED LIABILITY COMPANY—See Gold Peak Technology Group Limited; *Int'l*, pg. 3025
GP BATTERY MARKETING (HK) LTD.—See Gold Peak Technology Group Limited; *Int'l*, pg. 3025
GP BATTERY MARKETING (KOREA) LIMITED—See Gold Peak Technology Group Limited; *Int'l*, pg. 3025
GP BATTERY MARKETING (MALAYSIA) SDN. BHD.—See Gold Peak Technology Group Limited; *Int'l*, pg. 3025
GP BATTERY MARKETING (SINGAPORE) PTE. LTD.—See Gold Peak Technology Group Limited; *Int'l*, pg. 3025
GP BATTERY MARKETING (TAIWAN) LTD.—See Gold Peak Technology Group Limited; *Int'l*, pg. 3025
GP BATTERY (POLAND) SP. Z.O.O—See Gold Peak Technology Group Limited; *Int'l*, pg. 3025
GPB CAPITAL HOLDINGS, LLC; *U.S. Private*, pg. 1748
GPBC INC.; *U.S. Private*, pg. 1748
GPB-FACTORING LLC—See Gazprombank JSC; *Int'l*, pg. 2892

GPB FINANCIAL SERVICES LIMITED—See Gazprombank JSC; *Int'l*, pg. 2892
GPB INTERNATIONAL S.A—See Gazprombank JSC; *Int'l*, pg. 2892
GP BIS SP. Z O.O.—See Impel S.A.; *Int'l*, pg. 3631
GP BULLHOUND LLP; *Int'l*, pg. 3045
GP CAPITAL CO., LTD.; *Int'l*, pg. 3045
GPC ASIA PACIFIC HOLDINGS PTY LTD—See Genuine Parts Company; *U.S. Public*, pg. 932
GP CELLULOSE, LLC—See Koch Industries, Inc.; *U.S. Private*, pg. 2328
GPC FINANCE COMPANY—See Genuine Parts Company; *U.S. Public*, pg. 932
GPC INTERNATIONAL, INC.; *U.S. Private*, pg. 1748
GP COMMUNICATIONS, LLC—See Oblong, Inc.; *U.S. Public*, pg. 1560
GP COMPANIES INC.; *U.S. Private*, pg. 1747
GP CONSULTING PENZUGYI TANACSADO KFT.—See Assicurazioni Generali S.p.A.; *Int'l*, pg. 644
GPC PARTICIPACOES SA; *Int'l*, pg. 3046
GPD DRINA D.D.; *Int'l*, pg. 3046
GP DECORS BV—See Macintosh Retail Group NV; *Int'l*, pg. 4622
GP DECORS SNC—See Macintosh Retail Group NV; *Int'l*, pg. 4622
GP DESIGN, INC.; *U.S. Private*, pg. 1747
GPD GROUP; *U.S. Private*, pg. 1748
G-P DISTRIBUTING INC.; *U.S. Private*, pg. 1630
GPD, PC; *U.S. Private*, pg. 1748
G.P.E. (88/104 BISHOPSGATE) LIMITED—See Great Portland Estates Plc; *Int'l*, pg. 3065
GP ELECTRONICS (HONG KONG) LIMITED—See Gold Peak Technology Group Limited; *Int'l*, pg. 3025
GP ELECTRONICS (HUIZHOU) CO., LTD.—See Gold Peak Technology Group Limited; *Int'l*, pg. 3025
GP ELECTRONICS LIMITED—See Gold Peak Technology Group Limited; *Int'l*, pg. 3025
GP ELECTRONICS (SZ) LIMITED—See Gold Peak Technology Group Limited; *Int'l*, pg. 3025
G.P. EMBELTON & COMPANY PTY LTD.—See Embelton Limited; *Int'l*, pg. 2375
GPE-PLAST ENGINEERING GMBH—See capiton AG; *Int'l*, pg. 1314
G. PETER REBER MOBEL-LOGISTIK GMBH; *Int'l*, pg. 2864
GP FINANCE, INC.—See Global Payments Inc.; *U.S. Public*, pg. 943
GPG CONSTRUCTION & MODULAR HOMES, LLC.; *U.S. Private*, pg. 1748
G.P. GLOBAL POWERM LTD.; *Int'l*, pg. 2866
GPG LUPINE PARTNERS—See Greener Pastures Group LLC; *U.S. Private*, pg. 1777
GP GRENZACH PRODUKTIONS GMBH—See Bayer Aktiengesellschaft; *Int'l*, pg. 905
GP GUNTER PAPENBURG AG; *Int'l*, pg. 3045
G-P GYPSUM CORP. - ACME—See Koch Industries, Inc.; *U.S. Private*, pg. 2327
G-P GYPSUM CORP. - ANTIOCH—See Koch Industries, Inc.; *U.S. Private*, pg. 2327
G-P GYPSUM CORP. - BLUE RAPIDS—See Koch Industries, Inc.; *U.S. Private*, pg. 2327
G-P GYPSUM CORP. - CAMDEN—See Koch Industries, Inc.; *U.S. Private*, pg. 2327
G-P GYPSUM CORP. - NEWINGTON—See Koch Industries, Inc.; *U.S. Private*, pg. 2327
G-P GYPSUM CORPORATION—See Koch Industries, Inc.; *U.S. Private*, pg. 2327
G-P GYPSUM CORP. - SAN LEANDRO—See Koch Industries, Inc.; *U.S. Private*, pg. 2327
G-P GYPSUM CORP. - SAVANNAH—See Koch Industries, Inc.; *U.S. Private*, pg. 2327
G-P GYPSUM CORP. - WHEATFIELD—See Koch Industries, Inc.; *U.S. Private*, pg. 2327
G-PHARMA AG—See CSL Limited; *Int'l*, pg. 1866
GPH ISPAT LIMITED; *Int'l*, pg. 3046
GPH VILNIUS—See Nexans S.A.; *Int'l*, pg. 5240
GPI CHILE SPA—See GPI S.p.A.; *Int'l*, pg. 3046
GPIC LLC—See Genuine Parts Company; *U.S. Public*, pg. 932
GPI FL-H, LLC—See Group 1 Automotive, Inc.; *U.S. Public*, pg. 971
GPI FORANKRA SAS—See Axel Johnson Gruppen AB; *Int'l*, pg. 764
GPI GA-CGM, LLC—See Group 1 Automotive, Inc.; *U.S. Public*, pg. 971
GPI INTERNATIONAL LIMITED—See Gold Peak Technology Group Limited; *Int'l*, pg. 3025
GPI KRAKOW SP. Z O.O.—See Graphic Packaging Holding Company; *U.S. Public*, pg. 958
GPI LA-H, LLC—See Group 1 Automotive, Inc.; *U.S. Public*, pg. 971
G-PILE SISTEM SDN. BHD.—See CSC Holdings Limited; *Int'l*, pg. 1862
GPI MANAGEMENT SERVICES (PROPRIETARY) LIMITED—See Grand Parade Investments Limited; *Int'l*, pg. 3056
GP INDUSTRIES LIMITED—See Gold Peak Technology Group Limited; *Int'l*, pg. 3025

CORPORATE AFFILIATIONS

GPI NM-J, INC.—See Group 1 Automotive, Inc.; *U.S. Public*, pg. 971
GPI NM-LRII, INC.—See Group 1 Automotive, Inc.; *U.S. Public*, pg. 971
GP INSPECT GMBH—See centrotherm photovoltaics AG; *Int'l*, pg. 1415
GP INVESTIMENTOS LTDA.—See GP Investments, Ltd.; *Int'l*, pg. 3045
GP INVESTMENTS, LTD.; *Int'l*, pg. 3045
GPI (SAS)—See 3M Company; *U.S. Public*, pg. 6
GPI—See Angel Holdings Godo Kaisha; *Int'l*, pg. 459
GPI S.P.A.; *Int'l*, pg. 3046
GPI TX-AII, INC.—See Group 1 Automotive, Inc.; *U.S. Public*, pg. 971
GPI TX-DMIV, INC.—See Group 1 Automotive, Inc.; *U.S. Public*, pg. 971
GPI TX-EPGM, INC.—See Group 1 Automotive, Inc.; *U.S. Public*, pg. 971
GPI TX-HIII, INC.—See Group 1 Automotive, Inc.; *U.S. Public*, pg. 971
GPI TX-SKII, INC.—See Group 1 Automotive, Inc.; *U.S. Public*, pg. 971
GPI TX-SVIII INC.—See Group 1 Automotive, Inc.; *U.S. Public*, pg. 971
GPI UK—See Groupe Guillin SA; *Int'l*, pg. 3103
GPI USA INC.—See GPI S.p.A.; *Int'l*, pg. 3046
GP & J BAKER—See Kravet Fabrics Inc.; *U.S. Private*, pg. 2350
GPJ (SINGAPORE) PTE. LTD—See Project: Worldwide, Inc.; *U.S. Private*, pg. 3280
GP KRAJINA A.D.; *Int'l*, pg. 3046
GP LAND & CARPET CORPORATION; *U.S. Private*, pg. 1747
G-PLAN, INC.—See Hakuhodo DY Holdings Incorporated; *Int'l*, pg. 3221
GPL LIMPIEZAS, S.L.—See ACS, Actividades de Construccion y Servicios, S.A.; *Int'l*, pg. 112
GPLUSMEDIA INC.—See Gakken Holdings Co., Ltd.; *Int'l*, pg. 2869
G P MAINTENANCE SOLUTIONS, INC.—See Alexander & Baldwin, Inc.; *U.S. Public*, pg. 75
GPM ASSOCIATES LLC; *U.S. Private*, pg. 1748
GPM BUILDERS PTE. LTD.—See Goodland Group Limited; *Int'l*, pg. 3040
GPM-HENKEL LTD.—See Henkel AG & Co. KGaA; *Int'l*, pg. 3348
GPMI COMPANY—See Kelso & Company, L.P.; *U.S. Private*, pg. 2279
GPMI COMPANY—See Warburg Pincus LLC; *U.S. Private*, pg. 4436
GPM INDUSTRIES, INC.; *U.S. Private*, pg. 1748
GPM INVESTMENTS, LLC—See Haymaker Acquisition Corp.; *U.S. Private*, pg. 1885
GPML PTY LTD—See Wesfarmers Limited; *Int'l*, pg. 8381
GPM METALS INC.; *Int'l*, pg. 3046
GPM PETROLEUM LP—See Haymaker Acquisition Corp.; *U.S. Private*, pg. 1885
GPM SOUTHEAST, LLC—See Haymaker Acquisition Corp.; *U.S. Private*, pg. 1885
GPN GMBH—See Greiner Holding AG; *Int'l*, pg. 3079
GP NORTH AMERICA, LLC—See GP Investments, Ltd.; *Int'l*, pg. 3045
GPN STROJIRNA S.R.O.—See Greiner Holding AG; *Int'l*, pg. 3079
GPOD OF IDAHO; *U.S. Private*, pg. 1748
GPODS, INC.; *U.S. Private*, pg. 1748
GPO PLUS, INC.; *U.S. Public*, pg. 952
GPPC CHEMICAL CO., LTD—See Grand Pacific Petrochemical Corporation; *Int'l*, pg. 3055
GP PETROLEUMS LTD.; *Int'l*, pg. 3046
GP PLANUM AD BEOGRAD; *Int'l*, pg. 3046
GP PLANUM AD; *Int'l*, pg. 3046
GP PUT D.D. SARAJEVO; *Int'l*, pg. 3046
GP REINSURANCE EAD—See PPF Group N.V.; *Int'l*, pg. 5950
GP/RM PRESTRESS, LLC—See Alexander & Baldwin, Inc.; *U.S. Public*, pg. 75
GP ROADWAY SOLUTIONS, INC.—See Nan, Inc.; *U.S. Private*, pg. 2832
GPRO TITANIUM INDUSTRY CO., LTD.; *Int'l*, pg. 3046
GPROULX INC.; *U.S. Private*, pg. 1748
GPS ALLIANCE HOLDINGS LIMITED; *Int'l*, pg. 3046
GPS ALLIANCE HOLDINGS PTE. LTD.—See GPS Alliance Holdings Limited; *Int'l*, pg. 3047
GPS BODY REPAIRS LIMITED—See ZIGUP plc; *Int'l*, pg. 8682
GPS BULGARIA AD—See America Movil, S.A.B. de C.V.; *Int'l*, pg. 421
GPSC UK LIMITED—See General Motors Company; *U.S. Public*, pg. 928
GPS GLAS PRODUKTIONS SERVICE GMBH—See Compagnie de Saint-Gobain SA; *Int'l*, pg. 1735
GPS GMBH & CO KG—See Aliaxis S.A./N.V.; *Int'l*, pg. 324
GPS HOLDING GERMANY GMBH—See Aliaxis S.A./N.V.; *Int'l*, pg. 324
GPSHOPPER LLC—See Synchrony Financial; *U.S. Public*, pg. 1970
GPS IBERICA S.L.—See Aliaxis S.A./N.V.; *Int'l*, pg. 324

COMPANY NAME INDEX

GPSI HOLDINGS, LLC—See Ingersoll Rand Inc.; *U.S. Public*, pg. 1120
GPSI, INC.—See Ryman Hospitality Properties, Inc.; *U.S. Public*, pg. 1829
GPS INDUSTRIES, LLC—See Ingersoll Rand Inc.; *U.S. Public*, pg. 1120
GPS INSIGHT LLC—See Accel Partners L.P.; *U.S. Private*, pg. 48
GPS INSIGHT LLC—See KKR & Co. Inc.; *U.S. Public*, pg. 1238
GP SOLAR GMBH—See centrotherm photovoltaics AG; *Int'l*, pg. 1415
GPS SERVICES, INC.—See The Gap, Inc.; *U.S. Public*, pg. 2074
GPS SOURCE, INC.—See General Dynamics Corporation; *U.S. Public*, pg. 913
GP STRATEGIES CORP. - ALEXANDRIA—See Learning Technologies Group plc; *Int'l*, pg. 4435
GP STRATEGIES CORPORATION—See Learning Technologies Group plc; *Int'l*, pg. 4435
GP STRATEGIES DANYIMANLYK LIMITED SIRKETI—See Learning Technologies Group plc; *Int'l*, pg. 4435
GP STRATEGIES (HONG KONG) LIMITED—See Learning Technologies Group plc; *Int'l*, pg. 4435
GP STRATEGIES (INDIA) PVT. LIMITED—See Learning Technologies Group plc; *Int'l*, pg. 4435
GP STRATEGIES LTD.—See Learning Technologies Group plc; *Int'l*, pg. 4435
GP STRATEGIES MALAYSIA SDN BHD—See Learning Technologies Group plc; *Int'l*, pg. 4435
GP STRATEGIES NORDIC A/S—See Learning Technologies Group plc; *Int'l*, pg. 4435
GP STRATEGIES POLAND SP. Z.O.O—See Learning Technologies Group plc; *Int'l*, pg. 4435
GP STRATEGIES (SHANGHAI) CO., LTD.—See Learning Technologies Group plc; *Int'l*, pg. 4435
GP STRATEGIES SINGAPORE (ASIA) PTE., LTD.—See Learning Technologies Group plc; *Int'l*, pg. 4435
GP STRATEGIES SWITZERLAND GMBH—See Learning Technologies Group plc; *Int'l*, pg. 4435
GP STRATEGIES TRAINING LTD—See Learning Technologies Group plc; *Int'l*, pg. 4435
GPT CONCRETE PRODUCTS SOUTH AFRICA (PTY.) LIMITED—See GPT Infraprojects Limited; *Int'l*, pg. 3047
GPT GROUP; *Int'l*, pg. 3047
GPT HOUSTON—See Enpro Inc.; *U.S. Public*, pg. 774
GPT INFRAPROJECTS LIMITED; *Int'l*, pg. 3047
GPT NOMINEES PTY LIMITED—See GPT Group; *Int'l*, pg. 3047
GPT OPERATING PARTNERSHIP LP—See Blackstone Inc.; *U.S. Public*, pg. 350
GPT PTY LTD—See GPT Group; *Int'l*, pg. 3047
G&P TRUCKING COMPANY, INC.—See NFI Industries, Inc.; *U.S. Private*, pg. 2923
GPT-WEBSTER GREEN, LLC—See Equity Residential; *U.S. Public*, pg. 792
GPV AMERICAS MEXICO S.A.P.I DE CV—See Aktieselskabet Schouw & Co.; *Int'l*, pg. 266
GPV ASIA (HONG KONG), LTD.—See Aktieselskabet Schouw & Co.; *Int'l*, pg. 266
GPV ASIA (THAILAND) CO., LTD.—See Aktieselskabet Schouw & Co.; *Int'l*, pg. 266
GPV AUSTRIA CABLE GMBH—See Aktieselskabet Schouw & Co.; *Int'l*, pg. 266
GPV AUSTRIA GMBH—See Aktieselskabet Schouw & Co.; *Int'l*, pg. 266
GPV ESTONIA AS—See Aktieselskabet Schouw & Co.; *Int'l*, pg. 266
GPV GERMANY GMBH—See Aktieselskabet Schouw & Co.; *Int'l*, pg. 266
GPV GROUP A/S—See Aktieselskabet Schouw & Co.; *Int'l*, pg. 266
GPV INTERNATIONAL A/S—See Aktieselskabet Schouw & Co.; *Int'l*, pg. 266
GPV LANKA (PRIVATE), LTD.—See Aktieselskabet Schouw & Co.; *Int'l*, pg. 266
GPV SLOVAKIA (NOVA) S.R.O.—See Aktieselskabet Schouw & Co.; *Int'l*, pg. 266
GPV SLOVAKIA S.R.O.—See Aktieselskabet Schouw & Co.; *Int'l*, pg. 266
GPV SWEDEN AB—See Aktieselskabet Schouw & Co.; *Int'l*, pg. 266
GPV SWITZERLAND SA—See Aktieselskabet Schouw & Co.; *Int'l*, pg. 266
GPV ZHONGSHAN CO., LTD.—See Aktieselskabet Schouw & Co.; *Int'l*, pg. 266
GPW BENCHMARK S.A.—See Gielda Papierow Wartosciowych w Warszawie S.A.; *Int'l*, pg. 2968
GPW DEUTSCHLAND GMBH.—See YouGov plc; *Int'l*, pg. 8601
G-P WOOD & FIBER SUPPLY, LLC—See Koch Industries, Inc.; *U.S. Private*, pg. 2327
GP ZGP D.D. SARAJEVO; *Int'l*, pg. 3046
GQG PARTNERS (AUSTRALIA) PTY LTD.—See GQG Partners Inc.; *U.S. Public*, pg. 952
GQG PARTNERS INC.; *U.S. Public*, pg. 952
GRAAL S.A.; *Int'l*, pg. 3048

GRABADOS ESCHMANN INTERNATIONAL S.L.—See voestalpine AG; *Int'l*, pg. 8289
GRABAL ALOK IMPEX LIMITED—See Reliance - ADA Group Limited; *Int'l*, pg. 6261
GRABAL ALOK INTERNATIONAL LIMITED—See Reliance - ADA Group Limited; *Int'l*, pg. 6261
GRABAL ALOK (UK) LTD.—See Reliance - ADA Group Limited; *Int'l*, pg. 6261
GRABARZ & PARTNER WERBEAGENTUR GMBH; *Int'l*, pg. 3048
GRABBER, INC.—See Kobayashi Pharmaceutical Co., Ltd.; *Int'l*, pg. 4216
GRABENER PRESSENSYSTEME GMBH & CO. KG—See ANDRITZ AG; *Int'l*, pg. 456
GRAB HOLDINGS LIMITED; *Int'l*, pg. 3048
GRABIAK CHEVROLET, INC.; *U.S. Private*, pg. 1748
GRABILL CABINET COMPANY; *U.S. Private*, pg. 1748
GRABILL, INC.—See Pella Corporation; *U.S. Private*, pg. 3131
GRABLE & ASSOCIATES REALTY; *U.S. Private*, pg. 1748
GRAB ON GRIPS LLC—See Columbia Ventures Corporation; *U.S. Private*, pg. 978
GRABOYES COMMERCIAL WINDOW COMPANY; *U.S. Private*, pg. 1748
GRABTAXI PTE. LTD.; *Int'l*, pg. 3048
GRACE ALASKA INC.; *U.S. Private*, pg. 1748
GRACE ARGENTINA S.A.—See Standard Industries Holdings Inc.; *U.S. Private*, pg. 3779
GRACE AUSTRALIA PTY. LTD.—See Standard Industries Holdings Inc.; *U.S. Private*, pg. 3779
GRACE BAUPRODUKTE GMBH—See Standard Industries Holdings Inc.; *U.S. Private*, pg. 3779
GRACE BEHAVIORAL HEALTH, LLC—See KKR & Co. Inc.; *U.S. Public*, pg. 1249
GRACE BRASIL LTDA.—See Standard Industries Holdings Inc.; *U.S. Private*, pg. 3779
GRACE BREEDING LTD.; *Int'l*, pg. 3048
GRACE BROTHERS LTD.; *U.S. Private*, pg. 1748
GRACE CANADA, INC.—See Standard Industries Holdings Inc.; *U.S. Private*, pg. 3779
GRACE CATALYST AB—See Standard Industries Holdings Inc.; *U.S. Private*, pg. 3779
GRACE CATALYST AB—See Standard Industries Holdings Inc.; *U.S. Private*, pg. 3779
GRACE CHINA LTD.—See Standard Industries Holdings Inc.; *U.S. Private*, pg. 3779
GRACE COLOMBIA S.A.—See Standard Industries Holdings Inc.; *U.S. Private*, pg. 3779
GRACE CONSTRUCTION PRODUCTS N.V.—See Standard Industries Holdings Inc.; *U.S. Private*, pg. 3779
GRACE CONSTRUCTION PRODUCTS S.A.—See Standard Industries Holdings Inc.; *U.S. Private*, pg. 3779
GRACE CONSTRUCTION PRODUCTS—See Standard Industries Holdings Inc.; *U.S. Private*, pg. 3779
GRACE CONTAINER, S. A. DE C. V.—See Standard Industries Holdings Inc.; *U.S. Private*, pg. 3779
GRACE DAREX GMBH—See Standard Industries Holdings Inc.; *U.S. Private*, pg. 3779
GRACE DAVISON - CURTIS BAY (BALTIMORE) PLANT—See Standard Industries Holdings Inc.; *U.S. Private*, pg. 3779
GRACE DAVISON DISCOVERY SCIENCES—See Standard Industries Holdings Inc.; *U.S. Private*, pg. 3779
GRACE DAVISON DISCOVERY SCIENCES—See Standard Industries Holdings Inc.; *U.S. Private*, pg. 3779
GRACE DAVISON (PROPRIETARY) LIMITED—See Standard Industries Holdings Inc.; *U.S. Private*, pg. 3780
GRACE DAVISON—See Standard Industries Holdings Inc.; *U.S. Private*, pg. 3779
GRACE DISCOUNT FOODS INC.; *U.S. Private*, pg. 1748
GRACE ENERGY CORP.; *U.S. Private*, pg. 1748
GRACE FABRIC TECHNOLOGY CO., LTD.; *Int'l*, pg. 3048
GRACE FAMILY PRACTICE, LLC—See HCA Healthcare, Inc.; *U.S. Public*, pg. 997
GRACE FOOD PROCESSORS (CANNING) LTD.—See GraceKennedy Limited; *Int'l*, pg. 3048
GRACE FOOD PROCESSORS LTD.—See GraceKennedy Limited; *Int'l*, pg. 3048
GRACE FOODS INTERNATIONAL LTD.—See GraceKennedy Limited; *Int'l*, pg. 3048
GRACE FOODS & SERVICES COMPANY—See GraceKennedy Limited; *Int'l*, pg. 3048
GRACE FOODS UK LIMITED—See GraceKennedy Limited; *Int'l*, pg. 3048
GRACE FOODS (USA) INC.—See GraceKennedy Limited; *Int'l*, pg. 3049
GRACE GERMANY GMBH—See Standard Industries Holdings Inc.; *U.S. Private*, pg. 3780
GRACE GMBH & CO. KG—See Standard Industries Holdings Inc.; *U.S. Private*, pg. 3780
GRACE HEALTHCARE, LLC; *U.S. Private*, pg. 1749
GRACE HEALTHCARE MEDICAL, INC.—See AdaptHealth Corp.; *U.S. Public*, pg. 38
GRACE HEALTHCARE OF TUCKER—See Grace Healthcare, LLC; *U.S. Private*, pg. 1749
GRACE HEALTH; *U.S. Private*, pg. 1749

GRACE MEDICAL HOME, INC.

GRACE HEBERT CURTIS ARCHITECTS, LLC—See Bernhard Capital Partners Management, LP; *U.S. Private*, pg. 537
GRACE HELLAS E.P.E.—See Standard Industries Holdings Inc.; *U.S. Private*, pg. 3780
GRACE H-G, INC.—See Standard Industries Holdings Inc.; *U.S. Private*, pg. 3780
GRACE HILL, LLC—See Stone Point Capital LLC; *U.S. Private*, pg. 3825
GRACE HOLDINGS, S.A. DE C.V.—See Standard Industries Holdings Inc.; *U.S. Private*, pg. 3780
GRACE HOLMES, INC.—See Leonard Green & Partners, L.P.; *U.S. Private*, pg. 2426
GRACE HOLMES, INC.—See TPG Capital, L.P.; *U.S. Public*, pg. 2174
GRACE HOME FASHIONS LLC—See GHCL Limited; *Int'l*, pg. 2959
GRACE HOMES COLORADO; *U.S. Private*, pg. 1749
GRACE HOSPICE; *U.S. Private*, pg. 1749
GRACE HOSPITAL; *U.S. Private*, pg. 1749
GRACE INVESTMENT COMPANY, INC.; *U.S. Private*, pg. 1749
GRACE ITALY S.R.L.—See Standard Industries Holdings Inc.; *U.S. Private*, pg. 3780
GRACE JAPAN KABUSHIKI KAISHA—See Standard Industries Holdings Inc.; *U.S. Private*, pg. 3780
GRACE JAPAN K.K.—See Standard Industries Holdings Inc.; *U.S. Private*, pg. 3780
GRACE JOEL RETIREMENT VILLAGE LIMITED—See Ryman Healthcare Ltd.; *Int'l*, pg. 6439
GRACEKENNEDY (BELIZE) LTD.—See GraceKennedy Limited; *Int'l*, pg. 3048
GRACE KENNEDY CURRENCY TRADING SERVICES LIMITED—See GraceKennedy Limited; *Int'l*, pg. 3048
GRACEKENNEDY LIMITED; *Int'l*, pg. 3048
GRACEKENNEDY MONEY SERVICES (ANGUILLA) LIMITED—See GraceKennedy Limited; *Int'l*, pg. 3049
GRACEKENNEDY MONEY SERVICES CARIBBEAN SRL—See GraceKennedy Limited; *Int'l*, pg. 3049
GRACEKENNEDY MONEY SERVICES (UK) LIMITED—See GraceKennedy Limited; *Int'l*, pg. 3049
GRACEKENNEDY (ONTARIO) INC.—See GraceKennedy Limited; *Int'l*, pg. 3049
GRACE KENNEDY PAYMENT SERVICES LIMITED—See GraceKennedy Limited; *Int'l*, pg. 3048
GRACEKENNEDY REMITTANCE SERVICES (GUYANA) LIMITED—See GraceKennedy Limited; *Int'l*, pg. 3048
GRACE, KENNEDY REMITTANCE SERVICES (GUYANA) LIMITED—See GraceKennedy Limited; *Int'l*, pg. 3048
GRACEKENNEDY REMITTANCE SERVICES LIMITED—See GraceKennedy Limited; *Int'l*, pg. 3049
GRACEKENNEDY REMITTANCE SERVICES (TRINIDAD AND TOBAGO) LTD.—See GraceKennedy Limited; *Int'l*, pg. 3049
GRACEKENNEDY TRADE FINANCE LIMITED—See GraceKennedy Limited; *Int'l*, pg. 3049
GRACEKENNEDY (TRINIDAD AND TOBAGO) LIMITED—See GraceKennedy Limited; *Int'l*, pg. 3049
GRACE, KENNEDY (U.S.A.) INC.—See GraceKennedy Limited; *Int'l*, pg. 3048
GRACEKENNEDY (USA) INC.—See GraceKennedy Limited; *Int'l*, pg. 3049
GRACELAND CEMETERY DEVELOPMENT CO.—See Service Corporation International; *U.S. Public*, pg. 1869
GRACELAND COLLEGE CENTER FOR PROFESSIONAL DEVELOPMENT AND LIFELONG LEARNING, INC.; *U.S. Private*, pg. 1749
GRACELAND FRUIT INC.; *U.S. Private*, pg. 1749
GRACELAND SENIOR LIVING, INC.—See The Ensign Group, Inc.; *U.S. Public*, pg. 2071
GRACELAWN MEMORIAL PARK, INC—See Service Corporation International; *U.S. Public*, pg. 1869
GRACE LIFE-TECH HOLDINGS LIMITED; *Int'l*, pg. 3048
THE GRACE LIMITED—See Citizen Watch Co., Ltd.; *Int'l*, pg. 1625
GRACE LIMOUSINE, LLC; *U.S. Private*, pg. 1749
GRACELL BIOTECHNOLOGIES INC.—See AstraZeneca PLC; *Int'l*, pg. 661
GRACE LUTHERAN FOUNDATION; *U.S. Private*, pg. 1749
GRACE MANAGEMENT GROUP, LLC; *U.S. Private*, pg. 1749
GRACE MEDICAL HOME, INC.; *U.S. Private*, pg. 1749
GRACE NETHERLANDS B.V.—See Standard Industries Holdings Inc.; *U.S. Private*, pg. 3780
GRACE (NEW ZEALAND) LIMITED—See Standard Industries Holdings Inc.; *U.S. Private*, pg. 3779
GRACENOTE GMBH—See Brookfield Corporation; *Int'l*, pg. 1178
GRACENOTE GMBH—See Elliott Management Corporation; *U.S. Private*, pg. 1370
GRACENOTE, INC.—See Brookfield Corporation; *Int'l*, pg. 1178
GRACENOTE, INC.—See Elliott Management Corporation; *U.S. Private*, pg. 1370
GRACENOTE KK—See Brookfield Corporation; *Int'l*, pg. 1178
GRACENOTE KK—See Elliott Management Corporation; *U.S. Private*, pg. 1370

GRACENOTE KOREA LTD.—See Brookfield Corporation; *Int'l*, pg. 1178
GRACENOTE KOREA LTD.—See Elliott Management Corporation; *U.S. Private*, pg. 1371
GRACE PACIFIC LLC—See Nan, Inc.; *U.S. Private*, pg. 2832
GRACE PAR CORPORATION—See Standard Industries Holdings Inc.; *U.S. Private*, pg. 3780
GRACE PRODUCTIONS LLC—See National Amusements, Inc.; *U.S. Private*, pg. 2843
GRACE PRODUCTS (SINGAPORE) PRIVATE LIMITED—See Standard Industries Holdings Inc.; *U.S. Private*, pg. 3780
GRACE SILICA GMBH—See Standard Industries Holdings Inc.; *U.S. Private*, pg. 3780
GRACE SP. Z O.O.—See Standard Industries Holdings Inc.; *U.S. Private*, pg. 3780
GRACE TECHNOLOGY, INC.; *Int'l*, pg. 3048
GRACE TRADING (SHANGHAI) CO., LTD.—See Standard Industries Holdings Inc.; *U.S. Private*, pg. 3780
GRACE WINE HOLDINGS LTD.; *Int'l*, pg. 3048
GRACE YEAR ENTERPRISES LIMITED—See Wong's Kong King International (Holdings) Limited; *Int'l*, pg. 8447
GRACIANO CORPORATION; *U.S. Private*, pg. 1749
GRACIE SQUARE HOSPITAL; *U.S. Private*, pg. 1749
GRACO AUSTRALIA PTY LTD—See Graco, Inc.; *U.S. Public*, pg. 953
GRACO AUTOMOTIVE TECHNOLOGY CENTER—See Graco, Inc.; *U.S. Public*, pg. 953
GRACO BVBA—See Graco, Inc.; *U.S. Public*, pg. 953
GRACO CHILDREN'S PRODUCTS, INC.—See Newell Brands Inc.; *U.S. Public*, pg. 1514
GRACO DISTRIBUTION BVBA—See Graco, Inc.; *U.S. Public*, pg. 953
GRACO FLUID EQUIPMENT (SUZHOU) CO., LTD.—See Graco, Inc.; *U.S. Public*, pg. 953
GRACO HIGH PRESSURE EQUIPMENT INC.—See Graco, Inc.; *U.S. Public*, pg. 953
GRACO, INC.; *U.S. Public*, pg. 952
GRACO INDIA PRIVATE LIMITED—See Graco, Inc.; *U.S. Public*, pg. 953
GRACO KK—See Graco, Inc.; *U.S. Public*, pg. 953
GRACO KOREA, INC.—See Graco, Inc.; *U.S. Public*, pg. 953
GRACO MANUFACTURING CO. INC.—See Alfred Karcher GmbH & Co. KG; *Int'l*, pg. 316
GRACO MINNESOTA INC.—See Graco, Inc.; *U.S. Public*, pg. 953
GRACOM MASONRY—See Graham Group Ltd.; *Int'l*, pg. 3051
GRACON CORPORATION; *U.S. Private*, pg. 1749
GRACO N.V.—See Graco, Inc.; *U.S. Public*, pg. 953
GRACO OHIO INC.—See Graco, Inc.; *U.S. Public*, pg. 953
GRACO SHANGHAI OFFICE—See Graco, Inc.; *U.S. Public*, pg. 953
GRACO SOUTH DAKOTA INC.—See Graco, Inc.; *U.S. Public*, pg. 953
GRACO SUPPLY COMPANY—See Carl Marks & Co., Inc.; *U.S. Private*, pg. 762
GRACO UK & IRELAND—See Newell Brands Inc.; *U.S. Public*, pg. 1514
GRADAC FAVRO A.D.; *Int'l*, pg. 3049
GRADALL INDUSTRIES, INC.—See Alamo Group Inc.; *U.S. Public*, pg. 71
GRADBENI REMONT D.O.O.—See MHP SE; *Int'l*, pg. 4873
GRADBENO PO DJETJE IN KAMNOLOM GRASTO D.O.O.—See STRABAG SE; *Int'l*, pg. 7230
GRADCO HOLDINGS, LLC; *U.S. Private*, pg. 1749
GRADCO (JAPAN), LTD.—See Gradco Holdings, LLC; *U.S. Private*, pg. 1749
GRADCO (USA), INC.—See Gradco Holdings, LLC; *U.S. Private*, pg. 1749
GRADE A MARKET INC.; *U.S. Private*, pg. 1749
GRADE EIGHT CORP; *U.S. Private*, pg. 1750
GRADEVINAR A.D.; *Int'l*, pg. 3049
GRADEVINAR A.D.; *Int'l*, pg. 3049
GRADEVINSKO PREDUZECE PORR D.O.O.—See PORR AG; *Int'l*, pg. 5923
GRADEX INC.; *U.S. Private*, pg. 1750
GRADEZEN INSTITUT MAKEDONIJA; *Int'l*, pg. 3049
GRADIANT CORPORATION—See Gradiant Corporation; *Int'l*, pg. 3049
GRADIANT CORPORATION; *Int'l*, pg. 3049
GRADIENT.SYSTEMINTEGRATION GMBH—See IQVIA Holdings Inc.; *U.S. Public*, pg. 1171
GRADINA A.D.; *Int'l*, pg. 3049
GRADIP A.D. PRNJAVOR; *Int'l*, pg. 3049
GRADIR MONTENEGRO D.O.O. NIKSIC—See Stalprodukt S.A.; *Int'l*, pg. 7164
GRADIS IPGI, INDUSTRIJSKO PODJETJE GRADBENIH IZDELKOV, D.D.—See Zavarovalnica Triglav, d.d.; *Int'l*, pg. 8626
GRADISKA TRZNICA A.D.; *Int'l*, pg. 3049
GRADITELJ A.D.; *Int'l*, pg. 3049
GRADITELJSKO DIONICKO DRUSTVO VIADUKT; *Int'l*, pg. 3049
GRADNJA A.D.; *Int'l*, pg. 3050

GRADNJA GP A.D.; *Int'l*, pg. 3050
GRADSKA CISTOCA A.D.; *Int'l*, pg. 3050
GRADSKA LJEKARNA ZAGREB D.O.O.—See Zagrebacki holding d.o.o.; *Int'l*, pg. 8620
GRADSKA PLINARA BJELOVAR D.O.O.—See Zagrebacki holding d.o.o.; *Int'l*, pg. 8620
GRADSKA PLINARA ZAGREB D.O.O.—See Zagrebacki holding d.o.o.; *Int'l*, pg. 8620
GRADSKA PLINARA ZAGREB OPSKRBA D.O.O.—See Zagrebacki holding d.o.o.; *Int'l*, pg. 8620
GRADSKI TRGOVSKI CENTAR AD; *Int'l*, pg. 3050
GRADSKO STAMBENO KOMUNALNO GOSPODARSTVO D.O.O.—See Zagrebacki holding d.o.o.; *Int'l*, pg. 8620
GRADUATE PLASTICS, INC.; *U.S. Private*, pg. 1750
GRADUS AD-STARA ZAGORA; *Int'l*, pg. 3050
GRADY BRITTON, INC.; *U.S. Private*, pg. 1750
GRADY BROTHER'S, INC.; *U.S. Private*, pg. 1750
GRADY CRAWFORD CONSTRUCTION CO., INC. OF BATON ROUGE; *U.S. Private*, pg. 1750
GRADY CRAWFORD CONSTRUCTION CO.—See Grady Crawford Construction Co., Inc. of Baton Rouge; *U.S. Private*, pg. 1750
GRADY ELECTRIC MEMBERSHIP CORPORATION; *U.S. Private*, pg. 1750
GRADY-WHITE BOATS, INC.; *U.S. Private*, pg. 1750
GRAEBEL COMPANIES, INC.; *U.S. Private*, pg. 1750
GRAEBEL DENVER MOVERS, INC.; *U.S. Private*, pg. 1750
GRAEBENER PRESS SYSTEMS INC.—See ANDRITZ AG; *Int'l*, pg. 456
GRAE-CON CONSTRUCTION, INC.; *U.S. Private*, pg. 1750
GRAEF-USA, INC.; *U.S. Private*, pg. 1750
GRAETER'S, INC.; *U.S. Private*, pg. 1750
GRAETHEIDE BV—See Koninklijke DSM N.V.; *Int'l*, pg. 4264
GRAF AIR FREIGHT INCORPORATION; *U.S. Private*, pg. 1750
GRAFALCO EDICIONES S.L.—See Navneet Education Ltd; *Int'l*, pg. 5177
GRAF CARDSERVICES FAR EAST LTD.—See Rieter Holding Ltd.; *Int'l*, pg. 6338
GRAF + CIE AG—See Rieter Holding Ltd.; *Int'l*, pg. 6338
GRAFCO INDUSTRIES LIMITED PARTNERSHIP—See Berry Global Group, Inc; *U.S. Public*, pg. 321
GRAF CREAMERY INC.; *U.S. Private*, pg. 1750
GRAFENTAL GMBH & CO. KG—See ADLER Group SA; *Int'l*, pg. 150
GRAFF CAPITAL MANAGEMENT AG—See Basellandschaftliche Kantonalbank; *Int'l*, pg. 871
GRAFF CHEVROLET COMPANY; *U.S. Private*, pg. 1750
GRAFF DIAMONDS HONG KONG LIMITED—See Graff Diamonds International Ltd.; *Int'l*, pg. 3050
GRAFF DIAMONDS INTERNATIONAL LTD.; *Int'l*, pg. 3050
GRAFF DIAMONDS (NEW YORK) INC.—See Graff Diamonds International Ltd.; *Int'l*, pg. 3050
GRAFFITI BBDO SOFIA—See Omnicom Group Inc.; *U.S. Public*, pg. 1575
GRAFFITI BBDO—See Omnicom Group Inc.; *U.S. Public*, pg. 1575
GRAFFITI ENTERTAINMENT, INC.—See Azure Holding Group Corp.; *U.S. Private*, pg. 416
GRAFFITI FOODS, LTD.—See New Horizons Baking Company; *U.S. Private*, pg. 2897
GRAFFMANS INC.; *U.S. Private*, pg. 1750
GRAFF MOTOR SALES INC.; *U.S. Private*, pg. 1750
GRAFFO PARANAENSE DE EMBALAGENS, S.A.—See Sonoco Products Company; *U.S. Public*, pg. 1904
GRAF FRANCE SARL—See Rieter Holding Ltd.; *Int'l*, pg. 6338
GRAFF—See Meridian International Group, Inc.; *U.S. Private*, pg. 2673
GRAFF—See Hiolle Industries S.A.; *Int'l*, pg. 3401
GRAFF TRUCK CENTERS INC.; *U.S. Private*, pg. 1750
GRAF HOLLAND B.V.—See Rieter Holding Ltd.; *Int'l*, pg. 6338
GRAFICA EDITORA AQUARELA S.A.—See Cimpress plc; *Int'l*, pg. 1609
GRAFICAGROUP; *U.S. Private*, pg. 1750
GRAFICAINTER.ACTIVE, LTD.; *U.S. Private*, pg. 1750
GRAFICARBO S.R.L.—See Morgan Advanced Materials plc; *Int'l*, pg. 5041
GRAFICAS INTEGRADAS S.A.—See Dedalo Grupo Grafico, S.L.; *Int'l*, pg. 2002
GRAFIK MARKETING COMMUNICATIONS LTD.; *U.S. Private*, pg. 1750
GRAFIKPHARM, INC.—See Reese, Tomases & Ellick, Inc. (RT&E); *U.S. Private*, pg. 3383
GRAFILME - SOCIEDADE IMPRESSORA DE LEGENDAS, LDA.—See NOS SGPS, S.A.; *Int'l*, pg. 5448
GRAFINTEC OY—See Beowulf Mining plc; *Int'l*, pg. 978
GRAFIX GMBH—See Dr. Honle AG; *Int'l*, pg. 2192
GRAF-KRATZEN GMBH—See Rieter Holding Ltd.; *Int'l*, pg. 6338
GRAF MAQUINAS TEXTEIS IND. E COM. LTDA.—See Rieter Holding Ltd.; *Int'l*, pg. 6338
GRAF METALLIC OF AMERICA INC.—See Rieter Holding Ltd.; *Int'l*, pg. 6338

GRAFOID, INC.; *Int'l*, pg. 3050
GRAFOPROJEKT A.D.; *Int'l*, pg. 3050
GRAFOPROMET A.D.; *Int'l*, pg. 3050
GRAFO WIREMARKERS PTY. LTD.—See Brady Corporation; *U.S. Public*, pg. 379
GRAFTECH BRASIL PARTICIPACOES LTDA.—See Brookfield Corporation; *Int'l*, pg. 1187
GRAFTECH FRANCE S.N.C.—See Brookfield Corporation; *Int'l*, pg. 1187
GRAFTECH GERMANY GMBH—See Brookfield Corporation; *Int'l*, pg. 1187
GRAFTECH HONG KONG LIMITED—See Brookfield Corporation; *Int'l*, pg. 1187
GRAFTECH IBERICA S.L.—See Brookfield Corporation; *Int'l*, pg. 1187
GRAFTECH INTERNATIONAL LTD.—See Brookfield Corporation; *Int'l*, pg. 1187
GRAFTECH RUS LLC—See Brookfield Corporation; *Int'l*, pg. 1187
GRAFTECH SOUTH AFRICA (PTY) LTD.—See Brookfield Corporation; *Int'l*, pg. 1187
GRAFTECH S.P.A.—See Brookfield Corporation; *Int'l*, pg. 1187
GRAFTECH SWITZERLAND S.A.—See Brookfield Corporation; *Int'l*, pg. 1187
GRAFTECH UK LIMITED—See Brookfield Corporation; *Int'l*, pg. 1187
GRAFTECH USA LLC—See Brookfield Corporation; *Int'l*, pg. 1187
GRAFTON CAPITAL LIMITED; *Int'l*, pg. 3050
GRAFTON CITY HOSPITAL; *U.S. Private*, pg. 1751
GRAFTON FRASER, INC.; *Int'l*, pg. 3050
GRAFTON GROUP PLC; *Int'l*, pg. 3050
GRAFTON MERCHANTING GB LIMITED - BUILDBASE SUPPORT CENTRE DIVISION—See Grafton Group plc; *Int'l*, pg. 3050
GRAFTON MERCHANTING GB LIMITED - CIVILS & LINTELS DIVISION—See Grafton Group plc; *Int'l*, pg. 3051
GRAFTON MERCHANTING GB LIMITED—See Grafton Group plc; *Int'l*, pg. 3050
GRAFTON MERCHANTING ROI LIMITED—See Grafton Group plc; *Int'l*, pg. 3051
GRAFTON READY MIX CONCRETE—See Consumer Acquisitions, Inc.; *U.S. Private*, pg. 1025
GRAFT POLYMER (UK) PLC; *Int'l*, pg. 3050
GRAFT SALES AND SERVICE INC.; *U.S. Private*, pg. 1751
GRAGG ADVERTISING; *U.S. Private*, pg. 1751
GRAHAM ADVERTISING; *U.S. Private*, pg. 1751
GRAHAM ARCHITECTURAL PRODUCTS CORPORATION—See The Graham Group, Inc.; *U.S. Private*, pg. 4036
GRAHAM AUTOMALL; *U.S. Private*, pg. 1751
GRAHAM AUTOMOTIVE LLC—See Graham Holdings Company; *U.S. Public*, pg. 954
GRAHAM BROS. CONSTRUCTION LIMITED; *Int'l*, pg. 3051
GRAHAM CAPITAL GROUP, LLC; *U.S. Private*, pg. 1751
THE GRAHAM COMPANIES INC.; *U.S. Private*, pg. 4035
GRAHAM & COMPANY LIMITED—See Suncorp Group Limited; *Int'l*, pg. 7311
GRAHAM CONSTRUCTION CORP.—See The Graham Group, Inc.; *U.S. Private*, pg. 4036
GRAHAM CONSTRUCTION & MANAGEMENT, INC.—See Graham Group Ltd.; *Int'l*, pg. 3051
GRAHAM CONSTRUCTION - OMAHA—See Graham Group Ltd.; *Int'l*, pg. 3051
GRAHAM CONSTRUCTION SERVICES, INC.—See Graham Group Ltd.; *Int'l*, pg. 3051
GRAHAM CONTRACTING LTD.—See Graham Group Ltd.; *Int'l*, pg. 3051
GRAHAM CORNES MOTORS PTY. LTD.—See Eagers Automotive Limited; *Int'l*, pg. 2263
GRAHAM CORPORATION; *U.S. Public*, pg. 954
GRAHAM COUNTY ELECTRIC COOPERATIVE, INC.; *U.S. Private*, pg. 1751
GRAHAM C-STORES COMPANY; *U.S. Private*, pg. 1751
GRAHAM ENGINEERING CORPORATION—See The Graham Group, Inc.; *U.S. Private*, pg. 4036
GRAHAM ENTERPRISE INC.; *U.S. Private*, pg. 1751
THE GRAHAM GROUP, INC.; *U.S. Private*, pg. 4036
THE GRAHAM GROUP, INC.; *U.S. Private*, pg. 4036
GRAHAM GROUP LTD. - DELTA—See Graham Group Ltd.; *Int'l*, pg. 3051
GRAHAM GROUP LTD. - EDMONTON—See Graham Group Ltd.; *Int'l*, pg. 3051
GRAHAM GROUP LTD. - KELOWNA—See Graham Group Ltd.; *Int'l*, pg. 3051
GRAHAM GROUP LTD. - MISSISSAUGA—See Graham Group Ltd.; *Int'l*, pg. 3051
GRAHAM GROUP LTD. - REGINA—See Graham Group Ltd.; *Int'l*, pg. 3051
GRAHAM GROUP LTD. - SASKATOON—See Graham Group Ltd.; *Int'l*, pg. 3051
GRAHAM GROUP LTD.; *Int'l*, pg. 3051
THE GRAHAM GROUP; *U.S. Private*, pg. 4035
THE GRAHAM GROUP—See The Graham Group; *U.S. Private*, pg. 4036

COMPANY NAME INDEX

GRAHAM GULF, INC.; *U.S. Private*, pg. 1751
GRAHAM HEALTHCARE CAPITAL, LLC—See Graham Holdings Company; *U.S. Public*, pg. 954
GRAHAM HEALTHCARE GROUP, INC.—See Graham Holdings Company; *U.S. Public*, pg. 954
GRAHAM HOLDINGS COMPANY; *U.S. Public*, pg. 954
THE GRAHAM LEADER—See Alden Global Capital LLC; *U.S. Private*, pg. 156
GRAHAM LUMBER COMPANY, LLC—See Baillie Lumber Co., Inc.; *U.S. Private*, pg. 426
GRAHAM MEDIA GROUP, FLORIDA, INC.—See Graham Holdings Company; *U.S. Public*, pg. 955
GRAHAM MEDIA GROUP, HOUSTON, INC.—See Graham Holdings Company; *U.S. Public*, pg. 955
GRAHAM MEDIA GROUP, INC.—See Graham Holdings Company; *U.S. Public*, pg. 954
GRAHAM MEDIA GROUP, MICHIGAN, INC.—See Graham Holdings Company; *U.S. Public*, pg. 955
GRAHAM MEDIA GROUP, ORLANDO, INC.—See Graham Holdings Company; *U.S. Public*, pg. 955
GRAHAM MEDIA GROUP, SAN ANTONIO, INC.—See Graham Holdings Company; *U.S. Public*, pg. 955
GRAHAM MEDICAL TECHNOLOGIES, L.L.C.—See ADDvise Group AB; *Int'l*, pg. 136
GRAHAM MOTORS AND CONTROLS; *U.S. Private*, pg. 1751
GRAHAM NEWSPAPERS, INC.—See Alden Global Capital LLC; *U.S. Private*, pg. 156
GRAHAM PACKAGING COMPANY BV—See Pactiv Evergreen Inc.; *U.S. Public*, pg. 1633
GRAHAM PACKAGING COMPANY INC.—See Pactiv Evergreen Inc.; *U.S. Public*, pg. 1633
GRAHAM PACKAGING COMPANY ITALIA S.R.L.—See Pactiv Evergreen Inc.; *U.S. Public*, pg. 1633
GRAHAM PACKAGING COMPANY OY—See Pactiv Evergreen Inc.; *U.S. Public*, pg. 1633
GRAHAM PACKAGING FRANCE, S.A.S.—See Pactiv Evergreen Inc.; *U.S. Public*, pg. 1633
GRAHAM PACKAGING HOLDINGS COMPANY—See Pactiv Evergreen Inc.; *U.S. Public*, pg. 1633
GRAHAM PACKAGING PLASTICS LTD.—See Pactiv Evergreen Inc.; *U.S. Public*, pg. 1633
GRAHAM PACKAGING POLAND SP. Z.O.O.—See Pactiv Evergreen Inc.; *U.S. Public*, pg. 1633
GRAHAM PARTNERS, INC.—See The Graham Group, Inc.; *U.S. Private*, pg. 4036
GRAHAM PLASTPAK PLASTIK AMBALAJ SANAYI A.S.—See Pactiv Evergreen Inc.; *U.S. Public*, pg. 1633
GRAHAM-ROGERS, INC.—See Brown & Brown, Inc.; *U.S. Public*, pg. 398
GRAHAMS FUNERAL SERVICES LIMITED—See Propel Funeral Partners Limited; *Int'l*, pg. 5997
GRAHAM VACUUM AND HEAT TRANSFER TECHNOLOGY CO., LTD.—See Graham Corporation; *U.S. Public*, pg. 954
GRAHAM WOOD DOORS—See ASSA ABLOY AB; *Int'l*, pg. 636
GRAIL INSIGHTS—See Symphony Technology Group, LLC; *U.S. Private*, pg. 3900
GRAIL PARTNERS LLC; *U.S. Private*, pg. 1751
GRAINCOM GMBH—See AGRAVIS Raiffeisen AG; *Int'l*, pg. 215
GRAINCORP LIMITED; *Int'l*, pg. 3051
GRAINCORP LIQUID FEEDS PTY LTD—See GrainCorp Limited; *Int'l*, pg. 3052
GRAINCORP MALT—See GrainCorp Limited; *Int'l*, pg. 3052
GRAINCORP OPERATIONS LIMITED—See GrainCorp Limited; *Int'l*, pg. 3052
GRA, INC.; *U.S. Private*, pg. 1748
GRAIN DEALERS MUTUAL INSURANCE COMPANY INC.—See American Family Mutual Insurance Company; *U.S. Private*, pg. 233
GRAIN D'OR—See Vision Capital, LLP; *Int'l*, pg. 8251
GRAINES VOLTZ SA; *Int'l*, pg. 3052
GRAINGER CARIBE INC.—See W.W. Grainger, Inc.; *U.S. Public*, pg. 2319
GRAINGER CHINA LLC—See W.W. Grainger, Inc.; *U.S. Public*, pg. 2320
GRAINGER DOMINICANA SRL—See W.W. Grainger, Inc.; *U.S. Public*, pg. 2319
GRAINGER GUAM L.L.C.—See W.W. Grainger, Inc.; *U.S. Public*, pg. 2320
GRAINGER HONDA; *U.S. Private*, pg. 1751
GRAINGER INDUSTRIAL MRO DE COSTA RICA, S.R.L.—See W.W. Grainger, Inc.; *U.S. Public*, pg. 2320
GRAINGER INDUSTRIAL SUPPLY INDIA PVT. LTD.—See W.W. Grainger, Inc.; *U.S. Public*, pg. 2320
GRAINGER INTERNATIONAL HOLDINGS B.V.—See W.W. Grainger, Inc.; *U.S. Public*, pg. 2320
GRAINGER INTERNATIONAL, INC.—See W.W. Grainger, Inc.; *U.S. Public*, pg. 2320
GRAINGER LIMITED—See Grainger plc; *Int'l*, pg. 3052
GRAINGER LUXEMBOURG GERMANY HOLDINGS SARL—See Grainger plc; *Int'l*, pg. 3052
GRAINGER MANAGEMENT LLC—See W.W. Grainger, Inc.; *U.S. Public*, pg. 2320
GRAINGER PANAMA S.A.—See W.W. Grainger, Inc.; *U.S. Public*, pg. 2320

GRAINGER PERU S.R.L.—See W.W. Grainger, Inc.; *U.S. Public*, pg. 2320
GRAINGER PLC; *Int'l*, pg. 3052
GRAINGER RESIDENTIAL MANAGEMENT LIMITED—See Grainger plc; *Int'l*, pg. 3052
GRAINGER S.A. DE C.V.—See W.W. Grainger, Inc.; *U.S. Public*, pg. 2320
GRAINGER SERVICE HOLDING COMPANY, INC.—See W.W. Grainger, Inc.; *U.S. Public*, pg. 2320
GRAINGER STUTTGART PORTFOLIO 1 SARL & CO KG—See Grainger plc; *Int'l*, pg. 3052
GRAINGER & WORRALL LIMITED; *Int'l*, pg. 3052
GRAINGER & WORRALL MACHINING LTD—See Grainger & Worrall Limited; *Int'l*, pg. 3052
GRAINIT S.R.L.—See Corteva, Inc.; *U.S. Public*, pg. 584
GRAINLAND COOPERATIVE - AMHERST—See Grainland Cooperative; *U.S. Private*, pg. 1752
GRAINLAND COOPERATIVE; *U.S. Private*, pg. 1752
GRAINLAND COOPERATIVE; *U.S. Private*, pg. 1752
GRAINLI GMBH & CO. KG—See BayWa AG; *Int'l*, pg. 918
GRAIN MANAGEMENT, LLC; *U.S. Private*, pg. 1751
GRAIN MILLERS, INC.; *U.S. Private*, pg. 1751
GRAIN PROCESSING CORPORATION—See Kent Corporation; *U.S. Private*, pg. 2287
GRAIN SECURITIES LIMITED—See Saudi Arabian Mining Company - Ma'aden; *Int'l*, pg. 6589
GRAINS NOIR—See The Hain Celestial Group, Inc.; *U.S. Public*, pg. 2086
GRAINVEST B.V.—See BayWa AG; *Int'l*, pg. 918
GRAITEC GMBH—See Autodesk, Inc.; *U.S. Public*, pg. 229
GRAITEC SAS—See Autodesk, Inc.; *U.S. Public*, pg. 229
GRAKON, LLC—See Methode Electronics, Inc.; *U.S. Public*, pg. 1428
GRAMAG LLC; *U.S. Private*, pg. 1752
GRA-MAG TRUCK INTERIOR SYSTEMS LLC—See Grammer AG; *Int'l*, pg. 3053
GRAM A/S—See Amica S.A.; *Int'l*, pg. 427
GRAM CAR CARRIERS A.S.A.—See Mediterranean Shipping Company, S.A.; *Int'l*, pg. 4781
GRAM COMMERCIAL A/S—See Hoshizaki Corporation; *Int'l*, pg. 3483
GRAM COMMERCIAL BV—See Hoshizaki Corporation; *Int'l*, pg. 3483
GRAM COMMERCIAL NUF—See Hoshizaki Corporation; *Int'l*, pg. 3483
GRAM COMMERCIAL—See Hoshizaki Corporation; *Int'l*, pg. 3483
GRAM DEUTSCHLAND GMBH—See Hoshizaki Corporation; *Int'l*, pg. 3483
GRAMEDICA LTD.—See ADDvise Group AB; *Int'l*, pg. 136
GRAMEENPHONE LTD.—See Telenor ASA; *Int'l*, pg. 7539
GRAM EQUIPMENT A/S—See FSN Capital Partners AS; *Int'l*, pg. 2799
GRAM EQUIPMENT OF AMERICA INC.—See FSN Capital Partners AS; *Int'l*, pg. 2799
GRAMERCY OUTPATIENT SURGERY CENTER—See HCA Healthcare, Inc.; *U.S. Public*, pg. 997
GRAMERCY PROPERTY TRUST—See Blackstone Inc.; *U.S. Public*, pg. 350
GRAMMA PUBLICIDAD—See The Interpublic Group of Companies, Inc.; *U.S. Public*, pg. 2093
GRAMMARLY, INC.; *U.S. Private*, pg. 1752
GRAMMER AD—See Grammer AG; *Int'l*, pg. 3053
GRAMMER AG; *Int'l*, pg. 3053
GRAMMER ARGENTINA S.A.—See Grammer AG; *Int'l*, pg. 3053
GRAMMER AUTOMOTIVE CZ S.R.O.—See Grammer AG; *Int'l*, pg. 3053
GRAMMER AUTOMOTIVE ESPANOLA S.A.—See Grammer AG; *Int'l*, pg. 3053
GRAMMER AUTOMOTIVE METALL GMBH—See Grammer AG; *Int'l*, pg. 3053
GRAMMER AUTOMOTIVE PUEBLA S.A. DE C.V.—See Grammer AG; *Int'l*, pg. 3053
GRAMMER AUTOMOTIVE SLOVENIJA D.O.O.—See Grammer AG; *Int'l*, pg. 3053
GRAMMER CZ S.R.O.—See Grammer AG; *Int'l*, pg. 3053
GRAMMER DO BRASIL LTDA.—See Grammer AG; *Int'l*, pg. 3053
GRAMMER ELECTRONICS N.V.—See Grammer AG; *Int'l*, pg. 3053
GRAMMER FRANCE SARL—See Grammer AG; *Int'l*, pg. 3053
GRAMMER INC.—See Grammer AG; *Int'l*, pg. 3053
GRAMMER INDUSTRIES INC.—See Stellex Capital Management LP; *U.S. Private*, pg. 3800
GRAMMER INDUSTRIES, LLC—See Grammer AG; *Int'l*, pg. 3053
GRAMMER INTERIOR (BEIJING) CO., LTD.—See Grammer AG; *Int'l*, pg. 3053
GRAMMER INTERIOR (CHANGCHUN) CO., LTD.—See Grammer AG; *Int'l*, pg. 3053
GRAMMER INTERIOR COMPONENTS GMBH—See Grammer AG; *Int'l*, pg. 3053
GRAMMER INTERIOR (SHANGHAI) CO. LTD.—See Grammer AG; *Int'l*, pg. 3053
GRAMMER INTERIOR (TIANJIN) CO. LTD.—See Grammer AG; *Int'l*, pg. 3053

GRAND CAPITAL FOR FINANCIAL INVESTMENTS

GRAMMER JAPAN LTD.—See Grammer AG; *Int'l*, pg. 3053
GRAMMER KOLTUK SISTEMLERI SANAYI VE TICARET A.S.—See Grammer AG; *Int'l*, pg. 3053
GRAMMER MEXICANA S.A. DE C.V.—See Grammer AG; *Int'l*, pg. 3053
GRAMMER SEATING (JIANGSU) CO., LTD.—See Grammer AG; *Int'l*, pg. 3053
GRAMMER SEATING (SHAANXI) CO., LTD.—See Grammer AG; *Int'l*, pg. 3053
GRAMMER SEATING SYSTEMS LTD.—See Grammer AG; *Int'l*, pg. 3053
GRAMMER SYSTEM D.O.O.—See Grammer AG; *Int'l*, pg. 3053
GRAMMER TECHNICAL COMPONENTS GMBH—See Grammer AG; *Int'l*, pg. 3053
GRAMMER WACKERSDORF GMBH—See Grammer AG; *Int'l*, pg. 3053
GRAMON BAGO DE URUGUAY S.A.—See Bago Group; *Int'l*, pg. 799
GRAMPET SA; *Int'l*, pg. 3053
GRAMPIAN INTERNATIONAL FREIGHT B.V.—See DSV A/S; *Int'l*, pg. 2214
GRAM (UK) LTD.—See Hoshizaki Corporation; *Int'l*, pg. 3483
GRANADA GOLD MINE INC.; *Int'l*, pg. 3053
GRANADA INVESTMENT GMBH I.L.—See Commerzbank AG; *Int'l*, pg. 1718
GRANADILLA COUNTRY CLUB S.A.; *Int'l*, pg. 3054
GRANARD PHARMACEUTICAL—See Indukern, S.A.; *Int'l*, pg. 3661
GRANARIA HOLDINGS B.V.; *Int'l*, pg. 3054
GRANATH HAVAS WORLDWIDE—See Vivendi SE; *Int'l*, pg. 8268
GRANATHS HARDMETAL AS—See Investment AB Latour; *Int'l*, pg. 3782
GRANAT SA; *Int'l*, pg. 3054
GRANA Y ASOCIADOS CORREDORES DE SEGUROS SA—See Aon plc; *Int'l*, pg. 494
GRANBIO INVESTIMENTOS SA—See GranInvestimentos SA; *Int'l*, pg. 3059
GRANBURY HOSPITAL CORPORATION—See Community Health Systems, Inc.; *U.S. Public*, pg. 553
GRAN CIRCULO DE MADRID, S.A.—See Minor International PCL; *Int'l*, pg. 4911
GRAN COLOMBIA GOLD CORP.; *Int'l*, pg. 3053
GRAND AIRE EXPRESS INC.; *U.S. Private*, pg. 1752
GRANDALL SOLUTIONS INC.; *Int'l*, pg. 3057
GRAND AMERICA HOTELS & RESORTS—See HF Sinclair Corporation; *U.S. Public*, pg. 1034
GRAND AUTOS 2005 PTY LTD—See Eagers Automotive Limited; *Int'l*, pg. 2263
GRAND BAHAMA POWER COMPANY LIMITED—See Emera, Inc.; *Int'l*, pg. 2377
GRAND BAHAMA SHIP YARD LIMITED—See Carnival Corporation; *U.S. Public*, pg. 438
GRAND BANCORP, INC.; *U.S. Private*, pg. 1752
GRAND BANK CORPORATION; *U.S. Public*, pg. 956
GRAND BANKS YACHTS AUSTRALIA PTY LTD—See Grand Banks Yachts Limited; *Int'l*, pg. 3054
GRAND BANKS YACHTS LIMITED; *Int'l*, pg. 3054
GRAND BANKS YACHTS, LTD.—See Grand Banks Yachts Limited; *Int'l*, pg. 3054
GRAND BANKS YACHTS SDN. BHD.—See Grand Banks Yachts Limited; *Int'l*, pg. 3054
GRAND BAOXIN AUTO GROUP LIMITED—See Xinjiang Guanghui Industry Investment Group Co., Ltd.; *Int'l*, pg. 8531
GRAND BASKET, INC—See Z Capital Group, LLC; *U.S. Private*, pg. 4595
GRAND BAZAAR LTD.—See ANSA McAL Limited; *Int'l*, pg. 477
GRAND & BENEDICTS INC.; *U.S. Private*, pg. 1752
GRAND BLANC CEMENT PRODUCTS; *U.S. Private*, pg. 1752
GRAND BLANC PROCESSING, LLC—See Kobe Steel, Ltd.; *Int'l*, pg. 4217
GRANDBLUE ENVIRONMENT CO., LTD.; *Int'l*, pg. 3057
GRAND BRANDS (M) SDN. BHD.—See Hai-O Enterprise Berhad; *Int'l*, pg. 3209
GRAND BRETAGNE LTD.—See LAMPSA HELLENIC HOTELS S.A.; *Int'l*, pg. 4402
GRANDBRIDGE LIMITED; *Int'l*, pg. 3057
GRANDBRIDGE REAL ESTATE CAPITAL LLC—See Truist Financial Corporation; *U.S. Public*, pg. 2200
GRAND BRILLIANCE GROUP HOLDINGS LTD.; *Int'l*, pg. 3054
GRAND BUICK GMC KIA; *U.S. Private*, pg. 1752
GRAND BUICK, INC.; *U.S. Private*, pg. 1752
GRAND CANAL LAND PUBLIC COMPANY LIMITED—See Central Pattana Public Company Limited; *Int'l*, pg. 1409
GRAND CANYON EDUCATION, INC.; *U.S. Public*, pg. 956
GRAND CANYON RAILWAY INC.; *U.S. Private*, pg. 1752
GRAND CANYON UNIVERSITY—See Grand Canyon Education, Inc.; *U.S. Public*, pg. 957
GRAND CAPITAL FOR FINANCIAL INVESTMENTS; *Int'l*, pg. 3054

GRAND CAPITAL FOR FINANCIAL INVESTMENTS

CORPORATE AFFILIATIONS

GRAND CARPET INDUSTRIES SDN. BHD.—See SMIS Corporation Berhad; *Int'l*, pg. 7007

GRAND CASINOS OF BILOXI, LLC—See Caesars Entertainment, Inc.; *U.S. Public*, pg. 419

GRAND CATHAY SECURITIES CORPORATION—See KGI Financial Holding Co., Ltd.; *Int'l*, pg. 4150

GRAND CENTAR D.O.O—See Immofinanz AG; *Int'l*, pg. 3628

GRAND CENTRAL BAKERY; *U.S. Private*, pg. 1752

GRAND CENTRAL DISTRICT MANAGEMENT ASSOCIATION, INC.; *U.S. Private*, pg. 1752

GRAND CENTRAL ENTERPRISES BHD.; *Int'l*, pg. 3054

GRAND CENTRAL ENTERPRISES (SARAWAK) SDN. BHD.—See Grand Central Enterprises Bhd.; *Int'l*, pg. 3054

GRAND CENTRAL GLASGOW HOTEL OPCO LIMITED—See InterContinental Hotels Group PLC; *Int'l*, pg. 3736

GRAND CENTRAL (K.L.) SDN. BHD.—See Grand Central Enterprises Bhd.; *Int'l*, pg. 3054

GRAND CENTRAL RAILWAY COMPANY LIMITED—See Deutsche Bahn AG; *Int'l*, pg. 2051

GRAND CENTRAL SANITARY LANDFILL, INC.—See Waste Management, Inc.; *U.S. Public*, pg. 2331

GRAND CENTRAL TRANS-SERVICES SDN. BHD.—See Grand Central Enterprises Bhd.; *Int'l*, pg. 3054

GRANDCENTRIX GMBH—See Vodafone Group Plc; *Int'l*, pg. 8284

GRAND CHINA INDUSTRIAL LIMITED—See Legend Strategy International Holdings Group; *Int'l*, pg. 4444

GRAND CHINA PROJECT LOGISTICS CO., LTD—See Hainan Traffic Administration Holding Co., Ltd.; *Int'l*, pg. 3213

GRAND CIRCLE CORPORATION; *U.S. Private*, pg. 1752

GRAND CITY PROPERTIES SA; *Int'l*, pg. 3054

GRAND CONSTRUCTION LTD.; *Int'l*, pg. 3054

GRANDCORP INC—See Grandparents.com, Inc.; *U.S. Private*, pg. 1754

GRAND CRU SELECT WEINHANDELSGESELLSCHAFT MBH—See Hawesko Holding AG; *Int'l*, pg. 3288

GRAND DEPARTMENT STORE CO., LTD.; *Int'l*, pg. 3054

GRAND DESIGN RV, LLC—See Winnebago Industries, Inc.; *U.S. Public*, pg. 2374

GRANDE ASSET HOTELS & PROPERTY PUBLIC COMPANY LIMITED; *Int'l*, pg. 3057

GRANDE CACHE COAL CORPORATION—See CST Canada Coal Limited; *Int'l*, pg. 1868

GRANDE CHEESE COMPANY INC.; *U.S. Private*, pg. 1753

GRANDE CHEESE COMPANY LIMITED; *Int'l*, pg. 3057

GRANDE CHEESE COMPANY; *U.S. Private*, pg. 1753

GRANDE COMMUNICATIONS NETWORKS LLC—See Stonepeak Partners L.P.; *U.S. Private*, pg. 3829

GRANDECO WALLFASHION GROUP - BELGIUM NV—See Down2Earth Capital NV; *Int'l*, pg. 2185

GRANDE DIXENCE SA—See Alpiq Holding AG; *Int'l*, pg. 373

GRANDE DUNES SURGERY CENTER—See HCA Healthcare, Inc.; *U.S. Public*, pg. 997

GRANDEE BIOTECHNOLOGIES SDN. BHD.—See New Japan Chemical Co., Ltd.; *Int'l*, pg. 5225

GRAND EFFECTS, INC.—See The Carlyle Group Inc.; *U.S. Public*, pg. 2057

GRANDE FOODS CALIFORNIA CORPORATION; *U.S. Private*, pg. 1753

GRANDE FORD TRUCK SALES, INC.—See Cavender Auto Group; *U.S. Private*, pg. 795

GRANDE JOLLY, S.P.A.—See Minor International PCL; *Int'l*, pg. 4911

GRANDE LEASING OY—See Wulff-Group Plc; *Int'l*, pg. 8502

GRAND ELY LODGE LLC; *U.S. Private*, pg. 1752

GRAND ELY LODGE—See Grand Ely Lodge LLC; *U.S. Private*, pg. 1752

GRAND EMPEROR ENTERTAINMENT & HOTEL (MACAU) LIMITED—See Emperor Entertainment Hotel Limited; *Int'l*, pg. 2386

GRAND ENERGY, INC.; *U.S. Private*, pg. 1752

GRAND ENTRANCE; *U.S. Private*, pg. 1752

GRANDE PORTAGE RESOURCES LTD.; *Int'l*, pg. 3057

GRANDE PRAIRIE GENERATION, INC.—See Exelon Corporation; *U.S. Public*, pg. 807

GRANDE PRAIRIE SALVAGE LTD—See A. B. C. Recycling Ltd; *Int'l*, pg. 21

GRANDE SEMOULERIE DE L'OUEST A GOND-PONTOUVRE—See Vivescia; *Int'l*, pg. 8279

GRANDESIGN ADVERTISING FIRM, INC.; *U.S. Private*, pg. 1754

GRANDES INC.; *Int'l*, pg. 3057

GRANDES LIGNES INTERNATIONAL—See SNCF; *Int'l*, pg. 7026

GRANDEUR PARK SDN. BHD.—See Hua Yang Berhad; *Int'l*, pg. 3510

GRANDEUR PRODUCTS LIMITED; *Int'l*, pg. 3057

GRAND FIELD GROUP HOLDINGS LIMITED; *Int'l*, pg. 3054

GRAND-FLO ELECTRONIC SYSTEM SDN. BHD.—See NCT Alliance Berhad; *Int'l*, pg. 5182

GRAND-FLO SPRITVEST SDN. BHD.—See Radiant Globaltech Berhad; *Int'l*, pg. 6174

GRANDFLOW, INC.—See Smart Source of Georgia, LLC; *U.S. Private*, pg. 3691

GRAND FOOD CENTER—See D&D Management Inc.; *U.S. Private*, pg. 1137

GRAND FOODS (PTY) LTD.—See Grand Parade Investments Limited; *Int'l*, pg. 3056

GRAND FORKS GAZETTE—See Black Press Group Ltd.; *Int'l*, pg. 1059

GRAND FORKS HERALD—See Forum Communications Company; *U.S. Private*, pg. 1577

GRAND FORTUNE HIGH GRADE LIMITED; *Int'l*, pg. 3054

GRAND FOUNDRY LIMITED; *Int'l*, pg. 3054

GRAND FURNITURE DISCOUNT STORES; *U.S. Private*, pg. 1752

GRAND GENEVA, LLC—See The Marcus Corporation; *U.S. Public*, pg. 2112

GRAND GENEVA RESORT & SPA—See The Marcus Corporation; *U.S. Public*, pg. 2112

GRAND-GOURMET CO., LTD.—See Ship Healthcare Holdings, Inc.; *Int'l*, pg. 6852

THE GRAND GROUP AB—See FAM AB; *Int'l*, pg. 2611

GRAND GULF ENERGY INC.—See Grand Gulf Energy Limited; *Int'l*, pg. 3054

GRAND GULF ENERGY LIMITED; *Int'l*, pg. 3054

GRAND HALL ENTERPRISE COMPANY LTD.; *Int'l*, pg. 3055

GRAND HALL EUROPE B.V—See Grand Hall Enterprise Company Ltd.; *Int'l*, pg. 3055

GRAND HARBOR MANAGEMENT, LLC—See Icahn Enterprises L.P.; *U.S. Public*, pg. 1084

GRAND HARBOUR MARINA P.L.C.; *Int'l*, pg. 3055

GRAND HAVANA INC.; *U.S. Public*, pg. 957

GRAND HAVEN BOARD OF LIGHT & POWER; *U.S. Private*, pg. 1752

THE GRAND HEALTHCARE SYSTEM; *U.S. Private*, pg. 4037

GRAND HERITAGE HOTEL GROUP, LLC; *U.S. Private*, pg. 1752

GRAND HOLIDAY VILLA KHARTOUM CO. LTD.; *Int'l*, pg. 3055

GRAND HOME DIALYSIS, LLC—See DaVita Inc.; *U.S. Public*, pg. 639

GRAND HOME LOANS, LLC—See Hilltop Holdings Inc.; *U.S. Public*, pg. 1038

GRAND HOOVER PROPERTY SDN. BHD.—See PTT Synergy Group; *Int'l*, pg. 6093

GRANDHOPE BIOTECH CO., LTD.; *Int'l*, pg. 3058

GRANDHOPE BIOTECH (SHANGHAI) CO., LTD—See Grandhope Biotech Co., Ltd.; *Int'l*, pg. 3058

GRAND HOTEL BUCHAREST SA; *Int'l*, pg. 3055

GRAND HOTEL GROUP - GRAND HOTEL COMPANY PTY LIMITED—See Tuan Sing Holdings Limited; *Int'l*, pg. 7962

GRAND HOTEL GROUP LIMITED—See Hang Lung Group Limited; *Int'l*, pg. 3245

GRAND HOTEL INTER-CONTINENTAL PARIS SNC; *Int'l*, pg. 3055

GRAND HOTEL, LLC; *U.S. Private*, pg. 1752

GRAND HOTEL - MACKINAC ISLAND—See FAM AB; *Int'l*, pg. 2611

GRAND HOTEL TOPLICE BLED D.O.O.—See Sava d.d.; *Int'l*, pg. 6595

GRAND HOTEL UNION BUSINESS D.D.—See Grand Hotel Union d.d.; *Int'l*, pg. 3055

GRAND HOTEL UNION D.D.; *Int'l*, pg. 3055

GRAND HOTEL VICTORIA-JUNGFRAU AG—See AEVIS VICTORIA SA; *Int'l*, pg. 183

GRAND HYATT BERLIN GMBH—See Hyatt Hotels Corporation; *U.S. Public*, pg. 1077

GRAND HYATT SAN ANTONIO, L.L.C.—See Hyatt Hotels Corporation; *U.S. Public*, pg. 1077

GRAND HYATT SEOUL—See Hyatt Hotels Corporation; *U.S. Public*, pg. 1077

GRAND HYATT SF, L.L.C.—See Hyatt Hotels Corporation; *U.S. Public*, pg. 1077

GRAND HYATT SINGAPORE (PTE.) LIMITED—See Hyatt Hotels Corporation; *U.S. Public*, pg. 1077

GRANDIC INC.—See Ship Healthcare Holdings, Inc.; *Int'l*, pg. 6852

GRANDIMPIANTI I.L.E. ALI SPA.—See Ali Holding S.r.l; *Int'l*, pg. 251

GRANDI NAVI VELOCI S.P.A.; *Int'l*, pg. 3058

GRAND INCENTIVES, INC.; *U.S. Private*, pg. 1753

GRAND INDUSTRIAL HOLDING CO., LTD.; *Int'l*, pg. 3055

GRAND INVESTMENT INTERNATIONAL LIMITED; *Int'l*, pg. 3055

GRANDIS, INC.—See Samsung Group; *Int'l*, pg. 6512

THE GRAND ISLAND DAILY INDEPENDENT—See Lee Enterprises, Incorporated; *U.S. Public*, pg. 1298

GRAND ISLAND EXPRESS INC.; *U.S. Private*, pg. 1753

GRAND ISLAND HOTEL (LANGKAWI) SDN. BHD.—See Grand Central Enterprises Bhd.; *Int'l*, pg. 3054

GRAND ISLE SHIPYARD INC. - FABRICATION FACILITY—See Nana Regional Corporation, Inc.; *U.S. Private*, pg. 2832

GRAND ISLE SHIPYARD INC.—See Nana Regional Corporation, Inc.; *U.S. Private*, pg. 2832

GRANDI STAZIONI S.P.A.—See Ferrovie dello Stato Italiane S.p.A.; *Int'l*, pg. 2645

GRAND ITASCA CLINIC & HOSPITAL—See Fairview Health Services; *U.S. Private*, pg. 1464

GRANDJOUAN SACO SA—See Veolia Environnement S.A.; *Int'l*, pg. 8159

GRANDJOY HOLDINGS GROUP CO., LTD.—See COFCO Limited; *Int'l*, pg. 1692

GRAND JUNCTION CONCRETE PIPE CO.—See Ferguson plc; *Int'l*, pg. 2638

GRAND JUNCTION HARLEY DAVIDSON—See Morse Operations Inc.; *U.S. Private*, pg. 2790

GRAND JUNCTION NEWSPAPERS, INC.—See Apollo Global Management, Inc.; *U.S. Public*, pg. 163

GRAND KAHN ELECTRIC, LLC; *U.S. Private*, pg. 1753

GRAND KOREA LEISURE CO.LTD; *Int'l*, pg. 3055

GRAND LAKE MENTAL HEALTH CENTER, INC.; *U.S. Private*, pg. 1753

GRANDLAND HOLDINGS GROUP CO., LTD.; *Int'l*, pg. 3058

GRAND LAUNDRY, INC.—See MGM Resorts International; *U.S. Public*, pg. 1435

GRAND LIBERTY CO., LTD.—See Eson Precision Ind. Co., Ltd.; *Int'l*, pg. 2504

GRAND LIDO NEGRIL RESORT—See Sunwing Travel Group, Inc.; *Int'l*, pg. 7331

GRANDLINK LOGISTICS CO., LTD.—See Sonic Interfreight Public Co., Ltd.; *Int'l*, pg. 7099

THE GRAND LODGE OF MARYLAND; *U.S. Private*, pg. 4037

GRAND LUX CAFE LLC—See Cheesecake Factory Incorporated; *U.S. Public*, pg. 483

GRAND MARITIME TRASPORT LTD.—See Regional Container Lines Public Company Limited; *Int'l*, pg. 6254

GRANDMA'S COUNTRY FOODS; *U.S. Private*, pg. 1754

GRANDMA'S RESTAURANT CO.; *U.S. Private*, pg. 1754

GRAND MASSIF DOMAINES SKIABLES SA—See Compagnie des Alpes S.A.; *Int'l*, pg. 1738

GRANDMATE INDUSTRIAL COMPANY LIMITED—See China Automobile New Retail (Holdings) Limited; *Int'l*, pg. 1484

GRANDMA TRADING & AGENCIES LIMITED; *Int'l*, pg. 3058

GRAND MEMORIES PUNTA CANA—See Sunwing Travel Group, Inc.; *Int'l*, pg. 7331

GRAND MEMORIES SANTA MARIA—See Sunwing Travel Group, Inc.; *Int'l*, pg. 7331

GRAND MEMORIES SPLASH—See Sunwing Travel Group, Inc.; *Int'l*, pg. 7331

GRAND MEMORIES VARADERO—See Sunwing Travel Group, Inc.; *Int'l*, pg. 7331

GRAND MERIT RETAIL GROUP LIMITED—See Macau Legend Development Limited; *Int'l*, pg. 4620

GRAND MILLS COMPANY PJSC—See Agthia Group PJSC; *Int'l*, pg. 222

GRAND MING GROUP HOLDINGS LIMITED; *Int'l*, pg. 3055

GRAND MOTORS PRESTIGE PTY LTD.; *Int'l*, pg. 3055

GRAND NAWAPLASTIC MYANMAR CO., LTD.—See The Siam Cement Public Company Limited; *Int'l*, pg. 7682

GRAND OCEAN CLASSIC COMMERCIAL GROUP CO., LTD.—See Grand Ocean Retail Group Limited; *Int'l*, pg. 3055

GRAND OCEAN DEPARTMENT STORE GROUP CO., LTD.—See Grand Ocean Retail Group Limited; *Int'l*, pg. 3055

GRAND OCEAN RESOURCES COMPANY LIMITED; *Int'l*, pg. 3055

GRAND OCEAN RETAIL GROUP LIMITED; *Int'l*, pg. 3055

THE GRANDOE CORPORATION; *U.S. Private*, pg. 4037

GRAND OLE OPRY, LLC—See Ryman Hospitality Properties, Inc.; *U.S. Public*, pg. 1829

GRANDOR CORPORATION; *U.S. Private*, pg. 1754

GRANDPA BRANDS COMPANY; *U.S. Private*, pg. 1754

GRAND PACIFIC FINANCIAL CORP.—See Chailease Holding Company Limited; *Int'l*, pg. 1437

GRAND PACIFIC FINANCING CORP.—See Chailease Holding Company Limited; *Int'l*, pg. 1437

GRAND PACIFIC PETROCHEMICAL CORPORATION; *Int'l*, pg. 3055

GRAND PACIFIC WAREHOUSE LIMITED—See Eng Kong Holdings Pte Ltd.; *Int'l*, pg. 2426

GRAND PARADE INVESTMENTS LIMITED; *Int'l*, pg. 3056

GRANDPARENTS.COM, INC.; *U.S. Private*, pg. 1754

GRANDPARENTS INSURANCE SOLUTIONS LLC—See Grandparents.com, Inc.; *U.S. Private*, pg. 1754

GRAND PARKING CENTER CO., LTD.—See Mitsubishi Estate Co., Ltd.; *Int'l*, pg. 4946

GRAND PARTNERS SECURITIES LIMITED—See Wealthy Way Group Limited; *Int'l*, pg. 8363

GRANDPA SOAP COMPANY—See Grandpa Brands Company; *U.S. Private*, pg. 1754

GRAND PEACE GROUP HOLDINGS LIMITED; *Int'l*, pg. 3056

GRAND PEAK CAPITAL CORP.; *Int'l*, pg. 3056

GRAND PEQUOT TOWER—See Mashantucket Pequot Gaming Enterprise Inc.; *U.S. Private*, pg. 2601
GRAND PHARMACEUTICAL GROUP LIMITED; *Int'l*, pg. 3056
GRAND PHARMA (CHINA) CO., LTD.—See Grand Pharmaceutical Group Limited; *Int'l*, pg. 3056
GRAND PLACE CORPORATION—See Toyota Tsusho Corporation; *Int'l*, pg. 7877
GRANDPLAINS PROPERTIES, INC—See Linde plc; *Int'l*, pg. 4505
GRAND PLASTIC TECHNOLOGY CORP.; *Int'l*, pg. 3056
GRAND PLAZA HOTEL CORPORATION; *Int'l*, pg. 3056
GRAND POWER (2019) CO., LTD.—See Asia Green Energy Public Company Limited; *Int'l*, pg. 612
GRAND POWER EXPRESS INTERNATIONAL (CHINA) LIMITED—See Grand Power Logistics Group Limited; *Int'l*, pg. 3056
GRAND POWER EXPRESS INTERNATIONAL LIMITED—See Grand Power Logistics Group Limited; *Int'l*, pg. 3056
GRAND POWER EXPRESS INTERNATIONAL (SHENZHEN) LIMITED—See Grand Power Logistics Group Limited; *Int'l*, pg. 3056
GRAND POWER EXPRESS TOURISM CO., LTD.—See ZZLL Information Technology, Inc.; *Int'l*, pg. 8701
GRAND POWER LOGISTICS GROUP LIMITED; *Int'l*, pg. 3056
GRAND PRAIRIE DIALYSIS CENTER, LLC—See Nautic Partners, LLC; *U.S. Private*, pg. 2870
GRAND PRAIRIE SERVICES; *U.S. Private*, pg. 1753
GRAND PRAIRIE TRANSIT—See Cook-Illinois Corp.; *U.S. Private*, pg. 1038
GRAND PRIX INTERNATIONAL PUBLIC COMPANY LIMITED; *Int'l*, pg. 3056
GRANDPRIX LEISURE SYSTEM CO., LTD.—See Brother Industries, Ltd.; *Int'l*, pg. 1198
GRAND PRIX PERFORMANCE OF HICKSVILLE; *U.S. Private*, pg. 1753
GRAND RAPIDS AUTO AUCTION—See Huron Capital Partners LLC; *U.S. Private*, pg. 2012
GRAND RAPIDS FOAM TECHNOLOGIES, INC.; *U.S. Private*, pg. 1753
GRAND RAPIDS GRAVEL CO.; *U.S. Private*, pg. 1753
GRAND RAPIDS GRIFFINS—See DP Fox Ventures, LLC; *U.S. Private*, pg. 1270
GRAND RAPIDS LABEL CO.; *U.S. Private*, pg. 1753
GRAND RAPIDS PRINTING INK COMPANY; *U.S. Private*, pg. 1753
GRAND RAPIDS STATE BANK—See Wilcox Bancshares, Inc.; *U.S. Private*, pg. 4518
GRAND RAPIDS SURGICAL SUITES, LLC—See Tenet Healthcare Corporation; *U.S. Public*, pg. 2002
GRAND RAPIDS SYMPHONY SOCIETY; *U.S. Private*, pg. 1753
GRAND REAL ESTATE PROJECTS CO. K.S.C.C.; *Int'l*, pg. 3056
THE GRAND REHABILITATION AND NURSING AT RIVER VALLEY—See The Grand Healthcare System; *U.S. Private*, pg. 4037
GRAND REINSURANCE (PVT) LTD—See Masawara PLC; *Int'l*, pg. 4719
GRAND RESIDENCES BY MARRIOTT—See Marriott Vacations Worldwide Corporation; *U.S. Public*, pg. 1374
GRAND RIVER COMMERCE, INC.; *U.S. Public*, pg. 957
GRAND RIVER DAM AUTHORITY; *U.S. Private*, pg. 1753
GRAND RIVER FOODS; *Int'l*, pg. 3056
GRAND RIVER GATHERING, LLC—See Summit Midstream Partners, LP; *U.S. Private*, pg. 1960
GRAND RIVER, INC.; *U.S. Private*, pg. 1753
GRAND RIVER INFRASTRUCTURE—See Premarc Corporation; *U.S. Private*, pg. 3249
GRAND RIVER MUTUAL TELEPHONE CORPORATION; *U.S. Private*, pg. 1753
GRAND RIVER NAVIGATION COMPANY, INC.—See AIP, LLC; *U.S. Private*, pg. 135
GRAND ROYAL GROUP INTERNATIONAL COMPANY LIMITED—See Thai Beverage Public Company Limited; *Int'l*, pg. 7590
GRAND SAGA SDN. BHD.—See Taliworks Corporation Berhad; *Int'l*, pg. 7447
GRAND SAVINGS BANK—See Grand Bancorp, Inc.; *U.S. Private*, pg. 1752
GRANDS ELEVAGES DE KATONGOLA—See George Forrest International S.A.; *Int'l*, pg. 2938
GRANDS GARAGES DU LIMOUSIN—See Stellantis N.V.; *Int'l*, pg. 7202
GRANDSHORES TECHNOLOGY GROUP LIMITED; *Int'l*, pg. 3058
GRAND SIAM COMPOSITES CO., LTD.—See Mitsui Chemicals, Inc.; *Int'l*, pg. 4981
GRAND SIAM COMPOSITES CO., LTD.—See The Siam Cement Public Company Limited; *Int'l*, pg. 7683
GRANDS MILLESIMES DE FRANCE, S.A.—See Suntory Holdings Limited; *Int'l*, pg. 7326
GRANDS MOULINS DE PARIS S.A.—See Vivescia; *Int'l*, pg. 8279
GRAND SOLUTIONS LLC—See LST Marketing, LLC; *U.S. Private*, pg. 2509

GRANDSOUTH BANCORPORATION—See First Bancorp; *U.S. Public*, pg. 839
GRANDSOUTH BANK—See First Bancorp; *U.S. Public*, pg. 839
GRAND SPA LIETUVA, JSC—See Koncernas Achemos Grupe; *Int'l*, pg. 4246
GRAND STAR INDUSTRY CO., LTD.—See Saha Pathanapibul Public Company Limited; *Int'l*, pg. 6479
GRAND STORES—See GIBCA Limited; *Int'l*, pg. 2962
GRAND STRAND REGIONAL MEDICAL CENTER—See HCA Healthcare, Inc.; *U.S. Public*, pg. 997
GRAND STRAND SENIOR HEALTH CENTER, LLC—See HCA Healthcare, Inc.; *U.S. Public*, pg. 997
GRAND STRAND SPECIALTY ASSOCIATES, LLC—See HCA Healthcare, Inc.; *U.S. Public*, pg. 997
GRAND STRAND SURGICAL SPECIALISTS, LLC—See HCA Healthcare, Inc.; *U.S. Public*, pg. 997
GRAND STRAND WATER & SEWER AUTHORITY; *U.S. Private*, pg. 1753
GRANDS TRAVAUX OCEAN INDIEN (GTOI) SA—See Bouygues S.A.; *Int'l*, pg. 1123
GRANDSTREAM NETWORKS, INC.; *U.S. Private*, pg. 1754
GRAND TALENTS GROUP HOLDINGS LIMITED; *Int'l*, pg. 3057
GRANDTECH C.G.SYSTEM, INC.; *Int'l*, pg. 3058
GRAND TECH PRECISION MANUFACTURING (THAILAND) CORPORATION LIMITED—See Mayer Steel Pipe Corporation; *Int'l*, pg. 4744
GRAND-TEK TECHNOLOGY CO., LTD.; *Int'l*, pg. 3057
GRAND TERRACE APARTMENTS CALIFORNIA, LLC—See RAIT Financial Trust; *U.S. Private*, pg. 3348
GRAND TETON LODGE COMPANY, INC.—See Vail Resorts, Inc.; *U.S. Public*, pg. 2271
GRAND T G GOLD HOLDINGS LIMITED; *Int'l*, pg. 3057
GRAND TORONTO VENTURE, L.P.—See Hyatt Hotels Corporation; *U.S. Public*, pg. 1077
GRAND & TOY LIMITED—See The ODP Corporation; *U.S. Public*, pg. 2117
GRAND TRANSFORMERS INC.—See Blackford Capital LLC; *U.S. Private*, pg. 574
GRAND TRAVERSE MALL, LLC—See Brookfield Corporation; *Int'l*, pg. 1185
GRAND TREASURERS LIMITED—See Consolidated Hallmark Insurance Plc.; *Int'l*, pg. 1770
GRAND UNITY DEVELOPMENT COMPANY LIMITED—See Univentures Public Company Limited; *Int'l*, pg. 8077
GRAND VACATIONS SERVICES LLC—See Hilton Grand Vacations Inc.; *U.S. Public*, pg. 1040
GRAND VALLEY FORTIFIERS LIMITED; *Int'l*, pg. 3057
GRAND VENTURE TECHNOLOGY LIMITED; *Int'l*, pg. 3057
GRAND VENTURE TECHNOLOGY SDN. BHD.—See Grand Venture Technology Limited; *Int'l*, pg. 3057
GRAND VENTURE TECHNOLOGY (SUZHOU) CO., LTD.—See Grand Venture Technology Limited; *Int'l*, pg. 3057
GRANDVIEW HEALTH CARE CLINIC, LLC—See HCA Healthcare, Inc.; *U.S. Public*, pg. 997
GRAND VIEW HOTEL LIMITED—See Magnificent Hotel Investments Limited; *Int'l*, pg. 4641
GRANDVIEW HOTEL MACAU—See Kingston Financial Group Limited; *Int'l*, pg. 4179
GRAND VIEW MEDIA GROUP—See EBSCO Industries, Inc.; *U.S. Private*, pg. 1325
GRANDVIEW PHARMACY, LLC—See CVS Health Corporation; *U.S. Public*, pg. 616
GRANDVIEW PRODUCTS CO.; *U.S. Private*, pg. 1754
GRANDVIEW SURGERY CENTER, LTD.—See United Health Group Incorporated; *U.S. Public*, pg. 2250
GRAND VILLA PHX, INC.—See The Ensign Group, Inc.; *U.S. Public*, pg. 2071
GRANDVILLE EQUITIES CORP.; *Int'l*, pg. 3058
GRANDVILLE PRINTING COMPANY; *U.S. Private*, pg. 1754
GRAND VINCO CAPITAL LIMITED—See Zijing International Financial Holdings Limited; *Int'l*, pg. 8683
GRAND VIN LTD.; *U.S. Private*, pg. 1753
GRANDVISION B.V.—See Vision Group s.p.a.; *Int'l*, pg. 8252
GRAND VISION GAMING LLC—See Century Gaming Technologies; *U.S. Private*, pg. 833
GRAND VISION MEDIA HOLDINGS PLC; *Int'l*, pg. 3057
GRAND WIRELESS INC.; *U.S. Private*, pg. 1753
GRAND WORLDWIDE LOGISTICS CORP.—See The Jordan Company, L.P.; *U.S. Private*, pg. 4060
GRANDY AG—See Vicat S.A.; *Int'l*, pg. 8185
GRANDY ENVIRONMENTAL (H.K.) LIMITED—See Good Fellow Healthcare Holdings Limited; *Int'l*, pg. 3038
GRANDY HOUSE CORPORATION; *Int'l*, pg. 3058
GRANDY REFORM CO., LTD.—See Grandy House Corporation; *Int'l*, pg. 3058
GRANDY'S—See Sentinel Capital Partners, L.L.C.; *U.S. Private*, pg. 3609
GRANEFORS BRUK AB—See Outokumpu Oyj; *Int'l*, pg. 5667
GRANEL SA—See Firmenich International SA; *Int'l*, pg. 2681

GRANE TRANSPORTATION LINES; *U.S. Private*, pg. 1754
GRANEXPORT AD; *Int'l*, pg. 3058
GRANFORD MANUFACTURING, INC.—See The Goodyear Tire & Rubber Company; *U.S. Public*, pg. 2084
GRANGE CAPITAL PTY LTD—See Grange Resources Limited; *Int'l*, pg. 3058
THE GRANGE CARE HOME PERTH—See Balhousie Holdings Limited; *Int'l*, pg. 808
GRANGE COOPERATIVE SUPPLY ASSOCIATION; *U.S. Private*, pg. 1754
GRANGE FURNITURE INC.—See The Middleby Corporation; *U.S. Public*, pg. 2114
GRANGE INDEMNITY INSURANCE COMPANY—See Grange Mutual Casualty Company; *U.S. Private*, pg. 1754
GRANGE LIFE INSURANCE COMPANY—See Kansas City Life Insurance Company; *U.S. Public*, pg. 1214
GRANGE LUXEMBOURG SARL—See The Middleby Corporation; *U.S. Public*, pg. 2114
GRANGE MUTUAL CASUALTY COMPANY; *U.S. Private*, pg. 1754
GRANGE PROPERTY & CASUALTY INSURANCE COMPANY—See Grange Mutual Casualty Company; *U.S. Private*, pg. 1754
GRANGER ASSOCIATES, INC.; *U.S. Private*, pg. 1754
GRANGER COMPOST SERVICES—See Granger Associates, Inc.; *U.S. Private*, pg. 1754
GRANGER CONSTRUCTION COMPANY; *U.S. Private*, pg. 1754
GRANGER CONTAINER SERVICE, INC.—See Granger Associates, Inc.; *U.S. Private*, pg. 1754
GRANGE RESOURCES LIMITED; *Int'l*, pg. 3058
GRANGE RESOURCES (TASMANIA) PTY. LTD.—See Grange Resources Limited; *Int'l*, pg. 3058
GRANGER LAND DEVELOPMENT CO.—See Granger Associates, Inc.; *U.S. Private*, pg. 1754
GRANGER-LYNCH CORP.—See J.H. Lynch & Sons Inc.; *U.S. Private*, pg. 2166
GRANGE ROC PROPERTY PTY LTD—See Grange Resources Limited; *Int'l*, pg. 3058
GRANGER WASTE MANAGEMENT CO.—See Granger Associates, Inc.; *U.S. Private*, pg. 1754
GRANGES AB; *Int'l*, pg. 3058
GRANGES AMERICAS INC. - NEWPORT PLANT—See Granges AB; *Int'l*, pg. 3058
GRANGES AMERICAS INC.—See Granges AB; *Int'l*, pg. 3058
GRANGES FINSPANG AB—See Granges AB; *Int'l*, pg. 3058
GRANGES KONIN S.A.—See Granges AB; *Int'l*, pg. 3058
GRANGE STEELS LTD.—See Klockner & Co. SE; *Int'l*, pg. 4202
GRANGETTO FARM & GARDEN SUPPLY CO.; *U.S. Private*, pg. 1754
GRANHERNE PTY LTD—See KBR, Inc.; *U.S. Public*, pg. 1215
GRANICAR A.D.; *Int'l*, pg. 3058
GRANICUS INC.—See Vista Equity Partners, LLC; *U.S. Private*, pg. 4397
GRANI INSTALLATION INC.; *U.S. Private*, pg. 1755
GRANINGER & MAYR GESELLSCHAFT M.B.H—See BayWa AG; *Int'l*, pg. 918
GRANINVESTIMENTOS SA; *Int'l*, pg. 3058
GRANIOU ATEM SP.Z O.O.—See VINCI S.A.; *Int'l*, pg. 8237
GRANIOU AZUR SAS—See VINCI S.A.; *Int'l*, pg. 8222
GRANIOU ITELCOM—See VINCI S.A.; *Int'l*, pg. 8221
GRANIOU MOBILCOM—See VINCI S.A.; *Int'l*, pg. 8221
GRANIOU SERVICES CENTRE EAST—See VINCI S.A.; *Int'l*, pg. 8221
GRANIT AD; *Int'l*, pg. 3059
GRANIT-BRONZ, INC.—See Cold Spring Granite Company; *U.S. Public*, pg. 966
GRANIT CONSTRUCTION STOCK CO.; *Int'l*, pg. 3059
GRANIT D.D. JABLANICA; *Int'l*, pg. 3059
GRANITE ALLIANCE INSURANCE COMPANY—See Centene Corporation; *U.S. Public*, pg. 469
GRANITE AUSTRIA GMBH—See Granite Real Estate Investment Trust; *Int'l*, pg. 3059
GRANITE BANK; *U.S. Private*, pg. 1755
GRANITE BAY GOLF CLUB—See Apollo Global Management, Inc.; *U.S. Private*, pg. 149
GRANITE BRIDGE PARTNERS LLC; *U.S. Private*, pg. 1755
GRANITE BROADCASTING CORPORATION—See Silver Point Capital, L.P.; *U.S. Private*, pg. 3661
GRANITE BUSINESS SOLUTIONS, INC.—See ePlus Inc.; *U.S. Public*, pg. 784
GRANITE CITY CLINIC CORP.—See Quorum Health Corporation; *U.S. Private*, pg. 3330
GRANITE CITY - CREVE COEUR, INC.—See MTY Food Group Inc.; *Int'l*, pg. 5073
GRANITE CITY ELECTRIC SUPPLY CO., INC.; *U.S. Private*, pg. 1755
GRANITE CITY FOOD & BREWERY LTD—See MTY Food Group Inc.; *Int'l*, pg. 5073
GRANITE CITY HOME CARE SERVICES, LLC—See Community Health Systems, Inc.; *U.S. Public*, pg. 553

GRANITE CITY ELECTRIC SUPPLY CO., INC.

CORPORATE AFFILIATIONS

GRANITE CITY ILLINOIS HOSPITAL COMPANY, LLC—See Quorum Health Corporation; *U.S. Private*, pg. 3330

GRANITE CITY, INC.—See MTY Food Group Inc.; *Int'l*, pg. 5073

GRANITE CITY OF KANSAS LTD.—See MTY Food Group Inc.; *Int'l*, pg. 5073

GRANITE CITY OF OHIO, INC.—See MTY Food Group Inc.; *Int'l*, pg. 5073

GRANITE CITY - ORLAND PARK, INC.—See MTY Food Group Inc.; *Int'l*, pg. 5073

GRANITE CITY ORTHOPEDIC PHYSICIANS COMPANY, LLC—See Quorum Health Corporation; *U.S. Private*, pg. 3330

GRANITE CITY PHYSICIANS CORP.—See Quorum Health Corporation; *U.S. Private*, pg. 3330

GRANITE CITY RESTAURANT OPERATIONS, INC.—See MTY Food Group Inc.; *Int'l*, pg. 5073

GRANITE COMFORT, LP—See Tiger Infrastructure Partners LP; *U.S. Private*, pg. 4170

GRANITE CONSTRUCTION CO. - ARIZONA—See Granite Construction Incorporated; *U.S. Public*, pg. 957

GRANITE CONSTRUCTION CO. - BAKERSFIELD BRANCH—See Granite Construction Incorporated; *U.S. Public*, pg. 957

GRANITE CONSTRUCTION CO. - BAY AREA BRANCH—See Granite Construction Incorporated; *U.S. Public*, pg. 957

GRANITE CONSTRUCTION CO. - CENTRAL VALLEY BRANCH—See Granite Construction Incorporated; *U.S. Public*, pg. 957

GRANITE CONSTRUCTION CO. - MONTEREY BAY BRANCH—See Granite Construction Incorporated; *U.S. Public*, pg. 957

GRANITE CONSTRUCTION COMPANY—See Granite Construction Incorporated; *U.S. Public*, pg. 957

GRANITE CONSTRUCTION CO. - NEVADA—See Granite Construction Incorporated; *U.S. Public*, pg. 957

GRANITE CONSTRUCTION CO. - SACRAMENTO VALLEY BRANCH—See Granite Construction Incorporated; *U.S. Public*, pg. 957

GRANITE CONSTRUCTION CO. - SANTA BARBARA BRANCH—See Granite Construction Incorporated; *U.S. Public*, pg. 957

GRANITE CONSTRUCTION CO. - SOUTHERN CALIFORNIA BRANCH—See Granite Construction Incorporated; *U.S. Public*, pg. 957

GRANITE CONSTRUCTION CO. - STOCKTON BRANCH—See Granite Construction Incorporated; *U.S. Public*, pg. 957

GRANITE CONSTRUCTION CO. - UTAH—See Granite Construction Incorporated; *U.S. Public*, pg. 957

GRANITE CONSTRUCTION CO. - YAKIMA—See Granite Construction Incorporated; *U.S. Public*, pg. 957

GRANITE CONSTRUCTION INCORPORATED; *U.S. Public*, pg. 957

GRANITE CONSTRUCTION NORTHEAST, INC.—See Granite Construction Incorporated; *U.S. Public*, pg. 957

GRANITE CONSTRUCTION - WASHINGTON REGION—See Granite Construction Incorporated; *U.S. Public*, pg. 957

GRANITE CONTRACTING, LLC—See Reeves Construction Company; *U.S. Private*, pg. 3384

GRANITE CREEK CAPITAL PARTNERS, LLC; *U.S. Private*, pg. 1755

GRANITE CREEK COPPER INC.—See Metallic Group of Companies; *Int'l*, pg. 4847

GRANITE ELECTRICAL SUPPLY, INC.—See Edges Electrical Group; *U.S. Private*, pg. 1334

GRANITE ELECTRIC LIMITED—See Lynx Equity Limited; *Int'l*, pg. 4606

GRANITE EQUITY PARTNERS LLC; *U.S. Private*, pg. 1755

GRANITE FALLS ENERGY, LLC; *U.S. Private*, pg. 1755

GRANITE FURNITURE CO; *U.S. Private*, pg. 1755

GRANITE GEAR, INC.—See BRZZ Gear LLC; *U.S. Private*, pg. 674

GRANITE GROUP WHOLESALE LLC; *U.S. Private*, pg. 1755

GRANITE GROUP WHOLESALE, LLC—See Granite Group Wholesale LLC; *U.S. Private*, pg. 1755

GRANITE HACARMEL INVESTMENTS LTD.—See Azrieli Group Ltd.; *Int'l*, pg. 781

GRANITE INLINER, LLC—See Granite Construction Incorporated; *U.S. Public*, pg. 957

GRANITE MANAGEMENT CORP.—See Ford Motor Company; *U.S. Public*, pg. 866

GRANITE MANUFACTURING CO., LTD. - GRANIDA—See Phu Tai Joint Stock Company; *Int'l*, pg. 5857

GRANITE MICROSYSTEMS INC.; *U.S. Private*, pg. 1756

GRANITE MOUNTAIN STONE DESIGN—See Cold Spring Granite Company; *U.S. Private*, pg. 966

GRANITE OIL CORP.—See Lundin Group of Companies; *Int'l*, pg. 4583

GRANITE OPERATING COMPANY—See APA Corporation; *U.S. Public*, pg. 143

GRANITE PACKAGING SUPPLY ONE CO.; *U.S. Private*, pg. 1756

GRANITE POINT MORTGAGE TRUST INC.; *U.S. Public*, pg. 958

GRANITE PRECASTING & CONCRETE, INC.—See CRH plc; *Int'l*, pg. 1846

GRANITE REAL ESTATE INVESTMENT TRUST; *Int'l*, pg. 3059

GRANITE RE, INC.—See Federated Mutual Insurance Company; *U.S. Private*, pg. 1492

GRANITE REIT INC.—See Granite Real Estate Investment Trust; *Int'l*, pg. 3059

GRANITE RIDGE ENERGY, LLC—See Energy Capital Partners Management, LP; *U.S. Private*, pg. 1394

GRANITE RIDGE RESOURCES INC.; *U.S. Public*, pg. 958

GRANITE ROCK COMPANY; *U.S. Private*, pg. 1756

GRANITE RUN BUICK GMC, INC.; *U.S. Private*, pg. 1756

GRANITE STATE ELECTRIC COMPANY—See Algonquin Power & Utilities Corp.; *Int'l*, pg. 319

GRANITE STATE GAS TRANSMISSION, INC.—See Unitil Corporation; *U.S. Public*, pg. 2253

GRANITE STATE HEALTH PLAN, INC.—See Centene Corporation; *U.S. Public*, pg. 469

GRANITE STATE MANUFACTURING—See Allard Nazarian Group Inc.; *U.S. Private*, pg. 175

GRANITE STATE PLUMBING & HEATING, LLC—See Comfort Systems USA, Inc.; *U.S. Public*, pg. 544

GRANITE TELECOMMUNICATIONS, LLC; *U.S. Private*, pg. 1756

GRANITE WATER WORKS, INC.—See Core & Main, Inc.; *U.S. Public*, pg. 576

GRANITIFIANDRE S.P.A; *Int'l*, pg. 3059

GRANIT NEGOCE SA—See Axereal Union de Cooperatives Agricoles; *Int'l*, pg. 767

GRANITO ACQUISITION I, INC.; *U.S. Private*, pg. 1756

GRANIT PESACAR A.D.; *Int'l*, pg. 3059

GRANITUL SA; *Int'l*, pg. 3059

GRANNGARDEN AB—See Felleskjopet Agri SA; *Int'l*, pg. 2633

GRANOLIO D.D.; *Int'l*, pg. 3059

GRAN OPERADORA POSADAS, S.A. DE C.V.—See Grupo Posadas S.A.B. de C.V.; *Int'l*, pg. 3134

GRANOPT CO., LTD.—See Mitsubishi Gas Chemical Company, Inc.; *Int'l*, pg. 4948

GRANO RETAIL INVESTMENTS INC.; *Int'l*, pg. 3059

GRANOR S.A.S.—See Heidelberg Materials AG; *Int'l*, pg. 3310

GRANPORTUARIA S.A.—See Grupo TMM, S.A.B.; *Int'l*, pg. 3137

GRANQUARTZ, L.P.—See The Stephens Group, LLC; *U.S. Private*, pg. 4121

GRANSPORT AUTO EOOD—See Eurohold Bulgaria AD; *Int'l*, pg. 2553

GRANTA DESIGN LIMITED—See ANSYS, Inc.; *U.S. Public*, pg. 139

GRANT AVENUE CAPITAL, LLC; *U.S. Private*, pg. 1756

GRANT AVIATION INC.; *U.S. Private*, pg. 1756

GRANT BANCSHARES, INC.; *U.S. Private*, pg. 1756

GRANT-BLACKFORD MENTAL HEALTH, INC.; *U.S. Private*, pg. 1757

GRANT BROADCASTERS PTY. LTD.—See ARN Media Limited; *Int'l*, pg. 576

GRANT CENTER HOSPITAL OF OCALA, INC.—See HCA Healthcare, Inc.; *U.S. Public*, pg. 997

GRANT CONSTRUCTION, INC.; *U.S. Private*, pg. 1756

GRANT COOPER & ASSOCIATES, LLC—See Diversified Search, LLC; *U.S. Private*, pg. 1243

GRANT COUNTY FOODS INC.—See Castellini Company, Inc.; *U.S. Private*, pg. 784

GRANT DANIEL LONG PTY. LTD.—See Nutrien Ltd.; *Int'l*, pg. 5493

GRANT EMBLEMS LIMITED; *Int'l*, pg. 3059

GRANTHAM BOOK SERVICES LIMITED—See Bertelsmann SE & Co. KGaA; *Int'l*, pg. 992

GRANTHAM DISTRIBUTING COMPANY, INC.; *U.S. Private*, pg. 1757

GRANTHAM, MAYO, VAN OTTERLOO & CO. LLC - SAN FRANCISCO—See Grantham, Mayo, Van Otterloo & Co. LLC; *U.S. Private*, pg. 1757

GRANTHAM, MAYO, VAN OTTERLOO & CO. LLC; *U.S. Private*, pg. 1757

GRANTHAM VETS4PETS LIMITED—See Pets at Home Group Plc; *Int'l*, pg. 5833

GRANT HARTFORD CORPORATION; *U.S. Private*, pg. 1756

GRANT-HATCH & ASSOCIATES INC.—See Leavitt Group Enterprises, Inc.; *U.S. Private*, pg. 2409

GRAN TIERRA ENERGY COLOMBIA, LTD.—See Gran Tierra Energy Inc.; *Int'l*, pg. 3053

GRAN TIERRA ENERGY INC.; *Int'l*, pg. 3053

GRAN TIERRA EXCHANGECO INC.—See Gran Tierra Energy Inc.; *Int'l*, pg. 3053

GRANTIKA CESKE SPORITELNY, A.S.—See Erste Group Bank AG; *Int'l*, pg. 2499

GRANT INDUSTRIAL CONTROLS INC.; *U.S. Private*, pg. 1756

GRANT INDUSTRIES INCORPORATED; *U.S. Private*, pg. 1756

GRANT INDUSTRIES INC.; *U.S. Private*, pg. 1756

GRANT MARKETING; *U.S. Private*, pg. 1756

GRANT MEMORIAL HOSPITAL; *U.S. Private*, pg. 1756

GRANT PARK FUTURES FUND LIMITED PARTNERSHIP; *U.S. Public*, pg. 1756

GRANT PRIDECO, L.P.—See NOV, Inc.; *U.S. Public*, pg. 1544

GRANT PRIDECO NETHERLANDS B.V.—See NOV, Inc.; *U.S. Public*, pg. 1544

GRANT PRIDECO (SINGAPORE) PTE LTD—See NOV, Inc.; *U.S. Public*, pg. 1544

GRANT ROAD LUMBER CO. INC.; *U.S. Private*, pg. 1756

GRANT SAMUEL GROUP; *Int'l*, pg. 3059

GRANTS PASS SANITATION, INC.—See Republic Services, Inc.; *U.S. Public*, pg. 1786

GRANTS PASS SURGERY CENTER, LLC—See UnitedHealth Group Incorporated; *U.S. Public*, pg. 2241

GRANT THORNTON INTERNATIONAL LIMITED; *Int'l*, pg. 3059

GRANT THORNTON LLP - CANADA; *Int'l*, pg. 3059

GRANT THORNTON LLP - USA; *U.S. Private*, pg. 1756

GRANT THORNTON SOUTH AFRICA (PTY) LTD.; *Int'l*, pg. 3059

GRANT THORNTON UK LLP; *Int'l*, pg. 3059

GRANT VICTOR; *U.S. Private*, pg. 1757

GRANULAB (M) SDN BHD—See Reneuco Berhad; *Int'l*, pg. 6277

GRANULATS BOURGOGNE AUVERGNE—See Holcim Ltd.; *Int'l*, pg. 3449

GRANULATS DE BASSE NORMANDIE SAS—See VINCI S.A.; *Int'l*, pg. 8222

GRANULATS NEGOCE TRANSPORTS SAS—See VINCI S.A.; *Int'l*, pg. 8222

GRANULATS OUEST - GO—See Heidelberg Materials AG; *Int'l*, pg. 3316

GRANULATS RECYCLES DE NORMANDIE SAS—See VINCI S.A.; *Int'l*, pg. 8222

GRANULATS RHONE-ALPES S.A.S.—See Vicat S.A.; *Int'l*, pg. 8185

GRANULES INDIA LTD; *Int'l*, pg. 3059

GRANULES USA INC—See Granules India Ltd; *Int'l*, pg. 3060

GRANUM COMMUNICATIONS; *U.S. Private*, pg. 1757

GRANUM INC.; *U.S. Private*, pg. 1757

GRANUMIX B.V.—See Group de Cloedt SA; *Int'l*, pg. 3088

GRANVIA OPERATION S.R.O.—See VINCI S.A.; *Int'l*, pg. 8230

GRANVILLE GMBH; *Int'l*, pg. 3060

GRANVILLE TOYOTA; *Int'l*, pg. 3060

GRANZOW A/S—See Indutrade AB; *Int'l*, pg. 3679

GRAO CASTALIA, S.L.—See Banco de Sabadell, S.A.; *Int'l*, pg. 821

GRAPE BEGINNINGS, INC.—See The Winebow Group, LLC; *U.S. Private*, pg. 4137

GRAPE COMMUNICATIONS—See The Interpublic Group of Companies, Inc.; *U.S. Public*, pg. 2091

GRAPE EXPECTATIONS INC.; *U.S. Private*, pg. 1757

GRAPEFRUIT INC.; *U.S. Public*, pg. 958

GRAPE KING BIO LTD.; *Int'l*, pg. 3060

GRAPE ONE CO., LTD.—See Sumitomo Corporation; *Int'l*, pg. 7268

GRAPEVINE COMMUNICATIONS INTERNATIONAL INC.; *U.S. Private*, pg. 1757

GRAPEVINE CONCEPTS LIMITED—See Ireland Blyth Limited; *Int'l*, pg. 3807

GRAPEVINE DODGE CHRYSLER JEEP; *U.S. Private*, pg. 1757

GRAPEVINE LOGIC, INC.—See FNL Technologies, Inc.; *U.S. Private*, pg. 1555

GRAPEVINE MARKETING GMBH—See Stroer SE & Co. KGaA; *Int'l*, pg. 7242

GRAPEVINE MILLS—See Simon Property Group, Inc.; *U.S. Public*, pg. 1882

GRAPEVINE SOLUTIONS INC.—See DeepSpatial Inc.; *Int'l*, pg. 2003

GRAPEVINE SURGICARE PARTNERS, LTD.—See Tenet Healthcare Corporation; *U.S. Public*, pg. 2010

GRAPHANO ENERGY LTD.; *Int'l*, pg. 3060

GRAPHCOM, LLC—See Chatham Asset Management, LLC; *U.S. Private*, pg. 862

GRAPH-CORR—See Dunsirn Partners LLC; *U.S. Private*, pg. 1291

GRAPH-CORR—See Pfingsten Partners, LLC; *U.S. Private*, pg. 3164

GRAPHENE CORPORATION—See Elcora Advanced Materials Corp.; *Int'l*, pg. 2346

GRAPHENE MANUFACTURING GROUP LTD.; *Int'l*, pg. 3060

GRAPHENE NANOCHEM PLC; *Int'l*, pg. 3060

GRAPHENE & SOLAR TECHNOLOGIES LTD; *U.S. Public*, pg. 958

GRAPHENE SOLUTIONS PTE. LTD.—See Larsen & Toubro Limited; *Int'l*, pg. 4418

GRAPHEX GROUP LIMITED; *Int'l*, pg. 3060

GRAPHEX GROUP LIMITED; *Int'l*, pg. 3060

GRAPHIC ANGELS DESIGN GROUP; *U.S. Private*, pg. 1757

GRAPHICA PLUS LIMITED—See Litho Supplies Ltd; *Int'l*, pg. 4527

GRAPHIC ARTS COMMUNICATION CO., LTD.—See Nippon Paper Industries Co., Ltd.; *Int'l*, pg. 5327

COMPANY NAME INDEX

GRAPHIC ARTS MUTUAL INSURANCE CO.—See Utica National Insurance Group; *U.S. Private*, pg. 4325
GRAPHIC COMMUNICATIONS HOLDINGS, INC.—See Clayton, Dubilier & Rice, LLC; *U.S. Private*, pg. 929
GRAPHIC COMMUNICATIONS HOLDINGS; *U.S. Private*, pg. 1757
GRAPHIC COMMUNICATIONS UK—See Clayton, Dubilier & Rice, LLC; *U.S. Private*, pg. 928
GRAPHIC CONTROLS CANADA CO—See Nissha Co., Ltd.; *Int'l*, pg. 5371
GRAPHIC CONTROLS LLC—See Nissha Co., Ltd.; *Int'l*, pg. 5371
GRAPHIC CONTROLS PTY. LTD.—See Mitsubishi Heavy Industries, Ltd.; *Int'l*, pg. 4957
GRAPHIC CONVERTING INC.; *U.S. Private*, pg. 1757
GRAPHIC CREATION CO., LTD.—See MIMAKI ENGINEERING CO., LTD.; *Int'l*, pg. 4897
GRAPHIC DESIGN USA—See Kaye Publishing Corporation; *U.S. Private*, pg. 2266
THE GRAPHIC EDGE, INC.; *U.S. Private*, pg. 4037
GRAPHIC ENTERPRISES INC.—See Visual Edge Technology, Inc.; *U.S. Private*, pg. 4404
GRAPHIC INFORMATION SYSTEMS INC.; *U.S. Private*, pg. 1757
GRAPHIC INNOVATORS INC.; *U.S. Private*, pg. 1757
GRAPHIC LABEL, INC.—See Sole Source Capital LLC; *U.S. Private*, pg. 3708
GRAPHIC LAMINATING, INC.; *U.S. Private*, pg. 1757
GRAPHIC MATTER, INC.—See Baldwin & Obenauf, Inc.; *U.S. Private*, pg. 458
GRAPHIC MEDIA PRODUCTS INC.; *U.S. Private*, pg. 1757
GRAPHICODE INC.; *U.S. Private*, pg. 1758
GRAPHIC PACKAGING HOLDING COMPANY; *U.S. Public*, pg. 958
GRAPHIC PACKAGING INTERNATIONAL AUSTRALIA PTY LIMITED—See Graphic Packaging Holding Company; *U.S. Public*, pg. 958
GRAPHIC PACKAGING INTERNATIONAL BOX HOLDINGS LIMITED—See Graphic Packaging Holding Company; *U.S. Public*, pg. 958
GRAPHIC PACKAGING INTERNATIONAL BREMEN GMBH—See Graphic Packaging Holding Company; *U.S. Public*, pg. 958
GRAPHIC PACKAGING INTERNATIONAL CANADA CORPORATION—See Graphic Packaging Holding Company; *U.S. Public*, pg. 958
GRAPHIC PACKAGING INTERNATIONAL CANADA, ULC—See Graphic Packaging Holding Company; *U.S. Public*, pg. 958
GRAPHIC PACKAGING INTERNATIONAL DO BRASIL - EMBALAGENS LTDA.—See Graphic Packaging Holding Company; *U.S. Public*, pg. 959
GRAPHIC PACKAGING INTERNATIONAL EUROPE CARTONS B.V.—See Graphic Packaging Holding Company; *U.S. Public*, pg. 959
GRAPHIC PACKAGING INTERNATIONAL EUROPE NETHERLANDS B.V.—See CVC Capital Partners SICAV-FIS S.A.; *Int'l*, pg. 1881
GRAPHIC PACKAGING INTERNATIONAL FRANCE—See Graphic Packaging Holding Company; *U.S. Public*, pg. 959
GRAPHIC PACKAGING INTERNATIONAL GATESHEAD LIMITED—See Graphic Packaging Holding Company; *U.S. Public*, pg. 958
GRAPHIC PACKAGING INTERNATIONAL HOLDING SWEDEN AB—See Graphic Packaging Holding Company; *U.S. Public*, pg. 959
GRAPHIC PACKAGING INTERNATIONAL, INC. - CAROL STREAM—See Graphic Packaging Holding Company; *U.S. Public*, pg. 959
GRAPHIC PACKAGING INTERNATIONAL, INC. - CROSBY—See Graphic Packaging Holding Company; *U.S. Public*, pg. 959
GRAPHIC PACKAGING INTERNATIONAL, INC. - ELK GROVE VILLAGE—See Graphic Packaging Holding Company; *U.S. Public*, pg. 959
GRAPHIC PACKAGING INTERNATIONAL, INC. - SALT LAKE CITY—See Graphic Packaging Holding Company; *U.S. Public*, pg. 959
GRAPHIC PACKAGING INTERNATIONAL, INC. - WEST MONROE—See Graphic Packaging Holding Company; *U.S. Public*, pg. 959
GRAPHIC PACKAGING INTERNATIONAL JAPAN LTD.—See Graphic Packaging Holding Company; *U.S. Public*, pg. 959
GRAPHIC PACKAGING INTERNATIONAL LIMITED—See Graphic Packaging Holding Company; *U.S. Public*, pg. 959
GRAPHIC PACKAGING INTERNATIONAL, LLC - CLARKSVILLE—See Graphic Packaging Holding Company; *U.S. Public*, pg. 959
GRAPHIC PACKAGING INTERNATIONAL, LLC - PITTSTON—See Graphic Packaging Holding Company; *U.S. Public*, pg. 959
GRAPHIC PACKAGING INTERNATIONAL, LLC—See Graphic Packaging Holding Company; *U.S. Public*, pg. 958

GRAPHIC PACKAGING INTERNATIONAL MEXICANA, S. DE R.L. DE C.V.—See Graphic Packaging Holding Company; *U.S. Public*, pg. 959
GRAPHIC PACKAGING INTERNATIONAL PARTNERS, LLC—See Graphic Packaging Holding Company; *U.S. Public*, pg. 958
GRAPHIC PACKAGING INTERNATIONAL SPAIN, S.A.—See Graphic Packaging Holding Company; *U.S. Public*, pg. 959
GRAPHIC PACKAGING INTERNATIONAL S.P.A.—See Graphic Packaging Holding Company; *U.S. Public*, pg. 959
GRAPHIC PRESS GROUP SDN BHD—See Berjaya Corporation Berhad; *Int'l*, pg. 984
GRAPHIC PRODUCTS CORPORATION; *U.S. Private*, pg. 1757
GRAPHIC RESEARCH INC; *U.S. Private*, pg. 1757
GRAPHIC SCIENCES INC.; *U.S. Private*, pg. 1758
GRAPHICS EAST, INC.—See Detroit Legal News Company; *U.S. Private*, pg. 657
GRAPHICS GROUP LTD.; *U.S. Private*, pg. 1758
GRAPHICS INTERNATIONAL INC.; *U.S. Private*, pg. 1758
GRAPHICS PLUS, INC.—See Blooming Color, Inc.; *U.S. Private*, pg. 584
GRAPHICS RESEARCH CORPORATION LTD.—See QinetiQ Group plc; *Int'l*, pg. 6141
GRAPHICS SYSTEMS CORP. (GXSC); *U.S. Private*, pg. 1758
GRAPHICS WEST, INC.—See Nationwide Argosy Solutions, LLC; *U.S. Private*, pg. 2865
GRAPHIC SYSTEMS INC.; *U.S. Private*, pg. 1758
GRAPHIC SYSTEMS SERVICES, INC.—See Eastman Kodak Company; *U.S. Public*, pg. 707
GRAPHIC TECH, LLC—See Orora Limited; *Int'l*, pg. 5642
GRAPHIC TECHNOLOGY OF MARYLAND, INC.—See Chatham Asset Management, LLC; *U.S. Private*, pg. 862
GRAPHIC VILLAGE, LLC—See Revitalize Capital; *U.S. Private*, pg. 3416
GRAPHIC VISUAL SOLUTIONS, INC.; *U.S. Private*, pg. 1758
GRAPHIC WEST PACKAGING MACHINERY, LLC; *U.S. Private*, pg. 1758
GRAPHIK DIMENSIONS, LLC—See H.I.G. Capital, LLC; *U.S. Private*, pg. 1827
GRAPHISADS LIMITED; *Int'l*, pg. 3060
GRAPHISCHE BETRIEBE STAATS GMBH—See Triton Advisers Limited; *Int'l*, pg. 7929
GRAPHISOFT ASIA LTD.—See Nemetschek SE; *Int'l*, pg. 5194
GRAPHISOFT BRASIL SERVIGOS DE TECNOLOGIA DA INFORMACAO LTDA.—See Nemetschek SE; *Int'l*, pg. 5194
GRAPHISOFT CAD STUDIO KFT—See Nemetschek SE; *Int'l*, pg. 5194
GRAPHISOFT DEUTSCHLAND GMBH—See Nemetschek SE; *Int'l*, pg. 5194
GRAPHISOFT ITALIA S.R.L.—See Herbalife Nutrition Ltd.; *Int'l*, pg. 3359
GRAPHISOFT JAPAN, K.K.—See Nemetschek SE; *Int'l*, pg. 5194
GRAPHISOFT MEXICO S.A. DE C.V.—See Nemetschek SE; *Int'l*, pg. 5194
GRAPHISOFT NORTH AMERICA, INC.—See Nemetschek SE; *Int'l*, pg. 5194
GRAPHISOFT PARK KFT—See Graphisoft Park SE; *Int'l*, pg. 3060
GRAPHISOFT PARK SE; *Int'l*, pg. 3060
GRAPHISOFT R&D SZAMITASTECHNIKAI FEJLESZTO ZRT.—See Nemetschek SE; *Int'l*, pg. 5194
GRAPHISOFT SE—See Nemetschek SE; *Int'l*, pg. 5194
GRAPHISOFT SPAIN, S.L.—See Nemetschek SE; *Int'l*, pg. 5194
GRAPHISOFT UK LTD.—See Nemetschek SE; *Int'l*, pg. 5194
GRAPHISOFT U.S., INC.—See Nemetschek SE; *Int'l*, pg. 5194
GRAPHITE CAPITAL MANAGEMENT LLP; *Int'l*, pg. 3060
GRAPHITE CHEMICAL ENGINEERING CO. LTD.—See SGL Carbon SE; *Int'l*, pg. 6742
GRAPHITE CORP.; *U.S. Private*, pg. 1758
GRAPHITE COVA GMBH—See Graphite India Ltd; *Int'l*, pg. 3061
GRAPHITE DESIGN INC.; *Int'l*, pg. 3061
GRAPHITE DIE MOLD INC—See Morgan Advanced Materials plc; *Int'l*, pg. 5041
GRAPHITE INDIA LTD - GLASS REINFORCED PLASTIC (GRP) PIPES AND TANKS DIVISION—See Graphite India Ltd; *Int'l*, pg. 3061
GRAPHITE INDIA LTD - IMPERVIOUS GRAPHITE EQUIPMENT DIVISION—See Graphite India Ltd; *Int'l*, pg. 3061
GRAPHITE INDIA LTD; *Int'l*, pg. 3061
GRAPHITE INTERNATIONAL B.V.—See Graphite India Ltd; *Int'l*, pg. 3061
GRAPHITE METALLIZING CORPORATION; *U.S. Private*, pg. 1758
GRAPHITE ONE INC.; *Int'l*, pg. 3061
GRAPHITE SALES, INC.; *U.S. Private*, pg. 1758

GRAPHITES TECHNOLOGIE ET INDUSTRIE S.A.—See Toyo Tanso Co., Ltd.; *Int'l*, pg. 7858
GRAPHITE TYN SPOL. S R.O.—See AMG Critical Materials N.V.; *Int'l*, pg. 426
GRAPHIT KROPFMUHL AG—See AMG Critical Materials N.V.; *Int'l*, pg. 426
GRAPHIX PRODUCTS, INC.—See Kelmscott Communications, Inc.; *U.S. Private*, pg. 2277
GRAPHJET TECHNOLOGY; *Int'l*, pg. 3061
GRAPHLINE INC.—See Base-Line, Inc.; *U.S. Private*, pg. 484
GRAPHNET INC.; *U.S. Private*, pg. 1758
GRAPHO METRONIC MESS- UND REGELTECHNIK GMBH—See AIP, LLC; *U.S. Private*, pg. 134
GRAPHON CORPORATION—See hopTo Inc.; *U.S. Public*, pg. 1052
GRAPH SOLUTIONS PTY LTD—See Knill Holding GmbH; *Int'l*, pg. 4208
GRAPHTEC—See Chatham Asset Management, LLC; *U.S. Private*, pg. 862
GRASA Y TRANSPORTES CARVAJAL S.L.—See SODIM, SGPS, SA; *Int'l*, pg. 7049
GRASDORF GMBH; *Int'l*, pg. 3061
GRASEBY MEDICAL IRELAND LTD.—See ICU Medical, Inc.; *U.S. Public*, pg. 1087
GRASIM INDUSTRIES LIMITED—See The Aditya Birla Group; *Int'l*, pg. 7610
GRASIM INDUSTRIES LIMITED - VIKRAM WOOLLENS UNIT—See The Aditya Birla Group; *Int'l*, pg. 7611
GRASON-STADLER, INC.—See Demant A/S; *Int'l*, pg. 2023
GRASPHERE JAPAN CO., LTD.—See Central Security Patrols Co., Ltd.; *Int'l*, pg. 1410
GRASP SYSTEMS INTERNATIONAL INC.—See Koch Industries, Inc.; *U.S. Private*, pg. 2330
GRA SP. Z O. O.—See Agora S.A.; *Int'l*, pg. 212
GRASS-AIR COMPRESSOREN B.V.—See Atlas Copco AB; *Int'l*, pg. 680
GRASS-AIR HOLDING B.V.—See Atlas Copco AB; *Int'l*, pg. 679
GRASS AMERICA, INC.—See Wurth Verwaltungsgesellschaft mbH; *Int'l*, pg. 8505
GRASS AUSTRALIA/NEW ZEALAND PTY LTD.—See Wurth Verwaltungsgesellschaft mbH; *Int'l*, pg. 8505
GRAS SAVOYE ALGERIE SERVICES EURL—See Willis Towers Watson Public Limited Company; *Int'l*, pg. 8416
GRAS SAVOYE BELGIUM S.A. - HASSELT—See Willis Towers Watson Public Limited Company; *Int'l*, pg. 8416
GRAS SAVOYE BELGIUM S.A. - LIEGE—See Willis Towers Watson Public Limited Company; *Int'l*, pg. 8416
GRAS SAVOYE BELGIUM S.A.—See Willis Towers Watson Public Limited Company; *Int'l*, pg. 8416
GRAS SAVOYE BENIN SA—See Willis Towers Watson Public Limited Company; *Int'l*, pg. 8416
GRAS SAVOYE BROKERS AND CONSULTANTS LIMITED—See Willis Towers Watson Public Limited Company; *Int'l*, pg. 8416
GRAS SAVOYE BURKINA SA—See Willis Towers Watson Public Limited Company; *Int'l*, pg. 8416
GRAS SAVOYE CAMEROUN SA—See Willis Towers Watson Public Limited Company; *Int'l*, pg. 8416
GRAS SAVOYE CARAIBES—See Willis Towers Watson Public Limited Company; *Int'l*, pg. 8416
GRAS SAVOYE & CIE SAS—See Willis Towers Watson Public Limited Company; *Int'l*, pg. 8416
GRAS SAVOYE CONGO SA—See Willis Towers Watson Public Limited Company; *Int'l*, pg. 8416
GRAS SAVOYE COTE D'IVOIRE SA—See Willis Towers Watson Public Limited Company; *Int'l*, pg. 8416
GRAS SAVOYE EGYPTE SAE—See Willis Towers Watson Public Limited Company; *Int'l*, pg. 8416
GRAS SAVOYE GABON SA—See Willis Towers Watson Public Limited Company; *Int'l*, pg. 8416
GRAS SAVOYE GRAND SUD OUEST SAS—See Willis Towers Watson Public Limited Company; *Int'l*, pg. 8414
GRAS SAVOYE GUINEE SA—See Willis Towers Watson Public Limited Company; *Int'l*, pg. 8416
GRAS SAVOYE LUXEMBOURG SA—See Willis Towers Watson Public Limited Company; *Int'l*, pg. 8416
GRAS SAVOYE MALI SA—See Willis Towers Watson Public Limited Company; *Int'l*, pg. 8416
GRAS SAVOYE MAROC—See Willis Towers Watson Public Limited Company; *Int'l*, pg. 8416
GRAS SAVOYE MAURITANIE - REMA BROKING SA—See Willis Towers Watson Public Limited Company; *Int'l*, pg. 8416
GRAS SAVOYE NIGER SA—See Willis Towers Watson Public Limited Company; *Int'l*, pg. 8416
GRAS SAVOYE NOUVELLE CALEDONIE SA—See Willis Towers Watson Public Limited Company; *Int'l*, pg. 8416
GRAS SAVOYE NSA - GARANTIA E ASSISTANCIA AUTOMOVEL SA—See Willis Towers Watson Public Limited Company; *Int'l*, pg. 8414
GRAS SAVOYE NSA—See Willis Towers Watson Public Limited Company; *Int'l*, pg. 8414
GRAS SAVOYE OCEAN INDIEN—See Willis Towers Watson Public Limited Company; *Int'l*, pg. 8416
GRAS SAVOYE RDC SA—See Willis Towers Watson Public Limited Company; *Int'l*, pg. 8416

GRASDORF GMBH / CORPORATE AFFILIATIONS

GRAS SAVOYE ROMANIA SRL—See Willis Towers Watson Public Limited Company; *Int'l*, pg. 8416
GRAS SAVOYE SAS—See Willis Towers Watson Public Limited Company; *Int'l*, pg. 8416
GRAS SAVOYE SENEGAL SA—See Willis Towers Watson Public Limited Company; *Int'l*, pg. 8416
GRAS SAVOYE TAHITI NUI INSURANCE SA—See Willis Towers Watson Public Limited Company; *Int'l*, pg. 8416
GRAS SAVOYE TCHAD SA—See Willis Towers Watson Public Limited Company; *Int'l*, pg. 8416
GRAS SAVOYE TOGO SA—See Willis Towers Watson Public Limited Company; *Int'l*, pg. 8416
GRAS SAVOYE TUNISIE—See Willis Towers Watson Public Limited Company; *Int'l*, pg. 8416
GRAS SAVOYE UKRAINE LLC—See Willis Towers Watson Public Limited Company; *Int'l*, pg. 8416
GRAS SAVOYE WILLIS SA—See Willis Towers Watson Public Limited Company; *Int'l*, pg. 8416
GRAS SAVOYE WILLIS VIETNAM CO., LTD.—See Willis Towers Watson Public Limited Company; *Int'l*, pg. 8416
GRASSBURGER, LLC; *U.S. Private*, pg. 1758
GRASS CANADA INC.—See Wurth Verwaltungsgesellschaft mbH; *Int'l*, pg. 8505
GRASSCOR LAWN & LANDSCAPES, LLC—See Schill Landscaping & Lawn Services, Inc.; *U.S. Private*, pg. 3565
GRASS CZECH S.R.O.—See Wurth Verwaltungsgesellschaft mbH; *Int'l*, pg. 8505
GRASS GMBH & CO. KG—See Wurth Verwaltungsgesellschaft mbH; *Int'l*, pg. 8505
GRASS GMBH—See Wurth Verwaltungsgesellschaft mbH; *Int'l*, pg. 8504
GRASSHOPPER ENVIRONMENTAL PTY. LTD.—See Cleanaway Waste Management Limited; *Int'l*, pg. 1655
GRASSHOPPER GROUP, LLC—See Elliott Management Corporation; *U.S. Private*, pg. 1367
GRASSHOPPER GROUP, LLC—See Vista Equity Partners, LLC; *U.S. Private*, pg. 4396
GRASSHOPPERS EARLY LEARNING CENTRE PTY. LTD.—See G8 Education Ltd.; *Int'l*, pg. 2867
GRASS IBERIA, S.A.—See Wurth Verwaltungsgesellschaft mbH; *Int'l*, pg. 8505
GRASSINGER TECHNOLOGIES GMBH—See Leeport (Holdings) Limited; *Int'l*, pg. 4441
GRASS ITALIA SRL—See Wurth Verwaltungsgesellschaft mbH; *Int'l*, pg. 8505
GRASSLAND DAIRY PRODUCTS, INC.; *U.S. Private*, pg. 1758
GRASSLAND EQUIPMENT & IRRIGATION CORPORATION; *U.S. Private*, pg. 1758
GRASSLAND EQUIPMENT & IRRIGATION CORP.—See Grassland Equipment & Irrigation Corporation; *U.S. Private*, pg. 1758
GRASSLAND EQUIPMENT & IRRIGATION CORP.—See Grassland Equipment & Irrigation Corporation; *U.S. Private*, pg. 1758
GRASSLAND FERTILIZERS LIMITED—See Greencore Group plc; *Int'l*, pg. 3074
GRASSLAND HEALTHCARE AND REHABILITATION, INC.—See The Ensign Group, Inc.; *U.S. Public*, pg. 2071
GRASSLAND WATER SOLUTIONS, LLC—See NGL Energy Partners LP; *U.S. Public*, pg. 1527
GRASS & MORE OUTDOOR SERVICES, INC.; *U.S. Private*, pg. 1758
GRASS MOVEMENT SYSTEMS LTD.—See Wurth Verwaltungsgesellschaft mbH; *Int'l*, pg. 8505
GRASS NORDISKA AB—See Wurth Verwaltungsgesellschaft mbH; *Int'l*, pg. 8505
GRASSO COMPONENTES IBERIA LDA.—See GEA Group Aktiengesellschaft; *Int'l*, pg. 2903
GRASSO REFRIGERATION SYSTEMS SHANGHAI CO., LTD.—See GEA Group Aktiengesellschaft; *Int'l*, pg. 2903
GRASSROOTS ENTERPRISE, INC.; *U.S. Private*, pg. 1758
GRASSROOTS INC.; *Int'l*, pg. 3061
GRASS ROOTS SL—See P2 Capital Partners, LLC; *U.S. Private*, pg. 3061
GRASS ROOTS SL—See Silver Lake Group, LLC; *U.S. Private*, pg. 3656
GRASS (SHANGHAI) INTERNATIONAL TRADING CO., LTD.—See Wurth Verwaltungsgesellschaft mbH; *Int'l*, pg. 8505
GRASS SP. Z O.O.—See Wurth Verwaltungsgesellschaft mbH; *Int'l*, pg. 8505
GRASS TR MOBILYA AKSESUARLARI TICARET LIMITED SIRKETI—See Wurth Verwaltungsgesellschaft mbH; *Int'l*, pg. 8505
GRASS VALLEY AUSTRALIA PTY LTD—See Black Dragon Capital LLC; *U.S. Private*, pg. 571
GRASS VALLEY BELGIUM NV—See Black Dragon Capital LLC; *U.S. Private*, pg. 571
GRASS VALLEY CANADA, INC.—See Black Dragon Capital LLC; *U.S. Private*, pg. 571
GRASS VALLEY CANADA—See Black Dragon Capital LLC; *U.S. Private*, pg. 571
GRASS VALLEY CHINA CO. LTD.—See Black Dragon Capital LLC; *U.S. Private*, pg. 571

GRASS VALLEY DO BRASIL COMERCIO E SERVICOS DE EQUIPAMENTOS DE TELECOMUNICACOES LTDA—See Black Dragon Capital LLC; *U.S. Private*, pg. 571
GRASS VALLEY FRANCE S.A.—See Black Dragon Capital LLC; *U.S. Private*, pg. 571
GRASS VALLEY FRANCE SAS—See Black Dragon Capital LLC; *U.S. Private*, pg. 571
GRASS VALLEY GERMANY GMBH—See Black Dragon Capital LLC; *U.S. Private*, pg. 571
GRASS VALLEY INDIA PTE. LTD.—See Black Dragon Capital LLC; *U.S. Private*, pg. 571
GRASS VALLEY ITALIA S.R.L.—See Black Dragon Capital LLC; *U.S. Private*, pg. 571
GRASS VALLEY MALAYSIA SDN BHD—See Black Dragon Capital LLC; *U.S. Private*, pg. 571
GRASS VALLEY NEDERLAND B.V.—See Black Dragon Capital LLC; *U.S. Private*, pg. 571
GRASS VALLEY OUTPATIENT SURGERY CENTER, L.P.—See Tenet Healthcare Corporation; *U.S. Public*, pg. 2010
GRASS VALLEY USA, LLC—See Black Dragon Capital LLC; *U.S. Private*, pg. 571
GRASS ZA (PTY.) LTD.—See Wurth Verwaltungsgesellschaft mbH; *Int'l*, pg. 8505
GRATEKS LTD.—See Tekstilpromet d.d; *Int'l*, pg. 7528
GRATES CORPORATION; *U.S. Private*, pg. 1758
GRATEX INDUSTRIES LIMITED; *Int'l*, pg. 3061
GRATEX INTERNATIONAL, A.S.; *Int'l*, pg. 3061
GRATEX INTERNATIONAL AUST PTY LTD.—See Gratex International, a.s.; *Int'l*, pg. 3061
GRATISFILM PHOTOCOLOR CLUB SA—See CIL Group SL; *Int'l*, pg. 1607
GRATOMIC INC.; *Int'l*, pg. 3061
GRATTERPALM, LTD.; *Int'l*, pg. 3061
GRATWICK ENTERPRISES INC.; *U.S. Private*, pg. 1758
GRAUBUENDNER KANTONALBANK; *Int'l*, pg. 3061
GRAUER & WEIL INDIA LIMITED; *Int'l*, pg. 3061
GRAUER & WEIL INDIA LTD - DADRA PLANT—See Grauer & Weil India Limited; *Int'l*, pg. 3061
GRAUER & WEIL INDIA LTD - VAPI PLANT—See Grauer & Weil India Limited; *Int'l*, pg. 3061
GRAUPNER / SJ GMBH; *Int'l*, pg. 3061
GRAVA OF MEDFORD, INC.; *U.S. Private*, pg. 1758
GRAVELEIJS PRODUKTER AB—See FMCG Business Partner AB; *Int'l*, pg. 2717
GRAVEL SWEDEN AB—See Socialite US AB; *Int'l*, pg. 7031
GRAVER TECHNOLOGIES LLC—See Berkshire Hathaway Inc.; *U.S. Public*, pg. 311
GRAVER WATER SYSTEMS LLC—See Berkshire Hathaway Inc.; *U.S. Public*, pg. 311
GRAVES DE MER SAS—See VINCI S.A.; *Int'l*, pg. 8222
GRAVES & GRAVES CONSTRUCTION CO., INC.; *U.S. Private*, pg. 1758
GRAVES OIL COMPANY; *U.S. Private*, pg. 1759
GRAVES SUPER MARKETS INC.; *U.S. Private*, pg. 1759
GRAVIERE DE LA CLAIE-AUX-MOINES S.A.—See Implenia AG; *Int'l*, pg. 3636
GRAVIS COMPUTERVERTRIEBSGESELLSCHAF MBH—See freenet AG; *Int'l*, pg. 2770
GRAVIS-COMPUTERVERTRIEBSGESELLSCHAFT MBH—See Deutsche Post AG; *Int'l*, pg. 2080
GRAVIS ENERGY CORP.; *Int'l*, pg. 3061
GRAVIS FOOTWEAR INC.—See Burton Snowboard Company; *U.S. Private*, pg. 693
GRAVISS HOSPITALITY LIMITED; *Int'l*, pg. 3061
GRAVISS HOTELS & RESORTS LIMITED—See GRAVISS HOSPITALITY LIMITED; *Int'l*, pg. 3062
GRAVITA EXIM LTD—See Gravita India Limited; *Int'l*, pg. 3062
GRAVITA GEORGIA LIMITED—See Gravita India Limited; *Int'l*, pg. 3062
GRAVITA GHANA LTD—See Gravita India Limited; *Int'l*, pg. 3062
GRAVITA HONDURAS SA—See Gravita India Limited; *Int'l*, pg. 3062
GRAVITA INDIA LIMITED; *Int'l*, pg. 3062
GRAVITA MOZAMBIQUE LDA—See Gravita India Limited; *Int'l*, pg. 3062
GRAVITANT, INC.—See International Business Machines Corporation; *U.S. Public*, pg. 1145
GRAVITAS VENTURES LLC—See ProSiebenSat.1 Media SE; *Int'l*, pg. 6000
GRAVITA TANZANIA LIMITED—See Gravita India Limited; *Int'l*, pg. 3062
GRAVITA USA INC.—See Gravita India Limited; *Int'l*, pg. 3062
GRAVITON CAPITAL S.A.; *Int'l*, pg. 3062
GRAVITY CO., LTD.; *Int'l*, pg. 3062
GRAVITY COMMUNICATIONS CO., LTD.—See Gravity Co., Ltd.; *Int'l*, pg. 3062
GRAVITY GAME ARISE CO., LTD.—See Gravity Co., Ltd.; *Int'l*, pg. 3062
GRAVITY GAME HUB (GGH) PTE., LTD.—See Gravity Co., Ltd.; *Int'l*, pg. 3062
GRAVITY GAME TECH CO., LTD.—See Gravity Co., Ltd.; *Int'l*, pg. 3062

GRAVITY GAME VISION LIMITED—See Gravity Co., Ltd.; *Int'l*, pg. 3062
GRAVITY (INDIA) LIMITED; *Int'l*, pg. 3062
GRAVITY INTERACTIVE LLC—See Gravity Co., Ltd.; *Int'l*, pg. 3062
GRAVITY MEDIA GROUP LIMITED; *Int'l*, pg. 3062
GRAVITY NEOCYON INC.—See Gravity Co., Ltd.; *Int'l*, pg. 3062
GRAVITY PAYMENTS; *U.S. Private*, pg. 1759
GRAVITY PRODUCTIONS INC.—See National Amusements, Inc.; *U.S. Private*, pg. 2841
GRAVOGRAPH INDUSTRIE INTERNATIONAL S.A.—See LBO France S.a.r.l.; *Int'l*, pg. 4429
GRAVOGRAPH-NEW HERMES—See LBO France S.a.r.l.; *Int'l*, pg. 4429
GRAVUTEX ESCHMANN INTERNATIONAL LIMITED—See voestalpine AG; *Int'l*, pg. 8289
GRAVY ANALYTICS, INC.—See Unacast, Inc.; *U.S. Private*, pg. 4279
GRAVYMASTER INC.—See Founders Equity, Inc.; *U.S. Private*, pg. 1581
GRAY AMERICA CORP.; *U.S. Private*, pg. 1759
GRAYBACH, LLC; *U.S. Private*, pg. 1759
GRAYBAR CANADA LIMITED—See Graybar Electric Company, Inc.; *U.S. Private*, pg. 1760
GRAYBAR ELECTRIC CANADA LIMITED—See Graybar Electric Company, Inc.; *U.S. Private*, pg. 1760
GRAYBAR ELECTRIC COMPANY, INC.; *U.S. Private*, pg. 1759
GRAYBAR ENERGY LIMITED—See Graybar Electric Company, Inc.; *U.S. Private*, pg. 1760
GRAYBAR FINANCIAL SERVICES, INC.—See Graybar Electric Company, Inc.; *U.S. Private*, pg. 1760
GRAYBAR INTERNATIONAL, INC.—See Graybar Electric Company, Inc.; *U.S. Private*, pg. 1760
GRAY, BILL AUTOMOTIVE ENTERPRISES INC.; *U.S. Private*, pg. 1759
GRAYBOW COMMUNICATIONS GROUP, INC.; *U.S. Private*, pg. 1760
GRAYCLIFF ENTERPRISES, INC.; *U.S. Private*, pg. 1760
GRAYCLIFF ENTERPRISES, INC. - TUCSON OFFICE—See Graycliff Enterprises, Inc.; *U.S. Private*, pg. 1760
GRAYCLIFF EXPLORATION LIMITED; *Int'l*, pg. 3062
GRAYCLIFF PARTNERS LP; *U.S. Private*, pg. 1760
GRAYCO, INC.; *U.S. Private*, pg. 1761
GRAY & COMPANY; *U.S. Private*, pg. 1759
GRAY CONSTRUCTION, INC.—See Gray Inc.; *U.S. Private*, pg. 1759
GRAY CONSULTING INC.—See Thoma Bravo, L.P.; *U.S. Private*, pg. 4148
GRAYCOR BLASTING COMPANY INC.—See Graycor Inc.; *U.S. Private*, pg. 1761
GRAYCOR INC.; *U.S. Private*, pg. 1761
GRAYCOR INDUSTRIAL CONSTRUCTORS INC.—See Graycor Inc.; *U.S. Private*, pg. 1761
GRAYCOR INTERNATIONAL INC.—See Graycor Inc.; *U.S. Private*, pg. 1761
GRAY-DANIELS AUTO FAMILY—See Asbury Automotive Group, Inc.; *U.S. Public*, pg. 209
GRAY-DANIELS FORD; *U.S. Private*, pg. 1759
GRAY ENERGY SERVICES, LLC—See Centre Partners Management LLC; *U.S. Private*, pg. 828
GRAY, GRAY & GRAY, LLP—See Antares Group, Inc.; *U.S. Private*, pg. 287
GRAYHAWK LLC; *U.S. Private*, pg. 1761
GRAYHILL INC.; *U.S. Private*, pg. 1761
GRAY-HODGES CORPORATION; *U.S. Private*, pg. 1759
GRAY-I.C.E. BUILDERS—See Gray Inc.; *U.S. Private*, pg. 1759
GRAY INC.; *U.S. Private*, pg. 1759
GRAY INSURANCE COMPANY; *U.S. Private*, pg. 1759
GRAY LIFT INCORPORATED; *U.S. Private*, pg. 1759
GRAYLINE HOUSEWARES, INC.—See Panacea Products Corporation; *U.S. Private*, pg. 3084
GRAY LINE NEW YORK TOURS INC.—See Stagecoach Group plc; *Int'l*, pg. 7163
GRAY LINE OF ALASKA—See Carnival Corporation; *U.S. Public*, pg. 438
GRAY LINE OF SEATTLE—See Carnival Corporation; *U.S. Public*, pg. 438
GRAYLING AUSTRIA—See Clayton, Dubilier & Rice, LLC; *U.S. Private*, pg. 924
GRAYLING BARCELONA—See Clayton, Dubilier & Rice, LLC; *U.S. Private*, pg. 924
GRAYLING BELGIUM—See Clayton, Dubilier & Rice, LLC; *U.S. Private*, pg. 924
GRAYLING BULGARIA—See Clayton, Dubilier & Rice, LLC; *U.S. Private*, pg. 924
GRAYLING CHINA—See Clayton, Dubilier & Rice, LLC; *U.S. Private*, pg. 924
GRAYLING CROATIA—See Clayton, Dubilier & Rice, LLC; *U.S. Private*, pg. 924
GRAYLING CZECH REPUBLIC—See Clayton, Dubilier & Rice, LLC; *U.S. Private*, pg. 924
GRAYLING DEUTSCHLAND GMBH—See Clayton, Dubilier & Rice, LLC; *U.S. Private*, pg. 924
GRAYLING DEUTSCHLAND GMBH—See Clayton, Dubilier & Rice, LLC; *U.S. Private*, pg. 925

COMPANY NAME INDEX

GRAYLING DEUTSCHLAND GMBH—See Clayton, Dubilier & Rice, LLC; *U.S. Private*, pg. 925
GRAYLING FRANCE—See Clayton, Dubilier & Rice, LLC; *U.S. Private*, pg. 925
GRAYLING GENERATING STATION LIMITED PARTNERSHIP—See CMS Energy Corporation; *U.S. Public*, pg. 518
GRAYLING GLOBAL—See Clayton, Dubilier & Rice, LLC; *U.S. Private*, pg. 925
GRAYLING GLOBAL—See Clayton, Dubilier & Rice, LLC; *U.S. Private*, pg. 924
GRAYLING GLOBAL—See Clayton, Dubilier & Rice, LLC; *U.S. Private*, pg. 925
GRAYLING GLOBAL—See Clayton, Dubilier & Rice, LLC; *U.S. Private*, pg. 925
GRAYLING GLOBAL—See Clayton, Dubilier & Rice, LLC; *U.S. Private*, pg. 925
GRAYLING HUNGARY—See Clayton, Dubilier & Rice, LLC; *U.S. Private*, pg. 925
GRAYLING INDUSTRIES INC.; *U.S. Private*, pg. 1761
GRAYLING MADRID—See Clayton, Dubilier & Rice, LLC; *U.S. Private*, pg. 925
GRAYLING NETHERLANDS—See Clayton, Dubilier & Rice, LLC; *U.S. Private*, pg. 925
GRAYLING POLAND—See Clayton, Dubilier & Rice, LLC; *U.S. Private*, pg. 925
GRAYLING PORTUGAL—See Clayton, Dubilier & Rice, LLC; *U.S. Private*, pg. 925
GRAYLING ROMANIA—See Clayton, Dubilier & Rice, LLC; *U.S. Private*, pg. 925
GRAYLING RUSSIA—See Clayton, Dubilier & Rice, LLC; *U.S. Private*, pg. 925
GRAYLING SCHWEIZ AG—See Clayton, Dubilier & Rice, LLC; *U.S. Private*, pg. 925
GRAYLING SEVILLE—See Clayton, Dubilier & Rice, LLC; *U.S. Private*, pg. 925
GRAYLING SLOVAKIA—See Clayton, Dubilier & Rice, LLC; *U.S. Private*, pg. 925
GRAYLING SLOVENIA—See Clayton, Dubilier & Rice, LLC; *U.S. Private*, pg. 925
GRAYLING STOCKHOLM—See Clayton, Dubilier & Rice, LLC; *U.S. Private*, pg. 925
GRAYLING SUISSE SA—See Clayton, Dubilier & Rice, LLC; *U.S. Private*, pg. 925
GRAYLING UKRAINE—See Clayton, Dubilier & Rice, LLC; *U.S. Private*, pg. 925
GRAYLOC PRODUCTS CANADA LTD.—See Oceaneering International, Inc.; *U.S. Public*, pg. 1562
GRAYLOC PRODUCTS, L.L.C.—See Oceaneering International, Inc.; *U.S. Public*, pg. 1562
GRAYLOC PRODUCTS LTD.—See Oceaneering International, Inc.; *U.S. Public*, pg. 1562
GRAY LUMBER COMPANY INC.; *U.S. Private*, pg. 1759
GRAY MATTER AGENCY INC.—See Attivo group; *Int'l*, pg. 697
GRAY MATTER LTD.—See Reply S.p.A.; *Int'l*, pg. 6291
GRAY MATTER SYSTEMS, LLC—See Hamilton Robinson LLC; *U.S. Private*, pg. 1848
GRAY MEDIA GROUP, INC.—See Gray Television, Inc.; *U.S. Public*, pg. 959
GRAY MEDIA GROUP, INC.—See Gray Television, Inc.; *U.S. Public*, pg. 960
GRAYMILLS CORPORATION; *U.S. Private*, pg. 1761
GRAY MONK CELLARS LTD.—See Andrew Peller Limited; *Int'l*, pg. 451
GRAYMONT DOLIME (OH) INC.—See Graymont Limited; *Int'l*, pg. 3062
GRAYMONT INC.—See Graymont Limited; *Int'l*, pg. 3062
GRAYMONT LIMITED BEDFORD PLANT—See Graymont Limited; *Int'l*, pg. 3063
GRAYMONT LIMITED CRICKET MOUNTAIN PLANT—See Graymont Limited; *Int'l*, pg. 3063
GRAYMONT LIMITED EDEN PLANT—See Graymont Limited; *Int'l*, pg. 3063
GRAYMONT LIMITED EXSHAW PLANT—See Graymont Limited; *Int'l*, pg. 3063
GRAYMONT LIMITED FAULKNER PLANT—See Graymont Limited; *Int'l*, pg. 3063
GRAYMONT LIMITED GREEN BAY PLANT—See Graymont Limited; *Int'l*, pg. 3063
GRAYMONT LIMITED HAVELOCK PLANT—See Graymont Limited; *Int'l*, pg. 3063
GRAYMONT LIMITED INDIAN CREEK PLANT—See Graymont Limited; *Int'l*, pg. 3063
GRAYMONT LIMITED JOLIETTE PLANT—See Graymont Limited; *Int'l*, pg. 3063
GRAYMONT LIMITED - LAMONT COUNTY FACILITY—See Graymont Limited; *Int'l*, pg. 3062
GRAYMONT LIMITED MAKAREAO PLANT—See Graymont Limited; *Int'l*, pg. 3063
GRAYMONT LIMITED MARBLETON PLANT—See Graymont Limited; *Int'l*, pg. 3063
GRAYMONT LIMITED PAVILION PLANT—See Graymont Limited; *Int'l*, pg. 3063
GRAYMONT LIMITED PILOT PEAK PLANT—See Graymont Limited; *Int'l*, pg. 3063
GRAYMONT LIMITED PLEASANT GAP PLANT—See Graymont Limited; *Int'l*, pg. 3063

GRAYMONT LIMITED PORT INLAND PLANT—See Graymont Limited; *Int'l*, pg. 3063
GRAYMONT LIMITED - RIVERGATE FACILITY—See Graymont Limited; *Int'l*, pg. 3062
GRAYMONT LIMITED - SAINT-MARC-DES-CARRIERES FACILITY—See Graymont Limited; *Int'l*, pg. 3063
GRAYMONT LIMITED SCHUYLER FALLS PLANT—See Graymont Limited; *Int'l*, pg. 3063
GRAYMONT LIMITED; *Int'l*, pg. 3062
GRAYMONT LIMITED SUMMIT PLANT—See Graymont Limited; *Int'l*, pg. 3063
GRAYMONT LIMITED SUPERIOR PLANT—See Graymont Limited; *Int'l*, pg. 3063
GRAYMONT LIMITED TE KUITI PLANT—See Graymont Limited; *Int'l*, pg. 3063
GRAYMONT MATERIALS (NY) INC.—See Barrett Industries, Inc.; *U.S. Private*, pg. 480
GRAYMONT WESTERN LIME INC. - GREEN BAY—See Graymont Limited; *Int'l*, pg. 3063
GRAYMONT WESTERN LIME INC.—See Graymont Limited; *Int'l*, pg. 3063
GRAY & OSBORNE, INC.; *U.S. Private*, pg. 1759
GRAY & OSBOURN LIMITED—See N Brown Group plc; *Int'l*, pg. 5115
GRAY & PAPE, INC.; *U.S. Private*, pg. 1759
GRAY PLANTATION GOLF CLUB AND THE SPORT CLUB AT GRAYWOOD—See Escalante Golf, Inc.; *U.S. Private*, pg. 1424
GRAYROBINSON, P.A.; *U.S. Private*, pg. 1761
GRAYSCALE BITCOIN TRUST; *U.S. Public*, pg. 961
GRAYSCALE LITECOIN TRUST; *U.S. Public*, pg. 961
GRAYSCALE TECHNOLOGIES SDN. BHD.—See TechnoDex Berhad; *Int'l*, pg. 7510
GRAYS DISTILLING LTD.—See Terra Mauricia Limited; *Int'l*, pg. 7567
GRAYS ECOMMERCE GROUP LIMITED—See Quadrant Private Equity Pty. Ltd.; *Int'l*, pg. 6149
GRAY'S FOODS INC.; *U.S. Private*, pg. 1759
GRAYS HARBOR PUD NO. 1; *U.S. Private*, pg. 1761
GRAYSHOTT HALL LIMITED—See G. R. (Holdings) plc; *Int'l*, pg. 2864
GRAYS INC. LTD.—See Terra Mauricia Limited; *Int'l*, pg. 7567
GRAYS LEASING LIMITED; *Int'l*, pg. 3063
GRAYSON-COLLIN ELECTRIC COOPERATIVE, INC.; *U.S. Private*, pg. 1761
GRAYSON HYUNDAI-SUBARU; *U.S. Private*, pg. 1761
GRAYSON PRIMARY CARE, LLC—See HCA Healthcare, Inc.; *U.S. Public*, pg. 997
GRAYS PEAK CAPITAL LP; *U.S. Private*, pg. 1761
GRAYSTAR LLC; *U.S. Private*, pg. 1761
THE GRAYSTONE COMPANY, INC.; *U.S. Public*, pg. 2085
GRAY-STONE & COMPANY—See The Liberty Company Insurance Brokers, Inc.; *U.S. Private*, pg. 4069
GRAYSTONE TITLE COMPANY, LLC—See Stewart Information Services Corporation; *U.S. Public*, pg. 1947
GRAY SUPPLY CORP.; *U.S. Private*, pg. 1759
GRAY TELEVISION GROUP, INC.—See Gray Television, Inc.; *U.S. Public*, pg. 960
GRAY TELEVISION, INC.; *U.S. Public*, pg. 959
GRAY TRANSPORTATION INC.; *U.S. Private*, pg. 1759
GRAYWOLF INDUSTRIAL, INC.—See INNOVATE Corp.; *U.S. Public*, pg. 1126
GRAZER TRANSPORTBETON GESELLSCHAFT M.B.H.—See PORR AG; *Int'l*, pg. 5923
GRAZIANO TORTONA S.R.L.—See DMG MORI Co., Ltd.; *Int'l*, pg. 2144
GRAZIANO TRANSMISSIONI UK LTD.—See Dana Incorporated; *U.S. Public*, pg. 623
GRAZIANO TRASMISSIONI INDIA PVT. LTD.—See OC Oerlikon Corporation AG; *Int'l*, pg. 5514
GRAZIELLA GREEN POWER S.P.A; *Int'l*, pg. 3063
GRAZPER TECHNOLOGIES APS—See Yokogawa Electric Corporation; *Int'l*, pg. 8592
GRAZZIOTIN S.A.; *Int'l*, pg. 3063
GR CABLES LIMITED; *Int'l*, pg. 3047
GRC ELEARNING LIMITED—See Bloom Equity Partners Management, LLC; *U.S. Private*, pg. 583
GRC ENTERPRISES, INC.; *U.S. Private*, pg. 1761
GRC HOLDING, INC.—See RGP Holding, Inc.; *U.S. Private*, pg. 3420
GRC INC.; *U.S. Private*, pg. 1761
GRC INTERNATIONAL GROUP PLC—See Bloom Equity Partners Management, LLC; *U.S. Private*, pg. 583
GRC LOGISTICS LLP—See Globe International Carriers Ltd.; *Int'l*, pg. 3006
GRC MERLIN HOLDINGS, INC.—See TUV SUD AG; *Int'l*, pg. 7984
GR CONSULTING, INC.—See gremz, Inc.; *Int'l*, pg. 3080
GRCS INC.; *Int'l*, pg. 3063
GRDF—See ENGIE SA; *Int'l*, pg. 2434
GREAAT SCHOOLS INC.; *U.S. Private*, pg. 1761
GREASE MONKEY INTERNATIONAL, LLC—See Mid-Ocean Partners, LLP; *U.S. Private*, pg. 2716
GREAT AJAX CORP.; *U.S. Public*, pg. 961
GREAT ALPS INDUSTRY CO., LTD.—See Ossia International Limited; *Int'l*, pg. 5652
GREATAMERICA LEASING CORPORATION; *U.S. Private*, pg. 1768

GREAT BAY DISTRIBUTORS INC.

GREAT AMERICAN ADVISORS, INC.—See American Financial Group, Inc.; *U.S. Public*, pg. 102
GREAT AMERICAN ALLIANCE INSURANCE COMPANY—See American Financial Group, Inc.; *U.S. Public*, pg. 103
GREAT AMERICAN ASSURANCE COMPANY—See American Financial Group, Inc.; *U.S. Public*, pg. 103
GREAT AMERICAN BANCORP, INC.; *U.S. Public*, pg. 961
GREAT AMERICAN BANK; *U.S. Private*, pg. 1762
GREAT AMERICAN CAPITAL PARTNERS, LLC—See B. Riley Financial, Inc.; *U.S. Public*, pg. 261
GREAT AMERICAN CASUALTY INSURANCE COMPANY—See American Financial Group, Inc.; *U.S. Public*, pg. 103
GREAT AMERICAN CONTEMPORARY INSURANCE COMPANY—See American Financial Group, Inc.; *U.S. Public*, pg. 103
GREAT AMERICAN CUSTOM INSURANCE SERVICES, INC.—See American Financial Group, Inc.; *U.S. Public*, pg. 103
GREAT AMERICAN DELI, INC.—See The H.T. Hackney Company; *U.S. Private*, pg. 4041
GREAT AMERICAN DUCK RACES, INC.; *U.S. Private*, pg. 1762
GREAT AMERICAN FINANCIAL RESOURCES, INC.—See American Financial Group, Inc.; *U.S. Public*, pg. 102
GREAT AMERICAN FOOD CHAIN, INC.; *U.S. Public*, pg. 961
GREAT AMERICAN FOODS CORP.; *U.S. Private*, pg. 1762
GREAT AMERICAN FOODS, INC—See Alliance Global Group, Inc.; *Int'l*, pg. 339
GREAT AMERICAN GAMING CORPORATION—See Maverick Gold LLC; *U.S. Private*, pg. 2616
GREAT AMERICAN GROUP, LLC—See B. Riley Financial, Inc.; *U.S. Public*, pg. 261
THE GREAT AMERICAN HANGER COMPANY INC.; *U.S. Private*, pg. 4037
GREAT AMERICAN HOLDING, INC.—See American Financial Group, Inc.; *U.S. Public*, pg. 102
THE GREAT AMERICAN HOME STORE, INC.—See Rooms To Go, Inc.; *U.S. Private*, pg. 3479
GREAT AMERICAN INDUSTRIES, INC.; *U.S. Private*, pg. 1762
GREAT AMERICAN INSURANCE COMPANY—See American Financial Group, Inc.; *U.S. Public*, pg. 103
GREAT AMERICAN LIFE INSURANCE COMPANY—See Massachusetts Mutual Life Insurance Company; *U.S. Private*, pg. 2605
GREAT AMERICAN LINES, INC.—See Universal Logistics Holdings, Inc.; *U.S. Public*, pg. 2261
GREAT AMERICAN LLOYDS INC.—See Massachusetts Mutual Life Insurance Company; *U.S. Private*, pg. 2605
GREAT AMERICAN MARKETING CO.; *U.S. Private*, pg. 1762
GREAT AMERICAN OPPORTUNITIES, INC.—See The Southwestern Company; *U.S. Private*, pg. 4119
THE GREAT AMERICAN OUTDOORS GROUP LLC; *U.S. Private*, pg. 4037
GREAT AMERICAN PRODUCTS INC.—See Dyna Group International Inc.; *U.S. Public*, pg. 699
GREAT AMERICAN PROTECTION INSURANCE COMPANY—See American Financial Group, Inc.; *U.S. Public*, pg. 103
GREAT AMERICAN RESTAURANTS, INC.; *U.S. Private*, pg. 1762
THE GREAT AMERICAN SMOKED FISH CO.; *U.S. Private*, pg. 4038
GREAT AMERICAN SPIRIT INSURANCE CO.—See American Financial Group, Inc.; *U.S. Public*, pg. 103
GREAT AMERICAN TITLE AGENCY, INC.; *U.S. Private*, pg. 1762
GREAT AMERICA—See Six Flags Entertainment Corporation; *U.S. Public*, pg. 1890
THE GREAT ATLANTIC & PACIFIC TEA COMPANY, INC.; *U.S. Private*, pg. 4038
THE GREAT ATLANTIC PROPERTY MANAGEMENT COMPANY; *U.S. Private*, pg. 4038
GREAT ATLANTIC RESOURCES CORP.; *Int'l*, pg. 3063
GREAT BARRINGTON REHABILITATION AND NURSING CENTER—See Apollo Global Management, Inc.; *U.S. Public*, pg. 156
GREAT BASIN ENERGIES, INC.; *U.S. Public*, pg. 961
GREAT BASIN SCIENTIFIC, INC.; *U.S. Private*, pg. 1762
GREATBATCH-GLOBE TOOL, INC.—See Integer Holdings Corporation; *U.S. Public*, pg. 1135
GREATBATCH LTD. - PLYMOUTH PLANT—See Integer Holdings Corporation; *U.S. Public*, pg. 1135
GREATBATCH LTD.—See Integer Holdings Corporation; *U.S. Public*, pg. 1134
GREATBATCH MCSO, S. DE R.L. DE C.V—See Integer Holdings Corporation; *U.S. Public*, pg. 1135
GREATBATCH MEDICAL SA—See Integer Holdings Corporation; *U.S. Public*, pg. 1135
GREATBATCH MEDICAL SAS—See Integer Holdings Corporation; *U.S. Public*, pg. 1135
GREAT BAY DISTRIBUTORS INC.; *U.S. Private*, pg. 1762
GREAT BAY POWER MARKETING, INC.—See Tavistock Group, Inc.; *U.S. Private*, pg. 3937

GREAT BAY DISTRIBUTORS INC.
CORPORATE AFFILIATIONS

GREAT BEAR RESOURCES LTD.—See Kinross Gold Corporation; *Int'l*, pg. 4182
GREAT BEND COOPERATIVE ASSOCIATION; *U.S. Private*, pg. 1762
GREAT BEND INDUSTRIES—See Ligon Industries LLC; *U.S. Private*, pg. 2455
GREAT BIG PICTURES, INC.—See GSP Marketing Technologies, Inc.; *U.S. Private*, pg. 1801
GREAT BOULDER RESOURCES LIMITED; *Int'l*, pg. 3063
GREAT BRANDS LIMITED—See Thai Beverage Public Company Limited; *Int'l*, pg. 7590
GREAT BRITAIN TILE, INC.; *U.S. Private*, pg. 1762
GREATCALL, INC.—See Best Buy Co., Inc.; *U.S. Public*, pg. 326
GREAT CANADIAN CASINOS INC.—See Great Canadian Gaming Corporation; *Int'l*, pg. 3063
GREAT CANADIAN GAMING CORPORATION; *Int'l*, pg. 3063
GREAT CEDAR HOTEL—See Mashantucket Pequot Gaming Enterprise Inc.; *U.S. Private*, pg. 2601
GREATCELL SOLAR LTD.; *Int'l*, pg. 3066
GREAT CENTRAL LUMBER COMPANY—See Millman Lumber Company; *U.S. Private*, pg. 2737
GREAT CHINA HOLDINGS (HONG KONG) LIMITED; *Int'l*, pg. 3063
GREAT CHINA METAL IND. CO., LTD. - FUGANG PLANT—See Great China Metal Ind. Co., Ltd.; *Int'l*, pg. 3064
GREAT CHINA METAL IND. CO., LTD.; *Int'l*, pg. 3064
GREAT CHINA METAL IND. CO., LTD. - TOUFEN PLANT—See Great China Metal Ind. Co., Ltd.; *Int'l*, pg. 3064
GREAT CHINASOFT TECHNOLOGY CO., LTD.; *Int'l*, pg. 3064
GREAT CIRCLE FAMILY FOODS LLC; *U.S. Private*, pg. 1762
GREAT CIRCLE FLIGHT SERVICES, LLC—See Vitus Marine LLC; *U.S. Private*, pg. 4406
GREAT CIRCLE SHIPPING AGENCY LIMITED—See Precious Shipping Public Company Limited; *Int'l*, pg. 5956
GREAT CIRCLE; *U.S. Private*, pg. 1762
GREAT CLIPS, INC.; *U.S. Private*, pg. 1762
GREAT COMMUNICATORS, INC.; *U.S. Private*, pg. 1762
GREAT CONSTRUCTION SYSTEM, INC.—See Taiwan Tea Corporation; *Int'l*, pg. 7424
GREAT DANE POWER EQUIPMENT; *U.S. Private*, pg. 1762
GREAT DANE TRAILERS—See Henry Crown & Company; *U.S. Private*, pg. 1917
GREAT DANE TRAILERS—See Henry Crown & Company; *U.S. Private*, pg. 1917
GREAT DANE TRAILERS TENNESSEE, INC.—See Henry Crown & Company; *U.S. Private*, pg. 1917
GREAT DAY ADVERTISING—See Great Day Radio; *U.S. Private*, pg. 1762
GREAT DAY IMPROVEMENTS LLC; *U.S. Private*, pg. 1762
GREAT DAY RADIO; *U.S. Private*, pg. 1762
GREAT DESTINATIONS, INC.—See Marriott Vacations Worldwide Corporation; *U.S. Public*, pg. 1373
GREAT DESTINATIONS, INC.—See Marriott Vacations Worldwide Corporation; *U.S. Public*, pg. 1373
GREAT DIVIDE INSURANCE COMPANY—See W.R. Berkley Corporation; *U.S. Public*, pg. 2318
GREAT DIVIDE PIPELINE LIMITED—See Connacher Oil & Gas Limited; *Int'l*, pg. 1768
GREAT EAGLE HOLDINGS LIMITED; *Int'l*, pg. 3064
GREAT EAGLE HOTELS (AUCKLAND) LIMITED—See Great Eagle Holdings Limited; *Int'l*, pg. 3064
GREAT EAGLE HOTELS (CANADA) LIMITED—See Great Eagle Holdings Limited; *Int'l*, pg. 3064
GREAT EAGLE HOTELS (NEW ZEALAND) LIMITED—See Great Eagle Holdings Limited; *Int'l*, pg. 3064
GREAT EAGLE HOTELS (UK) LIMITED—See Great Eagle Holdings Limited; *Int'l*, pg. 3064
THE GREAT EAGLE PROPERTIES MANAGEMENT COMPANY, LIMITED—See Great Eagle Holdings Limited; *Int'l*, pg. 3064
GREATEARTH CONSTRUCTION PTE LTD—See Southern Capital Group Pte. Ltd.; *Int'l*, pg. 7118
GREATEARTH CORPORATION PTE LTD—See Southern Capital Group Pte. Ltd.; *Int'l*, pg. 7118
GREATEARTH PTE. LTD.—See Southern Capital Group Pte. Ltd.; *Int'l*, pg. 7118
THE GREAT EASTERN CHARTERING L.L.C.—See The Great Eastern Shipping Co., Ltd.; *Int'l*, pg. 7650
GREAT EASTERN COLOR LITHOGRAPHIC; *U.S. Private*, pg. 1762
GREAT EASTERN COMPANY USA INC.—See Wei-Chuan Food Corporation; *Int'l*, pg. 8369
GREAT EASTERN ENERGY CORPORATION LTD.; *Int'l*, pg. 3064
GREAT EASTERN GENERAL INSURANCE LTD—See Oversea-Chinese Banking Corporation Limited; *Int'l*, pg. 5671
GREAT EASTERN GENERAL INSURANCE (MALAYSIA) BERHAD—See Oversea-Chinese Banking Corporation Limited; *Int'l*, pg. 5671

GREAT EASTERN HOLDINGS LIMITED—See Oversea-Chinese Banking Corporation Limited; *Int'l*, pg. 5671
GREAT EASTERN INDUSTRIES LIMITED—See Feng Tay Enterprises Co., Ltd.; *Int'l*, pg. 2634
THE GREAT EASTERN LIFE ASSURANCE COMPANY LIMITED—See Oversea-Chinese Banking Corporation Limited; *Int'l*, pg. 5672
GREAT EASTERN LIFE ASSURANCE (MALAYSIA) BHD.—See Oversea-Chinese Banking Corporation Limited; *Int'l*, pg. 5671
THE GREAT EASTERN SHIPPING CO., LTD.; *Int'l*, pg. 7650
GREATECH INTEGRATION (M) SDN. BHD.—See Greatech Technology Berhad; *Int'l*, pg. 3067
GREATECH TECHNOLOGY BERHAD; *Int'l*, pg. 3067
GREAT ECOLOGY, INC.; *U.S. Private*, pg. 1763
GREAT ECOLOGY, INC.—See Great Ecology, Inc.; *U.S. Private*, pg. 1763
GREAT ECOLOGY, INC.—See Great Ecology, Inc.; *U.S. Private*, pg. 1763
GREAT ECOLOGY, INC.—See Great Ecology, Inc.; *U.S. Private*, pg. 1763
GREATEK ELECTRONICS INC.; *Int'l*, pg. 3067
GREATEK ELECTRONICS INC. - TOUFEN PLANT—See Greatek Electronics Inc.; *Int'l*, pg. 3067
GREAT ELM CAPITAL CORP.—See Forest Investments, Inc.; *U.S. Private*, pg. 1567
GREAT ELM GROUP, INC.; *U.S. Public*, pg. 961
GREATER AUSTIN DEVELOPMENT; *U.S. Private*, pg. 1769
GREATER BATON ROUGE FOOD BANK; *U.S. Private*, pg. 1769
GREATER BAY AREA DYNAMIC GROWTH HOLDINGS LIMITED; *Int'l*, pg. 3067
GREATER BELOIT PUBLISHING CO., INC.—See The Hagadone Corporation; *U.S. Private*, pg. 4041
GREATER BELOIT PUBLISHING CO.—See Adams Publishing Group, LLC; *U.S. Private*, pg. 75
GREATER BERKS FOOD BANK; *U.S. Private*, pg. 1769
GREATER BOSTON LEGAL SERVICES, INC.; *U.S. Private*, pg. 1769
THE GREATER CANNABIS COMPANY, INC.; *U.S. Public*, pg. 2085
GREATER CEDAR RAPIDS COMMUNITY FOUNDATION; *U.S. Private*, pg. 1769
GREATER CHICAGO AUTO AUCTION—See Cox Enterprises, Inc.; *U.S. Private*, pg. 1076
GREATER CHICAGO FOOD DEPOSITORY; *U.S. Private*, pg. 1769
GREATER CHINA APPRAISAL LIMITED—See Asia-Pac Financial Investment Company Limited; *Int'l*, pg. 616
GREATER CHINA ASSET SERVICES LIMITED—See Asia-Pac Financial Investment Company Limited; *Int'l*, pg. 616
GREATER CHINA CORPORATE CONSULTANCY & SERVICES LIMITED—See Asia-Pac Financial Investment Company Limited; *Int'l*, pg. 616
GREATER CHINA FINANCIAL HOLDINGS LTD.; *Int'l*, pg. 3067
THE GREATER CINCINNATI FOUNDATION; *U.S. Private*, pg. 4038
GREATER CLEVELAND REGIONAL TRANSIT AUTHORITY; *U.S. Private*, pg. 1769
GREATER DICKSON GAS AUTHORITY; *U.S. Private*, pg. 1769
THE GREATER FAIRBANKS COMMUNITY HOSPITAL FOUNDATION, INCORPORATED; *U.S. Private*, pg. 4038
GREATER FLORIDA ANESTHESIOLOGISTS, LLC—See KKR & Co. Inc.; *U.S. Public*, pg. 1245
GREATER GEORGIA PRINTERS, INC.; *U.S. Private*, pg. 1769
GREATER GIVING—See Global Payments Inc.; *U.S. Public*, pg. 944
GREATER GWINNETT INTERNAL MEDICINE ASSOCIATES, LLC—See HCA Healthcare, Inc.; *U.S. Public*, pg. 997
GREATER HARLEM NURSING HOME & REHABILITATION CENTER INC.; *U.S. Private*, pg. 1769
GREATER HOUSTON CONVENTION & VISITORS BUREAU—See Houston First Corporation; *U.S. Private*, pg. 1993
GREATER KANSAS CITY COMMUNITY FOUNDATION; *U.S. Private*, pg. 1769
GREATER LAS VEGAS DIALYSIS, LLC—See DaVita Inc.; *U.S. Public*, pg. 639
GREATER LAWRENCE COMMUNITY ACTION COUNCIL, INC.; *U.S. Private*, pg. 1769
GREATER LAWRENCE FAMILY HEALTH CENTER, INC.; *U.S. Private*, pg. 1769
GREATER LOS ANGELES DIALYSIS CENTERS, LLC—See DaVita Inc.; *U.S. Public*, pg. 639
GREATER LUCKY (H.K.) CO., LTD.—See Yue Xiu Enterprises (Holdings) Limited; *Int'l*, pg. 8610
GREATER LYNN SENIOR SERVICES, INC.; *U.S. Private*, pg. 1769
GREATER MANCHESTER BUSES SOUTH LTD.—See Stagecoach Group plc; *Int'l*, pg. 7163

GREATER MANCHESTER NEWSPAPERS—See The Scott Trust Limited; *Int'l*, pg. 7680
GREATER MIAMI CONVENTION & VISITORS BUREAU; *U.S. Private*, pg. 1769
GREATER MILWAUKEE FOUNDATION; *U.S. Private*, pg. 1769
GREATER MINNEAPOLIS CONVENTION & VISITORS ASSOCIATION; *U.S. Private*, pg. 1770
GREATER MISSOURI BUILDERS; *U.S. Private*, pg. 1770
GREATER NEVADA CREDIT UNION; *U.S. Private*, pg. 1770
GREATER NEW YORK HOSPITAL ASSOCIATION; *U.S. Private*, pg. 1770
GREATER NEW YORK MUTUAL INSURANCE COMPANY; *U.S. Private*, pg. 1770
GREATER NORTHWEST HOUSTON ENTERPRISES—See Tenet Healthcare Corporation; *U.S. Public*, pg. 2003
GREATER NY FINANCIAL CONSULTANTS—See Principal Financial Group, Inc.; *U.S. Public*, pg. 1721
GREATER OMAHA PACKING CO. INC.; *U.S. Private*, pg. 1770
GREATER ORLANDO AVIATION AUTHORITY INC.; *U.S. Private*, pg. 1770
GREATER PARK CITY COMPANY INC.—See Powdr Corp.; *U.S. Private*, pg. 3236
GREATER PEORIA SPECIALTY HOSPITAL, LLC—See Apollo Global Management, Inc.; *U.S. Public*, pg. 157
GREATER PHILADELPHIA HEALTH ACTION; *U.S. Private*, pg. 1770
GREATER PITTSBURGH CONVENTION & VISITORS BUREAU; *U.S. Private*, pg. 1770
GREATER RIDGEWOOD YOUTH COUNCIL INC.; *U.S. Private*, pg. 1770
GREATER SACRAMENTO SURGERY CENTER LIMITED PARTNERSHIP—See Centene Corporation; *U.S. Public*, pg. 469
GREATER SPRINGFIELD MRI, LP—See Akumin, Inc.; *U.S. Public*, pg. 70
GREATER TALENT NETWORK, INC.—See United Talent Agency, Inc.; *U.S. Private*, pg. 4301
GREATER TAMPA BAY PHYSICIAN NETWORK, LLC—See HCA Healthcare, Inc.; *U.S. Public*, pg. 997
GREATER TAMPA BAY PHYSICIAN SPECIALISTS, LLC—See HCA Healthcare, Inc.; *U.S. Public*, pg. 997
GREATER TAMPA BAY PHYSICIANS - PINELLAS, LLC—See HCA Healthcare, Inc.; *U.S. Public*, pg. 997
GREATER TAMPA CHAMBER OF COMMERCE; *U.S. Private*, pg. 1770
GREATER TEXAS FOUNDATION; *U.S. Private*, pg. 1770
GREATER TEXAS INSURANCE MANAGERS & AGENCY, INC.—See BKCW, L.P.; *U.S. Private*, pg. 568
GREATER THAN AB; *Int'l*, pg. 3067
GREATER THAN ONE, INC.; *U.S. Private*, pg. 1770
THE GREATER UNION ORGANISATION PTY LIMITED—See Event Hospitality & Entertainment Limited; *Int'l*, pg. 2562
THE GREATER VANCOUVER CONVENTION & VISITOR BUREAU; *Int'l*, pg. 7651
GREATER WASHINGTON ANESTHESIA ASSOCIATES, LLC—See WELL Health Technologies Corp.; *Int'l*, pg. 8372
THE GREATER WASHINGTON EDUCATIONAL TELECOMMUNICATIONS ASSOCIATION, INC.; *U.S. Private*, pg. 4038
GREATER WASHINGTON PUBLISHING, LLC—See Nash Holdings LLC; *U.S. Private*, pg. 2835
GREAT ESCAPE OF NITRO, LLC—See Cineworld Group plc; *Int'l*, pg. 1611
GREAT ESCAPE THEATRES OF NEW ALBANY, LLC—See Cineworld Group plc; *Int'l*, pg. 1611
GREAT EXPRESSIONS DENTAL CENTERS, P.C.—See Ontario Municipal Employees Retirement System; *Int'l*, pg. 5584
GREAT FALLS CLINIC SURGERY CENTER, LLC—See Bain Capital, LP; *U.S. Private*, pg. 445
GREAT FALLS DIALYSIS, LLC—See Nautic Partners, LLC; *U.S. Private*, pg. 2870
GREAT FALLS HEALTH CARE - BUTTE CENTER—See Formation Capital, LLC; *U.S. Private*, pg. 1570
GREAT FALLS HEALTH CARE COMPANY, L.L.C.—See Formation Capital, LLC; *U.S. Private*, pg. 1570
GREAT FALLS HEALTH CARE - DEER LODGE—See Formation Capital, LLC; *U.S. Private*, pg. 1570
GREAT FALLS HEALTH CARE - MISSOURI RIVER CENTER—See Formation Capital, LLC; *U.S. Private*, pg. 1570
GREAT FALLS TRIBUNE—See Gannett Co., Inc.; *U.S. Public*, pg. 897
THE GREAT FISH COMPANY—See Palladium Equity Partners, LLC; *U.S. Private*, pg. 3078
GREAT FLOORS, LLC—See The Sterling Group, L.P.; *U.S. Private*, pg. 4122
THE GREAT FRAME UP—See Franchise Concepts, Inc.; *U.S. Private*, pg. 1587
GREAT FRIDAYS INC.—See EPAM Systems, Inc.; *U.S. Public*, pg. 783
GREAT FRIDAYS LIMITED—See EPAM Systems, Inc.; *U.S. Public*, pg. 783

COMPANY NAME INDEX

GREAT GAME OF BUSINESS INC.—See SRC Holdings Corporation; *U.S. Private*, pg. 3767
GREAT GAS PETROLEUM (IRELAND) LIMITED—See DCC plc; *Int'l*, pg. 1991
GREAT GLOVE (THAILAND) CO. LTD.—See Top Glove Corporation Bhd.; *Int'l*, pg. 7812
GREAT GLOVE (XINGHUA) CO. LTD.—See Top Glove Corporation Bhd.; *Int'l*, pg. 7812
THE GREAT GOURMET, INC.; *U.S. Private*, pg. 4038
GREAT GROUP HOLDINGS LIMITED; *Int'l*, pg. 3064
GREAT HARVEST FRANCHISING, INC.; *U.S. Private*, pg. 1763
GREAT HARVEST MAETA HOLDINGS LIMITED; *Int'l*, pg. 3064
GREAT HILL PARTNERS, L.P.; *U.S. Private*, pg. 1763
GREAT HIRE INC.; *U.S. Private*, pg. 1764
GREAT IDEA CORP.; *U.S. Private*, pg. 1764
GREATIME INTERNATIONAL HOLDINGS LIMITED; *Int'l*, pg. 3067
GREAT LAKE CANNABIS CO.—See Biome Grow, Inc.; *Int'l*, pg. 1039
GREAT LAKES ADVISORS HOLDINGS, LLC—See Wintrust Financial Corporation; *U.S. Public*, pg. 2375
GREAT LAKES ASSEMBLIES, LLC—See TAG Holdings, LLC; *U.S. Private*, pg. 3922
GREAT LAKES AUTO AUCTION, INC.; *U.S. Private*, pg. 1764
GREAT LAKES AVIATION, LTD.; *U.S. Public*, pg. 961
GREAT LAKES BEHAVIORAL RESEARCH INSTITUTE; *U.S. Private*, pg. 1764
GREAT LAKES BEVERAGE; *U.S. Private*, pg. 1764
GREAT LAKES BOAT TOP, LLC—See Patrick Industries, Inc.; *U.S. Public*, pg. 1652
GREAT LAKES CASE & CABINET CO., INC.; *U.S. Private*, pg. 1764
GREAT LAKES CASTINGS CORPORATION—See Brittany Stamping, LLC; *U.S. Private*, pg. 657
THE GREAT LAKES CHEESE CO., INC.; *U.S. Private*, pg. 4038
GREAT LAKES CHEESE OF LA CROSSE WISCONSIN, INC.—See The Great Lakes Cheese Co., Inc.; *U.S. Private*, pg. 4038
GREAT LAKES CHEESE OF NEW YORK, INC.—See The Great Lakes Cheese Co., Inc.; *U.S. Private*, pg. 4038
GREAT LAKES CHEESE OF WISCONSIN—See The Great Lakes Cheese Co., Inc.; *U.S. Private*, pg. 4038
GREAT LAKES CHEMICAL (FAR EAST) LTD.—See LANXESS AG; *Int'l*, pg. 4415
GREAT LAKES CLEANING INC.; *U.S. Private*, pg. 1764
GREAT LAKES COATING LABORATORY—See Carl-Zeiss-Stiftung; *Int'l*, pg. 1335
GREAT LAKES COATING LABORATORY—See EQT AB; *Int'l*, pg. 2473
GREAT LAKES COMPUTER CORP.; *U.S. Private*, pg. 1764
GREAT LAKES COMPUTER SOURCE, INC.; *U.S. Private*, pg. 1764
THE GREAT LAKES CONSTRUCTION CO.; *U.S. Private*, pg. 4038
GREAT LAKES CONSULTING GROUP INC.—See Rockwood Holding Company Inc.; *U.S. Private*, pg. 3468
GREAT LAKES COPPER LTD.—See Mueller Industries, Inc.; *U.S. Public*, pg. 1484
GREAT LAKES CREDIT UNION; *U.S. Private*, pg. 1764
GREAT LAKES CUSTOM TOOL MFG, INC.; *U.S. Private*, pg. 1764
GREAT LAKES DIE CAST CORPORATION; *U.S. Private*, pg. 1764
GREAT LAKES DREDGE & DOCK COMPANY, LLC—See Great Lakes Dredge & Dock Corporation; *U.S. Public*, pg. 962
GREAT LAKES DREDGE & DOCK CORPORATION; *U.S. Public*, pg. 961
GREAT LAKES EDUCATIONAL LOAN SERVICES INC—See Nelnet, Inc.; *U.S. Public*, pg. 1504
GREAT LAKES ENERGY COOPERATIVE; *U.S. Private*, pg. 1764
GREAT LAKES ENERGY TECHNOLOGIES, LLC—See Orion Energy Systems, Inc.; *U.S. Public*, pg. 1618
GREAT LAKES FASTENERS, INC.; *U.S. Private*, pg. 1764
GREAT LAKES FILTERS—See Acme Mills Co. Inc.; *U.S. Private*, pg. 61
GREAT LAKES FISHERY COMMISSION; *U.S. Private*, pg. 1764
GREAT LAKES FOAM TECHNOLOGIES, INC.—See Taglich Private Equity LLC; *U.S. Private*, pg. 3922
GREAT LAKES GAS TRANSMISSION COMPANY—See TC Energy Corporation; *U.S. Public*, pg. 7482
GREAT LAKES GRAPHITE INC.; *Int'l*, pg. 3065
GREAT LAKES GYPSUM SUPPLY; *U.S. Private*, pg. 1764
GREAT LAKES HOME HEALTH SERVICES, INC.—See Blue Wolf Capital Partners LLC; *U.S. Private*, pg. 594
GREAT LAKES HOTEL SUPPLY CO.; *U.S. Private*, pg. 1764
GREAT LAKES ICE CREAM INC.; *U.S. Private*, pg. 1764
GREAT LAKES INSURANCE UK LIMITED—See Munchener Ruckversicherungs AG; *Int'l*, pg. 5088
GREAT LAKES INTEGRATED; *U.S. Private*, pg. 1764

GREAT LAKES MDF, LLC.; *U.S. Private*, pg. 1764
GREAT LAKES MECHANICAL CORP.—See Blue Point Capital Partners, LLC; *U.S. Private*, pg. 590
GREAT LAKES PACKAGING CORP.; *U.S. Private*, pg. 1765
GREAT LAKES PETERBILT, GMC; *U.S. Private*, pg. 1765
GREAT LAKES PETROLEUM CO.; *U.S. Private*, pg. 1765
GREAT LAKES PLUMBING & HEATING CO. INC.; *U.S. Private*, pg. 1765
GREAT LAKES POWER PRODUCTS INC.; *U.S. Private*, pg. 1765
GREAT LAKES PUBLISHING COMPANY; *U.S. Private*, pg. 1765
GREAT LAKES REALTY CORP.; *U.S. Private*, pg. 1765
GREAT LAKES REINSURANCE (UK) PLC.—See Munchener Ruckversicherungs AG; *Int'l*, pg. 5088
GREAT LAKES RUBBER CO. INC.—See MAC Valves, Inc.; *U.S. Private*, pg. 2531
GREAT LAKES RUBBER & SUPPLY; *U.S. Private*, pg. 1765
GREAT LAKES SCRIP CENTER, LLC—See Bold Orange Company, LLC; *U.S. Private*, pg. 610
GREAT LAKES SERVICES, LLC—See Centerbridge Partners, L.P.; *U.S. Private*, pg. 815
GREAT LAKES SERVICES LTD.—See Munchener Ruckversicherungs AG; *Int'l*, pg. 5088
GREAT LAKES SPECIALTY HOSPITAL-HACKLEY, LLC—See Select Medical Holdings Corporation; *U.S. Public*, pg. 1858
GREAT LAKES SURGICAL SUITES, LLC—See Tenet Healthcare Corporation; *U.S. Public*, pg. 2002
GREAT LAKES TEXTILES INCORPORATED; *U.S. Private*, pg. 1765
GREAT LAKES TISSUE COMPANY, INC.; *U.S. Private*, pg. 1765
GREAT LAKES VENEER INC.—See Marion Plywood Corporation; *U.S. Private*, pg. 2576
GREAT LAKES WINDOW, INC.—See Clayton, Dubilier & Rice, LLC; *U.S. Private*, pg. 921
GREAT LAKES WINE & SPIRITS, LLC; *U.S. Private*, pg. 1765
GREAT LAKES WIRE & CABLE, INC.; *U.S. Private*, pg. 1765
GREAT LAKE WOODS INC.; *U.S. Private*, pg. 1764
GREATLAND CORPORATION; *U.S. Private*, pg. 1770
GREATLAND GOLD PLC; *Int'l*, pg. 3067
GREAT LIFE FINANCIAL ASSURANCE CORPORATION—See Sun Life Financial Inc.; *Int'l*, pg. 7306
GREAT LIFE FINANCIAL ASSURANCE CORPORATION—See Yuchengco Group of Companies; *Int'l*, pg. 8610
GREAT LITTLE BOX COMPANY LTD.; *Int'l*, pg. 3065
GREATMATS.COM CORPORATION; *U.S. Private*, pg. 1770
GREAT MIDWEST BANK, S.S.B.; *U.S. Private*, pg. 1765
GREAT MIDWEST NEWS LLC; *U.S. Private*, pg. 1765
GREAT MILL ROCK LLC; *U.S. Private*, pg. 1765
GREAT NECK SAW MANUFACTURERS, INC.; *U.S. Private*, pg. 1766
GREAT NIGERIA INSURANCE PLC; *Int'l*, pg. 3065
GREAT NORTH EASTERN RAILWAY COMPANY LTD—See Deutsche Bahn AG; *Int'l*, pg. 2051
GREAT NORTHERN BREWING COMPANY—See The McKenzie River Corporation; *U.S. Private*, pg. 4077
GREAT NORTHERN BUILDING PRODUCTS, LLC; *U.S. Private*, pg. 1766
GREAT NORTHERN CORPORATION; *U.S. Private*, pg. 1766
GREAT NORTHERN INDUSTRIES INC.; *U.S. Private*, pg. 1766
GREAT NORTHERN INSURANCE COMPANY—See Chubb Limited; *Int'l*, pg. 1591
GREAT NORTHERN MINERALS LIMITED; *Int'l*, pg. 3065
GREAT NORTHERN PRODUCTS, LTD.; *U.S. Private*, pg. 1766
GREAT NORTHERN TRANSPORTATION SERVICES, LLC—See Roadrunner Transportation Systems, Inc.; *U.S. Public*, pg. 1802
GREAT NORTHWEST INSURANCE COMPANY; *U.S. Private*, pg. 1766
GREATOO (GUANGZHOU) ROBOT & INTELLIGENT MANUFACTURING CO., LTD.—See Greatoo Intelligent Equipment Inc.; *Int'l*, pg. 3067
GREATOO (INDIA) PRIVATE CO., LTD.—See Greatoo Intelligent Equipment Inc.; *Int'l*, pg. 3067
GREATOO INTELLIGENT EQUIPMENT INC.; *Int'l*, pg. 3067
GREAT OUTDOOR PROVISION CO.; *U.S. Private*, pg. 1766
GREAT PACIFIC INDUSTRIES, INC.—See The Jim Pattison Group; *Int'l*, pg. 7660
GREATPAC SDN. BHD.—See Doka Wawasan TKH Holdings Berhad; *Int'l*, pg. 2156
GREATPAC (S) PTE. LTD.—See Doka Wawasan TKH Holdings Berhad; *Int'l*, pg. 2156
GREAT PANTHER MINING LIMITED; *Int'l*, pg. 3065
GREAT PERFORMANCES/ARTISTS AS WAITRESSES, INC.; *U.S. Private*, pg. 1766

GREAT SOUTHERN INDUSTRIES INC.

GREAT PLACE TO WORK INSTITUTE, INC.—See Hellman & Friedman LLC; *U.S. Private*, pg. 1910
GREAT PLAINS ACCEPTANCE CORPORATION—See Kubota Corporation; *Int'l*, pg. 4320
GREAT PLAINS AG DIVISION—See Kubota Corporation; *Int'l*, pg. 4320
GREAT PLAINS AGRO—See Kubota Corporation; *Int'l*, pg. 4320
GREAT PLAINS COCA-COLA BOTTLING COMPANY—See Arca Continental, S.A.B. de C.V.; *Int'l*, pg. 540
GREAT PLAINS COMPANIES, INC.; *U.S. Private*, pg. 1766
GREAT PLAINS CORRECTIONAL FACILITY—See The GEO Group, Inc.; *U.S. Public*, pg. 2075
GREAT PLAINS FORD SALES; *Int'l*, pg. 3065
GREAT PLAINS HEALTH ALLIANCE INC.; *U.S. Private*, pg. 1767
GREAT PLAINS HEALTHCARE, INC.—See The Ensign Group, Inc.; *U.S. Public*, pg. 2071
GREAT PLAINS HOSPITAL, INC.—See Universal Health Services, Inc.; *U.S. Public*, pg. 2257
GREAT PLAINS INDUSTRIES, INC.—See Great Plains Ventures, Inc.; *U.S. Private*, pg. 1767
GREAT PLAINS INTERNATIONAL DIVISION—See Kubota Corporation; *Int'l*, pg. 4320
GREAT PLAINS LAND PRIDE DIVISION—See Kubota Corporation; *Int'l*, pg. 4320
GREAT PLAINS MANUFACTURING, INC. - ASSARIA PLANT—See Kubota Corporation; *Int'l*, pg. 4320
GREAT PLAINS MANUFACTURING, INC. - GRAIN DRILLS—See Kubota Corporation; *Int'l*, pg. 4320
GREAT PLAINS MANUFACTURING, INCORPORATED—See Kubota Corporation; *Int'l*, pg. 4320
GREAT PLAINS MANUFACTURING, INC. - PLANTING COMPONENTS—See Kubota Corporation; *Int'l*, pg. 4321
GREAT PLAINS MEDIA, INC.; *U.S. Private*, pg. 1767
GREAT PLAINS MEDIA - LAWRENCE—See Great Plains Media, Inc.; *U.S. Private*, pg. 1767
GREAT PLAINS OILFIELD RENTAL, L.L.C.—See Patterson-UTI Energy, Inc.; *U.S. Public*, pg. 1654
GREAT PLAINS ROOFING & SHEET METAL—See Western Construction Group; *U.S. Private*, pg. 4492
GREAT PLAINS SERVICE, INC.; *U.S. Private*, pg. 1767
GREAT PLAINS SIMBA—See Kubota Corporation; *Int'l*, pg. 4321
GREAT PLAINS TRUCKING DIVISION—See Kubota Corporation; *Int'l*, pg. 4321
GREAT PLAINS UKRAINE—See Kubota Corporation; *Int'l*, pg. 4321
GREAT PLAINS VENTURES, INC.; *U.S. Private*, pg. 1767
GREAT PLANES MODEL MANUFACTURING CO—See Hobbico, Inc.; *U.S. Private*, pg. 1958
GREAT POINT INVESTORS, LLC—See Washington Capital Management, Inc.; *U.S. Private*, pg. 4446
GREAT POINT PARTNERS, LLC; *U.S. Private*, pg. 1767
GREAT PORTLAND ESTATES PLC; *Int'l*, pg. 3065
GREAT POWER (ZHUHAI) BATTERY CO., LTD.—See Guangzhou Great Power Energy & Technology Co., Ltd.; *Int'l*, pg. 3165
GREAT QUEST GOLD LTD.; *Int'l*, pg. 3065
GREAT RANGE CAPITAL, LLC; *U.S. Private*, pg. 1767
GREAT RECIPES COMPANY, INC.; *U.S. Private*, pg. 1767
GREAT RICH TECHNOLOGIES LTD; *Int'l*, pg. 3065
GREAT RIVER ENERGY; *U.S. Private*, pg. 1767
GREAT RIVER HOLDING COMPANY; *U.S. Private*, pg. 1767
GREAT SALT LAKE ELECTRIC INCORPORATED; *U.S. Private*, pg. 1767
GREATS BRAND, INC.—See Unified Commerce Group; *U.S. Private*, pg. 4282
THE GREAT SCOTTISH & WESTERN RAILWAY COMPANY LTD.—See LVMH Moet Hennessy Louis Vuitton SE; *Int'l*, pg. 4591
GREATSHIP GLOBAL ENERGY SERVICES PTE. LTD—See The Great Eastern Shipping Co., Ltd.; *Int'l*, pg. 7650
GREATSHIP GLOBAL OFFSHORE SERVICES PTE. LTD.—See The Great Eastern Shipping Co., Ltd.; *Int'l*, pg. 7650
GREATSHIP (INDIA) LIMITED—See The Great Eastern Shipping Co., Ltd.; *Int'l*, pg. 7650
GREAT SLAVE HELICOPTERS LTD.—See Clairvest Group Inc.; *Int'l*, pg. 1641
GREATSOLUTIONS PTE. LTD.—See GS Holdings Limited; *Int'l*, pg. 3143
GREAT SOUTHERN BANCORP, INC.; *U.S. Public*, pg. 962
GREAT SOUTHERN BANK—See Great Southern Capital Corp.; *U.S. Private*, pg. 1768
GREAT SOUTHERN BANK—See Great Southern Bancorp, Inc.; *U.S. Public*, pg. 962
GREAT SOUTHERN CAPITAL CORP.; *U.S. Private*, pg. 1768
GREAT SOUTHERN COPPER PLC; *Int'l*, pg. 3065
GREAT SOUTHERN INDUSTRIES INC.; *U.S. Private*, pg. 1768

GREAT SOUTHERN INDUSTRIES INC.   CORPORATE AFFILIATIONS

GREAT SOUTHERN LIFE INSURANCE COMPANY—See Financial Holding Corp.; *U.S. Private*, pg. 1507
GREAT SOUTHERN MINING LIMITED; *Int'l*, pg. 3065
GREAT SOUTHERN RAIL LIMITED—See Quadrant Private Equity Pty. Ltd.; *Int'l*, pg. 6149
GREAT SOUTHERN RAIL TRAVEL PTY. LIMITED—See Quadrant Private Equity Pty. Ltd.; *Int'l*, pg. 6149
GREAT SOUTHERN TELEVISION LIMITED—See Seven West Media Limited; *Int'l*, pg. 6734
GREAT SOUTHERN WOOD PRESERVING, INCORPORATED; *U.S. Private*, pg. 1768
GREAT SOUTH TEXAS CORPORATION; *U.S. Private*, pg. 1768
GREAT SOUTHWEST AVIATION, INC.—See Leonard Green & Partners, L.P.; *U.S. Private*, pg. 2424
GREAT SOUTHWESTERN CONSTRUCTION, INC.—See MYR Group Inc.; *U.S. Public*, pg. 1489
GREAT SOUTHWEST PAPER CO., INC.—See Bain Capital, LP; *U.S. Private*, pg. 441
GREAT SPRING WATERS OF AMERICA—See Nestle S.A.; *Int'l*, pg. 5210
GREAT SPRING WATERS OF AMERICA—See Nestle S.A.; *Int'l*, pg. 5210
GREATSTAR GROUP CO., LTD.; *Int'l*, pg. 3067
GREAT STATES CORP.—See American Lawn Mower Company; *U.S. Private*, pg. 239
GREAT-SUN FOODS CO.,LTD.; *Int'l*, pg. 3066
THE GREAT TAIPEI GAS CORPORATION; *Int'l*, pg. 7650
GREAT TEAM BACKEND FOUNDRY, INC.—See Hong Tai Electric Industrial Co., Ltd.; *Int'l*, pg. 3469
GREATTOWN HOLDINGS LTD.; *Int'l*, pg. 3068
GREAT TREE PHARMACY CO., LTD.; *Int'l*, pg. 3065
GREAT UNIVERSAL CAPITAL CORP.—See Lee National Corporation; *U.S. Private*, pg. 2413
GREAT UNIVERSAL INCORPORATED; *U.S. Private*, pg. 1768
GREAT VALLEY ADVISOR GROUP, INC.; *U.S. Private*, pg. 1768
GREAT VALLEY RECYCLING INC.—See J. P. Mascaro & Sons; *U.S. Private*, pg. 2156
GREAT VICTORY CHEMICAL INDUSTRY CO., LTD.—See Formosan Union Chemical Corp.; *Int'l*, pg. 2736
GREATVIEW ASEPTIC PACKAGING COMPANY LIMITED; *Int'l*, pg. 3068
GREATVIEW ASEPTIC PACKAGING EUROPE GMBH—See Greatview Aseptic Packaging Company Limited; *Int'l*, pg. 3068
GREATVIEW ASEPTIC PACKAGING MANUFACTURING GMBH—See Greatview Aseptic Packaging Company Limited; *Int'l*, pg. 3068
GREATVIEW BEIJING TRADING CO., LTD.—See Greatview Aseptic Packaging Company Limited; *Int'l*, pg. 3068
GREAT WALL BROADBAND NETWORK SERVICE CO., LTD.—See CITIC Group Corporation; *Int'l*, pg. 1621
GREAT WALL BROADBAND NETWORK SERVICE CO., LTD.—See Dr. Peng Telecom & Media Group Co., Ltd.; *Int'l*, pg. 2194
GREAT WALL BUILDERS LTD.; *Int'l*, pg. 3065
GREAT WALL COMPUTER SOFTWARE & SYSTEMS CO., LTD—See China Electronics Corporation; *Int'l*, pg. 1499
GREATWALLE INC.; *Int'l*, pg. 3068
GREAT WALL (HOLDING) COMPANY LIMITED—See Cosmos Machinery Enterprises Limited; *Int'l*, pg. 1813
GREAT WALL INDIA RESEARCH & DEVELOPMENT PRIVATE LIMITED—See Great Wall Motor Company Limited; *Int'l*, pg. 3066
GREAT WALL INSURANCE SERVICES PTY LTD—See Steadfast Group Limited; *Int'l*, pg. 7187
GREAT WALL INTERNATIONAL ACG CO., LTD.; *Int'l*, pg. 3065
GREAT WALL JAPAN MOTOR CO., LTD.—See Great Wall Motor Company Limited; *Int'l*, pg. 3066
GREAT WALL MOTOR COMPANY LIMITED; *Int'l*, pg. 3065
GREAT WALL MOVIE AND TELEVISION CO., LTD.; *Int'l*, pg. 3066
GREAT WALL (OPTICAL) PLASTIC WORKS LTD.—See Cosmos Machinery Enterprises Limited; *Int'l*, pg. 1813
GREAT WALL PAN ASIA HOLDINGS LIMITED—See China Great Wall Asset Management Corporation; *Int'l*, pg. 1505
GREAT WALL PLASTIC INDUSTRIES BERHAD—See Scientex Berhad; *Int'l*, pg. 6648
GREAT WALL PRINTING CO., LTD.—See Prosperous Printing Company Limited; *Int'l*, pg. 6002
GREAT WALL SEAFOOD LA, LLC—See HF Foods Group Inc.; *U.S. Public*, pg. 1033
GREAT WALL SECURITIES CO., LTD.—See China Huaneng Group Co., Ltd.; *Int'l*, pg. 1509
GREAT WALL SEMICONDUCTOR CORP.—See Renesas Electronics Corporation; *Int'l*, pg. 6276
GREAT WALL TECHNOLOGY CO., LTD.—See China Electronics Corporation; *Int'l*, pg. 1499
GREAT WALL TERROIR HOLDINGS LIMITED; *Int'l*, pg. 3066
GREAT WEST CASUALTY COMPANY—See Old Republic International Corporation; *U.S. Public*, pg. 1567

GREAT WESTERN BANCORP, INC.; *U.S. Public*, pg. 962
GREAT WESTERN BANK—See Great Western Bancorp, Inc.; *U.S. Public*, pg. 962
THE GREAT WESTERN BREWING COMPANY; *Int'l*, pg. 7650
GREAT WESTERN CORPORATION PTY. LTD.; *Int'l*, pg. 3066
GREAT WESTERN DEVELOPMENT COMPANY—See The Broe Companies, Inc.; *U.S. Private*, pg. 4000
GREAT WESTERN DINING SERVICE, INC.; *U.S. Private*, pg. 1768
GREAT WESTERN ERECTORS CO.; *U.S. Private*, pg. 1768
GREAT WESTERN EXPLORATION LIMITED; *Int'l*, pg. 3066
GREAT WESTERN INK, INC.; *U.S. Private*, pg. 1768
GREAT WESTERN LEASING & SALES, LLC; *U.S. Private*, pg. 1768
GREAT WESTERN MALTING CO.—See GrainCorp Limited; *Int'l*, pg. 3052
GREAT WESTERN METALS INC.—See Four Winds Investment Corp.; *U.S. Private*, pg. 1583
GREAT WESTERN MINERALS GROUP LTD.; *Int'l*, pg. 3066
GREAT WESTERN MINING CORPORATION PLC; *Int'l*, pg. 3066
GREAT WESTERN OIL AND GAS COMPANY—See The Broe Companies, Inc.; *U.S. Private*, pg. 4001
GREAT WESTERN RAILWAY OF COLORADO, LLC—See The Broe Companies, Inc.; *U.S. Private*, pg. 4001
GREAT WESTERN SUPPLY, INC.; *U.S. Private*, pg. 1768
GREAT WESTERN TECHNOLOGIES INC.—See Great Western Minerals Group Ltd.; *Int'l*, pg. 3066
GREAT WESTERN TILLAGE—See Great Western Corporation Pty. Ltd.; *Int'l*, pg. 3066
GREAT-WEST FINANCIAL RETIREMENT PLAN SERVICES, LLC—See Power Corporation of Canada; *Int'l*, pg. 5943
GREAT WEST HOUSE LIMITED—See CLS Holdings plc; *Int'l*, pg. 1664
GREAT-WEST LIFE & ANNUITY INSURANCE COMPANY—See Power Corporation of Canada; *Int'l*, pg. 5943
GREAT-WEST LIFECO, INC.—See Power Corporation of Canada; *Int'l*, pg. 5943
GREAT WHITE ENERGY SERVICES, INC.—See Archer Limited; *Int'l*, pg. 548
GREAT WHITE FLEET, LTD.—See Banco Safra S.A.; *Int'l*, pg. 824
GREAT WHITE FLEET, LTD.—See Sucocitrico Cutrale Ltda.; *Int'l*, pg. 7251
GREAT WHITE PRESSURE CONTROL LLC—See Archer Limited; *Int'l*, pg. 548
GREAT WHITE SHARK ENTERPRISES, INC.; *U.S. Private*, pg. 1768
GREATWIDE AMERICAN TRANS-FREIGHT, LLC—See Centerbridge Partners, L.P.; *U.S. Private*, pg. 815
GREATWIDE CHEETAH TRANSPORTATION INC.—See Centerbridge Partners, L.P.; *U.S. Private*, pg. 815
GREATWIDE LOGISTICS SERVICES, INC.—See Centerbridge Partners, L.P.; *U.S. Private*, pg. 815
GREAT WOLF LODGE GRAND MOUND—See Centerbridge Partners, L.P.; *U.S. Private*, pg. 815
GREAT WOLF LODGE OF GRAPEVINE, LLC—See Centerbridge Partners, L.P.; *U.S. Private*, pg. 815
GREAT WOLF LODGE OF KANSAS CITY, LLC—See Centerbridge Partners, L.P.; *U.S. Private*, pg. 815
GREAT WOLF LODGE OF THE CAROLINAS, LLC—See Centerbridge Partners, L.P.; *U.S. Private*, pg. 815
GREAT WOLF LODGE OF TRAVERSE CITY, LLC—See Centerbridge Partners, L.P.; *U.S. Private*, pg. 815
GREAT WOLF RESORTS, INC.—See Centerbridge Partners, L.P.; *U.S. Private*, pg. 814
GREAT WORKPLACE RESEARCH & CONSULTING GMBH.—See YouGov plc; *Int'l*, pg. 8601
GREAT WORKS AB; *Int'l*, pg. 3066
GREAT WORKS CHINA CO., LTD.—See KAI Corporation; *Int'l*, pg. 4050
GREAT WORKS INC.—See KAI Corporation; *Int'l*, pg. 4050
GREAT WORKS INTERNET; *U.S. Private*, pg. 1768
GREAT WORLD COMPANY HOLDINGS LIMITED; *Int'l*, pg. 3066
GREAVES AIRCONDITIONING (PVT.) LTD—See Cherat Packaging Limited; *Int'l*, pg. 1471
GREAVES COTTON LTD.; *Int'l*, pg. 3068
GREAVES PAKISTAN (PVT) LTD—See Cherat Cement Company Limited; *Int'l*, pg. 1471
GREAVES TECHNOLOGIES INC.—See Greaves Cotton Ltd; *Int'l*, pg. 3068
GREAVES TECHNOLOGIES LIMITED—See Greaves Cotton Ltd; *Int'l*, pg. 3068
GREBSTAD HICKS COMMUNICATIONS LTD.—See Hakuhodo DY Holdings Incorporated; *Int'l*, pg. 3221
GRECAM S.A.S.—See CoStar Group, Inc.; *U.S. Public*, pg. 586
GREC CONVERSIONS—See Fortune Capital Partners, Inc.; *U.S. Private*, pg. 1577

GRECIAN DELIGHT FOODS INC.—See Entrepreneurial Equity Partners, LLC; *U.S. Private*, pg. 1406
GRECIAN MAGNESITE S.A; *Int'l*, pg. 3068
GRECO ALUMINUM RAILINGS, LTD.—See CSW Industrials, Inc.; *U.S. Public*, pg. 601
GRECO ALUMINUM RAILINGS (U.S.A.) INC.—See CSW Industrials, Inc.; *U.S. Public*, pg. 601
GRECO INTERNATIONAL HOLDING AG—See Marsh & McLennan Companies, Inc.; *U.S. Public*, pg. 1375
GREDE HOLDINGS LLC—See Gamut Capital Management, L.P.; *U.S. Private*, pg. 1641
GREE AIR CONDITIONER (VIETNAM) CO., LTD.—See Gree Electric Appliances, Inc. of Zhuhai; *Int'l*, pg. 3068
GREE AIRCONS LLP—See Gree Electric Appliances, Inc. of Zhuhai; *Int'l*, pg. 3068
GREEDYGUMS PTE. LTD.—See New Silkroutes Group Limited; *Int'l*, pg. 5227
GREE ELECTRIC APPLIANCES DO BRASIL LTDA—See Gree Electric Appliances, Inc. of Zhuhai; *Int'l*, pg. 3068
GREE ELECTRIC APPLIANCES, INC. OF ZHUHAI; *Int'l*, pg. 3068
GREE ELECTRIC (THAILAND) CO., LTD.—See Gree Electric Appliances, Inc. of Zhuhai; *Int'l*, pg. 3068
GREE GMBH—See Gree Electric Appliances, Inc. of Zhuhai; *Int'l*, pg. 3068
GREE GROUP CO., LTD.; *Int'l*, pg. 3069
GREE HOUSEHOLD ELECTRIC APPLIANCES CO., LTD.—See Gree Group Co., Ltd.; *Int'l*, pg. 3069
GREE INC.—See Gree Electric Appliances, Inc. of Zhuhai; *Int'l*, pg. 3068
GREE INC.; *Int'l*, pg. 3069
GREEINDIA AIR CONDITONERS & APPLIANCES LTD.—See Gree Electric Appliances, Inc. of Zhuhai; *Int'l*, pg. 3068
GREE INTERNATIONAL INC.—See RockYou, Inc.; *U.S. Private*, pg. 3469
GREEK BAKING SCHOOL S.A.—See Loulis Food Ingredients S.A.; *Int'l*, pg. 4563
GREEK CATHOLIC UNION OF THE U.S.A.; *U.S. Private*, pg. 1770
G REEKIE GROUP LTD; *Int'l*, pg. 2861
GREEK NATIONAL TOURIST ORGANIZATION—See Greek National Tourist Organization; *Int'l*, pg. 3069
GREEK NATIONAL TOURIST ORGANIZATION; *Int'l*, pg. 3069
GREEK NAVAL SHIPYARDS HOLDING S.A.—See ThyssenKrupp AG; *Int'l*, pg. 7724
GREEK ORGANISATION OF FOOTBALL PROGNOSTICS S.A.; *Int'l*, pg. 3069
GREEK RESOURCE SERVICES, INC.—See GI Manager L.P.; *U.S. Private*, pg. 1694
GREEK STEEL INDUSTRY (SERVISTEEL) S.A.—See Metlen Energy & Metals S.A.; *Int'l*, pg. 4855
GREEKTOWN CASINO HOTEL—See PENN Entertainment, Inc.; *U.S. Public*, pg. 1662
GREEKTOWN HOLDINGS, LLC; *U.S. Private*, pg. 1770
GREELEY CONTAINMENT AND REWORK INC.; *Int'l*, pg. 3069
GREELEY & HANSEN LLC, FT. MYERS—See T.Y. Lin International Group Ltd.; *U.S. Private*, pg. 3913
GREELEY & HANSEN LLC, GARY—See T.Y. Lin International Group Ltd.; *U.S. Private*, pg. 3913
GREELEY & HANSEN LLC, INDIANAPOLIS—See T.Y. Lin International Group Ltd.; *U.S. Private*, pg. 3913
GREELEY & HANSEN LLC, LAS VEGAS—See T.Y. Lin International Group Ltd.; *U.S. Private*, pg. 3913
GREELEY & HANSEN LLC, NEW YORK—See T.Y. Lin International Group Ltd.; *U.S. Private*, pg. 3913
GREELEY & HANSEN LLC, PHILADELPHIA—See T.Y. Lin International Group Ltd.; *U.S. Private*, pg. 3913
GREELEY & HANSEN LLC, PHOENIX—See T.Y. Lin International Group Ltd.; *U.S. Private*, pg. 3913
GREELEY & HANSEN LLC, RICHMOND—See T.Y. Lin International Group Ltd.; *U.S. Private*, pg. 3913
GREELEY & HANSEN LLC, SARASOTA—See T.Y. Lin International Group Ltd.; *U.S. Private*, pg. 3913
GREELEY & HANSEN LLC—See T.Y. Lin International Group Ltd.; *U.S. Private*, pg. 3913
GREELEY & HANSEN LLC, TAMPA—See T.Y. Lin International Group Ltd.; *U.S. Private*, pg. 3913
GREEMAK GROUP DOO—See Gree Electric Appliances, Inc. of Zhuhai; *Int'l*, pg. 3068
GREE MALAYSIA SDN. BHD.—See Gree Electric Appliances, Inc. of Zhuhai; *Int'l*, pg. 3068
GREEN 2 BLUE ENERGY CORP.; *Int'l*, pg. 3069
GREEN 711 THIRD AVENUE LLC—See SL Green Realty Corp.; *U.S. Public*, pg. 1894
GREEN ACRES CONTRACTING CO. INC.; *U.S. Private*, pg. 1771
GREENACRES DIALYSIS CENTER, LLC—See Nautic Partners, LLC; *U.S. Private*, pg. 2870
GREEN ACRES MALL, L.L.C.—See The Macerich Company; *U.S. Public*, pg. 2110
GREENACRES PET CREMATORIUM LIMITED—See CVS Group Plc; *Int'l*, pg. 1890
GREEN ADVERTISING—See WPP plc; *Int'l*, pg. 8483
GREENAFFAIR SAS—See VINCI S.A.; *Int'l*, pg. 8222
GREEN AGREVOLUTION PVT LTD.; *Int'l*, pg. 3069

COMPANY NAME INDEX

GREEN AIR CARE GROUP INC.—See Tiger Infrastructure Partners LP; *U.S. Private*, pg. 4170
GREEN AIR CO., LTD.—See Hyundai Steel Company; *Int'l*, pg. 3560
GREEN AIRPORTS INC.—See CCR S.A.; *Int'l*, pg. 1369
GREENALIA SA; *Int'l*, pg. 3073
GREEN AMERICA RECYCLING, LLC—See Summit Materials, Inc.; *U.S. Public*, pg. 1959
GREEN ANIMAL COMPANY—See Ship Healthcare Holdings, Inc.; *Int'l*, pg. 6852
GREEN AQUA COMPANY SGPS, S.A.; *Int'l*, pg. 3069
GREEN AQUA POVOA, S.A.—See GREEN AQUA Company SGPS, S.A.; *Int'l*, pg. 3069
GREEN ARROW RESOURCES INC.; *Int'l*, pg. 3069
GREEN ARROWS CENTRAL CO., LTD.—See Daiseki Eco. Solution Co., Ltd.; *Int'l*, pg. 1941
GREEN ARROWS KANSAI CO., LTD.—See Daiei Kankyo Co., Ltd.; *Int'l*, pg. 1924
GREEN & ARTS CO., LTD.—See Oriental Land Co., Ltd.; *Int'l*, pg. 5625
GREENAUER HOLDING INC.; *U.S. Private*, pg. 1774
GREEN AUTOMOTIVE COMPANY; *U.S. Private*, pg. 1771
GREENBACKER RENEWABLE ENERGY COMPANY LLC; *U.S. Private*, pg. 1774
GREENBACKER RENEWABLE ENERGY CORPORATION; *U.S. Private*, pg. 1774
GREEN BALLAST, INC.; *U.S. Private*, pg. 1771
GREENBALL CORPORATION; *U.S. Private*, pg. 1774
GREEN BANCORP, INC.—See Veritex Holdings, Inc.; *U.S. Public*, pg. 2283
GREENBANK CAPITAL INC.; *Int'l*, pg. 3073
GREENBANK HOLIDAYS LIMITED—See The Carlyle Group Inc.; *U.S. Public*, pg. 2047
GREEN BANK, N.A.—See Veritex Holdings, Inc.; *U.S. Public*, pg. 2283
GREENBANK VENTURES INC.; *Int'l*, pg. 3073
GREENBASE TECHNOLOGY CORP.—See NEXCOM International Co., Ltd.; *Int'l*, pg. 5242
GREEN BATTERY MINERALS INC.; *Int'l*, pg. 3069
GREENBAUM HOME FURNISHINGS; *U.S. Private*, pg. 1774
GREENBAX ENTERPRISES INC.; *U.S. Private*, pg. 1774
GREEN BAY DREDGED DEEP, LLC—See Rodono Diversified, Inc.; *U.S. Private*, pg. 3484
GREEN BAY NONWOVENS, INC.—See Suominen Oyj; *Int'l*, pg. 7334
GREEN BAY PACKAGING INC. - ARKANSAS KRAFT DIVISION—See Green Bay Packaging Inc.; *U.S. Private*, pg. 1771
GREEN BAY PACKAGING INC. - BAIRD DISPLAY DIVISION—See Green Bay Packaging Inc.; *U.S. Private*, pg. 1771
GREEN BAY PACKAGING INC. - BALTIMORE DIVISION—See Green Bay Packaging Inc.; *U.S. Private*, pg. 1771
GREEN BAY PACKAGING INC. - CALIFORNIA DIVISION—See Green Bay Packaging Inc.; *U.S. Private*, pg. 1771
GREEN BAY PACKAGING INC. - CHICKASHA DIVISION—See Green Bay Packaging Inc.; *U.S. Private*, pg. 1771
GREEN BAY PACKAGING INC. - CINCINNATI DIVISION—See Green Bay Packaging Inc.; *U.S. Private*, pg. 1771
GREEN BAY PACKAGING INC. - DE PERE DIVISION—See Green Bay Packaging Inc.; *U.S. Private*, pg. 1771
GREEN BAY PACKAGING INC. - EL PASO DIVISION—See Green Bay Packaging Inc.; *U.S. Private*, pg. 1771
GREEN BAY PACKAGING INC. - FIBER RESOURCE DIVISION—See Green Bay Packaging Inc.; *U.S. Private*, pg. 1771
GREEN BAY PACKAGING INC. - FOLDING CARTON DIVISION—See Green Bay Packaging Inc.; *U.S. Private*, pg. 1771
GREEN BAY PACKAGING INC. - FORT WORTH DIVISION—See Green Bay Packaging Inc.; *U.S. Private*, pg. 1771
GREEN BAY PACKAGING INC. - FREMONT DIVISION—See Green Bay Packaging Inc.; *U.S. Private*, pg. 1771
GREEN BAY PACKAGING INC. - GREEN BAY COATED PRODUCTS DIVISION—See Green Bay Packaging Inc.; *U.S. Private*, pg. 1771
GREEN BAY PACKAGING INC. - GREEN BAY DIVISION—See Green Bay Packaging Inc.; *U.S. Private*, pg. 1771
GREEN BAY PACKAGING INC. - GREEN BAY MILL DIVISION—See Green Bay Packaging Inc.; *U.S. Private*, pg. 1771
GREEN BAY PACKAGING INC. - KALAMAZOO DIVISION—See Green Bay Packaging Inc.; *U.S. Private*, pg. 1771
GREEN BAY PACKAGING INC. - KANSAS CITY DIVISION—See Green Bay Packaging Inc.; *U.S. Private*, pg. 1771

GREEN BAY PACKAGING INC. - MINNEAPOLIS DIVISION—See Green Bay Packaging Inc.; *U.S. Private*, pg. 1771
GREEN BAY PACKAGING INC. - PINECREST LUMBER DIVISION—See Green Bay Packaging Inc.; *U.S. Private*, pg. 1771
GREEN BAY PACKAGING INC.; *U.S. Private*, pg. 1771
GREEN BAY PACKAGING INC. - TULSA DIVISION—See Green Bay Packaging Inc.; *U.S. Private*, pg. 1771
GREEN BAY PACKAGING INC. - TWIN CITIES DIVISION—See Green Bay Packaging Inc.; *U.S. Private*, pg. 1771
GREEN BAY PACKAGING INC. - WAUSAU DIVISION—See Green Bay Packaging Inc.; *U.S. Private*, pg. 1771
GREEN BAY PACKAGING INC. - WINCHESTER DIVISION—See Green Bay Packaging Inc.; *U.S. Private*, pg. 1771
GREEN BAY PACKERS, INC.; *U.S. Private*, pg. 1771
GREEN BAY PRESS-GAZETTE—See Gannett Co., Inc.; *U.S. Public*, pg. 897
GREEN BAY REMODELING, INC.; *U.S. Private*, pg. 1771
GREEN BAY TERMINAL CORPORATION—See CHS INC.; *U.S. Public*, pg. 492
GREEN BAY TERMINAL CORPORATION—See Marathon Petroleum Corporation; *U.S. Public*, pg. 1364
GREEN BAY WATER UTILITY; *U.S. Private*, pg. 1771
GREEN BEANS COFFEE COMPANY, INC.; *U.S. Private*, pg. 1771
GREEN BELL BV—See LVMH Moet Hennessy Louis Vuitton SE; *Int'l*, pg. 4592
GREENBELT CAPITAL MANAGEMENT L.P.; *U.S. Private*, pg. 1774
GREENBELT RESOURCES CORP.; *U.S. Public*, pg. 964
GREENBERG FARROW ARCHITECTURE INC., CALIFORNIA—See Greenberg Farrow Architecture Incorporated; *U.S. Private*, pg. 1775
GREENBERG FARROW ARCHITECTURE INC., ILLINOIS—See Greenberg Farrow Architecture Incorporated; *U.S. Private*, pg. 1775
GREENBERG FARROW ARCHITECTURE INC., NEW YORK—See Greenberg Farrow Architecture Incorporated; *U.S. Private*, pg. 1775
GREENBERG FARROW ARCHITECTURE INCORPORATED; *U.S. Private*, pg. 1775
GREENBERG FARROW ARCHITECTURE INC., TEXAS—See Greenberg Farrow Architecture Incorporated; *U.S. Private*, pg. 1775
GREENBERG FRUIT COMPANY—See Wind Point Advisors LLC; *U.S. Private*, pg. 4534
GREENBERG INC.; *U.S. Private*, pg. 1775
GREENBERG ROOFING, INC.—See Altas Partners LP; *Int'l*, pg. 386
GREENBERG ROOFING, INC.—See Altas Partners LP; *Int'l*, pg. 386
GREENBERG'S JEWELERS INC.; *U.S. Private*, pg. 1775
GREENBERG SPORTS GROUP INC.; *U.S. Private*, pg. 1775
GREENBERG TRAURIG, LLP; *U.S. Private*, pg. 1775
GREENBERG TRAURIG, P.A.—See Greenberg Traurig, LLP; *U.S. Private*, pg. 1775
GREEN BITS, INC.—See Courier Plus, Inc.; *U.S. Private*, pg. 1068
GREEN & BLACK'S LIMITED—See Mondelez International, Inc.; *U.S. Public*, pg. 1461
GREEN BOX FOODS; *U.S. Private*, pg. 1771
GREENBRIAR CAPITAL CORP.; *Int'l*, pg. 3073
GREENBRIAR EQUITY GROUP, L.P.; *U.S. Private*, pg. 1775
GREENBRIAR OPERATIONS, LLC—See Apollo Global Management, Inc.; *U.S. Public*, pg. 156
GREEN BRICK MORTGAGE, LLC—See Hilltop Holdings Inc.; *U.S. Public*, pg. 1038
GREEN BRICK PARTNERS, INC.; *U.S. Public*, pg. 962
GREEN BRICK TITLE, LLC—See Green Brick Partners, Inc.; *U.S. Public*, pg. 962
GREENBRIER CHRYSLER-JEEP—See Southern Hospitality Auto Group of Virginia; *U.S. Private*, pg. 3732
THE GREENBRIER COMPANIES, INC.; *U.S. Public*, pg. 2085
GREENBRIER FARMS, INC.; *U.S. Private*, pg. 1776
GREENBRIER GERMANY GMBH—See The Greenbrier Companies, Inc.; *U.S. Public*, pg. 2085
GREENBRIER INTERNATIONAL, INC.—See Dollar Tree, Inc.; *U.S. Public*, pg. 672
GREENBRIER MALL, LLC—See CBL & Associates Properties, Inc.; *U.S. Public*, pg. 458
GREENBRIER-MAXION EQUIPAMENTOS E SERVICOS FERROVIARIOS S.A.—See The Greenbrier Companies, Inc.; *U.S. Public*, pg. 2086
GREENBRIER PET LOSS SERVICES, LLC—See Matthews International Corporation; *U.S. Public*, pg. 1399
GREENBRIER PETROLEUM CORPORATION—See MRC Global Inc.; *U.S. Public*, pg. 1481
GREENBRIER RAILCAR LLC—See The Greenbrier Companies, Inc.; *U.S. Public*, pg. 2086
GREENBRIER RAIL SERVICES WHEEL DIVISION—See The Greenbrier Companies, Inc.; *U.S. Public*, pg. 2086

GREEN CROSS HEALTH LIMITED

GREENBRIER REALTY, L.L.C.—See Acadia Healthcare Company, Inc.; *U.S. Public*, pg. 29
THE GREENBRIER—See Justice Family Group, LLC; *U.S. Private*, pg. 2246
GREENBROOK TMS, INC.; *Int'l*, pg. 3073
GREEN BUILDERS, INC.; *U.S. Private*, pg. 1772
GREEN BUILDING CERTIFICATION INSTITUTE; *U.S. Private*, pg. 1772
GREEN BUILD TECHNOLOGY LTD.; *Int'l*, pg. 3069
GREEN BULL—See Triton Advisers Limited; *Int'l*, pg. 7935
GREENBYTES, INC.—See Oracle Corporation; *U.S. Public*, pg. 1611
GREEN CALL SERVICE S.R.L.—See Gruppo MutuiOnline S.p.A; *Int'l*, pg. 3141
GREENCAP HOLDINGS LIMITED—See Wesfarmers Limited; *Int'l*, pg. 8381
GREENCAP LIMITED—See WSP Global, Inc.; *Int'l*, pg. 8496
GREENCAPS PHARMACEUTICAL CO., LTD.—See TOWA PHARMACEUTICAL CO. LTD.; *Int'l*, pg. 7849
GREENCASTLE RESOURCES LTD.; *Int'l*, pg. 3073
GREENCAT SP. Z O.O.—See The Timken Company; *U.S. Public*, pg. 2132
GREEN & CHAPMAN, INC.; *U.S. Private*, pg. 1771
GREENCHEM HOLDING B.V.—See Agrofert Holding, a.s.; *Int'l*, pg. 219
GREEN CHEMICAL CO., LTD.; *Int'l*, pg. 3069
GREENCHEM INDUSTRIES LLC; *U.S. Private*, pg. 1776
GREEN CHEVROLET-BUICK-GMC, INC.; *U.S. Private*, pg. 1772
GREEN CHEVROLET, INC.; *U.S. Private*, pg. 1772
GREEN CHIMNEYS CHILDREN'S SERVICES, INC.; *U.S. Private*, pg. 1772
GREEN CHINA HOLDINGS LIMITED; *Int'l*, pg. 3070
GREEN CIRCLE BIO ENERGY INC.; *U.S. Private*, pg. 1772
GREENCITY ACQUISITION CORPORATION; *Int'l*, pg. 3073
GREEN CLINIC, LLC—See Community Health Systems, Inc.; *U.S. Public*, pg. 553
GREEN CLOUD TECHNOLOGIES, LLC; *U.S. Private*, pg. 1772
GREENCLUSTER GMBH—See Voltabox AG; *Int'l*, pg. 8303
GREEN COAST ENTERPRISES LLC; *Int'l*, pg. 3070
GREENCOAT RENEWABLES PLC; *Int'l*, pg. 3073
GREENCOAT UK WIND PLC; *Int'l*, pg. 3073
GREEN COMPLIANCE WATER DIVISION LTD.—See Arjun Infrastructure Partners Limited; *Int'l*, pg. 568
GREENCORE DEVELOPMENTS LIMITED—See Greencore Group plc; *Int'l*, pg. 3074
GREENCORE FINANCE LIMITED—See Greencore Group plc; *Int'l*, pg. 3074
GREENCORE FOOD TO GO LIMITED—See Greencore Group plc; *Int'l*, pg. 3074
GREENCORE FROZEN FOODS LTD—See Greencore Group plc; *Int'l*, pg. 3074
GREENCORE GROCERY LIMITED—See Greencore Group plc; *Int'l*, pg. 3074
GREENCORE GROUP PLC - GREENCORE FOOD TO GO MANTON WOOD FACILITY—See Greencore Group plc; *Int'l*, pg. 3074
GREENCORE GROUP PLC; *Int'l*, pg. 3073
GREENCORE NORTHAMPTON—See Greencore Group plc; *Int'l*, pg. 3074
GREENCORE PREPARED MEALS-KIVETON—See Greencore Group plc; *Int'l*, pg. 3074
GREENCORE PREPARED MEALS—See Greencore Group plc; *Int'l*, pg. 3074
GREENCORE SANDWICHES LTD.—See Greencore Group plc; *Int'l*, pg. 3074
GREENCORE SAUCES AND SOUPS LTD.—See Greencore Group plc; *Int'l*, pg. 3074
GREENCORE UK HOLDINGS PLC—See Greencore Group plc; *Int'l*, pg. 3074
GREENCORE USA - CPG PARTNERS, LLC—See Charlesbank Capital Partners, LLC; *U.S. Private*, pg. 855
GREENCORE USA - CPG PARTNERS, LLC—See Partners Group Holding AG; *Int'l*, pg. 5749
GREEN COUNTRY PHYSICAL THERAPY, LIMITED PARTNERSHIP—See U.S. Physical Therapy, Inc.; *U.S. Public*, pg. 2214
GREEN COURTE PARTNERS, LLC; *U.S. Private*, pg. 1772
GREENCREST FINANCIAL SERVICES LIMITED; *Int'l*, pg. 3074
GREEN CRITICAL MINERALS LIMITED; *Int'l*, pg. 3070
GREEN CROSS CELL CORP.; *Int'l*, pg. 3070
GREEN CROSS CORPORATION - HWASUN PLANT—See GC Biopharma Corp.; *Int'l*, pg. 2894
GREEN CROSS CORPORATION - OCHANG PLANT—See GC Biopharma Corp.; *Int'l*, pg. 2894
GREEN CROSS HEALTH LIMITED; *Int'l*, pg. 3070
GREEN CROSS HEALTH SCIENCE—See GC Biopharma Corp.; *Int'l*, pg. 2894
GREEN CROSS HK HOLDINGS LIMITED—See China Resources Boya Bio-pharmaceutical Group Co., Ltd.; *Int'l*, pg. 1548

GREEN CROSS HOLDINGS CORP.

CORPORATE AFFILIATIONS

GREEN CROSS HOLDINGS CORP.; *Int'l*, pg. 3070
GREEN CROSS I-MED—See GC Biopharma Corp.; *Int'l*, pg. 2894
GREENCROSS LIMITED—See TPG Capital, L.P.; *U.S. Public*, pg. 2176
GREEN CROSS MEDICAL SCIENCE CORPORATION—See GC Biopharma Corp.; *Int'l*, pg. 2894
GREEN CROSS MEDICAL SCIENCE CORP.—See Green Cross WellBeing Corp.; *Int'l*, pg. 3070
GREEN CROSS MEDIS CORP.—See Green Cross WellBeing Corp.; *Int'l*, pg. 3070
GREENCROSS NSW PTY LTD.—See TPG Capital, L.P.; *U.S. Public*, pg. 2176
GREEN CROSS PROPERTY LIMITED—See Co-operative Group Limited; *Int'l*, pg. 1679
GREENCROSS VETS SOUTHCOAST PTY. LTD.—See TPG Capital, L.P.; *U.S. Public*, pg. 2176
GREEN CROSS WELLBEING CORP.; *Int'l*, pg. 3070
GREEN CROW CORPORATION; *U.S. Private*, pg. 1772
GREENDALE VETERINARY DIAGNOSTICS LIMITED—See CVS Group Plc; *Int'l*, pg. 1890
GREEN DELTA CAPITAL LTD.—See Green Delta Insurance Company Limited; *Int'l*, pg. 3070
GREEN DELTA INSURANCE COMPANY LIMITED; *Int'l*, pg. 3070
GREEN DIAMOND EQUIPMENT LTD.; *Int'l*, pg. 3070
GREEN DIAMOND RESOURCE COMPANY; *U.S. Private*, pg. 1772
GREEN DIAMOND SAND PRODUCTS INC.—See AAVIN, LLC; *U.S. Private*, pg. 33
GREEN DIAMOND SAND PRODUCTS INC.—See MSI Capital Partners LLC; *U.S. Private*, pg. 2807
GREEN DOT ADVERTISING & MARKETING; *U.S. Private*, pg. 1772
GREEN DOT BANK—See Green Dot Corporation; *U.S. Public*, pg. 963
GREEN DOT CORPORATION; *U.S. Public*, pg. 963
GREENEARTH CLEANING LIMITED—See Johnson Service Group PLC; *Int'l*, pg. 3993
GREEN EARTH INSTITUTE CO., LTD.; *Int'l*, pg. 3070
GREEN EARTH TECHNOLOGIES, INC.; *U.S. Private*, pg. 1772
GREENE BEVERAGE CO. INC.; *U.S. Private*, pg. 1776
THE GREENE COMPANY OF VIRGINIA INC.; *U.S. Private*, pg. 4039
GREEN ECONOMY DEVELOPMENT LIMITED; *Int'l*, pg. 3070
GREENE COUNTY BANCORP, INC.; *U.S. Public*, pg. 964
GREEN EDIBLE OIL SDN. BHD.—See Kretam Holdings Berhad; *Int'l*, pg. 4301
GREENE GROUP INC.; *U.S. Private*, pg. 1776
GREENE HOLCOMB & FISHER, LLC—See Bank of Montreal; *Int'l*, pg. 847
GREENE KING BREWING & RETAILING LIMITED—See CK Asset Holdings Limited; *Int'l*, pg. 1635
GREENE KING PLC—See CK Asset Holdings Limited; *Int'l*, pg. 1635
GREENE KING RETAILING LIMITED—See CK Asset Holdings Limited; *Int'l*, pg. 1635
GREENE KING RETAIL SERVICES LIMITED—See CK Asset Holdings Limited; *Int'l*, pg. 1635
GREENE KING SERVICES LIMITED—See CK Asset Holdings Limited; *Int'l*, pg. 1635
GREENELL CORP.; *U.S. Private*, pg. 1777
GREEN ENDEAVORS, INC.; *U.S. Private*, pg. 1772
GREEN ENERGY 4 SEASONS; *Int'l*, pg. 3071
GREEN ENERGY GROUP LIMITED; *Int'l*, pg. 3071
GREEN ENERGY INC.—See CDN Maverick Capital Corp.; *Int'l*, pg. 1371
GREENENERGY INTERNATIONAL INC.—See Shish Industries Limited; *Int'l*, pg. 6854
GREEN ENERGY MANAGEMENT SERVICES HOLDINGS, INC.; *U.S. Private*, pg. 1772
GREEN ENERGY RESOURCES INC.—See Noram Lithium Corp.; *Int'l*, pg. 5415
GREEN ENERGY SOLUTION INDUSTRIES, INC.; *Int'l*, pg. 3071
GREEN ENVIROTECH HOLDINGS CORP.; *U.S. Public*, pg. 963
THE GREENE ORGANIZATION, INC.—See Kynetic LLC; *U.S. Private*, pg. 2360
GREEN EQUIPMENT COMPANY—See Core & Main, Inc.; *U.S. Public*, pg. 576
GREENE RESOURCES, INC.; *U.S. Private*, pg. 1777
GREENERGY ASIA DMCC—See Trafigura Beheer B.V.; *Int'l*, pg. 7890
GREENERGY BRASIL TRADING SA—See Trafigura Beheer B.V.; *Int'l*, pg. 7890
GREENERGY HOLDINGS INC.; *Int'l*, pg. 3074
GREENERGY INTERNATIONAL LIMITED—See Trafigura Beheer B.V.; *Int'l*, pg. 7889
GREENERGY USA INC.—See Trafigura Beheer B.V.; *Int'l*, pg. 7890
GREENERITY GMBH—See Toray Industries, Inc.; *Int'l*, pg. 7823
GREENER PASTURES GROUP HLLC; *U.S. Private*, pg. 1777
GREENERPRINTER; *U.S. Private*, pg. 1777

GREENE RUBBER COMPANY; *U.S. Private*, pg. 1777
GREENERU, INC.—See Casella Waste Systems, Inc.; *U.S. Public*, pg. 446
GREENERY OF CHARLESTON, LLC—See Ruppert Landscape, LLC; *U.S. Private*, pg. 3504
GREENE'S ENERGY CORP.; *U.S. Private*, pg. 1777
GREENE TOOL SYSTEMS, INC.—See The Jordan Company, L.P.; *U.S. Private*, pg. 4060
THE GREENE TURTLE FRANCHISING CORPORATION—See Stone-Goff Partners, LLC; *U.S. Private*, pg. 3826
GREENE, TWEED & CO., BENELUX B.V.—See Greene, Tweed & Co.; *U.S. Private*, pg. 1777
GREENE, TWEED & CO FRANCE SAS—See Greene, Tweed & Co.; *U.S. Private*, pg. 1777
GREENE, TWEED & CO. GMBH—See Greene, Tweed & Co.; *U.S. Private*, pg. 1777
GREENE, TWEED & CO. ITALIA S.R.L.—See Greene, Tweed & Co.; *U.S. Private*, pg. 1777
GREENE, TWEED & CO. JAPAN—See Greene, Tweed & Co.; *U.S. Private*, pg. 1777
GREENE, TWEED & CO., KOREA LTD.—See Greene, Tweed & Co.; *U.S. Private*, pg. 1777
GREENE, TWEED & CO., LIMITED—See Greene, Tweed & Co.; *U.S. Private*, pg. 1777
GREENE, TWEED & CO. PTE LTD.—See Greene, Tweed & Co.; *U.S. Private*, pg. 1777
GREENE, TWEED & CO.; *U.S. Private*, pg. 1777
GREENE, TWEED & CO. (SUISSE) SA—See Greene, Tweed & Co.; *U.S. Private*, pg. 1777
GREENEVILLE LIGHT & POWER SYSTEM; *U.S. Private*, pg. 1777
GREENEVILLE OIL & PETROLEUM INC.; *U.S. Private*, pg. 1777
THE GREENEVILLE SUN—See Adams Publishing Group, LLC; *U.S. Private*, pg. 75
GREEN FAMILY STORES, INC.; *U.S. Private*, pg. 1772
GREENFIELD AG—See Atlas Copco AB; *Int'l*, pg. 677
GREENFIELD BANCORPORATION LTD.; *U.S. Private*, pg. 1777
GREENFIELD BANCSHARES INC.; *U.S. Private*, pg. 1777
GREENFIELD BANKING COMPANY—See Greenfield Bancshares Inc.; *U.S. Private*, pg. 1777
GREENFIELD BEVERAGE COMPANY INC—See Zink Distributing Inc; *U.S. Private*, pg. 4605
GREENFIELD GOLF, L.L.C.; *U.S. Private*, pg. 1777
GREENFIELD INDUSTRIES CANADA INC.—See Dalian Top-Eastern Group Co., Ltd.; *Int'l*, pg. 1953
GREENFIELD INDUSTRIES, INC.—See Dalian Top-Eastern Group Co., Ltd.; *Int'l*, pg. 1953
GREENFIELD PARTNERS LLC; *U.S. Private*, pg. 1777
GREENFIELD-PRODUTOS FARMACEUTICOS, LDA.—See Eli Lilly & Company; *U.S. Public*, pg. 733
GREENFIELD RESEARCH, INC.; *U.S. Private*, pg. 1777
GREENFIELDS ASSISTED LIVING LLC—See The Ensign Group, Inc.; *U.S. Public*, pg. 2071
GREENFIELD SAVINGS BANK; *U.S. Private*, pg. 1778
GREENFIELDS BV—See ABN AMRO Group N.V.; *Int'l*, pg. 64
GREENFIELDS BV—See Gilde Buy Out Partners B.V.; *Int'l*, pg. 2974
GREENFIELDS BV—See Parcom Capital Management B.V.; *Int'l*, pg. 5740
GREENFIELD SENIOR LIVING INC.; *U.S. Private*, pg. 1778
GREENFIELDS HOLDING BV—See ABN AMRO Group N.V.; *Int'l*, pg. 64
GREENFIELDS HOLDING BV—See Gilde Buy Out Partners B.V.; *Int'l*, pg. 2974
GREENFIELDS HOLDING BV—See Parcom Capital Management B.V.; *Int'l*, pg. 5740
GREENFIELD SPECIALTY ALCOHOLS INC.; *Int'l*, pg. 3074
GREENFIELDS PETROLEUM CORPORATION; *U.S. Private*, pg. 1778
GREENFIELDS SPORTS & LEISURE PTY LTD.—See ABN AMRO Group N.V.; *Int'l*, pg. 64
GREENFIELDS SPORTS & LEISURE PTY LTD.—See Gilde Buy Out Partners B.V.; *Int'l*, pg. 2974
GREENFIELDS SPORTS & LEISURE PTY LTD.—See Parcom Capital Management B.V.; *Int'l*, pg. 5740
GREENFIELDS SWISS AG—See ABN AMRO Group N.V.; *Int'l*, pg. 64
GREENFIELDS SWISS AG—See Gilde Buy Out Partners B.V.; *Int'l*, pg. 2974
GREENFIELDS SWISS AG—See Parcom Capital Management B.V.; *Int'l*, pg. 5740
THE GREENFIELD TOWN CRIER—See Alden Global Capital LLC; *U.S. Private*, pg. 155
GREENFIELD WINE COMPANY; *U.S. Private*, pg. 1778
GREEN FILL KOSAKA CO., LTD.—See Dowa Holdings Co., Ltd.; *Int'l*, pg. 2183
GREENFIRE RESOURCES INC.—See Greenfire Resources Ltd.; *Int'l*, pg. 3074
GREENFIRE RESOURCES LTD.; *Int'l*, pg. 3074
GREENFIRE RESOURCES OPERATING CORPORATION—See Greenfire Resources Ltd.; *Int'l*, pg. 3074

GREENFIRST FOREST PRODUCTS INC.; *Int'l*, pg. 3074
GREEN FLAG LIMITED—See Direct Line Insurance Group plc; *Int'l*, pg. 2129
GREENFLAME METALS INC.—See Troubadour Resources, Inc.; *Int'l*, pg. 7939
GREENFLEX ACTIRENT GROUP, S.L.—See TotalEnergies SE; *Int'l*, pg. 7836
GREENFLEX S.A.S.—See TotalEnergies SE; *Int'l*, pg. 7836
GREEN FORD INC.; *U.S. Private*, pg. 1773
GREEN FORD SALES INC.; *U.S. Private*, pg. 1773
GREEN FOR ENERGY, INC.; *U.S. Public*, pg. 963
GREEN FOREST (QINGXIN) PAPER INDUSTRIAL LIMITED—See Hop Fung Group Holdings Ltd; *Int'l*, pg. 3473
GREEN FUTURE FOOD HYDROCOLLOID MARINE SCIENCE COMPANY LIMITED; *Int'l*, pg. 3071
GREENGEEKS, LLC; *U.S. Private*, pg. 1778
GREEN GIANT INC.; *Int'l*, pg. 3071
GREEN GIFFORD MOTOR CORP.; *U.S. Private*, pg. 1773
GREEN GOLD CO., LTD.—See Asian Phytoceuticals Public Company Limited; *Int'l*, pg. 619
GREEN GRASS ECOLOGICAL TECHNOLOGY DEVELOPMENT CO., LTD.; *Int'l*, pg. 3071
GREEN GRASS FOODS, INC.—See MidOcean Partners, LLP; *U.S. Private*, pg. 2717
GREEN GRASS FOODS, INC.—See The Kroger Co.; *U.S. Public*, pg. 2108
GREENGRO TECHNOLOGIES INC.; *U.S. Public*, pg. 964
GREEN GROUP HOLDINGS LLC; *U.S. Private*, pg. 1773
GREEN GROWTH BRANDS, INC.; *Int'l*, pg. 3071
GREENHAM—See Bunzl plc; *Int'l*, pg. 1217
GREENHAVEN, INC.—See Apax Partners LLP; *Int'l*, pg. 506
GREENHAWK RESOURCES INC.; *Int'l*, pg. 3074
GREENHEART GROUP LIMITED; *Int'l*, pg. 3074
GREENHEART (SURINAME) N.V.—See Greenheart Group Limited; *Int'l*, pg. 3075
GREENHECK FAN CORPORATION; *U.S. Private*, pg. 1778
GREENHILL AIR, INC.; *U.S. Private*, pg. 1778
GREENHILL & CO. ASIA (SINGAPORE) PTE. LTD.—See Mizuho Financial Group, Inc.; *Int'l*, pg. 4997
GREENHILL & CO. AUSTRALIA PTY LIMITED—See Mizuho Financial Group, Inc.; *Int'l*, pg. 4997
GREENHILL & CO. CANADA LTD.—See Mizuho Financial Group, Inc.; *Int'l*, pg. 4997
GREENHILL & CO. DO BRASIL ASSESSORIA LTDA.—See Mizuho Financial Group, Inc.; *Int'l*, pg. 4997
GREENHILL & CO. EUROPE LLP—See Mizuho Financial Group, Inc.; *Int'l*, pg. 4997
GREENHILL COGENT—See Mizuho Financial Group, Inc.; *Int'l*, pg. 4997
GREENHILL & CO., INC.—See Mizuho Financial Group, Inc.; *Int'l*, pg. 4997
GREENHILL & CO. INTERNATIONAL LLP—See Mizuho Financial Group, Inc.; *Int'l*, pg. 4997
GREENHILL & CO. JAPAN LTD.—See Mizuho Financial Group, Inc.; *Int'l*, pg. 4997
GREENHILL & CO., LLC—See Mizuho Financial Group, Inc.; *Int'l*, pg. 4997
GREENHILL & CO. SWEDEN AB—See Mizuho Financial Group, Inc.; *Int'l*, pg. 4997
GREENHILL GERMANY GMBH—See Mizuho Financial Group, Inc.; *Int'l*, pg. 4997
GREEN HILL INC.; *U.S. Private*, pg. 1773
GREEN HILLS SOFTWARE AB—See Green Hills Software Inc.; *U.S. Private*, pg. 1773
GREEN HILLS SOFTWARE BV—See Green Hills Software Inc.; *U.S. Private*, pg. 1773
GREEN HILLS SOFTWARE GMBH—See Green Hills Software Inc.; *U.S. Private*, pg. 1773
GREEN HILLS SOFTWARE INC.; *U.S. Private*, pg. 1773
GREEN HILLS SOFTWARE (ISRAEL) LTD—See Green Hills Software Inc.; *U.S. Private*, pg. 1773
GREEN HILLS SOFTWARE, LAGUNA HILLS—See Green Hills Software Inc.; *U.S. Private*, pg. 1773
GREEN HILLS SOFTWARE LTD.—See Green Hills Software Inc.; *U.S. Private*, pg. 1773
GREEN HILLS SOFTWARE LTD.—See Green Hills Software Inc.; *U.S. Private*, pg. 1773
GREEN HILLS SOFTWARE, PALM HARBOR—See Green Hills Software Inc.; *U.S. Private*, pg. 1773
GREEN HILLS SOFTWARE S.A.R.L.—See Green Hills Software Inc.; *U.S. Private*, pg. 1773
GREENHOE, INC.—See Schilke Music Products, Inc.; *U.S. Private*, pg. 3565
GREEN HOLDING S.P.A.; *Int'l*, pg. 3071
GREENHOMES AMERICA, LLC—See ABM Industries, Inc.; *U.S. Public*, pg. 25
GREEN HOME SOLUTIONS LLC—See Grupe Holding Company; *U.S. Private*, pg. 1797
GREEN HOSPITAL SUPPLY, INC.—See Ship Healthcare Holdings, Inc.; *Int'l*, pg. 6852
GREEN HOUSE CAPITAL LIMITED—See Molecular Energies PLC; *Int'l*, pg. 5021
GREENHOUSE HOLDINGS, INC.—See root9B Holdings, Inc.; *U.S. Public*, pg. 1810

COMPANY NAME INDEX

GREEN HOUSER CO., LTD.—See JUTEC Holdings Corporation; *Int'l*, pg. 4032
GREENHOUSE REAL ESTATE, LLC—See AAC Holdings, Inc.; *U.S. Private*, pg. 31
GREENHOUSE SCHOLARS; *U.S. Private*, pg. 1778
GREENHOUSE SOFTWARE, INC.; *U.S. Private*, pg. 1778
GREENHOUSE SOLUTIONS INC.; *U.S. Public*, pg. 964
GREENHOUSE TREATMENT CENTER, LLC—See AAC Holdings, Inc.; *U.S. Private*, pg. 30
GREENHOUS GROUP LTD.; *Int'l*, pg. 3075
GREENHUNTER ENVIRONMENTAL SOLUTIONS, LLC—See GreenHunter Resources, Inc.; *U.S. Private*, pg. 1778
GREENHUNTER RESOURCES, INC.; *U.S. Private*, pg. 1778
GREENHUT CONSTRUCTION COMPANY, INC.; *U.S. Private*, pg. 1778
GREENHY2 LIMITED; *Int'l*, pg. 3075
GREEN HYDROGEN SYSTEMS A/S; *Int'l*, pg. 3071
GREEN HYGIENICS HOLDINGS INC.; *U.S. Public*, pg. 963
GREENIDGE GENERATION HOLDINGS INC.; *U.S. Public*, pg. 964
GREENIDGE GENERATION LLC—See Greenidge Generation Holdings Inc.; *U.S. Public*, pg. 964
GREEN IMPACT PARTNERS INC.; *Int'l*, pg. 3071
GREEN INDUSTRY SOLUTIONS INC.—See Munro Companies, Inc.; *U.S. Private*, pg. 2814
GREENING DONALD CO. LTD.—See ThyssenKrupp AG; *Int'l*, pg. 7729
GREEN INNOVATIONS LTD.; *U.S. Private*, pg. 1773
GREEN INTERNATIONAL HOLDINGS LIMITED; *Int'l*, pg. 3071
GREEN ISLE BRANDS LIMITED—See Boparan Holdings Limited; *Int'l*, pg. 1111
GREEN-IT TURF PRODUCTS INC.—See Central Garden & Pet Company; *U.S. Public*, pg. 473
GREENIX LLC; *U.S. Private*, pg. 1778
GREENJACKET INC.—See Hubbell Incorporated; *U.S. Public*, pg. 1066
GREEN KAIJI KAISHA, LTD.—See Mitsui O.S.K. Lines, Ltd.; *Int'l*, pg. 4989
GREENKO DUTCH B.V.; *Int'l*, pg. 3075
GREENKO ENERGIES PVT. LTD.—See Greenko Dutch B.V., *Int'l*, pg. 3075
GREENKRAFT, INC.; *U.S. Public*, pg. 964
GREEN LAKE EXCHANGE, LLC.—See Walsin Lihwa Corporation; *Int'l*, pg. 8334
GREEN LAKE RESORT, LLC—See The Marcus Corporation; *U.S. Public*, pg. 2112
GREENLAM AMERICA, INC.—See Greenply Industries Limited; *Int'l*, pg. 3076
GREENLAM ASIA PACIFIC PTE. LTD.—See Greenply Industries Limited; *Int'l*, pg. 3076
GREENLAM ASIA PACIFIC (THAILAND) CO LTD.—See Greenply Industries Limited; *Int'l*, pg. 3076
GREENLAM DECOLAN SA—See Greenlam Industries Limited; *Int'l*, pg. 3075
GREENLAM INDUSTRIES LIMITED; *Int'l*, pg. 3075
GREENLAM RUS LLC—See Greenlam Industries Limited; *Int'l*, pg. 3075
GREENLAND (AMERICA) INC.; *U.S. Private*, pg. 1778
GREENLAND FEDHA LTD—See Kenya Tea Development Agency Limited; *Int'l*, pg. 4129
GREENLAND HOLDING A/S; *Int'l*, pg. 3075
GREENLAND HOLDING GROUP CO., LTD.—See Greenland Holdings Corporation Limited; *Int'l*, pg. 3075
GREENLAND HOLDINGS CORPORATION LIMITED; *Int'l*, pg. 3075
GREENLAND HONG KONG HOLDINGS LIMITED—See Greenland Holdings Corporation Limited; *Int'l*, pg. 3075
GREENLAND RESORT COMPANY LIMITED; *Int'l*, pg. 3075
GREENLAND RESOURCES INC.; *Int'l*, pg. 3075
GREEN LANDSCAPING AB—See FSN Capital Partners AS; *Int'l*, pg. 2799
GREENLANDS REJSEBUREAU A/S—See Air Greenland A/S; *Int'l*, pg. 238
GREENLAND TECHNOLOGIES HOLDING CORPORATION; *Int'l*, pg. 3075
GREENLANE BIOGAS EUROPE LTD—See Pressure Technologies Plc; *Int'l*, pg. 5965
GREENLANE HOLDINGS, INC.; *U.S. Public*, pg. 964
GREENLANE IMAGING LTD—See BGH Capital Pty Ltd; *Int'l*, pg. 1008
GREENLANE IMAGING LTD—See Ontario Teachers' Pension Plan; *Int'l*, pg. 5586
GREENLANE RENEWABLES, INC.; *Int'l*, pg. 3075
GREEN LANTERN, INC.—See Blue Beacon International, Inc.; *U.S. Private*, pg. 585
GREEN LAWN FERTILIZING, INC.; *U.S. Private*, pg. 1773
GREENLAWN FUNERAL HOMES, INC.—See Carriage Services, Inc.; *U.S. Public*, pg. 439
GREEN LEADER HOLDINGS GROUP LIMITED; *Int'l*, pg. 3071
GREEN LEADS, LLC—See Next 15 Group plc; *Int'l*, pg. 5245
GREENLEAF AUTO RECYCLERS, LLC—See LKQ Corporation; *U.S. Public*, pg. 1334

GREENLEAF BOOK GROUP, LLC; *U.S. Private*, pg. 1778
GREENLEAF CAPITAL LLC—See HCI Group, Inc.; *U.S. Public*, pg. 1014
GREENLEAF CENTER, LLC—See Acadia Healthcare Company, Inc.; *U.S. Public*, pg. 29
GREENLEAF COMPACTION, INC.—See Waste Management, Inc.; *U.S. Public*, pg. 2331
THE GREENLEAF COMPANY INC.; *U.S. Private*, pg. 4039
GREENLEAF CORPORATION; *U.S. Private*, pg. 1778
GREENLEAF DIALYSIS, LLC—See DaVita Inc.; *U.S. Public*, pg. 639
GREENLEAF ENVIRONMENTAL GROUP, INC.; *U.S. Private*, pg. 1778
GREENLEAF GENETICS LLC—See China National Chemical Corporation; *Int'l*, pg. 1529
GREENLEAF, INC.—See Grace Management Group, LLC; *U.S. Private*, pg. 1749
GREEN LEAF INNOVATIONS, INC.; *U.S. Public*, pg. 963
GREEN LEAF LLC—See Ford Motor Company; *U.S. Public*, pg. 866
GREENLEAF NURSERY CO. INC.; *U.S. Private*, pg. 1778
GREEN LEAF PLANTS—See Aris Horticulture, Inc.; *U.S. Private*, pg. 323
GREENLEAF POWER—See Denham Capital Management LP; *U.S. Private*, pg. 1205
GREENLEAF-TNX SIKH SOLAR, LLC; *U.S. Private*, pg. 1778
GREENLEAF WHOLESALE FLORIST INC.; *U.S. Private*, pg. 1778
GREENLEE PLUMBING INC.—See Emerson Electric Co.; *U.S. Public*, pg. 741
GREENLEE PLUMBING INC.—See Emerson Electric Co.; *U.S. Public*, pg. 750
GREENLEE TOOLS, INC.—See Emerson Electric Co.; *U.S. Public*, pg. 741
GREENLEE TOOLS, INC.—See Emerson Electric Co.; *U.S. Public*, pg. 741
GREENLEE TOOLS, INC.—See Emerson Electric Co.; *U.S. Public*, pg. 750
GREENLEE TOOLS, INC.—See Emerson Electric Co.; *U.S. Public*, pg. 750
GREENLEE TOOLS, INC.—See Emerson Electric Co.; *U.S. Public*, pg. 750
GREEN LIFE CO., LTD.—See Ship Healthcare Holdings, Inc.; *Int'l*, pg. 6852
GREEN LIFE EAST CO., LTD.—See Ship Healthcare Holdings, Inc.; *Int'l*, pg. 6852
GREEN LIFE SCIENCE CO., LTD; *Int'l*, pg. 3071
GREENLIGHT ACQUISITION CORPORATION—See Verra Mobility Corporation; *U.S. Public*, pg. 2286
GREENLIGHT CAPITAL, INC.; *U.S. Private*, pg. 1778
GREENLIGHT CAPITAL RE, LTD.; *Int'l*, pg. 3075
GREENLIGHT COMMERCE LIMITED—See Brave Bison Group plc; *Int'l*, pg. 1141
GREENLIGHT DIGITAL LIMITED—See Brave Bison Group plc; *Int'l*, pg. 1141
GREEN LIGHT ENVIRONMENT PTY LIMITED—See Subsea 7 S.A.; *Int'l*, pg. 7249
GREENLIGHT MEDIA & MARKETING, LLC—See Live Nation Entertainment, Inc.; *U.S. Public*, pg. 1329
GREENLIGHT REINSURANCE IRELAND, LIMITED—See Greenlight Capital Re, Ltd.; *Int'l*, pg. 3075
GREENLIGHT REINSURANCE, LTD.—See Greenlight Capital Re, Ltd.; *Int'l*, pg. 3075
GREENLIGHT; *Int'l*, pg. 3075
GREENLINE A/S—See Brodrene A & O Johansen A/S; *Int'l*, pg. 1173
GREEN LINE EQUIPMENT - ALBION—See Green Line Equipment, Inc.; *U.S. Private*, pg. 1773
GREEN LINE EQUIPMENT, INC.; *U.S. Private*, pg. 1773
GREEN LINE EQUIPMENT - NORFOLK—See Green Line Equipment, Inc.; *U.S. Private*, pg. 1773
GREEN LINE EQUIPMENT - SPALDING—See Green Line Equipment, Inc.; *U.S. Private*, pg. 1773
GREEN LINE INVESTOR SERVICE—See The Toronto-Dominion Bank; *Int'l*, pg. 7694
GREEN LINE POLYMERS, INC.—See Advanced Drainage Systems, Inc.; *U.S. Public*, pg. 46
GREEN LINES TRANSPORTATION; *U.S. Private*, pg. 1773
GREENLINE SYNERGY CO., LTD.—See Bangkok Dusit Medical Services Public Company Limited; *Int'l*, pg. 834
GREENLINK FINANCIAL, LLC; *U.S. Private*, pg. 1779
GREENLINK INTERNATIONAL, INC.; *U.S. Public*, pg. 965
GREENLINKS GOLF VILLAS; *U.S. Private*, pg. 1779
GREENLIT BRANDS PROPRIETARY LIMITED—See Steinhoff International Holdings N.V.; *Int'l*, pg. 7194
GREENLIT VENTURES, INC.; *Int'l*, pg. 3075
GREENLOGIC ENERGY; *U.S. Private*, pg. 1779
GREENLOOP IT, INC.; *U.S. Private*, pg. 1779
GREENLOTS TECHNOLOGY INDIA LLP—See Shell plc; *Int'l*, pg. 6795
GREEN MANAGEMENT SP. Z O.O.—See Caiano AS; *Int'l*, pg. 1252
GREENMAN-PEDERSEN, INC.; *U.S. Private*, pg. 1779
GREEN MANUFACTURING, INC.—See ShoreView Industries, LLC; *U.S. Private*, pg. 3642

GREENPEACE, INC.

GREEN MESSAGE CO., LTD.—See Kewpie Corporation; *Int'l*, pg. 4144
GREEN METALS HOKURIKU INC.—See Toyota Tsusho Corporation; *Int'l*, pg. 7877
GREEN METALS UK LTD—See Toyota Tsusho Corporation; *Int'l*, pg. 7880
GREEN METHANE S.R.L.—See Rosetti Marino S.p.A.; *Int'l*, pg. 6400
GREEN MINERALS AS; *Int'l*, pg. 3071
GREEN MOBILITY INNOVATIONS LIMITED—See CN Innovations Holdings Limited; *Int'l*, pg. 1673
GREEN MOUNTAIN AS—See Azrieli Group Ltd.; *Int'l*, pg. 781
THE GREEN MOUNTAIN CORPORATION; *U.S. Private*, pg. 4039
GREEN MOUNTAIN DEVELOPMENT CORP.; *U.S. Public*, pg. 963
GREEN MOUNTAIN ENERGY COMPANY—See NRG Energy, Inc.; *U.S. Public*, pg. 1550
GREEN MOUNTAIN INSURANCE COMPANY.—See Concord General Mu; *U.S. Private*, pg. 1010
GREEN MOUNTAIN KNITTING INC.; *U.S. Private*, pg. 1773
GREEN MOUNTAIN LAWN & TREE CARE—See Senske Lawn & Tree Care, Inc.; *U.S. Private*, pg. 3608
GREEN MOUNTAIN MERGER, INC.; *U.S. Public*, pg. 963
GREEN MOUNTAIN POWER CORPORATION—See Caisse de Depot et Placement du Quebec; *Int'l*, pg. 1256
GREEN MOUNTAIN RIFLE BARREL CO. INC.—See EBSCO Industries, Inc.; *U.S. Private*, pg. 1325
GREEN NATURAL PRODUCT CO., LTD.—See Loxley Public Company Limited; *Int'l*, pg. 4567
GREEN OAK INVESTMENTS LLC—See Stellex Capital Management LP; *U.S. Private*, pg. 3800
GREENOAKS CAPITAL PARTNERS LLC; *U.S. Private*, pg. 1779
GREEN OAKS HOSPITAL—See HCA Healthcare, Inc.; *U.S. Public*, pg. 997
GREEN OAKS HOTEL—See Hostmark Hospitality Group; *U.S. Private*, pg. 1988
GREEN OAKS PHYSICAL THERAPY, LIMITED PARTNERSHIP—See U.S. Physical Therapy, Inc.; *U.S. Public*, pg. 2214
GREEN OCEAN CORPORATION BERHAD; *Int'l*, pg. 3072
GREEN OIL CO. INC.; *U.S. Private*, pg. 1773
GREEN OLEO SPA; *Int'l*, pg. 3072
GREENORBIT INC.—See Knosys Limited; *Int'l*, pg. 4212
GREENORBIT PTY. LTD.—See Knosys Limited; *Int'l*, pg. 4212
GREENORBIT SOFTWARE LIMITED—See Knosys Limited; *Int'l*, pg. 4212
GREENORDER, LLC—See Cleantech Group, Inc.; *U.S. Private*, pg. 931
GREENOUGH COMMUNICATIONS; *U.S. Private*, pg. 1779
GREENOVATION POWER CO., LTD.—See Gunkul Engineering Co., Ltd.; *Int'l*, pg. 3183
GREENOVATIVE S.A.—See Quality & Reliability S.A.; *Int'l*, pg. 6152
GREEN-OWENS INSURANCE—See Keystone Group, L.P.; *U.S. Private*, pg. 2299
GREEN PACKET (AUSTRALIA) PTY. LTD.—See Green Packet Berhad; *Int'l*, pg. 3072
GREEN PACKET BERHAD; *Int'l*, pg. 3072
GREEN PACKET, INC.—See Green Packet Berhad; *Int'l*, pg. 3072
GREEN PACKET NETWORKS (TAIWAN) PTE. LTD.—See Green Packet Berhad; *Int'l*, pg. 3072
GREEN PACKET NETWORKS W.L.L.—See Green Packet Berhad; *Int'l*, pg. 3072
GREEN PACKET (SHANGHAI) LTD.—See Green Packet Berhad; *Int'l*, pg. 3072
GREENPAGES, INC.; *U.S. Private*, pg. 1779
GREENPAGES—See GreenPages, Inc.; *U.S. Private*, pg. 1779
GREEN PANDA CAPITAL CORP.; *Int'l*, pg. 3072
GREEN PANEL PTY. LTD.—See Dominant Enterprise Berhad; *Int'l*, pg. 2161
GREEN PARTS INTERNATIONAL, INC.; *U.S. Private*, pg. 1773
GREENPATH INC; *U.S. Private*, pg. 1779
GREENPEACE; *U.S. Private*, pg. 1779
GREEN PEST MANAGEMENT PTE. LTD—See ISOTeam Ltd.; *Int'l*, pg. 3821
GREEN PHARMACY CO., LTD.—See Ship Healthcare Holdings, Inc.; *Int'l*, pg. 6852
GREENPHIRE, INC.—See Thoma Bravo, L.P.; *U.S. Private*, pg. 4148
GREENPIECE LANDSCAPES INDIA PRIVATE LIMITED—See Quess Corp Limited; *Int'l*, pg. 6160
GREEN, PLAGGE & SHAW, LTD.—See Savant Capital, LLC; *U.S. Private*, pg. 3556
GREEN PLAINS ATKINSON LLC—See Green Plains Inc.; *U.S. Public*, pg. 963
GREEN PLAINS BLUFFTON LLC—See Valero Energy Corporation; *U.S. Public*, pg. 2272
GREEN PLAINS CENTRAL CITY LLC—See Green Plains Inc.; *U.S. Public*, pg. 963

GREENPEACE, INC.

GREEN PLAINS COMMODITIES LLC—See Green Plains Inc.; *U.S. Public*, pg. 963
GREEN PLAINS ESSEX INC.—See Green Plains Inc.; *U.S. Public*, pg. 963
GREEN PLAINS FAIRMONT LLC—See Green Plains Inc.; *U.S. Public*, pg. 963
GREEN PLAINS GRAIN COMPANY TN LLC—See Green Plains Inc.; *U.S. Public*, pg. 963
GREEN PLAINS HEREFORD LLC—See Green Plains Inc.; *U.S. Public*, pg. 963
GREEN PLAINS INC.; *U.S. Public*, pg. 963
GREEN PLAINS MADISON LLC—See Green Plains Inc.; *U.S. Public*, pg. 963
GREEN PLAINS MOUNT VERNON LLC—See Green Plains Inc.; *U.S. Public*, pg. 963
GREEN PLAINS ORD LLC—See Green Plains Inc.; *U.S. Public*, pg. 963
GREEN PLAINS OTTER TAIL LLC—See Green Plains Inc.; *U.S. Public*, pg. 963
GREEN PLAINS PARTNERS LP—See Green Plains Inc.; *U.S. Public*, pg. 963
GREEN PLAINS SHENANDOAH LLC—See Green Plains Inc.; *U.S. Public*, pg. 963
GREEN PLAINS TRADE GROUP LLC—See Green Plains Inc.; *U.S. Public*, pg. 963
GREEN PLAINS WOOD RIVER LLC—See Green Plains Inc.; *U.S. Public*, pg. 964
GREEN PLAINS YORK LLC—See Green Plains Inc.; *U.S. Public*, pg. 963
GREEN PLANET BIOENGINEERING CO., LTD.; *U.S. Public*, pg. 964
GREEN PLANET GROUP, INC.; *U.S. Public*, pg. 964
GREEN PLANET INDUSTRIES LLC—See VVF Limited; *Int'l*, pg. 8319
GREEN PLUS CO., LTD.; *Int'l*, pg. 3072
GREENPLY INDUSTRIES LIMITED; *Int'l*, pg. 3076
GREENPOINT AG, LLC—See Tennessee Farmers Cooperative; *U.S. Private*, pg. 3967
GREENPOINT AG, LLC—See WinField United, LLC; *U.S. Private*, pg. 4541
GREEN POINT ASIA PACIFIC PTE. LTD.—See BITZER SE; *Int'l*, pg. 1052
GREEN POINT COMPRESSOR SERVICES & PARTS SDN. BHD.—See Far East Group Limited; *Int'l*, pg. 2616
GREEN POINT KOREA CO. LTD.—See BITZER SE; *Int'l*, pg. 1052
GREEN POINT PRECISION (M) SDN. BHD.—See Jabil Inc.; *U.S. Public*, pg. 1180
GREEN POINT PTY. LTD.—See BITZER SE; *Int'l*, pg. 1052
GREEN POINT (SINGAPORE) PTE. LTD.—See Far East Group Limited; *Int'l*, pg. 2616
GREEN POINT (SUZHOU) TECHNOLOGY CO., LTD.—See Jabil Inc.; *U.S. Public*, pg. 1180
GREENPOINT TECHNOLOGIES, INC.—See Safran SA; *Int'l*, pg. 6473
GREEN POINT TECHNOLOGY (SHENZHEN) CO., LTD.—See Jabil Inc.; *U.S. Public*, pg. 1180
GREEN POINT UK LIMITED—See BITZER SE; *Int'l*, pg. 1052
GREENPOINT US, LLC—See BITZER SE; *Int'l*, pg. 1052
GREEN POLKADOT BOX INC.; *U.S. Public*, pg. 964
GREEN POULTRY CO., LTD.—See Kobe Bussan Co., Ltd.; *Int'l*, pg. 4217
GREENPOWER ANLAGENERRICHTUNGS- UND BETRIEBS-GMBH—See PORR AG; *Int'l*, pg. 5922
GREEN POWER EMC; *U.S. Private*, pg. 1773
GREEN POWER GENERATION JSC; *Int'l*, pg. 3072
GREENPOWER GROUP PTY. LTD.—See Great Northern Minerals Limited; *Int'l*, pg. 3065
GREEN POWER ICHIHARA CO., LTD.—See Mitsui E&S Holdings Co., Ltd.; *Int'l*, pg. 4984
GREENPOWER INTERNATIONAL GROUP LIMITED; *U.S. Private*, pg. 1779
GREEN POWER KUZUMAKI CO., LTD.—See Electric Power Development Co., Ltd.; *Int'l*, pg. 2349
GREENPOWER MOTOR COMPANY, INC.—See GreenPower Motor Company Inc.; *Int'l*, pg. 3076
GREENPOWER MOTOR COMPANY INC.; *Int'l*, pg. 3076
GREEN POWER PLANT CO., LTD.—See Thai Polycons Public Company Limited; *Int'l*, pg. 7594
GREEN PRAIRIE INTERNATIONAL INC.; *Int'l*, pg. 3072
GREENPRINT HOLDINGS, INC.—See TA Associates, Inc.; *U.S. Private*, pg. 3917
GREENPRO CAPITAL CORP.; *Int'l*, pg. 3076
GREEN PRODUCTS CO. INC.; *U.S. Private*, pg. 1773
GREEN RADAR (HONG KONG) LIMITED—See Edvance International Holdings Limited; *Int'l*, pg. 2316
GREEN RADAR (SG) PTE LIMITED—See Edvance International Holdings Limited; *Int'l*, pg. 2316
GREEN RAIN SOLAR, INC.—See The Now Corporation; *U.S. Public*, pg. 2117
GREENRAY INDUSTRIES—See TechniCorp International II; *U.S. Private*, pg. 3954
GREENRECYCLE SRL—See Intek Group S.p.A.; *Int'l*, pg. 3732
GREEN REIT PLC—See Henderson Park Capital Partners UK LLP; *Int'l*, pg. 3345

GREEN REMANUFACTURING LLC—See Progressive Green Solutions, Inc.; *U.S. Public*, pg. 1726
GREEN RESOURCE, LLC; *U.S. Private*, pg. 1774
GREEN RESOURCES PUBLIC COMPANY LIMITED; *Int'l*, pg. 3072
GREENRIDGE INVESTMENT PARTNERS; *U.S. Private*, pg. 1779
GREENRIDGE WASTE SERVICES, LLC—See Republic Services, Inc.; *U.S. Public*, pg. 1786
GREENRISE GLOBAL BRANDS INC.; *Int'l*, pg. 3076
GREENRISE TECHNOLOGIES, LLC—See Boyne Capital Management, LLC; *U.S. Private*, pg. 629
GREEN RIVER GOLD CORP.; *Int'l*, pg. 3072
GREEN RIVER HOLDING CO., LTD.; *Int'l*, pg. 3072
GREENROC STRATEGIC MATERIALS PLC; *Int'l*, pg. 3076
GREENROPE, LLC; *U.S. Private*, pg. 1779
GREENROSE HOLDING CO INC.; *U.S. Public*, pg. 965
GREENRUBINO; *U.S. Private*, pg. 1779
GREEN SAN-AI INC.—See Sumitomo Corporation; *Int'l*, pg. 7268
GREEN SA—See VINCI S.A.; *Int'l*, pg. 8222
GREENSBORO COUNTRY CLUB; *U.S. Private*, pg. 1780
GREENSBORO MANOR, LP—See Brookdale Senior Living Inc.; *U.S. Public*, pg. 394
THE GREENSBORO NC ENDOSCOPY ASC, LLC—See KKR & Co. Inc.; *U.S. Public*, pg. 1247
THE GREENSBORO OPTHALMOLOGY ASC, LLC—See KKR & Co. Inc.; *U.S. Public*, pg. 1247
GREENSBORO TRACTOR COMPANY—See BobCo Inc.; *U.S. Private*, pg. 607
GREENSBURG WIND FARM, LLC—See Constellation Energy Corporation; *U.S. Public*, pg. 572
GREENSCAPE, INC.; *U.S. Private*, pg. 1780
GREENSCAPES OF SOUTHWEST FLORIDA, INC.; *U.S. Private*, pg. 1780
GREENS CO., LTD.; *Int'l*, pg. 3076
GREENS CREEK MINING CO.—See Hecla Mining Company; *U.S. Public*, pg. 1019
GREEN SEAL ENVIRONMENTAL, INC.—See Teachers Insurance Association - College Retirement Fund; *U.S. Private*, pg. 3945
GREEN SEAL HOLDING LIMITED; *Int'l*, pg. 3072
GREEN SECURITIES LIMITED—See Green International Holdings Limited; *Int'l*, pg. 3071
GREENS FARMS CAPITAL LLC; *U.S. Private*, pg. 1779
GREENSFELDER, HEMKER & GALE, P.C.—See UB Greensfelder LLP; *U.S. Private*, pg. 4273
GREEN'S GENERAL FOODS PTY. LIMITED; *Int'l*, pg. 3073
GREENSHADES SOFTWARE, INC.—See WayPoint Capital Partners; *U.S. Private*, pg. 4460
GREEN SHARE CO., LTD.—See Giga-Byte Technology Co., Ltd.; *Int'l*, pg. 2971
GREENS HEALTH & FITNESS LTD—See Nuffield Health; *Int'l*, pg. 5487
GREEN SHIELD CANADA; *Int'l*, pg. 3072
GREEN SHIFT COMMODITIES LTD.; *Int'l*, pg. 3072
GREEN SHIPPING LTD.—See Mitsui O.S.K. Lines, Ltd.; *Int'l*, pg. 4989
GREENSILL CAPITAL (UK) LIMITED; *Int'l*, pg. 3076
GREENSMART CORP.; *Int'l*, pg. 3076
GREEN & SMART HOLDINGS PLC; *Int'l*, pg. 3069
GREENSMITH ENERGY MANAGEMENT SYSTEMS, INC.—See Wartsila Corporation; *Int'l*, pg. 8346
GREENSMITH—See Arett Sales Corporation; *U.S. Private*, pg. 318
GREEN SOL INC.—See Frit Incorporated; *U.S. Private*, pg. 1612
GREENSONS BASEBALL II INC.—See Greenberg Sports Group Inc.; *U.S. Private*, pg. 1775
GREENSOURCE CORPORATION; *U.S. Private*, pg. 1780
GREEN SOURCE, LLC—See Bunzl plc; *Int'l*, pg. 1218
GREENSPACE BRANDS INC.; *Int'l*, pg. 3076
THE GREENSPAN COMPANY; *U.S. Private*, pg. 4039
GREENSPEED ENERGY SOLUTIONS, LLC—See Charge Enterprises, Inc.; *U.S. Public*, pg. 479
GREEN'S PLANET CO., LTD.—See Yoshinoya Holdings Co., Ltd.; *Int'l*, pg. 8600
GREENSPOON MARDER LLP; *U.S. Private*, pg. 1780
GREENS PORT CBR, LLC—See Kinder Morgan, Inc.; *U.S. Public*, pg. 1233
GREEN SPOT, INC.; *U.S. Private*, pg. 1774
GREENSPRING ASSOCIATES LIMITED PARTNERSHIP—See StepStone Group Inc.; *U.S. Public*, pg. 1945
GREENSPRING AT MT. SNOW HOMEOWNER'S ASSOCIATION, INC.; *U.S. Private*, pg. 1780
GREENSPRING COMPANY—See American Public Media Group; *U.S. Private*, pg. 244
GREENSPRING ENERGY LLC; *U.S. Private*, pg. 1780
GREENSPRING MEDIA LLC—See Hour Media Group, LLC; *U.S. Private*, pg. 1990
GREENSPRING STATION ENDOSCOPY, LLC—See KKR & Co. Inc.; *U.S. Public*, pg. 1245
THE GREENSPUN CORPORATION; *U.S. Private*, pg. 4039
GREENSPUN MEDIA GROUP, LLC—See The Greenspun Corporation; *U.S. Private*, pg. 4039

CORPORATE AFFILIATIONS

GREEN'S SUZUKI; *U.S. Private*, pg. 1774
GREEN STANDARD VANADIUM RESOURCES CORP.; *Int'l*, pg. 3072
GREENSTAR ALLENTOWN, LLC—See Waste Management, Inc.; *U.S. Public*, pg. 2331
GREEN STAR EXTERIORS, LLC; *U.S. Private*, pg. 1774
GREENSTAR LLC—See Waste Management, Inc.; *U.S. Public*, pg. 2333
GREENSTAR MANAGED SERVICES - CONNECTICUT, LLC—See Waste Management, Inc.; *U.S. Public*, pg. 2331
GREENSTAR MANAGED SERVICES - RLWM, LLC—See Waste Management, Inc.; *U.S. Public*, pg. 2331
GREENSTAR PATERSON, LLC—See Waste Management, Inc.; *U.S. Public*, pg. 2331
GREENSTAR PLANT PRODUCTS INC.—See Hydrofarm Holdings Group, Inc.; *U.S. Public*, pg. 1079
GREEN STAR PRODUCTS, INC.; *U.S. Public*, pg. 964
GREENSTONE ENTERTAINMENT GP LIMITED—See Live Nation Entertainment, Inc.; *U.S. Public*, pg. 1329
GREENSTONE FARM CREDIT SERVICES; *U.S. Private*, pg. 1780
GREENSTONE LLC—See Viatris Inc.; *U.S. Public*, pg. 2293
GREENSTONE MANAGEMENT SERVICES (PTY) LTD.—See Caledonia Mining Corporation Plc; *Int'l*, pg. 1263
GREENSTONE RESOURCES LTD.—See Horizon Minerals Limited; *Int'l*, pg. 3479
GREENSTONE RESOURCES (WA) PTY LTD.—See Red 5 Limited; *Int'l*, pg. 6243
GREEN STREAM HOLDINGS INC.; *U.S. Public*, pg. 964
GREEN STREET ADVISORS INC.—See Welsh, Carson, Anderson & Stowe; *U.S. Private*, pg. 4480
GREEN STREET CAPITAL CORP.; *U.S. Public*, pg. 964
GREEN STREET POWER PARTNERS LLC; *U.S. Private*, pg. 1774
GREENSTREET REAL ESTATE PARTNERS, L.P.; *U.S. Private*, pg. 1780
GREENSTRIPE MEDIA, INC.; *U.S. Private*, pg. 1780
GREEN SUN HOTEL MANAGEMENT INC.—See Solid Group, Inc.; *Int'l*, pg. 7072
GREENSVILLE COMPANY LIMITED—See Osotspa Co., Ltd.; *Int'l*, pg. 5652
GREENSWITCH WIND, LLC—See RWE AG; *Int'l*, pg. 6434
GREEN TEAM ADVERTISING, INC.; *U.S. Private*, pg. 1774
GREEN TEAM GROUP A/S—See Sydbank A/S; *Int'l*, pg. 7377
GREEN TEC CORPORATION; *Int'l*, pg. 3073
GREENTECH DENMARK APS—See Arrow Electronics, Inc.; *U.S. Public*, pg. 199
GREENTECH ENERGIESYSTEME GMBH—See Christof Holding AG; *Int'l*, pg. 1587
GREENTECH ENERGY SYSTEMS POLSKA SP. Z O.O.—See Athena Investments A/S; *Int'l*, pg. 669
GREENTECH ENVIRONMENTAL CO., LTD.; *Int'l*, pg. 3076
GREENTECH MALAYSIA FOUNDER SDN. BHD.—See PUC Berhad; *Int'l*, pg. 6115
GREENTECH METALS LIMITED; *Int'l*, pg. 3076
GREEN TECHNOLOGY MANAGEMENT PTY. LTD.—See SK Inc.; *Int'l*, pg. 6971
GREEN TECHNOLOGY METALS LIMITED; *Int'l*, pg. 3073
GREEN TECHNOLOGY SOLUTIONS, INC.; *U.S. Private*, pg. 1774
GREENTECHNO SEKIWA KANSAI, LTD—See Sekisui House, Ltd.; *Int'l*, pg. 6697
GREENTECHNO SEKIWA, LTD—See Sekisui House, Ltd.; *Int'l*, pg. 6697
GREENTECH SWEDEN AB—See Arrow Electronics, Inc.; *U.S. Public*, pg. 199
GREENTECH TECHNOLOGY INTERNATIONAL LIMITED; *Int'l*, pg. 3076
GREENTECH TRANSPORTATION INDUSTRIES INC.; *U.S. Private*, pg. 1780
GREENTEC INTERNATIONAL INC.; *Int'l*, pg. 3076
GREEN THREADS, LLC; *U.S. Private*, pg. 1774
GREEN THUMB INDUSTRIES, INC.; *U.S. Public*, pg. 964
GREEN TOTAL SOLUTIONS, INC.—See Huron Capital Partners LLC; *U.S. Private*, pg. 2011
GREEN TOWER PROPERTIES, INC.; *Int'l*, pg. 3073
GREENTOWN CHINA HOLDINGS LIMITED; *Int'l*, pg. 3076
GREENTOWN MANAGEMENT HOLDINGS COMPANY LIMITED—See Greentown China Holdings Limited; *Int'l*, pg. 3076
GREENTOWN PARKING SDN. BHD.—See Mega First Corporation Berhad; *Int'l*, pg. 4792
GREEN TOWN PROJECTS PLC; *Int'l*, pg. 3073
GREENTOWN REAL ESTATE GROUP CO., LTD.—See Greentown China Holdings Limited; *Int'l*, pg. 3077
GREENTOWN SERVICE GROUP CO. LTD.; *Int'l*, pg. 3077
GREEN TOYOTA OF LEXINGTON INC.; *U.S. Private*, pg. 1774
GREENTRANS CORPORATION—See China Motor Corporation; *Int'l*, pg. 1525

COMPANY NAME INDEX

GREEN TREE ELECTRONIC RECYCLING, LLC; *U.S. Private*, pg. 1774
GREENTREE GAS & OIL LTD.; *Int'l*, pg. 3077
GREENTREE HOSPITALITY GROUP LTD.; *Int'l*, pg. 3077
GREEN TREE MALL CO—See The Macerich Company; *U.S. Public*, pg. 2110
GREENTREE MORTGAGE COMPANY L P; *U.S. Private*, pg. 1780
GREENTREE MOTORS DANBURY INC.; *U.S. Private*, pg. 1780
GREEN TREE SERVICING LLC—See Ditech Holding Corporation; *U.S. Private*, pg. 1240
GREENTREE TRANSPORTATION COMPANY—See Transport Investments, Inc.; *U.S. Private*, pg. 4210
GREEN TRIANGLE PLANTATION FOREST COMPANY OF AUSTRALIA PTY. LTD.—See Oji Holdings Corporation; *Int'l*, pg. 5536
GREENTUBE INTERNET ENTERTAINMENT SOLUTIONS GMBH—See Novomatic AG; *Int'l*, pg. 5467
GREEN TURTLE AMERICAS, LTD—See Zurn Elkay Water Solutions Corporation; *U.S. Public*, pg. 2413
GREENVALE AP LIMITED—See Promethean Investments LLP; *Int'l*, pg. 5993
GREENVALE ENERGY LTD; *Int'l*, pg. 3077
GREENVAL INSURANCE DAC—See BNP Paribas SA; *Int'l*, pg. 1091
GREEN VALLEY CHEMICAL CORP.; *U.S. Private*, pg. 1774
GREEN VALLEY COAL COMPANY—See Alpha Natural Resources, Inc.; *U.S. Private*, pg. 199
GREEN VALLEY GROCERIES, INC.; *U.S. Private*, pg. 1774
GREEN VALLEY GROUP, LLC—See Zoned Properties, Inc.; *U.S. Public*, pg. 2411
GREEN VALLEY NUTRITION PTY LTD—See OSIM International Ltd.; *Int'l*, pg. 5650
GREEN VALLEY ONION COMPANY; *U.S. Private*, pg. 1774
GREEN VALLEY - UNITED KINGDOM—See Black Dragon Capital LLC; *U.S. Private*, pg. 571
GREEN VENTURES LIMITED; *Int'l*, pg. 3073
GREENVIEW DATA, INC.—See Open Text Corporation; *Int'l*, pg. 5598
GREEN VIEW DEVELOPMENT SERVICES LIMITED—See Dangote Group Limited; *Int'l*, pg. 1962
GREENVIEW LANDSCAPING, INC.; *U.S. Private*, pg. 1780
GREENVIEW PAVILION SDN. BHD.—See Infraharta Holdings Berhad; *Int'l*, pg. 3697
GREENVIEW REGIONAL HOSPITAL—See HCA Healthcare, Inc.; *U.S. Public*, pg. 997
GREENVIEW SPECIALTY ASSOCIATES, LLC—See HCA Healthcare, Inc.; *U.S. Public*, pg. 997
GREEN VIEW TECHNOLOGIES, INC.—See Clean Harbors, Inc.; *U.S. Public*, pg. 510
THE GREENVILLE ASC, LLC—See KKR & Co. Inc.; *U.S. Public*, pg. 1247
GREENVILLE CLINIC CORP.—See Quorum Health Corporation; *U.S. Private*, pg. 3330
GREENVILLE COLORANTS, LLC—See ChromaScape, LLC; *U.S. Private*, pg. 892
GREENVILLE COLORANTS LLC—See ChromaScape, LLC; *U.S. Private*, pg. 892
GREENVILLE COUNTRY CLUB; *U.S. Private*, pg. 1780
GREENVILLE DIALYSIS CLINIC, LLC—See Nautic Partners, LLC; *U.S. Private*, pg. 2870
GREENVILLE FEDERAL FINANCIAL CORPORATION; *U.S. Public*, pg. 965
GREENVILLE FEDERAL—See Greenville Federal Financial Corporation; *U.S. Public*, pg. 965
GREENVILLE HOSPITAL CORPORATION—See Quorum Health Corporation; *U.S. Private*, pg. 3330
GREENVILLE HOSPITAL SYSTEM INC.; *U.S. Private*, pg. 1780
GREENVILLE METALS, INC.—See Berkshire Hathaway Inc.; *U.S. Public*, pg. 315
GREENVILLE NATIONAL BANK; *U.S. Private*, pg. 1780
GREENVILLE NEWS—See Gannett Co., Inc.; *U.S. Public*, pg. 897
GREENVILLE READY MIX—See Martin Marietta Materials, Inc.; *U.S. Public*, pg. 1389
GREENVILLE REGIONAL HOSPITAL; *U.S. Private*, pg. 1780
GREENVILLE SURGERY CENTER, LLC—See UnitedHealth Group Incorporated; *U.S. Public*, pg. 2241
GREENVILLE TECHNOLOGY, INC.—See Moriroku Holdings Company, Ltd.; *Int'l*, pg. 5047
GREENVILLE TUBE COMPANY, LLC—See Berkshire Hathaway Inc.; *U.S. Public*, pg. 314
GREEN VISION BIOTECHNOLOGY CORP.; *Int'l*, pg. 3073
GREEN VISION RECYCLING LIMITED—See Downer EDI Limited; *Int'l*, pg. 2186
GREENVOLT - ENERGIAS RENOVAVEIS, S.A.—See KKR & Co. Inc.; *U.S. Public*, pg. 1252
GREENVOLT NEXT PORTUGAL, LDA.—See KKR & Co. Inc.; *U.S. Public*, pg. 1252
GREENWALD INDUSTRIES DIVISION—See The Eastern Company; *U.S. Public*, pg. 2069
GREENWASTE RECOVERY INC.; *U.S. Private*, pg. 1780

GREEN WASTE SOLUTIONS OF ALASKA, LLC—See Waste Connections, Inc.; *Int'l*, pg. 8353
GREEN WAVE LLC—See Ameresco, Inc.; *U.S. Public*, pg. 95
GREENWAVE REALITY, INC.; *U.S. Private*, pg. 1781
GREENWAVE TECHNOLOGY SOLUTIONS, INC.; *U.S. Public*, pg. 965
GREENWAY BANK; *U.S. Public*, pg. 965
GREENWAY CO-OP SERVICE COMPANY; *U.S. Private*, pg. 1781
GREENWAY ENTERPRISES INCORPORATED; *U.S. Private*, pg. 1781
GREENWAY EQUIPMENT, INC.; *U.S. Private*, pg. 1781
GREENWAY FORD, INC.; *U.S. Private*, pg. 1781
GREENWAY GRID GLOBAL PTE. LTD.—See Chubu Electric Power Co., Inc.; *Int'l*, pg. 1593
GREENWAY INVESTMENT COMPANY; *U.S. Private*, pg. 1781
GREENWAY-MALDEN EQUIPMENT CO.; *U.S. Private*, pg. 1781
GREENWAY MEDICAL TECHNOLOGIES, INC.—See Vista Equity Partners, LLC; *U.S. Private*, pg. 4398
GREENWAY MINING GROUP LIMITED; *Int'l*, pg. 3077
GREENWAY PARTNERS, LP; *U.S. Private*, pg. 1781
GREENWAY SURGICAL SUITES, LLC—See UnitedHealth Group Incorporated; *U.S. Public*, pg. 2241
GREENWAY TECHNOLOGIES, INC.; *U.S. Public*, pg. 965
GREENWAY TRANSPORTATION SERVICES; *U.S. Private*, pg. 1781
GREENWEB SERVICE CORP.—See NAVER Corporation; *Int'l*, pg. 5174
GREENWEEZ SAS—See Carrefour SA; *Int'l*, pg. 1345
GREENWEIZ PROJECTS LIMITED—See Weizmann Limited; *Int'l*, pg. 8371
GREENWELL ENERGY SOLUTIONS LLC; *U.S. Private*, pg. 1781
GREENWELL GLEESON GMBH—See Amadeus Fire AG; *Int'l*, pg. 405
GREENWELL GLEESON LTD.—See Amadeus Fire AG; *Int'l*, pg. 405
GREENWICH AEROGROUP, INC.; *U.S. Private*, pg. 1781
GREENWICH ASSOCIATES CANADA, ULC—See S&P Global Inc.; *U.S. Public*, pg. 1830
GREENWICH ASSOCIATES JAPAN K.K.—See S&P Global Inc.; *U.S. Public*, pg. 1830
GREENWICH ASSOCIATES LLC—See S&P Global Inc.; *U.S. Public*, pg. 1831
GREENWICH ASSOCIATES SINGAPORE PTE. LTD.—See S&P Global Inc.; *U.S. Public*, pg. 1830
GREENWICH ASSOCIATES UK LIMITED—See S&P Global Inc.; *U.S. Public*, pg. 1830
GREENWICH AUTOMOTIVE ENTERPRISES; *U.S. Private*, pg. 1781
GREENWICH BIOSCIENCES, INC.—See Jazz Pharmaceuticals plc; *Int'l*, pg. 3916
GREENWICH ENGLISH COLLEGE PTY LTD—See iCollege Limited; *Int'l*, pg. 3582
THE GREENWICH GROUP INTERNATIONAL LLC - CALIFORNIA—See The Greenwich Group International LLC; *U.S. Private*, pg. 4039
THE GREENWICH GROUP INTERNATIONAL LLC; *U.S. Private*, pg. 4039
THE GREENWICH GROUP INTERNATIONAL LLC - VIRGINIA—See The Greenwich Group International LLC; *U.S. Private*, pg. 4039
GREENWICH HONDA; *U.S. Private*, pg. 1781
GREENWICH, INC.—See Berkshire Partners LLC; *U.S. Private*, pg. 535
GREENWICH INSURANCE COMPANY—See AXA S.A.; *Int'l*, pg. 761
GREENWICH KAHALA AVIATION LTD.; *Int'l*, pg. 3077
GREENWICH LIFESCIENCES, INC.; *U.S. Public*, pg. 965
GREENWICH TIME—See The Hearst Corporation; *U.S. Private*, pg. 4047
GREENWICH VILLAGE GAZETTE—See Gilford Graphics International; *U.S. Private*, pg. 1699
GREENWICH WORKSHOP INC.; *U.S. Private*, pg. 1781
GREENWIND, S.A.—See EDP - Energias de Portugal, S.A.; *Int'l*, pg. 2314
GREENWING RESOURCES LTD.; *Int'l*, pg. 3077
GREENWOOD ASC, LLC—See Tenet Healthcare Corporation; *U.S. Public*, pg. 2010
GREENWOOD/ASHER & ASSOCIATES, LLC—See Kelly Services, Inc.; *U.S. Public*, pg. 1218
GREENWOOD COMMUNITIES & RESORTS, INC.—See GMI Holding, Inc.; *U.S. Public*, pg. 1722
GREENWOOD CREDIT UNION; *U.S. Private*, pg. 1781
GREENWOOD DIALYSIS, LLC—See DaVita Inc.; *U.S. Public*, pg. 639
GREENWOOD FABRICATING & PLATING; *U.S. Private*, pg. 1781
GREENWOOD GAMING & ENTERTAINMENT, INC.—See International Turf Investment Co., Inc.; *U.S. Private*, pg. 2121
GREENWOOD GENETIC CENTER INC.; *U.S. Private*, pg. 1781
GREENWOOD HOTEL (WA) PTY LTD—See Woolworths Group Limited; *Int'l*, pg. 8451
GREENWOOD INC.; *U.S. Public*, pg. 1782

GREER INDUSTRIES INC.

GREENWOOD INDUSTRIES; *U.S. Private*, pg. 1782
GREENWOOD INVESTMENT MANAGEMENT INC.—See Curi Holdings, Inc.; *U.S. Private*, pg. 1125
GREENWOOD MILLS, INC.—See GMI Holding, Inc.; *U.S. Private*, pg. 1722
GREENWOOD MOTOR LINES INC.—See R & L Carriers, Inc.; *U.S. Private*, pg. 3331
GREENWOOD MUSHROOMS—See AGF Management Limited; *Int'l*, pg. 207
GREENWOOD MUSHROOMS—See Instar Group Inc.; *Int'l*, pg. 3723
GREENWOOD PERSONAL CREDIT LIMITED—See Vanquis Banking Group plc; *Int'l*, pg. 8130
GREENWOOD PRODUCTS, INC.—See Jewett-Cameron Trading Company Ltd.; *U.S. Public*, pg. 1190
GREENWOOD PRODUCTS, INC.—See StoneCalibre, LLC; *U.S. Private*, pg. 3827
GREENWOOD RACING INC.—See International Turf Investment Co., Inc.; *U.S. Private*, pg. 2121
GREENWOODS COMMUNICATIONS LTD.; *Int'l*, pg. 3077
GREENWOODS FINANCIAL GROUP, INC.; *U.S. Private*, pg. 1782
THE GREENWOOD'S STATE BANK—See Greenwoods Financial Group, Inc.; *U.S. Private*, pg. 1782
GREENWOODS (ST IVES) LIMITED—See Heidelberg Materials AG; *Int'l*, pg. 3310
GREENWORKS CO., LTD.—See YG Plus Inc.; *Int'l*, pg. 8579
GREENWORKS (JIANGSU) CO., LTD.; *Int'l*, pg. 3077
GREENWORKS SERVICE COMPANY; *U.S. Private*, pg. 1782
GREEN WORLD HOTELS; *Int'l*, pg. 3073
GREENX METALS LIMITED; *Int'l*, pg. 3077
GREENYARD FLOWERS NETHERLANDS B.V.—See Greenyard N.V.; *Int'l*, pg. 3077
GREENYARD FRESH AUSTRIA GMBH—See Greenyard N.V.; *Int'l*, pg. 3077
GREENYARD FRESH BELGIUM N.V.—See Greenyard N.V.; *Int'l*, pg. 3077
GREENYARD FRESH BRAZIL LTDA.—See Greenyard N.V.; *Int'l*, pg. 3077
GREENYARD FRESH CHILE LTDA.—See Greenyard N.V.; *Int'l*, pg. 3077
GREENYARD FRESH COLOMBIA SAS—See Greenyard N.V.; *Int'l*, pg. 3077
GREENYARD FRESH DIRECT BELGIUM N.V.—See Greenyard N.V.; *Int'l*, pg. 3077
GREENYARD FRESH FRANCE S.A.S.—See Greenyard N.V.; *Int'l*, pg. 3077
GREENYARD FRESH GERMANY GMBH—See Greenyard N.V.; *Int'l*, pg. 3077
GREENYARD FRESH HOLDING NL B.V.—See Greenyard N.V.; *Int'l*, pg. 3077
GREENYARD FRESH ITALY S.R.L.—See Greenyard N.V.; *Int'l*, pg. 3077
GREENYARD FRESH PERU SAC—See Greenyard N.V.; *Int'l*, pg. 3077
GREENYARD FRESH UK LTD.—See Greenyard N.V.; *Int'l*, pg. 3077
GREENYARD FROZEN BELGIUM N.V.—See Greenyard N.V.; *Int'l*, pg. 3077
GREENYARD FROZEN BRAZIL LTDA.—See Greenyard N.V.; *Int'l*, pg. 3077
GREENYARD FROZEN COMINES S.A.S.—See Greenyard N.V.; *Int'l*, pg. 3077
GREENYARD FROZEN FRANCE S.A.S.—See Greenyard N.V.; *Int'l*, pg. 3077
GREENYARD FROZEN POLAND SP. Z O.O.—See Greenyard N.V.; *Int'l*, pg. 3077
GREENYARD FROZEN UK LTD.—See Greenyard N.V.; *Int'l*, pg. 3077
GREENYARD LOGISTICS BELGIUM N.V.—See Greenyard N.V.; *Int'l*, pg. 3077
GREENYARD LOGISTICS POLAND SP. Z O.O.—See Greenyard N.V.; *Int'l*, pg. 3078
GREENYARD LOGISTICS USA INC.—See Greenyard N.V.; *Int'l*, pg. 3078
GREENYARD N.V.; *Int'l*, pg. 3077
GREENYARD PREPARED BELGIUM N.V.—See Greenyard N.V.; *Int'l*, pg. 3078
GREENYARD PREPARED NETHERLANDS B.V.—See Greenyard N.V.; *Int'l*, pg. 3078
GREENYARD TRANSPORT BELGIUM N.V.—See Greenyard N.V.; *Int'l*, pg. 3078
GREENYIELD BERHAD; *Int'l*, pg. 3078
GREENYIELD INDUSTRIES (M) SDN. BHD.—See Greenyield Berhad; *Int'l*, pg. 3078
GREEN ZEBRA MEDIA; *U.S. Private*, pg. 1774
GREENZONE SOLUTIONS, INC.—See OceanSound Partners, LP; *U.S. Private*, pg. 2991
GREE PRODUCTS FRANCE SAS—See Gree Electric Appliances, Inc. of Zhuhai; *Int'l*, pg. 3068
GREE PRODUCTS, S.L.—See Gree Electric Appliances, Inc. of Zhuhai; *Int'l*, pg. 3068
GREE REAL ESTATE CO., LTD.; *Int'l*, pg. 3069
GREER INDUSTRIES INC.; *U.S. Private*, pg. 1782
GREER LABORATORIES, INC.—See B-FLEXION Group Holdings SA; *Int'l*, pg. 785

GREER INDUSTRIES INC.
CORPORATE AFFILIATIONS

GREER LIMESTONE COMPANY—See Greer Industries Inc.; *U.S. Private*, pg. 1782
GREER STEEL COMPANY—See Greer Industries Inc.; *U.S. Private*, pg. 1782
GREER-WILSON FUNERAL HOME, INC.—See Security National Financial Corporation; *U.S. Public*, pg. 1856
GREETEAT CORPORATION; *U.S. Public*, pg. 965
GREETZ B.V.—See Moonpig Group Plc; *Int'l*, pg. 5038
GREEVE LIMITED—See Elate Holdings Limited; *Int'l*, pg. 2343
GREFCO, INC.—See RGP Holding, Inc.; *U.S. Private*, pg. 3420
GREFUSA, S.L.—See Intersnack Group GmbH & Co. KG; *Int'l*, pg. 3760
GREGAN CONSTRUCTION CORP.; *U.S. Private*, pg. 1782
GREG BUICK PONTIAC CADILLAC; *U.S. Private*, pg. 1782
GREGERSON'S FOODS INC.; *U.S. Private*, pg. 1782
GREGER TOPSOIL—See Haines & Kibblehouse Inc.; *U.S. Private*, pg. 1841
GREGG APPLIANCES, INC.—See hhgregg, Inc.; *U.S. Public*, pg. 1034
GREGG COMMUNICATIONS SYSTEMS, INC.—See APLJ Capital Management LLC; *U.S. Private*, pg. 294
GREGG DRILLING & TESTING INC.; *U.S. Private*, pg. 1782
GREGG INDUSTRIAL INSULATORS—See Gregg Industries Inc.; *U.S. Private*, pg. 1782
GREGG INDUSTRIES INC.; *U.S. Private*, pg. 1782
GREGG INDUSTRIES, INC.—See Charlotte Pipe & Foundry Company; *U.S. Private*, pg. 857
GREGG MECHANICAL CORP.—See Brookfield Corporation; *Int'l*, pg. 1188
GREGGO & FERRARA INC.; *U.S. Private*, pg. 1782
GREGG'S GREENLAKE CYCLE INC.; *U.S. Private*, pg. 1782
GREGGS (LEASING) LIMITED—See Greggs plc; *Int'l*, pg. 3078
GREGG SMITH FORD LINCOLN MERCURY INC.; *U.S. Private*, pg. 1782
GREGGS PLC; *Int'l*, pg. 3078
GREG LEBLANC INC.; *U.S. Private*, pg. 1782
GREGMAR, INC.; *U.S. Private*, pg. 1782
THE GREG NORMAN COLLECTION—See Hellman & Friedman LLC; *U.S. Private*, pg. 1907
GREG NORMAN GOLF COURSE DESIGN COMPANY—See Great White Shark Enterprises, Inc.; *U.S. Private*, pg. 1768
GREGORIO, NUMO Y NOEL WERTHEIN S.A. - FRUIT DIVISION—See Gregorio, Numo y Noel Werthein S.A.; *Int'l*, pg. 3078
GREGORIO, NUMO Y NOEL WERTHEIN S.A.; *Int'l*, pg. 3078
GREGORIS NISSAN; *U.S. Private*, pg. 1783
GREGOR TECHNOLOGIES LLC—See Reliance Steel & Aluminum Co.; *U.S. Public*, pg. 1780
GREGORY COMMERCIAL FURNITURE PTY LIMITED—See Inventis Limited; *Int'l*, pg. 3773
GREGORY CONSTRUCTION INC.—See Pumford Construction Inc.; *U.S. Private*, pg. 3303
GREGORY DISTRIBUTION (HOLDINGS) LIMITED; *Int'l*, pg. 3078
GREGORY DISTRIBUTION—See Gregory Distribution (Holdings) Limited; *Int'l*, pg. 3078
GREGORY ELECTRIC CO. INC.; *U.S. Private*, pg. 1783
GREGORY FCA; *U.S. Private*, pg. 1783
GREGORY INDUSTRIES, INC.; *U.S. Private*, pg. 1783
GREGORY MOUNTAIN PRODUCTS, LLC—See Samsonite International S.A.; *Int'l*, pg. 6510
GREGORY PARTNERS, LLC—See I Squared Capital Advisors (US) LLC; *U.S. Private*, pg. 2025
GREGORY PEST CONTROL, INC.—See Rentokil Initial plc; *Int'l*, pg. 6289
GREGORY PEST CONTROL, LLC—See Rentokil Initial plc; *Int'l*, pg. 6289
GREGORY POOLE EQUIPMENT COMPANY INC.—See Panther Summit Industries Inc.; *U.S. Private*, pg. 3087
GREGORY, SHARER & STUART, P.A.; *U.S. Private*, pg. 1783
GREGSON & WEIGHT PTY LTD—See Propel Funeral Partners Limited; *Int'l*, pg. 5997
GREG WEBER, INC.; *U.S. Private*, pg. 1782
GREG WEEKS INC.; *U.S. Private*, pg. 1782
GREIF ARGENTINA S.A.—See Greif Inc.; *U.S. Public*, pg. 967
GREIF BELGIUM B.V.B.A.—See Greif Inc.; *U.S. Public*, pg. 967
GREIF BROTHERS CANADA, INC.—See Greif Inc.; *U.S. Public*, pg. 967
GREIF - CHILE—See Greif Inc.; *U.S. Public*, pg. 967
GREIF COLOMBIA S.A.—See Greif Inc.; *U.S. Public*, pg. 967
GREIF CONTAINERS, INC.—See Greif Inc.; *U.S. Public*, pg. 967
GREIF CORRUGATED PRODUCTS—See Greif Inc.; *U.S. Public*, pg. 967
GREIF COSTA RICA S.A.—See Greif Inc.; *U.S. Public*, pg. 967
GREIF CZECH REPUBLIC A/S—See Greif Inc.; *U.S. Public*, pg. 967
GREIF DENMARK A/S—See Greif Inc.; *U.S. Public*, pg. 967
GREIF EMBALAGENS INDUSTRIAIS DO BRASIL LTDA.—See Greif Inc.; *U.S. Public*, pg. 967
GREIFFENBERGER AG; *Int'l*, pg. 3078
GREIF FLEXIBLE PRODUCTS & SERVICES—See Greif Inc.; *U.S. Public*, pg. 967
GREIF FLEXIBLES BELGIUM N.V.—See Greif Inc.; *U.S. Public*, pg. 967
GREIF FLEXIBLES BENELUX B.V.—See Greif Inc.; *U.S. Public*, pg. 967
GREIF FLEXIBLES CHANGZHOU CO., LTD.—See Greif Inc.; *U.S. Public*, pg. 967
GREIF FLEXIBLES FINLAND OY—See Greif Inc.; *U.S. Public*, pg. 967
GREIF FLEXIBLES FRANCE SARL—See Greif Inc.; *U.S. Public*, pg. 967
GREIF FLEXIBLES GERMANY GMBH & CO, KG—See Greif Inc.; *U.S. Public*, pg. 967
GREIF FLEXIBLES GERMANY GMBH & CO.—See Greif Inc.; *U.S. Public*, pg. 967
GREIF FLEXIBLES ROMANIA SRL—See Greif Inc.; *U.S. Public*, pg. 967
GREIF FLEXIBLES TRADING HOLDING B.V.—See Greif Inc.; *U.S. Public*, pg. 968
GREIF FLEXIBLES UK LTD.—See Greif Inc.; *U.S. Public*, pg. 968
GREIF FLEXIBLES USA INC.—See Greif Inc.; *U.S. Public*, pg. 968
GREIF FRANCE HOLDINGS SAS—See Greif Inc.; *U.S. Public*, pg. 968
GREIF FRANCE S.A.S.—See Greif Inc.; *U.S. Public*, pg. 968
GREIF GERMANY GMBH—See Greif Inc.; *U.S. Public*, pg. 968
GREIF HELLAS—See Greif Inc.; *U.S. Public*, pg. 968
GREIF HUA I TAIWAN CO., LTD.—See Greif Inc.; *U.S. Public*, pg. 968
GREIF HUNGARY KFT—See Greif Inc.; *U.S. Public*, pg. 968
GREIF INC.; *U.S. Public*, pg. 965
GREIF INTERNATIONAL HOLDING SUPRA II C.V.—See Greif Inc.; *U.S. Public*, pg. 968
GREIF ITALIA SPA—See Greif Inc.; *U.S. Public*, pg. 968
GREIF JAMAICA LTD.—See Greif Inc.; *U.S. Public*, pg. 968
GREIF MALAYSIA SDN BHD—See Greif Inc.; *U.S. Public*, pg. 968
GREIF - MASSILLON—See Greif Inc.; *U.S. Public*, pg. 967
GREIF MEXICO, S.A. DE C.V.—See Greif Inc.; *U.S. Public*, pg. 968
GREIF MIMAYSAN AMBALAJ SANAYI AS—See Greif Inc.; *U.S. Public*, pg. 968
GREIF NEDERLAND B.V.—See Greif Inc.; *U.S. Public*, pg. 968
GREIF NORWAY AS—See Greif Inc.; *U.S. Public*, pg. 968
GREIF PACKAGING FRANCE INVESTMENTS SAS—See Greif Inc.; *U.S. Public*, pg. 968
GREIF PACKAGING LLC—See Greif Inc.; *U.S. Public*, pg. 968
GREIF PACKAGING MOROCCO S.A.—See Greif Inc.; *U.S. Public*, pg. 968
GREIF PACKAGING SPAIN SA—See Greif Inc.; *U.S. Public*, pg. 968
GREIF PLASTICS ITALY PACKAGING SERVICE—See Greif Inc.; *U.S. Public*, pg. 968
GREIF PLASTICS ITALY SRL—See Greif Inc.; *U.S. Public*, pg. 968
GREIF POLAND SP. Z.O.O.—See Greif Inc.; *U.S. Public*, pg. 968
GREIF PORTUGAL LTDA.—See Greif Inc.; *U.S. Public*, pg. 968
GREIF RIVERVILLE MILL—See Greif Inc.; *U.S. Public*, pg. 968
GREIF S.A. (PTY) LTD.—See Greif Inc.; *U.S. Public*, pg. 968
GREIF SINGAPORE PTE LTD—See Greif Inc.; *U.S. Public*, pg. 968
GREIF SOUTH AFRICA (PTY) LTD.—See Greif Inc.; *U.S. Public*, pg. 968
GREIF SWEDEN AB—See Greif Inc.; *U.S. Public*, pg. 968
GREIF THOLU B.V.—See Greif Inc.; *U.S. Public*, pg. 968
GREIF UK LTD.—See Greif Inc.; *U.S. Public*, pg. 968
GREIF VENEZUELA, C.A.—See Greif Inc.; *U.S. Public*, pg. 968
GREIF ZIMBABWE PRIVATE LTD.—See Greif Inc.; *U.S. Public*, pg. 968
GREIG MIDDLETON HOLDINGS LIMITED—See Barclays PLC; *Int'l*, pg. 862
GREINA TECHNOLOGIES, INC.—See Alps Alpine Co., Ltd.; *Int'l*, pg. 376
GREINER AEROSPACE INC.—See Greiner Holding AG; *Int'l*, pg. 3079
GREINER AEROSPACE (SHANGHAI) CO., LTD.—See Greiner Holding AG; *Int'l*, pg. 3079
GREINER ASSISTEC GMBH—See Greiner Holding AG; *Int'l*, pg. 3079
GREINER ASSISTEC LERESTI ROMANIA SA—See Greiner Holding AG; *Int'l*, pg. 3079
GREINER ASSISTEC, S. A. DE C. V.—See Greiner Holding AG; *Int'l*, pg. 3079
GREINER ASSISTEC S.R.L.—See Greiner Holding AG; *Int'l*, pg. 3079
GREINER ASSISTEC S.R.O.—See Greiner Holding AG; *Int'l*, pg. 3080
GREINER BIO-ONE BRASIL PRODUTOS MEDICOS HOSPITALARES LTDA.—See Greiner Holding AG; *Int'l*, pg. 3079
GREINER BIO-ONE B.V.—See Greiner Holding AG; *Int'l*, pg. 3079
GREINER BIO-ONE CO. LTD.—See Greiner Holding AG; *Int'l*, pg. 3079
GREINER BIO-ONE FRANCE S.A.S.—See Greiner Holding AG; *Int'l*, pg. 3079
GREINER BIO-ONE GMBH—See Greiner Holding AG; *Int'l*, pg. 3079
GREINER BIO-ONE GMBH—See Greiner Holding AG; *Int'l*, pg. 3079
GREINER BIO-ONE GMBH—See Greiner Holding AG; *Int'l*, pg. 3079
GREINER BIO-ONE HUNGARY KFT.—See Greiner Holding AG; *Int'l*, pg. 3079
GREINER BIO-ONE INDIA PRIVATE LIMITED—See Greiner Holding AG; *Int'l*, pg. 3079
GREINER BIO-ONE INTERNATIONAL GMBH—See Greiner Holding AG; *Int'l*, pg. 3079
GREINER BIO-ONE LTD.—See Greiner Holding AG; *Int'l*, pg. 3079
GREINER BIO-ONE NORTH AMERICA, INC.—See Greiner Holding AG; *Int'l*, pg. 3079
GREINER BIO-ONE SUNS CO., LTD.—See Greiner Holding AG; *Int'l*, pg. 3079
GREINER BIO-ONE (THAILAND) LTD.—See Greiner Holding AG; *Int'l*, pg. 3079
GREINER BIO-ONE VACUETTE SCHWEIZ GMBH—See Greiner Holding AG; *Int'l*, pg. 3079
GREINER EXTRUSION GROUP GMBH—See Greiner Holding AG; *Int'l*, pg. 3079
GREINER EXTRUSION TECHNOLOGY (SHANGHAI) CO., LTD.—See Greiner Holding AG; *Int'l*, pg. 3079
GREINER EXTRUSION US, INC.—See Greiner Holding AG; *Int'l*, pg. 3079
GREINER GMBH—See Marquard & Bahls AG; *Int'l*, pg. 4699
GREINER HOLDING AG; *Int'l*, pg. 3078
GREINER I JP PACKAGING D.O.O.—See Greiner Holding AG; *Int'l*, pg. 3079
GREINER INDUSTRIES, INC.—See IES Holdings, Inc.; *U.S. Public*, pg. 1094
GREINER MULTIFOAM SP. Z O.O.—See Greiner Holding AG; *Int'l*, pg. 3079
GREINER PACKAGING AG—See Greiner Holding AG; *Int'l*, pg. 3080
GREINER PACKAGING B.V.—See Greiner Holding AG; *Int'l*, pg. 3079
GREINER PACKAGING CORP.—See Greiner Holding AG; *Int'l*, pg. 3079
GREINER PACKAGING DISTRIBUTION SARL—See Greiner Holding AG; *Int'l*, pg. 3079
GREINER PACKAGING D.O.O.—See Greiner Holding AG; *Int'l*, pg. 3079
GREINER PACKAGING GMBH—See Greiner Holding AG; *Int'l*, pg. 3079
GREINER PACKAGING KFT.—See Greiner Holding AG; *Int'l*, pg. 3079
GREINER PACKAGING SLUSOVICE S.R.O—See Greiner Holding AG; *Int'l*, pg. 3080
GREINER PACKAGING SP. Z O.O.—See Greiner Holding AG; *Int'l*, pg. 3079
GREINER PACKAGING S.R.L—See Greiner Holding AG; *Int'l*, pg. 3079
GREINER PACKAGING S.R.O.—See Greiner Holding AG; *Int'l*, pg. 3080
GREINER PACKAGING VERTRIEBS GMBH—See Greiner Holding AG; *Int'l*, pg. 3079
GREINER PERFOAM GMBH—See Greiner Holding AG; *Int'l*, pg. 3079
GREINER PERFOAM GMBH—See Greiner Holding AG; *Int'l*, pg. 3079
GREINER PERFOAM SPOL. S R.O.—See Greiner Holding AG; *Int'l*, pg. 3079
GREINER PONTIAC-BUICK, INC.; *U.S. Private*, pg. 1783
GREINER PURTEC CZ SPOL. S.R.O.—See Greiner Holding AG; *Int'l*, pg. 3079
GREINER PURTEC GMBH—See Greiner Holding AG; *Int'l*, pg. 3079
GREINER REAL ESTATE SP. Z O.O.—See Greiner Holding AG; *Int'l*, pg. 3079
GREINER SCHMIDT MOTOR COMPANY; *U.S. Private*, pg. 1783
GREINER'S INC.; *U.S. Private*, pg. 1783
GREINER TOOL.TEC GMBH—See Greiner Holding AG; *Int'l*, pg. 3079
GREKA CHINA LTD—See G3 Exploration Limited; *Int'l*, pg. 2866

COMPANY NAME INDEX

GREKA DRILLING (INDIA) LTD—See Greka Drilling Limited; *Int'l*, pg. 3080
GREKA DRILLING LIMITED; *Int'l*, pg. 3080
GREKA ENERGY, CALIFORNIA—See Greka Energy Corporation; *U.S. Private*, pg. 1783
GREKA ENERGY, CHINA—See Greka Energy Corporation; *U.S. Private*, pg. 1783
GREKA ENERGY CORPORATION; *U.S. Private*, pg. 1783
GREKA ENGINEERING & TECHNOLOGY LTD.—See G3 Exploration Limited; *Int'l*, pg. 2866
GRELTON ELEVATOR INC.; *U.S. Private*, pg. 1783
GREMADA INDUSTRIES INC.; *U.S. Private*, pg. 1783
GREMESCO OF NEW JERSEY, LLC—See Brown & Brown, Inc.; *U.S. Public*, pg. 400
GREMI INWESTYCJE S.A.; *Int'l*, pg. 3080
GREMTEK SAS—See Diploma PLC; *Int'l*, pg. 2128
GREMZ, INC.; *Int'l*, pg. 3080
GREMZ POWER, INC.—See gremz, inc.; *Int'l*, pg. 3080
GREMZ SOLAR, INC.—See gremz, inc.; *Int'l*, pg. 3080
GRENADA BREWERIES LIMITED—See ANSA McAL Limited; *Int'l*, pg. 477
GRENADA ELECTRICITY SERVICES LIMITED; *Int'l*, pg. 3080
GRENADE (UK) LTD.—See Mondelez International, Inc.; *U.S. Public*, pg. 1461
GRENADIER HOLDINGS PLC—See Paragon Banking Group PLC; *Int'l*, pg. 5735
GRENADIER REALTY CORP.—See Starrett Corporation; *U.S. Private*, pg. 3787
GRENADIER—See Barkley; *U.S. Private*, pg. 475
GRENDENE ITALY S.R.L.—See Grendene S.A.; *Int'l*, pg. 3080
GRENDENE OGILVY & MATHER AG—See WPP plc; *Int'l*, pg. 8484
GRENDENE S.A.; *Int'l*, pg. 3080
GRENE AB OY—See SHV Holdings N.V.; *Int'l*, pg. 6872
GRENE AS—See SHV Holdings N.V.; *Int'l*, pg. 6872
GRENE DANMARK A/S—See SHV Holdings N.V.; *Int'l*, pg. 6872
GRENE DUSTRYBUCJA SP. Z O.O.—See SHV Holdings N.V.; *Int'l*, pg. 6872
GRENE KRAMP HOLDING A/S—See SHV Holdings N.V.; *Int'l*, pg. 6872
GRENERGY ERNEUERBARE ENERGIEN GMBH—See Grenergy Renovables SA, *Int'l*, pg. 0000
GRENERGY POLSKA SP. Z O.O.—See Grenergy Renovables SA; *Int'l*, pg. 3080
GRENERGY RENEWABLES UK LIMITED—See Grenergy Renovables SA; *Int'l*, pg. 3080
GRENERGY RENOVABLES SA; *Int'l*, pg. 3080
GRENE SP. Z O.O.—See SHV Holdings N.V.; *Int'l*, pg. 6872
GRENEVIA SA—See TDJ S.A.; *Int'l*, pg. 7486
GR ENGINEERING SERVICES LIMITED; *Int'l*, pg. 3047
GRENKE AG; *Int'l*, pg. 3080
GRENKE ALQUILER S.A—See Grenke AG; *Int'l*, pg. 3080
GRENKE BANK AG—See Grenke AG; *Int'l*, pg. 3081
GRENKE BUSINESS SOLUTIONS GMBH CO. KG—See Grenke AG; *Int'l*, pg. 3081
GRENKE DIGITAL GMBH—See Grenke AG; *Int'l*, pg. 3081
GRENKEFACTORING AG—See Grenke AG; *Int'l*, pg. 3081
GRENKEFACTORING GMBH—See Grenke AG; *Int'l*, pg. 3081
GRENKEFINANCE N.V.—See Grenke AG; *Int'l*, pg. 3081
GRENKE FINANCE PLC—See Grenke AG; *Int'l*, pg. 3081
GRENKE HRVATSKA D.O.O.—See Grenke AG; *Int'l*, pg. 3081
GRENKE INVESTITIONEN VERWALTUNGS KOMMANDITGESELLSCHAFT AUF AKTIEN—See Grenke AG; *Int'l*, pg. 3081
GRENKE KIRALAMA LTD. STI.—See Grenke AG; *Int'l*, pg. 3081
GRENKE LEASE SPRL—See Grenke AG; *Int'l*, pg. 3081
GRENKELEASING AB—See Grenke AG; *Int'l*, pg. 3081
GRENKELEASING AG—See Grenke AG; *Int'l*, pg. 3081
GRENKELEASING APS—See Grenke AG; *Int'l*, pg. 3081
GRENKELEASING D.O.O.—See Grenke AG; *Int'l*, pg. 3081
GRENKELEASING GMBH—See Grenke AG; *Int'l*, pg. 3081
GRENKE LEASING LTD.—See Grenke AG; *Int'l*, pg. 3081
GRENKELEASING MAGYARORSZAG KFT.—See Grenke AG; *Int'l*, pg. 3081
GRENKELEASING OY—See Grenke AG; *Int'l*, pg. 3081
GRENKELEASING SP. Z O.O.—See Grenke AG; *Int'l*, pg. 3081
GRENKELEASING S.R.O.—See Grenke AG; *Int'l*, pg. 3081
GRENKELEASING S.R.O.—See Grenke AG; *Int'l*, pg. 3081
GRENKE LIMITED—See Grenke AG; *Int'l*, pg. 3081
GRENKELOCATION SARL—See Grenke AG; *Int'l*, pg. 3081
GRENKE LOCATION SAS—See Grenke AG; *Int'l*, pg. 3081
GRENKE LOCAZIONE S.R.L.—See Grenke AG; *Int'l*, pg. 3081
GRENKE RENTING LTD.—See Grenke AG; *Int'l*, pg. 3081
GRENKE RENTING, S.A.—See Grenke AG; *Int'l*, pg. 3081

GRENKE RENTING S.R.L.—See Grenke AG; *Int'l*, pg. 3081
GRENKE RENT S.A.—See Grenke AG; *Int'l*, pg. 3081
GRENKE RENT S.L.—See Grenke AG; *Int'l*, pg. 3081
GRENOBLOISE D'ELECTRONIQUE ET D'AUTOMATISMES; *Int'l*, pg. 3081
GRENO INDUSTRIES INC.; *U.S. Private*, pg. 1783
GRENSEGUIDEN AS—See Eniro Group AB; *Int'l*, pg. 2439
GRENSON LIMITED; *Int'l*, pg. 3081
GRENSON SHOES LIMITED—See Grenson Limited; *Int'l*, pg. 3081
GRENTECH INDIA PVT LTD—See China GrenTech Corporation Limited; *Int'l*, pg. 1505
GRENTECH PAKISTAN (PVT.) LTD—See China GrenTech Corporation Limited; *Int'l*, pg. 1505
GRENTECH RF COMMUNICATION NIGERIA LIMITED—See China GrenTech Corporation Limited; *Int'l*, pg. 1506
GRENTECH RF COMMUNICATION NIGERIA LTD—See China GrenTech Corporation Limited; *Int'l*, pg. 1506
GRENTECH SA (PTY) LTD—See China GrenTech Corporation Limited; *Int'l*, pg. 1506
G RENT S.P.A.; *Int'l*, pg. 2861
GRENVILLE PRINTING LTD.; *Int'l*, pg. 3081
GRENZEBACH AUTOMATION GMBH—See Grenzebach Maschinenbau GmbH; *Int'l*, pg. 3081
GRENZEBACH BSH GMBH—See Grenzebach Maschinenbau GmbH; *Int'l*, pg. 3081
GRENZEBACH CORPORATION—See Grenzebach Maschinenbau GmbH; *Int'l*, pg. 3081
GRENZEBACH DO BRASIL—See Grenzebach Maschinenbau GmbH; *Int'l*, pg. 3082
GRENZEBACH - INOS AUTOMATION SOFTWARE INC.—See Grenzebach Maschinenbau GmbH; *Int'l*, pg. 3081
GRENZEBACH MACHINERY (INDIA) PVT. LTD.—See Grenzebach Maschinenbau GmbH; *Int'l*, pg. 3082
GRENZEBACH MACHINERY (JIASHAN) LTD.—See Grenzebach Maschinenbau GmbH; *Int'l*, pg. 3082
GRENZEBACH MACHINERY (SHANGHAI) LTD.—See Grenzebach Maschinenbau GmbH; *Int'l*, pg. 3082
GRENZEBACH MACHINERY TAIWAN LTD.—See Grenzebach Maschinenbau GmbH; *Int'l*, pg. 3082
GRENZEBACH MASCHINENBAU GMBH; *Int'l*, pg. 3081
GRENZEBACH MASHTECH, LLC—See Grenzebach Maschinenbau GmbH; *Int'l*, pg. 3082
GREPALIFE ASSET MANAGEMENT CORPORATION—See Sun Life Financial Inc.; *Int'l*, pg. 7306
GREPALIFE ASSET MANAGEMENT CORPORATION—See Yuchengco Group of Companies; *Int'l*, pg. 8610
GRESCO UTILITY SUPPLY INC.; *U.S. Private*, pg. 1783
G.RESEARCH, LLC—See Morgan Group Holding Co.; *U.S. Private*, pg. 1471
GRESGYING DIGITAL TECHNOLOGY CO., LTD.; *Int'l*, pg. 3082
GRESHAM & ASSOCIATES, INC.—See AmWINS Group, Inc.; *U.S. Private*, pg. 269
GRESHAM COMPUTER SERVICES LIMITED—See Symphony Technology Group, LLC; *U.S. Private*, pg. 3900
GRESHAM COSMETICS PTY. LTD.—See The Procter & Gamble Company; *U.S. Public*, pg. 2120
GRESHAM ENTERPRISE STORAGE INC—See Symphony Technology Group, LLC; *U.S. Private*, pg. 3900
GRESHAM FINANCIAL SYSTEMS LIMITED—See Symphony Technology Group, LLC; *U.S. Private*, pg. 3901
GRESHAM HOLDINGS, INC.—See Ault Alliance, Inc.; *U.S. Public*, pg. 227
GRESHAM HOUSE ENERGY STORAGE FUND PLC; *Int'l*, pg. 3082
GRESHAM HOUSE PLC—See Searchlight Capital Partners, L.P.; *U.S. Private*, pg. 3587
GRESHAM HOUSE STRATEGIC PLC; *Int'l*, pg. 3082
GRESHAM INVESTMENT MANAGEMENT LLC—See Teachers Insurance Association - College Retirement Fund; *U.S. Private*, pg. 3947
GRESHAM MINI & RV STORAGE, LLC—See National Storage Affiliates Trust; *U.S. Public*, pg. 1498
GRESHAM OUTLOOK; *U.S. Private*, pg. 1783
GRESHAM PARTNERS LTD.; *Int'l*, pg. 3082
GRESHAM PETROLEUM CO.; *U.S. Private*, pg. 1783
GRESHAM POWER ELECTRONICS LIMITED—See Ault Alliance, Inc.; *U.S. Public*, pg. 227
GRESHAM-PRUETT LUMBER EXCHANGE; *U.S. Private*, pg. 1784
GRESHAM, SMITH & PARTNERS, ATLANTA OFFICE—See Gresham, Smith & Partners; *U.S. Private*, pg. 1784
GRESHAM, SMITH & PARTNERS, BRIMINGHAM OFFICE—See Gresham, Smith & Partners; *U.S. Private*, pg. 1784
GRESHAM, SMITH & PARTNERS, CHARLOTTE OFFICE—See Gresham, Smith & Partners; *U.S. Private*, pg. 1784
GRESHAM, SMITH & PARTNERS, DALLAS OFFICE—See Gresham, Smith & Partners; *U.S. Private*, pg. 1784

GREY EAGLE DISTRIBUTORS INC.

GRESHAM, SMITH & PARTNERS, JACKSONVILLE OFFICE—See Gresham, Smith & Partners; *U.S. Private*, pg. 1784
GRESHAM, SMITH & PARTNERS, LOUISVILLE OFFICE—See Gresham, Smith & Partners; *U.S. Private*, pg. 1784
GRESHAM, SMITH & PARTNERS, MEMPHIS OFFICE—See Gresham, Smith & Partners; *U.S. Private*, pg. 1784
GRESHAM, SMITH & PARTNERS, RICHMOND OFFICE—See Gresham, Smith & Partners; *U.S. Private*, pg. 1784
GRESHAM, SMITH & PARTNERS; *U.S. Private*, pg. 1783
GRESHAM, SMITH & PARTNERS, TAMPA OFFICE—See Gresham, Smith & Partners; *U.S. Private*, pg. 1784
GRESHAM TECHNOLOGIES PLC—See Symphony Technology Group, LLC; *U.S. Private*, pg. 3900
GRESHAM TECHNOLOGIES (US) INC.—See Symphony Technology Group, LLC; *U.S. Private*, pg. 3901
GRESHAM WORLDWIDE, INC.—See Ault Alliance, Inc.; *U.S. Public*, pg. 227
G-RESOURCES GROUP LIMITED; *Int'l*, pg. 2862
GRES PANARIA PORTUGAL S.A.—See Panariagroup Industrie Ceramiche S.p.A.; *Int'l*, pg. 5717
GRES UNIVERSAL PTE. LTD.—See Hap Seng Consolidated Berhad; *Int'l*, pg. 3268
GRETEMAN GROUP; *U.S. Private*, pg. 1784
GRETEX CORPORATE SERVICES LTD; *Int'l*, pg. 3082
GRETEX INDUSTRIES LTD.; *Int'l*, pg. 3082
GRETTE ASSOCIATES, LLC—See Farallon Consulting, LLC; *U.S. Private*, pg. 1473
GRE VENTURES, INC.; *U.S. Private*, pg. 1761
GREVIN & CIE—See Compagnie des Alpes S.A.; *Int'l*, pg. 1738
GREVIN & CIE TOURAINE SAS—See Compagnie des Alpes S.A.; *Int'l*, pg. 1738
GREVIN DEUTSCHLAND GMBH—See Compagnie des Alpes S.A.; *Int'l*, pg. 1738
GREVSTAD & TVEDT AS—See Instalco AB; *Int'l*, pg. 3721
GREWALS (MAURITIUS) LIMITED—See ENL Limited; *Int'l*, pg. 2441
GREWALS RODRIGUES LTD.—See ENL Limited; *Int'l*, pg. 2441
GREXEL SYSTEMS OY—See Deutsche Borse AG; *Int'l*, pg. 2064
GREY AMSTERDAM—See WPP plc; *Int'l*, pg. 8470
GREY ARGENTINA—See WPP plc; *Int'l*, pg. 8470
GREY ATLANTA—See WPP plc; *Int'l*, pg. 8470
GREY BANGLADESH LTD.—See WPP plc; *Int'l*, pg. 8470
GREY BARCELONA—See WPP plc; *Int'l*, pg. 8471
GREY BEIJING—See WPP plc; *Int'l*, pg. 8470
GREYBULL CAPITAL LLP; *Int'l*, pg. 3082
GREY CANADA—See WPP plc; *Int'l*, pg. 8470
GREY CHILE—See WPP plc; *Int'l*, pg. 8470
GREYCOAT LUMLEYS LTD.—See Empresaria Group Plc; *Int'l*, pg. 2389
GREY DIRECT ARGENTINA—See WPP plc; *Int'l*, pg. 8470
GREY DIRECT CANADA—See WPP plc; *Int'l*, pg. 8464
GREY DIRECT GREECE—See WPP plc; *Int'l*, pg. 8470
GREY DIRECT SINGAPORE—See WPP plc; *Int'l*, pg. 8470
GREYDON, INC.—See Leonard Green & Partners, L.P.; *U.S. Private*, pg. 2427
GREY D.O.O. BELGRADE—See WPP plc; *Int'l*, pg. 8472
GREY EAGLE DISTRIBUTORS INC.; *U.S. Private*, pg. 1784
GREY FIRST SERVE ADVERTISING—See WPP plc; *Int'l*, pg. 8470
GREY GROUP ASIA PACIFIC—See WPP plc; *Int'l*, pg. 8470
GREY GROUP BELGIUM—See WPP plc; *Int'l*, pg. 8470
GREY GROUP BUDAPEST—See WPP plc; *Int'l*, pg. 8469
GREY GROUP BULGARIA—See WPP plc; *Int'l*, pg. 8470
GREY GROUP CROATIA—See WPP plc; *Int'l*, pg. 8470
GREY GROUP DENMARK—See WPP plc; *Int'l*, pg. 8470
GREY GROUP GERMANY—See WPP plc; *Int'l*, pg. 8470
GREY GROUP GREECE—See WPP plc; *Int'l*, pg. 8471
GREY GROUP HUNGARY—See WPP plc; *Int'l*, pg. 8471
GREY GROUP INDONESIA—See WPP plc; *Int'l*, pg. 8471
GREY GROUP JAPAN—See WPP plc; *Int'l*, pg. 8471
GREY GROUP KOREA—See WPP plc; *Int'l*, pg. 8471
GREY GROUP LATVIA—See WPP plc; *Int'l*, pg. 8471
GREY GROUP LUXEMBOURG—See WPP plc; *Int'l*, pg. 8471
GREY GROUP MACEDONIA—See WPP plc; *Int'l*, pg. 8471
GREY GROUP MALAYSIA—See WPP plc; *Int'l*, pg. 8471
GREY GROUP MIDDLE EAST NETWORK—See WPP plc; *Int'l*, pg. 8471
GREY GROUP POLAND—See WPP plc; *Int'l*, pg. 8471
GREY GROUP ROMANIA—See WPP plc; *Int'l*, pg. 8471
GREY GROUP—See WPP plc; *Int'l*, pg. 8464
GREY GROUP—See WPP plc; *Int'l*, pg. 8469
GREY GROUP SOUTH AFRICA—See WPP plc; *Int'l*, pg. 8471
GREY GROUP TAIWAN—See WPP plc; *Int'l*, pg. 8471
GREY GROUP UKRAINE—See WPP plc; *Int'l*, pg. 8471
GREY GROUP UZBEKISTAN—See WPP plc; *Int'l*, pg. 8471

GREY EAGLE DISTRIBUTORS INC.
CORPORATE AFFILIATIONS

GREY GUANGZHOU—See WPP plc; *Int'l*, pg. 8471
GREY HEALTHCARE PARIS—See WPP plc; *Int'l*, pg. 8470
GREY HEALTHCARE—See WPP plc; *Int'l*, pg. 8470
GREY HEALTHCARE—See WPP plc; *Int'l*, pg. 8470
GREY HONG KONG—See WPP plc; *Int'l*, pg. 8471
GREYHOUND AUSTRALIA PTY. LTD.; *Int'l*, pg. 3082
GREYHOUND CANADA TRANSPORTATION CORP.—See FlixMobility GmbH; *Int'l*, pg. 2706
GREYHOUND LINES, INC.—See FlixMobility GmbH; *Int'l*, pg. 2706
GREY (INDIA) PVT. LTD. (AHMEDABAD)—See WPP plc; *Int'l*, pg. 8470
GREY (INDIA) PVT. LTD. (CALCUTTA)—See WPP plc; *Int'l*, pg. 8470
GREY (INDIA) PVT. LTD.—See WPP plc; *Int'l*, pg. 8470
GREY (INDIA) PVT. PTY. LTD. (DELHI)—See WPP plc; *Int'l*, pg. 8470
GREY INTERACTIVE ARGENTINA AR—See WPP plc; *Int'l*, pg. 8470
GREY INTERACTIVE-HONG KONG—See WPP plc; *Int'l*, pg. 8470
GREY INTERACTIVE INDIA—See WPP plc; *Int'l*, pg. 8470
GREY INTERACTIVE ITALY—See WPP plc; *Int'l*, pg. 8470
GREY INTERACTIVE PORTUGAL—See WPP plc; *Int'l*, pg. 8470
GREY INTERACTIVE/TORONTO—See WPP plc; *Int'l*, pg. 8470
GREY ISTANBUL—See WPP plc; *Int'l*, pg. 8471
GREY ITALIA - ROME—See WPP plc; *Int'l*, pg. 8471
GREY ITALIA S.P.A—See WPP plc; *Int'l*, pg. 8471
GREYLINE INSTRUMENTS INC.—See Harbour Group Industries, Inc.; *U.S. Private*, pg. 1860
GREYLINE INSTRUMENTS, INC.—See Harbour Group Industries, Inc.; *U.S. Private*, pg. 1860
GREY LJUBLJANA D.O.O.—See WPP plc; *Int'l*, pg. 8471
GREYLOCK PARTNERS; *U.S. Private*, pg. 1784
GREYLOGIX GMBH—See E.ON SE; *Int'l*, pg. 2258
GREY LONDON—See WPP plc; *Int'l*, pg. 8471
GREY LOS ANGELES—See WPP plc; *Int'l*, pg. 8471
GREY MADRID—See WPP plc; *Int'l*, pg. 8471
GREYMART METAL COMPANY INC.; *U.S. Private*, pg. 1784
GREY MATTER (EMEA) LIMITED—See Climb Global Solutions, Inc.; *U.S. Public*, pg. 515
GREY MATTER LTD.; *Int'l*, pg. 3082
GREY MEXICO, S.A. DE C.V—See WPP plc; *Int'l*, pg. 8471
GREY MIDDLE EAST NETWORK—See WPP plc; *Int'l*, pg. 8471
GREY MOUNTAIN PARTNERS, LLC; *U.S. Private*, pg. 1784
GREY NEW YORK—See WPP plc; *Int'l*, pg. 8471
GREY NEW ZEALAND LIMITED—See WPP plc; *Int'l*, pg. 8471
GREY OAKS COUNTRY CLUB INC.—See Barron Collier Company, Ltd.; *U.S. Private*, pg. 480
GREY PERU—See WPP plc; *Int'l*, pg. 8471
GREY PTY. LTD.—See WPP plc; *Int'l*, pg. 8471
GREY PUERTO RICO—See WPP plc; *Int'l*, pg. 8471
GREYROCK CAPITAL GROUP, LLC; *U.S. Private*, pg. 1785
GREY SAN FRANCISCO—See WPP plc; *Int'l*, pg. 8471
GREY SHANGHAI—See WPP plc; *Int'l*, pg. 8471
GREY SHOPPER GMBH—See WPP plc; *Int'l*, pg. 8464
GREY SINGAPORE—See WPP plc; *Int'l*, pg. 8471
GREYSON INTERNATIONAL, INC.; *U.S. Public*, pg. 969
GREY—See WPP plc; *Int'l*, pg. 8470
GREYSTAR DEVELOPMENT & CONSTRUCTION, L.P.—See Greystar Real Estate Partners, LLC; *U.S. Private*, pg. 1785
GREYSTAR GROWTH & INCOME FUND, LP—See Greystar Real Estate Partners, LLC; *U.S. Private*, pg. 1785
GREYSTAR MANAGEMENT SERVICES, L.P.—See Greystar Real Estate Partners, LLC; *U.S. Private*, pg. 1785
GREYSTAR REAL ESTATE PARTNERS, LLC; *U.S. Private*, pg. 1785
GREY STOCKHOLM—See WPP plc; *Int'l*, pg. 8472
GREYSTON BAKERY INC.; *U.S. Private*, pg. 1785
GREYSTONE AFFORDABLE HOUSING INITIATIVES, LLC—See Greystone & Co., Inc.; *U.S. Private*, pg. 1785
GREYSTONE AMBIENT & STYLE GMBH & CO. KG—See Heidelberg Materials AG; *Int'l*, pg. 3310
GREYSTONE CAPITAL PARTNERS A/S; *Int'l*, pg. 3082
GREYSTONE & CO., INC.; *U.S. Private*, pg. 1785
GREYSTONE CONSTRUCTION COMPANY; *U.S. Private*, pg. 1786
GREYSTONE GRAPHICS, INC.; *U.S. Private*, pg. 1786
GREYSTONE HEALTHCARE MANAGEMENT CORP.; *U.S. Private*, pg. 1786
GREYSTONE HOUSING IMPACT INVESTORS LP—See Greystone & Co., Inc.; *U.S. Private*, pg. 1786
GREYSTONE INCORPORATED; *U.S. Private*, pg. 1786
GREYSTONE INTERNAL MEDICINE - BROOKWOOD, L.L.C.—See Tenet Healthcare Corporation; *U.S. Public*, pg. 2003
GREYSTONE LOGISTICS, INC.; *U.S. Public*, pg. 969

GREYSTONE POWER CORPORATION; *U.S. Private*, pg. 1786
GREYSTONE PROGRAMS, INC.; *U.S. Private*, pg. 1786
GREYSTONES CARGO SYSTEMS—See Carrix, Inc.; *U.S. Private*, pg. 773
GREYSTONE SERVICING CORPORATION, INC.—See Greystone & Co., Inc.; *U.S. Private*, pg. 1786
GREYTER WATER SYSTEMS; *Int'l*, pg. 3082
GREY THAILAND—See WPP plc; *Int'l*, pg. 8472
GREYTHORN, INC.—See Olympus Partners; *U.S. Private*, pg. 3014
GREYTHORN PTY LTD.—See ManpowerGroup Inc.; *U.S. Public*, pg. 1358
GREY & TRACE—See WPP plc; *Int'l*, pg. 8471
GREY & TRACE—See WPP plc; *Int'l*, pg. 8471
GREY TWO PR—See WPP plc; *Int'l*, pg. 8469
GREY VANCOUVER—See WPP plc; *Int'l*, pg. 8470
GREY VILNIUS—See WPP plc; *Int'l*, pg. 8472
GREYWALL CLUB L.L.C.—See Lennar Corporation; *U.S. Public*, pg. 1306
GREYWOLF ENERGY SERVICES LTD.—See TETRA Technologies, Inc.; *U.S. Public*, pg. 2024
GREY WORLDWIDE WARSAW—See WPP plc; *Int'l*, pg. 8469
GREZDIS; *Int'l*, pg. 3082
GR FINANCIAL LLC—See Radian Group, Inc.; *U.S. Public*, pg. 1759
GRG BANKING EQUIPMENT CO., LTD.—See Guangzhou Radio Group Co., Ltd.; *Int'l*, pg. 3167
GRG INTERNATIONAL CORPORATION—See GRG International Limited; *Int'l*, pg. 3082
GRG INTERNATIONAL LIMITED; *Int'l*, pg. 3082
GR GRUNDSTUCKS GMBH OBJEKT CORVUS & CO.—See Commerzbank AG; *Int'l*, pg. 1719
GR-HIGHLAND GLEN, L.P.—See Equity Residential; *U.S. Public*, pg. 792
G.R.H. MAIDEN INC.; *U.S. Private*, pg. 1631
G. R. (HOLDINGS) PLC; *Int'l*, pg. 2864
GRIBBLES VETERINARY PATHOLOGY LIMITED; *Int'l*, pg. 3082
GRIBETZ INTERNATIONAL, INC.—See Leggett & Platt, Incorporated; *U.S. Public*, pg. 1302
GRI BIO, INC.; *U.S. Public*, pg. 969
GRICHTING & VALTERIO ELECTRO SA—See Burkhalter Holding AG; *Int'l*, pg. 1225
GRID ALTERNATIVES; *U.S. Private*, pg. 1786
GRID BATTERY METALS INC; *Int'l*, pg. 3082
GRID BH D.O.O.—See PCC SE; *Int'l*, pg. 5766
GRID DYNAMICS HOLDINGS, INC.; *U.S. Public*, pg. 969
GRID INVESTMENT (CAMBODIA) CO., LTD.—See Troy Information Technology Co., Ltd.; *Int'l*, pg. 7940
GRIDIRON CAPITAL, LLC; *U.S. Private*, pg. 1786
GRID METALS CORP.; *Int'l*, pg. 3082
GRIDRESERVE LTD.—See Gresham House Energy Storage Fund PLC; *Int'l*, pg. 3082
GRIDSENSE INC.—See Franklin Electric Co., Inc.; *U.S. Public*, pg. 878
GRIDS INFORMATION TECHNOLOGIES, INC.—See Arlington Capital Partners LLC; *U.S. Private*, pg. 327
GRIDSMART TECHNOLOGIES, INC.—See Elliott Management Corporation; *U.S. Private*, pg. 1368
GRIDSMART TECHNOLOGIES, INC.—See Veritas Capital Fund Management, LLC; *U.S. Private*, pg. 4362
GRID SOLTUIONS OY—See General Electric Company; *U.S. Public*, pg. 918
GRID SOLUTIONS ENERJI ENDUSTRISI A.S—See General Electric Company; *U.S. Public*, pg. 918
GRID SOLUTIONS SAS—See General Electric Company; *U.S. Public*, pg. 917
GRID SOLUTIONS S.P.A—See General Electric Company; *U.S. Public*, pg. 918
GRID SOLUTIONS (U.S.) LLC—See General Electric Company; *U.S. Public*, pg. 920
GRIDSOURCE, INC.—See Hastings Equity Partners, LLC; *U.S. Private*, pg. 1879
GRIDSUM HOLDING INC.; *Int'l*, pg. 3083
GRIEG KALENDERFORLAG AS—See Sycamore Partners Management, LP; *U.S. Private*, pg. 3897
GRIEG SEAFOOD ASA; *Int'l*, pg. 3083
GRIEG SEAFOOD CANADA AS—See Grieg Seafood ASA; *Int'l*, pg. 3083
GRIEG SEAFOOD FINNMARK AS—See Grieg Seafood ASA; *Int'l*, pg. 3083
GRIEG SEAFOOD ROGALAND AS—See Grieg Seafood ASA; *Int'l*, pg. 3083
GRIEG TRIANGLE LOGISTICS B.V.—See DSV A/S; *Int'l*, pg. 2214
GRIESHABER GMBH & CO. KG—See Grieshaber Holding GmbH; *Int'l*, pg. 3083
GRIESHABER HOLDING GMBH; *Int'l*, pg. 3083
GRIESSON DE BEUKELAER GMBH & CO. KG—See Danone; *Int'l*, pg. 1968
GRIESSON DE BEUKELAER OSTERREICH GMBH—See Danone; *Int'l*, pg. 1968
THE GRIEVE CORPORATION; *U.S. Private*, pg. 4039
GRIFAL SPA; *Int'l*, pg. 3083
GRIFERIA SANITARIO (M) SDN. BHD.—See UNIMECH Group Berhad; *Int'l*, pg. 8049

GRIFFIN-AMERICAN HEALTHCARE REIT III, INC.—See American Healthcare Investors LLC; *U.S. Private*, pg. 236
GRIFFIN-AMERICAN HEALTHCARE REIT III, INC.—See Griffin Capital Corporation; *U.S. Private*, pg. 1787
GRIFFIN & ASSOCIATES; *U.S. Private*, pg. 1786
GRIFFIN & ASSOCIATES—See Griffin & Associates; *U.S. Private*, pg. 1787
GRIFFIN BEVERAGE CO.; *U.S. Private*, pg. 1787
GRIFFIN CAPITAL CORPORATION; *U.S. Private*, pg. 1787
GRIFFIN CAPITAL ESSENTIAL ASSET REIT II, INC.—See Griffin Capital Corporation; *U.S. Private*, pg. 1787
GRIFFIN CAPITAL SECURITIES, INC.—See Griffin Capital Corporation; *U.S. Private*, pg. 1787
GRIFFIN CATERING SERVICES LIMITED—See Fuller, Smith & Turner PLC; *Int'l*, pg. 2842
GRIFFIN CHRYSLER DODGE JEEP; *U.S. Private*, pg. 1787
GRIFFIN COMMUNICATIONS, LLC; *U.S. Private*, pg. 1787
GRIFFIN DEWATERING CORPORATION—See Crossplane Capital Management LP; *U.S. Private*, pg. 1107
GRIFFIN DIALYSIS, LLC—See DaVita Inc.; *U.S. Public*, pg. 639
GRIFFIN FOOD COMPANY—See Griffin Holdings Inc.; *U.S. Private*, pg. 1788
GRIFFIN FORD INC.; *U.S. Private*, pg. 1787
GRIFFIN FORD-LINCOLN-MERCURY, INC.; *U.S. Private*, pg. 1787
GRIFFIN GREENHOUSE & NURSERY SUPPLIES, INC. - CONNECTICUT—See Griffin Greenhouse & Nursery Supplies, Inc.; *U.S. Private*, pg. 1787
GRIFFIN GREENHOUSE & NURSERY SUPPLIES, INC. - MAINE—See Griffin Greenhouse & Nursery Supplies, Inc.; *U.S. Private*, pg. 1787
GRIFFIN GREENHOUSE & NURSERY SUPPLIES, INC. - NEW JERSEY—See Griffin Greenhouse & Nursery Supplies, Inc.; *U.S. Private*, pg. 1787
GRIFFIN GREENHOUSE & NURSERY SUPPLIES, INC. - NEW YORK-CENTRAL—See Griffin Greenhouse & Nursery Supplies, Inc.; *U.S. Private*, pg. 1788
GRIFFIN GREENHOUSE & NURSERY SUPPLIES, INC. - NEW YORK-EAST—See Griffin Greenhouse & Nursery Supplies, Inc.; *U.S. Private*, pg. 1788
GRIFFIN GREENHOUSE & NURSERY SUPPLIES, INC. - PENNSYLVANIA—See Griffin Greenhouse & Nursery Supplies, Inc.; *U.S. Private*, pg. 1788
GRIFFIN GREENHOUSE & NURSERY SUPPLIES, INC.; *U.S. Private*, pg. 1787
GRIFFIN GREENHOUSE & NURSERY SUPPLIES, INC. - VIRGINIA—See Griffin Greenhouse & Nursery Supplies, Inc.; *U.S. Private*, pg. 1788
THE GRIFFIN GROUP, LLC; *U.S. Private*, pg. 4039
GRIFFIN HEALTH SERVICES CORPORATION; *U.S. Private*, pg. 1788
GRIFFIN HOLDINGS INC.; *U.S. Private*, pg. 1788
GRIFFIN HOLDINGS, LLC; *U.S. Private*, pg. 1788
GRIFFIN IMAGING, INC.—See Cypress Partners, LLC; *U.S. Private*, pg. 1135
GRIFFIN INDUSTRIES, INC.—See Darling Ingredients Inc.; *U.S. Public*, pg. 634
GRIFFIN INDUSTRIES LLC—See Darling Ingredients Inc.; *U.S. Public*, pg. 634
GRIFFIN INFORMATION SYSTEMS LTD.; *Int'l*, pg. 3083
GRIFFIN INTEGRATED COMMUNICATIONS; *U.S. Private*, pg. 1788
GRIFFIN INTERNATIONAL COMPANIES; *U.S. Private*, pg. 1788
GRIFFIN KBIK STEPHENS & THOMPSON; *U.S. Private*, pg. 1788
GRIFFIN LAND—See Centerbridge Partners, L.P.; *U.S. Private*, pg. 815
GRIFFIN LAND—See GIC Pte. Ltd.; *Int'l*, pg. 2964
GRIFFIN-LEGGETT HEALEY & ROTH FUNERAL HOME—See Service Corporation International; *U.S. Public*, pg. 1871
GRIFFIN MEDICAL PRODUCTS INC.; *U.S. Private*, pg. 1788
GRIFFIN MINING LIMITED; *Int'l*, pg. 3083
GRIFFIN PARTNERS CO.—See ASIAN STAR CO.; *Int'l*, pg. 619
GRIFFIN PARTNERS, INC.; *U.S. Private*, pg. 1788
GRIFFIN PAVEMENT STRIPING, INC.—See The Sterling Group, L.P.; *U.S. Private*, pg. 4123
GRIFFIN PRESS PRINTING PTY. LTD.—See Lion Rock Group Ltd; *Int'l*, pg. 4519
GRIFFIN PRESS—See IVE Group Limited; *Int'l*, pg. 3846
GRIFFIN PUMP & EQUIPMENT, INC.—See Crossplane Capital Management LP; *U.S. Private*, pg. 1107
GRIFFIN'S FOODS LTD.—See Pacific Equity Partners Pty. Limited; *Int'l*, pg. 5688
GRIFFIN'S HUB CHRYSLER JEEP DODGE; *U.S. Private*, pg. 1788
GRIFFIN TECHNOLOGY, INC.—See Incipio, LLC; *U.S. Private*, pg. 2053
GRIFFIN TELEVISION, INC.; *U.S. Private*, pg. 1788
GRIFFIN THERMAL PRODUCTS INC.; *U.S. Private*, pg. 1788

COMPANY NAME INDEX

GRIFFIN TRAVEL (HK) LTD.—See EAC Invest AS; *Int'l*, pg. 2261
GRIFFIN UNDERWRITING SERVICES—See Ryan Specialty Holdings, Inc.; *U.S. Public*, pg. 1828
GRIFFIS BLESSING INC.; *U.S. Private*, pg. 1788
GRIFFIS INC.; *U.S. Private*, pg. 1788
GRIFFITH & COE ADVERTISING, INC.; *U.S. Private*, pg. 1788
GRIFFITH COLOMBIA S.A.—See Griffith Laboratories, Inc.; *U.S. Private*, pg. 1789
GRIFFITH COMPANY; *U.S. Private*, pg. 1789
GRIFFITH ELECTRIC SUPPLY COMPANY; *U.S. Private*, pg. 1789
GRIFFITH ENERGY, LLC—See ArcLight Capital Holdings, LLC; *U.S. Private*, pg. 312
GRIFFITH ENERGY SERVICES, INC.—See Star Group, L.P.; *U.S. Public*, pg. 1937
GRIFFITH HOLDINGS INC.; *U.S. Private*, pg. 1789
GRIFFITH, INC.—See KYOCERA Corporation; *Int'l*, pg. 4357
GRIFFITH LABORATORIES, INC. - INNOVA DIVISION—See Griffith Laboratories, Inc.; *U.S. Private*, pg. 1789
GRIFFITH LABORATORIES, INC.; *U.S. Private*, pg. 1789
GRIFFITH LABORATORIES, K.K.—See Griffith Laboratories, Inc.; *U.S. Private*, pg. 1789
GRIFFITH LABORATORIES LIMITED—See Griffith Laboratories, Inc.; *U.S. Private*, pg. 1789
GRIFFITH LABORATORIES LTD.—See Griffith Laboratories, Inc.; *U.S. Private*, pg. 1789
GRIFFITH LABORATORIES (PHILS.) INC.—See Griffith Laboratories, Inc.; *U.S. Private*, pg. 1789
GRIFFITH MOTOR COMPANY; *U.S. Private*, pg. 1789
GRIFFITH MOTORS INC.; *U.S. Private*, pg. 1789
GRIFFITH RUBBER MILLS INC.; *U.S. Private*, pg. 1789
GRIFFITH RUBBER MILLS OF GARRETT, INC.—See Griffith Rubber Mills Inc.; *U.S. Private*, pg. 1789
GRIFFITHS CORPORATION; *U.S. Private*, pg. 1789
GRIFFITHS EQUIPMENT LIMITED—See Amotiv Limited; *Int'l*, pg. 431
GRIFFITHS FORD; *Int'l*, pg. 3083
GRIFFITHS MCBURNEY (EUROPE) S.A.—See RF Capital Group Inc.; *Int'l*, pg. 6318
GRIFFON CORPORATION; *U.S. Public*, pg. 060
GRIFFS DIALYSIS, LLC—See DaVita Inc.; *U.S. Public*, pg. 639
GRIFOLS ARGENTINA, S.A.—See Grifols, S.A.; *Int'l*, pg. 3084
GRIFOLS ASIA PACIFIC PTE LTD—See Grifols, S.A.; *Int'l*, pg. 3084
GRIFOLS AUSTRALIA PTY LTD—See Grifols, S.A.; *Int'l*, pg. 3084
GRIFOLS BIOLOGICALS, INC.—See Grifols, S.A.; *Int'l*, pg. 3084
GRIFOLS CANADA LTD.—See Grifols, S.A.; *Int'l*, pg. 3084
GRIFOLS CHILE, S.A.—See Grifols, S.A.; *Int'l*, pg. 3084
GRIFOLS CHIRON DIAGNOSTICS CORP.—See Grifols, S.A.; *Int'l*, pg. 3084
GRIFOLS COLOMBIA, LTDA—See Grifols, S.A.; *Int'l*, pg. 3084
GRIFOLS DEUTSCHLAND GMBH—See Grifols, S.A.; *Int'l*, pg. 3084
GRIFOLS DEUTSCHLAND GMBH—See Grifols, S.A.; *Int'l*, pg. 3084
GRIFOLS DIAGNOSTICS EQUIPMENT TAIWAN LIMITED—See Grifols, S.A.; *Int'l*, pg. 3084
GRIFOLS ENGINEERING, S.A.—See Grifols, S.A.; *Int'l*, pg. 3084
GRIFOLS FRANCE, S.A.R.L.—See Grifols, S.A.; *Int'l*, pg. 3084
GRIFOLS (H.K.), LIMITED—See Grifols, S.A.; *Int'l*, pg. 3084
GRIFOLS, INC.—See Grifols, S.A.; *Int'l*, pg. 3084
GRIFOLS INDIA HEALTHCARE PRIVATE LTD.—See Grifols, S.A.; *Int'l*, pg. 3084
GRIFOLS INTERNATIONAL, S.A.—See Grifols, S.A.; *Int'l*, pg. 3084
GRIFOLS ITALIA S.P.A.—See Grifols, S.A.; *Int'l*, pg. 3084
GRIFOLS JAPAN K.K.—See Grifols, S.A.; *Int'l*, pg. 3084
GRIFOLS MALAYSIA SDN BHD—See Grifols, S.A.; *Int'l*, pg. 3084
GRIFOLS MEXICO, S.A. DE C.V.—See Grifols, S.A.; *Int'l*, pg. 3084
GRIFOLS MOVACO, S.A.—See Grifols, S.A.; *Int'l*, pg. 3084
GRIFOLS NORDIC AB—See Grifols, S.A.; *Int'l*, pg. 3084
GRIFOLS PHARMACEUTICAL TECHNOLOGY (SHANGHAI) CO., LTD.—See Grifols, S.A.; *Int'l*, pg. 3084
GRIFOLS POLSKA SP.Z.O.O—See Grifols, S.A.; *Int'l*, pg. 3084
GRIFOLS PORTUGAL PRODUCTOS FARMACEUTICOS E HOSPITALARES, LDA.—See Grifols, S.A.; *Int'l*, pg. 3084
GRIFOLS PORTUGAL PRODUTOS FARMACEUTICOS E HOSPITALARES, LDA.—See Grifols, S.A.; *Int'l*, pg. 3084
GRIFOLS, S.A.; *Int'l*, pg. 3083
GRIFOLS S.R.O.—See Grifols, S.A.; *Int'l*, pg. 3084

GRIFOLS THAILAND LTD.—See Grifols, S.A.; *Int'l*, pg. 3084
GRIFOLS U.K. LTD.—See Grifols, S.A.; *Int'l*, pg. 3084
GRIFOLS USA, INC.—See Grifols, S.A.; *Int'l*, pg. 3084
GRIFOLS VIAJES, S.A.—See Grifols, S.A.; *Int'l*, pg. 3084
GRIFOLS WORLDWIDE OPERATIONS LIMITED—See Grifols, S.A.; *Int'l*, pg. 3084
GRIGEO AB; *Int'l*, pg. 3085
GRIGEO BALTWOOD UAB—See Grigeo AB; *Int'l*, pg. 3085
GRIGEO KLAIPEDA AB—See Grigeo AB; *Int'l*, pg. 3085
GRIGGS NELSON MUTUAL INSURANCE CO.—See Walsh County Mutual Insurance Company; *U.S. Private*, pg. 4432
GRIID INFRASTRUCTURE INC.; *U.S. Public*, pg. 969
GRILL CONCEPTS-D.C., INC.—See Grill Concepts, Inc.; *U.S. Private*, pg. 1789
GRILL CONCEPTS, INC.; *U.S. Private*, pg. 1789
GRILLIT, INC.; *U.S. Public*, pg. 969
GRIMALDI COMMERCIAL REALTY CORP.; *U.S. Private*, pg. 1789
GRIMALDI GROUP SPA; *Int'l*, pg. 3085
GRIMALDI INDUSTRI AB; *Int'l*, pg. 3085
GRIMALDIS MEKANISKA VERKSTAD AB—See Grimaldi Industri AB; *Int'l*, pg. 3085
GRIMCO INC.; *U.S. Private*, pg. 1789
GRIMES ACE HARDWARE CO.; *U.S. Private*, pg. 1790
GRIMLEY FINANCIAL CORPORATION; *U.S. Private*, pg. 1790
GRIMM BROS. TRUCKING INC.—See Peoria Disposal Company/Area Disposal Service, Inc.; *U.S. Private*, pg. 3143
GRIMMER REALTY CO. INC.; *U.S. Private*, pg. 1790
GRIMM INDUSTRIES PTE. LTD.—See GDS Global Limited; *Int'l*, pg. 2896
GRIMMWAY ENTERPRISES INC.; *U.S. Private*, pg. 1790
GRIMSBY HYUNDAI—See Performance Auto Group; *Int'l*, pg. 5801
GRIMSHAW TRUCKING L.P.—See Mullen Group Ltd.; *Int'l*, pg. 5080
GRINAKER-LTA CONSTRUCTION AND DEVELOPMENT LIMITED; *Int'l*, pg. 3086
GRINAKER-LTA ENGINEERING AND MINING SERVICES LIMITED—See Aveng Limited; *Int'l*, pg. 738
GRINAKER-LTA (NAMIBIA) (PTY) LIMITED—See Aveng Limited; *Int'l*, pg. 738
GRINDEKS AS; *Int'l*, pg. 3086
GRINDER HAIZLIP CONSTRUCTION CO., INC.; *U.S. Private*, pg. 1790
GRINDEX AB—See Xylem Inc.; *U.S. Public*, pg. 2396
GRINDEX PUMPS LLC—See Xylem Inc.; *U.S. Public*, pg. 2396
GRINDING & DICING SERVICES, INC.—See Akoustis Technologies, Inc.; *U.S. Public*, pg. 69
GRINDING & SIZING COMPANY LLC—See American Securities LLC; *U.S. Private*, pg. 253
GRINDMASTER CORPORATION—See AB Electrolux; *Int'l*, pg. 40
GRINDMEDIA, LLC—See TEN: The Enthusiast Network, Inc.; *U.S. Private*, pg. 3964
GRINDR INC.; *U.S. Public*, pg. 969
GRINDROD BANK LIMITED—See Grindrod Limited; *Int'l*, pg. 3086
GRINDROD LIMITED - GRINDROD INTERMODAL DIVISION—See Grindrod Limited; *Int'l*, pg. 3086
GRINDROD LIMITED - GRINDROD LOGISTICS AUTO CARRIERS DIVISION—See Grindrod Limited; *Int'l*, pg. 3086
GRINDROD LIMITED - ISLAND VIEW SHIPPING DIVISION—See Grindrod Limited; *Int'l*, pg. 3086
GRINDROD LIMITED; *Int'l*, pg. 3086
GRINDROD LIMITED - UNICORN SHIPPING DIVISION—See Grindrod Limited; *Int'l*, pg. 3086
GRINDROD MANAGEMENT SERVICES (PTY) LIMITED—See Grindrod Limited; *Int'l*, pg. 3086
GRINDROD MARINE SERVICES—See Grindrod Limited; *Int'l*, pg. 3086
GRINDROD SHIPPING HOLDINGS LTD.; *Int'l*, pg. 3086
GRINDROD SHIPPING SERVICES UK LIMITED—See Grindrod Shipping Holdings Ltd.; *Int'l*, pg. 3086
GRINDROD SHIPPING (SOUTH AFRICA) PTY. LTD.—See Grindrod Shipping Holdings Ltd.; *Int'l*, pg. 3087
GRINDROD SHIPS AGENCIES LDA—See Albert Ballin KG; *Int'l*, pg. 294
GRINDROD SHIPS AGENCIES (PTY) LIMITED - KING & SONS DIVISION—See Grindrod Limited; *Int'l*, pg. 3086
GRINDROD SHIPS AGENCIES (PTY) LIMITED—See Grindrod Limited; *Int'l*, pg. 3086
GRINDROD (SOUTH AFRICA) (PTY) LTD - GRINDROD PCA DIVISION—See Grindrod Limited; *Int'l*, pg. 3086
GRINDROD (SOUTH AFRICA) (PTY) LTD - MITCHELL COTTS MARITIME DIVISION—See Grindrod Limited; *Int'l*, pg. 3086
GRINDROD TANK TERMINALS SA (PTY) LTD—See Grindrod Limited; *Int'l*, pg. 3086
GRINDROD TERMINALS (PTY) LTD - BAY STEVEDORES DIVISION—See Grindrod Limited; *Int'l*, pg. 3086
GRINDROD TERMINALS (PTY) LTD—See Grindrod Limited; *Int'l*, pg. 3086

GRINDROD TRAVEL (PTY) LIMITED—See Grindrod Limited; *Int'l*, pg. 3086
GRINDSTONE ENTERTAINMENT GROUP, LLC—See Lions Gate Entertainment Corp.; *Int'l*, pg. 4520
GRINDSTONE PARTNERS, LLC; *U.S. Private*, pg. 1790
GRINDWELL NORTON LTD.—See Compagnie de Saint-Gobain SA; *Int'l*, pg. 1730
GRINER DRILLING SERVICE INC.; *U.S. Private*, pg. 1790
GRINER PONTIAC CADILLAC NISSEN; *U.S. Private*, pg. 1790
G R INFRAPROJECTS LIMITED; *Int'l*, pg. 2861
GRINGO'S MEXICAN KITCHEN; *U.S. Private*, pg. 1790
GRINM ADVANCED MATERIALS CO., LTD.; *Int'l*, pg. 3087
GRINM ELECTRO-OPTIC MATERIALS CO., LTD.—See Grinm Advanced Materials Co., Ltd.; *Int'l*, pg. 3087
GRINNELL BANCSHARES, INC.; *U.S. Private*, pg. 1790
GRINNELL INFOSYSTEMS INC.—See Grinnell Mutual Reinsurance Company Inc.; *U.S. Private*, pg. 1790
GRINNELL LLC—See Johnson Controls International plc; *Int'l*, pg. 3988
GRINNELL MUTUAL REINSURANCE COMPANY INC.; *U.S. Private*, pg. 1790
GRINNELL SELECT INSURANCE COMPANY—See Grinnell Mutual Reinsurance Company Inc.; *U.S. Private*, pg. 1790
GRINNELL STATE BANK—See Grinnell Bancshares, Inc.; *U.S. Private*, pg. 1790
GRINO ECOLOGIC, S.A.; *Int'l*, pg. 3087
GRIP LIMITED—See Dentsu Group Inc.; *Int'l*, pg. 2036
GRIPLOCK SYSTEMS, LLC—See Salt Creek Capital Management, LLC; *U.S. Private*, pg. 3533
GRIPLOCK SYSTEMS, LLC—See Spell Capital Partners, LLC; *U.S. Private*, pg. 3754
GRIPPO POTATO CHIP COMPANY, INC.; *U.S. Private*, pg. 1790
GRIPROAD SPEZIALBELAGE UND BAUGESELLSCHAFT MBH—See STRABAG SE; *Int'l*, pg. 7230
GRIPSWARE DATENTECHNIK GMBH—See MEDIQON Group AG; *Int'l*, pg. 4780
GRI RENEWABLE INDUSTRIES, S.L.—See Mitsui & Co., Ltd.; *Int'l*, pg. 4973
GRISANTI, INC.; *U.S. Private*, pg. 1790
GRIS DECOUPAGE—See Societe Generale S.A.; *Int'l*, pg. 7042
GRISHAM FARM PRODUCTS, INC.; *U.S. Private*, pg. 1790
GRISTEDES FOODS, INC.—See Red Apple Group, Inc.; *U.S. Private*, pg. 3372
GRISTEDES SUPERMARKETS, INC.—See Red Apple Group, Inc.; *U.S. Private*, pg. 3372
GRIST MAGAZINE, INC.; *U.S. Private*, pg. 1790
GRIS UMFORMTECHNIK GMBH—See Societe Generale S.A.; *Int'l*, pg. 7042
GRISWOLD ACQUISITION COMPANY—See Dover Corporation; *U.S. Public*, pg. 681
GRISWOLD CONTROLS; *U.S. Private*, pg. 1790
GRISWOLD ENGINEERING, INC.—See Segula Technologies SA; *Int'l*, pg. 6683
GRISWOLD HOME CARE; *U.S. Private*, pg. 1790
GRISWOLD INDUSTRIES, INC.; *U.S. Private*, pg. 1790
GRISWOLD, LLC—See Rogers Corporation; *U.S. Public*, pg. 1808
GRITEE, INC.; *Int'l*, pg. 3087
GRIT GROUP HOLDINGS CO., LTD.—See SCALA Inc.; *Int'l*, pg. 6610
GRITIT; *Int'l*, pg. 3087
GRITMAN MEDICAL CENTER; *U.S. Private*, pg. 1791
GRIT REAL ESTATE INCOME GROUP LIMITED; *Int'l*, pg. 3087
GRITSTONE BIO, INC.; *U.S. Public*, pg. 970
GRIUL SA; *Int'l*, pg. 3087
GRIVALIA PROPERTIES REAL ESTATE INVESTMENTS COMPANY S.A.—See Eurobank Ergasias Services and Holdings S.A.; *Int'l*, pg. 2532
GRIZACO NV—See VINCI S.A.; *Int'l*, pg. 8222
GRIZZCO CAMP SERVICES INC—See Clean Harbors, Inc.; *U.S. Public*, pg. 510
GRIZZLY DISCOVERIES INC.; *Int'l*, pg. 3087
GRIZZLY ENERGY, LLC; *U.S. Public*, pg. 970
GRIZZLY EQUIPMENT COMPANY—See Surerus Pipeline Inc.; *Int'l*, pg. 7343
GRIZZLY INDUSTRIAL INC.; *U.S. Private*, pg. 1791
GRK CANADA LIMITED—See Illinois Tool Works Inc.; *U.S. Public*, pg. 1103
GRL B.V.—See Govind Rubber Ltd.; *Int'l*, pg. 3044
GRMEC A.D.; *Int'l*, pg. 3087
GRM INFORMATION MANAGEMENT SERVICES; *U.S. Private*, pg. 1791
G.R. MITCHELL INC.; *U.S. Private*, pg. 1631
GRM OVERSEAS LIMITED; *Int'l*, pg. 3087
GRN FUNDS, LLC; *U.S. Private*, pg. 1791
GRN HOLDING CORPORATION—See GRN Funds, LLC; *U.S. Private*, pg. 1791
GRO ALLIANCE; *U.S. Private*, pg. 1791
GRO ASIA AGRITECHNOLOGY SDN. BHD.—See Fintec Global Berhad; *Int'l*, pg. 2677

GRO ALLIANCE

GROBER INDUSTRIAL SERVICES SDN. BHD.—See Darco Water Technologies Limited; *Int'l*, pg. 1972
GROBET FILE COMPANY OF AMERICA, INC.—See Hammond, Kennedy, Whitney & Company, Inc.; *U.S. Private*, pg. 1850
THE GROB TEA COMPANY LIMITED; *Int'l*, pg. 7651
GROCERS INSURANCE AGENCY, INC.—See Brookfield Reinsurance Ltd.; *Int'l*, pg. 1194
THE GROCERS SUPPLY CO., INC; *U.S. Private*, pg. 4039
GROCERS SUPPLY INTERNATIONAL, INC.—See C&S Wholesale Grocers, Inc.; *U.S. Private*, pg. 704
GROCERY HAULERS INC.; *U.S. Private*, pg. 1791
GROCERY LOGISTICS OF SINGAPORE PTE LTD—See NTUC Fairprice Co-operative Ltd.; *Int'l*, pg. 5485
GROCERY MARKETING INC.; *U.S. Private*, pg. 1791
GROCERY OUTLET HOLDING CORP.; *U.S. Public*, pg. 970
GROCERY OUTLET INC.—See Hellman & Friedman LLC; *U.S. Private*, pg. 1908
THE GROCERY PEOPLE LTD.—See Federated Co-operatives Limited; *Int'l*, pg. 2631
GROCERY SUPPLY COMPANY-SAN ANTONIO—See GSC Enterprises, Inc.; *U.S. Private*, pg. 1800
GROCERY SUPPLY COMPANY—See GSC Enterprises, Inc.; *U.S. Private*, pg. 1800
GROCERY SUPPLY COMPANY-SOUTHEAST—See GSC Enterprises, Inc.; *U.S. Private*, pg. 1800
GROCERY WHOLESALERS PTY LTD—See Woolworths Group Limited; *Int'l*, pg. 8452
GROCLIN KARPATY SP. Z O.O.—See Groclin S.A.; *Int'l*, pg. 3087
GROCLIN S.A.; *Int'l*, pg. 3087
GROCLIN SEATING GMBH—See Groclin S.A.; *Int'l*, pg. 3087
GROCLIN SERVICE SP. Z O.O.—See Groclin S.A.; *Int'l*, pg. 3087
GROCON ERSTE GRUNDSTUCKSGESELLSCHAFT MBH—See Baloise Holding AG; *Int'l*, pg. 811
GROCON GROUP HOLDINGS PTY. LTD.; *Int'l*, pg. 3087
GRODAN B.V.—See ROCKWOOL A/S; *Int'l*, pg. 6380
GRODAN INC.—See ROCKWOOL A/S; *Int'l*, pg. 6380
GRODAN INC.—See ROCKWOOL A/S; *Int'l*, pg. 6380
GRODAN MED S.A.—See ROCKWOOL A/S; *Int'l*, pg. 6380
GRODAN S. DE R.L DE C.V.—See ROCKWOOL A/S; *Int'l*, pg. 6380
GRODAN SP. Z O.O.—See ROCKWOOL A/S; *Int'l*, pg. 6380
GRODITZ CELIK ENDUSTRI MALZ. SAN.VE TIC. A.S.—See Georgsmarienhutte Holding GmbH; *Int'l*, pg. 2940
GRODITZER VERTRIEBSGESELLSCHAFT MBH—See Georgsmarienhutte Holding GmbH; *Int'l*, pg. 2940
GRODNO AZOT JSC—See Concern Belneftekhim; *Int'l*, pg. 1764
GRODNO SA; *Int'l*, pg. 3087
GRODSKY SERVICE, INC.—See Harry Grodsky & Co., Inc.; *U.S. Private*, pg. 1871
GROEBNER & ASSOCIATES INC.; *U.S. Private*, pg. 1791
GROEDITZER KURBELWELLE WILDAU GMBH—See Georgsmarienhutte Holding GmbH; *Int'l*, pg. 2940
GROEDITZER WERKZEUGSTAHL BURG GMBH—See Georgsmarienhutte Holding GmbH; *Int'l*, pg. 2940
GROEIVERMOGEN N.V.—See ABN AMRO Group N.V.; *Int'l*, pg. 65
GROEN BROTHERS AVIATION, INC.; *U.S. Private*, pg. 1791
GROENDYKE TRANSPORT, INC.; *U.S. Private*, pg. 1791
GROENEVELD-BEKA CANADA INC.—See The Timken Company; *U.S. Public*, pg. 2132
GROENEVELD-BEKA GMBH—See The Timken Company; *U.S. Public*, pg. 2132
GROENEVELD BRILLEN EN CONTACTLENZEN B.V.—See Fielmann Group AG; *Int'l*, pg. 2658
GROENEVELD GROEP HOLDING B.V.—See The Timken Company; *U.S. Public*, pg. 2132
GROENEVELD ITALIA S.R.L.—See The Timken Company; *U.S. Public*, pg. 2132
GROENEVELD LUBRICATION SOLUTIONS INC.—See The Timken Company; *U.S. Public*, pg. 2132
GROENEVELD LUBRICATION SOLUTIONS INC.—See The Timken Company; *U.S. Public*, pg. 2132
GROENEVELD LUBRICATION SOLUTIONS LIMITED—See The Timken Company; *U.S. Public*, pg. 2132
GROENEVELD LUBRICATION SOLUTIONS LTD.—See The Timken Company; *U.S. Public*, pg. 2132
GROENEVELD LUBRICATION SOLUTIONS PTY LTD.—See The Timken Company; *U.S. Public*, pg. 2132
GROENEVELD LUBRICATION SOLUTIONS S.R.L.—See The Timken Company; *U.S. Public*, pg. 2132
GROENEVELD POLSKA SP Z O.O.—See The Timken Company; *U.S. Public*, pg. 2132
GROENEVELD UK LIMITED—See The Timken Company; *U.S. Public*, pg. 2132
GROENEVELD UK LIMITED—See The Timken Company; *U.S. Public*, pg. 2132

GROENEWOLD FUR & WOOL, CO.; *U.S. Private*, pg. 1791
GROENLEVEN B.V.—See BayWa AG; *Int'l*, pg. 918
GROEP HEYLEN BUSINESS & BUILDING BV; *Int'l*, pg. 3087
GROESBECK BANCSHARES, INC.; *U.S. Private*, pg. 1791
GROESBECK LUMBER & SUPPLY, INC.; *U.S. Private*, pg. 1791
G ROE WM & SONS INC.; *U.S. Private*, pg. 1628
GROFF TRACTOR & EQUIPMENT, INC; *U.S. Private*, pg. 1791
GROGANS TOWNE CHRYSLER DODGE INC.; *U.S. Private*, pg. 1791
GROGAN'S TOWNE CHRYSLER DODGE LLC—See Grogans Towne Chrysler Dodge Inc.; *U.S. Private*, pg. 1791
GROGENESIS, INC.; *U.S. Public*, pg. 970
GROGG'S HEATING & AIR CONDITIONING INC.—See NearU Services; *U.S. Private*, pg. 2878
GRO-GROUP INTERNATIONAL LIMITED—See Ping An Insurance (Group) Company of China, Ltd.; *Int'l*, pg. 5869
GROHE AG—See Development Bank of Japan, Inc.; *Int'l*, pg. 2087
GROHE AG—See LIXIL Group Corporation; *Int'l*, pg. 4533
GROHE AMERICA, INC.—See Development Bank of Japan, Inc.; *Int'l*, pg. 2088
GROHE AMERICA, INC.—See LIXIL Group Corporation; *Int'l*, pg. 4533
GROHE A/S—See Development Bank of Japan, Inc.; *Int'l*, pg. 2087
GROHE AS—See Development Bank of Japan, Inc.; *Int'l*, pg. 2088
GROHE A/S—See LIXIL Group Corporation; *Int'l*, pg. 4533
GROHE AS—See LIXIL Group Corporation; *Int'l*, pg. 4533
GROHEDAL SANITARSYSTEME GMBH & CO. KG—See Development Bank of Japan, Inc.; *Int'l*, pg. 2087
GROHEDAL SANITARSYSTEME GMBH & CO. KG—See LIXIL Group Corporation; *Int'l*, pg. 4533
GROHE DEUTSCHLAND VERTRIEBS GMBH—See Development Bank of Japan, Inc.; *Int'l*, pg. 2088
GROHE DEUTSCHLAND VERTRIEBS GMBH—See LIXIL Group Corporation; *Int'l*, pg. 4533
GROHE ESPANA, S.A.—See Development Bank of Japan, Inc.; *Int'l*, pg. 2088
GROHE ESPANA, S.A.—See LIXIL Group Corporation; *Int'l*, pg. 4533
GROHE GMBH—See Development Bank of Japan, Inc.; *Int'l*, pg. 2088
GROHE GMBH—See LIXIL Group Corporation; *Int'l*, pg. 4533
GROHE JAPAN LTD.—See Development Bank of Japan, Inc.; *Int'l*, pg. 2088
GROHE JAPAN LTD.—See LIXIL Group Corporation; *Int'l*, pg. 4533
GROHE LIMITED—See Development Bank of Japan, Inc.; *Int'l*, pg. 2088
GROHE LIMITED—See LIXIL Group Corporation; *Int'l*, pg. 4534
GROHE NEDERLAND B.V.—See Development Bank of Japan, Inc.; *Int'l*, pg. 2088
GROHE NEDERLAND B.V.—See LIXIL Group Corporation; *Int'l*, pg. 4534
GROHE N.V. S.A.—See Development Bank of Japan, Inc.; *Int'l*, pg. 2088
GROHE N.V. S.A.—See LIXIL Group Corporation; *Int'l*, pg. 4534
GROHE PACIFIC PTE. LTD.—See Development Bank of Japan, Inc.; *Int'l*, pg. 2088
GROHE PACIFIC PTE. LTD.—See LIXIL Group Corporation; *Int'l*, pg. 4534
GROHE POLSKA SP. ZO.O.—See Development Bank of Japan, Inc.; *Int'l*, pg. 2088
GROHE POLSKA SP. ZO.O.—See LIXIL Group Corporation; *Int'l*, pg. 4534
GROHE S.A.R.L.—See Development Bank of Japan, Inc.; *Int'l*, pg. 2088
GROHE S.A.R.L.—See LIXIL Group Corporation; *Int'l*, pg. 4534
GROHE S.P.A.—See Development Bank of Japan, Inc.; *Int'l*, pg. 2088
GROHE S.P.A.—See LIXIL Group Corporation; *Int'l*, pg. 4534
GROHE WATER TECHNOLOGY AG & CO. KG—See Development Bank of Japan, Inc.; *Int'l*, pg. 2088
GROHE WATER TECHNOLOGY AG & CO. KG—See LIXIL Group Corporation; *Int'l*, pg. 4534
GROHMANN ENGINEERING TRADING (SHANGHAI) CO. LTD.—See Tesla, Inc.; *U.S. Public*, pg. 2021
GROHMANN USA, INC.—See Tesla, Inc.; *U.S. Public*, pg. 2021
GROLIER INCORPORATED—See Scholastic Corporation; *U.S. Public*, pg. 1847
GROLIER INTERNATIONAL, INC.—See Scholastic Corporation; *U.S. Public*, pg. 1847
GROLIER INTERNATIONAL PRIVATE LIMITED—See Scholastic Corporation; *U.S. Public*, pg. 1847
GROLLEAU SAS—See Flex Ltd.; *Int'l*, pg. 2704

CORPORATE AFFILIATIONS

GROLLS AB—See Nordstjernan AB; *Int'l*, pg. 5425
GROLMUS ENTERPRISES INC.; *U.S. Private*, pg. 1791
GROLSCH INTERNATIONAL B.V.—See Asahi Group Holdings Ltd.; *Int'l*, pg. 593
GROMAX AGRI EQUIPMENT LIMITED—See Mahindra & Mahindra Limited; *Int'l*, pg. 4645
GROM SOCIAL ENTERPRISES, INC.; *U.S. Public*, pg. 970
GROMUTUAL BERHAD - MELAKA—See Gromutual Berhad; *Int'l*, pg. 3087
GROMUTUAL BERHAD; *Int'l*, pg. 3087
GRONDRECYCLAGE CENTRUM KALLO N.V.—See Ackermans & van Haaren NV; *Int'l*, pg. 105
GRONEMEYER IT GMBH; *Int'l*, pg. 3088
GRONG SPAREBANK; *Int'l*, pg. 3088
GRONLANDSBANKEN A/S; *Int'l*, pg. 3088
G-RONN S.R.O.—See MVV Energie AG; *Int'l*, pg. 5108
GRONN VEKST AS—See Cambi ASA; *Int'l*, pg. 1268
GROOME INDUSTRIAL SERVICE GROUP—See Argosy Capital Group, LLC; *U.S. Private*, pg. 321
GROOM ENERGY SOLUTIONS, LLC—See Electricite de France S.A.; *Int'l*, pg. 2350
GROOM & SONS' HARDWARE & LUMBER, INC.; *U.S. Private*, pg. 1791
GROOTE EYLANDT MINING COMPANY PTY. LTD.—See South32 Limited; *Int'l*, pg. 7117
GROOTHANDELSGEBOUWEN N.V.; *Int'l*, pg. 3088
GROOT HOSPITALITY LLC—See Live Nation Entertainment, Inc.; *U.S. Public*, pg. 1329
GROOT INDUSTRIES INC.—See Waste Connections, Inc.; *Int'l*, pg. 8353
GROOT RECYCLING & WASTE SERVICES, INC.—See Waste Connections, Inc.; *Int'l*, pg. 8353
GROOVE BOTANICALS INC.; *U.S. Public*, pg. 970
GROOVE LABS, INC.—See Clari, Inc.; *U.S. Private*, pg. 911
GROOVER SEMINARS, INC.; *U.S. Private*, pg. 1792
GROOV-PIN CORPORATION; *U.S. Private*, pg. 1792
GROOVY COMPANY, INC.—See ASAMA; *Int'l*, pg. 599
GROPPETTI AUTOMOTIVE; *U.S. Private*, pg. 1792
GROQ, INC.; *U.S. Private*, pg. 1792
GROSCHOPP AG; *Int'l*, pg. 3088
GROSCHOPP, INC.; *U.S. Private*, pg. 1792
GROSNOR DISTRIBUTION INC.; *Int'l*, pg. 3088
GROSOLAR INC.; *U.S. Private*, pg. 1792
GROSOUTH INC.; *U.S. Private*, pg. 1792
GROSSDUKENELSON & CO., P.C.—See Brady Ware & Schoenfeld Inc.; *U.S. Private*, pg. 633
GROSS ELECTRIC INC.; *U.S. Private*, pg. 1792
GROSSENBURG IMPLEMENT, INC.; *U.S. Private*, pg. 1792
GROSSGLOCKNER SARL—See CLS Holdings plc; *Int'l*, pg. 1664
GROSSINGER CITY AUTOPLEX, INC.; *U.S. Private*, pg. 1792
GROSSINGER'S NORTH AUTOCORP, INC.; *U.S. Private*, pg. 1792
GROSS & JANES CO.—See Koppers Holdings Inc.; *U.S. Public*, pg. 1271
GROSS-KOBRICK CORP.; *U.S. Private*, pg. 1792
GROSSLIGHT INSURANCE, INC.—See Peter C. Foy & Associates Insurance Services, Inc.; *U.S. Private*, pg. 3157
GROSS LOGISTICS INC.—See JSC Russian Railways; *Int'l*, pg. 4011
GROSSMAN CHEVROLET; *U.S. Private*, pg. 1792
GROSSMAN COMPANY PROPERTIES, INC.; *U.S. Private*, pg. 1792
GROSSMAN IRON & STEEL COMPANY; *U.S. Private*, pg. 1792
GROSSMAN MARKETING GROUP; *U.S. Private*, pg. 1792
GROSSMANS BARGAIN OUTLET—See E.C. Barton & Company; *U.S. Private*, pg. 1304
GROSSMAN Y ASOCIADOS, S.A. DE C.V.—See Arca Continental, S.A.B. de C.V.; *Int'l*, pg. 540
GROSS MOTORS AUTOMOTIVE GROUP; *U.S. Private*, pg. 1792
GROSSTAGEBAU KAMSDORF GMBH—See Koninklijke BAM Groep N.V.; *Int'l*, pg. 4261
GROSVENOR BUILDING SERVICES, INC.—See The Grosvenor Cleaning Services Ltd.; *Int'l*, pg. 7651
GROSVENOR CASINOS LIMITED—See The Rank Group Plc; *Int'l*, pg. 7678
GROSVENOR CLEANING SERVICES LIMITED—See The Grosvenor Cleaning Services Ltd.; *Int'l*, pg. 7651
THE GROSVENOR CLEANING SERVICES LTD.; *Int'l*, pg. 7651
GROSVENOR FINANCIAL SERVICES GROUP LTD.; *Int'l*, pg. 3088
THE GROSVENOR NUFFIELD HOSPITAL—See Nuffield Health; *Int'l*, pg. 5487
GROSVENOR PACIFIC PTY LTD—See Lee Kim Tah Holdings Ltd.; *Int'l*, pg. 4440
GROSVENOR RESOURCE CORPORATION; *Int'l*, pg. 3088
GROSVENOR TECHNOLOGY LIMITED—See Newmark Security Plc; *Int'l*, pg. 5235

COMPANY NAME INDEX

GROSVENOR TECHNOLOGY LLC—See Newmark Security Plc; *Int'l*, pg. 5235
GROSVENOR TRUST COMPANY LIMITED—See The Bank of N.T. Butterfield & Son Limited; *Int'l*, pg. 7616
GROSZEK SP.Z.O.O—See Emperia Holding S.A; *Int'l*, pg. 2385
GROT A.D.; *Int'l*, pg. 3088
GROTBERG ELECTRIC, INC. *U.S. Private*, pg. 1792
GROTECH VENTURES; *U.S. Private*, pg. 1793
GROTE ELECTRONICS—See Grote Industries, Inc.; *U.S. Private*, pg. 1793
GROTE INDUSTRIES, CO.—See Grote Industries, Inc.; *U.S. Private*, pg. 1793
GROTE INDUSTRIES DE MEXICO, S.A, DE C.V.—See Grote Industries, Inc.; *U.S. Private*, pg. 1793
GROTE INDUSTRIES EUROPE GMBH—See Grote Industries, Inc.; *U.S. Private*, pg. 1793
GROTE INDUSTRIES, INC.; *U.S. Private*, pg. 1792
GROTE (SHANGHAI) CO., LTD—See Grote Industries, Inc.; *U.S. Private*, pg. 1793
GROTE & WEIGEL INC.—See Rachael's Food Corporation; *U.S. Private*, pg. 3341
GROTH CORPORATION—See Tinicum Enterprises, Inc.; *U.S. Private*, pg. 4174
GROTHUSEN GESMBH; *Int'l*, pg. 3088
GROTON LANDMARK—See Alden Global Capital LLC; *U.S. Private*, pg. 157
GROTON WIND, LLC—See Iberdrola, S.A; *Int'l*, pg. 3570
GROTTES DE HAN-SUR-LESSE; *Int'l*, pg. 3088
GROTTO PIZZA INC.; *U.S. Private*, pg. 1793
THE GROUCHO CLUB LTD.—See Graphite Capital Management LLP; *Int'l*, pg. 3061
GROUND 2 AIR LTD.—See Ireland Blyth Limited; *Int'l*, pg. 3807
GROUND AIR SERVICE CO., LTD.—See Japan Airlines Co., Ltd.; *Int'l*, pg. 3881
GROUND CONTROL SYSTEMS, INC.—See Horizon Capital LLP; *Int'l*, pg. 3479
GROUND CREATE CO., LTD.—See MIRAIT ONE Corporation; *Int'l*, pg. 4917
GROUNDED PEOPLE APPAREL INC.; *Int'l*, pg. 3088
GROUND FREIGHT EXPEDITORS, LLC—See Allstates WorldCargo, Inc.; *U.S. Private*, pg. 193
GROUNDHEAT ENERGY SOLAR WIND CORP.; *Int'l*, pg. 3088
GROUND INVESTIGATION & PILING LIMITED; *Int'l*, pg. 3088
GROUNDLINK, INC.—See Comvest Group Holdings LLC; *U.S. Private*, pg. 1007
GROUND PENETRATING RADAR SYSTEMS, LLC—See Kohlberg & Company, LLC; *U.S. Private*, pg. 2338
GROUNDPROBE AUSTRALASIA PTY. LTD.—See Orica Limited; *Int'l*, pg. 5619
GROUNDPROBE (NANJING) MINING TECHNOLOGY CO., LTD.—See Orica Limited; *Int'l*, pg. 5619
GROUNDPROBE PERU S.A.C.—See Orica Limited; *Int'l*, pg. 5619
GROUNDPROBE PTY LTD—See Orica Limited; *Int'l*, pg. 5619
GROUNDPROBE SOUTH AFRICA (PROPRIETARY) LTD.—See Orica Limited; *Int'l*, pg. 5619
GROUNDPROBE SOUTH AMERICA S.A—See Orica Limited; *Int'l*, pg. 5619
GROUNDS FOR PLAY INC.—See Pfingsten Partners, LLC; *U.S. Private*, pg. 3164
GROUNDS FOR SCULPTURE; *U.S. Private*, pg. 1793
THE GROUNDS REAL ESTATE DEVELOPMENT AG; *Int'l*, pg. 7651
GROUNDSTAR RESOURCES LIMITED; *Int'l*, pg. 3088
GROUNDWATER & ENVIRONMENTAL SERVICES, INC.; *U.S. Private*, pg. 1793
GROUNDWATER PROTECTION—See Precision Assessment Technology Corporation; *Int'l*, pg. 5957
GROUND/WATER TREATMENT & TECHNOLOGY, LLC—See Keller Group plc; *Int'l*, pg. 4121
GROUNDWORK OPEN SOURCE, INC.—See HGGC, LLC; *U.S. Private*, pg. 1929
GROUP125 LLC; *U.S. Private*, pg. 1794
GROUP 1 AUTOMOTIVE, INC.; *U.S. Public*, pg. 970
GROUP 5 WEST, INC.; *U.S. Private*, pg. 1793
GROUP 5 WEST, INC.—See Group 5 West, Inc.; *U.S. Private*, pg. 1793
GROUP 6 METALS LIMITED; *Int'l*, pg. 3088
GROUP7 AG; *Int'l*, pg. 3090
GROUP9, INC.; *U.S. Private*, pg. 1794
GROUPAERO MEXICO—See Harlow Aerostructures, LLC; *U.S. Private*, pg. 1865
GROUP ALLIED LIMITED—See Sun Hung Kai Properties Limited; *Int'l*, pg. 7304
GROUP ALTERNATIVES INC.—See GTCR LLC; *U.S. Private*, pg. 1803
GROUPAMA ASIGURARI SA—See Groupama SA; *Int'l*, pg. 3090
GROUPAMA ASSET MANAGEMENT—See Groupama SA; *Int'l*, pg. 3090
GROUPAMA ASSICURAZIONI SPA—See Groupama SA; *Int'l*, pg. 3090
GROUPAMA ASSURANCES ET SERVICES—See Groupama SA; *Int'l*, pg. 3090
GROUPAMA EMEKLILIK A.S.—See Groupama SA; *Int'l*, pg. 3090
GROUPAMA GAN VIE—See Groupama SA; *Int'l*, pg. 3090
GROUPAMA GARANCIA BIZTOSITO ZRT—See Groupama SA; *Int'l*, pg. 3090
GROUPAMA GARANCIA POISTOVNA, A. S.—See Groupama SA; *Int'l*, pg. 3090
GROUPAMA IMMOBILIER—See Groupama SA; *Int'l*, pg. 3091
GROUPAMA INSURANCE (CHINA) LTD—See Groupama SA; *Int'l*, pg. 3091
GROUPAMA INSURANCE COMPANY LIMITED—See Ageas SA/NV; *Int'l*, pg. 205
GROUPAMA PHOENIX ASFALISTIKI—See Groupama SA; *Int'l*, pg. 3091
GROUPAMA PHOENIX ASFALISTIKI—See Groupama SA; *Int'l*, pg. 3091
GROUPAMA PJ SOCIETE DE PROTECTION JURIDIQUE—See Groupama SA; *Int'l*, pg. 3091
GROUPAMA SA; *Int'l*, pg. 3090
GROUPAMA SEGUROS PORTUGAL—See Groupama SA; *Int'l*, pg. 3091
GROUPAMA SEGUROS Y REASEGUROS SA—See Grupo Catalana Occidente, S.A.; *Int'l*, pg. 3124
GROUPAMA VIE BENIN—See Groupama SA; *Int'l*, pg. 3091
GROUPAMA ZASTRAHOVANE EAD—See Groupama SA; *Int'l*, pg. 3091
GROUP ASSOCIATES, INC.—See Marpai, Inc; *U.S. Public*, pg. 1370
GROUPAUTO UK & IRELAND LTD.—See Blackstone Inc.; *U.S. Public*, pg. 360
GROUP BENEFIT SERVICES INC.—See AmWINS Group, Inc.; *U.S. Private*, pg. 269
GROUP BENEFITS LLC—See Genstar Capital, LLC; *U.S. Private*, pg. 1674
GROUP BUILDERS INC.; *U.S. Private*, pg. 1793
GROUP DE CLOEDT SA; *Int'l*, pg. 3088
GROUP DEKKO - AVILLA—See Graham Holdings Company; *U.S. Public*, pg. 955
GROUP DEKKO, INC.—See Graham Holdings Company; *U.S. Public*, pg. 955
GROUP DEKKO - MERRIAM—See Graham Holdings Company; *U.S. Public*, pg. 955
GROUP DEKKO - NORTH WEBSTER—See Graham Holdings Company; *U.S. Public*, pg. 955
GROUP DE LABORATOIRE ALS MAIL SARL—See ALS Limited; *Int'l*, pg. 378
GROUP DELPHI, INC.; *U.S. Private*, pg. 1793
GROUPE AB S.A; *Int'l*, pg. 3091
GROUPE ACTICALL SAS—See Creadev SAS; *Int'l*, pg. 1830
GROUPE ADEO S.A.; *Int'l*, pg. 3091
GROUPE ADONIS INC.—See Metro Inc.; *Int'l*, pg. 4860
GROUPE AECON QUEBEC LTEE—See Aecon Group Inc.; *Int'l*, pg. 172
GROUPE AG3I SA; *Int'l*, pg. 3091
GROUPE AIRWELL SA; *Int'l*, pg. 3091
GROUPE APICIL; *Int'l*, pg. 3091
GROUPE ARCHAMBAULT INC.—See Groupe Renaud-Bray, Inc.; *Int'l*, pg. 3110
GROUPE ARNOULD SAS—See Legrand S.A.; *Int'l*, pg. 4444
GROUPE AXOR INC.; *Int'l*, pg. 3091
GROUPE BAUMGARTNER HOLDING SA—See Banque Cantonale Vaudoise; *Int'l*, pg. 853
GROUPE BEAUMANOIR; *Int'l*, pg. 3092
GROUPE BERKEM SA; *Int'l*, pg. 3092
GROUPE BERMEX INC.; *Int'l*, pg. 3092
GROUPE BERTRAND SARL; *Int'l*, pg. 3092
GROUPE B.M.R. INC.; *Int'l*, pg. 3091
GROUPE BOHLER SOUDAGE FRANCE S.A.S.—See voestalpine AG; *Int'l*, pg. 8291
GROUPE BPCE; *Int'l*, pg. 3092
GROUPE BRIAND SAS; *Int'l*, pg. 3099
GROUPE BRUXELLES LAMBERT SA; *Int'l*, pg. 3099
GROUPE CANAL+ S.A.—See Vivendi SE; *Int'l*, pg. 8266
GROUPE CANVAR INC.; *Int'l*, pg. 3101
GROUPE CASPERA SA; *Int'l*, pg. 3101
GROUPE CEGERCO INC.; *Int'l*, pg. 3101
GROUPE CENTENNIAL HOLDING SAH; *Int'l*, pg. 3101
GROUPE CIMENT QUEBEC, INC.; *Int'l*, pg. 3101
GROUPE CIOA SA; *Int'l*, pg. 3101
GROUPECONNECT LLC—See Publicis Groupe S.A.; *Int'l*, pg. 6099
GROUPEAERO-CONSEIL AON INC.—See Aon plc; *Int'l*, pg. 494
GROUPE CONSEIL DMR, INC.—See Fujitsu Limited; *Int'l*, pg. 2834
GROUPE CRIT, S.A.; *Int'l*, pg. 3101
GROUPE CT INC.—See Xerox Holdings Corporation; *U.S. Public*, pg. 2386
GROUPE DELOM INC.—See Wajax Corporation; *Int'l*, pg. 8331
GROUPE DES ASSURANCES DE TUNISIE (GAT)—See
GROUPE DESCHENES INC.; *Int'l*, pg. 3101
GROUPE DE SCIERIES G.D.S. INC.; *Int'l*, pg. 3101
GROUPE DUBREUIL SA; *Int'l*, pg. 3102
GROUPE DUTAILIER INC.; *Int'l*, pg. 3102
GROUPE DYNAMITE INC.; *Int'l*, pg. 3102
GROUPE EGIS S.A.; *Int'l*, pg. 3102
GROUPE ELYDAN; *Int'l*, pg. 3102
GROUPE ETAM SUISSE—See Etam Developpement SCA; *Int'l*, pg. 2520
GROUPE ETPO SA; *Int'l*, pg. 3102
GROUPE EUROPE HANDLING—See Groupe Crit, S.A.; *Int'l*, pg. 3101
GROUPE FLO SA—See Groupe Bertrand SARL; *Int'l*, pg. 3092
GROUPE FMC FRANCE SAS—See Ford Motor Company; *U.S. Public*, pg. 866
GROUPE FNAC S.A.; *Int'l*, pg. 3102
GROUPE GARNIER; *Int'l*, pg. 3103
GROUPE GILLETTE FRANCE S.A.—See The Procter & Gamble Company; *U.S. Public*, pg. 2124
GROUPE GLAXOSMITHKLINE SAS—See GSK plc; *Int'l*, pg. 3149
GROUPE GORGE S.A.; *Int'l*, pg. 3103
GROUPE GO SPORT SA—See Finatis SA; *Int'l*, pg. 2670
GROUPE GRIMAUD LA CORBIERE SA; *Int'l*, pg. 3103
GROUPE GUILBAULT LTEE; *Int'l*, pg. 3103
GROUPE GUILLIN SA; *Int'l*, pg. 3103
GROUPE HAMELIN S.A.; *Int'l*, pg. 3104
GROUPE HOMMELL; *Int'l*, pg. 3104
GROUPE INDUSPAC EMBALLAGE INC.; *Int'l*, pg. 3104
GROUPE INDUSTRIEL MARCEL DASSAULT S.A.; *Int'l*, pg. 3104
GROUPE INTERDECO—See Vivendi SE; *Int'l*, pg. 8274
GROUPE IRD SA; *Int'l*, pg. 3105
GROUPE LACASSE INC.; *Int'l*, pg. 3105
GROUPE LACTALIS SA; *Int'l*, pg. 3105
GROUPE LAGASSE INC.; *Int'l*, pg. 3106
GROUPE LEBEL INC.; *Int'l*, pg. 3106
GROUPE LE FIGARO—See Groupe Industriel Marcel Dassault S.A.; *Int'l*, pg. 3105
GROUPE LEGRIS INDUSTRIES; *Int'l*, pg. 3106
GROUPE LES ECHOS—See LVMH Moet Hennessy Louis Vuitton SE; *Int'l*, pg. 4592
GROUP ELEVEN RESOURCES CORP.; *Int'l*, pg. 3088
GROUPE LGS INC.—See International Business Machines Corporation; *U.S. Public*, pg. 1146
GROUPE LIMAGRAIN HOLDING SA; *Int'l*, pg. 3107
GROUPE LIMAGRAIN HOLDING—See Groupe Limagrain Holding SA; *Int'l*, pg. 3107
GROUPE LIMAGRAIN, PARIS OFFICE—See Groupe Limagrain Holding SA; *Int'l*, pg. 3107
GROUPE LOGISTICS IDL S.A.U.—See ID Logistics SAS; *Int'l*, pg. 3587
GROUP E LTD. INC.; *U.S. Private*, pg. 1793
GROUPE LUCIEN BARRIERE S.A.; *Int'l*, pg. 3108
GROUPE MARCELLE, INC.; *Int'l*, pg. 3108
GROUPE MARMARA SAS—See TUI AG; *Int'l*, pg. 7964
GROUPE MECALAC S.A.; *Int'l*, pg. 3108
GROUPEMENT D'ENTREPRISES ROUTIERES DE L'EST SAS—See VINCI S.A.; *Int'l*, pg. 8222
GROUPEMENT FLO; *Int'l*, pg. 3112
GROUPE MINOTERIES SA; *Int'l*, pg. 3108
GROUPE MONIN SAS; *Int'l*, pg. 3109
GROUPE MONITEUR HOLDING—See Bridgepoint Group Plc; *Int'l*, pg. 1155
GROUPE MTD FINANCE; *Int'l*, pg. 3109
GROUPE NOUVELLES FRONTIERES S.A.S.—See TUI AG; *Int'l*, pg. 7964
GROUPE OMERIN; *Int'l*, pg. 3109
GROUPE ONEPOINT SAS; *Int'l*, pg. 3109
GROUPE OPEN NEDERLAND B.V.—See Groupe OPEN S.A.; *Int'l*, pg. 3109
GROUPE OPEN S.A.; *Int'l*, pg. 3109
GROUPE OUELLET CANADA INC.; *Int'l*, pg. 3109
GROUPE PAROT SA; *Int'l*, pg. 3109
GROUPE PARTOUCHE INTERNATIONAL S.A.—See Groupe Partouche S.A.; *Int'l*, pg. 3109
GROUPE PARTOUCHE S.A.; *Int'l*, pg. 3109
GROUPE PETIT FORESTIER SAS; *Int'l*, pg. 3109
GROUPE PILARDIERE—See Archer-Daniels-Midland Company; *U.S. Public*, pg. 185
GROUPE PIZZORNO ENVIRONNEMENT S.A.N.; *Int'l*, pg. 3109
GROUPE PLAFOLIFT INC.; *Int'l*, pg. 3109
GROUPE PLOMBACTION INC; *Int'l*, pg. 3109
GROUPE PLUS VALUES SA; *Int'l*, pg. 3109
GROUPE PORCHER INDUSTRIES; *Int'l*, pg. 3109
GROUPE PREMIERE MOISSON INC.—See Metro Inc.; *Int'l*, pg. 4860
GROUPE PRIMONIAL SAS; *Int'l*, pg. 3110
GROUPE PSA AUTOMOTIV PAZARLAMA AS—See Stellantis N.V.; *Int'l*, pg. 7202
GROUPE PSYCHOLOGIES SA—See Vivendi SE; *Int'l*, pg. 8274
GROUPE RENAUD-BRAY, INC.; *Int'l*, pg. 3110
GROUPE RIVALIS SA—See Phosphore SARL; *Int'l*, pg. 5856
GROUPE ROBERT INC.—See Gestion Claude Robert Inc.; *Int'l*, pg. 2946
GROUPE ROBERT INC.—See Robert Bernard Pneus et Mecanique; *Int'l*, pg. 6358
GROUPE ROCHER OPERATIONS SAS; *Int'l*, pg. 3110

GROUPE ROCHER OPERATIONS SAS
CORPORATE AFFILIATIONS

GROUPE ROSSIGNOL CANADA INC.—See Altor Equity Partners AB; *Int'l*, pg. 396
GROUPE ROYER—See Apax Partners LLP; *Int'l*, pg. 504
GROUPE R.Y. BEAUDOIN, INC.; *Int'l*, pg. 3110
GROUPE SEB AUSTRALIA LTD.—See SEB S.A.; *Int'l*, pg. 6667
GROUPE SEB BELGIUM SA—See SEB S.A.; *Int'l*, pg. 6667
GROUPE SEB BULGARIA EOOD—See SEB S.A.; *Int'l*, pg. 6667
GROUPE SEB CANADA INC.—See SEB S.A.; *Int'l*, pg. 6667
GROUPE SEB CENTRAL EUROPE KFT—See SEB S.A.; *Int'l*, pg. 6667
GROUPE SEB COLOMBIA S.A.—See SEB S.A.; *Int'l*, pg. 6667
GROUPE SEB CR S.R.O.—See SEB S.A.; *Int'l*, pg. 6667
GROUPE SEB DANMARK AS—See SEB S.A.; *Int'l*, pg. 6667
GROUPE SEB DEUTSCHLAND GMBH—See SEB S.A.; *Int'l*, pg. 6667
GROUPE SEB D.O.O.—See SEB S.A.; *Int'l*, pg. 6668
GROUPE SEB HELLADOS S.A.—See SEB S.A.; *Int'l*, pg. 6667
GROUPE SEB IBERICA S.A.—See SEB S.A.; *Int'l*, pg. 6667
GROUPE SEB ISTANBUL EV ALETLERI TIC AS—See SEB S.A.; *Int'l*, pg. 6667
GROUPE SEB ITALIA SPA—See SEB S.A.; *Int'l*, pg. 6668
GROUPE SEB MAGYARORSZAG KFT—See SEB S.A.; *Int'l*, pg. 6668
GROUPE SEB MEXICANA SA DE CV—See SEB S.A.; *Int'l*, pg. 6668
GROUPE SEB MOULINEX SAS—See SEB S.A.; *Int'l*, pg. 6668
GROUPE SEB NEDERLAND BV—See SEB S.A.; *Int'l*, pg. 6668
GROUPE SEB NEDERLAND BV—See SEB S.A.; *Int'l*, pg. 6668
GROUPE SEB NORDIK AS—See SEB S.A.; *Int'l*, pg. 6668
GROUPE SEB PERU S.R.L.—See SEB S.A.; *Int'l*, pg. 6668
GROUPE SEB POLSKA SP. Z O.O.—See SEB S.A.; pg. 6668
GROUPE SEB PORTUGAL LDA—See SEB S.A.; *Int'l*, pg. 6668
GROUPE SEB SCHWEIZ GMBH—See SEB S.A.; *Int'l*, pg. 6668
GROUPE SEB SERVICIOS MEXICO—See SEB S.A.; *Int'l*, pg. 6668
GROUPE SEB SINGAPORE PTY LTD.—See SEB S.A.; *Int'l*, pg. 6668
GROUPE SEB SR, S.R.O.—See SEB S.A.; *Int'l*, pg. 6668
GROUPE SEB THAILAND CO., LTD.—See SEB S.A.; *Int'l*, pg. 6668
GROUPE SEB UK LTD.—See SEB S.A.; *Int'l*, pg. 6668
GROUPE SEB USA—See SEB S.A.; *Int'l*, pg. 6667
GROUPE SECHE SAS; *Int'l*, pg. 3110
GROUPE SFPI SA; *Int'l*, pg. 3111
GROUPE SIDEL—See Tetra Laval International S.A.; *Int'l*, pg. 7576
GROUPE SIPAREX; *Int'l*, pg. 3111
GROUPE SOLOTECH, INC.; *Int'l*, pg. 3111
GROUPE STAVIBEL INC.—See AtkinsRealis Group Inc.; *Int'l*, pg. 671
GROUPE ST-HUBERT INC.—See Fairfax Financial Holdings Limited; *Int'l*, pg. 2608
GROUPE TECHSOL MARINE INC.—See Electricite de France S.A.; *Int'l*, pg. 2351
GROUPE TELINDUS FRANCE SA—See Vivendi SE; *Int'l*, pg. 8266
GROUPE TERA SA; *Int'l*, pg. 3111
GROUPE TERRITORIAL—See Bridgepoint Group Plc; *Int'l*, pg. 1155
GROUPE THIRAN SA.—See Ackermans & van Haaren NV; *Int'l*, pg. 106
GROUPE UNIPEX SAS; *Int'l*, pg. 3112
GROUPE VENDOME ROME; *Int'l*, pg. 3112
GROUPE VIAL SA; *Int'l*, pg. 3112
GROUPE VISION OPTIQUE—See EssilorLuxottica SA; *Int'l*, pg. 2514
GROUPE VOLKSWAGEN FRANCE S.A.—See Porsche Automobil Holding SE; *Int'l*, pg. 5929
GROUP EXCELLENCE; *U.S. Private*, pg. 1793
GROUP FIVE BUILDING (PROPRIETARY) LIMITED—See Group Five Limited; *Int'l*, pg. 3089
GROUP FIVE CIVIL ENGINEERING (PROPRIETARY) LIMITED—See Group Five Limited; *Int'l*, pg. 3089
GROUP FIVE CONSTRUCTION (PROPRIETARY) LIMITED—See Group Five Limited; *Int'l*, pg. 3089
GROUP FIVE DESIGN AND PROJECT MANAGEMENT (PROPRIETARY) LIMITED—See Group Five Limited; *Int'l*, pg. 3089
GROUP FIVE ENERGY (PROPRIETARY) LIMITED—See Group Five Limited; *Int'l*, pg. 3089
GROUP FIVE HOUSING (PROPRIETARY) LIMITED—See Group Five Limited; *Int'l*, pg. 3089

GROUP FIVE INFRASTRUCTURE DEVELOPMENTS (PROPRIETARY) LIMITED—See Group Five Limited; *Int'l*, pg. 3089
GROUP FIVE KWAZULU-NATAL (PROPRIETARY) LIMITED—See Group Five Limited; *Int'l*, pg. 3089
GROUP FIVE LIMITED - BUILDING WESTERN CAPE BUSINESS UNIT—See Group Five Limited; *Int'l*, pg. 3089
GROUP FIVE LIMITED; *Int'l*, pg. 3088
GROUP FIVE OIL & GAS (PROPRIETARY) LIMITED—See Group Five Limited; *Int'l*, pg. 3089
GROUP FIVE PLANT & EQUIPMENT (PROPRIETARY) LIMITED—See Group Five Limited; *Int'l*, pg. 3089
GROUP FIVE PROJECTS (PROPRIETARY) LIMITED—See Group Five Limited; *Int'l*, pg. 3089
GROUP FIVE PROPERTY DEVELOPMENTS (PROPRIETARY) LIMITED—See Group Five Limited; *Int'l*, pg. 3089
GROUP FIVE WESTERN CAPE (PROPRIETARY) LIMITED—See Group Five Limited; *Int'l*, pg. 3089
GROUP HEALTH COOPERATIVE OF EAU CLAIRE; *U.S. Private*, pg. 1793
GROUP HEALTH COOPERATIVE OF SOUTH CENTRAL WISCONSIN; *U.S. Private*, pg. 1793
GROUPHEALTHFLORIDA.COM; *U.S. Private*, pg. 1794
GROUPHEALTH GLOBAL BENEFIT SYSTEMS INC.—See Munchener Ruckversicherungs AG; *Int'l*, pg. 5088
GROUP HEALTH, INC.—See EmblemHealth, Inc.; *U.S. Private*, pg. 1378
GROUP HEALTH SERVICE OF OKLAHOMA, INC.—See Health Care Service Corporation; *U.S. Private*, pg. 1892
GROUP HES LIMITED—See Flowtech Fluidpower plc; *Int'l*, pg. 2709
GROUP III INTERNATIONAL, LTD.; *U.S. Private*, pg. 1793
GROUPIMO S.A.; *Int'l*, pg. 3112
THE GROUP INC.; *U.S. Private*, pg. 4039
GROUP INSURANCE, INCORPORATED OF LOUISIANA—See Stone Point Capital LLC; *U.S. Private*, pg. 3819
GROUP KZ LLP—See DNOW Inc.; *U.S. Public*, pg. 671
GROUP LEASE PUBLIC COMPANY LIMITED—See Showa Holdings Co., Ltd.; *Int'l*, pg. 6861
GROUPLINE PROJECTS (PTY) LIMITED—See PSV Holdings Limited; *Int'l*, pg. 6018
GROUP LOGIC, INC.; *U.S. Private*, pg. 1793
GROUP LOTUS LIMITED—See Zhejiang Geely Holding Group Co., Ltd.; *Int'l*, pg. 8652
GROUP M5; *Int'l*, pg. 3089
GROUP MANUFACTURING SERVICES OF ARIZONA; *U.S. Private*, pg. 1793
GROUP MANUFACTURING SERVICES; *U.S. Private*, pg. 1793
GROUPM APAC HQ—See WPP plc; *Int'l*, pg. 8472
GROUP MARAIS SAS—See TESMEC S.p.A.; *Int'l*, pg. 7572
GROUPM ASIA PACIFIC HOLDINGS PTE. LTD.—See WPP plc; *Int'l*, pg. 8472
GROUPM CHINA—See WPP plc; *Int'l*, pg. 8472
GROUPM EMEA HQ—See WPP plc; *Int'l*, pg. 8472
GROUPM LATAM HQ—See WPP plc; *Int'l*, pg. 8474
GROUPM MALAYSIA—See WPP plc; *Int'l*, pg. 8474
GROUP MOBILE, INC.; *U.S. Private*, pg. 1793
GROUP MOBILE INTERNATIONAL, LLC—See Route1 Inc.; *Int'l*, pg. 6407
GROUP MONITEUR—See Bridgepoint Group Plc; *Int'l*, pg. 1155
GROUPM SINGAPORE PTE. LTD.—See WPP plc; *Int'l*, pg. 8472
GROUPM SINGAPORE—See WPP plc; *Int'l*, pg. 8474
GROUPM THAILAND—See WPP plc; *Int'l*, pg. 8474
GROUP M WORLDWIDE, INC.—See WPP plc; *Int'l*, pg. 8472
GROUP NINE ACQUISITION CORP.; *U.S. Public*, pg. 972
GROUP NINE MEDIA, INC.; *U.S. Private*, pg. 1793
GROUP O DIRECT INC.—See Group O Inc.; *U.S. Private*, pg. 1794
GROUP O INC.; *U.S. Private*, pg. 1793
GROUP ONE, INC.—See Daseke, Inc.; *U.S. Private*, pg. 1161
GROUP ONE THOUSAND ONE, LLC; *U.S. Private*, pg. 1794
GROUP ONE TRADING, L.P. - SAN FRANCISCO—See Group One Trading, L.P.; *U.S. Private*, pg. 1794
GROUP ONE TRADING, L.P.; *U.S. Private*, pg. 1794
GROUPON FRANCE SAS—See Groupon Inc.; *U.S. Public*, pg. 972
GROUPON GMBH—See Groupon Inc.; *U.S. Public*, pg. 972
GROUPON INC.; *U.S. Public*, pg. 972
GROUPON SPAIN, SLU—See Groupon Inc.; *U.S. Public*, pg. 972
GROUP & PENSION ADMINISTRATORS, INC.; *U.S. Private*, pg. 1793
GROUP PSAGOT FOR FINANCE AND INVESTMENTS LTD.; *Int'l*, pg. 3089
GROUP PUBLISHING INC.; *U.S. Private*, pg. 1794
GROUP RHI; *U.S. Private*, pg. 1794

GROUP SALES DIVISON—See Family Inns of America, Inc.; *U.S. Private*, pg. 1470
GROUP SENSE LIMITED—See Century Sunshine Group Holdings Limited; *Int'l*, pg. 1419
GROUP SENSE MOBILE-TECH LIMITED—See Century Sunshine Group Holdings Limited; *Int'l*, pg. 1419
GROUP SERVICES, LLC—See Genstar Capital, LLC; *U.S. Private*, pg. 1674
GROUP SIX CORPORATION; *U.S. Private*, pg. 1794
GROUP SJR; *U.S. Private*, pg. 1794
GROUP STEEL CORPORATION (M) SDN. BHD.—See China Steel Corporation; *Int'l*, pg. 1555
GROUP SUPECO MAXOR SL—See Carrefour SA; *Int'l*, pg. 1345
GROUPSYSTEMS CORPORATION; *U.S. Private*, pg. 1794
GROUP THERMOTE & VANHALST; *Int'l*, pg. 3089
GROUP TOOL & DIE CO. INC.; *U.S. Private*, pg. 1794
GROUP TRANSPORTATION SERVICES, INC.—See Roadrunner Transportation Systems, Inc.; *U.S. Public*, pg. 1802
GROUP TWO ADVERTISING, INC.; *U.S. Private*, pg. 1794
GROUP UNITED—See WPP plc; *Int'l*, pg. 8464
GROUP UP INDUSTRIAL CO., LTD.; *Int'l*, pg. 3090
GROUP VOYAGERS, INC.; *U.S. Private*, pg. 1794
GROUPWARE INTERNATIONAL INC.; *U.S. Private*, pg. 1794
GROUPWARE TECHNOLOGY, INC.—See American Securities LLC; *U.S. Private*, pg. 250
GROUP Z, INC.; *U.S. Private*, pg. 1794
THE GROUT MEDIC LLC—See Susquehanna International Group, LLP; *U.S. Private*, pg. 3885
GROUT TRADING CO., LTD.—See Kajima Corporation; *Int'l*, pg. 4054
GROVE ARCADE RESTORATION LLC—See Duke Energy Corporation; *U.S. Public*, pg. 691
GROVE/ATLANTIC, INC.; *U.S. Private*, pg. 1794
GROVE CAPITAL MANAGEMENT LIMITED—See Encore Capital Group, Inc.; *U.S. Public*, pg. 759
GROVE CITY DENTAL; *U.S. Private*, pg. 1794
GROVE CITY MEDICAL CENTER—See Allegheny Health Network; *U.S. Public*, pg. 176
GROVE COLLABORATIVE HOLDINGS, INC.; *U.S. Public*, pg. 972
GROVE COLLABORATIVE, INC.—See Grove Collaborative Holdings, Inc.; *U.S. Public*, pg. 972
GROVE ENERGY INC.—See Chesapeake Utilities Corporation; *U.S. Public*, pg. 485
GROVE FARM COMPANY INC.; *U.S. Private*, pg. 1794
GROVEHILL PTE. LTD.—See TA Corporation Ltd.; *Int'l*, pg. 7399
GROVE INDUSTRIES, INC.—See Pine Grove Holdings, LLC; *U.S. Private*, pg. 3182
GROVE INTERNATIONAL PTY LIMITED; *Int'l*, pg. 3112
GROVELAND TRANSFER AND RECYCLING, INC.—See Waste Connections, Inc.; *Int'l*, pg. 8353
GROVELEY DETECTION LIMITED—See Emerson Electric Co.; *U.S. Public*, pg. 747
GROVE LUMBER & BUILDING SUPPLIES INC.; *U.S. Private*, pg. 1794
GROVE MADSEN INDUSTRIES, A DIVISION OF CODALE—See Sonepar S.A.; *Int'l*, pg. 7093
GROVE MUELLER & SWANK PC—See Redw Stanley Financial Advisors LLC; *U.S. Private*, pg. 3380
GROVE MUSIC ONLINE—See Oxford University Press; *Int'l*, pg. 5675
GROVE PLACE SURGERY CENTER, LLC—See UnitedHealth Group Incorporated; *U.S. Public*, pg. 2241
GROVEPOINT CAPITAL LLP; *Int'l*, pg. 3112
GROVER CORPORATION; *U.S. Private*, pg. 1795
GROVE RESOURCE SOLUTIONS INCORPORATED—See DLH Holdings Corp.; *U.S. Public*, pg. 670
GROVER GAMING, INC.; *U.S. Private*, pg. 1795
GROVER INDUSTRIES INC.; *U.S. Private*, pg. 1795
GROVERT MOTOR CO.; *U.S. Private*, pg. 1795
GROVER ZAMPA VINEYARDS LIMITED; *Int'l*, pg. 3112
GROVES, JOHN & WESTRUP LIMITED—See Munchener Ruckversicherungs AG; *Int'l*, pg. 5088
GROVE SUPPLY INC.; *U.S. Private*, pg. 1795
GROVE U.S. LLC—See The Manitowoc Company, Inc.; *U.S. Public*, pg. 2111
GROVO LEARNING INC.—See Clearlake Capital Group, L.P.; *U.S. Private*, pg. 934
GROVY INDIA LIMITED; *Int'l*, pg. 3113
GROW AB—See Digitalist Group Oyj; *Int'l*, pg. 2123
GROW BIZ GAMES, INC.—See Winmark Corporation; *U.S. Public*, pg. 2374
GROW CAPITAL, INC.; *U.S. Public*, pg. 972
GROW COMPANY INC—See International Flavors & Fragrances Inc.; *U.S. Public*, pg. 1152
GRO-WELL BRANDS INC.; *U.S. Private*, pg. 1791
GROWEL SOFTECH LTD.—See Grauer & Weil India Limited; *Int'l*, pg. 3061
G. ROWE, M.D. , PLLC—See HCA Healthcare, Inc.; *U.S. Public*, pg. 996
GROWENS S.P.A.; *Int'l*, pg. 3112
GROWERIQ—See Wilcompute Systems Group, Inc.; *Int'l*, pg. 8409

COMPANY NAME INDEX

GROWERS DIRECT; *U.S. Private,* pg. 1795
GROWER SERVICES, LLC; *U.S. Private,* pg. 1795
GROWERS EXPRESS LLC; *U.S. Private,* pg. 1795
GROWERS FERTILIZER CORPORATION; *U.S. Private,* pg. 1795
GROWERS INTERNATIONAL ORGANIC SALES INC.—See Paterson GlobalFoods Inc.; *Int'l,* pg. 5756
GROWER'S ORGANIC LLC.; *U.S. Private,* pg. 1795
GROWERS REFRIGERATING COMPANY, INC.—See Naumes Inc.; *U.S. Private,* pg. 2868
GROWEST INC.; *U.S. Private,* pg. 1795
GROW FINANCIAL FEDERAL CREDIT UNION; *U.S. Private,* pg. 1795
GROWGENERATION CORP.; *U.S. Public,* pg. 972
GROWGENERATION OKLAHOMA CORP.—See GrowGeneration Corp.; *U.S. Public,* pg. 972
GROWGENIX SOLUTIONS LLC—See Nu Skin Enterprises, Inc.; *U.S. Public,* pg. 1551
GROWING IN VOICES; *U.S. Private,* pg. 1795
GROWING ROOM INC.; *U.S. Private,* pg. 1795
GROWINGTON VENTURES INDIA LIMITED; *Int'l,* pg. 3112
GROWIN' PARTNERS INC.—See Tanabe Consulting Group Co., Ltd.; *Int'l,* pg. 7454
GROW INTERACTIVE; *U.S. Private,* pg. 1795
GROWLIFE, INC.; *U.S. Public,* pg. 972
GROWMARK FS, LLC—See Growmark, Inc.; *U.S. Private,* pg. 1795
GROWMARK, INC.; *U.S. Private,* pg. 1795
GROWMAX AGRI CORP.—See Coloured Ties Capital Inc.; *Int'l,* pg. 1704
GROW MORE, INC.; *U.S. Private,* pg. 1795
GROWNERS S.A.; *Int'l,* pg. 3113
GROWN ROGUE INTERNATIONAL INC.; *Int'l,* pg. 3113
GROWN ROGUE UNLIMITED, LLC—See Grown Rogue International Inc.; *Int'l,* pg. 3113
GROWN UP GROUP INVESTMENT HOLDINGS LIMITED; *Int'l,* pg. 3113
GROW ON DEVELOPMENT LIMITED—See Great Eagle Holdings Limited; *Int'l,* pg. 3064
GROW PLATFORM GMBH—See Robert Bosch GmbH; *Int'l,* pg. 6368
GROW SOLUTIONS HOLDINGS, INC.; *U.S. Public,* pg. 972
GROW-TECH LLC—See Dummen Orange Holding B.V.; *Int'l,* pg. 2225
GROWTH ACCELERATION PARTNERS, LLC; *U.S. Private,* pg. 1795
GROWTH CATALYST PARTNERS, LLC; *U.S. Private,* pg. 1796
GROWTH COMPANY INVESTOR LTD—See Bonhill Group PLC; *Int'l,* pg. 1107
GROWTHCURVE CAPITAL LP; *U.S. Private,* pg. 1796
GROWTH ENERGY; *U.S. Private,* pg. 1796
GROWTH ENTERPRISE SDN. BHD.—See NPC Resources Berhad; *Int'l,* pg. 5472
GROWTHFORCE, LLC; *U.S. Private,* pg. 1796
THE GROWTH FOR GOOD ACQUISITION CORPORATION; *U.S. Private,* pg. 4040
GROWTH GEAR CO. LTD—See Digital Holdings, Inc.; *Int'l,* pg. 2122
GROWTHINK, INC.; *U.S. Private,* pg. 1796
GROWTH INVESTMENTS LTD.—See MAPFRE S.A.; *Int'l,* pg. 4685
GROWTH MANAGEMENT CORPORATION; *U.S. Private,* pg. 1796
GROWTHOPS LIMITED; *Int'l,* pg. 3113
GROWTH ORGANIZATION OF TOPEKA / SHAWNEE COUNTY, INC.; *U.S. Private,* pg. 1796
THE GROWTH PARTNERSHIP—See Engineered Tax Services, Inc; *U.S. Private,* pg. 1398
GROWTH PARTNERS, L.P.—See SVB Financial Group; *U.S. Public,* pg. 1968
GROWTHPLAY LLC; *U.S. Private,* pg. 1796
GROWTHPOINT BUILDING MANAGERS (PTY) LIMITED—See Growthpoint Properties Limited; *Int'l,* pg. 3113
GROWTHPOINT MANAGEMENT SERVICES (PTY) LIMITED—See Growthpoint Properties Limited; *Int'l,* pg. 3113
GROWTHPOINT PROPERTIES AUSTRALIA LIMITED—See Growthpoint Properties Limited; *Int'l,* pg. 3113
GROWTHPOINT PROPERTIES LIMITED; *Int'l,* pg. 3113
GROWTH POWER CO., LTD.—See Rentracks Co., Ltd.; *Int'l,* pg. 6289
GROWTH PROPERTIES INVESTMENT MANAGERS, INC.; *U.S. Private,* pg. 1796
GROWTH THROUGH SERVICE INTERIOR SUPPLY CO. INC.; *U.S. Private,* pg. 1796
GROWTHWORKS ATLANTIC LTD.—See Matrix Asset Management Inc.; *Int'l,* pg. 4728
GROWTHWORKS CAPITAL LTD.—See Matrix Asset Management Inc.; *Int'l,* pg. 4728
GROWTHWORKS LTD.—See Matrix Asset Management Inc.; *Int'l,* pg. 4728
GROWTHWORKS WV MANAGEMENT LTD.—See Matrix Asset Management Inc.; *Int'l,* pg. 4728

GROWTHZONE, INC.—See Greenridge Investment Partners; *U.S. Private,* pg. 1779
GROWWW MEDIA CO., LTD.—See Hakuhodo DY Holdings Incorporated; *Int'l,* pg. 3221
GROZ-BECKERT ASIA PRIVATE LIMITED—See Groz-Beckert KG; *Int'l,* pg. 3113
GROZ-BECKERT CARDING BELGIUM NV.—See Groz-Beckert KG; *Int'l,* pg. 3113
GROZ-BECKERT CARDING CHINA CO., LTD.—See Groz-Beckert KG; *Int'l,* pg. 3113
GROZ-BECKERT CARDING INDIA PRIVATE LIMITED—See Groz-Beckert KG; *Int'l,* pg. 3113
GROZ-BECKERT DE MEXICO S.A. DE C.V.—See Groz-Beckert KG; *Int'l,* pg. 3113
GROZ-BECKERT FRANCE S.A.—See Groz-Beckert KG; *Int'l,* pg. 3113
GROZ-BECKERT JAPAN K.K.—See Groz-Beckert KG; *Int'l,* pg. 3113
GROZ-BECKERT KG; *Int'l,* pg. 3113
GROZ-BECKERT KOREA CO., LTD.—See Groz-Beckert KG; *Int'l,* pg. 3113
GROZ-BECKERT SALES & SERVICES VIETNAM CO., LTD.—See Groz-Beckert KG; *Int'l,* pg. 3113
GROZ-BECKERT (SHANGHAI) TRADING CO., LTD.—See Groz-Beckert KG; *Int'l,* pg. 3113
GROZ-BECKERT SINGAPORE PTE. LTD.—See Groz-Beckert KG; *Int'l,* pg. 3113
GROZ-BECKERT TAIWAN LTD.—See Groz-Beckert KG; *Int'l,* pg. 3113
GROZ-BECKERT TRADING (SHENZHEN) CO., LTD.—See Groz-Beckert KG; *Int'l,* pg. 3113
GROZ-BECKERT TURKEY TEKSTIL MAKINE PARCALARI TICARET LIMITED SIRKETI—See Groz-Beckert KG; *Int'l,* pg. 3113
GROZ-BECKERT USA, INC.—See Groz-Beckert KG; *Int'l,* pg. 3113
GROZ-BECKERT (YANTAI) TRADING CO., LTD.—See Groz-Beckert KG; *Int'l,* pg. 3113
GRP CO.,LTD.—See Septeni Holdings Co., Ltd.; *Int'l,* pg. 6718
GR PHAGWARA EXPRESSWAY LIMITED—See G R Infraprojects Limited; *Int'l,* pg. 2861
GRP LIMITED; *Int'l,* pg. 3113
GRP LIMITED; *Int'l,* pg. 3113
GRP MEDIA, INC.; *U.S. Private,* pg. 1796
GRP PTE LTD—See Lian Ee Hydraulics Pte Ltd.; *Int'l,* pg. 4482
GRP PUBLIC RELATIONS LIMITED—See Providence Equity Partners L.L.C.; *U.S. Private,* pg. 3291
GRP RECORDS—See Universal Music Group N.V.; *Int'l,* pg. 8079
GR PROPERTIES LIMITED; *Int'l,* pg. 3047
GRP SDN. BHD.—See Kumpulan Jetson Berhad; *Int'l,* pg. 4332
GR. SARANTIS S.A.; *Int'l,* pg. 3047
GR SILVER MINING LTD.; *Int'l,* pg. 3047
GR SPRING & STAMPING INC.—See Gill Industries Inc.; *U.S. Private,* pg. 1700
GRS TITLE SERVICES, LLC—See Clayton, Dubilier & Rice, LLC; *U.S. Private,* pg. 927
GRS TITLE SERVICES, LLC—See Mubadala Investment Company PJSC; *Int'l,* pg. 5076
GRS TITLE SERVICES, LLC—See Stone Point Capital LLC; *U.S. Private,* pg. 3826
GRS VALTECH—See Veolia Environnement S.A.; *Int'l,* pg. 8159
GRT CORPORATION; *U.S. Private,* pg. 1796
GRTGAZ DEUTSCHLAND GMBH—See ENGIE SA; *Int'l,* pg. 2434
GRTGAZ SA—See ENGIE SA; *Int'l,* pg. 2434
GRT, INC.—See ConocoPhillips; *U.S. Public,* pg. 569
GRUBB & ELLIS COMPANY—See BGC Group, Inc.; *U.S. Public,* pg. 329
GRUBB & ELLIS MANAGEMENT SERVICES, INC.—See BGC Group, Inc.; *U.S. Public,* pg. 329
GRUBB & ELLIS NEW YORK, INC.—See BGC Group, Inc.; *U.S. Public,* pg. 329
GRUBBS INFINITI, LTD.; *U.S. Private,* pg. 1796
GRUBER GMBH & CO. KG; *Int'l,* pg. 3114
GRUBER HURST ELROD JOHANSEN HAIL SHANK LLP; *U.S. Private,* pg. 1796
GRUBER INDUSTRIES INC.; *U.S. Private,* pg. 1796
GRUBER & KAJA HIGH TECH METALS GMBH—See HTI High Tech Industries AG; *Int'l,* pg. 3508
GRUBER SYSTEMS INC.; *U.S. Private,* pg. 1797
GRUBER TECHNICAL INC.—See Gruber Industries Inc.; *U.S. Private,* pg. 1796
GRUBER UK LTD.—See Gruber GmbH & Co. KG; *Int'l,* pg. 3114
GRUBHUB, INC.—See Just Eat Takeaway.com N.V.; *Int'l,* pg. 4030
GRUBMARKET, INC.; *U.S. Private,* pg. 1797
GRU COMEDIL S.R.L.—See Terex Corporation; *U.S. Public,* pg. 2019
GRUENDLER GMBH—See ResMed Inc.; *U.S. Public,* pg. 1790
GRUENINGER MUSIC TOURS—See Grueninger Tours & Cruises Inc.; *U.S. Private,* pg. 1797

GRUNBERG REALTY

GRUENINGER TOURS & CRUISES INC.; *U.S. Private,* pg. 1797
GRUMA CORPORATION—See Gruma, S.A.B. de C.V.; *Int'l,* pg. 3114
GRUMA CORPORATION—See Gruma, S.A.B. de C.V.; *Int'l,* pg. 3114
GRUMAL GROUP SL—See Mondragon Corporation; *Int'l,* pg. 5029
GRUMA NETHERLANDS B.V.—See Gruma, S.A.B. de C.V.; *Int'l,* pg. 3114
GRUMA OCEANIA PTY. LTD.—See Gruma, S.A.B. de C.V.; *Int'l,* pg. 3114
GRUMA, S.A.B. DE C.V.; *Int'l,* pg. 3114
GRUMMAN HILL GROUP, LLC; *U.S. Private,* pg. 1797
GRUMS ROR AB—See Instalco AB; *Int'l,* pg. 3721
GRUNAU COMPANY, INC.—See API Group Corporation; *Int'l,* pg. 514
GRUNAU ILLERTISSEN GMBH—See BASF SE; *Int'l,* pg. 884
GRUNBERG REALTY; *U.S. Private,* pg. 1797
GRUNDBESITZGESELLSCHAFT BERLIN MBH—See Commerzbank AG; *Int'l,* pg. 1718
GRUNDER INGENIEURE AG—See BKW AG; *Int'l,* pg. 1055
GRUNDFOS AB—See The Poul Due Jensen Foundation; *Int'l,* pg. 7674
GRUNDFOS BIOBOOSTER A/S—See The Poul Due Jensen Foundation; *Int'l,* pg. 7675
GRUNDFOS BOSNA I HERZEGOVINA—See The Poul Due Jensen Foundation; *Int'l,* pg. 7675
GRUNDFOS CANADA INC.—See The Poul Due Jensen Foundation; *Int'l,* pg. 7675
GRUNDFOS CROATIA D.O.O.—See The Poul Due Jensen Foundation; *Int'l,* pg. 7675
GRUNDFOS DK A/S—See The Poul Due Jensen Foundation; *Int'l,* pg. 7675
GRUNDFOS GMBH—See The Poul Due Jensen Foundation; *Int'l,* pg. 7675
GRUNDFOS GULF DISTRIBUTION—See The Poul Due Jensen Foundation; *Int'l,* pg. 7675
GRUNDFOS HANDELS AG—See The Poul Due Jensen Foundation; *Int'l,* pg. 7675
GRUNDFOS HELLAS A.E.B.E.—See The Poul Due Jensen Foundation; *Int'l,* pg. 7675
GRUNDFOS HOLDING A/S—See The Poul Due Jensen Foundation; *Int'l,* pg. 7674
GRUNDFOS HUNGARIA KFT.—See The Poul Due Jensen Foundation; *Int'l,* pg. 7675
GRUNDFOS HUNGARY MANUFACTURING LTD.—See The Poul Due Jensen Foundation; *Int'l,* pg. 7675
GRUNDFOS (IRELAND) LTD.—See The Poul Due Jensen Foundation; *Int'l,* pg. 7674
GRUNDFOS ISTRA LLC—See The Poul Due Jensen Foundation; *Int'l,* pg. 7675
GRUNDFOS MANAGEMENT A/S—See The Poul Due Jensen Foundation; *Int'l,* pg. 7674
GRUNDFOS MANUFACTURING LTD.—See The Poul Due Jensen Foundation; *Int'l,* pg. 7675
GRUNDFOS NEDERLAND B.V.—See The Poul Due Jensen Foundation; *Int'l,* pg. 7675
GRUNDFOS OFIS BULGARIA—See The Poul Due Jensen Foundation; *Int'l,* pg. 7675
GRUNDFOS OOO—See The Poul Due Jensen Foundation; *Int'l,* pg. 7675
GRUNDFOS O.Z.—See The Poul Due Jensen Foundation; *Int'l,* pg. 7676
GRUNDFOS POMPA SAN. VE TIC. LTD. STI.—See The Poul Due Jensen Foundation; *Int'l,* pg. 7675
GRUNDFOS POMPA SANYI VE TICARET LTD. STI.—See The Poul Due Jensen Foundation; *Int'l,* pg. 7675
GRUNDFOS POMPE ITALIA S.R.L.—See The Poul Due Jensen Foundation; *Int'l,* pg. 7675
GRUNDFOS POMPE ROMANIA S.R.L.—See The Poul Due Jensen Foundation; *Int'l,* pg. 7675
GRUNDFOS POMPY SP. Z O.O.—See The Poul Due Jensen Foundation; *Int'l,* pg. 7675
GRUNDFOS (PTY) LTD.—See The Poul Due Jensen Foundation; *Int'l,* pg. 7674
GRUNDFOS PUMPEN AG—See The Poul Due Jensen Foundation; *Int'l,* pg. 7675
GRUNDFOS PUMPENFABRIK GMBH—See The Poul Due Jensen Foundation; *Int'l,* pg. 7675
GRUNDFOS PUMPEN VERTRIEB GES.M.B.H.—See The Poul Due Jensen Foundation; *Int'l,* pg. 7675
GRUNDFOS PUMPER A/S—See The Poul Due Jensen Foundation; *Int'l,* pg. 7675
GRUNDFOS PUMPS BALTIC SIA—See The Poul Due Jensen Foundation; *Int'l,* pg. 7674
GRUNDFOS PUMPS CORPORATION—See The Poul Due Jensen Foundation; *Int'l,* pg. 7675
GRUNDFOS PUMPS GHANA LTD.—See The Poul Due Jensen Foundation; *Int'l,* pg. 7675
GRUNDFOS PUMPS (HONG KONG) LTD.—See The Poul Due Jensen Foundation; *Int'l,* pg. 7675
GRUNDFOS PUMPS INDIA PRIVATE LTD.—See The Poul Due Jensen Foundation; *Int'l,* pg. 7675
GRUNDFOS PUMPS K.K.—See The Poul Due Jensen Foundation; *Int'l,* pg. 7675

GRUNBERG REALTY

CORPORATE AFFILIATIONS

GRUNDFOS PUMPS KOREA LTD.—See The Poul Due Jensen Foundation; *Int'l*, pg. 7675
GRUNDFOS PUMPS LATVIA LTD.—See The Poul Due Jensen Foundation; *Int'l*, pg. 7675
GRUNDFOS PUMPS LTD.—See The Poul Due Jensen Foundation; *Int'l*, pg. 7675
GRUNDFOS PUMPS MANUFACTURING CORPORATION—See The Poul Due Jensen Foundation; *Int'l*, pg. 7675
GRUNDFOS PUMPS NZ LTD.—See The Poul Due Jensen Foundation; *Int'l*, pg. 7675
GRUNDFOS PUMPS (PHILIPPINES) INC.—See The Poul Due Jensen Foundation; *Int'l*, pg. 7675
GRUNDFOS PUMPS PTE. LTD.—See The Poul Due Jensen Foundation; *Int'l*, pg. 7675
GRUNDFOS PUMPS PTY. LTD.—See The Poul Due Jensen Foundation; *Int'l*, pg. 7676
GRUNDFOS PUMPS SDN. BHD.—See The Poul Due Jensen Foundation; *Int'l*, pg. 7676
GRUNDFOS PUMPS (SHANGHAI) CO. LTD.—See The Poul Due Jensen Foundation; *Int'l*, pg. 7675
GRUNDFOS PUMPS (TAIWAN) LTD.—See The Poul Due Jensen Foundation; *Int'l*, pg. 7675
GRUNDFOS PUMPS UAB—See The Poul Due Jensen Foundation; *Int'l*, pg. 7676
GRUNDFOS PUMP VIETNAM—See The Poul Due Jensen Foundation; *Int'l*, pg. 7675
GRUNDFOS SERBIA—See The Poul Due Jensen Foundation; *Int'l*, pg. 7676
GRUNDFOS (SINGAPORE) PTE. LTD.—See The Poul Due Jensen Foundation; *Int'l*, pg. 7674
GRUNDFOS SLOVENIJA—See The Poul Due Jensen Foundation; *Int'l*, pg. 7676
GRUNDFOS SPOL. S.R.O.—See The Poul Due Jensen Foundation; *Int'l*, pg. 7676
GRUNDFOS SRBIJA D.O.O.—See The Poul Due Jensen Foundation; *Int'l*, pg. 7676
GRUNDFOS (THAILAND) LTD.—See The Poul Due Jensen Foundation; *Int'l*, pg. 7674
GRUNDFOS UKRAINE—See The Poul Due Jensen Foundation; *Int'l*, pg. 7676
GRUNDFOS WATER TREATMENT GMBH—See The Poul Due Jensen Foundation; *Int'l*, pg. 7676
GRUNDIA AB—See Nordisk Bergteknik AB; *Int'l*, pg. 5424
GRUNDIG AUSTRALIA PTY LIMITED—See Harvard International Ltd.; *Int'l*, pg. 3280
GRUNDIG INTERMEDIA GMBH—See Koc Holding A.S.; *Int'l*, pg. 4223
GRUNDIG MULTIMEDIA B.V.—See Koc Holding A.S.; *Int'l*, pg. 4223
GRUNDIG NORDIC AB.—See Koc Holding A.S.; *Int'l*, pg. 4223
GRUND- PFAHL- UND SONDERBAU GMBH—See PORR AG; *Int'l*, pg. 5923
GRUNDSTUCKSGESELLSCHAFT DER VEREINTEN VERSICHERUNGEN MBH—See Allianz SE; *Int'l*, pg. 353
GRUNDSTUCKSGESELLSCHAFT SIMON BESCHRANKT HAFTENDE KOMMANDITGESELLSCHAF—See UniCredit S.p.A.; *Int'l*, pg. 8039
GRUNDSTUCKSVERWALTUNG LINZ-MITTE GMBH—See UniCredit S.p.A.; *Int'l*, pg. 8037
GRUNDSTUCKSVERWALTUNG SALZBURG-MITTE GMBH—See Raiffeisen-Landesbank Steiermark AG; *Int'l*, pg. 6186
GRUNDSTUCKSVERWALTUNGSGESELLSCHAFT HENNE- UNIMOG GMBH & CO. OHG—See Mercedes-Benz Group AG; *Int'l*, pg. 4824
GRUNDSTUCKSVERWALTUNGSGESELLSCHAFT MERCEDES-BENZ AG & CO. OHG—See Mercedes-Benz Group AG; *Int'l*, pg. 4824
GRUNDSTUCKSVERWALTUNGS—See Helaba Landesbank Hessen-Thuringen; *Int'l*, pg. 3328
GRUNDY ELECTRIC COOPERATIVE, INC.; *U.S. Private*, pg. 1797
GRUNDY NATIONAL BANK; *U.S. Private*, pg. 1797
GRUNENTHAL B.V.—See Grunenthal GmbH; *Int'l*, pg. 3114
GRUNENTHAL CHILENA LTDA.—See Grunenthal GmbH; *Int'l*, pg. 3114
GRUNENTHAL COLOMBIANA S.A.—See Grunenthal GmbH; *Int'l*, pg. 3114
GRUNENTHAL DE MEXICO S.A. DE C.V.—See Grunenthal GmbH; *Int'l*, pg. 3115
GRUNENTHAL DENMARK APS—See Grunenthal GmbH; *Int'l*, pg. 3114
GRUNENTHAL ECUATORIANA C. LTDA.—See Grunenthal GmbH; *Int'l*, pg. 3114
GRUNENTHAL GES. M. B. H.—See Grunenthal GmbH; *Int'l*, pg. 3114
GRUNENTHAL GMBH; *Int'l*, pg. 3114
GRUNENTHAL ITALIA S.R.L.—See Grunenthal GmbH; *Int'l*, pg. 3114
GRUNENTHAL LTD.—See Grunenthal GmbH; *Int'l*, pg. 3114
GRUNENTHAL NORWAY AS—See Grunenthal GmbH; *Int'l*, pg. 3114
GRUNENTHAL PERUANA S.A.—See Grunenthal GmbH; *Int'l*, pg. 3114

GRUNENTHAL PHARMA AG—See Grunenthal GmbH; *Int'l*, pg. 3114
GRUNENTHAL PHARMA LTD.—See Grunenthal GmbH; *Int'l*, pg. 3114
GRUNENTHAL PHARMA SA—See Grunenthal GmbH; *Int'l*, pg. 3114
GRUNENTHAL S.A.—See Grunenthal GmbH; *Int'l*, pg. 3114
GRUNENTHAL SWEDEN AB—See Grunenthal GmbH; *Int'l*, pg. 3114
GRUNENTHAL USA, INC.—See Grunenthal GmbH; *Int'l*, pg. 3114
GRUNENTHAL VENEZOLANA FARMACEUTICA C.A.—See Grunenthal GmbH; *Int'l*, pg. 3115
GRUNER + JAHR AG (SCHWEIZ)—See Bertelsmann SE & Co. KGaA; *Int'l*, pg. 992
GRUNER + JAHR GMBH—See Bertelsmann SE & Co. KGaA; *Int'l*, pg. 992
GRUNES GMBH—See EnBW Energie Baden-Wurttemberg AG; *Int'l*, pg. 2401
GRUNLAND GMBH—See Hochland SE; *Int'l*, pg. 3437
GRUNLEY CONSTRUCTION CO. INC.; *U.S. Private*, pg. 1797
GRUNSKE METALL-RECYCLING GMBH & CO. KG—See Alba SE; *Int'l*, pg. 293
GRUNWALD EQUITY MANAGEMENT GMBH; *Int'l*, pg. 3115
GRUNWELL-CASHERO CO. INC.; *U.S. Private*, pg. 1797
GRUNWERKE GMBH—See EnBW Energie Baden-Wurttemberg AG; *Int'l*, pg. 2399
GRUPA ANIMEX S.A.—See WH Group Limited; *Int'l*, pg. 8395
GRUPA AZOTY ATT POLYMERS GMBH—See Grupa Azoty S.A.; *Int'l*, pg. 3115
GRUPA AZOTY AUTOMATYKA SP. Z O.O.—See Grupa Azoty S.A.; *Int'l*, pg. 3115
GRUPA AZOTY COMPOUNDING SP. Z O.O.—See Grupa Azoty S.A.; *Int'l*, pg. 3115
GRUPA AZOTY JEDNOSTKA RATOWNICTWA CHEMICZNEGO SP. Z.O.O.—See Grupa Azoty S.A.; *Int'l*, pg. 3115
GRUPA AZOTY KOLTAR SP. Z O.O.—See Grupa Azoty S.A.; *Int'l*, pg. 3115
GRUPA AZOTY KOPALNIE I ZAKIADY CHEMICZNE SIARKI SIARKOPOL S. A.—See Grupa Azoty S.A.; *Int'l*, pg. 3115
GRUPA AZOTY KOPALNIE I ZAKLADY CHEMICZNE SIARKI "SIARKOPOL" S.A.—See Grupa Azoty S.A.; *Int'l*, pg. 3115
GRUPA AZOTY POLICE SERWIS SP. Z O.O.—See Grupa Azoty S.A.; *Int'l*, pg. 3116
GRUPA AZOTY POLSKIE KONSORCJUM CHEMICZNE SP. Z O.O.—See Grupa Azoty S.A.; *Int'l*, pg. 3115
GRUPA AZOTY PROREM SP. Z O.O.—See Grupa Azoty S.A.; *Int'l*, pg. 3115
GRUPA AZOTY S.A.; *Int'l*, pg. 3115
GRUPA AZOTY TRANSTECH SP. Z O.O.—See Grupa Azoty S.A.; *Int'l*, pg. 3116
GRUPA AZOTY ZAKIADY AZOTOWE CHORZOW S. A.—See Grupa Azoty S.A.; *Int'l*, pg. 3116
GRUPA AZOTY ZAKIADY AZOTOWE KEDZIERZYN S. A.—See Grupa Azoty S.A.; *Int'l*, pg. 3115
GRUPA AZOTY ZAKIADY AZOTOWE PULAWY S. A.—See Grupa Azoty S.A.; *Int'l*, pg. 3115
GRUPA AZOTY ZAKIADY CHEMICZNE POLICE S. A.—See Grupa Azoty S.A.; *Int'l*, pg. 3116
GRUPA AZOTY ZAKLADY AZOTOWE CHORZOW S.A.—See Grupa Azoty S.A.; *Int'l*, pg. 3116
GRUPA AZOTY ZAKLADY AZOTOWE KEDZIERZYN S.A.—See Grupa Azoty S.A.; *Int'l*, pg. 3116
GRUPA AZQTY ZAKLADY CHEMICZNE "POLICE" S.A.—See Grupa Azoty S.A.; *Int'l*, pg. 3116
GRUPA FORTIS D.O.O. BANJA LUKA; *Int'l*, pg. 3116
GRUPA GRASS SP. Z O.O.; *Int'l*, pg. 3116
GRUPA KAPITALOWA IMMOBILE S.A.; *Int'l*, pg. 3116
GRUPA KETY S.A.; *Int'l*, pg. 3116
GRUPA KLEPSYDRA SA; *Int'l*, pg. 3117
GRUPA LOTOS S.A.; *Int'l*, pg. 3117
GRUPA MASPEX SP. Z O.O.; *Int'l*, pg. 3117
GRUPA NOKAUT S.A.; *Int'l*, pg. 3117
GRUPA OZAROW S.A.—See CRH plc; *Int'l*, pg. 1844
GRUPA PRACUJ S.A.; *Int'l*, pg. 3117
GRUPA RADIOWA AGORY SP. Z O.O.—See Agora S.A.; *Int'l*, pg. 212
GRUPA SMT S.A.; *Int'l*, pg. 3117
GRUPA WIRTUALNA POLSKA S.A.—See Wirtualna Polska Holding S.A.; *Int'l*, pg. 8434
GRUPA ZASTAVA VOZILA U RESTRUKTURIRANJU A.D.; *Int'l*, pg. 3117
GRUPA ZYWIEC S.A.; *Int'l*, pg. 3117
GRUPE COMMERCIAL COMPANY—See Grupe Holding Company; *U.S. Private*, pg. 1797
THE GRUPE COMPANY—See Grupe Holding Company; *U.S. Private*, pg. 1797
GRUPE HOLDING COMPANY; *U.S. Private*, pg. 1797
GRUPE MANAGEMENT COMPANY—See Grupe Holding Company; *U.S. Private*, pg. 1797
GRUPE, S.A.B. DE C.V.; *Int'l*, pg. 3118
GRUPEX D.D; *Int'l*, pg. 3118

GRUPO ABC LTDA.—See Omnicom Group Inc.; *U.S. Public*, pg. 1585
GRUPO ACERERO DEL NORTE S.A. DE C.V.; *Int'l*, pg. 3118
GRUPO AEROMEXICO, S.A.B. DE C.V.; *Int'l*, pg. 3118
GRUPO AEROPORTUARIO CENTRO NORTE, S.A. DE C.V.—See Empresas ICA S.A.B. de C.V.; *Int'l*, pg. 2390
GRUPO AEROPORTUARIO DEL CENTRO NORTE, S.A.B. DE C.V.; *Int'l*, pg. 3118
GRUPO AEROPORTUARIO DEL PACIFICO, S.A.B. DE C.V.; *Int'l*, pg. 3118
GRUPO AEROPORTUARIO DEL SURESTE, S.A.B. DE C.V.; *Int'l*, pg. 3118
GRUPO ALBION; *Int'l*, pg. 3119
GRUPO ALCIONE—See Sonepar S.A.; *Int'l*, pg. 7092
GRUPO ALIADO S.A.; *Int'l*, pg. 3119
GRUPO ALIMENTARIO ARGAL SA; *Int'l*, pg. 3119
GRUPO ANAYA SA—See Vivendi SE; *Int'l*, pg. 8272
GRUPO ANTOLIN-AMSTERDAM, B.V.—See Grupo Antolin-Irausa, S.A.; *Int'l*, pg. 3119
GRUPO ANTOLIN-ARAGUSA, S.A.U.—See Grupo Antolin-Irausa, S.A.; *Int'l*, pg. 3119
GRUPO ANTOLIN-ARA SL—See Grupo Antolin-Irausa, S.A.; *Int'l*, pg. 3119
GRUPO ANTOLIN-ARDASA, S.A.U.—See Grupo Antolin-Irausa, S.A.; *Int'l*, pg. 3119
GRUPO ANTOLIN-AUTOTRIM, S.A.U.—See Grupo Antolin-Irausa, S.A.; *Int'l*, pg. 3119
GRUPO ANTOLIN-BOHEMIA AS—See Grupo Antolin-Irausa, S.A.; *Int'l*, pg. 3119
GRUPO ANTOLIN-BRATISLAVA, S.R.O.—See Grupo Antolin-Irausa, S.A.; *Int'l*, pg. 3119
GRUPO ANTOLIN CAMBRAI S.A.S.—See Grupo Antolin-Irausa, S.A.; *Int'l*, pg. 3119
GRUPO ANTOLIN-DAPSA, S.A.U.—See Grupo Antolin-Irausa, S.A.; *Int'l*, pg. 3119
GRUPO ANTOLIN-DEUTSCHLAND, GMBH—See Grupo Antolin-Irausa, S.A.; *Int'l*, pg. 3119
GRUPO ANTOLIN-FRANCE, S.A.S.—See Grupo Antolin-Irausa, S.A.; *Int'l*, pg. 3119
GRUPO ANTOLIN IGA SAS—See Grupo Antolin-Irausa, S.A.; *Int'l*, pg. 3119
GRUPO ANTOLIN-ILLINOIS, INC.—See Grupo Antolin-Irausa, S.A.; *Int'l*, pg. 3120
GRUPO ANTOLIN INGENIERIE SIEGES, S.A.S.—See Grupo Antolin-Irausa, S.A.; *Int'l*, pg. 3119
GRUPO ANTOLIN-IRAUSA, S.A.; *Int'l*, pg. 3119
GRUPO ANTOLIN-ITALIA, S.R.L—See Grupo Antolin-Irausa, S.A.; *Int'l*, pg. 3119
GRUPO ANTOLIN-JAPAN, CO.—See Grupo Antolin-Irausa, S.A.; *Int'l*, pg. 3119
GRUPO ANTOLIN-JARNY, S.A.S.—See Grupo Antolin-Irausa, S.A.; *Int'l*, pg. 3119
GRUPO ANTOLIN KENTUCKY, INC.—See Grupo Antolin-Irausa, S.A.; *Int'l*, pg. 3119
GRUPO ANTOLIN-KOREA, L.L.C.—See Grupo Antolin-Irausa, S.A.; *Int'l*, pg. 3119
GRUPO ANTOLIN-LOGISTIK DEUTSCHLAND GMBH—See Grupo Antolin-Irausa, S.A.; *Int'l*, pg. 3120
GRUPO ANTOLIN LOIRE SAS—See Grupo Antolin-Irausa, S.A.; *Int'l*, pg. 3119
GRUPO ANTOLIN-LOUISIANA, INC.—See Grupo Antolin-Irausa, S.A.; *Int'l*, pg. 3119
GRUPO ANTOLIN-MAGNESIO, S.L.U.—See Grupo Antolin-Irausa, S.A.; *Int'l*, pg. 3120
GRUPO ANTOLIN MATORELL, S.A.U.—See Grupo Antolin-Irausa, S.A.; *Int'l*, pg. 3119
GRUPO ANTOLIN-MICHIGAN, INC.—See Grupo Antolin-Irausa, S.A.; *Int'l*, pg. 3120
GRUPO ANTOLIN MICHIGAN—See Grupo Antolin-Irausa, S.A.; *Int'l*, pg. 3119
GRUPO ANTOLIN-MISSOURI, LLC—See Grupo Antolin-Irausa, S.A.; *Int'l*, pg. 3120
GRUPO ANTOLIN-NAVARRA, S.A.U.—See Grupo Antolin-Irausa, S.A.; *Int'l*, pg. 3120
GRUPO ANTOLIN-NORTH AMERICA, INC.—See Grupo Antolin-Irausa, S.A.; *Int'l*, pg. 3120
GRUPO ANTOLIN-OSTRAVA, S.R.O.—See Grupo Antolin-Irausa, S.A.; *Int'l*, pg. 3120
GRUPO ANTOLIN-PLASBUR, S.A.U.—See Grupo Antolin-Irausa, S.A.; *Int'l*, pg. 3120
GRUPO ANTOLIN-PUNE PVT, LTD.—See Grupo Antolin-Irausa, S.A.; *Int'l*, pg. 3120
GRUPO ANTOLIN-RYA, S.A.U.—See Grupo Antolin-Irausa, S.A.; *Int'l*, pg. 3120
GRUPO ANTOLIN-SALTILLO, S. DE R.L.DE C.V.—See Grupo Antolin-Irausa, S.A.; *Int'l*, pg. 3120
GRUPO ANTOLIN SILAO SA DE CV—See Grupo Antolin-Irausa, S.A.; *Int'l*, pg. 3119
GRUPO ANTOLIN-SOUTH AFRICA, LTD.—See Grupo Antolin-Irausa, S.A.; *Int'l*, pg. 3120
GRUPO ANTOLIN-TURNOV, S.R.O.—See Grupo Antolin-Irausa, S.A.; *Int'l*, pg. 3120
GRUPO ANTOLIN-VALENCA COMPONENTES AUTO-MOVEL SOC. UNIPESSOAL, LDA.—See Grupo Antolin-Irausa, S.A.; *Int'l*, pg. 3120
GRUPO ANTOLIN-VALPLAS, S.A.U.—See Grupo Antolin-Irausa, S.A.; *Int'l*, pg. 3120

COMPANY NAME INDEX

GRUPO ANTOLIN-VIGO, S.L.U.—See Grupo Antolin-Irausa, S.A.; *Int'l*, pg. 3120
GRUPO ANTOLIN VOSGES—See Grupo Antolin-Irausa, S.A.; *Int'l*, pg. 3119
GRUPO ARBULU S.L; *Int'l*, pg. 3120
GRUPO ARGOS S.A.; *Int'l*, pg. 3120
GRUPO ASSA S.A.; *Int'l*, pg. 3121
GRUPO AVAL ACCIONES Y VALORES S.A.; *Int'l*, pg. 3121
GRUPO BAFAR, S.A.B DE C.V.; *Int'l*, pg. 3121
GRUPO BAL; *Int'l*, pg. 3121
GRUPO BANCO PROVINCIA S.A.—See Banco de la Provincia de Buenos Aires; *Int'l*, pg. 821
GRUPO BIMBO, S.A.B. DE C.V.; *Int'l*, pg. 3122
GRUPO BNS DE COSTA RICA, S.A.—See The Bank of Nova Scotia; *Int'l*, pg. 7617
GRUPO BOHLER SOLDADURA ESPANA S.A.—See voestalpine AG; *Int'l*, pg. 8288
GRUPO BOLIVAR S.A.; *Int'l*, pg. 3123
GRUPO BOLUDA; *Int'l*, pg. 3123
GRUPO BRASIL PARTICIPACOES; *Int'l*, pg. 3123
GRUPO BRAVO—See Corpfin Capital SA; *Int'l*, pg. 1802
GRUPO BRITT N.V.; *Int'l*, pg. 3123
GRUPO BUPA SANITAS SL—See The British United Provident Association Limited; *Int'l*, pg. 7629
GRUPO BURSATIL MEXICANO SA DE CV CASA DE BOLSA; *Int'l*, pg. 3123
GRUPO CALIDRA—See Lhoist S.A.; *Int'l*, pg. 4478
GRUPO CARE SA—See Emeis SA; *Int'l*, pg. 2376
GRUPO CARSO, S.A.B. DE C.V.; *Int'l*, pg. 3123
GRUPO CASA SABA S.A.B. DE C.V.—See Grupo Xtra S.A. de C.V.; *Int'l*, pg. 3139
GRUPO CATALANA OCCIDENTE, S.A.; *Int'l*, pg. 3124
GRUPO CATALANA OCCIDENTE SERVICIOS TECNOLOGICOS, AIE—See Grupo Catalana Occidente, S.A.; *Int'l*, pg. 3124
GRUPO CCRR; *Int'l*, pg. 3124
GRUPO CHEN, S. DE R.L. DE C.V.—See ALFA, S.A.B. de C.V.; *Int'l*, pg. 314
GRUPO CINEMEX SA DE CV—See Entretenimiento GM de Mexico SA de CV; *Int'l*, pg. 2453
GRUPO CINTAC S.A.—See CAP S.A.; *Int'l*, pg. 1300
GRUPO CLARIN, S.A.; *Int'l*, pg. 3124
GRUPO COLLADO S.A. DE C.V.; *Int'l*, pg. 3125
GRUPO COMERCIAL CHEDRAUI S.A.B. DE C.V.; *Int'l*, pg. 3125
GRUPO COMERCIAL GOMO, S.A. DE C.V.; *Int'l*, pg. 3125
GRUPO COMPONENTES VILANOVA, S.L.—See Cie Automotive S.A.; *Int'l*, pg. 1604
GRUPO CONCESIONARIO DEL OESTE, S.A.—See ACS, Actividades de Construccion y Servicios, S.A.; *Int'l*, pg. 112
GRUPO CONDUMEX, S. A. DE C. V.—See Grupo Carso, S.A.B. de C.V.; *Int'l*, pg. 3123
GRUPO CONTINENTAL, S.A.—See Arca Continental, S.A.B. de C.V.; *Int'l*, pg. 540
GRUPO CORPORATIVO GFI INFORMATICA S.A.—See Mannai Corporation QPSC; *Int'l*, pg. 4674
GRUPO CORPORATIVO INTERESTATAL, S.A. DE C.V.—See Promotora y Operadora de Infraestructura, S.A.B. de C.V.; *Int'l*, pg. 5996
GRUPO CORVI, S.A.B. DE C.V.; *Int'l*, pg. 3125
GRUPO DE INVERSIONES SURAMERICANA S.A.; *Int'l*, pg. 3125
GRUPO DE MODA SOMA S.A.; *Int'l*, pg. 3126
GRUPO DISTRIBUIDORAS INTERMEX, S.A. DE C.V.—See Grupo Televisa, S.A.B.; *Int'l*, pg. 3136
GRUPO DON MARIO; *Int'l*, pg. 3126
GRUPO EDITORIAL BRUNO S.L.—See Vivendi SE; *Int'l*, pg. 8272
GRUPO ELECTRO STOCKS, S.L.U.—See Wurth Verwaltungsgesellschaft mbH; *Int'l*, pg. 8505
GRUPO ELEKTRA S.A.B. DE C.V.—See Grupo Salinas, S.A. de C.V.; *Int'l*, pg. 3135
GRUPO EMES S.A.; *Int'l*, pg. 3126
GRUPO EMPRESARIAL ANGELES, S.A. DE C.V.; *Int'l*, pg. 3126
GRUPO EMPRESARIAL KALUZ S.A. DE C.V.; *Int'l*, pg. 3126
GRUPO EMPRESARIAL PALACIOS ALIMENTACION SA—See The Carlyle Group Inc.; *U.S. Public*, pg. 2047
GRUPO EMPRESARIAL SAN JOSE, S.A.—CENTRAL OFFICE—See Grupo Empresarial San Jose, S.A.; *Int'l*, pg. 3128
GRUPO EMPRESARIAL SAN JOSE, S.A.; *Int'l*, pg. 3128
GRUPO EMPRESAS NAVIERAS S.A.; *Int'l*, pg. 3128
GRUPO ENERGIA BOGOTA S.A. E.S.P.; *Int'l*, pg. 3128
GRUPO EROSKI; *Int'l*, pg. 3128
GRUPO ESCADA ESPANA S.A.U.—See Regent, L.P.; *U.S. Private*, pg. 3388
GRUPO EUROPRODUCCIONES, S.A.—See Vocento, S.A.; *Int'l*, pg. 8284
GRUPO EXP REALTORS MEXICO, S DE R.L. DE C.V.—see eXp World Holdings, Inc.; *U.S. Public*, pg. 808
GRUPO EZENTIS S.A.; *Int'l*, pg. 3129
GRUPO FAMSA S.A.B. DE C.V.; *Int'l*, pg. 3129

GRUPO FARMACEUTICO SOMAR—See Advent International Corporation; *U.S. Private*, pg. 102
GRUPO FERRER INTERNACIONAL, S.A.; *Int'l*, pg. 3129
GRUPO FERROATLANTICA, S.A.U.—See Sixth Street Partners LLC; *U.S. Private*, pg. 3677
GRUPO FERROMINERO, S.A. DE C.V.; *Int'l*, pg. 3129
GRUPO F.I.L.A.-DIXON, S.A. DE C.V.—See F.I.L.A. - Fabbrica Italiana Lapis ed Affini S.p.A.; *Int'l*, pg. 2597
GRUPO FINACCESS S.A.P.I. DE C.V.; *Int'l*, pg. 3129
GRUPO FINANCIERO BANAMEX, S.A. DE C.V.—See Citigroup Inc.; *U.S. Public*, pg. 504
GRUPO FINANCIERO BANORTE, S.A.B. DE C.V.; *Int'l*, pg. 3129
GRUPO FINANCIERO BARCLAYS MEXICO, S.A. DE C.V.—See Barclays PLC; *Int'l*, pg. 862
GRUPO FINANCIERO BBVA-BANCOMER, S.A.—See Banco Bilbao Vizcaya Argentaria, S.A.; *Int'l*, pg. 818
GRUPO FINANCIERO GALICIA S.A.; *Int'l*, pg. 3129
GRUPO FINANCIERO HSBC, S.A. DE C.V.—See HSBC Holdings plc; *Int'l*, pg. 3503
GRUPO FINANCIERO INBURSA, S.A. DE C.V.; *Int'l*, pg. 3129
GRUPO FINANCIERO INTERACCIONES, S.A. DE C.V.—See Grupo Financiero Banorte, S.A.B. de C.V.; *Int'l*, pg. 3129
GRUPO FINANCIERO SANTANDER MEXICO, S.A. DE C.V.—See Banco Santander, S.A.; *Int'l*, pg. 825
GRUPO FINANCIERO SCOTIABANK INVERLAT, S.A. DE C.V.—See The Bank of Nova Scotia; *Int'l*, pg. 7617
GRUPO GALLEGOS; *U.S. Private*, pg. 1797
GRUPO GAMESA S. DE R.L. DE C.V—See PepsiCo, Inc.; *U.S. Public*, pg. 1670
GRUPO GICSA, S.A.B. DE C.V.; *Int'l*, pg. 3129
GRUPO GIGANTE, S.A.B. DE C.V.; *Int'l*, pg. 3130
GRUPO GONVARRI—See Corporacion Gestamp SL; *Int'l*, pg. 1804
GRUPO HERDEZ, S.A.B. DE C.V.; *Int'l*, pg. 3130
GRUPO HIDROAPLICACIONES Y GAS, SL—See Aalberts N.V.; *Int'l*, pg. 34
GRUPO HIMA-SAN PABLO, INC.—See Metro Pavia Health System, Inc.; *U.S. Private*, pg. 2686
GRUPO HOTELERO QUERETARO, S.A. DE C.V.—See Minor International PCL; *Int'l*, pg. 4911
GRUPO HOTELERO SANTA FE, S.A.B. DE C.V.; *Int'l*, pg. 3130
GRUPO IBERDROLA MEXICO, S.A. DE C.V.—See Iberdrola, S.A.; *Int'l*, pg. 3571
GRUPO ICT II S.A.S.—See Salini Costruttori S.p.A.; *Int'l*, pg. 6493
GRUPO INDAL S.L.—See Koninklijke Philips N.V.; *Int'l*, pg. 4267
GRUPO INDUSTRIAL MASECA, S.A.B. DE C.V.—See Gruma, S.A.B. de C.V.; *Int'l*, pg. 3114
GRUPO INDUSTRIAL MINERA MEXICO, S.A. DE C.V.—See Grupo Mexico, S.A.B. de C.V.; *Int'l*, pg. 3132
GRUPO INDUSTRIAL MORGAN, S.A. DE C.V.—See Morgan Advanced Materials plc; *Int'l*, pg. 5041
GRUPO INDUSTRIAL SALTILLO S.A. DE C.V.; *Int'l*, pg. 3130
GRUPO INFFINIX, S.A. DE C.V.—See Equifax Inc.; *U.S. Public*, pg. 786
GRUPO INMOBILIARIO DE CAPITAL PRIVADO I (GICAP I) LTD.; *Int'l*, pg. 3130
GRUPO INTERNATIONAL, INC.; *U.S. Public*, pg. 972
GRUPO KONECTANET S.L.; *Int'l*, pg. 3130
GRUPO KUO, S.A.B. DE C.V.; *Int'l*, pg. 3130
GRUPO LACTALIS IBERIA S.A.—See Groupe Lactalis SA; *Int'l*, pg. 3106
GRUPO LALA S.A. DE C.V.; *Int'l*, pg. 3131
GRUPO LA MODERNA, S.A.B. DE C.V.; *Int'l*, pg. 3131
GRUPO LAMOSA S.A.B. DE C.V.; *Int'l*, pg. 3131
GRUPO LAMOSA, SA DE CV—See Grupo Lamosa S.A. de C.V.; *Int'l*, pg. 3131
GRUPO LAR INVERSIONES INMOBILIARIAS, SA; *Int'l*, pg. 3132
GRUPO LECHE PASCUAL S.A.; *Int'l*, pg. 3132
GRUPO LINDE GAS ARGENTINA S.A.—See Linde plc; *Int'l*, pg. 4505
GRUPO LINDE GAS ARGENTINA S.A.—See Linde plc; *Int'l*, pg. 4505
GRUPO MASSIMO DUTTI S.A.—See Industria de Diseno Textil, S.A.; *Int'l*, pg. 3666
GRUPO MATERIAS PRIMAS S. DE R. L. DE C. V.—See Covia Holdings Corporation; *U.S. Private*, pg. 1072
GRUPO MEDIA CAPITAL, SGPS, S.A.—See Promotora de Informaciones S.A.; *Int'l*, pg. 5996
GRUPO MELO S.A.; *Int'l*, pg. 3132
GRUPO MEXICANO DE DESARROLLO S.A.B. DE C.V.; *Int'l*, pg. 3132
GRUPO MEXICO, S.A.B. DE C.V.; *Int'l*, pg. 3132
GRUPO MINEROS DEL CARIBE, S. A. S.—See City View Green Holdings Inc.; *Int'l*, pg. 1628
GRUPO MINSA, S.A.B. DE C.V.; *Int'l*, pg. 3133
GRUPO MODELO, S.A. DE C.V.—See Anheuser-Busch InBev SA/NV; *Int'l*, pg. 466
GRUPO MRF CARTUJA SL; *Int'l*, pg. 3133
GRUPO MULTIASISTENCIA S.A.—See Allianz SE; *Int'l*, pg. 353

GRUPO MUNDIAL TENEDORA, S.A.; *Int'l*, pg. 3133
GRUPO MZ; *Int'l*, pg. 3133
GRUPO NACIONAL PROVINCIAL—See Grupo BAL; *Int'l*, pg. 3121
GRUPO NACION GN, S.A.; *Int'l*, pg. 3133
GRUPO NELSON—See Charlesbank Capital Partners, LLC; *U.S. Private*, pg. 854
GRUPO NET SLU—See Derichebourg S.A.; *Int'l*, pg. 2042
GRUPO NUEVA COMERCIAL TB, S.A. DE C.V.—See Grupo Televisa, S.A.B.; *Int'l*, pg. 3136
GRUPONUEVA S.A.; *Int'l*, pg. 3139
GRUPO NUTRESA S.A.; *Int'l*, pg. 3133
GRUPO OXYCHEM DE MEXICO, S.A. DE C.V.—See Occidental Petroleum Corporation; *U.S. Public*, pg. 1561
GRUPO PALACIO DE HIERRO, S.A. DE C.V.—See Grupo BAL; *Int'l*, pg. 3121
GRUPO PHOENIX—See Genstar Capital, LLC; *U.S. Private*, pg. 1678
GRUPO PILGRIM'S PRIDE FUNDING HOLDINGS, S. DE R.L. DE C.V.—See JBS S.A.; *Int'l*, pg. 3919
GRUPO POCHTECA S.A.B. DE C.V.; *Int'l*, pg. 3133
GRUPO POSADAS S.A.B. DE C.V.; *Int'l*, pg. 3134
GRUPO PRIVAL S.A.; *Int'l*, pg. 3134
GRUPO PROEZA, S.A.P.I. DE C.V.; *Int'l*, pg. 3134
GRUPO PROTEXA S.A. DE C.V.; *Int'l*, pg. 3134
GRUPO QUMMA, S.A. DE C.V.; *Int'l*, pg. 3134
GRUPO RADIO CENTRO, S.A. DE C.V.; *Int'l*, pg. 3134
GRUPO RADIO NOTICIAS S.R.L.; *Int'l*, pg. 3134
GRUPO RAF, S.A. DE C.V.; *Int'l*, pg. 3134
GRUPO REAL TURISMO S.A. DE C.V.; *Int'l*, pg. 3134
GRUPO REPSOL DE PERU, S.A.—See Repsol, S.A.; *Int'l*, pg. 6292
GRUPO ROCHE SYNTEX DE MEXICO S.A. DE C.V.—See Roche Holding AG; *Int'l*, pg. 6373
GRUPO ROMERO; *Int'l*, pg. 3134
GRUPO ROTOPLAS, S.A.B. DE C.V.; *Int'l*, pg. 3135
GRUPO SABRITAS, S. DE R.L. DE C.V.—See PepsiCo, Inc.; *U.S. Public*, pg. 1668
GRUPO SAKATA SEED DE MEXICO, S.A. DE C.V.—See Sakata Seed Corporation; *Int'l*, pg. 6488
GRUPO SALINAS, S.A. DE C.V.; *Int'l*, pg. 3135
GRUPO SALVADOR CAETANO (SGPS) S.A.; *Int'l*, pg. 3135
GRUPO SANBORNS, S.A. DE C.V.—See Grupo Carso, S.A.B. de C.V.; *Int'l*, pg. 3123
GRUPO SBF S.A.; *Int'l*, pg. 3135
GRUPO SEB DO BRASIL—See SEB S.A.; *Int'l*, pg. 6668
GRUPO SECURITAS MEXICO SA DE CV—See Securitas AB; *Int'l*, pg. 6675
GRUPO SECURITY S.A.; *Int'l*, pg. 3135
GRUPO SIEMENS S.A. DE C.V.—See Siemens Aktiengesellschaft; *Int'l*, pg. 6887
GRUPO SIMEC, S.A.B. DE C.V.—See Industrias CH, S.A.B. de C.V.; *Int'l*, pg. 3674
GRUPO SIRO S.L.; *Int'l*, pg. 3135
GRUPO SMURFIT MEXICO, S.A. DE C.V.—See Smurfit Kappa Group plc; *Int'l*, pg. 7017
GRUPO SPORTS WORLD, S. A. B. DE C. V.; *Int'l*, pg. 3135
GRUPO SUPERVIELLE S.A.; *Int'l*, pg. 3135
GRUPO TACA-GUATEMALA—See Synergy Group; *Int'l*, pg. 7384
GRUPO TACA—See Synergy Group; *Int'l*, pg. 7384
GRUPO TAPER, S.A.—See Banco Santander, S.A.; *Int'l*, pg. 826
GRUPO TECNOLOGICO E INDUSTRIAL GMV, S.A.; *Int'l*, pg. 3135
GRUPO TELESISTEMA, S.A. DE C.V.—See Grupo Televisa, S.A.B.; *Int'l*, pg. 3136
GRUPO TELEVISA, S.A.B.; *Int'l*, pg. 3136
GRUPO TELVISTA, S.A. DE C.V.—See America Movil, S.A.B. de C.V.; *Int'l*, pg. 421
GRUPO TERMOINDUSTRIAL ECA, S.A. DE C.V.; *Int'l*, pg. 3137
GRUPO TERRA S.A. DE C.V.; *Int'l*, pg. 3137
GRUPO TH MANTENIMIENTO, S.L.—See Helvetia Holding AG; *Int'l*, pg. 3339
GRUPO THYSSENKRUPP S.L.—See ThyssenKrupp AG; *Int'l*, pg. 7724
GRUPO TMM CIUDAD DEL CARMEN—See Grupo TMM, S.A.B.; *Int'l*, pg. 3137
GRUPO TMM, S.A.B.; *Int'l*, pg. 3137
GRUPO TRADEBE MEDIOAMBIENTE S.L.; *Int'l*, pg. 3138
GRUPO TRAXION, S. A. B. DE C. V.; *Int'l*, pg. 3138
GRUPO ULMA—See Mondragon Corporation; *Int'l*, pg. 5029
GRUPO VASCONIA, S.A.B.; *Int'l*, pg. 3138
GRUPO VENDAP, SA—See Magnum Industrial Partners, S.L.; *Int'l*, pg. 4641
GRUPO VILLAR MIR, S.A.U.; *Int'l*, pg. 3138
GRUPO VIPS—See Alsea, S.A.B. de C.V.; *Int'l*, pg. 379
GRUPO VISTEON, S. DE R.L. DE C.V.—See Visteon Corporation; *U.S. Public*, pg. 2305
GRUPO WACKENHUT S.A. DE C.V.—See Allied Universal Manager LLC; *U.S. Private*, pg. 189
GRUPO WILSON, S.A. DE C.V.—See ANTA Sports Products Limited; *Int'l*, pg. 480
GRUPO XTRA S.A. DE C.V.; *Int'l*, pg. 3139
GRUPO ZULIANO, C.A.; *Int'l*, pg. 3139

GRUPPA KOMPANIY RUSAGRO OOO; *Int'l*, pg. 3140
GRUPPO ATURIA S.P.A.—See WPIL Limited; *Int'l*, pg. 8462
GRUPPO CERAMICHE RICCHETTI S.P.A.—See QuattroR SGR S.p.A.; *Int'l*, pg. 6157
GRUPPO COIN S.P.A.; *Int'l*, pg. 3140
GRUPPO FORMULA S.P.A.; *Int'l*, pg. 3140
GRUPPO GENERALI SERVIZI S.R.L.—See Assicurazioni Generali S.p.A.; *Int'l*, pg. 647
GRUPPO GREEN POWER S.P.A.—See Alperia SpA; *Int'l*, pg. 366
GRUPPO INDUSTRIALE MACCAFERRI—See Societa Esercizi Commerciali Industriali; *Int'l*, pg. 7034
GRUPPO ITALIANO VINI S.P.A.—See Cantine Riunite & CIV S.C.Agr.; *Int'l*, pg. 1299
GRUPPO LACTALIS ITALIA S.P.A.—See Groupe Lactalis SA; *Int'l*, pg. 3106
GRUPPO LA PERLA FASHION SA—See Tennor Holding BV; *Int'l*, pg. 7561
GRUPPO MINERALI DO BRASIL LTDA—See Gruppo Minerali Maffei S.p.A.; *Int'l*, pg. 3140
GRUPPO MINERALI MAFFEI S.P.A.; *Int'l*, pg. 3140
GRUPPO MUTUIONLINE S.P.A.; *Int'l*, pg. 3140
GRUPPO PAM S.P.A.—See GECOS S.p.A.; *Int'l*, pg. 2909
GRUPPO PRO S.P.A.—See Solgenia S.p.A.; *Int'l*, pg. 7071
GRUPPO RIELLO SISTEMI FRANCE—See Gruppo Riello Sistemi S.p.A.; *Int'l*, pg. 3141
GRUPPO RIELLO SISTEMI GERMANY GMBH—See Gruppo Riello Sistemi S.p.A.; *Int'l*, pg. 3141
GRUPPO RIELLO SISTEMI NORTH AMERICA—See Gruppo Riello Sistemi S.p.A.; *Int'l*, pg. 3141
GRUPPO RIELLO SISTEMI S.P.A.; *Int'l*, pg. 3141
GRUPPO TRADE SERVICE POLSKA SP. Z O.O.—See ASM Group S.A.; *Int'l*, pg. 625
GRUPPO VENETO DIAGNOSTICA E RIABILITAZIONE S.R.L.—See Garofalo Health Care SpA; *Int'l*, pg. 2886
GRUPPO WASTE ITALIA S.P.A.; *Int'l*, pg. 3141
GRUPPO ZAFFIRO SRL—See Mittel S.p.A.; *Int'l*, pg. 4994
GRUP SIMEX S.R.L; *Int'l*, pg. 3115
GRUPUL EDITORILOR SI DIFUZORILOR DE PRESA SA; *Int'l*, pg. 3141
GRUPUTERQUE PORTUGAL CONFECCOES E ACESSORIOS LDA.—See Industria de Diseno Textil, S.A.; *Int'l*, pg. 3666
GRUSCHWITZ TEXTILWERKE AG; *Int'l*, pg. 3141
GRUSKIN GROUP; *U.S. Private*, pg. 1797
GRUS, LLC—See Gulfport Energy Corporation; *U.S. Public*, pg. 975
GRV GIBBS, INC.; *U.S. Private*, pg. 1797
GR VIETNAM INTERNATIONAL LIMITED—See Golden Resources Development International Limited; *Int'l*, pg. 3031
GRW ADVERTISING; *U.S. Private*, pg. 1798
GR WOOD INC.; *U.S. Private*, pg. 1748
GRY-ONLINE S.A.—See Penta Investments Limited; *Int'l*, pg. 5788
GRYPHON CAPITAL INCOME TRUST; *Int'l*, pg. 3141
GRYPHON DIGITAL MINING, INC.; *U.S. Public*, pg. 973
GRYPHON INVESTORS, LLC; *U.S. Private*, pg. 1798
GRYPHON MARINE, LLC—See AE Industrial Partners, LP; *U.S. Private*, pg. 112
GRYPHON SCIENTIFIC, LLC—See Deloitte LLP; *U.S. Private*, pg. 1198
GRYPHON SCIENTIFIC, LLC—See Deloitte Touche Tohmatsu Limited; *Int'l*, pg. 2015
GRYPHON TECHNOLOGIES, LC—See AE Industrial Partners, LP; *U.S. Private*, pg. 112
GRYYT, LLC; *U.S. Private*, pg. 1800
GRZA TURIST A.D.; *Int'l*, pg. 3141
GRZ IT CENTER LINZ GMBH—See Raiffeisenlandesbank Oberosterreich Aktiengesellschaft; *Int'l*, pg. 6187
GRZYBOWSKA CENTRUM SP. Z O.O.—See Atlas Estates Limited; *Int'l*, pg. 685
GS4 PERU, S.A.—See Allied Universal Manager LLC; *U.S. Private*, pg. 189
GSA GESELLSCHAFT FUR STRASSENANALYSE GMBH—See Sweco AB; *Int'l*, pg. 7363
GSA INSURANCE BROKERS PTY LTD—See Steadfast Group Limited; *Int'l*, pg. 7187
G.S. AUTO INTERNATIONAL LTD.; *Int'l*, pg. 2866
GSB & ASSOCIATES, INC.—See The Riverside Company; *U.S. Private*, pg. 4109
GS BATTERY (CHINA) CO., LTD.—See GS Yuasa Corporation; *Int'l*, pg. 3143
GS BATTERY TAIWAN CO., LTD.—See GS Yuasa Corporation; *Int'l*, pg. 3143
GS BATTERY (U.S.A.) INC.—See GS Yuasa Corporation; *Int'l*, pg. 3143
GS BATTERY VIETNAM CO., LTD.—See GS Yuasa Corporation; *Int'l*, pg. 3143
GSB DIGITAL INC.; *U.S. Private*, pg. 1800
GSB FINANCE LIMITED; *Int'l*, pg. 3143
G.S. BLODGETT CORPORATION—See The Middleby Corporation; *U.S. Public*, pg. 2114
GSB PROPERTIES SDN. BHD.—See Kerjaya Prospek Property Berhad; *Int'l*, pg. 4136
GSB SUMMIT CD (M) SDN. BHD.—See Kerjaya Prospek Property Berhad; *Int'l*, pg. 4137

GSC AIR LOGISTICS INC.—See GSC Logistics Inc.; *U.S. Private*, pg. 1800
GS CALTEX CORPORATION—See GS Holdings Corp.; *Int'l*, pg. 3141
GS CALTEX SINGAPORE PTE., LTD.—See GS Holdings Corp.; *Int'l*, pg. 3142
GS CAPITAL PARTNERS L.P.—See The Goldman Sachs Group, Inc.; *U.S. Public*, pg. 2076
GSC ARCHITECTS; *U.S. Private*, pg. 1800
GSC ENTERPRISES, INC.; *U.S. Private*, pg. 1800
GSC FOUNDRIES, INC.—See Berkshire Hathaway Inc.; *U.S. Public*, pg. 314
GSC GROUP; *U.S. Private*, pg. 1800
GS CHAIN PLC; *Int'l*, pg. 3141
G. SCHIRMER, INC.—See Music Sales Corporation; *U.S. Private*, pg. 2818
G. SCHNIDER, M.D., PLLC—See HCA Healthcare, Inc.; *U.S. Public*, pg. 996
GSC LOGISTICS INC.; *U.S. Private*, pg. 1800
G.S. COATING TECHNOLOGIES S.R.L.—See I.M.A. Industria Macchine Automatiche S.p.A.; *Int'l*, pg. 3565
GS CONSTRUCTION ARABIA CO., LTD.—See GS Holdings Corp.; *Int'l*, pg. 3142
G.S. CONTRACTS (JOINERY) LTD.—See MBH Corporation Plc; *Int'l*, pg. 4752
GSC PACKAGING, INC.; *U.S. Private*, pg. 1800
GSC TECHNOLOGIES INC.—See KL Outdoor LLC; *U.S. Private*, pg. 2317
GSD DENIZCILIK GAYRIMENKUL INSAAT SANAYI VE TICARET AS—See GSD Holding A.S.; *Int'l*, pg. 3144
GSD DIS TICARET A.S.—See GSD Holding A.S.; *Int'l*, pg. 3144
GSD EGITIM VAKFI BAHCELIEVLER ILKOKULU—See GSD Holding A.S.; *Int'l*, pg. 3144
GSD EGITIM VAKFI—See GSD Holding A.S.; *Int'l*, pg. 3144
GSD HOLDING A.S.; *Int'l*, pg. 3144
GSD&M CHICAGO—See Omnicom Group Inc.; *U.S. Public*, pg. 1585
GSD&M IDEA CITY LLC—See Omnicom Group Inc.; *U.S. Public*, pg. 1585
GSD YATIRIM BANKASI A.S.—See GSD Holding A.S.; *Int'l*, pg. 3144
G-SEARCH LTD.—See Fujitsu Limited; *Int'l*, pg. 2834
GSE AUSTRALIA PTY. LTD.—See Solmax International, Inc.; *Int'l*, pg. 7074
GS E&C CORP.—See GS Holdings Corp.; *Int'l*, pg. 3141
GS E&C INDIA PVT. LTD.—See GS Holdings Corp.; *Int'l*, pg. 3142
GS E&C NANJING CO., LTD.—See GS Holdings Corp.; *Int'l*, pg. 3142
GSE CO., LTD.; *Int'l*, pg. 3144
GS ECOMETAL CO., LTD.—See GS Holdings Corp.; *Int'l*, pg. 3142
GS E&C THAI CO., LTD.—See GS Holdings Corp.; *Int'l*, pg. 3142
GSE ENVIRONMENTAL, LLC—See Solmax International, Inc.; *Int'l*, pg. 7074
GSE ENVIRONMENTAL, LLC - SPEARFISH PLANT—See Solmax International, Inc.; *Int'l*, pg. 7074
GSE HOLDING, INC.—See Littlejohn & Co., LLC; *U.S. Private*, pg. 2470
GSE HOLDING, INC.—See Strategic Value Partners, LLC; *U.S. Private*, pg. 3836
GS-ELEKTROANLAGENMONTAGE GMBH; *Int'l*, pg. 3143
GSE LINING TECHNOLOGY CHILE, S.A.—See Solmax International, Inc.; *Int'l*, pg. 7074
GSE LINING TECHNOLOGY CO. - EGYPT S.A.E.—See Solmax International, Inc.; *Int'l*, pg. 7074
GSE LINING TECHNOLOGY CO., LTD.—See Solmax International, Inc.; *Int'l*, pg. 7074
GSE LINING TECHNOLOGY GMBH—See Solmax International, Inc.; *Int'l*, pg. 7074
GS ENERGY CORPORATION—See GS Holdings Corp.; *Int'l*, pg. 3141
GS ENGINEERING & CONSTRUCTION CORPORATION—See GS Holdings Corp.; *Int'l*, pg. 3142
G&S ENGINEERING SERVICES PTY. LTD.; *Int'l*, pg. 2862
GS ENTEC CORP.—See GS Holdings Corp.; *Int'l*, pg. 3142
G&S ENTERPRISES, INCORPORATED—See Pernix Therapeutics Holdings, Inc.; *U.S. Private*, pg. 3152
GS ENVIROSERVICES, INC.—See GreenSource Corporation; *U.S. Private*, pg. 1780
GSE POWER SYSTEMS AB—See GSE Systems, Inc.; *U.S. Public*, pg. 973
GS EPS CO., LTD.—See GS Holdings Corp.; *Int'l*, pg. 3141
GSE SYSTEMS, INC.; *U.S. Public*, pg. 973
GSEVEN; *Int'l*, pg. 3144
GSFC AGROTECH LIMITED—See Gujarat State Fertilizers & Chemicals Ltd.; *Int'l*, pg. 3177
GSF CAR PARTS LIMITED—See LKQ Corporation; *U.S. Public*, pg. 1336
GSF EUROPE B.V.—See Parker Hannifin Corporation; *U.S. Public*, pg. 1641

GSFM PTY LIMITED—See CI Financial Corporation; *Int'l*, pg. 1601
G.S. GALATARIOTIS & SONS LTD.; *Int'l*, pg. 2866
GSG DESIGN; *U.S. Private*, pg. 1800
GSG FASTENERS, LLC—See Morito Co., Ltd.; *Int'l*, pg. 5048
GSG FATENERS ASIA LIMITED—See Morito Co., Ltd.; *Int'l*, pg. 5048
GSG FATENERS INDIA LIMITED—See Morito Co., Ltd.; *Int'l*, pg. 5048
GSG FATENERS UK LIMITED—See Morito Co., Ltd.; *Int'l*, pg. 5048
GSG FINANCIAL—See Material Handling Services, LLC; *U.S. Private*, pg. 2609
GSG GEORGSMARIENHUETTE SERVICE GESELLSCHAFT MBH—See Georgsmarienhutte Holding GmbH; *Int'l*, pg. 2940
GSG GROUP INC.; *Int'l*, pg. 3144
GS GLOBAL AUSTRALIA PTY., LTD.—See GS Holdings Corp.; *Int'l*, pg. 3142
GS GLOBAL CORPORATION-KUALA LUMPUR—See GS Holdings Corp.; *Int'l*, pg. 3142
GS GLOBAL CORPORATION-NEW DELHI—See GS Holdings Corp.; *Int'l*, pg. 3142
GS GLOBAL CORP.—See GS Holdings Corp.; *Int'l*, pg. 3142
GS GLOBAL RESOURCES, INC.; *U.S. Private*, pg. 1800
GSG SCOVILL FASTENERS ASIA LIMITED—See The Gores Group, LLC; *U.S. Private*, pg. 4035
GS SOLAR BERLIN GMBH—See CPI Property Group, S.A.; *Int'l*, pg. 1825
GS HALL & COMPANY LIMITED—See Health and Plant Protein Group Limited; *Int'l*, pg. 3303
G-SHANK ENTERPRISE CO., LTD. - BANG PA-IN FACTORY—See G-Shank Enterprise Co., Ltd.; *Int'l*, pg. 2862
G-SHANK ENTERPRISE CO., LTD. - CHINA-SHANGHAI FACTORY—See G-Shank Enterprise Co., Ltd.; *Int'l*, pg. 2863
G-SHANK ENTERPRISE CO., LTD. - CHINA-SHENZHEN FACTORY—See G-Shank Enterprise Co., Ltd.; *Int'l*, pg. 2863
G-SHANK ENTERPRISE CO., LTD. - CHINA-SUZHOU FACTORY—See G-Shank Enterprise Co., Ltd.; *Int'l*, pg. 2863
G-SHANK ENTERPRISE CO., LTD. - DONGGUAN FACTORY—See G-Shank Enterprise Co., Ltd.; *Int'l*, pg. 2863
G-SHANK ENTERPRISE CO., LTD. - INDONESIA FACTORY—See G-Shank Enterprise Co., Ltd.; *Int'l*, pg. 2863
G-SHANK ENTERPRISE CO., LTD. - MALAYSIA FACTORY—See G-Shank Enterprise Co., Ltd.; *Int'l*, pg. 2863
G-SHANK ENTERPRISE CO., LTD. - MEXICO FACTORY—See G-Shank Enterprise Co., Ltd.; *Int'l*, pg. 2863
G-SHANK ENTERPRISE CO., LTD. - QINGDAO FACTORY—See G-Shank Enterprise Co., Ltd.; *Int'l*, pg. 2863
G-SHANK ENTERPRISE CO., LTD. - SHANGHAI FACTORY—See G-Shank Enterprise Co., Ltd.; *Int'l*, pg. 2863
G-SHANK ENTERPRISE CO., LTD. - SHENZHEN FACTORY—See G-Shank Enterprise Co., Ltd.; *Int'l*, pg. 2863
G-SHANK ENTERPRISE CO., LTD. - SHENZHEN G-BAO FACTORY—See G-Shank Enterprise Co., Ltd.; *Int'l*, pg. 2863
G-SHANK ENTERPRISE CO., LTD.; *Int'l*, pg. 2862
G-SHANK ENTERPRISE CO., LTD. - SUZHOU FACTORY—See G-Shank Enterprise Co., Ltd.; *Int'l*, pg. 2863
G-SHANK ENTERPRISE CO., LTD. - THAILAND FACTORY—See G-Shank Enterprise Co., Ltd.; *Int'l*, pg. 2863
G-SHANK ENTERPRISE CO., LTD. - TIANJIN FACTORY—See G-Shank Enterprise Co., Ltd.; *Int'l*, pg. 2863
G-SHANK ENTERPRISE CO., LTD. - XIAMEN FACTORY—See G-Shank Enterprise Co., Ltd.; *Int'l*, pg. 2863
G S HARRIS CO., INC.; *U.S. Private*, pg. 1628
GSH CORPORATION LIMITED; *Int'l*, pg. 3144
GSH DISTRIBUTION (CAMBODIA) PTE. LTD.—See Serial System Ltd.; *Int'l*, pg. 6722
GS HOLDINGS CORP.; *Int'l*, pg. 3141
GS HOLDINGS LIMITED; *Int'l*, pg. 3142
GS HOME SHOPPING, INC.—See GS Holdings Corp.; *Int'l*, pg. 3142
GS-HYDRO AB—See Ratos AB; *Int'l*, pg. 6218
GS-HYDRO AUSTRIA GMBH—See Ratos AB; *Int'l*, pg. 6218
GS-HYDRO BENELUX B.V.—See Ratos AB; *Int'l*, pg. 6218
GS-HYDRO DANMARK AS—See Ratos AB; *Int'l*, pg. 6218
GS-HYDRO DENMARK AS—See Interpump Group S.p.A.; *Int'l*, pg. 3755
GS HYDRO DO BRASIL SISTEMAS HIDRAULICOS LTDA—See Ratos AB; *Int'l*, pg. 6218

COMPANY NAME INDEX

GS-HYDRO FRANCE—See Ratos AB; *Int'l*, pg. 6218
GS-HYDRO HOLDING OY—See Ratos AB; *Int'l*, pg. 6218
GS-HYDRO KOREA LTD.—See Ratos AB; *Int'l*, pg. 6218
GS-HYDRO NORGE AS—See Ratos AB; *Int'l*, pg. 6218
GS-HYDRO OY—See Ratos AB; *Int'l*, pg. 6218
GS-HYDRO PIPING SYSTEMS (SHANGHAI) CO. LTD.—See Ratos AB; *Int'l*, pg. 6218
GS-HYDRO RUSSIA—See Ratos AB; *Int'l*, pg. 6218
GS-HYDRO S.A.U.—See Ratos AB; *Int'l*, pg. 6218
GS-HYDRO SINGAPORE PTE. LTD—See Ratos AB; *Int'l*, pg. 6218
GS-HYDRO SP. Z O.O.—See Ratos AB; *Int'l*, pg. 6218
GS-HYDRO SYSTEM GMBH—See Ratos AB; *Int'l*, pg. 6218
GS-HYDRO UK LTD.—See Ratos AB; *Int'l*, pg. 6218
GS-HYDRO U.S. INC.—See Ratos AB; *Int'l*, pg. 6218
GSI ABROS CO., LTD.—See GSI Creos Corporation; *Int'l*, pg. 3144
THE GSI ASIA GROUP SDN. BHD—See AGCO Corporation; *U.S. Public*, pg. 59
GSI BRASIL INDUSTRIA E COMERCIO DE EQUIPAMENTOS AGROPECUARIOS LTD—See AGCO Corporation; *U.S. Public*, pg. 58
GSI CREOS (BEIJING) CO., LTD—See GSI Creos Corporation; *Int'l*, pg. 3144
GSI CREOS BRASIL LTDA—See GSI Creos Corporation; *Int'l*, pg. 3144
GSI CREOS CORPORATION; *Int'l*, pg. 3144
GSI CREOS FIBER & TEXTILE PINGHU CO., LTD.—See GSI Creos Corporation; *Int'l*, pg. 3144
GSI CREOS KOREA CO., LTD.—See GSI Creos Corporation; *Int'l*, pg. 3144
GSI CREOS (THAILAND) CO., LTD.—See GSI Creos Corporation; *Int'l*, pg. 3144
GSI CUMBERLAND DE MEXICO, S. DE RL DE CV—See AGCO Corporation; *U.S. Public*, pg. 58
GSI ELECTRONIQUE INC—See AGCO Corporation; *U.S. Public*, pg. 58
G. SIEMPELKAMP GMBH & CO. KG; *Int'l*, pg. 2864
GSI ENVIRONNEMENT—See Colliers International Group Inc.; *Int'l*, pg. 1701
GSI EUROPE-IMPORT & EXPORT GMBH—See GSI Creos Corporation; *Int'l*, pg. 3144
GSI EXIM AMERICA INC.—See GSI Creos Corporation; *Int'l*, pg. 3144
GSI GROUP EUROPE GMBH—See Novanta Inc.; *U.S. Public*, pg. 1548
GSI GROUP, LLC—See AGCO Corporation; *U.S. Public*, pg. 58
GSI GROUP PRECISION TECHNOLOGIES (SUZHOU) CO., LTD.—See Novanta Inc.; *U.S. Public*, pg. 1548
THE GSI GROUP (SHANGHAI) CO. LTD—See AGCO Corporation; *U.S. Public*, pg. 59
GSI HEALTH, LLC—See Health Care Service Corporation; *U.S. Private*, pg. 1892
GSI HOLDING CORPORATION—See GSI Creos Corporation; *Int'l*, pg. 3144
GSI LEASING GMBH—See 7C Solarparken AG; *Int'l*, pg. 15
GSI LUCCHINI S.P.A—See JSW Steel Ltd.; *Int'l*, pg. 4015
GSI MARULONTEX CO., LTD.—See GSI Creos Corporation; *Int'l*, pg. 3144
GSI INIMA ENVIRONMENT, S.A.—See GS Holdings Corp.; *Int'l*, pg. 3142
GS INTER, INC.; *U.S. Private*, pg. 1800
GSI (SHENZHEN) LIMITED—See GSI Creos Corporation; *Int'l*, pg. 3144
GSI SYSTEMS INC.—See Gatekeeper Systems Inc.; *Int'l*, pg. 2889
GSI TECHNOLOGY, INC.; *U.S. Public*, pg. 973
GSI TRADING HONG KONG LIMITED—See GSI Creos Corporation; *Int'l*, pg. 3144
G&S JOINT VENTURE COMPANY LIMITED—See Pico (Thailand) Public Company Limited; *Int'l*, pg. 5860
GSJ SOLUTIONS, S.L.U.—See Grupo Empresarial San Jose, S.A.; *Int'l*, pg. 3128
GS KASEI KOGYO CO., LTD.—See GS Yuasa Corporation; *Int'l*, pg. 3143
GSK AZERBAIJAN—See GSK plc; *Int'l*, pg. 3145
GSK BELARUS—See GSK plc; *Int'l*, pg. 3145
GSK BIOLOGICALS—See GSK plc; *Int'l*, pg. 3146
GSK BUSINESS SERVICE CENTRE SDN BHD—See GSK plc; *Int'l*, pg. 3145
GSK CH KAZAKHSTAN LLP—See GSK plc; *Int'l*, pg. 3145
GSK COMMERCIAL SP. Z O.O.—See GSK plc; *Int'l*, pg. 3145
GSK CONSUMER HEALTHCARE CHILE SPA—See Haleon Plc; *Int'l*, pg. 3228
GSK CONSUMER HEALTHCARE LEVICE, S.R.O.—See GSK plc; *Int'l*, pg. 3145
GSK CONSUMER HEALTHCARE—See GSK plc; *Int'l*, pg. 3145
GSK CONSUMER HEALTHCARE TRINIDAD & TOBAGO LIMITED—See GSK plc; *Int'l*, pg. 3145
GSK CYPRUS—See GSK plc; *Int'l*, pg. 3145
GSK D.O.O.—See GSK plc; *Int'l*, pg. 3145
GSK KAZAKHSTAN LLP—See GSK plc; *Int'l*, pg. 3145
GSK MACEDONIA—See GSK plc; *Int'l*, pg. 3145
GSK MALTA—See GSK plc; *Int'l*, pg. 3145

GSK MOLDOVA—See GSK plc; *Int'l*, pg. 3145
GSK PLC; *Int'l*, pg. 3145
GSK PSC POLAND SP. Z O.O.—See GSK plc; *Int'l*, pg. 3145
GSK SERVICES SP. Z O.O.—See GSK plc; *Int'l*, pg. 3145
GSK UZBEKISTAN—See GSK plc; *Int'l*, pg. 3145
GSK VACCINES GMBH—See GSK plc; *Int'l*, pg. 3145
GSK VACCINES INSTITUTE FOR GLOBAL HEALTH S.R.L.—See GSK plc; *Int'l*, pg. 3145
GSL CORPORATION—See Compass Minerals International, Inc.; *U.S. Public*, pg. 560
GSL DARDAN LIMITED—See HAL Trust N.V.; *Int'l*, pg. 3226
G/S LEASING INC.; *U.S. Private*, pg. 1632
GSL ELECTRIC—See Great Salt Lake Electric Incorporated; *U.S. Private*, pg. 1768
GS&L ENTERPRISES INCORPORATED; *U.S. Private*, pg. 1800
GSL FINE LITHOGRAPHERS—See Chatham Asset Management, LLC; *U.S. Private*, pg. 862
GSL GM CITY; *Int'l*, pg. 3150
GSL SECURITIES LIMITED; *Int'l*, pg. 3150
GSL SOLUTIONS, INC.—See Becton, Dickinson & Company; *U.S. Public*, pg. 292
GS MARKETING, INC.; *U.S. Private*, pg. 1800
G-SMATT AMERICA CO., LTD.—See G-Smatt Global Co., Ltd.; *Int'l*, pg. 2863
G-SMATT EUROPE MEDIA LIMITED—See G-Smatt Global Co., Ltd.; *Int'l*, pg. 2863
G-SMATT GLOBAL CO., LTD.; *Int'l*, pg. 2863
G-SMATT HONG KONG LTD.—See G-Smatt Global Co., Ltd.; *Int'l*, pg. 2863
GS MBIZ CO., LTD.—See GS Holdings Corp.; *Int'l*, pg. 3142
GSM CONSULTING INC.—See Carl Marks & Co., Inc.; *U.S. Private*, pg. 763
G&S METAL PRODUCTS CO. INC.; *U.S. Private*, pg. 1629
GSM GESELLSCHAFT FUR SERVICE MANAGEMENT MBH—See UNIQA Insurance Group AG; *Int'l*, pg. 8057
GSM NATION LLC.; *U.S. Private*, pg. 1801
GS MOBILE, INC.—See GameStop Corp.; *U.S. Public*, pg. 895
GS NETVISION CO., LTD.—See GS Holdings Corp.; *Int'l*, pg. 3142
GSN GAMES—See Sony Group Corporation; *Int'l*, pg. 7105
GS NHA BE DEVELOPMENT ONE-MEMBER LLC—See GS Holdings Corp.; *Int'l*, pg. 3142
GSN MAQUINARIA-SERVICIOS-CNC, S.A. DE C.V.—See GSN Maschinen-Anlagen-Service GmbH; *Int'l*, pg. 3150
GSN MASCHINEN-ANLAGEN-SERVICE GMBH; *Int'l*, pg. 3150
GSN RETOOLING-MAINTENANCE, INC.—See GSN Maschinen-Anlagen-Service GmbH; *Int'l*, pg. 3150
GSO CAPITAL PARTNERS INTERNATIONAL LLP—See Blackstone Inc.; *U.S. Public*, pg. 360
GSO CAPITAL PARTNERS (TEXAS) LP—See Blackstone Inc.; *U.S. Public*, pg. 349
GSO EUROPEAN SENIOR DEBT ASSOCIATES LLC—See Blackstone Inc.; *U.S. Public*, pg. 349
GSOURCE, LLC—See The Jordan Company, L.P.; *U.S. Private*, pg. 4060
GSPANN TECHNOLOGIES, INC.; *U.S. Private*, pg. 1801
GS PAPERBOARD & PACKAGING SDN. BHD.—See Oji Holdings Corporation; *Int'l*, pg. 5536
GSPARK 24 CO., LTD.—See PARK24 Co. Ltd.; *Int'l*, pg. 5742
GSPARX SDN. BHD.—See Tenaga Nasional Berhad; *Int'l*, pg. 7557
GSP AUTOMOTIVE GROUP WENZHOU CO., LTD.; *Int'l*, pg. 3150
GSPC LNG LIMITED—See Gujarat State Petroleum Corporation Limited; *Int'l*, pg. 3177
GSP CO. LTD.—See Ireland Blyth Limited; *Int'l*, pg. 3807
GSPC PIPAVAV POWER COMPANY LIMITED—See Gujarat State Petroleum Corporation Limited; *Int'l*, pg. 3177
GSP EUROPE GMBH—See GSP Automotive Group Wenzhou Co., Ltd.; *Int'l*, pg. 3150
GSP FINANCE COMPANY (BANGLADESH) LIMITED; *Int'l*, pg. 3150
GS PHNOM PENH DEVELOPMENT CO., LTD.—See GS Holdings Corp.; *Int'l*, pg. 3142
GSP INTERNATIONAL AIRPORT; *U.S. Private*, pg. 1801
GSP INVESTMENTS LIMITED—See GSP Finance Company (Bangladesh) Limited; *Int'l*, pg. 3150
GSP LATIN AMERICA LTD.—See GSP Automotive Group Wenzhou Co., Ltd.; *Int'l*, pg. 3150
GSP LUS—See Signaux Girod S.A.; *Int'l*, pg. 6911
GSP MARKETING SERVICES, INC.; *U.S. Private*, pg. 1801
GSP MARKETING TECHNOLOGIES, INC.; *U.S. Private*, pg. 1801
GSP NANJING CO., LTD.—See GSP Automotive Group Wenzhou Co., Ltd.; *Int'l*, pg. 3150
GSP N.A.—See GSP Automotive Group Wenzhou Co., Ltd.; *Int'l*, pg. 3150
GS POWER CO.,LTD—See GS Holdings Corp.; *Int'l*, pg. 3142

GSP PRINT PTY LTD—See ARN Media Limited; *Int'l*, pg. 576
G.S. PRECISION, INC. - KEENE DIVISION—See AE Industrial Partners, LP; *U.S. Private*, pg. 112
G.S. PRECISION, INC.—See AE Industrial Partners, LP; *U.S. Private*, pg. 112
GSP RESOURCE CORP.; *Int'l*, pg. 3150
G&S REAL ESTATE, INC.—See Sysco Corporation; *U.S. Public*, pg. 1974
GS RETAIL CO., LTD.—See GS Holdings Corp.; *Int'l*, pg. 3142
GSR VENTILTECHNIK GMBH & CO. KG—See INDUS Holding AG; *Int'l*, pg. 3663
GSRX INDUSTRIES INC.—See Refined Energy Corp.; *Int'l*, pg. 6250
GS SAIGON DEVELOPMENT ONE-MEMBER LLC—See GS Holdings Corp.; *Int'l*, pg. 3142
G.S. SCHWARTZ & CO. INC.; *U.S. Private*, pg. 1631
GSS ENERGY LTD.; *Int'l*, pg. 3150
G&S SERVICES COMPANY; *U.S. Private*, pg. 1629
GSS INFOTECH LIMITED; *Int'l*, pg. 3150
GS SPORTS CORPORATION—See GS Holdings Corp.; *Int'l*, pg. 3142
GS SWISS PCB AG—See H2APEX Group SCA; *Int'l*, pg. 3199
GSTAAD CAPITAL CORP.; *Int'l*, pg. 3150
GST AMERICA INC.—See Global Standard Technology Co., Ltd.; *Int'l*, pg. 3001
GST CORPORATION—See Nippon Yusen Kabushiki Kaisha; *Int'l*, pg. 5360
GSTECHNOLOGIES LTD.; *Int'l*, pg. 3150
G STEEL PUBLIC COMPANY LIMITED; *Int'l*, pg. 2861
GSTEK, INC.; *U.S. Private*, pg. 1801
GS TELESERVICE INC—See GS Holdings Corp.; *Int'l*, pg. 3142
GST GRUPPO SOLUZIONI TECNOLOGICHE S R L—See Exprivia SpA; *Int'l*, pg. 2591
GST INFORMATION TECHNOLOGY SOLUTIONS; *U.S. Private*, pg. 1801
GSTM LLC—See The Goldman Sachs Group, Inc.; *U.S. Public*, pg. 2076
GST NET INC.; *U.S. Private*, pg. 1801
G.STONE MOTORS, INC.; *U.S. Private*, pg. 1631
G STREET FABRICS; *U.S. Private*, pg. 1628
GST TAIWAN LTD.—See Global Standard Technology Co., Ltd.; *Int'l*, pg. 3001
GSV, INC.; *U.S. Public*, pg. 973
GSV MATERIELUDLEJNING AS—See Access Capital Partners SA; *Int'l*, pg. 88
GSV MATERIELUDLEJNING AS—See Catacap Management AS; *Int'l*, pg. 1358
GSW IMMOBILIEN AG—See Deutsche Wohnen SE; *Int'l*, pg. 2085
GSW INTEGRATED SERVICES, LLC—See MYR Group Inc.; *U.S. Public*, pg. 1489
GSW PEGASUS GMBH—See Deutsche Wohnen SE; *Int'l*, pg. 2085
GSW WATER HEATERS—See A. O. Smith Corporation; *U.S. Public*, pg. 11
GS YUASA ACCOUNTING SERVICE LTD.—See GS Yuasa Corporation; *Int'l*, pg. 3143
GS YUASA BATTERY LTD.—See GS Yuasa Corporation; *Int'l*, pg. 3143
GS YUASA BATTERY SINGAPORE CO., PTE. LTD.—See GS Yuasa Corporation; *Int'l*, pg. 3143
GS YUASA CORPORATION; *Int'l*, pg. 3143
GS YUASA INTERNATIONAL LTD.—See GS Yuasa Corporation; *Int'l*, pg. 3143
GS YUASA LITHIUM POWER, INC—See GS Yuasa Corporation; *Int'l*, pg. 3143
GS YUASA POWER ELECTRONICS LTD.—See GS Yuasa Corporation; *Int'l*, pg. 3143
GS YUASA TECHNOLOGY LTD.—See GS Yuasa Corporation; *Int'l*, pg. 3143
GT ADVANCED CZ LLC—See GT Advanced Technologies Inc.; *U.S. Private*, pg. 1801
GT ADVANCED SAPPHIRE SYSTEMS GROUP LLC—See GT Advanced Technologies Inc.; *U.S. Private*, pg. 1801
GT ADVANCED TECHNOLOGIES INC. - POLYSILICON DIVISION—See GT Advanced Technologies Inc.; *U.S. Private*, pg. 1801
GT ADVANCED TECHNOLOGIES INC.; *U.S. Private*, pg. 1801
GT ADVANCED TECHNOLOGIES LIMITED—See GT Advanced Technologies Inc.; *U.S. Private*, pg. 1801
GT ADVANCED TECHNOLOGIES TAIWAN CO., LTD.—See GT Advanced Technologies Inc.; *U.S. Private*, pg. 1801
GTA FINANCECORP, INC.; *Int'l*, pg. 3151
GTA FINANCECORP INC.; *Int'l*, pg. 3151
GTA-NHT, INC.—See 3M Company; *U.S. Public*, pg. 8
GT AZUR SAS—See VINCI S.A.; *Int'l*, pg. 8221
GTB AGENCY, LLC—See WPP plc; *Int'l*, pg. 8469
GTBANK UK LTD.—See Guaranty Trust Holding Company PLC; *Int'l*, pg. 3169
GTB GASTRO TEAM BREMEN GMBH—See Aramark; *U.S. Public*, pg. 177
GT BIOPHARMA, INC.; *U.S. Public*, pg. 973

GT BIOPHARMA, INC.

CORPORATE AFFILIATIONS

GTB LIBERIA LIMITED—See Guaranty Trust Bank plc; *Int'l*, pg. 3169
GTB REGISTRARS LIMITED—See Guaranty Trust Bank plc; *Int'l*, pg. 3169
GT CAPITAL HOLDINGS, INC.; *Int'l*, pg. 3150
GT CAPITAL LIMITED—See GT Group Holdings Limited; *Int'l*, pg. 3151
GTC BULGARIA—See Globe Trade Centre S.A.; *Int'l*, pg. 3006
GTC CROATIA—See Globe Trade Centre S.A.; *Int'l*, pg. 3006
GTC CZECH REPUBLIC—See Globe Trade Centre S.A.; *Int'l*, pg. 3006
GTCHANNEL, INC.—See SEEEN plc; *Int'l*, pg. 6678
GTC HUNGARY—See Globe Trade Centre S.A.; *Int'l*, pg. 3006
GTC INVESTMENT B.V.—See Kardan N.V.; *Int'l*, pg. 4079
GTC OATS, INC.—See Ingredion Incorporated; *U.S. Public*, pg. 1123
GTCO CALCOMP, INC.—See Centre Lane Partners, LLC; *U.S. Private*, pg. 828
GT CONTRACTING CORP; *U.S. Private*, pg. 1801
GT COVERS—See Covercraft Direct, LLC; *U.S. Private*, pg. 1072
GTC REAL ESTATE INVESTMENTS BULGARIA B.V.—See Globe Trade Centre S.A.; *Int'l*, pg. 3006
GTC REAL ESTATE INVESTMENTS SERBIA B.V.—See Globe Trade Centre S.A.; *Int'l*, pg. 3006
GTC REAL ESTATE INVESTMENTS UKRAINE B.V.—See Globe Trade Centre S.A.; *Int'l*, pg. 3006
GTC REAL ESTATE MANAGEMENT, S.R.O.—See Globe Trade Centre S.A.; *Int'l*, pg. 3007
GTCR LLC; *U.S. Private*, pg. 1801
GTC ROMANIA—See Globe Trade Centre S.A.; *Int'l*, pg. 3007
GTC SERBIA—See Globe Trade Centre S.A.; *Int'l*, pg. 3007
GTC SYSTEMS INC.; *U.S. Private*, pg. 1801
GTC TECHNOLOGY US, LLC—See Sulzer Ltd.; *Int'l*, pg. 7257
GTD GRAPHIT TECHNOLOGIE GMBH—See Toyo Tanso Co., Ltd.; *Int'l*, pg. 7858
GT DIAGNOSTICS (UK) LIMITED—See Genting Berhad; *Int'l*, pg. 2928
GTECH AUSTRIA GMBH—See International Game Technology PLC; *Int'l*, pg. 3749
G-TECH INFO-TRAINING LTD.; *Int'l*, pg. 2863
G TECH MATERIAL CO., LTD.—See Wacoal Holdings Corp.; *Int'l*, pg. 8325
G-TECH METAL PTE. LTD.—See GT Steel Construction Group Limited; *Int'l*, pg. 3151
GTECH MONACO S.A.M.—See International Game Technology PLC; *Int'l*, pg. 3749
G-TECH OPTOELECTRONICS CORPORATION; *Int'l*, pg. 2863
GTECH PERU S.A.—See International Game Technology PLC; *Int'l*, pg. 3749
G-TECH SERVICES, INC.; *U.S. Private*, pg. 1630
GTECH S.P.A.—See International Game Technology PLC; *Int'l*, pg. 3748
G-TEC JAINX EDUCATION LTD.; *Int'l*, pg. 2863
GTE FINANCIAL; *U.S. Private*, pg. 1807
G-TEK; *Int'l*, pg. 2863
G-TEKT CO., LTD. - GUNMA PLANT—See G-TEKT Corporation; *Int'l*, pg. 2863
G-TEKT CO., LTD. - HAMURA PLANT—See G-TEKT Corporation; *Int'l*, pg. 2863
G-TEKT CO., LTD. - SAITAMA PLANT—See G-TEKT Corporation; *Int'l*, pg. 2863
G-TEKT CO., LTD. - SHIGA PLANT—See G-TEKT Corporation; *Int'l*, pg. 2863
G-TEKT CO., LTD. - TOCHIGI PLANT—See G-TEKT Corporation; *Int'l*, pg. 2863
G-TEKT CORPORATION; *Int'l*, pg. 2863
G-TEKT (DEUTSCHLAND) GMBH—See G-TEKT Corporation; *Int'l*, pg. 2863
G-TEKT EASTERN CO., LTD.—See G-TEKT Corporation; *Int'l*, pg. 2863
G-TEKT KCBPL EUROPE MANUFACTURING LTD.—See G-TEKT Corporation; *Int'l*, pg. 2863
G-TEKT (THAILAND) CO., LTD.—See G-TEKT Corporation; *Int'l*, pg. 2863
GT EMISSIONS SYSTEMS LTD.—See Knorr-Bremse AG; *Int'l*, pg. 4210
GT ENGINEERING & ASSOCIATES, LTD.—See Westinghouse Air Brake Technologies Corporation; *U.S. Public*, pg. 2358
G T EXHIBITIONS LIMITED—See DSV A/S; *Int'l*, pg. 2214
GT FORLUX SAS—See VINCI S.A.; *Int'l*, pg. 8221
GT GOLD CORP.—See Newmont Corporation; *U.S. Public*, pg. 1516
GT GOLF HOLDINGS, INC—See Kinzie Capital Partners LP; *U.S. Private*, pg. 2313
GT GRANDSTANDS, INC.—See Court Square Capital Partners, L.P.; *U.S. Private*, pg. 1070
GT GROUP HOLDINGS LIMITED; *Int'l*, pg. 3151
GT GROUP LTD.—See Knorr-Bremse AG; *Int'l*, pg. 4210
GTG TRAINING LIMITED—See Arnold Clark Automobiles Limited; *Int'l*, pg. 576

GTG VENTURES, INC.; *Int'l*, pg. 3151
GTG WELLNESS CO., LTD.; *Int'l*, pg. 3151
GTH CATERING A.S.—See Genesis Capital s.r.o.; *Int'l*, pg. 2921
GT HIRING SOLUTIONS (2005) INC.—See MAXIMUS, Inc.; *U.S. Public*, pg. 1402
G THREE HOLDINGS CORP.; *Int'l*, pg. 2861
GTIE AIR & DEFENSE—See VINCI S.A.; *Int'l*, pg. 8237
GTIE ARMORIQUE SAS—See VINCI S.A.; *Int'l*, pg. 8227
GTIE LORRAINE SAS—See VINCI S.A.; *Int'l*, pg. 8221
GTI ENERGY LTD; *Int'l*, pg. 3151
GTIE RENNES SAS—See VINCI S.A.; *Int'l*, pg. 8221
GTIE TELECOMS SAS—See VINCI S.A.; *Int'l*, pg. 8222
GTIE TERTIAIRE SAS—See VINCI S.A.; *Int'l*, pg. 8222
GTI HOLDINGS LIMITED; *Int'l*, pg. 3151
G&T INDUSTRIES INC.; *U.S. Private*, pg. 1629
G&T INDUSTRIES OF INDIANA INC.—See G&T Industries Inc.; *U.S. Private*, pg. 1629
GTI NEVADA, LLC—See Green Thumb Industries, Inc.; *U.S. Public*, pg. 964
GTI SOFTWARE & NETWORKING SARLAU—See Esprinet S.p.A.; *Int'l*, pg. 2506
GTIS PARTNERS BRAZIL—See GTIS Partners LP; *U.S. Private*, pg. 1807
GTIS PARTNERS LP; *U.S. Private*, pg. 1807
GTI TRANSPORT SOLUTIONS, INC.; *Int'l*, pg. 3151
GTJ CO. INC.; *U.S. Private*, pg. 1807
GTJ REIT, INC.; *U.S. Private*, pg. 1807
GTK ELECTRONICS GMBH—See Volex plc; *Int'l*, pg. 8301
G.T.K. (U.K.) LTD.—See Volex plc; *Int'l*, pg. 8301
GTL INFRASTRUCTURE LIMITED; *Int'l*, pg. 3151
GTL-LOT USLUGI LOTNISKOWE SP. Z O.O.—See LOT Polish Airlines S.A.; *Int'l*, pg. 4558
GTL RESOURCES PLC—See Harwood Capital LLP; *Int'l*, pg. 3282
GTL RESOURCES PLC—See Siem Industries Inc.; *Int'l*, pg. 6886
GTL SERVICIOS ADMINISTRATIVOS MEXICO, S.A. DE C.V.—See Metalurgica Gerdau S.A.; *Int'l*, pg. 4849
GTM BATIMENT AQUITAINE SAS—See VINCI S.A.; *Int'l*, pg. 8235
GTM BATIMENT—See VINCI S.A.; *Int'l*, pg. 8231
GTM DEVELOPMENT LTD.—See Aurelius Equity Opportunities SE & Co. KGaA; *Int'l*, pg. 708
GTM (EUROPE) LIMITED—See Gul Ahmed Textile Mills Ltd.; *Int'l*, pg. 3178
GTM HOLDINGS CORPORATION; *Int'l*, pg. 3151
GTM NORMANDIE CENTRE—See VINCI S.A.; *Int'l*, pg. 8222
GT MORBIHAN SAS—See VINCI S.A.; *Int'l*, pg. 8221
GTM OUEST SAS—See VINCI S.A.; *Int'l*, pg. 8235
GTM PAYROLL SERVICES INC.; *U.S. Private*, pg. 1807
GTM PLASTICS INC.; *U.S. Private*, pg. 1807
GTM SPORTSWEAR; *U.S. Private*, pg. 1807
GTM SUD-OUEST TPGC—See VINCI S.A.; *Int'l*, pg. 8222
GTM TERRASSEMENT—See VINCI S.A.; *Int'l*, pg. 8231
GTM TEXTILE CO., LTD.—See GTM HOLDINGS CORPORATION; *Int'l*, pg. 3151
GTM TRAVAUX SPECIAUX SAS—See VINCI S.A.; *Int'l*, pg. 8235
GTM USA CORP.—See Gul Ahmed Textile Mills Ltd.; *Int'l*, pg. 3178
GT NEXUS, INC. - NEW YORK OFFICE—See Koch Industries, Inc.; *U.S. Private*, pg. 2330
GT NEXUS, INC.—See Koch Industries, Inc.; *U.S. Private*, pg. 2330
GTN INDUSTRIES LTD; *Int'l*, pg. 3151
GTN LIMITED—See GTCR LLC; *U.S. Private*, pg. 1805
GTN TECHNICAL STAFFING; *U.S. Private*, pg. 1807
GTN TEXTILES LIMITED; *Int'l*, pg. 3151
GTO 2000, INC.—See Calera Capital Management, Inc.; *U.S. Private*, pg. 717
GTOWER SDN. BHD.—See IGB Berhad; *Int'l*, pg. 3601
GTP GREEN BELL INC.; *U.S. Private*, pg. 1807
GTPL HATHWAY LTD.; *Int'l*, pg. 3151
GTPL KCBPL BROADBAND PRIVATE LIMITED—See GTPL Hathway Ltd.; *Int'l*, pg. 3151
GTP SOUTH ACQUISITIONS II, LLC—See American Tower Corporation; *U.S. Public*, pg. 111
GT SALES & MANUFACTURING INC.; *U.S. Private*, pg. 1801
GT (SCOTLAND) CONSTRUCTION LIMITED—See Galliford Try Holdings plc; *Int'l*, pg. 2874
GTS DRYWALL SUPPLY COMPANY—See GMS Inc.; *U.S. Public*, pg. 948
GTS HOLDINGS, INC.; *U.S. Private*, pg. 1807
GTS HUNGARY TELECOMMUNICATION KFT.—See Deutsche Telekom AG; *Int'l*, pg. 2083
GTS JAPAN CO., LTD.—See Chubu Electric Power Co., Inc.; *Int'l*, pg. 1593
GT SOLAR (SHANGHAI) CO., LTD.—See GT Advanced Technologies Inc.; *U.S. Private*, pg. 1801
GT SRL—See Kering S.A.; *Int'l*, pg. 4134
GTS SERVICES, LLC—See Vista Equity Partners, LLC; *U.S. Private*, pg. 4400
G.T.S. SH.P.K.—See SOL S.p.A.; *Int'l*, pg. 7067

GT STEEL CONSTRUCTION GROUP LIMITED - SINGAPORE FACTORY—See GT Steel Construction Group Limited; *Int'l*, pg. 3151
GT STEEL CONSTRUCTION GROUP LIMITED; *Int'l*, pg. 3151
GTS TELECOM ROMANIA—See Deutsche Telekom AG; *Int'l*, pg. 2083
GTT COMMUNICATIONS HK LIMITED—See GTT Communications, Inc.; *U.S. Private*, pg. 1808
GTT COMMUNICATIONS, INC.; *U.S. Private*, pg. 1807
GT TECHNOLOGIES, INC.—See Industrial Opportunity Partners, LLC; *U.S. Private*, pg. 2067
GTT-EMEA, LTD.—See GTT Communications, Inc.; *U.S. Private*, pg. 1808
GTT GMBH—See GTT Communications, Inc.; *U.S. Private*, pg. 1808
GTTP—See FAYAT SAS; *Int'l*, pg. 2625
GTT TRAINING LTD.—See Gaztransport Et Technigaz SA; *Int'l*, pg. 2892
GTUIT, LLC—See Caterpillar, Inc.; *U.S. Public*, pg. 452
GT VENDEE SAS—See VINCI S.A.; *Int'l*, pg. 8221
GTV ENGINEERING LTD.; *Int'l*, pg. 3152
GTV PRODUCTIONS—See De Agostini S.p.A.; *Int'l*, pg. 1995
GTX SEF, LLC—See StoneX Group Inc.; *U.S. Public*, pg. 1952
GTY TECHNOLOGY HOLDINGS INC.—See GI Manager L.P.; *U.S. Private*, pg. 1692
GTY TIRE CO.—See The Yokohama Rubber Co., Ltd.; *Int'l*, pg. 7703
GTY TIRE CO.—See Toyo Tire Corporation; *Int'l*, pg. 7859
GUADALUPE-BLANCO RIVER AUTHORITY; *U.S. Private*, pg. 1808
GUADALUPE LUMBER CO.; *U.S. Private*, pg. 1808
GUADALUPE LUMBER & SUPPLY COMPANY, INC.; *U.S. Private*, pg. 1808
GUADALUPE POWER PARTNERS, LP—See Energy Capital Partners Management, LP; *U.S. Private*, pg. 1394
GUADALUPE VALLEY ELECTRIC COOP; *U.S. Private*, pg. 1808
GUADALUPE VALLEY TELECOMMUNICATIONS COOPERATIVE—See GVTC Communications; *U.S. Private*, pg. 1821
GUAGUAS GUMIDAFE, S.L.—See Mobico Group PLC; *Int'l*, pg. 5008
GUALA CLOSURES (CHENGDU) CO., LTD.—See Guala Closures S.p.A.; *Int'l*, pg. 3152
GUALA CLOSURES DEUTSCHLAND GMBH—See Guala Closures S.p.A.; *Int'l*, pg. 3152
GUALA CLOSURES NORTH AMERICA, INC.—See Guala Closures S.p.A.; *Int'l*, pg. 3152
GUALA CLOSURES S.P.A.; *Int'l*, pg. 3152
GUALA CLOSURES TECHNOLOGIA UKRAINE LLC—See Guala Closures S.p.A.; *Int'l*, pg. 3152
GUALA CLOSURES TURKEY AMBALAJ VE KAPAK SISTEMLERI SANAYI VE TICARET ANONIM SIRKETI—See Guala Closures S.p.A.; *Int'l*, pg. 3152
GUAM POWER AUTHORITY; *U.S. Private*, pg. 1808
GUAM PUBLICATIONS, INCORPORATED—See Gannett Co., Inc.; *U.S. Public*, pg. 897
GUAM REEF HOTEL, INC.—See H.I.S. Co., Ltd.; *Int'l*, pg. 3195
GUANACO COMPANIA MINERA SPA—See Austral Gold Limited; *Int'l*, pg. 719
GUANAJUATO GEAR & AXLE DE MEXICO S. DE R.L. DE C.V.—See American Axle & Manufacturing Holdings, Inc.; *U.S. Public*, pg. 96
GUANAJUATO SILVER COMPANY LTD.; *Int'l*, pg. 3152
GUAN CHAO HOLDINGS LIMITED; *Int'l*, pg. 3152
GUAN CHONG BERHAD; *Int'l*, pg. 3152
GUAN CHONG COCOA MANUFACTURER SDN. BHD.—See Guan Chong Berhad; *Int'l*, pg. 3152
GUANDAO PUER INVESTMENT CO., LTD.; *Int'l*, pg. 3152
GUANFU HOLDINGS CO., LTD.; *Int'l*, pg. 3152
GUANGBO GROUP STOCK CO., LTD.; *Int'l*, pg. 3152
GUANGDONG ADVERTISING GROUP CO., LTD.; *Int'l*, pg. 3152
GUANGDONG ADWAY CONSTRUCTION (GROUP) HOLDINGS COMPANY LIMITED; *Int'l*, pg. 3152
GUANGDONG AEON TEEN STORES CO., LTD.—See AEON Co., Ltd.; *Int'l*, pg. 177
GUANGDONG AIRTAC INTELLIGENT EQUIPMENT CO., LTD.—See Airtac International Group; *Int'l*, pg. 249
GUANGDONG ALL ACCESS NOTER COMMUNICATION TECHNOLOGY CO., LIMITED—See China All Access (Holdings) Limited; *Int'l*, pg. 1482
GUANGDONG ANJUBAO DIGITAL TECHNOLOGY CO., LTD.; *Int'l*, pg. 3152
GUANGDONG ANJUBAO DISPLAY TECHNOLOGY CO., LTD.—See Guangdong Anjubao Digital Technology Co., Ltd.; *Int'l*, pg. 3152
GUANGDONG AOFEI DATA TECHNOLOGY CO., LTD.; *Int'l*, pg. 3152
GUANGDONG AUTOMOTIVE TEST CENTER CO., LTD.—See China Automotive Engineering Research Institute Co., Ltd.; *Int'l*, pg. 1484

COMPANY NAME INDEX

GUANGDONG AVCIT TECHNOLOGY HOLDING CO., LTD.; *Int'l*, pg. 3152
GUANGDONG AVIC SPECIAL GLASS TECHNOLOGY CO., LTD.—See Hainan Development Holdings Nanhai Co., Ltd.; *Int'l*, pg. 3211
GUANGDONG BAOLIHUA NEW ENERGY STOCK CO., LTD.; *Int'l*, pg. 3153
GUANGDONG BIOLIGHT MEDITECH CO., LTD.; *Int'l*, pg. 3153
GUANGDONG BOBAOLON CO., LTD.; *Int'l*, pg. 3153
GUANGDONG BOLUO JIUNENG HIGH-NEW TECHNOLOGY ENGINEERING CO., LTD.—See China New Energy Limited; *Int'l*, pg. 1535
GUANGDONG BRANDMAX MARKETING CO., LTD.; *Int'l*, pg. 3153
GUANGDONG CHAMPION ASIA ELECTRONICS CO., LTD.; *Int'l*, pg. 3153
GUANGDONG CHANGHONG ELECTRONICS CO., LTD—See Sichuan Changhong Electric Co., Ltd.; *Int'l*, pg. 6877
GUANGDONG CHANGSHENG ENTERPRISES GROUP CO., LTD.—See Guangdong Rising Assets Management Co., Ltd.; *Int'l*, pg. 3159
GUANGDONG CHANGTONG WAREHOUSE & TERMINAL CO., LTD.—See China Merchants Group Limited; *Int'l*, pg. 1522
GUANGDONG CHANT GROUP CO., LTD.; *Int'l*, pg. 3153
GUANGDONG CHAOHUA TECHNOLOGY CO., LTD.; *Int'l*, pg. 3153
GUANGDONG CHEMICALS IMP. & EXP. CORPORATION (GROUP)—See Sinochem Corporation; *Int'l*, pg. 6949
GUANGDONG CHJ INDUSTRY CO., LTD.; *Int'l*, pg. 3153
GUANGDONG CHUANGFU METAL MANUFACTURING CO., LTD.—See Alconix Corporation; *Int'l*, pg. 302
GUANGDONG CONNECTEK IOT TECH CO., LTD.—See Super Telecom Co., Ltd.; *Int'l*, pg. 7335
GUANGDONG CREATE CENTURY INTELLIGENT EQUIPMENT GROUP CORPORATION LIMITED; *Int'l*, pg. 3153
GUANGDONG DABAOSHAN MINE CO., LTD.—See Guangdong Rising Assets Management Co., Ltd.; *Int'l*, pg. 3159
GUANGDONG DALI FOODS CO., LTD.—See Dali Foods Group Co. Ltd.; *Int'l*, pg. 1951
GUANGDONG DCENTI AUTO-PARTS STOCK LIMITED COMPANY; *Int'l*, pg. 3153
GUANGDONG DEDA BOW MA MOTOR SERVICE CO. LTD.—See Sime Darby Berhad; *Int'l*, pg. 6928
GUANGDONG DELIAN GROUP CO., LTD.; *Int'l*, pg. 3153
GUANGDONG DIAMET POWDER METALLURGY CO., LTD.—See Mitsubishi Materials Corporation; *Int'l*, pg. 4963
GUANGDONG DIC TOD RESINS CO., LTD.—See DIC India Ltd; *Int'l*, pg. 2111
GUANGDONG DINGFUNG PULP & PAPER CO., LTD.—See YFY, Inc.; *Int'l*, pg. 8579
GUANGDONG DONGFANG SCIENCE & TECHNOLOGY CO., LTD.; *Int'l*, pg. 3153
GUANGDONG DONGMU NEW MATERIALS CO., LTD.—See NBTM New Materials Group Co., Ltd.; *Int'l*, pg. 5179
GUANGDONG DOWSTONE TECHNOLOGY CO., LTD.; *Int'l*, pg. 3154
GUANGDONG DP CO., LTD.; *Int'l*, pg. 3154
GUANGDONG DTECH TECHNOLOGY CO., LTD.; *Int'l*, pg. 3154
GUANGDONG DX2 TECHNOLOGY CO., LTD.—See Shenzhen Hello Tech Energy Co., Ltd.; *Int'l*, pg. 6811
GUANGDONG EASTCROSS STATIONERY CO., LTD.—See Shantou Wanshun New Material Group Co., Ltd.; *Int'l*, pg. 6785
GUANGDONG ELECTRIC POWER DEVELOPMENT CO., LTD.—See Guangdong Yudean Group Co., Ltd.; *Int'l*, pg. 3162
GUANGDONG ELECTRONIC INFORMATION INDUSTRIAL GROUP CO., LTD.—See Guangdong Rising Assets Management Co., Ltd.; *Int'l*, pg. 3159
GUANGDONG ELLINGTON ELECTRONICS TECH CO., LTD.; *Int'l*, pg. 3154
GUANGDONG ENPACK PACKAGING CO., LTD.; *Int'l*, pg. 3154
GUANGDONG ETERNAL WAY INTERNATIONAL FREIGHT CO., LTD.—See China Merchants Group Limited; *Int'l*, pg. 1522
GUANGDONG EVER-RISING GROUP CORPORATION LTD.—See Guangdong Rising Assets Management Co., Ltd.; *Int'l*, pg. 3159
GUANGDONG EVERWIN PRECISION TECHNOLOGY CO., LTD.—See Shenzhen Everwin Precision Technology Co., Ltd.; *Int'l*, pg. 6809
GUANGDONG FAILONG CRYSTAL TECHNOLOGY CO., LTD.; *Int'l*, pg. 3154
GUANGDONG FENGHUA ADVANCED TECHNOLOGY (HOLDING) CO., LTD.; *Int'l*, pg. 3154
GUANGDONG FRESH JUICE BIOLOGICAL TECHNOLOGY COMPANY LTD.—See Sunjuice Holdings Co., Ltd.; *Int'l*, pg. 7317
GUANGDONG FUNDWAY TECHNOLOGY CO., LTD.—See PCI Technology Group Co., Ltd; *Int'l*, pg. 5768
GUANGDONG FUSION E-COMMERCE CO., LTD.—See ZRP Printing Group Co., Ltd.; *Int'l*, pg. 8691
GUANGDONG FUXIN TECHNOLOGY CO., LTD.; *Int'l*, pg. 3154
GUANGDONG GALANZ GROUP CO., LTD.; *Int'l*, pg. 3154
GUANGDONG GANHUA SCIENCE & INDUSTRY CO LTD.; *Int'l*, pg. 3154
GUANGDONG GDC CULTURAL PARK LIMITED—See Global Digital Creations Holdings Limited; *Int'l*, pg. 2994
GUANGDONG GENSHO LOGISTICS CO., LTD.; *Int'l*, pg. 3154
GUANGDONG GIANT LEAP CONSTRUCTION CO., LTD.—See Country Garden Holdings Company Limited; *Int'l*, pg. 1818
GUANGDONG GOLDEN DRAGON DEVELOPMENT INC.; *Int'l*, pg. 3154
GUANGDONG GOLDEN LEAF TECHNOLOGY DEVELOPMENT CO., LTD.—See Huabao International Holdings Limited; *Int'l*, pg. 3510
GUANGDONG GOWORLD CO., LTD.; *Int'l*, pg. 3154
GUANGDONG GREAT RIVER SMARTER LOGISTICS CO., LTD.; *Int'l*, pg. 3154
GUANGDONG GREEN PRECISION COMPONENTS CO., LTD.; *Int'l*, pg. 3154
GUANGDONG GUANGHONG HOLDINGS CO., LTD.; *Int'l*, pg. 3155
GUANGDONG GUANGHUA SCI-TECH CO., LTD.; *Int'l*, pg. 3155
GUANGDONG GUANGSHENG HOTEL GROUP CO., LTD.—See Guangdong Rising Assets Management Co., Ltd.; *Int'l*, pg. 3159
GUANGDONG GUANGSHENG METALLURGY CO., LTD.—See Guangdong Rising Assets Management Co., Ltd.; *Int'l*, pg. 3159
GUANGDONG GUANGSHENG POWER FUEL CO. LTD.—See Guangdong Rising Assets Management Co., Ltd.; *Int'l*, pg. 3159
GUANGDONG GUANGZHOU DAILY MEDIA CO., LTD.; *Int'l*, pg. 3155
GUANGDONG GUANHAO HIGH-TECH CO., LTD.; *Int'l*, pg. 3155
GUANGDONG HAID GROUP CO., LTD.; *Int'l*, pg. 3155
GUANGDONG HAIKONG SPECIAL GLASS TECHNOLOGY CO., LTD.—See Hainan Development Holdings Nanhai Co., Ltd.; *Int'l*, pg. 3211
GUANGDONG HANGXIAO STEEL STRUCTURE CO., LTD.—See Hangxiao Steel Structure Co., Ltd.; *Int'l*, pg. 3246
GUANGDONG HAOMEI NEW MATERIAL CO., LTD.; *Int'l*, pg. 3155
GUANGDONG HEC TECHNOLOGY HOLDING CO., LTD.; *Int'l*, pg. 3155
GUANGDONG HIGH DREAM INTELLECTUALIZED MACHINERY CO., LTD.; *Int'l*, pg. 3155
GUANGDONG HIGHSUN GROUP CO., LTD.; *Int'l*, pg. 3155
GUANGDONG HI LEX CABLE SYSTEM CO, LTD.—See Hi-Lex Corporation; *Int'l*, pg. 3380
GUANGDONG HNA LEWANJIA SUPERMARKET CO., LTD.—See Hainan Traffic Administration Holding Co., Ltd.; *Int'l*, pg. 3213
GUANGDONG HOMA APPLIANCES CO., LTD.; *Int'l*, pg. 3155
GUANGDONG HONGCHUAN SMART LOGISTICS CO., LTD.; *Int'l*, pg. 3155
GUANGDONG HONGDA HOLDINGS GROUP CO., LTD.; *Int'l*, pg. 3155
GUANGDONG HONG KONG GREATER BAY AREA HOLDINGS CO., LTD.; *Int'l*, pg. 3155
GUANGDONG HONGLING GROUP CO., LTD.—See Guangdong Rising Assets Management Co., Ltd.; *Int'l*, pg. 3159
GUANGDONG HONGMING INTELLIGENT JOINT STOCK CO., LTD.; *Int'l*, pg. 3155
GUANGDONG HONGTU TECHNOLOGY (HOLDINGS) CO., LTD.; *Int'l*, pg. 3155
GUANGDONG HONGWAN SUPPLY CHAIN TECHNOLOGY CO., LTD.—See Huali Industries Co Ltd; *Int'l*, pg. 3513
GUANGDONG HONGXING INDUSTRIAL CO., LTD.; *Int'l*, pg. 3156
GUANGDONG HOSHION INDUSTRIAL ALUMINIUM CO., LTD.; *Int'l*, pg. 3156
GUANGDONG HOTATA TECHNOLOGY GROUP CO., LTD.; *Int'l*, pg. 3156
GUANGDONG HUAFENG NEW ENERGY TECHNOLOGY CO., LTD.; *Int'l*, pg. 3156
GUANGDONG HUAJIAN ENTERPRISE GROUP CO., LTD.—See Guangdong Rising Assets Management Co., Ltd.; *Int'l*, pg. 3159
GUANGDONG HUARUN PAINTS CO., LTD.—See The Sherwin-Williams Company; *U.S. Public*, pg. 2127
GUANGDONG HUATE GAS CO., LTD.; *Int'l*, pg. 3156
GUANGDONG HUATIE TONGDA HIGH-SPEED RAILWAY EQUIPMENT CO., LTD.; *Int'l*, pg. 3156
GUANGDONG HUIYUN TITANIUM INDUSTRY CO., LTD.; *Int'l*, pg. 3156
GUANGDONG HYBRIBIO BIOTECH CO., LTD.; *Int'l*, pg. 3156
GUANGDONG INSIGHT BRAND MARKETING GROUP CO., LTD.; *Int'l*, pg. 3156
GUANGDONG INSTITUTE OF WORLD SOIL RESOURCES—See Hongda Xingye Co., Ltd.; *Int'l*, pg. 3470
GUANGDONG (INTERNATIONAL) HOTEL MANAGEMENT HOLDINGS LIMITED—See GDH Limited; *Int'l*, pg. 2896
GUANGDONG INVESTMENT LIMITED—See GDH Limited; *Int'l*, pg. 2896
GUANGDONG IVL PET POLYMER CO., LTD.—See Indorama Ventures Public Company Limited; *Int'l*, pg. 3658
GUANGDONG JADIETE HOLDINGS GROUP CO., LTD.; *Int'l*, pg. 3156
GUANGDONG JIAHAO FOODSTUFF CO., LTD.—See Huabao International Holdings Limited; *Int'l*, pg. 3510
GUANGDONG JIALONG FOOD CO., LTD.; *Int'l*, pg. 3156
GUANGDONG JIANGMEN CENTER FOR BIOTECH DEVELOPMENT CO., LTD.; *Int'l*, pg. 3156
GUANGDONG JIAYING PHARMACEUTICAL CO., LTD.; *Int'l*, pg. 3156
GUANGDONG JIA YUAN TECHNOLOGY SHARES CO., LTD.; *Int'l*, pg. 3156
GUANGDONG JIAYU DOOR,WINDOW & CURTAIN WALL CO., LTD.—See Jiayu Holding Co., Ltd.; *Int'l*, pg. 3962
GUANGDONG JINGYI METAL CO., LTD.; *Int'l*, pg. 3157
GUANGDONG JINMA ENTERTAINMENT CORPORATION LIMITED; *Int'l*, pg. 3157
GUANGDONG JINMING MACHINERY CO., LTD.; *Int'l*, pg. 3157
GUANGDONG JINMING MACHINERY CO., LTD.—See Guangdong Jinming Machinery Co., Ltd.; *Int'l*, pg. 3157
GUANGDONG JINMING MACHINERY CO., LTD.—See Guangdong Jinming Machinery Co., Ltd.; *Int'l*, pg. 3157
GUANGDONG JINMING MACHINERY CO., LTD.—See Guangdong Jinming Machinery Co., Ltd.; *Int'l*, pg. 3157
GUANGDONG JINPENG SECOM SECURITY CO., LTD.—See SECOM Co., Ltd.; *Int'l*, pg. 6671
GUANGDONG JOIN-SHARE FINANCING GUARANTEE INVESTMENT CO., LTD.; *Int'l*, pg. 3157
GUANGDONG JOTECH KONG YUE PRECISION INDUSTRIES LTD—See Jotech Metal Fabrication Industries Sdn. Bhd.; *Int'l*, pg. 4001
GUANGDONG JUSHEN LOGISTICS COMPANY LIMITED; *Int'l*, pg. 3157
GUANGDONG KAIPING KINGLY CAPSULE CO., LTD.—See The United Laboratories International Holdings Ltd.; *Int'l*, pg. 7697
GUANGDONG KANGHUA HEALTHCARE CO., LTD.; *Int'l*, pg. 3157
GUANGDONG KAWASAWA AUTOMOTIVE TRIM PARTS CO., LTD.—See Kasai Kogyo Co., Ltd.; *Int'l*, pg. 4086
GUANGDONG KEDA HYDRAULIC TECHNOLOGY CO., LTD.—See Keda Industrial Group Co., Ltd.; *Int'l*, pg. 4114
GUANGDONG KIBING ENERGY SAVING GLASS CO. LTD.—See Zhuzhou Kibing Group Co., Ltd.; *Int'l*, pg. 8680
GUANGDONG KINEX HARDWARE PRODUCTS CO., LTD.—See Guangdong Kinlong Hardware Prdcts Co., Ltd.; *Int'l*, pg. 3157
GUANGDONG KINGSHINE ELECTRONIC TECHNOLOGY COMPANY LIMITED; *Int'l*, pg. 3157
GUANGDONG KINGSTRONG TECHNOLOGY CO., LTD.; *Int'l*, pg. 3157
GUANGDONG KINLONG HARDWARE PRDCTS CO., LTD.; *Int'l*, pg. 3157
GUANGDONG KIN LONG HARDWARE PRODUCTS (HK) CO., LTD.—See Guangdong Kinlong Hardware Prdcts Co., Ltd.; *Int'l*, pg. 3157
GUANGDONG KITECH NEW MATERIAL HOLDING CO., LTD.; *Int'l*, pg. 3158
GUANGDONG KNORR-BREMSE GUO TONG RAILWAY VEHICLE SYSTEMS EQUIPMENT CO., LTD.—See Knorr-Bremse AG; *Int'l*, pg. 4210
GUANGDONG LAND HOLDINGS LIMITED—See GDH Limited; *Int'l*, pg. 2896
GUANGDONG LEADYO IC TESTING CO., LTD.; *Int'l*, pg. 3158
GUANGDONG LEARY NEW MATERIAL TECHNOLOGY CO., LTD.; *Int'l*, pg. 3158
GUANGDONG LEE & MAN PAPER MANUFACTURING LIMITED—See Lee & Man Paper Manufacturing Limited; *Int'l*, pg. 4440
GUANGDONG LIANTAI ENVIRONMENTAL PROTECTION CO., LTD.; *Int'l*, pg. 3158
GUANGDONG LIANXUN PRECISION MANUFACTURING CO., LTD.; *Int'l*, pg. 3158
GUANGDONG LIFESTRONG PHARMACY CO., LTD.; *Int'l*, pg. 3158
GUANGDONG LINGXIAO PUMP INDUSTRY CO., LTD.; *Int'l*, pg. 3158

GUANGDONG LINGXIAO PUMP INDUSTRY CO., LTD.

CORPORATE AFFILIATIONS

GUANGDONG LITE ARRAY COMPANY LIMITED—See Global-Tech Advanced Innovations Inc.; *Int'l*, pg. 3003
GUANGDONG LONGOOD INTELLIGENT ELECTRIC CO., LTD.—See Shenzhen Longood Intelligent Electric Co., Ltd.; *Int'l*, pg. 6817
GUANGDONG MARUBI BIOTECHNOLOGY CO., LTD.; *Int'l*, pg. 3158
GUANGDONG MEIYAN JIXIANG HYDROPOWER CO., LTD.; *Int'l*, pg. 3158
GUANGDONG MEIZHI PRECISE MANUFACTURE CO., LTD.—See Midea Group Co., Ltd.; *Int'l*, pg. 4884
GUANGDONG MEIZHI REFRIGERATION EQUIPMENT CO., LTD.—See Midea Group Co., Ltd.; *Int'l*, pg. 4884
GUANGDONG MIDEA REFRIGERATION EQUIPMENT CO., LTD.—See Midea Group Co., Ltd.; *Int'l*, pg. 4884
GUANGDONG MIDEA-SIIX ELECTRONICS CO., LTD.—See SIIX CORPORATION; *Int'l*, pg. 6913
GUANGDONG MIGAO CHEMICAL CO., LTD.—See Migao Corporation; *Int'l*, pg. 4890
GUANGDONG MINGZHU GROUP CO., LTD.; *Int'l*, pg. 3158
GUANGDONG MODERN HIGH-TECH FIBER CO., LTD.; *Int'l*, pg. 3158
GUANGDONG NBTM NEW MATERIALS CO., LTD.—See NBTM New Materials Group Co., Ltd.; *Int'l*, pg. 5179
GUANGDONG NEDFON AIR SYSTEM CO., LTD.; *Int'l*, pg. 3158
GUANGDONG NEW GRAND PACKING CO.,LTD.; *Int'l*, pg. 3158
GUANG DONG NIKON CAMERA CO., LTD.—See Nikon Corporation; *Int'l*, pg. 5292
GUANGDONG NORTEL TELECOMMUNICATIONS SWITCHING EQUIPMENT LIMITED—See Nortel Networks Corporation; *Int'l*, pg. 5438
GUANGDONG NT PHARMA CO., LTD.—See China NT Pharma Group Company Limited; *Int'l*, pg. 1536
GUANGDONG ORIENT ZIRCONIC INDUSTRY SCIENCE & TECHNOLOGY CO., LTD.; *Int'l*, pg. 3158
GUANGDONG OTSUKA PHARMACEUTICAL CO., LTD.—See Otsuka Holdings Co., Ltd.; *Int'l*, pg. 5659
GUANGDONG O'WATER ENVIRONMENTAL PROTECTIVE TECHNOLOGY CO., LTD.—See Beijing Origin Water Technology Co., Ltd.; *Int'l*, pg. 955
GUANGDONG PACIFIC MILLENNIUM PACKAGING & PAPER INDUSTRIES CO., LTD.—See Pacific Millennium Packaging Group Corporation; *Int'l*, pg. 5691
GUANGDONG PAISHENG INTELLIGENT TECHNOLOGY CO., LTD.; *Int'l*, pg. 3158
GUANGDONG PAK CORPORATION CO. LTD.; *Int'l*, pg. 3158
GUANGDONG (PANYU) PETROCHEMICAL STORAGE & TRANSPORTATION LTD.—See Guangzhou Development Group Incorporated; *Int'l*, pg. 3164
GUANGDONG PIANO CUSTOMIZED FURNITURE CO., LTD.; *Int'l*, pg. 3158
GUANGDONG PLASTICS EXCHANGE CO., LTD.—See Hongda Xingye Co., Ltd.; *Int'l*, pg. 3470
GUANGDONG POLY AUCTION CO., LTD—See China Poly Group Corporation; *Int'l*, pg. 1541
GUANGDONG POLY PHARMACEUTICAL CO., LTD.—See China Poly Group Corporation; *Int'l*, pg. 1541
GUANGDONG PROVINCE GUANGSHENG ASSETS MANAGEMENT CO., LTD—See Guangdong Rising Assets Management Co., Ltd.; *Int'l*, pg. 3159
GUANGDONG PROVINCIAL EXPRESSWAY DEVELOPMENT CO., LTD.; *Int'l*, pg. 3159
GUANGDONG QUANWEI TECHNOLOGY CO., LTD.; *Int'l*, pg. 3159
GUANGDONG QUNXING TOYS JOINT-STOCK CO., LTD.; *Int'l*, pg. 3159
GUANGDONG REAL-DESIGN INTELLIGENT TECHNOLOGY CO., LTD.; *Int'l*, pg. 3159
GUANGDONG REDWALL NEW MATERIALS LIMITED; *Int'l*, pg. 3159
GUANGDONG RENGO PACKAGING COMPANY LIMITED—See Hung Hing Printing Group Limited; *Int'l*, pg. 3535
GUANGDONG RIFENG ELECTRIC CABLE CO., LTD.; *Int'l*, pg. 3159
GUANGDONG RISING ASSETS MANAGEMENT CO., LTD.; *Int'l*, pg. 3159
GUANGDONG RISING GROUP INVESTMENT CO., LTD.—See Guangdong Rising Assets Management Co., Ltd.; *Int'l*, pg. 3159
GUANGDONG RISING MINING INVESTMENT DEVELOPMENT CO., LTD.—See Guangdong Rising Assets Management Co., Ltd.; *Int'l*, pg. 3159
GUANGDONG RONGTAI INDUSTRY CO., LTD.; *Int'l*, pg. 3159
GUANGDONG RUIQING CONTEMPORARY AMPEREX TECHNOLOGY LIMITED—See Contemporary Amperex Technology Co., Ltd.; *Int'l*, pg. 1779
GUANGDONG SACA PRECISION MANUFACTURING CO., LTD.; *Int'l*, pg. 3159
GUANGDONG SANHE PILE CO., LTD.; *Int'l*, pg. 3160
GUANGDONG SANSHUI T&H GLAZE CO., LTD.—See China Glaze Co., Ltd.; *Int'l*, pg. 1504

GUANGDONG SCAS AUTOMOBILE SALES SERVICES CO., LTD.—See China ZhengTong Auto Services Holdings Limited; *Int'l*, pg. 1566
GUANGDONG SECOM SECURITY CO., LTD.—See SECOM Co., Ltd.; *Int'l*, pg. 6671
GUANGDONG SENSSUN WEIGHING APPARATUS GROUP LTD.; *Int'l*, pg. 3160
GUANGDONG SHAONENG GROUP CO., LTD.; *Int'l*, pg. 3160
GUANGDONG SHENGLU TELECOMMUNICATION TECH CO., LTD.; *Int'l*, pg. 3160
GUANGDONG SHENLING ENVIRONMENTAL SYSTEMS CO., LTD.; *Int'l*, pg. 3160
GUANGDONG SHILIUYE CONSTRUCTION CO., LTD—See Guangdong Rising Assets Management Co., Ltd.; *Int'l*, pg. 3159
GUANGDONG SHIRONGZHAOYE CO., LTD.; *Int'l*, pg. 3160
GUANGDONG SHUN AN DA PACIFIC CONTAINER CO., LTD.; *Int'l*, pg. 3160
GUANGDONG SHUNDE NISSIN FOODS CO., LTD.—See Nissin Foods Holdings Co., Ltd.; *Int'l*, pg. 5376
GUANGDONG SHUNKONG DEVELOPMENT CO., LTD.; *Int'l*, pg. 3160
GUANGDONG SHUNNA ELECTRIC CO., LTD.; *Int'l*, pg. 3160
GUANGDONG SILVER AGE SCI & TECH CO., LTD.; *Int'l*, pg. 3160
GUANGDONG SINOFOCUS MEDIA LIMITED—See Huanxi Media Group Limited; *Int'l*, pg. 3513
GUANGDONG SITONG GROUP CO., LTD.; *Int'l*, pg. 3160
GUANGDONG SK ADVANCED POLYMER CO., LTD—See SK Innovation Co., Ltd.; *Int'l*, pg. 6973
GUANGDONG SONGFA CERAMICS CO., LTD.; *Int'l*, pg. 3160
GUANGDONG SONGYANG RECYCLE RESOURCES CO., LTD.; *Int'l*, pg. 3160
GUANGDONG SOUTHERN-CHINA SPECIALTY GASES INSTITUTE CO., LTD.—See Guangdong Huate Gas Co., Ltd.; *Int'l*, pg. 3156
GUANGDONG SOUTH NEW MEDIA CO., LTD.; *Int'l*, pg. 3160
GUANGDONG STARWAY BIO-TECHNOLOGY CO.,LTD—See INKON Life Technology Co., Ltd.; *Int'l*, pg. 3705
GUANGDONG STONESONIC DIGITAL TECHNIQUE CO., LTD.—See China Security & Surveillance Technology, Inc.; *Int'l*, pg. 1550
GUANGDONG SUNWILL PRECISING PLASTIC CO., LTD.; *Int'l*, pg. 3161
GUANGDONG TAIANTANG PHAMACEUTICAL CO., LTD.; *Int'l*, pg. 3161
GUANGDONG TAIENKANG PHARMACEUTICAL CO., LTD.; *Int'l*, pg. 3161
GUANGDONG TANABE PHARMACEUTICAL CO., LTD.—See Mitsubishi Chemical Group Corporation; *Int'l*, pg. 4935
GUANGDONG TAPAI GROUP CO., LTD.; *Int'l*, pg. 3161
GUANGDONG TDK RISING RARE EARTH HIGH TECHNOLOGY MATERIAL CO., LTD.—See TDK Corporation; *Int'l*, pg. 7487
GUANGDONG TECNON KEYI LIGHTING TECHNOLOGY CO., LTD.—See Tecnon Electronics Co., Ltd.; *Int'l*, pg. 7517
GUANGDONG TECSUN SCIENCE & TECHNOLOGY CO., LTD.; *Int'l*, pg. 3161
GUANGDONG TENGEN INDUSTRIAL GROUP CO., LTD.; *Int'l*, pg. 3161
GUANGDONG TIANAN NEW MATERIAL CO., LTD.; *Int'l*, pg. 3161
GUANGDONG TIANHE AGRICULTURAL MEANS OF PRODUCTION CO., LTD.; *Int'l*, pg. 3161
GUANGDONG TIANJI INDUSTRIAL INTELLIGENT SYSTEM CO., LTD.—See Shenzhen Everwin Precision Technology Co., Ltd.; *Int'l*, pg. 6809
GUANGDONG TIANJI ROBOT CO., LTD.—See Shenzhen Everwin Precision Technology Co., Ltd.; *Int'l*, pg. 6809
GUANGDONG TIANYIMA INFORMATION INDUSTRY CO., LTD.; *Int'l*, pg. 3161
GUANGDONG TLOONG TECHNOLOGY GROUP CO., LTD.; *Int'l*, pg. 3161
GUANGDONG TOPSTAR TECHNOLOGY CO., LTD.; *Int'l*, pg. 3161
GUANGDONG TOPSTRONG LIVING INNOVATION & INTEGRATION CO., LTD.; *Int'l*, pg. 3161
GUANGDONG TRANSPORT CO., LTD.—See China Merchants Group Limited; *Int'l*, pg. 1522
GUANGDONG TRANSTEK MEDICAL ELECTRONICS CO., LTD; *Int'l*, pg. 3161
GUANGDONG UCAN ROBOT TECHNOLOGY CO., LTD.—See Guangdong Dtech Technology Co., Ltd.; *Int'l*, pg. 3154
GUANGDONG VANWARD NEW ELECTRIC CO., LTD.; *Int'l*, pg. 3161
GUANGDONG VTR BIO-TECH CO., LTD.; *Int'l*, pg. 3161
GUANGDONG WACOAL INC.—See Wacoal Holdings Corp.; *Int'l*, pg. 8325

GUANGDONG WANHUA RONGWEI POLYURETHANES CO., LTD.—See Wanhua Chemical Group Co., Ltd.; *Int'l*, pg. 8341
GUANGDONG WANLIMA INDUSTRY CO LTD; *Int'l*, pg. 3161
GUANGDONG WEIHUA CORPORATION (MEIZHOU MEDIUM-DENSITY FIBERBOARD FACTORY)—See Chengxin Lithium Group Co., Ltd.; *Int'l*, pg. 1470
GUANGDONG WEISHI DATA TECHNOLOGY CO., LTD.—See VCREDIT Holdings Limited; *Int'l*, pg. 8140
GUANGDONG WELLING MOTOR MANUFACTURING CO., LTD.—See Midea Group Co., Ltd.; *Int'l*, pg. 4886
GUANGDONG WENCAN MOULD & TOOLING CO., LTD.—See Wencan Group Co., Ltd.; *Int'l*, pg. 8376
GUANGDONG WENKE GREEN TECHNOLOGY CORP., LTD.; *Int'l*, pg. 3161
GUANGDONG WENS DAHUANONG BIOTECHNOLOGY CO., LTD.; *Int'l*, pg. 3161
GUANGDONG XIANGDA CAMEL FEED CO., LTD—See Tangrenshen Group Co., Ltd.; *Int'l*, pg. 7458
GUANGDONG XIANGLU TUNGSTEN CO., LTD.; *Int'l*, pg. 3162
GUANGDONG XINBAO ELECTRICAL APPLIANCES HOLDINGS CO., LTD.; *Int'l*, pg. 3162
GUANGDONG XINGFA ALUMINIUM CO., LTD.—See Xingfa Aluminum Holdings Limited; *Int'l*, pg. 8529
GUANGDONG XINGFA ALUMINIUM (JIANGXI) CO., LTD.—See Xingfa Aluminum Holdings Limited; *Int'l*, pg. 8529
GUANGDONG XINHUI MEIDA NYLON CO., LTD.; *Int'l*, pg. 3162
GUANGDONG XIONGSU TECHNOLOGY GROUP CO., LTD.; *Int'l*, pg. 3162
GUANGDONG YANGSHAN UNITED PRECISION MANUFACTURING CO., LTD.; *Int'l*, pg. 3162
GUANGDONG YANTANG DAIRY CO., LTD.; *Int'l*, pg. 3162
GUANGDONG YLMF COMPUTER TECHNOLOGY CO., LTD.—See Zhewen Interactive Group Co Ltd; *Int'l*, pg. 8671
GUANGDONG YUDEAN GROUP CO., LTD.; *Int'l*, pg. 3162
GUANGDONG YUE AO SPORTS DEVELOPMENT CO., LTD.—See Li Ning Co., Ltd.; *Int'l*, pg. 4481
GUANGDONG YUEHAI FEEDS GROUP CO., LTD.; *Int'l*, pg. 3162
GUANGDONG YUEKE FINANCE GROUP CO., LTD.—See Guangdong Hongtu Technology (Holdings) Co., Ltd.; *Int'l*, pg. 3156
GUANGDONG YUEXING PHARMACEUTICAL CO., LTD.—See SINOPHARM Group Co., Ltd.; *Int'l*, pg. 6954
GUANGDONG YUEYUN TRANSPORTATION COMPANY LIMITED; *Int'l*, pg. 3162
GUANGDONG ZHAOQING L&V CO. LTD.—See Leggett & Platt, Incorporated; *U.S. Public*, pg. 1302
GUANGDONG ZHENYE TECHNOLOGY CO., LTD.; *Int'l*, pg. 3162
GUANGDONG ZHONGKE TIANYUAN NEW ENERGY TECHNOLOGY CO., LTD.—See China New Energy Limited; *Int'l*, pg. 1535
GUANGDONG ZHONGSHENG PHARMACEUTICAL CO., LTD.; *Int'l*, pg. 3162
GUANGHE LANDSCAPE CULTURE COMMUNICATION CO., LTD.; *Int'l*, pg. 3162
GUANGHUI ENERGY CO., LTD.—See Xinjiang Guanghui Industry Investment Group Co., Ltd.; *Int'l*, pg. 8531
GUANGHUI LOGISTICS CO., LTD.; *Int'l*, pg. 3162
GUANGLIAN AVIATION INDUSTRY CO., LTD.; *Int'l*, pg. 3162
GUANG-MING RIBAO SDN BHD—See Media Chinese International Limited; *Int'l*, pg. 4770
GUANGRAO JINQIAO MICRO CREDIT CO., LTD.—See Zhewen Interactive Group Co Ltd; *Int'l*, pg. 8671
GUANGSHEN RAILWAY COMPANY LIMITED; *Int'l*, pg. 3162
GUANGXHOU GAS GROUP CO., LTD.—See Guangzhou Development Group Incorporated; *Int'l*, pg. 3164
GUANGXI ARAKAWA CHEMICAL INDUSTRIES, LTD.—See Arakawa Chemical Industries, Ltd.; *Int'l*, pg. 534
GUANGXI BO HUAN ENVIRONMENTAL CONSULTING COMPANY—See Guangxi Bossco Environmental Protection Technology Co., Ltd.; *Int'l*, pg. 3163
GUANGXI BOKE PHARMACEUTICAL CO., LTD.—See AMERICAN ORIENTAL BIOENGINEERING, INC.; *Int'l*, pg. 422
GUANGXI BOQING FOOD CO., LTD—See The Garfield Weston Foundation; *Int'l*, pg. 7648
GUANGXI BOSSCO ENVIRONMENTAL PROTECTION TECHNOLOGY CO., LTD.; *Int'l*, pg. 3162
GUANGXI BOXUAN FOOD CO., LTD—See The Garfield Weston Foundation; *Int'l*, pg. 7648
GUANGXI FENGLIN WOOD INDUSTRY GROUP CO., LTD.; *Int'l*, pg. 3163
GUANGXI FPT SOFTWARE CO., LTD.—See FPT Corporation; *Int'l*, pg. 2758
GUANGXI GUIDONG ELECTRIC POWER CO., LTD.; *Int'l*, pg. 3163

GUANGXI (GUIGANG) AKR CONTAINER PORT CO LTD.—See PT AKR Corporindo Tbk; *Int'l*, pg. 6020
GUANGXI GUIGUAN ELECTRIC POWER CO., LTD.—See China Datang Corporation; *Int'l*, pg. 1497
GUANGXI HECHI CHEMICAL CO., LTD.—See China National Chemical Corporation; *Int'l*, pg. 1527
GUANGXI HEZHOU NIKKEI GUIYIN TECHNOLOGY CO., LTD.—See Nippon Light Metal Holdings Company, Ltd.; *Int'l*, pg. 5323
GUANGXI HUAXI NONFERROUS METALS CO., LTD; *Int'l*, pg. 3163
GUANGXI INVESTMENT GROUP CO., LTD.; *Int'l*, pg. 3163
GUANGXI IRON & STEEL GROUP CO., LTD.—See China Baowu Steel Group Corp., Ltd.; *Int'l*, pg. 1485
GUANGXI JICON ELECTRONICS CO., LTD.—See Shenzhen SDG Information Co., Ltd.; *Int'l*, pg. 6820
GUANGXI LIUGONG MACHINERY CO., LTD.; *Int'l*, pg. 3163
GUANGXI LIUZHOU PHARMACEUTICAL CO., LTD.; *Int'l*, pg. 3163
GUANGXI LUZHAI CQRC VILLAGE & TOWNSHIP BANK CO., LTD.—See Chongqing Rural Commercial Bank Co., Ltd.; *Int'l*, pg. 1581
GUANGXI NANNING CHEMICAL PHARMACEUTICAL CO., LTD.—See Roquette Freres SA; *Int'l*, pg. 6398
GUANGXI NANNING WATERWORKS CO., LTD.; *Int'l*, pg. 3163
GUANGXI OJI PLANTATION FOREST CO., LTD.—See Oji Holdings Corporation; *Int'l*, pg. 5536
GUANGXI ORIENTAL INTELLIGENT MANUFACTURING TECHNOLOGY CO., LTD; *Int'l*, pg. 3163
GUANGXI OVERLAND TOTAL LOGISTICS CO., LTD.—See Yamato Holdings Co., Ltd.; *Int'l*, pg. 8554
GUANGXI POLY YUANCHEN REAL ESTATE DEVELOPMENT CO., LTD—See China Poly Group Corporation; *Int'l*, pg. 1541
GUANGXI RADIO & TV NETWORK CORPORATION; *Int'l*, pg. 3163
GUANGXI RURAL INVESTMENT SUGAR INDUSTRY GROUP CO., LTD; *Int'l*, pg. 3163
GUANGXI SINGAMAS CONTAINER CO., LTD.—See Singamas Container Holdings Limited; *Int'l*, pg. 6030
GUANGXI START MANGANESE MATERIALS CO., LTD.—See CITIC Group Corporation; *Int'l*, pg. 1621
GUANGXI WUZHOU ARAKAWA CHEMICAL INDUSTRIES, LTD.—See Arakawa Chemical Industries, Ltd.; *Int'l*, pg. 534
GUANGXI WUZHOU COMMUNICATIONS CO., LTD.; *Int'l*, pg. 3164
GUANGXI WUZHOU ZHONGHENG GROUP CO., LTD.; *Int'l*, pg. 3164
GUANGXI XINXUNDA TECHNOLOGY GROUP CO., LTD.; *Int'l*, pg. 3164
GUANGXI YUCHAI MACHINERY CO. LTD.—See Hong Leong Investment Holdings Pte. Ltd.; *Int'l*, pg. 3469
GUANGXI YUEGUI GUANGYE HOLDINGS CO., LTD.; *Int'l*, pg. 3164
GUANGYUYUAN CHINESE HERBAL MEDICINE CO., LTD.; *Int'l*, pg. 3164
GUANGZHAO INDUSTRIAL FOREST BIOTECHNOLOGY GROUP LIMITED; *Int'l*, pg. 3164
GUANGZHENG EYE HOSPITAL GROUP CO., LTD.; *Int'l*, pg. 3164
GUANGZHOU AGILE HOTEL CO., LTD.—See Agile Group Holdings Limited; *Int'l*, pg. 209
GUANGZHOU AHRESTY CASTING CO., LTD.—See Ahresty Corporation; *Int'l*, pg. 226
GUANGZHOU ALCONIX (SHANGHAI) CORP.—See Alconix Corporation; *Int'l*, pg. 302
GUANGZHOU AMPHENOL ELECTRONICS CO., LTD.—See Amphenol Corporation; *U.S. Public*, pg. 130
GUANGZHOU AMPHENOL SINCERE FLEX CIRCUITS CO. LTD.—See Amphenol Corporation; *U.S. Public*, pg. 127
GUANGZHOU ANTOLIN AUTO-PARTS CO., LTD.—See Grupo Antolin-Irausa, S.A.; *Int'l*, pg. 3120
GUANGZHOU APPLE FOODS TECH CO., LTD.—See Apple Flavor & Fragrance Group Co., Ltd.; *Int'l*, pg. 520
GUANGZHOU ARCA VALVE LTD.—See ARCA Regler GmbH; *Int'l*, pg. 540
GUANGZHOU ARMITAGE COMPUTER SOFTWARE CO., LTD.—See Beijing Shiji Information Technology Co., Ltd.; *Int'l*, pg. 956
GUANGZHOU ARMITAGE TECHNOLOGIES LTD.—See Beijing Shiji Information Technology Co., Ltd.; *Int'l*, pg. 956
GUANGZHOU ASAHI DONGLING RESEARCH & DEVELOPMENT CO., LTD.—See Topy Industries, Ltd.; *Int'l*, pg. 7821
GUANGZHOU ASIA STEEL CO., LTD.—See China Metal Recycling (Holdings) Limited; *Int'l*, pg. 1524
GUANGZHOU AUTOMATED SYSTEMS LIMITED—See Beijing Teamsun Technology Co., Ltd.; *Int'l*, pg. 958
GUANGZHOU AUTOMOBILE GROUP BUSINESS CO., LTD.—See Guangzhou Automobile Industry Group Co., Ltd.; *Int'l*, pg. 3164

GUANGZHOU AUTOMOBILE GROUP COMPANY LIMITED—See Guangzhou Automobile Industry Group Co., Ltd.; *Int'l*, pg. 3164
GUANGZHOU AUTOMOBILE GROUP COMPONENT CO., LTD.—See Guangzhou Automobile Industry Group Co., Ltd.; *Int'l*, pg. 3164
GUANGZHOU AUTOMOBILE INDUSTRY GROUP CO., LTD.; *Int'l*, pg. 3164
GUANGZHOU BAIYUN ELECTRIC EQUIPMENT CO., LTD.; *Int'l*, pg. 3164
GUANGZHOU BAIYUN INTERNATIONAL AIRPORT COMPANY LIMITED; *Int'l*, pg. 3164
GUANGZHOU BAIYUN INTERNATIONAL LOGISTIC COMPANY LIMITED—See China Southern Airlines Co., Ltd.; *Int'l*, pg. 1553
GUANGZHOU BAIYUNSHAN PHARMACEUTICAL HOLDINGS COMPANY LIMITED; *Int'l*, pg. 3164
GUANGZHOU BAOTAIHANG AUTOMOBILE SALES SERVICES CO., LTD.—See China ZhengTong Auto Services Holdings Limited; *Int'l*, pg. 1566
GUANGZHOU BAOZE AUTOMOBILE SALES SERVICES CO., LTD.—See China ZhengTong Auto Services Holdings Limited; *Int'l*, pg. 1566
GUANGZHOU BEAUTY STAR CO., LTD.—See Shenzhen Leaguer Co., Ltd.; *Int'l*, pg. 6816
GUANGZHOU BIG-WANT FOODS LTD.—See Want Want China Holdings Ltd.; *Int'l*, pg. 8342
GUANGZHOU BOGUAN TELECOMMUNICATION TECHNOLOGY LIMITED—See NetEase, Inc.; *Int'l*, pg. 5214
GUANGZHOU BOTNY CHEMICAL CO., LTD.—See China Aluminum Cans Holdings Limited; *Int'l*, pg. 1482
GUANGZHOU BOZHAN HENGTENG INFORMATION TECHNOLOGY CO., LTD.—See NavInfo Co., Ltd.; *Int'l*, pg. 5175
GUANGZHOU BRIDON ROPES & LIFTING—See Ontario Teachers' Pension Plan; *Int'l*, pg. 5587
GUANGZHOU CABBEEN CLOTHING CO., LTD.—See Cabbeen Fashion Limited; *Int'l*, pg. 1245
GUANGZHOU CASA COMMUNICATION TECHNOLOGY LTD.—See Casa Systems, Inc.; *U.S. Private*, pg. 778
GUANGZHOU CHUNG SHUN CENTURY FIBRE GLASS CO., LTD.—See Kingboard Holdings Limited; *Int'l*, pg. 4171
GUANGZHOU CLOUDWALK INFORMATION TECHNOLOGY CO., LTD.—See PCI Technology Group Co., Ltd; *Int'l*, pg. 5768
GUANGZHOU CL SOLUTIONS LIMITED—See NCT Alliance Berhad; *Int'l*, pg. 5182
GUANGZHOU CPT M&E EQUIPMENT CO., LTD.—See Sichuan Dawn Precision Technology Co., Ltd.; *Int'l*, pg. 6878
GUANGZHOU DENSO CO., LTD.—See Denso Corporation; *Int'l*, pg. 2032
GUANGZHOU DEVELOPMENT GROUP INCORPORATED; *Int'l*, pg. 3164
GUANGZHOU DEVOTION DOMESTIC BOILERS MANUFACTURING CO. LTD.—See Devotion Energy Group Limited; *Int'l*, pg. 2090
GUANGZHOU DEVOTION THERMAL FACILITY CO., LTD.—See Devotion Energy Group Limited; *Int'l*, pg. 2090
GUANGZHOU DEVOTION THERMAL TECHNOLOGY CO., LTD.; *Int'l*, pg. 3165
GUANGZHOU DICASTAL ASAHI ALUMINIUM CO., LTD.—See Topy Industries, Ltd.; *Int'l*, pg. 7821
GUANGZHOU DIGITAL CHINA LIMITED—See Digital China Group Co., Ltd.; *Int'l*, pg. 2121
GUANGZHOU DIGITAL RISE CO., LTD.—See Guangdong Rising Assets Management Co., Ltd.; *Int'l*, pg. 3159
GUANGZHOU DONGSUNG CHEMICAL CO., LTD.—See Dongsung Chemical Co., Ltd.; *Int'l*, pg. 2170
GUANGZHOU DTS DIGITAL THEATER SYSTEM, CO. LTD—See Xperi Inc.; *U.S. Public*, pg. 2392
GUANGZHOU DYNAMIC INC.—See Excelsior Medical Co., Ltd.; *Int'l*, pg. 2579
GUANGZHOU ECHOM SCIENCE & TECHNOLOGY CO., LTD.; *Int'l*, pg. 3165
GUANGZHOU ELEC & ELTEK COMPANY LIMITED—See Kingboard Holdings Limited; *Int'l*, pg. 4170
GUANGZHOU ELEC & ELTEK HIGH DENSITY INTERCONNECT TECHNOLOGY NO.1 COMPANY LIMITED—See Kingboard Holdings Limited; *Int'l*, pg. 4171
GUANGZHOU EMHART FASTENING SYSTEM CO., LTD.—See Stanley Black & Decker, Inc.; *U.S. Public*, pg. 1932
GUANGZHOU EMHART FASTENING SYSTEMS CO., LTD.—See Stanley Black & Decker, Inc.; *U.S. Public*, pg. 1934
GUANGZHOU ENPLAS MECHATRONICS CO., LTD.—See ENPLAS CORPORATION; *Int'l*, pg. 2445
GUANGZHOU ETHICAL TRADING COMPANY—See Everlight Chemical Industry Co., Ltd.; *Int'l*, pg. 2567
GUANGZHOU FANGBANG ELECTRONICS CO., LTD.; *Int'l*, pg. 3165
GUANGZHOU FAN YA JIA RONG TRADING CO., LTD.—See BRENNTAG SE; *Int'l*, pg. 1149

GUANGZHOU FASTPRINT CIRCUIT TECH CO., LTD.—See Shenzhen Fastprint Circuit Tech Co., Ltd.; *Int'l*, pg. 6809
GUANGZHOU FENGZHONG ALUMINIUM SMELTING TECHNOLOGY CO., LTD.—See Toyota Tsusho Corporation; *Int'l*, pg. 7877
GUANGZHOU FIVE GOAT WATCH CO., LIMITED—See Citychamp Watch & Jewellery Group Limited; *Int'l*, pg. 1629
GUANGZHOU FORDA SIGNAL EQUIPMENT CO. LTD.—See Hongli Zhihui Group Co., Ltd.; *Int'l*, pg. 3471
GUANGZHOU FRIENDSHIP BALENO COMPANY LIMITED—See Texwinca Holdings Limited; *Int'l*, pg. 7584
GUANGZHOU FRIENDSHIP GROUP CO., LTD.; *Int'l*, pg. 3165
GUANGZHOU FRONTOP DIGITAL CREATIVE TECHNOLOGY CO., LTD.; *Int'l*, pg. 3165
GUANGZHOU FUTABA AUTO PARTS CO., LTD.—See Futaba Industrial Co., Ltd.; *Int'l*, pg. 2851
GUANGZHOU GEM-YEAR AUTO-PARTS CO., LTD.—See Gem-Year Industrial Co., Ltd.; *Int'l*, pg. 2915
GUANGZHOU GHW TRADING CO., LTD.—See GHW International; *Int'l*, pg. 2960
GUANGZHOU GLOBAL LOGISTICS CORP.—See ITOCHU Corporation; *Int'l*, pg. 3836
GUANGZHOU GOALAND ENERGY CONSERVATION TECH CO., LTD.; *Int'l*, pg. 3165
GUANGZHOU GRANDBUY CO., LTD.; *Int'l*, pg. 3165
GUANGZHOU GREAT POWER ENERGY & TECHNOLOGY CO., LTD.; *Int'l*, pg. 3165
GUANGZHOU GREAT WATER ENVIRONMENTAL PROTECTION CO., LTD.—See China TianYF Holdings Group Limited; *Int'l*, pg. 1559
GUANGZHOU GREEN HARBOUR ENVIRONMENTAL OPERATION LTD.—See Ecolab Inc.; *U.S. Public*, pg. 714
GUANGZHOU GRG METROLOGY & TEST CO., LTD.; *Int'l*, pg. 3165
GUANGZHOU GUANGRI STOCK CO., LTD.; *Int'l*, pg. 3165
GUANGZHOU GUANGYUE ASSETS MANAGEMENT CO., LTD.—See Guangzhou Automobile Industry Group Co., Ltd.; *Int'l*, pg. 3164
GUANGZHOU HAIGE COMMUNICATIONS GROUP INCORPORATED COMPANY; *Int'l*, pg. 3165
GUANGZHOU HANGXIN AVIATION TECHNOLOGY CO., LTD.; *Int'l*, pg. 3165
GUANGZHOU HANWA TRADING CO., LTD.—See Hanwa Co., Ltd.; *Int'l*, pg. 3262
GUANGZHOU HAOYANG ELECTRONIC CO., LTD.; *Int'l*, pg. 3165
GUANGZHOU HAOZHI INDUSTRIAL CO., LTD.; *Int'l*, pg. 3165
GUANGZHOU HENGYUN ENTERPRISES HOLDING LTD.; *Int'l*, pg. 3165
GUANGZHOU HENKEL SURFACE TECHNOLOGIES CO., LTD.—See Henkel AG & Co. KGaA; *Int'l*, pg. 3348
GUANGZHOU HIGHJET COMPUTER TECHNOLOGY CO., LTD.—See Yunnan Nantian Electronics Information Co., Ltd.; *Int'l*, pg. 8616
GUANGZHOU HITACHI UNISIA AUTOMOTIVE PARTS CO., LTD.—See Hitachi Astemo, Ltd.; *Int'l*, pg. 3408
GUANGZHOU HI-TARGET NAVIGATION TECH CO., LTD.; *Int'l*, pg. 3166
GUANGZHOU HOLIKE CREATIVE HOME CO., LTD.; *Int'l*, pg. 3166
GUANGZHOU HONGEN MEDICAL DIAGNOSTIC TECHNOLOGIES COMPANY LIMITED—See Yestar Healthcare Holdings Company Limited; *Int'l*, pg. 8578
GUANGZHOU HONGFAN TECHNOLOGY CO., LTD.—See CSSC Offshore & Marine Engineering Company Ltd.; *Int'l*, pg. 1868
GUANGZHOU HOPERUN SOFTWARE CO., LTD—See Jiangsu Hoperun Software Co., Ltd.; *Int'l*, pg. 3948
GUANGZHOU HOSHINO GAKKI MFG. CO., LTD.—See Hoshino Gakki Co., Ltd.; *Int'l*, pg. 3483
GUANGZHOU HOSHINO GAKKI TRADING CO., LTD.—See Hoshino Gakki Co., Ltd.; *Int'l*, pg. 3483
GUANGZHOU HOYER BULK TRANSPORT CO. LTD.—See Hoyer GmbH; *Int'l*, pg. 3498
GUANGZHOU HUALING AIR CONDITIONING EQUIPMENT CO., LTD—See Midea Group Co., Ltd.; *Int'l*, pg. 4884
GUANGZHOU HUAYAN PRECISION MACHINERY CO., LTD.; *Int'l*, pg. 3166
GUANGZHOU HYMSON LASER CO., LTD.—See Hymson Laser Technology Group Co Ltd; *Int'l*, pg. 3549
GUANGZHOU IMASEN ELECTRIC INDUSTRIAL CO., LTD.—See Imasen Electric Industrial Co., Ltd.; *Int'l*, pg. 3620
GUANGZHOU INABATA TRADING CO., LTD.—See Inabata & Co. Ltd.; *Int'l*, pg. 3643
GUANGZHOU INFORMA YI FAN EXHIBITIONS CO., LTD.; See Informa plc; *Int'l*, pg. 3691
GUANGZHOU INTEX AUTO PARTS CO., LTD.—See Toyota Boshoku Corporation; *Int'l*, pg. 7864
GUANGZHOU IWATANI TRADING CO., LTD—See Iwatani Corporation; *Int'l*, pg. 3850

GUANGZHOU JET BIO-FILTRATION CO., LTD.

GUANGZHOU JET BIO-FILTRATION CO., LTD.; *Int'l*, pg. 3166
GUANGZHOU JFE SHOJI STEEL PRODUCTS CO., LTD.—See JFE Holdings, Inc.; *Int'l*, pg. 3936
GUANGZHOU JFE STEEL SHEET CO., LTD.—See JFE Holdings, Inc.; *Int'l*, pg. 3937
GUANGZHOU JIACHENG INTERNATIONAL LOGISTICS CO., LTD.; *Int'l*, pg. 3166
GUANGZHOU JIAHONG INTERNATIONAL FREIGHT FORWARDING CO., LTD.—See CN Logistics International Holdings Limited; *Int'l*, pg. 1673
GUANGZHOU JIAJIAMAI OILS AND FATS CO., LTD.—See Great-Sun Foods Co.,LTD.; *Int'l*, pg. 3066
GUANGZHOU JINGHAO PHOTOELECTRIC TECHNOLOGY CO., LTD.—See Talant Optronics (suzhou) Co., Ltd.; *Int'l*, pg. 7443
GUANGZHOU JINPENG GROUP CO., LTD.—See Sanpower Group Co., Ltd.; *Int'l*, pg. 6554
GUANGZHOU JINYI MEDIA CORPORATION; *Int'l*, pg. 3166
GUANGZHOU JINZHONG AUTO PARTS MANUFACTURING CO., LTD.; *Int'l*, pg. 3166
GUANGZHOU JOINTAS CHEMICAL CO., LTD.; *Int'l*, pg. 3166
GUANGZHOU KAMHING TEXTILE DYEING CO., LTD.—See Kam Hing International Holdings Limited; *Int'l*, pg. 4059
GUANGZHOU KAM SING TEXTILE AND DYEING COMPANY LIMITED—See Kam Hing International Holdings Limited; *Int'l*, pg. 4059
GUANGZHOU KANSAI PAINT CO., LTD—See Kansai Paint Co., Ltd.; *Int'l*, pg. 4071
GUANGZHOU KASAI AUTOMOTIVE INTERIOR TRIM PARTS CO., LTD.—See Kasai Kogyo Co., Ltd.; *Int'l*, pg. 4086
GUANGZHOU KCF PLASTICS CO., LTD.—See Kurabo Industries Ltd.; *Int'l*, pg. 4335
GUANGZHOU KDT MACHINERY CO.,LTD; *Int'l*, pg. 3166
GUANGZHOU KEERUN PAPER CO., LTD.—See Xiamen ITG Group Corp., Ltd.; *Int'l*, pg. 8524
GUANGZHOU KINDLY MEDICAL DEVICES CO., LTD—See Shanghai Kindly Enterprise Development Group Co., Ltd; *Int'l*, pg. 6773
GUANGZHOU KINGMED DIAGNOSTICS CENTER CO., LTD.; *Int'l*, pg. 3166
GUANGZHOU KINGMED DIAGNOSTICS GROUP CO., LTD.; *Int'l*, pg. 3166
GUANGZHOU KINGTELLER TECHNOLOGY CO., LTD.; *Int'l*, pg. 3166
GUANGZHOU KINTE DESHENG INTELLIGENT EQUIPMENT CO., LTD.—See China National Electric Apparatus Research Institute Co., Ltd.; *Int'l*, pg. 1531
GUANGZHOU KINTE ELECTRIC INDUSTRIAL CO., LTD.—See China National Electric Apparatus Research Institute Co., Ltd.; *Int'l*, pg. 1531
GUANGZHOU KINTE INDUSTRIAL CO., LTD.—See China National Electric Apparatus Research Institute Co., Ltd.; *Int'l*, pg. 1531
GUANGZHOU KINTE MATERIAL TECHNOLOGY CO., LTD.—See China National Electric Apparatus Research Institute Co., Ltd.; *Int'l*, pg. 1531
GUANGZHOU KOITO AUTOMOTIVE LAMP CO., LTD.—See Koito Manufacturing Co., Ltd.; *Int'l*, pg. 4230
GUANGZHOU KORN/FERRY HUMAN CAPITAL COMPANY LTD.—See Korn Ferry; *U.S. Public*, pg. 1272
GUANGZHOU KUANGDA AUTOMOBILE FABRIC CO., LTD.—See Kuangda Technology Group Co., Ltd.; *Int'l*, pg. 4319
GUANGZHOU KURABO CHEMICALS CO., LTD.—See Kurabo Industries Ltd.; *Int'l*, pg. 4335
GUANGZHOU KYOSHA CIRCUIT TECHNOLOGY CO., LTD.—See KYOSHA CO., LTD.; *Int'l*, pg. 4365
GUANGZHOU LBP MEDICINE SCIENCE & TECHNOLOGY CO., LTD.; *Int'l*, pg. 3166
GUANGZHOU LIDYE RESIN CO., LTD.—See DIC Corporation; *Int'l*, pg. 2109
GUANGZHOU LINGNAN CABLE LTD.—See Guangzhou Zhiguang Electric Co., Ltd.; *Int'l*, pg. 3168
GUANGZHOU LINGNAN GROUP HOLDINGS COMPANY LIMITED; *Int'l*, pg. 3166
GUANGZHOU LINGWE TECHNOLOGY CO., LTD.; *Int'l*, pg. 3166
GUANGZHOU LUXVISIONS INNOVATION TECHNOLOGY LIMITED; *Int'l*, pg. 3166
GUANGZHOU LUXVISIONS INNOVATION TECHNOLOGY LIMITED—See Luxvisions Innovation Limited; *Int'l*, pg. 4589
GUANGZHOU MARUJUN CO., LTD.—See J-MAX Co., Ltd.; *Int'l*, pg. 3854
GUANGZHOU MAYER CORP., LIMITED—See Mayer Holdings Limited; *Int'l*, pg. 4744
GUANGZHOU MEADVILLE ELECTRONICS CO., LTD.; *Int'l*, pg. 3166
GUANGZHOU MEIBAOHANG AUTO SALES & SERVICES CO., LTD.—See China MeiDong Auto Holdings Limited; *Int'l*, pg. 1519
GUANGZHOU MEIJI CONFECTIONERY CO., LTD.—See Meiji Holdings Co., Ltd.; *Int'l*, pg. 4800

GUANGZHOU MELCO INDUSTRIAL SUPPLIES CO., LTD.—See Cosmos Machinery Enterprises Limited; *Int'l*, pg. 1813
GUANGZHOU METRO DESIGN & RESEARCH INSTITUTE CO., LTD.; *Int'l*, pg. 3167
GUANGZHOU MINHUI AUTO PARTS CO., LTD.—See Minth Group Limited; *Int'l*, pg. 4914
GUANGZHOU MITSUBA ELECTRIC CO., LTD.—See MITSUBA Corporation; *Int'l*, pg. 4928
GUANGZHOU MITSUBA ELECTRIC (WUHAN) CO., LTD.—See MITSUBA Corporation; *Int'l*, pg. 4928
GUANGZHOU MORIROKU TECHNOLOGY CO., LTD.—See Moriroku Holdings Company, Ltd.; *Int'l*, pg. 5047
GUANGZHOU MOST CROWN ELECTRONICS LIMITED—See Citizen Watch Co., Ltd.; *Int'l*, pg. 1625
GUANGZHOU MOTORS GROUP COMPANY—See Guangzhou Automobile Industry Group Co., Ltd.; *Int'l*, pg. 3164
GUANGZHOU NAGASE TRADING LTD.—See Nagase & Co., Ltd.; *Int'l*, pg. 5126
GUANGZHOU NANLAND AIR CATERING COMPANY LIMITED—See China Southern Airlines Co., Ltd.; *Int'l*, pg. 1553
GUANGZHOU NANTIAN COMPUTER SYSTEM CO., LTD.—See Yunnan Nantian Electronics Information Co., Ltd.; *Int'l*, pg. 8616
GUANGZHOU NATIONAL ADHESIVES CO., LTD.—See Henkel AG & Co. KGaA; *Int'l*, pg. 3348
GUANGZHOU NEPSTAR CHAIN CO., LTD.—See China Nepstar Chain Drugstore Ltd.; *Int'l*, pg. 1534
GUANGZHOU NETEASE INTERACTIVE ENTERTAINMENT CO., LTD.—See NetEase, Inc.; *Int'l*, pg. 5214
GUANGZHOU NEWLY MECHANICAL & ELECTRICAL CO., LTD.—See Daikin Industries, Ltd.; *Int'l*, pg. 1935
GUANGZHOU NICCA CHEMICAL CO., LTD.—See Nicca Chemical Co., Ltd.; *Int'l*, pg. 5263
GUANGZHOU NIPPON PAINT CO., LTD.—See Nippon Paint Holdings Co., Ltd.; *Int'l*, pg. 5325
GUANGZHOU NISHIKAWA SEALING SYSTEMS CO., LTD.—See Nishikawa Rubber Co., Ltd.; *Int'l*, pg. 5364
GUANGZHOU NISSHA HIGH PRECISION PLASTICS CO., LTD.—See Nissha Co., Ltd.; *Int'l*, pg. 5371
GUANGZHOU NISSIN INTERNATIONAL LOGISTICS, LTD.—See Nissin Corporation; *Int'l*, pg. 5375
GUANGZHOU NITTAN VALVE CO. LTD.—See Eaton Corporation plc; *Int'l*, pg. 2281
GUANGZHOU NOBLE JEWELRY LIMITED—See Central Development Holdings Ltd.; *Int'l*, pg. 1406
GUANGZHOU NOVOGENE MED LAB CO., LTD.—See Novogene Co., Ltd.; *Int'l*, pg. 5465
GUANGZHOU NTN-YULON DRIVETRAIN CO., LTD.—See Nissan Motor Co., Ltd.; *Int'l*, pg. 5370
GUANGZHOU NTN-YULON DRIVETRAIN CO., LTD.—See NTN Corporation; *Int'l*, pg. 5481
GUANGZHOU OPTEX INDUSTRIAL AUTOMATION CONTROL EQUIPMENT CO., LTD.—See Optex Group Co., Ltd.; *Int'l*, pg. 5602
GUANGZHOU OSTNOR SANITARY WARE LIMITED—See Ostnor AB; *Int'l*, pg. 5655
GUANGZHOU PANDA INT'L GROUP LTD.—See Panda Financial Holding Corp., Ltd.; *Int'l*, pg. 5726
GUANGZHOU PANYU DACHENG WOOD CO., LTD.—See Emerald Plantation Holdings Limited; *Int'l*, pg. 2377
GUANGZHOU PANYU GOLDEN FOUNTAIN IND., LTD.—See Tungtex (Holdings) Co. Ltd.; *Int'l*, pg. 7972
GUANGZHOU PANYU HUICHENG SMALL LOAN CO., LTD.—See PCI Technology Group Co., Ltd; *Int'l*, pg. 5768
GUANGZHOU PANYU JIU SHUI KENG FOSTER ELECTRIC FACTORY—See Foster Electric Co., Ltd.; *Int'l*, pg. 2750
GUANGZHOU PANYU MCP INDUSTRIES LIMITED—See CPMC Holdings Limited; *Int'l*, pg. 1826
GUANGZHOU PANYU SANKYO HOUSE CO., LTD.—See Sankyo Frontier. Co., Ltd.; *Int'l*, pg. 6543
GUANGZHOU PARKER AUTO PARTS CO, LTD.—See Nihon Parkerizing Co., Ltd.; *Int'l*, pg. 5286
GUANGZHOU PARKERIZING CO., LTD.—See Nihon Parkerizing Co., Ltd.; *Int'l*, pg. 5286
GUANGZHOU PARKLANE LIMOUSINE SERVICE LTD—See Brockman Mining Limited; *Int'l*, pg. 1173
GUANGZHOU PCI DATA SERVICE CO., LTD.—See PCI Technology Group Co., Ltd; *Int'l*, pg. 5768
GUANGZHOU PEARL RIVER INDUSTRIAL DEVELOPMENT HOLDINGS CO., LTD; *Int'l*, pg. 3167
GUANGZHOU PEARL RIVER PIANO GROUP CO., LTD.; *Int'l*, pg. 3167
GUANGZHOU PICO EXHIBITION SERVICES CO., LTD.—See Pico Far East Holdings Limited; *Int'l*, pg. 5860
GUANGZHOU PICO IES EXHIBITION SERVICES CO., LTD.—See Pico Far East Holdings Limited; *Int'l*, pg. 5861
GUANGZHOU POLY SOUTHEN CULTURE PROMULGATION CO., LTD—See China Poly Group Corporation; *Int'l*, pg. 1541
GUANGZHOU PORT GROUP CO., LTD.; *Int'l*, pg. 3167

GUANGZHOU POWER SUPPLY CO., LTD—See China Southern Power Grid Co., Ltd.; *Int'l*, pg. 1553
GUANGZHOU QIAN HU AQUARIUM & PETS ACCESSORIES MANUFACTURING CO., LTD.—See Qian Hu Corporation Limited; *Int'l*, pg. 6140
GUANGZHOU QIAN HU AQUARIUM & PETS CO., LTD.—See Qian Hu Corporation Limited; *Int'l*, pg. 6140
GUANGZHOU RADIO GROUP CO., LTD.; *Int'l*, pg. 3167
GUANGZHOU RESTAURANT GROUP CO., LTD.; *Int'l*, pg. 3167
GUANGZHOU R&F PROPERTIES CO., LTD.; *Int'l*, pg. 3167
GUANGZHOU RIB SOFTWARE COMPANY LIMITED—See Schneider Electric SE; *Int'l*, pg. 6624
GUANGZHOU RIDA MEDICAL INSTRUMENTS CO., LTD—See Improve Medical Instruments Co., Ltd; *Int'l*, pg. 3638
GUANGZHOU RINNAI GAS AND ELECTRIC APPLIANCE CO., LTD.—See Rinnai Corporation; *Int'l*, pg. 6344
GUANGZHOU RISING MICRO ELECTRONICS CO., LTD.—See Guangdong Rising Assets Management Co., Ltd.; *Int'l*, pg. 3159
GUANGZHOU RISONG INTELLIGENT TECHNOLOGY HOLDING CO., LTD.; *Int'l*, pg. 3167
GUANGZHOU RISONG WELDSTONE INTELLIGENT EQUIPMENT CO., LTD.—See Guangzhou Risong Intelligent Technology Holding Co., Ltd.; *Int'l*, pg. 3167
GUANGZHOU RUOYUCHEN TECHNOLOGY CO., LTD.; *Int'l*, pg. 3167
GUANGZHOU RURAL COMMERCIAL BANK CO., LTD.; *Int'l*, pg. 3167
GUANGZHOU SAIFU CHEMICAL CO., LTD.—See BRENNTAG SE; *Int'l*, pg. 1149
GUANGZHOU SAI YI CONVENIENCE STORES LTD.—See Jardine Matheson Holdings Limited; *Int'l*, pg. 3909
GUANGZHOU SANFU NEW MATERIALS TECHNOLOGY CO., LTD.; *Int'l*, pg. 3167
GUANGZHOU SANGO AUTOMOTIVE PARTS CO., LTD.—See Sango Co., Ltd.; *Int'l*, pg. 6537
GUANGZHOU SAN MIGUEL BREWERY CO., LTD.—See Top Frontier Investment Holdings, Inc.; *Int'l*, pg. 7812
GUANGZHOU SEAGULL KITCHEN & BATH PRODUCTS CO., LTD.; *Int'l*, pg. 3167
GUANGZHOU SECURITIES CO., LTD.—See CITIC Securities Co., Ltd.; *Int'l*, pg. 1622
GUANGZHOU SENKO LOGISTICS CO., LTD.—See Senko Group Holdings Co., Ltd.; *Int'l*, pg. 6709
GUANGZHOU SHANGPIN HOME COLLECTION CO., LTD.; *Int'l*, pg. 3167
GUANGZHOU SHENG SHI YUAN TRADING COMPANY LIMITED—See Yestar Healthcare Holdings Company Limited; *Int'l*, pg. 8578
GUANGZHOU SHINDENGEN ELECTRONIC CO., LTD.—See Shindengen Electric Manufacturing Co., Ltd.; *Int'l*, pg. 6841
GUANGZHOU SHIYUAN ELECTRONICS CO., LTD; *Int'l*, pg. 3168
GUANGZHOU SHIYUAN ELECTRONIC TECHNOLOGY CO., LTD.; *Int'l*, pg. 3168
GUANGZHOU SHIZHEN INFORMATION TECHNOLOGY CO., LTD.—See Guangzhou Shiyuan Electronics Co., Ltd; *Int'l*, pg. 3168
GUANGZHOU SHOWA AUTOPARTS CO., LTD.—See Hitachi Astemo, Ltd.; *Int'l*, pg. 3409
GUANGZHOU SIA ABRASIVES CO., LTD.—See Robert Bosch GmbH; *Int'l*, pg. 6364
GUANGZHOU SIE CONSULTING CO., LTD.; *Int'l*, pg. 3168
GUANGZHOU SINOBLE JEWELRY LIMITED—See Central Development Holdings Ltd.; *Int'l*, pg. 1406
GUANGZHOU SINO-MICROELECTRONICS CO., LTD.—See Jilin Sino-Microelectronics Co., Ltd.; *Int'l*, pg. 3964
GUANGZHOU SINTO ZHONGTONG MACHINERY CO., LTD.—See Sintokogio Ltd.; *Int'l*, pg. 6958
GUANGZHOU S.K AUTOMOTIVE INTERIOR CO., LTD.—See Kasai Kogyo Co., Ltd.; *Int'l*, pg. 4086
GUANGZHOU SKYTONE SMART TECHNOLOGIES CO., LTD.—See Anhui Tatfook Technology Co., Ltd; *Int'l*, pg. 469
GUANGZHOU SMART GRID INFORMATION TECHNOLOGY CO., LTD.—See Guangzhou Goaland Energy Conservation Tech Co., Ltd.; *Int'l*, pg. 3165
GUANGZHOU SONGFA HOTEL EQUIPMENT SUPPLIERS CO.—See Guangdong Songfa Ceramics Co., Ltd.; *Int'l*, pg. 3160
GUANGZHOU S.P.I DESIGN CO., LTD.; *Int'l*, pg. 3167
GUANGZHOU STANLEY ELECTRIC CO,.LTD—See Stanley Electric Co., Ltd.; *Int'l*, pg. 7170
GUANGZHOU STARLITE ENVIRONMENTAL FRIENDLY CENTER LTD.—See Starlite Holdings Limited; *Int'l*, pg. 7178
GUANGZHOU SUMIDA ELECTRIC CO., LTD.—See Sumida Corporation; *Int'l*, pg. 7261
GUANGZHOU TAIHUA MULTILAYER CIRCUIT BOARD CO., LTD.—See Guangdong Chaohua Technology Co., Ltd.; *Int'l*, pg. 3153

COMPANY NAME INDEX

GUANGZHOU TAI YI TRADING COMPANY LIMITED—See Tse Sui Luen Jewellery (International) Limited; *Int'l*, pg. 7950
GUANGZHOU TANDBERG ELECTRONIC COMPONENTS CO. LTD.—See Sphere 3D Corporation; *Int'l*, pg. 7134
GUANGZHOU TAOBO SPORTS DEVELOPMENT COMPANY LIMITED—See Hillhouse Investment Management Limited; *Int'l*, pg. 3392
GUANGZHOU TARGET-UNI DIGITAL MARKETING CO., LTD.—See Zhewen Interactive Group Co Ltd; *Int'l*, pg. 8671
GUANGZHOU TECH-LONG PACKAGING MACHINERY CO., LTD.; *Int'l*, pg. 3168
GUANGZHOU TERMBRAY ELECTRONICS TECHNOLOGIES COMPANY LIMITED—See TTM Technologies, Inc.; *U.S. Public*, pg. 2203
GUANGZHOU TIGERS POLYMER CO., LTD.—See Tigers Polymer Corporation; *Int'l*, pg. 7746
GUANGZHOU TINCI MATERIALS TECHNOLOGY COMPANY LIMITED; *Int'l*, pg. 3168
GUANGZHOU TINGJIN BEVERAGE CO., LTD.—See Tingyi (Cayman Islands) Holding Corp.; *Int'l*, pg. 7754
GUANGZHOU TINGYI FOOD CO., LTD.—See Tingyi (Cayman Islands) Holding Corp.; *Int'l*, pg. 7754
GUANGZHOU TONGDA AUTO ELECTRIC CO., LTD.; *Int'l*, pg. 3168
GUANGZHOU TOSHIBA BAIYUN CONTROL SYSTEM ENGINEERING CO., LTD.—See Japan Industrial Partners, Inc.; *Int'l*, pg. 3893
GUANGZHOU TOYOTETSU AUTOMOBILE PARTS CO., LTD.—See Toyoda Iron Works Co., Ltd.; *Int'l*, pg. 7863
GUANGZHOU TREDEGAR FILM PRODUCTS COMPANY LIMITED—See Tredegar Corporation; *U.S. Public*, pg. 2187
GUANGZHOU TS AUTOMOTIVE INTERIOR SYSTEMS CO., LTD.—See TS Tech Co Ltd; *Int'l*, pg. 7947
GUANGZHOU TS TECH AUTOMOTIVE INTERIOR RESEARCH & DEVELOPMENT CO., LTD.—See TS Tech Co Ltd; *Int'l*, pg. 7947
GUANGZHOU TUV INDUSTRIAL TECHNICAL SERVICES CO., LTD.—See TUV NORD AG; *Int'l*, pg. 7980
GUANGZHOU UNIQUE LOGISTICS INTERNATIONAL LIMITED—See Unique Logistics International Inc.; *U.S. Public*, pg. 2227
GUANGZHOU UNITED STEEL STRUCTURES LIMITED—See CSSC Offshore & Marine Engineering Company Ltd.; *Int'l*, pg. 1868
GUANGZHOU VANKE REAL ESTATE COMPANY LIMITED—See China Vanke Co., Ltd.; *Int'l*, pg. 1562
GUANGZHOU VBH CONSTRUCTION HARDWARE TRADING CO.,LTD.—See VBH Holding AG; *Int'l*, pg. 8139
GUANGZHOU WAHLAP TECHNOLOGY CORPORATION LIMITED; *Int'l*, pg. 3168
GUANGZHOU WANBAO GROUP CO., LTD.; *Int'l*, pg. 3168
GUANGZHOU WANRONG INFORMATION TECHNOLOGY CO., LTD.—See PacificNet Inc.; *Int'l*, pg. 5692
GUANGZHOU WENCHONG SHIPYARD CO., LTD.—See CSSC Offshore & Marine Engineering Company Ltd.; *Int'l*, pg. 1868
GUANGZHOU WESTMINSTER TRAVEL SERVICES LTD.—See Corporate Travel Management Limited; *Int'l*, pg. 1806
GUANGZHOU WICE LOGISTICS CO., LTD.—See WICE Logistics Public Company Limited; *Int'l*, pg. 8401
GUANGZHOU WONDFO BIOTECH CO., LTD.; *Int'l*, pg. 3168
GUANGZHOU XIN TIAN WEI TRANSPORTATION DEVELOPMENT CO., LTD.—See ComfortDelGro Corporation Limited; *Int'l*, pg. 1713
GUANGZHOU XX-MOTOR INFORMATION TECHNOLOGYCO., LTD.—See PCI Technology Group Co., Ltd; *Int'l*, pg. 5768
GUANGZHOU YAKULT CO., LTD.—See Yakult Honsha Co., Ltd.; *Int'l*, pg. 8546
GUANGZHOU YAMAHA-PEARL RIVER PIANO INC.—See Yamaha Corporation; *Int'l*, pg. 8549
GUANGZHOU YI-LIANG TRADING CO., LTD.—See Everlight Electronics Co., Ltd.; *Int'l*, pg. 2567
GUANGZHOU YONGTONG METRO ADS CO., LTD.—See JCDecaux S.A.; *Int'l*, pg. 3921
GUANGZHOU YOROZU BAO MIT AUTOMOTIVE CO., LTD.—See Yorozu Corporation; *Int'l*, pg. 8599
GUANGZHOU YUETAI GROUP CO., LTD.; *Int'l*, pg. 3168
GUANGZHOU YUEXIU CAPITAL HOLDINGS GROUP CO., LTD.; *Int'l*, pg. 3168
GUANGZHOU YUSHIN PRECISION EQUIPMENT CO., LTD.—See YUSHIN PRECISION EQUIPMENT CO. LTD.; *Int'l*, pg. 8617
GUANGZHOU ZHAOKE LIAN FA PHARMACEUTICAL LIMITED—See Lee's Pharmaceutical Holdings Limited; *Int'l*, pg. 4441
GUANGZHOU ZHENGTONG LOGISTICS CO. LTD.—See Great-Sun Foods Co.,LTD.; *Int'l*, pg. 3066
GUANGZHOU ZHIGUANG ELECTRIC CO., LTD.; *Int'l*, pg. 3168
GUANGZHOU ZHIGUANG ELECTRIC LTD.—See Guangzhou Zhiguang Electric Co., Ltd.; *Int'l*, pg. 3168

GUANGZHOU ZHIGUANG ENERGY SAVING CO., LTD.—See Guangzhou Zhiguang Electric Co., Ltd.; *Int'l*, pg. 3168
GUANGZHOU ZHUJIANG BREWERY GROUP CO., LTD.; *Int'l*, pg. 3168
GUANHAES ENERGIA S.A.—See Light S.A.; *Int'l*, pg. 4496
GUANHUA CORP.; *U.S. Private*, pg. 1808
GUANNAN ZHONGYU GAS CO., LTD.—See Zhongyu Energy Holdings Limited; *Int'l*, pg. 8675
GUANO-WERKE GMBH & CO. KG—See BASF SE; *Int'l*, pg. 884
GUANWEI RECYCLING CORP.; *Int'l*, pg. 3169
GUANZE MEDICAL INFORMATION INDUSTRY (HOLDING) CO., LTD.; *Int'l*, pg. 3169
GUAN ZHI HOLDINGS LTD.—See Gunze Limited; *Int'l*, pg. 3185
GUARAGUAO TRUCK SALES INC.; *U.S. Private*, pg. 1808
THE GUARANTEE COMPANY OF NORTH AMERICA—See Intact Financial Corporation; *Int'l*, pg. 3727
THE GUARANTEE COMPANY OF NORTH AMERICA—See Intact Financial Corporation; *Int'l*, pg. 3727
GUARANTEED HOME MORTGAGE, INC.; *U.S. Private*, pg. 1809
GUARANTEED INDUSTRIES LIMITED; *Int'l*, pg. 3169
GUARANTEED RATE, INC.; *U.S. Private*, pg. 1809
GUARANTEE ELECTRICAL COMPANY; *U.S. Private*, pg. 1808
GUARANTEE INSURANCE COMPANY—See Guarantee Insurance Group, Inc.; *U.S. Private*, pg. 1809
GUARANTEE INSURANCE GROUP, INC.; *U.S. Private*, pg. 1809
GUARANTEE INTERIORS INC.; *U.S. Private*, pg. 1809
GUARANTEE RV; *Int'l*, pg. 3169
GUARANTEE SPECIALTIES INC.; *U.S. Private*, pg. 1809
GUARANTEE TITLE & TRUST COMPANY; *U.S. Private*, pg. 1809
GUARANTY BANCORP—See Independent Bank Group, Inc.; *U.S. Public*, pg. 1116
GUARANTY BANCSHARES, INC.; *U.S. Public*, pg. 973
GUARANTY BANK AND TRUST COMPANY—See Guaranty Capital Corp; *U.S. Private*, pg. 1809
GUARANTY BANK—See QCR Holdings, Inc.; *U.S. Public*, pg. 1742
GUARANTY BANK & TRUST COMPANY—See Independent Bank Group, Inc.; *U.S. Public*, pg. 1116
GUARANTY BANK & TRUST, N.A.—See Guaranty Bancshares, Inc.; *U.S. Public*, pg. 973
GUARANTY BROADCASTING COMPANY, LLC—See Guaranty Corporation; *U.S. Public*, pg. 973
GUARANTY CAPITAL CORP; *U.S. Private*, pg. 1809
GUARANTY CHEVROLET-PONTIAC; *U.S. Private*, pg. 1809
GUARANTY CORPORATION; *U.S. Public*, pg. 973
GUARANTY DEVELOPMENT COMPANY; *U.S. Private*, pg. 1809
GUARANTY FEDERAL BANCSHARES, INC.—See QCR Holdings, Inc.; *U.S. Public*, pg. 1742
GUARANTY FINANCIAL CORP.; *U.S. Public*, pg. 973
GUARANTY INCOME LIFE INSURANCE COMPANY—See Kuvare US Holdings, Inc.; *U.S. Private*, pg. 2358
GUARANTY REAL ESTATE MANAGEMENT COMPANY, LLC—See Guaranty Corporation; *U.S. Public*, pg. 973
GUARANTY REALTY, INC.—See QCR Holdings, Inc.; *U.S. Public*, pg. 1742
GUARANTY RV CENTERS; *U.S. Private*, pg. 1809
GUARANTY TRUST BANK (GAMBIA) LIMITED—See Guaranty Trust Bank plc; *Int'l*, pg. 3169
GUARANTY TRUST BANK PLC; *Int'l*, pg. 3169
GUARANTY TRUST BANK (SIERRA LEONE) LIMITED—See Guaranty Trust Bank plc; *Int'l*, pg. 3169
GUARANTY TRUST BANK (UK) LIMITED—See Guaranty Trust Bank plc; *Int'l*, pg. 3169
GUARANTY TRUST HOLDING COMPANY PLC; *Int'l*, pg. 3169
GUARARAPES CONFECCOES S.A.; *Int'l*, pg. 3169
GUARDAMIGLIO S.R.L.—See Cremonini S.p.A.; *Int'l*, pg. 1838
GUARDANT HEALTH, INC.; *U.S. Public*, pg. 973
GUARDCAP ASSET MANAGEMENT LIMITED—See Guardian Capital Group Limited; *Int'l*, pg. 3169
GUARDFORCE AI CO., LIMITED; *Int'l*, pg. 3169
GUARDFORCE LIMITED—See China Security Co., Ltd.; *Int'l*, pg. 1550
GUARDFORCE (MACAU) LIMITED—See China Security Co., Ltd.; *Int'l*, pg. 1550
GUARDIAN 8 HOLDINGS; *U.S. Private*, pg. 1809
GUARDIAN AFRICA CORP (PTY) LTD.—See Koch Industries, Inc.; *U.S. Private*, pg. 2329
GUARDIAN ALARM COMPANY; *U.S. Private*, pg. 1809
GUARDIAN ALARM OF TOLEDO—See Guardian Alarm Company; *U.S. Private*, pg. 1809
GUARDIAN ANALYTICS, INC.—See NICE Ltd.; *Int'l*, pg. 5265
GUARDIAN ANGELS HOMECARE, LLC; *U.S. Private*, pg. 1809

GUARDIAN HOLDINGS LIMITED

GUARDIAN A SHAWCOR COMPANY—See ShawCor Ltd.; *Int'l*, pg. 6791
GUARDIAN ASSET MANAGEMENT LTD—See Guardian Holdings Limited; *Int'l*, pg. 3171
GUARDIAN AUTOGLAS GMBH—See Parter Capital Group GmbH; *Int'l*, pg. 5748
GUARDIAN CAPITAL ADVISORS LP—See Guardian Capital Group Limited; *Int'l*, pg. 3169
GUARDIAN CAPITAL ENTERPRISES LIMITED—See Guardian Capital Group Limited; *Int'l*, pg. 3169
GUARDIAN CAPITAL GROUP LIMITED; *Int'l*, pg. 3169
GUARDIAN CAPITAL LP—See Guardian Capital Group Limited; *Int'l*, pg. 3169
GUARDIAN CAPITAL PARTNERS, LLC; *U.S. Private*, pg. 1810
GUARDIAN CARE OF AHOSKIE—See Apollo Global Management, Inc.; *U.S. Public*, pg. 156
GUARDIAN CARE OF ROANOKE RAPIDS—See Apollo Global Management, Inc.; *U.S. Public*, pg. 156
GUARDIAN COMMERCIAL REALTY; *U.S. Private*, pg. 1810
GUARDIAN COMPANIES INC.; *U.S. Private*, pg. 1810
GUARDIAN COMPANIES INC.—See Guardian Companies Inc.; *U.S. Private*, pg. 1810
GUARDIAN CONTROLS LTD.; *Int'l*, pg. 3170
GUARDIAN COUPLINGS LLC—See Regal Rexnord Corporation; *U.S. Public*, pg. 1772
GUARDIAN DO BRASIL VIDROS PLANOS LTDA—See Koch Industries, Inc.; *U.S. Private*, pg. 2329
GUARDIAN ELECTRIC MANUFACTURING COMPANY—See Kelco Industries Inc.; *U.S. Private*, pg. 2274
GUARDIAN ENGINEERING LIMITED—See Vistar Holdings Limited; *Int'l*, pg. 8254
GUARDIAN EUROPE S.A.R.L.—See Koch Industries, Inc.; *U.S. Private*, pg. 2329
GUARDIAN EXPLORATION INC.; *Int'l*, pg. 3170
GUARDIAN FALL PROTECTION, INC.; *U.S. Private*, pg. 1810
GUARDIAN FIRE ENGINEERS & CONSULTANTS LIMITED—See Vistar Holdings Limited; *Int'l*, pg. 8254
GUARDIAN FIRE PROTECTION SERVICE, LLC—See Knox Lane LP; *U.S. Private*, pg. 2324
GUARDIAN FLACHGLAS GMBH—See Koch Industries, Inc.; *U.S. Private*, pg. 2329
GUARDIAN FLIGHT, LLC—See KKR & Co. Inc.; *U.S. Public*, pg. 1252
GUARDIANFP LIMITED—See Suncorp Group Limited; *Int'l*, pg. 7311
GUARDIAN FUELING TECHNOLOGIES; *U.S. Private*, pg. 1810
GUARDIAN FUNERAL HOME—See Service Corporation International; *U.S. Public*, pg. 1871
GUARDIAN GATE HARDWARE, LLC—See The Duchossois Group, Inc.; *U.S. Private*, pg. 4023
GUARDIAN GENERAL INSURANCE LTD—See Guardian Holdings Limited; *Int'l*, pg. 3171
GUARDIAN GENERAL LTD—See Guardian Holdings Limited; *Int'l*, pg. 3171
GUARDIAN GLASS CO. - CORSICANA PLANT—See Koch Industries, Inc.; *U.S. Private*, pg. 2329
GUARDIAN GLASS CO. - KINGSBURY PLANT—See Koch Industries, Inc.; *U.S. Private*, pg. 2329
GUARDIAN GLASS CO. - MILLBURY PLANT—See Koch Industries, Inc.; *U.S. Private*, pg. 2329
GUARDIAN GLASS COMPANY—See Koch Industries, Inc.; *U.S. Private*, pg. 2329
GUARDIAN GLASS ESPANA CENTRAL VIDRIERA S.L.—See Koch Industries, Inc.; *U.S. Private*, pg. 2329
GUARDIAN GLOBAL SECURITY PLC; *Int'l*, pg. 3170
GUARDIAN GROUP, INC.—See YOUNG & Associates; *U.S. Private*, pg. 4592
GUARDIAN HEALTH AND BEAUTY SDN BHD—See Jardine Matheson Holdings Limited; *Int'l*, pg. 3909
GUARDIAN HEALTH CARE, INC.—See KKR & Co. Inc.; *U.S. Public*, pg. 1249
GUARDIAN HEALTH SERVICES, L.L.C.—See Apollo Global Management, Inc.; *U.S. Public*, pg. 155
GUARDIAN HOLDINGS INC.; *U.S. Private*, pg. 1810
GUARDIAN HOLDINGS LIMITED; *Int'l*, pg. 3170
GUARDIAN HOME CARE, INC.—See Encompass Health Corporation; *U.S. Public*, pg. 756
GUARDIAN HYGIENE SERVICES LIMITED—See Rollins, Inc.; *U.S. Public*, pg. 1809
GUARDIAN IB LIMITED—See Brown & Brown, Inc.; *U.S. Public*, pg. 400
GUARDIAN IND., INC.—See Regal Rexnord Corporation; *U.S. Public*, pg. 1772
GUARDIAN INDUSTRIE FRANCE SAS—See Koch Industries, Inc.; *U.S. Private*, pg. 2329
GUARDIAN INDUSTRIES CORP. LTD.—See Koch Industries, Inc.; *U.S. Private*, pg. 2329
GUARDIAN INDUSTRIES CORP - RICHBURG PLANT—See Koch Industries, Inc.; *U.S. Private*, pg. 2329
GUARDIAN INDUSTRIES CORP.—See Koch Industries, Inc.; *U.S. Private*, pg. 2329
GUARDIAN INDUSTRIES POLAND SP.Z.O.O.—See Koch Industries, Inc.; *U.S. Private*, pg. 2329

GUARDIAN HOLDINGS LIMITED

GUARDIAN INDUSTRIES UK LTD—See Koch Industries, Inc.; *U.S. Private*, pg. 2329
GUARDIAN INDUSTRIES VP, S. DE R.L. DE C.V.—See Koch Industries, Inc.; *U.S. Private*, pg. 2329
GUARDIAN INSPECTION S.A. DE C.V.—See ShawCor Ltd.; *Int'l*, pg. 6791
THE GUARDIAN INSURANCE & ANNUITY COMPANY, INC.—See The Guardian Life Insurance Company of America; *U.S. Private*, pg. 4040
GUARDIAN INSURANCE COMPANY, INC.—See Lockhart Companies Inc.; *U.S. Private*, pg. 2478
GUARDIAN INVESTOR SERVICES LLC—See The Guardian Life Insurance Company of America; *U.S. Private*, pg. 4040
GUARDIAN/KW HAYWARD LLC—See Kennedy-Wilson Holdings, Inc.; *U.S. Public*, pg. 1223
GUARDIAN LABORATORIES DIVISION—See United-Guardian, Inc.; *U.S. Public*, pg. 2238
THE GUARDIAN LIFE INSURANCE COMPANY OF AMERICA; *U.S. Private*, pg. 4040
GUARDIAN LIFE OF THE CARIBBEAN LTD—See Guardian Holdings Limited; *Int'l*, pg. 3171
GUARDIANLINK; *U.S. Private*, pg. 1810
GUARDIAN LLODIO UNO, S.L.—See Koch Industries, Inc.; *U.S. Private*, pg. 2329
GUARDIAN LUXGUARD I S.A.—See Koch Industries, Inc.; *U.S. Private*, pg. 2329
GUARDIAN MEDIA GROUP PLC—See The Scott Trust Limited; *Int'l*, pg. 7680
GUARDIAN MEDIA LIMITED—See ANSA McAL Limited; *Int'l*, pg. 477
GUARDIAN MORTGAGE—See FirstSun Capital Bancorp; *U.S. Public*, pg. 850
GUARDIAN MOVING & STORAGE CO., INC.; *U.S. Private*, pg. 1810
GUARDIAN NAVARRA S.L.—See Koch Industries, Inc.; *U.S. Private*, pg. 2329
GUARDIAN OILFIELD SERVICES—See ShawCor Ltd.; *Int'l*, pg. 6791
GUARDIAN OROSHAZA CO. LTD.—See Koch Industries, Inc.; *U.S. Private*, pg. 2329
GUARDIAN PACKAGING INDUSTRIES, LP—See Conner Industries, Inc.; *U.S. Private*, pg. 1017
GUARDIAN PEST CONTROL LIMITED—See Rollins, Inc.; *U.S. Public*, pg. 1809
GUARDIAN PHARMACIES AUSTRALIA PTY. LTD.—See Sigma Healthcare Ltd.; *Int'l*, pg. 6907
GUARDIAN PHARMACY, LLC; *U.S. Private*, pg. 1810
GUARDIAN PHARMACY OF DALLAS-FORT WORTH—See Guardian Pharmacy, LLC; *U.S. Private*, pg. 1810
GUARDIAN PIPELINE, L.L.C.—See ONEOK, Inc.; *U.S. Public*, pg. 1603
GUARDIAN PROPERTY MANAGEMENT LIMITED—See Savills plc; *Int'l*, pg. 6598
GUARDIAN PROTECTION PRODUCTS, INC.—See On-Point Warranty Solutions, LLC; *U.S. Private*, pg. 3027
GUARDIAN PROTECTION SERVICES, INC.—See Armstrong Holdings, Inc.; *U.S. Private*, pg. 331
GUARDIAN ROYAL EXCHANGE PLC—See AXA S.A.; *Int'l*, pg. 758
GUARDIAN SAVINGS BANK FSB; *U.S. Private*, pg. 1810
GUARDIAN SECURITY SYSTEMS, INC.; *U.S. Private*, pg. 1810
GUARDIAN SMART INFRASTRUCTURE MANAGEMENT INC.—See Guardian Capital Group Limited; *Int'l*, pg. 3170
THE GUARDIAN—See The Scott Trust Limited; *Int'l*, pg. 7680
GUARDIAN SOUTH EAST ASIA PTE. LTD.—See V.S. Industry Berhad; *Int'l*, pg. 8106
GUARDIAN STEKLO ROSTOV LLC—See Koch Industries, Inc.; *U.S. Private*, pg. 2329
GUARDIAN STEKLO RYAZAN LLC—See Koch Industries, Inc.; *U.S. Private*, pg. 2329
GUARDIAN SURVIVAL GEAR, INC.; *U.S. Private*, pg. 1810
GUARDIAN TECHNOLOGIES LLC—See Lasko Products, LLC; *U.S. Private*, pg. 2395
GUARDIAN TITLE AGENCY, LLC—See Anywhere Real Estate Inc.; *U.S. Public*, pg. 141
GUARDIAN TITLE COMPANY—See Anywhere Real Estate Inc.; *U.S. Public*, pg. 142
GUARDIAN TRACKING, LLC—See Envisage Technologies, LLC; *U.S. Private*, pg. 1410
GUARDIAN TRAFFIC SYSTEMS, LLC—See The Duchossois Group, Inc.; *U.S. Private*, pg. 4023
GUARDIAN TRAVEL, INC.—See Assurant, Inc.; *U.S. Public*, pg. 215
GUARDIAN ZOUJAJ INTERNATIONAL FLOAT GLASS CO. LLC—See Koch Industries, Inc.; *U.S. Private*, pg. 2329
GUARDIAR USA LLC; *U.S. Private*, pg. 1810
GUARD INSURANCE GROUP, INC.—See Berkshire Hathaway Inc.; *U.S. Public*, pg. 302
GUARDION HEALTH SCIENCES, INC.; *U.S. Public*, pg. 973
GUARDIUM, INC.—See International Business Machines Corporation; *U.S. Public*, pg. 1145
GUARD ONE SECURITY, INC.—See Security Solutions of America; *U.S. Private*, pg. 3596
GUARD PUBLISHING COMPANY; *U.S. Private*, pg. 1809
GUARDRISK ALLIED PRODUCTS & SERVICES PROPRIETARY LIMITED—See Alexander Forbes Group Holdings Limited; *Int'l*, pg. 307
GUARDSIGHT, INC.—See Iron Bow Technologies LLC; *U.S. Private*, pg. 2139
GUARDSMAN AUSTRALIA PTY LIMITED—See The Sherwin-Williams Company; *U.S. Public*, pg. 2127
GUARDSMAN INDUSTRIES LIMITED—See The Sherwin-Williams Company; *U.S. Public*, pg. 2128
GUARD-SYSTEMS, INC.; *U.S. Private*, pg. 1809
GUARD THERAPEUTICS INTERNATIONAL AB; *Int'l*, pg. 3169
GUAR GLOBAL LTD.; *U.S. Private*, pg. 1808
GUAVA LTD.—See Ardian SAS; *Int'l*, pg. 554
GUAVUS, INC.—See Thales S.A.; *Int'l*, pg. 7606
GUAY INC.; *Int'l*, pg. 3171
GUBER A.D.; *Int'l*, pg. 3171
GUBRA A/S; *Int'l*, pg. 3171
GUBRE FABRIKALARI T.A.S.; *Int'l*, pg. 3171
GUCCI AMERICA INC.—See Kering S.A.; *Int'l*, pg. 4135
GUCCI AUSTRALIA PTY LTD—See Kering S.A.; *Int'l*, pg. 4134
GUCCI AUSTRIA GMBH.—See Kering S.A.; *Int'l*, pg. 4135
GUCCI BELGIUM SA—See Kering S.A.; *Int'l*, pg. 4134
GUCCI (CHINA) TRADING LTD—See Kering S.A.; *Int'l*, pg. 4135
GUCCI FINANZIARIA SPA—See Kering S.A.; *Int'l*, pg. 4135
GUCCI GARDEN SRL—See Kering S.A.; *Int'l*, pg. 4134
GUCCI GROUP JAPAN HOLDING LIMITED—See Kering S.A.; *Int'l*, pg. 4135
GUCCI GROUP JAPAN LIMITED—See Kering S.A.; *Int'l*, pg. 4135
GUCCI (HONG KONG) LTD.—See Kering S.A.; *Int'l*, pg. 4134
GUCCI HUNGARY KFT—See Kering S.A.; *Int'l*, pg. 4135
GUCCI HUNGARY RETAIL LTD.—See Kering S.A.; *Int'l*, pg. 4134
GUCCI INDIA PRIVATE LTD—See Kering S.A.; *Int'l*, pg. 4135
GUCCI IRELAND LIMITED—See Kering S.A.; *Int'l*, pg. 4135
GUCCI LOGISTICA SPA—See Kering S.A.; *Int'l*, pg. 4135
GUCCI MEXICO S.A. DE C.V.—See Kering S.A.; *Int'l*, pg. 4135
GUCCI NEW ZEALAND LTD—See Kering S.A.; *Int'l*, pg. 4135
GUCCI OSTERIA JAPAN G.K.—See Kering S.A.; *Int'l*, pg. 4134
GUCCI PARTICIPATION BV—See Kering S.A.; *Int'l*, pg. 4135
GUCCI SAM—See Kering S.A.; *Int'l*, pg. 4135
GUCCI SHOPS OF CANADA INC.—See Kering S.A.; *Int'l*, pg. 4135
GUCCI SINGAPORE PTE LIMITED—See Kering S.A.; *Int'l*, pg. 4135
GUCCI SWEDEN AB—See Kering S.A.; *Int'l*, pg. 4135
GUCHENG ZHONGYU GAS CO., LTD.—See Zhongyu Energy Holdings Limited; *Int'l*, pg. 8676
GUCKENHEIMER ENTERPRISE, INC.—See EQT AB; *Int'l*, pg. 2476
GUCKENHEIMER ENTERPRISE, INC.—See The Goldman Sachs Group, Inc.; *U.S. Public*, pg. 2077
G.U. CO., LTD.—See Fast Retailing Co., Ltd.; *Int'l*, pg. 2621
GUCO N.V.—See Rudisa Holdingmaatschappij N.V.; *Int'l*, pg. 6424
GUDECO ELEKTRONIK HANDELS GMBH; *Int'l*, pg. 3171
GUDEL A.S.—See Gudel Group AG; *Int'l*, pg. 3171
GUDEL AUTOMATION GMBH—See Gudel Group AG; *Int'l*, pg. 3171
GUDEL CONTROLS GMBH—See Gudel Group AG; *Int'l*, pg. 3171
GUDEL GMBH—See Gudel Group AG; *Int'l*, pg. 3171
GUDEL GMBH—See Gudel Group AG; *Int'l*, pg. 3171
GUDEL GROUP AG; *Int'l*, pg. 3171
GUDEL INC.—See Gudel Group AG; *Int'l*, pg. 3171
GUDEL INDIA PVT. LTD.—See Gudel Group AG; *Int'l*, pg. 3171
GUDEL INTERNATIONAL TRADING CO. LTD.—See Gudel Group AG; *Int'l*, pg. 3171
GUDEL INTRALOGISTICS GMBH—See Gudel Group AG; *Int'l*, pg. 3171
GUDEL LINEARTEC CO., LTD.—See Gudel Group AG; *Int'l*, pg. 3171
GUDEL LINEARTEC CO. LTD.—See Gudel Group AG; *Int'l*, pg. 3171
GUDEL LINEARTEC INC.—See Gudel Group AG; *Int'l*, pg. 3171
GUDEL LINEARTEC (U.K.) LTD.—See Gudel Group AG; *Int'l*, pg. 3171
GUDEL OTOMASYON LTD. STI.—See Gudel Group AG; *Int'l*, pg. 3171
GUDEL SAS—See Gudel Group AG; *Int'l*, pg. 3171
GUDEL SP. Z O.O.—See Gudel Group AG; *Int'l*, pg. 3171
GUDEL S.R.L.—See Gudel Group AG; *Int'l*, pg. 3171
GUDEL SUMER SAS—See Gudel Group AG; *Int'l*, pg. 3171
GUDEL TSC S.A. DE C.V.—See Gudel Group AG; *Int'l*, pg. 3171
GUDENKAUF CORPORATION—See Crestview Partners, L.P.; *U.S. Private*, pg. 1098
GUD FILTERS PTY. LTD.; *Int'l*, pg. 3171
GUD GERAER UMWELTDIENSTE GMBH & CO. KG—See Veolia Environnement S.A.; *Int'l*, pg. 8160
GUD (NZ) LIMITED—See Amotiv Limited; *Int'l*, pg. 431
GUDOU HOLDINGS LIMITED; *Int'l*, pg. 3171
GUELPH NISSAN; *Int'l*, pg. 3172
GUELPH-S, LP—See Lithia Motors, Inc.; *U.S. Public*, pg. 1322
GUELPH TOOL INC.; *Int'l*, pg. 3172
GUELPH TOOL SALES INC.—See Guelph Tool Inc.; *Int'l*, pg. 3172
GUELPH UTILITY POLE COMPANY LTD.—See Stella-Jones, Inc.; *Int'l*, pg. 7196
GUELPH VOLKSWAGEN; *Int'l*, pg. 3172
GUENTHER BAKERIES UK LIMITED—See The Pritzker Group - Chicago, LLC; *U.S. Private*, pg. 4098
GUENTHER-VORRUCKEN, INC.; *U.S. Private*, pg. 1810
GUERBET AG—See Guerbet SA; *Int'l*, pg. 3172
GUERBET ARGENTINA LIMITED - ARGENTINA BRANCH OFFICE—See Guerbet SA; *Int'l*, pg. 3172
GUERBET ARGENTINA LIMITED—See Guerbet SA; *Int'l*, pg. 3172
GUERBET ASIA PACIFIC LTD—See Guerbet SA; *Int'l*, pg. 3172
GUERBET COLOMBIA S.A.S.—See Guerbet SA; *Int'l*, pg. 3172
GUERBET FRANCE, SA—See Guerbet SA; *Int'l*, pg. 3172
GUERBET GMBH—See Guerbet SA; *Int'l*, pg. 3172
GUERBET GROSSHANDEL MIT PHARMAZEUTISCHEN PRODUKTEN GES.M.B.H.—See Guerbet SA; *Int'l*, pg. 3172
GUERBET ILAC TIBBI A.S.—See Guerbet SA; *Int'l*, pg. 3172
GUERBET IMAGING PANAMA S. A.—See Guerbet SA; *Int'l*, pg. 3172
GUERBET JAPAN KK—See Guerbet SA; *Int'l*, pg. 3172
GUERBET KOREA LTD.—See Guerbet SA; *Int'l*, pg. 3172
GUERBET LABORATORIES LTD.—See Guerbet SA; *Int'l*, pg. 3172
GUERBET LLC—See Guerbet SA; *Int'l*, pg. 3172
GUERBET MEXICANA S. A. DE C. V.—See Guerbet SA; *Int'l*, pg. 3172
GUERBET NEDERLAND B.V.—See Guerbet SA; *Int'l*, pg. 3172
GUERBET N.V.—See Guerbet SA; *Int'l*, pg. 3172
GUERBET POLAND SP. Z O.O.—See Guerbet SA; *Int'l*, pg. 3172
GUERBET PRODUTOS RADIOLOGICOS LTDA.—See Guerbet SA; *Int'l*, pg. 3172
GUERBET SA; *Int'l*, pg. 3172
GUERBET S.P.A.—See Guerbet SA; *Int'l*, pg. 3172
GUERBET TAIWAN CO., LTD.—See Guerbet SA; *Int'l*, pg. 3172
GUERIN S.A.—See Sonepar S.A.; *Int'l*, pg. 7092
GUERLAIN ARGENTINA (FACSA)—See LVMH Moet Hennessy Louis Vuitton SE; *Int'l*, pg. 4594
GUERLAIN ASIA PACIFIC LTD—See LVMH Moet Hennessy Louis Vuitton SE; *Int'l*, pg. 4594
GUERLAIN BENELUX S.A.—See LVMH Moet Hennessy Louis Vuitton SE; *Int'l*, pg. 4594
GUERLAIN BENELUX S.A.—See LVMH Moet Hennessy Louis Vuitton SE; *Int'l*, pg. 4594
GUERLAIN CANADA LTD.—See LVMH Moet Hennessy Louis Vuitton SE; *Int'l*, pg. 4594
GUERLAIN DE PORTUGAL LDA.—See LVMH Moet Hennessy Louis Vuitton SE; *Int'l*, pg. 4594
GUERLAIN GES. M.B.H.—See LVMH Moet Hennessy Louis Vuitton SE; *Int'l*, pg. 4594
GUERLAIN GMBH—See LVMH Moet Hennessy Louis Vuitton SE; *Int'l*, pg. 4594
GUERLAIN, INC.—See LVMH Moet Hennessy Louis Vuitton SE; *Int'l*, pg. 4594
GUERLAIN KK—See LVMH Moet Hennessy Louis Vuitton SE; *Int'l*, pg. 4594
GUERLAIN KOREA—See LVMH Moet Hennessy Louis Vuitton SE; *Int'l*, pg. 4594
GUERLAIN LTD.—See LVMH Moet Hennessy Louis Vuitton SE; *Int'l*, pg. 4594
GUERLAIN PARFUMEUR GMBH—See LVMH Moet Hennessy Louis Vuitton SE; *Int'l*, pg. 4594
GUERLAIN S.A.E.—See LVMH Moet Hennessy Louis Vuitton SE; *Int'l*, pg. 4594
GUERLAIN S.A.—See LVMH Moet Hennessy Louis Vuitton SE; *Int'l*, pg. 4594
GUERLAIN SPA—See LVMH Moet Hennessy Louis Vuitton SE; *Int'l*, pg. 4594
GUERLAIN TAIWAN CO. LTD.—See LVMH Moet Hennessy Louis Vuitton SE; *Int'l*, pg. 4594
GUERNSEY BEL INC.—See Kerry Group plc; *Int'l*, pg. 4138
GUERNSEY INTERNATIONAL FUND MANAGERS LIMITED—See ING Groep N.V.; *Int'l*, pg. 3699

GUERNSEY OFFICE PRODUCTS INC.; *U.S. Private*, pg. 1810
GUERNSEY STONE COMPANY—See Martin Marietta Materials, Inc.; *U.S. Public*, pg. 1389
GUERRERO EXPLORATION INC.; *Int'l*, pg. 3172
GUERRILLA RF, INC.; *U.S. Public*, pg. 973
GUERRILLA RF OPERATING CORPORATION—See Guerrilla RF, Inc.; *U.S. Public*, pg. 974
GUESS? ASIA LIMITED—See Guess? Inc.; *U.S. Public*, pg. 974
GUESS? CANADA CORPORATION—See Guess? Inc.; *U.S. Public*, pg. 974
GUESS.COM, INC.—See Guess? Inc.; *U.S. Public*, pg. 974
GUESS? DEUTSCHLAND GMBH—See Guess? Inc.; *U.S. Public*, pg. 974
GUESS? EUROPE SAGL—See Guess? Inc.; *U.S. Public*, pg. 974
GUESS FORD, INC.—See Guess Motors, Inc.; *U.S. Private*, pg. 1810
GUESS? INC.; *U.S. Public*, pg. 974
GUESS? ITALIA, SRL—See Guess? Inc.; *U.S. Public*, pg. 974
GUESS MOTORS, INC.; *U.S. Private*, pg. 1810
GUESS? PORTUGAL, LDA—See Guess? Inc.; *U.S. Public*, pg. 974
GUESTLOGIX INC.; *Int'l*, pg. 3173
GUEST PACKAGING, LLC—See Sysco Corporation; *U.S. Public*, pg. 1974
GUEST SERVICES COMPANY OF VIRGINIA—See Guest Services, Inc.; *U.S. Private*, pg. 1811
GUEST SERVICES, INC.; *U.S. Private*, pg. 1810
GUEST SUPPLY ASIA, LIMITED—See Sysco Corporation; *U.S. Public*, pg. 1976
GUEST-TEK INTERACTIVE ENTERTAINMENT INC—See Guest-Tek Interactive Entertainment Ltd.; *Int'l*, pg. 3172
GUEST-TEK INTERACTIVE ENTERTAINMENT LTD.; *Int'l*, pg. 3172
GUEST-TEK INTERACTIVE ENTERTAINMENT SP. Z O.O—See Guest-Tek Interactive Entertainment Ltd.; *Int'l*, pg. 3172
GUEST-TEK INTERACTIVE ENTERTAINMENT GROUP LTD—See Guest-Tek Interactive Entertainment Ltd.; *Int'l*, pg. 3172
GUFIC BIOSCIENCES LIMITED; *Int'l*, pg. 3173
GUGGENHEIM BASEBALL MANAGEMENT, L.P.; *U.S. Private*, pg. 1811
GUGGENHEIM CREDIT ALLOCATION FUND; *U.S. Public*, pg. 974
GUGGENHEIM CREDIT INCOME FUND—See Guggenheim Partners, LLC; *U.S. Private*, pg. 1811
GUGGENHEIM ENHANCED EQUITY INCOME FUND; *U.S. Public*, pg. 974
GUGGENHEIM FUNDS DISTRIBUTORS, LLC—See Guggenheim Partners, LLC; *U.S. Private*, pg. 1812
GUGGENHEIM LIFE AND ANNUITY COMPANY—See Guggenheim Partners, LLC; *U.S. Private*, pg. 1811
GUGGENHEIM PARTNERS, LLC; *U.S. Private*, pg. 1811
GUGGENHEIM STRATEGIC OPPORTUNITIES FUND; *U.S. Public*, pg. 974
GUGGENHEIM TAXABLE MUNICIPAL BOND & INVESTMENT GRADE DEBT TRUST—See Guggenheim Partners, LLC; *U.S. Private*, pg. 1812
GUGGISBERG KURZ AG—See BKW AG; *Int'l*, pg. 1055
GUH CIRCUIT INDUSTRY (PG) SDN. BHD.—See GUH Holdings Berhad; *Int'l*, pg. 3173
GUH CIRCUIT INDUSTRY (SUZHOU) CO., LTD.—See GUH Holdings Berhad; *Int'l*, pg. 3173
GUH DEVELOPMENT SDN. BHD.—See GUH Holdings Berhad; *Int'l*, pg. 3173
GUH ELECTRICAL (BW) SDN. BHD.—See GUH Holdings Berhad; *Int'l*, pg. 3173
GUHESWORI MERCHANT BANKING & FINANCE LIMITED; *Int'l*, pg. 3173
GUH HOLDINGS BERHAD; *Int'l*, pg. 3173
GUHL IKEBANA COSMETICS B.V.—See Kao Corporation; *Int'l*, pg. 4073
GUHL IKEBANA GMBH—See Kao Corporation; *Int'l*, pg. 4073
GUH PLANTATIONS SDN. BHD.—See GUH Holdings Berhad; *Int'l*, pg. 3173
GUH PROPERTIES SDN. BHD.—See GUH Holdings Berhad; *Int'l*, pg. 3173
GUIAN S.A.—See Marsh & McLennan Companies, Inc.; *U.S. Public*, pg. 1375
GUIDANCE AUTOMATION LIMITED—See Matthews International Corporation; *U.S. Public*, pg. 1399
GUIDANCE MARINE LLC—See Wartsila Corporation; *Int'l*, pg. 8346
GUIDANCE MARINE LTD.—See Wartsila Corporation; *Int'l*, pg. 8346
GUIDANCE MARINE PTE. LTD.—See Wartsila Corporation; *Int'l*, pg. 8346
GUIDANT EUROPE SA/NV—See Boston Scientific Corporation; *U.S. Public*, pg. 374
GUIDANT FINANCIAL GROUP, INC.; *U.S. Private*, pg. 1813
GUIDANT GROUP, INC.—See HFBG Holding B.V.; *Int'l*, pg. 3375
GUIDANT PARTNERS; *U.S. Private*, pg. 1813

THE GUIDA-SEIBERT DAIRY COMPANY INC.; *U.S. Private*, pg. 4040
GUIDED DISCOVERIES INC.; *U.S. Private*, pg. 1813
GUIDED INSURANCE SOLUTIONS, LLC—See The Baldwin Insurance Group, Inc.; *U.S. Public*, pg. 2036
GUIDEDRAW LTD.; *Int'l*, pg. 3173
GUIDED THERAPEUTICS, INC.; *U.S. Public*, pg. 974
GUIDED WAVE ASIA PTE. LTD.—See Advanced Holdings Ltd.; *Int'l*, pg. 159
GUIDED WAVE EUROPE BVBA—See Advanced Holdings Ltd.; *Int'l*, pg. 159
GUIDED WAVE INC.—See IGP Industries, LLC; *U.S. Private*, pg. 2040
GUIDEHOUSE INC.—See Bain Capital, LP; *U.S. Private*, pg. 432
GUIDEHOUSE LLP—See Bain Capital, LP; *U.S. Private*, pg. 432
GUIDELINE GEO AB; *Int'l*, pg. 3173
GUIDELINE GEO AMERICAS, INC.—See Guideline Geo AB; *Int'l*, pg. 3173
GUIDELINE GROUP INFORMATION TECHNOLOGIES LTD.; *Int'l*, pg. 3173
GUIDELINE, INC.—See Lake Capital Management LLC; *U.S. Private*, pg. 2374
GUIDENT CORP.—See Tekcapital plc; *Int'l*, pg. 7526
GUIDEONE INSURANCE COMPANY; *U.S. Private*, pg. 1813
GUIDEPOST GROWTH MANAGEMENT COMPANY LLC; *U.S. Private*, pg. 1813
GUIDEPOSTS ASSOCIATES, INC.; *U.S. Private*, pg. 1813
GUIDER MEDIA GROUP EUROPE AB—See Kinnevik AB; *Int'l*, pg. 4181
GUIDESPARK, INC.; *U.S. Private*, pg. 1813
GUIDESTAR DIRECT CORP.; *U.S. Private*, pg. 1813
GUIDESTAR USA, INC.; *U.S. Private*, pg. 1813
GUIDEWELL INC.—See GuideWell Mutual Holding Corporation; *U.S. Private*, pg. 1813
GUIDEWELL MUTUAL HOLDING CORPORATION; *U.S. Private*, pg. 1813
GUIDEWIRE CANADA LTD.—See Guidewire Software, Inc.; *U.S. Public*, pg. 974
GUIDEWIRE SOFTWARE ASIA LTD.—See Guidewire Software, Inc.; *U.S. Public*, pg. 974
GUIDEWIRE SOFTWARE (BEIJING) CO., LTD.—See Guidewire Software, Inc.; *U.S. Public*, pg. 974
GUIDEWIRE SOFTWARE CANADA LTD.—See Guidewire Software, Inc.; *U.S. Public*, pg. 974
GUIDEWIRE SOFTWARE DENMARK APS—See Guidewire Software, Inc.; *U.S. Public*, pg. 974
GUIDEWIRE SOFTWARE FRANCE SAS—See Guidewire Software, Inc.; *U.S. Public*, pg. 974
GUIDEWIRE SOFTWARE GMBH—See Guidewire Software, Inc.; *U.S. Public*, pg. 974
GUIDEWIRE SOFTWARE, INC.; *U.S. Public*, pg. 974
GUIDEWIRE SOFTWARE (IRELAND) LIMITED—See Guidewire Software, Inc.; *U.S. Public*, pg. 974
GUIDEWIRE SOFTWARE JAPAN K.K.—See Guidewire Software, Inc.; *U.S. Public*, pg. 974
GUIDEWIRE SOFTWARE LTD.—See Guidewire Software, Inc.; *U.S. Public*, pg. 974
GUIDEWIRE SOFTWARE (MALAYSIA) SDN. BHD—See Guidewire Software, Inc.; *U.S. Public*, pg. 974
GUIDEWIRE SOFTWARE PTY. LTD.—See Guidewire Software, Inc.; *U.S. Public*, pg. 974
GUIDEWIRE SOFTWARE (SWITZERLAND) GMBH—See Guidewire Software, Inc.; *U.S. Public*, pg. 974
GUIDEWORKS, LLC—See Comcast Corporation; *U.S. Public*, pg. 538
GUIDING EYES FOR THE BLIND, INC.; *U.S. Private*, pg. 1814
GUIDO & COMPANIES; *U.S. Private*, pg. 1814
GUIDON PARTNERS, LP; *U.S. Private*, pg. 1814
GUILBAUD SAS—See VINCI S.A.; *Int'l*, pg. 8222
GUILBERT LUXEMBOURG S.A.R.L.—See Aurelius Equity Opportunities SE & Co. KGaA; *Int'l*, pg. 709
GUILBERT PROPRETE; *Int'l*, pg. 3173
GUILD ASSOCIATES INC.; *U.S. Private*, pg. 1814
GUILD CLAIMS SERVICE—See Loss Management Group Ltd.; *Int'l*, pg. 4558
GUILD ELECTRIC LTD.; *Int'l*, pg. 3173
GUILD ESPORTS PLC; *Int'l*, pg. 3173
GUILDFORD MOTORS INC; *Int'l*, pg. 3173
THE GUILDFORD NUFFIELD HOSPITAL—See Nuffield Health; *Int'l*, pg. 5487
GUILDFORD VETS4PETS LIMITED—See Pets at Home Group Plc; *Int'l*, pg. 5833
THE GUILD FOR EXCEPTIONAL CHILDREN, INC.; *U.S. Private*, pg. 4040
THE GUILD FOR HUMAN SERVICES, INC.; *U.S. Private*, pg. 4040
GUILD GUITARS—See TPG Capital, L.P.; *U.S. Public*, pg. 2173
GUILD HOLDINGS COMPANY—See McCarthy Group, LLC; *U.S. Private*, pg. 2626
THE GUILD INC.; *U.S. Private*, pg. 4040
GUILDMASTER, INC.; *U.S. Private*, pg. 1814
GUILD MORTGAGE COMPANY, LLC—See McCarthy Group, LLC; *U.S. Private*, pg. 2626

GUILD MORTGAGE—See McCarthy Group, LLC; *U.S. Private*, pg. 2627
THE GUILD OF VALUERS & JEWELLERS—See Loss Management Group Ltd.; *Int'l*, pg. 4558
GUILDPRIME SPECIALIST CONTRACTS LTD.—See MBH Corporation Plc; *Int'l*, pg. 4752
GUILFORD AUTOMOCION IBERICA, S.L.—See Lear Corporation; *U.S. Public*, pg. 1297
GUILFORD CHILD DEVELOPMENT; *U.S. Public*, pg. 1814
GUILFORD DEUTSCHLAND GMBH—See Lear Corporation; *U.S. Public*, pg. 1297
GUILFORD EUROPE LTD.—See Lear Corporation; *U.S. Public*, pg. 1297
GUILFORD FRANCE—See Lear Corporation; *U.S. Public*, pg. 1297
GUILFORD GAS—See UGI Corporation; *U.S. Public*, pg. 2221
GUILFORD MILLS AUTOMOTIVE (CZECH REPUBLIC) LIMITED—See Lear Corporation; *U.S. Public*, pg. 1296
GUILFORD MILLS AUTOMOTIVE (PORTUGAL) LIMITED—See Lear Corporation; *U.S. Public*, pg. 1296
GUILFORD MILLS - AUTOMOTIVE & UPHOLSTERY FABRICS—See Lear Corporation; *U.S. Public*, pg. 1297
GUILFORD MILLS EUROPE LIMITED—See Lear Corporation; *U.S. Public*, pg. 1297
GUILFORD MILLS, INC.—See Lear Corporation; *U.S. Public*, pg. 1297
GUILFORD PERFORMANCE TEXTILES, INC.—See Lear Corporation; *U.S. Public*, pg. 1297
GUILFORD SAVINGS BANK; *U.S. Private*, pg. 1814
GUILFORD SHANGHAI TRADING CO., LTD.—See Lear Corporation; *U.S. Public*, pg. 1297
GUILFORD SPECIALTY GROUP, INC.—See IFG Companies; *U.S. Private*, pg. 2038
GUILIN ANXIN SOFTWARE CO., LTD.—See Japan System Techniques Co., Ltd.; *Int'l*, pg. 3905
GUILIN DAEWOO HOTEL CO. LTD.—See Korea Development Bank; *Int'l*, pg. 4282
GUILIN FUDA CO., LTD.; *Int'l*, pg. 3173
GUILIN HENKEL DETERGENTS & CLEANING PRODUCTS CO. LTD.—See Henkel AG & Co. KGaA; *Int'l*, pg. 3348
GUILIN LAYN NATURAL INGREDIENTS CORP.; *Int'l*, pg. 3173
GUILIN SANJIN PHARMACEUTICAL CO., LTD.; *Int'l*, pg. 3173
GUILIN SEAMILD FOODS CO., LTD.; *Int'l*, pg. 3173
GUILIN TOURISM CORPORATION LIMITED; *Int'l*, pg. 3174
GUILLEMOT CORPORATION S.A.; *Int'l*, pg. 3174
GUILLEMOT SA—See Guillemot Corporation S.A.; *Int'l*, pg. 3174
GUILLEMOT SPAIN SL—See Guillemot Corporation S.A.; *Int'l*, pg. 3174
GUILLIN DEUTSCHLAND GMBH—See Groupe Guillin SA; *Int'l*, pg. 3103
GUILLIN EMBALLAGES—See Groupe Guillin SA; *Int'l*, pg. 3103
GUILLIN ESPANA SL—See Groupe Guillin SA; *Int'l*, pg. 3104
GUILLIN ITALIA SPA—See Groupe Guillin SA; *Int'l*, pg. 3104
GUILLIN NEDERLAND B.V.—See Groupe Guillin SA; *Int'l*, pg. 3104
GUILLIN POLSKA NIEPRUSZEWO SP. Z O.O.—See Groupe Guillin SA; *Int'l*, pg. 3104
GUILLIN PORTUGAL—See Groupe Guillin SA; *Int'l*, pg. 3104
GUILLIN PORTUGAL, UNIPESSOAL, LDA—See Groupe Guillin SA; *Int'l*, pg. 3104
GUILLIN ROMANIA SRL—See Groupe Guillin SA; *Int'l*, pg. 3104
GUILLOT COBREDA S.A.S.—See LDC SA; *Int'l*, pg. 4431
GUILN FUDA ALFING LARGE CRANKSAFT CO., LTD.—See Guilin Fuda Co., Ltd.; *Int'l*, pg. 3173
GUILVIDIS—See Carrefour SA; *Int'l*, pg. 1345
GUIMA FRANCE S.A.S.—See Palfinger AG; *Int'l*, pg. 5707
GUIMAR ENGENHARIA LTDA.—See Jacobs Engineering Group, Inc.; *U.S. Public*, pg. 1184
GUINEA INSURANCE PLC; *Int'l*, pg. 3174
GUINNESS GHANA BREWERIES PLC—See Diageo plc; *Int'l*, pg. 2102
GUINNESS NIGERIA PLC—See Diageo plc; *Int'l*, pg. 2102
GUINNESS NORTHERN COUNTIES LTD; *Int'l*, pg. 3174
GUINNESS STOREHOUSE LIMITED—See Diageo plc; *Int'l*, pg. 2102
GUINNESS WORLD RECORDS LTD.—See The Jim Pattison Group; *Int'l*, pg. 7660
GUINOT JAPAN CORPORATION—See Mandom Corporation; *Int'l*, pg. 4668
GUIPUZCOANO CAPITAL, S.A.—See Banco de Sabadell, S.A.; *Int'l*, pg. 821
GUIPUZCOANO CORREDURIA DE SEGUROS DEL GRUPO BANCO GUIPUZCOANO, S.A.—See Banco de Sabadell, S.A.; *Int'l*, pg. 821

GUIPUZCOANO ENTIDAD GESTORA DE FONDOS DE PENSIONES, S.A.—See Banco de Sabadell, S.A.; *Int'l*, pg. 821
GUIRENNIAO CO., LTD.; *Int'l*, pg. 3174
GUIRYS INC.; *U.S. Private*, pg. 1814
THE GUITAMMER COMPANY; *U.S. Private*, pg. 4040
GUITAR CENTER HOLDINGS, INC.—See Bain Capital, LP; *U.S. Private*, pg. 440
GUITAR CENTER, INC.—See Bain Capital, LP; *U.S. Private*, pg. 440
GUITAR SALON INTERNATIONAL; *U.S. Private*, pg. 1814
GUITING QUARRY LIMITED—See SigmaRoc Plc; *Int'l*, pg. 6909
GUITTARD CHOCOLATE COMPANY; *U.S. Private*, pg. 1814
GUIYANG LONGMASTER INFORMATION & TECHNOLOGY CO., LTD.; *Int'l*, pg. 3174
GUIYANG SUNLORD XUNDA ELECTRONICS CO., LTD.—See Shenzhen Sunlord Electronics Co., Ltd.; *Int'l*, pg. 6822
GUIYANG VANKE REAL ESTATE COMPANY LIMITED—See China Vanke Co., Ltd.; *Int'l*, pg. 1562
GUIYANG XINTIAN PHARMACEUTICAL CO., LTD.; *Int'l*, pg. 3174
GUIZHOU AIRLINES COMPANY LIMITED—See China Southern Airlines Co., Ltd.; *Int'l*, pg. 1553
GUIZHOU BAILING GROUP PHARMACEUTICAL CO., LTD.; *Int'l*, pg. 3174
GUIZHOU BROADCASTING & TV INFORMATION NETWORK CO., LTD.; *Int'l*, pg. 3174
GUIZHOU CHANFERT ENTERPRISE CO., LTD.—See Guizhou Chanhen Chemical Corporation; *Int'l*, pg. 3174
GUIZHOU CHANGZHENG TIANCHENG HOLDING CO., LTD.; *Int'l*, pg. 3174
GUIZHOU CHANHEN CHEMICAL CORPORATION; *Int'l*, pg. 3174
GUIZHOU CHINA INTERNATIONAL TRAVEL SERVICE CO., LTD.—See China Tourism Group Duty Free Corporation Limited; *Int'l*, pg. 1560
GUIZHOU CRYSTAL CHEMICAL CO LTD—See China National Chemical Corporation; *Int'l*, pg. 1527
GUIZHOU CRYSTAL ORGANIC CHEMICAL (GROUP) CO., LTD.—See China National Chemical Corporation; *Int'l*, pg. 1527
GUIZHOU EAST CHINA ENGINEERING CO., LTD.—See East China Engineering Science & Technology Co., Ltd.; *Int'l*, pg. 2269
GUIZHOU GAS GROUP CORPORATION, LTD.; *Int'l*, pg. 3174
GUIZHOU GUIHANG AOTOMOTIVE COMPONENTS CO., LTD.; *Int'l*, pg. 3174
GUIZHOU HONGXING DEVELOPMENT CO., LTD.—See Guizhou Redstar Development Co., Ltd.; *Int'l*, pg. 3175
GUIZHOU HUACHANG AUTOMOBILE ELECTRICS CO. LTD.—See Mobase Co., Ltd.; *Int'l*, pg. 5007
GUIZHOU MACCURA SCIENCE & TECHNOLOGY CO., LTD—See Maccura Biotechnology Co., Ltd.; *Int'l*, pg. 4620
GUIZHOU NEW SHUANGLONG CEMENT CO., LTD.—See Anhui Conch Cement Company Limited; *Int'l*, pg. 467
GUIZHOU PANJIANG REFINED COAL CO., LTD.; *Int'l*, pg. 3174
GUIZHOU QIANYUAN POWER CO., LTD.; *Int'l*, pg. 3174
GUIZHOU REDSTAR DEVELOPMENT CO., LTD.; *Int'l*, pg. 3175
GUIZHOU RED STAR DEVELOPMENT DRAGON CHEMICAL INDUSTRY CO., LTD.—See Guizhou Redstar Development Co., Ltd.; *Int'l*, pg. 3175
GUIZHOU RED STAR DEVELOPMENT FANJINGSHAN COLD WATER FISHERIES CO., LTD.—See Guizhou Redstar Development Co., Ltd.; *Int'l*, pg. 3175
GUIZHOU RED STAR DEVELOPMENT IMPORT & EXPORT CO., LTD.—See Guizhou Redstar Development Co., Ltd.; *Int'l*, pg. 3175
GUIZHOU RONBAY LITHIUM BATTERY MATERIALS CO., LTD.—See Ningbo Ronbay New Energy Technology Co., Ltd.; *Int'l*, pg. 5305
GUIZHOU SANLI PHARMACEUTICAL CO., LTD.; *Int'l*, pg. 3175
GUIZHOU SHUI ON CEMENT DEVELOPMENT MANAGEMENT CO. LTD—See Shui On Company Limited; *Int'l*, pg. 6869
GUIZHOU SPACE APPLIANCE CO., LTD.; *Int'l*, pg. 3175
GUIZHOU TAIYONG-CHANGZHENG TECHNOLOGY CO., LTD.; *Int'l*, pg. 3175
GUIZHOU TONGJITANG PHARMACEUTICAL CO., LTD.—See Tongjitang Chinese Medicines Company; *Int'l*, pg. 7808
GUIZHOU TONGJITANG PHARMACEUTICAL DISTRIBUTION CO., LTD.—See Tongjitang Chinese Medicines Company; *Int'l*, pg. 7808
GUIZHOU TONGREN PARKSON RETAIL CO., LTD.—See Uni-Bio Science Group Ltd; *Int'l*, pg. 8028
GUIZHOU TRANSPORTATION PLANNING SURVEY & DESIGN ACADEME CO., LTD.; *Int'l*, pg. 3175
GUI ZHOU TYRE CO., LTD.; *Int'l*, pg. 3173
GUIZHOU WIRE ROPE INCORPORATED COMPANY; *Int'l*, pg. 3175

GUIZHOU XIANGDA CAMEL FEED CO., LTD—See Tangrenshen Group Co., Ltd.; *Int'l*, pg. 7458
GUIZHOU XINBANG PHARMACEUTICAL CO., LTD.; *Int'l*, pg. 3175
GUIZHOU YIBAI PHARMACEUTICAL CO., LTD.; *Int'l*, pg. 3175
GUIZHOU ZUNYI PARKSON RETAIL DEVELOPMENT CO., LTD.—See Parkson Retail Group Limited; *Int'l*, pg. 5744
GUJARAT AKRUTI-TCG BIOTECH LIMITED—See Hubtown Limited; *Int'l*, pg. 3521
GUJARAT ALKALIES & CHEMICALS LTD; *Int'l*, pg. 3175
GUJARAT AMBUJA EXPORTS LTD. - AKOLA DIVISION—See Gujarat Ambuja Exports Ltd.; *Int'l*, pg. 3175
GUJARAT AMBUJA EXPORTS LTD. - COTTON YARN DIVISION—See Gujarat Ambuja Exports Ltd.; *Int'l*, pg. 3175
GUJARAT AMBUJA EXPORTS LTD. - KADI DIVISION—See Gujarat Ambuja Exports Ltd.; *Int'l*, pg. 3175
GUJARAT AMBUJA EXPORTS LTD. - KARNATAKA DIVISION—See Gujarat Ambuja Exports Ltd.; *Int'l*, pg. 3175
GUJARAT AMBUJA EXPORTS LTD. - MANDSAUR DIVISION—See Gujarat Ambuja Exports Ltd.; *Int'l*, pg. 3175
GUJARAT AMBUJA EXPORTS LTD. - PITHAMPUR DIVISION—See Gujarat Ambuja Exports Ltd.; *Int'l*, pg. 3175
GUJARAT AMBUJA EXPORTS LTD.; *Int'l*, pg. 3175
GUJARAT AMBUJA EXPORTS LTD. - UTTRANCHAL DIVISION—See Gujarat Ambuja Exports Ltd.; *Int'l*, pg. 3175
GUJARAT APOLLO INDUSTRIES LIMITED; *Int'l*, pg. 3175
GUJARAT CEMENT PLANT—See The Aditya Birla Group; *Int'l*, pg. 7611
GUJARAT CONTAINERS LIMITED; *Int'l*, pg. 3176
GUJARAT CONTAINERS LIMITED - UNIT II—See GUJARAT CONTAINERS LIMITED; *Int'l*, pg. 3176
GUJARAT CONTAINERS LIMITED - UNIT I—See GUJARAT CONTAINERS LIMITED; *Int'l*, pg. 3176
GUJARAT COTEX LIMITED; *Int'l*, pg. 3176
GUJARAT CRAFT INDUSTRIES LIMITED; *Int'l*, pg. 3176
GUJARAT ENERGY RESEARCH AND MANAGEMENT INSTITUTE—See Gujarat State Petroleum Corporation Limited; *Int'l*, pg. 3177
GUJARAT FLUOROCHEMICALS LIMITED—See INOX Leasing & Finance Limited; *Int'l*, pg. 3715
GUJARAT GAS LIMITED—See Gujarat State Petroleum Corporation Limited; *Int'l*, pg. 3177
GUJARAT GUARDIAN LTD.—See Koch Industries, Inc.; *U.S. Private*, pg. 2329
GUJARAT GUARDIAN LTD.—See Modi Rubber Limited; *Int'l*, pg. 5016
GUJARAT HOTELS LIMITED; *Int'l*, pg. 3176
GUJARAT HYSPIN LIMITED; *Int'l*, pg. 3176
GUJARAT INDUSTRIES POWER COMPANY LIMITED; *Int'l*, pg. 3176
GUJARAT INJECT (KERALA) LTD.; *Int'l*, pg. 3176
GUJARAT INSECTICIDES LIMITED—See Gharda Chemicals Limited; *Int'l*, pg. 2958
GUJARAT INTRUX LIMITED; *Int'l*, pg. 3176
GUJARAT INVESTA LIMITED; *Int'l*, pg. 3176
GUJARAT LEASE FINANCING LIMITED; *Int'l*, pg. 3176
GUJARAT MEDITECH LTD; *Int'l*, pg. 3176
GUJARAT METALLIC COAL & COKE LIMITED; *Int'l*, pg. 3176
GUJARAT MINERAL DEVELOPMENT CORPORATION LIMITED; *Int'l*, pg. 3176
GUJARAT NARMADA VALLEY FERTILIZERS & CHEMICALS LIMITED; *Int'l*, pg. 3176
GUJARAT NATURAL RESOURCES LIMITED; *Int'l*, pg. 3176
GUJARAT NCODE SOLUTIONS LIMITED—See Gujarat Narmada Valley Fertilizers & Chemicals Limited; *Int'l*, pg. 3176
GUJARAT NRE COKE LTD.; *Int'l*, pg. 3177
GUJARAT ORGANICS LIMITED; *Int'l*, pg. 3177
GUJARAT PAGUTHAN ENERGY CORPORATION PRIVATE LIMITED—See CLP Holdings Limited; *Int'l*, pg. 1663
GUJARAT PERSTORP ELECTRONICS LTD.; *Int'l*, pg. 3177
GUJARAT PETROSYNTHESE LTD; *Int'l*, pg. 3177
GUJARAT PIPAVAV PORT LIMITED—See A.P. Moller-Maersk A/S; *Int'l*, pg. 25
GUJARAT POLY ELECTRONICS LIMITED—See Polychem Limited; *Int'l*, pg. 5914
GUJARAT RAFFIA INDUSTRIES LIMITED; *Int'l*, pg. 3177
GUJARAT SIDHEE CEMENT LIMITED; *Int'l*, pg. 3177
GUJARAT STATE FERTILIZERS & CHEMICALS LTD.; *Int'l*, pg. 3177
GUJARAT STATE FINANCIAL CORPORATION LTD.; *Int'l*, pg. 3177
GUJARAT STATE PETROLEUM CORPORATION LIMITED; *Int'l*, pg. 3177

GUJARAT TERCE LABORATORIES LIMITED; *Int'l*, pg. 3177
GUJARAT THEMIS BIOSYN LIMITED; *Int'l*, pg. 3177
GUJARAT TOOLROOM LIMITED; *Int'l*, pg. 3177
GUJCHEM DISTILLERIES INDIA LTD.; *Int'l*, pg. 3177
GUJCHEM DISTILLERS INDIA LIMITED; *Int'l*, pg. 3177
GUJ INFO PETRO LIMITED—See Gujarat State Petroleum Corporation Limited; *Int'l*, pg. 3177
GUK-FALZMASCHINEN GRIESSER & KUNZMANN GMBH & CO. KG; *Int'l*, pg. 3177
GUKO TECH GMBH—See Greiner Holding AG; *Int'l*, pg. 3079
GUL AHMED INTERNATIONAL LIMITED FZC—See Gul Ahmed Textile Mills Ltd.; *Int'l*, pg. 3178
GUL AHMED TEXTILE MILLS LTD.; *Int'l*, pg. 3177
GULER YATIRIM HOLDING A.S.; *Int'l*, pg. 3178
GULE SIDER AS—See Eniro Group AB; *Int'l*, pg. 2439
GULE SIDER INTERNETT AS—See Eniro Group AB; *Int'l*, pg. 2439
GULF AGENCY CO. (BAHRAIN) W.L.L.—See Gulf Agency Company Ltd.; *Int'l*, pg. 3179
GULF AGENCY COMPANY (AUSTRALIA) PTY LTD—See Gulf Agency Company Ltd.; *Int'l*, pg. 3179
GULF AGENCY COMPANY (CYPRUS) LTD—See Gulf Agency Company Ltd.; *Int'l*, pg. 3179
GULF AGENCY COMPANY (EGYPT) LTD—See Gulf Agency Company Ltd.; *Int'l*, pg. 3179
GULF AGENCY COMPANY (FUJAIRAH) PVT. WLL.—See Gulf Agency Company Ltd.; *Int'l*, pg. 3179
GULF AGENCY COMPANY (HONG KONG) LTD.—See Gulf Agency Company Ltd.; *Int'l*, pg. 3179
GULF AGENCY COMPANY (JORDAN) LTD—See Gulf Agency Company Ltd.; *Int'l*, pg. 3179
GULF AGENCY COMPANY LTD.; *Int'l*, pg. 3178
GULF AGENCY COMPANY (OMAN) L.L.C—See Gulf Agency Company Ltd.; *Int'l*, pg. 3179
GULF AGENCY COMPANY QATAR (W.L.L.)—See Gulf Agency Company Ltd.; *Int'l*, pg. 3179
GULF AGENCY COMPANY (RAS AL KHAIMAH) L.L.C.—See Gulf Agency Company Ltd.; *Int'l*, pg. 3179
GULF AGENCY COMPANY SAUDI ARABIA—See Gulf Agency Company Ltd.; *Int'l*, pg. 3179
GULF AGENCY COMPANY (THAILAND) LTD.—See Thoresen Thai Agencies Public Company Limited; *Int'l*, pg. 7718
GULF AGENCY CO. SHARJAH W.L.L.—See Gulf Agency Company Ltd.; *Int'l*, pg. 3179
GULF AGENCY DENIZCILIK A.S.—See Gulf Agency Company Ltd.; *Int'l*, pg. 3179
GULFA GENERAL INVESTMENT COMPANY; *Int'l*, pg. 3182
GULF AIR COMPANY B.S.C.; *Int'l*, pg. 3179
GULF AIR CONDITIONING MANUFACTURING INDUSTRIES L.L.C—See GIBCA Limited; *Int'l*, pg. 2962
GULF AIR—See Gulf Air Company B.S.C.; *Int'l*, pg. 3179
GULF AND ARAB WORLD RESTAURANTS CO.—See Adeptio LLC; *Int'l*, pg. 143
GULF ASHLEY MOTORS LIMITED—See Hinduja Group Ltd.; *Int'l*, pg. 3398
GULF ASIA INTERNATIONAL CORPORATION—See EEI Corporation; *Int'l*, pg. 2317
GULF ASSIST E.C.—See MAPFRE S.A.; *Int'l*, pg. 4684
GULF AUTOMOBILES & TRADING CO. W.L.L.—See Kassem Darwish Fakhro & Sons; *Int'l*, pg. 4088
GULF BANK ALGERIA—See Kuwait Projects Company (Holding) K.S.C.P.; *Int'l*, pg. 4346
GULF BANK K.S.C.P.; *Int'l*, pg. 3179
GULF & BASCO—See Kodiak Building Partners LLC; *U.S. Private*, pg. 2336
GULF BAY GROUP OF COMPANIES; *U.S. Private*, pg. 1814
GULF BAY HOTELS INC.; *U.S. Private*, pg. 1814
GULF BAYPORT CHEMICALS L.P.—See Platte River Ventures, LLC; *U.S. Private*, pg. 3211
GULF BREEZE REAL ESTATE; *U.S. Private*, pg. 1814
GULF BUILDING CORP.; *U.S. Private*, pg. 1815
GULF BUSINESS MACHINES B.S.C. (C)—See Gulf Business Machines EC; *Int'l*, pg. 3179
GULF BUSINESS MACHINES EC; *Int'l*, pg. 3179
GULF BUSINESS MACHINES (GBM) L.L.C.—See Gulf Business Machines EC; *Int'l*, pg. 3179
GULF BUSINESS MACHINES (OMAN) CO. L.L.C.—See Gulf Business Machines EC; *Int'l*, pg. 3179
GULF BUSINESS MACHINES PERSONAL SYSTEMS DIVISION—See Gulf Business Machines EC; *Int'l*, pg. 3179
GULF BUSINESS MACHINES W.L.L.—See Gulf Business Machines EC; *Int'l*, pg. 3179
GULF BUSSINESS FORMS COMPANY W.L.L.—See First Investment Company K.S.C.C.; *Int'l*, pg. 2685
GULF CABLE & ELECTRICAL INDUSTRIES CO. K.S.C.; *Int'l*, pg. 3179
GULF CAPITAL PJSC; *Int'l*, pg. 3179
GULF CEMENT COMPANY P.S.C.; *Int'l*, pg. 3180
GULF CHEMICAL & METALLURGICAL CORPORATION—See Eramet SA; *Int'l*, pg. 2489
GULF CHLORINE W.L.L—See Oman Chlorine S.A.O.G.; *Int'l*, pg. 5559

COMPANY NAME INDEX

GULF CITY CLEANING COMPANY—See Abdulla Ahmed Nass Group WLL; *Int'l*, pg. 58
GULF CLOSURES W.L.L.—See AptarGroup, Inc.; *U.S. Public*, pg. 174
GULF COAST BANK; *U.S. Private*, pg. 1815
GULF COAST BANK & TRUST COMPANY; *U.S. Private*, pg. 1815
GULF COAST BILLING—See CareCloud, Inc.; *U.S. Public*, pg. 435
GULF COAST BLENDERS, INC.—See L.H. Hayward & Co., LLC; *U.S. Private*, pg. 2366
GULFCOAST COIN & JEWELRY, LLC; *U.S. Private*, pg. 1817
GULF COAST COLLECTION BUREAU, INC.; *U.S. Private*, pg. 1815
GULF COAST COMMUNITY SERVICES ASSOCIATION; *U.S. Private*, pg. 1815
GULF COAST DIVISION, INC.—See HCA Healthcare, Inc.; *U.S. Public*, pg. 997
GULF COAST ELECTRIC COOPERATIVE INC.; *U.S. Private*, pg. 1815
GULF COAST EXPRESS PIPELINE LLC; *U.S. Private*, pg. 1815
GULF COAST GALVANIZING INC.—See AZZ, Inc.; *U.S. Public*, pg. 259
GULF COAST HMA PHYSICIAN MANAGEMENT, LLC—See Community Health Systems, Inc.; *U.S. Public*, pg. 553
GULF COAST INSULATION LLC—See Installed Building Products, Inc.; *U.S. Public*, pg. 1132
GULF COAST MARINE SUPPLY COMPANY INC.; *U.S. Private*, pg. 1815
GULF COAST MEDICAL CENTER, LLC—See Community Health Systems, Inc.; *U.S. Public*, pg. 553
GULF COAST MEDICAL CENTER PRIMARY CARE, LLC—See HCA Healthcare, Inc.; *U.S. Public*, pg. 997
GULF COAST MEDICAL CENTER—See Lee Memorial Health System; *U.S. Private*, pg. 2413
GULF COAST NEWSPAPERS, LLC—See Osteen Publishing Company; *U.S. Private*, pg. 3048
GULF COAST NUTRITIONALS, INC.; *U.S. Private*, pg. 1815
GULF COAST OBSTETRICS AND GYNECOLOGY OF SARASOTA, LLC, *U.S. Private*, pg. 1816
GULF COAST OFFICE PRODUCTS, INC.; *U.S. Private*, pg. 1815
GULF COAST PET SUPPLIES, INC.; *U.S. Private*, pg. 1815
GULF COAST PHYSICIAN ADMINISTRATORS, INC.—See HCA Healthcare, Inc.; *U.S. Public*, pg. 997
GULF COAST PIPE LINE, L.P.—See Industry Super Holdings Pty. Ltd.; *Int'l*, pg. 3676
GULF COAST POWER & CONTROL OF LOUISIANA LLC—See CSE Global Ltd.; *Int'l*, pg. 1864
GULF COAST PRE-STRESS, INC.; *U.S. Private*, pg. 1815
GULF COAST RENAISSANCE CORPORATION; *U.S. Private*, pg. 1815
GULF COAST SOCIAL SERVICES; *U.S. Private*, pg. 1815
GULFCOAST SPINE INSTITUTE, PA; *U.S. Private*, pg. 1817
GULF COAST STABILIZED MATERIALS LLC—See Heidelberg Materials AG; *Int'l*, pg. 3310
GULF COAST SUPPLY & MFG INC.; *U.S. Private*, pg. 1815
GULF COAST SURGERY CENTER—See HCA Healthcare, Inc.; *U.S. Public*, pg. 997
GULF COAST TOWN CENTER CMBS, LLC—See CBL & Associates Properties, Inc.; *U.S. Public*, pg. 458
GULF COAST TREATMENT CENTER, INC.—See Universal Health Services, Inc.; *U.S. Public*, pg. 2257
GULF COAST TRUCK & EQUIPMENT CO., INC.; *U.S. Private*, pg. 1815
GULF COAST ULTRA DEEP ROYALTY TRUST; *U.S. Public*, pg. 974
GULF COAST UTILITIES, INC.—See Keystone Group, L.P.; *U.S. Private*, pg. 2297
GULF COAST UTILITIES, INC.—See Pamlico Capital Management, L.P.; *U.S. Private*, pg. 3083
GULF COAST WATER AUTHORITY; *U.S. Private*, pg. 1815
GULF COAST YACHT SALES INCORPORATED; *U.S. Private*, pg. 1815
GULF COMMERCIAL BANK; *Int'l*, pg. 3180
GULF COMPRESS; *U.S. Private*, pg. 1816
GULF CONSOLIDATED CONTRACTORS CO. LTD.; *Int'l*, pg. 3180
GULF CONTROLS CO. - ACTION HYDRAULICS DIVISION—See Employee Owned Holdings, Inc.; *U.S. Private*, pg. 1386
GULF CONTROLS COMPANY, LLC—See Employee Owned Holdings, Inc.; *U.S. Private*, pg. 1386
GULF CO-OPERATION INSURANCE COMPANY LTD., EC—See Dabbagh Group Holding Company Ltd.; *Int'l*, pg. 1902
GULF COPPER & MANUFACTURING CORP; *U.S. Private*, pg. 1816
GULF CORPORATION FOR TECHNOLOGY; *Int'l*, pg. 3180

GULF COURT HOTEL BUSINESS BAY LLC—See Gulf Hotels Group B.S.C.; *Int'l*, pg. 3180
GULF CREDIT UNION; *U.S. Private*, pg. 1816
GULFDETECTION LLC—See Bhatia Brothers Group; *Int'l*, pg. 1014
GULF DEVELOPMENT CORPORATION—See Abdulla Ahmed Nass Group WLL; *Int'l*, pg. 58
GULF DISTRIBUTING COMPANY OF MOBILE LLC—See Gulf Distributing Holdings LLC; *U.S. Private*, pg. 1816
GULF DISTRIBUTING HOLDINGS LLC; *U.S. Private*, pg. 1816
GULF DREDGING AND GENERAL CONTRACTING COMPANY KSE—See Heavy Engineering Industries & Shipbuilding Co. K.S.C.; *Int'l*, pg. 3305
GULF DRILLING INTERNATIONAL LIMITED Q.S.C.—See Gulf International Services QSC; *Int'l*, pg. 3181
GULF DUNES LANDSCAPING & AGRICULTURAL SERVICES L.L.C.—See International Holdings Company PJSC; *Int'l*, pg. 3750
GULF DUNES LLC—See Fairfax Financial Holdings Limited; *Int'l*, pg. 2608
GULF DURA INDUSTRIES L.L.C—See Gulf General Investment Company PSC; *Int'l*, pg. 3180
GULF DYNAMIC SERVICES LLC (GDS)—See Dubai Investments PJSC; *Int'l*, pg. 2219
GULFEAGLE SUPPLY, INC.; *U.S. Private*, pg. 1817
GULF EGYPT FOR HOTELS & TOURISM S.A.E—See Kuwait Projects Company (Holding) K.S.C.P.; *Int'l*, pg. 4347
GULF ELECTRIC PUBLIC CO. LTD—See EGAT Public Company Limited; *Int'l*, pg. 2322
GULF ELECTROQUIP LTD.; *U.S. Private*, pg. 1816
GULF ENERGY DEVELOPMENT PUBLIC COMPANY LIMITED; *Int'l*, pg. 3180
GULF ENERGY INFORMATION; *U.S. Private*, pg. 1816
GULF ENERGY SAOC—See National Energy Services Reunited Corp.; *U.S. Public*, pg. 1494
GULF ENGINEERING, LLC; *U.S. Private*, pg. 1816
GULF EQUIPMENT CORPORATION; *U.S. Private*, pg. 1816
GULF EXTRUSIONS CO. (LLC)—See Al Ghurair Group; *Int'l*, pg. 277
GULF FERRO ALLOYS COMPANY (SABAYEK) W.L.L.—See United Gulf Investment Corporation B.S.C.; *Int'l*, pg. 8068
GULF FINANCE CORPORATION PJSC—See SHUAA Capital psc; *Int'l*, pg. 6868
GULF FOOD INDUSTRIES COMPANY—See Adeptio LLC; *Int'l*, pg. 143
GULF FRANCHISING HOLDING COMPANY K.S.C.C.; *Int'l*, pg. 3180
GULFGATE DODGE, INC.—See Stellantis N.V.; *Int'l*, pg. 7200
GULF GENERAL COOPERATIVE INSURANCE COMPANY; *Int'l*, pg. 3180
GULF GENERAL INVESTMENT COMPANY PSC - REAL ESTATE DIVISION—See Gulf General Investment Company PSC; *Int'l*, pg. 3180
GULF GENERAL INVESTMENT COMPANY PSC; *Int'l*, pg. 3180
GULF GLASS FIBER TECHNOLOGICAL INDUSTRIES COMPANY; *Int'l*, pg. 3180
GULF GLASS INDUSTRIES LLC—See GIBCA Limited; *Int'l*, pg. 2962
GULF GLASS MANUFACTURING CO. K.S.C.; *Int'l*, pg. 3180
GULF-GREAT LAKES PACKAGING CORPORATION; *U.S. Private*, pg. 1817
GULF GROUP CO. (W.L.L)—See Kuwait Commercial Markets Complex Co. (S.A.K.); *Int'l*, pg. 4344
GULF HELICOPTER COMPANY—See Qatar Petroleum; *Int'l*, pg. 6135
GULF HILL & KNOWLTON—See WPP plc; *Int'l*, pg. 8477
GULF HILL & KNOWLTON—See WPP plc; *Int'l*, pg. 8477
GULF HILL & KNOWLTON—See WPP plc; *Int'l*, pg. 8477
GULF HOLDING COMPANY KSCC—See GFH Financial Group B.S.C.; *Int'l*, pg. 2956
GULF HOTEL LAUNDRY SERVICES W.L.L—See Gulf Hotels Group B.S.C.; *Int'l*, pg. 3181
GULF HOTELS GROUP B.S.C.; *Int'l*, pg. 3180
GULF HOTELS (OMAN) COMPANY LIMITED SAOG; *Int'l*, pg. 3180
GULF INDUSTRIES FOR REFRIGERATION AND CATERING COMPANY O.P.C—See Salam International Investment Limited; *Int'l*, pg. 6491
GULF INSURANCE COMPANY—See The Travelers Companies, Inc.; *U.S. Public*, pg. 2136
GULF INSURANCE CO.; *Int'l*, pg. 3181
GULF INSURANCE GROUP (GIG) GULF—See AXA S.A.; *Int'l*, pg. 759
GULF INSURANCE GROUP K.S.C.P.—See Fairfax Financial Holdings Limited; *Int'l*, pg. 2606
GULF INSURANCE LIMITED—See Assuria N.V.; *Int'l*, pg. 650
GULF INTERNATIONAL BANK B.S.C.; *Int'l*, pg. 3181
GULF INTERNATIONAL BANK (UK) LTD.—See Gulf International Bank B.S.C.; *Int'l*, pg. 3181
GULF INTERNATIONAL CHEMICALS SAOG; *Int'l*, pg. 3181

GULF & PACIFIC EQUITIES CORP.

GULF INTERNATIONAL CORPORATION; *U.S. Private*, pg. 1816
GULF INTERNATIONAL SERVICES QSC; *Int'l*, pg. 3181
GULF INTERNATIONAL TRUCKS; *U.S. Private*, pg. 1816
GULF INTERSTATE ENGINEERING COMPANY—See Gulf International Corporation; *U.S. Private*, pg. 1816
GULF INTERSTATE FIELD SERVICES, INC.—See Gulf International Corporation; *U.S. Private*, pg. 1816
GULFINVEST INTERNATIONAL K.S.C.C.; *Int'l*, pg. 3182
GULF INVESTMENT HOUSE K.S.C.P.; *Int'l*, pg. 3181
GULF INVESTMENT SERVICES HOLDING COMPANY SAOG—See Oman Investment & Finance Co. SAOG; *Int'l*, pg. 5560
GULF ISLAND FABRICATION, INC.; *U.S. Public*, pg. 975
GULF ISLAND, LLC—See Gulf Island Fabrication, Inc.; *U.S. Public*, pg. 975
GULF ISLAND SHIPYARDS, LLC—See Gulf Island Fabrication, Inc.; *U.S. Public*, pg. 975
GULF KEYSTONE PETROLEUM INTERNATIONAL LTD.—See Gulf Keystone Petroleum Limited; *Int'l*, pg. 3181
GULF KEYSTONE PETROLEUM LIMITED; *Int'l*, pg. 3181
GULF KEYSTONE PETROLEUM (UK) LIMITED—See Gulf Keystone Petroleum Limited; *Int'l*, pg. 3181
GULF LIFE INSURANCE COMPANY—See Fairfax Financial Holdings Limited; *Int'l*, pg. 2607
GULF LINE TRANSPORTATION—See US 1 Industries, Inc.; *U.S. Private*, pg. 4317
GULF LUBRICANTS UK LTD—See Hinduja Group Ltd.; *Int'l*, pg. 3398
GULF MANAGEMENT,INC.—See AutoNation, Inc.; *U.S. Public*, pg. 235
GULF MANGANESE CORPORATION LIMITED; *Int'l*, pg. 3181
GULF MARINE FABRICATORS, L.P.—See Gulf Island Fabrication, Inc.; *U.S. Public*, pg. 975
GULF MARINE FAR EAST PTE. LTD.—See Tidewater Inc.; *U.S. Public*, pg. 2158
GULF MARINE REPAIR CORPORATION; *U.S. Private*, pg. 1816
GULF MARINE SAUDI ARABIA CO. LIMITED—See Gulf Marine Services Plc; *Int'l*, pg. 3181
GULF MARINE SERVICES PLC; *Int'l*, pg. 3181
GULFMARK AMERICAS, INC.—See Tidewater Inc.; *U.S. Public*, pg. 2158
GULFMARK ASIA PTE., LTD.—See Tidewater Inc.; *U.S. Public*, pg. 2158
GULFMARK AS—See Tidewater Inc.; *U.S. Public*, pg. 2158
GULFMARK ENERGY, INC.—See Adams Resources & Energy, Inc.; *U.S. Public*, pg. 38
GULF MARKETING & SERVICES COMPANY LLC; *Int'l*, pg. 3181
GULFMARK MANAGEMENT, INC.—See Tidewater Inc.; *U.S. Public*, pg. 2158
GULFMARK OFFSHORE INC.—See Tidewater Inc.; *U.S. Public*, pg. 2158
GULFMARK REDERI AS—See Tidewater Inc.; *U.S. Public*, pg. 2158
GULFMARK U.K. LTD.—See Tidewater Inc.; *U.S. Public*, pg. 2158
GULF MEDICAL PROJECTS COMPANY PJSC; *Int'l*, pg. 3181
GULF METAL CRAFT (GMC)—See Dubai Investments PJSC; *Int'l*, pg. 2219
GULF MUSHROOM PRODUCTS CO. SAOG; *Int'l*, pg. 3181
GULF NAVIGATION HOLDING PJSC; *Int'l*, pg. 3181
GULF NAVIGATION POLIMAR MARITIME LLC—See Gulf Navigation Holding PJSC; *Int'l*, pg. 3181
GULF NORTH AFRICA HOLDING CO. K.S.C.; *Int'l*, pg. 3181
GULF OAKS THERAPEUTIC DAY SCHOOL, LLC—See Community Health Systems, Inc.; *U.S. Public*, pg. 553
GULF OFFSHORE NORGE AS—See Tidewater Inc.; *U.S. Public*, pg. 2158
GULF OFFSHORE N.S. LTD.—See Tidewater Inc.; *U.S. Public*, pg. 2158
GULF OIL ARGENTINA SA—See Hinduja Group Ltd.; *Int'l*, pg. 3398
GULF OIL CORPN. LTD. - LUBES DIVISION—See Hinduja Group Ltd.; *Int'l*, pg. 3398
GULF OIL INTERNATIONAL LTD.—See Hinduja Group Ltd.; *Int'l*, pg. 3398
GULF OIL, LP—See ArcLight Capital Holdings, LLC; *U.S. Private*, pg. 312
GULF OIL LUBRICANTS INDIA LIMITED—See Hinduja Group Ltd.; *Int'l*, pg. 3399
GULF OIL MIDDLE EAST LTD - JEBEL ALI FACILITY—See Hinduja Group Ltd.; *Int'l*, pg. 3399
GULF OIL MIDDLE EAST LTD—See Hinduja Group Ltd.; *Int'l*, pg. 3399
GULF OIL NEDERLAND B.V.—See Hinduja Group Ltd.; *Int'l*, pg. 3399
GULF OIL PHILIPPINES, INC.—See Hinduja Group Ltd.; *Int'l*, pg. 3398
GULF OVERSEAS EXCHANGE COMPANY LLC—See National Bank Limited; *Int'l*, pg. 5151
GULF & PACIFIC EQUITIES CORP.; *Int'l*, pg. 3178

GULF PACIFIC INC.   CORPORATE AFFILIATIONS

GULF PACIFIC INC.; U.S. Private, pg. 1816
GULF PAPER MANUFACTURING COMPANY K.S.C.; Int'l, pg. 3181
GULF PETROCHEMICAL INDUSTRIES CO.—See Kuwait Petroleum Corporation; Int'l, pg. 4345
GULF PETROLEUM INVESTMENT CO. S.A.K.C.; Int'l, pg. 3182
GULF PHARMACEUTICAL INDUSTRIES P.S.C.; Int'l, pg. 3182
GULF PLASTICS INDUSTRIES COMPANY SAOG; Int'l, pg. 3182
GULF POINTE SURGERY CENTER—See HCA Healthcare, Inc.; U.S. Public, pg. 997
GULFPORT ENERGY CORPORATION; U.S. Public, pg. 975
GULF POWERBEAT WLL—See Time Technoplast Limited; Int'l, pg. 7751
GULF POWER INTERNATIONAL LTD.—See Dabbagh Group Holding Company Ltd.; Int'l, pg. 1902
GULF PREFAB HOUSES FACTORY LTD.—See Gulf General Investment Company PSC; Int'l, pg. 3180
GULF PUBLISHING COMPANY, INC.—See Chatham Asset Management, LLC; U.S. Private, pg. 866
GULF PUBLISHING COMPANY—See Main Street Capital Corporation; U.S. Public, pg. 1355
GULF RAK OIL LLC—See Hinduja Group Ltd.; Int'l, pg. 3399
GULF REINSURANCE LIMITED—See Arch Capital Group Ltd.; Int'l, pg. 547
GULF RESOURCES, INC.; Int'l, pg. 3182
GULF RICE ARKANSAS, LLC.; U.S. Private, pg. 1816
GULF ROCKS K.S.C.; Int'l, pg. 3182
GULF ROPE & PLASTIC PRODUCTS LLC—See Sharjah Cement & Industrial Development Company P.S.C.; Int'l, pg. 6790
GULF RUBBER AUSTRALIA PTY LIMITED—See Skellerup Holdings Limited; Int'l, pg. 6980
GULF RUBBER (MALAYSIA) SDN BHD—See ecoWise Holdings Limited; Int'l, pg. 2300
GULFSANDS PETROLEUM PLC; Int'l, pg. 3182
GULFSAT COMMUNICATIONS COMPANY K.S.C.—See Kuwait Projects Company (Holding) K.S.C.P.; Int'l, pg. 4346
GULF SCIENTIFIC CORPORATION—See Waters Corporation; U.S. Public, pg. 2334
GULF SCIENTIFIC CORPORATION—See Waters Corporation; U.S. Public, pg. 2334
GULF SECURITY TECHNOLOGY CO., LTD.—See Carrier Global Corporation; U.S. Public, pg. 441
GULF SEMICONDUCTOR LTD.—See Sintronic Technology Inc.; Int'l, pg. 6959
GULF SEMICONDUCTOR (SHAN DONG) CO., LTD.—See Sintronic Technology Inc.; Int'l, pg. 6959
GULFSHORE BUSINESS—See Open Sky Media Inc.; U.S. Private, pg. 3029
GULFSHORE ENDOSCOPY CENTER, LLC—See Tenet Healthcare Corporation; U.S. Public, pg. 2002
GULFSHORE INSURANCE, INC.; U.S. Private, pg. 1817
GULFSHORE LIFE—See Open Sky Media Inc.; U.S. Private, pg. 3029
GULF SHORE TEL-COM INC.; U.S. Private, pg. 1816
GULFSIDE SUPPLY INC.; U.S. Private, pg. 1817
GULF SIGORTA A.S.—See Fairfax Financial Holdings Limited; Int'l, pg. 2607
GULFSLOPE ENERGY, INC.; U.S. Public, pg. 975
GULF SOUTH PIPELINE COMPANY, LP—See Loews Corporation; U.S. Public, pg. 1339
GULF SOUTH SURGERY CENTER, LLC—See Community Health Systems, Inc.; U.S. Public, pg. 553
GULF SOUTH TECHNOLOGY SOLUTIONS, LLC.; U.S. Private, pg. 1816
GULF SPECIAL SERVICES, INC.; U.S. Private, pg. 1816
GULF STABILIZERS INDUSTRIES LTD.—See Zamil Group Holding Company; Int'l, pg. 8623
GULF STANDARD ENERGY COMPANY, LLC; U.S. Private, pg. 1816
GULF STATE PIPE LINE COMPANY—See Balmoral Funds LLC; U.S. Private, pg. 462
GULF STATES CANNERS INC.; U.S. Private, pg. 1816
GULF STATES FINANCIAL SERVICES, INC.; U.S. Private, pg. 1817
GULF STATES HOLDINGS, INC.; U.S. Private, pg. 1817
GULF STATES INSURANCE COMPANY, INC.—See Gulf States Holdings, Inc.; U.S. Private, pg. 1817
GULF STATES TOYOTA, INC.—See The Friedkin Group, Inc.; U.S. Private, pg. 4031
GULF STONE COMPANY SAOG.; Int'l, pg. 3182
GULFSTREAM AEROSPACE CORPORATION OF TEXAS—See General Dynamics Corporation; U.S. Public, pg. 916
GULFSTREAM AEROSPACE CORPORATION—See General Dynamics Corporation; U.S. Public, pg. 913
GULFSTREAM AEROSPACE SERVICES CORPORATION—See General Dynamics Corporation; U.S. Public, pg. 916
GULF STREAM BUILDERS SUPPLY, INC.; U.S. Private, pg. 1817
GULFSTREAM - CALIFORNIA, INC.—See General Dynamics Corporation; U.S. Public, pg. 916

GULFSTREAM CAPITAL CORPORATION; Int'l, pg. 3182
GULF STREAM COACH INC.; U.S. Private, pg. 1817
GULF STREAM MARINE INC.—See Blue Wolf Capital Partners LLC; U.S. Private, pg. 595
GULFSTREAM NATURAL GAS SYSTEM, L.L.C.—See The Williams Companies, Inc.; U.S. Public, pg. 2143
GULFSTREAM PARK RACING ASSOCIATION, INC.—See The Stronach Group Inc.; Int'l, pg. 7689
GULF SYSTEMS INC.; U.S. Private, pg. 1817
GULFTAINER COMPANY LIMITED; Int'l, pg. 3182
GULF TECHNICAL CONSTRUCTION COMPANY L.L.C—See Drake & Scull International PJSC; Int'l, pg. 2200
GULFTEL COMMUNICATIONS—See Lumen Technologies, Inc.; U.S. Public, pg. 1346
GULF TILE DISTRIBUTORS OF FLORIDA, INC.; U.S. Private, pg. 1817
GULF TOTAL TRACTEBEL POWER COMPANY; Int'l, pg. 3182
GULF TRADING STORES—See Mohammed Jalal & Sons WLL; Int'l, pg. 5018
GULF UNION ALAHLIA COOPERATIVE INSURANCE CO.; Int'l, pg. 3182
GULF UNITED REAL ESTATE INVESTMENTS COMPANY—See Zad Holding Company S.A.Q.; Int'l, pg. 8619
GULF UNITED REAL ESTATE & TOURISM INVESTMENT COMPANY - K.S.C.—See Sultan Center Food Products Co. KSCC; Int'l, pg. 7256
GULF UTILITY SERVICE INC.—See Ember Infrastructure Management, LP; U.S. Private, pg. 1378
GULF VEGETABLE OIL COMPANY (NABATI)—See Ajwa Group for Food Industries Holding Ltd. Co.; Int'l, pg. 259
GULF VIEW SQUARE, LLC—See Washington Prime Group Inc.; U.S. Private, pg. 4448
GULF WAREHOUSING COMPANY QSC; Int'l, pg. 3182
GULF WARRANTIES W.L.L.—See Arab Insurance Group B.S.C.; Int'l, pg. 530
GULF WASTE SYSTEMS, INC.—See Watts Trucking Service, Inc.; U.S. Private, pg. 4456
GULF WEST LANDFILL TX, LP—See Republic Services, Inc.; U.S. Public, pg. 1786
GULF WEST SECUTIRY NETWORK, INC.; U.S. Public, pg. 975
GULF WINDS INTERNATIONAL INC.; U.S. Private, pg. 1817
GULGONG PTY LIMITED—See ARN Media Limited; Int'l, pg. 576
GULISTAN CARPET INC.; U.S. Private, pg. 1817
GULISTAN GROUP; Int'l, pg. 3182
GULISTAN SPINNING MILLS LIMITED—See Gulistan Group; Int'l, pg. 3182
GULISTAN TEXTILE MILLS LIMITED—See Gulistan Group; Int'l, pg. 3182
GULLANGETS MEKANISKA VERKSTAD AB—See Storskogen Group AB; Int'l, pg. 7227
GULLBERG & JANSSON AB; Int'l, pg. 3182
GULLBERGS SVERIGE AB—See Litorina Capital Management AB; Int'l, pg. 4527
GULLERS GROUP PORTER NOVELLI—See Omnicom Group Inc.; U.S. Public, pg. 1590
GULLEWA LIMITED; Int'l, pg. 3182
GULLEY ENTERPRISES INC.; U.S. Private, pg. 1818
GULL GMBH—See 7Days Group GmbH & Co. KG; Int'l, pg. 15
GULL HOLDINGS, LTD.; U.S. Private, pg. 1817
GULLIVER ENERGY LTD.; Int'l, pg. 3183
GULLIVER KERESKEDELMI ES SZOLGALTATO KFT.—See KBC Group NV; Int'l, pg. 4104
GULLIVERS SPORTS TRAVEL LIMITED—See TUI AG; Int'l, pg. 7965
GULLIVER TRAVEL D.O.O.—See TUI AG; Int'l, pg. 7964
GULL NEW ZEALAND LTD.—See Ampol Limited; Int'l, pg. 436
GULLWING BEACH RESORT—See SunStream, Inc.; U.S. Private, pg. 3873
GULLY TRANSPORTATION INC.; U.S. Private, pg. 1818
GULP INFORMATION SERVICES GMBH—See Randstad N.V.; Int'l, pg. 6203
GULP SCHWEIZ AG—See Randstad N.V.; Int'l, pg. 6201
GULP SOLUTION SERVICES GMBH & CO. KG—See Randstad N.V.; Int'l, pg. 6201
GULSHAN POLYOLS LTD.; Int'l, pg. 3183
GULSKOGEN PROSJEKT & EIENDOM AS—See BNP Paribas SA; Int'l, pg. 1091
GULTECH INTERNATIONAL PTE LTD—See Gul Technologies Singapore Ltd.; Int'l, pg. 3178
GUL TECHNOLOGIES SINGAPORE LTD.; Int'l, pg. 3178
GULTECH (SUZHOU) ELECTRONICS CO., LTD.—See Gul Technologies Singapore Ltd.; Int'l, pg. 3178
GULTECH (WUXI) ELECTRONICS CO., LTD.—See Gul Technologies Singapore Ltd.; Int'l, pg. 3178
GUMA GROUP; Int'l, pg. 3183
GUMAS ADVERTISING; U.S. Private, pg. 1818
GUM BASE COMPANY S.P.A.—See Perfetti Van Melle Holding B.V.; Int'l, pg. 5800
GUM BASE SHANGHAI FOOD CO., LTD.—See Perfetti Van Melle Holding B.V.; Int'l, pg. 5800

GUMBLE BROTHERS INC.; U.S. Private, pg. 1818
GUMBY'S PIZZA SYSTEMS INC.; U.S. Private, pg. 1818
GUMI INC.; Int'l, pg. 3183
GUMMER WHOLESALE CO. INC.; U.S. Private, pg. 1818
GUMP'S BY MAIL, INC.—See Gump's Corp.; U.S. Private, pg. 1818
GUMP'S CORP.; U.S. Private, pg. 1818
GUMSTIX INC.—See Altium Limited; Int'l, pg. 394
GUM TREE FABRICS INC.; U.S. Private, pg. 1818
GUMTREE WHOLESALE INSURANCE BROKERS, INC.—See Caisse de Depot et Placement du Quebec; Int'l, pg. 1256
GUMTREE WHOLESALE INSURANCE BROKERS, INC.—See KKR & Co. Inc.; U.S. Public, pg. 1265
GUNAY BANK OJSC; Int'l, pg. 3183
GUNAYDIN ET SANAYI VE TICARET A.S.—See Dogus Holding AS; Int'l, pg. 2155
GUNDA CORPORATION, LLC—See Littlejohn & Co., LLC; U.S. Private, pg. 2469
GUNDAKER COMMERCIAL GROUP, INC.; U.S. Private, pg. 1818
GUNDELACH GMBH—See AGRAVIS Raiffeisen AG; Int'l, pg. 215
GUNDERMANN & GUNDERMANN—See Keystone Group, L.P.; U.S. Private, pg. 2297
GUNDERSEN LUTHERAN HEALTH SYSTEMS, INC.; U.S. Private, pg. 1818
GUNDERSON - GIMSA S. A. DE C.V.—See The Greenbrier Companies, Inc.; U.S. Public, pg. 2086
GUNDERSON LLC—See The Greenbrier Companies, Inc.; U.S. Public, pg. 2086
GUNDERSON MARINE LLC; U.S. Private, pg. 1818
GUNDERSON RAIL SERVICES, LLC—See The Greenbrier Companies, Inc.; U.S. Public, pg. 2086
GUNDERSON'S JEWELERS; U.S. Private, pg. 1818
GUND, INC.—See Spin Master Corp.; Int'l, pg. 7136
GUNDLACH CHAMPION, INC.—See Champion, Inc.; U.S. Private, pg. 847
GUNDLACH EQUIPMENT CORPORATION—See Hillenbrand, Inc.; U.S. Public, pg. 1036
GUNDLE GEO SYNTHETICS (PTY) LIMITED—See Winhold Limited; Int'l, pg. 8428
GUNDLE LIMITED—See Winhold Limited; Int'l, pg. 8428
GUNDLE PLASTIC GROUP (PTY) LIMITED—See Winhold Limited; Int'l, pg. 8428
GUN EI CHEMICAL INDUSTRY CO., LTD. - SHIGA PLANT—See Gun Ei Chemical Industry Co., Ltd.; Int'l, pg. 3183
GUN EI CHEMICAL INDUSTRY CO., LTD.; Int'l, pg. 3183
GUNES SIGORTA AS—See Turkiye Vakiflar Bankasi T.A.O.; Int'l, pg. 7977
GUNES SIGORTA—See Groupama SA; Int'l, pg. 3091
GUNGHO ONLINE ENTERTAINMENT AMERICA, INC.—See GungHo Online Entertainment, Inc.; Int'l, pg. 3183
GUNGHO ONLINE ENTERTAINMENT, INC.; Int'l, pg. 3183
THE GUNGIN CARD CO., LTD.—See The Gunma Bank, Ltd.; Int'l, pg. 7651
GUNGIN GENERAL MAINTENANCE CO., LTD.—See The Gunma Bank, Ltd.; Int'l, pg. 7651
THE GUNGIN JCB CARD CO., LTD.—See The Gunma Bank, Ltd.; Int'l, pg. 7651
GUNGIN LEASE COMPANY LIMITED—See The Gunma Bank, Ltd.; Int'l, pg. 7651
GUNGIN SECURITIES CO., LTD.—See The Gunma Bank, Ltd.; Int'l, pg. 7651
GUNGIN SYSTEM SERVICE CO., LTD.—See The Gunma Bank, Ltd.; Int'l, pg. 7651
GUNGNIR RESOURCES INC.; Int'l, pg. 3183
GUNHOKU DAIICHI TRAFFIC CO., LTD.—See Daiichi Koutsu Sangyo Co., Ltd.; Int'l, pg. 1928
GUNIMPERM-BAUVEG SA—See PORR AG; Int'l, pg. 5923
GUN.IO INCORPORATED; U.S. Private, pg. 1818
GUNITE CORPORATION—See Crestview Partners, L.P.; U.S. Private, pg. 1098
GUNKUL ENGINEERING CO., LTD.; Int'l, pg. 3183
THE GUNLOCKE COMPANY—See HNI Corporation; U.S. Public, pg. 1043
THE GUNMA BANK, LTD.; Int'l, pg. 7651
GUNMA CAPITAL CO., LTD.—See The Gunma Bank, Ltd.; Int'l, pg. 7651
GUNMA FINANCE (HONG KONG) LIMITED—See The Gunma Bank, Ltd.; Int'l, pg. 7651
GUNMA GRANDY HOUSE CO., LTD.—See Grandy House Corporation; Int'l, pg. 3058
GUNMA ISUZU CORPORATION—See Mitsubishi Corporation; Int'l, pg. 4938
GUNMA ISUZU CORPORATION - TAKASAKI FACTORY—See Mitsubishi Corporation; Int'l, pg. 4938
GUNMA KASAI CO., LTD. - QTA PLANT—See Kasai Kogyo Co., Ltd.; Int'l, pg. 4086
GUNMA KASAI CO., LTD.—See Kasai Kogyo Co., Ltd.; Int'l, pg. 4086
GUNMA KOIKE CO., LTD.—See Koike Sanso Kogyo Co., Ltd.; Int'l, pg. 4230
GUNMA K-TECHNO CO., LTD—See Kandenko Co., Ltd.; Int'l, pg. 4065

COMPANY NAME INDEX

GUNMA MORI SHIGYO CO., LTD.—See Oji Holdings Corporation; *Int'l*, pg. 5536
GUNMA SEKISUI HEIM CO., LTD.—See Sekisui Chemical Co., Ltd.; *Int'l*, pg. 6693
GUNMA SHINYO HOSHO CO., LTD.—See The Gunma Bank, Ltd.; *Int'l*, pg. 7651
GUNNAN SANGYO CO., LTD.—See Nippon Kayaku Co., Ltd.; *Int'l*, pg. 5320
GUNNARN MINING AB—See Orex Minerals Inc.; *Int'l*, pg. 5616
GUNNEBO AB; *Int'l*, pg. 3184
GUNNEBO A/S—See Gunnebo AB; *Int'l*, pg. 3184
GUNNEBO AUSTRALIA PTY LTD—See Gunnebo AB; *Int'l*, pg. 3184
GUNNEBO BALTIC SP Z O O—See Gunnebo AB; *Int'l*, pg. 3184
GUNNEBO CANADA INC.—See Gunnebo AB; *Int'l*, pg. 3184
GUNNEBO CZ S.R.O.—See Gunnebo AB; *Int'l*, pg. 3184
GUNNEBO DEUTSCHLAND GMBH—See Gunnebo AB; *Int'l*, pg. 3184
GUNNEBO DO BRASIL LTDA—See Gunnebo AB; *Int'l*, pg. 3184
GUNNEBO ENTRANCE CONTROL, INC.—See Gunnebo AB; *Int'l*, pg. 3184
GUNNEBO ENTRANCE CONTROL LTD.—See Gunnebo AB; *Int'l*, pg. 3184
GUNNEBO ENTRANCE CONTROL SARL—See Gunnebo AB; *Int'l*, pg. 3184
GUNNEBO ESPANA SA—See Gunnebo AB; *Int'l*, pg. 3184
GUNNEBO HOLDING GMBH—See Gunnebo AB; *Int'l*, pg. 3184
GUNNEBO INDIA LTD—See Gunnebo AB; *Int'l*, pg. 3184
GUNNEBO INDONESIA—See Gunnebo AB; *Int'l*, pg. 3184
GUNNEBO INDUSTRIES—See Gunnebo AB; *Int'l*, pg. 3184
GUNNEBO INTRANCE CONTROL S.P.A.—See Gunnebo AB; *Int'l*, pg. 3184
GUNNEBO ITALIA S.P.A—See Gunnebo AB; *Int'l*, pg. 3184
GUNNEBO JOHNSON CORPORATION—See Gunnebo AB; *Int'l*, pg. 3184
GUNNEBO LTD.—See Gunnebo AB; *Int'l*, pg. 3184
GUNNEBO MAGYARORSZAG KFT.—See Gunnebo AB; *Int'l*, pg. 3184
GUNNEBO MIDDLE EAST FZE—See Gunnebo AB; *Int'l*, pg. 3184
GUNNEBO NEDERLAND BV—See Gunnebo AB; *Int'l*, pg. 3184
GUNNEBO NORDIC AB—See Gunnebo AB; *Int'l*, pg. 3184
GUNNEBO NORDIC OY—See Gunnebo AB; *Int'l*, pg. 3184
GUNNEBO OSTERREICH GMBH—See Gunnebo AB; *Int'l*, pg. 3184
GUNNEBO PERIMETER PROTECTION AB—See Gunnebo AB; *Int'l*, pg. 3184
GUNNEBO POLSKA SP. Z O.O.—See Gunnebo AB; *Int'l*, pg. 3184
GUNNEBO PORTUGAL S.A.—See Gunnebo AB; *Int'l*, pg. 3184
GUNNEBO SAFEPAY AB—See Gunnebo AB; *Int'l*, pg. 3184
GUNNEBO SECURITY (CHINA) CO., LTD—See Gunnebo AB; *Int'l*, pg. 3184
GUNNEBO SINGAPORE PTE LTD—See Gunnebo AB; *Int'l*, pg. 3184
GUNNEBO SOUTH AFRICA (PTY) LTD—See Gunnebo AB; *Int'l*, pg. 3184
GUNNEBO (SUISSE) SA—See Gunnebo AB; *Int'l*, pg. 3184
GUNNEBO TREASURY SA—See Gunnebo AB; *Int'l*, pg. 3184
GUNNEBO UK LTD—See Gunnebo AB; *Int'l*, pg. 3184
GUNN-MOWERY, LLC; *U.S. Private*, pg. 1818
GUNN PONTIAC GMC, INC.—See Curtis C. Gunn, Inc.; *U.S. Private*, pg. 1126
GUNN'S HOMEMADE CAKES & PASTRY LTD.; *Int'l*, pg. 3184
GUNN, STEERS & COMPANY, LLC—See Keystone Group, L.P.; *U.S. Private*, pg. 2299
GUNOSY INC.; *Int'l*, pg. 3185
GUNPOINT EXPLORATION LTD.; *Int'l*, pg. 3185
GUNSAN EXPORTADORA E IMPORTADORA LTDA.—See GSI Creos Corporation; *Int'l*, pg. 3144
GUNSAN PORT PIER 7 OPERATION CO., LTD.—See Sebang Co., Ltd.; *Int'l*, pg. 6669
GUNSEN CO., LTD.—See Seiren Co., Ltd.; *Int'l*, pg. 6691
GUNSTER, YOAKLEY & STEWART, P.A.; *U.S. Private*, pg. 1818
GUNSTOCK RECREATION AREA; *U.S. Private*, pg. 1818
GUNSTONES BAKERY—See Boparan Holdings Limited; *Int'l*, pg. 1111
GUNSYND PLC; *Int'l*, pg. 3185
G-UNTERNEHMENSBETEILIGUNG GMBH—See Vonovia SE; *Int'l*, pg. 8305
GUNTERSVILLE DIALYSIS, LLC—See DaVita Inc.; *U.S. Public*, pg. 639
GUNTHER DOUGLAS, INC.; *U.S. Private*, pg. 1818
GUNTHER GRANT, INC.; *U.S. Public*, pg. 975
GUNTHER KALTETECHNIK GMBH—See DZ BANK AG Deutsche Zentral-Genossenschaftsbank; *Int'l*, pg. 2244
GUNTHER LUBSEN GMBH—See BGC Group, Inc.; *U.S. Public*, pg. 329
GUNTHER MELE LIMITED; *Int'l*, pg. 3185
GUNTHER MELE PACKAGING, INC.—See Gunther Mele Limited; *Int'l*, pg. 3185
GUNTHER MOTOR COMPANY; *U.S. Private*, pg. 1818
GUNTHER NASH INCORPORATED—See Alberici Corporation; *U.S. Private*, pg. 152
GUNTHER'S ATHLETIC SERVICE, INC.—See Fenway Partners, LLC; *U.S. Private*, pg. 1495
GUNTHER SCHRAMM GMBH—See Jacquet Metal Service SA; *Int'l*, pg. 3866
GUNTHER TOOLS S.A.S.—See Sandvik AB; *Int'l*, pg. 6534
GUNTHER VOLKSWAGON OF COCONUT CREEK; *U.S. Private*, pg. 1818
GUNTON CORPORATION; *U.S. Private*, pg. 1819
GUNVOR DEUTSCHLAND GMBH—See Gunvor Group Ltd.; *Int'l*, pg. 3185
GUNVOR GROUP LTD.; *Int'l*, pg. 3185
GUNVOR INTERNATIONAL B.V.—See Gunvor Group Ltd.; *Int'l*, pg. 3185
GUNVOR RAFFINERIE INGOLSTADT GMBH—See Gunvor Group Ltd.; *Int'l*, pg. 3185
GUNVOR SA—See Gunvor Group Ltd.; *Int'l*, pg. 3185
GUNZE DISTRIBUTION CO., LTD.—See Gunze Limited; *Int'l*, pg. 3185
GUNZE ELECTRONICS USA CORP.—See Gunze Limited; *Int'l*, pg. 3185
GUNZE ENGINEERING CO., LTD.—See Gunze Limited; *Int'l*, pg. 3185
GUNZE GREEN CO., LTD.—See Gunze Limited; *Int'l*, pg. 3185
GUNZE INTERNATIONAL HONG KONG LIMITED—See Gunze Limited; *Int'l*, pg. 3185
GUNZE INTERNATIONAL USA INC.—See Gunze Limited; *Int'l*, pg. 3185
GUNZE KOBUNSHI CORPORATION—See Gunze Limited; *Int'l*, pg. 3185
GUNZE LIMITED; *Int'l*, pg. 3185
GUNZE OFFICE SERVICES CO., LTD.—See Gunze Limited; *Int'l*, pg. 3185
GUNZE PACKAGING SYSTEMS CO., LTD.—See Gunze Limited; *Int'l*, pg. 3185
GUNZE PLASTICS & ENGINEERING CORPORATION OF AMERICA—See Gunze Limited; *Int'l*, pg. 3185
GUNZE PLASTICS & ENGINEERING CORPORATION—See Gunze Limited; *Int'l*, pg. 3185
GUNZE (SHANGHAI) INTERNATIONAL TRADING CO., LTD.—See Gunze Limited; *Int'l*, pg. 3185
GUNZE SPORTS CO., LTD.—See Gunze Limited; *Int'l*, pg. 3186
GUO ANDA CO., LTD.; *Int'l*, pg. 3186
GUOAN INTERNATIONAL LIMITED—See CITIC Group Corporation; *Int'l*, pg. 1620
GUOCHANG ELECTRONICS (DONGGUAN) LTD.—See Laser Tek Taiwan Co., Ltd.; *Int'l*, pg. 4420
GUOCHENG MINING CO., LTD.; *Int'l*, pg. 3186
GUOCHUANG SOFTWARE CO., LTD; *Int'l*, pg. 3186
GUOCO GROUP LTD.—See Hong Leong Investment Holdings Pte. Ltd.; *Int'l*, pg. 3467
GUOCOLAND BINH DUONG PROPERTY CO., LTD.—See Hong Leong Investment Holdings Pte. Ltd.; *Int'l*, pg. 3468
GUOCOLAND LIMITED—See Hong Leong Investment Holdings Pte. Ltd.; *Int'l*, pg. 3468
GUOCOLAND (MALAYSIA) BERHAD—See Hong Leong Investment Holdings Pte. Ltd.; *Int'l*, pg. 3468
GUOCOLAND (SINGAPORE) PTE. LTD.—See Hong Leong Investment Holdings Pte. Ltd.; *Int'l*, pg. 3468
GUODIAN CHONGQING HENGTAI POWER GENERATION CO., LTD.—See China Guodian Corporation; *Int'l*, pg. 1506
GUODIAN JINGMEN JIANGSHAN POWER GENERATION CO., LTD.—See China Guodian Corporation; *Int'l*, pg. 1506
GUODIAN NANJING AUTOMATION CO., LTD.; *Int'l*, pg. 3186
GUODIAN TECHNOLOGY & ENVIRONMENT GROUP CORPORATION LIMITED; *Int'l*, pg. 3186
GUODIAN UNITED POWER TECHNOLOGY (BAODING) CO., LTD.—See Guodian Technology & Environment Group Corporation Limited; *Int'l*, pg. 3186
GUODIAN YUYUAN POWER GENERATION CO., LTD.—See China Guodian Corporation; *Int'l*, pg. 1506
GUOEN HOLDINGS LIMITED; *Int'l*, pg. 3186
GUOGUANG ELECTRIC COMPANY LIMITED; *Int'l*, pg. 3186
GUOLIAN CAPITAL CO., LTD.—See Guolian Securities Co., Ltd; *Int'l*, pg. 3186
GUOLIAN SECURITIES CO., LTD; *Int'l*, pg. 3186
GUOMAI CULTURE & MEDIA CO., LTD; *Int'l*, pg. 3186
GUOMAI TECHNOLOGIES, INC.; *Int'l*, pg. 3186
GUOMAN HOTEL MANAGEMENT (UK) LIMITED—See Hong Leong Investment Holdings Pte. Ltd.; *Int'l*, pg. 3468
GUOSEN SECURITIES CO. LTD.; *Int'l*, pg. 3187
GUOSHENG FINANCIAL HOLDING INC.; *Int'l*, pg. 3187
GUOTAI JUNAN ALLIANZ FUND MANAGEMENT CO., LTD.—See Allianz SE; *Int'l*, pg. 346
GUOTAI JUNAN ALLIANZ FUND MANAGEMENT CO., LTD.—See Guotai Junan Securities Co., Ltd.; *Int'l*, pg. 3187
GUOTAI JUNAN CAPITAL LIMITED—See Guotai Junan Securities Co., Ltd.; *Int'l*, pg. 3187
GUOTAI JUNAN FINANCIAL HOLDINGS CO., LTD—See Guotai Junan Securities Co., Ltd.; *Int'l*, pg. 3187
GUOTAI JUNAN FUTURES CO., LTD.—See Guotai Junan Securities Co., Ltd.; *Int'l*, pg. 3187
GUOTAI JUNAN FUTURES (HONG KONG) LIMITED—See Guotai Junan Securities Co., Ltd.; *Int'l*, pg. 3187
GUOTAI JUNAN FX LIMITED—See Guotai Junan Securities Co., Ltd.; *Int'l*, pg. 3187
GUOTAI JUNAN INNOVATION INVESTMENT CO., LTD.—See Guotai Junan Securities Co., Ltd.; *Int'l*, pg. 3187
GUOTAI JUNAN INTERNATIONAL HOLDINGS LIMITED—See Guotai Junan Securities Co., Ltd.; *Int'l*, pg. 3187
GUOTAI JUNAN SECURITIES CO., LTD.; *Int'l*, pg. 3187
GUOTAI JUNAN SECURITIES (HONG KONG) LIMITED—See Guotai Junan Securities Co., Ltd.; *Int'l*, pg. 3187
GUOTAI JUNAN SECURITIES (VIETNAM) CORPORATION—See Guotai Junan Securities Co., Ltd.; *Int'l*, pg. 3187
GUOTAI JUNAN SECURITIES (VIETNAM) CORP.; *Int'l*, pg. 3187
GUOTAI JUNAN ZHENGYU INVESTMENT CO., LTD.—See Guotai Junan Securities Co., Ltd.; *Int'l*, pg. 3187
GUOYUAN SECURITIES CO., LTD.; *Int'l*, pg. 3187
GUOZI ZHONGYU CAPITAL HOLDINGS COMPANY; *U.S. Public*, pg. 975
GUPPY MEDIA INC; *U.S. Private*, pg. 1819
GUPTA PERMOLD CORPORATION; *U.S. Private*, pg. 1819
GURALP SYSTEMS LIMITED—See Primary Capital Limited; *Int'l*, pg. 5975
GURANS LIFE INSURANCE COMPANY LTD.; *Int'l*, pg. 3187
GURAS BETEILIGUNGS GMBH & CO. VERMIETUNGS-KG—See INA-Holding Schaeffler GmbH & Co. KG; *Int'l*, pg. 3639
GURENERJI ELEKTRIK URETIM LTD. STI.—See Parsan Makina Parcalari Sanayii AS; *Int'l*, pg. 5747
GU, RENSOW LTD.; *Int'l*, pg. 3152
GURIS HOLDING A.S.—See Parsan Makina Parcalari Sanayii AS; *Int'l*, pg. 5747
GURIS HOLDING CO. INC.—See Parsan Makina Parcalari Sanayii AS; *Int'l*, pg. 5747
GURIS IS MAKINALARI ENDUSTRI A.S—See Parsan Makina Parcalari Sanayii AS; *Int'l*, pg. 5747
GURIT AMERICAS INC.—See Gurit Holding AG; *Int'l*, pg. 3188
GURIT (ASIA PACIFIC) LTD.—See Gurit Holding AG; *Int'l*, pg. 3187
GURIT (AUSTRALIA) PTY LTD—See Gurit Holding AG; *Int'l*, pg. 3187
GURIT BALSA, S.L.—See Gurit Holding AG; *Int'l*, pg. 3188
GURIT (CANADA) INC—See Gurit Holding AG; *Int'l*, pg. 3187
GURIT COMPOSITE COMPONENTS LIMITED—See Gurit Holding AG; *Int'l*, pg. 3188
GURIT COMPOSITE COMPONENTS LTD.—See Gurit Holding AG; *Int'l*, pg. 3188
GURIT HOLDING AG; *Int'l*, pg. 3187
GURIT (HUNGARY) KFT.—See CARBOPRESS S.p.A.; *Int'l*, pg. 1321
GURIT (INDIA) PVT. LTD—See Gurit Holding AG; *Int'l*, pg. 3187
GURIT ITALY S.R.L.—See Gurit Holding AG; *Int'l*, pg. 3188
GURIT (KASSEL) GMBH—See Gurit Holding AG; *Int'l*, pg. 3187
GURIT SCANDINAVIA APS—See Gurit Holding AG; *Int'l*, pg. 3188
GURIT SERVICES AG—See Gurit Holding AG; *Int'l*, pg. 3188
GURIT—See Gurit Holding AG; *Int'l*, pg. 3187
GURIT (SPAIN) LTD—See Gurit Holding AG; *Int'l*, pg. 3188
GURIT (TIANJIN) COMPOSITE MATERIAL CO., LTD.—See Gurit Holding AG; *Int'l*, pg. 3188
GURIT TOOLING (TAICANG) CO., LTD.—See Gurit Holding AG; *Int'l*, pg. 3188
GURIT (UK) LIMITED—See Gurit Holding AG; *Int'l*, pg. 3188
GURIT (UK) LTD—See Gurit Holding AG; *Int'l*, pg. 3188
GURIT (USA) INC—See Gurit Holding AG; *Int'l*, pg. 3188
GURIT (ZULLWIL) AG—See Gurit Holding AG; *Int'l*, pg. 3188
GURKHAS FINANCE LIMITED; *Int'l*, pg. 3188
GURKTALER AKTIENGESELLSCHAFT; *Int'l*, pg. 3188
GURLEY-LEEP BUICK-GMC TRUCK, INC; *U.S. Private*, pg. 1819
GURLEY MOTOR COMPANY; *U.S. Private*, pg. 1819
GURMETUM S.R.O.—See AMBRA S.A.; *Int'l*, pg. 415

GURNEE DODGE CHRYSLER JEEP, INC. CORPORATE AFFILIATIONS

Company Index

GURNEE DODGE CHRYSLER JEEP, INC.; *U.S. Private*, pg. 1819
GURNEE HYUNDAI MOTORS; *U.S. Private*, pg. 1819
THE GURNET GROUP LLC—See Praecipio Consulting LLC; *U.S. Private*, pg. 3241
GURNET POINT CAPITAL LLC; *U.S. Private*, pg. 1819
GURNEY PRODUCTIONS, INC.—See ITV plc; *Int'l*, pg. 3845
GURTLER INDUSTRIES INC; *U.S. Private*, pg. 1819
GURTNER—See Gevelot S.A.; *Int'l*, pg. 2954
GURU APP FACTORY CORP.; *Int'l*, pg. 3188
GURU.COM; *U.S. Private*, pg. 1819
GURU DENIM, INC.—See TowerBrook Capital Partners, L.P.; *U.S. Private*, pg. 4196
GURUM COMPANY INC.; *Int'l*, pg. 3188
GURUNAVI, INC.; *Int'l*, pg. 3188
GURU ORGANIC ENERGY CORP.; *Int'l*, pg. 3188
THE GURWIN JEWISH GERIATRIC CENTER; *U.S. Private*, pg. 4040
GURWITCH PRODUCTS, L.L.C.—See Shiseido Company, Limited; *Int'l*, pg. 6854
GUSBOURNE PLC; *Int'l*, pg. 3188
GUS GROUP AG & CO KG; *Int'l*, pg. 3188
GUSHENGTANG HOLDINGS LIMITED; *Int'l*, pg. 3188
GUSHEN, INC.; *U.S. Public*, pg. 975
GUSHER PUMPS, INC.—See Ruthman Pump & Engineering Inc.; *U.S. Private*, pg. 3508
GUSHER PUMPS (SHANGHAI) CO., LTD.—See Ruthman Pump & Engineering Inc.; *U.S. Private*, pg. 3508
GUSKIN GOLD CORP.; *U.S. Public*, pg. 975
GUS MACHADO ENTERPRISES, INC.; *U.S. Private*, pg. 1819
GUS MACHADO FORD, INC.—See Gus Machado Enterprises, Inc.; *U.S. Private*, pg. 1819
GUSMER ENTERPRISES, INC.; *U.S. Private*, pg. 1819
GUSMER ENTERPRISES, INC.—See Gusmer Enterprises, Inc.; *U.S. Private*, pg. 1819
GUSMER-EUROPE—See Graco, Inc.; *U.S. Public*, pg. 953
GUSMER SUDAMERICA S.A.—See Graco, Inc.; *U.S. Public*, pg. 953
GUSSCO MANUFACTURING, INC.—See Selco Industries, Inc.; *U.S. Private*, pg. 3600
GUSTAF FAGERBERG A/S—See Indutrade AB; *Int'l*, pg. 3679
GUSTAF FAGERBERG HOLDING AB—See Indutrade AB; *Int'l*, pg. 3679
GUSTAFSON'S KIA; *Int'l*, pg. 3188
GUSTAVE A. LARSON COMPANY; *U.S. Private*, pg. 1819
GUSTAV. F. HUEBENER GMBH—See Kuehne + Nagel International AG; *Int'l*, pg. 4324
GUSTAV KLAUKE GMBH—See Emerson Electric Co.; *U.S. Public*, pg. 750
GUSTAV RAETZ GERUSTBAU GMBH—See Aurelius Equity Opportunities SE & Co. KGaA; *Int'l*, pg. 708
GUSTAVSON ASSOCIATES LLC—See WSP Global, Inc.; *Int'l*, pg. 8496
GUSTOMSC B.V.—See NOV, Inc.; *U.S. Public*, pg. 1545
GUSTOMSC INC.—See SBM Offshore N.V.; *Int'l*, pg. 6607
GUSTO PACKING CO., INC.—See Maxwell Foods, LLC; *U.S. Private*, pg. 2619
GUSTO PACKING CO., INC.—See Seaboard Corporation; *U.S. Public*, pg. 1850
GUSWEILER GM CENTER; *U.S. Private*, pg. 1819
G&U SYSTEM SERVICE, LTD.—See BIPROGY Inc.; *Int'l*, pg. 1045
G&U SYSTEM SERVICE, LTD.—See Gunze Limited; *Int'l*, pg. 3185
GUTA-BANK JSC; *Int'l*, pg. 3188
GUTEFRAGE.NET GMBH—See Verlagsgruppe Georg von Holtzbrinck GmbH; *Int'l*, pg. 8172
GUTEHOFFNUNGSHUTTE RADSATZ GMBH—See Bonatrans Group a.s.; *Int'l*, pg. 1105
GUTENBERG COMMUNICATIONS; *U.S. Private*, pg. 1820
GUTENBERG COMMUNICATIONS—See Gutenberg Communications; *U.S. Private*, pg. 1820
GUTERMANN & PRYM CONSUMER ITALIA S.R.L.—See William Prym GmbH & Co. KG; *Int'l*, pg. 8413
GUTERTERMINAL WERNDORF PROJEKT GMBH—See OBB-Holding AG; *Int'l*, pg. 5509
GUTH HIGH VOLTAGE GMBH—See XP Power Limited; *Int'l*, pg. 8537
THE GUTHRIE CLINIC; *U.S. Private*, pg. 4040
GUTHRIE CONSTRUCTION & RETROFITTING (S) PTE LTD—See Guthrie GTS Limited; *Int'l*, pg. 3188
GUTHRIE CONSULTANCY SERVICES PTE LTD—See Guthrie GTS Limited; *Int'l*, pg. 3188
GUTHRIE COUNTY RURAL ELECTRIC COOPERATIVE ASSOCIATION; *U.S. Private*, pg. 1820
GUTHRIE ENGINEERING (S) PTE LTD—See Guthrie GTS Limited; *Int'l*, pg. 3188
GUTHRIE FMC PTE LTD—See Guthrie GTS Limited; *Int'l*, pg. 3188
GUTHRIE GTS LIMITED; *Int'l*, pg. 3188
GUTHRIE LUMBER SALES INC.; *U.S. Private*, pg. 1820
GUTHRIE MARKETING (S) PTE LTD—See Guthrie GTS Limited; *Int'l*, pg. 3188
GUTHRIE/MAYES; *U.S. Private*, pg. 1820
GUTHRIE OVERSEAS INVESTMENTS PTE LTD—See Guthrie GTS Limited; *Int'l*, pg. 3189
GUTHRIE PMS (S) PTE LTD—See Guthrie GTS Limited; *Int'l*, pg. 3189
GUTHY-RENKER CORPORATION; *U.S. Private*, pg. 1820
GUTHY-RENKER CORP. - SANTA MONICA OFFICE—See Guthy-Renker Corporation; *U.S. Private*, pg. 1820
THE GUTIERREZ COMPANY; *U.S. Private*, pg. 4040
GUTJAHR SYSTEMTECHNIK GMBH; *Int'l*, pg. 3189
GUTKNECHT CONSTRUCTION COMPANY; *U.S. Private*, pg. 1820
GUTMANN AG—See ALCO Hellas S.A.; *Int'l*, pg. 301
GUTMANN ALUMINIUM DRAHT GMBH—See ALCO Hellas S.A.; *Int'l*, pg. 301
THE GUTMANN COMPANY—See Elica S.p.A.; *Int'l*, pg. 2361
GUTOR ELECTRONIC ASIA PACIFIC SDN BHD—See Schneider Electric SE; *Int'l*, pg. 6627
GUTOR ELECTRONIC GMBH—See Latour Capital Management SAS; *Int'l*, pg. 4423
GUTOR ELECTRONIC LLC—See Latour Capital Management SAS; *Int'l*, pg. 4423
GUTSCHE ENVIRONMENTAL TECHNOLOGY (YIXING) CO. LTD.—See Lydall, Inc.; *U.S. Public*, pg. 1349
GUTS GROUP INC.; *Int'l*, pg. 3189
GUTS INVESTIGATION CO., LTD.—See Guts Group Inc.; *Int'l*, pg. 3189
GUTS OPERATION CO., LTD.—See Guts Group Inc.; *Int'l*, pg. 3189
GUTS SECURITECH CO., LTD.—See Guts Group Inc.; *Int'l*, pg. 3189
GUTTMAN ENERGY, INC.—See Guttman Holdings, Inc.; *U.S. Private*, pg. 1820
GUTTMAN HOLDINGS, INC.; *U.S. Private*, pg. 1820
GUTTOMAT SEKTIONALTORE GMBH—See Atrya SAS; *Int'l*, pg. 694
GUYANA AMERICAS MERCHANT BANK INC.—See Edward B. Beharry & Co. Ltd.; *Int'l*, pg. 2316
GUYANA BANK FOR TRADE & INDUSTRY LTD.—See Edward B. Beharry & Co. Ltd.; *Int'l*, pg. 2316
GUYANA FRONTIER MINING CORP.; *Int'l*, pg. 3189
GUYANA GOLD CORP.; *U.S. Public*, pg. 975
GUYANA GOLDFIELDS INC.—See Zijin Mining Group Company Limited; *Int'l*, pg. 8683
GUYANA GOLDSTRIKE INC.; *Int'l*, pg. 3189
GUYANA LOTTERY COMPANY LIMITED—See Canadian Bank Note Company Limited; *Int'l*, pg. 1282
GUYANA TELEPHONE & TELEGRAPH CO (GT&T)—See ATN International, Inc.; *U.S. Public*, pg. 225
GUYAN INTERNATIONAL INC.; *U.S. Private*, pg. 1820
GUY BENNETT LUMBER COMPANY; *U.S. Private*, pg. 1820
GUY BROWN PRODUCTS; *U.S. Private*, pg. 1820
GUY CARPENTER BERMUDA LTD.—See Marsh & McLennan Companies, Inc.; *U.S. Public*, pg. 1375
GUY CARPENTER & CIA., S.A.—See Marsh & McLennan Companies, Inc.; *U.S. Public*, pg. 1375
GUY CARPENTER & CO. LABUAN LTD.—See Marsh & McLennan Companies, Inc.; *U.S. Public*, pg. 1375
GUY CARPENTER & CO. LABUAN LTD.—See Marsh & McLennan Companies, Inc.; *U.S. Public*, pg. 1375
GUY CARPENTER COLOMBIA LTDA.—See Marsh & McLennan Companies, Inc.; *U.S. Public*, pg. 1375
GUY CARPENTER & COMPANY AB—See Marsh & McLennan Companies, Inc.; *U.S. Public*, pg. 1375
GUY CARPENTER & COMPANY B.V.—See Marsh & McLennan Companies, Inc.; *U.S. Public*, pg. 1375
GUY CARPENTER & COMPANY CORREDORES DE REASEGUROS LTDA—See Marsh & McLennan Companies, Inc.; *U.S. Public*, pg. 1375
GUY CARPENTER & COMPANY CORRETORA DE RESSEGUROS LTDA.—See Marsh & McLennan Companies, Inc.; *U.S. Public*, pg. 1375
GUY CARPENTER & COMPANY GMBH—See Marsh & McLennan Companies, Inc.; *U.S. Public*, pg. 1375
GUY CARPENTER & COMPANY INC. OF PENNSYLVANIA—See Marsh & McLennan Companies, Inc.; *U.S. Public*, pg. 1375
GUY CARPENTER & COMPANY LIMITED—See Marsh & McLennan Companies, Inc.; *U.S. Public*, pg. 1375
GUY CARPENTER & COMPANY LIMITED—See Marsh & McLennan Companies, Inc.; *U.S. Public*, pg. 1375
GUY CARPENTER & COMPANY, LIMITED—See Marsh & McLennan Companies, Inc.; *U.S. Public*, pg. 1375
GUY CARPENTER & COMPANY, LIMITED—See Marsh & McLennan Companies, Inc.; *U.S. Public*, pg. 1375
GUY CARPENTER & COMPANY, LLC—See Marsh & McLennan Companies, Inc.; *U.S. Public*, pg. 1375
GUY CARPENTER & COMPANY, LTDA.—See Marsh & McLennan Companies, Inc.; *U.S. Public*, pg. 1375
GUY CARPENTER & COMPANY, LTD.—See Marsh & McLennan Companies, Inc.; *U.S. Public*, pg. 1375
GUY CARPENTER & COMPANY PERU CORREDORES DE REASEGUROS S.A.—See Marsh & McLennan Companies, Inc.; *U.S. Public*, pg. 1375
GUY CARPENTER & COMPANY PRIVATE LIMITED—See Marsh & McLennan Companies, Inc.; *U.S. Public*, pg. 1375
GUY CARPENTER & COMPANY (PTY) LIMITED—See Marsh & McLennan Companies, Inc.; *U.S. Public*, pg. 1375
GUY CARPENTER & COMPANY PTY. LIMITED—See Marsh & McLennan Companies, Inc.; *U.S. Public*, pg. 1375
GUY CARPENTER & COMPANY, S.A.—See Marsh & McLennan Companies, Inc.; *U.S. Public*, pg. 1375
GUY CARPENTER & COMPANY, S.A.—See Marsh & McLennan Companies, Inc.; *U.S. Public*, pg. 1375
GUY CARPENTER & COMPANY, S.A.—See Marsh & McLennan Companies, Inc.; *U.S. Public*, pg. 1375
GUY CARPENTER & COMPANY S.A.—See Marsh & McLennan Companies, Inc.; *U.S. Public*, pg. 1375
GUY CARPENTER & COMPANY, S.A.S.—See Marsh & McLennan Companies, Inc.; *U.S. Public*, pg. 1375
GUY CARPENTER & COMPANY S.R.L.—See Marsh & McLennan Companies, Inc.; *U.S. Public*, pg. 1375
GUY CARPENTER INSURANCE BROKERS (BEIJING) CO. LTD.—See Marsh & McLennan Companies, Inc.; *U.S. Public*, pg. 1375
GUY CARPENTER JAPAN, INC.—See Marsh & McLennan Companies, Inc.; *U.S. Public*, pg. 1376
GUY CARPENTER MEXICO INTERMEDIARIO DE REASEGURO, S.A. DE C.V.—See Marsh & McLennan Companies, Inc.; *U.S. Public*, pg. 1376
GUY CARPENTER MEXICO, INTERMEDIARO DE REASUGURO, S.A. DE C.V.—See Marsh & McLennan Companies, Inc.; *U.S. Public*, pg. 1376
GUY CARPENTER (MIDDLE EAST) LIMITED—See Marsh & McLennan Companies, Inc.; *U.S. Public*, pg. 1375
GUY CHEMICAL COMPANY, INC.; *U.S. Private*, pg. 1820
GUY DEGRENNE S.A.—See Vorwerk & Co. KG; *Int'l*, pg. 8307
GUYENNE ET GASCOGNE SA—See Carrefour SA; *Int'l*, pg. 1345
GUYER WARME UND WASSER AG—See Burkhalter Holding AG; *Int'l*, pg. 1225
GUYETTE, SCHMIDT & DEETER; *U.S. Private*, pg. 1820
GUY F. ATKINSON CONSTRUCTION, LLC - NORTHWEST DIVISION—See Clark Enterprises, Inc.; *U.S. Private*, pg. 913
GUY F. ATKINSON CONSTRUCTION, LLC—See Clark Enterprises, Inc.; *U.S. Private*, pg. 912
GUY F. ATKINSON CONSTRUCTION, LLC - SOUTHERN CALIFORNIA DIVISION—See Clark Enterprises, Inc.; *U.S. Private*, pg. 913
GUY HOPKINS CONSTRUCTION CO., INC.; *U.S. Private*, pg. 1820
GUY LAROCHE SA—See Societe BIC S.A.; *Int'l*, pg. 7037
GUYMARK UK LIMITED—See Demant A/S; *Int'l*, pg. 2023
GUYMON EXTRACTS INC.—See Riken Vitamin Co., Ltd.; *Int'l*, pg. 6341
GUY M. TURNER INC.; *U.S. Private*, pg. 1820
GUYO ENTERTAINMENT, INC.—See Live Nation Entertainment, Inc.; *U.S. Public*, pg. 1329
GUYOMARC'H - VCN COMPANY LIMITED—See Archer-Daniels-Midland Company; *U.S. Public*, pg. 185
GUY & O'NEILL, INC.—See Centre Partners Management LLC; *U.S. Private*, pg. 828
GUYOT-WALSER INFORMATIQUE S.A.R.L.—See GPI S.p.A.; *Int'l*, pg. 3046
GUYOUNG TECH. CO., LTD - ALABAMA FACTORY—See Guyoung Tech. Co., Ltd; *Int'l*, pg. 3189
GUYOUNG TECH. CO., LTD - DAEGU PLANT—See Guyoung Tech. Co., Ltd; *Int'l*, pg. 3189
GUYOUNG TECH. CO., LTD; *Int'l*, pg. 3189
GUYOUNG TECH. CO., LTD - YEONGCHEON PLANT—See Guyoung Tech. Co., Ltd; *Int'l*, pg. 3189
GUY SALMON HONDA LIMITED—See Penske Automotive Group, Inc.; *U.S. Public*, pg. 1666
GUY SALMON JAGUAR STOCKPORT—See Penske Automotive Group, Inc.; *U.S. Public*, pg. 1666
GUY SALMON LIMITED—See Penske Automotive Group, Inc.; *U.S. Public*, pg. 1666
GUYS FLOOR SERVICE INCORPORATED; *U.S. Private*, pg. 1820
GUYSON CN—See Guyson International Limited; *Int'l*, pg. 3189
GUYSON CORPORATION OF U.S.A.—See Guyson International Limited; *Int'l*, pg. 3189
GUYSON INTERNATIONAL LIMITED - HOSE & COUPLINGS DIVISION—See Guyson International Limited; *Int'l*, pg. 3189
GUYSON INTERNATIONAL LIMITED; *Int'l*, pg. 3189
GUYSON SA—See Guyson International Limited; *Int'l*, pg. 3189
GUYSON SDN BHD—See Guyson International Limited; *Int'l*, pg. 3189
GUZEL SANATLAR SAATCHI & SAATCHI—See Publicis Groupe S.A.; *Int'l*, pg. 6108
GUZIP BIOMARKERS CORPORATION—See Win Semiconductors Corp.; *Int'l*, pg. 8424
GUZZLER MANUFACTURING INC.—See Federal Signal Corporation; *U.S. Public*, pg. 826
GVA CONSULTANTS AB—See KBR, Inc.; *U.S. Public*, pg. 1216
GVA OXFORD—See Oxford Development Company; *U.S. Private*, pg. 3057
GVA TRANSFERS.COM SARL—See Mobico Group PLC.; *Int'l*, pg. 5008

COMPANY NAME INDEX

GVC CORPORATION B.V.—See Entain PLC; *Int'l*, pg. 2449
GVD INDUSTRIES LLC; *U.S. Private*, pg. 1820
G-VEST CORPORATION SDN. BHD.—See PLC Financial Solutions Limited; *Int'l*, pg. 5895
GV FILMS LTD; *Int'l*, pg. 3189
GV (GEUMVIT CORP.) JAPAN CO., LTD.—See GeumVit Corp.; *Int'l*, pg. 2954
GV (GEUMVIT CORP.) (YANTAI) CO., LTD.—See GeumVit Corp.; *Int'l*, pg. 2954
GVG GESELLSCHAFT ZUR VERWERTUNG VON GRUNDBESITZ MIT BESCHRANKTER HAFTUNG—See Commerzbank AG; *Int'l*, pg. 1718
GVG RHEIN-ERFT GMBH—See E.ON SE; *Int'l*, pg. 2257
GVH MANAGEMENT; *U.S. Private*, pg. 1821
GVIC COMMUNICATIONS CORP.; *Int'l*, pg. 3189
G-VISION INTERNATIONAL (HOLDINGS) LIMITED; *Int'l*, pg. 2864
GVK AIRPORT DEVELOPERS PRIVATE LIMITED—See GVK Power and Infrastructure Limited; *Int'l*, pg. 3190
GVK BIOSCIENCES PVT. LTD.—See GVK Power and Infrastructure Limited; *Int'l*, pg. 3190
GVK INDUSTRIES LIMITED—See GVK Power and Infrastructure Limited; *Int'l*, pg. 3190
GVK JAIPUR EXPRESSWAY PRIVATE LIMITED—See GVK Power and Infrastructure Limited; *Int'l*, pg. 3190
GVK POWER AND INFRASTRUCTURE LIMITED; *Int'l*, pg. 3189
GVL RECHENZENTRUM GMBH—See Arzneiwerk AG VIDA; *Int'l*, pg. 589
GV MANAGEMENT COMPANY, LLC—See Alphabet Inc.; *U.S. Public*, pg. 82
GV MEDIA GROUP LIMITED—See Radio Jamaica Limited; *Int'l*, pg. 6176
GVM INC.; *U.S. Private*, pg. 1820
G.V. MOORE LUMBER CO., INC.; *U.S. Private*, pg. 1631
GVNA HEALTHCARE, INC.; *U.S. Private*, pg. 1821
GVO, D.O.O.—See Telekom Slovenije, d.d.; *Int'l*, pg. 7538
G. VOLKL GMBH—See Dr. Aichhorn GmbH; *Int'l*, pg. 2190
GVS ARGENTINA SA—See GVS S.p.A.; *Int'l*, pg. 3190
GVS FILTRATION CO., LTD.—See GVS S.p.A.; *Int'l*, pg. 3190
GVS FILTRATION SDN. BHD.—See GVS S.p.A.; *Int'l*, pg. 3190
GVS GIFT VOUCHER SHOP LIMITED—See P2 Capital Partners, LLC; *U.S. Private*, pg. 3061
GVS GIFT VOUCHER SHOP LIMITED—See Silver Lake Group, LLC; *U.S. Private*, pg. 3656
GVS JAPAN KK—See GVS S.p.A.; *Int'l*, pg. 3190
GVS KOREA LTD.—See GVS S.p.A.; *Int'l*, pg. 3190
GVS MICROFILTRAZIONE S.R.L.—See GVS S.p.A.; *Int'l*, pg. 3190
GVS NETZ GMBH—See EnBW Energie Baden-Wurttemberg AG; *Int'l*, pg. 2399
GVS RUSSIA LLC—See GVS S.p.A.; *Int'l*, pg. 3190
GVS S.P.A.; *Int'l*, pg. 3190
GVS TECHNOLOGY (SUZHOU) CO., LTD.—See GVS S.p.A.; *Int'l*, pg. 3190
GVTC COMMUNICATIONS; *U.S. Private*, pg. 1821
GVW GROUP, LLC; *U.S. Private*, pg. 1821
GWA GROUP LIMITED; *Int'l*, pg. 3190
GWANAK CONSTRUCTION AND EQUIPMENT SERVICE CO LTD; *Int'l*, pg. 3190
GWANDA, LLC—See iVenture Solutions, Inc.; *U.S. Private*, pg. 2151
GWANGJU SHINSEGAE. CO., LTD.—See Shinsegae Inc.; *Int'l*, pg. 6848
GWA TRADING (SHANGHAI) CO., LTD.—See GWA Group Limited; *Int'l*, pg. 3190
GWAVA EMEA GMBH—See Micro Focus International plc; *Int'l*, pg. 4876
G.W. BERKHEIMER CO. INC.; *U.S. Private*, pg. 1631
GWB IMMOBILIEN AG; *Int'l*, pg. 3190
G&W CANADA CORPORATION—See G&W Electric Company; *U.S. Private*, pg. 1629
GWC GLOBAL TRANSPORT LLC—See Gulf Warehousing Company QSC; *Int'l*, pg. 3182
GWC MARINE SERVICES W.L.L.—See Gulf Warehousing Company QSC; *Int'l*, pg. 3182
G&W COMMERCIAL FLOORING, INC.—See Lynx Equity Limited; *Int'l*, pg. 4606
G & W CONCRETE PRODUCTS PTE LTD—See Koh Brothers Group Limited; *Int'l*, pg. 4228
GWC WARRANTY CORPORATION—See Ontario Teachers' Pension Plan; *Int'l*, pg. 5587
GWE BUDAFILTER KFT.—See BAUER Aktiengesellschaft; *Int'l*, pg. 893
GWE FRANCE S.A.S.—See BAUER Aktiengesellschaft; *Int'l*, pg. 893
G&W ELECTRIC COMPANY; *U.S. Private*, pg. 1629
GWE POL-BUD SP.Z.O.O—See BAUER Aktiengesellschaft; *Int'l*, pg. 893
GWE PUMPENBOESE GMBH.—See BAUER Aktiengesellschaft; *Int'l*, pg. 893
G&W EQUIPMENT, INC.; *U.S. Private*, pg. 1629
GWE TUBOMIN S.A.—See BAUER Aktiengesellschaft; *Int'l*, pg. 893
GWE WARME- UND ENERGIETECHNIK GMBH & CO. KG—See CEZ, a.s.; *Int'l*, pg. 1428

GWFACT - INVOICE SOLUTIONS, LDA.—See Grenke AG; *Int'l*, pg. 3081
GW FOODS INC.; *U.S. Private*, pg. 1821
GW FREIGHT MANAGEMENT BRAZIL—See SNCF; *Int'l*, pg. 7025
GWG GREVENBROICH GMBH—See RWE AG; *Int'l*, pg. 6434
GWG HOLDINGS, INC.; *U.S. Public*, pg. 975
G+W GMBH—See AVK Holding A/S; *Int'l*, pg. 748
GWH AUFZUGE GMBH—See ThyssenKrupp AG; *Int'l*, pg. 7724
GWH BAUPROJEKTE GMBH—See Helaba Landesbank Hessen-Thuringen; *Int'l*, pg. 3327
GW HEALTH NETWORK, LLC—See Universal Health Services, Inc.; *U.S. Public*, pg. 2257
GWH IMMOBILIEN HOLDING GMBH—See Helaba Landesbank Hessen-Thuringen; *Int'l*, pg. 3328
G.W. HOFFMAN MARKETING & COMMUNICATIONS; *U.S. Private*, pg. 1631
GW-HOTEL INC.—See Hilton Worldwide Holdings Inc.; *U.S. Public*, pg. 1040
GWH WERTINVEST GMBH—See Helaba Landesbank Hessen-Thuringen; *Int'l*, pg. 3328
GWI ACQUISITIONS PTY LTD—See Brookfield Infrastructure Partners L.P.; *Int'l*, pg. 1191
GWI ACQUISITIONS PTY LTD—See GIC Pte. Ltd.; *Int'l*, pg. 2966
GWI BAUUNTERNEHMUNG GMBH—See Erbud S.A.; *Int'l*, pg. 2489
GWI HOLDING BV—See Brookfield Infrastructure Partners L.P.; *Int'l*, pg. 1191
GWI HOLDING BV—See GIC Pte. Ltd.; *Int'l*, pg. 2966
GWI, INC.; *U.S. Private*, pg. 1821
G. WILLI-FOOD INTERNATIONAL LTD.—See Willi-Food Investments Ltd.; *Int'l*, pg. 8412
GWIN DOBSON & FOREMAN INC.; *U.S. Private*, pg. 1821
G & W INDUSTRIAL CORPORATION PTE LTD—See Koh Brothers Group Limited; *Int'l*, pg. 4228
G & W INDUSTRIES (M) SDN. BHD.—See Koh Brothers Group Limited; *Int'l*, pg. 4228
G & W INDUSTRIES PTE LTD—See Koh Brothers Group Limited; *Int'l*, pg. 4228
GWINNETT DAILY POST—See Southern Community Newspapers Inc.; *U.S. Private*, pg. 3730
GWINNETT HOSPITAL SYSTEM, INC.; *U.S. Private*, pg. 1821
GWINNETT PLACE HONDA—See The Hendrick Companies, LLC; *U.S. Private*, pg. 4051
GW INSTEK INDIA LLP—See Good Will Instrument Co., Ltd.; *Int'l*, pg. 3039
GW&K INVESTMENT MANAGEMENT, LLC—See Affiliated Managers Group, Inc.; *U.S. Public*, pg. 55
GWK TRAVELEX N.V.—See Travelex Holdings Limited; *Int'l*, pg. 7907
G&W LABORATORIES INC.; *U.S. Private*, pg. 1630
G.W. LISK COMPANY, INC.; *U.S. Private*, pg. 1631
GWL REALTY ADVISORS, INC.—See Power Corporation of Canada; *Int'l*, pg. 5943
G.W. PALMER LOGISTICS, LLC.; *U.S. Private*, pg. 1631
GW PHARMACEUTICALS PLC—See Jazz Pharmaceuticals plc; *Int'l*, pg. 3916
GW PHARMA LIMITED—See Jazz Pharmaceuticals plc; *Int'l*, pg. 3916
GWP INDUSTRIES INC.; *U.S. Private*, pg. 1821
GW PLASTICS (DONGGUAN) LTD.—See Nolato AB; *Int'l*, pg. 5407
GW PLASTICS INC.—See Nolato AB; *Int'l*, pg. 5407
GW PLASTICS MEXICANA S DE RL DE CV—See Nolato AB; *Int'l*, pg. 5407
GW PLASTICS SAN ANTONIO INC.—See Nolato AB; *Int'l*, pg. 5407
GW PLASTICS SOUTHWEST INC.—See Nolato AB; *Int'l*, pg. 5407
GW PLASTICS TUCSON INCORPORATED—See Nolato AB; *Int'l*, pg. 5407
G & W PRECAST PTE LTD—See Koh Brothers Group Limited; *Int'l*, pg. 4228
GWQ GESELLSCHAFT FUR WERKSTOFFPRUFUNG UND QUALITATSSICHERUNG MBH—See TUV NORD AG; *Int'l*, pg. 7980
G & W READY-MIX PTE LTD—See Koh Brothers Group Limited; *Int'l*, pg. 4228
GWR GROUP LIMITED; *Int'l*, pg. 3190
GW SERVICES, LLC—See Primo Water Corporation; *U.S. Public*, pg. 1718
GW SILICONES INC.—See Nolato AB; *Int'l*, pg. 5407
G.W. SPRINKLER A/S—See Carrier Global Corporation; *U.S. Public*, pg. 441
GWS PRINTING SYSTEMS B.V.—See L. Possehl & Co. mbH; *Int'l*, pg. 4382
GWS TECHNOLOGIES LTD.—See Ireland Blyth Limited; *Int'l*, pg. 3807
GWS TOOL GROUP, LLC—See L Squared Capital Management LP; *U.S. Private*, pg. 2361
GWS TOOL LLC—See Sandvik AB; *Int'l*, pg. 6529
GW TRANSPORTATION SERVICES—See Stan Koch & Sons Trucking; *U.S. Private*, pg. 3777

GYOR-SOPRON-EBENFURTI VASUT RT.

THE G.W. VAN KEPPEL CO. - KANSAS CITY, MISSOURI—See The G.W. Van Keppel Company; *U.S. Private*, pg. 4031
THE G.W. VAN KEPPEL COMPANY; *U.S. Private*, pg. 4031
THE G.W. VAN KEPPEL CO. - OKLAHOMA CITY—See The G.W. Van Keppel Company; *U.S. Private*, pg. 4031
GW VITEK CO., LTD.; *Int'l*, pg. 3190
GW & WADE; *U.S. Private*, pg. 1821
GWYNT Y MOR OFTO PLC—See Balfour Beatty plc; *Int'l*, pg. 808
GXC COATINGS GMBH; *Int'l*, pg. 3190
GXO LOGISTICS, INC.; *U.S. Public*, pg. 975
GXP AUTOMATION LLC.—See Huron Capital Partners LLC; *U.S. Private*, pg. 2011
GXP GERMAN PROPERTIES AG; *Int'l*, pg. 3190
GX SCIENCES, LLC—See Fagron NV; *Int'l*, pg. 2603
GXS INC.—See Open Text Corporation; *Int'l*, pg. 5597
GXS, INC.—See Open Text Corporation; *Int'l*, pg. 5597
GXS INDIA TECHNOLOGY CENTRE PRIVATE LIMITED—See Open Text Corporation; *Int'l*, pg. 5597
GXS INTERNATIONAL, INC.—See Open Text Corporation; *Int'l*, pg. 5597
GXS LTD.—See Open Text Corporation; *Int'l*, pg. 5597
GXS - RALEIGH—See Open Text Corporation; *Int'l*, pg. 5597
GXS SAS—See Open Text Corporation; *Int'l*, pg. 5597
GXS UK HOLDING LIMITED—See Open Text Corporation; *Int'l*, pg. 5597
GX TECHNOLOGY AUSTRALIA PTY LTD.—See ION Geophysical Corporation; *U.S. Public*, pg. 1166
GX TECHNOLOGY CANADA, LTD.—See ION Geophysical Corporation; *U.S. Public*, pg. 1166
GX TECHNOLOGY CORPORATION—See ION Geophysical Corporation; *U.S. Public*, pg. 1166
GX TECHNOLOGY EAME LIMITED—See ION Geophysical Corporation; *U.S. Public*, pg. 1166
GX TECHNOLOGY PROCESSAMENTO DE DADOS LTDA.—See ION Geophysical Corporation; *U.S. Public*, pg. 1166
GX TECHNOLOGY TRINIDAD, LTD.—See ION Geophysical Corporation; *U.S. Public*, pg. 1166
GYAN DEVELOPERS & BUILDERS LIMITED; *Int'l*, pg. 3190
GYANSYS INC.; *U.S. Private*, pg. 1821
GYAO CORPORATION—See SoftBank Group Corp.; *Int'l*, pg. 7052
GYARMATHY & PARTNERS LTD.; *Int'l*, pg. 3190
GY COMMERCE CO LTD; *Int'l*, pg. 3190
GYD IBERICA S.A.—See Giesecke & Devrient GmbH; *Int'l*, pg. 2970
GYD LATINOAMERICANA S.A.—See Giesecke & Devrient GmbH; *Int'l*, pg. 2970
GYEONGJU WORLD RESORT CO., LTD.—See Asia Holdings Co., Ltd.; *Int'l*, pg. 613
GYG PLC; *Int'l*, pg. 3190
GYK ANTLER; *U.S. Private*, pg. 1821
GYLDENDAL A/S; *Int'l*, pg. 3191
GYMA FOOD INDUSTRIES FZ-LLC—See Savola Group; *Int'l*, pg. 6602
GYMBOGLOBAL CORPORATION; *U.S. Private*, pg. 1821
THE GYM GROUP PLC; *Int'l*, pg. 7651
THE GYM LIMITED; *Int'l*, pg. 7651
GYMPIE & DISTRICT VETERINARY SERVICES PTY. LTD.—See Apiam Animal Health Limited; *Int'l*, pg. 515
GYMPIE FUNERAL SERVICES PTY LTD—See Propel Funeral Partners Limited; *Int'l*, pg. 5997
GYMPIE PRIVATE HOSPITAL PTY. LTD.—See Luye Medical Group; *Int'l*, pg. 4589
GYMTECH FEEDMILL (M) SDN. BHD.—See Emivest Berhad; *Int'l*, pg. 2383
GYNAE-SCREEN LIMITED—See Eurofins Scientific S.E.; *Int'l*, pg. 2550
GYNECOLOGIC ONCOLOGY ASSOCIATES, INC.—See KKR & Co. Inc.; *U.S. Public*, pg. 1245
GYNOPHARM DE VENEZUELA, C.A.—See Abbott Laboratories; *U.S. Public*, pg. 20
GYNOPHARM S.A.—See Abbott Laboratories; *U.S. Public*, pg. 20
GYOGYITO PATIKUS BT.—See PHOENIX Pharmahandel GmbH & Co. KG; *Int'l*, pg. 5854
GYOGYSZERIPARI ELLENORZO ES FEJLESTO LABORATORIUM—See Gedeon Richter Plc.; *Int'l*, pg. 2910
GYOMAI KNER NYOMDA ZRT.—See ANY Security Printing Company PLC; *Int'l*, pg. 486
GYOR-SOPRON-EBENFURTI VASUT RT.; *Int'l*, pg. 3191
GYOZA KEIKAKU CO., LTD.—See CJ Corporation; *Int'l*, pg. 1634
GYPCO SHANGHAI—See Compagnie de Saint-Gobain SA; *Int'l*, pg. 1725
GYP PROPERTIES LIMITED—See Rumah & Co. Pte. Ltd.; *Int'l*, pg. 6427
GYPROC AB—See Compagnie de Saint-Gobain SA; *Int'l*, pg. 1725
GYPROC A/S—See Compagnie de Saint-Gobain SA; *Int'l*, pg. 1725
GYPROC AS—See Compagnie de Saint-Gobain SA; *Int'l*, pg. 1725

1161

GYPRO CO., LTD.—See Takeei Corporation; *Int'l*, pg. 7440
GYPROC OY—See Heidelberg Materials AG; *Int'l*, pg. 3315
GYPSUM CREEK HEALTHCARE, INC.—See The Ensign Group, Inc.; *U.S. Public*, pg. 2071
GYPSUM EXPRESS LTD.; *U.S. Private*, pg. 1821
GYPSUM INDUSTRIES (IRELAND) LIMITED—See Compagnie de Saint-Gobain SA; *Int'l*, pg. 1725
GYPSUM INDUSTRIES (PVT) LTD.—See Compagnie de Saint-Gobain SA; *Int'l*, pg. 1725
GYPSUM INDUSTRIES (UK) LTD.—See Compagnie de Saint-Gobain SA; *Int'l*, pg. 1725
GYPSUM MANAGEMENT & SUPPLY, INC.—See GMS Inc.; *U.S. Public*, pg. 947
GYPSUM PRODUCTS INC.; *U.S. Private*, pg. 1821
GYPSUM SUPPLY COMPANY—See GMS Inc.; *U.S. Public*, pg. 948
GYPSUM SUPPLY CO.; *U.S. Private*, pg. 1821
GYPSUM WALLBOARD SUPPLY INC.—See American Securities LLC; *U.S. Private*, pg. 249
GYRE THERAPEUTICS, INC.—See GNI Group Ltd.; *Int'l*, pg. 3017
GYRO BENELUX B.V.—See Gyro Communications Ltd; *Int'l*, pg. 3191
GYRO CHICAGO—See Gyro Communications Ltd; *Int'l*, pg. 3191
GYRO CINCINNATI—See Gyro Communications Ltd; *Int'l*, pg. 3191
GYRO COMMUNICATIONS LTD; *Int'l*, pg. 3191
GYRODATA, INC.—See Schlumberger Limited; *U.S. Public*, pg. 1844
GYRO DENVER—See Gyro Communications Ltd; *Int'l*, pg. 3191
GYRO DEUTSCHLAND GMBH—See Gyro Communications Ltd; *Int'l*, pg. 3191
GYRODYNE, LLC; *U.S. Public*, pg. 976
GYROMETRIC SYSTEMS LIMITED—See Nanosynth Group PLC; *Int'l*, pg. 5144
GYRO MUNICH—See Gyro Communications Ltd; *Int'l*, pg. 3191
GYRO NEW YORK—See Gyro Communications Ltd; *Int'l*, pg. 3191
GYRO PARIS—See Gyro Communications Ltd; *Int'l*, pg. 3191
GYRO SCANDINAVIA AB—See Gyro Communications Ltd; *Int'l*, pg. 3191
GYROSCOPE THERAPEUTICS HOLDINGS PLC; *Int'l*, pg. 3191
GYROSCOPE THERAPEUTICS LIMITED—See Novartis AG; *Int'l*, pg. 5457
GYROS PROTEIN TECHNOLOGIES AB—See Mesa Laboratories, Inc.; *U.S. Public*, pg. 1426
GYROS PROTEIN TECHNOLOGY AB—See Mesa Laboratories, Inc.; *U.S. Public*, pg. 1426
GYROS U.S. INC.—See Mesa Laboratories, Inc.; *U.S. Public*, pg. 1426
GYRO TECHNOLOGIES, INC.—See Imdex Limited; *Int'l*, pg. 3623
GYRO TECHNOLOGIES, INC.—See Lime Rock Partners, LLC; *U.S. Private*, pg. 2456
GYROTRON TECHNOLOGY INC.; *U.S. Private*, pg. 1821
GYRUS ACMI ENT—See Olympus Corporation; *Int'l*, pg. 5558
GYRUS ACMI STAMFORD DIVISION—See Olympus Corporation; *Int'l*, pg. 5558
GYRUS ACMI-SURGICAL DIVISION—See Olympus Corporation; *Int'l*, pg. 5558
GYRUS GROUP LIMITED—See Olympus Corporation; *Int'l*, pg. 5556
GYUAN CO., LTD.—See Zensho Holdings Co., Ltd.; *Int'l*, pg. 8634
GYXIS CORPORATION—See Idemitsu Kosan Co., Ltd.; *Int'l*, pg. 3590
GZ6G TECHNOLOGIES CORP.; *U.S. Public*, pg. 976
GZA GEOENVIRONMENTAL INC.; *U.S. Private*, pg. 1821
G. ZARA HOME URUGUAY, S.A.—See Industria de Diseno Textil, S.A.; *Int'l*, pg. 3665
G.ZARA URUGUAY, S.A.—See Industria de Diseno Textil, S.A.; *Int'l*, pg. 3665
GZK INC.; *U.S. Private*, pg. 1822
GZNF FOSFORY SP Z.O.O.—See Kulczyk Investments S.A.; *Int'l*, pg. 4328
GZP DOM A.D.; *Int'l*, pg. 3191
GZS DIGITAL GMBH—See Zech Group SE; *Int'l*, pg. 8628

H

H20 CREATIVE—See H2O Creative; *Int'l*, pg. 3200
H20 NATIONWIDE LIMITED—See Cap10 Partners LLP; *Int'l*, pg. 1301
H2APEX GROUP SCA; *Int'l*, pg. 3199
H2 EQUITY PARTNERS B.V.; *Int'l*, pg. 3199
H2G GREEN LIMITED; *Int'l*, pg. 3200
H2I GROUP, INC.; *U.S. Private*, pg. 1836
H2M ARCHITECTS + ENGINEERS; *U.S. Private*, pg. 1837
H2M AM ASIA PTE LTD.—See Groupe BPCE; *Int'l*, pg. 3098

H2O ASSET MANAGEMENT LLP—See Groupe BPCE; *Int'l*, pg. 3098
H2OCEAN, INC.; *U.S. Private*, pg. 1837
H2O COMMUNICATION NEXT CORPORATION—See H2O Retailing Corp.; *Int'l*, pg. 3200
H2O CREATIVE; *Int'l*, pg. 3200
H2O ENGINEERING, INC.—See Newterra Ltd.; *Int'l*, pg. 5238
H2O HYDROPONICS, LLC—See GrowGeneration Corp.; *U.S. Public*, pg. 972
H2O, INC.; *U.S. Private*, pg. 1837
H2O INNOVATION INC.—See Ember Infrastructure Management, LP; *U.S. Private*, pg. 1378
H2O INNOVATION INC.—See Ember Infrastructure Management, LP; *U.S. Private*, pg. 1378
H2O INNOVATION INC.—See Ember Infrastructure Management, LP; *U.S. Private*, pg. 1378
H2O INNOVATION OPERATION & MAINTENANCE, LLC—See Ember Infrastructure Management, LP; *U.S. Private*, pg. 1378
H2O NATIONWIDE LIMITED—See Cap10 Partners LLP; *Int'l*, pg. 1301
H2O PLUS, LLC—See The Goldman Sachs Group, Inc.; *U.S. Public*, pg. 2081
H2O PLUS, LLC—See The Williams Capital Group, L.P.; *U.S. Private*, pg. 4136
H2O POWER LIMITED PARTNERSHIP—See Public Sector Pension Investment Board; *Int'l*, pg. 6096
H2O PRODUCTIONS SAS—See LOV Group Invest SAS; *Int'l*, pg. 4563
H2O (PRO) LIMITED—See E. Bon Holdings Ltd; *Int'l*, pg. 2250
H2O RETAILING CORP.; *Int'l*, pg. 3200
H2O SHOPPING CENTER DEVELOPMENT CO., LTD.—See H2O Retailing Corp.; *Int'l*, pg. 3200
H2O SMILE CO., LTD.—See H2O Retailing Corp.; *Int'l*, pg. 3200
H2O SUPPLY INC.—See Winsupply, Inc.; *U.S. Private*, pg. 4545
H2O SYSTEM CO., LTD.—See H2O Retailing Corp.; *Int'l*, pg. 3200
H2O TO GO/OPAL SPRINGS WATER COMPANY INC.; *U.S. Private*, pg. 1837
H2 PERFORMANCE CONSULTING; *U.S. Private*, pg. 1836
H2 POWER TECH, LLC—See Chung-Hsin Electric & Machinery Manufacturing Corp.; *Int'l*, pg. 1597
H2SCAN CORPORATION; *U.S. Private*, pg. 1837
H2U WELLNESS CENTERS - CONROE REGIONAL MEDICAL CENTER, PLLC—See HCA Healthcare, Inc.; *U.S. Public*, pg. 997
H2U WELLNESS CENTERS - DEL SOL MEDICAL CENTER, PLLC—See HCA Healthcare, Inc.; *U.S. Public*, pg. 997
H2U WELLNESS CENTERS, LLC—See HCA Healthcare, Inc.; *U.S. Public*, pg. 997
H2X GMBH—See BayWa AG; *Int'l*, pg. 918
H365 HEALTH PRODUCTS LIMITED—See Shunten International (Holdings) Limited; *Int'l*, pg. 6870
H3 BIOMEDICINE INC.—See Eisai Co., Ltd.; *Int'l*, pg. 2335
H3 SPORTGEAR LLC—See Mainland Headwear Holdings Ltd.; *Int'l*, pg. 4651
H 47 GMBH & CO. KG—See Commerzbank AG; *Int'l*, pg. 1718
H 47 VERWALTUNGSGESELLSCHAFT MBH—See Commerzbank AG; *Int'l*, pg. 1718
H4B LONDON LIMITED—See Vivendi SE; *Int'l*, pg. 8268
HAADTHIP DEVELOPMENT CO., LTD.—See Haad Thip Public Company Limited; *Int'l*, pg. 3201
HAAD THIP PUBLIC COMPANY LIMITED; *Int'l*, pg. 3201
HAAF SPEDITION GMBH & CO. KG; *Int'l*, pg. 3201
HAAGEN-DAZS ARRAS SNC—See General Mills, Inc.; *U.S. Public*, pg. 922
HAAGEN-DAZS BELGIUM (SPRL)—See General Mills, Inc.; *U.S. Public*, pg. 922
HAAGEN-DAZS EUROPE—See General Mills, Inc.; *U.S. Public*, pg. 922
HAAGEN-DAZS JAPAN, INC.—See General Mills, Inc.; *U.S. Public*, pg. 922
HAAGEN-DAZS JAPAN, INC.—See Suntory Holdings Limited; *Int'l*, pg. 7326
HAAGEN-DAZS JAPAN, INC.—See Takanashi Milk Products Co., Ltd.; *Int'l*, pg. 7430
THE HAAGEN-DAZS SHOPPE COMPANY, INC.—See Nestle S.A.; *Int'l*, pg. 5208
HAAG-STREIT AG—See Metall Zug AG; *Int'l*, pg. 4847
HAAG-STREIT AG VERKAUF SCHWEIZ—See Metall Zug AG; *Int'l*, pg. 4847
HAAG-STREIT DEUTSCHLAND GMBH—See Metall Zug AG; *Int'l*, pg. 4847
HAAG-STREIT FAR EAST LTD.—See Metall Zug AG; *Int'l*, pg. 4847
HAAG-STREIT HOLDING AG—See Metall Zug AG; *Int'l*, pg. 4846
HAAG-STREIT SURGICAL GMBH—See Metall Zug AG; *Int'l*, pg. 4847
HAAG-STREIT UK LTD.—See Metall Zug AG; *Int'l*, pg. 4847

HAAG-STREIT USA, INC.—See Metall Zug AG; *Int'l*, pg. 4847
HAAGTECHNO—See Rexel, S.A.; *Int'l*, pg. 6317
HAAKON AG—See Howden Group Holdings Limited; *Int'l*, pg. 3493
HAAKON (ASIA) LTD—See Howden Group Holdings Limited; *Int'l*, pg. 3493
HAAKON INDUSTRIES (CANADA) LTD.; *Int'l*, pg. 3201
HAAL USA INC—See The Aditya Birla Group; *Int'l*, pg. 7611
HAAR AUSTRALIA PTY LTD—See Alfons Haar Maschinenbau GmbH & Co. KG; *Int'l*, pg. 315
HAAR CZ S.R.O.—See Alfons Haar Maschinenbau GmbH & Co. KG; *Int'l*, pg. 315
HAAR FRANCE SAS—See Alfons Haar Maschinenbau GmbH & Co. KG; *Int'l*, pg. 315
HAARLANDER GMBH—See LEONI AG; *Int'l*, pg. 4462
HAAR NEDERLAND CV—See Alfons Haar Maschinenbau GmbH & Co. KG; *Int'l*, pg. 315
HAAR PENINSULAR S.L.—See Alfons Haar Maschinenbau GmbH & Co, KG; *Int'l*, pg. 315
HAAR POLSKA SP. Z O.O.—See Alfons Haar Maschinenbau GmbH & Co. KG; *Int'l*, pg. 316
HAAR SALZBURG GMBH & CO. KG—See Alfons Haar Maschinenbau GmbH & Co. KG; *Int'l*, pg. 316
HAARSLEV INC.—See Altor Equity Partners AB; *Int'l*, pg. 394
HAARSLEV INDUSTRIES A/S—See Altor Equity Partners AB; *Int'l*, pg. 394
HAARSLEV INDUSTRIES GMBH—See Altor Equity Partners AB; *Int'l*, pg. 395
HAARSLEV INDUSTRIES LTDA.—See Altor Equity Partners AB; *Int'l*, pg. 395
HAARSLEV INDUSTRIES LTD.—See Altor Equity Partners AB; *Int'l*, pg. 395
HAARSLEV INDUSTRIES SAC—See Altor Equity Partners AB; *Int'l*, pg. 395
HAARSLEV INDUSTRIES S.A.U.—See Altor Equity Partners AB; *Int'l*, pg. 395
HAARSLEV INDUSTRIES SDN BHD—See Altor Equity Partners AB; *Int'l*, pg. 395
HAARSLEV INDUSTRIES—See Altor Equity Partners AB; *Int'l*, pg. 394
HAARSLEV MACHINERY XUZHOU CO.—See Altor Equity Partners AB; *Int'l*, pg. 395
HAARSLEV UK LTD.—See Altor Equity Partners AB; *Int'l*, pg. 395
HAART INC.; *U.S. Private*, pg. 1837
THE HAARTZ CORPORATION - BLOOMFIELD HILLS—See The Haartz Corporation; *U.S. Private*, pg. 4041
THE HAARTZ CORPORATION; *U.S. Private*, pg. 4041
HAARTZ GMBH—See The Haartz Corporation; *U.S. Private*, pg. 4041
HAAS-ANDERSON CONSTRUCTION; *U.S. Private*, pg. 1837
HAAS BROTHERS, LTD.; *U.S. Private*, pg. 1837
HAAS CABINET CO. INC.; *U.S. Private*, pg. 1837
HAAS CARRIAGE CO.—See Haas Cabinet Co. Inc.; *U.S. Private*, pg. 1837
HAAS DOOR COMPANY; *U.S. Private*, pg. 1837
HAAS FACTORY OUTLET LLC—See Morris Group, Inc.; *U.S. Private*, pg. 2787
HAAS FACTORY OUTLET—See Gerotech Inc.; *U.S. Private*, pg. 1687
HAAS FACTORY OUTLET—See Gerotech Inc.; *U.S. Private*, pg. 1687
HAAS FINECHEM (SHANGHAI) CO. LTD.—See Platinum Equity, LLC; *U.S. Private*, pg. 3210
HAAS GROUP AUSTRALIA PTY LIMITED—See Platinum Equity, LLC; *U.S. Private*, pg. 3210
HAAS GROUP INTERNATIONAL GMBH—See Platinum Equity, LLC; *U.S. Private*, pg. 3210
HAAS GROUP INTERNATIONAL INC.—See Platinum Equity, LLC; *U.S. Private*, pg. 3210
HAAS GROUP INTERNATIONAL SCM IRELAND LIMITED—See Platinum Equity, LLC; *U.S. Private*, pg. 3210
HAAS GROUP INTERNATIONAL SCM LIMITED—See Platinum Equity, LLC; *U.S. Private*, pg. 3210
HAAS GROUP, LLC—See Platinum Equity, LLC; *U.S. Private*, pg. 3210
HAAS & HAAS, LLC; *U.S. Private*, pg. 1837
HAAS HOLDINGS, LLC—See Platinum Equity, LLC; *U.S. Private*, pg. 3210
HAAS INDUSTRIES, INC.—See Lynden Incorporated; *U.S. Private*, pg. 2521
HAAS, JEFF MAZDA; *U.S. Private*, pg. 1837
HAAS OUTDOORS INC.; *U.S. Private*, pg. 1837
HAAS-PUBLIKATIONEN GMBH—See Knightec AB; *Int'l*, pg. 4207
HAAS TCM GROUP OF THE UK LIMITED—See Platinum Equity, LLC; *U.S. Private*, pg. 3210
HAAS TCM ITALIA SRL—See Platinum Equity, LLC; *U.S. Private*, pg. 3210
HAAS TCM OF ISRAEL INC.—See Platinum Equity, LLC; *U.S. Private*, pg. 3210
HAAS TCM SINGAPORE PTE. LTD.—See Platinum Equity, LLC; *U.S. Private*, pg. 3210

COMPANY NAME INDEX

HAASZ AUTO MALL, LLC—See Sarchione Automotive Group; *U.S. Private*, pg. 3550
HAATZ INC.; *Int'l*, pg. 3201
HA BAC NITROGENOUS FERTILIZER AND CHEMICAL LIMITED COMPANY—See Masan Consumer Corp.; *Int'l*, pg. 4719
HABA COMPUTER AKTIENGESELLSCHAFT—See CompuGroup Medical SE & Co. KGaA; *Int'l*, pg. 1756
HABA CREATION CO., LTD.—See Medipal Holdings Corporation; *Int'l*, pg. 4779
HABA HONG KONG LIMITED—See HABA LABORATORIES, INC.; *Int'l*, pg. 3201
HABA LABORATORIES, INC.; *Int'l*, pg. 3201
HABARANA LODGE LTD.—See John Keells Holdings PLC; *Int'l*, pg. 3978
HABARANA WALK INN LTD.—See John Keells Holdings PLC; *Int'l*, pg. 3978
HABASIT AB—See Habasit AG; *Int'l*, pg. 3201
HABASIT AB—See Habasit AG; *Int'l*, pg. 3201
HABASIT AG; *Int'l*, pg. 3201
HABASIT AMERICA - BUFFALO—See Habasit AG; *Int'l*, pg. 3202
HABASIT AMERICA, INC.—See Habasit AG; *Int'l*, pg. 3202
HABASIT AMERICA - MIDDLETOWN—See Habasit AG; *Int'l*, pg. 3202
HABASIT AMERICA - READING—See Habasit AG; *Int'l*, pg. 3202
HABASIT ARGENTINA S.A.—See Habasit AG; *Int'l*, pg. 3202
HABASIT (AUSTRALIA) PTY LIMITED—See Habasit AG; *Int'l*, pg. 3202
HABASIT BELGIUM N.V.—See Habasit AG; *Int'l*, pg. 3202
HABASIT BULGARIA—See Habasit AG; *Int'l*, pg. 3202
HABASIT CANADA LIMITED—See Habasit AG; *Int'l*, pg. 3202
HABASIT DO BRASIL IND. E COM. DE CORREIAS LTDA.—See Habasit AG; *Int'l*, pg. 3202
HABASIT FAR EAST PTE. LTD.—See Habasit AG; *Int'l*, pg. 3202
HABASIT FRANCE S.A.S.—See Habasit AG; *Int'l*, pg. 3202
HABASIT GESELLSCHAFT M.B.H.—See Habasit AG; *Int'l*, pg. 3202
HABASIT GMBH—See Habasit AG; *Int'l*, pg. 3201
HABASIT GMBH—See Habasit AG; *Int'l*, pg. 3202
HABASIT HISPANICA S.A.—See Habasit AG; *Int'l*, pg. 3202
HABASIT HUNGARIA KFT.—See Habasit AG; *Int'l*, pg. 3202
HABASIT ITALIANA SPA—See Habasit AG; *Int'l*, pg. 3202
HABASIT KAYIS SAN VE TIC. LTD.—See Habasit AG; *Int'l*, pg. 3202
HABASIT MOSCOW—See Habasit AG; *Int'l*, pg. 3202
HABASIT NETHERLANDS BV—See Habasit AG; *Int'l*, pg. 3202
HABASIT NIPPON CO. LTD—See Habasit AG; *Int'l*, pg. 3202
HABASIT NORGE A/S—See Habasit AG; *Int'l*, pg. 3201
HABASIT POLSKA SP. Z O.O.—See Habasit AG; *Int'l*, pg. 3202
HABASIT ROSSI (TAIWAN) LIMITED—See Habasit AG; *Int'l*, pg. 3202
HABASIT (SHANGHAI) CO. LTD.—See Habasit AG; *Int'l*, pg. 3201
HABASIT (UK) LIMITED—See Habasit AG; *Int'l*, pg. 3201
HABASIT UKRAINE LLC—See Habasit AG; *Int'l*, pg. 3202
HABAU HOCH- UND TIEFBAUGESELLSCHAFT M.B.H.; *Int'l*, pg. 3202
HABBERSTAD BMW INC.; *U.S. Private*, pg. 1837
THE HABEGGER CORPORATION; *U.S. Private*, pg. 4041
HABERER REGISTERED INVESTMENT ADVISOR, INC.—See Huntington Bancshares Incorporated; *U.S. Public*, pg. 1071
HABERKORN ABDICHTUNGSSYSTEME GMBH—See Sika AG; *Int'l*, pg. 6914
HABERKORN D.O.O.—See Haberkorn Holding AG; *Int'l*, pg. 3202
HABERKORN EOOD—See Haberkorn Holding AG; *Int'l*, pg. 3202
HABERKORN FAIRTOOL KFT.—See KTR Kupplungstechnik GmbH; *Int'l*, pg. 4317
HABERKORN HOLDING AG; *Int'l*, pg. 3202
HABERKORN SP. Z O.O.—See Haberkorn Holding AG; *Int'l*, pg. 3202
HABERKORN S.R.O.—See Haberkorn Holding AG; *Int'l*, pg. 3202
HABERMAN & ASSOCIATES, INC.; *U.S. Private*, pg. 1837
HABERSHAM HARDWARE & DISTRIBUTING COMPANY—See Tyndale Advisors, LLC; *U.S. Private*, pg. 4268
HABIA BENELUX BV—See Beijer Alma AB; *Int'l*, pg. 942
HABIA CABLE AB—See Beijer Alma AB; *Int'l*, pg. 942
HABIA CABLE AB—See Beijer Alma AB; *Int'l*, pg. 942
HABIA CABLE ASIA LTD—See Beijer Alma AB; *Int'l*, pg. 942
HABIA CABLE CHINA LTD—See Beijer Alma AB; *Int'l*, pg. 942

HABIA CABLE CS TECHNOLOGY AB—See Beijer Alma AB; *Int'l*, pg. 942
HABIA CABLE INDIA LTD—See Beijer Alma AB; *Int'l*, pg. 942
HABIA CABLE LTD—See Beijer Alma AB; *Int'l*, pg. 942
HABIA CABLE NORDIC AB—See Beijer Alma AB; *Int'l*, pg. 942
HABIA CABLE PRODUCTION AB—See Beijer Alma AB; *Int'l*, pg. 942
HABIA CABLE SA—See Beijer Alma AB; *Int'l*, pg. 942
HABIA CABLE SP.Z.O.O—See Beijer Alma AB; *Int'l*, pg. 943
HABIA KABEL GMBH—See HEW-KABEL Holding GmbH; *Int'l*, pg. 3367
HABIA KABEL PRODUKTIONS GMBH & CO.KG—See Beijer Alma AB; *Int'l*, pg. 943
HABIB ALLIED INTERNATIONAL BANK PLC.—See Habib Bank Limited; *Int'l*, pg. 3203
HABIB AMERICAN BANK; *U.S. Private*, pg. 1837
HABIB BANK AG ZURICH; *Int'l*, pg. 3202
HABIB BANK LIMITED; *Int'l*, pg. 3202
HABIB FINANCE INTERNATIONAL LIMITED—See Habib Bank Limited; *Int'l*, pg. 3203
HABIB GROUP OF COMPANIES; *Int'l*, pg. 3203
HABIB GULZAR MOTORS LTD.—See Bridgestone Corporation; *Int'l*, pg. 1160
HABIB INSURANCE COMPANY LIMITED—See Habib Group of Companies; *Int'l*, pg. 3203
HABIB IT SOLUTIONS PVT LTD—See Habib Group of Companies; *Int'l*, pg. 3203
HABIB METRO PAKISTAN (PRIVATE) LIMITED—See House of Habib; *Int'l*, pg. 3491
HABIB METROPOLITAN BANK LIMITED—See Habib Bank AG Zurich; *Int'l*, pg. 3202
HABIB METROPOLITAN FINANCIAL SERVICES LIMITED—See Habib Bank AG Zurich; *Int'l*, pg. 3202
HABIB RICE PRODUCT LIMITED; *Int'l*, pg. 3203
HABIBSONS BANK LIMITED—See Habib Group of Companies; *Int'l*, pg. 3203
HABIBSONS BANK LIMITED—See Habib Bank Limited; *Int'l*, pg. 3203
HABIB SUGAR MILLS LIMITED—See Habib Group of Companies; *Int'l*, pg. 3203
HABILITATION CENTER, INC.—See Acadia Healthcare Company, Inc.; *U.S. Public*, pg. 30
HABILITATIVE SERVICES, INC.—See Centerbridge Partners, L.P.; *U.S. Private*, pg. 813
HAB, INC.—See GI Manager L.P.; *U.S. Private*, pg. 1693
HABITASUL FLORESTAL S.A.—See Irani Papel e Embalagem S.A.; *Int'l*, pg. 3805
HABITAT BAIX, S.L.—See Sacyr, S.A.; *Int'l*, pg. 6465
HABITAT BEAUJOLAIS VAL DE SAONE; *Int'l*, pg. 3203
THE HABITAT COMPANY INC.; *U.S. Private*, pg. 4041
HABITAT DU GARD; *Int'l*, pg. 3203
HABITAT EN REGION SERVICES SAS—See Groupe BPCE; *Int'l*, pg. 3098
HABITAT FRANCE SA—See Cafom SA; *Int'l*, pg. 1250
HABITAT INTERNATIONAL—See Cafom SA; *Int'l*, pg. 1250
HABITATION DOMAINE DES TREMBLES INC.—See Welltower Inc.; *U.S. Public*, pg. 2348
HABITATION FAUBOURG GIFFARD INC.—See Welltower Inc.; *U.S. Public*, pg. 2348
HABITAT NETWORK, S.A.—See Sacyr, S.A.; *Int'l*, pg. 6465
HABITAT PROIECT S.A.; *Int'l*, pg. 3203
HABITAT PROPERTIES (SHANGHAI) LTD.—See Tuan Sing Holdings Limited; *Int'l*, pg. 7962
HABITATSOFT S.L.U.—See Vocento, S.A.; *Int'l*, pg. 8284
HABITAT; *Int'l*, pg. 3203
HABITAT UK LTD.—See Hilco Trading, LLC; *U.S. Private*, pg. 1944
HABITEC SECURITY INC.; *U.S. Private*, pg. 1837
HABIT HOLDINGS, INC.—See Acadia Healthcare Company, Inc.; *U.S. Public*, pg. 29
THE HABIT RESTAURANTS, INC.—See Yum! Brands, Inc.; *U.S. Public*, pg. 2400
HABO DANMARK A/S—See Volati AB; *Int'l*, pg. 8300
HABO FINLAND OY—See Volati AB; *Int'l*, pg. 8300
HABO GRUPPEN AB—See Volati AB; *Int'l*, pg. 8300
HABO NORGE AS—See Volati AB; *Int'l*, pg. 8300
HABRINOL DECIN S.R.O. (GMBH)—See Huettenes-Albertus Chemische Werke GmbH; *Int'l*, pg. 3523
HABROK MINING PTY LTD.; *Int'l*, pg. 3203
H.A. BRUNO LLC—See Charterhouse Capital Partners LLP; *Int'l*, pg. 1455
HABTEC ENGENHARIA SANITARIA E AMBIENTAL LTDA—See Mott MacDonald Group Ltd.; *Int'l*, pg. 5055
HABTECH COMMUNICATIONS—See APi Group Corporation; *Int'l*, pg. 514
HACCO, INC.—See Neogen Corporation; *U.S. Public*, pg. 1505
HACCP JAPAN CO., LTD.—See 4Cs Holdings Co., Ltd.; *Int'l*, pg. 11
HACES INVERSIONES Y SERVICIOS S.A.S.—See Lundbeckfonden; *Int'l*, pg. 4582
HACH COMPANY—See Danaher Corporation; *U.S. Public*, pg. 627

HACHIK DISTRIBUTORS, INC.

HACHETTE AUSTRALIA PTY. LTD.—See Vivendi SE; *Int'l*, pg. 8272
HACHETTE BOOK GROUP CANADA LTD.—See Vivendi SE; *Int'l*, pg. 8272
HACHETTE BOOK GROUP, INC.—See Vivendi SE; *Int'l*, pg. 8273
HACHETTE BOOK PUBLISHING INDIA PVT LTD—See Vivendi SE; *Int'l*, pg. 8272
HACHETTE CANADA—See Vivendi SE; *Int'l*, pg. 8272
HACHETTE COLLECTIONS JAPAN K.K.—See Vivendi SE; *Int'l*, pg. 8271
HACHETTE COLLECTIONS S.N.C.—See Vivendi SE; *Int'l*, pg. 8272
HACHETTE DIGITAL INC.—See Vivendi SE; *Int'l*, pg. 8273
HACHETTE DISTRIBUTION SERVICES POLSKA—See Vivendi SE; *Int'l*, pg. 8272
HACHETTE EDUCATION S.A.-N.V.—See Vivendi SE; *Int'l*, pg. 8272
HACHETTE FASCICOLI SRL—See Vivendi SE; *Int'l*, pg. 8272
HACHETTE FILIPACCHI 2000—See Vivendi SE; *Int'l*, pg. 8272
HACHETTE FILIPACCHI GLOBAL ADVERTISING ITALIE—See Vivendi SE; *Int'l*, pg. 8272
HACHETTE FILIPACCHI GLOBAL USA—See Vivendi SE; *Int'l*, pg. 8274
HACHETTE FILIPACCHI HOLDINGS, INC.—See Vivendi SE; *Int'l*, pg. 8274
HACHETTE FILIPACCHI NORGE A/S—See Hjemmet Mortensen As; *Int'l*, pg. 3428
HACHETTE FILIPACCHI PRESSE SA—See Czech Media Invest as; *Int'l*, pg. 1898
HACHETTE FILIPACCHI PRESSE Z.A.O.—See Vivendi SE; *Int'l*, pg. 8272
HACHETTE FILIPACCHI S.A.—See Vivendi SE; *Int'l*, pg. 8272
HACHETTE FILIPACCHI UK LTD.—See Vivendi SE; *Int'l*, pg. 8273
HACHETTE INDUSTRIE ET SERVICES—See Vivendi SE; *Int'l*, pg. 8273
HACHETTE LATINO AMERICA S.A. DE C.V.—See Vivendi SE; *Int'l*, pg. 8273
HACHETTE LIVRE ESPANA SA—See Vivendi SE; *Int'l*, pg. 8273
HACHETTE LIVRE SA—See Vivendi SE; *Int'l*, pg. 8272
HACHETTE LIVRE—See Vivendi SE; *Int'l*, pg. 8273
HACHETTE LIVRE USA, INC.—See Vivendi SE; *Int'l*, pg. 8273
HACHETTE NEW ZEALAND LTD—See Vivendi SE; *Int'l*, pg. 8273
HACHETTE PARTWORKS LTD.—See Vivendi SE; *Int'l*, pg. 8271
HACHETTE-PHOENIX CULTURAL DEVELOPMENT (BEIJING) CO., LTD.—See Jiangsu Phoenix Publishing & Media Corporation Ltd.; *Int'l*, pg. 3952
HACHETTE POLSKA SP. Z O.O.—See Vivendi SE; *Int'l*, pg. 8271
HACHETTE UK HOLDING LIMITED—See Vivendi SE; *Int'l*, pg. 8273
HACHETTE UK LTD—See Vivendi SE; *Int'l*, pg. 8273
HACHI-BAN CO., LTD.; *Int'l*, pg. 3203
HACHIBAN TRADING (THAILAND) CO., LTD.—See HACHI-BAN CO., LTD.; *Int'l*, pg. 3203
HACHIJUNI AUTO LEASE CO., LTD.—See The Hachijuni Bank Ltd.; *Int'l*, pg. 7651
THE HACHIJUNI BANK LTD.; *Int'l*, pg. 7651
HACHIJUNI BUSINESS SERVICE CO., LTD.—See The Hachijuni Bank Ltd.; *Int'l*, pg. 7651
HACHIJUNI CAPITAL CO., LTD.—See The Hachijuni Bank Ltd.; *Int'l*, pg. 7651
HACHIJUNI CREDIT GUARANTEE CO., LTD.—See The Hachijuni Bank Ltd.; *Int'l*, pg. 7651
HACHIJUNI DC CARD CO., LTD.; *Int'l*, pg. 3203
HACHIJUNI LEASE CO., LTD; *Int'l*, pg. 3203
HACHIJUNI SECURITIES CO., LTD—See The Hachijuni Bank Ltd.; *Int'l*, pg. 7651
HACHIJUNI STAFF SERVICE CO., LTD.—See The Hachijuni Bank Ltd.; *Int'l*, pg. 7651
HACHIJUNI SYSTEM DEVELOPMENT CO., LTD.—See The Hachijuni Bank Ltd.; *Int'l*, pg. 7651
HACHIKAN CO., LTD.—See Nissui Corporation; *Int'l*, pg. 5378
HACHIK DISTRIBUTORS, INC.; *U.S. Private*, pg. 1838
HACHIMANTAI GEOTHERMAL CORPORATION—See Mitsubishi Materials Corporation; *Int'l*, pg. 4963
HACHIMANTAI GREEN ENERGY CORPORATION—See Mitsubishi Gas Chemical Company, Inc.; *Int'l*, pg. 4948
HACHIMENROPPI, INC.—See Vector Inc.; *Int'l*, pg. 8144
HACHINOHE CEMENT CO., LTD.—See Sumitomo Osaka Cement Co Ltd; *Int'l*, pg. 7296
HACHINOHE MINING CO., LTD.—See Nittetsu Mining Co., Ltd.; *Int'l*, pg. 5383
HACHINOHE PAPER PROCESSING CO., LTD.—See Mitsubishi Paper Mills Limited; *Int'l*, pg. 4967
HACHINOHE TOYO CO., LTD.—See Toyo Suisan Kaisha, Ltd.; *Int'l*, pg. 7858
HACH INTERNATIONAL FOREIGN SALES CO., INC.—See Danaher Corporation; *U.S. Public*, pg. 627

1163

HACHIK DISTRIBUTORS, INC.

CORPORATE AFFILIATIONS

HACHITA ENTERPRISE SDN. BHD.—See Engtex Group Berhad; *Int'l*, pg. 2436
HACHIUMA STEAMSHIP CO., LTD.—See Nippon Yusen Kabushiki Kaisha; *Int'l*, pg. 5357
HACH LANGE APS—See Danaher Corporation; *U.S. Public*, pg. 627
HACH LANGE FINANCE GMBH—See Danaher Corporation; *U.S. Public*, pg. 627
HACH LANGE FRANCE S.A.S.—See Danaher Corporation; *U.S. Public*, pg. 627
HACH LANGE GMBH—See Danaher Corporation; *U.S. Public*, pg. 626
HACH LANGE S.L.—See Danaher Corporation; *U.S. Public*, pg. 627
HACH LANGE SPAIN S.L.—See Danaher Corporation; *U.S. Public*, pg. 627
HACH LANGE S.R.L.—See Danaher Corporation; *U.S. Public*, pg. 627
HACH SALES & SERVICE CANADA LTD.—See Danaher Corporation; *U.S. Public*, pg. 627
HACHSHARA INSURANCE COMPANY LTD.; *Int'l*, pg. 3203
HACHSHARAT HAYISHUV HOTELS LTD.—See The Israel Land Development Co., Ltd.; *Int'l*, pg. 7657
HACH ULTRA JAPAN KK—See Danaher Corporation; *U.S. Public*, pg. 627
HACIENDA HEIGHTS HIGHLANDER—See Alden Global Capital LLC; *U.S. Private*, pg. 158
HACIENDA HOME CENTERS INC.; *U.S. Private*, pg. 1838
HACIENDA LIGHTING, INCORPORATED; *U.S. Private*, pg. 1838
HACIENDA OUTPATIENT SURGERY CENTER, LLC—See Tenet Healthcare Corporation; *U.S. Public*, pg. 2010
HACI OMER SABANCI HOLDING A.S.; *Int'l*, pg. 3203
HACKBARTH DELIVERY SERVICE, INC.; *U.S. Private*, pg. 1838
HACKBRIGHT ACADEMY, INC.—See Strategic Education, Inc.; *U.S. Public*, pg. 1954
HACKENSACK MERIDIAN HEALTH, INC.; *U.S. Private*, pg. 1838
HACKENSACK UNIVERSITY MEDICAL CENTER—See Hackensack Meridian Health, Inc.; *U.S. Private*, pg. 1838
HACKERAGENCY, INC.—See The Interpublic Group of Companies, Inc.; *U.S. Public*, pg. 2093
HACKER INSTRUMENTS & INDUSTRIES INC.; *U.S. Private*, pg. 1838
HACKER, JOHNSON & SMITH PA; *U.S. Private*, pg. 1838
THE HACKETT GROUP AUSTRALIA PTY. LTD.—See The Hackett Group, Inc.; *U.S. Public*, pg. 2086
THE HACKETT GROUP BV—See The Hackett Group, Inc.; *U.S. Public*, pg. 2086
THE HACKETT GROUP GMBH—See The Hackett Group, Inc.; *U.S. Public*, pg. 2086
THE HACKETT GROUP, INC.; *U.S. Public*, pg. 2086
HACKETT GROUP (INDIA) LTD.—See The Hackett Group, Inc.; *U.S. Public*, pg. 2086
HACKETT-REL LIMITED—See The Hackett Group, Inc.; *U.S. Public*, pg. 2086
HACKETTSTOWN MEDICAL CENTER—See Atlantic Health System Inc.; *U.S. Private*, pg. 373
HACKETT VALINE & MACDONALD, INC.—See Aon plc; *Int'l*, pg. 496
HACKLEY COMMUNITY CARE; *U.S. Private*, pg. 1838
HACKMAN OYJ ABP—See Ali Holding S.r.l.; *Int'l*, pg. 321
HACKNEY CONTRACT FURNITURE—See The H.T. Hackney Company; *U.S. Private*, pg. 4041
HACKNEY HOME FURNISHINGS—See The H.T. Hackney Company; *U.S. Private*, pg. 4041
HACKNEY INTERNATIONAL—See Temasek Holdings (Private) Limited; *Int'l*, pg. 7552
HACKNEY PETROLEUM, INC.—See The H.T. Hackney Company; *U.S. Private*, pg. 4041
HACKNEY—See Temasek Holdings (Private) Limited; *Int'l*, pg. 7552
HACKNEY USA—See Temasek Holdings (Private) Limited; *Int'l*, pg. 7552
HACKWORTH REPROGRAPHICS, INC.; *U.S. Private*, pg. 1838
HACO A.S.—See Haco N.V.; *Int'l*, pg. 3204
HACO-ATLANTIC, INC.—See Haco N.V.; *Int'l*, pg. 3205
HACO AUSTRALIA PERTH—See Haco N.V.; *Int'l*, pg. 3204
HACO (AUSTRALIA) PTY LTD—See Haco N.V.; *Int'l*, pg. 3205
HACO B.V—See Haco N.V.; *Int'l*, pg. 3204
HACO CANADA INC—See Haco N.V.; *Int'l*, pg. 3204
HACO FAR EAST PTE LTD—See Haco N.V.; *Int'l*, pg. 3204
HACO G. KOUZARIS LTD.—See Haco N.V.; *Int'l*, pg. 3204
HACO MACHINERY (MALAYSIA) SDN BHD—See Haco N.V.; *Int'l*, pg. 3205
HACO MACHINERY PRIVATE LIMITED—See Haco N.V.; *Int'l*, pg. 3204
HACO - MUBEA SYSTEME GMBH—See Haco N.V.; *Int'l*, pg. 3204
HACO (NINGBO) INTERNATIONAL TRADING CO., LTD—See Haco N.V.; *Int'l*, pg. 3204

HACON INGENIEURGESELLSCHAFT MBH—See Siemens Aktiengesellschaft; *Int'l*, pg. 6887
HACO N.V.; *Int'l*, pg. 3204
HACO SAS—See Haco N.V.; *Int'l*, pg. 3204
HACO SL—See Haco N.V.; *Int'l*, pg. 3204
HACO TRADING COMPANY NV—See Haco N.V.; *Int'l*, pg. 3204
HADADY CORPORATION; *U.S. Private*, pg. 1838
HADAPT INC.—See Teradata Corporation; *U.S. Public*, pg. 2017
HADARA FOR TECHNOLOGICAL INVESTMENT LTD.—See Palestine Telecommunications Company P.L.C.; *Int'l*, pg. 5707
HADASIT BIO-HOLDINGS LTD.; *Int'l*, pg. 3205
HADASSAH, THE WOMEN'S ZIONIST ORGANIZATION OF AMERICA, INC.; *U.S. Private*, pg. 1838
HADCO CORPORATION—See Sanmina Corporation; *U.S. Public*, pg. 1840
HADCO LIMITED; *Int'l*, pg. 3205
HADCO METAL TRADING CO., LLC—See Scope Metals Group Ltd.; *Int'l*, pg. 6650
HADCO—See Signify N.V.; *Int'l*, pg. 6912
HADDAD APPAREL GROUP, LTD.; *U.S. Private*, pg. 1838
HADDAD DODGE; *U.S. Private*, pg. 1838
HADDAD ORGANIZATION LTD.; *U.S. Private*, pg. 1839
HADDAD RESTAURANT GROUP, INC.; *U.S. Private*, pg. 1839
HADDAD SPECIALTY RESTAURANTS, INC.—See Haddad Restaurant Group, Inc.; *U.S. Private*, pg. 1839
HADDENS IGA—See W. Lee Flowers & Company Inc.; *U.S. Private*, pg. 4418
HADDON HOUSE FOOD PRODUCTS, INC.—See United Natural Foods, Inc.; *U.S. Public*, pg. 2231
HADDON-MCCLELLAN ASSOCIATES INC.; *U.S. Private*, pg. 1839
HADDON SAVINGS BANK; *U.S. Private*, pg. 1839
HADEED SAUDI IRON & STEEL CO.—See Saudi Basic Industries Corporation; *Int'l*, pg. 6590
HADEF FRANCE MANUTENTION ET LEVAGE INDUSTRIEL SARL—See HEINRICH DE FRIES GmbH; *Int'l*, pg. 3324
HADER INC.—See Hader Industries Inc.; *U.S. Private*, pg. 1839
HADER INDUSTRIES INC.; *U.S. Private*, pg. 1839
HADER SA—See Fagron NV; *Int'l*, pg. 2603
HADER-SEITZ INC.—See Hader Industries Inc.; *U.S. Private*, pg. 1839
HADFIELD ELEVATOR—See 3Phase Elevator Corp; *U.S. Private*, pg. 14
HADINGER CARPET INC.; *U.S. Private*, pg. 1839
HADLEY CAPITAL LLC; *U.S. Private*, pg. 1839
HADLEY EXHIBITS INC.; *U.S. Private*, pg. 1839
HADLEY HOUSE COMPANY; *U.S. Private*, pg. 1839
HADLEY INDUSTRIES PLC; *Int'l*, pg. 3205
HADLEY INSURIT GROUP INSURANCE, INC.—See Narragansett Financial Corp.; *U.S. Private*, pg. 2835
HADLEY & LYDEN, INC.—See World Insurance Associates LLC; *U.S. Private*, pg. 4566
HADLEY MEDIA INC.—See Grandesign Advertising Firm, Inc.; *U.S. Private*, pg. 1754
HA DO GROUP JOINT STOCK COMPANY; *Int'l*, pg. 3201
HADRIAN EIENDOM AS—See Storebrand ASA; *Int'l*, pg. 7226
HADRIAN SOLUTIONS ULC—See Zurn Elkay Water Solutions Corporation; *U.S. Public*, pg. 2413
HADRIAN'S WALL SECURED INVESTMENTS LTD.; *Int'l*, pg. 3205
HADRILL INSURANCE BROKERS PTY LTD—See Wesfarmers Limited; *Int'l*, pg. 8382
HADROKOR SP. Z O.O.—See Fabryka Farb i Lakierow Sniezka S.A.; *Int'l*, pg. 2600
H/ADVISORS ABERNATHY—See Vivendi SE; *Int'l*, pg. 8267
HADWIN WHITE PONTIAC - BUICK - GMC TRUCK; *U.S. Private*, pg. 1839
HAD YAI (THAILAND) CO., LTD.—See Central Group Company Limited; *Int'l*, pg. 1407
H A ECKHART & ASSOCIATES, INC.—See Arsenal Capital Management LP; *U.S. Private*, pg. 338
HAECO CABIN SYSTEMS—See John Swire & Sons Limited; *Int'l*, pg. 3980
HAEDONG SS PHARMACEUTICAL CO., LTD—See CMIC Holdings Co., Ltd.; *Int'l*, pg. 1670
HAEDRICH & CO., INC.—See Capital Rivers Commercial LLC; *U.S. Private*, pg. 742
HAEDUK POWERWAY CO., LTD.; *Int'l*, pg. 3205
HAEFELI SAS—See VINCI S.A.; *Int'l*, pg. 8222
HAEFELY TEST AG—See PFIFFNER International AG; *Int'l*, pg. 5835
HAEGER INDUSTRIES, INC.; *U.S. Private*, pg. 1839
HAEGER POTTERIES, INC.—See Haeger Industries, Inc.; *U.S. Private*, pg. 1839
HAEGER POTTERIES OF MACOMB INC—See Haeger Industries, Inc.; *U.S. Private*, pg. 1839
HAE IN CORP.; *Int'l*, pg. 3205
HAEIN RESOURCES CO., LTD.—See Hae In Corp.; *Int'l*, pg. 3205
HAE INSURANCE SERVICES LIMITED—See Marsh & McLennan Companies, Inc.; *U.S. Public*, pg. 1376

HAELSSEN & LYON NORTH AMERICA CORPORATION—See Halssen & Lyon GmbH; *Int'l*, pg. 3233
HAEMA AG—See Grifols, S.A.; *Int'l*, pg. 3085
HAEMATO AG—See M1 Kliniken AG; *Int'l*, pg. 4617
HAEMATOLOGIC TECHNOLOGIES, LLC—See Edgewater Capital Partners, L.P.; *U.S. Private*, pg. 1335
HAEMATO MED GMBH—See M1 Kliniken AG; *Int'l*, pg. 4617
HAEMATO PHARM GMBH—See M1 Kliniken AG; *Int'l*, pg. 4617
HAEMONETICS ASIA, INC.—See Haemonetics Corporation; *U.S. Public*, pg. 979
HAEMONETICS BELGIUM N.V.—See Haemonetics Corporation; *U.S. Public*, pg. 979
HAEMONETICS CANADA, LTD.—See Haemonetics Corporation; *U.S. Public*, pg. 979
HAEMONETICS CORPORATION; *U.S. Public*, pg. 979
HAEMONETICS CZ, SPOL.S.R.O—See Haemonetics Corporation; *U.S. Public*, pg. 979
HAEMONETICS FRANCE S.A.R.L.—See Haemonetics Corporation; *U.S. Public*, pg. 979
HAEMONETICS, GMBH—See Haemonetics Corporation; *U.S. Public*, pg. 979
HAEMONETICS HONG KONG LTD.—See Haemonetics Corporation; *U.S. Public*, pg. 979
HAEMONETICS HOSPITALAR EIRELI—See Haemonetics Corporation; *U.S. Public*, pg. 979
HAEMONETICS ITALIA, S.R.L.—See Haemonetics Corporation; *U.S. Public*, pg. 979
HAEMONETICS JAPAN CO., LTD.—See Haemonetics Corporation; *U.S. Public*, pg. 979
HAEMONETICS JAPAN GK—See Haemonetics Corporation; *U.S. Public*, pg. 979
HAEMONETICS LTD.—See Haemonetics Corporation; *U.S. Public*, pg. 979
HAEMONETICS MANUFACTURING, INC.—See Haemonetics Corporation; *U.S. Public*, pg. 979
HAEMONETICS MEDICAL DEVICES (SHANGHAI) TRADING CO., LTD.—See Haemonetics Corporation; *U.S. Public*, pg. 979
HAEMONETICS PUERTO RICO, LLC—See Haemonetics Corporation; *U.S. Public*, pg. 979
HAEMONETICS SCANDINAVIA AB—See Haemonetics Corporation; *U.S. Public*, pg. 979
HAEMONETICS (SHANGHAI) MANAGEMENT CO. LTD.—See Haemonetics Corporation; *U.S. Public*, pg. 979
HAEMONETICS SINGAPORE PTE. LTD.—See Haemonetics Corporation; *U.S. Public*, pg. 979
HAEMOPHARM BIOFLUIDS S.R.L.—See Medtronic plc; *Int'l*, pg. 4787
HAEMOPHARM INC—See Kedrion S.p.A.; *Int'l*, pg. 4115
HAEMOSTATIX LIMITED—See Permira Advisers LLP; *Int'l*, pg. 5804
HA.EM OSTRAVA S.R.O.—See CEZ, a.s.; *Int'l*, pg. 1428
HAERTEREI HAUCK GAIDORF GMBH—See Aalberts N.V.; *Int'l*, pg. 34
HAERTEREI HAUCK GMBH—See Aalberts N.V.; *Int'l*, pg. 34
HAESUNG DS CO., LTD. - CHANGWON FACTORY—See HAESUNG DS Co., Ltd.; *Int'l*, pg. 3205
HAESUNG DS CO., LTD.; *Int'l*, pg. 3205
HAESUNG INDUSTRIAL CO., LTD.; *Int'l*, pg. 3205
HAESUNG OPTICS CO., LTD.; *Int'l*, pg. 3206
HAEWAYTIAN CAKE HOUSE SDN BHD—See Oversea Enterprise Berhad; *Int'l*, pg. 5671
HAFA BATHROOM GROUP AB; *Int'l*, pg. 3206
HAFA BATHROOM GROUP OY—See Hafa Bathroom Group AB; *Int'l*, pg. 3206
HAFARY BALESTIER SHOWROOM PTE. LTD.—See Hap Seng Consolidated Berhad; *Int'l*, pg. 3268
HAFARY HOLDINGS LIMITED—See Hap Seng Consolidated Berhad; *Int'l*, pg. 3268
HAFELE AMERICA CO. INC.; *U.S. Private*, pg. 1839
HAFENBOGEN GMBH & CO. KG—See Helaba Landesbank Hessen-Thuringen; *Int'l*, pg. 3328
HAFENBRACK MARKETING & PUBLIC RELATIONS, INC.—See Oxiem, LLC; *U.S. Private*, pg. 3057
HAFEN UND GUTERVERKEHR KOLN AG—See Stadtwerke Koln GmbH; *Int'l*, pg. 7161
HAFFMANS B.V.—See Pentair plc; *Int'l*, pg. 5789
HAFFMANS NORTH AMERICA, INC.—See Pentair plc; *Int'l*, pg. 5789
HAFFNER ENERGY SA; *Int'l*, pg. 3206
HAFFNER'S SERVICE STATIONS, INC.—See Energy North Incorporated; *U.S. Private*, pg. 1395
HAF HAMBURGER AKADEMIE FUR FERNSTUDIEN GMBH—See Ernst Klett AG; *Int'l*, pg. 2495
HAFIZ LIMITED; *Int'l*, pg. 3206
HA FLEET PTY LTD.—See Hertz Global Holdings, Inc.; *U.S. Public*, pg. 1029
HAFNIA LIMITED—See BW Group Ltd.; *Int'l*, pg. 1231
HA FOUNDRY CORE (CHANGCHUN) CO., LTD.—See Huettenes-Albertus Chemische Werke GmbH; *Int'l*, pg. 3523
HA FOUNDRY MATERIAL (SHANGHAI) CO., LTD.—See Huettenes-Albertus Chemische Werke GmbH; *Int'l*, pg. 3522

COMPANY NAME INDEX

HA FRANCE S.A.R.L—See Huettenes-Albertus Chemische Werke GmbH; *Int'l*, pg. 3522
HAFSA CORPORATION; *U.S. Private*, pg. 1839
HAFSLUND ASA; *Int'l*, pg. 3206
HAFSLUND DRIFTSSENTRAL AS—See Hafslund ASA; *Int'l*, pg. 3206
HAFSLUND EIENDOM AS—See Hafslund ASA; *Int'l*, pg. 3206
HAFSLUND ENERGI AB—See Fortum Oyj; *Int'l*, pg. 2742
HAFSLUND ENERGY TRADING AS—See Hafslund ASA; *Int'l*, pg. 3206
HAFSLUND FAKTURASERVICE AS—See Hafslund ASA; *Int'l*, pg. 3206
HAFSLUND FJERNVARME AS—See Hafslund ASA; *Int'l*, pg. 3206
HAFSLUND HEDGING AS—See Hafslund ASA; *Int'l*, pg. 3206
HAFSLUND KUNDESENTER AS—See Hafslund ASA; *Int'l*, pg. 3206
HAFSLUND NETT AS—See Hafslund ASA; *Int'l*, pg. 3206
HAFSLUND PRODUKSJON AS—See Hafslund ASA; *Int'l*, pg. 3206
HAFSLUND STROM AS—See Hafslund ASA; *Int'l*, pg. 3206
HAGA & BERG ENTREPRENOR AS—See AF Gruppen ASA; *Int'l*, pg. 184
THE HAGADONE CORPORATION; *U.S. Private*, pg. 4041
HAGADONE DIRECTORIES INC.—See The Hagadone Corporation; *U.S. Private*, pg. 4041
HAGADONE HOSPITALITY INC.—See The Hagadone Corporation; *U.S. Private*, pg. 4041
HAGADONE PHOTOGRAPHY INC.—See The Hagadone Corporation; *U.S. Private*, pg. 4041
HAGADONE PRINTING COMPANY INC.—See The Hagadone Corporation; *U.S. Private*, pg. 4041
HAGAG GROUP REAL ESTATE ENTREPRENEURSHIP LTD.; *Int'l*, pg. 3206
HAGARD: HAL, SPOL. S R.O.—See Wurth Verwaltungsgesellschaft mbH; *Int'l*, pg. 8505
HAGAR HF.; *Int'l*, pg. 3206
HAGART SP. Z O.O.—See Figene Capital SA; *Int'l*, pg. 2661
HAGA S/A INDUSTRIA E COMERCIO; *Int'l*, pg. 3206
HAGEMEYER AUSTRIA—See Sonepar S.A.; *Int'l*, pg. 7090
HAGEMEYER CANADA—See Nautic Partners, LLC; *U.S. Private*, pg. 2872
HAGEMEYER COMMERCE & TRADE (SHANGHAI) CO., LTD.—See Sonepar S.A.; *Int'l*, pg. 7090
HAGEMEYER DEUTSCHLAND GMBH & CO. KG—See Rexel, S.A.; *Int'l*, pg. 6317
HAGEMEYER NEDERLAND B.V.—See Rexel, S.A.; *Int'l*, pg. 6317
HAGEMEYER NORTH AMERICA—See Nautic Partners, LLC; *U.S. Private*, pg. 2872
HAGEMEYER NORTH AMERICA—See Nautic Partners, LLC; *U.S. Private*, pg. 2872
HAGEMEYER NORTH AMERICA—See Nautic Partners, LLC; *U.S. Private*, pg. 2872
HAGEMEYER NORTH AMERICA—See Nautic Partners, LLC; *U.S. Private*, pg. 2872
HAGEMEYER-PPS (THAILAND) LTD.—See Sonepar S.A.; *Int'l*, pg. 7091
HAGEMEYER SINGAPORE PPS PTE LTD.—See Sonepar S.A.; *Int'l*, pg. 7090
HAGEN DEUTSCHLAND GMBH & CO. KG—See Rolf C. Hagen, Inc.; *Int'l*, pg. 6391
HAGENUK MARINEKOMMUNIKATION GMBH—See Airbus SE; *Int'l*, pg. 242
HAGENUK MARINEKOMMUNIKATION GMBH—See ThyssenKrupp AG; *Int'l*, pg. 7723
HAGER CABINETS INCORPORATED; *U.S. Private*, pg. 1839
HAGER GROUP INC.; *U.S. Private*, pg. 1839
HAGER MACHINE & TOOL INC.—See Atec, Inc.; *U.S. Private*, pg. 365
HAGERMAN CONSTRUCTION CORPORATION; *U.S. Private*, pg. 1839
THE HAGERMAN GROUP—See Hagerman Construction Corporation; *U.S. Private*, pg. 1839
HAGER MOSS FILM GMBH—See Highlight Communications AG; *Int'l*, pg. 3388
HAGER OIL COMPANY INC.—See AIP, LLC; *U.S. Private*, pg. 136
HAGER SHARP INC.; *U.S. Private*, pg. 1839
HAGERSTOWN OUTBACK, INC.—See Bloomin' Brands, Inc.; *U.S. Public*, pg. 363
HAGERSTOWN SURGERY CENTER, LLC—See Tenet Healthcare Corporation; *U.S. Public*, pg. 2002
THE HAGERTY GROUP, LLC—See Hagerty, Inc.; *U.S. Public*, pg. 979
HAGERTY, INC.; *U.S. Public*, pg. 979
HAGERTY INSURANCE AGENCY, LLC—See Hagerty, Inc.; *U.S. Public*, pg. 979
HAGERTY INTERNATIONAL LIMITED—See Hagerty, Inc.; *U.S. Public*, pg. 979
HAGERTY, LOCKENVITZ ADVERTISING, INC.; *U.S. Private*, pg. 1840

HAGERTY STEEL & ALUMINUM CO.—See Reliance Steel & Aluminum Co.; *U.S. Public*, pg. 1780
HAGGAR CANADA CO.—See Perseus LLC; *U.S. Private*, pg. 3155
HAGGAR CLOTHING CO.—See Randa Corp.; *U.S. Private*, pg. 3353
HAGGAR CORPORATION—See Perseus LLC; *U.S. Private*, pg. 3155
HAGGARD & STOCKING ASSOCIATES INC.; *U.S. Private*, pg. 1840
HAGGEN, INC.—See Comvest Group Holdings LLC; *U.S. Private*, pg. 1007
HAGGLUNDS DRIVES SOUTH AFRICA (PTY.) LTD.—See Robert Bosch GmbH; *Int'l*, pg. 6361
HAGGLUNDS VEHICLE GMBH—See BAE Systems plc; *Int'l*, pg. 798
HA GIANG MINERAL MECHANICS JOINT STOCK COMPANY; *Int'l*, pg. 3201
HAGIBOR OFFICE BUILDING, A.S.—See CPI Property Group, S.A.; *Int'l*, pg. 1825
HAGIE MANUFACTURING COMPANY—See Deere & Company; *U.S. Public*, pg. 646
HAGIHANA MACHINERY (SHANGHAI) CO., LTD.—See Hagihara Industries Inc.; *Int'l*, pg. 3207
HAGIHARA INDUSTRIES INC.; *Int'l*, pg. 3206
HAGIMORI INDUSTRIES, LTD.—See UBE Corporation; *Int'l*, pg. 8000
HAGIMORI LOGISTICS, LTD.—See UBE Corporation; *Int'l*, pg. 8000
HAGIN INVESTMENT MANAGMENT; *U.S. Private*, pg. 1840
HAGIWARA AMERICA, INC.—See Hagiwara Electric Holdings Co., Ltd.; *Int'l*, pg. 3207
HAGIWARA ELECTRIC EUROPE GMBH—See Hagiwara Electric Holdings Co., Ltd.; *Int'l*, pg. 3207
HAGIWARA ELECTRIC HOLDINGS CO., LTD.; *Int'l*, pg. 3207
HAGIWARA ELECTRIC KOREA CO., LTD.—See Hagiwara Electric Holdings Co., Ltd.; *Int'l*, pg. 3207
HAGIWARA ELECTRIC (SHANGHAI) CO., LTD.—See Hagiwara Electric Holdings Co., Ltd.; *Int'l*, pg. 3207
HAGIWARA ELECTRIC (THAILAND) CO., LTD.—See Hagiwara Electric Holdings Co., Ltd.; *Int'l*, pg. 3207
HAGIWARA ELECTRONICS CO., LTD.—See Hagiwara Electric Holdings Co., Ltd.; *Int'l*, pg. 3207
HAGIWARA ELECTRONICS INDIA PRIVATE LIMITED—See Hagiwara Electric Holdings Co., Ltd.; *Int'l*, pg. 3207
HAGIWARA ENGINEERING CO., LTD.—See Hagiwara Electric Holdings Co., Ltd.; *Int'l*, pg. 3207
HAGIWARA HOKUTO TECHNO CO., LTD.—See Hagiwara Electric Holdings Co., Ltd.; *Int'l*, pg. 3207
HAGIWARA (SHANGHAI) CO., LTD.—See Hagiwara Electric Holdings Co., Ltd.; *Int'l*, pg. 3207
HAGIWARA TECHNO SOLUTIONS CO. LTD.—See Hagiwara Electric Holdings Co., Ltd.; *Int'l*, pg. 3207
HAGIWARA TECHNO SOLUTIONS (SHANGHAI) CO., LTD.—See Hagiwara Electric Holdings Co., Ltd.; *Int'l*, pg. 3207
HAGLEITNER HYGIENE BOSNE I HERCEGOVINE D.O.O.—See Hagleitner Hygiene International GmbH; *Int'l*, pg. 3207
HAGLEITNER HYGIENE BULGARIA EOOD—See Hagleitner Hygiene International GmbH; *Int'l*, pg. 3207
HAGLEITNER HYGIENE CESKO S.R.O.—See Hagleitner Hygiene International GmbH; *Int'l*, pg. 3207
HAGLEITNER HYGIENE DEUTSCHLAND GMBH—See Hagleitner Hygiene International GmbH; *Int'l*, pg. 3207
HAGLEITNER HYGIENE D.O.O.—See Hagleitner Hygiene International GmbH; *Int'l*, pg. 3207
HAGLEITNER HYGIENE HRVATSKA D.O.O.—See Hagleitner Hygiene International GmbH; *Int'l*, pg. 3207
HAGLEITNER HYGIENE INTERNATIONAL GMBH; *Int'l*, pg. 3207
HAGLEITNER HYGIENE ITALIA S.R.L.—See Hagleitner Hygiene International GmbH; *Int'l*, pg. 3207
HAGLEITNER HYGIENE MAGYARORSZAG KFT.—See Hagleitner Hygiene International GmbH; *Int'l*, pg. 3207
HAGLEITNER HYGIENE ROMANIA S.R.L.—See Hagleitner Hygiene International GmbH; *Int'l*, pg. 3207
HAGLEITNER HYGIENE SLOVENSKO S.R.O.—See Hagleitner Hygiene International GmbH; *Int'l*, pg. 3207
HAGLEITNER HYGIENE SRBIJA D.O.O.—See Hagleitner Hygiene International GmbH; *Int'l*, pg. 3207
HAGLEITNER ITALIA S.R.L.—See Hagleitner Hygiene International GmbH; *Int'l*, pg. 3207
HAGLEITNER NWO DEUTSCHLAND GMBH—See Hagleitner Hygiene International GmbH; *Int'l*, pg. 3207
HAGLE LUMBER COMPANY, INC.; *U.S. Private*, pg. 1840
HAGLER BAILLY PAKISTAN (PRIVATE) LIMITED—See Tetra Tech, Inc.; *U.S. Public*, pg. 2023
HAGLOFS AB—See LionRock Capital Limited; *Int'l*, pg. 4520
HAGL RUBBER JSC—See Hoang Anh Gia Lai Joint Stock Company; *Int'l*, pg. 3436
HAGLUND & HELLBERG BIL I HANINGE AB—See Bilia AB; *Int'l*, pg. 1029
HAGMANS TAK OST AB—See Kingspan Group PLC; *Int'l*, pg. 4178

HAGOLD HEFE GMBH—See Lallemand, Inc.; *Int'l*, pg. 4399
HAGOPIAN WORLD OF RUGS INC.; *U.S. Private*, pg. 1840
HAGO PU GMBH—See Sika AG; *Int'l*, pg. 6914
HAGOR NV—See Udea B.V.; *Int'l*, pg. 8014
HAGOROMO FOODS CORPORATION; *Int'l*, pg. 3207
HAGSTROM I NAS AB—See Peab AB; *Int'l*, pg. 5771
HAGSTROM MAP COMPANY—See Langenscheidt Kommanditgesellschaft; *Int'l*, pg. 4409
HAGU CO., LTD.—See AB&Company Co., Ltd.; *Int'l*, pg. 47
HAGUE AND LONDON OIL PLC; *Int'l*, pg. 3207
HAHA GENERATION CORP.; *Int'l*, pg. 3207
HAHL FILAMENTS GMBH—See Global Equity Partners Beteiligungs-Management AG; *Int'l*, pg. 2996
HAHL INC.—See Global Equity Partners Beteiligungs-Management AG; *Int'l*, pg. 2996
HAHN AUTOMATION AG—See RAG-Stiftung; *Int'l*, pg. 6179
HAHN AUTOMATION COMPONENTS GMBH—See RAG-Stiftung; *Int'l*, pg. 6179
HAHN AUTOMATION D.O.O.—See RAG-Stiftung; *Int'l*, pg. 6179
HAHN AUTOMATION GMBH—See RAG-Stiftung; *Int'l*, pg. 6179
HAHN AUTOMATION, INC.—See RAG-Stiftung; *Int'l*, pg. 6179
HAHN AUTOMATION (KUNSHAN) CO. LTD.—See RAG-Stiftung; *Int'l*, pg. 6179
HAHN AUTOMATION SAN VE TIC. LTD. STI.—See RAG-Stiftung; *Int'l*, pg. 6179
HAHN AUTOMATION, S.R.O.—See RAG-Stiftung; *Int'l*, pg. 6179
HAHN AUTOMOTIVE WAREHOUSE, INC.; *U.S. Private*, pg. 1840
HAHN & CLAY, LTD.; *U.S. Private*, pg. 1840
HAHN & COMPANY; *Int'l*, pg. 3207
HAHN ENERSAVE GMBH—See RAG-Stiftung; *Int'l*, pg. 6179
HAHNER FOREMAN & HARNESS INC.; *U.S. Private*, pg. 1840
HAHN GASFEDERN GMBH—See Triton Advisers Limited; *Int'l*, pg. 7933
HAHN GROUP GMBH; *Int'l*, pg. 3208
HAHN HOLDING CO.; *U.S. Private*, pg. 1840
HAHN I KOLB INSTRUMENTI EOOD—See Wurth Verwaltungsgesellschaft mbH; *Int'l*, pg. 8505
HAHN INVESTMENT STEWARDS & COMPANY INC.—See iA Financial Corporation Inc.; *Int'l*, pg. 3567
HAHN + KOLB D.O.O.—See Wurth Verwaltungsgesellschaft mbH; *Int'l*, pg. 8505
HAHN KOLB ENDUSTRI URUNLERI TIC. LTD. STI—See Wurth Verwaltungsgesellschaft mbH; *Int'l*, pg. 8505
HAHN + KOLB (GUANGZHOU) TOOLS CO., LTD.—See Wurth Verwaltungsgesellschaft mbH; *Int'l*, pg. 8505
HAHN + KOLB HUNGARIA KFT.—See Wurth Verwaltungsgesellschaft mbH; *Int'l*, pg. 8505
HAHN+KOLB MEXICO, S. DE R.L DE CV.—See Wurth Verwaltungsgesellschaft mbH; *Int'l*, pg. 8505
HAHN + KOLB POLSKA SP. Z O.O.—See Wurth Verwaltungsgesellschaft mbH; *Int'l*, pg. 8505
HAHN + KOLB ROMANIA SRL—See Wurth Verwaltungsgesellschaft mbH; *Int'l*, pg. 8505
HAHN + KOLB SOVECO S.A.R.L—See Wurth Verwaltungsgesellschaft mbH; *Int'l*, pg. 8505
HAHN + KOLB (TIANJIN) INTERNATIONAL TRADE CO., LTD.—See Wurth Verwaltungsgesellschaft mbH; *Int'l*, pg. 8505
HAHN+KOLB TOOLS PVT. LTD.—See Wurth Verwaltungsgesellschaft mbH; *Int'l*, pg. 8505
HAHN + KOLB WERKZEUGE GMBH—See Wurth Verwaltungsgesellschaft mbH; *Int'l*, pg. 8505
HAHN OTOMASYON LTD. STI.—See RAG-Stiftung; *Int'l*, pg. 6179
HAHN SYSTEMS, LLC—See Descours & Cabaud SA; *Int'l*, pg. 2044
HA-HO KFT.—See Aiphone Co., Ltd.; *Int'l*, pg. 235
HA HOWARD SERVICES LLC—See Hannon Armstrong Sustainable Infrastructure Capital, Inc.; *U.S. Public*, pg. 983
HAI AGROCHEM JOINT STOCK COMPANY; *Int'l*, pg. 3208
HAI AGROCHEM JOINT STOCK COMPANY—See HAI Agrochem Joint Stock Company; *Int'l*, pg. 3208
HAIBARA MACHINE & TOOLS CO., LTD.—See Koito Manufacturing Co., Ltd.; *Int'l*, pg. 4230
HAIBO HEAVY ENGINERNG SCNC & TECH CO LTD; *Int'l*, pg. 3209
HAICHANG OCEAN PARK HOLDINGS LTD.; *Int'l*, pg. 3209
HAICHENG HUAYIN HIGH-TECH MATERIALS CO., LTD.—See Puyang Refractories Group Co., Ltd.; *Int'l*, pg. 6124
HAICHENG LINLI MINING CO., LTD.; *Int'l*, pg. 3209
HAI CHEUNG TRADING CO.—See Daeyang Electric Co., Ltd.; *Int'l*, pg. 1911
HAIDACKER PROJEKTENTWICKLUNG GMBH—See PORR AG; *Int'l*, pg. 5923

HAIDEMENOS S.A. CORPORATE AFFILIATIONS

HAIDEMENOS S.A.; *Int'l*, pg. 3209
HAIDILAO INTERNATIONAL HOLDING LTD.; *Int'l*, pg. 3209
HAIDKOPF GMBH—See BASF SE; *Int'l*, pg. 885
HAI DUONG PUMP MANUFACTURING JOINT STOCK COMPANY; *Int'l*, pg. 3208
HAIER AMERICA TRADING, LLC—See Haier Smart Home Co., Ltd.; *Int'l*, pg. 3210
HAIER ELECTRONICS GROUP CO., LTD.—See Haier Smart Home Co., Ltd.; *Int'l*, pg. 3210
HAIER SMART HOME CO., LTD.; *Int'l*, pg. 3209
HAIER US APPLIANCE SOLUTIONS, INC.—See Haier Smart Home Co., Ltd.; *Int'l*, pg. 3210
HAIFA CHEMICALS LTD.—See Trans-Resources, Inc.; *U.S. Private*, pg. 4206
HAIFA NORTH AMERICA INCORPORATED—See Trans-Resources, Inc.; *U.S. Private*, pg. 4206
THE HAIGH ENGINEERING COMPANY LIMITED; *Int'l*, pg. 7651
HAIGH-FARR, INC.—See Videndum plc; *Int'l*, pg. 8190
HAIGHT BROWN & BONESTEEL, LLP; *U.S. Private*, pg. 1840
HAIGHTS CROSS COMMUNICATIONS, INC.; *U.S. Private*, pg. 1840
HAIGOOD & CAMPBELL LLC; *U.S. Private*, pg. 1840
HAIG'S SERVICE CORPORATION; *U.S. Private*, pg. 1840
HAIHA CONFECTIONERY JOINT STOCK COMPANY; *Int'l*, pg. 3210
HAIHAO HIGH FASHION CO., LTD.—See Haixin Group Company Ltd.; *Int'l*, pg. 3219
HAIKE CHEMICAL GROUP LTD; *Int'l*, pg. 3210
HAIKE TRADING HONGKONG LIMITED—See HaiKe Chemical Group Ltd; *Int'l*, pg. 3211
HAIKOU PEACE BASE INDUSTRY DEVELOPMENT CO. LTD.—See CAQ Holdings Limited; *Int'l*, pg. 1319
HAIKOU ZHONGFU CONTAINER CO., LTD.—See Zhuhai Zhongfu Enterprise Co., Ltd.; *Int'l*, pg. 8679
HAIKUI SEAFOOD AG; *Int'l*, pg. 3211
HAIKU LEARNING SYSTEMS, INC.—See Vista Equity Partners, LLC; *U.S. Private*, pg. 4398
HAI KWANG ENTERPRISE CORPORATION; *Int'l*, pg. 3208
HAIL AGRICULTURAL DEVELOPMENT COMPANY—See Almarai Company Ltd.; *Int'l*, pg. 363
HAILAN HOLDINGS LIMITED; *Int'l*, pg. 3211
HAIL CEMENT COMPANY—See Qassim Cement Co.; *Int'l*, pg. 6133
HAIL & COTTON INC.—See Luckett Tobaccos Inc.; *U.S. Private*, pg. 2511
HAIL & COTTON—See Luckett Tobaccos Inc.; *U.S. Private*, pg. 2511
HAIL CREEK COAL PTY LTD—See Rio Tinto plc; *Int'l*, pg. 6347
HAI LECK ENGINEERING PTE LTD—See Hai Leck Holdings Limited; *Int'l*, pg. 3208
HAI LECK HOLDINGS LIMITED; *Int'l*, pg. 3208
HAILE GOLD MINE INC.—See OceanaGold Corporation; *Int'l*, pg. 5517
HAILE SHAW & PFAFFENBERGER, P.A.—See Nason, Yeager, Gerson, Harris & Fumero P.A.; *U.S. Private*, pg. 2837
HAILIANG AMERICA CORPORATION—See Zhejiang Hailiang Co., Ltd.; *Int'l*, pg. 8655
HAILIANG EDUCATION GROUP INC.; *Int'l*, pg. 3211
HAILIANG GROUP CO. LTD.; *Int'l*, pg. 3211
HAILIANG INTERNATIONAL HOLDINGS LIMITED—See Hailiang Group Co. Ltd.; *Int'l*, pg. 3211
HAILIR PESTICIDES & CHEMICALS GROUP; *Int'l*, pg. 3211
HAI LUEN TRADING CO., LTD.—See China Merchants Group Limited; *Int'l*, pg. 1521
HAILUN PIANO CO., LTD.; *Int'l*, pg. 3211
HAIMA AUTOMOBILE CO., LTD.; *Int'l*, pg. 3211
HAI MING INDUSTRIES SDN. BHD—See KPS Consortium Berhad; *Int'l*, pg. 4299
HAI MING PAPER MILLS SDN. BHD.—See KPS Consortium Berhad; *Int'l*, pg. 4299
HAI MING TRADING CO. SDN. BHD.—See KPS Consortium Berhad; *Int'l*, pg. 4299
HAI MINH CORPORATION; *Int'l*, pg. 3208
HAI MINH LOGISTICS CO.,LTD.—See Hai Minh Corporation; *Int'l*, pg. 3208
HAI MINH PORT SERVICE JOINT STOCK COMPANY—See Hai Minh Corporation; *Int'l*, pg. 3209
HAIMO AMERICA, INC.—See Haimo Technologies Group Corp.; *Int'l*, pg. 3211
HAIMO INTERNATIONAL FZE—See Haimo Technologies Group Corp.; *Int'l*, pg. 3211
HAIMO OILFIELD SERVICES CO., LTD.—See Haimo Technologies Group Corp.; *Int'l*, pg. 3211
HAIMO SUBSEA TECHNOLOLY (SHANGHAI) CO., LTD.—See Haimo Technologies Group Corp.; *Int'l*, pg. 3211
HAIMO TECHNOLOGIES GROUP CORP.; *Int'l*, pg. 3211
HAIMURUBUSHI CO., LTD.—See Mitsui Fudosan Co., Ltd.; *Int'l*, pg. 4986
HAINA INTELLIGENT EQUIPMENT INTERNATIONAL HOLDINGS LIMITED; *Int'l*, pg. 3211

HAINAN AIRLINES HOLDING CO., LTD.—See Hainan Traffic Administration Holding Co., Ltd.; *Int'l*, pg. 3215
HAINAN AIRLINES SALES CO., LTD.—See Hainan Traffic Administration Holding Co., Ltd.; *Int'l*, pg. 3215
HAINAN AIRPORT INFRASTRUCTURE CO LTD; *Int'l*, pg. 3211
HAINAN BESTCHAIN INFORMATION SYSTEM CO., LTD—See Hainan Traffic Administration Holding Co., Ltd.; *Int'l*, pg. 3215
HAINAN DADONGHAI TOURISM CENTRE (HOLDINGS) CO., LTD.; *Int'l*, pg. 3211
HAINAN DEVELOPMENT HOLDINGS NANHAI CO., LTD.; *Int'l*, pg. 3211
HAINAN DFS RETAIL COMPANY LIMITED—See LVMH Moet Hennessy Louis Vuitton SE; *Int'l*, pg. 4592
HAINAN DIC MICROALGAE CO., LTD.—See DIC Corporation; *Int'l*, pg. 2109
HAINAN DRINDA NEW ENERGY TECHNOLOGY CO., LTD.; *Int'l*, pg. 3212
HAINAN EKING TECHNOLOGY CO., LTD.—See Hainan Traffic Administration Holding Co., Ltd.; *Int'l*, pg. 3215
HAINAN EXPRESSWAY CO., LTD.; *Int'l*, pg. 3212
HAINAN GENERAL SANYANG PHARMACEUTICAL CO., LTD.—See China Meheco Group Co., Ltd.; *Int'l*, pg. 1519
HAINAN GOLDEN GULF INVESTMENT & DEVELOPMENT CO., LTD.—See Hainan Traffic Administration Holding Co., Ltd.; *Int'l*, pg. 3215
HAINAN HAIDE CAPITAL MANAGEMENT CO., LTD.; *Int'l*, pg. 3212
HAINAN HAIQI TRANSPORTATION GROUP CO., LTD.; *Int'l*, pg. 3212
HAINAN HAIYAO CO., LTD.; *Int'l*, pg. 3212
HAINAN HITACHI ELEVATOR SERVICE CO., LTD.—See Hitachi, Ltd.; *Int'l*, pg. 3416
HAINAN HNA DRINK CO., LTD—See Hainan Traffic Administration Holding Co., Ltd.; *Int'l*, pg. 3215
HAINAN HNA ZHONGMIAN DUTY FREE CO., LTD—See Hainan Traffic Administration Holding Co., Ltd.; *Int'l*, pg. 3215
HAINAN HULUWA PHARMACEUTICAL GROUP CO., LTD.; *Int'l*, pg. 3212
HAINAN I.R.E. LETIAN CONSTRUCTION & DECORATION ENGINEERING CO., LTD.—See Sapphire Corporation Limited; *Int'l*, pg. 6572
HAINAN JINGLIANG HOLDINGS CO., LTD.; *Int'l*, pg. 3212
HAINAN JINPAN SMART TECHNOLOGY CO., LTD.; *Int'l*, pg. 3212
HAINAN JUI LI INDUSTRY CO., LTD.—See Jui Li Enterprise Co., Ltd.; *Int'l*, pg. 4022
HAINAN LONGAO INVESTMENT CO., LTD.—See Zhewen Interactive Group Co Ltd; *Int'l*, pg. 8671
HAINAN MANASLU CORP.; *Int'l*, pg. 3212
HAINAN MEILAN INTERNATIONAL AIRPORT COMPANY LIMITED; *Int'l*, pg. 3212
HAINAN MINING CO., LTD.—See Fosun International Limited; *Int'l*, pg. 2751
HAINAN ORG PACKAGING INDUSTRY CO., LTD.—See ORG Technology Co., Ltd.; *Int'l*, pg. 5617
HAINAN POLY. CO., LTD.—See Hainan Poly Pharm.Co.,Ltd.; *Int'l*, pg. 3212
HAINAN POLY PHARM.CO.,LTD.; *Int'l*, pg. 3212
HAINAN POWER GRID COMPANY—See China Southern Power Grid Co., Ltd.; *Int'l*, pg. 1553
HAINAN RUIZE NEW BUILDING MATERIAL CO.; *Int'l*, pg. 3212
HAINAN SCAS AUTOMOBILE SALES CO., LTD.—See China ZhengTong Auto Services Holdings Limited; *Int'l*, pg. 1566
HAINAN SHENNONG SEED TECHNOLOGY CO., LTD.; *Int'l*, pg. 3212
HAINAN SHINER INDUSTRIAL CO., LTD.—See Shiner International, Inc.; *Int'l*, pg. 6843
HAINAN SHUANGCHENG PHARMACEUTICALS CO., LTD.; *Int'l*, pg. 3212
HAINAN STRAIT SHIPPING CO., LTD.; *Int'l*, pg. 3212
HAINAN SUNDIRO-KAWASAKI ENGINE CO., LTD.—See Kawasaki Heavy Industries, Ltd.; *Int'l*, pg. 4095
HAINAN TECHNIK CO., LTD.—See Hainan Traffic Administration Holding Co., Ltd.; *Int'l*, pg. 3215
HAINAN TRAFFIC ADMINISTRATION HOLDING CO., LTD.; *Int'l*, pg. 3212
HAINAN WEN-SHENG HIGH-TECH MATERIALS CO., LTD.—See Shenghe Resources Holding Co., Ltd.; *Int'l*, pg. 6801
HAINAN XIANFENG ELECTRIC IMP. & EXP. CO., LTD.—See Korea Electric Terminal Co., Ltd.; *Int'l*, pg. 4284
HAINAN YEDAO (GROUP) CO., LTD.; *Int'l*, pg. 3216
HAINAN YUANYANG CO., LTD.—See ORG Technology Co., Ltd.; *Int'l*, pg. 5617
HAINAN ZAMBON PHARMACEUTICAL CO., LTD—See Zambon Company S.p.A.; *Int'l*, pg. 8622
HAINAN ZHONGSHENG STAR AUTOMOBILE SALES & SERVICE CO., LTD.—See Zhongsheng Group Holdings Limited; *Int'l*, pg. 8674
HAIN BPC, INC.—See The Hain Celestial Group, Inc.; *U.S. Public*, pg. 2086

HAIN CELESTIAL BELGIUM BVBA—See The Hain Celestial Group, Inc.; *U.S. Public*, pg. 2086
HAIN CELESTIAL EUROPE B.V.—See The Hain Celestial Group, Inc.; *U.S. Public*, pg. 2086
THE HAIN CELESTIAL GROUP, INC.; *U.S. Public*, pg. 2086
HAIN CELESTIAL UK LIMITED—See The Hain Celestial Group, Inc.; *U.S. Public*, pg. 2087
THE HAIN DANIELS GROUP LIMITED—See The Hain Celestial Group, Inc.; *U.S. Public*, pg. 2087
HAINES CITY HMA URGENT CARE, LLC—See Community Health Systems, Inc.; *U.S. Public*, pg. 553
HAINES & COMPANY, INC. - AMERICALIST DIVISION—See Haines & Company, Inc.; *U.S. Private*, pg. 1840
HAINES & COMPANY, INC. - HAINES DIRECT DIVISION—See Haines & Company, Inc.; *U.S. Private*, pg. 1840
HAINES & COMPANY, INC.; *U.S. Private*, pg. 1840
HAINES & KIBBLEHOUSE INC.; *U.S. Private*, pg. 1840
HAINES NZ LIMITED—See WPP plc; *Int'l*, pg. 8462
HAINING CHINA LEATHER MARKET CO., LTD.; *Int'l*, pg. 3216
HAINING DILONG YONGFU NEW MATERIAL CO., LTD.—See Zhejiang Juli Culture Development Co., Ltd.; *Int'l*, pg. 8658
HAINING MINGYI ELECTRONIC TECHNOLOGY CO., LTD.—See Zhejiang Chenfeng Science & Technology Co., Ltd.; *Int'l*, pg. 8649
HAINING MY HOME MECHANISM CO., LTD.—See Phoenix Mecano AG; *Int'l*, pg. 5852
HAIN LIFESCIENCES S.A. PTY. LTD.—See Bruker Corporation; *U.S. Public*, pg. 406
HAIN LIFESCIENCE UK LTD.—See Bruker Corporation; *U.S. Public*, pg. 406
HAIN PURE PROTEIN CORPORATION—See Aterian Investment Management, L.P.; *U.S. Public*, pg. 366
H+A INTERNATIONAL, INC.; *U.S. Private*, pg. 1824
HA INTERNATIONAL LLC—See Huettenes-Albertus Chemische Werke GmbH; *Int'l*, pg. 3522
HAINZ-KIMBERLY DEUTSCHLAND GMBH—See Kimberly-Clark Corporation; *U.S. Public*, pg. 1230
HAI-O ENTERPRISE BERHAD; *Int'l*, pg. 3209
HAI-O MARKETING SDN. BHD.—See Hai-O Enterprise Berhad; *Int'l*, pg. 3209
HAI-O MEDICINE SDN. BHD.—See Hai-O Enterprise Berhad; *Int'l*, pg. 3209
HAI-O RAYA BHD.—See Hai-O Enterprise Berhad; *Int'l*, pg. 3209
HAI PHAT INVESTMENT JSC; *Int'l*, pg. 3209
HAI PHONG ELECTRICAL MECHANICAL JSC; *Int'l*, pg. 3209
HAI PHONG ELECTRICITY WATER MACHINE ASSEMBLY JOINT STOCK; *Int'l*, pg. 3209
HAI PHONG HOANG HA PAPER JOINT STOCK COMPANY; *Int'l*, pg. 3209
HAI PHONG PETROLIMEX TRANSPORTATION & SERVICES JSC—See Vietnam National Petroleum Corporation; *Int'l*, pg. 8201
HAI PHONG PORT OPERATIONS AND ENGINEERING TRAINING ONE MEMBER LIMITED COMPANY—See Port of Hai Phong Joint Stock Company; *Int'l*, pg. 5933
HAIPHONG SECURITIES JOINT STOCK COMPANY; *Int'l*, pg. 3216
HAI PLASTIC LTD.—See Bram Industries Ltd.; *Int'l*, pg. 1138
HAIR CLUB FOR MEN, LLC—See Aderans Co., Ltd.; *Int'l*, pg. 143
HAIR CLUB FOR MEN, LTD., INC.—See Aderans Co., Ltd.; *Int'l*, pg. 143
HAIR CLUB FOR MEN, LTD., INC.—See Aderans Co., Ltd.; *Int'l*, pg. 143
THE HAIR CUTTERY—See The Ratner Companies; *U.S. Private*, pg. 4102
HAIRGROUP AG; *Int'l*, pg. 3216
HAIRHOUSE WAREHOUSE ONLINE PTY. LTD.; *Int'l*, pg. 3217
HAIRSTYLISTS MANAGEMENT SYSTEMS; *U.S. Private*, pg. 1841
HAISAN RESOURCES BERHAD; *Int'l*, pg. 3217
HAISAN SDN. BHD.—See Haisan Resources Berhad; *Int'l*, pg. 3217
HAI SAN & SONS SDN. BHD.—See Haisan Resources Berhad; *Int'l*, pg. 3217
HAISCH AUFZUGE GMBH—See ThyssenKrupp AG; *Int'l*, pg. 7724
HAISCO PHARMACEUTICAL GROUP CO., LTD.; *Int'l*, pg. 3217
HAISUNG TPC CO., LTD.; *Int'l*, pg. 3217
HAITAI CONFECTIONERY AND FOODS CO.,LTD. - CHEONAN FACTORY—See Haitai Confectionery And Foods Co.,ltd.; *Int'l*, pg. 3217
HAITAI CONFECTIONERY AND FOODS CO.,LTD. - CHONGJU FACTORY—See Haitai Confectionery And Foods Co.,ltd.; *Int'l*, pg. 3217
HAITAI CONFECTIONERY AND FOODS CO.,LTD. - DAGUE FACTORY—See Haitai Confectionery And Foods Co.,ltd.; *Int'l*, pg. 3217

COMPANY NAME INDEX

HAITAI CONFECTIONERY AND FOODS CO.,LTD. - KWANGJU FACTORY—See Haitai Confectionery And Foods Co.,ltd.; *Int'l*, pg. 3217
HAITAI CONFECTIONERY AND FOODS CO.,LTD.; *Int'l*, pg. 3217
HAITAI, INC.; *U.S. Private*, pg. 1841
HA ITALIA S.P.A.—See Huettenes-Albertus Chemische Werke GmbH; *Int'l*, pg. 3523
HAITEX CO., LTD.—See Hayashi Telempu Co., Ltd.; *Int'l*, pg. 3289
HAITIAN ENERGY INTERNATIONAL LIMITED; *Int'l*, pg. 3217
HAITIAN HUAYUAN (JAPAN) MACHINERY CO., LTD—See Haitian International Holdings Ltd.; *Int'l*, pg. 3217
HAITIAN HUAYUAN MACHINERY (INDIA) PRIVATE LIMITED—See Haitian International Holdings Ltd.; *Int'l*, pg. 3217
HAITIAN HUAYUAN MIDDLE EAST MAKINA DIS TI-CARET LIMITED SIRKETI—See Haitian International Holdings Ltd.; *Int'l*, pg. 3217
HAITIAN HUAYUAN SOUTH AMERICA COMERCIO DE MAQUINAS LTDA.—See Haitian International Holdings Ltd.; *Int'l*, pg. 3217
HAITIAN IBERICA, S.L.—See Haitian International Holdings Ltd.; *Int'l*, pg. 3217
HAITIAN INTERNATIONAL GERMANY GMBH—See Haitian International Holdings Ltd.; *Int'l*, pg. 3217
HAITIAN INTERNATIONAL HOLDINGS LTD.; *Int'l*, pg. 3217
HAITIAN MIDDLE EAST FZC—See Haitian International Holdings Ltd.; *Int'l*, pg. 3217
HAITIAN PLASTICS MACHINERY GROUP CO., LTD.—See Haitian International Holdings Ltd.; *Int'l*, pg. 3217
HAITIAN PRECISION MACHINERY (MALAYSIA) PRIVATE LIMITED—See Ningbo Haitian Precision Machinery Co.,Ltd.; *Int'l*, pg. 5302
HAITIAN PRECISION MACHINERY MEXICO S.DE R.L.DE C.V.—See Ningbo Haitian Precision Machinery Co.,Ltd.; *Int'l*, pg. 5302
HAITIAN PRECISION MACHINERY (TURKEY) PRIVATE LIMITED—See Ningbo Haitian Precision Machinery Co.,Ltd.; *Int'l*, pg. 5302
HAITIAN PRECISION MACHINERY (VIETNAM) COMPANY LIMITED—See Ningbo Haitian Precision Machinery Co.,Ltd.; *Int'l*, pg. 5302
HAITIAN RUSSIA LTD—See Haitian International Holdings Ltd.; *Int'l*, pg. 3217
HAITIAN WATER GROUP CO., LTD.; *Int'l*, pg. 3217
HAITI ENTREPRENEURIAL INITIATIVE; *U.S. Private*, pg. 1841
HAITONG BANCO DE INVESTIMENTO DO BRASIL S.A.—See Haitong Securities Co., Ltd.; *Int'l*, pg. 3218
HAITONG BANK, S.A.—See Haitong Securities Co., Ltd.; *Int'l*, pg. 3218
HAITONG BANK, S.A. - SPAIN BRANCH—See Haitong Securities Co., Ltd.; *Int'l*, pg. 3218
HAITONG BANK, S.A. - WARSAW BRANCH—See Haitong Securities Co., Ltd.; *Int'l*, pg. 3218
HAITONG CAPITAL INVESTMENT CO., LTD.—See Haitong Securities Co., Ltd.; *Int'l*, pg. 3218
HAITONG-FORTIS PRIVATE EQUITY FUND MANAGEMENT CO., LTD.—See Haitong Securities Co., Ltd.; *Int'l*, pg. 3218
HAITONG FUTURES CO., LTD.—See Haitong Securities Co., Ltd.; *Int'l*, pg. 3218
HAITONG INNOVATION SECURITIES INVESTMENT CO., LTD.—See Haitong Securities Co., Ltd.; *Int'l*, pg. 3218
HAITONG INTERNATIONAL HOLDINGS LIMITED—See Haitong Securities Co., Ltd.; *Int'l*, pg. 3218
HAITONG INTERNATIONAL HOLDINGS (UK) LIMITED—See Haitong Securities Co., Ltd.; *Int'l*, pg. 3218
HAITONG INTERNATIONAL SECURITIES GROUP LIMITED—See Haitong Securities Co., Ltd.; *Int'l*, pg. 3218
HAITONG INTERNATIONAL SECURITIES KK—See Haitong Securities Co., Ltd.; *Int'l*, pg. 3218
HAITONG INTERNATIONAL SECURITIES (UK) LIMITED—See Haitong Securities Co., Ltd.; *Int'l*, pg. 3218
HAITONG INVESTMENT IRELAND PLC—See Haitong Securities Co., Ltd.; *Int'l*, pg. 3218
HAITONG SECURITIES CO., LTD.; *Int'l*, pg. 3218
HAITONG SECURITIES (UK) LIMITED—See Haitong Securities Co., Ltd.; *Int'l*, pg. 3218
HAITONG UNITRUST INTERNATIONAL FINANCIAL LEASING CO., LTD.—See Haitong Securities Co., Ltd.; *Int'l*, pg. 3218
HAITONG UNITRUST INTERNATIONAL LEASING CORPORATION—See Feishang Anthracite Resources Limited; *Int'l*, pg. 2632
HAITSMA BETON B.V.—See Ronesans Holding A.S.; *Int'l*, pg. 6396
HAIVISION NETWORK VIDEO GMBH—See HaiVision Systems, Inc.; *Int'l*, pg. 3218
HAIVISION NETWORK VIDEO INC.—See HaiVision Systems, Inc.; *Int'l*, pg. 3218

HAIVISION NETWORK VIDEO - INTERNET MEDIA DIVISION—See HaiVision Systems, Inc.; *Int'l*, pg. 3218
HAIVISION SYSTEMS, INC.; *Int'l*, pg. 3218
HAIWAN INTERNATIONAL DEVELOPMENT CO., LTD.; *Int'l*, pg. 3218
HAIXIN FOODS CO., LTD.; *Int'l*, pg. 3218
HAIXIN GROUP COMPANY LTD.; *Int'l*, pg. 3218
HAIXIN (H.K.) INT'L TRADING CO.—See Shanghai Haixin Group Co., Ltd.; *Int'l*, pg. 6769
HAIXIN OHTSU CO., LTD.—See Haixin Group Company Ltd.; *Int'l*, pg. 3219
HAIXIN PLUSH CO., LTD.—See Haixin Group Company Ltd.; *Int'l*, pg. 3219
HAIXIN TOYS CO., LTD.—See Haixin Group Company Ltd.; *Int'l*, pg. 3219
HAIYUAN PROPERTY CO., LTD.—See Hubei Jumpcan Pharmaceutical Co., Ltd.; *Int'l*, pg. 3518
HAJDUCICA A.D.; *Int'l*, pg. 3219
HAJI ABDULLAH ALIREZA & CO. LTD.—See Albert Ballin KG; *Int'l*, pg. 294
HAJI HUSEIN ALIREZA & CO. LTD.; *Int'l*, pg. 3219
HAJIME CONSTRUCTION CO., LTD.—See Iida Group Holdings Co., Ltd.; *Int'l*, pg. 3607
HAJI MOHAMMAD ISMAIL MILLS LIMITED; *Int'l*, pg. 3219
HAJNAL BT.—See PHOENIX Pharmahandel GmbH & Co. KG; *Int'l*, pg. 5854
HAJOCA CORP. - COSTA MESA—See Blackfriars Corp.; *U.S. Private*, pg. 575
HAJOCA CORP. - HAWTHORNE—See Blackfriars Corp.; *U.S. Private*, pg. 575
HAJOCA CORP. - LOS ANGELES—See Blackfriars Corp.; *U.S. Private*, pg. 575
HAJOCA CORPORATION—See Blackfriars Corp.; *U.S. Private*, pg. 575
HAJOCA CORP. - STROUDSBURG—See Blackfriars Corp.; *U.S. Private*, pg. 575
HAK ALGAHTANI GROUP OF COMPANIES; *Int'l*, pg. 3219
HAKAMA AG—See INDUS Holding AG; *Int'l*, pg. 3663
HAKA MOTORS—See HAK Algahtani Group of Companies; *Int'l*, pg. 3219
HAKATA BUS TERMINAL CO., LTD.—See Nishi-Nippon Railroad Co., Ltd.; *Int'l*, pg. 5364
THE HAKATA DAIMARU, INC.—See J. Front Retailing Co., Ltd.; *Int'l*, pg. 3855
HAKATA IZUMI CO., LTD.—See The Sumitomo Warehouse Co. Ltd.; *Int'l*, pg. 7689
HAKATA MARUKITA SUISAN CO., LTD—See Nissui Corporation; *Int'l*, pg. 5378
HAKATA SANSO-BUTSURYU CO., LTD.—See Mitsui-Soko Holdings Co., Ltd.; *Int'l*, pg. 4992
HAKATA TAKUMI KOUGEI INC.; *Int'l*, pg. 3219
HAK B.V.—See SHV Holdings N.V.; *Int'l*, pg. 6871
HAKERS ENTERPRISE CO., LTD.; *Int'l*, pg. 3219
HAKIMIANPOUR RESTAURANT GROUP; *U.S. Private*, pg. 1841
HAKIM OPTICAL LABORATORY LIMITED; *Int'l*, pg. 3219
HAKI SAFETY AB; *Int'l*, pg. 3219
HAKKANI CORPORATION—See Hakkani Group; *Int'l*, pg. 3219
HAKKANI GROUP; *Int'l*, pg. 3219
HAKKANI MOTORS LTD.—See Hakkani Group; *Int'l*, pg. 3219
HAKKANI PAPER & BOARD MILLS (PVT.) LTD.—See Hakkani Group; *Int'l*, pg. 3219
HAKKANI PAPER MILLS (PVT.) LTD.—See Hakkani Group; *Int'l*, pg. 3219
HAKKANI PULP & PAPER MILLS LTD.—See Hakkani Group; *Int'l*, pg. 3219
HAKKASAN LTD.; *Int'l*, pg. 3219
HAKKEN CAPITAL CORP.; *Int'l*, pg. 3219
HAKKIM TEXTILE MILLS LIMITED; *Int'l*, pg. 3219
HAKKODA DENSHI CO., LTD.—See Ferrotec Holdings Corporation; *Int'l*, pg. 2643
HAKKO ELECTRONICS CO., LTD.—See Fuji Electric Co., Ltd.; *Int'l*, pg. 2812
HAKKO TSUSHO CO., LTD. - KASHIMA PLANT—See Manac Incorporated; *Int'l*, pg. 4666
HAKKO TSUSHO CO., LTD.—See Manac Incorporated; *Int'l*, pg. 4666
HAKLIFT ABT OY—See Axel Johnson Gruppen AB; *Int'l*, pg. 764
HAKLIFT BALTIC OU—See Axel Johnson Gruppen AB; *Int'l*, pg. 764
HAKO AUSTRALIA PTY. LTD.—See L. Possehl & Co. mbH; *Int'l*, pg. 4382
HAKO B.V.—See L. Possehl & Co. mbH; *Int'l*, pg. 4382
HAKO CLEANING SYSTEM (SHANGHAI) CO., LTD.—See L. Possehl & Co. mbH; *Int'l*, pg. 4382
HAKODATE CARL RAYMON CO., LTD.—See NH Foods Ltd.; *Int'l*, pg. 5256
THE HAKODATE DOCK CO., LTD.—See Namura Shipbuilding Co., Ltd.; *Int'l*, pg. 5136
HAKODATE KOKUSAI HOTEL, CO., LTD.; *Int'l*, pg. 3219
HAKODATE MARUI IMAI LTD.—See Isetan Mitsukoshi Holdings Ltd.; *Int'l*, pg. 3814
HAKODATE MAZDA CO., LTD.—See Mazda Motor Corporation; *Int'l*, pg. 4748

HAKUHODO DY HOLDINGS INCORPORATED

HAKODATE NDK CO., LTD.—See NIHON DEMPA KOGYO Co Ltd; *Int'l*, pg. 5283
HAKO ESPANA S.A.—See L. Possehl & Co. mbH; *Int'l*, pg. 4382
HAKO GMBH—See L. Possehl & Co. mbH; *Int'l*, pg. 4382
HAKO GROUND & GARDEN AB—See L. Possehl & Co. mbH; *Int'l*, pg. 4382
HAKO GROUND & GARDEN A/S—See L. Possehl & Co. mbH; *Int'l*, pg. 4382
HAKO GROUP EAST ASIA LTD.—See L. Possehl & Co. mbH; *Int'l*, pg. 4382
HAKO MACHINES LTD.—See L. Possehl & Co. mbH; *Int'l*, pg. 4382
HAKONE ROPEWAY CO., LTD—See Odakyu Electric Railway Co., Ltd.; *Int'l*, pg. 5523
HAKONE TOZAN RAILWAY CO., LTD.—See Odakyu Electric Railway Co., Ltd.; *Int'l*, pg. 5523
HAKO POLSKA SP. Z O.O.—See L. Possehl & Co. mbH; *Int'l*, pg. 4382
HAKO SCHWEIZ AG—See L. Possehl & Co. mbH; *Int'l*, pg. 4382
HAKO TECHNOLOGY SP. Z O.O.—See L. Possehl & Co. mbH; *Int'l*, pg. 4382
HA KOVOCHEM SPOL S.R.O.—See Huettenes-Albertus Chemische Werke GmbH; *Int'l*, pg. 3523
HAKO-WERKE GMBH—See L. Possehl & Co. mbH; *Int'l*, pg. 4382
HAKOZAKI KAMI RYUTSU CENTER CO., LTD.—See Japan Pulp and Paper Company Limited; *Int'l*, pg. 3903
HAKRO-OOSTERBERG-NIJKERK B.V.—See TD Synnex Corp; *U.S. Public*, pg. 1986
HAKSAN PUBLISHING CO., LTD.—See Daewon Media Co., Ltd.; *Int'l*, pg. 1910
HAKUAI NURSING VILLA CO., LTD.—See Toyota Industries Corporation; *Int'l*, pg. 7866
HAKUBA RESORT DEVELOPMENT, CO., LTD.—See Nippon Ski Resort Development Co., Ltd.; *Int'l*, pg. 5334
HAKUBUNDO, INC.—See TOHAN CORPORATION; *Int'l*, pg. 7775
HAKUDO CO., LTD. - FUKUSHIMA PLANT—See Hakudo Co., Ltd.; *Int'l*, pg. 3219
HAKUDO CO., LTD. - KANAGAWA PLANT—See Hakudo Co., Ltd.; *Int'l*, pg. 3220
HAKUDO CO., LTD. - KYUSHU PLANT—See Hakudo Co., Ltd.; *Int'l*, pg. 3220
HAKUDO CO., LTD. - SHIGA PLANT—See Hakudo Co., Ltd.; *Int'l*, pg. 3220
HAKUDO CO., LTD.; *Int'l*, pg. 3219
HAKUDO (THAILAND) CO., LTD.—See Hakudo Co., Ltd.; *Int'l*, pg. 3219
HAKUGEN EARTH CO., LTD.—See Earth Corporation; *Int'l*, pg. 2268
HAKUHODO AUSTRALIA PTY. LTD.—See Hakuhodo DY Holdings Incorporated; *Int'l*, pg. 3221
HAKUHODO BANGKOK CO., LTD.—See Hakuhodo DY Holdings Incorporated; *Int'l*, pg. 3221
HAKUHODO-CEIL, INC.—See Hakuhodo DY Holdings Incorporated; *Int'l*, pg. 3221
HAKUHODO-CEIL, INC.—See Samsung Group; *Int'l*, pg. 6511
HAKUHODO CO., LTD. TOHOKU—See Hakuhodo DY Holdings Incorporated; *Int'l*, pg. 3221
HAKUHODO COMMUNICATIONS, INC.—See Hakuhodo DY Holdings Incorporated; *Int'l*, pg. 3221
HAKUHODO CREATIVE VOX, INC.—See Hakuhodo DY Holdings Incorporated; *Int'l*, pg. 3221
HAKUHODO DEUTSCHLAND GMBH-HAMBURG OFFICE—See Hakuhodo DY Holdings Incorporated; *Int'l*, pg. 3221
HAKUHODO DEUTSCHLAND GMBH-MUNICH OFFICE—See Hakuhodo DY Holdings Incorporated; *Int'l*, pg. 3221
HAKUHODO DEUTSCHLAND GMBH—See Hakuhodo DY Holdings Incorporated; *Int'l*, pg. 3221
HAKUHODO DY CAPCO—See Hakuhodo DY Holdings Incorporated; *Int'l*, pg. 3221
HAKUHODO DY HOLDINGS INCORPORATED; *Int'l*, pg. 3220
HAKUHODO DY I.O INC.—See Hakuhodo DY Holdings Incorporated; *Int'l*, pg. 3221
HAKUHODO DY MEDIA PARTNERS INC.—See Hakuhodo DY Holdings Incorporated; *Int'l*, pg. 3221
HAKUHODO DY TOTAL SUPPORT INC.—See Hakuhodo DY Holdings Incorporated; *Int'l*, pg. 3221
HAKUHODO ERG, INC.—See Hakuhodo DY Holdings Incorporated; *Int'l*, pg. 3221
HAKUHODO FRANCE S.A.—See Hakuhodo DY Holdings Incorporated; *Int'l*, pg. 3221
HAKUHODO HONG KONG LTD.—See Hakuhodo DY Holdings Incorporated; *Int'l*, pg. 3221
HAKUHODO INC. CHUBU OFFICE—See Hakuhodo DY Holdings Incorporated; *Int'l*, pg. 3221
HAKUHODO INC. KANSAI OFFICE—See Hakuhodo DY Holdings Incorporated; *Int'l*, pg. 3221
HAKUHODO INC. KYUSHU OFFICE—See Hakuhodo DY Holdings Incorporated; *Int'l*, pg. 3221
HAKUHODO INCORPORATED—See Hakuhodo DY Holdings Incorporated; *Int'l*, pg. 3220

HAKUHODO I.O. CO., LTD.—See Hakuhodo DY Holdings Incorporated; *Int'l*, pg. 3221
HAKUHODO I-STUDIO, INC.—See Hakuhodo DY Holdings Incorporated; *Int'l*, pg. 3221
HAKUHODO MALAYSIA SDN. BHD.—See Hakuhodo DY Holdings Incorporated; *Int'l*, pg. 3221
HAKUHODO PERCEPT PVT. LTD.—See Hakuhodo DY Holdings Incorporated; *Int'l*, pg. 3221
HAKUHODO & SAIGON ADVERTISING CO., LTD.—See Hakuhodo DY Holdings Incorporated; *Int'l*, pg. 3221
HAKUHODO SINGAPORE PTE. LTD.—See Hakuhodo DY Holdings Incorporated; *Int'l*, pg. 3221
HAKUI MURATA MANUFACTURING CO., LTD.—See Murata Manufacturing Co., Ltd.; *Int'l*, pg. 5097
HAKURYO KOUN CO.,LTD.—See Mitsubishi Logistics Corporation; *Int'l*, pg. 4962
HAKUSAN TEC CO., LTD.—See NOK Corporation; *Int'l*, pg. 5401
HAKUSEISHA CO., LTD.—See AEON Co., Ltd.; *Int'l*, pg. 177
HAKUTEN CORPORATION; *Int'l*, pg. 3222
HAKUTO ENTERPRISES LTD.—See STMicroelectronics N.V.; *Int'l*, pg. 7217
HAKUYOSHA COMPANY LTD.; *Int'l*, pg. 3222
HALABI INC.; *U.S. Private*, pg. 1841
HALA ENTERPRISES LIMITED; *Int'l*, pg. 3227
H.A. LANGER & ASSOCIATES; *U.S. Private*, pg. 1825
HALBERG A/S; *Int'l*, pg. 3227
HALBERG KAPITAL A/S—See Halberg A/S; *Int'l*, pg. 3227
H. ALBERT GMBH; *Int'l*, pg. 3194
HALCO INDUSTRIES, LLC; *U.S. Private*, pg. 1841
HALCOM VIETNAM JSC; *Int'l*, pg. 3227
HALCON ENERGY PROPERTIES, INC.—See Battalion Oil Corp.; *U.S. Public*, pg. 279
HALCON FIELD SERVICES, LLC—See Battalion Oil Corp.; *U.S. Public*, pg. 279
HALCORE GROUP, INC.—See AIP, LLC; *U.S. Private*, pg. 135
HALCO SERVICE CORP.—See Blue Sea Capital Management LLC; *U.S. Private*, pg. 592
HALCO USA LLC—See Robit Plc; *Int'l*, pg. 6370
HALCROW CHINA LIMITED—See Jacobs Engineering Group, Inc.; *U.S. Public*, pg. 1184
HALCROW GROUP IRELAND LIMITED—See Jacobs Engineering Group, Inc.; *U.S. Public*, pg. 1184
HALCROW HOLDINGS LIMITED—See Jacobs Engineering Group, Inc.; *U.S. Public*, pg. 1184
HALCROW, INC.—See Jacobs Engineering Group, Inc.; *U.S. Public*, pg. 1184
HALCYON AGRI CORPORATION LTD.—See China Hainan Rubber Industry Group Co., Ltd.; *Int'l*, pg. 1506
HALCYON COAST INVESTMENT (CANADA) LTD.; *Int'l*, pg. 3227
HALCYON CREEK INC.; *U.S. Private*, pg. 1842
HALCYON HOSPICE OF AIKEN, LLC—See UnitedHealth Group Incorporated; *U.S. Public*, pg. 2245
HALCYON HOSPICE—See UnitedHealth Group Incorporated; *U.S. Public*, pg. 2245
HALCYON KNIGHTS NEW ZEALAND LTD.—See PeopleIn Limited; *Int'l*, pg. 5794
HALCYON KNIGHTS PTE LTD—See PeopleIn Limited; *Int'l*, pg. 5794
HALCYON KNIGHTS PTY LTD—See PeopleIn Limited; *Int'l*, pg. 5794
HALCYON METAL COMPANY LIMITED—See Halcyon Technology Public Company Limited; *Int'l*, pg. 3227
HALCYON TECHNOLOGY (M) SDN. BHD.—See Halcyon Technology Public Company Limited; *Int'l*, pg. 3227
HALCYON TECHNOLOGY (PHILIPPINES) INC.—See Halcyon Technology Public Company Limited; *Int'l*, pg. 3227
HALCYON TECHNOLOGY PUBLIC COMPANY LIMITED; *Int'l*, pg. 3227
HALCYON UNDERWRITERS, INC.—See Brown & Brown, Inc.; *U.S. Public*, pg. 400
HALDANE FISHER LTD.; *Int'l*, pg. 3227
HALDANE MCCALL PLC; *Int'l*, pg. 3227
HALDEMAN LINCOLN MERCURY, INC.; *U.S. Private*, pg. 1842
HALDER BETEILIGUNGSBERATUNG GMBH; *Int'l*, pg. 3227
HALDER SCHNEIDTECHNIK GMBH—See Erwin Halder KG; *Int'l*, pg. 2500
HALDER VENTURES LIMITED; *Int'l*, pg. 3227
HALDEX AB; *Int'l*, pg. 3228
HALDEX AIR MANAGEMENT—See Haldex AB; *Int'l*, pg. 3228
HALDEX ANAND INDIA LTD.—See Haldex AB; *Int'l*, pg. 3228
HALDEX BRAKE PRODUCTS AB—See Haldex AB; *Int'l*, pg. 3228
HALDEX BRAKE PRODUCTS CORPORATION - LITTLE ROCK PLANT—See Haldex AB; *Int'l*, pg. 3228
HALDEX BRAKE PRODUCTS CORPORATION—See Haldex AB; *Int'l*, pg. 3228
HALDEX BRAKE PRODUCTS GMBH—See Haldex AB; *Int'l*, pg. 3228
HALDEX BRAKE PRODUCTS PTY. LTD.—See Haldex AB; *Int'l*, pg. 3228
HALDEX CONCENTRIC PLC.—See Haldex AB; *Int'l*, pg. 3228
HALDEX DO BRASIL IND. E COMERCIO LTDA.—See Haldex AB; *Int'l*, pg. 3228
HALDEX DO BRASIL INDUSTRIA E COMERCIO LTDA.—See Haldex AB; *Int'l*, pg. 3228
HALDEX ESPANA S.A.—See Haldex AB; *Int'l*, pg. 3228
HALDEX EUROPE SAS—See Haldex AB; *Int'l*, pg. 3228
HALDEX GMBH—See Haldex AB; *Int'l*, pg. 3228
HALDEX HUNGARY KFT—See Haldex AB; *Int'l*, pg. 3228
HALDEX INDIA LIMITED—See Haldex AB; *Int'l*, pg. 3228
HALDEX INTERNATIONAL TRADING (SHANGHAI) CO., LTD.—See Haldex AB; *Int'l*, pg. 3228
HALDEX INT TRADING CO LTD—See Haldex AB; *Int'l*, pg. 3228
HALDEX ITALIA SRL.—See Haldex AB; *Int'l*, pg. 3228
HALDEX KOREA LTD.—See Haldex AB; *Int'l*, pg. 3228
HALDEX LIMITED—See Haldex AB; *Int'l*, pg. 3228
HALDEX LIMITED—See Haldex AB; *Int'l*, pg. 3228
HALDEX NV—See Haldex AB; *Int'l*, pg. 3228
HALDEX PRODUCTS DE MEXICO S.A. DE C.V.—See Haldex AB; *Int'l*, pg. 3228
HALDEX RUSSIA OOO—See Haldex AB; *Int'l*, pg. 3228
HALDEX SP. Z.O.O.—See Haldex AB; *Int'l*, pg. 3228
HALDEX VEHICLE PRODUCTS (SUZHOU) CO. LTD.—See Haldex AB; *Int'l*, pg. 3228
HALDEX WIEN GES.M.B.H.—See Haldex AB; *Int'l*, pg. 3228
HALDIA PETROCHEMICALS LIMITED—See The Chatterjee Group; *U.S. Private*, pg. 4007
HALDIA WATER SERVICES PVT. LTD.—See Shristi Infrastructure Development Corporation Ltd.; *Int'l*, pg. 6867
HALDIMAND MOTORS LTD.—See AutoCanada Inc.; *Int'l*, pg. 726
HALDOR TOPSOE AMERICA LATINA S.A.—See Topsoe A/S; *Int'l*, pg. 7821
HALDOR TOPSOE A/S—See Topsoe A/S; *Int'l*, pg. 7821
HALDOR TOPSOE CANADA LIMITED—See Topsoe A/S; *Int'l*, pg. 7821
HALDOR TOPSOE, INC.—See Topsoe A/S; *Int'l*, pg. 7821
HALDOR TOPSOE, INC.—See Topsoe A/S; *Int'l*, pg. 7821
HALDOR TOPSOE INDIA PRIVATE LIMITED—See Topsoe A/S; *Int'l*, pg. 7821
HALDOR TOPSOE INTERNATIONAL A/S—See Topsoe A/S; *Int'l*, pg. 7821
HALDOR TOPSOE INTERNATIONAL A/S—See Topsoe A/S; *Int'l*, pg. 7821
HALDOR TOPSOE INTERNATIONAL A/S—See Topsoe A/S; *Int'l*, pg. 7821
HALDOR TOPSOE SA (PTY) LTD.—See Topsoe A/S; *Int'l*, pg. 7821
HALDOR TOPSOE SDN. BHD.—See Topsoe A/S; *Int'l*, pg. 7821
HALDYN GLASS LTD.; *Int'l*, pg. 3228
HALE & ASSOCIATES, INC.—See PCF Insurance Services of The West, LLC; *U.S. Private*, pg. 3120
HALE BROTHERS SUMMIT, LLC—See Performance Food Group Company; *U.S. Public*, pg. 1674
HALE CAPITAL PARTNERS, L.P.; *U.S. Private*, pg. 1842
HALE ENERGY LIMITED—See Thor Energy PLC; *Int'l*, pg. 7717
THE HALE HAND CENTER, LIMITED PARTNERSHIP—See U.S. Physical Therapy, Inc.; *U.S. Public*, pg. 2216
HALE KAUAI, LTD.; *U.S. Private*, pg. 1842
HALEKULANI CORPORATION—See Mitsui Fudosan Co., Ltd.; *Int'l*, pg. 4986
HALE MAKUA; *U.S. Private*, pg. 1842
HALEON ITALY S.R.L.—See Haleon Plc; *Int'l*, pg. 3228
HALEON NETHERLANDS B.V.—See Haleon Plc; *Int'l*, pg. 3228
HALEON NEW ZEALAND ULC—See Haleon Plc; *Int'l*, pg. 3228
HALEON PAKISTAN LIMITED—See Haleon Plc; *Int'l*, pg. 3228
HALEON PLC; *Int'l*, pg. 3228
HALE PRODUCTS INC.—See IDEX Corp; *U.S. Public*, pg. 1090
HALES AUSTRALIA PTY. LTD.—See Punch Industry Co., Ltd.; *Int'l*, pg. 6118
HALE TRAILER BRAKE & WHEEL; *U.S. Private*, pg. 1842
HALEWOOD INTERNATIONAL LTD.; *Int'l*, pg. 3228
HALEX BIOTECHNOLOGIES SDN. BHD.—See Hextar Global Berhad; *Int'l*, pg. 3373
HALEX CORPORATION—See Standard Industries Holdings Inc.; *U.S. Private*, pg. 3779
HALEX INDUSTRIES (M) SDN. BHD.—See Hextar Global Berhad; *Int'l*, pg. 3373
HALEX—See Berkshire Hathaway Inc.; *U.S. Public*, pg. 300
HALEX WOOLTON (M) SDN. BHD.—See Hextar Global Berhad; *Int'l*, pg. 3373
HALEY & ALDRICH CONSTRUCTION SERVICES, INC.—See Haley & Aldrich Inc.; *U.S. Private*, pg. 1842
HALEY & ALDRICH INC.; *U.S. Private*, pg. 1842
HALEY CONSTRUCTION INC.; *U.S. Private*, pg. 1842
HALEY-GREER INC.; *U.S. Private*, pg. 1842

HALEY INDUSTRIES LIMITED—See Magellan Aerospace Corporation; *Int'l*, pg. 4637
HALEY MECHANICAL, LLC—See Apex Service Partners LLC; *U.S. Private*, pg. 293
HALEY MIRANDA GROUP; *U.S. Private*, pg. 1842
HALEY OF FARMVILLE, INC.; *U.S. Private*, pg. 1842
HALEY & WARD, INC.—See CES, Inc.; *U.S. Private*, pg. 842
HALFACRE CONSTRUCTION COMPANY; *U.S. Private*, pg. 1842
HALFAKER & ASSOCIATES, LLC—See Science Applications International Corporation; *U.S. Public*, pg. 1848
HALFEN AS—See CRH plc; *Int'l*, pg. 1844
HALFEN GMBH—See CRH plc; *Int'l*, pg. 1844
HALFEN S.R.L.—See CRH plc; *Int'l*, pg. 1844
HALFF ASSOCIATES, INC.; *U.S. Private*, pg. 1842
HALFON CANDY COMPANY, INC.—See Harbor Foods Group Inc.; *U.S. Private*, pg. 1859
HALFORD, NIEMIEC & FREEMAN, L.L.P.; *U.S. Private*, pg. 1842
HALFORDS BELGIUM NV—See Macintosh Retail Group NV; *Int'l*, pg. 4622
HALFORDS FINANCE LIMITED—See Halfords Group plc; *Int'l*, pg. 3229
HALFORDS GROUP PLC; *Int'l*, pg. 3229
HALFORDS NEDERLAND BV; *Int'l*, pg. 3229
HALF PRICE BOOKS RECORDS MAGAZINES INC.; *U.S. Private*, pg. 1842
HALF-TIDE MARINE PTY LTD—See Peabody Energy Corporation; *U.S. Public*, pg. 1659
HALFWAY MOTORS 1989 LTD; *Int'l*, pg. 3229
HAL HAYS CONSTRUCTION, INC.; *U.S. Private*, pg. 1841
HAL HOLDING N.V.—See HAL Trust N.V.; *Int'l*, pg. 3223
HALI BUROMOBEL GMBH; *Int'l*, pg. 3229
HALIEUTIS FISH & CO.S.A.S—See Nissui Corporation; *Int'l*, pg. 5378
HALIFAX CHRYSLER DODGE; *Int'l*, pg. 3229
HALIFAX ELECTRIC MEMBERSHIP CORP.; *U.S. Private*, pg. 1842
THE HALIFAX EVENING COURIER LTD—See JPIMedia Holdings Limited; *Int'l*, pg. 4007
THE HALIFAX GROUP LLC; *U.S. Private*, pg. 4041
HALIFAX MEDIA HOLDINGS, LLC—See Gannett Co., Inc.; *U.S. Public*, pg. 905
HALIFAX MEDICAL CENTER; *U.S. Private*, pg. 1843
HALIFAX PLC—See Lloyds Banking Group plc; *Int'l*, pg. 4537
HALIFAX PORT AUTHORITY; *Int'l*, pg. 3229
HALIFAX RACK AND SCREW NORTH AMERICA—See Halifax Rack & Screw Cutting Co. Ltd.; *Int'l*, pg. 3229
HALIFAX RACK & SCREW CUTTING CO. LTD.; *Int'l*, pg. 3229
HAL INVESTMENTS BV—See HAL Trust N.V.; *Int'l*, pg. 3223
HALIS LLC—See Peak Rock Capital LLC; *U.S. Private*, pg. 3124
HALITRON, INC.; *U.S. Public*, pg. 979
HALJOHN INC.; *U.S. Private*, pg. 1843
HALJOHN-SAN ANTONIO, INC.—See Haljohn Inc.; *U.S. Private*, pg. 1843
HAL JONES CONTRACTORS INC.; *U.S. Private*, pg. 1841
HALKBANK AD—See Turkiye Halk Bankasi A.S.; *Int'l*, pg. 7976
HALKEY-ROBERTS CORPORATION—See Nordson Corporation; *U.S. Public*, pg. 1532
HALK FAKTORING A.S.—See Turkiye Halk Bankasi A.S.; *Int'l*, pg. 7976
HALK FINANSAL KIRALAMA A.S.; *Int'l*, pg. 3229
HALK GAYRIMENKUL YATIRIM ORTAKLIGI A.S.; *Int'l*, pg. 3229
HALK OSIGURUVANJE A.D.—See Turkiye Halk Bankasi A.S.; *Int'l*, pg. 7976
HALK SIGORTA A.S.—See Turkiye Varlik Fonu Yonetimi AS; *Int'l*, pg. 7978
HALK VARLIK KIRALAMA AS; *Int'l*, pg. 3229
HALK YATIRIM MENKUL DEGERLER A.S.—See Turkiye Halk Bankasi A.S.; *Int'l*, pg. 7976
HALLADAY MOTORS INC.; *U.S. Private*, pg. 1843
HALLADOR ENERGY COMPANY; *U.S. Public*, pg. 980
HALLA GROUP; *Int'l*, pg. 3229
HALLA MEISTER LTD.—See Halla Group; *Int'l*, pg. 3229
HALLA MEISTER SHANGHAI TRADING CO., LTD.—See Halla Group; *Int'l*, pg. 3229
HALLA MEISTER SUZHOU LOGISTICS CO., LTD—See Halla Group; *Int'l*, pg. 3229
HALLAM LAND MANAGEMENT LIMITED—See Henry Boot PLC; *Int'l*, pg. 3355
HALLAMORE CORPORATION; *U.S. Private*, pg. 1844
HALL AND PARTNERS—See Omnicom Group Inc.; *U.S. Public*, pg. 1585
HALLA SHOPPING FASTIGHETS AB—See Stenhus Fastigheter I Norden AB; *Int'l*, pg. 7207
HALLA STACKPOLE CORPORATION—See Johnson Electric Holdings Limited; *Int'l*, pg. 3990
HALL AUTOMOTIVE; *U.S. Private*, pg. 1843
HALL AUTO WORLD INC.; *U.S. Private*, pg. 1843
HALLA VISTEON CLIMATE CONTROL (NANCHANG) CO., LTD.—See Hahn & Company; *Int'l*, pg. 3208

COMPANY NAME INDEX

HALL CAPITAL, LLC; *U.S. Private*, pg. 1843
HALL CAPITAL PARTNERS LLC—See Lovell Minnick Partners LLC; *U.S. Private*, pg. 2503
HALL CAPITAL PARTNERS, LP—See Hall Capital, LLC; *U.S. Private*, pg. 1843
THE HALL CHINA COMPANY; *U.S. Private*, pg. 4042
HALL CONSTRUCTION SERVICES LTD; *Int'l*, pg. 3229
HALL CONTRACTING CORP.; *U.S. Private*, pg. 1843
HALL CONTRACTING OF KENTUCKY; *U.S. Private*, pg. 1843
HALL COUNTY TRANSFER STATION, LLC—See Waste Management, Inc.; *U.S. Public*, pg. 1753
HALLECK-WILLARD, INC.—See Inflexion Private Equity Partners LLP; *Int'l*, pg. 3689
HALLE ENTERPRISES INC.; *U.S. Private*, pg. 1844
THE HALLEN CONSTRUCTION CO. INC.—See Quanta Services, Inc.; *U.S. Public*, pg. 1753
HALLENSTEIN BROS LIMITED—See Hallenstein Glasson Holdings Limited; *Int'l*, pg. 3230
HALLENSTEIN GLASSON HOLDINGS LIMITED; *Int'l*, pg. 3230
HALL ENTERPRISES, INC.—See Providence Equity Partners L.L.C.; *U.S. Private*, pg. 3292
HAL LEONARD CORPORATION—See Francisco Partners Management, LP; *U.S. Private*, pg. 1590
HALLER BUSBETRIEB GMBH—See Deutsche Bahn AG; *Int'l*, pg. 2051
HALLESCHE MITTELDEUTSCHE BAU - A.G.—See Tekfen Holding A.S.; *Int'l*, pg. 7526
HALLETT ROOFING SERVICES PTY LTD—See Brickworks Limited; *Int'l*, pg. 1152
HALLEY ELEVATOR COMPANY, INC.—See 3Phase Elevator Corp; *U.S. Private*, pg. 14
HALLEY HOMES PTY LTD.—See Onterran Limited; *Int'l*, pg. 5591
HALL FINANCIAL GROUP, LTD.; *U.S. Private*, pg. 1843
HALL FUNERAL SERVICES PTY LTD—See Propel Funeral Partners Limited; *Int'l*, pg. 5997
HALL & HOUSE LUMBER CO. INC.; *U.S. Private*, pg. 1843
THE HALLIARD PROPERTY CO. LIMITED—See Centremanor Ltd.; *Int'l*, pg. 1412
HALLIBURTON ARGENTINA S.A.—See Halliburton Company; *U.S. Public*, pg. 980
HALLIBURTON AS—See Halliburton Company; *U.S. Public*, pg. 980
HALLIBURTON CANADA CORP.—See Halliburton Company; *U.S. Public*, pg. 980
HALLIBURTON COMPANY GERMANY GMBH—See Halliburton Company; *U.S. Public*, pg. 980
HALLIBURTON COMPANY; *U.S. Public*, pg. 980
HALLIBURTON DE MEXICO S.A. DE C.V.—See Halliburton Company; *U.S. Public*, pg. 980
HALLIBURTON DRILLING & EVALUATION—See Halliburton Company; *U.S. Public*, pg. 980
HALLIBURTON ENERGY SERVICES, INC.—See Halliburton Company; *U.S. Public*, pg. 980
HALLIBURTON ENERGY SERVICES, INC.—See Halliburton Company; *U.S. Public*, pg. 980
HALLIBURTON ENERGY SERVICES LIMITED—See Halliburton Company; *U.S. Public*, pg. 980
HALLIBURTON GLOBAL AFFILIATES HOLDINGS B.V.—See Halliburton Company; *U.S. Public*, pg. 980
HALLIBURTON GROUP CANADA INC.—See Halliburton Company; *U.S. Public*, pg. 980
HALLIBURTON INTERNATIONAL, INC.—See Halliburton Company; *U.S. Public*, pg. 980
HALLIBURTON LIMITED—See Halliburton Company; *U.S. Public*, pg. 980
HALLIBURTON MANUFACTURING & SERVICES LIMITED—See Halliburton Company; *U.S. Public*, pg. 980
HALLIBURTON NETHERLANDS HOLDINGS B.V.—See Halliburton Company; *U.S. Public*, pg. 981
HALLIBURTON NIGERIA LIMITED—See Halliburton Company; *U.S. Public*, pg. 980
HALLIBURTON SECURITY DBS—See Halliburton Company; *U.S. Public*, pg. 980
HALLIBURTON TRINIDAD LIMITED—See Halliburton Company; *U.S. Public*, pg. 980
HALLIBURTON/WELLDYNAMICS—See Halliburton Company; *U.S. Public*, pg. 981
HALLIBURTON/WELLDYNAMICS—See Shell plc; *Int'l*, pg. 6796
HALLIBURTON WORLDWIDE GMBH—See Halliburton Company; *U.S. Public*, pg. 981
HALLIDIE MACHINE TOOL SALES, INC.; *U.S. Private*, pg. 1844
HALLIM MACHINERY CO., LTD.—See Daifuku Co., Ltd.; *Int'l*, pg. 1926
HALL IMPORTS—See Hall Automotive; *U.S. Private*, pg. 1843
HALLINGKRAFT AS—See Hafslund ASA; *Int'l*, pg. 3206
HALLINK MOULDS, INC.—See The Eastern Company; *U.S. Public*, pg. 2069
HALLIN MARINE PTE. LTD.—See Superior Energy Services, Inc.; *U.S. Private*, pg. 3877
HALLIN MARINE SINGAPORE PTE LTD.—See Superior Energy Services, Inc.; *U.S. Private*, pg. 3877

HALL-IRWIN CORPORATION; *U.S. Private*, pg. 1843
HALLITE (FRANCE) LIMITED—See Compagnie Generale des Etablissements Michelin SCA; *Int'l*, pg. 1745
HALLITE ITALIA SRL—See Compagnie Generale des Etablissements Michelin SCA; *Int'l*, pg. 1745
HALLITE SEALING SOLUTIONS INDIA PRIVATE LIMITED—See Compagnie Generale des Etablissements Michelin SCA; *Int'l*, pg. 1742
HALLITE SEALS AMERICAS, LLC—See Compagnie Generale des Etablissements Michelin SCA; *Int'l*, pg. 1742
HALLITE SEALS AUSTRALIA PTY LIMITED—See Compagnie Generale des Etablissements Michelin SCA; *Int'l*, pg. 1742
HALLITE SEALS (CANADA) LIMITED—See Compagnie Generale des Etablissements Michelin SCA; *Int'l*, pg. 1745
HALLITE SEALS INTERNATIONAL LTD—See Compagnie Generale des Etablissements Michelin SCA; *Int'l*, pg. 1745
HALLITE SEALS INTERNATIONAL LTD—See Compagnie Generale des Etablissements Michelin SCA; *Int'l*, pg. 1745
HALLITE SHANGHAI COMPANY LIMITED—See Compagnie Generale des Etablissements Michelin SCA; *Int'l*, pg. 1742
HALL & KAY FIRE ENGINEERING—See Carrier Global Corporation; *U.S. Public*, pg. 441
HALL LONGMORE (PROPRIETARY) LIMITED; *Int'l*, pg. 3229
HALL MANAGEMENT COMPANY; *U.S. Private*, pg. 1843
HALLMAN LINDSAY PAINTS INC.; *U.S. Private*, pg. 1844
HALLMAN & LORBER ASSOCIATES, INC.; *U.S. Private*, pg. 1844
HALLMAN WOOD PRODUCTS INC.; *U.S. Private*, pg. 1844
HALLMARK AVIATION SERVICES LP; *U.S. Private*, pg. 1844
HALLMARK BUILDING SUPPLIES, INC.; *U.S. Private*, pg. 1844
HALLMARK BUSINESS CONNECTIONS, INC.—See Interactive Communications Inc; *U.S. Private*, pg. 2108
HALLMARK CANADA, INC.—See Hallmark Cards, Inc.; *U.S. Private*, pg. 1844
HALLMARK CARDS AUSTRALIA LTD.—See Hallmark Cards, Inc.; *U.S. Private*, pg. 1844
HALLMARK CARDS BELGIUM NV—See Hallmark Cards, Inc.; *U.S. Private*, pg. 1844
HALLMARK CARDS, INC. - CENTER FIXTURE OPERATIONS—See Hallmark Cards, Inc.; *U.S. Private*, pg. 1844
HALLMARK CARDS, INC. - ENFIELD—See Hallmark Cards, Inc.; *U.S. Private*, pg. 1844
HALLMARK CARDS, INC. - LAWRENCE PRODUCTION CENTER—See Hallmark Cards, Inc.; *U.S. Private*, pg. 1844
HALLMARK CARDS, INC. - LEAVENWORTH PRODUCTION CENTER—See Hallmark Cards, Inc.; *U.S. Private*, pg. 1844
HALLMARK CARDS, INC. - LIBERTY DISTRIBUTION CENTER—See Hallmark Cards, Inc.; *U.S. Private*, pg. 1844
HALLMARK CARDS, INC.; *U.S. Private*, pg. 1844
HALLMARK CARDS NEDERLAND, B.V.—See Hallmark Cards, Inc.; *U.S. Private*, pg. 1844
HALLMARK CARDS NEW ZEALAND LTD.—See Hallmark Cards, Inc.; *U.S. Private*, pg. 1844
HALLMARK CLAIMS SERVICE INC.—See Hallmark Financial Services, Inc.; *U.S. Public*, pg. 981
HALLMARK COMPANY LIMITED—See TELECARD LIMITED; *Int'l*, pg. 7529
HALLMARK DATA SYSTEMS, INC.—See Omeda Communications, Inc.; *U.S. Private*, pg. 3015
HALLMARK DEVELOPMENT OF FLORIDA, INC.; *U.S. Private*, pg. 1845
HALLMARK ESCROW CO., INC.—See First Team Real Estate-Orange County Inc.; *U.S. Private*, pg. 1529
HALLMARK FINANCIAL SERVICES, INC.; *U.S. Public*, pg. 981
HALL-MARK FIRE APPARATUS, INC.—See AIP, LLC; *U.S. Private*, pg. 135
HALL-MARK FIRE APPARATUS - TEXAS, LLC—See AIP, LLC; *U.S. Private*, pg. 135
HALLMARK FORD SALES LIMITED; *Int'l*, pg. 3230
HALLMARK INSURANCE COMPANY—See Hallmark Financial Services, Inc.; *U.S. Public*, pg. 981
HALLMARK INTERNATIONAL—See Hallmark Cards, Inc.; *U.S. Private*, pg. 1844
HALLMARK JEEP INC.; *U.S. Private*, pg. 1845
HALLMARK PARTNERS INC.; *U.S. Private*, pg. 1845
HALLMARK POULTRY PROCESSORS LTD.; *Int'l*, pg. 3230
HALLMARK PUERTO RICO INC.—See Hallmark Cards, Inc.; *U.S. Private*, pg. 1844
HALLMARK SPECIALTY INSURANCE COMPANY—See Hallmark Financial Services, Inc.; *U.S. Public*, pg. 981
HALLMARK SYSTEMS INC.; *U.S. Private*, pg. 1845
HALLMARK VENTURE GROUP, INC.; *U.S. Public*, pg. 981

HALO TECHNOLOGY HOLDINGS, INC.

HALLMARK VOLKSWAGEN MITSUBISHI; *U.S. Private*, pg. 1845
HALLMARK YOUTHCARE-RICHMOND, LLC—See Petra Capital Partners, LLC; *U.S. Private*, pg. 3161
HALL NISSAN VIRGINIA BEACH; *U.S. Private*, pg. 1843
HALLOCK AGENCY; *U.S. Private*, pg. 1845
HALL OF FAME BEVERAGES, INC.; *U.S. Public*, pg. 979
HALL OF FAME RESORT & ENTERTAINMENT COMPANY; *U.S. Public*, pg. 980
HALLOREN SCHOKOLADENFABRIK AG; *Int'l*, pg. 3230
HALLOSONNE GMBH—See Verbund AG; *Int'l*, pg. 8165
HALLOWELL MANUFACTURING LLC—See Orica Limited; *Int'l*, pg. 5619
HALLS DRIVE INS INC.; *U.S. Private*, pg. 1845
HALL SHEET METAL WORKS, INC.; *U.S. Private*, pg. 1843
HALL SIGNS, INC.; *U.S. Private*, pg. 1843
HALLS MERCHANDISING INC.—See Hallmark Cards, Inc.; *U.S. Private*, pg. 1844
THE HALLSTAR COMPANY; *U.S. Private*, pg. 4042
HALLSTROM CONSTRUCTION INC.; *U.S. Private*, pg. 1845
HALL STRUCTURED FINANCE—See Hall Financial Group, Ltd.; *U.S. Private*, pg. 1843
HALLS WAREHOUSE CORP.; *U.S. Private*, pg. 1845
HALL TECHNOLOGIES INC.; *U.S. Private*, pg. 1843
HALLUM INC.; *U.S. Private*, pg. 1845
HALLVARSSON & HALVARSSON AB; *Int'l*, pg. 3230
HALL WINES OF NAPA, L.P.—See Hall Financial Group, Ltd.; *U.S. Private*, pg. 1843
HALLWOOD GROUP, LLC; *U.S. Private*, pg. 1845
HALLYEO ENERGY RESOURCE—See Dongkuk S&C Co., Ltd.; *Int'l*, pg. 2169
HALMA AUSTRALASIA PTY LTD—See Halma plc; *Int'l*, pg. 3231
HALMA HOLDINGS INC.—See Halma plc; *Int'l*, pg. 3231
HALMA INDIA PRIVATE LTD.—See Halma plc; *Int'l*, pg. 3232
HALMAN-ALDUBI INVESTMENT HOUSE LTD.; *Int'l*, pg. 3233
HAL MANN PROPERTIES LTD.—See Hal Mann Vella Group PLC; *Int'l*, pg. 3223
HAL MANN VELLA GROUP PLC; *Int'l*, pg. 3222
HALMA PLC; *Int'l*, pg. 3230
HALMA TRADING AND SERVICES INDIA PVT LTD—See Halma plc; *Int'l*, pg. 3232
HAL MCBRIDE CAR SALES INCORPORATED; *U.S. Private*, pg. 1841
HALMEK HOLDINGS CO., LTD.; *Int'l*, pg. 3233
HALMONT PROPERTIES CORPORATION; *Int'l*, pg. 3233
HALMOS CAPITAL PARTNERS; *U.S. Private*, pg. 1845
HALO BRANDED SOLUTIONS, INC.—See TPG Capital, L.P.; *U.S. Public*, pg. 2176
HALOCARBON LABORATORIES—See Halocarbon Products Corporation; *U.S. Private*, pg. 1846
HALOCARBON PRODUCTS CORPORATION; *U.S. Private*, pg. 1846
HALO COLLECTIVE INC.; *Int'l*, pg. 3233
HALO COMPANIES, INC.; *U.S. Public*, pg. 981
HALO ELECTRONICS INC.; *U.S. Private*, pg. 1845
HAL OFFSHORE LIMITED; *Int'l*, pg. 3223
HALO FOOD CO. LIMITED; *Int'l*, pg. 3233
HALO FOODS LTD.—See Peak Rock Capital LLC; *U.S. Private*, pg. 3124
HALOGEN RESPONSE MEDIA—See Publicis Groupe S.A.; *Int'l*, pg. 6111
HA LOGISTICS, INC.; *U.S. Private*, pg. 1837
HALO GROUP, INC.—See Halo Companies, Inc.; *U.S. Public*, pg. 981
THE HALO GROUP, LLC—See Global Employment Holdings, Inc.; *U.S. Private*, pg. 1713
HALON BANKING SYSTEMS—See APi Group Corporation; *Int'l*, pg. 514
HALONG CANNED FOOD JOINT STOCK CORPORATION; *Int'l*, pg. 3233
HALO PHARMACEUTICAL, INC.—See Permira Advisers LLP; *Int'l*, pg. 5803
HALO PHOTONICS LTD.—See Lumibird Group; *Int'l*, pg. 4578
HALOPOLYMER KIROVO-CHEPETSK LLC; *Int'l*, pg. 3233
HALOPOLYMER PERM, OJSC; *Int'l*, pg. 3233
HALO PORTFOLIO ADVISORS, LLC—See Halo Companies, Inc.; *U.S. Public*, pg. 981
HALO, PURELY FOR PETS, INC.—See Better Choice Company, Inc.; *U.S. Public*, pg. 326
HALOS CORPORATION—See Hanwa Co., Ltd.; *Int'l*, pg. 3262
HALOSOURCE CORP.; *U.S. Private*, pg. 1846
HALOSOURCE, INC.—See Halosource Corp.; *U.S. Private*, pg. 1846
HALOSOURCE TECHNOLOGIES PVT. LTD.—See Halosource Corp.; *U.S. Private*, pg. 1846
HALOSOURCE WATER PURIFICATION TECHNOLOGY (SHANGHAI) CO. LTD.—See Halosource Corp.; *U.S. Private*, pg. 1846
HALO TECHNOLOGIES HOLDINGS LTD.; *Int'l*, pg. 3233
HALO TECHNOLOGY HOLDINGS, INC.; *U.S. Private*, pg. 1845

HALO TECHNOLOGY HOLDINGS, INC. CORPORATE AFFILIATIONS

HALOTRON, INC.—See H.I.G. Capital, LLC; *U.S. Private*, pg. 1829
HALOWS CO., LTD; *Int'l*, pg. 3233
HALOX—See Israel Corporation Ltd.; *Int'l*, pg. 3823
HALOX TECHNOLOGIES, INC.—See IDEX Corp; *U.S. Public*, pg. 1090
HALOZYME THERAPEUTICS, INC.; *U.S. Public*, pg. 981
HALPERN ENTERPRISES, INC.; *U.S. Private*, pg. 1846
HALPERN IMPORT COMPANY INC.; *U.S. Private*, pg. 1846
HALPERN LTD.—See CHI & Partners Limited; *Int'l*, pg. 1474
HALPERN'S STEAK & SEAFOOD CO.; *U.S. Private*, pg. 1846
HALPRIN, INCORPORATED—See AdaptHealth Corp.; *U.S. Public*, pg. 39
HALQUIST STONE COMPANY, INC.; *U.S. Private*, pg. 1846
HAL REAL ESTATE INC.—See HAL Trust N.V.; *Int'l*, pg. 3227
HALREC INC.; *U.S. Private*, pg. 1846
HALRON LUBRICANTS INC.; *U.S. Private*, pg. 1846
HALS-DEVELOPMENT JSC; *Int'l*, pg. 3233
HALSE MARTIN CONSTRUCTION CO LTD; *Int'l*, pg. 3233
HALSEY ASSOCIATES, INC.—See Washington Trust Bancorp, Inc.; *U.S. Public*, pg. 2329
HALSEY TAYLOR—See Zurn Elkay Water Solutions Corporation; *U.S. Public*, pg. 7346
HALSINGEBYGG I HUDIKSVALL AB—See Peab AB; *Int'l*, pg. 5771
HALSKI SYSTEMS, LLC—See The Riverside Company; *U.S. Private*, pg. 4109
HAL SMITH RESTAURANT GROUP, INC.; *U.S. Private*, pg. 1841
HALSNOY DOKK AS; *Int'l*, pg. 3233
HALSSEN & LYON GMBH; *Int'l*, pg. 3233
HALSTAD ELEVATOR COMPANY; *U.S. Private*, pg. 1846
HALSTEAD BROOKLYN, LLC—See Halstead Property, LLC.; *U.S. Private*, pg. 1846
HALSTEAD EAST HAMPTON, LLC—See Halstead Property, LLC.; *U.S. Private*, pg. 1846
HALSTEAD FLOORING CONCEPTS PTY LIMITED—See James Halstead PLC; *Int'l*, pg. 3877
HALSTEAD INSURANCE AGENCY, INC.—See GTCR LLC; *U.S. Private*, pg. 1803
HALSTEAD PROPERTY CONNECTICUT, LLC—See Halstead Property, LLC.; *U.S. Private*, pg. 1846
HALSTEAD PROPERTY HUDSON VALLEY, LLC—See Halstead Property, LLC.; *U.S. Private*, pg. 1846
HALSTEAD PROPERTY, LLC.; *U.S. Private*, pg. 1846
HALSTEAD PROPERTY NEW JERSEY, LLC—See Halstead Property, LLC.; *U.S. Private*, pg. 1846
HALSTEAD PROPERTY RIVERDALE, LLC—See Halstead Property, LLC.; *U.S. Private*, pg. 1846
HALT BUZAS & POWELL LTD—See Sikich LLP; *U.S. Private*, pg. 3651
HALTEC HALE SP. Z O.O.—See HALTEC Hallensysteme GmbH; *Int'l*, pg. 3233
HALTEC HALLENSYSTEME AG—See HALTEC Hallensysteme GmbH; *Int'l*, pg. 3233
HALTEC HALLENSYSTEME GMBH; *Int'l*, pg. 3233
HALTEC HALLENSYSTEME GMBH—See HALTEC Hallensysteme GmbH; *Int'l*, pg. 3234
HALTEC NEDERLAND B.V.—See HALTEC Hallensysteme GmbH; *Int'l*, pg. 3234
HALTEC SAS—See HALTEC Hallensysteme GmbH; *Int'l*, pg. 3234
HALTERMANN CARLESS DEUTSCHLAND GMBH—See H.I.G. Capital, LLC; *U.S. Private*, pg. 1828
HALTERM LIMITED—See Temasek Holdings (Private) Limited; *Int'l*, pg. 7549
HALTOM'S JEWELERS INC.; *U.S. Private*, pg. 1846
HALTON AS—See Oy Halton Group Ltd.; *Int'l*, pg. 5677
HALTON COMPANY—See Oy Halton Group Ltd.; *Int'l*, pg. 5677
HALTON GLOBAL SERVICES, INC.—See Oy Halton Group Ltd.; *Int'l*, pg. 5677
HALTON GROUP ASIA SDN BHD—See Oy Halton Group Ltd.; *Int'l*, pg. 5677
HALTON HILLS HYDRO INC.; *Int'l*, pg. 3234
HALTON KLIMATECHNIK GMBH—See Oy Halton Group Ltd.; *Int'l*, pg. 5677
HALTON OY—See Oy Halton Group Ltd.; *Int'l*, pg. 5677
HALTON SAS—See Oy Halton Group Ltd.; *Int'l*, pg. 5677
HALTON VENT MASTER LIMITED—See Oy Halton Group Ltd.; *Int'l*, pg. 5677
HAL TRUST N.V.; *Int'l*, pg. 3223
HALUCO B.V.—See Dole plc; *Int'l*, pg. 2158
HALUL OFFSHORE SERVICES COMPANY W.L.L.—See Qatar Navigation (Milaha) Q.P.S.C.; *Int'l*, pg. 6135
HALUS POWER SYSTEMS; *U.S. Private*, pg. 1846
HALVIK CORP.; *U.S. Private*, pg. 1846
HALVORSEN HOLDINGS LLC; *U.S. Private*, pg. 1847
HALVORSON DESIGN PARTNERSHIP—See Tighe & Bond, Inc.; *U.S. Private*, pg. 4170
HALVORSON & PARTNERS, INC.—See WSP Global, Inc.; *Int'l*, pg. 8497
HALWANI BROS; *Int'l*, pg. 3234

HALYARD BELGIUM BVBA—See Avanos Medical, Inc.; *U.S. Public*, pg. 241
HALYARD CAPITAL MANAGEMENT, LLC; *U.S. Private*, pg. 1847
HALYARD CHINA CO., LTD.—See Avanos Medical, Inc.; *U.S. Public*, pg. 241
HALYARD DEUTSCHLAND GMBH—See Avanos Medical, Inc.; *U.S. Public*, pg. 241
HALYARD HEALTH INDIA PRIVATE LIMITED—See Avanos Medical, Inc.; *U.S. Public*, pg. 241
HALYARD NEDERLAND B.V.—See Avanos Medical, Inc.; *U.S. Public*, pg. 241
HALYARD SINGAPORE PTE. LTD.—See Avanos Medical, Inc.; *U.S. Public*, pg. 241
HALYK BANK OF KAZAKHSTAN JSC; *Int'l*, pg. 3234
HALYK FINANCE JSC—See Halyk Bank of Kazakhstan JSC; *Int'l*, pg. 3234
HALYPS BUILDING MATERIALS S.A.—See Heidelberg Materials AG; *Int'l*, pg. 3316
HAMA B.V.—See Hama GmbH & Co KG; *Int'l*, pg. 3234
HAMADAN GLASS COMPANY LLP; *Int'l*, pg. 3234
HAMADEN P.S CO., LTD.—See Denso Corporation; *Int'l*, pg. 2032
HAMA DISTRIBUTION ROMANIA SRL—See Hama GmbH & Co KG; *Int'l*, pg. 3234
HAMAD MEDICAL CORPORATION—See Dar Al Dawa Development & Investment Co.; *Int'l*, pg. 1971
HAMA EURL—See Hama GmbH & Co KG; *Int'l*, pg. 3234
HAMA FINANCIAL INSTITUTION LIMITED; *Int'l*, pg. 3234
HAMAGA AS; *Int'l*, pg. 3234
HAMAGIN FINANCE CO., LTD.—See Concordia Financial Group, Ltd.; *Int'l*, pg. 1765
HAMAGIN RESEARCH INSTITUTE LTD—See Concordia Financial Group, Ltd.; *Int'l*, pg. 1765
HAMAGIN TOKAI TOKYO SECURITIES CO., LTD.—See Concordia Financial Group, Ltd.; *Int'l*, pg. 1765
HAMA GMBH & CO KG; *Int'l*, pg. 3234
HAMAGOMU AICOM INC.—See The Yokohama Rubber Co., Ltd.; *Int'l*, pg. 7702
HAMAI CO., LTD. - ASHIKAGA FACTORY—See Hamai Co., Ltd.; *Int'l*, pg. 3235
HAMAI CO., LTD.; *Int'l*, pg. 3235
HAMAI FUCHU FACTORY LTD.—See HAMAI INDUSTRIES LIMITED; *Int'l*, pg. 3235
HAMAI INDUSTRIES LIMITED; *Int'l*, pg. 3235
HAMAI OTAKI FACTORY LTD.—See HAMAI INDUSTRIES LIMITED; *Int'l*, pg. 3235
HAMA KFT.—See Hama GmbH & Co KG; *Int'l*, pg. 3234
HAMAK GOLD LIMITED; *Int'l*, pg. 3235
HAMAKYOREX CO., LTD.; *Int'l*, pg. 3235
HA MALAYSIA SDN. BHD—See Durr AG; *Int'l*, pg. 2232
HAMAMA MEIR TRADING (1996) LTD.; *Int'l*, pg. 3235
HAMAMATSU CORPORATION - FACTORY—See Hamamatsu Photonics K.K.; *Int'l*, pg. 3235
HAMAMATSU CORPORATION—See Hamamatsu Photonics K.K.; *Int'l*, pg. 3235
HAMAMATSU ELECTRONIC PRESS CO., LTD.—See Hamamatsu Photonics K.K.; *Int'l*, pg. 3235
HAMAMATSU MANUFACTURING FACILITY—See Honda Motor Co., Ltd.; *Int'l*, pg. 3460
HAMAMATSU NDS CO., LTD.—See COMSYS Holdings Corporation; *Int'l*, pg. 1761
HAMAMATSU PHOTONICS (CHINA) CO., LTD.—See Hamamatsu Photonics K.K.; *Int'l*, pg. 3235
HAMAMATSU PHOTONICS DEUTSCHLAND GMBH—See Hamamatsu Photonics K.K.; *Int'l*, pg. 3235
HAMAMATSU PHOTONICS FRANCE S.A.R.L.—See Hamamatsu Photonics K.K.; *Int'l*, pg. 3235
HAMAMATSU PHOTONICS ITALIA S.R.L.—See Hamamatsu Photonics K.K.; *Int'l*, pg. 3235
HAMAMATSU PHOTONICS K.K. - ELECTRON TUBE DIVISION—See Hamamatsu Photonics K.K.; *Int'l*, pg. 3235
HAMAMATSU PHOTONICS K.K. - SOLID STATE DIVISION—See Hamamatsu Photonics K.K.; *Int'l*, pg. 3235
HAMAMATSU PHOTONICS K.K.; *Int'l*, pg. 3235
HAMAMATSU PHOTONICS K.K. - SYSTEMS DIVISION—See Hamamatsu Photonics K.K.; *Int'l*, pg. 3235
HAMAMATSU PHOTONICS NORDEN AB—See Hamamatsu Photonics K.K.; *Int'l*, pg. 3235
HAMAMATSU PHOTONICS TAIWAN CO., LTD.—See Hamamatsu Photonics K.K.; *Int'l*, pg. 3235
HAMAMATSU PHOTONICS UK LIMITED—See Hamamatsu Photonics K.K.; *Int'l*, pg. 3235
HAMAMATSU PIPE CO., LTD.—See Suzuki Motor Corporation; *Int'l*, pg. 7354
HAMAMATSU PROPANE STAND LTD.—See Sala Corporation; *Int'l*, pg. 6490
HAMAMATSU TERMINAL DEVELOPMENT CO., LTD.—See Central Japan Railway Company; *Int'l*, pg. 1408
HAMAMURA YUATSU CO., LTD.—See NANYO Corporation; *Int'l*, pg. 5146
HAMANAKODENSO CO., LTD.—See Denso Corporation; *Int'l*, pg. 2032
HAMANO LEATHER CRAFTS CO., LTD.—See TRIIS, Inc.; *Int'l*, pg. 7922

HAMA NV—See Hama GmbH & Co KG; *Int'l*, pg. 3234
HAMAOKA SOKEN CO., LTD.—See Soken Chemical & Engineering Co.,Ltd.; *Int'l*, pg. 7066
HAMAOKA TOSHIBA ELECTRONICS CORP.—See Japan Industrial Partners, Inc.; *Int'l*, pg. 3889
H. A. MAPES, INC.—See Nouria Energy Corp.; *U.S. Private*, pg. 2965
HAMA POLSKA SP. Z.O.O.—See Hama GmbH & Co KG; *Int'l*, pg. 3234
HAMAR-QUANDT CO. INC.; *U.S. Private*, pg. 1847
HAMAR STORSENTER AS—See BNP Paribas SA; *Int'l*, pg. 1091
HAMASHIN CO., LTD.—See Japan Airport Terminal Co., Ltd.; *Int'l*, pg. 3885
HAMA SLOVAKIA SPOL.S.R.O.—See Hama GmbH & Co KG; *Int'l*, pg. 3234
HAMASPIK OF ROCKLAND COUNTY, INC.; *U.S. Private*, pg. 1847
HAMA SPOL. S R.O.—See Hama GmbH & Co KG; *Int'l*, pg. 3234
HAMA TECHNICS AG—See Hama GmbH & Co KG; *Int'l*, pg. 3234
HAMA TECHNICS HANDELS GMBH—See Hama GmbH & Co KG; *Int'l*, pg. 3234
HAMA TECHNICS S.L.—See Hama GmbH & Co KG; *Int'l*, pg. 3234
HAMATECH USA, INC.—See SUSS MicroTec SE; *Int'l*, pg. 7346
HAMAT GROUP LTD.; *Int'l*, pg. 3236
HAMATON AUTOMOTIVE TECHNOLOGY CO., LTD.; *Int'l*, pg. 3236
HAMA (UK) LTD.—See Hama GmbH & Co KG; *Int'l*, pg. 3234
HAMAYUU CO., LTD.; *Int'l*, pg. 3236
HAMAZUSHI CO., LTD.—See Zensho Holdings Co., Ltd.; *Int'l*, pg. 8634
HAMBLEDON MINING COMPANY LIMITED—See Altyn-Gold plc; *Int'l*, pg. 400
THE HAMBLETONIAN SOCIETY, INC.; *U.S. Private*, pg. 4042
HAMBLIN WATSA INVESTMENT COUNSEL LTD.—See Fairfax Financial Holdings Limited; *Int'l*, pg. 2607
HAMBORNBERG IMMOBILIEN- UND VERWALTUNGS-GMBH—See Hamborner REIT AG; *Int'l*, pg. 3236
HAMBORNER REIT AG; *Int'l*, pg. 3236
HAMBRO PERKS ACQUISITION COMPANY LIMITED; *Int'l*, pg. 3236
HAMBURG BROTHERS; *U.S. Private*, pg. 1847
HAMBURG COMMERCIAL BANK AG—See Cerberus Capital Management, L.P.; *U.S. Private*, pg. 838
HAMBURG COMMERCIAL BANK AG—See GoldenTree Asset Management LP; *U.S. Private*, pg. 1734
HAMBURG COMMERCIAL BANK AG—See J.C. Flowers & Co. LLC; *U.S. Private*, pg. 2159
HAMBURGER ALUMINIUM-WERK GMBH—See TRIMET Aluminium SE; *Int'l*, pg. 7923
HAMBURGER GESELLSCHAFT FUR FLUGHAFENANLAGEN MBH—See Deutsche Lufthansa AG; *Int'l*, pg. 2070
HAMBURGER HAFEN UND LOGISTIK AG; *Int'l*, pg. 3236
HAMBURGER HOF VERSICHERUNGS-AKTIENGESELLSCHAFT—See E.ON SE; *Int'l*, pg. 2258
HAMBURGER SPARKASSE AG; *Int'l*, pg. 3237
HAMBURGISCHE SEEHANDLUNG GESELLSCHAFT FUR SCHIFFSBETEILIGUNGEN MBH & CO. KG—See M.M. Warburg & Co. KGaA; *Int'l*, pg. 4616
HAMBURG-MANNHEIMER FILIAL AF HAMBURG-MANNHEIMER VERSICHERUNGS-AG TYSK FORSIKRINGSSELSKAB—See Munchener Ruckversicherungs AG; *Int'l*, pg. 5087
HAMBURG-MANNHEIMER RECHTSSCHUTZ SCHADEN-SERVICE GMBH—See Munchener Ruckversicherungs AG; *Int'l*, pg. 5088
HAMBURG-MANNHEIMER RECHTSSCHUTZVERSICHERUNGS-AG—See Munchener Ruckversicherungs AG; *Int'l*, pg. 5087
HAMBURG-MANNHEIMER SACHVERSICHERUNGS-AG—See Munchener Ruckversicherungs AG; *Int'l*, pg. 5087
HAMBURG-MANNHEIMER SKADE FILIAL AF HAMBURG-MANNHEIMER SACHVERSICHERUNGS-AG TYSK FORSIKRINGSSELSKAB—See Munchener Ruckversicherungs AG; *Int'l*, pg. 5087
HAMBURG-MANNHEIMER VERSICHERUNGS-AG—See Munchener Ruckversicherungs AG; *Int'l*, pg. 5087
HAMBURG MARRIOTT HOTELMANAGEMENT GMBH—See Marriott International, Inc.; *U.S. Public*, pg. 1370
HAMBURG SUDAMERIKANISCHE DAMPFSCHIFFFAHRTS-GESELLSCHAFT A/S & CO KG—See A.P. Moller-Maersk A/S; *Int'l*, pg. 27
HAMBURG SUDAMERIKANISCHE DAMPFSCHIFFFAHRTS-GESELLSCHAFT A/S & CO KG—See A.P. Moller-Maersk A/S; *Int'l*, pg. 26
HAMBY CHEVROLET-BUICK-GMC TRUCK; *U.S. Private*, pg. 1847
HAMCO, INC.—See Crown Crafts, Inc.; *U.S. Public*, pg. 596

COMPANY NAME INDEX

HAMCO MANUFACTURING & DISTRIBUTING LLC—See Griffin Holdings, LLC; *U.S. Private*, pg. 1788
HAMCOS IT SERVICE GMBH—See Kontron AG; *Int'l*, pg. 4276
HAMEE CORP.; *Int'l*, pg. 3237
HAMEE INDIA PVT. LTD.—See Hamee Corp.; *Int'l*, pg. 3237
HAMEE KOREA CO., LTD.—See Hamee Corp.; *Int'l*, pg. 3237
HAMEENKYLAN KAUPPA OY—See Kesko Corporation; *Int'l*, pg. 4142
HAMEE SHANGHAI TRADE CO., LTD.—See Hamee Corp.; *Int'l*, pg. 3237
HAMEE TAIWAN, CORP.—See Hamee Corp.; *Int'l*, pg. 3237
HAMEE US, CORP.—See Hamee Corp.; *Int'l*, pg. 3237
HAMEG INSTRUMENTS GMBH—See Rohde & Schwarz GmbH & Co. KG; *Int'l*, pg. 6384
HAMEL BUILDERS; *U.S. Private*, pg. 1847
HAMELEX WHITE PTY LTD—See MaxiPARTS Limited; *Int'l*, pg. 4742
HAMEL FOREST PRODUCTS, INC.; *U.S. Private*, pg. 1847
HAMELIN A/S—See Groupe Hamelin S.A.; *Int'l*, pg. 3104
HAMELIN BRANDS LTD—See Groupe Hamelin S.A.; *Int'l*, pg. 3104
HAMELIN B.V.—See Groupe Hamelin S.A.; *Int'l*, pg. 3104
HAMELIN B.V.—See Groupe Hamelin S.A.; *Int'l*, pg. 3104
HAMELIN GMBH—See Groupe Hamelin S.A.; *Int'l*, pg. 3104
HAMELIN GOLD LIMITED; *Int'l*, pg. 3237
HAMELIN, LDA.—See Groupe Hamelin S.A.; *Int'l*, pg. 3104
HAMELIN POLSKA SP. Z O.O.—See Groupe Hamelin S.A.; *Int'l*, pg. 3104
HAMELIN S.A.—See Groupe Hamelin S.A.; *Int'l*, pg. 3104
HAMELIN S.A.S.—See Groupe Hamelin S.A.; *Int'l*, pg. 3104
HAMELIN S.P.A.—See Groupe Hamelin S.A.; *Int'l*, pg. 3104
HAMEL & MCALISTER INC.; *U.S. Private*, pg. 1847
HAMELN GROUP GMBH; *Int'l*, pg. 3237
HAMELN PHAMA PLUS GMBH—See Hameln Group GmbH; *Int'l*, pg. 3237
HAMELN PHARMACEUTICALS GMBH—See Siegfried Holding AG; *Int'l*, pg. 6884
HAMELN PHARMACEUTICALS LTD.—See Hameln Group GmbH; *Int'l*, pg. 3237
HAMELN RDS GMBH—See Siegfried Holding AG; *Int'l*, pg. 6884
HAMER ENVIRONMENTAL L.P.—See Environmental Enginuity Group LLC; *U.S. Private*, pg. 1407
HAMER-FISCHBEIN LLC - FISCHBEIN DIVISION—See Warburg Pincus LLC; *U.S. Private*, pg. 4437
HAMER-FISCHBEIN LLC—See Warburg Pincus LLC; *U.S. Private*, pg. 4437
HAMERSLEY HOLDINGS LIMITED—See Rio Tinto plc; *Int'l*, pg. 6346
HAMERSLEY INTERNATIONAL BV—See CLS Holdings plc; *Int'l*, pg. 1664
HAMERSLEY IRON PTY LTD—See Rio Tinto plc; *Int'l*, pg. 6347
HAMER TOYOTA INC.; *U.S. Private*, pg. 1847
HAMID FABRICS LTD.; *Int'l*, pg. 3237
HAMID TEXTILE MILLS LIMITED; *Int'l*, pg. 3237
HAMILTON-ACORN LTD.—See Orkla ASA; *Int'l*, pg. 5638
HAMILTON ARMS CENTER—See Formation Capital, LLC; *U.S. Private*, pg. 1570
HAMILTON BEACH BRANDS CANADA, INC.—See Hamilton Beach Brands Holding Company; *U.S. Public*, pg. 981
HAMILTON BEACH BRANDS HOLDING COMPANY; *U.S. Public*, pg. 981
HAMILTON BEACH BRANDS, INC.—See Hamilton Beach Brands Holding Company; *U.S. Public*, pg. 981
HAMILTON BEACH, INC.—See Hamilton Beach Brands Holding Company; *U.S. Public*, pg. 981
HAMILTON BEACH/PROCTOR SILEX, INC.—See Hamilton Beach Brands Holding Company; *U.S. Public*, pg. 981
HAMILTON BONADUZ AG—See Hamilton Co., Inc.; *U.S. Private*, pg. 1847
HAMILTON BOND LIMITED—See Marsh & McLennan Companies, Inc.; *U.S. Public*, pg. 1376
HAMILTON BRANDS (PTY) LIMITED—See Kansai Paint Co., Ltd.; *Int'l*, pg. 4072
HAMILTON CASTER & MFG. CO.; *U.S. Private*, pg. 1847
HAMILTON CENTER, INC.; *U.S. Private*, pg. 1847
HAMILTON CO., INC.; *U.S. Private*, pg. 1847
THE HAMILTON COLLECTION, INC.—See The Bradford Group; *U.S. Private*, pg. 3999
HAMILTON COMMUNICATIONS GROUP, INC.; *U.S. Private*, pg. 1847
HAMILTON COMMUNITY NEWS—See Torstar Corporation; *Int'l*, pg. 7831
HAMILTON & COMPANY LIMITED; *Int'l*, pg. 3237
HAMILTON CONSTRUCTION CO. OREGON INC.; *U.S. Private*, pg. 1847
HAMILTON COUNTY ELECTRIC COOPERATIVE; *U.S. Private*, pg. 1847

HAMILTON DATA SERVICES EOOD—See Iron Mountain Incorporated; *U.S. Public*, pg. 1172
HAMILTON ENGINEERING, INC.—See Harlow Aerostructures, LLC; *U.S. Private*, pg. 1865
HAMILTON EQUIPMENT, INC.; *U.S. Private*, pg. 1847
HAMILTON EXHIBITS LLC; *U.S. Private*, pg. 1847
HAMILTON FORM CO., LTD.; *U.S. Private*, pg. 1847
HAMILTON FUNERAL CHAPEL, INC.—See Service Corporation International; *U.S. Public*, pg. 1869
HAMILTON GLOBAL OPPORTUNITIES PLC; *Int'l*, pg. 3237
HAMILTON HEALTH CARE SYSTEM, INC.; *U.S. Private*, pg. 1848
HAMILTON HOTEL PARTNERS LTD—See Pyramid Hotels & Resorts, Inc.; *U.S. Private*, pg. 3310
HAMILTON IMPORTS; *U.S. Private*, pg. 1848
HAMILTON INSURANCE GROUP, LTD.; *Int'l*, pg. 3238
HAMILTON INTERNATIONAL AG—See The Swatch Group Ltd.; *Int'l*, pg. 7691
HAMILTON INVESTMENTS, INC.—See Kingsway Financial Services Inc.; *U.S. Public*, pg. 1234
HAMILTON KENT INC—See Aliaxis S.A./N.V.; *Int'l*, pg. 324
HAMILTON LANE ADVISORS, LLC; *U.S. Private*, pg. 1848
HAMILTON LANE ALLIANCE HOLDINGS I, INC.—See Hamilton Lane Incorporated; *U.S. Public*, pg. 982
HAMILTON LANE (AUSTRALIA) PTY LIMITED—See Hamilton Lane Incorporated; *U.S. Public*, pg. 982
HAMILTON LANE DO BRASIL LTDA.—See Hamilton Lane Advisors, LLC; *U.S. Private*, pg. 1848
HAMILTON LANE (HONG KONG) LIMITED—See Hamilton Lane Advisors, LLC; *U.S. Private*, pg. 1848
HAMILTON LANE INCORPORATED; *U.S. Public*, pg. 981
HAMILTON LANE INVESTIMENTOS LTDA.—See Hamilton Lane Incorporated; *U.S. Public*, pg. 982
HAMILTON LANE ISRAEL LTD.—See Hamilton Lane Advisors, LLC; *U.S. Private*, pg. 1848
HAMILTON LANE (JAPAN) CO., LTD.—See Hamilton Lane Advisors, LLC; *U.S. Private*, pg. 1848
HAMILTON LANE (JAPAN) GK—See Hamilton Lane Incorporated; *U.S. Public*, pg. 982
HAMILTON LANE (UK) LIMITED—See Hamilton Lane Advisors, LLC; *U.S. Private*, pg. 1848
HAMILTON MATERIALS INC.; *U.S. Private*, pg. 1848
HAMILTON MEDICALLY ASSISTED TREATMENT ASSOCIATES, LLC—See AAC Holdings, Inc.; *U.S. Private*, pg. 31
HAMILTON MEMORIAL HOSPITAL, INC.—See HCA Healthcare, Inc.; *U.S. Public*, pg. 998
HAMILTON MESSTECHNIK GMBH—See Hamilton Co., Inc.; *U.S. Private*, pg. 1847
HAMILTON METALS INC.; *U.S. Private*, pg. 1848
HAMILTON MUTUAL INSURANCE COMPANY—See Employers Mutual Casualty Company; *U.S. Private*, pg. 1387
HAMILTON-PARKER COMPANY; *U.S. Private*, pg. 1848
HAMILTON PARTNERS, INC.; *U.S. Private*, pg. 1848
HAMILTON PHYSICAL THERAPY, LIMITED PARTNERSHIP—See U.S. Physical Therapy, Inc.; *U.S. Public*, pg. 2214
HAMILTON PLACE MALL GENERAL PARTNERSHIP—See CBL & Associates Properties, Inc.; *U.S. Public*, pg. 458
HAMILTON POWER SOLUTIONS—See Palmer Johnson Enterprises, Inc.; *U.S. Private*, pg. 3081
HAMILTON PRECISION METALS, INC.—See AMETEK, Inc.; *U.S. Public*, pg. 116
HAMILTON PUBLIC RELATIONS—See Bodden Partners; *U.S. Private*, pg. 607
HAMILTON RENTALS LTD.; *Int'l*, pg. 3238
HAMILTON RISK MANAGEMENT CO.—See Kingsway Financial Services Inc.; *U.S. Public*, pg. 1234
HAMILTON ROBINSON LLC; *U.S. Private*, pg. 1848
HAMILTON-RYKER COMPANY; *U.S. Private*, pg. 1848
HAMILTON SAFE CO.—See Gunnebo AB; *Int'l*, pg. 3185
HAMILTON SCIENTIFIC LLC—See OpenGate Capital Management, LLC; *U.S. Private*, pg. 3030
HAMILTON SORTER, INC—See H.S. Morgan Limited Partnership; *U.S. Private*, pg. 1836
HAMILTON SPECIALTY BAR CORP.—See Woodside Capital Partners; *U.S. Private*, pg. 4560
THE HAMILTON SPECTATOR—See Torstar Corporation; *Int'l*, pg. 7831
HAMILTON & SPILL LTD; *Int'l*, pg. 3237
HAMILTON SUNDSTRAND CORPORATION—See RTX Corporation; *U.S. Public*, pg. 1821
HAMILTON SUNDSTRAND SPACE SYSTEMS INTERNATIONAL, INC.—See RTX Corporation; *U.S. Public*, pg. 1821
HAMILTON'S UNIFORMS LLC; *U.S. Private*, pg. 1848
HAMILTON SYSTEM DISTRIBUTORS; *U.S. Private*, pg. 1848
HAMILTON TELECOMMUNICATIONS—See Nedelco Inc.; *U.S. Private*, pg. 2879
HAMILTON TELECOMMUNICATIONS—See Nedelco Inc.; *U.S. Private*, pg. 2879
HAMILTON THORNE LTD.—See Astorg Partners S.A.S.; *Int'l*, pg. 656

HAMMERSMITH DATA MANAGEMENT, INC.

HAMILTON VALLEY MANAGEMENT, INC.—See BHHH Companies Inc.; *U.S. Private*, pg. 549
HAMILTON-WENHAM CHRONICLE—See Gannett Co., Inc.; *U.S. Public*, pg. 902
HA MINERALS GMBH—See Huettenes-Albertus Chemische Werke GmbH; *Int'l*, pg. 3523
HAMISHMAR INSURANCE AGENCY LTD.—See Harel Insurance Investments & Financial Services Ltd.; *Int'l*, pg. 3273
THE HAMISTER GROUP, INC.; *U.S. Private*, pg. 4042
HAM-LET (ISRAEL-CANADA) LTD.—See Ultra Clean Holdings, Inc.; *U.S. Public*, pg. 2223
HAMLETT ENGINEERING SALES COMPANY—See Brixey & Meyer, Inc.; *U.S. Public*, pg. 658
HAMLEYS ASIA LIMITED—See Reliance - ADA Group Limited; *Int'l*, pg. 6263
HAMLEYS FINLAND OY—See Reliance - ADA Group Limited; *Int'l*, pg. 6263
THE HAMLEYS GROUP LIMITED—See Reliance - ADA Group Limited; *Int'l*, pg. 6262
HAMLEYS NORWAY AS—See Reliance - ADA Group Limited; *Int'l*, pg. 6263
HAMLEYS OF LONDON LIMITED—See Reliance - ADA Group Limited; *Int'l*, pg. 6263
HAMLEYS SWENDEN AB—See Reliance - ADA Group Limited; *Int'l*, pg. 6263
HAMLEYS TOYS (IRELAND) LIMITED—See Reliance - ADA Group Limited; *Int'l*, pg. 6263
HAMLIN BANK & TRUST COMPANY; *U.S. Public*, pg. 982
HAMLIN ELECTRONICS EUROPE LTD.—See Littelfuse, Inc.; *U.S. Public*, pg. 1327
HAMLIN ELECTRONICS (SUZHOU) LIMITED—See Littelfuse, Inc.; *U.S. Public*, pg. 1327
HAMLIN, INC.—See Littelfuse, Inc.; *U.S. Public*, pg. 1327
HAMLIN NEWCO, LLC; *U.S. Private*, pg. 1848
HAMLON PTY LTD—See Hancock & Gore Ltd.; *Int'l*, pg. 3242
HAMLYN PUBLISHING—See Vivendi SE; *Int'l*, pg. 8274
HAMMACHER SCHLEMMER & CO., INC.; *U.S. Private*, pg. 1849
HAMM AG—See Deere & Company; *U.S. Public*, pg. 647
HAMMAN-MILLER-BEAUCHAMP-DEEBLE, INC.—See Hellman & Friedman LLC; *U.S. Private*, pg. 1909
HAMMASLAAKARIKESKUS MANDIPULA OY—See Pihlajalinna Oy; *Int'l*, pg. 5865
HAMM CONSTRUCTION LTD.; *Int'l*, pg. 3238
HAMMEL, GREEN & ABRAHAMSON, INC.; *U.S. Private*, pg. 1849
HAMMELMANN AUSTRALIA PTY LTD—See Interpump Group S.p.A.; *Int'l*, pg. 3755
HAMMELMANN CORPORATION—See Interpump Group S.p.A.; *Int'l*, pg. 3755
HAMMELMANN FRANCE S.A.R.L.—See Interpump Group S.p.A.; *Int'l*, pg. 3755
HAMMELMANN GMBH—See Interpump Group S.p.A.; *Int'l*, pg. 3755
HAMMELMANN MASCHINENFABRIK GMBH—See Interpump Group S.p.A.; *Int'l*, pg. 3755
HAMMELMANN PUMPS SYSTEMS CO LTD—See Interpump Group S.p.A.; *Int'l*, pg. 3755
HAMMELMANN S. L.—See Interpump Group S.p.A.; *Int'l*, pg. 3755
HAMMELMANN SWISS GMBH—See Interpump Group S.p.A.; *Int'l*, pg. 3755
HAMMERBERG INVESTMENTS, INC.—See Arthur J. Gallagher & Co.; *U.S. Public*, pg. 205
HAMMER COMMERCIAL, INC.; *U.S. Private*, pg. 1849
HAMMER CONSTRUCTION, INC.; *U.S. Private*, pg. 1849
HAMMER CREATIVE; *U.S. Private*, pg. 1849
HAMMERFEST INDUSTRIFISKE AS—See Austevoll Seafood ASA; *Int'l*, pg. 717
HAMMERHEAD ENERGY INC.; *Int'l*, pg. 3238
HAMMERITE PRODUCTS LIMITED—See Akzo Nobel N.V.; *Int'l*, pg. 274
HAMMERL GMBH & CO. KG—See CRH plc; *Int'l*, pg. 1844
HAMMERMAN & GAINER INC.; *U.S. Private*, pg. 1849
HAMMER METALS AUSTRALIA PTY. LTD.—See Hammer Metals Limited; *Int'l*, pg. 3238
HAMMER METALS LIMITED; *Int'l*, pg. 3238
HAMMERMILL PAPER—See International Paper Company; *U.S. Public*, pg. 1155
HAMMER PACKAGING CORP.—See Advent International Corporation; *U.S. Private*, pg. 101
HAMMER RETEX AG; *Int'l*, pg. 3238
HAMMERS LLC; *U.S. Private*, pg. 1849
HAMMERSMITH DATA MANAGEMENT, INC.; *U.S. Private*, pg. 1849
HAMMERSON (BRENT CROSS) LTD—See Hammerson plc; *Int'l*, pg. 3238
HAMMERSON CENTRE COMMERCIAL ITALIE SAS—See Hammerson plc; *Int'l*, pg. 3238
HAMMERSON GROUP MANAGEMENT LTD—See Hammerson plc; *Int'l*, pg. 3238
HAMMERSON INTERNATIONAL HOLDINGS LTD—See Hammerson plc; *Int'l*, pg. 3238
HAMMERSON MADELEINE SAS—See Hammerson plc; *Int'l*, pg. 3238

HAMMERSMITH DATA MANAGEMENT, INC.

HAMMERSON MARKETING ET COMMUNICATION SAS—See Hammerson plc; *Int'l*, pg. 3238
HAMMERSON ORACLE INVESTMENTS LTD—See Hammerson plc; *Int'l*, pg. 3238
HAMMERSON PLC; *Int'l*, pg. 3238
HAMMERSON PROPERTY LTD—See Hammerson plc; *Int'l*, pg. 3238
HAMMERSON SAS—See Hammerson plc; *Int'l*, pg. 3238
HAMMERSTONE CORPORATION—See Brookfield Corporation; *Int'l*, pg. 1187
HAMMER TAEPPER A/S—See Egetaepper A/S; *Int'l*, pg. 2324
HAMMER TECHNOLOGY HOLDINGS; *U.S. Public*, pg. 982
HAMMERT'S IRON WORKS, INC.—See Stupp Bros., Inc.; *U.S. Private*, pg. 3844
HAMMER-WILLIAMS COMPANY; *U.S. Private*, pg. 1849
HAMMES PARTNERS WISCONSIN LP; *U.S. Private*, pg. 1849
HAMMILL MANUFACTURING COMPANY INC.; *U.S. Private*, pg. 1849
HAMM, INC.—See Summit Materials, Inc.; *U.S. Public*, pg. 1960
HAMM MANAGEMENT CO.; *U.S. Private*, pg. 1849
HAMMOCK LANDING/WEST MELBOURNE, LLC—See CBL & Associates Properties, Inc.; *U.S. Public*, pg. 458
HAMMONASSET FORD-LINCOLN-MERCURY INC.; *U.S. Private*, pg. 1849
HAMMOND DAILY STAR PUBLISHING CO. INC.—See Paxton Media Group LLC; *U.S. Private*, pg. 3116
HAMMOND DIALYSIS CLINIC, LLC—See Nautic Partners, LLC; *U.S. Private*, pg. 2870
HAMMOND ELECTRONICS INC.; *U.S. Private*, pg. 1849
HAMMOND ELECTRONICS LIMITED—See Hammond Manufacturing Co. Ltd.; *Int'l*, pg. 3238
HAMMOND ELECTRONICS PTY. LIMITED—See Hammond Manufacturing Co. Ltd.; *Int'l*, pg. 3238
HAMMOND EXPANDERS DIVISION - MALAYSIA PLANT—See Hammond Group, Inc.; *U.S. Private*, pg. 1849
HAMMOND GROUP, INC.; *U.S. Private*, pg. 1849
HAMMOND HANLON CAMP LLC—See Fifth Third Bancorp; *U.S. Public*, pg. 833
HAMMOND, KENNEDY, WHITNEY & COMPANY, INC. - INDIANAPOLIS—See Hammond, Kennedy, Whitney & Company, Inc.; *U.S. Private*, pg. 1850
HAMMOND, KENNEDY, WHITNEY & COMPANY, INC.; *U.S. Private*, pg. 1850
HAMMOND LEAD PRODUCTS DIVISION - POTTSTOWN PLANT—See Hammond Group, Inc.; *U.S. Private*, pg. 1850
HAMMOND LEAD PRODUCTS—See Hammond Group, Inc.; *U.S. Private*, pg. 1849
HAMMOND LUMBER COMPANY; *U.S. Private*, pg. 1850
HAMMOND MACHINERY, INC.; *U.S. Private*, pg. 1850
HAMMOND MANUFACTURING CO. LTD.; *Int'l*, pg. 3238
HAMMOND MANUFACTURING COMPANY INC—See Hammond Manufacturing Co. Ltd.; *Int'l*, pg. 3238
HAMMOND POWER SOLUTIONS, INC.; *U.S. Private*, pg. 1850
HAMMOND POWER SOLUTIONS INC.; *Int'l*, pg. 3238
HAMMOND POWER SOLUTIONS, INC.—See Hammond Power Solutions Inc.; *Int'l*, pg. 3239
HAMMOND POWER SOLUTIONS S.A. DE C.V.—See Hammond Power Solutions Inc.; *Int'l*, pg. 3239
HAMMOND TRACTOR COMPANY; *U.S. Private*, pg. 1850
HAMMOND VALVE CORP.—See Milwaukee Valve Company, Inc.; *U.S. Private*, pg. 2739
HAMMONS PRODUCTS CO. - ARKANSAS—See Hammons Products Company; *U.S. Private*, pg. 1851
HAMMONS PRODUCTS COMPANY; *U.S. Private*, pg. 1850
HAMM & PHILLIPS SERVICE COMPANY—See Hamm Management Co.; *U.S. Private*, pg. 1849
THE HAMNER INSTITUTES FOR HEALTH SCIENCES; *U.S. Private*, pg. 4042
HAMNES INVESTMENTS BV—See Barclays PLC; *Int'l*, pg. 862
HAMON & CIE S.A.; *Int'l*, pg. 3239
HAMON CORPORATION—See Hamon & Cie S.A.; *Int'l*, pg. 3239
HAMON DELTAK, INC.—See Hamon & Cie S.A.; *Int'l*, pg. 3239
HAMO SWITZERLAND AG/SA/LTD.—See STERIS plc; *Int'l*, pg. 7209
HAMPDEN AGENCIES LIMITED—See Hampden Holdings Limited; *Int'l*, pg. 3239
HAMPDEN CAPITAL PLC—See Hampden Holdings Limited; *Int'l*, pg. 3239
HAMPDEN CORPORATE MEMBER LIMITED—See Helios Underwriting PLC; *Int'l*, pg. 3330
HAMPDEN HOLDINGS LIMITED; *Int'l*, pg. 3239
HAMPDEN INSURANCE GROUP BV—See Hampden Holdings Limited; *Int'l*, pg. 3239
HAMPDEN INVESTMENT CORPORATION II—See Berkshire Hills Bancorp, Inc.; *U.S. Public*, pg. 320
HAMPDEN PAPERS INC.—See LLFlex, LLC; *U.S. Private*, pg. 2475

HAMPDEN PLC—See Hampden Holdings Limited; *Int'l*, pg. 3239
HAMPEL OIL DISTRIBUTORS INC.; *U.S. Private*, pg. 1851
HAMPERS WITH BITE PTY. LTD.—See Pental Limited; *Int'l*, pg. 5791
HAMPIDJAN AUSTRALIA PTY LTD—See Hampidjan hf; *Int'l*, pg. 3239
HAMPIDJAN BALTIC UAB—See Hampidjan hf; *Int'l*, pg. 3239
HAMPIDJAN CANADA LTD.—See Hampidjan hf; *Int'l*, pg. 3239
HAMPIDJAN HF; *Int'l*, pg. 3239
HAMPIDJAN NEW ZEALAND LTD—See Hampidjan hf; *Int'l*, pg. 3239
HAMPIDJAN RUSSIA LTD.—See Hampidjan hf; *Int'l*, pg. 3239
HAMPIDJAN USA INC.—See Hampidjan hf; *Int'l*, pg. 3239
HAMPSHIRE BRANDS—See Hampshire Group Limited; *U.S. Private*, pg. 1851
HAMPSHIRE DESIGNERS, INC. NY—See Hampshire Group Limited; *U.S. Private*, pg. 1851
HAMPSHIRE DESIGNERS, INC. SC—See Hampshire Group Limited; *U.S. Private*, pg. 1851
HAMPSHIRE EQUITY PARTNERS; *U.S. Private*, pg. 1851
HAMPSHIRE GAS COMPANY—See AltaGas Ltd.; *Int'l*, pg. 384
HAMPSHIRE GROUP LIMITED; *U.S. Private*, pg. 1851
THE HAMPSHIRE & ISLE OF WIGHT REHABILITATION COMPANY LTD.—See Interserve Plc; *Int'l*, pg. 3760
HAMPSHIRE PET PRODUCTS, LLC—See Red Collar Pet Foods, Inc.; *U.S. Private*, pg. 3374
HAMPSHIRE PROPERTIES LLC—See Heidelberg Materials AG; *Int'l*, pg. 3311
HAMPSON INDUSTRIES PLC; *Int'l*, pg. 3239
HAMPSON PRECISION AUTOMOTIVE (INDIA) PRIVATE LIMITED—See Hampson Industries PLC; *Int'l*, pg. 3239
HAMPSON RUSSEL LIMITED PARTNERSHIP—See CGG; *Int'l*, pg. 1431
HAMPSON-RUSSELL SOFTWARE SERVICES LP—See CGG; *Int'l*, pg. 1431
HAMPTON AFFILIATES - MORTON - COWLITZ DIVISION—See Hampton Affiliates; *U.S. Private*, pg. 1851
HAMPTON AFFILIATES - RANDLE - COWLITZ DIVISION—See Hampton Affiliates; *U.S. Private*, pg. 1851
HAMPTON AFFILIATES; *U.S. Private*, pg. 1851
HAMPTON AFFILIATES - WARRENTON DIVISION—See Hampton Affiliates; *U.S. Private*, pg. 1851
HAMPTON AFFILIATES - WASHINGTON MILLS—See Hampton Affiliates; *U.S. Private*, pg. 1851
HAMPTON ASSOCIATES LTD.; *Int'l*, pg. 3239
HAMPTON BAY CAPITAL, INC.; *Int'l*, pg. 3239
HAMPTON CHEVROLET MAZDA; *U.S. Private*, pg. 1851
THE HAMPTON COUNTY GUARDIAN—See Shivers Trading & Operating Company; *U.S. Private*, pg. 3638
HAMPTON DISTRIBUTING CO.; *U.S. Private*, pg. 1851
HAMPTON ENTERPRISES INC.; *U.S. Private*, pg. 1851
HAMPTON FINANCIAL CORPORATION; *Int'l*, pg. 3239
HAMPTON FORGE, LTD.—See Centre Lane Partners, LLC; *U.S. Private*, pg. 827
HAMPTON HALL CLUB, INC.—See Toll Brothers, Inc.; *U.S. Public*, pg. 2161
HAMPTON HILL MINING NL; *Int'l*, pg. 3239
HAMPTON HOMES, LLC; *U.S. Private*, pg. 1851
HAMPTON HYDRAULICS, LLC—See Ligon Industries LLC; *U.S. Private*, pg. 2455
HAMPTON HYDRAULICS LLC—See Ligon Industries LLC; *U.S. Private*, pg. 2455
HAMPTON INN - FOOTHILL RANCH—See Stonebridge Realty Advisors, Inc.; *U.S. Private*, pg. 3827
HAMPTON INN - LAKEWOOD—See Stonebridge Realty Advisors, Inc.; *U.S. Private*, pg. 3827
HAMPTON INNS LLC—See Hilton Worldwide Holdings Inc.; *U.S. Public*, pg. 1040
HAMPTON INN & SUITES - CHERRY CREEK—See Stonebridge Realty Advisors, Inc.; *U.S. Private*, pg. 3827
HAMPTON ROADS COMMUNITY FOUNDATION; *U.S. Private*, pg. 1851
HAMPTON ROADS ECONOMIC DEVELOPMENT ALLIANCE; *U.S. Private*, pg. 1851
HAMPTON ROADS RECOVERY CENTER, LLC—See Waste Connections, Inc.; *Int'l*, pg. 8352
HAMPTON RUBBER COMPANY INC.—See AEA Investors LP; *U.S. Private*, pg. 115
HAMPTON S.A.—See Industria de Diseno Textil, S.A.; *Int'l*, pg. 3666
HAMPTON SECURITIES LIMITED—See Hampton Financial Corporation; *Int'l*, pg. 3239
THE HAMPTONS (NEWCASTLE) RESIDENT MANAGEMENT COMPANY LIMITED—See Persimmon plc; *Int'l*, pg. 5817
HAMPTON SPORTSWEAR (PTY) LIMITED—See AVI Limited; *Int'l*, pg. 740
HAMPTON STEEL LTD.; *Int'l*, pg. 3240
HAMPTON TEDDER ELECTRIC CO.; *U.S. Private*, pg. 1851

CORPORATE AFFILIATIONS

HAMPTON TEXTILE PRINTING—See Safer Prints Inc.; *U.S. Private*, pg. 3524
HAMPTON TOYOTA; *U.S. Private*, pg. 1851
HAMPTON TREE FARMS, INC.—See Hampton Affiliates; *U.S. Private*, pg. 1851
HAMRICK INC.; *U.S. Private*, pg. 1851
HAMRO BIKAS BANK LIMITED; *Int'l*, pg. 3240
HAMSAR DIVERSCO INC.—See Methode Electronics, Inc.; *U.S. Public*, pg. 1428
HAMSDALE AUSTRALIA PTY LTD.—See QAF Limited; *Int'l*, pg. 6132
HAMSHAW LUMBER INC.; *U.S. Private*, pg. 1851
HAMS—See The Interpublic Group of Companies, Inc.; *U.S. Public*, pg. 2100
HAMSTRA GROUP, INC.; *U.S. Private*, pg. 1851
HAMWORTHY BALTIC DESIGN CENTRE LIMITED—See Wartsila Corporation; *Int'l*, pg. 8349
HAMWORTHY B.V.—See Wartsila Corporation; *Int'l*, pg. 8349
HAMWORTHY COMBUSTION ENGINEERING (KOREA) CO. LTD.—See Koch Industries, Inc.; *U.S. Private*, pg. 2331
HAMWORTHY COMBUSTION ENGINEERING LIMITED—See Koch Industries, Inc.; *U.S. Private*, pg. 2331
HAMWORTHY COMBUSTION ENGINEERING S.R.L.—See Koch Industries, Inc.; *U.S. Private*, pg. 2331
HAMWORTHY GREENSHIP BV—See Wartsila Corporation; *Int'l*, pg. 8350
HAMWORTHY HEATING LIMITED—See Atlantic Societe Francaise Develop Thermique S.A.; *Int'l*, pg. 675
HAMWORTHY INC.—See Wartsila Corporation; *Int'l*, pg. 8350
HAMWORTHY INDIA PVT LTD—See Wartsila Corporation; *Int'l*, pg. 8350
HAMWORTHY KOREA LIMITED—See Wartsila Corporation; *Int'l*, pg. 8350
HAMWORTHY MIDDLE EAST (FZC)—See Wartsila Corporation; *Int'l*, pg. 8350
HAMWORTHY PEABODY COMBUSTION INC.—See Koch Industries, Inc.; *U.S. Private*, pg. 2331
HAMWORTHY PTE LIMITED—See Wartsila Corporation; *Int'l*, pg. 8350
HAMWORTHY PUMP SYSTEMS AS—See Wartsila Corporation; *Int'l*, pg. 8350
HAMWORTHY SERCK COMO GMBH—See Wartsila Corporation; *Int'l*, pg. 8350
HAMWORTHY (SUZHOU) LIMITED—See Wartsila Corporation; *Int'l*, pg. 8349
HANA ALTERNATIVE ASSET MANAGEMENT CO., LTD.—See Hana Financial Group, Inc.; *Int'l*, pg. 3240
HANA ASIA LIMITED—See Hana Financial Group, Inc.; *Int'l*, pg. 3240
HANA ASSET TRUST CO., LTD.—See Hana Financial Group, Inc.; *Int'l*, pg. 3240
HANA BANK (CHINA) CO., LTD.—See Hana Financial Group, Inc.; *Int'l*, pg. 3240
HANACANS JOINT STOCK COMPANY—See Resonac Holdings Corporation; *Int'l*, pg. 6298
HANA CAPITAL CO., LTD.—See Hana Financial Group, Inc.; *Int'l*, pg. 3240
HANAC, INC.; *U.S. Private*, pg. 1852
HANA DAETOO SECURITIES CO., LTD.—See Hana Financial Group, Inc.; *Int'l*, pg. 3240
HANAE MORI ASSOCIATES CO., LTD—See Mitsui & Co., Ltd.; *Int'l*, pg. 4973
HANA F&I, INC.—See Hana Financial Group, Inc.; *Int'l*, pg. 3240
HANA FINANCIAL GROUP, INC.; *Int'l*, pg. 3240
HANA FINANCIAL INVESTMENT CO., LTD.—See Hana Financial Group, Inc.; *Int'l*, pg. 3240
HANA HSBC LIFE INSURANCE CO., LTD.—See Hana Financial Group, Inc.; *Int'l*, pg. 3240
HANA HSBC LIFE INSURANCE CO., LTD.—See HSBC Holdings plc; *Int'l*, pg. 3506
HANA INSTITUTE OF FINANCE—See Hana Financial Group, Inc.; *Int'l*, pg. 3240
HANA INSURANCE. CO., LTD.—See Hana Financial Group, Inc.; *Int'l*, pg. 3240
HA-NA-IRO CO., LTD.—See Hitachi Zosen Corporation; *Int'l*, pg. 3412
HANA I&S—See Hana Financial Group, Inc.; *Int'l*, pg. 3240
HANALL BIOPHARMA CO., LTD. - BUSINESS DEVELOPMENT DIVISION—See HanAll BioPharma Co., Ltd.; *Int'l*, pg. 3241
HANALL BIOPHARMA CO., LTD. - INTERNATIONAL EXPORTS DIVISION—See HanAll BioPharma Co., Ltd.; *Int'l*, pg. 3241
HANALL BIOPHARMA CO., LTD.; *Int'l*, pg. 3241
HANAMARU, INC.—See Yoshinoya Holdings Co., Ltd.; *Int'l*, pg. 8600
HANA MATERIALS INC.; *Int'l*, pg. 3241
HANA MICRODISPLAY TECHNOLOGIES, INC.—See Hana Microelectronics Public Company Limited; *Int'l*, pg. 3241
HANA MICROELECTRONICS, INC.—See Hana Microelectronics Public Company Limited; *Int'l*, pg. 3241

COMPANY NAME INDEX

HANA MICROELECTRONICS (JIAXING) CO., LTD.—See Hana Microelectronics Public Company Limited; *Int'l*, pg. 3241
HANA MICROELECTRONICS PUBLIC CO., LTD.—See Hana Microelectronics Public Company Limited; *Int'l*, pg. 3241
HANA MICROELECTRONICS PUBLIC COMPANY LIMITED; *Int'l*, pg. 3241
HANA MICRON INC.; *Int'l*, pg. 3241
HANA MUST SEVEN SPECIAL PURPOSE ACQUISITION COMPANY; *Int'l*, pg. 3241
HANA MUST SPECIAL PURPOSE ACQUISITION COMPANY; *Int'l*, pg. 3241
HANAN MOR GROUP - HOLDING LTD.; *Int'l*, pg. 3241
HANA PHARM CO., LTD.; *Int'l*, pg. 3241
HANAPIN MARKETING, LLC—See Brain Labs Digital Ltd.; *Int'l*, pg. 1137
HANASAB INSURANCE SERVICES, INC.—See ABRY Partners, LLC; *U.S. Private*, pg. 42
HANASAKU LIFE INSURANCE CO., LTD.—See Nippon Life Insurance Company; *Int'l*, pg. 5322
HANA SAVINGS BANK CO., LTD.—See Hana Financial Group, Inc.; *Int'l*, pg. 3240
HANA SEMICONDUCTOR (AYUTTHAYA) CO., LTD.—See Hana Microelectronics Public Company Limited; *Int'l*, pg. 3241
HANA SEMICONDUCTOR (BKK) CO., LTD.—See Hana Microelectronics Public Company Limited; *Int'l*, pg. 3241
HANA SK CARD—See Hana Financial Group, Inc.; *Int'l*, pg. 3240
HANA SPORTS INC.; *U.S. Private*, pg. 1852
HANA TECHNOLOGY CO., LTD.—See Adtec Plasma Technology Co., Ltd.; *Int'l*, pg. 154
HANA TI CO., LTD.—See Hana Financial Group, Inc.; *Int'l*, pg. 3240
HANATOUR JAPAN CO., LTD.—See Hanatour Service, Inc.; *Int'l*, pg. 3241
HANATOUR SERVICE, INC.; *Int'l*, pg. 3241
HANA VENTURES LLC—See Hana Financial Group, Inc.; *Int'l*, pg. 3240
HANA WLS INC—See Hana Micron Inc.; *Int'l*, pg. 3241
HANAZONO TOOLS MFG. CO., LTD.—See Yuasa Trading Co., Ltd.; *Int'l*, pg. 8609
HANBELL PRECISE MACHINERY CO., LTD.—See Shanghai Hanbell Precise Machinery Co., Ltd.; *Int'l*, pg. 6769
HANBELL PRECISE MACHINERY KOREA CO., LTD.—See Shanghai Hanbell Precise Machinery Co., Ltd.; *Int'l*, pg. 6769
HANBIT SOFT INC.; *Int'l*, pg. 3241
HANBUL ENERGY MANAGEMENT CO. LTD.—See Veolia Environnement S.A.; *Int'l*, pg. 8158
HANCAP AB; *Int'l*, pg. 3241
HANCHANG CORPORATION; *Int'l*, pg. 3242
HANCHANG INDUSTRY CO., LTD.; *Int'l*, pg. 3242
HANCHANG PAPER CO., LTD; *Int'l*, pg. 3242
HANCHETT ENTRY SYSTEMS INC.—See ASSA ABLOY AB; *Int'l*, pg. 639
HANCHIH ELECTRONICS (SHENZHEN) CO., LTD.—See Hanpin Electron Co., Ltd.; *Int'l*, pg. 3258
HANCOCK CLAIMS CONSULTANTS, LLC; *U.S. Private*, pg. 1852
HANCOCK CONCRETE PRODUCTS INC.—See CRH plc; *Int'l*, pg. 1846
HANCOCK COUNTY SAVINGS BANK, F.S.B.; *U.S. Private*, pg. 1852
HANCOCK FABRICS, INC.; *U.S. Private*, pg. 1852
HANCOCK & GORE LTD.; *Int'l*, pg. 3242
HANCOCK LUMBER COMPANY, INC.; *U.S. Private*, pg. 1852
HANCOCK & MOORE INC.; *U.S. Private*, pg. 1852
HANCOCK NATURAL RESOURCE GROUP INC.—See Manulife Financial Corporation; *Int'l*, pg. 4678
HANCOCK PARK ASSOCIATES, LP; *U.S. Private*, pg. 1852
HANCOCK PARK CORPORATE INCOME, INC.; *U.S. Private*, pg. 1852
HANCOCK PROSPECTING PTY. LTD.; *Int'l*, pg. 3242
HANCOCK SIGMA SENSING INC—See Synex Renewable Energy Corporation; *Int'l*, pg. 7385
HANCOCKS PHARMACY & SURGICAL; *U.S. Private*, pg. 1852
HANCOCK TIMBER RESOURCE GROUP—See Manulife Financial Corporation; *Int'l*, pg. 4678
HANCOCK WHITNEY BANK—See Hancock Whitney Corporation; *U.S. Public*, pg. 982
HANCOCK WHITNEY CORPORATION; *U.S. Public*, pg. 982
HANCOCK WHITNEY INVESTMENT SERVICES, INC.—See Hancock Whitney Corporation; *U.S. Public*, pg. 982
HANCOCK-WOOD ELECTRIC COOP INC.; *U.S. Private*, pg. 1852
HANCOM FINTECH, INC.—See Hancom, Inc.; *Int'l*, pg. 3242
HANCOM GMD INC.—See Hancom With Inc.; *Int'l*, pg. 3242
HANCOM, INC.; *Int'l*, pg. 3242

HANCOM INTERFREE, INC.—See Hancom, Inc.; *Int'l*, pg. 3243
HANCOM LIFECARE INC.; *Int'l*, pg. 3242
HANCOM MDS (SHENZHEN) TECHNOLOGY LTD. CO.—See Hancom, Inc.; *Int'l*, pg. 3243
HANCOMM INC.—See Hanwha Group; *Int'l*, pg. 3264
HANCOM TALKAFE INC.—See Hancom, Inc.; *Int'l*, pg. 3243
HANCOM WITH INC.; *Int'l*, pg. 3242
HANDA CASTING COMPANY—See Toyota Industries Corporation; *Int'l*, pg. 7866
HANDAL & ASSOCIATES, INC.—See Greenspoon Marder LLP; *U.S. Private*, pg. 1780
HANDAL ENERGY BERHAD; *Int'l*, pg. 3243
HANDA MINING CORPORATION; *Int'l*, pg. 3243
HANDAN BAOHE AUTOMOBILE SALES AND SERVICE CO., LTD.—See China Yongda Automobiles Services Holdings Limited; *Int'l*, pg. 1564
HANDAN CHENGUANG PRECIOUS OIL CO., LTD—See Chenguang Biotech Group Co., Ltd.; *Int'l*, pg. 1470
HANDAN JISHAN REAL ESTATE DEVELOPMENT CO., LTD.—See China Jishan Holdings Limited; *Int'l*, pg. 1513
HANDAN XURI COMMERCIAL & INDUSTRIAL CO., LTD.; *Int'l*, pg. 3243
HANDA PHARMACEUTICALS, INC.; *U.S. Private*, pg. 1852
HAND ARNOLD TRINIDAD LIMITED—See Agostini's Limited; *Int'l*, pg. 213
HANDAV KFT.—See Nayax Ltd.; *Int'l*, pg. 5178
HAND CONSTRUCTION, LLC.; *U.S. Private*, pg. 1852
HANDCRAFT CLEANERS AND LAUNDERERS INC.—See Puritan Cleaners; *U.S. Private*, pg. 3306
HANDCRAFTED HOMES, LLC—See Innovative Building Systems LLC; *U.S. Private*, pg. 2082
HANDCRAFTED WINES, LLC; *U.S. Private*, pg. 1852
HANDE AS—See Veidekke ASA; *Int'l*, pg. 8148
HANDEE MART FOOD STORES INC.; *U.S. Private*, pg. 1852
HANDEE MARTS, INC.—See Seven & i Holdings Co., Ltd.; *Int'l*, pg. 6731
HANDELSBANKEN ASSET MANAGEMENT—See Svenska Handelsbanken AB; *Int'l*, pg. 7358
HANDELSBANKEN CAPITAL MARKETS—See Svenska Handelsbanken AB; *Int'l*, pg. 7358
HANDELSBANKEN DENMARK—See Svenska Handelsbanken AB; *Int'l*, pg. 7358
HANDELSBANKEN FINANS AB—See Svenska Handelsbanken AB; *Int'l*, pg. 7358
HANDELSBANKEN FINLAND—See Svenska Handelsbanken AB; *Int'l*, pg. 7358
HANDELSBANKEN FONDBOLAG AB—See Svenska Handelsbanken AB; *Int'l*, pg. 7358
HANDELSBANKEN FONDER AB—See Svenska Handelsbanken AB; *Int'l*, pg. 7358
HANDELSBANKEN INFORMATION SYSTEMS DEPARTMENT—See Svenska Handelsbanken AB; *Int'l*, pg. 7358
HANDELSBANKEN KAPITALFORVALTNING AS—See Svenska Handelsbanken AB; *Int'l*, pg. 7358
HANDELSBANKEN LIV FORSAKRINGS AB—See Svenska Handelsbanken AB; *Int'l*, pg. 7358
HANDELSBANKEN LIV—See Svenska Handelsbanken AB; *Int'l*, pg. 7358
HANDELSBANKEN MARKETS SECURITIES, INC—See Svenska Handelsbanken AB; *Int'l*, pg. 7358
HANDELSBANKEN NORWAY—See Svenska Handelsbanken AB; *Int'l*, pg. 7358
HANDELSBANKEN RAHOITUS OY—See Oma Saastopankki Oyj; *Int'l*, pg. 5559
HANDELSBANKEN WEALTH & ASSET MANAGEMENT LIMITED—See Svenska Handelsbanken AB; *Int'l*, pg. 7358
HANDELSBLATT-DOW JONES GMBH—See Verlagsgruppe Georg von Holtzbrinck GmbH; *Int'l*, pg. 8172
HANDELSGESELLSCHAFT HEINRICH HEINE GMBH—See Otto GmbH & Co. KG; *Int'l*, pg. 5662
HANDELSINVEST INVESTERINGSFORVALTNING A/S—See Svenska Handelsbanken AB; *Int'l*, pg. 7358
HANDENI GOLD INC.; *Int'l*, pg. 3243
HANDENKO CORPORATION—See Kandenko Co., Ltd.; *Int'l*, pg. 4065
HANDEN SP. Z O.O.—See EnBW Energie Baden-Wurttemberg AG; *Int'l*, pg. 2400
HAND ENTERPRISE SOLUTIONS CO., LTD.; *Int'l*, pg. 3243
HAND ENTERPRISE USA, INC.—See Hand Enterprise Solutions Co., Ltd.; *Int'l*, pg. 3243
HANDEX CONSULTING AND REMEDIATION, LLC; *U.S. Private*, pg. 1852
HANDFORD GENERAL CONTRACTORS; *U.S. Private*, pg. 1852
HANDFORTH VETS4PETS LIMITED—See Pets at Home Group Plc; *Int'l*, pg. 5834
HANDGARDS INC.—See Wind Point Advisors LLC; *U.S. Private*, pg. 4534
HANDHELD GERMANY GMBH—See MilDef Group AB; *Int'l*, pg. 4894

THE HANDY/KENLIN GROUP

HAND HELD PRODUCTS, INC—See Honeywell International Inc.; *U.S. Public*, pg. 1047
HANDHELD SWISS GMBH—See MilDef Group AB; *Int'l*, pg. 4894
HANDICAPPED PETS, INC.—See Inflexion Private Equity Partners LLP; *Int'l*, pg. 3689
HANDICARE AS—See Savaria Corporation; *Int'l*, pg. 6596
HANDICARE GROUP AB—See Savaria Corporation; *Int'l*, pg. 6596
HANDI-HOUSE MANUFACTURING CO.; *U.S. Private*, pg. 1852
HANDI QUILTER, INC.—See Branford Castle, Inc.; *U.S. Private*, pg. 639
HANDI-RAMP; *U.S. Private*, pg. 1852
HANDISOFT SOFTWARE (PTY) LTD—See The Sage Group plc; *Int'l*, pg. 7679
HANDLERY HOTELS INC.; *U.S. Private*, pg. 1853
HANDLEY FUNERALS PTY LTD—See Propel Funeral Partners Limited; *Int'l*, pg. 5997
HANDLING COUNTS GMBH—See Deutsche Lufthansa AG; *Int'l*, pg. 2066
HANDLING SYSTEMS INC.; *U.S. Private*, pg. 1853
HANDLING SYSTEMS SAS—See VINCI S.A.; *Int'l*, pg. 8222
HANDL-IT INC.; *U.S. Private*, pg. 1852
H AND M HENNES AND MAURITZ PROPRIETARY LIMITED—See H&M Hennes & Mauritz AB; *Int'l*, pg. 3192
HANDOK CLEAN TECH CO., LTD.; *Int'l*, pg. 3243
HANDOK INC. - HANDOK EUMSEONG FACTORY—See Handok Inc.; *Int'l*, pg. 3243
HANDOK INC.; *Int'l*, pg. 3243
HANDPIECE HEADQUARTERS CORP.—See Henry Schein, Inc.; *U.S. Public*, pg. 1025
HAND-PROD SP. Z O. O.—See Interogo Holding AG; *Int'l*, pg. 3754
HANDS CORPORATION LTD. - HANDS 1 PLANT—See Hands Corporation Ltd.; *Int'l*, pg. 3243
HANDS CORPORATION LTD. - HANDS 2 PLANT—See Hands Corporation Ltd.; *Int'l*, pg. 3243
HANDS CORPORATION LTD. - HANDS 3 PLANT—See Hands Corporation Ltd.; *Int'l*, pg. 3243
HANDS CORPORATION LTD. - HANDS 5 PLANT—See Hands Corporation Ltd.; *Int'l*, pg. 3243
HANDS CORPORATION LTD. - HANDS 6 PLANT—See Hands Corporation Ltd.; *Int'l*, pg. 3243
HANDS CORPORATION LTD. - HANDS MECHANIC PLANT—See Hands Corporation Ltd.; *Int'l*, pg. 3243
HANDS CORPORATION LTD. - HANDS THUMB PLANT—See Hands Corporation Ltd.; *Int'l*, pg. 3243
HANDS CORPORATION LTD.; *Int'l*, pg. 3243
HANDS FORM HOLDINGS LIMITED; *Int'l*, pg. 3243
HANDSHAKE NETWORKING CO., LTD.—See Guardforce AI Co., Limited; *Int'l*, pg. 3169
HANDSMAN CO., LTD.; *Int'l*, pg. 3243
HANDSOME CHEMICAL DEVELOPMENT LIMITED—See Yips Chemical Holdings Limited; *Int'l*, pg. 8585
HANDSOME CHEMICAL SERVICES LIMITED—See Yips Chemical Holdings Limited; *Int'l*, pg. 8585
HANDSOME CORP.; *Int'l*, pg. 3243
HANDSOME REWARDS—See Starcrest Products of California; *U.S. Private*, pg. 3786
HANDSON3, LLC; *U.S. Private*, pg. 1853
HANDS ON EDUCATION CONSULTANTS CO., LTD.—See Graham Holdings Company; *U.S. Public*, pg. 955
HANDS-ON LEARNING SOLUTIONS LLC; *U.S. Private*, pg. 1853
HANDSON PARTICIPACOES S.A.—See Cosan S.A.; *Int'l*, pg. 1809
HANDSTAND INNOVATIONS LLC; *U.S. Private*, pg. 1853
HAND THERAPY ASSOCIATES, INC.—See Select Medical Holdings Corporation; *U.S. Public*, pg. 1858
HANDVAERKERGARDEN A/S—See Per Aarsleff Holding A/S; *Int'l*, pg. 5795
HANDWERKER PROMOTION E. GMBH—See DEAG Deutsche Entertainment AG; *Int'l*, pg. 1998
HANDY BUICK-GMC-CADILLAC INC.; *U.S. Private*, pg. 1853
HANDY BUTTON MACHINE COMPANY—See The Handy/Kenlin Group; *U.S. Private*, pg. 4043
HANDY CHEMICALS LTD.—See Rain Industries Limited; *Int'l*, pg. 6189
HANDY FOOD STORES INC.—See B&B Corporate Holdings, Inc.; *U.S. Private*, pg. 417
HANDY HARDWARE WHOLESALE INC.—See Littlejohn & Co.; *U.S. Private*, pg. 2470
HANDY & HARMAN GROUP, LTD.—See Steel Partners Holdings L.P.; *U.S. Public*, pg. 1942
HANDY & HARMAN LTD.—See Steel Partners Holdings L.P.; *U.S. Public*, pg. 1942
HANDY & HARMAN LTD.—See Steel Partners Holdings L.P.; *U.S. Public*, pg. 1942
HANDY & HARMAN MANUFACTURING (SINGAPORE) PTE. LTD.—See Steel Partners Holdings L.P.; *U.S. Public*, pg. 1942
HANDY & HARMAN TUBE CO., INC.—See Steel Partners Holdings L.P.; *U.S. Public*, pg. 1942
THE HANDY/KENLIN GROUP; *U.S. Private*, pg. 4042

THE HANDY/KENLIN GROUP

CORPORATE AFFILIATIONS

HANDYMAN—See Momar, Inc.; *U.S. Private*, pg. 2768
THE HANDYMAN VAN LIMITED—See Franchise Brands plc; *Int'l*, pg. 2760
HANDY NETWORK INTERNATIONAL CO., LTD.; *Int'l*, pg. 3244
HANDYSOFT, INC.; *Int'l*, pg. 3244
HANDY STORE FIXTURES, INC.; *U.S. Private*, pg. 1853
HANDYTUBE CORPORATION—See Steel Partners Holdings L.P.; *U.S. Public*, pg. 1943
HANDY TV INC.; *U.S. Private*, pg. 1853
HANDY WACKS CORPORATION; *U.S. Private*, pg. 1853
HANE CO., LTD.—See Kaneka Corporation; *Int'l*, pg. 4067
HANEDA FUTURE RESEARCH INSTITUTE INCORPORATED—See Japan Airport Terminal Co., Ltd.; *Int'l*, pg. 3885
HANEDA KEIKYU BUS CO., LTD.—See Keikyu Corporation; *Int'l*, pg. 4117
HANEDA ZENITH HOLDINGS CO., LTD.; *Int'l*, pg. 3244
HANEI.LIMITED—See Sapporo Holdings Limited; *Int'l*, pg. 6573
HANEKAMP BUSREISEN GMBH—See Deutsche Bahn AG; *Int'l*, pg. 2051
HANENKRATT GRAIN CO., INC.; *U.S. Private*, pg. 1853
HANERGY AMERICA SOLAR SOLUTIONS—See Hanergy Holding Group Limited; *Int'l*, pg. 3244
HANERGY HOLDING GROUP LIMITED; *Int'l*, pg. 3244
HANERGY SOLAR POWER (EUROPE) B. V.—See Hanergy Holding Group Limited; *Int'l*, pg. 3244
HANERGY SOLAR POWER (ITALY) S.R.L.—See Hanergy Holding Group Limited; *Int'l*, pg. 3244
HANERON CO., LTD.—See Soft99 Corporation; *Int'l*, pg. 7051
HANES AUSTRALASIA PTY LTD—See Hanesbrands Inc.; *U.S. Public*, pg. 983
HANES AUSTRIA GMBH—See Hanesbrands Inc.; *U.S. Public*, pg. 983
HANES BODYWEAR GERMANY GMBH—See Hanesbrands Inc.; *U.S. Public*, pg. 983
HANESBRANDS BRAZIL TEXTIL LTDA.—See Hanesbrands Inc.; *U.S. Public*, pg. 983
HANESBRANDS DIRECT, LLC—See Hanesbrands Inc.; *U.S. Public*, pg. 983
HANESBRANDS INC.; *U.S. Public*, pg. 982
HANESBRANDS PHILIPPINES INC.—See Hanesbrands Inc.; *U.S. Public*, pg. 983
HANESBRANDS ROH ASIA LTD.—See Hanesbrands Inc.; *U.S. Public*, pg. 983
HANES COMPANIES, INC.—See Leggett & Platt, Incorporated; *U.S. Public*, pg. 1302
HANES COMPANIES - NEW JERSEY, LLC—See Leggett & Platt, Incorporated; *U.S. Public*, pg. 1302
HANES DYE & FINISHING—See Leggett & Platt, Incorporated; *U.S. Public*, pg. 1302
HANES FRANCE S.A.S.—See Hanesbrands Inc.; *U.S. Public*, pg. 982
HANES GEO COMPONENTS—See Leggett & Platt, Incorporated; *U.S. Public*, pg. 1302
HANES GERMANY GMBH—See Hanesbrands Inc.; *U.S. Public*, pg. 983
HANES INDUSTRIES—See Leggett & Platt, Incorporated; *U.S. Public*, pg. 1302
HANES ITALY SRL—See Hanesbrands Inc.; *U.S. Public*, pg. 983
HANES POLAND SP. Z O.O.—See Hanesbrands Inc.; *U.S. Public*, pg. 983
HANES SOUTH AFRICA (PTY) LIMITED—See Hanesbrands Inc.; *U.S. Public*, pg. 983
HANES SUPPLY INC.; *U.S. Private*, pg. 1853
HANEXPRESS CO, LTD.; *Int'l*, pg. 3244
HAN EXPRESS ENERGY SDN. BHD.—See HANEXPRESS CO, LTD.; *Int'l*, pg. 3244
HANEXPRESS LOGISTICS (NINGBO) CO., LTD—See HANEXPRESS CO, LTD.; *Int'l*, pg. 3244
HAN EXPRESS VIETNAM CO., LTD.—See HANEXPRESS CO, LTD.; *Int'l*, pg. 3244
HANEY BUILDERS' SUPPLIES (1971) LTD.; *Int'l*, pg. 3244
HANEY TRUCK LINE LLC - PORTLAND—See Evergreen Pacific Partners Management Co., Inc.; *U.S. Private*, pg. 1440
HANEY TRUCK LINE LLC—See Evergreen Pacific Partners Management Co., Inc.; *U.S. Private*, pg. 1440
HANFANG TRADING COMPANY LIMITED—See Hua Han Health Industry Holdings Limited; *Int'l*, pg. 3509
HAN FENG, INC.—See HF Foods Group Inc; *U.S. Public*, pg. 1033
HANFORD CHRYSLER-DODGE-JEEP, INC.; *U.S. Private*, pg. 1853
HANFORD DIALYSIS, LLC—See DaVita Inc.; *U.S. Public*, pg. 639
HANFORD HOTELS INC.; *U.S. Private*, pg. 1853
HANFORD SENTINEL, INC.—See Lee Enterprises, Incorporated; *U.S. Public*, pg. 1299
HANFT RABOY & PARTNERS; *U.S. Private*, pg. 1853
HANGAR 8 ENGINEERING LIMITED—See Gama Aviation plc; *Int'l*, pg. 2876
HANGAR 8 MANAGEMENT LIMITED—See Gama Aviation plc; *Int'l*, pg. 2876

HANGARTNER TERMINAL S.R.L.—See Deutsche Bahn AG; *Int'l*, pg. 2051
HANGCHA GROUP CO., LTD.—See GreatStar Group Co., Ltd.; *Int'l*, pg. 3067
HANG CHEUNG COATINGS (ZHEJIANG) LIMITED—See Yips Chemical Holdings Limited; *Int'l*, pg. 8585
HANG CHI HOLDINGS LIMITED; *Int'l*, pg. 3244
HANG CHUI COMPANY LIMITED—See Hang Lung Group Limited; *Int'l*, pg. 3245
HANGER ADVANCED BIO-MECHANICS INC.—See Patient Square Capital, L.P.; *U.S. Private*, pg. 3107
HANGER CLINIC-MOBILE; *U.S. Private*, pg. 1853
HANGERDORREN AB—See Ratos AB; *Int'l*, pg. 6220
HANGER FABRICATION NETWORK LLC—See Patient Square Capital, L.P.; *U.S. Private*, pg. 3107
HANGER, INC.—See Patient Square Capital, L.P.; *U.S. Private*, pg. 3106
THE HANGER LIMITED—See Minor International PCL; *Int'l*, pg. 4913
HANGER PROSTHETIC & ORTHOTICS, INC.—See Patient Square Capital, L.P.; *U.S. Private*, pg. 3107
HANGER PROSTHETICS & ORTHOTICS EAST, INC.—See Patient Square Capital, L.P.; *U.S. Private*, pg. 3107
HANG FAR COMPANY LIMITED—See Hang Lung Group Limited; *Int'l*, pg. 3245
HANG FINE COMPANY LIMITED—See Hang Lung Group Limited; *Int'l*, pg. 3245
HANG FUNG INTERNATIONAL INDUSTRIAL CO., LTD.; *Int'l*, pg. 3244
HANGGU CRANETEK CO., LTD.—See Mitsui & Co., Ltd.; *Int'l*, pg. 4980
HANG JIAN TECHNOLOGY CO., LTD.—See Wha Yu Industrial Co., Ltd.; *Int'l*, pg. 8396
HANGJI GLOBAL LIMITED; *Int'l*, pg. 3246
HANG JIN TECHNOLOGY CO., LTD.; *Int'l*, pg. 3244
HANG KWOK COMPANY LIMITED—See Hang Lung Group Limited; *Int'l*, pg. 3245
HANG LUNG (ADMINISTRATION) LIMITED—See Hang Lung Group Limited; *Int'l*, pg. 3245
HANG LUNG FINANCIAL SERVICES LIMITED—See Hang Lung Group Limited; *Int'l*, pg. 3245
HANG LUNG GROUP LIMITED; *Int'l*, pg. 3244
HANG LUNG PROJECT MANAGEMENT LIMITED—See Hang Lung Group Limited; *Int'l*, pg. 3245
HANG LUNG PROPERTIES LIMITED—See Hang Lung Group Limited; *Int'l*, pg. 3245
HANG LUNG PROPERTY MANAGEMENT LIMITED—See Hang Lung Group Limited; *Int'l*, pg. 3245
HANG LUNG REAL ESTATE AGENCY LIMITED—See Hang Lung Group Limited; *Int'l*, pg. 3245
HANG LUNG TREASURY LIMITED—See Hang Lung Group Limited; *Int'l*, pg. 3245
HANGOOK MCDONALD'S CO. LTD.—See McDonald's Corporation; *U.S. Public*, pg. 1406
HANGOUT HOTELS INTERNATIONAL PTE LTD—See Cathay Organisation Holdings Ltd; *Int'l*, pg. 1360
HANGOVER JOE'S HOLDING CORPORATION; *U.S. Private*, pg. 1853
HANG PIN LIVING TECHNOLOGY COMPANY LIMITED; *Int'l*, pg. 3245
HANG SANG (SIU PO) INTERNATIONAL HOLDING COMPANY LIMITED; *Int'l*, pg. 3245
HANG SENG BANK (CHINA) LIMITED—See HSBC Holdings plc; *Int'l*, pg. 3506
HANG SENG BANK LIMITED—See HSBC Holdings plc; *Int'l*, pg. 3507
HANG SENG INSURANCE COMPANY LIMITED—See HSBC Holdings plc; *Int'l*, pg. 3506
HANG SENG INVESTMENT MANAGEMENT LIMITED—See HSBC Holdings plc; *Int'l*, pg. 3506
HANG TAI YUE GROUP HOLDINGS LIMITED; *Int'l*, pg. 3245
HANG TEN ENTERPRISES (M) SDN BHD—See Li & Fung Limited; *Int'l*, pg. 4479
HANG TEN ENTERPRISES (PTE) LTD.—See Li & Fung Limited; *Int'l*, pg. 4479
HANG TEN GROUP HOLDINGS LIMITED—See Li & Fung Limited; *Int'l*, pg. 4479
HANG TEN PHILS., CORP.—See Li & Fung Limited; *Int'l*, pg. 4479
HANG UP SHOPPES INC.; *U.S. Private*, pg. 1853
HANG XANH MOTORS SERVICE JOINT STOCK COMPANY; *Int'l*, pg. 3245
HANGXIAO STEEL STRUCTURE CO., LTD.; *Int'l*, pg. 3246
HANG YICK HOLDINGS COMPANY LIMITED; *Int'l*, pg. 3245
HANG YICK PROPERTIES MANAGEMENT LIMITED—See Henderson Land Development Co. Ltd.; *Int'l*, pg. 3344
HANG YUE TONG COMPANY LIMITED—See Xiamen C&D Inc.; *Int'l*, pg. 8523
HANGZHI MACHINERY & ELECTRONICS CO., LTD.—See Japan Industrial Partners, Inc.; *Int'l*, pg. 3889
HANGZHOU ADVANCE FORGING CO., LTD.—See Hangzhou Advance Gearbox Group Co., Ltd.; *Int'l*, pg. 3246

HANGZHOU ADVANCE FOUNDRY CO., LTD.—See Hangzhou Advance Gearbox Group Co., Ltd.; *Int'l*, pg. 3246
HANGZHOU ADVANCE GEARBOX GROUP CO., LTD.; *Int'l*, pg. 3246
HANGZHOU ADVANCE GENERAL MACHINERY CO., LTD.—See Hangzhou Advance Gearbox Group Co., Ltd.; *Int'l*, pg. 3246
HANGZHOU ADVANCE MASSON MARINE TRANSMISSION CO., LTD.—See Hangzhou Advance Gearbox Group Co., Ltd.; *Int'l*, pg. 3246
HANGZHOU ADVANCE WIND-POWER GEARBOX CO., LTD.—See Hangzhou Advance Gearbox Group Co., Ltd.; *Int'l*, pg. 3246
HANGZHOU AGS MED TECH CO. LTD.—See Da An Gene Co., Ltd.; *Int'l*, pg. 1901
HANGZHOU ALLTEST BIOTECH CO., LTD.; *Int'l*, pg. 3246
HANGZHOU AMPHENOL JET INTERCONNECT TECHNOLOGY CO. LTD.—See Amphenol Corporation; *U.S. Public*, pg. 130
HANGZHOU AMPHENOL PHOENIX TELECOM PARTS CO., LTD.—See Amphenol Corporation; *U.S. Public*, pg. 128
HANGZHOU AMPHENOL PHOENIX TELECOM PARTS CO. LTD.—See Amphenol Corporation; *U.S. Public*, pg. 130
HANGZHOU ANOW MICROFILTRATION CO., LTD.—See Entegris, Inc.; *U.S. Public*, pg. 777
HANGZHOU ANYSOFT INFORMATION TECH CO LTD; *Int'l*, pg. 3246
HANGZHOU AOYI POLLEN PHARMACEUTICAL CO., LTD.—See Shanxi C&Y Pharmaceutical Group Co., Ltd.; *Int'l*, pg. 6786
HANGZHOU ARCVIDEO TECHNOLOGY CO., LTD.; *Int'l*, pg. 3246
HANGZHOU ASAHIKASEI SPANDEX CO., LTD.—See Asahi Kasei Corporation; *Int'l*, pg. 596
HANGZHOU ASAHIKASEI TEXTILES CO., LTD.—See Asahi Kasei Corporation; *Int'l*, pg. 596
HANGZHOU ASLE E, CO. LTD.—See Onamba Co., Ltd.; *Int'l*, pg. 5573
HANGZHOU AUCHAN HYPERMARKET CO., LTD.—See Alibaba Group Holding Limited; *Int'l*, pg. 326
HANGZHOU BINJIANG REAL ESTATE GROUP CO., LTD.; *Int'l*, pg. 3246
HANGZHOU BIO-SINCERITY PHARMA-TECH CO., LTD.; *Int'l*, pg. 3246
HANGZHOU BOILER GROUP ENGINEERING TRADING CO., LTD.—See Xizi Clean Energy Equipment Manufacturing Co., Ltd.; *Int'l*, pg. 8535
HANGZHOU BOILER GROUP GENERAL EQUIPMENT CO., LTD.—See Xizi Clean Energy Equipment Manufacturing Co., Ltd.; *Int'l*, pg. 8535
HANGZHOU BOILER GROUP INDUSTRIAL BOILER CO., LTD.—See Xizi Clean Energy Equipment Manufacturing Co., Ltd.; *Int'l*, pg. 8535
HANGZHOU BONYEE DAILY NECESSITY TECHNOLOGY CO., LTD.—See Hangzhou Nbond Nonwoven Co.,Ltd; *Int'l*, pg. 3249
HANGZHOU CABLE CO., LTD.; *Int'l*, pg. 3246
HANGZHOU CAIZHIXIN TECHNOLOGY CO., LTD.—See Dalian Thermal Power Co., Ltd.; *Int'l*, pg. 1952
HANGZHOU CENTURY CO., LTD.; *Int'l*, pg. 3246
HANGZHOU CHANG CHUAN TECHNOLOGY CO., LTD.; *Int'l*, pg. 3246
HANGZHOU CHUHUAN SCIENCE & TECHNOLOGY COMPANY LIMITED; *Int'l*, pg. 3246
HANGZHOU CITY INVESTMENT CONSTRUCTION CO., LTD.—See Long Yuan Construction Group Co., Ltd; *Int'l*, pg. 4549
HANGZHOU CNCR-IT CO., LTD.; *Int'l*, pg. 3247
HANGZHOU CNP-TSURUMI PUMP CO., LTD.—See Tsurumi Manufacturing Co., Ltd.; *Int'l*, pg. 7958
HANGZHOU COCO HEALTHCARE PRODUCTS CO., LTD.; *Int'l*, pg. 3247
HANGZHOU CONBA PHARMACEUTICAL CO., LTD.—See Zhejiang CONBA Pharmaceutical Co., Ltd.; *Int'l*, pg. 8650
HANGZHOU DADI HAIYANG ENVIRONMENTAL PROTECTION CO., LTD.; *Int'l*, pg. 3247
HANGZHOU DAHE THERMO-MAGNETICS CO., LTD. (FTH)—See Ferrotec Holdings Corporation; *Int'l*, pg. 2643
HANGZHOU DAHE THERMO-MAGNETICS CO., LTD. - QUARTZ DIVISION—See Ferrotec Holdings Corporation; *Int'l*, pg. 2643
HANGZHOU DAHE THERMO-MAGNETICS CO., LTD. - TE DIVISION—See Ferrotec Holdings Corporation; *Int'l*, pg. 2643
HANGZHOU DAHE THERMO-MAGNETICS CO., LTD. - VF DIVISION—See Ferrotec Holdings Corporation; *Int'l*, pg. 2643
HANGZHOU DAHUI FOAM PUMP COMPANY LTD—See Daiwa Can Company; *Int'l*, pg. 1944
HANGZHOU DANBI FOOD CO., LTD.—See Christine International Holdings Limited; *Int'l*, pg. 1587

COMPANY NAME INDEX

HANGZHOU DANWEI BIOLOGICAL TECHNOLOGY CO., LTD.—See Zhejiang Orient Gene Biotech Co., Ltd.; *Int'l*, pg. 8661

HANGZHOU DANWEI BIOTECHNOLOGY CO. LTD.—See Zhejiang Orient Gene Biotech Co., Ltd.; *Int'l*, pg. 8661

HANGZHOU DIGITAL CHINA LIMITED—See Digital China Holdings Limited; *Int'l*, pg. 2121

HANGZHOU DPTECH TECHNOLOGIES CO., LTD.; *Int'l*, pg. 3247

HANGZHOU EASTCOM CITY CO.LTD.—See Eastern communications Co., LTD.; *Int'l*, pg. 2272

HANGZHOU ELECTRONIC SOUL NETWORK TECHNOLOGY CO., LTD.; *Int'l*, pg. 3247

HANGZHOU ENERGY & ENVIRONMENTAL ENGINEERING CO,. LTD.—See WELLE Environmental Group Co., Ltd.; *Int'l*, pg. 8374

HANGZHOU EN'S GENE TECHNOLOGY DEVELOPEMENT CO., LTD.—See Shanxi C&Y Pharmaceutical Group Co., Ltd.; *Int'l*, pg. 6786

HANGZHOU EVERFINE PHOTO-E-INFO CO., LTD.; *Int'l*, pg. 3247

HANGZHOU FAIR FINE ELECTROMECHANICS CO., LTD.—See Fair Friend Group; *Int'l*, pg. 2604

HANGZHOU FEELER TAKAMATSU MACHINERY CO., LTD—See Takamatsu Machinery Co., Ltd.; *Int'l*, pg. 7430

HANGZHOU FIRST APPLIED MATERIAL CO., LTD.; *Int'l*, pg. 3247

HANGZHOU FREELY COMMUNICATION CO., LTD.; *Int'l*, pg. 3247

HANGZHOU FUJIKURA RUBBER LTD.—See Fujikura Composites Inc.; *Int'l*, pg. 2826

HANGZHOU FUSHENG ELECTRICAL APPLIANCE CO., LTD.—See Shanghai Highly (Group) Co., Ltd.; *Int'l*, pg. 6770

HANGZHOU GAOXIN RUBBER & PLASTIC MATERIALS CO., LTD.; *Int'l*, pg. 3247

HANGZHOU GLORY FRIEND MACHINERY TECHNOLOGY CO., LTD.—See Fair Friend Group; *Int'l*, pg. 2604

HANGZHOU GREAT STAR INDUSTRIAL CO., LTD.—See GreatStar Group Co., Ltd.; *Int'l*, pg. 3067

HANGZHOU GREENDA ELECTRONIC MATERIALS CO., LTD.; pg. 3247

HANGZHOU HANGGUO ELECTRIC TECHNOLOGY CO., LTD.—See Xizi Clean Energy Equipment Manufacturing Co., Ltd.; *Int'l*, pg. 8535

HANGZHOU HANGGUO TESTING TECHNOLOGY CO., LTD.—See Xizi Clean Energy Equipment Manufacturing Co., Ltd.; *Int'l*, pg. 8535

HANGZHOU HANGHUA-HARIMA CHEMICALS CO., LTD.—See Harima Chemicals Group, Inc.; *Int'l*, pg. 3276

HANGZHOU HANGMIN DAMEI DYEING & FINISHING CO. LTD.—See Zhejiang Hangmin Co., Ltd.; *Int'l*, pg. 8655

HANGZHOU HANGMIN MEISHIDA PRINTING & DYEING CO., LTD.—See Zhejiang Hangmin Co., Ltd.; *Int'l*, pg. 8655

HANGZHOU HANGMIN THERMAL ELECTRICITY CO., LTD.—See Zhejiang Hangmin Co., Ltd.; *Int'l*, pg. 8655

HANGZHOU HANGXIAO STEEL STRUCTURE CO. LTD.—See Hangxiao Steel Structure Co., Ltd.; *Int'l*, pg. 3246

HANGZHOU HAOYUE PERSONAL CARE CO., LTD.; *Int'l*, pg. 3247

HANGZHOU HAVECO AUTOMOTIVE TRANSMISSION CO., LTD.—See Hangzhou Advance Gearbox Group Co., Ltd.; *Int'l*, pg. 3246

HANGZHOU HESHUN TECHNOLOGY CO., LTD.; *Int'l*, pg. 3247

HANGZHOU HIKROBOT TECHNOLOGY CO., LTD.—See Hangzhou Hikvision Digital Technology Co., Ltd.; *Int'l*, pg. 3247

HANGZHOU HIKVISION DIGITAL TECHNOLOGY CO., LTD.; *Int'l*, pg. 3247

HANGZHOU HI-LEX CABLE SYSTEMS CO., LTD.—See Hi-Lex Corporation; *Int'l*, pg. 3380

HANGZHOU HI-TECH CONTROL TECHNOLOGY CO., LTD.—See Shanghai Hi-Tech Control System CO., LTD.; *Int'l*, pg. 6770

HANGZHOU HOLYCORE COMPOSITE MATERIAL CO., LTD.—See Zhejiang Wazam New Materials Group Co., Ltd.; *Int'l*, pg. 8665

HANGZHOU HONGSHENG ZHONGHONG NEW ENERGY CO., LTD.—See Hongsheng Heat Exchanger Manufacturing Co.,ltd; *Int'l*, pg. 3471

HANGZHOU HOPECHART IOT TECHNOLOGY CO., LTD.; *Int'l*, pg. 3248

HANGZHOU HOTA M & E HOLDINGS CO., LTD.; *Int'l*, pg. 3248

HANGZHOU HUAAN TESTING TECHNOLOGY CO., LTD.—See Centre Testing International Corporation; *Int'l*, pg. 1411

HANGZHOU HUADIAN BANSHAN POWER GENERATION COMPANY LIMITED—See Huadian Power International Corporation Limited; *Int'l*, pg. 3511

HANGZHOU HUAGUANG ADVANCED WELDING MATERIALS CO., LTD.; *Int'l*, pg. 3248

HANGZHOU HUAWANG NEW MATERIAL TECHNOLOGY CO., LTD.; *Int'l*, pg. 3248

HANGZHOU HUAXING CHUANGYE COMMUNICATION TECHNOLOGY STOCK CO., LTD.; *Int'l*, pg. 3248

HANGZHOU HUAXIN MECHANICAL & ELECTRICAL ENGINEERING CO., LTD.—See Zhuzhou Tianqiao Crane Co., Ltd.; *Int'l*, pg. 8680

HANGZHOU HUIKANG HUAZHUO IMPORT & EXPORT TRADE CO., LTD.—See JNBY Design Limited; *Int'l*, pg. 3976

HANGZHOU HUNING ELEVATOR PARTS CO., LTD.; *Int'l*, pg. 3248

HANGZHOU HUVIS YONGSHENG DYEING & FINISHING COMPANY LIMITED—See Yongsheng Advanced Materials Company Limited; *Int'l*, pg. 8597

HANGZHOU IECHO SCIENCE & TECHNOLOGY CO., LTD.; *Int'l*, pg. 3248

HANGZHOU INNOVER TECHNOLOGY CO., LTD.; *Int'l*, pg. 3248

HANGZHOU IRON & STEEL CO., LTD.; *Int'l*, pg. 3248

HANGZHOU JALCO ELECTRONICS CO., LTD.—See Tohoku Tatsumi KK; *Int'l*, pg. 7777

HANGZHOU JIEBAI GROUP CO., LTD.; *Int'l*, pg. 3248

HANGZHOU JIHUA POLYMER MATERIAL CO., LTD.—See Jihua Group Corporation Limited; *Int'l*, pg. 3963

HANGZHOU JINCHEN MEDICAL SUPPLIES MANUFACTURE CO., LTD.—See Medtecs International Corporation Limited; *Int'l*, pg. 4786

HANGZHOU JIUZHOU GRAND PHARMACY CHAIN CO., LTD.—See CHINA JO-JO DRUGSTORES, INC.; *Int'l*, pg. 1513

HANGZHOU JIZHI MECHATRONIC CO., LTD.; *Int'l*, pg. 3249

HANGZHOU JOYSHINE IMP.& EXP. CO., LTD.—See Joy Kie Corporation Limited; *Int'l*, pg. 4004

HANGZHOU JUHESHUN NEW MATERIAL CO., LTD.; *Int'l*, pg. 3249

HANGZHOU JUI LI JIAHE AUTO PARTS CO., LTD.—See Jui Li Enterprise Co., Ltd.; *Int'l*, pg. 4022

HANGZHOU KANGJI MEDICAL INSTRUMENT LTD.—See Kangji Medical Holdings Limited; *Int'l*, pg. 4070

HANGZHOU KELIN ELECTRIC CO., LTD.; *Int'l*, pg. 3249

HANGZHOU KEWPIE CORPORATION—See Kewpie Corporation; *Int'l*, pg. 4144

HANGZHOU KOBELCO CONSTRUCTION MACHINERY CO., LTD.—See Kobe Steel, Ltd.; *Int'l*, pg. 4217

HANGZHOU LANDSCAPE ARCHITECTURE DESIGN INSTITUTE CO., LTD.; *Int'l*, pg. 3249

HANGZHOU LANDSCAPING CO., LTD.; *Int'l*, pg. 3249

HANGZHOU LANTRO CO., LTD.—See MIRAIT ONE Corporation; *Int'l*, pg. 4917

HANGZHOU LIANLUO INTERACTIVE INFORMATION TECHNOLOGY CO., LTD.; *Int'l*, pg. 3249

HANGZHOU LIANSHENG INSULATION CO., LTD.—See Zhejiang Wazam New Materials Group Co., Ltd.; *Int'l*, pg. 8665

HANGZHOU LION ELECTRONICS CO., LTD.; *Int'l*, pg. 3249

HANGZHOU LONGSHAN CHEMICAL INDUSTRY LTD.—See Zhejiang Longsheng Group Co., Ltd.; *Int'l*, pg. 8659

HANGZHOU MARY KAY COSMETICS CO. LTD.—See Mary Kay Holding Corporation; *U.S. Private*, pg. 2599

HANGZHOU MCN PAPER TECH CO., LTD.—See Huazhang Technology Holding Limited; *Int'l*, pg. 3516

HANGZHOU MDK OPTO ELECTRONIC CORP., LTD.; *Int'l*, pg. 3249

HANGZHOU MEIBAH PRECISION MACHINERY CO., LTD.; *Int'l*, pg. 3249

HANGZHOU MPS SEMICONDUCTOR TECHNOLOGY LTD.—See Monolithic Power Systems, Inc.; *U.S. Public*, pg. 1464

HANGZHOU MULTI-COLOR OPTOELECTRICAL CO., LTD.—See Hangzhou Silan Microelectronics Co., Ltd.; *Int'l*, pg. 3250

HANGZHOU NBOND NONWOVEN CO.,LTD; *Int'l*, pg. 3249

HANGZHOU NEOHALO BIOTECHNOLOGY LIMITED—See New Horizon Health Limited; *Int'l*, pg. 5225

HANGZHOU NEW CENTURY ENERGY ENVIRONMENTAL PROTECTION ENGINEERING CO., LTD.—See Xizi Clean Energy Equipment Manufacturing Co., Ltd.; *Int'l*, pg. 8535

HANGZHOU NEW HUAHAI BUSINESS & TRADING CO., LTD.—See ITOCHU Corporation; *Int'l*, pg. 3836

HANGZHOU NIAGRA REAL ESTATES COMPANY LIMITED—See China City Infrastructure Group Limited; *Int'l*, pg. 1489

HANG ZHOU NIKON CAMERA CO., LTD.—See Nikon Corporation; *Int'l*, pg. 5292

HANGZHOU OLEOCHEMICALS CO.,LTD.—See Zanyu Technology Group Co., Ltd.; *Int'l*, pg. 8624

HANGZHOU ONECHANCE TECHNOLOGY CORP.; *Int'l*, pg. 3249

HANGZHOU OPTCLA MEDICAL INSTRUMENT CO., LTD.—See Mindray Medical International Ltd.; *Int'l*, pg. 4901

HANGZHOU OXYGEN PLANT GROUP CO., LTD.; pg. 3249

HANGZHOU PAX ELECTRONIC TECHNOLOGY LIMITED—See Hi Sun Technology (China) Limited; *Int'l*, pg. 3380

HANGZHOU PINMING SOFTWARE CO., LTD.; pg. 3249

HANGZHOU PREVAIL OPTOELECTRONIC EQUIPMENT CO., LTD.; *Int'l*, pg. 3249

HANGZHOU QIANJIANG PRINTING & DYEING CO., LTD.—See Zhejiang Hangmin Co., Ltd.; *Int'l*, pg. 8655

HANGZHOU QIANJING TECHNOLOGY CO., LTD.—See Shenzhen Megmeet Electrical Co.,Ltd; *Int'l*, pg. 6817

HANGZHOU QINGSHAN LAKE FOREST SILICON VALLEY DEVELOPMENT CO., LTD.—See Long Yuan Construction Group Co., Ltd; *Int'l*, pg. 4549

HANGZHOU RADICAL ENERGY SAVING TECHNOLOGY CO., LTD.; *Int'l*, pg. 3249

HANGZHOU RAYCLOUD TECHNOLOGY CO., LTD.; *Int'l*, pg. 3250

HANGZHOU RICHAO MACHINERY & ELECTRONICS CO., LTD.—See Ningbo Henghe Precision Industry Co., Ltd.; *Int'l*, pg. 5302

HANGZHOU ROBAM APPLIANCES CO., LTD.; *Int'l*, pg. 3250

HANGZHOU SANXIANG IMPRESSION REAL ESTATE CO., LTD.—See Sanxiang Impression Co., Ltd.; *Int'l*, pg. 6561

HANGZHOU SECK INTELLIGENT TECHNOLOGY CO., LTD.; *Int'l*, pg. 3250

HANGZHOU SEI-FUTONG OPTICAL FIBER CO., LTD.—See Sumitomo Electric Industries, Ltd.; *Int'l*, pg. 7278

HANGZHOU SEMICONDUCTOR WAFER CO., LTD.—See Ferrotec Holdings Corporation; *Int'l*, pg. 2643

HANGZHOU SF INTRA-CITY INDUSTRIAL CO., LTD.; *Int'l*, pg. 3250

HANGZHOU SHENHAO TECHNOLOGY CO., LTD.; pg. 3250

HANGZHOU SHINEDO TECHNOLOGY CO.,LTD.—See Zhejiang Orient Gene Biotech Co., Ltd.; *Int'l*, pg. 8661

HANGZHOU SHINIH FIBER PRODUCTS CO., LTD.—See Shinih Enterprise Co., Ltd.; *Int'l*, pg. 6845

HANGZHOU SHUNWANG TECHNOLOGY CO., LTD.; *Int'l*, pg. 3250

HANGZHOU SILAN AZURE CO., LTD.—See Hangzhou Silan Microelectronics Co., Ltd.; *Int'l*, pg. 3250

HANGZHOU SILAN INTEGRATED CIRCUIT CO., LTD.—See Hangzhou Silan Microelectronics Co., Ltd.; *Int'l*, pg. 3250

HANGZHOU SILAN MICROELECTRONICS CO., LTD.; *Int'l*, pg. 3250

HANGZHOU SILAN OPTRONICS TECHNOLOGY CO., LTD.—See Hangzhou Silan Microelectronics Co., Ltd.; *Int'l*, pg. 3250

HANGZHOU SIME DARBY TRADING CO. LTD.—See Sime Darby Berhad; *Int'l*, pg. 6928

HANGZHOU SIMO CO., LTD.—See Hangzhou Tigermed Consulting Co., Ltd.; *Int'l*, pg. 3250

HANGZHOU STAR SHUAIER ELECTRIC APPLIANCE CO., LTD.; *Int'l*, pg. 3250

HANGZHOU STEAM TURBINE CO., LTD.; *Int'l*, pg. 3250

HANGZHOU SUNRISE TECHNOLOGY COMPANY LIMITED; *Int'l*, pg. 3250

HANGZHOU SUNYARD COMPUTER SERVICES CO., LTD.—See Sunyard Technology Co., Ltd; *Int'l*, pg. 7333

HANGZHOU SUNYARD SANJIA SYSTEM ENGINEERING CO., LTD.—See Sunyard Technology Co., Ltd; *Int'l*, pg. 7333

HANGZHOU SUPERSTRENGTH NEW MATERIALS TECHNOLOGY CO., LTD.—See Zhejiang Orient Financial Holdings Group Co., Ltd.; *Int'l*, pg. 8661

HANGZHOU TAIKU TECHNOLOGIES CO., LTD.—See Sky-mobi Limited; *Int'l*, pg. 6993

HANGZHOU TBK-APG AUTO BRAKES CO., LTD.—See TBK Co. Ltd.; *Int'l*, pg. 7480

HANGZHOU TIANMING ENVIRONMENTAL PROTECTION ENGINEERING CO., LTD.—See Sunyard Technology Co., Ltd; *Int'l*, pg. 7333

HANGZHOU TIANMUSHAN PHARMACEUTICAL ENTERPRISE CO., LTD.; *Int'l*, pg. 3250

HANGZHOU TIANSHUN FOOD CO., LTD.—See Apple Flavor & Fragrance Group Co., Ltd.; *Int'l*, pg. 520

HANGZHOU TIANYUAN PET PRODUCTS CO., LTD.; *Int'l*, pg. 3250

HANGZHOU TIGERMED CONSULTING CO., LTD.; pg. 3250

HANGZHOU TIGERS POLYMER CO., LTD.—See Tigers Polymer Corporation; *Int'l*, pg. 7746

HANGZHOU TODAYTEC DIGITAL CO., LTD.; *Int'l*, pg. 3251

HANGZHOU TOKA INK CHEMICAL CO., LTD.—See T&K TOKA Corporation; *Int'l*, pg. 7395

HANGZHOU TRANSTECNO POWER TRANSMISSIONS CO. LTD.—See Interpump Group S.p.A.; *Int'l*, pg. 3755

HANGZHOU WAGEN PRECISION TOOLING CO., LTD.—See Ferrotec Holdings Corporation; *Int'l*, pg. 2643

HANGZHOU WAHAHA GROUP CO., LTD.; *Int'l*, pg. 3251

HANGZHOU WAHAHA GROUP CO., LTD.
CORPORATE AFFILIATIONS

HANGZHOU WALSIN POWER CABLE & WIRE CO., LTD.—See Sumitomo Electric Industries, Ltd.; *Int'l*, pg. 7278
HANGZHOU WAZAM NEW MATERIALS CO., LTD.—See Zhejiang Wazam New Materials Group Co., Ltd.; *Int'l*, pg. 8665
HANGZHOU WEIGUANG ELECTRONIC CO., LTD.; *Int'l*, pg. 3251
HANGZHOU WENSLI SILK CULTURE CO., LTD.; *Int'l*, pg. 3251
HANGZHOU WINMATION AUTOMATION COMPANY LIMITED—See ABB Ltd.; *Int'l*, pg. 49
HANGZHOU XIAOSHAN HANGMIN NON-WOVEN FABRIC CO., LTD.—See Zhejiang Hangmin Co., Ltd.; *Int'l*, pg. 8655
HANGZHOU XIAOSHAN ZHONG'AN HOLIDAY INN CO., LTD.—See Zhong An Group Limited; *Int'l*, pg. 8671
HANGZHOU XILI INTELLIGENT TECHNOLOGY CO., LTD.; *Int'l*, pg. 3251
HANGZHOU XZB TECH CO.,LTD; *Int'l*, pg. 3251
HANGZHOU YAMAHA MUSICAL INSTRUMENTS CO., LTD.—See Yamaha Corporation; *Int'l*, pg. 8549
HANG ZHOU YITONG NEW MATERIALS CO., LTD.; *Int'l*, pg. 3246
HANGZHOU YOUNGSUN INTELLIGENT EQUIPMENT CO., LTD.; *Int'l*, pg. 3251
HANGZHOU YOUWANG ELECTRONICS CO., LTD.—See Hangzhou Silan Microelectronics Co., Ltd.; *Int'l*, pg. 3250
HANGZHOU YUEXI BUS MANUFACTURE CO., LTD.—See Coslight Technology International Group Limited; *Int'l*, pg. 1810
HANGZHOU ZHANGWEI TECHNOLOGY CO., LTD.—See Simei Media Co. Ltd.; *Int'l*, pg. 6931
HANGZHOU ZHENGQIANG CORPORATION LIMITED; *Int'l*, pg. 3251
HANGZHOU ZHIGUANG YICHUANG TECHNOLOGIES LTD.—See Guangzhou Zhiguang Electric Co., Ltd.; *Int'l*, pg. 3168
HANGZHOU ZHONGFU CONTAINER CO., LTD.—See Zhuhai Zhongfu Enterprise Co., Ltd.; *Int'l*, pg. 8679
HANGZHOU ZHONGHENG ELECTRIC CO., LTD.; *Int'l*, pg. 3251
HANGZHOU ZHONGSHENG STAR AUTOMOBILE SALES & SERVICE CO., LTD.—See Zhongsheng Group Holdings Limited; *Int'l*, pg. 8674
HANGZHOU ZHONGSHENG XINGQI AUTOMOBILE SALES & SERVICES CO., LTD.—See Zhongsheng Group Holdings Limited; *Int'l*, pg. 8674
HANGZHOU ZHONGTAI CRYOGENIC TECHNOLOGY CORPORATION; *Int'l*, pg. 3251
HANGZHOU ZHONGYA MACHINERY CO., LTD.; *Int'l*, pg. 3252
HANHUA FINANCIAL HOLDING CO., LTD.; *Int'l*, pg. 3252
HANIEL REEDEREI HOLDING GMBH—See Franz Haniel & Cie. GmbH; *Int'l*, pg. 2763
HANIEL TEXTILE SERVICE GMBH—See Franz Haniel & Cie. GmbH; *Int'l*, pg. 2762
HANIGAN CHEVROLET; *U.S. Private*, pg. 1853
HANIG'S FOOTWEAR INC.; *U.S. Private*, pg. 1853
HANIL CAN CO LIMITED—See Ball Corporation; *U.S. Public*, pg. 267
HANIL CEMENT CO., LTD.—See Hanil Holdings Co., Ltd; *Int'l*, pg. 3252
HANIL CHEMICAL IND. CO., LTD.; *Int'l*, pg. 3252
HANIL FEED CO., LTD.; *Int'l*, pg. 3252
HANIL FORGING INDUSTRIAL CO., LTD. - JINCHEON FACTORY—See Hanil Forging Industrial Co., Ltd.; *Int'l*, pg. 3252
HANIL FORGING INDUSTRIAL CO., LTD.; *Int'l*, pg. 3252
HANIL FORGING INDUSTRIAL CO., LTD. - THAILAND FACTORY—See Hanil Forging Industrial Co., Ltd.; *Int'l*, pg. 3252
HANIL HOLDINGS CO., LTD; *Int'l*, pg. 3252
HANIL HYUNDAI CEMENT CO., LTD.—See Hanil Holdings Co., Ltd; *Int'l*, pg. 3252
HANIL IRON & STEEL CO., LTD.; *Int'l*, pg. 3252
HANIL NETWORKS CO., LTD.—See Hanil Holdings Co., Ltd; *Int'l*, pg. 3252
HANIL TOYO CO., LTD.—See Toyo Ink SC Holdings Co., Ltd.; *Int'l*, pg. 7853
HANIL VACUUM CO., LTD.; *Int'l*, pg. 3252
HANISON CONSTRUCTION HOLDINGS LIMITED; *Int'l*, pg. 3252
HANITA COATINGS USA, INC.—See Avery Dennison Corporation; *U.S. Public*, pg. 244
HANITA METAL WORKS, LTD.—See Kennametal Inc.; *U.S. Public*, pg. 1221
HANITA PACIFIC PTY LTD.—See Avery Dennison Corporation; *U.S. Public*, pg. 244
HANITATEK, LLC—See Avery Dennison Corporation; *U.S. Public*, pg. 244
HANJIA DESIGN GROUP CO., LTD.; *Int'l*, pg. 3252
HANJI ELECTRONIC ENGINEERING CO., LTD.—See Japan Industrial Partners, Inc.; *Int'l*, pg. 3889
HANJIN ARKAS LOGISTICS & TRADING S.A.—See Eusu Holdings Co., Ltd.; *Int'l*, pg. 2559
HANJIN CITY GAS—See HJ Shipbuilding & Construction Company, Ltd.; *Int'l*, pg. 3428

HANJIN GLOBAL LOGISTICS (DALIAN) CO., LIMITED—See Hanjin Transportation Co., Ltd.; *Int'l*, pg. 3253
HANJIN GLOBAL LOGISTICS (GUANGZHOU) CO., LIMITED—See Hanjin Transportation Co., Ltd.; *Int'l*, pg. 3253
HANJIN GLOBAL LOGISTICS (HONG KONG) LIMITED—See Hanjin Transportation Co., Ltd.; *Int'l*, pg. 3253
HANJIN GLOBAL LOGISTICS (SHANGHAI) CO., LIMITED—See Hanjin Transportation Co., Ltd.; *Int'l*, pg. 3253
HANJIN GLOBAL LOGISTICS (SHENZHEN) CO., LIMITED—See Hanjin Transportation Co., Ltd.; *Int'l*, pg. 3253
HANJIN HEAVY INDUSTRIES & CONSTRUCTION CO., LTD. - DADAEPO FACTORY—See Hanjin Heavy Industries & Construction Co., Ltd.; *Int'l*, pg. 3252
HANJIN HEAVY INDUSTRIES & CONSTRUCTION CO., LTD.; *Int'l*, pg. 3252
HANJIN HEAVY INDUSTRIES & CONSTRUCTION CO., LTD. - ULSAN FACTORY—See HJ Shipbuilding & Construction Company, Ltd.; *Int'l*, pg. 3428
HANJIN HEAVY INDUSTRIES & CONSTRUCTION CO., LTD. - YULDO FACTORY—See Hanjin Heavy Industries & Construction Co., Ltd.; *Int'l*, pg. 3252
HANJIN HEAVY INDUSTRIES & CONSTRUCTION CO., LTD. - YULDO FACTORY—See HJ Shipbuilding & Construction Company, Ltd.; *Int'l*, pg. 3428
HANJIN HEAVY INDUSTRIES & CONSTRUCTION - CONSTRUCTION DIVISION—See HJ Shipbuilding & Construction Company, Ltd.; *Int'l*, pg. 3428
HANJIN INFORMATION SYSTEMS & TELECOMMUNICATION CO., LTD.—See Korean Air Lines Co., Ltd.; *Int'l*, pg. 4288
HANJIN INTERNATIONAL CORP.—See Korean Air Lines Co., Ltd.; *Int'l*, pg. 4288
HANJIN KAL CORP.; *Int'l*, pg. 3252
HANJIN TRANSPORTATION CO., LTD.; *Int'l*, pg. 3252
HANJOO METAL CO., LTD.; *Int'l*, pg. 3253
HANJUNGNCS CO., LTD.; *Int'l*, pg. 3253
HANJUNG POWER CO., LTD.—See Doosan Corporation; *Int'l*, pg. 2174
HANKE TISSUE SP. Z O.O.—See MBB SE; *Int'l*, pg. 4751
HANKEY GROUP; *U.S. Private*, pg. 1853
HANKIN GROUP; *U.S. Private*, pg. 1853
HANKINS LUMBER COMPANY, INC.; *U.S. Private*, pg. 1853
HANKISON INTERNATIONAL; *U.S. Private*, pg. 1853
HAN KOOK CAPITAL CO., LTD.; *Int'l*, pg. 3240
HANKOOK CAR & LIFE CO., LTD.—See Hankook Tire & Technology Co.,Ltd.; *Int'l*, pg. 3253
HANKOOK & COMPANY CO., LTD.; *Int'l*, pg. 3253
HANKOOK COSMETICS CO., LTD.—See Hankook Cosmetics Manufacturing Co., Ltd.; *Int'l*, pg. 3253
HANKOOK COSMETICS MANUFACTURING CO., LTD.; *Int'l*, pg. 3253
HANKOOK DONGGEURAMI PARTNERS CO., LTD.—See Hankook Tire & Technology Co.,Ltd.; *Int'l*, pg. 3253
HANKOOK ENGINEERING WORKS CO., LTD.—See Hankook Tire & Technology Co.,Ltd.; *Int'l*, pg. 3253
HANKOOK ESI—See Keysight Technologies, Inc.; *U.S. Public*, pg. 1227
HANKOOK ESPANA S.A.—See Hankook Tire & Technology Co.,Ltd.; *Int'l*, pg. 3254
HANKOOK FRANCE SARL—See Hankook Tire & Technology Co.,Ltd.; *Int'l*, pg. 3253
HANKOOK FURNITURE CO., LTD.; *Int'l*, pg. 3253
HANKOOK MOTORS INC.; *U.S. Private*, pg. 1854
HANKOOK NETWORKS AMERICA, INC.—See Hankook Tire & Technology Co.,Ltd.; *Int'l*, pg. 3253
HANKOOK NETWORKS CO., LTD.—See Hankook Tire & Technology Co.,Ltd.; *Int'l*, pg. 3253
HANKOOK OTIS ELEVATOR COMPANY—See Otis Worldwide Corporation; *U.S. Public*, pg. 1623
HANKOOK PRECISION WORKS CO., LTD.—See Hankook Tire & Technology Co.,Ltd.; *Int'l*, pg. 3253
HANKOOK REIFEN DEUTSCHLAND GMBH—See Hankook Tire & Technology Co.,Ltd.; *Int'l*, pg. 3254
HANKOOK SHELL OIL CO., LTD.—See Shell plc; *Int'l*, pg. 6795
HANKOOK STEEL CO., LTD.—See Hankook Tire & Technology Co.,Ltd.; *Int'l*, pg. 3253
HAN KOOK STEEL & MILL CO., LTD.—See HNK Machine Tool Co., Ltd.; *Int'l*, pg. 3434
HANKOOK TECHNOLOGY INC.; *Int'l*, pg. 3253
HANKOOK TIRE AMERICA CORP.—See Hankook Tire & Technology Co.,Ltd.; *Int'l*, pg. 3253
HANKOOK TIRE AUSTRIA GMBH—See Hankook Tire & Technology Co.,Ltd.; *Int'l*, pg. 3253
HANKOOK TIRE BUDAPEST KERESKEDELMI KFT—See Hankook Tire & Technology Co.,Ltd.; *Int'l*, pg. 3253
HANKOOK TIRE CANADA CORP.—See Hankook Tire & Technology Co.,Ltd.; *Int'l*, pg. 3253
HANKOOK TIRE CESKA REPUBLIKA S.R.O.—See Hankook Tire & Technology Co.,Ltd.; *Int'l*, pg. 3254
HANKOOK TIRE COLOMBIA LTDA.—See Hankook Tire & Technology Co.,Ltd.; *Int'l*, pg. 3254

HANKOOK TIRE CO., LTD. - PANAMA OFFICE—See Hankook Tire & Technology Co.,Ltd.; *Int'l*, pg. 3253
HANKOOK TIRE CO., LTD.—See Hankook & Company Co., Ltd.; *Int'l*, pg. 3253
HANKOOK TIRE CO., LTD.—See Hankook Tire & Technology Co.,Ltd.; *Int'l*, pg. 3254
HANKOOK TIRE CO., LTD.—See Hankook Tire & Technology Co.,Ltd.; *Int'l*, pg. 3254
HANKOOK TIRE CO., LTD.—See Hankook Tire & Technology Co.,Ltd.; *Int'l*, pg. 3254
HANKOOK TIRE DE MEXICO, S.A. DE C.V—See Hankook Tire & Technology Co.,Ltd.; *Int'l*, pg. 3253
HANKOOK TIRE DO BRASIL LTDA.—See Hankook Tire & Technology Co.,Ltd.; *Int'l*, pg. 3253
HANKOOK TIRE D.O.O—See Hankook Tire & Technology Co.,Ltd.; *Int'l*, pg. 3254
HANKOOK TIRE EUROPE GMBH—See Hankook Tire & Technology Co.,Ltd.; *Int'l*, pg. 3254
HANKOOK TIRE FRANCE SARL—See Hankook Tire & Technology Co.,Ltd.; *Int'l*, pg. 3254
HANKOOK TIRE ITALIA S.R.L.—See Hankook Tire & Technology Co.,Ltd.; *Int'l*, pg. 3254
HANKOOK TIRE JAPAN CORP.—See Hankook Tire & Technology Co.,Ltd.; *Int'l*, pg. 3254
HANKOOK TIRE MALAYSIA SDN. BHD.—See Hankook Tire & Technology Co.,Ltd.; *Int'l*, pg. 3254
HANKOOK TIRE MIDDLE EAST & AFRICA FZE—See Hankook Tire & Technology Co.,Ltd.; *Int'l*, pg. 3254
HANKOOK TIRE NETHERLANDS B.V—See Hankook Tire & Technology Co.,Ltd.; *Int'l*, pg. 3254
HANKOOK TIRE PANAMA LTDA.—See Hankook Tire & Technology Co.,Ltd.; *Int'l*, pg. 3254
HANKOOK TIRE POLSKA SP. Z O.O.—See Hankook Tire & Technology Co.,Ltd.; *Int'l*, pg. 3254
HANKOOK TIRE RUS LLC—See Hankook Tire & Technology Co.,Ltd.; *Int'l*, pg. 3254
HANKOOK TIRES INDIA LLP—See Hankook Tire & Technology Co.,Ltd.; *Int'l*, pg. 3254
HANKOOK TIRE SWEDEN AB—See Hankook Tire & Technology Co.,Ltd.; *Int'l*, pg. 3254
HANKOOK TIRE & TECHNOLOGY CO.,LTD.; *Int'l*, pg. 3253
HANKOOK TIRE THAILAND CO., LTD.—See Hankook Tire & Technology Co.,Ltd.; *Int'l*, pg. 3254
HANKOOK TIRE UKRAINE LLC—See Hankook Tire & Technology Co.,Ltd.; *Int'l*, pg. 3254
HANKOOK TIRE VIETNAM CO., LTD.—See Hankook Tire & Technology Co.,Ltd.; *Int'l*, pg. 3254
HANKOOK TYRE AUSTRALIA PTY. LTD.—See Hankook Tire & Technology Co.,Ltd.; *Int'l*, pg. 3254
HANKOOK TYRE U.K. LTD.—See Hankook Tire & Technology Co.,Ltd.; *Int'l*, pg. 3254
HANK PRODUCTIONS LLC—See Dolphin Entertainment, Inc.; *U.S. Public*, pg. 673
HANKSCRAFT INC.; *U.S. Private*, pg. 1854
HANK'S FURNITURE INC.; *U.S. Private*, pg. 1853
HANKS MACHINERY MOVERS, INC.—See Olympus Partners; *U.S. Private*, pg. 3013
HANKUK ADVANCED MATERIALS CO., LTD.—See HANKUK CARBON Co., Ltd.; *Int'l*, pg. 3254
HANKUK CARBON CO., LTD. - HAMYANG PLANT—See HANKUK CARBON Co., Ltd.; *Int'l*, pg. 3254
HANKUK CARBON CO., LTD.; *Int'l*, pg. 3254
HANKUK CHAIN INDUSTRIAL CO., LTD.—See Daedong Corporation; *Int'l*, pg. 1906
HANKUK ELECTRIC GLASS CO., LTD.—See AGC Inc.; *Int'l*, pg. 204
HANKUK GLASS INDUSTRIES INC.; *Int'l*, pg. 3254
HANKUK PACKAGE CO., LTD.; *Int'l*, pg. 3254
HANKUK PAPER MFG CO LTD - ONSAN PLANT—See Haesung Industrial Co., Ltd.; *Int'l*, pg. 3205
HANKUK PAPER MFG CO LTD—See Haesung Industrial Co., Ltd.; *Int'l*, pg. 3205
HANKUK PAPER USA, INC.—See Haesung Industrial Co., Ltd.; *Int'l*, pg. 3205
HANKUK STEEL WIRE CO., LTD.; *Int'l*, pg. 3254
HANKYU ACT FOR—See H2O Retailing Corp.; *Int'l*, pg. 3200
HANKYU ADVERTISING AGENCY INC.—See Hankyu Hanshin Holdings Inc.; *Int'l*, pg. 3255
HANKYU BAKERY CO LTD—See H2O Retailing Corp.; *Int'l*, pg. 3200
HANKYU BUS CO., LTD.—See Hankyu Hanshin Holdings Inc.; *Int'l*, pg. 3255
HANKYU BUSINESS ASSOCIATE CO., LTD.—See Hankyu Hanshin Holdings Inc.; *Int'l*, pg. 3255
HANKYU CARGO SERVICE CO., LTD.—See PLUS Corporation; *Int'l*, pg. 5898
HANKYU COMMUNITY SERVICE CO., LTD.—See Hankyu Hanshin Holdings Inc.; *Int'l*, pg. 3255
HANKYU CORPORATION—See Hankyu Hanshin Holdings Inc.; *Int'l*, pg. 3255
HANKYU DELICA I, INC.—See H2O Retailing Corp.; *Int'l*, pg. 3200
HANKYU DELICA INC.—See H2O Retailing Corp.; *Int'l*, pg. 3200
HANKYU EYEWEAR CO LTD—See H2O Retailing Corp.; *Int'l*, pg. 3200

HANKYU FACILITIES CO., LTD.—See Hankyu Hanshin Holdings Inc.; *Int'l*, pg. 3255
HANKYU FOOD PROCESS CO., LTD.—See H2O Retailing Corp.; *Int'l*, pg. 3200
HANKYU FOODS INC—See H2O Retailing Corp.; *Int'l*, pg. 3200
HANKYU HANSHIN BUILDING MANAGEMENT CO., LTD.—See Sika AG; *Int'l*, pg. 6917
HANKYU HANSHIN CLEAN SERVICE CO., LTD.—See Hankyu Hanshin Holdings Inc.; *Int'l*, pg. 3255
HANKYU HANSHIN DEPARTMENT STORES, INC—See H2O Retailing Corp.; *Int'l*, pg. 3200
HANKYU HANSHIN EXPRESS CO., LTD.—See Hankyu Hanshin Holdings Inc.; *Int'l*, pg. 3255
HANKYU HANSHIN EXPRESS SOUTHEAST ASIA PTE. LTD.—See Hankyu Hanshin Holdings Inc.; *Int'l*, pg. 3255
HANKYU HANSHIN EXPRESS (USA) INC.—See Hankyu Hanshin Holdings Inc.; *Int'l*, pg. 3255
HANKYU HANSHIN FINANCIAL SUPPORT CO., LTD.—See Hankyu Hanshin Holdings Inc.; *Int'l*, pg. 3255
HANKYU HANSHIN HOLDINGS INC.; *Int'l*, pg. 3254
HANKYU HANSHIN HOTELS CO., LTD.—See Hankyu Hanshin Holdings Inc.; *Int'l*, pg. 3255
HANKYU HANSHIN MARKETING SOLUTIONS INC.—See Hankyu Hanshin Holdings Inc.; *Int'l*, pg. 3255
HANKYU HANSHIN RESTAURANTS CO., LTD.—See Hankyu Hanshin Holdings Inc.; *Int'l*, pg. 3255
HANKYU HANSHIN SECURITY SERVICE CO., LTD.—See Hankyu Hanshin Holdings Inc.; *Int'l*, pg. 3255
HANKYU HANSHIN TECHNO SERVICE CO., LTD.—See Hankyu Hanshin Holdings Inc.; *Int'l*, pg. 3255
HANKYU HELLO DOG CO., LTD.—See H2O Retailing Corp.; *Int'l*, pg. 3200
HANKYU HOME STYLING CO, LTD.—See H2O Retailing Corp.; *Int'l*, pg. 3200
HANKYU INTERNATIONAL TRANSPORT (DEUTSCHLAND) GMBH—See Hankyu Hanshin Holdings Inc.; *Int'l*, pg. 3255
HANKYU INTERNATIONAL TRANSPORT (NETHERLANDS) B.V.—See Hankyu Hanshin Holdings Inc.; *Int'l*, pg. 3255
HANKYU INTERNATIONAL TRANSPORT (TAIWAN) LTD.—See Hankyu Hanshin Holdings Inc.; *Int'l*, pg. 3255
HANKYU INVESTMENT PARTNERS, INC.—See Hankyu Hanshin Holdings Inc.; *Int'l*, pg. 3255
HANKYU JOB YELL CO LTD—See H2O Retailing Corp.; *Int'l*, pg. 3200
HANKYU KANKO BUS CO., LTD.—See Hankyu Hanshin Holdings Inc.; *Int'l*, pg. 3255
HANKYU KENSOU CO., LTD.—See H2O Retailing Corp.; *Int'l*, pg. 3200
HANKYU KITCHEN YELL, INC—See H2O Retailing Corp.; *Int'l*, pg. 3200
HANKYU KITCHEN YELL KANSAI, INC.—See H2O Retailing Corp.; *Int'l*, pg. 3200
HANKYU MAINTENANCE SERVICE CO LTD—See H2O Retailing Corp.; *Int'l*, pg. 3200
HANKYU OASIS CO., LTD.—See H2O Retailing Corp.; *Int'l*, pg. 3200
HANKYU QUALITY SUPPORT—See H2O Retailing Corp.; *Int'l*, pg. 3200
HANKYU REALTY CO., LTD.—See Hankyu Hanshin Holdings Inc.; *Int'l*, pg. 3255
HANKYU REIT, INC.—See Hankyu Hanshin Holdings Inc.; *Int'l*, pg. 3255
HANKYU RETAILS CORPORATION—See Hankyu Hanshin Holdings Inc.; *Int'l*, pg. 3255
HANKYU SEKKEI CONSULTANT CO., LTD.—See Hankyu Hanshin Holdings Inc.; *Int'l*, pg. 3255
HANKYU SHOPPING CENTER DEVELOPMENT CO LTD—See H2O Retailing Corp.; *Int'l*, pg. 3200
HANKYU TAXI INC.—See Hankyu Hanshin Holdings Inc.; *Int'l*, pg. 3255
HANKYU TRAVEL SUPPORT CO., LTD.—See Hankyu Hanshin Holdings Inc.; *Int'l*, pg. 3255
HANLA IMS CO., LTD.; *Int'l*, pg. 3256
HANLA M&E CO., LTD.—See HANLA IMS LTD.; *Int'l*, pg. 3256
HAN LANGUAGE CENTRE PTE. LTD.—See Singapore Press Holdings Ltd.; *Int'l*, pg. 6942
HANLEES HILLTOP TOYOTA; *U.S. Private*, pg. 1854
HANLEIGH MANAGEMENT INC.—See Truist Financial Corporation; *U.S. Public*, pg. 2200
HANLEY ECONOMIC BUILDING SOCIETY; *Int'l*, pg. 3256
HANLEY WOOD MEDIA, INC.—See MidOcean Partners, LLP; *U.S. Private*, pg. 2717
HANLY MOIR PATHOLOGY PTY LIMITED—See Sonic Healthcare Limited; *Int'l*, pg. 7097
HANMAN FIT LIMITED; *Int'l*, pg. 3256
HANMA TECHNOLOGY GROUP CO., LTD.; *Int'l*, pg. 3256
HANMERE POLYTHENE LTD—See Chiltern Capital LLP; *Int'l*, pg. 1479
HANMER & PARTNERS—See Publicis Groupe S.A.; *Int'l*, pg. 6099

HANMI BANK—See Hanmi Financial Corporation; *U.S. Public*, pg. 983
HANMI FINANCIAL CORPORATION; *U.S. Public*, pg. 983
HANMI FINE CHEMICAL CO., LTD—See Hanmi Pharmaceutical Co., Ltd.; *Int'l*, pg. 3256
HANMIGLOBAL CO., LTD.; *Int'l*, pg. 3256
HANMIGLOBAL CONSTRUCTION CONSULTING (SHANGHAI) CO., LTD.—See HanmiGlobal Co., LTD.; *Int'l*, pg. 3257
HANMIGLOBAL CONSULTING (SHANGHAI) CO., LTD.—See HanmiGlobal Co., LTD.; *Int'l*, pg. 3257
HANMIGLOBAL INDIA PRIVATE LTD.—See HanmiGlobal Co., LTD.; *Int'l*, pg. 3257
HANMIGLOBAL SAUDI (LLC)—See HanmiGlobal Co., LTD.; *Int'l*, pg. 3257
HANMIGLOBAL UK LIMITED—See HanmiGlobal Co., LTD.; *Int'l*, pg. 3257
HANMIGLOBAL VIETNAM CO., LTD.—See HanmiGlobal Co., LTD.; *Int'l*, pg. 3257
HANMI IT CO., LTD.—See Hanmi Pharmaceutical Co., Ltd.; *Int'l*, pg. 3256
HANMI JAPAN PHARMACEUTICAL CO., LTD—See Hanmi Pharmaceutical Co., Ltd.; *Int'l*, pg. 3256
HANMI PHARMACEUTICAL CO., LTD.; *Int'l*, pg. 3256
HANMI SCIENCE CO., LTD.; *Int'l*, pg. 3256
HANMI SEMICONDUCTOR CO., LTD.; *Int'l*, pg. 3256
HANMO CORPORATION—See BELIMO Holding AG; *Int'l*, pg. 965
HANNA ANDERSSON LLC—See Catterton Management Company, LLC; *U.S. Private*, pg. 793
HANNA & ASSOCIATES INC.; *U.S. Private*, pg. 1854
HANNABERY ELECTRIC INC.; *U.S. Private*, pg. 1855
HANNA CAPITAL CORP.; *Int'l*, pg. 3257
HANNA COMMERCIAL REAL ESTATE—See Hanna Holdings, Inc.; *U.S. Private*, pg. 1854
HANNA CYLINDERS; *U.S. Private*, pg. 1854
HANNAFORD BROS. CO., LLC—See Koninklijke Ahold Delhaize N.V.; *Int'l*, pg. 4260
HANNAH MOTOR COMPANY INCORPORATED; *U.S. Private*, pg. 1855
HANNA HOLDINGS, INC.; *U.S. Private*, pg. 1854
HANNA INSTRUMENTS INC.; *U.S. Private*, pg. 1854
HANNA LEE COMMUNICATIONS, INC.; *U.S. Private*, pg. 1854
HANNAM CHAIN USA INC.; *U.S. Private*, pg. 1855
HANNAN METALS LTD.; *Int'l*, pg. 3257
HANNANS LIMITED; *Int'l*, pg. 3257
HANNAN SUPPLY COMPANY; *U.S. Private*, pg. 1855
HANNAN TANK TERMINAL CO., LTD.—See Fuji Oil Holdings Inc.; *Int'l*, pg. 2815
HANNA RUBBER CO., INC.—See AEA Investors LP; *U.S. Private*, pg. 115
HANNA STEEL CORPORATION; *U.S. Private*, pg. 1855
HANNA TRUCK LINE, INC.—See Hanna Steel Corporation; *U.S. Private*, pg. 1855
HANNAY REELS INC.; *U.S. Private*, pg. 1855
HANN ENTERPRISES, INC.; *U.S. Private*, pg. 1854
HANNER CHEVROLET PONTIAC; *U.S. Private*, pg. 1855
HANNET CO., LTD.; *Int'l*, pg. 3257
HANNIBAL COURIER-POST—See Gannett Co., Inc.; *U.S. Public*, pg. 903
HANNIG CONSTRUCTION, INC.—See Central State Construction, Corporation; *U.S. Private*, pg. 825
HANNING & KAHL GMBH & CO KG; *Int'l*, pg. 3257
HANNING & KAHL L.P.—See HANNING & KAHL GmbH & Co KG; *Int'l*, pg. 3257
HANNIS T. BOURGEOIS, LLP; *U.S. Private*, pg. 1855
HANNON ARMSTRONG SECURITIES, LLC—See Hannon Armstrong Sustainable Infrastructure Capital, Inc.; *U.S. Public*, pg. 983
HANNON ARMSTRONG SUSTAINABLE INFRASTRUCTURE CAPITAL, INC.; *U.S. Public*, pg. 983
HANNON COMPANY; *U.S. Private*, pg. 1855
HANNONG CHEMICALS INC; *Int'l*, pg. 3257
HANNON HILL CORPORATION; *U.S. Private*, pg. 1855
HANNON'S KENTUCKY FRIED CHICKEN, INC.; *U.S. Private*, pg. 1855
HANNOUSH JEWELERS INC.; *U.S. Private*, pg. 1855
HANNOVER CONSULTANCY B.V.—See Deutsche Messe AG; *Int'l*, pg. 2071
HANNOVER FAIRS AUSTRALIA PTY. LTD.—See Deutsche Messe AG; *Int'l*, pg. 2071
HANNOVER FAIRS DO BRASIL S/C LTDA—See Deutsche Messe AG; *Int'l*, pg. 2071
HANNOVER FAIRS TURKEY FUARCILIK A.S.—See Deutsche Messe AG; *Int'l*, pg. 2071
HANNOVER FAIRS USA INC.—See Deutsche Messe AG; *Int'l*, pg. 2071
HANNOVER FINANZ GMBH; *Int'l*, pg. 3257
HANNOVER HOUSE, INC.—See Crimson Forest Entertainment Group Inc.; *U.S. Private*, pg. 1100
HANNOVER LEASING GMBH & CO. KG—See Helaba Landesbank Hessen-Thuringen; *Int'l*, pg. 3328
HANNOVER LEASING INVESTMENT GMBH—See COR-ESTATE Capital Holding SA; *Int'l*, pg. 1800
HANNOVER LEASING WACHSTUMSWERTE ASIEN 1 GMBH & CO. KG—See Helaba Landesbank Hessen-Thuringen; *Int'l*, pg. 3328

HANNOVER LIFE REASSURANCE AFRICA LTD.—See Talanx AG; *Int'l*, pg. 7444
HANNOVER LIFE REASSURANCE COMPANY OF AMERICA—See Talanx AG; *Int'l*, pg. 7444
HANNOVER LIFE REASSURANCE (IRELAND) LTD.—See Talanx AG; *Int'l*, pg. 7444
HANNOVER LIFE REASSURANCE (UK) LTD.—See Talanx AG; *Int'l*, pg. 7444
HANNOVER LIFE RE OF AUSTRALASIA LTD.—See Talanx AG; *Int'l*, pg. 7444
HANNOVERMASSANS SVERIGEKONTOR AB—See Deutsche Messe AG; *Int'l*, pg. 2071
HANNOVER MILANO FAIRS CHINA LTD.—See Deutsche Messe AG; *Int'l*, pg. 2071
HANNOVER MILANO FAIRS INDIA PVT. LTD.—See Deutsche Messe AG; *Int'l*, pg. 2071
HANNOVER MILANO FAIRS SHANGHAI LTD.—See Deutsche Messe AG; *Int'l*, pg. 2071
HANNOVER RE (BERMUDA) LTD.—See Talanx AG; *Int'l*, pg. 7444
HANNOVER REINSURANCE AFRICA LTD.—See Talanx AG; *Int'l*, pg. 7444
HANNOVER REINSURANCE GROUP AFRICA (PTY) LIMITED—See Talanx AG; *Int'l*, pg. 7444
HANNOVER RE (IRELAND) DESIGNATED ACTIVITY COMPANY—See Talanx AG; *Int'l*, pg. 7444
HANNOVER RE (IRELAND) LIMITED—See Talanx AG; *Int'l*, pg. 7444
HANNOVER RE SERVICES ITALY S.R.L.—See Talanx AG; *Int'l*, pg. 7444
HANNOVER RE SERVICES JAPAN KK—See Talanx AG; *Int'l*, pg. 7444
HANNOVER RUCK SE—See Talanx AG; *Int'l*, pg. 7444
HANNOVER SERVICES MEXICO S.A. DE C.V.—See Talanx AG; *Int'l*, pg. 7444
HANNOVER SERVICES (UK) LTD.—See Talanx AG; *Int'l*, pg. 7444
HANNO WERK GMBH & CO. KG; *Int'l*, pg. 3257
HANNS GLASS GMBH & CO. KG—See Freudenberg SE; *Int'l*, pg. 2789
HANNSPREE DISPLAY TECHNOLOGY (NANJING) INC.—See HannStar Display Corporation; *Int'l*, pg. 3257
HANNSPREE EUROPE GMBH—See HannStar Display Corporation; *Int'l*, pg. 3258
HANNSPREE EUROPE HOLDINGS B.V.—See HannStar Display Corporation; *Int'l*, pg. 3258
HANNSPREE, INC.—See HannStar Display Corporation; *Int'l*, pg. 3257
HANNSTAR BOARD CORPORATION; *Int'l*, pg. 3257
HANNSTAR BOARD INTERNATIONAL HOLDINGS LIMITED; *Int'l*, pg. 3257
HANNSTAR DISPLAY CORPORATION - NEIHU PLANT—See HannStar Display Corporation; *Int'l*, pg. 3257
HANNSTAR DISPLAY CORPORATION; *Int'l*, pg. 3257
HANNSTAR DISPLAY CORPORATION - TAINAN PLANT—See HannStar Display Corporation; *Int'l*, pg. 3257
HANNSTAR DISPLAY (NANJING) CORPORATION—See HannStar Display Corporation; *Int'l*, pg. 3257
HANNSTOUCH SOLUTION INC.; *Int'l*, pg. 3258
HANNUMS HARLEY-DAVIDSON SALES, INC.; *U.S. Private*, pg. 1855
HA NOI BATTERY JOINT STOCK COMPANY; *Int'l*, pg. 3201
HANOI BEER ALCOHOL & BEVERAGE JOINT STOCK CORPORATION; *Int'l*, pg. 3258
HANOI BEER TRADING JSC; *Int'l*, pg. 3258
HANOI EDUCATION DEVELOPMENT & INVESTMENT JSC; *Int'l*, pg. 3258
HANOI - HAI DUONG BEER JSC; *Int'l*, pg. 3258
HANOI INVESTMENT GENERAL CORPORATION; *Int'l*, pg. 3258
HA NOI - KINH BAC AGRICULTURE AND FOOD JOINT STOCK COMPANY; *Int'l*, pg. 3201
HANOIMILK JSC; *Int'l*, pg. 3258
HANOI REINSURANCE JOINT STOCK CORPORATION—See PVI Holdings; *Int'l*, pg. 6125
HANOI SAVICO JSC—See Saigon General Service Corporation; *Int'l*, pg. 6483
HANOI SOAP JOINT STOCK COMPANY—See Masan Consumer Corp.; *Int'l*, pg. 4719
HA NOI SOUTH HOUSING AND URBAN DEVELOPMENT CORPORATION; *Int'l*, pg. 3201
HANOI STEEL CENTER CO., LTD. - FACTORY 1—See Sumitomo Corporation; *Int'l*, pg. 7268
HANOI STEEL CENTER CO., LTD.—See Sumitomo Corporation; *Int'l*, pg. 7268
HA NOI TRANSFORMER MANUFACTURING; *Int'l*, pg. 3201
HANON CLIMATE SYSTEMS INDIA PRIVATE LIMITED—See Hahn & Company; *Int'l*, pg. 3208
HANON SYSTEMS ALABAMA CORP.—See Hahn & Company; *Int'l*, pg. 3208
HANON SYSTEMS (BEIJING) CO., LTD.—See Hahn & Company; *Int'l*, pg. 3208
HANON SYSTEMS CANADA, INC.—See Hahn & Company; *Int'l*, pg. 3208

HA NOI TRANSFORMER MANUFACTURING

HANON SYSTEMS PORTUGAL, S.A.—See Hahn & Company; *Int'l*, pg. 3208
HANON SYSTEMS—See Hahn & Company; *Int'l*, pg. 3207
HANON SYSTEMS (THAILAND) CO. LTD.—See Hahn & Company; *Int'l*, pg. 3208
HANORA SPINNING—See The First Republic Corporation of America; *U.S. Public*, pg. 2074
THE HANOR COMPANY, INC.; *U.S. Private*, pg. 4043
HANOTRANS LIMITED CO.,—See The Van Cargoes & Foreign Trade Logistics Joint Stock Company; *Int'l*, pg. 7698
HANOVER ACCEPTANCES LIMITED; *Int'l*, pg. 3258
HANOVER BANCORP INC.; *U.S. Public*, pg. 983
HANOVER COMMUNITY BANK—See Hanover Bancorp Inc.; *U.S. Public*, pg. 984
THE HANOVER COMPANY—See Hanover R.S. Limited Partnership; *U.S. Private*, pg. 1855
HANOVER COMPANY STORE, LLC—See Chelsey Direct, LLC; *U.S. Private*, pg. 870
THE HANOVER CONSUMER COOPERATIVE SOCIETY, INC.; *U.S. Private*, pg. 4043
HANOVER DIRECT, INC.—See Chelsey Direct, LLC; *U.S. Private*, pg. 870
HANOVER ENGINEERS PC INC.; *U.S. Private*, pg. 1855
HANOVER EXCESS & SURPLUS, INC.—See Arthur J. Gallagher & Co.; *U.S. Public*, pg. 205
HANOVER FINANCIAL MANAGEMENT LIMITED—See The Ince Group Plc; *Int'l*, pg. 7654
HANOVER FIRE & CASUALTY INSURANCE COMPANY; *U.S. Private*, pg. 1855
HANOVER FOODS CORPORATION; *U.S. Public*, pg. 984
HANOVER FOODS CORP.—See Hanover Foods Corporation; *U.S. Public*, pg. 984
HANOVER FOODS—See Hanover Foods Corporation; *U.S. Public*, pg. 984
HANOVER HOUSE—See Communicare, Inc.; *U.S. Private*, pg. 988
THE HANOVER INSURANCE COMPANY—See The Hanover Insurance Group, Inc.; *U.S. Public*, pg. 2087
THE HANOVER INSURANCE GROUP, INC.; *U.S. Public*, pg. 2087
HANOVER INVESTORS MANAGEMENT LLP; *Int'l*, pg. 3258
HANOVER IRON WORKS, INC.—See Highland Roofing Co.; *U.S. Private*, pg. 1939
HANOVER LAND SERVICES, INC.-PENNSYLVANIA OFFICE—See Hanover Land Services, Inc.; *U.S. Private*, pg. 1855
HANOVER LAND SERVICES, INC.; *U.S. Private*, pg. 1855
HANOVER LANTERN INC.—See Signify N.V.; *Int'l*, pg. 6912
HANOVER LLOYD'S INSURANCE COMPANY—See The Hanover Insurance Group, Inc.; *U.S. Public*, pg. 2087
HANOVER MANUFACTURING PLANT—See REA Magnet Wire Company, Inc.; *U.S. Private*, pg. 3365
HANOVER MARINER—See Gannett Co., Inc.; *U.S. Public*, pg. 902
THE HANOVER NJ ENDOSCOPY ASC, LLC—See KKR & Co. Inc.; *U.S. Public*, pg. 1247
HANOVER PARTNERS, INC.; *U.S. Private*, pg. 1855
HANOVER PENSIONS LIMITED—See The Ince Group Plc; *Int'l*, pg. 7654
HANOVER R.S. LIMITED PARTNERSHIP; *U.S. Private*, pg. 1855
HANOVIA LIMITED—See Halma plc; *Int'l*, pg. 3232
HANPIN BVI INTERNATIONAL CO., LTD.—See Hanpin Electron Co., Ltd.; *Int'l*, pg. 3258
HANPIN BVI INTL CO., LTD.—See Hanpin Electron Co., Ltd.; *Int'l*, pg. 3258
HANP INC.; *Int'l*, pg. 3258
HANPIN ELECTRON CO., LTD.; *Int'l*, pg. 3258
HANRYO KIGYO CO.,LTD.—See Mitsubishi Logistics Corporation; *Int'l*, pg. 4962
HANRYU HOLDINGS, INC.; *Int'l*, pg. 3258
HAN RYUK ELECTRONICS CO., LTD.—See Hokuriku Electric Industry Co., Ltd.; *Int'l*, pg. 3444
THE HANRYU TIMES CO., LTD.; *Int'l*, pg. 7651
HANSABATTERY OY—See Addtech AB; *Int'l*, pg. 131
HANSA BIOPHARMA AB; *Int'l*, pg. 3259
HANSAB UAB—See Nayax Ltd.; *Int'l*, pg. 5178
HANSA CHEMIE HOLLAND BV—See Hansa Chemie International AG; *Int'l*, pg. 3259
HANSA CHEMIE INTERNATIONAL AG; *Int'l*, pg. 3259
HANSAE CO., LTD.—See Hansae Yes24 Holdings Co., Ltd.; *Int'l*, pg. 3259
HANSAEMK CO.,LTD.; *Int'l*, pg. 3259
HANSAE YES24 HOLDINGS CO., LTD.; *Int'l*, pg. 3259
HANSA HAMBURG SHIPPING INTERNATIONAL GMBH & CO. KG—See M.M. Warburg & Co. KGaA; *Int'l*, pg. 4616
HANSA INVESTMENT COMPANY LIMITED; *Int'l*, pg. 3259
HANSA LOGISTIK EG—See Arla Foods amba; *Int'l*, pg. 573
HANSA LUFTBILD AG; *Int'l*, pg. 3259
HANSA MARINE LOGISTICS GMBH—See Bremer Lagerhaus-Gesellschaft; *Int'l*, pg. 1145
HANSAMATRIX AS; *Int'l*, pg. 3259

HANSA MELASSE HANDELSGESELLSCHAFT MBH—See W&R Barnett Ltd.; *Int'l*, pg. 8320
HANS ANDERS NEDERLAND B.V.—See 3i Group plc; *Int'l*, pg. 9
HANSAPORT HAFENBETRIEBSGESELLSCHAFT MBH—See Salzgitter AG; *Int'l*, pg. 6496
HANSAPOST OU; *Int'l*, pg. 3259
HANSAPRINT AB—See Sanoma Oyj; *Int'l*, pg. 6553
HANSAPRINT ELANDERS KFT—See Hansaprint Oy; *Int'l*, pg. 3259
HANSAPRINT OY; *Int'l*, pg. 3259
HANSARD EUROPE DESIGNATED ACTIVITY COMPANY—See Hansard Global plc; *Int'l*, pg. 3259
HANSARD EUROPE LIMITED—See Hansard Global plc; *Int'l*, pg. 3259
HANSARD GLOBAL PLC; *Int'l*, pg. 3259
HANSATON AKUSTISCHE GERATE GES.M.B.H.—See Sonova Holding AG; *Int'l*, pg. 7100
HANS BELL EQUIPMENT LTD.—See Daeyang Electric Co., Ltd.; *Int'l*, pg. 1911
HANSBERGER GROWTH INVESTORS, LP—See Groupe BPCE; *Int'l*, pg. 3096
HANS BINDER MASCHINENBAU GMBH—See EnWave Corporation; *Int'l*, pg. 2456
HANSBIOMED CHINA, INC.—See Hans Biomed Corporation; *Int'l*, pg. 3258
HANS BIOMED CORPORATION; *Int'l*, pg. 3258
HANSBIOMED USA, INC.—See Hans Biomed Corporation; *Int'l*, pg. 3258
HANSCO CAPITAL CORP.; *Int'l*, pg. 3259
HANSEA NV—See Deutsche Bank Aktiengesellschaft; *Int'l*, pg. 2057
HANSEATICA SECHZEHNTE GRUNDBESITZ INVESTITIONSGESELLSCHAFT MBH & CO. KG—See DZ BANK AG Deutsche Zentral-Genossenschaftsbank; *Int'l*, pg. 2244
HANSEATIC BANK GMBH & CO KG—See Societe Generale S.A.; *Int'l*, pg. 7039
HANSEATIC BANK GMBH & CO.—See Societe Generale S.A.; *Int'l*, pg. 7039
HANSEATIC VERSICHERUNGSDIENST GMBH—See Otto GmbH & Co. KG; *Int'l*, pg. 5662
HANSEATISCHE IMMOBILIEN MANAGEMENT GMBH—See Ernst Russ AG; *Int'l*, pg. 2496
HANSEATISCHE IMMOBILIEN MANAGEMENT NIEDERLANDE GMBH—See Ernst Russ AG; *Int'l*, pg. 2496
HANSEATISCHES WEIN- UND SEKT-KONTOR HAWESKO GMBH & CO. KG—See Hawesko Holding AG; *Int'l*, pg. 3288
HANSEAT REISEBURO GMBH—See Global Business Travel Group, Inc.; *U.S. Public*, pg. 941
HANSE BEREEDERUNG GMBH—See Schoeller Holdings Ltd.; *Int'l*, pg. 6637
HANSECOM PUBLIC TRANSPORT TICKETING SOLUTIONS GMBH—See init innovation in traffic systems SE; *Int'l*, pg. 3704
HANSE (DEUTSCHLAND) VERTRIEBS GMBH & CO, KG—See Aurelius Equity Opportunities SE & Co. KGaA; *Int'l*, pg. 708
HANSE HAUS GMBH & CO. KG—See Equistone Partners Europe Limited; *Int'l*, pg. 2486
HANS EINHELL (CHINA) CHONGQING CO., LTD.—See Einhell Germany AG; *Int'l*, pg. 2333
HANS EINHELL OSTERREICH GMBH—See Einhell Germany AG; *Int'l*, pg. 2333
HANS EINHELL UKRAINE TOV—See Einhell Germany AG; *Int'l*, pg. 2333
HANSEL HONDA; *U.S. Private*, pg. 1856
HANSELLS MASTERTON LTD.; *Int'l*, pg. 3259
HANSEL 'N GRETEL BRAND INC.; *U.S. Private*, pg. 1856
HANSEL TEXTIL INTERLINING GMBH—See Freudenberg SE; *Int'l*, pg. 2789
HANSEL TEXTILROM SRL—See Freudenberg SE; *Int'l*, pg. 2789
HANSEN BEVERAGE COMPANY—See Monster Beverage Corporation; *U.S. Public*, pg. 1465
HANSEN CHEVROLET, INC.; *U.S. Private*, pg. 1856
HANSEN COMPANY INC.; *U.S. Private*, pg. 1856
HANSEN CORPORATION EUROPE LIMITED—See Hansen Technologies Limited; *Int'l*, pg. 3260
HANSEN CORPORATION INVESTMENTS PTY LIMITED—See Hansen Technologies Limited; *Int'l*, pg. 3260
HANSEN CORPORATION PTY. LTD.—See Hansen Technologies Limited; *Int'l*, pg. 3260
HANSEN CORPORATION—See Delany Capital Management Corp.; *U.S. Private*, pg. 1194
HANSEN CORPORATION USA LIMITED—See Hansen Technologies Limited; *Int'l*, pg. 3260
HANSEN ENGINEERING CO. INC.; *U.S. Private*, pg. 1856
HANS ENERGY COMPANY LIMITED; *Int'l*, pg. 3259
HANSENET TELEKOMMUNIKATION GMBH—See Telefonica, S.A.; *Int'l*, pg. 7535
HANS ENG CO., LTD.; *Int'l*, pg. 3259
HANSEN HELLAS ABEE—See Novonesis A/S; *Int'l*, pg. 5468
HANSEN HELLAS A/S—See Novonesis A/S; *Int'l*, pg. 5468

CORPORATE AFFILIATIONS

HANSEN INDUSTRIAL TRANSMISSIONS NV—See Sumitomo Heavy Industries, Ltd.; *Int'l*, pg. 7286
HANSEN INTERNATIONAL INC.; *U.S. Private*, pg. 1856
HANSEN INTERNATIONAL INC.—See Marsh & McLennan Companies, Inc.; *U.S. Public*, pg. 1376
HANSEN MANUFACTURING CORP.—See Ag Growth International Inc.; *Int'l*, pg. 198
HANSEN MECHANICAL CONTRACTORS, INC.—See EMCOR Group, Inc.; *U.S. Public*, pg. 737
HANSEN MEDICAL DEUTSCHLAND GMBH—See Johnson & Johnson; *U.S. Public*, pg. 1194
HANSEN MEDICAL, INC.—See Johnson & Johnson; *U.S. Public*, pg. 1194
HANSEN MEDICAL UK LTD.—See Johnson & Johnson; *U.S. Public*, pg. 1194
HANSEN-MUELLER CO. INC.; *U.S. Private*, pg. 1856
HANSEN NEW ZEALAND LIMITED—See Hansen Technologies Limited; *Int'l*, pg. 3260
HANSEN OIL CO.; *U.S. Private*, pg. 1856
HANSENS IGA INCORPORATED; *U.S. Private*, pg. 1856
HANSEN TECHNOLOGIES CANADA, INC.—See Hansen Technologies Limited; *Int'l*, pg. 3260
HANSEN TECHNOLOGIES CDE LIMITED—See Hansen Technologies Limited; *Int'l*, pg. 3260
HANSEN TECHNOLOGIES DENMARK A/S—See Hansen Technologies Limited; *Int'l*, pg. 3260
HANSEN TECHNOLOGIES LIMITED; *Int'l*, pg. 3260
HANSEN TECHNOLOGIES NORWAY AS—See Hansen Technologies Limited; *Int'l*, pg. 3260
HANSEN TECHNOLOGIES (SHANGHAI) COMPANY LIMITED—See Hansen Technologies Limited; *Int'l*, pg. 3260
HANSEN TECHNOLOGIES SWEDEN AB—See Hansen Technologies Limited; *Int'l*, pg. 3260
HANSEN TECHNOLOGIES VIETNAM LLC—See Hansen Technologies Limited; *Int'l*, pg. 3260
HANSEN WIND ENERGY DRIVES (CHINA) CO. LTD.—See ZF Friedrichshafen AG; *Int'l*, pg. 8647
HANSEN YUNCKEN PTY LTD; *Int'l*, pg. 3260
HANSER & ASSOCIATES PUBLIC RELATIONS; *U.S. Private*, pg. 1856
HANSER & ASSOCIATES PUBLIC RELATIONS—See Hanser & Associates Public Relations; *U.S. Private*, pg. 1856
HANSER HOLDINGS INTERNATIONAL; *U.S. Private*, pg. 1856
HANSETANK SPEDITION GMBH; *Int'l*, pg. 3260
HANSEVISION GMBH—See Bechtle AG; *Int'l*, pg. 938
HANSEWERK AG—See E.ON SE; *Int'l*, pg. 2253
HANSE WINDKRAFT GMBH—See Stadtwerke Munchen GmbH; *Int'l*, pg. 7162
HANSEYACHTS AG—See Aurelius Equity Opportunities SE & Co. KGaA; *Int'l*, pg. 708
HANS FOLSGAARD A/S—See Addtech AB; *Int'l*, pg. 133
HANSGROHE A.B.—See Masco Corporation; *U.S. Public*, pg. 1390
HANSGROHE ARMATUR SANAYI VE TICARET LIMITED SIRKETI—See Masco Corporation; *U.S. Public*, pg. 1390
HANSGROHE BRASIL METAIS SANITARIOS LTDA.—See Masco Corporation; *U.S. Public*, pg. 1390
HANSGROHE DEUTSCHLAND VERTRIEBS GMBH—See Masco Corporation; *U.S. Public*, pg. 1390
HANSGROHE D.O.O.—See Masco Corporation; *U.S. Public*, pg. 1391
HANSGROHE HANDELSGES.MBH—See Masco Corporation; *U.S. Public*, pg. 1390
HANSGROHE INTERNATIONAL GMBH—See Masco Corporation; *U.S. Public*, pg. 1390
HANSGROHE JAPAN KK—See Masco Corporation; *U.S. Public*, pg. 1390
HANSGROHE LIMITED—See Masco Corporation; *U.S. Public*, pg. 1390
HANSGROHE N.V.—See Masco Corporation; *U.S. Public*, pg. 1390
HANSGROHE OOO—See Masco Corporation; *U.S. Public*, pg. 1391
HANSGROHE PTY LTD—See Masco Corporation; *U.S. Public*, pg. 1390
HANSGROHE SA (PTY) LTD.—See Masco Corporation; *U.S. Public*, pg. 1390
HANSGROHE S.A.—See Masco Corporation; *U.S. Public*, pg. 1390
HANSGROHE S.A.U.—See Masco Corporation; *U.S. Public*, pg. 1390
HANSGROHE SE7—See Masco Corporation; *U.S. Public*, pg. 1390
HANSGROHE SE—See Masco Corporation; *U.S. Public*, pg. 1390
HANSGROHE SP. Z.O.O.—See Masco Corporation; *U.S. Public*, pg. 1390
HANS-GUNTER BERNER GMBH & CO. KG; *Int'l*, pg. 3259
HANS HAGEN HOMES INC.; *U.S. Private*, pg. 1855
HANSHANG GROUP CO., LTD.; *Int'l*, pg. 3260
HANS HELD TIEFBAU GMBH & CO—See Swietelsky Baugesellschaft m.b.H.; *Int'l*, pg. 7367
HANS HEPP GMBH & CO. KG; *Int'l*, pg. 3259

COMPANY NAME INDEX

HANSHIN BUS CO., LTD.—See Hankyu Hanshin Holdings Inc.; *Int'l*, pg. 3255
HANSHIN CONSTRUCTION CO., LTD.; *Int'l*, pg. 3260
HANSHIN CONTENTS LINK CORPORATION—See Hankyu Hanshin Holdings Inc.; *Int'l*, pg. 3255
HANSHIN DELICA CO., LTD.—See Kewpie Corporation; *Int'l*, pg. 4144
THE HANSHIN DIESEL WORKS, LTD. - AKASHI FACTORY—See The Hanshin Diesel Works, Ltd.; *Int'l*, pg. 7652
THE HANSHIN DIESEL WORKS, LTD. - HARIMA FACTORY—See The Hanshin Diesel Works, Ltd.; *Int'l*, pg. 7652
THE HANSHIN DIESEL WORKS, LTD.; *Int'l*, pg. 7651
THE HANSHIN DIESEL WORKS, LTD. - TAMATSU FACTORY—See The Hanshin Diesel Works, Ltd.; *Int'l*, pg. 7652
HANSHIN ELECTRIC RAILWAY CO., LTD.—See Hankyu Hanshin Holdings Inc.; *Int'l*, pg. 3255
HANSHIN HOTEL SYSTEMS CO., LTD.—See Hankyu Hanshin Holdings Inc.; *Int'l*, pg. 3255
HANSHIN-IMPORTS SARL LLC—See WEDS CO., LTD.; *Int'l*, pg. 8367
HANSHIN LOGISTIC SYSTEMS CORP.—See Japan Logistic Systems Corp.; *Int'l*, pg. 3898
HANSHIN LOGI-SUPPORT CORP.—See Japan Logistic Systems Corp.; *Int'l*, pg. 3898
HANSHIN MACHINERY CO., LTD.; *Int'l*, pg. 3260
HANSHIN REAL ESTATE CO., LTD.—See Hankyu Hanshin Holdings Inc.; *Int'l*, pg. 3256
HANSHIN SENKO TRANSPORT CO., LTD.—See Senko Group Holdings Co., Ltd.; *Int'l*, pg. 6709
HANSHIN SILO CO., LTD.—See Sojitz Corporation; *Int'l*, pg. 7061
HANSHIN SPECIAL STEEL CO., LTD.—See Sato shoji Corporation; *Int'l*, pg. 6586
HANSHIN TAXI CO., LTD.—See Hankyu Hanshin Holdings Inc.; *Int'l*, pg. 3256
HANSHIN TIGERS BASEBALL CLUB—See Hankyu Hanshin Holdings Inc.; *Int'l*, pg. 3256
HANSHIN TRANSPORTATION CO., LTD.—See Senko Group Holdings Co., Ltd.; *Int'l*, pg. 6709
HANS H. MEYER GMBH—See Hyster-Yale Materials Handling, Inc.; *U.S. Public*, pg. 1080
HANS HOLTERBOSCH, INC.; *U.S. Private*, pg. 1856
HANSI ANHAI FAR EAST LTD.—See Einhell Germany AG; *Int'l*, pg. 2333
HANS-JURGEN KEIL ANLAGENBAU GMBH & CO. KG; *Int'l*, pg. 3259
HANS KASPAR AG—See Orkla ASA; *Int'l*, pg. 5637
HANS KISSLE COMPANY, LLC—See Mitsui & Co., Ltd.; *Int'l*, pg. 4973
HAN'S LASER TECHNOLOGY INDUSTRY GROUP CO., LTD.; *Int'l*, pg. 3240
HANSLER INDUSTRIES; *Int'l*, pg. 3260
HANSLER MANUTENTION, INC—See Hansler Industries; *Int'l*, pg. 3260
HANS LUTZ MASCHINENFABRIK GMBH & CO. KG; *Int'l*, pg. 3259
HANSMENS MARKETING SDN BHD—See P-Duke Technology Co., Ltd.; *Int'l*, pg. 5681
HANSOL CHEMICAL CO. LTD.—See Hansol Group; *Int'l*, pg. 3260
HANSOL DEVELOPMENT CO. LTD.—See Hansol Group; *Int'l*, pg. 3260
HANSOL EME CO. LTD.—See Hansol Group; *Int'l*, pg. 3260
HANSOL GROUP; *Int'l*, pg. 3260
HANSOL HOMEDECO CO. LTD.—See Hansol Group; *Int'l*, pg. 3260
HANSOL INTICUBE CO., LTD.; *Int'l*, pg. 3261
HANSOL IONES CO., LTD; *Int'l*, pg. 3261
HANSOL LCD INC.—See Hansol Group; *Int'l*, pg. 3260
HANSOL LOGISTICS CO., LTD.—See Hansol Group; *Int'l*, pg. 3260
HANSOL PAPER CO., LTD.—See Hansol Group; *Int'l*, pg. 3260
HANSOL PNS CO., LTD.—See Hansol Group; *Int'l*, pg. 3260
HANSOL SEENTEC CO., LTD. - NO 1 FACTORY—See Seen Tec Co., Ltd.; *Int'l*, pg. 6679
HANSOL SEENTEC CO., LTD. - NO 2 FACTORY—See Seen Tec Co., Ltd.; *Int'l*, pg. 6679
HANSOL SEENTEC CO., LTD. - NO 3 FACTORY—See Seen Tec Co., Ltd.; *Int'l*, pg. 6679
HANSOL TECHNICS CO., LTD.; *Int'l*, pg. 3261
HANSOL TELECOM CO. LTD.—See Hansol Group; *Int'l*, pg. 3261
HANSON AGGREGATES BMC, INC.—See Heidelberg Materials AG; *Int'l*, pg. 3313
HANSON AGGREGATES DAVON LLC—See Heidelberg Materials AG; *Int'l*, pg. 3313
HANSON AGGREGATES EAST LLC—See Heidelberg Materials AG; *Int'l*, pg. 3313
HANSON AGGREGATES HOLDING NEDERLAND B.V.—See Heidelberg Materials AG; *Int'l*, pg. 3311
HANSON AGGREGATES LIMITED—See Heidelberg Materials AG; *Int'l*, pg. 3312

HANSON AGGREGATES LLC—See Heidelberg Materials AG; *Int'l*, pg. 3313
HANSON AGGREGATES MID-PACIFIC, INC.—See Heidelberg Materials AG; *Int'l*, pg. 3313
HANSON AGGREGATES MIDWEST LLC—See Heidelberg Materials AG; *Int'l*, pg. 3313
HANSON AGGREGATES NEDERLAND B.V.—See Heidelberg Materials AG; *Int'l*, pg. 3313
HANSON AGGREGATES NORTH AMERICA—See Heidelberg Materials AG; *Int'l*, pg. 3313
HANSON AGGREGATES (NORTH) LIMITED—See Heidelberg Materials AG; *Int'l*, pg. 3311
HANSON AGGREGATES PACIFIC SOUTHWEST, INC.—See Heidelberg Materials AG; *Int'l*, pg. 3313
HANSON AGGREGATES PENNSYLVANIA LLC—See Heidelberg Materials AG; *Int'l*, pg. 3313
HANSON AGGREGATES SOUTHEAST LLC—See Heidelberg Materials AG; *Int'l*, pg. 3313
HANSON AGGREGATES SOUTH WALES HOLDINGS LIMITED—See Heidelberg Materials AG; *Int'l*, pg. 3311
HANSON AGGREGATES UK - SOUTH WEST—See Heidelberg Materials AG; *Int'l*, pg. 3312
HANSON AGGREGATES WRP, INC.—See Heidelberg Materials AG; *Int'l*, pg. 3313
HANSON ALASKA LLC—See Hanson Professional Services, Inc.; *U.S. Private*, pg. 1856
HANSON AMALGAMATED INDUSTRIES LIMITED—See Heidelberg Materials AG; *Int'l*, pg. 3311
HANSON AUSTRALIA CEMENT PTY LIMITED—See Heidelberg Materials AG; *Int'l*, pg. 3311
HANSON AUSTRALIA (HOLDINGS) PTY. LIMITED—See Heidelberg Materials AG; *Int'l*, pg. 3311
HANSON AUSTRALIA INVESTMENTS PTY LIMITED—See Heidelberg Materials AG; *Int'l*, pg. 3311
HANSON AUSTRALIA PTY LIMITED—See Heidelberg Materials AG; *Int'l*, pg. 3311
HANSON BATH AND PORTLAND STONE LIMITED—See Heidelberg Materials AG; *Int'l*, pg. 3311
HANSON BATTERIES LIMITED—See Heidelberg Materials AG; *Int'l*, pg. 3311
HANSON BETON NEDERLAND B.V.—See Heidelberg Materials AG; *Int'l*, pg. 3311
HANSON BRICK EAST, LLC—See Heidelberg Materials AG; *Int'l*, pg. 3313
HANSON BRICK LIMITED—See Heidelberg Materials AG; *Int'l*, pg. 3311
HANSON BUILDING MATERIALS CARTAGE SDN BHD—See Heidelberg Materials AG; *Int'l*, pg. 3311
HANSON BUILDING MATERIALS EUROPE LIMITED—See Heidelberg Materials AG; *Int'l*, pg. 3311
HANSON BUILDING MATERIALS INDUSTRIES SDN BHD—See Heidelberg Materials AG; *Int'l*, pg. 3312
HANSON BUILDING MATERIALS-KTPC SDN BHD—See Heidelberg Materials AG; *Int'l*, pg. 3312
HANSON BUILDING MATERIALS LIMITED—See Heidelberg Materials AG; *Int'l*, pg. 3312
HANSON BUILDING MATERIALS MALAYSIA SDN BHD—See Heidelberg Materials AG; *Int'l*, pg. 3312
HANSON BUILDING MATERIALS MANUFACTURING SDN BHD—See Heidelberg Materials AG; *Int'l*, pg. 3312
HANSON BUILDING MATERIALS PRODUCTION SDN BHD—See Heidelberg Materials AG; *Int'l*, pg. 3312
HANSON BUILDING MATERIALS SERVICES SDN BHD—See Heidelberg Materials AG; *Int'l*, pg. 3312
HANSON CEMENT LTD.—See Heidelberg Materials AG; *Int'l*, pg. 3308
HANSON CEMENT - RIBBLESDALE WORKS—See Heidelberg Materials AG; *Int'l*, pg. 3308
HANSON COLD STORAGE, LLC—See Bay Grove Capital LLC; *U.S. Private*, pg. 493
HANSON COMMUNICATIONS INC.; *U.S. Private*, pg. 1856
HANSON CONCRETE (M) SDN BHD—See Heidelberg Materials AG; *Int'l*, pg. 3312
HANSON CONCRETE PRODUCTS—See Heidelberg Materials AG; *Int'l*, pg. 3313
HANSON CONCRETE PRODUCTS—See Heidelberg Materials AG; *Int'l*, pg. 3313
HANSON CONSTRUCTION CO, INC.; *U.S. Private*, pg. 1856
HANSON CONSTRUCTION MATERIALS PTY LTD.—See Heidelberg Materials AG; *Int'l*, pg. 3311
HANSON CREWING SERVICES LIMITED—See Heidelberg Materials AG; *Int'l*, pg. 3312
HANSON DIRECTORY SERVICE, INC.—See DirecTech LLC; *U.S. Private*, pg. 1236
HANSON DISTRIBUTING COMPANY; *U.S. Private*, pg. 1856
HANSON DODGE INC.; *U.S. Private*, pg. 1856
HANSON ELECTRIC OF BEMIDJI; *U.S. Private*, pg. 1856
HANSON FINANCE AUSTRALIA LTD—See Heidelberg Materials AG; *Int'l*, pg. 3312
HANSON FINANCE LIMITED—See Heidelberg Materials AG; *Int'l*, pg. 3312
HANSON FINANCIAL SERVICES LIMITED—See Heidelberg Materials AG; *Int'l*, pg. 3312
HANSON FOODS LIMITED—See Heidelberg Materials AG; *Int'l*, pg. 3312

HANSONGNEOTECH CO., LTD.; *Int'l*, pg. 3261
HANSON & HANSON ENTERPRISES LLC; *U.S. Private*, pg. 1856
HANSON HISPANIA S.A.—See Heidelberg Materials AG; *Int'l*, pg. 3312
HANSON IM-UND EXPORT GMBH—See Li & Fung Limited; *Int'l*, pg. 4479
HANSON INDUSTRIAL (ENGINEERING HOLDINGS) LIMITED—See Heidelberg Materials AG; *Int'l*, pg. 3312
HANSON INDUSTRIAL LIMITED—See Heidelberg Materials AG; *Int'l*, pg. 3312
HANSON INTERNATIONAL HOLDINGS LIMITED—See Heidelberg Materials AG; *Int'l*, pg. 3312
HANSON INTERNATIONAL INC.; *U.S. Private*, pg. 1856
HANSON ISLAND MANAGEMENT LIMITED—See Heidelberg Materials AG; *Int'l*, pg. 3312
HANSON (ISRAEL) LTD.—See Heidelberg Materials AG; *Int'l*, pg. 3311
HANSON LANDFILL SERVICES PTY LTD—See Heidelberg Materials AG; *Int'l*, pg. 3312
HANSON LHA LIMITED—See Heidelberg Materials AG; *Int'l*, pg. 3312
HANSON LIMITED—See Heidelberg Materials AG; *Int'l*, pg. 3311
HANSON LOGISTICS; *U.S. Private*, pg. 1856
HANSON MARINE LIMITED—See Heidelberg Materials AG; *Int'l*, pg. 3312
HANSON MATERIAL SERVICE—See Heidelberg Materials AG; *Int'l*, pg. 3313
HANSON PEABODY LIMITED—See Heidelberg Materials AG; *Int'l*, pg. 3312
HANSON PIPE & PRECAST QUEBEC LTD.—See Heidelberg Materials AG; *Int'l*, pg. 3312
HANSON PRECAST PTY LTD - MULGRAVE FACTORY—See Heidelberg Materials AG; *Int'l*, pg. 3312
HANSON PRECAST PTY LTD—See Heidelberg Materials AG; *Int'l*, pg. 3312
HANSON PROFESSIONAL SERVICES, INC.; *U.S. Private*, pg. 1856
HANSON PTY LIMITED—See Heidelberg Materials AG; *Int'l*, pg. 3312
HANSON QUARRY PRODUCTS (BATU PAHAT) SDN BHD—See Heidelberg Materials AG; *Int'l*, pg. 3312
HANSON QUARRY PRODUCTS EUROPE LTD.—See Heidelberg Materials AG; *Int'l*, pg. 3312
HANSON QUARRY PRODUCTS (HOLDINGS) SDN BHD—See Heidelberg Materials AG; *Int'l*, pg. 3312
HANSON QUARRY PRODUCTS (ISRAEL) LTD—See Heidelberg Materials AG; *Int'l*, pg. 3312
HANSON QUARRY PRODUCTS (KUANTAN) SDN BHD—See Heidelberg Materials AG; *Int'l*, pg. 3312
HANSON QUARRY PRODUCTS (KULAI) SDN BHD—See Heidelberg Materials AG; *Int'l*, pg. 3312
HANSON QUARRY PRODUCTS (PERAK) SDN BHD—See Heidelberg Materials AG; *Int'l*, pg. 3312
HANSON QUARRY PRODUCTS (RAWANG) SDN BHD—See Heidelberg Materials AG; *Int'l*, pg. 3312
HANSON QUARRY PRODUCTS SDN. BHD.—See Heidelberg Materials AG; *Int'l*, pg. 3313
HANSON QUARRY PRODUCTS (SEGAMAT) SDN BHD—See Heidelberg Materials AG; *Int'l*, pg. 3312
HANSON QUARRY PRODUCTS (TERENGGANU) SDN BHD—See Heidelberg Materials AG; *Int'l*, pg. 3312
HANSON QUARRY PRODUCTS VENTURES LIMITED—See Heidelberg Materials AG; *Int'l*, pg. 3313
HANSON RBS TRUSTEES LIMITED—See Heidelberg Materials AG; *Int'l*, pg. 3313
HANSON READY MIX, INC. - ARNPRIOR PLANT—See Heidelberg Materials AG; *Int'l*, pg. 3317
HANSON READY MIX, INC. - ASHTON PLANT—See Heidelberg Materials AG; *Int'l*, pg. 3317
HANSON READY MIX, INC. - AYLMER PLANT—See Heidelberg Materials AG; *Int'l*, pg. 3317
HANSON READY MIX, INC. - BRADDOCK PLANT—See Heidelberg Materials AG; *Int'l*, pg. 3317
HANSON READY MIX, INC. - CHARLESTON PLANT—See Heidelberg Materials AG; *Int'l*, pg. 3317
HANSON READY MIX, INC. - HUNTINGTON PLANT—See Heidelberg Materials AG; *Int'l*, pg. 3317
HANSON READY MIX, INC. - OTTAWA PLANT—See Heidelberg Materials AG; *Int'l*, pg. 3317
HANSON READY MIX, INC. - OTTAWA—See Heidelberg Materials AG; *Int'l*, pg. 3317
HANSON READY MIX, INC. - PARKERSBURG PLANT—See Heidelberg Materials AG; *Int'l*, pg. 3317
HANSON READY MIX, INC. - PEMBROKE PLANT—See Heidelberg Materials AG; *Int'l*, pg. 3317
HANSON READY MIX, INC. - PITTSBURGH PLANT—See Heidelberg Materials AG; *Int'l*, pg. 3317
HANSON READY MIX, INC. - STATE COLLEGE—See Heidelberg Materials AG; *Int'l*, pg. 3317
HANSON READY MIX, INC. - THURSO PLANT—See Heidelberg Materials AG; *Int'l*, pg. 3317
HANSON READY MIX, INC.- WHEELING PLANT—See Heidelberg Materials AG; *Int'l*, pg. 3317
HANSON READY MIX, INC. - WINFIELD PLANT—See Heidelberg Materials AG; *Int'l*, pg. 3317

HANSON PROFESSIONAL SERVICES, INC.

CORPORATE AFFILIATIONS

HANSON RESEARCH CORP.—See Teledyne Technologies Incorporated; *U.S. Public*, pg. 1993
HANSON RESOURCE MANAGEMENT LIMITED—See The Pritzker Organization, LLC; *U.S. Private*, pg. 4100
HANSON RETAIL LIMITED—See Heidelberg Materials AG; *Int'l*, pg. 3313
HANSON'S AUTO & IMPLEMENT INC.; *U.S. Private*, pg. 1857
HANSON'S WATER TREATMENT INC.—See Roto-Gro International Limited; *Int'l*, pg. 6405
HANSON SYSTEMS, LLC—See Crestview Partners, L.P.; *U.S. Private*, pg. 1098
HANSON THERMALITE LIMITED—See Heidelberg Materials AG; *Int'l*, pg. 3313
HANSON TIS HOLDINGS LIMITED—See Heidelberg Materials AG; *Int'l*, pg. 3313
HANSON TIS LIMITED—See Heidelberg Materials AG; *Int'l*, pg. 3313
HANSON TRUSS INCORPORATED; *U.S. Private*, pg. 1857
HANSON, WALTER & ASSOCIATES, INC.; *U.S. Private*, pg. 1857
HANSON WATSON ASSOCIATES; *U.S. Private*, pg. 1857
HANSORD AGENCY INC.—See Luther Holding Company; *U.S. Private*, pg. 2517
H.A.N.S. PREFA A.S.—See Bain Capital, LP; *U.S. Private*, pg. 438
HANSSAK CO., LTD.; *Int'l*, pg. 3261
HANS SCHWARZKOPF & HENKEL GMBH & CO. KG—See Henkel AG & Co. KGaA; *Int'l*, pg. 3348
HANSSEM CO., LTD. - ANSAN PLANT 1—See Hanssem Co., Ltd.; *Int'l*, pg. 3261
HANSSEM CO., LTD. - ANSAN PLANT 2—See Hanssem Co., Ltd.; *Int'l*, pg. 3261
HANSSEM CO., LTD. - ANSAN PLANT 3—See Hanssem Co., Ltd.; *Int'l*, pg. 3261
HANSSEM CO., LTD. - SIHEUNG PLANT 1—See Hanssem Co., Ltd.; *Int'l*, pg. 3261
HANSSEM CO., LTD. - SIHEUNG PLANT 2—See Hanssem Co., Ltd.; *Int'l*, pg. 3261
HANSSEM CO., LTD.; *Int'l*, pg. 3261
HANSSEM CORPORATION - NEW JERSEY PLANT 2—See Hanssem Co., Ltd.; *Int'l*, pg. 3261
HANSSEM CORPORATION—See Hanssem Co., Ltd.; *Int'l*, pg. 3261
HANSSEM INC.—See Hanssem Co., Ltd.; *Int'l*, pg. 3261
HANSSEM (SHANGHAI) HOME FURNISHINGS CO., LTD.—See Hanssem Co., Ltd.; *Int'l*, pg. 3261
HANSSON & KNUDSEN A/S—See Per Aarsleff Holding A/S; *Int'l*, pg. 5795
HANSSON PYROTECH AB—See Patria Oyj; *Int'l*, pg. 5758
HANSTEEL COMPANY LTD.—See HBIS Group Co., Ltd.; *Int'l*, pg. 3296
HANSTEEN HOLDINGS PLC—See Blackstone Inc.; *U.S. Public*, pg. 350
HANSTONE GOLD CORP.; *Int'l*, pg. 3261
HANS TURCK GMBH & CO. KG—See Turck Holding GmbH; *Int'l*, pg. 7974
HANSU CO., LTD.—See Kurita Water Industries Ltd.; *Int'l*, pg. 4340
HANSUI CO., LTD.—See Yokohama Maruuo Co.; *Int'l*, pg. 8595
HAN SUNG ENTERPRISE CO., LTD. - DANGGIIN FACTORY—See Han Sung Enterprise Co., Ltd.; *Int'l*, pg. 3240
HAN SUNG ENTERPRISE CO., LTD. - GURYONGPO FACTORY—See Han Sung Enterprise Co., Ltd.; *Int'l*, pg. 3240
HAN SUNG ENTERPRISE CO., LTD.; *Int'l*, pg. 3240
HANSUNG TECH CO., LTD.—See Komax Holding AG; *Int'l*, pg. 4240
HANSU TECHNICAL SERVICE LTD.—See Kurita Water Industries Ltd.; *Int'l*, pg. 4340
HANS ZIEGLER AG—See Poenina Holding AG; *Int'l*, pg. 5903
HANTANG CULTURE & EDUCATION HOLDING GROUP LIMITED; *Int'l*, pg. 3261
HAN TANG TECHNOLOGY, INC.; *U.S. Public*, pg. 982
HANTONG METAL COMPONENT (KL) SDN BHD—See CFM Holdings Limited; *Int'l*, pg. 1430
HANTONG METAL COMPONENT (PENANG) SDN. BHD.—See EasyIO Engineering Pte Ltd.; *Int'l*, pg. 2276
HANTONG METAL COMPONENT SDN BHD—See CFM Holdings Limited; *Int'l*, pg. 1430
HAN TONG METAL COMPONENT SDN BHD—See CFM Holdings Limited; *Int'l*, pg. 1430
HANTOP INC.; *Int'l*, pg. 3261
HANTOVER INC.; *U.S. Private*, pg. 1857
HANTRONG INVESTMENT CO., LTD.—See China Hi-Tech Group Co., Ltd.; *Int'l*, pg. 1507
HANTZ AIR, LLC—See Hantz Group, Inc.; *U.S. Private*, pg. 1857
HANTZ FINANCIAL SERVICES, INC.—See Hantz Group, Inc.; *U.S. Private*, pg. 1857
HANTZ GROUP, INC.; *U.S. Private*, pg. 1857
HANUMAN MACHINE TOOLS CORPORATION—See Quaser Machine Tools, Inc.; *Int'l*, pg. 6157
HANUNG TOYS AND TEXTILES LIMITED; *Int'l*, pg. 3261
HANURL AUTOMOTIVE PVT. LTD.—See Korea Electric Terminal Co., Ltd.; *Int'l*, pg. 4284
HANU SOFTWARE SOLUTIONS, INC.—See Insight Enterprises, Inc.; *U.S. Public*, pg. 1129
HANU SOFTWARE SOLUTIONS (INDIA) PRIVATE LTD.—See Insight Enterprises, Inc.; *U.S. Public*, pg. 1129
HANVEY GROUP HOLDINGS LTD.; *Int'l*, pg. 3261
HANVON C-PEN TECHNOLOGY CO., LTD.—See Hanwang Technology Co., Ltd.; *Int'l*, pg. 3264
HANVON MANUFACTURER CO., LTD—See Hanwang Technology Co., Ltd.; *Int'l*, pg. 3264
HANVON TECHNOLOGY COMPANY LTD—See Hanwang Technology Co., Ltd.; *Int'l*, pg. 3264
HANVON TECHNOLOGY (DEUTSCHLAND) GMBH—See Hanwang Technology Co., Ltd.; *Int'l*, pg. 3264
HANWA AEROSPACE USA—See Hanwha Group; *Int'l*, pg. 3264
HANWA ALPHA BUSINESS CO., LTD.—See Hanwa Co., Ltd.; *Int'l*, pg. 3262
HANWA AMERICAN CORP.—See Hanwa Co., Ltd.; *Int'l*, pg. 3262
HANWA AMERICAN CORP.—See Hanwa Co., Ltd.; *Int'l*, pg. 3262
HANWA (BEIJING) CO., LTD.—See Hanwa Co., Ltd.; *Int'l*, pg. 3262
HANWA CANADA CORP.—See Hanwa Co., Ltd.; *Int'l*, pg. 3262
HANWA CHILE LIMITADA—See Hanwa Co., Ltd.; *Int'l*, pg. 3262
HANWA CO., (HONG KONG) LTD.—See Hanwa Co., Ltd.; *Int'l*, pg. 3262
HANWA CO., LTD.; *Int'l*, pg. 3261
HANWA CO., LTD.—See Hanwa Co., Ltd.; *Int'l*, pg. 3262
HANWA CO., LTD.—See Hanwa Co., Ltd.; *Int'l*, pg. 3262
HANWA CO., LTD.—See Hanwa Co., Ltd.; *Int'l*, pg. 3262
HANWA DAISUN CO., LTD.—See Hanwa Co., Ltd.; *Int'l*, pg. 3262
HANWA (DALIAN) CO., LTD.—See Hanwa Co., Ltd.; *Int'l*, pg. 3262
HANWA ECO STEEL CO., LTD.—See Hanwa Co., Ltd.; *Int'l*, pg. 3262
HANWA EUROPE B.V.—See Hanwa Co., Ltd.; *Int'l*, pg. 3262
HANWA EUROPE B.V.—See Hanwa Co., Ltd.; *Int'l*, pg. 3262
HANWA FELLOWS ENGINEERING (CHINA) CO., LTD.—See Hanwa Co., Ltd.; *Int'l*, pg. 3262
HANWA FELLOWS ENGINEERING (THAILAND) CO., LTD.—See Hanwa Co., Ltd.; *Int'l*, pg. 3262
HANWA FOODS CO., LTD.—See Hanwa Co., Ltd.; *Int'l*, pg. 3262
HANWA INDIA PRIVATE LTD.—See Hanwa Co., Ltd.; *Int'l*, pg. 3262
HANWA (KOREA) CO., LTD.—See Hanwa Co., Ltd.; *Int'l*, pg. 3262
HANWA KOZAI CO., LTD.—See JFE Holdings, Inc.; *Int'l*, pg. 3936
HANWA LOGISTICS GROUP CO., LTD.—See Hanwa Co., Ltd.; *Int'l*, pg. 3262
HANWA LOGISTICS NAGOYA CO., LTD.—See Hanwa Co., Ltd.; *Int'l*, pg. 3262
HANWA LOGISTICS OSAKA CO., LTD.—See Hanwa Co., Ltd.; *Int'l*, pg. 3262
HANWA LOGISTICS TOKYO CO., LTD. - SENDAI FACTORY—See Hanwa Co., Ltd.; *Int'l*, pg. 3262
HANWA (MALAYSIA) SDN. BHD.—See Hanwa Co., Ltd.; *Int'l*, pg. 3262
HANWA METALS CO., LTD.—See Hanwa Co., Ltd.; *Int'l*, pg. 3262
HANWA MEXICANA, S.A. DE C.V.—See Hanwa Co., Ltd.; *Int'l*, pg. 3262
HANWA MIDDLE EAST FZE—See Hanwa Co., Ltd.; *Int'l*, pg. 3262
HANWANG TECHNOLOGY CO., LTD.; *Int'l*, pg. 3263
HANWA (QINGDAO) CO., LTD.—See Hanwa Co., Ltd.; *Int'l*, pg. 3262
HANWA SINGAPORE (PRIVATE) LTD.—See Hanwa Co., Ltd.; *Int'l*, pg. 3262
HANWA SMC STEEL SERVICE HA NOI CO., LTD.—See Hanwa Co., Ltd.; *Int'l*, pg. 3262
HANWA STEEL CENTRE (M) SDN. BHD.—See Hanwa Co., Ltd.; *Int'l*, pg. 3262
HANWA STEEL SERVICE (DONGGUAN) CO., LTD.—See Hanwa Co., Ltd.; *Int'l*, pg. 3262
HANWA STEEL SERVICE LTD.—See Hanwa Co., Ltd.; *Int'l*, pg. 3262
HANWA STEEL SERVICE MEXICANA, S.A. DE C.V.—See Hanwa Co., Ltd.; *Int'l*, pg. 3263
HANWA STEEL SERVICE (THAILAND) CO., LTD.—See Hanwa Co., Ltd.; *Int'l*, pg. 3262
HANWA THAILAND CO., LTD.—See Hanwa Co., Ltd.; *Int'l*, pg. 3262
HANWA TRADING (SHANGHAI) CO., LTD.—See Hanwa Co., Ltd.; *Int'l*, pg. 3263
HANWA VIETNAM CO., LTD.—See Hanwa Co., Ltd.; *Int'l*, pg. 3263
HANWECK ASSOCIATES, LLC—See Cboe Global Markets, Inc.; *U.S. Public*, pg. 459
HANWEI ELECTRONICS GROUP CORPORATION; *Int'l*, pg. 3264
HANWEI ENERGY SERVICES CORP.; *Int'l*, pg. 3264
HANWEL BELGIE N.V.—See Indutrade AB; *Int'l*, pg. 3679
HANWEL NEDERLAND B.V.—See Indutrade AB; *Int'l*, pg. 3679
HANWHA ACE SPECIAL PURPOSE ACQUISITION 2ND CO., LTD.; *Int'l*, pg. 3264
HANWHA ADVANCED MATERIALS ALABAMA LLC—See Hanwha Group; *Int'l*, pg. 3264
HANWHA ADVANCED MATERIALS (BEIJING) CO., LTD.—See Hanwha Group; *Int'l*, pg. 3264
HANWHA ADVANCED MATERIALS CO., LTD.—See Hanwha Group; *Int'l*, pg. 3264
HANWHA ADVANCED MATERIALS CZECH S.R.O.—See Hanwha Group; *Int'l*, pg. 3264
HANWHA ADVANCED MATERIALS (SHANGHAI) CO., LTD.—See Hanwha Group; *Int'l*, pg. 3264
HANWHA AEROSPACE CO., LTD.—See Hanwha Group; *Int'l*, pg. 3264
HANWHA AMERICA DEVELOPMENT INC.—See Hanwha Group; *Int'l*, pg. 3265
HANWHA ASSET MANAGEMENT CO., LTD.—See Hanwha Group; *Int'l*, pg. 3264
HANWHA AZDEL, INC.—See Hanwha Group; *Int'l*, pg. 3265
HANWHA BANK HUNGARY LTD.—See Hanwha Group; *Int'l*, pg. 3266
HANWHA CANADA DEVELOPMENT INC.—See Hanwha Group; *Int'l*, pg. 3265
HANWHA CHEMICAL MALAYSIA SDN. BHD.—See Hanwha Group; *Int'l*, pg. 3265
HANWHA CHEMICAL (NINGBO) CO., LTD.—See Hanwha Group; *Int'l*, pg. 3265
HANWHA CHEMICAL (THAILAND) CO., LTD.—See Hanwha Group; *Int'l*, pg. 3265
HANWHA CHEMICAL TRADING (SHANGHAI) CO., LTD.—See Hanwha Group; *Int'l*, pg. 3265
HANWHA CHINA—See Hanwha Group; *Int'l*, pg. 3265
HANWHA CORPORATION—See Hanwha Group; *Int'l*, pg. 3265
HANWHA DEFENSE SYSTEMS CO., LTD.—See Hanwha Group; *Int'l*, pg. 3265
HANWHA DEVELOPMENT CO., LTD.—See Hanwha Group; *Int'l*, pg. 3265
HANWHA ENERGY CORP.—See Hanwha Group; *Int'l*, pg. 3265
HANWHA ENGINE CO., LTD.; *Int'l*, pg. 3264
HANWHA ENGINEERING & CONSTRUCTION CORP.—See Hanwha Group; *Int'l*, pg. 3265
HANWHA EUROPE GMBH—See Hanwha Group; *Int'l*, pg. 3265
HANWHA GALLERIA CO., LTD.—See Hanwha Group; *Int'l*, pg. 3265
HANWHA GALLERIA TIMEWORLD CO., LTD.—See Hanwha Group; *Int'l*, pg. 3265
HANWHA GENERAL CHEMICAL CO., LTD.—See Hanwha Group; *Int'l*, pg. 3265
HANWHA GENERAL INSURANCE CO., LTD.—See Hanwha Group; *Int'l*, pg. 3266
HANWHA GROUP; *Int'l*, pg. 3264
HANWHA (H.K.) CO., LTD.—See Hanwha Group; *Int'l*, pg. 3265
HANWHA HOTELS & RESORTS CO., LTD.—See Hanwha Group; *Int'l*, pg. 3266
HANWHA INTERNACIONAL DO BRASIL LTDA—See Hanwha Group; *Int'l*, pg. 3265
HANWHA INTERNATIONAL INDIA PVT. LTD.—See Hanwha Group; *Int'l*, pg. 3265
HANWHA INTERNATIONAL LLC—See Hanwha Group; *Int'l*, pg. 3265
HANWHA INTERNATIONAL (S) PTE LTD.—See Hanwha Group; *Int'l*, pg. 3265
HANWHA INVESTMENT & SECURITIES CO., LTD.; *Int'l*, pg. 3266
HANWHA INVESTMENT TRUST MANAGEMENT CO., LTD.—See Hanwha Group; *Int'l*, pg. 3266
HANWHA JAPAN CO., LTD.—See Hanwha Group; *Int'l*, pg. 3265
HANWHA LIFE CO., LTD—See Hanwha Group; *Int'l*, pg. 3266
HANWHA LIFE INSURANCE CO., LTD.—See Hanwha Group; *Int'l*, pg. 3266
HANWHA LIFE INSURANCE VIETNAM LTD.—See Hanwha Group; *Int'l*, pg. 3266
HANWHA LIFE INVESTMENT (AMERICA) LTD.—See Hanwha Group; *Int'l*, pg. 3266
HANWHA MACHINERY AMERICA INC.—See Hanwha Group; *Int'l*, pg. 3266
HANWHA MACHINERY CO., LTD.—See Hanwha Group; *Int'l*, pg. 3266
HANWHA OCEAN CO., LTD.; *Int'l*, pg. 3266
HANWHA POLYDREAMER CO., LTD.—See Hanwha Group; *Int'l*, pg. 3266
HANWHA Q CELLS AUSTRALIA PTY. LTD.—See Hanwha Group; *Int'l*, pg. 3265

HANWHA Q CELLS CO., LTD.—See Hanwha Group; *Int'l*, pg. 3265
HANWHA Q CELLS GMBH—See Hanwha Group; *Int'l*, pg. 3265
HANWHA Q CELLS JAPAN CO., LTD.—See Hanwha Group; *Int'l*, pg. 3265
HANWHA Q CELLS MALAYSIA—See Hanwha Group; *Int'l*, pg. 3265
HANWHA Q CELLS USA CORP.—See Hanwha Group; *Int'l*, pg. 3265
HANWHA RESORT CO., LTD.—See Hanwha Group; *Int'l*, pg. 3266
HANWHA SAUDI CONTRACTING CO., LTD.—See Hanwha Group; *Int'l*, pg. 3265
HANWHA SAVINGS BANK—See Hanwha Group; *Int'l*, pg. 3266
HANWHA S&C CO., LTD.—See Hanwha Group; *Int'l*, pg. 3266
HANWHA SECURITIES CO., LTD.—See Hanwha Group; *Int'l*, pg. 3266
HANWHA SOLAR AMERICA LLC—See Hanwha Group; *Int'l*, pg. 3265
HANWHA SOLARONE GMBH—See Hanwha Group; *Int'l*, pg. 3265
HANWHA SOLARONE (SHANGHAI) CO., LTD.—See Hanwha Group; *Int'l*, pg. 3265
HANWHA SOLARONE TECHNOLOGY CO., LTD.—See Hanwha Group; *Int'l*, pg. 3265
HANWHA SOLUTIONS CORPORATION; *Int'l*, pg. 3267
HANWHA SOLUTIONS CORP.—See Hanwha Group; *Int'l*, pg. 3266
HANWHA STORES CO., LTD.—See Hanwha Group; *Int'l*, pg. 3266
HANWHA SYSTEMS CO., LTD.; *Int'l*, pg. 3267
HANWHA TECHM CO., LTD. - ASAN 1 PLANT—See Hanwha Group; *Int'l*, pg. 3266
HANWHA TECHM CO., LTD. - CHANGWON PLANT—See Hanwha Group; *Int'l*, pg. 3266
HANWHA TECHM CO., LTD.—See Hanwha Group; *Int'l*, pg. 3266
HANWHA TECHM (SUZHOU) CO., LTD.—See Hanwha Group; *Int'l*, pg. 3266
HANWHA TECHM USA LLC—See Hanwha Group; *Int'l*, pg. 3266
HANWOOK TECH INO GLASS CO., LTD.—See AGC Inc.; *Int'l*, pg. 204
HANXING METALLURGICAL MINE ADMINISTRATION—See China Rare Earth Resources And Technology Co., Ltd.; *Int'l*, pg. 1545
HANXING PRINTEC CO., LTD.—See Synopex Inc.; *Int'l*, pg. 7386
HANXX MEDIA GMBH—See Stroer SE & Co. KGaA; *Int'l*, pg. 7242
HANYANG CONSTRUCTION(DALIAN) CO., LTD.—See Hanyang Eng Co., Ltd.; *Int'l*, pg. 3267
HANYANG DIGITECH CO., LTD.; *Int'l*, pg. 3267
HANYANG ENG CO., LTD.; *Int'l*, pg. 3267
HANYANG NAVICOM CO., LTD—See Hanyang Eng Co., Ltd.; *Int'l*, pg. 3267
HANYANG SECURITIES CO., LTD.; *Int'l*, pg. 3267
HANYANG (XIAN) ENGINEERING CO., LTD.—See Hanyang Eng Co., Ltd.; *Int'l*, pg. 3267
HANYUAN TECHNICAL SERVICE CENTER GMBH—See China COSCO Shipping Corporation Limited; *Int'l*, pg. 1494
HANYU GROUP JOINT-STOCK CO., LTD.; *Int'l*, pg. 3267
HANYU PLASTICS INDUSTRIES LTD.—See Sekisui Chemical Co., Ltd.; *Int'l*, pg. 6693
HANZA AB; *Int'l*, pg. 3267
HANZA ALFARAM ELECTRIC (SUZHOU) CO., LTD.—See Hanza AB; *Int'l*, pg. 3267
HANZA CZECH REPUBLIC S.R.O—See Hanza AB; *Int'l*, pg. 3267
HANZA ELECTRIC (SUZHOU) CO., LTD.—See Hanza AB; *Int'l*, pg. 3267
HANZA ELEKTROMEKAN AB—See Hanza AB; *Int'l*, pg. 3267
HANZA GMBH—See Hanza AB; *Int'l*, pg. 3267
HANZA LEVYPROFIILI OY—See Hanza AB; *Int'l*, pg. 3267
HANZA MECHANICS - ARJANG—See Hanza AB; *Int'l*, pg. 3267
HANZA MECHANICS KUNOVICE S.R.O—See Hanza AB; *Int'l*, pg. 3267
HANZA MECHANICS NARVA AS—See Hanza AB; *Int'l*, pg. 3267
HANZA MECHANICS SWEDEN AB—See Hanza AB; *Int'l*, pg. 3267
HANZA MECHANICS TARTU AS—See Hanza AB; *Int'l*, pg. 3267
HANZA MECHANICS TOREBODA—See Hanza AB; *Int'l*, pg. 3267
HANZA METALLISET OY—See Hanza AB; *Int'l*, pg. 3267
HANZA POLAND SP. Z.O.O—See Hanza AB; *Int'l*, pg. 3267
HANZA TECH SOLUTIONS GMBH—See Hanza AB; *Int'l*, pg. 3267
HANZA TOOLFAC OY—See Hanza AB; *Int'l*, pg. 3267
HANZHONG YAOBAI CEMENT CO. LTD—See West China Cement Limited; *Int'l*, pg. 8383

HAO BAI INTERNATIONAL (CAYMAN) LIMITED; *Int'l*, pg. 3267
HAOERSAI TECHNOLOGY GROUP CORP., LTD.; *Int'l*, pg. 3268
HAOHUA CHEMICAL SCIENCE & TECHNOLOGY CORP.—See China National Chemical Corporation; *Int'l*, pg. 1526
HAOHUA EAST CHINA CHEMICAL CO., LTD.—See China National Chemical Corporation; *Int'l*, pg. 1527
HAOHUA HITONE INVESTMENT MANAGEMENT CO., LTD.—See China National Chemical Corporation; *Int'l*, pg. 1527
HAOHUA HONGHE CHEMICAL CO., LTD.—See China National Chemical Corporation; *Int'l*, pg. 1527
HAOHUA JUNHUA GROUP CO., LTD.—See China National Chemical Corporation; *Int'l*, pg. 1527
HAOHUA YUHANG CHEMICAL CO., LTD.—See China National Chemical Corporation; *Int'l*, pg. 1528
HAOMA MINING NL; *Int'l*, pg. 3268
HAOSEN AUTOMATION GMBH—See Dalian Haosen Equipment Manufacturing Co., Ltd.; *Int'l*, pg. 1952
HAOSEN AUTOMATION INDIA PRIVATE LIMITED—See Dalian Haosen Equipment Manufacturing Co., Ltd.; *Int'l*, pg. 1952
HAOSEN AUTOMATION NORTH AMERICA, INC.—See Dalian Haosen Equipment Manufacturing Co., Ltd.; *Int'l*, pg. 1952
HAOSEN HONG KONG LIMITED—See Dalian Haosen Equipment Manufacturing Co., Ltd.; *Int'l*, pg. 1952
HAOSEN INTELLIGENT EQUIPMENT (SHENZHEN) CO., LTD.—See Dalian Haosen Equipment Manufacturing Co., Ltd.; *Int'l*, pg. 1952
HAOSEN RUNBO INTELLIGENT MANUFACTURING CHANGZHOU CO., LTD.—See Dalian Haosen Equipment Manufacturing Co., Ltd.; *Int'l*, pg. 1952
HAOSEN ULTRA-PRECISION CO., LTD.—See Dalian Haosen Equipment Manufacturing Co., Ltd.; *Int'l*, pg. 1952
HAO TIAN INTERNATIONAL CONSTRUCTION INVESTMENT GROUP LIMITED; *Int'l*, pg. 3267
HAO WEN HOLDINGS LIMITED; *Int'l*, pg. 3267
HAOXIANGNI HEALTH FOOD CO., LTD.; *Int'l*, pg. 3268
HAO YONG AUTOMOTIVE CONTROLS LTD.; *Int'l*, pg. 3268
HAOYUN TECHNOLOGIES CO., LTD.; *Int'l*, pg. 3268
HAOYIN TECHNOLOGY CO., LTD.; *Int'l*, pg. 3268
HAPA AG—See Coesia S.p.A.; *Int'l*, pg. 1690
HAPAC-LLOYD (SCHWEIZ) AG—See Albert Ballin KG; *Int'l*, pg. 294
HAPACO GROUP JOINT STOCK COMPANY; *Int'l*, pg. 3268
HAPAG-LLOYD (AFRICA) PTY. LTD.—See Albert Ballin KG; *Int'l*, pg. 294
HAPAG-LLOYD AGENCY LLC—See Albert Ballin KG; *Int'l*, pg. 295
HAPAG-LLOYD AG—See Albert Ballin KG; *Int'l*, pg. 294
HAPAG-LLOYD (AMERICA) INC.—See Albert Ballin KG; *Int'l*, pg. 294
HAPAG-LLOYD(AMERICA) LLC—See Albert Ballin KG; *Int'l*, pg. 295
HAPAG-LLOYD ANTWERPEN—See Albert Ballin KG; *Int'l*, pg. 295
HAPAG-LLOYD ARGENTINA S.R.L.—See Albert Ballin KG; *Int'l*, pg. 295
HAPAG-LLOYD (AUSTRALIA) PTY. LTD.—See Albert Ballin KG; *Int'l*, pg. 294
HAPAG-LLOYD AUSTRIA GMBH—See Albert Ballin KG; *Int'l*, pg. 295
HAPAG-LLOYD BRAZIL—See Albert Ballin KG; *Int'l*, pg. 295
HAPAG-LLOYD (CANADA) INC.—See Albert Ballin KG; *Int'l*, pg. 294
HAPAG-LLOYD CHILE AG. MAR. LTDA.—See Albert Ballin KG; *Int'l*, pg. 295
HAPAG-LLOYD (CHINA) LTD.—See Albert Ballin KG; *Int'l*, pg. 294
HAPAG-LLOYD (CHINA) SHIPPING LTD.—See Albert Ballin KG; *Int'l*, pg. 294
HAPAG-LLOYD COLOMBIA LTDA.—See Albert Ballin KG; *Int'l*, pg. 295
HAPAG-LLOYD COSTA RICA S.A.—See Albert Ballin KG; *Int'l*, pg. 295
HAPAG-LLOYD DENAMRK—See Albert Ballin KG; *Int'l*, pg. 295
HAPAG-LLOYD DENIZASIRI NAKLIYAT A.S.—See Albert Ballin KG; *Int'l*, pg. 295
HAPAG-LLOYD (EASTWIND) PTE. LTD.—See Albert Ballin KG; *Int'l*, pg. 295
HAPAG-LLOYD EXECUTIVE GMBH—See TUI AG; *Int'l*, pg. 7965
HAPAG-LLOYD FLUGGESELLSCHAFT MBH—See TUI AG; *Int'l*, pg. 7967
HAPAG-LLOYD (FRANCE) SAS—See Albert Ballin KG; *Int'l*, pg. 295
HAPAG-LLOYD GLOBAL SERVICES PVT. LTD.—See Albert Ballin KG; *Int'l*, pg. 295
HAPAG-LLOYD GUATAMALA S.A.—See Albert Ballin KG; *Int'l*, pg. 295
HAPAG-LLOYD (IRELAND) LTD.—See Albert Ballin KG; *Int'l*, pg. 295

HAPAG-LLOYD (ITALY) S.R.L.—See Albert Ballin KG; *Int'l*, pg. 295
HAPAG-LLOYD (JAPAN) K.K.—See Albert Ballin KG; *Int'l*, pg. 295
HAPAG-LLOYD (KOREA) LTD.—See Albert Ballin KG; *Int'l*, pg. 295
HAPAG-LLOYD KREUZFAHRTEN GMBH—See Royal Caribbean Cruises Ltd.; *U.S. Public*, pg. 1815
HAPAG-LLOYD KREUZFAHRTEN GMBH—See TUI AG; *Int'l*, pg. 7967
HAPAG-LLOYD LANKA (PVT.) LTD.—See Albert Ballin KG; *Int'l*, pg. 295
HAPAG-LLOYD (MALAYSIA) SDN. BHD.—See Albert Ballin KG; *Int'l*, pg. 295
HAPAG-LLOYD MEXICO S.A. DE C.V.—See Albert Ballin KG; *Int'l*, pg. 295
HAPAG-LLOYD (NEW ZEALAND) LTD.—See Albert Ballin KG; *Int'l*, pg. 295
HAPAG-LLOYD OVERSEAS TRANSPORT (HELLAS) SA—See Albert Ballin KG; *Int'l*, pg. 295
HAPAG-LLOYD OVERSEAS TRANSPORT S.A.—See Albert Ballin KG; *Int'l*, pg. 295
HAPAG-LLOYD PERU S.A.C.—See Albert Ballin KG; *Int'l*, pg. 295
HAPAG-LLOYD (PHILIPPINES) INC.—See Albert Ballin KG; *Int'l*, pg. 295
HAPAG-LLOYD POLSKA SP. Z.O.O.—See Albert Ballin KG; *Int'l*, pg. 295
HAPAG-LLOYD PORTUGAL LDA.—See Albert Ballin KG; *Int'l*, pg. 295
HAPAG-LLOYD PTE. LTD.—See Albert Ballin KG; *Int'l*, pg. 295
HAPAG-LLOYD ROTTERDAM—See Albert Ballin KG; *Int'l*, pg. 295
HAPAG-LLOYD SPAIN S.L.—See Albert Ballin KG; *Int'l*, pg. 295
HAPAG-LLOYD SWEDEN AB—See Albert Ballin KG; *Int'l*, pg. 295
HAPAG-LLOYD TAIWAN LTD.—See Albert Ballin KG; *Int'l*, pg. 295
HAPAG-LLOYD (THAILAND) LTD.—See Albert Ballin KG; *Int'l*, pg. 295
HAPAG-LLOYD (UK) LTD.—See Albert Ballin KG; *Int'l*, pg. 295
HAPAG-LLOYD VENEZUELA, C.A.—See Albert Ballin KG; *Int'l*, pg. 295
HAPAG-LLOYD (VIETNAM)—See Albert Ballin KG; *Int'l*, pg. 295
HAPBEE TECHNOLOGIES INC.; *Int'l*, pg. 3268
HAPCO FARMS INC.; *U.S. Private*, pg. 1857
HAPCO REAL ESTATE INVESTMENT; *U.S. Private*, pg. 1857
HAPCO—See The Dyson-Kissner-Moran Corporation; *U.S. Private*, pg. 4024
HAPILOGI, INC.—See CRE, Inc.; *Int'l*, pg. 1830
HAPINS CO., LTD.—See RIZAP GROUP, Inc.; *Int'l*, pg. 6354
HAPO COMMUNITY CREDIT UNION; *U.S. Private*, pg. 1857
HAP O'NEILL, INC.; *U.S. Private*, pg. 1857
HAPPENINGS COMMUNICATIONS GROUP, INC.—See JRjr33, Inc.; *U.S. Private*, pg. 2240
HAPPIEST MINDS TECHNOLOGIES PVT. LTD.; *Int'l*, pg. 3268
HAPPIMINDSHARE—See WPP plc; *Int'l*, pg. 8475
HAPPINESS AND D CO., LTD.; *Int'l*, pg. 3268
HAPPINESS INC.; *U.S. Private*, pg. 1857
HAPPINET CORPORATION; *Int'l*, pg. 3269
HAPPINET LOGISTICS SERVICE CORPORATION—See Happinet Corporation; *Int'l*, pg. 3269
HAPPINET MARKETING CORPORATION—See Happinet Corporation; *Int'l*, pg. 3269
HAPPINET PHANTOM STUDIOS CORPORATION—See Happinet Corporation; *Int'l*, pg. 3269
HAPPINET VENDING SERVICE CORPORATION—See Happinet Corporation; *Int'l*, pg. 3269
HAPPOLD INGENIEURBURO GMBH—See Buro Happold Engineers Limited; *Int'l*, pg. 1226
HAPPO TELEVISION, INC.—See Fuji Media Holdings, Inc.; *Int'l*, pg. 2814
HAPPU BUS CO., LTD.—See Mie Kotsu Group Holdings, Inc.; *Int'l*, pg. 4888
HAPPY APPLE COMPANY; *U.S. Private*, pg. 1857
HAPPY BANCSHARES, INC.—See Home BancShares, Inc.; *U.S. Public*, pg. 1045
HAPPY BELLY FOOD GROUP INC.; *Int'l*, pg. 3269
HAPPY CHEF SYSTEMS, INC.; *U.S. Private*, pg. 1857
THE HAPPY COMPANY—See Tender Loving Things Inc.; *U.S. Private*, pg. 3966
HAPPY CREEK MINERALS LTD.; *Int'l*, pg. 3269
HAPPY DAY CORPORATION; *U.S. Private*, pg. 1857
HAPPYDOO SA; *Int'l*, pg. 3269
HAPPYFAMILY; *U.S. Private*, pg. 1857
HAPPY FOODS, INC.; *U.S. Private*, pg. 1857
HAPPY FORGING LIMITED; *Int'l*, pg. 3269
HAPPY FORSMAN & BODENFORS AB—See Stagwell, Inc.; *U.S. Public*, pg. 1927

Company Index

HAPPY FORGING LIMITED

CORPORATE AFFILIATIONS

HAPPY HARRY'S DISCOUNT DRUG STORES, INC.—See Walgreens Boots Alliance, Inc.; *U.S. Public*, pg. 2323
HAPPY HARRY'S INC.—See Walgreens Boots Alliance, Inc.; *U.S. Public*, pg. 2323
HAPPY JACK INC.; *U.S. Private*, pg. 1857
HAPPY JAPAN INC.—See Platinum Equity, LLC; *U.S. Private*, pg. 3208
HAPPY JOE'S PIZZA AND ICE CREAM PARLOR, INC.; *U.S. Private*, pg. 1857
HAPPY LAND ENTERTAINMENT (W.L.L.)—See Future Kid Entertainment and Real Estate Co. K.S.C.C.; *Int'l*, pg. 2856
HAPPY LIFE INSURANCE CO., LTD.—See China Cinda Asset Management Co., Ltd.; *Int'l*, pg. 1488
HAPPY MCGARRYBOWEN—See Dentsu Group Inc.; *Int'l*, pg. 2036
HAPPY MOTORING CO. SDN. BHD.—See Oriental Holdings Berhad; *Int'l*, pg. 5624
HAPPYNARAE AMERICA LLC—See SK hynix Inc.; *Int'l*, pg. 6970
HAPPYNEURON INC.—See Scientific Brain Training SA; *Int'l*, pg. 6648
HAPPYNEURON SAS; *Int'l*, pg. 3269
HAPPY ON SUPPLY CHAIN MANAGEMENT LTD.—See Promate Electronic Co., Ltd.; *Int'l*, pg. 5992
HAPPY PLANET FOODS, INC.—See Agrifoods International Cooperative LTD; *Int'l*, pg. 217
HAPPY VALLEY NUTRITION LIMITED; *Int'l*, pg. 3269
H&A PRESTIGE BOTTLING LTD.—See Halewood International Ltd.; *Int'l*, pg. 3229
HAPRO DEUTSCHLAND GMBH—See VDL Groep B.V.; *Int'l*, pg. 8140
HAPRO INTERNATIONAL BV—See VDL Groep B.V.; *Int'l*, pg. 8140
HAP SENG CONSOLIDATED BERHAD; *Int'l*, pg. 3268
HAP SENG CREDIT SDN. BHD.—See Hap Seng Consolidated Berhad; *Int'l*, pg. 3268
HAP SENG FERTILIZERS SDN. BHD.—See Hap Seng Consolidated Berhad; *Int'l*, pg. 3268
HAP SENG LAND SDN. BHD.—See Hap Seng Consolidated Berhad; *Int'l*, pg. 3268
HAP SENG PLANTATIONS HOLDINGS BERHAD—See Hap Seng Consolidated Berhad; *Int'l*, pg. 3268
HAP SENG PROPERTIES DEVELOPMENT SDN. BHD.—See Hap Seng Consolidated Berhad; *Int'l*, pg. 3268
HAP SENG REALTY (KK I) SDN. BHD.—See Hap Seng Consolidated Berhad; *Int'l*, pg. 3268
HAP SENG STAR SDN. BHD.—See Hap Seng Consolidated Berhad; *Int'l*, pg. 3268
HAP SENG TRUCKS DISTRIBUTION SDN. BHD.—See Hap Seng Consolidated Berhad; *Int'l*, pg. 3268
HAPUGASTENNE PLANTATIONS LTD—See John Swire & Sons Limited; *Int'l*, pg. 3980
HAPVIDA PARTICIPACOES E INVESTIMENTOS S.A.; *Int'l*, pg. 3269
HARA CORPORATION—See Toyota Industries Corporation; *Int'l*, pg. 7866
HARADA ASIA-PACIFIC LTD.—See HARADA INDUSTRY CO., LTD.; *Int'l*, pg. 3269
HARADA AUTOMOTIVE ANTENNA (PHILIPPINES), INC.—See HARADA INDUSTRY CO., LTD.; *Int'l*, pg. 3269
HARADA COMMUNICATION SYSTEMS CO., LTD.—See HARADA INDUSTRY CO., LTD.; *Int'l*, pg. 3269
HARADA INDUSTRIES (EUROPE) LIMITED—See HARADA INDUSTRY CO., LTD.; *Int'l*, pg. 3269
HARADA INDUSTRIES (MEXICO), S.A.DE C.V.—See HARADA INDUSTRY CO., LTD.; *Int'l*, pg. 3269
HARADA INDUSTRIES VIETNAM LIMITED—See HARADA INDUSTRY CO., LTD.; *Int'l*, pg. 3269
HARADA INDUSTRY CO., LTD.; *Int'l*, pg. 3269
HARADA INDUSTRY OF AMERICA, INC.—See HARADA INDUSTRY CO., LTD.; *Int'l*, pg. 3269
HARADEN MOTORCAR CORP.; *U.S. Private*, pg. 1857
HARALAMBOS DISTRIBUTING CO.; *U.S. Private*, pg. 1857
HARALD A. MOLLER AS—See MollerGruppen AS; *Int'l*, pg. 5022
HARALD QUANDT HOLDING GMBH; *Int'l*, pg. 3269
HARAM TRANSPORTATION CO. S.A.E.—See Ghabbour Auto S.A.E.; *Int'l*, pg. 2958
HARANGA RESOURCES LIMITED; *Int'l*, pg. 3270
HARARI INC.; *U.S. Private*, pg. 1857
HAR AS—See MillerKnoll, Inc.; *U.S. Public*, pg. 1447
HARATECHS CORPORATION—See Toyota Industries Corporation; *Int'l*, pg. 7866
HARBACH GILLAN & NIXON INC.; *U.S. Private*, pg. 1857
HARBERT MANAGEMENT CORPORATION; *U.S. Private*, pg. 1857
HARBERT MEZZANINE CAPITAL—See Harbert Management Corporation; *U.S. Private*, pg. 1858
HARBERT VENTURE PARTNERS—See Harbert Management Corporation; *U.S. Private*, pg. 1858
HARBIN AIR CONDITIONING CO., LTD.; *Int'l*, pg. 3270
HARBIN BANK CO., LTD.; *Int'l*, pg. 3270
HARBIN BOILER COMPANY LIMITED—See Harbin Electric Corporation; *Int'l*, pg. 3270
HARBIN BOSHI AUTOMATION CO., LTD.; *Int'l*, pg. 3270
HARBIN CHANGFANGYUAN HI-TECH ENVIRONMENT-FRIENDLY INDUSTRIAL CO., LTD—See CHINA GREEN MATERIAL TECHNOLOGIES, INC.; *Int'l*, pg. 1505
HARBIN CHURIN GROUP JOINTSTOCK CO., LTD.; *Int'l*, pg. 3270
HARBIN CLINIC LLC; *U.S. Private*, pg. 1858
HARBIN COSLIGHT ELECTRIC AUTOMATION COMPANY LIMITED—See Coslight Technology International Group Limited; *Int'l*, pg. 1810
HARBIN COSLIGHT ELECTRIC WIRE & CABLE CO., LTD.—See Coslight Technology International Group Limited; *Int'l*, pg. 1810
HARBIN COSLIGHT POWER CO., LTD.—See Coslight Technology International Group Limited; *Int'l*, pg. 1810
HARBIN COSLIGHT STORAGE BATTERY COMPANY LIMITED—See Coslight Technology International Group Limited; *Int'l*, pg. 1810
HARBIN COSLIGHT SWITCH COMPANY LIMITED—See Coslight Technology International Group Limited; *Int'l*, pg. 1810
HARBIN DONGAN AUTO ENGINE CO., LTD.; *Int'l*, pg. 3270
HARBIN ELECTRICAL MACHINERY COMPANY LIMITED—See Harmonicare Medical Holdings Ltd.; *Int'l*, pg. 3278
HARBIN ELECTRIC COMPANY LIMITED—See Harbin Electric Corporation; *Int'l*, pg. 3270
HARBIN ELECTRIC CORPORATION; *Int'l*, pg. 3270
HARBIN ELECTRIC GROUP JIAMUSI ELECTRIC MACHINE CO., LTD.; *Int'l*, pg. 3270
HARBIN ELECTRIC (H.E) CORPORATION—See Harbin Electric Corporation; *Int'l*, pg. 3270
HARBIN ELECTRIC INTERNATIONAL CO., LTD.—See Harbin Electric Corporation; *Int'l*, pg. 3270
HARBIN ELECTRIC MACHINERY CO., LTD.—See Harbin Electric Corporation; *Int'l*, pg. 3270
HARBIN FIBER GLASS—See NOV, Inc.; *U.S. Public*, pg. 1544
HARBIN GAOMEI PRINTING CO., LTD.—See Tesson Holdings Limited; *Int'l*, pg. 7575
HARBINGER CAPITAL PARTNERS LLC; *U.S. Private*, pg. 1858
HARBINGER GROUP INC.; *Int'l*, pg. 3271
HARBINGER KNOWLEDGE PRODUCTS, INC.—See Harbinger Group Inc.; *Int'l*, pg. 3271
HARBINGER KNOWLEDGE PRODUCTS PVT. LTD.—See Harbinger Group Inc.; *Int'l*, pg. 3271
HARBINGER PARTNERS, INC.; *U.S. Private*, pg. 1858
HARBINGER TECHNOLOGY CORP.—See Cub Elecparts Inc.; *Int'l*, pg. 1875
HARBIN GLORIA PHARMACEUTICAL CO., LTD.; *Int'l*, pg. 3270
HARBIN GONG DA HIGH-TECH ENTERPRISE DEVELOPMENT CO., LTD.; *Int'l*, pg. 3270
HARBIN HATOU INVESTMENT CO., LTD.; *Int'l*, pg. 3270
HARBIN JIARUN HOSPITAL CO., LTD—See JRSIS Health Care Corporation; *Int'l*, pg. 4008
HARBIN JIUZHOU GROUP CO., LTD.; *Int'l*, pg. 3270
HARBIN LUMBER COMPANY INCORPORATED; *U.S. Private*, pg. 1858
HARBIN MAURI YEAST CO., LTD—See The Garfield Weston Foundation; *Int'l*, pg. 7648
HARBIN MEDISAN PHARMACEUTICAL CO., LTD.; *Int'l*, pg. 3270
HARBIN PHARMACEUTICAL GROUP SANJING PHARMACEUTICAL CO., LTD; *Int'l*, pg. 3271
HARBIN POLY REAL ESTATE COMPREHENSIVE DEVELOPMENT CO., LTD—See China Poly Group Corporation; *Int'l*, pg. 1541
HARBIN SAMICK CORP.—See Samick Musical Instrument Co., Ltd.; *Int'l*, pg. 6505
HARBIN SAYYAS WINDOWS CO., LTD.; *Int'l*, pg. 3271
HARBIN SONGBEI SHANGRI-LA HOTEL CO., LIMITED—See Shangri-La Asia Limited; *Int'l*, pg. 6783
HARBIN TIAN DI REN MEDICAL SCIENCE AND TECHNOLOGY COMPANY—See China Sky One Medical, Inc.; *Int'l*, pg. 1552
HARBIN VITI ELECTRONICS CO., LTD.; *Int'l*, pg. 3271
HARBIN XINGUANG OPTIC-ELECTRONICS TECHNOLOGY CO., LTD.; *Int'l*, pg. 3271
HARBIN YANMAR AGRICULTURAL EQUIPMENT CO., LTD.—See Yanmar Co., Ltd.; *Int'l*, pg. 8563
HARBIN YEW SCIENCE AND TECHNOLOGY DEVELOPMENT CO., LTD.—See Yew Bio-Pharm Group, Inc.; *U.S. Private*, pg. 4589
HARBIN YIFENG ECO-ENVIRONMENT CO., LTD.—See EASTERN ENVIRONMENT SOLUTIONS, CORP.; *Int'l*, pg. 2272
HARBIN ZHONGFU IN-LINE CONTAINER CO., LTD.—See Zhuhai Zhongfu Enterprise Co., Ltd.; *Int'l*, pg. 8679
HARBIN ZHONGQIANG POWER-TECH CO., LTD.—See Advanced Battery Technologies, Inc.; *U.S. Private*, pg. 88
HARBISON CORPORATION; *U.S. Private*, pg. 1858
HARBISONWALKER INTERNATIONAL, INC.—See Platinum Equity, LLC; *U.S. Private*, pg. 3203
HARBISON-WALKER REFRACTORIES COMPANY—See Platinum Equity, LLC; *U.S. Private*, pg. 3203
HARBOES BRYGGERI A/S; *Int'l*, pg. 3271
HARBOE SVERIGE AB—See Harboes Bryggeri A/S; *Int'l*, pg. 3271
HARBORAGE MARINA, LLC—See International Marina Group, LP; *U.S. Private*, pg. 2118
HARBOR AMERICA; *U.S. Private*, pg. 1858
THE HARBOR BANK OF MARYLAND—See Harbor Bankshares Corporation; *U.S. Public*, pg. 984
HARBOR BANKSHARES CORPORATION; *U.S. Public*, pg. 984
HARBOR BEACH CAPITAL, LLC; *U.S. Private*, pg. 1858
HARBOR BEACH COMMUNITY HOSPITAL, INC.; *U.S. Private*, pg. 1858
HARBOR BRIDGE INTERMODAL INC—See US 1 Industries, Inc.; *U.S. Private*, pg. 4317
HARBOR BUSINESS COMPLIANCE CORPORATION; *U.S. Private*, pg. 1858
HARBOR CAPITAL ADVISORS, INC.—See ORIX Corporation; *Int'l*, pg. 5634
HARBOR COMMUNICATIONS, LLC—See Telapex Inc.; *U.S. Private*, pg. 3959
HARBOR CORP.; *U.S. Private*, pg. 1858
HARBOR CREDIT UNION—See Southland Credit Union; *U.S. Private*, pg. 3736
HARBOR CUSTOM DEVELOPMENT, INC.; *U.S. Public*, pg. 984
HARBOR DEVELOPMENTAL DISABILITIES FOUNDATION, INC.; *U.S. Private*, pg. 1859
HARBOR DISTRIBUTING LLC—See Reyes Holdings, LLC; *U.S. Private*, pg. 3418
HARBOR DIVERSIFIED, INC.; *U.S. Public*, pg. 984
HARBOR ELECTRIC ENERGY COMPANY—See Eversource Energy; *U.S. Public*, pg. 801
HARBOR ELECTRONICS, INC.—See Technoprobe S.p.A.; *Int'l*, pg. 7511
HARBOR FOODS GROUP INC.; *U.S. Private*, pg. 1859
HARBOR FOOTWEAR GROUP, LTD.; *U.S. Private*, pg. 1859
HARBOR FREIGHT TOOLS USA; *U.S. Private*, pg. 1859
HARBOR GROUP INCORPORATED; *U.S. Private*, pg. 1859
HARBOR GROUP INC; *U.S. Private*, pg. 1859
HARBOR HEIGHTS SURGERY CENTER, LLC—See Tenet Healthcare Corporation; *U.S. Public*, pg. 2002
HARBOR INDUSTRIES INC.; *U.S. Private*, pg. 1859
HARBOR INN OF CS ASSOCIATES—See MSL Property Management; *U.S. Private*, pg. 2807
HARBORLIGHT CAPITAL GROUP, LLC; *U.S. Private*, pg. 1859
HARBORLIGHT CAPITAL MANAGEMENT, LLC—See HarborLight Capital Group, LLC; *U.S. Private*, pg. 1859
HARBOR MEDICAL ASSOCIATES P.C.—See Partners HealthCare System, Inc.; *U.S. Private*, pg. 3101
HARBOR MOTORS; *U.S. Private*, pg. 1859
HARBORONE BANCORP, INC.; *U.S. Public*, pg. 984
HARBORONE BANK—See HarborOne Bancorp, Inc.; *U.S. Public*, pg. 984
HARBORONE MORTGAGE, LLC—See HarborOne Bancorp, Inc.; *U.S. Public*, pg. 984
HARBOR PAYMENTS, INC.—See American Express Company; *U.S. Public*, pg. 100
HARBOR PHYSICAL THERAPY, LIMITED PARTNERSHIP—See U.S. Physical Therapy, Inc.; *U.S. Public*, pg. 2214
HARBOR POINT BEHAVIORAL HEALTH CENTER, INC.—See Universal Health Services, Inc.; *U.S. Public*, pg. 2257
HARBOR RETIREMENT ASSOCIATES, LLC; *U.S. Private*, pg. 1859
HARBOR SEAFOOD, INC.; *U.S. Private*, pg. 1859
HARBOR STAR SHIPPING SERVICES INC.; *Int'l*, pg. 3271
HARBOR STEEL & SUPPLY CORPORATION—See Harbor Group Incorporated; *U.S. Private*, pg. 1859
HARBORSTONE CREDIT UNION; *U.S. Private*, pg. 1859
HARBOR THERAPEUTICS, INC.—See Harbor Diversified, Inc.; *U.S. Public*, pg. 984
HARBOR-UCLA FACULTY PRACTICE PLAN, A MEDICAL GROUP, INC.—See Harbor-UCLA Medical Foundation, Inc.; *U.S. Private*, pg. 1859
HARBOR-UCLA MEDICAL FOUNDATION, INC.; *U.S. Private*, pg. 1859
HARBOR URBAN, LLC—See Urban Partners, LLC; *U.S. Private*, pg. 4314
HARBOR VIEW BEHAVIORAL HEALTH CENTER—See Formation Capital, LLC; *U.S. Private*, pg. 1570
HARBOR VIEW HOLDINGS INC.; *U.S. Private*, pg. 1859
HARBORWAY INSURANCE AGENCY, LLC—See The Travelers Companies, Inc.; *U.S. Public*, pg. 2136
HARBOR WHOLESALE GROCERY INC.—See Harbor Foods Group Inc.; *U.S. Private*, pg. 1859
HARBOUR AGENCIES (SABAH) SDN. BHD.—See Harbour-Link Group Berhad; *Int'l*, pg. 3272
HARBOUR AGENCIES (SARAWAK) SDN. BHD.—See Harbour-Link Group Berhad; *Int'l*, pg. 3272
HARBOUR AGENCIES (SIBU) SDN. BHD.—See Harbour-Link Group Berhad; *Int'l*, pg. 3272

COMPANY NAME INDEX

HARBOUR CENTRE DEVELOPMENT LIMITED—See Wheelock & Company Limited; *Int'l*, pg. 8397
HARBOUR CONTRACTORS, INC.; *U.S. Private*, pg. 1859
HARBOUR DIGITAL ASSET CAPITAL LIMITED; *Int'l*, pg. 3271
HARBOUR ENERGY LTD.—See EIG Global Energy Partners, LLC; *U.S. Private*, pg. 1347
HARBOUR ENERGY PLC; *Int'l*, pg. 3271
HARBOUR EQUINE HOLDINGS LIMITED; *Int'l*, pg. 3271
HARBOUR FULL GROUP LIMITED—See Liaoning Port Co., Ltd.; *Int'l*, pg. 4483
HARBOUR GRAND HONG KONG LIMITED—See CK Asset Holdings Limited; *Int'l*, pg. 1635
HARBOUR GROUP INDUSTRIES, INC.; *U.S. Private*, pg. 1860
HARBOUR GROUP LIMITED OF DELAWARE—See Harbour Group Industries, Inc.; *U.S. Private*, pg. 1860
HARBOUR HOMES LLC; *U.S. Private*, pg. 1861
HARBOUR INDUSTRIES CANADA LTD.—See Berkshire Hathaway Inc.; *U.S. Public*, pg. 310
HARBOUR INDUSTRIES, INC.—See Berkshire Hathaway Inc.; *U.S. Public*, pg. 310
HARBOUR-LINK GROUP BERHAD; *Int'l*, pg. 3272
HARBOUR-LINK LINES (JB) SDN. BHD.—See Harbour-Link Group Berhad; *Int'l*, pg. 3272
HARBOUR-LINK LINES (PK) SDN. BHD.—See Harbour-Link Group Berhad; *Int'l*, pg. 3272
HARBOUR-LINK LOGISTICS SDN. BHD.—See Harbour-Link Group Berhad; *Int'l*, pg. 3272
HARBOUR-LINK LOGISTICS (S) SDN. BHD.—See Harbour-Link Group Berhad; *Int'l*, pg. 3272
HARBOUR LINK SHIPPING SDN. BHD.—See Albert Ballin KG; *Int'l*, pg. 295
HARBOUR MARINE PRODUCTS INC.; *Int'l*, pg. 3272
HARBOUR PLAZA 8 DEGREES LIMITED—See CK Hutchison Holdings Limited; *Int'l*, pg. 1637
HARBOUR PLAZA CHONGQING COMPANY LIMITED—See CK Asset Holdings Limited; *Int'l*, pg. 1635
HARBOUR PLAZA DEGREES LIMITED—See CK Asset Holdings Limited; *Int'l*, pg. 1635
HARBOUR PLAZA HOTEL MANAGEMENT LIMITED—See CK Asset Holdings Limited; *Int'l*, pg. 1635
HARBOUR PLAZA METROPOLIS LIMITED—See CK Asset Holdings Limited; *Int'l*, pg. 1635
HARBOUR PLAZA RESORT CITY LIMITED—See CK Asset Holdings Limited; *Int'l*, pg. 1635
HARBOUR POINT MANAGEMENT LLC; *U.S. Private*, pg. 1861
HARBOUR RACING LIMITED—See Harbour Equine Holdings Limited; *Int'l*, pg. 3272
HARBOUR SERVICES CORPORATION SDN. BHD.—See Harbour-Link Group Berhad; *Int'l*, pg. 3272
HARBOURVEST GLOBAL PRIVATE EQUITY LIMITED; *Int'l*, pg. 3272
HARBOURVEST HORIZON—See HarbourVest Partners, LLC; *U.S. Private*, pg. 1861
HARBOURVEST INVESTMENT CONSULTING (BEIJING) COMPANY LIMITED—See HarbourVest Partners, LLC; *U.S. Private*, pg. 1861
HARBOURVEST PARTNERS (ASIA) LIMITED—See HarbourVest Partners, LLC; *U.S. Private*, pg. 1861
HARBOURVEST PARTNERS (JAPAN) LIMITED—See HarbourVest Partners, LLC; *U.S. Private*, pg. 1861
HARBOURVEST PARTNERS, LLC; *U.S. Private*, pg. 1861
HARBOURVEST PARTNERS, LLC—See HarbourVest Partners, LLC; *U.S. Private*, pg. 1861
HARBOURVEST PARTNERS (U.K.) LIMITED—See HarbourVest Partners, LLC; *U.S. Private*, pg. 1861
HARBOURVIEW AUTOHAUS LTD.; *Int'l*, pg. 3272
HARBOUR WATER CORPORATION—See Veolia Water Indianapolis, LLC; *U.S. Private*, pg. 4358
HARBRIDGE CONSULTING GROUP, LLC—See Community Bank System, Inc.; *U.S. Public*, pg. 549
HARBRIDGE + CROSS LIMITED; *Int'l*, pg. 3272
HARBURGER/SCOTT ADVERTISING; *U.S. Private*, pg. 1861
HARBURG-FREUDENBERGER BELISCE D.O.O.—See L. Possehl & Co. mbH; *Int'l*, pg. 4383
HARBURG-FREUDENBERGER (FRANCE) S.A.R.L.—See L. Possehl & Co. mbH; *Int'l*, pg. 4383
HARBURG-FREUDENBERGER MACHINERY (CHINA) CO., LTD.—See L. Possehl & Co. mbH; *Int'l*, pg. 4383
HARBURG-FREUDENBERGER MASCHINENBAU GMBH—See L. Possehl & Co. mbH; *Int'l*, pg. 4383
HARBURG-FREUDENBERGER MASCHINENBAU GMBH—See L. Possehl & Co. mbH; *Int'l*, pg. 4383
HARCHELROAD MOTORS INC.; *U.S. Private*, pg. 1861
HARCOB CO., LTD.—See Senko Group Holdings Co., Ltd.; *Int'l*, pg. 6709
HARCO DISTRIBUTORS INC.; *U.S. Private*, pg. 1861
HARCO, INC.—See New Rite Aid, LLC; *U.S. Private*, pg. 2905
HARCO INSURANCE SERVICES; *U.S. Private*, pg. 1861
HARCO LABORATORIES INC.—See TransDigm Group Incorporated; *U.S. Public*, pg. 2182
HARCO, LLC; *U.S. Private*, pg. 1862
HARCO MANUFACTURING COMPANY INC.; *U.S. Private*, pg. 1862

HARCO NATIONAL INSURANCE COMPANY, INC.—See IAT Reinsurance Company, Ltd.; *U.S. Private*, pg. 2028
HARCON INC.; *U.S. Private*, pg. 1862
HARCOSEMCO LLC—See TransDigm Group Incorporated; *U.S. Public*, pg. 2181
HARCOURT EDUCATION LTD.—See Pearson plc; *Int'l*, pg. 5776
HARCOURT INVESTMENT CONSULTING AG—See Vontobel Holding AG; *Int'l*, pg. 8306
HARCOURTS INTERNATIONAL LTD; *Int'l*, pg. 3272
HARCROS CHEMICALS INC. - ORGANICS DIVISION—See Harcros Chemicals Inc.; *U.S. Private*, pg. 1862
HARCROS CHEMICALS INC.; *U.S. Private*, pg. 1862
HARDAGE HOTELS V LLC—See Hardage Investments, Inc.; *U.S. Private*, pg. 1862
HARDAGE INVESTMENTS, INC.; *U.S. Private*, pg. 1862
HARDAWAY CONSTRUCTION CORP.—See Hardaway Group, Inc.; *U.S. Private*, pg. 1862
HARDAWAY GROUP, INC.; *U.S. Private*, pg. 1862
HARDAWAY REALTY CO. INC.—See Hardaway Group, Inc.; *U.S. Private*, pg. 1862
HARDBALL CAPITAL; *U.S. Private*, pg. 1862
HARD BEAT COMMUNICATIONS; *U.S. Private*, pg. 1862
HARDCASTLE RESTAURANTS PRIVATE LIMITED—See Westlife Development Limited; *Int'l*, pg. 8391
HARDCASTLE & WAUD MANUFACTURING COMPANY LIMITED; *Int'l*, pg. 3272
HARD-CO CONSTRUCTION LTD.; *Int'l*, pg. 3272
HARDCORE DISCOVERIES LTD.; *Int'l*, pg. 3272
HARD-CO SAND & GRAVEL LTD.—See Hard-Co Construction Ltd.; *Int'l*, pg. 3272
HARD DOLLAR CORPORATION; *U.S. Private*, pg. 1862
HARD DRIVES NORTHWEST, INC.; *U.S. Private*, pg. 1862
HARDEE BY EVH MANUFACTURING COMPANY, LLC; *U.S. Private*, pg. 1862
HARDEE'S FOOD SYSTEMS, INC.—See Roark Capital Group Inc.; *U.S. Private*, pg. 3454
HARDEES SOUTHWEST MISSOURI INC.; *U.S. Private*, pg. 1862
HARDEL BUILDERS CENTER—See Hardel Mutual Plywood Corporation; *U.S. Private*, pg. 1862
HARDEL MUTUAL PLYWOOD CORPORATION; *U.S. Private*, pg. 1862
HARDEMAN LANDSCAPE NURSERY, INC.; *U.S. Private*, pg. 1862
HARDEN & ASSOCIATES, INC.—See Arthur J. Gallagher & Co.; *U.S. Public*, pg. 205
HARDENBERGH INSURANCE GROUP, INC.; *U.S. Private*, pg. 1862
HARDENBURGH TITLE AGENCY—See Hill-N-Dale Abstracters, Inc.; *U.S. Private*, pg. 1946
HARDEN FURNITURE INC.; *U.S. Private*, pg. 1862
HARDEN MANUFACTURING CORP.—See Linsalata Capital Partners, Inc.; *U.S. Private*, pg. 2463
HARDEN TECHNOLOGIES INC.; *Int'l*, pg. 3272
HARDER CORP.; *U.S. Private*, pg. 1862
HARDER MECHANICAL CONTRACTORS INC.; *U.S. Private*, pg. 1863
HARDER & STEENBECK GMBH & CO. KG—See ANEST IWATA Corporation; *Int'l*, pg. 458
HARDESTY & HANOVER, LLC; *U.S. Private*, pg. 1863
HARD EVENTS LLC—See Live Nation Entertainment, Inc.; *U.S. Public*, pg. 1329
HARDI AUSTRALIA PTY. LTD.—See Exel Industries SA; *Int'l*, pg. 2582
HARDI CROP PROTECTION SA LTD.—See Exel Industries SA; *Int'l*, pg. 2582
HARDIDE COATINGS INCORPORATED—See Hardide Plc; *Int'l*, pg. 3273
HARDIDE COATINGS LIMITED—See Hardide Plc; *Int'l*, pg. 3273
HARDIDE PLC; *Int'l*, pg. 3272
HARDIE GRANT PUBLISHING PTY. LTD.; *Int'l*, pg. 3273
HARDIE'S FRUIT & VEGETABLE CO., LP—See The Chefs' Warehouse, Inc.; *U.S. Public*, pg. 2059
HARDI EVRARD SA—See Exel Industries SA; *Int'l*, pg. 2582
HARDIGG FRANCE SAS—See Platinum Equity, LLC; *U.S. Private*, pg. 3207
HARDIGG UK LIMITED—See Platinum Equity, LLC; *U.S. Private*, pg. 3207
HARDI GMBH—See Exel Industries SA; *Int'l*, pg. 2582
HARDI GMBH—See Exel Industries SA; *Int'l*, pg. 2582
HARDI INC.—See Exel Industries SA; *Int'l*, pg. 2582
HARDI INTERNATIONAL AS—See Exel Industries SA; *Int'l*, pg. 2582
HARDI KENYA LTD.—See Exel Industries SA; *Int'l*, pg. 2582
HARDI LTD.—See Exel Industries SA; *Int'l*, pg. 2582
HARDIN BUICK PONTIAC GMC; *U.S. Private*, pg. 1863
HARDIN COMPLIANCE CONSULTING, LLC—See Genstar Capital, LLC; *U.S. Private*, pg. 1677
HARDIN COUNTY BANCORPORATION; *U.S. Private*, pg. 1863
HARDIN COUNTY SAVINGS BANK—See Hardin County Bancorporation; *U.S. Private*, pg. 1863

HARDING COMPANY INC.—See ALP Industries, Inc.; *U.S. Private*, pg. 196
HARDINGE BROTHERS, INC.—See Privet Fund Management, LLC; *U.S. Private*, pg. 3269
HARDINGE GMBH—See Privet Fund Management, LLC; *U.S. Private*, pg. 3269
HARDINGE INC.—See Privet Fund Management, LLC; *U.S. Private*, pg. 3269
HARDINGE MACHINE (SHANGHAI) CO., LTD.—See Privet Fund Management, LLC; *U.S. Private*, pg. 3269
HARDINGE MACHINE TOOLS B.V.—See Privet Fund Management, LLC; *U.S. Private*, pg. 3269
HARDINGE MACHINE TOOLS B.V. - TAIWAN REPRESENTATIVE OFFICE—See Privet Fund Management, LLC; *U.S. Private*, pg. 3269
HARDINGER TRANSFER CO. INC.; *U.S. Private*, pg. 1863
HARDING & HILL INC.; *U.S. Private*, pg. 1863
HARDING HOLDINGS INC.; *U.S. Private*, pg. 1863
HARDINGS MARKET-WEST INC.; *U.S. Private*, pg. 1863
HARDINGS THOMAS MANAGEMENT; *U.S. Private*, pg. 1863
HARDIN HONDA; *U.S. Private*, pg. 1863
HARDI NORTH AMERICA INC—See Exel Industries SA; *Int'l*, pg. 2582
HARDIN SANITATION, INC.—See Waste Connections, Inc.; *Int'l*, pg. 8353
HARDISON/DOWNEY CONSTRUCTION INC.; *U.S. Private*, pg. 1863
HARDISON/DOWNEY, INC.—See Kitchell Corporation; *U.S. Private*, pg. 2316
THE HARDMAN GROUP LIMITED; *Int'l*, pg. 7652
HARDMAN GROUP—See The Hardman Group Limited; *Int'l*, pg. 7652
HARDMAN GROUP—See The Hardman Group Limited; *Int'l*, pg. 7652
HARDMAN SUPPLY COMPANY; *U.S. Private*, pg. 1863
HARDMAN WHOLESALE LLC—See Hardwoods Distribution Inc.; *Int'l*, pg. 3273
HARD OFF CORPORATION CO., LTD.; *Int'l*, pg. 3272
HARDOX WEARPARTS CENTER STIRLING LTD.—See SSAB AB; *Int'l*, pg. 7153
HARD PARTS DIRECT B.V.—See Dover Corporation; *U.S. Public*, pg. 681
HARDRIVES, INC.; *U.S. Private*, pg. 1863
HARDRIVES OF DELRAY, INC.; *U.S. Private*, pg. 1863
HARD ROCK CAFE INTERNATIONAL CHICAGO—See Seminole Tribe of Florida, Inc.; *U.S. Private*, pg. 3604
HARD ROCK CAFE INTERNATIONAL INC. GEORGIA—See Seminole Tribe of Florida, Inc.; *U.S. Private*, pg. 3605
HARD ROCK CAFE INTERNATIONAL, INC.—See Seminole Tribe of Florida, Inc.; *U.S. Private*, pg. 3604
HARD ROCK CAFE INTERNATIONAL LA JOLLA—See Seminole Tribe of Florida, Inc.; *U.S. Private*, pg. 3605
HARD ROCK CAFE INTERNATIONAL LAS VEGAS—See Seminole Tribe of Florida, Inc.; *U.S. Private*, pg. 3605
HARD ROCK CAFE INTERNATIONAL MAUI—See Seminole Tribe of Florida, Inc.; *U.S. Private*, pg. 3605
HARD ROCK CAFE INTERNATIONAL MIAMI—See Seminole Tribe of Florida, Inc.; *U.S. Private*, pg. 3605
HARD ROCK CAFE INTERNATIONAL NEW JERSEY—See Seminole Tribe of Florida, Inc.; *U.S. Private*, pg. 3605
HARD ROCK CAFE INTERNATIONAL NEWPORT BEACH—See Seminole Tribe of Florida, Inc.; *U.S. Private*, pg. 3605
HARD ROCK CAFE INTERNATIONAL NEW YORK—See Seminole Tribe of Florida, Inc.; *U.S. Private*, pg. 3605
HARD ROCK CAFE INTERNATIONAL SAN ANTONIO—See Seminole Tribe of Florida, Inc.; *U.S. Private*, pg. 3605
HARD ROCK CAFE INTERNATIONAL—See Seminole Tribe of Florida, Inc.; *U.S. Private*, pg. 3604
HARD ROCK CAFE INTERNATIONAL—See Seminole Tribe of Florida, Inc.; *U.S. Private*, pg. 3604
HARD ROCK CAFE INTERNATIONAL SOUTH CAROLINA—See Seminole Tribe of Florida, Inc.; *U.S. Private*, pg. 3605
HARD ROCK CAFE INTERNATIONAL TENNESSEE—See Seminole Tribe of Florida, Inc.; *U.S. Private*, pg. 3605
HARD ROCK CAFE INTERNATIONAL TEXAS—See Seminole Tribe of Florida, Inc.; *U.S. Private*, pg. 3605
HARD ROCK CAFE INTERNATIONAL UNIVERSAL CITY—See Seminole Tribe of Florida, Inc.; *U.S. Private*, pg. 3605
HARD ROCK CAFE INTERNATIONAL USA—See Seminole Tribe of Florida, Inc.; *U.S. Private*, pg. 3605
HARD ROCK CAFE KEY WEST—See Seminole Tribe of Florida, Inc.; *U.S. Private*, pg. 3605
HARD ROCK CAFE PUERTO RICO—See Seminole Tribe of Florida, Inc.; *U.S. Private*, pg. 3605
HARD ROCK TOOL INC.; *U.S. Private*, pg. 1862
HARDSCRABBLE WIND POWER, LLC—See Iberdrola, S.A.; *Int'l*, pg. 3570
HARDSTAFF BARRIERS LIMITED—See Hill & Smith PLC; *Int'l*, pg. 3391
HARDT GROUP ADVISORS, INC.—See HARDT GROUP Global Management AG; *Int'l*, pg. 3273

HARDT GROUP GLOBAL MANAGEMENT AG

HARDT GROUP GLOBAL MANAGEMENT AG; *Int'l*, pg. 3273
HARDT GROUP GMBH—See HARDT GROUP Global Management AG; *Int'l*, pg. 3273
HARDWARE CONSULTANTS—See Platinum Equity, LLC; *U.S. Private*, pg. 3208
HARDWARE DISTRIBUTION WAREHOUSES, INC.; *U.S. Private*, pg. 1863
HARDWARE HOLDINGS—See Littlejohn & Co., LLC; *U.S. Private*, pg. 2470
HARDWARE IMAGINATION-TECH; *U.S. Private*, pg. 1863
HARDWARE & LUMBER LIMITED—See GraceKennedy Limited; *Int'l*, pg. 3049
HARDWARE PRODUCTS, LP—See SEI MetalTek; *U.S. Private*, pg. 3599
HARDWARE SALES INC.; *U.S. Private*, pg. 1863
HARDWARE SPECIALTY CO. INC.; *U.S. Private*, pg. 1863
HARDWARE SUPPLIERS OF AMERICA; *U.S. Private*, pg. 1864
HARDWICK CLOTHES INC.; *U.S. Private*, pg. 1864
HARDWIRE LLC; *U.S. Private*, pg. 1864
HARDWOOD CREATIONS; *U.S. Private*, pg. 1864
HARDWOOD FUNDING LLC—See National Basketball Association; *U.S. Private*, pg. 2848
HARDWOOD INDUSTRIES INC.; *U.S. Private*, pg. 1864
HARDWOOD MARKET REPORT L.P.—See Astorg Partners S.A.S.; *Int'l*, pg. 656
HARDWOODS DISTRIBUTION INC.; *Int'l*, pg. 3273
HARDWOODS INCORPORATED—See Atlanta Hardwood Corporation; *U.S. Private*, pg. 370
HARDWOODS OF MICHIGAN, INC.—See Hardwoods Distribution Inc.; *Int'l*, pg. 3273
HARDWOODS SPECIALTY PRODUCTS US LP—See Hardwoods Distribution Inc.; *Int'l*, pg. 3273
HARDWYN INDIA LIMITED; *Int'l*, pg. 3273
HARDY CAPITAL CORPORATION; *Int'l*, pg. 3273
HARDY CHEVROLET, INC.; *U.S. Private*, pg. 1864
HARDY COMMUNICATIONS DEVELOPMENT; *U.S. Private*, pg. 1864
THE HARDY CORPORATION; *U.S. Private*, pg. 4043
HARDY DIAGNOSTICS; *U.S. Private*, pg. 1864
HARDY ENTERPRISES INCORPORATED; *U.S. Private*, pg. 1864
HARDYFLEX INDUSTRIES SDN BHD—See Armstrong Industrial Corporation Ltd.; *Int'l*, pg. 575
HARDY GUERNSEY LIMITED—See Loews Corporation; *U.S. Public*, pg. 1340
HARDY OIL AND GAS PLC—See Blake Holdings Limited; *Int'l*, pg. 1062
HARDY PROCESS SOLUTIONS, INC.—See Technology for Energy Corporation; *U.S. Private*, pg. 3955
HARDY'S TINTARA WINERY—See The Carlyle Group Inc.; *U.S. Public*, pg. 2044
HARDY UNDERWRITING BERMUDA LIMITED—See Loews Corporation; *U.S. Public*, pg. 1340
HARDY UNDERWRITING LIMITED—See Loews Corporation; *U.S. Public*, pg. 1340
HAREBELL MEADOWS AND HARTBURN GRANGE RESIDENTS MANAGEMENT COMPANY LIMITED—See Persimmon plc; *Int'l*, pg. 5816
HAREL FINANCE OPERATING SERVICES LTD.—See Harel Insurance Investments & Financial Services Ltd.; *Int'l*, pg. 3274
HAREL HAMISHMAR COMPUTERS LTD.—See Harel Insurance Investments & Financial Services Ltd.; *Int'l*, pg. 3274
HAREL INSURANCE COMPANY LTD.—See Harel Insurance Investments & Financial Services Ltd.; *Int'l*, pg. 3274
HAREL INSURANCE, FINANCING & ISSUING LTD.—See Harel Insurance Investments & Financial Services Ltd.; *Int'l*, pg. 3274
HAREL INSURANCE INVESTMENTS & FINANCIAL SERVICES LTD.; *Int'l*, pg. 3273
HAREL MALLAC BUREAUTIQUE LTD—See Harel Mallac & Co. Ltd.; *Int'l*, pg. 3274
HAREL MALLAC & CO. LTD.; *Int'l*, pg. 3274
HAREL MALLAC ENGINEERING LTD—See Harel Mallac & Co. Ltd.; *Int'l*, pg. 3274
HAREL MALLAC OUTSOURCING LTD—See Harel Mallac & Co. Ltd.; *Int'l*, pg. 3274
HAREL MALLAC TECHNOLOGIES LTD—See Harel Mallac & Co. Ltd.; *Int'l*, pg. 3274
HAREL MALLAC TRAVEL AND LEISURE LTD—See Harel Mallac & Co. Ltd.; *Int'l*, pg. 3274
HAREL MUTUAL FUNDS LTD.—See Harel Insurance Investments & Financial Services Ltd.; *Int'l*, pg. 3274
HAREL (UK) LTD.—See Harel Insurance Investments & Financial Services Ltd.; *Int'l*, pg. 3274
HAREN CONSTRUCTION COMPANY INC; *U.S. Private*, pg. 1864
HAREWOOD ASSET MANAGEMENT (US) INC.—See BNP Paribas SA; *Int'l*, pg. 1088
HARFANG EXPLORATION INC.; *Int'l*, pg. 3274
HARFORD BANK; *U.S. Public*, pg. 984
THE HARFORD MUTUAL INSURANCE COMPANY INC.; *U.S. Private*, pg. 4043

HARFORD SYSTEMS, INC.—See Bio Medic Corporation; *U.S. Private*, pg. 561
HARGER HOWE ADVERTISING; *U.S. Private*, pg. 1864
HARGER HOWE ADVERTISING—See Harger Howe Advertising; *U.S. Private*, pg. 1864
HARGER HOWE ADVERTISING—See Harger Howe Advertising; *U.S. Private*, pg. 1864
HARGER INC.—See TE Connectivity Ltd.; *Int'l*, pg. 7494
HARGIS INDUSTRIES INC—See Hillman Solutions Corp.; *U.S. Public*, pg. 1038
HARGRAVE POWER, INC.—See Quanta Services, Inc.; *U.S. Public*, pg. 1751
HARGRAY COMMUNICATIONS GROUP, INC.—See Cable One, Inc.; *U.S. Public*, pg. 416
HARGREAVE HALE AIM VCT PLC; *Int'l*, pg. 3274
HARGREAVES DUCTWORK LIMITED—See M+W Group GmbH; *Int'l*, pg. 4613
HARGREAVES INDUSTRIAL SERVICES (HK) LIMITED—See Hargreaves Services plc; *Int'l*, pg. 3275
HARGREAVES LANSDOWN ASSET MANAGEMENT LTD—See Hargreaves Lansdown PLC; *Int'l*, pg. 3274
HARGREAVES LANSDOWN EBT TRUSTEES LTD—See Hargreaves Lansdown PLC; *Int'l*, pg. 3274
HARGREAVES LANSDOWN FUND MANAGERS LTD—See Hargreaves Lansdown PLC; *Int'l*, pg. 3274
HARGREAVES LANSDOWN NOMINEES LTD—See Hargreaves Lansdown PLC; *Int'l*, pg. 3274
HARGREAVES LANSDOWN PENSIONS DIRECT LTD—See Hargreaves Lansdown PLC; *Int'l*, pg. 3274
HARGREAVES LANSDOWN PENSIONS TRUSTEES LTD—See Hargreaves Lansdown PLC; *Int'l*, pg. 3275
HARGREAVES LANSDOWN PLC; *Int'l*, pg. 3274
HARGREAVES LANSDOWN STOCKBROKERS LTD—See Hargreaves Lansdown PLC; *Int'l*, pg. 3275
HARGREAVES LANSDOWN TRUSTEE COMPANY LTD—See Hargreaves Lansdown PLC; *Int'l*, pg. 3275
HARGREAVES POWER SERVICES (HK) LIMITED—See Hargreaves Services plc; *Int'l*, pg. 3275
HARGREAVES SERVICES PLC; *Int'l*, pg. 3275
HARGROVE ENGINEERS & CONSTRUCTORS; *U.S. Private*, pg. 1864
HARGROVE ENGINEERS + CONSTRUCTORS; *U.S. Private*, pg. 1864
HARIA APPARELS LIMITED—See Haria Exports Limited; *Int'l*, pg. 3275
HARIA EXPORTS LIMITED; *Int'l*, pg. 3275
HARI BHOOMI COMMUNICATIONS PRIVATE LIMITED—See SINDHU TRADE LINKS LIMITED; *Int'l*, pg. 6938
HARIBO AUSTRALIA PTY LIMITED—See HARIBO GmbH & Co. KG; *Int'l*, pg. 3275
HARIBO BELGIE B.V.B.A.—See HARIBO GmbH & Co. KG; *Int'l*, pg. 3275
HARIBO DUNHILLS (PONTEFRACT) PLC—See HARIBO GmbH & Co. KG; *Int'l*, pg. 3275
HARIBO ESPANA S.A.U—See HARIBO GmbH & Co. KG; *Int'l*, pg. 3275
HARIBO ESPANA S.A.U.—See HARIBO GmbH & Co. KG; *Int'l*, pg. 3275
HARIBO GMBH & CO. KG; *Int'l*, pg. 3275
HARIBO HUNGARIA KFT.—See HARIBO GmbH & Co. KG; *Int'l*, pg. 3275
HARIBO IRELAND LTD.—See HARIBO GmbH & Co. KG; *Int'l*, pg. 3275
HARIBO ITALIA S.P.A.—See HARIBO GmbH & Co. KG; *Int'l*, pg. 3275
HARIBO KONFETY OOO—See HARIBO GmbH & Co. KG; *Int'l*, pg. 3275
HARIBO LAKRIDS A/S—See HARIBO GmbH & Co. KG; *Int'l*, pg. 3275
HARIBO LAKRIDS OY AB—See HARIBO GmbH & Co. KG; *Int'l*, pg. 3275
HARIBO LAKRIS AS—See HARIBO GmbH & Co. KG; *Int'l*, pg. 3275
HARIBO LAKRITS AB—See HARIBO GmbH & Co. KG; *Int'l*, pg. 3275
HARIBO LAKRITZEN - HANS RIEGEL BETRIEBSGES.M.B.H.—See HARIBO GmbH & Co. KG; *Int'l*, pg. 3275
HARIBO NEDERLAND B.V.—See HARIBO GmbH & Co. KG; *Int'l*, pg. 3275
HARIBO OF AMERICA INC.—See HARIBO GmbH & Co. KG; *Int'l*, pg. 3275
HARIBO RICQLES-ZAN S.A.—See HARIBO GmbH & Co. KG; *Int'l*, pg. 3275
HARIBO SEKERLEME SAN. VE TIC. LTD. STI—See HARIBO GmbH & Co. KG; *Int'l*, pg. 3275
HARIG CRANKSHAFTS LIMITED; *Int'l*, pg. 3275
HARI GOVIND INTERNATIONAL LIMITED; *Int'l*, pg. 3275
HARIMA B-STEM CORPORATION; *Int'l*, pg. 3276
HARIMA CHEMICALS GROUP, INC.; *Int'l*, pg. 3276
HARIMA CHEMICALS, INC.—See Harima Chemicals Group, Inc.; *Int'l*, pg. 3276
HARIMA CHEMICALS (SHANGHAI) CO., LTD.—See Harima Chemicals Group, Inc.; *Int'l*, pg. 3276
HARIMA DO BRASIL INDUSTRIA QUIMICA LTDA—See Harima Chemicals Group, Inc.; *Int'l*, pg. 3276
HARIMA KASEI POLYMER CO., LTD.—See Harima Chemicals Group, Inc.; *Int'l*, pg. 3276

CORPORATE AFFILIATIONS

HARIMA-KYOWA CO., LTD.; *Int'l*, pg. 3276
HARIMA M.I.D., INC.—See Harima Chemicals Group, Inc.; *Int'l*, pg. 3276
HARIMA PAPER TECH. CORPORATION—See Daio Paper Corporation; *Int'l*, pg. 1940
HARIMA SANSO ELECTRIC CO., LTD.—See Sanso Electric Co., Ltd.; *Int'l*, pg. 6557
HARIMATEC CZECH S.R.O.—See Harima Chemicals Group, Inc.; *Int'l*, pg. 3276
HARIMATEC HANGZHOU CO., LTD.—See Harima Chemicals Group, Inc.; *Int'l*, pg. 3276
HARIMATEC INC.—See Harima Chemicals Group, Inc.; *Int'l*, pg. 3276
HARIMATEC MALAYSIA SDN. BHD.—See Harima Chemicals Group, Inc.; *Int'l*, pg. 3276
HARIMA TRADING, INC.—See Harima Chemicals Group, Inc.; *Int'l*, pg. 3276
HARIMA USA, INC.—See Harima Chemicals Group, Inc.; *Int'l*, pg. 3276
HARIM CO., LTD.—See Harim Holdings Co., Ltd.; *Int'l*, pg. 3275
HARIM HOLDINGS CO., LTD.; *Int'l*, pg. 3275
HARIMIC (MALAYSIA) SDN. BHD.—See Nippon Steel Corporation; *Int'l*, pg. 5335
HARINAS DE CHIHUAHUA, S.A. DE C.V.—See Grupo Xtra S.A. de C.V.; *Int'l*, pg. 3139
HARINERA DE MAIZ DE JALISCO, S.A. DE C.V.—See Gruma, S.A.B. de C.V.; *Int'l*, pg. 3114
HARINERA DE MAIZ DE MEXICALI, S.A. DE C.V.—See Gruma, S.A.B. de C.V.; *Int'l*, pg. 3114
HARINERA LOS PIRINEOS, S.A. DE C.V.—See Grupo La Moderna, S.A.B. de C.V.; *Int'l*, pg. 3131
HARIOM PIPE INDUSTRIES LIMITED; *Int'l*, pg. 3276
HARISH TEXTILE ENGINEERS LTD.; *Int'l*, pg. 3276
HARISON TOSHIBA LIGHTING CORP.; *Int'l*, pg. 3277
HARISON TOSHIBA USA INC—See Harison Toshiba Lighting Corp.; *Int'l*, pg. 3277
HARITA FEHRER LIMITED—See Uno Minda Limited; *Int'l*, pg. 8084
HARITA-NTI LIMITED—See Northern Technologies International Corporation; *U.S. Public*, pg. 1538
HARITA SEATING SYSTEMS LIMITED—See Uno Minda Limited; *Int'l*, pg. 8084
HARITA TECHSERV PRIVATE LIMITED—See TVS Electronics Limited; *Int'l*, pg. 7989
HARIWOOD SDN. BHD.—See Ta Ann Holdings Berhad; *Int'l*, pg. 7398
HARIYALI INSURANCE BROKING LIMITED—See DCM Shriram Limited; *Int'l*, pg. 1992
HARIYANA METALS INDUSTRIES LIMITED; *Int'l*, pg. 3277
HARIYANA SHIP BREAKERS LTD.; *Int'l*, pg. 3277
HARJU ELEKTER AS; *Int'l*, pg. 3277
HARKCON INC.; *U.S. Private*, pg. 1864
HARKEL OFFICE FURNITURE LTD.; *Int'l*, pg. 3277
HARKEMA SERVICES, INC.—See Universal Corporation; *U.S. Public*, pg. 2254
HARKEN, INCORPORATED; *U.S. Private*, pg. 1864
HARKINS AMUSEMENT ENTERPRISES, INC.; *U.S. Private*, pg. 1864
HARKINS BUILDERS, INC.—See Harkins Builders, Inc.; *U.S. Private*, pg. 1864
HARKINS BUILDERS, INC.; *U.S. Private*, pg. 1864
HARKINS BUILDERS, INC. VIRGINIA—See Harkins Builders, Inc.; *U.S. Private*, pg. 1864
HARKINS THEATRES, INC.—See Harkins Amusement Enterprises, Inc.; *U.S. Private*, pg. 1864
HARKNESS AUTO GROUP, INC.—See Pete Harkness Auto Group, Inc.; *U.S. Private*, pg. 3157
HARKNESS JIM EQUIPMENT LTD.—See Tym Corporation; *Int'l*, pg. 7994
HARLAN BAKERIES LLC; *U.S. Private*, pg. 1864
HARLAN-CUMBERLAND COAL COMPANY; *U.S. Private*, pg. 1865
HARLAND CLARKE CORP.—See MacAndrews & Forbes Incorporated; *U.S. Private*, pg. 2532
HARLAND & WOLFF (APPLEDORE) LIMITED—See Harland & Wolff Group Holdings plc; *Int'l*, pg. 3277
HARLAND & WOLFF (BELFAST) LIMITED—See Harland & Wolff Group Holdings plc; *Int'l*, pg. 3277
HARLAND & WOLFF GROUP HOLDINGS PLC; *Int'l*, pg. 3277
HARLAND & WOLFF (METHIL) LIMITED—See Harland & Wolff Group Holdings plc; *Int'l*, pg. 3277
HARLAN ELECTRIC COMPANY INC.; *U.S. Private*, pg. 1865
HARLAN ELECTRIC COMPANY—See MYR Group Inc.; *U.S. Public*, pg. 1489
HARLAN SPRAGUE DAWLEY INC.; *U.S. Private*, pg. 1865
HARLECH-PPM LIMITED—See Japan Pulp and Paper Company Limited; *Int'l*, pg. 3903
HARLEM CHILDREN'S ZONE, INC.; *U.S. Private*, pg. 1865
HARLEM GLOBETROTTERS INTERNATIONAL, INC.—See Herschend Family Entertainment Corp.; *Int'l*, pg. 1926
HARLEQUIN ENTERPRISES (AUSTRALIA) PTY LTD—See News Corporation; *U.S. Public*, pg. 1519

COMPANY NAME INDEX

HARLEQUIN ENTERPRISES LIMITED—See Charlesbank Capital Partners, LLC; *U.S. Private*, pg. 854
HARLEQUIN KFT. (AKA HARLEQUIN MAGYARORSZAG KORLATOLT FELELOSSEGU TARSASAG)—See News Corporation; *U.S. Public*, pg. 1519
HARLEQUIN MAGAZINES INC—See Charlesbank Capital Partners, LLC; *U.S. Private*, pg. 854
HARLEQUIN RETAIL INC.—See News Corporation; *U.S. Public*, pg. 1519
HARLEQUIN S.A.—See News Corporation; *U.S. Public*, pg. 1519
HARLEQUIN (UK) LIMTED—See Charlesbank Capital Partners, LLC; *U.S. Private*, pg. 854
HARLEY & ASSOCIATES COMMERCIAL REAL ESTATE, INC.—See Sun Coast Partners, LLC; *U.S. Private*, pg. 3862
HARLEY-DAVIDSON AUSTRALIA PTY. LIMITED—See Harley-Davidson, Inc.; *U.S. Public*, pg. 984
HARLEY-DAVIDSON BENELUX B.V.—See Harley-Davidson, Inc.; *U.S. Public*, pg. 984
HARLEY-DAVIDSON CANADA GP INC—See Harley-Davidson, Inc.; *U.S. Public*, pg. 985
HARLEY-DAVIDSON CANADA LP—See Harley-Davidson, Inc.; *U.S. Public*, pg. 984
HARLEY-DAVIDSON CENTRAL AND EASTERN EUROPE S.R.O.—See Harley-Davidson, Inc.; *U.S. Public*, pg. 985
HARLEY-DAVIDSON DEALER SYSTEMS, INC.—See Harley-Davidson, Inc.; *U.S. Public*, pg. 984
HARLEY-DAVIDSON ESPANA S.L.—See Harley-Davidson, Inc.; *U.S. Public*, pg. 985
HARLEY-DAVIDSON EUROPE LIMITED—See Harley-Davidson, Inc.; *U.S. Public*, pg. 984
HARLEY-DAVIDSON FINANCIAL SERVICES CANADA, INC.—See Harley-Davidson, Inc.; *U.S. Public*, pg. 985
HARLEY-DAVIDSON FINANCIAL SERVICES EUROPE LTD.—See Harley-Davidson, Inc.; *U.S. Public*, pg. 985
HARLEY-DAVIDSON FINANCIAL SERVICES, INC.—See Harley-Davidson, Inc.; *U.S. Public*, pg. 985
HARLEY-DAVIDSON FINANCIAL SERVICES INTERNATIONAL, INC.—See Harley-Davidson, Inc.; *U.S. Public*, pg. 985
HARLEY-DAVIDSON FRANCE SAS—See Harley-Davidson, Inc.; *U.S. Public*, pg. 985
HARLEY-DAVIDSON GMBH—See Harley-Davidson, Inc.; *U.S. Public*, pg. 985
HARLEY-DAVIDSON HOLDING CO., INC.—See Harley-Davidson, Inc.; *U.S. Public*, pg. 985
HARLEY-DAVIDSON, INC.; *U.S. Public*, pg. 984
HARLEY-DAVIDSON INSURANCE SERVICES, INC.—See Harley-Davidson, Inc.; *U.S. Public*, pg. 985
HARLEY-DAVIDSON INSURANCE SERVICES OF ILLINOIS, INC.—See Harley-Davidson, Inc.; *U.S. Public*, pg. 985
HARLEY-DAVIDSON ITALIA S.R.L.—See Harley-Davidson, Inc.; *U.S. Public*, pg. 985
HARLEY-DAVIDSON MOTOR COMPANY, INC.—See Harley-Davidson, Inc.; *U.S. Public*, pg. 985
HARLEY-DAVIDSON MOTOR COMPANY OPERATIONS, INC.—See Harley-Davidson, Inc.; *U.S. Public*, pg. 985
HARLEY-DAVIDSON MOTORCYCLE TRUST 2013-1—See Harley-Davidson, Inc.; *U.S. Public*, pg. 985
HARLEY-DAVIDSON OF CHARLOTTE; *U.S. Private*, pg. 1865
HARLEY DAVIDSON OF FORT SMITH; *U.S. Private*, pg. 1865
HARLEY DAVIDSON OF GLENDALE; *U.S. Private*, pg. 1865
HARLEY-DAVIDSON OF MIAMI LLC; *U.S. Private*, pg. 1865
HARLEY DAVIDSON OF VICTORVILLE, INC.—See Wise Automotive, Inc.; *U.S. Private*, pg. 4549
HARLEY-DAVIDSON OF WASHINGTON, DC; *U.S. Private*, pg. 1865
HARLEY-DAVIDSON RETAIL, INC.—See Harley-Davidson, Inc.; *U.S. Public*, pg. 985
HARLEY-DAVIDSON SWITZERLAND GMBH—See Harley-Davidson, Inc.; *U.S. Public*, pg. 985
HARLEY-DAVIDSON (THAILAND) COMPANY LIMITED—See Harley-Davidson, Inc.; *U.S. Public*, pg. 985
HARLEY ELLIS DEVEREAUX CORPORATION; *U.S. Private*, pg. 1865
HARLEY HOLLAN COMPANIES, INC.—See Superior Waste Industries LLC; *U.S. Private*, pg. 3881
HARLEY MARINE SERVICES INC.; *U.S. Private*, pg. 1865
HARLEY STANFIELD, INC.; *U.S. Private*, pg. 1865
THE HARLEY STREET CLINIC—See HCA Healthcare, Inc.; *U.S. Public*, pg. 1012
THE HARLEY STREET CLINIC—See HCA Healthcare, Inc.; *U.S. Public*, pg. 998
HARLEY STREET CLINIC @ THE GROVES LLP—See HCA Healthcare, Inc.; *U.S. Public*, pg. 998
HARLEY STREET MEDICAL CENTRE LLC—See Aster DM Healthcare Ltd.; *Int'l*, pg. 654
HARLEYSVILLE FINANCIAL CORPORATION; *U.S. Public*, pg. 985

HARLEYSVILLE SAVINGS BANK—See Harleysville Financial Corporation; *U.S. Public*, pg. 985
HARLINGEN HEALTHCARE, INC.—See The Ensign Group, Inc.; *U.S. Public*, pg. 2071
HARLINGEN MEDICAL CENTER, LP—See Prime Healthcare Services, Inc.; *U.S. Private*, pg. 3261
HARLINGEN PHYSICIAN NETWORK, INC.—See Tenet Healthcare Corporation; *U.S. Public*, pg. 2014
HARLO CORPORATION; *U.S. Private*, pg. 1865
HARLOW AEROSTRUCTURES, LLC; *U.S. Private*, pg. 1865
HARLOW HILL GRANGE (HARROGATE) MANAGEMENT COMPANY LIMITED—See Persimmon plc; *Int'l*, pg. 5816
HARLOW-HRK, LLC—See CI Capital Partners LLC; *U.S. Private*, pg. 895
HARMA-BIO SERV PR, INC.—See PHARMA-BIO SERV, INC.; *U.S. Public*, pg. 1684
HARMAC MEDICAL PRODUCTS INC.; *U.S. Private*, pg. 1865
HARMAN BECKER AUTOLOGIC SYSTEMS GMBH—See Samsung Group; *Int'l*, pg. 6512
HARMAN BECKER AUTOMOTIVE SYSTEMS GMBH—See Samsung Group; *Int'l*, pg. 6512
HARMAN BECKER AUTOMOTIVE SYSTEMS GMBH—See Samsung Group; *Int'l*, pg. 6512
HARMAN BECKER AUTOMOTIVE SYSTEMS ITALY S.R.L.—See Samsung Group; *Int'l*, pg. 6512
HARMAN BECKER AUTOMOTIVE SYSTEMS S.A. DE C.V.—See Samsung Group; *Int'l*, pg. 6512
HARMAN BELGIUM NV—See Samsung Group; *Int'l*, pg. 6512
HARMAN DEUTSCHLAND GMBH—See Samsung BioLogics Co., Ltd.; *Int'l*, pg. 6510
HARMAN EMBEDDED AUDIO, LLC—See Samsung Group; *Int'l*, pg. 6512
HARMAN HOLDING GMBH & CO. KG—See Samsung Group; *Int'l*, pg. 6512
HARMAN INTERNATIONAL INDUSTRIES, INCORPORATED—See Samsung Group; *Int'l*, pg. 6512
HARMAN INTERNATIONAL INDUSTRIES LTD.—See Samsung Group; *Int'l*, pg. 6512
HARMAN INTERNATIONAL JAPAN CO. LTD.—See Samsung Group; *Int'l*, pg. 6512
HARMAN INTERNATIONAL SINGAPORE PTE. LTD.—See Samsung Group; *Int'l*, pg. 6512
HARMAN PROFESSIONAL DENMARK APS—See Samsung BioLogics Co., Ltd.; *Int'l*, pg. 6510
HARMAN PROFESSIONAL, INC.—See Samsung Group; *Int'l*, pg. 6512
HARMAN TECHNOLOGY, LTD.—See DH Private Equity Partners LLP; *Int'l*, pg. 2097
HARMAR; *U.S. Private*, pg. 1866
HARMATHAZ KFT.—See Swietelsky Baugesellschaft m.b.H.; *Int'l*, pg. 7367
HARMELIN MEDIA; *U.S. Private*, pg. 1866
HARMER & SIMMONS—See 3W Power S.A.; *Int'l*, pg. 10
HARMON CITY, INC.; *U.S. Private*, pg. 1866
HARMON CONSTRUCTION INCORPORATED—See Harmon Group; *U.S. Private*, pg. 1866
HARMONEY CORP LIMITED; *Int'l*, pg. 3277
HARMON FOODS INC; *U.S. Private*, pg. 1866
HARMON GROUP; *U.S. Private*, pg. 1866
HARMONIA, INC; *U.S. Private*, pg. 1866
HARMONIC AD, INC.—See Harmonic Drive Systems Inc.; *Int'l*, pg. 3277
HARMONICARE MEDICAL HOLDINGS LTD.; *Int'l*, pg. 3278
HARMONIC DRIVE ESPANA, S.L.U.—See Harmonic Drive Systems Inc.; *Int'l*, pg. 3277
HARMONIC DRIVE FRANCE SAS—See Harmonic Drive Systems Inc.; *Int'l*, pg. 3277
HARMONIC DRIVE L.L.C.—See Harmonic Drive Systems Inc.; *Int'l*, pg. 3277
HARMONIC DRIVE SE—See Harmonic Drive Systems Inc.; *Int'l*, pg. 3277
HARMONIC DRIVE SYSTEMS INC.; *Int'l*, pg. 3277
HARMONIC DRIVE SYSTEMS (SHANGHAI) CO., LTD.—See Harmonic Drive Systems Inc.; *Int'l*, pg. 3277
HARMONIC DRIVE UK LIMITED—See Harmonic Drive Systems Inc.; *Int'l*, pg. 3277
HARMONIC EUROPE S.A.S.—See Harmonic, Inc.; *U.S. Public*, pg. 985
HARMONIC FRANCE SAS—See Harmonic, Inc.; *U.S. Public*, pg. 985
HARMONIC, INC.; *U.S. Public*, pg. 985
HARMONIC INTERNATIONAL AUSTRALIA PTY. LTD.—See Harmonic, Inc.; *U.S. Public*, pg. 985
HARMONIC INTERNATIONAL LIMITED—See Harmonic, Inc.; *U.S. Public*, pg. 985
HARMONIC LIMITED—See KBR, Inc.; *U.S. Public*, pg. 1215
HARMONIC PRECISION CORPORATION—See Harmonic Drive Systems Inc.; *Int'l*, pg. 3277
HARMONIC TECHNOLOGIES (BEIJING) CO. LTD.—See Harmonic, Inc.; *U.S. Public*, pg. 986

HARMONIC TECHNOLOGIES (HK) LIMITED—See Harmonic, Inc.; *U.S. Public*, pg. 986
HARMONIC (UK) LIMITED—See Harmonic, Inc.; *U.S. Public*, pg. 985
HARMONIC VIDEO SYSTEMS LTD.—See Harmonic, Inc.; *U.S. Public*, pg. 986
HARMONIE CLUB OF THE CITY OF NEW YORK; *U.S. Private*, pg. 1866
HARMON.IE CORP. - BOSTON OFFICE—See Cukierman & Co. Investment House Ltd.; *Int'l*, pg. 1876
HARMON.IE CORP. - ISRAEL OFFICE—See Cukierman & Co. Investment House Ltd.; *Int'l*, pg. 1876
HARMON.IE CORPORATION—See Cukierman & Co. Investment House Ltd.; *Int'l*, pg. 1876
HARMON, INC.—See Apogee Enterprises, Inc.; *U.S. Public*, pg. 145
HARMON, INC.—See Apogee Enterprises, Inc.; *U.S. Public*, pg. 145
HARMONIX MUSIC SYSTEMS, INC.—See National Amusements, Inc.; *U.S. Private*, pg. 2841
HARMON STEEL, INC.—See Harmon Group; *U.S. Private*, pg. 1866
HARMON STORES, INC.—See 20230930-DK-Butterfly-1, Inc.; *U.S. Private*, pg. 5
HARMON & SULLIVAN ASSOCIATES, INC.—See Cincon Electronics Co., Ltd.; *Int'l*, pg. 1610
HARMONY AGRICULTURAL PRODUCTS IN OHIO, LLC—See Honda Motor Co., Ltd.; *Int'l*, pg. 3462
HARMONY BIOSCIENCES HOLDINGS, INC.; *U.S. Public*, pg. 986
HARMONY CAPITAL SERVICES LIMITED; *Int'l*, pg. 3278
HARMONY CASTINGS, LLC—See Ligon Industries LLC; *U.S. Private*, pg. 2455
HARMONYCHAIN AS; *Int'l*, pg. 3278
HARMONY COUNTRY COOPERATIVE; *U.S. Private*, pg. 1866
HARMONY DEVELOPMENT CO., LLC; *U.S. Private*, pg. 1866
HARMONY DIALYSIS, LLC—See DaVita Inc.; *U.S. Public*, pg. 639
HARMONY ELECTRONICS CORP—See Daishinku Corp.; *Int'l*, pg. 1942
HARMONY ELECTRONICS (DONGGUAN) CO., LTD.—See Daishinku Corp.; *Int'l*, pg. 1942
HARMONY ELECTRONICS (THAILAND) CO LTD—See Daishinku Corp.; *Int'l*, pg. 1942
HARMONY GOLD (AUSTRALIA) PTY. LTD.—See Harmony Gold Mining Company Limited; *Int'l*, pg. 3278
HARMONY GOLD MINES—See Harmony Gold Mining Company Limited; *Int'l*, pg. 3278
HARMONY GOLD MINING COMPANY LIMITED; *Int'l*, pg. 3278
HARMONY GOLD (PNG SERVICES) (PROPRIETARY) LIMITED—See Harmony Gold Mining Company Limited; *Int'l*, pg. 3278
HARMONY HEALTHCARE INTERNATIONAL, INC.; *U.S. Private*, pg. 1866
HARMONY HEALTHCARE, LLC—See Odyssey Investment Partners, LLC; *U.S. Public*, pg. 2994
HARMONY HEALTH PLAN INC.—See Centene Corporation; *U.S. Public*, pg. 471
HARMONY HEALTH PLAN OF INDIANA—See Centene Corporation; *U.S. Public*, pg. 471
HARMONY HOME HEALTH, LLC; *U.S. Private*, pg. 1866
HARMONY LLC—See Turner Industries Group, L.L.C.; *U.S. Private*, pg. 4260
HARMONY MERGER CORP.—See NextDecade Corporation; *U.S. Public*, pg. 1526
HARMONY PROPERTY SDN. BHD.—See Brem Holding Berhad; *Int'l*, pg. 1144
HARMS OIL COMPANY; *U.S. Private*, pg. 1866
HARNDEN GROUP, LLC—See Haines & Kibblehouse Inc.; *U.S. Private*, pg. 1841
HARN ENGINEERING SOLUTIONS PUBLIC COMPANY LIMITED; *Int'l*, pg. 3278
HARNESS MASTER WIRING SYSTEMS (NSW) PTY LIMITED—See SubZero Group Limited; *Int'l*, pg. 7250
HARNISH GROUP INC.; *U.S. Private*, pg. 1866
HARN LEN CORPORATION BHD; *Int'l*, pg. 3278
HARNOIS GROUPE PETROLIER INC.; *Int'l*, pg. 3278
H. ARNOLD WOOD TURNING INC.; *U.S. Private*, pg. 1824
HARN R/O SYSTEMS, INC.—See Komline-Sanderson Corporation; *U.S. Private*, pg. 2342
HARNUM INDUSTRIES, LTD.—See Olympus Partners; *U.S. Private*, pg. 3013
HARODITE INDUSTRIES, INC.; *U.S. Private*, pg. 1866
HARODITE INDUSTRIES, INC. - SOUTH CAROLINA—See Harodite Industries, Inc.; *U.S. Private*, pg. 1866
HARODITE S.A. DE C.V.—See Harodite Industries, Inc.; *U.S. Private*, pg. 1866
HARODITE S.A. DE C.V.—See Harodite Industries, Inc.; *U.S. Private*, pg. 1866
HARO FINANCIAL CORPORATION—See Crown Investments Corporation of Saskatchewan; *Int'l*, pg. 1857
HAROL BROTHERS LLC; *U.S. Private*, pg. 1866
HAROLD ALLEN'S MOBILE HOMES INC.; *U.S. Private*, pg. 1867

HAROLD A. O'NEIL CO., INC.; *U.S. Private*, pg. 1866
HAROLD DIERS & CO.—See Brown & Brown, Inc.; *U.S. Public*, pg. 397
HAROLD FRIEDMAN INC.; *U.S. Private*, pg. 1867
HAROLD GRINSPOON FOUNDATION; *U.S. Private*, pg. 1867
HAROLD JOHNSON OPTICAL LABORATORIES, INC.—See Truist Financial Corporation; *U.S. Public*, pg. 2200
HAROLD LEMAY ENTERPRISES, INC.—See Waste Connections, Inc.; *Int'l*, pg. 8353
HAROLD LEVINSON ASSOCIATES; *U.S. Private*, pg. 1867
HAROLD MATTHEWS NISSAN INC.; *U.S. Private*, pg. 1867
HAROLD M. PITMAN COMPANY, INC.—See Agfa-Gevaert N.V.; *Int'l*, pg. 208
HAROLD T. ILLING CO. INC.; *U.S. Private*, pg. 1867
HAROLD ZEIGLER AUTO GROUP, INC.; *U.S. Private*, pg. 1867
HAROLD ZEIGLER FORD LINCOLN MERCURY -ELKHART—See Harold Zeigler Lincoln-Mercury; *U.S. Private*, pg. 1867
HAROLD ZEIGLER LINCOLN-MERCURY; *U.S. Private*, pg. 1867
HA ROMANIA S.R.L.—See Huettenes-Albertus Chemische Werke GmbH; *Int'l*, pg. 3523
HAROON ENGINEERING LTD.—See Daikin Industries, Ltd.; *Int'l*, pg. 1935
HAROON OILS LIMITED; *Int'l*, pg. 3278
HARPAK-ULMA ENGINEERING—See Harpak-ULMA Packaging, LLC; *U.S. Private*, pg. 1867
HARPAK-ULMA PACKAGING, LLC.—See Mondragon Corporation; *Int'l*, pg. 5029
HARPAK-ULMA PACKAGING, LLC; *U.S. Private*, pg. 1867
HARPEL OIL COMPANY INC.; *U.S. Private*, pg. 1867
HARPENDEN BUILDING SOCIETY; *Int'l*, pg. 3278
HARPER BRUSH WORKS INCORPORATED—See Griffon Corporation; *U.S. Public*, pg. 969
HARPER CHEVROLET-BUICK-GMC; *U.S. Private*, pg. 1867
HARPERCOLLINS CANADA LIMITED—See News Corporation; *U.S. Public*, pg. 1519
HARPERCOLLINS CHILDREN'S BOOKS GROUP - U.S.—See Charlesbank Capital Partners, LLC; *U.S. Private*, pg. 854
HARPERCOLLINS CHRISTIAN PUBLISHING, INC.—See News Corporation; *U.S. Public*, pg. 1519
HARPERCOLLINS GENERAL BOOKS GROUP - U.S.—See Charlesbank Capital Partners, LLC; *U.S. Private*, pg. 854
HARPERCOLLINS ITALIA S.P.A—See Charlesbank Capital Partners, LLC; *U.S. Private*, pg. 854
HARPERCOLLINS PUBLISHERS AUSTRALIA PTY. LIMITED—See News Corporation; *U.S. Public*, pg. 1519
HARPERCOLLINS PUBLISHERS (HOLDINGS) PTY. LIMITED—See News Corporation; *U.S. Public*, pg. 1519
HARPERCOLLINS PUBLISHERS INDIA LIMITED—See News Corporation; *U.S. Public*, pg. 1519
HARPERCOLLINS PUBLISHERS LIMITED—See News Corporation; *U.S. Public*, pg. 1519
HARPERCOLLINS PUBLISHERS L.L.C.—See Charlesbank Capital Partners, LLC; *U.S. Private*, pg. 854
HARPERCOLLINS PUBLISHERS LTD—See News Corporation; *U.S. Public*, pg. 1519
HARPERCOLLINS (UK)—See News Corporation; *U.S. Public*, pg. 1519
THE HARPER COMPANY; *U.S. Private*, pg. 4043
HARPER CONSTRUCTION COMPANY; *U.S. Private*, pg. 1867
HARPER CORPORATION OF AMERICA; *U.S. Private*, pg. 1867
THE HARPER CORPORATION; *U.S. Private*, pg. 4043
HARPER CREEK MINING CORPORATION—See Taseko Mines Limited; *Int'l*, pg. 7465
HARPER DENNIS HOBBS LIMITED—See Newmark Group, Inc.; *U.S. Public*, pg. 1515
HARPE REALTY—See Henderson Properties Inc.; *U.S. Private*, pg. 1914
HARPER ENGRAVING & PRINTING CO.; *U.S. Private*, pg. 1867
HARPER HOLDING SARL—See Enstar Group Limited; *Int'l*, pg. 2449
HARPER HYGIENICS S.A.—See iCotton SIA; *Int'l*, pg. 3586
HARPER INDUSTRIES INC.; *U.S. Private*, pg. 1867
HARPER INDUSTRIES, INC.; *U.S. Private*, pg. 1867
HARPER INDUSTRIES INC.; *U.S. Private*, pg. 1867
HARPER LIMBACH LLC—See Limbach Holdings, Inc.; *U.S. Public*, pg. 1316
HARPER-LOVE ADHESIVES CORPORATION—See HBM Holdings Company; *U.S. Private*, pg. 1887
HARPER MACLEOD LLP; *Int'l*, pg. 3278
HARPER OIL PRODUCTS INC.; *U.S. Private*, pg. 1867
HARPERONE—See Charlesbank Capital Partners, LLC; *U.S. Private*, pg. 854

HARPER'S BAZAAR—See The Hearst Corporation; *U.S. Private*, pg. 4046
HARPER + SCOTT, LLC; *U.S. Private*, pg. 1867
HARPER'S MAGAZINE FOUNDATION; *U.S. Private*, pg. 1868
HARPERS SEA FREIGHT CO., LTD.—See Yamatane Corporation; *Int'l*, pg. 8553
HARPER TRUCKS, INC.; *U.S. Private*, pg. 1868
HARPER & TWO; *U.S. Private*, pg. 1867
HARPETH VALLEY UTILITIES DISTRICT OF DAVIDSON & WILLIAMSON COUNTIES; *U.S. Private*, pg. 1868
HARPIA OMEGA PARTICIPACOES S.A.; *Int'l*, pg. 3278
HARP INTERNATIONAL LIMITED; *Int'l*, pg. 3278
HARP MIDDLE EAST L.L.C.—See Harp International Limited; *Int'l*, pg. 3278
HARPO, INC.; *U.S. Private*, pg. 1868
HARPOON MEDICAL, INC.—See Edwards Lifesciences Corporation; *U.S. Public*, pg. 721
HARPOON THERAPEUTICS, INC.—See Merck & Co., Inc.; *U.S. Public*, pg. 1416
HARPO PRODUCTIONS, INC.—See Harpo, Inc.; *U.S. Private*, pg. 1868
HARPS FOOD STORES, INC.; *U.S. Private*, pg. 1868
HARPURE ENTERPRISES INC.; *U.S. Private*, pg. 1868
HARP USA INC.—See Harp International Limited; *Int'l*, pg. 3278
HARRAH MFG. CO.—See The Bloomfield Manufacturing Co., Inc.; *U.S. Private*, pg. 3995
HARRAH'S ARIZONA CORPORATION—See Caesars Entertainment, Inc.; *U.S. Public*, pg. 419
HARRAH'S ATLANTIC CITY OPERATING COMPANY, LLC—See Caesars Entertainment, Inc.; *U.S. Public*, pg. 420
HARRAH'S BOSSIER CITY MANAGEMENT COMPANY, LLC—See Caesars Entertainment, Inc.; *U.S. Public*, pg. 419
HARRAH'S COUNCIL BLUFFS LLC—See VICI Properties Inc.; *U.S. Public*, pg. 2295
HARRAH'S ILLINOIS CORPORATION—See Caesars Entertainment, Inc.; *U.S. Public*, pg. 419
HARRAH'S JOLIET LANDCO LLC—See VICI Properties Inc.; *U.S. Public*, pg. 2295
HARRAH'S LAKE TAHOE LLC—See VICI Properties Inc.; *U.S. Public*, pg. 2295
HARRAH'S LAS VEGAS, LLC—See Caesars Entertainment, Inc.; *U.S. Public*, pg. 420
HARRAH'S LAUGHLIN, LLC—See Caesars Entertainment, Inc.; *U.S. Public*, pg. 420
HARRAH'S RENO—See Caesars Entertainment, Inc.; *U.S. Public*, pg. 419
HARRAMIENTAS TULTITLIN S.A.—See Klein Tools Inc.; *U.S. Private*, pg. 2319
HARRANOVA BESI VE TARIM URUNLERI A.S.—See Koc Holding A.S.; *Int'l*, pg. 4223
HARRELD CHEVROLET CO.; *U.S. Private*, pg. 1868
HARRELL HALL ENTERPRISES INC.; *U.S. Private*, pg. 1868
HARRELL & HARRELL INC.; *U.S. Private*, pg. 1868
HARRELL OIL CO. OF MOUNT AIRY; *U.S. Private*, pg. 1868
HARRELL'S CAR WASH SYSTEMS—See Generation Growth Capital, Inc.; *U.S. Private*, pg. 1668
HARRELLS INC.; *U.S. Private*, pg. 1868
HARREMS TOOLS B.V.—See LKQ Corporation; *U.S. Public*, pg. 1334
HARREN EQUITY PARTNERS; *U.S. Private*, pg. 1868
HARRICK SCIENTIFIC PRODUCTS, INC.—See Ampersand Management LLC; *U.S. Private*, pg. 265
HARRIER LLC—See District Photo Inc.; *U.S. Private*, pg. 1239
HARRIET CARTER GIFTS, INC.—See JH Partners LLC; *U.S. Private*, pg. 2207
HARRIET CARTER GIFTS, INC.—See Prudential Financial, Inc.; *U.S. Public*, pg. 1732
HARRIET (ONYX) PTY LTD—See APA Corporation; *U.S. Public*, pg. 143
HARRIMAN ASSOCIATES; *U.S. Private*, pg. 1868
HARRIMAN CREATIVE, INC; *U.S. Private*, pg. 1868
HARRIMAN PROPERTY MANAGEMENT LIMITED—See Wheelock & Company Limited; *Int'l*, pg. 8397
HARRIMAN UTILITY BOARD; *U.S. Private*, pg. 1868
HARRINGTON BENEFIT SERVCES, INC.—See Fiserv, Inc.; *U.S. Public*, pg. 851
HARRINGTON BOTTLING COMPANY; *U.S. Private*, pg. 1868
HARRINGTON COLLEGE OF DESIGN—See Perdoceo Education Corporation; *U.S. Public*, pg. 1673
HARRINGTON & CORTELYOU, INC.—See Burns & McDonnell, Inc.; *U.S. Private*, pg. 690
HARRINGTON ENGINEERING, INC.; *U.S. Private*, pg. 1868
HARRINGTON GENERATORS INTERNATIONAL—See Melrose Industries PLC; *Int'l*, pg. 4813
HARRINGTON HEALTHCARE SYSTEM; *U.S. Private*, pg. 1868
HARRINGTON HOISTS, INC.—See The Carlyle Group Inc.; *U.S. Public*, pg. 2055
HARRINGTON HOUSE BEACHFRONT BED & BREAKFAST INN; *U.S. Private*, pg. 1868

HARRINGTON INDUSTRIAL PLASTICS LLC—See Bain Capital, LP; *U.S. Private*, pg. 432
HARRINGTON INSTITUTE OF INTERIOR DESIGN, INC.—See Perdoceo Education Corporation; *U.S. Public*, pg. 1673
HARRINGTON & KING PERFORATING COMPANY, INC.; *U.S. Private*, pg. 1868
HARRINGTON & KING SOUTH, INC.—See Harrington & King Perforating Company, Inc.; *U.S. Private*, pg. 1868
HARRINGTON, RIGHTER & PARSONS, LLC—See Apollo Global Management, Inc.; *U.S. Public*, pg. 163
HARRINGTONS OF VERMONT, INC.; *U.S. Private*, pg. 1869
HARRIS/ARIZONA REBAR, INC.—See Nucor Corporation; *U.S. Public*, pg. 1553
HARRIS ASIA PACIFIC (M) SDN. BHD—See L3Harris Technologies, Inc.; *U.S. Public*, pg. 1279
HARRIS ASSOCIATES, L.P.—See Groupe BPCE; *Int'l*, pg. 3096
HARRIS, BAIO & McCULLOUGH INC.; *U.S. Private*, pg. 1870
HARRIS BATTERY CO., INC.; *U.S. Private*, pg. 1869
HARRISBURG NEWS COMPANY INC.-HARRISBURG, PA—See Harrisburg News Company Inc.; *U.S. Private*, pg. 1870
HARRISBURG NEWS COMPANY INC.; *U.S. Private*, pg. 1870
HARRISBURG STAMP CO.—See American Marking Systems, Inc.; *U.S. Private*, pg. 241
HARRIS BUSINESS GROUP INC.; *U.S. Private*, pg. 1869
HARRIS CALORIFIC GMBH—See Lincoln Electric Holdings, Inc.; *U.S. Public*, pg. 1317
HARRIS CALORIFIC INTERNATIONAL SP. Z O.O.—See Lincoln Electric Holdings, Inc.; *U.S. Public*, pg. 1317
HARRIS CALORIFIC S.R.L.—See Lincoln Electric Holdings, Inc.; *U.S. Public*, pg. 1317
HARRIS CANADA HOLDINGS INC.—See L3Harris Technologies, Inc.; *U.S. Public*, pg. 1279
HARRIS CANADA, INC.—See L3Harris Technologies, Inc.; *U.S. Public*, pg. 1279
HARRIS CANADA SYSTEMS, INC.—See L3Harris Technologies, Inc.; *U.S. Public*, pg. 1279
HARRIS CAPITAL GROUP, INC.; *U.S. Private*, pg. 1869
HARRIS COMMUNICATION ARGENTINA SA—See Aviat Networks, Inc.; *U.S. Public*, pg. 246
HARRIS COMMUNICATIONS (AUSTRALIA) PTY. LTD.—See L3Harris Technologies, Inc.; *U.S. Public*, pg. 1279
HARRIS COMMUNICATIONS EGYPT, LLC—See L3Harris Technologies, Inc.; *U.S. Public*, pg. 1279
HARRIS COMMUNICATIONS FZCO—See L3Harris Technologies, Inc.; *U.S. Public*, pg. 1279
HARRIS COMPANIES - HARRIS MECHANICAL SOUTHWEST DIVISION—See Harris Companies; *U.S. Private*, pg. 1869
HARRIS COMPANIES; *U.S. Private*, pg. 1869
HARRIS COMPANIES - WASATCH CONTROLS DIVISION—See Harris Companies; *U.S. Private*, pg. 1869
HARRIS COMUNICACOES PARTICIPACOES DO BRASIL LTDA.—See L3Harris Technologies, Inc.; *U.S. Public*, pg. 1279
HARRIS CONNECT, LLC; *U.S. Private*, pg. 1869
HARRIS CORP. - COMMUNICATIONS DIVISION—See L3Harris Technologies, Inc.; *U.S. Public*, pg. 1279
HARRIS CORP. - ELECTRONIC SYSTEMS DIVISION - AMITYVILLE—See L3Harris Technologies, Inc.; *U.S. Public*, pg. 1279
HARRIS CORP. - ELECTRONIC SYSTEMS DIVISION - ELECTRONIC WARFARE SYSTEMS - CLIFTON—See L3Harris Technologies, Inc.; *U.S. Public*, pg. 1279
HARRIS CORP. - ELECTRONIC SYSTEMS DIVISION - RADAR & RECONNAISSANCE SYSTEMS - VAN NUYS—See L3Harris Technologies, Inc.; *U.S. Public*, pg. 1279
HARRIS CORP. - ELECTRONIC SYSTEMS DIVISION - RECONNAISSANCE & SURVEILLANCE SYSTEMS - MORGAN HILL—See L3Harris Technologies, Inc.; *U.S. Public*, pg. 1280
HARRIS CORP. - ELECTRONIC SYSTEMS DIVISION - SONAR & COMMAND SYSTEMS - CHESAPEAKE—See L3Harris Technologies, Inc.; *U.S. Public*, pg. 1280
HARRIS CORP. - ELECTRONIC SYSTEMS DIVISION—See L3Harris Technologies, Inc.; *U.S. Public*, pg. 1279
HARRIS CORP. - GEOSPATIAL SYSTEMS DIVISION—See L3Harris Technologies, Inc.; *U.S. Public*, pg. 1280
HARRIS CORP. - NIGHT VISION & COMMUNICATIONS SOLUTIONS DIVISION—See L3Harris Technologies, Inc.; *U.S. Public*, pg. 1279
HARRIS CORP. - NIGHT VISION—See Elbit Systems Limited; *Int'l*, pg. 2344
HARRIS CORP. - SPACE & INTELLIGENCE SYSTEMS DIVISION—See L3Harris Technologies, Inc.; *U.S. Public*, pg. 1280
HARRIS CORP. - WASHINGTON OPERATIONS—See L3Harris Technologies, Inc.; *U.S. Public*, pg. 1280

COMPANY NAME INDEX

HARRIS COUNTY EMERGENCY CORPS; *U.S. Private,* pg. 1869
HARRIS DATA SERVICES OF WISCONSIN—See Harris Business Group Inc.; *U.S. Private,* pg. 1869
HARRIS DIALYSIS, LLC—See DaVita Inc.; *U.S. Public,* pg. 639
HARRIS D. MCKINNEY, INC.; *U.S. Private,* pg. 1869
HARRIS ELECTRIC SUPPLY CO., INC.—See Border States Industries, Inc.; *U.S. Private,* pg. 618
HARRIS EURO S.L.—See Lincoln Electric Holdings, Inc.; *U.S. Public,* pg. 1317
HARRIS EXPLORATION, INC.; *U.S. Public,* pg. 986
HARRIS FARMS, INC.; *U.S. Private,* pg. 1869
HARRIS FEEDING CO.—See Central Valley Meat Holding Company; *U.S. Private,* pg. 826
HARRIS FIRE PROTECTION CO INC.—See Knox Lane LP; *U.S. Private,* pg. 2324
HARRIS FORD, INC.; *U.S. Private,* pg. 1869
HARRIS & FORD, LLC; *U.S. Private,* pg. 1869
HARRIS FOWLER INSURANCE COMPANY, INC.—See Leavitt Group Enterprises, Inc.; *U.S. Private,* pg. 2409
HARRIS FRASER GROUP LIMITED—See Mason Group Holdings Limited; *Int'l,* pg. 4722
HARRIS FREEMAN & CO. LP; *U.S. Private,* pg. 1869
HARRIS GEOSPATIAL SOLUTIONS GMBH—See L3Harris Technologies, Inc.; *U.S. Public,* pg. 1280
HARRIS GEOSPATIAL SOLUTIONS, INC.—See L3Harris Technologies, Inc.; *U.S. Public,* pg. 1280
HARRIS GEOSPATIAL SOLUTIONS ITALIA SRL—See L3Harris Technologies, Inc.; *U.S. Public,* pg. 1280
HARRIS GEOSPATIAL SOLUTIONS SARL—See L3Harris Technologies, Inc.; *U.S. Public,* pg. 1280
HARRIS GEOSPATIAL SOLUTIONS UK LIMITED—See L3Harris Technologies, Inc.; *U.S. Public,* pg. 1280
HARRIS GROUP INC.; *U.S. Private,* pg. 1869
HARRIS HOLDINGS INC.; *U.S. Private,* pg. 1869
HARRIS INDUSTRIAL PRODUCTS & PACKAGING—See Jackson Paper Company; *U.S. Private,* pg. 2178
HARRIS INTERACTIVE AG—See Verlinvest S.A.; *Int'l,* pg. 8172
HARRIS INTERACTIVE SAS—See Verlinvest S.A.; *Int'l,* pg. 8172
HARRIS INTERACTIVE UK LIMITED—See Verlinvest S.A.; *Int'l,* pg. 8172
HARRIS MARKETING GROUP; *U.S. Private,* pg. 1869
HARRIS MAZDA; *Int'l,* pg. 3278
HARRIS MECHANICAL SERVICE, LLC—See Harris Companies; *U.S. Private,* pg. 1869
HARRIS MEDICAL CLINICS, INC.—See Community Health Systems, Inc.; *U.S. Public,* pg. 553
HARRIS METALS COMPANY, LLC; *U.S. Private,* pg. 1869
HARRIS MORAN SEED CO.—See Groupe Limagrain Holding SA; *Int'l,* pg. 3108
HARRIS MYCFO, INC.—See Bank of Montreal; *Int'l,* pg. 846
HARRIS NORGE AS—See L3Harris Technologies, Inc.; *U.S. Public,* pg. 1280
HARRIS OIL COMPANY INC.—See Heartland, Inc.; *U.S. Private,* pg. 1901
HARRIS OLDSMOBILE, INCORPORATED; *U.S. Private,* pg. 1870
HARRISON AND STAR—See Omnicom Group Inc.; *U.S. Public,* pg. 1586
HARRISONBURG AUTO AUCTION—See Cox Enterprises, Inc.; *U.S. Private,* pg. 1076
HARRISON COMMUNITY HOSPITAL, INC.—See Wheeling Hospital, Inc.; *U.S. Private,* pg. 4506
HARRISON CREATIVE DIRECTION; *U.S. Private,* pg. 1870
HARRISON ENDO SURGICAL CENTER, LLC—See UnitedHealth Group Incorporated; *U.S. Public,* pg. 2241
HARRISON FORD, INC.; *U.S. Private,* pg. 1870
HARRISON FRENCH & ASSOCIATES, LTD.; *U.S. Private,* pg. 1870
HARRISON GYPSUM, LLC—See Arcosa, Inc.; *U.S. Public,* pg. 186
HARRISON & HETHERINGTON LIMITED—See H&H Group plc; *Int'l,* pg. 3191
HARRISON HMA, INC.—See Community Health Systems, Inc.; *U.S. Public,* pg. 553
HARRISON-HOGE INDUSTRIES, INC.; *U.S. Private,* pg. 1871
HARRISON HOUSE; *U.S. Private,* pg. 1870
HARRISON INTERESTS LTD.; *U.S. Private,* pg. 1870
HARRISON LEIFER DIMARCO, INC.; *U.S. Private,* pg. 1870
HARRISON LEIFER DIMARCO PUBLIC RELATIONS—See Harrison Leifer DiMarco, Inc.; *U.S. Private,* pg. 1870
HARRISON MEDICAL CENTER—See Franciscan Health System; *U.S. Private,* pg. 1587
HARRISON OIL & TIRE CO.; *U.S. Private,* pg. 1870
HARRISON-ORR AIR CONDITIONING, INC.; *U.S. Private,* pg. 1871
HARRISON PAINT COMPANY - EXCELSIOR COATINGS DIVISION—See Harrison Paint Company; *U.S. Private,* pg. 1870
HARRISON PAINT COMPANY; *U.S. Private,* pg. 1870
HARRISON POULTRY INC.; *U.S. Private,* pg. 1870

HARRISON RESOURCES, LLC—See Oxford Mining Company, LLC; *U.S. Private,* pg. 3057
HARRISONS ESTATE AGENTS LIMITED—See The Skipton Building Society; *Int'l,* pg. 7686
HARRISONS HOLDINGS (MALAYSIA) BERHAD; *Int'l,* pg. 3278
HARRISON & SHRIFTMAN LLC—See Omnicom Group Inc.; *U.S. Public,* pg. 1585
HARRISON & SHRIFTMAN—See Omnicom Group Inc.; *U.S. Public,* pg. 1585
HARRISON & SHRIFTMAN—See Omnicom Group Inc.; *U.S. Public,* pg. 1585
HARRISONS MALAYALAM LIMITED; *Int'l,* pg. 3279
HARRISONS MARKETING & SERVICES SDN BHD—See Harrisons Holdings (Malaysia) Berhad; *Int'l,* pg. 3279
HARRISONS PENINSULAR SDN. BHD.—See Harrisons Holdings (Malaysia) Berhad; *Int'l,* pg. 3279
HARRISONS SABAH SDN. BHD.—See Harrisons Holdings (Malaysia) Berhad; *Int'l,* pg. 3279
HARRISONS SARAWAK SDN BHD—See Harrisons Holdings (Malaysia) Berhad; *Int'l,* pg. 3279
HARRISON STEEL CASTINGS CO.; *U.S. Private,* pg. 1870
HARRISONS TRADING (PENINSULAR) SDN BHD—See Harrisons Holdings (Malaysia) Berhad; *Int'l,* pg. 3279
HARRISONS TRADING (SABAH) SDN BHD—See Harrisons Holdings (Malaysia) Berhad; *Int'l,* pg. 3279
HARRISONS TRAVEL SDN. BHD.—See Harrisons Holdings (Malaysia) Berhad; *Int'l,* pg. 3279
HARRISON STREET REAL ESTATE CAPITAL LLC—See Colliers International Group Inc.; *Int'l,* pg. 1701
HARRISON TRANSPORTATION SERVICES, INC.—See Marcou Transportation Group LLC; *U.S. Private,* pg. 2572
HARRISON TRUCK CENTERS, INC.—See Omaha Truck Center Inc.; *U.S. Private,* pg. 3014
HARRISON, VICKERS & WATERMAN, INC.—See Attitude Drinks Incorporated; *U.S. Private,* pg. 383
HARRISON WALKER & HARPER LP; *U.S. Private,* pg. 1870
HARRIS ORIGINALS OF NY., INC.; *U.S. Private,* pg. 1870
HARRIS ORTHOGON GMBH—See L3Harris Technologies, Inc.; *U.S. Public,* pg. 1280
HARRIS PACKAGING CORPORATION; *U.S. Private,* pg. 1870
HARRIS PREFERRED CAPITAL CORPORATION; *U.S. Private,* pg. 1870
HARRIS RANCH BEEF COMPANY—See Central Valley Meat Holding Company; *U.S. Private,* pg. 826
HARRIS RANCH BEEF HOLDING COMPANY—See Central Valley Meat Holding Company; *U.S. Private,* pg. 826
HARRIS RANCH INN & RESTAURANT—See Harris Farms, Inc.; *U.S. Private,* pg. 1869
HARRIS REBAR - ATLANTIC—See Nucor Corporation; *U.S. Public,* pg. 1553
HARRIS REBAR BOISE, INC—See Nucor Corporation; *U.S. Public,* pg. 1553
HARRIS REBAR CARSON CITY, INC—See Nucor Corporation; *U.S. Public,* pg. 1553
HARRIS REBAR SEATTLE, INC.—See Nucor Corporation; *U.S. Public,* pg. 1553
HARRIS REBAR—See Nucor Corporation; *U.S. Public,* pg. 1553
HARRIS REBAR—See Nucor Corporation; *U.S. Public,* pg. 1553
HARRIS RESEARCH, INC.—See Baird Financial Group, Inc.; *U.S. Private,* pg. 453
HARRIS RIA HOLDINGS, INC.—See Bank of Montreal; *Int'l,* pg. 846
HARRIS SALINAS REBAR , INC.—See Nucor Corporation; *U.S. Public,* pg. 1553
HARRIS SCARFE AUSTRALIA PTY LTD.; *Int'l,* pg. 3278
HARRISS & COVINGTON HOSIERY MILLS; *U.S. Private,* pg. 1871
HARRIS SOFTWARE SYSTEMS PTY. LTD.—See L3Harris Technologies, Inc.; *U.S. Public,* pg. 1280
HARRIS SOLDAS ESPECIAIS S.A.—See Lincoln Electric Holdings, Inc.; *U.S. Public,* pg. 1317
HARRIS & SON TRUCKING CO. INC.; *U.S. Private,* pg. 1869
THE HARRIS SOUP COMPANY—See Kainos Capital, LLC; *U.S. Private,* pg. 2255
HARRIS STEEL CO.; *U.S. Private,* pg. 1870
HARRIS STEEL ULC—See Nucor Corporation; *U.S. Public,* pg. 1553
HARRIS STEEL ULC—See Nucor Corporation; *U.S. Public,* pg. 1553
HARRIS SYSTEMS LIMITED—See L3Harris Technologies, Inc.; *U.S. Public,* pg. 1280
HARRIS TECHNOLOGY GROUP LIMITED; *Int'l,* pg. 3278
HARRIS TECHNOLOGY (NZ) PTY LTD—See Wesfarmers Limited; *Int'l,* pg. 8381
HARRIS TEETER, INC.—See The Kroger Co.; *U.S. Public,* pg. 2108
HARRIS TEETER SUPERMARKETS, INC.—See The Kroger Co.; *U.S. Public,* pg. 2108
HARRIS TIRE COMPANY; *U.S. Private,* pg. 1870

HARRISTOWN DEVELOPMENT CORPORATION; *U.S. Private,* pg. 1871
HARRIS TRANSPORTATION COMPANY, LLC—See Trimac Transportation Ltd.; *Int'l,* pg. 7923
HARRISVACCINES, INC.—See Merck & Co., Inc.; *U.S. Public,* pg. 1416
HARRIS VENTURES, INC.; *U.S. Private,* pg. 1870
HARRIS WASTE MANAGEMENT GROUP, INC.—See Melrose Industries PLC; *Int'l,* pg. 4813
HARRIS WILLIAMS & CO.—See The PNC Financial Services Group, Inc.; *U.S. Public,* pg. 2119
HARR MOTOR COMPANY; *U.S. Private,* pg. 1868
HARROD MANAGEMENT INC.; *U.S. Private,* pg. 1871
HARRODS AVIATION—See Harrods Ltd.; *Int'l,* pg. 3279
HARRODS BANK LTD—See Harrods Ltd.; *Int'l,* pg. 3279
HARRODS CASINO—See Harrods Ltd.; *Int'l,* pg. 3279
HARRODS ESTATES—See Harrods Ltd.; *Int'l,* pg. 3279
HARRODS LTD.; *Int'l,* pg. 3279
HARROGATE, INC.; *U.S. Private,* pg. 1871
HARRON COMMUNICATIONS, L.P.; *U.S. Private,* pg. 1871
HARROP INDUSTRIES, INC.; *U.S. Private,* pg. 1871
HARROW ESTATES PLC—See Barratt Developments PLC; *Int'l,* pg. 868
HARROW GREEN LIMITED—See Restore plc; *Int'l,* pg. 6304
HARROW STORES INC.; *U.S. Private,* pg. 1871
HARRSELE AB—See Statkraft AS; *Int'l,* pg. 7185
THE HARRY ALTER COMPANY—See Carrier Global Corporation; *U.S. Public,* pg. 444
THE HARRY ALTER COMPANY—See Watsco, Inc.; *U.S. Public,* pg. 2337
HARRY BARLOW LTD.; *Int'l,* pg. 3279
HARRY BOCK COMPANY INC.; *U.S. Private,* pg. 1871
HARRY COOPER SUPPLY COMPANY; *U.S. Private,* pg. 1871
HARRY & DAVID HOLDINGS, INC.—See 1-800-FLOWERS.COM, Inc.; *U.S. Public,* pg. 1
HARRY & DAVID, LLC—See 1-800-FLOWERS.COM, Inc.; *U.S. Public,* pg. 1
HARRY & DAVID OPERATIONS, INC.—See 1-800-FLOWERS.COM, Inc.; *U.S. Public,* pg. 1
HARRY E. FERRYMAN ENTERPRISES; *U.S. Private,* pg. 1871
HARRY E. ROBBINS ASSOCIATES, INC.; *U.S. Private,* pg. 1871
HARRY FAIRBAIRN LIMITED—See Arnold Clark Automobiles Limited; *Int'l,* pg. 576
HARRY F. ORTLIP COMPANY INC.; *U.S. Private,* pg. 1871
HARRY FOURTUNIS INC.; *U.S. Private,* pg. 1871
THE HARRY FOX AGENCY, INC.—See Blackstone Inc.; *U.S. Public,* pg. 357
HARRY GRODSKY & CO., INC.-HARTFORD OFFICE—See Harry Grodsky & Co., Inc.; *U.S. Private,* pg. 1871
HARRY GRODSKY & CO., INC.; *U.S. Private,* pg. 1871
HARRY HOLLAND & SON, INC.; *U.S. Private,* pg. 1871
HARRY J. BOSWORTH COMPANY; *U.S. Private,* pg. 1871
HARRY J. KLOEPPEL & ASSOCIATES; *U.S. Private,* pg. 1871
HARRY J. LAWALL & SON; *U.S. Private,* pg. 1871
HARRY J. RASHTI & CO. INC.; *U.S. Private,* pg. 1872
HARRY KRANTZ COMPANY; *U.S. Private,* pg. 1872
HARRY LONDON CANDIES, INC.—See Ferrero International S.A.; *Int'l,* pg. 2640
HARRY MAJOR MACHINE & TOOL CO.; *U.S. Private,* pg. 1872
HARRY NORMAN REALTORS—See Berkshire Hathaway Inc.; *U.S. Public,* pg. 306
HARRY O. HEFTER ASSOCIATES, INC.—See The HOH Group; *U.S. Private,* pg. 4054
HARRY PEPPER & ASSOCIATES, INC.—See EMCOR Group, Inc.; *U.S. Public,* pg. 738
HARRY RITCHIE JEWELER INC.; *U.S. Private,* pg. 1872
HARRY ROBINSON BUICK GMC; *U.S. Private,* pg. 1872
HARRY ROSEN INC.; *Int'l,* pg. 3279
HARRY'S BAR LTD.—See LVMH Moet Hennessy Louis Vuitton SE; *Int'l,* pg. 4591
HARRY S. EKLOF JR. & ASSOCIATES INC.; *U.S. Private,* pg. 1872
HARRY'S ELECTRONICS INC.; *U.S. Private,* pg. 1872
HARRY S ESPLANADE PTE. LTD.—See Everstone Capital Advisors Pvt. Ltd.; *Int'l,* pg. 2569
HARRY'S HARDWARE INC.; *U.S. Private,* pg. 1872
HARRY'S HOLDINGS LTD.—See Everstone Capital Advisors Pvt. Ltd.; *Int'l,* pg. 2569
HARRYS INTERNATIONAL MANUFACTURING INC.—See Harrys Manufacturing Inc.; *Int'l,* pg. 3279
HARRY S INTERNATIONAL PTE. LTD.—See Everstone Capital Advisors Pvt. Ltd.; *Int'l,* pg. 2569
HARRY SJOGREN AB—See Castellum AB; *Int'l,* pg. 1356
HARRYS MANUFACTURING INC.; *Int'l,* pg. 3279
HARRY'S OF AMERICA INC.; *U.S. Private,* pg. 1872
HARRY'S ON THE HILL; *U.S. Private,* pg. 1872
HARRY S. PETERSON COMPANY—See Western Construction Group; *U.S. Private,* pg. 4492

HARRY'S ON THE HILL

HARRY'S RESTAURATION SAS—See Barilla Holding S.p.A.; *Int'l*, pg. 865
HARRYSSON ENTREPRENAD AKTIEBOLAG—See Storskogen Group AB; *Int'l*, pg. 7227
HARRY VIOLA ADVERTISING; *U.S. Private*, pg. 1872
HARRY WALKER AGENCY INC.—See Silver Lake Group, LLC; *U.S. Private*, pg. 3654
HARRY WINSTON (HONG KONG) LIMITED—See The Swatch Group Ltd.; *Int'l*, pg. 7691
HARRY WINSTON, INC.—See The Swatch Group Ltd.; *Int'l*, pg. 7693
HARRY WINSTON JAPAN K.K.—See The Swatch Group Ltd.; *Int'l*, pg. 7693
HARSCH INVESTMENT CORP.; *U.S. Private*, pg. 1872
HARSCH INVESTMENT INC.—See Harsch Investment Corp.; *U.S. Private*, pg. 1872
HARSCO ASEAN—See Enviri Corporation; *U.S. Public*, pg. 780
HARSCO IKG, LLC—See KPS Capital Partners, LP; *U.S. Private*, pg. 2347
HARSCO INDIA SERVICES PRIVATE LTD.—See Enviri Corporation; *U.S. Public*, pg. 780
HARSCO INDUSTRIAL AIR-X-CHANGERS—See Chart Industries, Inc.; *U.S. Public*, pg. 481
HARSCO INDUSTRIAL PATTERSON-KELLEY—See Enviri Corporation; *U.S. Public*, pg. 780
HARSCO INFRASTRUCTURE B.V.—See Enviri Corporation; *U.S. Public*, pg. 780
HARSCO INFRASTRUCTURE CONSTRUCTION SERVICES B.V.—See Brand Industrial Services, Inc.; *U.S. Private*, pg. 636
HARSCO INFRASTRUCTURE GROUP LIMITED—See Brand Industrial Services, Inc.; *U.S. Private*, pg. 636
HARSCO INFRASTRUCTURE LOGISTIC SERVICES B.V.—See Brand Industrial Services, Inc.; *U.S. Private*, pg. 636
HARSCO INFRASTRUCTURE—See Brand Industrial Services, Inc.; *U.S. Private*, pg. 636
HARSCO METALS FRANCE S.A.S.—See Enviri Corporation; *U.S. Public*, pg. 780
HARSCO METALS GROUP LIMITED—See Enviri Corporation; *U.S. Public*, pg. 780
HARSCO METALS INDIA—See Enviri Corporation; *U.S. Public*, pg. 781
HARSCO METALS LOGISTIQUE ET SERVICES SPECIALISES S.A.S.—See Enviri Corporation; *U.S. Public*, pg. 780
HARSCO METALS LUXEMBOURG S.A.—See Enviri Corporation; *U.S. Public*, pg. 780
HARSCO METALS MIDDLE EAST FZE—See Enviri Corporation; *U.S. Public*, pg. 781
HARSCO METALS & MINERALS SAS—See Enviri Corporation; *U.S. Public*, pg. 780
HARSCO METALS & MINERALS—See Enviri Corporation; *U.S. Public*, pg. 780
HARSCO METALS OOSTELIJK STAAL INTERNATIONAL B.V.—See Enviri Corporation; *U.S. Public*, pg. 781
HARSCO METALS SWEDEN A.B.—See Enviri Corporation; *U.S. Public*, pg. 780
HARSCO MINERAIS LIMITADA—See Enviri Corporation; *U.S. Public*, pg. 781
HARSCO MINERALS DEUTSCHLAND GMBH—See Enviri Corporation; *U.S. Public*, pg. 781
HARSCO MINERALS PA LLC—See Enviri Corporation; *U.S. Public*, pg. 781
HARSCO RAIL LTDA.—See Enviri Corporation; *U.S. Public*, pg. 781
HARSCO RAIL PTY. LTD.—See Enviri Corporation; *U.S. Public*, pg. 781
HARSCO RAIL—See Enviri Corporation; *U.S. Public*, pg. 781
HARSHA ENGINEERS EUROPE SRL—See Harsha Engineers International Limited; *Int'l*, pg. 3279
HARSHA ENGINEERS INTERNATIONAL LIMITED; *Int'l*, pg. 3279
HARSHA PRECISION BEARING COMPONENTS (CHINA) CO. LTD.—See Harsha Engineers International Limited; *Int'l*, pg. 3279
HARSHAW SERVICE INC.; *U.S. Private*, pg. 1872
HARSH INTERNATIONAL, INC.; *U.S. Private*, pg. 1872
HARSON TRADING (CHINA) CO., LTD.; *Int'l*, pg. 3279
HARTA DISTRIBUTION NETWORK SDN. BHD.—See HPI Resources Berhad; *Int'l*, pg. 3500
HARTA FLEKSIPAK SDN. BHD.—See HPI Resources Berhad; *Int'l*, pg. 3500
HARTALEGA HOLDINGS BERHAD; *Int'l*, pg. 3279
HARTAMAS GROUP BHD.; *Int'l*, pg. 3279
HARTAMAS REAL ESTATE (KD) SDN BHD—See Hartamas Group Bhd.; *Int'l*, pg. 3279
HARTAMAS REAL ESTATE (OUG) SDN BHD—See Hartamas Group Bhd.; *Int'l*, pg. 3280
HARTAMAS REAL ESTATE SDN. BHD.—See Hartamas Group Bhd.; *Int'l*, pg. 3279
HARTAMAS REAL ESTATE (SETIA ALAM) SDN BHD—See Hartamas Group Bhd.; *Int'l*, pg. 3280
HARTA PACKAGING INDUSTRIES (CAMBODIA) LIMITED—See HPI Resources Berhad; *Int'l*, pg. 3500
HARTA PACKAGING INDUSTRIES (MALACCA) SDN. BHD.—See HPI Resources Berhad; *Int'l*, pg. 3500

HARTA PACKAGING INDUSTRIES (PERAK) SDN. BHD.—See HPI Resources Berhad; *Int'l*, pg. 3500
HARTA PACKAGING INDUSTRIES SDN. BHD.—See HPI Resources Berhad; *Int'l*, pg. 3500
HART ASSOCIATES, INC.; *U.S. Private*, pg. 1872
HART CABLE, INC.—See Lintel Inc.; *U.S. Private*, pg. 2463
HARTCHROM SCHOCH GMBH.—See Arbonia AG; *Int'l*, pg. 538
HARTCHROM TEIKURO AUTOMOTIVE GMBH.—See Arbonia AG; *Int'l*, pg. 538
HARTCO INC.; *U.S. Private*, pg. 3280
HARTCO, INC.—See Osceola Capital Management, LLC; *U.S. Private*, pg. 3047
HART COMMUNICATIONS INC.—See Lintel Inc.; *U.S. Private*, pg. 2463
HART CONSUMER PRODUCTS, INC.—See Techtronic Industries Co., Ltd.; *Int'l*, pg. 7512
HART & COOLEY, INC.—See Egeria Capital Management B.V.; *Int'l*, pg. 2323
THE HARTCOURT COMPANIES, INC.; *Int'l*, pg. 7652
HART CROWSER, INC.—See Haley & Aldrich Inc.; *U.S. Private*, pg. 1842
HARTE GOLD CORP.; *Int'l*, pg. 3280
HARTE-HANKS BELGIUM NV—See Harte Hanks, Inc.; *U.S. Public*, pg. 986
HARTE HANKS CONSULTING—See Harte Hanks, Inc.; *U.S. Public*, pg. 986
HARTE-HANKS CRM SERVICES BELGIUM N.V.—See Harte Hanks, Inc.; *U.S. Public*, pg. 986
HARTE-HANKS DATA TECHNOLOGIES, INC.—See Harte Hanks, Inc.; *U.S. Public*, pg. 986
HARTE-HANKS DIRECT, INC.—See Harte Hanks, Inc.; *U.S. Public*, pg. 986
HARTE-HANKS DIRECT MARKETING/BALTIMORE, INC.—See Harte Hanks, Inc.; *U.S. Public*, pg. 986
HARTE HANKS DIRECT MARKETING/CINCINNATI, INC.—See Harte Hanks, Inc.; *U.S. Public*, pg. 986
HARTE-HANKS DIRECT MARKETING/DALLAS, INC.—See Harte Hanks, Inc.; *U.S. Public*, pg. 986
HARTE-HANKS DIRECT MARKETING/DALLAS, L.P.—See Harte Hanks, Inc.; *U.S. Public*, pg. 986
HARTE-HANKS DIRECT MARKETING/FULLERTON, INC.—See Harte Hanks, Inc.; *U.S. Public*, pg. 986
HARTE-HANKS DIRECT MARKETING/JACKSONVILLE, LLC—See Harte Hanks, Inc.; *U.S. Public*, pg. 986
HARTE-HANKS DIRECT MARKETING/KANSAS CITY, LLC—See Harte Hanks, Inc.; *U.S. Public*, pg. 986
HARTE-HANKS DIRECT MARKETING—See Harte Hanks, Inc.; *U.S. Public*, pg. 986
HARTE-HANKS FLORIDA, INC.—See Harte Hanks, Inc.; *U.S. Public*, pg. 986
HARTE-HANKS FLYER, INC.—See Harte Hanks, Inc.; *U.S. Public*, pg. 986
HARTE HANKS, INC.; *U.S. Public*, pg. 986
HARTE-HANKS, INC.—See Harte Hanks, Inc.; *U.S. Public*, pg. 986
HARTE-HANKS, INC.—See Harte Hanks, Inc.; *U.S. Public*, pg. 986
HARTE HANKS LOGISTICS, LLC—See Harte Hanks, Inc.; *U.S. Public*, pg. 986
HARTE-HANKS MARKET INTELLIGENCE EUROPE B.V.—See Harte Hanks, Inc.; *U.S. Public*, pg. 986
HARTE-HANKS RESPONSE MANAGEMENT/BOSTON, INC.—See Harte Hanks, Inc.; *U.S. Public*, pg. 986
HARTE-HANKS SHOPPERS INC.—See Harte Hanks, Inc.; *U.S. Public*, pg. 986
HARTE-HANKS STOCK PLAN, INC.—See Harte Hanks, Inc.; *U.S. Public*, pg. 986
HARTE-HANKS TAMPA FLYER INC.—See Harte Hanks, Inc.; *U.S. Public*, pg. 986
HARTE INFINITI INC.; *U.S. Private*, pg. 1873
HART ELECTRIC MEMBERSHIP CORPORATION; *U.S. Private*, pg. 1872
HART ENERGY PUBLISHING LP—See Wiegers Capital Partners; *U.S. Private*, pg. 4516
HART ENGINEERING CORPORATION; *U.S. Private*, pg. 1872
HARTE NISSAN, INC.; *U.S. Private*, pg. 1873
HARTER AEROSPACE, LLC—See HEICO Corporation; *U.S. Public*, pg. 1020
HARTEREI HAUCK SUD GMBH—See Aalberts N.V.; *Int'l*, pg. 34
HARTEREITECHNIK ROSENBLATTL GMBH—See Semperit AG Holding; *Int'l*, pg. 6706
HARTEREI VTN WITTEN GMBH—See E.ON SE; *Int'l*, pg. 2255
HARTER HOUSE-GLENSTONE, INC.; *U.S. Private*, pg. 1873
HARTER—See JSJ Corporation; *U.S. Public*, pg. 2241
HARTEST PRECISION INSTRUMENTS INDIA PRIVATE LIMITED—See Checkit plc; *Int'l*, pg. 1459
HARTEST PRECISION INSTRUMENTS LIMITED—See Checkit plc; *Int'l*, pg. 1459
HARTFIEL AUTOMATION; *U.S. Private*, pg. 1873
HARTFIELD LOUISVILLE, LLC—See Aon plc; *Int'l*, pg. 496
HARTFIELD, TITUS & DONNELLY LLC—See CME Group, Inc.; *U.S. Public*, pg. 517

CORPORATE AFFILIATIONS

HARTFORD ADVOCATE—See Tribune Publishing Company; *U.S. Private*, pg. 4228
HARTFORD BAKERY, INC.—See Lewis Brothers Bakeries, Inc.; *U.S. Private*, pg. 2438
HARTFORD CITY NEWS TIMES INC.—See Community Media Group; *U.S. Private*, pg. 995
HARTFORD CITY PAPER LLC; *U.S. Private*, pg. 1873
HARTFORD COMPRESSORS INC.—See Berjaya Corporation Berhad; *Int'l*, pg. 984
THE HARTFORD COURANT COMPANY—See Tribune Publishing Company; *U.S. Private*, pg. 4228
HARTFORD CPL CO-OP, INC.; *U.S. Private*, pg. 1873
THE HARTFORD DISPENSARY; *U.S. Private*, pg. 4043
HARTFORD DISTRIBUTORS INC.; *U.S. Private*, pg. 1873
HARTFORD ELECTRIC SUPPLY CO.; *U.S. Private*, pg. 1873
HARTFORD ESCROW INC.—See Tarbell Financial Corporation; *U.S. Private*, pg. 3933
THE HARTFORD FINANCIAL SERVICES GROUP, INC.; *U.S. Public*, pg. 2087
HARTFORD FIRE INSURANCE CO.—See The Hartford Financial Services Group, Inc.; *U.S. Public*, pg. 2088
HARTFORD FOUNDATION FOR PUBLIC GIVING; *U.S. Private*, pg. 1873
HARTFORD FUNDS MANAGEMENT COMPANY, LLC—See The Hartford Financial Services Group, Inc.; *U.S. Public*, pg. 2088
HARTFORD FUNDS MANAGEMENT GROUP, INC.—See The Hartford Financial Services Group, Inc.; *U.S. Public*, pg. 2088
HARTFORD GREAT HEALTH CORP.; *U.S. Public*, pg. 986
HARTFORD HEALTHCARE CORPORATION; *U.S. Private*, pg. 1873
HARTFORD INTERNATIONAL INSURANCE COMPANY—See The Hartford Financial Services Group, Inc.; *U.S. Public*, pg. 2088
HARTFORD INVESTMENT MANAGEMENT COMPANY—See The Hartford Financial Services Group, Inc.; *U.S. Public*, pg. 2088
HARTFORD LIFE & ACCIDENT INSURANCE COMPANY—See Sixth Street Specialty Lending, Inc.; *U.S. Public*, pg. 1891
HARTFORD LIFE INSURANCE K.K.—See ORIX Corporation; *Int'l*, pg. 5635
HART FORD LINCOLN, INC.; *U.S. Private*, pg. 1873
HARTFORD STEAM BOILER COLOMBIA LTDA.—See Munchener Ruckversicherungs AG; *Int'l*, pg. 5089
THE HARTFORD STEAM BOILER INSPECTION AND INSURANCE COMPANY—See Munchener Ruckversicherungs AG; *Int'l*, pg. 5090
HARTFORD STEAM BOILER INTERNATIONAL-GMBH—See Munchener Ruckversicherungs AG; *Int'l*, pg. 5089
HARTFORD STEAM BOILER (M) SDN. BHD—See Munchener Ruckversicherungs AG; *Int'l*, pg. 5088
HARTFORD STEAM BOILER (SINGAPORE), PTE LTD.—See Munchener Ruckversicherungs AG; *Int'l*, pg. 5089
HARTFORD STEAM BOILER UK LIMITED—See Munchener Ruckversicherungs AG; *Int'l*, pg. 5089
THE HARTFORD STEAM COMPANY—See Iberdrola, S.A.; *Int'l*, pg. 3571
HARTFORD SYMPHONY ORCHESTRA INC.; *U.S. Private*, pg. 1873
HARTFORD TOYOTA SUPERSTORE; *U.S. Private*, pg. 1873
HARTFORD WOLFPACK, LLC—See Madison Square Garden Sports Corp.; *U.S. Public*, pg. 1354
HARTFORD-WOOD RIVER TERMINAL LLC—See Piasa Motor Fuels LLC; *U.S. Private*, pg. 3175
HART FURNITURE COMPANY INC.; *U.S. Private*, pg. 1873
HARTGERS DIAMONDS, LTD.; *U.S. Private*, pg. 1873
HART HOTELS, INC.—See WPH Airport Associates; *U.S. Private*, pg. 4571
HART INDUSTRIES INC.; *U.S. Private*, pg. 1873
HART INTERCIVIC INC.; *U.S. Private*, pg. 1873
HARTLAGE MANUFACTURING, INC.—See Maxey Logistics, Inc.; *U.S. Private*, pg. 2617
HARTLAND CONTROLS LLC—See Littelfuse, Inc.; *U.S. Public*, pg. 1327
HARTLAND FUEL PRODUCTS, LLC; *U.S. Private*, pg. 1874
HARTLEY COMPANY; *U.S. Private*, pg. 1874
HARTLEY CYLKE PACIFIC INSURANCE SERVICES, INC.—See Arthur J. Gallagher & Co.; *U.S. Public*, pg. 205
HARTLEY GRANGE (WHITTLESEY) RESIDENTS MANAGEMENT COMPANY LIMITED—See Persimmon plc; *Int'l*, pg. 5816
THE HARTLINE ALARM CO, LLC—See Pye-Barker Fire & Safety, LLC; *U.S. Private*, pg. 3309
HARTMAN 400 NORTH BELT LLC—See SILVER STAR PROPERTIES REIT, INC.; *U.S. Private*, pg. 3662
HARTMAN & CO. INC.; *U.S. Private*, pg. 1874
HARTMAN COOPER STREET PLAZA, LLC—See SILVER STAR PROPERTIES REIT, INC.; *U.S. Private*, pg. 3662

HARTMAN CORPORATE PARK PLACE LLC—See SILVER STAR PROPERTIES REIT, INC.; *U.S. Private*, pg. 3662
HARTMAN FIJNMECHANISCHE INDUSTRIE B.V.; *Int'l*, pg. 3280
HARTMAN MITCHELLDALE BUSINESS PARK, LLC—See SILVER STAR PROPERTIES REIT, INC.; *U.S. Private*, pg. 3662
HARTMANN-BABOLNA PACKAGING KFT.—See Thornico A/S; *Int'l*, pg. 7719
HARTMANN BETEILIGUNGEN GMBH—See PAUL HARTMANN AG; *Int'l*, pg. 5760
HARTMANN BILOKALNIK AMBALAZA D.O.O.—See Thornico A/S; *Int'l*, pg. 7719
HARTMANN CANADA INC.—See Thornico A/S; *Int'l*, pg. 7719
HARTMANN CODIER GMBH—See Phoenix Mecano AG; *Int'l*, pg. 5852
HARTMANN CZ S.R.O.—See Thornico A/S; *Int'l*, pg. 7719
HARTMANN D.O.O.—See Thornico A/S; *Int'l*, pg. 7719
HARTMANN DRUCKFARBEN GMBH—See DIC Corporation; *Int'l*, pg. 2110
HARTMANN ELECTRIC COMPANY INC.; *U.S. Private*, pg. 1874
HARTMANN ELECTRONIC GMBH—See Phoenix Mecano AG; *Int'l*, pg. 5852
HARTMANN ELEKTRONIK GMBH—See Phoenix Mecano AG; *Int'l*, pg. 5852
HARTMAN NEWSPAPERS INC.; *U.S. Private*, pg. 1874
HARTMANN & FORBES; *U.S. Private*, pg. 1874
HARTMANN FRANCE S.A.R.L.—See Thornico A/S; *Int'l*, pg. 7719
HARTMANN-HUNGARY KFT.—See Thornico A/S; *Int'l*, pg. 7719
HARTMANN INDIA LTD.—See Thornico A/S; *Int'l*, pg. 7719
HARTMANN ITALIANA S.R.L.—See Thornico A/S; *Int'l*, pg. 7719
HARTMANN-MAI LTD.—See Thornico A/S; *Int'l*, pg. 7719
HARTMANN PAPIRNA AMBALAZA D.O.O.—See Thornico A/S; *Int'l*, pg. 7719
HARTMANN PARDES GMBH—See PAUL HARTMANN AG; *Int'l*, pg. 5760
HARTMANN POLSKA SP. Z.O.O.—See Thornico A/S; *Int'l*, pg. 7719
HARTMANN-RICO A.S.—See PAUL HARTMANN AG; *Int'l*, pg. 5760
HARTMANN-RICO HUNGARIA KFT.—See PAUL HARTMANN AG; *Int'l*, pg. 5760
HARTMANN-RICO S.R.O.—See PAUL HARTMANN AG; *Int'l*, pg. 5760
HARTMANN-SCANDICARE AB—See PAUL HARTMANN AG; *Int'l*, pg. 5760
HARTMANN-SCHWEDT GMBH—See Thornico A/S; *Int'l*, pg. 7719
HARTMANN-SUN CHEMICAL EOOD—See DIC Corporation; *Int'l*, pg. 2110
HARTMANN TRESORE AG; *Int'l*, pg. 3280
HARTMANN TRESORE FRANCE S.A.R.L.—See HARTMANN TRESORE AG; *Int'l*, pg. 3280
HARTMANN TRESORE ITALIA SRL—See HARTMANN TRESORE AG; *Int'l*, pg. 3280
HARTMANN TRESORE MIDDLE EAST LLC—See HARTMANN TRESORE AG; *Int'l*, pg. 3280
HARTMANN TRESORE POLSKA SP. Z O.O.—See HARTMANN TRESORE AG; *Int'l*, pg. 3280
HARTMANN TRESORE SCHWEIZ AG—See HARTMANN TRESORE AG; *Int'l*, pg. 3280
HARTMANN USA, INC.—See PAUL HARTMANN AG; *Int'l*, pg. 5760
HARTMANN VERPACKUNG AG—See Thornico A/S; *Int'l*, pg. 7719
HARTMANN VERPACKUNG GMBH—See Thornico A/S; *Int'l*, pg. 7719
HARTMANN-VITAMED (PTY) LTD.—See PAUL HARTMANN AG; *Int'l*, pg. 5760
HARTMAN SKYMARK TOWER LLC—See SILVER STAR PROPERTIES REIT, INC.; *U.S. Private*, pg. 3662
HARTMAN THREE FOREST PLAZA, LLC—See SILVER STAR PROPERTIES REIT, INC.; *U.S. Private*, pg. 3662
HARTMAN-WALSH CORPORATION; *U.S. Private*, pg. 1874
HARTMAN WESTWAY ONE, LLC—See SILVER STAR PROPERTIES REIT, INC.; *U.S. Private*, pg. 3662
HART METALS, INC.—See Luxfer Holdings PLC; *Int'l*, pg. 4588
HARTNESS INTERNATIONAL EUROPE, GMBH—See Illinois Tool Works Inc.; *U.S. Public*, pg. 1103
HARTNESS INTERNATIONAL INC.—See Illinois Tool Works Inc.; *U.S. Public*, pg. 1103
HARTREE PARTNERS, LP—See Brookfield Corporation; *Int'l*, pg. 1182
HARTSHEAD RESOURCES NL; *Int'l*, pg. 3280
HARTSHORNE MINING GROUP, LLC—See Paringa Resources Limited; *U.S. Private*, pg. 3094
HARTS INTERNATIONAL LLC—See The Emirates Group; *Int'l*, pg. 7639

HARTSON-KENNEDY CABINET TOP CO. INC. - LUKE AFB—See Hartson-Kennedy Cabinet Top Co. Inc.; *U.S. Private*, pg. 1874
HARTSON-KENNEDY CABINET TOP CO. INC. - MACON—See Hartson-Kennedy Cabinet Top Co. Inc.; *U.S. Private*, pg. 1874
HARTSON-KENNEDY CABINET TOP CO. INC.; *U.S. Private*, pg. 1874
THE HARTSTONE GROUP LIMITED; *Int'l*, pg. 7652
HART STORES INC.; *Int'l*, pg. 3279
HARTSTRINGS LLC—See Parigi Group Ltd; *U.S. Private*, pg. 3094
HARTSVILLE HMA, INC.—See Apollo Global Management, Inc.; *U.S. Public*, pg. 154
HARTSVILLE OIL MILL; *U.S. Private*, pg. 1874
HART SYSTEMS, INC.—See Zebra Technologies Corporation; *U.S. Public*, pg. 2401
HART SYSTEMS UK LTD.—See Zebra Technologies Corporation; *U.S. Public*, pg. 2401
HART TELEPHONE COMPANY INC.—See Lintel Inc.; *U.S. Private*, pg. 2463
HARTTERGRUPPE GMBH—See Axxiome AG; *Int'l*, pg. 773
HARTU ELECTRONIQUE S.A.R.L.—See Phoenix Mecano AG; *Int'l*, pg. 5852
HARTUNG BROTHERS INC. - BOWLING GREEN CUCUMBER PLANT—See Hartung Brothers Inc.; *U.S. Private*, pg. 1874
HARTUNG BROTHERS INC. - MADISON SEED PLANT—See Hartung Brothers Inc.; *U.S. Private*, pg. 1874
HARTUNG BROTHERS INC. - MUNCIE ILLINOIS SEED PRODUCTION AND DISTRIBUTION PLANT—See Hartung Brothers Inc.; *U.S. Private*, pg. 1874
HARTUNG BROTHERS INC.; *U.S. Private*, pg. 1874
HARTUNG BROTHERS, INC.-UVALDE CUCUMBER OPERATIONS—See Hartung Brothers Inc.; *U.S. Private*, pg. 1874
HARTUNG GLASS INDUSTRIES, INC.; *U.S. Private*, pg. 1874
HARTU S.A.R.L.—See Phoenix Mecano AG; *Int'l*, pg. 5852
HART & VOGT INC.; *U.S. Private*, pg. 1872
HARTWELL CORPORATION—See TransDigm Group Incorporated; *U.S. Public*, pg. 2183
HARTWELL ENVIRONMENTAL CORP.—See DXP Enterprises, Inc.; *U.S. Public*, pg. 697
HARTWELL HEALTH HOLDINGS LLC—See The Ensign Group, Inc.; *U.S. Public*, pg. 2071
HARTWELL OILFIELD LTD.—See Vertex Resource Group Ltd.; *Int'l*, pg. 8174
HARTWELL PLC; *Int'l*, pg. 3280
HARTWICK O'SHEA & CARTWRIGHT LIMITED; *Int'l*, pg. 3280
HARTWIG INC.; *U.S. Private*, pg. 1874
HARTWIG TRANSIT INC.; *U.S. Private*, pg. 1874
THE HARTY PRESS INC.; *U.S. Private*, pg. 4043
HARTY TRACTOR SERVICES, INC.; *U.S. Private*, pg. 1874
HARTZ CONSTRUCTION CO. INC.; *U.S. Private*, pg. 1874
HARTZ CONSTRUCTION CORP.—See Scott and Murphy, Inc.; *U.S. Public*, pg. 3576
HARTZELL ENGINE TECHNOLOGIES LLC—See Arcline Investment Management LP; *U.S. Private*, pg. 313
HARTZELL FAN, INC.—See Hartzell Industries, Inc.; *U.S. Private*, pg. 1874
HARTZELL HARDWOODS, INC.—See Hartzell Industries, Inc.; *U.S. Private*, pg. 1874
HARTZELL INDUSTRIES, INC.; *U.S. Private*, pg. 1874
HARTZELL INSURANCE ASSOCIATES, INC.—See ABRY Partners, LLC; *U.S. Private*, pg. 42
HARTZELL PROPELLER INC.—See Tailwind Technologies Inc.; *U.S. Private*, pg. 3924
HARTZELL VENEER PRODUCTS, LLC—See Hartzell Industries, Inc.; *U.S. Private*, pg. 1874
THE HARTZ GROUP, INC.; *U.S. Private*, pg. 4043
THE HARTZ MOUNTAIN CORPORATION—See Sumitomo Corporation; *Int'l*, pg. 7274
THE HARTZ MOUNTAIN CORPORATION—See Unicharm Corporation; *Int'l*, pg. 8032
HARTZ MOUNTAIN INDUSTRIES, INC.—See The Hartz Group, Inc.; *U.S. Private*, pg. 4043
HARU AMSTERDAM AVENUE CORP.—See TPG Capital, L.P.; *U.S. Public*, pg. 2167
HARU GRAMERCY PARK CORP.—See TPG Capital, L.P.; *U.S. Public*, pg. 2167
HARU HOLDING CORP.—See TPG Capital, L.P.; *U.S. Public*, pg. 2167
HARUM BIDANG SDN. BHD.—See KKB Engineering Berhad; *Int'l*, pg. 4198
HARUM INTISARI SDN BHD—See Gamuda Berhad; *Int'l*, pg. 2879
HARU THIRD AVENUE CORP.—See TPG Capital, L.P.; *U.S. Public*, pg. 2167
HARU WALL STREET CORP.—See TPG Capital, L.P.; *U.S. Public*, pg. 2167
HARUYAMA HOLDINGS INC.; *Int'l*, pg. 3280
HARVARD APPARATUS LIMITED—See Harvard Bioscience, Inc.; *U.S. Public*, pg. 987

HARVARD APPARATUS REGENERATIVE TECHNOLOGY, INC.; *U.S. Public*, pg. 987
HARVARD APPARATUS S.A.R.L.—See Harvard Bioscience, Inc.; *U.S. Public*, pg. 987
HARVARD BIOSCIENCE, INC.; *U.S. Public*, pg. 987
HARVARD BIOSCIENCE (SHANGHAI) CO. LTD.—See Harvard Bioscience, Inc.; *U.S. Public*, pg. 987
HARVARD BUSINESS REVIEW—See Harvard Business School Publishing Corporation; *U.S. Private*, pg. 1875
HARVARD BUSINESS SCHOOL PUBLISHING CORPORATION; *U.S. Private*, pg. 1874
HARVARD COMMON PRESS—See The Quarto Group, Inc.; *Int'l*, pg. 7677
HARVARD COOPERATIVE SOCIETY INC.; *U.S. Private*, pg. 1875
HARVARD DEVELOPMENT COMPANY LLC; *U.S. Private*, pg. 1875
THE HARVARD DRUG GROUP, LLC—See Cardinal Health, Inc.; *U.S. Public*, pg. 434
HARVARD HILLSIDE—See Alden Global Capital LLC; *U.S. Private*, pg. 157
HARVARD ILLINOIS BANCORP, INC.; *U.S. Private*, pg. 1875
HARVARD IN-HOUSE AGENCY; *U.S. Private*, pg. 1875
HARVARD INTERNATIONAL (HONG KONG) LIMITED—See Harvard International Ltd.; *Int'l*, pg. 3280
HARVARD INTERNATIONAL LTD.; *Int'l*, pg. 3280
HARVARD JOLLY, INC.; *U.S. Private*, pg. 1875
HARVARD JOLLY INC.—See Harvard Jolly, Inc.; *U.S. Private*, pg. 1875
HARVARD MAINTENANCE, INC.; *U.S. Private*, pg. 1875
HARVARD MARITIME LIMITED—See Harvard International Ltd.; *Int'l*, pg. 3280
HARVARD PARK SURGERY CENTER, LLC—See Tenet Healthcare Corporation; *U.S. Public*, pg. 2010
HARVARD PILGRIM HEALTH CARE, INC.; *U.S. Private*, pg. 1875
HARVARD STUDENT AGENCIES, INC.; *U.S. Private*, pg. 1875
HARVARD UNIVERSITY PRESS - LONDON—See Harvard University Press; *U.S. Private*, pg. 1875
HARVARD UNIVERSITY PRESS; *U.S. Private*, pg. 1875
HARVATEK CORPORATION; *Int'l*, pg. 3280
HARVER B.V.—See Rubicon Technology Partners, LLC; *U.S. Private*, pg. 3500
HARVEST CAPITAL CREDIT CORPORATION; *U.S. Public*, pg. 987
HARVEST CAPITAL MANAGEMENT PUBLIC LTD.; *Int'l*, pg. 3280
HARVEST CAPITAL STRATEGIES LLC—See Citizens Financial Group, Inc.; *U.S. Public*, pg. 505
HARVEST CHOICE AUSTRALIA PTY. LTD.—See Lamb Weston Holdings, Inc.; *U.S. Public*, pg. 1291
HARVEST CONSUMER INSULATION, INC.; *U.S. Private*, pg. 1875
HARVEST CREATIVE; *U.S. Private*, pg. 1875
HARVEST ENTERPRISES, INC.—See Trulieve Cannabis Corp.; *U.S. Public*, pg. 2201
HARVESTERS - THE COMMUNITY FOOD NETWORK; *U.S. Private*, pg. 1877
HARVEST FOOD COMPANY—See Sand Dollar Holdings Incorporated; *U.S. Private*, pg. 3542
HARVEST FOODS—See URM Stores, Inc.; *U.S. Private*, pg. 4316
HARVEST FUND ADVISORS, LLC—See Blackstone Inc.; *U.S. Public*, pg. 354
HARVEST GARDEN PRO, LLC—See Harvest Power Inc.; *U.S. Private*, pg. 1877
HARVEST GROUP FINANCIAL SERVICES, CORP.—See The Goldman Sachs Group, Inc.; *U.S. Public*, pg. 2082
HARVEST HEALTHCARE LEADERS INCOME ETF; *Int'l*, pg. 3280
HARVEST HEALTH & RECREATION INC.—See Trulieve Cannabis Corp.; *U.S. Public*, pg. 2201
HARVEST HILL BEVERAGE COMPANY—See Brynwood Partners Management LLC; *U.S. Private*, pg. 674
HARVEST, INC.; *U.S. Private*, pg. 1877
HARVEST INTERNATIONAL INC.; *U.S. Private*, pg. 1875
HARVEST LAND COOPERATIVE; *U.S. Private*, pg. 1875
HARVEST LAND CO-OP INC.; *U.S. Private*, pg. 1875
HARVEST LAND CO-OP INC.—See Harvest Land Co-Op Inc.; *U.S. Private*, pg. 1875
HARVESTLAND DEVELOPMENT PTE LTD—See Keppel Corporation Limited; *Int'l*, pg. 4130
HARVEST MANOR FARMS LLC—See Conagra Brands, Inc.; *U.S. Public*, pg. 564
HARVEST MEDICINE INC.—See MediPharm Labs Corp.; *Int'l*, pg. 4779
HARVEST MINERALS LIMITED; *Int'l*, pg. 3280
HARVEST MIRACLE CAPITAL BERHAD; *Int'l*, pg. 3280
HARVEST OIL & GAS CORP.—See EnerVest, Ltd.; *U.S. Private*, pg. 1397
HARVESTONE GROUP LLC; *U.S. Private*, pg. 1877
HARVEST OPERATIONS CORP.—See Korea National Oil Corporation; *Int'l*, pg. 4286
HARVEST PARTNERS L.P.; *U.S. Private*, pg. 1876
HARVEST PORTFOLIOS GROUP INC.; *Int'l*, pg. 3281
HARVEST POWER INC.; *U.S. Private*, pg. 1877

HARVEST POWER INC.

HARVEST RETIREMENT COMMUNITY INC.—See Extendicare Inc.; *Int'l*, pg. 2591
HARVEST S.A.—See Rothschild & Co SCA; *Int'l*, pg. 6403
HARVEST STAR INTERNATIONAL LIMITED—See Great Eagle Holdings Limited; *Int'l*, pg. 3064
HARVEST SUPERMARKETS INC.; *U.S. Private*, pg. 1877
HARVEST SUSTAINABLE INCOME FUND—See Harvest Portfolios Group Inc.; *Int'l*, pg. 3281
HARVEST TECHNOLOGIES CORP.—See Terumo Corporation; *Int'l*, pg. 7569
HARVEST TECHNOLOGY GROUP LTD.; *Int'l*, pg. 3281
HARVEST TECHNOLOGY PLC; *Int'l*, pg. 3281
HARVEST VINCCLER, S.C.A.; *Int'l*, pg. 3281
HARVEST WEALTHPTY. LTD.—See Azimut Holding SpA; *Int'l*, pg. 779
HARVEY ALPERT & CO. INC.; *U.S. Private*, pg. 1877
HARVEY CADILLAC COMPANY; *U.S. Private*, pg. 1877
HARVEY CADILLAC; *U.S. Private*, pg. 1877
HARVEY CAMERON GROUP LIMITED—See Attivo group; *Int'l*, pg. 697
HARVEY CHEVROLET CORPORATION; *U.S. Private*, pg. 1877
HARVEY-CLEARY BUILDERS—See David E. Harvey Builders Inc.; *U.S. Private*, pg. 1170
HARVEY-CLEARY BUILDERS—See David E. Harvey Builders Inc.; *U.S. Private*, pg. 1170
HARVEY & DAUGHTERS, INC./ H&D BRANDING; *U.S. Private*, pg. 1877
HARVEY DONALDSON & GIBSON LIMITED—See The Skipton Building Society; *Int'l*, pg. 7686
HARVEY FERTILIZER & GAS CO.; *U.S. Private*, pg. 1877
HARVEY FRESH (1994) LTD.—See Groupe Lactalis SA; *Int'l*, pg. 3106
HARVEY GM, LLC—See Group 1 Automotive, Inc.; *U.S. Public*, pg. 971
HARVEY INDUSTRIES, INC. - DARTMOUTH MANUFACTURING FACILITY—See Clayton, Dubilier & Rice, LLC; *U.S. Private*, pg. 920
HARVEY INDUSTRIES, LLC.; *U.S. Private*, pg. 1878
HARVEY INDUSTRIES, LLC—See Clayton, Dubilier & Rice, LLC; *U.S. Private*, pg. 920
HARVEY M. HARPER CO.; *U.S. Private*, pg. 1878
HARVEY NASH AG—See DBAY Advisors Limited; *Int'l*, pg. 1987
HARVEY NASH BV—See DBAY Advisors Limited; *Int'l*, pg. 1987
HARVEY NASH GMBH—See DBAY Advisors Limited; *Int'l*, pg. 1987
HARVEY NASH GROUP LTD—See DBAY Advisors Limited; *Int'l*, pg. 1987
HARVEY NASH INC—See DBAY Advisors Limited; *Int'l*, pg. 1987
HARVEY NASH (IRELAND) LTD—See DBAY Advisors Limited; *Int'l*, pg. 1987
HARVEY NASH IT CONSULTING NV—See DBAY Advisors Limited; *Int'l*, pg. 1987
HARVEY NASH LIMITED—See DBAY Advisors Limited; *Int'l*, pg. 1987
HARVEY NASH NV—See DBAY Advisors Limited; *Int'l*, pg. 1987
HARVEY NASH (VIETNAM) LTD—See DBAY Advisors Limited; *Int'l*, pg. 1987
HARVEY NICHOLS GROUP LIMITED; *Int'l*, pg. 3281
HARVEY NORMAN CROATIA D.O.O.—See Harvey Norman Holdings Ltd; *Int'l*, pg. 3281
HARVEY NORMAN HOLDINGS LTD; *Int'l*, pg. 3281
HARVEY NORMAN SINGAPORE PTE. LIMITED—See Harvey Norman Holdings Ltd; *Int'l*, pg. 3281
HARVEY NORMAN TRADING D.O.O.—See Harvey Norman Holdings Ltd; *Int'l*, pg. 3281
HARVEY NORMAN TRADING (IRELAND) LIMITED—See Harvey Norman Holdings Ltd; *Int'l*, pg. 3281
HARVEY PALLETS, INC.; *U.S. Private*, pg. 1878
HARVEY SALT COMPANY INC; *U.S. Private*, pg. 1878
HARVEYS TAHOE MANAGEMENT COMPANY, INC.—See Caesars Entertainment, Inc.; *U.S. Public*, pg. 419
HARVEY & THOMPSON LTD.—See H&T Group Plc; *Int'l*, pg. 3193
HARVEY TOOL COMPANY, LLC—See Summit Partners, L.P.; *U.S. Private*, pg. 3855
HARVEY WORLD TRAVEL GROUP PTY. LTD.—See Helloworld Travel Limited; *Int'l*, pg. 3337
HARVEY WORLD TRAVEL SOUTHERN AFRICA (PTY) LIMITED—See Helloworld Travel Limited; *Int'l*, pg. 3337
HARVIA OYJ; *Int'l*, pg. 3281
HARWICH HOLDING GMBH—See Aptiv PLC; *Int'l*, pg. 525
HARWICH INTERNATIONAL PORT LIMITED—See CK Hutchison Holdings Limited; *Int'l*, pg. 1637
HARWICH ORACLE—See Gannett Co., Inc.; *U.S. Public*, pg. 902
HARWICK STANDARD DISTRIBUTION CORPORATION; *U.S. Private*, pg. 1878
HARWOOD CAPITAL LLP; *Int'l*, pg. 3282
HARWOOD WEALTH MANAGEMENT GROUP PLC—See The Carlyle Group Inc.; *U.S. Public*, pg. 2047
HARWORTH GROUP PLC; *Int'l*, pg. 3282

HARWORTH INSURANCE COMPANY LIMITED—See Harworth Group plc; *Int'l*, pg. 3282
HARYANA CAPFIN LIMITED; *Int'l*, pg. 3282
HARYANA FINANCIAL CORPORATION LTD.; *Int'l*, pg. 3282
HARYANA LEATHER CHEMICALS LTD.; *Int'l*, pg. 3282
HARYANA TEXPRINTS (OVERSEAS) LTD.; *Int'l*, pg. 3282
HARZGERODE GUSS GMBH—See TRIMET Aluminium SE; *Int'l*, pg. 7923
HARZ GUSS ZORGE GMBH—See Georgsmarienhutte Holding GmbH; *Int'l*, pg. 2940
HASA, INC.—See GHK Capital Partners LP; *U.S. Private*, pg. 1690
HASAN & PARTNERS OY—See The Interpublic Group of Companies, Inc.; *U.S. Public*, pg. 2098
HASBRO AUSTRALIA PTY LTD—See Hasbro, Inc.; *U.S. Public*, pg. 987
HASBRO AUSTRALIA—See Hasbro, Inc.; *U.S. Public*, pg. 987
HASBRO BRADLEY FAR EAST LTD.—See Hasbro, Inc.; *U.S. Public*, pg. 987
HASBRO B.V.—See Hasbro, Inc.; *U.S. Public*, pg. 987
HASBRO CANADA CORPORATION—See Hasbro, Inc.; *U.S. Public*, pg. 988
HASBRO DE MEXICO S.R.L. DE C.V.—See Hasbro, Inc.; *U.S. Public*, pg. 988
HASBRO DEUTSCHLAND GMBH—See Hasbro, Inc.; *U.S. Public*, pg. 988
HASBRO FRANCE—See Hasbro, Inc.; *U.S. Public*, pg. 988
HASBRO HELLAS INDUSTRIAL & COMMERCIAL COMPANY S.A.—See Hasbro, Inc.; *U.S. Public*, pg. 988
HASBRO HONG KONG LIMITED—See Hasbro, Inc.; *U.S. Public*, pg. 988
HASBRO, INC.; *U.S. Public*, pg. 987
HASBRO INTERNATIONAL HOLDINGS, B.V.—See Hasbro, Inc.; *U.S. Public*, pg. 988
HASBRO MANAGERIAL SERVICES LLC—See Hasbro, Inc.; *U.S. Public*, pg. 988
HASBRO NETHERLANDS HOLDINGS, B.V.—See Hasbro, Inc.; *U.S. Public*, pg. 988
HASBRO S.A.—See Hasbro, Inc.; *U.S. Public*, pg. 988
HASBRO TOYS & GAMES HOLDINGS, S.L.—See Hasbro, Inc.; *U.S. Public*, pg. 988
HASBRO UK LTD—See Hasbro, Inc.; *U.S. Public*, pg. 988
HASCALL STEEL COMPANY-ECORSE PLANT—See Hascall Steel Company Inc.; *U.S. Private*, pg. 1878
HASCALL STEEL COMPANY INC. - BENTON PLANT—See Hascall Steel Company Inc.; *U.S. Private*, pg. 1878
HASCALL STEEL COMPANY INC. - NASHVILLE PLANT—See Hascall Steel Company Inc.; *U.S. Private*, pg. 1878
HASCALL STEEL COMPANY INC.; *U.S. Private*, pg. 1878
HASCALL STEEL COMPANY INC. - STRONG STREET PLANT—See Hascall Steel Company Inc.; *U.S. Private*, pg. 1878
HASC CENTER INC.; *U.S. Private*, pg. 1878
H. ASCHEHOUG & CO. W. NYGAARD AS; *Int'l*, pg. 3194
H.A. SCHLATTER AG—See Schlatter Industries AG; *Int'l*, pg. 6622
H.A. SCHLATTER, INC.—See Schlatter Industries AG; *Int'l*, pg. 6622
HASC, LLC—See Harley-Davidson, Inc.; *U.S. Public*, pg. 985
HASCO AMERICA INC.—See Berndorf AG; *Int'l*, pg. 987
HASCO AUSTRIA GESELLSCHAFT M.B.H—See Berndorf AG; *Int'l*, pg. 987
HASCO CANADA INC.—See Berndorf AG; *Int'l*, pg. 987
HASCO ENCOUNTER LTD.—See Berndorf AG; *Int'l*, pg. 987
HASCO FORM-SERVICE AB—See Berndorf AG; *Int'l*, pg. 987
HASCO FRANCE S.A.R.L.—See Berndorf AG; *Int'l*, pg. 987
HASCO HASENCLEVER GMBH & CO. KG—See Berndorf AG; *Int'l*, pg. 987
HASCO IBERICA S.L.U.—See Berndorf AG; *Int'l*, pg. 987
HASCO INDIA PVT. LTD.—See Berndorf AG; *Int'l*, pg. 987
HASCO INTERNORM LTD.—See Berndorf AG; *Int'l*, pg. 987
HASCOL PETROLEUM LIMITED; *Int'l*, pg. 3282
HASCO NORMALIEN MEXICO S.A. DE C.V.—See Berndorf AG; *Int'l*, pg. 987
HASCO OIL COMPANY, INC.; *U.S. Private*, pg. 1878
HASCO POLSKA SP ZO.O.—See Berndorf AG; *Int'l*, pg. 987
HASCO PORTUGUESA LDA.—See Berndorf AG; *Int'l*, pg. 987
HASCO SINGAPORE (PTE) LTD.—See Berndorf AG; *Int'l*, pg. 987
HASCO SUISSE AG—See Berndorf AG; *Int'l*, pg. 987
HASCO TRADING (SHENZHEN) CO., LTD.—See Berndorf AG; *Int'l*, pg. 987
HAS CZ A.S.—See WAMGROUP S.p.A.; *Int'l*, pg. 8337
HASEEB WAQAS GROUP OF COMPANIES; *Int'l*, pg. 3282
HASEEB WAQAS SUGAR MILLS LTD.—See Haseeb Waqas Group of Companies; *Int'l*, pg. 3282

HASEE COMPUTER CO., LTD.; *Int'l*, pg. 3282
HASEGAWA CO., LTD.; *Int'l*, pg. 3282
HASEKE GMBH & CO. KG—See Gesco AG; *Int'l*, pg. 2945
HASEKO AMERICA, INC.—See Haseko Corporation; *Int'l*, pg. 3283
HASEKO ANESIS CORPORATION—See Haseko Corporation; *Int'l*, pg. 3283
HASEKO BUSINESS PROXY, INC.—See Haseko Corporation; *Int'l*, pg. 3283
HASEKO COMMUNITY, INC.—See Haseko Corporation; *Int'l*, pg. 3283
HASEKO COMMUNITY OKINAWA INC.—See Haseko Corporation; *Int'l*, pg. 3283
HASEKO CORPORATION; *Int'l*, pg. 3282
HASEKO FURNISHING CO.,LTD.—See Haseko Corporation; *Int'l*, pg. 3283
HASEKO HOMELOANS, LLC—See Central Pacific Financial Corporation; *U.S. Public*, pg. 473
HASEKO INTECH, INC.—See Haseko Corporation; *Int'l*, pg. 3283
HASEKO LIVENET, INC.—See Haseko Corporation; *Int'l*, pg. 3283
HASEKO PROPERTY MANAGEMENT HOLDINGS INC.—See Haseko Corporation; *Int'l*, pg. 3283
HASEKO REFORM INC.—See Haseko Corporation; *Int'l*, pg. 3283
HASEKO SENIOR HOLDINGS CO., LTD.—See Haseko Corporation; *Int'l*, pg. 3283
HASEKO SENIOR WELL DESIGN CO., LTD.—See Haseko Corporation; *Int'l*, pg. 3283
HASEKO SYSTEMS INC.—See Haseko Corporation; *Int'l*, pg. 3283
HASEKO URBAN CO., LTD.—See Haseko Corporation; *Int'l*, pg. 3283
HASEKO URBEST, INC.—See Haseko Corporation; *Int'l*, pg. 3283
THE HASELDEN COMPANY, INC.—See Komline-Sanderson Corporation; *U.S. Private*, pg. 2342
HASELDEN CONSTRUCTION LLC; *U.S. Private*, pg. 1878
HAS ELECTRONIC COMPANY LIMITED—See S.A.S. Dragon Holdings Limited; *Int'l*, pg. 6449
HASELHOFER FEINMECHANIK GMBH—See AUMA Riester GmbH & Co. KG; *Int'l*, pg. 705
HASENTREE—See Apollo Global Management, Inc.; *U.S. Public*, pg. 149
HASE PETROLEUM WAX CO. INC.; *U.S. Private*, pg. 1878
HASGO GROUP LTD.; *Int'l*, pg. 3283
HASGROVE PLC; *Int'l*, pg. 3283
H.A. SHAR & SONS LTD.—See HORIBA Ltd; *Int'l*, pg. 3475
HASHAVSHEVET LTD.—See Hilan Ltd.; *Int'l*, pg. 3390
HASHICORP, INC.; *U.S. Public*, pg. 988
HASHIMI CAN COMPANY LIMITED; *Int'l*, pg. 3283
HASHIMOTO SOGYO HOLDINGS CO., LTD.; *Int'l*, pg. 3283
HASH SPACE ACQUISITION CORP.; *Int'l*, pg. 3283
HASHWANI GROUP; *Int'l*, pg. 3283
HASIBAT INFORMATION TECHNOLOGIST COMPANY—See Arabi Holding Group Company K.S.C.C.; *Int'l*, pg. 532
HASIL A.S.—See ASSA ABLOY AB; *Int'l*, pg. 633
HASIL S.R.O.—See ASSA ABLOY AB; *Int'l*, pg. 633
HASIS SP. Z.O.O.—See Marie Brizard Wine & Spirits S.A.; *Int'l*, pg. 4693
HASKEL EUROPE LTD. - ABERDEEN—See BC Partners LLP; *Int'l*, pg. 922
HASKEL EUROPE LTD. - ABERDEEN—See The Carlyle Group Inc.; *U.S. Public*, pg. 2044
HASKEL EUROPE LTD.—See BC Partners LLP; *Int'l*, pg. 922
HASKEL EUROPE LTD.—See The Carlyle Group Inc.; *U.S. Public*, pg. 2044
HASKEL FRANCE SAS—See BC Partners LLP; *Int'l*, pg. 922
HASKEL FRANCE SAS—See The Carlyle Group Inc.; *U.S. Public*, pg. 2044
HASKEL INTERNATIONAL, LLC—See BC Partners LLP; *Int'l*, pg. 922
HASKEL INTERNATIONAL, LLC—See The Carlyle Group Inc.; *U.S. Public*, pg. 2044
THE HASKELL COMPANY; *U.S. Private*, pg. 4043
HASKELL CORPORATION; *U.S. Private*, pg. 1878
HASKELL DE MEXICO, S.A. DE C.V.—See The Haskell Company; *U.S. Private*, pg. 4043
HASKELL LEMON CONSTRUCTION CO.; *U.S. Private*, pg. 1878
HASKEL SISTEMAS DE FLUIDOS ESPANA, S.R.L.—See BC Partners LLP; *Int'l*, pg. 922
HASKEL SISTEMAS DE FLUIDOS ESPANA, S.R.L.—See The Carlyle Group Inc.; *U.S. Public*, pg. 2044
HASKINS ELECTRIC INC.; *U.S. Private*, pg. 1878
HASKINS STEEL CO., INC.; *U.S. Private*, pg. 1878
HASKONING CAMBODIA LTD.—See Koninklijke HaskoningDHV Groep B.V.; *Int'l*, pg. 4266
HASKONING CARIBBEAN B.V.—See Koninklijke HaskoningDHV Groep B.V.; *Int'l*, pg. 4266

HASKONINGDHV INDIA PVT LTD.—See Koninklijke HaskoningDHV Groep B.V.; *Int'l*, pg. 4266
HASKONINGDHV (MALAYSIA) SDN BHD.—See Koninklijke HaskoningDHV Groep B.V.; *Int'l*, pg. 4266
HASKONINGDHV NEDERLAND B.V.—See Koninklijke HaskoningDHV Groep B.V.; *Int'l*, pg. 4266
HASKONING INTERNATIONAL SERVICES B.V.—See Koninklijke HaskoningDHV Groep B.V.; *Int'l*, pg. 4266
HASKONING LIBYA JSC—See Koninklijke HaskoningDHV Groep B.V.; *Int'l*, pg. 4266
HASKONING PHILIPPINES INC.—See Koninklijke HaskoningDHV Groep B.V.; *Int'l*, pg. 4266
HASKO TRADING INC.; *U.S. Private*, pg. 1878
HASK TOILETRIES—See Inspired Beauty Brands Inc.; *U.S. Private*, pg. 2092
HASLAM'S BOOK STORE, INC.; *U.S. Private*, pg. 1878
HASLER & COMPANY INCORPORATED; *U.S. Private*, pg. 1878
HASLER FENSTER AG—See Atrya SAS; *Int'l*, pg. 694
HASLER OIL COMPANY INCORPORATED; *U.S. Private*, pg. 1878
HAS LIFESTYLE LIMITED; *Int'l*, pg. 3282
HASLIMANN TAYLOR PUBLIC RELATIONS—See Clayton, Dubilier & Rice, LLC; *U.S. Private*, pg. 925
HASLINGER ACELSZERKEZETEPITO KFT—See Hutter & Schrantz PMS Ges.m.b.H; *Int'l*, pg. 3540
HASLINGER PROJEKT GMBH—See Hutter & Schrantz PMS Ges.m.b.H; *Int'l*, pg. 3540
HASLINGER STAHLBAU GMBH—See Hutter & Schrantz PMS Ges.m.b.H; *Int'l*, pg. 3540
HASPER EQUIPMENT CO.—See Cloverdale Equipment Co.; *U.S. Private*, pg. 948
HASRAT MERANTI (CHEMOR) SDN. BHD.—See KYM Holdings Bhd.; *Int'l*, pg. 4355
HASRAT MERANTI SDN. BHD.—See KYM Holdings Bhd.; *Int'l*, pg. 4355
HASRAT MERANTI (TAPAH) SDN. BHD.—See KYM Holdings Bhd.; *Int'l*, pg. 4355
HASSAD FOOD CO.—See Qatar Investment Authority; *Int'l*, pg. 6134
HASSAS BAGLAMA EKIPMANLARI TIC LTD. STI—See Georg Fischer AG; *Int'l*, pg. 2935
HASSEI SHOKAI CO., LTD.—See Nippon Thompson Co., Ltd.; *Int'l*, pg. 5350
HASSELBLAD A/S—See Victor Hasselblad AB; *Int'l*, pg. 8187
HASSELBLAD BRON INC.—See Victor Hasselblad AB; *Int'l*, pg. 8188
HASSELBLAD FRANCE S.A.—See Victor Hasselblad AB; *Int'l*, pg. 8188
HASSELBLAD JAPAN KK—See Victor Hasselblad AB; *Int'l*, pg. 8188
HASSELBLAD (UK) LTD.—See Victor Hasselblad AB; *Int'l*, pg. 8187
HASSELBLAD USA, INC.—See Victor Hasselblad AB; *Int'l*, pg. 8188
HASSELBLAD VERTRIEBSGESELLSCHAFT GMBH—See Victor Hasselblad AB; *Int'l*, pg. 8188
HASSELL & HUGHES LUMBER COMPANY, INC.; *U.S. Private*, pg. 1878
HASSEL MOTORS INC.—See Group 1 Automotive, Inc.; *U.S. Public*, pg. 971
HASSERODER BRAUEREI GMBH—See Anheuser-Busch InBev SA/NV; *Int'l*, pg. 466
HASSETT AIR EXPRESS; *U.S. Private*, pg. 1878
HASSETT AIR EXPRESS—See Hassett Air Express; *U.S. Private*, pg. 1878
HASSE & WREDE CVS DALIAN, CHINA LTD.—See Knorr-Bremse AG; *Int'l*, pg. 4210
HASSE & WREDE GMBH—See Knorr-Bremse AG; *Int'l*, pg. 4210
HASSIA PACKAGING PVT. LTD.—See I.M.A. Industria Macchine Automatiche S.p.A.; *Int'l*, pg. 3565
HASSINGER COMPANIES; *U.S. Private*, pg. 1879
HASSLEN CONSTRUCTION COMPANY; *U.S. Private*, pg. 1879
HASSO PLATTNER VENTURES AFRICA (PTY) LTD.; *Int'l*, pg. 3283
HASSO PLATTNER VENTURES MANAGEMENT GMBH; *Int'l*, pg. 3284
HASTANAS DEVELOPMENT SDN. BHD.—See Insas Berhad; *Int'l*, pg. 3718
HASTEN SYSTEMS—See AC Corporation; *U.S. Private*, pg. 45
HASTI FINANCE LIMITED; *Int'l*, pg. 3284
HASTINGS + COHN REAL ESTATE, LLC; *U.S. Private*, pg. 1879
HASTINGS CO-OP CREAMERY COMPANY; *U.S. Private*, pg. 1879
HASTINGS DEERING (AUSTRALIA) LIMITED—See Sime Darby Berhad; *Int'l*, pg. 6930
HASTINGS DEERING (PNG) LTD.—See Sime Darby Berhad; *Int'l*, pg. 6930
HASTINGS DEERING (SOLOMON ISLANDS) LIMITED—See Sime Darby Berhad; *Int'l*, pg. 6930
HASTINGS DESIGN CO; *U.S. Private*, pg. 1879
HASTINGS EAST MANUFACTURING CO., LTD.—See RFE Investment Partners; *U.S. Private*, pg. 3419

HASTINGS EQUITY PARTNERS, LLC; *U.S. Private*, pg. 1879
HASTINGS FUNDS MANAGEMENT LIMITED—See Westpac Banking Corporation; *Int'l*, pg. 8391
HASTINGS FUNDS MANAGEMENT (UK) LIMITED—See Westpac Banking Corporation; *Int'l*, pg. 8391
HASTINGS GROUP HOLDINGS LIMITED—See Sampo plc; *Int'l*, pg. 6507
HASTINGS INVESTMENT MANAGEMENT PTY. LTD.—See Westpac Banking Corporation; *Int'l*, pg. 8391
HASTINGS LANDSCAPE & DESIGN GROUP—See H.G. Hastings Co.; *U.S. Private*, pg. 1826
HASTINGS MANUFACTURING COMPANY—See RFE Investment Partners; *U.S. Private*, pg. 3419
HASTINGS NATURE & GARDEN CENTER—See H.G. Hastings Co.; *U.S. Private*, pg. 1826
HASTINGS TECHNOLOGY METALS LIMITED; *Int'l*, pg. 3284
HASTINGS TECHNOLOGY METALS PTE LTD—See Hastings Technology Metals Limited; *Int'l*, pg. 3284
HASTINGS TILE & BATH, INC.; *U.S. Private*, pg. 1879
HASWELL PTY LIMITED—See ARN Media Limited; *Int'l*, pg. 576
HATA FOODS CO., LTD.—See Kobe Bussan Co., Ltd.; *Int'l*, pg. 4217
HA TAY PHARMACEUTICAL JOINT STOCK COMPANY; *Int'l*, pg. 3201
HA TAY TRADING JOINT STOCK COMPANY; *Int'l*, pg. 3201
HATCH64; *Int'l*, pg. 3284
HATCHASIA INC.; *Int'l*, pg. 3284
HATCH ASSOCIATES PTY. LTD.—See Hatch Ltd.; *Int'l*, pg. 3284
HATCH & BAILEY COMPANY; *U.S. Private*, pg. 1879
HATCHBEAUTY AGENCY LLC—See American Exchange Group; *U.S. Private*, pg. 232
HATCHER CHEVROLET BUICK PONTIAC OLDS GMC INC.; *U.S. Private*, pg. 1879
HATCHER CONSTRUCTION SERVICES LLC; *U.S. Private*, pg. 1879
HATCHER GROUP LTD.; *Int'l*, pg. 3284
THE HATCHER GROUP; *U.S. Private*, pg. 4043
HATCHET RIDGE WIND, LLC—See Canada Pension Plan Investment Board; *Int'l*, pg. 1281
HATCH IAS—See Hatch Ltd.; *Int'l*, pg. 3284
HATCH, INC.—See Wall Family Enterprise, Inc.; *U.S. Private*, pg. 4430
HATCH INSIGHT KK—See Aflac Incorporated; *U.S. Public*, pg. 57
HATCH & KIRK, INC.; *U.S. Private*, pg. 1879
HATCH LTD.; *Int'l*, pg. 3284
HATCH MOTT MACDONALD, LLC—See Mott MacDonald Group Ltd.; *Int'l*, pg. 5055
HATCH STAMPING COMPANY INC.; *U.S. Private*, pg. 1879
HATCH WORK CO., LTD.—See Vector Inc.; *Int'l*, pg. 8144
THE HAT CLUB, LLC; *U.S. Private*, pg. 4043
HATCO CORPORATION; *U.S. Private*, pg. 1879
HATEKS HATAY TEKSTIL ISLETMELERI A.S.; *Int'l*, pg. 3284
HATENA CO., LTD.; *Int'l*, pg. 3284
HATFASH LIMITED—See Young An Hat Co., Ltd.; *Int'l*, pg. 8602
HATFIELD & COMPANY INC.; *U.S. Private*, pg. 1879
HATFIELD PHILIPS DEUTSCHLAND GMBH—See Starwood Property Trust, Inc.; *U.S. Public*, pg. 1939
HATFIELD QUALITY MEATS, INC.—See Clemens Family Corporation; *U.S. Private*, pg. 940
HATFIELD SPAIN, S.L.—See Starwood Property Trust, Inc.; *U.S. Public*, pg. 1939
HATHAWAY AGENCY, INC.—See NBT Bancorp Inc.; *U.S. Public*, pg. 1500
HATHAWAY CONSTRUCTION COMPANY, INC.; *U.S. Private*, pg. 1879
HATHAWAY DEVELOPMENT CORP.; *U.S. Private*, pg. 1879
HATHAWAY DINWIDDIE CONSTRUCTION COMPANY; *U.S. Private*, pg. 1880
HATHAWAY INC.; *U.S. Private*, pg. 1880
HATHAWAY LLC; *U.S. Private*, pg. 1880
HATHAWAY & SONS, INC.—See GMS Inc.; *U.S. Public*, pg. 948
HATHAWAY SYSTEMS CORPORATION—See Allient Inc.; *U.S. Public*, pg. 80
HATHEWAY (TRACADIE) LTEE; *Int'l*, pg. 3284
HA THUAN HUNG CONSTRUCTION - TRADE - SERVICE LTD. COMPANY—See Dat Xanh Group Joint Stock Company; *Int'l*, pg. 1975
HATHWAY BHAWANI CABLETEL & DATACOM LIMITED; *Int'l*, pg. 3284
HATHWAY CABLE & DATACOM LTD.; *Int'l*, pg. 3284
HATHWAY INC.—See Bounteous, Inc.; *U.S. Private*, pg. 624
HATILLO PAPER BOARD CORP.—See Borinquen Container Corp.; *U.S. Private*, pg. 618
HA TINH BOOK & EDUCATIONAL EQUIPMENT JOINT STOCK COMPANY; *Int'l*, pg. 3201

HATLING FLINT—See Flint Communications, Inc. & Adfarm; *U.S. Private*, pg. 1545
HATO REY PLASTICS INC.—See Vaqueria Tres Monjitas Inc.; *U.S. Private*, pg. 4345
HAT SICAF S.P.A.; *Int'l*, pg. 3284
HATSTAND LTD.—See Synechron Inc.; *U.S. Private*, pg. 3903
HATSUHO SHOUJI CO., LTD.; *Int'l*, pg. 3284
HATSUN AGRO PRODUCTS LTD; *Int'l*, pg. 3284
HATTELAND DISPLAY AS—See Norautron Group AS; *Int'l*, pg. 5415
HATTEN LAND LIMITED; *Int'l*, pg. 3284
HATTERAS FUNDS LLC—See RCAP Holdings, LLC; *U.S. Private*, pg. 3361
HATTERAS PRESS INC.; *U.S. Private*, pg. 1880
HATTERAS YACHTS—See Brunswick Corporation; *U.S. Public*, pg. 407
HATTERSLY NEWMAN HENDER LTD.—See Crane NXT, Co.; *U.S. Public*, pg. 591
HATTIESBURG AMERICAN—See Gannett Co., Inc.; *U.S. Public*, pg. 898
HATTINGTON CAPITAL LLP; *Int'l*, pg. 3284
HATTON PLANTATIONS PLC; *Int'l*, pg. 3285
HATTON POINT, INC.; *U.S. Private*, pg. 1880
HATTORI GUMI CO., LTD.—See The Sumitomo Warehouse Co. Ltd.; *Int'l*, pg. 7689
HATTORI KOUN CO., LTD.—See Okaya & Co., Ltd.; *Int'l*, pg. 5546
HAT WORLD, INC.—See Genesco Inc.; *U.S. Public*, pg. 930
HATZEL & BUEHLER, INC.—See Construction Management Service; *U.S. Private*, pg. 1023
HAUCK & AUFHAUSER ASSET MANAGEMENT SERVICES S.A R.L.—See Deutsche Bank Aktiengesellschaft; *Int'l*, pg. 2062
HAUCK & AUFHAUSER FUND PLATFORMS S.A.—See Fosun International Limited; *Int'l*, pg. 2751
HAUCK & AUFHAUSER INVESTMENT GESELLSCHAFT S.A.—See Fosun International Limited; *Int'l*, pg. 2751
HAUCK & AUFHAUSER LAMPE PRIVATBANK AG—See Fosun International Limited; *Int'l*, pg. 2751
HAUCK & AUFHAUSER PRIVATBANKIERS AG—See Fosun International Limited; *Int'l*, pg. 2751
HAUCK & AUFHAUSER (SCHWEIZ) AG—See Fosun International Limited; *Int'l*, pg. 2751
HAUCK HEAT TREATMENT LIMITED—See Aalberts N.V.; *Int'l*, pg. 34
HAUCK MANUFACTURING COMPANY—See Honeywell International Inc.; *U.S. Public*, pg. 1048
HAUENSTEIN & BURMEISTER, INC.; *U.S. Private*, pg. 1880
HAUFF-TECHNIK GMBH & CO. KG—See INDUS Holding AG; *Int'l*, pg. 3663
HAUG IMPLEMENT CO. INC; *U.S. Private*, pg. 1880
HAUHINCO LP—See Hauhinco Maschinenfabrik G. Hausherr Jochums GmbH & Co. KG; *Int'l*, pg. 3285
HAUHINCO MASCHINENFABRIK G. HAUSHERR JOCHUMS GMBH & CO. KG; *Int'l*, pg. 3285
HAULERS INSURANCE COMPANY, INC.—See Shelter Mutual Insurance Company; *U.S. Private*, pg. 3631
HAULGAUGE, INC.—See LCI Industries; *U.S. Public*, pg. 1295
HAULMARK INDUSTRIES INC.; *U.S. Private*, pg. 1880
HAULOTTE ARGENTINA S.A.—See Haulotte Group SA; *Int'l*, pg. 3285
HAULOTTE AUSTRALIA PTY LTD.—See Haulotte Group SA; *Int'l*, pg. 3285
HAULOTTE CHILE SPA—See Haulotte Group SA; *Int'l*, pg. 3285
HAULOTTE DO BRAZIL LTD.A—See Haulotte Group SA; *Int'l*, pg. 3285
HAULOTTE FRANCE SARL—See Haulotte Group SA; *Int'l*, pg. 3285
HAULOTTE GROUP SA; *Int'l*, pg. 3285
HAULOTTE HUBARBEITSBUHNEN GMBH—See Haulotte Group SA; *Int'l*, pg. 3285
HAULOTTE IBERICA S.L.—See Haulotte Group SA; *Int'l*, pg. 3285
HAULOTTE INDIA PRIVATE LIMITED—See Haulotte Group SA; *Int'l*, pg. 3285
HAULOTTE ITALIA S.R.L.—See Haulotte Group SA; *Int'l*, pg. 3285
HAULOTTE MEXICO S.A. DE C.V.—See Haulotte Group SA; *Int'l*, pg. 3285
HAULOTTE MIDDLE EAST FZE—See Haulotte Group SA; *Int'l*, pg. 3285
HAULOTTE NETHERLANDS B.V—See Haulotte Group SA; *Int'l*, pg. 3285
HAULOTTE NORTH AMERICA MANUFACTURING L.L.C—See Haulotte Group SA; *Int'l*, pg. 3285
HAULOTTE POLSKA SP. Z O.O.—See Haulotte Group SA; *Int'l*, pg. 3285
HAULOTTE SCANDINAVIA AB—See Haulotte Group SA; *Int'l*, pg. 3285
HAULOTTE SHANGHAI CO., LTD.—See Haulotte Group SA; *Int'l*, pg. 3285
HAULOTTE SINGAPORE PTE LTD.—See Haulotte Group SA; *Int'l*, pg. 3285

HAULOTTE GROUP SA

Company Index

HAULOTTE TRADING (SHANGHAI) CO., LTD.—See Haulotte Group SA; *Int'l*, pg. 3285
HAULOTTE UK LTD.—See Haulotte Group SA; *Int'l*, pg. 3285
HAULOTTE VOSTOK OOO—See Haulotte Group SA; *Int'l*, pg. 3285
HAUNI DO BRASIL LTDA.—See Korber AG; *Int'l*, pg. 4280
HAUNI FAR EAST LIMITED—See Korber AG; *Int'l*, pg. 4280
HAUNI HUNGARIA GEPGYARTO KFT.—See Korber AG; *Int'l*, pg. 4280
HAUNI JAPAN CO., LTD.—See Korber AG; *Int'l*, pg. 4280
HAUNI MALAYSIA SDN. BHD.—See Korber AG; *Int'l*, pg. 4280
HAUNI MASCHINENBAU AG—See Korber AG; *Int'l*, pg. 4280
HAUNI PRIMARY GMBH—See Korber AG; *Int'l*, pg. 4280
HAUNI RICHMOND, INC.—See Korber AG; *Int'l*, pg. 4280
HAUNI SINGAPORE PTE. LTD.—See Korber AG; *Int'l*, pg. 4280
HAUNI TECHNICAL SERVICES AND TRADING COMPANY LTD.—See Korber AG; *Int'l*, pg. 4280
HAUNI TRADING (SHANGHAI) CO., LTD.—See Korber AG; *Int'l*, pg. 4280
HAUN WELDING SUPPLY INC.; *U.S. Private*, pg. 1880
HAUPPAUGE COMPUTER WORKS GMBH—See HAUPPAUGE DIGITAL, INC.; *U.S. Public*, pg. 988
HAUPPAUGE COMPUTER WORKS INC.—See HAUPPAUGE DIGITAL, INC.; *U.S. Public*, pg. 988
HAUPPAUGE COMPUTER WORKS SARL—See HAUPPAUGE DIGITAL, INC.; *U.S. Public*, pg. 988
HAUPPAUGE COMPUTER WORKS SARL—See HAUPPAUGE DIGITAL, INC.; *U.S. Public*, pg. 988
HAUPPAUGE COMPUTER WORKS UK LTD.—See HAUPPAUGE DIGITAL, INC.; *U.S. Public*, pg. 988
HAUPPAUGE DIGITAL ASIA PTE LTD.—See HAUPPAUGE DIGITAL, INC.; *U.S. Public*, pg. 988
HAUPPAUGE DIGITAL, INC.; *U.S. Public*, pg. 988
HAUPPAUGE DIGITAL INC.—See HAUPPAUGE DIGITAL, INC.; *U.S. Public*, pg. 988
HAUPT PHARMA AG—See BC Partners LLP; *Int'l*, pg. 922
HAUPT PHARMA AMAREG GMBH—See BC Partners LLP; *Int'l*, pg. 922
HAUPT PHARMA BERLIN GMBH - BRACKENHEIM—See BC Partners LLP; *Int'l*, pg. 922
HAUPT PHARMA BERLIN GMBH—See BC Partners LLP; *Int'l*, pg. 922
HAUPT PHARMA DEVELOPMENT GMBH—See BC Partners LLP; *Int'l*, pg. 922
HAUPT PHARMA INC.—See BC Partners LLP; *Int'l*, pg. 922
HAUPT PHARMA LATINA S.R.L.—See BC Partners LLP; *Int'l*, pg. 922
HAUPT PHARMA LIVRON S.A.S.—See BC Partners LLP; *Int'l*, pg. 922
HAUPT PHARMA MUNSTER GMBH—See BC Partners LLP; *Int'l*, pg. 922
HAUPT PHARMA SALES GMBH—See BC Partners LLP; *Int'l*, pg. 922
HAUPT PHARMA TORIDE CO., LTD.—See BC Partners LLP; *Int'l*, pg. 922
HAUPT PHARMA WOLFRATSHAUSEN GMBH—See BC Partners LLP; *Int'l*, pg. 922
HAUPT PHARMA WULFING GMBH—See BC Partners LLP; *Int'l*, pg. 923
HAUS AM BRUSSELER PLATZ GMBH & CO. KG—See Helaba Landesbank Hessen-Thuringen; *Int'l*, pg. 3328
HAUS AMSELHOF SENIORENRESIDENZ GMBH—See Clariane SE; *Int'l*, pg. 1643
HAUSBAU FINANZ GMBH—See HELMA Eigenheimbau AG; *Int'l*, pg. 3338
HAUSER CAPITAL MARKETS LLC—See Art Hauser Insurance, Inc.; *U.S. Private*, pg. 339
THE HAUSER GROUP—See Ames Scullin O'Haire; *U.S. Private*, pg. 262
HAUS FURNISHINGS & INTERIORS PTE. LTD.—See SDAI Limited; *Int'l*, pg. 6657
HAUSHAHN AUFZUG GMBH—See Schindler Holding AG; *Int'l*, pg. 6619
HAUSHAHN GMBH & CO.—See Schindler Holding AG; *Int'l*, pg. 6619
HAUS KURFURST GMBH—See ATON GmbH; *Int'l*, pg. 689
HAUSLICHE KRANKENPFLEGE CHARLOTTE KONIG GMBH & CO.—See Clariane SE; *Int'l*, pg. 1643
HAUSMANN INDUSTRIES, INC.—See Dynatronics Corporation; *U.S. Public*, pg. 700
HAUSMANN INTERNATIONAL PTE LTD.—See Shin Tai Industry Co., Ltd.; *Int'l*, pg. 6838
HAUSMANN JOHNSON INSURANCE, INC.—See The Benefit Services Group, Inc.; *U.S. Private*, pg. 3993
HAUSNER HARD - CHROME, INC.; *U.S. Private*, pg. 1880
HAUS SAALETAL GMBH—See Asklepios Kliniken GmbH & Co. KGaA; *Int'l*, pg. 624
HAUS TALK, INC.; *Int'l*, pg. 3285
HAUSWARTPROFIS AG—See PHM Group Holding Oyj; *Int'l*, pg. 5848

HAUT BUYS (PVT) LTD—See Hi-Tech Lubricants Ltd.; *Int'l*, pg. 3381
HAUTECOEUR FRANCE; *Int'l*, pg. 3285
HAUTELOOK, INC.—See Nordstrom, Inc.; *U.S. Public*, pg. 1535
HAUTE-NORMANDIE VEHICULES INDUSTRIELS; *Int'l*, pg. 3285
HAUTEVILLE INSURANCE COMPANY LTD.—See Allianz SE; *Int'l*, pg. 342
HAUZER TECHNO COATING B.V.—See IHI Corporation; *Int'l*, pg. 3604
HAVAL MOTORS AUSTRALIA PTY. LTD.—See Great Wall Motor Company Limited; *Int'l*, pg. 3066
HAVAL MOTORS SOUTH AFRICA PROPRIETARY LIMITED—See Great Wall Motor Company Limited; *Int'l*, pg. 3066
HAVAM AUTOMOTIVE B.V.—See LKQ Corporation; *U.S. Public*, pg. 1334
HAVANA AUTO PARTS INC.; *U.S. Private*, pg. 1880
THE HAVANA NATIONAL BANK—See Community Investment Group, Ltd.; *U.S. Private*, pg. 995
HAVANA YAYINCILIK TURIZM VE GIDA PAZARLAMA TICARET A.S.—See Dogus Holding AS; *Int'l*, pg. 2155
HAVA PTY. LTD.—See World Kinect Corporation; *U.S. Public*, pg. 2380
HAVAS 10—See Vivendi SE; *Int'l*, pg. 8266
HAVAS AG—See Vivendi SE; *Int'l*, pg. 8268
HAVAS BRUSSELS—See Vivendi SE; *Int'l*, pg. 8267
HAVAS CREATIVE BANGALORE—See Vivendi SE; *Int'l*, pg. 8268
HAVAS CREATIVE GROUP—See Vivendi SE; *Int'l*, pg. 8267
HAVAS CREATIVE GURGAON—See Vivendi SE; *Int'l*, pg. 8268
HAVAS CREATIVE MUMBAI—See Vivendi SE; *Int'l*, pg. 8268
HAVAS DANMARK A/S—See Vivendi SE; *Int'l*, pg. 8268
HAVAS DESIGN + PORTUGAL LDA.—See Vivendi SE; *Int'l*, pg. 8268
HAVAS DISCOVERY, LLC - BALTIMORE—See Vivendi SE; *Int'l*, pg. 8267
HAVAS DISCOVERY, LLC - RICHMOND—See Vivendi SE; *Int'l*, pg. 8267
HAVAS DISCOVERY, LLC—See Vivendi SE; *Int'l*, pg. 8267
HAVAS DUSSELDORF GMBH—See Vivendi SE; *Int'l*, pg. 8268
HAVAS EDGE BOSTON LLC—See Vivendi SE; *Int'l*, pg. 8267
HAVAS EDGE LLC—See Vivendi SE; *Int'l*, pg. 8267
HAVAS EDITION—See Vivendi SE; *Int'l*, pg. 8266
HAVAS EHS DISCOVERY LTD.—See Vivendi SE; *Int'l*, pg. 8268
HAVAS EHS LIMITED - CIRENCESTER—See Vivendi SE; *Int'l*, pg. 8268
HAVAS ENGAGE PAZARLAMA VE ILETISIM HIZMETLERI A.S.—See Vivendi SE; *Int'l*, pg. 8268
HAVAS EVENTS—See Vivendi SE; *Int'l*, pg. 8266
HAVAS FINANCES SERVICES SNC—See Vivendi SE; *Int'l*, pg. 8266
HAVAS FORMULA - EL SEGUNDO—See Vivendi SE; *Int'l*, pg. 8267
HAVAS FORMULA, LLC—See Vivendi SE; *Int'l*, pg. 8267
HAVAS FORMULA - NEW YORK—See Vivendi SE; *Int'l*, pg. 8267
HAVAS GMBH—See Vivendi SE; *Int'l*, pg. 8268
HAVAS GUATEMALA—See Vivendi SE; *Int'l*, pg. 8269
HAVAS HAMBURG GMBH—See Vivendi SE; *Int'l*, pg. 8268
HAVAS HEALTH, INC.—See Vivendi SE; *Int'l*, pg. 8267
HAVAS HELIA LIMITED—See Vivendi SE; *Int'l*, pg. 8268
HAVAS HOLDING DEUTSCHLAND GMBH—See Vivendi SE; *Int'l*, pg. 8268
HAVAS IMPACT, LLC - OPERATIONS & TRAINING CENTER—See Vivendi SE; *Int'l*, pg. 8267
HAVAS IMPACT, LLC—See Vivendi SE; *Int'l*, pg. 8267
HAVAS IRELAND LIMITED—See Vivendi SE; *Int'l*, pg. 8270
HAVAS IT—See Vivendi SE; *Int'l*, pg. 8266
HAVAS JAPAN—See Vivendi SE; *Int'l*, pg. 8267
HAVAS LEMZ BV—See Vivendi SE; *Int'l*, pg. 8267
HAVAS LIFE AB—See Vivendi SE; *Int'l*, pg. 8267
HAVAS LIFE ITALY S.R.L.—See Vivendi SE; *Int'l*, pg. 8267
HAVAS LIFE - LISBON—See Vivendi SE; *Int'l*, pg. 8267
HAVAS LIFE MEDICOM—See Vivendi SE; *Int'l*, pg. 8267
HAVAS LIFE METRO - CHICAGO—See Vivendi SE; *Int'l*, pg. 8267
HAVAS LIFE METRO - NEW YORK—See Vivendi SE; *Int'l*, pg. 8267
HAVAS LIFE - MUNICH—See Vivendi SE; *Int'l*, pg. 8267
HAVAS LIFE - PARIS—See Vivendi SE; *Int'l*, pg. 8267
HAVAS LIFE PR - PARIS—See Vivendi SE; *Int'l*, pg. 8267
HAVAS LIFE S.A.—See Vivendi SE; *Int'l*, pg. 8267
HAVAS LIFE—See Vivendi SE; *Int'l*, pg. 8269
HAVAS LIFE TORONTO, INC.—See Vivendi SE; *Int'l*, pg. 8269
HAVAS LIFE TORONTO—See Vivendi SE; *Int'l*, pg. 8267
HAVAS MANAGEMENT ESPANA, S.L.—See Vivendi SE; *Int'l*, pg. 8266
HAVAS MEDELLIN—See Vivendi SE; *Int'l*, pg. 8269

HAVAS MEDIA AG—See Vivendi SE; *Int'l*, pg. 8270
HAVAS MEDIA ARGENTINA—See Vivendi SE; *Int'l*, pg. 8270
HAVAS MEDIA BELGIUM S.A.—See Vivendi SE; *Int'l*, pg. 8270
HAVAS MEDIA BOSTON—See Vivendi SE; *Int'l*, pg. 8270
HAVAS MEDIA CHICAGO—See Vivendi SE; *Int'l*, pg. 8270
HAVAS MEDIA COLOMBIA SAS—See Vivendi SE; *Int'l*, pg. 8270
HAVAS MEDIA CZECH REPUBLIC, S.R.O.—See Vivendi SE; *Int'l*, pg. 8270
HAVAS MEDIA ECUADOR—See Vivendi SE; *Int'l*, pg. 8270
HAVAS MEDIA FRANCE GROUP—See Vivendi SE; *Int'l*, pg. 8269
HAVAS MEDIA FRANCE—See Vivendi SE; *Int'l*, pg. 8270
HAVAS MEDIA HUNGARY KFT.—See Vivendi SE; *Int'l*, pg. 8270
HAVAS MEDIA INTERNATIONAL—See Vivendi SE; *Int'l*, pg. 8270
HAVAS MEDIA IRELAND—See Vivendi SE; *Int'l*, pg. 8270
HAVAS MEDIA LATVIA—See Vivendi SE; *Int'l*, pg. 8270
HAVAS MEDIA LIMITED—See Vivendi SE; *Int'l*, pg. 8270
HAVAS MEDIA MADRID—See Vivendi SE; *Int'l*, pg. 8270
HAVAS MEDIA MADRID—See Vivendi SE; *Int'l*, pg. 8270
HAVAS MEDIA MEXICO—See Vivendi SE; *Int'l*, pg. 8270
HAVAS MEDIA MUMBAI—See Vivendi SE; *Int'l*, pg. 8270
HAVAS MEDIA NEDERLAND B.V.—See Vivendi SE; *Int'l*, pg. 8270
HAVAS MEDIA NEW YORK—See Vivendi SE; *Int'l*, pg. 8270
HAVAS MEDIA NICARAGUA—See Vivendi SE; *Int'l*, pg. 8270
HAVAS MEDIA NORTH AMERICA—See Vivendi SE; *Int'l*, pg. 8270
HAVAS MEDIA PANAMA—See Vivendi SE; *Int'l*, pg. 8270
HAVAS MEDIA PORTUGAL HOLDING SGPS, S.A.—See Vivendi SE; *Int'l*, pg. 8270
HAVAS MEDIA REGIONES, S.A. DE C.V.—See Vivendi SE; *Int'l*, pg. 8270
HAVAS MEDIA ROMANIA SL—See Vivendi SE; *Int'l*, pg. 8270
HAVAS MEDIA RUSSIA—See Vivendi SE; *Int'l*, pg. 8270
HAVAS MEDIA SAN FRANCISCO—See Vivendi SE; *Int'l*, pg. 8270
HAVAS MEDIA SERVICES S.A. DE C.V.—See Vivendi SE; *Int'l*, pg. 8270
HAVAS MEDIA SINGAPORE—See Vivendi SE; *Int'l*, pg. 8270
HAVAS MEDIA SLOVAKIA—See Vivendi SE; *Int'l*, pg. 8270
HAVAS MEDIA, S.L.—See Vivendi SE; *Int'l*, pg. 8269
HAVAS MEDIA SP. Z.O.O—See Vivendi SE; *Int'l*, pg. 8270
HAVAS MEDIA S.R.L.—See Vivendi SE; *Int'l*, pg. 8270
HAVAS MEDIA UKRAINE—See Vivendi SE; *Int'l*, pg. 8270
HAVAS PEOPLE LIMITED - BIRMINGHAM—See Vivendi SE; *Int'l*, pg. 8268
HAVAS PEOPLE LIMITED - CARDIFF—See Vivendi SE; *Int'l*, pg. 8268
HAVAS PEOPLE LIMITED—See Vivendi SE; *Int'l*, pg. 8268
HAVAS PR MILAN SRL—See Vivendi SE; *Int'l*, pg. 8268
HAVAS PR NORTH AMERICA, INC.—See Vivendi SE; *Int'l*, pg. 8267
HAVAS PR PRAGUE S.R.O.—See Vivendi SE; *Int'l*, pg. 8268
HAVAS PR - TALLINN—See Vivendi SE; *Int'l*, pg. 8268
HAVAS PR WARSAW SP. Z O.O.—See Vivendi SE; *Int'l*, pg. 8268
HAVAS RH—See Vivendi SE; *Int'l*, pg. 8270
HAVAS RIVERORCHID—See Vivendi SE; *Int'l*, pg. 8270
HAVAS S.A.—See Vivendi SE; *Int'l*, pg. 8266
HAVAS SHARED SERVICES LIMITED—See Vivendi SE; *Int'l*, pg. 8270
HAVAS SINGAPORE PTE. LTD.—See Vivendi SE; *Int'l*, pg. 8267
HAVAS SPORTS ARGENTINA S.A.—See Vivendi SE; *Int'l*, pg. 8270
HAVAS SPORTS & ENTERTAINMENT SA—See Vivendi SE; *Int'l*, pg. 8270
HAVAS SPORTS ENTERTAINMENT—See Vivendi SE; *Int'l*, pg. 8270
HAVAS SPORTS LIMITED—See Vivendi SE; *Int'l*, pg. 8270
HAVAS SPORTS, S.A.—See Vivendi SE; *Int'l*, pg. 8270
HAVASU NEWSPAPERS INC.—See Western Newspapers, Inc.; *U.S. Private*, pg. 4495
HAVASU REGIONAL MEDICAL CENTER, LLC—See Apollo Global Management, Inc.; *U.S. Public*, pg. 155
HAVASU SURGERY CENTER, INC.—See Apollo Global Management, Inc.; *U.S. Public*, pg. 155
HAVAS VILLAGE BOGOTA—See Vivendi SE; *Int'l*, pg. 8267
HAVAS WARSAW SP. Z O.O.—See Vivendi SE; *Int'l*, pg. 8268
HAVAS WIEN GMBH—See Vivendi SE; *Int'l*, pg. 8268
HAVAS WORLDWIDE AG - GENEVA—See Vivendi SE; *Int'l*, pg. 8268
HAVAS WORLDWIDE AMSTERDAM B.V.—See Vivendi SE; *Int'l*, pg. 8268

HAVAS WORLDWIDE ARABIA—See Vivendi SE; *Int'l*, pg. 8269
HAVAS WORLDWIDE ASIA PACIFIC—See Vivendi SE; *Int'l*, pg. 8267
HAVAS WORLDWIDE BRUSSELS SA—See Vivendi SE; *Int'l*, pg. 8268
HAVAS WORLDWIDE BUCHAREST—See Vivendi SE; *Int'l*, pg. 8268
HAVAS WORLDWIDE BUDAPEST KOMMUNIKACIOS ZRT.—See Vivendi SE; *Int'l*, pg. 8268
HAVAS WORLDWIDE BUENOS AIRES S.A.—See Vivendi SE; *Int'l*, pg. 8269
HAVAS WORLDWIDE CHICAGO, INC.—See Vivendi SE; *Int'l*, pg. 8268
HAVAS WORLDWIDE COLOMBIA S.A.S.—See Vivendi SE; *Int'l*, pg. 8269
HAVAS WORLDWIDE (CREATIVE) INDIA PVT. LTD.—See Vivendi SE; *Int'l*, pg. 8268
HAVAS WORLDWIDE DALLAS, LLC—See Vivendi SE; *Int'l*, pg. 8268
HAVAS WORLDWIDE EUROPE & AFRICA—See Vivendi SE; *Int'l*, pg. 8268
HAVAS WORLDWIDE GURISA—See Vivendi SE; *Int'l*, pg. 8269
HAVAS WORLDWIDE HELSINKI OY—See Vivendi SE; *Int'l*, pg. 8268
HAVAS WORLDWIDE ISTANBUL ILETISIM HIZMETLERI A.S.—See Vivendi SE; *Int'l*, pg. 8268
HAVAS WORLDWIDE JAPAN K.K.—See Vivendi SE; *Int'l*, pg. 8268
HAVAS WORLDWIDE JOHANNESBURG (PTY) LTD.—See Vivendi SE; *Int'l*, pg. 8269
HAVAS WORLDWIDE KIEV—See Vivendi SE; *Int'l*, pg. 8269
HAVAS WORLDWIDE KOREA CO., LTD.—See Vivendi SE; *Int'l*, pg. 8268
HAVAS WORLDWIDE LATIN AMERICA—See Vivendi SE; *Int'l*, pg. 8269
HAVAS WORLDWIDE, LLC—See Vivendi SE; *Int'l*, pg. 8267
HAVAS WORLDWIDE LONDON LIMITED—See Vivendi SE; *Int'l*, pg. 8269
HAVAS WORLDWIDE MEXICO S.A. DE C.V.—See Vivendi SE; *Int'l*, pg. 8269
HAVAS WORLDWIDE MIDDLE EAST—See Vivendi SE; *Int'l*, pg. 8269
HAVAS WORLDWIDE MILAN S.R.L.—See Vivendi SE; *Int'l*, pg. 8269
HAVAS WORLDWIDE MOSCOW—See Vivendi SE; *Int'l*, pg. 8269
HAVAS WORLDWIDE MUNCHEN GMBH—See Vivendi SE; *Int'l*, pg. 8269
HAVAS WORLDWIDE NETHERLANDS B.V.—See Vivendi SE; *Int'l*, pg. 8269
HAVAS WORLDWIDE NEW YORK, INC.—See Vivendi SE; *Int'l*, pg. 8269
HAVAS WORLDWIDE PORTUGAL LDA.—See Vivendi SE; *Int'l*, pg. 8269
HAVAS WORLDWIDE PRAGUE A.S—See Vivendi SE; *Int'l*, pg. 8269
HAVAS WORLDWIDE PUERTO RICO, INC.—See Vivendi SE; *Int'l*, pg. 8269
HAVAS WORLDWIDE SAN FRANCISCO, LLC—See Vivendi SE; *Int'l*, pg. 8269
HAVAS WORLDWIDE SANTIAGO S.A.—See Vivendi SE; *Int'l*, pg. 8269
HAVAS WORLDWIDE SOFIA—See Vivendi SE; *Int'l*, pg. 8269
HAVAS WORLDWIDE SPAIN S.A.—See Vivendi SE; *Int'l*, pg. 8269
HAVAS WORLDWIDE TONIC—See Vivendi SE; *Int'l*, pg. 8269
HAVAS WORLDWIDE TORONTO INC.—See Vivendi SE; *Int'l*, pg. 8269
HAVAS WORLDWIDE UKRAINE—See Vivendi SE; *Int'l*, pg. 8269
HAVAS WORLDWIDE VALE SA DE CV—See Vivendi SE; *Int'l*, pg. 8269
HAVAY INDUSTRY INC.—See GHW International; *Int'l*, pg. 2960
HAVCO WOOD PRODUCTS LLC; *U.S. Private*, pg. 1880
HAVELAAR ET VAN STOLK B.V.—See Allianz SE; *Int'l*, pg. 353
HAVELI INVESTMENT MANAGEMENT LLC—See Whanau Interests LLC.; *U.S. Private*, pg. 4503
HAVELLANDISCHE EISENBAHN AG; *Int'l*, pg. 3286
HAVELL'S HOLDINGS INTERNATIONAL, LLC—See Havell's India Ltd.; *Int'l*, pg. 3286
HAVELL'S INDIA LTD. - ALWAR WORKS—See Havell's India Ltd.; *Int'l*, pg. 3286
HAVELL'S INDIA LTD. - FARIDABAD WORKS—See Havell's India Ltd.; *Int'l*, pg. 3286
HAVELL'S INDIA LTD. - HARIDWAR WORKS—See Havell's India Ltd.; *Int'l*, pg. 3286
HAVELL'S INDIA LTD.; *Int'l*, pg. 3285
HAVELLS SYLVANIA ARGENTINA S.A.—See Havell's India Ltd.; *Int'l*, pg. 3286
HAVELLS SYLVANIA BELGIUM B.V.B.A.—See Havell's India Ltd.; *Int'l*, pg. 3286

HAVELLS SYLVANIA BRASIL ILUMINACAO LTDA.—See Havell's India Ltd.; *Int'l*, pg. 3286
HAVELLS SYLVANIA COLOMBIA S.A.—See Havell's India Ltd.; *Int'l*, pg. 3286
HAVELLS SYLVANIA-CONCORD:MARLIN—See Havell's India Ltd.; *Int'l*, pg. 3286
HAVELLS SYLVANIA COSTA RICA S.A.—See Havell's India Ltd.; *Int'l*, pg. 3286
HAVELLS SYLVANIA DUBAI FZCO—See Havell's India Ltd.; *Int'l*, pg. 3286
HAVELLS SYLVANIA EUROPE LTD—See Havell's India Ltd.; *Int'l*, pg. 3286
HAVELLS SYLVANIA FIXTURES UK LTD—See Havell's India Ltd.; *Int'l*, pg. 3286
HAVELLS SYLVANIA FRANCE S.A.S.—See Havell's India Ltd.; *Int'l*, pg. 3286
HAVELL'S SYLVANIA (GERMANY) GMBH—See Havell's India Ltd.; *Int'l*, pg. 3286
HAVELLS SYLVANIA GREECE A.E.E.E.—See Havell's India Ltd.; *Int'l*, pg. 3286
HAVELLS SYLVANIA (GUANGZHOU) ENTERPRISE LTD—See Havell's India Ltd.; *Int'l*, pg. 3286
HAVELLS SYLVANIA GUATEMALA S.A.—See Havell's India Ltd.; *Int'l*, pg. 3286
HAVELLS SYLVANIA ITALY S.P.A.—See Havell's India Ltd.; *Int'l*, pg. 3286
HAVELLS SYLVANIA LIGHTING FRANCE SAS—See Havell's India Ltd.; *Int'l*, pg. 3286
HAVELL'S SYLVANIA NETHERLANDS B.V.—See Havell's India Ltd.; *Int'l*, pg. 3286
HAVELLS SYLVANIA N.V.—See Havell's India Ltd.; *Int'l*, pg. 3286
HAVELLS SYLVANIA SPAIN LOGISTICS S.L.—See Havell's India Ltd.; *Int'l*, pg. 3286
HAVELLS SYLVANIA SPAIN S.A.—See Havell's India Ltd.; *Int'l*, pg. 3286
HAVELLS SYLVANIA SWEDEN A.B.—See Havell's India Ltd.; *Int'l*, pg. 3286
HAVELLS SYLVANIA SWITZERLAND A.G.—See Havell's India Ltd.; *Int'l*, pg. 3286
HAVELLS SYLVANIA TUNISIA S.A.R.L.—See Havell's India Ltd.; *Int'l*, pg. 3286
HAVELLS SYLVANIA UK LTD.—See Havell's India Ltd.; *Int'l*, pg. 3286
HAVELLS SYLVANIA VENEZUELA C.A.—See Havell's India Ltd.; *Int'l*, pg. 3286
HAVELOCK CITY (PVT) LTD.—See Overseas Realty (Ceylon) PLC; *Int'l*, pg. 5673
HAVELOCK EUROPA PLC; *Int'l*, pg. 3287
HAVELOCK NEWS—See Gannett Co., Inc.; *U.S. Public*, pg. 906
HAVELSAN HAVA ELEKTRONIK SANAYI VE TICARET AS; *Int'l*, pg. 3287
HAVEL—See EMCOR Group, Inc.; *U.S. Public*, pg. 739
HAVEN AUTOMATION INDUSTRIES (S) PTE. LTD.—See Hanwha Group; *Int'l*, pg. 3264
HAVEN AUTOMATION INDUSTRIES (S) PTE. LTD.—See Hanwha Ocean Co., Ltd.; *Int'l*, pg. 3266
HAVEN BANCORP, INC.—See Haven Bancorp, MHC; *U.S. Private*, pg. 1880
HAVEN BANCORP, MHC; *U.S. Private*, pg. 1880
HAVEN COMMODITIES LLC—See Mid-Kansas Co-op Association; *U.S. Private*, pg. 2708
HAVENCREST CAPITAL MANAGEMENT, LLC; *U.S. Private*, pg. 1880
HAVEN FOR HOPE OF BEXAR COUNTY; *U.S. Private*, pg. 1880
HAVEN HOSPICE—See SantaFe Healthcare, Inc.; *U.S. Private*, pg. 3547
HAVEN LEISURE LTD.—See Blackstone Inc.; *U.S. Public*, pg. 352
HAVEN MORTGAGES LTD.—See AIB Group plc; *Int'l*, pg. 228
HAVEN POWER LIMITED—See Drax Group plc; *Int'l*, pg. 2200
HAVEN SAVINGS BANK—See Haven Bancorp, MHC; *U.S. Private*, pg. 1880
THE HAVEN SDN. BHD.; *Int'l*, pg. 7652
HAVENTREE BANK—See Smoothwater Capital Corporation; *Int'l*, pg. 7014
HAVENWOOD-HERITAGE HEIGHTS RETIREMENT COMMUNITY; *U.S. Private*, pg. 1880
HAVENWYCK HOSPITAL INC.—See Universal Health Services, Inc.; *U.S. Public*, pg. 2257
HAVE OUR PLASTIC INC.—See Tah Hsin Industrial Corporation; *Int'l*, pg. 7407
HAVERFIELD INTERNATIONAL INCORPORATED—See Quanta Services, Inc.; *U.S. Public*, pg. 1751
HAVERFORD PLACE APARTMENTS OWNER, LLC—See Independence Realty Trust, Inc.; *U.S. Public*, pg. 1115
HAVERFORD SYSTEMS; *U.S. Private*, pg. 1880
HAVERHILL GAZETTE—See The Retirement Systems of Alabama; *U.S. Private*, pg. 4105
HAVERHILL NORTH COKE COMPANY—See SunCoke Energy, Inc.; *U.S. Public*, pg. 1963
HAVERLAND CARTER LIFESTYLE GROUP; *U.S. Private*, pg. 1880
HAVERSTICK CONSULTING, INC.—See Kratos Defense & Security Solutions, Inc.; *U.S. Public*, pg. 1276

HAVERTON WTV LIMITED—See EQTEC plc; *Int'l*, pg. 2483
HAVERTY FURNITURE COMPANIES, INC.; *U.S. Public*, pg. 988
HAVERTYS CREDIT SERVICES, INC.—See Haverty Furniture Companies, Inc.; *U.S. Public*, pg. 988
HAVFISK ASA—See Austevoll Seafood ASA; *Int'l*, pg. 717
HAVI FOOD DISTRIBUTION (THAILAND) CO., LTD.—See Thai Beverage Public Company Limited; *Int'l*, pg. 7590
HAVILA HOLDING AS; *Int'l*, pg. 3287
HAVILAH RESOURCES LIMITED; *Int'l*, pg. 3287
HAVILA KYSTRUTEN AS; *Int'l*, pg. 3287
HAVILAND CONSUMER PRODUCTS, INC.—See Haviland Enterprises Inc.; *U.S. Private*, pg. 1880
HAVILAND ENTERPRISES INC.; *U.S. Private*, pg. 1880
HAVILAND PRODUCTS COMPANY—See Haviland Enterprises Inc.; *U.S. Private*, pg. 1880
HAVILAND TELEPHONE COMPANY, INC.—See LICT Corporation; *U.S. Public*, pg. 1312
HAVILA SHIPPING ASA—See Havila Holding AS; *Int'l*, pg. 3287
HAVILL-SPOERL FORD LINCOLN, INC.; *U.S. Private*, pg. 1881
HAVILL-SPOERL MOTOR SALES, LTD.; *U.S. Private*, pg. 1881
HAVIS, INC.; *U.S. Private*, pg. 1881
HAVIX CORPORATION; *Int'l*, pg. 3287
HAVLIK GEAR—See Mill City Capital, L.P.; *U.S. Private*, pg. 2730
HAVLIK INTERNATIONAL MACHINERY INC.—See Mill City Capital, L.P.; *U.S. Private*, pg. 2730
HAVN LIFE SCIENCES, INC.; *Int'l*, pg. 3287
HAVRE DAILY NEWS INC.—See Pioneer Newspapers Inc.; *U.S. Private*, pg. 3187
HAVRE PIPELINE COMPANY, LLC—See NorthWestern Corporation; *U.S. Public*, pg. 1543
HAVSFRUN CAPITAL AB—See Havsfrun Investment AB; *Int'l*, pg. 3287
HAVSFRUN INVESTMENT AB; *Int'l*, pg. 3287
HAWA ENGINEERS LTD.; *Int'l*, pg. 3288
HAWAIIANA GROUP, INC.—See NIPPON KANZAI Holdings Co.,Ltd.; *Int'l*, pg. 5319
HAWAIIANA GROUP, INC.—See Swell International Inc; *U.S. Private*, pg. 3892
HAWAIIAN AIRLINES, INC.—See Alaska Air Group, Inc.; *U.S. Public*, pg. 72
HAWAIIAN BEACH RENTALS—See RealVoice LLC; *U.S. Private*, pg. 3369
HAWAIIAN CEMENT; *U.S. Private*, pg. 1881
HAWAIIAN CEMENT—See MDU Resources Group, Inc.; *U.S. Public*, pg. 1410
HAWAIIAN COOL WATER, LLC; *U.S. Private*, pg. 1881
HAWAIIAN DREDGING CONSTRUCTION COMPANY, INC.—See Kajima Corporation; *Int'l*, pg. 4055
HAWAIIAN ELECTRIC COMPANY, INC.—See Hawaiian Electric Industries, Inc.; *U.S. Public*, pg. 989
HAWAIIAN ELECTRIC INDUSTRIES, INC.; *U.S. Public*, pg. 988
HAWAIIAN EXPRESS SERVICE INC.; *U.S. Private*, pg. 1881
HAWAIIAN FRUIT SPECIALTIES LLC; *U.S. Private*, pg. 1882
HAWAIIAN GARDENS DIALYSIS, LLC—See DaVita Inc.; *U.S. Public*, pg. 639
HAWAIIAN HOLDINGS, INC.—See Alaska Air Group, Inc.; *U.S. Public*, pg. 71
HAWAIIAN HOSPITALITY GROUP, INC.; *U.S. Public*, pg. 989
HAWAIIAN HOST INC.; *U.S. Private*, pg. 1882
HAWAIIAN INSURANCE & GUARANTY COMPANY, LTD.—See Great Northwest Insurance Company; *U.S. Private*, pg. 1766
HAWAIIAN ISLAND CREATIONS; *U.S. Private*, pg. 1882
HAWAIIAN ISLES ENTERPRISES, INC.; *U.S. Private*, pg. 1882
HAWAIIAN MACADAMIA NUT ORCHARDS, L.P.; *U.S. Private*, pg. 1882
HAWAIIAN MEMORIAL LIFE PLAN, LTD.—See Service Corporation International; *U.S. Public*, pg. 1869
HAWAIIAN OCEAN TRANSPORT, INC.—See The Jordan Company, L.P.; *U.S. Private*, pg. 4060
HAWAIIAN PACIFIC RESTAURANT GROUP, INC.; *U.S. Private*, pg. 1882
HAWAIIAN SPRINGS, LLC; *U.S. Private*, pg. 1882
HAWAIIAN SUN PRODUCTS INC.; *U.S. Private*, pg. 1882
HAWAIIAN TELCOM COMMUNICATIONS, INC.—See Macquarie Group Limited; *Int'l*, pg. 4628
HAWAIIAN TELCOM HOLDCO, INC.—See Macquarie Group Limited; *Int'l*, pg. 4628
HAWAIIAN TELCOM, INC.—See Macquarie Group Limited; *Int'l*, pg. 4628
HAWAIIAN TUG & BARGE—See Saltchuk Resources Inc.; *U.S. Private*, pg. 3534
HAWAII CARPENTERS VACATION & HOLIDAY FUND; *U.S. Private*, pg. 1881
HAWAII COFFEE COMPANY—See Paradise Beverages, Inc.; *U.S. Private*, pg. 3090
HAWAII COMMERCIAL REAL ESTATE, LLC—See Elite Pacific, LLC; *U.S. Private*, pg. 1361

HAWAII CARPENTERS VACATION & HOLIDAY FUND
CORPORATE AFFILIATIONS

HAWAII DIVERSIFIED INNOVATION FUND, LLC—See Bank of Hawaii Corporation; *U.S. Public*, pg. 273
HAWAII ELECTRIC LIGHT COMPANY, INC.—See Hawaiian Electric Industries, Inc.; *U.S. Public*, pg. 989
HAWAII EMPLOYERS' MUTUAL INSURANCE COMPANY, INC.; *U.S. Private*, pg. 1881
HAWAII ENERGY CONNECTION—See Hercules Capital, Inc.; *U.S. Public*, pg. 1028
HAWAII ENERGY CONNECTION—See Northern Pacific Group; *U.S. Private*, pg. 2954
THE HAWAII FOODBANK; *U.S. Public*, pg. 4043
HAWAII GROWER PRODUCTS, INC.—See J.R. Simplot Company; *U.S. Private*, pg. 2170
HAWAII HEALTH CONNECTOR; *U.S. Private*, pg. 1881
HAWAII HUMAN RESOURCES, INC.—See ProService Hawaii; *U.S. Private*, pg. 3287
HAWAII INFORMATION CONSORTIUM, LLC—See Tyler Technologies, Inc.; *U.S. Public*, pg. 2208
HAWAII INSURANCE CONSULTANTS, LTD.—See Zurich Insurance Group Limited; *Int'l*, pg. 8698
HAWAII LIBRARY BINDERY INC.—See The HF Group LLC; *U.S. Private*, pg. 4052
HAWAII LIFE REAL ESTATE BROKERS; *U.S. Private*, pg. 1881
HAWAII LIFE; *U.S. Private*, pg. 1881
HAWAII MEDICAL SERVICE ASSOCIATION; *U.S. Private*, pg. 1881
HAWAII MEGA-COR., INC.—See Patterson Companies, Inc.; *U.S. Public*, pg. 1653
HAWAII NATIONAL BANCSHARES, INC.; *U.S. Private*, pg. 1881
HAWAII NATIONAL BANK—See Hawaii National Bancshares, Inc.; *U.S. Private*, pg. 1881
HAWAII PACIFIC TELEPORT, LP—See Calian Group Ltd.; *Int'l*, pg. 1264
HAWAII PETROLEUM INC.; *U.S. Private*, pg. 1881
HAWAII PIZZA HUT, INC.—See Grupo Finaccess S.A.P.I. de C.V.; *Int'l*, pg. 3129
HAWAII PLANING MILL LTD.; *U.S. Private*, pg. 1881
HAWAII PRINCE HOTEL WAIKIKI; *U.S. Private*, pg. 1881
HAWAII TOURISM AUSTRALIA PTY LIMITED—See Southern Travel Holdings Limited; *Int'l*, pg. 7121
HAWAII TRANSFER CO. LTD.; *U.S. Private*, pg. 1881
HAWAII TRIBUNE HERALD—See Gannett Co., Inc.; *U.S. Public*, pg. 903
HAWAII VINTAGE CHOCOLATE CO.; *U.S. Public*, pg. 988
HAWAII WATER SERVICE COMPANY—See California Water Service Group; *U.S. Public*, pg. 424
HA WAINWRIGHT (GROUP) LIMITED—See Diploma PLC; *Int'l*, pg. 2128
HAWA MUNTERS CO. LTD.—See Munters AB; *Int'l*, pg. 5093
HAWBAKER ENGINEERING, LLC—See Glenn O. Hawbaker, Inc.; *U.S. Private*, pg. 1710
HAWCO LTD.—See Bay Tree Private Equity LLP; *Int'l*, pg. 901
HAWE FINLAND OY—See HAWE Hydraulik SE; *Int'l*, pg. 3288
HAWE HIDRAULICA, S.L.U.—See HAWE Hydraulik SE; *Int'l*, pg. 3288
HAWE HIDRAVLIKA D.O.O.—See HAWE Hydraulik SE; *Int'l*, pg. 3288
HAWE HOLDING GMBH—See HAWE Hydraulik SE; *Int'l*, pg. 3288
HAWE-HYDRATEC AG—See HAWE Hydraulik SE; *Int'l*, pg. 3288
HAWE HYDRAULICS AUSTRALIA PTY LTD—See HAWE Hydraulik SE; *Int'l*, pg. 3288
HAWE HYDRAULICS PVT. LTD.—See HAWE Hydraulik SE; *Int'l*, pg. 3288
HAWE HYDRAULIK SE; *Int'l*, pg. 3288
HAWE HYDRAULIK SINGAPORE PTE. LTD.—See HAWE Hydraulik SE; *Int'l*, pg. 3288
HAWE ITALIANA S.R.L.—See HAWE Hydraulik SE; *Int'l*, pg. 3288
HAWE JAPAN LTD.—See HAWE Hydraulik SE; *Int'l*, pg. 3288
HAWE KOREA CO., LTD.—See HAWE Hydraulik SE; *Int'l*, pg. 3288
HAWE NORTH AMERICA, INC.—See HAWE Hydraulik SE; *Int'l*, pg. 3288
HAWE OIL-HYDRAULIC TECHNOLOGY (SHANGHAI) CO., LTD.—See HAWE Hydraulik SE; *Int'l*, pg. 3288
HAWE OSTERREICH GMBH—See HAWE Hydraulik SE; *Int'l*, pg. 3288
HAWE-OTELEC S.A.S.—See HAWE Hydraulik SE; *Int'l*, pg. 3288
HAWERA PROBST GMBH—See Robert Bosch GmbH; *Int'l*, pg. 6361
HAWE S.A.; *Int'l*, pg. 3288
HAWES GROUP, LLC—See S.A.I. Leisure Group Company Limited; *Int'l*, pg. 6449
HAWESKO HOLDING AG; *Int'l*, pg. 3288
HAWESTA-FEINKOST HANS WESTPHAL GMBH & CO. KG—See Thai Union Group Public Company Limited; *Int'l*, pg. 7597
HAW HAVELLANDISCHE ABFALLWIRTSCHAFTSGESELLSCHAFT MBH—See Alba SE; *Int'l*, pg. 293
HAWK AUTO GROUP; *U.S. Private*, pg. 1882

HAWKE ASIA PACIFIC PTE. LTD.—See Hubbell Incorporated; *U.S. Public*, pg. 1066
HAWKE INTERNATIONAL—See Hubbell Incorporated; *U.S. Public*, pg. 1066
HAWKE MEDIA, LLC; *U.S. Private*, pg. 1882
HAWKER BEECHCRAFT GLOBAL CUSTOMER SUPPORT, LLC—See Textron Inc.; *U.S. Public*, pg. 2028
HAWKER BRITTON GROUP PTY LIMITED—See WPP plc; *Int'l*, pg. 8462
HAWKER ENERGY, INC.; *U.S. Private*, pg. 1882
HAWKER GMBH—See EnerSys; *U.S. Public*, pg. 767
HAWKER PACIFIC AEROSPACE—See Deutsche Lufthansa AG; *Int'l*, pg. 2070
HAWKER PACIFIC AIRSERVICES LIMITED—See General Dynamics Corporation; *U.S. Public*, pg. 916
HAWKER POWERSOURCE, INC.—See EnerSys; *U.S. Public*, pg. 767
HAWKER RICHARDSON LTD.—See Nylex Limited; *Int'l*, pg. 5500
HAWKER SIDDELEY CANADA INC.—See GVIC Communications Corp.; *Int'l*, pg. 3189
HAWKER SIDDELEY SWITCHGEAR LIMITED TECHNOLOGY CENTRE—See Melrose Industries PLC; *Int'l*, pg. 4813
HAWKER SIDDELEY SWITCHGEAR LTD—See Melrose Industries PLC; *Int'l*, pg. 4813
HAWKER SIDDELEY SWITCHGEAR LTD, SOUTH AMERICA—See Melrose Industries PLC; *Int'l*, pg. 4813
HAWKER SIDDELEY SWITCHGEAR PTY AUSTRALIA—See Melrose Industries PLC; *Int'l*, pg. 4813
HAWKES BAY GLASS & GLAZING LIMITED—See Metro Performance Glass Limited; *Int'l*, pg. 4861
THE HAWKES BAY MOTOR COMPANY LTD.—See The Colonial Motor Company Limited; *Int'l*, pg. 7635
HAWKES MOTORS; *U.S. Private*, pg. 1882
HAWK-E SP. Z O.O.—See Jastrzebska Spolka Weglowa S.A.; *Int'l*, pg. 3913
HAWKEYE CORRUGATED BOX CO.—See Buckeye Corrugated Inc.; *U.S. Private*, pg. 677
HAWKEYE DISTRIBUTION INC.; *U.S. Private*, pg. 1882
HAWKEYE ELECTRONIC SECURITY LTD.; *Int'l*, pg. 3289
HAWKEYE ENERGY HOLDINGS LLC—See Thomas H. Lee Partners, L.P.; *U.S. Private*, pg. 4156
HAWKEYE FFWD—See Hawkeye, Inc.; *U.S. Private*, pg. 1883
HAWKEYE FOREST PRODUCTS INC.; *U.S. Private*, pg. 1882
HAWKEYE GOLD & DIAMOND INC.; *Int'l*, pg. 3289
HAWKEYE, INC.; *U.S. Private*, pg. 1883
HAWKEYE PROPERTIES, INC.; *U.S. Private*, pg. 1882
HAWKEYE—See Hawkeye, Inc.; *U.S. Private*, pg. 1883
HAWKEYE STEEL PRODUCTS, INC. - PRIDE OF THE FARM DIVISION—See Hawkeye Steel Products, Inc.; *U.S. Private*, pg. 1882
HAWKEYE STEEL PRODUCTS, INC.; *U.S. Private*, pg. 1882
HAWKEYE STEEL PRODUCTS, INC. - SPAN-TECH DIVISION—See Hawkeye Steel Products, Inc.; *U.S. Private*, pg. 1883
HAWKEYE SYSTEMS, INC.; *U.S. Public*, pg. 989
HAWKEYE WASTE SYSTEMS, INC.—See Watts Trucking Service, Inc.; *U.S. Private*, pg. 4456
HAWK HOLDING COMPANY, LLC—See KSL Capital Partners, LLC; *U.S. Private*, pg. 2354
HAWK INCENTIVES HOLDINGS LIMITED—See P2 Capital Partners, LLC; *U.S. Private*, pg. 3061
HAWK INCENTIVES HOLDINGS LIMITED—See Silver Lake Group, LLC; *U.S. Private*, pg. 3656
HAWKINS ASSOCIATES INC.; *U.S. Private*, pg. 1883
HAWKINS BUILDING SERVICES OF SAINT LOUIS, LLC—See Hercules Window Cleaning Co.; *U.S. Private*, pg. 1921
HAWKINS CHEVROLET INC.; *U.S. Private*, pg. 1883
HAWKINS CONRAD & CO., PLLC—See BGW CPA, PLLC; *U.S. Private*, pg. 549
HAWKINS CONSTRUCTION COMPANY; *U.S. Private*, pg. 1883
HAWKINS CONSTRUCTION, INC.; *U.S. Private*, pg. 1883
HAWKINS COOKERS LIMITED; *Int'l*, pg. 3289
HAWKINS COUNTY GAS UTILITY DISTRICT; *U.S. Private*, pg. 1883
HAWKINS, INC.; *U.S. Public*, pg. 989
HAWKINSON NISSAN, LLC; *U.S. Private*, pg. 1883
HAWKINS TERMINAL I—See Hawkins, Inc.; *U.S. Public*, pg. 989
HAWKLEY OIL & GAS LIMITED—See Persist Oil And Gas Inc.; *Int'l*, pg. 5818
HAWK MANAGEMENT & FINANCIAL SERVICES INC.; *U.S. Private*, pg. 1882
HAWK RIDGE SYSTEMS, LLC; *U.S. Private*, pg. 1882
HAWKS ACQUISITION CORP.; *U.S. Public*, pg. 989
HAWKSBILL BEACH HOTEL—See Marketing & Reservations International Ltd.; *Int'l*, pg. 4696
HAWK SEARCH, INC.—See Bridgeline Digital, Inc.; *U.S. Public*, pg. 382
HAWKSFORD INTERNATIONAL; *Int'l*, pg. 3289
HAWKSMERE LIMITED—See Graham Holdings Company; *U.S. Public*, pg. 955

HAWKSTONE ASSOCIATES, INC.; *U.S. Private*, pg. 1883
HAWK STREET ACQUISITION CORPORATION; *U.S. Private*, pg. 1882
HAWLEY & HAZEL CHEMICAL CO., (HK) LTD.—See Colgate-Palmolive Company; *U.S. Public*, pg. 532
HAWLEY, LLC; *U.S. Private*, pg. 1883
HAWORTH BUROEINRICHTUNGEN GMBH—See Haworth, Inc.; *U.S. Private*, pg. 1883
HAWORTH FRANCE—See Haworth, Inc.; *U.S. Private*, pg. 1883
HAWORTH GMBH—See Haworth, Inc.; *U.S. Private*, pg. 1883
HAWORTH HONG KONG LTD.—See Haworth, Inc.; *U.S. Private*, pg. 1883
HAWORTH, INC.; *U.S. Private*, pg. 1883
HAWORTH LTD.—See Haworth, Inc.; *U.S. Private*, pg. 1883
HAWORTH MARKETING & MEDIA COMPANY; *U.S. Private*, pg. 1883
HAWORTH MARKETING & MEDIA COMPANY—See Haworth Marketing & Media Company; *U.S. Private*, pg. 1883
HAWORTH PORTUGAL—See Haworth, Inc.; *U.S. Private*, pg. 1883
HAWORTH U.K. LTD.—See Haworth, Inc.; *U.S. Private*, pg. 1883
HAW PAR CORPORATION LIMITED; *Int'l*, pg. 3287
HAW PAR HEALTHCARE LIMITED—See Haw Par Corporation Limited; *Int'l*, pg. 3287
HAW PAR LAND (MALAYSIA) SDN. BHD.—See Haw Par Corporation Limited; *Int'l*, pg. 3287
HAW PAR LAND (M) SDN. BHD.—See Haw Par Corporation Limited; *Int'l*, pg. 3287
HAW PAR LEISURE PTE LTD—See Haw Par Corporation Limited; *Int'l*, pg. 3287
HAW PAR PROPERTIES (SINGAPORE) PRIVATE LIMITED—See Haw Par Corporation Limited; *Int'l*, pg. 3287
HAW PAR SECURITIES (PRIVATE) LIMITED—See Haw Par Corporation Limited; *Int'l*, pg. 3287
HAWS AG—See Haws Corporation; *U.S. Private*, pg. 1884
HAWS AVLIS DO BRASIL—See Haws Corporation; *U.S. Private*, pg. 1884
HAWS CORPORATION; *U.S. Private*, pg. 1883
HAWSGOODWIN INVESTMENT MANAGEMENT, LLC—See Genstar Capital, LLC; *U.S. Private*, pg. 1677
HAWSGOODWIN INVESTMENT MANAGEMENT, LLC—See Keystone Group, L.P.; *U.S. Private*, pg. 2298
HAWS MANUFACTURING PTE. LTD.—See Haws Corporation; *U.S. Private*, pg. 1884
HAWSONS IRON LIMITED; *Int'l*, pg. 3289
HAWTAI MOTOR GROUP LIMITED; *Int'l*, pg. 3289
HAWTHORN BANCSHARES, INC.; *U.S. Public*, pg. 989
HAWTHORN BANK—See Hawthorn Bancshares, Inc.; *U.S. Public*, pg. 989
HAWTHORNE AUTOMOBILE SALES CO.; *U.S. Private*, pg. 1884
HAWTHORNE COAL COMPANY, INC.—See Arch Resources, Inc.; *U.S. Public*, pg. 180
HAWTHORNECOMMONSPLUS, LLC—See Welltower Inc.; *U.S. Public*, pg. 2348
HAWTHORNE CORPORATION—See Moelis Asset Management LP; *U.S. Private*, pg. 2764
HAWTHORNE DIRECT INC.; *U.S. Private*, pg. 1884
HAWTHORNE GLOBAL AVIATION SERVICES, LLC—See Moelis Asset Management LP; *U.S. Private*, pg. 2764
HAWTHORNE LIFT SYSTEMS—See HCI Equity Management, L.P.; *U.S. Private*, pg. 1889
HAWTHORNE MACHINERY COMPANY; *U.S. Private*, pg. 1884
HAWTHORNE PAINT COMPANY, INC.—See SK Capital Partners, LP; *U.S. Private*, pg. 3679
HAWTHORNE POWER SYSTEMS—See Hawthorne Machinery Company; *U.S. Private*, pg. 1884
HAWTHORN KIDNEY CENTER, LLC—See Nautic Partners, LLC; *U.S. Private*, pg. 2870
HAWTHORN LEARNING PTY LTD.—See Navitas Limited; *Int'l*, pg. 5176
HAWTHORN OIL TRANSPORTATION, INC.—See EOG Resources, Inc.; *U.S. Public*, pg. 782
HAWTHORN RESOURCES CORP.; *Int'l*, pg. 3289
HAWTHORN RESOURCES LIMITED; *Int'l*, pg. 3289
HAXC HOLDINGS (BEIJING) CO., LTD.; *Int'l*, pg. 3289
HAYAH INSURANCE COMPANY P.J.S.C—See AXA S.A.; *Int'l*, pg. 759
HAYAKAWA DENSEN KOGYO CO., LTD.; *Int'l*, pg. 3289
HAYAKITA COUNTRY CLUB CO., LTD.—See Meiji Shipping Co., Ltd.; *Int'l*, pg. 4801
HAYAMA BONJOUR CO., LTD.—See Sotetsu Holdings, Inc.; *Int'l*, pg. 7112
HAYAMA INDUSTRIES CO., LTD.—See AOI Electronics Co., Ltd.; *Int'l*, pg. 488
HAYAMIZUDENKI CO., LTD.—See Chudenko Corporation; *Int'l*, pg. 1594
HAYAN PETROLEUM COMPANY—See INA-Industrija Nafte, d.d.; *Int'l*, pg. 3642
HAY APS—See MillerKnoll, Inc.; *U.S. Public*, pg. 1447

HAYASHIBARA CO., LTD.—See Nagase & Co., Ltd.; *Int'l*, pg. 5126
HAYASHI CANADA INC.—See Hayashi Telempu Co., Ltd.; *Int'l*, pg. 3289
HAYASHIKANE SANGYO CO., LTD.; *Int'l*, pg. 3290
HAYASHI KOGYO CO., LTD.—See Sanwa Holdings Corporation; *Int'l*, pg. 6560
HAYASHI LOST-WAX INDUSTRIES CO., LTD.—See Kawakin Holdings Co., Ltd.; *Int'l*, pg. 4094
HAYASHI METAL CORP.—See Alconix Corporation; *Int'l*, pg. 302
HAYASHI SHIPPING, CO., LTD.—See Daicel Corporation; *Int'l*, pg. 1919
HAYASHI TELEMPU CO., LTD. - HAMAMATSU PLANT—See Hayashi Telempu Co., Ltd.; *Int'l*, pg. 3289
HAYASHI TELEMPU CO., LTD. - MAIN PLANT—See Hayashi Telempu Co., Ltd.; *Int'l*, pg. 3289
HAYASHI TELEMPU CO., LTD. - MIZUSHIMA PLANT—See Hayashi Telempu Co., Ltd.; *Int'l*, pg. 3289
HAYASHI TELEMPU CO., LTD. - NAGOYA PLANT—See Hayashi Telempu Co., Ltd.; *Int'l*, pg. 3289
HAYASHI TELEMPU CO., LTD.; *Int'l*, pg. 3289
HAYASHI TELEMPU CO., LTD. - TOYOHASHI PLANT—See Hayashi Telempu Co., Ltd.; *Int'l*, pg. 3289
HAYASHI TELEMPU NORTH AMERICA CORPORATION - ALABAMA PLANT—See Hayashi Telempu Co., Ltd.; *Int'l*, pg. 3289
HAYASHI TELEMPU NORTH AMERICA CORPORATION - KENTUCKY PLANT—See Hayashi Telempu Co., Ltd.; *Int'l*, pg. 3289
HAYASHI TELEMPU NORTH AMERICA CORPORATION - OHIO PLANT—See Hayashi Telempu Co., Ltd.; *Int'l*, pg. 3290
HAYASHI TELEMPU NORTH AMERICA CORPORATION—See Hayashi Telempu Co., Ltd.; *Int'l*, pg. 3289
HAYAT COMMICATIONS COMPANY W.L.L.—See Hayat Communications Co. K.S.C.C.; *Int'l*, pg. 3290
HAYAT COMMICATIONS (MEA) FZCO—See Hayat Communications Co. K.S.C.C.; *Int'l*, pg. 3290
HAYAT COMMUNICATIONS CO. K.S.C.C; *Int'l*, pg. 3290
HAYATELE KANTO CO., LTD.—See Hayashi Telempu Co., Ltd.; *Int'l*, pg. 3290
HAYATELE KYUSHU K.K.—See Hayashi Telempu Co., Ltd.; *Int'l*, pg. 3290
HAYATELE TOUHOKU CO., LTD.—See Hayashi Telempu Co., Ltd.; *Int'l*, pg. 3290
HAYAT PHARMACEUTICAL INDUSTRIES; *Int'l*, pg. 3290
HAYATSUKI ASUKON CO., LTD.—See NIPPON CARBIDE INDUSTRIES CO., INC.; *Int'l*, pg. 5311
HAYATSUKI NAMAKON CO., LTD.—See NIPPON CARBIDE INDUSTRIES CO., INC.; *Int'l*, pg. 5311
HAY CANYON WIND, LLC—See Iberdrola, S.A.; *Int'l*, pg. 3570
HAYCARB HOLDINGS AUSTRALIA (PTY) LTD.—See Hayleys PLC; *Int'l*, pg. 3291
HAYCHEM (BANGLADESH) LTD.—See Hayleys PLC; *Int'l*, pg. 3291
HAYCO MANUFACTURING LTD.; *Int'l*, pg. 3290
HAYDALE CERAMIC TECHNOLOGIES, LLC—See Haydale Graphene Industries plc; *Int'l*, pg. 3290
HAYDALE GRAPHENE INDUSTRIES PLC; *Int'l*, pg. 3290
HAYDALE LTD.—See Haydale Graphene Industries plc; *Int'l*, pg. 3290
HAYDALE TECHNOLOGIES, INC.—See Haydale Graphene Industries plc; *Int'l*, pg. 3290
HAYDALE TECHNOLOGIES KOREA CO., LTD.—See Haydale Graphene Industries plc; *Int'l*, pg. 3290
HAYDALE TECHNOLOGIES THAILAND LTD.—See Haydale Graphene Industries plc; *Int'l*, pg. 3290
HAYDARI CONSTRUCTION COMPANY LIMITED; *Int'l*, pg. 3290
HAYDEN AUTOMOTIVE—See Standard Motor Products, Inc.; *U.S. Public*, pg. 1929
HAYDEN BUILDING MAINTENANCE CORP.; *U.S. Private*, pg. 1884
HAYDEN HOMES INC.; *U.S. Private*, pg. 1884
HAYDOCK CASTER COMPANY—See E.R. Wagner Manufacturing Co.; *U.S. Private*, pg. 1307
HAYDOCY PONTIAC-GMC TRUCK INC.; *U.S. Private*, pg. 1884
HAYDON BUILDING CORP.; *U.S. Private*, pg. 1884
HAYDON KERK MOTION SOLUTIONS, INC.-HAYDON PRODUCTS DIVISION—See AMETEK, Inc.; *U.S. Public*, pg. 116
HAYDON KERK MOTION SOLUTIONS, INC.-KERK PRODUCTS DIVISION—See AMETEK, Inc.; *U.S. Public*, pg. 116
HAYDON LINEAR MOTORS (CHANGZHOU) CO., LTD.—See AMETEK, Inc.; *U.S. Public*, pg. 120
HAYDON MECHANICAL AND ELECTRICAL LIMITED—See Mears Group PLC; *Int'l*, pg. 4763
HAYEL SAEED ANAM & ASSOCIATES WELFARE CORPORATION—See Hayel Saeed Anam Group of Companies; *Int'l*, pg. 3290
HAYEL SAEED ANAM GROUP OF COMPANIES; *Int'l*, pg. 3290
HAYES CHRYSLER PLYMOUTH, INC.; *U.S. Private*, pg. 1884

HAYES CITY CORPORATION; *U.S. Private*, pg. 1884
HAYES DISTRIBUTING, INC.—See Alvarez & Marsal, Inc.; *U.S. Private*, pg. 213
HAYES DISTRIBUTING, INC.—See Highview Capital, LLC; *U.S. Private*, pg. 1942
HAYES E-GOVERNMENT RESOURCES, INC.; *U.S. Private*, pg. 1884
HAYES FORD - LINCOLN MERCURY; *U.S. Private*, pg. 1884
HAYES INDUSTRIES, LTD.—See Enerpac Tool Group Corp.; *U.S. Public*, pg. 765
HAYES & JARVIS (TRAVEL) LIMITED—See TUI AG; *Int'l*, pg. 7968
HAYES LOCUMS LLC; *U.S. Private*, pg. 1884
HAYES & LUNSFORD ELECTRIC, LLC—See Comfort Systems USA, Inc.; *U.S. Public*, pg. 544
HAYES MACHINE COMPANY INC.—See Sacmi Imola S.C.A.R.L.; *Int'l*, pg. 6463
HAYES MANAGEMENT CONSULTING; *U.S. Private*, pg. 1884
HAYES PROPERTY MANAGEMENT CO.; *U.S. Private*, pg. 1884
HAYES PUMP, INC.; *U.S. Private*, pg. 1884
HAYES SOFTWARE SYSTEMS, INC.—See Roper Technologies, Inc.; *U.S. Public*, pg. 1811
HAYES SPECIALTY MACHINING, LTD.—See Enerpac Tool Group Corp.; *U.S. Public*, pg. 765
HAYES WELDING INC.; *U.S. Private*, pg. 1884
HAYFIN CAPITAL MANAGEMENT LLP—See British Columbia Investment Management Corp.; *Int'l*, pg. 1169
HAYGARTH COMMUNICATIONS LIMITED—See Omnicom Group Inc.; *U.S. Public*, pg. 1592
HAY GROUP LIMITADA—See Korn Ferry; *U.S. Public*, pg. 1274
HAY GROUP LLC—See Korn Ferry; *U.S. Public*, pg. 1272
HAY GROUP OY—See Korn Ferry; *U.S. Public*, pg. 1274
HAY GROUP S.A.—See Korn Ferry; *U.S. Public*, pg. 1274
HAY GROUP S.R.O.—See Korn Ferry; *U.S. Public*, pg. 1272
HAY GROUP UAB—See Korn Ferry; *U.S. Public*, pg. 1272
HAY HOUSE, LLC—See Bertelsmann SE & Co. KGaA; *Int'l*, pg. 990
HAY INTERNATIONAL DE GMBH B.V.—See MillerKnoll, Inc.; *U.S. Public*, pg. 1447
HAY ISLAND HOLDING CORPORATION; *U.S. Private*, pg. 1884
HAYLETT AUTO COMPANY, INC.—See Bish's RV, Inc.; *U.S. Private*, pg. 565
HAYLEX B.V.—See Hayleys PLC; *Int'l*, pg. 3292
HAYLEYS ADVANTIS LTD—See Hayleys PLC; *Int'l*, pg. 3292
HAYLEYS AGRICULTURE HOLDINGS LIMITED—See Hayleys PLC; *Int'l*, pg. 3292
HAYLEYS AGRO BIO-TECH (PVT) LTD.—See Hayleys PLC; *Int'l*, pg. 3292
HAYLEYS AGRO FARMS (PVT) LTD.—See Hayleys PLC; *Int'l*, pg. 3292
HAYLEYS AGRO FERTILIZERS (PVT) LTD.—See Hayleys PLC; *Int'l*, pg. 3292
HAYLEYS AGRO PRODUCTS LIMITED—See Hayleys PLC; *Int'l*, pg. 3292
HAYLEYS BUSINESS SOLUTIONS INTERNATIONAL (PVT) LTD.—See Hayleys PLC; *Int'l*, pg. 3292
HAYLEYS CONSUMER PRODUCTS LTD.—See Hayleys PLC; *Int'l*, pg. 3292
HAYLEYS ELECTRONICS LTD—See Hayleys PLC; *Int'l*, pg. 3292
HAYLEYS ENGINEERING LTD—See Hayleys PLC; *Int'l*, pg. 3292
HAYLEYS FABRIC PLC; *Int'l*, pg. 3291
HAYLEYS GROUP SERVICES LTD.—See Hayleys PLC; *Int'l*, pg. 3292
HAYLEYS INDUSTRIAL SOLUTIONS LIMITED—See Hayleys PLC; *Int'l*, pg. 3292
HAYLEYS LEISURE PLC; *Int'l*, pg. 3291
HAYLEYS LIFESCIENCES (PVT) LTD.—See Hayleys PLC; *Int'l*, pg. 3292
HAYLEYS PHOTOPRINT LTD—See Hayleys PLC; *Int'l*, pg. 3292
HAYLEYS PLC; *Int'l*, pg. 3291
HAYLEYS TRAVELS (PVT) LTD.—See Hayleys PLC; *Int'l*, pg. 3292
HAYLIX PTY LIMITED—See WPP plc; *Int'l*, pg. 8462
HAYMAKER ACQUISITION CORP. II—See Haymaker Acquisition Corp.; *U.S. Private*, pg. 1885
HAYMAKER ACQUISITION CORP.; *U.S. Private*, pg. 1885
HAYMAN COMPANY; *U.S. Private*, pg. 1885
HAYMARKET EXHIBITIONS LTD.—See Haymarket Group Limited; *Int'l*, pg. 3292
HAYMARKET GROUP LIMITED; *Int'l*, pg. 3292
HAYMARKET MEDIA ASIA PTE LTD—See Haymarket Group Limited; *Int'l*, pg. 3292
HAYMARKET MEDIA GMBH & CO. KG—See Haymarket Group Limited; *Int'l*, pg. 3292
HAYMARKET MEDIA GROUP LTD.—See Haymarket Group Limited; *Int'l*, pg. 3292
HAYMARKET MEDIA, INC.—See Haymarket Group Limited; *Int'l*, pg. 3293

HAYMARKET MEDIA (INDIA) PVT LTD—See Haymarket Group Limited; *Int'l*, pg. 3292
HAYMARKET MEDIA LIMITED—See Haymarket Group Limited; *Int'l*, pg. 3292
HAYMARKET SURGERY CENTER, LLC—See Tenet Healthcare Corporation; *U.S. Public*, pg. 2002
HAYMARK INC.—See Hayleys PLC; *Int'l*, pg. 3292
HAYNEEDLE, INC.; *U.S. Private*, pg. 1885
HAYNES & BOONE LLP; *U.S. Private*, pg. 1885
HAYNES BROTHERS LUMBER CO. LTD. PARTNER; *U.S. Private*, pg. 1885
HAYNES CORPORATION—See Caterpillar, Inc.; *U.S. Public*, pg. 452
HAYNES-EAGLIN-WATERS, LLP; *U.S. Private*, pg. 1885
HAYNES FURNITURE COMPANY INCORPORATED; *U.S. Private*, pg. 1885
HAYNES FURNITURE COMPANY INC.—See Haynes Furniture Company Incorporated; *U.S. Private*, pg. 1885
HAYNES INTERNATIONAL, AG—See Acerinox, S.A.; *Int'l*, pg. 100
HAYNES INTERNATIONAL (CHINA) LTD.—See Acerinox, S.A.; *Int'l*, pg. 101
HAYNES INTERNATIONAL, INC.—See Acerinox, S.A.; *Int'l*, pg. 100
HAYNES INTERNATIONAL, INC.—See Acerinox, S.A.; *Int'l*, pg. 100
HAYNES INTERNATIONAL K. K.—See Acerinox, S.A.; *Int'l*, pg. 101
HAYNES INTERNATIONAL, LTD.—See Acerinox, S.A.; *Int'l*, pg. 100
HAYNES INTERNATIONAL SARL—See Acerinox, S.A.; *Int'l*, pg. 100
HAYNES INTERNATIONAL S.R.L.—See Acerinox, S.A.; *Int'l*, pg. 100
HAYNES MARKETING NETWORK, INC.; *U.S. Private*, pg. 1885
HAYNES MECHANICAL SYSTEMS; *U.S. Private*, pg. 1885
HAYNES NORTH AMERICA, INC—See Apax Partners LLP; *Int'l*, pg. 502
HAYNES NORTH AMERICA, INC—See TowerBrook Capital Partners, L.P.; *U.S. Private*, pg. 4195
HAYNES PACIFIC PTE LTD—See Acerinox, S.A.; *Int'l*, pg. 101
HAYNES PUBLISHING GROUP PLC—See Apax Partners LLP; *Int'l*, pg. 502
HAYNES PUBLISHING GROUP PLC—See TowerBrook Capital Partners, L.P.; *U.S. Private*, pg. 4195
HAYNES SECURITY INC.; *U.S. Private*, pg. 1885
HAYNES WIRE COMPANY—See Acerinox, S.A.; *Int'l*, pg. 101
HAYNES WIRE ROPE, INC.—See Dot Family Holdings LLC; *U.S. Private*, pg. 1264
HAYNIE INCORPORATED; *U.S. Private*, pg. 1885
HAYS AG—See Hays PLC; *Int'l*, pg. 3293
HAYS BELGIUM NV—See Hays PLC; *Int'l*, pg. 3293
HAYS BUSINESS SOLUTIONS PRIVATE LIMITED—See Hays PLC; *Int'l*, pg. 3293
HAYS BV—See Hays PLC; *Int'l*, pg. 3293
HAYS COLOMBIA SAS—See Hays PLC; *Int'l*, pg. 3293
HAYS COMPANIES INC.—See Brown & Brown, Inc.; *U.S. Public*, pg. 400
HAYS COMPANIES OF NEW JERSEY, INC.—See Brown & Brown, Inc.; *U.S. Public*, pg. 401
HAYS COOLING & HEATING LLC—See Brookfield Corporation; *Int'l*, pg. 1188
HAYS CZECH REPUBLIC, S.R.O.—See Hays PLC; *Int'l*, pg. 3293
HAYS ENERGY LIMITED PARTNERSHIP—See ENGIE SA; *Int'l*, pg. 2433
HAYS EXECUTIVE SASU—See Hays PLC; *Int'l*, pg. 3293
HAYS FLUID CONTROLS—See Romac Industries, Inc.; *U.S. Private*, pg. 3475
HAYS FOOD TOWN INC.; *U.S. Private*, pg. 1885
HAYS FOOD TOWN—See Hays Food Town Inc.; *U.S. Private*, pg. 1885
HAYS FZ-LLC—See Hays PLC; *Int'l*, pg. 3293
HAYS GROUP OF WISCONSIN LLC—See Brown & Brown, Inc.; *U.S. Public*, pg. 401
HAYS HEALTHCARE LIMITED—See Hays PLC; *Int'l*, pg. 3293
HAYS HOLDING GMBH—See Hays PLC; *Int'l*, pg. 3293
HAYS HOLDINGS BV—See Hays PLC; *Int'l*, pg. 3293
HAYS HOLDINGS LIMITED—See Hays PLC; *Int'l*, pg. 3293
HAYS HONG KONG LIMITED—See Hays PLC; *Int'l*, pg. 3293
HAYS HUNGARY KFT—See Hays PLC; *Int'l*, pg. 3293
HAYS INSURANCE BROKERAGE OF NEW ENGLAND, LLC—See Brown & Brown, Inc.; *U.S. Public*, pg. 401
HAYS INTERNATIONAL HOLDINGS LIMITED—See Hays PLC; *Int'l*, pg. 3293
HAYSITE REINFORCED PLASTICS, LLC—See Dunes Point Capital, LLC; *U.S. Private*, pg. 1288
HAYSITE REINFORCED PLASTICS LTD.—See Dunes Point Capital, LLC; *U.S. Private*, pg. 1288
HAYS LIFE SCIENCES UK—See Hays PLC; *Int'l*, pg. 3293
HAYS MEDICAL CENTER; *U.S. Private*, pg. 1885
HAYS NORD EST SASU—See Hays PLC; *Int'l*, pg. 3293

HAYS MEDICAL CENTER   CORPORATE AFFILIATIONS

HAYS OF UTAH INSURANCE SERVICES INC—See Brown & Brown, Inc.; *U.S. Public*, pg. 401
HAYS OSTERREICH GMBH—See Hays PLC; *Int'l*, pg. 3293
HAYS OUEST SASU—See Hays PLC; *Int'l*, pg. 3293
HAYS OVERSEAS HOLDINGS LIMITED—See Hays PLC; *Int'l*, pg. 3293
HAYS OVERSEAS (PORTUGAL) SGPS LDA—See Hays PLC; *Int'l*, pg. 3293
HAYS PERSONNEL ESPANA EMPRESA DE TRABOJO TEMPORAL SA—See Hays PLC; *Int'l*, pg. 3293
HAYS PERSONNEL SERVICES ESPANA SA—See Hays PLC; *Int'l*, pg. 3293
HAYS PLC; *Int'l*, pg. 3293
HAYS POLAND SP Z.O.O—See Hays PLC; *Int'l*, pg. 3293
HAYSP - RECRUTAMENTO, SELECCAO E EMPRESA DE TRABALHO TEMPORARIO, UNIPESSOAL, LDA—See Hays PLC; *Int'l*, pg. 3294
HAYS PROFESSIONAL SOLUTIONS OSTERREICH GMBH—See Hays PLC; *Int'l*, pg. 3293
HAYS RESOURCE MANAGEMENT JAPAN K.K.—See Hays PLC; *Int'l*, pg. 3293
HAYS S.A. DE C.V.—See Hays PLC; *Int'l*, pg. 3293
HAYS S.A.R.L—See Hays PLC; *Int'l*, pg. 3293
HAYS SASU—See Hays PLC; *Int'l*, pg. 3293
HAYS (SCHWEIZ) AG—See Hays PLC; *Int'l*, pg. 3293
HAYSSEN PACKING TECHNOLOGIES, INC.—See Barry-Wehmiller Companies, Inc.; *U.S. Private*, pg. 482
HAYS SERVICES NV—See Hays PLC; *Int'l*, pg. 3293
HAYS SLOVAKIA S.R.O.—See Hays PLC; *Int'l*, pg. 3293
HAYS SOCIAL CARE LIMITED—See Hays PLC; *Int'l*, pg. 3293
HAYS SOLUTIONS S.R.L—See Hays PLC; *Int'l*, pg. 3293
HAYS SPECIALIST RECRUITMENT (AUSTRALIA) PTY LIMITED—See Hays PLC; *Int'l*, pg. 3294
HAYS SPECIALIST RECRUITMENT BELGIUM—See Hays PLC; *Int'l*, pg. 3294
HAYS SPECIALIST RECRUITMENT BRAZIL—See Hays PLC; *Int'l*, pg. 3294
HAYS SPECIALIST RECRUITMENT CANADA—See Hays PLC; *Int'l*, pg. 3294
HAYS SPECIALIST RECRUITMENT DENMARK—See Hays PLC; *Int'l*, pg. 3294
HAYS SPECIALIST RECRUITMENT DUBAI UAE—See Hays PLC; *Int'l*, pg. 3294
HAYS SPECIALIST RECRUITMENT FRANCE—See Hays PLC; *Int'l*, pg. 3294
HAYS SPECIALIST RECRUITMENT (HOLDINGS) LIMITED—See Hays PLC; *Int'l*, pg. 3294
HAYS SPECIALIST RECRUITMENT HONG KONG—See Hays PLC; *Int'l*, pg. 3294
HAYS SPECIALIST RECRUITMENT HUNGARY—See Hays PLC; *Int'l*, pg. 3294
HAYS SPECIALIST RECRUITMENT IRELAND—See Hays PLC; *Int'l*, pg. 3294
HAYS SPECIALIST RECRUITMENT ITALY—See Hays PLC; *Int'l*, pg. 3294
HAYS SPECIALIST RECRUITMENT JAPAN KK—See Hays PLC; *Int'l*, pg. 3294
HAYS SPECIALIST RECRUITMENT LIMITED—See Hays PLC; *Int'l*, pg. 3294
HAYS SPECIALIST RECRUITMENT LUXEMBOURG—See Hays PLC; *Int'l*, pg. 3294
HAYS SPECIALIST RECRUITMENT NETHERLANDS—See Hays PLC; *Int'l*, pg. 3294
HAYS SPECIALIST RECRUITMENT NEW ZEALAND—See Hays PLC; *Int'l*, pg. 3294
HAYS SPECIALIST RECRUITMENT PORTUGAL—See Hays PLC; *Int'l*, pg. 3294
HAYS SPECIALIST RECRUITMENT PRIVATE LIMITED—See Hays PLC; *Int'l*, pg. 3294
HAYS SPECIALIST RECRUITMENT PTE LIMITED—See Hays PLC; *Int'l*, pg. 3294
HAYS SPECIALIST RECRUITMENT (SHANGHAI) CO. LIMITED—See Hays PLC; *Int'l*, pg. 3294
HAYS SPECIALIST RECRUITMENT SPAIN—See Hays PLC; *Int'l*, pg. 3294
HAYS SPECIALIST RECRUITMENT SWEDEN—See Hays PLC; *Int'l*, pg. 3294
HAYS SPECIALIST RECRUITMENT WARSAW—See Hays PLC; *Int'l*, pg. 3294
HAYS S.R.L—See Hays PLC; *Int'l*, pg. 3293
HAYS SUD OUEST SASU—See Hays PLC; *Int'l*, pg. 3294
HAYS (SWITZERLAND) LTD.—See Hays PLC; *Int'l*, pg. 3293
HAYSTACKID LLC—See Quad-C Management, Inc.; *U.S. Private*, pg. 3315
HAYSTACK MOUNTAIN GOAT DAIRY, INC.—See The Stage Fund, LLC; *U.S. Private*, pg. 4120
HAYS TALENT SOLUTIONS ESPANA S.L—See Hays PLC; *Int'l*, pg. 3294
HAYS TALENT SOLUTIONS GMBH—See Hays PLC; *Int'l*, pg. 3294
HAYSTAX TECHNOLOGY, INC.—See Edgewater Services, LLC; *U.S. Private*, pg. 1335
HAYS TECHNOLOGY SOLUTIONS GMBH—See Hays PLC; *Int'l*, pg. 3294
HAYS TECHNOLOGY SOLUTIONS ROMANIA S.R.L.—See Hays PLC; *Int'l*, pg. 3294

HAYS TRAVAIL TEMPORAIRE LUXEMBOURG S.A.R.L—See Hays PLC; *Int'l*, pg. 3294
HAYTER LIMITED—See The Toro Company; *U.S. Public*, pg. 2135
HAYTER OIL COMPANY, INC.; *U.S. Private*, pg. 1885
HAY TOR CAPITAL LLP; *Int'l*, pg. 3289
HAYWARD BAKER INC.—See Keller Group plc; *Int'l*, pg. 4119
HAYWARD GORDON LTD—See Ebara Corporation; *Int'l*, pg. 2284
HAYWARD HOLDINGS, INC.; *U.S. Public*, pg. 990
HAYWARD/IMG—See CCMP Capital Advisors, LP; *U.S. Private*, pg. 800
HAYWARD/IMG—See MSD Capital, L.P.; *U.S. Private*, pg. 2807
HAYWARD INDUSTRIAL PRODUCTS, INC.—See CCMP Capital Advisors, LP; *U.S. Private*, pg. 800
HAYWARD INDUSTRIAL PRODUCTS, INC.—See MSD Capital, L.P.; *U.S. Private*, pg. 2807
HAYWARD INDUSTRIES, INC.—See CCMP Capital Advisors, LP; *U.S. Private*, pg. 800
HAYWARD INDUSTRIES, INC.—See MSD Capital, L.P.; *U.S. Private*, pg. 2807
HAYWARD LABORATORIES—See E.T. Browne Drug Company, Inc.; *U.S. Private*, pg. 1307
HAYWARD POOL EUROPE—See CCMP Capital Advisors, LP; *U.S. Private*, pg. 800
HAYWARD POOL EUROPE—See MSD Capital, L.P.; *U.S. Private*, pg. 2807
HAYWARD POOL PRODUCTS CANADA, INC.—See CCMP Capital Advisors, LP; *U.S. Private*, pg. 800
HAYWARD POOL PRODUCTS CANADA, INC.—See MSD Capital, L.P.; *U.S. Private*, pg. 2807
HAYWARD POOL PRODUCTS, INC.—See CCMP Capital Advisors, LP; *U.S. Private*, pg. 800
HAYWARD POOL PRODUCTS, INC.—See CCMP Capital Advisors, LP; *U.S. Private*, pg. 800
HAYWARD POOL PRODUCTS, INC.—See MSD Capital, L.P.; *U.S. Private*, pg. 2807
HAYWARD POOL PRODUCTS, INC.—See MSD Capital, L.P.; *U.S. Private*, pg. 2807
HAYWARD TYLER FLUID HANDLING LTD—See Avingtrans plc; *Int'l*, pg. 744
HAYWARD TYLER GROUP LIMITED—See Avingtrans plc; *Int'l*, pg. 743
HAYWARD TYLER GROUP PLC—See Avingtrans plc; *Int'l*, pg. 743
HAYWARD TYLER HOLDINGS LIMITED—See Avingtrans plc; *Int'l*, pg. 744
HAYWARD TYLER INC.—See Avingtrans plc; *Int'l*, pg. 744
HAYWARD TYLER INDIA PRIVATE LIMITED—See Avingtrans plc; *Int'l*, pg. 744
HAYWARD TYLER PUMPS (KUNSHAN) CO., LTD—See Avingtrans plc; *Int'l*, pg. 744
HAYWOOD B. HYMAN JR. INC.; *U.S. Private*, pg. 1886
HAYWOOD BUILDERS SUPPLY COMPANY—See Building Industry Partners LLC; *U.S. Private*, pg. 683
HAYWOOD ELECTRIC MEMBERSHIP CORPORATION; *U.S. Private*, pg. 1886
HAZAMA ANDO CORPORATION; *Int'l*, pg. 3294
HAZAMA ANDO THAILAND CO., LTD.—See Hazama Ando Corporation; *Int'l*, pg. 3294
HAZAMA CORPORATION—See Hazama Ando Corporation; *Int'l*, pg. 3294
HAZAMA CORPORATION—See Hazama Ando Corporation; *Int'l*, pg. 3294
HAZAMA KOGYO CO., LTD.—See Hazama Ando Corporation; *Int'l*, pg. 3295
HAZAMA PHILIPPINES, INC.—See Hazama Ando Corporation; *Int'l*, pg. 3295
HAZARA PHOSPHATE FERTILIZERS (PRIVATE) LIMITED—See Azgard Nine Limited; *Int'l*, pg. 778
HAZCHEM LOGISTICS MANAGEMENT CO., LTD.—See Triple i Logistics Public Company Limited; *Int'l*, pg. 7926
HAZCHEM TRANS MANAGEMENT CO., LTD.—See Triple i Logistics Public Company Limited; *Int'l*, pg. 7926
HAZELDEN BETTY FORD FOUNDATION; *U.S. Private*, pg. 1886
HAZELDENE'S CHICKEN FARM PTY. LTD.; *Int'l*, pg. 3295
HAZELDEN/NEW YORK—See Hazelden Betty Ford Foundation; *U.S. Private*, pg. 1886
HAZELDEN—See Hazelden Betty Ford Foundation; *U.S. Private*, pg. 1886
HAZELETT STRIP-CASTING CORP.—See Stave Island Ltd. Partnership; *U.S. Private*, pg. 3794
HAZEL FOLD RESIDENTS MANAGEMENT COMPANY LIMITED—See Bellway plc; *Int'l*, pg. 968
HAZEL LESSEE LLC—See Pebblebrook Hotel Trust; *U.S. Public*, pg. 1660
HAZELNUT GROWERS OF OREGON; *U.S. Private*, pg. 1886
HAZEL'S HOT SHOT, INC.; *U.S. Private*, pg. 1886
HAZELTON DIALYSIS, LLC—See DaVita Inc.; *U.S. Public*, pg. 950
HAZELTREE FUND SERVICES INC—See Bendigo Partners, LLC; *U.S. Private*, pg. 524

HAZELWOOD POWER PARTNERSHIP—See ENGIE SA; *Int'l*, pg. 2432
HAZEN MEMORIAL HOSPITAL ASSOCIATION; *U.S. Private*, pg. 1886
HAZEN PAPER COMPANY; *U.S. Private*, pg. 1886
HAZEN & SAWYER; *U.S. Private*, pg. 1886
HAZEN TRANSPORT INC.—See Storage & Transportation Co., Inc.; *U.S. Private*, pg. 3831
HAZER GROUP LIMITED; *Int'l*, pg. 3295
HAZET BAUUNTERNEHMUNG GMBH—See ALPINE Bau GmbH; *Int'l*, pg. 371
HAZ HOLDINGS, INC.; *U.S. Public*, pg. 990
HAZIRA PORT PRIVATE LIMITED—See Shell plc; *Int'l*, pg. 6795
HAZLEHURST INVESTORS, INC.; *U.S. Private*, pg. 1886
HAZLETON MATERIALS, L.L.C.—See Haines & Kibblehouse Inc.; *U.S. Private*, pg. 1841
HAZLETON SITE CONTRACTORS—See Haines & Kibblehouse Inc.; *U.S. Private*, pg. 1841
HAZLETON STANDARD-SPEAKER INC; *U.S. Private*, pg. 1886
HAZLEWOOD CONVENIENCE FOOD GROUP LIMITED—See Greencore Group plc; *Int'l*, pg. 3074
HAZLEWOOD CONVENIENCE GROUP 1 LIMITED—See Greencore Group plc; *Int'l*, pg. 3074
HAZLEWOOD GROCERY LIMITED—See Greencore Group plc; *Int'l*, pg. 3074
HAZMASTERS INC.—See WESCO International, Inc.; *U.S. Public*, pg. 2351
HAZMAT ENVIRONMENTAL GROUP, INC.; *U.S. Private*, pg. 1886
HAZMATPAC, INC.—See Cleveland Steel Container Corporation; *U.S. Private*, pg. 941
HAZMED INC.; *U.S. Private*, pg. 1886
HAZNEDAR REFRAKTER SANAYII A.S.—See Groupe Bruxelles Lambert SA; *Int'l*, pg. 3100
HAZOOR MULTI PROJECTS LIMITED; *Int'l*, pg. 3295
HAZ-TANK FABRICATORS, INC.—See Johnson Controls International plc; *Int'l*, pg. 3986
HAZTEK, INC.; *U.S. Private*, pg. 1886
HBA HUTCHINSON BRASIL AUTOMOTIVE LTDA.—See TotalEnergies SE; *Int'l*, pg. 7836
HBANCORPORATION INC.; *U.S. Public*, pg. 990
H. BAUER PUBLISHING LTD.—See Heinrich Bauer Verlag KG; *Int'l*, pg. 3323
HBA UNION HOTEL CONSULTANTS LIMITED—See Suzhou Gold Mantis Construction Decoration Co., Ltd.; *Int'l*, pg. 7350
HB BOYS, LLC; *U.S. Private*, pg. 1886
HBC ACQUISITION CORP.; *U.S. Private*, pg. 1886
H.B. CARBIDE COMPANY—See Star Cutter Company; *U.S. Private*, pg. 3784
HB CLARK & CO (SUCCESSORS) LIMITED—See Kitwave Group Plc; *Int'l*, pg. 4196
HB CONSTRUCTION COMPANY LTD.—See The Williams Companies, Inc.; *U.S. Public*, pg. 2142
HBCT (AUST) PTY LTD.—See ST Group Food Industries Holdings Limited; *Int'l*, pg. 7158
HBD CONSTRUCTION, INC.; *U.S. Private*, pg. 1887
H.B.D. CONTRACTING INC.; *U.S. Private*, pg. 1825
H&B DESIGN CO., LTD.; *Int'l*, pg. 3191
HBD INDUSTRIES, INC.; *U.S. Private*, pg. 1887
HBD/THERMOID, INC.—See HBD Industries, Inc.; *U.S. Private*, pg. 1887
HBE ADAM'S RIB—See HBE Corporation; *U.S. Private*, pg. 1887
H. BECK, INC.—See Warburg Pincus LLC; *U.S. Private*, pg. 4439
HBE CORPORATION; *U.S. Private*, pg. 1887
HBE LLP; *U.S. Private*, pg. 1887
H. BENTZ ELECTRONICS LTD.—See ESPEC Corp.; *Int'l*, pg. 2505
HB EQUITY PARTNERS, L.P.; *U.S. Private*, pg. 1886
HB ESTATE DEVELOPERS LTD.; *Int'l*, pg. 3295
H. BETTI INDUSTRIES, INC.; *U.S. Private*, pg. 1824
H.B. FENN AND COMPANY LTD.; *Int'l*, pg. 3195
H&B FERTIGUNGSTECHNIK GMBH—See Wuppermann AG; *Int'l*, pg. 8503
HBF HEALTH LTD.; *Int'l*, pg. 3295
H.B. FRAZER COMPANY; *U.S. Private*, pg. 1825
H.B. FULLER ADHESIVES DEUTSCHLAND GMBH—See H.B. Fuller Company; *U.S. Public*, pg. 977
H.B. FULLER ADHESIVES FRANCE SAS—See H.B. Fuller Company; *U.S. Public*, pg. 977
H.B. FULLER ADHESIVES HONG KONG LIMITED—See H.B. Fuller Company; *U.S. Public*, pg. 977
H.B. FULLER ADHESIVES ITALIA S.P.A.—See H.B. Fuller Company; *U.S. Public*, pg. 977
H.B. FULLER ADHESIVES NETHERLANDS B.V.—See H.B. Fuller Company; *U.S. Public*, pg. 977
H.B. FULLER ADHESIVES ROMANIA SRL—See H.B. Fuller Company; *U.S. Public*, pg. 977
H.B. FULLER ARGENTINA, S.A.I.C—See H.B. Fuller Company; *U.S. Public*, pg. 977
H.B. FULLER BELGIE BVBA—See H.B. Fuller Company; *U.S. Public*, pg. 977
H.B. FULLER CANADA (PARTNERSHIP)—See H.B. Fuller Company; *U.S. Public*, pg. 977

COMPANY NAME INDEX

H.B. FULLER CENTROAMERICA, S.A.—See H.B. Fuller Company; *U.S. Public*, pg. 977
H.B. FULLER CHILE, S.A.—See H.B. Fuller Company; *U.S. Public*, pg. 977
H.B. FULLER (CHINA) ADHESIVES, LTD.—See H.B. Fuller Company; *U.S. Public*, pg. 977
H.B. FULLER COLOMBIA S.A.S.—See H.B. Fuller Company; *U.S. Public*, pg. 977
H.B. FULLER COMPANY AUSTRALIA PTY. LTD.—See H.B. Fuller Company; *U.S. Public*, pg. 977
H.B. FULLER COMPANY; *U.S. Public*, pg. 976
H.B. FULLER CONSTRUCTION PRODUCTS INC. - LA MIRADA—See H.B. Fuller Company; *U.S. Public*, pg. 977
H.B. FULLER CONSTRUCTION PRODUCTS INC.—See H.B. Fuller Company; *U.S. Public*, pg. 977
H.B. FULLER DEUTSCHLAND GMBH—See H.B. Fuller Company; *U.S. Public*, pg. 978
H.B. FULLER DEUTSCHLAND HOLDING GMBH—See H.B. Fuller Company; *U.S. Public*, pg. 977
H.B. FULLER DEUTSCHLAND PRODUKTIONS GMBH—See H.B. Fuller Company; *U.S. Public*, pg. 978
H.B. FULLER ESPANA, S.A.—See H.B. Fuller Company; *U.S. Public*, pg. 978
H.B. FULLER GREECE S.A.I.C.—See H.B. Fuller Company; *U.S. Public*, pg. 978
H.B. FULLER GROUP LIMITED—See H.B. Fuller Company; *U.S. Public*, pg. 978
H.B. FULLER (GUANGZHOU) ADHESIVES CO., LTD—See H.B. Fuller Company; *U.S. Public*, pg. 977
H.B. FULLER HUNGARY KFT.—See H.B. Fuller Company; *U.S. Public*, pg. 978
H.B. FULLER INTERNATIONAL, INC.—See H.B. Fuller Company; *U.S. Public*, pg. 978
H.B. FULLER (NEW ZEALAND) LIMITED—See H.B. Fuller Company; *U.S. Public*, pg. 978
H.B. FULLER PENSION TRUSTEES LIMITED—See H.B. Fuller Company; *U.S. Public*, pg. 978
H.B. FULLER (PHILIPPINES), INC.—See H.B. Fuller Company; *U.S. Public*, pg. 977
H.B. FULLER (PHILS.) INC.—See Filinvest Development Corporation; *Int'l*, pg. 2663
H.B. FULLER POLAND SP.Z.O.O.—See H.B. Fuller Company; *U.S. Public*, pg. 978
H.B. FULLER RUS LTD.—See H.B. Fuller Company; *U.S. Public*, pg. 978
H.B. FULLER (SHANGHAI) CO. LTD.—See H.B. Fuller Company; *U.S. Public*, pg. 977
H.B. FULLER SOUTH AFRICA (PTY) LTD.—See H.B. Fuller Company; *U.S. Public*, pg. 978
H.B. FULLER TAIWAN CO., LTD.—See H.B. Fuller Company; *U.S. Public*, pg. 978
H.B. FULLER (THAILAND) CO.—See H.B. Fuller Company; *U.S. Public*, pg. 977
HB&G BUILDING PRODUCTS, INC.; *U.S. Private*, pg. 1886
HB GLOBAL LIMITED; *Int'l*, pg. 3295
HB GRANDI HF; *Int'l*, pg. 3295
HBI CESKA REPUBLIKA, S.R.O.—See Ratos AB; *Int'l*, pg. 6216
H & B IMMOBILIEN GMBH & CO. OBJEKTE KG—See UniCredit S.p.A.; *Int'l*, pg. 8039
H & B INTERTEX CO., LTD.—See Saha Pathanapibul Public Company Limited; *Int'l*, pg. 6479
HBI POLSKA SP. Z.O.O.—See Ratos AB; *Int'l*, pg. 6217
HBI RECEIVABLES LLC—See Hanesbrands Inc.; *U.S. Public*, pg. 983
HBIS BEIJING INTERNATIONAL TRADE CO., LTD.—See HBIS Group Co., Ltd.; *Int'l*, pg. 3295
HBIS CARBON ASSETS MANAGEMENT CO., LTD.—See HBIS Group Co., Ltd.; *Int'l*, pg. 3295
HBIS COMMERCIAL FACTORING CO., LTD.—See HBIS Group Co., Ltd.; *Int'l*, pg. 3296
HBIS DIGITAL TECHNOLOGY CO., LTD.—See HBIS Group Co., Ltd.; *Int'l*, pg. 3296
HBIS DUFERCO INTERNATIONAL TRADING HOLDING S.A.—See HBIS Group Co., Ltd.; *Int'l*, pg. 3296
HBIS FINANCIAL LEASING CO., LTD.—See HBIS Group Co., Ltd.; *Int'l*, pg. 3296
HBIS GROUP CHENGDE IRON & STEEL COMPANY—See HBIS Group Co., Ltd.; *Int'l*, pg. 3296
HBIS GROUP CO., LTD.; *Int'l*, pg. 3295
HBIS GROUP ELECTRICITY SALES CO., LTD.—See HBIS Group Co., Ltd.; *Int'l*, pg. 3296
HBIS GROUP FINANCE CO., LTD.—See HBIS Group Co., Ltd.; *Int'l*, pg. 3296
HBIS GROUP FINANCIAL MANAGEMENT CLOUD TECHNOLOGY CO., LTD.—See HBIS Group Co., Ltd.; *Int'l*, pg. 3296
HBIS GROUP HANDAN IRON & STEEL COMPANY—See HBIS Group Co., Ltd.; *Int'l*, pg. 3296
HBIS GROUP HENGSTRIP COMPANY—See HBIS Group Co., Ltd.; *Int'l*, pg. 3296
HBIS GROUP INVESTMENT HOLDING CO., LTD.—See HBIS Group Co., Ltd.; *Int'l*, pg. 3296
HBIS GROUP PURCHASING CORPORATION—See HBIS Group Co., Ltd.; *Int'l*, pg. 3296
HBIS GROUP SALES CORPORATION—See HBIS Group Co., Ltd.; *Int'l*, pg. 3296
HBIS GROUP SHIJIAZHUANG IRON & STEEL COMPANY—See HBIS Group Co., Ltd.; *Int'l*, pg. 3296
HBIS GROUP SUPPLY CHAIN MANAGEMENT CO., LTD.—See HBIS Group Co., Ltd.; *Int'l*, pg. 3296
HBIS GROUP TANGSHAN IRON & STEEL COMPANY—See HBIS Group Co., Ltd.; *Int'l*, pg. 3296
HBIS GROUP WUYANG IRON & STEEL COMPANY—See HBIS Group Co., Ltd.; *Int'l*, pg. 3296
HBIS GROUP XUANHUA CONSTRUCTION MACHINERY CO., LTD.—See HBIS Group Co., Ltd.; *Int'l*, pg. 3296
HBIS GROUP XUANHUA IRON & STEEL COMPANY—See HBIS Group Co., Ltd.; *Int'l*, pg. 3296
HBIS INDUSTRIAL TECHNOLOGY SERVICE CO., LTD.—See HBIS Group Co., Ltd.; *Int'l*, pg. 3296
HBIS LIMITED—See HBIS Group Co., Ltd.; *Int'l*, pg. 3296
HBIS MINING—See HBIS Group Co., Ltd.; *Int'l*, pg. 3296
HBIS RESOURCES CO., LTD.; *Int'l*, pg. 3296
HBIS SALES CO. LTD.—See HBIS Group Co., Ltd.; *Int'l*, pg. 3296
HBIS SERBIA IRON & STEEL D.O.O.—See HBIS Group Co., Ltd.; *Int'l*, pg. 3296
HBIS SERBIA LTD.—See HBIS Group Co., Ltd.; *Int'l*, pg. 3296
HBI TITLE SERVICES, INC.—See Huntington Bancshares Incorporated; *U.S. Public*, pg. 1071
HBK CPAS & CONSULTANTS—See Hill, Barth & King LLC; *U.S. Private*, pg. 1945
HBK ENGINEERING, LLC—See Quanta Services, Inc.; *U.S. Public*, pg. 1751
HBL ASSET MANAGEMENT LIMITED—See Habib Bank Limited; *Int'l*, pg. 3202
HB LEASING & FINANCE COMPANY LIMITED; *Int'l*, pg. 3295
HBL GERMANY GMBH—See HBL Power Systems Ltd.; *Int'l*, pg. 3296
HBL HOLDING GMBH—See Mechel PAO; *Int'l*, pg. 4766
HBL HONG KONG LTD.—See HBL Power Systems Ltd.; *Int'l*, pg. 3296
HBL, LLC—See Penske Automotive Group, Inc.; *U.S. Public*, pg. 1665
HBL, LTD.—See Herbalife Nutrition Ltd.; *Int'l*, pg. 3359
HBL POWER SYSTEMS LTD.; *Int'l*, pg. 3296
HBL PRODUCTS S.A.—See Herbalife Nutrition Ltd.; *Int'l*, pg. 3359
HBMA HOLDINGS LLC—See Heidelberg Materials AG; *Int'l*, pg. 3310
HB MANAGEMENT GROUP, INC.; *U.S. Private*, pg. 1886
HB MANAGEMENT LLC; *U.S. Private*, pg. 1886
H.B. MCCLURE COMPANY; *U.S. Private*, pg. 1825
HBM DANMARK APS—See Spectris Plc; *Int'l*, pg. 7130
H.B. MELLOTT ESTATE, INC.; *U.S. Private*, pg. 1825
HBM FIBERSENSING SA—See Spectris Plc; *Int'l*, pg. 7130
HBM FRANCE SAS—See Spectris Plc; *Int'l*, pg. 7130
HBM HEALTHCARE INVESTMENTS AG; *Int'l*, pg. 3296
HBM HEALTHCARE INVESTMENTS (CAYMAN) LTD.—See HBM Healthcare Investments AG; *Int'l*, pg. 3296
HBM HOLDINGS COMPANY; *U.S. Private*, pg. 1887
HBM IBERICA, S. L.U.—See Spectris Plc; *Int'l*, pg. 7130
HBM ITALIA S.R.L.—See Spectris Plc; *Int'l*, pg. 7131
HBM LTD.—See VINCI S.A.; *Int'l*, pg. 8232
HBM NCODE FEDERAL LLC—See Spectris Plc; *Int'l*, pg. 7131
HBM NORGE AS—See Spectris Plc; *Int'l*, pg. 7131
HBM PARTNERS LTD.—See HBM Healthcare Investments AG; *Int'l*, pg. 3297
HBM PHARMA S.R.O.—See GRINDEKS AS; *Int'l*, pg. 3086
HBM PRENSCIA INC.—See Spectris Plc; *Int'l*, pg. 7130
HBM PRENSCIA PTE. LTD.—See Spectris Plc; *Int'l*, pg. 7130
HBM PRENSCIA S.P. Z.O.O.—See Spectris Plc; *Int'l*, pg. 7130
HB&M SPORTS, INC.—See Harris, Baio & McCullough Inc.; *U.S. Private*, pg. 1870
HBM UNITED KINGDOM LIMITED—See Spectris Plc; *Int'l*, pg. 7131
HB NETWORK SOLUTIONS, INC.—See The Innovation Institute; *U.S. Private*, pg. 4056
HBO ENTERTAINMENT—See Warner Bros. Discovery, Inc.; *U.S. Public*, pg. 2327
HBO EUROPE HOLDINGS, INC.—See Warner Bros. Discovery, Inc.; *U.S. Public*, pg. 2327
HBO FILMS—See Warner Bros. Discovery, Inc.; *U.S. Public*, pg. 2327
HBOIL JSC; *Int'l*, pg. 3297
HBO INTERNATIONAL DISTRIBUTION—See Warner Bros. Discovery, Inc.; *U.S. Public*, pg. 2327
HBO INTERNATIONAL—See Warner Bros. Discovery, Inc.; *U.S. Public*, pg. 2327
HBO LATIN AMERICA MEDIA SERVICES, INC.—See Warner Bros. Discovery, Inc.; *U.S. Public*, pg. 2327
HBO SERVICES, INC.—See Warner Bros. Discovery, Inc.; *U.S. Public*, pg. 2327
HBOS INSURANCE & INVESTMENT GROUP LIMITED—See Lloyds Banking Group plc; *Int'l*, pg. 4537
HBOS INVESTMENT FUND MANAGERS LIMITED—See Lloyds Banking Group plc; *Int'l*, pg. 4537
HBOS PLC—See Lloyds Banking Group plc; *Int'l*, pg. 4536
HBO SPORTS—See Warner Bros. Discovery, Inc.; *U.S. Public*, pg. 2327
HBO VIDEO—See Warner Bros. Discovery, Inc.; *U.S. Public*, pg. 2327
HBP ENERGY CORP.; *Int'l*, pg. 3297
HBP, INC.; *U.S. Private*, pg. 1887
HBP OF SAN DIEGO, INC.—See Konica Minolta, Inc.; *Int'l*, pg. 4258
HBPO GMBH—See Burelle S.A.; *Int'l*, pg. 1222
HB PORTFOLIO LTD.; *Int'l*, pg. 3295
HBR CONSULTING LLC; *U.S. Private*, pg. 1888
H.B. REESE CANDY CO.—See The Hershey Co.; *U.S. Public*, pg. 2088
H.B. RENTALS, L.C.—See Superior Energy Services, Inc.; *U.S. Private*, pg. 3877
HB RENTALS LIMITED—See Superior Energy Services, Inc.; *U.S. Private*, pg. 3877
HB RENTALS—See Superior Energy Services, Inc.; *U.S. Private*, pg. 3877
H. BRUCE AND SONS INC.; *U.S. Private*, pg. 1824
H. BRUNNER GMBH—See Chequers SA; *Int'l*, pg. 1471
H.B. SMITH CO., INC.; *U.S. Private*, pg. 1825
HB SOLUTION CO., LTD.; *Int'l*, pg. 3295
HB SOLUTION CO., LTD.; *Int'l*, pg. 3295
HBS REALTORS PVT. LTD.; *Int'l*, pg. 3297
H.B. S.R.L.—See Dana Incorporated; *U.S. Public*, pg. 623
HBS SYSTEMS, INC.; *U.S. Private*, pg. 1888
HBS STOCKHOLDINGS LIMITED; *Int'l*, pg. 3295
H&B STORES LTD.—See Dabur India Ltd; *Int'l*, pg. 1903
H.B. STUBBS COMPANY; *U.S. Private*, pg. 1825
HB SVENSKA DAGBLADETS AB & CO—See Schibsted ASA; *Int'l*, pg. 6616
HB TECHNOLOGY INC. - CHEONAN-SI PLANT—See HB Technology Inc.; *Int'l*, pg. 3295
HB TECHNOLOGY INC.; *Int'l*, pg. 3295
HBT FINANCIAL, INC.; *U.S. Public*, pg. 990
HBV HOLDING UND BETEILIGUNGSVERWALTUNG GMBH—See BAWAG Group AG; *Int'l*, pg. 900
H.B. WHITE CANADA CORP.—See MasTec, Inc.; *U.S. Public*, pg. 1393
HCA FLORIDA WEST TAMPA HOSPITAL—See HCA Healthcare, Inc.; *U.S. Public*, pg. 997
HCA GULF COAST DIVISION—See HCA Healthcare, Inc.; *U.S. Public*, pg. 997
HCA HEALTHCARE, INC.; *U.S. Public*, pg. 990
HCA HEALTHCARE MISSION FUND, LLC—See HCA Healthcare, Inc.; *U.S. Public*, pg. 997
HCA HEALTHCARE UK LIMITED—See HCA Healthcare, Inc.; *U.S. Public*, pg. 998
HCA-HEALTHONE, LLC—See HCA Healthcare, Inc.; *U.S. Public*, pg. 998
HCA HEALTH SERVICES OF OKLAHOMA, INC.—See HCA Healthcare, Inc.; *U.S. Public*, pg. 997
HCA HEALTH SERVICES OF TENNESSEE, INC.—See HCA Healthcare, Inc.; *U.S. Public*, pg. 997
HCA HEALTH SERVICES OF VIRGINIA—See HCA Healthcare, Inc.; *U.S. Public*, pg. 997
HCA HOUSTON ER 24/7 - CYPRESS FAIRBANKS—See HCA Healthcare, Inc.; *U.S. Public*, pg. 998
HCA HOUSTON HEALTHCARE-MAINLAND—See HCA Healthcare, Inc.; *U.S. Public*, pg. 998
HCA HOUSTON HEALTHCARE - SOUTHEAST—See HCA Healthcare, Inc.; *U.S. Public*, pg. 998
HCA HOUSTON HEALTHCARE TOMBALL—See HCA Healthcare, Inc.; *U.S. Public*, pg. 998
HCA HOUSTON HEALTHCARE WEST—See HCA Healthcare, Inc.; *U.S. Public*, pg. 998
HCA INTERNATIONAL HOLDINGS LIMITED—See HCA Healthcare, Inc.; *U.S. Public*, pg. 998
HCA INTERNATIONAL LIMITED—See HCA Healthcare, Inc.; *U.S. Public*, pg. 998
H&C ANIMAL HEALTH, LLC; *U.S. Private*, pg. 1822
HCAP PARTNERS, LLC; *U.S. Private*, pg. 1888
HCA - RALEIGH COMMUNITY HOSPITAL, INC.—See HCA Healthcare, Inc.; *U.S. Public*, pg. 997
HCA RICHMOND CARDIAC CLINICAL CO-MANAGEMENT COMPANY, LLC—See HCA Healthcare, Inc.; *U.S. Public*, pg. 998
H. CARR & SONS INC.; *U.S. Private*, pg. 1824
HC ASIA HOLDING GMBH—See Heidelberg Materials AG; *Int'l*, pg. 3310
HCAS THAI TRADING CO., LTD.—See Proterial, Ltd.; *Int'l*, pg. 6005
HCA SWITZERLAND FINANCE GMBH—See HCA Healthcare, Inc.; *U.S. Public*, pg. 998
HC AURORA, LLC—See PENN Entertainment, Inc.; *U.S. Public*, pg. 1662
HC BANGOR, LLC—See PENN Entertainment, Inc.; *U.S. Public*, pg. 1662
HC BERLIN PHARMA AG; *Int'l*, pg. 3297
HC BETONS SIA—See Heidelberg Materials AG; *Int'l*, pg. 3310

HC BETOON AS—See Heidelberg Materials AG; *Int'l*, pg. 3310
H.C.B. FINANCIAL CORP.; *U.S. Public*, pg. 978
HC&B HEALTHCARE COMMUNICATIONS INC.; *U.S. Private*, pg. 1888
HCB HEALTH CHICAGO—See HC&B Healthcare Communications Inc.; *U.S. Private*, pg. 1888
HCB HOSPITALITY COMPETENCE BERLIN GMBH—See MRP Consult GmbH; *Int'l*, pg. 5064
HC BRANDS; *U.S. Private*, pg. 1888
HCB TECHNOLOGIES LIMITED—See Bapcor Limited; *Int'l*, pg. 857
HCC AEGIS INC.—See AMETEK, Inc.; *U.S. Public*, pg. 116
HCC CASUALTY INSURANCE SERVICES, INC.—See Tokio Marine Holdings, Inc.; *Int'l*, pg. 7783
HCC CREDIT GROUP, INC.—See Tokio Marine Holdings, Inc.; *Int'l*, pg. 7783
HCC GLOBAL FINANCIAL PRODUCTS LLC—See Tokio Marine Holdings, Inc.; *Int'l*, pg. 7783
HCC HANSEATIC CRUISE CENTERS GMBH—See Hamburger Hafen und Logistik AG; *Int'l*, pg. 3236
HCC, INC.; *U.S. Private*, pg. 1888
HCC INC.—See Taiheiyo Kouhatsu Incorporated; *Int'l*, pg. 7412
HCC INDEMNITY GUARANTY AGENCY, INC.—See Tokio Marine Holdings, Inc.; *Int'l*, pg. 7783
HCC INDUSTRIES INTERNATIONAL—See AMETEK, Inc.; *U.S. Public*, pg. 116
HCC INDUSTRIES INTERNATIONAL—See AMETEK, Inc.; *U.S. Public*, pg. 116
HCC INDUSTRIES INTERNATIONAL—See Windward Capital Partners LP; *U.S. Private*, pg. 4539
HCC INSURANCE HOLDINGS, INC.—See Tokio Marine Holdings, Inc.; *Int'l*, pg. 7783
HCC INTERNATIONAL INSURANCE COMPANY PLC—See Tokio Marine Holdings, Inc.; *Int'l*, pg. 7783
HCC LIFE INSURANCE COMPANY—See Tokio Marine Holdings, Inc.; *Int'l*, pg. 7783
HCC MEDICAL INSURANCE SERVICES, LLC—See Tokio Marine Holdings, Inc.; *Int'l*, pg. 7784
THE HC COMPANIES, INC.—See Platinum Equity, LLC; *U.S. Private*, pg. 3207
HCC PUBLIC RISK CLAIM SERVICE, INC.—See Tokio Marine Holdings, Inc.; *Int'l*, pg. 7784
HCCR HAMBURGER CONTAINER- UND CHASSIS-REPARATUR-GESELLSCHAFT MBH—See Hamburger Hafen und Logistik AG; *Int'l*, pg. 3236
HCC RISK MANAGEMENT CORPORATION—See Tokio Marine Holdings, Inc.; *Int'l*, pg. 7784
HCC SPECIALTY UNDERWRITERS, INC.—See Tokio Marine Holdings, Inc.; *Int'l*, pg. 7784
HCC SURETY GROUP; *U.S. Private*, pg. 1888
HCC UNDERWRITING AGENCY LTD.—See Tokio Marine Holdings, Inc.; *Int'l*, pg. 7784
HCD INVESTMENT PRODUCING & TRADING JOINT STOCK CO; *Int'l*, pg. 3297
HC DURACLEAN SDN. BHD.—See Damansara Realty Berhad; *Int'l*, pg. 1955
H. CEGIELSKI - POZNAN S.A.; *Int'l*, pg. 3194
HC ENERGIA—See EDP - Energias de Portugal, S.A.; *Int'l*, pg. 2314
HCENTIVE, INC.—See UnitedHealth Group Incorporated; *U.S. Public*, pg. 2253
HCF HOLDINGS INC.—See Big Fresh Media, Inc.; *U.S. Private*, pg. 553
HC FINANCIAL ADVISORS INC.—See The Mather Group, LLC; *U.S. Private*, pg. 4075
HC FORKLIFT AMERICA CORPORATION—See GreatStar Group Co., Ltd.; *Int'l*, pg. 3067
HCFS HEALTH CARE FINANCIAL SERVICES, LLC—See Blackstone Inc.; *U.S. Public*, pg. 359
HCFS, INC.—See ABRY Partners, LLC; *U.S. Private*, pg. 41
HCG EKO ONCOLOGY LLP—See Healthcare Global Enterprises Limited; *Int'l*, pg. 3304
HCG ENERGY CORPORATION; *U.S. Private*, pg. 1888
HCGI HARTFORD—See Avnet, Inc.; *U.S. Public*, pg. 253
HC GROUP, INC.; *Int'l*, pg. 3297
HC GROUP SEARCH INC.—See HC Group, Inc.; *Int'l*, pg. 3297
HC GROUP SEARCH LTD.—See HC Group, Inc.; *Int'l*, pg. 3297
HC GROUP SEARCH PTE. LTD.—See HC Group, Inc.; *Int'l*, pg. 3297
HCG TECHNOLOGIES INC.; *U.S. Private*, pg. 1888
HCH BEARING AMERICAS—See China Huanchi Bearing Group Co., Ltd.; *Int'l*, pg. 1509
HCH BEARING GERMANY GMBH—See China Huanchi Bearing Group Co., Ltd.; *Int'l*, pg. 1509
HCH BEARING ITALY SRL—See China Huanchi Bearing Group Co., Ltd.; *Int'l*, pg. 1509
H&C HEADWEAR-ATLANTA CAPCO SPORTSWEAR—See H&C Headwear Inc.; *U.S. Private*, pg. 1822
H&C HEADWEAR-CHICAGO—See H&C Headwear Inc.; *U.S. Private*, pg. 1822
H&C HEADWEAR-DALLAS—See H&C Headwear Inc.; *U.S. Private*, pg. 1822

H&C HEADWEAR INC.; *U.S. Private*, pg. 1822
H&C HEADWEAR-NEW YORK—See H&C Headwear Inc.; *U.S. Private*, pg. 1822
HCH. KETTELHACK GMBH & CO. KG; *Int'l*, pg. 3297
HC HOODCO, INC.—See Platinum Equity, LLC; *U.S. Private*, pg. 3208
H.C. HOSPITAL CONSULTING S.P.A.—See Fresenius SE & Co. KGaA; *Int'l*, pg. 2778
HCI ASSET GMBH—See Ernst Russ AG; *Int'l*, pg. 2495
HCI CARE SERVICES; *U.S. Private*, pg. 1888
HCI CENTRAL EUROPE HOLDING B.V.—See BRENNTAG SE; *Int'l*, pg. 1149
H.C.I. CHEMICALS NEDERLAND B.V.—See BRENNTAG SE; *Int'l*, pg. 1149
HCI CHEMTEC, INC.; *U.S. Private*, pg. 1888
HCI EQUITY MANAGEMENT, L.P.; *U.S. Private*, pg. 1888
HCI GROUP, INC.; *U.S. Public*, pg. 1014
HCI HAMMONIA SHIPPING AG; *Int'l*, pg. 3297
HCI HANSEATISCHE CAPITALBERATUNGSGESELLSCHAFT FUR BETEILIGUNGSKAPITAL MBH—See Ernst Russ AG; *Int'l*, pg. 2495
HCI HANSEATISCHE CAPITALBERATUNGSGESELLSCHAFT MBH—See Ernst Russ AG; *Int'l*, pg. 2495
HCI HANSEATISCHE CAPITALBERATUNGSGESELLSCHAFT MBH—See Ernst Russ AG; *Int'l*, pg. 2495
HCI HANSEATISCHE IMMOBILIENBETEILIGUNGSGESELLSCHAFT MBH—See Ernst Russ AG; *Int'l*, pg. 2495
HCI HANSEATISCHE SCHIFFSCONSULT GMBH—See Ernst Russ AG; *Int'l*, pg. 2495
HCI HOLLAND COATINGS INDUSTRIES—See 3G Capital Partners L.P.; *U.S. Private*, pg. 11
HCI IMMOBILIEN GESCHAFTSFUHRUNGSGESELLSCHAFT MBH—See Ernst Russ AG; *Int'l*, pg. 2495
HCI INSTITUTIONAL FUNDS GMBH—See Ernst Russ AG; *Int'l*, pg. 2495
HCI INVEST 3 HOLDCO PROPRIETARY LIMITED—See E Media Holdings Limited; *Int'l*, pg. 2246
HCI KHUSELA COAL (PROPRIETARY) LIMITED—See Hosken Consolidated Investments Limited; *Int'l*, pg. 3485
H. CILLEKENS & B.V.—See dormakaba Holding AG; *Int'l*, pg. 2179
HC INTERNATIONAL HOLDINGS, INC—See InterContinental Hotels Group PLC; *Int'l*, pg. 3737
HC INTERNATIONAL; *U.S. Private*, pg. 1888
HCI REAL ESTATE FINANCE I GMBH & CO. KG—See Ernst Russ AG; *Int'l*, pg. 2496
HCI SOLUTIONS LTD.—See CSL Limited; *Int'l*, pg. 1866
HCI ITALIA SRL—See Heidelberg Materials AG; *Int'l*, pg. 3310
HCI TREUHAND GMBH—See Ernst Russ AG; *Int'l*, pg. 2496
HCK2 PARTNERS; *U.S. Private*, pg. 1889
HCK CAPITAL GROUP BERHAD; *Int'l*, pg. 3297
HCK COMMUNICATIONS SDN. BHD.—See HCK Capital Group Berhad; *Int'l*, pg. 3297
HCKP B.V.—See SIG plc; *Int'l*, pg. 6906
H.C. LA MARCHE ENTERPRISES; *U.S. Private*, pg. 1825
HCL AMERICA, INC.—See HCL Technologies Ltd.; *Int'l*, pg. 3298
HCL AMERICA, INC.—See HCL Technologies Ltd.; *Int'l*, pg. 3298
HC LAND COMPANY L.C.—See The ODP Corporation; *U.S. Public*, pg. 2117
HC LANGUAGE SOLUTIONS, INC.—See Honyaku Center Inc.; *Int'l*, pg. 3472
HCL ARGENTINA S.A.—See HCL Technologies Ltd.; *Int'l*, pg. 3298
H CLARKSON & COMPANY LIMITED—See Clarkson PLC; *Int'l*, pg. 1651
HCL AUSTRALIA SERVICES PTY. LTD.—See HCL Technologies Ltd.; *Int'l*, pg. 3298
HCL AUSTRALIA SERVICES PTY. LTD.—See HCL Technologies Ltd.; *Int'l*, pg. 3298
HCL AVITAS PRIVATE LIMITED—See HCL Infosystems Limited; *Int'l*, pg. 3297
HCL AXON (PTY) LTD.—See HCL Technologies Ltd.; *Int'l*, pg. 3298
HCL BBL MEDICAL LIMITED—See Ares Management Corporation; *U.S. Public*, pg. 188
HCL BBL MEDICAL LIMITED—See Old Oak Holdings Limited; *Int'l*, pg. 5552
HCL BERMUDA LIMITED—See HCL Technologies Ltd.; *Int'l*, pg. 3298
HCL BPO SERVICES (NI) LIMITED—See HCL Technologies Ltd.; *Int'l*, pg. 3298
HCL CLIENT/SERVER APPLICATIONS DIVISION—See HCL Technologies Ltd.; *Int'l*, pg. 3298
HCL COMNET LIMITED—See HCL Infosystems Limited; *Int'l*, pg. 3297
HCL COMNET SYSTEMS AND SERVICES LIMITED—See HCL Infosystems Limited; *Int'l*, pg. 3297
HCL CORE TECHNOLOGIES DIVISION—See HCL Technologies Ltd.; *Int'l*, pg. 3298
HCL EAS LIMITED—See HCL Technologies Ltd.; *Int'l*, pg. 3298
H&C, LEO BURNETT—See Publicis Groupe S.A.; *Int'l*, pg. 6100

H. CLEVELAND AND CO., LTD.—See Kamei Corporation; *Int'l*, pg. 4061
H.C. LEWIS OIL COMPANY INC.; *U.S. Private*, pg. 1825
HCL EXPENSE MANAGEMENT SERVICES INC.—See HCL Technologies Ltd.; *Int'l*, pg. 3298
HCL GPS LIMITED—See Ares Management Corporation; *U.S. Public*, pg. 188
HCL GPS LIMITED—See Old Oak Holdings Limited; *Int'l*, pg. 5552
HCL GREAT BRITAIN LTD.—See HCL Technologies Ltd.; *Int'l*, pg. 3298
HCL HEALTHCARE LIMITED—See Ares Management Corporation; *U.S. Public*, pg. 188
HCL HEALTHCARE LIMITED—See Old Oak Holdings Limited; *Int'l*, pg. 5552
HCL HONG KONG SAR LTD.—See HCL Technologies Ltd.; *Int'l*, pg. 3298
HCL INFOSYSTEMS LIMITED; *Int'l*, pg. 3297
HCL INFOSYSTEMS MEA FZE—See Pacific Century Group Holdings Limited; *Int'l*, pg. 5687
HCL INSURANCE BPO SERVICES LTD.—See HCL Technologies Ltd.; *Int'l*, pg. 3298
HCL INSYS PTE LIMITED—See Pacific Century Group Holdings Limited; *Int'l*, pg. 5687
HCL JAPAN LTD.—See HCL Technologies Ltd.; *Int'l*, pg. 3299
HCL LEARNING LIMITED—See HCL Infosystems Limited; *Int'l*, pg. 3297
HCL NETHERLANDS B.V.—See HCL Technologies Ltd.; *Int'l*, pg. 3299
HCL NETWORKING PRODUCTS DIVISION—See HCL Technologies Ltd.; *Int'l*, pg. 3299
HCL NEW ZEALAND LTD.—See HCL Technologies Ltd.; *Int'l*, pg. 3298
HCL NEW ZEALAND LTD.—See HCL Technologies Ltd.; *Int'l*, pg. 3298
HCL POLAND SP.Z.O.O.—See HCL Technologies Ltd.; *Int'l*, pg. 3299
HCL SAFETY LIMITED—See MSA Safety Incorporated; *U.S. Public*, pg. 1481
HCL SERVICES LIMITED—See HCL Infosystems Limited; *Int'l*, pg. 3297
HCL TALENT CARE PRIVATE LIMITED—See HCL Infosystems Limited; *Int'l*, pg. 3297
HCL TECHNOLOGIES BELGIUM SA/NV—See HCL Technologies Ltd.; *Int'l*, pg. 3298
HCL TECHNOLOGIES BPO SERVICES LTD—See HCL Technologies Ltd.; *Int'l*, pg. 3299
HCL TECHNOLOGIES DENMARK APS.—See HCL Technologies Ltd.; *Int'l*, pg. 3299
HCL TECHNOLOGIES EUROPE LTD.—See HCL Technologies Ltd.; *Int'l*, pg. 3299
HCL TECHNOLOGIES GMBH—See HCL Technologies Ltd.; *Int'l*, pg. 3299
HCL TECHNOLOGIES LTD.; *Int'l*, pg. 3298
HCL TECHNOLOGIES (MASS) INC.—See HCL Technologies Ltd.; *Int'l*, pg. 3298
HCL TECHNOLOGIES NORWAY AS—See HCL Technologies Ltd.; *Int'l*, pg. 3299
HCL TECHNOLOGIES (SHANGHAI) LIMITED—See HCL Technologies Ltd.; *Int'l*, pg. 3299
HCL TECHNOLOGIES (SINGAPORE) LTD.—See HCL Technologies Ltd.; *Int'l*, pg. 3299
HCL TECHNOLOGIES SWEDEN AB—See HCL Technologies Ltd.; *Int'l*, pg. 3299
HCL THAMES MEDICS LIMITED—See Ares Management Corporation; *U.S. Public*, pg. 188
HCL THAMES MEDICS LIMITED—See Old Oak Holdings Limited; *Int'l*, pg. 5552
HCL TOUCH INC.—See HCL Infosystems Limited; *Int'l*, pg. 3297
HCM ACQUISITION CORP.; *U.S. Public*, pg. 1014
HC MATERIALEN B.V.—See Heidelberg Materials AG; *Int'l*, pg. 3311
HCMC INVESMENT & DEVELOPMENT JSC—See Dat Xanh Group Joint Stock Company; *Int'l*, pg. 1975
HCM ENGINEERING SDN BHD—See Protasco Berhad; *Int'l*, pg. 6003
H.C. MILLER COMPANY; *U.S. Private*, pg. 1825
H & C MOTORS, INC.; *U.S. Private*, pg. 1822
HCMS GROUP, LLC—See UPMC WorkPartners; *U.S. Private*, pg. 4312
HCM SYSTEMS, INC.; *U.S. Private*, pg. 1890
HC NATURGAS COMERCIALIZADORA DE ULTIMO RECURSO, S.A.—See EDP - Energias de Portugal, S.A.; *Int'l*, pg. 2314
HCN DOWNREIT MEMBER, LLC—See Welltower Inc.; *U.S. Public*, pg. 2348
H&C NETWORK CO. LTD.—See KT Corporation; *Int'l*, pg. 4315
HCN-REVERA LESSEE (ARNPRIOR VILLA) GP INC.—See Welltower Inc.; *U.S. Public*, pg. 2348
HCN-REVERA LESSEE (INGLEWOOD) LP—See Welltower Inc.; *U.S. Public*, pg. 2348
HCN-REVERA LESSEE (JARDINS DU COUVENT) LP—See Welltower Inc.; *U.S. Public*, pg. 2348
HCN-REVERA LESSEE (MANOIR LAFONTAINE) LP—See Welltower Inc.; *U.S. Public*, pg. 2348

COMPANY NAME INDEX

HCN-REVERA LESSEE (MCKENZIE TOWNE) LP—See Welltower Inc.; *U.S. Public*, pg. 2348
HCN-REVERA LESSEE (RIVER RIDGE) GP INC.—See Welltower Inc.; *U.S. Public*, pg. 2348
HCN-REVERA LESSEE (SCENIC ACRES) GP INC.—See Welltower Inc.; *U.S. Public*, pg. 2348
HCN-REVERA LESSEE (THE CHURCHILL) GP INC.—See Welltower Inc.; *U.S. Public*, pg. 2348
HCOA HOSPITAL HOLDINGS (AUSTRALIA) PTY LIMITED—See Ramsay Health Care Limited; *Int'l*, pg. 6199
HCOA OPERATIONS (AUSTRALIA) PTY LIMITED—See Ramsay Health Care Limited; *Int'l*, pg. 6199
HC-ONE LIMITED—See Court Cavendish Limited; *Int'l*, pg. 1819
HC ORTHOPAEDIC SURGERY PTE. LTD.—See LYC Healthcare Berhad; *Int'l*, pg. 4605
H.C. PARTNERSHIP—See Universal Health Services, Inc.; *U.S. Public*, pg. 2257
H.C. PETERSEN & CO.S EFTF. A/S—See Iseki & Co., Ltd.; *Int'l*, pg. 3814
H.C. PHARMACY CENTRAL, INC.—See University of Pittsburgh Medical Center; *U.S. Private*, pg. 4309
HCP LIFE SCIENCE ESTATES, INC.—See Healthpeak Properties, Inc.; *U.S. Public*, pg. 1016
HCP MOB SCOTTSDALE LLC—See Healthpeak Properties, Inc.; *U.S. Public*, pg. 1016
HCP PACKAGING FRANCE SAS—See TPG Capital, L.P.; *U.S. Public*, pg. 2173
HCP PACKAGING GROUP—See TPG Capital, L.P.; *U.S. Public*, pg. 2173
HCP PACKAGING HONG KONG LTD.—See TPG Capital, L.P.; *U.S. Public*, pg. 2173
HCP PACKAGING (HUAI AN) CO., LTD.—See TPG Capital, L.P.; *U.S. Public*, pg. 2173
HCP PACKAGING (SHANGHAI) CO. LTD.—See TPG Capital, L.P.; *U.S. Public*, pg. 2173
HCP PACKAGING UK LTD.—See TPG Capital, L.P.; *U.S. Public*, pg. 2173
HCP PACKAGING USA, INC. - HINSDALE PLANT—See TPG Capital, L.P.; *U.S. Public*, pg. 2174
HCP PACKAGING USA, INC.—See TPG Capital, L.P.; *U.S. Public*, pg. 2174
HCP PLASTENE BULKPACK LTD.; *Int'l*, pg. 3299
HCP PROPERTIES, INC.—See JPMorgan Chase & Co.; *U.S. Public*, pg. 1207
HC PRIVATE INVESTMENTS LLC; *U.S. Private*, pg. 1888
HCPRO, INC; *U.S. Private*, pg. 1890
HC QUERETARO S.A. DE C.V.—See Hitachi, Ltd.; *Int'l*, pg. 3413
HCR CO., LTD.; *Int'l*, pg. 3299
HCR, INC.—See Jamison Door Company; *U.S. Private*, pg. 2186
H. C. RUSTIN CORPORATION; *U.S. Private*, pg. 1824
HCS BETEILIGUNGSGESELLSCHAFT MBH; *Int'l*, pg. 3299
HCSC INSURANCE SERVICES COMPANY—See Health Care Service Corporation; *U.S. Private*, pg. 1892
HCS CORPORATION—See Compagnie de Saint-Gobain SA; *Int'l*, pg. 1730
HC SEMITEK CORPORATION; *Int'l*, pg. 3297
HCS HEAD START, INC.; *U.S. Private*, pg. 1890
HCS - HEALTH COMMUNICATION SERVICE GMBH—See CompuGroup Medical SE & Co. KGaA; *Int'l*, pg. 1757
HC SHIPPING AND CHARTERING LTD—See Clarkson PLC; *Int'l*, pg. 1651
HCS HOLDINGS CO., LTD.—See LTS, Inc.; *Int'l*, pg. 4571
HCS LANCASTER LLC—See Linde plc; *Int'l*, pg. 4505
HC SLINGSBY PLC; *Int'l*, pg. 3297
HCSS, INC.; *U.S. Private*, pg. 1890
H.C. STARCK GMBH & CO. KG—See Advent International Corporation; *U.S. Private*, pg. 102
H.C. STARCK GMBH & CO. KG—See The Carlyle Group Inc.; *U.S. Public*, pg. 2047
H.C. STARCK INC—See Advent International Corporation; *U.S. Private*, pg. 102
H.C. STARCK INC—See The Carlyle Group Inc.; *U.S. Public*, pg. 2047
H.C. STARCK, INC.—See Advent International Corporation; *U.S. Private*, pg. 102
H.C. STARCK, INC.—See The Carlyle Group Inc.; *U.S. Public*, pg. 2047
H.C. STARCK, INC.—See Advent International Corporation; *U.S. Private*, pg. 102
H.C. STARCK, INC.—See The Carlyle Group Inc.; *U.S. Public*, pg. 2047
H.C. STARCK INC—See Advent International Corporation; *U.S. Private*, pg. 102
H.C. STARCK INC—See The Carlyle Group Inc.; *U.S. Public*, pg. 2047
HC SURGICAL SPECIALISTS LIMITED; *Int'l*, pg. 3297
HCT2 CO.—See HealthStream, Inc.; *U.S. Public*, pg. 1017
HCT AMERICA LLC—See HCT Co., Ltd.; *U.S. Private*, pg. 3299
HCT ASIA SERVICES PTE. LTD.—See Heidelberg Materials AG; *Int'l*, pg. 3311
HCT CO., LTD.; *Int'l*, pg. 3299
HCTEC PARTNERS LLC—See TruArc Partners, L.P.; *U.S. Private*, pg. 4245

HCTEC PARTNERS—See TruArc Partners, L.P.; *U.S. Private*, pg. 4245
HC TRADING B.V.—See Heidelberg Materials AG; *Int'l*, pg. 3310
HC TRADING MALTA LIMITED—See Heidelberg Materials AG; *Int'l*, pg. 3311
HCT SERVICES ASIA PTE. LTD.—See Heidelberg Materials AG; *Int'l*, pg. 3311
HCV DATA MANAGEMENT GMBH—See Bechtle AG; *Int'l*, pg. 938
HCV UNDERWRITING MANAGERS (PTY) LIMITED—See Hollard Insurance Company Ltd; *Int'l*, pg. 3451
H.C. WAINWRIGHT & CO., LLC; *U.S. Private*, pg. 1825
HCW BIOLOGICS INC.; *U.S. Public*, pg. 1014
HCW DISTRIBUTING CORP.—See HAUPPAUGE DIGITAL, INC.; *U.S. Public*, pg. 988
H-D ADVANCED MANUFACTURING COMPANY—See Hicks Holdings, LLC; *U.S. Private*, pg. 1934
H-D ADVANCED MANUFACTURING COMPANY—See The Riverside Company; *U.S. Private*, pg. 4108
H-D ADVANCED MANUFACTURING COMPANY—See Weinberg Capital Group, Inc.; *U.S. Private*, pg. 4471
HD AMERICAN ROAD LLC; *U.S. Private*, pg. 1890
HD CAFE LTD—See Hadco Limited; *Int'l*, pg. 3205
HDC DATA CENTRE LIMITED—See Henderson Land Development Co. Ltd.; *Int'l*, pg. 3344
HDC HOLDINGS CO., LTD.; *Int'l*, pg. 3300
HDC HYUNDAI DEVELOPMENT COMPANY; *Int'l*, pg. 3300
HDC HYUNDAI ENGINEERING PLASTICS CO., LTD.; *Int'l*, pg. 3300
HDC LABS CO., LTD.; *Int'l*, pg. 3300
HDC WASSERBAU NORD GMBH—See HAL Trust N.V.; *Int'l*, pg. 3226
HD DUNAV AD; *Int'l*, pg. 3299
HDEC CONSTRUCTION CORPORATION—See Continental Holdings Corp.; *Int'l*, pg. 1784
H.D. EICHELBERG & CO. GMBH—See Development Bank of Japan, Inc.; *Int'l*, pg. 2088
H.D. EICHELBERG & CO. GMBH—See LIXIL Group Corporation; *Int'l*, pg. 4534
HDFC ASSET MANAGEMENT COMPANY LIMITED—See Housing Development Finance Corporation Limited; *Int'l*, pg. 3491
HDFC BANK LIMITED—See Housing Development Finance Corporation Limited; *Int'l*, pg. 3491
HDFC CAPITAL ADVISORS LTD.—See Housing Development Finance Corporation Limited; *Int'l*, pg. 3492
HDFC CREDILA FINANCIAL SERVICES LTD.—See Housing Development Finance Corporation Limited; *Int'l*, pg. 3492
HDFC EDUCATION & DEVELOPMENT SERVICES PVT. LTD.—See Vama Sundari Investments (Delhi) Private Limited; *Int'l*, pg. 8125
HDFC ERGO GENERAL INSURANCE COMPANY LTD.—See Housing Development Finance Corporation Limited; *Int'l*, pg. 3492
HDFC MUTUAL FUND—See Housing Development Finance Corporation Limited; *Int'l*, pg. 3491
HDFC REALTY LIMITED—See Housing Development Finance Corporation Limited; *Int'l*, pg. 3492
HDFC SALES—See Housing Development Finance Corporation Limited; *Int'l*, pg. 3492
HDFC SECURITIES LIMITED—See Housing Development Finance Corporation Limited; *Int'l*, pg. 3492
HDFC STANDARD LIFE INSURANCE COMPANY LTD.—See abrdn PLC; *Int'l*, pg. 68
HDFC STANDARD LIFE INSURANCE COMPANY LTD.—See Housing Development Finance Corporation Limited; *Int'l*, pg. 3492
HDFC TRUSTEE COMPANY LIMITED—See Housing Development Finance Corporation Limited; *Int'l*, pg. 3492
HDF INVESTMENTS LIMITED—See Cabot Corporation; *U.S. Public*, pg. 417
HDFI PTY LIMITED—See Mulpha International Bhd.; *Int'l*, pg. 5081
HDG ASSOCIATES—See Hyatt Hotels Corporation; *U.S. Public*, pg. 1077
HD GLOBAL (HK) ENGINEERING SERVICES LTD. (HONG KONG)—See Hyundai Group; *Int'l*, pg. 3557
HD-GLOBAL (HK) ENGINEERING SERVICES LTD. - SHENZHEN—See Hyundai Group; *Int'l*, pg. 3557
H-D GROUP LLC—See Harley-Davidson, Inc.; *U.S. Public*, pg. 984
HD HOSPITAL DISPOSABLES INCORPORATED—See DeRoyal Industries Inc.; *Int'l*, pg. 1210
HD HOTEL LLC—See Meyer Jabara Hotels, LLC; *U.S. Private*, pg. 2692
HDH THORACIC SURGEONS, LLC—See HCA Healthcare, Inc.; *U.S. Public*, pg. 998
H.D. HUDSON ASIA LIMITED—See H.D. Hudson Manufacturing Company; *U.S. Private*, pg. 1825
H.D. HUDSON MANUFACTURING COMPANY; *U.S. Private*, pg. 1825
HD HYUNDAI CO., LTD; *Int'l*, pg. 3299
HD HYUNDAI ENERGY SOLUTIONS CO.,LTD.; *Int'l*, pg. 3299
HD HYUNDAI INFRACORE CO., LTD.; *Int'l*, pg. 3299
HDI DEUTSCHLAND AG—See Talanx AG; *Int'l*, pg. 7443

HDI-GERLING AMERICA INSURANCE COMPANY—See Talanx AG; *Int'l*, pg. 7444
HDI-GERLING AMERICA INSURANCE COMPANY—See Talanx AG; *Int'l*, pg. 7444
HDI-GERLING DE MEXICO SEGUROS, S.A.—See Talanx AG; *Int'l*, pg. 7444
HDI-GERLING INDUSTRIE VERSICHERUNG AG - FRANCE OFFICE—See Talanx AG; *Int'l*, pg. 7444
HDI-GERLING INDUSTRIE VERSICHERUNG AG - NORWAY OFFICE—See Talanx AG; *Int'l*, pg. 7444
HDI-GERLING INDUSTRIE VERSICHERUNG AG—See Talanx AG; *Int'l*, pg. 7444
HDI-GERLING INDUSTRIE VERSICHERUNG AG - SWITZERLAND OFFICE—See Talanx AG; *Int'l*, pg. 7444
HDI-GERLING INSURANCE OF SOUTH AFRICA LIMITED—See Talanx AG; *Int'l*, pg. 7444
HDI GLOBAL INSURANCE COMPANY—See Talanx AG; *Int'l*, pg. 7443
HDI GLOBAL INSURANCE LIMITED LIABILITY COMPANY—See Talanx AG; *Int'l*, pg. 7443
HDI GLOBAL SA LTD.—See Talanx AG; *Int'l*, pg. 7444
HDI GLOBAL SEGUROS SA—See PBG S/A; *Int'l*, pg. 5765
HDI GLOBAL SE—See Talanx AG; *Int'l*, pg. 7444
HDI GLOBAL SPECIALTY SE—See Talanx AG; *Int'l*, pg. 7444
HDI ITALIA, S.P.A.—See Talanx AG; *Int'l*, pg. 7444
HDI LANDING GEAR USA, INC.—See Heroux-Devtek Inc.; *Int'l*, pg. 3364
HDI LEBENSVERSICHERUNG AG - AUSTRIA—See Talanx AG; *Int'l*, pg. 7445
HDI LEBENSVERSICHERUNG AG—See Talanx AG; *Int'l*, pg. 7445
H-D INTERNATIONAL HOLDINGS GROUP COMPANY; *U.S. Private*, pg. 976
HDI SEGUROS S.A.—See Talanx AG; *Int'l*, pg. 7444
HDI SEGUROS S.A.—See Talanx AG; *Int'l*, pg. 7444
HDI SOLUTIONS, INC.; *U.S. Private*, pg. 1890
HDI VERSICHERUNG AG, ORGANIZACNI SLOZKA—See Talanx AG; *Int'l*, pg. 7444
HDI VERSICHERUNG AG - SLOVAKIA OFFICE—See Talanx AG; *Int'l*, pg. 7444
HDI VERSICHERUNG AG—See Talanx AG; *Int'l*, pg. 7445
HDJ DESIGN GROUP—See PBS Engineering & Envrnmntl; *U.S. Private*, pg. 3119
HDK AMERICA INC.—See Hokuriku Electric Industry Co., Ltd.; *Int'l*, pg. 3444
HDK CHINA LTD.—See Hokuriku Electric Industry Co., Ltd.; *Int'l*, pg. 3444
HDK INDUSTRIES, INC.—See Branford Castle, Inc.; *U.S. Private*, pg. 639
HDK MICRO DEVICES CO., LTD.—See Hokuriku Electric Industry Co., Ltd.; *Int'l*, pg. 3444
HDK (THAILAND) CO., LTD.—See Hokuriku Electric Industry Co., Ltd.; *Int'l*, pg. 3444
THE H.D. LEE COMPANY, INC.—See V. F. Corporation; *U.S. Public*, pg. 2268
HD LOGISTICS, INC.—See Harmonic Drive Systems Inc.; *Int'l*, pg. 3277
HDM CAPITAL SDN BHD—See Hwang Capital (Malaysia) Berhad; *Int'l*, pg. 3542
HD MEDIA COMPANY, LLC; *U.S. Private*, pg. 1890
HDM ELQUITECNICA CIA LTDA.—See HORIBA Ltd; *Int'l*, pg. 3477
HDM HYDRAULICS, LLC—See Ligon Industries LLC; *U.S. Private*, pg. 2455
HDM PRIVATE EQUITY SDN. BHD.—See Hwang Capital (Malaysia) Berhad; *Int'l*, pg. 3542
HDM PROPERTIES SDN BHD—See Hwang Capital (Malaysia) Berhad; *Int'l*, pg. 3542
HDM RETAIL, INC.—See Heritage Home Group, LLC; *U.S. Private*, pg. 1924
HDOS ENTERPRISES—See Fog Cutter Capital Group Inc.; *U.S. Private*, pg. 1557
H-DO (THAILAND) LIMITED; *Int'l*, pg. 3194
HD PLUS GMBH—See SES S.A.; *Int'l*, pg. 6727
HDP TRADING B.V.—See The Scotts Miracle-Gro Company; *U.S. Public*, pg. 2126
HDR ARCHITECTURE INC.—See HDR, Inc.; *U.S. Private*, pg. 1890
HDR CONSTRUCTION CONTROL CORPORATION—See HDR, Inc.; *U.S. Private*, pg. 1890
HDR ENGINEERING INC.—See HDR, Inc.; *U.S. Private*, pg. 1890
HDR ENGINEERING INC.—See HDR, Inc.; *U.S. Private*, pg. 1890
HD RESOURCES MANAGEMENT CORPORATION—See CTCI Corporation; *Int'l*, pg. 1870
HDR, INC.; *U.S. Private*, pg. 1890
HDS DEUTSCHLAND GMBH—See Vivendi SE; *Int'l*, pg. 8276
H.D. SHELDON & COMPANY INC.; *U.S. Private*, pg. 1825
HDS INMEDIO ROMANIA—See Vivendi SE; *Int'l*, pg. 8276
HDS MARKETING, INC.; *U.S. Private*, pg. 1890
H.D. SMITH WHOLESALE DRUG CO. INC.; *U.S. Private*, pg. 1825
H.D. SMITH WHOLESALE DRUG CO. INC.—See H.D. Smith Wholesale Drug Co. Inc.; *U.S. Private*, pg. 1825
HDS POLSKA SP. Z O.O.—See Vivendi SE; *Int'l*, pg. 8276

H.D. SMITH WHOLESALE DRUG CO. INC. CORPORATE AFFILIATIONS

HDS RETAIL ASIA PACIFIC—See Vivendi SE; *Int'l*, pg. 8272
HDS RETAIL CZ A.S.—See Vivendi SE; *Int'l*, pg. 8276
HDS RETAIL NORTH AMERICA—See Vivendi SE; *Int'l*, pg. 8272
H&D STEEL SERVICE, INC.; *U.S. Private*, pg. 1822
HD SUPPLY CANADA INC.—See Clayton, Dubilier & Rice, LLC; *U.S. Private*, pg. 930
HD SUPPLY FACILITIES MAINTENANCE, LTD.—See The Home Depot, Inc.; *U.S. Public*, pg. 2089
HD SUPPLY HOLDINGS, INC.—See The Home Depot, Inc.; *U.S. Public*, pg. 2089
HD SUPPLY, INC.—See The Home Depot, Inc.; *U.S. Public*, pg. 2089
HD SUPPLY REPAIR & REMODEL, LLC—See Clayton, Dubilier & Rice, LLC; *U.S. Private*, pg. 930
HD SYMMCO INC.—See Symmco Group Inc.; *U.S. Private*, pg. 3899
HD TECHNOLOGY SDN BHD—See Zavarco PLC; *Int'l*, pg. 8626
HDT ENGINEERED TECHNOLOGIES, INC.—See Metalmark Capital Holdings LLC; *U.S. Private*, pg. 2681
HDT EXPEDITIONARY SYSTEMS, INC.—See Metalmark Capital Holdings LLC; *U.S. Private*, pg. 2681
HDT GLOBAL EUROPE LTD—See Metalmark Capital Holdings LLC; *U.S. Private*, pg. 2681
HDT GLOBAL, INC.—See Nexus Capital Management LP; *U.S. Private*, pg. 2922
H-D TOMAHAWK INDUSTRIAL PARK, LLC—See Harley-Davidson, Inc.; *U.S. Public*, pg. 985
HDT SRL—See Ningbo Techmation Co., Ltd.; *Int'l*, pg. 5306
HDTV SUPPLY, INC.; *U.S. Private*, pg. 1890
H-D U.S.A., LLC—See Harley-Davidson, Inc.; *U.S. Public*, pg. 984
H.D. VEST, INC.—See Genstar Capital, LLC; *U.S. Private*, pg. 1676
HDV HOLDINGS, INC.—See Genstar Capital, LLC; *U.S. Private*, pg. 1676
HD VIEW 360, INC.; *U.S. Private*, pg. 1890
HDW BV—See Group Thermote & Vanhalst; *Int'l*, pg. 3089
HDW-GREENWOOD DISTRIBUTION CENTER—See Hardware Distribution Warehouses, Inc.; *U.S. Private*, pg. 1863
HEACHEON MACHINERY CO., LTD.—See Seoam Machinery Industry Co., Ltd.; *Int'l*, pg. 6715
HEAD ASSET MANAGEMENT OY—See Head Invest Oy; *Int'l*, pg. 3300
HEAD-BECKHAN AMERINSURANCE, INC.—See MAPFRE S.A.; *Int'l*, pg. 4683
HEAD B.V.; *Int'l*, pg. 3300
HEAD CANADA INC.—See Head B.V.; *Int'l*, pg. 3300
HEADCO INDUSTRIES; *U.S. Private*, pg. 1891
HEADCO MACHINE WORKS, INC.—See Headco Industries; *U.S. Private*, pg. 1891
HEADCOUNT MANAGEMENT, INC.; *U.S. Private*, pg. 1891
HEAD COUNTRY INC.—See Gladstone Management Corporation; *U.S. Private*, pg. 1705
HEADER PRODUCTS INC.; *U.S. Private*, pg. 1891
HEAD FAME COMPANY LIMITED—See Golden Ponder Holdings Limited; *Int'l*, pg. 3031
HEAD FRANCE S.A.S.—See Head B.V.; *Int'l*, pg. 3300
HEAD GERMANY GMBH—See Head B.V.; *Int'l*, pg. 3300
HEADHAUL CAPITAL PARTNERS LLC; *U.S. Private*, pg. 1891
HEAD HOLDING UNTERNEHMENSBETEILIGUNG GMBH—See Head B.V.; *Int'l*, pg. 3300
HEADHUNTER GROUP PLC; *Int'l*, pg. 3301
THE HEADHUNTERS RECRUITMENT, INC.—See Hire Technologies, Inc.; *Int'l*, pg. 3404
HEAD INJURY ASSOCIATION, INC.; *U.S. Private*, pg. 1891
HEAD INVEST OY; *Int'l*, pg. 3300
HEAD JAPAN CO., LTD.—See Head B.V.; *Int'l*, pg. 3300
HEADLAM BV—See Headlam Group plc; *Int'l*, pg. 3301
HEADLAM GROUP PLC; *Int'l*, pg. 3301
HEADLAND CAPITAL PARTNERS (INDIA) PRIVATE LIMITED—See Headland Capital Partners Limited; *Int'l*, pg. 3301
HEADLAND CAPITAL PARTNERS LIMITED; *Int'l*, pg. 3301
HEADLAND CAPITAL PARTNERS (SHANGHAI) LIMITED—See Headland Capital Partners Limited; *Int'l*, pg. 3301
HEADLAND INVESTMENT CONSULTING (SHANGHAI) CORPORATION LIMITED—See Headland Capital Partners Limited; *Int'l*, pg. 3301
HEADLANDS DIALYSIS, LLC—See DaVita Inc.; *U.S. Public*, pg. 639
HEADLANDS RESEARCH, INC.—See KKR & Co. Inc.; *U.S. Public*, pg. 1252
HEADLINE BOOK PUBLISHING LIMITED—See Vivendi SE; *Int'l*, pg. 8273
HEADLINE DAILY LIMITED—See SING TAO NEWS CORPORATION LIMITED; *Int'l*, pg. 6939
HEADLINE PUBLISHING AGENCY—See Omnicom Group Inc.; *U.S. Public*, pg. 1596
HEADLINE PUBLISHING GROUP LTD—See Vivendi SE; *Int'l*, pg. 8273
HEAD/PENN RACQUET SPORTS—See Head B.V.; *Int'l*, pg. 3300
HEADQUARTERS ADVERTISING INC.; *U.S. Private*, pg. 1891
HEADQUARTERS ADVISORY GROUP, LLC—See Genstar Capital, LLC; *U.S. Private*, pg. 1676
HEADQUARTERS LIMITED—See Century Legend Holdings Ltd; *Int'l*, pg. 1418
HEADQUARTER TOYOTA; *U.S. Private*, pg. 1891
HEADS & ALLTHREADS PRIVATE LIMITED—See Park-Ohio Holdings Corp.; *U.S. Public*, pg. 1639
HEADSENT AB; *Int'l*, pg. 3301
HEADSETS.COM, INC.; *U.S. Private*, pg. 1891
HEADSET SOLUTIONS AFRICA PROPRIETARY LIMITED—See AYO Technology Solutions Ltd.; *Int'l*, pg. 775
HEADSPACE INC.; *U.S. Private*, pg. 1891
HEAD SPAIN S.A.—See Head B.V.; *Int'l*, pg. 3300
HEAD SPORT GMBH—See Head B.V.; *Int'l*, pg. 3300
HEADSTART FOR LIFE PTE. LTD.—See OUE Limited; *Int'l*, pg. 5666
HEADSTART NURSERY INC.; *U.S. Private*, pg. 1891
HEADSTART (PRIVATE) LIMITED—See Axiata Group Berhad; *Int'l*, pg. 768
HEADSTREAM INC; *U.S. Private*, pg. 1891
HEADSTRONG BUSINESS SERVICES, INC.—See Genpact Limited; *Int'l*, pg. 2927
HEADSTRONG CORPORATION—See Genpact Limited; *Int'l*, pg. 2927
HEADSTRONG PHILIPPINES, INC.—See Genpact Limited; *Int'l*, pg. 2927
HEADSUP ENTERTAINMENT INTERNATIONAL, INC.; *Int'l*, pg. 3301
HEADS UP TECHNOLOGIES, INC.—See JLL Partners, LLC; *U.S. Private*, pg. 2212
HEADS UP VENTURES LIMITED—See GB Global Limited; *Int'l*, pg. 2892
HEAD TECHNOLOGY GMBH—See Head B.V.; *Int'l*, pg. 3300
HEAD UK LTD—See Head B.V.; *Int'l*, pg. 3300
HEADUP GMBH—See Thunderful Group AB; *Int'l*, pg. 7722
HEADWALL PHOTONICS, INC.; *U.S. Private*, pg. 1891
HEADWATER COMPANIES, LLC—See Franklin Electric Co., Inc.; *U.S. Public*, pg. 878
HEADWATER EQUIPMENT SALES LTD; *Int'l*, pg. 3301
HEADWATER EXPLORATION INC.; *Int'l*, pg. 3301
HEADWATER HOLIDAYS LIMITED—See TUI AG; *Int'l*, pg. 7965
HEADWATERS CO.; *Int'l*, pg. 3302
HEADWATERS ENERGY SERVICES CORP.—See Seven Group Holdings Limited; *Int'l*, pg. 6733
HEADWATERS INCORPORATED—See Seven Group Holdings Limited; *Int'l*, pg. 6733
HEADWATERS MB LLC—See Huntington Bancshares Incorporated; *U.S. Public*, pg. 1071
HEADWAY ADVANCED MATERIALS INC.; *Int'l*, pg. 3302
HEADWAY ADVANCED MATERIALS (SHANGHAI) CO., LTD.—See Headway Advanced Materials Inc.; *Int'l*, pg. 3302
HEADWAY ADVANCED MATERIALS (VIETNAM) CO., LTD.—See Headway Advanced Materials Inc.; *Int'l*, pg. 3302
HEADWAY CAPITAL, LLC—See Enova International, Inc.; *U.S. Public*, pg. 769
HEADWAY CORPORATE RESOURCES INC.; *U.S. Private*, pg. 1891
HEADWAY CORPORATE STAFFING SERVICES OF NORTH CAROLINA INC.—See Headway Corporate Resources Inc.; *U.S. Private*, pg. 1891
HEADWAY HOLDING GMBH—See Empresaria Group Plc; *Int'l*, pg. 2389
HEADWAY POLYURETHANE CO., LTD.—See Headway Advanced Materials Inc.; *Int'l*, pg. 3302
HEADWAY TECHNOLOGIES INC.—See TDK Corporation; *Int'l*, pg. 7488
HEADWAY WORKFORCE SOLUTIONS, INC.—See Staffing 360 Solutions, Inc.; *U.S. Public*, pg. 1925
HEADWORKS INTERNATIONAL INC.; *U.S. Private*, pg. 1891
HEAG SUDHESSISCHE ENERGIE AG; *Int'l*, pg. 3302
HEALEY BROTHERS AUTOMOTIVE; *U.S. Private*, pg. 1891
HEALEY RAILROAD CORPORATION; *U.S. Private*, pg. 1891
HEALGEN SCIENTIFIC LIMITED LIABILITY COMPANY—See Zhejiang Orient Gene Biotech Co., Ltd.; *Int'l*, pg. 8661
THE HEALING COMPANY INC.; *U.S. Public*, pg. 2088
HEALING SOLUTIONS (REMEDY) LLC—See Aterian, Inc.; *U.S. Public*, pg. 221
HEALING TOUCH HOLDINGS, INC.; *Int'l*, pg. 3302
HEALIOS K.K.; *Int'l*, pg. 3302
HEALIUS LIMITED; *Int'l*, pg. 3302
HEALIUS PATHOLOGY PTY. LTD.—See Healius Limited; *Int'l*, pg. 3302
HEALIXA INC.; *U.S. Public*, pg. 1014
HEALOGICS, INC.—See Clayton, Dubilier & Rice, LLC; *U.S. Private*, pg. 924
HEALSTONE BIOTECH INC.—See Zhejiang Orient Gene Biotech Co., Ltd.; *Int'l*, pg. 8661
HEALTECH S.R.L.—See GPI S.p.A.; *Int'l*, pg. 3046
HEALTH 2.0, LLC—See Healthcare Information & Management Systems Society; *U.S. Private*, pg. 1895
HEALTH ACCESS NETWORK; *U.S. Private*, pg. 1892
HEALTH ACQUISITION CORP.—See Blue Wolf Capital Partners LLC; *U.S. Private*, pg. 595
HEALTH ADVANCE INC.; *U.S. Public*, pg. 1014
HEALTH ADVANCES GMBH—See Pamplona Capital Management LLP; *Int'l*, pg. 5712
HEALTH ADVANCES LLC—See Pamplona Capital Management LLP; *Int'l*, pg. 5712
HEALTH ADVOCATE, INC.—See Teleperformance SE; *Int'l*, pg. 7540
HEALTH ADVOCATES NETWORK, INC.; *U.S. Private*, pg. 1892
HEALTH AFFILIATES MAINE; *U.S. Private*, pg. 1892
HEALTH ALLIANCE PLAN OF MICHIGAN—See Henry Ford Health System; *U.S. Private*, pg. 1918
HEALTHAMERICA HEALTH INSURANCE—See CVS Health Corporation; *U.S. Public*, pg. 615
HEALTHAMERICA PENNSYLVANIA, INC.—See CVS Health Corporation; *U.S. Public*, pg. 615
HEALTH AND HAPPINESS (H&H) INTERNATIONAL HOLDINGS LIMITED; *Int'l*, pg. 3303
HEALTH AND PLANT PROTEIN GROUP LIMITED; *Int'l*, pg. 3303
HEALTH AND SPORTS NUTRITION GROUP HSNG AB—See Orkla ASA; *Int'l*, pg. 5637
HEALTHANSWERS EDUCATION LLC—See WPP plc; *Int'l*, pg. 8492
HEALTH ASSURANCE ACQUISITION CORP.; *U.S. Public*, pg. 1014
HEALTH AT HOME—See LCS Holdings Inc.; *U.S. Private*, pg. 2404
HEALTHAXIS GROUP, LLC; *U.S. Private*, pg. 1895
HEALTHBABY BIOTECH (MACAU) CO., LIMITED—See Cordlife Group Limited; *Int'l*, pg. 1796
HEALTHBANK HOLDINGS LIMITED; *Int'l*, pg. 3303
HEALTHBEACON PLC; *Int'l*, pg. 3303
HEALTH BIOSCIENCES SPA; *Int'l*, pg. 3303
HEALTHCAP GP SA—See Odlander Fredrikson & Co. AB; *Int'l*, pg. 5527
HEALTHCARE ACTIVOS YIELD SOCIMI, S.A.; *Int'l*, pg. 3303
HEALTHCARE AI ACQUISITION CORP.; *Int'l*, pg. 3303
HEALTH CARE AND REHABILITATION SERVICES; *U.S. Private*, pg. 1892
HEALTHCARE ASSOCIATES CREDIT UNION; *U.S. Private*, pg. 1895
HEALTHCARE ASSOCIATION OF NEW YORK STATE; *U.S. Private*, pg. 1895
HEALTHCARE AT HOME LTD.; *Int'l*, pg. 3303
THE HEALTH CARE AUTHORITY OF THE CITY OF ANNISTON; *U.S. Private*, pg. 4043
HEALTHCARE BILLING SYSTEMS LLC—See Varsity Management Company, LP; *U.S. Private*, pg. 4347
HEALTH CARE CAPITAL CONSOLIDATED; *U.S. Private*, pg. 1892
HEALTHCARE CAPITAL CORP.; *U.S. Public*, pg. 1015
HEALTHCARE CO., LTD.; *Int'l*, pg. 3304
HEALTHCARE COMMUNICATIONS UK LTD.—See Cisco Systems, Inc.; *U.S. Public*, pg. 499
HEALTH CARE COMPLIANCE STRATEGIES, INC.—See HealthStream, Inc.; *U.S. Public*, pg. 1017
HEALTH CARE CONCEPT GMBH—See Asklepios Kliniken GmbH & Co. KGaA; *Int'l*, pg. 623
HEALTHCARE CONSULTANCY GROUP—See Omnicom Group Inc.; *U.S. Public*, pg. 1586
HEALTHCARE CORPORATION OF AMERICA; *U.S. Public*, pg. 1015
HEALTH CARE CORPORATION PTY LIMITED—See Ramsay Health Care Limited; *Int'l*, pg. 6199
HEALTH CARE ENTERPRISES, LLC—See Centene Corporation; *U.S. Public*, pg. 469
HEALTHCAREFIRST, INC.—See ResMed Inc.; *U.S. Public*, pg. 1790
HEALTH CARE FOR THE HOMELESS; *U.S. Private*, pg. 1892
HEALTH CARE FOUNDATION OF GREATER KANSAS CITY; *U.S. Private*, pg. 1892
HEALTH CARE FUTURES, L.P.—See Northlane Capital Partners, LLC; *U.S. Private*, pg. 2956
HEALTHCARE GATEWAY LIMITED—See EMIS Group plc; *Int'l*, pg. 2383
HEALTHCARE GLOBAL ENTERPRISES LIMITED; *Int'l*, pg. 3304
HEALTH & CARE GROUP LIMITED—See HKR International Limited; *Int'l*, pg. 3429
HEALTHCARE GROWTH PARTNERS; *U.S. Private*, pg. 1895
HEALTHCARE IKKOU CORPORATION—See Medical Ikkou Co., Ltd.; *Int'l*, pg. 4775
HEALTHCARE IMAGING SERVICES PTY LTD—See Healius Limited; *Int'l*, pg. 3302

COMPANY NAME INDEX

HEALTHCARE IMAGING SERVICES (VICTORIA) PTY LTD—See Healius Limited; *Int'l*, pg. 3302
HEALTHCARE INFORMATION & MANAGEMENT SYSTEMS SOCIETY; *U.S. Private*, pg. 1895
HEALTHCARE INNOVATIONS OF OKLAHOMA, L.L.C.—See Encompass Health Corporation; *U.S. Public*, pg. 756
HEALTHCARE INNOVATIONS OF WESTERN OKLAHOMA, L.L.C.—See Encompass Health Corporation; *U.S. Public*, pg. 756
HEALTHCARE INNOVATIONSTRAVERTINE HEALTH SERVICES, L.L.C.—See Encompass Health Corporation; *U.S. Public*, pg. 756
HEALTHCARE INSURANCE PROFESSIONALS, INC.—See Brown & Brown, Inc.; *U.S. Public*, pg. 401
HEALTHCARE INTEGRATED TECHNOLOGIES INC.; *U.S. Public*, pg. 1015
HEALTHCARE LINEN SERVICES GROUP—See York Capital Management Global Advisors, LLC; *U.S. Private*, pg. 4590
HEALTHCARE LOCUMS PLC—See Ares Management Corporation; *U.S. Public*, pg. 188
HEALTHCARE LOCUMS PLC—See Old Oak Holdings Limited; *Int'l*, pg. 5552
HEALTH CARE MANAGEMENT, INC.—See Key Family of Companies; *U.S. Private*, pg. 2293
HEALTHCARE MANAGEMENT OF AMERICA, INC.—See Healthcare Realty Trust Incorporated; *U.S. Public*, pg. 1015
HEALTHCARE MANAGEMENT PARTNERS, INC.—See Mitsubishi HC Capital Inc.; *Int'l*, pg. 4951
HEALTHCARE & MEDICAL INVESTMENT CORPORATION; *Int'l*, pg. 3303
HEALTHCARE NETWORK HOSPITALS, INC.—See Tenet Healthcare Corporation; *U.S. Public*, pg. 2004
HEALTHCARE NETWORK OF SOUTHWEST FLORIDA; *U.S. Private*, pg. 1895
HEALTHCARE OF TODAY, INC; *U.S. Private*, pg. 1895
HEALTHCARE PARTNERS ASC-LB, LLC—See DaVita Inc.; *U.S. Public*, pg. 639
HEALTHCARE PARTNERS COLORADO, LLC—See DaVita Inc.; *U.S. Public*, pg. 639
HEALTHCARE PARTNERS HOLDINGS LLC—See DaVita Inc.; *U.S. Public*, pg. 639
HEALTHCARE PARTNERS INVESTMENTS LLC; *U.S. Private*, pg. 1895
HEALTHCARE PARTNERS, LLC—See DaVita Inc.; *U.S. Public*, pg. 639
HEALTHCARE PARTNERS SOUTH FLORIDA, LLC—See DaVita Inc.; *U.S. Public*, pg. 639
HEALTHCARE PERFORMANCE PARTNERS—See Vizient, Inc.; *U.S. Private*, pg. 4407
HEALTHCARE REALTY HOLDINGS, L.P.—See Healthcare Realty Trust Incorporated; *U.S. Public*, pg. 1015
HEALTHCARE REALTY SERVICES INCORPORATED—See Healthcare Realty Trust Incorporated; *U.S. Public*, pg. 1015
HEALTHCARE REALTY TRUST INCORPORATED; *U.S. Public*, pg. 1015
HEALTHCARE REGIONAL MARKETING (HRM); *U.S. Private*, pg. 1895
HEALTH CARE REIT, LLC—See Welltower Inc.; *U.S. Public*, pg. 2348
HEALTHCARE RESOURCE NETWORK LLC; *U.S. Private*, pg. 1895
HEALTHCARE REVENUE RECOVERY GROUP, LLC—See Blackstone Inc.; *U.S. Public*, pg. 359
HEALTHCARE RISK SPECIALISTS, LLC—See Captive Resources, LLC; *U.S. Private*, pg. 747
HEALTHCARE ROYALTY, INC.; *U.S. Public*, pg. 1015
HEALTH CARE SERVICE CORPORATION; *U.S. Private*, pg. 1892
HEALTHCARE SERVICES ACQUISITION CORPORATION; *U.S. Public*, pg. 1015
HEALTHCARE SERVICES GROUP, INC.; *U.S. Public*, pg. 1015
HEALTH CARE SOLUTIONS AT HOME INC.—See Linde plc; *Int'l*, pg. 4505
HEALTHCARE SOLUTIONS HOLDING, LLC—See Cardinal Health, Inc.; *U.S. Public*, pg. 434
HEALTHCARE SOLUTIONS, INC.—See UnitedHealth Group Incorporated; *U.S. Public*, pg. 2247
HEALTHCARE SOLUTIONS MANAGEMENT GROUP, INC.—See Cardinal Health, Inc.; *U.S. Public*, pg. 434
HEALTHCARE SOLUTIONS TEAM, LLC—See The Allstate Corporation; *U.S. Public*, pg. 2033
HEALTHCARESOURCE HR, INC.—See Clearlake Capital Group, L.P.; *U.S. Private*, pg. 937
HEALTHCARESOURCE HR, INC.—See SkyKnight Capital LLC; *U.S. Private*, pg. 3685
HEALTHCARE SPECIAL OPPORTUNITIES FUND; *Int'l*, pg. 3304
HEALTHCARE STAFFING INC; *U.S. Private*, pg. 1895
HEALTHCARE STAFFING, INC.—See Novation Companies, Inc.; *U.S. Public*, pg. 1548
HEALTHCARE STRATEGY GROUP, LLC; *U.S. Private*, pg. 1895
HEALTHCARE SUPPORT SERVICES, LLC—See HCA Healthcare, Inc.; *U.S. Public*, pg. 998

HEALTHCARE SUPPORT STAFFING, INC.; *U.S. Private*, pg. 1895
HEALTHCARE SYSTEMS & TECHNOLOGIES, LLC; *U.S. Private*, pg. 1895
HEALTHCARE-TECH CORPORATION—See Air Water Inc.; *Int'l*, pg. 240
HEALTHCARE TECHNICAL SERVICES SDN. BHD.—See Johor Corporation; *Int'l*, pg. 3994
HEALTHCARE TRIANGLE, INC.; *U.S. Public*, pg. 1015
THE HEALTHCARE UNDERWRITING COMPANY, A RISK RETENTION GROUP—See Tenet Healthcare Corporation; *U.S. Public*, pg. 2009
HEALTHCARE USA OF MISSOURI, LLC—See CVS Health Corporation; *U.S. Public*, pg. 615
HEALTH CAROUSEL, LLC; *U.S. Private*, pg. 1892
HEALTH CATALYST, INC.; *U.S. Public*, pg. 1014
THE HEALTH CENTER OF HERMITAGE, LLC—See National HealthCare Corporation; *U.S. Public*, pg. 1496
THE HEALTHCENTRAL NETWORK, INC.—See Topspin Partners, L.P.; *U.S. Private*, pg. 4188
HEALTHCHAMPION PARTNERS LLC; *U.S. Private*, pg. 1895
HEALTHCHANNELS, INC.; *U.S. Private*, pg. 1895
HEALTH-CHEM CORP.; *U.S. Public*, pg. 1015
HEALTH-CHEM DIAGNOSTICS LLC—See PL Development, Inc.; *U.S. Private*, pg. 3194
HEALTH CIRCLE, INC.—See Acreage Holdings, Inc.; *U.S. Public*, pg. 36
HEALTHCITY LUXEMBOURG S.A.—See Basic-Fit NV; *Int'l*, pg. 886
HEALTHCLICK CO., LTD.—See CMIC Holdings Co., Ltd.; *Int'l*, pg. 1670
HEALTH CLUB ACQUISITIONS LTD—See Nuffield Health; *Int'l*, pg. 5487
HEALTH COEVO AG—See BAWAG Group AG; *Int'l*, pg. 900
HEALTHCO HEALTHCARE & WELLNESS REIT; *Int'l*, pg. 3304
HEALTH COMMUNICATION NETWORK PTY LIMITED—See Affinity Equity Partners (HK) Ltd.; *Int'l*, pg. 186
HEALTHCOMMUNITIES.COM, INC.; *U.S. Private*, pg. 1895
HEALTHCOMPARE INSURANCE SERVICES, INC.—See The Allstate Corporation; *U.S. Public*, pg. 2033
HEALTH COMPLEX MEDICAL, INC.—See AdaptHealth Corp.; *U.S. Public*, pg. 39
HEALTHCOMP LLC—See New Mountain Capital, LLC; *U.S. Private*, pg. 2902
HEALTHCONN CORP.; *Int'l*, pg. 3304
HEALTH CORE, INC.—See Elevance Health, Inc.; *U.S. Public*, pg. 730
HEALTHCREST SURGICAL PARTNERS, LLC; *U.S. Private*, pg. 1896
HEALTH DATA MANAGEMENT PARTNERS SA—See Cegedim S.A.; *Int'l*, pg. 1390
HEALTH DATA & MANAGEMENT SOLUTIONS, INC.—See CVS Health Corporation; *U.S. Public*, pg. 614
HEALTH DATA & MANAGEMENT SOLUTIONS, INC.—See CVS Health Corporation; *U.S. Public*, pg. 615
HEALTHDATIX, INC.—See NUTEX HEALTH INC.; *U.S. Public*, pg. 1555
HEALTH DELIVERY INC.; *U.S. Private*, pg. 1893
HEALTH DESIGNS, INC.; *U.S. Private*, pg. 1893
HEALTH DIAGNOSTICS MANAGEMENT, LLC—See FONAR Corporation; *U.S. Public*, pg. 863
HEALTH DIALOG ANALYTIC SOLUTIONS CORP.—See New Rite Aid, LLC; *U.S. Private*, pg. 2905
HEALTH DIALOG SERVICES CORP.—See New Rite Aid, LLC; *U.S. Private*, pg. 2905
HEALTH DIMENSIONS GROUP; *U.S. Private*, pg. 1893
HEALTH DIRECT, INC.—See American International Group, Inc.; *U.S. Public*, pg. 107
HEALTH DIRECTIONS INC.; *U.S. Private*, pg. 1893
HEALTH DISCOVERY CORPORATION; *U.S. Public*, pg. 1014
HEALTHDRIVE CORPORATION—See Cressey & Company, LP; *U.S. Private*, pg. 1095
HEALTHEASE OF FLORIDA INC.—See Centene Corporation; *U.S. Public*, pg. 471
HEALTHEAST CARE SYSTEM—See Fairview Health Services; *U.S. Private*, pg. 1464
HEALTHEAST ST. JOHN'S HOSPITAL—See Fairview Health Services; *U.S. Private*, pg. 1464
HEALTHE CARE AUSTRALIA PTY LTD.—See Luye Medical Group; *Int'l*, pg. 4589
HEALTHEDGE INVESTMENT PARTNERS, LLC; *U.S. Private*, pg. 1896
HEALTHEDGE SOFTWARE, INC.—See Blackstone Inc.; *U.S. Public*, pg. 354
HEALTH EDUCATION SERVICES, LLC—See Community Health Systems, Inc.; *U.S. Public*, pg. 553
HEALTH EDUCATION SOLUTIONS, INC.—See Nelnet, Inc.; *U.S. Public*, pg. 1504
HEALTHE GOODS; *U.S. Private*, pg. 1896
HEALTH EMPIRE CORPORATION PUBLIC COMPANY LIMITED; *Int'l*, pg. 3303
HEALTH ENTERPRISE PARTNERS LLC; *U.S. Private*, pg. 1893

HEALTHEQUITY, INC.; *U.S. Public*, pg. 1015
HEALTH E SYSTEMS, LLC; *U.S. Private*, pg. 1893
HEALTH EVOLUTION PARTNERS, LLC; *U.S. Private*, pg. 1893
HEALTH FACILITY SOLUTIONS CO., (HFS); *U.S. Private*, pg. 1893
HEALTH FEDERATION OF PHILADELPHIA; *U.S. Private*, pg. 1893
HEALTH FIDELITY, INC.—See Edifecs, Inc.; *U.S. Private*, pg. 1336
HEALTHFIELD HOME HEALTH, LLC—See Humana, Inc.; *U.S. Public*, pg. 1069
HEALTHFINCH, LLC—See Health Catalyst, Inc.; *U.S. Public*, pg. 1014
HEALTHFIRST BLUEGRASS; *U.S. Private*, pg. 1896
HEALTHFIRST CORP.; *U.S. Private*, pg. 1896
HEALTHFIRST, INC.; *U.S. Private*, pg. 1896
HEALTHFIRST NETWORK; *U.S. Private*, pg. 1896
HEALTH FITNESS CONCEPTS RN, LLC—See Cardiac Imaging Solutions, LLC; *U.S. Private*, pg. 749
HEALTH FITNESS CORPORATION—See Trustmark Mutual Holding Company; *U.S. Private*, pg. 4251
HEALTHFLEX HOME HEALTH SERVICES; *U.S. Private*, pg. 1896
HEALTH FOCUS HOLDINGS INC.—See OSIM International Ltd.; *Int'l*, pg. 5650
HEALTH FOOD ASSOCIATES, INC.—See AMCON Distributing Company; *U.S. Public*, pg. 93
HEALTHFUSION HOLDINGS, INC.—See Thoma Bravo, L.P.; *U.S. Private*, pg. 4150
HEALTHFUSION, INC.—See Thoma Bravo, L.P.; *U.S. Private*, pg. 4150
HEALTHGRADES OPERATING COMPANY, INC.—See Vestar Capital Partners, LLC; *U.S. Private*, pg. 4371
HEALTH GRID, LLC—See Veradigm Inc.; *U.S. Public*, pg. 2280
HEALTHGUARD HEALTH BENEFITS FUND LTD—See HBF Health Ltd.; *Int'l*, pg. 3295
HEALTHGUARD OF LANCASTER—See Highmark Health; *U.S. Private*, pg. 1940
HEALTH & HAPPINESS (H&H) TRADING INDIA PRIVATE LIMITED—See Health and Happiness (H&H) International Holdings Limited; *Int'l*, pg. 3303
HEALTH HAVEN PTY LTD—See Sigma Healthcare Ltd.; *Int'l*, pg. 6907
HEALTH HORIZONS ENTERPRISES PTE. LTD.—See Bumrungrad Hospital Public Company Limited; *Int'l*, pg. 1215
HEALTH HOUSE INTERNATIONAL LIMITED—See Melodiol Global Health Limited; *Int'l*, pg. 4812
HEALTHIA LIMITED—See Pacific Equity Partners Pty. Limited; *Int'l*, pg. 5688
HEALTHIER CHOICES MANAGEMENT CORP.; *U.S. Public*, pg. 1016
HEALTH IMAGING & CHECK-UP CENTRE LIMITED—See Kato (Hong Kong) Holdings Limited; *Int'l*, pg. 4090
HEALTH IMPERATIVES, INC.; *U.S. Private*, pg. 1893
HEALTH INFORMATION DESIGNS, INC.—See HDI Solutions, Inc.; *U.S. Private*, pg. 1890
HEALTH INNOVATION TECHNOLOGIES INC.; *U.S. Private*, pg. 1893
HEALTHINSIGHT MANAGEMENT CORPORATION; *U.S. Private*, pg. 1896
HEALTHINSIGHT NEW MEXICO—See HealthInsight Management Corporation; *U.S. Private*, pg. 1896
HEALTHINSIGHT OF NEVADA—See HealthInsight Management Corporation; *U.S. Private*, pg. 1896
HEALTHINSIGHT OREGON—See HealthInsight Management Corporation; *U.S. Private*, pg. 1896
HEALTHINSIGHT UTAH—See HealthInsight Management Corporation; *U.S. Private*, pg. 1896
HEALTH INSURANCE PLAN OF GREATER NEW YORK—See EmblemHealth, Inc.; *U.S. Private*, pg. 1378
HEALTH INTEGRATED, INC.—See ExlService Holdings, Inc.; *U.S. Public*, pg. 807
HEALTH INTELLIGENCE COMPANY LLC—See GuideWell Mutual Holding Corporation; *U.S. Private*, pg. 1814
HEALTH ITALIA S.P.A.; *Int'l*, pg. 3303
HEALTHIX, INC.; *U.S. Private*, pg. 1896
HEALTHJUMP, INC.; *U.S. Private*, pg. 1897
HEALTHKEEPERS, INC.—See Elevance Health, Inc.; *U.S. Public*, pg. 729
HEALTHLAND, INC. - GLENWOOD—See TruBridge, Inc.; *U.S. Public*, pg. 2198
HEALTHLAND, INC.—See TruBridge, Inc.; *U.S. Public*, pg. 2198
HEALTH LANGUAGE, INC.—See Wolters Kluwer n.v.; *Int'l*, pg. 8444
HEALTHLIFT MEDICAL TRANSPORTATION, INC.—See The Ensign Group, Inc.; *U.S. Public*, pg. 2071
HEALTHLINC, INC.; *U.S. Private*, pg. 1897
HEALTHLINE MEDICAL EQUIPMENT, INC.—See AdaptHealth Corp.; *U.S. Public*, pg. 39
HEALTHLINE NETWORKS, INC.; *U.S. Private*, pg. 1897
HEALTHLINK HMO, INC.—See Elevance Health, Inc.; *U.S. Public*, pg. 730
HEALTHLINK, INC.—See Elevance Health, Inc.; *U.S. Public*, pg. 730

HEALTHLINE NETWORKS, INC. — CORPORATE AFFILIATIONS

HEALTHLINK NEW ZEALAND GROUP LIMITED—See HFBG Holding B.V.; *Int'l*, pg. 3375
HEALTHLOGIC SYSTEMS CORPORATION—See Bank of America Corporation; *U.S. Public*, pg. 271
HEALTH LOGISTICS GMBH—See PHOENIX Pharmahandel GmbH & Co. KG; *Int'l*, pg. 5854
HEALTHLYNKED CORP.; *U.S. Public*, pg. 1016
HEALTH-LYNX, INC.—See The Cigna Group; *U.S. Public*, pg. 2061
HEALTH MANAGEMENT ASSOCIATES, INC.; *U.S. Private*, pg. 1893
HEALTH MANAGEMENT ASSOCIATES, LLC—See Community Health Systems, Inc.; *U.S. Public*, pg. 553
HEALTH MANAGEMENT ASSOCIATES OF WEST VIRGINIA, INC.—See Community Health Systems, Inc.; *U.S. Public*, pg. 553
HEALTH MANAGEMENT CORPORATION OF AMERICA—See FONAR Corporation; *U.S. Public*, pg. 863
HEALTH MANAGEMENT CORPORATION—See Elevance Health, Inc.; *U.S. Public*, pg. 730
THE HEALTH MANAGEMENT GROUP, INC.; *U.S. Private*, pg. 4043
HEALTH MANAGEMENT INTERNATIONAL LTD.—See EQT AB; *Int'l*, pg. 2475
HEALTH MANAGEMENT LIMITED—See MAXIMUS, Inc.; *U.S. Public*, pg. 1402
HEALTH MANAGEMENT SERVICES INC.; *U.S. Private*, pg. 1894
HEALTH MANAGEMENT SYSTEMS, INC.—See Veritas Capital Fund Management, LLC; *U.S. Private*, pg. 4362
HEALTHMARKETS, INC.—See Blackstone Inc.; *U.S. Public*, pg. 354
HEALTHMARK INDUSTRIES CO. INC.—See Getinge AB; *Int'l*, pg. 2951
HEALTH MEDIA VENTURES INC. - LOS ANGELES—See Meredith Corporation; *U.S. Public*, pg. 1423
HEALTH MEDIA VENTURES INC.—See Meredith Corporation; *U.S. Public*, pg. 1422
HEALTHNBIO, INC.—See UbiVelox Co., Ltd.; *Int'l*, pg. 8004
HEALTH NET ACCESS, INC.—See Centene Corporation; *U.S. Public*, pg. 469
HEALTH NET FEDERAL SERVICES, LLC—See Centene Corporation; *U.S. Public*, pg. 469
HEALTHNET, INC.; *U.S. Private*, pg. 1897
HEALTHNET INTERNATIONAL (PVT) LTD.—See Hemas Holdings PLC; *Int'l*, pg. 3340
HEALTH NET, LLC—See Centene Corporation; *U.S. Public*, pg. 469
HEALTH NETWORK GROUP, LLC—See The Allstate Corporation; *U.S. Public*, pg. 2033
HEALTH NETWORK ONE, INC.—See H.I.G. Capital, LLC; *U.S. Private*, pg. 1833
HEALTH & NUTRITION TECHNOLOGY, INC.—See CalNutri, Inc.; *U.S. Private*, pg. 723
HEALTHOME INC.; *U.S. Private*, pg. 1897
HEALTHONE CLINIC SERVICES - CANCER SPECIALTIES, LLC—See HCA Healthcare, Inc.; *U.S. Public*, pg. 998
HEALTHONE CLINIC SERVICES - PRIMARY CARE, LLC—See HCA Healthcare, Inc.; *U.S. Public*, pg. 998
HEALTHONE COLORADO CARE PARTNERS ACO LLC—See HCA Healthcare, Inc.; *U.S. Public*, pg. 998
HEALTHONE HEART CARE LLC—See HCA Healthcare, Inc.; *U.S. Public*, pg. 998
HEALTHONE MENTAL HEALTH THERAPY CENTER, LLC—See HCA Healthcare, Inc.; *U.S. Public*, pg. 998
HEALTHONE OF DENVER, INC.—See HCA Healthcare, Inc.; *U.S. Public*, pg. 998
HEALTHONE RIDGE VIEW ENDOSCOPY CENTER, LLC—See HCA Healthcare, Inc.; *U.S. Public*, pg. 998
HEALTH OPTIONS, INC.—See GuideWell Mutual Holding Corporation; *U.S. Private*, pg. 1814
HEALTHPAC COMPUTER SYSTEMS, INC.; *U.S. Private*, pg. 1897
HEALTHPARTNERS, INC.; *U.S. Private*, pg. 1897
HEALTH PARTNERS, INC.; *U.S. Private*, pg. 1894
HEALTH PARTNERS OF KANSAS, INC.—See HCA Healthcare, Inc.; *U.S. Public*, pg. 998
HEALTHPEAK OP, LLC—See Healthpeak Properties, Inc.; *U.S. Public*, pg. 1016
HEALTHPEAK PROPERTIES, INC.; *U.S. Public*, pg. 1016
HEALTH PHARMA SPA—See Health Biosciences SpA; *Int'l*, pg. 3303
HEALTH PLAN ADMINISTRATORS, INC.—See Geneve Holdings Corp.; *U.S. Private*, pg. 1670
HEALTHPLAN HOLDINGS, INC.—See Water Street Healthcare Partners, LLC; *U.S. Private*, pg. 4452
HEALTH PLAN OF NEVADA, INC.—See UnitedHealth Group Incorporated; *U.S. Public*, pg. 2252
HEALTHPLANONE, LLC—See Peloton Equity LLC; *U.S. Private*, pg. 3131
HEALTHPLAN SERVICES, INC.—See Wipro Limited; *Int'l*, pg. 8432
HEALTH PLANS, INC.—See Harvard Pilgrim Health Care, Inc.; *U.S. Private*, pg. 1875
HEALTHPLEX, INC.—See Managed Care of North America, Inc.; *U.S. Private*, pg. 2559

HEALTH PLUS MANAGEMENT, LLC—See Investcorp Holdings B.S.C.; *Int'l*, pg. 3775
HEALTHPOINTCAPITAL, LLC; *U.S. Private*, pg. 1897
HEALTHPOINT, LTD.—See Smith & Nephew plc; *Int'l*, pg. 7009
HEALTHPOINT MEDICAL GROUP—See BayCare Health System Inc.; *U.S. Private*, pg. 495
HEALTHPOINT OF NORTH CAROLINA, L.L.C.—See Tenet Healthcare Corporation; *U.S. Public*, pg. 2003
HEALTHPOINT; *U.S. Private*, pg. 1897
HEALTH PRODUCTS CORPORATION; *U.S. Private*, pg. 1894
HEALTH PRODUCTS PLUS, INC.—See AdaptHealth Corp.; *U.S. Public*, pg. 39
HEALTH PROFESSIONS EDUCATION FOUNDATION; *U.S. Private*, pg. 1894
HEALTHPRO LIFE SDN. BHD.—See Medi Lifestyle Limited; *Int'l*, pg. 4769
HEALTHPRO MARKETING SDN. BHD.—See Medi Lifestyle Limited; *Int'l*, pg. 4769
HEALTH PROOF INTERNATIONAL COMPANY LIMITED—See Shunten International (Holdings) Limited; *Int'l*, pg. 6870
HEALTHPRO PHARMA PTE. LTD.—See Medi Lifestyle Limited; *Int'l*, pg. 4769
HEALTH QUEST SYSTEMS, INC.; *U.S. Private*, pg. 1894
HEALTHREACH COMMUNITY HEALTH CENTERS; *U.S. Private*, pg. 1897
HEALTH RECOVERY SOLUTIONS INC.; *U.S. Private*, pg. 1894
HEALTH RESEARCH INC.; *U.S. Private*, pg. 1894
HEALTH RESOURCES NORTHWEST; *U.S. Private*, pg. 1894
HEALTH RESOURCES OF EMERY, L.L.C.—See Welltower Inc.; *U.S. Public*, pg. 2348
HEALTH RESOURCES OF GLASTONBURY, INC.—See Welltower Inc.; *U.S. Public*, pg. 2348
HEALTH REVENUE ASSURANCE HOLDINGS, INC.; *U.S. Public*, pg. 1015
HEALTHRIGHT 360; *U.S. Private*, pg. 1897
HEALTH-RIGHT DISCOVERIES, INC.; *U.S. Private*, pg. 1894
HEALTH RISK RESOURCE GROUP INC.—See Principal Financial Group, Inc.; *U.S. Public*, pg. 1720
HEALTH & SAFETY INSTITUTE INC.—See Waud Capital Partners LLC; *U.S. Private*, pg. 4457
HEALTH SCIENCE COMMUNICATIONS—See Omnicom Group Inc.; *U.S. Public*, pg. 1586
HEALTH SCIENCES CORPORATION—See SMK Imaging, LLC; *U.S. Private*, pg. 3698
HEALTH SCIENCES GROUP, INC.; *U.S. Public*, pg. 1015
HEALTHSCIENCES INTERNATIONAL PTE. LTD.—See New Silkroutes Group Limited; *Int'l*, pg. 5227
HEALTH SCIENCES SOUTH CAROLINA; *U.S. Private*, pg. 1894
HEALTHSCOPE BENEFITS, INC.; *U.S. Private*, pg. 1897
HEALTHSCOPE NEW ZEALAND LIMITED—See Brookfield Corporation; *Int'l*, pg. 1176
HEALTHSCOPE OPERATIONS PTY. LTD.—See Brookfield Corporation; *Int'l*, pg. 1176
HEALTHSCOPE PTY. LTD.—See Brookfield Corporation; *Int'l*, pg. 1176
HEALTHSCOPE (TASMANIA) PTY. LTD.—See Brookfield Corporation; *Int'l*, pg. 1176
HEALTH SERVICES GROUP, INC.; *U.S. Private*, pg. 1894
HEALTH SERVICES MANAGEMENT, INC.; *U.S. Private*, pg. 1894
HEALTH SERVICES NETWORK HOSPITALS, INC.—See Tenet Healthcare Corporation; *U.S. Public*, pg. 2002
HEALTH SERVICES OF NORTHERN NEW YORK, INC.—See The Hamister Group, Inc.; *U.S. Private*, pg. 4042
HEALTH SHARE OF OREGON; *U.S. Private*, pg. 1894
HEALTHSMART BENEFIT SOLUTIONS, INC.—See HealthSmart Holdings, Inc.; *U.S. Private*, pg. 1897
HEALTHSMART CASUALTY CLAIMS SOLUTIONS—See HealthSmart Holdings, Inc.; *U.S. Private*, pg. 1897
HEALTHSMART HOLDINGS, INC.; *U.S. Private*, pg. 1897
HEALTH SMART LIMITED—See Hong Kong Economic Times Holdings Ltd; *Int'l*, pg. 3465
HEALTH SOLUTIONS, LLC; *U.S. Private*, pg. 1894
HEALTH SOLUTIONS (MALAYSIA) SDN. BHD—See PSC Corporation Ltd.; *Int'l*, pg. 6015
HEALTH SOLUTIONS SERVICES SDN. BHD—See PSC Corporation Ltd.; *Int'l*, pg. 6015
HEALTHSOURCE GLOBAL STAFFING, INC.—See AMN Healthcare Services, Inc.; *U.S. Public*, pg. 125
HEALTHSOURCE OF OHIO; *U.S. Private*, pg. 1897
HEALTHSOURCE; *U.S. Private*, pg. 1897
HEALTHSOUTH CLINICAL TECHNOLOGIES, LLC—See Encompass Health Corporation; *U.S. Public*, pg. 756
HEALTHSOUTH EAST VALLEY REHABILITATION HOSPITAL, LLC—See Encompass Health Corporation; *U.S. Public*, pg. 756
HEALTHSOUTH HARMARVILLE REHABILITATION HOSPITAL, LLC—See Encompass Health Corporation; *U.S. Public*, pg. 756

HEALTHSOUTH LITTLETON REHABILITATION, LLC—See Encompass Health Corporation; *U.S. Public*, pg. 756
HEALTHSOUTH MESA REHABILITATION HOSPITAL, LLC—See Encompass Health Corporation; *U.S. Public*, pg. 756
HEALTHSOUTH MIDDLETOWN REHABILITATION HOSPITAL, LLC—See Encompass Health Corporation; *U.S. Public*, pg. 756
HEALTHSOUTH OF AUSTIN, INC.—See Encompass Health Corporation; *U.S. Public*, pg. 757
HEALTHSOUTH OF DOTHAN, INC.—See Encompass Health Corporation; *U.S. Public*, pg. 758
HEALTHSOUTH OF EAST TENNESSEE, LLC—See Encompass Health Corporation; *U.S. Public*, pg. 758
HEALTHSOUTH OF HOUSTON, INC.—See Encompass Health Corporation; *U.S. Public*, pg. 758
HEALTHSOUTH OF LARGO LIMITED PARTNERSHIP—See Encompass Health Corporation; *U.S. Public*, pg. 758
HEALTHSOUTH OF MIDLAND, INC.—See Encompass Health Corporation; *U.S. Public*, pg. 758
HEALTHSOUTH OF NITTANY VALLEY, INC.—See Encompass Health Corporation; *U.S. Public*, pg. 758
HEALTHSOUTH OF PHENIX CITY, INC.—See Encompass Health Corporation; *U.S. Public*, pg. 758
HEALTHSOUTH OF READING, LLC—See Encompass Health Corporation; *U.S. Public*, pg. 758
HEALTHSOUTH OF SAN ANTONIO, INC.—See Encompass Health Corporation; *U.S. Public*, pg. 758
HEALTHSOUTH OF SEA PINES LIMITED PARTNERSHIP—See Encompass Health Corporation; *U.S. Public*, pg. 758
HEALTHSOUTH OF SOUTH CAROLINA, INC.—See Encompass Health Corporation; *U.S. Public*, pg. 758
HEALTHSOUTH OF SPRING HILL, INC.—See Encompass Health Corporation; *U.S. Public*, pg. 758
HEALTHSOUTH OF TEXARKANA, INC.—See Encompass Health Corporation; *U.S. Public*, pg. 758
HEALTHSOUTH OF TEXAS, INC.—See Encompass Health Corporation; *U.S. Public*, pg. 758
HEALTHSOUTH OF TOMS RIVER, LLC—See Encompass Health Corporation; *U.S. Public*, pg. 758
HEALTHSOUTH OF TREASURE COAST, INC.—See Encompass Health Corporation; *U.S. Public*, pg. 758
HEALTHSOUTH OF UTAH, INC.—See Encompass Health Corporation; *U.S. Public*, pg. 758
HEALTHSOUTH PLANO REHABILITATION HOSPITAL, LLC—See Encompass Health Corporation; *U.S. Public*, pg. 756
HEALTHSOUTH REHABILITATION CENTER, INC.—See Encompass Health Corporation; *U.S. Public*, pg. 756
HEALTHSOUTH REHABILITATION CENTER OF NEW HAMPSHIRE, INC.—See Encompass Health Corporation; *U.S. Public*, pg. 756
HEALTHSOUTH REHABILITATION HOSPITAL OF ARLINGTON, LLC—See Encompass Health Corporation; *U.S. Public*, pg. 756
HEALTHSOUTH REHABILITATION HOSPITAL OF AUSTIN, INC.—See Encompass Health Corporation; *U.S. Public*, pg. 756
HEALTHSOUTH REHABILITATION HOSPITAL OF BEAUMONT, LLC—See Encompass Health Corporation; *U.S. Public*, pg. 756
HEALTHSOUTH REHABILITATION HOSPITAL OF CHARLESTON, LLC—See Encompass Health Corporation; *U.S. Public*, pg. 757
HEALTHSOUTH REHABILITATION HOSPITAL OF CYPRESS, LLC—See Encompass Health Corporation; *U.S. Public*, pg. 757
HEALTHSOUTH REHABILITATION HOSPITAL OF DESERT CANYON, LLC—See Encompass Health Corporation; *U.S. Public*, pg. 757
HEALTHSOUTH REHABILITATION HOSPITAL OF FORT WORTH, LLC—See Encompass Health Corporation; *U.S. Public*, pg. 757
HEALTHSOUTH REHABILITATION HOSPITAL OF HENDERSON, LLC—See Encompass Health Corporation; *U.S. Public*, pg. 757
HEALTHSOUTH REHABILITATION HOSPITAL OF HUMBLE, LLC—See Encompass Health Corporation; *U.S. Public*, pg. 757
HEALTHSOUTH REHABILITATION HOSPITAL OF JONESBORO, LLC—See Encompass Health Corporation; *U.S. Public*, pg. 757
HEALTHSOUTH REHABILITATION HOSPITAL OF LARGO, LLC—See Encompass Health Corporation; *U.S. Public*, pg. 757
HEALTHSOUTH REHABILITATION HOSPITAL OF MANATI, INC.—See Encompass Health Corporation; *U.S. Public*, pg. 757
HEALTHSOUTH REHABILITATION HOSPITAL OF MARTIN COUNTY, LLC—See Encompass Health Corporation; *U.S. Public*, pg. 757
HEALTHSOUTH REHABILITATION HOSPITAL OF MECHANICSBURG, LLC—See Encompass Health Corporation; *U.S. Public*, pg. 757

COMPANY NAME INDEX

HEALTHSOUTH REHABILITATION HOSPITAL OF MIDLAND/ODESSA, LLC—See Encompass Health Corporation; *U.S. Public*, pg. 757
HEALTHSOUTH REHABILITATION HOSPITAL OF NEW MEXICO, INC.—See Encompass Health Corporation; *U.S. Public*, pg. 757
HEALTHSOUTH REHABILITATION HOSPITAL OF NEWNAN, LLC—See Encompass Health Corporation; *U.S. Public*, pg. 757
HEALTHSOUTH REHABILITATION HOSPITAL OF NORTH HOUSTON, LP—See Encompass Health Corporation; *U.S. Public*, pg. 757
HEALTHSOUTH REHABILITATION HOSPITAL OF PETERSBURG, LLC—See Encompass Health Corporation; *U.S. Public*, pg. 757
HEALTHSOUTH REHABILITATION HOSPITAL OF READING, LLC—See Encompass Health Corporation; *U.S. Public*, pg. 757
HEALTHSOUTH REHABILITATION HOSPITAL OF SAN JUAN, INC.—See Encompass Health Corporation; *U.S. Public*, pg. 757
HEALTHSOUTH REHABILITATION HOSPITAL OF SARASOTA, LLC—See Encompass Health Corporation; *U.S. Public*, pg. 757
HEALTHSOUTH REHABILITATION HOSPITAL OF SEMINOLE COUNTY, LLC—See Encompass Health Corporation; *U.S. Public*, pg. 757
HEALTHSOUTH REHABILITATION HOSPITAL OF SEWICKLEY, LLC—See Encompass Health Corporation; *U.S. Public*, pg. 757
HEALTHSOUTH REHABILITATION HOSPITAL OF SOUTH JERSEY, LLC—See Encompass Health Corporation; *U.S. Public*, pg. 757
HEALTHSOUTH REHABILITATION HOSPITAL OF TALLAHASSEE, LLC—See Encompass Health Corporation; *U.S. Public*, pg. 757
HEALTHSOUTH REHABILITATION HOSPITAL OF TEXARKANA, INC.—See Encompass Health Corporation; *U.S. Public*, pg. 757
HEALTHSOUTH REHABILITATION HOSPITAL OF UTAH, LLC—See Encompass Health Corporation; *U.S. Public*, pg. 757
HEALTHSOUTH REHABILITATION HOSPITAL THE WOODLANDS, INC.—See Encompass Health Corporation; *U.S. Public*, pg. 756
HEALTHSOUTH REHABILITATION INSTITUTE OF SAN ANTONIO (RIOSA), INC.—See Encompass Health Corporation; *U.S. Public*, pg. 757
HEALTHSOUTH REHABILITATION INSTITUTE OF TUCSON, LLC—See Encompass Health Corporation; *U.S. Public*, pg. 757
HEALTHSOUTH SCOTTSDALE REHABILITATION HOSPITAL, LLC—See Encompass Health Corporation; *U.S. Public*, pg. 757
HEALTHSOUTH SUNRISE REHABILITATION HOSPITAL, LLC—See Encompass Health Corporation; *U.S. Public*, pg. 757
HEALTHSOUTH VALLEY OF THE SUN REHABILITATION HOSPITAL, LLC—See Encompass Health Corporation; *U.S. Public*, pg. 757
HEALTHSOUTH WALTON REHABILITATION HOSPITAL, LLC—See Encompass Health Corporation; *U.S. Public*, pg. 757
HEALTHSPAN, INC.—See Catholic Healthcare Partners; *U.S. Private*, pg. 792
HEALTHSPARQ, INC.—See Cambia Health Solutions, Inc.; *U.S. Private*, pg. 726
HEALTH SPAS GUIDE (PTY) LTD.—See Caxton and CTP Publishers and Printers Ltd.; *Int'l*, pg. 1363
HEALTH SPECIAL RISK, INC.—See Brown & Brown, Inc.; *U.S. Public*, pg. 401
HEALTHSPRING, INC.—See The Cigna Group; *U.S. Public*, pg. 2061
HEALTHSPRING OF FLORIDA, INC.—See The Cigna Group; *U.S. Public*, pg. 2061
HEALTHSTAR COMMUNICATIONS, INC.; *U.S. Private*, pg. 1898
HEALTHSTAT, INC.—See New Enterprise Associates, LLC; *U.S. Private*, pg. 2895
HEALTHSTREAM, INC.; *U.S. Public*, pg. 1016
HEALTHSTREAM RESEARCH—See HealthStream, Inc.; *U.S. Public*, pg. 1017
HEALTHSTREAM RESEARCH—See HealthStream, Inc.; *U.S. Public*, pg. 1017
HEALTHSTRONG PTY LTD—See Medibank Private Limited; *Int'l*, pg. 4774
HEALTHSTYLE PRESS—See Interactivation Health Networks LLC; *U.S. Private*, pg. 2108
HEALTHSUN HEALTH PLANS, INC.—See Elevance Health, Inc.; *U.S. Public*, pg. 730
HEALTH SUPPORT LIMITED—See EBOS Group Limited; *Int'l*, pg. 2285
HEALTH SYSTEMS COOPERATIVE LAUNDRIES; *U.S. Private*, pg. 1894
HEALTH SYSTEMS INTERNATIONAL, LLC—See Great Point Partners, LLC; *U.S. Private*, pg. 1767
HEALTH SYSTEMS SOLUTIONS, INC.—See Sandata Holdings, Inc.; *U.S. Private*, pg. 3542

HEALTH SYSTEM TECHNOLOGIES (PTY) LTD—See African Equity Empowerment Investmts Limited; *Int'l*, pg. 191
HEALTHTAP, INC.; *U.S. Private*, pg. 1898
HEALTH TECHNOLOGY RESOURCES, LLC—See Quipt Home Medical Corp.; *U.S. Public*, pg. 1757
HEALTH TECHNOLOGY SOLUTIONS, INC.—See Rennova Health, Inc.; *U.S. Public*, pg. 1783
HEALTHTECH SOLUTIONS, INC.; *U.S. Public*, pg. 1017
HEALTH TESTING CENTERS, INC.—See Laboratory Corporation of America Holdings; *U.S. Public*, pg. 1287
HEALTHTIQUE DURHAM LLC—See Healthtique Group LLC; *U.S. Private*, pg. 1898
HEALTHTIQUE GROUP LLC; *U.S. Private*, pg. 1898
HEALTHTIQUE WINSTON SALEM LLC—See Healthtique Group LLC; *U.S. Private*, pg. 1898
HEALTHTRACK SPORTS & WELLNESS, LLC—See Northwestern Memorial HealthCare; *U.S. Private*, pg. 2962
HEALTHTRACK SPORTS & WELLNESS, LLC—See Wheaton-Oaks Sport Center, Inc.; *U.S. Private*, pg. 4505
HEALTHTRAX INC.; *U.S. Private*, pg. 1898
HEALTHTRAX INTERNATIONAL INC.—See Healthtrax Inc.; *U.S. Private*, pg. 1898
HEALTHTRIO, LLC; *U.S. Private*, pg. 1898
HEALTHTRONICS, INC.—See Altaris Capital Partners, LLC; *U.S. Private*, pg. 206
HEALTHTRUST EUROPE COMPANY LIMITED—See HCA Healthcare, Inc.; *U.S. Public*, pg. 998
HEALTHTRUST - EUROPE LLP—See HCA Healthcare, Inc.; *U.S. Public*, pg. 998
HEALTHTRUST, L.L.C.—See Sabra Health Care REIT, Inc.; *U.S. Public*, pg. 1833
HEALTHTRUST PURCHASING GROUP, L.P.—See HCA Healthcare, Inc.; *U.S. Public*, pg. 1005
THE HEALTH TRUST; *U.S. Private*, pg. 4044
HEALTHTRUST WORKFORCE SOLUTIONS, LLC—See HCA Healthcare, Inc.; *U.S. Public*, pg. 998
HEALTH UNION, LLC; *U.S. Private*, pg. 1894
HEALTH UNLIMITED LLC—See Accenture plc; *Int'l*, pg. 87
HEALTHWAREHOUSE.COM, INC.; *U.S. Public*, pg. 1017
HEALTHWARE SOLUTIONS, LLC—See MD On-Line Inc.; *U.S. Private*, pg. 2646
HEALTH WATER BOTTLING CO. LTD.—See The Olayan Group; *Int'l*, pg. 7672
HEALTHWAY HOME PRODUCTS, INC.—See AE Industrial Partners, LP; *U.S. Private*, pg. 112
HEALTHWAY MEDICAL CORPORATION LIMITED—See OUE Limited; *Int'l*, pg. 5665
HEALTHWAY MEDICAL ENTERPRISES PTE LTD—See OUE Limited; *Int'l*, pg. 5666
HEALTHWAYS HEALTH SUPPORT—See Stone Point Capital LLC; *U.S. Private*, pg. 3825
HEALTHWAY SHOPPING NETWORK, INC.; *U.S. Private*, pg. 1898
HEALTHWAYS INTERNATIONAL, GMBH—See Stone Point Capital LLC; *U.S. Private*, pg. 3825
HEALTHWAYS WHOLEHEALTH NETWORKS, INC.—See Stone Point Capital LLC; *U.S. Private*, pg. 3825
HEALTHWELL FOUNDATION; *U.S. Private*, pg. 1898
HEALTHWELL MEDICAL INC.—See CU Medical Systems Inc.; *Int'l*, pg. 1875
HEALTH & WELLNESS SURGERY CENTER, L.P.—See Tenet Healthcare Corporation; *U.S. Public*, pg. 2003
HEALTHWISE, INCORPORATED—See KKR & Co. Inc.; *U.S. Public*, pg. 1254
HEALTHWISE; *U.S. Private*, pg. 1898
HEALTHWORLD COMMUNICATIONS GROUP (NETHERLANDS) BV—See WPP plc; *Int'l*, pg. 8489
HEALTHWORLD PAN GULF/DUBAI—See WPP plc; *Int'l*, pg. 8489
HEALTHWORLD (SCHWEIZ) AG—See WPP plc; *Int'l*, pg. 8489
HEALTH WRIGHT PRODUCTS, INC.—See International Flavors & Fragrances Inc.; *U.S. Public*, pg. 1152
HEALTHWYSE, LLC; *U.S. Private*, pg. 1898
HEALTHX, INC.—See Frontier Capital LLC; *U.S. Private*, pg. 1615
THE HEALTHY BACK INSTITUTE; *U.S. Private*, pg. 4044
HEALTHY COFFEE INTERNATIONAL, INC.; *U.S. Private*, pg. 1898
HEALTHYDAYS GROUP PLC; *Int'l*, pg. 3304
HEALTHY DIRECTIONS, LLC—See Helen of Troy Limited; *Int'l*, pg. 3328
HEALTHY EXTRACTS INC.; *U.S. Public*, pg. 1017
HEALTHY HOLDINGS, INC.—See North Castle Partners, LLC; *U.S. Private*, pg. 2943
HEALTHY LIFE AGRITEC LIMITED; *Int'l*, pg. 3304
HEALTHY LIFE GROUP PTY. LTD.—See Eu Yan Sang International Ltd.; *Int'l*, pg. 2525
HEALTHY NATURAL INC.—See RICEBRAN TECHNOLOGIES; *U.S. Public*, pg. 1797
HEALTHY NEIGHBORHOODS, INC.; *U.S. Private*, pg. 1898
HEALTHY PAWS PET INSURANCE LLC—See Aon plc; *Int'l*, pg. 495
HEALTHY PET, L.P.—See Kinderhook Industries, LLC; *U.S. Private*, pg. 2307

THE HEARST CORPORATION

HEALTHYPHARM B.V.—See Bain Capital, LP; *U.S. Private*, pg. 443
HEALTHYPHARM B.V.—See Cinven Limited; *Int'l*, pg. 1613
HEALTHY PHARMS, INC.—See 4Front Ventures Corp.; *U.S. Public*, pg. 9
HEALTHY PLANET PRODUCTS PUBLISHING, INC.; *U.S. Private*, pg. 1898
HEALTHY RETAIL LIMITED—See Whitbread PLC; *Int'l*, pg. 8398
HEALTHY SOFTWARE LTD.—See Vista Equity Partners, LLC; *U.S. Private*, pg. 4394
HEALTHY STATE, INC.—See HCA Healthcare, Inc.; *U.S. Public*, pg. 998
HEALTHY TIMES. INC.—See Health and Happiness (H&H) International Holdings Limited; *Int'l*, pg. 3303
HEA LUGU OU—See AS Ekspress Grupp; *Int'l*, pg. 590
HEALWELL AI INC.; *Int'l*, pg. 3304
HEALY TIBBITTS BUILDERS, INC.—See Kiewit Corp.; *U.S. Private*, pg. 2304
HEANY INDUSTRIES, INC.—See Crawford United Corporation; *U.S. Public*, pg. 592
HEAP SENG HENG (M) SDN. BHD.—See Mercury Industries Berhad; *Int'l*, pg. 4834
HEAP WAH BARAKAH SDN. BHD.—See PTT Synergy Group; *Int'l*, pg. 6093
HEAP WAH ENTERPRISE SDN. BHD.—See PTT Synergy Group; *Int'l*, pg. 6093
HEAR ATLAST HOLDINGS, INC.; *Int'l*, pg. 3304
HEAR.COM N.V.; *Int'l*, pg. 3304
HEARING HEALTHCARE MANAGEMENT, INC.—See Demant A/S; *Int'l*, pg. 2023
HEARING HELP EXPRESS, INC.—See IntriCon Corporation; *U.S. Public*, pg. 1159
HEARING HOLDING BELGIUM NV—See Demant A/S; *Int'l*, pg. 2023
HEARINGLIFE CANADA LTD.—See Demant A/S; *Int'l*, pg. 2023
HEARING RETAIL GROUP PTY. LTD.—See Sonova Holding AG; *Int'l*, pg. 7100
HEARING SCREENING ASSOCIATES LLC—See Demant A/S; *Int'l*, pg. 2023
HEARING SUPPLIES SA—See Amplifon S.p.A.; *Int'l*, pg. 435
HEARMEOUT LIMITED; *Int'l*, pg. 3304
THE HEARN COMPANY; *U.S. Private*, pg. 4044
HEARRON SALES, INC.—See Platinum Equity, LLC; *U.S. Private*, pg. 3209
HEARSAY SOCIAL, INC.—See Yext, Inc.; *U.S. Public*, pg. 2398
HEARST BALTIMORE RADIO MANAGEMENT—See The Hearst Corporation; *U.S. Private*, pg. 4048
HEARST BOOKS—See The Hearst Corporation; *U.S. Private*, pg. 4046
HEARST BRAND DEVELOPMENT—See The Hearst Corporation; *U.S. Private*, pg. 4044
HEARST BUSINESS MEDIA—See The Hearst Corporation; *U.S. Private*, pg. 4044
HEARST BUSINESS PUBLISHING, INC.—See The Hearst Corporation; *U.S. Private*, pg. 4045
HEARST COMMUNICATIONS, INC.—See The Hearst Corporation; *U.S. Private*, pg. 4045
THE HEARST CORPORATION; *U.S. Private*, pg. 4044
HEARST EDIMPRESA - EDITORA DE PUBLICACOES, LDA.—See Impresa SGPS S.A.; *Int'l*, pg. 3637
HEARST ELECTRONICS GROUP—See The Hearst Corporation; *U.S. Private*, pg. 4045
HEARST ENTERTAINMENT, INC.—See The Hearst Corporation; *U.S. Private*, pg. 4045
HEARST ENTERTAINMENT & SYNDICATION—See The Hearst Corporation; *U.S. Private*, pg. 4045
HEARST FUJINGAHO CO., LTD.—See Vivendi SE; *Int'l*, pg. 8274
HEARST INTEGRATED MEDIA—See The Hearst Corporation; *U.S. Private*, pg. 4046
HEARST INTERACTIVE MEDIA—See The Hearst Corporation; *U.S. Private*, pg. 4046
HEARST MAGAZINES DIGITAL MEDIA—See The Hearst Corporation; *U.S. Private*, pg. 4046
HEARST MAGAZINES INTERNATIONAL—See The Hearst Corporation; *U.S. Private*, pg. 4046
HEARST MAGAZINES NETHERLANDS—See Vivendi SE; *Int'l*, pg. 8273
HEARST MAGAZINES—See The Hearst Corporation; *U.S. Private*, pg. 4046
HEARST NEWSPAPERS—See The Hearst Corporation; *U.S. Private*, pg. 4047
HEARST NEWS SERVICE—See The Hearst Corporation; *U.S. Private*, pg. 4047
HEARST RANCH—See The Hearst Corporation; *U.S. Private*, pg. 4048
THE HEARST SERVICE CENTER, IN CHARLOTTE, N.C.—See The Hearst Corporation; *U.S. Private*, pg. 4049
HEARST TELEVISION, INC.—See The Hearst Corporation; *U.S. Private*, pg. 4048
HEART 102.4—See Global Radio Group Limited; *Int'l*, pg. 3000

1203

THE HEARST CORPORATION

CORPORATE AFFILIATIONS

HEART 103—See Global Radio Group Limited; *Int'l*, pg. 3000

THE HEART AND VASCULAR CLINIC, L.L.C.—See Tenet Healthcare Corporation; *U.S. Public*, pg. 2008

HEARTBEAM, INC.; *U.S. Public*, pg. 1017

HEARTBEAT DIGITAL; *U.S. Private*, pg. 1899

HEART DINING INC.—See H2O Retailing Corp.; *Int'l*, pg. 3200

HEARTFELT CREATIONS; *U.S. Private*, pg. 1899

HEART FM—See Global Radio Group Limited; *Int'l*, pg. 3000

THE HEART GROUP OF LANCASTER GENERAL HEALTH; *U.S. Private*, pg. 4049

HEARTH & CARE OF GREENFIELD, LLC—See Regional Health Properties, Inc.; *U.S. Public*, pg. 1775

HEARTH & HOME OF URBANA, LLC—See Regional Health Properties, Inc.; *U.S. Public*, pg. 1776

HEARTH & HOME OF VANDALIA, INC.—See Regional Health Properties, Inc.; *U.S. Public*, pg. 1776

HEARTH & HOME OF VAN WERT, LLC—See Regional Health Properties, Inc.; *U.S. Public*, pg. 1776

HEARTH & HOME TECHNOLOGIES, INC.—See HNI Corporation; *U.S. Public*, pg. 1043

HEARTHMARK, LLC—See Newell Brands Inc.; *U.S. Public*, pg. 1514

HEART HOME COUNTIES—See Global Radio Group Limited; *Int'l*, pg. 3000

HEART HOSPITAL OF AUSTIN, A CAMPUS OF ST. DAVIDS MEDICAL CENTER—See HCA Healthcare, Inc.; *U.S. Public*, pg. 998

HEART HOSPITAL OF NEW MEXICO, LLC—See Ventas, Inc.; *U.S. Public*, pg. 2278

HEARTHSIDE FOOD SOLUTIONS, LLC - GIBSON CITY—See Charlesbank Capital Partners, LLC; *U.S. Private*, pg. 855

HEARTHSIDE FOOD SOLUTIONS, LLC - GIBSON CITY—See Partners Group Holding AG; *Int'l*, pg. 5749

HEARTHSIDE FOOD SOLUTIONS, LLC - MCCOMB—See Charlesbank Capital Partners, LLC; *U.S. Private*, pg. 855

HEARTHSIDE FOOD SOLUTIONS, LLC - MCCOMB—See Partners Group Holding AG; *Int'l*, pg. 5749

HEARTHSIDE FOOD SOLUTIONS, LLC—See Charlesbank Capital Partners, LLC; *U.S. Private*, pg. 855

HEARTHSIDE FOOD SOLUTIONS, LLC—See Partners Group Holding AG; *Int'l*, pg. 5749

HEARTHSIDE HOMES, INC.—See California Coastal Communities, Inc.; *U.S. Private*, pg. 718

HEARTHSONG, INC.—See Evergreen Enterprises, Inc.; *U.S. Private*, pg. 1439

HEARTHSTONE ENTERPRISES, INC.; *U.S. Private*, pg. 1899

HEARTHSTONE INC.; *U.S. Private*, pg. 1899

HEARTHSTONE; *U.S. Private*, pg. 1899

HEARTHSTONE UTILITIES, INC.—See First Reserve Management, L.P.; *U.S. Private*, pg. 1525

HEARTLAND AG INC.; *U.S. Private*, pg. 1899

HEARTLAND AMERICA, INC.; *U.S. Private*, pg. 1899

HEARTLAND AUTOMOTIVE LLC.; *U.S. Private*, pg. 1899

HEARTLAND AVIATION, LLC—See Moelis Asset Management LP; *U.S. Private*, pg. 2764

HEARTLAND BANCCORP; *U.S. Public*, pg. 1017

HEARTLAND BANK LIMITED; *Int'l*, pg. 3304

HEARTLAND BANK—See Heartland BancCorp; *U.S. Public*, pg. 1017

HEARTLAND BANK & TRUST COMPANY—See HBT Financial, Inc.; *U.S. Public*, pg. 990

HEARTLAND BLOOD CENTERS; *U.S. Private*, pg. 1899

HEARTLAND BUILDING CENTER INC.; *U.S. Private*, pg. 1899

HEARTLAND BUSINESS CREDIT CORPORATION—See Midland States Bancorp, Inc.; *U.S. Public*, pg. 1445

HEARTLAND BUSINESS SYSTEMS; *U.S. Private*, pg. 1899

HEARTLAND CATFISH COMPANY, INC.; *U.S. Private*, pg. 1899

HEARTLAND CATFISH - GREENSBORO—See Heartland Catfish Company, Inc.; *U.S. Private*, pg. 1899

HEARTLAND COMMUNICATIONS GROUP—See Heartland Community Group Inc; *U.S. Private*, pg. 1899

HEARTLAND COMMUNITY GROUP INC; *U.S. Private*, pg. 1899

HEARTLAND COOPERATIVE SERVICES; *U.S. Private*, pg. 1899

HEARTLAND COOPERATIVE; *U.S. Private*, pg. 1899

HEARTLAND CREDIT UNION; *U.S. Private*, pg. 1899

HEARTLAND DENTAL, LLC—See KKR & Co. Inc.; *U.S. Public*, pg. 1252

HEARTLAND DERMATOLOGY AND SKIN CANCER CENTER, P.A.; *U.S. Private*, pg. 1899

HEARTLAND ENGINEERED PRODUCTS, LLC; *U.S. Private*, pg. 1900

HEARTLAND EQUIPMENT, INC.; *U.S. Private*, pg. 1900

HEARTLAND EQUITY MANAGEMENT LLC; *U.S. Private*, pg. 1900

HEARTLAND EXPRESS, INC., OF IOWA—See Heartland Express, Inc.; *U.S. Public*, pg. 1017

HEARTLAND EXPRESS, INC.; *U.S. Public*, pg. 1017

HEARTLAND FAMILY SERVICE; *U.S. Private*, pg. 1900

HEARTLAND FARMS INC.; *U.S. Private*, pg. 1900

HEARTLAND FINANCIAL GROUP, INC—See Integrity Marketing Group LLC; *U.S. Private*, pg. 2103

HEARTLAND FINANCIAL USA, INC.; *U.S. Public*, pg. 1017

HEARTLAND FOOD PRODUCTS, LLC—See BOK Financial Corporation; *U.S. Public*, pg. 367

HEARTLAND FOOD SERVICES INC.; *U.S. Private*, pg. 1900

HEARTLAND FOR CHILDREN; *U.S. Private*, pg. 1900

HEARTLAND FORD SALES, INC.; *Int'l*, pg. 3304

HEARTLAND GROUP HOLDINGS LIMITED; *Int'l*, pg. 3304

HEARTLAND HEART & VASCULAR, LLC—See United Health Group Incorporated; *U.S. Public*, pg. 2241

HEARTLAND HOMECARE SERVICES, INC.; *U.S. Private*, pg. 1900

HEARTLAND HOME SERVICES, INC.; *U.S. Private*, pg. 1900

HEARTLAND HONDA; *U.S. Private*, pg. 1900

HEARTLAND HOTEL CORP.; *U.S. Private*, pg. 1900

HEARTLAND, INC.; *U.S. Private*, pg. 1901

HEARTLAND INFORMATION SERVICES, INC.—See Microsoft Corporation; *U.S. Public*, pg. 1443

HEARTLAND LABEL PRINTERS, INC.; *U.S. Private*, pg. 1900

HEARTLAND LIVESTOCK SERVICES—See Nilsson Bros., Inc.; *Int'l*, pg. 5295

HEARTLAND, LLC—See Laird Norton Company, LLC; *U.S. Private*, pg. 2374

HEARTLAND MEAT CO. INC.; *U.S. Private*, pg. 1900

HEARTLAND MEDIA ACQUISITION CORP.; *U.S. Public*, pg. 1018

HEARTLAND MEDIA, LLC; *U.S. Private*, pg. 1900

HEARTLAND MEDICAL CORPORATION—See AIN Holdings Inc.; *Int'l*, pg. 234

HEARTLAND PAYMENT SYSTEMS, LLC—See Global Payments Inc.; *U.S. Public*, pg. 944

HEARTLAND PAYROLL SOLUTIONS, INC.—See Global Payments Inc.; *U.S. Public*, pg. 944

HEARTLAND PET FOOD MANUFACTURING IOWA, INC.—See General Mills, Inc.; *U.S. Public*, pg. 922

HEARTLAND PHARMACY OF ILLINOIS LLC—See CVS Health Corporation; *U.S. Public*, pg. 616

HEARTLAND PROPERTIES, INC.; *U.S. Private*, pg. 1900

HEARTLAND PROPERTIES (PTY) LIMITED—See Shanghai Zendai Property Limited; *Int'l*, pg. 6783

HEARTLAND PUBLICATIONS, LLC; *U.S. Private*, pg. 1900

HEARTLAND PUMP RENTAL & SALES, INC.—See Xylem Inc.; *U.S. Public*, pg. 2396

HEARTLAND RECREATIONAL VEHICLES, LLC—See Thor Industries, Inc.; *U.S. Public*, pg. 2156

HEARTLAND REHABILITATION SERVICES, LLC—See American Healthcare Systems Corp., Inc.; *U.S. Private*, pg. 236

HEARTLAND RURAL ELECTRIC COOPERATIVE, INC.; *U.S. Private*, pg. 1900

HEARTLAND RURAL HEALTHCARE, LLC—See Quorum Health Corporation; *U.S. Public*, pg. 3330

HEARTLANDS ASSISTED LIVING AT SEVERNA PARK—See AlerisLife Inc.; *U.S. Private*, pg. 161

HEARTLAND SCHOOL SOLUTIONS—See Global Payments Inc.; *U.S. Public*, pg. 944

HEARTLAND SERVICES, INC.; *U.S. Private*, pg. 1900

HEARTLAND SPECIALTY INSURANCE—See Texans Credit Union; *U.S. Private*, pg. 3974

HEARTLAND STEEL PRODUCTS, LLC—See LFM Capital LLC; *U.S. Private*, pg. 2441

HEARTLAND TANNING INC.; *U.S. Private*, pg. 1900

HEARTLAND VETERINARY PHARMACY LLC—See Pet Assistant Holdings, LLC; *U.S. Private*, pg. 3156

HEARTLAND VILLA CENTER—See Formation Capital, LLC; *U.S. Private*, pg. 1570

HEARTLASS INC.—See Digital Holdings, Inc.; *Int'l*, pg. 2122

HEART LIFE CORPORATION—See Ship Healthcare Holdings, Inc.; *Int'l*, pg. 6852

HEARTLINE FITNESS SYSTEMS; *U.S. Private*, pg. 1901

HEART MEDICAL CARE CO., LTD.—See EQT AB; *Int'l*, pg. 2467

HEARTNUT GROVE WWT INC.—See Water Ways Technologies Inc.; *Int'l*, pg. 8356

HEART OF AMERICA ASC, LLC—See HCA Healthcare, Inc.; *U.S. Public*, pg. 998

HEART OF AMERICA BEVERAGE COMPANY; *U.S. Private*, pg. 1898

HEART OF AMERICA TITLE & ESCROW, LLC—See Stewart Information Services Corporation; *U.S. Public*, pg. 1947

HEART OF COMPASSION DISTRIBUTION, INC.; *U.S. Private*, pg. 1898

HEART OF ENGLAND CO-OPERATIVE SOCIETY LIMITED; *Int'l*, pg. 3304

HEART OF ENGLAND HOUSING AND CARE LIMITED—See Sanctuary Housing Association; *Int'l*, pg. 6523

HEART OF FLORIDA SURGERY CENTER, LLC—See Adventist Health System Sunbelt Healthcare Corporation; *U.S. Private*, pg. 108

HEART OF GEORGIA RAILROAD, INC.—See Brookfield Infrastructure Partners L.P.; *Int'l*, pg. 1191

HEART OF GEORGIA RAILROAD, INC.—See GIC Pte. Ltd.; *Int'l*, pg. 2966

HEART OF TEXAS ELECTRIC COOPERATIVE INC.; *U.S. Private*, pg. 1899

HEARTS AND MINDS INVESTMENTS LIMITED; *Int'l*, pg. 3304

HEARTSINE TECHNOLOGIES LIMITED—See Stryker Corporation; *U.S. Public*, pg. 1955

HEARTSINE TECHNOLOGIES, LLC—See Stryker Corporation; *U.S. Public*, pg. 1955

HEARTSOFT, INC.; *U.S. Public*, pg. 1018

HEARTS ON FIRE COMPANY LLC—See Chow Tai Fook Enterprises Limited; *Int'l*, pg. 1584

HEART TEST LABORATORIES, INC.; *U.S. Public*, pg. 1017

HEART THAMES VALLEY—See Global Radio Group Limited; *Int'l*, pg. 3000

HEART TO HEART INTERNATIONAL INC.; *U.S. Private*, pg. 1899

HEART TRUSS & ENGINEERING; *U.S. Private*, pg. 1899

HEART & VASCULAR CENTER OF ARIZONA, PLLC—See Webster Equity Partners, LLC; *U.S. Private*, pg. 4467

HEART & VASCULAR INSTITUTE OF MICHIGAN—See Tenet Healthcare Corporation; *U.S. Public*, pg. 2015

HEART & VASCULAR INSTITUTE OF TEXAS, INC.—See Tenet Healthcare Corporation; *U.S. Public*, pg. 2014

HEART WALES—See Global Radio Group Limited; *Int'l*, pg. 3000

HEARTWARE INTERNATIONAL, INC.—See Medtronic plc; *Int'l*, pg. 4787

HEARTWARE PTY. LIMITED—See Medtronic plc; *Int'l*, pg. 4787

HEARTWOOD PARTNERS, LLC; *U.S. Private*, pg. 1901

HEARTWOOD STUDIOS, INC.; *U.S. Private*, pg. 1901

HEARTWOOD WEALTH MANAGEMENT LIMITED—See Svenska Handelsbanken AB; *Int'l*, pg. 7358

HEARUSA, INC.—See Siemens Aktiengesellschaft; *Int'l*, pg. 6890

HEARX WEST LLC—See Siemens Aktiengesellschaft; *Int'l*, pg. 6889

HEASON TECHNOLOGY LIMITED—See discoverIE Group plc; *Int'l*, pg. 2133

THE HEAT AND WARMTH FUND; *U.S. Private*, pg. 4050

HEAT AUTHORITY, LLC—See Thermon Group Holdings, Inc.; *U.S. Public*, pg. 2155

HEAT & CONTROL, INC.; *U.S. Private*, pg. 1901

HEAT & CONTROL INC.—See Heat & Control, Inc.; *U.S. Private*, pg. 1901

HEAT CONTROLLER, INC.—See Motors & Armatures, Inc.; *U.S. Private*, pg. 2797

HEATCRAFT GEELONG PTY LTD—See Lennox International Inc.; *U.S. Public*, pg. 1307

HEATCRAFT REFRIGERATION (WUXI) CO. LTD.—See Lennox International Inc.; *U.S. Public*, pg. 1307

HEATCRAFT TASMANIA PTY LTD—See Lennox International Inc.; *U.S. Public*, pg. 1307

HEATEC GUANGZHOU CO., LTD.—See Heatec JieTong Holdings Ltd; *Int'l*, pg. 3305

HEATEC, INC.—See Astec Industries, Inc.; *U.S. Public*, pg. 216

HEATEC JIETONG HOLDINGS LTD; *Int'l*, pg. 3304

HEATEC JIETONG PTE. LTD.—See Heatec JieTong Holdings Ltd; *Int'l*, pg. 3305

HEATEC SHANGHAI CO., LTD.—See Heatec JieTong Holdings Ltd; *Int'l*, pg. 3305

HEATEC VESLINK MARINE SERVICES CORP.—See Heatec JieTong Holdings Ltd; *Int'l*, pg. 3305

HEATEFLEX CORPORATION; *U.S. Private*, pg. 1901

HEATER SPECIALISTS LLC; *U.S. Private*, pg. 1902

HEAT-FLO, INC.—See Bradford-White Corporation; *U.S. Private*, pg. 632

HEATH & ASSOCIATES INC.—See Warren Equity Partners, LLC; *U.S. Private*, pg. 4443

HEATH COMM AS—See Lagercrantz Group AB; *Int'l*, pg. 4394

HEATH CONSULTANTS INC. DAMAGE PREVENTION SERVICES—See Heath Consultants Incorporated; *U.S. Private*, pg. 1902

HEATH CONSULTANTS INCORPORATED - CENTRAL DIVISON—See Heath Consultants Incorporated; *U.S. Private*, pg. 1902

HEATH CONSULTANTS INCORPORATED, INTERNATIONAL SALES—See Heath Consultants Incorporated; *U.S. Private*, pg. 1902

HEATH CONSULTANTS INCORPORATED - NORTHEAST DIVISON—See Heath Consultants Incorporated; *U.S. Private*, pg. 1902

HEATH CONSULTANTS INCORPORATED; *U.S. Private*, pg. 1902

HEATH CONSULTANTS INCORPORATED - SOUTHEAST DIVISION—See Heath Consultants Incorporated; *U.S. Private*, pg. 1902

COMPANY NAME INDEX

HEATH CONSULTANTS INCORPORATED - WESTERN DIVISION—See Heath Consultants Incorporated; *U.S. Private*, pg. 1902
HEATH CONSULTANTS—See Heath Consultants Incorporated; *U.S. Private*, pg. 1902
HEATHCOTE COMMUNICATIONS; *U.S. Private*, pg. 1902
HEATHCOTT ASSOCIATES, INC.—See Cranford Johnson Robinson Woods, Inc.; *U.S. Private*, pg. 1085
HEATHERBRAE INC; *Int'l*, pg. 3305
HEATHER CREEK APARTMENTS MESQUITE, LTD—See American Realty Investors, Inc.; *U.S. Public*, pg. 108
HEATHER HEIGHTS OF PITTSFORD, INC.—See The Hamister Group, Inc.; *U.S. Private*, pg. 4042
HEATHER HIGHLANDS MOBILE HOME VILLAGE ASSOCIATES, LP—See UMH Properties, Inc.; *U.S. Public*, pg. 2224
HEATHER PAINTING & DECORATING LTD—See Davian Construction Ltd.; *Int'l*, pg. 1983
HEATHERWOOD CONSTRUCTION COMPANY; *U.S. Private*, pg. 1902
HEATH FARM ENERGY LIMITED—See Aviva plc; *Int'l*, pg. 746
HEATHGATE RESOURCES PTY, LTD.—See General Atomics; *U.S. Private*, pg. 1663
HEATHPATCH LTD.; *Int'l*, pg. 3305
HEATHROW AIRPORT HOLDINGS LIMITED—See Ferrovial S.A.; *Int'l*, pg. 2644
HEATHROW AIRPORT LTD.—See Ferrovial S.A.; *Int'l*, pg. 2644
HEATHROW COUNTRY CLUB—See Concert Golf Partners, LLC; *U.S. Private*, pg. 1009
HEATHROW INTERNAL MEDICINE, LLC—See HCA Healthcare, Inc.; *U.S. Public*, pg. 998
HEATHROW LIMITED—See Berjaya Corporation Berhad; *Int'l*, pg. 983
HEATHROW TRUCK CENTRE LTD—See Ballyvesey Holdings Limited; *Int'l*, pg. 809
HEATH VILLAGE RETIREMENT COMMUNITY; *U.S. Private*, pg. 1902
HEATH XS, LLC—See Hallmark Financial Services, Inc.; *U.S. Public*, pg. 981
THE HEATING COMPANY DENMARK A/S—See Vaessen Industries nv; *Int'l*, pg. 8108
THE HEATING COMPANY FRANCE SARL—See Vaessen Industries nv; *Int'l*, pg. 8108
THE HEATING COMPANY GERMANY GMBH—See Vaessen Industries nv; *Int'l*, pg. 8108
HEATING & COOLING SUPPLY LLC—See Watsco, Inc.; *U.S. Public*, pg. 2336
HEATING GROUP INTERNATIONAL B.V.—See NIBE Industrier AB; *Int'l*, pg. 5261
HEATING & PLUMBING ENGINEERS INC.; *U.S. Private*, pg. 1902
HEATLEYS SAFETY & INDUSTRIAL LIMITED—See Stealth Global Holdings Ltd.; *Int'l*, pg. 7188
HEATLINK GROUP, INC.—See Mueller Industries, Inc.; *U.S. Public*, pg. 1484
HEATLINK GROUP USA, LLC—See Mueller Industries, Inc.; *U.S. Public*, pg. 1484
HEATMASTERS OY—See Panostaja Oyj; *Int'l*, pg. 5729
HEATMASTERS SP.ZOO—See Panostaja Oyj; *Int'l*, pg. 5729
HEATMAX, INC.—See Kobayashi Pharmaceutical Co., Ltd.; *Int'l*, pg. 4216
HEATMERCHANTS—See Ferguson plc; *Int'l*, pg. 2638
HEAT PIPE TECHNOLOGY, INC.—See Berkshire Hathaway Inc.; *U.S. Public*, pg. 312
HEATPOINT B.V.—See NIBE Industrier AB; *Int'l*, pg. 5261
HEATRAE SAIDIA HEATING LTD.—See BDR Thermea Group B.V.; *Int'l*, pg. 930
HEATRIC—See Parker Hannifin Corporation; *U.S. Public*, pg. 1641
HEATROD ELEMENTS LTD.—See NIBE Industrier AB; *Int'l*, pg. 5261
HEATRON, INC.—See NIBE Industrier AB; *Int'l*, pg. 5261
HEAT SEAL LLC; *U.S. Private*, pg. 1901
HEAT SOFTWARE FRANCE SAS—See Clearlake Capital Group, L.P.; *U.S. Private*, pg. 935
HEAT SOFTWARE USA INC.—See Clearlake Capital Group, L.P.; *U.S. Private*, pg. 935
HEAT—See Deloitte LLP; *U.S. Private*, pg. 1198
HEAT—See Deloitte Touche Tohmatsu Limited; *Int'l*, pg. 2014
HEATSOURCE, INC.—See HS Holdings, LLC; *U.S. Private*, pg. 1998
HEAT & SURFACE TREATMENT B.V.—See Aalberts N.V.; *Int'l*, pg. 34
HEAT TRANSFER PRODUCTS GROUP, LLC - COLDZONE—See Paloma Industries Limited; *Int'l*, pg. 5709
HEAT TRANSFER PRODUCTS GROUP, LLC - KRAMER—See Paloma Industries Limited; *Int'l*, pg. 5709
HEAT TRANSFER PRODUCTS GROUP, LLC—See Paloma Industries Limited; *Int'l*, pg. 5709
HEAT TRANSFER SYSTEMS S.R.O.—See LU-VE SpA; *Int'l*, pg. 4572
HEAT TREATING SERVICES CORPORATION OF AMERICA; *U.S. Private*, pg. 1901

HEAT WAVES HOT OIL SERVICE, LLC—See Enservco Corporation; *U.S. Public*, pg. 775
HEAVAC B.V.—See INDUS Holding AG; *Int'l*, pg. 3663
HEAVENER DIALYSIS, LLC—See DaVita Inc.; *U.S. Public*, pg. 639
HEAVEN HILL DISTILLERIES, INC.; *U.S. Private*, pg. 1902
HEAVENLY VALLEY, LIMITED PARTNERSHIP—See Vail Resorts, Inc.; *U.S. Public*, pg. 2271
HEAVEN-SENT CAPITAL MANAGEMENT GROUP CO. LTD.; *Int'l*, pg. 3305
HEAVEN'S PETS AT LAKELAWN METAIRIE, LLC—See Service Corporation International; *U.S. Public*, pg. 1869
HEAVENSTONE CORP.; *U.S. Private*, pg. 1902
HEAVILAND ENTERPRISES, INC.—See BrightView Holdings, Inc.; *U.S. Public*, pg. 384
THE HEAVITREE BREWERY PLC; *Int'l*, pg. 7652
HEAVYBAG MEDIA; *U.S. Private*, pg. 1902
HEAVYBAG WEST—See HeavyBag Media; *U.S. Private*, pg. 1902
HEAVY CONSTRUCTORS INC.; *U.S. Private*, pg. 1902
HEAVY CRUDE HAULING L.P.—See Mullen Group Ltd.; *Int'l*, pg. 5080
HEAVY DUTY RAMPS, LLC—See Rotunda Capital Partners LLC; *U.S. Private*, pg. 3488
HEAVY ENGINEERING INDUSTRIES & SHIPBUILDING CO. K.S.C. - INDUSTRIAL CONTRACTS DIVISION—See Heavy Engineering Industries & Shipbuilding Co. K.S.C.; *Int'l*, pg. 3305
HEAVY ENGINEERING INDUSTRIES & SHIPBUILDING CO. K.S.C.; *Int'l*, pg. 3305
HEAVY EQUIPMENT SERVICES, INC.—See The Helm Group; *U.S. Private*, pg. 4051
HEAVY & HIGHWAY INC.—See Trierweiler Construction & Supply Co. Inc.; *U.S. Private*, pg. 1902
HEAVY IRON STUDIOS, INC.—See Canada Pension Plan Investment Board; *Int'l*, pg. 1280
HEAVY IRON STUDIOS, INC.—See EQT AB; *Int'l*, pg. 2482
HEAVY IRON STUDIOS, INC.—See Temasek Holdings (Private) Limited; *Int'l*, pg. 7548
HEAVY MACHINES, INC. - FINLEY LLC DIVISION—See Heavy Machines, Inc.; *U.S. Private*, pg. 1902
HEAVY MACHINES, INC.; *U.S. Private*, pg. 1902
HEAVY MAINTENANCE SINGAPORE SERVICES PTE. LTD.—See Temasek Holdings (Private) Limited; *Int'l*, pg. 7551
HEAVY MATERIALS LLC—See Vulcan Materials Company; *U.S. Public*, pg. 2314
HEAVYMECH PTY. LTD.—See E&A Limited; *Int'l*, pg. 2247
HEAVY MINERALS LIMITED; *Int'l*, pg. 3305
HEAVY-NET SP. Z O.O—See WDX S.A.; *Int'l*, pg. 8362
HEAVY RARE EARTHS LIMITED; *Int'l*, pg. 3305
HEAVY TRANSPORT, INC.—See Bragg Investment Company, Inc.; *U.S. Private*, pg. 634
HEAVYWATER, INC.—See Intercontinental Exchange, Inc.; *U.S. Public*, pg. 1141
HEBA FASTIGHETS AB; *Int'l*, pg. 3305
HEBAT ABADI SDN BHD—See Kumpulan Darul Ehsan Berhad; *Int'l*, pg. 4331
HEBBERD KULOW ENTERPRISES; *U.S. Private*, pg. 1902
HEB CONSTRUCTION LTD.—See VINCI S.A.; *Int'l*, pg. 8222
HEBEI CHANGSHAN BIOCHEMICAL PHARMACEUTICAL CO. LTD.; *Int'l*, pg. 3305
HEBEI CHANGSHAN KAIKUDE BIOTECHNOLOGY CO., LTD.—See Hebei Changshan Biochemical Pharmaceutical Co. Ltd.; *Int'l*, pg. 3305
HEBEI CHANGSHAN KAILA BIOTECHNOLOGY CO., LTD.—See Hebei Changshan Biochemical Pharmaceutical Co. Ltd.; *Int'l*, pg. 3305
HEBEI CHANGSHAN KAILUONITE BIOTECHNOLOGY CO., LTD.—See Hebei Changshan Biochemical Pharmaceutical Co. Ltd.; *Int'l*, pg. 3305
HEBEI CHANGSHAN LONG KANG BIOTECHNOLOGY CO., LTD.—See Hebei Changshan Biochemical Pharmaceutical Co. Ltd.; *Int'l*, pg. 3305
HE BEI CHENG DE LOLO COMPANY LIMITED; *Int'l*, pg. 3300
HEBEI CHENGXIN CO., LTD.; *Int'l*, pg. 3305
HEBEI CONSTRUCTION GROUP CORPORATION LIMITED; *Int'l*, pg. 3305
HEBEI DALI FOODS CO., LTD.—See Dali Foods Group Co. Ltd.; *Int'l*, pg. 1951
HEBEI GONGDA KEYA ENERGY TECHNOLOGY CO., LTD.; *Int'l*, pg. 3305
HEBEI HANGXIAO STEEL STRUCTURE CO., LTD.—See Hangxiao Steel Structure Co., Ltd.; *Int'l*, pg. 3246
HEBEI HANLIN BIOTECHNOLOGY CO., LTD.—See SSY Group Limited; *Int'l*, pg. 7157
HEBEI HENGSHUI LAOBAIGAN LIQUOR CO., LTD.; *Int'l*, pg. 3305
HEBEI HEZHONG BUILDING MATERIALS CO., LTD.—See Beijing Hanjian Heshan Pipeline Co.,LTD.; *Int'l*, pg. 951
HEBEI HONGSONG WIND POWER CO., LTD.—See China Ruifeng Renewable Energy Holdings Limited; *Int'l*, pg. 1549

HECKLER AG

HEBEI HUADIAN SHIJIAZHUANG THERMAL POWER COMPANY LIMITED—See Huadian Power International Corporation Limited; *Int'l*, pg. 3511
HEBEI HUATONG WIRES & CABLES GROUP CO., LTD.; *Int'l*, pg. 3306
HEBEI HUAXIA ENTERPRISE CO.LTD.—See Avery Dennison Corporation; *U.S. Public*, pg. 245
HEBEI HUIJIN GROUP CO., LTD.; *Int'l*, pg. 3306
HEBEI JIANXIN CHEMICAL CO., LTD.; *Int'l*, pg. 3306
HEBEI JINNIU CHEMICAL INDUSTRY CO., LTD.—See Jizhong Energy Resources Co., Ltd.; *Int'l*, pg. 3972
HEBEI JINXI IRON & STEEL GROUP CO., LTD.—See China Oriental Group Company Limited; *Int'l*, pg. 1538
HEBEI LIHUA HAT MANUFACTURING GROUP CO., LTD.; *Int'l*, pg. 3306
HEBEI MAURI FOOD CO., LTD—See The Garfield Weston Foundation; *Int'l*, pg. 7648
HEBEI MEISHAN POLYSACCHARIDE & POLYPEPTIDE TECHNOLOGY CO., LTD.—See Hebei Changshan Biochemical Pharmaceutical Co. Ltd.; *Int'l*, pg. 3305
HEBEI NOTER COMMUNICATION TECHNOLOGY CO., LIMITED—See China All Access (Holdings) Limited; *Int'l*, pg. 1482
HEBEI O.R.G PACKAGING CO., LTD.—See ORG Technology Co., Ltd.; *Int'l*, pg. 5617
HEBEI SAILHERO ENVIRONMENTAL PROTECTION HIGH-TECH CO., LTD.; *Int'l*, pg. 3306
HEBEI SERCEL-JUNFENG GEOPHYSICAL PROSPECTING EQUIPMENT CO., LTD.—See CGG; *Int'l*, pg. 1432
HEBEI SHENGHUA CHEMICAL CO., LTD.—See China National Chemical Corporation; *Int'l*, pg. 1528
HEBEI SINOPACK ELECTRONIC TECHNOLOGY CO., LTD.; *Int'l*, pg. 3306
HEBEI TIANWEI HUARI ELECTRIC CO., LTD.—See Advanced Technology & Materials Co., Ltd.; *Int'l*, pg. 162
HEBEI YANGYUAN ZHIHUI BEVERAGE CO., LTD.; *Int'l*, pg. 3306
HEBEI YICHEN INDUSTRIAL GROUP CORPORATION LIMITED; *Int'l*, pg. 3306
HEBEI YONGLE TAPE CO., LTD.—See Avery Dennison Corporation; *U.S. Public*, pg. 244
HEBELER CORPORATION; *U.S. Private*, pg. 1902
HEBELER PROCESS SOLUTIONS, LLC—See Hebeler Corporation; *U.S. Private*, pg. 1902
HEBERT CANDIES; *U.S. Private*, pg. 1902
HEBERT KANNEGIESSER GMBH; *Int'l*, pg. 3306
HEBERT STEEL CO. INC.; *U.S. Private*, pg. 1903
HEBETEC ENGINEERING A.G.—See VINCI S.A.; *Int'l*, pg. 8232
HEBETECHNIK GESELLSCHAFT GMBH—See Columbus McKinnon Corporation; *U.S. Public*, pg. 535
THE HEBETS COMPANY—See Aon plc; *Int'l*, pg. 497
HEBI HAICHANG SPECIAL EQUIPMENT CO LTD—See China Auto Electronics Group Limited; *Int'l*, pg. 1483
H-E-B, LP; *U.S. Private*, pg. 1824
HEBOLD SYSTEMS GMBH—See L. Possehl & Co. mbH; *Int'l*, pg. 4383
HEBO LIMITED—See Hang Lung Group Limited; *Int'l*, pg. 3245
THE HEBREW HOME AT RIVERDALE; *U.S. Private*, pg. 4050
HEBRO CHEMIE ZWEIGNIEDERLASSUNG DER ROCKWOOD SPECIALTIES GROUP GMBH—See Albemarle Corporation; *U.S. Public*, pg. 74
HEBRON S.A.—See Otsuka Holdings Co., Ltd.; *Int'l*, pg. 5659
HEBRON SAVINGS BANK; *U.S. Private*, pg. 1903
HEBS DIGITAL; *U.S. Private*, pg. 1903
HEBSON HOLDINGS PLC; *Int'l*, pg. 3306
H.E. BUTT GROCERY COMPANY; *U.S. Private*, pg. 1826
H.E. CALLAHAN CONSTRUCTION CO.; *U.S. Private*, pg. 1826
HECATE ENERGY, LLC; *U.S. Private*, pg. 1903
HECATE EXPLORATION; *U.S. Private*, pg. 1903
HECHENG VEHICLE PARTS (TAICANG) CO., LTD.—See Hwaseung Industries Co., Ltd.; *Int'l*, pg. 3542
HECHO STUDIOS LLC—See Stagwell, Inc.; *U.S. Public*, pg. 1927
HECHT & HECHT INSURANCE AGENCY, INC.—See Stone Point Capital LLC; *U.S. Private*, pg. 3819
HEC INFRA PROJECTS LTD.; *Int'l*, pg. 3306
HECKENKEMPER HOMES, LLC.; *U.S. Private*, pg. 1903
HECK ENTERPRISES INC.; *U.S. Private*, pg. 1903
HECK ESTATES—See F. Korbel Bros. Inc.; *U.S. Private*, pg. 1455
HECKETHORN MANUFACTURING COMPANY, INC.—See The Rosewood Corporation; *U.S. Private*, pg. 4112
HECKLER AG; *Int'l*, pg. 3307
HECKLER & KOCH GMBH—See BAE Systems plc; *Int'l*, pg. 798
HECKLER & KOCH INC.—See BAE Systems plc; *Int'l*, pg. 798
HECKLER ROMANIA S.R.L.—See Heckler AG; *Int'l*, pg. 3307
HECKMANN WATER RESOURCES (CVR), INC.—See Select Water Solutions, Inc.; *U.S. Public*, pg. 1862
HEC KOREA CO., LTD.—See Compucase Enterprise Co., Ltd.; *Int'l*, pg. 1754

HECK WALL SYSTEMS GMBH & CO. KG—See ROCK-WOOL A/S; *Int'l*, pg. 6380
HECK WALL SYSTEMS VERWALTUNGS-GMBH—See ROCKWOOL A/S; *Int'l*, pg. 6380
HECLA CANADA LTD.—See Hecla Mining Company; *U.S. Public*, pg. 1019
HECLA GREENS CREEK MINING COMPANY—See Hecla Mining Company; *U.S. Public*, pg. 1019
HECLA LIMITED - LUCKY FRIDAY MINE—See Hecla Mining Company; *U.S. Public*, pg. 1019
HECLA MINING COMPANY; *U.S. Public*, pg. 1018
HECNY TRANSPORTATION INC.; *U.S. Private*, pg. 1903
HECO AUDIO-PRODUKTE GMBH—See VOXX International Corporation; *U.S. Public*, pg. 2311
HECO NORDISKA AB—See Volati AB; *Int'l*, pg. 8300
HECO SCHRAUBEN GMBH & CO. KG—See SFS Group AG; *Int'l*, pg. 6738
HECO SCHRAUBEN S.R.L.—See SFS Group AG; *Int'l*, pg. 6738
HEC PHARM CO., LTD.; *Int'l*, pg. 3307
HEC RESOURCES LIMITED—See Empresaria Group Plc; *Int'l*, pg. 2389
HECTAS GEBAUDEDIENSTE GES.M.B.H & CO. KG—See Vorwerk & Co. KG; *Int'l*, pg. 8307
HECTAS GEBAUDEDIENSTE STIFTUNG & CO. KG—See Vorwerk & Co. KG; *Int'l*, pg. 8307
HECTAS GEBAUDEMANAGEMENT GMBH & CO. KG—See Vorwerk & Co. KG; *Int'l*, pg. 8307
HECTAS GROEP C.V.—See Vorwerk & Co. KG; *Int'l*, pg. 8307
HECTAS SICHERHEITSDIENSTE GMBH—See Vorwerk & Co. KG; *Int'l*, pg. 8307
HECTAS TECHNICKE A BEZPECNOSTNI SLUZBY S.R.O.—See Vorwerk & Co. KG; *Int'l*, pg. 8307
HECTO FINANCIAL CO., LTD.; *Int'l*, pg. 3307
HECTO INNOVATION CO., LTD; *Int'l*, pg. 3307
HECTOR COMMUNICATIONS CORPORATION—See Arvig Enterprises, Inc.; *U.S. Private*, pg. 344
HECTOR COMMUNICATIONS CORPORATION—See Blue Earth Valley Communications; *U.S. Private*, pg. 588
HECTOR COMMUNICATIONS CORPORATION—See Nuvera Communications, Inc.; *U.S. Public*, pg. 1556
HECTOR RAIL AB—See EQT AB; *Int'l*, pg. 2475
HECTRONIC AB—See discoverIE Group plc; *Int'l*, pg. 2133
HEDAHLS INC.; *U.S. Private*, pg. 1903
HEDBERG DATA SYSTEMS INC.—See Steelcase Inc.; *U.S. Public*, pg. 1944
HEDBERGS BILSKROT AB—See Bilia AB; *Int'l*, pg. 1029
HEDCO DIV.—See The Dewey Electronics Corporation; *U.S. Public*, pg. 2067
HEDDINGER BROKERAGE INC.; *U.S. Private*, pg. 1903
HEDEDANMARK A/S—See Det Danske Hedeselskab; *Int'l*, pg. 2047
HEDEF GIRISIM SERMAYESI YATI ORTAK; *Int'l*, pg. 3307
HEDEF INTERNATIONAL HOLDINGS BV—See Walgreens Boots Alliance, Inc.; *U.S. Public*, pg. 2322
HEDEGAARD A/S—See Danish Agro AmbA; *Int'l*, pg. 1963
HEDEMORA DIESEL AB—See Engenco Limited; *Int'l*, pg. 2427
HEDEMORA TURBO & DIESEL AB—See Engenco Limited; *Int'l*, pg. 2427
HEDERA CONSULTING BVBA—See Cognizant Technology Solutions Corporation; *U.S. Public*, pg. 524
HEDERMAN BROTHERS, LLC; *U.S. Private*, pg. 1903
HEDESELSKABET SP. Z.O.O.—See Det Danske Hedeselskab; *Int'l*, pg. 2047
HEDGEBROOK; *U.S. Private*, pg. 1903
HEDGE CONNECTION INC.; *U.S. Private*, pg. 1903
HEDGES BUILDING SUPPLIES LIMITED—See Fletcher Building Limited; *Int'l*, pg. 2700
HEDGEWORLD—See Thomson Reuters Corporation; *Int'l*, pg. 7715
HEDGEYE POTOMAC RESEARCH—See Hedgeye Risk Management LLC; *U.S. Private*, pg. 1903
HEDGEYE RISK MANAGEMENT LLC; *U.S. Private*, pg. 1903
HEDINN SCHINDLER LYFTUR H.F.—See Schindler Holding AG; *Int'l*, pg. 6619
HEDLEY TECHNOLOGIES LTD.—See BioSyent Inc.; *Int'l*, pg. 1042
HEDLEY TECHNOLOGIES (USA) INC.—See BioSyent Inc.; *Int'l*, pg. 1042
HEDNO S.A—See Public Power Corporation S.A.; *Int'l*, pg. 6095
HEDOSOPHIA EUROPEAN GROWTH; *Int'l*, pg. 3307
HEDRICK BROTHERS CONSTRUCTION CO., INC.; *U.S. Private*, pg. 1903
HEDRICK INDUSTRIES INC.; *U.S. Private*, pg. 1903
HEDSON NORTH AMERICA, INC.—See Storskogen Group AB; *Int'l*, pg. 7227
HEDSON TECHNOLOGIES AB—See Storskogen Group AB; *Int'l*, pg. 7227
HEDWIN DIVISION OF ZACROS AMERICA—See ZACROS Corporation; *Int'l*, pg. 8619
HEE ENVIRONMENTAL ENGINEERING, LLC—See CECO Environmental Corp.; *U.S. Public*, pg. 463
HEEL BELGIUM NV—See Delton AG; *Int'l*, pg. 2021

HEEL BIOLOGISCHE GENEESMIDDELEN B.V.—See Delton AG; *Int'l*, pg. 2021
HEEL CANADA INC.; *Int'l*, pg. 3307
HEEL DO BRASIL BIOMEDICA LTDA.—See Delton AG; *Int'l*, pg. 2021
HEELING HOLDING CORPORATION—See Sequential Brands Group, Inc.; *U.S. Public*, pg. 1868
HEELING SPORTS LIMITED—See Sequential Brands Group, Inc.; *U.S. Public*, pg. 1868
HEEL POLSKA SP. Z.O.O.—See Delton AG; *Int'l*, pg. 2021
HEELY-BROWN COMPANY INC.; *U.S. Private*, pg. 1903
HEELYS, INC.—See Sequential Brands Group, Inc.; *U.S. Public*, pg. 1868
H&E EQUIPMENT SERVICES (CALIFORNIA), LLC—See H&E Equipment Services, Inc.; *U.S. Public*, pg. 976
H&E EQUIPMENT SERVICES INC. - PHOENIX—See H&E Equipment Services, Inc.; *U.S. Public*, pg. 976
H&E EQUIPMENT SERVICES, INC.; *U.S. Public*, pg. 976
H&E EQUIPMENT SERVICES LLC—See H&E Equipment Services, Inc.; *U.S. Public*, pg. 976
H&E EQUIPMENT SERVICES (MID-ATLANTIC), INC.—See H&E Equipment Services, Inc.; *U.S. Public*, pg. 976
H&E EQUIPMENT SERVICES (MIDWEST), INC.—See H&E Equipment Services, Inc.; *U.S. Public*, pg. 976
HEERA ISPAT LTD.; *Int'l*, pg. 3307
HEERIM ARCHITECTS & PLANNERS CO., LTD.; *Int'l*, pg. 3307
HEETCO INC.; *U.S. Private*, pg. 1903
HEETER PRINTING CO., INC.; *U.S. Private*, pg. 1903
HEETON ESTATE PTE LTD—See Heeton Holdings Limited; *Int'l*, pg. 3307
HEETON HOLDINGS LIMITED; *Int'l*, pg. 3307
HEETON SG50 LIMITED—See Heeton Holdings Limited; *Int'l*, pg. 3307
HEFA AB—See New Wave Group AB; *Int'l*, pg. 5229
HEFAL SERWIS S.A.; *Int'l*, pg. 3307
HEFEFABRIK GIELGOLD—See Lallemand, Inc.; *Int'l*, pg. 4399
HEFEI AHRESTY CASTING CO., LTD.—See Ahresty Corporation; *Int'l*, pg. 226
HEFEI BOE OPTOELECTRONICS TECHNOLOGY CO., LTD.—See BOE Technology Group Co., Ltd.; *Int'l*, pg. 1099
HEFEI CHANG QING MACHINERY CO., LTD.; *Int'l*, pg. 3307
HEFEI CHIA TAI CO., LTD.—See Charoen Pokphand Foods Public Company Limited; *Int'l*, pg. 1452
HEFEI CR CONTAINER CO., LTD.—See Zhuhai Zhongfu Enterprise Co., Ltd.; *Int'l*, pg. 8679
HEFEI DANSUN PACKAGING CO., LTD—See PSC Corporation Ltd.; *Int'l*, pg. 6015
HEFEI DEPARTMENT STORE GROUP CO., LTD.; *Int'l*, pg. 3307
HEFEI DEREN ELECTRONIC DEVICE CO., LTD.—See Shenzhen Deren Electronic Co., Ltd.; *Int'l*, pg. 6808
HEFEI DONGJIN SEMICHEM CO., LTD.—See Dongjin Semichem Co., Ltd.; *Int'l*, pg. 2168
HEFEI EAGLE AUTOMATION ENGINEERING TECHNOLOGY CO., LTD.—See Saimo Technology Co., Ltd.; *Int'l*, pg. 6484
HEFEI ECRIEE-TAMURA ELECTRIC CO., LTD.—See Tamura Corporation; *Int'l*, pg. 7451
HEFEI FENGLE SEED CO., LTD.; *Int'l*, pg. 3307
HEFEI HENGCHANG AUTOMATION CONTROL CO., LTD.—See Endress+Hauser (International) Holding AG; *Int'l*, pg. 2408
HEFEI JIANGHANG AIRCRAFT EQUIPMENT CO., LTD.; *Int'l*, pg. 3307
HEFEI LIFEON PHARMACEUTICAL CO., LTD.; *Int'l*, pg. 3307
HEFEI METALFORMING INTELLIGENT MANUFACTURING CO., LTD.; *Int'l*, pg. 3307
HEFEI MEYER OPTOELECTRONIC TECHNOLOGY INC.; *Int'l*, pg. 3307
HEFEI MIDEA-SIIX ELECTRONICS CO., LTD.—See SIIX CORPORATION; *Int'l*, pg. 6913
HEFEI NSK CO., LTD.—See NSK Ltd.; *Int'l*, pg. 5478
HEFEI OVAL INSTRUMENT CO. LTD.—See OVAL Corporation; *Int'l*, pg. 5670
HEFEI PARAGON PLASTIC PACKAGING CO., LTD.—See PT. Berlina Tbk; *Int'l*, pg. 6085
HEFEI POLY GRAND THEATRE MANAGEMENT CORPORATION LIMITED—See Poly Culture Group Corporation Limited; *Int'l*, pg. 5913
HEFEI QUNYING SCIENCE & TECHNOLOGY CO., LTD.—See Endress+Hauser (International) Holding AG; *Int'l*, pg. 2408
HEFEI RONG AN POWER MACHINERY CO., LTD.—See China Huarong Energy Co. Ltd.; *Int'l*, pg. 1509
HEFEI SUNWIN INTELLIGENT CO., LTD—See Shenzhen Sunwin Intelligent Co., Ltd.; *Int'l*, pg. 6822
HEFEI TAIHE OPTOELECTRONIC TECHNOLOGY CO., LTD; *Int'l*, pg. 3308
HEFEI TONGZHI ELECTROMECHANICAL CONTROL TECHNOLOGY CO., LTD.—See Jiangsu Yinhe Electronics Co., Ltd.; *Int'l*, pg. 3956

HEFEI TRISTATE GARMENT MANUFACTURING COMPANY LIMITED—See Tristate Holdings Limited; *Int'l*, pg. 7927
HEFEI URBAN CONSTRUCTION DEVEL CO., LTD.; *Int'l*, pg. 3308
HEFEI XINHAI ELECTRONIC TECHNOLOGY CO., LTD.—See Chipsea Technologies (Shenzhen) Corp.; *Int'l*, pg. 1573
HEFEI XINSHENG OPTOELECTRONICS TECHNOLOGY CO., LTD.—See BOE Technology Group Co., Ltd.; *Int'l*, pg. 1099
HEFFERNAN INSURANCE BROKERS; *U.S. Private*, pg. 1903
HEFFERNAN NETWORK INSURANCE BROKERS—See Heffernan Insurance Brokers; *U.S. Private*, pg. 1904
HEFFNER MOTORS LIMITED; *Int'l*, pg. 3308
HEF & HIJS NEDERLAND B.V.—See ABIRD Holding BV; *Int'l*, pg. 62
HEFREN-TILLOTSON, INC.; *U.S. Private*, pg. 1904
HEFTER SYSTEMFORM GMBH—See Francotyp-Postalia Holding AG; *Int'l*, pg. 2761
HEG HOPFENEXTRAKTION GMBH—See S.S. Steiner Inc.; *U.S. Private*, pg. 3518
HEG LIMITED; *Int'l*, pg. 3308
HEGMATAN CEMENT CO.—See Tehran Cement Company; *Int'l*, pg. 7522
HE HARBIN POWER PLANT VALVE CO., LTD.—See Harbin Electric Corporation; *Int'l*, pg. 3270
HEHEIST CO., LTD.; *Int'l*, pg. 3308
HEHMEYER, LLC; *U.S. Private*, pg. 1904
HEHR GLASS COMPANY INC.—See LCI Industries; *U.S. Public*, pg. 1295
HEHR INTERNATIONAL INC. - INDIANA WINDOW PLANT—See LCI Industries; *U.S. Public*, pg. 1295
HEHR INTERNATIONAL INC. - KANSAS GLASS PLANT—See LCI Industries; *U.S. Public*, pg. 1295
HEHR INTERNATIONAL INC. - KANSAS WINDOW PLANT—See LCI Industries; *U.S. Public*, pg. 1295
HEHR INTERNATIONAL INC. - MICHIGAN WINDOW PLANT—See LCI Industries; *U.S. Public*, pg. 1295
HEHR INTERNATIONAL INC.—See LCI Industries; *U.S. Public*, pg. 1295
H.E. HUNEWILL CONSTRUCTION CO.; *U.S. Private*, pg. 1826
HEIAN CEREMONY SERVICE CO., LTD.; *Int'l*, pg. 3308
HEIBER SCHRODER GMBH—See INDUS Holding AG; *Int'l*, pg. 3663
HEICO AEROSPACE CORPORATION—See HEICO Corporation; *U.S. Public*, pg. 1019
HEICO AEROSPACE HOLDINGS CORP.—See HEICO Corporation; *U.S. Public*, pg. 1019
HEICO AEROSPACE PARTS CORP.—See HEICO Corporation; *U.S. Public*, pg. 1019
THE HEICO COMPANIES, L.L.C.; *U.S. Private*, pg. 4050
HEICO COMPONENT REPAIR GROUP—See HEICO Corporation; *U.S. Public*, pg. 1019
HEICO CORPORATION; *U.S. Public*, pg. 1019
HEICO ELECTRONIC TECHNOLOGIES CORP.—See HEICO Corporation; *U.S. Public*, pg. 1020
HEICO FLIGHT SUPPORT CORP.—See HEICO Corporation; *U.S. Public*, pg. 1021
HEICO PARTS GROUP, INC.—See HEICO Corporation; *U.S. Public*, pg. 1019
HEICO WIRE GROUP—See HEICO Corporation; *U.S. Public*, pg. 1019
HEIDEBLUME MOLKEREI ELSDORF-ROTENBURG AG—See J. Bauer GmbH & Co. KG; *Int'l*, pg. 3854
HEIDEBREICHT, INC.; *U.S. Private*, pg. 1904
HEIDECK DIALYSIS, LLC—See DaVita Inc.; *U.S. Public*, pg. 639
HEIDE & COOK, LTD.—See Heide & Cook Mechanical Contractors; *U.S. Private*, pg. 1904
HEIDE & COOK MECHANICAL CONTRACTORS; *U.S. Private*, pg. 1904
HEIDEGESELLASCHAFT G.M.B.H.—See Det Danske Hedeselskab; *Int'l*, pg. 2047
HEIDELBERG ASIA PTE LTD.—See Heidelberger Druckmaschinen AG; *Int'l*, pg. 3321
HEIDELBERG BALTIC FINLAND OU—See Heidelberger Druckmaschinen AG; *Int'l*, pg. 3321
HEIDELBERG BENELUX BVBA—See Heidelberger Druckmaschinen AG; *Int'l*, pg. 3321
HEIDELBERG BENELUX B.V.—See Heidelberger Druckmaschinen AG; *Int'l*, pg. 3321
HEIDELBERG CANADA GRAPHIC EQUIPMENT LTD.—See Heidelberger Druckmaschinen AG; *Int'l*, pg. 3321
HEIDELBERG CATERING SERVICES GMBH—See Heidelberger Druckmaschinen AG; *Int'l*, pg. 3321
HEIDELBERGCEMENT ASIA PTE LTD—See Heidelberg Materials AG; *Int'l*, pg. 3314
HEIDELBERGCEMENT BANGLADESH LIMITED—See Heidelberg Materials AG; *Int'l*, pg. 3314
HEIDELBERGCEMENT CENTRAL EUROPE EAST HOLDING B.V.—See Heidelberg Materials AG; *Int'l*, pg. 3314
HEIDELBERGCEMENT CHINA—See Heidelberg Materials AG; *Int'l*, pg. 3310

COMPANY NAME INDEX

HEIDELBERGCEMENT GRUNDSTUCKSGESELLSCHAFT MBH & CO. KG—See Heidelberg Materials AG; *Int'l*, pg. 3314
HEIDELBERGCEMENT GRUNDSTUCKSVERWALTUNGSGESELLSCHAFT MBH—See Heidelberg Materials AG; *Int'l*, pg. 3314
HEIDELBERG CEMENT, INC.—See Heidelberg Materials AG; *Int'l*, pg. 3314
HEIDELBERGCEMENT INDIA LTD.—See Heidelberg Materials AG; *Int'l*, pg. 3314
HEIDELBERGCEMENT INTERNATIONAL HOLDING GMBH—See Heidelberg Materials AG; *Int'l*, pg. 3315
HEIDELBERGCEMENT MILJO AB - PRODUCTION PLANT—See Heidelberg Materials AG; *Int'l*, pg. 3315
HEIDELBERGCEMENT MILJO AB—See Heidelberg Materials AG; *Int'l*, pg. 3314
HEIDELBERGCEMENT NETHERLANDS HOLDING B.V.—See Heidelberg Materials AG; *Int'l*, pg. 3315
HEIDELBERGCEMENT NORTHERN EUROPE AB—See Heidelberg Materials AG; *Int'l*, pg. 3315
HEIDELBERGCEMENT NORWAY A.S.—See Heidelberg Materials AG; *Int'l*, pg. 3315
HEIDELBERGCEMENT PUMPS & TRUCKS AS—See Heidelberg Materials AG; *Int'l*, pg. 3315
HEIDELBERGCEMENT ROMANIA SA—See Heidelberg Materials AG; *Int'l*, pg. 3315
HEIDELBERGCEMENT SHARED SERVICE CENTRE AB—See Heidelberg Materials AG; *Int'l*, pg. 3315
HEIDELBERGCEMENT SHARED SERVICES GMBH—See Heidelberg Materials AG; *Int'l*, pg. 3315
HEIDELBERGCEMENT SWEDEN AB—See Heidelberg Materials AG; *Int'l*, pg. 3315
HEIDELBERGCEMENT TECHNOLOGY CENTER GMBH—See Heidelberg Materials AG; *Int'l*, pg. 3315
HEIDELBERGCEMENT UK HOLDING II LIMITED—See Heidelberg Materials AG; *Int'l*, pg. 3315
HEIDELBERGCEMENT UK LIMITED—See Heidelberg Materials AG; *Int'l*, pg. 3315
HEIDELBERG CHINA LTD.—See Heidelberger Druckmaschinen AG; *Int'l*, pg. 3321
HEIDELBERG DISTRICT COMMUNITY ENTERPRISE LIMITED—See Bendigo & Adelaide Bank Ltd.; *Int'l*, pg. 971
HEIDELBERG DO BRASIL SISTEMAS GRAFICOS E SERVICOS LTDA—See Heidelberger Druckmaschinen AG; *Int'l*, pg. 3322
HEIDELBERG ENGINEERING GMBH—See EssilorLuxottica SA; *Int'l*, pg. 2514
HEIDELBERG ENGINEERING INC.—See EssilorLuxottica SA; *Int'l*, pg. 2514
HEIDELBERG ENGINEERING LTD.—See EssilorLuxottica SA; *Int'l*, pg. 2514
HEIDELBERG ENGINEERING PTY. LTD.—See EssilorLuxottica SA; *Int'l*, pg. 2514
HEIDELBERGER BETEILIGUNGSHOLDING AG; *Int'l*, pg. 3321
HEIDELBERGER BETON ASCHAFFENBURG VERWALTUNGS-GMBH—See Heidelberg Materials AG; *Int'l*, pg. 3315
HEIDELBERGER BETON DONAU-ILLER VERWALTUNGS-GMBH—See Heidelberg Materials AG; *Int'l*, pg. 3315
HEIDELBERGER BETON DONAU-NAAB GMBH & CO. KG—See Heidelberg Materials AG; *Int'l*, pg. 3315
HEIDELBERGER BETONELEMENTE VERWALTUNGS-GMBH—See Heidelberg Materials AG; *Int'l*, pg. 3316
HEIDELBERGER BETON ELSTER-SPREE GMBH & CO. KG—See Heidelberg Materials AG; *Int'l*, pg. 3316
HEIDELBERGER BETON GMBH—See Heidelberg Materials AG; *Int'l*, pg. 3316
HEIDELBERGER BETON INNTAL GMBH & CO. KG—See Heidelberg Materials AG; *Int'l*, pg. 3316
HEIDELBERGER BETON KURPFALZ GMBH & CO. KG—See Heidelberg Materials AG; *Int'l*, pg. 3316
HEIDELBERGER BETONPUMPEN RHEIN-MAIN-NAHE GMBH & CO. KG—See Heidelberg Materials AG; *Int'l*, pg. 3316
HEIDELBERGER BETONPUMPEN RHEIN-MAIN-NAHE VERWALTUNGS-GMBH—See Heidelberg Materials AG; *Int'l*, pg. 3316
HEIDELBERGER BETONPUMPEN SIMONIS GMBH & CO. KG—See Heidelberg Materials AG; *Int'l*, pg. 3316
HEIDELBERGER BETON RHEIN-NAHE GMBH & CO.KG—See Heidelberg Materials AG; *Int'l*, pg. 3316
HEIDELBERGER BETON SCHWANDORF GMBH—See Heidelberg Materials AG; *Int'l*, pg. 3316
HEIDELBERGER BETON ZWICKAU GMBH & CO. KG—See Heidelberg Materials AG; *Int'l*, pg. 3316
HEIDELBERGER BETON ZWICKAU VERWALTUNGS-GMBH—See Heidelberg Materials AG; *Int'l*, pg. 3316
HEIDELBERGER CIS OOO—See Heidelberger Druckmaschinen AG; *Int'l*, pg. 3322
HEIDELBERGER DRUCKMASCHINEN AG; *Int'l*, pg. 3321
HEIDELBERGER DRUCKMASCHINEN AUSTRIA VERTRIEBS-GMBH—See Heidelberger Druckmaschinen AG; *Int'l*, pg. 3322
HEIDELBERGER DRUCKMASCHINEN OSTEUROPA VERTRIEBS-GMBH 4—See Heidelberger Druckmaschinen AG; *Int'l*, pg. 3322

HEIDELBERGER DRUCKMASCHINEN UKRAINA LTD.—See Heidelberger Druckmaschinen AG; *Int'l*, pg. 3322
HEIDELBERGER DRUCKMASCHINEN VERTRIEB DEUTSCHLAND GMBH—See Heidelberger Druckmaschinen AG; *Int'l*, pg. 3322
HEIDELBERGER FLIESSESTRICH SUDWEST GMBH—See Heidelberg Materials AG; *Int'l*, pg. 3316
HEIDELBERGER KS BETEILIGUNGEN DEUTSCHLAND VERWALTUNGSGESELLSCHAFT MBH—See Heidelberg Materials AG; *Int'l*, pg. 3316
HEIDELBERGER LEBENSVERSICHERUNG AG—See Cinven Limited; *Int'l*, pg. 1616
HEIDELBERGER LEBENSVERSICHERUNG AG—See Talanx AG; *Int'l*, pg. 7445
HEIDELBERGER SAND UND KIES HANDEL & LOGISTIK GMBH—See Heidelberg Materials AG; *Int'l*, pg. 3316
HEIDELBERGER SAND UND KIES HANDELS- UND VERTRIEBS-GMBH—See Heidelberg Materials AG; *Int'l*, pg. 3316
HEIDELBERGER WESERKIES VERWALTUNGS-GMBH—See Heidelberg Materials AG; *Int'l*, pg. 3316
HEIDELBERG FRANCE S.A.S.—See Heidelberger Druckmaschinen AG; *Int'l*, pg. 3321
HEIDELBERG GRAFIK TICARET SERVIS LIMITED SIRKETI—See Heidelberger Druckmaschinen AG; *Int'l*, pg. 3321
HEIDELBERG GRAPHIC EQUIPMENT LIMITED—See Heidelberger Druckmaschinen AG; *Int'l*, pg. 3321
HEIDELBERG GRAPHIC EQUIPMENT LTD.—See Heidelberger Druckmaschinen AG; *Int'l*, pg. 3321
HEIDELBERG GRAPHIC EQUIPMENT LTD.—See Heidelberger Druckmaschinen AG; *Int'l*, pg. 3321
HEIDELBERG GRAPHIC EQUIPMENT (SHANGHAI) CO. LTD.—See Heidelberger Druckmaschinen AG; *Int'l*, pg. 3321
HEIDELBERG GRAPHICS TAIWAN LTD.—See Heidelberger Druckmaschinen AG; *Int'l*, pg. 3321
HEIDELBERG GRAPHICS (THAILAND) LTD.—See Heidelberger Druckmaschinen AG; *Int'l*, pg. 3321
HEIDELBERG GRAPHIC SYSTEMS SOUTHERN AFRICA (PTY) LTD—See Heidelberger Druckmaschinen AG; *Int'l*, pg. 3321
HEIDELBERG HELLAS A.E.E.—See Heidelberger Druckmaschinen AG; *Int'l*, pg. 3321
HEIDELBERG HONG KONG—See EAC Invest AS; *Int'l*, pg. 2261
HEIDELBERG INDIA PRIVATE LTD.—See Heidelberger Druckmaschinen AG; *Int'l*, pg. 3321
HEIDELBERG INNOVATION FONDS MANAGEMENT GMBH; *Int'l*, pg. 3308
HEIDELBERG INTERNATIONAL LTD. A/S—See Heidelberger Druckmaschinen AG; *Int'l*, pg. 3321
HEIDELBERG ITALIA S.R.L.—See Heidelberger Druckmaschinen AG; *Int'l*, pg. 3321
HEIDELBERG JAPAN K.K.—See Heidelberger Druckmaschinen AG; *Int'l*, pg. 3321
HEIDELBERG KOREA LTD.—See Heidelberger Druckmaschinen AG; *Int'l*, pg. 3321
HEIDELBERG MAGYARORSZAG KFT.—See Heidelberger Druckmaschinen AG; *Int'l*, pg. 3321
HEIDELBERG MALAYSIA SDN BHD—See Heidelberger Druckmaschinen AG; *Int'l*, pg. 3321
HEIDELBERG MANUFACTURING DEUTSCHLAND GMBH—See Heidelberger Druckmaschinen AG; *Int'l*, pg. 3321
HEIDELBERG MATERIALS AG; *Int'l*, pg. 3308
HEIDELBERG MATERIALS ALKMAAR BETON B.V.—See Heidelberg Materials AG; *Int'l*, pg. 3314
HEIDELBERG MATERIALS BETON DE GMBH—See Heidelberg Materials AG; *Int'l*, pg. 3314
HEIDELBERG MATERIALS BETONG NORGE AS—See Heidelberg Materials AG; *Int'l*, pg. 3314
HEIDELBERG MATERIALS BETONG SVERIGE AB—See Heidelberg Materials AG; *Int'l*, pg. 3314
HEIDELBERG MATERIALS BETOON AS—See Heidelberg Materials AG; *Int'l*, pg. 3314
HEIDELBERG MATERIALS CEMENT SVERIGE AB—See Heidelberg Materials AG; *Int'l*, pg. 3314
HEIDELBERG MATERIALS DIGITAL HUB BRNO, S.R.O.—See Heidelberg Materials AG; *Int'l*, pg. 3314
HEIDELBERG MATERIALS DIGITAL HUB VARNA EAD—See Heidelberg Materials AG; *Int'l*, pg. 3314
HEIDELBERG MATERIALS FRANCE S.A.S.—See Heidelberg Materials AG; *Int'l*, pg. 3314
HEIDELBERG MATERIALS- HELWAN CEMENT S.A.E.—See Heidelberg Materials AG; *Int'l*, pg. 3314
HEIDELBERG MATERIALS HISPANIA CEMENTOS, S.A.—See Heidelberg Materials AG; *Int'l*, pg. 3314
HEIDELBERG MATERIALS KAZAKHSTAN LLP—See Heidelberg Materials AG; *Int'l*, pg. 3314
HEIDELBERG MATERIALS KUNDA AS—See Heidelberg Materials AG; *Int'l*, pg. 3314
HEIDELBERG MATERIALS LATVIJA BETONS SIA—See Heidelberg Materials AG; *Int'l*, pg. 3314
HEIDELBERG MATERIALS LATVIJA SSC SIA—See Heidelberg Materials AG; *Int'l*, pg. 3314
HEIDELBERG MATERIALS LIETUVA CEMENTAS UAB—See Heidelberg Materials AG; *Int'l*, pg. 3314

HEIDELBERG MATERIALS MILJO AS—See Heidelberg Materials AG; *Int'l*, pg. 3314
HEIDELBERG MATERIALS MINERALIK DE GMBH—See Heidelberg Materials AG; *Int'l*, pg. 3314
HEIDELBERG MATERIALS NEDERLAND BETON B.V.—See Heidelberg Materials AG; *Int'l*, pg. 3314
HEIDELBERG MATERIALS NORWAY AS—See Heidelberg Materials AG; *Int'l*, pg. 3314
HEIDELBERG MATERIALS PRECAST ABETONG AB—See Heidelberg Materials AG; *Int'l*, pg. 3314
HEIDELBERG MATERIALS PRECAST CONTIGA AB—See Heidelberg Materials AG; *Int'l*, pg. 3314
HEIDELBERG MATERIALS PRECAST DENMARK A/S—See Heidelberg Materials AG; *Int'l*, pg. 3314
HEIDELBERG MATERIALS PREFAB NORGE AS—See Heidelberg Materials AG; *Int'l*, pg. 3314
HEIDELBERG MATERIALS ROMANIA S.A.—See Heidelberg Materials AG; *Int'l*, pg. 3314
HEIDELBERG MATERIALS- TOURAH CEMENT S.A.E.—See Heidelberg Materials AG; *Int'l*, pg. 3314
HEIDELBERG MATERIALS UK LIMITED—See Heidelberg Materials AG; *Int'l*, pg. 3314
HEIDELBERG MATERIALS US, INC.—See Heidelberg Materials AG; *Int'l*, pg. 3313
HEIDELBERG MEXICO S. DE R.L. DE C.V.—See Heidelberger Druckmaschinen AG; *Int'l*, pg. 3321
HEIDELBERG PASTRY SHOPPE, INC.; *U.S. Private*, pg. 1904
HEIDELBERG PHARMA AG; *Int'l*, pg. 3321
HEIDELBERG PHILIPPINES, INC.—See Heidelberger Druckmaschinen AG; *Int'l*, pg. 3321
HEIDELBERG POLSKA SP Z.O.O.—See Heidelberger Druckmaschinen AG; *Int'l*, pg. 3321
HEIDELBERG POSTPRESS DEUTSCHLAND GMBH—See Heidelberger Druckmaschinen AG; *Int'l*, pg. 3321
HEIDELBERG PRAHA SPOL S.R.O.—See Heidelberger Druckmaschinen AG; *Int'l*, pg. 3322
HEIDELBERG PRINT FINANCE AMERICAS, INC—See Heidelberger Druckmaschinen AG; *Int'l*, pg. 3322
HEIDELBERG PROMINENT FLUID CONTROLS INDIA PVT. LTD.—See Verder International B.V.; *Int'l*, pg. 8166
HEIDELBERG SCHWEIZ AG—See Heidelberger Druckmaschinen AG; *Int'l*, pg. 3322
HEIDELBERG SLOVENSKO S.H.U.—See Heidelberger Druckmaschinen AG; *Int'l*, pg. 3322
HEIDELBERG SPAIN S.L.U.—See Heidelberger Druckmaschinen AG; *Int'l*, pg. 3322
HEIDELBERG SVERIGE AB—See Heidelberger Druckmaschinen AG; *Int'l*, pg. 3322
HEIDELBERG USA, INC.—See Heidelberger Druckmaschinen AG; *Int'l*, pg. 3322
HEIDELBERG WEB CARTON CONVERTING GMBH—See Heidelberger Druckmaschinen AG; *Int'l*, pg. 3322
HEIDE PARK SOLTAU GMBH—See Merlin Entertainments plc; *Int'l*, pg. 4837
HEIDLER HOLDINGS, INC.—See Core & Main, Inc.; *U.S. Public*, pg. 576
HEIDRICK & STRUGGLES AB—See Heidrick & Struggles International, Inc.; *U.S. Public*, pg. 1022
HEIDRICK & STRUGGLES AG—See Heidrick & Struggles International, Inc.; *U.S. Public*, pg. 1022
HEIDRICK & STRUGGLES A/S—See Heidrick & Struggles International, Inc.; *U.S. Public*, pg. 1022
HEIDRICK & STRUGGLES AUSTRALIA, LTD.—See Heidrick & Struggles International, Inc.; *U.S. Public*, pg. 1022
HEIDRICK & STRUGGLES BV—See Heidrick & Struggles International, Inc.; *U.S. Public*, pg. 1022
HEIDRICK & STRUGGLES CANADA, INC.—See Heidrick & Struggles International, Inc.; *U.S. Public*, pg. 1022
HEIDRICK & STRUGGLES DE CHILE LIMITADA—See Heidrick & Struggles International, Inc.; *U.S. Public*, pg. 1023
HEIDRICK & STRUGGLES DO BRASIL LTDA.—See Heidrick & Struggles International, Inc.; *U.S. Public*, pg. 1023
HEIDRICK & STRUGGLES ESPANA, INC.—See Heidrick & Struggles International, Inc.; *U.S. Public*, pg. 1022
HEIDRICK & STRUGGLES HONG KONG LTD.—See Heidrick & Struggles International, Inc.; *U.S. Public*, pg. 1022
HEIDRICK & STRUGGLES, INC.—See Heidrick & Struggles International, Inc.; *U.S. Public*, pg. 1023
HEIDRICK & STRUGGLES (INDIA) PRIVATE LIMITED—See Heidrick & Struggles International, Inc.; *U.S. Public*, pg. 1022
HEIDRICK & STRUGGLES INTERIM EXECUTIVE GMBH—See Heidrick & Struggles International, Inc.; *U.S. Public*, pg. 1022
HEIDRICK & STRUGGLES INTERNATIONAL, INC.; *U.S. Public*, pg. 1022
HEIDRICK & STRUGGLES INTERNATIONAL SRL—See Heidrick & Struggles International, Inc.; *U.S. Public*, pg. 1022
HEIDRICK & STRUGGLES IRELAND, LIMITED—See Heidrick & Struggles International, Inc.; *U.S. Public*, pg. 1022

HEIDRICK & STRUGGLES JAPAN, LTD.—See Heidrick & Struggles International, Inc.; *U.S. Public*, pg. 1022
HEIDRICK & STRUGGLES KOREA, INC.—See Heidrick & Struggles International, Inc.; *U.S. Public*, pg. 1022
HEIDRICK & STRUGGLES (MIDDLE EAST) LLC—See Heidrick & Struggles International, Inc.; *U.S. Public*, pg. 1022
HEIDRICK & STRUGGLES (NZ) LIMITED—See Heidrick & Struggles International, Inc.; *U.S. Public*, pg. 1022
HEIDRICK & STRUGGLES RECRUITMENT THAILAND CO., LTD.—See Heidrick & Struggles International, Inc.; *U.S. Public*, pg. 1022
HEIDRICK & STRUGGLES RUSSIA LLC—See Heidrick & Struggles International, Inc.; *U.S. Public*, pg. 1023
HEIDRICK & STRUGGLES S.A. DE C.V.—See Heidrick & Struggles International, Inc.; *U.S. Public*, pg. 1023
HEIDRICK & STRUGGLES (SHP) LIMITED—See Heidrick & Struggles International, Inc.; *U.S. Public*, pg. 1022
HEIDRICK & STRUGGLES SINGAPORE PTE LTD.—See Heidrick & Struggles International, Inc.; *U.S. Public*, pg. 1023
HEIDRICK & STRUGGLES SP. Z O.O.—See Heidrick & Struggles International, Inc.; *U.S. Public*, pg. 1023
HEIDRICK & STRUGGLES UK LTD.—See Heidrick & Struggles International, Inc.; *U.S. Public*, pg. 1023
HEIDRICK & STRUGGLES UNTERNEHMENSBERATUNG GMBH—See Heidrick & Struggles International, Inc.; *U.S. Public*, pg. 1023
HEIDRICK & STRUGGLES UNTERNEHMENSBERATUNG VERWALTUNG- GMBH—See Heidrick & Struggles International, Inc.; *U.S. Public*, pg. 1022
HEIDRIVE GMBH—See Allient Inc.; *U.S. Public*, pg. 80
HEIDRIVE S.R.O.—See Allient Inc.; *U.S. Public*, pg. 80
HEIDT DESIGN LLC; *U.S. Private*, pg. 1904
HEIDTMAN STEEL PRODUCTS, INC.; *U.S. Private*, pg. 1904
HEIFERMAN, INC.—See Dubin Clark & Company, Inc.; *U.S. Private*, pg. 1283
HEIGHTS FINANCE CORPORATION—See CURO Group Holdings Corp.; *U.S. Public*, pg. 611
THE HEIGHTS PTY LTD—See Bonatla Property Holdings Limited; *Int'l*, pg. 1105
HEI HOSPITALITY, LLC; *U.S. Private*, pg. 1904
HEIJMANS BESTCON B.V.—See Heijmans N.V.; *Int'l*, pg. 3322
HEIJMANS BETON- EN WATERBOUW B.V.—See Heijmans N.V.; *Int'l*, pg. 3322
HEIJMANS (B) N.V.—See Orascom Construction PLC; *Int'l*, pg. 5612
HEIJMANS BOUW N.V.—See Orascom Construction PLC; *Int'l*, pg. 5612
HEIJMANS BURGH HAAMSTEDE B.V.—See Heijmans N.V.; *Int'l*, pg. 3322
HEIJMANS BURGH HAAMSTEDE B.V.—See Heijmans N.V.; *Int'l*, pg. 3323
HEIJMANS ENERGIE B.V.—See Heijmans N.V.; *Int'l*, pg. 3322
HEIJMANS INFRA GEINTEGREERDE PROJECTEN B.V.—See Heijmans N.V.; *Int'l*, pg. 3322
HEIJMANS NEDERLAND B.V.—See Heijmans N.V.; *Int'l*, pg. 3322
HEIJMANS N.V.; *Int'l*, pg. 3322
HEIJMANS TECHNIEK EN MOBILITEIT B.V.—See Heijmans N.V.; *Int'l*, pg. 3322
HEIJMANS TECHNISCHE INFRA B.V.—See Heijmans N.V.; *Int'l*, pg. 3322
HEIJMANS VASTGOED B.V.—See Heijmans N.V.; *Int'l*, pg. 3322
HEIJMANS VASTGOED PARTICIPATIES B.V.—See Heijmans N.V.; *Int'l*, pg. 3322
HEIJMANS VASTGOED REALISATIE B.V.—See Heijmans N.V.; *Int'l*, pg. 3322
HEIJMANS WONINGBOUW B.V.—See Heijmans N.V.; *Int'l*, pg. 3322
HEIJMANS WONINGBOUW B.V.—See Heijmans N.V.; *Int'l*, pg. 3322
HEIJMANS WONINGBOUW B.V.—See Heijmans N.V.; *Int'l*, pg. 3322
HEIJMANS WONINGBOUW B.V.—See Heijmans N.V.; *Int'l*, pg. 3323
H. EIKENHOUT & SONS, INC.; *U.S. Private*, pg. 1824
HEIK HOLDING COMPANY INC.; *U.S. Private*, pg. 1904
HEIKINTORI OY—See Citycon Oyj; *Int'l*, pg. 1629
HEIKKINEN & PULJULA LTD.—See REISSWOLF International AG; *Int'l*, pg. 6257
HEIKO PACK CO., LTD.—See Shimojima Co., Ltd.; *Int'l*, pg. 6836
HEILAND GMBH—See Vimian Group AB; *Int'l*, pg. 8208
HEIL ASIA LIMITED—See Terex Corporation; *U.S. Public*, pg. 2019
HEILBAD BAD NEUSTADT GMBH—See Asklepios Kliniken GmbH & Co. KGaA; *Int'l*, pg. 624
HEILBAD SAUERBRUNN BETRIEBSGESELLSCHAFT M.B.H.—See Fresenius SE & Co. KGaA; *Int'l*, pg. 2779
HEILBRICE; *U.S. Private*, pg. 1904
THE HEIL CO. - ALABAMA—See Terex Corporation; *U.S. Public*, pg. 2019
THE HEIL CO. - MISSISSIPPI—See Terex Corporation; *U.S. Public*, pg. 2019

THE HEIL CO.—See Terex Corporation; *U.S. Public*, pg. 2019
HEIL FARID EUROPEAN COMPANY LIMITED—See Terex Corporation; *U.S. Public*, pg. 2019
HEILIND ELECTRONICS, INC.; *U.S. Private*, pg. 1904
HEILMAN HOLDING COMPANY INC.; *U.S. Private*, pg. 1904
HEILONGJIANG AGRICLTURE COMPANY LIMITED; *Int'l*, pg. 3323
HEILONGJIANG CHEMICAL GROUP CO., LTD.—See China National Chemical Corporation; *Int'l*, pg. 1528
HEILONGJIANG CHINA INTERNATIONAL TRAVEL SERVICE LIMITED—See China Tourism Group Duty Free Corporation Limited; *Int'l*, pg. 1560
HEILONGJIANG FEIHE DAIRY CO., LIMITED—See Feihe International, Inc.; *Int'l*, pg. 2632
HEILONGJIANG FUJIN KAMA VEHICLE WHEEL MANUFACTURING CO., LTD.—See China Hi-Tech Group Corporation; *Int'l*, pg. 1508
HEILONGJIANG HAOHUA CHEMICAL CO., LTD.—See China National Chemical Corporation; *Int'l*, pg. 1528
HEILONGJIANG INTERCHINA WATER TREATMENT CO., LTD.; *Int'l*, pg. 3323
HEILONGJIANG KINGDOM ENTERPRISE CO, LTD.—See Kingdom Holdings Limited; *Int'l*, pg. 4172
HEILONGJIANG RILUBEIDA FOODSTUFFS CO., LTD.—See Maruha Nichiro Corporation; *Int'l*, pg. 4711
HEILONGJIANG TRANSPORT DEVELOPMENT CO., LTD.; *Int'l*, pg. 3323
HEILONGJIANG YABULI ON SNOW ASIAN GAME VILLAGE HOTEL CO. LTD.—See Mountain China Resorts (Holding) Limited; *Int'l*, pg. 5057
HEILONGJIANG ZBD PHARMACEUTICAL CO., LTD.; *Int'l*, pg. 3323
HEILONGJIANG ZHONGSHENG STAR AUTOMOBILE SALES & SERVICE CO., LTD.—See Zhongsheng Group Holdings Limited; *Int'l*, pg. 8674
HEIL TRAILER INTERNATIONAL, CO. - HEIL ATHENS MANUFACTURING FACILITY—See AIP, LLC; *U.S. Private*, pg. 134
HEIL TRAILER INTERNATIONAL, CO. - HEIL TANK SERVICE - MANUFACTURING FACILITY—See AIP, LLC; *U.S. Private*, pg. 134
HEIL TRAILER INTERNATIONAL, CO.—See AIP, LLC; *U.S. Private*, pg. 134
HEIL TRAILER INTERNATIONAL, CO. - TEXAS—See AIP, LLC; *U.S. Private*, pg. 134
HEIMAR HF.; *Int'l*, pg. 3323
HEIM BEARINGS COMPANY—See RBC Bearings Incorporated; *U.S. Public*, pg. 1766
HEIMBS KAFEE GMBH & CO KG—See Nestle S.A.; *Int'l*, pg. 5205
HEIMBS KAFFEE GMBH & CO. KG—See Alois Dallmayr KG; *Int'l*, pg. 365
THE HEIMBURG GROUP, INC.—See Hardesty & Hanover, LLC; *U.S. Private*, pg. 1863
HEIM & BURO VERSAND GMBH—See Metro AG; *Int'l*, pg. 4857
HEIMERLE + MEULE GMBH—See L. Possehl & Co. mbH; *Int'l*, pg. 4383
HEIMON KALA OY—See Kalanevuos Oy; *Int'l*, pg. 4057
HEIMSOFT SOLUTIONS AG—See NEXUS AG; *Int'l*, pg. 5250
HEIMSTADEN AB; *Int'l*, pg. 3323
HEIN DE WINDT B.V.—See FUCHS SE; *Int'l*, pg. 2804
HEINEKEN FRANCE S.A.—See L'Arche Green N.V.; *Int'l*, pg. 4377
HEINEKEN HOLDING N.V.—See L'Arche Green N.V.; *Int'l*, pg. 4376
HEINEKEN HUNGARIA SORGYARAK ZRT.—See L'Arche Green N.V.; *Int'l*, pg. 4377
HEINEKEN IRELAND—See L'Arche Green N.V.; *Int'l*, pg. 4377
HEINEKEN ITALIA S.P.A.—See L'Arche Green N.V.; *Int'l*, pg. 4377
HEINEKEN MALAYSIA BERHAD—See L'Arche Green N.V.; *Int'l*, pg. 4377
HEINEKEN NEDERLAND BV—See L'Arche Green N.V.; *Int'l*, pg. 4377
HEINEKEN N.V.—See L'Arche Green N.V.; *Int'l*, pg. 4376
HEINEKEN SWITZERLAND AG—See L'Arche Green N.V.; *Int'l*, pg. 4377
HEINEKEN UK LIMITED—See L'Arche Green N.V.; *Int'l*, pg. 4377
HEINEKEN USA INC.—See L'Arche Green N.V.; *Int'l*, pg. 4377
HEINEMANN ASIA PACIFIC PTE. LTD.—See Gebr. Heinemann SE & Co. KG; *Int'l*, pg. 2905
HEINEMANN PUBLISHERS, LTD.—See Pearson plc; *Int'l*, pg. 5776
HEINEMANN PUBLISHERS (PTY) LTD—See Pearson plc; *Int'l*, pg. 5775
HEINEMANN-RAINTREE—See Coughlan Companies, Inc.; *U.S. Private*, pg. 1065
HEINEMANN'S BAKERIES L.L.C.; *U.S. Private*, pg. 1904
HEINEMANN—See Veritas Capital Fund Management, LLC; *U.S. Private*, pg. 4363
HEINEN & ASSOCIATES LLC; *U.S. Private*, pg. 1904
HEINEN'S INC.; *U.S. Private*, pg. 1904

HEINE RESISTORS GMBH—See Knorr-Bremse AG; *Int'l*, pg. 4210
HEINER GOSSEN HOTELBETRIEB GMBH—See Minor International PCL; *Int'l*, pg. 4911
HEINKEL FILTERING SYSTEMS INC.—See HEINKEL Process Technology GmbH; *Int'l*, pg. 3323
HEINKEL PROCESS TECHNOLOGY GMBH; *Int'l*, pg. 3323
HEINKE TECHNOLOGY INC.—See PCE, Inc.; *U.S. Private*, pg. 3120
HEINN CHAPMAN CORPORATION; *U.S. Private*, pg. 1905
HEINRICH BAUER EDICIONES S.L.—See Hubert Burda Media Holding Kommanditgesellschaft; *Int'l*, pg. 3519
HEINRICH BAUER PRODUKTIONS KG—See Heinrich Bauer Verlag KG; *Int'l*, pg. 3324
HEINRICH BAUER VERLAG KG; *Int'l*, pg. 3323
HEINRICH BRUNING GMBH—See BayWa AG; *Int'l*, pg. 918
HEINRICH CHEVROLET; *U.S. Private*, pg. 1905
HEINRICH CO.—See Ace Stamping & Machine Co, Inc.; *U.S. Private*, pg. 57
HEINRICH DE FRIES GMBH; *Int'l*, pg. 3324
HEINRICH DEHN INTERNATIONALE SPEDITION GMBH; *Int'l*, pg. 3324
HEINRICH DURST MALZFABRIKEN GMBH & CO. KG—See Etablissements J. Soufflet; *Int'l*, pg. 2519
HEINRICH ENVELOPE CORPORATION—See Taylor Corporation; *U.S. Private*, pg. 3938
HEINRICH GEISSLER GMBH—See Georgsmarienhutte Holding GmbH; *Int'l*, pg. 2940
HEINRICH GEUTHER KINDERMOBEL UND -GERATE GMBH & CO. KG; *Int'l*, pg. 3324
HEINRICH HAGNER GMBH & CO.; *Int'l*, pg. 3324
HEINRICH HAWAII—See Heinrich Marketing; *U.S. Private*, pg. 1905
HEINRICH HEINE GMBH—See Otto GmbH & Co. KG; *Int'l*, pg. 5662
HEINRICH HEINE HANDELSGESELLSCHAFT AG—See Otto GmbH & Co. KG; *Int'l*, pg. 5662
HEINRICH HIRDES GMBH—See HAL Trust N.V.; *Int'l*, pg. 3226
HEINRICH HIRDES KAMPFMITTELRAUMUNG GMBH—See HAL Trust N.V.; *Int'l*, pg. 3226
HEINRICH HISPANIDAD—See Heinrich Marketing; *U.S. Private*, pg. 1905
HEINRICH HUHN GMBH + CO.KG; *Int'l*, pg. 3324
HEINRICH KOHLER AUCTIONSHAUS GMBH & CO. KG—See Global Philatelic Network; *Int'l*, pg. 3000
HEINRICH KOPP GMBH—See Alfanar Trading Co.; *Int'l*, pg. 315
HEINRICH KUPER GMBH & CO. KG; *Int'l*, pg. 3324
HEINRICH MARKETING; *U.S. Private*, pg. 1905
HEINRICH NAGEL GMBH & CO. KG—See RETHMANN AG & Co. KG; *Int'l*, pg. 6306
HEINRICH RENNER GMBH; *Int'l*, pg. 3324
HEINRICH SCHMID MASCHINEN-UND WERKZEUGBAU AG—See Artemis Holding AG; *Int'l*, pg. 582
HEINRICH SCHMIDT GMBH & CO. KG; *Int'l*, pg. 3325
HEINRICH'S SYNDICATE LIMITED—See Anheuser-Busch InBev SA/NV; *Int'l*, pg. 464
HEINRICH WAGNER SINTO MASCHINENFABRIK GMBH—See Sintokogio Ltd.; *Int'l*, pg. 6958
HEINS & CO. GMBH—See Linde plc; *Int'l*, pg. 4505
HEINTZ AUTOMOTIVE; *U.S. Private*, pg. 1905
HEINTZMANN AUSTRALIA PTY. LTD.—See Sandvik AB; *Int'l*, pg. 6529
HEINZE GRUPPE GMBH; *Int'l*, pg. 3325
HEINZE KUNSTSTOFFTECHNIK GMBH & CO. KG—See Heinze Gruppe GmbH; *Int'l*, pg. 3325
HEINZEL DEUTSCHLAND GMBH—See Heinzel Holding GmbH; *Int'l*, pg. 3325
HEINZEL GRAPHIC PAPER ITALIA S.R.L.—See Heinzel Holding GmbH; *Int'l*, pg. 3325
HEINZEL GRAPHIC PAPER POLSKA SP. Z.O.O.—See Heinzel Holding GmbH; *Int'l*, pg. 3325
HEINZEL HOLDING GMBH; *Int'l*, pg. 3325
HEINZEL IMPORT-EXPORT, INC.—See Heinzel Holding GmbH; *Int'l*, pg. 3326
HEINZEL SALES ASIA PACIFIC SDN. BHD.—See Heinzel Holding GmbH; *Int'l*, pg. 3325
HEINZEL SALES CANADA INC.—See Heinzel Holding GmbH; *Int'l*, pg. 3325
HEINZEL SALES FRANCE S.A.S.—See Heinzel Holding GmbH; *Int'l*, pg. 3325
HEINZEL SALES ITALY S.R.L.—See Heinzel Holding GmbH; *Int'l*, pg. 3326
HEINZERLING FOUNDATION; *U.S. Private*, pg. 1905
HEINZ ESSMANN GMBH—See Skanska AB; *Int'l*, pg. 6978
HEINZ EUROPEAN HOLDING B.V.—See 3G Capital Inc.; *U.S. Private*, pg. 9
HEINZ EUROPEAN HOLDING B.V.—See Berkshire Hathaway Inc.; *U.S. Public*, pg. 317
HEINZ FIEGE GMBH—See KEBA AG; *Int'l*, pg. 4113
HEINZ-GLAS GMBH & CO. KGAA; *Int'l*, pg. 3325
HEINZ HANGGI GMBH—See OEP Capital Advisors, L.P.; *U.S. Private*, pg. 2999

COMPANY NAME INDEX

HEINZ IBERICA, S.A.—See 3G Capital Inc.; *U.S. Private*, pg. 10
HEINZ IBERICA, S.A.—See Berkshire Hathaway Inc.; *U.S. Public*, pg. 317
HEINZ ITALIA S.P.A.—See 3G Capital Inc.; *U.S. Private*, pg. 10
HEINZ ITALIA S.P.A.—See Berkshire Hathaway Inc.; *U.S. Public*, pg. 317
HEINZ KETTLER GMBH & CO.KG - HANWEILER FACTORY—See Lafayette Mittelstand Capital; *Int'l*, pg. 4392
HEINZ KETTLER GMBH & CO.KG - KAMEN I FACTORY—See Lafayette Mittelstand Capital; *Int'l*, pg. 4392
HEINZ KETTLER GMBH & CO.KG - MERSCH FACTORY—See Lafayette Mittelstand Capital; *Int'l*, pg. 4392
HEINZ KETTLER GMBH & CO.KG—See Lafayette Mittelstand Capital; *Int'l*, pg. 4392
HEINZ NORTH AMERICA—See 3G Capital Inc.; *U.S. Private*, pg. 10
HEINZ NORTH AMERICA—See Berkshire Hathaway Inc.; *U.S. Public*, pg. 317
HEINZ SOYER BOLZENSCHWEISSTECHNIK GMBH; *Int'l*, pg. 3325
HEINZ-UFE LTD.—See 3G Capital Inc.; *U.S. Private*, pg. 10
HEINZ-UFE LTD.—See Berkshire Hathaway Inc.; *U.S. Public*, pg. 318
HEINZ WATTIE'S LIMITED—See 3G Capital Inc.; *U.S. Private*, pg. 9
HEINZ WATTIE'S LIMITED—See Berkshire Hathaway Inc.; *U.S. Public*, pg. 317
HEIQ AEONIQ GMBH—See HeiQ Plc; *Int'l*, pg. 3326
HEIQ CHEMTEX INC.—See HeiQ Plc; *Int'l*, pg. 3326
HEIQ (CHINA) MATERIAL TECH LTD.—See HeiQ Plc; *Int'l*, pg. 3326
HEIQ COMPANY LIMITED—See HeiQ Plc; *Int'l*, pg. 3326
HEIQ IBERIA UNIPESSOAL LDA.—See HeiQ Plc; *Int'l*, pg. 3326
HEIQ MATERIALS AG—See HeiQ Plc; *Int'l*, pg. 3326
HEIQ PLC; *Int'l*, pg. 3326
HEIQ RAS AG—See HeiQ Plc; *Int'l*, pg. 3326
HEIRLER CENOVIO GMBH—See Coop Gruppo Genossenschaft; *Int'l*, pg. 1790
HEIRLOOM RESTAURANT GROUP; *U.S. Private*, pg. 1905
HEISEI CERAMICS CO LTD—See NGK Insulators, Ltd.; *Int'l*, pg. 5254
HEISEI CORPORATION—See Nihon Parkerizing Co., Ltd.; *Int'l*, pg. 5286
HEISEIDO CO., LTD.—See Restar Holdings Corporation; *Int'l*, pg. 6303
HEISER AUTOMOTIVE GROUP INC.; *U.S. Private*, pg. 1905
HEISER TOYOTA, INC.; *U.S. Private*, pg. 1905
HEISEY MECHANICAL, LTD.—See Cemtrex, Inc.; *U.S. Public*, pg. 466
HEISLER GORDON & ASSOCIATES; *U.S. Private*, pg. 1905
HEISTER HOUSE MILLWORKS, INC.; *U.S. Private*, pg. 1905
HEITECH I-SOLUTIONS SDN. BHD.—See HeiTech Padu Berhad; *Int'l*, pg. 3326
HEITECH MANAGED SERVICES SDN. BHD—See HeiTech Padu Berhad; *Int'l*, pg. 3326
HEITECH PADU BERHAD; *Int'l*, pg. 3326
HEITECH SERVICES, INC.; *U.S. Private*, pg. 1905
HEITKAMP, INC.—See Michels Corporation; *U.S. Private*, pg. 2700
HEITKAMP INGENIEUR- UND KRAFTWERKSBAU GMBH—See Zech Group SE; *Int'l*, pg. 8629
HEITKAMP & THUMANN KG; *Int'l*, pg. 3326
HEITKAMP & THUMANN (S) PTE LTD.—See Heitkamp & Thumann KG; *Int'l*, pg. 3326
HEITMAN LLC; *U.S. Private*, pg. 1905
HEITS BUILDING SERVICES, INC.; *U.S. Private*, pg. 1905
HEIWA CORPORATION; *Int'l*, pg. 3327
HEIWADO CO., LTD.; *Int'l*, pg. 3327
HEIWA IRONWORKS CO., LTD.—See Hirayama Holdings Co., Ltd.; *Int'l*, pg. 3404
HEIWA KINZOKU CO., LTD.—See Alconix Corporation; *Int'l*, pg. 302
HEIWA KISEN KAISHA, LTD.—See Idemitsu Kosan Co., Ltd.; *Int'l*, pg. 3590
HEIWA PAPER CO., LTD.; *Int'l*, pg. 3327
HEIWA REAL ESTATE ASSET MANAGEMENT CO., LTD.—See HEIWA REAL ESTATE CO. LTD.; *Int'l*, pg. 3327
HEIWA REAL ESTATE CO. LTD.; *Int'l*, pg. 3327
HEIWA REAL ESTATE REIT,INC.; *Int'l*, pg. 3327
HEIWA SERVICE CO., LTD.—See HEIWA REAL ESTATE CO. LTD.; *Int'l*, pg. 3327
HEIWA TECHNOS CORPORATION—See Sankyu, Inc.; *Int'l*, pg. 6543
HEIWA TOKEI MANUFACTURING CO., LTD.—See Citizen Watch Co., Ltd.; *Int'l*, pg. 1625

HEIZKORPER PROLUX AG—See Arbonia AG; *Int'l*, pg. 538
HEIZUNGS- UND SANITARBAU WIJA GMBH—See RWE AG; *Int'l*, pg. 6434
HEJIANG JINCAI PRINTING & PACKAGING CO., LTD.—See MYS Group Co., Ltd.; *Int'l*, pg. 5114
HEKA ELECTRONIK DR. SCHULZE GMBH—See Harvard Bioscience, Inc.; *U.S. Public*, pg. 987
HEKA INSTRUMENTS INCORPORATED—See Harvard Bioscience, Inc.; *U.S. Public*, pg. 987
HEKI CO., LTD.; *Int'l*, pg. 3327
HEKINAN UNSO CO., LTD.—See AISIN Corporation; *Int'l*, pg. 253
HEKMAN FURNITURE COMPANY—See Howard Miller Company; *U.S. Private*, pg. 1995
HEKTAR REAL ESTATE INVESTMENT TRUST; *Int'l*, pg. 3327
HEKTAS TICARET T.A.S.; *Int'l*, pg. 3327
HEKTOEN INSTITUTE, LLC.; *U.S. Private*, pg. 1905
HEKUMA GMBH—See SMS Holding GmbH; *Int'l*, pg. 7016
HELABA ASSET SERVICES—See Helaba Landesbank Hessen-Thuringen; *Int'l*, pg. 3328
HELABA BETEILIGUNGS-MANAGEMENT GESELLSCHAFT MBH—See Helaba Landesbank Hessen-Thuringen; *Int'l*, pg. 3328
HELABA DIGITAL GMBH & CO. KG—See Helaba Landesbank Hessen-Thuringen; *Int'l*, pg. 3328
HELABA DUBLIN LANDESBANK HESSEN-THURINGEN INTERNATIONAL—See Helaba Landesbank Hessen-Thuringen; *Int'l*, pg. 3328
HELABA GESELLSCHAFT FUR IMMOBILIENBEWERTUNG MBH—See Helaba Landesbank Hessen-Thuringen; *Int'l*, pg. 3328
HELABA INTERNATIONAL FINANCE PLC—See Helaba Landesbank Hessen-Thuringen; *Int'l*, pg. 3328
HELABA INVEST KAPITALANLAGEGESELLSCHAFT MBH—See Helaba Landesbank Hessen-Thuringen; *Int'l*, pg. 3328
HELABA LANDESBANK HESSEN-THURINGEN GIROZENTRALE—See Helaba Landesbank Hessen-Thuringen; *Int'l*, pg. 3328
HELABA LANDESBANK HESSEN-THURINGEN; *Int'l*, pg. 3327
HELABA LANDESBANK HESSEN THURINGEN—See Helaba Landesbank Hessen-Thuringen; *Int'l*, pg. 3328
HELADOS Y POSTRES S.A.—See Nestle S.A.; *Int'l*, pg. 5203
HELAKOR D.O.O.—See Kansai Paint Co., Ltd.; *Int'l*, pg. 4071
HELBIO S.A.—See Amasten Fastighets AB; *Int'l*, pg. 412
HELBOR EMPREENDIMENTOS S.A.; *Int'l*, pg. 3328
HELDENFELS ENTERPRISES INC.; *U.S. Private*, pg. 1905
HELD ENLOE & ASSOCIATES, LLC—See Lovell Minnick Partners LLC; *U.S. Private*, pg. 2503
HELD SYSTEMS GMBH—See INDUS Holding AG; *Int'l*, pg. 3663
HELECTOR CYPRUS—See ELLAKTOR S.A.; *Int'l*, pg. 2365
HELECTOR GMBH—See ELLAKTOR S.A.; *Int'l*, pg. 2365
HELECTOR SA—See ELLAKTOR S.A.; *Int'l*, pg. 2365
HELENA ABREU, UNIPESSOAL, LDA.—See Zur Rose Group AG; *Int'l*, pg. 8696
HELENA AGRI-ENTERPRISES, LLC—See Marubeni Corporation; *Int'l*, pg. 4706
HELENA CHEMICAL COMPANY—See Marubeni Corporation; *Int'l*, pg. 4706
HELENA LABORATORIES (AUSTRALIA) PTY. LTD.—See Helena Laboratories Corporation; *U.S. Private*, pg. 1906
HELENA LABORATORIES CORPORATION; *U.S. Private*, pg. 1906
HELENA LABORATORIES (UK) LIMITED—See Helena Laboratories Corporation; *U.S. Private*, pg. 1906
HELENA MOTORS LLC; *U.S. Private*, pg. 1906
HELENA PLASTICS—See Helena Laboratories Corporation; *U.S. Private*, pg. 1906
HELENA SAND & GRAVEL, INC.—See CRH plc; *Int'l*, pg. 1847
HELEN GORDON INTERESTS LTD.; *U.S. Private*, pg. 1905
HELEN GRACE CHOCOLATES, INC.—See Hilton Grand Vacations Inc.; *U.S. Public*, pg. 1040
HELEN OF TROY CANADA, INC.—See Helen of Troy Limited; *Int'l*, pg. 3328
HELEN OF TROY CONSUMER PRODUCTS DIVISION—See Helen of Troy Limited; *Int'l*, pg. 3328
HELEN OF TROY LIMITED; *Int'l*, pg. 3328
HELEN OF TROY L.P.—See Helen of Troy Limited; *Int'l*, pg. 3328
HELEN OF TROY PROFESSIONAL SALON DIVISION—See Helen of Troy Limited; *Int'l*, pg. 3329
HELEN OF TROY TEXAS CORPORATION—See Helen of Troy Limited; *Int'l*, pg. 3328
HELEN ROSS MCNABB CENTER, INC.; *U.S. Private*, pg. 1905
HELENS INTERNATIONAL HOLDINGS COMPANY LIMITED; *Int'l*, pg. 3329

HELIO S.A.

HELENS ROR AB—See Benteler International AG; *Int'l*, pg. 977
HELENS ROR A/S—See Benteler International AG; *Int'l*, pg. 977
HELEN THOMPSON MEDIA; *U.S. Private*, pg. 1905
HELEN WOODWARD ANIMAL CENTER; *U.S. Private*, pg. 1906
HELESI ITALIA S.R.L.—See Helesi Plc; *Int'l*, pg. 3329
HELESI PLC - KOMOTINI PLANT—See Helesi Plc; *Int'l*, pg. 3329
HELESI PLC; *Int'l*, pg. 3329
HELESI S.A.—See Helesi Plc; *Int'l*, pg. 3329
HELEVETIUS S.R.L.—See Krka, d.d., Novo Mesto; *Int'l*, pg. 4302
HELEXIA SOLAR I S.L.—See Voltalia S.A.; *Int'l*, pg. 8303
HELEX, LLC—See PHI, Inc.; *U.S. Private*, pg. 3168
HELFMAN DODGE CHRYSLER JEEP FIAT; *U.S. Private*, pg. 1906
HELFMAN ENTERPRISES INC.; *U.S. Private*, pg. 1906
HELGELAND PLAST AS—See Egersund Group AS; *Int'l*, pg. 2323
HELGELAND SPAREBANK; *Int'l*, pg. 3329
HELGESEN INDUSTRIES INC.—See Standard Iron & Wire Works Inc.; *U.S. Private*, pg. 3780
HELGESEN TEKNISKE BYGG AS—See AF Gruppen ASA; *Int'l*, pg. 184
HELGET SAFETY SUPPLY INC.; *U.S. Private*, pg. 1906
HELIAD AG; *Int'l*, pg. 3329
HELIAD EQUITY PARTNERS GMBH & CO. KGAA—See Heliad AG; *Int'l*, pg. 3329
HELIA GROUP LIMITED; *Int'l*, pg. 3329
HELI AMERICA INC.—See Anhui Heli Co., Ltd.; *Int'l*, pg. 467
HELIATEK GMBH; *Int'l*, pg. 3329
HELIBRAS—See Airbus SE; *Int'l*, pg. 244
HELICAL AUTO-TECHNOLOGY PVT LTD—See Helical Technology Limited; *Int'l*, pg. 3330
HELICAL BAR DEVELOPMENTS (SOUTH EAST) LTD—See Helical Plc; *Int'l*, pg. 3330
HELICAL BAR (REX HOUSE) LTD—See Helical Plc; *Int'l*, pg. 3329
HELICAL BAR (WALES) LTD—See Helical Plc; *Int'l*, pg. 3330
HELICAL (BRAMSHOTT PLACE) LTD—See Helical Plc; *Int'l*, pg. 3329
HELICAL (CARDIFF) LTD—See Helical Plc; *Int'l*, pg. 3329
HELICAL (CRAWLEY) LTD—See Helical Plc; *Int'l*, pg. 3329
HELICAL (HAILSHAM) LTD—See Helical Plc; *Int'l*, pg. 3329
HELICAL PLC; *Int'l*, pg. 3329
HELICAL PRODUCTS COMPANY—See American Securities LLC; *U.S. Private*, pg. 249
HELICAL RETAIL LTD—See Helical Plc; *Int'l*, pg. 3330
HELICAL (SEVENOAKS) LTD—See Helical Plc; *Int'l*, pg. 3329
HELICAL TECHNOLOGY LIMITED; *Int'l*, pg. 3330
HELICAL WROCLAW SP. Z.O.O.—See Helical Plc; *Int'l*, pg. 3330
HELICOMB INTERNATIONAL, INC.—See Berkshire Hathaway Inc.; *U.S. Public*, pg. 314
HELICONIA CAPITAL MANAGEMENT PTE. LTD.—See Temasek Holdings (Private) Limited; *Int'l*, pg. 7547
HELICOPTER CONSULTANTS OF MAUI, LLC—See American Securities LLC; *U.S. Private*, pg. 247
HELICOPTERS INC.; *U.S. Private*, pg. 1906
HELIFOR INDUSTRIES LIMITED—See Interfor Corporation; *Int'l*, pg. 3741
HELIJET INTERNATIONAL INC.; *Int'l*, pg. 3330
HELI-LYNX HELICOPTER SERVICES INC.; *Int'l*, pg. 3329
HELI-MART INC.; *U.S. Private*, pg. 1906
HELINET AVIATION SERVICES LLC; *U.S. Private*, pg. 1906
HELIOGEN, INC.; *U.S. Public*, pg. 1023
HELIOGRAPH HOLDING GMBH; *Int'l*, pg. 3330
HELIO LLC—See EchoStar Corporation; *U.S. Public*, pg. 711
HELI-ONE COLORADO—See First Reserve Management, L.P.; *U.S. Private*, pg. 1525
HELI-ONE EUROPE—See First Reserve Management, L.P.; *U.S. Private*, pg. 1525
HELI-ONE—See First Reserve Management, L.P.; *U.S. Private*, pg. 1525
HELION SAS—See Orano SA; *Int'l*, pg. 5611
HELIO PRECISION PRODUCTS INC.; *U.S. Private*, pg. 1906
HELIOS AGNES-KARLL KRANKENHAUS GMBH—See Fresenius SE & Co. KGaA; *Int'l*, pg. 2779
HELIOS AIRWAYS LIMITED—See Libra Holidays Group Public Ltd.; *Int'l*, pg. 4486
HELIOS AND MATHESON ANALYTICS INC.; *U.S. Public*, pg. 1023
HELIO S.A.; *Int'l*, pg. 3330
HELIOS AUKAMM-KLINIK WIESBADEN GMBH—See Fresenius SE & Co. KGaA; *Int'l*, pg. 2779
HELIOS BH D.O.O.—See Kansai Paint Co., Ltd.; *Int'l*, pg. 4071
HELIOS BORDEKLINIK GMBH—See Fresenius SE & Co. KGaA; *Int'l*, pg. 2779

HELIO S.A.
CORPORATE AFFILIATIONS

HELIOS COATINGS DEUTSCHLAND GMBH—See Kansai Paint Co., Ltd.; *Int'l*, pg. 4071
HELIOS COATINGS INC.—See Kansai Paint Co., Ltd.; *Int'l*, pg. 4071
HELIOS COATINGS ROMANIA S.R.L.—See Kansai Paint Co., Ltd.; *Int'l*, pg. 4071
HELIOS D.D; *Int'l*, pg. 3330
HELIOS DOMZALE, D.O.O.—See Kansai Paint Co., Ltd.; *Int'l*, pg. 4071
HELIOS EDUCATION FOUNDATION; *U.S. Private*, pg. 1906
HELIOS ENERGY LTD.; *Int'l*, pg. 3330
HELIOS ENERGY USA LTD.—See Helios Energy Ltd.; *Int'l*, pg. 3330
HELIOS FACHKLINIKEN HILDBURGHAUSEN GMBH—See Fresenius SE & Co. KGaA; *Int'l*, pg. 2779
HELIOS FACHKLINIK VOGELSANG-GOMMERN GMBH—See Fresenius SE & Co. KGaA; *Int'l*, pg. 2779
HELIOS FAIRFAX PARTNERS CORPORATION—See Helios Investment Partners LLP; *Int'l*, pg. 3330
HELIOS FRANKENWALDKLINIK KRONACH GMBH—See Fresenius SE & Co. KGaA; *Int'l*, pg. 2779
HELIOS HANSEKLINIKUM STRALSUND GMBH—See Fresenius SE & Co. KGaA; *Int'l*, pg. 2779
HELIOS HEALTH GMBH—See Fresenius SE & Co. KGaA; *Int'l*, pg. 2779
HELIOS HR, LLC; *U.S. Private*, pg. 1906
HELIOS INVESTMENT PARTNERS LLP; *Int'l*, pg. 3330
HELIOS ITALIA S.P.A.—See Kansai Paint Co., Ltd.; *Int'l*, pg. 4071
HELIOS KEMOSTIK D.O.O.—See Kansai Paint Co., Ltd.; *Int'l*, pg. 4071
HELIOS KLINIK BAD BERLEBURG GMBH—See Fresenius SE & Co. KGaA; *Int'l*, pg. 2779
HELIOS KLINIK BAD EMS GMBH—See Fresenius SE & Co. KGaA; *Int'l*, pg. 2779
HELIOS KLINIK BLANKENHAIN GMBH—See Fresenius SE & Co. KGaA; *Int'l*, pg. 2779
HELIOS KLINIK BLEICHERODE GMBH—See Fresenius SE & Co. KGaA; *Int'l*, pg. 2779
HELIOS KLINIKEN BREISGAU HOCHSCHWARZWALD GMBH—See Fresenius SE & Co. KGaA; *Int'l*, pg. 2779
HELIOS KLINIKEN GMBH—See Fresenius SE & Co. KGaA; *Int'l*, pg. 2778
HELIOS KLINIKEN MANSFELD-SUDHARZ GMBH—See Fresenius SE & Co. KGaA; *Int'l*, pg. 2779
HELIOS KLINIKEN MITTELWESER GMBH—See Fresenius SE & Co. KGaA; *Int'l*, pg. 2779
HELIOS KLINIK HERZBERG/OSTERODE GMBH—See Fresenius SE & Co. KGaA; *Int'l*, pg. 2779
HELIOS KLINIK JERICHOWER LAND GMBH—See Fresenius SE & Co. KGaA; *Int'l*, pg. 2779
HELIOS KLINIK KOTHEN GMBH—See Fresenius SE & Co. KGaA; *Int'l*, pg. 2779
HELIOS KLINIK LEEZEN GMBH—See Fresenius SE & Co. KGaA; *Int'l*, pg. 2779
HELIOS KLINIK LEISNIG GMBH—See Fresenius SE & Co. KGaA; *Int'l*, pg. 2779
HELIOS KLINIK LENGERICH GMBH—See Fresenius SE & Co. KGaA; *Int'l*, pg. 2779
HELIOS KLINIK ROTTWEIL GMBH—See Fresenius SE & Co. KGaA; *Int'l*, pg. 2779
HELIOS KLINIK SCHKEUDITZ GMBH—See Fresenius SE & Co. KGaA; *Int'l*, pg. 2779
HELIOS KLINIK SCHLESWIG GMBH—See Fresenius SE & Co. KGaA; *Int'l*, pg. 2779
HELIOS KLINIKUM AUE GMBH—See Fresenius SE & Co. KGaA; *Int'l*, pg. 2780
HELIOS KLINIKUM BAD SAAROW GMBH—See Fresenius SE & Co. KGaA; *Int'l*, pg. 2780
HELIOS KLINIKUM BERLIN-BUCH GMBH—See Fresenius SE & Co. KGaA; *Int'l*, pg. 2780
HELIOS KLINIKUM ERFURT GMBH—See Fresenius SE & Co. KGaA; *Int'l*, pg. 2780
HELIOS KLINIKUM GIFHORN GMBH—See Fresenius SE & Co. KGaA; *Int'l*, pg. 2780
HELIOS KLINIKUM GOTHA GMBH—See Fresenius SE & Co. KGaA; *Int'l*, pg. 2780
HELIOS KLINIKUM HILDESHEIM GMBH—See Fresenius SE & Co. KGaA; *Int'l*, pg. 2780
HELIOS KLINIKUM MEININGEN GMBH—See Fresenius SE & Co. KGaA; *Int'l*, pg. 2780
HELIOS KLINIKUM PFORZHEIM GMBH—See Fresenius SE & Co. KGaA; *Int'l*, pg. 2778
HELIOS KLINIKUM PIRNA GMBH—See Fresenius SE & Co. KGaA; *Int'l*, pg. 2778
HELIOS KLINIKUM SCHWELM GMBH—See Fresenius SE & Co. KGaA; *Int'l*, pg. 2780
HELIOS KLINIKUM SIEGBURG GMBH—See Fresenius SE & Co. KGaA; *Int'l*, pg. 2780
HELIOS KLINIKUM UELZEN GMBH—See Fresenius SE & Co. KGaA; *Int'l*, pg. 2780
HELIOS KLINIKUM WARBURG GMBH—See Fresenius SE & Co. KGaA; *Int'l*, pg. 2778
HELIOS KLINIK WESERMARSCH GMBH—See Fresenius SE & Co. KGaA; *Int'l*, pg. 2778
HELIOS KLINIK WIPPERFURTH GMBH—See Fresenius SE & Co. KGaA; *Int'l*, pg. 2779

HELIOS KLINIK ZERBST/ANHALT GMBH—See Fresenius SE & Co. KGaA; *Int'l*, pg. 2779
HELIOSLOUGH LIMITED—See SEGRO plc; *Int'l*, pg. 6683
HELIOS MAKEDONIJA DOOEL—See Kansai Paint Co., Ltd.; *Int'l*, pg. 4071
HELIOS & MATHESON INFORMATION TECHNOLOGY LIMITED; *Int'l*, pg. 3330
HELIOS MB S.R.O.—See RWE AG; *Int'l*, pg. 6434
HELIOS PARK-KLINIKUM LEIPZIG GMBH—See Fresenius SE & Co. KGaA; *Int'l*, pg. 2780
HELIOSPECTRA AB; *Int'l*, pg. 3330
HELIOSPECTRA INC.—See Heliospectra AB; *Int'l*, pg. 3330
HELIOS POLSKA SP. Z.O.O—See Kansai Paint Co., Ltd.; *Int'l*, pg. 4071
HELIOS POWER SOLUTIONS FZE—See P-Duke Technology Co., Ltd.; *Int'l*, pg. 5681
HELIOS POWER SOLUTIONS LTD.—See P-Duke Technology Co., Ltd.; *Int'l*, pg. 5681
HELIOS POWER SOLUTIONS PTE LTD—See P-Duke Technology Co., Ltd.; *Int'l*, pg. 5681
HELIOS POWER SOLUTIONS PTY LTD—See P-Duke Technology Co., Ltd.; *Int'l*, pg. 5681
HELIOS REHAKLINIKEN BAD BERLEBURG GMBH—See Fresenius SE & Co. KGaA; *Int'l*, pg. 2780
HELIOS S.A.—See EL. D. MOUZAKIS S.A.; *Int'l*, pg. 2341
HELIOS S.A.—See Agora S.A.; *Int'l*, pg. 212
HELIOS SLOVAKIA S.R.O—See Kansai Paint Co., Ltd.; *Int'l*, pg. 4071
HELIOS SPITAL UBERLINGEN GMBH—See Fresenius SE & Co. KGaA; *Int'l*, pg. 2780
HELIOS SRBIJA AD—See Kansai Paint Co., Ltd.; *Int'l*, pg. 4071
HELIOS ST. ELISABETH KLINIK OBERHAUSEN GMBH—See Fresenius SE & Co. KGaA; *Int'l*, pg. 2780
HELIOS ST. ELISABETH-KRANKENHAUS BAD KISSINGEN GMBH—See Fresenius SE & Co. KGaA; *Int'l*, pg. 2780
HELIOS ST. MARIENBERG KLINIK HELMSTEDT GMBH—See Fresenius SE & Co. KGaA; *Int'l*, pg. 2780
HELIOSTAR METALS LTD.; *Int'l*, pg. 3330
HELIOS TBLUS, D.O.O.—See Kansai Paint Co., Ltd.; *Int'l*, pg. 4071
HELIOS TECHNO HOLDING CO., LTD.; *Int'l*, pg. 3330
HELIOS TECHNOLOGIES, INC.; *U.S. Public*, pg. 1023
HELIOS TOVARNA BARV LAKOV IN UMETNIH SMOL KOLIEVO D.O.O.—See Kansai Paint Co., Ltd.; *Int'l*, pg. 4071
HELIOS TOWERS PLC; *Int'l*, pg. 3330
HELIOS UNDERWRITING PLC; *Int'l*, pg. 3330
HELIOS VERSORGUNGSZENTREN GMBH—See Fresenius SE & Co. KGaA; *Int'l*, pg. 2780
HELIOS VOGTLAND-KLINIKUM PLAUEN GMBH—See Fresenius SE & Co. KGaA; *Int'l*, pg. 2780
HELIOS WEISSERITZTAL-KLINIKEN GMBH—See Fresenius SE & Co. KGaA; *Int'l*, pg. 2778
HELIO VISION GERMANY GMBH—See Aldeyra Therapeutics, Inc.; *U.S. Public*, pg. 74
HELIQWEST AVIATION INC; *Int'l*, pg. 3331
HELISIM—See Airbus SE; *Int'l*, pg. 244
HELI SOUTHEAST ASIA CO., LTD.—See Anhui Heli Co., Ltd.; *Int'l*, pg. 467
HELIS SAS—See Econocom Group SA; *Int'l*, pg. 2298
HELI-TECH, INC.—See Bristow Group, Inc.; *U.S. Public*, pg. 388
HELIUM ONE GLOBAL LTD.; *Int'l*, pg. 3331
HELIUM SERVICES S.A.—See L'Air Liquide S.A.; *Int'l*, pg. 4375
HELIUS MEDICAL TECHNOLOGIES, INC.; *U.S. Public*, pg. 1024
HELIVIA AERO TAXI SA—See Greenwich AeroGroup, Inc.; *U.S. Private*, pg. 1781
HELIX BIOMEDIX, INC.; *U.S. Public*, pg. 1024
HELIX BIOPHARMA CORP.; *Int'l*, pg. 3331
HELIX CO., LTD.—See Ananda Development Public Company Limited; *Int'l*, pg. 447
HELIX ELECTRIC INC.; *U.S. Private*, pg. 1906
HELIX ENERGY SOLUTIONS GROUP, INC.; *U.S. Public*, pg. 1024
HELIX FINANCIAL SYSTEMS, L.P.—See Cantor Fitzgerald, L.P.; *U.S. Private*, pg. 736
HELIX HEALTHCARE B.V.—See Aurobindo Pharma Ltd.; *Int'l*, pg. 712
HELIX INDUSTRIES LTD.—See Cinven Limited; *Int'l*, pg. 1612
HELIX LIMITED; *U.S. Private*, pg. 1906
HELIX MEDICAL LLC - BALDWIN PARK—See Freudenberg SE; *Int'l*, pg. 2789
HELIX MEDICAL LLC—See Freudenberg SE; *Int'l*, pg. 2789
HELIXMITH CO., LTD.; *Int'l*, pg. 3331
HELIX OFFSHORE INTERNATIONAL HOLDINGS S.A R.L.—See Helix Energy Solutions Group, Inc.; *U.S. Public*, pg. 1024
HELIX RESOURCES LIMITED; *Int'l*, pg. 3331
HELIX SLEEP, INC.—See Cerberus Capital Management, L.P.; *U.S. Private*, pg. 838
HELIX TECHNOLOGIES, INC.—See Forian Inc.; *U.S. Public*, pg. 868

HELIX UNIFORMED LTD.—See Preformed Line Products Company; *U.S. Public*, pg. 1714
HELIX WATER DISTRICT; *U.S. Private*, pg. 1906
HELIX WIND, CORP.—See Better For You Wellness, Inc.; *U.S. Public*, pg. 326
HELKAMA-AUTO OY; *Int'l*, pg. 3331
HELLA AGLAIA MOBILE VISION GMBH—See Hella GmbH & Co. KGaA; *Int'l*, pg. 3331
HELLA ASIA SINGAPORE PTE. LTD.—See Hella GmbH & Co. KGaA; *Int'l*, pg. 3331
HELLA A/S—See Hella GmbH & Co. KGaA; *Int'l*, pg. 3331
HELLA AUSTRALIA PTY LTD.—See Hella GmbH & Co. KGaA; *Int'l*, pg. 3331
HELLA AUTOMOTIVE SALES, INC.—See Hella GmbH & Co. KGaA; *Int'l*, pg. 3331
HELLA AUTOMOTIVE SOUTH AFRICA (PTY) LTD—See Metair Investments Limited; *Int'l*, pg. 4844
HELLA AUTOTECHNIK NOVA S.R.O.—See Hella GmbH & Co. KGaA; *Int'l*, pg. 3331
HELLA-BEKTO INDUSTRIES D.O.O.—See Hella GmbH & Co. KGaA; *Int'l*, pg. 3332
HELLA CENTRO CORPORATIVO MEXICO S.A. DE C.V.—See Hella GmbH & Co. KGaA; *Int'l*, pg. 3331
HELLA CHANGCHUN TOOLING CO., LTD.—See Hella GmbH & Co. KGaA; *Int'l*, pg. 3331
HELLA CORPORATE CENTER (CHINA) CO., LTD.—See Hella GmbH & Co. KGaA; *Int'l*, pg. 3331
HELLA CORPORATE CENTER USA, INC.—See Hella GmbH & Co. KGaA; *Int'l*, pg. 3332
HELLA CZ. S.R.O.—See Hella GmbH & Co. KGaA; *Int'l*, pg. 3331
HELLA DISTRIBUTION GMBH—See Hella GmbH & Co. KGaA; *Int'l*, pg. 3331
HELLA DO BRAZIL AUTOMOTIVE LTDA.—See Hella GmbH & Co. KGaA; *Int'l*, pg. 3332
HELLA ELECTRONICS ENGINEERING GMBH—See Hella GmbH & Co. KGaA; *Int'l*, pg. 3331
HELLA ENGINEERING FRANCE S.A.S.—See Hella GmbH & Co. KGaA; *Int'l*, pg. 3331
HELLA FAHRZEUGKOMPONENTEN GMBH—See Hella GmbH & Co. KGaA; *Int'l*, pg. 3331
HELLA FAHRZEUGTEILE AUSTRIA GMBH—See Hella GmbH & Co. KGaA; *Int'l*, pg. 3331
HELLA FAST FORWARD SHANGHAI CO., LTD.—See Hella GmbH & Co. KGaA; *Int'l*, pg. 3332
HELLA FINANCE NEDERLAND—See Hella GmbH & Co. KGaA; *Int'l*, pg. 3332
HELLA GMBH & CO. KGAA; *Int'l*, pg. 3331
HELLA GUTMANN ANLAGENVERMIETUNG GMBH—See Hella GmbH & Co. KGaA; *Int'l*, pg. 3332
HELLA GUTMANN HOLDING GMBH—See Hella GmbH & Co. KGaA; *Int'l*, pg. 3332
HELLA GUTMANN MOBILITY GMBH—See Hella GmbH & Co. KGaA; *Int'l*, pg. 3332
HELLA GUTMANN SOLUTIONS A/S—See Hella GmbH & Co. KGaA; *Int'l*, pg. 3332
HELLA GUTMANN SOLUTIONS INTERNATIONAL AG—See Hella GmbH & Co. KGaA; *Int'l*, pg. 3332
HELLA HANDEL AUSTRIA GMBH—See Hella GmbH & Co. KGaA; *Int'l*, pg. 3332
HELLA HUNGARIA KFT.—See Hella GmbH & Co. KGaA; *Int'l*, pg. 3332
HELLA INC—See Hella GmbH & Co. KGaA; *Int'l*, pg. 3332
HELLA INDIA AUTOMOTIVE PRIVATE LIMITED—See Hella GmbH & Co. KGaA; *Int'l*, pg. 3332
HELLA INDIA AUTOMOTIVE PRIVATE LIMITITED—See Hella GmbH & Co. KGaA; *Int'l*, pg. 3332
HELLA INDIA LIGHTING LTD.; *Int'l*, pg. 3333
HELLA INDUPERM A/S—See Hella GmbH & Co. KGaA; *Int'l*, pg. 3332
HELLA INFRA MARKET PRIVATE LIMITED; *Int'l*, pg. 3333
HELLA INNENLEUCHTEN-SYSTEME BRATISLAVA, S.R.O.—See Hella GmbH & Co. KGaA; *Int'l*, pg. 3332
HELLA INNENLEUCHTEN-SYSTEME GMBH—See Hella GmbH & Co. KGaA; *Int'l*, pg. 3332
HELLA IRELAND LIMITED—See Hella GmbH & Co. KGaA; *Int'l*, pg. 3332
HELLA JAPAN INC.—See Hella GmbH & Co. KGaA; *Int'l*, pg. 3332
HELLA KGAA HUECK & CO. - NELLINGEN PLANT—See Hella GmbH & Co. KGaA; *Int'l*, pg. 3332
HELLA KGAA HUECK & CO. - PLANT 4—See Hella GmbH & Co. KGaA; *Int'l*, pg. 3332
HELLA KGAA HUECK & CO. - PLANT 5—See Hella GmbH & Co. KGaA; *Int'l*, pg. 3332
HELLA KOREA INC.—See Hella GmbH & Co. KGaA; *Int'l*, pg. 3332
HELLA LIGHTING FINLAND OY—See Hella GmbH & Co. KGaA; *Int'l*, pg. 3332
HELLA MIDDLE EAST FZE—See Hella GmbH & Co. KGaA; *Int'l*, pg. 3332
HELLA MINING LLC—See Hella GmbH & Co. KGaA; *Int'l*, pg. 3332
HELLA-NEW ZEALAND LIMITED—See Hella GmbH & Co. KGaA; *Int'l*, pg. 3332
HELLANOR AS—See Aurelius Equity Opportunities SE & Co. KGaA; *Int'l*, pg. 708

COMPANY NAME INDEX

HELLA-PHIL., INC.—See Stanley Electric Co., Ltd.; *Int'l*, pg. 7170
HELLA POLSKA SP. Z O.O.—See Hella GmbH & Co. KGaA; *Int'l*, pg. 3332
HELLA ROMANIA S.R.L.—See Hella GmbH & Co. KGaA; *Int'l*, pg. 3332
HELLA S.A.—See Hella GmbH & Co. KGaA; *Int'l*, pg. 3332
HELLA S.A.S.—See Hella GmbH & Co. KGaA; *Int'l*, pg. 3332
HELLA SATURNUS SLOVENIJA D.O.O.—See Hella GmbH & Co. KGaA; *Int'l*, pg. 3332
HELLASCOM S.A.—See Hellenic Telecommunications Organization S.A.; *Int'l*, pg. 3333
HELLAS GOLD SA—See Eldorado Gold Corporation; *Int'l*, pg. 2347
HELLA SHANGHAI ELECTRONICS CO., LTD.—See Hella GmbH & Co. KGaA; *Int'l*, pg. 3332
HELLA SLOVAKIA FRONT-LIGHTING S.R.O.—See Hella GmbH & Co. KGaA; *Int'l*, pg. 3332
HELLA SLOVAKIA LIGHTING S.R.O.—See Hella GmbH & Co. KGaA; *Int'l*, pg. 3332
HELLA SLOVAKIA SIGNAL-LIGHTING S.R.O.—See Hella GmbH & Co. KGaA; *Int'l*, pg. 3332
HELLAS ONLINE S.A.—See Vodafone Group Plc; *Int'l*, pg. 8286
HELLA S.P.A.—See Hella GmbH & Co. KGaA; *Int'l*, pg. 3332
HELLAS SAT CONSORTIUM LIMITED—See Arab Satellite Communications Organization; *Int'l*, pg. 531
HELLAS SAT S.A.—See Arab Satellite Communications Organization; *Int'l*, pg. 531
HELLASTIR MARITIME S.A.—See Israel Corporation Ltd.; *Int'l*, pg. 3823
HELLA TRADING (SHANGHAI) CO., LTD.—See Hella GmbH & Co. KGaA; *Int'l*, pg. 3332
HELLA UK HOLDINGS LIMITED—See Hella GmbH & Co. KGaA; *Int'l*, pg. 3332
HELLA VENTURES, LLC—See Hella GmbH & Co. KGaA; *Int'l*, pg. 3332
HELLA VIETNAM COMPANY LIMITED—See Hella GmbH & Co. KGaA; *Int'l*, pg. 3332
HELLA WERKZEUG TECHNOLOGIEZENTRUM GMBH—See Hella GmbH & Co. KGaA; *Int'l*, pg. 3332
HELLA (XIAMEN) AUTOMOTIVE ELECTRONICS CO. LTD.—See Hella GmbH & Co. KGaA; *Int'l*, pg. 3331
HELLA (XIAMEN) ELECTRONIC DEVICE CO., LTD—See Hella GmbH & Co. KGaA; *Int'l*, pg. 3331
HELLBERG SAFETY AB—See Investment AB Latour; *Int'l*, pg. 3781
HELLEMANS CONSULTANCY B.V.—See Triton Advisers Limited; *Int'l*, pg. 7935
HELLENDOORN AVONTUREN PARK BV—See Compagnie des Alpes S.A.; *Int'l*, pg. 1738
HELLENIC ALICO LIFE INSURANCE COMPANY LTD—See Hellenic Bank Public Company Ltd.; *Int'l*, pg. 3333
HELLENIC AVIATION FUEL COMPANY S.A.—See World Kinect Corporation; *U.S. Public*, pg. 2380
HELLENIC BANK (INVESTMENTS) LTD—See Hellenic Bank Public Company Ltd.; *Int'l*, pg. 3333
HELLENIC BANK PUBLIC COMPANY LTD.; *Int'l*, pg. 3333
HELLENIC BANK TRUST AND FINANCE CORP. LTD—See Hellenic Bank Public Company Ltd.; *Int'l*, pg. 3333
HELLENIC CABLES S.A.—See Viohalco SA/NV; *Int'l*, pg. 8243
HELLENIC CATERING S.A.—See Marfin Investment Group Holdings S.A.; *Int'l*, pg. 4691
HELLENIC COMPANY FOR TELECOMMUNICATIONS & TELEMATIC APPLICATIONS S.A.; *Int'l*, pg. 3333
HELLENIC DEFENCE VEHICLE SYSTEMS S.A.—See Krauss-Maffei Wegmann GmbH & Co. KG; *Int'l*, pg. 4300
HELLENIC DISTRIBUTIONS S.A.—See Folli Follie S.A.; *Int'l*, pg. 2721
HELLENIC EXCHANGES-ATHENS STOCK EXCHANGE S.A.; *Int'l*, pg. 3333
HELLENIC FABRICS S.A.; *Int'l*, pg. 3333
HELLENIC FISHFARMING S.A.; *Int'l*, pg. 3333
HELLENIC PETROLEUM CYPRUS LTD.—See HELLENiQ ENERGY Holdings S.A.; *Int'l*, pg. 3334
HELLENIC PETROLEUM INTERNATIONAL AG—See HELLENiQ ENERGY Holdings S.A.; *Int'l*, pg. 3334
HELLENIC QUALITY FOODS S.A.—See Vis Containers Manufacturing Co., Ltd.; *Int'l*, pg. 8249
HELLENIC QUARRIES SA—See ELLAKTOR S.A.; *Int'l*, pg. 2364
HELLENIC SAILING HOLIDAYS SA—See TUI AG; *Int'l*, pg. 7965
HELLENIC SEAWAYS SINGLE MEMBER MARITIME S.A.—See Attica Group; *Int'l*, pg. 696
HELLENIC SUGAR INDUSTRY S.A.—See Piraeus Financial Holdings S.A.; *Int'l*, pg. 5873
HELLENIC TELECOMMUNICATIONS ORGANIZATION S.A.; *Int'l*, pg. 3333
HELLENIC TELEVISION LTD.; *Int'l*, pg. 3334
HELLENIC TOURS S.A.—See EQT AB; *Int'l*, pg. 2478

HELLENIC VEHICLE INDUSTRY S.A.—See Metlen Energy & Metals S.A.; *Int'l*, pg. 4854
THE HELLENIC WOMEN'S BENEVOLENT ASSOCIATION, INC.; *U.S. Private*, pg. 4051
HELLENIQ ENERGY HOLDINGS S.A.; *Int'l*, pg. 3334
HELLENIQ ENERGY HOLDINGS S.A; *Int'l*, pg. 3334
HELLER AUTO GROUP; *U.S. Private*, pg. 1906
HELLER BROS. PACKING CORP.; *U.S. Private*, pg. 1906
HELLER DISTRIBUTING CO. INC.; *U.S. Private*, pg. 1906
HELLER HOLZ GMBH—See Pfleiderer GmbH; *Int'l*, pg. 5836
HELLER INDUSTRIES INC.; *U.S. Private*, pg. 1907
HELLERMANNTYTON AB DANMARK—See Aptiv PLC; *Int'l*, pg. 525
HELLERMANNTYTON AB—See Aptiv PLC; *Int'l*, pg. 525
HELLERMANNTYTON AS—See Aptiv PLC; *Int'l*, pg. 525
HELLERMANNTYTON AUSTRALIA PTY LTD—See Aptiv PLC; *Int'l*, pg. 525
HELLERMANNTYTON B.V.—See Aptiv PLC; *Int'l*, pg. 525
HELLERMANNTYTON CO., LTD.—See Aptiv PLC; *Int'l*, pg. 525
HELLERMANNTYTON CORPORATION—See Aptiv PLC; *Int'l*, pg. 525
HELLERMANNTYTON DATA LTD.—See Aptiv PLC; *Int'l*, pg. 525
HELLERMANNTYTON ESPANA SL—See Aptiv PLC; *Int'l*, pg. 525
HELLERMANNTYTON GMBH - AUSTRIA—See Aptiv PLC; *Int'l*, pg. 525
HELLERMANNTYTON GMBH—See Aptiv PLC; *Int'l*, pg. 525
HELLERMANNTYTON GROUP PLC—See Aptiv PLC; *Int'l*, pg. 525
HELLERMANNTYTON INDIA PVT. LTD.—See Aptiv PLC; *Int'l*, pg. 526
HELLERMANNTYTON LTDA.—See Aptiv PLC; *Int'l*, pg. 526
HELLERMANNTYTON LTD. - MANCHESTER—See Aptiv PLC; *Int'l*, pg. 525
HELLERMANNTYTON LTD. - PLYMOUTH—See Aptiv PLC; *Int'l*, pg. 526
HELLERMANNTYTON (MEXICO) S. DE R.L. DE C.V.—See Aptiv PLC; *Int'l*, pg. 525
HELLERMANNTYTON OY—See Aptiv PLC; *Int'l*, pg. 526
HELLERMANNTYTON PTE LTD.—See Aptiv PLC; *Int'l*, pg. 526
HELLERMANNTYTON (PTY.) LTD.—See Aptiv PLC; *Int'l*, pg. 525
HELLERMANNTYTON S.A.S.—See Aptiv PLC; *Int'l*, pg. 526
HELLERMANNTYTON S.L.—See Aptiv PLC; *Int'l*, pg. 526
HELLERMANNTYTON SP. Z.O.O.—See Aptiv PLC; *Int'l*, pg. 526
HELLERMANNTYTON SRL-ARGENTINA—See Aptiv PLC; *Int'l*, pg. 526
HELLERMANNTYTON SRL—See Aptiv PLC; *Int'l*, pg. 526
HELLERMANNTYTON (WUXI) ELECTRICAL ACCESSORIES CO., LTD.—See Aptiv PLC; *Int'l*, pg. 525
HELLER MOTORS, INC.; *U.S. Private*, pg. 1907
HELLER TOOLS GMBH—See Serafin Unternehmensgruppe GmbH; *Int'l*, pg. 6720
HELLIER NDT, INC.—See Rockwood Holdings Limited Partnership; *U.S. Private*, pg. 3468
HELLIX VENTURES INC.; *Int'l*, pg. 3334
HELLMA (ASIA PACIFIC) PTE LTD—See Hellma GmbH & Co. KG; *Int'l*, pg. 3334
HELLMA AXIOM, INC.—See Hellma GmbH & Co. KG; *Int'l*, pg. 3334
HELLMA BENELUX BVBA—See Hellma GmbH & Co. KG; *Int'l*, pg. 3334
HELLMA CANADA LIMITED—See Hellma GmbH & Co. KG; *Int'l*, pg. 3334
HELLMA-FRANCE S.A.R.L.—See Hellma GmbH & Co. KG; *Int'l*, pg. 3335
HELLMA GMBH & CO. KG; *Int'l*, pg. 3334
HELLMA ITALIA S.R.L.—See Hellma GmbH & Co. KG; *Int'l*, pg. 3334
HELLMA MATERIALS GMBH—See Hellma GmbH & Co. KG; *Int'l*, pg. 3334
HELLMAN ASSOCIATES, INC.; *U.S. Private*, pg. 1911
HELLMAN & FRIEDMAN EUROPE LIMITED—See Hellman & Friedman LLC; *U.S. Private*, pg. 1910
HELLMAN & FRIEDMAN LLC; *U.S. Private*, pg. 1907
HELLMANN EAST EUROPE LLC—See Hellmann Worldwide Logistics GmbH & Co. KG; *Int'l*, pg. 3335
HELLMANN EAST EUROPE OVERSEAS LTD—See Hellmann Worldwide Logistics GmbH & Co. KG; *Int'l*, pg. 3335
HELLMANN EAST EUROPE SOOO—See Hellmann Worldwide Logistics GmbH & Co. KG; *Int'l*, pg. 3335
HELLMANN NETWORK INC.—See Hellmann Worldwide Logistics GmbH & Co. KG; *Int'l*, pg. 3335
HELLMANN PERISHABLE LOGISTICS INC.—See Hellmann Worldwide Logistics GmbH & Co. KG; *Int'l*, pg. 3336
HELLMANN PERISHABLE LOGISTICS—See Hellmann Worldwide Logistics GmbH & Co. KG; *Int'l*, pg. 3335
HELLMANN PERISHABLE LOGISTICS—See Hellmann Worldwide Logistics GmbH & Co. KG; *Int'l*, pg. 3335

HELLMANN PERISHABLE LOGISTICS—See Hellmann Worldwide Logistics GmbH & Co. KG; *Int'l*, pg. 3335
HELLMANN PERISHABLE LOGISTICS—See Hellmann Worldwide Logistics GmbH & Co. KG; *Int'l*, pg. 3336
HELLMANN PERISHABLE LOGISTICS—See Hellmann Worldwide Logistics GmbH & Co. KG; *Int'l*, pg. 3336
HELLMANN SAUDI ARABIA LLC—See Hellmann Worldwide Logistics GmbH & Co. KG; *Int'l*, pg. 3335
HELLMANN WORLDWIDE LOGISTICS AS—See Hellmann Worldwide Logistics GmbH & Co. KG; *Int'l*, pg. 3335
HELLMANN WORLDWIDE LOGISTICS A/S—See Hellmann Worldwide Logistics GmbH & Co. KG; *Int'l*, pg. 3335
HELLMANN WORLDWIDE LOGISTICS B.V.—See Hellmann Worldwide Logistics GmbH & Co. KG; *Int'l*, pg. 3335
HELLMANN WORLDWIDE LOGISTICS (CAMBODIA) LLC—See Hellmann Worldwide Logistics GmbH & Co. KG; *Int'l*, pg. 3335
HELLMANN WORLDWIDE LOGISTICS (CHINA) LTD.—See Hellmann Worldwide Logistics GmbH & Co. KG; *Int'l*, pg. 3335
HELLMANN WORLDWIDE LOGISTICS CO., LTD.—See Hellmann Worldwide Logistics GmbH & Co. KG; *Int'l*, pg. 3335
HELLMANN WORLDWIDE LOGISTICS (CUBA) GMBH—See Hellmann Worldwide Logistics GmbH & Co. KG; *Int'l*, pg. 3335
HELLMANN WORLDWIDE LOGISTICS DO BRASIL LTDA.—See Hellmann Worldwide Logistics GmbH & Co. KG; *Int'l*, pg. 3335
HELLMANN WORLDWIDE LOGISTICS GMBH & CO. KG; *Int'l*, pg. 3335
HELLMANN WORLDWIDE LOGISTICS GMBH—See Hellmann Worldwide Logistics GmbH & Co. KG; *Int'l*, pg. 3335
HELLMANN WORLDWIDE LOGISTICS INC.—See Hellmann Worldwide Logistics GmbH & Co. KG; *Int'l*, pg. 3335
HELLMANN WORLDWIDE LOGISTICS INC.—See Hellmann Worldwide Logistics GmbH & Co. KG; *Int'l*, pg. 3335
HELLMANN WORLDWIDE LOGISTICS, INC.—See Hellmann Worldwide Logistics GmbH & Co. KG; *Int'l*, pg. 3336
HELLMANN WORLDWIDE LOGISTICS INDIA PRIVATE LIMITED—See Hellmann Worldwide Logistics GmbH & Co. KG; *Int'l*, pg. 3335
HELLMANN WORLDWIDE LOGISTICS KAZAKHSTAN LLP—See Hellmann Worldwide Logistics GmbH & Co. KG; *Int'l*, pg. 3335
HELLMANN WORLDWIDE LOGISTICS KFT.—See Hellmann Worldwide Logistics GmbH & Co. KG; *Int'l*, pg. 3335
HELLMANN WORLDWIDE LOGISTICS LIMITED—See Hellmann Worldwide Logistics GmbH & Co. KG; *Int'l*, pg. 3335
HELLMANN WORLDWIDE LOGISTICS LLC—See Hellmann Worldwide Logistics GmbH & Co. KG; *Int'l*, pg. 3335
HELLMANN WORLDWIDE LOGISTICS LLP—See Hellmann Worldwide Logistics GmbH & Co. KG; *Int'l*, pg. 3335
HELLMANN WORLDWIDE LOGISTICS LTDA.—See Hellmann Worldwide Logistics GmbH & Co. KG; *Int'l*, pg. 3336
HELLMANN WORLDWIDE LOGISTICS LTD.—See Hellmann Worldwide Logistics GmbH & Co. KG; *Int'l*, pg. 3336
HELLMANN WORLDWIDE LOGISTICS LTD.—See Hellmann Worldwide Logistics GmbH & Co. KG; *Int'l*, pg. 3336
HELLMANN WORLDWIDE LOGISTICS LTD.—See Hellmann Worldwide Logistics GmbH & Co. KG; *Int'l*, pg. 3336
HELLMANN WORLDWIDE LOGISTICS LTD.—See Hellmann Worldwide Logistics GmbH & Co. KG; *Int'l*, pg. 3336
HELLMANN WORLDWIDE LOGISTICS LTD.—See Hellmann Worldwide Logistics GmbH & Co. KG; *Int'l*, pg. 3336
HELLMANN WORLDWIDE LOGISTICS LTD.—See Hellmann Worldwide Logistics GmbH & Co. KG; *Int'l*, pg. 3336
HELLMANN WORLDWIDE LOGISTICS LTD.—See Hellmann Worldwide Logistics GmbH & Co. KG; *Int'l*, pg. 3336
HELLMANN WORLDWIDE LOGISTICS LTD.—See Hellmann Worldwide Logistics GmbH & Co. KG; *Int'l*, pg. 3336
HELLMANN WORLDWIDE LOGISTICS LTD. STI—See Hellmann Worldwide Logistics GmbH & Co. KG; *Int'l*, pg. 3336
HELLMANN WORLDWIDE LOGISTICS MADAGASCAR SARL—See Hellmann Worldwide Logistics GmbH & Co. KG; *Int'l*, pg. 3336

HELLMANN WORLDWIDE LOGISTICS GMBH & CO. KG

HELLMANN WORLDWIDE LOGISTICS N.V.—See Hellmann Worldwide Logistics GmbH & Co. KG; *Int'l*, pg. 3336
HELLMANN WORLDWIDE LOGISTICS OU—See Hellmann Worldwide Logistics GmbH & Co. KG; *Int'l*, pg. 3336
HELLMANN WORLDWIDE LOGISTICS POLSKA SPOLKA Z OGRANICZONA ODPOWIEDZIALNOSCIA—See Hellmann Worldwide Logistics GmbH & Co. KG; *Int'l*, pg. 3336
HELLMANN WORLDWIDE LOGISTICS (PTY) LTD—See Hellmann Worldwide Logistics GmbH & Co. KG; *Int'l*, pg. 3335
HELLMANN WORLDWIDE LOGISTICS (PTY) LTD.—See Hellmann Worldwide Logistics GmbH & Co. KG; *Int'l*, pg. 3335
HELLMANN WORLDWIDE LOGISTICS PTY LTD—See Hellmann Worldwide Logistics GmbH & Co. KG; *Int'l*, pg. 3336
HELLMANN WORLDWIDE LOGISTICS (PVT) LTD—See Hellmann Worldwide Logistics GmbH & Co. KG; *Int'l*, pg. 3335
HELLMANN WORLDWIDE LOGISTICS (PVT) LTD—See Hellmann Worldwide Logistics GmbH & Co. KG; *Int'l*, pg. 3335
HELLMANN WORLDWIDE LOGISTICS S.A.C.—See Hellmann Worldwide Logistics GmbH & Co. KG; *Int'l*, pg. 3336
HELLMANN WORLDWIDE LOGISTICS S.A. DE C.V.—See Hellmann Worldwide Logistics GmbH & Co. KG; *Int'l*, pg. 3336
HELLMANN WORLDWIDE LOGISTICS SARL—See Hellmann Worldwide Logistics GmbH & Co. KG; *Int'l*, pg. 3336
HELLMANN WORLDWIDE LOGISTICS S.A.—See Hellmann Worldwide Logistics GmbH & Co. KG; *Int'l*, pg. 3336
HELLMANN WORLDWIDE LOGISTICS S.A.—See Hellmann Worldwide Logistics GmbH & Co. KG; *Int'l*, pg. 3336
HELLMANN WORLDWIDE LOGISTICS SDN. BHD.—See Hellmann Worldwide Logistics GmbH & Co. KG; *Int'l*, pg. 3336
HELLMANN WORLDWIDE LOGISTICS (SHANGHAI) LTD.—See Hellmann Worldwide Logistics GmbH & Co. KG; *Int'l*, pg. 3335
HELLMANN WORLDWIDE LOGISTICS SIA—See Hellmann Worldwide Logistics GmbH & Co. KG; *Int'l*, pg. 3336
HELLMANN WORLDWIDE LOGISTICS S.P.A.—See Hellmann Worldwide Logistics GmbH & Co. KG; *Int'l*, pg. 3336
HELLMANN WORLDWIDE LOGISTICS SRL—See Hellmann Worldwide Logistics GmbH & Co. KG; *Int'l*, pg. 3336
HELLMANN WORLDWIDE LOGISTICS S.R.O.—See Hellmann Worldwide Logistics GmbH & Co. KG; *Int'l*, pg. 3336
HELLMANN WORLDWIDE LOGISTICS (T) LTD.—See Hellmann Worldwide Logistics GmbH & Co. KG; *Int'l*, pg. 3335
HELLMANN WORLDWIDE LOGISTICS UAB—See Hellmann Worldwide Logistics GmbH & Co. KG; *Int'l*, pg. 3336
HELLMANN WORLDWIDE LOGISTICS (VIETNAM) CO., LTD—See Hellmann Worldwide Logistics GmbH & Co. KG; *Int'l*, pg. 3335
HELLMANN WORLDWIDE LOGISTICS WLL—See Hellmann Worldwide Logistics GmbH & Co. KG; *Int'l*, pg. 3336
HELLMANN WORLDWIDE LOGISTICS ZAMBIA LIMITED—See Hellmann Worldwide Logistics GmbH & Co. KG; *Int'l*, pg. 3336
HELLMAN—See Hellman Associates, Inc.; *U.S. Private*, pg. 1911
HELLMA OPTIK GMBH—See Hellma GmbH & Co. KG; *Int'l*, pg. 3334
HELLMA SCHWEIZ AG—See Hellma GmbH & Co. KG; *Int'l*, pg. 3334
HELLMA UK LTD—See Hellma GmbH & Co. KG; *Int'l*, pg. 3334
HELLMA USA INC.—See Hellma GmbH & Co. KG; *Int'l*, pg. 3335
HELLMUTH, OBATA & KASSABAUM, INC.; *U.S. Private*, pg. 1911
HELLO! CALIFORNIA—See Hello! Florida Destination Management, Inc.; *U.S. Private*, pg. 1911
HELLO DESIGN, LLC—See Stagwell, Inc.; *U.S. Public*, pg. 1927
HELLO DIGIT, LLC—See Oportun Financial Corporation; *U.S. Public*, pg. 1608
HELLO DIRECT, INC.—See Synergy Communications Management; *U.S. Private*, pg. 3904
HELLO FIOUL SA—See Financiere de L'Odet; *Int'l*, pg. 2667
HELLO! FLORIDA DESTINATION MANAGEMENT, INC.; *U.S. Private*, pg. 1911
HELLOFRESH SE—See Rocket Internet SE; *Int'l*, pg. 6378
HELLO GROUP INC.; *Int'l*, pg. 3336

HELLO, INC.; *U.S. Private*, pg. 1911
HELLO METRO; *U.S. Private*, pg. 1911
HELLO NET INC.—See Aucnet Inc.; *Int'l*, pg. 700
HELLO PAL INTERNATIONAL, INC.; *Int'l*, pg. 3337
HELLO PRODUCTS LLC—See Colgate-Palmolive Company; *U.S. Public*, pg. 532
HELLO!; *U.S. Private*, pg. 1911
HELLO THERE HOLDING AB—See Stampen AB; *Int'l*, pg. 7166
HELLOWALLET, LLC—See KeyCorp; *U.S. Public*, pg. 1225
HELLOWORLD, INC.—See Dentsu Group Inc.; *Int'l*, pg. 2036
HELLOWORLD TECHNOLOGIES INDIA PRIVATE LIMITED—See Aurum PropTech Ltd.; *Int'l*, pg. 715
HELLOWORLD TRAVEL LIMITED; *Int'l*, pg. 3337
HELLYER MILL OPERATIONS PTY LTD; *Int'l*, pg. 3337
HELLY HANSEN AS—See Canadian Tire Corporation Limited; *Int'l*, pg. 1286
HELLY HANSEN BENELUX B.V.—See Canadian Tire Corporation Limited; *Int'l*, pg. 1286
HELLY-HANSEN DEUTSCHLAND GMBH—See Canadian Tire Corporation Limited; *Int'l*, pg. 1286
HELLY HANSEN GROUP AS—See Canadian Tire Corporation Limited; *Int'l*, pg. 1286
HELLY HANSEN SCHWEIZ AG—See Canadian Tire Corporation Limited; *Int'l*, pg. 1286
HELLY-HANSEN (UK) LTD.—See Canadian Tire Corporation Limited; *Int'l*, pg. 1286
HELLY-HANSEN (US), INC.—See Canadian Tire Corporation Limited; *Int'l*, pg. 1286
HELM43, LLC—See Banyan Technologies Group, LLC; *U.S. Private*, pg. 470
HELMA EIGENHEIMBAU AG; *Int'l*, pg. 3338
HELMA FERIENIMMOBILIEN GMBH—See HELMA Eigenheimbau AG; *Int'l*, pg. 3338
HELM AGRO US, INC.—See HELM AG; *Int'l*, pg. 3337
HELM AG; *Int'l*, pg. 3337
HELM ANDINA LTDA.—See HELM AG; *Int'l*, pg. 3337
HELM ARGENTINA S.R.L.—See HELM AG; *Int'l*, pg. 3337
HELMARK STEEL, INC.; *U.S. Private*, pg. 1911
HELM AUSTRIA GES.M.B.H.—See HELM AG; *Int'l*, pg. 3337
HELM BANK USA; *U.S. Private*, pg. 1911
HELM CHEMICALS B.V.—See HELM AG; *Int'l*, pg. 3337
HELM CHINA LTD.—See HELM AG; *Int'l*, pg. 3337
HELM D3 SAS—See HELM AG; *Int'l*, pg. 3337
HELM DE MEXICO, S.A.—See HELM AG; *Int'l*, pg. 3337
HELM DUNGEMITTEL GMBH—See HELM AG; *Int'l*, pg. 3337
HELM ENGRAIS FRANCE S.A.R.L.—See HELM AG; *Int'l*, pg. 3337
HELMER DIALYSIS, LLC—See DaVita Inc.; *U.S. Public*, pg. 639
HELMERICH AND PAYNE MEXICO DRILLING, S. DE R.L. DE C.V.—See Helmerich & Payne, Inc.; *U.S. Public*, pg. 1024
HELMERICH & PAYNE (COLOMBIA) DRILLING CO.—See Helmerich & Payne, Inc.; *U.S. Public*, pg. 1024
HELMERICH & PAYNE DEL ECUADOR, INC.—See Helmerich & Payne, Inc.; *U.S. Public*, pg. 1024
HELMERICH & PAYNE DE VENEZUELA C.A.—See Helmerich & Payne, Inc.; *U.S. Public*, pg. 1024
HELMERICH & PAYNE, INC.; *U.S. Public*, pg. 1024
HELMERICH & PAYNE INC—See Helmerich & Payne, Inc.; *U.S. Public*, pg. 1024
HELMERICH & PAYNE INTERNATIONAL DRILLING CO.—See Helmerich & Payne, Inc.; *U.S. Public*, pg. 1024
HELMERICH & PAYNE PROPERTIES, INC.—See Helmerich & Payne, Inc.; *U.S. Public*, pg. 1024
HELMERICH & PAYNE RASCO, INC.—See Helmerich & Payne, Inc.; *U.S. Public*, pg. 1024
HELMES INC.; *U.S. Private*, pg. 1912
HELM FERTILIZER CORP—See HELM AG; *Int'l*, pg. 3337
HELM FERTILIZER GREAT BRITAIN LTD.—See HELM AG; *Int'l*, pg. 3337
HELM FERTILIZER HELENA TERMINAL INC.—See HELM AG; *Int'l*, pg. 3337
HELM FERTILIZER TERMINAL INC.—See HELM AG; *Int'l*, pg. 3337
HELM FRANCE S.A.R.L.—See HELM AG; *Int'l*, pg. 3337
HELM GREAT BRITAIN LTD.—See HELM AG; *Int'l*, pg. 3337
THE HELM GROUP; *U.S. Private*, pg. 4051
HELM HOLDING COMPANY; *U.S. Private*, pg. 1911
THE HELMHOLTZ ASSOCIATION; *Int'l*, pg. 7652
HELMHOLTZ-ZENTRUM HEREON; *Int'l*, pg. 3338
HELM HONG KONG LTD.—See HELM AG; *Int'l*, pg. 3337
HELM IBERICA, S.A.—See HELM AG; *Int'l*, pg. 3337
HELMICK CORPORATION; *U.S. Private*, pg. 1912
HELM ITALIA S.R.L.—See HELM AG; *Int'l*, pg. 3337
HELMITIN INC.—See ITOCHU Corporation; *Int'l*, pg. 3836
HELMITIN INC.—See ITOCHU Corporation; *Int'l*, pg. 3836
HELM JAPAN LTD.—See HELM AG; *Int'l*, pg. 3337
HELMKAMP CONSTRUCTION CO.; *U.S. Private*, pg. 1912
HELM KIMYA LTD. SIRKETI—See HELM AG; *Int'l*, pg. 3337

HELM KOREA LTD.—See HELM AG; *Int'l*, pg. 3337
HELMONDSE METAAL INDUSTRIE BV—See VDL Groep B.V.; *Int'l*, pg. 8140
HELM POLSKA SP. Z O.O—See HELM AG; *Int'l*, pg. 3338
HELM PORTUGAL, LDA.—See HELM AG; *Int'l*, pg. 3338
HELMSBRISCOE INC; *U.S. Private*, pg. 1912
HELM SKANDINAVIEN A/S—See HELM AG; *Int'l*, pg. 3338
THE HELMSLEY CARLTON HOUSE—See Helmsley Enterprises, Inc.; *U.S. Private*, pg. 1912
HELMSLEY ENTERPRISES, INC.; *U.S. Private*, pg. 1912
HELMSLEY-NOYES CO., LLC—See Helmsley Enterprises, Inc.; *U.S. Private*, pg. 1912
THE HELMSLEY PARK LANE—See Helmsley Enterprises, Inc.; *U.S. Private*, pg. 1912
THE HELMSLEY SANDCASTLE—See Helmsley Enterprises, Inc.; *U.S. Private*, pg. 1912
HELMSLEY-SPEAR, LLC; *U.S. Private*, pg. 1912
HELMSMAN MANAGEMENT SERVICES, LLC—See Liberty Mutual Holding Company Inc.; *U.S. Private*, pg. 2445
HELMSTEDTER REVIER GMBH—See Energeticky a Prumyslovy Holding, a.s.; *Int'l*, pg. 2420
HELMS TMT-CENTRET A/S—See Tym Corporation; *Int'l*, pg. 7995
HELM U.S. CORPORATION—See HELM AG; *Int'l*, pg. 3338
HELMUT GEISSLER GLASINSTRUMENTE GMBH—See Johnson Controls International plc; *Int'l*, pg. 3987
HELMUT LOSER GMBH & CO. KG WAFFELFABRIK—See Zertus GmbH; *Int'l*, pg. 8639
HELMUT RUBSAMEN GMBH & CO. KG—See INDUS Holding AG; *Int'l*, pg. 3663
HELNAN INTERNATIONAL HOTELS A/S; *Int'l*, pg. 3338
HELNAN MARINA HOTEL—See Helnan International Hotels A/S; *Int'l*, pg. 3338
HELO CORP.; *U.S. Public*, pg. 1024
HELONGJIANG POLY AOYU REAL ESTATE DEVELOPMENT CO., LTD—See China Poly Group Corporation; *Int'l*, pg. 1541
HELPAGE FINLEASE LTD.; *Int'l*, pg. 3338
HELP AT HOME, LLC—See Centerbridge Partners, L.P.; *U.S. Private*, pg. 815
HELP AT HOME, LLC—See The Vistria Group, LP; *U.S. Private*, pg. 4131
HELPE ARTA PREVEZA SA—See HELLENiQ ENERGY Holdings S.A.; *Int'l*, pg. 3334
HELPFUL ALLIANCE COMPANY; *U.S. Private*, pg. 1912
THE HELP GROUP; *U.S. Private*, pg. 4051
HELPHIRE LEGAL SERVICES LIMITED—See ZIGUP plc; *Int'l*, pg. 8682
HELPHIRE (UK) LIMITED—See ZIGUP plc; *Int'l*, pg. 8682
HELPING HAND CENTER; *U.S. Private*, pg. 1912
HELPING HAND FOR RELIEF & DEVELOPMENT; *U.S. Private*, pg. 1912
HELPING HANDS MINISTRIES, INC.; *U.S. Private*, pg. 1912
HELPING RESTORE ABILITY; *U.S. Private*, pg. 1912
HELP INTERNATIONAL CORPORATION BERHAD—See Southern Capital Group Pte. Ltd.; *Int'l*, pg. 7118
HELPLINE BV—See Serviceware SE; *Int'l*, pg. 6726
HELPLINE GMBH—See Serviceware SE; *Int'l*, pg. 6726
HELPLINE IT SOLUTIONS GMBH—See Serviceware SE; *Int'l*, pg. 6726
HELP-LINE SAS—See Neurones S.A.; *Int'l*, pg. 5219
HELP LINE S.P.A.—See Nexi SpA; *Int'l*, pg. 5244
HELP-LINK UK LTD.—See Brookfield Corporation; *Int'l*, pg. 1188
HELPMAN CAPITAL BV—See Alfa Laval AB; *Int'l*, pg. 310
HELPNET INGENIERIA Y SERVICIOS DE RECURSOS HUMANOS S.A.—See Bain Capital, LP; *U.S. Private*, pg. 434
HELP - NEW MEXICO, INC.; *U.S. Private*, pg. 1912
HELP PHILADELPHIA—See Help USA Inc.; *U.S. Private*, pg. 1912
HELP SEGUROS DE VIDA S.A.—See UnitedHealth Group Incorporated; *U.S. Public*, pg. 2241
HELP/SYSTEMS, LLC—See HGGC, LLC; *U.S. Private*, pg. 1929
HELP USA INC.; *U.S. Private*, pg. 1912
HELSER INDUSTRIES INC.; *U.S. Private*, pg. 1912
HELSINGEN PANTTI-OSAKEYHTIO—See Nordea Bank Abp; *Int'l*, pg. 5417
HELSINGIN HUUTOKAUPPAKAMARI OY—See Lone Star Global Acquisitions, LLC; *U.S. Private*, pg. 2487
HELSINGIN ITAMERENKATU 21 KOY—See Blackstone Inc.; *U.S. Public*, pg. 351
HELSINGOR DAGBLAD A/S—See North Media A/S; *Int'l*, pg. 5440
HELSINKI COOPERATIVE SOCIETY ELANTO—See Suomen Osuuskauppojen Keskuskunta; *Int'l*, pg. 7333
HELSINKI FOODSTOCK OY—See Orkla ASA; *Int'l*, pg. 5637
HELSINKI MEMORY TECHNOLOGIES OY—See Pendrell Corporation; *U.S. Public*, pg. 1661
HELSTON GARAGES GROUP; *Int'l*, pg. 3338
HELTON INDUSTRIES LTD.—See ASSA ABLOY AB; *Int'l*, pg. 639
HELTOR LIMITED; *Int'l*, pg. 3338

HELUKABEL AB—See HELUKABEL GmbH; *Int'l*, pg. 3338
HELUKABEL AG—See HELUKABEL GmbH; *Int'l*, pg. 3338
HELUKABEL AUSTRIA GMBH—See HELUKABEL GmbH; *Int'l*, pg. 3338
HELUKABEL BELGIUM BVBA.—See HELUKABEL GmbH; *Int'l*, pg. 3338
HELUKABEL B.V.—See HELUKABEL GmbH; *Int'l*, pg. 3338
HELUKABEL CANADA INC.—See HELUKABEL GmbH; *Int'l*, pg. 3338
HELUKABEL CZ S.R.O.—See HELUKABEL GmbH; *Int'l*, pg. 3338
HELUKABEL FRANCE SARL—See HELUKABEL GmbH; *Int'l*, pg. 3338
HELUKABEL GMBH; *Int'l*, pg. 3338
HELUKABEL INDIA PVT.LTD.—See HELUKABEL GmbH; *Int'l*, pg. 3338
HELUKABEL INT TRADING (SHANGHAI) CO., LTD.—See HELUKABEL GmbH; *Int'l*, pg. 3338
HELUKABEL ITALIA S.R.L.—See HELUKABEL GmbH; *Int'l*, pg. 3338
HELUKABEL KABLO SAN. VE TIC. LTD. STI.—See HELUKABEL GmbH; *Int'l*, pg. 3338
HELUKABEL KOREA CO., LTD.—See HELUKABEL GmbH; *Int'l*, pg. 3338
HELUKABEL MALAYSIA SDN BHD—See HELUKABEL GmbH; *Int'l*, pg. 3338
HELUKABEL POLSKA SP.Z O.O.—See HELUKABEL GmbH; *Int'l*, pg. 3338
HELUKABEL RUSSIA—See HELUKABEL GmbH; *Int'l*, pg. 3338
HELUKABEL SINGAPORE PTE. LTD.—See HELUKABEL GmbH; *Int'l*, pg. 3338
HELUKABEL SOUTH AFRICA (PTY) LTD.—See HELUKABEL GmbH; *Int'l*, pg. 3338
HELUKABEL (THAILAND) CO. LTD.—See HELUKABEL GmbH; *Int'l*, pg. 3338
HELUKABEL (UK) LTD.—See HELUKABEL GmbH; *Int'l*, pg. 3338
HELUKABEL USA, INC.—See HELUKABEL GmbH; *Int'l*, pg. 3338
HELUSTA UAB—See HELUKABEL GmbH; *Int'l*, pg. 3338
HELUVA GOOD, LLC—See Catamount Dairy Holdings L.P.; *U.S. Private*, pg. 787
HELVAR AB—See Helvar Merca Oy AB; *Int'l*, pg. 3339
HELVAR GMBH—See Helvar Merca Oy AB; *Int'l*, pg. 3339
HELVAR KFT.—See Helvar Merca Oy AB; *Int'l*, pg. 3339
HELVAR LIGHTING (SUZHOU) CO., LTD.—See Helvar Merca Oy AB; *Int'l*, pg. 3339
HELVAR LTD—See Helvar Merca Oy AB; *Int'l*, pg. 3339
HELVAR MERCA OY AB; *Int'l*, pg. 3339
HELVAR OY AB—See Helvar Merca Oy AB; *Int'l*, pg. 3339
HELVAR SRL—See Helvar Merca Oy AB; *Int'l*, pg. 3339
HEL VED BOLIG AS—See Honkarakenne Oyj; *Int'l*, pg. 3471
HELVETIA ASSET MANAGEMENT AG—See Helvetia Holding AG; *Int'l*, pg. 3339
HELVETIA ASSURANCES S.A. - LE HAVRE—See Helvetia Holding AG; *Int'l*, pg. 3339
HELVETIA ASSURANCES S.A.—See Helvetia Holding AG; *Int'l*, pg. 3339
HELVETIA COMPAGNIE SUISSE D'ASSURANCES SA—See Helvetia Holding AG; *Int'l*, pg. 3339
HELVETIA COMPANIA SUIZA SOCIEDAD ANONIMA DE SEGUROS Y REASEGUROS—See Helvetia Holding AG; *Int'l*, pg. 3339
HELVETIA CONSULTA AG—See Helvetia Holding AG; *Int'l*, pg. 3339
HELVETIA CONSULTA GESELLSCHAFT FUR VORSORGEBERATUNG AG—See Helvetia Holding AG; *Int'l*, pg. 3339
HELVETIA CONSULTING AG—See Helvetia Holding AG; *Int'l*, pg. 3339
HELVETIA HOLDING AG; *Int'l*, pg. 3339
HELVETIA INVESTMENT FOUNDATION—See Helvetia Holding AG; *Int'l*, pg. 3339
HELVETIA ITALIA ASSICURAZIONI S.P.A.—See Helvetia Holding AG; *Int'l*, pg. 3339
HELVETIA LATIN AMERICA LLC—See Helvetia Holding AG; *Int'l*, pg. 3339
HELVETIA LEBEN MAKLERSERVICE GMBH—See Helvetia Holding AG; *Int'l*, pg. 3339
HELVETIA SCHWEIZERISCHE LEBENSVERSICHERUNGS AG—See Helvetia Holding AG; *Int'l*, pg. 3339
HELVETIA SCHWEIZERISCHE LEBENSVERSICHERUNGSGESELLSCHAFT AG—See Helvetia Holding AG; *Int'l*, pg. 3339
HELVETIA SCHWEIZERISCHE VERSICHERUNGSGESELLSCHAFT AG—See Helvetia Holding AG; *Int'l*, pg. 3339
HELVETIA SPORT LTD.—See ENL Limited; *Int'l*, pg. 2441
HELVETIA SWISS INSURANCE COMPANY IN LIECHTENSTEIN LTD.—See Helvetia Holding AG; *Int'l*, pg. 3340
HELVETIA SWISS INSURANCE COMPANY (LABUAN BRANCH) LTD.—See Helvetia Holding AG; *Int'l*, pg. 3340
HELVETIA SWISS INSURANCE COMPANY LTD—See Helvetia Holding AG; *Int'l*, pg. 3340

HELVETIA SWISS LIFE INSURANCE COMPANY LTD.—See Helvetia Holding AG; *Int'l*, pg. 3340
HELVETIA VERSICHERUNGEN AG—See Helvetia Holding AG; *Int'l*, pg. 3340
HELVETIA VERSICHERUNGEN—See Helvetia Holding AG; *Int'l*, pg. 3340
HELVETIA VERSICHERUNGS-AG—See Helvetia Holding AG; *Int'l*, pg. 3340
HELVETIA VITA - COMPAGNIA ITALO SVIZZERA DI ASSICURAZIONI SULLA VITA S.P.A.—See Helvetia Holding AG; *Int'l*, pg. 3340
HELVETICA CAPITAL AG—See Resonac Holdings Corporation; *Int'l*, pg. 6298
HELVETICA CREATIVE; *U.S. Private*, pg. 1912
HELVETIC WARRANTY GMBH—See Helvetia Holding AG; *Int'l*, pg. 3340
HELVIASS VERZEKERINGEN B.V.—See Allianz SE; *Int'l*, pg. 353
HELVITA SENIORENZENTREN GMBH—See Clariane SE; *Int'l*, pg. 1643
HELVITIA VITA COMPAGNIA SA—See Helvetia Holding AG; *Int'l*, pg. 3340
HELVOET PHARMA N.V.—See Pema Holding AG; *Int'l*, pg. 5784
HELVOET RUBBER & PLASTIC TECHNOLOGIES BV—See Hydratec Industries NV; *Int'l*, pg. 3546
HELVOET RUBBER & PLASTIC TECHNOLOGIES GMBH—See RF Plast GmbH; *Int'l*, pg. 6318
HELVOET RUBBER & PLASTIC TECHNOLOGIES NV—See Hydratec Industries NV; *Int'l*, pg. 3546
HELVOET (TILBURG) B.V.—See Pema Holding AG; *Int'l*, pg. 5784
HELWAN CEMENT COMPANY S.A.E.—See Heidelberg Materials AG; *Int'l*, pg. 3316
HELWIG CARBON PRODUCTS DE MEXICO, S. DE R.L. DE C.V.—See Helwig Carbon Products, Inc.; *U.S. Private*, pg. 1912
HELWIG CARBON PRODUCTS, INC.; *U.S. Private*, pg. 1912
HELWIG CARBON PRODUCTS OF CANADA, INC.—See Helwig Carbon Products, Inc.; *U.S. Private*, pg. 1912
HELZBERG'S DIAMOND SHOPS, INC.—See Berkshire Hathaway Inc.; *U.S. Public*, pg. 306
HEMABH TECHNOLOGY PRIVATE LIMITED—See CMS Info Systems Limited; *Int'l*, pg. 1672
HEMA B.V.—See Ramphastos Investments Management BV; *Int'l*, pg. 6199
HEMACARE CORPORATION—See Charles River Laboratories International, Inc.; *U.S. Public*, pg. 480
HEMA DIAGNOSTIC SYSTEMS, LLC—See Generex Biotechnology Corporation; *U.S. Public*, pg. 930
HEMAGEN DIAGNOSTICS, INC.; *U.S. Public*, pg. 1025
HEMAIR SYSTEMS INDIA LTD.—See AIRTECH JAPAN, LTD.; *Int'l*, pg. 249
HEMANG RESOURCES LIMITED; *Int'l*, pg. 3340
HEMANT SURGICAL INDUSTRIES LIMITED; *Int'l*, pg. 3340
HEMARAJ LAND & DEVELOPMENT PUBLIC COMPANY LIMITED—See WHA Corporation Public Company Limited; *Int'l*, pg. 8396
HEMARAJ LEASEHOLD REAL ESTATE INVESTMENT TRUST; *Int'l*, pg. 3340
HEMARAJ WATER COMPANY LIMITED—See WHA Corporation Public Company Limited; *Int'l*, pg. 8396
HEMAS AIR SERVICES (PTE) LTD—See Hemas Holdings PLC; *Int'l*, pg. 3340
HEMAS AIR SERVICES (PVT.) LTD.—See Hemas Holdings PLC; *Int'l*, pg. 3340
HEMAS DEVELOPMENTS (PTE) LTD—See Hemas Holdings PLC; *Int'l*, pg. 3340
HEMAS HOLDINGS PLC; *Int'l*, pg. 3340
HEMAS HOSPITALS (PVT) LTD.—See Hemas Holdings PLC; *Int'l*, pg. 3340
HEMAS MANUFACTURING (PTE) LTD—See Hemas Holdings PLC; *Int'l*, pg. 3340
HEMAS MARITIME (PVT) LTD.—See Hemas Holdings PLC; *Int'l*, pg. 3340
HEMASOFT AMERICA CORP.—See GPI S.p.A.; *Int'l*, pg. 3046
HEMASOURCE, INC.—See Ridgemont Partners Management LLC; *U.S. Private*, pg. 3433
HEMAS PHARMACEUTICALS (PVT.) LTD.—See Hemas Holdings PLC; *Int'l*, pg. 3340
HEMAS POWER LIMITED—See Hemas Holdings PLC; *Int'l*, pg. 3340
HEMAS SURGICALS & DIAGNOSTICS (PVT.) LTD.—See Hemas Holdings PLC; *Int'l*, pg. 3340
HEMAS TRAVELS (PTE) LTD—See Hemas Holdings PLC; *Int'l*, pg. 3340
HEMATECH, INC.—See Kirin Holdings Company, Limited; *Int'l*, pg. 4188
HEMA-TRW OTOMOTIV DIREKSIYON SISTEMLERI A.S.—See ZF Friedrichshafen AG; *Int'l*, pg. 8645
HEMBLA AB—See Vonovia SE; *Int'l*, pg. 8305
HEMBREE & ASSOCIATES, INC.; *U.S. Private*, pg. 1913
HEMCHECK SWEDEN AB; *Int'l*, pg. 3341
HEMCON MEDICAL TECHNOLOGIES EUROPE, LTD.—See Weifang Tricol Trading Co. Ltd. *Int'l*, pg. 8370

HEMERIA SASU; *Int'l*, pg. 3341
HEMFOSA FASTIGHETER AB—See Samhallsbyggnadsbolaget I Norden AB; *Int'l*, pg. 6504
HEM HOLDINGS & TRADING LTD.; *Int'l*, pg. 3340
HEMI HEATING AB—See NIBE Industrier AB; *Int'l*, pg. 5261
HEMIJSKA INDUSTRIJA VRANJE A.D.; *Int'l*, pg. 3341
HEMINA SPA—See IDEX Corp; *U.S. Public*, pg. 1090
HEM INC.; *U.S. Private*, pg. 1913
HEMISPHERE ENERGY CORPORATION; *Int'l*, pg. 3341
HEMISPHERE FASHION GROUP; *Int'l*, pg. 3341
HEMISPHERE GNSS (USA) INC.—See CNH Industrial N.V.; *Int'l*, pg. 1675
HEMISPHERE MEDIA GROUP, INC.; *U.S. Private*, pg. 1913
HEMISPHERE PROPERTIES INDIA LIMITED; *Int'l*, pg. 3341
HEMISPHERX BIOPHARMA EUROPE—See AIM ImmunoTech Inc.; *U.S. Public*, pg. 63
HEM JAARBEURSPLEIN UTRECHT, B.V.—See Minor International PCL; *Int'l*, pg. 4911
HEMKOPSKEDJAN AB—See Axel Johnson Gruppen AB; *Int'l*, pg. 764
HEMLOCK EQUIPMENT LLC—See Evergreen Marine Corporation (Taiwan) Ltd.; *Int'l*, pg. 2566
HEMLOCK SEMICONDUCTOR, LLC—See Corning Incorporated; *U.S. Public*, pg. 579
HEMLOCK SEMICONDUCTOR, LLC—See Dow Inc.; *U.S. Public*, pg. 684
HEMLOCK SEMICONDUCTOR, LLC—See Shin-Etsu Chemical Co. Ltd.; *Int'l*, pg. 6839
HEMLOCK SEMICONDUCTOR OPERATIONS LLC—See Corning Incorporated; *U.S. Public*, pg. 579
HEMLOCK SEMICONDUCTOR OPERATIONS LLC—See Dow Inc.; *U.S. Public*, pg. 684
HEMLOCK SEMICONDUCTOR OPERATIONS LLC—See Shin-Etsu Chemical Co. Ltd.; *Int'l*, pg. 6839
HEMMAFONSTER SVERIGE AB—See Ratos AB; *Int'l*, pg. 6219
HEMMELRATH AUTOMOTIVE COATINGS (JILIN) CO., LTD.—See PPG Industries, Inc.; *U.S. Public*, pg. 1707
HEMMERLIN POLSKA SP. Z O.O.—See Hemmerlin S.A.; *Int'l*, pg. 3341
HEMMERLIN ROMANIA DUNAROM SPED. S.R.L.—See Hemmerlin S.A.; *Int'l*, pg. 3341
HEMMERLIN S.A.; *Int'l*, pg. 3341
HEMMERLIN SWISS AG—See Hemmerlin S.A.; *Int'l*, pg. 3341
HEMMERS-ITEX TEXTIL IMPORT EXPORT GMBH—See BENCIS Capital Partners B.V.; *Int'l*, pg. 970
HEMMING MORSE, INC.; *U.S. Private*, pg. 1913
HEMMY AB—See BHG Group AB; *Int'l*, pg. 1015
HEMOCUE AB—See Danaher Corporation; *U.S. Public*, pg. 630
HEMOCUE AUSTRALIA PTY. LTD.—See Danaher Corporation; *U.S. Public*, pg. 630
HEMOCUE GMBH—See Danaher Corporation; *U.S. Public*, pg. 630
HEMOCUE HOLDING AB—See Quest Diagnostics, Inc.; *U.S. Public*, pg. 1755
HEMOCUE, INC.—See Danaher Corporation; *U.S. Public*, pg. 630
HEMOCUE OY—See Danaher Corporation; *U.S. Public*, pg. 630
HEMOFARM A.D.—See Bain Capital, LP; *U.S. Private*, pg. 443
HEMOFARM A.D.—See Cinven Limited; *Int'l*, pg. 1613
HEMOFARM BANJA LUKA D.O.O.—See Bain Capital, LP; *U.S. Private*, pg. 443
HEMOFARM BANJA LUKA D.O.O.—See Cinven Limited; *Int'l*, pg. 1613
HEMOFARM KONCERN A.D.—See Bain Capital, LP; *U.S. Private*, pg. 443
HEMOFARM KONCERN A.D.—See Cinven Limited; *Int'l*, pg. 1613
HEMOGENYX PHARMACEUTICALS PLC; *Int'l*, pg. 3341
HEMOMAK HEM UROS DOOEL—See BASF SE; *Int'l*, pg. 884
HEMOMONT D.O.O.—See Bain Capital, LP; *U.S. Private*, pg. 443
HEMOMONT D.O.O.—See Cinven Limited; *Int'l*, pg. 1613
HEMO ORGANIC LIMITED; *Int'l*, pg. 3341
HEMOPHARM GMBH—See Bain Capital, LP; *U.S. Private*, pg. 443
HEMOPHARM GMBH—See Cinven Limited; *Int'l*, pg. 1613
HEMOPHILIA CENTER OF WESTERN NEW YORK, INC.; *U.S. Private*, pg. 1913
HEMOPHILIA SERVICES CONSORTIUM, INC.; *U.S. Private*, pg. 1913
HEMOPLAST JSC; *Int'l*, pg. 3341
HEMOSONICS, LLC—See Diagnostica Stago S.A.S.; *Int'l*, pg. 2103
HEMOSTASIS REFERENCE LABORATORY INC.—See Universal Biosensors, Inc.; *Int'l*, pg. 8077
HEMOSTEMIX INC.; *Int'l*, pg. 3341
HEMOTEK RENAL CENTER, INC.—See Euro-Med Laboratories Phil., Inc.; *Int'l*, pg. 2532
HEMOTEQ AG; *Int'l*, pg. 3341

HEMOVENT GMBH—See MicroPort Scientific Corporation; *Int'l*, pg. 4880
HEMPACCO CO., INC.; *U.S. Public*, pg. 1025
HEMPEL A/S; *Int'l*, pg. 3341
HEMPEL (CHINA) LTD.—See Hempel A/S; *Int'l*, pg. 3341
HEMPEL-HAI HONG COATINGS (KUNSHAN) CO., LTD—See China Merchants Group Limited; *Int'l*, pg. 1521
HEMPEL (USA) INC.—See Hempel A/S; *Int'l*, pg. 3341
HEMPHILL CORPORATION; *U.S. Private*, pg. 1913
HEMP, INC; *U.S. Public*, pg. 1025
HEMPLER FOODS GROUP LLC—See Premium Brands Holdings Corporation; *Int'l*, pg. 5963
HEMPLIFE TODAY; *U.S. Public*, pg. 1025
HEMP NATURALS, INC.; *U.S. Public*, pg. 1025
HEMPRO A.D.; *Int'l*, pg. 3341
THE HEMPSHIRE GROUP, INC.; *Int'l*, pg. 7652
HEMPSTEAD AUTO CO. INC.; *U.S. Private*, pg. 1913
HEMPSTEAD FORD LINCOLN; *U.S. Private*, pg. 1913
HEMPT BROTHERS, INC.; *U.S. Private*, pg. 1913
HEMPTOWN ORGANICS CORP.; *Int'l*, pg. 3341
HEMSEDAL BOOKING AS—See SkiStar AB; *Int'l*, pg. 6990
HEMSEDAL SKISENTER A/S—See SkiStar AB; *Int'l*, pg. 6990
HEMSLEY FRASER AUSTRALIA PTY LTD—See Demos S.A.; *Int'l*, pg. 2026
HEMSLEY FRASER GROUP LIMITED—See Demos S.A.; *Int'l*, pg. 2026
HEMSLEY FRASER US—See Demos S.A.; *Int'l*, pg. 2026
HEMSTREET DEVELOPMENT CORP.; *U.S. Private*, pg. 1913
HEMSWORTH VETS4PETS LIMITED—See Pets at Home Group Plc; *Int'l*, pg. 5834
HEMTEX AB—See ICA Gruppen AB; *Int'l*, pg. 3577
H.E. MURDOCK CO. INC.; *U.S. Private*, pg. 1826
HENA, INC.; *U.S. Private*, pg. 1913
HENAN ANCAI HI-TECH CO., LTD.; *Int'l*, pg. 3342
HENAN ARMCO & METAWISE TRADING CO., LTD.—See Armco Metals Holdings, Inc.; *U.S. Private*, pg. 330
HENAN BCCY ENVIRONMENTAL ENERGY CO., LTD.; *Int'l*, pg. 3342
HENAN CARVE ELECTRONICS TECHNOLOGY CO., LTD.; *Int'l*, pg. 3342
HENAN CHENG LOONG PACKING PRODUCTS CO., LTD.—See Cheng Loong Corp.; *Int'l*, pg. 1466
HENAN COMMUNICATIONS PLANNING AND DESIGN INSTITUTE CO., LTD.; *Int'l*, pg. 3342
HENAN DALI FOODS CO., LTD.—See Dali Foods Group Co. Ltd.; *Int'l*, pg. 1951
HENAN DAYOU ENERGY CO., LTD.; *Int'l*, pg. 3342
HENAN ELECTRIC POWER COMPANY—See State Grid Corporation of China; *Int'l*, pg. 7182
HENAN ENERGY & CHEMICAL INDUSTRY GROUP CO., LTD.; *Int'l*, pg. 3342
HENAN GAOJIAN PROJECT MANAGEMENT CO., LTD.—See Henan Communications Planning and Design Institute Co., Ltd; *Int'l*, pg. 3342
HENAN GREAT POWER ENERGY CO., LTD.—See Guangzhou Great Power Energy & Technology Co., Ltd.; *Int'l*, pg. 3165
HENAN GREAT POWER ENERGY & TECHNOLOGY CO., LTD.—See Guangzhou Great Power Energy & Technology Co., Ltd.; *Int'l*, pg. 3165
HENAN HANGXIAO STEEL STRUCTURE CO., LTD.—See Hangxiao Steel Structure Co., Ltd.; *Int'l*, pg. 3246
HENAN HENGXING SCIENCE & TECHNOLOGY CO., LTD.; *Int'l*, pg. 3342
HENAN HUALONG AROMA CHEMICALS CO., LTD.—See Apple Flavor & Fragrance Group Co., Ltd.; *Int'l*, pg. 520
HENAN HUAMAO NEW MATERIAL TECHNOLOGY DEVELOPMENT CO., LTD.—See Zhengzhou Sino-Crystal Diamond Co., Ltd.; *Int'l*, pg. 8670
HENAN HUANGHE WHIRLWIND CO., LTD.; *Int'l*, pg. 3342
HENAN HUAYING AGRICULTURE DEVELOPMENT CO., LTD.; *Int'l*, pg. 3342
HENAN JAKE NEW MATERIAL CO., LTD.—See Henan Shijia Photons Technology Co., Ltd.; *Int'l*, pg. 3343
HENAN JINDAN LACTIC ACID TECHNOLOGY CO., LTD.; *Int'l*, pg. 3342
HENAN JINMA ENERGY COMPANY LIMITED; *Int'l*, pg. 3342
HENAN JINTANGSHENG AUTOMOBILE CO., LTD.—See China ZhengTong Auto Services Holdings Limited; *Int'l*, pg. 1566
HENAN KEDI DAIRY INDUSTRY CO., LTD.; *Int'l*, pg. 3342
HENAN LANTIAN GAS CO., LTD.; *Int'l*, pg. 3342
HENAN LILIANG DIAMOND CO., LTD.; *Int'l*, pg. 3342
HENAN LINGRUI PHARMACEUTICAL CO., LTD.; *Int'l*, pg. 3342
HENAN MACHINERY & ELECTRIC IMPORT & EXPORT CO., LTD.—See China Machinery Engineering Corporation; *Int'l*, pg. 1516
HENAN MINGTAI ALUMINUM CO., LTD.; *Int'l*, pg. 3342
HENAN MUTONG ENVIRONMENTAL INDUSTRY CO., LTD.—See GEM Co., Ltd.; *Int'l*, pg. 2914

HENAN NEWLAND PHARMACEUTICAL CO., LTD.; *Int'l*, pg. 3342
HENAN NINTH METALLURGICAL CONSTRUCTION CO., LTD.—See China Aluminum International Engineering Corporation Limited; *Int'l*, pg. 1482
HENAN PINGGAO ELECTRIC CO., LTD—See State Grid Corporation of China; *Int'l*, pg. 7183
HENAN PINGGAO TOSHIBA HIGH-VOLTAGE SWITCH-GEAR CO., LTD.—See Japan Industrial Partners, Inc.; *Int'l*, pg. 3889
HENAN PINGGAO TOSHIBA HIGH-VOLTAGE SWITCH-GEAR CO., LTD.—See State Grid Corporation of China; *Int'l*, pg. 7183
HENAN POLY ART CENTER MANAGEMENT CORPORATION LIMITED—See Poly Culture Group Corporation Limited; *Int'l*, pg. 5914
HENAN PROVINCE ACADEMY OF ENGINEERING DETECT CROSS REINFORCEMENT LTD.—See Henan Communications Planning and Design Institute Co., Ltd; *Int'l*, pg. 3342
HENAN PROVINCE PHARMACEUTICAL CO., LTD.—See China Meheco Group Co., Ltd.; *Int'l*, pg. 1519
HENAN QINGSHUIYUAN TECHNOLOGY CO., LTD.; *Int'l*, pg. 3342
HENAN REBECCA HAIR PRODUCTS CO., LTD.; *Int'l*, pg. 3343
HENAN SENYUAN ELECTRIC CO., LTD.; *Int'l*, pg. 3343
HENAN SHEN HUO COAL INDUSTRY & ELECTRICITY POWER CO., LTD.; *Int'l*, pg. 3343
HENAN SHIJIA COMMUNICATION TECHNOLOGY CO., LTD.—See Henan Shijia Photons Technology Co., Ltd.; *Int'l*, pg. 3343
HENAN SHIJIA ELECTRONIC TECHNOLOGY CO., LTD.—See Henan Shijia Photons Technology Co., Ltd.; *Int'l*, pg. 3343
HENAN SHIJIA OPTOELECTRONIC DEVICES CO., LTD.—See Henan Shijia Photons Technology Co., Ltd.; *Int'l*, pg. 3343
HENAN SHIJIA PHOTONS TECHNOLOGY CO., LTD.; *Int'l*, pg. 3343
HENAN SHUANGHUI INVESTMENT & DEVELOPMENT CO., LTD.—See WH Group Limited; *Int'l*, pg. 8394
HENAN SPLENDOR SCIENCE & TECHNOLOGY CO., LTD.; *Int'l*, pg. 3343
HENAN TALOPH PHARMACEUTICAL STOCK CO., LTD.; *Int'l*, pg. 3343
HENAN THINKER AUTOMATIC EQUIPMENT CO., LTD.; *Int'l*, pg. 3343
HENAN TONG-DA CABLE CO., LTD.; *Int'l*, pg. 3343
HENAN TOPFOND PHARMACEUTICAL CO.,LTD.; *Int'l*, pg. 3343
HENAN UNIVERSE INTRAOCULAR LENS RESEARCH AND MANUFACTURE CO., LTD.—See Shanghai Haohai Biological Technology Co., Ltd.; *Int'l*, pg. 6769
HENAN XINFEI ELECTRIC CO., LTD.—See Hong Leong Investment Holdings Pte. Ltd.; *Int'l*, pg. 3469
HENAN XINLIANXIN BLUE ENVIRONMENTAL PROTECTION TECHNOLOGY CO., LTD.—See China XLX Fertiliser Ltd; *Int'l*, pg. 1563
HENAN XINNING MODERN LOGISICS CO., LTD.; *Int'l*, pg. 3343
HENAN XINYE TEXTILE CO., LTD.; *Int'l*, pg. 3343
HENAN YICHENG NEW ENERGY CO., LTD.; *Int'l*, pg. 3343
HENAN YINGE INDUSTRIAL INVESTMENT CO., LTD.; *Int'l*, pg. 3343
HENAN YUGUANG GOLD & LEAD CO., LTD; *Int'l*, pg. 3344
HENAN YUNENG HOLDINGS CO., LTD.; *Int'l*, pg. 3344
HENAN YUXING SINO-CRYSTAL MIRO CO., LTD.—See Zhengzhou Sino-Crystal Diamond Co., Ltd.; *Int'l*, pg. 8670
HENAN ZHONGCHUANG CITY SERVICE CO., LTD.—See Xiamen Zhongchuang Environmental Technology Co., Ltd.; *Int'l*, pg. 8526
HENAN ZHONGFU INDUSTRY CO., LTD.; *Int'l*, pg. 3344
HENAN ZHONGFU PREFORM CO., LTD.—See Zhuhai Zhongfu Enterprise Co., Ltd.; *Int'l*, pg. 8679
HENAN ZHONGPIN IMPORT AND EXPORT TRADING COMPANY—See Zhongpin Inc.; *Int'l*, pg. 8674
HENAN ZHONGYUAN EXPRESSWAY COMPANY LIMITED; *Int'l*, pg. 3344
HENAN ZHONGYU GAS ENGINEERING DESIGN CO., LTD.—See Zhongyu Energy Holdings Limited; *Int'l*, pg. 8676
HENCH ENTERPRISES INC.; *U.S. Private*, pg. 1913
HENCO FLOOR N.V.—See Aalberts N.V.; *Int'l*, pg. 34
HENCO INDUSTRIES N.V.—See Aalberts N.V.; *Int'l*, pg. 34
HENDALE CAPITAL; *Int'l*, pg. 3344
HENDAYA S.A.—See Compania Electro Metalurgica S.A.; *Int'l*, pg. 1749
HENDELS INCORPORATED; *U.S. Private*, pg. 1913
THE HENDERSON ALTERNATIVE STRATEGIES TRUST PLC; *Int'l*, pg. 7652
HENDERSON ANUSA, LLC—See AutoNation, Inc.; *U.S. Public*, pg. 235
HENDERSON AUCTIONS—See JAH Enterprises, Inc.; *U.S. Private*, pg. 2182

HENDERSON BANCSHARES, INC.; *U.S. Private*, pg. 1913
HENDERSON BAS PARTNERSHIP—See Stagwell, Inc.; *U.S. Public*, pg. 1928
HENDERSON COFFEE CORP—See Huron Capital Partners LLC; *U.S. Private*, pg. 2012
HENDERSON COLLISION, INC.—See AutoNation, Inc.; *U.S. Public*, pg. 235
HENDERSON COMBINED GROUP OF COMPANIES, INC.; *U.S. Private*, pg. 1913
THE HENDERSON CORPORATION; *U.S. Private*, pg. 4051
HENDERSON DIVERSIFIED INCOME TRUST PLC; *Int'l*, pg. 3344
HENDERSON ENGINEERS INC.; *U.S. Private*, pg. 1913
HENDERSON EQUITY PARTNERS LIMITED—See Janus Henderson Group plc; *Int'l*, pg. 3881
HENDERSON EUROPEAN TRUST PLC; *Int'l*, pg. 3344
HENDERSON FAR EAST INCOME LIMITED; *Int'l*, pg. 3344
HENDERSON, FRANKLIN, STARNES & HOLT, P.A.; *U.S. Private*, pg. 1914
HENDERSON GLOBAL INVESTORS (HOLDINGS) LIMITED—See Janus Henderson Group plc; *Int'l*, pg. 3881
HENDERSON GLOBAL INVESTORS (INTERNATIONAL HOLDINGS) BV—See Janus Henderson Group plc; *Int'l*, pg. 3881
HENDERSON GLOBAL INVESTORS (NORTH AMERICA) INC.—See Janus Henderson Group plc; *Int'l*, pg. 3881
HENDERSON HIGH INCOME TRUST PLC; *Int'l*, pg. 3344
HENDERSON HOLDINGS GROUP BV—See Janus Henderson Group plc; *Int'l*, pg. 3881
HENDERSON-HY, LLC—See Lithia Motors, Inc.; *U.S. Public*, pg. 1322
HENDERSON IMPLEMENT CO. INC.; *U.S. Private*, pg. 1914
HENDERSON INVESTMENT LIMITED—See Henderson Land Development Co. Ltd.; *Int'l*, pg. 3344
HENDERSON-JOHNSON CO. INC.; *U.S. Private*, pg. 1914
HENDERSON, JOSEPH J. & SONS; *U.S. Private*, pg. 1914
HENDERSON LAND DEVELOPMENT CO. LTD.; *Int'l*, pg. 3344
HENDERSON NEDERLAND BV—See ASSA ABLOY AB; *Int'l*, pg. 635
HENDERSON NEDERLANDS BV—See ASSA ABLOY AB; *Int'l*, pg. 639
HENDERSON OPPORTUNITIES TRUST PLC; *Int'l*, pg. 3345
HENDERSON PARK CAPITAL PARTNERS UK LLP; *Int'l*, pg. 3345
HENDERSON PRODUCTS, INC.—See Douglas Dynamics, Inc.; *U.S. Public*, pg. 677
HENDERSON PROPERTIES INC.; *U.S. Private*, pg. 1914
HENDERSON SERVICES LLC; *U.S. Private*, pg. 1914
HENDERSON SMALLER COMPANIES INVESTMENT TRUST PLC; *Int'l*, pg. 3345
HENDERSONS PRINTING INC.; *U.S. Private*, pg. 1914
HENDERSONVILLE HOSPITAL CORPORATION—See HCA Healthcare, Inc.; *U.S. Public*, pg. 998
HENDERSONVILLE MEDICAL CENTER—See HCA Healthcare, Inc.; *U.S. Public*, pg. 998
HENDERSONVILLE NEWSPAPER CORPORATION—See Gannett Co., Inc.; *U.S. Public*, pg. 905
HENDERSONVILLE OB/GYN, LLC—See HCA Healthcare, Inc.; *U.S. Public*, pg. 998
HENDOR MINING SUPPLIES (PTY) LTD—See ARGENT INDUSTRIAL LIMITED; *Int'l*, pg. 560
HENDRICK BMW—See The Hendrick Companies, LLC; *U.S. Private*, pg. 4051
HENDRICK CANCER CENTER—See Hendrick Health System; *U.S. Private*, pg. 1914
HENDRICK CHEVROLET CADILLAC; *U.S. Private*, pg. 1914
HENDRICK CHRYSLER JEEP; *U.S. Private*, pg. 1914
THE HENDRICK COMPANIES, LLC; *U.S. Private*, pg. 4051
HENDRICK CORPORATION, LLC—See The Hendrick Companies, LLC; *U.S. Private*, pg. 4051
HENDRICK HEALTH SYSTEM; *U.S. Private*, pg. 1914
HENDRICK MANUFACTURING COMPANY; *U.S. Private*, pg. 1914
HENDRICK MOTORS OF CHARLOTTE—See The Hendrick Companies, LLC; *U.S. Private*, pg. 4051
HENDRICK MOTORSPORTS, LLC—See The Hendrick Companies, LLC; *U.S. Private*, pg. 4051
HENDRICK PROVIDER NETWORK—See Hendrick Health System; *U.S. Private*, pg. 1914
HENDRICKS & CO GMBH—See Howden Group Holdings Limited; *Int'l*, pg. 3493
HENDRICK SCREEN CO.—See Hendrick Manufacturing Company; *U.S. Private*, pg. 1914
HENDRICKS HOLDING COMPANY, INC.; *U.S. Private*, pg. 1914
HENDRICKS LOVELL LTD.—See Grafton Group plc; *Int'l*, pg. 3051

HENDRICKSON ASIA PACIFIC PTY. LTD.—See The Boler Company; *U.S. Private*, pg. 3996
HENDRICKSON AUSTRIA GMBH—See The Boler Company; *U.S. Private*, pg. 3996
HENDRICKSON AUXILIARY AXLE SYSTEMS—See The Boler Company; *U.S. Private*, pg. 3996
HENDRICKSON BUMPER & TRIM—See The Boler Company; *U.S. Private*, pg. 3996
HENDRICKSON CANADA—See The Boler Company; *U.S. Private*, pg. 3996
HENDRICKSON CHINA - JINAN PLANT—See The Boler Company; *U.S. Private*, pg. 3996
HENDRICKSON CHINA—See The Boler Company; *U.S. Private*, pg. 3996
HENDRICKSON COMMERCIAL VEHICLE SYSTEMS UK—See The Boler Company; *U.S. Private*, pg. 3996
HENDRICKSON FRANCE S.A.S.—See The Boler Company; *U.S. Private*, pg. 3996
HENDRICKSON INDIA—See The Boler Company; *U.S. Private*, pg. 3996
HENDRICKSON INTERNATIONAL CORPORATION—See The Boler Company; *U.S. Private*, pg. 3996
HENDRICKSON JAPAN GK—See The Boler Company; *U.S. Private*, pg. 3996
HENDRICKSON MEXICANA—See The Boler Company; *U.S. Private*, pg. 3996
HENDRICKSON ROMANIA—See The Boler Company; *U.S. Private*, pg. 3996
HENDRICKSON TRAILER COMMERCIAL VEHICLE SYSTEMS—See The Boler Company; *U.S. Private*, pg. 3996
HENDRICKSON TRUCK COMMERCIAL VEHICLE SYSTEMS—See The Boler Company; *U.S. Private*, pg. 3996
HENDRICKSON TRUCKING, INC.; *U.S. Private*, pg. 1915
HENDRICKSON USA LLC—See The Boler Company; *U.S. Private*, pg. 3996
HENDRICKS & PARTNERS, INC.; *U.S. Private*, pg. 1914
HENDRICKS RIVER LOGISTICS, LLC—See Hendricks Holding Company, Inc.; *U.S. Private*, pg. 1915
HENDRIX BUSINESS SYSTEMS, INC.; *U.S. Private*, pg. 1915
HENDRIX GENETICS B.V.; *Int'l*, pg. 3345
HENDRIX HOTEL & RESTAURANT EQUIPMENT & SUPPLIES LTD.—See Blue Point Capital Partners, LLC; *U.S. Private*, pg. 590
HENDRIX LONDON—See Blue Point Capital Partners, LLC; *U.S. Private*, pg. 590
HENDRIX MARMON UTILITY LLC—See Berkshire Hathaway Inc.; *U.S. Public*, pg. 310
HENDRY ALUMINUM, INC.; *U.S. Private*, pg. 1916
HENDY GROUP LTD.; *Int'l*, pg. 3345
HENEGHAN PR—See WPP plc; *Int'l*, pg. 8468
HENEGHAN WRECKING & EXCAVATING CO., INC.—See J.F. Lehman & Company, Inc.; *U.S. Private*, pg. 2164
H.E. NEUMANN CO.; *U.S. Private*, pg. 1916
HENGAN INTERNATIONAL GROUP CO. LTD.; *Int'l*, pg. 3345
HENGAN PHARMACARE COMPANY LIMITED—See Hengan International Group Co. Ltd.; *Int'l*, pg. 3345
HENG ASSET MANAGEMENT LIMITED—See NOIZ Group Limited; *Int'l*, pg. 5401
HENGBAO CO., LTD.; *Int'l*, pg. 3346
HENGBAO INTERNATIONAL PTE LTD—See Hengbao Co., Ltd.; *Int'l*, pg. 3346
HENG CLINIC FOR WOMEN PTE. LTD.—See Singapore O&G Ltd.; *Int'l*, pg. 6941
HENGDELI HOLDINGS LIMITED; *Int'l*, pg. 3346
HENGDIAN ENTERTAINMENT CO., LTD.; *Int'l*, pg. 3346
HENGDIAN GROUP DMEGC MAGNETICS CO., LTD.; *Int'l*, pg. 3346
HENGDIAN GROUP TOSPO LIGHTING CO LTD; *Int'l*, pg. 3346
HENGERDA NEW MATERIALS (FUJIAN) CO., LTD.; *Int'l*, pg. 3346
HENGFENG INFORMATION TECHNOLOGY CO. LTD.; *Int'l*, pg. 3346
HENGGELER COMPUTER CONSULTANTS, INC.—See RTX Corporation; *U.S. Public*, pg. 1824
HENGGUANG HOLDING CO., LIMITED; *Int'l*, pg. 3346
HENG HUP HOLDINGS LTD.; *Int'l*, pg. 3345
HENGI CHEMICAL CO., LTD.—See Coremax Corp.; *Int'l*, pg. 1798
HENGLI AMERICA CORPORATION—See Jiangsu Hengli Hydraulic Co., Ltd.; *Int'l*, pg. 3947
HENGLI GROUP CO.,LTD.; *Int'l*, pg. 3346
HENGLI HYDRAULIC INDIA SYSTEM SOLUTIONS PVT. LTD.—See Jiangsu Hengli Hydraulic Co., Ltd.; *Int'l*, pg. 3947
HENGLI INDUSTRIAL DEVELOPMENT GROUP CO., LTD.; *Int'l*, pg. 3346
HENGLIN HOME FURNISHINGS CO., LTD.; *Int'l*, pg. 3346
HENGLI PETROCHEMICAL CO., LTD.; *Int'l*, pg. 3346
HENG LONG INTERNATIONAL LTD.—See LVMH Moet Hennessy Louis Vuitton SE; *Int'l*, pg. 4594
HENG LONG LEATHER CO (PTE) LTD—See LVMH Moet Hennessy Louis Vuitton SE; *Int'l*, pg. 4594

HENGLONG USA CORPORATION—See China Automotive Systems, Inc.; *Int'l*, pg. 1484
HENGMEI OPTOELECTRONIC CORPORATION—See Cheng Mei Materials Technology Corporation; *Int'l*, pg. 1466
HENGNENG CAR CO., LTD.—See Sichuan Western Resources Holding Co., Ltd.; *Int'l*, pg. 6881
HENGSHAN GEAR CO., LTD—See Hunan Oil Pump Co., Ltd.; *Int'l*, pg. 3533
HENG SHENG HOLDING GROUP LTD.; *Int'l*, pg. 3345
HENG SHI CHENG (HONG KONG) INTERNATIONAL HOLDING LIMITED—See Suzhou Hengmingda Electronic Technology Co., Ltd.; *Int'l*, pg. 7350
HENGSHUI ZHONGYU GAS CO., LTD.—See Zhongyu Energy Holdings Limited; *Int'l*, pg. 8676
HENGST ASIA PACIFIC PTE. LTD.—See Hengst SE & Co. KG; *Int'l*, pg. 3347
HENGST FILTER SYSTEMS (KUNSHAN) CO., LTD.—See Hengst SE & Co. KG; *Int'l*, pg. 3347
HENGST INDUSTRIA DE FILTROS LTDA.—See Hengst SE & Co. KG; *Int'l*, pg. 3347
HENGSTLER GMBH—See Fortive Corporation; *U.S. Public*, pg. 870
HENGST-LUMAN INDIA PVT. LTD.—See Hengst SE & Co. KG; *Int'l*, pg. 3347
HENGST MIDDLE EAST FZE—See Hengst SE & Co. KG; *Int'l*, pg. 3347
HENGST OF NORTH AMERICA, INC.—See Hengst SE & Co. KG; *Int'l*, pg. 3347
HENGST POLAND SP. Z O.O.—See Hengst SE & Co. KG; *Int'l*, pg. 3347
HENGST SE & CO. KG - BERLIN PLANT—See Hengst SE & Co. KG; *Int'l*, pg. 3347
HENGST SE & CO. KG - NORDWALDE PLANT—See Hengst SE & Co. KG; *Int'l*, pg. 3347
HENGST SE & CO. KG; *Int'l*, pg. 3347
HENGTAI CAPITAL INVESTMENT CO., LTD.—See HengTai Securities Co., LTD; *Int'l*, pg. 3347
HENGTAI CHANGCAI SECURITIES CO., LTD.—See HengTai Securities Co., LTD; *Int'l*, pg. 3347
HENG TAI CONSUMABLES GROUP LIMITED; *Int'l*, pg. 3345
HENGTAI FUTURES CO., LTD.—See HengTai Securities Co., LTD; *Int'l*, pg. 3347
HENGTAI PIONEER INVESTMENTS CO., LTD.—See HengTai Securities Co., LTD; *Int'l*, pg. 3347
HENGTAI SECURITIES CO., LTD; *Int'l*, pg. 3347
HENGTAI YINGWO ASSET MANAGEMENT CO., LTD.—See HengTai Securities Co., LTD; *Int'l*, pg. 3347
HENGTONG LOGISTICS CO., LTD.; *Int'l*, pg. 3347
HENGTONG OPTIC-ELECTRIC CO., LTD.; *Int'l*, pg. 3347
HENG XIN CHINA HOLDINGS LIMITED; *Int'l*, pg. 3345
HENGXING GOLD HOLDING COMPANY LIMITED; *Int'l*, pg. 3347
HENGXIN SHAMBOLA CULTURE CO., LTD.; *Int'l*, pg. 3347
HENGXIN TECHNOLOGY LTD.; *Int'l*, pg. 3347
HENG YA ELECTRIC (DONGGUAN) LTD.—See Ta Ya Electric Wire & Cable Co., Ltd.; *Int'l*, pg. 7400
HENG YA ELECTRIC (KUNSHAN) LTD.—See Ta Ya Electric Wire & Cable Co., Ltd.; *Int'l*, pg. 7400
HENG YANG KINGBOARD CHEMICAL CO., LTD.—See Kingboard Holdings Limited; *Int'l*, pg. 4171
HENGYANG LUZE AUTOMOBILE SALES SERVICES CO., LTD.—See China ZhengTong Auto Services Holdings Limited; *Int'l*, pg. 1566
HENGYANG MEIBAOHANG AUTO SALES & SERVICES CO., LTD.—See China MeiDong Auto Holdings Limited; *Int'l*, pg. 1519
HENGYANG XIANGDA CAMEL FEED CO., LTD—See Tangrenshen Group Co., Ltd.; *Int'l*, pg. 7458
HENG YI DA MACHINE (YINCHUAN) CO., LTD.—See Daikin Industries, Ltd.; *Int'l*, pg. 1935
HENGYI INTERNATIONAL INDUSTRIES GROUP, INC.; *Int'l*, pg. 3347
HENGYI PETROCHEMICAL CO., LTD.; *Int'l*, pg. 3347
HENG YUI (MACAO) COMMERCIAL OFFSHORE LIMITED—See Heng Tai Consumables Group Limited; *Int'l*, pg. 3345
HENIFF TRANSPORTATION SYSTEMS INC.; *U.S. Private*, pg. 1916
HENIG FURS INC.; *U.S. Private*, pg. 1916
HENINGER TOYOTA; *Int'l*, pg. 3348
HENKEL ABLESTIK JAPAN LTD.—See Henkel AG & Co. KGaA; *Int'l*, pg. 3349
HENKEL ABLESTIK KOREA LTD.—See Henkel AG & Co. KGaA; *Int'l*, pg. 3353
HENKEL ADHESIVES CO., LTD.—See Henkel AG & Co. KGaA; *Int'l*, pg. 3348
HENKEL ADHESIVES CORPORATION—See Henkel AG & Co. KGaA; *Int'l*, pg. 3353
HENKEL ADHESIVES TECHNOLOGIES (GUANGDONG) CO. LIMITED—See Henkel AG & Co. KGaA; *Int'l*, pg. 3348
HENKEL ADHESIVES TECHNOLOGIES INDIA PRIVATE LIMITED—See Henkel AG & Co. KGaA; *Int'l*, pg. 3348
HENKEL ADHESIVE TECHNOLOGIES CANADA—See Henkel AG & Co. KGaA; *Int'l*, pg. 3350

HENKEL ADHESIVE TECHNOLOGIES (MALAYSIA) HOLDINGS B.V.—See Henkel AG & Co. KGaA; *Int'l*, pg. 3348
HENKEL ADHESIVE TECHNOLOGIES NORDEN AB—See Henkel AG & Co. KGaA; *Int'l*, pg. 3351
HENKEL ADHESIVE TECHNOLOGIES SDN. BHD.—See Henkel AG & Co. KGaA; *Int'l*, pg. 3348
HENKEL AG & CO. KGAA; *Int'l*, pg. 3348
HENKEL ALGERIE S.P.A.—See Henkel AG & Co. KGaA; *Int'l*, pg. 3352
HENKEL ALKI DISTRIBUTION S.A.R.L.—See Henkel AG & Co. KGaA; *Int'l*, pg. 3352
HENKEL ANAND INDIA PVT. LTD.—See Henkel AG & Co. KGaA; *Int'l*, pg. 3348
HENKEL ARABIA FOR HOME AND PERSONAL CARE PRODUCTS CO. LTD.—See Henkel AG & Co. KGaA; *Int'l*, pg. 3352
HENKEL ARGENTINA S.A.—See Henkel AG & Co. KGaA; *Int'l*, pg. 3349
HENKEL ASIA-PACIFIC LTD.—See Henkel AG & Co. KGaA; *Int'l*, pg. 3348
HENKEL AUSTRALIA PTY. LTD.—See Henkel AG & Co. KGaA; *Int'l*, pg. 3349
HENKEL AUSTRIA GROUP—See Henkel AG & Co. KGaA; *Int'l*, pg. 3350
HENKEL BALTI OPERATIONS OU—See Henkel AG & Co. KGaA; *Int'l*, pg. 3349
HENKEL BALTI OU—See Henkel AG & Co. KGaA; *Int'l*, pg. 3350
HENKEL BALTI—See Henkel AG & Co. KGaA; *Int'l*, pg. 3349
HENKEL BAUTECHNIK KAZAKHSTAN LLP—See Henkel AG & Co. KGaA; *Int'l*, pg. 3350
HENKEL BAUTECHNIK KAZAKHSTAN TOO—See Henkel AG & Co. KGaA; *Int'l*, pg. 3350
HENKEL BAUTECHNIK TAA—See Henkel AG & Co. KGaA; *Int'l*, pg. 3349
HENKEL BAUTECHNIK (UKRAINA) TOB—See Henkel AG & Co. KGaA; *Int'l*, pg. 3349
HENKEL BELGIUM N.V.—See Henkel AG & Co. KGaA; *Int'l*, pg. 3350
HENKEL BELGIUM OPERATIONS N.V.—See Henkel AG & Co. KGaA; *Int'l*, pg. 3350
HENKEL BH D.O.O.—See Henkel AG & Co. KGaA; *Int'l*, pg. 3349
HENKEL BULGARIA EOOD—See Henkel AG & Co. KGaA; *Int'l*, pg. 3350
HENKEL CANADA CORPORATION—See Henkel AG & Co. KGaA; *Int'l*, pg. 3350
HENKEL CAPITAL S.A. DE C.V.—See Henkel AG & Co. KGaA; *Int'l*, pg. 3350
HENKEL CAPITAL S.A. DE C.V.—See Henkel AG & Co. KGaA; *Int'l*, pg. 3350
HENKEL CENTRAL ASIA & CAUCASUS TOO—See Henkel AG & Co. KGaA; *Int'l*, pg. 3350
HENKEL CENTRAL EASTERN EUROPE GMBH—See Henkel AG & Co. KGaA; *Int'l*, pg. 3350
HENKEL CENTROAMERICANA S.A.—See Henkel AG & Co. KGaA; *Int'l*, pg. 3350
HENKEL CHEMBOND SURFACE TECHNOLOGIES LTD.—See Henkel AG & Co. KGaA; *Int'l*, pg. 3350
HENKEL CHEMICAL TECHNOLOGIES (SHANGHAI) LTD.—See Henkel AG & Co. KGaA; *Int'l*, pg. 3348
HENKEL CHILE LTDA.—See Henkel AG & Co. KGaA; *Int'l*, pg. 3350
HENKEL CHILE S.A.—See Henkel AG & Co. KGaA; *Int'l*, pg. 3350
HENKEL (CHINA) CO. LTD.—See Henkel AG & Co. KGaA; *Int'l*, pg. 3348
HENKEL (CHINA) INVESTMENT CO. LTD.—See Henkel AG & Co. KGaA; *Int'l*, pg. 3348
HENKEL CHRYSLER JEEP INC.; *U.S. Private*, pg. 1916
HENKEL & CIE AG - LAESSER KLEBSTOFFE DIVISION—See Henkel AG & Co. KGaA; *Int'l*, pg. 3348
HENKEL & CIE AG—See Henkel AG & Co. KGaA; *Int'l*, pg. 3348
HENKEL COLOMBIANA S.A.—See Henkel AG & Co. KGaA; *Int'l*, pg. 3350
HENKEL CONSTRUCTION COMPANY; *U.S. Private*, pg. 1916
HENKEL CONSUMER ADHESIVES, INC.—See Henkel AG & Co. KGaA; *Int'l*, pg. 3353
HENKEL CONSUMER GOODS CANADA, INC.—See Henkel AG & Co. KGaA; *Int'l*, pg. 3350
HENKEL CONSUMER GOODS INC.—See Henkel AG & Co. KGaA; *Int'l*, pg. 3353
HENKEL CONSUMER GOODS, INC.—See Henkel AG & Co. KGaA; *Int'l*, pg. 3353
HENKEL CORPORATION, ONTARIO—See Henkel AG & Co. KGaA; *Int'l*, pg. 3350
HENKEL COSMETICS (ZHAOQING) CO., LTD.—See Henkel AG & Co. KGaA; *Int'l*, pg. 3348
HENKEL COSTA RICA LTDA.—See Henkel AG & Co. KGaA; *Int'l*, pg. 3350
HENKEL CROATIA D.O.O.—See Henkel AG & Co. KGaA; *Int'l*, pg. 3350
HENKEL CR SPOL.S.R.O.—See Henkel AG & Co. KGaA; *Int'l*, pg. 3350

HENKEL CONSTRUCTION COMPANY

HENKEL DENMARK A/S—See Henkel AG & Co. KGaA; *Int'l*, pg. 3350
HENKEL DETERGENTS SAUDI ARABIA LTD.—See Henkel AG & Co. KGaA; *Int'l*, pg. 3350
HENKEL DONGSUNG (THAILAND) LTD.—See Henkel AG & Co. KGaA; *Int'l*, pg. 3349
HENKEL DONGSUNG VIETNAM CO. LTD.—See Henkel AG & Co. KGaA; *Int'l*, pg. 3349
HENKEL EASTERN EUROPE GMBH—See Henkel AG & Co. KGaA; *Int'l*, pg. 3350
HENKEL ECUATORIANA S.A.—See Henkel AG & Co. KGaA; *Int'l*, pg. 3350
HENKEL EGYPT FOR INDUSTRY & TRADE SAE—See Henkel AG & Co. KGaA; *Int'l*, pg. 3351
HENKEL ELECTRONIC MATERIALS (BELGIUM) N.V.—See Henkel AG & Co, KGaA; *Int'l*, pg. 3350
HENKEL ELECTRONIC MATERIALS LLC—See Henkel AG & Co. KGaA; *Int'l*, pg. 3353
HENKEL ELECTRONICS MATERIALS N.V.—See Henkel AG & Co. KGaA; *Int'l*, pg. 3353
HENKEL FINANCE AUSTRALIA L.P.—See Henkel AG & Co. KGaA; *Int'l*, pg. 3349
HENKEL FINLAND OY—See Henkel AG & Co. KGaA; *Int'l*, pg. 3351
HENKEL FRANCE OPERATIONS S.A.—See Henkel AG & Co. KGaA; *Int'l*, pg. 3351
HENKEL FRANCE S.A.—See Henkel AG & Co. KGaA; *Int'l*, pg. 3351
HENKEL GENTHIN GMBH—See Henkel AG & Co. KGaA; *Int'l*, pg. 3351
HENKEL + GERLACH GMBH & CO. KG; *Int'l*, pg. 3348
HENKEL GLOBAL SUPPLY CHAIN B.V.—See Henkel AG & Co. KGaA; *Int'l*, pg. 3351
HENKEL HAKUSUI CORPORATION—See Henkel AG & Co. KGaA; *Int'l*, pg. 3349
HENKELHAUSEN GMBH & CO. KG; *Int'l*, pg. 3354
HENKEL HELLAS SA—See Henkel AG & Co. KGaA; *Int'l*, pg. 3350
HENKEL HOME CARE KOREA LTD. - ANSAN PLANT—See Henkel AG & Co. KGaA; *Int'l*, pg. 3349
HENKEL HOME CARE KOREA LTD.—See Henkel AG & Co. KGaA; *Int'l*, pg. 3349
HENKEL HONG KONG HOLDING LTD.—See Henkel AG & Co. KGaA; *Int'l*, pg. 3349
HENKEL HONG KONG LTD.—See Henkel AG & Co. KGaA; *Int'l*, pg. 3349
HENKEL IBERICA PORTUGAL, UNIPESSOAL LDA.—See Henkel AG & Co. KGaA; *Int'l*, pg. 3351
HENKEL IBERICA S.A.—See Henkel AG & Co. KGaA; *Int'l*, pg. 3351
HENKEL INDUSTRIAL ADHESIVES PAKISTAN PVT. LTD.—See Henkel AG & Co. KGaA; *Int'l*, pg. 3352
HENKEL INDUSTRIE AG—See Henkel AG & Co. KGaA; *Int'l*, pg. 3351
HENKEL IP MANAGEMENT AND IC SERVICES GMBH—See Henkel AG & Co. KGaA; *Int'l*, pg. 3351
HENKEL IRELAND LTD.—See Henkel AG & Co. KGaA; *Int'l*, pg. 3351
HENKEL ITALIA OPERATIONS S.R.L.—See Henkel AG & Co. KGaA; *Int'l*, pg. 3351
HENKEL ITALIA S.R.L.—See Henkel AG & Co. KGaA; *Int'l*, pg. 3351
HENKEL JAMAICA LIMITED—See Henkel AG & Co. KGaA; *Int'l*, pg. 3351
HENKEL JAPAN LTD.—See Henkel AG & Co. KGaA; *Int'l*, pg. 3349
HENKEL JEBEL ALI FZCO—See Henkel AG & Co. KGaA; *Int'l*, pg. 3351
HENKEL (JIANGSU) AUTO PARTS CO., LTD.—See Henkel AG & Co. KGaA; *Int'l*, pg. 3348
HENKEL JORDAN PSC—See Henkel AG & Co. KGaA; *Int'l*, pg. 3352
HENKEL KENYA LTD.—See Henkel AG & Co. KGaA; *Int'l*, pg. 3351
HENKEL KOREA LTD.—See Henkel AG & Co. KGaA; *Int'l*, pg. 3349
HENKEL LABORATORIES—See Henkel AG & Co. KGaA; *Int'l*, pg. 3353
HENKEL LA LUZ S.A.—See Henkel AG & Co. KGaA; *Int'l*, pg. 3351
HENKEL LATVIA SIA—See Henkel AG & Co. KGaA; *Int'l*, pg. 3351
HENKELL & CO. SEKTKELLEREI KG—See Dr. August Oetker KG; *Int'l*, pg. 2190
HENKEL LEBANON S.A.L.—See Henkel AG & Co. KGaA; *Int'l*, pg. 3351
HENKEL LOCTITE BRASIL LTDA.—See Henkel AG & Co. KGaA; *Int'l*, pg. 3351
HENKEL LOCTITE (CHINA) CO. LTD.—See Henkel AG & Co. KGaA; *Int'l*, pg. 3349
HENKEL LOCTITE DEUTSCHLAND GMBH—See Henkel AG & Co. KGaA; *Int'l*, pg. 3351
HENKEL LOCTITE DE VENEZUELA, C.A.—See Henkel AG & Co. KGaA; *Int'l*, pg. 3352
HENKEL LOCTITE ESPANA, S.A.—See Henkel AG & Co. KGaA; *Int'l*, pg. 3351
HENKEL LOCTITE FRANCE SAS—See Henkel AG & Co. KGaA; *Int'l*, pg. 3351
HENKEL LOCTITE HONG KONG LIMITED—See Henkel AG & Co. KGaA; *Int'l*, pg. 3349
HENKEL LOCTITE ITALIA S.P.A.—See Henkel AG & Co. KGaA; *Int'l*, pg. 3352
HENKEL LOCTITE-KID GMBH—See Henkel AG & Co. KGaA; *Int'l*, pg. 3351
HENKEL LOCTITE KOREA LTD.—See Henkel AG & Co. KGaA; *Int'l*, pg. 3349
HENKEL LTDA.—See Henkel AG & Co. KGaA; *Int'l*, pg. 3351
HENKEL LTD., LINTON—See Henkel AG & Co. KGaA; *Int'l*, pg. 3353
HENKEL LTD.—See Henkel AG & Co. KGaA; *Int'l*, pg. 3351
HENKEL MAGYARORSZAG KFT.—See Henkel AG & Co. KGaA; *Int'l*, pg. 3350
HENKEL MAKROFLEX OY—See Henkel AG & Co. KGaA; *Int'l*, pg. 3351
HENKEL (MALAYSIA) SDN. BHD.—See Henkel AG & Co. KGaA; *Int'l*, pg. 3349
HENKEL MANAGEMENT AG—See Henkel AG & Co. KGaA; *Int'l*, pg. 3351
HENKEL MARIBOR D.O.O.—See Henkel AG & Co. KGaA; *Int'l*, pg. 3351
HENKEL MERIMA A.D.—See Henkel AG & Co. KGaA; *Int'l*, pg. 3350
HENKEL MEXICANA S.A. DE C.V.—See Henkel AG & Co. KGaA; *Int'l*, pg. 3352
HENKEL NEDERLAND B.V., SCHEEMDA—See Henkel AG & Co. KGaA; *Int'l*, pg. 3353
HENKEL NEDERLAND B.V.—See Henkel AG & Co. KGaA; *Int'l*, pg. 3351
HENKEL NEDERLAND OPERATIONS B.V.—See Henkel AG & Co. KGaA; *Int'l*, pg. 3351
HENKEL NEW ZEALAND LTD.—See Henkel AG & Co. KGaA; *Int'l*, pg. 3349
HENKEL NORDEN AB—See Henkel AG & Co. KGaA; *Int'l*, pg. 3351
HENKEL NORDEN OY—See Henkel AG & Co. KGaA; *Int'l*, pg. 3352
HENKEL NORGE AB—See Henkel AG & Co. KGaA; *Int'l*, pg. 3352
HENKEL OBERFLACHENTECHNIK GMBH—See Henkel AG & Co. KGaA; *Int'l*, pg. 3352
HENKEL OF AMERICA INC.—See Henkel AG & Co. KGaA; *Int'l*, pg. 3352
HENKELORBSEAL—See Henkel AG & Co. KGaA; *Int'l*, pg. 3353
HENKEL PDC EGYPT SAE—See Henkel AG & Co. KGaA; *Int'l*, pg. 3352
HENKEL PERUANA S.A.—See Henkel AG & Co. KGaA; *Int'l*, pg. 3352
HENKEL PHILIPPINES INC.—See Henkel AG & Co. KGaA; *Int'l*, pg. 3352
HENKEL POLSKA OPERATIONS SP. Z O.O.—See Henkel AG & Co. KGaA; *Int'l*, pg. 3352
HENKEL POLSKA S.A.—See Henkel AG & Co. KGaA; *Int'l*, pg. 3350
HENKEL POLYBIT INDUSTRIES LTD.—See Henkel AG & Co. KGaA; *Int'l*, pg. 3352
HENKEL PUERTO RICO, INC.—See Henkel AG & Co. KGaA; *Int'l*, pg. 3352
HENKEL REPUBLICA DOMINICANA SRL—See Henkel AG & Co. KGaA; *Int'l*, pg. 3352
HENKEL ROMANIA SRL—See Henkel AG & Co. KGaA; *Int'l*, pg. 3351
HENKEL SAUDI ARABIA DETERGENTS CO. LTD.—See Henkel AG & Co. KGaA; *Int'l*, pg. 3352
HENKEL (SIAM) ADHESIVE TECHNOLOGIES LTD.—See Henkel AG & Co. KGaA; *Int'l*, pg. 3348
HENKEL SINGAPORE PTE., LTD.—See Henkel AG & Co. KGaA; *Int'l*, pg. 3349
HENKEL SLOVENIJA D.O.O.—See Henkel AG & Co. KGaA; *Int'l*, pg. 3350
HENKEL SLOVENSKO SPOL. S.R.O.—See Henkel AG & Co. KGaA; *Int'l*, pg. 3350
HENKELS & MCCOY CANADA, INC.—See MasTec, Inc.; *U.S. Public*, pg. 1393
HENKELS & MCCOY, INC.—See MasTec, Inc.; *U.S. Public*, pg. 1393
HENKEL SOAD LTD.—See Henkel AG & Co. KGaA; *Int'l*, pg. 3352
HENKEL SOUTH AFRICA (PTY.) LTD.—See Henkel AG & Co. KGaA; *Int'l*, pg. 3352
HENKEL S.P.A.—See Henkel AG & Co. KGaA; *Int'l*, pg. 3352
HENKEL SRBIJA D.O.O. - INDJIJA PLANT—See Henkel AG & Co. KGaA; *Int'l*, pg. 3352
HENKEL SRBIJA D.O.O. - KRUSEVAC PLANT—See Henkel AG & Co. KGaA; *Int'l*, pg. 3352
HENKEL SRBIJA D.O.O.—See Henkel AG & Co. KGaA; *Int'l*, pg. 3352
HENKEL-STORITVE D.O.O.—See Henkel AG & Co. KGaA; *Int'l*, pg. 3354
HENKEL SURFACE TECHNOLOGIES GMBH—See Henkel AG & Co. KGaA; *Int'l*, pg. 3352
HENKEL SURFACE TECHNOLOGIES NORDIC AB—See Henkel AG & Co. KGaA; *Int'l*, pg. 3351

CORPORATE AFFILIATIONS

HENKEL SURFACE TECHNOLOGIES—See Henkel AG & Co. KGaA; *Int'l*, pg. 3352
HENKEL SURFACE TECHNOLOGIES—See Henkel AG & Co. KGaA; *Int'l*, pg. 3352
HENKEL SWEDEN OPERATIONS AB—See Henkel AG & Co. KGaA; *Int'l*, pg. 3352
HENKEL SWITZERLAND OPERATIONS AG—See Henkel AG & Co. KGaA; *Int'l*, pg. 3352
HENKEL TAIWAN LTD. - P'INGCHEN—See Henkel AG & Co. KGaA; *Int'l*, pg. 3349
HENKEL TAIWAN LTD.—See Henkel AG & Co. KGaA; *Int'l*, pg. 3349
HENKEL TECHNOLOGIES FRANCE SAS—See Henkel AG & Co. KGaA; *Int'l*, pg. 3351
HENKEL TECHNOLOGIES (KOREA) LTD. - BUSAN PLANT—See Henkel AG & Co. KGaA; *Int'l*, pg. 3349
HENKEL TECHNOLOGIES (KOREA) LTD. - CHUNAN PLANT—See Henkel AG & Co. KGaA; *Int'l*, pg. 3349
HENKEL TECHNOLOGIES (KOREA) LTD. - EUMSUNG PLANT—See Henkel AG & Co. KGaA; *Int'l*, pg. 3349
HENKEL TECHNOLOGIES (KOREA) LTD.—See Henkel AG & Co. KGaA; *Int'l*, pg. 3349
HENKEL TECHNOLOGIES—See Henkel AG & Co. KGaA; *Int'l*, pg. 3353
HENKEL TEROSON GMBH—See Henkel AG & Co. KGaA; *Int'l*, pg. 3351
HENKEL (THAILAND) LTD.—See Henkel AG & Co. KGaA; *Int'l*, pg. 3349
HENKEL TRADING MAGHREB S.A.R.L.—See Henkel AG & Co. KGaA; *Int'l*, pg. 3352
HENKEL TUNISIE S.A.—See Henkel AG & Co. KGaA; *Int'l*, pg. 3352
HENKEL UKRAINE TOW—See Henkel AG & Co. KGaA; *Int'l*, pg. 3352
HENKEL US OPERATIONS CORPORATION—See Henkel AG & Co. KGaA; *Int'l*, pg. 3352
HENKEL US OPERATIONS CORPORATION - TCLAD DIVISION—See Henkel AG & Co. KGaA; *Int'l*, pg. 3353
HENKEL VENEZOLANA S.A.—See Henkel AG & Co, KGaA; *Int'l*, pg. 3352
HENKEL VIETNAM CO. LTD. - BINH DUONG COSMETICS PLANT—See Henkel AG & Co. KGaA; *Int'l*, pg. 3349
HENKEL VIETNAM CO. LTD.—See Henkel AG & Co. KGaA; *Int'l*, pg. 3349
HENKEL WASCH- UND REINIGUNGSMITTEL GMBH—See Henkel AG & Co. KGaA; *Int'l*, pg. 3352
HENKEL XIANGHUA ADHESIVES CO. LTD.—See Henkel AG & Co. KGaA; *Int'l*, pg. 3349
HENKE MACHINE - BUFFALO EQUIPMENT—See Sinca Industries, Inc.; *U.S. Private*, pg. 3669
HENLEY ARCH PTY. LTD.—See Sumitomo Forestry Co., Ltd.; *Int'l*, pg. 7285
HENLEY ENTERPRISES, INC.; *U.S. Private*, pg. 1916
HENLEY MANAGEMENT COMPANY; *U.S. Private*, pg. 1916
HENLEY PARK ACQUISITION CORP.; *U.S. Public*, pg. 1025
HENLOPEN MEMORIAL PARK LLC—See Axar Capital Management L.P.; *U.S. Private*, pg. 411
HENMAN ENGINEERING & MACHINE INC.—See JD Norman Industries, Inc.; *U.S. Private*, pg. 2195
HENNEBERRY HILL TECHNOLOGIES; *U.S. Private*, pg. 1916
HENNECKE GMBH—See Capvis AG; *Int'l*, pg. 1318
HENNECKE INC. POLYURETHANE TECHNOLOGY—See Capvis AG; *Int'l*, pg. 1318
HENNECKE SYSTEMS GMBH—See Meyer Burger Technology AG; *Int'l*, pg. 4869
THE HENNEGAN COMPANY—See Chatham Asset Management, LLC; *U.S. Private*, pg. 863
HENNEN FURNITURE; *U.S. Private*, pg. 1916
HENNEO MEDIA, SA; *Int'l*, pg. 3354
HENNEPIN HEALTHCARE SYSTEM, INC.; *U.S. Private*, pg. 1916
HENNES MAURITZ (SHANGHAI) COMMERCIAL LTD CO—See H&M Hennes & Mauritz AB; *Int'l*, pg. 3192
HENNESSEE GROUP LLC—See Terrapin Partners LLC; *U.S. Private*, pg. 3972
HENNESSEN & POTTHOFF, GMBH—See Inapa - Investimentos, Participacoes e Gestao, SA; *Int'l*, pg. 3645
HENNESSEY'S TAVERN, INC.; *U.S. Private*, pg. 1916
HENNESSY ADVISORS, INC.; *U.S. Public*, pg. 1025
HENNESSY CADILLAC INC.; *U.S. Private*, pg. 1916
HENNESSY CONSTRUCTION SERVICES CORP.; *U.S. Private*, pg. 1916
HENNESSY INDUSTRIES CANADA—See Vontier Corporation; *U.S. Public*, pg. 2309
HENNESSY INDUSTRIES, LLC—See Vontier Corporation; *U.S. Public*, pg. 2309
HENNESSY LEXUS OF ATLANTA; *U.S. Private*, pg. 1916
HENNESSY'S RIVER VIEW FORD; *U.S. Private*, pg. 1916
HENNESY MECHANICAL SALES, LLC—See DXP Enterprises, Inc.; *U.S. Public*, pg. 697
HENNE-UNIMOG GMBH—See Mercedes-Benz Group AG; *Int'l*, pg. 4824
HENNGE K.K.; *Int'l*, pg. 3354
HENNIGES AUTOMOTIVE, INC. - FREDERICK—See Aviation Industry Corporation of China; *Int'l*, pg. 742

COMPANY NAME INDEX

HENNIGES AUTOMOTIVE INC. - GOMEZ PALACIO—See Aviation Industry Corporation of China; *Int'l*, pg. 742

HENNIGES AUTOMOTIVE INC. - GUADALAJARA—See Aviation Industry Corporation of China; *Int'l*, pg. 742

HENNIGES AUTOMOTIVE, INC. - NEW HAVEN—See Aviation Industry Corporation of China; *Int'l*, pg. 742

HENNIGES AUTOMOTIVE, INC. - OAKVILLE—See Aviation Industry Corporation of China; *Int'l*, pg. 742

HENNIGES AUTOMOTIVE, INC. - REIDSVILLE PLANT—See Aviation Industry Corporation of China; *Int'l*, pg. 742

HENNIGES AUTOMOTIVE, INC.—See Aviation Industry Corporation of China; *Int'l*, pg. 742

HENNIGES AUTOMOTIVE INC. - TORREON—See Aviation Industry Corporation of China; *Int'l*, pg. 742

HENNIKER SCIENTIFIC LTD.—See Judges Scientific plc; *Int'l*, pg. 4021

HENNING CONSTRUCTION COMPANY LLC; *U.S. Private*, pg. 1917

HENNINGER D.C., L.L.C.—See Henninger Media Services Inc.; *U.S. Private*, pg. 1917

HENNINGER MEDIA SERVICES INC.; *U.S. Private*, pg. 1917

HENNING LARSEN ARCHITECTS A/S—See Ramboll Gruppen A/S; *Int'l*, pg. 6197

HENNINGSEN COLD STORAGE COMPANY; *U.S. Private*, pg. 1917

HENNINGSEN FOODS, INC.—See Post Holdings, Inc.; *U.S. Public*, pg. 1704

HENNINGSEN NEDERLAND B.V.—See ARIAKE JAPAN Co., Ltd.; *Int'l*, pg. 564

HENNINGSONS ELEKTRISKA AB—See Instalco AB; *Int'l*, pg. 3721

HENNLICH INDUSTRIETECHNIK SPOLECNOST S.R.O—See THK CO., LTD.; *Int'l*, pg. 7711

HENNLICH INDUSTRIETECHNIK SPOL. SRO—See THK CO., LTD.; *Int'l*, pg. 7711

HENNLICH INDUSTRIJSKA TEHNIKA D.O.O.—See THK CO., LTD.; *Int'l*, pg. 7711

HENNLICH INUDSTRIJSKA TEHNIKA D.O.O.—See THK CO., LTD.; *Int'l*, pg. 7711

HENNLICH OOD—See THK CO., LTD.; *Int'l*, pg. 7711

HENNLICH SP. Z O.O.—See THK CO., LTD.; *Int'l*, pg. 7711

HENNLICH & ZEBISCH GMBH—See THK CO., LTD.; *Int'l*, pg. 7711

HENREDON DESIGNER SHOWROOMS, INC.—See Heritage Home Group, LLC; *U.S. Private*, pg. 1924

HENREDON FURNITURE INDUSTRIES, INC.—See Heritage Home Group, LLC; *U.S. Private*, pg. 1924

HENRICKSEN & COMPANY INC.; *U.S. Private*, pg. 1917

HENRICO DOCTORS' HOSPITAL—See HCA Healthcare, Inc.; *U.S. Public*, pg. 997

HENRICO RADIATION ONCOLOGY, LLC—See HCA Healthcare, Inc.; *U.S. Public*, pg. 998

HENRIETTA BUILDING SUPPLIES, INC—See American Securities LLC; *U.S. Private*, pg. 248

HENRIKSEN-BUTLER DESIGN GROUP; *U.S. Private*, pg. 1917

HENRIQUEZ ELECTRIC CORP.; *U.S. Private*, pg. 1917

HENRI SELMER PARIS—See Argos Wityu S.A.; *Int'l*, pg. 563

HENROB CORPORATION—See Atlas Copco AB; *Int'l*, pg. 681

HENROB CORPORATION—See Atlas Copco AB; *Int'l*, pg. 681

HENRY AVOCADO CORP; *U.S. Private*, pg. 1917

HENRY BATH B.V.—See CMST Development Co., Ltd.; *Int'l*, pg. 1672

HENRY BATH B.V.—See Mercuria Energy Group Holding SA; *Int'l*, pg. 4833

HENRY BATH LLC—See CMST Development Co., Ltd.; *Int'l*, pg. 1672

HENRY BATH LLC—See Mercuria Energy Group Holding SA; *Int'l*, pg. 4833

HENRY BATH SINGAPORE PTE. LTD.—See CMST Development Co., Ltd.; *Int'l*, pg. 1672

HENRY BATH SINGAPORE PTE. LTD.—See Mercuria Energy Group Holding SA; *Int'l*, pg. 4833

HENRY BATH & SON LIMITED—See CMST Development Co., Ltd.; *Int'l*, pg. 1672

HENRY BATH & SON LIMITED—See Mercuria Energy Group Holding SA; *Int'l*, pg. 4833

HENRY BOOT CONSTRUCTION (UK) LIMITED—See Henry Boot PLC; *Int'l*, pg. 3355

HENRY BOOT DEVELOPMENTS LIMITED—See Henry Boot PLC; *Int'l*, pg. 3355

HENRY BOOT ESTATES LIMITED—See Henry Boot PLC; *Int'l*, pg. 3355

HENRY BOOT 'K' LTD—See Henry Boot PLC; *Int'l*, pg. 3355

HENRY BOOT PLC; *Int'l*, pg. 3354

HENRY BOOT PROJECTS LIMITED—See Henry Boot PLC; *Int'l*, pg. 3355

HENRY BOOT TAMWORTH LIMITED—See Henry Boot PLC; *Int'l*, pg. 3355

HENRY BROCH & CO.—See Sunridge Partners (UK), LLP; *Int'l*, pg. 7321

HENRY BROS. ELECTRONICS, INC.—See Kratos Defense & Security Solutions, Inc.; *U.S. Public*, pg. 1276

HENRY BROS. ELECTRONICS, INC.—See Kratos Defense & Security Solutions, Inc.; *U.S. Public*, pg. 1276

HENRY BROS. ELECTRONICS, INC.—See Kratos Defense & Security Solutions, Inc.; *U.S. Public*, pg. 1276

HENRY CARLSON COMPANY; *U.S. Private*, pg. 1917

HENRY COMPANY LLC - KIMBERTON—See Carlisle Companies Incorporated; *U.S. Public*, pg. 437

HENRY COMPANY LLC—See Carlisle Companies Incorporated; *U.S. Public*, pg. 437

HENRY COUNTY BANK—See Civista Bancshares, Inc.; *U.S. Public*, pg. 507

HENRY COUNTY HOSPITAL; *U.S. Private*, pg. 1917

HENRY CROWN & COMPANY; *U.S. Private*, pg. 1917

HENRY DAY FORD, INC.; *U.S. Private*, pg. 1918

HENRY DENNY & SONS (NI) LIMITED—See Kerry Group plc; *Int'l*, pg. 4138

HENRY ESTATE WINERY; *U.S. Private*, pg. 1918

HENRY FARM CENTER, INC.—See SunSouth LLC; *U.S. Private*, pg. 3872

HENRY FARMERS COOPERATIVE INC.; *U.S. Private*, pg. 1918

HENRY FILTERS (EUROPE) LTD.—See Durr AG; *Int'l*, pg. 2233

HENRY FILTERS, INC.—See Komline-Sanderson Corporation; *U.S. Private*, pg. 2342

HENRY F. MICHELL COMPANY INC.; *U.S. Private*, pg. 1918

HENRY FORD ALLEGIANCE HEALTH—See Henry Ford Health System; *U.S. Private*, pg. 1918

HENRY FORD HEALTH SYSTEM; *U.S. Private*, pg. 1918

HENRY FORD MUSEUM AND GREENFIELD VILLAGE; *U.S. Private*, pg. 1918

HENRY FORD & SONS LTD—See Ford Motor Company; *U.S. Public*, pg. 865

HENRY FORD VILLAGE; *U.S. Private*, pg. 1918

HENRY F. TEICHMANN INCORPORATED; *U.S. Private*, pg. 1918

HENRY GILL COMMUNICATIONS; *U.S. Private*, pg. 1918

HENRY G. MEIGS, LLC—See Heritage Group; *U.S. Private*, pg. 1923

HENRY GORDY INTERNATIONAL INC.—See EXX Inc.; *U.S. Private*, pg. 1453

HENRY HEYINK CONSTRUCTION LTD.; *Int'l*, pg. 3355

HENRY H. LEWIS CONTRACTORS LLC—See Stewart & Tate, Inc.; *U.S. Private*, pg. 3811

HENRY HOLT & CO. PUBLISHING—See Verlagsgruppe Georg von Holtzbrinck GmbH; *Int'l*, pg. 8170

HENRY H. OTTENS MANUFACTURING CO., INC.—See International Flavors & Fragrances Inc.; *U.S. Public*, pg. 1152

HENRY J. AUSTIN HEALTH CENTER, INC.; *U.S. Private*, pg. 1918

HENRY J. LEE DISTRIBUTORS INC.—See Reyes Holdings, LLC; *U.S. Private*, pg. 3418

HENRY JONES FOODS PTY LTD—See Perma Funds Management; *Int'l*, pg. 5802

HENRY JONES FOODS PTY LTD—See Perma Funds Management; *Int'l*, pg. 5802

HENRY JONES FOODS PTY LTD—See The Eights Group Pty Ltd.; *Int'l*, pg. 7638

HENRY JONES FOODS PTY LTD—See The Eights Group Pty Ltd.; *Int'l*, pg. 7638

HENRY LAMOTTE FOOD GMBH—See Henry Lamotte GmbH; *Int'l*, pg. 3355

HENRY LAMOTTE GMBH; *Int'l*, pg. 3355

HENRY LAMOTTE OILS GMBH—See Henry Lamotte GmbH; *Int'l*, pg. 3355

HENRY LAMOTTE SERVICES GMBH—See Henry Lamotte GmbH; *Int'l*, pg. 3355

HENRY LEE WILLIS COMMUNITY CENTER INC; *U.S. Private*, pg. 1918

HENRY LUST REAL ESTATE CO., INC.; *U.S. Private*, pg. 1918

HENRY MEMORIAL PARK LLC—See Axar Capital Management L.P.; *U.S. Private*, pg. 411

HENRY M. JACKSON FOUNDATION FOR THE ADVANCEMENT OF MILITARY MEDICINE, INC.; *U.S. Private*, pg. 1918

HENRY MODELL & COMPANY, INC.; *U.S. Private*, pg. 1919

HENRY MOTORS INCORPORADO; *U.S. Private*, pg. 1919

HENRY OIL COMPANY INC.; *U.S. Private*, pg. 1919

HENRY PRATT COMPANY, LLC—See Mueller Water Products, Inc.; *U.S. Public*, pg. 1485

HENRY PRODUCTION INCORPORATED; *U.S. Private*, pg. 1919

HENRY PRODUCTS INCORPORATED; *U.S. Private*, pg. 1919

HENRY QUENTZEL PLUMBING SUPPLY CO., INC.; *U.S. Private*, pg. 1919

HENRY SCHEIN ANIMAL HEALTH HOLDINGS LIMITED—See Clayton, Dubilier & Rice, LLC; *U.S. Private*, pg. 921

HENRY SCHEIN ANIMAL HEALTH HOLDINGS LIMITED—See TPG Capital, L.P.; *U.S. Public*, pg. 2170

HENRY SCHEIN ANIMAL HEALTH—See Clayton, Dubilier & Rice, LLC; *U.S. Private*, pg. 921

HENRY SCHEIN ANIMAL HEALTH—See TPG Capital, L.P.; *U.S. Public*, pg. 2170

HENRY SCHEIN ARCONA, INC.—See Henry Schein, Inc.; *U.S. Public*, pg. 1025

HENRY SCHEIN CANADA, INC.—See Henry Schein, Inc.; *U.S. Public*, pg. 1025

HENRY SCHEIN DENTAL WAREHOUSE (PTY) LTD.—See Henry Schein, Inc.; *U.S. Public*, pg. 1025

HENRY SCHEIN ESPANA, S.L.—See Henry Schein, Inc.; *U.S. Public*, pg. 1025

HENRY SCHEIN HEMAO GUANGZHOUMEDICAL DEVICE CO., LTD.—See Henry Schein, Inc.; *U.S. Public*, pg. 1025

HENRY SCHEIN HOLDING GMBH—See Henry Schein, Inc.; *U.S. Public*, pg. 1025

HENRY SCHEIN HONG KONG LIMITED—See Henry Schein, Inc.; *U.S. Public*, pg. 1025

HENRY SCHEIN, INC. - ATLANTA, GA—See Henry Schein, Inc.; *U.S. Public*, pg. 1026

HENRY SCHEIN, INC. - BIRMINGHAM, AL—See Henry Schein, Inc.; *U.S. Public*, pg. 1026

HENRY SCHEIN, INC. - BOISE, ID—See Henry Schein, Inc.; *U.S. Public*, pg. 1026

HENRY SCHEIN, INC. - BOSTON, MA—See Henry Schein, Inc.; *U.S. Public*, pg. 1026

HENRY SCHEIN, INC. - BUFFALO, NY—See Henry Schein, Inc.; *U.S. Public*, pg. 1026

HENRY SCHEIN, INC. - CHICAGO, IL—See Henry Schein, Inc.; *U.S. Public*, pg. 1026

HENRY SCHEIN, INC. - CINCINNATI, OH—See Henry Schein, Inc.; *U.S. Public*, pg. 1026

HENRY SCHEIN, INC. - COLUMBUS, OH—See Henry Schein, Inc.; *U.S. Public*, pg. 1026

HENRY SCHEIN, INC.-DENVER, PENNSYLVANIA—See Henry Schein, Inc.-*U.S. Public*, pg. 1026

HENRY SCHEIN, INC. - DETROIT, MI—See Henry Schein, Inc.; *U.S. Public*, pg. 1026

HENRY SCHEIN, INC.-FLORIDA—See Henry Schein, Inc.; *U.S. Public*, pg. 1026

HENRY SCHEIN, INC.-FLORIDA—See Henry Schein, Inc.; *U.S. Public*, pg. 1026

HENRY SCHEIN, INC.-FLORIDA SOUTH—See Henry Schein, Inc.; *U.S. Public*, pg. 1027

HENRY SCHEIN, INC.-FT. WAYNE, INDIANA—See Henry Schein, Inc.; *U.S. Public*, pg. 1026

HENRY SCHEIN, INC. - GRAND RAPIDS, MI—See Henry Schein, Inc.; *U.S. Public*, pg. 1026

HENRY SCHEIN, INC. - GRAPEVINE, TX—See Henry Schein, Inc.; *U.S. Public*, pg. 1026

HENRY SCHEIN, INC. - GREENVILLE, SC—See Henry Schein, Inc.; *U.S. Public*, pg. 1026

HENRY SCHEIN INC.-INDIANA—See Henry Schein, Inc.; *U.S. Public*, pg. 1025

HENRY SCHEIN, INC. - JACKSON, MS—See Henry Schein, Inc.; *U.S. Public*, pg. 1026

HENRY SCHEIN, INC.-KANSAS—See Henry Schein, Inc.; *U.S. Public*, pg. 1027

HENRY SCHEIN, INC. - LAS VEGAS, NV—See Henry Schein, Inc.; *U.S. Public*, pg. 1026

HENRY SCHEIN, INC. - LIVERMORE, CA—See Henry Schein, Inc.; *U.S. Public*, pg. 1026

HENRY SCHEIN, INC.-LOUISVILLE, KENTUCKY—See Henry Schein, Inc.; *U.S. Public*, pg. 1027

HENRY SCHEIN, INC. - MEMPHIS, TN—See Henry Schein, Inc.; *U.S. Public*, pg. 1026

HENRY SCHEIN, INC. - MILWAUKEE, WI—See Henry Schein, Inc.; *U.S. Public*, pg. 1026

HENRY SCHEIN, INC. - MINNEAPOLIS/ST. PAUL, MN—See Henry Schein, Inc.; *U.S. Public*, pg. 1026

HENRY SCHEIN, INC.-MURRAY, UTAH—See Henry Schein, Inc.; *U.S. Public*, pg. 1027

HENRY SCHEIN, INC. - NASHVILLE, TN—See Henry Schein, Inc.; *U.S. Public*, pg. 1026

HENRY SCHEIN, INC.-NEVADA RENO—See Henry Schein, Inc.; *U.S. Public*, pg. 1027

HENRY SCHEIN, INC.-NEVADA SPARKS—See Henry Schein, Inc.; *U.S. Public*, pg. 1027

HENRY SCHEIN, INC.-NEW MEXICO—See Henry Schein, Inc.; *U.S. Public*, pg. 1027

HENRY SCHEIN, INC.-NEW YORK—See Henry Schein, Inc.; *U.S. Public*, pg. 1027

HENRY SCHEIN, INC.-NEW YORK—See Henry Schein, Inc.; *U.S. Public*, pg. 1027

HENRY SCHEIN, INC.-NORTH CAROLINA—See Henry Schein, Inc.; *U.S. Public*, pg. 1027

HENRY SCHEIN, INC.-NORTH CAROLINA—See Henry Schein, Inc.; *U.S. Public*, pg. 1027

HENRY SCHEIN, INC. - OMAHA, NE—See Henry Schein, Inc.; *U.S. Public*, pg. 1026

HENRY SCHEIN, INC. - ORANGE, CA—See Henry Schein, Inc.; *U.S. Public*, pg. 1026

HENRY SCHEIN, INC.-PENNSYLVANIA—See Henry Schein, Inc.; *U.S. Public*, pg. 1027

HENRY SCHEIN, INC.-PENNSYLVANIA—See Henry Schein, Inc.; *U.S. Public*, pg. 1027

HENRY SCHEIN, INC. - PHILADELPHIA, PA—See Henry Schein, Inc.; *U.S. Public*, pg. 1026

HENRY QUENTZEL PLUMBING SUPPLY CO., INC. CORPORATE AFFILIATIONS

HENRY SCHEIN, INC. - RICHMOND, VA—See Henry Schein, Inc.; *U.S. Public*, pg. 1026
HENRY SCHEIN, INC. - SAN ANTONIO, TX—See Henry Schein, Inc.; *U.S. Public*, pg. 1026
HENRY SCHEIN, INC. - SAN FRANCISCO—See Henry Schein, Inc.; *U.S. Public*, pg. 1026
HENRY SCHEIN, INC. - SAN JOSE, CA—See Henry Schein, Inc.; *U.S. Public*, pg. 1026
HENRY SCHEIN, INC. - SOLON—See Henry Schein, Inc.; *U.S. Public*, pg. 1026
HENRY SCHEIN, INC.; *U.S. Public*, pg. 1025
HENRY SCHEIN, INC.—See Henry Schein, Inc.; *U.S. Public*, pg. 1026
HENRY SCHEIN, INC.—See Henry Schein, Inc.; *U.S. Public*, pg. 1026
HENRY SCHEIN, INC. - TAMPA, FL—See Henry Schein, Inc.; *U.S. Public*, pg. 1026
HENRY SCHEIN, INC.-TEXAS—See Henry Schein, Inc.; *U.S. Public*, pg. 1027
HENRY SCHEIN, INC.-TOLEDO, OHIO—See Henry Schein, Inc.; *U.S. Public*, pg. 1026
HENRY SCHEIN, INC. - TULSA, OK—See Henry Schein, Inc.; *U.S. Public*, pg. 1026
HENRY SCHEIN, INC.-WILSONVILLE, OREGON—See Henry Schein, Inc.; *U.S. Public*, pg. 1027
HENRY SCHEIN, INC. - WISCONSIN—See Henry Schein, Inc.; *U.S. Public*, pg. 1026
HENRY SCHEIN MEDICAL—See Henry Schein, Inc.; *U.S. Public*, pg. 1025
HENRY SCHEIN MEDICAL—See Henry Schein, Inc.; *U.S. Public*, pg. 1026
HENRY SCHEIN ONE AUSTRALIA—See Henry Schein, Inc.; *U.S. Public*, pg. 1025
HENRY SCHEIN ONE, LLC—See Henry Schein, Inc.; *U.S. Public*, pg. 1025
HENRY SCHEIN PRACTICE SOLUTIONS INC.—See Henry Schein, Inc.; *U.S. Public*, pg. 1026
HENRY SCHEIN REGIONAL LIMITED—See Henry Schein, Inc.; *U.S. Public*, pg. 1026
HENRY SCHEIN REGIONAL PTY LTD—See Henry Schein, Inc.; *U.S. Public*, pg. 1026
HENRY SCHEIN SUNSHINE (BEIJING) MEDICAL DEVICE CO., LTD.—See Henry Schein, Inc.; *U.S. Public*, pg. 1026
HENRY SCHEIN TRADING (SHANGHAI) CO., LTD.—See Henry Schein, Inc.; *U.S. Public*, pg. 1026
HENRY SCHEIN UK HOLDINGS LIMITED—See Henry Schein, Inc.; *U.S. Public*, pg. 1026
HENRY'S FOODS, INC.—See AMCON Distributing Company; *U.S. Public*, pg. 93
HENRY S. MILLER BROKERAGE, LLC—See Henry S. Miller Management Corp.; *U.S. Private*, pg. 1919
HENRY S. MILLER COMMERCIAL AUSTIN, INC.—See Henry S. Miller Management Corp.; *U.S. Private*, pg. 1919
HENRY S. MILLER CONSULTING, LLC—See Henry S. Miller Management Corp.; *U.S. Private*, pg. 1919
HENRY S. MILLER FUNDING CORPORATION—See Henry S. Miller Management Corp.; *U.S. Private*, pg. 1919
HENRY S. MILLER INVESTMENT SERVICES, LLC—See Henry S. Miller Management Corp.; *U.S. Private*, pg. 1919
HENRY S. MILLER MANAGEMENT CORP.; *U.S. Private*, pg. 1919
HENRY S. MILLER REALTY MANAGEMENT, LLC—See Henry S. Miller Management Corp.; *U.S. Private*, pg. 1919
HENRY S. MILLER REALTY SERVICES, LLC—See Henry S. Miller Management Corp.; *U.S. Private*, pg. 1919
HENRY'S TACKLE LLC—See Peak Global Holdings, LLC; *U.S. Private*, pg. 3123
HENRY STREET SETTLEMENT; *U.S. Private*, pg. 1919
HENRY'S WRECKER SERVICE FAIRFAX COUNTY; *U.S. Private*, pg. 1919
HENRY TECHNOLOGIES CANADA—See Hendricks Holding Company, Inc.; *U.S. Private*, pg. 1915
HENRY TECHNOLOGIES - CHATHAM PLANT—See Hendricks Holding Company, Inc.; *U.S. Private*, pg. 1915
HENRY-TECHNOLOGIES GMBH—See Hendricks Holding Company, Inc.; *U.S. Private*, pg. 1915
HENRY TECHNOLOGIES, INC.—See Hendricks Holding Company, Inc.; *U.S. Private*, pg. 1915
HENRY TECHNOLOGIES LIMITED—See Hendricks Holding Company, Inc.; *U.S. Private*, pg. 1915
HENRY-THE ART OF LIVING GMBH—See DO & CO Aktiengesellschaft; *Int'l*, pg. 2152
HENRY TROEMNER LLC—See Mettler-Toledo International, Inc.; *U.S. Public*, pg. 1432
HENRY VON OESEN & ASSOCIATES, INC.—See Littlejohn & Co., LLC; *U.S. Private*, pg. 2469
THE HENRY WINE GROUP—See The Winebow Group, LLC; *U.S. Private*, pg. 4137
HENRY WURST INC.; *U.S. Private*, pg. 1919
HENSALL DISTRICT CO-OPERATIVE, INC.; *Int'l*, pg. 3355
HENSCHEL STEINAU INC.; *U.S. Private*, pg. 1919
HENSEL AG ELEKTROTECHNISCHE UNTERNEHMUNGEN—See BKW AG; *Int'l*, pg. 1055

HENSEL PHELPS CONSTRUCTION CO.; *U.S. Private*, pg. 1919
HENSEL PHELPS INTERNATIONAL LLC—See Hensel Phelps Construction Co.; *U.S. Private*, pg. 1920
HENSLEY & CO.; *U.S. Private*, pg. 1920
HENSLEY INDUSTRIES, INC. - ATTACHMENTS DIVISION—See Komatsu Ltd.; *Int'l*, pg. 4235
HENSLEY INDUSTRIES, INC.—See Komatsu Ltd.; *Int'l*, pg. 4235
HENSLEY LINGFENG CO., LTD.—See Komatsu Ltd.; *Int'l*, pg. 4235
HENSOLDT AG; *Int'l*, pg. 3355
HENSOLDT AUSTRALIA PTY LTD—See HENSOLDT AG; *Int'l*, pg. 3355
HENSOLDT CYBER GMBH—See HENSOLDT AG; *Int'l*, pg. 3355
HENSOLDT DO BRASIL SEGURANCA E DEFESA ELECTRONICA E OPTICA LTDA—See HENSOLDT AG; *Int'l*, pg. 3355
HENSOLDT FRANCE S.A.S.—See HENSOLDT AG; *Int'l*, pg. 3355
HENSOLDT HOLDING GERMANY GMBH—See HENSOLDT AG; *Int'l*, pg. 3355
HENSOLDT OPTRONICS GMBH—See HENSOLDT AG; *Int'l*, pg. 3355
HENSOLDT OPTRONICS (PTY) LTD.—See HENSOLDT AG; *Int'l*, pg. 3355
HENSOLDT PRIVATE LTD.—See HENSOLDT AG; *Int'l*, pg. 3355
HENSOLDT SENSORS GMBH—See HENSOLDT AG; *Int'l*, pg. 3355
HENSOLDT SINGAPORE PTE LTD.—See HENSOLDT AG; *Int'l*, pg. 3355
HENSOLDT SPACE CONSULTING S.A.S.—See HENSOLDT AG; *Int'l*, pg. 3356
HENSON FARM SUPPLY INC.—See Tym Corporation; *Int'l*, pg. 7995
HENSON FORD INC.—See Henson Motor Company Inc.; *U.S. Private*, pg. 1920
HENSON LUMBER LTD.; *U.S. Private*, pg. 1920
HENSON MOTOR COMPANY INC.; *U.S. Private*, pg. 1920
HENSON SALES GROUP LTD.—See Cinpak, Inc.; *U.S. Private*, pg. 898
HENSON TIMBER PRODUCTS CORP.—See Stonecutter Mills Corp.; *U.S. Private*, pg. 3828
H ENTERPRISES INTERNATIONAL INC.; *U.S. Private*, pg. 1822
HENTGES GLASS COMPANY INC.—See Brin Northwestern Glass Company Inc.; *U.S. Private*, pg. 654
HENTSCHELL & ASSOCIATES INC.; *U.S. Private*, pg. 1920
HENTY OIL LIMITED—See World Kinect Corporation; *U.S. Public*, pg. 2380
HENTZEN COATINGS INC.; *U.S. Private*, pg. 1920
HENZETEAM GMBH; *Int'l*, pg. 3356
HEOSCONT HUNGARIA KFT.—See SWARCO AG; *Int'l*, pg. 7360
HEPAC B.V.—See Darling Ingredients Inc.; *U.S. Public*, pg. 634
HEPACO INC.—See Gryphon Investors, LLC; *U.S. Private*, pg. 1798
HEPAHOPE, INC.; *U.S. Private*, pg. 1920
HEPAHOPE KOREA, INC.; *Int'l*, pg. 3356
H-E PARTS INTERNATIONAL LLC—See Hitachi, Ltd.; *Int'l*, pg. 3415
HEPCO HEAVY EQUIPMENT PRODUCTION COMPANY; *Int'l*, pg. 3356
HEP EL DORADO LLC—See HF Sinclair Corporation; *U.S. Public*, pg. 1033
HEP ENERGIJA D.O.O.—See Hrvatska elektroprivreda d.d.; *Int'l*, pg. 3502
HEP ESCO D.O.O.—See Hrvatska elektroprivreda d.d.; *Int'l*, pg. 3502
HEP GMBH—See HEP Tech Co., Ltd.; *Int'l*, pg. 3356
HEPHAESTUS HOLDINGS LIMITED—See ITI Industrial Investments (UK) Ltd.; *Int'l*, pg. 3833
HEPHAESTUS HOLDINGS LIMITED; *Int'l*, pg. 3356
HEPHAIST SEIKO CO., LTD. - AKITA FACTORY—See Heheist Co., Ltd.; *Int'l*, pg. 3308
HEPHAIST SEIKO (SHANGHAI) CO., LTD.—See Heheist Co., Ltd.; *Int'l*, pg. 3308
HEPION PHARMACEUTICALS, INC.; *U.S. Public*, pg. 1027
HEPITES SA; *Int'l*, pg. 3356
HEP MATERIALS CORP.; *U.S. Private*, pg. 1920
HEP-NOC VELIKA—See Hrvatska elektroprivreda d.d.; *Int'l*, pg. 3502
HEP-OBNOVLJIVI IZVORI ENERGIJE D.O.O.—See Hrvatska elektroprivreda d.d.; *Int'l*, pg. 3502
HEP-ODMOR I REKREACIJA D.O.O.—See Hrvatska elektroprivreda d.d.; *Int'l*, pg. 3502
HEP-OPERATOR DISTRIBUCIJSKOG SUSTAVA D.O.O.—See Hrvatska elektroprivreda d.d.; *Int'l*, pg. 3502
HEP-OPERATOR PRIJENOSNOG SUSTAVA D.O.O.—See Hrvatska elektroprivreda d.d.; *Int'l*, pg. 3502
HEP OPSKRBA D.O.O.—See Hrvatska elektroprivreda d.d.; *Int'l*, pg. 3502

HEP-PLIN D.O.O.—See Hrvatska elektroprivreda d.d.; *Int'l*, pg. 3502
HEP-PROIZVODNJA D.O.O.—See Hrvatska elektroprivreda d.d.; *Int'l*, pg. 3502
H.E. PROPERTIES, INC.—See Hyatt Hotels Corporation; *U.S. Public*, pg. 1077
HEPTA GROUP PUBLICIS—See Publicis Groupe S.A.; *Int'l*, pg. 6099
HEPTARES THERAPEUTICS LTD.—See Nxera Pharma Co., Ltd.; *Int'l*, pg. 5499
HEP TECH CO., LTD.; *Int'l*, pg. 3356
HEP-TELEKOMUNIKACIJE D.O.O.—See Hrvatska elektroprivreda d.d.; *Int'l*, pg. 3502
HEP-TOPLINARSTVO D.O.O.—See Hrvatska elektroprivreda d.d.; *Int'l*, pg. 3502
HEP-TRGOVINA D.O.O.—See Hrvatska elektroprivreda d.d.; *Int'l*, pg. 3502
HEP-UPRAVLJANJE IMOVINOM D.O.O.—See Hrvatska elektroprivreda d.d.; *Int'l*, pg. 3502
HEPWORTH BUILDING PRODUCTS LIMITED—See Bharti Enterprises Limited; *Int'l*, pg. 1012
HEPWORTH PME LLC; *Int'l*, pg. 3356
HEPWORTH PME QATAR WLL—See Hepworth PME LLC; *Int'l*, pg. 3356
HEPWORTH WLL—See Hepworth PME LLC; *Int'l*, pg. 3356
HERACLES GENERAL CEMENT COMPANY S.A.—See Holcim Ltd.; *Int'l*, pg. 3446
HERACLES SA; *Int'l*, pg. 3357
HERA COMM MEDITERRANEA S.R.L.—See Hera S.p.A.; *Int'l*, pg. 3356
HERA COMM S.P.A.—See Hera S.p.A.; *Int'l*, pg. 3356
HERA ENERGIE BOLOGNA S.R.L.—See Hera S.p.A.; *Int'l*, pg. 3356
HERAEUS AMBA AUSTRALIA PTY. LTD.—See Heraeus Holding GmbH; *Int'l*, pg. 3357
HERAEUS AMBA LTD.—See Heraeus Holding GmbH; *Int'l*, pg. 3357
HERAEUS CATALYSTS (DANYANG) CO. LTD.—See Heraeus Holding GmbH; *Int'l*, pg. 3357
HERAEUS CONTACT MATERIALS DIVISION—See Heraeus Holding GmbH; *Int'l*, pg. 3358
HERAEUS CZ S.R.O.—See Heraeus Holding GmbH; *Int'l*, pg. 3357
HERAEUS DENTAL KOREA CO., LTD.—See Mitsui Chemicals, Inc.; *Int'l*, pg. 4981
HERAEUS DEUTSCHLAND GMBH & CO. KG—See Heraeus Holding GmbH; *Int'l*, pg. 3357
HERAEUS DRIJFHOUT BV—See Heraeus Holding GmbH; *Int'l*, pg. 3357
HERAEUS ELECTRO-NITE AB—See Heraeus Holding GmbH; *Int'l*, pg. 3357
HERAEUS ELECTRO-NITE (AUST.) PTY. LTD.—See Heraeus Holding GmbH; *Int'l*, pg. 3357
HERAEUS ELECTRO-NITE CANADA LTD.—See Heraeus Holding GmbH; *Int'l*, pg. 3357
HERAEUS ELECTRO-NITE CHELYABINSK LLC—See Heraeus Holding GmbH; *Int'l*, pg. 3357
HERAEUS ELECTRO-NITE CO., LLC—See Heraeus Holding GmbH; *Int'l*, pg. 3357
HERAEUS ELECTRO-NITE ESPANA, S.L.—See Heraeus Holding GmbH; *Int'l*, pg. 3357
HERAEUS ELECTRO-NITE FRANCE S.A.R.L.—See Heraeus Holding GmbH; *Int'l*, pg. 3357
HERAEUS ELECTRO-NITE INSTRUMENTOS LTDA.—See Heraeus Holding GmbH; *Int'l*, pg. 3357
HERAEUS ELECTRO-NITE INTERNATIONAL N.V.—See Heraeus Holding GmbH; *Int'l*, pg. 3357
HERAEUS ELECTRO-NITE ITALY S.R.L.—See Heraeus Holding GmbH; *Int'l*, pg. 3357
HERAEUS ELECTRO-NITE JAPAN LTD.—See Heraeus Holding GmbH; *Int'l*, pg. 3357
HERAEUS ELECTRO-NITE MEXICANA S.A. DE C.V.—See Heraeus Holding GmbH; *Int'l*, pg. 3357
HERAEUS ELECTRO-NITE POLSKA SP. Z O.O.—See Heraeus Holding GmbH; *Int'l*, pg. 3357
HERAEUS ELECTRO-NITE SHENYANG CO. LTD.—See Heraeus Holding GmbH; *Int'l*, pg. 3357
HERAEUS ELECTRO-NITE—See Heraeus Holding GmbH; *Int'l*, pg. 3357
HERAEUS ELECTRO-NITE TAIWAN LTD.—See Heraeus Holding GmbH; *Int'l*, pg. 3357
HERAEUS ELECTRO-NITE (U.K.) LTD.—See Heraeus Holding GmbH; *Int'l*, pg. 3357
HERAEUS ELECTRO-NITE UKRAINA LLC—See Heraeus Holding GmbH; *Int'l*, pg. 3357
HERAEUS HOLDING GMBH; *Int'l*, pg. 3357
HERAEUS INC.—See Heraeus Holding GmbH; *Int'l*, pg. 3357
HERAEUS KULZER AUSTRALIA PTY. LTD.—See Heraeus Holding GmbH; *Int'l*, pg. 3357
HERAEUS KULZER AUSTRIA GMBH—See Mitsui Chemicals, Inc.; *Int'l*, pg. 4981
HERAEUS KULZER BENELUX B.V.—See Mitsui Chemicals, Inc.; *Int'l*, pg. 4981
HERAEUS KULZER DENTAL LTD.—See Mitsui Chemicals, Inc.; *Int'l*, pg. 4981
HERAEUS KULZER GMBH—See Mitsui Chemicals, Inc.; *Int'l*, pg. 4981

COMPANY NAME INDEX

HERAEUS KULZER HUNGARY KFT.—See Mitsui Chemicals, Inc.; *Int'l*, pg. 4981
HERAEUS KULZER IBERIA—See Mitsui Chemicals, Inc.; *Int'l*, pg. 4981
HERAEUS KULZER JAPAN KABUSHIKI KAISHA—See Mitsui Chemicals, Inc.; *Int'l*, pg. 4981
HERAEUS KULZER LLC—See Mitsui Chemicals, Inc.; *Int'l*, pg. 4981
HERAEUS KULZER LTD.—See Mitsui Chemicals, Inc.; *Int'l*, pg. 4981
HERAEUS KULZER MEXICO S.A. DE C.V.—See Mitsui Chemicals, Inc.; *Int'l*, pg. 4981
HERAEUS KULZER NORDIC AB—See Mitsui Chemicals, Inc.; *Int'l*, pg. 4981
HERAEUS KULZER SOUTH AMERICA LTDA.—See Mitsui Chemicals, Inc.; *Int'l*, pg. 4981
HERAEUS KULZER S.R.L.—See Mitsui Chemicals, Inc.; *Int'l*, pg. 4981
HERAEUS LTD.—See Heraeus Holding GmbH; *Int'l*, pg. 3357
HERAEUS MATERIALS S.A.—See Heraeus Holding GmbH; *Int'l*, pg. 3357
HERAEUS MATERIALS SINGAPORE PTE. LTD. - CONTACT MATERIALS—See Heraeus Holding GmbH; *Int'l*, pg. 3358
HERAEUS MATERIALS SINGAPORE PTE. LTD.—See Heraeus Holding GmbH; *Int'l*, pg. 3357
HERAEUS MATERIALS TECHNOLOGY NORTH AMERICA LLC—See Heraeus Holding GmbH; *Int'l*, pg. 3357
HERAEUS MATERIALS TECHNOLOGY SHANGHAI LTD.—See Heraeus Holding GmbH; *Int'l*, pg. 3357
HERAEUS MATERIALS TECHNOLOGY TAIWAN LTD.—See Heraeus Holding GmbH; *Int'l*, pg. 3357
HERAEUS MEDICAL AUSTRALIA PTY LIMITED—See Heraeus Holding GmbH; *Int'l*, pg. 3358
HERAEUS MEDICAL COMPONENTS CARIBE—See Heraeus Holding GmbH; *Int'l*, pg. 3358
HERAEUS MEDICAL COMPONENTS, INC.—See Heraeus Holding GmbH; *Int'l*, pg. 3358
HERAEUS MEDICAL GMBH—See Heraeus Holding GmbH; *Int'l*, pg. 3358
HERAEUS METAL PROCESSING, LLC—See Heraeus Holding GmbH; *Int'l*, pg. 3357
HERAEUS METAL PROCESSING, LTD.—See Heraeus Holding GmbH; *Int'l*, pg. 3358
HERAEUS METALS HONG KONG LTD.—See Heraeus Holding GmbH; *Int'l*, pg. 3358
HERAEUS METALS NEW YORK LLC—See Heraeus Holding GmbH; *Int'l*, pg. 3357
HERAEUS METALS (SHANGHAI) CO., LTD.—See Heraeus Holding GmbH; *Int'l*, pg. 3358
HERAEUS NOBLELIGHT AMERICA LLC—See AEA Investors LP; *U.S. Private*, pg. 113
HERAEUS NOBLELIGHT ANALYTICS LTD.—See AEA Investors LP; *U.S. Private*, pg. 113
HERAEUS ORIENTAL HITEC CO. LTD.—See Heraeus Holding GmbH; *Int'l*, pg. 3358
HERAEUS PRECIOUS METALS MANAGEMENT INC.—See Heraeus Holding GmbH; *Int'l*, pg. 3357
HERAEUS PRECIOUS METALS NORTH AMERICA CONSHOHOCKEN LLC—See Heraeus Holding GmbH; *Int'l*, pg. 3357
HERAEUS PRECIOUS METALS NORTH AMERICA DAYCHEM LLC—See Heraeus Holding GmbH; *Int'l*, pg. 3357
HERAEUS QUARTZ AMERICA, LLC—See Heraeus Holding GmbH; *Int'l*, pg. 3358
HERAEUS QUARTZ UK LTD.—See Heraeus Holding GmbH; *Int'l*, pg. 3358
HERAEUS QUARZGLAS GMBH & CO. KG—See Heraeus Holding GmbH; *Int'l*, pg. 3358
HERAEUS RECYCLING TECHNOLOGY (TAICANG) CO., LTD.—See Heraeus Holding GmbH; *Int'l*, pg. 3358
HERAEUS S.A.—See Heraeus Holding GmbH; *Int'l*, pg. 3358
HERAEUS SENSOR TECHNOLOGY GMBH—See Heraeus Holding GmbH; *Int'l*, pg. 3358
HERAEUS SHIN-ETSU AMERICA, INC.—See Shin-Etsu Chemical Co. Ltd.; *Int'l*, pg. 6838
HERAEUS SHINETSU QUARTZ CHINA INC.—See Heraeus Holding GmbH; *Int'l*, pg. 3358
HERAEUS SOUTH AFRICA (PTY.) LTD.—See Heraeus Holding GmbH; *Int'l*, pg. 3358
HERAEUS S.P.A.—See Heraeus Holding GmbH; *Int'l*, pg. 3358
HERAEUS ZHAOYUAN CHANGSHU LTD.—See Heraeus Holding GmbH; *Int'l*, pg. 3358
HERAEUS ZHAOYUAN PRECIOUS METAL MATERIALS CO. LTD.—See Heraeus Holding GmbH; *Int'l*, pg. 3358
HERAKLES S.A.—See Safran SA; *Int'l*, pg. 6473
HERAKLES SHIPPING CO., LTD—See Thoresen Thai Agencies Public Company Limited; *Int'l*, pg. 7718
THE HERALD AND WEEKLY TIMES PTY. LIMITED—See News Corporation; *U.S. Public*, pg. 1520
HERALD DATANETICS LIMITED—See Herald Holdings Limited; *Int'l*, pg. 3358
THE HERALD-DISPATCH—See HD Media Company, LLC; *U.S. Private*, pg. 1890

HERALD ELECTRONICS LIMITED—See Herald Holdings Limited; *Int'l*, pg. 3358
HERALD ENGINEERING SERVICES INC.—See Herald Holdings Limited; *Int'l*, pg. 3358
HERALD HOLDINGS LIMITED; *Int'l*, pg. 3358
HERALD HOUSEWARE LIMITED—See Herald Holdings Limited; *Int'l*, pg. 3358
THE HERALD, INC.; *U.S. Private*, pg. 4051
HERALD INVESTMENT MANAGEMENT LIMITED; *Int'l*, pg. 3358
HERALD INVESTMENTS (CHINA) COMPANY LIMITED—See Herald Holdings Limited; *Int'l*, pg. 3358
HERALD MEDIA INC.; *U.S. Private*, pg. 1920
HERALD METAL AND PLASTIC WORKS LIMITED—See Herald Holdings Limited; *Int'l*, pg. 3358
HERALD NATIONAL BANK—See BankUnited, Inc.; *U.S. Public*, pg. 274
THE HERALD NEWS—See Gannett Co., Inc.; *U.S. Public*, pg. 903
THE HERALD NEWS—See Chicago Public Media, Inc.; *U.S. Private*, pg. 879
HERALDO DE ARAGON SA—See Henneo Media, SA; *Int'l*, pg. 3354
HERALD OFFICE SUPPLY COMPANY; *U.S. Private*, pg. 1920
HERALD RESOURCES LIMITED—See PT Bumi Resources Tbk; *Int'l*, pg. 6031
HERALD & REVIEW—See Lee Enterprises, Incorporated; *U.S. Public*, pg. 1299
THE HERALD—See Chatham Asset Management, LLC; *U.S. Private*, pg. 867
HERALD SQUARE DIALYSIS , LLC—See Nautic Partners, LLC; *U.S. Private*, pg. 2870
HERALD TECHNOLOGY INC.—See Herald Holdings Limited; *Int'l*, pg. 3358
HERALD TIMES REPORTER—See Gannett Co., Inc.; *U.S. Public*, pg. 898
HERALD-TRIBUNE COMPANY—See Gannett Co., Inc.; *U.S. Public*, pg. 905
THE HERALD & WEEKLY TIMES LTD.—See News Corporation; *U.S. Public*, pg. 1520
HERA LUCE S.R.L.—See Hera S.p.A.; *Int'l*, pg. 3356
HERAMBIENTE SPA—See Hera S.p.A.; *Int'l*, pg. 3356
HERAMED LIMITED; *Int'l*, pg. 3358
HERANBA INDUSTRIES LIMITED; *Int'l*, pg. 3358
HERANTIS PHARMA PLC; *Int'l*, pg. 3359
HERAS-ADRONIT GMBH—See CRH plc; *Int'l*, pg. 1844
HERAS B.V.—See Equistone Partners Europe Limited; *Int'l*, pg. 2486
HERAS CLOTURE S.A.R.L.—See CRH plc; *Int'l*, pg. 1843
HERA SERVIZI ENERGIA SRL—See Hera S.p.A.; *Int'l*, pg. 3356
HERAS MOBILZAUN GMBH—See CRH plc; *Int'l*, pg. 1844
HERA S.P.A.; *Int'l*, pg. 3356
HERAS SKS GMBH—See CRH plc; *Int'l*, pg. 1844
HERA TRADING S.R.L.—See Hera S.p.A.; *Int'l*, pg. 3356
HERBA BANGKOK, S.L.—See Ebro Foods S.A.; *Int'l*, pg. 2286
HERBA CHEMOSAN APOTHEKER-AG—See McKesson Corporation; *U.S. Public*, pg. 1408
HERBACOS RECORDATI S.R.O.—See Recordati S.p.A.; *Int'l*, pg. 6239
HERBA EGYPT RICEMILLS, LTD.—See Ebro Foods S.A.; *Int'l*, pg. 2286
HERBAFOOD INGREDIENTS GMBH—See Herbstreith & Fox KG Pektin-Fabriken; *Int'l*, pg. 3360
HERBA INGREDIENTS, B.V.—See Ebro Foods S.A.; *Int'l*, pg. 2286
HERBAL DISPATCH INC.; *Int'l*, pg. 3359
HERBALIFE AUSTRALASIA PTY. LTD.—See Herbalife Nutrition Ltd.; *Int'l*, pg. 3359
HERBALIFE BELA, LLC—See Herbalife Nutrition Ltd.; *Int'l*, pg. 3359
HERBALIFE BOLIVIA, LTDA.—See Herbalife Nutrition Ltd.; *Int'l*, pg. 3359
HERBALIFE (CAMBODIA) CO., LTD.—See Herbalife Nutrition Ltd.; *Int'l*, pg. 3359
HERBALIFE CHINA, LLC—See Herbalife Nutrition Ltd.; *Int'l*, pg. 3359
HERBALIFE CZECH REPUBLIC, S.R.O—See Herbalife Nutrition Ltd.; *Int'l*, pg. 3359
HERBALIFE DEL ECUADOR, S.A.—See Herbalife Nutrition Ltd.; *Int'l*, pg. 3359
HERBALIFE DENMARK APS—See Herbalife Nutrition Ltd.; *Int'l*, pg. 3359
HERBALIFE EUROPE LIMITED—See Herbalife Nutrition Ltd.; *Int'l*, pg. 3359
HERBALIFE INTERNACIONAL DE MEXICO, S.A. DE C.V.—See Herbalife Nutrition Ltd.; *Int'l*, pg. 3359
HERBALIFE INTERNAITONAL (THAILAND), LTD.—See Herbalife Nutrition Ltd.; *Int'l*, pg. 3359
HERBALIFE INTERNATIONAL ARGENTINA, S.A.—See Herbalife Nutrition Ltd.; *Int'l*, pg. 3359
HERBALIFE INTERNATIONAL COMMUNICATIONS, INC.—See Herbalife Nutrition Ltd.; *Int'l*, pg. 3359
HERBALIFE INTERNATIONAL DEL COLOMBIA—See Herbalife Nutrition Ltd.; *Int'l*, pg. 3359
HERBALIFE INTERNATIONAL DEL ECUADOR, S.A.—See Herbalife Nutrition Ltd.; *Int'l*, pg. 3359

HERBERT C. HAYNES INC.

HERBALIFE INTERNATIONAL DE MEXICO, S.A.DE C.V.—See Herbalife Nutrition Ltd.; *Int'l*, pg. 3360
HERBALIFE INTERNATIONAL DEUTSCHLAND GMBH—See Herbalife Nutrition Ltd.; *Int'l*, pg. 3359
HERBALIFE INTERNATIONAL DO BRASIL LTDA.—See Herbalife Nutrition Ltd.; *Int'l*, pg. 3359
HERBALIFE INTERNATIONAL ESPANA, S.A.—See Herbalife Nutrition Ltd.; *Int'l*, pg. 3360
HERBALIFE INTERNATIONAL FINLAND OY—See Herbalife Nutrition Ltd.; *Int'l*, pg. 3359
HERBALIFE INTERNATIONAL FRANCE S.A.—See Herbalife Nutrition Ltd.; *Int'l*, pg. 3360
HERBALIFE INTERNATIONAL GREECE S.A.—See Herbalife Nutrition Ltd.; *Int'l*, pg. 3359
HERBALIFE INTERNATIONAL-HONG KONG—See Herbalife Nutrition Ltd.; *Int'l*, pg. 3360
HERBALIFE INTERNATIONAL ISRAEL LTD.—See Herbalife Nutrition Ltd.; *Int'l*, pg. 3360
HERBALIFE INTERNATIONAL LUXEMBOURG NETHERLANDS BRANCH—See Herbalife Nutrition Ltd.; *Int'l*, pg. 3360
HERBALIFE INTERNATIONAL OF AMERICA, INC.—See Herbalife Nutrition Ltd.; *Int'l*, pg. 3359
HERBALIFE INTERNATIONAL OF AMERICA, INC. - TORRANCE—See Herbalife Nutrition Ltd.; *Int'l*, pg. 3360
HERBALIFE INTERNATIONAL OF HONG KONG LIMITED—See Herbalife Nutrition Ltd.; *Int'l*, pg. 3360
HERBALIFE INTERNATIONAL OF ISRAEL (1990) LTD.—See Herbalife Nutrition Ltd.; *Int'l*, pg. 3360
HERBALIFE INTERNATIONAL PHILIPPINES—See Herbalife Nutrition Ltd.; *Int'l*, pg. 3360
HERBALIFE INTERNATIONAL RS LLC—See Herbalife Nutrition Ltd.; *Int'l*, pg. 3359
HERBALIFE INTERNATIONAL, S.A.-PORTUGAL—See Herbalife Nutrition Ltd.; *Int'l*, pg. 3360
HERBALIFE INTERNATIONAL SOUTH AFRICA, LTD.—See Herbalife Nutrition Ltd.; *Int'l*, pg. 3359
HERBALIFE INTERNATIONAL (THAILAND), LTD.—See Herbalife Nutrition Ltd.; *Int'l*, pg. 3359
HERBALIFE ITALIA S.P.A.—See Herbalife Nutrition Ltd.; *Int'l*, pg. 3360
HERBALIFE KAZAKHSTAN LLP—See Herbalife Nutrition Ltd.; *Int'l*, pg. 3360
HERBALIFE NORWAY PRODUCTS AS—See Herbalife Nutrition Ltd.; *Int'l*, pg. 3360
HERBALIFE NUTRITION LTD.; *Int'l*, pg. 3359
HERBALIFE (N.Z.) LIMITED—See Herbalife Nutrition Ltd.; *Int'l*, pg. 3359
HERBALIFE OF CANADA LTD.—See Herbalife Nutrition Ltd.; *Int'l*, pg. 3360
HERBALIFE OF GHANA LIMITED—See Herbalife Nutrition Ltd.; *Int'l*, pg. 3360
HERBALIFE OF JAPAN K.K.—See Herbalife Nutrition Ltd.; *Int'l*, pg. 3360
HERBALIFE PARAGUAY S.R.L.—See Herbalife Nutrition Ltd.; *Int'l*, pg. 3360
HERBALIFE PERU S.R.L.—See Herbalife Nutrition Ltd.; *Int'l*, pg. 3360
HERBALIFE POLSKA SP.Z.O.O—See Herbalife Nutrition Ltd.; *Int'l*, pg. 3360
HERBALIFE RO S.R.L.—See Herbalife Nutrition Ltd.; *Int'l*, pg. 3360
HERBALIFE SLOVAKIA, S.R.O.—See Herbalife Nutrition Ltd.; *Int'l*, pg. 3360
HERBALIFE TAIWAN, INC.—See Herbalife Nutrition Ltd.; *Int'l*, pg. 3360
HERBALIFE (U.K.) LIMITED—See Herbalife Nutrition Ltd.; *Int'l*, pg. 3359
HERBALIFE VIETNAM SMLLC—See Herbalife Nutrition Ltd.; *Int'l*, pg. 3360
HERBAL WELLNESS CENTER, LLC—See Vext Science, Inc.; *Int'l*, pg. 8182
HERBA NUTRICION, S.L.U.—See Ebro Foods S.A.; *Int'l*, pg. 2286
HERBAPOL LUBLIN S.A.; *Int'l*, pg. 3360
HERBA RICEMILLS ROM S.R.L.—See Ebro Foods S.A.; *Int'l*, pg. 2286
HERBA RICEMILLS, S.L.U.—See Ebro Foods S.A.; *Int'l*, pg. 2286
HERB CHAMBERS HONDA OF SEEKONK—See Herb Chambers of Somerville, Inc.; *U.S. Private*, pg. 1920
HERB CHAMBERS OF NATICK, INC.—See Herb Chambers of Somerville, Inc.; *U.S. Private*, pg. 1920
HERB CHAMBERS OF SOMERVILLE, INC.; *U.S. Private*, pg. 1920
HERB EASLEY MOTORS INC.; *U.S. Private*, pg. 1920
HERBEIN + COMPANY, INC.; *U.S. Private*, pg. 1920
H. ERBEN LIMITED—See Keystone Group, L.P.; *U.S. Private*, pg. 2297
HERBER ENGINEERING AB—See Duc Long Gia Lai Group JSC; *Int'l*, pg. 2222
HERBERGER'S, INC.—See The Bon Ton Stores, Inc.; *U.S. Public*, pg. 2041
HERBERT (1) PLC—See Paragon Banking Group PLC; *Int'l*, pg. 5735
HERBERT C. HAYNES INC.; *U.S. Private*, pg. 1920
HERBERT KANNEGIESSER GES. MBH—See Hebert Kannegiesser GmbH; *Int'l*, pg. 3306

HERBERT C. HAYNES INC.

HERBERT L. JAMISON & CO., LLC—See GTCR LLC; *U.S. Private*, pg. 1803
HERBERT PARKINSON LIMITED—See John Lewis Partnership plc; *Int'l*, pg. 3979
HERBERTS ROR AB—See Bravida Holding AB; *Int'l*, pg. 1142
HERBERT YENTIS & COMPANY; *U.S. Private*, pg. 1920
HERB GORDON MERCEDES-BENZ—See Atlantic Automotive Corp.; *U.S. Private*, pg. 371
HERB HALLMAN CHEVROLET INC.; *U.S. Private*, pg. 1920
HERBICIDES PRODUCTION COMPANY; *Int'l*, pg. 3360
HERBIE WILES INSURANCE, INC.; *U.S. Private*, pg. 1921
HERBITEC (M) SDN. BHD.—See Tanco Holdings Berhad; *Int'l*, pg. 7456
HERB JONES CHEVROLET, INC.; *U.S. Private*, pg. 1920
HERBOLD MECKESHEIM GMBH—See Hillenbrand, Inc.; *U.S. Public*, pg. 1036
HERBORIUM GROUP, INC.; *U.S. Public*, pg. 1027
HERBOS-INVEST D.D.; *Int'l*, pg. 3360
HERB PHILIPSON'S ARMY & NAVY; *U.S. Private*, pg. 1920
HERB RITSEMA CO.—See RDR Properties Inc.; *U.S. Private*, pg. 3364
HERB SHAW & SONS LIMITED; *Int'l*, pg. 3359
HERBS OF GOLD PTY LIMITED—See Vita Life Sciences Limited; *Int'l*, pg. 8257
HERBSPRO.COM—See Universal Herbs Inc.; *U.S. Private*, pg. 4305
HERBSTREITH & FOX INC.—See Herbstreith & Fox KG Pektin-Fabriken; *Int'l*, pg. 3360
HERBSTREITH & FOX KFT.—See Herbstreith & Fox KG Pektin-Fabriken; *Int'l*, pg. 3360
HERBSTREITH & FOX KG PEKTIN-FABRIKEN; *Int'l*, pg. 3360
HERBY INDUSTRIE S.A.—See Leifheit AG; *Int'l*, pg. 4446
HER CAMPUS MEDIA, LLC; *U.S. Private*, pg. 1920
HERCEGOVINA A.D.; *Int'l*, pg. 3360
HERCEGOVINA AUTO D.D.; *Int'l*, pg. 3361
HERCEGOVINAPUTEVI A.D.; *Int'l*, pg. 3361
HER CHEE INDUSTRIAL CO., LTD.; *Int'l*, pg. 3356
HERC HOLDINGS INC.; *U.S. Public*, pg. 1027
HERCON ENVIRONMENTAL CORPORATION—See Aberdeen Road Company; *U.S. Private*, pg. 38
HERCON PHARMACEUTICALS LLC—See Zydus Lifesciences Limited; *Int'l*, pg. 8700
HERC RENTALS INC.—See Herc Holdings Inc.; *U.S. Public*, pg. 1027
HERCULES ARGENTINA S.A.—See Ashland Inc.; *U.S. Public*, pg. 212
HERCULES CAPITAL, INC.; *U.S. Public*, pg. 1028
HERCULES CHEMICAL CO., INC.; *U.S. Private*, pg. 1921
HERCULES CHEMICALS SOLUTION PTE. LTD.—See Ashland Inc.; *U.S. Public*, pg. 212
HERCULES CHEMICALS (TAIWAN) CO., LTD.—See Ashland Inc.; *U.S. Public*, pg. 212
HERCULES CHILE LIMITADA—See Ashland Inc.; *U.S. Public*, pg. 212
HERCULES CLEAN TECHNOLOGY CAPITAL, INC.; *U.S. Private*, pg. 1921
HERCULES CLOROBEN CORP.—See Hercules Chemical Co., Inc.; *U.S. Private*, pg. 1921
HERCULES DO BRASIL PRODUTOS QUIMICOS LTDA.—See Ashland Inc.; *U.S. Public*, pg. 212
HERCULES DOEL BVBA—See Ashland Inc.; *U.S. Public*, pg. 212
HERCULES DRILLING COMPANY, LLC—See Hercules Offshore, Inc.; *U.S. Private*, pg. 1921
HERCULES ENGINE COMPONENTS LLC; *U.S. Private*, pg. 1921
HERCULES EQUIPAMENTOS DE PROTECAO LTDA.—See Ansell Limited; *Int'l*, pg. 478
HERCULES EUROPE BV—See Diploma PLC; *Int'l*, pg. 2128
HERCULES FENCE; *U.S. Private*, pg. 1921
HERCULES FUNDING I LLC—See Hercules Capital, Inc.; *U.S. Public*, pg. 1028
HERCULES GRUNDLAGGNING AB—See Nordstjernan AB; *Int'l*, pg. 5425
HERCULES HOISTS LIMITED—See Bajaj Auto Ltd.; *Int'l*, pg. 804
HERCULES HOLDING SPECIALTY MATERIALS B.V.—See Ashland Inc.; *U.S. Public*, pg. 212
HERCULES HYDROCARBON HOLDINGS, INC.—See Ashland Inc.; *U.S. Public*, pg. 212
HERCULES INCORPORATED—See Ashland Inc.; *U.S. Public*, pg. 212
HERCULES INDUSTRIES INC.; *U.S. Private*, pg. 1921
HERCULES MACHINERY GASES SDN BHD—See Mitsubishi Chemical Group Corporation; *Int'l*, pg. 4936
HERCULES OFFSHORE, INC.; *U.S. Private*, pg. 1921
HERCULES OFFSHORE LABUAN CORPORATION—See Hercules Offshore, Inc.; *U.S. Private*, pg. 1921
HERCULES OFFSHORE UK LIMITED—See Hercules Offshore, Inc.; *U.S. Private*, pg. 1921
HERCULES PORTUGUESA, LDA.—See Ashland Inc.; *U.S. Public*, pg. 212

HERCULES S.A. - FABRICA DE TALHERES—See Mundial S.A.; *Int'l*, pg. 5093
HERCULES SAGEMANN GMBH—See New-York Hamburger Gummi-Waaren Compagnie AG; *Int'l*, pg. 5232
HERCULES SEALING PRODUCTS INC.—See Diploma PLC; *Int'l*, pg. 2128
HERCULES SILVER CORP.; *Int'l*, pg. 3361
HERCULES SITE SERVICES PLC; *Int'l*, pg. 3361
HERCULES—See Vivendi SE; *Int'l*, pg. 8266
HERCULES STEEL COMPANY INC.; *U.S. Private*, pg. 1921
HERCULES TECHNOLOGY SBIC MANAGEMENT, LLC—See Hercules Capital, Inc.; *U.S. Public*, pg. 1028
HERCULES TIANPU CHEMICALS COMPANY LIMITED—See Ashland Inc.; *U.S. Public*, pg. 212
THE HERCULES TIRE & RUBBER COMPANY—See TPG Capital, L.P.; *U.S. Public*, pg. 2166
HERCULES TIRE SALES INC.; *U.S. Private*, pg. 1921
HERCULES TRANSPORT INC.; *U.S. Private*, pg. 1921
HERCULES WINDOW CLEANING CO.; *U.S. Private*, pg. 1921
HERCULES WIRE ROPE & SLING CO., INC.; *U.S. Private*, pg. 1921
HERC-U-LIFT, INC.; *U.S. Private*, pg. 1921
HERCULITE PRODUCTS, INC.—See Aberdeen Road Company; *U.S. Private*, pg. 38
HERDADE DE RIO FRIO, S.A.—See CORTICEIRA AMORIM, S.G.P.S., S.A.; *Int'l*, pg. 1807
HERD ENTERPRISES INC.; *U.S. Private*, pg. 1921
HERDER B.V.—See Alamo Group Inc.; *U.S. Public*, pg. 71
HERDER IMPLEMENTOS E MAQUINAS AGRICOLAS LTDA.—See Alamo Group Inc.; *U.S. Public*, pg. 71
HERDRICH PETROLEUM CORP.; *U.S. Private*, pg. 1921
HERDSMAN LAKE TAVERN (WA) PTY LTD—See Woolworths Group Limited; *Int'l*, pg. 8451
HEREAUS PRECIOUS METALS GMBH & CO. KG—See Heraeus Holding GmbH; *Int'l*, pg. 3358
HERE MEDIA INC.; *U.S. Private*, pg. 1921
HERENCIA RESOURCES PLC.; *Int'l*, pg. 3361
HEREN HEALTH CO., LTD.; *Int'l*, pg. 3361
HERE TO SERVE HOLDING CORP.; *U.S. Public*, pg. 1028
HERFF JONES CANADA—See Bain Capital, LP; *U.S. Private*, pg. 452
HERFF JONES FINE PAPERS - IOLA—See Bain Capital, LP; *U.S. Private*, pg. 452
HERFF JONES FINE PAPERS—See Bain Capital, LP; *U.S. Private*, pg. 452
HERFF JONES, INC. - CAP & GOWN DIVISION—See Bain Capital, LP; *U.S. Private*, pg. 451
HERFF JONES, INC. - COLLEGIATE CAP & GOWN, ARCOLA—See Bain Capital, LP; *U.S. Private*, pg. 452
HERFF JONES, INC. - JEWELRY—See Bain Capital, LP; *U.S. Private*, pg. 452
HERFF JONES, INC.—See Bain Capital, LP; *U.S. Private*, pg. 451
HERFF JONES, INC. - YEARBOOK MARKETING—See Bain Capital, LP; *U.S. Private*, pg. 452
HERFF JONES, INC. - YEARBOOKS—See Bain Capital, LP; *U.S. Private*, pg. 452
HERFF JONES, INC. - YEARBOOKS—See Bain Capital, LP; *U.S. Private*, pg. 452
HERFF JONES, INC. - YEARBOOKS—See Bain Capital, LP; *U.S. Private*, pg. 452
HERFORDER BRAUEREI GMBH & CO. KG—See Warsteiner Brauerei Haus Cramer KG; *Int'l*, pg. 8346
HERFY FOOD SERVICES COMPANY LTD.—See Savola Group; *Int'l*, pg. 6602
HERGA TECHNOLOGY LIMITED—See discoverIE Group plc; *Int'l*, pg. 2133
HERGERT MILLING INC.; *U.S. Private*, pg. 1921
HERGO ERGONOMIC SUPPORT SYSTEMS, INC.; *U.S. Private*, pg. 1921
HERGOTT FARM EQUIPMENT LTD.; *Int'l*, pg. 3361
HERHOF GMBH—See ELLAKTOR S.A.; *Int'l*, pg. 2365
HERHOF RECYCLING CENTER OSNABRUCK GMBH—See ELLAKTOR S.A.; *Int'l*, pg. 2365
HERIGE SA; *Int'l*, pg. 3361
HER IMPORTS; *U.S. Public*, pg. 1027
HERING AG—See BAVARIA Industries Group AG; *Int'l*, pg. 899
HERING SCHUPPENER CONSULTING—See WPP plc; *Int'l*, pg. 8469
HERING SCHUPPENER-FRANKFORT AMMAIN—See WPP plc; *Int'l*, pg. 8469
HERION SYSTEMTECHNIK GMBH—See IMI plc; *Int'l*, pg. 3625
HERIOT REIT LTD.; *Int'l*, pg. 3361
HERITABLE DEVELOPMENT FINANCE LIMITED—See OneSavings Bank plc; *Int'l*, pg. 5577
HERITAGE AUTO MALL OF BEL AIR INC.—See Atlantic Automotive Corp.; *U.S. Private*, pg. 371
HERITAGE AUTOMOTIVE GROUP INC.; *U.S. Private*, pg. 1922
HERITAGE AVIATION LTD.—See Patriarch Partners, LLC; *U.S. Public*, pg. 3109
HERITAGE AWALI GOLF & SPA RESORT—See Rogers & Company Limited; *Int'l*, pg. 6383

CORPORATE AFFILIATIONS

HERITAGE BABY PRODUCTS LLC; *U.S. Private*, pg. 1922
HERITAGE BAG COMPANY - FAIRFIELD—See Apollo Global Management, Inc.; *U.S. Public*, pg. 153
HERITAGE BAG COMPANY - LOGAN TOWNSHIP—See Apollo Global Management, Inc.; *U.S. Public*, pg. 153
HERITAGE BAG COMPANY - RANCHO CUCAMONGA—See Apollo Global Management, Inc.; *U.S. Public*, pg. 153
HERITAGE BAG COMPANY—See Apollo Global Management, Inc.; *U.S. Public*, pg. 153
HERITAGE BAG COMPANY - VILLA RICA—See Apollo Global Management, Inc.; *U.S. Public*, pg. 154
HERITAGE BANCSHARES GROUP, INC.; *U.S. Private*, pg. 1922
HERITAGE BANK INC.; *U.S. Private*, pg. 1922
HERITAGE BANK LIMITED; *Int'l*, pg. 3361
HERITAGE BANK N.A.—See Heritage Bancshares Group, Inc.; *U.S. Private*, pg. 1922
HERITAGE BANK OF COMMERCE—See Heritage Commerce Corp; *U.S. Public*, pg. 1028
HERITAGE BANK OF ST. TAMMANY—See Heritage NOLA Bancorp, Inc.; *U.S. Public*, pg. 1028
THE HERITAGE BANK; *U.S. Private*, pg. 4051
HERITAGE BANK—See Heritage Financial Corporation; *U.S. Public*, pg. 1028
HERITAGE BANK—See Heritage Group, Inc.; *U.S. Private*, pg. 1923
HERITAGE BRANDS LIMITED; *Int'l*, pg. 3361
HERITAGE BROADCASTING GROUP, INC.; *U.S. Private*, pg. 1922
HERITAGE BUSINESS SYSTEMS, INC.—See Xerox Holdings Corporation; *U.S. Public*, pg. 2388
HERITAGE CADILLAC, INC.; *U.S. Private*, pg. 1922
HERITAGE CANNABIS HOLDINGS CORP.; *Int'l*, pg. 3361
HERITAGE CAPITAL GROUP, INC.; *U.S. Private*, pg. 1922
HERITAGE CHEVROLET, INC.; *U.S. Private*, pg. 1922
HERITAGE CHEVROLET, INC.—See Atlantic Automotive Corp.; *U.S. Private*, pg. 371
HERITAGE CHRISTIAN SERVICES, INC.; *U.S. Private*, pg. 1922
HERITAGE CHRYSLER DODGE JEEP RAM—See Atlantic Automotive Corp.; *U.S. Private*, pg. 371
HERITAGE COMMERCE CORP; *U.S. Public*, pg. 1028
HERITAGE COMMUNITIES L.P.—See UDR, Inc.; *U.S. Public*, pg. 2218
HERITAGE CONSTRUCTION CO. INC.; *U.S. Private*, pg. 1922
HERITAGE COOPERATIVE INC.; *U.S. Private*, pg. 1922
THE HERITAGE CO.; *U.S. Private*, pg. 4052
HERITAGE-CRYSTAL CLEAN, INC.—See J.F. Lehman & Company, Inc.; *U.S. Private*, pg. 2163
HERITAGE DAIRY STORES INC.; *U.S. Private*, pg. 1922
HERITAGE DEVELOPMENT GROUP INC.; *U.S. Private*, pg. 1922
HERITAGE DIALYSIS CENTER LLC—See Nautic Partners, LLC; *U.S. Private*, pg. 2870
HERITAGE DISTILLING COMPANY, INC.—See Heritage Distilling Holding Company, Inc.; *U.S. Private*, pg. 1922
HERITAGE DISTILLING HOLDING COMPANY, INC.; *U.S. Private*, pg. 1922
HERITAGE DISTRIBUTION HOLDINGS—See Beijer Ref AB; *Int'l*, pg. 944
HERITAGE ENVIRONMENTAL SERVICES, LLC—See EQT AB; *Int'l*, pg. 2482
HERITAGE EQUIPMENT INC.; *U.S. Private*, pg. 1922
THE HERITAGE ESCROW COMPANY—See First American Financial Corporation; *U.S. Public*, pg. 838
HERITAGE ETC GP, L.L.C.—See Energy Transfer LP; *U.S. Public*, pg. 763
HERITAGE FAMILY SPECIALTY FOODS, INC.; *U.S. Private*, pg. 1922
HERITAGE FEDERAL CREDIT UNION; *U.S. Private*, pg. 1922
HERITAGE FINANCIAL CONSULTANTS, LLC; *U.S. Private*, pg. 1922
HERITAGE FINANCIAL CORPORATION; *U.S. Public*, pg. 1028
HERITAGE FINANCIAL GROUP, INC.; *U.S. Private*, pg. 1922
HERITAGE FINANCIAL SYSTEMS—See ConsenSys, Inc.; *U.S. Private*, pg. 1019
HERITAGE FOOD SERVICE GROUP, INC.—See Windjammer Capital Investors, LLC; *U.S. Private*, pg. 4537
HERITAGE FOODS INDIA LTD. - DAIRY DIVISION—See Heritage Foods Ltd.; *Int'l*, pg. 3361
HERITAGE FOODS LTD.; *Int'l*, pg. 3361
HERITAGE FORD INC.; *U.S. Private*, pg. 1923
HERITAGE FOREST PRODUCTS INC.—See Baillie Lumber Co., Inc.; *U.S. Private*, pg. 426
HERITAGE FOREST PRODUCTS—See Baillie Lumber Co., Inc.; *U.S. Private*, pg. 426
HERITAGE FS INC.; *U.S. Private*, pg. 1923
HERITAGE GLOBAL INC.—See RFA Capital Holdings Inc.; *Int'l*, pg. 6318
HERITAGE GOLF GROUP LLC—See KSL Capital Partners, LLC; *U.S. Private*, pg. 2355
HERITAGE GROUP, INC.; *U.S. Private*, pg. 1923

1220

COMPANY NAME INDEX

HERITAGE GROUP, LLC; *U.S. Private*, pg. 1923
HERITAGE GROUP LTD.; *Int'l*, pg. 3361
HERITAGE GROUP; *U.S. Private*, pg. 1923
HERITAGE HEALTH AND HOUSING; *U.S. Private*, pg. 1923
HERITAGE HEALTHCARE INNOVATION FUND II, LP—See Community Health Systems, Inc.; *U.S. Public*, pg. 553
HERITAGE HEALTH CARE SERVICES, INC.; *U.S. Private*, pg. 1923
HERITAGE HEALTH TPA PRIVATE LIMITED—See S K Bajoria Group; *Int'l*, pg. 6442
HERITAGE HILLS GOLF COURSE—See Orscheln Group; *U.S. Private*, pg. 3045
HERITAGE HOME GROUP, LLC; *U.S. Private*, pg. 1923
HERITAGE HOMES INC.; *U.S. Private*, pg. 1924
HERITAGE HOUSE FABRICS INC.—See Jeffrey Fabrics Inc.; *U.S. Private*, pg. 2198
HERITAGE IMPORTS INC.—See Atlantic Automotive Corp.; *U.S. Private*, pg. 371
HERITAGE INSURANCE HOLDINGS, INC.; *U.S. Public*, pg. 1028
HERITAGE INSURANCE INC—See Covenant Logistics Group, Inc.; *U.S. Public*, pg. 588
HERITAGE INSURANCE SERVICE INC.—See Marsh & McLennan Companies, Inc.; *U.S. Public*, pg. 1380
HERITAGE INTERACTIVE SERVICES, LLC—See EQT AB; *Int'l*, pg. 2482
HERITAGE INTERIORS, INC.; *U.S. Private*, pg. 1924
HERITAGE INTERNATIONAL FUND SERVICES (MALTA) LIMITED—See Heritage Group Ltd.; *Int'l*, pg. 3362
HERITAGE LACE, INC.; *U.S. Private*, pg. 1924
HERITAGE LANDSCAPE SUPPLY GROUP, INC.—See Leonard Green & Partners, L.P.; *U.S. Private*, pg. 2429
HERITAGE LINKS—See Lexicon, Inc.; *U.S. Private*, pg. 2440
HERITAGE LOGISTICS, LLC—See Vulcan Materials Company; *U.S. Public*, pg. 2314
HERITAGE MANAGEMENT CORP.; *U.S. Private*, pg. 1924
HERITAGE MECHANICAL SERVICES, INC.—See EMCOR Group, Inc.; *U.S. Public*, pg. 738
HERITAGE MEDICAL GROUP OF HILTON HEAD, L.L.C.—See Tenet Healthcare Corporation; *U.S. Public*, pg. 2008
HERITAGE MINING LTD.; *Int'l*, pg. 3362
HERITAGENERGY (NY) INC.; *U.S. Private*, pg. 1925
HERITAGE NEWSPAPERS, INC.—See Alden Global Capital LLC; *U.S. Private*, pg. 156
HERITAGE NOLA BANCORP, INC.; *U.S. Public*, pg. 1028
HERITAGE NUTRIVET LIMITED—See Heritage Foods Ltd.; *Int'l*, pg. 3361
HERITAGE OAK FLOORING—See Mid America Hardwoods Inc.; *U.S. Private*, pg. 2705
HERITAGE OF GAINESVILLE INC.—See RNMC Inc.; *U.S. Private*, pg. 3453
HERITAGE OIL CORPORATION—See Heritage Oil Plc; *Int'l*, pg. 3362
HERITAGE OIL & GAS LIMITED—See Heritage Oil Plc; *Int'l*, pg. 3362
HERITAGE OIL PLC; *Int'l*, pg. 3362
HERITAGE OPERATING, L.P.—See UGI Corporation; *U.S. Public*, pg. 2221
HERITAGE PACKAGING, LLC—See Welch Packaging Group, Inc.; *U.S. Private*, pg. 4473
HERITAGE PALMS GOLF & COUNTRY CLUB INC.; *U.S. Private*, pg. 1924
HERITAGE PAPER COMPANY, INC.; *U.S. Private*, pg. 1924
HERITAGE PAPER CO.—See Pioneer Packing Inc.; *U.S. Private*, pg. 3187
HERITAGE PARK SURGICAL HOSPITAL, LLC—See Tenet Healthcare Corporation; *U.S. Public*, pg. 2010
HERITAGE PARTNERS, INC.; *U.S. Private*, pg. 1924
HERITAGE PETROLEUM; *U.S. Private*, pg. 1924
HERITAGE PLASTICS, INC.—See Clayton, Dubilier & Rice, LLC; *U.S. Private*, pg. 919
HERITAGE PLASTICS, INC. - TAMPA—See Clayton, Dubilier & Rice, LLC; *U.S. Private*, pg. 919
HERITAGE POINTE PROPERTIES INC.—See Upper Lakes Group Inc.; *Int'l*, pg. 8093
HERITAGE POULTRY LTD.; *Int'l*, pg. 3362
HERITAGE PROPERTY & CASUALTY INSURANCE COMPANY—See Heritage Insurance Holdings, Inc.; *U.S. Public*, pg. 1028
HERITAGE RESOURCE LP—See Ontario Teachers' Pension Plan; *Int'l*, pg. 5590
HERITAGE RESOURCES LTD.—See Ascendis Health Limited; *Int'l*, pg. 601
HERITAGE SCHOOLS, INC.; *U.S. Private*, pg. 1924
HERITAGE SEEDS PTY. LTD.—See Barenbrug Holding B.V.; *Int'l*, pg. 864
HERITAGE SOUTH COMMUNITY CREDIT UNION; *U.S. Private*, pg. 1924
HERITAGE SOUTHEAST BANCORPORATION, INC.—See The First Bancshares, Inc.; *U.S. Public*, pg. 2073
HERITAGE SPORTSWEAR, INC.; *U.S. Private*, pg. 1924
HERITAGE STATE BANK—See HBancorporation Inc.; *U.S. Public*, pg. 990
HERITAGE TECHNOLOGIES, LLC; *U.S. Private*, pg. 1924
HERITAGE TERMITE & PEST SERVICES—See Rentokil Initial plc; *Int'l*, pg. 6289
HERITAGE TEXAS PROPERTIES, LLC—See Anywhere Real Estate Inc.; *U.S. Public*, pg. 140
HERITAGE TRACE APARTMENTS VIRGINIA, LLC—See RAIT Financial Trust; *U.S. Private*, pg. 6383
HERITAGE TRANSPORT LLC—See EQT AB; *Int'l*, pg. 2482
HERITAGE WAY ADVISORS, LLC—See Creative Planning, LLC; *U.S. Private*, pg. 1090
HERITAGE WHOLESALERS INC.; *U.S. Private*, pg. 1925
HERITAGE-WTI, INC.—See EQT AB; *Int'l*, pg. 2482
THE HERJAVEC GROUP, INC.; *Int'l*, pg. 7652
HERKER INDUSTRIES INC.; *U.S. Private*, pg. 1925
HERKULES CAPITAL AS; *Int'l*, pg. 3362
HERKULES HEBETECHNIK GMBH—See Storskogen Group AB; *Int'l*, pg. 7227
HERKULES S.A.; *Int'l*, pg. 3362
HERKY HAWK FINANCIAL CORP.; *U.S. Private*, pg. 1925
HERLEY CTI—See Advent International Corporation; *U.S. Private*, pg. 101
HERLEY GMI EYAL LTD.—See Kratos Defense & Security Solutions, Inc.; *U.S. Public*, pg. 1276
HERLEY LANCASTER—See Advent International Corporation; *U.S. Private*, pg. 101
HERLEY NEW ENGLAND—See Advent International Corporation; *U.S. Private*, pg. 101
HERLITZ BENELUX BV—See Pelikan International Corporation Berhad; *Int'l*, pg. 5782
HERLITZ BULGARIA EOOD—See Pelikan International Corporation Berhad; *Int'l*, pg. 5782
HERLITZ HUNGARIA KFT.—See Pelikan International Corporation Berhad; *Int'l*, pg. 5782
HERLITZ PBS AG—See Pelikan International Corporation Berhad; *Int'l*, pg. 5782
HERLITZ ROMANIA SRL—See Pelikan International Corporation Berhad; *Int'l*, pg. 5782
HERLITZ SLOVAKIA S.R.O.—See Pelikan International Corporation Berhad; *Int'l*, pg. 5782
HERLITZ SPOLKA Z.O.O.—See Pelikan International Corporation Berhad; *Int'l*, pg. 5783
HERLITZ SPOL. S.R.O.—See Pelikan International Corporation Berhad; *Int'l*, pg. 5783
HERLITZ UK LTD.—See Pelikan International Corporation Berhad; *Int'l*, pg. 5783
HERMALUX SARL—See CLS Holdings plc; *Int'l*, pg. 1664
HERMAN AGENCY INC.—See Principal Financial Group, Inc.; *U.S. Public*, pg. 1721
HERMAN ANDERSSON OY—See Stora Enso Oyj; *Int'l*, pg. 7222
HERMAN ASSOCIATES, INC.; *U.S. Private*, pg. 1925
HERMAN ASSOCIATES PUBLIC RELATIONS—See Herman Associates, Inc.; *U.S. Private*, pg. 1925
HERMAN CONSTRUCTION GROUP, INC.—See Bristol Bay Native Corporation; *U.S. Private*, pg. 656
HERMAN CONSTRUCTION SERVICES, INC.; *U.S. Private*, pg. 1925
HERMAN COOK VOLKSWAGEN; *U.S. Private*, pg. 1925
HERMAN ELECTRONICS, INC.; *U.S. Private*, pg. 1925
HERMAN GOLDNER COMPANY INC.; *U.S. Private*, pg. 1925
HERMAN INTEGRATION SERVICES LLC—See Resideo Technologies, Inc.; *U.S. Public*, pg. 1789
HERMAN KAY BROMLEY INC.; *U.S. Private*, pg. 1925
HERMAN MILLER ASIA (PTE.) LTD.—See MillerKnoll, Inc.; *U.S. Public*, pg. 1447
HERMAN MILLER (AUSTRALIA) PTY. LTD.—See MillerKnoll, Inc.; *U.S. Public*, pg. 1447
HERMAN MILLER CANADA—See MillerKnoll, Inc.; *U.S. Public*, pg. 1447
HERMAN MILLER DO BRASIL, LTDA.—See MillerKnoll, Inc.; *U.S. Public*, pg. 1447
HERMAN MILLER FURNITURE (INDIA) PVT. LTD.—See MillerKnoll, Inc.; *U.S. Public*, pg. 1447
HERMAN MILLER ITALIA S.P.A.—See MillerKnoll, Inc.; *U.S. Public*, pg. 1447
HERMAN MILLER JAPAN, LTD.—See MillerKnoll, Inc.; *U.S. Public*, pg. 1447
HERMAN MILLER, LTD.—See MillerKnoll, Inc.; *U.S. Public*, pg. 1447
HERMAN MILLER MEXICO S.A. DE C.V. - MONTERREY—See MillerKnoll, Inc.; *U.S. Public*, pg. 1447
HERMAN MILLER MEXICO S.A. DE C.V.—See MillerKnoll, Inc.; *U.S. Public*, pg. 1447
HERMANN AUTOMATION GMBH—See Hormann KG Verkaufsgesellschaf; *Int'l*, pg. 3480
HERMANN COMPANIES INC.; *U.S. Private*, pg. 1925
HERMANN DRIVE SURGICAL HOSPITAL, LP—See Nobilis Health Corp.; *U.S. Private*, pg. 2932
HERMANN ENGELMANN GREENHOUSES INC.; *U.S. Private*, pg. 1925
HERMANN FRANK GMBH & CO. KG.—See Uzin Utz AG; *Int'l*, pg. 8103
HERMANN GROSSKUCHENTECHNIK HOTEL- UND GASTRONOMIEBEDARF GMBH—See Metro AG; *Int'l*, pg. 4857
HERMANN KIRCHNER BAUUNTERNEHMUNG GMBH—See STRABAG SE; *Int'l*, pg. 7230
HERMANN KIRCHNER HOCH- UND INGENIEURBAU GMBH—See STRABAG SE; *Int'l*, pg. 7230
HERMANN KIRCHNER PROJEKTGESELLSCHAFT MBH—See STRABAG SE; *Int'l*, pg. 7230
HERMANN LANGE GMBH & CO. KG; *Int'l*, pg. 3362
HERMANN SCHWELLING MASCHINENBAU GMBH & CO. KG; *Int'l*, pg. 3362
HERMANN SEIPPEL-UNTERSTUTZUNGSEINRICHTUNG GMBH—See E.ON SE; *Int'l*, pg. 2258
HERMANN SERVICES INCORPORATED; *U.S. Private*, pg. 1925
HERMANN VAN DILLEN ASIATEX GMBH - GLOBAL LABELS DIVISION—See Steilmann Holding AG; *Int'l*, pg. 7193
HERMANN VAN DILLEN ASIATEX GMBH—See Steilmann Holding AG; *Int'l*, pg. 7193
HERMANOS LOPEZ INC.; *U.S. Private*, pg. 1925
HERMANOS SANTIAGO CASH & CARRY; *U.S. Private*, pg. 1925
HERMAN R. EWELL INC.; *U.S. Private*, pg. 1925
HERMAN SEEKAMP INC.; *U.S. Private*, pg. 1925
HERMANS GROEP B.V.—See Tengelmann Warenhandelsgesellschaft KG; *Int'l*, pg. 7560
HERMAN STRAUSS INC.; *U.S. Private*, pg. 1925
HERM. DAUELSBERG GMBH & CO. KG; *Int'l*, pg. 3362
HERMED INGENIERIA CLINICA ESPANA, S.L.—See Fresenius SE & Co. KGaA; *Int'l*, pg. 2780
HERMED MEDIZINTECHNIK SCHWEIZ AG—See Fresenius SE & Co. KGaA; *Int'l*, pg. 2780
HERMED MEDROTT MEDICAL BVBA—See Fresenius SE & Co. KGaA; *Int'l*, pg. 2780
HERMED MEDROTT MEDICAL B.V.—See Fresenius SE & Co. KGaA; *Int'l*, pg. 2780
HERMED TECHNISCHE BERATUNGS GMBH—See Fresenius SE & Co. KGaA; *Int'l*, pg. 2780
HERMES ABRASIVES (CANADA) LTD.—See Hermes Schleifmittel GmbH & Co. KG; *Int'l*, pg. 3363
HERMES ABRASIVES LTD.—See Hermes Schleifmittel GmbH & Co. KG; *Int'l*, pg. 3363
HERMES ABRASIVES (SHANGHAI) CO., LTD.—See Hermes Schleifmittel GmbH & Co. KG; *Int'l*, pg. 3363
HERMES ARGENTINA SRL—See Hermes International SCA; *Int'l*, pg. 3362
HERMES ASIA PACIFIC LIMITED—See Hermes International SCA; *Int'l*, pg. 3362
HERMES AVIATION, INC.—See Mercury Air Group Inc.; *U.S. Private*, pg. 2670
HERMES BENELUX NORDICS SA—See Hermes International SCA; *Int'l*, pg. 3362
HERMES CENTRE JOINT STOCK COMPANY; *Int'l*, pg. 3362
HERMES CHINA CO. LTD.—See Hermes International SCA; *Int'l*, pg. 3362
HERMES DENMARK APS—See Hermes International SCA; *Int'l*, pg. 3362
HERMES DE PARIS MEXICO, S.A. DE C.V.—See Hermes International SCA; *Int'l*, pg. 3363
HERMES DO BRASIL INDUSTRIA E COMERCIO LTDA.—See Hermes International SCA; *Int'l*, pg. 3362
HERMES EINRICHTUNGS SERVICE GMBH & CO.KG—See Otto GmbH & Co. KG; *Int'l*, pg. 5662
HERMES EQUITY OWNERSHIP SERVICES LIMITED—See Federated Hermes, Inc.; *U.S. Public*, pg. 827
HERMES EUROPE GMBH—See Otto GmbH & Co. KG; *Int'l*, pg. 5662
HERMES FINANCIAL MANAGEMENT EGYPT, LTD.—See EFG Holding; *Int'l*, pg. 2319
HERMES FULFILMENT GMBH—See Otto GmbH & Co. KG; *Int'l*, pg. 5663
HERMES FUND MANAGERS LIMITED—See Federated Hermes, Inc.; *U.S. Public*, pg. 827
HERMES GMBH—See Hermes International SCA; *Int'l*, pg. 3362
HERMES GPE LLP—See Federated Hermes, Inc.; *U.S. Public*, pg. 827
HERMES GPE (SINGAPORE) PTE. LIMITED—See Federated Hermes, Inc.; *U.S. Public*, pg. 827
HERMES GPE (USA) INC.—See Federated Hermes, Inc.; *U.S. Public*, pg. 827
HERMES GRECE S.A.—See Hermes International SCA; *Int'l*, pg. 3362
HERMES IMMOBILIER GENEVE SA—See Hermes International SCA; *Int'l*, pg. 3362
HERMES INDIA RETAIL & DISTRIBUTORS PRIVATE LIMITED—See Hermes International SCA; *Int'l*, pg. 3362
HERMES INTERNACIONAL PORTUGAL LDA—See Hermes International SCA; *Int'l*, pg. 3362
HERMES INTERNATIONAL SCA; *Int'l*, pg. 3362
HERMES INVESTMENT MANAGEMENT LTD.—See Federated Hermes, Inc.; *U.S. Public*, pg. 827
HERMES ITALIA S.P.A.—See Otto GmbH & Co. KG; *Int'l*, pg. 5663
HERMES ITALIE S.P.A.—See Hermes International SCA; *Int'l*, pg. 3363

HERMES INTERNATIONAL SCA

HERMES I TICKETS PTE, LTD.—See Wirecard AG; *Int'l*, pg. 8434
HERMES JAPON CO., LTD.—See Hermes International SCA; *Int'l*, pg. 3363
HERMES LOGISTIK GMBH & CO. KG—See Otto GmbH & Co. KG; *Int'l*, pg. 5663
HERMES LOGISTIK GMBH & CO KG—See Otto GmbH & Co. KG; *Int'l*, pg. 5663
HERMES MICROVISION, INC.—See ASML Holding N.V.; *Int'l*, pg. 628
HERMES-MICROVISION, INC.—See ASML Holding N.V.; *Int'l*, pg. 628
HERMES MUSIC S.A. DE C.V.; *Int'l*, pg. 3363
HERMES NEXTEC GMBH—See Otto GmbH & Co. KG; *Int'l*, pg. 5663
HERMES OF PARIS, INC.—See Hermes International SCA; *Int'l*, pg. 3363
HERMES PARCELNET LIMITED—See Otto GmbH & Co. KG; *Int'l*, pg. 5663
HERMES PRAGUE, A.S.—See Hermes International SCA; *Int'l*, pg. 3363
HERMES REAL ESTATE INVESTMENT MANAGEMENT LTD.—See Federated Hermes, Inc.; *U.S. Public*, pg. 827
HERMES RUSSIA—See Otto GmbH & Co. KG; *Int'l*, pg. 5663
HERMES SCHLEIFKORPER GMBH—See Hermes Schleifmittel GmbH & Co. KG; *Int'l*, pg. 3363
HERMES SCHLEIFMITTEL GMBH & CO. KG; *Int'l*, pg. 3363
HERMES SECURITIES BROKERAGE—See EFG Holding; *Int'l*, pg. 2319
HERMES SELLIER SAS—See Hermes International SCA; *Int'l*, pg. 3363
HERMES S.L.—See Assicurazioni Generali S.p.A.; *Int'l*, pg. 644
HERMES SYSTEMS INC.—See Shindengen Electric Manufacturing Co., Ltd.; *Int'l*, pg. 6841
HERMES TRADING CO. INC.—See Hermes Music S.A. de C.V.; *Int'l*, pg. 3363
HERMES TRANSPORTES BLINDADOS SA; *Int'l*, pg. 3363
HERMES VIET NAM MACHINERY COMPANY—See Shanghai Hanbell Precise Machinery Co., Ltd.; *Int'l*, pg. 6769
HERMETIC SEAL—See AMETEK, Inc.; *U.S. Public*, pg. 116
HERMETIC SOLUTIONS GROUP, LLC—See Windjammer Capital Investors, LLC; *U.S. Private*, pg. 4537
HERM HUGHES & SONS, INC.; *U.S. Private*, pg. 1925
HERMILL INVESTMENTS PTE LTD—See Hotel Properties Limited; *Int'l*, pg. 3488
HERMIONE RAIFFEISEN-IMMOBILIEN-LEASING GMBH—See Raiffeisen Bank International AG; *Int'l*, pg. 6182
HERMISTON FOODS, LLC—See Norpac Foods, Inc.; *U.S. Private*, pg. 2939
HERMISTON HERALD—See East Oregonian Publishing Co.; *U.S. Private*, pg. 1317
HERMITAGE OFFSHORE SERVICES LTD.; *Int'l*, pg. 3363
HERMITAGE PRIMARY CARE, LLC—See HCA Healthcare, Inc.; *U.S. Public*, pg. 998
HERMLE CHINA CO LTD.—See Maschinenfabrik Berthold Hermle AG; *Int'l*, pg. 4720
HERMLE ITALIA S.R.L.—See Maschinenfabrik Berthold Hermle AG; *Int'l*, pg. 4720
HERMLE-LEIBINGER SYSTEMTECHNIK GMBH—See Maschinenfabrik Berthold Hermle AG; *Int'l*, pg. 4720
HERMLE MACHINE CO—See Maschinenfabrik Berthold Hermle AG; *Int'l*, pg. 4720
HERMLE MACHINE (SHANGHAI) CO. LTD.—See Maschinenfabrik Berthold Hermle AG; *Int'l*, pg. 4720
HERMLE MASCHINENBAU GMBH—See Maschinenfabrik Berthold Hermle AG; *Int'l*, pg. 4720
HERMLE MEXIKO S DE R.L. DE C.V.—See Maschinenfabrik Berthold Hermle AG; *Int'l*, pg. 4720
HERMLE NEDERLAND B.V.—See Maschinenfabrik Berthold Hermle AG; *Int'l*, pg. 4720
HERMLE NORDIC—See Maschinenfabrik Berthold Hermle AG; *Int'l*, pg. 4720
HERMLE OSTERREICH AG—See Maschinenfabrik Berthold Hermle AG; *Int'l*, pg. 4720
HERMLE + PARTNER VERTRIEBS GMBH—See Maschinenfabrik Berthold Hermle AG; *Int'l*, pg. 4720
HERMLE (SCHWEIZ) AG—See Maschinenfabrik Berthold Hermle AG; *Int'l*, pg. 4720
HERMLE SEA CO., LTD.—See Maschinenfabrik Berthold Hermle AG; *Int'l*, pg. 4720
HERMLE SOUTHEAST EUROPE—See Maschinenfabrik Berthold Hermle AG; *Int'l*, pg. 4720
HERMLE USA INC.—See Maschinenfabrik Berthold Hermle AG; *Int'l*, pg. 4720
HERMLE WWE AG—See Maschinenfabrik Berthold Hermle AG; *Int'l*, pg. 4720
HERMODS AB—See AcadeMedia AB; *Int'l*, pg. 76
HERMOS AG—See CEZ, a.s.; *Int'l*, pg. 1428
HERMOS GESELLSCHAFT FUR STEUER-, MESS- UND REGELTECHNIK MBH—See CEZ, a.s.; *Int'l*, pg. 1428
HERMOS SP. Z O.O.—See CEZ, a.s.; *Int'l*, pg. 1428

HERMOS SYSTEMS GMBH—See CEZ, a.s.; *Int'l*, pg. 1428
HERNALSER HOF BETEILIGUNGSVERWALTUNGS GMBH & CO. KG—See PORR AG; *Int'l*, pg. 5923
HERNALSER HOF BETEILIGUNGSVERWALTUNGS GMBH—See PORR AG; *Int'l*, pg. 5923
HERNANDEZ CONSULTING; *U.S. Private*, pg. 1925
HERNANDO HMA, INC.—See Community Health Systems, Inc.; *U.S. Public*, pg. 553
HERNANDO HMA, INC.—See Community Health Systems, Inc.; *U.S. Public*, pg. 553
HERNDON PRODUCTS, INC.—See HCI Equity Management, L.P.; *U.S. Private*, pg. 1889
HERNER GLAS - BERND HOFFBAUER GMBH; *Int'l*, pg. 3363
HERNING UNDERGROUND SUPPLY INC.—See WESCO International, Inc.; *U.S. Public*, pg. 2351
HERNIS SCAN SYSTEMS - ASIA PTE LTD.—See Eaton Corporation plc; *Int'l*, pg. 2282
HERNIS SCAN SYSTEMS A/S—See Eaton Corporation plc; *Int'l*, pg. 2282
HERNON MANUFACTURING, INC.; *U.S. Private*, pg. 1925
HERO AG; *Int'l*, pg. 3363
HERO ASIA INVESTMENT LIMITED—See China Longyuan Power Group Corp Ltd.; *Int'l*, pg. 1515
HERO BENELUX B.V.—See Hero AG; *Int'l*, pg. 3363
HERO CORP.; *Int'l*, pg. 3363
HERO CZECH S.R.O.—See Hero AG; *Int'l*, pg. 3363
HERO DIGITAL LLC—See AEA Investors LP; *U.S. Private*, pg. 114
HERO ECO LIMITED—See Hero Corp.; *Int'l*, pg. 3363
H.E.R.O.E.S. CARE; *U.S. Private*, pg. 1826
HEROES, INC.; *U.S. Private*, pg. 1925
HERO ESPANA, S.A.—See Hero AG; *Int'l*, pg. 3363
HEROES TECHNOLOGY LTD.; *Int'l*, pg. 3364
HERO EUROPE S.R.L.—See I.C.T.C. Holdings Corporation; *Int'l*, pg. 3565
HEROFLON S.P.A.—See Daikin Industries, Ltd.; *Int'l*, pg. 1935
HERO INTERNATIONAL USA HOLDING CORP.; *U.S. Public*, pg. 1029
HERO ITALIA SPA—See Hero AG; *Int'l*, pg. 3363
HEROKU, INC.—See Salesforce, Inc.; *U.S. Public*, pg. 1837
HERO LATIN AMERICA SISTEMAS TINTOMETRICOS LTDA—See I.C.T.C. Holdings Corporation; *Int'l*, pg. 3565
HEROLEADS (THAILAND) CO., LTD.—See Transcosmos Inc.; *Int'l*, pg. 7898
HERO MOTOCORP LTD.—See Hero Corp.; *Int'l*, pg. 3363
HERON EVIDENCE DEVELOPMENT AB—See Pamplona Capital Management LLP; *Int'l*, pg. 5712
HERON FOODS LTD.—See B&M European Value Retail S.A.; *Int'l*, pg. 784
HERON HEALTH PVT. LTD—See Pamplona Capital Management LLP; *Int'l*, pg. 5712
HERON LAKE BIOENERGY, LLC—See Granite Falls Energy, LLC; *U.S. Private*, pg. 1755
HERON RESOURCES LIMITED; *Int'l*, pg. 3364
HERON SHIPPING CO.,LTD—See Thoresen Thai Agencies Public Company Limited; *Int'l*, pg. 7718
HERON STREET ACQUISITION CORPORATION; *U.S. Private*, pg. 1926
HERON SYSTEMS, INC.—See Shield AI Inc.; *U.S. Private*, pg. 3635
HERON THERAPEUTICS, INC.; *U.S. Public*, pg. 1029
HERO POLSKA SP. Z O.O.—See Hero AG; *Int'l*, pg. 3363
HERO PORTUGAL LDA.—See Hero AG; *Int'l*, pg. 3363
HERO PRODUCTS INDIA PVT. LTD.—See I.C.T.C. Holdings Corporation; *Int'l*, pg. 3565
HEROSE GMBH; *Int'l*, pg. 3364
HEROSE IBERICA SL—See HEROSE GMBH; *Int'l*, pg. 3364
HEROSE LIMITED—See HEROSE GMBH; *Int'l*, pg. 3364
HEROSE TRADING CO., LTD.—See HEROSE GMBH; *Int'l*, pg. 3364
HERO SLOVAKIA S.R.O.—See Hero AG; *Int'l*, pg. 3363
HERO TECHNOLOGIES INC.; *U.S. Public*, pg. 1029
HEROUX-DEVTEK INC.; *Int'l*, pg. 3364
HEROUX-DEVTEK - LONGUEUIL PLANT—See Heroux-Devtek Inc.; *Int'l*, pg. 3364
HEROUX-DEVTEK - SCARBOROUGH PLANT—See Heroux-Devtek Inc.; *Int'l*, pg. 3364
HEROZ, INC.; *Int'l*, pg. 3364
HERRAJES HETTICH, S.A. DE C.V.—See Hettich Holding GmbH & Co. oHG; *Int'l*, pg. 3365
HERRAJES Y ACABADOS METALICOS, S.A. DE C.V.—See KPS Capital Partners, LP; *U.S. Private*, pg. 2347
HERRAMIENTAS CLEVELAND, S.A. DE C.V.—See Dalian Top-Eastern Group Co., Ltd.; *Int'l*, pg. 1953
HERRAMIENTAS PREZISS, S.L.—See Sandvik AB; *Int'l*, pg. 6529
HERREGAN DISTRIBUTORS, INC.; *U.S. Private*, pg. 1926
HERREN ENTERPRISES, INC.—See KKR & Co. Inc.; *U.S. Public*, pg. 1249

HERREN GLOBUS—See The Federation of Migros Cooperatives; *Int'l*, pg. 7642
HERR FOODS INC.; *U.S. Private*, pg. 1926
THE HERRICK CORPORATION; *U.S. Private*, pg. 4052
HERRICK, FEINSTEIN LLP; *U.S. Private*, pg. 1926
HERR INDUSTRIAL INC.; *U.S. Private*, pg. 1926
HERRING BANCORP, INC.; *U.S. Private*, pg. 1926
HERRING BANK—See Herring Bancorp, Inc.; *U.S. Private*, pg. 1926
HERRING FORD, INC.; *U.S. Private*, pg. 1926
HERRING GAS COMPANY INC.; *U.S. Private*, pg. 1926
HERRMAN & GOETZ INC.; *U.S. Private*, pg. 1926
HERRMAN LUMBER COMPANY; *U.S. Private*, pg. 1926
HERRON VALVE, INC.—See Proconex Management Group Inc.; *U.S. Private*, pg. 3272
HERROZ SDN. BHD.—See HPMT Holding Berhad; *Int'l*, pg. 3501
HERRSCHNERS, INC.; *U.S. Private*, pg. 1926
HERSAM ACORN NEWSPAPERS LLC; *U.S. Private*, pg. 1926
HERSAM ACORN NEWSPAPERS—See Hersam Acorn Newspapers LLC; *U.S. Private*, pg. 1926
HERSCHEL PARTS, INC.—See F.P. Bourgault Industries Ltd.; *Int'l*, pg. 2597
HERSCHEND FAMILY ENTERTAINMENT CORP.; *U.S. Private*, pg. 1926
HERSCHMAN ARCHITECTS, INC.; *U.S. Private*, pg. 1926
HERSHA ENTERPRISES, LTD.; *U.S. Private*, pg. 1926
HERSHA HOSPITALITY MANAGEMENT CO.—See Hersha Enterprises, Ltd.; *U.S. Private*, pg. 1926
HERSHA HOSPITALITY TRUST—See KSL Capital Partners, LLC; *U.S. Private*, pg. 2355
HERSHEY ASIA PACIFIC PTE. LTD.—See The Hershey Co.; *U.S. Public*, pg. 2088
HERSHEY CANADA, INC.—See The Hershey Co.; *U.S. Public*, pg. 2088
HERSHEY CHOCOLATE & CONFECTIONERY COMPANY—See The Hershey Co.; *U.S. Public*, pg. 2088
HERSHEY CHOCOLATE OF VIRGINIA, INC.—See The Hershey Co.; *U.S. Public*, pg. 2088
THE HERSHEY CO.; *U.S. Public*, pg. 2088
HERSHEY CREAMERY COMPANY; *U.S. Public*, pg. 1029
HERSHEY ENGINEERING COMPANY, LTD.—See Formosan Union Chemical Corp.; *Int'l*, pg. 2736
HERSHEY ENTERTAINMENT & RESORTS COMPANY; *U.S. Private*, pg. 1926
HERSHEY ENVIRONMENTAL TECHNOLOGY CO., LTD.—See Formosan Union Chemical Corp.; *Int'l*, pg. 2736
HERSHEY FOODS CORP.-HAZLETON PLANT—See The Hershey Co.; *U.S. Public*, pg. 2088
HERSHEY FOODS INTERNATIONAL TRADE (SHANGHAI) CO, LTD.—See The Hershey Co.; *U.S. Public*, pg. 2088
HERSHEY INDIA CONFECTIONERY PRIVATE LIMITED—See The Hershey Co.; *U.S. Public*, pg. 2089
HERSHEY INDIA PRIVATE LIMITED—See The Hershey Co.; *U.S. Public*, pg. 2089
HERSHEY INTERNATIONAL LTD.—See The Hershey Co.; *U.S. Public*, pg. 2089
HERSHEY JAPAN CO., LTD.—See The Hershey Co.; *U.S. Public*, pg. 2089
HERSHEY MEXICO, S.A. DE C.V.—See The Hershey Co.; *U.S. Public*, pg. 2089
HERSHEY OUTPATIENT SURGERY CENTER, L.P.—See Tenet Healthcare Corporation; *U.S. Public*, pg. 2010
HERSHEY'S MILL GOLF CLUB INC.—See Wooldridge Construction Co., Inc.; *U.S. Private*, pg. 4562
HERSHEY'S MILL RESTAURANT SERVICE INC.—See Wooldridge Construction Co., Inc.; *U.S. Private*, pg. 4562
HERSHMAN CAPITAL CORP.; *U.S. Private*, pg. 1927
HERSHOCKS INC.; *U.S. Private*, pg. 1927
HERSMAN SERLES ALMOND PLLC; *U.S. Private*, pg. 1927
HERSMEX S. DE R.L. DE C.V.—See The Hershey Co.; *U.S. Public*, pg. 2089
HERSRUD CO. INC.; *U.S. Private*, pg. 1927
HERSTAL, S.A.; *Int'l*, pg. 3364
HERTA GMBH—See Nestle S.A.; *Int'l*, pg. 5205
HERTART APS—See Vitrolife AB; *Int'l*, pg. 8262
HERTA S.A.—See Nestle S.A.; *Int'l*, pg. 5205
HERTECANT FLANGES N.V.—See Wise Equity SGR S.p.A.; *Int'l*, pg. 8435
HERTI AD; *Int'l*, pg. 3365
HERTI FRANCE—See Herti AD; *Int'l*, pg. 3365
HERTI GERMANY GMBH—See Herti AD; *Int'l*, pg. 3365
HERTIG HAUSTECHNIK AG—See BKW AG; *Int'l*, pg. 1055
HERTI GROUP INTERNATIONAL—See Herti AD; *Int'l*, pg. 3365
HERTI UK LTD.—See Herti AD; *Int'l*, pg. 3365
HERTLI & BERTSCHY AG, ELEKTRISCHE ANLAGEN—See BKW AG; *Int'l*, pg. 1055
HERTRICH NISSAN JEEP EAGLE; *U.S. Private*, pg. 1927
HERTWICH ENGINEERING GMBH—See SMS Holding GmbH; *Int'l*, pg. 7015

HERTZ ASIA PACIFIC PTE. LTD.—See Hertz Global Holdings, Inc.; *U.S. Public*, pg. 1029
HERTZ AUSTRALIA PTY. LIMITED—See Hertz Global Holdings, Inc.; *U.S. Public*, pg. 1029
HERTZ AUTOVERMIETUNG GMBH—See Hertz Global Holdings, Inc.; *U.S. Public*, pg. 1029
HERTZ BELGIUM B.V.B.A.—See Hertz Global Holdings, Inc.; *U.S. Public*, pg. 1029
HERTZBERG-NEW METHOD INC.; *U.S. Private*, pg. 1927
HERTZ CAR SALES LLC—See Hertz Global Holdings, Inc.; *U.S. Public*, pg. 1029
HERTZ CLAIM MANAGEMENT B.V.—See Hertz Global Holdings, Inc.; *U.S. Public*, pg. 1029
HERTZ CLAIM MANAGEMENT GMBH—See Hertz Global Holdings, Inc.; *U.S. Public*, pg. 1029
THE HERTZ CORPORATION—See Hertz Global Holdings, Inc.; *U.S. Public*, pg. 1029
HERTZ DO BRASIL LTDA.—See Hertz Global Holdings, Inc.; *U.S. Public*, pg. 1029
HERTZ GLOBAL HOLDINGS, INC.; *U.S. Public*, pg. 1029
HERTZ HOLDINGS NETHERLANDS B.V.—See Hertz Global Holdings, Inc.; *U.S. Public*, pg. 1029
HERTZ LITHIUM INC.; *Int'l*, pg. 3365
HERTZ LOCAL EDITION CORP.—See Hertz Global Holdings, Inc.; *U.S. Public*, pg. 1029
HERTZ SYSTEMTECHNIK GMBH—See CEWE Stiftung & Co. KGaA; *Int'l*, pg. 1425
HERWALDT AUTOMOTIVE GROUP, INC.; *U.S. Private*, pg. 1927
HERZFELD CARIBBEAN BASIN FUND, INC.; *U.S. Public*, pg. 1029
HERZING, INC.; *U.S. Private*, pg. 1927
HERZOG COILEX GMBH—See ThyssenKrupp AG; *Int'l*, pg. 7734
HERZOG CONTRACTING CORP.; *U.S. Private*, pg. 1927
HERZOG & DE MEURON BASEL LTD.; *Int'l*, pg. 3365
HERZOG-MEIER INC.; *U.S. Private*, pg. 1927
HERZOG MEIER VOLKSWAGEN; *U.S. Private*, pg. 1927
HERZOG TRUE VALUE HOME CENTER INC.; *U.S. Private*, pg. 1927
HERZ-UND GEFASS-KLINIK GMBH—See Asklepios Kliniken GmbH & Co. KGaA; *Int'l*, pg. 624
HERZZENTRUM LAHR/BADEN GMBH & CO. KG—See Asklepios Kliniken GmbH & Co. KGaA; *Int'l*, pg. 623
HERZZENTRUM LEIPZIG GMBH—See Fresenius SE & Co. KGaA; *Int'l*, pg. 2778
HESAI GROUP; *Int'l*, pg. 3365
H.E.S. BEHEER N.V.; *Int'l*, pg. 3195
HESCHONG MAHONE GROUP, INC.; *U.S. Private*, pg. 1927
HESCO ARMOR, INC.—See CVC Capital Partners SICAV-FIS S.A.; *Int'l*, pg. 1886
HESCO BASTION, INC.—See CVC Capital Partners SICAV-FIS S.A.; *Int'l*, pg. 1886
HESCO BASTION LTD.—See CVC Capital Partners SICAV-FIS S.A.; *Int'l*, pg. 1886
HESCO GROUP LIMITED—See CVC Capital Partners SICAV-FIS S.A.; *Int'l*, pg. 1885
HESCO INC.; *U.S. Private*, pg. 1927
HESCO PARTS CORPORATION; *U.S. Private*, pg. 1927
HESCO PARTS—See Hesco Parts Corporation; *U.S. Private*, pg. 1927
HESCO SERVICES INC.—See Hoj Engineering & Sales Co., LLC; *U.S. Private*, pg. 1961
HES ELEVATOR SERVICES INC.—See Savaria Corporation; *Int'l*, pg. 6596
HE SERVICES CO. INC.; *U.S. Private*, pg. 1890
HESHAN DEREN ELECTRONIC SCIENCE&TECHNOLOGY CO., LTD.—See Shenzhen Deren Electronic Co., Ltd.; *Int'l*, pg. 6808
HESHAN GOLIK METAL MANUFACTURING CO. LIMITED—See Golik Holdings Limited; *Int'l*, pg. 3036
HESHAN HANG KEI STEEL WIRE MANUFACTURING CO., LIMITED—See Golik Holdings Limited; *Int'l*, pg. 3036
HESHAN JIANGCI WIRE & CABLE CO., LTD.—See Lingyi iTech (Guangdong) Company; *Int'l*, pg. 4512
HESKA AG—See Mars, Incorporated; *U.S. Private*, pg. 2588
HESKA CORPORATION—See Mars, Incorporated; *U.S. Private*, pg. 2588
HESKA IMAGING INTERNATIONAL, LLC—See Mars, Incorporated; *U.S. Private*, pg. 2588
HESKA IMAGING US, LLC—See Mars, Incorporated; *U.S. Private*, pg. 2588
HESPERIA HOSPITAL MODENA S.P.A.—See Garofalo Health Care SpA; *Int'l*, pg. 2886
HESPERIA STAR—See Gannett Co., Inc.; *U.S. Public*, pg. 904
HESS AMERICA—See Ragni SAS; *Int'l*, pg. 6181
HESS AUSTRIA GMBH—See Gauselmann AG; *Int'l*, pg. 2890
HESS BAKKEN INVESTMENTS II L.L.C.—See Hess Corporation; *U.S. Public*, pg. 1030
HESS BROTHER'S FRUIT COMPANY; *U.S. Private*, pg. 1928
HESS CASH SYSTEMS GMBH & CO. KG—See Gauselmann AG; *Int'l*, pg. 2890
HESSCOR, INC.; *U.S. Private*, pg. 1927

HESS CORP. - HOUSTON REGIONAL OFFICE—See Hess Corporation; *U.S. Public*, pg. 1030
HESS CORPORATION; *U.S. Public*, pg. 1030
HESS CORP. - PORT READING REFINERY & TERMINAL—See Hess Corporation; *U.S. Public*, pg. 1030
HESSCO; *U.S. Private*, pg. 1927
HESS (DENMARK) APS—See INEOS Limited; *Int'l*, pg. 3682
THE HESSE COMPANIES; *U.S. Private*, pg. 4052
HESSE INDUSTRIAL SALES INC.; *U.S. Private*, pg. 1928
HESSELBEIN TIRE CO. INC.—See Dunlap & Kyle Co. Inc.; *U.S. Private*, pg. 1290
THE HESSEL GROUP LIMITED—See News Corporation; *U.S. Public*, pg. 1519
HESSEL HOLDING CO. INC.; *U.S. Private*, pg. 1928
HESSENATIE LOGISTICS NV—See Compagnie Maritime Belge S.A.; *Int'l*, pg. 1746
HESSE & PATRNER, AG—See Arthur J. Gallagher & Co.; *U.S. Public*, pg. 206
HESS EQUATORIAL GUINEA INC.—See Kosmos Energy Ltd.; *U.S. Public*, pg. 1275
HESS EQUATORIAL GUINEA INC.—See Warburg Pincus LLC; *U.S. Private*, pg. 4440
HESSER OLDSMOBILE PONTIAC INC.; *U.S. Private*, pg. 1928
HESSER TOYOTA INC.—See Bill Hesser Enterprises Inc.; *U.S. Private*, pg. 557
HESS EXPLORATION AUSTRALIA PTY LIMITED—See Hess Corporation; *U.S. Public*, pg. 1030
HESS FINE ARTS, INC.; *U.S. Private*, pg. 1927
HESS GMBH LICHT + FORM—See Ragni SAS; *Int'l*, pg. 6181
HESS GROUP AG; *Int'l*, pg. 3365
HESS INDUSTRIES, INC.; *U.S. Private*, pg. 1927
HESS INDUSTRIES, INC.—See Hess Industries, Inc.; *U.S. Private*, pg. 1927
HESSLE FORK TRUCKS LTD—See CorpAcq Holdings Limited; *Int'l*, pg. 1802
HESSLER'S, INC.; *U.S. Private*, pg. 1928
HESS LTD.—See Hess Corporation; *U.S. Public*, pg. 1030
HESS MALAYSIA SDN. BHD.—See Hess Corporation; *U.S. Public*, pg. 1030
HESS MIDSTREAM LP; *U.S. Public*, pg. 1030
HESS MIDSTREAM PARTNERS LP—See Hess Corporation; *U.S. Public*, pg. 1030
HESS ROUNTREE INC—See Bowman Consulting Group Ltd.; *U.S. Public*, pg. 376
HESS SCHWEIZ AG—See Gauselmann AG; *Int'l*, pg. 2890
HESS TRADING CORPORATION—See Hess Corporation; *U.S. Public*, pg. 1030
HESTA AG; *Int'l*, pg. 3365
HESTA BETEILIGUNGS-GMBH—See Hesta AG; *Int'l*, pg. 3365
HESTA IMMOBILIEN GMBH—See Hesta AG; *Int'l*, pg. 3365
HESTER BIOSCIENCES LIMITED; *Int'l*, pg. 3365
HESTER BIOSCIENCES NEPAL PRIVATE LIMITED—See Hester Biosciences Limited; *Int'l*, pg. 3365
HESTIA INSIGHT, INC.; *U.S. Public*, pg. 1030
HESTIA KONTAKT SP. Z O.O.—See Munchener Ruckversicherungs AG; *Int'l*, pg. 5089
HESTIA LOSS CONTROL SP. Z O.O.—See Munchener Ruckversicherungs AG; *Int'l*, pg. 5089
HESTIKA FRANCE S.A.S—See Citizen Watch Co., Ltd.; *Int'l*, pg. 1625
HESTIS SAS—See Blackfin Capital Partners SAS; *Int'l*, pg. 1060
HESTO HARNESSES (PTY) LTD.—See Metair Investments Limited; *Int'l*, pg. 4844
HESTYA ENERGY BV—See Riverstone Holdings LLC; *U.S. Private*, pg. 3447
HE SYSTEM ELECTRONIC GMBH & CO. KG—See Magna International Inc.; *U.S. Private*, pg. 4639
HETAG FYN A/S—See Kingspan Group PLC; *Int'l*, pg. 4178
HETAG JK TAGENTREPRISE A/S—See Kingspan Group PLC; *Int'l*, pg. 4178
HETAG NORDJYSK TAG A/S—See Kingspan Group PLC; *Int'l*, pg. 4178
HETAG TAGMATERIALER A/S—See Kingspan Group PLC; *Int'l*, pg. 4178
HETAT HOLDINGS PTE. LTD.—See SHS Holdings Ltd.; *Int'l*, pg. 6867
HET HUIS OPTICIENS—See CVC Capital Partners SICAV-FIS S.A.; *Int'l*, pg. 1886
HETLANDHUS AS—See OBOS BBL; *Int'l*, pg. 5512
HETMOS MOSTAR HOTELI D.D.; *Int'l*, pg. 3365
HET PAROOL B.V.—See DPG Media Group NV; *Int'l*, pg. 2188
HETRAS DEUTSCHLAND GMBH—See Beijing Shiji Information Technology Co., Ltd.; *Int'l*, pg. 956
HETRICK COMMUNICATIONS, INC.; *U.S. Private*, pg. 1928
HETROGENOUS, INC.—See Infospectrum, Inc.; *U.S. Private*, pg. 2074
HETRONIC ASIA—See Methode Electronics, Inc.; *U.S. Public*, pg. 1428

HETRONIC INTERNATIONAL, INC.—See Methode Electronics, Inc.; *U.S. Public*, pg. 1428
HETRONIC ITALY S.R.L.—See Methode Electronics, Inc.; *U.S. Public*, pg. 1428
HETRONIC MIDWEST, LLC—See Methode Electronics, Inc.; *U.S. Public*, pg. 1428
HETRONIC SWISS AG—See Methode Electronics, Inc.; *U.S. Public*, pg. 1428
HETRONIC USA, INC.—See Methode Electronics, Inc.; *U.S. Public*, pg. 1428
HETSCO, INC.—See The Toronto-Dominion Bank; *Int'l*, pg. 7696
H&E TSURUMI PUMP CO., LTD.—See Tsurumi Manufacturing Co., Ltd.; *Int'l*, pg. 7958
HETTICH AMERICA, L.P.—See Hettich Holding GmbH & Co. oHG; *Int'l*, pg. 3365
HETTICH AUSTRALIA PTY LTD—See Hettich Holding GmbH & Co. oHG; *Int'l*, pg. 3365
HETTICH CANADA L.P.—See Hettich Holding GmbH & Co. oHG; *Int'l*, pg. 3365
HETTICH CR K.S.—See Hettich Holding GmbH & Co. oHG; *Int'l*, pg. 3365
HETTICH FRANCE SCS—See Hettich Holding GmbH & Co. oHG; *Int'l*, pg. 3365
HETTICH FRANKE GMBH & CO. KG—See Hettich Holding GmbH & Co. oHG; *Int'l*, pg. 3365
HETTICH FURNTECH GMBH & CO. KG—See Hettich Holding GmbH & Co. oHG; *Int'l*, pg. 3365
HETTICH HARDWARE ACCESSORIES (SHANGHAI) CO. LTD.—See Hettich Holding GmbH & Co. oHG; *Int'l*, pg. 3365
HETTICH HOLDING GMBH & CO. OHG; *Int'l*, pg. 3365
HETTICH IBERIA S.L. EN COM.—See Hettich Holding GmbH & Co. oHG; *Int'l*, pg. 3365
HETTICH ITALIA SRL—See Hettich Holding GmbH & Co. oHG; *Int'l*, pg. 3365
HETTICH JAPAN K.K.—See Hettich Holding GmbH & Co. oHG; *Int'l*, pg. 3365
HETTICH LABINSTRUMENT AB—See ADDvise Group AB; *Int'l*, pg. 136
HETTICH LOGISTIK SERVICE GMBH & CO. KG—See Hettich Holding GmbH & Co. oHG; *Int'l*, pg. 3365
HETTICH MARKETING- UND VERTRIEBS GMBH & CO. KG—See Hettich Holding GmbH & Co. oHG; *Int'l*, pg. 3366
HETTICH MIDDLE EAST JLT.—See Hettich Holding GmbH & Co. oHG; *Int'l*, pg. 3366
HETTICH-ONI GMBH & CO. KG—See Hettich Holding GmbH & Co. oHG; *Int'l*, pg. 3366
HETTICH POLSKA SP. Z O.O.—See Hettich Holding GmbH & Co. oHG; *Int'l*, pg. 3366
HETTICH SINGAPORE (S.E.A.) PTE LTD—See Hettich Holding GmbH & Co. oHG; *Int'l*, pg. 3366
HETTICH SKANDINAVISKA AB—See Hettich Holding GmbH & Co. oHG; *Int'l*, pg. 3366
HETTICH SR S.R.O.—See Hettich Holding GmbH & Co. oHG; *Int'l*, pg. 3366
HETTICH STROTHMANN GMBH & CO. KG—See Hettich Holding GmbH & Co. oHG; *Int'l*, pg. 3366
HETTICH TR MOBILYA TEKNIK MALZEMELERI SAN. VE TIC. LTD. STI.—See Hettich Holding GmbH & Co. oHG; *Int'l*, pg. 3366
HETTICH (UK) LTD—See Hettich Holding GmbH & Co. oHG; *Int'l*, pg. 3365
HETTY SAS—See TotalEnergies SE; *Int'l*, pg. 7836
H.E. TURNER & CO., INC.; *U.S. Private*, pg. 1826
HEUBACH TOYO COLOUR PVT. LTD.—See Toyo Ink SC Holdings Co., Ltd.; *Int'l*, pg. 7853
HEUCOTECH LTD.; *U.S. Private*, pg. 1928
HEUGH HALL (COXHOE) RESIDENTS MANAGEMENT COMPANY LIMITED—See Persimmon plc; *Int'l*, pg. 5816
HEUMAN PHARMAN GMBH & CO., LTD.—See Torrent Pharmaceuticals Limited; *Int'l*, pg. 7831
HEUNET PHARMA GMBH—See Torrent Pharmaceuticals Limited; *Int'l*, pg. 7831
HEUNG-A LOGISTICS CO., LTD.; *Int'l*, pg. 3366
HEUNG-A LOGISTICS (SHANGHAI) CO., LTD.—See Heung-A Shipping Company Limited; *Int'l*, pg. 3366
HEUNG-A (M) SDN. BHD.—See Heung-A Shipping Company Limited; *Int'l*, pg. 3366
HEUNG-A SHIPPING (CHINA) CO., LTD.—See Heung-A Shipping Company Limited; *Int'l*, pg. 3366
HEUNG-A SHIPPING COMPANY LIMITED; *Int'l*, pg. 3366
HEUNG-A SHIPPING (THAILAND) CO., LTD.—See Heung-A Shipping Company Limited; *Int'l*, pg. 3366
HEUNG-A SHIPPING VIETNAM CO., LTD.—See Heung-A Shipping Company Limited; *Int'l*, pg. 3366
HEUNG-A (SINGAPORE) PTE LTD.—See Heung-A Shipping Company Limited; *Int'l*, pg. 3366
HEUNGGU OIL CO., LTD.; *Int'l*, pg. 3366
HEUNGKUK FIRE & MARINE INSURANCE CO., LTD.; *Int'l*, pg. 3366
HEUNGKUK METALTECH CO., LTD.; *Int'l*, pg. 3366
HEUREKA-GAMMA AG—See E.ON SE; *Int'l*, pg. 2258
HEURTEY PETROCHEM BRASIL LTDA.—See Heurtey Petrochem SA; *Int'l*, pg. 3366
HEURTEY PETROCHEM GMBH—See Heurtey Petrochem SA; *Int'l*, pg. 3366

HEURTEY PETROCHEM INDIA PVT LTD—See Heurtey Petrochem SA; *Int'l*, pg. 3366
HEURTEY PETROCHEM MANUFACTURING S.A.—See Heurtey Petrochem SA; *Int'l*, pg. 3366
HEURTEY PETROCHEM ROMANIA SRL—See Heurtey Petrochem SA; *Int'l*, pg. 3366
HEURTEY PETROCHEM SA; *Int'l*, pg. 3366
HEURTEY PETROCHEM SOUTH AFRICA (PTY) LTD—See Heurtey Petrochem SA; *Int'l*, pg. 3366
HEURTEY PETROCHEM TECHNOLOGY (BEIJING) LTD.—See Heurtey Petrochem SA; *Int'l*, pg. 3366
HEUSEL TEXTILHANDELSGESELLSCHAFT MBH—See Li & Fung Limited; *Int'l*, pg. 4479
HEUS MANUFACTURING COMPANY, INC.; *U.S. Private*, pg. 1928
HEUSSER NEWEIGH METROLOGY SERVICES—See Rice Lake Weighing Systems, Inc; *U.S. Private*, pg. 3425
HEUTS HANDEL B.V.—See LKQ Corporation; *U.S. Public*, pg. 1334
HEVEABOARD BERHAD; *Int'l*, pg. 3367
HEVEA B.V.; *Int'l*, pg. 3366
HEVEAFIL SDN. BERHAD—See Permodalan Nasional Berhad; *Int'l*, pg. 5809
HEVEAGRO SDN. BHD.—See HeveaBoard Berhad; *Int'l*, pg. 3367
HEVEAMART SDN. BHD.—See HeveaBoard Berhad; *Int'l*, pg. 3367
HEVEAPAC SDN. BHD.—See HeveaBoard Berhad; *Int'l*, pg. 3367
HEV HOHENLOHER ENERGIE VERSORGUNG GMBH—See EnBW Energie Baden-Wurttemberg AG; *Int'l*, pg. 2399
HEVOL SERVICES GROUP CO. LIMITED; *Int'l*, pg. 3367
HEWES MANUFACTURING CO.—See Maverick Boat Co. Inc.; *U.S. Private*, pg. 2615
H.E. WHITLOCK INC.; *U.S. Private*, pg. 1826
H.E. WILLIAMS, INC.; *U.S. Private*, pg. 1826
HEWING GMBH—See Rettig Group Ltd.; *Int'l*, pg. 6310
HEWITT ASSOCIATES (CHILE) LTDA.—See Alight, Inc.; *U.S. Public*, pg. 76
HEWITT ASSOCIATES GMBH—See Alight, Inc.; *U.S. Public*, pg. 76
HEWITT ASSOCIATES KABUSHIKI GAISYA—See Alight, Inc.; *U.S. Public*, pg. 76
HEWITT ASSOCIATES KOREA YUHAN HOESA—See Alight, Inc.; *U.S. Public*, pg. 76
HEWITT ASSOCIATES SARL—See Alight, Inc.; *U.S. Public*, pg. 76
HEWITT ASSOCIATES S.A.—See Alight, Inc.; *U.S. Public*, pg. 76
HEWITT ASSOCIATES SDN BHD—See Alight, Inc.; *U.S. Public*, pg. 76
HEWITT ASSOCIATES SRL—See Alight, Inc.; *U.S. Public*, pg. 76
HEW-KABEL GMBH & CO. KG—See HEW-KABEL Holding GmbH; *Int'l*, pg. 3367
HEW-KABEL HOLDING GMBH; *Int'l*, pg. 3367
HEWLAND ENGINEERING LTD; *Int'l*, pg. 3367
HEWLETT-PACKARD APS—See Hewlett Packard Enterprise Company; *U.S. Public*, pg. 1031
HEWLETT-PACKARD ARABIA LLC—See HP Inc.; *U.S. Public*, pg. 1063
HEWLETT-PACKARD ASIA PACIFIC PTE. LTD.—See Hewlett Packard Enterprise Company; *U.S. Public*, pg. 1031
HEWLETT-PACKARD AUSTRALIA PTY. LTD.—See Hewlett Packard Enterprise Company; *U.S. Public*, pg. 1031
HEWLETT-PACKARD AUSTRALIA PTY. LTD.—See Hewlett Packard Enterprise Company; *U.S. Public*, pg. 1031
HEWLETT-PACKARD BELGIUM SPRL/BVBA—See Hewlett Packard Enterprise Company; *U.S. Public*, pg. 1031
HEWLETT-PACKARD BRASIL LTDA.—See Hewlett Packard Enterprise Company; *U.S. Public*, pg. 1032
HEWLETT-PACKARD - BUSINESS INTELLIGENCE—See HP Inc.; *U.S. Public*, pg. 1063
HEWLETT-PACKARD DEVELOPMENT COMPANY, L.P.—See HP Inc.; *U.S. Public*, pg. 1063
HEWLETT-PACKARD ENTERPRISE BV—See Hewlett Packard Enterprise Company; *U.S. Public*, pg. 1031
HEWLETT PACKARD ENTERPRISE CANADA CO.—See Hewlett Packard Enterprise Company; *U.S. Public*, pg. 1031
HEWLETT PACKARD ENTERPRISE (CHINA) CO., LTD.—See Hewlett Packard Enterprise Company; *U.S. Public*, pg. 1031
HEWLETT PACKARD ENTERPRISE COMPANY; *U.S. Public*, pg. 1030
HEWLETT PACKARD ENTERPRISE GLOBALSOFT PRIVATE LIMITED—See Hewlett Packard Enterprise Company; *U.S. Public*, pg. 1031
HEWLETT-PACKARD ENTERPRISES, LLC—See HP Inc.; *U.S. Public*, pg. 1063
HEWLETT-PACKARD ESPANOLA, S.A.—See HP Inc.; *U.S. Public*, pg. 1063
HEWLETT-PACKARD ESPANOLA, S.A.—See HP Inc.; *U.S. Public*, pg. 1063
HEWLETT-PACKARD ESPANOLA, S.A.—See HP Inc.; *U.S. Public*, pg. 1063
HEWLETT-PACKARD ESPANOLA S.L.—See HP Inc.; *U.S. Public*, pg. 1063
HEWLETT-PACKARD EUROPA HOLDING B.V.—See HP Inc.; *U.S. Public*, pg. 1063
HEWLETT-PACKARD FINANCIAL SERVICES CANADA COMPANY—See Hewlett Packard Enterprise Company; *U.S. Public*, pg. 1031
HEWLETT-PACKARD FINANCIAL SERVICES (INDIA) PRIVATE LIMITED—See Hewlett Packard Enterprise Company; *U.S. Public*, pg. 1031
HEWLETT-PACKARD FRANCE SAS—See Hewlett Packard Enterprise Company; *U.S. Public*, pg. 1031
HEWLETT-PACKARD FRANCE—See Hewlett Packard Enterprise Company; *U.S. Public*, pg. 1031
HEWLETT-PACKARD GESELLSCHAFT MBH—See Hewlett Packard Enterprise Company; *U.S. Public*, pg. 1031
HEWLETT-PACKARD GMBH—See Hewlett Packard Enterprise Company; *U.S. Public*, pg. 1031
HEWLETT-PACKARD GMBH—See Hewlett Packard Enterprise Company; *U.S. Public*, pg. 1031
HEWLETT-PACKARD GMBH—See Hewlett Packard Enterprise Company; *U.S. Public*, pg. 1031
HEWLETT-PACKARD GMBH—See Hewlett Packard Enterprise Company; *U.S. Public*, pg. 1031
HEWLETT-PACKARD GMBH—See Hewlett Packard Enterprise Company; *U.S. Public*, pg. 1031
HEWLETT-PACKARD GMBH—See Hewlett Packard Enterprise Company; *U.S. Public*, pg. 1031
HEWLETT-PACKARD HK SAR LIMITED—See Hewlett Packard Enterprise Company; *U.S. Public*, pg. 1031
HEWLETT-PACKARD INDIA SALES PVT. LTD.—See HP Inc.; *U.S. Public*, pg. 1063
HEWLETT-PACKARD INDIGO B.V.—See HP Inc.; *U.S. Public*, pg. 1063
HEWLETT-PACKARD INDIGO LTD.—See HP Inc.; *U.S. Public*, pg. 1064
HEWLETT-PACKARD INDUSTRIAL PRINTING LTD.—See HP Inc.; *U.S. Public*, pg. 1064
HEWLETT-PACKARD INTERNATIONAL PTE. LTD.—See HP Inc.; *U.S. Public*, pg. 1064
HEWLETT-PACKARD INTERNATIONAL SARL—See Hewlett Packard Enterprise Company; *U.S. Public*, pg. 1031
HEWLETT-PACKARD IRELAND LTD.—See HP Inc.; *U.S. Public*, pg. 1064
HEWLETT-PACKARD (ISRAEL) LTD.—See Hewlett Packard Enterprise Company; *U.S. Public*, pg. 1031
HEWLETT-PACKARD ITALIANA S.R.L.—See Hewlett Packard Enterprise Company; *U.S. Public*, pg. 1031
HEWLETT-PACKARD JAPAN, LTD.—See Hewlett Packard Enterprise Company; *U.S. Public*, pg. 1031
HEWLETT-PACKARD KOREA LTD.—See Hewlett Packard Enterprise Company; *U.S. Public*, pg. 1031
HEWLETT-PACKARD LATIN AMERICA—See Hewlett Packard Enterprise Company; *U.S. Public*, pg. 1032
HEWLETT-PACKARD LIMITED—See Hewlett Packard Enterprise Company; *U.S. Public*, pg. 1032
HEWLETT-PACKARD LIMITED—See Hewlett Packard Enterprise Company; *U.S. Public*, pg. 1032
HEWLETT-PACKARD LUXEMBOURG S.C.A.—See HP Inc.; *U.S. Public*, pg. 1064
HEWLETT-PACKARD MANUFACTURING LTD.—See Hewlett Packard Enterprise Company; *U.S. Public*, pg. 1032
HEWLETT-PACKARD MEXICO - MONTERREY/NUEVO LEON—See Hewlett Packard Enterprise Company; *U.S. Public*, pg. 1032
HEWLETT-PACKARD MEXICO S. DE R.L. DE C.V.—See Hewlett Packard Enterprise Company; *U.S. Public*, pg. 1032
HEWLETT-PACKARD MIDDLE EAST FZ-LLC—See Hewlett Packard Enterprise Company; *U.S. Public*, pg. 1032
HEWLETT-PACKARD (M) SDN. BHD.—See Hewlett Packard Enterprise Company; *U.S. Public*, pg. 1031
HEWLETT-PACKARD NEDERLAND B.V.—See Hewlett Packard Enterprise Company; *U.S. Public*, pg. 1032
HEWLETT-PACKARD NEW ZEALAND—See Hewlett Packard Enterprise Company; *U.S. Public*, pg. 1032
HEWLETT-PACKARD (NIGERIA) LIMITED—See Hewlett Packard Enterprise Company; *U.S. Public*, pg. 1031
HEWLETT-PACKARD NORGE A/S—See Hewlett Packard Enterprise Company; *U.S. Public*, pg. 1032
HEWLETT-PACKARD OPERATIONS MEXICO, S. DE R.L. DE C.V.—See Hewlett Packard Enterprise Company; *U.S. Public*, pg. 1032
HEWLETT-PACKARD OY—See Hewlett Packard Enterprise Company; *U.S. Public*, pg. 1032
HEWLETT-PACKARD PHILIPPINES CORPORATION—See Hewlett Packard Enterprise Company; *U.S. Public*, pg. 1032
HEWLETT-PACKARD POLSKA SP. Z.O.O.—See HP Inc.; *U.S. Public*, pg. 1064
HEWLETT-PACKARD PORTUGAL LDA.—See Hewlett Packard Enterprise Company; *U.S. Public*, pg. 1032
HEWLETT-PACKARD S.A.R.L.—See Hewlett Packard Enterprise Company; *U.S. Public*, pg. 1032
HEWLETT-PACKARD (SCHWEIZ) GMBH—See Hewlett Packard Enterprise Company; *U.S. Public*, pg. 1031
HEWLETT-PACKARD (SCHWEIZ) GMBH—See Hewlett Packard Enterprise Company; *U.S. Public*, pg. 1031
HEWLETT-PACKARD (SCHWEIZ) GMBH—See Hewlett Packard Enterprise Company; *U.S. Public*, pg. 1031
HEWLETT-PACKARD SERVICES SAUDI ARABIA COMPANY—See HP Inc.; *U.S. Public*, pg. 1064
HEWLETT-PACKARD SERVICIOS ESPANA S.L.—See Hewlett Packard Enterprise Company; *U.S. Public*, pg. 1032
HEWLETT-PACKARD SINGAPORE (PRIVATE) LIMITED—See HP Inc.; *U.S. Public*, pg. 1064
HEWLETT-PACKARD SINGAPORE (SALES) PTE. LTD.—See Hewlett Packard Enterprise Company; *U.S. Public*, pg. 1031
HEWLETT-PACKARD SOUTH AFRICA (PROPRIETARY) LIMITED—See Hewlett Packard Enterprise Company; *U.S. Public*, pg. 1032
HEWLETT-PACKARD S.R.O.—See Hewlett Packard Enterprise Company; *U.S. Public*, pg. 1032
HEWLETT-PACKARD SVERIGE AB—See Hewlett Packard Enterprise Company; *U.S. Public*, pg. 1032
HEWLETT PACKARD TAIWAN LTD.—See Hewlett Packard Enterprise Company; *U.S. Public*, pg. 1031
HEWLETT-PACKARD TECHNOLOGY (SHANGHAI) CO. LTD.—See HP Inc.; *U.S. Public*, pg. 1064
HEWLETT-PACKARD TEKNOLOJI COZUMLERI LIMITED SIRKETI—See Hewlett Packard Enterprise Company; *U.S. Public*, pg. 1032
HEWLETT-PACKARD TRADING (SHANGHAI) CO., LTD.—See HP Inc.; *U.S. Public*, pg. 1064
HEWLETT-PACKARD VIETNAM LTD.—See HP Inc.; *U.S. Public*, pg. 1064
HEWS COMPANY LLC; *U.S. Private*, pg. 1928
HEWTECH (BANGKOK) CO., LTD.—See Hirakawa Hewtech Corp.; *Int'l*, pg. 3403
HEWTECH HONG KONG LTD.—See Hirakawa Hewtech Corp.; *Int'l*, pg. 3403
HEWTECH (LIANYUNGANG) ELECTRONICS CO., LTD.—See Hirakawa Hewtech Corp.; *Int'l*, pg. 3403
HEWTECH PHILIPPINES CORP.—See Hirakawa Hewtech Corp.; *Int'l*, pg. 3403
HEWTECH PHILIPPINES ELECTRONICS CORP.—See Hirakawa Hewtech Corp.; *Int'l*, pg. 3403
HEWTECH SHANGHAI TRADING CO., LTD.—See Hirakawa Hewtech Corp.; *Int'l*, pg. 3403
HEWTECH (SHENZHEN) ELECTRONICS CO., LTD.—See Hirakawa Hewtech Corp.; *Int'l*, pg. 3403
HEWTECH (THAILAND) CO., LTD.—See Hirakawa Hewtech Corp.; *Int'l*, pg. 3403
HEXA AMERICAS INC.—See ITOCHU Corporation; *Int'l*, pg. 3836
HEXA ANALISA SDN. BHD.—See Fibon Berhad; *Int'l*, pg. 2652
HEXACHASE CORPORATION SDN. BHD.—See Mega First Corporation Berhad; *Int'l*, pg. 4792
HEXACHASE FLEXIPACK SDN. BHD.—See Mega First Corporation Berhad; *Int'l*, pg. 4792
HEXACOMB CORPORATION—See Packaging Corporation of America; *U.S. Public*, pg. 1633
HEXACON CONSTRUCTION PTE LIMITED—See IJM Corporation Berhad; *Int'l*, pg. 3608
HEXAGON AB; *Int'l*, pg. 3367
HEXAGON COMPOSITES ASA; *Int'l*, pg. 3369
HEXAGON COMPOSITE SDN. BHD.—See Hexagon Holdings Berhad; *Int'l*, pg. 3370
HEXAGON DIGITAL WAVE, LLC—See Hexagon Composites ASA; *Int'l*, pg. 3370
HEXAGON DISTRIBUTORS SDN. BHD.—See Hexagon Holdings Berhad; *Int'l*, pg. 3370
HEXAGON ENERGY BV—See Koninklijke DSM N.V.; *Int'l*, pg. 4264
HEXAGON ENERGY MATERIALS LIMITED; *Int'l*, pg. 3370
HEXAGON ENGINEERING AND DESIGN INC.—See Kiraca Holding A.S.; *Int'l*, pg. 4185
HEXAGON HOLDINGS BERHAD; *Int'l*, pg. 3370
HEXAGON LINCOLN, INC.—See Hexagon Composites ASA; *Int'l*, pg. 3370
HEXAGON MEASUREMENT TECHNOLOGIES—See Hexagon AB; *Int'l*, pg. 3367
HEXAGON METROLOGY FRANCE S.A.—See Hexagon AB; *Int'l*, pg. 3367
HEXAGON METROLOGY GMBH—See Hexagon AB; *Int'l*, pg. 3367
HEXAGON METROLOGY NORDIC AB—See Hexagon AB; *Int'l*, pg. 3367
HEXAGON METROLOGY SERVICES LTD.—See Hexagon AB; *Int'l*, pg. 3367
HEXAGON MIDCO INDIA PVT. LTD.—See Hexagon Holdings Berhad; *Int'l*, pg. 3370
HEXAGON PPM - CADWORX & ANALYSIS SOLUTIONS—See Hexagon AB; *Int'l*, pg. 3368
HEXAGON PPM—See Hexagon AB; *Int'l*, pg. 3368
HEXAGON PURUS ASA; *Int'l*, pg. 3370
HEXAGON RAUFOSS AS—See Hexagon Composites ASA; *Int'l*, pg. 3370
HEXAGON SHOP SYSTEM SDN. BHD.—See Hexagon Holdings Berhad; *Int'l*, pg. 3370
HEXAGON SOCIEDAD ANONIMA—See John Wood Group PLC; *Int'l*, pg. 3983

COMPANY NAME INDEX

HEXAGON-TATSUNO ENGINEERING SDN. BHD.—See Hexagon Holdings Berhad; *Int'l*, pg. 3370
HEXAGON TOWER PHILIPPINES INC.—See Hexagon Holdings Berhad; *Int'l*, pg. 3370
HEXAGON TOWER (TIANJIN) ENGINEERING CO., LTD.—See Hexagon Holdings Berhad; *Int'l*, pg. 3370
HEXAGON VETEC SDN. BHD.—See Hexagon Holdings Berhad; *Int'l*, pg. 3370
HEXAL AG—See Sandoz Group AG; *Int'l*, pg. 6526
HEXATECH, INC.—See Stanley Electric Co., Ltd.; *Int'l*, pg. 7170
HEXATIER LTD.—See Huawei Investment & Holding Co., Ltd.; *Int'l*, pg. 3515
HEXA TRADEX LIMITED—See Jindal Holdings Limited; *Int'l*, pg. 3966
HEXATRONIC AUSTRALIA PTY. LTD.—See Hexatronic Group AB; *Int'l*, pg. 3370
HEXATRONIC CABLES & INTERCONNECT AB—See Hexatronic Group AB; *Int'l*, pg. 3370
HEXATRONIC CANADA INC—See Hexatronic Group AB; *Int'l*, pg. 3370
HEXATRONIC FIBEROPTIC AB—See Hexatronic Group AB; *Int'l*, pg. 3370
HEXATRONIC GMBH—See Hexatronic Group AB; *Int'l*, pg. 3371
HEXATRONIC GROUP AB; *Int'l*, pg. 3370
HEXATRONIC NEW ZEALAND LTD.—See Hexatronic Group AB; *Int'l*, pg. 3371
HEXATRONIC SECURITY & SURVEILLANCE AB—See Hexatronic Group AB; *Int'l*, pg. 3371
HEXATRONIC UK LTD.—See Hexatronic Group AB; *Int'l*, pg. 3371
HEXAWARE TECHNOLOGIES INC.—See EQT AB; *Int'l*, pg. 2470
HEXAWARE TECHNOLOGIES LTD—See EQT AB; *Int'l*, pg. 2470
HEXCEL-CHINA HOLDINGS CORP.—See Hexcel Corporation; *U.S. Public*, pg. 1033
HEXCEL COMPOSITES GMBH & CO. KG—See Hexcel Corporation; *U.S. Public*, pg. 1032
HEXCEL COMPOSITES GMBH—See Hexcel Corporation; *U.S. Public*, pg. 1032
HEXCEL COMPOSITES LIMITED—See Hexcel Corporation; *U.S. Public*, pg. 1032
HEXCEL COMPOSITES S.A.—See Hexcel Corporation; *U.S. Public*, pg. 1032
HEXCEL COMPOSITES SASU—See Hexcel Corporation; *U.S. Public*, pg. 1032
HEXCEL COMPOSITES S.P.R.L.—See Hexcel Corporation; *U.S. Public*, pg. 1032
HEXCEL CORP. - DUBLIN—See Hexcel Corporation; *U.S. Public*, pg. 1033
HEXCEL CORPORATION; *U.S. Public*, pg. 1032
HEXCEL EUROPE LIMITED—See Hexcel Corporation; *U.S. Public*, pg. 1033
HEXCEL FIBERS INC.—See Hexcel Corporation; *U.S. Public*, pg. 1033
HEXCEL HOLDING GMBH—See Hexcel Corporation; *U.S. Public*, pg. 1033
HEXCEL POTTSVILLE CORPORATION—See Hexcel Corporation; *U.S. Public*, pg. 1033
HEXCEL REINFORCEMENTS CORP.—See Hexcel Corporation; *U.S. Public*, pg. 1033
HEXCEL REINFORCEMENTS SASU—See Hexcel Corporation; *U.S. Public*, pg. 1033
HEXCEL REINFORCEMENTS—See Hexcel Corporation; *U.S. Public*, pg. 1033
HEXCEL REINFORCEMENTS UK LIMITED—See Hexcel Corporation; *U.S. Public*, pg. 1033
HEXCEL REINFORCEMENTS UK LIMITED—See Hexcel Corporation; *U.S. Public*, pg. 1033
HEXICO ENTERPRISE CO., LTD.—See San Shing Fastech Corp.; *Int'l*, pg. 6521
HEXICON AB; *Int'l*, pg. 3371
HEXIMA LIMITED; *Int'l*, pg. 3371
HEXING ELECTRICAL CO LTD; *Int'l*, pg. 3371
HEXION B.V. - ROTTERDAM, BOTLEK—See American Securities LLC; *U.S. Private*, pg. 249
HEXION B.V.—See American Securities LLC; *U.S. Private*, pg. 249
HEXION CANADA INC.—See American Securities LLC; *U.S. Private*, pg. 249
HEXION GMBH—See American Securities LLC; *U.S. Private*, pg. 249
HEXION HOLDINGS CORPORATION—See American Securities LLC; *U.S. Private*, pg. 249
HEXION INC.—See American Securities LLC; *U.S. Private*, pg. 249
HEXION SPECIALTY CHEMICALS IBERICA, S.A.—See American Securities LLC; *U.S. Private*, pg. 249
HEXION TOPCO, LLC—See Apollo Global Management, Inc.; *U.S. Public*, pg. 151
HEXION UK LTD. - PETERLEE—See American Securities LLC; *U.S. Private*, pg. 249
HEXION UK LTD.—See American Securities LLC; *U.S. Private*, pg. 249
HEXION UK LTD. - STIRLING—See American Securities LLC; *U.S. Private*, pg. 249
HEXIS AG; *Int'l*, pg. 3371

HEXIS CIENTIFICA S.A.—See Danaher Corporation; *U.S. Public*, pg. 627
HEXIS GMBH—See Hexis AG; *Int'l*, pg. 3371
HEXO CORP.—See Tilray Brands, Inc.; *Int'l*, pg. 7748
HEXONIA GMBH; *Int'l*, pg. 3371
HEXO OPERATIONS INC.—See Tilray Brands, Inc.; *Int'l*, pg. 7748
HEXPOL AB; *Int'l*, pg. 3371
HEXPOL COMPOUNDING CA INC.—See HEXPOL AB; *Int'l*, pg. 3372
HEXPOL COMPOUNDING (FOSHAN) CO., LTD.—See HEXPOL AB; *Int'l*, pg. 3372
HEXPOL COMPOUNDING GMBH—See HEXPOL AB; *Int'l*, pg. 3372
HEXPOL COMPOUNDING HQ SA—See HEXPOL AB; *Int'l*, pg. 3372
HEXPOL COMPOUNDING HQ SPRL—See HEXPOL AB; *Int'l*, pg. 3372
HEXPOL COMPOUNDING LESINA S.R.O.—See HEXPOL AB; *Int'l*, pg. 3372
HEXPOL COMPOUNDING LLC—See HEXPOL AB; *Int'l*, pg. 3372
HEXPOL COMPOUNDING NC INC.—See HEXPOL AB; *Int'l*, pg. 3372
HEXPOL COMPOUNDING (QINGDAO) CO., LTD.—See HEXPOL AB; *Int'l*, pg. 3371
HEXPOL COMPOUNDING QUERETARO S.A. DE C.V.—See HEXPOL AB; *Int'l*, pg. 3372
HEXPOL COMPOUNDING S.A. DE C.V.—See HEXPOL AB; *Int'l*, pg. 3372
HEXPOL COMPOUNDING S.L.U.—See HEXPOL AB; *Int'l*, pg. 3372
HEXPOL COMPOUNDING SPRL—See HEXPOL AB; *Int'l*, pg. 3372
HEXPOL COMPOUNDING S.R.O.—See HEXPOL AB; *Int'l*, pg. 3372
HEXPOL COMPOUNDING (UK) LTD.—See HEXPOL AB; *Int'l*, pg. 3372
HEXPOL SERVICES COMPOUNDING S.A DE C.V—See HEXPOL AB; *Int'l*, pg. 3372
HEXPOL TPE AB—See HEXPOL AB; *Int'l*, pg. 3372
HEXPOL TPE GMBH—See HEXPOL AB; *Int'l*, pg. 3372
HEXPOL TPE LTD.—See HEXPOL AB; *Int'l*, pg. 3372
HEXTAR CHEMICALS SDN. BHD.—See Hextar Holdings Sdn. Bhd.; *Int'l*, pg. 3373
HEXTAR FERTILIZERS SDN. BHD.—See Hextar Holdings Sdn. Bhd.; *Int'l*, pg. 3373
HEXTAR GLOBAL BERHAD; *Int'l*, pg. 3373
HEXTAR HEALTHCARE BERHAD—See Hextar Global Berhad; *Int'l*, pg. 3373
HEXTAR HOLDINGS SDN. BHD.; *Int'l*, pg. 3373
HEXTAR INDUSTRIES BERHAD; *Int'l*, pg. 3373
HEXTAR RUBBER SDN. BHD.—See Hextar Global Berhad; *Int'l*, pg. 3373
HEXTAR TECHNOLOGIES SOLUTIONS BHD—See Hextar Holdings Sdn. Bhd.; *Int'l*, pg. 3373
HEXTER-FAIR / FIRST AMERICAN TITLE COMPANY, LLC—See First American Financial Corporation; *U.S. Public*, pg. 838
HEXZACHEM SARAWAK SDN. BHD.—See Hexza Corporation Berhad; *Int'l*, pg. 3373
HEXZACHEM SARAWAK SDN. BHD.—See Hexza Corporation Berhad; *Int'l*, pg. 3373
HEXZACHEM SARAWAK SDN. BHD.—See Hexza Corporation Berhad; *Int'l*, pg. 3373
HEXZACHEM SARAWAK SDN. BHD.—See Hexza Corporation Berhad; *Int'l*, pg. 3373
HEXZA CORPORATION BERHAD; *Int'l*, pg. 3373
HEXZA-MATHER SDN. BHD.—See Hexza Corporation Berhad; *Int'l*, pg. 3373
HEYBRYAN MEDIA, INC.; *Int'l*, pg. 3374
HEYBURN DIALYSIS, LLC—See DaVita Inc.; *U.S. Public*, pg. 634
HEYCARTER (PTY.) LTD.—See PSG Group Limited; *Int'l*, pg. 6016
HEYCO INC.; *U.S. Public*, pg. 1928
HEYDAY5 PTY. LIMITED—See Southern Cross Electrical Engineering Limited; *Int'l*, pg. 7119
HEYDE COMPANIES; *U.S. Private*, pg. 1928
HEYDERHOFF GMBH—See Aiphone Co., Ltd.; *Int'l*, pg. 235
HEYDEVELD BVBA—See Clariane SE; *Int'l*, pg. 1643
HEYE GMBH—See Omnicom Group Inc.; *U.S. Public*, pg. 1581
HEYE INTERNATIONAL GMBH—See Ardagh Group S.A.; *Int'l*, pg. 553
HEYE MEDIA OMD GMBH—See Omnicom Group Inc.; *U.S. Public*, pg. 1582
HEYE & PARTNER GMBH - HAMBURG—See Omnicom Group Inc.; *U.S. Public*, pg. 1581
HEYER CORP.; *U.S. Private*, pg. 1928
HEYE SPECIAL STEEL CO., LTD.—See Advanced Technology & Materials Co., Ltd.; *Int'l*, pg. 162
HEYE & SUMMIT TOOLS CO., LTD—See Advanced Technology & Materials Co., Ltd.; *Int'l*, pg. 162
HEYFORM BRAMSCHE GMBH—See NORD Holding Unternehmensbeteiligungsgesellschaft mbH; *Int'l*, pg. 5416

HEYL CHEMISCH-PHARMAZEUTISCHE FABRIK GMBH UND CO. KG; *Int'l*, pg. 3374
HEYL LOGISTICS—See Heyl Truck Lines Inc.; *U.S. Private*, pg. 1928
HEYLTEX CORPORATION—See HEYL Chemisch-pharmazeutische Fabrik GmbH und Co. KG; *Int'l*, pg. 3374
HEYL TRUCK LINES INC.; *U.S. Private*, pg. 1928
HEYMANN CONSTRUCTION COMPANY; *U.S. Private*, pg. 1928
HEYMO INGENIERIA, S. A.—See Tecnicas Reunidas, S.A.; *Int'l*, pg. 7515
HEYSHAM PORT LTD.—See Peel Holdings Ltd.; *Int'l*, pg. 5779
HEY-SONG CORPORATION; *Int'l*, pg. 3373
HEYSONG FOOD (SUZHOU) CO., LTD.—See Hey-Song Corporation; *Int'l*, pg. 3374
HEYUAN GUANFENGHANG AUTO CO., LTD.—See China MeiDong Auto Holdings Limited; *Int'l*, pg. 1519
HEYUAN KIBING SILICON INDUSTRY CO. LIMITED—See Zhuzhou Kibing Group Co., Ltd.; *Int'l*, pg. 8680
HE YUAN SKY WEALTH ELECTRONIC & PLASTIC COMPANY LIMITED—See Keen Ocean International Holding Ltd.; *Int'l*, pg. 4115
HEYWIRE, INC.—See Salesforce, Inc.; *U.S. Public*, pg. 1837
HEYWOOD HOSPITAL; *U.S. Private*, pg. 1928
HEYWOOD LIMITED—See Sincere Navigation Corporation; *Int'l*, pg. 6937
HEYWOOD METAL FINISHERS LTD.—See Coil S.A./N.V.; *Int'l*, pg. 1696
HEYWOOD WILLIAMS COMPONENTS LIMITED—See ASSA ABLOY AB; *Int'l*, pg. 639
HEYWOOD WILLIAMS COMPONENTS LIMITED—See ASSA ABLOY AB; *Int'l*, pg. 639
HEZHONG INTERNATIONAL (HOLDING) LIMITED; *Int'l*, pg. 3374
HEZHOU BOSSCO ENVIRONMENTAL INVESTMENT & CONSTRUCTION CO., LTD.—See Guangxi Bossco Environmental Protection Technology Co., Ltd.; *Int'l*, pg. 3163
HEZHOU PINGGUI PGMA CEMENT CO. LTD—See China Nonferrous Metal Mining (Group) Co., Ltd.; *Int'l*, pg. 1535
HEZHOU PINGGUI PGMA TRANSPORTATION CO. LTD—See China Nonferrous Metal Mining (Group) Co., Ltd.; *Int'l*, pg. 1535
HFACTOR, INC.; *U.S. Public*, pg. 1034
H-FARM SPA; *Int'l*, pg. 3194
H-FARM S.P.A.; *Int'l*, pg. 3194
HFB FINANCIAL CORPORATION; *U.S. Public*, pg. 1034
HFB FINANCIAL PLANNING LTD.; *Int'l*, pg. 3374
HFBG HOLDING B.V.; *Int'l*, pg. 3374
HFB BANK LIMITED—See HSBC Holdings plc; *Int'l*, pg. 3505
HFC CONTROLS. CORP.—See Doosan Corporation; *Int'l*, pg. 2174
HFCL LIMITED; *Int'l*, pg. 3375
HF COMPANY; *Int'l*, pg. 3374
HFCONTROLS—See Doosan Corporation; *Int'l*, pg. 2173
HFCS TRANSPORT INC.—See P&S Investment Company Inc.; *U.S. Private*, pg. 3059
HF DANYKO AS—See Addtech AB; *Int'l*, pg. 133
HFD LTD—See Headlam Group plc; *Int'l*, pg. 3301
H&F EUROPE LIMITED—See Hitachi Zosen Corporation; *Int'l*, pg. 3410
HFF, INC.—See Jones Lang LaSalle Incorporated; *U.S. Public*, pg. 1202
HF FOODS GROUP INC.; *U.S. Public*, pg. 1033
HFG BENEFITS CORP.—See Arthur J. Gallagher & Co.; *U.S. Public*, pg. 205
HF GROUP INC. - HOUSTON FEARLESS 76 DIVISION—See HF Group Inc.; *U.S. Private*, pg. 1928
HF GROUP INC.; *U.S. Private*, pg. 1928
THE HF GROUP LLC - BOOK PARTNER DIVISION—See The HF Group LLC; *U.S. Public*, pg. 4052
THE HF GROUP LLC; *U.S. Public*, pg. 4052
HF GROUP PLC; *Int'l*, pg. 3374
HFG (SINGAPORE) PTE. LTD.—See High Finance Ltd.; *Int'l*, pg. 3385
HFG SVERIGE AB—See Hilton Food Group plc; *Int'l*, pg. 3395
H&F GULF INC.; *U.S. Private*, pg. 1822
HF HEALTHCARE LIMITED—See Walgreens Boots Alliance, Inc.; *U.S. Public*, pg. 2322
HFI INC.; *U.S. Private*, pg. 1928
H.F. LONG AND ASSOCIATES, INC.; *U.S. Private*, pg. 1826
HF MANUFACTURING CORP.; *U.S. Private*, pg. 1928
HF MIXING GROUP SERVICES (S.E.A.) SDN. BHD.—See L. Possehl & Co. mbH; *Int'l*, pg. 4382
HF NAJUS, A.S.—See L. Possehl & Co. mbH; *Int'l*, pg. 4383
HFO CHICAGO, LLC—See Morris Group, Inc.; *U.S. Private*, pg. 2787
HFOTCO LLC—See Energy Transfer LP; *U.S. Public*, pg. 764
HFO TELECOM AG; *Int'l*, pg. 3375

HFO TELECOM AG
CORPORATE AFFILIATIONS

HFP ACOUSTICAL CONSULTANTS CORP.—See Charterhouse Capital Partners LLP; *Int'l*, pg. 1456
H. FREEMAN & SON, INC.; *U.S. Private*, pg. 1824
HFR INC.; *Int'l*, pg. 3375
HF RUBBER MACHINERY INC.—See L. Possehl & Co. mbH; *Int'l*, pg. 4383
HF SCIENTIFIC, INC.—See Watts Water Technologies, Inc.; *U.S. Public*, pg. 2337
HFS.COM REAL ESTATE INCORPORATED—See Anywhere Real Estate Inc.; *U.S. Public*, pg. 142
HFS.COM REAL ESTATE LLC—See Anywhere Real Estate Inc.; *U.S. Public*, pg. 142
H&F SERVICES (THAILAND) CO., LTD.—See Hitachi Zosen Corporation; *Int'l*, pg. 3410
HFS HELVETIC FINANCIAL SERVICES AG—See CORESTATE Capital Holding SA; *Int'l*, pg. 1800
H&F SHOES (THAILAND) CO., LTD.—See Aurelius Equity Opportunities SE & Co. KGaA; *Int'l*, pg. 708
HFS HOLDING CORPORATION—See Magnetic Ticket & Label Corp.; *U.S. Private*, pg. 2547
H.F.S. HYPO-FONDSBETEILIGUNGEN FUR SACHWERTE GMBH—See UniCredit S.p.A.; *Int'l*, pg. 8041
H.F.S. IMMOBILIENFONDS EUROPA 2 BETEILIGUNGS GMBH—See UniCredit S.p.A.; *Int'l*, pg. 8034
HF SINCLAIR CASPER REFINING LLC—See HF Sinclair Corporation; *U.S. Public*, pg. 1033
HF SINCLAIR CORPORATION; *U.S. Public*, pg. 1033
HF SINCLAIR EL DORADO REFINING LLC—See HF Sinclair Corporation; *U.S. Public*, pg. 1033
HF SINCLAIR PARCO REFINING LLC—See HF Sinclair Corporation; *U.S. Public*, pg. 1033
HF SINCLAIR PUGET SOUND REFINING LLC—See HF Sinclair Corporation; *U.S. Public*, pg. 1033
HF SUPPLIERS (SCOTLAND) LIMITED—See W.W. Grainger, Inc.; *U.S. Public*, pg. 2320
H.F.S. ZWEITMARKTFONDS DEUTSCHLAND 4 GMBH & CO. KG—See UniCredit S.p.A.; *Int'l*, pg. 8041
H.F.T. INDUSTRIAL LTD.—See Funai Electric Co., Ltd.; *Int'l*, pg. 2844
HFT INTL. (GUERNSEY) LTD—See Banque Heritage (Suisse) S.A.; *Int'l*, pg. 854
HFT INVESTMENT MANAGEMENT CO., LTD.—See Haitong Securities Co., Ltd.; *Int'l*, pg. 3218
HF VERMOGENSVERWALTUNGSGESELLSCHAFT IM RUHRTAL GMBH—See ThyssenKrupp AG; *Int'l*, pg. 7724
HFX HOLDING CORP.; *Int'l*, pg. 3375
HGA INC; *U.S. Private*, pg. 1928
HGA MID-ATLANTIC, INC.—See Hammel, Green & Abrahamson, Inc.; *U.S. Private*, pg. 1849
HGCAPITAL LLP—See HgCapital Trust plc; *Int'l*, pg. 3376
HGCAPITAL TRUST PLC; *Int'l*, pg. 3376
HGC HAMBURG GAS CONSULT GMBH—See E.ON SE; *Int'l*, pg. 2254
HGC, INC.—See Chevron Corporation; *U.S. Public*, pg. 487
HG CONSTRUCTION STEEL PTE LTD.—See HG Metal Manufacturing Limited; *Int'l*, pg. 3375
HG DATA CO.—See Clarion Capital Partners, LLC; *U.S. Private*, pg. 911
HGEARS AG; *Int'l*, pg. 3378
HGEARS PADOVA S.P.A.—See hGears AG; *Int'l*, pg. 3378
HGEARS (SUZHOU) CO., LTD.—See hGears AG; *Int'l*, pg. 3378
H. GEIGER GMBH; *Int'l*, pg. 3194
HGGC, LLC; *U.S. Private*, pg. 1928
H.G. HASTINGS CO.; *U.S. Private*, pg. 1826
HGH HARDWARE SUPPLY INC.; *U.S. Private*, pg. 1930
HGH HOLDINGS LTD.; *Int'l*, pg. 3378
H&G HIGH CONVICTION LIMITED; *Int'l*, pg. 3191
HGH INFRARED SYSTEMS INC.; *U.S. Private*, pg. 1930
HG HOLDINGS, INC.; *U.S. Public*, pg. 1034
HGI IMMOBILIEN GMBH & CO. GB I KG—See DZ BANK AG Deutsche Zentral-Genossenschaftsbank; *Int'l*, pg. 2244
HGIM HOLDINGS, LLC—See The Jordan Company, L.P.; *U.S. Private*, pg. 4061
HG INDUSTRIES LIMITED—See Greenlam Industries Limited; *Int'l*, pg. 3075
H&G INFOTECH OFFICE—See Herrman & Goetz Inc.; *U.S. Private*, pg. 1926
H.G. INFRA ENGINEERING LTD.; *Int'l*, pg. 3195
HGI REALTY, INC.—See Heritage Group, Inc.; *U.S. Private*, pg. 1923
HG LOGISTICS, LLC—See Hill & Griffith Company; *U.S. Private*, pg. 1944
H.G. MAKELIM COMPANY; *U.S. Private*, pg. 1826
HG METAL MANUFACTURING LIMITED; *Int'l*, pg. 3375
HG METAL MANUFACTURING SDN. BHD.—See HG Metal Manufacturing Limited; *Int'l*, pg. 3375
HG METAL PTE LTD—See HG Metal Manufacturing Limited; *Int'l*, pg. 3375
HGNH INTERNATIONAL FINANCIAL (SINGAPORE) PTE. LTD.—See Nanhua Futures Co., Ltd.; *Int'l*, pg. 5139
H GOODWIN & SON (NEWCASTLE) LIMITED—See Co-operative Group Limited; *Int'l*, pg. 1679
H.G. PAGE REALTY CORPORATION—See Page Bros Enterprises Ltd.; *U.S. Private*, pg. 3074

H.G. PAGE & SONS INC.—See Page Bros Enterprises Ltd.; *U.S. Private*, pg. 3074
HGP INTERNATIONAL BV—See Eneraqua Technologies Plc; *Int'l*, pg. 2418
HG POWER TRANSMISSION SDN. BHD.—See Rohas Tecnic Berhad; *Int'l*, pg. 6384
H.G.P. SASU—See L-Acoustics SAS; *Int'l*, pg. 4381
H. GREENBERG & SON INC.; *U.S. Private*, pg. 1824
HGREG.COM; *U.S. Private*, pg. 1930
HGREG NISSAN BUENA PARK—See HGreg.com; *U.S. Private*, pg. 1931
H.G. REYNOLDS CO. INC.; *U.S. Private*, pg. 1826
H.GRINGOIRE S.A.R.L.—See Pranda Jewelry Public Company Limited; *Int'l*, pg. 5954
THE H GROUP; *U.S. Private*, pg. 4040
H&G SALES INC.; *U.S. Private*, pg. 1822
HG SEMICONDUCTOR LIMITED; *Int'l*, pg. 3375
H.G.S. GMBH & CO. KG—See ENGIE SA; *Int'l*, pg. 2429
HGS HOLDINGS, INC.—See Kratos Defense & Security Solutions, Inc.; *U.S. Public*, pg. 1276
HGS-LITO KFT.—See Hella GmbH & Co. KGaA; *Int'l*, pg. 3332
HGST EUROPE, LTD.—See Western Digital Corporation; *U.S. Public*, pg. 2355
HGST, INC.—See Western Digital Corporation; *U.S. Public*, pg. 2355
HGST JAPAN CO., LTD.—See Western Digital Corporation; *U.S. Public*, pg. 2355
HGST PHILIPPINES CORP.—See Western Digital Corporation; *U.S. Public*, pg. 2355
HGST SINGAPORE PTE. LTD.—See Western Digital Corporation; *U.S. Public*, pg. 2355
HGST (THAILAND) LTD.—See Western Digital Corporation; *U.S. Public*, pg. 2355
HGS USA—See Hinduja Global Solutions Ltd.; *Int'l*, pg. 3398
HGT AS—See Peab AB; *Int'l*, pg. 5771
HG TECHNOLOGIES CO., LTD.; *Int'l*, pg. 3375
HGTRADE, TRZENJE BARV, D.O.O.—See Kansai Paint Co., Ltd.; *Int'l*, pg. 4071
HGTV MAGAZINE—See The Hearst Corporation; *U.S. Private*, pg. 4046
HGV HAMBURGER GESELLSCHAFT FUR VERMOGENS- UND BETEILIGUNGSMANAGEMENT MBH; *Int'l*, pg. 3378
HGV HANSEATISCHE GESELLSCHAFT FUR VERLAGS-SERVICE MBH—See Verlagsgruppe Georg von Holtzbrinck GmbH; *Int'l*, pg. 8169
HG YANGON COMPANY LIMITED—See HG Metal Manufacturing Limited; *Int'l*, pg. 3375
H&H AGENCY, INC.; *U.S. Private*, pg. 1822
HH ASSOCIATES US, INC.—See HH Global Group Limited; *Int'l*, pg. 3378
H.H. BENFIELD ELECTRIC SUPPLY COMPANY INC. - BENFIELD DATA COMM DIVISION—See H.H. Benfield Electric Supply Company Inc.; *U.S. Private*, pg. 1826
H.H. BENFIELD ELECTRIC SUPPLY COMPANY INC.; *U.S. Private*, pg. 1826
HH BIOTECHNOLOGY HOLDINGS COMPANY; *Int'l*, pg. 3378
H H BIRCH & SON LIMITED—See Co-operative Group Limited; *Int'l*, pg. 1679
H.H. BROWN SHOE COMPANY, INC.—See Berkshire Hathaway Inc.; *U.S. Public*, pg. 299
HHC AUGUSTA, INC.—See Universal Health Services, Inc.; *U.S. Public*, pg. 2257
HH-CDJR MOTORS, INC.—See AutoNation, Inc.; *U.S. Public*, pg. 235
HHC FOCUS FLORIDA, INC.—See Universal Health Services, Inc.; *U.S. Public*, pg. 2257
H & H CHEVROLET OLDSMOBILE PONTIAC & CADILLAC; *U.S. Private*, pg. 1822
HHC INDIANA, INC.—See Universal Health Services, Inc.; *U.S. Public*, pg. 2257
HH-COLLISION, INC.—See AutoNation, Inc.; *U.S. Public*, pg. 235
H&H CONSTRUCTORS OF FAYETTEVILLE, LLC—See Dream Finders Homes, Inc.; *U.S. Public*, pg. 687
H&H CONTINENTAL MOTORS INC.; *U.S. Private*, pg. 1822
HHC POPLAR SPRINGS, INC.—See Universal Health Services, Inc.; *U.S. Public*, pg. 2257
HHC RIVER PARK, INC.—See Universal Health Services, Inc.; *U.S. Public*, pg. 2257
HHC S CAROLINA, INC.—See Universal Health Services, Inc.; *U.S. Public*, pg. 2257
HHCS HANDHELD USA INC.—See MilDef Group AB; *Int'l*, pg. 4894
HHC SOUTH CAROLINA, INC.—See Universal Health Services, Inc.; *U.S. Public*, pg. 2257
HHC ST. SIMONS, INC.—See Universal Health Services, Inc.; *U.S. Public*, pg. 2257
HHC TRS BALTIMORE II LLC—See Ashford Hospitality Trust, Inc.; *U.S. Public*, pg. 211
H+H DANMARK A/S—See H+H International A/S; *Int'l*, pg. 3193
H+H DEUTSCHLAND GMBH—See H+H International A/S; *Int'l*, pg. 3193

H&H DISTRIBUTING COMPANY, INC.; *U.S. Private*, pg. 1822
H&H DOOR CO., INC.—See Platinum Equity, LLC; *U.S. Private*, pg. 3208
HHE (DEUTSCHLAND) GMBH—See Hankyu Hanshin Holdings Inc.; *Int'l*, pg. 3255
H. HEITZ FURNIERKANTENWERK GMBH & CO. KG—See INDUS Holding AG; *Int'l*, pg. 3663
H&H ENGINEERING CONSTRUCTION—See Wind Point Advisors LLC; *U.S. Private*, pg. 4535
H HERITAGE LICENSING, LLC—See XCel Brands, Inc.; *U.S. Public*, pg. 2385
HHE (USA) INC.—See Hankyu Hanshin Holdings Inc.; *Int'l*, pg. 3255
H+H FINLAND OY—See H+H International A/S; *Int'l*, pg. 3194
HH FLUORESCENT PARTS INCORPORATED; *U.S. Private*, pg. 1931
H.-H. FOCKE GMBH & CO. KG—See Focke & Co. (GmbH & Co.) Verpackungsmaschinen; *Int'l*, pg. 2718
HHG CAPITAL CORPORATION; *Int'l*, pg. 3379
HHG DISTRIBUTING LLC—See hhgregg, Inc.; *U.S. Public*, pg. 1034
HH GLOBAL GROUP LIMITED; *Int'l*, pg. 3378
HHGREGG, INC.; *U.S. Public*, pg. 1034
H&H GROUP INC.; *U.S. Private*, pg. 1822
H&H GROUP PLC; *Int'l*, pg. 3191
H&H GUN RANGE-SHOOTING SPORTS OUTLET; *U.S. Private*, pg. 1822
HH HOLDINGS INC.; *U.S. Private*, pg. 1931
HH HOTELS (EMEA) BV—See InterContinental Hotels Group PLC; *Int'l*, pg. 3737
H.H. HUNT CORPORATION; *U.S. Private*, pg. 1826
HHHUNT PROPERTY MANAGEMENT, INC.; *U.S. Private*, pg. 1931
HHIC-HONG KONG LTD.—See Hanjin Heavy Industries & Construction Co., Ltd.; *Int'l*, pg. 3252
HHIC-PHIL INC.—See Cerberus Capital Management, L.P.; *U.S. Private*, pg. 838
HHI FORMTECH, LLC—See American Axle & Manufacturing Holdings, Inc.; *U.S. Public*, pg. 96
HHI GROUP HOLDINGS, LLC—See American Axle & Manufacturing Holdings, Inc.; *U.S. Public*, pg. 96
H&H INDUSTRIAL CORPORATION; *U.S. Private*, pg. 1823
H+H INTERNATIONAL A/S; *Int'l*, pg. 3193
H&H INT'L LOGISTICS (FUJIAN) CO., LTD.—See Eusu Holdings Co., Ltd.; *Int'l*, pg. 2559
HHJ HOLDINGS LIMITED; *U.S. Private*, pg. 1931
H+H KALKSANDSTEIN GMBH—See H+H International A/S; *Int'l*, pg. 3193
HHK DATEBTECHNIK GMBH—See Trimble, Inc.; *U.S. Public*, pg. 2190
HHLA CONTAINER-TERMINAL ALTENWERDER GMBH—See Hamburger Hafen und Logistik AG; *Int'l*, pg. 3236
HHLA CONTAINER TERMINAL BURCHARDKAI GMBH—See Hamburger Hafen und Logistik AG; *Int'l*, pg. 3236
HHLA CONTAINER TERMINALS GMBH—See Hamburger Hafen und Logistik AG; *Int'l*, pg. 3236
HHLA CONTAINER TERMINAL TOLLERORT GMBH—See Hamburger Hafen und Logistik AG; *Int'l*, pg. 3236
HH&L ACQUISITION CO.; *Int'l*, pg. 3379
HHLA FRUCHT- UND KUHL-ZENTRUM GMBH—See Hamburger Hafen und Logistik AG; *Int'l*, pg. 3236
HHLA INTERMODAL GMBH—See Hamburger Hafen und Logistik AG; *Int'l*, pg. 3236
HHLA INTERMODAL VERWALTUNG GMBH—See Hamburger Hafen und Logistik AG; *Int'l*, pg. 3236
HHLA LOGISTICS ALTENWERDER GMBH & CO. KG—See Hamburger Hafen und Logistik AG; *Int'l*, pg. 3236
HHLA LOGISTICS ALTENWERDER VERWALTUNGSGESELLSCHAFT MBH—See Hamburger Hafen und Logistik AG; *Int'l*, pg. 3236
HHLA LOGISTICS GMBH—See Hamburger Hafen und Logistik AG; *Int'l*, pg. 3236
HHLA NEXT GMBH—See Hamburger Hafen und Logistik AG; *Int'l*, pg. 3236
HHLA PLT ITALY S.R.L.—See Hamburger Hafen und Logistik AG; *Int'l*, pg. 3236
HHLA PROJECT LOGISTICS LLC—See Hamburger Hafen und Logistik AG; *Int'l*, pg. 3236
HHLA TK ESTONIA AS—See Hamburger Hafen und Logistik AG; *Int'l*, pg. 3236
HHLA TK ESTONIA AS—See Hamburger Hafen und Logistik AG; *Int'l*, pg. 3236
HHLP BRIDGEWATER ASSOCIATES, LLC—See KSL Capital Partners, LLC; *U.S. Private*, pg. 2355
HHLP COCONUT GROVE ASSOCIATES, LLC—See KSL Capital Partners, LLC; *U.S. Private*, pg. 2355
HHLP PRESCOTT ASSOCIATES, LLC—See KSL Capital Partners, LLC; *U.S. Private*, pg. 2355
HHLP WHITE PLAINS ASSOCIATES, LLC—See KSL Capital Partners, LLC; *U.S. Private*, pg. 2355
H&H LTD.—See Steel Partners Holdings L.P.; *U.S. Public*, pg. 1942

H&H LUMBER CO., INC.—See Bain Capital, LP; *U.S. Private,* pg. 450
H&H MEDICAL CORPORATION—See Water Street Healthcare Partners, LLC; *U.S. Private,* pg. 4452
HHMI CORP.; *U.S. Private,* pg. 1931
H+H NEDERLAND B.V.—See H+H International A/S; *Int'l,* pg. 3194
H+H NORGE AS—See H+H International A/S; *Int'l,* pg. 3194
HHP INC.; *U.S. Private,* pg. 1931
H+H POLSKA SP. Z O.O.—See H+H International A/S; *Int'l,* pg. 3194
HH REHAB ASSOCIATES, INC.—See U.S. Physical Therapy, Inc.; *U.S. Public,* pg. 2214
HHRG BERHAD; *Int'l,* pg. 3379
HHR HOLDINGS PTY LTD.—See Host Hotels & Resorts, Inc.; *U.S. Public,* pg. 1055
HH ROBERTSON FLOOR SYSTEMS—See Clayton, Dubilier & Rice, LLC; *U.S. Private,* pg. 920
H & H ROOFING SUPPLY, LLC—See Beacon Roofing Supply, Inc.; *U.S. Public,* pg. 286
HH RUSEAU, LLC—See MillerKnoll, Inc.; *U.S. Public,* pg. 1447
HHS CONSTRUCTION, INC.—See Crestview Partners, L.P.; *U.S. Private,* pg. 1098
H&H SHOOTING SPORTS COMPLEX; *U.S. Private,* pg. 1823
H+H SLOVENSKA REPUBLIKA S.R.O.—See H+H International A/S; *Int'l,* pg. 3194
H&H SPAS & TRUCK COVERS—See Harrell Hall Enterprises Inc.; *U.S. Private,* pg. 1868
H+H SVERIGE AB—See H+H International A/S; *Int'l,* pg. 3194
H&H SYSTEMS AND DESIGN INC.; *U.S. Private,* pg. 1823
HHT CONSTRUCTION CO., LTD.—See BTS Group Holdings Public Company Limited; *Int'l,* pg. 1205
H&H TRAILER, LLC; *U.S. Private,* pg. 1823
H+H UK LIMITED—See H+H International A/S; *Int'l,* pg. 3194
H.H.V. WHITCHURCH & CO. LTD.; *Int'l,* pg. 3195
HHW HOMMEL HERCULES PL SP. Z O.O.—See Wurth Verwaltungsgesellschaft mbH; *Int'l,* pg. 8505
HHW-HOMMEL HEROULEO WERKZEUGHANDEL CZ/SK S.R.O.—See Wurth Verwaltungsgesellschaft mbH; *Int'l,* pg. 8505
HHY FUND; *Int'l,* pg. 3379
HIAB AB—See Cargotec Corporation; *Int'l,* pg. 1326
HIAB AUSTRIA GMBH—See Cargotec Corporation; *Int'l,* pg. 1327
HIAB BENELUX B.V.—See Cargotec Corporation; *Int'l,* pg. 1327
HIAB CHILE S.A.—See Cargotec Corporation; *Int'l,* pg. 1326
HIAB CRANES, S.L.—See Cargotec Corporation; *Int'l,* pg. 1326
HIAB DENMARK A/S—See Cargotec Corporation; *Int'l,* pg. 1326
HIAB GERMANY GMBH—See Cargotec Corporation; *Int'l,* pg. 1328
HIAB GMBH—See Cargotec Corporation; *Int'l,* pg. 1326
HIAB HANA CO. LTD.—See Cargotec Corporation; *Int'l,* pg. 1326
HIAB IBERIA, S.L.—See Cargotec Corporation; *Int'l,* pg. 1328
HIAB ITALIA S.R.L.—See Cargotec Corporation; *Int'l,* pg. 1328
HIAB KK—See Cargotec Corporation; *Int'l,* pg. 1326
HIAB LOAD HANDLING EQUIPMENT (SHANGHAI) CO., LTD—See Cargotec Corporation; *Int'l,* pg. 1328
HIAB LTD.—See Cargotec Corporation; *Int'l,* pg. 1327
HIAB NORWAY AS—See Cargotec Corporation; *Int'l,* pg. 1328
HIAB (PTY) LTD—See Cargotec Corporation; *Int'l,* pg. 1327
HIAB S.A. DE C.V.—See Cargotec Corporation; *Int'l,* pg. 1327
HIAB S.A./N.V.—See Cargotec Corporation; *Int'l,* pg. 1327
HIAB S.A.—See Cargotec Corporation; *Int'l,* pg. 1327
HIAB SDN BHD—See Cargotec Corporation; *Int'l,* pg. 1328
HI-ACE TRADING CO., LTD.—See Chun Yu Works & Co., Ltd.; *Int'l,* pg. 1596
HIADVANCE INC.; *U.S. Private,* pg. 1932
HIADVANCE (KOREA) CO., LTD.—See HiAdvance Inc.; *U.S. Private,* pg. 1932
HIADVANCE PHILIPPINES INC.—See HiAdvance Inc.; *U.S. Private,* pg. 1932
HIAG HANDEL AG—See Holzwerkstoff Holding AG; *Int'l,* pg. 3454
HIAG HANDEL IMMOBILIEN AG—See HIAG Immobilen Holding AG; *Int'l,* pg. 3382
HIAG HOLDING AG—See HIAG Immobilen Holding AG; *Int'l,* pg. 3382
HIAG IMMOBILEN HOLDING AG; *Int'l,* pg. 3382
HIAG IMMOBILIEN BETA GMBH—See Hornbach Holding AG & Co. KGaA; *Int'l,* pg. 3481
HIAG IMMOBILIEN DELTA GMBH—See Hornbach Holding AG & Co. KGaA; *Int'l,* pg. 3481

HIAG IMMOBILIEN SCHWEIZ AG—See HIAG Immobilen Holding AG; *Int'l,* pg. 3382
HI AI 1ST SPECIAL PURPOSE ACQUISITION CO; *Int'l,* pg. 3379
HI AIR KOREA CO., LTD.; *Int'l,* pg. 3379
HIALEAH HOSPITAL, INC.—See Tenet Healthcare Corporation; *U.S. Public,* pg. 2003
HIALEAH INCORPORATED; *U.S. Private,* pg. 1932
HI-ALLOY VALVE LLC—See Movement Industries Corp.; *U.S. Public,* pg. 1480
HIAP HOE LIMITED; *Int'l,* pg. 3382
HIAP HUAT HOLDINGS BHD; *Int'l,* pg. 3382
HIAP SENG ENGINEERING LIMITED; *Int'l,* pg. 3382
HIAP SENG ENGINEERING (M) SDN. BHD.—See Hiap Seng Engineering Limited; *Int'l,* pg. 3382
HIAP SENG ENGINEERING (THAILAND) CO., LTD.—See Hiap Seng Engineering Limited; *Int'l,* pg. 3382
HIAP SENG-SANKO TPM PTE. LTD.—See Hiap Seng Engineering Limited; *Int'l,* pg. 3382
HIAP TECK HARDWARE SDN BHD—See Hiap Teck Venture Berhad; *Int'l,* pg. 3382
HIAP TECK VENTURE BERHAD; *Int'l,* pg. 3382
HIAP TONG CORPORATION LTD.; *Int'l,* pg. 3382
HIAS INC.; *U.S. Private,* pg. 1932
HIATUS SPA & RETREAT; *U.S. Private,* pg. 1932
HIAWASSEE HARDWARE & BUILDING SUPPLY, INC.—See Tyndale Advisors, LLC; *U.S. Private,* pg. 4268
HIAWATHA COMMUNITY HOSPITAL; *U.S. Private,* pg. 1932
HIAWATHA, INC.—See Activar, Inc.; *U.S. Private,* pg. 68
HIAWATHA, INC.; *U.S. Private,* pg. 1932
HIAWATHA MANOR ASSOCIATION AT LAKE TANSI—See Crown Resorts, Ltd.; *U.S. Private,* pg. 1112
HIAWATHA NATIONAL BANK; *U.S. Private,* pg. 1932
HIBAR CHINA CO. LTD.—See Tesla, Inc.; *U.S. Public,* pg. 2021
HIBARI DEVELOPMENT CO., LTD.—See Bain Capital, LP; *U.S. Private,* pg. 444
HIBAR SYSTEMS EUROPE GMBH—See Tesla, Inc.; *U.S. Public,* pg. 2021
HIBAR SYSTEMS LIMITED—See Tesla, Inc.; *U.S. Public,* pg. 2021
THE HIBBERT GROUP; *U.S. Private,* pg. 4052
HIBBETT, INC.—See Pentland Group Limited; *Int'l,* pg. 5792
HIBBETT SPORTING GOODS INC.—See Pentland Group Limited; *Int'l,* pg. 5792
HIBBING CHRYSLER CENTER, LLC; *U.S. Private,* pg. 1932
HIBBING DAILY TRIBUNE—See American Consolidated Media LP; *U.S. Private,* pg. 228
HIBBING TACONITE COMPANY—See United States Steel Corporation; *U.S. Public,* pg. 2236
HIBBS-HALLMARK & COMPANY; *U.S. Private,* pg. 1932
HIBCO PLASTICS INCORPORATED; *U.S. Private,* pg. 1933
HIBER ALI SPA—See Ali Holding S.r.l; *Int'l,* pg. 321
HIBERCELL, INC.—See Arch Venture Partners; *U.S. Private,* pg. 310
HIBERNIA ATLANTIC CABLE SYSTEM LIMITED—See GTT Communications, Inc.; *U.S. Public,* pg. 1808
HIBERNIAN FOOTBALL CLUB LTD.; *Int'l,* pg. 3383
HIBERNIA REIT PLC—See Brookfield Corporation; *Int'l,* pg. 1188
HIBIKINADA GREENFARM CO LTD—See Kagome Co., Ltd.; *Int'l,* pg. 4050
HIBINO ASIA PACIFIC LIMITED—See Hibino Corporation; *Int'l,* pg. 3383
HIBINO ASIA PACIFIC (SHANGHAI) LIMITED—See Hibino Corporation; *Int'l,* pg. 3383
HIBINO BESCO CORPORATION—See Hibino Corporation; *Int'l,* pg. 3383
HIBINO CORPORATION; *Int'l,* pg. 3383
HIBINO IMAGINEERING CORPORATION—See Hibino Corporation; *Int'l,* pg. 3383
HIBINO LIGHTING INC.—See Hibino Corporation; *Int'l,* pg. 3383
HIBINO MEDIA TECHNICAL CORPORATION—See Hibino Corporation; *Int'l,* pg. 3383
HIBINO SPACETECH CORPORATION—See Hibino Corporation; *Int'l,* pg. 3383
HIBINO USA, INC.—See Hibino Corporation; *Int'l,* pg. 3383
HIBINO WINES & SPIRITS CO.—See Suntory Holdings Limited; *Int'l,* pg. 7326
HIBISCUS PETROLEUM BERHAD; *Int'l,* pg. 3383
HI-BIS GMBH—See Honshu Chemical Industry Co., Ltd.; *Int'l,* pg. 3472
HIBIYA COMPUTER SYSTEM CO., LTD.—See LTS, Inc.; *Int'l,* pg. 4571
HIBIYA ENGINEERING LTD; *Int'l,* pg. 3383
HIBIYA-KADAN FLORAL CO., LTD.; *Int'l,* pg. 3383
HIBIYA RESOURCE PLANNING CO., LTD.—See LTS, Inc.; *Int'l,* pg. 4571
HIBIYA TSUSHOU CO., LTD.—See Hibiya Engineering Ltd; *Int'l,* pg. 3383
HIBLEAD INC.; *Int'l,* pg. 3383
HIBON CORPORATION SDN. BHD.—See Kossan Rubber Industries Bhd; *Int'l,* pg. 4291

HIBON INC.—See Ingersoll Rand Inc.; *U.S. Public,* pg. 1120
HI-BOY GROUP INC.; *U.S. Private,* pg. 1931
HIB TRIM PART SOLUTIONS GMBH—See Ningbo Huaxiang Electronic Co., Ltd.; *Int'l,* pg. 5302
HIBU GROUP 2013 LIMITED; *Int'l,* pg. 3383
HIBU INC.—See H.I.G. Capital, LLC; *U.S. Private,* pg. 1834
HIBU (UK) LIMITED—See hibu Group 2013 Limited; *Int'l,* pg. 3383
HICA EDUCATION LOAN CORPORATION—See SLM Corporation; *U.S. Public,* pg. 1894
HICAPS, INC.; *U.S. Private,* pg. 1933
HICHAIN LOGISTICS CO., LTD.; *Int'l,* pg. 3383
HICHEM PAINT TECHNOLOGIES PTY. LIMITED—See RPM International Inc.; *U.S. Public,* pg. 1817
HICHROM LIMITED—See Avantor, Inc.; *U.S. Public,* pg. 242
HICKEL INVESTMENT COMPANY INC.; *U.S. Private,* pg. 1933
HICKEY & ASSOCIATES, LLC.; *U.S. Private,* pg. 1933
HICKEY FREEMAN TAILERED CLOTHING, INC.—See Grano Retail Investments Inc.; *Int'l,* pg. 3059
HICKINGBOTHAM INVESTMENTS, INC.; *U.S. Private,* pg. 1933
HICKMAN INDUSTRIES LIMITED—See Owens Corning; *U.S. Public,* pg. 1626
HICKMAN INVESTMENTS INC.; *U.S. Private,* pg. 1933
HICKMAN, WILLIAMS CANADA, INC.—See Hickman, Williams & Company; *U.S. Private,* pg. 1933
HICKMAN, WILLIAMS & COMPANY; *U.S. Private,* pg. 1933
HICKMAN, WILLIAMS & COMPANY—See Hickman, Williams & Company; *U.S. Private,* pg. 1933
HICKMAN, WILLIAMS & COMPANY—See Hickman, Williams & Company; *U.S. Private,* pg. 1933
HICKOK AE LLC—See Crawford United Corporation; *U.S. Public,* pg. 592
HICKORY BRANDS, INC.; *U.S. Private,* pg. 1933
HICKORY BUSINESS FURNITURE—See HNI Corporation; *U.S. Public,* pg. 1043
HICKORY CHAIR COMPANY—See Heritage Home Group, LLC; *U.S. Private,* pg. 1924
HICKORY CONSTRUCTION COMPANY; *U.S. Private,* pg. 1933
HICKORY CREEK NURSERY INC.; *U.S. Private,* pg. 1933
HICKORY DAILY RECORD—See Lee Enterprises, Incorporated; *U.S. Public,* pg. 1298
HICKORY FARMS, LLC—See Sun Capital Partners, Inc.; *U.S. Private,* pg. 3859
HICKORY FOODS, INC.; *U.S. Private,* pg. 1933
HICKORY HERITAGE OF FALLING CREEK, INC.; *U.S. Private,* pg. 1933
HICKORY HILLS VILLAGE, LLC—See Sun Communities, Inc.; *U.S. Public,* pg. 1961
HICKORY POINT BANK & TRUST FSB; *U.S. Private,* pg. 1933
HICKORY PRINTING SOLUTIONS—See Chatham Asset Management, LLC; *U.S. Private,* pg. 862
HICKORY PRINTING—See Chatham Asset Management, LLC; *U.S. Private,* pg. 862
HICKORY SPRINGS MANUFACTURING COMPANY; *U.S. Private,* pg. 1933
HICKORY SPRINGS MANUFACTURING COMPANY—See Hickory Springs Manufacturing Company; *U.S. Private,* pg. 1933
HICKORY SPRINGS MANUFACTURING COMPANY—See Hickory Springs Manufacturing Company; *U.S. Private,* pg. 1933
HICKORY SPRINGS OF CALIFORNIA, INC.—See Hickory Springs Manufacturing Company; *U.S. Private,* pg. 1933
HICKORY SPRINGS WATER, LLC—See Silver Springs Bottled Water Co.; *U.S. Private,* pg. 3662
HICKORY TRAIL HOSPITAL, L.P.—See Universal Health Services, Inc.; *U.S. Public,* pg. 2258
HICKSGAS, LLC—See DCC plc; *Int'l,* pg. 1989
HICKS HOLDINGS, LLC; *U.S. Private,* pg. 1934
HICKS LIGHTNING PROTECTION, INC.; *U.S. Private,* pg. 1934
HICKS OIL-HICKS GAS, INC.; *U.S. Private,* pg. 1934
HICKSON LTD.—See Lonza Group AG; *Int'l,* pg. 4553
HICKS & OTIS PRINTS INC.; *U.S. Private,* pg. 1934
HICKS PLASTICS COMPANY, INC.—See New Water Capital, L.P.; *U.S. Private,* pg. 2908
HICKS SPORTS GROUP, LLC—See Hicks Holdings, LLC; *U.S. Private,* pg. 1934
HICLASST, INC.; *Int'l,* pg. 3383
HI-CLEARANCE, INC.; *Int'l,* pg. 3380
HICL INFRASTRUCTURE PLC; *Int'l,* pg. 3383
HICO AMERICA SALES & TECHNOLOGY, INC.—See Hyosung Corporation; *Int'l,* pg. 3551
HICOM AUTOMOTIVE MANUFACTURERS (MALAYSIA) SDN BHD—See DRB-HICOM Berhad; *Int'l,* pg. 2201
HICOM DIECASTINGS SDN. BHD.—See DRB-HICOM Berhad; *Int'l,* pg. 2201
HICOM HOLDINGS BHD—See DRB-HICOM Berhad; *Int'l,* pg. 2201

HICOM TECHNOLOGY LIMITED—See Vitalhub Corp.; *Int'l*, pg. 8258
HICONICS ECO-ENERGY TECHNOLOGY CO., LTD.; *Int'l*, pg. 3384
HI CORPORATION—See Micware Co. Ltd.; *Int'l*, pg. 4882
HI-COUNTRY CHEVROLET INC.; *U.S. Private*, pg. 1931
HI-CRUSH CHAMBERS LLC—See Atlas Energy Solutions Inc.; *U.S. Public*, pg. 224
HI-CRUSH INC.—See Atlas Energy Solutions Inc.; *U.S. Public*, pg. 223
HI-CRUSH OPERATING LLC—See Atlas Energy Solutions Inc.; *U.S. Public*, pg. 224
HIDADA LTD.—See Xenel Industries Ltd.; *Int'l*, pg. 8521
HIDA JAPANESE RESTAURANT—See Gasho of Japan International Ltd.; *U.S. Private*, pg. 1648
HIDAKA TOSHI GAS CO., LTD.—See Sinanen Holdings Co., Ltd.; *Int'l*, pg. 6936
HIDALGO COUNTY CLINICAL SERVICES INC.; *U.S. Private*, pg. 1934
HIDALGO INDUSTRIAL SERVICES, INC.; *U.S. Private*, pg. 1934
HID ASIA PACIFIC LTD.—See ASSA ABLOY AB; *Int'l*, pg. 637
HIDAYAT YAKIN SDN. BHD.; *Int'l*, pg. 3384
HIDAY HIDAKA CORP.; *Int'l*, pg. 3384
HID CHINA LTD.—See ASSA ABLOY AB; *Int'l*, pg. 637
HID CORPORATION LTD.—See ASSA ABLOY AB; *Int'l*, pg. 637
HID CORPORATION LTD.—See ASSA ABLOY AB; *Int'l*, pg. 637
HIDDEN CHAMPIONS CAPITAL MANAGEMENT PTE. LTD.—See 8I Holdings Limited; *Int'l*, pg. 16
HIDDEN HARBOR CAPITAL PARTNERS; *U.S. Private*, pg. 1934
HIDDEN HEARING LIMITED—See Demant A/S; *Int'l*, pg. 2024
HIDDEN HEARING (PORTUGAL), UNIPESSOAL LDA.—See Demant A/S; *Int'l*, pg. 2023
HIDDEN HEARING (UK) LTD.—See Demant A/S; *Int'l*, pg. 2023
HIDDEN RIDGE AN RV COMMUNITY, LLC—See Sun Communities, Inc.; *U.S. Public*, pg. 1961
HIDDEN VALLEY GOLF AND SKI, INC.—See Vail Resorts, Inc.; *U.S. Public*, pg. 2271
HIDDEN VALLEY RESORT—See The Nutting Company, Inc.; *U.S. Private*, pg. 4086
HIDD POWER COMPANY BSC—See ENGIE SA; *Int'l*, pg. 2432
HIDD POWER COMPANY BSC—See MMC Corporation Berhad; *Int'l*, pg. 5005
HIDD POWER COMPANY BSC—See Sumitomo Corporation; *Int'l*, pg. 7268
HIDEAWAY AT ROYALTON NEGRIL—See Sunwing Travel Group, Inc.; *Int'l*, pg. 7332
HIDEAWAY AT ROYALTON PUNTA CANA—See Sunwing Travel Group, Inc.; *Int'l*, pg. 7332
HIDEAWAY AT ROYALTON RIVIERA CANCUN—See Sunwing Travel Group, Inc.; *Int'l*, pg. 7332
HIDEAWAY AT SAINT LUCIA—See Sunwing Travel Group, Inc.; *Int'l*, pg. 7332
HIDEAWAY BAY MARINA, INC.—See Sun Communities, Inc.; *U.S. Public*, pg. 1963
HIDE-AWAY STORAGE SERVICES INC.; *U.S. Private*, pg. 1934
HIDEEP INC.; *Int'l*, pg. 3384
HIDEF LIFESTYLE; *U.S. Private*, pg. 1934
HIDEKI ELECTRONICS LIMITED—See K & P International Holdings Limited; *Int'l*, pg. 4037
THE HIDE & LEATHER HOUSE; *U.S. Private*, pg. 4052
HI-DE LINERS, LLC—See Sole Source Capital LLC; *U.S. Private*, pg. 3708
HIDEO NAKAYAMA IMP. EXP. COM. E INDUSTRIA LTDA.—See Riken Keiki Co., Ltd.; *Int'l*, pg. 6340
HIDEPITO ZRT.—See VINCI S.A.; *Int'l*, pg. 8231
HI-DESERT PUBLISHING CO. INC.—See Brehm Communications Inc.; *U.S. Private*, pg. 644
HI DEVELOPMENT CORPORATION; *U.S. Private*, pg. 1931
HID GLOBAL CORPORATION—See ASSA ABLOY AB; *Int'l*, pg. 637
HID GLOBAL GMBH—See ASSA ABLOY AB; *Int'l*, pg. 637
HID GLOBAL GMBH—See ASSA ABLOY AB; *Int'l*, pg. 637
HID GLOBAL IRELAND TEORANTA LTD.—See ASSA ABLOY AB; *Int'l*, pg. 637
HID GLOBAL RASTEDE GMBH—See ASSA ABLOY AB; *Int'l*, pg. 637
HID GLOBAL SAS—See ASSA ABLOY AB; *Int'l*, pg. 639
HID GLOBAL SDN. BHD.—See ASSA ABLOY AB; *Int'l*, pg. 637
HID GLOBAL SWITZERLAND S.A.—See ASSA ABLOY AB; *Int'l*, pg. 637
HID HAMBURGER IMMOBILIENDIENSTE GMBH—See Fielmann Group AG; *Int'l*, pg. 2658
HIDILI INDUSTRY INTERNATIONAL DEVELOPMENT LIMITED; *Int'l*, pg. 3384
HID INDIA PRIVATE LTD.—See ASSA ABLOY AB; *Int'l*, pg. 637
HIDIRECT—See Saratoga Partners L.P.; *U.S. Private*, pg. 3549

HIDIS GMBH; *Int'l*, pg. 3384
HIDIV ELEKTRIK ENERJISI TOPTAN SATIS A.S—See EnBW Energie Baden-Wurttemberg AG; *Int'l*, pg. 2399
HIDOC PTE. LTD.—See Singapore Medical Group Limited; *Int'l*, pg. 6940
HIDONG ESTATE PLC; *Int'l*, pg. 3384
HIDRA STIL D.D.; *Int'l*, pg. 3384
HIDRAULICA DEL CHIRIQUI, S.A.—See ACS, Actividades de Construccion y Servicios, S.A.; *Int'l*, pg. 114
HIDRAULICA INDL. S.A. IND. E COM—See WEG S.A.; *Int'l*, pg. 8367
HIDRIA AET D.O.O.—See Hidria d.o.o.; *Int'l*, pg. 3384
HIDRIA BAUSCH GMBH—See Hidria d.o.o.; *Int'l*, pg. 3384
HIDRIA BAUSCH KFT—See Hidria d.o.o.; *Int'l*, pg. 3384
HIDRIA BH D.O.O.—See Hidria d.o.o.; *Int'l*, pg. 3384
HIDRIA C.Z.—See Hidria d.o.o.; *Int'l*, pg. 3384
HIDRIA D.O.O.E.L.—See Hidria d.o.o.; *Int'l*, pg. 3384
HIDRIA D.O.O.; *Int'l*, pg. 3384
HIDRIA GIF GMBH—See Hidria d.o.o.; *Int'l*, pg. 3384
HIDRIA HEATEC D.O.O.—See Hidria d.o.o.; *Int'l*, pg. 3384
HIDRIA IMP KLIMA D.O.O.—See Hidria d.o.o.; *Int'l*, pg. 3384
HIDRIA LC D.O.O.—See Hidria d.o.o.; *Int'l*, pg. 3384
HIDRIA PODGORICA D.O.O.—See Hidria d.o.o.; *Int'l*, pg. 3384
HIDRIA POLSKA SP. Z O.O.—See Hidria d.o.o.; *Int'l*, pg. 3384
HIDRIA ROTOMATIKA D.O.O.—See Hidria d.o.o.; *Int'l*, pg. 3384
HIDRIA TEHNOLOSKI CENTER D. O. O.—See Hidria d.o.o.; *Int'l*, pg. 3384
HIDRIA USA INC.—See Hidria d.o.o.; *Int'l*, pg. 3384
HIDROBIRO A.D.; *Int'l*, pg. 3384
HIDROCANTABRICO COGENERACION, S.L.—See EDP - Energias de Portugal, S.A.; *Int'l*, pg. 2314
HIDROCANTABRICO ENERGIA, S.A.U.—See EDP - Energias de Portugal, S.A.; *Int'l*, pg. 2314
HIDROCHICAPA S.A.—See PJSC Alrosa; *Int'l*, pg. 5878
HIDRO DIZAYN MUHENDISLIK MUSAVIRLIK INSAAT VE TICARET A.S.—See Lahmeyer Holding GmbH; *Int'l*, pg. 4395
HIDROECOLOGICA DEL TERIBE S.A.—See Empresas Publicas de Medellin ESP; *Int'l*, pg. 2392
HIDROELECTRICA DEL CANTABRICO, S.A.—See EDP - Energias de Portugal, S.A.; *Int'l*, pg. 2314
HIDROELECTRICA IBERICA, S.L.—See Iberdrola, S.A.; *Int'l*, pg. 3572
HIDROELECTRICIDAD DEL PACIFICO SRL DE CV—See Enel S.p.A.; *Int'l*, pg. 2414
HIDROELEKTRANE NA DRINI A.D.; *Int'l*, pg. 3384
HIDROELEKTRANE NA VRBASU A.D; *Int'l*, pg. 3384
HIDROELEKTRA NISKOGRADNJA D.D.; *Int'l*, pg. 3384
HIDROGESTION, S.A.—See ACS, Actividades de Construccion y Servicios, S.A.; *Int'l*, pg. 114
HIDROGRADEVINAR A.D.; *Int'l*, pg. 3384
HIDROGRADNJA A.D.; *Int'l*, pg. 3384
HIDROGRADNJA D.D. SARAJEVO; *Int'l*, pg. 3384
HIDROLIN HIDRODIZAYN & LINERJI ENERJI MUHENDISLIK VE MUSAVIRLIK LTD. STI.—See Lahmeyer Holding GmbH; *Int'l*, pg. 4395
HIDROPNEVMOTEHNIKA AD; *Int'l*, pg. 3384
HIDROSTAL S.A.; *Int'l*, pg. 3384
HIDROTEHNIKA-HIDROENERGETIKA A.D.; *Int'l*, pg. 3385
HID ULTRAVIOLET, LLC—See Amergraph Corporation; *U.S. Private*, pg. 219
HIDY MOTORS, INC.; *U.S. Private*, pg. 1934
THE HIEBING GROUP, INC.; *U.S. Private*, pg. 4052
HI-EISAI PHARMACEUTICALS, INC.—See Eisai Co., Ltd.; *Int'l*, pg. 2335
HIELKEMA TESTEQUIPMENT B.V.—See ESPEC Corp.; *Int'l*, pg. 2505
HIEP QUANG TRADING CO., LTD—See DABACO Group Joint Stock Company; *Int'l*, pg. 1902
HIEROJAKOULU RELAXI OY—See Terveystalo PLC; *Int'l*, pg. 7571
HIERROS DEL EBRO S.A.—See Klockner & Co. SE; *Int'l*, pg. 4202
HIERROS DEL TURIA S.A.—See Klockner & Co. SE; *Int'l*, pg. 4202
HIESTAND AUSTRIA GMBH—See ARYZTA AG; *Int'l*, pg. 589
HIESTAND BETEILIGUNGSHOLDING GMBH & CO. KG—See ARYZTA AG; *Int'l*, pg. 589
HIESTAND DEUTSCHLAND GMBH—See ARYZTA AG; *Int'l*, pg. 589
HIESTAND HOLDINGS (SWITZERLAND) AG—See ARYZTA AG; *Int'l*, pg. 588
HIESTAND MALAYSIA SDN BHD—See ARYZTA AG; *Int'l*, pg. 589
HIESTAND & SUHR HANDELS UND LOGISTIK GMBH—See ARYZTA AG; *Int'l*, pg. 588
HIFAB GROUP AB; *Int'l*, pg. 3385
HIFAB INTERNATIONAL AB—See Hifab Group AB; *Int'l*, pg. 3385
HIFAB OY—See Hifab Group AB; *Int'l*, pg. 3385
HIFFMAN SHAFFER ASSOCIATES, INC.—See Island Capital Group LLC; *U.S. Private*, pg. 2144

HI-FI ENGINEERING INC.—See Enbridge Inc.; *Int'l*, pg. 2397
HIFI ORIENT THAI PLC—See Hon Hai Precision Industry Co., Ltd.; *Int'l*, pg. 3459
HIFLEX DENMARK A/S—See Alfagomma S.p.A.; *Int'l*, pg. 315
HIFLY AIRLINES; *Int'l*, pg. 3385
HIFM LIMITED—See Euronet Worldwide, Inc.; *U.S. Public*, pg. 798
HIFSA—See Airtificial Intelligence Structures SA; *Int'l*, pg. 249
HIFX AUSTRALIA PTY LTD—See Euronet Worldwide, Inc.; *U.S. Public*, pg. 798
HIFX EUROPE LIMITED—See Euronet Worldwide, Inc.; *U.S. Public*, pg. 798
HIFX LIMITED—See Euronet Worldwide, Inc.; *U.S. Public*, pg. 798
HIFX SPAIN S.L.—See Euronet Worldwide, Inc.; *U.S. Public*, pg. 798
H.I.G. ACQUISITION CORP.; *U.S. Public*, pg. 979
HIGASHI CHUGOKU RYOJU ESTATE CO., LTD.—See Mitsubishi Heavy Industries, Ltd.; *Int'l*, pg. 4953
HIGASHIFUJI (MALAYSIA) SDN. BHD.—See Nidec Corporation; *Int'l*, pg. 5278
HIGASHI HOKKAIDO HINO MOTOR LTD.—See Toyota Motor Corporation; *Int'l*, pg. 7870
HIGASHIMARU CO., LTD.; *Int'l*, pg. 3385
HIGASHI-MATSUYAMA SKYLARK—See Bain Capital, LP; *U.S. Private*, pg. 444
HIGASHI MURAYAMA FACTORY OF KANTOH DIET EGG CO., LTD.—See Kenko Mayonnaise Co., Ltd.; *Int'l*, pg. 4127
HIGASHINE SHINDENGEN CO., LTD.—See Shindengen Electric Manufacturing Co., Ltd.; *Int'l*, pg. 6841
HIGASHI-NIHON CONTAINER SERVICE CO., LTD.—See Taiyo Kogyo Corporation; *Int'l*, pg. 7425
HIGASHINIHON DIECASTING INDUSTRY CO., LTD.—See MITSUBA Corporation; *Int'l*, pg. 4928
HIGASHINIHON FUDOSAN CO., LTD.—See First Brothers Co., Ltd.; *Int'l*, pg. 2682
HIGASHINIHON GAS CORPORATION—See Nippon Gas Co., Ltd.; *Int'l*, pg. 5318
HIGASHI NIHON INOAC CO. LTD.—See INOAC Corporation; *Int'l*, pg. 3714
HIGASHINIHON KAIHATSU CO., LTD.—See Mitsubishi Estate Co., Ltd.; *Int'l*, pg. 4946
HIGASHI NIHON KOUGYOU CO., INC.—See Tohoku Electric Power Co., Inc.; *Int'l*, pg. 7777
HIGASHI NIHON MITSUBISHI MOTORS SALES CO., LTD.—See Mitsubishi Motors Corporation; *Int'l*, pg. 4966
THE HIGASHI-NIPPON BANK, LTD.—See Concordia Financial Group, Ltd.; *Int'l*, pg. 1765
HIGASHI NIPPON FOOD, INC.—See Nissin Foods Holdings Co., Ltd.; *Int'l*, pg. 5376
HIGASHI TWENTY ONE CO., LTD.; *Int'l*, pg. 3385
HIGASHIYAMA FELT CO., LTD.—See Nippon Felt Co., Ltd.; *Int'l*, pg. 5317
HIGBEE & ASSOCIATES; *U.S. Private*, pg. 1934
H.I.G. BIOVENTURES, LLC—See H.I.G. Capital, LLC; *U.S. Private*, pg. 1827
H.I.G. BRAZIL INVESTMENT ADVISORY LTDA.—See H.I.G. Capital, LLC; *U.S. Private*, pg. 1828
H.I.G. CAPITAL, LLC - BOSTON OFFICE—See H.I.G. Capital, LLC; *U.S. Private*, pg. 1828
H.I.G. CAPITAL, LLC; *U.S. Private*, pg. 1826
HIGDON FURNITURE CO.; *U.S. Private*, pg. 1934
H.I.G. EUROPEAN CAPITAL PARTNERS GMBH—See H.I.G. Capital, LLC; *U.S. Private*, pg. 1828
H.I.G. EUROPEAN CAPITAL PARTNERS LLP—See H.I.G. Capital, LLC; *U.S. Private*, pg. 1828
H.I.G. EUROPEAN CAPITAL PARTNERS SAS—See H.I.G. Capital, LLC; *U.S. Private*, pg. 1828
H.I.G. EUROPEAN CAPITAL PARTNERS SPAIN, S.L.U.—See H.I.G. Capital, LLC; *U.S. Private*, pg. 1828
HIGGERSON-BUCHANAN INC.; *U.S. Private*, pg. 1934
HIGGINBOTHAM-BARTLETT COMPANY LTD.—See Higginbotham Bros. & Company; *U.S. Private*, pg. 1935
HIGGINBOTHAM BROS. & CO., LLC - GATESVILLE—See Bain Capital, LP; *U.S. Private*, pg. 450
HIGGINBOTHAM BROS. & CO., LLC—See Bain Capital, LP; *U.S. Private*, pg. 450
HIGGINBOTHAM BROS. & COMPANY; *U.S. Private*, pg. 1935
HIGGINBOTHAM INSURANCE AGENCY, LLC—See Galiot Insurance Services, Inc.; *U.S. Private*, pg. 1637
HIGGINBOTHAM INSURANCE GROUP, INC.—See Galiot Insurance Services, Inc.; *U.S. Private*, pg. 1638
HIGGINBOTHAM OIL CO., INC.; *U.S. Private*, pg. 1935
HIGGINS CHEVROLET INC.; *U.S. Private*, pg. 1935
HIGGINS DEVELOPMENT PARTNERS, LLC; *U.S. Private*, pg. 1935
HIGGINS ELECTRIC, INC. OF DOTHAN; *U.S. Private*, pg. 1935
HIGGINS ERECTORS & HAULERS INC; *U.S. Private*, pg. 1935
HIGGINS GROUP HOLDINGS LIMITED—See Fletcher Building Limited; *Int'l*, pg. 2700
THE HIGGINS GROUP, INC.; *U.S. Private*, pg. 4052

COMPANY NAME INDEX

HIGGINS PROPERTIES LLC—See Equity Commonwealth; *U.S. Public*, pg. 790
HIGGS INTERNATIONAL LIMITED—See Deutsche Post AG; *Int'l*, pg. 2080
HIGGS INTERNATIONAL PUBLISHING LOGISTICS LTD—See Deutsche Post AG; *Int'l*, pg. 2080
HIGGSTEC, INC.; *Int'l*, pg. 3385
HIGH-5 CONGLOMERATE BERHAD; *Int'l*, pg. 3386
HIGHAIM (KUNSHAN) TECHNOLOGY INC.—See Ennoconn Corporation; *Int'l*, pg. 2443
HIGHAIM TECHNOLOGY INC.—See Ennoconn Corporation; *Int'l*, pg. 2443
HIGHAMS RECRUITMENT LIMITED—See Ridgecrest Plc; *Int'l*, pg. 6337
HIGH AND MIGHTY LIMITED—See N Brown Group plc; *Int'l*, pg. 5115
HIGH ARCTIC ENERGY SERVICES INC.; *Int'l*, pg. 3385
HIGH ARCTIC ENERGY SERVICES LP—See High Arctic Energy Services Inc.; *Int'l*, pg. 3385
HIGH ARCTIC ENERGY SERVICES PNG LIMITED—See High Arctic Energy Services Inc.; *Int'l*, pg. 3385
HIGHBANK RESOURCES LTD.; *Int'l*, pg. 3386
HIGHBAR MANAGEMENT, LLC; *U.S. Private*, pg. 1937
HIGHBRIDGE ADVISORY COUNCIL FAMILY SERVICES, INC.; *U.S. Private*, pg. 1937
HIGHBRIDGE CAPITAL MANAGEMENT (HONG KONG), LIMITED—See JPMorgan Chase & Co.; *U.S. Public*, pg. 1207
HIGHBRIDGE CAPITAL MANAGEMENT, LLC—See JPMorgan Chase & Co.; *U.S. Public*, pg. 1207
HIGHBRIDGE CAPITAL MANAGEMENT (UK), LTD.—See JPMorgan Chase & Co.; *U.S. Public*, pg. 1207
HIGHBROAD ADVANCED MATERIAL (HEFEI) CO., LTD.; *Int'l*, pg. 3386
HIGHBURY FORD SALES LIMITED; *Int'l*, pg. 3386
HIGHCO BENELUX—See HighCo S.A.; *Int'l*, pg. 3387
HIGHCO BOX, S.A.S—See HighCo S.A.; *Int'l*, pg. 3387
HIGHCO DATA BENELUX NV—See HighCo S.A.; *Int'l*, pg. 3387
HIGHCO DATA, S.A.S—See HighCo S.A.; *Int'l*, pg. 3387
HIGHCO EDITING SAS—See HighCo S.A.; *Int'l*, pg. 3387
HIGHCO MINDOZA SAS—See HighCo S.A.; *Int'l*, pg. 3387
HIGH COMPONENTS AOMORI CO., LTD.—See AOI Electronics Co., Ltd.; *Int'l*, pg. 488
HIGHCO MRM—See HighCo S.A.; *Int'l*, pg. 3387
HIGHCON AB—See Instalco AB; *Int'l*, pg. 3721
HIGH CONCRETE GROUP LLC—See High Industries, Inc.; *U.S. Private*, pg. 1935
HIGH CONCRETE TECHNOLOGY LLC—See High Industries, Inc.; *U.S. Private*, pg. 1935
HIGH CONNEXION, S.A.S—See HighCo S.A.; *Int'l*, pg. 3387
HIGH CONNEXION SRL—See HighCo S.A.; *Int'l*, pg. 3386
HIGHCON SYSTEMS LTD.; *Int'l*, pg. 3387
HIGHCO S.A.; *Int'l*, pg. 3386
HIGHCO SHELF SERVICE NV—See HighCo S.A.; *Int'l*, pg. 3387
HIGHCO SHOPPER SAS—See HighCo S.A.; *Int'l*, pg. 3387
HIGHCO SHOPPER SL—See HighCo S.A.; *Int'l*, pg. 3387
HIGHCO SPAIN—See HighCo S.A.; *Int'l*, pg. 3387
HIGH COUNTRY BANCORP, INC.; *U.S. Public*, pg. 1034
HIGH COUNTRY BANK—See High Country Bancorp, Inc.; *U.S. Public*, pg. 1035
HIGH COUNTRY BEVERAGE CORP.; *U.S. Private*, pg. 1935
HIGH COUNTRY CHEVROLET LTD.; *Int'l*, pg. 3385
HIGH COUNTRY FUSION COMPANY, INC.; *U.S. Private*, pg. 1935
HIGH COUNTRY INVESTOR, INC.; *U.S. Private*, pg. 1935
HIGH COUNTRY LINE CONSTRUCTION, INC.—See MYR Group Inc.; *U.S. Public*, pg. 1489
HIGH COUNTRY LINENS INC.; *U.S. Private*, pg. 1935
HIGH COUNTRY LUMBER INC.; *U.S. Private*, pg. 1935
HIGHCROFT INVESTMENTS PLC; *Int'l*, pg. 3387
HIGH DESERT BROADCASTING LLC—See Point Broadcasting Company; *U.S. Private*, pg. 3221
HIGH DESERT CAPITAL, LLC; *U.S. Private*, pg. 1935
HIGH DESERT HOLDING CORP.; *U.S. Private*, pg. 1935
HIGH DESERT HUNT CLUB LLC—See Tejon Ranch Company; *U.S. Public*, pg. 1991
HIGH DESERT MINERAL RESOURCES, INC.—See Royal Gold, Inc.; *U.S. Public*, pg. 1815
HIGH DESERT PARTNERSHIP IN ACADEMIC EXCELLENCE FOUNDATION, INC.; *U.S. Private*, pg. 1935
HIGH END SYSTEMS, INC.—See Electronic Theatre Controls, Inc.; *U.S. Private*, pg. 1356
HIGH ENERGY BATTERIES (INDIA) LTD—See Seshasayee Paper & Boards Ltd; *Int'l*, pg. 6729
HIGH ENERGY INC.; *U.S. Private*, pg. 1935
HIGH ENPLA CO., LTD.—See YAMAICHI ELECTRONICS Co Ltd; *Int'l*, pg. 8552
HIGHER EDUCATION SERVICES, INC.—See Dream Center Foundation, a California Nonprofit Corp.; *U.S. Private*, pg. 1273
HIGHER EDUCATION & VOCATIONAL BOOK JSC; *Int'l*, pg. 3387
HIGHER LEARNING COMMISSION; *U.S. Private*, pg. 1937

HIGHER LOGIC, LLC; *U.S. Private*, pg. 1937
HIGHER POWER INC.—See Qurate Retail, Inc.; *U.S. Public*, pg. 1757
HIGHER POWER MARKETING (HPM); *U.S. Private*, pg. 1937
HIGHER WAY ELECTRONIC CO., LTD.; *Int'l*, pg. 3387
HIGHEST PERFORMANCES HOLDINGS INC.; *Int'l*, pg. 3387
HIGH FALLS OIL COMPANY INC.; *U.S. Private*, pg. 1935
HIGH FASHION (CHINA) CO., LTD.—See High Fashion International Limited; *Int'l*, pg. 3385
HIGH FASHION GARMENTS COMPANY LIMITED—See High Fashion International Limited; *Int'l*, pg. 3385
HIGH FASHION GARMENTS, INC.—See High Fashion International Limited; *Int'l*, pg. 3385
HIGH FASHION INTERNATIONAL LIMITED; *Int'l*, pg. 3385
HIGH FASHION KNIT COMPANY LIMITED—See High Fashion International Limited; *Int'l*, pg. 3385
HIGH FASHION (UK) LIMITED—See High Fashion International Limited; *Int'l*, pg. 3385
HIGHFIELD COMMUNICATIONS LLC—See Kearney O'Doherty Public Affairs, LLC; *U.S. Private*, pg. 2271
HIGHFIELD RESOURCES LIMITED; *Int'l*, pg. 3387
HIGHFIELDS CAPITAL MANAGEMENT LP; *U.S. Private*, pg. 1937
HIGH FINANCE LTD.; *Int'l*, pg. 3385
HIGH FLYER INTERNATIONAL LIMITED—See Samson Paper Holdings Limited; *Int'l*, pg. 6509
HIGHGATE HOSPITAL LLP—See Tenet Healthcare Corporation; *U.S. Public*, pg. 2004
HIGHGATE HOTELS, L.P.; *U.S. Private*, pg. 1937
HIGHGOLD MINING, INC.; *Int'l*, pg. 3387
HIGH GRADE BEVERAGE; *U.S. Private*, pg. 1935
HIGH-GRADE BRICK-TILE JOINT STOCK COMPANY; *Int'l*, pg. 3386
HIGH GRADE MATERIALS COMPANY; *U.S. Private*, pg. 1935
HIGH GRADE TECHNOLOGIES & ENERGY SYSTEMS NIGERIA LTD.—See Transition Evergreen; *Int'l*, pg. 7901
HIGH GROUND ENTERPRISE LIMITED; *Int'l*, pg. 3385
HIGH HOPE AGI ORY LIMITED—See Jiangsu High Hope International Group Corporation; *Int'l*, pg. 3947
HIGH HOPE GROUP JIANGSU TONGTAI CO., LTD.—See Jiangsu High Hope International Group Corporation; *Int'l*, pg. 3947
HIGH HOPE INTERNATIONAL GROUP JIANGSU MEDICINES AND HEALTH PRODUCTS IMPORT & EXPORT CO., LTD.—See Jiangsu High Hope International Group Corporation; *Int'l*, pg. 3947
HIGH HOPE INTL GROUP JIANGSU ASSET MANAGEMENT CO., LTD.—See Jiangsu High Hope International Group Corporation; *Int'l*, pg. 3947
HIGH HOPE INTL GROUP JIANGSU CHAMPION HOLDINGS LTD.—See Jiangsu High Hope International Group Corporation; *Int'l*, pg. 3947
HIGH HOPE INTL GROUP JIANGSU MEDICINES & HEALTH PRODUCTS IMPORT & EXPORT CORP. LTD.—See Jiangsu High Hope International Group Corporation; *Int'l*, pg. 3947
HIGH HOPE ZHONGDING CORPORATION—See Jiangsu High Hope International Group Corporation; *Int'l*, pg. 3947
HIGH HOPE ZHONGTIAN CORPORATION—See Jiangsu High Hope International Group Corporation; *Int'l*, pg. 3947
HIGH INDUSTRIES, INC.; *U.S. Private*, pg. 1935
HIGH INTENSITY PRODUCTS, INC.—See Sally Beauty Holdings, Inc.; *U.S. Public*, pg. 1838
HIGHJUMP SOFTWARE INC.—See Accellos, Inc.; *U.S. Private*, pg. 50
HIGHLAND ACQUISITION CORPORATION—See Highland Capital Management, L.P.; *U.S. Private*, pg. 1938
HIGHLAND ASSOCIATES, INC.—See Regions Financial Corporation; *U.S. Public*, pg. 1776
HIGHLAND BANKSHARES INC.; *U.S. Private*, pg. 1938
HIGHLAND BANK—See Highland Bankshares Inc.; *U.S. Private*, pg. 1938
HIGHLAND BOLT & NUT—See MNP Corporation; *U.S. Private*, pg. 2756
HIGHLAND CAPITAL BROKERAGE, INC.—See Reverence Capital Partners LLC; *U.S. Private*, pg. 3414
HIGHLAND CAPITAL HOLDING CORP.—See Reverence Capital Partners LLC; *U.S. Private*, pg. 3414
HIGHLAND CAPITAL MANAGEMENT, LLC—See Argent Financial Group, Inc.; *U.S. Private*, pg. 320
HIGHLAND CAPITAL MANAGEMENT, L.P.; *U.S. Private*, pg. 1938
HIGHLAND CAPITAL PARTNERS, LLC; *U.S. Private*, pg. 1938
HIGHLAND CHEVROLET BUICK GMC CADILLAC; *Int'l*, pg. 3387
HIGHLAND COMMERCIAL ROOFING—See HCI Equity Management, L.P.; *U.S. Private*, pg. 1889
HIGHLAND COMPUTER FORMS INC.; *U.S. Private*, pg. 1938

HIGHLAND CONSUMER PARTNERS MANAGEMENT COMPANY LLC—See Highland Capital Partners, LLC; *U.S. Private*, pg. 1938
HIGHLAND COPPER COMPANY INC.; *Int'l*, pg. 3387
HIGHLAND CORPORATION; *U.S. Private*, pg. 1938
HIGHLAND ELECTROPLATERS LTD.—See DMI UK Ltd.; *Int'l*, pg. 2146
HIGHLANDER OIL & GAS ASSET LLC—See Magnolia Oil & Gas Corporation; *U.S. Public*, pg. 1354
HIGHLANDER PARTNERS, LP.; *U.S. Private*, pg. 1939
HIGHLANDER PARTNERS SP. Z O.O—See Highlander Partners, LP.; *U.S. Private*, pg. 1939
HIGHLANDER SILVER CORP.; *Int'l*, pg. 3387
HIGHLANDER SOLAR 1, LLC—See Duke Energy Corporation; *U.S. Public*, pg. 691
HIGHLAND EUROPE (UK) LLP—See Highland Capital Partners, LLC; *U.S. Private*, pg. 1938
HIGHLAND-EXCHANGE PETROLEUM SUPPLY CO. INC.—See Highland-Exchange Service Cooperative Inc.; *U.S. Private*, pg. 1939
HIGHLAND-EXCHANGE SERVICE COOPERATIVE INC.; *U.S. Private*, pg. 1939
HIGHLAND FABRICATORS INC.—See Hickory Springs Manufacturing Company; *U.S. Private*, pg. 1933
HIGHLAND FINANCIAL TRUST—See Highland Capital Management, L.P.; *U.S. Private*, pg. 1938
HIGHLAND FORWARDING, INC.; *U.S. Private*, pg. 1938
HIGHLAND FOUNDRY LTD.; *Int'l*, pg. 3387
HIGHLAND FUELS LTD.; *Int'l*, pg. 3387
HIGHLAND GOLD MINING LIMITED—See Fortiana Holdings Ltd; *Int'l*, pg. 2738
HIGHLAND GROUP HOLDINGS LIMITED—See Sanpower Group Co., Ltd.; *Int'l*, pg. 6554
HIGHLAND HEALTHCARE LLC—See The Ensign Group, Inc.; *U.S. Public*, pg. 2071
HIGHLAND HELICOPTERS LTD.; *Int'l*, pg. 3387
HIGHLAND HOLDINGS, INC.—See Berkshire Hathaway Inc.; *U.S. Public*, pg. 304
HIGHLAND HOMELOANS, LLC—See Hilltop Holdings Inc.; *U.S. Public*, pg. 1038
HIGHLAND HOMES LTD.; *U.S. Private*, pg. 1938
HIGHLAND HYDRAULICS, INC.—See Headco Industries; *U.S. Private*, pg. 1891
HIGHLAND INDUSTRIES INC.—See Takata Global Group; *U.S. Private*, pg. 3925
HIGHLAND INTERNATIONAL, INC.—See Henkel AG & Co. KGaA; *Int'l*, pg. 3354
HIGHLAND KACKELL PTY LTD—See Eagers Automotive Limited; *Int'l*, pg. 2263
HIGHLAND LAKES CENTER, LLC—See Washington Prime Group Inc.; *U.S. Private*, pg. 4448
HIGHLAND LEASE CORPORATION—See M&T Bank Corporation; *U.S. Public*, pg. 1350
HIGHLAND MEMORIAL PARK, INC.—See Axar Capital Management L.P.; *U.S. Private*, pg. 411
HIGHLAND MILLS INC.; *U.S. Private*, pg. 1938
HIGHLAND MINI STORAGE—See TKG-StorageMart Partners Portfolio, LLC; *U.S. Private*, pg. 4178
HIGHLAND MOUNTAIN WATER—See Primo Water Corporation; *U.S. Public*, pg. 1718
HIGHLAND NEWS-LEADER—See Chatham Asset Management, LLC; *U.S. Private*, pg. 866
HIGHLAND PACKAGING SOLUTIONS, LLC—See Sonoco Products Company; *U.S. Public*, pg. 1904
HIGHLAND PARK DISTILLERY—See The Edrington Group; *Int'l*, pg. 7638
HIGHLAND PARK HOSPITAL—See NorthShore University HealthSystem; *U.S. Private*, pg. 2957
HIGHLAND PRODUCTIONS, LLC; *U.S. Private*, pg. 1938
HIGHLAND RISK SERVICES LLC—See AmWINS Group, Inc.; *U.S. Private*, pg. 269
HIGHLAND ROOFING CO.; *U.S. Private*, pg. 1939
THE HIGHLANDS AT WYOMISSING; *U.S. Private*, pg. 4052
HIGHLANDS BANCORP, INC.—See Provident Financial Services, Inc.; *U.S. Public*, pg. 1730
HIGHLANDS BANKSHARES, INC.—See First Community Bankshares, Inc.; *U.S. Public*, pg. 842
HIGHLANDS HOSPITAL; *U.S. Private*, pg. 1940
HIGHLANDS INSURANCE GROUP INC.; *U.S. Private*, pg. 1940
HIGHLANDS MUTUAL HOUSING CORPORATION, INC.; *U.S. Private*, pg. 1940
THE HIGHLANDS NEWS-SUN—See Sun Coast Media Group, Inc.; *U.S. Private*, pg. 3862
HIGHLANDS PACIFIC AUSTRALIA PTY LIMITED—See Pala Investments Limited; *Int'l*, pg. 5705
HIGHLANDS PACIFIC LIMITED—See Pala Investments Limited; *Int'l*, pg. 5705
HIGHLANDS PHYSICAL THERAPY & SPORTS MEDICINE, LIMITED PARTNERSHIP—See U.S. Physical Therapy, Inc.; *U.S. Public*, pg. 2214
HIGHLANDS RANCH COMMUNITY ASSOCIATION, INC.; *U.S. Private*, pg. 1940
HIGHLANDS REIT, INC.; *U.S. Private*, pg. 1940
HIGHLANDS STATE BANK—See Provident Financial Services, Inc.; *U.S. Public*, pg. 1730
HIGHLAND SUGARWORKS, INCORPORATED; *U.S. Private*, pg. 1939

HIGHLAND SUPPLY CORPORATION

CORPORATE AFFILIATIONS

HIGHLAND SUPPLY CORPORATION; *U.S. Private,* pg. 1939
HIGHLAND SURPRISE CONSOLIDATED MINING CO.; *U.S. Public,* pg. 1035
HIGHLAND TANK & MANUFACTURING CO.; *U.S. Private,* pg. 1939
HIGHLAND TELEPHONE COOPERATIVE, INC,; *U.S. Private,* pg. 1939
HIGHLAND TEXAS ENERGY CO; *U.S. Private,* pg. 1939
HIGHLAND TRANSCEND PARTNERS I CORP.; *U.S. Public,* pg. 1035
HIGHLAND VENTURES, LTD.; *U.S. Private,* pg. 1939
HIGHLAND WATER COMPANY, INC.—See Pinnacle West Capital Corporation; *U.S. Public,* pg. 1692
HIGH LIFTER PRODUCTS, INC.—See Morgan Stanley; *U.S. Public,* pg. 1474
HIGHLIGHT COMMUNICATIONS AG; *Int'l,* pg. 3388
HIGHLIGHT EVENT AG—See Highlight Event & Entertainment AG; *Int'l,* pg. 3388
HIGHLIGHT EVENT & ENTERTAINMENT AG; *Int'l,* pg. 3388
HIGHLIGHTS FOR CHILDREN, INC.; *U.S. Private,* pg. 1940
HIGHLIGHTS FOR CHILDREN INTERNATIONAL, INC.—See Highlights for Children, Inc.; *U.S. Private,* pg. 1940
HIGHLIGHT S.R.L.—See Gek Terna Societe Anonyme Holdings Real Estate Constructions; *Int'l,* pg. 2913
HIGHLINE ELECTRIC ASSOCIATION; *U.S. Private,* pg. 1940
HIGHLINE INTERNATIONAL LTD.—See BRF S.A.; *Int'l,* pg. 1151
HIGHLINE PRODUCE LIMITED - HIGHLINE DISTRIBUTION FACILITY—See Sumitomo Corporation; *Int'l,* pg. 7268
HIGHLINE PRODUCE LIMITED - KINGSVILLE MUSHROOM FARM FACILITY—See Sumitomo Corporation; *Int'l,* pg. 7268
HIGHLINE PRODUCE LIMITED—See Sumitomo Corporation; *Int'l,* pg. 7268
HIGHLINE PRODUCE LIMITED - WELLINGTON MUSHROOM FARM FACILITY—See Sumitomo Corporation; *Int'l,* pg. 7268
HIGHLINE QUEST SDN. BHD.—See Hubline Berhad; *Int'l,* pg. 3520
HIGH LINER FOODS INCORPORATED; *Int'l,* pg. 3385
HIGH LINER FOODS (USA) INCORPORATED—See High Liner Foods Incorporated; *Int'l,* pg. 3385
HIGHLINES CONSTRUCTION COMPANY, INC.—See Asplundh Tree Expert Co.; *U.S. Private,* pg. 353
HIGHLINE SHIPPING SDN. BHD.—See Hubline Berhad; *Int'l,* pg. 3520
HIGH LUCK GROUP LIMITED—See New Times Energy Corporation Limited; *Int'l,* pg. 5228
HIGHMAG TECHNOLOGY (SHENZHEN), LTD.—See Advanced Technology & Materials Co., Ltd.; *Int'l,* pg. 162
HIGHMARK BLUE CROSS BLUE SHIELD DELAWARE—See Highmark Health; *U.S. Private,* pg. 1940
HIGHMARK BLUE CROSS BLUE SHIELD WEST VIRGINIA—See Highmark Health; *U.S. Private,* pg. 1940
HIGHMARK CARING PLACE—See Highmark Health; *U.S. Private,* pg. 1940
HIGHMARK HEALTH; *U.S. Private,* pg. 1940
HIGHMARK HOOFDDORP, B.V.—See Minor International PCL; *Int'l,* pg. 4911
HIGHMARK INC.—See Highmark Health; *U.S. Private,* pg. 1940
HIGHMARK INTERACTIVE; *Int'l,* pg. 3388
HIGHMARK SENIOR RESOURCES INC.—See Highmark Health; *U.S. Private,* pg. 1941
HIGHMARK TRAFFIC SERVICES, INC.—See Federal Signal Corporation; *U.S. Public,* pg. 826
HIGHNOON LABORATORIES LIMITED; *Int'l,* pg. 3388
HIGH NOON PRODUCTIONS, LLC—See ITV plc; *Int'l,* pg. 3845
HIGH NOON SALOON LLC—See Live Nation Entertainment, Inc.; *U.S. Public,* pg. 1329
HIGH NOON SOLAR, LLC—See Duke Energy Corporation; *U.S. Public,* pg. 691
HIGH NOON SOLAR PROJECT LLC—See Enel S.p.A.; *Int'l,* pg. 2414
HIGHPEAK ENERGY ACQUISITION CORP.—See HighPeak Energy, Inc.; *U.S. Public,* pg. 1035
HIGHPEAK ENERGY, INC.; *U.S. Public,* pg. 1035
HIGH PEAK ROYALTIES LIMITED; *Int'l,* pg. 3385
HIGH PERFORMANCE COPPER FOIL, INC.—See ENEOS Holdings, Inc.; *Int'l,* pg. 2416
HIGH PERFORMANCE PHYSICAL THERAPY, LLC—See U.S. Physical Therapy, Inc.; *U.S. Public,* pg. 2214
HIGH PERFORMANCE REAL ESTATE INVESTMENTS COMPANY PLC; *Int'l,* pg. 3386
HIGH PLAINS BANK—See First Keyes Bancshares, Inc.; *U.S. Private,* pg. 1520
HIGH PLAINS BIOENERGY, LLC—See Seaboard Corporation; *U.S. Public,* pg. 1850
HIGH PLAINS COMPUTING, INC.; *U.S. Private,* pg. 1936
HIGH PLAINS COOPERATIVE; *U.S. Private,* pg. 1936

HIGH PLAINS DISPOSAL, INC.—See Superior Energy Services, Inc.; *U.S. Private,* pg. 3877
HIGH PLAINS DRILLING, INC.—See Terracon Consultants, Inc.; *U.S. Private,* pg. 3971
HIGH PLAINS PHYSICAL THERAPY, LIMITED PARTNERSHIP—See U.S. Physical Therapy, Inc.; *U.S. Public,* pg. 2214
HIGH PLAINS POWER INC.; *U.S. Private,* pg. 1936
HIGH PLAINS TRANSPORT LLC—See Seaboard Corporation; *U.S. Public,* pg. 1850
HIGH POINT ENTERPRISE; *U.S. Private,* pg. 1936
HIGH POINT FURNITURE INDUSTRIES; *U.S. Private,* pg. 1936
HIGH POINT GAS TRANSMISSION, LLC—See ArcLight Capital Holdings, LLC; *U.S. Private,* pg. 312
HIGHPOINT GLOBAL, LLC; *U.S. Private,* pg. 1941
HIGHPOINT HOLDINGS, LLC; *U.S. Private,* pg. 1941
HIGHPOINT INVESTMENTS, LLC—See The GEO Group, Inc.; *U.S. Public,* pg. 2075
HIGH POINT MANOR, LP—See Brookdale Senior Living Inc.; *U.S. Public,* pg. 394
HIGH POINT OIL CO.; *U.S. Private,* pg. 1936
HIGH POINT, RANDLEMAN, ASHEBORO AND SOUTHERN RAILROAD CO.—See Norfolk Southern Corporation; *U.S. Public,* pg. 1536
HIGHPOINT RESOURCES CORPORATION—See Civitas Resources, Inc.; *U.S. Public,* pg. 507
HIGHPOINT SERVICE NETWORK CORPORATION—See Acer Incorporated; *Int'l,* pg. 99
HIGHPOINT SERVICE NETWORK SDN BHD—See Acer Incorporated; *Int'l,* pg. 99
HIGH POINT SOLUTIONS, INC.; *U.S. Private,* pg. 1936
HIGHPOINT SOLUTIONS, LLC; *U.S. Private,* pg. 1941
HIGHPOINT SOLUTIONS, LLC—See IQVIA Holdings Inc.; *U.S. Public,* pg. 1168
HIGHPOINT TECHNOLOGY SOLUTIONS, INC.; *U.S. Private,* pg. 1941
HIGH POINT TREATMENT CENTER; *U.S. Private,* pg. 1936
HIGH POOL TANKERS LTD—See d'Amico International Shipping S.A.; *Int'l,* pg. 1899
HIGHPOST CAPITAL, LLC; *U.S. Private,* pg. 1941
HIGH POWER EQUIPMENT AFRICA (PTY.) LTD.—See Invicta Holdings Limited; *Int'l,* pg. 3788
HIGHPOWER INTERNATIONAL, INC.; *Int'l,* pg. 3388
HIGH POWER LIGHTING CORP.; *Int'l,* pg. 3386
HIGH POWER TECHNICAL SERVICES; *U.S. Private,* pg. 1936
HIGH PRECISION DEVICES, INC.—See FormFactor, Inc.; *U.S. Public,* pg. 868
HIGH PRESSURE EQUIPMENT COMPANY—See Graco, Inc.; *U.S. Public,* pg. 953
HIGH-PURITY SILICON AMERICA CORPORATION—See SUMCO Corporation; *Int'l,* pg. 7260
HIGH Q LASER GMBH—See MKS Instruments, Inc.; *U.S. Public,* pg. 1453
HIGH QUALITY FOOD S.P.A.; *Int'l,* pg. 3386
HIGHRADIUS CORPORATION; *U.S. Private,* pg. 1941
HIGH REAL ESTATE GROUP LLC; *U.S. Private,* pg. 1936
HIGH RIDGE BRANDS CO.—See Clayton, Dubilier & Rice, LLC; *U.S. Private,* pg. 924
HIGHRIDGE—See Plantscapes, Inc.; *U.S. Private,* pg. 3198
HIGH RIVER FORD; *Int'l,* pg. 3386
HIGH ROAD CAPITAL PARTNERS, LLC; *U.S. Private,* pg. 1936
HIGH ROAD COMMUNICATIONS—See Omnicom Group Inc.; *U.S. Public,* pg. 1585
HIGH ROAD COMMUNICATIONS—See Omnicom Group Inc.; *U.S. Public,* pg. 1585
HIGH ROAD COMMUNICATIONS—See Omnicom Group Inc.; *U.S. Public,* pg. 1585
HIGH ROAD CRAFT ICE CREAM, INC.—See PMC Capital Partners, LLC; *U.S. Private,* pg. 3217
HIGHROAD SOLUTION; *U.S. Private,* pg. 1941
HIGHROCK RESOURCES LTD.; *Int'l,* pg. 3388
HIGHSCENE LIMITED—See Fountain Set (Holdings) Limited; *Int'l,* pg. 2754
HIGHSCORE, INC.—See Septeni Holdings Co., Ltd.; *Int'l,* pg. 6718
HIGH SEAS MARINE & INDUSTRIAL SERVICES CO. LTD.—See Ali Abdullah Al Tamimi Company; *Int'l,* pg. 319
HIGH SEAS TECHNOLOGY, INC.—See Pipe Welders Inc.; *U.S. Public,* pg. 3189
HIGH SEA SUGAR INC.; *U.S. Private,* pg. 1936
HIGH SECURITY SYSTEM CO., LTD.—See Hankyu Hanshin Holdings Inc.; *Int'l,* pg. 3256
HIGH SIERRA CRUDE OIL & MARKETING, LLC—See NGL Energy Partners LP; *U.S. Public,* pg. 1527
HIGH SIERRA ELECTRONICS, INC.—See Onerain, Inc.; *U.S. Private,* pg. 3025
HIGH SIERRA SPORT COMPANY—See Samsonite International S.A.; *Int'l,* pg. 6510
HIGH SIERRA TECHNOLOGIES, INC.; *U.S. Public,* pg. 1035
HIGHSMITH, LLC—See Wall Family Enterprise, Inc.; *U.S. Private,* pg. 4430
HIGH'S OF BALTIMORE INC.; *U.S. Private,* pg. 1937

HIGH SPARK PROPERTIES LIMITED—See Tern Properties Company Limited; *Int'l,* pg. 7566
HIGH SPEED RAIL CORPORATION OF INDIA LTD.—See Rail Vikas Nigam Ltd.; *Int'l,* pg. 6188
HIGHSTANDARD CO., LTD.—See Curves Holdings Co., Ltd.; *Int'l,* pg. 1880
HIGH STANDARD, INC.—See RFE Investment Partners; *U.S. Private,* pg. 3419
HIGH STANDARDS TECHNOLOGY, INC.—See Vector Choice Technology Solutions, Corp.; *U.S. Private,* pg. 4353
HIGH STEEL SERVICE CENTER LLC—See High Industries, Inc.; *U.S. Private,* pg. 1935
HIGH STEEL STRUCTURES INC.—See High Industries, Inc.; *U.S. Private,* pg. 1936
HIGHSTREET ASSET MANAGEMENT INC.—See AGF Management Limited; *Int'l,* pg. 206
HIGH STREET CAPITAL MANAGEMENT, INC.; *U.S. Private,* pg. 1936
HIGHSTREET CRUISES & ENTERTAINMENT PRIVATE LIMITED—See Delta Corp Ltd.; *Int'l,* pg. 2016
HIGH STREET FILATEX LTD; *Int'l,* pg. 3386
HIGH STREET INSURANCE PARTNERS, INC.—See ABRY Partners, LLC; *U.S. Private,* pg. 41
HIGH STREET VOUCHERS LIMITED—See PayPoint plc; *Int'l,* pg. 5763
HIGHSUN HOLDING GROUP CO., LTD.; *Int'l,* pg. 3388
HIGHSYSTEM AG—See NEXUS AG; *Int'l,* pg. 5250
HIGHT CHEVROLET BUICK GMC; *U.S. Private,* pg. 1941
HIGH TEAM INTERNATIONAL LIMITED—See SEA Holdings Limited; *Int'l,* pg. 6660
HIGH TECH CAMPUS EINDHOVEN U.A.—See Koninklijke Philips N.V.; *Int'l,* pg. 4268
HIGH-TECH CLIMA S.A.—See CEZ, a.s.; *Int'l,* pg. 1428
HIGH TECH COATINGS GMBH—See Miba AG; *Int'l,* pg. 4873
HIGH TECH COMPUTER ASIA PACIFIC PTE. LTD.—See HTC Corporation; *Int'l,* pg. 3508
HIGH TECH COMPUTER (H.K.) LIMITED—See HTC Corporation; *Int'l,* pg. 3508
HIGH TECH CRIME INSTITUTE INC.; *U.S. Private,* pg. 1937
HIGH TECH HOME CARE AG—See Healthcare at Home Ltd.; *Int'l,* pg. 3304
HIGH TECH IRRIGATION INC.; *U.S. Private,* pg. 1937
HIGH-TECH METALS LIMITED; *Int'l,* pg. 3386
HIGH TECHNOLOGY INSTITUTE LLP—See JSC National Atomic Company Kazatomprom; *Int'l,* pg. 4009
HIGH TECHNOLOGY SOURCES LIMITED—See James Fisher & Sons Public Limited Company; *Int'l,* pg. 3876
HIGH TECHNOLOGY SYSTEMS LTD.; *Int'l,* pg. 3386
HIGHTECH PAYMENT SYSTEMS S A; *Int'l,* pg. 3388
HIGH TECH PHARM CO., LTD.; *Int'l,* pg. 3386
HIGHTECH POLYMER SDN. BHD.—See Wah Lee Industrial Corp.; *Int'l,* pg. 8329
HIGH-TEK HARNESS ENTERPRISE CO., LTD.; *Int'l,* pg. 3386
HIGHTEL TOWERS SPA; *Int'l,* pg. 3388
HIGH TEMPERATURE SUPERCONDUCTORS, INC.; *U.S. Private,* pg. 1937
HIGHTEMP FURNACES LTD.—See Dowa Holdings Co., Ltd.; *Int'l,* pg. 2184
HIGHT ENTERPRISES, LTD. INC.; *U.S. Private,* pg. 1941
HIGHTEX GMBH; *Int'l,* pg. 3389
HIGH TIDE, INC.; *Int'l,* pg. 3386
HIGHTIMES HOLDING CORP.; *U.S. Private,* pg. 1941
HIGH-TOUCH COMMUNICATIONS INC.; *Int'l,* pg. 3386
HIGH TOUCH, INC.; *U.S. Private,* pg. 1937
HIGH TOUCH, INC.—See High Touch, Inc.; *U.S. Private,* pg. 1937
HIGHTOWER ADVISORS, LLC—See HighTower Holding LLC; *U.S. Private,* pg. 1941
HIGH TOWER ENGINEERING LLC—See SMC Corporation; *Int'l,* pg. 7003
HIGHTOWER HOLDING LLC; *U.S. Private,* pg. 1941
HIGHTOWERS PETROLEUM COMPANY; *U.S. Private,* pg. 1941
HIGHVIEW CAPITAL, LLC; *U.S. Private,* pg. 1941
HIGHVISTA GOLD INC.; *Int'l,* pg. 3389
HIGH VOLTAGE MAINTENANCE CORPORATION—See Emerson Electric Co.; *U.S. Public,* pg. 748
HIGH VOLTAGE MAINTENANCE CORP.—See Emerson Electric Co.; *U.S. Public,* pg. 748
HIGH VOLTAGE MAINTENANCE CORP.—See Emerson Electric Co.; *U.S. Public,* pg. 748
HIGH VOLTAGE MAINTENANCE CORP.—See Emerson Electric Co.; *U.S. Public,* pg. 748
HIGH VOLTAGE MAINTENANCE CORP.—See Emerson Electric Co.; *U.S. Public,* pg. 748
HIGH VOLTAGE MAINTENANCE - NORTHEAST ELECTRICAL TESTING—See Emerson Electric Co.; *U.S. Public,* pg. 748
HIGH VOLTAGE SOFTWARE, INC.—See Canada Pension Plan Investment Board; *Int'l,* pg. 1280
HIGH VOLTAGE SOFTWARE, INC.—See EQT AB; *Int'l,* pg. 2482
HIGH VOLTAGE SOFTWARE, INC.—See Temasek Holdings (Private) Limited; *Int'l,* pg. 7548

COMPANY NAME INDEX HILCO INC.

Company Index

HIGH VOLTAGE TECHNOLOGY LIMITED—See HEICO Corporation; *U.S. Public*, pg. 1020
HIGHWATER ETHANOL, LLC; *U.S. Private*, pg. 1942
HIGHWAY 50 GOLD CORP.; *Int'l*, pg. 3389
HIGHWAY 97 MINI STORAGE, LLC—See National Storage Affiliates Trust; *U.S. Public*, pg. 1498
HIGHWAY 99 MINI STORAGE, LLC—See National Storage Affiliates Trust; *U.S. Public*, pg. 1498
HIGHWAY CAPITAL PLC; *Int'l*, pg. 3389
HIGHWAY EQUIPMENT COMPANY; *U.S. Private*, pg. 1942
HIGHWAY EQUIPMENT COMPANY; *U.S. Private*, pg. 1942
HIGHWAY EQUIPMENT & SUPPLY CO.; *U.S. Private*, pg. 1942
HIGHWAY HOLDINGS LIMITED; *Int'l*, pg. 3389
HIGHWAY INSURANCE HOLDINGS PLC; *Int'l*, pg. 3389
HIGHWAY MAIL (PTY) LTD.—See Caxton and CTP Publishers and Printers Ltd.; *Int'l*, pg. 1363
HIGHWAY MARINE SERVICE INC.; *U.S. Private*, pg. 1942
HIGHWAY MOTORS INC.; *U.S. Private*, pg. 1942
HIGHWAY SAFETY LLC—See Race Rock GP, L.L.C; *U.S. Private*, pg. 3341
HIGHWAY SERVICE VENTURES INC.; *U.S. Private*, pg. 1942
HIGHWAYS, INC.; *U.S. Private*, pg. 1943
HIGHWAYS & SKYWAYS, INC.—See Radiant Logistics, Inc.; *U.S. Public*, pg. 1759
HIGHWAYS & SKYWAYS OF NC, INC.—See Radiant Logistics, Inc.; *U.S. Public*, pg. 1759
HIGHWAY SUPPLY, LLC—See Investcorp Holdings B.S.C.; *Int'l*, pg. 3777
HIGHWAY SUPPLY, LLC—See Trilantic Capital Management L.P.; *U.S. Private*, pg. 4231
HIGHWAY TECHNOLOGIES, INC.—See Wynnchurch Capital, L.P.; *U.S. Private*, pg. 4577
HIGHWAY TO HEALTH, INC.; *U.S. Private*, pg. 1942
HIGHWAY TOLL ADMINISTRATION, LLC—See Platinum Equity, LLC; *U.S. Private*, pg. 3203
HIGHWEALTH CONSTRUCTION CORP.; *Int'l*, pg. 3389
HIGH WEST DISTILLERY, LLC—See Constellation Brands, Inc.; *U.S. Public*, pg. 571
HIGH WEST ENERGY, INC.; *U.S. Private*, pg. 1937
HIGHWINDS NETWORK GROUP INC.—See ABRY Partners, LLC; *U.S. Private*, pg. 42
HIGH WIRE NETWORKS, INC.; *U.S. Private*, pg. 1937
HIGH WIRE NETWORKS INC.; *U.S. Public*, pg. 1035
HIGHWOOD ASSET MANAGEMENT LTD.; *Int'l*, pg. 3389
HIGHWOODS PROPERTIES, INC.; *U.S. Public*, pg. 1035
HIGHWOODS REALTY LIMITED PARTNERSHIP—See Highwoods Properties, Inc.; *U.S. Public*, pg. 1035
HIGH WYCOMBE - FOOD TECHNOLOGY CENTRE—See Premier Foods plc; *Int'l*, pg. 5960
HIGHYAG LASERTECHNOLOGIE GMBH—See Coherent Corp.; *U.S. Public*, pg. 528
HIGIENE INFANTIL DE MEXICO, S.A. DE C.V.—See Corporativo Copamex, S.A. de C.V.; *Int'l*, pg. 1806
HIGIJENA A.D.; *Int'l*, pg. 3389
HIGLEY HEALTHCARE, INC.—See The Ensign Group, Inc.; *U.S. Public*, pg. 2071
HIGMAN BARGE LINES INC.—See Higman Marine Inc.; *U.S. Private*, pg. 1943
HIGMAN MARINE INC.; *U.S. Private*, pg. 1943
THE HIGNELL COMPANIES; *U.S. Private*, pg. 4052
THE HIGO BANK, LTD.—See Kyushu Financial Group, Inc; *Int'l*, pg. 4368
HIGO DAIICHI TRAFFIC LTD—See Daiichi Koutsu Sangyo Co., Ltd.; *Int'l*, pg. 1928
HI GOLD OCEAN KMARIN NO.12 SHIP INVESTMENT COMPANY; *Int'l*, pg. 3379
H.I.G. PRIVATE EQUITY—See H.I.G. Capital, LLC; *U.S. Private*, pg. 1828
HI-GREAT GROUP HOLDING CO.; *U.S. Public*, pg. 1034
HI-GREEN CARBON LIMITED; *Int'l*, pg. 3380
THE HIGRO GROUP LLC; *U.S. Private*, pg. 4052
HIG SERVICES US INC—See Howden Group Holdings Limited; *Int'l*, pg. 3493
HIGUERA HARDWOODS LLC; *U.S. Private*, pg. 1943
HIHCL HP AMSTERDAM AIRPORT B.V.—See Hyatt Hotels Corporation; *U.S. Public*, pg. 1077
HI-HEALTH SUPERMART CORPORATION; *U.S. Private*, pg. 1931
HI-HEALTH SUPERMART—See Hi-Health Supermart Corporation; *U.S. Private*, pg. 1931
HI-HEVI RIGGING LTD.—See Vertex Resource Group Ltd.; *Int'l*, pg. 8174
HI-HO INC.—See Internet Initiative Japan Inc.; *Int'l*, pg. 3753
HI-HO PETROLEUM CO.—See D'Addario Industries Inc.; *U.S. Private*, pg. 1138
HII INDUSTRIES, INC.; *U.S. Private*, pg. 1943
HI INVESTMENT & SECURITIES CO., LTD.—See DGB Financial Group Co., Ltd.; *Int'l*, pg. 2096
H.I. (IRELAND) LIMITED—See InterContinental Hotels Group PLC; *Int'l*, pg. 3737
HIIT REPUBLIC AUSTRALIA PTY. LIMITED—See Viva Leisure Limited; *Int'l*, pg. 8264
HIJOS DE ANTONIO BARCELO, S.A.—See Acciona, S.A.; *Int'l*, pg. 90
HIJOS DE J. BARRERAS, S.A.—See Petroleos Mexicanos; *Int'l*, pg. 5828
HI-KALIBRE EQUIPMENT LTD.; *Int'l*, pg. 3380
HIKAL LIMITED; *Int'l*, pg. 3389
HIKAM AMERICA,INC.—See Hirakawa Hewtech Corp.; *Int'l*, pg. 3403
HIKAM ELECTRONICA DE MEXICO, S.A.DE C.V.—See Hirakawa Hewtech Corp.; *Int'l*, pg. 3403
HIKAMI MANUFACTURING CO., INC.—See Shizuki Electric Company, Inc.; *Int'l*, pg. 6855
HIKAM TECNOLOGIA DE SINALOA, S.A.DE C.V.—See Hirakawa Hewtech Corp.; *Int'l*, pg. 3403
HIKARI BUSINESS FORM CO., LTD.; *Int'l*, pg. 3389
HIKARI FURNITURE CO., LTD.; *Int'l*, pg. 3389
HIKARIGAOKA CORPORATION—See Maeda Corporation; *Int'l*, pg. 4635
HIKARI GLASS (CHANGZHOU) OPTICS CO., LTD.—See Nikon Corporation; *Int'l*, pg. 5292
HIKARI GLASS CO., LTD—See Nikon Corporation; *Int'l*, pg. 5292
HIKARI HEIGHTS-VARUS CO., LTD.; *Int'l*, pg. 3389
HIKARI HOLDINGS CO., LTD.; *Int'l*, pg. 3389
HIKARI PRIVATE EQUITY INC—See Hikari Tsushin, Inc.; *Int'l*, pg. 3390
HIKARI SEIKI INDUSTRY CO., LTD.—See NTN Corporation; *Int'l*, pg. 5481
HIKARI SHOES CO., LTD.—See Kuraray Co., Ltd.; *Int'l*, pg. 4336
HIKARI TSUSHIN, INC.; *Int'l*, pg. 3389
HIKING GROUP SHANDONG HAISHUN INTERNATIONAL CO., LTD.—See Shandong Hiking International Co., Ltd.; *Int'l*, pg. 6754
HIKING TEXTILE (SHANDONG) CO., LTD.—See Shandong Hiking International Co., Ltd.; *Int'l*, pg. 6754
HIKKADUWA BEACH RESORT PLC—See Citrus Leisure PLC; *Int'l*, pg. 1626
HI-KLASS TRADING & INVESTMENT LIMITED; *Int'l*, pg. 3380
HIKMA EMERGING MARKETS & ASIA PACIFIC FZ LLC—See Hikma Pharmaceuticals PLC; *Int'l*, pg. 3390
HIKMA FARMACEUTICA S.A.—See Hikma Pharmaceuticals PLC; *Int'l*, pg. 3390
HIKMA ITALIA S.P.A.—See Hikma Pharmaceuticals PLC; *Int'l*, pg. 3390
HIKMA LIBAN S.A.R.L—See Hikma Pharmaceuticals PLC; *Int'l*, pg. 3390
HIKMA PHARMA ALGERIA S.A.R.L—See Hikma Pharmaceuticals PLC; *Int'l*, pg. 3390
HIKMA PHARMACEUTICALS LLC—See Hikma Pharmaceuticals PLC; *Int'l*, pg. 3390
HIKMA PHARMACEUTICALS PLC; *Int'l*, pg. 3390
HIKMA PHARMACEUTICALS USA INC.—See Hikma Pharmaceuticals PLC; *Int'l*, pg. 3390
HIKMA PHARMA GMBH—See Hikma Pharmaceuticals PLC; *Int'l*, pg. 3390
HIKMA PHARMA SAE—See Hikma Pharmaceuticals PLC; *Int'l*, pg. 3390
HIKMA SLOVAKIA S.R.O.—See Hikma Pharmaceuticals PLC; *Int'l*, pg. 3390
HIKMA SPECIALITY USA INC.—See Hikma Pharmaceuticals PLC; *Int'l*, pg. 3390
HIKO ENERGY, LLC—See Via Renewables, Inc.; *U.S. Public*, pg. 2290
HIKOKI POWER TOOLS ASIA CO., LTD.—See KKR & Co. Inc.; *U.S. Public*, pg. 1257
HIKOKI POWER TOOLS BELGIUM N.V./S.A.—See KKR & Co. Inc.; *U.S. Public*, pg. 1257
HIKOKI POWER TOOLS DEUTSCHLAND GMBH—See KKR & Co. Inc.; *U.S. Public*, pg. 1257
HIKOKI POWER TOOLS FRANCE S.A.S.—See KKR & Co. Inc.; *U.S. Public*, pg. 1257
HIKOKI POWER TOOLS HUNGARY KFT.—See KKR & Co. Inc.; *U.S. Public*, pg. 1257
HIKOKI POWER TOOLS IBERICA, S.A.—See KKR & Co. Inc.; *U.S. Public*, pg. 1257
HIKOKI POWER TOOLS INDIA PRIVATE LTD.—See KKR & Co. Inc.; *U.S. Public*, pg. 1257
HIKOKI POWER TOOLS ITALIA SPA—See KKR & Co. Inc.; *U.S. Public*, pg. 1257
HIKOKI POWER TOOLS (MALAYSIA) SDN. BHD.—See KKR & Co. Inc.; *U.S. Public*, pg. 1257
HIKOKI POWER TOOLS NETHERLANDS B.V.—See KKR & Co. Inc.; *U.S. Public*, pg. 1257
HIKOKI POWER TOOLS NORWAY AS—See KKR & Co. Inc.; *U.S. Public*, pg. 1257
HIKOKI POWER TOOLS OSTERREICH GMBH—See KKR & Co. Inc.; *U.S. Public*, pg. 1257
HIKOKI POWER TOOLS ROMANIA S.R.L.—See KKR & Co. Inc.; *U.S. Public*, pg. 1257
HIKOKI POWER TOOLS RUS L.L.C.—See KKR & Co. Inc.; *U.S. Public*, pg. 1257
HIKOKI POWER TOOLS (SINGAPORE) PTE.LTD.—See KKR & Co. Inc.; *U.S. Public*, pg. 1257
HIKOKI POWER TOOLS SWEDEN AB—See KKR & Co. Inc.; *U.S. Public*, pg. 1257
HIKOKI POWER TOOLS (THAILAND) CO.,LTD.—See KKR & Co. Inc.; *U.S. Public*, pg. 1257
HIKOKI POWER TOOLS (U.K.) LTD.—See KKR & Co. Inc.; *U.S. Public*, pg. 1257
HI KOREA & CO.—See Micware Co. Ltd.; *Int'l*, pg. 4882
HIKU BRANDS COMPANY LTD.—See Canopy Growth Corporation; *Int'l*, pg. 1298
HIKVISION AUSTRALIA PTY CO., LTD.—See Hangzhou Hikvision Digital Technology Co., Ltd.; *Int'l*, pg. 3247
HIKVISION AZERBAIJAN LIMITED LIABILITY—See Hangzhou Hikvision Digital Technology Co., Ltd.; *Int'l*, pg. 3247
HIKVISION CANADA INC.—See Hangzhou Hikvision Digital Technology Co., Ltd.; *Int'l*, pg. 3247
HIKVISION CZECH S.R.O.—See Hangzhou Hikvision Digital Technology Co., Ltd.; *Int'l*, pg. 3247
HIKVISION DEUTSCHLAND GMBH—See Hangzhou Hikvision Digital Technology Co., Ltd.; *Int'l*, pg. 3247
HIKVISION DO BRASIL COMERCIO DE EQUIPAMENTOS DE SEGURANCA LTDA.—See Hangzhou Hikvision Digital Technology Co., Ltd.; *Int'l*, pg. 3248
HIKVISION EUROPE B.V.—See Hangzhou Hikvision Digital Technology Co., Ltd.; *Int'l*, pg. 3247
HIKVISION FRANCE SAS—See Hangzhou Hikvision Digital Technology Co., Ltd.; *Int'l*, pg. 3247
HIKVISION FZE—See Hangzhou Hikvision Digital Technology Co., Ltd.; *Int'l*, pg. 3247
HIKVISION ITALY S.R.L—See Hangzhou Hikvision Digital Technology Co., Ltd.; *Int'l*, pg. 3247
HIKVISION KAZAKHSTAN LIMITED LIABILITY PARTNERSHIP—See Hangzhou Hikvision Digital Technology Co., Ltd.; *Int'l*, pg. 3247
HIKVISION KOREA LIMITED—See Hangzhou Hikvision Digital Technology Co., Ltd.; *Int'l*, pg. 3247
HIKVISION LLC—See Hangzhou Hikvision Digital Technology Co., Ltd.; *Int'l*, pg. 3248
HIKVISION (MALAYSIA) SDN. BHD.—See Hangzhou Hikvision Digital Technology Co., Ltd.; *Int'l*, pg. 3247
HIKVISION MEXICO S.A.DE C.V.—See Hangzhou Hikvision Digital Technology Co., Ltd.; *Int'l*, pg. 3248
HIKVISION NEW ZEALAND LIMITED—See Hangzhou Hikvision Digital Technology Co., Ltd.; *Int'l*, pg. 3248
HIKVISION PAKISTAN (SMC-PRIVATE) LIMITED—See Hangzhou Hikvision Digital Technology Co., Ltd.; *Int'l*, pg. 3248
HIKVISION POLAND SPOLKA Z OGRANICZONA ODPOWIEDZIALNOSCIA—See Hangzhou Hikvision Digital Technology Co., Ltd.; *Int'l*, pg. 3248
HIKVISION SINGAPORE PTE. LTD.—See Hangzhou Hikvision Digital Technology Co., Ltd.; *Int'l*, pg. 3248
HIKVISION SOUTH AFRICA (PTY) CO., LTD.—See Hangzhou Hikvision Digital Technology Co., Ltd.; *Int'l*, pg. 3248
HIKVISION SPAIN, S.L.—See Hangzhou Hikvision Digital Technology Co., Ltd.; *Int'l*, pg. 3248
HIKVISION TECHNOLOGY EGYPT JSC—See Hangzhou Hikvision Digital Technology Co., Ltd.; *Int'l*, pg. 3248
HIKVISION TECHNOLOGY ISRAEL CO., LTD.—See Hangzhou Hikvision Digital Technology Co., Ltd.; *Int'l*, pg. 3248
HIKVISION TURKEY TECHNOLOGY & SECURITY SYSTEMS COMMERCE CORPORATION—See Hangzhou Hikvision Digital Technology Co., Ltd.; *Int'l*, pg. 3248
HIKVISION UK LIMITED—See Hangzhou Hikvision Digital Technology Co., Ltd.; *Int'l*, pg. 3248
HIKVISION USA, INC.—See Hangzhou Hikvision Digital Technology Co., Ltd.; *Int'l*, pg. 3248
HI-LAI FOODS CO., LTD.; *Int'l*, pg. 3380
HILAL CEMENT COMPANY K.S.C.C.; *Int'l*, pg. 3390
HILAND DAIRY FOODS COMPANY, LLC—See Dairy Farmers of America, Inc.; *U.S. Private*, pg. 1146
HILAND DAIRY FOODS COMPANY, LLC—See Prairie Farms Dairy, Inc.; *U.S. Private*, pg. 3242
HI-LAND TECHNO CORPORATION—See Takashima & Co., Ltd.; *Int'l*, pg. 7435
HILAN LTD.; *Int'l*, pg. 3390
HILBER SOLAR GMBH; *Int'l*, pg. 3391
THE HILB GROUP, LLC—See ABRY Partners, LLC; *U.S. Private*, pg. 43
THE HILB GROUP OF INDIANA, LLC—See ABRY Partners, LLC; *U.S. Private*, pg. 43
THE HILB GROUP OF VIRGINIA, LLC—See ABRY Partners, LLC; *U.S. Private*, pg. 43
HILBIG SERVICES INC.—See Southland Industries; *U.S. Private*, pg. 3737
HILBISH FORD; *U.S. Private*, pg. 1943
HILBROY ADVISORY INC.; *Int'l*, pg. 3391
HILCO APPRAISAL LIMITED—See Hilco Trading, LLC; *U.S. Private*, pg. 1943
HILCO APPRAISAL SERVICES, LLC—See Hilco Trading, LLC; *U.S. Private*, pg. 1943
HILCO CONSUMER CAPITAL, LLC—See Hilco Trading, LLC; *U.S. Private*, pg. 1943
HILCO CORPORATE FINANCE, LLC—See Hilco Trading, LLC; *U.S. Private*, pg. 1943
HILCO ELECTRIC COOPERATIVE; *U.S. Private*, pg. 1943
HILCO EQUITY MANAGEMENT, LLC—See Hilco Trading, LLC; *U.S. Private*, pg. 1943
HILCO EUROPE—See Windjammer Capital Investors, LLC; *U.S. Private*, pg. 4538
HILCO INC.; *U.S. Private*, pg. 1943
HILCO INDUSTRIAL, LLC—See Hilco Trading, LLC; *U.S. Private*, pg. 1943

HILCO INC.

HILCO INDUSTRIAL ONLINE, LLC—See Hilco Trading, LLC; *U.S. Private*, pg. 1943
HILCO MERCHANT RESOURCES LLC; *U.S. Private*, pg. 1943
HILCONA CONVENIENCE AG—See Coop-Gruppe Genossenschaft; *Int'l*, pg. 1790
HILCONA FRESH EXPRESS—See Coop-Gruppe Genossenschaft; *Int'l*, pg. 1790
HILCO REAL ESTATE, LLC—See Hilco Trading, LLC; *U.S. Private*, pg. 1943
HILCO RECEIVABLES EUROPE B.V.—See Hilco Trading, LLC; *U.S. Private*, pg. 1944
HILCO RECEIVABLES LLC—See Hilco Trading, LLC; *U.S. Private*, pg. 1944
HILCORP ALASKA LLC; *U.S. Private*, pg. 1944
HILCORP ENERGY CO.; *U.S. Private*, pg. 1944
HILCO TRADING CO., INC.—See Hilco Trading, LLC; *U.S. Private*, pg. 1943
HILCO TRADING, LLC; *U.S. Private*, pg. 1943
HILCO TRANSPORT INC.; *U.S. Private*, pg. 1944
HILCO UK LTD.—See Hilco Trading, LLC; *U.S. Private*, pg. 1944
HILDA ROSS RETIREMENT VILLAGE LIMITED—See Ryman Healthcare Ltd.; *Int'l*, pg. 6439
HILDEBRAND FRANCE S.A.R.L.—See Metall Zug AG; *Int'l*, pg. 4847
HILDEBRAND MOTORS LTD.; *Int'l*, pg. 3391
HILDEBRANDT NETHERLANDS B.V.—See August Hildebrandt GmbH; *Int'l*, pg. 703
HILDEBRANDT USA, INC.—See August Hildebrandt GmbH; *Int'l*, pg. 703
HILDEN AMERICA, INC.; *U.S. Private*, pg. 1944
HILDESHEIMER STAHLHANDEL GMBH & CO. KG—See Salzgitter AG; *Int'l*, pg. 6496
HILDI INCORPORATED—See Caisse de Depot et Placement du Quebec; *Int'l*, pg. 1256
HILDI INCORPORATED—See KKR & Co. Inc.; *U.S. Public*, pg. 1265
HILD SAMEN GMBH—See Bayer Aktiengesellschaft; *Int'l*, pg. 908
HILEC, LLC—See Delfingen Industry, S.A.; *Int'l*, pg. 2013
HILER INDUSTRIES; *U.S. Private*, pg. 1944
HI-LEVEL TECHNOLOGY LIMITED—See S.A.S. Dragon Holdings Limited; *Int'l*, pg. 6449
HI-LEX AMERICA, INC.—See Hi-Lex Corporation; *Int'l*, pg. 3380
HI-LEX AUTO PARTS SPAIN, S.L.—See Hi-Lex Corporation; *Int'l*, pg. 3380
HI-LEX CABLE SYSTEM CO.,LTD.—See Hi-Lex Corporation; *Int'l*, pg. 3380
HI-LEX CONTROLS, INC.—See Hi-Lex Corporation; *Int'l*, pg. 3380
HI-LEX CORPORATION - KAIBARA PLANT—See Hi-Lex Corporation; *Int'l*, pg. 3380
HI-LEX CORPORATION - MIKKABI PLANT—See Hi-Lex Corporation; *Int'l*, pg. 3380
HI-LEX CORPORATION - SANDA-NISHI PLANT—See Hi-Lex Corporation; *Int'l*, pg. 3380
HI-LEX CORPORATION - SANDA PLANT—See Hi-Lex Corporation; *Int'l*, pg. 3380
HI-LEX CORPORATION; *Int'l*, pg. 3380
HI-LEX CZECH, S.R.O.—See Hi-Lex Corporation; *Int'l*, pg. 3380
HI LEX DO BRASIL LTDA.—See Hi-Lex Corporation; *Int'l*, pg. 3380
HI-LEX EUROPE GMBH—See Hi-Lex Corporation; *Int'l*, pg. 3380
HI-LEX HUNGARY CABLE SYSTEM MANUFACTURING LLC—See Hi-Lex Corporation; *Int'l*, pg. 3380
HI-LEX HUNGARY KFT—See Hi-Lex Corporation; *Int'l*, pg. 3380
HI-LEX INDIA (P) LTD.—See Hi-Lex Corporation; *Int'l*, pg. 3380
HI-LEX ITALY S.P.A.—See Hi-Lex Corporation; *Int'l*, pg. 3380
HI-LEX KANTO, INC—See Hi-Lex Corporation; *Int'l*, pg. 3380
HI-LEX MEXICANA S.A. DE C.V.—See Hi-Lex Corporation; *Int'l*, pg. 3380
HI-LEX MIYAGI, INC.—See Hi-Lex Corporation; *Int'l*, pg. 3380
HILEX POLY CO. LLC - NORTH VERNON—See Apollo Global Management, Inc.; *U.S. Public*, pg. 154
HILEX POLY CO. LLC—See Apollo Global Management, Inc.; *U.S. Public*, pg. 154
HI-LEX RUS LLC—See Hi-Lex Corporation; *Int'l*, pg. 3381
HI-LEX SAITAMA, INC.—See Hi-Lex Corporation; *Int'l*, pg. 3381
HI-LEX SERBIA D.O.O.—See Hi-Lex Corporation; *Int'l*, pg. 3381
HI-LEX SHIMANE, INC.—See Hi-Lex Corporation; *Int'l*, pg. 3381
HI-LEX VIETNAM CO., LTD—See Hi-Lex Corporation; *Int'l*, pg. 3380
HILEY AUTO DEALERSHIPS, INC.; *U.S. Private*, pg. 1944
HILFIGER STORES DENMARK APS—See PVH Corp.; *U.S. Public*, pg. 1739

HILFIGER STORES SPZOO—See PVH Corp.; *U.S. Public*, pg. 1739
HILFIGER STORES SRO—See PVH Corp.; *U.S. Public*, pg. 1739
HILFORT PLASTICS (PTY) LTD—See Berry Global Group, Inc; *U.S. Public*, pg. 324
HILGER CRYSTALS LTD.—See Dynasil Corporation of America; *U.S. Private*, pg. 1299
HI-LIFE TOOLS—See Berkshire Hathaway Inc.; *U.S. Public*, pg. 315
HILIFT JACK CO.—See The Bloomfield Manufacturing Co., Inc.; *U.S. Private*, pg. 3995
HI-LIGHT ELECTRICAL PTE LTD—See Kingsmen Creatives Ltd.; *Int'l*, pg. 4175
HILIKS TECHNOLOGIES LTD.; *Int'l*, pg. 3391
HIL INDUSTRIS BERHAD; *Int'l*, pg. 3390
HI-LINE COOPERATIVE INC.; *U.S. Private*, pg. 1931
HI-LINE INDUSTRIES II, INC.—See Sciens Capital Management LLC; *U.S. Private*, pg. 3574
HI-LINE MOVING SERVICES INC.; *U.S. Private*, pg. 1931
HI-LINE UTILITY SUPPLY COMPANY—See WESCO International, Inc.; *U.S. Public*, pg. 2351
HILI PREMIER ESTATE ROMANIA SRL—See Hili Properties PLC; *Int'l*, pg. 3391
HILI PROPERTIES PLC; *Int'l*, pg. 3391
HI-LITE CAMERA COMPANY LIMITED—See Highway Holdings Limited; *Int'l*, pg. 3389
HILITE GERMANY GMBH—See Aviation Industry Corporation of China; *Int'l*, pg. 742
HILITE GERMANY GMBH—See Aviation Industry Corporation of China; *Int'l*, pg. 742
HILITE INTERNATIONAL, INC. - WHITEHALL—See Aviation Industry Corporation of China; *Int'l*, pg. 742
HILI VENTURES LTD; *Int'l*, pg. 3391
HILL-ACME—See Magnum Integrated Technologies, Inc.; *Int'l*, pg. 4642
HILL AEROSYSTEMS INC.—See Acorn Growth Companies, LC; *U.S. Private*, pg. 63
HILLANDALE FARMS OF PA INC.; *U.S. Private*, pg. 1946
HILLARD HEINTZE, LLC—See Gryphon Investors, LLC; *U.S. Private*, pg. 1798
HILL ASSOCIATES INC.; *U.S. Private*, pg. 1944
HILL & ASSOCIATES (INDIA) PVT. LTD.—See Allied Universal Manager LLC; *U.S. Private*, pg. 190
HILL & ASSOCIATES LIMITED—See Allied Universal Manager LLC; *U.S. Private*, pg. 190
HILL & ASSOCIATES (PRC) LTD.—See Allied Universal Manager LLC; *U.S. Private*, pg. 190
HILL, BARTH & KING LLC; *U.S. Private*, pg. 1945
HILL BARTON VALE EXETER MANAGEMENT COMPANY LIMITED—See Persimmon plc; *Int'l*, pg. 5816
HILL BROTHERS CHEMICAL COMPANY INC. - CITY OF INDUSTRY—See Hill Brothers Chemical Company Inc.; *U.S. Private*, pg. 1944
HILL BROTHERS CHEMICAL COMPANY INC. - SALT LAKE CITY—See Hill Brothers Chemical Company Inc.; *U.S. Private*, pg. 1944
HILL BROTHERS CHEMICAL COMPANY INC.; *U.S. Private*, pg. 1944
HILL BROTHERS CONSTRUCTION & ENGINEERING CO.; *U.S. Private*, pg. 1944
HILL BROTHERS, INC.; *U.S. Private*, pg. 1945
HILL BROTHERS INTERMODAL LOGISTICS INC.—See Hill Brothers, Inc.; *U.S. Private*, pg. 1945
HILL CADILLAC; *U.S. Private*, pg. 1945
HILL CITY OIL COMPANY INC.; *U.S. Private*, pg. 1945
HILL CITY WHOLESALE CO. INC.; *U.S. Private*, pg. 1945
HILL CONSTRUCTION CORPORATION, *U.S. Private*, pg. 1945
THE HILLCORE GROUP; *Int'l*, pg. 7652
HILL COUNTRY BAKERY; *U.S. Private*, pg. 1945
HILL COUNTRY COMMUNITY ACTION ASSOCIATION, INC.; *U.S. Private*, pg. 1945
HILL COUNTRY DAIRIES INC.; *U.S. Private*, pg. 1945
HILL COUNTRY ELECTRIC SUPPLY, L.P.—See WESCO International, Inc.; *U.S. Public*, pg. 2351
HILL COUNTRY ENTERPRISES; *U.S. Private*, pg. 1945
HILL COUNTRY SURGERY CENTER, LLC—See Tenet Healthcare Corporation; *U.S. Public*, pg. 2004
HILL COUNTRY WHOLESALE INC.—See Peter Pan Bus Lines, Inc.; *U.S. Private*, pg. 3159
HILL & COX CORPORATION; *U.S. Private*, pg. 1944
HILL CRAFT FURNITURE CO.; *U.S. Private*, pg. 1945
HILLCREST AUTOMOTIVE SERVICES; *U.S. Private*, pg. 1946
HILLCREST BANK—See National Bank Holdings Corporation; *U.S. Public*, pg. 1493
HILLCREST CAPITAL PARTNERS LP; *U.S. Private*, pg. 1946
HILLCREST CENTER—See Formation Capital, LLC; *U.S. Private*, pg. 1570
HILLCREST DEVELOPMENT INC.; *U.S. Private*, pg. 1946
HILL CREST DEVELOPMENT; *U.S. Private*, pg. 1945
HILLCREST EDUCATIONAL CENTERS, INC.; *U.S. Private*, pg. 1946
HILLCREST ENERGY TECHNOLOGIES LTD.; *Int'l*, pg. 3392
HILLCREST FOODS INC.; *U.S. Private*, pg. 1946

CORPORATE AFFILIATIONS

HILLCREST GOLF & COUNTRY CLUB, LTD.—See Pulte-Group, Inc.; *U.S. Public*, pg. 1737
HILLCREST HEALTHCARE SYSTEM—See Ventas, Inc.; *U.S. Public*, pg. 2279
HILLCREST LABORATORIES, INC.—See CEVA, Inc.; *U.S. Public*, pg. 476
HILLCREST; *U.S. Private*, pg. 1946
HILLCREST VOLKSWAGEN (1979) LTD; *Int'l*, pg. 3392
HILL DISTRIBUTING COMPANY; *U.S. Private*, pg. 1945
HILLDRUP TRANSFER & STORAGE, INC.; *U.S. Private*, pg. 1946
HILLEBRAND GORI HONG KONG LIMITED—See Deutsche Post AG; *Int'l*, pg. 2080
HILLEBRAND GORI JAPAN K.K.—See Deutsche Post AG; *Int'l*, pg. 2080
HILLEBRAND GORI KOREA LTD.—See Deutsche Post AG; *Int'l*, pg. 2080
HILLEBRAND KENYA LIMITED—See Deutsche Post AG; *Int'l*, pg. 2080
HILLEL: THE FOUNDATION FOR JEWISH CAMPUS LIFE; *U.S. Private*, pg. 1946
HILLE & MULLER GMBH—See Tata Sons Limited; *Int'l*, pg. 7472
HILLE & MULLER (U.S.A.), INC—See Tata Sons Limited; *Int'l*, pg. 7473
HILLENBRAND GERMANY HOLDING GMBH—See Hillenbrand, Inc.; *U.S. Public*, pg. 1036
HILLENBRAND, INC.; *U.S. Public*, pg. 1035
HILL ENGINEERING CONSULTANCY, LLC—See Global Infrastructure Solutions, Inc.; *U.S. Private*, pg. 1715
HILL ENGINEERING, INC.—See Mestek, Inc.; *U.S. Public*, pg. 1426
THE HILLER COMPANIES, INC.—See Littlejohn & Co., LLC; *U.S. Private*, pg. 2471
HILLER COMPANY INCORPORATED; *U.S. Private*, pg. 1946
THE HILLER GROUP, INC.—See World Kinect Corporation; *U.S. Public*, pg. 2381
HILLERICH & BRADSBY CO., INC.; *U.S. Private*, pg. 1946
HILLER PLUMBING, HEATING & COOLING COMPANY; *U.S. Private*, pg. 1946
HILLERS INC; *U.S. Private*, pg. 1946
HILLEVAX, INC.; *U.S. Public*, pg. 1037
HILLFIELD MEADOWS (SUNDERLAND) MANAGEMENT COMPANY LIMITED—See Persimmon plc; *Int'l*, pg. 5816
HILL & FOSS, INC.—See Berkshire Partners LLC; *U.S. Private*, pg. 535
HILL & GRIFFITH COMPANY; *U.S. Private*, pg. 1944
THE HILL GROUP; *U.S. Private*, pg. 4052
HILLGROVE MINES PTY LTD.—See Larvotto Resources Limited; *Int'l*, pg. 4420
HILLGROVE RESOURCES LIMITED; *Int'l*, pg. 3392
HILL HOLLIDAY/NEW YORK—See Attivo group; *Int'l*, pg. 697
HILL HOLLIDAY—See Attivo group; *Int'l*, pg. 697
HILLHOUSE INVESTMENT MANAGEMENT LIMITED; *Int'l*, pg. 3392
HILLHOUSE NATURALS FARM, LTD.; *U.S. Private*, pg. 1946
HILLIARD CORPORATION; *U.S. Public*, pg. 1038
HILLIARD GRAND APARTMENTS, LLC—See Independence Realty Trust, Inc.; *U.S. Public*, pg. 1115
HILLIARD'S BEER—See Odin Brewing Co.; *U.S. Private*, pg. 2993
HILLIES VIEW (WOMBWELL) MANAGEMENT COMPANY LIMITED—See Persimmon plc; *Int'l*, pg. 5816
HIL LIMITED—See CK Birla Group; *Int'l*, pg. 1636
HILL INCORPORATED; *Int'l*, pg. 3392
HILL INTERNATIONAL BH DO.O—See Global Infrastructure Solutions, Inc.; *U.S. Private*, pg. 1715
HILL INTERNATIONAL (BUCHAREST) S.R.L.—See Global Infrastructure Solutions, Inc.; *U.S. Private*, pg. 1715
HILL INTERNATIONAL (COLOMBIA) SAS—See Global Infrastructure Solutions, Inc.; *U.S. Private*, pg. 1715
HILL INTERNATIONAL DE MEXICO, S.A. DE C.V.—See Global Infrastructure Solutions, Inc.; *U.S. Private*, pg. 1715
HILL INTERNATIONAL ENGINEERING CONSULTANCY, LLC—See Global Infrastructure Solutions, Inc.; *U.S. Private*, pg. 1715
HILL INTERNATIONAL (GERMANY) GMBH—See Global Infrastructure Solutions, Inc.; *U.S. Private*, pg. 1715
HILL INTERNATIONAL (HELLAS) S.A.—See Global Infrastructure Solutions, Inc.; *U.S. Private*, pg. 1715
HILL INTERNATIONAL (HONG KONG) LTD.—See Global Infrastructure Solutions, Inc.; *U.S. Private*, pg. 1715
HILL INTERNATIONAL INC.- ABU DHABI, U.A.E.—See Global Infrastructure Solutions, Inc.; *U.S. Private*, pg. 1715
HILL INTERNATIONAL INC.-CALIFORNIA—See Global Infrastructure Solutions, Inc.; *U.S. Private*, pg. 1715
HILL INTERNATIONAL INC.-DISTRICT OF COLUMBIA—See Global Infrastructure Solutions, Inc.; *U.S. Private*, pg. 1715
HILL INTERNATIONAL INC.-FLORIDA—See Global Infrastructure Solutions, Inc.; *U.S. Private*, pg. 1715

COMPANY NAME INDEX

HILL INTERNATIONAL INC.-GREECE—See Global Infrastructure Solutions, Inc.; *U.S. Private*, pg. 1715
HILL INTERNATIONAL INC.-NEW YORK—See Global Infrastructure Solutions, Inc.; *U.S. Private*, pg. 1715
HILL INTERNATIONAL INC.-PENNSYLVANIA—See Global Infrastructure Solutions, Inc.; *U.S. Private*, pg. 1715
HILL INTERNATIONAL INC.—See Global Infrastructure Solutions, Inc.; *U.S. Private*, pg. 1715
HILL INTERNATIONAL (LIBYA) LTD.—See Global Infrastructure Solutions, Inc.; *U.S. Private*, pg. 1715
HILL INTERNATIONAL (NEW ENGLAND) INC.—See Global Infrastructure Solutions, Inc.; *U.S. Private*, pg. 1715
HILL INTERNATIONAL (NORTH AFRICA) LTD.—See Global Infrastructure Solutions, Inc.; *U.S. Private*, pg. 1715
HILL INTERNATIONAL PROJECT MANAGEMENT (INDIA) PRIVATE LIMITED—See Global Infrastructure Solutions, Inc.; *U.S. Private*, pg. 1715
HILL INTERNATIONAL PROJE YONETIMI VE DANISMANLIK A.S.—See Global Infrastructure Solutions, Inc.; *U.S. Private*, pg. 1715
HILL INTERNATIONAL—See Global Infrastructure Solutions, Inc.; *U.S. Private*, pg. 1715
HILL INTERNATIONAL (SPAIN) S.A.—See Global Infrastructure Solutions, Inc.; *U.S. Private*, pg. 1715
HILL INTERNATIONAL TRUCKS LLC; *U.S. Private*, pg. 1945
HILL INTERNATIONAL (UK), LTD.—See Global Infrastructure Solutions, Inc.; *U.S. Private*, pg. 1715
HILL INTERNATIONAL VIETNAM CO. LIMITED—See Global Infrastructure Solutions, Inc.; *U.S. Private*, pg. 1715
HILLIS-CARNES ENGINEERING ASSOCIATES, INC.; *U.S. Private*, pg. 1946
HILL & KNOWLTON AUSTRALIA PTY. LTD.—See WPP plc; *Int'l*, pg. 8477
HILL & KNOWLTON BRAZIL—See WPP plc; *Int'l*, pg. 8477
HILL & KNOWLTON (CANADA) LIMITED—See WPP plc; *Int'l*, pg. 8478
HILL & KNOWLTON CAPTIVA—See WPP plc; *Int'l*, pg. 8477
HILL & KNOWLTON (CHINA) PUBLIC RELATIONS CO. LTD—See WPP plc; *Int'l*, pg. 8477
HILL & KNOWLTON (CHINA) PUBLIC RELATIONS CO. LTD.—See WPP plc; *Int'l*, pg. 8477
HILL & KNOWLTON DE ARGENTINA—See WPP plc; *Int'l*, pg. 8478
HILL & KNOWLTON DE GUATEMALA—See WPP plc; *Int'l*, pg. 8478
HILL & KNOWLTON EESTI AS—See WPP plc; *Int'l*, pg. 8478
HILL & KNOWLTON ESPANA, S.A.—See WPP plc; *Int'l*, pg. 8477
HILL & KNOWLTON ESPANA, S.A.—See WPP plc; *Int'l*, pg. 8478
HILL & KNOWLTON FRANKFURT—See WPP plc; *Int'l*, pg. 8478
HILL & KNOWLTON HONG KONG LTD.—See WPP plc; *Int'l*, pg. 8478
HILL & KNOWLTON, INC—See WPP plc; *Int'l*, pg. 8478
HILL & KNOWLTON, INC.—See WPP plc; *Int'l*, pg. 8477
HILL & KNOWLTON, INC.—See WPP plc; *Int'l*, pg. 8478
HILL & KNOWLTON, INC.—See WPP plc; *Int'l*, pg. 8478
HILL & KNOWLTON, INC.—See WPP plc; *Int'l*, pg. 8478
HILL & KNOWLTON, INC.—See WPP plc; *Int'l*, pg. 8478
HILL & KNOWLTON, INC.—See WPP plc; *Int'l*, pg. 8478
HILL & KNOWLTON, INC.—See WPP plc; *Int'l*, pg. 8478
HILL & KNOWLTON, INC.—See WPP plc; *Int'l*, pg. 8478
HILL & KNOWLTON INTERNATIONAL BELGIUM S.A./N.V.—See WPP plc; *Int'l*, pg. 8478
HILL & KNOWLTON ITALY—See WPP plc; *Int'l*, pg. 8478
HILL & KNOWLTON JAPAN, LTD.—See WPP plc; *Int'l*, pg. 8478
HILL & KNOWLTON LATVIA—See WPP plc; *Int'l*, pg. 8478
HILL & KNOWLTON MEXICO—See WPP plc; *Int'l*, pg. 8478
HILL & KNOWLTON NEDERLAND B.V.—See WPP plc; *Int'l*, pg. 8478
HILL & KNOWLTON RESULT, INC.—See WPP plc; *Int'l*, pg. 8478
HILL & KNOWLTON (SEA) PVT. LTD.—See WPP plc; *Int'l*, pg. 8477
HILL & KNOWLTON (SEA) SDN. BHD.—See WPP plc; *Int'l*, pg. 8477
HILL & KNOWLTON—See WPP plc; *Int'l*, pg. 8477
HILL & KNOWLTON—See WPP plc; *Int'l*, pg. 8478
HILL & KNOWLTON STRATEGIES GMBH-FRANKFURT—See WPP plc; *Int'l*, pg. 8478
HILL & KNOWLTON STRATEGIES GMBH—See WPP plc; *Int'l*, pg. 8478
HILL + KNOWLTON STRATEGIES ITALY S.R.L.—See WPP plc; *Int'l*, pg. 8478
HILL & KNOWLTON SWEDEN AB—See WPP plc; *Int'l*, pg. 8478
HILL & KNOWLTON THAILAND—See WPP plc; *Int'l*, pg. 8478

HILL & KNOWLTON/THOMPSON CORP.—See WPP plc; *Int'l*, pg. 8479
HILL & KNOWLTON (UK) LTD.—See WPP plc; *Int'l*, pg. 8477
HILL MANAGEMENT SERVICES INC.—See The Home Sales Company; *U.S. Private*, pg. 4054
THE HILLMAN COMPANIES, INC.—See Hillman Solutions Corp.; *U.S. Public*, pg. 1038
THE HILLMAN COMPANY; *U.S. Private*, pg. 4052
THE HILLMAN FLUID POWER GROUP—See The Hillman Company; *U.S. Private*, pg. 4053
THE HILLMAN GROUP, INC.—See Hillman Solutions Corp.; *U.S. Public*, pg. 1038
THE HILLMAN GROUP - TEMPE—See Hillman Solutions Corp.; *U.S. Public*, pg. 1038
HILLMAN OYSTER COMPANY; *U.S. Private*, pg. 1946
HILLMAN SOLUTIONS CORP.; *U.S. Public*, pg. 1038
HILLMAN'S TRANSFER LIMITED—See Armour Transportation Systems; *Int'l*, pg. 575
HILLMER INC.; *U.S. Private*, pg. 1946
THE HILLMONT ASC, L.P.—See KKR & Co. Inc.; *U.S. Public*, pg. 1247
HILL-N-DALE ABSTRACTERS, INC.; *U.S. Private*, pg. 1946
HILL NISSAN, INC.; *U.S. Private*, pg. 1945
HILLPARK DEVELOPMENT SDN. BHD.—See Gromutual Berhad; *Int'l*, pg. 3087
HILL PETROLEUM INC.; *U.S. Private*, pg. 1945
HILL PETROLEUM, INC.; *U.S. Private*, pg. 1945
HILL PETROLEUM—See Hill Petroleum, Inc.; *U.S. Private*, pg. 1945
HILL PHOENIX COSTA RICA, SOCIEDAD DE RESPONSABILIDAD LIMITADA—See Dover Corporation; *U.S. Public*, pg. 681
HILL PHOENIX INC.—See Dover Corporation; *U.S. Public*, pg. 679
HILL PHYSICIANS MEDICAL GROUP, INC.—See Primed Management Consulting Services Inc.; *U.S. Private*, pg. 3262
HILL REGIONAL CLINIC CORP.—See Community Health Systems, Inc.; *U.S. Public*, pg. 553
HILL-ROM AB—See Baxter International Inc.; *U.S. Public*, pg. 282
HILL-ROM AUSTRIA GMBH—See Baxter International Inc.; *U.S. Public*, pg. 282
HILLROM BELGIUM B.V.—See Baxter International Inc.; *U.S. Public*, pg. 283
HILL-ROM B.V.—See Baxter International Inc.; *U.S. Public*, pg. 283
HILL-ROM CANADA, LTD.—See Baxter International Inc.; *U.S. Public*, pg. 283
HILL-ROM CANADA RESPIRATORY, LTD.—See Baxter International Inc.; *U.S. Public*, pg. 283
HILL-ROM - CHARLESTON—See Baxter International Inc.; *U.S. Public*, pg. 283
HILL-ROM COMERCIALIZADOR A DE MEXICO S DE RL DE CV—See Baxter International Inc.; *U.S. Public*, pg. 283
HILL-ROM COMPANY, INC.—See Baxter International Inc.; *U.S. Public*, pg. 283
HILL-ROM DTC, INC.—See Baxter International Inc.; *U.S. Public*, pg. 283
HILL-ROM GMBH—See Baxter International Inc.; *U.S. Public*, pg. 283
HILL-ROM HOLDINGS, INC.—See Baxter International Inc.; *U.S. Public*, pg. 282
HILL-ROM IBERIA S.L.—See Baxter International Inc.; *U.S. Public*, pg. 283
HILL-ROM, INC.—See Baxter International Inc.; *U.S. Public*, pg. 282
HILL-ROM INDUSTRIES SA—See Baxter International Inc.; *U.S. Public*, pg. 283
HILL-ROM JAPAN KK—See Baxter International Inc.; *U.S. Public*, pg. 283
HILL-ROM LOGISTICS, LLC—See Baxter International Inc.; *U.S. Public*, pg. 283
HILL-ROM LTD.—See Baxter International Inc.; *U.S. Public*, pg. 283
HILL-ROM MANUFACTURING, INC.—See Baxter International Inc.; *U.S. Public*, pg. 283
HILL-ROM PTY, LTD—See Baxter International Inc.; *U.S. Public*, pg. 283
HILL-ROM SARL—See Baxter International Inc.; *U.S. Public*, pg. 283
HILL-ROM S.A.S.—See Baxter International Inc.; *U.S. Public*, pg. 283
HILL-ROM SERVICES PTE, LTD.—See Baxter International Inc.; *U.S. Public*, pg. 283
HILL-ROM SERVICIOS S DE RL DE CV—See Baxter International Inc.; *U.S. Public*, pg. 283
HILL-ROM SHANGHAI LTD.—See Baxter International Inc.; *U.S. Public*, pg. 283
HILL-ROM SOCIEDADE UNIPESSOAL, LDA A PORTUGUESE CORPORATION—See Baxter International Inc.; *U.S. Public*, pg. 283
HILL-ROM SOCIEDADE UNIPESSOAL, LDA—See Baxter International Inc.; *U.S. Public*, pg. 282
HILL-ROM SOCIEDADE UNIPESSOAL, LDA—See Baxter International Inc.; *U.S. Public*, pg. 283

HILL-ROM, S.P.A—See Baxter International Inc.; *U.S. Public*, pg. 283
HILL-ROM SPRL—See Baxter International Inc.; *U.S. Public*, pg. 283
HILL-ROM TURKEY MEDIKAL URUNLER DAGITIM VE TICARET LIMITED SIRKETI—See Baxter International Inc.; *U.S. Public*, pg. 283
HILL-ROM UK (HOLDINGS) LTD.—See Baxter International Inc.; *U.S. Public*, pg. 283
HILLROSS ALLIANCES LIMITED—See AMP Limited; *Int'l*, pg. 432
HILLROSS FINANCIAL SERVICES LIMITED—See AMP Limited; *Int'l*, pg. 432
HILLROSS INNISFAIL PTY LIMITED—See AMP Limited; *Int'l*, pg. 432
HILLS ACE HARDWARE & LUMBER CENTER; *U.S. Private*, pg. 1946
HILLS AND DALES GENERAL HOSPITAL; *U.S. Private*, pg. 1947
HILLS BANCORPORATION; *U.S. Public*, pg. 1038
HILLS BANK & TRUST COMPANY—See Hills Bancorporation; *U.S. Public*, pg. 1038
HILLSBORO AREA HOSPITAL; *U.S. Private*, pg. 1947
HILLSBORO ARGUS—See Advance Publications, Inc.; *U.S. Private*, pg. 86
HILLSBORO BANK; *U.S. Private*, pg. 1947
HILLSBORO CLUB, LLC—See Alecta pensionsforsakring, omsesidigt; *Int'l*, pg. 305
HILLSBORO EQUIPMENT INCORPORATED; *U.S. Private*, pg. 1947
HILLSBORO LANDFILL INC.—See Waste Management, Inc.; *U.S. Public*, pg. 2331
HILLSBORO TELEPHONE COMPANY, INC.—See Lumen Technologies, Inc.; *U.S. Public*, pg. 1346
HILLSBORO TERRACE, LLC—See Alecta pensionsforsakring, omsesidigt; *Int'l*, pg. 305
HILLSBORO TOWN SOLAR, LLC—See United Renewable Energy Co., LLC; *Int'l*, pg. 8073
HILLSBORO TRANSPORTATION CO.; *U.S. Private*, pg. 1947
HILLSBOROUGH COUNTY AVIATION AUTHORITY; *U.S. Private*, pg. 1947
HILLSBOROUGH TITLE INC.; *U.S. Private*, pg. 1947
HILLSBUS CO PTY. LTD.—See ComfortDelGro Corporation Limited; *Int'l*, pg. 1713
HILL'S-COLGATE JAPAN LTD.—See Colgate-Palmolive Company; *U.S. Public*, pg. 533
HILLSDALE CO-OPERATIVE ELEVATOR CO.; *U.S. Private*, pg. 1947
HILLSDALE DAILY NEWS—See Gannett Co., Inc.; *U.S. Public*, pg. 903
HILLSDALE FABRICATORS—See Alberici Corporation; *U.S. Private*, pg. 152
HILLSDALE FURNITURE LLC—See Brookside International Incorporated; *U.S. Private*, pg. 665
HILLSDALE STRUCTURES, LP.—See Alberici Corporation; *U.S. Private*, pg. 152
HILL'S ENVIRONMENTAL LIMITED—See Arthur J. Gallagher & Co.; *U.S. Public*, pg. 203
THE HILLSHIRE BRANDS COMPANY—See Tyson Foods, Inc.; *U.S. Public*, pg. 2210
HILLSIDE CANDY, LLC—See Highlander Partners, LP.; *U.S. Private*, pg. 1939
HILLSIDE CAPITAL INCORPORATED—See Brookside International Incorporated; *U.S. Private*, pg. 665
HILLSIDE HOSPITAL, LLC—See Apollo Global Management, Inc.; *U.S. Public*, pg. 155
HILLSIDE PLASTICS CORPORATION; *U.S. Private*, pg. 1947
HILLSIDE PLASTICS INC.—See Behrman Brothers Management Corp.; *U.S. Private*, pg. 515
HILLS INDUSTRIES ANTENNA & TV SYSTEMS—See Hills Limited; *Int'l*, pg. 3393
HILLS INDUSTRIES DIRECT ALARM SUPPLIES—See Hills Limited; *Int'l*, pg. 3393
HILLS LIMITED; *Int'l*, pg. 3393
HILL & SMITH, INC.—See Hill & Smith PLC; *Int'l*, pg. 3391
HILL & SMITH INFRASTRUCTURE PRODUCTS INDIA PRIVATE LIMITED—See Hill & Smith PLC; *Int'l*, pg. 3391
HILL & SMITH LTD—See Hill & Smith PLC; *Int'l*, pg. 3391
HILL & SMITH PLC; *Int'l*, pg. 3391
HILL & SMITH PTY LIMITED—See Hill & Smith PLC; *Int'l*, pg. 3391
HILL'S PET NUTRITION ASIA-PACIFIC, PTE. LTD.—See Colgate-Palmolive Company; *U.S. Public*, pg. 532
HILL'S PET NUTRITION B.V.—See Colgate-Palmolive Company; *U.S. Public*, pg. 532
HILL'S PET NUTRITION CANADA INC.—See Colgate-Palmolive Company; *U.S. Public*, pg. 533
HILL'S PET NUTRITION DE MEXICO, S.A. DE C.V.—See Colgate-Palmolive Company; *U.S. Public*, pg. 533
HILL'S PET NUTRITION DENMARK APS—See Colgate-Palmolive Company; *U.S. Public*, pg. 533
HILL'S PET NUTRITION ESPANA, S.L.—See Colgate-Palmolive Company; *U.S. Public*, pg. 533
HILL'S PET NUTRITION GMBH—See Colgate-Palmolive Company; *U.S. Public*, pg. 533

HILL & SMITH PLC
CORPORATE AFFILIATIONS
Company Index

HILL'S PET NUTRITION, INC.—See Colgate-Palmolive Company; *U.S. Public*, pg. 533
HILL'S PET NUTRITION INDIANA, INC.—See Colgate-Palmolive Company; *U.S. Public*, pg. 533
HILL'S PET NUTRITION ITALIA, S.R.L.—See Colgate-Palmolive Company; *U.S. Public*, pg. 533
HILL'S PET NUTRITION KOREA LTD.—See Colgate-Palmolive Company; *U.S. Public*, pg. 533
HILL'S PET NUTRITION LIMITED—See Colgate-Palmolive Company; *U.S. Public*, pg. 533
HILL'S PET NUTRITION MANUFACTURING, B.V.—See Colgate-Palmolive Company; *U.S. Public*, pg. 533
HILL'S PET NUTRITION NORWAY AS—See Colgate-Palmolive Company; *U.S. Public*, pg. 533
HILL'S PET NUTRITION (NZ) LIMITED—See Colgate-Palmolive Company; *U.S. Public*, pg. 532
HILL'S PET NUTRITION PTY. LTD.—See Colgate-Palmolive Company; *U.S. Public*, pg. 533
HILL'S PET NUTRITION SALES, INC.—See Colgate-Palmolive Company; *U.S. Public*, pg. 533
HILL'S PET NUTRITION S.N.C.—See Colgate-Palmolive Company; *U.S. Public*, pg. 533
HILL'S PET NUTRITION SOUTH AFRICA PROPRIETARY LIMITED—See Colgate-Palmolive Company; *U.S. Public*, pg. 533
HILL'S PET NUTRITION S.R.O.—See Colgate-Palmolive Company; *U.S. Public*, pg. 533
HILL'S PET NUTRITION SWEDEN AB—See Colgate-Palmolive Company; *U.S. Public*, pg. 533
HILL'S PET NUTRITION SWITZERLAND GMBH—See Colgate-Palmolive Company; *U.S. Public*, pg. 533
HILLSPIRE LLC; *U.S. Private*, pg. 1947
HILLS PRODUCTS GROUP, INC.—See Northwestern Engineering Company; *U.S. Private*, pg. 2962
HILLS; *U.S. Private*, pg. 1946
HILL'S SUPPLY CO.; *U.S. Private*, pg. 1945
HILLSTONE INTERNATIONAL, LLC—See Global Infrastructure Solutions, Inc.; *U.S. Private*, pg. 1715
HILLSTONE NETWORKS CO., LTD.; *Int'l*, pg. 3393
HILLSTRAND DEVELOPMENT SDN BHD—See Gadang Holdings Berhad; *Int'l*, pg. 2868
HILLSTREET FUND LP; *U.S. Private*, pg. 1947
HILLS WASTE SOLUTIONS LIMITED; *Int'l*, pg. 3393
HILL TECHNICAL SOLUTIONS, INC.—See D.C. Capital Partners, LLC; *U.S. Private*, pg. 1141
HILLTIP GMBH—See Sdiptech AB; *Int'l*, pg. 6658
HILLTIP INC.—See Sdiptech AB; *Int'l*, pg. 6658
HILL TIRE COMPANY—See Continental Aktiengesellschaft; *Int'l*, pg. 1783
HILLTOP AVIATION SERVICES; *U.S. Private*, pg. 1947
HILLTOP BASIC RESOURCES, INC.; *U.S. Private*, pg. 1947
HILLTOP BUICK GMC INC.; *U.S. Private*, pg. 1947
HILL TOP COUNTRY CLUB LIMITED—See ENM Holdings Limited; *Int'l*, pg. 2442
HILLTOP ENERGY INC.—See D.W. Dickey & Sons Inc.; *U.S. Private*, pg. 1143
HILLTOP GARDENS RETIREMENT VILLAGE LIMITED—See AX Investments PLC; *Int'l*, pg. 754
HILLTOP HOLDINGS INC.; *U.S. Public*, pg. 1038
HILL TOP OIL COMPANY INC.—See Nittany Oil Company Inc.; *U.S. Private*, pg. 2930
HILLTOP PRIVATE CAPITAL, LLC; *U.S. Private*, pg. 1947
HILLTOP QUARRY—See Haines & Kibblehouse Inc.; *U.S. Private*, pg. 1841
HILL TOP RESEARCH INC.; *U.S. Private*, pg. 1945
HILLTOP SECURITIES HOLDINGS LLC—See Hilltop Holdings Inc.; *U.S. Public*, pg. 1038
HILLTOP SECURITIES INC.—See Hilltop Holdings Inc.; *U.S. Public*, pg. 1038
HILLTOP SECURITIES INDEPENDENT NETWORK INC.—See Hilltop Holdings Inc.; *U.S. Public*, pg. 1039
HILLTOP SERVICES LLC—See Comcast Corporation; *U.S. Public*, pg. 538
HILLTOP VILLAGE—See Sava Senior Care LLC; *U.S. Private*, pg. 3555
HILL TRUCK SALES INC.; *U.S. Private*, pg. 1945
HILL & VALLEY, INC.—See J&J Snack Foods Corporation; *U.S. Public*, pg. 1179
HILL VALLEY, S.L.—See Vocento, S.A.; *Int'l*, pg. 8284
HILLVIEW MOTORS; *U.S. Private*, pg. 1947
HILL WARD HENDERSON; *U.S. Private*, pg. 1945
HILLWOOD COUNTRY CLUB; *U.S. Private*, pg. 1947
HILLYARD, INC.; *U.S. Private*, pg. 1947
HILLYARD-ROVIC—See Hillyard, Inc.; *U.S. Private*, pg. 1947
HILLYER'S MID CITY FORD INC.; *U.S. Private*, pg. 1947
HILL YORK CORPORATION; *U.S. Private*, pg. 1945
HILMAN, INC.; *U.S. Private*, pg. 1947
HILMAR CHEESE COMPANY; *U.S. Private*, pg. 1947
HIL MEDIC SDN. BHD.—See HIL Industris Berhad; *Int'l*, pg. 3390
HILO DIRECT SEGUROS Y REASEGUROS S.A.—See AXA S.A.; *Int'l*, pg. 757
HI-LO FOOD STORES (JA) LTD.—See GraceKennedy Limited; *Int'l*, pg. 3049
HI LOGISTICS CO., LTD.—See LG Corp.; *Int'l*, pg. 4475
HI LOGISTICS EGYPT S.A.E.—See LX Holdings Corp.; *Int'l*, pg. 4604
HILOGISTICS EUROPE B.V.—See LG Corp.; *Int'l*, pg. 4474
HI-LO INDUSTRIES INC.; *U.S. Private*, pg. 1932
HILO MAINTENANCE SYSTEMS, INC.; *U.S. Private*, pg. 1948
HILONG (COLOMBIA) OIL SERVICE & ENGINEERING CO., LTD.—See Hilong Holding Limited; *Int'l*, pg. 3393
HILONG DRILL PIPE (WUXI) CO., LTD.—See Hilong Holding Limited; *Int'l*, pg. 3393
HILONG ENERGY LIMITED—See Hilong Holding Limited; *Int'l*, pg. 3393
HILONG HOLDING LIMITED; *Int'l*, pg. 3393
HILONG MARINE ENGINEERING (HONG KONG) LIMITED—See Hilong Holding Limited; *Int'l*, pg. 3393
HILONG OIL SERVICE & ENGINEERING CO., LTD.—See Hilong Holding Limited; *Int'l*, pg. 3393
HILONG OIL SERVICE & ENGINEERING ECUADOR CIA. LTDA.—See Hilong Holding Limited; *Int'l*, pg. 3393
HILONG OIL SERVICE & ENGINEERING NIGERIA LTD.—See Hilong Holding Limited; *Int'l*, pg. 3393
HILONG OIL SERVICE & ENGINEERING PAKISTAN (PRIVATE) LIMITED—See Hilong Holding Limited; *Int'l*, pg. 3393
HILONG PETROLEUM COMPANY LLC—See Hilong Holding Limited; *Int'l*, pg. 3393
HILONG PETROLEUM PIPE COMPANY LLC—See Hilong Holding Limited; *Int'l*, pg. 3393
HILONG PETROPIPE CO., LTD.—See Hilong Holding Limited; *Int'l*, pg. 3393
HILONG USA LLC.—See Hilong Holding Limited; *Int'l*, pg. 3393
HILO PRODUCTS INC.; *U.S. Private*, pg. 1948
HILOS A&E DE COSTA RICA, S.A.—See The Kroger Co.; *U.S. Public*, pg. 2108
HILOS A&E DE EL SALVADOR, S.A. DE C.V.—See The Kroger Co.; *U.S. Public*, pg. 2108
HILOS A&E DE HONDURAS, S.A.—See Platinum Equity, LLC; *U.S. Private*, pg. 3201
HILOS A&E DE MEXICO SA DE CV—See Platinum Equity, LLC; *U.S. Private*, pg. 3201
HILOS A&E DOMINICANA LTD—See Platinum Equity, LLC; *U.S. Private*, pg. 3201
HILOS AMERICAN & EFIRD DE HONDURAS, S.A. DE C.V.—See The Kroger Co.; *U.S. Public*, pg. 2108
HILOS AMERICAN & EFIRD DE MEXICO, S.A. DE C.V.—See The Kroger Co.; *U.S. Public*, pg. 2108
HILPERT ELECTRONICS GMBH—See ViTrox Corporation Berhad; *Int'l*, pg. 8262
HILSCHER-CLARKE ELECTRIC COMPANY; *U.S. Private*, pg. 1948
THE HILSINGER COMPANY PARENT, LLC—See Windjammer Capital Investors, LLC; *U.S. Private*, pg. 4538
HILSINGER MENDELSON PUBLIC RELATIONS; *U.S. Private*, pg. 1948
HILSINGER MENDELSON PUBLIC RELATIONS—See Hilsinger Mendelson Public Relations; *U.S. Private*, pg. 1948
HILTAP FITTINGS LTD.—See Dover Corporation; *U.S. Public*, pg. 681
HILTI AG; *Int'l*, pg. 3394
HILTI AG, WERK THURINGEN—See Hilti AG; *Int'l*, pg. 3394
HILTI ALBANIA SHPK—See Hilti AG; *Int'l*, pg. 3394
HILTI ARGENTINA, S.A.—See Hilti AG; *Int'l*, pg. 3394
HILTI (AUST.) PTY. LTD.—See Hilti AG; *Int'l*, pg. 3394
HILTI AUSTRIA GMBH—See Hilti AG; *Int'l*, pg. 3394
HILTI BAHRAIN W.L.L—See Hilti AG; *Int'l*, pg. 3394
HILTI BELGIUM N.V.—See Hilti AG; *Int'l*, pg. 3394
HILTI (BULGARIA) EOOD—See Hilti AG; *Int'l*, pg. 3394
HILTI BY FLLC—See Hilti AG; *Int'l*, pg. 3394
HILTI (CANADA) CORPORATION—See Hilti AG; *Int'l*, pg. 3394
HILTI CARIBE INC.—See Hilti AG; *Int'l*, pg. 3394
HILTI CHILE LIMITADA—See Hilti AG; *Int'l*, pg. 3394
HILTI (CHINA) LTD.—See Hilti AG; *Int'l*, pg. 3394
HILTI COLOMBIA S.A.—See Hilti AG; *Int'l*, pg. 3394
HILTI COMPLETE SYSTEMS UAB—See Hilti AG; *Int'l*, pg. 3394
HILTI CONSTRUCTION EQUIPMENTS EURL—See Hilti AG; *Int'l*, pg. 3394
HILTI CROATIA D.O.O.—See Hilti AG; *Int'l*, pg. 3394
HILTI CR SPOL. S.R.O.—See Hilti AG; *Int'l*, pg. 3394
HILTI DENMARK A/S—See Hilti AG; *Int'l*, pg. 3394
HILTI DEUTSCHLAND GMBH—See Hilti AG; *Int'l*, pg. 3394
HILTI DISTRIBUTION LTD.—See Hilti AG; *Int'l*, pg. 3394
HILTI DO BRASIL COMERCIAL LTDA.—See Hilti AG; *Int'l*, pg. 3395
HILTI EESTI OU—See Hilti AG; *Int'l*, pg. 3394
HILTI ENTWICKLUNG BEFESTIGUNGSTECHNIK GMBH—See Hilti AG; *Int'l*, pg. 3394
HILTI ENTWICKLUNG ELEKTROWERZEUGE GMBH—See Hilti AG; *Int'l*, pg. 3394
HILTI ESPANOLA S.A.—See Hilti AG; *Int'l*, pg. 3394
HILTI FAR EAST PRIVATE LTD.—See Hilti AG; *Int'l*, pg. 3394
HILTI (FASTENING SYSTEMS) LTD.—See Hilti AG; *Int'l*, pg. 3394
HILTI FRANCE S.A.—See Hilti AG; *Int'l*, pg. 3394
HILTI (GT. BRITAIN) LIMITED—See Hilti AG; *Int'l*, pg. 3394
HILTI HELLAS S.A.—See Hilti AG; *Int'l*, pg. 3394
HILTI HOLDING GMBH—See Hilti AG; *Int'l*, pg. 3395
HILTI (HONG KONG) LTD.—See Hilti AG; *Int'l*, pg. 3394
HILTI HUNGARIA SZOLGALTATO KFT.—See Hilti AG; *Int'l*, pg. 3395
HILTI, INC.—See Hilti AG; *Int'l*, pg. 3395
HILTI INDIA PRIVATE LIMITED—See Hilti AG; *Int'l*, pg. 3395
HILTI INSAAT MALZEMELERI TICARET A.S.—See Hilti AG; *Int'l*, pg. 3395
HILTI ITALIA S.P.A.—See Hilti AG; *Int'l*, pg. 3395
HILTI (JAPAN) LTD.—See Hilti AG; *Int'l*, pg. 3394
HILTI (KOREA) COMPANY LTD.—See Hilti AG; *Int'l*, pg. 3394
HILTI KUNSTSTOFFTECHNIK GMBH—See Hilti AG; *Int'l*, pg. 3395
HILTI (MALAYSIA) SDN. BHD.—See Hilti AG; *Int'l*, pg. 3394
HILTI MAROC S.A.—See Hilti AG; *Int'l*, pg. 3395
HILTI MEXICANA, S.A. DE C.V.—See Hilti AG; *Int'l*, pg. 3395
HILTI MIDDLE EAST FZE—See Hilti AG; *Int'l*, pg. 3395
HILTI NEDERLAND B.V.—See Hilti AG; *Int'l*, pg. 3395
HILTI (PHILIPPINES), INC.—See Hilti AG; *Int'l*, pg. 3394
HILTI (POLAND) SP. ZO.O.—See Hilti AG; *Int'l*, pg. 3394
HILTI (PORTUGAL), PRODUCTOS E SERVICOS LDA.—See Hilti AG; *Int'l*, pg. 3394
HILTI QATAR W.L.L.—See Hilti AG; *Int'l*, pg. 3395
HILTI ROMANIA S.R.L.—See Hilti AG; *Int'l*, pg. 3395
HILTI (SCHWEIZ) AG—See Hilti AG; *Int'l*, pg. 3394
HILTI SERVICES LIMITED—See Hilti AG; *Int'l*, pg. 3395
HILTI SLOVAKIA SPOL. S.R.O.—See Hilti AG; *Int'l*, pg. 3395
HILTI SLOVENIJA D.O.O.—See Hilti AG; *Int'l*, pg. 3395
HILTI SMN DOO—See Hilti AG; *Int'l*, pg. 3395
HILTI (SOUTH AFRICA) PTY. LTD.—See Hilti AG; *Int'l*, pg. 3394
HILTI (SUOMI) OY—See Hilti AG; *Int'l*, pg. 3394
HILTI SVENSKA AB—See Hilti AG; *Int'l*, pg. 3395
HILTI-SYRIA L.L.C.—See Hilti AG; *Int'l*, pg. 3395
HILTI SYSTEMS BH SARAJEVO D.O.O.—See Hilti AG; *Int'l*, pg. 3395
HILTI TAIWAN CO., LTD.—See Hilti AG; *Int'l*, pg. 3395
HILTI (UKRAINE) LTD.—See Hilti AG; *Int'l*, pg. 3394
HILTI VIETNAM CO. LTD—See Hilti AG; *Int'l*, pg. 3395
HILTON CANADA INC.—See Hilton Worldwide Holdings Inc.; *U.S. Public*, pg. 1040
HILTON CAPITAL MANAGEMENT, LLC—See Rafferty Holdings, LLC; *U.S. Private*, pg. 3345
HILTON DENVER INVERNESS—See Commune Hotels & Resorts, LLC; *U.S. Private*, pg. 987
HILTON EL CONQUISTADOR GOLF & TENNIS RESORT—See Hilton Worldwide Holdings Inc.; *U.S. Public*, pg. 1041
HILTON FOOD GROUP PLC; *Int'l*, pg. 3395
HILTON FOODS LIMITED SP. Z.O.O.—See Hilton Food Group plc; *Int'l*, pg. 3395
HILTON GARDEN INN - ANCHORAGE—See Stonebridge Realty Advisors, Inc.; *U.S. Private*, pg. 3827
HILTON GARDEN INN - CHERRY CREEK—See Stonebridge Realty Advisors, Inc.; *U.S. Private*, pg. 3827
HILTON GARDEN INN - GARDEN GROVE—See Stonebridge Realty Advisors, Inc.; *U.S. Private*, pg. 3827
HILTON GARDEN INNS MANAGEMENT LLC—See Hilton Worldwide Holdings Inc.; *U.S. Public*, pg. 1040
THE HILTON GARDEN INN—See Hilton Worldwide Holdings Inc.; *U.S. Public*, pg. 1041
HILTON GRAND VACATIONS COMPANY, LLC—See Hilton Grand Vacations Inc.; *U.S. Public*, pg. 1040
HILTON GRAND VACATIONS INC.; *U.S. Public*, pg. 1039
HILTON HAWAIIAN VILLAGE—See Hilton Worldwide Holdings Inc.; *U.S. Public*, pg. 1041
HILTON HEAD HEALTH SYSTEM, L.P.—See Tenet Healthcare Corporation; *U.S. Public*, pg. 2008
HILTON HEAD REGIONAL OB/GYN PARTNERS, L.L.C.—See Tenet Healthcare Corporation; *U.S. Public*, pg. 2008
HILTON HEAD REGIONAL PHYSICIAN NETWORK - GEORGIA, LLC—See Tenet Healthcare Corporation; *U.S. Public*, pg. 2004
HILTON HOMES LTD.; *Int'l*, pg. 3395
HILTON HONORS WORLDWIDE LLC—See Hilton Worldwide Holdings Inc.; *U.S. Public*, pg. 1040
HILTON HOTELS OF AUSTRALIA (MELBOURNE) PTY. LTD.—See Hilton Worldwide Holdings Inc.; *U.S. Public*, pg. 1040
HILTON HOTELS OF AUSTRALIA PTY. LTD.—See Hilton Worldwide Holdings Inc.; *U.S. Public*, pg. 1040
HILTON HOUSTON HOBBY AIRPORT HOTEL—See Gal-Tex Hotel Corporation; *U.S. Private*, pg. 1635
HILTON INTERNATIONAL HOTELS (UK) LIMITED—See Hilton Worldwide Holdings Inc.; *U.S. Public*, pg. 1040
HILTON INTERNATIONAL (SWITZERLAND) GMBH—See Hilton Worldwide Holdings Inc.; *U.S. Public*, pg. 1041
HILTON INTERNATIONAL WIEN GMBH—See Hilton Worldwide Holdings Inc.; *U.S. Public*, pg. 1041
HILTON LONDON—See Clarke Inc.; *Int'l*, pg. 1650

COMPANY NAME INDEX

HILTON MALTA LIMITED—See Hilton Worldwide Holdings Inc.; *U.S. Public*, pg. 1041
HILTON MANAGEMENT LLC—See Hilton Worldwide Holdings Inc.; *U.S. Public*, pg. 1041
HILTON MCLEAN TYSONS CORNER—See Hilton Worldwide Holdings Inc.; *U.S. Public*, pg. 1041
HILTON MEATS (RETAIL) LIMITED—See Hilton Food Group plc; *Int'l*, pg. 3395
HILTON MEATS ZAANDAM B.V.—See Hilton Food Group plc; *Int'l*, pg. 3395
HILTON METAL FORGING LTD.; *Int'l*, pg. 3395
HILTON MIAMI DOWNTOWN—See Argent Ventures, LLC; *U.S. Private*, pg. 320
HILTON MUNICH AIRPORT HOTEL MANAGE GMBH—See Hilton Worldwide Holdings Inc.; *U.S. Public*, pg. 1041
HILTON NAIROBI LIMITED—See Hilton Worldwide Holdings Inc.; *U.S. Public*, pg. 1041
HILTON NEW YORK—See Hilton Worldwide Holdings Inc.; *U.S. Public*, pg. 1041
HILTON OF PANAMA LIMITED—See Hilton Worldwide Holdings Inc.; *U.S. Public*, pg. 1041
HILTON ON THE PARK MELBOURNE—See Brookfield Corporation; *Int'l*, pg. 1189
HILTON PALM SPRINGS HOTEL & RESORT—See Hilton Worldwide Holdings Inc.; *U.S. Public*, pg. 1041
HILTON RESERVATIONS & CUSTOMER CARE—See Hilton Worldwide Holdings Inc.; *U.S. Public*, pg. 1041
HILTON RESERVATIONS WORLDWIDE LLC—See Hilton Worldwide Holdings Inc.; *U.S. Public*, pg. 1041
HILTON SAN DIEGO LLC—See Hilton Worldwide Holdings Inc.; *U.S. Public*, pg. 1041
HILTON SINGER ISLAND OCEANFRONT/PALM BEACHES RESORT—See Hilton Worldwide Holdings Inc.; *U.S. Public*, pg. 1041
HILTON SUPPLY MANAGEMENT LLC—See Hilton Worldwide Holdings Inc.; *U.S. Public*, pg. 1041
HILTON VALVE, INC.—See Granite Equity Partners LLC; *U.S. Private*, pg. 1755
HILTON VIENNA DANUBE—See Hilton Worldwide Holdings Inc.; *U.S. Public*, pg. 1041
HILTON WORLDWIDE HOLDINGS INC.; *U.S. Public*, pg. 1040
HILTON WORLDWIDE - MEMPHIS OPERATIONS CENTER—See Hilton Worldwide Holdings Inc.; *U.S. Public*, pg. 1041
HILZINGER FENSTER + TUEREN GMBH—See hilzinger Holding GmbH; *Int'l*, pg. 3395
HILZINGER HOLDING GMBH; *Int'l*, pg. 3395
HIMA CEMENT LTD.—See Holcim Ltd.; *Int'l*, pg. 3446
HIMACHAL ENERGY PRIVATE LIMITED—See HPL Electric & Power Limited; *Int'l*, pg. 3501
HIMACHAL FIBRES LIMITED; *Int'l*, pg. 3396
HIMACS, LTD.; *Int'l*, pg. 3396
HIMADRI SPECIALTY CHEMICAL LTD.; *Int'l*, pg. 3396
HIMAG MAGNETIC CORPORATION—See China Steel Corporation; *Int'l*, pg. 1555
THE HIMALAYA DRUG COMPANY FZCO—See Himalaya Drug Company; *Int'l*, pg. 3396
THE HIMALAYA DRUG COMPANY L.L.C.—See Himalaya Drug Company; *Int'l*, pg. 3396
THE HIMALAYA DRUG COMPANY PTE LTD—See Himalaya Drug Company; *Int'l*, pg. 3396
THE HIMALAYA DRUG COMPANY (PTY) LTD—See Himalaya Drug Company; *Int'l*, pg. 3396
HIMALAYA DRUG COMPANY; *Int'l*, pg. 3396
HIMALAYA FOOD INTERNATIONAL LIMITED; *Int'l*, pg. 3396
HIMALAYA HOMES INC.; *U.S. Private*, pg. 1948
HIMALAYAN BANK LIMITED; *Int'l*, pg. 3396
HIMALAYAN DISTILLERY LIMITED; *Int'l*, pg. 3396
HIMALAYAN EVEREST INSURANCE LIMITED; *Int'l*, pg. 3396
HIMALAYA SHIPPING LTD.; *Int'l*, pg. 3396
HIMALAYA TECHNOLOGIES, INC.; *U.S. Public*, pg. 1041
HIMAL POWER LIMITED—See Statkraft AS; *Int'l*, pg. 7185
HIMAL REFRIGERATION & ELECTRICAL INDUSTRIES PVT. LTD.—See Daikin Industries, Ltd.; *Int'l*, pg. 1935
HIMARAYA CO., LTD.; *Int'l*, pg. 3396
HI-MAR SPECIALTY CHEMICALS, LLC—See Elementis plc; *Int'l*, pg. 2359
HIMATSINGKA AMERICA INC.—See Himatsingka Seide Limited; *Int'l*, pg. 3396
HIMATSINGKA LINENS—See Himatsingka Seide Limited; *Int'l*, pg. 3396
HIMATSINGKA SEIDE LIMITED; *Int'l*, pg. 3396
HIMATSINGKA SINGAPORE PTE. LTD.—See Himatsingka Seide Limited; *Int'l*, pg. 3396
HIMAX ANALOGIC, INC.—See Himax Technologies, Inc.; *Int'l*, pg. 3396
HIMAX CORPORATION—See Scroll Corporation; *Int'l*, pg. 6656
HIMAX DISPLAY (USA) INC.—See Himax Technologies, Inc.; *Int'l*, pg. 3396
HIMAX IGI PRECISION LTD.—See Himax Technologies, Inc.; *Int'l*, pg. 3396
HIMAX IMAGING, INC.—See Himax Technologies, Inc.; *Int'l*, pg. 3396

HIMAX IMAGING, LTD.—See Himax Technologies, Inc.; *Int'l*, pg. 3396
HIMAX MEDIA SOLUTIONS, INC.—See Himax Technologies, Inc.; *Int'l*, pg. 3397
HIMAX TECHNOLOGIES, INC.; *Int'l*, pg. 3396
HIMAX TECHNOLOGIES JAPAN LTD.—See Himax Technologies, Inc.; *Int'l*, pg. 3397
HIMAX TECHNOLOGIES KOREA LTD.—See Himax Technologies, Inc.; *Int'l*, pg. 3397
HIMAX TECHNOLOGIES (SHENZHEN) CO., LTD.—See Himax Technologies, Inc.; *Int'l*, pg. 3397
HIMAX TECHNOLOGIES (SUZHOU) CO., LTD.—See Himax Technologies, Inc.; *Int'l*, pg. 3397
HIMCO DISTRIBUTION SERVICES COMPANY—See The Hartford Financial Services Group, Inc.; *U.S. Public*, pg. 2088
HIM CONNECTIONS, LLC; *U.S. Private*, pg. 1948
HIMEC CONVEYORS INC—See Harris Companies; *U.S. Private*, pg. 1869
HI-MECHA CO., LTD.—See Citizen Watch Co., Ltd.; *Int'l*, pg. 1625
HIMEC INC.; *U.S. Private*, pg. 1948
HI-MEDIA BELGIUM SPRL—See AdUX SA; *Int'l*, pg. 155
HI-MEDIA DEUTSCHLAND AG—See AdUX SA; *Int'l*, pg. 155
HI-MEDIA ITALY SRL—See AdUX SA; *Int'l*, pg. 155
HI-MEDIA LTD—See AdUX SA; *Int'l*, pg. 155
HI-MEDIA NEDERLAND BV—See AdUX SA; *Int'l*, pg. 155
HI-MEDIA NETWORK INTERNET ESPANA SL—See AdUX SA; *Int'l*, pg. 155
HI-MEDIA PERFOMANCE GMBH—See AdUX SA; *Int'l*, pg. 155
HI-MEDIA PORTUGAL LDA—See AdUX SA; *Int'l*, pg. 155
HI-MEDIA SALES AB—See AdUX SA; *Int'l*, pg. 155
HIMEDIC INC.—See RESORT TRUST INC.; *Int'l*, pg. 6301
HIMEGIN BUSINESS SERVICE CO., LTD.—See The Ehime Bank, Ltd.; *Int'l*, pg. 7638
HIMEGIN LEASE CO., LTD.—See The Ehime Bank, Ltd.; *Int'l*, pg. 7638
HIMEGIN SOFT CO., LTD.—See The Ehime Bank, Ltd.; *Int'l*, pg. 7638
HIMEGIN STAFF SUPPORT CO., LTD.—See The Ehime Bank, Ltd.; *Int'l*, pg. 7638
HIMEJI DAIICHI TRAFFIC CO., LTD.—See Daiichi Koutsu Sangyo Co., Ltd.; *Int'l*, pg. 1928
HIMEJI TOSHIBA E.P. CORPORATION—See Japan Industrial Partners, Inc.; *Int'l*, pg. 3889
HIMEYURI TOTAL WORK CO., LTD.—See Kureha Corporation; *Int'l*, pg. 4338
HIM GMBH; *Int'l*, pg. 3395
HIMIKO CO., LTD.—See WA, Inc.; *Int'l*, pg. 8322
HIMILE EUROPE, LLC—See Himile Mechanical Science & Technology Co., Ltd; *Int'l*, pg. 3397
HIMILE (LIAONING) SCIENCE & TECHNOLOGY CO., LTD.—See Himile Mechanical Science & Technology Co., Ltd; *Int'l*, pg. 3397
HIMILE MECHANICAL SCIENCE & TECHNOLOGY CO., LTD; *Int'l*, pg. 3397
HIMILE MECHANICAL SCIENCE & TECHNOLOGY (KUNSHAN) CO., LTD.—See Himile Mechanical Science & Technology Co., Ltd; *Int'l*, pg. 3397
HIMILE MOLD (TIANJIN) CO., LTD.—See Himile Mechanical Science & Technology Co., Ltd; *Int'l*, pg. 3397
HIMILE (THAILAND) CO., LTD.—See Himile Mechanical Science & Technology Co., Ltd; *Int'l*, pg. 3397
HIMI MURATA MANUFACTURING CO., LTD.—See Murata Manufacturing Co., Ltd.; *Int'l*, pg. 5097
HIM INTERNATIONAL MUSIC; *Int'l*, pg. 3397
HI-MIRROR CO., LTD.—See Nippon Sheet Glass Co. Ltd.; *Int'l*, pg. 5331
HIMMER AG; *Int'l*, pg. 3397
HIMS CO., LTD.; *Int'l*, pg. 3397
HIMS & HERS HEALTH, INC.; *U.S. Public*, pg. 1041
HIMS INTERNATIONAL CORPORATION—See Selvas AI Co., Ltd.; *Int'l*, pg. 6701
HIM TEKNOFORGE LIMITED; *Int'l*, pg. 3396
HI NABOR SUPERMARKET INC.; *U.S. Private*, pg. 1931
HINATUAN MINING CORPORATION—See Nickel Asia Corporation; *Int'l*, pg. 5271
HINCHCLIFF PRODUCTS COMPANY; *U.S. Private*, pg. 1948
HINCKLEY, ALLEN & SNYDER LLP; *U.S. Private*, pg. 1948
HINCKLEY AND RUGBY BUILDING SOCIETY; *Int'l*, pg. 3397
HINCKLEYS INCORPORATED; *U.S. Private*, pg. 1948
HINDA, INC.; *U.S. Private*, pg. 1948
HINDALCO-ALMEX AEROSPACE LIMITED—See The Aditya Birla Group; *Int'l*, pg. 7611
HINDALCO INDUSTRIES LTD.—See The Aditya Birla Group; *Int'l*, pg. 7611
HIND ALUMINIUM INDUSTRIES LIMITED; *Int'l*, pg. 3397
HIND COMMERCE LIMITED; *Int'l*, pg. 3397
HINDCON CHEMICALS LIMITED; *Int'l*, pg. 3397
HIND ELECTRONIKA INDIA PRIVATE LIMITED—See HIOKI E.E. Corporation; *Int'l*, pg. 3401
HINDLEY MANUFACTURING COMPANY, INC.; *U.S. Private*, pg. 1948
HINDMAN MANUFACTURING CO.; *U.S. Private*, pg. 1948

HINES GLOBAL INCOME TRUST, INC.

HINDOOSTAN MILLS LIMITED; *Int'l*, pg. 3397
HINDPRAKASH INDUSTRIES LTD.; *Int'l*, pg. 3397
HIND RECTIFIERS LIMITED; *Int'l*, pg. 3397
HINDS-BOCK CORPORATION—See The Middleby Corporation; *U.S. Public*, pg. 2114
HINDS COUNTY HUMAN RESOURCE AGENCY; *U.S. Private*, pg. 1948
HIND SECURITIES & CREDITS LIMITED; *Int'l*, pg. 3397
HINDS INSTRUMENTS, INC.; *U.S. Private*, pg. 1948
HIND SYNTEX LIMITED; *Int'l*, pg. 3397
HINDUJA BANK (MIDDLE EAST) LTD.—See Hinduja Group Ltd.; *Int'l*, pg. 3399
HINDUJA BANK (SCHWEIZ) AG.—See Hinduja Group Ltd.; *Int'l*, pg. 3399
HINDUJA BANK (SWITZERLAND) LTD—See Hinduja Group Ltd.; *Int'l*, pg. 3399
HINDUJA FOUNDRIES LTD—See Hinduja Group Ltd.; *Int'l*, pg. 3398
HINDUJA GLOBAL SOLUTIONS LTD.; *Int'l*, pg. 3397
HINDUJA GLOBAL SOLUTIONS (UK) LIMITED—See Hinduja Global Solutions Ltd.; *Int'l*, pg. 3398
HINDUJA GROUP LTD.; *Int'l*, pg. 3398
HINDUJA INDIA MAURITIUS HOLDINGS LTD.—See Hinduja Group Ltd.; *Int'l*, pg. 3399
HINDUJA LEYLAND FINANCE LIMITED—See Hinduja Group Ltd.; *Int'l*, pg. 3398
HINDUJA NATIONAL POWER CORPORATION LTD.—See Hinduja Group Ltd.; *Int'l*, pg. 3399
HINDUJA TECH GMBH—See Hinduja Group Ltd.; *Int'l*, pg. 3398
HINDUJA TECH, INC.—See Hinduja Group Ltd.; *Int'l*, pg. 3398
HINDUJA TECH LIMITED—See Hinduja Group Ltd.; *Int'l*, pg. 3398
HINDUSTAN ADHESIVES LTD.; *Int'l*, pg. 3399
HINDUSTAN AERONAUTICS LIMITED; *Int'l*, pg. 3399
HINDUSTAN AGRIGENETICS LIMITED; *Int'l*, pg. 3399
HINDUSTAN BIO SCIENCES LIMITED; *Int'l*, pg. 3399
HINDUSTAN CARGO LTD.—See Allcargo Logistics Limited; *Int'l*, pg. 334
HINDUSTAN COLAS PVT. LTD.—See Bouygues S.A.; *Int'l*, pg. 1123
HINDUSTAN COLAS PVT. LTD.—See Oil & Natural Gas Corporation Limited; *Int'l*, pg. 5534
HINDUSTAN COMPOSITES LIMITED; *Int'l*, pg. 3399
HINDUSTAN CONSTRUCTION CO. LTD; *Int'l*, pg. 3399
HINDUSTAN COPPER LIMITED; *Int'l*, pg. 3399
HINDUSTAN DORR-OLIVER LTD; *Int'l*, pg. 3399
HINDUSTAN FLUOROCARBONS LIMITED—See Hindustan Organic Chemicals Limited; *Int'l*, pg. 3400
HINDUSTAN FOODS LIMITED; *Int'l*, pg. 3399
HINDUSTAN HARDY LIMITED; *Int'l*, pg. 3400
THE HINDUSTAN HOUSING COMPANY LIMITED; *Int'l*, pg. 7652
HINDUSTAN MEDIA VENTURES LIMITED; *Int'l*, pg. 3400
HINDUSTAN MOTORS LIMITED; *Int'l*, pg. 3400
HINDUSTAN OIL EXPLORATION COMPANY LTD; *Int'l*, pg. 3400
HINDUSTAN ORGANIC CHEMICALS LIMITED; *Int'l*, pg. 3400
HINDUSTAN PETROLEUM CORPORATION LIMITED—See Oil & Natural Gas Corporation Limited; *Int'l*, pg. 5534
HINDUSTAN PHOTO FILMS MANUFACTURING COMPANY LIMITED; *Int'l*, pg. 3400
HINDUSTAN SANITARYWARE & INDUSTRIES LTD (CD II)—See AGI Greenpac Limited; *Int'l*, pg. 209
HINDUSTAN SANITARYWARE & INDUSTRIES LTD (CD I)—See AGI Greenpac Limited; *Int'l*, pg. 209
HINDUSTAN TIN WORKS LTD.; *Int'l*, pg. 3400
HINDUSTAN UNILEVER LTD.—See Unilever PLC; *Int'l*, pg. 8044
HINDUSTAN WIRES LIMITED; *Int'l*, pg. 3400
HINDUSTAN ZINC LIMITED—See Vedanta Resources Ltd; *Int'l*, pg. 8146
HINDUSTHAN NATIONAL GLASS & INDUSTRIES LIMITED; *Int'l*, pg. 3400
HINDUSTHAN NATIONAL GLASS & INDUSTRIES LTD. - BAHADURGARH PLANT—See Hindusthan National Glass & Industries Limited; *Int'l*, pg. 3400
HINDUSTHAN NATIONAL GLASS & INDUSTRIES LTD. - RISHIKESH PLANT—See Hindusthan National Glass & Industries Limited; *Int'l*, pg. 3400
HINDUSTHAN NATIONAL GLASS & INDUSTRIES LTD. - RISHRA PLANT—See Hindusthan National Glass & Industries Limited; *Int'l*, pg. 3400
HINDUSTHAN SPECIALITY CHEMICALS LTD.—See Hindusthan Urban Infrastructure Ltd.; *Int'l*, pg. 3400
HINDUSTHAN UDYOG LIMITED; *Int'l*, pg. 3400
HINDUSTHAN URBAN INFRASTRUCTURE LTD.; *Int'l*, pg. 3400
HINDWARE HOME INNOVATION LIMITED; *Int'l*, pg. 3400
HINER TRANSPORT, INC.—See Service First Corporation; *U.S. Private*, pg. 3615
HINES BUILDING SUPPLY - US LBM, LLC—See Bain Capital, LP; *U.S. Private*, pg. 450
HINES CORPORATION; *U.S. Private*, pg. 1948
HINES GLOBAL INCOME TRUST, INC.; *U.S. Public*, pg. 1041

HINES GLOBAL REIT, INC.   CORPORATE AFFILIATIONS

HINES GLOBAL REIT, INC.; *U.S. Private*, pg. 1949
HINES GLOBAL REIT MARLBOROUGH CAMPUS I LLC—See Hines Global REIT, Inc.; *U.S. Private*, pg. 1949
THE HINES GROUP, INC.; *U.S. Private*, pg. 4053
HINES INTERESTS LIMITED PARTNERSHIP; *U.S. Private*, pg. 1949
HINES PARK LINCOLN MERCURY; *U.S. Private*, pg. 1949
HINES REAL ESTATE INVESTMENT TRUST, INC.; *U.S. Private*, pg. 1949
HINES-RINALDI FUNERAL HOME, INC.—See Service Corporation International; *U.S. Public*, pg. 1871
HINES SECURITIES, INC.; *U.S. Private*, pg. 1949
HING CHEONG METALS (CHINA & HONG KONG) LIMITED—See Shougang Century Holdings Limited; *Int'l*, pg. 6860
HINGE, INCORPORATED; *U.S. Private*, pg. 1949
HINGHAM INSTITUTION FOR SAVINGS; *U.S. Public*, pg. 1042
HINGHAM JOURNAL—See Gannett Co., Inc.; *U.S. Public*, pg. 902
HING LEE (HK) HOLDINGS LIMITED; *Int'l*, pg. 3400
HING LEE SECURITIES LIMITED—See Global Token Limited; *Int'l*, pg. 3001
HING MING HOLDINGS LIMITED; *Int'l*, pg. 3401
HINGTEX HOLDINGS LTD.; *Int'l*, pg. 3401
HINIARATAKAN CORPORATION—See Daifuku Co., Ltd.; *Int'l*, pg. 1926
HINIKER COMPANY - COSTER ENGINEERING DIVISION—See Hiniker Company; *U.S. Private*, pg. 1949
HINIKER COMPANY; *U.S. Private*, pg. 1949
HINKE TANKBAU GMBH—See VEKTOR Management GmbH & Co Erste KG; *Int'l*, pg. 8148
HINKLE BLOCK & MASONRY—See Summit Materials, Inc.; *U.S. Public*, pg. 1960
HINKLE CONTRACTING CO., LLC - JACKSON—See Summit Materials, Inc.; *U.S. Public*, pg. 1960
HINKLE CONTRACTING CO., LLC - LEXINGTON—See Summit Materials, Inc.; *U.S. Public*, pg. 1960
HINKLE CONTRACTING CO., LLC - SOMERSET—See Summit Materials, Inc.; *U.S. Public*, pg. 1960
HINKLE CONTRACTING COMPANY, LLC—See Summit Materials, Inc.; *U.S. Public*, pg. 1960
HINKLE INSULATION & DRYWALL COMPANY, INCORPORATED—See Installed Building Products, Inc.; *U.S. Public*, pg. 1132
HINKLE MANUFACTURING INC; *U.S. Private*, pg. 1949
HINKLE METALS & SUPPLY CO. INC.; *U.S. Private*, pg. 1949
HINKLE'S PHARMACY; *U.S. Private*, pg. 1949
HINKLE TRANSFER STATION, LLC—See Waste Management, Inc.; *U.S. Public*, pg. 2331
HINKLEY LIGHTING INC.; *U.S. Private*, pg. 1949
HINNI AG—See BKW AG; *Int'l*, pg. 1055
HINODE SHIKI KOGYO CO., LTD.—See Rengo Co., Ltd.; *Int'l*, pg. 6279
HINO DIESEL TRUCKS (U.S.A.), INC.-NEW YORK—See Toyota Motor Corporation; *Int'l*, pg. 7870
HINO ENGINEERING ANNEX, LTD.—See Toyota Motor Corporation; *Int'l*, pg. 7871
HINO HUTECH CO., LTD.—See Toyota Motor Corporation; *Int'l*, pg. 7871
HINOKI WOOD WORK COMPANY LIMITED—See Demeter Corporation Public Company Limited; *Int'l*, pg. 2025
HINOKIYA GROUP CO., LTD.—See Yamada Holdings Co., Ltd.; *Int'l*, pg. 8548
HINO LOGISTICS AND PACKING, LTD.—See Toyota Motor Corporation; *Int'l*, pg. 7871
HINOMARU CO., LTD.—See Sekisui Chemical Co., Ltd.; *Int'l*, pg. 6693
HINOMARU EXPRESS CO., LTD.—See SBS Holdings Inc.; *Int'l*, pg. 6607
HINOMARU SEINO TRANSPORTATION CO., LTD.—See Seino Holdings Co., Ltd.; *Int'l*, pg. 6690
HINO MOTOR SALES AUSTRALIA PTY. LTD.—See Toyota Motor Corporation; *Int'l*, pg. 7871
HINO MOTOR SALES (CANADA) LTD.—See Toyota Motor Corporation; *Int'l*, pg. 7871
HINO MOTOR SALES (THAILAND) LIMITED—See Toyota Motor Corporation; *Int'l*, pg. 7871
HINO MOTOR SALES USA, INC.—See Toyota Motor Corporation; *Int'l*, pg. 7871
HINO MOTOR SALES USA, INC.—See Toyota Motor Corporation; *Int'l*, pg. 7871
HINO MOTORS CANADA, LTD.—See Toyota Motor Corporation; *Int'l*, pg. 7871
HINO MOTORS (CHINA) CO., LTD.—See Toyota Motor Corporation; *Int'l*, pg. 7871
HINO MOTORS DE VENEZUELA, C.A.—See Toyota Motor Corporation; *Int'l*, pg. 7871
HINO MOTORS (EUROPE) N.V.—See Toyota Motor Corporation; *Int'l*, pg. 7871
HINO MOTORS, LTD. - HAMURA PLANT—See Toyota Motor Corporation; *Int'l*, pg. 7871
HINO MOTORS, LTD. - KOGA PLANT—See Toyota Motor Corporation; *Int'l*, pg. 7871

HINO MOTORS, LTD. - NITTA PLANT—See Toyota Motor Corporation; *Int'l*, pg. 7871
HINO MOTORS, LTD.—See Toyota Motor Corporation; *Int'l*, pg. 7870
HINO MOTORS (MALAYSIA) SDN. BHD.—See Toyota Motor Corporation; *Int'l*, pg. 7871
HINO MOTORS MANUFACTURING COLOMBIA, S.A.—See Toyota Motor Corporation; *Int'l*, pg. 7871
HINO MOTORS MANUFACTURING USA, INC.—See Toyota Motor Corporation; *Int'l*, pg. 7871
HINO MOTORS PHILIPPINES CORPORATION—See Toyota Motor Corporation; *Int'l*, pg. 7871
HINO MOTORS SALES (THAILAND) LTD.—See Toyota Motor Corporation; *Int'l*, pg. 7871
HINO MOTORS VIETNAM, LTD.—See Toyota Motor Corporation; *Int'l*, pg. 7871
HINOPAK MOTORS LIMITED—See Toyota Motor Corporation; *Int'l*, pg. 7871
HINO SEIKI CO., LTD.—See TOA Corporation; *Int'l*, pg. 7768
HINO U-TRUCK & ENGINEERING, LTD.—See Toyota Motor Corporation; *Int'l*, pg. 7871
HINOWA S.P.A.—See Oshkosh Corporation; *U.S. Public*, pg. 1620
HINRICHS FLANAGAN FINANCIAL; *U.S. Private*, pg. 1949
HINRICHS TRADING LLC—See Cargill, Inc.; *U.S. Private*, pg. 754
HINRICHS TRADING LLC—See CHS INC.; *U.S. Public*, pg. 491
HINRICHS TRADING LLC—See Conagra Brands, Inc.; *U.S. Public*, pg. 563
HIN SANG GROUP (INTERNATIONAL) HOLDING CO. LTD.; *Int'l*, pg. 3397
HIN SANG HONG COMPANY LIMITED—See Hin Sang Group (International) Holding Co. Ltd.; *Int'l*, pg. 3397
HINSDALE BANK & TRUST COMPANY, N.A.—See Wintrust Financial Corporation; *U.S. Public*, pg. 2375
HINSDALE SURGICAL CENTER, LLC—See Tenet Healthcare Corporation; *U.S. Public*, pg. 2010
HINSHAW & CULBERTSON LLP; *U.S. Private*, pg. 1950
HINSON GALLERIES, INC.; *U.S. Private*, pg. 1950
HINSTEC CO., LTD.—See HIOKI E.E. Corporation; *Int'l*, pg. 3401
HINTO ENERGY, INC.; *U.S. Private*, pg. 1950
HINTTECH BV—See Tahzoo LLC; *U.S. Private*, pg. 3923
HINXHILL PARK (ASHFORD) MANAGEMENT COMPANY LIMITED—See Bellway plc; *Int'l*, pg. 968
HINZE INC.; *U.S. Private*, pg. 1950
HIOKI E.E. CORPORATION; *Int'l*, pg. 3401
HIOKI ENGINEERING SERVICE CORPORATION—See HIOKI E.E. Corporation; *Int'l*, pg. 3401
HIOKI EUROPE GMBH—See HIOKI E.E. Corporation; *Int'l*, pg. 3401
HIOKI FOREST PLAZA CORPORATION—See HIOKI E.E. Corporation; *Int'l*, pg. 3401
HIOKI INDIA ENGINEERING PRIVATE LIMITED—See HIOKI E.E. Corporation; *Int'l*, pg. 3401
HIOKI KOREA CO., LTD.—See HIOKI E.E. Corporation; *Int'l*, pg. 3401
HIOKI (SHANGHAI) MEASUREMENT TECHNOLOGIES CO., LTD.—See HIOKI E.E. Corporation; *Int'l*, pg. 3401
HIOKI (SHANGHAI) MEASURING INSTRUMENTS CO., LTD.—See HIOKI E.E. Corporation; *Int'l*, pg. 3401
HIOKI (SHANGHAI) SALES & TRADING CO., LTD.—See HIOKI E.E. Corporation; *Int'l*, pg. 3401
HIOKI (SHANGHAI) TECHNOLOGY DEVELOPMENT CO., LTD.—See HIOKI E.E. Corporation; *Int'l*, pg. 3401
HIOKI SINGAPORE PTE. LTD.—See HIOKI E.E. Corporation; *Int'l*, pg. 3401
HIOKI TAIWAN CO., LTD.—See HIOKI E.E. Corporation; *Int'l*, pg. 3401
HIOKI USA CORPORATION—See HIOKI E.E. Corporation; *Int'l*, pg. 3401
HIOLLE INDUSTRIES S.A.; *Int'l*, pg. 3401
HIOLLE LOGISTICS JSC—See Hiolle Industries S.A.; *Int'l*, pg. 3401
HIOLLE TECHNOLOGIES SAS—See Hiolle Industries S.A.; *Int'l*, pg. 3401
HIOSSEN CHILE SPA—See MBK Partners Ltd.; *Int'l*, pg. 4753
HIOSSEN CHILE SPA—See Unison Capital, Inc.; *Int'l*, pg. 8061
HIOSSEN CHINA CO., LTD.—See MBK Partners Ltd.; *Int'l*, pg. 4753
HIOSSEN CHINA CO., LTD.—See Unison Capital, Inc.; *Int'l*, pg. 8061
HIOSSEN DE MEXICO, S.A. DE C.V.—See MBK Partners Ltd.; *Int'l*, pg. 4753
HIOSSEN DE MEXICO, S.A. DE C.V.—See Unison Capital, Inc.; *Int'l*, pg. 8061
HIOSSEN IMPLANT CANADA INC.—See MBK Partners Ltd.; *Int'l*, pg. 4753
HIOSSEN IMPLANT CANADA INC.—See Unison Capital, Inc.; *Int'l*, pg. 8061
HIOSSEN INC.—See MBK Partners Ltd.; *Int'l*, pg. 4753
HIOSSEN INC.—See Unison Capital, Inc.; *Int'l*, pg. 8061
HIPACK CO., LTD.—See Resonac Holdings Corporation; *Int'l*, pg. 6298

HI-PACK GROUP FOR PACKAGING SOLUTION—See Hayel Saeed Anam Group of Companies; *Int'l*, pg. 3290
HIPAC LIMITED—See Goddard Enterprises Limited; *Int'l*, pg. 3019
HIPAGES GROUP HOLDINGS LIMITED; *Int'l*, pg. 3402
HIPARION DISTRIBUTION SA; *Int'l*, pg. 3402
HIPAY SAS—See GibMedia S.a.r.l.; *Int'l*, pg. 2963
HI-P (CHENGDU) MOLD BASE MANUFACTURING CO., LTD.—See Hi-P International Limited; *Int'l*, pg. 3381
HI-P (CHENGDU) PRECISION PLASTIC MANUFACTURING CO., LTD.—See Hi-P International Limited; *Int'l*, pg. 3381
HIP CORPORATION; *Int'l*, pg. 3402
HIP DIGITAL MEDIA, INC.—See Snipp Interactive Inc.; *Int'l*, pg. 7028
HI-P ELECTRONICS PTE. LTD.—See Hi-P International Limited; *Int'l*, pg. 3381
HIPERCOR, S.A.—See El Corte Ingles, S.A.; *Int'l*, pg. 2340
HI-PERFORMANCE FASTENING SYSTEMS—See American Securities LLC; *U.S. Private*, pg. 249
HIPER GLOBAL LTD.; *Int'l*, pg. 3402
HIPER GLOBAL UK LTD.—See HIPER Global Ltd.; *Int'l*, pg. 3402
HIPER GLOBAL US LTD.—See HIPER Global Ltd.; *Int'l*, pg. 3402
HIPERMARC S.A.; *Int'l*, pg. 3402
HIPEROS, LLC—See Thoma Bravo, L.P.; *U.S. Private*, pg. 4147
HIPERSCAN GMBH—See Fagron NV; *Int'l*, pg. 2603
HI-P INTERNATIONAL LIMITED; *Int'l*, pg. 3381
HIP & JOINT SPECIALISTS OF NORTH TEXAS, PLLC—See HCA Healthcare, Inc.; *U.S. Public*, pg. 998
HI-PLAINS BAG & BAGGING CO., INC.—See Langston Companies, Inc.; *U.S. Private*, pg. 2390
HI-PLAINS COOPERATIVE ASSOCIATION; *U.S. Private*, pg. 1932
HI-P LENS TECHNOLOGY (SHANGHAI) CO., LTD.—See Hi-P International Limited; *Int'l*, pg. 3381
HI-P MANAGEMENT SERVICES PTE. LTD.—See Hi-P International Limited; *Int'l*, pg. 3381
HI-P NORTH AMERICA, INC.—See Hi-P International Limited; *Int'l*, pg. 3381
HIPODROMO DE LA ZARZUELA, S.A.—See Sociedad Estatal de Participaciones Industriales; *Int'l*, pg. 7032
HIPOL A.D.; *Int'l*, pg. 3402
HIPOLIN LIMITED; *Int'l*, pg. 3402
HIPOTECARIA CRUZ DEL SUR PRINCIPAL, S.A.—See Principal Financial Group, Inc.; *U.S. Public*, pg. 1720
HIPOTECARIA SECURITY PRINCIPAL, S.A.—See Principal Financial Group, Inc.; *U.S. Public*, pg. 1720
HIPOTECARIOS ATACAS SL—See Tessi S.A.; *Int'l*, pg. 7574
HIPOTRONICS, INC.—See Hubbell Incorporated; *U.S. Public*, pg. 1066
HI-POWER LIMITED—See Flowtech Fluidpower plc; *Int'l*, pg. 2709
HIP-PETROHEMIJA A.D.; *Int'l*, pg. 3402
HIPPIE CAMPER LTD.—See Tourism Holdings Limited; *Int'l*, pg. 7848
HIPPIE CAMPER PTY. LTD.—See Tourism Holdings Limited; *Int'l*, pg. 7848
HIPPO HOLDINGS INC.; *U.S. Public*, pg. 1042
HI-P POLAND SP. Z O.O.—See Hi-P International Limited; *Int'l*, pg. 3381
HIPPO MARINE LTD—See James Fisher & Sons Public Limited Company; *Int'l*, pg. 3875
HIPPO VALLEY ESTATES LIMITED—See Tongaat Hulett Limited; *Int'l*, pg. 7807
HI-PRO FEEDS—See Friona Industries, LP; *U.S. Private*, pg. 1612
HI-P (SHANGHAI) HOUSING APPLIANCE CO., LTD.—See Hi-P International Limited; *Int'l*, pg. 3381
HI-P (SHANGHAI) TECHNOLOGY CO., LTD.—See Hi-P International Limited; *Int'l*, pg. 3381
HIPS (TRUSTEES) LIMITED—See Heidelberg Materials AG; *Int'l*, pg. 3311
HI-P (SUZHOU) ELECTRONICS TECHNOLOGY CO., LTD.—See Hi-P International Limited; *Int'l*, pg. 3381
HI-P (THAILAND) CO., LTD.—See Hi-P International Limited; *Int'l*, pg. 3381
HI-P TIANJIN ELECTRONICS CO., LTD.—See Hi-P International Limited; *Int'l*, pg. 3381
HI-P (TIANJIN) TECHNOLOGY CO., LTD.—See Hi-P International Limited; *Int'l*, pg. 3381
HIP TRIPS GMBH—See ProSiebenSat.1 Media SE; *Int'l*, pg. 6000
HIPUS CO., LTD.—See Infosys Limited; *Int'l*, pg. 3696
HI-P (XIAMEN) PRECISION PLASTIC MANUFACTURING CO., LTD.—See Hi-P International Limited; *Int'l*, pg. 3381
HIQ ACCELERATED CONCEPT EVALUATION AB—See HiQ International AB; *Int'l*, pg. 3402
HIQ APPROVE AB—See HiQ International AB; *Int'l*, pg. 3402
HI-Q AUTOMOTIVE (PTY) LTD—See The Goodyear Tire & Rubber Company; *U.S. Public*, pg. 2084

COMPANY NAME INDEX

HIQ CORPORATE SERVICES, INC.—See Apax Partners LLP; *Int'l*, pg. 503
HIQ FINLAND OY—See HiQ International AB; *Int'l*, pg. 3402
HI-Q GLOBAL SDN. BHD.—See Neo Group Limited; *Int'l*, pg. 5196
HIQ GOTEBORG AB—See HiQ International AB; *Int'l*, pg. 3402
HIQ INTERNATIONAL AB; *Int'l*, pg. 3402
HIQ KARLSKRONA AB—See HiQ International AB; *Int'l*, pg. 3402
HIQ KOBENHAVN A/S—See HiQ International AB; *Int'l*, pg. 3402
HIQ MALARDALEN AB—See HiQ International AB; *Int'l*, pg. 3402
HIQ MOBILEYES AB—See HiQ International AB; *Int'l*, pg. 3402
HIQ SKANE AB—See HiQ International AB; *Int'l*, pg. 3402
HIQ SOFTPLAN OY—See HiQ International AB; *Int'l*, pg. 3402
HIQ STOCKHOLM AB—See HiQ International AB; *Int'l*, pg. 3402
HIQ WISE A/S—See HiQ International AB; *Int'l*, pg. 3402
HIRA AUTOMOBILES LIMITED; *Int'l*, pg. 3402
HIRA ENERGY LIMITED—See Godawari Power & Ispat Ltd.; *Int'l*, pg. 3018
HIRA FERRO ALLOYS LTD.; *Int'l*, pg. 3402
HIRAFUKU ELECTRIC MFG.CO.,LTD.—See Teikoku Electric Mfg. Co., Ltd.; *Int'l*, pg. 7524
HIRAGA CO., LTD.; *Int'l*, pg. 3402
HIRAKAWA HEWTECH CORP. - FUKUSHIMA FACTORY—See Hirakawa Hewtech Corp.; *Int'l*, pg. 3403
HIRAKAWA HEWTECH CORP. - KOGA GENERAL R&D PLANT—See Hirakawa Hewtech Corp.; *Int'l*, pg. 3403
HIRAKAWA HEWTECH CORP. - MONOU FACTORY—See Hirakawa Hewtech Corp.; *Int'l*, pg. 3403
HIRAKAWA HEWTECH CORP. - NIIGATA FACTORY—See Hirakawa Hewtech Corp.; *Int'l*, pg. 3403
HIRAKAWA HEWTECH CORP; *Int'l*, pg. 3402
HIRAKAWA SINGAPORE PTE. LTD.—See The Furukawa Electric Co., Ltd.; *Int'l*, pg. 7646
HIRAKI CO., LTD.; *Int'l*, pg. 3403
HIRAMATSU INC.; *Int'l*, pg. 3403
HIRAM HOLLOW REGENERATION CORP.—See Casella Waste Systems, Inc.; *U.S. Public*, pg. 446
HIRAM WALKER & SONS LTD.—See Pernod Ricard S.A.; *Int'l*, pg. 5811
HIRAN ORGOCHEM LTD.; *Int'l*, pg. 3403
HIRANO TECSEED CO., LTD.; *Int'l*, pg. 3403
HIRATA AUTOMATED MACHINERY (SHANGHAI) CO., LTD.—See Hirata Corporation; *Int'l*, pg. 3403
HIRATA CORPORATION - EAST PLANT—See Hirata Corporation; *Int'l*, pg. 3403
HIRATA CORPORATION - KANSAI PLANT—See Hirata Corporation; *Int'l*, pg. 3403
HIRATA CORPORATION - KANTO PLANT—See Hirata Corporation; *Int'l*, pg. 3403
HIRATA CORPORATION - KUMAMOTO PLANT—See Hirata Corporation; *Int'l*, pg. 3403
HIRATA CORPORATION - KUSUNO PLANT—See Hirata Corporation; *Int'l*, pg. 3403
HIRATA CORPORATION OF AMERICA—See Hirata Corporation; *Int'l*, pg. 3403
HIRATA CORPORATION OF EUROPE LTD—See Hirata Corporation; *Int'l*, pg. 3403
HIRATA CORPORATION; *Int'l*, pg. 3403
HIRATA ENGINEERING EUROPE GMBH—See Hirata Corporation; *Int'l*, pg. 3403
HIRATA ENGINEERING, INC.—See Hirata Corporation; *Int'l*, pg. 3403
HIRATA ENGINEERING S.A. DE C.V.—See Hirata Corporation; *Int'l*, pg. 3403
HIRATA ENGINEERING (THAILAND) CO., LTD.—See Hirata Corporation; *Int'l*, pg. 3403
HIRATA FA ENGINEERING (M) SDN. BHD.—See Hirata Corporation; *Int'l*, pg. 3403
HIRATA FA ENGINEERING (S) PTE LTD—See Hirata Corporation; *Int'l*, pg. 3403
HIRATA FIELD ENGINEERING CO., LTD.—See Hirata Corporation; *Int'l*, pg. 3403
HIRATA FIELD ENGINEERING CO., LTD.—See Hirata Corporation; *Int'l*, pg. 3403
HIRATA MECHANICAL EQUIPMENT SALES (SHANGHAI) CO., LTD.—See Hirata Corporation; *Int'l*, pg. 3404
HIRATA SOFTWARE TECHNOLOGY CO., LTD.—See Hirata Corporation; *Int'l*, pg. 3404
HIRA TEXTILE MILLS LIMITED; *Int'l*, pg. 3402
HIRATSUKA DAIICHI TRAFFIC & CO., LTD.—See Daiichi Koutsu Sangyo Co., Ltd.; *Int'l*, pg. 1928
HIRAYAMA CO., LTD.—See Hirayama Holdings Co., Ltd.; *Int'l*, pg. 3404
HIRAYAMA GLOBAL SUPPORTER CO., LTD.—See Hirayama Holdings Co., Ltd.; *Int'l*, pg. 3404
HIRAYAMA HOLDINGS CO., LTD.; *Int'l*, pg. 3404
HIRAYAMA LACC CO., LTD.—See Hirayama Holdings Co., Ltd.; *Int'l*, pg. 3404
HIRAYAMA (THAILAND) CO., LTD.—See Hirayama Holdings Co., Ltd.; *Int'l*, pg. 3404

HIRAYAMA VIETNAM COMPANY LIMITED—See Hirayama Holdings Co., Ltd.; *Int'l*, pg. 3404
HIREAHELPER LLC; *U.S. Private*, pg. 1950
HI REAL SPA; *Int'l*, pg. 3379
HIREASE, INC.; *U.S. Private*, pg. 1950
HIRED HANDS, INC.; *U.S. Private*, pg. 1950
HIRE DYNAMICS, LLC.—See Apollo Global Management, Inc.; *U.S. Public*, pg. 151
HIREGY; *U.S. Private*, pg. 1950
HIRE INTELLIGENCE INTERNATIONAL LIMITED; *Int'l*, pg. 3404
HI-REL ALLOYS LTD.—See Windjammer Capital Investors, LLC; *U.S. Private*, pg. 4537
HI-REL GROUP, LLC—See Windjammer Capital Investors, LLC; *U.S. Private*, pg. 4537
HIRELIFESCIENCE LLC—See Aequor Technologies, LLC; *U.S. Private*, pg. 117
HI-REL LIDS LTD.—See Windjammer Capital Investors, LLC; *U.S. Private*, pg. 4538
HI-REL PRODUCTS, LLC—See Windjammer Capital Investors, LLC; *U.S. Private*, pg. 4538
HIREL SYSTEMS, LLC-MARSHALL—See Vishay Intertechnology, Inc.; *U.S. Public*, pg. 2302
HIREL SYSTEMS LLC—See Vishay Intertechnology, Inc.; *U.S. Public*, pg. 2302
HIREMETHODS; *U.S. Private*, pg. 1950
HIREMII LIMITED; *Int'l*, pg. 3404
HIRENETWORKS; *U.S. Private*, pg. 1950
HIRE ONE LTD.—See Renew Holdings plc; *Int'l*, pg. 6278
HIRE POWER, INC.; *U.S. Private*, pg. 1950
HIREQUEST, INC.; *U.S. Public*, pg. 1042
HIRERIGHT AU PTY LTD—See General Atlantic Service Company, L.P.; *U.S. Private*, pg. 1663
HIRERIGHT AU PTY LTD—See Stone Point Capital LLC; *U.S. Private*, pg. 3825
HIRERIGHT BACKGROUND SCREENING INDIA LLP—See General Atlantic Service Company, L.P.; *U.S. Private*, pg. 1663
HIRERIGHT BACKGROUND SCREENING INDIA LLP—See Stone Point Capital LLC; *U.S. Private*, pg. 3825
HIRERIGHT CANADA CORPORATION—See Corporate Risk Holdings LLC; *U.S. Private*, pg. 1056
HIRFRIGHT ESTONIA AS—See Corporate Risk Holdings LLC; *U.S. Private*, pg. 1056
HIRERIGHT HOLDINGS CORPORATION—See General Atlantic Service Company, L.P.; *U.S. Private*, pg. 1662
HIRERIGHT HOLDINGS CORPORATION—See Stone Point Capital LLC; *U.S. Private*, pg. 3825
HIRERIGHT, INC.—See Corporate Risk Holdings LLC; *U.S. Private*, pg. 1056
HIRERIGHT, LLC; *U.S. Private*, pg. 1950
HIRERIGHT POLAND SP. Z O.O.—See Corporate Risk Holdings LLC; *U.S. Private*, pg. 1056
HIRERIGHT PTE LTD—See Corporate Risk Holdings LLC; *U.S. Private*, pg. 1056
HIRERIGHT SOLUTIONS, INC.—See Corporate Risk Holdings LLC; *U.S. Private*, pg. 1056
HIRERIGHT UK HOLDING LIMITED—See General Atlantic Service Company, L.P.; *U.S. Private*, pg. 1663
HIRERIGHT UK HOLDING LIMITED—See Stone Point Capital LLC; *U.S. Private*, pg. 3825
HI RESOLUTION PRODUCTION—See WPP plc; *Int'l*, pg. 8474
HIRE STATION LIMITED—See Vp PLC; *Int'l*, pg. 8312
HIRESTRATEGY, INC.—See Odyssey Investment Partners, LLC; *U.S. Private*, pg. 2994
HIRESYNERGY, INC.—See Odyssey Investment Partners, LLC; *U.S. Private*, pg. 2994
HIRE TECHNOLOGIES, INC.; *Int'l*, pg. 3404
HIRE VELOCITY, LLC; *U.S. Private*, pg. 1950
HIREVERGENCE LLC—See My Job Matcher, Inc.; *U.S. Private*, pg. 2823
HIREVUE, INC.—See The Carlyle Group Inc.; *U.S. Public*, pg. 2047
HIREWELL; *U.S. Private*, pg. 1950
HIREX ENGINEERING SAS—See TUV NORD AG; *Int'l*, pg. 7980
HIRKER ZRT—See Vivendi SE; *Int'l*, pg. 8276
HIRNING PONTIAC BUICK GMC; *U.S. Private*, pg. 1950
HIROBISHI SOKOUNYU CO., LTD.—See Sankyu, Inc.; *Int'l*, pg. 6544
HIROCA HOLDINGS LTD.; *Int'l*, pg. 3404
HIROGIN AREA DESIGN CO., LTD.—See Hirogin Holdings, Inc.; *Int'l*, pg. 3404
HIROGIN AUTO LEASE CO. LTD—See Mitsubishi HC Capital Inc.; *Int'l*, pg. 4951
HIROGIN CAPITAL PARTNERS CO., LTD.—See Hirogin Holdings, Inc.; *Int'l*, pg. 3404
HIROGIN HOLDINGS, INC.; *Int'l*, pg. 3404
HIROGIN HUMAN RESOURCES CO., LTD.—See Hirogin Holdings, Inc.; *Int'l*, pg. 3404
HIROGIN IT SOLUTIONS CO., LTD.—See Hirogin Holdings, Inc.; *Int'l*, pg. 3404
HIROGIN LEASE CO., LTD.—See Hirogin Holdings, Inc.; *Int'l*, pg. 3404
HIROGIN SECURITIES CO., LTD.—See Hirogin Holdings, Inc.; *Int'l*, pg. 3404

HIRSCH INTERNATIONAL CORP.

HIROJI CENTER CO., LTD.—See Mitsubishi Heavy Industries, Ltd.; *Int'l*, pg. 4953
HIROKURA CO., LTD.—See Nippon Yusen Kabushiki Kaisha; *Int'l*, pg. 5357
HI-ROLLERS SPORTSWEAR LTD.—See E.S. Sutton Inc.; *U.S. Private*, pg. 1307
HIRONIC CO., LTD.; *Int'l*, pg. 3405
HIRONS & COMPANY; *U.S. Private*, pg. 1950
HIRONS & COMPANY—See Hirons & Company; *U.S. Private*, pg. 1950
HIRONS; *U.S. Private*, pg. 1950
HIRON TRADE INVESTMENT & INDUSTRIAL BUILDINGS LTD.; *Int'l*, pg. 3404
HIROSE ELECTRIC CO., LTD., EUROPEAN BRANCH—See Hirose Electric Co., Ltd.; *Int'l*, pg. 3405
HIROSE ELECTRIC CO., LTD.; *Int'l*, pg. 3405
HIROSE ELECTRIC EUROPE B.V—See Hirose Electric Co., Ltd.; *Int'l*, pg. 3405
HIROSE ELECTRIC HONG KONG CO., LTD.—See Hirose Electric Co., Ltd.; *Int'l*, pg. 3405
HIROSE ELECTRIC HONG KONG TRADING CO., LTD.—See Hirose Electric Co., Ltd.; *Int'l*, pg. 3405
HIROSE ELECTRIC MALAYSIA SDN BHD—See Hirose Electric Co., Ltd.; *Int'l*, pg. 3405
HIROSE ELECTRIC SINGAPORE PTE.LTD—See Hirose Electric Co., Ltd.; *Int'l*, pg. 3405
HIROSE ELECTRIC TAIWAN CO., LTD—See Hirose Electric Co., Ltd.; *Int'l*, pg. 3405
HIROSE ELECTRIC TRADING (SHANGHAI) CO., LTD—See Hirose Electric Co., Ltd.; *Int'l*, pg. 3405
HIROSE ELECTRIC UK LTD—See Hirose Electric Co., Ltd.; pg. 3405
HIROSE ELECTRIC (U.S.A.), INC.—See Hirose Electric Co., Ltd.; *Int'l*, pg. 3405
HIROSE HOLDINGS & CO.,LTD.; *Int'l*, pg. 3405
HIROSEKI KAKO CO., LTD.—See Sekisui Chemical Co., Ltd.; *Int'l*, pg. 6693
HIROSE KOREA CO. LTD.—See Hirose Electric Co., Ltd.; *Int'l*, pg. 3405
HIROSE OPTROCNIS CO., LTD.—See Wuhan Jingce Electronic Group Co., Ltd.; *Int'l*, pg. 8500
HIROSE SANGYO KAIUN CO., LTD.—See Tradia Corporation; *Int'l*, pg. 7889
HIROSE SEIKO CO., LTD.—See Honda Motor Co., Ltd.; *Int'l*, pg. 3460
HIROSE TECHNOLOGY CO. LTD.—See Suncall Corporation; *Int'l*, pg. 7310
HIROSE TUSYO, INC.; *Int'l*, pg. 3405
THE HIROSHIMA BANK, LTD.; *Int'l*, pg. 7652
HIROSHIMA DAIICHI TRAFFIC CO., LTD.—See Daiichi Koutsu Sangyo Co., Ltd.; *Int'l*, pg. 1928
HIROSHIMA EAGLE CO., LTD.—See Eagle Industry Co., Ltd.; *Int'l*, pg. 2265
HIROSHIMA ELECTRIC RAILWAY CO.,LTD.; *Int'l*, pg. 3405
HIROSHIMA GAS CO., LTD. - BINGO PLANT—See Hiroshima Gas Co., Ltd.; *Int'l*, pg. 3405
HIROSHIMA GAS CO., LTD.; *Int'l*, pg. 3405
HIROSHIMA GAS LIVING CO., LTD.—See Hiroshima Gas Co., Ltd.; *Int'l*, pg. 3405
HIROSHIMA GRINDING INDUSTRIES CO., LTD.—See Noritake Co., Limited; *Int'l*, pg. 5428
HIROSHIMAGUMI CO., LTD.—See TENOX CO., LTD.; *Int'l*, pg. 7561
HIROSHIMA MITSUKOSHI LTD.—See Isetan Mitsukoshi Holdings Ltd.; *Int'l*, pg. 3814
HIROSHIMA NICHIREI SERVICE INC.—See Nichirei Corporation; *Int'l*, pg. 5270
HIROSHIMA RYOJU ENGINEERING CO., LTD.—See Mitsubishi Heavy Industries, Ltd.; *Int'l*, pg. 4953
HIROSHIMA RYOJU ESTATE CO., LTD.—See Mitsubishi Heavy Industries, Ltd.; *Int'l*, pg. 4961
HIROSHIMA SUBARU INC.—See SUBARU CO., LTD.; *Int'l*, pg. 7246
HIROSHIMA TOKUYAMA READY MIXED CONCRETE CO., LTD.—See Tokuyama Corporation; *Int'l*, pg. 7787
HIROSHIMA TOYO CARP, K.K.; *Int'l*, pg. 3405
HIROSS ZANDER DIVISION—See Parker Hannifin Corporation; *U.S. Public*, pg. 1649
HIROTAKO ACOUSTICS SDN. BHD.—See MBM Resources Berhad; *Int'l*, pg. 4754
HIROTAKO HOLDINGS BERHAD—See MBM Resources Berhad; *Int'l*, pg. 4754
HIROUCHI ATSUEN KOGYO CO., LTD.—See Hanwa Co., Ltd.; *Int'l*, pg. 3263
HIROUCHI STEEL CO., LTD.—See Hanwa Co., Ltd.; *Int'l*, pg. 3263
HIRSCHBACH MOTOR LINES, INC.; *U.S. Private*, pg. 1951
HIRSCH BEDNER ASSOCIATES INC.—See Suzhou Gold Mantis Construction Decoration Co., Ltd.; *Int'l*, pg. 7350
HIRSCH BUSINESS CONCEPTS, LLC—See Hirsch International Corp.; *U.S. Private*, pg. 1950
HIRSCHER MONEYSYSTEMS GMBH—See Novomatic AG; *Int'l*, pg. 5467
HIRSCHFELD INDUSTRIES, INC.—See Berkshire Hathaway Inc.; *U.S. Public*, pg. 298
HIRSCH INTERNATIONAL CORP.; *U.S. Private*, pg. 1950

1237

HIRSCH INTERNATIONAL CORP.

CORPORATE AFFILIATIONS

HIRSCH ITALIA S.R.L.—See Hirsch Servo AG; *Int'l*, pg. 3405
HIRSCHLER FLEISCHER, A PROFESSIONAL CORPORATION; *U.S. Private*, pg. 1951
HIRSCHMANN AUTOMATION & CONTROL GMBH—See Belden, Inc.; *U.S. Public*, pg. 294
HIRSCHMANN & LUMBERG AUTOMATION USA—See Belden, Inc.; *U.S. Public*, pg. 294
HIRSCH MASCHINENBAU GMBH—See Hirsch Servo AG; *Int'l*, pg. 3405
HIRSCH METALS CORPORATION; *U.S. Private*, pg. 1951
HIRSCH PIPE & SUPPLY CO., INC.; *U.S. Private*, pg. 1951
HIRSCH POROZELL GMBH—See Hirsch Servo AG; *Int'l*, pg. 3405
HIRSCH POROZELL KFT—See Hirsch Servo AG; *Int'l*, pg. 3406
HIRSCH POROZELL SP. Z O.O.—See Hirsch Servo AG; *Int'l*, pg. 3406
HIRSCH POROZELL S.R.L.—See Hirsch Servo AG; *Int'l*, pg. 3406
HIRSCH SERVO AG; *Int'l*, pg. 3405
HIRSHFIELD'S INC.; *U.S. Private*, pg. 1951
HIRSHFIELD'S PAINT MANUFACTURING INC.—See Hirshfield's Inc.; *U.S. Private*, pg. 1951
HIRSH INDUSTRIES DOVER DIVISION—See Hirsh Industries, Inc.; *U.S. Private*, pg. 1951
HIRSH INDUSTRIES, INC.; *U.S. Private*, pg. 1951
HIRSH INDUSTRIES LLC—See Hirsh Industries, Inc.; *U.S. Private*, pg. 1951
HIRSLANDEN AG—See Remgro Limited; *Int'l*, pg. 6269
HIRSLANDEN CLINIQUE LA COLLINE S.A.—See Remgro Limited; *Int'l*, pg. 6269
HIRSLANDEN KLINIK AM ROSENBERG AG—See Remgro Limited; *Int'l*, pg. 6270
HIRSLANDEN PRIVATE HOSPITAL GROUP—See Remgro Limited; *Int'l*, pg. 6270
HIRSONDIS; *Int'l*, pg. 3406
HIRTENBERGER HOLDING GMBH; *Int'l*, pg. 3406
HIRTLE CALLAGHAN & CO.; *U.S. Private*, pg. 1951
HIRTLER SEIFEN GMBH—See L. Possehl & Co. mbH; *Int'l*, pg. 4382
HIRU CORP.; *U.S. Public*, pg. 1042
HIRZEL CANNING CO & FARMS; *U.S. Private*, pg. 1951
HIRZU, INC.—See WPP plc; *Int'l*, pg. 8469
HISAKA AUTOMATION SDN. BHD.—See Regal International Group Ltd.; *Int'l*, pg. 6251
HISAKA (CHINA) CO., LTD.—See Hisaka Works, Ltd.; *Int'l*, pg. 3406
HISAKA KOREA CO., LTD.—See Hisaka Works, Ltd.; *Int'l*, pg. 3406
HISAKA MIDDLE EAST CO., LTD—See Hisaka Works, Ltd.; *Int'l*, pg. 3406
HISAKA SHANGHAI CO., LTD.—See Regal International Group Ltd.; *Int'l*, pg. 6251
HISAKA (SINGAPORE) PTE. LTD.—See Regal International Group Ltd.; *Int'l*, pg. 6251
HISAKA WORKS (CHINA) CO., LTD.—See Hisaka Works, Ltd.; *Int'l*, pg. 3406
HISAKA WORKS, LTD. - KONOIKE PLANT—See Hisaka Works, Ltd.; *Int'l*, pg. 3406
HISAKA WORKS, LTD.; *Int'l*, pg. 3406
HISAKAWORKS S.E.A. SDN. BHD.—See Hisaka Works, Ltd.; *Int'l*, pg. 3406
HISAKA WORKS (SINGAPORE) PTE LTD.—See Hisaka Works, Ltd.; *Int'l*, pg. 3406
HISAKA WORKS (THAILAND) CO., LTD.—See Hisaka Works, Ltd.; *Int'l*, pg. 3406
HISA KINZOKU KOGYO CO., LTD.—See Ishizuka Glass Co., Ltd.; *Int'l*, pg. 3818
HISAMITSU AMERICA, INC.—See Hisamitsu Pharmaceutical Co., Inc.; *Int'l*, pg. 3406
HISAMITSU FARMACEUTICA DO BRASIL LTDA.—See Hisamitsu Pharmaceutical Co., Inc.; *Int'l*, pg. 3406
HISAMITSU PHARMACEUTICAL CO., INC.; *Int'l*, pg. 3406
HISAMITSU UK LTD.—See Hisamitsu Pharmaceutical Co., Inc.; *Int'l*, pg. 3406
HISAMITSU VIETNAM PHARMACEUTICAL CO., LTD.—See Hisamitsu Pharmaceutical Co., Inc.; *Int'l*, pg. 3406
HISARLAR MAKINA SANAYI VE TICARET ANONIM SIRKETI—See Mahindra & Mahindra Limited; *Int'l*, pg. 4645
HISAR MADEN A.S.—See Bera Holding A.S.; *Int'l*, pg. 978
HISAR METAL INDUSTRIES LIMITED; *Int'l*, pg. 3406
HISAR SPINNING MILLS LIMITED; *Int'l*, pg. 3406
H.I.S. AUSTRALIA PTY. LTD.—See H.I.S. Co., Ltd.; *Int'l*, pg. 3195
H.I.S. CANADA INC.—See H.I.S. Co., Ltd.; *Int'l*, pg. 3195
HISCO, INC.—See Q.E.P. Co., Inc.; *U.S. Public*, pg. 1741
HISCO, INC.—See Distribution Solutions Group, Inc.; *U.S. Public*, pg. 668
H.I.S. CO., LTD.; *Int'l*, pg. 3195
HIS COMPANY, INC. - HISCOMEX DIVISION—See Distribution Solutions Group, Inc.; *U.S. Public*, pg. 668
HIS COMPANY, INC.—See Distribution Solutions Group, Inc.; *U.S. Public*, pg. 668

HISCOX INSURANCE COMPANY (GUERNSEY) LIMITED—See Hiscox Ltd.; *Int'l*, pg. 3407
HISCOX INSURANCE COMPANY INC.—See Hiscox Ltd.; *Int'l*, pg. 3407
HISCOX LTD.; *Int'l*, pg. 3406
HISCOX RE INSURANCE LINKED STRATEGIES LTD.—See Hiscox Ltd.; *Int'l*, pg. 3407
H.I.S. DEUTSCHLAND TOURISTIK GMBH—See H.I.S. Co., Ltd.; *Int'l*, pg. 3195
HI-SEAS OF DULAC INC.; *U.S. Private*, pg. 1932
HISENSE CO., LTD.; *Int'l*, pg. 3407
HISENSE KELON ELECTRICAL HOLDINGS CO., LTD.—See Hisense Co., Ltd.; *Int'l*, pg. 3407
HISENSE USA CORPORATION—See Hisense Co., Ltd.; *Int'l*, pg. 3408
HISENSE VISUAL TECHNOLOGY CO., LTD.—See Hisense Co., Ltd.; *Int'l*, pg. 3408
HISENSE-WHIRLPOOL (ZHEJIANG) ELECTRIC APPLIANCES CO., LTD.—See Hisense Co., Ltd.; *Int'l*, pg. 3408
HISENSE-WHIRLPOOL (ZHEJIANG) ELECTRIC APPLIANCES CO., LTD.—See Whirlpool Corporation; *U.S. Public*, pg. 2367
HIS EQUIPMENT MARKETING CO.; *U.S. Private*, pg. 1951
H.I.S. EUROPE ITALY S.R.L.—See H.I.S. Co., Ltd.; *Int'l*, pg. 3195
H.I.S. EUROPE LIMITED—See H.I.S. Co., Ltd.; *Int'l*, pg. 3195
HI SHARP ELECTRONICS CO., LTD.; *Int'l*, pg. 3379
HI-SHEAR CORPORATION—See LISI S.A.; *Int'l*, pg. 4524
HISHIKO CORPORATION—See Koike Sanso Kogyo Co., Ltd.; *Int'l*, pg. 4230
HISHI PLASTICS U.S.A., INC.—See Mitsubishi Chemical Group Corporation; *Int'l*, pg. 4931
HIS (HONG KONG) COMPANY LIMITED—See H.I.S. Co., Ltd.; *Int'l*, pg. 3195
H.I.S. HOTEL HOLDINGS CO., LTD.—See H.I.S. Co., Ltd.; *Int'l*, pg. 3195
HIS INTERNATIONAL TOURS FRANCE SAS—See H.I.S. Co., Ltd.; *Int'l*, pg. 3195
H.I.S. INTERNATIONAL TRAVEL PTE. LTD.—See H.I.S. Co., Ltd.; *Int'l*, pg. 3195
H.I.S.-MERIT TRAVEL INC.—See H.I.S. Co., Ltd.; *Int'l*, pg. 3195
H-I-S PAINT MANUFACTURING COMPANY INC.; *U.S. Private*, pg. 1824
HISPANA DOS S.A.—See FAES Farma, S.A.; *Int'l*, pg. 2601
HISPANIA ACTIVOS INMOBILIARIOS SOCIMI, S.A.—See Blackstone Inc.; *U.S. Public*, pg. 354
HISPANIC ASSOCIATION OF COLLEGES AND UNIVERSITIES; *U.S. Private*, pg. 1951
HISPANIC BUSINESS INC.; *U.S. Private*, pg. 1951
HISPANIC BUSINESS MAGAZINE—See Hispanic Business Inc.; *U.S. Private*, pg. 1951
HISPANIC EXPRESS, INC.; *U.S. Public*, pg. 1042
HISPANIC SCHOLARSHIP FUND; *U.S. Private*, pg. 1951
HISPANO SUIZA (S.A.)—See Safran SA; *Int'l*, pg. 6473
HISPASAT, S.A.—See Redeia Corporation, S.A.; *Int'l*, pg. 6246
HISPAVIC IBERICA S.L.—See Solvay S.A.; *Int'l*, pg. 7078
HI SPECIAL PURPOSE ACQUISITION COMPANY; *Int'l*, pg. 3379
H.I.S.-RED LABEL VACATIONS INC.—See H.I.S. Co., Ltd.; *Int'l*, pg. 3195
HISSAB LASANTECH SAS—See HORIBA Ltd; *Int'l*, pg. 3477
HISSAN TRADING CO., LTD.—See Denki Company Limited; *Int'l*, pg. 2027
HISSHO SUSHI; *U.S. Private*, pg. 1951
HISSONG GROUP INC.; *U.S. Private*, pg. 1951
H.I.S. SUPER POWER CO., LTD.—See H.I.S. Co., Ltd.; *Int'l*, pg. 3195
HISTEEL CO., LTD.; *Int'l*, pg. 3408
HISTION LLC—See Inotiv, Inc.; *U.S. Public*, pg. 1128
HISTOGEN, INC.; *U.S. Public*, pg. 1042
HISTOIRE D'OR S.A.S.—See Bridgepoint Group Plc; *Int'l*, pg. 1155
HISTOLAB PRODUCTS AB—See Algol Oy; *Int'l*, pg. 318
HISTON SWEET SPREADS LIMITED—See The Hain Celestial Group, Inc.; *U.S. Public*, pg. 2087
HISTORICAL EMPORIUM, INC.; *U.S. Private*, pg. 1952
HISTORIC CONSTRUCTION INC.—See Historic Restoration, Inc.; *U.S. Private*, pg. 1952
THE HISTORIC CRAGS LODGE—See Apollo Global Management, Inc.; *U.S. Public*, pg. 150
THE HISTORIC CRAGS LODGE—See Reverence Capital Partners LLC; *U.S. Private*, pg. 3415
HISTORIC HUDSON VALLEY; *U.S. Private*, pg. 1951
HISTORIC PRESERVATION PARTNERS, INC.; *U.S. Private*, pg. 1951
HISTORIC PROPERTIES INC.—See Apartment Investment and Management Company; *U.S. Public*, pg. 144
HISTORIC PROPERTY MANAGEMENT LLC—See Duke Energy Corporation; *U.S. Public*, pg. 691
HISTORIC RESTORATION, INC.; *U.S. Private*, pg. 1952
HISTORIC TOURS OF AMERICA INC.; *U.S. Private*, pg. 1952

HISTORY ASSOCIATES INC.; *U.S. Private*, pg. 1952
HISTORY BOOK CLUB—See Bertelsmann SE & Co. KGaA; *Int'l*, pg. 992
THE HISTORY CHANNEL—See The Hearst Corporation; *U.S. Private*, pg. 4045
THE HISTORY CHANNEL—See The Walt Disney Company; *U.S. Public*, pg. 2137
HISTORYNET, LLC—See Regent, L.P.; *U.S. Private*, pg. 3388
THE HISTORY PRESS, INC.—See Arcadia Publishing, Inc.; *U.S. Private*, pg. 309
HISTOTOX LABS, INC.—See Inotiv, Inc.; *U.S. Public*, pg. 1128
H.I.S. TOURS CO., LTD.—See H.I.S. Co., Ltd.; *Int'l*, pg. 3195
HIS ULUSLARARASI TURIZM SEYAHAT ACENTASI LIMITED SIRKETI—See H.I.S. Co., Ltd.; *Int'l*, pg. 3195
HI SUN TECHNOLOGY (CHINA) LIMITED; *Int'l*, pg. 3379
HISWAY PARTNERS, INC.; *U.S. Private*, pg. 1952
HITACHI ABB POWER GRIDS AG—See Hitachi, Ltd.; *Int'l*, pg. 3413
HITACHI ACADEMY CO., LTD.—See Hitachi, Ltd.; *Int'l*, pg. 3413
HITACHI ALOKA MEDICAL, LTD.—See Hitachi, Ltd.; *Int'l*, pg. 3413
HITACHI AMERICA, LTD.—See Hitachi, Ltd.; *Int'l*, pg. 3413
HITACHI APPLIANCES TECHNO SERVICE, LTD.—See Hitachi, Ltd.; *Int'l*, pg. 3414
HITACHI AQUA-TECH ENGINEERING PTE. LTD.—See Hitachi, Ltd.; *Int'l*, pg. 3414
HITACHI ARCHITECTS & ENGINEERS CO., LTD.—See Hitachi, Ltd.; *Int'l*, pg. 3414
HITACHI ARCHITECTS & ENGINEERS (SHANGHAI) CO., LTD.—See Hitachi, Ltd.; *Int'l*, pg. 3414
HITACHI ASIA LTD.—See Hitachi, Ltd.; *Int'l*, pg. 3414
HITACHI ASIA (M) SDN BHD—See Hitachi, Ltd.; *Int'l*, pg. 3414
HITACHI ASIA (VIETNAM) COMPANY LIMITED—See Hitachi, Ltd.; *Int'l*, pg. 3414
HITACHI ASTEMO, LTD.; *Int'l*, pg. 3408
HITACHI AUSTRALIA PTY LTD.—See Hitachi, Ltd.; *Int'l*, pg. 3414
HITACHI AUTOMOTIVE PRODUCTS (SUZHOU) LTD.—See Hitachi Astemo, Ltd.; *Int'l*, pg. 3408
HITACHI AUTOMOTIVE SYSTEMS AMERICAS, INC. - ALLEN PARK—See Hitachi Astemo, Ltd.; *Int'l*, pg. 3408
HITACHI AUTOMOTIVE SYSTEMS AMERICAS, INC. - BEREA PLANT—See Hitachi Astemo, Ltd.; *Int'l*, pg. 3408
HITACHI AUTOMOTIVE SYSTEMS AMERICAS, INC. - FARMINGTON HILLS—See Hitachi Astemo, Ltd.; *Int'l*, pg. 3408
HITACHI AUTOMOTIVE SYSTEMS AMERICAS, INC. - GEORGIA PLANT—See Hitachi Astemo, Ltd.; *Int'l*, pg. 3408
HITACHI AUTOMOTIVE SYSTEMS AMERICAS, INC. - LOS ANGELES—See Hitachi Astemo, Ltd.; *Int'l*, pg. 3408
HITACHI AUTOMOTIVE SYSTEMS AMERICAS, INC.—See Hitachi Astemo, Ltd.; *Int'l*, pg. 3408
HITACHI AUTOMOTIVE SYSTEMS ASIA, LTD.—See Hitachi Astemo, Ltd.; *Int'l*, pg. 3408
HITACHI AUTOMOTIVE SYSTEMS (CHINA) LTD.—See Hitachi Astemo, Ltd.; *Int'l*, pg. 3408
HITACHI AUTOMOTIVE SYSTEMS CHONBURI LTD.—See Hitachi, Ltd.; *Int'l*, pg. 3415
HITACHI AUTOMOTIVE SYSTEMS ESPELKAMP GMBH—See Hitachi, Ltd.; *Int'l*, pg. 3415
HITACHI AUTOMOTIVE SYSTEMS EUROPE (FRANCE)—See Hitachi Astemo, Ltd.; *Int'l*, pg. 3408
HITACHI AUTOMOTIVE SYSTEMS EUROPE GMBH - DUSSELDORF—See Hitachi Astemo, Ltd.; *Int'l*, pg. 3408
HITACHI AUTOMOTIVE SYSTEMS EUROPE GMBH—See Hitachi Astemo, Ltd.; *Int'l*, pg. 3408
HITACHI AUTOMOTIVE SYSTEMS EUROPE LTD.—See Hitachi Astemo, Ltd.; *Int'l*, pg. 3408
HITACHI AUTOMOTIVE SYSTEMS KORAT, LTD.—See Hitachi, Ltd.; *Int'l*, pg. 3415
HITACHI AUTOMOTIVE SYSTEMS PUNE (INDIA) PVT. LTD.—See Hitachi, Ltd.; *Int'l*, pg. 3415
HITACHI AUTOMOTIVE SYSTEMS (S) PTE LTD.—See Hitachi Astemo, Ltd.; *Int'l*, pg. 3408
HITACHI BRASIL LTDA.—See Hitachi, Ltd.; *Int'l*, pg. 3415
HITACHI BUILDING SYSTEMS BUSINESS SUPPORT CO., LTD.—See Hitachi, Ltd.; *Int'l*, pg. 3415
HITACHI BUILDING SYSTEMS CO., LTD.—See Hitachi, Ltd.; *Int'l*, pg. 3415
HITACHI BUILDING SYSTEMS ENGINEERING CO., LTD.—See Hitachi, Ltd.; *Int'l*, pg. 3415
HITACHI CABLE AMERICA, INC. - FLORIDA PLANT—See Proterial, Ltd.; *Int'l*, pg. 6005
HITACHI CABLE AMERICA, INC. - INDIANA PLANT—See Proterial, Ltd.; *Int'l*, pg. 6005
HITACHI CABLE AMERICA, INC. - MANCHESTER PLANT—See Proterial, Ltd.; *Int'l*, pg. 6005
HITACHI CABLE AMERICA, INC.—See Proterial, Ltd.; *Int'l*, pg. 6005

COMPANY NAME INDEX

HITACHI CABLE (CHINA) TRADING CO., LTD.—See Proterial, Ltd.; *Int'l*, pg. 6005
HITACHI CABLE (JOHOR) SDN. BHD.—See Hitachi, Ltd.; *Int'l*, pg. 3415
HITACHI CABLE (JOHOR) SDN BH—See Proterial, Ltd.; *Int'l*, pg. 6005
HITACHI CABLE PHILIPPINES INC.—See Hitachi, Ltd.; *Int'l*, pg. 3415
HITACHI CABLE (SUZHOU) CO., LTD.—See Proterial, Ltd.; *Int'l*, pg. 6005
HITACHI CABLE TRADING (DALIAN F.T.Z.) CO., LTD.—See Proterial, Ltd.; *Int'l*, pg. 6005
HITACHI CABLE VIETNAM CO., LTD.—See Proterial, Ltd.; *Int'l*, pg. 6005
HITACHI CANADA LTD. - CALGARY POWER AND INDUSTRY DIVISION—See Hitachi, Ltd.; *Int'l*, pg. 3415
HITACHI CANADA—See Hitachi, Ltd.; *Int'l*, pg. 3415
HITACHI CAPITAL AMERICA CORP.—See Hitachi, Ltd.; *Int'l*, pg. 3413
HITACHI CAPITAL AMERICA VENDOR SERVICES—See Hitachi, Ltd.; *Int'l*, pg. 3413
HITACHI CAPITAL ASIA PACIFIC PTE LTD.—See Mitsubishi HC Capital Inc.; *Int'l*, pg. 4951
HITACHI CAPITAL AUTO LEASE CORPORATION—See Mitsubishi HC Capital Inc.; *Int'l*, pg. 4951
HITACHI CAPITAL CANADA CORP.—See Mitsubishi HC Capital Inc.; *Int'l*, pg. 4951
HITACHI CAPITAL CORPORATION—See Mitsubishi HC Capital Inc.; *Int'l*, pg. 4951
HITACHI CAPITAL INSURANCE CORP.—See Mitsubishi HC Capital Inc.; *Int'l*, pg. 4951
HITACHI CAPITAL LEASING (CHINA) CO., LTD.—See Mitsubishi HC Capital Inc.; *Int'l*, pg. 4951
HITACHI CAPITAL MALAYSIA SDN. BHD.—See Mitsubishi HC Capital Inc.; *Int'l*, pg. 4951
HITACHI CAPITAL NBL CORPORATION—See Mitsubishi HC Capital Inc.; *Int'l*, pg. 4951
HITACHI CAPITAL (THAILAND) CO., LTD.—See Mitsubishi HC Capital Inc.; *Int'l*, pg. 4951
HITACHI CAPITAL (UK) - BUSINESS FINANCE DIVISION—See Mitsubishi HC Capital Inc.; *Int'l*, pg. 4951
HITACHI CAPITAL (UK) - CONSUMER FINANCE DIVISION—See Mitsubishi HC Capital Inc.; *Int'l*, pg. 4951
HITACHI CAPITAL (UK) - INVOICE FINANCE DIVISION—See Mitsubishi HC Capital Inc.; *Int'l*, pg. 4951
HITACHI CAPITAL (UK) PLC—See Mitsubishi HC Capital Inc.; *Int'l*, pg. 4951
HITACHI CAPITAL VEHICLE SOLUTIONS LTD. - COMMERCIAL VEHICLE SERVICES DIVISION—See Mitsubishi HC Capital Inc.; *Int'l*, pg. 4951
HITACHI CAPITAL VEHICLE SOLUTIONS LTD—See Mitsubishi HC Capital Inc.; *Int'l*, pg. 4951
HITACHI CHEMICAL ASIA-PACIFIC PTE LTD.—See Resonac Holdings Corporation; *Int'l*, pg. 6299
HITACHI CHEMICAL (CHINA) CO., LTD.—See Resonac Holdings Corporation; *Int'l*, pg. 6298
HITACHI CHEMICAL CO. AMERICA LTD.—See Resonac Holdings Corporation; *Int'l*, pg. 6298
HITACHI CHEMICAL CO. (HONG KONG) LTD.—See Resonac Holdings Corporation; *Int'l*, pg. 6299
HITACHI CHEMICAL CO., LTD. - GOI WORKS—See Resonac Holdings Corporation; *Int'l*, pg. 6299
HITACHI CHEMICAL CO., LTD. - SHIMODATE WORKS—See Resonac Holdings Corporation; *Int'l*, pg. 6299
HITACHI CHEMICAL CO., LTD. - YAMAZAKI WORKS—See Resonac Holdings Corporation; *Int'l*, pg. 6299
HITACHI CHEMICAL DIAGNOSTICS, INC.—See Resonac Holdings Corporation; *Int'l*, pg. 6299
HITACHI CHEMICAL DIAGNOSTICS SYSTEMS CO., LTD.- FUJI PLANT—See Resonac Holdings Corporation; *Int'l*, pg. 6299
HITACHI CHEMICAL DIAGNOSTICS SYSTEMS CO., LTD.—See Resonac Holdings Corporation; *Int'l*, pg. 6299
HITACHI CHEMICAL DIAGNOSTICS SYSTEMS (SHANGHAI) CO., LTD.—See Resonac Holdings Corporation; *Int'l*, pg. 6299
HITACHI CHEMICAL (DONGGUAN) CO. LTD.—See Resonac Holdings Corporation; *Int'l*, pg. 6298
HITACHI CHEMICAL ELECTRONIC MATERIALS (KOREA) CO., LTD.—See Resonac Holdings Corporation; *Int'l*, pg. 6299
HITACHI CHEMICAL EUROPE GMBH—See Resonac Holdings Corporation; *Int'l*, pg. 6299
HITACHI CHEMICAL INTERNATIONAL CO., (TAIWAN) LTD.—See Resonac Holdings Corporation; *Int'l*, pg. 6299
HITACHI CHEMICAL (JOHOR) SDN BHD—See Resonac Holdings Corporation; *Int'l*, pg. 6299
HITACHI CHEMICAL MEXICO S.A. DE C.V.—See Resonac Holdings Corporation; *Int'l*, pg. 6299
HITACHI CHEMICAL (M) SDN BHD—See Resonac Holdings Corporation; *Int'l*, pg. 6298

HITACHI CHEMICAL RESEARCH CENTER, INC.—See Resonac Holdings Corporation; *Int'l*, pg. 6299
HITACHI CHEMICAL (SHANGHAI) CO., LTD.—See Resonac Holdings Corporation; *Int'l*, pg. 6298
HITACHI CHEMICAL SINGAPORE PTE LTD.—See Resonac Holdings Corporation; *Int'l*, pg. 6299
HITACHI CHEMICAL STORAGE BATTERY (THAILAND) PLC.; *Int'l*, pg. 3410
HITACHI CHEMICAL SUMIDEN POWER PRODUCTS, LTD.—See Sumitomo Electric Industries, Ltd.; *Int'l*, pg. 7278
HITACHI CHEMICAL (THAILAND) CO., LTD.—See Resonac Holdings Corporation; *Int'l*, pg. 6299
HITACHI CHEMICAL (YANTAI) CO., LTD.—See Resonac Holdings Corporation; *Int'l*, pg. 6299
HITACHI (CHINA), LTD.—See Hitachi, Ltd.; *Int'l*, pg. 3413
HITACHI (CHINA) RESEARCH & DEVELOPMENT CORPORATION—See Hitachi, Ltd.; *Int'l*, pg. 3413
HITACHI COLLABONEXT TRANSPORT SYSTEM CO., LTD.—See KKR & Co. Inc.; *U.S. Public*, pg. 1258
HITACHI COMMUNICATION TECHNOLOGIES AMERICA, INC. - HCTA PACKET CORE DIVISION—See Hitachi, Ltd.; *Int'l*, pg. 3413
HITACHI COMMUNICATION TECHNOLOGIES AMERICA, INC.—See Hitachi, Ltd.; *Int'l*, pg. 3413
HITACHI COMPUTER PRODUCTS (AMERICA), INC.—See Hitachi, Ltd.; *Int'l*, pg. 3413
HITACHI COMPUTER PRODUCTS (EUROPE) S.A.S.—See Hitachi, Ltd.; *Int'l*, pg. 3415
HITACHI CONSTRUCTION MACHINERY AFRICA PTY. LTD.—See Hitachi, Ltd.; *Int'l*, pg. 3415
HITACHI CONSTRUCTION MACHINERY ASIA AND PACIFIC PTE LTD.—See Hitachi, Ltd.; *Int'l*, pg. 3415
HITACHI CONSTRUCTION MACHINERY AUSTRALIA PTY. LTD.—See Hitachi, Ltd.; *Int'l*, pg. 3416
HITACHI CONSTRUCTION MACHINERY (CHINA) CO., LTD.—See Hitachi, Ltd.; *Int'l*, pg. 3415
HITACHI CONSTRUCTION MACHINERY CO., LTD.—See Hitachi, Ltd.; *Int'l*, pg. 3415
HITACHI CONSTRUCTION MACHINERY EURASIA SALES LLC—See Hitachi, Ltd.; *Int'l*, pg. 3416
HITACHI CONSTRUCTION MACHINERY (EUROPE) N.V.—See Hitachi, Ltd.; *Int'l*, pg. 3415
HITACHI CONSTRUCTION MACHINERY HOLDING U.S.A CORPORATION.—See Hitachi, Ltd.; *Int'l*, pg. 3416
HITACHI CONSTRUCTION MACHINERY JAPAN CO., LTD.—See Hitachi, Ltd.; *Int'l*, pg. 3416
HITACHI CONSTRUCTION MACHINERY LOADERS AMERICA INC.—See Hitachi, Ltd.; *Int'l*, pg. 3416
HITACHI CONSTRUCTION MACHINERY MIDDLE EAST CORPORATION FZE—See Hitachi, Ltd.; *Int'l*, pg. 3416
HITACHI CONSTRUCTION MACHINERY MOZAMBIQUE LIMITED—See Hitachi, Ltd.; *Int'l*, pg. 3416
HITACHI CONSTRUCTION MACHINERY (M) SDN BHD—See Hitachi, Ltd.; *Int'l*, pg. 3415
HITACHI CONSTRUCTION MACHINERY N.V.—See Hitachi, Ltd.; *Int'l*, pg. 3416
HITACHI CONSTRUCTION MACHINERY SALES AND SERVICE FRANCE S.A.S.—See Hitachi, Ltd.; *Int'l*, pg. 3416
HITACHI CONSTRUCTION MACHINERY (SHANGHAI) CO., LTD.—See Hitachi, Ltd.; *Int'l*, pg. 3415
HITACHI CONSTRUCTION MACHINERY SOUTHERN AFRICA CO., LTD.—See Hitachi, Ltd.; *Int'l*, pg. 3416
HITACHI CONSTRUCTION MACHINERY (THAILAND) CO., LTD.—See Hitachi, Ltd.; *Int'l*, pg. 3415
HITACHI CONSTRUCTION MACHINERY (UK) LIMITED—See Hitachi, Ltd.; *Int'l*, pg. 3415
HITACHI CONSTRUCTION MACHINERY ZAMBIA CO., LTD.—See Hitachi, Ltd.; *Int'l*, pg. 3416
HITACHI CONSTRUCTION TRUCK MANUFACTURING, LTD.—See Hitachi, Ltd.; *Int'l*, pg. 3416
HITACHI CONSULTING ASIA PACIFIC PTE. LTD.—See Hitachi, Ltd.; *Int'l*, pg. 3416
HITACHI CONSULTING AUSTRALIA PTY. LTD.—See Hitachi, Ltd.; *Int'l*, pg. 3416
HITACHI CONSULTING (CHINA) CO., LTD.—See Hitachi, Ltd.; *Int'l*, pg. 3413
HITACHI CONSULTING CORPORATION—See Hitachi, Ltd.; *Int'l*, pg. 3413
HITACHI CONSULTING INDIA PRIVATE LIMITED—See Hitachi, Ltd.; *Int'l*, pg. 3413
HITACHI CONSULTING PORTUGAL S.A.—See Hitachi, Ltd.; *Int'l*, pg. 3413
HITACHI CONSULTING SINGAPORE PTE LTD.—See Hitachi, Ltd.; *Int'l*, pg. 3413
HITACHI CONSULTING UK LIMITED—See Hitachi, Ltd.; *Int'l*, pg. 3413
HITACHI CONSUMER ELECTRONICS CO., LTD.—See Hitachi, Ltd.; *Int'l*, pg. 3416
HITACHI CONSUMER ELECTRONICS CO., LTD. - YOKOHAMA WORKS—See Hitachi, Ltd.; *Int'l*, pg. 3416
HITACHI CONSUMER MARKETING (CHINA) LTD.—See Hitachi, Ltd.; *Int'l*, pg. 3416
HITACHI CONSUMER PRODUCTS (THAILAND), LTD.—See Hitachi, Ltd.; *Int'l*, pg. 3416
HITACHI CRITICAL FACILITIES PROTECTION PTE. LTD.—See Hitachi, Ltd.; *Int'l*, pg. 3416

HITACHI DATA SYSTEMS AB (GOTHENBURG)—See Hitachi, Ltd.; *Int'l*, pg. 3413
HITACHI DATA SYSTEMS AG—See Hitachi, Ltd.; *Int'l*, pg. 3413
HITACHI DATA SYSTEMS AS—See Hitachi, Ltd.; *Int'l*, pg. 3413
HITACHI DATA SYSTEMS A/S—See Hitachi, Ltd.; *Int'l*, pg. 3413
HITACHI DATA SYSTEMS A/S—See Hitachi, Ltd.; *Int'l*, pg. 3413
HITACHI DATA SYSTEMS AUSTRALIA PTY LTD—See Hitachi, Ltd.; *Int'l*, pg. 3413
HITACHI DATA SYSTEMS BELGIUM NV/SA—See Hitachi, Ltd.; *Int'l*, pg. 3414
HITACHI DATA SYSTEMS B.V.—See Hitachi, Ltd.; *Int'l*, pg. 3414
HITACHI DATA SYSTEMS (CHILE) LIMITADA—See Hitachi, Ltd.; *Int'l*, pg. 3413
HITACHI DATA SYSTEMS CORPORATION—See Hitachi, Ltd.; *Int'l*, pg. 3413
HITACHI DATA SYSTEMS CREDIT CORPORATION—See Hitachi, Ltd.; *Int'l*, pg. 3414
HITACHI DATA SYSTEMS GMBH—See Hitachi, Ltd.; *Int'l*, pg. 3414
HITACHI DATA SYSTEMS HOLDING CORPORATION—See Hitachi, Ltd.; *Int'l*, pg. 3414
HITACHI DATA SYSTEMS INC.—See Hitachi, Ltd.; *Int'l*, pg. 3414
HITACHI DATA SYSTEMS INDIA PVT. LTD.—See Hitachi, Ltd.; *Int'l*, pg. 3414
HITACHI DATA SYSTEMS ISRAEL LTD.—See Hitachi, Ltd.; *Int'l*, pg. 3414
HITACHI DATA SYSTEMS ITALIA S.R.L.—See Hitachi, Ltd.; *Int'l*, pg. 3414
HITACHI DATA SYSTEMS KOREA LIMITED—See Hitachi, Ltd.; *Int'l*, pg. 3414
HITACHI DATA SYSTEMS LIMITED—See Hitachi, Ltd.; *Int'l*, pg. 3414
HITACHI DATA SYSTEMS LTD.—See Hitachi, Ltd.; *Int'l*, pg. 3414
HITACHI DATA SYSTEMS LTD.—See Hitachi, Ltd.; *Int'l*, pg. 3414
HITACHI DATA SYSTEMS NEDERLAND BV—See Hitachi, Ltd.; *Int'l*, pg. 3414
HITACHI DATA SYSTEMS OY—See Hitachi, Ltd.; *Int'l*, pg. 3414
HITACHI DATA SYSTEMS (POLSKA) SP. Z.O.O.—See Hitachi, Ltd.; *Int'l*, pg. 3413
HITACHI DATA SYSTEMS PTE. LTD.—See Hitachi, Ltd.; *Int'l*, pg. 3414
HITACHI DATA SYSTEMS S.A. (BARCELONA)—See Hitachi, Ltd.; *Int'l*, pg. 3414
HITACHI DATA SYSTEMS S.A.S—See Hitachi, Ltd.; *Int'l*, pg. 3414
HITACHI DATA SYSTEMS SDN BHD—See Hitachi, Ltd.; *Int'l*, pg. 3414
HITACHI DATA SYSTEMS (SPAIN)—See Hitachi, Ltd.; *Int'l*, pg. 3413
HITACHI DE VENEZUELA, C.A.—See Hitachi, Ltd.; *Int'l*, pg. 3422
HITACHI DIGITAL HOST SDN. BHD.—See Hitachi, Ltd.; *Int'l*, pg. 3416
HITACHI DIGITAL MEDIA GROUP - RUSSIA—See Hitachi, Ltd.; *Int'l*, pg. 3416
HITACHI DIGITAL PAYMENT SOLUTIONS LIMITED—See Hitachi, Ltd.; *Int'l*, pg. 3416
HITACHI DIGITAL PAYMENT SOLUTIONS PHILIPPINES, INC.—See Hitachi, Ltd.; *Int'l*, pg. 3416
HITACHI DIGITAL PRODUCTS CHINA CO., LTD.—See Hitachi, Ltd.; *Int'l*, pg. 3416
HITACHI DISTRIBUTION SOFTWARE (SHANGHAI) CO., LTD.—See KKR & Co. Inc.; *U.S. Public*, pg. 1258
HITACHI DOCUMENT PRINTING CO., LTD.—See Hitachi, Ltd.; *Int'l*, pg. 3416
HITACHI DRIVES & AUTOMATION GMBH—See Hitachi, Ltd.; *Int'l*, pg. 3416
HITACHI EAST ASIA LTD.—See Hitachi, Ltd.; *Int'l*, pg. 3416
HITACHI EBWORX (INDO-CHINA) CO. LTD.—See Hitachi, Ltd.; *Int'l*, pg. 3422
HITACHI EBWORX INTERNATIONAL PTE. LTD.—See Hitachi, Ltd.; *Int'l*, pg. 3422
HITACHI EBWORX SDN. BHD.—See Hitachi, Ltd.; *Int'l*, pg. 3422
HITACHI EBWORX TECHNOLOGY (CHENGDU) CO. LTD.—See Hitachi, Ltd.; *Int'l*, pg. 3422
HITACHI ELECTRONIC DEVICES (WUJIANG) CO., LTD.—See Hitachi, Ltd.; *Int'l*, pg. 3416
HITACHI ELECTRONIC PRODUCTS (M) SDN BHD—See Hitachi, Ltd.; *Int'l*, pg. 3416
HITACHI ELECTRONICS ENGINEERING AMERICA—See Hitachi, Ltd.; *Int'l*, pg. 3414
HITACHI ELEVATOR ASIA PTE. LTD.—See Hitachi, Ltd.; *Int'l*, pg. 3416
HITACHI ELEVATOR (CAMBODIA) CO., LTD.—See Hitachi, Ltd.; *Int'l*, pg. 3416
HITACHI ELEVATOR (CHENGDU) CO., LTD.—See Hitachi, Ltd.; *Int'l*, pg. 3416

HITACHI CHEMICAL STORAGE BATTERY (THAILAND) PLC. CORPORATE AFFILIATIONS

HITACHI ELEVATOR (CHINA) CO., LTD.—See Hitachi, Ltd.; *Int'l*, pg. 3416
HITACHI ELEVATOR ENGINEERING COMPANY (HONG KONG) LIMITED—See Hitachi, Ltd.; *Int'l*, pg. 3416
HITACHI ELEVATOR ENGINEERING (MALAYSIA) SDN. BHD.—See Hitachi, Ltd.; *Int'l*, pg. 3417
HITACHI ELEVATOR (GUANGZHOU) ESCALATOR CO., LTD.—See Hitachi, Ltd.; *Int'l*, pg. 3417
HITACHI ELEVATOR MOTOR (GUANGZHOU) CO., LTD—See Hitachi, Ltd.; *Int'l*, pg. 3416
HITACHI ELEVATOR PHILIPPINES CORPORATION—See Hitachi, Ltd.; *Int'l*, pg. 3417
HITACHI ELEVATOR SAUDI ARABIA LIMITED—See Hitachi, Ltd.; *Int'l*, pg. 3417
HITACHI ELEVATOR VIETNAM CO., LTD.—See Hitachi, Ltd.; *Int'l*, pg. 3417
HITACHI ENERGY UK LIMITED—See ABB Ltd.; *Int'l*, pg. 52
HITACHI ENERGY USA INC.—See ABB Ltd.; *Int'l*, pg. 52
HITACHI ENGINEERING & SERVICES CO., LTD.—See Hitachi, Ltd.; *Int'l*, pg. 3417
HITACHI ENVIRONMENTAL TECHNOLOGY (YIXING) CO., LTD.—See Hitachi, Ltd.; *Int'l*, pg. 3417
HITACHI EUROPE A.B. (GREECE)—See Hitachi, Ltd.; *Int'l*, pg. 3417
HITACHI EUROPE GMBH - DIGITAL MEDIA GROUP—See Hitachi, Ltd.; *Int'l*, pg. 3417
HITACHI EUROPE GMBH - EUROPEAN PROCUREMENT & SOURCING GROUP—See Hitachi, Ltd.; *Int'l*, pg. 3417
HITACHI EUROPE GMBH—See Hitachi, Ltd.; *Int'l*, pg. 3417
HITACHI EUROPE LTD. - AIR CONDITIONING AND REFRIGERATION GROUP DIVISION—See Hitachi, Ltd.; *Int'l*, pg. 3417
HITACHI EUROPE LTD. - DIGITAL MEDIA GROUP DIVISION—See Hitachi, Ltd.; *Int'l*, pg. 3417
HITACHI EUROPE LTD. - INFORMATION SYSTEMS GROUP DIVISION—See Hitachi, Ltd.; *Int'l*, pg. 3417
HITACHI EUROPE LTD. - POWER DEVICE DIVISION—See Hitachi, Ltd.; *Int'l*, pg. 3417
HITACHI EUROPE LTD.—See Hitachi, Ltd.; *Int'l*, pg. 3417
HITACHI EUROPE S.A.—See Hitachi, Ltd.; *Int'l*, pg. 3417
HITACHI EUROPE S.R.L.—See Hitachi, Ltd.; *Int'l*, pg. 3417
HITACHI FERRITE ELECTRONICS, LTD.—See Proterial, Ltd.; *Int'l*, pg. 6005
HITACHI FINANCIAL EQUIPMENT SYSTEM(SHENZHEN) CO., LTD.—See Hitachi, Ltd.; *Int'l*, pg. 3417
HITACHI FOODS & LOGISTICS SYSTEMS INC.—See Hitachi, Ltd.; *Int'l*, pg. 3417
HITACHI-GE NUCLEAR ENERGY, LTD.—See Hitachi, Ltd.; *Int'l*, pg. 3422
HITACHI GLOBAL AIR POWER US, LLC—See Hitachi, Ltd.; *Int'l*, pg. 3417
HITACHI GLOBAL LIFE SOLUTIONS, INC,—See Hitachi, Ltd.; *Int'l*, pg. 3417
HITACHI GLOBAL STORAGE PRODUCTS (SHENZHEN) CO., LTD.—See Western Digital Corporation; *U.S. Public*, pg. 2355
HITACHI GLOBAL STORAGE TECHNOLOGIES CONSULTING (SHANGHAI) CO., LTD.—See Western Digital Corporation; *U.S. Public*, pg. 2355
HITACHI GLOBAL STORAGE TECHNOLOGIES MALAYSIA SDN. BHD.—See Western Digital Corporation; *U.S. Public*, pg. 2355
HITACHI GLOBAL STORAGE TECHNOLOGIES PHILIPPINES CORP.—See Western Digital Corporation; *U.S. Public*, pg. 2355
HITACHI GLOBAL STORAGE TECHNOLOGIES (SHENZHEN) CO., LTD.—See Western Digital Corporation; *U.S. Public*, pg. 2355
HITACHI HANBELL(SHANGHAI) PRECISE MACHINERY CO., LTD.—See Hitachi, Ltd.; *Int'l*, pg. 3417
HITACHI HEALTHCARE AMERICAS CORPORATION—See Hitachi, Ltd.; *Int'l*, pg. 3414
HITACHI HIGHLY AUTOMOTIVE PRODUCTS (SHANGHAI) LTD.—See Hitachi Astemo, Ltd.; *Int'l*, pg. 3408
HITACHI HIGH-TECH AMERICA, INC.—See Hitachi, Ltd.; *Int'l*, pg. 3418
HITACHI HIGH-TECH ANALYTICAL SCIENCE AMERICA, INC.—See Hitachi, Ltd.; *Int'l*, pg. 3418
HITACHI HIGH-TECH ANALYTICAL SCIENCE FINLAND OY—See Hitachi, Ltd.; *Int'l*, pg. 3418
HITACHI HIGH-TECH ANALYTICAL SCIENCE GMBH—See Hitachi, Ltd.; *Int'l*, pg. 3418
HITACHI HIGH-TECH ANALYTICAL SCIENCE LIMITED—See Hitachi, Ltd.; *Int'l*, pg. 3418
HITACHI HIGH-TECH ANALYTICAL SCIENCE SHANGHAI CO., LTD.—See Hitachi, Ltd.; *Int'l*, pg. 3418
HITACHI HIGH-TECH CORPORATION—See Hitachi, Ltd.; *Int'l*, pg. 3418
HITACHI HIGH-TECH DIAGNOSTICS (SHANGHAI) CO., LTD.—See Hitachi, Ltd.; *Int'l*, pg. 3418
HITACHI HIGH-TECH FIELDING CORPORATION—See Hitachi, Ltd.; *Int'l*, pg. 3418
HITACHI HIGH-TECH FINE SYSTEMS CORPORATION—See Hitachi, Ltd.; *Int'l*, pg. 3418
HITACHI HIGH-TECH HONG KONG LIMITED—See Hitachi, Ltd.; *Int'l*, pg. 3418
HITACHI HIGH-TECH INDIA PRIVATE LIMITED—See Hitachi, Ltd.; *Int'l*, pg. 3418
HITACHI HIGH-TECH IPC (MALAYSIA) SDN. BHD.—See Hitachi, Ltd.; *Int'l*, pg. 3418
HITACHI HIGH-TECH ISRAEL, LTD.—See Hitachi, Ltd.; *Int'l*, pg. 3418
HITACHI HIGH-TECH KYUSHU CORPORATION—See Hitachi, Ltd.; *Int'l*, pg. 3418
HITACHI HIGH-TECH MANUFACTURING & SERVICE CORPORATION—See Hitachi, Ltd.; *Int'l*, pg. 3418
HITACHI HIGH-TECH MEXICO, S.A. DE C.V.—See Hitachi, Ltd.; *Int'l*, pg. 3418
HITACHI HIGH-TECH NEXUS CORPORATION—See Hitachi, Ltd.; *Int'l*, pg. 3418
HITACHI HIGH TECHNOLOGIES AMERICA, INC. - DALLAS—See Hitachi, Ltd.; *Int'l*, pg. 3418
HITACHI HIGH TECHNOLOGIES AMERICA, INC. - PLEASANTON—See Hitachi, Ltd.; *Int'l*, pg. 3418
HITACHI HIGH TECHNOLOGIES AMERICA, INC.—See Hitachi, Ltd.; *Int'l*, pg. 3418
HITACHI HIGH-TECHNOLOGIES CANADA INC.—See Hitachi, Ltd.; *Int'l*, pg. 3418
HITACHI HIGH-TECHNOLOGIES CORPORATION—See Hitachi, Ltd.; *Int'l*, pg. 3418
HITACHI HIGH TECHNOLOGIES DO BRASIL LTDA.—See Hitachi, Ltd.; *Int'l*, pg. 3418
HITACHI HIGH TECHNOLOGIES EUROPE GMBH—See Hitachi, Ltd.; *Int'l*, pg. 3418
HITACHI HIGH-TECHNOLOGIES HONG KONG LTD.—See Hitachi, Ltd.; *Int'l*, pg. 3418
HITACHI HIGH-TECHNOLOGIES IPC (M) SDN. BHD.—See Hitachi, Ltd.; *Int'l*, pg. 3418
HITACHI HIGH-TECHNOLOGIES KOREA CO., LTD.—See Hitachi, Ltd.; *Int'l*, pg. 3419
HITACHI HIGH-TECHNOLOGIES (S) PTE. LTD.—See Hitachi, Ltd.; *Int'l*, pg. 3418
HITACHI HIGH-TECHNOLOGIES TAIWAN CORPORATION—See Hitachi, Ltd.; *Int'l*, pg. 3419
HITACHI HIGH-TECHNOLOGIES (THAILAND) LTD.—See Hitachi, Ltd.; *Int'l*, pg. 3418
HITACHI HIGH-TECH RUS LIMITED LIABILITY COMPANY—See Hitachi, Ltd.; *Int'l*, pg. 3418
HITACHI HIGH-TECH SCIENCE AMERICA, INC.—See Hitachi, Ltd.; *Int'l*, pg. 3418
HITACHI HIGH-TECH SCIENTIFIC SOLUTIONS (BEIJING) CO., LTD.—See Hitachi, Ltd.; *Int'l*, pg. 3418
HITACHI HIGH-TECH SCIENTIFIC SOLUTIONS CO., LTD.—See Hitachi, Ltd.; *Int'l*, pg. 3418
HITACHI HIGH-TECH (SHANGHAI) CO., LTD.—See Hitachi, Ltd.; *Int'l*, pg. 3418
HITACHI HIGH-TECH (SHENZHEN) CO., LTD.—See Hitachi, Ltd.; *Int'l*, pg. 3418
HITACHI HIGH-TECH STEEL DO BRASIL LTDA.—See Hitachi, Ltd.; *Int'l*, pg. 3418
HITACHI HIGH-TECH SUPPORT CORPORATION—See Hitachi, Ltd.; *Int'l*, pg. 3418
HITACHI HI-REL POWER ELECTRONICS PVT. LTD.—See Hitachi, Ltd.; *Int'l*, pg. 3417
HITACHI HI-SYSTEM21 CO., LTD.—See Hitachi, Ltd.; *Int'l*, pg. 3417
HITACHI HOME ELECTRONICS ASIA (S) PTE. LTD.—See Hitachi, Ltd.; *Int'l*, pg. 3414
HITACHI HOME ELECTRONICS VIETNAM CO., LTD.—See Hitachi, Ltd.; *Int'l*, pg. 3419
HITACHI (HONG KONG) LTD.—See Hitachi, Ltd.; *Int'l*, pg. 3413
HITACHI HVB, INC.—See Hitachi, Ltd.; *Int'l*, pg. 3414
HITACHI IBARAKI TECHNICAL SERVICE LTD.—See Hitachi, Ltd.; *Int'l*, pg. 3419
HITACHI ICT BUSINESS SERVICES, LTD.—See Hitachi, Ltd.; *Int'l*, pg. 3419
HITACHI ID SYSTEMS HOLDING, INC—See Hitachi, Ltd.; *Int'l*, pg. 3415
HITACHI INDIA PVT. LTD.—See Hitachi, Ltd.; *Int'l*, pg. 3419
HITACHI INDIA TRADING PVT. LTD.—See Hitachi, Ltd.; *Int'l*, pg. 3419
HITACHI INDUSTRIAL EQUIPMENT DRIVE & SOLUTIONS CO., LTD.—See Hitachi, Ltd.; *Int'l*, pg. 3419
HITACHI INDUSTRIAL EQUIPMENT (MALAYSIA) SDN. BHD.—See Hitachi, Ltd.; *Int'l*, pg. 3419
HITACHI INDUSTRIAL EQUIPMENT MEXICO, S.A. DE C.V.—See Hitachi, Ltd.; *Int'l*, pg. 3419
HITACHI INDUSTRIAL EQUIPMENT NAKAJO ENGINEERING CO., LTD.—See Hitachi, Ltd.; *Int'l*, pg. 3419
HITACHI INDUSTRIAL EQUIPMENT (NANJING) CO., LTD.—See Hitachi, Ltd.; *Int'l*, pg. 3419
HITACHI INDUSTRIAL EQUIPMENT (SUZHOU) COMPRESSOR CO., LTD.—See Hitachi, Ltd.; *Int'l*, pg. 3419
HITACHI INDUSTRIAL EQUIPMENT SYSTEMS (CHINA) CO., LTD.—See Hitachi, Ltd.; *Int'l*, pg. 3419
HITACHI INDUSTRIAL EQUIPMENT SYSTEMS CO., LTD. - AIR COMPRESSOR SYSTEM DIVISION—See Hitachi, Ltd.; *Int'l*, pg. 3419
HITACHI INDUSTRIAL EQUIPMENT SYSTEMS CO., LTD. - EBINA DIVISION—See Hitachi, Ltd.; *Int'l*, pg. 3419
HITACHI INDUSTRIAL EQUIPMENT SYSTEMS CO., LTD. - NARASHINO DIVISION—See Hitachi, Ltd.; *Int'l*, pg. 3419
HITACHI INDUSTRIAL EQUIPMENT SYSTEMS CO., LTD. - SAGAMI DIVISION—See Hitachi, Ltd.; *Int'l*, pg. 3419
HITACHI INDUSTRIAL EQUIPMENT SYSTEMS CO., LTD.—See Hitachi, Ltd.; *Int'l*, pg. 3419
HITACHI INDUSTRIAL EQUIPMENT SYSTEMS CO., LTD. - TAGA DIVISION—See Hitachi, Ltd.; *Int'l*, pg. 3419
HITACHI INDUSTRIAL EQUIPMENT SYSTEMS (HONG KONG) CO., LTD.—See Hitachi, Ltd.; *Int'l*, pg. 3419
HITACHI INDUSTRIAL EQUIPMENT TECHNOLOGY SERVICE, CO., LTD.—See Hitachi, Ltd.; *Int'l*, pg. 3419
HITACHI INDUSTRIAL PRODUCTS, LTD.—See Hitachi, Ltd.; *Int'l*, pg. 3419
HITACHI INDUSTRIAL TECHNOLOGY (THAILAND), LTD.—See Hitachi, Ltd.; *Int'l*, pg. 3419
HITACHI INDUSTRY & CONTROL SOLUTIONS, LTD.—See Hitachi, Ltd.; *Int'l*, pg. 3419
HITACHI INFORMATION & CONTROL SOLUTIONS, LTD.—See Hitachi, Ltd.; *Int'l*, pg. 3419
HITACHI INFORMATION CONTROL SYSTEMS EUROPE LTD.—See Hitachi, Ltd.; *Int'l*, pg. 3419
HITACHI INFORMATION ENGINEERING, LTD.—See Hitachi, Ltd.; *Int'l*, pg. 3419
HITACHI INFORMATION SYSTEMS (SHANGHAI), LTD—See Hitachi, Ltd.; *Int'l*, pg. 3419
HITACHI INFRASTRUCTURE SYSTEMS (ASIA) PTE. LTD.—See Hitachi, Ltd.; *Int'l*, pg. 3419
HITACHI INSTRUMENT (DALIAN) CO., LTD.—See Hitachi, Ltd.; *Int'l*, pg. 3419
HITACHI INSURANCE AGENCY (CHINA) LIMITED—See Hitachi, Ltd.; *Int'l*, pg. 3419
HITACHI INSURANCE SERVICES (HONG KONG) LTD.—See Hitachi, Ltd.; *Int'l*, pg. 3419
HITACHI INSURANCE SERVICES, LTD.—See Hitachi, Ltd.; *Int'l*, pg. 3419
HITACHI INTERNATIONAL (HOLLAND) B.V.—See Hitachi, Ltd.; *Int'l*, pg. 3419
HITACHI INTERNATIONAL TREASURY LTD.—See Hitachi, Ltd.; *Int'l*, pg. 3414
HITACHI INTERNATIONAL TREASURY (MALAYSIA) SDN. BHD.—See Hitachi, Ltd.; *Int'l*, pg. 3419
HITACHI INVESTMENT MANAGEMENT, LTD.—See Hitachi, Ltd.; *Int'l*, pg. 3420
HITACHI KASEI SHOJI CO., LTD.—See Resonac Holdings Corporation; *Int'l*, pg. 6299
HITACHI KASHIWA REYSOL CO., LTD.—See Hitachi, Ltd.; *Int'l*, pg. 3420
HITACHI KE SYSTEMS, LTD.—See Hitachi, Ltd.; *Int'l*, pg. 3419
HITACHI KOKUSAI ELECTRIC AMERICA, LTD.—See KKR & Co. Inc.; *U.S. Public*, pg. 1257
HITACHI KOKUSAI ELECTRIC CANADA, LTD.—See KKR & Co. Inc.; *U.S. Public*, pg. 1257
HITACHI KOKUSAI ELECTRIC COMARK LLC—See Nisshinbo Holdings Inc.; *Int'l*, pg. 5373
HITACHI KOKUSAI ELECTRIC EUROPE GMBH—See KKR & Co. Inc.; *U.S. Public*, pg. 1257
HITACHI KOKUSAI ELECTRIC, INC.—See KKR & Co. Inc.; *U.S. Public*, pg. 1257
HITACHI KOKUSAI ELECTRIC SERVICES INC.—See KKR & Co. Inc.; *U.S. Public*, pg. 1257
HITACHI KOKUSAI LINEAR EQUIPAMENTOS ELETRONICOS S/A—See Hitachi, Ltd.; *Int'l*, pg. 3415
HITACHI KOREA LTD.—See Hitachi, Ltd.; *Int'l*, pg. 3420
HITACHI-LG DATA STORAGE (HUIZHOU) LTD.—See Hitachi, Ltd.; *Int'l*, pg. 3422
HITACHI-LG DATA STORAGE, INC.—See Hitachi, Ltd.; *Int'l*, pg. 3422
HITACHI-LG DATA STORAGE KOREA, INC.—See Hitachi, Ltd.; *Int'l*, pg. 3422
HITACHI LIFE, LTD.—See Hitachi, Ltd.; *Int'l*, pg. 3420
HITACHI LIFT INDIA PVT. LTD.—See Hitachi, Ltd.; *Int'l*, pg. 3420
HITACHI, LTD.; *Int'l*, pg. 3412
HITACHI MANAGEMENT PARTNER, CORP.—See Hitachi, Ltd.; *Int'l*, pg. 3420
HITACHI MEDIA ELECTRONICS CO., LTD.—See Hitachi, Ltd.; *Int'l*, pg. 3420
HITACHI MEDICAL (GUANGZHOU) CO., LTD.—See Hitachi, Ltd.; *Int'l*, pg. 3420
HITACHI MEDICAL SYSTEMS B.V.—See Hitachi, Ltd.; *Int'l*, pg. 3420
HITACHI MEDICAL SYSTEMS EUROPE HOLDING AG—See Hitachi, Ltd.; *Int'l*, pg. 3420
HITACHI MEDICAL SYSTEMS GMBH—See Hitachi, Ltd.; *Int'l*, pg. 3420
HITACHI MEDICAL SYSTEMS GMBH—See Hitachi, Ltd.; *Int'l*, pg. 3420
HITACHI MEDICAL SYSTEMS KFT.—See Hitachi, Ltd.; *Int'l*, pg. 3420
HITACHI MEDICAL SYSTEMS N.V.—See Hitachi, Ltd.; *Int'l*, pg. 3420
HITACHI MEDICAL SYSTEMS S.A.S.—See Hitachi, Ltd.; *Int'l*, pg. 3420
HITACHI MEDICAL SYSTEMS S.L.—See Hitachi, Ltd.; *Int'l*, pg. 3420

COMPANY NAME INDEX

HITACHI, LTD.

HITACHI MEDICAL SYSTEMS (S) PTE. LTD.—See Hitachi, Ltd.; *Int'l*, pg. 3420
HITACHI MEDICAL SYSTEMS UK LTD.—See Hitachi, Ltd.; *Int'l*, pg. 3420
HITACHI METALS ADMET, LTD.—See Proterial, Ltd.; *Int'l*, pg. 6005
HITACHI METALS ADVANCED MACHINING, LTD.—See Hitachi, Ltd.; *Int'l*, pg. 3420
HITACHI METALS AMERICA, LTD.—See Proterial, Ltd.; *Int'l*, pg. 6005
HITACHI METALS AUTOMOTIVE COMPONENTS USA, LLC - LAWRENCEVILLE FACILITY—See Proterial, Ltd.; *Int'l*, pg. 6005
HITACHI METALS AUTOMOTIVE COMPONENTS, USA, LLC—See Proterial, Ltd.; *Int'l*, pg. 6005
HITACHI METALS (DONG GUAN) SPECIALTY STEEL CO., LTD.—See Proterial, Ltd.; *Int'l*, pg. 6005
HITACHI METALS EUROPE GMBH—See Proterial, Ltd.; *Int'l*, pg. 6005
HITACHI METALS FINETECH, LTD.—See Proterial, Ltd.; *Int'l*, pg. 6005
HITACHI METALS HONG KONG LTD. - PANYU FACTORY—See Proterial, Ltd.; *Int'l*, pg. 6005
HITACHI METALS HONG KONG LTD.—See Proterial, Ltd.; *Int'l*, pg. 6005
HITACHI METALS (INDIA) PVT. LTD.—See Proterial, Ltd.; *Int'l*, pg. 6005
HITACHI METALS KOREA CO., LTD.—See Hitachi, Ltd.; *Int'l*, pg. 3420
HITACHI METALS, LTD. - KUMAGAYA DIVISION—See Proterial, Ltd.; *Int'l*, pg. 6005
HITACHI METALS, LTD. - KUWANA WORKS—See Proterial, Ltd.; *Int'l*, pg. 6005
HITACHI METALS, LTD. - METGLAS YASUGI WORKS—See Proterial, Ltd.; *Int'l*, pg. 6005
HITACHI METALS, LTD. - MOKA WORKS—See Proterial, Ltd.; *Int'l*, pg. 6005
HITACHI METALS, LTD. - SAGA WORKS—See Proterial, Ltd.; *Int'l*, pg. 6005
HITACHI METALS, LTD. - TOTTORI WORKS—See Proterial, Ltd.; *Int'l*, pg. 6006
HITACHI METALS MMC SUPERALLOY LTD.—See Proterial, Ltd.; *Int'l*, pg. 6005
HITACHI METALS NEOMATERIAL, LTD.—See Proterial, Ltd.; *Int'l*, pg. 0005
HITACHI METALS NORTH CAROLINA, LTD.—See Proterial, Ltd.; *Int'l*, pg. 6005
HITACHI METALS PRECISION INSTRUMENTS (SHENZHEN) LTD.—See Hitachi, Ltd.; *Int'l*, pg. 3420
HITACHI METALS PRECISION, LTD.—See Proterial, Ltd.; *Int'l*, pg. 6005
HITACHI METALS PRECISION, LTD. - YASUGI WORKS—See Proterial, Ltd.; *Int'l*, pg. 6005
HITACHI METALS SAN HUAN MAGNETIC MATERIALS (NANTONG) CO., LTD.—See Hitachi, Ltd.; *Int'l*, pg. 3420
HITACHI METALS (SHANGHAI) LTD.—See Proterial, Ltd.; *Int'l*, pg. 6005
HITACHI METALS SINGAPORE PTE LTD.—See Proterial, Ltd.; *Int'l*, pg. 6005
HITACHI METALS (SUZHOU) TECHNOLOGY, LTD.—See Proterial, Ltd.; *Int'l*, pg. 6005
HITACHI METALS (SUZHOU) TECHNOLOGY, LTD. - SPECIALTY STEEL DIVISION—See Proterial, Ltd.; *Int'l*, pg. 6005
HITACHI METALS TAIWAN, LTD.—See Hitachi, Ltd.; *Int'l*, pg. 3420
HITACHI METALS (THAILAND) LTD.—See Hitachi, Ltd.; *Int'l*, pg. 3420
HITACHI METALS TOOL STEEL, LTD.—See Proterial, Ltd.; *Int'l*, pg. 6005
HITACHI METALS TRADING, LTD.—See Hitachi, Ltd.; *Int'l*, pg. 3420
HITACHI METALS WAKAMATSU, LTD.—See Proterial, Ltd.; *Int'l*, pg. 6005
HITACHI METGLAS (INDIA) PVT. LTD.—See Proterial, Ltd.; *Int'l*, pg. 6005
HITACHI MEXICO, S.A. DE C.V.—See Hitachi, Ltd.; *Int'l*, pg. 3420
HITACHI MITSUBISHI HYDRO CORPORATION—See Mitsubishi Electric Corporation; *Int'l*, pg. 4944
HITACHI MORI SHIGYO CO., LTD.—See Oji Holdings Corporation; *Int'l*, pg. 5536
HITACHI-MYCOM MAINTENANCE & SOLUTIONS LTDA.—See Hitachi, Ltd.; *Int'l*, pg. 3422
HITACHINAKA-TOKAI HIGH TRUST CO., LTD.—See Takuma Co., Ltd.; *Int'l*, pg. 7442
HITACHI NICO TRANSMISSION CO., LTD.—See Hitachi, Ltd.; *Int'l*, pg. 3420
HITACHI-OMRON TERMINAL SOLUTIONS, CORP.—See Hitachi, Ltd.; *Int'l*, pg. 3422
HITACHI OPERATION & MAINTENANCE - EGYPT S.A.E.—See Hitachi, Ltd.; *Int'l*, pg. 3420
HITACHI PAYMENT SERVICES PRIVATE LIMITED—See Hitachi, Ltd.; *Int'l*, pg. 3420
HITACHI PLANT CONSTRUCTION, LTD.—See Hitachi, Ltd.; *Int'l*, pg. 3420
HITACHI PLANT ENGINEERING & CONSTRUCTION (SUZHOU) CO., LTD.—See Hitachi, Ltd.; *Int'l*, pg. 3420

HITACHI PLANT MECHANICS CO., LTD.—See Hitachi, Ltd.; *Int'l*, pg. 3420
HITACHI PLANT SERVICES CO., LTD.—See Hitachi, Ltd.; *Int'l*, pg. 3420
HITACHI PLANT TECHNOLOGIES LTD - CSR PROMOTION DIVISION—See Hitachi, Ltd.; *Int'l*, pg. 3420
HITACHI PLANT TECHNOLOGIES, LTD.—See Hitachi, Ltd.; *Int'l*, pg. 3420
HITACHI PLANT TECHNOLOGIES (VIETNAM) CO., LTD.—See Hitachi, Ltd.; *Int'l*, pg. 3420
HITACHI POWDERED METALS CO., LTD.—See Resonac Holdings Corporation; *Int'l*, pg. 6299
HITACHI POWDERED METALS (S) PTE LTD.—See Resonac Holdings Corporation; *Int'l*, pg. 6299
HITACHI POWDERED METALS (THAILAND) CO., LTD.—See Resonac Holdings Corporation; *Int'l*, pg. 6299
HITACHI POWDERED METALS (USA), INC.—See Resonac Holdings Corporation; *Int'l*, pg. 6299
HITACHI POWER SOLUTIONS CO., LTD.—See Hitachi, Ltd.; *Int'l*, pg. 3420
HITACHI POWER SYSTEMS AMERICA, LTD.—See Hitachi, Ltd.; *Int'l*, pg. 3414
HITACHI PUMP MANUFACTURE (WUXI) CO., LTD.—See Hitachi, Ltd.; *Int'l*, pg. 3420
HITACHI QIANDIAN (HANGZHOU) TRANSFORMER CO., LTD.—See Hitachi, Ltd.; *Int'l*, pg. 3419
HITACHI RAIL ESPANA, S.L.U.—See Hitachi, Ltd.; *Int'l*, pg. 3421
HITACHI RAIL EUROPE LTD.—See Hitachi, Ltd.; *Int'l*, pg. 3417
HITACHI RAIL ITALY S.P.A—See Hitachi, Ltd.; *Int'l*, pg. 3420
HITACHI RAIL STS AUSTRALIA PTY LTD—See Hitachi, Ltd.; *Int'l*, pg. 3421
HITACHI RAIL STS MALAYSIA SDN. BHD.—See Hitachi, Ltd.; *Int'l*, pg. 3421
HITACHI RAIL STS—See Hitachi, Ltd.; *Int'l*, pg. 3417
HITACHI RAIL STS USA—See Hitachi, Ltd.; *Int'l*, pg. 3417
HITACHI REAL ESTATE PARTNERS, LTD.—See Hitachi, Ltd.; *Int'l*, pg. 3421
HITACHI SALES (MACAU) LTD.—See Hitachi, Ltd.; *Int'l*, pg. 3421
HITACHI SALES (M) SDN BHD—See Hitachi, Ltd.; *Int'l*, pg. 3414
HITACHI SALES (THAILAND), LTD.—See Hitachi, Ltd.; *Int'l*, pg. 3421
HITACHI SC, LTD.—See Hitachi, Ltd.; *Int'l*, pg. 3421
HITACHI (SHANGHAI) TRADING CO., LTD.—See Hitachi, Ltd.; *Int'l*, pg. 3413
HITACHI SISTEMA DE TRANSPORTE MEXICO, S.A. DE C.V.—See KKR & Co. Inc.; *U.S. Public*, pg. 1258
HITACHI SISTEMAS MEDICOS DO BRASIL LTDA.—See Hitachi, Ltd.; *Int'l*, pg. 3421
HITACHI SOE ELECTRIC & MACHINERY CO., LTD.—See Hitachi, Ltd.; *Int'l*, pg. 3421
HITACHI SOLUTIONS AMERICA - BUSINESS SOLUTIONS GROUP—See Hitachi, Ltd.; *Int'l*, pg. 3421
HITACHI SOLUTIONS AMERICA, LTD.—See Hitachi, Ltd.; *Int'l*, pg. 3421
HITACHI SOLUTIONS ASIA PACIFIC PTE. LTD.—See Hitachi, Ltd.; *Int'l*, pg. 3421
HITACHI SOLUTIONS (CHINA) CO., LTD.—See Hitachi, Ltd.; *Int'l*, pg. 3421
HITACHI SOLUTIONS CREATE, LTD.—See Hitachi, Ltd.; *Int'l*, pg. 3421
HITACHI SOLUTIONS EAST JAPAN, LTD.—See Hitachi, Ltd.; *Int'l*, pg. 3421
HITACHI SOLUTIONS EUROPE A.G.—See Hitachi, Ltd.; *Int'l*, pg. 3421
HITACHI SOLUTIONS EUROPE LTD.—See Hitachi, Ltd.; *Int'l*, pg. 3421
HITACHI SOLUTIONS EUROPE S.A.S—See Hitachi, Ltd.; *Int'l*, pg. 3421
HITACHI SOLUTIONS GERMANY GMBH—See Hitachi, Ltd.; *Int'l*, pg. 3421
HITACHI SOLUTIONS INDIA PRIVATE LIMITED—See Hitachi, Ltd.; *Int'l*, pg. 3421
HITACHI SOLUTIONS, LTD.—See Hitachi, Ltd.; *Int'l*, pg. 3421
HITACHI SOLUTIONS PHILIPPINES CORPORATION—See Hitachi, Ltd.; *Int'l*, pg. 3421
HITACHI SOLUTIONS TECHNOLOGY, LTD.—See Hitachi, Ltd.; *Int'l*, pg. 3421
HITACHI SOLUTIONS (THAILAND) LTD.—See Hitachi, Ltd.; *Int'l*, pg. 3421
HITACHI SOLUTIONS WEST JAPAN, LTD.—See Hitachi, Ltd.; *Int'l*, pg. 3421
HITACHI SOUTH AMERICA, ARGENTINA S.A.—See Hitachi, Ltd.; *Int'l*, pg. 3421
HITACHI STEEL CENTER CO., LTD.—See Okaya & Co., Ltd.; *Int'l*, pg. 5546
HITACHI STORAGE BATTERY (THAILAND) CO., LTD.—See Hitachi, Ltd.; *Int'l*, pg. 3421
HITACHI SUNWAY DATA CENTRE SERVICES SDN. BHD.—See Hitachi, Ltd.; *Int'l*, pg. 3421
HITACHI SUNWAY INFORMATION SYSTEMS SDN. BHD.—See Hitachi, Ltd.; *Int'l*, pg. 3421

HITACHI SUNWAY INFORMATION SYSTEMS (SINGAPORE) PTE. LTD.—See Hitachi, Ltd.; *Int'l*, pg. 3421
HITACHI SUNWAY INFORMATION SYSTEMS (THAILAND), LTD.—See Hitachi, Ltd.; *Int'l*, pg. 3421
HITACHI SYSTEMS DIGITAL SERVICES (MALAYSIA) SDN. BHD.—See Hitachi, Ltd.; *Int'l*, pg. 3421
HITACHI SYSTEMS DIGITAL SERVICES (SINGAPORE) PTE. LTD.—See Hitachi, Ltd.; *Int'l*, pg. 3421
HITACHI SYSTEMS ENGINEERING SERVICES, LTD.—See Hitachi, Ltd.; *Int'l*, pg. 3421
HITACHI SYSTEMS FIELD SERVICES, LTD.—See Hitachi, Ltd.; *Int'l*, pg. 3421
HITACHI SYSTEMS, LTD.—See Hitachi, Ltd.; *Int'l*, pg. 3422
HITACHI SYSTEMS MICRO CLINIC PVT. LTD.—See Hitachi, Ltd.; *Int'l*, pg. 3421
HITACHI SYSTEMS POWER SERVICIES, LTD.—See Hitachi, Ltd.; *Int'l*, pg. 3421
HITACHI SYSTEMS SECURITY EUROPE SA—See Hitachi, Ltd.; *Int'l*, pg. 3421
HITACHI SYSTEMS SECURITY INC.—See Hitachi, Ltd.; *Int'l*, pg. 3421
HITACHI SYSTEMS VIETNAM COMPANY LIMITED—See Hitachi, Ltd.; *Int'l*, pg. 3422
HITACHI T&D SOLUTIONS, INC.—See Hitachi, Ltd.; *Int'l*, pg. 3422
HITACHI T&D SYSTEMS ASIA PTE. LTD.—See Hitachi, Ltd.; *Int'l*, pg. 3422
HITACHI T&D SYSTEMS SAUDI ARABIA, LTD.—See Hitachi, Ltd.; *Int'l*, pg. 3422
HITACHI TECHNOLOGIES AND SERVICES LTD.—See Hitachi, Ltd.; *Int'l*, pg. 3422
HITACHI TELECOM (USA), INC.—See Hitachi, Ltd.; *Int'l*, pg. 3414
HITACHI TERMINAL MECHATRONICS, CORP.—See Hitachi, Ltd.; *Int'l*, pg. 3422
HITACHI TERMINALS MECHATRONICS PHILIPPINES CORPORATION—See Hitachi, Ltd.; *Int'l*, pg. 3422
HITACHI TERMINAL SOLUTIONS INDIA PRIVATE LIMITED—See Hitachi, Ltd.; *Int'l*, pg. 3422
HITACHI TERMINAL SOLUTIONS KOREA CO., LTD.—See Hitachi, Ltd.; *Int'l*, pg. 3422
HITACHI TERMINAL SOLUTIONS (THAILAND) COMPANY LIMITED—See Hitachi, Ltd.; *Int'l*, pg. 3422
HITACHI TRANSPORT SYSTEEM (NEDERLAND) BV—See KKH & Co. Inc.; *U.S. Public*, pg. 1258
HITACHI TRANSPORT SYSTEM (ASIA) PTE. LTD.—See KKR & Co. Inc.; *U.S. Public*, pg. 1258
HITACHI TRANSPORT SYSTEM (AUSTRALIA) PTY. LTD.—See KKR & Co. Inc.; *U.S. Public*, pg. 1258
HITACHI TRANSPORT SYSTEM (EUROPE) B.V.—See KKR & Co. Inc.; *U.S. Public*, pg. 1258
HITACHI TRANSPORT SYSTEM (EUROPE) GMBH—See KKR & Co. Inc.; *U.S. Public*, pg. 1258
HITACHI TRANSPORT SYSTEM (HONG KONG) LTD.—See KKR & Co. Inc.; *U.S. Public*, pg. 1258
HITACHI TRANSPORT SYSTEM INDIA PVT. LTD.—See KKR & Co. Inc.; *U.S. Public*, pg. 1259
HITACHI TRANSPORT SYSTEM (KOREA), LTD.—See KKR & Co. Inc.; *U.S. Public*, pg. 1258
HITACHI TRANSPORT SYSTEM (M) SDN. BHD.—See KKR & Co. Inc.; *U.S. Public*, pg. 1258
HITACHI TRANSPORT SYSTEMS (FRANCE) S.A.R.L.—See KKR & Co. Inc.; *U.S. Public*, pg. 1259
HITACHI TRANSPORT SYSTEM (SHANGHAI), LTD—See KKR & Co. Inc.; *U.S. Public*, pg. 1259
HITACHI TRANSPORT SYSTEMS LTD.—See KKR & Co. Inc.; *U.S. Public*, pg. 1259
HITACHI TRANSPORT SYSTEMS S.A.R.L.—See KKR & Co. Inc.; *U.S. Public*, pg. 1259
HITACHI TRANSPORT SYSTEM (TAIWAN) LTD.—See KKR & Co. Inc.; *U.S. Public*, pg. 1259
HITACHI TRANSPORT SYSTEM (THAILAND), LTD.—See KKR & Co. Inc.; *U.S. Public*, pg. 1259
HITACHI TRANSPORT SYSTEM (UK) LTD.—See KKR & Co. Inc.; *U.S. Public*, pg. 1259
HITACHI TRAVEL BUREAU SHANGHAI CO., LTD.—See KKR & Co. Inc.; *U.S. Public*, pg. 1259
HITACHI URBAN INVESTMENT, LTD.—See Hitachi, Ltd.; *Int'l*, pg. 3422
HITACHI URBAN SUPPORT, LTD.—See Hitachi, Ltd.; *Int'l*, pg. 3422
HITACHI VALVE, LTD.—See Proterial, Ltd.; *Int'l*, pg. 6006
HITACHI VANTARA A/S—See Hitachi, Ltd.; *Int'l*, pg. 3422
HITACHI VANTARA A/S—See Hitachi, Ltd.; *Int'l*, pg. 3422
HITACHI VANTARA (CHILE) LIMITADA—See Hitachi, Ltd.; *Int'l*, pg. 3422
HITACHI VANTARA (CHINA) CO., LTD.—See Hitachi, Ltd.; *Int'l*, pg. 3422
HITACHI VANTARA DIGITAL SOLUTIONS JAPAN, K.K.—See Hitachi, Ltd.; *Int'l*, pg. 3422
HITACHI VANTARA GMBH—See Hitachi, Ltd.; *Int'l*, pg. 3422
HITACHI VANTARA (IRELAND) LIMITED—See Hitachi, Ltd.; *Int'l*, pg. 3422
HITACHI VANTARA ISRAEL LTD.—See Hitachi, Ltd.; *Int'l*, pg. 3422
HITACHI VANTARA KENYA LIMITED—See Hitachi, Ltd.; *Int'l*, pg. 3422

HITACHI, LTD.

CORPORATE AFFILIATIONS

HITACHI VANTARA KOREA LIMITED—See Hitachi, Ltd.; *Int'l*, pg. 3422
HITACHI VANTARA LLC—See Hitachi, Ltd.; *Int'l*, pg. 3422
HITACHI VANTARA LTD.—See Hitachi, Ltd.; *Int'l*, pg. 3422
HITACHI VANTARA NIGERIA LIMITED—See Hitachi, Ltd.; *Int'l*, pg. 3422
HITACHI VANTARA OOO—See Hitachi, Ltd.; *Int'l*, pg. 3422
HITACHI VANTARA OY—See Hitachi, Ltd.; *Int'l*, pg. 3422
HITACHI VANTARA (POLSKA) SP. Z O.O.—See Hitachi, Ltd.; *Int'l*, pg. 3422
HITACHI VANTARA S.A.—See Hitachi, Ltd.; *Int'l*, pg. 3422
HITACHI VIA MECHANICS (USA), INC.—See Hitachi, Ltd.; *Int'l*, pg. 3414
HITACHI XINXIN GLOBAL LOGISTICS (HENAN) CO., LTD—See KKR & Co. Inc.; *U.S. Public*, pg. 1259
HITACHI ZOSEN CHUGOKU CONSTRUCTION WORKS CO., LTD.—See Hitachi Zosen Corporation; *Int'l*, pg. 3410
HITACHI ZOSEN CORPORATION; *Int'l*, pg. 3410
HITACHI ZOSEN CORPORATION - TOKYO OFFICE—See Hitachi Zosen Corporation; *Int'l*, pg. 3410
HITACHI ZOSEN DIESEL & ENGINEERING CO., LTD.—See Hitachi Zosen Corporation; *Int'l*, pg. 3410
HITACHI ZOSEN ENGINEERING SINGAPORE (PTE.) LTD.—See Hitachi Zosen Corporation; *Int'l*, pg. 3410
HITACHI ZOSEN EUROPE LTD.—See Hitachi Zosen Corporation; *Int'l*, pg. 3410
HITACHI ZOSEN EUROPE LTD.—See Hitachi Zosen Corporation; *Int'l*, pg. 3411
HITACHI ZOSEN FUKUI CORPORATION—See Hitachi Zosen Corporation; *Int'l*, pg. 3411
HITACHI ZOSEN FUKUI U.S.A., INC.—See Hitachi Zosen Corporation; *Int'l*, pg. 3411
HITACHI ZOSEN HANDLING SYSTEM CO., LTD.—See Hitachi Zosen Corporation; *Int'l*, pg. 3411
HITACHI ZOSEN INOVA AG—See Hitachi Zosen Corporation; *Int'l*, pg. 3411
HITACHI ZOSEN INOVA AG - SWEDEN BRANCH—See Hitachi Zosen Corporation; *Int'l*, pg. 3411
HITACHI ZOSEN INOVA AUSTRALIA PTY LTD—See Hitachi Zosen Corporation; *Int'l*, pg. 3411
HITACHI ZOSEN INOVA BIOMETHAN FRANCE S.A.R.L.—See Hitachi Zosen Corporation; *Int'l*, pg. 3411
HITACHI ZOSEN INOVA BIOMETHAN GMBH—See Hitachi Zosen Corporation; *Int'l*, pg. 3411
HITACHI ZOSEN INOVA DEUTSCHLAND GMBH—See Hitachi Zosen Corporation; *Int'l*, pg. 3411
HITACHI ZOSEN INOVA ETOGAS GMBH—See Hitachi Zosen Corporation; *Int'l*, pg. 3411
HITACHI ZOSEN INOVA KRAFTWERKSTECHNIK GMBH—See Hitachi Zosen Corporation; *Int'l*, pg. 3411
HITACHI ZOSEN INOVA RUS LLC—See Hitachi Zosen Corporation; *Int'l*, pg. 3411
HITACHI ZOSEN INOVA SLOVAKIA S.R.O.—See Hitachi Zosen Corporation; *Int'l*, pg. 3411
HITACHI ZOSEN INOVA UK LTD.—See Hitachi Zosen Corporation; *Int'l*, pg. 3411
HITACHI ZOSEN INOVA U.S.A. LLC—See Hitachi Zosen Corporation; *Int'l*, pg. 3411
HITACHI ZOSEN KRB AG—See Hitachi Zosen Corporation; *Int'l*, pg. 3411
HITACHI ZOSEN MARINE ENGINE CO., LTD.—See Hitachi Zosen Corporation; *Int'l*, pg. 3412
HITACHI-ZOSEN PLANT TECHNO-SERVICE CORPORATION—See Hitachi Zosen Corporation; *Int'l*, pg. 3411
HITACHI ZOSEN SERVICES (MALAYSIA) SDN. BHD.—See Hitachi Zosen Corporation; *Int'l*, pg. 3411
HITACHI ZOSEN SUS ENVIRONMENT TECHNOLOGY CO., LTD.—See Hitachi Zosen Corporation; *Int'l*, pg. 3412
HITACHI ZOSEN TRADING (SHANGHAI) CO., LTD.—See Hitachi Zosen Corporation; *Int'l*, pg. 3412
HITACHI ZOSEN U.S.A. LTD.—See Hitachi Zosen Corporation; *Int'l*, pg. 3411
HITACHI ZOSEN U.S.A. LTD.—See Hitachi Zosen Corporation; *Int'l*, pg. 3411
HITACHI ZOSEN VIETNAM CO., LTD.—See Hitachi Zosen Corporation; *Int'l*, pg. 3411
HITACHI ZOSEN YANGLING CO., LTD.—See Hitachi Zosen Corporation; *Int'l*, pg. 3411
HITADO GMBH—See Sysmex Corporation; *Int'l*, pg. 7388
HITAY INVESTMENT HOLDINGS A.S.; *Int'l*, pg. 3425
HITCENTS—See Houchens Industries, Inc.; *U.S. Private*, pg. 1990
HITCHCOCK AUTOMOTIVE RESOURCES; *U.S. Private*, pg. 1952
HITCHCOCK CHAIR COMPANY LTD.; *U.S. Private*, pg. 1952
HITCHCOCK CHAIR COMPANY LTD. - STILL RIVER ANTIQUES DIVISION—See Hitchcock Chair Company Ltd.; *U.S. Private*, pg. 1952
HITCHCOCK FLEMING & ASSOCIATES, INC.; *U.S. Private*, pg. 1952
HITCHCOCK HEALTHCARE, INC.—See Universal Health Services, Inc.; *U.S. Public*, pg. 2258
HITCHCOCK SHOES, INC.; *U.S. Private*, pg. 1953

HITCHED WEDDINGS & EVENTS LLC—See Minted LLC.; *U.S. Private*, pg. 2745
HITCHEN FOODS LTD—See Bakkavor Group plc; *Int'l*, pg. 806
HITCH ENTERPRISES INC.; *U.S. Private*, pg. 1952
HITCH FEEDERS INC.—See Hitch Enterprises Inc.; *U.S. Private*, pg. 1952
HITCHINER FRANCE—See Hitchiner Manufacturing Company Inc.; *U.S. Private*, pg. 1953
HITCHINER MANUFACTURING COMPANY DE MEXICO S. DE R.L. DE C.V.—See Hitchiner Manufacturing Company Inc.; *U.S. Private*, pg. 1953
HITCHINER MANUFACTURING COMPANY INC. - FERROUS DIVISION—See Hitchiner Manufacturing Company Inc.; *U.S. Private*, pg. 1953
HITCHINER MANUFACTURING COMPANY INC.; *U.S. Private*, pg. 1953
HITCHINER S.A. DE C.V.—See Hitchiner Manufacturing Company Inc.; *U.S. Private*, pg. 1953
HITCHING POST INC.; *U.S. Private*, pg. 1953
HITCH PORK PRODUCERS, INC.—See Hitch Enterprises Inc.; *U.S. Private*, pg. 1952
HITCO CARBON COMPOSITES, INC.—See SGL Carbon SE; *Int'l*, pg. 6742
HI-TEC ESPANA S.A.—See Hi-Tec Sports PLC; *Int'l*, pg. 3381
HI-TECH ASSET PROTECTION PROPRIETARY LIMITED—See CSG Holdings Limited; *Int'l*, pg. 1864
HITECH ASSETS LLC—See Caretta Partners, LLC; *U.S. Private*, pg. 754
HI-TECH CARE, INC.—See Amedisys, Inc.; *U.S. Public*, pg. 94
HI-TECH COLOR, INC.—See Dainichiseika Color & Chemicals Mfg. Co., Ltd.; *Int'l*, pg. 1939
HI-TECH COLOR (SHANGHAI) CO., LTD.—See Dainichiseika Color & Chemicals Mfg. Co., Ltd.; *Int'l*, pg. 1939
HI-TECH COMPONENT DISTRIBUTORS; *U.S. Private*, pg. 1932
HI-TECH CONCRETE PRODUCTS LLC—See Alpha Dhabi Holding PJSC; *Int'l*, pg. 367
HI-TECH CONSTRUCTION COMPANY; *U.S. Private*, pg. 1932
HITECH CORPORATION LTD.; *Int'l*, pg. 3425
HITECH & DEVELOPMENT WIRELESS SWEDEN HOLDING AB; *Int'l*, pg. 3425
HI-TECH DURAVENT, INC.—See Smiths Group plc; *Int'l*, pg. 7009
HI-TECH ELECTRIC INC.; *U.S. Private*, pg. 1932
HI-TECH ELECTRONIC MANUFACTURING, INC.; *U.S. Private*, pg. 1932
HI-TECH FABRICATION INC.; *U.S. Private*, pg. 1932
HI-TECH FABRICATION LTD.—See Manoir Industries; *Int'l*, pg. 4675
HI-TECH FIBER GROUP CORPORATION—See China Hi-Tech Group Co., Ltd.; *Int'l*, pg. 1507
HI-TECH GEARS LTD; *Int'l*, pg. 3381
HITECH GROUP AUSTRALIA LIMITED - HITECH PERSONNEL DIVISION—See HiTech Group Australia Limited; *Int'l*, pg. 3425
HITECH GROUP AUSTRALIA LIMITED; *Int'l*, pg. 3425
HI-TECH HEALTHCARE; *U.S. Private*, pg. 1932
HI-TECH HOME; *U.S. Private*, pg. 1932
HI TECH HONEYCOMB INC.; *U.S. Private*, pg. 1931
HI-TECH INSTRUMENTS SDN BHD—See HORIBA Ltd; *Int'l*, pg. 3477
HI-TECH LUBRICANTS LTD.; *Int'l*, pg. 3381
HI-TECH METALS, INC.—See ESCO Technologies, Inc.; *U.S. Public*, pg. 794
HI-TECH MOLD & ENGINEERING; *U.S. Private*, pg. 1932
HI-TECH NELSPRUIT PROPRIETARY LIMITED—See CSG Holdings Limited; *Int'l*, pg. 1864
HI-TECH NITTSU (THAILAND) CO., LTD.—See Nippon Express Holdings, Inc.; *Int'l*, pg. 5316
HITEC HOLDING B.V.—See Air Water Inc.; *Int'l*, pg. 240
HI-TECH PIPES LTD.; *Int'l*, pg. 3382
HI-TECH POLYMER (CHINA) INC.—See K & P International Holdings Limited; *Int'l*, pg. 4037
HI-TECH PRECISION INDUSTRIAL LIMITED—See K & P International Holdings Limited; *Int'l*, pg. 4037
HITECH PRINT SYSTEMS LTD.—See Anjani Portland Cement Ltd.; *Int'l*, pg. 472
HITECHPROS S.A.; *Int'l*, pg. 3425
HI-TECH RUBBER PRODUCTS CO., LTD.—See Inabata & Co. Ltd.; *Int'l*, pg. 3643
HITECH SEMICONDUCTOR (WUXI) CO., LTD.—See Wuxi Taiji Industry Co., Ltd.; *Int'l*, pg. 8516
HI-TECH SERVICES & SUPPLIES LLC—See Al Hassan Engineering Company S.A.O.G.; *Int'l*, pg. 279
HITECH SPORTS PTY LTD—See Hi-Tec Sports PLC; *Int'l*, pg. 3381
HI-TECH SPRAY EQUIPMENT, S.A.—See Graco, Inc.; *U.S. Public*, pg. 953
HITECH STAGES LTD.; *Int'l*, pg. 3425
HI-TECH STEEL SERVICES LTD.; *Int'l*, pg. 3382
HI-TECH WINDING SYSTEMS LTD.; *Int'l*, pg. 3382
HITEC, INC.—See CVC Capital Partners SICAV-FIS S.A.; *Int'l*, pg. 1885
HI TECMETAL GROUP, INC.; *U.S. Private*, pg. 1931

HI-TEC NEDERLAND BV—See Hi-Tec Sports PLC; *Int'l*, pg. 3381
THE HITE COMPANY; *U.S. Private*, pg. 4053
HITEC POWER PROTECTION (BEIJING) CO., LTD.—See Air Water Inc.; *Int'l*, pg. 240
HITEC POWER PROTECTION B.V.—See Air Water Inc.; *Int'l*, pg. 240
HITEC POWER PROTECTION IBERICA S.L.—See Air Water Inc.; *Int'l*, pg. 240
HITEC POWER PROTECTION LTD.—See Air Water Inc.; *Int'l*, pg. 240
HITEC POWER PROTECTION (MALAYSIA) SDN. BHD.—See Air Water Inc.; *Int'l*, pg. 240
HITEC POWER PROTECTION TAIWAN LTD.—See Air Water Inc.; *Int'l*, pg. 240
HITECS B.V.—See Fluor Corporation; *U.S. Public*, pg. 860
HITEC SENSOR SOLUTIONS, INC.—See Bridgepoint Group Plc; *Int'l*, pg. 1155
HI-TEC SPORTS CANADA LTD.—See Hi-Tec Sports PLC; *Int'l*, pg. 3381
HI-TEC SPORTS INTERNATIONAL HOLDINGS B.V.—See Apex Global Brands Inc.; *U.S. Private*, pg. 292
HI-TEC SPORTS PLC; *Int'l*, pg. 3381
HI-TEC SPORTS USA, INC.—See Hi-Tec Sports PLC; *Int'l*, pg. 3381
HITEC SYSTEMS CORPORATION—See CAC Holdings Corporation; *Int'l*, pg. 1247
HITEC VASTGOED B.V.—See Air Water Inc.; *Int'l*, pg. 240
HITECVISION AS; *Int'l*, pg. 3425
HITE ELECTRIC TECHNOLOGY CO., LTD.—See Sonepar S.A.; *Int'l*, pg. 7091
HITE JINRO CO., LTD. - CHEONGJU DISTILLERY FACTORY—See Hite Jinro Co., Ltd.; *Int'l*, pg. 3425
HITE JINRO CO., LTD. - GANGWON BREWERY FACTORY—See Hite Jinro Co., Ltd.; *Int'l*, pg. 3425
HITE JINRO CO., LTD. - ICHEON DISTILLERY FACTORY—See Hite Jinro Co., Ltd.; *Int'l*, pg. 3425
HITE JINRO CO., LTD. - IKSAN DISTILLERY FACTORY—See Hite Jinro Co., Ltd.; *Int'l*, pg. 3425
HITE JINRO CO., LTD. - JEONJU BREWERY FACTORY—See Hite Jinro Co., Ltd.; *Int'l*, pg. 3425
HITE JINRO CO., LTD. - MASAN BREWERY FACTORY—See Hite Jinro Co., Ltd.; *Int'l*, pg. 3425
HITE JINRO CO., LTD.; *Int'l*, pg. 3425
HITEJINRO HOLDINGS CO., LTD.; *Int'l*, pg. 3426
HITEK GLOBAL, INC.; *Int'l*, pg. 3426
HI-TEK INTERNATIONAL INC.—See TOWA Corporation; *Int'l*, pg. 7849
HITEK LIMITED—See Diploma PLC; *Int'l*, pg. 2128
HITEK POWER LTD. U.K.—See Advanced Energy Industries, Inc.; *U.S. Public*, pg. 47
HI TEMP INSULATION INC.; *U.S. Private*, pg. 1931
HITENDRA NAGAR SAHAKARI VASAHAT LTD.—See Mazda Ltd; *Int'l*, pg. 4748
HIT ENTERTAINMENT, INC.—See Mattel, Inc.; *U.S. Public*, pg. 1398
HIT ENTERTAINMENT LTD.—See Mattel, Inc.; *U.S. Public*, pg. 1398
HITEVISION CO., LTD.; *Int'l*, pg. 3426
HI-TEX FOUNDED BY TEFRON LTD.—See Tefron Ltd.; *Int'l*, pg. 7520
HITEX GMBH—See Infineon Technologies AG; *Int'l*, pg. 3685
HITEX (UK) LIMITED—See Infineon Technologies AG; *Int'l*, pg. 3685
HIT FRISCHE GMBH & CO. KG—See Dohle Handelsgruppe Holding GmbH & Co. KG; *Int'l*, pg. 2155
HITGEN INC.; *Int'l*, pg. 3426
HIT HANDELSGRUPPE GMBH & CO. KG—See Dohle Handelsgruppe Holding GmbH & Co. KG; *Int'l*, pg. 2155
HITHINK ROYALFLUSH INFORMATION NETWORK CO., LTD.; *Int'l*, pg. 3426
HITI DIGITAL AMERICA, INC.—See HiTi Digital Inc.; *Int'l*, pg. 3426
HITI DIGITAL EUROPE S.R.L—See HiTi Digital Inc.; *Int'l*, pg. 3426
HITI DIGITAL INC.; *Int'l*, pg. 3426
HITI DIGITAL, INC.—See HiTi Digital Inc.; *Int'l*, pg. 3426
HITI DIGITAL SINGAPORE PTE LTD—See HiTi Digital Inc.; *Int'l*, pg. 3426
HITI DIGITAL (SUZHOU), INC.—See HiTi Digital Inc.; *Int'l*, pg. 3426
HITIM GROUP; *Int'l*, pg. 3426
HIT, INC.; *U.S. Private*, pg. 1952
HITIQ LIMITED; *Int'l*, pg. 3426
HITIT AYAKKABI SAAT MUCEVHERAT TURIZM INSAAT PETROL SAN. VE TIC. LTD.STI.—See Hitit Holding A.S.; *Int'l*, pg. 3426
HITIT CONSTRUCTION COMPANY—See Hitit Holding A.S.; *Int'l*, pg. 3427
HITIT GOLD KUYUMCULUK VE MUCEVHERAT SAN. VE TIC. A.S.—See Hitit Holding A.S.; *Int'l*, pg. 3426
HITIT HOLDING A.S.; *Int'l*, pg. 3426
HITIT MODA TASARIM MAGAZACLK GIYIM MUCEVHERAT SAN.TIC.LTD.STI.—See Hitit Holding A.S.; *Int'l*, pg. 3427
HIT KIT GLOBAL SOLUTIONS LIMITED; *Int'l*, pg. 3408
HITMA BV—See Indutrade AB; *Int'l*, pg. 3679

COMPANY NAME INDEX

HITMA FILTRATIE B.V.—See Indutrade AB; *Int'l*, pg. 3679
HITMA INSTRUMENTATIE B.V.—See Indutrade AB; *Int'l*, pg. 3679
HITMA INSTRUMENTATIE B.V.—See Indutrade AB; *Int'l*, pg. 3679
HITMA PROCESS B.V.—See Indutrade AB; *Int'l*, pg. 3679
HITMA ULTRAPURE B.V.—See Indutrade AB; *Int'l*, pg. 3679
HITO COMMUNICATIONS HOLDINGS, INC.; *Int'l*, pg. 3427
HITO-COMMUNICATIONS, INC.—See Nomura Holdings, Inc.; *Int'l*, pg. 5412
HITOOLS INC.—See Infineon Technologies AG; *Int'l*, pg. 3685
HITOPS INC.; *U.S. Private*, pg. 1953
HIT PROMOTIONAL PRODUCTS INC.; *U.S. Private*, pg. 1952
HITRADIO RTL SACHSEN GMBH—See Bertelsmann SE & Co. KGaA; *Int'l*, pg. 994
HIT RADIO VERONICA—See Bertelsmann SE & Co. KGaA; *Int'l*, pg. 994
HITRA VIND AS—See Statkraft AS; *Int'l*, pg. 7185
HITRON SYSTEMS INC. - CHINA FACTORY—See Hitron Systems Inc.; *Int'l*, pg. 3427
HITRON SYSTEMS INC.; *Int'l*, pg. 3427
HITRON TECHNOLOGIES AMERICAS INC.—See Hitron Technologies Inc.; *Int'l*, pg. 3427
HITRON TECHNOLOGIES EUROPE HOLDING B.V.—See Hitron Technologies Inc.; *Int'l*, pg. 3427
HITRON TECHNOLOGIES INC.; *Int'l*, pg. 3427
HITRON TECHNOLOGIES (SIP) INC.—See Hitron Technologies Inc.; *Int'l*, pg. 3427
HITS, INC; *U.S. Private*, pg. 1953
HITTAPUNKTSE AB—See Sponsor Capital Oy; *Int'l*, pg. 7142
HITT CONTRACTING, INC.; *U.S. Private*, pg. 1953
HITTCO TOOLS LIMITED; *Int'l*, pg. 3427
HIT UNION COMPANY LTD.; *Int'l*, pg. 3408
HIT WELDING INDUSTRY CO., LTD.; *Int'l*, pg. 3408
HITZ ENVIRONMENT SERVICE COMPANY LIMITED—See Hitachi Zosen Corporation; *Int'l*, pg. 3411
HITZ ENVIRONMENT TAKAMATSU CO., LTD.—See Hitachi Zosen Corporation; *Int'l*, pg. 3411
HITZ HOLDINGS U.S.A. INC.—See Hitachi Zosen Corporation; *Int'l*, pg. 3411
HITZINGER GMBH—See Dr. Aichhorn GmbH; *Int'l*, pg. 2190
HITZINGER UK LIMITED—See Dr. Aichhorn GmbH; *Int'l*, pg. 2190
HI-VAC CORPORATION; *U.S. Private*, pg. 1932
HIVE BLOCKCHAIN TECHNOLOGIES LTD.; *Int'l*, pg. 3427
HIVECREATION CO., LTD.—See Sega Sammy Holdings, Inc.; *Int'l*, pg. 6680
HIVELOCITY VENTURES CORP.; *U.S. Private*, pg. 1953
HIVEN OY—See Orion Corporation; *Int'l*, pg. 5631
HIVEST CAPITAL PARTNERS SAS; *Int'l*, pg. 3427
HIVI ACOUSTICS TECHNOLOGY CO., LTD.; *Int'l*, pg. 3427
HIVIEW LOGISTICS CO., LTD.—See T3EX Global Holdings Corp.; *Int'l*, pg. 7398
HI-VIEW RESOURCES INC.; *Int'l*, pg. 3382
HIVINT PTY LIMITED—See Temasek Holdings (Private) Limited; *Int'l*, pg. 7553
HIWA ROTTERDAM PORT COLD STORES B.V.—See Nichirei Corporation; *Int'l*, pg. 5270
HIWAVE (HONG KONG) LIMITED—See FLAT Audio Technologies, LLC; *U.S. Private*, pg. 1541
HI-WAY 9 EXPRESS LTD.—See Mullen Group Ltd.; *Int'l*, pg. 5080
HI-WAY CO., LTD.—See TISCO Financial Group Public Company Limited; *Int'l*, pg. 7758
HI-WAY EQUIPMENT COMPANY INC.—See Midwesco Industries Inc.; *U.S. Private*, pg. 2719
HIWAY TEXTILES LIMITED—See Fountain Set (Holdings) Limited; *Int'l*, pg. 2754
HIWIN GMBH—See Hiwin Technologies Corp.; *Int'l*, pg. 3427
HIWIN JAPAN—See Hiwin Technologies Corp.; *Int'l*, pg. 3427
HIWIN MIKROSYSTEM CORP.; *Int'l*, pg. 3427
HIWIN SINGAPORE PTE. LTD.—See Hiwin Technologies Corp.; *Int'l*, pg. 3427
HIWIN S.R.L.—See Hiwin Technologies Corp.; *Int'l*, pg. 3427
HIWIN S.R.O.—See Hiwin Technologies Corp.; *Int'l*, pg. 3427
HIWIN TECHNOLOGIES CORP.; *Int'l*, pg. 3427
HIWIN USA—See Hiwin Technologies Corp.; *Int'l*, pg. 3427
HI-WIRE LTD (GLASGOW)—See Nexans S.A.; *Int'l*, pg. 5242
HIW-KC ORLANDO, LLC—See Highwoods Properties, Inc.; *U.S. Public*, pg. 1035
HIXARDT TECHNOLOGIES, INC.; *U.S. Private*, pg. 1953
HIXSON AUTOPLEX OF ALEXANDRIA; *U.S. Private*, pg. 1953
HIXSON FORD MONROE; *U.S. Private*, pg. 1953
HIXSON LUMBER SALES, INC.; *U.S. Private*, pg. 1953

HIYES INTERNATIONAL CO., LTD.; *Int'l*, pg. 3427
HIZEAERO CO.,LTD.; *Int'l*, pg. 3427
H. JASON JONES & CO. LIMITED—See Kensington Court Limited; *Int'l*, pg. 4128
H.J. BAKER & BRO., INC.; *U.S. Private*, pg. 1834
H.J. BAKER & BRO., INC. - SULPHUR PLANT—See H.J. Baker & Bro., Inc.; *U.S. Private*, pg. 1834
H.J. BERKHOUT VERSSNIJLIJN BV—See What's Cooking Group NV; *Int'l*, pg. 8396
H & J CHEVROLET INC.—See Gill Automotive Group, Inc.; *U.S. Private*, pg. 1700
HJEMMET MORTENSEN AS; *Int'l*, pg. 3428
H. JESSEN JURGENSEN AB—See Beijer Ref AB; *Int'l*, pg. 944
H. JESSEN JURGENSEN A/S—See Beijer Ref AB; *Int'l*, pg. 944
HJ FOUNDATION, INC.—See Keller Group plc; *Int'l*, pg. 4119
H.J. HATFIELD & SONS LIMITED—See The Stanley Gibbons Group Plc; *Int'l*, pg. 7688
H.J. HEINZ BELGIUM N.V.—See 3G Capital Inc.; *U.S. Private*, pg. 9
H.J. HEINZ BELGIUM N.V.—See Berkshire Hathaway Inc.; *U.S. Public*, pg. 317
H.J. HEINZ B.V.—See 3G Capital Inc.; *U.S. Private*, pg. 9
H.J. HEINZ B.V.—See Berkshire Hathaway Inc.; *U.S. Public*, pg. 317
H.J. HEINZ COMPANY AUSTRALIA LTD.—See 3G Capital Inc.; *U.S. Private*, pg. 9
H.J. HEINZ COMPANY AUSTRALIA LTD.—See Berkshire Hathaway Inc.; *U.S. Public*, pg. 317
H.J. HEINZ COMPANY (IRELAND) LIMITED—See 3G Capital Inc.; *U.S. Private*, pg. 10
H.J. HEINZ COMPANY (IRELAND) LIMITED—See Berkshire Hathaway Inc.; *U.S. Public*, pg. 317
H.J. HEINZ COMPANY LIMITED—See 3G Capital Inc.; *U.S. Private*, pg. 10
H.J. HEINZ COMPANY LIMITED—See Berkshire Hathaway Inc.; *U.S. Public*, pg. 317
H.J. HEINZ COMPANY, L.P.—See 3G Capital Inc.; *U.S. Private*, pg. 9
H.J. HEINZ COMPANY, L.P.—See Berkshire Hathaway Inc.; *U.S. Public*, pg. 317
H.J. HEINZ COMPANY OF CANADA LTD.—See 3G Capital Inc.; *U.S. Private*, pg. 9
H.J. HEINZ COMPANY OF CANADA LTD.—See Berkshire Hathaway Inc.; *U.S. Public*, pg. 317
H.J. HEINZ CR/SR A.S.—See 3G Capital Inc.; *U.S. Private*, pg. 9
H.J. HEINZ CR/SR A.S.—See Berkshire Hathaway Inc.; *U.S. Public*, pg. 317
H.J. HEINZ FINANCE UK PLC—See 3G Capital Inc.; *U.S. Private*, pg. 10
H.J. HEINZ FINANCE UK PLC—See Berkshire Hathaway Inc.; *U.S. Public*, pg. 318
H.J. HEINZ FOODSERVICE—See 3G Capital Inc.; *U.S. Private*, pg. 10
H.J. HEINZ FOODSERVICE—See Berkshire Hathaway Inc.; *U.S. Public*, pg. 317
H.J. HEINZ FRANCE S.A.S.—See 3G Capital Inc.; *U.S. Private*, pg. 10
H.J. HEINZ FRANCE S.A.S.—See Berkshire Hathaway Inc.; *U.S. Public*, pg. 317
H.J. HEINZ FROZEN & CHILLED FOODS LIMITED—See 3G Capital Inc.; *U.S. Private*, pg. 10
H.J. HEINZ FROZEN & CHILLED FOODS LIMITED—See Berkshire Hathaway Inc.; *U.S. Public*, pg. 317
H.J. HEINZ GMBH—See 3G Capital Inc.; *U.S. Private*, pg. 10
H.J. HEINZ GMBH—See Berkshire Hathaway Inc.; *U.S. Public*, pg. 317
HJ HEINZ POLSKA SP. Z O.O.—See 3G Capital Inc.; *U.S. Private*, pg. 10
HJ HEINZ POLSKA SP. Z O.O.—See Berkshire Hathaway Inc.; *U.S. Public*, pg. 317
HJ HOLDINGS, INC.—See Nippon Television Holdings Inc.; *Int'l*, pg. 5356
H&J INC.—See The Hagadone Corporation; *U.S. Private*, pg. 4041
H.J. KALIKOW & CO. LLC; *U.S. Private*, pg. 1834
HJM ENTERPRISES, INC.—See BMS CAT, Inc.; *U.S. Private*, pg. 601
H.J. OLDENKAMP CO.; *U.S. Private*, pg. 1834
H.J. RUSSELL & COMPANY; *U.S. Private*, pg. 1834
HJS CONDIMENTS LIMITED—See Hayleys PLC; *Int'l*, pg. 3291
HJ SHIPBUILDING & CONSTRUCTION COMPANY, LTD.; *Int'l*, pg. 3428
HJS MOTOREN GMBH—See 2G Energy AG; *Int'l*, pg. 5
H.J. TINSLEY & CO. LIMITED—See Morgan Advanced Materials plc; *Int'l*, pg. 5041
HJT STEEL TOWER (AUSTRALIA) PTY. LTD.—See Qingdao Huijintong Power Equipment Co., Ltd.; *Int'l*, pg. 6144
HJULEX AB—See Addtech AB; *Int'l*, pg. 133
H.J. WALKER OIL CO. INC.; *U.S. Private*, pg. 1834
HK01 COMPANY LIMITED—See Nan Hai Corporation Limited; *Int'l*, pg. 5137
HK ACQUISITION CORPORATION; *Int'l*, pg. 3428

HKA ENTERPRISES, LLC—See Cenergy Partners LLC; *U.S. Private*, pg. 808
HKA GLOBAL HOLDINGS LTD—See PAI Partners S.A.S.; *Int'l*, pg. 5700
HKA GLOBAL LTD—See PAI Partners S.A.S.; *Int'l*, pg. 5700
HK AMERICA INC.—See HK Co., Ltd.; *Int'l*, pg. 3428
HK ASIA HOLDINGS LTD.; *Int'l*, pg. 3428
HK BATTERY TECHNOLOGY, INC.; *U.S. Public*, pg. 1042
HKB KETELBOUW BV—See Viessmann Werke GmbH & Co. KG; *Int'l*, pg. 8196
HKBN LTD.—See Hong Kong Technology Venture Company Limited; *Int'l*, pg. 3467
H.K. CASTINGS, INC.—See Hatch & Kirk, Inc.; *U.S. Private*, pg. 1879
HK CHINA GROUP LIMITED—See SEMIKRON International GmbH; *Int'l*, pg. 6705
HKC (HOLDINGS) LIMITED; *Int'l*, pg. 3428
HKC INTERNATIONAL HOLDINGS LIMITED; *Int'l*, pg. 3428
HKC INTERNATIONAL (THAILAND) CO. LTD.—See HKC International Holdings Limited; *Int'l*, pg. 3428
HK CO., LTD.; *Int'l*, pg. 3428
H-K CONTRACTORS INC.; *U.S. Private*, pg. 1824
HKC TECHNOLOGY LIMITED—See HKC International Holdings Limited; *Int'l*, pg. 3428
HKC TECHNOLOGY (SHANGHAI) CO. LTD.—See HKC International Holdings Limited; *Int'l*, pg. 3428
HKDP COMMUNICATIONS & PUBLIC AFFAIRS—See WPP plc; *Int'l*, pg. 8477
HKDP COMMUNICATIONS & PUBLIC AFFAIRS—See WPP plc; *Int'l*, pg. 8477
HKE HOLDINGS LTD.; *Int'l*, pg. 3428
HK ELECTRIC INVESTMENTS LIMITED; *Int'l*, pg. 3428
H & K EQUIPMENT COMPANY INC.—See Diamond Group Inc.; *U.S. Private*, pg. 1223
HK FAMILY CLINIC & SURGERY PTE. LTD.—See New Silkroutes Group Limited; *Int'l*, pg. 5227
HKFE CLEARING CORPORATION LIMITED—See Hong Kong Exchanges & Clearing Limited; *Int'l*, pg. 3466
HK FIBRE SDN. BHD.—See HHRG Berhad; *Int'l*, pg. 3379
HK FINANCIAL—See Pure Financial Advisors, Inc.; *U.S. Private*, pg. 3305
HKF INC.; *U.S. Private*, pg. 1953
HKFOODS PLC; *Int'l*, pg. 3428
HK GLOBAL TRADING LTD.; *U.S. Private*, pg. 1953
HK GRAPHENE TECHNOLOGY CORPORATION; *U.S. Public*, pg. 1042
H&K GRAPHICS; *U.S. Private*, pg. 1823
HK GUA MUSANG SDN. BHD.—See HHRG Berhad; *Int'l*, pg. 3379
HKH HOLDINGS SDN. BHD.—See Keck Seng (Malaysia) Berhad; *Int'l*, pg. 4114
HK HOLDINGS (NO.1) LIMITED—See Heidelberg Materials AG; *Int'l*, pg. 3311
HK IMMOBILIEN GMBH—See Storskogen Group AB; *Int'l*, pg. 7227
HK INNO.N CORP.; *Int'l*, pg. 3428
HK INSTRUMENTS OY—See Investment AB Latour; *Int'l*, pg. 3781
HK JINGQUANHUA DEVELOPMENT LTD.—See Shenzhen JingQuanHua Electronics Co., Ltd.; *Int'l*, pg. 6814
HK KITARAN SDN. BHD.—See HHRG Berhad; *Int'l*, pg. 3379
HK KOMGRAP AD; *Int'l*, pg. 3428
H.K. LANE PALM DESERT, INC.; *U.S. Private*, pg. 1835
HKL (ESPLANADE) PTE LIMITED—See Jardine Matheson Holdings Limited; *Int'l*, pg. 3910
HKL (PRINCE'S BUILDING) LTD.—See Hong Kong Land Holdings Ltd.; *Int'l*, pg. 3466
HKL (THAI DEVELOPMENTS) LIMITED—See Hong Kong Land Holdings Ltd.; *Int'l*, pg. 3466
HKL (VIETNAM) CONSULTANCY & MANAGEMENT COMPANY LIMITED—See Hong Kong Land Holdings Ltd.; *Int'l*, pg. 3466
H&K MATERIALS—See Haines & Kibblehouse Inc.; *U.S. Private*, pg. 1841
HKM INC.; *U.S. Private*, pg. 1953
HKNET COMPANY LIMITED—See Nippon Telegraph & Telephone Corporation; *Int'l*, pg. 5344
HKN, INC.; *U.S. Public*, pg. 1042
HKN, INC.; *U.S. Private*, pg. 1953
H. KRAMER & CO.; *U.S. Private*, pg. 1824
HK RESOURCES, LLC—See Battalion Oil Corp.; *U.S. Public*, pg. 279
HKR INTERNATIONAL LIMITED; *Int'l*, pg. 3429
HKSCAN DENMARK A/S—See HKFoods Plc; *Int'l*, pg. 3429
HKSCAN FINLAND OY—See HKFoods Plc; *Int'l*, pg. 3429
HKSCAN LATVIA AS—See HKFoods Plc; *Int'l*, pg. 3429
HKSCAN SWEDEN AB—See HKFoods Plc; *Int'l*, pg. 3429
HKSCC NOMINEES LIMITED—See Hong Kong Exchanges & Clearing Limited; *Int'l*, pg. 3466
HKS CO., LTD.; *Int'l*, pg. 3429
HKS ENTERPRISES INC.; *U.S. Private*, pg. 1953
HKS EUROPE, LTD.—See HKS CO., LTD.; *Int'l*, pg. 3429
HKS, INC.; *U.S. Private*, pg. 1953
HKS METALS B.V.—See Alfa Acciai SpA; *Int'l*, pg. 307

HKS, INC.   CORPORATE AFFILIATIONS

HKS METALS B.V.—See CRONIMET Holding GmbH; *Int'l*, pg. 1855
HKS METALS B.V.—See RETHMANN AG & Co. KG; *Int'l*, pg. 6307
HK SPORTS & GOLF AKTIEBOLAG—See Frasers Group plc; *Int'l*, pg. 2765
HKS-PROZESSTECHNIK GMBH—See Enovis Corporation; *U.S. Public*, pg. 773
HKS SCRAP METALS B.V.—See Alfa Acciai SpA; *Int'l*, pg. 307
HKS SCRAP METALS B.V.—See CRONIMET Holding GmbH; *Int'l*, pg. 1855
HKS SCRAP METALS B.V.—See RETHMANN AG & Co. KG; *Int'l*, pg. 6307
HKS (SHANGHAI) TRADING CO., LTD—See HKS CO., LTD.; *Int'l*, pg. 3429
HKS TECHNICAL FACTORY CO., LTD.—See HKS CO., LTD.; *Int'l*, pg. 3429
HKS (THAILAND) CO., LTD.—See HKS CO.,LTD.; *Int'l*, pg. 3429
HKT GLOBAL (SINGAPORE) PTE. LTD.—See Pacific Century Group Holdings Limited; *Int'l*, pg. 5686
HK TRACKS (WUXI) CO. LTD.—See Heungkuk Metaltech Co., Ltd.; *Int'l*, pg. 3366
HKTT LIMITED—See Open Up Group Inc; *Int'l*, pg. 5598
HKT TRUST & HKT LIMITED—See Pacific Century Group Holdings Limited; *Int'l*, pg. 5686
H.K. WENTWORTH (INDIA) PRIVATE LIMITED—See Element Solutions Inc.; *U.S. Public*, pg. 726
H.K. WENTWORTH LIMITED—See Element Solutions Inc.; *U.S. Public*, pg. 726
H.K. WENTWORTH PTY LIMITED—See Element Solutions Inc.; *U.S. Public*, pg. 726
H.K. WIRING SYSTEMS, LTD.—See Sumitomo Electric Industries, Ltd.; *Int'l*, pg. 7284
HK WUSEJIE GROUP CO. LTD.; *Int'l*, pg. 3428
HKX INC.—See Diploma PLC; *Int'l*, pg. 2128
HK XZJ DIGITAL CO., LTD.—See Supreme Electronics Co., Ltd.; *Int'l*, pg. 7340
HL 93—See Vivendi SE; *Int'l*, pg. 8272
HLA COMPANY INC.; *U.S. Private*, pg. 1954
HLA CONTAINER SERVICES PTE. LTD.—See LHN Limited; *Int'l*, pg. 4477
HLA CORP., LTD.; *Int'l*, pg. 3430
HL ACQUISITIONS CORP.; *U.S. Public*, pg. 1042
HLADNJACA A.D.; *Int'l*, pg. 3430
HL ADVANCE TECHNOLOGIES (M) SDN. BHD.—See HLT Global Berhad; *Int'l*, pg. 3431
HLAVINKA EQUIPMENT COMPANY; *U.S. Private*, pg. 1954
HLB AZERBAIJAN LLC; *Int'l*, pg. 3430
HLB BIOSTEP CO., LTD.; *Int'l*, pg. 3430
HLB CHILE - CONSULTORES Y AUDITORES DE EMPRESAS LTDA.; *Int'l*, pg. 3430
HLB CINNAMON, JANG, WILLOUGHBY & CO.; *Int'l*, pg. 3430
HLB DEUTSCHLAND GMBH; *Int'l*, pg. 3430
HLB EL SALVADOR, S.A. DE C.V.; *Int'l*, pg. 3430
HLB GLOBAL CO LTD; *Int'l*, pg. 3430
HLB INC.; *Int'l*, pg. 3430
HLB INNOVATION CO.,LTD; *Int'l*, pg. 3430
HLB INTERNATIONAL LIMITED; *Int'l*, pg. 3430
HLB LIFE SCIENCE CO.,LTD.; *Int'l*, pg. 3430
H & L BLOOM, INC.; *U.S. Private*, pg. 1822
HLB MANN JUDD AUSTRALASIAN ASSOCIATION; *Int'l*, pg. 3430
HLB MANN JUDD (WA) PTY LTD—See HLB Mann Judd Australasian Association; *Int'l*, pg. 3430
HLB PANAGENE CO., LTD.; *Int'l*, pg. 3430
HLB PHARMACEUTICAL CO LTD; *Int'l*, pg. 3430
HLB TECHNOLOGIES (MUMBAI) PRIVATE LIMITED; *Int'l*, pg. 3430
HLB (THAILAND) LTD.; *Int'l*, pg. 3430
HLB THERAPEUTICS CO., LTD.; *Int'l*, pg. 3431
HLB UKRAINE LLC; *Int'l*, pg. 3431
HLB USA, INC.; *U.S. Private*, pg. 1954
HL CAPITAL CORP.—See Zurn Elkay Water Solutions Corporation; *U.S. Public*, pg. 2413
H.L. CHAPMAN PIPELINE CONSTRUCTION, INC.—See Quanta Services, Inc.; *U.S. Public*, pg. 1751
H & L CHEVROLET, INC.; *U.S. Private*, pg. 1822
HLC, INC.—See MiddleGround Management, LP; *U.S. Private*, pg. 2712
HL CLINIC PTE. LTD.—See New Silkroutes Group Limited; *Int'l*, pg. 5227
HL CORP - HANDLEBAR DIVISION—See HL CORP.; *Int'l*, pg. 3429
HL CORP (HONG KONG) LIMITED—See HL CORP.; *Int'l*, pg. 3429
HL CORP - MEDICAL EQUIPMENT DIVISION—See HL CORP.; *Int'l*, pg. 3429
HL CORP.; *Int'l*, pg. 3429
HL CORP - SPORTING GOODS AND FITNESS DIVISION—See HL CORP.; *Int'l*, pg. 3429
HL CORP (TAICANG)—See HL CORP.; *Int'l*, pg. 3429
HL CORP (USA) , INC.—See HL CORP.; *Int'l*, pg. 3429
HLD ASSOCIES SA; *Int'l*, pg. 3431
HL DERMAHEALTH AESTHETIC CLINIC PTE. LTD.—See New Silkroutes Group Limited; *Int'l*, pg. 5227

HL D&I HALLA CORPORATION—See Halla Group; *Int'l*, pg. 3229
HL DISPLAY AB—See Ratos AB; *Int'l*, pg. 6218
HL DISPLAY (ASIA) PTE LTD.—See Ratos AB; *Int'l*, pg. 6219
HL DISPLAY AUSTRALIA PTY LTD.—See Ratos AB; *Int'l*, pg. 6219
HL DISPLAY BELGIUM NV—See Ratos AB; *Int'l*, pg. 6219
HL DISPLAY BENELUX B.V.—See Ratos AB; *Int'l*, pg. 6219
HL DISPLAY CESKA REPUBLIKA S.R.O.—See Ratos AB; *Int'l*, pg. 6219
HL DISPLAY DEUTSCHLAND GMBH—See Ratos AB; *Int'l*, pg. 6219
HL DISPLAY D.O.O.—See Ratos AB; *Int'l*, pg. 6219
HL DISPLAY D.O.O.—See Ratos AB; *Int'l*, pg. 6219
HL DISPLAY ESPANA S.L—See Ratos AB; *Int'l*, pg. 6219
HL DISPLAY FALKENBERG AB—See Ratos AB; *Int'l*, pg. 6219
HL DISPLAY FRANCE SAS—See Ratos AB; *Int'l*, pg. 6219
HL DISPLAY HOLDING AB—See Ratos AB; *Int'l*, pg. 6218
HL DISPLAY HONG KONG LTD—See Ratos AB; *Int'l*, pg. 6219
HL DISPLAY INDIA PVT LTD—See Ratos AB; *Int'l*, pg. 6219
HL DISPLAY KARLSKOGA AB—See Ratos AB; *Int'l*, pg. 6219
HL DISPLAY KOREA CO LTD—See Ratos AB; *Int'l*, pg. 6219
HL DISPLAY LATVIA SIA—See Ratos AB; *Int'l*, pg. 6219
HL DISPLAY LTD STI—See Ratos AB; *Int'l*, pg. 6219
HL DISPLAY MALAYSIA SDN BHD—See Ratos AB; *Int'l*, pg. 6219
HL DISPLAY MIDDLE EAST JLT—See Ratos AB; *Int'l*, pg. 6219
HL DISPLAY NEDERLAND BV—See Ratos AB; *Int'l*, pg. 6219
HL DISPLAY NORGE A/S—See Ratos AB; *Int'l*, pg. 6219
HL DISPLAY OOO—See Ratos AB; *Int'l*, pg. 6219
HL DISPLAY OSTERREICH GMBH—See Ratos AB; *Int'l*, pg. 6219
HL DISPLAY POLSKA SP. Z O.O.—See Ratos AB; *Int'l*, pg. 6219
HL DISPLAY ROMANIA SRL—See Ratos AB; *Int'l*, pg. 6219
HL DISPLAY (SHANGHAI) CO LTD—See Ratos AB; *Int'l*, pg. 6219
HL DISPLAY SLOVENSKO S.R.O.—See Ratos AB; *Int'l*, pg. 6219
HL DISPLAY SUNDSVALL AB—See Ratos AB; *Int'l*, pg. 6219
HL DISPLAY SUOMI OY—See Ratos AB; *Int'l*, pg. 6219
HL DISPLAY SUZHOU LTD—See Ratos AB; *Int'l*, pg. 6219
HL DISPLAY SVERIGE AB—See Ratos AB; *Int'l*, pg. 6219
HL DISPLAY SWIZERLAND AG—See Ratos AB; *Int'l*, pg. 6219
HL DISPLAY TAIWAN LTD—See Ratos AB; *Int'l*, pg. 6219
HL DISPLAY (THAILAND) LTD.—See Ratos AB; *Int'l*, pg. 6219
HLE CONSTRUCTION & ENGINEERING SDN. BHD.—See Chasen Holdings Limited; *Int'l*, pg. 1457
H. LEE MOFFITT CANCER CENTER & RESEARCH INSTITUTE; *U.S. Private*, pg. 1824
THE H. LEFF ELECTRIC COMPANY; *U.S. Private*, pg. 4040
HLE GLASCOAT LIMITED; *Int'l*, pg. 3431
H L EQUIPMENTS INC.—See HLE Glascoat Limited; *Int'l*, pg. 3431
HL FAMILY CLINIC & SURGERY (BEDOK) PTE. LTD.—See New Silkroutes Group Limited; *Int'l*, pg. 5227
HL FARM CORP.—See Liebherr-International AG; *Int'l*, pg. 4489
HLF COLOMBIA LTD.—See Herbalife Nutrition Ltd.; *Int'l*, pg. 3359
HL FINANCES SARL—See Vivendi SE; *Int'l*, pg. 8272
H&L GARAGES LIMITED; *Int'l*, pg. 3191
HLG HEALTH COMMUNICATIONS; *U.S. Private*, pg. 1954
HL GLOBAL ENTERPRISES LIMITED; *Int'l*, pg. 3429
HLH AGRICULTURE (CAMBODIA) CO., LTD.—See Hong Lai Huat Group Limited; *Int'l*, pg. 3467
HLH AGRI INTERNATIONAL PTE LTD—See Hong Lai Huat Group Limited; *Int'l*, pg. 3467
HLH AGRI R&D PTE LTD—See Hong Lai Huat Group Limited; *Int'l*, pg. 3467
HL HAMBURGER LEISTUNGSFUTTER GMBH—See AGRAVIS Raiffeisen AG; *Int'l*, pg. 215
HLH DEVELOPMENT PTE LTD—See Hong Lai Huat Group Limited; *Int'l*, pg. 3467
HLH GLOBAL TRADING PTE LTD—See Hong Lai Huat Group Limited; *Int'l*, pg. 3467
HLHI (CAMBODIA) CO., LTD.—See Hong Lai Huat Group Limited; *Int'l*, pg. 3467
H & L HIGH-TECH MOULD (THAILAND) CO., LTD.—See Kumpulan H & L High-Tech Berhad; *Int'l*, pg. 4331
HL HOLDINGS CORPORATION—See Halla Group; *Int'l*, pg. 3229
H.L. HUDSON FURNITURE INC.; *U.S. Private*, pg. 1835

HLI-HUME MANAGEMENT COMPANY—See Hong Leong Investment Holdings Pte. Ltd.; *Int'l*, pg. 3468
H-LINE OGILVY COMMUNICATIONS CO LTD—See WPP plc; *Int'l*, pg. 8490
H-LINE OGILVY COMMUNICATIONS CO LTD—See WPP plc; *Int'l*, pg. 8490
HLI SOLUTIONS, INC.—See AIP, LLC; *U.S. Private*, pg. 134
HLK BIOTECH HOLDING GROUP, INC.; *U.S. Public*, pg. 1042
HL KOMM TELEKOMMUNIKATIONS GMBH—See Morgan Stanley; *U.S. Public*, pg. 1473
HL MANDO CO, LTD.—See Halla Group; *Int'l*, pg. 3229
HLM DU COTENTIN; *Int'l*, pg. 3431
H&L MESABI COMPANY; *U.S. Private*, pg. 1823
HLM MANAGEMENT CO., INC.; *U.S. Private*, pg. 1954
HLM MANAGEMENT CO., LLC—See HLM Management Co., Inc.; *U.S. Private*, pg. 1954
HL MULTI-FAMILY HOLDINGS, LLC—See Howard Hughes Holdings Inc.; *U.S. Public*, pg. 1060
HLN METAL (SHENZHEN) CO., LTD.—See Sinjia Land Limited; *Int'l*, pg. 6945
HLN METAL (SUZHOU) CO., LTD—See Sinjia Land Limited; *Int'l*, pg. 6945
HLN RUBBER PRODUCTS PTE. LTD.; *Int'l*, pg. 3431
HLN (SUZHOU) RUBBER PRODUCTS CO., LTD.—See HLN Rubber Products Pte. Ltd.; *Int'l*, pg. 3431
HLN TECHNOLOGIES SDN BHD—See Sinjia Land Limited; *Int'l*, pg. 6945
H. LOIDL WURSTPRODUKTIONS- UND VERTRIEBSGESELLSCHAFT M.B.H. & CO. KG—See Raiffeisenlandesbank Oberosterreich Aktiengesellschaft; *Int'l*, pg. 6187
HL OPERATING LLC—See Samsonite International S.A.; *Int'l*, pg. 6510
HLP (CHINA) LIMITED—See Hang Lung Group Limited; *Int'l*, pg. 3245
HL PLASTICS LTD.—See Quanex Building Products Corp.; *U.S. Public*, pg. 1749
HLP TREASURY SERVICES LIMITED—See Hang Lung Group Limited; *Int'l*, pg. 3245
HLRB BROILER FARM SDN. BHD.—See Huat Lai Resources Berhad; *Int'l*, pg. 3514
HLRB PROCESSING SDN. BHD.—See Huat Lai Resources Berhad; *Int'l*, pg. 3514
HL RUBBER INDUSTRIES SDN. BHD.—See HLT Global Berhad; *Int'l*, pg. 3431
HL SCIENCE CO., LTD.; *Int'l*, pg. 3430
HLS CZECH S. R. O.—See Midea Group Co., Ltd.; *Int'l*, pg. 4884
HLS ELECTRONICS PTE LTD—See Enviro-Hub Holdings Ltd.; *Int'l*, pg. 2454
HLS INGENIEURBURO GMBH—See Midea Group Co., Ltd.; *Int'l*, pg. 4884
HLSP LIMITED—See Mott MacDonald Group Ltd.; *Int'l*, pg. 5055
HL S.R.L.—See El.En. S.p.A.; *Int'l*, pg. 2342
HLS THERAPEUTICS, INC.; *Int'l*, pg. 3431
HLTC INC; *U.S. Private*, pg. 1954
HL TECH SP. Z O.O.—See Hargreaves Lansdown PLC; *Int'l*, pg. 3274
HLT GLOBAL BERHAD; *Int'l*, pg. 3431
HL THORNE & CO., LTD.; *Int'l*, pg. 3430
H&L TOOL COMPANY, INC.—See Chicago Rivet & Machine Company; *U.S. Public*, pg. 488
H&L TOOTH COMPANY; *U.S. Private*, pg. 1823
H. LUNDBECK AB—See Lundbeckfonden; *Int'l*, pg. 4581
H. LUNDBECK A/S LUMSAS—See Lundbeckfonden; *Int'l*, pg. 4581
H. LUNDBECK A/S - SAUDI ARABIA—See Lundbeckfonden; *Int'l*, pg. 4581
H. LUNDBECK AS—See Lundbeckfonden; *Int'l*, pg. 4581
H. LUNDBECK A/S—See Lundbeckfonden; *Int'l*, pg. 4581
HLV LTD.; *Int'l*, pg. 3431
HLW INTERNATIONAL LLP; *U.S. Private*, pg. 1954
HLW INTERNATIONAL LLP—See HLW International LLP; *U.S. Private*, pg. 1954
HLW INTERNATIONAL LTD.—See HLW International LLP; *U.S. Private*, pg. 1954
HMA AGRO INDUSTRIES LIMITED; *Int'l*, pg. 3431
HMA BAYFLITE SERVICES, LLC—See Community Health Systems, Inc.; *U.S. Public*, pg. 553
HMA SANTA ROSA MEDICAL CENTER, INC.—See Community Health Systems, Inc.; *U.S. Public*, pg. 553
HMB CONSTRUCTION AB—See AF Gruppen ASA; *Int'l*, pg. 184
HMB CONSTRUCTION OREBRO AB—See AF Gruppen ASA; *Int'l*, pg. 184
HMB, SPOL. S R.O.—See FERMAT Group, a.s.; *Int'l*, pg. 2639
HMC ADVERTISING LLC; *U.S. Private*, pg. 1954
HMC CAPITAL LIMITED; *Int'l*, pg. 3431
HMC CONSULTING (SHANGHAI) CO. LTD—See Hospitality Marketing Concepts, Inc.; *U.S. Private*, pg. 1987
HMC CORPORATION—See HMC Corp.; *U.S. Private*, pg. 1955
HMC CORP.; *U.S. Private*, pg. 1954
HMC GATEWAY, INC.—See Host Hotels & Resorts, Inc.; *U.S. Public*, pg. 1055

COMPANY NAME INDEX

HMC HOME HEALTH, LLC—See UnitedHealth Group Incorporated; *U.S. Public*, pg. 2245
HMC INVESTORS, LLC—See Harbert Management Corporation; *U.S. Private*, pg. 1858
HM.CLAUSE ITALIA S.P.A.—See Groupe Limagrain Holding SA; *Int'l*, pg. 3108
HMCM, INC.—See FONAR Corporation; *U.S. Public*, pg. 863
HMC NGL LP—See Host Hotels & Resorts, Inc.; *U.S. Public*, pg. 1055
H&M COMPANY INC.; *U.S. Private*, pg. 1823
H & M CONSTRUCTORS CO.; *U.S. Private*, pg. 1822
HMC POLYMERS COMPANY LIMITED—See LyondellBasell Industries N.V.; *Int'l*, pg. 4608
H.M. CRAGG CO.; *U.S. Private*, pg. 1835
HMD TRANSPORT, INC.; *U.S. Private*, pg. 1955
H.M. DUNN COMPANY INC.; *U.S. Private*, pg. 1835
HME CONSTRUCTION, INC.—See Ukpeagvik Inupiat Corporation; *U.S. Private*, pg. 4275
HME, INC.—See Valley Truck Parts, Inc.; *U.S. Private*, pg. 4335
HM ELECTRONICS INCORPORATED; *U.S. Private*, pg. 1954
H. MEYER DAIRY—See Capitol Peak Partners, LLC; *U.S. Private*, pg. 744
H. MEYER DAIRY—See KKR & Co. Inc.; *U.S. Public*, pg. 1242
HMF MAKINA VE SERVIS SAN. VE TIC. A.S—See Nigbas Nigde Beton Sanayi ve Ticaret A.S.; *Int'l*, pg. 5282
HMG/COURTLAND PROPERTIES, INC.; *U.S. Public*, pg. 1042
HMG GROUP; *U.S. Private*, pg. 1955
HMG HARDCHROME PTY. LTD.—See Sime Darby Berhad; *Int'l*, pg. 6928
HM GORAZDZE PREFABRYKACJA SP.Z.O.O.—See Heidelberg Materials AG; *Int'l*, pg. 3311
HMG-PCMS LIMITED—See Arthur J. Gallagher & Co.; *U.S. Public*, pg. 205
HM GRAPHICS INC.—See Color Ink, Inc.; *U.S. Private*, pg. 972
H&M HENNES LTD—See H&M Hennes & Mauritz AB, *Int'l*, pg. 3192
H&M HENNES & MAURITZ AB; *Int'l*, pg. 3192
H&M HENNES & MAURITZ A.E.—See H&M Hennes & Mauritz AB; *Int'l*, pg. 3192
H&M HENNES & MAURITZ AS—See H&M Hennes & Mauritz AB; *Int'l*, pg. 3192
H&M HENNES & MAURITZ A/S—See H&M Hennes & Mauritz AB; *Int'l*, pg. 3192
H&M HENNES & MAURITZ BELGIUM NV—See H&M Hennes & Mauritz AB; *Int'l*, pg. 3192
H&M HENNES & MAURITZ B.V. & CO.KG—See H&M Hennes & Mauritz AB; *Int'l*, pg. 3192
H & M HENNES & MAURITZ CZ, S.R.O.—See H&M Hennes & Mauritz AB; *Int'l*, pg. 3192
H&M HENNES & MAURITZ FAR EAST LTD—See H&M Hennes & Mauritz AB; *Int'l*, pg. 3192
H&M HENNES & MAURITZ GESMBH—See H&M Hennes & Mauritz AB; *Int'l*, pg. 3192
H&M HENNES & MAURITZ (HK) LTD—See H&M Hennes & Mauritz AB; *Int'l*, pg. 3192
H&M HENNES & MAURITZ HOLDING BV—See H&M Hennes & Mauritz AB; *Int'l*, pg. 3192
H&M HENNES & MAURITZ INC.—See H&M Hennes & Mauritz AB; *Int'l*, pg. 3192
H&M HENNES & MAURITZ INTERNATIONAL B.V.—See H&M Hennes & Mauritz AB; *Int'l*, pg. 3192
H & M HENNES & MAURITZ LLP—See H&M Hennes & Mauritz AB; *Int'l*, pg. 3192
H & M HENNES & MAURITZ LOGISTICS AB CO. KG—See H&M Hennes & Mauritz AB; *Int'l*, pg. 3192
H & M HENNES & MAURITZ LOGISTICS GBC NV—See H&M Hennes & Mauritz AB; *Int'l*, pg. 3192
H & M HENNES & MAURITZ LOGISTICS GBC—See H&M Hennes & Mauritz AB; *Int'l*, pg. 3192
H & M HENNES & MAURITZ LOGISTICS SP. Z.O.O.—See H&M Hennes & Mauritz AB; *Int'l*, pg. 3192
H&M HENNES & MAURITZ LP—See H&M Hennes & Mauritz AB; *Int'l*, pg. 3192
H & M HENNES & MAURITZ MANAGEMENT B.V.—See H&M Hennes & Mauritz AB; *Int'l*, pg. 3192
H&M HENNES & MAURITZ NETHERLANDS BV—See H&M Hennes & Mauritz AB; *Int'l*, pg. 3192
H&M HENNES & MAURITZ OY—See H&M Hennes & Mauritz AB; *Int'l*, pg. 3192
H&M HENNES & MAURITZ SARL—See H&M Hennes & Mauritz AB; *Int'l*, pg. 3192
H&M HENNES & MAURITZ SA—See H&M Hennes & Mauritz AB; *Int'l*, pg. 3192
H&M HENNES & MAURITZ SP.Z.O.O.—See H&M Hennes & Mauritz AB; *Int'l*, pg. 3192
H&M HENNES & MAURITZ S.R.L.—See H&M Hennes & Mauritz AB; *Int'l*, pg. 3192
H & M HENNES & MAURITZ TR TEKSTIL LTD SIRKETI—See H&M Hennes & Mauritz AB; *Int'l*, pg. 3192
H&M HENNES & MAURITZ UK LTD.—See H&M Hennes & Mauritz AB; *Int'l*, pg. 3192

H&M HENNES & MAURITZ USA BV—See H&M Hennes & Mauritz AB; *Int'l*, pg. 3192
H & M HENNES & MAURITZ VIETNAM LLC—See H&M Hennes & Mauritz AB; *Int'l*, pg. 3192
HMH INTERNATIONAL, INC.—See Vivendi SE; *Int'l*, pg. 8271
HMH PUBLISHERS LLC—See Veritas Capital Fund Management, LLC; *U.S. Private*, pg. 4363
HMIA PTY LTD—See Steadfast Group Limited; *Int'l*, pg. 7187
HMI BUYING GROUP INC.; *U.S. Private*, pg. 1955
HMI CONSTRUCTION INC.—See ANDRITZ AG; *Int'l*, pg. 455
HMI ELECTRIC—See Heavy Machines, Inc.; *U.S. Private*, pg. 1902
HMIH CEDAR CREST, LLC—See Acadia Healthcare Company, Inc.; *U.S. Public*, pg. 29
HMI INDUSTRIES INC.; *U.S. Private*, pg. 1955
HMI INSTITUTE OF HEALTH SCIENCES PTE. LTD.—See EQT AB; *Int'l*, pg. 2475
H&M INDUSTRIAL SERVICE INC.—See H&M Company Inc.; *U.S. Private*, pg. 1823
HMIN, INC.—See Corporate Partners LLC; *U.S. Private*, pg. 1055
HM INSURANCE GROUP, INC.—See Highmark Health; *U.S. Private*, pg. 1940
HM INTERNATIONAL HOLDINGS LIMITED; *Int'l*, pg. 3431
HM INTERNATIONAL; *U.S. Private*, pg. 1954
H&M INTERNATIONAL TRANSPORTATION INC.; *U.S. Private*, pg. 1823
HM INWEST S.A.; *Int'l*, pg. 3431
HMIS, INC.—See Hillenbrand, Inc.; *U.S. Public*, pg. 1035
HMI SP. Z O O.—See Munchener Ruckversicherungs AG; *Int'l*, pg. 5088
HMJ INC.; *U.S. Private*, pg. 1955
HMK AUTOMATION GROUP LIMITED; *Int'l*, pg. 3431
HMK ENTERPRISES, INC.; *U.S. Private*, pg. 1955
HMK INSURANCE—See Genstar Capital, LLC; *U.S. Private*, pg. 1674
HML ANDERTONS LIMITED—See HML Holdings plc; *Int'l*, pg. 3432
HML HOLDINGS PLC; *Int'l*, pg. 3432
HM LIFE INSURANCE COMPANY—See Highmark Health; *U.S. Private*, pg. 1940
HML SHAW LIMITED—See HML Holdings plc; *Int'l*, pg. 3432
HM MANAGEMENT COMPANY INC; *U.S. Private*, pg. 1954
H.M. MARKETING RESEARCH, INC.—See Macromill Embrain Co., Ltd.; *Int'l*, pg. 4632
HMM CO., LTD.; *Int'l*, pg. 3432
H & M MECHANICAL, INC.—See Comfort Systems USA, Inc.; *U.S. Public*, pg. 544
H & M METALS, LLC—See OEP Capital Advisors, L.P.; *U.S. Private*, pg. 2999
HMN FINANCIAL, INC.—See Alerus Financial Corporation; *U.S. Public*, pg. 75
HMN INC.; *U.S. Private*, pg. 1955
HMO LUXEMBOURG S.A.R.L.—See maxingvest ag; *Int'l*, pg. 4741
HMO MISSOURI, INC.—See Elevance Health, Inc.; *U.S. Public*, pg. 730
HMO OF LOUISIANA, INC.—See Louisiana Health Service & Indemnity Company, Inc.; *U.S. Private*, pg. 2499
H.M. PALLHUBER GMBH & CO. KG—See Orlando Management AG; *Int'l*, pg. 5639
HM PLANT LTD.—See Hitachi, Ltd.; *Int'l*, pg. 3415
HMP PROPERTIES, INC.—See JPMorgan Chase & Co.; *U.S. Public*, pg. 1207
HMR ACQUISITION COMPANY INC.; *U.S. Private*, pg. 1955
HM RETAILINGS CO., LTD.—See Yamano Holdings Corporation; *Int'l*, pg. 8553
H&M ROWELLS AB—See H&M Hennes & Mauritz AB; *Int'l*, pg. 3192
HM ROYAL INC.; *U.S. Private*, pg. 1954
HMR PLAN LLC—See Profile Development, LLC; *U.S. Private*, pg. 3277
H&M RUBBER INC—See Recipharm AB; *Int'l*, pg. 6236
HMS BERGBAU AFRICA (PTY.) LTD.—See HMS Bergbau AG; *Int'l*, pg. 3432
HMS BERGBAU AG OIL & GAS DIVISION—See HMS Bergbau AG; *Int'l*, pg. 3432
HMS BERGBAU AG; *Int'l*, pg. 3432
HMS BERGBAU FZCO DUBAI LLC—See HMS Bergbau AG; *Int'l*, pg. 3432
HMS BERGBAU SINGAPORE (PTE.) LTD.—See HMS Bergbau AG; *Int'l*, pg. 3432
HMS BERGBAU USA CORP.—See HMS Bergbau AG; *Int'l*, pg. 3432
HM SCIENCE INC.—See China National Pharmaceutical Group Corporation; *Int'l*, pg. 1534
HM SCIENCE INC.—See Hoyu Co., Ltd.; *Int'l*, pg. 3499
HMS CORPORATE—See Videlio SA; *Int'l*, pg. 8190
HMS EMPLOYER SOLUTIONS—See Veritas Capital Fund Management, LLC; *U.S. Private*, pg. 4362
HMS ENTERPRISES INC.; *U.S. Private*, pg. 1955
HMS GLOBAL MARITIME, INC.; *U.S. Private*, pg. 1955

HMS HEALTHCARE MANAGEMENT SOLUTIONS, INC.—See HealthEdge Investment Partners, LLC; *U.S. Private*, pg. 1896
HMS HOLDINGS CORP.—See Veritas Capital Fund Management, LLC; *U.S. Private*, pg. 4362
HMSHOST CORPORATION—See Avolta AG; *Int'l*, pg. 749
HMS HYDRAULIC MACHINES & SYSTEMS GROUP PLC; *Int'l*, pg. 3432
HMS INDUSTRIAL NETWORKS AB—See HMS Networks AB; *Int'l*, pg. 3432
HMS INDUSTRIAL NETWORKS APS—See HMS Networks AB; *Int'l*, pg. 3433
HMS INDUSTRIAL NETWORKS GMBH—See HMS Networks AB; *Int'l*, pg. 3433
HMS INDUSTRIAL NETWORKS INC.—See HMS Networks AB; *Int'l*, pg. 3433
HMS INDUSTRIAL NETWORKS INDIA PRIVATE LTD.—See HMS Networks AB; *Int'l*, pg. 3433
HMS INDUSTRIAL NETWORKS K.K.—See HMS Networks AB; *Int'l*, pg. 3433
HMS INDUSTRIAL NETWORKS LTD—See HMS Networks AB; *Int'l*, pg. 3433
HMS INDUSTRIAL NETWORKS PTY. LTD.—See HMS Networks AB; *Int'l*, pg. 3433
HMS INDUSTRIAL NETWORKS SAS—See HMS Networks AB; *Int'l*, pg. 3433
HMS INDUSTRIAL NETWORKS S.R.L.—See HMS Networks AB; *Int'l*, pg. 3433
HMS INSURANCE ASSOCIATES, INC.—See Marsh & McLennan Companies, Inc.; *U.S. Public*, pg. 1380
HMS IT S.P.A.—See Cassa Depositi e Prestiti S.p.A.; *Int'l*, pg. 1355
HMS LIVHYDROMASH JSC—See HMS Hydraulic Machines & Systems Group plc; *Int'l*, pg. 3432
HMS NEFTEMASH JSC—See HMS Hydraulic Machines & Systems Group plc; *Int'l*, pg. 3432
HMS NETWORKS AB; *Int'l*, pg. 3432
H M S PRODUCTIONS, INC.—See Bruderman & Co., LLC; *U.S. Public*, pg. 671
HMS PRODUCTS CO.; *U.S. Private*, pg. 1955
HMS SERVICE CO. INC.; *U.S. Private*, pg. 1955
HMS TECHNOLOGIES, INC.; *U.S. Private*, pg. 1955
HMT AUSTRALIA PTY LTD—See Tailwind Capital Group, LLC; *U.S. Private*, pg. 3924
HMT INTERNATIONAL LIMITED—See HMT Limited; *Int'l*, pg. 3433
HMT LIMITED; *Int'l*, pg. 3433
HMT, LLC—See Tailwind Capital Group, LLC; *U.S. Private*, pg. 3924
HMT MACHINE TOOLS LIMITED—See HMT Limited; *Int'l*, pg. 3433
HMT PTE LTD.—See Tailwind Capital Group, LLC; *U.S. Private*, pg. 3924
HM TRADING GLOBAL GMBH—See Heidelberg Materials AG; *Int'l*, pg. 3311
HMT RUBBAGLAS, LTD.—See Tailwind Capital Group, LLC; *U.S. Private*, pg. 3924
HMTV, LLC—See Hemisphere Media Group, Inc.; *U.S. Private*, pg. 1913
HMTV TV DOMINICANA, LLC—See Hemisphere Media Group, Inc.; *U.S. Private*, pg. 1913
HMT (XIAMEN) NEW TECHNICAL MATERIALS CO., LTD.; *Int'l*, pg. 3433
H. MUEHLSTEIN AND CO. INC.—See Ravago Holding S.A.; *Int'l*, pg. 6222
HMV CANADA, INC.—See Hilco Trading, LLC; *U.S. Private*, pg. 1944
HMVOD LTD.; *Int'l*, pg. 3433
H&M WAGNER & SONS INC.; *U.S. Private*, pg. 1823
H.M. WHITE LLC; *U.S. Private*, pg. 1835
H&M WHOLESALE INC.; *U.S. Private*, pg. 1823
HMY, LTD.—See Hitachi, Ltd.; *Int'l*, pg. 3413
HMY YACHT SALES, INC.; *U.S. Private*, pg. 1955
HNA CAPITAL GROUP CO., LTD.—See Hainan Traffic Administration Holding Co., Ltd.; *Int'l*, pg. 3213
HNA CAPITAL HOLDING CO., LTD.—See Hainan Traffic Administration Holding Co., Ltd.; *Int'l*, pg. 3213
HNA CARGO CO., LTD.—See Hainan Traffic Administration Holding Co., Ltd.; *Int'l*, pg. 3213
HNAC TECHNOLOGY CO., LTD.; *Int'l*, pg. 3433
HNA DAJI INVESTMENT & DEVELOPMENT CO., LTD.—See Hainan Traffic Administration Holding Co., Ltd.; *Int'l*, pg. 3213
H. NAGEL & SON CO.; *U.S. Private*, pg. 1825
HNA GROUP CO., LTD.—See Hainan Traffic Administration Holding Co., Ltd.; *Int'l*, pg. 3212
HNA GROUP (HONG KONG) CO., LTD.—See Hainan Traffic Administration Holding Co., Ltd.; *Int'l*, pg. 3213
HNA INNOVATION HAINAN CO., LTD.; *Int'l*, pg. 3433
HNA INTERNATIONAL INVESTMENT HOLDINGS LIMITED; *Int'l*, pg. 3433
HNA INVESTMENT GROUP CO., LTD.; *Int'l*, pg. 3433
HNA PROPERTY MANAGEMENT CO., LTD.—See Hainan Traffic Administration Holding Co., Ltd.; *Int'l*, pg. 3213
HNA SAFE CAR RENTAL CO., LTD.—See Hainan Traffic Administration Holding Co., Ltd.; *Int'l*, pg. 3213
HNA SOUTHERN TOURISM HOLDING GROUP CO., LTD.—See Hainan Traffic Administration Holding Co., Ltd.; *Int'l*, pg. 3213

HNA INVESTMENT GROUP CO., LTD.   CORPORATE AFFILIATIONS

HNA STORKOKSSERVICE AB—See Bravida Holding AB; *Int'l*, pg. 1142
HNA TECHNOLOGY CO., LTD.—See Hainan Traffic Administration Holding Co., Ltd.; *Int'l*, pg. 3213
HNA TOPWIN FUTURES CO., LTD.—See Hainan Traffic Administration Holding Co., Ltd.; *Int'l*, pg. 3215
HN AUTOTRANSPORT N.V.—See Hoedlmayr International AG; *Int'l*, pg. 3439
HNA YAJEE PERFORMING ARTS INTERNATIONAL CO., LTD.—See Hainan Traffic Administration Holding Co., Ltd.; *Int'l*, pg. 3215
HNB ASSURANCE PLC; *Int'l*, pg. 3433
HNB GENERAL INSURANCE LIMITED—See HNB Assurance PLC; *Int'l*, pg. 3434
HNB NATIONAL BANK; *U.S. Private*, pg. 1955
H&N CHEVROLET BUICK CO. INC.; *U.S. Private*, pg. 1823
HNE HUNTLEIGH NESBIT EVANS HEALTH CARE GMBH.—See Getinge AB; *Int'l*, pg. 2951
HNE MEDICAL SA—See Getinge AB; *Int'l*, pg. 2948
H&N FOODS INTERNATIONAL, INC.; *U.S. Private*, pg. 1823
H.N. FUNKHOUSER & COMPANY INC.; *U.S. Private*, pg. 1835
HNG CAPITAL SDN BHD; *Int'l*, pg. 3434
HNG FLOAT GLASS LIMITED—See Hindusthan National Glass & Industries Limited; *Int'l*, pg. 3400
HNG STORAGE LP; *U.S. Private*, pg. 1955
HNH INTERNATIONAL LTD.; *Int'l*, pg. 3434
HNI ASIA L.L.C.—See HNI Corporation; *U.S. Public*, pg. 1043
HNI ASIA TECHNOLOGY SERVICES (SHENZHEN) LIMITED—See HNI Corporation; *U.S. Public*, pg. 1043
HNI CORPORATION; *U.S. Public*, pg. 1042
HNI OFFICE INDIA LTD.—See HNI Corporation; *U.S. Public*, pg. 1043
HNK MACHINE TOOL CO., LTD.; *Int'l*, pg. 3434
HNLC, INC.—See Douglas Emmett, Inc.; *U.S. Public*, pg. 678
HNMC, INC.—See Tenet Healthcare Corporation; *U.S. Public*, pg. 2002
HNM SYSTEMS, INC.; *U.S. Private*, pg. 1955
HNO INTERNATIONAL, INC.; *U.S. Public*, pg. 1043
HNP CAPITAL, LLC—See Financial Institutions, Inc.; *U.S. Public*, pg. 834
H&N PRINTING & GRAPHICS, INC.—See Chatham Asset Management, LLC; *U.S. Private*, pg. 862
HNR ACQUISITION CORP.; *U.S. Public*, pg. 1044
HNRY LOGISTICS, INC.—See Yellow Corporation; *U.S. Public*, pg. 2398
HNS AMERICAS COMMUNICACOES, LTDA.—See EchoStar Corporation; *U.S. Public*, pg. 711
HNS DE MEXICO S.A. DE C.V.—See EchoStar Corporation; *U.S. Public*, pg. 711
HNSPOWERTECH CORP.—See H&S HighTech Corp.; *Int'l*, pg. 3193
HNTB ARCHITECTURE—See HNTB Corporation; *U.S. Private*, pg. 1956
HNTB-ARLINGTON—See HNTB Corporation; *U.S. Private*, pg. 1956
HNTB-ATLANTA—See HNTB Corporation; *U.S. Private*, pg. 1956
HNTB-AUSTIN—See HNTB Corporation; *U.S. Private*, pg. 1956
HNTB-BATON ROUGE—See HNTB Corporation; *U.S. Private*, pg. 1956
HNTB-BOSTON—See HNTB Corporation; *U.S. Private*, pg. 1956
HNTB-CHARLOTTE—See HNTB Corporation; *U.S. Private*, pg. 1956
HNTB-COLUMBIA—See HNTB Corporation; *U.S. Private*, pg. 1957
HNTB CORPORATION - PARSIPPANY—See HNTB Corporation; *U.S. Private*, pg. 1956
HNTB CORPORATION, SANTA ANA BRANCH—See HNTB Corporation; *U.S. Private*, pg. 1956
HNTB CORPORATION; *U.S. Private*, pg. 1955
HNTB CORPORATION—See HNTB Corporation; *U.S. Private*, pg. 1956
HNTB CORPORATION—See HNTB Corporation; *U.S. Private*, pg. 1956
HNTB CORPORATION—See HNTB Corporation; *U.S. Private*, pg. 1956
HNTB-DALLAS—See HNTB Corporation; *U.S. Private*, pg. 1957
HNTB-DENVER—See HNTB Corporation; *U.S. Private*, pg. 1957
HNTB-DETROIT—See HNTB Corporation; *U.S. Private*, pg. 1957
HNTB-HARTFORD—See HNTB Corporation; *U.S. Private*, pg. 1957
HNTB-INDIANA—See HNTB Corporation; *U.S. Private*, pg. 1957
HNTB-JACKSONVILLE—See HNTB Corporation; *U.S. Private*, pg. 1957
HNTB-LOS ANGELES—See HNTB Corporation; *U.S. Private*, pg. 1957
HNTB-MADISON—See HNTB Corporation; *U.S. Private*, pg. 1957

HNTB-MIAMI—See HNTB Corporation; *U.S. Private*, pg. 1957
HNTB MICHIGAN INC—See HNTB Corporation; *U.S. Private*, pg. 1956
HNTB-MILWAUKEE—See HNTB Corporation; *U.S. Private*, pg. 1957
HNTB-MINNEAPOLIS—See HNTB Corporation; *U.S. Private*, pg. 1957
HNTB-MORGANTOWN—See HNTB Corporation; *U.S. Private*, pg. 1957
HNTB-NEW YORK—See HNTB Corporation; *U.S. Private*, pg. 1957
HNTB-OAKLAND—See HNTB Corporation; *U.S. Private*, pg. 1957
HNTB-OHIO,INC—See HNTB Corporation; *U.S. Private*, pg. 1957
HNTB-OHIO INC—See HNTB Corporation; *U.S. Private*, pg. 1957
HNTB-ORLANDO—See HNTB Corporation; *U.S. Private*, pg. 1957
HNTB-OVERLAND PARK—See HNTB Corporation; *U.S. Private*, pg. 1957
HNTB-PLANO—See HNTB Corporation; *U.S. Private*, pg. 1957
HNTB-PORTLAND—See HNTB Corporation; *U.S. Private*, pg. 1957
HNTB-RALEIGH—See HNTB Corporation; *U.S. Private*, pg. 1957
HNTB-SAINT LOUIS—See HNTB Corporation; *U.S. Private*, pg. 1957
HNTB-SALT LAKE CITY—See HNTB Corporation; *U.S. Private*, pg. 1957
HNTB-SAN ANTONIO—See HNTB Corporation; *U.S. Private*, pg. 1957
HNTB-SAN BERNARDINO—See HNTB Corporation; *U.S. Private*, pg. 1957
HNTB-SAN JOSE—See HNTB Corporation; *U.S. Private*, pg. 1957
HNTB-SANTA ANA—See HNTB Corporation; *U.S. Private*, pg. 1957
HNTB-SEATTLE—See HNTB Corporation; *U.S. Private*, pg. 1957
HNTB—See HNTB Corporation; *U.S. Private*, pg. 1956
HNTB-TAMPA—See HNTB Corporation; *U.S. Private*, pg. 1957
HNTB-TOLEDO—See HNTB Corporation; *U.S. Private*, pg. 1957
HNT (DONGGUAN) COMPANY LIMITED—See HNT Electronics Co.,Ltd; *Int'l*, pg. 3434
HNT ELECTRONICS CO.,LTD; *Int'l*, pg. 3434
HNTI LIMITED—See Northern Technologies International Corporation; *U.S. Public*, pg. 1538
H&N TRANSPORT—See Hartung Brothers Inc.; *U.S. Private*, pg. 1874
HNT (VINA) COMPANY LIMITED—See HNT Electronics Co.,Ltd; *Int'l*, pg. 3434
HNZ AUSTRALIA PTY LTD.—See PHI, Inc.; *U.S. Private*, pg. 3168
HNZ NEW ZEALAND LTD.—See PHI, Inc.; *U.S. Private*, pg. 3168
HOA AN JOINT STOCK COMPANY; *Int'l*, pg. 3435
HOA BINH 479 JOINT STOCK COMPANY—See Hoa Binh Construction Group JSC; *Int'l*, pg. 3435
HOA BINH ARCHITECTURE CO., LTD.—See Hoa Binh Construction Group JSC; *Int'l*, pg. 3435
HOA BINH CONSTRUCTION GROUP JSC; *Int'l*, pg. 3435
HOA BINH HOUSE JSC—See Hoa Binh Construction Group JSC; *Int'l*, pg. 3435
HOA BINH INFRASTRUCTURE INVESTMENT & CONSTRUCTION JSC—See Hoa Binh Construction Group JSC; *Int'l*, pg. 3435
HOA BINH MECHANICAL ELECTRICAL (HBE) JSC—See Hoa Binh Construction Group JSC; *Int'l*, pg. 3435
HOA BINH PAINT CO., LTD.—See Hoa Binh Construction Group JSC; *Int'l*, pg. 3435
HOA BINH RENEWABLE ENERGY & INVESTMENT JOINT STOCK COMPANY—See Hoa Binh Construction Group JSC; *Int'l*, pg. 3435
HOA BINH SECURITIES JOINT STOCK COMPANY; *Int'l*, pg. 3435
HOA BINH URBAN ENVIRONMENTAL SERVICES JOINT STOCK COMPANY; *Int'l*, pg. 3435
HOA CAM CONCRETE JSC; *Int'l*, pg. 3435
HOAD, INC. - SAN JUAN DIVISION—See John Wood Group PLC; *Int'l*, pg. 3984
HOAD, INC.—See John Wood Group PLC; *Int'l*, pg. 3984
HOAG HOSPITAL FOUNDATION; *U.S. Private*, pg. 1957
HOAG & SONS BOOK BINDERY INC.—See The HF Group LLC; *U.S. Private*, pg. 4052
HOAK MOTORS INC.; *U.S. Private*, pg. 1957
HOA LAM-SHANGRI-LA HEALTHCARE LTD. LIABILITY CO—See Aseana Properties Ltd.; *Int'l*, pg. 605
HOANG ANH GIA LAI JOINT STOCK COMPANY; *Int'l*, pg. 3436
HOANGHA JOINT STOCK COMPANY; *Int'l*, pg. 3436
HOANG KIM TAY NGUYEN GROUP JOINT STOCK COMPANY; *Int'l*, pg. 3436
HOANG LONG GROUP JOINT STOCK COMPANY; *Int'l*, pg. 3436

HOANG PHUC MINERAL TRADING & CONSTRUCTION JSC; *Int'l*, pg. 3436
HOANG QUAN APPRAISAL CO., LTD.—See Hoang Quan Consulting - Trading - Service Real Estate Corporation; *Int'l*, pg. 3436
HOANG QUAN BINH THUAN CONSULTING - TRADING - SERVICE REAL ESTATE CORPORATION—See Hoang Quan Consulting - Trading - Service Real Estate Corporation; *Int'l*, pg. 3436
HOANG QUAN CAN THO INVESTMENT REAL ESTATE CORPORATION—See Hoang Quan Consulting - Trading - Service Real Estate Corporation; *Int'l*, pg. 3436
HOANG QUAN CONSULTING - TRADING - SERVICE REAL ESTATE CORPORATION; *Int'l*, pg. 3436
HOAN PHARMACEUTICALS—See Bora Pharmaceuticals; *Int'l*, pg. 1112
HOANSUPPLY CO., LTD.—See Nippon Rietec Co., Ltd.; *Int'l*, pg. 5329
HOA PHAT DOOR JSC—See Hoa Phat Group Joint Stock Company; *Int'l*, pg. 3435
HOA PHAT DUNG QUAT STEEL JSC—See Hoa Phat Group Joint Stock Company; *Int'l*, pg. 3435
HOA PHAT ENERGY JSC—See Hoa Phat Group Joint Stock Company; *Int'l*, pg. 3435
HOA PHAT EQUIPMENT & ACCESSORIES CO., LTD.—See Hoa Phat Group Joint Stock Company; *Int'l*, pg. 3435
HOA PHAT FURNITURE JSC—See Hoa Phat Group Joint Stock Company; *Int'l*, pg. 3435
HOA PHAT GROUP JOINT STOCK COMPANY; *Int'l*, pg. 3435
HOA PHAT HAI DUONG STEEL JSC—See Hoa Phat Group Joint Stock Company; *Int'l*, pg. 3435
HOA PHAT HOME APPLIANCES JSC—See Hoa Phat Group Joint Stock Company; *Int'l*, pg. 3435
HOA PHAT METAL PRODUCING CO., LTD.—See Hoa Phat Group Joint Stock Company; *Int'l*, pg. 3435
HOA PHAT MINING JSC—See Hoa Phat Group Joint Stock Company; *Int'l*, pg. 3435
HOA PHAT REFRIGERATION ENGINEERING CO., LTD.—See Hoa Phat Group Joint Stock Company; *Int'l*, pg. 3435
HOA PHAT STEEL JSC—See Hoa Phat Group Joint Stock Company; *Int'l*, pg. 3435
HOA PHAT STEEL ONE MEMBER CO., LTD.—See Hoa Phat Group Joint Stock Company; *Int'l*, pg. 3435
HOA PHAT STEEL PIPE CO., LTD.—See Hoa Phat Group Joint Stock Company; *Int'l*, pg. 3435
HOA PHAT STEEL SHEET CO., LTD.—See Hoa Phat Group Joint Stock Company; *Int'l*, pg. 3435
HOA PHAT TRADING CO., LTD.—See Hoa Phat Group Joint Stock Company; *Int'l*, pg. 3435
HOA PHAT URBAN DEVELOPMENT AND CONSTRUCTION JSC—See Hoa Phat Group Joint Stock Company; *Int'l*, pg. 3435
HOAR CONSTRUCTION LLC; *U.S. Private*, pg. 1957
HOARDBURST LIMITED—See Barclays PLC; *Int'l*, pg. 862
HOARD-IT LIMITED—See Billington Holdings Plc; *Int'l*, pg. 1031
HOA SEN BINHDINH ONE MEMBER CO., LTD.—See Hoa Sen Group; *Int'l*, pg. 3436
HOA SEN BUILDING MATERIAL ONE MEMBER LIMITED LIABILITIES COMPANY—See Hoa Sen Group; *Int'l*, pg. 3436
HOA SEN GROUP; *Int'l*, pg. 3436
HOA SEN NGHE AN ONE MEMBER LIMITED LIABILITIES COMPANY—See Hoa Sen Group; *Int'l*, pg. 3436
HOA SEN NHON HOI - BINH DINH ONE MEMBER LIMITED LIABILITIES COMPANY—See Hoa Sen Group; *Int'l*, pg. 3436
HOA SEN PLASTICS JOINT STOCK COMPANY—See Hoa Sen Group; *Int'l*, pg. 3436
HOA SEN STEEL SHEET ONE MEMBER LIMITED LIABILITIES COMPANY—See Hoa Sen Group; *Int'l*, pg. 3436
HOA SEN YEN BAI BUILDING MATERIAL CO., LTD.—See Hoa Sen Group; *Int'l*, pg. 3436
HOBAN & ASSOCIATES, LLC; *U.S. Private*, pg. 1958
HOBAN RECRUITMENT PTY. LTD.—See Bain Capital, LP; *U.S. Private*, pg. 435
HOBART ANDINA S.A.S.—See Illinois Tool Works Inc.; *U.S. Public*, pg. 1103
HOBART BROTHERS COMPANY—See Illinois Tool Works Inc.; *U.S. Public*, pg. 1103
HOBART CANADA CORP.—See Illinois Tool Works Inc.; *U.S. Public*, pg. 1103
HOBART CORPORATION—See Illinois Tool Works Inc.; *U.S. Public*, pg. 1103
HOBART DAYTON MEXICANA, S. DE R.L. DE C.V.—See Illinois Tool Works Inc.; *U.S. Public*, pg. 1104
HOBART DO BRASIL LTD.—See Illinois Tool Works Inc.; *U.S. Public*, pg. 1104
HOBART ENTERPRISES LTD; *Int'l*, pg. 3436
HOBART FOOD EQUIPMENT CO., LTD.—See Illinois Tool Works Inc.; *U.S. Public*, pg. 1104
HOBART FOOD EQUIPMENT GROUP CANADA—See Illinois Tool Works Inc.; *U.S. Public*, pg. 1103
HOBART FOSTER BELGIUM B.V.B.A.—See Illinois Tool Works Inc.; *U.S. Public*, pg. 1104

COMPANY NAME INDEX

HOBART GESELLSCHAFT MIT BESCHRANKTER HAFTUNG—See Illinois Tool Works Inc.; *U.S. Public*, pg. 1103
HOBART GMBH—See Illinois Tool Works Inc.; *U.S. Public*, pg. 1104
HOBART GROUND POWER—See Illinois Tool Works Inc.; *U.S. Public*, pg. 1103
HOBART INTERNATIONAL (SINGAPORE) PTE. LTD.—See Illinois Tool Works Inc.; *U.S. Public*, pg. 1104
HOBART IVF PTY. LTD.—See Monash IVF Group Limited; *Int'l*, pg. 5025
HOBART (JAPAN) K.K.—See Illinois Tool Works Inc.; *U.S. Public*, pg. 1103
HOBART KOREA CO. LTD.—See Illinois Tool Works Inc.; *U.S. Public*, pg. 1104
HOBART NEDERLAND B.V.—See Illinois Tool Works Inc.; *U.S. Public*, pg. 1104
HOBART NEDERLAND B.V.—See Illinois Tool Works Inc.; *U.S. Public*, pg. 1104
HOBART PRIVATE HOSPITAL—See Brookfield Corporation; *Int'l*, pg. 1176
HOBART REVENUE MANAGEMENT LIMITED; *Int'l*, pg. 3437
HOBART SALES & SERVICE, INC.—See Illinois Tool Works Inc.; *U.S. Public*, pg. 1104
HOBART SCANDINAVIA APS—See Illinois Tool Works Inc.; *U.S. Public*, pg. 1104
HOBART SPECIALIST DAY HOSPITAL PTY LIMITED—See Virtus Health Limited; *Int'l*, pg. 8248
HOBART UK LIMITED—See Illinois Tool Works Inc.; *U.S. Public*, pg. 1104
HOBAS AUSTRALIA PTY. LTD.—See Knoch, Kern & Co. KG; *Int'l*, pg. 4209
HOBAS BENELUX B.V.—See Knoch, Kern & Co. KG; *Int'l*, pg. 4209
HOBAS BULGARIA EOOD—See Knoch, Kern & Co. KG; *Int'l*, pg. 4209
HOBAS CZ SPOL. S R. O.—See Knoch, Kern & Co. KG; *Int'l*, pg. 4209
HOBAS ENGINEERING GMBH—See Knoch, Kern & Co. KG; *Int'l*, pg. 4209
HOBAS ENGINEERING + ROHRE AG—See Knoch, Kern & Co. KG; *Int'l*, pg. 4209
HOBAS FRANCE SAS—See Knoch, Kern & Co. KG; *Int'l*, pg. 4209
HOBAS HUNGARIA KFT.—See Knoch, Kern & Co. KG; *Int'l*, pg. 4209
HOBAS (MALAYSIA) SDN. BHD.—See Knoch, Kern & Co. KG; *Int'l*, pg. 4209
HOBAS PIPE HONG KONG LTD.—See Knoch, Kern & Co. KG; *Int'l*, pg. 4209
HOBAS PIPE SYSTEMS SRL—See Knoch, Kern & Co. KG; *Int'l*, pg. 4209
HOBAS PIPE USA, LP—See Knoch, Kern & Co. KG; *Int'l*, pg. 4209
HOBAS QUEBEC INC.—See Knoch, Kern & Co. KG; *Int'l*, pg. 4209
HOBAS ROHRE GMBH—See Knoch, Kern & Co. KG; *Int'l*, pg. 4209
HOBAS ROHRE GMBH—See Knoch, Kern & Co. KG; *Int'l*, pg. 4209
HOBAS SCANDINAVIA AB—See Knoch, Kern & Co. KG; *Int'l*, pg. 4209
HOBAS SINGAPORE PTE. LTD.—See Knoch, Kern & Co. KG; *Int'l*, pg. 4209
HOBAS SK SPOL. S R. O.—See Knoch, Kern & Co. KG; *Int'l*, pg. 4209
HOBAS SYSTEM POLSKA SP. Z O. O.—See Knoch, Kern & Co. KG; *Int'l*, pg. 4209
HOBAS TUBI S.R.L.—See Knoch, Kern & Co. KG; *Int'l*, pg. 4209
HOBATEX GMBH—See AUCTUS Capital Partners AG; *Int'l*, pg. 700
HOBBICO, INC.; *U.S. Private*, pg. 1958
HOB BIOTECH GROUP CORP., LTD.; *Int'l*, pg. 3436
HOBBS AND ASSOCIATES INC.—See Madison Dearborn Partners, LLC; *U.S. Private*, pg. 2541
HOBBS & CURRY FAMILY LIMITED PARTNERSHIP; *U.S. Private*, pg. 1958
HOBBS INCORPORATED; *U.S. Private*, pg. 1958
HOBBY HALL SUOMI OY—See Hansapost OU; *Int'l*, pg. 3259
HOBBY LOBBY MANUFACTURING—See Hob-Lob Limited Partnership; *U.S. Private*, pg. 1958
HOBBY LOBBY STORES INC.—See Hob-Lob Limited Partnership; *U.S. Private*, pg. 1958
HOBBY-POOL TECHNOLOGIES GMBH—See BWT Aktiengesellschaft; *Int'l*, pg. 1233
HOBBYRA HOBBYRE CORPORATION—See Mitsubishi Pencil Co., Ltd.; *Int'l*, pg. 4967
HOBBY TOWN UNLIMITED, INC.; *U.S. Private*, pg. 1958
HOBBYTYME DISTRIBUTORS; *U.S. Private*, pg. 1958
HOB CO., LTD.; *Int'l*, pg. 3436
HO BEE LAND LTD; *Int'l*, pg. 3434
HOBEN INTERNATIONAL LTD.—See Goodwin PLC; *Int'l*, pg. 3041
HOB ENTERTAINMENT, INC.—See Live Nation Entertainment, Inc.; *U.S. Public*, pg. 1329

HOBERG LUXEMBOURG AG—See Groupe SFPI SA; *Int'l*, pg. 3111
HOBERG N.V.—See Groupe SFPI SA; *Int'l*, pg. 3111
HOBE SOUND GOLF CLUB, INC.; *U.S. Private*, pg. 1958
HOB HOUSE OF BEAUTY LTD.—See N.K. Shacolas (Holdings) Ltd.; *Int'l*, pg. 5116
HOBIE BAG COMPANY—See Hobie Cat Company; *U.S. Private*, pg. 1958
HOBIE CAT AUSTRALASIA PTY LTD—See Hobie Cat Company; *U.S. Private*, pg. 1958
HOBIE CAT COMPANY; *U.S. Private*, pg. 1958
HOBIE KAYAK EUROPE BV—See Hobie Cat Company; *U.S. Private*, pg. 1958
HOBI KOZMETIK IMALAT SANAYI VE—See Dabur India Ltd; *Int'l*, pg. 1903
HOBI OUTDOOR POWER EQUIPMENT—See The Pape Group, Inc.; *U.S. Private*, pg. 4090
HOB-LOB LIMITED PARTNERSHIP; *U.S. Private*, pg. 1958
HOBO CORP.—See Mitsubishi UFJ Financial Group, Inc.; *Int'l*, pg. 4971
HOBONICHI CO., LTD.; *Int'l*, pg. 3437
HOBSON FABRICATING CORPORATION; *U.S. Private*, pg. 1958
HOBSON GALVANIZING, INC.—See AZZ, Inc.; *U.S. Public*, pg. 259
HOBSONS, INC.—See Daily Mail & General Trust plc; *Int'l*, pg. 1938
HOBSONS PLC—See Daily Mail & General Trust plc; *Int'l*, pg. 1937
HOBUM OELE UND FETTE GMBH—See Vandemoortele N.V.; *Int'l*, pg. 8128
HO CHAI KUNG MEDICINE MANUFACTORY LIMITED—See Jacobson Pharma Corporation Limited; *Int'l*, pg. 3865
HOCHATOWN DIALYSIS, LLC—See DaVita Inc.; *U.S. Public*, pg. 639
HOCHDORF HOLDING AG—See HOCHDORF Holding AG; *Int'l*, pg. 3437
HOCHDORF HOLDING AG; *Int'l*, pg. 3437
HOCHDORF NUTRICARE LTD.—See HOCHDORF Holding AG; *Int'l*, pg. 3437
HOCHDORF NUTRIFOOD LTD.—See HOCHDORF Holding AG; *Int'l*, pg. 3437
HOCHDORF SWISS MILK LTD.—See HOCHDORF Holding AG; *Int'l*, pg. 3437
HOCHENG CO., LTD.—See Hocheng Corporation; *Int'l*, pg. 3437
HOCHENG CORPORATION; *Int'l*, pg. 3437
HOCHENG PHILIPPINES CORPORATION—See Hocheng Corporation; *Int'l*, pg. 3437
HOCHHEIM PRAIRIE FARM MUTUAL INSURANCE; *U.S. Private*, pg. 1958
HOCHIKI AMERICA CORPORATION—See Hochiki Corporation; *Int'l*, pg. 3437
HOCHIKI ASIA PACIFIC PTE. LTD.—See Hochiki Corporation; *Int'l*, pg. 3437
HOCHIKI AUSTRALIA PTY LTD—See Hochiki Corporation; *Int'l*, pg. 3437
HOCHIKI CORPORATION; *Int'l*, pg. 3437
HOCHIKI EUROPE (U.K.) LTD.—See Hochiki Corporation; *Int'l*, pg. 3437
HOCHIKI MIDDLE EAST FZE—See Hochiki Corporation; *Int'l*, pg. 3437
HOCHIKI SERVICIOS, S. DE R.L. DE C.V.—See Hochiki Corporation; *Int'l*, pg. 3437
HOCHIKI THAILAND CO., LTD.—See Hochiki Corporation; *Int'l*, pg. 3437
HO CHI MINH CITY INFRASTRUCTURE INVESTMENT JOINT STOCK COMPANY; *Int'l*, pg. 3434
HO CHI MINH CITY SECURITIES CORPORATION; *Int'l*, pg. 3434
HOCHKONIG BERGBAHNEN GES.M.B.H—See Erste Group Bank AG; *Int'l*, pg. 2499
HOCHLAND DEUTSCHLAND GMBH—See Hochland SE; *Int'l*, pg. 3437
HOCHLAND ESPANOLA S. A.—See Hochland SE; *Int'l*, pg. 3437
HOCHLAND NATEC GMBH—See Hochland SE; *Int'l*, pg. 3437
HOCHLAND ROMANIA SRL—See Hochland SE; *Int'l*, pg. 3437
HOCHLAND SE; *Int'l*, pg. 3437
HOCH.REIN BETEILIGUNGEN GMBH—See RWE AG; *Int'l*, pg. 6433
HOCHSCHILD MINING ARES (UK) LTD.—See Hochschild Mining plc; *Int'l*, pg. 3438
HOCHSCHILD MINING PLC; *Int'l*, pg. 3437
HOCHSCHILD MINING—See Hochschild Mining plc; *Int'l*, pg. 3438
HOCHTIEF AG—See ACS, Actividades de Construccion y Servicios, S.A.; *Int'l*, pg. 112
HOCHTIEF AKTIENGESELLSCHAFT VORM. GEBR. HELFMAN GES. M.B.H.—See ACS, Actividades de Construccion y Servicios, S.A.; *Int'l*, pg. 113
HOCHTIEF AMERICAS GMBH—See ACS, Actividades de Construccion y Servicios, S.A.; *Int'l*, pg. 113
HOCHTIEF ASIA PACIFIC GMBH—See ACS, Actividades de Construccion y Servicios, S.A.; *Int'l*, pg. 113

HOCH-TIEF-BAU IMST GESELLSCHAFT M.B.H.—See Swietelsky Baugesellschaft m.b.H.; *Int'l*, pg. 7367
HOCHTIEF CONCESSIONS AG—See ACS, Actividades de Construccion y Servicios, S.A.; *Int'l*, pg. 113
HOCHTIEF CONSTRUCCIONES S.A.—See ACS, Actividades de Construccion y Servicios, S.A.; *Int'l*, pg. 113
HOCHTIEF CONSTRUCTION AUSTRIA GMBH & CO KG—See ACS, Actividades de Construccion y Servicios, S.A.; *Int'l*, pg. 114
HOCHTIEF CZ A.S.—See ACS, Actividades de Construccion y Servicios, S.A.; *Int'l*, pg. 113
HOCHTIEF ENGINEERING GMBH—See ACS, Actividades de Construccion y Servicios, S.A.; *Int'l*, pg. 114
HOCHTIEF INFRASTRUCTURE GMBH—See ACS, Actividades de Construccion y Servicios, S.A.; *Int'l*, pg. 114
HOCHTIEF INSURANCE BROKING & RISK MANAGEMENT SOLUTIONS GMBH—See ACS, Actividades de Construccion y Servicios, S.A.; *Int'l*, pg. 114
HOCHTIEF-LUXEMBOURG S.A.—See ACS, Actividades de Construccion y Servicios, S.A.; *Int'l*, pg. 114
HOCHTIEF POLSKA SP. Z.O.O.—See ACS, Actividades de Construccion y Servicios, S.A.; *Int'l*, pg. 114
HOCHTIEF PPP SOLUTIONS GMBH—See ACS, Actividades de Construccion y Servicios, S.A.; *Int'l*, pg. 114
HOCHTIEF PPP SOLUTIONS (UK) LTD.—See ACS, Actividades de Construccion y Servicios, S.A.; *Int'l*, pg. 114
HOCHTIEF PROJEKTENTWICKLUNG GMBH—See ACS, Actividades de Construccion y Servicios, S.A.; *Int'l*, pg. 114
HOCHTIEF PROJEKTENTWICKLUNG HELFMANN PARK GMBH & CO. KG—See ACS, Actividades de Construccion y Servicios, S.A.; *Int'l*, pg. 114
HOCHTIEF SOLUTIONS AG—See ACS, Actividades de Construccion y Servicios, S.A.; *Int'l*, pg. 114
HOCHTIEF (UK) CONSTRUCTION LTD.—See ACS, Actividades de Construccion y Servicios, S.A.; *Int'l*, pg. 114
HOCHTIEF VERKEHRSWEGEBAU GMBH—See ACS, Actividades de Construccion y Servicios, S.A.; *Int'l*, pg. 114
HOCHTIEF VSB A/S—See ACS, Actividades de Construccion y Servicios, S.A.; *Int'l*, pg. 114
HOC INDUSTRIES INC.; *U.S. Private*, pg. 1958
HOCK ANN METAL SCAFFOLDING PTE. LTD.—See Union Steel Holdings Limited; *Int'l*, pg. 8053
HOCKENBERG EQUIPMENT & SUPPLY CO., INC.; *U.S. Private*, pg. 1958
HOCKENBERGS EQUIPMENT & SUPPLY CO., INC.—See Warburg Pincus LLC; *U.S. Private*, pg. 4440
HOCKENHEIM RIGID PAPER—See Sonoco Products Company; *U.S. Public*, pg. 1904
HOCKEY WESTERN NEW YORK, LLC; *U.S. Private*, pg. 1958
HOCK HENG GRANITE SDN. BHD—See DFCITY Group Berhad; *Int'l*, pg. 2094
HOCK HENG MARKETING (KL) SDN. BHD.—See DFCITY Group Berhad; *Int'l*, pg. 2094
HOCK HENG MARKETING (KL) SDN BHD—See DFCITY Group Berhad; *Int'l*, pg. 2094
HOCK HENG MARKETING (SOUTHERN REGION) SDN BHD—See DFCITY Group Berhad; *Int'l*, pg. 2094
HOCK HENG STONE (EAST COAST) SDN BHD—See DFCITY Group Berhad; *Int'l*, pg. 2094
HOCK HENG STONE—See DFCITY Group Berhad; *Int'l*, pg. 2094
HOCKING ATHENS PERRY COMMUNITY ACTION; *U.S. Private*, pg. 1959
HOCKING VALLEY BANCSHARES, INC.; *U.S. Public*, pg. 1044
HOCKING VALLEY BANK—See Hocking Valley Bancshares, Inc.; *U.S. Public*, pg. 1044
HOCK LEONG SHIPPING SDN. BHD.—See Shin Yang Shipping Corporation Berhad; *Int'l*, pg. 6838
HOCKLEY & O'DONNELL INSURANCE AGENCY, LLC—See ACNB Corporation; *U.S. Public*, pg. 35
HOCK LIAN SENG CONTRACTORS PTE LTD—See Hock Lian Seng Holdings Limited; *Int'l*, pg. 3438
HOCK LIAN SENG HOLDINGS LIMITED; *Int'l*, pg. 3438
HOCK LIAN SENG INFRASTRUCTURE PTE LTD—See Hock Lian Seng Holdings Limited; *Int'l*, pg. 3438
HOCK LIAN SENG PROPERTIES PTE. LTD.—See Hock Lian Seng Holdings Limited; *Int'l*, pg. 3438
HOCKMAN INSURANCE AGENCY, INC.—See ABRY Partners, LLC; *U.S. Private*, pg. 43
HOCKMAN-LEWIS LIMITED; *U.S. Private*, pg. 1959
HOCKS.COM, INC.—See HealthWarehouse.com, Inc.; *U.S. Public*, pg. 1017
HOCK SENG FOOD (M) SDN BHD—See Hosen Group Ltd; *Int'l*, pg. 3482
HOCK SENG FOOD PTE LTD—See Hosen Group Ltd; *Int'l*, pg. 3482
HOCK SENG LEE BERHAD; *Int'l*, pg. 3438
HOCK SIN LEONG GROUP BERHAD; *Int'l*, pg. 3438
HOCK THAI MOTOR CO.—See Bridgestone Corporation; *Int'l*, pg. 1160
HOCKWAY MIDDLE EAST FZE—See New Mountain Capital, LLC; *U.S. Private*, pg. 2899

HOCMON TRADE JOINT STOCK COMPANY; *Int'l*, pg. 3438
HOCO BETON B.V.—See Ronesans Holding A.S.; *Int'l*, pg. 6396
HOC USA INC.—See Hartwick O'shea & Cartwright Limited; *Int'l*, pg. 3280
HOD-ASSAF INDUSTRIES LTD.; *Int'l*, pg. 3438
HODDER EDUCATION LTD—See Vivendi SE; *Int'l*, pg. 8273
HODDER HEADLINE IRELAND—See Vivendi SE; *Int'l*, pg. 8273
HODDER HEADLINE LTD—See Vivendi SE; *Int'l*, pg. 8273
HODDER & STOUGHTON EDUCATIONAL LTD.—See Vivendi SE; *Int'l*, pg. 8271
HODDER & STOUGHTON LTD—See Vivendi SE; *Int'l*, pg. 8273
HODDER WAYLAND—See Vivendi SE; *Int'l*, pg. 8273
HODELL-NATCO INDUSTRIES INC.—See Nautic Partners, LLC; *U.S. Private*, pg. 2871
HODEN SEIMITSU KAKO KENKYUSHO CO., LTD.; *Int'l*, pg. 3438
HODESS CLEANROOM CONSTRUCTION, LLC; *U.S. Private*, pg. 1959
HODGDON POWDER COMPANY; *U.S. Private*, pg. 1959
HODGDON YACHT SERVICES, LLC—See Hodgdon Yachts, Inc.; *U.S. Private*, pg. 1959
HODGDON YACHTS, INC.; *U.S. Private*, pg. 1959
HODGE FOUNDRY, INC.—See Silverhawk Capital Partners, LLC; *U.S. Private*, pg. 3663
HODGEN CONSTRUCTION & DEVELOPMENT GROUP INC.; *U.S. Private*, pg. 1959
HODGES BADGE COMPANY INC.; *U.S. Private*, pg. 1959
HODGE SCHINDLER INTEGRATED COMMUNICATIONS; *U.S. Private*, pg. 1959
HODGES SUPPLY COMPANY; *U.S. Private*, pg. 1959
HODGSON AUTOMOTIVE LIMITED—See Group 1 Automotive, Inc.; *U.S. Public*, pg. 971
HODGSON CUSTOM ROLLING INC.; *Int'l*, pg. 3438
HODGSON/MEYERS ADVERTISING, INC.; *U.S. Private*, pg. 1959
HODGSON MILL, INC.—See Siemer Milling Company; *U.S. Private*, pg. 3646
HODGSON RUSS LLP; *U.S. Private*, pg. 1959
HODIJ COATINGS B.V.—See PPG Industries, Inc.; *U.S. Public*, pg. 1707
HODLMAYR LOGISTICS CZECH REPUBLIC A.S.—See Hoedlmayr International AG; *Int'l*, pg. 3439
HODLMAYR LOGISTICS GMBH—See Hoedlmayr International AG; *Int'l*, pg. 3439
HODLMAYR ZASTAVA D.O.O.—See Hoedlmayr International AG; *Int'l*, pg. 3439
HODOGAYA CHEMICAL CO., LTD. - KORIYAMA PLANT—See Hodogaya Chemical Co., Ltd.; *Int'l*, pg. 3438
HODOGAYA CHEMICAL CO., LTD. - NANYO PLANT—See Hodogaya Chemical Co., Ltd.; *Int'l*, pg. 3438
HODOGAYA CHEMICAL CO., LTD.; *Int'l*, pg. 3438
HODOGAYA CHEMICAL CO., LTD. - YOKOHAMA PLANT—See Hodogaya Chemical Co., Ltd.; *Int'l*, pg. 3438
HODOGAYA CHEMICAL EUROPE GMBH—See Hodogaya Chemical Co., Ltd.; *Int'l*, pg. 3438
HODOGAYA CHEMICAL KOREA CO., LTD.—See Hodogaya Chemical Co., Ltd.; *Int'l*, pg. 3438
HODOGAYA CHEMICAL (U.S.A.), INC.—See Hodogaya Chemical Co., Ltd.; *Int'l*, pg. 3438
HODOGAYA CONTRACT LABORATORY CO., LTD.—See Hodogaya Chemical Co., Ltd.; *Int'l*, pg. 3438
HODOGAYA LOGISTICS CO., LTD.—See Hodogaya Chemical Co., Ltd.; *Int'l*, pg. 3438
HODOGAYA (SHANGHAI) TRADING CO., LTD.—See Hodogaya Chemical Co., Ltd.; *Int'l*, pg. 3438
HODOGAYA UPL CO., LTD.—See Hodogaya Chemical Co., Ltd.; *Int'l*, pg. 3438
HODYON L.P.—See Fallbrook Technologies Inc.; *U.S. Private*, pg. 1467
HOEC BARDAHL INDIA LIMITED—See Hindustan Oil Exploration Company Ltd; *Int'l*, pg. 3400
HOECHSTETTER PRINTING—See Chatham Asset Management, LLC; *U.S. Private*, pg. 863
HOECHST GMBH—See Sanofi; *Int'l*, pg. 6550
HOECHST PAKISTAN LIMITED; *Int'l*, pg. 3439
HOEDLMAYR INTERNATIONAL AG; *Int'l*, pg. 3439
HOEDLMAYR-LAZAR ROMANIA S.R.L.—See Hoedlmayr International AG; *Int'l*, pg. 3439
HOED MYSTERY SHOPPING NEW ZEALAND LTD.—See WPP plc; *Int'l*, pg. 8462
HOED RESEARCH PTY LTD—See WPP plc; *Int'l*, pg. 8462
HOEGANAES CORPORATION EUROPE GMBH—See GKN plc; *Int'l*, pg. 2986
HOEGANAES CORP—See GKN plc; *Int'l*, pg. 2986
HOEGEMEYER HYBRIDS, INC.—See Corteva, Inc.; *U.S. Public*, pg. 584
HOEGH LNG ASIA PTE. LTD.—See Hoegh LNG Holding Ltd.; *Int'l*, pg. 3439
HOEGH LNG COLOMBIA S.A.S.—See Hoegh LNG Holding Ltd.; *Int'l*, pg. 3439

HOEGH LNG EGYPT LCC.—See Hoegh LNG Holding Ltd.; *Int'l*, pg. 3439
HOEGH LNG HOLDING LTD.; *Int'l*, pg. 3439
HOEGH LNG PARTNERS LP—See Hoegh LNG Holding Ltd.; *Int'l*, pg. 3439
HOEHN MOTORS; *U.S. Private*, pg. 1959
HOEI DENKI CO., LTD.—See Fuji Electric Co., Ltd.; *Int'l*, pg. 2812
HOEI ELECTRONICS (S) PRIVATE LTD.—See Fuji Electric Co., Ltd.; *Int'l*, pg. 2812
HOEI HONG KONG CO., LTD.—See Fuji Electric Co., Ltd.; *Int'l*, pg. 2812
HOEI INDUSTRIES CO., LTD.—See Ryobi Limited; *Int'l*, pg. 6440
HOEI PLASTICS CO., LTD.—See Fuji Electric Co., Ltd.; *Int'l*, pg. 2812
HOEI SANGYO CO., LTD.; *Int'l*, pg. 3439
HOEI SHOJI CO., LTD.—See Dowa Holdings Co., Ltd.; *Int'l*, pg. 2184
HOEK HOVENIERS B.V.; *Int'l*, pg. 3439
HOEKSTRA TRUCK EQUIPMENT COMPANY INC.; *U.S. Private*, pg. 1959
HOE LEONG CORPORATION LTD.; *Int'l*, pg. 3439
HOE LEONG MACHINERY (H.K.) LIMITED—See Hoe Leong Corporation Ltd.; *Int'l*, pg. 3439
HOEN CO., LTD.—See Howa Machinery, Ltd.; *Int'l*, pg. 3493
H.O. ENGINEERING CO., LTD.—See Okaya & Co., Ltd.; *Int'l*, pg. 5546
HOENLE UV TECHNOLOGY (SHANGHAI) TRADING LTD.—See Dr. Honle AG; *Int'l*, pg. 2192
HOE PHARMACEUTICALS SDN. BHD.—See Taisho Pharmaceutical Holdings Co., Ltd; *Int'l*, pg. 7417
HOEPHARMA HOLDINGS SDN BHD—See Taisho Pharmaceutical Holdings Co., Ltd; *Int'l*, pg. 7417
HOEPPNER PHYSICAL THERAPY, LIMITED PARTNERSHIP—See U.S. Physical Therapy, Inc.; *U.S. Public*, pg. 2214
HOERBIGER ANTRIEBSTECHNIK HOLDING GMBH—See Hoerbiger Holding AG; *Int'l*, pg. 3440
HOERBIGER AUSTRALIA PTY LTD.—See Hoerbiger Holding AG; *Int'l*, pg. 3440
HOERBIGER AUTOMATISIERUNGSTECHNIK GMBH—See Hoerbiger Holding AG; *Int'l*, pg. 3440
HOERBIGER AUTOMOTIVE KOMFORTSYSTEME GMBH—See Hoerbiger Holding AG; *Int'l*, pg. 3440
HOERBIGER CANADA LTD.—See Hoerbiger Holding AG; *Int'l*, pg. 3440
HOERBIGER CORPORATION OF AMERICA, INC.—See Hoerbiger Holding AG; *Int'l*, pg. 3440
HOERBIGER DE ARGENTINA S.A.—See Hoerbiger Holding AG; *Int'l*, pg. 3440
HOERBIGER DE CHILE S.A.—See Hoerbiger Holding AG; *Int'l*, pg. 3440
HOERBIGER DE COLOMBIA LTDA.—See Hoerbiger Holding AG; *Int'l*, pg. 3440
HOERBIGER DEL ECUADOR, S.A.—See Hoerbiger Holding AG; *Int'l*, pg. 3440
HOERBIGER DRIVE TECHNOLOGY (CHANGZHOU) CO. LTD.—See Hoerbiger Holding AG; *Int'l*, pg. 3440
HOERBIGER FRANCE SAS—See Hoerbiger Holding AG; *Int'l*, pg. 3440
HOERBIGER HOLDING AG; *Int'l*, pg. 3439
HOERBIGER INDIA PRIVATE LTD.—See Hoerbiger Holding AG; *Int'l*, pg. 3440
HOERBIGER INTERNATIONAL MANAGEMENT SERVICES GMBH—See Hoerbiger Holding AG; *Int'l*, pg. 3440
HOERBIGER MICRO FLUID GMBH—See Hoerbiger Holding AG; *Int'l*, pg. 3440
HOERBIGER-ORIGA CORP.—See Hoerbiger Holding AG; *Int'l*, pg. 3440
HOERBIGER PENZBERG GMBH—See Hoerbiger Holding AG; *Int'l*, pg. 3440
HOERBIGER SERVICE EGYPT, LLC—See Hoerbiger Holding AG; *Int'l*, pg. 3440
HOERBIGER SERVICE GMBH—See Hoerbiger Holding AG; *Int'l*, pg. 3440
HOERBIGER SERVICE HUNGARIA KFT.—See Hoerbiger Holding AG; *Int'l*, pg. 3440
HOERBIGER SYNCHRONTECHNIK GMBH & CO. KG—See Hoerbiger Holding AG; *Int'l*, pg. 3440
HOERBIGER TURBOMACHINERY SERVICES B.V.B.A.—See Hoerbiger Holding AG; *Int'l*, pg. 3440
HOERBIGER VALVES (CHANGZHOU) CO., LTD.—See Hoerbiger Holding AG; *Int'l*, pg. 3440
HOERBIGER (WUXI) AUTOMATION TECHNOLOGY CO., LTD.—See Hoerbiger Holding AG; *Int'l*, pg. 3440
HOERBIGER ZANDOV S.R.O.—See Hoerbiger Holding AG; *Int'l*, pg. 3440
HOERMANN (HK) LIMITED—See Hormann KG Verkaufsgesellschaft; *Int'l*, pg. 3480
HOESCH BAUSYSTEME GESELLSCHAFT M.B.H.—See ThyssenKrupp AG; *Int'l*, pg. 7724
HOESCH BAUSYSTEME GMBH—See ThyssenKrupp AG; *Int'l*, pg. 7730
HOESCH DESIGN GMBH—See ThyssenKrupp AG; *Int'l*, pg. 7730

HOESCH HOHENLIMBURG GMBH—See ThyssenKrupp AG; *Int'l*, pg. 7730
HOESCH IMPORMOL-INDUSTRIA PORTUGUESA DE MOLAS S.A.—See ThyssenKrupp AG; *Int'l*, pg. 7732
HOESCH SCHWERTER PROFILE GMBH—See Calvi Holding S.r.l.; *Int'l*, pg. 1266
HOE SENG HUAT PTE LTD—See HupSteel Limited; *Int'l*, pg. 3538
HOETING INC.; *U.S. Private*, pg. 1959
HOEV CO., LTD—See Hoya Corporation; *Int'l*, pg. 3495
HOFD ASHVILLE PARK LLC—See Jefferies Financial Group Inc.; *U.S. Public*, pg. 1188
HOFER POWERTAIN PRODUCTS UK LTD.—See ElringKlinger AG; *Int'l*, pg. 2370
HOFER POWERTRAIN PRODUCTS GMBH—See ElringKlinger AG; *Int'l*, pg. 2370
HOFF COMPANIES INC.; *U.S. Private*, pg. 1959
HOFF COMPANIES, INC; *U.S. Private*, pg. 1959
HOFF DIAMONDS & GEMS; *U.S. Private*, pg. 1959
HOFFER PLASTICS CORPORATION; *U.S. Private*, pg. 1959
HOFFINGER INDUSTRIES, INC.; *U.S. Private*, pg. 1959
THE HOFFMAN AGENCY; *U.S. Private*, pg. 4053
THE HOFFMAN AGENCY—See The Hoffman Agency; *U.S. Private*, pg. 4053
THE HOFFMAN AGENCY—See The Hoffman Agency; *U.S. Private*, pg. 4053
THE HOFFMAN AGENCY—See The Hoffman Agency; *U.S. Private*, pg. 4053
THE HOFFMAN AGENCY—See The Hoffman Agency; *U.S. Private*, pg. 4053
THE HOFFMAN AGENCY—See The Hoffman Agency; *U.S. Private*, pg. 4053
THE HOFFMAN AGENCY—See The Hoffman Agency; *U.S. Private*, pg. 4053
THE HOFFMAN AGENCY—See The Hoffman Agency; *U.S. Private*, pg. 4053
THE HOFFMAN AGENCY—See The Hoffman Agency; *U.S. Private*, pg. 4053
HOFFMAN ARCHITECTS, P.A.; *U.S. Private*, pg. 1960
HOFFMAN BEVERAGE CO., INC.—See Old Dominion Tobacco Company Inc.; *U.S. Private*, pg. 3008
HOFFMAN BROS AUTO ELECTRIC; *U.S. Private*, pg. 1960
HOFFMAN CHRYSLER PLYMOUTH JEEP; *U.S. Private*, pg. 1960
HOFFMAN CONSTRUCTION COMPANY OF WASHINGTON—See Hoffman Corporation; *U.S. Private*, pg. 1960
HOFFMAN CORPORATION; *U.S. Private*, pg. 1960
HOFFMAN ENCLOSURES INC.—See Pentair plc; *Int'l*, pg. 5790
HOFFMAN ENGINEERING CORPORATION—See HWH Investments Limited; *Int'l*, pg. 3543
HOFFMAN ESTATES PARK DISTRICT; *U.S. Private*, pg. 1960
HOFFMAN FORD SALES INC.; *U.S. Private*, pg. 1960
HOFFMAN FUEL COMPANY OF BRIDGEPORT INC.—See Star Group, L.P.; *U.S. Public*, pg. 1937
HOFFMAN FUEL COMPANY OF DANBURY INC.—See Star Group, L.P.; *U.S. Public*, pg. 1938
HOFFMAN FUEL COMPANY OF STAMFORD—See Star Group, L.P.; *U.S. Public*, pg. 1937
HOFFMAN & HOFFMAN INC.; *U.S. Private*, pg. 1959
HOFFMAN INSTRUMENTATION SUPPLY, INC.—See Ultra Clean Holdings, Inc.; *U.S. Public*, pg. 2223
HOFFMAN/LEWIS; *U.S. Private*, pg. 1960
HOFFMAN/LEWIS—See Hoffman/Lewis; *U.S. Private*, pg. 1960
HOFFMAN MECHANICAL CORPORATION—See Hoffman Corporation; *U.S. Private*, pg. 1960
HOFFMAN MILLS INC.; *U.S. Private*, pg. 1960
HOFFMANN ARCHITECTS, INC.—See Wannemacher Jensen Architects Inc.; *U.S. Private*, pg. 4435
HOFFMANN A/S—See Veidekke ASA; *Int'l*, pg. 8148
HOFFMANN AUSTRIA QUALITATSWERKZEUGE GMBH—See SFS Group AG; *Int'l*, pg. 6738
HOFFMANN & CO. ELEKTROKOHLE AG—See Schunk GmbH; *Int'l*, pg. 6642
HOFFMANN DANMARK APS—See SFS Group AG; *Int'l*, pg. 6738
HOFFMANN DIE CAST CORPORATION; *U.S. Private*, pg. 1960
HOFFMANN ENGINEERING SERVICES GMBH—See SFS Group AG; *Int'l*, pg. 6738
HOFFMANN ESSEN QUALITATSWERKZEUGE GMBH—See SFS Group AG; *Int'l*, pg. 6738
HOFFMANN/NEW YORKER INC.; *U.S. Private*, pg. 1960
THE HOFFMANN FAMILY OF COMPANIES; *U.S. Private*, pg. 4053
HOFFMANN FRANCE S.A.S.—See SFS Group AG; *Int'l*, pg. 6738
HOFFMANN GMBH—See SFS Group AG; *Int'l*, pg. 6739
HOFFMANN GOPPINGEN QUALITATSWERKZEUGE GMBH—See SFS Group AG; *Int'l*, pg. 6739
HOFFMANN GREEN CEMENT TECHNOLOGIES SAS; *Int'l*, pg. 3440
HOFFMANN GROUP SYSTEM GMBH—See SFS Group AG; *Int'l*, pg. 6739

COMPANY NAME INDEX

HOFFMANN HUNGARY QUALITY TOOLS KFT.—See SFS Group AG; *Int'l*, pg. 6739
HOFFMANN IBERIA QUALITY TOOLS S.L.—See SFS Group AG; *Int'l*, pg. 6739
HOFFMANN INDUSTRIAL TOOLS S.R.L.—See SFS Group AG; *Int'l*, pg. 6739
HOFFMANN ITALIA S.P.A.—See SFS Group AG; *Int'l*, pg. 6739
HOFFMANN KVALITETNA ORODJA D.O.O.—See SFS Group AG; *Int'l*, pg. 6739
HOFFMANN-LA ROCHE AG—See Roche Holding AG; *Int'l*, pg. 6373
HOFFMANN-LA ROCHE INC.—See Roche Holding AG; *Int'l*, pg. 6373
HOFFMANN-LA ROCHE LIMITED—See Roche Holding AG; *Int'l*, pg. 6373
HOFFMANN NEOPAC; *Int'l*, pg. 3440
HOFFMANN NURNBERG GMBH—See SFS Group AG; *Int'l*, pg. 6739
HOFFMANN QUALITATSWERKZEUGE CZ S.R.O—See SFS Group AG; *Int'l*, pg. 6739
HOFFMANN QUALITATSWERKZEUGE SK S.R.O.—See SFS Group AG; *Int'l*, pg. 6739
HOFFMANN QUALITY TOOLS B.V.—See SFS Group AG; *Int'l*, pg. 6739
HOFFMANN QUALITY TOOLS INDIA PVT. LTD.—See SFS Group AG; *Int'l*, pg. 6739
HOFFMANN QUALITY TOOLS (MALAYSIA) SDN. BHD.—See SFS Group AG; *Int'l*, pg. 6739
HOFFMANN QUALITY TOOLS MEXICO S. DE R.L. DE C.V.—See SFS Group AG; *Int'l*, pg. 6739
HOFFMANN QUALITY TOOLS TRADING CO., LTD.—See SFS Group AG; *Int'l*, pg. 6739
HOFFMANN SUPPLY CHAIN GMBH—See SFS Group AG; *Int'l*, pg. 6739
HOFFMAN PLANNING, DESIGN & CONSTRUCTION, INC.; *U.S. Private*, pg. 1960
HOFFMAN PLASTIC COMPOUNDS, INC.; *U.S. Private*, pg. 1960
HOFFMAN & REED INC.; *U.S. Private*, pg. 1959
HOFFMANS CHOCOLATE, LLC—See Hilton Grand Vacations Inc.; *U.S. Public*, pg. 1039
HOFFMAN SCHROFF PTE LTD—See Pentair plc; *Int'l*, pg. 5790
HOFFMAN SPECIALTY—See Xylem Inc.; *U.S. Public*, pg. 2396
HOFFMAN STRUCTURES, INC.—See Hoffman Corporation; *U.S. Private*, pg. 1960
HOFFMAN TRANSPORT INC.; *U.S. Private*, pg. 1960
HOFFMAN VACATION RENTALS LLC; *U.S. Private*, pg. 1960
HOFFMAN WEBER CONSTRUCTION; *U.S. Private*, pg. 1960
HOFFMAN YORK, INC.; *U.S. Private*, pg. 1960
HOFFMASTER GROUP, INC.—See Wellspring Capital Management LLC; *U.S. Private*, pg. 4477
HOFFMEISTER-LEUCHTEN GMBH—See Societe d'Application des Methodes Modernes d'Eclairage SA; *Int'l*, pg. 7037
HOFFMEYER COMPANY INC.; *U.S. Private*, pg. 1960
HOF HAUS; *U.S. Private*, pg. 1959
HOF HOORNEMAN BANKIERS NV—See Van Lanschot Kempen NV; *Int'l*, pg. 8126
HOFLAND OPTIEK B.V.—See Fielmann Group AG; *Int'l*, pg. 2659
HOFLANDT AUTOMOBILE; *Int'l*, pg. 3440
HOFLER YANTAI SERVICE CO., LTD.—See Klingelnberg AG; *Int'l*, pg. 4201
HOFMANN CERAMIC CZ S.R.O.—See S K Bajoria Group; *Int'l*, pg. 6443
HOFMANN CERAMIC GMBH—See S K Bajoria Group; *Int'l*, pg. 6443
HOFMANN CERAMIC LIMITED—See S K Bajoria Group; *Int'l*, pg. 6443
HOFMANN INDUSTRIES, INC. - EAU CLAIRE DIVISION—See Hofmann Industries, Inc.; *U.S. Private*, pg. 1961
HOFMANN INDUSTRIES, INC.; *U.S. Private*, pg. 1960
HOFMANN PRUFTECHNIK GMBH—See HWH Investments Limited; *Int'l*, pg. 3543
HOFMANN SAUSAGE CO., INC.—See Trivest Partners, LP; *U.S. Private*, pg. 4241
HOFNETZ UND IT SERVICES GMBH—See CPI Property Group, S.A.; *Int'l*, pg. 1825
HOFPLEIN OFFICES ROTTERDAM B.V.—See PPF Group N.V.; *Int'l*, pg. 5950
HOFSETH BIOCARE AS; *Int'l*, pg. 3440
HOF'S HUT RESTAURANTS INC.; *U.S. Private*, pg. 1959
HOFTEX GROUP AG; *Int'l*, pg. 3440
HOFT PROPERTIES LLC—See InterContinental Hotels Group PLC; *Int'l*, pg. 3737
HOFU PORTBUILDING CO., LTD.—See Sankyu, Inc.; *Int'l*, pg. 6544
HOGANAS AB; *Int'l*, pg. 3441
HOGANAS BELGIUM S.A.—See Hoganas AB; *Int'l*, pg. 3441
HOGANAS BRASIL LTDA.—See Hoganas AB; *Int'l*, pg. 3441

HOGANAS CERAMIQUES FRANCE SA—See QuattroR SGR S.p.A.; *Int'l*, pg. 6157
HOGANAS (CHINA) LTD—See Hoganas AB; *Int'l*, pg. 3441
HOGANAS EAST EUROPE LLC—See Hoganas AB; *Int'l*, pg. 3441
HOGANAS FRANCE S.A.S.—See Hoganas AB; *Int'l*, pg. 3441
HOGANAS GMBH—See Hoganas AB; *Int'l*, pg. 3441
HOGANAS GREAT BRITAIN UK—See Hoganas AB; *Int'l*, pg. 3441
HOGANAS HAMNBYGGNADS AB—See Hoganas AB; *Int'l*, pg. 3441
HOGANAS IBERICA S.A.—See Hoganas AB; *Int'l*, pg. 3441
HOGANAS INDIA LTD—See Hoganas AB; *Int'l*, pg. 3441
HOGANAS JAPAN K.K.—See Hoganas AB; *Int'l*, pg. 3441
HOGANAS KOREA LTD.—See Hoganas AB; *Int'l*, pg. 3441
HOGANAS SWEDEN AB—See Hoganas AB; *Int'l*, pg. 3441
HOGANAS TAIWAN LTD.—See Hoganas AB; *Int'l*, pg. 3441
HOGAN CHEVROLET BUICK GMC LIMITED; *Int'l*, pg. 3441
THE HOGAN COMPANY; *U.S. Private*, pg. 4053
HOGAN HOMES INC; *U.S. Private*, pg. 1961
HOGAN LOVELLS (ALICANTE) S.L. & CIA.—See Hogan Lovells International LLP; *Int'l*, pg. 3441
HOGAN LOVELLS BSTL, S.C.—See Hogan Lovells International LLP; *Int'l*, pg. 3441
HOGAN LOVELLS CIS LLC—See Hogan Lovells International LLP; *Int'l*, pg. 3441
HOGAN LOVELLS INTERNATIONAL LLP; *Int'l*, pg. 3441
HOGAN LOVELLS (LUXEMBOURG) LLP—See Hogan Lovells International LLP; *Int'l*, pg. 3441
HOGAN LOVELLS (MIDDLE EAST) LLP—See Hogan Lovells International LLP; *Int'l*, pg. 3441
HOGAN LOVELLS (MONGOLIA) LLP—See Hogan Lovells International LLP; *Int'l*, pg. 3441
HOGAN LOVELLS (PARIS) LLP—See Hogan Lovells International LLP; *Int'l*, pg. 3441
HOGAN LOVELLS SOUTH AFRICA—See Hogan Lovells International LLP; *Int'l*, pg. 3441
HOGAN LOVELLS STUDIO LEGALE—See Hogan Lovells International LLP; *Int'l*, pg. 3441
HOGAN LOVELLS US LLP—See Hogan Lovells International LLP; *Int'l*, pg. 3441
HOGAN LOVELLS (WARSZAWA) LLP—See Hogan Lovells International LLP; *Int'l*, pg. 3441
HOGAN MANUFACTURING INC.; *U.S. Private*, pg. 1961
HOGAN MOTOR LEASING INC.; *U.S. Private*, pg. 1961
HOGAR CREA INC.; *U.S. Private*, pg. 1961
HOGEBUILT, INC.—See Berkshire Hathaway Inc.; *U.S. Public*, pg. 310
HOGE LUMBER COMPANY; *U.S. Private*, pg. 1961
HOGG CONSTRUCTION INC.; *U.S. Private*, pg. 1961
HOGGETT BOWERS—See PSD Group plc; *Int'l*, pg. 6016
HOGG ROBINSON AUSTRALIA PTY LIMITED—See Global Business Travel Group, Inc.; *U.S. Public*, pg. 941
HOGG ROBINSON GERMANY GMBH & CO. KG—See Global Business Travel Group, Inc.; *U.S. Public*, pg. 941
HOGG ROBINSON GROUP LIMITED—See Global Business Travel Group, Inc.; *U.S. Public*, pg. 941
HOGG ROBINSON GROUP POLAND—See Global Business Travel Group, Inc.; *U.S. Public*, pg. 941
HOGG ROBINSON LIMITED—See Global Business Travel Group, Inc.; *U.S. Public*, pg. 941
HOGG ROBINSON MAGYARORSZAG KFT.—See Global Business Travel Group, Inc.; *U.S. Public*, pg. 941
HOGG ROBINSON NORDIC AB—See Global Business Travel Group, Inc.; *U.S. Public*, pg. 941
HOGG ROBINSON NORDIC OY—See Global Business Travel Group, Inc.; *U.S. Public*, pg. 941
HOGG ROBINSON SINGAPORE PTE LIMITED—See Global Business Travel Group, Inc.; *U.S. Public*, pg. 941
HOGG ROBINSON (TRAVEL) LIMITED—See Global Business Travel Group, Inc.; *U.S. Public*, pg. 941
HOGIA AB; *Int'l*, pg. 3441
HOGIA FERRY SYSTEMS OY—See Hogia AB; *Int'l*, pg. 3441
HOGIA LONN AS—See Hogia AB; *Int'l*, pg. 3441
HOGIA TRANSPORT SYSTEMS LTD.—See Hogia AB; *Int'l*, pg. 3441
HOGLA-KIMBERLY LTD.—See Kimberly-Clark Corporation; *U.S. Public*, pg. 1229
HOGLUND BUS CO. INC.; *U.S. Private*, pg. 1961
HOG SLAT INC.; *U.S. Private*, pg. 1961
HOGUE & ASSOCIATES INC.; *U.S. Private*, pg. 1961
HOGY MEDICAL ASIA PACIFIC PTE. LTD.—See Mitsubishi Corporation; *Int'l*, pg. 4938
HOGY MEDICAL CO. LTD. - MIHO PLANT NO. 1—See Hogy Medical Co., Ltd.; *Int'l*, pg. 3442
HOGY MEDICAL CO., LTD. - MIHO PLANT NO. 2—See Hogy Medical Co., Ltd.; *Int'l*, pg. 3442
HOGY MEDICAL CO., LTD.; *Int'l*, pg. 3442

HOJGAARD HOLDING A/S

HOH ARCHITECTS, INC.—See The HOH Group; *U.S. Private*, pg. 4053
HOH BIRGER CHRISTENSEN AS—See BWT Aktiengesellschaft; *Int'l*, pg. 1233
HOH ENGINEERS, INC.—See The HOH Group; *U.S. Private*, pg. 4053
THE HOH GROUP; *U.S. Private*, pg. 4053
HOHL-FINDLAY, LLC—See Lazydays Holdings, Inc.; *U.S. Public*, pg. 1295
HOHL INDUSTRIAL SERVICES CO.; *U.S. Private*, pg. 1961
HOHMANN & BARNARD, INC.—See Berkshire Hathaway Inc.; *U.S. Public*, pg. 312
HOHMAN PLATING & MANUFACTURING, LLC—See KKR & Co. Inc.; *U.S. Public*, pg. 1262
HOHMEIER ANLAGENBAU GMBH—See MINDA Industrieanlagen GmbH; *Int'l*, pg. 4900
HOHNER, INC./HSS—See Matth. Hohner AG; *Int'l*, pg. 4731
HOHNER MAQUINARIA DE ARTES GRAFICAS S.L.—See Hohner Maschinenbau GmbH; *Int'l*, pg. 3442
HOHNER MASCHINENBAU GMBH; *Int'l*, pg. 3442
HOHNER MUSIKINSTRUMENTE GMBH & CO. KG—See Matth. Hohner AG; *Int'l*, pg. 4731
HOHNER S.A.—See Matth. Hohner AG; *Int'l*, pg. 4731
HOHNER STITCHING PRODUCTS INC.—See Hohner Maschinenbau GmbH; *Int'l*, pg. 3442
HOHNER STITCHING TECHNOLOGY (NANJING) CO., LTD.—See Hohner Maschinenbau GmbH; *Int'l*, pg. 3442
HOHNER UK LTD.—See Hohner Maschinenbau GmbH; *Int'l*, pg. 3442
HOHN GMBH—See Prysmian S.p.A.; *Int'l*, pg. 6012
HOH SEPARTEC OY—See BWT Aktiengesellschaft; *Int'l*, pg. 1233
HOHSUI CORPORATION—See Nissui Corporation; *Int'l*, pg. 5378
HO HUP CONSTRUCTION COMPANY BERHAD; *Int'l*, pg. 3434
HO HUP (MYANMAR) E&C CO., LTD.—See Ho Hup Construction Company Berhad; *Int'l*, pg. 3434
HOH VATTENTEKNIK AB—See BWT Aktiengesellschaft; *Int'l*, pg. 1233
HOH WATER TECHNOLOGY A/S—See BWT Aktiengesellschaft; *Int'l*, pg. 1233
H-O-H WATER TECHNOLOGY, INC.; *U.S. Private*, pg. 1824
HOI AN TOURIST SERVICE JOINT STOCK COMPANY; *Int'l*, pg. 3442
HOIAX AS—See NIBE Industrier AB; *Int'l*, pg. 5261
HOIGAARD'S, INC.—See Vail Resorts, Inc.; *U.S. Public*, pg. 2271
HOI PRODUCTIONS GERMANY GMBH—See CTS Eventim AG & Co. KGAA; *Int'l*, pg. 1873
HOI SANG LIMITED—See Hang Lung Group Limited; *Int'l*, pg. 3245
HOIST FINANCE AB; *Int'l*, pg. 3442
HOIST FINANCE CRAIOVA S.R.L.—See Hoist Finance AB; *Int'l*, pg. 3442
HOIST FINANCE SPAIN S.L.—See Hoist Finance AB; *Int'l*, pg. 3442
HOIST FINANCE UK LIMITED—See Permira Advisers LLP; *Int'l*, pg. 5807
HOIST FITNESS SYSTEMS INC.; *U.S. Private*, pg. 1961
HOIST HELLAS S.A—See Hoist Finance AB; *Int'l*, pg. 3442
HOIST HELLAS S.L.D.S.A.—See Hoist Finance AB; *Int'l*, pg. 3442
HOIST ITALIA S.R.L.—See Hoist Finance AB; *Int'l*, pg. 3442
HOIST MATERIAL HANDLING, INC.—See Toyota Industries Corporation; *Int'l*, pg. 7869
HOIST POLSKA SP. Z O.O.—See Hoist Finance AB; *Int'l*, pg. 3442
HOI TAI TOURS LIMITED—See Transport International Holdings Limited; *Int'l*, pg. 7905
HOI TIN UNIVERSAL LIMITED; *Int'l*, pg. 3442
HOI TUNG MARINE MACHINERY SUPPLIERS LIMITED—See China Merchants Group Limited; *Int'l*, pg. 1521
HOI TUNG (SHANGHAI) LIMITED—See China Merchants Group Limited; *Int'l*, pg. 1521
HOI TUNG (SHENZHEN) CO., LTD.—See China Merchants Group Limited; *Int'l*, pg. 1521
HOIVATILAT OYJ; *Int'l*, pg. 3442
HOJALATA MEXICANA, S.A. DE C.V.—See Grupo Acerero del Norte S.A. de C.V.; *Int'l*, pg. 3118
HOJALATA Y LAMINADOS S.A.—See JFE Holdings, Inc.; *Int'l*, pg. 3937
HOJBJERG DYREKLINIK APS—See Vimian Group AB; *Int'l*, pg. 8208
HOJEIJ BRANDED FOODS LLC—See Vivendi SE; *Int'l*, pg. 8276
HOJ ENGINEERING & SALES CO., LLC; *U.S. Private*, pg. 1961
HOJEON LIMITED; *Int'l*, pg. 3442
HOJ FORKLIFT SYSTEMS—See Hoj Engineering & Sales Co., LLC; *U.S. Private*, pg. 1961
HOJGAARD HOLDING A/S; *Int'l*, pg. 3442

HOJGAARD HOLDING A/S

HOJGAARD INDUSTRI A/S—See Hojgaard Holding A/S; *Int'l*, pg. 3442
HOJU UNYU CO., LTD.—See Tomoku Co., Ltd.; *Int'l*, pg. 7801
HOKANSON, INC.—See Scott Group Custom Carpets, Inc.; *U.S. Private*, pg. 3577
HOKE, INC.—See KKR & Co. Inc.; *U.S. Public*, pg. 1242
HOKE INC.; *U.S. Private*, pg. 1961
HOKENDOHJINSHA INC.—See Polaris Capital Group Co., Ltd.; *Int'l*, pg. 5907
HOKEN HIROBA, LTD.—See Yamaguchi Financial Group Inc.; *Int'l*, pg. 8548
HOKENMINAOSHIHONPO CO., LTD.—See WebCrew Inc.; *Int'l*, pg. 8365
HOKENSO SDN. BHD.—See Hitachi, Ltd.; *Int'l*, pg. 3422
HOKKAIDO AIR SERVICE CO., LTD.—See Japan Airlines Co., Ltd.; *Int'l*, pg. 3881
HOKKAIDO AIR SYSTEM CO., LTD.—See Japan Airlines Co., Ltd.; *Int'l*, pg. 3884
HOKKAIDO AJINOMOTO CO., INC.—See Ajinomoto Company, Inc.; *Int'l*, pg. 257
HOKKAIDO AKEBONO SHOKUHIN, CO., LTD.—See Maruha Nichiro Corporation; *Int'l*, pg. 4711
HOKKAIDO AOKI KAGAKU CO., LTD.—See Matsuda Sangyo Co., Ltd.; *Int'l*, pg. 4729
HOKKAIDO BALLPARK CORPORATION—See Dentsu Group Inc.; *Int'l*, pg. 2039
HOKKAIDO BANK, LTD.—See Hokuhoku Financial Group, Inc.; *Int'l*, pg. 3444
THE HOKKAIDO BANK, LTD.—See Hokuhoku Financial Group, Inc.; *Int'l*, pg. 3444
HOKKAIDO CHUO BUS CO., LTD.; *Int'l*, pg. 3442
HOKKAIDO COCA-COLA BOTTLING CO., LTD.—See Dai Nippon Printing Co., Ltd.; *Int'l*, pg. 1915
HOKKAIDO CSK CORPORATION—See Sumitomo Corporation; *Int'l*, pg. 7270
HOKKAIDO CUBE SYSTEM INC.—See Cube System Inc.; *Int'l*, pg. 1875
HOKKAIDO DRY-CHEMICAL CO., LTD.—See Nippon Dry-Chemical Co., Ltd.; *Int'l*, pg. 5314
HOKKAIDO ECO RECYCLE SYSTEMS CO., LTD.—See Hitachi, Ltd.; *Int'l*, pg. 3422
HOKKAIDO ELECTRIC INDUSTRIES LTD.—See Sumitomo Electric Industries, Ltd.; *Int'l*, pg. 7278
HOKKAIDO ELECTRIC METERS INDUSTRY—See Hokkaido Electric Power Co., Inc.; *Int'l*, pg. 3443
HOKKAIDO ELECTRIC POWER CO., INC.; *Int'l*, pg. 3442
HOKKAIDO FUJI ELECTRIC CO., LTD.—See Fuji Electric Co., Ltd.; *Int'l*, pg. 2812
HOKKAIDO GAS CO LTD; *Int'l*, pg. 3443
HOKKAIDO GLORY CO., LTD.—See GLORY Ltd.; *Int'l*, pg. 3010
HOKKAIDO HAKUHODO, INC.—See Hakuhodo DY Holdings Incorporated; *Int'l*, pg. 3221
HOKKAIDO HINO MOTOR LTD.—See Toyota Motor Corporation; *Int'l*, pg. 7871
HOKKAIDO HITACHI SYSTEMS, LTD.—See Hitachi, Ltd.; *Int'l*, pg. 3422
HOKKAIDO INOAC CO., LTD. - MINAMI PLANT—See INOAC Corporation; *Int'l*, pg. 3714
HOKKAIDO INOAC CO., LTD.—See INOAC Corporation; *Int'l*, pg. 3714
HOKKAIDO INSTITUTE OF PAHRMACY BENEFIT CO., LTD.—See Medical System Network Co., Ltd.; *Int'l*, pg. 4775
HOKKAIDO KANZAI CO., LTD.—See Kurimoto Ltd; *Int'l*, pg. 4339
HOKKAIDO KIKKOMAN COMPANY—See Kikkoman Corporation; *Int'l*, pg. 4160
HOKKAIDO KOSAN CO., LTD.—See The Japan Steel Works, Ltd.; *Int'l*, pg. 7658
HOKKAIDO KUBOTA CORPORATION—See Kubota Corporation; *Int'l*, pg. 4321
HOKKAIDO LIME CO., LTD.—See Nittetsu Mining Co., Ltd.; *Int'l*, pg. 5383
HOKKAIDO LINER CO., LTD.—See NIPPON CARBIDE INDUSTRIES CO., INC.; *Int'l*, pg. 5311
HOKKAIDO MARUICHI STEEL TUBE LTD. - SAPPORO POLE PLANT—See Maruichi Steel Tube Ltd; *Int'l*, pg. 4713
HOKKAIDO MARUICHI STEEL TUBE LTD.—See Maruichi Steel Tube Ltd; *Int'l*, pg. 4713
HOKKAIDO MEIHAN CO., LTD.—See Meiji Holdings Co., Ltd.; *Int'l*, pg. 4800
HOKKAIDO MITSUBISHI MOTOR SALES CO., LTD.—See Mitsubishi Motors Corporation; *Int'l*, pg. 4966
HOKKAIDO MITSUI CHEMICALS, INC.—See Mitsui Chemicals, Inc.; *Int'l*, pg. 4981
HOKKAIDO MORI SHIGYO CO., LTD.—See Oji Holdings Corporation; *Int'l*, pg. 5537
HOKKAIDO MORITA CORPORATION—See Morita Holdings Corporation; *Int'l*, pg. 5048
HOKKAIDO NICHIMO CO., LTD.—See NICHIMO CO. LTD.; *Int'l*, pg. 5269
HOKKAIDO NIKKAN SPORTS SHIMBUNSHA K.K.—See The Asahi Shimbun Company; *Int'l*, pg. 7614
HOKKAIDO NIPPON HAM FIGHTERS BASEBALL CLUB—See NH Foods Ltd.; *Int'l*, pg. 5256

HOKKAIDO NISSIN CO., LTD.—See Nissin Corporation; *Int'l*, pg. 5375
HOKKAIDO NISSUI CO., LTD.—See Nissui Corporation; *Int'l*, pg. 5378
HOKKAIDO NOF CORPORATION—See NOF Corporation; *Int'l*, pg. 5399
HOKKAIDO NOHMI CO., LTD.—See Nohmi Bosai Ltd.; *Int'l*, pg. 5400
HOKKAIDO NS SOLUTIONS CORPORATION—See Nippon Steel Corporation; *Int'l*, pg. 5334
HOKKAIDO ORIGIN CO., LTD.—See Origin Co., Ltd.; *Int'l*, pg. 5629
HOKKAIDO OSAKI ELECTRIC CO., LTD.—See Osaki Electric Co., Ltd.; *Int'l*, pg. 5647
HOKKAIDO PHARMARISE CO., LTD.—See Pharmarise Holdings Corporation; *Int'l*, pg. 5841
HOKKAIDO POWER ENGINEERING CO., INC.—See Hokkaido Electric Power Co., Inc.; *Int'l*, pg. 3443
HOKKAIDO PRIMA MEAT PACKERS, LTD.—See Prima Meat Packers Ltd.; *Int'l*, pg. 5975
HOKKAIDO RECORDS MANAGEMENT CO., INC.—See Hokkaido Electric Power Co., Inc.; *Int'l*, pg. 3443
HOKKAIDO-SAINT-GERMAIN CO., LTD.—See create restaurants holdings inc.; *Int'l*, pg. 1832
HOKKAIDO SANITARY MAINTENANCE CO., LTD.—See Takuma Co., Ltd.; *Int'l*, pg. 7442
HOKKAIDO SANPLUS CO., LTD.—See ITOCHU Corporation; *Int'l*, pg. 3835
HOKKAIDO SAPPORO LION LIMITED—See Sapporo Holdings Limited; *Int'l*, pg. 6573
HOKKAIDO SEINO TRANSPORTATION CO., LTD.—See Seino Holdings Co., Ltd.; *Int'l*, pg. 6690
HOKKAIDO SEKISUI FAMI S CO.—See Sekisui Chemical Co., Ltd.; *Int'l*, pg. 6693
HOKKAIDO SEKISUI SHOJI CO., LTD.—See Sekisui Chemical Co., Ltd.; *Int'l*, pg. 6693
HOKKAIDO SENKO CO., LTD.—See Senko Group Holdings Co., Ltd.; *Int'l*, pg. 6709
HOKKAIDO SERVICE ENGINEERING CO., LTD.—See Mitsubishi Heavy Industries, Ltd.; *Int'l*, pg. 4953
HOKKAIDO SODA CO., LTD.—See AGC Inc.; *Int'l*, pg. 204
HOKKAIDO SUBARU INC.—See SUBARU CO., LTD.; *Int'l*, pg. 7246
HOKKAIDO SUMIDEN DENGYO CO., LTD.—See Sumitomo Densetsu Co., Ltd.; *Int'l*, pg. 7276
HOKKAIDO SUMIDEN PRECISION CO., LTD.—See Sumitomo Electric Industries, Ltd.; *Int'l*, pg. 7278
HOKKAIDO SUMIDEN STEEL WIRE CO., LTD.—See Sumitomo Electric Industries, Ltd.; *Int'l*, pg. 7278
HOKKAIDO SUN AGRO CO., LTD.—See Nissan Chemical Corporation; *Int'l*, pg. 5366
HOKKAIDO SUPERBAG CO., LTD.—See Superbag Co., Ltd.; *Int'l*, pg. 7336
HOKKAIDO TELECOMMUNICATION NETWORK—See Hokkaido Electric Power Co., Inc.; *Int'l*, pg. 3443
HOKKAIDO UBE CO., LTD.—See UBE Corporation; *Int'l*, pg. 8000
HOKKAI ELECTRICAL CONSTRUCTION CO., INC.—See Hokkaido Electric Power Co., Inc.; *Int'l*, pg. 3443
HOKKAI ELECTRONICS CO., LTD.—See Renesas Electronics Corporation; *Int'l*, pg. 6277
HOKKAI SHIGYO CO., LTD.—See Japan Pulp and Paper Company Limited; *Int'l*, pg. 3903
HOKKAI TAIYO PLASTIC CO., LTD.—See Sumitomo Bakelite Co., Ltd.; *Int'l*, pg. 7263
HOKKAI TRANSPORTATION CO., LTD.—See Kawasaki Kisen Kaisha, Ltd.; *Int'l*, pg. 4099
THE HOKKAI YASUDA LOGISTICS CO., LTD.—See Yasuda Logistics Corporation; *Int'l*, pg. 8571
HOKKAN HOLDINGS LIMITED; *Int'l*, pg. 3443
HOKKO CHEMICAL CO., LTD.—See Sojitz Corporation; *Int'l*, pg. 7061
HOKKO CHEMICAL INDUSTRY CO., LTD. - OKAYAMA FACTORY—See HOKKO CHEMICAL INDUSTRY CO., LTD.; *Int'l*, pg. 3443
HOKKO CHEMICAL INDUSTRY CO., LTD.; *Int'l*, pg. 3443
HOKKOH TRANSPORTATION INC.—See Sumitomo Electric Industries, Ltd.; *Int'l*, pg. 7278
THE HOKKOKU BANK, LTD.; *Int'l*, pg. 7652
THE HOKKOKU CAPITAL CO., LTD.—See The Hokkoku Bank, Ltd.; *Int'l*, pg. 7652
HOKKOKU CO., LTD.; *Int'l*, pg. 3443
THE HOKKOKU CREDIT SERVICE CO., LTD.—See The Hokkoku Bank, Ltd.; *Int'l*, pg. 7652
HOKKOKU FINANCIAL HOLDINGS, INC.; *Int'l*, pg. 3443
THE HOKKOKU GENERAL LEASE CO., LTD.—See The Hokkoku Bank, Ltd.; *Int'l*, pg. 7652
HOKKOKU GENERAL LEASING CO., LTD.—See Hokkoku Financial Holdings, Inc.; *Int'l*, pg. 3443
HOKKOKU HOSO KIZAI CO., LTD.—See Rengo Co., Ltd.; *Int'l*, pg. 6279
HOKKOKU INTEC SERVICE INC.—See TIS Inc.; *Int'l*, pg. 7757
THE HOKKOKU MANAGEMENT, LTD.—See The Hokkoku Bank, Ltd.; *Int'l*, pg. 7652
HOKKO SANGYO CO., LTD.—See HOKKO CHEMICAL INDUSTRY CO., LTD.; *Int'l*, pg. 3443
HOKKO SHOUJI, INC.—See Topy Industries, Ltd.; *Int'l*, pg. 7821

HOKO CO., LTD.—See NH Foods Ltd.; *Int'l*, pg. 5256
HO KOK SUN COLORECTAL PTE. LTD.—See Alliance Healthcare Group Limited; *Int'l*, pg. 340
HOKTO KINOKO COMPANY—See Hokuto Corporation; *Int'l*, pg. 3445
HOKUBU CO., LTD.—See MIRAIT ONE Corporation; *Int'l*, pg. 4917
HOKUDEN ASSOCIA CO., INC.—See Hokkaido Electric Power Co., Inc.; *Int'l*, pg. 3443
HOKUDEN ECO-ENERGY CO., LTD.—See Hokkaido Electric Power Co., Inc.; *Int'l*, pg. 3443
HOKUDEN INFORMATION SYSTEM SERVICE COMPANY, INC.—See Hokuriku Electric Power Co.; *Int'l*, pg. 3445
HOKUDEN INFORMATION TECHNOLOGY—See Hokkaido Electric Power Co., Inc.; *Int'l*, pg. 3443
HOKUDEN KOGYO—See Hokkaido Electric Power Co., Inc.; *Int'l*, pg. 3443
HOKUDEN LIFE SYSTEM—See Hokkaido Electric Power Co., Inc.; *Int'l*, pg. 3443
HOKUDEN (MALAYSIA) SDN. BHD.—See Hokuriku Electric Industry Co., Ltd.; *Int'l*, pg. 3444
HOKUDEN PARTNER SERVICE INC.—See Hokuriku Electric Power Co.; *Int'l*, pg. 3445
HOKUDEN SERVICE CO., LTD.—See Hokkaido Electric Power Co., Inc.; *Int'l*, pg. 3443
HOKUDEN SOGO SEKKEI—See Hokkaido Electric Power Co., Inc.; *Int'l*, pg. 3443
THE HOKUETSU BANK, LTD.—See Daishi Hokuetsu Financial Group, Inc.; *Int'l*, pg. 1941
THE HOKUETSU CARD CO., LTD.—See Daishi Hokuetsu Financial Group, Inc.; *Int'l*, pg. 1941
HOKUETSU CORPORATION; *Int'l*, pg. 3443
HOKUETSU ENGINEERING CO., LTD.—See Hokuetsu Corporation; *Int'l*, pg. 3443
HOKUETSU FOREST CO., LTD.—See Hokuetsu Corporation; *Int'l*, pg. 3443
HOKUETSU INDUSTRIES CO., LTD.; *Int'l*, pg. 3444
HOKUETSU INDUSTRIES EUROPE B.V.—See Hokuetsu Industries Co., Ltd.; *Int'l*, pg. 3444
HOKUETSU KASEI CO., LTD.—See Tosoh Corporation; *Int'l*, pg. 7832
HOKUETSU KISHU PAPER CO., LTD. - OSAKA MILL—See Hokuetsu Corporation; *Int'l*, pg. 3443
HOKUETSU KISHU SALES CO., LTD.—See Hokuetsu Corporation; *Int'l*, pg. 3443
HOKUETSU KOGYO, LTD.—See Topy Industries, Ltd.; *Int'l*, pg. 7821
THE HOKUETSU LEASING CO., LTD.—See Daishi Hokuetsu Financial Group, Inc.; *Int'l*, pg. 1941
HOKUETSU METAL CO., LTD.; *Int'l*, pg. 3444
HOKUETSU PACKAGE CO., LTD.—See Hokuetsu Corporation; *Int'l*, pg. 3444
HOKUETSU PAPER SALES CO., LTD.—See Hokuetsu Corporation; *Int'l*, pg. 3444
HOKUETSU TOYO FIBRE CO., LTD.—See Hokuetsu Corporation; *Int'l*, pg. 3444
HOKUETSU TRADING CORPORATION—See Hokuetsu Corporation; *Int'l*, pg. 3444
HOKUETSU TURNBUCKLE CO., LTD.—See Topy Industries, Ltd.; *Int'l*, pg. 7821
HOKUGIN BUSINESS SERVICES CO., LTD.—See Hokuhoku Financial Group, Inc.; *Int'l*, pg. 3444
THE HOKUGIN ECONOMIC RESEARCH INSTITUTE LTD—See Daishi Hokuetsu Financial Group, Inc.; *Int'l*, pg. 1941
HOKUGIN LEASE CO., LTD.—See Hokuhoku Financial Group, Inc.; *Int'l*, pg. 3444
HOKUGIN REAL ESTATE SERVICES CO., LTD.—See Hokuhoku Financial Group, Inc.; *Int'l*, pg. 3444
HOKUGIN SOFTWARE CO., LTD.—See Hokuhoku Financial Group, Inc.; *Int'l*, pg. 3444
HOKUHOKU FINANCIAL GROUP, INC.; *Int'l*, pg. 3444
HOKUHOKU TOKAI TOKYO SECURITIES CO., LTD.—See Hokuhoku Financial Group, Inc.; *Int'l*, pg. 3444
HOKUMEI ELECTRIC INDUSTRY CO., LTD.—See Nippon Signal Co., Ltd.; *Int'l*, pg. 5333
HOKUO TOKYO CO., LTD.—See Odakyu Electric Railway Co., Ltd.; *Int'l*, pg. 5523
HOKURIKU BANDO, INC.—See Bando Chemical Industries, Ltd.; *Int'l*, pg. 830
THE HOKURIKU BANK, LTD.—See Hokuhoku Financial Group, Inc.; *Int'l*, pg. 3444
THE HOKURIKU BANK, LTD.—See Hokuhoku Financial Group, Inc.; *Int'l*, pg. 3444
HOKURIKU CARD CO., LTD.—See Hokuhoku Financial Group, Inc.; *Int'l*, pg. 3444
HOKURIKU CERAMICS CO., LTD.—See NIPPON CARBIDE INDUSTRIES CO., INC.; *Int'l*, pg. 5311
HOKURIKU CHEMICAL INDUSTRIAL CO., LTD.—See Kowa Co., Ltd.; *Int'l*, pg. 4294
HOKURIKU COCA-COLA BOTTLING CO., LTD.; *Int'l*, pg. 3444
HOKURIKU COLOR CO., LTD.—See Kowa Co., Ltd.; *Int'l*, pg. 4294
HOKURIKU COLUMN CO., LTD.—See Hanwa Co., Ltd.; *Int'l*, pg. 3263

HOKURIKU DAISEKI CO., LTD.—See Daiseki Co. Ltd.; *Int'l*, pg. 1941
HOKURIKU DENWA KOUJI CO., LTD.—See COMSYS Holdings Corporation; *Int'l*, pg. 1761
HOKURIKU (DONGGUAN) CO., LTD - 2ND FACTORY—See Hokuriku Electric Industry Co., Ltd.; *Int'l*, pg. 3444
HOKURIKU ELECTRICAL CONSTRUCTION CO., LTD.; *Int'l*, pg. 3445
HOKURIKU ELECTRIC (GUANG DONG) CO., LTD. - 1ST FACTORY—See Hokuriku Electric Industry Co., Ltd.; *Int'l*, pg. 3445
HOKURIKU ELECTRIC INDUSTRY CO., LTD.; *Int'l*, pg. 3444
HOKURIKU ELECTRIC POWER CO.; *Int'l*, pg. 3445
HOKURIKU ENERGYS CO., LTD.—See NGK Insulators, Ltd.; *Int'l*, pg. 5254
HOKURIKU FRESH FOODS CO., LTD—See Nissui Corporation; *Int'l*, pg. 5378
HOKURIKU GAS CO., LTD.; *Int'l*, pg. 3445
HOKURIKU HAKUHODO, INC.—See Hakuhodo DY Holdings Incorporated; *Int'l*, pg. 3221
HOKURIKU HEAVY INDUSTRIES, LTD.—See Kyokuto Kaihatsu Kogyo Co. Ltd.; *Int'l*, pg. 4363
HOKURIKU HITACHI CO., LTD.—See Hitachi, Ltd.; *Int'l*, pg. 3423
HOKURIKU HONG KONG CO., LTD.—See Hokuriku Electric Industry Co., Ltd.; *Int'l*, pg. 3445
HOKURIKU HOSHO SERVICES CO., LTD.—See Hokuhoku Financial Group, Inc.; *Int'l*, pg. 3444
HOKURIKU INTERNATIONAL (THAILAND) CO., LTD.—See Hokuriku Electric Industry Co., Ltd.; *Int'l*, pg. 3445
HOKURIKU KINZOKU CO., LTD.—See Nachi-Fujikoshi Corp.; *Int'l*, pg. 5121
HOKURIKU KOGYO CORPORATION—See JFE Holdings, Inc.; *Int'l*, pg. 3936
HOKURIKU KOSAN CO., LTD.—See Hokuriku Electric Industry Co., Ltd.; *Int'l*, pg. 3445
HOKURIKU KYOEI SYSTEMS INC.—See KYCOM Holdings Co., Ltd.; *Int'l*, pg. 4355
HOKURIKU (MALAYSIA), SDN. BHD.—See Hokuriku Electric Industry Co., Ltd.; *Int'l*, pg. 3445
HOKURIKU MAZDA CO., LTD.—See Mazda Motor Corporation; *Int'l*, pg. 4748
HOKURIKU MORI SHIGYO CO., LTD.—See Oji Holdings Corporation; *Int'l*, pg. 5536
HOKURIKU RYOSHOKU LTD.—See Mitsubishi Corporation; *Int'l*, pg. 4942
HOKURIKU SANKYO SEIKO CO., LTD.—See Sankyo Seiko Co., Ltd.; *Int'l*, pg. 6543
HOKURIKU SEIKI CO., LTD.—See Hokuriku Electric Industry Co., Ltd.; *Int'l*, pg. 3445
HOKURIKU SENKO TRANSPORT CO., LTD.—See Senko Group Holdings Co., Ltd.; *Int'l*, pg. 6709
HOKURIKU (SHANGHAI) INTERNATIONAL TRADING CO., LTD.—See Hokuriku Electric Industry Co., Ltd.; *Int'l*, pg. 3445
HOKURIKU SHIKI CO., LTD.—See Rengo Co., Ltd.; *Int'l*, pg. 6279
HOKURIKU (SINGAPORE) PTE., LTD.—See Hokuriku Electric Industry Co., Ltd.; *Int'l*, pg. 3445
HOKURIKU STEEL CO., LTD.—See JFE Holdings, Inc.; *Int'l*, pg. 3936
HOKURIKU TELECOMMUNICATION NETWORK CO., INC.—See Hokuriku Electric Power Co.; *Int'l*, pg. 3445
HOKURIKU UBE CONCRETE CO., LTD.—See UBE Corporation; *Int'l*, pg. 8000
HOKURIKU U.S.A. LTD.—See Hokuriku Electric Industry Co., Ltd.; *Int'l*, pg. 3445
HOKURIKU WACOAL SEWING CORP.—See Wacoal Holdings Corp.; *Int'l*, pg. 8325
HOKURIKU YUKEN CO., LTD.—See Yuken Kogyo Co., Ltd.; *Int'l*, pg. 8612
HOKURYO CITY SERVICE CO., LTD.—See Mitsubishi Estate Co., Ltd.; *Int'l*, pg. 4946
HOKURYO CO., LTD.; *Int'l*, pg. 3445
HOKURYO MOLD CO., LTD.—See Mitsubishi Chemical Group Corporation; *Int'l*, pg. 4931
HOKUSEI KOGYO CO., LTD—See KITAGAWA SEIKI CO., LTD.; *Int'l*, pg. 4194
HOKUSHIN CLINICAL LABORATORY, INC.—See H.U. Group Holdings, Inc.; *Int'l*, pg. 3197
HOKUSHIN CO., LTD.; *Int'l*, pg. 3445
HOKUSHINFOODS INC.—See Rohto Pharmaceutical Co. Ltd.; *Int'l*, pg. 6387
HOKUSHIN INDUSTRY CO., LTD.—See Konoike Transport Co., Ltd.; *Int'l*, pg. 4274
HOKUSHIN KIZAI CO., LTD.—See Mitsubishi Corporation; *Int'l*, pg. 4942
HOKUSHIN KOUN CO., LTD.—See Nissin Corporation; *Int'l*, pg. 5375
HOKUSHINKYUKO RAILWAY CO., LTD.—See Hankyu Hanshin Holdings, Inc.; *Int'l*, pg. 3256
HOKUSO KOHATSU K.K.—See Mitsui O.S.K. Lines, Ltd.; *Int'l*, pg. 4989
HOKUTAN HIGH TRUST CO., LTD.—See Takuma Co., Ltd.; *Int'l*, pg. 7442

THE HOKUTO BANK, LTD.—See FIDEA Holdings Co. Ltd.; *Int'l*, pg. 2653
HOKUTO CORPORATION; *Int'l*, pg. 3445
HOKUTO DENKO CORPORATION - ATSUGI FACTORY—See Meidensha Corporation; *Int'l*, pg. 4797
HOKUTO DENKO CORPORATION—See Meidensha Corporation; *Int'l*, pg. 4797
HOKUTOH GIKEN KOGYO CORPORATION—See KITZ CORPORATION; *Int'l*, pg. 4196
HOKUTO KOGYO CO.,LTD.—See Cosmo Energy Holdings Co., Ltd.; *Int'l*, pg. 1812
HOKUTO PRINTING CO., LTD.; *Int'l*, pg. 3445
HOKUTO TSUSHIN CO., LTD.—See Yamato Kogyo Co. Ltd.; *Int'l*, pg. 8555
HOKUYAKU CO., LTD.—See Sala Corporation; *Int'l*, pg. 6490
HOKUYAKU TAKEYAMA HOLDINGS, INC.; *Int'l*, pg. 3445
HOKUYO BUSINESS SERVICE CO., LTD.—See North Pacific Bank, Ltd.; *Int'l*, pg. 5441
HOKUYO CO., LTD.—See Tomoku Co., Ltd.; *Int'l*, pg. 7801
HOKUYO GLASS CO., LTD.—See Ishizuka Glass Co., Ltd.; *Int'l*, pg. 3818
HOKUYO INFORMATION SYSTEM., LTD—See Systena Corporation; *Int'l*, pg. 7393
HOKUYO KOEKI CO., LTD.—See Tomoku Co., Ltd.; *Int'l*, pg. 7801
HOKUYU LUCKY CO., LTD.; *Int'l*, pg. 3445
HOLADAY CIRCUITS, INC.—See Firan Technology Group Corporation; *Int'l*, pg. 2678
HOLADAY-PARKS FABRICATORS INC.; *U.S. Private*, pg. 1961
HOLAD HOLDING & ADMINISTRATION AG—See Porsche Automobil Holding SE; *Int'l*, pg. 5929
HOLADOCTOR, INC.—See Pan-American Life Insurance Group, Inc.; *U.S. Private*, pg. 3084
HOLALUZ-CLIDOM SA; *Int'l*, pg. 3445
HOLANDA VENEZUELA C.A.—See BRENNTAG SE; *Int'l*, pg. 1149
HOLAND OG SETSKOG SPAREBANK; *Int'l*, pg. 3445
HOLBAT SAS—See GCC SAS; *Int'l*, pg. 2894
HOLBEN, MARTIN & WHITE, INC.—See John A. Martin & Associates, Incorporated; *U.S. Private*, pg. 2219
HOLBORN COLLEGE LIMITED—See Graham Holdings Company; *U.S. Public*, pg. 955
HOLBROOK LTD.—See Deckers Outdoor Corporation; *U.S. Public*, pg. 645
HOLBROOK LUMBER COMPANY; *U.S. Private*, pg. 1961
HOLBROOK & MANTER INC.; *U.S. Private*, pg. 1961
HOLBROOK MFG., INC.; *U.S. Private*, pg. 1961
HOLBROOK SUN—See Gannett Co., Inc.; *U.S. Public*, pg. 902
HOLCHEM LABORATORIES LIMITED—See Ecolab Inc.; *U.S. Public*, pg. 714
HOLCIBEL S.A.—See Holcim Ltd.; *Int'l*, pg. 3446
HOLCIM AGGREGATI CALCESTRUZZI S.R.L.—See Holcim Ltd.; *Int'l*, pg. 3448
HOLCIM (AUSTRALIA) PTY., LTD.—See Holcim Ltd.; *Int'l*, pg. 3446
HOLCIM (AZERBAIJAN) O.J.S.C.—See Holcim Ltd.; *Int'l*, pg. 3446
HOLCIM (BELGIQUE) S.A.—See Holcim Ltd.; *Int'l*, pg. 3446
HOLCIM BETEILIGUNGS GMBH—See Holcim Ltd.; *Int'l*, pg. 3448
HOLCIM BETON UND ZUSCHLAGSTOFFE GMBH—See Holcim Ltd.; *Int'l*, pg. 3447
HOLCIM BF+P SA—See Holcim Ltd.; *Int'l*, pg. 3447
HOLCIM (BULGARIA) AD—See Holcim Ltd.; *Int'l*, pg. 3447
HOLCIM CEMENTS (BANGLADESH) LTD.—See Holcim Ltd.; *Int'l*, pg. 3448
HOLCIM COLOMBIA S.A.—See Holcim Ltd.; *Int'l*, pg. 3448
HOLCIM (COSTA RICA) S.A. - CARTAGO PLANT—See Holcim Ltd.; *Int'l*, pg. 3448
HOLCIM COSTA RICA S.A.—See Holcim Ltd.; *Int'l*, pg. 3448
HOLCIM (DEUTSCHLAND) GMBH - BREMEN GRINDING PLANT—See Holcim Ltd.; *Int'l*, pg. 3447
HOLCIM (DEUTSCHLAND) GMBH - HOVER PLANT—See Holcim Ltd.; *Int'l*, pg. 3447
HOLCIM (DEUTSCHLAND) GMBH - LAGERDORF PLANT—See Holcim Ltd.; *Int'l*, pg. 3447
HOLCIM (DEUTSCHLAND) GMBH—See Holcim Ltd.; *Int'l*, pg. 3447
HOLCIM EL SALVADOR S.A. DE C.V. - EL RONCO PLANT—See Holcim Ltd.; *Int'l*, pg. 3448
HOLCIM EL SALVADOR S.A. DE C.V. - MAYA PLANT—See Holcim Ltd.; *Int'l*, pg. 3448
HOLCIM EL SALVADOR S.A. DE C.V.—See Holcim Ltd.; *Int'l*, pg. 3448
HOLCIM (ESPANA) S.A. - JEREZ PLANT—See Holcim Ltd.; *Int'l*, pg. 3449
HOLCIM FINANCE (LUXEMBOURG) S.A.—See Holcim Ltd.; *Int'l*, pg. 3448
HOLCIM GROUP SERVICES LTD—See Holcim Ltd.; *Int'l*, pg. 3448
HOLCIM GRUPPO (ITALIA) S.P.A. - TERNATE PLANT—See Holcim Ltd.; *Int'l*, pg. 3448
HOLCIM (HRVATSKA) D.O.O.—See Holcim Ltd.; *Int'l*, pg. 3447

HOLCIM KIES UND BETON AG—See Holcim Ltd.; *Int'l*, pg. 3447
HOLCIM KIES UND BETON GMBH—See Holcim Ltd.; *Int'l*, pg. 3447
HOLCIM (LIBAN) S.A.L.—See Holcim Ltd.; *Int'l*, pg. 3447
HOLCIM LTD.; *Int'l*, pg. 3446
HOLCIM (MADAGASCAR) S.A.—See Holcim Ltd.; *Int'l*, pg. 3447
HOLCIM (MALAYSIA) SDN BHD - PASIR GUDANG PLANT—See Holcim Ltd.; *Int'l*, pg. 3447
HOLCIM (MALAYSIA) SDN. BHD.—See Holcim Ltd.; *Int'l*, pg. 3447
HOLCIM MEXICO S.A. DE C.V.—See Holcim Ltd.; *Int'l*, pg. 3448
HOLCIM (NEDERLAND) B.V.—See Holcim Ltd.; *Int'l*, pg. 3447
HOLCIM (NEW ZEALAND) LTD.—See Holcim Ltd.; *Int'l*, pg. 3447
HOLCIM (NICARAGUA) S.A.—See Holcim Ltd.; *Int'l*, pg. 3447
HOLCIM (PHILIPPINES) INC.—See Holcim Ltd.; *Int'l*, pg. 3447
HOLCIM PRECONTRAINT S.A.—See Holcim Ltd.; *Int'l*, pg. 3447
HOLCIM (REUNION) S.A.—See Holcim Ltd.; *Int'l*, pg. 3447
HOLCIM (ROMANIA) S.A. - ALESD PLANT—See Holcim Ltd.; *Int'l*, pg. 3447
HOLCIM (ROMANIA) S.A. - CAMPULUNG PLANT—See Holcim Ltd.; *Int'l*, pg. 3447
HOLCIM (ROMANIA) S.A.—See Holcim Ltd.; *Int'l*, pg. 3447
HOLCIM (ROMANIA) S.A. - TURDA GRINDING PLANT—See Holcim Ltd.; *Int'l*, pg. 3447
HOLCIM (RUS) CM LTD. - SHUROVO PLANT—See Holcim Ltd.; *Int'l*, pg. 3449
HOLCIM (RUS) OOO- VOLSK PLANT—See Holcim Ltd.; *Int'l*, pg. 3449
HOLCIM (SCHWEIZ) AG - SIGGENTHAL PLANT—See Holcim Ltd.; *Int'l*, pg. 3447
HOLCIM (SCHWEIZ) AG—See Holcim Ltd.; *Int'l*, pg. 3447
HOLCIM (SCHWEIZ) AG - UNTERVAZ PLANT—See Holcim Ltd.; *Int'l*, pg. 3447
HOLCIM (SINGAPORE) LIMITED—See Holcim Ltd.; *Int'l*, pg. 3447
HOLCIM (SUDDEUTSCHLAND) GMBH - DOTTERNHAUSEN PLANT—See Holcim Ltd.; *Int'l*, pg. 3447
HOLCIM (SUDDEUTSCHLAND) GMBH—See Holcim Ltd.; *Int'l*, pg. 3447
HOLCIM TRADING INC.—See Holcim Ltd.; *Int'l*, pg. 3448
HOLCIM TRADING S.A.—See Holcim Ltd.; *Int'l*, pg. 3448
HOLCIM (US) INC. - ADA PLANT—See Holcim Ltd.; *Int'l*, pg. 3447
HOLCIM (US) INC. - ARTESIA PLANT—See Holcim Ltd.; *Int'l*, pg. 3447
HOLCIM (US) INC. - BIRMINGHAM PLANT—See Holcim Ltd.; *Int'l*, pg. 3447
HOLCIM (US) INC. - HAGERSTOWN PLANT—See Holcim Ltd.; *Int'l*, pg. 3447
HOLCIM (US) INC. - HOLLY HILL PLANT—See Holcim Ltd.; *Int'l*, pg. 3447
HOLCIM (US) INC. - MIDLOTHIAN PLANT—See Holcim Ltd.; *Int'l*, pg. 3447
HOLCIM (US) INC. - PORTLAND PLANT—See Holcim Ltd.; *Int'l*, pg. 3447
HOLCIM (US) INC.—See Holcim Ltd.; *Int'l*, pg. 3447
HOLCIM (US) INC. - STE. GENEVIEVE PLANT—See Holcim Ltd.; *Int'l*, pg. 3447
HOLCIM (US) INC. - THEODORE PLANT—See Holcim Ltd.; *Int'l*, pg. 3447
HOLCIM (VENEZUELA) C.A.; *Int'l*, pg. 3446
HOLCOMB ENTERPRISES; *U.S. Private*, pg. 1961
HOLCOMBE USA INC.; *U.S. Private*, pg. 1962
HOLCOMB & HOKE MANUFACTURING COMPANY, INC.; *U.S. Private*, pg. 1961
HOLDAHL INC.; *U.S. Private*, pg. 1962
HOLDAL S.A.L.; *Int'l*, pg. 3449
HOLDAN BENELUX B.V.—See Midwich Group Plc; *Int'l*, pg. 4887
HOLDAN LIMITED—See Midwich Group Plc; *Int'l*, pg. 4887
HOLD BROTHERS INC.; *U.S. Private*, pg. 1962
HOLDCO NUVO GROUP D.G LTD.; *U.S. Public*, pg. 1044
HOLDEN EMPLOYEES SUPERANNUATION FUND PTY LTD—See General Motors Company; *U.S. Public*, pg. 926
HOLDEN GRAPHIC SERVICES; *U.S. Private*, pg. 1962
HOLDEN INDUSTRIES, INC.; *U.S. Private*, pg. 1962
HOLDEN NEW ZEALAND LIMITED—See General Motors Company; *U.S. Public*, pg. 926
HOLDEN OIL, INC.—See Superior Plus Corp.; *Int'l*, pg. 7338
HOLDER CONSTRUCTION COMPANY; *U.S. Private*, pg. 1962
HOLDER ELECTRIC SUPPLY, INC.; *U.S. Private*, pg. 1962
HOLDERFIN B.V.—See Holcim Ltd.; *Int'l*, pg. 3448
HOLDER HOSPITALITY GROUP INC.; *U.S. Private*, pg. 1962
HOLDERNESS BUILDING MATERIALS, INC.—See Bain Capital, LP; *U.S. Private*, pg. 451

HOLDER HOSPITALITY GROUP INC.

CORPORATE AFFILIATIONS

HOLDERS COMPONENTS LIMITED—See Holders Technology plc; *Int'l*, pg. 3449
HOLDERS TECHNOLOGY GMBH—See Holders Technology plc; *Int'l*, pg. 3450
HOLDERS TECHNOLOGY PLC; *Int'l*, pg. 3449
HOLDERS TECHNOLOGY UK LTD—See Holders Technology plc; *Int'l*, pg. 3450
HOLD-E-ZEE, LTD.—See Channellock, Inc.; *U.S. Private*, pg. 848
HOLDFAST INSURANCE BROKERS PTY. LTD.—See Steadfast Group Limited; *Int'l*, pg. 7187
HOLDFAST TECHNOLOGIES, LLC—See The Sterling Group, L.P.; *U.S. Private*, pg. 4122
HOLDIAL SA—See L'Oreal S.A.; *Int'l*, pg. 4378
HOLDIMAN MOTOR, INC.; *U.S. Private*, pg. 1962
HOLDINA D.O.O.—See INA-Industrija Nafte, d.d.; *Int'l*, pg. 3642
HOLDING BERCY INVESTISSEMENT SCA—See Charterhouse Capital Partners LLP; *Int'l*, pg. 1455
HOLDING CENTER AD; *Int'l*, pg. 3450
HOLDING CO ADMIE (IPTO) SA; *Int'l*, pg. 3450
HOLDING COOP-YUG AD; *Int'l*, pg. 3450
HOLDING DA INDUSTRIA TRANSFORMADORA DO TOMATE, SGPS S.A.—See Kagome Co., Ltd.; *Int'l*, pg. 4050
HOLDING D'INFRASTRUCTURES DE TRANSPORT SAS—See ACS, Actividades de Construccion y Servicios, S.A.; *Int'l*, pg. 112
HOLDING DRINATRANS AD—See Kompanija BOBAR d.o.o.; *Int'l*, pg. 4244
HOLDING FINANCIERE DIMOTRANS SA; *Int'l*, pg. 3450
HOLDING GONDOMAR 3 SAS—See BNP Paribas SA; *Int'l*, pg. 1091
HOLDING LE DUFF SA; *Int'l*, pg. 3450
HOLDING NOV VEK AD; *Int'l*, pg. 3450
HOLDING SOCOTEC S.A.S.—See Cobepa S.A.; *Int'l*, pg. 1683
HOLDING SOLINA SA—See Ardian SAS; *Int'l*, pg. 555
HOLDING SVETA SOFIA AD; *Int'l*, pg. 3450
HOLDING TEXTILE HERMES SAS—See Hermes International SCA; *Int'l*, pg. 3363
HOLDING VARNA AD-VARNA; *Int'l*, pg. 3450
HOLDINTER S.A.R.L.—See Toyota Tsusho Corporation; *Int'l*, pg. 7876
HOLD IT—See LOV Group Invest SAS; *Int'l*, pg. 4565
HOLD KEY ELECTRIC WIRE & CABLE, CO. LTD.; *Int'l*, pg. 3449
HOLD KEY ELECTRIC WIRE & CABLE, CO. LTD. - TAIWAN FACTORY1—See Hold Key Electric Wire & Cable, Co. Ltd.; *Int'l*, pg. 3449
HOLD KEY ELECTRIC WIRE & CABLE, CO. LTD. - TAIWAN FACTORY2—See Hold Key Electric Wire & Cable, Co. Ltd.; *Int'l*, pg. 3449
HOLD KEY ELECTRIC WIRE & CABLE, CO. LTD. - TAIWAN FACTORY3—See Hold Key Electric Wire & Cable, Co. Ltd.; *Int'l*, pg. 3449
HOLD ME LTD.; *Int'l*, pg. 3449
HOLDUX BETEILIGUNGSGESELLSCHAFT—See Assicurazioni Generali S.p.A.; *Int'l*, pg. 646
HOLE-IN-THE- WALL EDUCATION LIMITED—See Coforge Ltd.; *Int'l*, pg. 1693
HOLE MONTES, INC.—See Bowman Consulting Group Ltd.; *U.S. Public*, pg. 376
HO LEONG TRACTORS SDN. BHD.—See Hoe Leong Corporation Ltd.; *Int'l*, pg. 3439
HOLES, INC.; *U.S. Private*, pg. 1962
HOLFORD GAS STORAGE LIMITED—See E.ON SE; *Int'l*, pg. 2256
HOLGATE INFRASTRUCTURE & MOTORWAY SERVICES LIMITED—See Siteserv Investments Limited; *Int'l*, pg. 6965
HOLGATES NUTRITIONAL FOODS LIMITED—See Raisio PLC; *Int'l*, pg. 6190
HOLGER CHRISTIANSEN A/S—See Robert Bosch GmbH; *Int'l*, pg. 6361
HOLGER CHRISTIANSEN DEUTSCHLAND GMBH—See Robert Bosch GmbH; *Int'l*, pg. 6361
HOLGER CHRISTIANSEN FRANCE SAS—See Robert Bosch GmbH; *Int'l*, pg. 6361
HOLGER CHRISTIANSEN ITALIA S.R.L.—See Robert Bosch GmbH; *Int'l*, pg. 6361
HOLGER CHRISTIANSEN SVERIGE AB—See Robert Bosch GmbH; *Int'l*, pg. 6361
HOLGER CHRISTIANSEN UK LTD.—See Robert Bosch GmbH; *Int'l*, pg. 6361
HOLIDAY AUTO & TRUCK INC.; *U.S. Private*, pg. 1962
HOLIDAYBREAK LTD.—See Cox & Kings Limited; *Int'l*, pg. 1822
HOLIDAYBREAK REISEVERMITTLUNG GMBH—See Cox & Kings Limited; *Int'l*, pg. 1822
HOLIDAY BUILDERS INC.; *U.S. Private*, pg. 1962
HOLIDAY CARPET & FLOOR COVERINGS; *U.S. Private*, pg. 1962
HOLIDAY CENTER S.A.—See TUI AG; *Int'l*, pg. 7965
HOLIDAYCHECK AG—See Hubert Burda Media Holding Kommanditgesellschaft; *Int'l*, pg. 3520
HOLIDAYCHECK GROUP AG—See Hubert Burda Media Holding Kommanditgesellschaft; *Int'l*, pg. 3520
HOLIDAY CHEVROLET, LLC; *U.S. Private*, pg. 1962

HOLIDAY CLUB RESORTS OY—See Mahindra & Mahindra Limited; *Int'l*, pg. 4645
HOLIDAY COMPANIES; *U.S. Private*, pg. 1962
HOLIDAY CVS, L.L.C.—See CVS Health Corporation; *U.S. Public*, pg. 616
HOLIDAY DIALYSIS, LLC—See DaVita Inc.; *U.S. Public*, pg. 639
HOLIDAY DIVER INC.; *U.S. Private*, pg. 1963
HOLIDAY ENTERTAINMENT CO., LTD.; *Int'l*, pg. 3450
HOLIDAY EXPRESS CORPORATION; *U.S. Private*, pg. 1963
HOLIDAY FOODS & GROCERIES INC.; *U.S. Private*, pg. 1963
HOLIDAY FORD SALES (1980) LIMITED; *Int'l*, pg. 3450
HOLIDAY HOMES INC.; *U.S. Private*, pg. 1963
HOLIDAY HOUSE, INC.; *U.S. Private*, pg. 1963
HOLIDAY IMAGE, INC.; *U.S. Private*, pg. 1963
HOLIDAY INN AUSTIN MIDTOWN—See Jones Lang LaSalle Incorporated; *U.S. Public*, pg. 1204
HOLIDAY INN CAIRNS PTY LTD—See InterContinental Hotels Group PLC; *Int'l*, pg. 3737
HOLIDAY INN DOWNTOWN BEIJING COMPANY LIMITED—See Beijing Properties (Holdings) Limited; *Int'l*, pg. 955
HOLIDAY INN EXPRESS BOSTON—See KSL Capital Partners, LLC; *U.S. Private*, pg. 2355
HOLIDAY INN EXPRESS - DENVER INTERNATIONAL AIRPORT—See Stonebridge Realty Advisors, Inc.; *U.S. Private*, pg. 3827
HOLIDAY INN EXPRESS - WHITBY—See Northampton Group Inc.; *Int'l*, pg. 5442
HOLIDAY INN KUALA LUMPUR GLENMARIE—See InterContinental Hotels Group PLC; *Int'l*, pg. 3737
HOLIDAY INN MEXICANA S.A.—See InterContinental Hotels Group PLC; *Int'l*, pg. 3737
HOLIDAY INN OAKVILLE CENTRE HOTEL—See Clarke Inc.; *Int'l*, pg. 1650
HOLIDAY INN - PRINCETON—See Northampton Group Inc.; *Int'l*, pg. 5442
HOLIDAY INNS (BEIJING) LTD.—See InterContinental Hotels Group PLC; *Int'l*, pg. 3737
HOLIDAY INNS (CHONGQING), INC.—See InterContinental Hotels Group PLC; *Int'l*, pg. 3737
HOLIDAY INNS DE ESPANA S.A.—See InterContinental Hotels Group PLC; *Int'l*, pg. 3737
HOLIDAY INNS HOLDINGS (AUSTRALIA) PTY LTD.—See InterContinental Hotels Group PLC; *Int'l*, pg. 3737
HOLIDAY INNS (MACAU) LTD.—See InterContinental Hotels Group PLC; *Int'l*, pg. 3737
HOLIDAY INNS OF AMERICA (UK) LTD.—See InterContinental Hotels Group PLC; *Int'l*, pg. 3737
HOLIDAY ISLE RESORT & MARINA; *U.S. Private*, pg. 1963
HOLIDAY LETTINGS LIMITED—See TripAdvisor, Inc.; *U.S. Public*, pg. 2195
HOLIDAY MALTA CO. LTD.—See SMS Group Limited; *Int'l*, pg. 7014
HOLIDAY MALTA (HELLAS) TOURISM EPE—See Ryanair Holdings PLC; *Int'l*, pg. 6438
HOLIDAY ON ICE PRODUCTIONS B.V.—See CTS Eventim AG & Co. KGAA; *Int'l*, pg. 1873
HOLIDAY PACIFIC EQUITY CORPORATION—See InterContinental Hotels Group PLC; *Int'l*, pg. 3737
HOLIDAY PACIFIC LIMITED LIABILITY COMPANY—See InterContinental Hotels Group PLC; *Int'l*, pg. 3738
HOLIDAY PROPERTIES; *U.S. Private*, pg. 1963
HOLIDAY QUALITY FOODS, INC.—See North State Grocery Inc.; *U.S. Private*, pg. 2948
HOLIDAY RETIREMENT (CLEVEDON) LIMITED—See Welltower Inc.; *U.S. Public*, pg. 2348
HOLIDAY RETIREMENT CORP.—See SoftBank Group Corp.; *Int'l*, pg. 7053
HOLIDAYS SELECT LIMITED—See Emerson Developments (Holdings) Limited; *Int'l*, pg. 2379
HOLIDAY STATIONSTORES, LLC—See Alimentation Couche-Tard Inc.; *Int'l*, pg. 328
HOLIDAY SUPPORT FACILITY 2099; *U.S. Private*, pg. 1963
HOLIDAY TOURS & TRAVEL (KOREA) LIMITED—See Qantas Airways Limited; *Int'l*, pg. 6132
HOLIDAY TOURS & TRAVEL LIMITED—See Qantas Airways Limited; *Int'l*, pg. 6132
HOLIDAY TOURS & TRAVEL LTD—See Qantas Airways Limited; *Int'l*, pg. 6132
HOLIDAY TOURS & TRAVEL PTE. LTD.—See Qantas Airways Limited; *Int'l*, pg. 6132
HOLIDAY TOURS & TRAVEL (SINGAPORE) PTE. LTD.—See Qantas Airways Limited; *Int'l*, pg. 6132
HOLIDAY VACATIONS, LLC—See The Anschutz Corporation; *U.S. Private*, pg. 3987
HOLIDAY VILLAGE OF SANDPIPER INC.—See Fosun International Limited; *Int'l*, pg. 2750
HOLIDAY WHOLESALE INC.; *U.S. Private*, pg. 1963
HOLIDAY WORLD OF DALLAS LTD.; *U.S. Private*, pg. 1963
HOLIEN INC.; *U.S. Private*, pg. 1963
HOLISTA BIOTECH SDN BHD—See Holista CollTech Limited; *Int'l*, pg. 3450
HOLISTA COLLTECH LIMITED; *Int'l*, pg. 3450

HOLISTIC CARE HOME HEALTH AGENCY, INC.—See Astrana Health Inc.; *U.S. Public*, pg. 217
HOLISTIC PET SOURCE—See Summit Partners, L.P.; *U.S. Private*, pg. 3855
HOLITECH TECHNOLOGY CO., LTD.; *Int'l*, pg. 3451
HOLJERON CORPORATION—See Matthews International Corporation; *U.S. Public*, pg. 1400
HOLLADAY CORPORATION; *U.S. Private*, pg. 1963
HOLLADAY MEMORIAL PARK, INC.—See Security National Financial Corporation; *U.S. Public*, pg. 1856
HOLLAND AMERICA LINE INC.—See Carnival Corporation; *U.S. Public*, pg. 438
HOLLAND AMERICA LINE N.V.—See Carnival Corporation; *U.S. Public*, pg. 438
HOLLAND BANCORP, INC.; *U.S. Private*, pg. 1964
HOLLAND & BARRETT RETAIL LIMITED—See KKR & Co. Inc.; *U.S. Public*, pg. 1264
HOLLAND COLOURS AMERICAS INC—See Holland Colours NV; *Int'l*, pg. 3451
HOLLAND COLOURS CANADA INC—See Holland Colours NV; *Int'l*, pg. 3451
HOLLAND COLOURS CHINA LTD—See Holland Colours NV; *Int'l*, pg. 3451
HOLLAND COLOURS EUROPE BV—See Holland Colours NV; *Int'l*, pg. 3451
HOLLAND COLOURS HUNGARIA KFT—See Holland Colours NV; *Int'l*, pg. 3451
HOLLAND COLOURS MEXICANA SA DE CV—See Holland Colours NV; *Int'l*, pg. 3451
HOLLAND COLOURS NV; *Int'l*, pg. 3451
HOLLAND COLOURS UK LTD—See Holland Colours NV; *Int'l*, pg. 3451
THE HOLLAND COMPANY, INC.; *U.S. Private*, pg. 4054
HOLLAND CONSTRUCTION COMPANY, INC.; *U.S. Private*, pg. 1964
HOLLAND CORPORATION INC.; *U.S. Private*, pg. 1964
HOLLAND ELECTRONICS, INC.—See Amphenol Corporation; *U.S. Public*, pg. 130
HOLLANDER EN VAN DER MEY/MS&L—See Publicis Groupe S.A.; *Int'l*, pg. 6103
HOLLANDER INTERNATIONAL SYSTEMS LIMITED—See Vista Equity Partners, LLC; *U.S. Private*, pg. 4400
HOLLANDER SLEEP PRODUCTS LLC—See Centre Lane Partners, LLC; *U.S. Private*, pg. 827
HOLLAND GRAPHIC OCCASIONS B.V.—See Koenig & Bauer AG; *Int'l*, pg. 4226
HOLLAND & HART LLP; *U.S. Private*, pg. 1963
HOLLAND HEATING B.V.—See Systemair AB; *Int'l*, pg. 7391
HOLLAND HERSTEL GROEP / URECO B.V.—See Rentokil Initial plc; *Int'l*, pg. 6287
HOLLAND HOUSE FURNITURE—See The H.T. Hackney Company; *U.S. Private*, pg. 4041
HOLLANDIA DAIRY, INC.; *U.S. Private*, pg. 1964
HOLLANDIA SUNROOFS DE MEXICO, S.A. DE C.V.—See Webasto SE; *Int'l*, pg. 8364
THE HOLLAND, INC.; *U.S. Private*, pg. 4054
HOLLAND & KNIGHT LLP; *U.S. Private*, pg. 1963
HOLLAND LP—See Curran Group, Inc.; *U.S. Private*, pg. 1125
HOLLAND MOUNTING SYSTEMS B.V.—See Brady Corporation; *U.S. Public*, pg. 379
HOLLAND OPTICAL INSTRUMENTS BV—See EssilorLuxottica SA; *Int'l*, pg. 2514
HOLLAND PANEL PRODUCTS, INC.—See Panel Processing, Inc.; *U.S. Private*, pg. 3086
HOLLAND PARK LIMITED—See Berjaya Corporation Berhad; *Int'l*, pg. 983
HOLLAND PUMP MFG., INC.—See Arcus Infrastructure Partners LLP; *Int'l*, pg. 553
HOLLAND PUMP OF LOUISIANA, INC—See Arcus Infrastructure Partners LLP; *Int'l*, pg. 553
THE HOLLAND SENTINEL—See Gannett Co., Inc.; *U.S. Public*, pg. 904
HOLLAND SERVICES, LLC—See H.I.G. Capital, LLC; *U.S. Private*, pg. 1829
HOLLAND TRANSPORTATION MANAGEMENT INC.; *U.S. Private*, pg. 1964
THE HOLLAR COMPANY INC.; *U.S. Private*, pg. 4054
HOLLARD BOTSWANA (PTY) LTD—See Hollard Insurance Company Ltd; *Int'l*, pg. 3451
HOLLARD INSURANCE COMPANY LTD; *Int'l*, pg. 3451
HOLLARD INSURANCE COMPANY OF NAMIBIA LIMITED—See Hollard Insurance Company Ltd; *Int'l*, pg. 3451
HOLLARD INSURANCE ZAMBIA LIMITED—See Hollard Insurance Company Ltd; *Int'l*, pg. 3451
HOLLARD LIFE ASSURANCE ZAMBIA LIMITED—See Hollard Insurance Company Ltd; *Int'l*, pg. 3451
HOLLARD LIFE PROPERTIES (PTY) LIMITED—See Hollard Insurance Company Ltd; *Int'l*, pg. 3451
HOLLARD MOCAMBIQUE COMPANHIA DE SEGUROS SARL—See Hollard Insurance Company Ltd; *Int'l*, pg. 3451
HOLLARD SPECIALIST INSURANCE LIMITED—See Hollard Insurance Company Ltd; *Int'l*, pg. 3451
HOLLARD SPECIALIST LIFE LIMITED—See Hollard Insurance Company Ltd; *Int'l*, pg. 3451

COMPANY NAME INDEX

HOLLAR & GREENE PRODUCE CO. INC.; *U.S. Private*, pg. 1964
HOLLENBACH CONSTRUCTION, INC.; *U.S. Private*, pg. 1964
HOLLENFELS RE SA—See The Toronto-Dominion Bank; *Int'l*, pg. 7695
HOLLER DIGITAL LTD.—See Publicis Groupe S.A.; *Int'l*, pg. 6100
HOLLER DRIVER'S MART; *U.S. Private*, pg. 1964
HOLLESTELLE VASTGOED ONTWIKKELING B.V.—See Ronesans Holding A.S.; *Int'l*, pg. 6396
HOLLEWAY CAPITAL PARTNERS LLC; *U.S. Private*, pg. 1964
HOLLEY COMMUNICATIONS CO. LTD.—See Holley Holding, Ltd.; *Int'l*, pg. 3451
HOLLEY GROUP CO., LTD.—See Holley Holding, Ltd.; *Int'l*, pg. 3451
HOLLEY HOLDING, LTD.; *Int'l*, pg. 3451
HOLLEY HOLLAND LIMITED; *Int'l*, pg. 3451
HOLLEY INC.; *U.S. Public*, pg. 1044
HOLLEY METERING LTD.—See Holley Holding, Ltd.; *Int'l*, pg. 3451
HOLLEY PERFORMANCE PRODUCTS INC.—See Holley Inc.; *U.S. Public*, pg. 1044
HOLLIDAY CHEMICAL ESPANA S.A.—See Huntsman Corporation; *U.S. Public*, pg. 1073
HOLLIDAY FRANCE S.A.S.—See Huntsman Corporation; *U.S. Public*, pg. 1073
HOLLIDAY GROUP, LLC; *U.S. Private*, pg. 1965
HOLLIDAY ROCK CO., INC.; *U.S. Private*, pg. 1965
HOLLIDAY'S GENERAL SERVICE CORP.; *U.S. Private*, pg. 1965
HOLLIMANN S.A.—See Hubert Burda Media Holding Kommanditgesellschaft; *Int'l*, pg. 3519
HOLLINGER-HANNA LIMITED—See Labrador Iron Ore Royalty Corporation; *Int'l*, pg. 4390
HOLLINGSWORTH OIL CO. INC.; *U.S. Private*, pg. 1965
HOLLINGSWORTH OIL CO.—See Hollingsworth Oil Co. Inc.; *U.S. Private*, pg. 1965
HOLLINGSWORTH RICHARDS MAZDA; *U.S. Private*, pg. 1965
HOLLIS D. SEGUR INC.; *U.S. Private*, pg. 1965
HOLLISTER ASIA INCORPORATED—See Hollister Incorporated; *U.S. Private*, pg. 1965
HOLLISTER BELGIUM—See Hollister Incorporated; *U.S. Private*, pg. 1965
HOLLISTER & BLACKSMITH, INC.—See American Cannabis Company, Inc.; *U.S. Public*, pg. 98
HOLLISTER B.V.—See Hollister Incorporated; *U.S. Private*, pg. 1965
HOLLISTER CO., LTD.—See Hollister Incorporated; *U.S. Private*, pg. 1965
HOLLISTER CONSTRUCTION SERVICES, LLC; *U.S. Private*, pg. 1965
HOLLISTER CO.—See Abercrombie & Fitch Co.; *U.S. Public*, pg. 25
HOLLISTER DO BRASIL LTDA—See Hollister Incorporated; *U.S. Private*, pg. 1966
HOLLISTER EUROPE LIMITED—See Hollister Incorporated; *U.S. Private*, pg. 1965
HOLLISTER FASHION L.L.C—See Abercrombie & Fitch Co.; *U.S. Public*, pg. 25
HOLLISTER FREE LANCE—See Metro Publishing, Inc.; *U.S. Private*, pg. 2686
HOLLISTER GMBH—See Hollister Incorporated; *U.S. Private*, pg. 1965
HOLLISTER GREECE MEDICAL PRODUCTS COMMERCIAL S.A.—See Hollister Incorporated; *U.S. Private*, pg. 1965
HOLLISTER IBERICA, SA—See Hollister Incorporated; *U.S. Private*, pg. 1965
HOLLISTER INCORPORATED NIEDERLASSUNG DEUTSCHLAND—See Hollister Incorporated; *U.S. Private*, pg. 1965
HOLLISTER INCORPORATED; *U.S. Private*, pg. 1965
HOLLISTER KFT—See Hollister Incorporated; *U.S. Private*, pg. 1965
HOLLISTER LANDSCAPE SUPPLY—See Assured Aggregates Company; *U.S. Private*, pg. 359
HOLLISTER LATIN AMERICA—See Hollister Incorporated; *U.S. Private*, pg. 1965
HOLLISTER LIBERTY MEDICAL (SWITZERLAND) AG—See Hollister Incorporated; *U.S. Private*, pg. 1965
HOLLISTER LIMITED—See Hollister Incorporated; *U.S. Private*, pg. 1965
HOLLISTER LIMITED—See Hollister Incorporated; *U.S. Private*, pg. 1965
HOLLISTER LIMITED—See Hollister Incorporated; *U.S. Private*, pg. 1965
HOLLISTER MEDICAL INDIA PRIVATE LIMITED—See Hollister Incorporated; *U.S. Private*, pg. 1965
HOLLISTER NORGE—See Hollister Incorporated; *U.S. Private*, pg. 1965
HOLLISTER S.A. DE C.V.—See Hollister Incorporated; *U.S. Private*, pg. 1965
HOLLISTER SCANDINAVIA INC., SUOMEN SIVULIIKE—See Hollister Incorporated; *U.S. Private*, pg. 1965
HOLLISTER—See Hollister Incorporated; *U.S. Private*, pg. 1965
HOLLISTER SOUTH AFRICA (PTY) LTD—See Hollister Incorporated; *U.S. Private*, pg. 1966
HOLLISTER S.P.A.—See Hollister Incorporated; *U.S. Private*, pg. 1965
HOLLISTER SP. ZO.O.—See Hollister Incorporated; *U.S. Private*, pg. 1966
HOLLISTER S.R.O—See Hollister Incorporated; *U.S. Private*, pg. 1966
HOLLISTER SUPER INCORPORATED; *U.S. Private*, pg. 1966
HOLLISTER SVERIGE—See Hollister Incorporated; *U.S. Private*, pg. 1966
HOLLISTER ULC—See Hollister Incorporated; *U.S. Private*, pg. 1966
HOLLISTON, LLC; *U.S. Private*, pg. 1966
HOLLISTON TAB—See Gannett Co., Inc.; *U.S. Public*, pg. 902
HOLLISWEALTH ADVISORY SERVICES INC.—See iA Financial Corporation Inc.; *Int'l*, pg. 3567
HOLLI-TEX SUPPLY CO.; *U.S. Private*, pg. 1965
HOLLMAN INC.; *U.S. Private*, pg. 1966
HOLLOMAN CORPORATION; *U.S. Private*, pg. 1966
HOLLON OIL COMPANY; *U.S. Private*, pg. 1966
HOLLOWAY LODGING CORPORATION—See Clarke Inc.; *Int'l*, pg. 1650
HOLLOWAY SPORTSWEAR, INC.—See Platinum Equity, LLC; *U.S. Private*, pg. 3207
HOLLOW METAL SPECIALISTS, INC.—See Platinum Equity, LLC; *U.S. Private*, pg. 3208
HOLLSTADT & ASSOCIATES, INC.; *U.S. Private*, pg. 1966
HOLLUND INDUSTRIAL MARINE, INC.; *U.S. Public*, pg. 1044
HOLLYBERRY PROPS 12 (PROPRIETARY) LIMITED—See Hosken Consolidated Investments Limited; *Int'l*, pg. 3485
HOLLY CITY DEVELOPMENT CORPORATION; *U.S. Private*, pg. 1966
HOLLY CONNECTS, INC.—See Apollo Global Management, Inc.; *U.S. Public*, pg. 152
HOLLYCORP AVIATION, LLC—See HF Sinclair Corporation; *U.S. Public*, pg. 1034
HOLLY ENERGY PARTNERS, L.P.—See HF Sinclair Corporation; *U.S. Public*, pg. 1033
HOLLY FAYE MHP LLC—See Manufactured Housing Properties Inc.; *U.S. Public*, pg. 1362
HOLLYFRONTIER ASPHALT COMPANY LLC—See HF Sinclair Corporation; *U.S. Public*, pg. 1033
HOLLYFRONTIER CORPORATION—See HF Sinclair Corporation; *U.S. Public*, pg. 1033
HOLLYFRONTIER EL DORADO REFINING LLC—See HF Sinclair Corporation; *U.S. Public*, pg. 1033
HOLLYFRONTIER NAVAJO REFINING LLC—See HF Sinclair Corporation; *U.S. Public*, pg. 1033
HOLLYFRONTIER REFINING & MARKETING LLC—See HF Sinclair Corporation; *U.S. Public*, pg. 1033
HOLLY FUTURES CO., LTD.; *Int'l*, pg. 3451
HOLLY HILL HOSPITAL, LLC—See Universal Health Services, Inc.; *U.S. Public*, pg. 2258
HOLLY HUNT DO BRASIL IMPORTACAO E COMERCIO DE MOBILIARIOS LTDA—See MillerKnoll, Inc.; *U.S. Public*, pg. 1447
HOLLY HUNT ENTERPRISES, INC.—See MillerKnoll, Inc.; *U.S. Public*, pg. 1447
HOLLYLAND (CHINA) ELECTRONICS TECHNOLOGY CORPORATION LIMITED—See Hollyland Group Holdings Limited; *Int'l*, pg. 3452
HOLLYLAND CO., LTD.—See Hollyland Group Holdings Limited; *Int'l*, pg. 3452
HOLLYLAND GROUP HOLDINGS LIMITED; *Int'l*, pg. 3452
HOLLY LOGISTIC SERVICES, L.L.C.—See HF Sinclair Corporation; *U.S. Public*, pg. 1033
HOLLYMATIC CORPORATION; *U.S. Private*, pg. 1966
HOLLY PETROLEUM, INC.—See HF Sinclair Corporation; *U.S. Public*, pg. 1033
HOLLY REFINING COMMUNICATIONS, INC.—See HF Sinclair Corporation; *U.S. Public*, pg. 1033
HOLLY REFINING & MARKETING COMPANY—See HF Sinclair Corporation; *U.S. Public*, pg. 1033
HOLLY REFINING & MARKETING COMPANY - WOODS CROSS LLC—See HF Sinclair Corporation; *U.S. Public*, pg. 1033
HOLLY REFINING & MARKETING-TULSA LLC—See HF Sinclair Corporation; *U.S. Public*, pg. 1033
HOLLY'S CUSTOM PRINT, INC.; *U.S. Private*, pg. 1966
HOLLY SEED, LLC—See Southern Minnesota Beet Sugar Cooperative; *U.S. Private*, pg. 3733
HOLLY SU FUTURES (HONGKONG) CO., LTD.—See Holly Futures Co., Ltd.; *Int'l*, pg. 3451
HOLLYSYS (ASIA PACIFIC) PTE. LIMITED—See Hollysys Automation Technologies Ltd.; *Int'l*, pg. 3452
HOLLYSYS AUTOMATION TECHNOLOGIES LTD.; *Int'l*, pg. 3452
HOLLYWALL ENTERTAINMENT INC.; *U.S. Public*, pg. 1044
HOLLYWOOD BOWL GROUP PLC; *Int'l*, pg. 3452
HOLLYWOOD BRANDED INC.; *U.S. Private*, pg. 1966
HOLLYWOOD CHRYSLER PLYMOUTH INC.; *U.S. Private*, pg. 1966
HOLLYWOOD CLASSICS NETWORK, INC.; *U.S. Private*, pg. 1966
HOLLYWOOD ENTERTAINMENT EDU HOLDING, INC.; *U.S. Private*, pg. 1966
HOLLYWOOD FOREIGN PRESS ASSOCIATION; *U.S. Private*, pg. 1966
HOLLYWOOD IMPORTS LIMITED, INC.—See AutoNation, Inc.; *U.S. Public*, pg. 235
HOLLYWOOD KIA, INC.—See Morgan Auto Group, LLC; *U.S. Private*, pg. 2783
HOLLYWOOD LIFE MEDIA, LLC—See Penske Media Corporation; *U.S. Private*, pg. 3139
HOLLYWOOD RECORDS INC.—See The Walt Disney Company; *U.S. Public*, pg. 2138
HOLLYWOOD RENTALS PRODUCTION SERVICES LLC; *U.S. Private*, pg. 1966
HOLLYWOOD RENTAL SP.Z.O.O.—See Hollywood SA; *Int'l*, pg. 3452
THE HOLLYWOOD REPORTER, LLC—See Valence Media Group; *U.S. Private*, pg. 4330
HOLLYWOOD RIBBON INDUSTRIES INC.—See IG Design Group Plc; *Int'l*, pg. 3600
HOLLYWOOD SA; *Int'l*, pg. 3452
HOLLYWOOD SUPER MARKET INC.; *U.S. Private*, pg. 1966
HOLLYWOOD TANNING SYSTEMS, INC.; *U.S. Private*, pg. 1966
HOLLYWOOD TEXTILE SERVICE SP.Z.O.O.—See Hollywood SA; *Int'l*, pg. 3452
HOLLYWOOD TRUCKS, LLC—See Base Craft LLC; *U.S. Private*, pg. 484
HOLLYWOOD WOODWORK, INC.; *U.S. Private*, pg. 1966
HOL-MAC CORPORATION; *U.S. Private*, pg. 1961
HOLMAK HEATX B.V.—See CENTROTEC SE; *Int'l*, pg. 1414
HOLMAN AUTOMOTIVE GROUP, INC.; *U.S. Private*, pg. 1967
HOLMAN CADILLAC—See Holman Automotive Group, Inc.; *U.S. Private*, pg. 1967
HOLMAN COOKING EQUIPMENT INC.—See The Middleby Corporation; *U.S. Public*, pg. 2115
HOLMAN DISTRIBUTION CENTER OF OREGON; *U.S. Private*, pg. 1967
HOLMAN DISTRIBUTION CENTER OF WASHINGTON; *U.S. Private*, pg. 1967
HOLMAN'S INCORPORATED; *U.S. Private*, pg. 1967
HOLMARC OPTO-MECHATRONICS LTD.; *Int'l*, pg. 3452
HOLMATRO, INC.—See Madison Industries Holdings LLC; *U.S. Private*, pg. 2543
HOLMATRO N.V.—See Madison Industries Holdings LLC; *U.S. Private*, pg. 2543
HOLM AUTOMOTIVE CENTER; *U.S. Private*, pg. 1966
HOLMBERG FRANCE SAS—See Holmberg GmbH & Co. KG; *Int'l*, pg. 3452
HOLMBERG GMBH & CO. KG; *Int'l*, pg. 3452
HOLMEDALS KANTINESERVICE AS—See Oy Karl Fazer Ab; *Int'l*, pg. 5677
HOLMED, LLC—See NN, Inc.; *U.S. Public*, pg. 1531
HOLMEN AB; *Int'l*, pg. 3452
HOLMEN B.V.—See Holmen AB; *Int'l*, pg. 3452
HOLMEN DATA AB—See Holmen AB; *Int'l*, pg. 3452
HOLMEN ENERGI AB—See Holmen AB; *Int'l*, pg. 3452
HOLMEN ENERGI ELNAT AB—See Holmen AB; *Int'l*, pg. 3452
HOLMEN FRANCE S.A.S.—See Holmen AB; *Int'l*, pg. 3452
HOLMEN GMBH—See Holmen AB; *Int'l*, pg. 3452
HOLMEN ITALIA SRL—See Holmen AB; *Int'l*, pg. 3452
HOLMEN NEDERLAND B.V.—See Holmen AB; *Int'l*, pg. 3452
HOLMEN PAPER AB—See Holmen AB; *Int'l*, pg. 3452
HOLMEN PAPER AG—See Holmen AB; *Int'l*, pg. 3453
HOLMEN PAPER IBERICA SL—See Holmen AB; *Int'l*, pg. 3453
HOLMEN PAPER LTD.—See Holmen AB; *Int'l*, pg. 3453
HOLMEN PAPER MADRID S.L.—See Holmen AB; *Int'l*, pg. 3453
HOLMEN PAPIERS—See Holmen AB; *Int'l*, pg. 3453
HOLMEN S.A.S.—See Holmen AB; *Int'l*, pg. 3453
HOLMEN SKOG AB-IGGESUND—See Holmen AB; *Int'l*, pg. 3453
HOLMEN SKOG AB-LYCKSELE—See Holmen AB; *Int'l*, pg. 3453
HOLMEN SKOG AB-ORNSKOLDSVIK—See Holmen AB; *Int'l*, pg. 3453
HOLMEN SKOG AB-ROBERTSFORS—See Holmen AB; *Int'l*, pg. 3453
HOLMEN SKOG AB—See Holmen AB; *Int'l*, pg. 3453
HOLMEN TIMBER AB/IGGESUND SAWMILL—See Holmen AB; *Int'l*, pg. 3453
HOLMEN TIMBER UK—See Holmen AB; *Int'l*, pg. 3453
HOLMER MASCHINENBAU GMBH—See Exel Industries SA; *Int'l*, pg. 2582
HOLMES & ASSOCIATES LLC; *U.S. Private*, pg. 1967
HOLMES BODY SHOP INC.; *U.S. Private*, pg. 1967

HOLMES CHAPEL TRADING LTD—See Solvay S.A.; *Int'l*, pg. 7078
HOLMES COMPANY OF JACKSON; *U.S. Private*, pg. 1967
HOLMES CONSTRUCTION CO. LP; *U.S. Private*, pg. 1967
HOLMES FOODS INC.; *U.S. Private*, pg. 1967
HOLMES FREIGHT LINES INC.; *Int'l*, pg. 3453
HOLMES FUNERAL DIRECTORS, INC.—See Service Corporation International; *U.S. Public*, pg. 1869
HOLMES LANDSCAPE COMPANY—See Landscape Developmental Inc.; *U.S. Private*, pg. 2387
HOLMES LUMBER & BUILDING CENTER INC.—See Carter Lumber Co.; *U.S. Private*, pg. 776
HOLMES MOTORS, INC.; *U.S. Private*, pg. 1967
HOLMES MURPHY & ASSOCIATES, INC.; *U.S. Private*, pg. 1967
HOLMES OIL COMPANY INC.; *U.S. Private*, pg. 1968
HOLMES PACKAGING AUSTRALIA PTY. LTD—See Sealed Air Corporation; *U.S. Public*, pg. 1853
HOLMES PLACE INTERNATIONAL LTD.; *Int'l*, pg. 3453
HOLMES SHAW, INC.—See PointeNorth Insurance Group LLC; *U.S. Private*, pg. 3222
HOLMES TUTTLE FORD, INC.—See Tuttle-Click Automotive Group; *U.S. Private*, pg. 4263
HOLMGREN & ASSOCIATES; *U.S. Private*, pg. 1968
HOLMGRENS METALL AKTIEBOLAGET—See Aalberts N.V.; *Int'l*, pg. 34
HOLMGRENS TRUCK-MOTOR AB—See Bilia AB; *Int'l*, pg. 1029
HOLM & HALBY A/S—See Addtech AB; *Int'l*, pg. 133
HOLM KK EXTRUSIONS PVT. LTD.—See Ilpea Inc.; *U.S. Private*, pg. 2043
HOLMQUIST FEEDMILL INC.; *U.S. Private*, pg. 1968
HOLMQUIST LUMBER CO.; *U.S. Private*, pg. 1968
HOLMSKOV RUSTFRI STAINLESS STEEL COMPANY A/S—See Per Aarsleff Holding A/S; *Int'l*, pg. 5795
THE HOLMS SAND & GRAVEL COMPANY (1985)—See Heidelberg Materials AG; *Int'l*, pg. 3320
HOLM TRAVAROR AB; *Int'l*, pg. 3453
HOLOBUILDER, INC.—See FARO Technologies, Inc.; *U.S. Public*, pg. 823
HOLOGENIX, LLC; *U.S. Private*, pg. 1968
HOLOGIC ASIA PACIFIC LIMITED—See Hologic, Inc.; *U.S. Public*, pg. 1045
HOLOGIC (AUSTRALIA) PTY LIMITED—See Hologic, Inc.; *U.S. Public*, pg. 1045
HOLOGIC AUSTRIA GMBH—See Hologic, Inc.; *U.S. Public*, pg. 1045
HOLOGIC DEUTSCHLAND GMBH—See Hologic, Inc.; *U.S. Public*, pg. 1045
HOLOGIC FRANCE, SARL—See Hologic, Inc.; *U.S. Public*, pg. 1045
HOLOGIC FRANCE S.A.—See Hologic, Inc.; *U.S. Public*, pg. 1045
HOLOGIC HITEC-IMAGING GMBH—See Hologic, Inc.; *U.S. Public*, pg. 1045
HOLOGIC IBERIA, S.L.—See Hologic, Inc.; *U.S. Public*, pg. 1045
HOLOGIC, INC. - BREAST IMAGING SOLUTIONS—See Hologic, Inc.; *U.S. Public*, pg. 1045
HOLOGIC, INC.; *U.S. Public*, pg. 1044
HOLOGIC INTERNATIONAL HOLDINGS B.V.—See Hologic, Inc.; *U.S. Public*, pg. 1045
HOLOGIC ITALIA S.R.L.—See Hologic, Inc.; *U.S. Public*, pg. 1045
HOLOGIC JAPAN, INC.—See Hologic, Inc.; *U.S. Public*, pg. 1045
HOLOGIC MEDICOR SUISSE GMBH—See Hologic, Inc.; *U.S. Public*, pg. 1045
HOLOGIC NETHERLANDS B.V.—See Hologic, Inc.; *U.S. Public*, pg. 1045
HOLOGIC N.V.—See Hologic, Inc.; *U.S. Public*, pg. 1045
HOLOGIC SA—See Hologic, Inc.; *U.S. Public*, pg. 1045
HOLOGIC SUISSE SA—See Hologic, Inc.; *U.S. Public*, pg. 1045
HOLOGIC SURGICAL PRODUCTS COSTA RICA S.A.—See Hologic, Inc.; *U.S. Public*, pg. 1045
HOLOGIC SWEDEN AB—See Hologic, Inc.; *U.S. Public*, pg. 1045
HOLOGRAM. INDUSTRIES RESEARCH GMBH—See Hologram. Industries SA; *Int'l*, pg. 3453
HOLOGRAM. INDUSTRIES SA; *Int'l*, pg. 3453
HOLOGRAM USA NETWORKS INC.; *U.S. Private*, pg. 1968
HOLOGRAPHIC STORAGE LTD.; *U.S. Public*, pg. 1045
HOLOGRAPHIX LLC—See Headwall Photonics, Inc.; *U.S. Private*, pg. 1891
HOLO-KROME COMPANY—See Fastenal Company; *U.S. Public*, pg. 824
HOLOMETRIC TECHNOLOGIES FORSCHUNGS- UND ENTWICKLUNGS-GMBH—See Carl-Zeiss-Stiftung; *Int'l*, pg. 1336
HOLON CO., LTD.—See A&D Co., Ltd.; *Int'l*, pg. 19
HOLOPHANE EUROPE LTD.—See Acuity Brands, Inc.; *U.S. Public*, pg. 37
HOLOPHANE LIGHTING LTD.—See Acuity Brands, Inc.; *U.S. Public*, pg. 37

HOLOPHANE, S.A. DE C.V.—See Acuity Brands, Inc.; *U.S. Public*, pg. 37
HOLOSFIND S.A.; *Int'l*, pg. 3453
HOLOTEK TECHNOLOGY CO., LTD.—See Shenzhen Jinjia Group Co., Ltd.; *Int'l*, pg. 6814
HOLROYD PRECISION LTD.—See Chongqing Machinery & Electronics Holding (Group) Co., Ltd.; *Int'l*, pg. 1580
HOLSOTHERM GMBH; *Int'l*, pg. 3453
HOLSTEIN ASSOCIATION USA, INC.; *U.S. Private*, pg. 1968
HOLSTEINER HUMUS UND ERDEN GMBH—See L. Possehl & Co. mbH; *Int'l*, pg. 4383
HOLSTEN-BRAUEREI AG—See Carlsberg A/S; *Int'l*, pg. 1340
HOLSTON ELECTRIC COOPERATIVE INC.; *U.S. Private*, pg. 1968
HOLSTON GASES INC.; *U.S. Private*, pg. 1968
HOLSTON UNITED METHODIST HOME FOR CHILDREN; *U.S. Private*, pg. 1968
HOLSTON VALLEY AMBULATORY SURGERY CENTER, LLC—See Tenet Healthcare Corporation; *U.S. Public*, pg. 2004
HOLSUM BAKERY, INC.—See Flowers Foods, Inc.; *U.S. Public*, pg. 855
HOLT & BUGBEE COMPANY; *U.S. Private*, pg. 1968
HOLT CAT COMPANY OF TEXAS INC.; *U.S. Private*, pg. 1968
HOLT CONSTRUCTION CORP.; *U.S. Private*, pg. 1968
HOLTEC INTERNATIONAL; *U.S. Private*, pg. 1969
HOLTEK SEMICONDUCTOR (CHINA) INC.—See Holtek Semiconductor Inc.; *Int'l*, pg. 3453
HOLTEK SEMICONDUCTOR INC.; *Int'l*, pg. 3453
HOLTEK SEMICONDUCTOR INC.—See Holtek Semiconductor Inc.; *Int'l*, pg. 3454
HOLTEK SEMICONDUCTOR (INDIA) PVT. LTD.—See Holtek Semiconductor Inc.; *Int'l*, pg. 3453
HOLTEK SEMICONDUCTOR (USA), INC.—See Holtek Semiconductor Inc.; *Int'l*, pg. 3453
HOLT ELECTRIC INC.; *U.S. Private*, pg. 1968
HOLTEN DIALYSIS, LLC—See DaVita Inc.; *U.S. Public*, pg. 639
HOLTER REGELARMATUREN GMBH & CO. KG; *Int'l*, pg. 3454
HOLT & HOLT, INC.; *U.S. Private*, pg. 1968
HOLT HOSIERY MILLS, INC.; *U.S. Private*, pg. 1968
HOLTHOUSE CARLIN VAN TRIGT LLP; *U.S. Private*, pg. 1969
HOLT INTERNATIONAL CHILDREN'S SERVICES; *U.S. Private*, pg. 1968
HOLT JAPAN INC.—See Hoya Corporation; *Int'l*, pg. 3494
HOLT LLOYD INTERNATIONAL LTD—See Rank Group Ltd.; *Int'l*, pg. 6208
HOLT LUMBER INC.; *U.S. Private*, pg. 1968
HOLT MOTOR INC.; *U.S. Private*, pg. 1968
HOLT MOTORS, INC.; *U.S. Private*, pg. 1968
HOLT OF CALIFORNIA INC.; *U.S. Private*, pg. 1968
HOLTON COMMUNITY HOSPITAL; *U.S. Private*, pg. 1969
HOLTON FOOD PRODUCTS COMPANY—See RPM International Inc.; *U.S. Public*, pg. 1817
HOLTON SENTIVAN + GURY; *U.S. Private*, pg. 1969
HOLTRY'S LLC—See Tym Corporation; *Int'l*, pg. 7995
HOLT'S CIGAR HOLDINGS, INC.; *U.S. Private*, pg. 1969
HOLT TEXAS, LTD.; *U.S. Private*, pg. 1968
HOLTZBRINCK DIGITAL GMBH—See Verlagsgruppe Georg von Holtzbrinck GmbH; *Int'l*, pg. 8169
HOLTZBRINCK PUBLISHERS, LLC—See Verlagsgruppe Georg von Holtzbrinck GmbH; *Int'l*, pg. 8170
HOLTZMAN OIL CORP.; *U.S. Private*, pg. 1969
HOLTZMAN PROPANE LLC—See Holtzman Oil Corp.; *U.S. Private*, pg. 1969
HOLU ENERGY LLC—See EnSync, Inc.; *U.S. Public*, pg. 776
HOLUX LIGHTING SYSTEM CO. LTD.—See A.A.G. STUCCHI s.r.l.; *Int'l*, pg. 23
HOLY CROSS ENERGY; *U.S. Private*, pg. 1969
HOLY CROSS HEALTH SYSTEM—See Trinity Health Corporation; *U.S. Private*, pg. 4233
HOLY CROSS HOSPITAL—See Ascension Health Alliance; *U.S. Private*, pg. 347
THE HOLY LAND INSURANCE CO.; *Int'l*, pg. 7652
HOLY LANDS SUN TOURS—See Isram Wholesale Tours & Travel Ltd.; *U.S. Private*, pg. 2147
HOLY NAME MEDICAL CENTER; *U.S. Private*, pg. 1969
HOLYOKE FINE HOMES—See Lease Crutcher Lewis; *U.S. Private*, pg. 2408
HOLYOKE GAS & ELECTRIC DEPARTMENT; *U.S. Private*, pg. 1969
HOLYOKE HEALTHCARE CENTER, LLC—See National HealthCare Corporation; *U.S. Public*, pg. 1495
HOLYOKE NEWS CO. INC.; *U.S. Private*, pg. 1969
HOLYROOD COMMUNICATIONS LTD.—See Biteback Publishing Ltd.; *Int'l*, pg. 1050
HOLY STONE ENTERPRISE CO., LTD. - DONGGUAN PLANT—See Holy Stone Enterprise Co., Ltd.; *Int'l*, pg. 3454
HOLY STONE ENTERPRISE CO., LTD.; *Int'l*, pg. 3454
HOLY STONE (EUROPE) LTD.—See Holy Stone Enterprise Co., Ltd.; *Int'l*, pg. 3454

HOLY STONE HEALTHCARE CO., LTD.—See Holy Stone Enterprise Co., Ltd.; *Int'l*, pg. 3454
HOLY STONE HOLDINGS CO., LTD.—See Holy Stone Enterprise Co., Ltd.; *Int'l*, pg. 3454
HOLY STONE INTERNATIONAL TRADING (SHANGHAI) CO., LTD.—See Holy Stone Enterprise Co., Ltd.; *Int'l*, pg. 3454
HOLYWORLD SA—See MPX International Corporation; *Int'l*, pg. 5063
HOLZER HEALTH SYSTEM; *U.S. Private*, pg. 1969
HOLZHAUER AUTO & TRUCK SALES, INC.; *U.S. Private*, pg. 1969
HOLZ-HER GMBH—See Michael Weinig AG; *Int'l*, pg. 4874
HOLZ-HER MASCHINENBAU GMBH—See Michael Weinig AG; *Int'l*, pg. 4874
HOLZINDUSTRIE BRUCHSAL GMBH—See Draexlmaier Gruppe; *Int'l*, pg. 2198
HOLZMA PLATTENAUFTEILTECHNIK GMBH—See Durr AG; *Int'l*, pg. 2232
HOLZMA PLATTENAUFTEILTECHNIK S.A.—See Durr AG; *Int'l*, pg. 2232
HOLZMA TECH GMBH—See Durr AG; *Int'l*, pg. 2232
HOLZ MOTORS, INC.; *U.S. Private*, pg. 1969
HOLZWARME GRINDELWALD AG—See BKW AG; *Int'l*, pg. 1055
HOLZWERKSTOFF HOLDING AG; *Int'l*, pg. 3454
HOLZWORTH INSTRUMENTATION, INC.—See Artemis Capital Partners Management Co., LLC; *U.S. Private*, pg. 341
HOMAC MANUFACTURING COMPANY INC.; *U.S. Private*, pg. 1969
HOMAC NICOT CORP.—See DCM Holdings Co., Ltd.; *Int'l*, pg. 1992
HOM/ADE FOODS, INC.—See J&J Snack Foods Corporation; *U.S. Public*, pg. 1179
HOMAG ASIA (PTE) LTD—See Durr AG; *Int'l*, pg. 2232
HOMAG ASIA (THAILAND) CO., LTD.—See Durr AG; *Int'l*, pg. 2233
HOMAG AUSTRALIA PTY LTD—See Durr AG; *Int'l*, pg. 2232
HOMAG AUSTRIA GESELLSCHAFT M.B.H.—See Durr AG; *Int'l*, pg. 2233
HOMAG AUTOMATION GMBH—See Durr AG; *Int'l*, pg. 2233
HOMAG BOHRSYSTEME GMBH—See Durr AG; *Int'l*, pg. 2233
HOMAG CANADA INC—See Durr AG; *Int'l*, pg. 2232
HOMAG DANMARK A/S—See Durr AG; *Int'l*, pg. 2232
HOMAG ESOLUTION GMBH—See Durr AG; *Int'l*, pg. 2232
HOMAG ESPANA S.A.—See Durr AG; *Int'l*, pg. 2233
HOMAG FINANCE GMBH—See Durr AG; *Int'l*, pg. 2232
HOMAG FRANCE S.A—See Durr AG; *Int'l*, pg. 2232
HOMAG GMBH—See Durr AG; *Int'l*, pg. 2233
HOMAG GROUP AG—See Durr AG; *Int'l*, pg. 2232
HOMAG HOLZBEARBEITUNGSSYSTEME GMBH—See Durr AG; *Int'l*, pg. 2232
HOMAG INDIA PRIVATE LTD—See Durr AG; *Int'l*, pg. 2232
HOMAG ITALIA S.P.A—See Durr AG; *Int'l*, pg. 2232
HOMAG JAPAN CO. LTD—See Durr AG; *Int'l*, pg. 2232
HOMAG KANTENTECHNIK GMBH—See Durr AG; *Int'l*, pg. 2233
HOMAG KOREA CO., LTD.—See Durr AG; *Int'l*, pg. 2232
HOMAG MACHINERY (SHANGHAI) CO., LTD.—See Durr AG; *Int'l*, pg. 2232
HOMAG MACHINERY SRODA SP. Z O.O.—See Durr AG; *Int'l*, pg. 2232
HOMAG PLATTENAUFTEILTECHNIK GMBH—See Durr AG; *Int'l*, pg. 2233
HOMAG POLSKA SP.Z O.O—See Durr AG; *Int'l*, pg. 2232
HOMAG (SCHWEIZ) AG—See Durr AG; *Int'l*, pg. 2232
HOMAG SERVICES POLAND SP. Z O.O.—See Durr AG; *Int'l*, pg. 2233
HOMAG SOUTH AMERICA LTDA—See Durr AG; *Int'l*, pg. 2232
HOMAG TRADING AND SERVICES SDN. BHD.—See Durr AG; *Int'l*, pg. 2233
HOMAG U.K. LTD.—See Durr AG; *Int'l*, pg. 2232
HOMAG VERTRIEBS-BETEILIGUNGS GMBH—See Durr AG; *Int'l*, pg. 2232
HOMAG VERTRIEB & SERVICE GMBH—See Durr AG; *Int'l*, pg. 2232
HOMAG VIETNAM COMPANY LIMITED—See Durr AG; *Int'l*, pg. 2233
HOMAIR VACANCES SA—See The Carlyle Group Inc.; *U.S. Public*, pg. 2047
HOMAN AUTO SALES, INC.; *U.S. Private*, pg. 1969
HOMAN LUMBER MART, INC.; *U.S. Private*, pg. 1970
HOMANS ASSOCIATES LLC—See Watsco, Inc.; *U.S. Public*, pg. 2336
HOMA POMPEN B.V.—See HOMA Pumpenfabrik GmbH; *Int'l*, pg. 3454
HOMA PUMPENFABRIK GMBH; *Int'l*, pg. 3454
HOMASOTE COMPANY; *U.S. Public*, pg. 1045
THE HOMAX GROUP, INC.—See PPG Industries, Inc.; *U.S. Public*, pg. 1710
HOMAX OIL SALES INC.; *U.S. Private*, pg. 1970

COMPANY NAME INDEX

HOMAX PRODUCTS, INC.—See PPG Industries, Inc.; *U.S. Public*, pg. 1708
HOME24 OUTLET GMBH—See XXXLutz KG; *Int'l*, pg. 8542
HOME24 SE—See XXXLutz KG; *Int'l*, pg. 8542
HOME ACCESS HEALTH CORPORATION—See Everlywell, Inc.; *U.S. Private*, pg. 1440
HOME ACRES BUILDING SUPPLY CO., LLC; *U.S. Private*, pg. 1970
HOMEADVISOR, INC.—See IAC Inc.; *U.S. Public*, pg. 1081
HOME AFRIKA LIMITED; *Int'l*, pg. 3454
THE HOME AGENCY; *U.S. Private*, pg. 4054
HOMEAMERICAN MORTGAGE CORP.—See Sekisui House, Ltd.; *Int'l*, pg. 6697
HOME APPLIANCE MART INC.; *U.S. Private*, pg. 1970
HOME A/S—See Danske Bank A/S; *Int'l*, pg. 1969
HOME ATTENDANT SERVICE OF HYDE PARK; *U.S. Private*, pg. 1970
HOME AUTOMATION (FE) PTE. LTD.—See Hi Sharp Electronics Co., Ltd.; *Int'l*, pg. 3379
HOME AUTOMATION, INC.—See Leviton Manufacturing Company, Inc.; *U.S. Private*, pg. 2436
HOMEAWAY, INC.—See Expedia Group, Inc.; *U.S. Public*, pg. 809
HOMEAWAY PTY LTD—See Expedia Group, Inc.; *U.S. Public*, pg. 809
HOME BANCGROUP, INC.; *U.S. Private*, pg. 1970
HOME BANCORP, INC.; *U.S. Public*, pg. 1045
HOME BANCORP WISCONSIN, INC.; *U.S. Public*, pg. 1045
HOME BANCSHARES, INC.; *U.S. Public*, pg. 1045
HOME BANK, NATIONAL ASSOCIATION—See Home Bancorp, Inc.; *U.S. Public*, pg. 1045
HOME BANK SB; *U.S. Private*, pg. 1970
HOMEBASE GROUP LTD.—See Hilco Trading, LLC; *U.S. Private*, pg. 1944
HOMEBAY RESIDENTIAL PRIVATE LIMITED—See Jones Lang LaSalle Incorporated; *U.S. Public*, pg. 1202
HOME BISTRO, INC.; *U.S. Public*, pg. 1045
HOME BOX OFFICE, INC.—See Warner Bros. Discovery, Inc.; *U.S. Public*, pg. 2327
HOMEBOY ELECTRONICS RECYCLING—See Homeboy Industries; *U.S. Private*, pg. 1972
HOMEBOY INDUSTRIES; *U.S. Private*, pg. 1972
HOME BRANDS, LLC—See Tuff Shed, Inc.; *U.S. Private*, pg. 4257
HOME BREW MART, INC.—See Kings & Convicts Brewing Co.; *U.S. Private*, pg. 2311
HOMEBRIDGE FINANCIAL SERVICES, INC. - SHERMAN OAKS—See HomeBridge Financial Services, Inc.; *U.S. Private*, pg. 1973
HOMEBRIDGE FINANCIAL SERVICES, INC.; *U.S. Private*, pg. 1973
HOMEBRIDGE FINANCIAL SERVICES, INC.—See HomeBridge Financial Services, Inc.; *U.S. Private*, pg. 1973
HOME BUILDERS & SUPPLY CO. INC.; *U.S. Private*, pg. 1970
HOMECALL OF FREDERICK—See UnitedHealth Group Incorporated; *U.S. Public*, pg. 2245
HOME & CAPITAL ADVISERS LIMITED—See Grainger plc; *Int'l*, pg. 3052
HOME CAPITAL GROUP INC.—See Smith Financial Corporation; *Int'l*, pg. 7009
HOME & CAPITAL TRUSTEE COMPANY LIMITED—See Grainger plc; *Int'l*, pg. 3052
THE HOME & CAPITAL TRUST GROUP LIMITED—See Grainger plc; *Int'l*, pg. 3052
HOME & CAPITAL TRUST LIMITED—See Grainger plc; *Int'l*, pg. 3052
HOME CARE ASSISTANCE CORPORATION; *U.S. Private*, pg. 1970
HOME CARE CONNECTIONS, INC.—See UnitedHealth Group Incorporated; *U.S. Public*, pg. 2245
HOME CARE CONNECT LLC; *U.S. Private*, pg. 1970
HOME CARE DELIVERED, INC.—See Beecken Petty O'Keefe & Company, LLC; *U.S. Private*, pg. 514
HOME CARE EQUIPMENT, INC.—See Lundbeckfonden; *Int'l*, pg. 4580
HOMECARE HEALTH SOLUTIONS, INC.—See Humana, Inc.; *U.S. Public*, pg. 1069
HOMECARE HOMEBASE, LLC—See The Hearst Corporation; *U.S. Private*, pg. 4045
HOMECARE & HOSPICE OF THE VALLEY; *U.S. Private*, pg. 1973
HOME CARE MEDICAL, INC.—See Linde plc; *Int'l*, pg. 4508
HOME CARE PHARMACY, LLC—See CVS Health Corporation; *U.S. Public*, pg. 616
HOMECARE PREFERRED CHOICE, INC.—See Amedisys, Inc.; *U.S. Public*, pg. 94
HOMECARE PRODUCTS, INC.; *U.S. Private*, pg. 1973
HOME CARE PULSE LLC—See In The Know, Inc.; *U.S. Private*, pg. 2052
HOMECARE SOFTWARE SOLUTIONS LLC; *U.S. Private*, pg. 1973
HOME CARE SPECIALISTS, INC.; *U.S. Private*, pg. 1970
HOMECAST CO., LTD.; *Int'l*, pg. 3455
HOME CENTER HOLDINGS CO., LTD.; *Int'l*, pg. 3454

HOME CENTER, INC.; *U.S. Private*, pg. 1970
HOME CENTER SANKO CO., LTD.—See DCM Holdings Co., Ltd.; *Int'l*, pg. 1992
HOME CENTRE LLC—See Landmark Retail Holdings 1 Limited; *Int'l*, pg. 4407
HOMECHOICE PARTNERS, INC—See Option Care Health, Inc.; *U.S. Public*, pg. 1609
HOME CITY ICE COMPANY INC.; *U.S. Private*, pg. 1970
HOMECO DAILY NEEDS REIT; *Int'l*, pg. 3455
HOME CONCEPT SA; *Int'l*, pg. 3454
HOME CONNECT GMBH—See Robert Bosch GmbH; *Int'l*, pg. 6361
HOME CONSORTIUM LIMITED—See HMC Capital Limited; *Int'l*, pg. 3431
HOME CONTROL INTERNATIONAL LIMITED; *Int'l*, pg. 3454
HOME COUNTIES INSURANCE SERVICES LIMITED—See Brown & Brown, Inc.; *U.S. Public*, pg. 401
HOME CREDIT CONSUMER FINANCE CO., LTD.—See PPF Group N.V.; *Int'l*, pg. 5950
HOME CREDIT & FINANCE BANK LLC—See PPF Group N.V.; *Int'l*, pg. 5950
HOME CREDIT INDIA FINANCE PRIVATE LTD.—See PPF Group N.V.; *Int'l*, pg. 5950
HOME CREDIT INDONESIA PT—See Mitsubishi UFJ Financial Group, Inc.; *Int'l*, pg. 4969
HOME CREDIT INTERNATIONAL A.S.—See PPF Group N.V.; *Int'l*, pg. 5950
HOME CREDIT SLOVAKIA, A.S.—See PPF Group N.V.; *Int'l*, pg. 5950
HOME CREDIT VIETNAM FINANCE COMPANY LTD.—See PPF Group N.V.; *Int'l*, pg. 5950
HOMECREST OUTDOOR LIVING LLC; *U.S. Private*, pg. 1973
HOMEDALE HEALTHCARE, INC.—See The Ensign Group, Inc.; *U.S. Public*, pg. 2071
HOME DECO CO., LTD.—See Nitori Holdings Co., Ltd.; *Int'l*, pg. 5381
HOME DECORATORS COLLECTION INC.—See The Home Depot, Inc.; *U.S. Public*, pg. 2089
HOME DECOR HOLDING COMPANY—See Kohlberg & Company, LLC; *U.S. Private*, pg. 2338
HOME DECOR INNOVATIONS, INC.; *U.S. Private*, pg. 1970
HOME DECOR LIQUIDATORS FURNITURE & FLOORING; *U.S. Private*, pg. 1970
HOME DELIVERY INCONTINENT SUPPLIES CO., INC.—See PT Sinar Mas Group; *Int'l*, pg. 6073
HOME DEPOT DIRECT—See The Home Depot, Inc.; *U.S. Public*, pg. 2089
THE HOME DEPOT, INC.; *U.S. Public*, pg. 2089
HOME DEPOT MEXICO, S. DE R.L. DE C.V.—See The Home Depot, Inc.; *U.S. Public*, pg. 2089
HOME DEPOT OF CANADA INC.—See The Home Depot, Inc.; *U.S. Public*, pg. 2089
HOME DEPOT U.S.A., INC.—See The Home Depot, Inc.; *U.S. Public*, pg. 2089
HOME DESIGN OUTLET CENTER; *U.S. Private*, pg. 1970
HOME DESIGN STUDIO; *U.S. Private*, pg. 1970
HOMEDICS USA LLC; *U.S. Private*, pg. 1973
HOME & DRY LIMITED—See Fletcher Building Limited; *Int'l*, pg. 2700
HOME DYNAMIX LLC—See H.I.G. Capital, LLC; *U.S. Private*, pg. 1832
HOMEEASE INDUSTRIAL CO. LTD.; *Int'l*, pg. 3455
HOME ESSENTIALS & BEYOND INC.; *U.S. Private*, pg. 1970
HOME ETC; *U.S. Private*, pg. 1970
HOMEEXCHANGE.COM INC.; *U.S. Private*, pg. 1973
HOME FARM HAMPERS LIMITED—See PayPoint plc; *Int'l*, pg. 5763
HOMEFED CORPORATION—See Jefferies Financial Group Inc.; *U.S. Public*, pg. 1188
HOME FEDERAL BANCORP, INC. OF LOUISIANA; *U.S. Public*, pg. 1046
HOME FEDERAL BANK CORPORATION—See HFB Financial Corporation; *U.S. Public*, pg. 1034
HOME FEDERAL BANK OF HOLLYWOOD—See Home BancGroup, Inc.; *U.S. Private*, pg. 1970
HOME FEDERAL BANK OF TENNESSEE FSB; *U.S. Private*, pg. 1970
HOME FEDERAL BANK—See Home Federal Bancorp, Inc. of Louisiana; *U.S. Public*, pg. 1046
HOME FEDERAL PRIVATE BANKING—See Alerus Financial Corporation; *U.S. Public*, pg. 75
HOME FEDERAL SAVINGS AND LOAN ASSOCIATION OF NILES—See First Niles Financial, Inc.; *U.S. Public*, pg. 846
HOME FEDERAL SAVINGS BANK—See Alerus Financial Corporation; *U.S. Public*, pg. 75
HOMEFED RESOURCES CORPORATION—See Jefferies Financial Group Inc.; *U.S. Public*, pg. 1188
HOME FINANCE COMPANY GAMBIA LTD.—See Trust Bank Limited; *Int'l*, pg. 7944
HOME FINANCE COMPANY LIMITED—See Fiji National Provident Fund; *Int'l*, pg. 2661
HOME FINANCIAL BANCORP; *U.S. Public*, pg. 1046
HOMEFINDER.COM, LLC—See Placester, Inc.; *U.S. Private*, pg. 3194

HOME LUMBER & SUPPLY CO.

HOME FIRST FINANCE COMPANY INDIA LIMITED; *Int'l*, pg. 3454
HOMEFIX CORPORATION; *U.S. Private*, pg. 1973
HOME FOOD SERVICE OF PA; *U.S. Private*, pg. 1970
HOME FORWARD; *U.S. Private*, pg. 1970
HOME FRAGRANCE ITALIA S.R.L.—See Newell Brands Inc.; *U.S. Public*, pg. 1514
HOME FRANCHISE CONCEPTS, INC.—See JM Family Enterprises Inc.; *U.S. Private*, pg. 2214
HOME FROM HOME LIMITED—See The Skipton Building Society; *Int'l*, pg. 7686
HOME FRONT COMMUNICATIONS, LLC; *U.S. Private*, pg. 1971
HOME FURNITURE COMPANY INC.—See Home Furniture Company of Lafayette Inc.; *U.S. Private*, pg. 1971
HOME FURNITURE COMPANY OF LAFAYETTE INC.; *U.S. Private*, pg. 1971
HOME FURNITURE CO. OF LAKE CHARLES INC.—See Home Furniture Company of Lafayette Inc.; *U.S. Private*, pg. 1971
HOMEGAIN.COM, INC.—See Reply! Inc.; *U.S. Private*, pg. 3401
HOME & GARDEN PARTY, LTD.; *U.S. Private*, pg. 1970
HOME & GARDEN SHOWPLACE—See ACON Investments, LLC; *U.S. Private*, pg. 63
HOMEGATE AG—See TX Group AG; *Int'l*, pg. 7992
HOMEGENIUS REAL ESTATE LLC—See Radian Group, Inc.; *U.S. Public*, pg. 1759
HOMEGOODS, INC.—See The TJX Companies, Inc.; *U.S. Public*, pg. 2134
HOME GROUP DEVELOPMENTS LIMITED—See Home Group Limited; *Int'l*, pg. 3454
HOME GROUP LIMITED; *Int'l*, pg. 3454
HOME GROWN INDUSTRIES OF GEORGIA, INC.; *U.S. Private*, pg. 1971
HOMEGROWN NATURAL FOODS INC.; *U.S. Private*, pg. 1973
HOMEGROWN SHRIMP (USA), LLC—See Charoen Pokphand Foods Public Company Limited; *Int'l*, pg. 1452
HOMEGURU PTY LTD.—See News Corporation; *U.S. Public*, pg. 1520
HOME HARDWARE CENTER; *U.S. Private*, pg. 1971
HOME HARDWARE STORES LIMITED; *Int'l*, pg. 3454
HOME HEALTHCARE LABORATORY OF AMERICA, LLC—See Laboratory Corporation of America Holdings; *U.S. Public*, pg. 1287
HOME HEALTH DEPOT, INC.; *U.S. Private*, pg. 1971
HOME HEALTH OF ALEXANDRIA, L.L.C.—See Amedisys, Inc.; *U.S. Public*, pg. 94
HOME HEALTH OF RURAL TEXAS, INC.—See Apollo Global Management, Inc.; *U.S. Public*, pg. 156
HOME HELPERS OF TAMPA; *U.S. Private*, pg. 1971
HOMEINNS HOTEL GROUP; *Int'l*, pg. 3455
HOME IN SCOTLAND LIMITED—See Home Group Limited; *Int'l*, pg. 3454
HOME INSTEAD SENIOR CARE; *U.S. Private*, pg. 1971
HOME INSTRUCTION FOR PARENTS OF PRESCHOOL YOUNGSTERS (HIPPY); *U.S. Private*, pg. 1971
HOMEINSURANCE.COM LLC—See Red Ventures, LLC; *U.S. Private*, pg. 3376
HOME INVEST BELGIUM SA; *Int'l*, pg. 3454
HOME JUICE CORP.—See National Beverage Corp.; *U.S. Public*, pg. 1494
HOMELAND CREDIT UNION, INC.; *U.S. Private*, pg. 1973
HOMELAND ENERGY SOLUTIONS, LLC; *U.S. Private*, pg. 1973
HOMELAND HEALTHCARE, INC.; *U.S. Private*, pg. 1973
HOMELAND INTERACTIVE TECHNOLOGY LTD.; *Int'l*, pg. 3455
HOMELAND SAFETY SYSTEMS INC.—See Alpine Investors; *U.S. Private*, pg. 201
HOMELAND SECURITY CORPORATION; *U.S. Public*, pg. 1046
HOMELAND SECURITY SOLUTIONS, INC. (HSSI); *U.S. Private*, pg. 1973
HOMELAND STORES, INC.—See Associated Wholesale Grocers, Inc.; *U.S. Private*, pg. 357
HOME & LEGACY INSURANCE SERVICES LIMITED—See Allianz SE; *Int'l*, pg. 353
HOMELIFE/BAYVIEW REALTY INC.; *Int'l*, pg. 3455
HOME/LIFE SERVICES, INC.; *U.S. Private*, pg. 1972
HOME LINE FURNITURE INDUSTRIES INC.; *U.S. Private*, pg. 1971
HOMELITE CONSUMER PRODUCTS, INC.—See Techtronic Industries Co., Ltd.; *Int'l*, pg. 7513
HOME LOAN FINANCIAL CORPORATION; *U.S. Public*, pg. 1046
HOME LOAN & INVESTMENT BANK FSB INC.—See Home Loan & Investment Bank; *U.S. Private*, pg. 1971
HOME LOAN & INVESTMENT BANK; *U.S. Private*, pg. 1971
HOMELOAN MANAGEMENT LIMITED—See Computershare Limited; *Int'l*, pg. 1760
THE HOME LOAN SAVINGS BANK—See Home Loan Financial Corporation; *U.S. Public*, pg. 1046
HOME LOGISTICS CO., LTD.—See Nitori Holdings Co., Ltd.; *Int'l*, pg. 5381
HOME LUMBER & SUPPLY CO.; *U.S. Private*, pg. 1971

HOMEMAID AB — CORPORATE AFFILIATIONS

HOMEMAID AB; *Int'l*, pg. 3455
HOMEMAKER MEGAMALL AUBURN PTY LTD—See AMP Limited; *Int'l*, pg. 432
HOMEMAKERS PLAZA, INC.—See Berkshire Hathaway Inc.; *U.S. Public*, pg. 313
HOME MANAGEMENT KFT.—See Duna House Holding Public Company Limited; *Int'l*, pg. 2225
HOME MARKET FOODS INCORPORATED; *U.S. Private*, pg. 1971
HOME MEAL REPLACEMENT SA; *Int'l*, pg. 3455
HOME MEDICAL EXPRESS, INC.—See AdaptHealth Corp.; *U.S. Public*, pg. 39
HOME MEDICAL SERVICES LLC; *U.S. Private*, pg. 1971
HOME MERIDIAN INTERNATIONAL, INC.—See Hooker Furnishings Corporation; *U.S. Public*, pg. 1052
HOME MOBILITY SOLUTIONS, INC.—See Rockwood Equity Partners, LLC; *U.S. Private*, pg. 3468
HOME MORTGAGE BANK; *Int'l*, pg. 3455
HOMEMOVEBOX LTD.—See Citipost Group; *Int'l*, pg. 1623
HOMEMUSEUM.COM—See Nissha Co., Ltd.; *Int'l*, pg. 5372
HOMENEMA TECHNOLOGY INCORPORATION; *Int'l*, pg. 3455
HOMENET AUTOMOTIVE LLC—See Cox Enterprises, Inc.; *U.S. Private*, pg. 1076
HOME NEWS ENTERPRISES, LLC; *U.S. Private*, pg. 1971
HOME NEWS TRIBUNE—See Gannett Co., Inc.; *U.S. Public*, pg. 898
HOME NURSING AGENCY; *U.S. Private*, pg. 1971
HOME OF ECONOMY INC.; *U.S. Private*, pg. 1972
HOME & OFFICE FURNITURE SDN. BHD.—See TAFI Industries Berhad; *Int'l*, pg. 7406
HOME OF HEART (SHANGHAI) E-COMMERCE CO., LTD.—See Sika AG; *Int'l*, pg. 6914
HOME OF HOPE, INC; *U.S. Private*, pg. 1972
HOME OF LIVING BRANDS GROUP LIMITED—See The Bidvest Group Limited; *Int'l*, pg. 7624
HOME OF LIVING BRANDS HOLDINGS LIMITED—See The Bidvest Group Limited; *Int'l*, pg. 7624
HOME OIL CO. INC.; *U.S. Private*, pg. 1972
HOME OIL COMPANY INCORPORATED; *U.S. Private*, pg. 1972
HOME OIL & GAS COMPANY INC.; *U.S. Private*, pg. 1972
HOMEOSTYLE INC.—See SBI Holdings, Inc.; *Int'l*, pg. 6604
HOME OUTFITTERS—See Abrams Capital, LLC; *U.S. Private*, pg. 40
HOME OUTFITTERS—See Rhone Group, LLC; *U.S. Private*, pg. 3423
HOME OUTFITTERS—See WeWork Inc.; *U.S. Public*, pg. 2364
HOMEOWNERS CHOICE PROPERTY & CASUALTY INSURANCE COMPANY, INC.—See HCI Group, Inc.; *U.S. Public*, pg. 1014
HOME-OWNERS INSURANCE CO.—See Auto-Owners Insurance Group; *U.S. Private*, pg. 397
HOMEOWNERS OF AMERICA HOLDING CORPORATION—See Porch Group, Inc.; *U.S. Public*, pg. 1702
HOMEPAGES, LLC—See BV Investment Partners, LLC; *U.S. Private*, pg. 699
HOME PARAMONT PEST CONTROL COMPANIES; *U.S. Private*, pg. 1972
HOME PERFECT RESTORATION, INC.; *U.S. Private*, pg. 1972
HOMEPLACE OF BURLINGTON—See AlerisLife Inc.; *U.S. Private*, pg. 161
HOME PLATE ACQUISITION CORPORATION; *U.S. Public*, pg. 1046
HOME.PL S.A.—See United Internet AG; *Int'l*, pg. 8069
HOMEPLUS CO., LIMITED—See Canada Pension Plan Investment Board; *Int'l*, pg. 1279
HOMEPLUS CO., LIMITED—See MBK Partners Ltd.; *Int'l*, pg. 4753
HOMEPLUS CO., LIMITED—See Public Sector Pension Investment Board; *Int'l*, pg. 6096
HOMEPLUS CO., LIMITED—See Temasek Holdings (Private) Limited; *Int'l*, pg. 7547
HOME POINT CAPITAL INC.—See Mr. Cooper Group Inc.; *U.S. Public*, pg. 1480
HOME POINT CAPITAL LP—See Stone Point Capital LLC; *U.S. Private*, pg. 3825
HOME POINT FINANCIAL CORPORATION—See Mr. Cooper Group Inc.; *U.S. Public*, pg. 1480
HOME POTTERY PUBLIC COMPANY LIMITED; *Int'l*, pg. 3455
HOME PRODUCT CENTER (MALAYSIA) SDN. BHD.—See Home Product Center Public Company Limited; *Int'l*, pg. 3455
HOME PRODUCT CENTER PLC—See Land & Houses Public Company Limited; *Int'l*, pg. 4403
HOME PRODUCT CENTER PUBLIC COMPANY LIMITED; *Int'l*, pg. 3455
HOME PRODUCTS INTERNATIONAL, INC.—See Quaestus Holdings, LLC; *U.S. Private*, pg. 3316

HOME PROPERTIES 1200 EAST WEST, LLC—See Lone Star Global Acquisitions, LLC; *U.S. Private*, pg. 2488
HOME PROPERTIES CAMBRIDGE COURT, LLC—See Lone Star Global Acquisitions, LLC; *U.S. Private*, pg. 2488
HOME PROPERTIES CAMBRIDGE VILLAGE, LLC—See Lone Star Global Acquisitions, LLC; *U.S. Private*, pg. 2488
HOME PROPERTIES CHARLESTON, LLC—See Lone Star Global Acquisitions, LLC; *U.S. Private*, pg. 2488
HOME PROPERTIES CIDER MILL, LLC—See Lone Star Global Acquisitions, LLC; *U.S. Private*, pg. 2488
HOME PROPERTIES COUNTRY VILLAGE LLC—See Lone Star Global Acquisitions, LLC; *U.S. Private*, pg. 2488
HOME PROPERTIES CRESCENT CLUB, LLC—See Lone Star Global Acquisitions, LLC; *U.S. Private*, pg. 2488
HOME PROPERTIES DE WOODMONT, LLC—See Lone Star Global Acquisitions, LLC; *U.S. Private*, pg. 2488
HOME PROPERTIES FALCON CREST TOWNHOUSES, LLC—See Lone Star Global Acquisitions, LLC; *U.S. Private*, pg. 2488
HOME PROPERTIES FALKLAND CHASE, LLC—See Lone Star Global Acquisitions, LLC; *U.S. Private*, pg. 2488
HOME PROPERTIES HERITAGE SQUARE, LLC—See Lone Star Global Acquisitions, LLC; *U.S. Private*, pg. 2488
HOME PROPERTIES HOLIDAY SQUARE, LLC—See Lone Star Global Acquisitions, LLC; *U.S. Private*, pg. 2488
HOME PROPERTIES HUNTERS GLEN, LLC—See Lone Star Global Acquisitions, LLC; *U.S. Private*, pg. 2488
HOME PROPERTIES LAKE GROVE, LLC—See Lone Star Global Acquisitions, LLC; *U.S. Private*, pg. 2488
HOME PROPERTIES, L.P.—See Lone Star Global Acquisitions, LLC; *U.S. Private*, pg. 2488
HOME PROPERTIES MID-ISLAND, LLC—See Lone Star Global Acquisitions, LLC; *U.S. Private*, pg. 2488
HOME PROPERTIES MORNINGSIDE HEIGHTS LLC—See Lone Star Global Acquisitions, LLC; *U.S. Private*, pg. 2488
HOME PROPERTIES NEWPORT VILLAGE, LLC—See Lone Star Global Acquisitions, LLC; *U.S. Private*, pg. 2488
HOME PROPERTIES PLEASANT VIEW, LLC—See Lone Star Global Acquisitions, LLC; *U.S. Private*, pg. 2488
HOME PROPERTIES RIDGEVIEW AT WAKEFIELD VALLEY—See Lone Star Global Acquisitions, LLC; *U.S. Private*, pg. 2488
HOME PROPERTIES SAYVILLE, LLC—See Lone Star Global Acquisitions, LLC; *U.S. Private*, pg. 2488
HOME PROPERTIES SOUTH BAY MANOR, LLC—See Lone Star Global Acquisitions, LLC; *U.S. Private*, pg. 2488
HOME PROPERTIES TAMARRON, LLC—See Lone Star Global Acquisitions, LLC; *U.S. Private*, pg. 2488
HOME PROPERTIES TOPFIELD, LLC—See Lone Star Global Acquisitions, LLC; *U.S. Private*, pg. 2488
HOME PROPERTIES VILLAGE SQUARE, LLC—See Lone Star Global Acquisitions, LLC; *U.S. Private*, pg. 2488
HOME PROPERTIES WESTBROOKE, LLC—See Lone Star Global Acquisitions, LLC; *U.S. Private*, pg. 2488
HOME PROPERTIES WESTCHESTER WEST, LLC—See Lone Star Global Acquisitions, LLC; *U.S. Private*, pg. 2488
HOME PROPERTIES WOODHOLME MANOR, LLC—See Lone Star Global Acquisitions, LLC; *U.S. Private*, pg. 2488
HOME PROPERTIES WOODMONT VILLAGE, LLC—See Lone Star Global Acquisitions, LLC; *U.S. Private*, pg. 2488
HOMEQ CORPORATION—See Birch Hill Equity Partners Management Inc.; *Int'l*, pg. 1046
HOMER CITY COAL PROCESSING CO.—See CLI Corporation; *U.S. Public*, pg. 942
HOME REAL ESTATE INC.—See Berkshire Hathaway Inc.; *U.S. Public*, pg. 306
HOMER ELECTRIC ASSOCIATION, INC.; *U.S. Private*, pg. 1973
HOME RENT SP. Z O.O.—See City Service SE; *Int'l*, pg. 1627
HOME RESIDENCE DU PLATEAU SPRL—See Clariane SE; *Int'l*, pg. 1643
HOME RETAIL GROUP (UK) LIMITED—See J Sainsbury plc; *Int'l*, pg. 3852
THE HOMER GROUP; *U.S. Private*, pg. 4054
HOME RIGHT—See Diversified Dynamics Corporation; *U.S. Private*, pg. 1242
HOMERITZ CORPORATION BERHAD; *Int'l*, pg. 3455
THE HOMER LAUGHLIN CHINA COMPANY; *U.S. Private*, pg. 4054
HOMER NEWS, LLC—See Gannett Co., Inc.; *U.S. Public*, pg. 903
HOMER OPTICAL COMPANY, INC.—See EssilorLuxottica SA; *Int'l*, pg. 2513
HOMER SKELTON FORD, INC.; *U.S. Private*, pg. 1973
HOMER T. HAYWARD LUMBER CO. INC.; *U.S. Private*, pg. 1973

HOMERUNBYNET OY—See SmartCraft ASA; *Int'l*, pg. 7002
HOMERUN ELECTRONICS, INC.—See Vangeo Technology Group, LLC; *U.S. Private*, pg. 4343
HOME RUN INN, INC.; *U.S. Private*, pg. 1972
HOMERUN RESOURCES INC.; *Int'l*, pg. 3455
HOMER WARREN PROCTOR INC.; *U.S. Private*, pg. 1973
HOMERWOOD HARDWOOD FLOORING COMPANY—See Armstrong World Industries, Inc.; *U.S. Public*, pg. 194
HOMESALE LENDING, LLC—See Wells Fargo & Company; *U.S. Public*, pg. 2343
THE HOME SALES COMPANY; *U.S. Private*, pg. 4054
HOME SAVINGS BANK—See Home Bancorp Wisconsin, Inc.; *U.S. Public*, pg. 1045
HOMES BY AVI INC.; *Int'l*, pg. 3455
HOMES BY DAVID POWERS; *U.S. Private*, pg. 1973
HOMES BY JOHN C. FOWKE, INC.; *U.S. Private*, pg. 1974
HOMES BY TOWNE, A ZILBER COMPANY, LLC—See Zilber Ltd.; *U.S. Private*, pg. 4604
HOMES BY WESTBAY, LLC; *U.S. Private*, pg. 1974
HOMES BY WHITTAKER; *U.S. Private*, pg. 1974
HOMES.COM, INC.—See Irish Times; *U.S. Private*, pg. 2138
HOMESCRIPTS.COM, LLC—See Centene Corporation; *U.S. Public*, pg. 469
HOME SECURITY OF AMERICA, INC.—See frontdoor, inc.; *U.S. Public*, pg. 887
HOMESERVE ASSISTANCE LIMITED—See Brookfield Corporation; *Int'l*, pg. 1188
HOMESERVE CARE SOLUTIONS LIMITED—See Brookfield Corporation; *Int'l*, pg. 1188
HOMESERVE CLAIMS MANAGEMENT—See Brookfield Corporation; *Int'l*, pg. 1188
HOMESERVE ENTERPRISES LIMITED—See Brookfield Corporation; *Int'l*, pg. 1188
HOMESERVE GB LIMITED—See Brookfield Corporation; *Int'l*, pg. 1188
HOMESERVE MEMBERSHIP LIMITED—See Brookfield Corporation; *Int'l*, pg. 1188
HOMESERVE PLC—See Brookfield Corporation; *Int'l*, pg. 1188
HOMESERVE SERVOWARM LIMITED—See Brookfield Corporation; *Int'l*, pg. 1188
HOMESERVE SPAIN SLU—See Brookfield Corporation; *Int'l*, pg. 1188
HOMESERVE USA CORP.—See Brookfield Corporation; *Int'l*, pg. 1188
HOMESERVE USA ENERGY SERVICES LLC—See Brookfield Corporation; *Int'l*, pg. 1188
HOMESERVE USA ENERGY SERVICES (NEW ENGLAND) LLC—See Brookfield Corporation; *Int'l*, pg. 1188
HOMESERVE USA REPAIR MANAGEMENT CORP.—See Brookfield Corporation; *Int'l*, pg. 1188
HOME SERVICE OIL CO. INC. - DONIPHAN DIVISION—See Home Service Oil Co. Inc.; *U.S. Private*, pg. 1972
HOME SERVICE OIL CO. INC. - POPLAR BLUFF DIVISION—See Home Service Oil Co. Inc.; *U.S. Private*, pg. 1972
HOME SERVICE OIL CO. INC. - REYNO DIVISION—See Home Service Oil Co. Inc.; *U.S. Private*, pg. 1972
HOME SERVICE OIL CO. INC.; *U.S. Private*, pg. 1972
HOME SERVICE PUBLICATIONS, INC.—See RDA Holding Co.; *U.S. Private*, pg. 3363
HOMESERVICES LENDING, LLC—See Wells Fargo & Company; *U.S. Public*, pg. 2343
HOMESERVICES OF AMERICA, INC.—See Berkshire Hathaway Inc.; *U.S. Public*, pg. 306
HOME SERVICES SYSTEMS INC; *U.S. Private*, pg. 1972
HOMES FOR AMERICA HOLDINGS; *U.S. Private*, pg. 1974
HOMES & HOLIDAY AG; *Int'l*, pg. 3455
HOME SHOPPING EUROPE GMBH—See Providence Equity Partners L.L.C.; *U.S. Private*, pg. 3292
HOMESIDE FINANCIAL, LLC; *U.S. Private*, pg. 1974
HOMESMART CONSTRUCTION—See Berkshire Hathaway Inc.; *U.S. Public*, pg. 304
HOMESMART HOLDINGS, INC.; *U.S. Private*, pg. 1974
HOMESMART INTERNATIONAL LLC; *U.S. Private*, pg. 1974
HOME SOURCE INTERNATIONAL, INC.; *U.S. Private*, pg. 1972
HOMESPAN REALTY CO., INC.—See Commerce Group Corp.; *U.S. Public*, pg. 545
HOMESQUARE HOLDINGS LLC; *U.S. Private*, pg. 1974
HOMESQUARE PRO, LLC—See Homesquare Holdings LLC; *U.S. Private*, pg. 1974
HOMES & SON CONTRACTORS, INC.; *U.S. Private*, pg. 1973
HOME STATE BANCORP, INC.; *U.S. Private*, pg. 1972
HOME STATE BANK, N.A.—See Home State Bancorp, Inc.; *U.S. Private*, pg. 1972
HOMESTEAD BUILDING SYSTEMS INC.—See Bain Capital, LP; *U.S. Public*, pg. 451
HOMESTEAD CENTER—See Formation Capital, LLC; *U.S. Private*, pg. 1570

COMPANY NAME INDEX

HOMESTEAD ENTERPRISES INC.; *U.S. Private*, pg. 1974
HOMESTEADERS LIFE CO. INC.; *U.S. Private*, pg. 1974
HOMESTEAD GARDENS INC.; *U.S. Private*, pg. 1974
HOMESTEAD GOLD & SILVER LTD.; *U.S. Public*, pg. 1046
HOMESTEAD HOSPITAL—See Baptist Health South Florida, Inc.; *U.S. Private*, pg. 471
HOMESTEAD INTERNATIONAL GROUP LTD.—See Li & Fung Limited; *Int'l*, pg. 4480
HOMESTEAD-MIAMI SPEEDWAY, LLC—See National Association for Stock Car Auto Racing, Inc.; *U.S. Private*, pg. 2845
HOMESTEAD NURSING, LLC—See Regional Health Properties, Inc.; *U.S. Private*, pg. 1776
HOMESTEAD PUBLISHING CO.—See Tribune Publishing Company; *U.S. Private*, pg. 4228
HOMESTEAD SHOP (M) SDN BHD—See Digilife Technologies Limited; *Int'l*, pg. 2119
HOMESTREET BANK—See HomeStreet, Inc.; *U.S. Public*, pg. 1046
HOMESTREET CAPITAL CORPORATION—See HomeStreet, Inc.; *U.S. Public*, pg. 1046
HOMESTREET, INC.; *U.S. Public*, pg. 1046
HOMESTRONGUSA; *U.S. Private*, pg. 1975
HOMESTYLE DINING, LLC—See Fog Cutter Capital Group Inc.; *U.S. Private*, pg. 1557
HOME SWEET HOME HOLDINGS INC.; *U.S. Private*, pg. 1972
HOMESYS MEDIA KFT.—See OTT-ONE Plc.; *Int'l*, pg. 5661
HOMESYS MEDIA LTD.—See OTT-ONE Plc.; *Int'l*, pg. 5661
HOMETEAM PEST DEFENSE, LLC—See Rollins, Inc.; *U.S. Public*, pg. 1809
HOME TEAM SERVICES,LLC; *U.S. Private*, pg. 1972
HOME-TECH CONSOLIDATED, INC.; *U.S. Private*, pg. 1972
HOMETECH, INC.—See VIQ Solutions Inc.; *Int'l*, pg. 8245
HOME TELEPHONE COMPANY INC.; *U.S. Private*, pg. 1972
HOMETOGO SE; *Int'l*, pg. 3455
HOMETOWN AMERICA MANAGEMENT CORP.; *U.S. Private*, pg. 1975
HOMETOWN AUTO RETAILERS, INC.; *U.S. Private*, pg 1975
HOMETOWN BANK, NATIONAL ASSOCIATION; *U.S. Private*, pg. 1975
HOMETOWN BANKSHARES CORPORATION—See Atlantic Union Bankshares Corporation; *U.S. Public*, pg. 223
HOMETOWN BANK—See Atlantic Union Bankshares Corporation; *U.S. Public*, pg. 223
HOMETOWN BANK; *U.S. Private*, pg. 1975
HOMETOWN BANK—See Hometown Financial Group, Inc.; *U.S. Private*, pg. 1975
HOMETOWN CABLE COMPANY, LLC—See Schurz Communications, Inc.; *U.S. Private*, pg. 3571
HOMETOWN COMMUNITY BANCORP, INC.; *U.S. Private*, pg. 1975
HOMETOWN FINANCIAL GROUP, INC.; *U.S. Private*, pg. 1975
HOMETOWN FOOD COMPANY—See Brynwood Partners Management LLC; *U.S. Private*, pg. 674
HOME TOWN FUNDING, INC.—See Canandaigua National Corporation; *U.S. Private*, pg. 428
HOMETOWN HEARING CENTRE INC.—See Amplifon S.p.A.; *Int'l*, pg. 435
HOMETOWN INVESTMENT SERVICES, INC.—See Great Western Bancorp, Inc.; *U.S. Public*, pg. 962
HOME TOWN MORTGAGE INC.; *U.S. Private*, pg. 1972
HOMETOWN NATIONAL BANK—See LaSalle Bancorp, Inc.; *U.S. Private*, pg. 2394
HOMETOWN OXYGEN, CHARLOTTE, LLC—See The Halifax Group LLC; *U.S. Private*, pg. 4042
HOMETOWN PLUMBING & HEATING CO.; *U.S. Private*, pg. 1975
HOMETOWN REALTY SERVICES INC.; *U.S. Private*, pg. 1975
HOMETOWN TELECOM; *U.S. Private*, pg. 1975
HOMETRACK AUSTRALIA PTY LIMITED—See News Corporation; *U.S. Public*, pg. 1521
HOMETRACK DATA SYSTEMS LIMITED; *Int'l*, pg. 3456
HOME TRADE CENTER CO., LTD.—See Iida Group Holdings Co., Ltd.; *Int'l*, pg. 3607
HOME & TRAVEL LIMITED—See Arthur J. Gallagher & Co.; *U.S. Public*, pg. 206
HOME TRENDS & DESIGN, INC.; *U.S. Private*, pg. 1972
HOMETRUST BANCSHARES, INC.; *U.S. Public*, pg. 1046
HOMETRUST BANK—See HomeTrust Bancshares, Inc.; *U.S. Public*, pg. 1046
HOME TRUST COMPANY—See Smith Financial Corporation; *Int'l*, pg. 7009
HOMETRUST LIMITED—See Rentokil Initial plc; *Int'l*, pg. 6287
HOMETTE CORPORATION—See Champion Homes, Inc.; *U.S. Public*, pg. 477
HOME UPHOLSTERY INDUSTRIES SDN. BHD.—See Homeritz Corporation Berhad; *Int'l*, pg. 3455
HOMEVALET, INC.; *U.S. Private*, pg. 1975

HOMEVESTORS OF AMERICA, INC.—See Levine Leichtman Capital Partners, LLC; *U.S. Private*, pg. 2436
HOMEVISIT, LLC—See Urbanimmersive, Inc.; *Int'l*, pg. 8095
HOMEWARD LEGAL LIMITED—See NAHL Group plc; *Int'l*, pg. 5130
HOME WARRANTY OF AMERICA, INC.—See NRG Energy, Inc.; *U.S. Public*, pg. 1549
HOMEWATCH INTERNATIONAL, INC.—See Apax Partners LLP; *Int'l*, pg. 502
HOMEWAY GMBH—See Hexatronic Group AB; *Int'l*, pg. 3371
HOME WELLNESS, INC.—See AdaptHealth Corp.; *U.S. Public*, pg. 38
HOMEWETBAR; *U.S. Private*, pg. 1975
HOMEWOOD AT BROOKMONT TERRACE, LLC—See Brookdale Senior Living Inc.; *U.S. Public*, pg. 394
HOMEWOOD CORPORATION; *U.S. Private*, pg. 1975
HOMEWOOD HOLDINGS, LLC—See Bain Capital, LP; *U.S. Private*, pg. 450
HOMEWOOD MOUNTAIN RESORT—See JMA Ventures, LLC; *U.S. Private*, pg. 2214
HOMEWOOD SUITES - ANCHORAGE—See Stonebridge Realty Advisors, Inc.; *U.S. Private*, pg. 3827
HOMEWOOD SUITES BY HILTON—See Hilton Worldwide Holdings Inc.; *U.S. Public*, pg. 1041
HOMEWOOD SUITES MANAGEMENT LLC—See Hilton Worldwide Holdings Inc.; *U.S. Public*, pg. 1041
HOMEWORKS ASIA LIMITED—See Li & Fung Limited; *Int'l*, pg. 4479
HOMEWORKS INC.; *U.S. Private*, pg. 1976
HOMEWORLD—See C.S. Wo & Sons Ltd.; *U.S. Private*, pg. 709
HOMEX ATIZAPAN, S.A. DE C.V.—See Desarrolladora Homex, S.A. de C.V.; *Int'l*, pg. 2044
HOMEX CENTRAL MARCARIA, S.A. DE C.V.—See Desarrolladora Homex, S.A. de C.V.; *Int'l*, pg. 2044
HOMEX INFRAESTRUCTURA OBRAS, S.A. DE C.V.—See Desarrolladora Homex, S.A. de C.V.; *Int'l*, pg. 2044
HOMEX INFRAESTRUCTURA, S.A. DE C.V.—See Desarrolladora Homex, S.A. de C.V.; *Int'l*, pg. 2044
HOMEXTERIOR BUILDING SUPPLY, INC.—See Hendricks Holding Company, Inc.; *U.S. Private*, pg. 1914
HOM FURNITURE, INC.; *U.S. Private*, pg. 1969
HOMIER DISTRIBUTING COMPANY; *U.S. Private*, pg. 1976
HOMIER & SONS INC.; *U.S. Private*, pg. 1976
HOMIZY S.P.A.; *Int'l*, pg. 3456
HOMMEL-ETAMIC AMERICA CORP—See Jenoptik AG; *Int'l*, pg. 3928
HOMMEL-ETAMIC ESPANA S.A—See Jenoptik AG; *Int'l*, pg. 3928
HOMMEL-ETAMIC FRANCE SA—See Jenoptik AG; *Int'l*, pg. 3928
HOMMEL GMBH—See Quaser Machine Tools, Inc.; *Int'l*, pg. 6157
HOMMEL HERCULES FRANCE, S.R.O.—See Wurth Verwaltungsgesellschaft mbH; *Int'l*, pg. 8505
HOMMEL HERCULES-WERKZEUGHANDEL GMBH & CO. KG—See Wurth Verwaltungsgesellschaft mbH; *Int'l*, pg. 8505
HOMMEL & SEITZ GMBH—See Wurth Verwaltungsgesellschaft mbH; *Int'l*, pg. 8505
HOMOGENEOUS METALS INC.—See RTX Corporation; *U.S. Public*, pg. 1823
HOMOLJE A.D.; *Int'l*, pg. 3456
HONASA CONSUMER LIMITED; *Int'l*, pg. 3459
HONAT BANCORP INC.; *U.S. Public*, pg. 1046
HONAZ FZCO.—See Xaar PLC; *Int'l*, pg. 8518
HONBRIDGE HOLDINGS LTD.; *Int'l*, pg. 3459
HON CHUAN ENTERPRISE (CHANGSHA) CO., LTD.—See Taiwan Hon Chuan Enterprise Co., Ltd.; *Int'l*, pg. 7420
HON CHUAN FOOD PACKING (ANYANG) CO., LTD.—See Taiwan Hon Chuan Enterprise Co., Ltd.; *Int'l*, pg. 7420
HON CHUAN FOOD PACKING (CHUZHOU) CO., LTD.—See Taiwan Hon Chuan Enterprise Co., Ltd.; *Int'l*, pg. 7420
HON CHUAN FOOD PACKING (JINAN) CO., LTD.—See Taiwan Hon Chuan Enterprise Co., Ltd.; *Int'l*, pg. 7420
HON CHUAN FOOD PACKING (QINGXIN) CO., LTD.—See Taiwan Hon Chuan Enterprise Co., Ltd.; *Int'l*, pg. 7421
HON CHUAN FOOD PACKING (TAIYUAN) CO., LTD.—See Taiwan Hon Chuan Enterprise Co., Ltd.; *Int'l*, pg. 7421
HON CHUAN FOOD PACKING (XIANTAO) CO., LTD.—See Taiwan Hon Chuan Enterprise Co., Ltd.; *Int'l*, pg. 7421
HON CHUAN FOOD PACKING (ZHANGZHOU) CO., LTD.—See Taiwan Hon Chuan Enterprise Co., Ltd.; *Int'l*, pg. 7421
HONC INDUSTRIES, INC.; *U.S. Private*, pg. 1976
HONC MARINE CONTRACTING, INC.; *U.S. Private*, pg. 1976
HONCO INC.; *Int'l*, pg. 3459

THE HON COMPANY, LLC—See HNI Corporation; *U.S. Public*, pg. 1043
HON CORPORATION LTD.; *Int'l*, pg. 3456
THE HON CO.—See HNI Corporation; *U.S. Public*, pg. 1043
HONDA ACCESS CORPORATION—See Honda Motor Co., Ltd.; *Int'l*, pg. 3460
HONDA ACCESS EUROPE N.V.—See Honda Motor Co., Ltd.; *Int'l*, pg. 3460
HONDA AERO, INC.—See Honda Motor Co., Ltd.; *Int'l*, pg. 3460
HONDA AIRCRAFT COMPANY, LLC—See Honda Motor Co., Ltd.; *Int'l*, pg. 3460
HONDA AIRWAYS CO., LTD.—See Honda Motor Co., Ltd.; *Int'l*, pg. 3460
HONDA ATLAS CARS PAKISTAN LTD.—See Atlas Group of Companies; *Int'l*, pg. 685
HONDA ATLAS CARS PAKISTAN LTD.—See Honda Motor Co., Ltd.; *Int'l*, pg. 3460
HONDA ATLAS POWER PRODUCT (PRIVATE) LTD.—See Honda Motor Co., Ltd.; *Int'l*, pg. 3460
HONDA AUSTRALIA M. & P.E. PTY. LTD.—See Honda Motor Co., Ltd.; *Int'l*, pg. 3460
HONDA AUSTRALIA PTY., LTD.—See Honda Motor Co., Ltd.; *Int'l*, pg. 3460
HONDA AUSTRIA G.M.B.H.—See Honda Motor Co., Ltd.; *Int'l*, pg. 3460
HONDA AUTO BODY CO., LTD.—See Honda Motor Co., Ltd.; *Int'l*, pg. 3460
HONDA AUTOMOBILE (CHINA) CO., LTD.—See Guangzhou Automobile Industry Group Co., Ltd.; *Int'l*, pg. 3164
HONDA AUTOMOBILES OF BARTLESVILLE; *U.S. Private*, pg. 1976
HONDA AUTOMOBILE WESTERN AFRICA LTD.—See Honda Motor Co., Ltd.; *Int'l*, pg. 3460
HONDA AUTOMOVEIS DO BRASIL LTDA.—See Honda Motor Co., Ltd.; *Int'l*, pg. 3460
HONDA AUTOMOVILES ESPANA S.A.—See Honda Motor Co., Ltd.; *Int'l*, pg. 3460
HONDA BANK GMBH—See Honda Motor Co., Ltd.; *Int'l*, pg. 3460
HONDA BELGIUM N.V.—See Honda Motor Co., Ltd.; *Int'l*, pg. 3460
HONDA CANADA FINANCE, INC.—See Honda Motor Co., Ltd.; *Int'l*, pg. 3461
HONDA CANADA INC.—See Honda Motor Co., Ltd.; *Int'l*, pg. 3461
HONDA CAR SALES NAGAOKA CO., LTD.—See Nippon Seiki Co., Ltd.; *Int'l*, pg. 5329
HONDA CARS CEBU, INC.—See Ayala Corporation; *Int'l*, pg. 774
HONDA CARS MAKATI, INC.—See Ayala Corporation; *Int'l*, pg. 773
HONDA CARS OF CORONA; *U.S. Private*, pg. 1976
HONDA CARS OF ROCK HILL; *U.S. Private*, pg. 1976
HONDA CARS PHILIPPINES INC.—See Honda Motor Co., Ltd.; *Int'l*, pg. 3461
HONDA CARS SAITAMA KITA CO., LTD.—See Hitachi Astemo, Ltd.; *Int'l*, pg. 3409
HONDA CARS SATIAMAKITA CO., LTD.—See TS Tech Co Ltd; *Int'l*, pg. 7947
HONDA CARS TOKAI CO., LTD.—See VT Holdings Co., Ltd.; *Int'l*, pg. 8315
HONDA CENTRE (2010) PVT. LTD.—See Honda Motor Co., Ltd.; *Int'l*, pg. 3461
HONDA CLIO SHIN TOKYO CO., LTD.—See Honda Motor Co., Ltd.; *Int'l*, pg. 3461
HONDA CZECH REPUBLIC LTD.—See Honda Motor Co., Ltd.; *Int'l*, pg. 3461
HONDA DEL PERU S.A.—See Honda Motor Co., Ltd.; *Int'l*, pg. 3461
HONDA DE MEXICO, S.A. DE C.V.—See Honda Motor Co., Ltd.; *Int'l*, pg. 3463
HONDA DEVELOPMENT & MANUFACTURING OF AMERICA, LLC—See Honda Motor Co., Ltd.; *Int'l*, pg. 3461
HONDA EAST—See Beechmont Automotive Group; *U.S. Private*, pg. 513
HONDA ELECTRON CO., LTD.—See G Three Holdings Corp.; *Int'l*, pg. 2862
HONDA ENGINEERING ASIAN CO., LTD.—See Honda Motor Co., Ltd.; *Int'l*, pg. 3461
HONDA ENGINEERING CHINA CO., LTD.—See Honda Motor Co., Ltd.; *Int'l*, pg. 3461
HONDA ENGINEERING EUROPE LTD.—See Honda Motor Co., Ltd.; *Int'l*, pg. 3461
HONDA ENGINEERING NORTH AMERICA—See Honda Motor Co., Ltd.; *Int'l*, pg. 3461
HONDA EUROPE N.V.—See Honda Motor Co., Ltd.; *Int'l*, pg. 3461
HONDA FINANCE EUROPE PLC—See Honda Motor Co., Ltd.; *Int'l*, pg. 3462
HONDA FOUNDRY CO., LTD.—See Honda Motor Co., Ltd.; *Int'l*, pg. 3461
HONDA FRANCE MANUFACTURING S.A.S—See Honda Motor Co., Ltd.; *Int'l*, pg. 3461
HONDA FRANCE S.A.S.—See Honda Motor Co., Ltd.; *Int'l*, pg. 3461

HONDA GABRIEL

CORPORATE AFFILIATIONS

HONDA GABRIEL; *Int'l*, pg. 3459
HONDA GULF FZE—See Honda Motor Co., Ltd.; *Int'l*, pg. 3461
HONDA HUNGARY KFT.—See Honda Motor Co., Ltd.; *Int'l*, pg. 3461
HONDA ILE PERROT; *Int'l*, pg. 3459
HONDA INDIA POWER PRODUCTS LIMITED—See Honda Motor Co., Ltd.; *Int'l*, pg. 3461
HONDA INDIA POWER PRODUCTS LIMITED—See Siddharth Shriram Group; *Int'l*, pg. 6883
HONDA INTERNATIONAL TRADING CO. (H.I.T.)—See Honda Motor Co., Ltd.; *Int'l*, pg. 3459
HONDA ITALIA INDUSTRIALE S.P.A.—See Honda Motor Co., Ltd.; *Int'l*, pg. 3461
HONDA KAIHATSU CO., LTD.—See Honda Motor Co., Ltd.; *Int'l*, pg. 3461
HONDA KOREA CO., LTD.—See Honda Motor Co., Ltd.; *Int'l*, pg. 3461
HONDA LOCK THAI CO., LTD.—See Honda Motor Co., Ltd.; *Int'l*, pg. 3460
HONDA LOGISTIC CENTER AUSTRIA G.M.B.H.—See Honda Motor Co., Ltd.; *Int'l*, pg. 3461
HONDA LOGISTIC CENTRE (U.K.) LTD.—See Honda Motor Co., Ltd.; *Int'l*, pg. 3461
HONDA LOGISTICS INC.—See Honda Motor Co., Ltd.; *Int'l*, pg. 3461
HONDA MALAYSIA SDN BHD—See Honda Motor Co., Ltd.; *Int'l*, pg. 3461
HONDA MALIWAN COMPANY LIMITED—See Autocorp Holding Public Company Limited; *Int'l*, pg. 726
HONDA MALMO—See Honda Motor Co., Ltd.; *Int'l*, pg. 3461
HONDA MANUFACTURING OF ALABAMA, LLC—See Honda Motor Co., Ltd.; *Int'l*, pg. 3461
HONDA MANUFACTURING OF INDIANA, LLC—See Honda Motor Co., Ltd.; *Int'l*, pg. 3461
HONDA MOTOR (CHINA) CO., LTD.—See Honda Motor Co., Ltd.; *Int'l*, pg. 3461
HONDA MOTOR (CHINA) INVESTMENT CO., LTD.—See Honda Motor Co., Ltd.; *Int'l*, pg. 3461
HONDA MOTOR CO., LTD. - HAMAMATSU HOSOE FACTORY—See Honda Motor Co., Ltd.; *Int'l*, pg. 3461
HONDA MOTOR CO., LTD. - KUMAMOTO FACTORY—See Honda Motor Co., Ltd.; *Int'l*, pg. 3461
HONDA MOTOR CO., LTD.; *Int'l*, pg. 3459
HONDA MOTOR CO., LTD.—See Honda Motor Co., Ltd.; *Int'l*, pg. 3461
HONDA MOTOR CO., LTD.—See Honda Motor Co., Ltd.; *Int'l*, pg. 3461
HONDA MOTOR CO., LTD. - SUZUKA FACTORY—See Honda Motor Co., Ltd.; *Int'l*, pg. 3461
HONDA MOTORCYCLE & SCOOTER INDIA PVT. LTD.—See Honda Motor Co., Ltd.; *Int'l*, pg. 3462
HONDA MOTOR DE ARGENTINA S.A.—See Honda Motor Co., Ltd.; *Int'l*, pg. 3462
HONDA MOTOR DE CHILE S.A.—See Honda Motor Co., Ltd.; *Int'l*, pg. 3462
HONDA MOTOR EUROPE LIMITED—See Honda Motor Co., Ltd.; *Int'l*, pg. 3461
HONDA MOTOR EUROPE (NORTH) GMBH—See Honda Motor Co., Ltd.; *Int'l*, pg. 3461
HONDA MOTOR RUS LLC—See Honda Motor Co., Ltd.; *Int'l*, pg. 3462
HONDA MOTORS INC.; *U.S. Private*, pg. 1976
HONDA MOTORS SOUTHERN AFRICA (PTY.) LTD.—See Honda Motor Co., Ltd.; *Int'l*, pg. 3462
HONDA NEDERLAND B.V.—See Honda Motor Co., Ltd.; *Int'l*, pg. 3462
HONDA NEW ZEALAND LTD.—See Honda Motor Co., Ltd.; *Int'l*, pg. 3462
HONDA NORTH AMERICA INC.—See Honda Motor Co., Ltd.; *Int'l*, pg. 3459
HONDA OF AMERICA MANUFACTURING, INC.—See Honda Motor Co., Ltd.; *Int'l*, pg. 3460
HONDA OF AMES—See Lithia Motors, Inc.; *U.S. Public*, pg. 1322
HONDA OF CANADA MFG.—See Honda Motor Co., Ltd.; *Int'l*, pg. 3463
HONDA OF ITHACA; *U.S. Private*, pg. 1976
HONDA OF SALEM; *U.S. Private*, pg. 1976
HONDA OF SOUTH CAROLINA MANUFACTURING—See Honda Motor Co., Ltd.; *Int'l*, pg. 3463
HONDA OF STATEN ISLAND; *U.S. Private*, pg. 1976
HONDA OF THE U.K. MANUFACTURING LIMITED—See Honda Motor Co., Ltd.; *Int'l*, pg. 3461
HONDA OF TIFFANY SPRINGS—See A&L Holding Company Inc.; *U.S. Private*, pg. 20
HONDA PARTS MFG. CORP.—See Honda Motor Co., Ltd.; *Int'l*, pg. 3462
HONDA PERFORMANCE DEVELOPMENT—See Honda Motor Co., Ltd.; *Int'l*, pg. 3462
HONDA PHILIPPINES INC.—See Honda Motor Co., Ltd.; *Int'l*, pg. 3462
HONDA POLAND LTD.—See Honda Motor Co., Ltd.; *Int'l*, pg. 3462
HONDA POWER EQUIPMENT MANUFACTURING, INC.—See Honda Motor Co., Ltd.; *Int'l*, pg. 3460
HONDA POWER EQUIPMENT SWEDEN A.B.—See Honda Motor Co., Ltd.; *Int'l*, pg. 3462

HONDA PRECISION PARTS OF GEORGIA, LLC—See Honda Motor Co., Ltd.; *Int'l*, pg. 3462
HONDA RACING DEVELOPMENT LTD.—See Honda Motor Co., Ltd.; *Int'l*, pg. 3462
HONDA R&D AMERICAS, INC.—See Honda Motor Co., Ltd.; *Int'l*, pg. 3462
HONDA R & D ASIA PACIFIC CO., LTD.—See Honda Motor Co., Ltd.; *Int'l*, pg. 3462
HONDA R&D EUROPE (DEUTSCHLAND) GMBH—See Honda Motor Co., Ltd.; *Int'l*, pg. 3462
HONDA R & D EUROPE (U.K.) LTD.—See Honda Motor Co., Ltd.; *Int'l*, pg. 3462
HONDA R & D (INDIA) PVT. LTD.—See Honda Motor Co., Ltd.; *Int'l*, pg. 3462
HONDA R & D SOUTHEAST ASIA CO., LTD. (HRS)—See Honda Motor Co., Ltd.; *Int'l*, pg. 3462
HONDA RESEARCH INSTITUTE EUROPE G.M.B.H.—See Honda Motor Co., Ltd.; *Int'l*, pg. 3462
HONDA RESEARCH INSTITUTE JAPAN CO., LTD.—See Honda Motor Co., Ltd.; *Int'l*, pg. 3462
HONDA RESEARCH INSTITUTE USA, INC.—See Honda Motor Co., Ltd.; *Int'l*, pg. 3462
HONDA SALES OPERATIONS JAPAN CO., LTD.—See Honda Motor Co., Ltd.; *Int'l*, pg. 3462
HONDA SIEL CARS INDIA LTD.—See Honda Motor Co., Ltd.; *Int'l*, pg. 3462
HONDA SIEL CARS INDIA LTD.—See Siddharth Shriram Group; *Int'l*, pg. 6883
HONDA SLOVAKIA SPOL. S.R.O.—See Honda Motor Co., Ltd.; *Int'l*, pg. 3462
HONDA SOUTH AMERICA LTDA.—See Honda Motor Co., Ltd.; *Int'l*, pg. 3462
HONDA (SUISSE) S.A.—See Honda Motor Co., Ltd.; *Int'l*, pg. 3460
HONDA TAIWAN CO., LTD.—See Honda Motor Co., Ltd.; *Int'l*, pg. 3462
HONDA TAIWAN MOTOR CO., LTD.—See Honda Motor Co., Ltd.; *Int'l*, pg. 3462
HONDA TRADING AMERICA CORP.—See Honda Motor Co., Ltd.; *Int'l*, pg. 3462
HONDA TRADING ASIA CO., LTD.—See Honda Motor Co., Ltd.; *Int'l*, pg. 3462
HONDA TRADING CANADA, INC.—See Honda Motor Co., Ltd.; *Int'l*, pg. 3462
HONDA TRADING (CHINA) CO., LTD.—See Honda Motor Co., Ltd.; *Int'l*, pg. 3462
HONDA TRADING CORP.—See Honda Motor Co., Ltd.; *Int'l*, pg. 3462
HONDA TRADING DE MEXICO S.A. DE C.V.—See Honda Motor Co., Ltd.; *Int'l*, pg. 3463
HONDA TRADING DO BRASIL LTDA.—See Honda Motor Co., Ltd.; *Int'l*, pg. 3462
HONDA TRADING EUROPE LTD.—See Honda Motor Co., Ltd.; *Int'l*, pg. 3462
HONDA TRADING (GUANGZHOU) CO., LTD.—See Honda Motor Co., Ltd.; *Int'l*, pg. 3462
HONDA TRADING (SOUTH CHINA) CO., LTD.—See Honda Motor Co., Ltd.; *Int'l*, pg. 3462
HONDA TRANSMISSION MANUFACTURING OF AMERICA, INC.—See Honda Motor Co., Ltd.; *Int'l*, pg. 3463
HONDA TSUSHIN KOGYO CO., LTD.—See Minebea Mitsumi Inc.; *Int'l*, pg. 4902
HONDA TURKIYE A.S.—See Honda Motor Co., Ltd.; *Int'l*, pg. 3463
HONDA UGANDA LTD.—See Honda Motor Co., Ltd.; *Int'l*, pg. 3463
HONDA U-TEC CO., LTD.—See Honda Motor Co., Ltd.; *Int'l*, pg. 3463
HONDA VIETNAM CO., LTD.—See Honda Motor Co., Ltd.; *Int'l*, pg. 3463
HONDURAS AMERICAN TABACO, S.A. DE C.V.—See Skandinavisk Holding A/S; *Int'l*, pg. 6976
H-ONE CO. LTD. - KAMEYAMA FACTORY—See H-One Co., Ltd.; *Int'l*, pg. 3194
H-ONE CO. LTD. - KARASUYAMA PLANT—See H-One Co., Ltd.; *Int'l*, pg. 3194
H-ONE CO. LTD. - KORIYAMA FACTORY—See H-One Co., Ltd.; *Int'l*, pg. 3194
H-ONE CO. LTD. - MAEBASHI FACTORY—See H-One Co., Ltd.; *Int'l*, pg. 3194
H-ONE CO., LTD.; *Int'l*, pg. 3194
H-ONE INDIA PVT. LTD.—See H-One Co., Ltd.; *Int'l*, pg. 3194
HONE OIL COMPANY INC.; *U.S. Private*, pg. 1976
H-ONE PARTS SRIRACHA CO., LTD.—See H-One Co., Ltd.; *Int'l*, pg. 3194
H-ONE PARTS (THAILAND) CO., LTD.—See H-One Co., Ltd.; *Int'l*, pg. 3194
H ONE (PRIVATE) LIMITED—See Axiata Group Berhad; *Int'l*, pg. 768
THE HONESDALE NATIONAL BANK—See Honat Bancorp Inc.; *U.S. Public*, pg. 1046
HONEST COMPANY, INC.; *U.S. Public*, pg. 1046
THE HONEST KITCHEN, INC.; *U.S. Private*, pg. 4054
HONEST TEA—See The Coca-Cola Company; *U.S. Public*, pg. 2065
HONESTY SHIPPING CO., LIMITED—See Xiamen Xiangyu Co., Ltd.; *Int'l*, pg. 8526

HONEU LEASING GESELLSCHAFT M.B.H—See UniCredit S.p.A.; *Int'l*, pg. 8036
HONEY BADGER SILVER INC.; *Int'l*, pg. 3465
HONEYBAKED HAM CO. OF OHIO; *U.S. Private*, pg. 1976
HONEY BUN (1982) LTD.; *Int'l*, pg. 3465
HONEY-CAN-DO INTERNATIONAL; *U.S. Private*, pg. 1976
HONEY CREEK MALL, LLC—See CBL & Associates Properties, Inc.; *U.S. Public*, pg. 458
HONEY DEW ASSOCIATES, INC.; *U.S. Private*, pg. 1976
HONEY FARMS INC.; *U.S. Private*, pg. 1976
HONEY GARDENS, INC.—See HGGC, LLC; *U.S. Private*, pg. 1930
HONEY HOPE HONESTY ENTERPRISE CO., LTD.; *Int'l*, pg. 3465
HONEY LAKE PLANTATION RESORT & SPA; *U.S. Private*, pg. 1976
HONEY MONSTER FOODS LIMITED—See Raisio PLC; *Int'l*, pg. 6191
HONEYMOON PAPER PRODUCTS, INC.—See Southern Champion Tray Co. Inc.; *U.S. Private*, pg. 3730
HONEYS HOLDINGS CO., LTD.; *Int'l*, pg. 3465
HONEYVILLE GRAIN INC.; *U.S. Private*, pg. 1976
HONEYWELL ACCESS—See Honeywell International Inc.; *U.S. Public*, pg. 1049
HONEYWELL ADEMCO SECURITY—See Honeywell International Inc.; *U.S. Public*, pg. 1049
HONEYWELL AEROSPACE AVIONICS MALAYSIA SDN BHD.—See Honeywell International Inc.; *U.S. Public*, pg. 1047
HONEYWELL AEROSPACE - BOYNE CITY—See Honeywell International Inc.; *U.S. Public*, pg. 1047
HONEYWELL AEROSPACE DE MEXICO, S. DE R.L. DE C.V.—See Honeywell International Inc.; *U.S. Public*, pg. 1047
HONEYWELL AEROSPACE ELECTRONIC SYSTEMS—See Honeywell International Inc.; *U.S. Public*, pg. 1047
HONEYWELL AEROSPACE GMBH—See Honeywell International Inc.; *U.S. Public*, pg. 1047
HONEYWELL AEROSPACE - HOUSTON, AIR CENTER BOULEVARD—See Honeywell International Inc.; *U.S. Public*, pg. 1047
HONEYWELL AEROSPACE - MOORESTOWN—See Honeywell International Inc.; *U.S. Public*, pg. 1047
HONEYWELL AEROSPACE - NORCROSS—See Honeywell International Inc.; *U.S. Public*, pg. 1047
HONEYWELL AEROSPACE—See Honeywell International Inc.; *U.S. Public*, pg. 1047
HONEYWELL AEROSPACE - TORRANCE—See Honeywell International Inc.; *U.S. Public*, pg. 1047
HONEYWELL AEROSPACE - URBANA—See Honeywell International Inc.; *U.S. Public*, pg. 1047
HONEYWELL AEROSPACE YEOVIL—See Honeywell International Inc.; *U.S. Public*, pg. 1047
HONEYWELL AIRCRAFT LANDING SYSTEMS—See Honeywell International Inc.; *U.S. Public*, pg. 1047
HONEYWELL AIRPORT SYSTEM—See Honeywell International Inc.; *U.S. Public*, pg. 1047
HONEYWELL AIR TRANSPORT SYSTEMS—See Honeywell International Inc.; *U.S. Public*, pg. 1047
HONEYWELL ANALYTICS AG—See Honeywell International Inc.; *U.S. Public*, pg. 1048
HONEYWELL ANALYTICS AG—See Honeywell International Inc.; *U.S. Public*, pg. 1048
HONEYWELL ANALYTICS ASIA PACIFIC CO., LTD.—See Honeywell International Inc.; *U.S. Public*, pg. 1047
HONEYWELL ANALYTICS FRANCE S.A.—See Honeywell International Inc.; *U.S. Public*, pg. 1048
HONEYWELL ANALYTICS INSTRUMENTATION—See Honeywell International Inc.; *U.S. Public*, pg. 1048
HONEYWELL ANALYTICS LIMITED—See Honeywell International Inc.; *U.S. Public*, pg. 1048
HONEYWELL ANALYTICS—See Honeywell International Inc.; *U.S. Public*, pg. 1048
HONEYWELL ASCA INC.—See Honeywell International Inc.; *U.S. Public*, pg. 1051
HONEYWELL AUTOMATION & CONTROL SOLUTIONS—See Honeywell International Inc.; *U.S. Public*, pg. 1047
HONEYWELL AUTOMATION INDIA LTD.—See Honeywell International Inc.; *U.S. Public*, pg. 1051
HONEYWELL AUTOMOTIVE PARTS SERVICES (SHANGHAI) CO., LTD.—See Garrett Motion Inc.; *Int'l*, pg. 2886
HONEYWELL AVIONICS SYSTEMS LIMITED—See Honeywell International Inc.; *U.S. Public*, pg. 1051
HONEYWELL BUILDING SOLUTIONS—See Honeywell International Inc.; *U.S. Public*, pg. 1048
HONEYWELL BURDICK & JACKSON—See Honeywell International Inc.; *U.S. Public*, pg. 1051
HONEYWELL CANADA, INC.—See Honeywell International Inc.; *U.S. Public*, pg. 1051
HONEYWELL (CHINA) CO., LTD.—See Honeywell International Inc.; *U.S. Public*, pg. 1047
HONEYWELL CO., LTD.—See Honeywell International Inc.; *U.S. Public*, pg. 1051

HONEYWELL COMMERCIAL ELECTRONIC SYSTEMS—See Honeywell International Inc.; *U.S. Public*, pg. 1047
HONEYWELL CONTROL SYSTEMS LTD.—See Honeywell International Inc.; *U.S. Public*, pg. 1047
HONEYWELL DEFENSE AND SPACE ELECTRONIC SYSTEMS—See Honeywell International Inc.; *U.S. Public*, pg. 1047
HONEYWELL DEFENSE AVIONICS SYSTEMS—See Honeywell International Inc.; *U.S. Public*, pg. 1047
HONEYWELL ELECTRONIC MATERIALS—See Honeywell International Inc.; *U.S. Public*, pg. 1047
HONEYWELL ELECTRONIC MATERIALS (THAILAND) CO., LTD.—See Honeywell International Inc.; *U.S. Public*, pg. 1051
HONEYWELL ENGINE SYSTEMS & SERVICES—See Honeywell International Inc.; *U.S. Public*, pg. 1047
HONEYWELL ENRAF AMERICAS, INC.—See Honeywell International Inc.; *U.S. Public*, pg. 1049
HONEYWELL ENVIRONMENTAL & COMBUSTION CONTROLS—See Honeywell International Inc.; *U.S. Public*, pg. 1048
HONEYWELL EUROPE NV—See Honeywell International Inc.; *U.S. Public*, pg. 1051
HONEYWELL FEDERAL MANUFACTURING TECHNOLOGY—See Honeywell International Inc.; *U.S. Public*, pg. 1047
HONEYWELL FIRST RESPONDER PRODUCTS—See Honeywell International Inc.; *U.S. Public*, pg. 1049
HONEYWELL FLOUR MILLS PLC; *Int'l*, pg. 3465
HONEYWELL GARRETT S.A.—See Garrett Motion Inc.; *Int'l*, pg. 2886
HONEYWELL GLOBAL TRACKING—See Honeywell International Inc.; *U.S. Public*, pg. 1047
HONEYWELL HOLDINGS PTY. LTD.—See Honeywell International Inc.; *U.S. Public*, pg. 1051
HONEYWELL INTERNATIONAL, INC. - PUERTO RICO OFFICE—See Honeywell International Inc.; *U.S. Public*, pg. 1051
HONEYWELL INTERNATIONAL INC.; *U.S. Public*, pg. 1046
HONEYWELL INTERNATIONAL SDN. BHD.—See Honeywell International Inc.; *U.S. Public*, pg. 1051
HONEYWELL JAPAN INC. See Honeywell International Inc.; *U.S. Public*, pg. 1051
HONEYWELL KOREA, LTD.—See Honeywell International Inc.; *U.S. Public*, pg. 1051
HONEYWELL LIFE SAFETY ROMANIA SRL—See Honeywell International Inc.; *U.S. Public*, pg. 1051
HONEYWELL LIFE SAFETY—See Honeywell International Inc.; *U.S. Public*, pg. 1048
HONEYWELL LIMITED—See Honeywell International Inc.; *U.S. Public*, pg. 1051
HONEYWELL NORTH SAFETY PRODUCTS CANADA—See Honeywell International Inc.; *U.S. Public*, pg. 1049
HONEYWELL NYLON LLC—See Honeywell International Inc.; *U.S. Public*, pg. 1051
HONEYWELL PROCESS SOLUTIONS—See Honeywell International Inc.; *U.S. Public*, pg. 1049
HONEYWELL PTE. LTD.—See Honeywell International Inc.; *U.S. Public*, pg. 1051
HONEYWELL SAFETY PRODUCTS AUSTRALIA PTY LTD—See Honeywell International Inc.; *U.S. Public*, pg. 1049
HONEYWELL SAFETY PRODUCTS EMERGENCY EYEWASH—See Honeywell International Inc.; *U.S. Public*, pg. 1049
HONEYWELL SAFETY PRODUCTS EUROPE SAS—See Honeywell International Inc.; *U.S. Public*, pg. 1051
HONEYWELL SAFETY PRODUCTS GLOVES USA, LLC—See Honeywell International Inc.; *U.S. Public*, pg. 1049
HONEYWELL SAFETY PRODUCTS HEARING PROTECTION, LLC—See Honeywell International Inc.; *U.S. Public*, pg. 1049
HONEYWELL SAFETY PRODUCTS ITALIA SRL—See Honeywell International Inc.; *U.S. Public*, pg. 1049
HONEYWELL SAFETY PRODUCTS RESPIRATORY PROTECTION USA, LLC—See Honeywell International Inc.; *U.S. Public*, pg. 1049
HONEYWELL SAFETY PRODUCTS—See Honeywell International Inc.; *U.S. Public*, pg. 1049
HONEYWELL SAFETY PRODUCTS USA, INC.—See Honeywell International Inc.; *U.S. Public*, pg. 1048
HONEYWELL SALISBURY ELECTRICAL SAFETY—See Honeywell International Inc.; *U.S. Public*, pg. 1049
HONEYWELL SCANNING & MOBILITY—See Honeywell International Inc.; *U.S. Public*, pg. 1050
HONEYWELL SECURITY & COMMUNICATIONS - CANADA—See Honeywell International Inc.; *U.S. Public*, pg. 1050
HONEYWELL SECURITY—See Honeywell International Inc.; *U.S. Public*, pg. 1050
HONEYWELL SECURITY UK LIMITED—See Honeywell International Inc.; *U.S. Public*, pg. 1050
HONEYWELL SENSING & CONTROL—See Honeywell International Inc.; *U.S. Public*, pg. 1050

HONEYWELL SENSING & CONTROL—See Honeywell International Inc.; *U.S. Public*, pg. 1050
HONEYWELL SENSORS, INC.—See Honeywell International Inc.; *U.S. Public*, pg. 1051
HONEYWELL SPACE SYSTEMS—See Honeywell International Inc.; *U.S. Public*, pg. 1047
HONEYWELL SPECIALTY CHEMICALS SEELZE GMBH—See Honeywell International Inc.; *U.S. Public*, pg. 1051
HONEYWELL SPOL. SR.O.—See Honeywell International Inc.; *U.S. Public*, pg. 1051
HONEYWELL TCAS INC.—See L3Harris Technologies, Inc.; *U.S. Public*, pg. 1281
HONEYWELL TECHNOLOGIES SARL—See Honeywell International Inc.; *U.S. Public*, pg. 1051
HONEYWELL TECHNOLOGY SOLUTIONS LAB PVT. LTD.—See Honeywell International Inc.; *U.S. Public*, pg. 1051
HONEYWELL TECHNOLOGY SOLUTIONS QATAR LTD.—See Honeywell International Inc.; *U.S. Public*, pg. 1051
HONEYWELL TEKNOLOJI ANONIM SIRKETI—See Honeywell International Inc.; *U.S. Public*, pg. 1051
HONEYWELL UK LIMITED—See Honeywell International Inc.; *U.S. Public*, pg. 1051
HONEYWELL VIDEO SYSTEMS—See Honeywell International Inc.; *U.S. Public*, pg. 1051
HONEYWELL VIDEO SYSTEMS—See Honeywell International Inc.; *U.S. Public*, pg. 1050
HONGBANG DIE CASTING (NANTONG) CO., LTD.—See Wencan Group Co., Ltd.; *Int'l*, pg. 8376
HONGBAOLI GROUP CO., LTD; *Int'l*, pg. 3469
HONGBO CO., LTD.; *Int'l*, pg. 3469
HONGCHANG INTERNATIONAL CO LTD.; *Int'l*, pg. 3470
HONGCHENG ENVIRONMENTAL TECHNOLOGY CO., LTD.; *Int'l*, pg. 3470
HONGDA FINANCIAL HOLDING LIMITED; *Int'l*, pg. 3470
HONGDA HIGH-TECH HOLDING CO., LTD.; *Int'l*, pg. 3470
HONGDA XINGYE CO., LTD.; *Int'l*, pg. 3470
HONGDUK INDUSTRIAL CO., LTD. - GEOCHANG STEEL CORD FACTORY—See KISWIRE LTD; *Int'l*, pg. 4193
HONGDUK INDUSTRIAL CO., LTD. - HAMAN STEEL CORD FACTORY—See KISWIRE LTD; *Int'l*, pg. 4193
HONGDUK INDUSTRIAL CO., LTD. - MACHINERY MANUFACTURING DIVISION—See KISWIRE LTD; *Int'l*, pg. 4193
HONGDUK INDUSTRIAL CO., LTD. - POHANG BEAD WIRE FACTORY—See KISWIRE LTD; *Int'l*, pg. 4193
HONGDUK INDUSTRIAL CO., LTD. - POHANG SILK WIRE FACTORY—See KISWIRE LTD; *Int'l*, pg. 4193
HONGDUK INDUSTRIAL CO., LTD. - POHANG SPRING WIRE FACTORY—See KISWIRE LTD; *Int'l*, pg. 4193
HONGDUK INDUSTRIAL CO., LTD.—See KISWIRE LTD; *Int'l*, pg. 4193
HONGFA AMERICA, INC.—See Hongfa Technology Co Ltd; *Int'l*, pg. 3470
HONGFA ELECTROACOUSTIC (HONGKONG) CO., LTD.—See Hongfa Technology Co Ltd; *Int'l*, pg. 3470
HONGFA EUROPE GMBH—See Hongfa Technology Co Ltd; *Int'l*, pg. 3470
HONGFA ITALY S.R.L.—See Hongfa Technology Co Ltd; *Int'l*, pg. 3470
HONGFA TECHNOLOGY CO LTD; *Int'l*, pg. 3470
HONGFENG COMPOSITE MATERIALS CORP.—See Wenzhou Hongfeng Electrical Alloy Co., Ltd.; *Int'l*, pg. 8377
HONGFENG ELEKTROWERKSTOFFE GMBH—See Wenzhou Hongfeng Electrical Alloy Co., Ltd.; *Int'l*, pg. 8377
HONG FOK CORPORATION LIMITED; *Int'l*, pg. 3465
HONG FOK LAND PTE. LTD.—See Hong Fok Corporation Limited; *Int'l*, pg. 3465
HONG HA LONG AN JOINT STOCK COMPANY; *Int'l*, pg. 3465
HONG HENG SHENG ELECTRONICAL TECHNOLOGY (HUAIAN) CO., LTD.—See Zhen Ding Technology Holding Limited; *Int'l*, pg. 8669
HONG HO PRECISION TEXTILES CO., LTD.; *Int'l*, pg. 3465
HONGHUA AMERICA, LLC—See Honghua Group Ltd; *Int'l*, pg. 3470
HONGHUA GOLDEN COAST EQUIPMENT FZE—See Honghua Group Ltd; *Int'l*, pg. 3470
HONGHUA GROUP LTD; *Int'l*, pg. 3470
HONGHUA INTERNATIONAL CO., LTD.—See Honghua Group Ltd; *Int'l*, pg. 3470
HONGHUA INTERNATIONAL DE VENEZUELA, C.A.—See Honghua Group Ltd; *Int'l*, pg. 3471
HONGHUA INTERNATIONAL SUCURSAL COLOMBIA—See Honghua Group Ltd; *Int'l*, pg. 3470
HONGHUA INTERNATIONAL UKRAINE CO., LTD.—See Honghua Group Ltd; *Int'l*, pg. 3470
HONGHUASHENG PRECISION ELECTRONICS (YANTAI) CO., LTD.—See Pan-International Industrial Corporation; *Int'l*, pg. 5715
HONGHUA SUCURSAL BOLIVIA—See Honghua Group Ltd; *Int'l*, pg. 3471

HONGKANG (JIUJIANG) AGRICULTURAL DEVELOPMENT CO., LTD.—See Heng Tai Consumables Group Limited; *Int'l*, pg. 3345
HONGKONG ACE PILLAR CO., LTD—See ACE PILLAR Co., Ltd; *Int'l*, pg. 94
HONG KONG ACE PILLAR ENTERPRISE CO., LTD.—See ACE PILLAR Co., Ltd; *Int'l*, pg. 94
HONG KONG AEROSPACE TECHNOLOGY GROUP LIMITED—See Hong Kong Aerospace Technology Holdings Limited; *Int'l*, pg. 3465
HONG KONG AEROSPACE TECHNOLOGY HOLDINGS LIMITED; *Int'l*, pg. 3465
HONG KONG AIC LIMITED—See Hitachi, Ltd.; *Int'l*, pg. 3423
HONG KONG AIR CARGO INDUSTRY SERVICES LIMITED—See Jardine Matheson Holdings Limited; *Int'l*, pg. 3908
HONG KONG AIR CARGO TERMINALS LTD.—See Jardine Matheson Holdings Limited; *Int'l*, pg. 3908
HONG KONG AIRCRAFT ENGINEERING CO.—See John Swire & Sons Limited; *Int'l*, pg. 3980
HONG KONG AIRLINES LIMITED—See Hainan Traffic Administration Holding Co., Ltd.; *Int'l*, pg. 3215
HONG KONG AIRPORT SERVICES LTD.—See Cathay Pacific Airways Limited; *Int'l*, pg. 1360
THE HONG KONG AND SHANGHAI BANKING CORPORATION LIMITED—See HSBC Holdings plc; *Int'l*, pg. 3506
THE HONGKONG AND SHANGHAI HOTELS LIMITED; *Int'l*, pg. 7652
THE HONGKONG AND YAUMATI FERRY COMPANY LIMITED—See Henderson Land Development Co. Ltd.; *Int'l*, pg. 3345
HONG KONG ASSET MANAGEMENT GROUP LIMITED—See Value Partners Group Limited; *Int'l*, pg. 8124
HONGKONG BAY SECURITIES LIMITED—See Bay Area Gold Group Limited; *Int'l*, pg. 900
HONG KONG BUSINESS AVIATION CENTRE LIMITED—See Sun Hung Kai Properties Limited; *Int'l*, pg. 7304
HONG KONG CHAOSHANG GROUP LIMITED; *Int'l*, pg. 3465
HONG KONG CHEMI-CON LTD.—See Nippon Chemi-Con Corporation; *Int'l*, pg. 5312
HONG KONG & CHINA GAS COMPANY LIMITED—See Henderson Land Development Co. Ltd.; *Int'l*, pg. 3344
HONGKONG CHINESE LIMITED—See Lippo Limited; *Int'l*, pg. 4522
HONG KONG COMMUNICATIONS COMPANY LIMITED—See HKC International Holdings Limited; *Int'l*, pg. 3428
HONG KONG COSCO HOTEL MANAGEMENT CO., LTD.—See China COSCO Shipping Corporation Limited; *Int'l*, pg. 1492
HONG KONG DESCENTE TRADING LTD.—See ITOCHU Corporation; *Int'l*, pg. 3836
HONG KONG DISNEYLAND MANAGEMENT LIMITED—See The Walt Disney Company; *U.S. Public*, pg. 2139
HONG KONG DRAGON AIRLINES LIMITED—See Cathay Pacific Airways Limited; *Int'l*, pg. 1360
HONG KONG ECONOMIC TIMES HOLDINGS LTD; *Int'l*, pg. 3465
HONG KONG ECONOMIC TIMES LIMITED—See Hong Kong Economic Times Holdings Ltd; *Int'l*, pg. 3466
THE HONGKONG ELECTRIC CO., LTD.—See Power Assets Holdings Limited; *Int'l*, pg. 5943
HONGKONG ELECTRIC INTERNATIONAL LTD.—See Power Assets Holdings Limited; *Int'l*, pg. 5943
THE HONGKONG EXCELLEN SCIENCE & TECHNOLOGY LTD.—See Shanghai Putailai New Energy Technology Co., Ltd.; *Int'l*, pg. 6777
HONG KONG EXCHANGES & CLEARING LIMITED; *Int'l*, pg. 3466
HONG KONG FERRY (HOLDINGS) CO. LTD.—See Henderson Land Development Co. Ltd.; *Int'l*, pg. 3344
HONG KONG FINANCE GROUP LIMITED; *Int'l*, pg. 3466
HONG KONG FLOUR MILLS LIMITED—See LAM SOON (HONG KONG) LIMITED; *Int'l*, pg. 4400
HONG KONG FOOD INVESTMENT HOLDINGS LIMITED; *Int'l*, pg. 3466
HONG KONG FOUR SEAS TOURS LIMITED—See Orient Victory Smart urban Services Holding Limited; *Int'l*, pg. 5623
HONG KONG FUJIDENKI CO., LTD.—See Fuji Electric Co., Ltd.; *Int'l*, pg. 2812
HONG KONG FUTURES EXCHANGE LTD.—See Hong Kong Exchanges & Clearing Limited; *Int'l*, pg. 3466
HONG KONG GOURMET LIMITED—See Vitasoy International Holdings Ltd.; *Int'l*, pg. 8259
HONGKONG GREAT INTERNATIONAL ENTERPRISE CO., LIMITED—See Daeyang Electric Co., Ltd.; *Int'l*, pg. 1911
HONG KONG HIGHPOWER INTERNATIONAL CO., LTD.—See Highpower International, Inc.; *Int'l*, pg. 3388
HONG KONG HIGHPOWER TECHNOLOGY CO., LTD.—See Highpower International, Inc.; *Int'l*, pg. 3388

HONG KONG FOOD INVESTMENT HOLDINGS LIMITED

CORPORATE AFFILIATIONS

HONG KONG HOSIDEN LTD—See Hosiden Corporation; *Int'l*, pg. 3484

HONG KONG HUNG HING METAL MANUFACTURING COMPANY LIMITED—See Karrie International Holdings Limited; *Int'l*, pg. 4085

HONG KONG INTERNATIONAL AVIATION LEASING CO., LTD.—See Hainan Traffic Administration Holding Co., Ltd.; *Int'l*, pg. 3215

HONG KONG INTERNATIONAL STEP ELECTRIC HOLDINGS CO., LTD.—See Shanghai STEP Electric Corporation; *Int'l*, pg. 6779

HONGKONG INTERNATIONAL TRADE FINANCE (JAPAN) KK—See HSBC Holdings plc; *Int'l*, pg. 3507

HONG KONG ISLAND LANDSCAPE COMPANY LIMITED—See FSE Services Group Limited; *Int'l*, pg. 2798

HONG KONG ITALIVING INTERNATIONAL CO., LIMITED—See Qi-House Holdings Limited; *Int'l*, pg. 6139

HONG KONG IT ALLIANCE LIMITED—See Champion Technology Holdings Ltd; *Int'l*, pg. 1440

HONG KONG I.V.A. CONSULTANTS LIMITED—See Credit Intelligence Limited; *Int'l*, pg. 1835

HONG KONG JIYE HOLDINGS LIMITED—See Redco Properties Group Limited; *Int'l*, pg. 6246

HONG KONG JOHNSON HOLDINGS COMPANY LIMITED; *Int'l*, pg. 3466

HONG KONG KAM HING THREADS LIMITED—See Kam Hing International Holdings Limited; *Int'l*, pg. 4059

HONG KONG KAM KEE FOODSTUFFS TRADING CO., LTD.; *Int'l*, pg. 3466

HONG KONG KANSAI PAINT CO., LTD.—See Kansai Paint Co., Ltd.; *Int'l*, pg. 4072

HONG KONG KNITTERS LIMITED—See Yangtzekiang Garment Limited; *Int'l*, pg. 8561

HONG KONG KONKA LIMITED—See Konka Group Co., Ltd.; *Int'l*, pg. 4274

HONGKONG LAND (ASIA MANAGEMENT) LIMITED—See Jardine Matheson Holdings Limited; *Int'l*, pg. 3910

HONGKONG LAND (BEIJING) MANAGEMENT CO LTD—See Jardine Matheson Holdings Limited; *Int'l*, pg. 3910

HONGKONG LAND (CHENGDU) INVESTMENT & DEVELOPMENT COMPANY LIMITED—See Hong Kong Land Holdings Ltd.; *Int'l*, pg. 3466

HONGKONG LAND (CHONGQING) INVESTMENT & HOLDING CO. LTD.—See Hong Kong Land Holdings Ltd.; *Int'l*, pg. 3466

HONGKONG LAND (CHONGQING) MANAGEMENT CO LTD—See Jardine Matheson Holdings Limited; *Int'l*, pg. 3910

HONGKONG LAND (HANGZHOU) SHENGYUE MANAGEMENT CO., LTD.—See Hong Kong Land Holdings Ltd.; *Int'l*, pg. 3466

HONGKONG LAND HOLDINGS LIMITED—See Jardine Matheson Holdings Limited; *Int'l*, pg. 3910

HONG KONG LAND HOLDINGS LTD.; *Int'l*, pg. 3466

HONGKONG LAND LIMITED—See Jardine Matheson Holdings Limited; *Int'l*, pg. 3910

HONGKONG LAND (NANJING) PUZHI MANAGEMENT CO., LTD.—See Hong Kong Land Holdings Ltd.; *Int'l*, pg. 3466

HONGKONG LAND (PHILIPPINES) CONSULTANCY, INC.—See Hong Kong Land Holdings Ltd.; *Int'l*, pg. 3466

HONGKONG LAND (PREMIUM INVESTMENTS) LIMITED—See Hong Kong Land Holdings Ltd.; *Int'l*, pg. 3466

THE HONGKONG LAND PROPERTY COMPANY, LIMITED—See Jardine Matheson Holdings Limited; *Int'l*, pg. 3910

HONGKONG LAND (SHANGHAI) MANAGEMENT COMPANY LIMITED—See Hong Kong Land Holdings Ltd.; *Int'l*, pg. 3466

HONGKONG LAND (SINGAPORE) PTE. LIMITED—See Jardine Matheson Holdings Limited; *Int'l*, pg. 3910

HONGKONG LAND (WUHAN) INVESTMENT & DEVELOPMENT COMPANY LIMITED—See Hong Kong Land Holdings Ltd.; *Int'l*, pg. 3467

HONG KONG LIFE SCIENCES & TECHNOLOGIES GROUP LIMITED; *Int'l*, pg. 3467

HONG KONG MARKET PLACE INC.; *U.S. Private*, pg. 1976

HONGKONG MAYTIME INTERNATIONAL INDUSTRY CO., LTD.—See Ningbo Jintian Copper (Group) Co., Ltd.; *Int'l*, pg. 5302

HONG KONG MEDICAL CONSULTANTS LIMITED—See Town Health International Medical Group Limited; *Int'l*, pg. 7851

HONG KONG MING WAH SHIPPING CO., LTD.—See China Merchants Group Limited; *Int'l*, pg. 1521

HONG KONG MONETARY AUTHORITY; *Int'l*, pg. 3467

HONG KONG NICCA CHEMICAL LTD.—See Nicca Chemical Co., Ltd.; *Int'l*, pg. 5263

HONG KONG NIPPON SEIKI CO., LTD.—See Nippon Seiki Co., Ltd.; *Int'l*, pg. 5329

HONG KONG NUCLEAR INVESTMENT COMPANY LIMITED—See CLP Holdings Limited; *Int'l*, pg. 1663

HONG KONG OOTOYA CO., LTD.—See OOTOYA Holdings Co., Ltd.; *Int'l*, pg. 5595

HONG KONG PERFECT JEWELLERY DMCC—See Perfect Group International Holdings Ltd.; *Int'l*, pg. 5798

HONG KONG PROPERTY SERVICES (AGENCY) LTD.—See Midland Holdings Limited; *Int'l*, pg. 4886

HONG KONG PROPERTY SERVICES IC&I) LIMITED—See Legend Upstar Holdings Limited; *Int'l*, pg. 4444

HONG KONG QUAM SECURITIES COMPANY LIMITED—See Quam Plus International Financial Limited; *Int'l*, pg. 6152

HONGKONG RATON INTERNATIONAL CO., LTD.—See Shenzhen Prolto Supply Chain Management Co., Ltd.; *Int'l*, pg. 6819

HONG KONG REGAL SHOE CO., LTD.—See REGAL CORPORATION; *Int'l*, pg. 6251

HONG KONG RESOURCES HOLDINGS COMPANY LIMITED—See Luk Fook Holdings (International) Limited; *Int'l*, pg. 4576

HONGKONG SALVAGE & TOWAGE—See CK Hutchison Holdings Limited; *Int'l*, pg. 1637

HONGKONG SALVAGE & TOWAGE—See John Swire & Sons Limited; *Int'l*, pg. 3980

HONG KONG SATORI CO., LTD.—See SATORI ELECTRIC CO., LTD.; *Int'l*, pg. 6586

THE HONG KONG SCHOOL OF MOTORING LIMITED—See The Cross-Harbour (Holdings) Limited; *Int'l*, pg. 7636

HONG KONG SECURITIES CLEARING COMPANY LIMITED—See Hong Kong Exchanges & Clearing Limited; *Int'l*, pg. 3466

HONG KONG SECURITY PRINTING LIMITED—See YGM Trading Ltd; *Int'l*, pg. 8580

HONG KONG SEIBU ENTERPRISE COMPANY LIMITED—See Dickson Concepts (International) Limited; *Int'l*, pg. 2112

HONG KONG SEMBA LTD.—See SEMBA Corporation; *Int'l*, pg. 6702

HONG KONG SENSORS TECHNOLOGIES LIMITED—See TE Connectivity Ltd.; *Int'l*, pg. 7495

HONG KONG SENSORS TECHNOLOGIES LIMITED—See TE Connectivity Ltd.; *Int'l*, pg. 7495

HONG KONG SHANGHAI ALLIANCE HOLDINGS LIMITED; *Int'l*, pg. 3467

THE HONG KONG & SHANGHAI BANKING CORPORATION LTD.-TAIWAN—See HSBC Holdings plc; *Int'l*, pg. 3507

THE HONG KONG & SHANGHAI BANKING CORPORATION LTD.-THAILAND—See HSBC Holdings plc; *Int'l*, pg. 3507

THE HONG KONG SHIPYARD LIMITED—See Henderson Land Development Co. Ltd.; *Int'l*, pg. 3345

HONG KONG SINBON ELECTRONICS CO., LTD.—See SINBON Electronics Co., Ltd.; *Int'l*, pg. 6936

HONG KONG SKY DECK LIMITED—See Sun Hung Kai Properties Limited; *Int'l*, pg. 7304

HONG KONG SUMIRUBBER LTD.—See Sumitomo Rubber Industries, Ltd.; *Int'l*, pg. 7299

HONG KONG SUPERMARKET INC.; *U.S. Private*, pg. 1976

HONG KONG TAIYO YUDEN COMPANY LTD.—See Taiyo Yuden Company Ltd.; *Int'l*, pg. 7426

HONG KONG TAKUNG ART COMPANY LIMITED—See Takung Art Co., Ltd.; *Int'l*, pg. 7443

HONG KONG TECHNOLOGY VENTURE COMPANY LIMITED; *Int'l*, pg. 3467

HONG KONG THREE-CIRCLE ELECTRONIC CO., LTD.—See Chaozhou Three-Circle Group Co., Ltd.; *Int'l*, pg. 1447

HONG KONG TOKHE LOGISTICS CO., LTD.—See SBS Holdings Inc.; *Int'l*, pg. 6607

HONG KONG TOURISM BOARD - NEW YORK—See Hong Kong Tourism Board; *Int'l*, pg. 3467

HONG KONG TOURISM BOARD; *Int'l*, pg. 3467

HONG KONG TRANSLATIONS LIMITED—See Straker Limited; *Int'l*, pg. 7235

HONG KONG ULVAC CO., LTD.—See ULVAC, Inc.; *Int'l*, pg. 8020

HONG KONG VICTORIA WELL INDUSTRIAL LIMITED—See Doshisha Co., Ltd.; *Int'l*, pg. 2180

HONG KONG WEI—See China Security Co., Ltd.; *Int'l*, pg. 1550

HONG KONG WINALITE GROUP, INC.; *U.S. Public*, pg. 1052

HONG KONG YAMAZAKI BAKING CO., LTD.—See Yamazaki Baking Co., Ltd.; *Int'l*, pg. 8556

HONG LAI HUAT CONSTRUCTION PTE LTD—See Hong Lai Huat Group Limited; *Int'l*, pg. 3467

HONG LAI HUAT GROUP LIMITED; *Int'l*, pg. 3467

HONG LEONG ASIA LTD.—See Hong Leong Investment Holdings Pte. Ltd.; *Int'l*, pg. 3468

HONG LEONG ASSURANCE BHD.—See Hong Leong Investment Holdings Pte. Ltd.; *Int'l*, pg. 3468

HONG LEONG BANK BERHAD—See Hong Leong Investment Holdings Pte. Ltd.; *Int'l*, pg. 3468

HONG LEONG CAPITAL BERHAD—See Hong Leong Investment Holdings Pte. Ltd.; *Int'l*, pg. 3468

HONG LEONG COMPANY (MALAYSIA) BERHAD—See Hong Leong Investment Holdings Pte. Ltd.; *Int'l*, pg. 3467

HONG LEONG CORPORATION HOLDINGS PTE. LTD.—See Hong Leong Investment Holdings Pte. Ltd.; *Int'l*, pg. 3468

HONG LEONG FINANCE LIMITED—See Hong Leong Investment Holdings Pte. Ltd.; *Int'l*, pg. 3469

HONG LEONG FINANCIAL GROUP BERHAD—See Hong Leong Investment Holdings Pte. Ltd.; *Int'l*, pg. 3468

HONG LEONG HOLDINGS LTD.—See Hong Leong Investment Holdings Pte. Ltd.; *Int'l*, pg. 3469

HONG LEONG INDUSTRIES BERHAD—See Hong Leong Investment Holdings Pte. Ltd.; *Int'l*, pg. 3468

HONG LEONG INVESTMENT HOLDINGS PTE. LTD.; *Int'l*, pg. 3467

HONG LEONG MSIG TAKAFUL BERHAD—See MS&AD Insurance Group Holdings, Inc.; *Int'l*, pg. 5066

HONGLI CLEAN ENERGY TECHNOLOGIES CORP.; *Int'l*, pg. 3471

HONGLI GROUP INC.; *Int'l*, pg. 3471

HONGLING FINANCIAL LEASING CO., LTD.—See Mitsubishi Corporation; *Int'l*, pg. 4938

HONGLI ZHIHUI GROUP CO., LTD.; *Int'l*, pg. 3471

HONGLK CO., LTD—See AK Holdings, Inc.; *Int'l*, pg. 259

HONG MING TERMINAL & STEVEDORING CORP.—See Yang Ming Marine Transport Corporation; *Int'l*, pg. 8560

HONG NAM INDUSTRY (M) SDN BHD—See Print N Etch Pte. Ltd.; *Int'l*, pg. 5981

HONG PHAT CONSTRUCTION INVESTMENT JSC; *Int'l*, pg. 3469

HONG QI SHENG PRECISION ELECTRONICS (QINHUANGDAO) CO., LTD.—See Zhen Ding Technology Holding Limited; *Int'l*, pg. 8669

HONG RI DA TECHNOLOGY COMPANY LIMITED; *Int'l*, pg. 3469

HONGRONG LIGHT INDUSTRY CO., LTD.—See China Hongxing Sports Limited; *Int'l*, pg. 1508

HONGRUN CONSTRUCTION GROUP CO., LTD.; *Int'l*, pg. 3471

HONG SENG CONSOLIDATED BERHAD; *Int'l*, pg. 3469

HONG SENG GLOVES SDN. BHD.—See Hong Seng Consolidated Berhad; *Int'l*, pg. 3469

HONGSHENG HEAT EXCHANGER MANUFACTURING CO., LTD; *Int'l*, pg. 3471

HONG SHENG LEATHER IND. CO., LTD.—See WW Holding Inc; *Int'l*, pg. 8517

HONG TAI ELECTRIC INDUSTRIAL CO., LTD.; *Int'l*, pg. 3469

HONGTA SECURITIES CO., LTD.; *Int'l*, pg. 3471

HONGTECH ELECTRONICS CO., LTD.—See WT Microelectronics Co., Ltd.; *Int'l*, pg. 8498

HONG WEI (ASIA) HOLDINGS COMPANY LIMITED; *Int'l*, pg. 3469

HONG WEI ELECTRICAL INDUSTRY CO., LTD.; *Int'l*, pg. 3469

HONGWEI TECHNOLOGIES LIMITED; *Int'l*, pg. 3471

HONGXING ERKE SPORTS GOODS CO., LTD—See China Hongxing Sports Limited; *Int'l*, pg. 1508

HONG YI FIBER INDUSTRY CO., LTD.; *Int'l*, pg. 3469

HONG YI FIBER INDUSTRY CO., LTD. - YINGGE FACTORY—See Hong Yi Fiber Industry Co., Ltd.; *Int'l*, pg. 3469

HONG YI INTERNATION CO., LTD.—See Hong Yi Fiber Industry Co., Ltd.; *Int'l*, pg. 3469

HONGYUAN HARDWARE INDUSTRY & TRADING CO. LTD.; *Int'l*, pg. 3471

HONGYUAN HUIZHI INVESTMENT CO., LTD.—See Shenwan Hongyuan Group Co., Ltd.; *Int'l*, pg. 6803

HONG YUEN ELECTRONICS LIMITED—See China Aerospace International Holdings Limited; *Int'l*, pg. 1481

HONG YU MATERIALS CO., LTD.—See Headway Advanced Materials Inc.; *Int'l*, pg. 3302

HONGZE SAINTY FORTUNE GARMENT MANUFACTURING CO., LTD.—See Jiangsu Sainty Corp., Ltd.; *Int'l*, pg. 3953

HONGZHI MECH. & ELECT. (SZ) CO., LTD.—See SEMIKRON International GmbH; *Int'l*, pg. 6705

HONGZHI TECHNOLOGY CO., LTD.—See Beyondsoft Corporation; *Int'l*, pg. 1006

HON HAI PRECISION INDUSTRY CO., LTD.; *Int'l*, pg. 3456

HON HAI PRECISION INDUSTRY CO., LTD. - TAIPEI OFFICE—See Hon Hai Precision Industry Co., Ltd.; *Int'l*, pg. 3457

HONIGMAN MILLER SCHWARTZ & COHN LLP - CHICAGO—See Honigman Miller Schwartz & Cohn LLP; *U.S. Private*, pg. 1977

HONIGMAN MILLER SCHWARTZ & COHN LLP; *U.S. Private*, pg. 1976

HONIG MERKARTIKELEN—See 3G Capital Inc.; *U.S. Private*, pg. 9

HONIG MERKARTIKELEN—See Berkshire Hathaway Inc.; *U.S. Public*, pg. 317

HONING INC.—See Dril-Quip, Inc.; *U.S. Public*, pg. 687

HONJO CHEMICAL CORPORATION - NAOSHIMA FACTORY—See Honjo Chemical Corporation; *Int'l*, pg. 3471

HONJO CHEMICAL CORPORATION; *Int'l*, pg. 3471

COMPANY NAME INDEX

HONJO CHEMICAL (SINGAPORE) PTE LTD—See Honjo Chemical Corporation; *Int'l*, pg. 3471
HONKA FINLAND HOUSES EOOD—See Honkarakenne Oyj; *Int'l*, pg. 3471
HONKA JAPAN INC.—See Honkarakenne Oyj; *Int'l*, pg. 3471
HONKA LOG HOME LLC—See Honkarakenne Oyj; *Int'l*, pg. 3471
HONKAMP KRUEGER & CO., PC; *U.S. Private*, pg. 1977
HONKARAKENNE OYJ; *Int'l*, pg. 3471
HON KWOK LAND INVESTMENT CO., LTD.; *Int'l*, pg. 3459
HONLE UV FRANCE S.A.R.L.—See Dr. Honle AG; *Int'l*, pg. 2192
HONLIV HEALTHCARE MANAGEMENT GROUP COMPANY LIMITED; *Int'l*, pg. 3471
HONLY FOOD & BEVERAGE CO., LTD.—See Taiwan Hon Chuan Enterprise Co., Ltd.; *Int'l*, pg. 7421
HONMA GOLF LIMITED; *Int'l*, pg. 3471
HONMA GOLF U.S., LTD.—See Honma Golf Limited; *Int'l*, pg. 3472
HONMYUE ENTERPRISE CO., LTD.; *Int'l*, pg. 3472
HONMYUE ENTERPRISE (ZHEJIANG) CO., LTD.—See Honmyue Enterprise Co., Ltd.; *Int'l*, pg. 3472
HONNEN EQUIPMENT CO.—See 4 Rivers Equipment LLC; *U.S. Private*, pg. 14
HONOLD & LA PAGE, INC.; *U.S. Private*, pg. 1977
HONOLUA SURF CO. INTERNATIONAL LTD.—See Leonard Green & Partners, L.P.; *U.S. Private*, pg. 2424
HONOLULU FORD, INC.—See Lithia Motors, Inc.; *U.S. Public*, pg. 1322
HONOLULU FREIGHT SERVICE INC.; *U.S. Private*, pg. 1977
HONOLULU SPINE CENTER, LLC—See Bain Capital, LP; *U.S. Private*, pg. 445
HONOLULU STAR-ADVERTISER—See Black Press Group Ltd; *Int'l*, pg. 1059
HONOR CAPITAL CORP.—See Geneve Holdings Corp.; *U.S. Private*, pg. 1671
HONOR CREDIT UNION; *U.S. Private*, pg. 1977
HONOR FINANCE LLC—See CIVC Partners LLC; *U.S. Private*, pg. 907
HONOR FOODS, INC.—See Burris Logistics; *U.S. Private*, pg. 692
HONORS CONTRACTORS, INC.; *U.S. Private*, pg. 1977
HONOR SEIKI CO., LTD.—See Tong-Tai Machine Tool Co., Ltd.; *Int'l*, pg. 7806
HONOR STATE BANK; *U.S. Private*, pg. 1977
HONOR TONE LIMITED—See Valuetronics Holdings Limited; *Int'l*, pg. 8125
HONOURS GOLF COMPANY, LLC—See Troon Golf L.L.C.; *U.S. Private*, pg. 4242
HONSADOR LUMBER LLC—See Grey Mountain Partners, LLC; *U.S. Private*, pg. 1784
HONSEN ENERGY & RESOURCES INTERNATIONAL LTD.; *Int'l*, pg. 3472
HONSHU CHEMICAL INDUSTRY CO., LTD.; *Int'l*, pg. 3472
HONSHU CHEMICAL INDUSTRY CO., LTD. - WAKAYAMA WORKS—See Honshu Chemical Industry Co., Ltd.; *Int'l*, pg. 3472
HONSHU ELECTRICAL MATERIALS SALES CO., LTD.—See Japan Pulp and Paper Company Limited; *Int'l*, pg. 3903
HONSHU RHEEM CO., LTD.—See Nagase & Co., Ltd.; *Int'l*, pg. 5126
HONSHU SEIKAN CO., LTD.—See Toyo Seikan Group Holdings, Ltd.; *Int'l*, pg. 7856
HONSIN APPAREL SDN. BHD.—See Techbase Industries Berhad; *Int'l*, pg. 7503
HONTEX INTERNATIONAL HOLDINGS CO., LTD.; *Int'l*, pg. 3472
HONTZSCH GMBH—See TUV NORD AG; *Int'l*, pg. 7980
HONU KATO COFFEE INC.—See Key Coffee Inc.; *Int'l*, pg. 4145
HONWORLD GROUP LIMITED; *Int'l*, pg. 3472
HONYAKU CENTER INC.; *Int'l*, pg. 3472
HONY CAPITAL ACQUISITION CORP.; *Int'l*, pg. 3472
HONY CAPITAL (BEIJING) CO., LTD.—See Legend Holdings Corporation; *Int'l*, pg. 4443
HONY CAPITAL LTD.—See Legend Holdings Corporation; *Int'l*, pg. 4443
HONYE FINANCIAL SERVICES LTD.; *Int'l*, pg. 3472
HONYI INTERNATIONA CO., LTD.; *Int'l*, pg. 3472
HONZ PHARMACEUTICAL CO., LTD.; *Int'l*, pg. 3472
HOOAH LLC; *U.S. Private*, pg. 1977
HOOBER INCORPORATED; *U.S. Private*, pg. 1977
HOOD CONTAINER CORPORATION; *U.S. Private*, pg. 1977
HOOD DISTRIBUTION MCEWEN GROUP—See Hood Industries Inc.; *U.S. Private*, pg. 1977
HOOD DISTRIBUTION—See Hood Industries Inc.; *U.S. Private*, pg. 1977
HOOD HOME HEALTH SERVICE, LLC—See UnitedHealth Group Incorporated; *U.S. Public*, pg. 2245
HOOD INDUSTRIES INC.; *U.S. Private*, pg. 1977
HOOD INDUSTRIES—See The Carpenter Group; *U.S. Private*, pg. 4005

HOOD MEDICAL GROUP—See Community Health Systems, Inc.; *U.S. Public*, pg. 553
HOOD NORTHLAKE; *U.S. Private*, pg. 1977
HOODOO LAND AND CATTLE COMPANY—See Hunt Consolidated, Inc.; *U.S. Private*, pg. 2008
HOOD PACKAGING CORPORATION - GRAPHICS FACILITY—See Hood Packaging Corporation; *U.S. Private*, pg. 1977
HOOD PACKAGING CORPORATION - PLASTIC PACKAGING - GLOPAK DIVISION—See Hood Packaging Corporation; *U.S. Private*, pg. 1977
HOOD PACKAGING CORPORATION; *U.S. Private*, pg. 1977
HOOD RIVER DISTILLERS INC.; *U.S. Private*, pg. 1978
HOOG CATHARIJNE BV—See Klepierre SA; *Int'l*, pg. 4200
HOOGENBOSCH RETAIL GROUP BV—See Macintosh Retail Group NV; *Int'l*, pg. 4622
HOOGESTEGER B.V.—See PanJam Investment Limited; *Int'l*, pg. 5728
HOOGHLY MET COKE & POWER CO. LTD.—See Tata Sons Limited; *Int'l*, pg. 7471
HOOGHLY PRINTING COMPANY LTD.—See Andrew Yule & Company Ltd.; *Int'l*, pg. 452
HOOKED MEDIA, LLC; *U.S. Private*, pg. 1978
HOOKER FURNISHINGS CORPORATION; *U.S. Public*, pg. 1052
HOOKER & HOLCOMBE, INC.—See Caisse de Depot et Placement du Quebec; *Int'l*, pg. 1257
HOOKER & HOLCOMBE, INC.—See KKR & Co. Inc.; *U.S. Public*, pg. 1265
HOOKER NATIONAL BANCSHARES, INC.; *U.S. Private*, pg. 1978
HOOKIPA PHARMA INC.; *U.S. Public*, pg. 1052
HOOK'S CHEESE COMPANY, INC.; *U.S. Private*, pg. 1978
HOOKSETT KAWASAKI, INC.; *U.S. Private*, pg. 1978
HOOKS-YENSON LLC—See Parnassus Books LLC; *U.S. Private*, pg. 3099
HOOLEON CORPORATION; *U.S. Private*, pg. 1978
HOOMARK ARTEX SP. Z O.O—See IG Design Group Plc; *Int'l*, pg. 3600
HOOMARK B.V.—See IG Design Group Plc; *Int'l*, pg. 3600
HOOMARK GIFT-WRAP PARTNERS BV—See IG Design Group Plc; *Int'l*, pg. 3600
HOONVED ALI SPA—See Ali Holding S.r.l; *Int'l*, pg. 321
HOOPER CORPORATION; *U.S. Private*, pg. 1978
HOOPER, SPUHLER & STURGEON INSURANCE SERVICES, INC.—See Aquiline Capital Partners LLC; *U.S. Private*, pg. 305
HOOPLAH INC.; *Int'l*, pg. 3472
HOOPS SCOUTING USA; *U.S. Public*, pg. 1052
HOORAY SECURITIES LIMITED—See Universal Technologies Holdings Limited; *Int'l*, pg. 8082
HOOSIER CARE PROPERTIES, INC.; *U.S. Private*, pg. 1978
HOOSIER ENERGY RURAL ELECTRIC COOPERATIVE INC.; *U.S. Private*, pg. 1978
HOOSIER EQUIPMENT BROKERS, INC.; *U.S. Private*, pg. 1978
HOOSIER HILLS CREDIT UNION; *U.S. Private*, pg. 1978
HOOSIER INVESTMENT LLC; *U.S. Private*, pg. 1978
HOOSIER MAGNETICS INC.; *U.S. Private*, pg. 1978
HOOSIER PARK, LLC—See Caesars Entertainment, Inc.; *U.S. Public*, pg. 420
HOOSIERS CORPORATION—See Hoosiers Holdings; *Int'l*, pg. 3472
HOOSIERS HOLDINGS; *Int'l*, pg. 3472
HOOSIERS LIVING SERVICE CO., LTD.—See Hoosiers Holdings; *Int'l*, pg. 3472
HOOSIER-TIMES, INC.—See Gannett Co., Inc.; *U.S. Public*, pg. 903
HOOSIER UPLANDS ECONOMIC DEVELOPMENT CORPORATION; *U.S. Private*, pg. 1978
HOOT AUSTRALIA PTY LTD—See Sonnet BioTherapeutics Holdings, Inc.; *U.S. Public*, pg. 1904
HOOTECH INC.; *Int'l*, pg. 3472
HOOTEN'S, LLC.; *U.S. Private*, pg. 1978
HOOTERS BRAZIL—See Sonnet BioTherapeutics Holdings, Inc.; *U.S. Public*, pg. 1904
HOOTERS MANAGEMENT CORPORATION; *U.S. Private*, pg. 1978
HOOTERS OF AMERICA, LLC—See The Toronto-Dominion Bank; *Int'l*, pg. 7696
HOOTERS OF CAPE CORAL, INC.—See LTP Management Group, Inc.; *U.S. Private*, pg. 2510
HOOTERS OF CRYSTAL LAKE, INC.—See LTP Management Group, Inc.; *U.S. Private*, pg. 2510
HOOTERS OF CYPRESS CREEK, INC.—See LTP Management Group, Inc.; *U.S. Private*, pg. 2510
HOOTERS OF DORAL, INC.—See LTP Management Group, Inc.; *U.S. Private*, pg. 2510
HOOT PARRAMATTA PTY LTD—See Sonnet BioTherapeutics Holdings, Inc.; *U.S. Public*, pg. 1904
HOOTSUITE MEDIA, INC.; *Int'l*, pg. 3472
HOOVER BUILDING SUPPLY INC.—See BHHH Companies Inc.; *U.S. Private*, pg. 549
HOOVER CHRYSLER JEEP INC.; *U.S. Private*, pg. 1978

HOPEWELL INDUSTRIES INC.

HOOVER COLOR CORPORATION—See Cathay Industries Europe N.V.; *Int'l*, pg. 1360
HOOVER CONSTRUCTION COMPANY; *U.S. Private*, pg. 1978
HOOVER CONTAINER SOLUTIONS NORWAY AS—See First Reserve Management, L.P.; *U.S. Private*, pg. 1526
HOOVER CONTAINER SOLUTIONS PTY. LTD.—See First Reserve Management, L.P.; *U.S. Private*, pg. 1526
HOOVER DODGE JEEP CHRYSLER, INC.; *U.S. Private*, pg. 1978
HOOVER FERGUSON GROUP, INC.—See First Reserve Management, L.P.; *U.S. Private*, pg. 1525
HOOVER INC.; *U.S. Private*, pg. 1978
HOOVER LTD.—See Haier Smart Home Co., Ltd.; *Int'l*, pg. 3210
HOOVER MANAGEMENT SDN. BHD.—See PTT Synergy Group; *Int'l*, pg. 6093
HOOVER MATERIALS HANDLING GROUP, INC.—See First Reserve Management, L.P.; *U.S. Private*, pg. 1526
HOOVER MECHANICAL PLUMBING & HEATING LTD.; *Int'l*, pg. 3472
HOOVER'S, INC.—See Cannae Holdings, Inc.; *U.S. Public*, pg. 430
HOOVER'S, INC.—See CC Capital Partners, LLC; *U.S. Private*, pg. 798
HOOVER'S, INC.—See Intercontinental Exchange, Inc.; *U.S. Public*, pg. 1142
HOOVER TILING TRADING SDN. BHD.—See PTT Synergy Group; *Int'l*, pg. 6093
HOOVER TREATED WOOD PRODUCTS, INC.—See Graham Holdings Company; *U.S. Public*, pg. 955
HOOVER UNIVERSAL, INC.—See Adient plc; *Int'l*, pg. 148
HOOVER WELLS, INC.; *U.S. Private*, pg. 1978
HOOYU LTD.—See Mitek Systems, Inc.; *U.S. Public*, pg. 1452
HOP CHEONG TECHNOLOGY (INTERNATIONAL) LIMITED—See HNA International Investment Holdings Limited; *Int'l*, pg. 3433
HOP CHEONG TECHNOLOGY LIMITED—See HNA International Investment Holdings Limited; *Int'l*, pg. 3433
HOPE BANCORP, INC.; *U.S. Public*, pg. 1052
HOPE BAY MINING LTD.—See Newmont Corporation; *U.S. Public*, pg. 1516
HOPE BULKSHIP S.A.—See Uni-Asia Group Limited; *Int'l*, pg. 8028
HOPE COMMUNITY TV INC.—See Wehco Media, Inc.; *U.S. Private*, pg. 4469
HOPEDALE MEDICAL FOUNDATION; *U.S. Private*, pg. 1979
HOPE EDUCATION GROUP CO., LTD.; *Int'l*, pg. 3473
HOPEFLUENT GROUP HOLDINGS LTD; *Int'l*, pg. 3473
HOPEFLUENT PROPERTIES LIMITED—See Hopefluent Group Holdings Ltd; *Int'l*, pg. 3473
HOPE GAS, INC.—See Ullico Inc.; *U.S. Private*, pg. 4276
HOPE GROUP CORPORATION; *U.S. Private*, pg. 1979
HOPEHEALTH, INC.; *U.S. Private*, pg. 1979
HOPEHEALTH, INC.; *U.S. Private*, pg. 1979
HOPE HOSPICE AND COMMUNITY SERVICES INC.; *U.S. Private*, pg. 1979
HOPE HOSPICE INC.—See University of California San Francisco Medical Center; *U.S. Private*, pg. 4308
HOPE, INC.; *Int'l*, pg. 3473
HOPE LIFE INTERNATIONAL HOLDINGS LIMITED; *Int'l*, pg. 3473
HOP ENERGY LLC—See Delos Capital, LLC; *U.S. Private*, pg. 1198
HOPE NET CO., LTD.—See MIRAIT ONE Corporation; *Int'l*, pg. 4917
HOPENING SA; *Int'l*, pg. 3473
H.O. PENN MACHINERY COMPANY INC.; *U.S. Private*, pg. 1835
HOPE OF LIFE INTERNATIONAL; *U.S. Private*, pg. 1979
HOPE RESTORATION MINISTRIES, INC.; *U.S. Private*, pg. 1979
HOPERUN SOFTWARE SINGAPORE PTE. LTD.—See Jiangsu Hoperun Software Co., Ltd.; *Int'l*, pg. 3948
HOPERUN TECHNOLOGY CORPORATION—See Jiangsu Hoperun Software Co., Ltd.; *Int'l*, pg. 3948
HOPE'S WINDOWS, INC.; *U.S. Private*, pg. 1979
HOPETECH SDN. BHD.; *Int'l*, pg. 3473
HOPE UTILITIES LLC—See Ullico Inc.; *U.S. Private*, pg. 4276
HOPEWELL CENTRE MANAGEMENT LIMITED—See Hopewell Holdings Limited; *Int'l*, pg. 3473
HOPEWELL COGENERATION LP—See ENGIE SA; *Int'l*, pg. 2433
HOPEWELL CONSTRUCTION COMPANY LIMITED—See Hopewell Holdings Limited; *Int'l*, pg. 3473
HOPEWELL HEALTHCARE, INC.—See The Ensign Group, Inc.; *U.S. Public*, pg. 2071
HOPEWELL HEALTH CENTERS INC.; *U.S. Private*, pg. 1979
HOPEWELL HEALTH CENTERS INC.—See Hopewell Health Centers Inc.; *U.S. Private*, pg. 1979
HOPEWELL HOLDINGS LIMITED; *Int'l*, pg. 3473
HOPEWELL HOTELS MANAGEMENT LIMITED—See Hopewell Holdings Limited; *Int'l*, pg. 3473
HOPEWELL INDUSTRIES INC.; *U.S. Private*, pg. 1979

HOPEWELL INDUSTRIES INC.   CORPORATE AFFILIATIONS

HOPEWELL PROPERTY MANAGEMENT COMPANY LIMITED—See Hopewell Holdings Limited; *Int'l*, pg. 3473
HOPEWELL REAL ESTATE AGENCY LIMITED—See Hopewell Holdings Limited; *Int'l*, pg. 3473
HOPE WORLDWIDE, LTD.; *U.S. Private*, pg. 1979
HOP FAT YUK YING ENGINEERING LIMITED—See Silver Tide Holdings Limited; *Int'l*, pg. 6924
HOP FUNG GROUP HOLDINGS LTD; *Int'l*, pg. 3472
HOP HING GROUP HOLDINGS LIMITED; *Int'l*, pg. 3473
HOP HING MARINE INDUSTRIAL (HONG KONG) LIMITED—See China COSCO Shipping Corporation Limited; *Int'l*, pg. 1494
HOP INDUSTRIES CORPORATION; *U.S. Private*, pg. 1979
HOPIN LTD.—See Bending Spoons S.p.A.; *Int'l*, pg. 971
HOPITAL SERVICES SYSTEMES S.A.—See Illinois Tool Works Inc.; *U.S. Public*, pg. 1104
HOPIUM S.A.; *Int'l*, pg. 3473
HOPKINS AUTO SUPPLY INC.; *U.S. Private*, pg. 1979
HOPKINS CENTER—See Formation Capital, LLC; *U.S. Private*, pg. 1570
HOPKINS CONSTRUCTION (LACOMBE) LTD.; *Int'l*, pg. 3473
HOPKINS FINANCIAL CORPORATION; *U.S. Private*, pg. 1979
HOPKINS FORD, INC.; *U.S. Private*, pg. 1979
HOPKINS HILL SAND & STONE, LLC—See Cardi Corporation; *U.S. Public*, pg. 749
HOPKINS MANOR LTD.—See Tryko Partners, LLC; *U.S. Private*, pg. 4251
HOPKINS MANUFACTURING CORPORATION—See ONEX Corporation; *Int'l*, pg. 5578
HOPKINSONS LIMITED—See The Weir Group PLC; *Int'l*, pg. 7699
HOPKINS PONTIAC-GMC TRUCKS; *U.S. Private*, pg. 1979
HOPKINS STEEL WORKS LIMITED—See Supreme Group; *Int'l*, pg. 7341
HOPKINSVILLE ELEVATOR COMPANY, INC.; *U.S. Private*, pg. 1979
HOPKINSVILLE MILLING CO.; *U.S. Private*, pg. 1979
HOPKINTON CRIER—See Gannett Co., Inc.; *U.S. Public*, pg. 902
HOP LUN (HONG KONG) LIMITED—See Platinum Equity, LLC; *U.S. Private*, pg. 3203
HOP-ON, INC.; *U.S. Public*, pg. 1052
HOPPENSTEDT360 GMBH—See Ratos AB; *Int'l*, pg. 6217
HOPPENSTEDT FIRMENINFORMATIONEN GMBH; *Int'l*, pg. 3473
HOPPENSTEDT KREDITINFORMATIONEN GMBH—See Ratos AB; *Int'l*, pg. 6217
HOPPINGS SOFTWOOD PRODUCTS PLC; *Int'l*, pg. 3474
H & O PRODUCTS PTY LIMITED—See Oldfields Holdings Limited; *Int'l*, pg. 5553
HOPSCOTCH AFRICA S.A.—See Hopscotch Groupe S.A.; *Int'l*, pg. 3474
HOPSCOTCH EUROPE LTD.—See Hopscotch Groupe S.A.; *Int'l*, pg. 3474
HOPSCOTCH GROUPE S.A.; *Int'l*, pg. 3474
HOPS EXTRACT CORPORATION OF AMERICA—See S.S. Steiner Inc.; *U.S. Private*, pg. 3518
HOPSON DEVELOPMENT HOLDINGS LIMITED; *Int'l*, pg. 3474
HOPSON HOLDINGS INCORPORATED; *U.S. Private*, pg. 1979
HOPSON OIL CO. INC.; *U.S. Private*, pg. 1980
HOPSTEINER TRADING (ZHUHAI) CO., LTD.—See S.S. Steiner Inc.; *U.S. Private*, pg. 3518
HOPTO INC.; *U.S. Public*, pg. 1052
HOPU INVESTMENT MANAGEMENT CO., LTD.; *Int'l*, pg. 3474
HOQUIAM HEALTHCARE, INC.—See The Ensign Group, Inc.; *U.S. Public*, pg. 2071
HORACE G. ILDERTON INC.; *U.S. Private*, pg. 1980
HORACE MANN EDUCATORS CORPORATION; *U.S. Public*, pg. 1052
HORACE MANN INSURANCE COMPANY—See Horace Mann Educators Corporation; *U.S. Public*, pg. 1053
HORACE MANN LIFE INSURANCE COMPANY—See Horace Mann Educators Corporation; *U.S. Public*, pg. 1053
HORACE SMALL APPAREL COMPANY—See V. F. Corporation; *U.S. Public*, pg. 2269
HORACIO ICAZA Y CIA, S.A.—See HORIBA Ltd.; *Int'l*, pg. 3477
HORAI CO., LTD.; *Int'l*, pg. 3474
HORAK INSURANCE, INC—See Arthur J. Gallagher & Co.; *U.S. Public*, pg. 206
HORANA PLANTATIONS PLC—See Lanka Walltile PLC; *Int'l*, pg. 4412
HORAN CAPITAL MANAGEMENT, LLC; *U.S. Private*, pg. 1980
HORAN CONSTRUCTION; *U.S. Private*, pg. 1980
HORATIO ALGER ASSOCIATION OF DISTINGUISHED AMERICANS, INC.; *U.S. Private*, pg. 1980
HORBACH WIRTSCHAFTSBERATUNG GMBH—See Swiss Life Holding; *Int'l*, pg. 7368
HORBACH WIRTSCHAFTSBERATUNG GMBH—See Swiss Life Holding; *Int'l*, pg. 7369

HORBUCH HAMBURG HHV GMBH—See Bonnier AB; *Int'l*, pg. 1108
HORCHATA FROZEN DESSERT SANDWICH FARCHITECTURE BB, LLC; *U.S. Private*, pg. 1980
HORDAGRUPPEN AB; *Int'l*, pg. 3474
HORD COPLAN MACHT, INC.; *U.S. Private*, pg. 1980
HORDENER HOLZWERK GMBH; *Int'l*, pg. 3474
HORD FAMILY FARMS LLC—See Hord Livestock Company, Inc.; *U.S. Private*, pg. 1980
HORD LIVESTOCK COMPANY, INC.; *U.S. Private*, pg. 1980
HORECA MANAGEMENT CO., LTD.—See Thai Beverage Public Company Limited; *Int'l*, pg. 7590
HORECA TRADE LLC—See The Bidvest Group Limited; *Int'l*, pg. 7624
HOREN DEVENTER BV—See Amplifon S.p.A.; *Int'l*, pg. 435
HOREN NEDERLAND BEHEER BV—See Amplifon S.p.A.; *Int'l*, pg. 435
HORIBA ABX DIAGNOSTICS THAILAND LTD.—See HORIBA Ltd; *Int'l*, pg. 3475
HORIBA ABX LTDA.—See HORIBA Ltd; *Int'l*, pg. 3475
HORIBA ABX S.A.S—See HORIBA Ltd; *Int'l*, pg. 3475
HORIBA ABX S.A.S—See HORIBA Ltd; *Int'l*, pg. 3476
HORIBA ABX S.A.S—See HORIBA Ltd; *Int'l*, pg. 3476
HORIBA ABX SAS—See HORIBA Ltd; *Int'l*, pg. 3476
HORIBA ABX SP. Z. O.O.—See HORIBA Ltd; *Int'l*, pg. 3476
HORIBA ADVANCED TECHNO CO., LTD. - KYOTO FACTORY—See HORIBA Ltd; *Int'l*, pg. 3476
HORIBA ADVANCED TECHNO CO., LTD.—See HORIBA Ltd; *Int'l*, pg. 3476
HORIBA (AUSTRIA) GMBH—See HORIBA Ltd; *Int'l*, pg. 3475
HORIBA AUTOMOTIVE TEST SYSTEMS INC.—See HORIBA Ltd; *Int'l*, pg. 3476
HORIBA AUTOMOTIVE TEST SYSTEMS LTD.—See HORIBA Ltd; *Int'l*, pg. 3476
HORIBA CANADA, INC.—See HORIBA Ltd; *Int'l*, pg. 3476
HORIBA (CHINA) TRADING CO., LTD.—See HORIBA Ltd; *Int'l*, pg. 3475
HORIBA EUROPE AUTOMATION DIVISION GMBH—See HORIBA Ltd; *Int'l*, pg. 3476
HORIBA EUROPE GMBH - LEICHLINGEN FACILITY—See HORIBA Ltd; *Int'l*, pg. 3476
HORIBA EUROPE GMBH—See HORIBA Ltd; *Int'l*, pg. 3477
HORIBA EUROPE GMBH—See HORIBA Ltd; *Int'l*, pg. 3477
HORIBA EUROPE GMBH—See HORIBA Ltd; *Int'l*, pg. 3476
HORIBA EUROPE GMBH—See HORIBA Ltd; *Int'l*, pg. 3477
HORIBA FRANCE SARL—See HORIBA Ltd; *Int'l*, pg. 3476
HORIBA FUELCON GMBH—See HORIBA Ltd; *Int'l*, pg. 3476
HORIBA GMBH—See HORIBA Ltd; *Int'l*, pg. 3476
HORIBA INDIA PRIVATE LTD.—See HORIBA Ltd; *Int'l*, pg. 3476
HORIBA INSTRUMENTS BRASIL, LTDA.—See HORIBA Ltd; *Int'l*, pg. 3476
HORIBA INSTRUMENTS INC.- ANN ARBOR FACILITY—See HORIBA Ltd; *Int'l*, pg. 3476
HORIBA INSTRUMENTS INC. - IRVINE FACILITY—See HORIBA Ltd; *Int'l*, pg. 3476
HORIBA INSTRUMENTS INC. - TEMPE FACILITY—See HORIBA Ltd; *Int'l*, pg. 3476
HORIBA INSTRUMENTS INC. - TROY FACILITY—See HORIBA Ltd; *Int'l*, pg. 3476
HORIBA INSTRUMENTS (SHANGHAI) CO., LTD.—See HORIBA Ltd; *Int'l*, pg. 3476
HORIBA INSTRUMENTS (SINGAPORE) PTE, LTD.—See HORIBA Ltd; *Int'l*, pg. 3476
HORIBA ITALIA SRL—See HORIBA Ltd; *Int'l*, pg. 3476
HORIBA JOBIN YVON GMBH - RAMAN DIVISION—See HORIBA Ltd; *Int'l*, pg. 3476
HORIBA JOBIN YVON GMBH IBH LTD.—See HORIBA Ltd; *Int'l*, pg. 3476
HORIBA JOBIN YVON LTD.—See HORIBA Ltd; *Int'l*, pg. 3476
HORIBA JOBIN YVON S.A.S - RAMAN DIVISION—See HORIBA Ltd; *Int'l*, pg. 3476
HORIBA JOBIN YVON S.A.S.—See HORIBA Ltd; *Int'l*, pg. 3476
HORIBA JOBIN YVON S.A.S. - THIN FILM DIVISION—See HORIBA Ltd; *Int'l*, pg. 3476
HORIBA KOREA CO., LTD. - BUCHEON FACTORY—See HORIBA Ltd; *Int'l*, pg. 3476
HORIBA KOREA LTD. - HORIBA CZECH OLOMOUC FACTORY—See HORIBA Ltd; *Int'l*, pg. 3476
HORIBA LTD; *Int'l*, pg. 3474
HORIBA MIRA LTD.—See HORIBA Ltd; *Int'l*, pg. 3476
HORIBA OOO—See HORIBA Ltd; *Int'l*, pg. 3476
HORIBA PRECISION INSTRUMENTS (BEIJING) CO., LTD.—See HORIBA Ltd; *Int'l*, pg. 3477
HORIBA SCIENTIFIC—See HORIBA Ltd; *Int'l*, pg. 3476

HORIBA STEC, CO., LTD. - ASO FACTORY—See HORIBA Ltd; *Int'l*, pg. 3476
HORIBA STEC, CO., LTD.—See HORIBA Ltd; *Int'l*, pg. 3476
HORIBA STEC KOREA LTD.—See HORIBA Ltd; *Int'l*, pg. 3476
HORIBA TAIWAN, INC.—See HORIBA Ltd; *Int'l*, pg. 3476
HORIBA TECHNOLOGY (SUZHOU) CO.,LTD.—See HORIBA Ltd; *Int'l*, pg. 3476
HORIBA TECHNO SERVICE CO., LTD.—See HORIBA Ltd; *Int'l*, pg. 3476
HORIBA TEST AUTOMATION LTD.—See HORIBA Ltd; *Int'l*, pg. 3477
HORIBA (THAILAND) LIMITED—See HORIBA Ltd; *Int'l*, pg. 3475
HORIBA TOCADERO GMBH—See HORIBA Ltd; *Int'l*, pg. 3477
HORIBA TRADING (SHANGHAI) CO., LTD.—See HORIBA Ltd; *Int'l*, pg. 3477
HORIBA UK LIMITED—See HORIBA Ltd; *Int'l*, pg. 3477
HORIBA VIETNAM COMPANY LIMITED—See HORIBA Ltd; *Int'l*, pg. 3477
HORICH PARKS LEBOW ADVERTISING; *U.S. Private*, pg. 1980
HORICON STATE BANK; *U.S. Private*, pg. 1980
HORII FOODSERVICE CO., LTD.; *Int'l*, pg. 3478
HORIKIRI, INC—See NHK Spring Co., Ltd.; *Int'l*, pg. 5257
HORIPRO INC.; *Int'l*, pg. 3478
HORISONT ENERGI AS; *Int'l*, pg. 3478
HORIS SAS—See Illinois Tool Works Inc.; *U.S. Public*, pg. 1104
HORIX MANUFACTURING COMPANY; *U.S. Private*, pg. 1980
HORIZAL; *Int'l*, pg. 3478
HORIZON ACQUISITION CORPORATION II; *U.S. Public*, pg. 1053
HORIZON ACQUISITION CORPORATION; *U.S. Public*, pg. 1053
HORIZON AGENCY, INC.—See Hellman & Friedman LLC; *U.S. Private*, pg. 1909
HORIZON AIR INDUSTRIES—See Alaska Air Group, Inc.; *U.S. Public*, pg. 72
HORIZON BANCORP, INC.; *U.S. Public*, pg. 1053
HORIZON BANK—See Horizon Bancorp, Inc.; *U.S. Public*, pg. 1053
HORIZON BEHAVIORAL SERVICES, INC.—See CVS Health Corporation; *U.S. Public*, pg. 615
HORIZON BEVERAGE CO.; *U.S. Private*, pg. 1980
HORIZON BUSINESS SERVICES, INC.; *U.S. Private*, pg. 1980
HORIZON CAPITAL LLP; *Int'l*, pg. 3479
HORIZON CAPITAL LLP; *Int'l*, pg. 3479
HORIZON CHEVROLET, INC.—See AutoNation, Inc.; *U.S. Public*, pg. 235
HORIZON CHILLICOTHE TELEPHONE—See Novacap Management Inc.; *Int'l*, pg. 5454
HORIZON COMMODITIES & FUTURES COMPANY LIMITED—See Lee Kee Holdings Limited; *Int'l*, pg. 4440
HORIZON CONSTRUCTION MANAGEMENT LTD.—See Canadian Natural Resources Ltd.; *Int'l*, pg. 1284
HORIZON CONSULTANTS, INC.—See Mangan, Inc.; *U.S. Private*, pg. 2563
HORIZON COPPER CORP.; *Int'l*, pg. 3479
HORIZON CREDIT UNION; *U.S. Private*, pg. 1980
HORIZON CSA LLC—See Cressey & Company, LP; *U.S. Private*, pg. 1095
HORIZON CSA LLC—See Health Enterprise Partners LLC; *U.S. Private*, pg. 1893
HORIZON DEVELOPMENT GROUP, INC.; *U.S. Private*, pg. 1980
HORIZON DIRECT—See Horizon Media, Inc.; *U.S. Private*, pg. 1982
HORIZON DISCOVERY GROUP, PLC—See Revvity, Inc.; *U.S. Public*, pg. 1794
HORIZON DISTRIBUTION, INC.; *U.S. Private*, pg. 1980
HORIZON DISTRIBUTORS, INC.—See Pool Corporation; *U.S. Public*, pg. 1701
HORIZON DOWNING LLC—See Downing Displays Inc.; *U.S. Private*, pg. 1269
HORIZON DRAFTFCB DUBAI—See The Interpublic Group of Companies, Inc.; *U.S. Public*, pg. 2093
HORIZON DRAFTFCB JEDDAH—See The Interpublic Group of Companies, Inc.; *U.S. Public*, pg. 2093
HORIZON.DRAFTFCB KUWAIT—See The Interpublic Group of Companies, Inc.; *U.S. Public*, pg. 2093
HORIZON.DRAFTFCB RIYADH—See The Interpublic Group of Companies, Inc.; *U.S. Public*, pg. 2093
HORIZON DRILLING INC.—See Western Energy Services Corp.; *Int'l*, pg. 8388
HORIZON ENERGY DISTRIBUTION LIMITED—See Eastern Bay Energy Trust; *Int'l*, pg. 2271
HORIZON ENGINEERING GROUP, INC.—See Greenman-Pedersen, Inc.; *U.S. Private*, pg. 1779
HORIZON EQUIPMENT; *U.S. Private*, pg. 1980
HORIZON FOOD GROUP, INC.; *U.S. Private*, pg. 1980
HORIZON FOODS COMPANY; *U.S. Private*, pg. 1980
HORIZON FOREST PRODUCTS LP—See Baillie Lumber Co., Inc.; *U.S. Private*, pg. 426

COMPANY NAME INDEX

HORIZON FREIGHT SYSTEM INC.; *U.S. Private*, pg. 1980
HORIZON FREIGHT SYSTEM—See Horizon Freight System Inc.; *U.S. Private*, pg. 1980
HORIZON GLOBAL CORPORATION—See Crowne Group LLC; *U.S. Private*, pg. 1112
HORIZON GLOBEX GMBH—See Touchpoint Group Holdings, Inc.; *U.S. Public*, pg. 2165
HORIZON GOLD LIMITED—See ICM Limited; *Int'l*, pg. 3582
HORIZON GROUP PROPERTIES, INC.; *U.S. Public*, pg. 1053
HORIZON GROUP USA INC.; *U.S. Private*, pg. 1981
HORIZON HEALTH CARE, INC.; *U.S. Private*, pg. 1981
HORIZON HEALTHCARE SERVICES, INC.; *U.S. Private*, pg. 1981
HORIZON HEALTH CORPORATION—See Universal Health Services, Inc.; *U.S. Public*, pg. 2258
HORIZON HEALTH SERVICES, INC.; *U.S. Private*, pg. 1981
HORIZON HOBBY DISTRIBUTORS; *U.S. Private*, pg. 1981
HORIZON HOLDINGS, INC.; *U.S. Private*, pg. 1981
HORIZON HOLDINGS LLC; *U.S. Private*, pg. 1981
HORIZON HOLDINGS—See The Interpublic Group of Companies, Inc.; *U.S. Public*, pg. 2093
HORIZON HOSPICE AND PALLIATIVE CARE; *U.S. Private*, pg. 1981
HORIZON HOTELS LTD.; *U.S. Private*, pg. 1981
HORIZON HOUSE PUBLICATIONS INC.; *U.S. Private*, pg. 1981
HORIZON HOUSE; *U.S. Private*, pg. 1981
HORIZON IMMOBILIEN AG—See Solvay S.A.; *Int'l*, pg. 7078
HORIZON INSURANCE SERVICES, INC.—See Horizon Bancorp, Inc.; *U.S. Public*, pg. 1053
HORIZON INVESTMENTS, LLC; *U.S. Private*, pg. 1981
HORIZON KEYSTONE FINANCIAL LLC—See HPS Investment Partners, LLC; *U.S. Private*, pg. 1997
HORIZON LAMPS, INC.—See Forsyth Capital Investors LLC; *U.S. Private*, pg. 1573
HORIZON MANAGEMENT GROUP, LLC—See The Hartford Financial Services Group, Inc.; *U.S. Public*, pg. 2088
HORIZON MARINE, INO.—See Collecte Localication Satellites; *Int'l*, pg. 1699
HORIZON MEAT & SEAFOOD DISTRIBUTORS INC.; *U.S. Private*, pg. 1981
HORIZON MEAT & SEAFOOD OF GEORGIA INC.—See Horizon Meat & Seafood Distributors Inc.; *U.S. Private*, pg. 1981
HORIZON MEDIA, INC. - LOS ANGELES—See Horizon Media, Inc.; *U.S. Private*, pg. 1982
HORIZON MEDIA, INC.; *U.S. Private*, pg. 1981
HORIZON MENTAL HEALTH MANAGEMENT, LLC—See Universal Health Services, Inc.; *U.S. Public*, pg. 2258
HORIZON METALLIC INDUSTRIES L.L.C—See Gulf General Investment Company PSC; *Int'l*, pg. 3180
HORIZON MINERALS CORP.; *U.S. Public*, pg. 1053
HORIZON MINERALS LIMITED; *Int'l*, pg. 3479
HORIZON MORTGAGE CORPORATION; *U.S. Private*, pg. 1982
HORIZON NORTH DAKOTA PUBLICATIONS INC.—See Horizon Publications Inc.; *U.S. Private*, pg. 1982
HORIZON NUCLEAR POWER LIMITED—See Hitachi, Ltd.; *Int'l*, pg. 3420
HORIZON OGILVY—See WPP plc; *Int'l*, pg. 8484
HORIZON OIL LIMITED; *Int'l*, pg. 3479
HORIZON OPTICAL COMPANY LTD—See EssilorLuxottica SA; *Int'l*, pg. 2515
HORIZON ORGANIC DAIRY, LLC—See Danone; *Int'l*, pg. 1967
HORIZON OUT-OF-HOME—See Horizon Media, Inc.; *U.S. Private*, pg. 1982
HORIZON PAPER CO., INC.; *U.S. Private*, pg. 1982
HORIZON PARTNERS LTD.; *U.S. Private*, pg. 1982
HORIZON PETROLEUM LTD.; *Int'l*, pg. 3479
HORIZON PHARMA AG—See Amgen Inc.; *U.S. Public*, pg. 123
HORIZON PHARMACEUTICAL LLC—See Amgen Inc.; *U.S. Public*, pg. 123
HORIZON PHARMA GMBH—See Amgen Inc.; *U.S. Public*, pg. 123
HORIZON PHARMA, INC.—See Amgen Inc.; *U.S. Public*, pg. 123
HORIZON PHARMA SWITZERLAND GMBH—See Amgen Inc.; *U.S. Public*, pg. 123
HORIZON PHARMA USA, INC. - ROSWELL, GEORGIA OFFICE—See Amgen Inc.; *U.S. Public*, pg. 123
HORIZON PHARMA USA, INC.—See Amgen Inc.; *U.S. Public*, pg. 123
HORIZON PLASTICS INTERNATIONAL INC.—See Core Molding Technologies, Inc.; *U.S. Public*, pg. 576
HORIZON POWER, INC.—See National Fuel Gas Company; *U.S. Public*, pg. 1494
HORIZON PRINT SERVICES GROUP—See Horizon Media, Inc.; *U.S. Private*, pg. 1982
HORIZON PROPERTIES OF PENSACOLA; *U.S. Private*, pg. 1982

HORIZON PUBLICATIONS INC.; *U.S. Private*, pg. 1982
HORIZON REMIT SDN. BHD.—See The Western Union Company; *U.S. Public*, pg. 2141
HORIZON RESOURCES; *U.S. Private*, pg. 1982
HORIZON RIDGE SURGERY CENTER, LLC—See Tenet Healthcare Corporation; *U.S. Public*, pg. 2004
HORIZON ROOFING; *U.S. Private*, pg. 1982
HORIZON SALES, INC.; *U.S. Private*, pg. 1982
HORIZONS ALPHAPRO GARTMAN ETF; *Int'l*, pg. 3479
HORIZONS BEHAVIORAL HEALTH LLC—See Centegra Health System; *U.S. Private*, pg. 809
HORIZON SCIENTIFIC, INC.—See Standex International; *U.S. Public*, pg. 1930
HORIZON SERVICES CORPORATION—See O2 Investment Partners, LLC; *U.S. Private*, pg. 2982
HORIZON SERVICES LIMITED—See Eastern Bay Energy Trust; *Int'l*, pg. 2272
HORIZON SERVICES, LLC—See New Mountain Capital, LLC; *U.S. Private*, pg. 2902
HORIZONS ETFS MANAGEMENT (CANADA) INC.—See Mirae Asset Financial Group; *Int'l*, pg. 4916
HORIZONS FOUNDATION; *U.S. Private*, pg. 1983
HORIZON SHIPPING LIMITED—See GraceKennedy Limited; *Int'l*, pg. 3049
HORIZONS HOLDINGS INTERNATIONAL, INC.; *U.S. Public*, pg. 1053
HORIZONS INCORPORATED; *U.S. Private*, pg. 1983
HORIZON SINGAPORE TERMINALS PRIVATE LIMITED—See Emirates National Oil Company Limited; *Int'l*, pg. 2381
HORIZON SNACK FOODS OF CAL—See Horizon Food Group, Inc.; *U.S. Private*, pg. 1980
HORIZON SOFTWARE INTERNATIONAL LLC—See Roper Technologies, Inc.; *U.S. Public*, pg. 1813
HORIZON SOLUTIONS CORP.; *U.S. Private*, pg. 1982
HORIZON—See Pool Corporation; *U.S. Public*, pg. 1701
HORIZON STAFFING INC.; *U.S. Private*, pg. 1982
HORIZON STEEL COMPANY; *U.S. Private*, pg. 1982
HORIZON STONE LLC; *U.S. Private*, pg. 1982
HORIZON SURVEY COMPANY (FZE)—See HAL Trust N.V.; *Int'l*, pg. 3226
HORIZON SYSTEMS, INC.; *U.S. Private*, pg. 1982
HORIZONTAL DRILLING INTERNATIONAL (HDI) S.A.—See VINCI S.A.; *Int'l*, pg. 8217
HORIZONTAL INTEGRATION; *U.S. Private*, pg. 1983
HORIZONTAL SOFTWARE SAS; *Int'l*, pg. 3479
HORIZONTAL UNIP. LDA—See Horizal; *Int'l*, pg. 3479
HORIZON TANK LINES, INC.—See Heniff Transportation Systems Inc.; *U.S. Private*, pg. 1916
HORIZONT DOM, D.O.O.—See Tulikivi Corporation; *Int'l*, pg. 7969
HORIZON TECHNOLOGY FINANCE CORPORATION; *U.S. Public*, pg. 1053
HORIZON TECHNOLOGY FINANCE MANAGEMENT LLC—See Monroe Capital LLC; *U.S. Private*, pg. 2773
HORIZON TECHNOLOGY, INC.—See Biotage AB; *Int'l*, pg. 1042
HORIZON TELECOM INC.—See Novacap Management Inc.; *Int'l*, pg. 5454
HORIZON TELECOM INC.—See Novacap Management Inc.; *Int'l*, pg. 5454
HORIZONTE MINERALS PLC; *Int'l*, pg. 3479
HORIZON TERMINALS LIMITED—See Emirates National Oil Company Limited; *Int'l*, pg. 2381
HORIZONTES ENERGIA S.A.—See Companhia Energetica de Minas Gerais - CEMIG; *Int'l*, pg. 1747
HORIZON THERAPEUTICS PLC—See Amgen Inc.; *U.S. Public*, pg. 123
HORIZON TOURISM (NEW ZEALAND) LIMITED—See Skycity Entertainment Group Limited; *Int'l*, pg. 6993
HORIZONT PERSONAL- TEAM- UND ORGANISATIONSENTWICKLUNG GMBH—See Vienna Insurance Group AG Wiener Versicherung Gruppe; *Int'l*, pg. 8194
HORIZON TRANSPORT INC.; *U.S. Private*, pg. 1982
HORIZONT SOFTWARE GMBH—See SPARTA AG; *Int'l*, pg. 7127
HORIZON WINE & SPIRITS, INC.—See Berkshire Hathaway Inc.; *U.S. Public*, pg. 312
HORIZON WINE & SPIRITS - NASHVILLE, INC.—See Berkshire Hathaway Inc.; *U.S. Public*, pg. 307
HOR KEW CORPORATION LIMITED; *Int'l*, pg. 3474
HOR KEW PRIVATE LIMITED—See Hor Kew Corporation Limited; *Int'l*, pg. 3474
HORLEMANN AUTOMATION & IT GMBH—See VINCI S.A.; *Int'l*, pg. 8222
HORLEMANN ELEKTROBAU GMBH—See VINCI S.A.; *Int'l*, pg. 8222
HORLEMANN ROHRLEITUNGS- UND ANLAGENBAU GMBH—See VINCI S.A.; *Int'l*, pg. 8222
HORLGE SAINT BENOIT S.A.—See Onward Holdings Co., Ltd.; *Int'l*, pg. 5592
HORLICKS LIMITED—See GSK plc; *Int'l*, pg. 3149
HORLOGE SAINT BENOIT S.A.S.—See Onward Holdings Co., Ltd.; *Int'l*, pg. 5592
HORMANN ALKMAAR B.V.—See Hormann KG Verkaufsgesellschaf; *Int'l*, pg. 3480
HORMANN AUTOMATIONSSERVICE GMBH—See Hormann Holding GmbH & Co. KG; *Int'l*, pg. 3480

HORMANN AUTOMOTIVE BIELEFELD GMBH—See Hormann Holding GmbH & Co. KG; *Int'l*, pg. 3480
HORMANN AUTOMOTIVE EISLINGEN GMBH—See Hormann Holding GmbH & Co. KG; *Int'l*, pg. 3480
HORMANN AUTOMOTIVE GMBH—See Hormann Holding GmbH & Co. KG; *Int'l*, pg. 3480
HORMANN AUTOMOTIVE GUSTAVSBURG GMBH—See Hormann Holding GmbH & Co. KG; *Int'l*, pg. 3480
HORMANN AUTOMOTIVE PENZBERG GMBH—See Hormann Holding GmbH & Co. KG; *Int'l*, pg. 3480
HORMANN AUTOMOTIVE SAARBRUCKEN GMBH—See Hormann Holding GmbH & Co. KG; *Int'l*, pg. 3480
HORMANN AUTOMOTIVE SLOVAKIA S.R.O.—See Hormann Holding GmbH & Co. KG; *Int'l*, pg. 3480
HORMANN AUTOMOTIVE ST. WENDEL GMBH—See Hormann Holding GmbH & Co. KG; *Int'l*, pg. 3480
HORMANN AUTOMOTIVE WACKERSDORF GMBH—See Hormann Holding GmbH & Co. KG; *Int'l*, pg. 3480
HORMANN BALTIC, UAB—See Hormann KG Verkaufsgesellschaf; *Int'l*, pg. 3480
HORMANN BEIJING DOOR PRODUCTION CO. LTD.—See Hormann KG Verkaufsgesellschaf; *Int'l*, pg. 3480
HORMANN BELGIUM NV/SA—See Hormann KG Verkaufsgesellschaf; *Int'l*, pg. 3480
HORMANN BRASIL PORTAS LTDA—See Hormann KG Verkaufsgesellschaf; *Int'l*, pg. 3480
HORMANN CESKA REPUBLIKA S.R.O.—See Hormann KG Verkaufsgesellschaf; *Int'l*, pg. 3480
HORMANN CHANGSHU DOOR PRODUCTION CO. LTD.—See Hormann KG Verkaufsgesellschaf; *Int'l*, pg. 3480
HORMANN DANMARK AS—See Hormann KG Verkaufsgesellschaf; *Int'l*, pg. 3480
HORMANN DOORS MALAYSIA SDN BHD—See Hormann KG Verkaufsgesellschaf; *Int'l*, pg. 3480
HORMANN EESTI OU—See Hormann KG Verkaufsgesellschaf; *Int'l*, pg. 3480
HORMANN ESPANA, S.A.—See Hormann KG Verkaufsgesellschaf; *Int'l*, pg. 3480
HORMANN FLEXON, LLC—See Hormann KG Verkaufsgesellschaf; *Int'l*, pg. 3481
HORMANN FRANCE S.A.—See Hormann KG Verkaufsgesellschaf; *Int'l*, pg. 3481
HORMANN HELLAS LTD—See Hormann KG Verkaufsgesellschaf; *Int'l*, pg. 3481
HORMANN HOLDING GMBH & CO. KG; *Int'l*, pg. 3479
HORMANN HRVATSKA D.O.O.—See Hormann KG Verkaufsgesellschaf; *Int'l*, pg. 3481
HORMANN HUNGARIA KFT.—See Hormann KG Verkaufsgesellschaf; *Int'l*, pg. 3481
HORMANN INDUSTRIESERVICE GMBH—See Hormann Holding GmbH & Co. KG; *Int'l*, pg. 3480
HORMANN ITALIA S.R.L.—See Hormann KG Verkaufsgesellschaf; *Int'l*, pg. 3481
HORMANN KAZAKHSTAN LLP—See Hormann KG Verkaufsgesellschaf; *Int'l*, pg. 3480
HORMANN KG VERKAUFSGESELLSCHAF; *Int'l*, pg. 3480
HORMANN KMT KOMMUNIKATIONS- UND MELDETECHNIK GMBH—See Hormann Holding GmbH & Co. KG; *Int'l*, pg. 3480
HORMANN KOMMUNIKATINSNETZTE GMBH—See Hormann Holding GmbH & Co. KG; *Int'l*, pg. 3480
HORMANN LEGNICA SP. ZO.O—See Hormann KG Verkaufsgesellschaf; *Int'l*, pg. 3481
HORMANN LLC—See Hormann KG Verkaufsgesellschaf; *Int'l*, pg. 3481
HORMANN LOGISTIK GMBH—See Hormann Holding GmbH & Co. KG; *Int'l*, pg. 3480
HORMANN MAROC SARL—See Hormann KG Verkaufsgesellschaf; *Int'l*, pg. 3481
HORMANN MEXICO, S.A.DE C.V—See Hormann KG Verkaufsgesellschaf; *Int'l*, pg. 3480
HORMANN MIDDLE EAST FZE—See Hormann KG Verkaufsgesellschaf; *Int'l*, pg. 3481
HORMANN NEDERLAND B.V.—See Hormann KG Verkaufsgesellschaf; *Int'l*, pg. 3481
HORMANN NORGE AS—See Hormann KG Verkaufsgesellschaf; *Int'l*, pg. 3481
HORMANN OENSINGEN AG—See Hormann KG Verkaufsgesellschaf; *Int'l*, pg. 3481
HORMANN POLSKA SP. Z O.O.—See Hormann KG Verkaufsgesellschaf; *Int'l*, pg. 3481
HORMANN PORTUGAL, LDA.—See Hormann KG Verkaufsgesellschaf; *Int'l*, pg. 3481
HORMANN RAWEMA ENGINEERING & CONSULTING GMBH—See Hormann Holding GmbH & Co. KG; *Int'l*, pg. 3480
HORMANN ROMANIA SRL—See Hormann KG Verkaufsgesellschaf; *Int'l*, pg. 3481
HORMANN SCHWEIZ AG—See Hormann KG Verkaufsgesellschaf; *Int'l*, pg. 3481
HORMANN SERBIA—See Hormann KG Verkaufsgesellschaf; *Int'l*, pg. 3480
HORMANNSHOFER FASSADEN GMBH & CO. HALLE KG—See BayernLB Holding AG; *Int'l*, pg. 914
HORMANNSHOFER FASSADEN SUD GMBH & CO. KG—See BayernLB Holding AG; *Int'l*, pg. 914

HORMANN SLOVENSKA REPUBLIKA S.R.O.—See Hormann KG Verkaufsgesellschaf; *Int'l*, pg. 3481
HORMANN SVENSKA AB—See Hormann KG Verkaufsgesellschaf; *Int'l*, pg. 3481
HORMANN TIANJIN DOOR PRODUCTION CO. LTD.—See Hormann KG Verkaufsgesellschaf; *Int'l*, pg. 3481
HORMANN (UK) LIMITED—See Hormann KG Verkaufsgesellschaf; *Int'l*, pg. 3480
HORMANN VEHICLE ENGINEERING GMBH—See Hormann Holding GmbH & Co. KG; *Int'l*, pg. 3480
HORMANN WARNSYSTEME GMBH—See Hormann Holding GmbH & Co. KG; *Int'l*, pg. 3480
HORMANN YAPI ELEMANLARI TIC. LTD. STI.—See Hormann KG Verkaufsgesellschaf; *Int'l*, pg. 3481
HORMEL CANADA LTD.—See Hormel Foods Corporation; *U.S. Public*, pg. 1054
HORMEL FOODS AUSTRALIA PTY LTD.—See Hormel Foods Corporation; *U.S. Public*, pg. 1054
HORMEL FOODS CORP. - DELI DIVISION—See Hormel Foods Corporation; *U.S. Public*, pg. 1054
HORMEL FOODS CORP. - FOODSERVICE DIVISION—See Hormel Foods Corporation; *U.S. Public*, pg. 1054
HORMEL FOODS CORP. - GROCERY PRODUCTS DIVISION—See Hormel Foods Corporation; *U.S. Public*, pg. 1054
HORMEL FOODS CORPORATE SERVICES, LLC—See Hormel Foods Corporation; *U.S. Public*, pg. 1054
HORMEL FOODS CORPORATION; *U.S. Public*, pg. 1053
HORMEL FOODS CORP. - REFRIGERATED FOODS DIVISION—See Hormel Foods Corporation; *U.S. Public*, pg. 1054
HORMEL FOODS CORP. - SPECIALTY PRODUCTS DIVISION—See Hormel Foods Corporation; *U.S. Public*, pg. 1054
HORMEL FOODS INTERNATIONAL CORPORATION—See Hormel Foods Corporation; *U.S. Public*, pg. 1054
HORMEL FOODS JAPAN K.K.—See Hormel Foods Corporation; *U.S. Public*, pg. 1054
HORMEL HEALTHLABS, INC.—See Hormel Foods Corporation; *U.S. Public*, pg. 1054
HORMEN CE A.S.—See CEZ, a.s.; *Int'l*, pg. 1428
HORMIGONES HERCULES S.L.—See Camargo Correa S.A.; *Int'l*, pg. 1268
HORMIGONES LOS SERRANOS S.L—See Eiffage S.A.; *Int'l*, pg. 2331
HORMIGONES Y ARIDOS, S.A.—See Heidelberg Materials AG; *Int'l*, pg. 3316
HORMIGONES Y MINAS S.A.—See Heidelberg Materials AG; *Int'l*, pg. 3317
HORMIGONES Y MORTEROS SERRANO SL—See Eiffage S.A.; *Int'l*, pg. 2331
HORMOSAN PHARMA GMBH—See Lupin Limited; *Int'l*, pg. 4586
HORMOZGAN CEMENT CO.; *Int'l*, pg. 3481
HORNADY MANUFACTURING COMPANY; *U.S. Private*, pg. 1983
HORNADY TRANSPORTATION, LLC—See Daseke, Inc.; *U.S. Private*, pg. 1161
HORNADY TRUCK LINE, INC.—See Daseke, Inc.; *U.S. Private*, pg. 1161
HORNBACH BAUMARKT AG—See Hornbach Holding AG & Co. KGaA; *Int'l*, pg. 3481
HORNBACH BAUMARKT CS SPOL S.R.O.—See Hornbach Holding AG & Co. KGaA; *Int'l*, pg. 3482
HORNBACH BAUMARKT LUXEMBURG SARL—See Hornbach Holding AG & Co. KGaA; *Int'l*, pg. 3482
HORNBACH BAUMARKT (SCHWEIZ) AG—See Hornbach Holding AG & Co. KGaA; *Int'l*, pg. 3482
HORNBACH BAUSTOFF UNION GMBH—See Hornbach Holding AG & Co. KGaA; *Int'l*, pg. 3481
HORNBACH BOUWMARKT (NEDERLAND) B.V.—See Hornbach Holding AG & Co. KGaA; *Int'l*, pg. 3482
HORNBACH CENTRALA SRL—See Hornbach Holding AG & Co. KGaA; *Int'l*, pg. 3481
HORNBACHER'S PHARMACIES, INC.—See United Natural Foods, Inc.; *U.S. Public*, pg. 2231
HORNBACHERS—See United Natural Foods, Inc.; *U.S. Public*, pg. 2231
HORNBACH HOLDING AG & CO. KGAA; *Int'l*, pg. 3481
HORNBACH IMMOBILIEN AG—See Hornbach Holding AG & Co. KGaA; *Int'l*, pg. 3481
HORNBECK OFFSHORE OPERATORS, LLC—See Hornbeck Offshore Services, Inc.; *U.S. Private*, pg. 1983
HORNBECK OFFSHORE SERVICES, INC.; *U.S. Private*, pg. 1983
HORNBECK OFFSHORE SERVICES, LLC—See Hornbeck Offshore Services, Inc.; *U.S. Private*, pg. 1983
HORNBLOWER CRUISES & EVENTS; *U.S. Private*, pg. 1983
HORNBY AMERICA INC.—See Phoenix Asset Management Partners Ltd.; *Int'l*, pg. 5849
HORNBY BAY MINERAL EXPLORATION LTD.; *Int'l*, pg. 3482
HORNBY DEUTSCHLAND GMBH—See Phoenix Asset Management Partners Ltd.; *Int'l*, pg. 5849

HORNBY ESPANA S.A—See Phoenix Asset Management Partners Ltd.; *Int'l*, pg. 5849
HORNBY FRANCE S.A.S.—See Phoenix Asset Management Partners Ltd.; *Int'l*, pg. 5849
HORNBY HOBBIES LIMITED—See Phoenix Asset Management Partners Ltd.; *Int'l*, pg. 5849
HORNBY ITALIA S.R.L.—See Phoenix Asset Management Partners Ltd.; *Int'l*, pg. 5849
HORNBY PLC—See Phoenix Asset Management Partners Ltd.; *Int'l*, pg. 5849
HORN & CO POLSKA SP. Z O.O.—See RHI Magnesita N.V.; *Int'l*, pg. 6325
HORNE AUTO CENTER INC.; *U.S. Private*, pg. 1983
HORNE BROTHERS CONSTRUCTION INC—See Pine Gate Renewables LLC; *U.S. Private*, pg. 3182
HORNE BUILDING SPECIALTIES; *U.S. Private*, pg. 1983
HORNE CREATIVE GROUP, INC.—See The Hatcher Group; *U.S. Private*, pg. 4043
HORNE FORD INC.; *U.S. Private*, pg. 1983
HORNE INTERNATIONAL, INC.; *U.S. Private*, pg. 1983
HORNELL BREWING CO., INC.—See Ferolito, Vultaggio & Sons; *U.S. Private*, pg. 1498
HORNE LLP; *U.S. Private*, pg. 1983
HORNER INDUSTRIAL GROUP; *U.S. Private*, pg. 1983
HORNER MILLWORK CORP.; *U.S. Private*, pg. 1983
HORNER PONTIAC BUICK INC.; *U.S. Private*, pg. 1983
HORNER-RAUSCH EAST, INC.; *U.S. Private*, pg. 1983
HORNETS BASKETBALL, LLC; *U.S. Private*, pg. 1984
HORNETS SPORTS & ENTERTAINMENT—See MJ Basketball Holdings, LLC; *U.S. Private*, pg. 2752
HORN GLASS ASIA PACIFIC SDN. BHD.—See Certina Holding AG; *Int'l*, pg. 1423
HORN GLASS INDUSTRIES AG—See Certina Holding AG; *Int'l*, pg. 1423
HORN GLASS TECHNOLOGY (BEIJING) CO., LTD—See Certina Holding AG; *Int'l*, pg. 1423
HORN GMBH & CO. KG—See INDUS Holding AG; *Int'l*, pg. 3663
HORNGROUP HOLDING GMBH & CO. KG—See INDUS Holding AG; *Int'l*, pg. 3663
HORN GROUP INC.—See Ruder Finn Group, Inc.; *U.S. Private*, pg. 3501
HORN GROUP - NEW YORK—See Ruder Finn Group, Inc.; *U.S. Private*, pg. 3501
HORNG SHIUE HOLDING CO., LTD.; *Int'l*, pg. 3482
HORNG TONG ENTERPRISE CO., LTD.; *Int'l*, pg. 3482
HORN INDUSTRIAL SERVICES—See Charlesbank Capital Partners, LLC; *U.S. Private*, pg. 855
HORN INTERNATIONAL FORWARDING—See Horn Packaging Corporation; *U.S. Private*, pg. 1983
HORN INTERNATIONAL PACKAGING—See Horn Packaging Corporation; *U.S. Private*, pg. 1983
HORNOR, TOWNSEND & KENT, INC.—See The Penn Mutual Life Insurance Company; *U.S. Private*, pg. 4092
HORN PACKAGING CORPORATION; *U.S. Private*, pg. 1983
HORNSCHUCH FRANCE SARL—See Continental Aktiengesellschaft; *Int'l*, pg. 1780
HORNSCHUCH ITALIA S.R.L.—See Continental Aktiengesellschaft; *Int'l*, pg. 1780
HORNSCHUCH UK LTD.—See Continental Aktiengesellschaft; *Int'l*, pg. 1780
HORN'S OUTDOOR INC.—See Tym Corporation; *Int'l*, pg. 7995
HORNWOOD INC.; *U.S. Private*, pg. 1984
HORNWOOD INC.—See Hornwood Inc.; *U.S. Private*, pg. 1984
HOROQUARTZ S.A.—See Amano Corporation; *Int'l*, pg. 411
HO-RO TRUCKING COMPANY INC.; *U.S. Private*, pg. 1957
HOROVITZ, RUDOY & ROTEMAN, LLC; *U.S. Private*, pg. 1984
HORRIGAN COLE ENTERPRISES, INC.—See Centerbridge Partners, L.P.; *U.S. Private*, pg. 813
HORRISON RESOURCES INC.; *Int'l*, pg. 3482
HORROCKS ENGINEERS, INC.; *U.S. Private*, pg. 1984
HORRY COUNTY SOLID WASTE AUTHORITY INC.; *U.S. Private*, pg. 1984
HORRY ELECTRIC COOPERATIVE INC.; *U.S. Private*, pg. 1984
HORRY TELEPHONE LONG DISTANCE—See HTC Inc.; *U.S. Private*, pg. 1999
HORSAM AB; *Int'l*, pg. 3482
THE HORSBURGH & SCOTT CO.—See GenNx360 Capital Partners, L.P.; *U.S. Private*, pg. 1672
HORSEBRIDGE NETWORK SYSTEMS LIMITED—See Persimmon plc; *Int'l*, pg. 5816
HORSECITY.COM—See Shivers Trading & Operating Company; *U.S. Private*, pg. 3638
HORSEHEAD CORP.—See Befesa S.A.; *Int'l*, pg. 939
HORSEHEAD METALS DEVELOPMENT, LLC—See Befesa S.A.; *Int'l*, pg. 939
HORSEHEADS AUTOMOTIVE RECYCLING, INC.—See Stellex Capital Management LP; *U.S. Private*, pg. 3800
HORSE HILL DEVELOPMENTS LTD.—See UK Oil & Gas Plc; *Int'l*, pg. 8016

HORSELESS CARRIAGE CARRIERS, INC.—See McCollister's Transportation Group Inc.; *U.S. Private*, pg. 2629
HORSEMEN, INC.; *U.S. Private*, pg. 1984
HORSEMEN'S QUARTER HORSE RACING ASSOCIATION, INC.—See Quarter Horse Racing Inc.; *U.S. Private*, pg. 3324
HORSE & RIDER—See Active Interest Media, Inc.; *U.S. Private*, pg. 69
HORSESHOE BAY RESORT LTD.; *U.S. Private*, pg. 1984
HORSESHOE BOSSIER CITY PROP LLC—See VICI Properties Inc.; *U.S. Public*, pg. 2295
HORSESHOE COUNCIL BLUFFS LLC—See VICI Properties Inc.; *U.S. Public*, pg. 2295
HORSESHOE ENTERTAINMENT, INC.—See Caesars Entertainment, Inc.; *U.S. Public*, pg. 420
HORSESHOE INSURANCE SERVICES HOLDINGS LTD.—See Arthur J. Gallagher & Co.; *U.S. Public*, pg. 206
HORSESHOE METALS LIMITED; *Int'l*, pg. 3482
HORSESHOE TUNICA LLC—See VICI Properties Inc.; *U.S. Public*, pg. 2295
THE HORSESHU HOTEL & CASINO—See PENN Entertainment, Inc.; *U.S. Public*, pg. 1662
HORSETOOTH FINANCIAL LLC—See SageView Advisory Group LLC; *U.S. Private*, pg. 3527
HORSKY HOTEL TATRA, SPOL. S.R.O.—See Terex Corporation; *U.S. Public*, pg. 2019
HORST CONSTRUCTION COMPANY INC.—See The Horst Group Inc.; *U.S. Private*, pg. 4054
THE HORST GROUP INC.; *U.S. Private*, pg. 4054
HORST INSURANCE AGENCY—See The Horst Group Inc.; *U.S. Private*, pg. 4054
HORST LANGE GMBH—See Deufol SE; *Int'l*, pg. 2048
HORSTMAN DEFENCE SYSTEMS LIMITED—See HWH Investments Limited; *Int'l*, pg. 3543
HORST PROPERTY MANAGEMENT—See The Horst Group Inc.; *U.S. Private*, pg. 4054
HORST SPRENGER GMBH RECYCLING-TOOLS—See Stanley Black & Decker, Inc.; *U.S. Public*, pg. 1932
HORST WELLNESS GMBH & CO. KG; *Int'l*, pg. 3482
HORST-ZIMMERMAN INC.; *U.S. Private*, pg. 1984
HOR TECHNOLOGIE GMBH—See DZ BANK AG Deutsche Zentral-Genossenschaftsbank; *Int'l*, pg. 2244
HORTENSE & LOUIS RUBIN DIALYSIS CENTER, INC.; *U.S. Private*, pg. 1984
HORTEN VERWALTUNGS GMBH & CO. OBJEKT INGOLSTADT KG—See Metro AG; *Int'l*, pg. 4857
HORTICA INSURANCE; *U.S. Private*, pg. 1984
HORTICASH PLANTES; *Int'l*, pg. 3482
HORTIFRUT SA; *Int'l*, pg. 3482
HORTI MILANO SRL—See BNP Paribas SA; *Int'l*, pg. 1091
HORTIM SK, S.R.O.—See Dole plc; *Int'l*, pg. 2158
HORTON AUTOMATICS, LTD.—See Sanwa Holdings Corporation; *Int'l*, pg. 6560
HORTON AUTOMATICS—See Sanwa Holdings Corporation; *Int'l*, pg. 6560
HORTON CBI, LIMITED—See McDermott International, Inc.; *U.S. Public*, pg. 1405
HORTON CBI, LIMITED—See McDermott International, Inc.; *U.S. Public*, pg. 1405
HORTON CBI, LIMITED—See McDermott International, Inc.; *U.S. Public*, pg. 1405
HORTON CBI, LIMITED—See McDermott International, Inc.; *U.S. Public*, pg. 1405
HORTON CBI, LIMITED—See McDermott International, Inc.; *U.S. Public*, pg. 1405
THE HORTON FRUIT COMPANY, INC.; *U.S. Private*, pg. 4054
THE HORTON GROUP INC.—See Marsh & McLennan Companies, Inc.; *U.S. Public*, pg. 1382
HORTON HOMES, INC.—See Horton Industries, Inc.; *U.S. Private*, pg. 1984
HORTON HYGIENE CO.—See Elsan Ltd.; *Int'l*, pg. 2370
HORTON INC—See Horton Inc.; *U.S. Private*, pg. 1984
HORTON INC.; *U.S. Private*, pg. 1984
HORTON INDUSTRIES, INC.; *U.S. Private*, pg. 1984
HORTON MEXICO, S. DE RL DE CV—See Horton Inc.; *U.S. Private*, pg. 1984
HORTONWORKS INC.—See Clayton, Dubilier & Rice, LLC; *U.S. Private*, pg. 920
HORTONWORKS INC.—See KKR & Co. Inc.; *U.S. Public*, pg. 1243
HORTORS STATIONERY (PTY) LIMITED—See The Bidvest Group Limited; *Int'l*, pg. 7624
HORUS B.V.—See Merck & Co., Inc.; *U.S. Public*, pg. 1416
HORUS VISION, LLC; *U.S. Private*, pg. 1984
HORVIK LIMITED; *Int'l*, pg. 3482
HORWATH & CO. INC.—See S&H Packing & Sales Co. Inc.; *U.S. Private*, pg. 3513
HORWATH HTL LIMITED—See Beijing Shiji Information Technology Co., Ltd.; *Int'l*, pg. 956
HORWITZ NS/I INC.; *U.S. Private*, pg. 1984
HORWOOD HOMEWARES LIMITED—See TTK Prestige Limited; *Int'l*, pg. 7961
HORY CORPORATION—See Takamiya Co., Ltd.; *Int'l*, pg. 7430
HORY VIETNAM CO., LTD.—See Takamiya Co., Ltd.; *Int'l*, pg. 7430

COMPANY NAME INDEX

HOSA INTERNATIONAL LIMITED; *Int'l*, pg. 3482
HOS BROTHERS CONSTRUCTION, INC.; *U.S. Private*, pg. 1984
H. O. SCHLUTER GMBH & CO. KG; *Int'l*, pg. 3194
HOSCO FITTINGS LLC—See Carlisle Companies Incorporated; *U.S. Public*, pg. 436
HOSCOTE RUBBER ESTATES LIMITED—See Sime Darby Berhad; *Int'l*, pg. 6929
HOSEA O. WEAVER AND SONS INC.; *U.S. Private*, pg. 1985
HOSEASONS HOLIDAYS LIMITED—See Travel & Leisure Co.; *U.S. Public*, pg. 2185
HOSE & FITTINGS ETC.; *U.S. Private*, pg. 1984
HOSEI BRAKE INDUSTRY CO., LTD. - OKAZAKI FACTORY—See AISIN Corporation; *Int'l*, pg. 253
HOSEI BRAKE INDUSTRY CO., LTD.—See AISIN Corporation; *Int'l*, pg. 253
HOSEI BRAKE INDUSTRY CO., LTD. - TAKAHAMA FACTORY—See AISIN Corporation; *Int'l*, pg. 253
HOSELMANN STAHL GMBH—See Jacquet Metal Service SA; *Int'l*, pg. 3867
HOSELTON CHEVROLET INCORPORATED; *U.S. Private*, pg. 1985
HOSEN GROUP LTD; *Int'l*, pg. 3482
HOSHAKU INRYO CO., LTD.—See Aseed Holdings Co., Ltd.; *Int'l*, pg. 605
HOSHIENU PHARMACEUTICAL CO., LTD.—See Mitsubishi Chemical Group Corporation; *Int'l*, pg. 4935
HOSHI INDUSTRIES CO., LTD.—See Sumitomo Electric Industries, Ltd.; *Int'l*, pg. 7278
HOSHIIRYO-SANKI CO., LTD.; *Int'l*, pg. 3482
HOSHI KINZOKU CORPORATION—See JFE Holdings, Inc.; *Int'l*, pg. 3936
HOSHINE SILICON INDUSTRY CO., LTD.; *Int'l*, pg. 3482
HOSHINE SILICON (JIAXING) INDUSTRY CO., LTD.—See Hoshine Silicon Industry Co., Ltd.; *Int'l*, pg. 3482
HOSHINE SILICON (LUZHOU) INDUSTRY CO., LTD.—See Hoshine Silicon Industry Co., Ltd.; *Int'l*, pg. 3482
HOSHINE SILICON (SHANSHAN) INDUSTRY CO., LTD.—See Hoshine Silicon Industry Co., Ltd.; *Int'l*, pg. 3482
HOSHIN GIGAMEDIA CENTER INC.—See GigaMedia Limited; *Int'l*, pg. 2971
HOSHIN GOSEI CO., LTD.—See Toyoda Gosei Co., Ltd.; *Int'l*, pg. 7861
HOSHINO BENELUX B.V.—See Hoshino Gakki Co., Ltd.; *Int'l*, pg. 3483
HOSHINO GAKKI CO., LTD. - AKATSUKI FACTORY—See Hoshino Gakki Co., Ltd.; *Int'l*, pg. 3483
HOSHINO GAKKI CO., LTD.; *Int'l*, pg. 3483
HOSHINO GAKKI HANBAI CO., LTD.—See Hoshino Gakki Co., Ltd.; *Int'l*, pg. 3483
HOSHINO RESORTS INC.; *Int'l*, pg. 3483
HOSHINO RESORTS OMO7 ASAHIKAWA HOTEL—See Hoshino Resorts Inc.; *Int'l*, pg. 3483
HOSHINO RESORTS REIT, INC.—See Hoshino Resorts Inc.; *Int'l*, pg. 3483
HOSHINO (USA) INC.—See Hoshino Gakki Co., Ltd.; *Int'l*, pg. 3483
HOSHIZAKI AMERICA, INC.—See Hoshizaki Corporation; *Int'l*, pg. 3484
HOSHIZAKI CHUGOKU CO., LTD.—See Hoshizaki Corporation; *Int'l*, pg. 3483
HOSHIZAKI CORPORATION; *Int'l*, pg. 3483
HOSHIZAKI EUROPE B.V.—See Hoshizaki Corporation; *Int'l*, pg. 3483
HOSHIZAKI EUROPE HOLDINGS B.V.—See Hoshizaki Corporation; *Int'l*, pg. 3483
HOSHIZAKI EUROPE LTD.—See Hoshizaki Corporation; *Int'l*, pg. 3483
HOSHIZAKI HOKKAIDO K.K.—See Hoshizaki Corporation; *Int'l*, pg. 3483
HOSHIZAKI HOKUSHINETSU K.K.—See Hoshizaki Corporation; *Int'l*, pg. 3483
HOSHIZAKI KANTO K.K.—See Hoshizaki Corporation; *Int'l*, pg. 3483
HOSHIZAKI KEIHAN K.K.—See Hoshizaki Corporation; *Int'l*, pg. 3483
HOSHIZAKI KITAKANTO CO LTD.—See Hoshizaki Corporation; *Int'l*, pg. 3483
HOSHIZAKI KITAKYU K.K.—See Hoshizaki Corporation; *Int'l*, pg. 3483
HOSHIZAKI LANCER PTY LTD.—See Hoshizaki Corporation; *Int'l*, pg. 3483
HOSHIZAKI MALAYSIA SDN. BHD.—See Hoshizaki Corporation; *Int'l*, pg. 3483
HOSHIZAKI NANKYU K.K.—See Hoshizaki Corporation; *Int'l*, pg. 3483
HOSHIZAKI OKINAWA CO LTD.—See Hoshizaki Corporation; *Int'l*, pg. 3483
HOSHIZAKI PHILIPPINES CORPORATION—See Hoshizaki Corporation; *Int'l*, pg. 3484
HOSHIZAKI SHANGHAI CO., LTD.—See Hoshizaki Corporation; *Int'l*, pg. 3484
HOSHIZAKI SHIKOKU K.K.—See Hoshizaki Corporation; *Int'l*, pg. 3484

HOSHIZAKI SINGAPORE PTE LTD.—See Hoshizaki Corporation; *Int'l*, pg. 3484
HOSHIZAKI SUZHOU CO., LTD.—See Hoshizaki Corporation; *Int'l*, pg. 3484
HOSHIZAKI (THAILAND) LIMITED—See Hoshizaki Corporation; *Int'l*, pg. 3483
HOSHIZAKI TOHOKU K.K.—See Hoshizaki Corporation; *Int'l*, pg. 3484
HOSHIZAKI TOKAI CO., LTD.—See Hoshizaki Corporation; *Int'l*, pg. 3484
HOSHIZAKI TOKYO K.K.—See Hoshizaki Corporation; *Int'l*, pg. 3484
HOSHIZAKI USA HOLDINGS, INC.—See Hoshizaki Corporation; *Int'l*, pg. 3484
HOSIDEN AMERICA CORP—See Hosiden Corporation; *Int'l*, pg. 3484
HOSIDEN BESSON LTD—See Hosiden Corporation; *Int'l*, pg. 3484
HOSIDEN CORPORATION - CHINA HOSIDEN LCD FACTORY—See Hosiden Corporation; *Int'l*, pg. 3484
HOSIDEN CORPORATION (M) SDN. BHD—See Hosiden Corporation; *Int'l*, pg. 3484
HOSIDEN CORPORATION; *Int'l*, pg. 3484
HOSIDEN CORPORATION-TOKYO FACTORY—See Hosiden Corporation; *Int'l*, pg. 3484
HOSIDEN ELECTRONICS (MALAYSIA) SDN. BHD—See Hosiden Corporation; *Int'l*, pg. 3484
HOSIDEN ELECTRONICS (SHANGHAI) CO., LTD.—See Hosiden Corporation; *Int'l*, pg. 3484
HOSIDEN ELECTRONICS (SHENZHEN) CO., LTD.—See Hosiden Corporation; *Int'l*, pg. 3484
HOSIDEN EUROPE GMBH—See Hosiden Corporation; *Int'l*, pg. 3484
HOSIDEN F.D. CORPORATION—See Hosiden Corporation; *Int'l*, pg. 3484
HOSIDEN KYUSHU CORPORATION—See Hosiden Corporation; *Int'l*, pg. 3484
HOSIDEN PLASTICS CORPORATION—See Hosiden Corporation; *Int'l*, pg. 3484
HOSIDEN SEIKO CORPORATION—See Hosiden Corporation; *Int'l*, pg. 3484
HOSIDEN SERVICE CORPORATION—See Hosiden Corporation; *Int'l*, pg. 3484
HOSIDEN (SHANGHAI) CO., LTD.—See Hosiden Corporation; *Int'l*, pg. 3484
HOSIDEN (SHENZHEN) CO., LTD.—See Hosiden Corporation; *Int'l*, pg. 3484
HOSIDEN SINGAPORE PTE. LTD.—See Hosiden Corporation; *Int'l*, pg. 3484
HOSIDEN TECHNOLOGY (QINGDAO) CO., LTD.—See Hosiden Corporation; *Int'l*, pg. 3484
HOSIDEN (THAILAND) CO., LTD—See Hosiden Corporation; *Int'l*, pg. 3484
HOSIDEN VIETNAM (BAC GIANG) CO., LTD.—See Hosiden Corporation; *Int'l*, pg. 3484
HOSIDEN WAKAYAMA CORPORATION—See Hosiden Corporation; *Int'l*, pg. 3484
HOSKEN CONSOLIDATED INVESTMENTS LIMITED; *Int'l*, pg. 3485
HOSKING PARTNERS LLP; *Int'l*, pg. 3485
HOSKIN & MUIR, INC.; *U.S. Private*, pg. 1985
HOSKINS PEST CONTROL INC.—See Certus Pest, Inc.; *U.S. Private*, pg. 842
HOSLEY INTERNATIONAL TRADING CORPORATION; *U.S. Private*, pg. 1985
HOSMER-DORRANCE CORPORATION—See Patient Square Capital, L.P.; *U.S. Private*, pg. 3107
HOSODA CORPORATION—See Haseko Corporation; *Int'l*, pg. 3283
HOSOKAWA ALPINE AKTIENGESELLSCHAFT & CO. OHG—See Hosokawa Micron Corporation; *Int'l*, pg. 3486
HOSOKAWA ALPINE AMERICAN INC.—See Hosokawa Micron Corporation; *Int'l*, pg. 3485
HOSOKAWA ALPINE JAPAN CO., LTD.—See Hosokawa Micron Corporation; *Int'l*, pg. 3485
HOSOKAWA ALPINE POLAND SP. Z O.O.—See Hosokawa Micron Corporation; *Int'l*, pg. 3486
HOSOKAWA BEPEX GMBH—See Hosokawa Micron Corporation; *Int'l*, pg. 3486
HOSOKAWA DE MEXICO S.A. DE C.V.—See Hosokawa Micron Corporation; *Int'l*, pg. 3486
HOSOKAWA FOODS CO., LTD.—See Yoshimura Food Holdings K.K.; *Int'l*, pg. 8600
HOSOKAWA MICRON B.V.—See Hosokawa Micron Corporation; *Int'l*, pg. 3486
HOSOKAWA MICRON CORPORATION; *Int'l*, pg. 3485
HOSOKAWA MICRON FRANCE—See Hosokawa Micron Corporation; *Int'l*, pg. 3486
HOSOKAWA MICRON GMBH—See Hosokawa Micron Corporation; *Int'l*, pg. 3486
HOSOKAWA MICRON INDIA PVT. LTD.—See Hosokawa Micron Corporation; *Int'l*, pg. 3486
HOSOKAWA MICRON INTERNATIONAL INC.—See Hosokawa Micron Corporation; *Int'l*, pg. 3486
HOSOKAWA MICRON (KOREA) LTD—See Hosokawa Micron Corporation; *Int'l*, pg. 3486
HOSOKAWA MICRON LTD.—See Hosokawa Micron Corporation; *Int'l*, pg. 3486

HOSPICE SAVANNAH, INC.

HOSOKAWA MICRON LTD.—See Hosokawa Micron Corporation; *Int'l*, pg. 3486
HOSOKAWA MICRON POWDERS GMBH—See Hosokawa Micron Corporation; *Int'l*, pg. 3486
HOSOKAWA MICRON POWDER SYSTEMS—See Hosokawa Micron Corporation; *Int'l*, pg. 3486
HOSOKAWA MICRON (SHANGHAI) POWDER MACHINERY CO. LTD—See Hosokawa Micron Corporation; *Int'l*, pg. 3486
HOSOKAWA POLYMER SYSTEMS—See Hosokawa Micron Corporation; *Int'l*, pg. 3486
HOSOKAWA SOLIDS CHILE SPA—See Hosokawa Micron Corporation; *Int'l*, pg. 3486
HOSOKAWA SOLIDS MEXICO S.A. DE C.V.—See Hosokawa Micron Corporation; *Int'l*, pg. 3486
HOSOKAWA SOLIDS S.L.—See Hosokawa Micron Corporation; *Int'l*, pg. 3486
HOSOKAWA SOLIDS SOLUTIONS GMBH—See Hosokawa Micron Corporation; *Int'l*, pg. 3486
HOSOKURA METAL MINING CO., LTD.—See Mitsubishi Materials Corporation; *Int'l*, pg. 4963
HOSOSHIMAKO NIYAKU SHINKO CO., LTD.—See Senko Group Holdings Co., Ltd.; *Int'l*, pg. 6709
HOSOYA PYRO-ENGINEERING CO., LTD.; *Int'l*, pg. 3486
HOSPAL S.A.—See Baxter International Inc.; *U.S. Public*, pg. 282
HOSPARUS INC.; *U.S. Private*, pg. 1985
HOSPECO BRANDS GROUP; *U.S. Private*, pg. 1985
HOSPEDIA HOLDINGS LIMITED—See Marlin Equity Partners, LLC; *U.S. Private*, pg. 2584
HOSPEDIA LIMITED—See Marlin Equity Partners, LLC; *U.S. Private*, pg. 2584
HOSPICE AND PALLIATIVE CARE CENTER OF ALAMANCE-CASWELL; *U.S. Private*, pg. 1985
HOSPICE AT GREENSBORO, INC.; *U.S. Private*, pg. 1985
HOSPICE AUSTIN; *U.S. Private*, pg. 1985
HOSPICE BUFFALO; *U.S. Private*, pg. 1985
HOSPICE CARE INC.—See Chemed Corporation; *U.S. Public*, pg. 484
HOSPICE CARE OF SOUTHWEST MICHIGAN; *U.S. Private*, pg. 1985
HOSPICE & COMMUNITY CARE; *U.S. Private*, pg. 1985
HOSPICE EL PASO; *U.S. Private*, pg. 1985
HOSPICE HAWAII; *U.S. Private*, pg. 1985
HOSPICE INC.; *U.S. Private*, pg. 1985
HOSPICE OF AMERICA, INC.—See Dorilton Capital Advisors LLC; *U.S. Private*, pg. 1263
HOSPICE OF ARIZONA—See The Riverside Company; *U.S. Private*, pg. 4107
HOSPICE OF CENTRAL ARKANSAS, LLC—See UnitedHealth Group Incorporated; *U.S. Public*, pg. 2245
HOSPICE OF CENTRAL PENNSYLVANIA; *U.S. Private*, pg. 1985
HOSPICE OF CHATTANOOGA, INC.; *U.S. Private*, pg. 1985
HOSPICE OF CITRUS COUNTY, INC.—See Chemed Corporation; *U.S. Public*, pg. 484
HOSPICE OF CLEVELAND COUNTY, INC.; *U.S. Private*, pg. 1985
HOSPICE OF DAYTON, INC.; *U.S. Private*, pg. 1986
HOSPICE OF EAST TEXAS; *U.S. Private*, pg. 1986
HOSPICE OF HOPE; *U.S. Private*, pg. 1986
HOSPICE OF LAURENS COUNTY, INC.; *U.S. Private*, pg. 1986
HOSPICE OF MARION COUNTY; *U.S. Private*, pg. 1986
HOSPICE OF MESILLA VALLEY, LLC—See Humana, Inc.; *U.S. Public*, pg. 1069
HOSPICE OF MICHIGAN INC.; *U.S. Private*, pg. 1986
HOSPICE OF NEW JERSEY—See The Riverside Company; *U.S. Private*, pg. 4107
HOSPICE OF NORTHWEST OHIO; *U.S. Private*, pg. 1986
HOSPICE OF RUTHERFORD COUNTY, INC.; *U.S. Private*, pg. 1986
HOSPICE OF SOUTHERN ILLINOIS, INC.; *U.S. Private*, pg. 1986
HOSPICE OF THE BLUEGRASS; *U.S. Private*, pg. 1986
HOSPICE OF THE COMFORTER, INC.; *U.S. Private*, pg. 1986
HOSPICE OF THE PIEDMONT, INC.; *U.S. Private*, pg. 1986
HOSPICE OF THE PIEDMONT; *U.S. Private*, pg. 1986
HOSPICE OF THE RED RIVER VALLEY; *U.S. Private*, pg. 1986
HOSPICE OF THE SACRED HEART; *U.S. Private*, pg. 1986
HOSPICE OF THE VALLEY; *U.S. Private*, pg. 1986
HOSPICE OF THE WESTERN RESERVE, INC.; *U.S. Private*, pg. 1987
HOSPICE OF VIRGINIA—See The Riverside Company; *U.S. Private*, pg. 4107
HOSPICE OF WAKE COUNTY; *U.S. Private*, pg. 1987
HOSPICE & PALLIATIVE CARECENTER; *U.S. Private*, pg. 1985
HOSPICE & PALLIATIVE CARE CHARLOTTE REGION—See Hospice of Laurens County, Inc.; *U.S. Private*, pg. 1986
HOSPICE SAVANNAH, INC.; *U.S. Private*, pg. 1987

HOSPICE SAVANNAH, INC.

CORPORATE AFFILIATIONS

HOSPICE SOURCE LLC—See New Mountain Capital, LLC; *U.S. Private*, pg. 2903
HOSPICIO Y HOME CARE SAN LUCAS; *U.S. Private*, pg. 1987
HOSPIDANA A/S—See AddLife AB; *Int'l*, pg. 129
HOSPIRA ASEPTIC SERVICES LIMITED—See Pfizer Inc.; *U.S. Public*, pg. 1680
HOSPIRA - AUSTIN—See Pfizer Inc.; *U.S. Public*, pg. 1680
HOSPIRA AUSTRALIA PTY. LTD.—See Pfizer Inc.; *U.S. Public*, pg. 1680
HOSPIRA DEUTSCHLAND GMBH—See Pfizer Inc.; *U.S. Public*, pg. 1680
HOSPIRA, INC.—See Pfizer Inc.; *U.S. Public*, pg. 1680
HOSPIRA INVICTA SA—See Pfizer Inc.; *U.S. Public*, pg. 1680
HOSPIRA ITALIA S.R.L.—See Pfizer Inc.; *U.S. Public*, pg. 1680
HOSPIRA PHILIPPINES, INC.—See Pfizer Inc.; *U.S. Public*, pg. 1680
HOSPIRA PTY LIMITED—See Pfizer Inc.; *U.S. Public*, pg. 1680
HOSPIRA SLOVAKIA, S.R.O.—See Pfizer Inc.; *U.S. Public*, pg. 1680
HOSPIRA UK LIMITED—See Pfizer Inc.; *U.S. Public*, pg. 1680
HOSPIRA WORLDWIDE, LLC—See Pfizer Inc.; *U.S. Public*, pg. 1680
HOSPITAL ALVORADA DE TAGUATINGA LTDA.—See UnitedHealth Group Incorporated; *U.S. Public*, pg. 2241
HOSPITAL AMA S.A.—See UnitedHealth Group Incorporated; *U.S. Public*, pg. 2241
HOSPITAL ANA COSTA S.A.—See UnitedHealth Group Incorporated; *U.S. Public*, pg. 2241
HOSPITALARES S.A. + CORMEDICA S.A.—See Werfen Life Group, S.A.U.; *Int'l*, pg. 8379
HOSPITAL BILLING & COLLECTION SERVICE, LTD.; *U.S. Private*, pg. 1987
HOSPITAL BUEN SAMARITANO, INC.; *U.S. Private*, pg. 1987
HOSPITAL BUILDING & EQUIPMENT CO.—See HBE Corporation; *U.S. Private*, pg. 1887
HOSPITAL CARLOS CHAGAS S.A.—See UnitedHealth Group Incorporated; *U.S. Public*, pg. 2241
HOSPITAL CENTRAL SERVICES, INC.; *U.S. Private*, pg. 1987
HOSPITAL CORPORATION AUSTRALIA PTY LIMITED—See Ramsay Health Care Limited; *Int'l*, pg. 6199
HOSPITAL CORPORATION OF AMERICA; *U.S. Private*, pg. 1987
HOSPITAL CORPORATION OF CHINA LIMITED; *Int'l*, pg. 3486
HOSPITAL CUF CASCAIS, S.A.—See Jose de Mello, SGPS, S.A.; *Int'l*, pg. 4001
HOSPITAL CUF DESCOBERTAS, S.A.—See Jose de Mello, SGPS, S.A.; *Int'l*, pg. 4001
HOSPITAL CUF INFANTE SANTO, S.A.—See Jose de Mello, SGPS, S.A.; *Int'l*, pg. 4001
HOSPITAL CUF PORTO, S.A.—See Jose de Mello, SGPS, S.A.; *Int'l*, pg. 4001
HOSPITAL CUF TORRES VEDRAS, S.A.—See Jose de Mello, SGPS, S.A.; *Int'l*, pg. 4001
HOSPITAL DA ARRABIDA - GAIA, S.A.—See Fosun International Limited; *Int'l*, pg. 2751
HOSPITAL DA LUZ, S.A.—See Fosun International Limited; *Int'l*, pg. 2751
HOSPITAL DE CLINICAS DE JACAREPAGUA LTDA.—See UnitedHealth Group Incorporated; *U.S. Public*, pg. 2241
HOSPITAL DE LA CONCEPCION; *U.S. Private*, pg. 1987
HOSPITAL DE MAJADAHONDA, S.A.—See DIF Management Holding B.V.; *Int'l*, pg. 2118
HOSPITAL DESIGNERS, INC.—See HBE Corporation; *U.S. Private*, pg. 1887
HOSPITAL DEVELOPMENT OF WEST PHOENIX, INC.—See Tenet Healthcare Corporation; *U.S. Public*, pg. 2014
HOSPITAL DEVELOPMENTS PTY LIMITED—See Ramsay Health Care Limited; *Int'l*, pg. 6199
HOSPITAL E MATERNIDADE SAINT-VIVANT LTDA.—See UnitedHealth Group Incorporated; *U.S. Public*, pg. 2241
HOSPITAL E MATERNIDADE SAMARITANO LTDA.—See Hapvida Participacoes e Investimentos S.A.; *Int'l*, pg. 3269
HOSPITAL FOR SPECIAL CARE; *U.S. Private*, pg. 1987
HOSPITAL GERAL E MATERNIDADE MADRE MARIA THEODORA LTDA.—See UnitedHealth Group Incorporated; *U.S. Public*, pg. 2241
HOSPITALIA INTERNATIONAL GMBH—See Fresenius SE & Co. KGaA; *Int'l*, pg. 2780
HOSPITALISTS AT FAIRVIEW PARK, LLC—See HCA Healthcare, Inc.; *U.S. Public*, pg. 998
HOSPITALISTS AT STONECREST, LLC—See HCA Healthcare, Inc.; *U.S. Public*, pg. 999
HOSPITALISTS OF NORTHERN MICHIGAN; *U.S. Private*, pg. 1987

HOSPITALITY DESIGN GROUP—See ONEX Corporation; *Int'l*, pg. 5579
HOSPITALITY DIGITAL GMBH—See Metro AG; *Int'l*, pg. 4857
HOSPITALITY INT. THAILANDE—See Accor S.A.; *Int'l*, pg. 91
HOSPITALITY INVESTMENTS LP; *U.S. Private*, pg. 1987
HOSPITALITY INVESTORS TRUST, INC.—See AR Global Investments, LLC; *U.S. Private*, pg. 306
HOSPITALITY MARKETING CONCEPTS, (ASIA PACIFIC) INC—See Hospitality Marketing Concepts, Inc.; *U.S. Private*, pg. 1987
HOSPITALITY MARKETING CONCEPTS, INC.; *U.S. Private*, pg. 1987
HOSPITALITY MARKETING CONCEPTS, INC.—See Hospitality Marketing Concepts, Inc.; *U.S. Private*, pg. 1987
HOSPITALITY MINTS LLC—See Mount Franklin Foods, LLC; *U.S. Private*, pg. 2798
HOSPITALITY NETWORK CORPORATION—See Tsukada Global Holdings Inc.; *Int'l*, pg. 7956
HOSPITALITY NETWORKS AND SERVICES ESPANA SA—See Swisscom AG; *Int'l*, pg. 7373
HOSPITALITY NETWORKS AND SERVICES UK LTD—See Swisscom AG; *Int'l*, pg. 7373
HOSPITALITY PARTNERS; *U.S. Private*, pg. 1987
HOSPITALITY PROPERTY FUND LTD.—See Hosken Consolidated Investments Limited; *Int'l*, pg. 3485
HOSPITALITY PURVEYOR INC.; *U.S. Private*, pg. 1988
HOSPITALITY RESOURCES S.P.C.—See Gulf Hotels Group B.S.C.; *Int'l*, pg. 3181
HOSPITALITY SERVICES ITALIA S.R.L.—See Swisscom AG; *Int'l*, pg. 7373
HOSPITALITY SERVICES PLUS SA—See Swisscom AG; *Int'l*, pg. 7373
HOSPITALITY SERVICES S.A.R.L.—See Westmont Hospitality Group; *Int'l*, pg. 8391
HOSPITALITY SPECIALISTS, INC.; *U.S. Private*, pg. 1988
HOSPITALITY STAFFING SOLUTIONS, LLC—See Cerberus Capital Management, L.P.; *U.S. Private*, pg. 839
HOSPITALITY TECHNOLOGY—See RFE Investment Partners; *U.S. Private*, pg. 3419
HOSPITALITY USA INVESTMENT GROUP, INC.; *U.S. Private*, pg. 1988
HOSPITALITY WEST LLC; *U.S. Private*, pg. 1988
HOSPITAL LAUNDRY SERVICES, INC.—See Community Health Systems, Inc.; *U.S. Public*, pg. 553
HOSPITAL LAUNDRY SERVICES; *U.S. Private*, pg. 1987
HOSPITAL MONTE KLINIKUM S/S LTDA.—See UnitedHealth Group Incorporated; *U.S. Public*, pg. 2241
HOSPITAL OF BARSTOW, INC.—See Quorum Health Corporation; *U.S. Private*, pg. 3330
HOSPITAL OF FULTON, INC.—See Community Health Systems, Inc.; *U.S. Public*, pg. 553
HOSPITAL OF LOUISA, INC.—See Quorum Health Corporation; *U.S. Private*, pg. 3330
HOSPITAL OF MORRISTOWN, INC.—See Community Health Systems, Inc.; *U.S. Public*, pg. 553
HOSPITAL PANTAI AYER KEROH SDN. BHD.—See Khazanah Nasional Berhad; *Int'l*, pg. 4152
HOSPITAL POLUSA, S.A.—See Centene Corporation; *U.S. Public*, pg. 469
HOSPITAL POVISA, S.A.—See Centene Corporation; *U.S. Public*, pg. 469
HOSPITAL PRACTICE—See JTE Multimedia, LLC; *U.S. Private*, pg. 2241
HOSPITAL SAMARITANO DE SAO PAULO LTDA.—See UnitedHealth Group Incorporated; *U.S. Public*, pg. 2241
HOSPITAL SAN CARLOS BORROMEO; *U.S. Private*, pg. 1987
HOSPITAL SANTA HELENA S.A.—See UnitedHealth Group Incorporated; *U.S. Public*, pg. 2241
HOSPITAL SISTERS HEALTH SYSTEM; *U.S. Private*, pg. 1987
HOSPITAL SOLUTIONS, INC.; *U.S. Private*, pg. 1987
HOSPITALS PROJEKTENTWICKLUNGSGES.M.B.H.—See PORR AG; *Int'l*, pg. 5923
HOSPITAL UNDERWRITING GROUP, INC.—See Tenet Healthcare Corporation; *U.S. Public*, pg. 2004
HOSPITHERA N.V.—See Viatris Inc.; *U.S. Public*, pg. 2293
HOSPOR - HOSPITAIS PORTUGUESES, S.A.—See Fosun International Limited; *Int'l*, pg. 2751
HOS PORT, LLC—See Hornbeck Offshore Services, Inc.; *U.S. Private*, pg. 1983
HOSS INDUSTRIAL LLC; *U.S. Private*, pg. 1988
HOSS'S STEAK & SEA HOUSE, INC.; *U.S. Private*, pg. 1988
HOSS VALUE CARS & TRUCKS INC.; *U.S. Private*, pg. 1988
HOST ANALYTICS, INC.—See Vector Capital Management, L.P.; *U.S. Private*, pg. 4351
HOSTBASKET—See Liberty Global plc; *Int'l*, pg. 4485
HOSTDIME.COM, INC.; *U.S. Private*, pg. 1988
HOSTED SOLUTIONS CHARLOTTE, LLC—See Windstream Holdings, Inc.; *U.S. Public*, pg. 2373
HOSTELLING INTERNATIONAL USA; *U.S. Private*, pg. 1988

HOSTER BINDERY, INC.—See The HF Group LLC; *U.S. Private*, pg. 4052
HOSTESS BRANDS, INC.—See The J.M. Smucker Company; *U.S. Public*, pg. 2107
HOSTESS BRANDS, LLC—See The J.M. Smucker Company; *U.S. Public*, pg. 2107
HOSTETLERS SALES & CONSTRUCTION LLC; *U.S. Private*, pg. 1988
HOST EUROPE GMBH—See KKR & Co. Inc.; *U.S. Public*, pg. 1252
HOST EUROPE GMBH—See Silver Lake Group, LLC; *U.S. Private*, pg. 3657
HOST EUROPE GMBH—See TCMI, Inc.; *U.S. Private*, pg. 3943
HOST EUROPE GROUP LIMITED—See KKR & Co. Inc.; *U.S. Public*, pg. 1252
HOST EUROPE GROUP LIMITED—See Silver Lake Group, LLC; *U.S. Private*, pg. 3657
HOST EUROPE GROUP LIMITED—See TCMI, Inc.; *U.S. Private*, pg. 3943
HOSTGATOR.COM LLC—See Clearlake Capital Group, L.P.; *U.S. Private*, pg. 934
HOSTGATOR.COM LLC—See Siris Capital Group, LLC; *U.S. Private*, pg. 3673
HOST HEALTHCARE, INC.—See TPG Capital, L.P.; *U.S. Public*, pg. 2176
HOST HOTELS & RESORTS, INC.; *U.S. Public*, pg. 1054
HOST HOTELS & RESORTS L.P.—See Host Hotels & Resorts, Inc.; *U.S. Public*, pg. 1055
HOSTI INTERNATIONAL GMBH; *Int'l*, pg. 3486
HOSTIN D.O.O.—See INA-Industrija Nafte, d.d.; *Int'l*, pg. 3642
HOSTING.COM, INC.; *U.S. Private*, pg. 1988
HOSTMARK HOSPITALITY GROUP; *U.S. Private*, pg. 1988
HOSTMORE PLC; *Int'l*, pg. 3486
HOSTMYSITE.COM; *U.S. Private*, pg. 1988
HOST.NET—See Novacap Management Inc.; *Int'l*, pg. 5454
HOSTOPIA.COM INC.—See Deluxe Corporation; *U.S. Public*, pg. 653
HOSTPAPA, INC.; *Int'l*, pg. 3487
HOST-PLUS PTY. LIMITED; *Int'l*, pg. 3486
HOST PTE LTD—See Sonepar S.A.; *Int'l*, pg. 7091
HOST; *Int'l*, pg. 3486
HOSTVENTURES.COM, INC.; *U.S. Private*, pg. 1988
HOSTWAY SERVICES, INC.—See Hosting.com, Inc.; *U.S. Private*, pg. 1988
HOT 91 PTY LIMITED—See Seven West Media Limited; *Int'l*, pg. 6734
HOTAI DEVELOPMENT CO., LTD.—See Daikin Industries, Ltd.; *Int'l*, pg. 1935
HO-TAI MOTOR CO. LTD.—See Toyota Motor Corporation; *Int'l*, pg. 7871
HOTAI MOTOR CO., LTD.; *Int'l*, pg. 3487
HOTA INDUSTRIAL MFG. CO., LTD.; *Int'l*, pg. 3487
HOTAN CORP.—See CMC Magnetics Corporation; *Int'l*, pg. 1669
HOTARD COACHES, INC.; *U.S. Private*, pg. 1989
HOTATECH, INC.—See Hota Industrial Mfg. Co., Ltd.; *Int'l*, pg. 3487
HOTBATH SRL—See FM Mattsson Mora Group AB; *Int'l*, pg. 2717
HOTBED LIMITED; *Int'l*, pg. 3487
HOTCAM NEW YORK INC.—See Procam Television Ltd.; *Int'l*, pg. 5986
HOT CHILI LIMITED; *Int'l*, pg. 3487
HOTCHKISS INSURANCE AGENCY; *U.S. Private*, pg. 1989
HOTDOCS CORPORATION—See Ontario Teachers' Pension Plan; *Int'l*, pg. 5586
HOTDOCS LIMITED—See Ontario Teachers' Pension Plan; *Int'l*, pg. 5586
HOTEIS OTHON S.A.; *Int'l*, pg. 3487
HOTEL 101 MANAGEMENT CORPORATION—See DoubleDragon Corporation; *Int'l*, pg. 2181
HOTEL ALEXANDER, S.A.S.—See Melia Hotels International, S.A.; *Int'l*, pg. 4810
HOTEL AL KHOZAMA—See Chow Tai Fook Enterprises Limited; *Int'l*, pg. 1585
HOTEL AMENITIES SUPPLIERS PROPRIETARY LIMITED—See The Bidvest Group Limited; *Int'l*, pg. 7624
HOTEL AM KANZLERAMT VERWALTUNGS GMBH—See PORR AG; *Int'l*, pg. 5923
HOTEL ANNUPURI CO., LTD.—See Meiji Shipping Co., Ltd.; *Int'l*, pg. 4801
HOTEL ARCTIC A/S—See Air Greenland A/S; *Int'l*, pg. 238
HOTEL ARTS BARCELONA—See Marriott International, Inc.; *U.S. Public*, pg. 1371
HOTELBEDS GROUP, S.L.U.—See Canada Pension Plan Investment Board; *Int'l*, pg. 1279
HOTELBEDS GROUP, S.L.U.—See Cinven Limited; *Int'l*, pg. 1612
HOTELBEDS HONG KONG LIMITED—See Canada Pension Plan Investment Board; *Int'l*, pg. 1279
HOTELBEDS HONG KONG LIMITED—See Cinven Limited; *Int'l*, pg. 1612

COMPANY NAME INDEX

HOTELBEDS PTE. LTD.—See Canada Pension Plan Investment Board; *Int'l*, pg. 1279
HOTELBEDS PTE. LTD.—See Cinven Limited; *Int'l*, pg. 1612
HOTELBEDS SPAIN, S.L.U.—See Canada Pension Plan Investment Board; *Int'l*, pg. 1279
HOTELBEDS SPAIN, S.L.U.—See Cinven Limited; *Int'l*, pg. 1612
HOTEL BELA LADA A.D.; *Int'l*, pg. 3487
HOTEL BELLVER, S.A.—See Melia Hotels International, S.A.; *Int'l*, pg. 4809
HOTEL BENITO MANAGEMENT LIMITED—See Southeast Asia Properties & Finance Limited; *Int'l*, pg. 7117
HOTEL BENIYA CO., LTD.—See KITZ CORPORATION; *Int'l*, pg. 4196
HOTELBIRD GMBH—See 029 Group SE; *Int'l*, pg. 1
HOTEL BOHLERSTERN GESELLSCHAFT M.B.H.—See voestalpine AG; *Int'l*, pg. 8287
HOTEL BOSNA A.D. BANJA LUKA; *Int'l*, pg. 3487
HOTELBUSINESS ZUG AG—See Zug Estates Holding AG; *Int'l*, pg. 8693
HOTEL CAMPOS DE GUADALMINA S.L.—See Barcelo Corporacion Empresarial S.A.; *Int'l*, pg. 859
HOTEL CAPRI CARIBE, S. DE R.L. DE C.V.—See Playa Hotels & Resorts N.V.; *Int'l*, pg. 5894
HOTEL CARDOSO SARL—See Lonrho Limited; *Int'l*, pg. 4552
HOTEL CARUSO S.R.L.—See LVMH Moet Hennessy Louis Vuitton SE; *Int'l*, pg. 4590
HOTEL & CASINO RESORT ADMIRAL—See Novomatic AG; *Int'l*, pg. 5467
HOTEL CHANCELLOR @ ORCHARD PTE. LTD.—See Hotel Grand Central Limited; *Int'l*, pg. 3487
HOTEL CHINZANSO TOKYO—See Fujita Kanko Inc.; *Int'l*, pg. 2831
HOTEL CHOCOLAT GROUP LIMITED—See Mars, Incorporated; *U.S. Private*, pg. 2589
HOTEL CIPRIANI S.R.L.—See LVMH Moet Hennessy Louis Vuitton SE; *Int'l*, pg. 4590
HOTEL CLUB ESTIVAL 2002 SA; *Int'l*, pg. 3487
HOTEL COLBERT SAS—See Melia Hotels International, S.A.; *Int'l*, pg. 4809
HOTEL COMPANY INC.; *U.S. Private*, pg. 1989
HOTEL CONSULTING SERVICES INC.; *U.S. Private*, pg. 1909
HOTEL CONVENTO EXTREMADURA, S.A.—See Melia Hotels International, S.A.; *Int'l*, pg. 4809
HOTEL CORPORATION OF INDIA LIMITED—See Air India Limited; *Int'l*, pg. 238
HOTEL CRESCENT COURT—See Chow Tai Fook Enterprises Limited; *Int'l*, pg. 1585
HOTEL DE EDGE LIMITED—See Kai Yuan Holdings Limited; *Int'l*, pg. 4051
HOTEL DEL CORONADO—See KSL Capital Partners, LLC; *U.S. Private*, pg. 2355
HOTEL DEVELOPERS (LANKA) PLC; *Int'l*, pg. 3487
HOTEL DU PONT COMPANY—See The Buccini/Pollin Group, Inc.; *U.S. Private*, pg. 4002
HOTELEIRA BRASIL LTDA.—See Minor International PCL; *Int'l*, pg. 4911
HOTEL EQUIPMENT & DESIGN GMBH—See H World Group Limited; *Int'l*, pg. 3191
HOTEL EQUITIES, INC.; *U.S. Private*, pg. 1989
HOTELERA ADMINISTRADORA DE MONTERREY, S.A. DE C.V.—See Grupo Posadas S.A.B. de C.V.; *Int'l*, pg. 3134
HOTELERA DE LA PARRA, S.A. DE C.V.—See Minor International PCL; *Int'l*, pg. 4911
HOTELERA INMOBILIARIA DE MONCLOVA, S.A. DE C.V.—See Grupo Posadas S.A.B. de C.V.; *Int'l*, pg. 3134
HOTELES BESTPRICE S.A.; *Int'l*, pg. 3489
HOTELES CANCUN K20, S. DE R.L. DE C.V.—See Marriott Vacations Worldwide Corporation; *U.S. Public*, pg. 1373
HOTELES CITY EXPRESS, S.A.B. DE C.V.; *Int'l*, pg. 3489
HOTELES ESTELAR DE COLOMBIA S.A.—See InterContinental Hotels Group PLC; *Int'l*, pg. 3737
HOTELES HESPERIA, S.A.—See Minor International PCL; *Int'l*, pg. 4911
HOTELES SOL MELIA, S.L.—See Melia Hotels International, S.A.; *Int'l*, pg. 4809
HOTEL FLORA A.S.; *Int'l*, pg. 3487
HOTEL FUERTEVENTURA PLAYA, S.L—See Barcelo Corporacion Empresarial S.A.; *Int'l*, pg. 859
HOTEL GOLUBACKI GRAD A.D.; *Int'l*, pg. 3487
HOTEL GRAND CENTRAL LIMITED; *Int'l*, pg. 3487
HOTEL GRAND CHANCELLOR (ADELAIDE) PTY. LIMITED—See Hotel Grand Central Limited; *Int'l*, pg. 3487
HOTEL GRAND CHANCELLOR (AUCKLAND CITY) LIMITED—See Hotel Grand Central Limited; *Int'l*, pg. 3487
HOTEL GRAND CHANCELLOR (BRISBANE) PTY. LIMITED—See Hotel Grand Central Limited; *Int'l*, pg. 3487
HOTEL GRAND CHANCELLOR (HOBART) PTY. LIMITED—See Hotel Grand Central Limited; *Int'l*, pg. 3487

HOTEL GRAND CHANCELLOR (LAUNCESTON) PTY. LIMITED—See Hotel Grand Central Limited; *Int'l*, pg. 3487
HOTEL GRAND CHANCELLOR (MELBOURNE) PTY. LIMITED—See Hotel Grand Central Limited; *Int'l*, pg. 3488
HOTEL GRAND CHANCELLOR (PALM COVE) PTY. LIMITED—See Hotel Grand Central Limited; *Int'l*, pg. 3488
HOTEL GRAND CHANCELLOR (TOWNSVILLE) PTY. LIMITED—See Hotel Grand Central Limited; *Int'l*, pg. 3488
HOTEL GRANVIA HIROSHIMA CO., LTD.—See West Japan Railway Company; *Int'l*, pg. 8386
HOTEL GRANVIA OKAYAMA CO., LTD.—See West Japan Railway Company; *Int'l*, pg. 8386
HOTEL GROUP INTERNATIONAL, INC.; *U.S. Private*, pg. 1989
HOTEL HDC CO., LTD.—See HDC Hyundai Development Company; *Int'l*, pg. 3300
HOTEL HOLIDAY GARDEN; *Int'l*, pg. 3488
HOTEL HUM D.O.O.—See Adris Grupa d.d.; *Int'l*, pg. 153
HOTEL HYUNDAI CO., LTD.—See Hahn & Company; *Int'l*, pg. 3208
HOTEL HYUNDAI ULSAN—See Hahn & Company; *Int'l*, pg. 3208
HOTELI BERNARDIN D.D.; *Int'l*, pg. 3489
HOTELI DUBROVACKA RIVIJERA D.D.—See Adris Grupa d.d.; *Int'l*, pg. 153
HOTELIGA INT. SP. Z O.O.—See Epsilon Net S.A.; *Int'l*, pg. 2466
HOTELI MAESTRAL D.D; *Int'l*, pg. 3489
HOTELI-METROPOL AD—See Fersped A.D.; *Int'l*, pg. 2646
HOTELIM SA; *Int'l*, pg. 3489
HOTEL INTERNATIONAL DE LYON S.A.; *Int'l*, pg. 3488
HOTELI PIRAN D.D.—See NFD Holding d.d.; *Int'l*, pg. 5252
HOTELI VODICE D.D.; *Int'l*, pg. 3489
HOTEL KAJIMA NO MORI CO., LTD.—See Kajima Corporation; *Int'l*, pg. 4054
HOTEL KEIHAN CO., LTD.—See Keihan Holdings Co., Ltd.; *Int'l*, pg. 4116
HOTEL KYOCERA CO., LTD—See KYOCERA Corporation; *Int'l*, pg. 4355
HOTEL LE GEORGESVILLE—See Pomerleau Inc.; *Int'l*, pg. 5917
HOTEL LOTTE CO., LTD.—See Lotte Co., Ltd.; *Int'l*, pg. 4559
HOTEL LOWEN SCHRUNS GMBH—See Liebherr-International AG; *Int'l*, pg. 4488
HOTEL MADELEINE PALACE, S.A.S.—See Melia Hotels International, S.A.; *Int'l*, pg. 4809
HOTEL MAJESTIC CANNES SA; *Int'l*, pg. 3488
HOTEL MAJESTIC LLC—See Kennedy-Wilson Holdings, Inc.; *U.S. Public*, pg. 1223
HOTEL MANAGEMENT INTERNATIONAL CO., LTD.; *Int'l*, pg. 3488
HOTEL MAX; *U.S. Private*, pg. 1989
HOTEL METROPOLE SAM; *Int'l*, pg. 3488
HOTEL METROPOLITAN NAGANO CO., LTD.—See East Japan Railway Company; *Int'l*, pg. 2270
HOTEL METROPOLITAN TOKYO—See East Japan Railway Company; *Int'l*, pg. 2270
HOTEL MONTELEONE INC.; *U.S. Private*, pg. 1989
HOTEL MOSKVA BELGRADE; *Int'l*, pg. 3488
HOTEL NARVIK A.D.; *Int'l*, pg. 3488
HOTEL NEWGROND CO., LTD.; *Int'l*, pg. 3488
HOTEL NEW HANKYU KOCHI CO., LTD.—See Hankyu Hanshin Holdings Inc.; *Int'l*, pg. 3255
HOTEL NEWMARKET PTY LTD—See Reading International, Inc.; *U.S. Public*, pg. 1768
HOTEL NEW OJI CO., LTD.—See Oji Holdings Corporation; *Int'l*, pg. 5536
HOTEL NIKKO CHITOSE—See Japan Airlines Co., Ltd.; *Int'l*, pg. 3882
HOTEL NIKKO OF SAN FRANCISCO, INC.—See Japan Airlines Co., Ltd.; *Int'l*, pg. 3882
HOTEL NIKKO OSAKA CO., LTD.—See Japan Airlines Co., Ltd.; *Int'l*, pg. 3882
HOTEL NIKKO PRINCESS KYOTO CO., LTD.—See KYOCERA Corporation; *Int'l*, pg. 4355
THE HOTEL OF LAN KWAI FONG LIMITED—See Far East Consortium International Limited; *Int'l*, pg. 2615
HOTEL OKURA CO., LTD.; *Int'l*, pg. 3488
HOTEL OKURA ENTERPRISE CO., LTD.—See Hotel Okura, Co., Ltd.; *Int'l*, pg. 3488
HOTEL OKURA FUKUOKA—See Hotel Okura Co., Ltd.; *Int'l*, pg. 3488
HOTEL OKURA KOBE—See Hotel Okura Co., Ltd.; *Int'l*, pg. 3488
HOTEL OKURA NIIGATA—See Hotel Okura Co., Ltd.; *Int'l*, pg. 3488
HOTEL OKURA SAPPORO—See Hotel Okura Co., Ltd.; *Int'l*, pg. 3488
HOTEL OKURA TOKYO—See Hotel Okura Co., Ltd.; *Int'l*, pg. 3488
HOTELOPIA SL—See Canada Pension Plan Investment Board; *Int'l*, pg. 1279

H.O. TRERICE COMPANY

HOTELOPIA SL—See Cinven Limited; *Int'l*, pg. 1612
HOTEL PALAS A.D. BANJA LUKA; *Int'l*, pg. 3488
HOTELPLAN SUISSE, MTCG AG—See The Federation of Migros Cooperatives; *Int'l*, pg. 7642
HOTEL POLANA LTDA—See Aga Khan Development Network; *Int'l*, pg. 199
HOTEL PRAG A.D.; *Int'l*, pg. 3488
HOTEL PRECEDE KORIYAMA CO. LTD.—See Taisei Corporation; *Int'l*, pg. 7415
HOTEL PRIJEDOR A.D.; *Int'l*, pg. 3488
HOTEL PRINCESS KYOTO CO., LTD.—See KYOCERA Corporation; *Int'l*, pg. 4356
HOTEL PROPERTIES LIMITED; *Int'l*, pg. 3488
HOTEL PROPERTY INVESTMENTS LIMITED; *Int'l*, pg. 3488
HOTEL REGINA PARIS S.A.; *Int'l*, pg. 3489
HOTEL & RESTAURANT SUPPLY; *U.S. Private*, pg. 1989
HOTEL ROUGE—See Pebblebrook Hotel Trust; *U.S. Public*, pg. 1660
HOTEL ROYAL LIMITED; *Int'l*, pg. 3489
HOTEL ROYAL - NIKKO TAIPEI—See Japan Airlines Co., Ltd.; *Int'l*, pg. 3882
HOTEL ROYAL @ QUEENS (SINGAPORE) PTE LTD—See Hotel Royal Limited; *Int'l*, pg. 3489
HOTEL SAN MARCO SRL—See Radici Partecipazioni S.p.A.; *Int'l*, pg. 6175
HOTELS COLOMBO (1963) LIMITED—See Bank of Ceylon; *Int'l*, pg. 841
HOTELS.COM GP, LLC—See Expedia Group, Inc.; *U.S. Public*, pg. 809
HOTELS.COM, L.P.—See Expedia Group, Inc.; *U.S. Public*, pg. 809
HOTEL SELESA (JB) SDN BHD—See Johor Corporation; *Int'l*, pg. 3994
HOTEL SFERA SDN. BHD.—See YNH Property Bhd; *Int'l*, pg. 8590
HOTELS FOR HOPE, INC.—See Liberty Media Corporation; *U.S. Public*, pg. 1311
HOTEL SHILLA CO., LTD.; *Int'l*, pg. 3489
HOTEL SIGIRIYA PLC; *Int'l*, pg. 3489
HOTELS ILIDZA D.D. ILIDZA; *Int'l*, pg. 3489
HOTELS MANAGEMENT COMPANY INTERNATIONAL SAOG; *Int'l*, pg. 3489
HOTEL SPLENDIDO S.R.L.—See LVMH Moet Hennessy Louis Vuitton SE; *Int'l*, pg. 4591
HOTEL SYSTEM 21 CO., LTD.—See MBK Co., Ltd.; *Int'l*, pg. 4753
HOTEL TROPICO, S.A.—See Teixeira Duarte SA; *Int'l*, pg. 7525
HOTEL UNION SQUARE—See Engage Hospitality LLC; *U.S. Private*, pg. 1397
HOTEL U PARKU, S.R.O.—See CPI Property Group, S.A.; *Int'l*, pg. 1825
HOTEL VALBELLA INN AG—See Kirkbi A/S; *Int'l*, pg. 4189
HOTEL VANITIES INTERNATIONAL, LLC; *U.S. Private*, pg. 1989
HOTEL VENTURE LP—See Circa Capital Corporation; *U.S. Private*, pg. 899
HOTEL VICTOR - SOUTH BEACH—See KRC Capital B.V.; *Int'l*, pg. 4300
HOTEL WASHINGTON, INC.—See Dubai World Corporation; *Int'l*, pg. 2222
HOTEL YOUNTVILLE—See Braemar Hotels & Resorts, Inc.; *U.S. Public*, pg. 379
HOT FROG PRINT MEDIA LLC; *U.S. Private*, pg. 1988
THE HOTH CORP.; *U.S. Private*, pg. 4054
HOT HOUSE CO. LTD.—See Relo Group, Inc.; *Int'l*, pg. 6265
HOTH THERAPEUTICS, INC.; *U.S. Public*, pg. 1055
HOTLAND CO., LTD.; *Int'l*, pg. 3489
HOT-LINE FREIGHT SYSTEM, INC.—See TFI International, Inc.; *Int'l*, pg. 7586
HOT-LINE INTERNATIONAL TRANSPORT (CHINA) LIMITED—See Toyota Tsusho Corporation; *Int'l*, pg. 7877
HOT-LINE INTERNATIONAL TRANSPORT (H.K.) LIMITED—See Toyota Tsusho Corporation; *Int'l*, pg. 7877
HOT-LINE INTERNATIONAL TRANSPORT LTD.—See Toyota Tsusho Corporation; *Int'l*, pg. 7877
HOT-LINE LOGISTICS CENTER—See Toyota Tsusho Corporation; *Int'l*, pg. 7877
HOTLINE PRODUCTS—See Brown & Bigelow, Inc.; *U.S. Private*, pg. 666
HOTLINES EUROPE LTD.—See The American Bicycle Group LLC; *U.S. Private*, pg. 3985
HOTLINE TELECOMMUNICATIONS; *U.S. Private*, pg. 1989
HOTLINE TO HR INC.; *Int'l*, pg. 3489
HOT MAMA'S FOODS, INC.; *U.S. Private*, pg. 1988
HOTMAN CO., LTD.; *Int'l*, pg. 3489
HOTMIX ASPHALT EQUIPMENT CO.; *U.S. Private*, pg. 1989
HOTMIX PARTS; *U.S. Private*, pg. 1989
HOT OFF THE PRESS, INC.; *U.S. Private*, pg. 1988
HOTOKU CO., LTD.—See Nippon Paper Industries Co., Ltd.; *Int'l*, pg. 5327
HOTONDO BUILDING PTY. LTD.; *Int'l*, pg. 3489
H.O. TRERICE COMPANY; *U.S. Private*, pg. 1835

HOTRON PRECISION ELECTRONIC (FUQING) CO., LTD.—See Hotron Precision Electronic Industrial Co. Ltd.; *Int'l*, pg. 3489
HOTRON PRECISION ELECTRONIC INDUSTRIAL CO. LTD.; *Int'l*, pg. 3489
HOTRON PRECISION ELECTRONIC (SUZHOU) CO., LTD.—See Hotron Precision Electronic Industrial Co. Ltd.; *Int'l*, pg. 3489
HOTSCHEDULES; *U.S. Private*, pg. 1989
HOT SHOT DELIVERY INC.; *U.S. Private*, pg. 1988
HOT SHOT EXPRESS INC.; *U.S. Private*, pg. 1988
HOT SOX COMPANY, INC.; *U.S. Private*, pg. 1988
HOTSPOT INTERNATIONAL, S DE R.L. DE C.V.; *Int'l*, pg. 3489
HOT SPRING POWER COMPANY, LLC—See ENGIE SA; *Int'l*, pg. 2433
HOT SPRINGS CONVENTION & VISITORS BUREAU; *U.S. Private*, pg. 1988
HOT SPRINGS COUNTY MEMORIAL HOSPITAL; *U.S. Private*, pg. 1989
HOT SPRINGS ON THE GO!—See Wehco Media, Inc.; *U.S. Private*, pg. 4470
HOT SPRING SPA AUSTRALASIA PTY LTD—See Masco Corporation; *U.S. Public*, pg. 1392
HOT SPRING SPAS NEW ZEALAND—See Masco Corporation; *U.S. Public*, pg. 1392
HOTSPUR TECHNOLOGIES, INC.—See Teleflex Incorporated; *U.S. Public*, pg. 1995
HOT STUDIO, INC.; *U.S. Private*, pg. 1989
THE HOTSY CORPORATION—See Alfred Karcher GmbH & Co. KG; *Int'l*, pg. 316
HOT TELECOMMUNICATION SYSTEMS LTD.; *Int'l*, pg. 3487
HOTTINGER BALDWIN MEASUREMENT INC.—See Spectris Plc; *Int'l*, pg. 7131
HOTTINGER BALDWIN MEASUREMENT (SUZHOU) CO. LTD.—See Spectris Plc; *Int'l*, pg. 7131
HOTTINGER BALDWIN MESSTECHNIK AG—See Spectris Plc; *Int'l*, pg. 7131
HOTTINGER BALDWIN MESSTECHNIK GMBH—See Spectris Plc; *Int'l*, pg. 7130
HOTTINGER BALDWIN MESSTECHNIK GMBH—See Spectris Plc; *Int'l*, pg. 7131
HOTTINGER BALDWIN (SUZHOU) ELECTRONIC MEASUREMENT TECHNOLOGY LTD.—See Spectris Plc; *Int'l*, pg. 7130
HOTTINGER BRUEL & KJAER AUSTRIA GMBH—See Spectris Plc; *Int'l*, pg. 7131
HOTTINGER BRUEL & KJAER BENELUX B.V.—See Spectris Plc; *Int'l*, pg. 7131
HOTTINGER BRUEL & KJAER CO., LTD.—See Spectris Plc; *Int'l*, pg. 7131
HOTTINGER BRUEL & KJAER GMBH—See Spectris Plc; *Int'l*, pg. 7131
HOTTINGER BRUEL & KJAER IBERICA, S.L.U.—See Spectris Plc; *Int'l*, pg. 7131
HOTTINGER BRUEL & KJAER ITALY S.R.L.—See Spectris Plc; *Int'l*, pg. 7131
HOTTINGER BRUEL & KJAER NORWAY AS—See Spectris Plc; *Int'l*, pg. 7131
HOTTINGER BRUEL & KJAER POLAND SP. Z.O.O.—See Spectris Plc; *Int'l*, pg. 7131
HOTTINGER BRUEL & KJAER UK LIMITED—See Spectris Plc; *Int'l*, pg. 7131
HOTTO LINK INC.; *Int'l*, pg. 3489
HOTTOPIC.COM, INC.—See Sycamore Partners Management, LP; *U.S. Private*, pg. 3896
HOT TOPIC, INC.—See Sycamore Partners Management, LP; *U.S. Private*, pg. 3895
HOT TUNA AUSTRALIA PTY LTD.—See Concha plc; *Int'l*, pg. 1764
HOT (UK) LIMITED—See Helen of Troy Limited; *Int'l*, pg. 3328
HO TUNG CHEMICAL CORP.; *Int'l*, pg. 3434
HOTUNG INVESTMENT HOLDINGS LIMITED; *Int'l*, pg. 3490
HOTUSA HOTELS SA; *Int'l*, pg. 3490
HOTWAY TECHNOLOGY CORPORATION—See Ban Leong Technologies Limited; *Int'l*, pg. 814
HOTWIRE, INC.—See Expedia Group, Inc.; *U.S. Public*, pg. 809
HOTWIRE PUBLIC RELATION ITALY S.R.L.—See Enero Group Limited; *Int'l*, pg. 2424
HOTWIRE PUBLIC RELATIONS GMBH—See Enero Group Limited; *Int'l*, pg. 2424
HOTWIRE PUBLIC RELATIONS LIMITED—See Enero Group Limited; *Int'l*, pg. 2424
HOTWIRE PUBLIC RELATIONS SARL—See Enero Group Limited; *Int'l*, pg. 2424
HOTWIRE PUBLIC RELATIONS SL—See Enero Group Limited; *Int'l*, pg. 2424
HOUAY HO POWER COMPANY LIMITED—See PTT Public Company Limited; *Int'l*, pg. 6092
HOUCHENS INDUSTRIES, INC.; *U.S. Private*, pg. 1989
HOUCHENS MARKETS—See Houchens Industries, Inc.; *U.S. Private*, pg. 1990
HOUCHIN COMMUNITY BLOOD BANK; *U.S. Private*, pg. 1990
HOUCK INDUSTRIES, INC.; *U.S. Private*, pg. 1990

HOUDARD; *Int'l*, pg. 3490
HOUDEBINE S.A.—See Nestle S.A.; *Int'l*, pg. 5205
HOU ELECTRONICS INC.; *U.S. Private*, pg. 1989
HOUFF TRANSFER INC.; *U.S. Private*, pg. 1990
HOUGEN MANUFACTURING INC.; *U.S. Private*, pg. 1990
HOUGHTON ASIA PACIFIC CO., LTD.—See Quaker Chemical Corporation; *U.S. Public*, pg. 1746
HOUGHTON AUSTRALIA PTY. LTD.—See Quaker Chemical Corporation; *U.S. Public*, pg. 1746
HOUGHTON BRAZIL LTDA.—See Quaker Chemical Corporation; *U.S. Public*, pg. 1746
HOUGHTON CANADA INC.—See Quaker Chemical Corporation; *U.S. Public*, pg. 1746
HOUGHTON CHEMICAL CORPORATION - ALLSTON FACILITY—See Houghton Chemical Corporation; *U.S. Private*, pg. 1990
HOUGHTON CHEMICAL CORPORATION; *U.S. Private*, pg. 1990
HOUGHTON CHEMICAL—See Houghton Chemical Corporation; *U.S. Private*, pg. 1990
HOUGHTON CZ S.R.O.—See Quaker Chemical Corporation; *U.S. Public*, pg. 1746
HOUGHTON DENMARK A/S—See Quaker Chemical Corporation; *U.S. Public*, pg. 1746
HOUGHTON DEUTSCHLAND GMBH—See Quaker Chemical Corporation; *U.S. Public*, pg. 1746
HOUGHTON EUROPE BV—See Hinduja Group Ltd.; *Int'l*, pg. 3399
HOUGHTON IBERICA S.A.—See Quaker Chemical Corporation; *U.S. Public*, pg. 1746
HOUGHTON INTERNATIONAL INC.—See Quaker Chemical Corporation; *U.S. Public*, pg. 1745
HOUGHTON ITALIA S.P.A.—See Quaker Chemical Corporation; *U.S. Public*, pg. 1746
HOUGHTON JAPAN CO., LTD.—See Quaker Chemical Corporation; *U.S. Public*, pg. 1746
HOUGHTON KIMYA SAN A.S.—See Quaker Chemical Corporation; *U.S. Public*, pg. 1746
HOUGHTON KIMYA SANAYI AS—See Hinduja Group Ltd.; *Int'l*, pg. 3399
HOUGHTON MEXICO S.A. DE C.V.—See Quaker Chemical Corporation; *U.S. Public*, pg. 1746
HOUGHTON MEXICO S.A. DE C.V.—See Hinduja Group Ltd.; *Int'l*, pg. 3399
HOUGHTON MIFFLIN COMPANY INTERNATIONAL, INC.—See Veritas Capital Fund Management, LLC; *U.S. Private*, pg. 4363
HOUGHTON MIFFLIN HARCOURT COMPANY—See Veritas Capital Fund Management, LLC; *U.S. Private*, pg. 4362
HOUGHTON MIFFLIN HARCOURT INTERNATIONAL PUBLISHERS—See Veritas Capital Fund Management, LLC; *U.S. Private*, pg. 4363
HOUGHTON MIFFLIN HARCOURT LEARNING TECHNOLOGY—See Veritas Capital Fund Management, LLC; *U.S. Private*, pg. 4363
HOUGHTON MIFFLIN HARCOURT PUBLISHING CO. - AUSTIN—See Veritas Capital Fund Management, LLC; *U.S. Private*, pg. 4363
HOUGHTON MIFFLIN HARCOURT PUBLISHING CO. - LEWISVILLE—See Veritas Capital Fund Management, LLC; *U.S. Private*, pg. 4363
HOUGHTON MIFFLIN HARCOURT PUBLISHING COMPANY—See Veritas Capital Fund Management, LLC; *U.S. Private*, pg. 4363
HOUGHTON MIFFLIN HARCOURT PUBLISHING CO. - ORLANDO—See Veritas Capital Fund Management, LLC; *U.S. Private*, pg. 4363
HOUGHTON MIFFLIN HARCOURT TRADE & REFERENCE PUBLISHERS—See Veritas Capital Fund Management, LLC; *U.S. Private*, pg. 4363
HOUGHTON MIFFLIN HARCOURT TRADE & REFERENCE PUBLISHERS—See Veritas Capital Fund Management, LLC; *U.S. Private*, pg. 4363
HOUGHTON OIL (MALAYSIA) SDN, BHD.—See Quaker Chemical Corporation; *U.S. Public*, pg. 1746
HOUGHTON PLC—See Quaker Chemical Corporation; *U.S. Public*, pg. 1746
HOUGHTON POLSKA SP. Z O.O.—See Quaker Chemical Corporation; *U.S. Public*, pg. 1746
HOUGHTON ROMANIA S.R.L.—See Quaker Chemical Corporation; *U.S. Public*, pg. 1746
HOUGHTON (SHANGHAI) SPECIALTY INDUSTRIAL FLUIDS CO. LTD.—See Quaker Chemical Corporation; *U.S. Public*, pg. 1745
HOUGHTON (SHANGHAI) SPECIALTY INDUSTRIAL FLUIDS CO. LTD.—See Hinduja Group Ltd.; *Int'l*, pg. 3399
HOUGHTON SINGAPORE—See Quaker Chemical Corporation; *U.S. Public*, pg. 1746
HOUGHTON SVERIGE AB—See Quaker Chemical Corporation; *U.S. Public*, pg. 1746
HOUGHTON TAIWAN CO. LTD.—See Quaker Chemical Corporation; *U.S. Public*, pg. 1746
HOUGHTON UKRAINE LTD.—See Quaker Chemical Corporation; *U.S. Public*, pg. 1746
HOUGHTON WINES—See The Carlyle Group Inc.; *U.S. Public*, pg. 2044
HOUG SPECIAL SERVICES, INC.; *U.S. Private*, pg. 1990

HOUKO CO., LTD.—See JTEKT Corporation; *Int'l*, pg. 4017
HOULDER INSURANCE SERVICES LTD.; *Int'l*, pg. 3490
HOULE ELECTRIC LIMITED; *Int'l*, pg. 3490
HOULE RESTAURATION; *Int'l*, pg. 3490
HOULIHAN LAWRENCE INC.—See Berkshire Hathaway Inc.; *U.S. Public*, pg. 306
HOULIHAN LOKEY CAPITAL, INC.—See Houlihan Lokey, Inc.; *U.S. Public*, pg. 1055
HOULIHAN LOKEY (CHINA) LIMITED—See Houlihan Lokey, Inc.; *U.S. Public*, pg. 1055
HOULIHAN LOKEY (CORPORATE FINANCE) LIMITED—See Houlihan Lokey, Inc.; *U.S. Public*, pg. 1055
HOULIHAN LOKEY EMEA, LLP—See Houlihan Lokey, Inc.; *U.S. Public*, pg. 1055
HOULIHAN LOKEY (ESPANA) S.A.—See Houlihan Lokey, Inc.; *U.S. Public*, pg. 1055
HOULIHAN LOKEY (EUROPE) LIMITED—See Houlihan Lokey, Inc.; *U.S. Public*, pg. 1055
HOULIHAN LOKEY FINANCIAL ADVISORS, INC.—See Houlihan Lokey, Inc.; *U.S. Public*, pg. 1055
HOULIHAN LOKEY GMBH—See Houlihan Lokey, Inc.; *U.S. Public*, pg. 1055
HOULIHAN LOKEY, INC.; *U.S. Public*, pg. 1055
HOULIHAN LOKEY (NETHERLANDS) B.V.—See Houlihan Lokey, Inc.; *U.S. Public*, pg. 1055
HOULIHAN'S RESTAURANTS, INC.—See Fertitta Entertainment, Inc.; *U.S. Private*, pg. 1499
HOULTON REGIONAL HOSPITAL; *U.S. Private*, pg. 1990
HOUMA ARMATURE WORKS & SUPPLY, INC.—See Arcline Investment Management LP; *U.S. Private*, pg. 313
THE HOUMA COURIER NEWSPAPER CORPORATION—See Gannett Co., Inc.; *U.S. Public*, pg. 905
HOUPU CLEAN ENERGY GROUP CO., LTD; *Int'l*, pg. 3490
HOURGLASS ACQUISITION I, LLC—See Apollo Global Management, Inc.; *U.S. Public*, pg. 165
HOURGLASS ANGEL; *U.S. Private*, pg. 1991
THE HOUR GLASS (AUSTRALIA) PTY LTD—See The Hour Glass Limited; *Int'l*, pg. 7653
THE HOUR GLASS HOLDING (THAILAND) CO LTD—See The Hour Glass Limited; *Int'l*, pg. 7653
THE HOUR GLASS JAPAN LTD.—See The Hour Glass Limited; *Int'l*, pg. 7653
THE HOUR GLASS LIMITED; *Int'l*, pg. 7653
THE HOUR GLASS SDN BHD—See The Hour Glass Limited; *Int'l*, pg. 7653
THE HOUR GLASS (THAILAND) CO LTD—See The Hour Glass Limited; *Int'l*, pg. 7653
HOURIGAN CONSTRUCTION CORP.; *U.S. Private*, pg. 1991
HOUR LOOP, INC.; *U.S. Public*, pg. 1056
HOUR MEDIA GROUP, LLC; *U.S. Private*, pg. 1990
HOUR MEDIA, LLC—See Hour Media Group, LLC; *U.S. Private*, pg. 1991
HOUR PASSION SAS—See The Swatch Group Ltd.; *Int'l*, pg. 7691
HOUR PUBLISHING COMPANY; *U.S. Private*, pg. 1991
HOUSATONIC PARTNERS MANAGEMENT CO., INC.; *U.S. Private*, pg. 1991
HOUSATONIC PUBLICATIONS INC.—See Warburg Pincus LLC; *U.S. Private*, pg. 4438
HOUSE 2 HOME SHOWCASE—See MacAndrews & Forbes Incorporated; *U.S. Private*, pg. 2532
HOUSE AI-FACTORY CORPORATION—See House Foods Group Inc.; *Int'l*, pg. 3490
HOUSE-AUTRY MILLS INC.; *U.S. Private*, pg. 1992
HOUSE BEAUTIFUL—See The Hearst Corporation; *U.S. Private*, pg. 4046
HOUSE BUILDING SPA—See Uni Land S.p.A.; *Int'l*, pg. 8028
HOUSE BUSINESS PARTNERS CORPORATION—See House Foods Group Inc.; *Int'l*, pg. 3490
HOUSE CALLS OF NEW MEXICO, LLC—See Addus HomeCare Corporation; *U.S. Public*, pg. 40
HOUSECOM CORPORATION—See Daito Trust Construction Co., Ltd.; *Int'l*, pg. 1944
HOUSECOMP INGATLANSTUDIO—See TCS TurControlSysteme AG; *Int'l*, pg. 7485
HOUSECOM TECHNOLOGIES CO., LTD.—See Daito Trust Construction Co., Ltd.; *Int'l*, pg. 1944
HOUSE DEPOT PARTNERS CO., LTD.—See Mitsui & Co., Ltd.; *Int'l*, pg. 4973
HOUSE FOOD ANALYTICAL LABORATORY INC.—See House Foods Group Inc.; *Int'l*, pg. 3490
HOUSE FOODS AMERICA CORPORATION—See House Foods Group Inc.; *Int'l*, pg. 3490
HOUSE FOODS CHINA INC.—See House Foods Group Inc.; *Int'l*, pg. 3490
HOUSE FOODS CORPORATION—See House Foods Group Inc.; *Int'l*, pg. 3490
HOUSE FOODS GROUP INC.; *Int'l*, pg. 3490
HOUSE FOODS VIETNAM CO., LTD.—See House Foods Group Inc.; *Int'l*, pg. 3490
HOUSEFREEDOM CO., LTD.; *Int'l*, pg. 3491

COMPANY NAME INDEX

HOUSE-HASSON HARDWARE COMPANY-PERSINGER—See House-Hasson Hardware Company; *U.S. Private*, pg. 1992
HOUSE-HASSON HARDWARE COMPANY; *U.S. Private*, pg. 1992
HOUSEHOLD CREDIT SERVICES INC.—See HSBC Holdings plc; *Int'l*, pg. 3505
HOUSEHOLDER GROUP INC.; *U.S. Private*, pg. 1992
HOUSE LEAVE CO., LTD.—See Daito Trust Construction Co., Ltd.; *Int'l*, pg. 1943
HOUSE LOGISTICS SERVICE CORPORATION—See House Foods Group Inc.; *Int'l*, pg. 3490
HOUSEMARKET SA—See FOURLIS HOLDINGS S.A.; *Int'l*, pg. 2755
THE HOUSE OF AGRICULTURE SPIROY S.A. - SEEDLING PRODUCTION UNIT—See THE HOUSE OF AGRICULTURE SPIROY S.A.; *Int'l*, pg. 7653
THE HOUSE OF AGRICULTURE SPIROY S.A.; *Int'l*, pg. 7653
HOUSE OF ANTIQUE HARDWARE; *U.S. Private*, pg. 1991
HOUSE OF BANFI—See Banfi Product Corp.; *U.S. Private*, pg. 465
HOUSE OF BATH—See N Brown Group plc; *Int'l*, pg. 5115
HOUSE OF BLUES CONCERTS, INC.—See Live Nation Entertainment, Inc.; *U.S. Public*, pg. 1329
HOUSE OF BLUES DALLAS RESTAURANT CORP.—See Live Nation Entertainment, Inc.; *U.S. Public*, pg. 1329
HOUSE OF BLUES HOUSTON RESTAURANT CORP.—See Live Nation Entertainment, Inc.; *U.S. Public*, pg. 1329
HOUSE OF BLUES LAS VEGAS RESTAURANT CORP.—See Live Nation Entertainment, Inc.; *U.S. Public*, pg. 1329
HOUSE OF BLUES MYRTLE BEACH RESTAURANT CORP.—See Live Nation Entertainment, Inc.; *U.S. Public*, pg. 1329
HOUSE OF BLUES NEW ORLEANS RESTAURANT CORP.—See Live Nation Entertainment, Inc.; *U.S. Public*, pg. 1329
HOUSE OF BLUES ORLANDO RESTAURANT CORP.—See Live Nation Entertainment, Inc.; *U.S. Public*, pg. 1329
HOUSE OF BODS FITNESS, INC.; *U.S. Private*, pg. 1991
HOUSE OF BRANDS GMBH—See Otto GmbH & Co. KG; *Int'l*, pg. 5663
HOUSE OF BRICK TECHNOLOGIES LLC—See OpsCompass, LLC; *U.S. Private*, pg. 3034
HOUSE OF BRIDES INC.; *U.S. Private*, pg. 1991
THE HOUSE OF CAMPBELL, INC.—See Welltower Inc.; *U.S. Public*, pg. 2349
HOUSE OF COOL INTERNATIONAL INC.—See WildBrain Ltd.; *Int'l*, pg. 8409
HOUSE OF FLAVORS, INC.; *U.S. Private*, pg. 1991
HOUSE OF FRASER (STORES) LIMITED—See Frasers Group plc; *Int'l*, pg. 2765
HOUSE OF FULLER, S. DE RL DE CV—See Tupperware Brands Corporation; *U.S. Public*, pg. 2204
HOUSE OF HABIB; *Int'l*, pg. 3491
HOUSE OF HARLEY-DAVIDSON INC.; *U.S. Private*, pg. 1991
HOUSE OF IMPORTS INC.; *U.S. Private*, pg. 1991
HOUSE OF INSURTECH SWITZERLAND AG—See Assicurazioni Generali S.p.A.; *Int'l*, pg. 644
HOUSE OF INVESTMENTS INC.—See Yuchengco Group of Companies; *Int'l*, pg. 8609
HOUSE OF JANE, INC.—See Visitalk Capital Corporation; *U.S. Private*, pg. 4392
THE HOUSE OF KAIZEN LIMITED—See House of Kaizen LLC; *U.S. Private*, pg. 1991
HOUSE OF KAIZEN LLC; *U.S. Private*, pg. 1991
THE HOUSE OF KWONG SANG HONG LIMITED—See Chinese Estates Holdings Limited; *Int'l*, pg. 1569
HOUSE OF LEARNING PTY LTD—See Simonds Group Limited; *Int'l*, pg. 6933
HOUSE OF MONATIC (PTY) LTD.—See Brimstone Investment Corporation Ltd.; *Int'l*, pg. 1164
HOUSE OF OLIVER TWIST A/S—See Philip Morris International Inc.; *U.S. Public*, pg. 1687
HOUSE OF PACKAGING INC.; *U.S. Private*, pg. 1991
HOUSE OF PERFECTION, INC.; *U.S. Private*, pg. 1991
HOUSE OF RAEFORD FARMS, INC.; *U.S. Private*, pg. 1991
HOUSE OF ROSE CO., LTD.; *Int'l*, pg. 3491
HOUSE OF SPICES INDIA INC.; *U.S. Private*, pg. 1991
HOUSE OF THREADS INC.—See Wurth Verwaltungsgesellschaft mbH; *Int'l*, pg. 8511
HOUSE OF TOOLS & ENGINEERING; *U.S. Private*, pg. 1992
HOUSE OF WESLEY, INC.; *U.S. Private*, pg. 1992
HOUSE OF WYOMING VALLEY INC.; *U.S. Private*, pg. 1992
HOUSE OSOTSPA FOODS CO., LTD.—See House Foods Group Inc.; *Int'l*, pg. 3490
HOUSE PARTY, INC.; *U.S. Private*, pg. 1992
HOUSE PAYMENT CO., LTD.—See Daito Trust Construction Co., Ltd.; *Int'l*, pg. 1943
HOUSEPLUS CORPORATION, INC.—See Tokyo Electric Power Company Holdings, Incorporated; *Int'l*, pg. 7790

HOUSERATE LIMITED—See Heidelberg Materials AG; *Int'l*, pg. 3316
HOUSE RESEARCH INSTITUTE; *U.S. Private*, pg. 1992
HOUSER SHOES INCORPORATED; *U.S. Private*, pg. 1992
HOUSE SAISON ENTERPRISE CO., LTD.—See Meiho Enterprise Co., Ltd.; *Int'l*, pg. 4799
HOUSETEC INC.—See Yamada Holdings Co., Ltd.; *Int'l*, pg. 8548
HOUSE VIET NAM JOINT STOCK COMPANY; *Int'l*, pg. 3491
HOUSE WELLNESS FOODS CORPORATION—See House Foods Group Inc.; *Int'l*, pg. 3490
HOUSEWORKS CO PTY LTD—See Wesfarmers Limited; *Int'l*, pg. 8381
HOUSEWORKS, LLC; *U.S. Private*, pg. 1992
HOUSING AND URBAN DEVELOPMENT CORPORATION LIMITED; *Int'l*, pg. 3491
HOUSING ASSISTANCE COUNCIL; *U.S. Private*, pg. 1992
HOUSING ASSISTANCE OF ORANGE CITY, LTD.—See Apartment Investment and Management Company; *U.S. Public*, pg. 144
HOUSING AUTHORITY NEW ORLEANS (HANO); *U.S. Private*, pg. 1992
HOUSING AUTHORITY OF THE CITY OF CHARLOTTE; *U.S. Private*, pg. 1992
HOUSING AUTHORITY RISK RETENTION GROUP INC.; *U.S. Private*, pg. 1992
THE HOUSING BANK FOR TRADE & FINANCE; *Int'l*, pg. 7653
HOUSING CAPITAL COMPANY—See U.S. Bancorp; *U.S. Public*, pg. 2212
HOUSING & DEVELOPMENT BANK SAE; *Int'l*, pg. 3491
HOUSING DEVELOPMENT CORPORATION LIMITED—See Maldives Transport & Contracting Company Plc; *Int'l*, pg. 4662
HOUSING DEVELOPMENT FINANCE CORPORATION BANK OF SRI LANKA; *Int'l*, pg. 3491
HOUSING DEVELOPMENT FINANCE CORPORATION LIMITED; *Int'l*, pg. 3491
HOUSING DEVELOPMENT & INFRASTRUCTURE LIMITED; *Int'l*, pg. 3491
THE HOUSING FINANCE CORPORATION LIMITED; *Int'l*, pg. 7653
HOUSING HELPERS OF COLORADO, LLC; *U.S. Private*, pg. 1992
HOUSING MART INC.; *U.S. Private*, pg. 1992
HOUSING NETWORK OF HAMILTON COUNTY INC.; *U.S. Private*, pg. 1992
HOUSING NEW YORK CORPORATION—See New York City Housing Development Corporation; *U.S. Private*, pg. 2909
THE HOUSING PARTNERSHIP NETWORK; *U.S. Private*, pg. 4054
HOUSING SUPPORT CORPORATION—See Asahi Broadcasting Group Holdings Corporation; *Int'l*, pg. 592
HOUSING TECHNOLOGY CORP.—See Europtronic Group Ltd.; *Int'l*, pg. 2557
HOUSING TRUST SILICON VALLEY; *U.S. Private*, pg. 1992
HOUSKA INSURANCE SERVICES INC.—See New Mountain Capital, LLC; *U.S. Private*, pg. 2901
HOUSLEY COMMUNICATIONS LIMITED; *U.S. Private*, pg. 1992
HOUSTON 2-WAY RADIO, INC.—See Littlejohn & Co., LLC; *U.S. Private*, pg. 2472
HOUSTON AMBULATORY SURGICAL ASSOCIATES, L.P.—See Tenet Healthcare Corporation; *U.S. Public*, pg. 2010
HOUSTON AMERICAN ENERGY CORPORATION; *U.S. Public*, pg. 1056
HOUSTON ANUSA, LLC—See AutoNation, Inc.; *U.S. Public*, pg. 235
HOUSTON AREA COMMUNITY SERVICES; *U.S. Private*, pg. 1992
HOUSTON ARMATURE WORKS INC.; *U.S. Private*, pg. 1993
HOUSTON ASSET MANAGEMENT, INC.—See Lightyear Capital LLC; *U.S. Private*, pg. 2454
HOUSTON ASSET MANAGEMENT, INC.—See Ontario Teachers' Pension Plan; *Int'l*, pg. 5586
HOUSTON ASTROS, LLC—See Houston Baseball Partners LLC; *U.S. Private*, pg. 1993
HOUSTON AUTO AUCTION, INC.—See E Automotive Inc.; *Int'l*, pg. 2245
HOUSTON AUTO M. IMPORTS GREENWAY, LTD.—See AutoNation, Inc.; *U.S. Public*, pg. 235
HOUSTON AUTO M. IMPORTS GREENWAY, LTD.—See AutoNation, Inc.; *U.S. Public*, pg. 235
HOUSTON AUTO M. IMPORTS NORTH, LTD.—See AutoNation, Inc.; *U.S. Public*, pg. 235
HOUSTON BALLET FOUNDATION INC.; *U.S. Private*, pg. 1993
HOUSTON BASEBALL PARTNERS LLC; *U.S. Private*, pg. 1993
HOUSTON BUSINESS INSURANCE AGENCY, INC.—See GTCR LLC; *U.S. Private*, pg. 1803

HOUSTON BUSINESS JOURNAL, INC.—See Advance Publications, Inc.; *U.S. Private*, pg. 84
HOUSTON CAPITAL MORTGAGE—See Paragon Global Resources, Inc.; *U.S. Private*, pg. 3091
HOUSTON CASUALTY COMPANY—See Tokio Marine Holdings, Inc.; *Int'l*, pg. 7784
THE HOUSTON CHEESECAKE FACTORY CORPORATION—See Cheesecake Factory Incorporated; *U.S. Public*, pg. 483
HOUSTON CHRONICLE—See The Hearst Corporation; *U.S. Private*, pg. 4047
HOUSTON COMMUNITY NEWSPAPERS—See The Hearst Corporation; *U.S. Private*, pg. 4047
HOUSTON CONTINENTOIL INC.—See MBI & Partners U.K. Limited; *Int'l*, pg. 4752
HOUSTON COPART SALVAGE AUTO AUCTIONS LP—See Copart, Inc.; *U.S. Public*, pg. 575
HOUSTON COUNTY PROPANE—See UGI Corporation; *U.S. Public*, pg. 2221
HOUSTON CRATING, INC.—See Olympus Partners; *U.S. Private*, pg. 3013
HOUSTON DISTRIBUTING COMPANY; *U.S. Private*, pg. 1993
HOUSTON FIRST CORPORATION; *U.S. Private*, pg. 1993
HOUSTON FREIGHTLINER INC.—See Mercedes-Benz Group AG; *Int'l*, pg. 4823
HOUSTON FUEL OIL TERMINAL COMPANY LLC—See Energy Transfer LP; *U.S. Public*, pg. 764
HOUSTON GOLF ASSOCIATION; *U.S. Private*, pg. 1993
HOUSTON GRAND OPERA ASSOCIATION; *U.S. Private*, pg. 1993
HOUSTON HARVEST GIFT PRODUCTS LLC—See Marvin Traub Associates, Inc.; *U.S. Private*, pg. 2598
HOUSTON HEART, PLLC—See HCA Healthcare, Inc.; *U.S. Public*, pg. 999
HOUSTON HOTEL ASSOCIATES L.P., L.L.P.—See Sotherly Hotels Inc.; *U.S. Public*, pg. 1910
THE HOUSTONIAN GOLF & COUNTRY CLUB—See The Redstonian Companies, L.P.; *U.S. Private*, pg. 4103
HOUSTON KIDNEY CENTER/TOTAL RENAL CARE INTEGRATED SERVICE NETWORK LIMITED PARTNERSHIP—See DaVita Inc.; *U.S. Public*, pg. 639
HOUSTON LIVESTOCK SHOW AND RODEO; *U.S. Private*, pg. 1993
HOUSTON METRO ORTHO AND SPINE SURGERY CENTER, LLC—See Nobilis Health Corp.; *U.S. Private*, pg. 2932
HOUSTON MOTOR & CONTROL, INC.; *U.S. Private*, pg. 1993
HOUSTON NATURAL RESOURCES CORP.; *U.S. Public*, pg. 1056
HOUSTON NORTHWEST MEDICAL CENTER, INC.—See HCA Healthcare, Inc.; *U.S. Public*, pg. 999
HOUSTON NORTHWEST OPERATING COMPANY, L.L.C.—See HCA Healthcare, Inc.; *U.S. Public*, pg. 999
HOUSTON OCTG GROUP, INC—See WSP Holdings Limited; *Int'l*, pg. 8498
HOUSTON OFFSHORE ENGINEERING, LLC—See AtkinsRealis Group Inc.; *Int'l*, pg. 673
THE HOUSTON PALM—See Palm Restaurant Group; *U.S. Private*, pg. 3080
HOUSTON PEDIATRIC SPECIALTY GROUP, PLLC—See HCA Healthcare, Inc.; *U.S. Public*, pg. 999
HOUSTON PILOTS; *U.S. Private*, pg. 1993
HOUSTON PIPE LINE COMPANY, L.P.—See Energy Transfer LP; *U.S. Public*, pg. 763
HOUSTON PIZZA VENTURE LP; *U.S. Private*, pg. 1993
HOUSTON PLANTS AND GARDEN WORLD; *U.S. Private*, pg. 1993
HOUSTON POST TENSION, INC.; *U.S. Private*, pg. 1994
HOUSTON REFINING LP—See LyondellBasell Industries N.V.; *Int'l*, pg. 4608
HOUSTON REGIONAL HIV/AIDS RESOURCE GROUP, INC.; *U.S. Private*, pg. 1994
HOUSTON SPECIALTY HOSPITAL, INC.—See Tenet Healthcare Corporation; *U.S. Public*, pg. 2008
HOUSTON'S RESTAURANTS INC.; *U.S. Private*, pg. 1994
HOUSTON SURPLUS LINES, INC.—See XPT Group LLC; *U.S. Private*, pg. 4582
HOUSTON TEXANS, L.P.; *U.S. Private*, pg. 1994
HOUSTON UROLOGIC SURGICENTER, LLC—See HCA Healthcare, Inc.; *U.S. Public*, pg. 999
HOUSTON VENTURES; *U.S. Private*, pg. 1994
HOUSTON WASTE SOLUTIONS, LLC—See Fomento de Construcciones y Contratas, S.A.; *Int'l*, pg. 2723
HOUSTON WELL SCREEN COMPANY—See Weatherford International plc; *U.S. Public*, pg. 2339
HOUSTON WIRE & CABLE COMPANY—See Dot Family Holdings LLC; *U.S. Private*, pg. 1264
HOUTSCHILD INTERNATIONALE BOEKHANDEL BV—See Aurelius Equity Opportunities SE & Co. KGaA; *Int'l*, pg. 708
HOUTTUIN B.V.—See KKR & Co. Inc.; *U.S. Public*, pg. 1242
HOVDE GROUP, LLC; *U.S. Private*, pg. 1994
HOVDE PRIVATE EQUITY ADVISORS LLC; *U.S. Private*, pg. 1994
HOVDING SVERIGE AB; *Int'l*, pg. 3492

HOVDING SVERIGE AB

HOVE AMERICAS INC.—See Hove A/S; *Int'l*, pg. 3492
HOVE A/S; *Int'l*, pg. 3492
HOVE BRASIL EQUIPAMENTOS E SERVICOS DE LUBRIFICACAO LTDA.—See Hove A/S; *Int'l*, pg. 3492
HOVE BUICK-NISSAN; *U.S. Private*, pg. 1994
HOVELMANN & CO. EISENGROSSHANDLUNG GMBH—See ThyssenKrupp AG; *Int'l*, pg. 7724
HOVELMANN & LUEG GMBH—See Salzgitter AG; *Int'l*, pg. 6496
HOVE LUBRICANTS INDIA PRIVATE LIMITED—See Hove A/S; *Int'l*, pg. 3492
HOVE MEDICAL SYSTEMS AS—See PatientSky Group AS; *Int'l*, pg. 5756
HOV ENVIRONMENT SOLUTIONS PRIVATE LIMITED—See HOV Services Limited; *Int'l*, pg. 3492
HOVER-DAVIS, INC.—See Francisco Partners Management, LP; *U.S. Private*, pg. 1590
HOVERINK BIOTECHNOLOGIES, INC.; *U.S. Private*, pg. 1994
HOVEROUND CORP.—See Jordan Industries, Inc.; *U.S. Private*, pg. 2235
HOVG, LLC—See Exela Technologies, Inc.; *U.S. Public*, pg. 806
HOVID BERHAD; *Int'l*, pg. 3492
HOVID INC.—See Hovid Berhad; *Int'l*, pg. 3492
HOVID LIMITED—See Hovid Berhad; *Int'l*, pg. 3492
HOVID MARKETING SDN. BHD.—See Hovid Berhad; *Int'l*, pg. 3492
HOVIONE FARMA CIENCIA S.A.; *Int'l*, pg. 3492
HOVIONE LIMITED—See Hovione Farma Ciencia S.A.; *Int'l*, pg. 3492
HOVIONE LIMITED—See Hovione Farma Ciencia S.A.; *Int'l*, pg. 3492
HOVIONE LLC—See Hovione Farma Ciencia S.A.; *Int'l*, pg. 3492
HOVIONE PHARMASCIENCE LTD.—See Hovione Farma Ciencia S.A.; *Int'l*, pg. 3492
HOVIONE SA—See Hovione Farma Ciencia S.A.; *Int'l*, pg. 3492
HOVIS & ASSOCIATES—See Integrity Marketing Group LLC; *U.S. Private*, pg. 2103
HOVIS LTD.—See The Gores Group, LLC; *U.S. Private*, pg. 4034
HOVIS PRECISION PRODUCTS INC.—See DRT Mfg. Company; *U.S. Private*, pg. 1279
HOVNANIAN ENTERPRISES, INC.; *U.S. Public*, pg. 1056
HOV SERVICES LIMITED; *Int'l*, pg. 3492
HOVSITE FIRENZE LLC—See Hovnanian Enterprises, Inc.; *U.S. Public*, pg. 1056
HOWA BANK LTD.; *Int'l*, pg. 3492
HOWA CORPORATION; *Int'l*, pg. 3492
HO WAH GENTING BERHAD; *Int'l*, pg. 3434
HO WAH GENTING TRADING SDN. BHD.—See Ho Wah Genting Berhad; *Int'l*, pg. 3435
HOWA MACHINERY, LTD.; *Int'l*, pg. 3492
HOWA MACHINERY SINGAPORE PTE. LTD.—See Sojitz Corporation; *Int'l*, pg. 7061
HOWA MATAI PACKAGING (THAILAND) CO., LTD.—See Rengo Co., Ltd.; *Int'l*, pg. 6280
HOWARD BANCORP, INC.—See F.N.B. Corporation; *U.S. Public*, pg. 818
HOWARD BANK—See F.N.B. Corporation; *U.S. Public*, pg. 818
HOWARD BENTLEY BUICK GMC, INC.; *U.S. Private*, pg. 1994
HOWARD BERGER CO. LLC—See Littlejohn & Co., LLC; *U.S. Private*, pg. 2470
HOWARD BROWN HEALTH CENTER; *U.S. Private*, pg. 1994
HOWARD BUILDING CORPORATION; *U.S. Private*, pg. 1994
HOWARD COUNTY GASTROINTESTINAL DIAGNOSTIC CENTER, LLC—See Tenet Healthcare Corporation; *U.S. Public*, pg. 2004
HOWARD FARMERS COOP ASSOCIATION; *U.S. Private*, pg. 1994
HOWARD FERTILIZER COMPANY INC.; *U.S. Private*, pg. 1994
HOWARD FINISHING LLC; *U.S. Private*, pg. 1994
HOWARD FISCHER ASSOCIATES INTERNATIONAL; *U.S. Private*, pg. 1994
HOWARD GROUP; *U.S. Private*, pg. 1994
HOWARD HANNA CO. - MENTOR—See Hanna Holdings, Inc.; *U.S. Private*, pg. 1854
HOWARD HANNA COMPANY—See Hanna Holdings, Inc.; *U.S. Private*, pg. 1854
HOWARD HOTELS LTD.; *Int'l*, pg. 3493
HOWARD HUGHES HOLDINGS INC.; *U.S. Public*, pg. 1060
HOWARD HUGHES MANAGEMENT SERVICES COMPANY, LLC—See Howard Hughes Holdings Inc.; *U.S. Public*, pg. 1060
HOWARD INDUSTRIES INC.; *U.S. Private*, pg. 1994
HOWARD INDUSTRIES, INC.; *U.S. Private*, pg. 1995
HOWARD INDUSTRIES—See Howard Industries, Inc.; *U.S. Private*, pg. 1995
HOWARD INDUSTRIES; *U.S. Private*, pg. 1994
HOWARD JOHNSON INTERNATIONAL, INC.—See Travel & Leisure Co.; *U.S. Public*, pg. 2185

HOWARD JOHNSON'S ENTERPRISES INC.; *U.S. Private*, pg. 1995
HOWARD LEASING INC.; *U.S. Private*, pg. 1995
HOWARD LIGHTING PRODUCTS—See Howard Industries, Inc.; *U.S. Private*, pg. 1995
HOWARD LUMBER COMPANY; *U.S. Private*, pg. 1995
HOWARD MEMORIAL HOSPITAL; *U.S. Private*, pg. 1995
HOWARD, MERRELL & PARTNERS, INC.; *U.S. Private*, pg. 1995
HOWARD MIDSTREAM PARTNERS, LP; *U.S. Private*, pg. 1995
HOWARD MILLER COMPANY; *U.S. Private*, pg. 1995
HOWARD M. SCHWARTZ & ASSOCIATES, INC.; *U.S. Private*, pg. 1995
HOWARD P. FAIRFIELD, LLC; *U.S. Private*, pg. 1995
HOWARD PRECISION METALS, INC.—See Ryerson Holding Corporation; *U.S. Public*, pg. 1829
HOWARD'S APPLIANCES, INC.; *U.S. Private*, pg. 1995
HOWARD S.A.—See Kongskilde Industries A/S; *Int'l*, pg. 4257
HOWARDS (ESTATE AGENTS) LIMITED—See HAL Trust N.V.; *Int'l*, pg. 3226
HOWARD SHEPPARD INC.; *U.S. Private*, pg. 1995
HOWARD SMITH PAPER GROUP LIMITED—See KPP Group Holdings Co., Ltd.; *Int'l*, pg. 4298
HOWARD SMITH PAPER LIMITED—See KPP Group Holdings Co., Ltd.; *Int'l*, pg. 4298
HOWARD'S TV & APPLIANCES, INC.; *U.S. Private*, pg. 1995
HOWARD SYSTEMS INTERNATIONAL INC.; *U.S. Private*, pg. 1995
HOWARD TECHNOLOGY SOLUTIONS, INC.—See Howard Industries, Inc.; *U.S. Private*, pg. 1995
HOWARD TERNES PACKAGING CO.; *U.S. Private*, pg. 1995
HOWARD TRANSPORTATION, INC.—See Howard Industries, Inc.; *U.S. Private*, pg. 1995
HOWARD UNIVERSITY DIALYSIS CENTER, LLC—See Nautic Partners, LLC; *U.S. Private*, pg. 2870
HOWARD WEIL, INC.—See The Bank of Nova Scotia; *Int'l*, pg. 7618
HOWARD WEIL, INC.—See The Bank of Nova Scotia; *Int'l*, pg. 7618
HOWA SANGYO CO., LTD.—See Rengo Co., Ltd.; *Int'l*, pg. 6280
HOWA (SHANGHAI) CO., LTD.—See Rengo Co., Ltd.; *Int'l*, pg. 6279
HOWA TAIWAN CO., LTD.—See Rengo Co., Ltd.; *Int'l*, pg. 6280
HOWA (TIANJIN) MACHINERY CO., LTD.—See Howa Machinery, Ltd.; *Int'l*, pg. 3493
HOWA TRADING CO., LTD.—See China Baowu Steel Group Corp., Ltd.; *Int'l*, pg. 1485
HOWCO DISTRIBUTING CO.—See Bantec, Inc.; *U.S. Public*, pg. 275
HOWCO GROUP PLC; *Int'l*, pg. 3493
HOWCOM CO., LTD.—See Persol Holdings Co., Ltd.; *Int'l*, pg. 5819
HOWCO METALS INC.; *U.S. Private*, pg. 1995
HOWDEN AFRICA HOLDINGS LIMITED—See Chart Industries, Inc.; *U.S. Public*, pg. 482
HOWDEN AIR & GAS INDIA PRIVATE LIMITED—See Chart Industries, Inc.; *U.S. Public*, pg. 481
HOWDEN ALPHAIR VENTILATING SYSTEMS INC.—See Chart Industries, Inc.; *U.S. Public*, pg. 481
HOWDEN AUSTRALIA PTY LIMITED—See Chart Industries, Inc.; *U.S. Public*, pg. 481
HOWDEN AXIAL FANS AB—See Chart Industries, Inc.; *U.S. Public*, pg. 481
HOWDEN AXIAL FANS APS—See Chart Industries, Inc.; *U.S. Public*, pg. 481
HOWDEN BC COMPRESSORS—See Chart Industries, Inc.; *U.S. Public*, pg. 481
HOWDEN BROKING GROUP LIMITED—See Howden Group Holdings Limited; *Int'l*, pg. 3493
HOWDEN CKD COMPRESSORS S.R.O—See Chart Industries, Inc.; *U.S. Public*, pg. 481
HOWDEN COMPRESSORS INC—See Chart Industries, Inc.; *U.S. Public*, pg. 482
HOWDEN COMPRESSORS LIMITED—See Chart Industries, Inc.; *U.S. Public*, pg. 481
HOWDEN CORRETORA DE RESSEGUROS LTDA—See Howden Group Holdings Limited; *Int'l*, pg. 3493
HOWDEN COVENT FANS INC.—See Chart Industries, Inc.; *U.S. Public*, pg. 481
HOWDEN DONKIN (PROPRIETARY) LIMITED—See Chart Industries, Inc.; *U.S. Public*, pg. 481
HOWDEN EMPLOYEE BENEFITS LIMITED—See Howden Group Holdings Limited; *Int'l*, pg. 3494
HOWDEN FFP (PROPRIETARY) LIMITED—See Chart Industries, Inc.; *U.S. Public*, pg. 481
HOWDEN FORSIKRINGSMEGLING AS—See Howden Group Holdings Limited; *Int'l*, pg. 3493
HOWDEN FRANCE—See Chart Industries, Inc.; *U.S. Public*, pg. 482
HOWDEN GROUP BV—See Chart Industries, Inc.; *U.S. Public*, pg. 482
HOWDEN GROUP HOLDINGS LIMITED; *Int'l*, pg. 3493

CORPORATE AFFILIATIONS

HOWDEN GROUP LTD.—See Chart Industries, Inc.; *U.S. Public*, pg. 481
HOWDEN GROUP SOUTH AFRICA LIMITED—See Chart Industries, Inc.; *U.S. Public*, pg. 482
HOWDEN IBERIA S.A.—See Howden Group Holdings Limited; *Int'l*, pg. 3493
HOWDEN INSURANCE BROKERS (2002) LIMITED—See Howden Group Holdings Limited; *Int'l*, pg. 3493
HOWDEN INSURANCE BROKERS AB—See Howden Group Holdings Limited; *Int'l*, pg. 3494
HOWDEN INSURANCE BROKERS (BERMUDA) LIMITED—See Howden Group Holdings Limited; *Int'l*, pg. 3494
HOWDEN INSURANCE BROKERS (HK) LIMITED—See Howden Group Holdings Limited; *Int'l*, pg. 3494
HOWDEN INSURANCE BROKERS LIMITED—See Howden Group Holdings Limited; *Int'l*, pg. 3494
HOWDEN INSURANCE BROKERS LIMITED—See Howden Group Holdings Limited; *Int'l*, pg. 3494
HOWDEN INSURANCE BROKERS NEDERLAND B.V.—See Howden Group Holdings Limited; *Int'l*, pg. 3494
HOWDEN INSURANCE BROKERS OY—See Howden Group Holdings Limited; *Int'l*, pg. 3494
HOWDEN INSURANCE BROKERS (S.) PTE. LIMITED—See Howden Group Holdings Limited; *Int'l*, pg. 3494
HOWDEN INSURANCE, LLC—See Howden Group Holdings Limited; *Int'l*, pg. 3494
HOWDEN INSURANCE & REINSURANCE BROKERS (PHIL.), INC.—See Howden Group Holdings Limited; *Int'l*, pg. 3493
HOWDEN INSURANCE SERVICES, INC—See Howden Group Holdings Limited; *Int'l*, pg. 3494
HOWDEN JAPAN LIMITED—See Chart Industries, Inc.; *U.S. Public*, pg. 482
HOWDEN JOINERY GROUP PLC; *Int'l*, pg. 3494
HOWDEN JOINERY LIMITED—See Howden Joinery Group Plc; *Int'l*, pg. 3494
HOWDEN MELBOURNE PTY LIMITED—See Chart Industries, Inc.; *U.S. Public*, pg. 482
HOWDEN MIDDLE EAST FZE—See Chart Industries, Inc.; *U.S. Public*, pg. 482
HOWDEN NORTH AMERICA, INC.—See Chart Industries, Inc.; *U.S. Public*, pg. 482
HOWDEN RISK MANAGEMENT CONSULTANTS SDN. BHD.—See Howden Group Holdings Limited; *Int'l*, pg. 3494
HOWDEN SIGORTA BROKERLIGI ANONIM SIRKETI—See Howden Group Holdings Limited; *Int'l*, pg. 3494
HOWDENS OF HARROGATE LIMITED—See Lookers plc; *Int'l*, pg. 4555
HOWDEN SOLYVENT (INDIA) PVT LTD—See Chart Industries, Inc.; *U.S. Public*, pg. 482
HOWDEN THOMASSEN COMPRESSORS INDIA PRIVATE LIMITED—See Chart Industries, Inc.; *U.S. Public*, pg. 482
HOWDEN THOMASSEN COMPRESSORS—See Chart Industries, Inc.; *U.S. Public*, pg. 482
HOWDEN THOMASSEN FAR EAST PTE LTD—See Chart Industries, Inc.; *U.S. Public*, pg. 482
HOWDEN THOMASSEN MIDDLE EAST FZCO—See Chart Industries, Inc.; *U.S. Public*, pg. 482
HOWDEN TURBO FANS OY—See Chart Industries, Inc.; *U.S. Public*, pg. 482
HOWDEN TURBOMACHINERY S.R.L.—See Chart Industries, Inc.; *U.S. Public*, pg. 482
HOWDEN TURBOWERKE GMBH—See Chart Industries, Inc.; *U.S. Public*, pg. 482
HOWDEN UK GROUP LIMITED—See Howden Group Holdings Limited; *Int'l*, pg. 3494
HOWDEN UK LIMITED - CARCROFT DIVISION—See Chart Industries, Inc.; *U.S. Public*, pg. 482
HOWDEN UK LIMITED - CONSTRUCTION & MAINTENANCE DIVISION—See Chart Industries, Inc.; *U.S. Public*, pg. 482
HOWDEN UK LIMITED—See Chart Industries, Inc.; *U.S. Public*, pg. 482
HOWDEN URUGUAY CORREDORES DE REASEGUROS S.A—See Howden Group Holdings Limited; *Int'l*, pg. 3494
HOWDEN USA COMPANY—See Chart Industries, Inc.; *U.S. Public*, pg. 482
HOWDEN VENTILATOREN GMBH—See Chart Industries, Inc.; *U.S. Public*, pg. 482
HOWE A/S—See Whippoorwill Associates, Inc.; *U.S. Private*, pg. 4507
HOWE BARNES CAPITAL MANAGEMENT, INC.—See Raymond James Financial, Inc.; *U.S. Public*, pg. 1764
HOWE BARNES INVESTMENTS, INC.; *U.S. Private*, pg. 1995
HOWE & CO PTY LTD—See Schaffer Corporation Limited; *Int'l*, pg. 6615
HOWE ELECTRIC INC.; *U.S. Private*, pg. 1996
HOWE FURNITURE CORPORATION—See Whippoorwill Associates, Inc.; *U.S. Private*, pg. 4507
HOWE & HOWE TECHNOLOGIES, INC.—See Textron Inc.; *U.S. Public*, pg. 2029

COMPANY NAME INDEX

HOWE LEATHER (SHANGHAI) CO. LTD.—See Schaffer Corporation Limited; *Int'l*, pg. 6615
HOWELL & HOWELL CONTRACTORS, INC.; *U.S. Private*, pg. 1996
HOWELL INSTRUMENTS INC.; *U.S. Private*, pg. 1996
HOWELL METAL COMPANY—See Mueller Industries, Inc.; *U.S. Public*, pg. 1485
HOWELL METAL COMPANY—See Commercial Metals Company; *U.S. Public*, pg. 546
HOWELL-OREGON ELECTRIC COOPERATIVE, INC.; *U.S. Private*, pg. 1996
HOWELL SHONE INSURANCE BROKERS LIMITED—See Marsh & McLennan Companies, Inc.; *U.S. Public*, pg. 1376
HOWELL TRACTOR AND EQUIPMENT LLC—See Lanco International Inc.; *U.S. Private*, pg. 2382
HOWE SLOVENSKO S.R.O.—See Schaffer Corporation Limited; *Int'l*, pg. 6615
HOWE SOUND PULP & PAPER CORPORATION—See PT Sinar Mas Group; *Int'l*, pg. 6074
HOWESTEMCO, LLC—See NN, Inc.; *U.S. Public*, pg. 1531
HOWKINGTECH INTERNATIONAL HOLDING LIMITED; *Int'l*, pg. 3494
HOWLAND PUMP & SUPPLY CO. INC.; *U.S. Private*, pg. 1996
HOWLETT LUMBER CO. INC.; *U.S. Private*, pg. 1996
HOWMEDICA OSTEONICS CORP.—See Stryker Corporation; *U.S. Public*, pg. 1955
HOWMET AEROSPACE INC.; *U.S. Public*, pg. 1061
HOWMET ALUMINUM CASTING LTD.—See Howmet Aerospace Inc.; *U.S. Public*, pg. 1061
HOWMET CASTINGS & SERVICES, INC. - DOVER ALLOY—See Howmet Aerospace Inc.; *U.S. Public*, pg. 1061
HOWMET CASTINGS & SERVICES, INC. - DOVER—See Howmet Aerospace Inc.; *U.S. Public*, pg. 1061
HOWMET CASTINGS & SERVICES, INC. - HAMPTON—See Howmet Aerospace Inc.; *U.S. Public*, pg. 1061
HOWMET CASTINGS & SERVICES, INC. - LA PORTE—See Howmet Aerospace Inc.; *U.S. Public*, pg. 1061
HOWMET CASTINGS & SERVICES, INC. - MORRISTOWN—See Howmet Aerospace Inc.; *U.S. Public*, pg. 1061
HOWMET CASTINGS & SERVICES, INC.—See Howmet Aerospace Inc.; *U.S. Public*, pg. 1061
HOWMET CASTINGS & SERVICES, INC. - STRUCTURAL CASTING—See Howmet Aerospace Inc.; *U.S. Public*, pg. 1061
HOWMET CASTINGS & SERVICES, INC. - TITANIUM CASTINGS—See Howmet Aerospace Inc.; *U.S. Public*, pg. 1061
HOWMET CASTINGS & SERVICES, INC. - WHITEHALL CASTING—See Howmet Aerospace Inc.; *U.S. Public*, pg. 1061
HOWMET CASTINGS & SERVICES, INC. - WICHITA FALLS—See Howmet Aerospace Inc.; *U.S. Public*, pg. 1061
HOWMET CIRAL S.N.C—See Howmet Aerospace Inc.; *U.S. Public*, pg. 1061
HOWMET CORPORATION—See Howmet Aerospace Inc.; *U.S. Public*, pg. 1061
HOWMET HOLDINGS CORPORATION—See Howmet Aerospace Inc.; *U.S. Public*, pg. 1061
HOWMET INTERNATIONAL, INC.—See Howmet Aerospace Inc.; *U.S. Public*, pg. 1061
HOWMET LAVAL CASTING LTD.—See Howmet Aerospace Inc.; *U.S. Public*, pg. 1061
HOWMET LIMITED—See Howmet Aerospace Inc.; *U.S. Public*, pg. 1061
HOWMET RESEARCH CORPORATION—See Howmet Aerospace Inc.; *U.S. Public*, pg. 1061
HOWMET S.A.S.—See Howmet Aerospace Inc.; *U.S. Public*, pg. 1061
HOWROYD-WRIGHT EMPLOYMENT AGENCY INC.; *U.S. Private*, pg. 1996
HOWS MARKETS LLC; *U.S. Private*, pg. 1996
HOWSTUFFWORKS, INC.—See Genstar Capital, LLC; *U.S. Private*, pg. 1676
HOWTEH TECHNOLOGY CO., LTD.; *Int'l*, pg. 3494
HOWTELEVISION, INC.; *Int'l*, pg. 3494
HOWW MANUFACTURING COMPANY INC.—See Arch Promo Group LLC; *U.S. Private*, pg. 310
HOYA CANDEO OPTRONICS CORPORATION—See Hoya Corporation; *Int'l*, pg. 3494
HOYA CORPORATION - AKISHIMA FACILITY—See Hoya Corporation; *Int'l*, pg. 3494
HOYA CORPORATION - ATLANTA FACILITY—See Hoya Corporation; *Int'l*, pg. 3497
HOYA CORPORATION - CLEVELAND FACILITY—See Hoya Corporation; *Int'l*, pg. 3497
HOYA CORPORATION - DALLAS FACILITY—See Hoya Corporation; *Int'l*, pg. 3497
HOYA CORPORATION - DAYTON FACILITY—See Hoya Corporation; *Int'l*, pg. 3497
HOYA CORPORATION - EUGENE FACILITY—See Hoya Corporation; *Int'l*, pg. 3497
HOYA CORPORATION - HARTFORD FACILITY—See Hoya Corporation; *Int'l*, pg. 3497
HOYA CORPORATION - KNOXVILLE FACILITY—See Hoya Corporation; *Int'l*, pg. 3497
HOYA CORPORATION - LARGO FACILITY—See Hoya Corporation; *Int'l*, pg. 3497
HOYA CORPORATION - LEWISTON FACILITY—See Hoya Corporation; *Int'l*, pg. 3497
HOYA CORPORATION - MIYAGI FACTORY—See Hoya Corporation; *Int'l*, pg. 3494
HOYA CORPORATION - MODESTO FACILITY—See Hoya Corporation; *Int'l*, pg. 3497
HOYA CORPORATION - NEW ORLEANS FACILITY—See Hoya Corporation; *Int'l*, pg. 3497
HOYA CORPORATION - OGAWA FACTORY—See Hoya Corporation; *Int'l*, pg. 3494
HOYA CORPORATION - PENTAX LIFECARE DIVISION, MEDICAL INSTRUMENT SBU—See Hoya Corporation; *Int'l*, pg. 3495
HOYA CORPORATION - PENTAX LIFECARE DIVISION—See Hoya Corporation; *Int'l*, pg. 3494
HOYA CORPORATION - PORTLAND FACILITY—See Hoya Corporation; *Int'l*, pg. 3497
HOYA CORPORATION - SAN ANTONIO FACILITY—See Hoya Corporation; *Int'l*, pg. 3497
HOYA CORPORATION - SAN DIEGO FACILITY—See Hoya Corporation; *Int'l*, pg. 3497
HOYA CORPORATION; *Int'l*, pg. 3494
HOYA CORPORATION - USA OPTICS DIVISION—See Hoya Corporation; *Int'l*, pg. 3497
HOYA CORPORATION USA—See Hoya Corporation; *Int'l*, pg. 3496
HOYA CORPORATION - YAMAGATA FACTORY—See Hoya Corporation; *Int'l*, pg. 3494
HOYA DIGITAL SOLUTIONS CORPORATION—See Hoya Corporation; *Int'l*, pg. 3495
HOYA ELECTRONICS KOREA CO., LTD.—See Hoya Corporation; *Int'l*, pg. 3495
HOYA ELECTRONICS MALAYSIA SDN. BHD.—See Hoya Corporation; *Int'l*, pg. 3495
HOYA ELECTRONICS SINGAPORE PTE. LTD.—See Hoya Corporation; *Int'l*, pg. 3495
HOYA GLASS DISK PHILIPPINES, INC.—See Hoya Corporation; *Int'l*, pg. 3495
HOYA GLASS DISK (THAILAND) LTD.—See Hoya Corporation; *Int'l*, pg. 3495
HOYA GLASS DISK VIETNAM II LTD.—See Hoya Corporation; *Int'l*, pg. 3495
HOYA GLASS DISK VIETNAM LTD.—See Hoya Corporation; *Int'l*, pg. 3495
HOYA HEALTHCARE (SHANGHAI) CO., LTD.—See Hoya Corporation; *Int'l*, pg. 3495
HOYA HILL OPTICS SOUTH AFRICA (PTY) LTD.—See Hoya Corporation; *Int'l*, pg. 3494
HOYA HOLDINGS (ASIA) B.V.—See Hoya Corporation; *Int'l*, pg. 3496
HOYA HOLDINGS ASIA PACIFIC PTE LTD.—See Hoya Corporation; *Int'l*, pg. 3495
HOYA HOLDINGS, INC.—See Hoya Corporation; *Int'l*, pg. 3496
HOYA HOLDINGS N.V.—See Hoya Corporation; *Int'l*, pg. 3496
HOYA LAMPHUN LTD.—See Hoya Corporation; *Int'l*, pg. 3497
HOYA LAOS CO., LTD.—See Hoya Corporation; *Int'l*, pg. 3497
HOYA LENS AUSTRALIA PTY. LTD.—See Hoya Corporation; *Int'l*, pg. 3495
HOYA LENS BELGIUM N.V.—See Hoya Corporation; *Int'l*, pg. 3496
HOYA LENS BELGUIM B.V.—See Hoya Corporation; *Int'l*, pg. 3496
HOYA LENS CANADA, INC. - MONTREAL FACILITY—See Hoya Corporation; *Int'l*, pg. 3496
HOYA LENS CANADA, INC.—See Hoya Corporation; *Int'l*, pg. 3496
HOYA LENS CANADA, INC. - TORONTO FACILITY—See Hoya Corporation; *Int'l*, pg. 3496
HOYA LENS CANADA, INC. - VANCOUVER FACILITY—See Hoya Corporation; *Int'l*, pg. 3496
HOYA LENS CZ A.S—See Hoya Corporation; *Int'l*, pg. 3496
HOYA LENS DENMARK A/S—See Hoya Corporation; *Int'l*, pg. 3496
HOYA LENS DEUTSCHLAND GMBH—See Hoya Corporation; *Int'l*, pg. 3496
HOYA LENS FINLAND OY—See Hoya Corporation; *Int'l*, pg. 3496
HOYA LENS FRANCE S.A.—See Hoya Corporation; *Int'l*, pg. 3496
HOYA LENS GUANGZHOU LTD.—See Hoya Corporation; *Int'l*, pg. 3495
HOYA LENS HONG KONG LTD.—See Hoya Corporation; *Int'l*, pg. 3495
HOYA LENS HUNGARY RT—See Hoya Corporation; *Int'l*, pg. 3496
HOYA LENS IBERIA S.A.—See Hoya Corporation; *Int'l*, pg. 3496

HOYA LENS IBERIA S.A.—See Hoya Corporation; *Int'l*, pg. 3496
HOYA LENS INDIA PVT.LTD—See Hoya Corporation; *Int'l*, pg. 3495
HOYA LENS ITALIA S.P.A.—See Hoya Corporation; *Int'l*, pg. 3496
HOYA LENS KOREA CO., LTD.—See Hoya Corporation; *Int'l*, pg. 3495
HOYA LENS MANUFACTURING HUNGARY PRIVATE CO.—See Hoya Corporation; *Int'l*, pg. 3497
HOYA LENS MANUFACTURING HUNGARY RT—See Hoya Corporation; *Int'l*, pg. 3496
HOYA LENS MANUFACTURING MALAYSIA SDN. BHD.—See Hoya Corporation; *Int'l*, pg. 3495
HOYA LENS NEDERLAND B.V.—See Hoya Corporation; *Int'l*, pg. 3496
HOYA LENS OF AMERICA INC.—See Hoya Corporation; *Int'l*, pg. 3496
HOYA LENS OF CHICAGO, INC.—See Hoya Corporation; *Int'l*, pg. 3497
HOYA LENS PHILIPPINES, INC.—See Hoya Corporation; *Int'l*, pg. 3495
HOYA LENS POLAND SP. Z.O.O.—See Hoya Corporation; *Int'l*, pg. 3496
HOYA LENS RUSSIA LLC—See Hoya Corporation; *Int'l*, pg. 3498
HOYA LENS SHANGHAI LTD.—See Hoya Corporation; *Int'l*, pg. 3495
HOYA LENS (S) PTE. LTD.—See Hoya Corporation; *Int'l*, pg. 3495
HOYA LENS SWEDEN AB—See Hoya Corporation; *Int'l*, pg. 3496
HOYA LENS TAIWAN LTD.—See Hoya Corporation; *Int'l*, pg. 3496
HOYA LENS THAILAND LTD.—See Hoya Corporation; *Int'l*, pg. 3496
HOYA LENS U.K. LIMITED—See Hoya Corporation; *Int'l*, pg. 3496
HOYA LENS VIETNAM LTD.—See Hoya Corporation; *Int'l*, pg. 3496
HOYA MEDICAL DEVICE CONSULTING CO., LTD.—See Hoya Corporation; *Int'l*, pg. 3498
HOYA MEDICAL INDIA PVT. LTD.—See Hoya Corporation; *Int'l*, pg. 3498
HOYA MEDICAL SINGAPORE PTE. LTD.—See Hoya Corporation; *Int'l*, pg. 3496
HOYA MEMORY DISK TECHNOLOGIES LTD.—See Hoya Corporation; *Int'l*, pg. 3498
HOYA MICROELECTRONICS (SUZHOU) LTD.—See Hoya Corporation; *Int'l*, pg. 3496
HOYA MICROELECTRONICS TAIWAN CO., LTD.—See Hoya Corporation; *Int'l*, pg. 3496
HOYA OPTICAL (ASIA) CO., LTD—See Hoya Corporation; *Int'l*, pg. 3496
HOYA OPTICAL LABORATORIES—See Hoya Corporation; *Int'l*, pg. 3497
HOYA OPTICAL LABORATORIES—See Hoya Corporation; *Int'l*, pg. 3497
HOYA OPTICAL TECHNOLOGY (SUZHOU) LTD.—See Hoya Corporation; *Int'l*, pg. 3496
HOYA OPTICAL TECHNOLOGY (WEIHAI) CO., LTD.—See Hoya Corporation; *Int'l*, pg. 3496
HOYA OPTICS (THAILAND) LTD.—See Hoya Corporation; *Int'l*, pg. 3496
HOYA OPTO-ELECTRONICS QINGDAO LTD.—See Hoya Corporation; *Int'l*, pg. 3496
HOYA RESORT HOTEL GROUP; *Int'l*, pg. 3498
HOYA SERVICE CORPORATION—See Hoya Corporation; *Int'l*, pg. 3494
HOYAS LESSEE LLC—See Pebblebrook Hotel Trust; *U.S. Public*, pg. 1660
HOYA SURGICAL OPTICS GMBH—See Hoya Corporation; *Int'l*, pg. 3496
HOYA SURGICAL OPTICS, INC. - ATLANTA FACILITY—See Hoya Corporation; *Int'l*, pg. 3497
HOYA SURGICAL OPTICS, INC. - CHICAGO FACILITY—See Hoya Corporation; *Int'l*, pg. 3497
HOYA SURGICAL OPTICS, INC. - CLEVELAND FACILITY—See Hoya Corporation; *Int'l*, pg. 3497
HOYA SURGICAL OPTICS, INC. - DALLAS FACILITY—See Hoya Corporation; *Int'l*, pg. 3497
HOYA SURGICAL OPTICS, INC. - DAYTON FACILITY—See Hoya Corporation; *Int'l*, pg. 3497
HOYA SURGICAL OPTICS, INC. - EUGENE FACILITY—See Hoya Corporation; *Int'l*, pg. 3497
HOYA SURGICAL OPTICS, INC. - HARTFORD FACILITY—See Hoya Corporation; *Int'l*, pg. 3497
HOYA SURGICAL OPTICS, INC. - KNOXVILLE FACILITY—See Hoya Corporation; *Int'l*, pg. 3497
HOYA SURGICAL OPTICS, INC. - LARGO FACILITY—See Hoya Corporation; *Int'l*, pg. 3497
HOYA SURGICAL OPTICS, INC. - LEWISTON FACILITY—See Hoya Corporation; *Int'l*, pg. 3497
HOYA SURGICAL OPTICS, INC. - MODESTO FACILITY—See Hoya Corporation; *Int'l*, pg. 3497
HOYA SURGICAL OPTICS, INC. - PORTLAND FACILITY—See Hoya Corporation; *Int'l*, pg. 3497
HOYA SURGICAL OPTICS, INC. - SAN ANTONIO FACILITY—See Hoya Corporation; *Int'l*, pg. 3497

HOYA RESORT HOTEL GROUP

CORPORATE AFFILIATIONS

HOYA SURGICAL OPTICS, INC. - SAN DIEGO FACILITY—See Hoya Corporation; *Int'l*, pg. 3497
HOYA SURGICAL OPTICS, INC.—See Hoya Corporation; *Int'l*, pg. 3497
HOYA SURGICAL OPTICS, INC. - ST. LOUIS FACILITY—See Hoya Corporation; *Int'l*, pg. 3497
HOYA TECHNOSURGICAL CORPORATION—See Hoya Corporation; *Int'l*, pg. 3498
HOYA TURKEY OPTIK LENS SAN. VE TIC. A.S.—See Hoya Corporation; *Int'l*, pg. 3498
HOYA VISION CARE COMPANY - SEATTLE FACILITY—See Hoya Corporation; *Int'l*, pg. 3497
HOYA VISION CARE COMPANY—See Hoya Corporation; *Int'l*, pg. 3497
HOYA VISION CARE NORTH AMERICA INC.—See Hoya Corporation; *Int'l*, pg. 3497
HOY BROS. FISH & CRAB CO. INC.—See Dulcich, Inc.; *U.S. Private*, pg. 1286
HOYER AUSTRIA GES. M.B.H.—See Hoyer GmbH; *Int'l*, pg. 3498
HOYER BALTIC EXPEDITION UAB—See Hoyer GmbH; *Int'l*, pg. 3498
HOYER BELGIE N.V.—See Hoyer GmbH; *Int'l*, pg. 3498
HOYER BITUMEN-LOGISTIK GMBH—See Hoyer GmbH; *Int'l*, pg. 3498
HOYER BULGARIA EOOD—See Hoyer GmbH; *Int'l*, pg. 3498
HOYER BULK TRANSPORT CO. LTD. GUANGZHOU—See Hoyer GmbH; *Int'l*, pg. 3498
HOYER DANMARK A/S—See Hoyer GmbH; *Int'l*, pg. 3498
HOYER DEEPSEA MALAYSIA SDN. BHD.—See Hoyer GmbH; *Int'l*, pg. 3498
HOYER ESPANA, S.A.—See Hoyer GmbH; *Int'l*, pg. 3498
HOYER ESTONIA OU—See Hoyer GmbH; *Int'l*, pg. 3498
HOYER FINLAND OY—See Hoyer GmbH; *Int'l*, pg. 3498
HOYER FRANCE S.A.—See Hoyer GmbH; *Int'l*, pg. 3499
HOYER GASLOG GMBH—See Hoyer GmbH; *Int'l*, pg. 3499
HOYER GLOBAL (BRASIL) TRANSPORTES LTDA.—See Hoyer GmbH; *Int'l*, pg. 3499
HOYER GLOBAL BRAZIL LTDA—See Hoyer GmbH; *Int'l*, pg. 3499
HOYER GLOBAL INC.—See Hoyer GmbH; *Int'l*, pg. 3499
HOYER GLOBAL SHANGHAI BV—See Hoyer GmbH; *Int'l*, pg. 3498
HOYER GLOBAL SINGAPORE PTE LTD.—See Hoyer GmbH; *Int'l*, pg. 3499
HOYER GLOBAL TRANSPORT BV—See Hoyer GmbH; *Int'l*, pg. 3498
HOYER GLOBAL TRANSPORT FZE—See Hoyer GmbH; *Int'l*, pg. 3498
HOYER GMBH; *Int'l*, pg. 3498
HOYER HUNGARIA KFT—See Hoyer GmbH; *Int'l*, pg. 3499
HOYER IRELAND LTD.—See Hoyer GmbH; *Int'l*, pg. 3499
HOYER ITALIA S.R.L.—See Hoyer GmbH; *Int'l*, pg. 3499
HOYER LIQUID DRUMMING B.V.—See Hoyer GmbH; *Int'l*, pg. 3499
HOYER LOGISTICS AUSTRALIA PTY. LTD.—See Hoyer GmbH; *Int'l*, pg. 3499
HOYER LUXEMBOURG S.A.R.L.—See Hoyer GmbH; *Int'l*, pg. 3498
HOYER MEDNARODNA SPEDICIJA D.O.O.—See Hoyer GmbH; *Int'l*, pg. 3498
HOYER MIDDLE EAST LTD.—See Hoyer GmbH; *Int'l*, pg. 3499
HOYER MINERALOL LOGISTIK GMBH—See Hoyer GmbH; *Int'l*, pg. 3499
HOYER NEDERLAND B.V.—See Hoyer GmbH; *Int'l*, pg. 3498
HOYER-ODFJELL INC.—See Hoyer GmbH; *Int'l*, pg. 3499
HOYER POLSKA SP.Z O.O.—See Hoyer GmbH; *Int'l*, pg. 3499
HOYER POLSKA SP. Z O. O.—See Hoyer GmbH; *Int'l*, pg. 3499
HOYER PORTUGAL UNIPESSOAL LDA.—See Hoyer GmbH; *Int'l*, pg. 3499
HOYER SLOVENSKA REPUBLIKA S.R.O.—See Hoyer GmbH; *Int'l*, pg. 3498
HOYER SVENSKA AB—See Hoyer GmbH; *Int'l*, pg. 3498
HOYER (SVIZZERA) SA—See Hoyer GmbH; *Int'l*, pg. 3498
HOYER UK LTD.—See Hoyer GmbH; *Int'l*, pg. 3499
HOYER UKRAINE TOV—See Hoyer GmbH; *Int'l*, pg. 3498
HOYE'S PHARMACY; *U.S. Private*, pg. 1996
HOYLES FIRE & SAFETY LIMITED—See London Security PLC; *Int'l*, pg. 4547
HOYLU AB; *Int'l*, pg. 3499
HOYNE FINANCIAL CORPORATION; *U.S. Private*, pg. 1996
HOYNE SAVINGS BANK—See Hoyne Financial Corporation; *U.S. Private*, pg. 1996
HOYOS CONSULTING LLC; *U.S. Private*, pg. 1996
HOY PUBLICATIONS, LLC—See Tribune Publishing Company; *U.S. Private*, pg. 4228
HOYT BRUMM & LINK, INC.; *U.S. Private*, pg. 1996
HOYTE DODGE LTD.; *U.S. Private*, pg. 1996
THE HOYTS CORPORATION PTY LTD.; *Int'l*, pg. 7653

HOYT, SHEPSTON & SCIARONI INC.; *U.S. Private*, pg. 1996
HOYUAN GREEN ENERGY CO.,LTD; *Int'l*, pg. 3499
HOYU CO., LTD.; *Int'l*, pg. 3499
HOZELOCK LTD.—See Exel Industries SA; *Int'l*, pg. 2582
H.O. ZIMMAN, INC.; *U.S. Private*, pg. 1835
HOZTORG LLC—See Gr. Sarantis, S.A.; *Int'l*, pg. 3047
HP ADHESIVES LIMITED; *Int'l*, pg. 3499
H PARK GERMANY LP GMBH—See Jones Lang LaSalle Incorporated; *U.S. Public*, pg. 1201
H. PAULIN & CO., LIMITED—See Hillman Solutions Corp.; *U.S. Public*, pg. 1038
H. PAULIN & CO., LTD. - CAPITAL METAL INDUSTRIES—See Hillman Solutions Corp.; *U.S. Public*, pg. 1038
H. PAULIN & CO., LTD. - DOMINION FITTINGS—See Hillman Solutions Corp.; *U.S. Public*, pg. 1038
H. PAULIN & CO., LTD. - JEYCO MACHINE PRODUCTS—See Hillman Solutions Corp.; *U.S. Public*, pg. 1038
H. PAULIN & CO., LTD. - LONG-LOK CANADA—See Hillman Solutions Corp.; *U.S. Public*, pg. 1038
H. PAULIN & CO., LTD. - PRECISION FASTENERS—See Hillman Solutions Corp.; *U.S. Public*, pg. 1038
H. PAULIN & CO., LTD. - PRO-TIP—See Hillman Solutions Corp.; *U.S. Public*, pg. 1038
HP AUSTRIA GMBH—See HP Inc.; *U.S. Public*, pg. 1062
HP BELGIUM BVBA—See HP Inc.; *U.S. Public*, pg. 1062
HPB INSURANCE GROUP, INC.—See Pinnacle Financial Partners, Inc.; *U.S. Public*, pg. 1692
HPB INVEST D.O.O.—See Hrvatska Postanska banka d.d.; *Int'l*, pg. 3502
HPB NEKRETNINE D.O.O.—See Hrvatska Postanska banka d.d.; *Int'l*, pg. 3502
H. P. BRANDT FUNERAL HOME, INC.—See Service Corporation International; *U.S. Public*, pg. 1869
HP BRASIL INDUSTRIA E COMERCIO DE EQUIPAMENTOS ELETRONICOS LTDA—See HP Inc.; *U.S. Public*, pg. 1062
HPB STAMBENA STEDIONICA D.D.—See Hrvatska Postanska banka d.d.; *Int'l*, pg. 3502
H.P. BULMER LIMITED—See L'Arche Green N.V.; *Int'l*, pg. 4377
HPC AG; *Int'l*, pg. 3500
HPC AMERICA LLC—See Cognizant Technology Solutions Corporation; *U.S. Public*, pg. 525
HPC AUSTRIA GMBH—See HPC AG; *Int'l*, pg. 3500
HPC BIOSCIENCES LIMITED; *Int'l*, pg. 3500
HPC BULGARIA EOOD—See HPC AG; *Int'l*, pg. 3500
HPC DIERING ROMANIA SRL—See HPC AG; *Int'l*, pg. 3500
HPC ENGINEERING (THAILAND) CO., LTD.—See Hitachi, Ltd.; *Int'l*, pg. 3413
HPC ENVIROTEC S.A.—See HPC AG; *Int'l*, pg. 3500
HPC FOODS, LTD.; *U.S. Private*, pg. 1996
HPC HAMBURG PORT CONSULTING GMBH—See Hamburger Hafen und Logistik AG; *Int'l*, pg. 3236
HPC HOLDINGS LIMITED; *Int'l*, pg. 3500
HPC INDUSTRIAL SERVICES, LLC—See Clean Harbors, Inc.; *U.S. Public*, pg. 510
HPC INDUSTRIES LLC; *U.S. Private*, pg. 1996
HPC ITALIA S.R.L.—See HPC AG; *Int'l*, pg. 3500
HPCKAL, LLC—See Huntington Bancshares Incorporated; *U.S. Public*, pg. 1071
HPCL BIOFUELS LIMITED—See Oil & Natural Gas Corporation Limited; *Int'l*, pg. 5534
HPCL MIDDLE EAST FZCO—See Oil & Natural Gas Corporation Limited; *Int'l*, pg. 5534
HPCL-MITTAL ENERGY LIMITED—See SMCore Inc.; *Int'l*, pg. 7006
HP COLORSPAN—See HP Inc.; *U.S. Public*, pg. 1063
HP COMPUTING AND PRINTING D.O.O.—See HP Inc.; *U.S. Public*, pg. 1062
HP COMPUTING AND PRINTING SYSTEMS INDIA PRIVATE LIMITED—See HP Inc.; *U.S. Public*, pg. 1062
H.P COTTON TEXTILE MILLS LTD.; *Int'l*, pg. 3196
HPC PASECO SP LTD.—See HPC AG; *Int'l*, pg. 3500
HPCP-COMPUTING AND PRINTING PORTUGAL, UNIPESSOAL, LDA.—See HP Inc.; *U.S. Public*, pg. 1063
HPC POLSKA SP.Z.O,O.—See HPC AG; *Int'l*, pg. 3500
HPC PRODUCKTIONS GMBH—See Tong-Tai Machine Tool Co., Ltd.; *Int'l*, pg. 7806
HPC PRODUKTIONS GMBH—See Tong-Tai Machine Tool Co., Ltd.; *Int'l*, pg. 7806
HPC SEKURE GMBH—See Phoenix Mecano AG; *Int'l*, pg. 5852
HPC SOLUTIONS CO., LTD.—See Argo Graphics Inc.; *Int'l*, pg. 562
HPC SOLUTIONS; *U.S. Private*, pg. 1996
HPC SYSTEMS, INC.; *Int'l*, pg. 3500
H.P. CUMMINGS CONSTRUCTION COMPANY INC.; *U.S. Private*, pg. 1835
HPC VENEZUELA C.A.—See Hitachi, Ltd.; *Int'l*, pg. 3413
HPC WIRELESS SERVICES; *U.S. Private*, pg. 1996
HP DEUTSCHLAND GMBH—See HP Inc.; *U.S. Public*, pg. 1062
HPD HOLDINGS CORP.—See WD-40 Company; *U.S. Public*, pg. 2338

HPE INC.—See The Gibson Group Inc.; *U.S. Private*, pg. 4033
HPE SECURITY - DATA SECURITY—See Veritas Capital Fund Management, LLC; *U.S. Private*, pg. 4364
HPE S.P.A.—See Barnes Group Inc.; *U.S. Public*, pg. 277
HP EXSTREAM SOFTWARE—See HP Inc.; *U.S. Public*, pg. 1063
HP FINLAND OY—See HP Inc.; *U.S. Public*, pg. 1063
HP FIRE PREVENTION SPRL—See London Security PLC; *Int'l*, pg. 4547
HPG INC.—See Balder Danmark A/S; *Int'l*, pg. 807
HPG LLC—See Spectrum Brands Holdings, Inc.; *U.S. Public*, pg. 1916
HPG SOLUTIONS, LLC—See HCA Healthcare, Inc.; *U.S. Public*, pg. 998
H-PHAR SA—See Floridienne SA; *Int'l*, pg. 2708
H-PHOENIX PROPERTY COMPANY LIMITED—See WHA Corporation Public Company Limited; *Int'l*, pg. 8396
HP HOOD LLC—See Catamount Dairy Holdings L.P.; *U.S. Public*, pg. 787
HPI AG; *Int'l*, pg. 3500
HPI ASIA PACIFIC LTD.—See HPI AG; *Int'l*, pg. 3500
HPI COLLIER PARK LLC—See Independence Realty Trust, Inc.; *U.S. Public*, pg. 1115
HPI DISTRIBUTION GMBH—See HPI AG; *Int'l*, pg. 3500
HPI HARTSHIRE LLC—See Independence Realty Trust, Inc.; *U.S. Public*, pg. 1115
HPI INTERNATIONAL INC.; *U.S. Private*, pg. 1997
HPI INT. TRADING & CHEMICAL GMBH—See HPI AG; *Int'l*, pg. 3500
HPI KENSINGTON COMMONS LLC—See Independence Realty Trust, Inc.; *U.S. Public*, pg. 1115
HPIL HOLDING; *U.S. Public*, pg. 1065
HPI LIMITED—See Vista Equity Partners, LLC; *U.S. Private*, pg. 4400
HPI, LLC; *U.S. Private*, pg. 1997
HPI LOGISTICS GMBH & CO. KG—See HPI AG; *Int'l*, pg. 3500
HP IMAGING & PRINTING GROUP—See HP Inc.; *U.S. Public*, pg. 1063
HP INC ARGENTINA S.R.L.—See HP Inc.; *U.S. Public*, pg. 1063
HP INC CHILE COMERCIAL LIMITADA—See HP Inc.; *U.S. Public*, pg. 1063
HP INC COSTA RICA LIMITADA—See HP Inc.; *U.S. Public*, pg. 1063
HP INC CZECH REPUBLIC S.R.O.—See HP Inc.; *U.S. Public*, pg. 1063
HP INC DANMARK APS—See HP Inc.; *U.S. Public*, pg. 1063
HP INC MAGYARORSZAG KFT.—See HP Inc.; *U.S. Public*, pg. 1063
HP INC POLSKA SP. Z O.O.—See HP Inc.; *U.S. Public*, pg. 1063
HP INC ROMANIA SRL—See HP Inc.; *U.S. Public*, pg. 1063
HP INC SLOVAKIA, S.R.O.—See HP Inc.; *U.S. Public*, pg. 1063
HP INC.; *U.S. Public*, pg. 1062
HP INC TUNISIE SARL—See HP Inc.; *U.S. Public*, pg. 1063
HP INGREDIENTS; *U.S. Private*, pg. 1996
HP INSPECTIONS, INC.; *U.S. Private*, pg. 1996
H PIO CO., LTD.; *Int'l*, pg. 3191
HPI RESOURCES BERHAD; *Int'l*, pg. 3500
HPI RESOURCES (OVERSEAS) SDN. BHD.—See HPI Resources Berhad; *Int'l*, pg. 3500
HPI RIVERCHASE LLC—See Independence Realty Trust, Inc.; *U.S. Public*, pg. 1115
HPI SCHIRM FARMS LLC—See Independence Realty Trust, Inc.; *U.S. Public*, pg. 1115
HP SOURCING GMBH & CO. KG—See HPI AG; *Int'l*, pg. 3500
HP ITALY S.R.L.—See HP Inc.; *U.S. Public*, pg. 1063
HPK A.D.; *Int'l*, pg. 3501
H.P. KOPPLEMANN INC.; *U.S. Private*, pg. 1835
HP KSA LTD.—See HP Inc.; *U.S. Public*, pg. 1063
HPL ELECTRIC & POWER LIMITED; *Int'l*, pg. 3501
HPL ESTATES LIMITED—See Heidelberg Materials AG; *Int'l*, pg. 3311
HPL HOTELS & RESORTS PTE LTD—See Hotel Properties Limited; *Int'l*, pg. 3488
HPL STAMPINGS INC.; *U.S. Private*, pg. 1997
HPM AMERICA DIVISION—See Taylor's Industrial Services, L.L.C.; *U.S. Private*, pg. 3941
HP MARKETING CORP.—See Gepe Holding AG; *Int'l*, pg. 2942
HPM CABLES SARL—See TKH Group N.V.; *Int'l*, pg. 7764
HPM CORP.—See Workcare, Inc.; *U.S. Private*, pg. 4563
HP MIDDLE EAST HOLDINGS LIMITED COMPANY—See Helmerich & Payne, Inc.; *U.S. Public*, pg. 1024
HPMT DEUTSCHLAND GMBH—See HPMT Holding Berhad; *Int'l*, pg. 3501
HPMT HOLDING BERHAD; *Int'l*, pg. 3501
HPMT (SHENZHEN) LIMITED—See HPMT Holding Berhad; *Int'l*, pg. 3501
HP NEDERLAND B.V.—See HP Inc.; *U.S. Public*, pg. 1063
H.P. NEMENZ FOOD STORES INC.; *U.S. Private*, pg. 1835

COMPANY NAME INDEX

HPN HOLDINGS, INC.; *U.S. Public*, pg. 1065
HP NORGE AS—See HP Inc.; *U.S. Public*, pg. 1063
HPOI CORPORATION—See OPTOFLUX GMBH; *Int'l*, pg. 5606
HPP A.C.E.—See UnitedHealth Group Incorporated; *U.S. Public*, pg. 2241
HPP ALGARVE, S.A.—See UnitedHealth Group Incorporated; *U.S. Public*, pg. 2241
HPP BOAVISTA, S.A.—See UnitedHealth Group Incorporated; *U.S. Public*, pg. 2241
HPP HOLDINGS BERHAD; *Int'l*, pg. 3501
HPP - HOSPITAIS PRIVADOS DE PORTUGAL, SGPS, S.A.—See UnitedHealth Group Incorporated; *U.S. Public*, pg. 2241
HPP - MEDICINA MOLECULAR, S.A.—See UnitedHealth Group Incorporated; *U.S. Public*, pg. 2241
HP POLYMERS, LTD.—See PPG Industries, Inc.; *U.S. Public*, pg. 1711
HP PPS AUSTRALIA PTY LTD—See HP Inc.; *U.S. Public*, pg. 1063
HP-PPS ECUADOR CIA. LTDA—See HP Inc.; *U.S. Public*, pg. 1063
HP PPS MALAYSIA SDN. BHD.—See HP Inc.; *U.S. Public*, pg. 1063
HP PPS MAROC SARL—See HP Inc.; *U.S. Public*, pg. 1063
HP PPS MULTIMEDIA SDN. BHD.—See HP Inc.; *U.S. Public*, pg. 1063
HP PPS SINGAPORE (SALES) PTE. LTD.—See HP Inc.; *U.S. Public*, pg. 1063
HP PPS SVERIGE AB—See HP Inc.; *U.S. Public*, pg. 1063
HP PRINTING AND PERSONAL SYSTEMS HELLAS EPE—See HP Inc.; *U.S. Public*, pg. 1063
HP PRINTING & COMPUTING SOLUTIONS, S.L.U.—See HP Inc.; *U.S. Public*, pg. 1063
HP PRODUCTS CORPORATION; *U.S. Private*, pg. 1996
H-P PRODUCTS, INC.; *U.S. Private*, pg. 1824
HPP SAUDE - PARCERIAS CASCAIS, S.A.—See UnitedHealth Group Incorporated; *U.S. Public*, pg. 2241
HPQ HOLDINGS, LLC—See HP Inc.; *U.S. Public*, pg. 1063
HPQ-SILICON RESOURCES INC.; *Int'l*, pg. 3501
HP RESOURCES INC., U.O. Private, pg. 1006
HPR, INC.; *U.S. Private*, pg. 1997
HPR, INC.—See HPR, Inc.; *U.S. Private*, pg. 1997
H-PRODUKTER AS—See Flakk Holding AS; *Int'l*, pg. 2698
HP SCHWEIZ GMBH—See HP Inc.; *U.S. Public*, pg. 1063
HPS EUROPE—See Hightech Payment Systems S A; *Int'l*, pg. 3388
HPS INVESTMENT PARTNERS, LLC; *U.S. Private*, pg. 1997
HPS INVESTMENT PARTNERS (UK) LLP—See HPS Investment Partners, LLC; *U.S. Private*, pg. 1997
HPSI PURCHASING SERVICES, LLC—See Aramark; *U.S. Public*, pg. 177
HPS MECHANICAL, INC.; *U.S. Private*, pg. 1997
HP SOLUTIONS CREATION AND DEVELOPMENT SERVICES S.L.U.—See HP Inc.; *U.S. Public*, pg. 1063
HP SOUTH AFRICA PROPRIETARY LIMITED—See HP Inc.; *U.S. Public*, pg. 1063
HPS PLUMBING SERVICE, INC.; *U.S. Private*, pg. 1997
H.P.S. S.P.A.—See Sacmi Imola S.C.A.R.L.; *Int'l*, pg. 6463
HPS S.R.L.—See Hammond Power Solutions Inc.; *Int'l*, pg. 3239
H.P. STARR LUMBER COMPANY LLC; *U.S. Private*, pg. 1835
HPS TECHNOLOGIES, INC.; *U.S. Private*, pg. 1997
HP TAIWAN INFORMATION TECHNOLOGY LTD.—See HP Inc.; *U.S. Public*, pg. 1063
HPTEC GMBH—See Hunan Nonferrous Metals Corporation Ltd.; *Int'l*, pg. 3533
HP TECHNOLOGY IRELAND LIMITED—See HP Inc.; *U.S. Public*, pg. 1063
HPTI HAMBURG PORT TRAINING INSTITUTE GMBH—See Hamburger Hafen und Logistik AG; *Int'l*, pg. 3236
HP VALVES B.V—See Indutrade AB; *Int'l*, pg. 3679
H.P. WHITE LABORATORY, INC.—See Intertek Group plc; *Int'l*, pg. 3763
HQ AB; *Int'l*, pg. 3501
H&Q ASIA PACIFIC, LTD.; *U.S. Private*, pg. 1823
HQ CAPITAL (DEUTSCHLAND) GMBH—See Harald Quandt Holding GmbH; *Int'l*, pg. 3269
HQ CAPITAL GMBH & CO. KG—See Harald Quandt Holding GmbH; *Int'l*, pg. 3269
HQ CAPITAL PRIVATE EQUITY LLC—See Harald Quandt Holding GmbH; *Int'l*, pg. 3269
HQ CAPITAL REAL ESTATE L.P.—See Harald Quandt Holding GmbH; *Int'l*, pg. 3269
HQDA ELDERLY LIFE NETWORK CORP.; *U.S. Public*, pg. 1065
HQ DIRECT AB—See HQ AB; *Int'l*, pg. 3501
HQ ENERGY SERVICES (U.S.) INC.—See Hydro-Quebec; *Int'l*, pg. 3547
HQ EQUITA GMBH—See Harald Quandt Holding GmbH; *Int'l*, pg. 3269
HQ GLOBAL EDUCATION INC.; *Int'l*, pg. 3501

HQ GLOBAL WORKPLACES, LLC—See IWG Plc; *Int'l*, pg. 3850
HQ INSURANCE CORPORATION—See HireQuest, Inc.; *U.S. Public*, pg. 1042
HQ REALTY, INC.—See Lumen Technologies, Inc.; *U.S. Public*, pg. 1347
HR ACCESS SOLUTIONS SAS—See FMR LLC; *U.S. Private*, pg. 1555
HR ACCESS SOLUTIONS S.L.—See FMR LLC; *U.S. Private*, pg. 1555
H&R AGRI-POWER, INC.; *U.S. Private*, pg. 1823
HR AMERICA INC.; *U.S. Private*, pg. 1997
HRAM HOLDING DD; *Int'l*, pg. 3501
HRANSWERLINK; *U.S. Private*, pg. 1998
H&R ANZ PTY. LTD.—See H&R KGaA; *Int'l*, pg. 3193
HRA PHARMA DEUTSCHLAND, GMBH—See Astorg Partners S.A.S.; *Int'l*, pg. 656
HRA PHARMA DEUTSCHLAND, GMBH—See The Goldman Sachs Group, Inc.; *U.S. Public*, pg. 2077
HRA PHARMA IBERIA S.L.—See Astorg Partners S.A.S.; *Int'l*, pg. 656
HRA PHARMA IBERIA S.L.—See The Goldman Sachs Group, Inc.; *U.S. Public*, pg. 2077
HRA PHARMA ITALIA S.R.L.—See Astorg Partners S.A.S.; *Int'l*, pg. 656
HRA PHARMA ITALIA S.R.L.—See The Goldman Sachs Group, Inc.; *U.S. Public*, pg. 2077
HRA PHARMA, SA—See Astorg Partners S.A.S.; *Int'l*, pg. 656
HRA PHARMA, SA—See The Goldman Sachs Group, Inc.; *U.S. Public*, pg. 2077
HRA PHARMA UK & IRELAND LTD—See Astorg Partners S.A.S.; *Int'l*, pg. 656
HRA PHARMA UK & IRELAND LTD—See The Goldman Sachs Group, Inc.; *U.S. Public*, pg. 2077
H&R AUTO RADIO SERVICE INCORPORATED; *U.S. Private*, pg. 1823
HRB CORPORATE SERVICES LLC—See H&R Block, Inc.; *U.S. Public*, pg. 976
HRB DIGITAL LLC—See H&R Block, Inc.; *U.S. Public*, pg. 976
H&R BENELUX B.V.—See H&R KGaA; *Int'l*, pg. 3193
HRB FLORICULTURE LIMITED; *Int'l*, pg. 3501
H.R. BLACK CO. INC.—See Komline-Sanderson Corporation; *U.S. Private*, pg. 2342
H&R BLOCK COMPANY OF UTAH—See H&R Block, Inc.; *U.S. Public*, pg. 976
H&R BLOCK EASTERN ENTERPRISES, INC.—See H&R Block, Inc.; *U.S. Public*, pg. 976
H&R BLOCK GROUP, INC.—See H&R Block, Inc.; *U.S. Public*, pg. 976
H&R BLOCK, INC.; *U.S. Public*, pg. 976
H&R BLOCK (INDIA) PRIVATE LIMITED—See H&R Block, Inc.; *U.S. Public*, pg. 976
H&R BLOCK TAX AND BUSINESS SERVICES, INC.—See H&R Block, Inc.; *U.S. Public*, pg. 976
H&R BLOCK TAX RESOLUTION SERVICES, INC.—See H&R Block, Inc.; *U.S. Public*, pg. 976
H&R BLOCK TAX SERVICES LLC—See H&R Block, Inc.; *U.S. Public*, pg. 976
HRB RESOURCES LLC—See H&R Block, Inc.; *U.S. Public*, pg. 976
HRC ENERGY RESOURCES (WV), INC.—See Battalion Oil Corp.; *U.S. Public*, pg. 279
H&R CENTURY UNION CORPORATION; *Int'l*, pg. 3192
HR CERTIFICATION INSTITUTE; *U.S. Private*, pg. 1997
HRC FERTILITY MANAGEMENT, LLC—See Jinxin Fertility Group Limited; *Int'l*, pg. 3970
H&R CHEMPHARM GMBH—See H&R KGaA; *Int'l*, pg. 3193
H&R CHEMPHARM (THAILAND) LTD.—See H&R KGaA; *Int'l*, pg. 3193
H&R CHEMPHARM (UK) LTD.—See H&R KGaA; *Int'l*, pg. 3193
H&R CHINA (DAXIE) CO., LTD.—See H&R KGaA; *Int'l*, pg. 3193
H&R CHINA (FUSHUN) CO., LTD.—See H&R KGaA; *Int'l*, pg. 3193
H&R CHINA (HONG KONG) CO., LTD.—See H&R KGaA; *Int'l*, pg. 3193
H&R CONSTRUCTION PARTS & EQUIPMENT, INC.—See Kinderhook Industries, LLC; *U.S. Private*, pg. 2306
HR CONSULTANCY PARTNERS SAS—See Randstad N.V.; *Int'l*, pg. 6201
H.R. CURRY COMPANY, INC.; *U.S. Private*, pg. 1835
HRD AERO SYSTEMS, INC.; *U.S. Private*, pg. 1998
HR FOCAL POINT, LLC; *U.S. Private*, pg. 1998
HR FORCE, INC.—See Funai Soken Holdings Incorporated; *Int'l*, pg. 2845
HRG BELGIUM NV—See Global Business Travel Group, Inc.; *U.S. Public*, pg. 941
HRG DEBTCO LIMITED—See Global Business Travel Group, Inc.; *U.S. Public*, pg. 941
HRGM CORPORATION; *U.S. Private*, pg. 1998
H&R GROUP US, INC.—See H&R KGaA; *Int'l*, pg. 3193
H&R GRUNDSTUCKSVERWALTUNGS-BETEILIGUNGSGESELLSCHAFT MBH—See H&R KGaA; *Int'l*, pg. 3193

H&R GRUNDSTUCKSVERWALTUNGS GMBH—See H&R KGaA; *Int'l*, pg. 3193
H.R. HANNAPEL DOOR CO.; *U.S. Private*, pg. 1835
HR HANNOVER RE, CORREDURIA DE REASEGUROS, S.A.—See Talanx AG; *Int'l*, pg. 7444
H.R. HARMER, GLOBAL PHILATELIC NETWORK, INC.—See Global Philatelic Network; *Int'l*, pg. 3000
HRH CONSTRUCTION LLC; *U.S. Private*, pg. 1998
HRH MEDIA; *U.S. Private*, pg. 1998
HRH NEXT SERVICES LIMITED; *Int'l*, pg. 3501
HRI HOSPITAL, INC.—See Universal Health Services, Inc.; *U.S. Public*, pg. 2257
HRI, INC.—See Apollo Global Management, Inc.; *U.S. Public*, pg. 166
HRI IT-CONSULTING GMBH—See H&R KGaA; *Int'l*, pg. 3193
HR IMMOBILIEN RHO GMBH—See Hornbach Holding AG & Co. KGaA; *Int'l*, pg. 3481
HR, INC.; *U.S. Private*, pg. 1998
H&R INFOTECH GMBH—See H&R KGaA; *Int'l*, pg. 3193
H&R INTERNATIONAL GMBH—See H&R KGaA; *Int'l*, pg. 3193
H. R. JASPER & SON LTD.—See Dunbia Group; *Int'l*, pg. 2225
H&R KGAA; *Int'l*, pg. 3193
H.R. LEWIS PETROLEUM CO.; *U.S. Private*, pg. 1835
HRL HOLDINGS LIMITED; *Int'l*, pg. 3501
HRL LABORATORIES, LLC—See General Motors Company; *U.S. Public*, pg. 926
HRL LABORATORIES, LLC—See The Boeing Company; *U.S. Public*, pg. 2041
H&R LUBE BLENDING GMBH—See H&R KGaA; *Int'l*, pg. 3193
H&R LUBETECH GMBH—See H&R KGaA; *Int'l*, pg. 3193
HR MACHINERY INC.; *U.S. Private*, pg. 1998
H&R MALAYSIA SDN. BHD.—See LPKF Laser & Electronics AG; *Int'l*, pg. 4568
HRMALL INC.—See Ayala Corporation; *Int'l*, pg. 774
HR MAX—See Legacy Partners Inc.; *U.S. Private*, pg. 2416
HR MC HOTEL COMPANY, S. DE R.L. DE C.V.—See Hyatt Hotels Corporation; *U.S. Public*, pg. 1077
HRM ENTERPRISES INC.; *U.S. Private*, pg. 1998
HRNETGROUP LIMITED; *Int'l*, pg. 3501
HRO INC.; *U.S. Private*, pg. 1998
H&R OLWERKE SCHINDLER GMBH—See H&R KGaA; *Int'l*, pg. 3193
HR OWEN INSURANCE SERVICES LIMITED—See Arthur J. Gallagher & Co.; *U.S. Public*, pg. 205
H.R. OWEN PLC—See Berjaya Corporation Berhad; *Int'l*, pg. 983
HR PARTNERS PTY LIMITED—See Randstad N.V.; *Int'l*, pg. 6201
HR PATH SAS; *Int'l*, pg. 3501
HR PHARMACEUTICALS, INC.; *U.S. Private*, pg. 1998
HRP LIMITED—See Beijer Ref AB; *Int'l*, pg. 944
HRQ, INC.; *U.S. Private*, pg. 1998
H&R REAL ESTATE INVESTMENT TRUST; *Int'l*, pg. 3193
HRR ENTERPRISES, INC.—See Kane-Miller Corp.; *U.S. Private*, pg. 2260
HRS CO., LTD. - ASAN FACTORY—See HRS Co., Ltd.; *Int'l*, pg. 3502
HRS CO., LTD. - PYEONGTAEK FACTORY—See HRS Co., Ltd.; *Int'l*, pg. 3502
HRS CO., LTD.; *Int'l*, pg. 3502
HRS CO., LTD. - SUZHOU FACTORY—See HRS Co., Ltd.; *Int'l*, pg. 3502
HRS EDUCATION SERVICES, INC.—See Hawk Management & Financial Services Inc.; *U.S. Private*, pg. 1882
HRS ERASE INC.; *U.S. Private*, pg. 1998
HR-SERVICE NEDERLAND B.V.—See Darling Ingredients Inc.; *U.S. Public*, pg. 634
H&R SINGAPORE PTE. LTD.—See H&R KGaA; *Int'l*, pg. 3193
HRS LOGISTICS, INC.—See Derry Enterprises Inc.; *U.S. Private*, pg. 1210
HR SOLUTION DCS CO., LTD.—See Mitsubishi Research Institute, Inc.; *Int'l*, pg. 4968
HR SOLUTIONS CORP.—See SoftBank Group Corp.; *Int'l*, pg. 7051
H&R SOUTH AFRICA GMBH—See H&R KGaA; *Int'l*, pg. 3193
H&R SOUTH AFRICA (PTY) LIMITED—See H&R KGaA; *Int'l*, pg. 3193
H&R SOUTH AFRICA SALES (PTY) LIMITED—See H&R KGaA; *Int'l*, pg. 3193
H. R. SPINNER CORPORATION; *U.S. Private*, pg. 1825
HRST, INC.; *U.S. Private*, pg. 1998
HR STRATEGIES COMPANY; *U.S. Private*, pg. 1998
HRT AMERICA INC.—See Petro Rio S.A.; *Int'l*, pg. 5825
HRTI, LLC—See Healthcare Realty Trust Incorporated; *U.S. Public*, pg. 1015
HRT O&G EXPLORACAO E PRODUCAO DE PETROLEO LTDA.—See Petro Rio S.A.; *Int'l*, pg. 5825
H & R TRANSPORT LTD.; *Int'l*, pg. 3191
HRVATSKA BANKA ZA OBNOVU I RAZVITAK; *Int'l*, pg. 3502
HRVATSKA ELEKTROPRIVREDA D.D.; *Int'l*, pg. 3502
HRVATSKA NORADNA BANKA; *Int'l*, pg. 3502

HRVATSKA POSTANSKA BANKA D.D.   CORPORATE AFFILIATIONS

HRVATSKA POSTANSKA BANKA D.D.; *Int'l*, pg. 3502
HRVATSKI TELEKOM D.D.—See Deutsche Telekom AG; *Int'l*, pg. 2083
H&R WAX MALAYSIA SDN. BHD.—See H&R KGaA; *Int'l*, pg. 3193
HRW LLC—See Majestic Construction LLC; *U.S. Private*, pg. 2554
HR WORKS, INC.; *U.S. Private*, pg. 1998
HRX PTY, LTD.—See TrueBlue, Inc.; *U.S. Public*, pg. 2198
HSA COMMERCIAL REAL ESTATE; *U.S. Private*, pg. 1999
HS AD INC.; *Int'l*, pg. 3502
HS AD, INC.—See WPP plc; *Int'l*, pg. 8491
HS AD, INC.—See WPP plc; *Int'l*, pg. 8491
HS AD, INC.—See WPP plc; *Int'l*, pg. 8491
H. SALB INTERNATIONAL; *Int'l*, pg. 3195
H. SALT OF SOUTHERN CALIFORNIA, INC.; *U.S. Private*, pg. 1825
H. SARTORIUS NACHF. GMBH & CO. KG—See Wurth Verwaltungsgesellschaft mbH; *Int'l*, pg. 8505
HS AUTOMOTIVE ALABAMA INC.—See Hwaseung Industries Co., Ltd.; *Int'l*, pg. 3542
H+S AVIATION LIMITED—See BlackRock, Inc.; *U.S. Public*, pg. 346
H+S AVIATION LIMITED—See Blackstone Inc.; *U.S. Public*, pg. 358
H+S AVIATION LIMITED—See Cascade Investment LLC; *U.S. Private*, pg. 780
H&S BAKERY INC.; *U.S. Private*, pg. 1823
HSB ASSOCIATES, INC—See Munchener Ruckversicherungs AG; *Int'l*, pg. 5088
HSBC ALGERIA—See HSBC Holdings plc; *Int'l*, pg. 3503
HSBC AMANAH MALAYSIA BERHAD—See HSBC Holdings plc; *Int'l*, pg. 3506
HSBC ARGENTINA HOLDINGS S.A.—See HSBC Holdings plc; *Int'l*, pg. 3503
HSBC ASSET FINANCE (UK) LIMITED—See HSBC Holdings plc; *Int'l*, pg. 3503
HSBC ASSET MANAGEMENT (INDIA) PRIVATE LIMITED—See HSBC Holdings plc; *Int'l*, pg. 3503
HSBC AUTO FINANCE—See HSBC Holdings plc; *Int'l*, pg. 3505
HSBC BANK ARGENTINA SA—See HSBC Holdings plc; *Int'l*, pg. 3503
HSBC BANK ARMENIA CJSC—See HSBC Holdings plc; *Int'l*, pg. 3503
HSBC BANK A.S.—See HSBC Holdings plc; *Int'l*, pg. 3503
HSBC BANK AUSTRALIA LIMITED—See HSBC Holdings plc; *Int'l*, pg. 3506
HSBC BANK (BAHAMAS) LTD.—See HSBC Holdings plc; *Int'l*, pg. 3503
HSBC BANK CANADA—See Royal Bank of Canada; *Int'l*, pg. 6409
HSBC BANK (CHILE) SA—See HSBC Holdings plc; *Int'l*, pg. 3503
HSBC BANK (CHINA) COMPANY LIMITED—See HSBC Holdings plc; *Int'l*, pg. 3506
HSBC BANK EGYPT (SAE)—See HSBC Holdings plc; *Int'l*, pg. 3503
HSBC BANK INTERNATIONAL LIMITED—See HSBC Holdings plc; *Int'l*, pg. 3503
HSBC BANK MALAYSIA BERHAD—See HSBC Holdings plc; *Int'l*, pg. 3506
HSBC BANK MALTA P.L.C.—See HSBC Holdings plc; *Int'l*, pg. 3503
HSBC BANK MIDDLE EAST LIMITED—See HSBC Holdings plc; *Int'l*, pg. 3503
HSBC BANK OMAN S.A.O.G.—See Sohar International Bank SAOG; *Int'l*, pg. 7059
HSBC BANK PLC, LUXEMBOURG BRANCH—See HSBC Holdings plc; *Int'l*, pg. 3503
HSBC BANK PLC—See HSBC Holdings plc; *Int'l*, pg. 3503
HSBC BANK POLSKA S.A.—See HSBC Holdings plc; *Int'l*, pg. 3503
HSBC BANK UK PLC—See HSBC Holdings plc; *Int'l*, pg. 3503
HSBC BANK (URUGUAY) S.A.—See HSBC Holdings plc; *Int'l*, pg. 3503
HSBC BANK USA, N.A.—See HSBC Holdings plc; *Int'l*, pg. 3505
HSBC BANK (VIETNAM) LTD.—See HSBC Holdings plc; *Int'l*, pg. 3506
HSBC BOOKING SECURITIES ASIA LTD.—See HSBC Holdings plc; *Int'l*, pg. 3506
HSBC BRASIL HOLDING S.A.—See HSBC Holdings plc; *Int'l*, pg. 3505
HSBC BROKING SERVICES ASIA LTD—See HSBC Holdings plc; *Int'l*, pg. 3506
HSBC CAPITAL MARKETS CORPORATION—See HSBC Holdings plc; *Int'l*, pg. 3505
HSBC CONTINENTAL EUROPE S.A.—See HSBC Holdings plc; *Int'l*, pg. 3505
HSBC CORPORATE BANKING SWITZERLAND—See HSBC Holdings plc; *Int'l*, pg. 3505
HSBC CORPORATE FINANCE LIMITED—See HSBC Holdings plc; *Int'l*, pg. 3505
HSBC CORPORATION (ISLE OF MAN) LIMITED—See HSBC Holdings plc; *Int'l*, pg. 3504

HSBC ELECTRONIC DATA PROCESSING INDIA PRIVATE LIMITED—See HSBC Holdings plc; *Int'l*, pg. 3505
HSBC EQUATOR BANK PLC—See HSBC Holdings plc; *Int'l*, pg. 3505
HSBC EXPAT—See HSBC Holdings plc; *Int'l*, pg. 3504
HSBC FINANCE (BRUNEI) BERHAD—See HSBC Holdings plc; *Int'l*, pg. 3506
HSBC FINANCE CORPORATION—See HSBC Holdings plc; *Int'l*, pg. 3505
HSBC FINANCIAL SERVICES (CAYMAN) LIMITED—See HSBC Holdings plc; *Int'l*, pg. 3504
HSBC FORFAITING LTD.—See HSBC Holdings plc; *Int'l*, pg. 3504
HSBC FRANCE—See HSBC Holdings plc; *Int'l*, pg. 3504
HSBC GERMANY HOLDINGS GMBH—See HSBC Holdings plc; *Int'l*, pg. 3505
HSBC GLOBAL ASSET MANAGEMENT (CANADA) LIMITED—See HSBC Holdings plc; *Int'l*, pg. 3504
HSBC GLOBAL ASSET MANAGEMENT (DEUTSCHLAND) GMBH—See HSBC Holdings plc; *Int'l*, pg. 3504
HSBC GLOBAL ASSET MANAGEMENT (HONG KONG) LIMITED—See HSBC Holdings plc; *Int'l*, pg. 3506
HSBC GLOBAL ASSET MANAGEMENT (JAPAN) K.K.—See HSBC Holdings plc; *Int'l*, pg. 3504
HSBC GLOBAL ASSET MANAGEMENT LIMITED—See HSBC Holdings plc; *Int'l*, pg. 3504
HSBC GLOBAL ASSET MANAGEMENT (MALTA) LTD—See HSBC Holdings plc; *Int'l*, pg. 3504
HSBC GLOBAL ASSET MANAGEMENT (OESTERREICH) GMBH—See HSBC Holdings plc; *Int'l*, pg. 3504
HSBC GLOBAL ASSET MANAGEMENT (SINGAPORE) LTD.—See HSBC Holdings plc; *Int'l*, pg. 3506
HSBC GLOBAL ASSET MANAGEMENT (SWITZERLAND) AG—See HSBC Holdings plc; *Int'l*, pg. 3504
HSBC GLOBAL ASSET MANAGEMENT (UK) LIMITED—See HSBC Holdings plc; *Int'l*, pg. 3504
HSBC GLOBAL ASSET MANAGEMENT (USA) INC.—See HSBC Holdings plc; *Int'l*, pg. 3504
HSBC GLOBAL SERVICES (UK) LIMITED—See HSBC Holdings plc; *Int'l*, pg. 3504
HSBC GUYERZELLER TRUST COMPANY SA—See HSBC Holdings plc; *Int'l*, pg. 3504
HSBC HIRE PURCHASE & LEASING LTD.—See HSBC Holdings plc; *Int'l*, pg. 3506
HSBC HOLDINGS BV—See HSBC Holdings plc; *Int'l*, pg. 3504
HSBC HOLDINGS PLC; *Int'l*, pg. 3503
HSBC HOLDINGS PLC; *Int'l*, pg. 3507
HSBC INSTITUTIONAL TRUST SERVICES (IRELAND) LIMITED—See HSBC Holdings plc; *Int'l*, pg. 3505
HSBC INSTITUTIONAL TRUST SERVICES SINGAPORE LIMITED—See HSBC Holdings plc; *Int'l*, pg. 3504
HSBC INSURANCE (ASIA) LIMITED—See HSBC Holdings plc; *Int'l*, pg. 3505
HSBC INSURANCE (ASIA-PACIFIC) HOLDINGS LIMITED—See HSBC Holdings plc; *Int'l*, pg. 3506
HSBC INSURANCE (IRELAND) LIMITED—See HSBC Holdings plc; *Int'l*, pg. 3505
HSBC INSURANCE SERVICES—See HSBC Holdings plc; *Int'l*, pg. 3505
HSBC INSURANCE (SINGAPORE) PTE. LIMITED—See HSBC Holdings plc; *Int'l*, pg. 3505
HSBC INTERNATIONAL FINANCE CORPORATION LIMITED—See HSBC Holdings plc; *Int'l*, pg. 3504
HSBC INTERNATIONAL TRUSTEE (BVI) LIMITED—See HSBC Holdings plc; *Int'l*, pg. 3505
HSBC INTERNATIONAL TRUSTEE LIMITED—See HSBC Holdings plc; *Int'l*, pg. 3504
HSBC INTERNATIONAL TRUSTEE (SINGAPORE) LIMITED—See HSBC Holdings plc; *Int'l*, pg. 3506
HSBC INVESTMENT BANK ASIA LIMITED—See HSBC Holdings plc; *Int'l*, pg. 3506
HSBC INVESTMENT BANK PLC—See HSBC Holdings plc; *Int'l*, pg. 3504
HSBC INVESTMENT TRUST (JAPAN) K.K.—See HSBC Holdings plc; *Int'l*, pg. 3506
HSBC INVOICE FINANCE UK LTD—See HSBC Holdings plc; *Int'l*, pg. 3504
HSBC IRELAND—See HSBC Holdings plc; *Int'l*, pg. 3504
HSBC (KUALA LUMPUR) NOMINEES SDN BHD—See HSBC Holdings plc; *Int'l*, pg. 3506
HSBC LIFE ASSURANCE (MALTA) LIMITED—See HSBC Holdings plc; *Int'l*, pg. 3505
HSBC LIFE UK LIMITED—See HSBC Holdings plc; *Int'l*, pg. 3504
HSBC MEXICO S.A.—See HSBC Holdings plc; *Int'l*, pg. 3503
HSBC MORTGAGE SERVICES—See HSBC Holdings plc; *Int'l*, pg. 3505
HSBC NORTH AMERICA HOLDINGS INC.—See HSBC Holdings plc; *Int'l*, pg. 3505
HSBC PRIVATE BANK (C.I.) LIMITED—See HSBC Holdings plc; *Int'l*, pg. 3505
HSBC PRIVATE BANK INTERNATIONAL—See HSBC Holdings plc; *Int'l*, pg. 3505
HSBC PRIVATE BANK (JERSEY) LIMITED—See HSBC Holdings plc; *Int'l*, pg. 3504

HSBC PRIVATE BANK NOMINEES LTD—See HSBC Holdings plc; *Int'l*, pg. 3504
HSBC PRIVATE BANK (SUISSE) S.A.—See HSBC Holdings plc; *Int'l*, pg. 3504
HSBC PRIVATE BANK (UK) LTD—See HSBC Holdings plc; *Int'l*, pg. 3504
HSBC PRIVATE TRUSTEE (HONG KONG) LIMITED—See HSBC Holdings plc; *Int'l*, pg. 3505
HSBC QIANHAI SECURITIES LIMITED—See HSBC Holdings plc; *Int'l*, pg. 3505
HSBC REINSURANCE LTD—See HSBC Holdings plc; *Int'l*, pg. 3505
HSBC SAUDI ARABIA LIMITED—See The Saudi British Bank; *Int'l*, pg. 7680
THE HSBC SAVINGS BANK—See HSBC Holdings plc; *Int'l*, pg. 3506
HSBC SECURITIES AND CAPITAL MARKETS (INDIA) PRIVATE LIMITED—See HSBC Holdings plc; *Int'l*, pg. 3506
HSBC SECURITIES ASIA LTD.—See HSBC Holdings plc; *Int'l*, pg. 3506
HSBC SECURITIES BROKERS (ASIA) LIMITED—See HSBC Holdings plc; *Int'l*, pg. 3506
HSBC SECURITIES, INC.—See HSBC Holdings plc; *Int'l*, pg. 3505
HSBC SECURITIES JAPAN LIMITED—See HSBC Holdings plc; *Int'l*, pg. 3506
HSBC SECURITIES SERVICES (IRELAND) LIMITED—See HSBC Holdings plc; *Int'l*, pg. 3506
HSBC SECURITIES SERVICES (MALTA) LTD—See HSBC Holdings plc; *Int'l*, pg. 3506
HSBC SECURITIES (SOUTH AFRICA) (PTY) LIMITED—See HSBC Holdings plc; *Int'l*, pg. 3505
HSBC SECURITIES (TAIWAN) CORPORATION LIMITED—See HSBC Holdings plc; *Int'l*, pg. 3505
HSBC SECURITY SERVICES (MAURITIUS) LIMITED—See HSBC Holdings plc; *Int'l*, pg. 3505
HSBC SERVICE DELIVERY (POLSKA) SP. Z O.O.—See HSBC Holdings plc; *Int'l*, pg. 3506
HSBC SHIPPING SERVICES LTD.—See HSBC Holdings plc; *Int'l*, pg. 3507
HSBC (SINGAPORE) LTD.—See HSBC Holdings plc; *Int'l*, pg. 3506
HSBC (SINGAPORE) NOMINEES PTE. LTD.—See HSBC Holdings plc; *Int'l*, pg. 3506
HSBC TRANSACTION SERVICES GMBH—See HSBC Holdings plc; *Int'l*, pg. 3506
HSBC TRINKAUS & BURKHARDT AG—See HSBC Holdings plc; *Int'l*, pg. 3505
HSBC TRINKAUS & BURKHARDT (INTERNATIONAL) S.A.—See HSBC Holdings plc; *Int'l*, pg. 3504
HSBC TRINKAUS CAPITAL MANAGEMENT GMBH—See HSBC Holdings plc; *Int'l*, pg. 3504
HSBC TRINKAUS INVESTMENT MANAGERS S.A.—See HSBC Holdings plc; *Int'l*, pg. 3506
HSBC TRUSTEE (C.I.) LIMITED—See HSBC Holdings plc; *Int'l*, pg. 3504
HSBC TRUSTEE (CI) LIMITED—See HSBC Holdings plc; *Int'l*, pg. 3505
HSBC TRUSTEE (HONG KONG) LIMITED—See HSBC Holdings plc; *Int'l*, pg. 3507
HSBC TRUSTEE (JERSEY) LIMITED—See HSBC Holdings plc; *Int'l*, pg. 3504
HSBC TRUSTEE (SINGAPORE) LIMITED—See HSBC Holdings plc; *Int'l*, pg. 3506
HSBC UNIT TRUST MANAGEMENT LIMITED—See HSBC Holdings plc; *Int'l*, pg. 3504
HSBC USA, INC.—See HSBC Holdings plc; *Int'l*, pg. 3505
HSBC YATIRIM MENKUL DEGERLER A.S.—See HSBC Holdings plc; *Int'l*, pg. 3506
HSB ENGINEERING INSURANCE LIMITED—See Munchener Ruckversicherungs AG; *Int'l*, pg. 5090
HSB ENGINEERING INSURANCE SERVICES LIMITED—See Munchener Ruckversicherungs AG; *Int'l*, pg. 5088
HSB GROUP, INC.—See Munchener Ruckversicherungs AG; *Int'l*, pg. 5090
HSB HEIZSYSTEME UND BRENNER AG—See Max Weishaupt GmbH; *Int'l*, pg. 4735
HS BIO SDN. BHD.—See Hong Seng Consolidated Berhad; *Int'l*, pg. 3469
HSB JAPAN KK—See Munchener Ruckversicherungs AG; *Int'l*, pg. 5088
HSBK EUROPE B.V.—See Halyk Bank of Kazakhstan JSC; *Int'l*, pg. 3234
HSB PROFESSIONAL LOSS CONTROL—See Munchener Ruckversicherungs AG; *Int'l*, pg. 5090
HS BRANDS INC.—See SponsorsOne, Inc.; *Int'l*, pg. 7142
HS BRANDS INTERNATIONAL; *U.S. Private*, pg. 1998
HSB SOLOMON ASSOCIATES LLC—See Munchener Ruckversicherungs AG; *Int'l*, pg. 5088
HSB SOLOMON L.L.C.—See Munchener Ruckversicherungs AG; *Int'l*, pg. 5090
HSB TECHNICAL CONSULTING & SERVICES (SHANGHAI) COMPANY, LTD.—See Munchener Ruckversicherungs AG; *Int'l*, pg. 5088
HSC HANSEATISCHE MANAGEMENT GMBH—See Ernst Russ AG; *Int'l*, pg. 2496

HSC HANSEATISCHE SACHWERT CONCEPT GMBH—See Ernst Russ AG; *Int'l*, pg. 2496
HS COMPRESSION & PROCESS PTE LTD—See Hiap Seng Engineering Limited; *Int'l*, pg. 3382
H&S CONSTRUCTORS INC.; *U.S. Private*, pg. 1824
H.S. CROCKER CO., INC.; *U.S. Private*, pg. 1835
H.S. CROCKER CO., INC.—See H.S. Crocker Co., Inc.; *U.S. Private*, pg. 1835
HS DESIGN, INC.—See Inflexion Private Equity Partners LLP; *Int'l*, pg. 3689
HS DIE & ENGINEERING, INC.; *U.S. Private*, pg. 1998
HSD MARINE INDUSTRY(DALIAN) CO., LTD.—See Hanwha Engine Co., Ltd.; *Int'l*, pg. 3264
HS DOMS GMBH—See Metall Zug AG; *Int'l*, pg. 4846
HSD S.P.A.—See Biesse S.p.A.; *Int'l*, pg. 1020
HSD USA, INC.—See Biesse S.p.A.; *Int'l*, pg. 1020
HSE24—See IAC Inc.; *U.S. Public*, pg. 1082
HSE GROUP PTY LTD—See John Swire & Sons Limited; *Int'l*, pg. 3980
HSE INTEGRATED LTD.—See DXP Enterprises, Inc.; *U.S. Public*, pg. 697
HSE LTD.—See Mitsubishi HC Capital Inc.; *Int'l*, pg. 4951
HSF BETEILIGUNGS GMBH—See DFDS A/S; *Int'l*, pg. 2095
HSF ENTERPRISES INC.; *U.S. Private*, pg. 1999
H&S FOREST PRODUCTS INC.; *U.S. Private*, pg. 1824
H.S.F. SAMENWERKENDE FABRIEKEN B.V.—See Aalberts N.V.; *Int'l*, pg. 34
H.S. GERE & SONS INCORPORATED; *U.S. Private*, pg. 1835
HS GOVTECH SOLUTIONS INC.—See Banneker Partners, LLC; *U.S. Private*, pg. 468
HSG ZANDER FS GMBH—See EQT AB; *Int'l*, pg. 2469
HSH FACILITY MANAGEMENT GMBH—See Cerberus Capital Management, L.P.; *U.S. Private*, pg. 838
HSH FACILITY MANAGEMENT GMBH—See GoldenTree Asset Management LP; *U.S. Private*, pg. 1734
HSH FACILITY MANAGEMENT GMBH—See J.C. Flowers & Co. LLC; *U.S. Private*, pg. 2159
H&S HIGHTECH CORP. - CHINA FACTORY—See H&S HighTech Corp.; *Int'l*, pg. 3193
H&S HIGHTECH CORP.; *Int'l*, pg. 3193
HSH MANAGEMENT SERVICES LIMITED—See The Hongkong and Shanghai Hotels Limited; *Int'l*, pg. 7652
HSH MOVE+MORE GMBH—See Cerberus Capital Management, L.P.; *U.S. Private*, pg. 838
HSH MOVE+MORE GMBH—See GoldenTree Asset Management LP; *U.S. Private*, pg. 1734
HSH MOVE+MORE GMBH—See J.C. Flowers & Co. LLC; *U.S. Private*, pg. 2159
HSH N FINANCIAL SECURITIES LLC—See Cerberus Capital Management, L.P.; *U.S. Private*, pg. 838
HSH N FINANCIAL SECURITIES LLC—See GoldenTree Asset Management LP; *U.S. Private*, pg. 1734
HSH N FINANCIAL SECURITIES LLC—See J.C. Flowers & Co. LLC; *U.S. Private*, pg. 2159
HSH NORDBANK AG (LUXEMBOURG)—See Cerberus Capital Management, L.P.; *U.S. Private*, pg. 838
HSH NORDBANK AG (LUXEMBOURG)—See GoldenTree Asset Management LP; *U.S. Private*, pg. 1734
HSH NORDBANK AG (LUXEMBOURG)—See J.C. Flowers & Co. LLC; *U.S. Private*, pg. 2159
HSH NORDBANK SECURITIES S.A.—See Cerberus Capital Management, L.P.; *U.S. Private*, pg. 838
HSH NORDBANK SECURITIES S.A.—See GoldenTree Asset Management LP; *U.S. Private*, pg. 1734
HSH NORDBANK SECURITIES S.A.—See J.C. Flowers & Co. LLC; *U.S. Private*, pg. 2159
HS HOLDINGS CO., LTD.; *Int'l*, pg. 3503
HS HOLDINGS, LLC; *U.S. Private*, pg. 1998
HSHS MEDICAL GROUP INC.—See Hospital Sisters Health System; *U.S. Private*, pg. 1987
HSH-SYSTEME FUR PROZESS-IT GMBH—See AZO GmbH & Co. KG; *Int'l*, pg. 780
HSIA HOSPITALITY SERVICES NETHERLANDS B.V.—See Swisscom AG; *Int'l*, pg. 7373
HSIA HOSPITALITY SERVICES PORTUGAL SA—See Swisscom AG; *Int'l*, pg. 7373
HSI AUTOMOTIVES LTD.—See Hwaseung Industries Co., Ltd.; *Int'l*, pg. 3542
HSIN BA BA CORPORATION; *Int'l*, pg. 3507
HSIN CHONG GROUP HOLDINGS LIMITED; *Int'l*, pg. 3507
HSIN DAR ENVIRONMENT CORPORATION—See Continental Holdings Corp.; *Int'l*, pg. 1784
H.S. INDIA LTD.; *Int'l*, pg. 3196
HSIN FENG BUFF FACTORY CO., LTD.—See Jason Industries, Inc.; *U.S. Private*, pg. 2190
HSING LUNG SDN BHD—See Karyon Industries Berhad; *Int'l*, pg. 4086
HSING TA CEMENT CO., LTD.; *Int'l*, pg. 3507
HSINJING HOLDING CO., LTD.; *Int'l*, pg. 3507
HSIN KAO GAS CO., LTD.; *Int'l*, pg. 3507
HSIN KUANG STEEL CO., LTD.; *Int'l*, pg. 3507
HSIN-LI CHEMICAL INDUSTRIAL CORP.; *Int'l*, pg. 3507
HSIN SIN TEXTILE CO., LTD.; *Int'l*, pg. 3507
HSIN TAI GAS CO., LTD.; *Int'l*, pg. 3507
HSIN YUNG CHIEN CO., LTD.; *Int'l*, pg. 3507

HSIN YUNG CHIEN RUBBER CO.,LTD.—See Hsin Yung Chien Co., Ltd.; *Int'l*, pg. 3507
HSIN YUNG CHIEN (TIANJIN) CO.,LTD.—See Hsin Yung Chien Co., Ltd.; *Int'l*, pg. 3507
HSK PARTNERS; *Int'l*, pg. 3507
HSL ELECTRONICS CORP.—See SL Corporation; *Int'l*, pg. 6995
HSL PATHOLOGY LLP—See Sonic Healthcare Limited; *Int'l*, pg. 7097
HSLS RUBBER INDUSTRIES SDA. BHD.—See Hwaseung Industries Co., Ltd.; *Int'l*, pg. 3542
H&S MANUFACTURING CO. INC.—See Heik Holding Company Inc.; *U.S. Private*, pg. 1904
HS MARSTON AEROSPACE LIMITED—See RTX Corporation; *U.S. Public*, pg. 1821
HSMC ORIZON LLC; *U.S. Private*, pg. 1999
HSM DEVELOPMENT, INC.—See Henry S. Miller Management Corp.; *U.S. Private*, pg. 1919
HSM DO BRASIL S.A.—See Anima Holding SA; *Int'l*, pg. 471
H.S. MORGAN LIMITED PARTNERSHIP; *U.S. Private*, pg. 1835
HSN CATALOG SERVICES, INC.—See Qurate Retail, Inc.; *U.S. Public*, pg. 1758
HS NETWORKS INDIA PVT LTD—See Hwaseung Industries Co., Ltd.; *Int'l*, pg. 3542
HSN IMPROVEMENTS, LLC—See Qurate Retail, Inc.; *U.S. Private*, pg. 1758
HSN, INC.—See Qurate Retail, Inc.; *U.S. Public*, pg. 1758
HSN, LLC—See IAC Inc.; *U.S. Public*, pg. 1082
H&S OIL COMPANY INC.; *U.S. Private*, pg. 1824
HS OPTIMUS HOLDINGS LIMITED; *Int'l*, pg. 3503
HS ORKA HF—See Innergex Renewable Energy Inc.; *Int'l*, pg. 3708
H-SOURCE HOLDINGS LTD.; *Int'l*, pg. 3194
HS PENTA AFRICA PTY LTD—See Interpump Group S.p.A.; *Int'l*, pg. 3755
HSP EPI ACQUISITIONS, LLC—See Augeo Affinity Marketing, Inc.; *U.S. Private*, pg. 392
HSP GROUP LIMITED—See Sumitomo Corporation; *Int'l*, pg. 7273
HSP HOCHSPANNUNGSGERATE GMBH—See Siemens Energy AG; *Int'l*, pg. 6902
HSP HOESCH SPUNDWAND UND PROFIL GMBH—See Salzgitter AG; *Int'l*, pg. 6496
HSP, INC.—See Brookfield Corporation; *Int'l*, pg. 1183
HS PIPEQUIPMENT (ABERDEEN) LIMITED—See Sumitomo Corporation; *Int'l*, pg. 7273
HS PIPEQUIPMENT (NORTHERN) LIMITED—See Sumitomo Corporation; *Int'l*, pg. 7273
HSPI S.P.A.—See TXT e-Solutions S.p.A.; *Int'l*, pg. 7993
H&S PRODUCTIONS, LLC—See CJ Corporation; *Int'l*, pg. 1634
H&S PROPERTIES DEVELOPMENT CORPORATION—See H&S Bakery Inc.; *U.S. Private*, pg. 1823
HSQ TECHNOLOGY INC—See Wind Point Advisors LLC; *U.S. Private*, pg. 4535
H. SQUARED, INC.; *U.S. Private*, pg. 1825
HSR BELGIUM S.A./N.V.—See Wurth Verwaltungsgesellschaft mbH; *Int'l*, pg. 8505
HSR GMBH HOCHDRUCK SCHLAUCH + ROHRVERBINDUNGEN—See Wurth Verwaltungsgesellschaft mbH; *Int'l*, pg. 8505
HSR GMBH—See Wurth Verwaltungsgesellschaft mbH; *Int'l*, pg. 8506
HSR ITALIA S.R.L.—See Wurth Verwaltungsgesellschaft mbH; *Int'l*, pg. 8505
HSRL HOLDINGS LLC—See Ampersand Management LLC; *U.S. Private*, pg. 265
HSR PROPERTY CONSULTANTS PTE LTD—See 3Cnergy Limited; *Int'l*, pg. 7
HSS BIM SOLUTIONS PRIVATE LIMITED—See HSS Engineers Berhad; *Int'l*, pg. 3507
HSS ENGINEERS BERHAD; *Int'l*, pg. 3507
HSS HIRE GROUP PLC—See Exponent Private Equity LLP; *Int'l*, pg. 2589
HSS SYSTEMS, LLC—See HCA Healthcare, Inc.; *U.S. Public*, pg. 998
H & S STAHLBAU AG—See Hutter & Schrantz PMS Ges.m.b.H; *Int'l*, pg. 3540
H. & S. SWANSONS' TOOL COMPANY—See The Jordan Company, L.P.; *U.S. Private*, pg. 4060
HST BETEILIGUNGS GMBH—See Raiffeisen-Landesbank Steiermark AG; *Int'l*, pg. 6186
HST CO, LTD.—See Hirose Electric Co., Ltd.; *Int'l*, pg. 3405
HS TECHNOLOGY CO., LTD.—See DY Corporation; *Int'l*, pg. 2237
H.STERN BUENOS AIRES—See H. Stern Com & Ind., S.A.; *Int'l*, pg. 3195
H. STERN COM & IND., S.A.; *Int'l*, pg. 3195
H.STERN ISRAEL—See H. Stern Com & Ind., S.A.; *Int'l*, pg. 3195
H. STERN JEWELERS, INC.—See H. Stern Com & Ind., S.A.; *Int'l*, pg. 3195
H.STERN LIMA—See H. Stern Com & Ind., S.A.; *Int'l*, pg. 3195

HST GLOBAL, INC.; *U.S. Public*, pg. 1065
HST (HONGKONG) LTD—See Hirose Electric Co., Ltd.; *Int'l*, pg. 3405
HST MASCHINENBAU GMBH—See Krones AG; *Int'l*, pg. 4305
HST MATERIALS, INC.—See JBC Technologies, Inc.; *U.S. Private*, pg. 2193
H&S TRANSPORTATION CO. INC.—See EverArc Holdings Limited; *Int'l*, pg. 2563
HSU DEVELOPMENT; *U.S. Private*, pg. 1999
HSU FU CHI INTERNATIONAL LIMITED—See Nestle S.A.; *Int'l*, pg. 5203
H. SUKOPP GESELLSCHAFT MBH—See Nicolas Correa S.A.; *Int'l*, pg. 5273
HSUS GINSENG ENTERPRISES, INC.; *U.S. Private*, pg. 1999
HS VALVE CO., LTD - FACTORY III—See HS VALVE CO., LTD; *Int'l*, pg. 3503
HS VALVE CO., LTD - FACTORY II—See HS VALVE CO., LTD; *Int'l*, pg. 3503
HS VALVE CO., LTD; *Int'l*, pg. 3503
HSW GMBH; *Int'l*, pg. 3507
HSW INC.—See Balfour Beatty plc; *Int'l*, pg. 808
HT-315 TRUMBULL STREET ASSOCIATES, LLC—See KSL Capital Partners, LLC; *U.S. Private*, pg. 2355
HTAG HAFEN UND TRANSPORT AG—See Stadtwerke Koln GmbH; *Int'l*, pg. 7161
HT AUTOMOTIVE, LLC—See Penske Automotive Group, Inc.; *U.S. Public*, pg. 1665
HTB ENERGY CO., LTD.—See H.I.S. Co., Ltd.; *Int'l*, pg. 3195
HTB ENGENHARIA E CONSTRCAO S.A.—See Zech Group SE; *Int'l*, pg. 8628
H.T. BERRY CO. INC.—See Kelso & Company, L.P.; *U.S. Private*, pg. 2279
H.T. BERRY CO. INC.—See Warburg Pincus LLC; *U.S. Private*, pg. 4436
HTB - HOCH-TIEF-BAU SRL—See Swietelsky Baugesellschaft m.b.H.; *Int'l*, pg. 7367
HTC-AED, A.S.—See HTC holding a.s.; *Int'l*, pg. 3508
HTC AMERICA, INC.—See HTC Corporation; *Int'l*, pg. 3508
HTC CORPORATION; *Int'l*, pg. 3508
HTC EUROPE CO., LTD.—See HTC Corporation; *Int'l*, pg. 3508
HTC GLOBAL SERVICES INC.; *U.S. Private*, pg. 1999
HTC HOLDING A.S.; *Int'l*, pg. 3508
HTC HOLDING COMPANY; *U.S. Private*, pg. 1999
HTC HYDROGEN TECHNOLOGIES CORP.—See HTC Purenergy Inc.; *Int'l*, pg. 3508
HTC INC.; *U.S. Private*, pg. 1999
HTC NETHERLANDS B.V.—See HTC Corporation; *Int'l*, pg. 3508
HT CONCEPTS, INCORPORATED; *U.S. Private*, pg. 1999
HTC PURENERGY INC.; *Int'l*, pg. 3508
HTC U.S.A., INC.—See HTC holding a.s.; *Int'l*, pg. 3508
HTC VAN CENTRE LTD—See Ballyvesey Holdings Limited; *Int'l*, pg. 809
HTEC LTD—See TA Associates, Inc.; *U.S. Private*, pg. 3917
HTE GMBH—See BASF SE; *Int'l*, pg. 886
HTE NORTHEAST—See Charterhouse Capital Partners LLP; *Int'l*, pg. 1456
HTG MANAGED SERVICES LIMITED—See Helios Towers PLC; *Int'l*, pg. 3330
HTG MOLECULAR DIAGNOSTICS, INC.; *U.S. Public*, pg. 1065
H&T GROUP PLC; *Int'l*, pg. 3193
HTG STEVEDORING OY—See AS Infortar; *Int'l*, pg. 590
THE H.T. HACKNEY COMPANY; *U.S. Private*, pg. 4041
THE H.T. HACKNEY CO.—See The H.T. Hackney Company; *U.S. Private*, pg. 4041
THE H.T. HACKNEY CO.—See The H.T. Hackney Company; *U.S. Private*, pg. 4041
THE H.T. HACKNEY CO.—See The H.T. Hackney Company; *U.S. Private*, pg. 4041
THE H.T. HACKNEY CO.—See The H.T. Hackney Company; *U.S. Private*, pg. 4041
THE H.T. HACKNEY CO.—See The H.T. Hackney Company; *U.S. Private*, pg. 4041
HTH CORPORATION; *U.S. Private*, pg. 1999
HT HEIZEELEMENTE DEUTSCHLAND GMBH—See NIBE Industrier AB; *Int'l*, pg. 5260
HTH EKSPERT W. KUCHNI S.P.Z.O.O.—See Nobia AB; *Int'l*, pg. 5395
HTH GOR DET SELV VIBORG A.P.S.—See Nobia AB; *Int'l*, pg. 5395
HTH GRUPPEN FYN A/S—See Nobia AB; *Int'l*, pg. 5395
HTH HEATECH INC.; *Int'l*, pg. 3508
HTH KOKKENER A/S—See Nobia AB; *Int'l*, pg. 5395
HTH KOKKENFORUM AABENRAA A/S—See Nobia AB; *Int'l*, pg. 5395
HTH KOKKENFORUM ARHUS A/S—See Nobia AB; *Int'l*, pg. 5395
HTH KOKKENFORUM HOLSTEBRO A.P.S.—See Nobia AB; *Int'l*, pg. 5395
HTH KOKKENFORUM KOGE A/S—See Nobia AB; *Int'l*, pg. 5395
HTH KOKKENFORUM NAESTVED A/S—See Nobia AB; *Int'l*, pg. 5395

HTH HEATECH INC. — CORPORATE AFFILIATIONS

HTH KOKKENFORUM VIBORG A.P.S.—See Nobia AB; *Int'l*, pg. 5395
HTH KUCHEN GMBH—See Nobia AB; *Int'l*, pg. 5395
HTH OST A/S—See Nobia AB; *Int'l*, pg. 5395
HTH SKIVE-SILKEBORG A/S—See Nobia AB; *Int'l*, pg. 5395
HTI HIGH TECH INDUSTRIES AG; *Int'l*, pg. 3508
HTK C&H ASIA PACIFIC PTE LTD.—See Minebea Mitsumi Inc.; *Int'l*, pg. 4902
HTK C&H (THAILAND) LTD.—See Minebea Mitsumi Inc.; *Int'l*, pg. 4902
HTK ENGINEERING CO., LTD.—See Minebea Mitsumi Inc.; *Int'l*, pg. 4902
HTK EUROPE LTD.—See Minebea Mitsumi Inc.; *Int'l*, pg. 4902
HTK HONG KONG LTD.—See Minebea Mitsumi Inc.; *Int'l*, pg. 4902
HTK/HUNT TRAINA KENNARD INSURANCE AGENCY, INC.—See World Insurance Associates LLC; *U.S. Private*, pg. 4566
HT KOREA CO., LTD—See Haitian International Holdings Ltd.; *Int'l*, pg. 3217
HTL AUSTRALASIA PTY. LTD.—See Enerpac Tool Group Corp.; *U.S. Public*, pg. 765
HTL AUSTRALIA PTY LTD—See Yihua Lifestyle Technology Co., Ltd.; *Int'l*, pg. 8582
HTL FURNITURE (CHANGSHU) CO., LTD.—See Yihua Lifestyle Technology Co., Ltd.; *Int'l*, pg. 8582
HTL FURNITURE (HUAI AN) CO., LTD.—See Yihua Lifestyle Technology Co., Ltd.; *Int'l*, pg. 8582
H.T.L. FURNITURE, INC—See Yihua Lifestyle Technology Co., Ltd.; *Int'l*, pg. 8582
HTL FURNITURE (KUNSHAN) CO., LTD.—See Yihua Lifestyle Technology Co., Ltd.; *Int'l*, pg. 8582
HTL FURNITURE (YANGZHOU) CO., LTD.—See Yihua Lifestyle Technology Co., Ltd.; *Int'l*, pg. 8582
HTL HOME (JIANG SU) CO., LTD.—See Yihua Lifestyle Technology Co., Ltd.; *Int'l*, pg. 8582
HTL INTERNATIONAL GMBH—See Yihua Lifestyle Technology Co., Ltd.; *Int'l*, pg. 8582
HTL INTERNATIONAL HOLDINGS PTE LTD—See Yihua Lifestyle Technology Co., Ltd.; *Int'l*, pg. 8582
HTL INTERNATIONAL PTE LTD—See Yihua Lifestyle Technology Co., Ltd.; *Int'l*, pg. 8582
HTL KOREA CO., LTD.—See Yihua Lifestyle Technology Co., Ltd.; *Int'l*, pg. 8582
HTL LEATHER (CHINA) CO., LTD.—See Yihua Lifestyle Technology Co., Ltd.; *Int'l*, pg. 8582
HTL LIMITED—See HFCL Limited; *Int'l*, pg. 3375
HTL MANUFACTURING PTE LTD—See Yihua Lifestyle Technology Co., Ltd.; *Int'l*, pg. 8582
HTL (UK) LIMITED—See Yihua Lifestyle Technology Co., Ltd.; *Int'l*, pg. 8582
HTL VERPACKUNG, GMBH—See Inapa - Investimentos, Participacoes e Gestao, SA; *Int'l*, pg. 3645
H.T. LYONS, INC.—See ENGIE SA; *Int'l*, pg. 2429
H&T MARSBERG GMBH & CO. KG—See Heitkamp & Thumann KG; *Int'l*, pg. 3326
HT MEDIA LIMITED; *Int'l*, pg. 3508
HT MICRON—See Hana Micron Inc.; *Int'l*, pg. 3241
HTM INTERNATIONAL HOLDING LTD.; *Int'l*, pg. 3508
HT MMOBILE INC—See Sunplus Technology Co., Ltd.; *Int'l*, pg. 7320
HTM USA HOLDINGS INC.—See Head B.V.; *Int'l*, pg. 3300
HT MUSIC AND ENTERTAINMENT COMPANY LIMITED—See HT Media Limited; *Int'l*, pg. 3508
H-TPA KFT.—See STRABAG SE; *Int'l*, pg. 7230
HTP FONTANA A.D.; *Int'l*, pg. 3508
HTP HIGH TECH PLASTICS GMBH—See Nanogate SE; *Int'l*, pg. 5143
HTP HUISAPOTHEEK B.V.—See Bain Capital, LP; *U.S. Private*, pg. 443
HTP HUISAPOTHEEK B.V.—See Cinven Limited; *Int'l*, pg. 1613
H.T.P. INVESTMENTS BV; *Int'l*, pg. 3196
HTP KORCULA D.D.; *Int'l*, pg. 3509
HTP OREBIC D.D.; *Int'l*, pg. 3509
HTR CORPORATION LTD.—See Sino-Thai Engineering & Construction Public Company Limited; *Int'l*, pg. 6949
HTS AMA SP.Z.O.O.—See Hollywood SA; *Int'l*, pg. 3452
HTS BALTICA SP.Z.O.O.—See Hollywood SA; *Int'l*, pg. 3452
HTS BAXTER SP.Z.O.O.—See Hollywood SA; *Int'l*, pg. 3452
H & T SEAFOOD, INC.; *U.S. Private*, pg. 1822
HTS ENGINEERING LTD.; *Int'l*, pg. 3509
HTS FORWARDING MALAYSIA SDN. BHD.—See KKR & Co. Inc.; *U.S. Public*, pg. 1258
HTS-LOAN SERVICING, INC.—See Hyatt Hotels Corporation; *U.S. Public*, pg. 1077
HTS MEDIJ SP.Z.O.O.—See Hollywood SA; *Int'l*, pg. 3452
HT S.P.A.—See NIBE Industrier AB; *Int'l*, pg. 5261
HTSS, INC.; *U.S. Private*, pg. 1999
HTS STARGARD SP.Z.O.O.—See Hollywood SA; *Int'l*, pg. 3452
HTS TARGATZ GMBH—See Hollywood SA; *Int'l*, pg. 3452
HTS (USA) INC.—See OMNIQ Corp.; *U.S. Public*, pg. 1600

HT SWEENEY & SON INC.—See Southwest Gas Holdings, Inc.; *U.S. Public*, pg. 1913
HT&T COMPANY—See C. Brewer & Co. Ltd.; *U.S. Private*, pg. 705
HTT, INC.; *U.S. Private*, pg. 1999
H.T.U.P. PARK A.D.; *Int'l*, pg. 3196
HT USA INC.—See Hidria d.o.o.; *Int'l*, pg. 3384
HTV GMBH; *Int'l*, pg. 3509
H&T WATERBURY INC.—See Heitkamp & Thumann KG; *Int'l*, pg. 3326
HT WINDOW FASHIONS; *U.S. Private*, pg. 1999
HUAAN ASSET MANAGEMENT (HONG KONG) LIMITED—See Guotai Junan Securities Co., Ltd.; *Int'l*, pg. 3187
HUAAN FUNDS MANAGEMENT CO., LTD.—See Guotai Junan Securities Co., Ltd.; *Int'l*, pg. 3187
HUAAN SECURITIES CO. LTD; *Int'l*, pg. 3510
HUABANG CORPORATE FINANCE LIMITED—See Huabang Technology Holdings Limited; *Int'l*, pg. 3510
HUABANG SECURITIES LIMITED—See Huabang Technology Holdings Limited; *Int'l*, pg. 3510
HUABANG TECHNOLOGY HOLDINGS LIMITED; *Int'l*, pg. 3510
HUABAO FLAVOURS & FRAGRANCES CO., LTD.—See Huabao International Holdings Limited; *Int'l*, pg. 3510
HUABAO FLAVOURS & FRAGRANCES (HK) LIMITED—See Huabao International Holdings Limited; *Int'l*, pg. 3510
HUABAO INTERNATIONAL HOLDINGS LIMITED; *Int'l*, pg. 3510
HUABO BIOPHARM (SHANGHAI) CO., LTD.; *Int'l*, pg. 3511
HUA CAPITAL MANAGEMENT CO., LTD.; *Int'l*, pg. 3509
HUACHANGDA INTELLIGENT EQUIPMENT GROUP CO., LTD.; *Int'l*, pg. 3511
HUACHENG REAL ESTATE SA; *Int'l*, pg. 3511
HUACHENG TOKO ELECTRONICS CO., LTD.—See Murata Manufacturing Co., Ltd.; *Int'l*, pg. 5098
HUACHEN PRECISION EQUIPMENT (KUNSHAN) CO., LTD.; *Int'l*, pg. 3511
HUADA AUTOMOTIVE TECHNOLOGY CO.,LTD.; *Int'l*, pg. 3511
HUADIAN ENERGY COMPANY LIMITED—See China Huadian Corporation Ltd.; *Int'l*, pg. 1508
HUADIAN FUXIN ENERGY CORPORATION LIMITED—See China Huadian Corporation Ltd.; *Int'l*, pg. 1508
HUADIAN HEAVY INDUSTRIES CO.,LTD.; *Int'l*, pg. 3511
HUADIAN LIAONING ENERGY DEVELOPMENT CO., LTD.; *Int'l*, pg. 3511
HUADIAN POWER INTERNATIONAL CORPORATION LIMITED; *Int'l*, pg. 3511
HUADI INTERNATIONAL GROUP CO., LTD.; *Int'l*, pg. 3511
HUADONG MEDICINE CO., LTD.; *Int'l*, pg. 3511
HUA ENG WIRE & CABLE CO., LTD. - KAO-NAN FACTORY—See Hua Eng Wire & Cable Co., Ltd.; *Int'l*, pg. 3509
HUA ENG WIRE & CABLE CO., LTD.; *Int'l*, pg. 3509
HUAFA INDUSTRIAL CO., LTD.—See Zhuhai Huafa Group Co., Ltd; *Int'l*, pg. 8677
HUAFANG CO., LTD.; *Int'l*, pg. 3511
HUAFA PROPERTY SERVICES GROUP COMPANY LIMITED; *Int'l*, pg. 3511
HUAFENG SMITHS INTERCONNECT (SICHUAN) CO., LTD.—See Smiths Group plc; *Int'l*, pg. 7009
HUAFENG TEST & CONTROL TECHNOLOGY (TIANJIN) CO., LTD.—See Beijing Huafeng Test & Control Technology Co., Ltd.; *Int'l*, pg. 952
HUAFENG TRADING MACAO COMMERCIAL OFFSHORE LIMITED—See Blockchain Group Company Limited; *Int'l*, pg. 1064
HUAFON CHEMICAL CO., LTD.; *Int'l*, pg. 3511
HUAFON FOREIGN TRADE CO., LTD.—See Huafon Chemical Co., Ltd.; *Int'l*, pg. 3511
HUAFON MICROFIBRE (SHANGHAI) CO., LTD.; *Int'l*, pg. 3511
HUAFU FASHION CO., LTD.; *Int'l*, pg. 3512
HUA GANG INTERNATIONAL TRADING CO., LTD.—See Wah Lee Industrial Corp.; *Int'l*, pg. 8329
HUAGONG TECH COMPANY LIMITED; *Int'l*, pg. 3512
HUAHAI JAPAN PHARM CO., LTD.—See Zhejiang Huahai Pharmaceutical Co., Ltd.; *Int'l*, pg. 8655
HUAHAI PHARMACEUTICAL SALES CO., LTD.—See Zhejiang Huahai Pharmaceutical Co., Ltd.; *Int'l*, pg. 8655
HUAHAI US INC.—See Zhejiang Huahai Pharmaceutical Co., Ltd.; *Int'l*, pg. 8655
HUA HAN HEALTH INDUSTRY HOLDINGS LIMITED; *Int'l*, pg. 3509
HUAHIN POOL SUITE CO., LTD.—See Veranda Resort Public Company Limited; *Int'l*, pg. 8164
HUA HONG SEMICONDUCTOR LIMITED; *Int'l*, pg. 3509
HUAHUI EDUCATION GROUP LIMITED; *Int'l*, pg. 3512
HUAIAN FEILI SUPPLY CHAIN MANAGEMENT CO., LTD.—See Jiangsu Feiliks International Logistics Inc.; *Int'l*, pg. 3946

HUAIAN FUYANG ELECTRONIC MATERIAL CO., LIMITED—See Long Young Electronic (Kunshan) Co., Ltd.; *Int'l*, pg. 4549
HUAIAN GLORY CHEMICAL CO., LTD.—See Jiangsu Flag Chemical Industry Co., Ltd.; *Int'l*, pg. 3946
HUAIAN HONGFU HANHAN SCIENCE AND TECHNOLOGY CO., LTD.—See Shenzhen Hongfuhan Technology Co., Ltd.; *Int'l*, pg. 6812
HUAIAN LIANFA TEXTILES CO., LTD.—See Jiangsu Lianfa Textile Co., Ltd.; *Int'l*, pg. 3950
HUAIAN WANBANG AROMATIC CHEMICALS INDUSTRY CO., LTD—See Wanxiang International Limited; *Int'l*, pg. 8343
HUAIAN WANT WANT FOODS LTD.—See Want Want China Holdings Ltd; *Int'l*, pg. 8342
HUAIBEI GREENGOLD INDUSTRY INVESTMENT CO., LTD.; *Int'l*, pg. 3512
HUAIBEI MINING HOLDINGS CO., LTD.; *Int'l*, pg. 3512
HUAIHE ENERGY (GROUP) CO., LTD.; *Int'l*, pg. 3512
HUAIHUA XIANGDA CAMEL FEED CO., LTD—See Tangrenshen Group Co., Ltd.; *Int'l*, pg. 7458
HUAIJI DENGYUN AUTO-PARTS (HOLDING) CO., LTD.; *Int'l*, pg. 3512
HUAIZHONG HEALTH GROUP, INC.; *Int'l*, pg. 3512
HUAJIN FINANCIAL (INTERNATIONAL) HOLDINGS LIMITED—See Huafa Property Services Group Company Limited; *Int'l*, pg. 3511
HUAJIN (HONG KONG) LIMITED—See Huayou Cobalt Co., Ltd.; *Int'l*, pg. 3516
HUAJIN INTERNATIONAL HOLDINGS LIMITED; *Int'l*, pg. 3512
HUA JUNG COMPONENTS CO., LTD.; *Int'l*, pg. 3509
HUA JUNG ELECTRONICS (GUANG DONG) CO., LTD.—See Hua Jung Components Co., Ltd.; *Int'l*, pg. 3509
HUA JUNG ELECTRONICS (SHANGHAI) CO., LTD.—See Hua Jung Components Co., Ltd.; *Int'l*, pg. 3509
HUAKANG BIOMEDICAL HOLDINGS CO., LTD.; *Int'l*, pg. 3512
HUAKAN INTERNATIONAL MINING INC.; *Int'l*, pg. 3512
HUAKE HOLDING BIOLOGY CO., LTD.; *Int'l*, pg. 3512
HUAKU DEVELOPMENT CO., LTD.; *Int'l*, pg. 3512
HUALAN BIOLOGICAL ENGINEERING INC.; *Int'l*, pg. 3512
HUALAN GROUP CO., LTD.; *Int'l*, pg. 3512
HUALE ACOUSTICS CORPORATION; *Int'l*, pg. 3512
HUA LIEN INTERNATIONAL (HOLDING) COMPANY LIMITED—See China National Complete Plant Import & Export Corporation; *Int'l*, pg. 1531
HUALI INDUSTRIAL GROUP COMPANY LIMITED; *Int'l*, pg. 3512
HUALI INDUSTRIES CO LTD; *Int'l*, pg. 3513
HUALU ENGINEERING & TECHNOLOGY CO., LTD.—See China National Chemical Engineering Co., Ltd.; *Int'l*, pg. 1531
HUALU OPTICAL STORAGE INSTITUTE (DALIAN) CO., LTD.—See Beijing E-Hualu Information Technology Co., Ltd.; *Int'l*, pg. 949
HUALU SENIOR CARE & HEALTH DEVELOPMENT CO., LTD.—See Beijing E-Hualu Information Technology Co., Ltd.; *Int'l*, pg. 949
HUA MEDICINE LTD.; *Int'l*, pg. 3509
HUAMING POWER EQUIPMENT CO., LTD.; *Int'l*, pg. 3513
HUA NAN ASSETS MANAGEMENT CO., LTD.—See Hua Nan Financial Holdings Co., Ltd.; *Int'l*, pg. 3509
HUA NAN COMMERCIAL BANK, LTD. - OFFSHORE BANKING—See Hua Nan Financial Holdings Co., Ltd.; *Int'l*, pg. 3509
HUA NAN COMMERCIAL BANK, LTD. - SINGAPORE—See Hua Nan Financial Holdings Co., Ltd.; *Int'l*, pg. 3509
HUA NAN COMMERCIAL BANK, LTD.—See Hua Nan Financial Holdings Co., Ltd.; *Int'l*, pg. 3509
HUA NAN COMMERCIAL BANK, LTD.—See Hua Nan Financial Holdings Co., Ltd.; *Int'l*, pg. 3509
HUA NAN FINANCIAL HOLDINGS CO., LTD.; *Int'l*, pg. 3509
HUA NAN INVESTMENT TRUST CORPORATION—See Hua Nan Financial Holdings Co., Ltd.; *Int'l*, pg. 3509
HUA NAN MANAGEMENT & CONSULTING CO., LTD.—See Hua Nan Financial Holdings Co., Ltd.; *Int'l*, pg. 3509
HUA NAN SECURITIES CO., LTD.—See Hua Nan Financial Holdings Co., Ltd.; *Int'l*, pg. 3510
HUA NAN SECURITIES INVESTMENT TRUST CO., LTD.—See Hua Nan Financial Holdings Co., Ltd.; *Int'l*, pg. 3510
HUA NAN VENTURE CAPITAL CO., LTD.—See Hua Nan Financial Holdings Co., Ltd.; *Int'l*, pg. 3510
HU AN CABLE HOLDINGS LTD.; *Int'l*, pg. 3509
HUANCHUN CEMENT INTERNATIONAL CORPORATION LTD.—See Universal Cement Corporation; *Int'l*, pg. 8078
HUANENG CAPITAL SERVICES CO., LTD.—See China Huaneng Group Co., Ltd.; *Int'l*, pg. 1509
HUANENG GUICHENG TRUST CO., LTD.—See China Huaneng Group Co., Ltd.; *Int'l*, pg. 1509

COMPANY NAME INDEX

HUANENG INVESCO WLR INVESTMENT CONSULTING CO., LTD.—See China Huaneng Group Co., Ltd.; *Int'l*, pg. 1509
HUANENG LANCANG RIVER HYDROPOWER CO., LTD.—See China Huaneng Group Co., Ltd.; *Int'l*, pg. 1509
HUANENG POWER INTERNATIONAL, INC.—See China Huaneng Group Co., Ltd.; *Int'l*, pg. 1509
HUANENG RENEWABLES CORPORATION LIMITED—See China Huaneng Group Co., Ltd.; *Int'l*, pg. 1509
HUANG HSIANG CONSTRUCTION CORPORATION; *Int'l*, pg. 3513
HUANGHUA JUJIN HARDWARE PRODUCTS CO., LTD.—See Tycoons Group Enterprise Co., Ltd.; *Int'l*, pg. 7994
HUANGHUA SEWON AUTOMATIVE TECHHNOLOGY CO., LTD.—See Sewon Precision Industry Co., Ltd.; *Int'l*, pg. 6737
HUANGHUA SEWON AUTOMATIVE TECHNOLOGY CO., LTD.—See SEWON CORPORATION Co., Ltd.; *Int'l*, pg. 6736
HUANG LONG CO., LTD.—See Square Enix Holdings Co. Ltd.; *Int'l*, pg. 7147
HUANGSHAN CHINA INTERNATIONAL TRAVEL SERVICE CO., LTD.—See China Tourism Group Duty Free Corporation Limited; *Int'l*, pg. 1560
HUANGSHAN CHINA OVERSEAS TRAVEL SERVICE MANAGEMENT CO., LTD.—See Huangshan Tourism Development Co., Ltd.; *Int'l*, pg. 3513
HUANGSHAN HUAJIA SURFACE TECHNOLOGY CO., LTD.—See PPG Industries, Inc.; *U.S. Public*, pg. 1707
HUANGSHAN HUASHAN MYSTERY CAVE TOURISM DEVELOPMENT CO., LTD.—See Huangshan Tourism Development Co., Ltd.; *Int'l*, pg. 3513
HUANGSHAN INTERNATIONAL HOTEL CO., LTD.—See Huangshan Tourism Development Co., Ltd.; *Int'l*, pg. 3513
HUANGSHAN LONGSHENG CHEMICAL CO., LTD.—See Zhejiang Longsheng Group Co., Ltd.; *Int'l*, pg. 8659
HUANGSHAN NOVEL CO., LTD.; *Int'l*, pg. 3513
HUANGSHAN PROCUREMENT AND DISTRIBUTION CENTER CO.—See Huangshan Tourism Development Co., Ltd.; *Int'l*, pg. 3513
HUANGSHAN TAIPING LAKE CULTURAL TOURISM CO., LTD.—See Huangshan Tourism Development Co., Ltd.; *Int'l*, pg. 3513
HUANGSHAN TOURISM DEVELOPMENT CO., LTD.; *Int'l*, pg. 3513
HUANGSHAN TUMAMART TOURISM E-COMMERCE CO., LTD.—See Huangshan Tourism Development Co., Ltd.; *Int'l*, pg. 3513
HUANGSHAN XIHAI HOTEL CO., LTD.—See Huangshan Tourism Development Co., Ltd.; *Int'l*, pg. 3513
HUANGSHAN YUCHENG CROWNE PLAZA HOTELS & RESORTS LTD.—See Huangshan Tourism Development Co., Ltd.; *Int'l*, pg. 3513
HUANGSHI DONGBEI ELECTRICAL APPLIANCE CO., LTD.; *Int'l*, pg. 3513
HUANGSHI G&D WANDA SECURITY CARD CO. LTD.—See Giesecke & Devrient GmbH; *Int'l*, pg. 2970
HUANGSHI JIUFENG INTELLIGENT MECHANICAL & ELECTRICAL CO., LTD.—See SanFeng Intelligent Equipment Group Co., Ltd.; *Int'l*, pg. 6536
HUAN HSIN HOLDINGS LTD.; *Int'l*, pg. 3513
HUANLEJIA FOOD GROUP CO., LTD.; *Int'l*, pg. 3513
HUAN MING (SHANGHAI) INTERNATIONAL SHIPPING AGENCY CO., LTD.—See Yang Ming Marine Transport Corporation; *Int'l*, pg. 8560
HUANXI MEDIA GROUP LIMITED; *Int'l*, pg. 3513
HUAPENG GLASS (HEZE) CO., LTD.—See Shangdong Huapeng Glass Co., Ltd.; *Int'l*, pg. 6760
HUAPONT LIFE SCIENCES CO., LTD.; *Int'l*, pg. 3514
HUAREN PHARMACEUTICAL CO., LTD.; *Int'l*, pg. 3514
HUARONG CAPITAL MANAGEMENT CO., LTD.—See China CITIC Financial Asset Management Co., Ltd.; *Int'l*, pg. 1489
HUARONG CHEMICAL CO., LTD.; *Int'l*, pg. 3514
HUARONG CONSUMER FINANCE CO., LTD.—See Bank of Ningbo Co., Ltd.; *Int'l*, pg. 847
HUARONG FINANCIAL LEASING CO., LTD.—See China CITIC Financial Asset Management Co., Ltd.; *Int'l*, pg. 1489
HUARONG FINANCIAL (SHENZHEN) EQUITY INVESTMENT FUND MANAGEMENT CO., LTD.—See China CITIC Financial Asset Management Co., Ltd.; *Int'l*, pg. 1489
HUARONG FUTURES CO., LTD.—See China CITIC Financial Asset Management Co., Ltd.; *Int'l*, pg. 1489
HUARONG (HK) INTERNATIONAL HOLDINGS LIMITED—See China CITIC Financial Asset Management Co., Ltd.; *Int'l*, pg. 1489
HUARONG HUITONG ASSET MANAGEMENT CO., LTD.—See China CITIC Financial Asset Management Co., Ltd.; *Int'l*, pg. 1489
HUARONG INDUSTRIAL INVESTMENT & MANAGEMENT CO., LTD.—See China CITIC Financial Asset Management Co., Ltd.; *Int'l*, pg. 1489

HUARONG INTERNATIONAL ASSET MANAGEMENT LIMITED—See China CITIC Financial Asset Management Co., Ltd.; *Int'l*, pg. 1489
HUARONG INTERNATIONAL FINANCIAL HOLDINGS LIMITED—See China CITIC Financial Asset Management Co., Ltd.; *Int'l*, pg. 1489
HUARONG INTERNATIONAL SECURITIES LIMITED—See China CITIC Financial Asset Management Co., Ltd.; *Int'l*, pg. 1489
HUARONG INTERNATIONAL TRUST CO., LTD.—See China CITIC Financial Asset Management Co., Ltd.; *Int'l*, pg. 1489
HUARONG INVESTMENT STOCK CORPORATION LIMITED—See China CITIC Financial Asset Management Co., Ltd.; *Int'l*, pg. 1489
HUARONG REAL ESTATE CO., LTD.—See China CITIC Financial Asset Management Co., Ltd.; *Int'l*, pg. 1489
HUARONG RONGTONG (BEIJING) TECHNOLOGY CO., LTD.—See China CITIC Financial Asset Management Co., Ltd.; *Int'l*, pg. 1489
HUARONG RUITONG EQUITY INVESTMENT MANAGEMENT CO., LTD.—See China CITIC Financial Asset Management Co., Ltd.; *Int'l*, pg. 1489
HUARONG SECURITIES CO., LTD.—See China CITIC Financial Asset Management Co., Ltd.; *Int'l*, pg. 1489
HUARONG TIANHAI (SHANGHAI) INVESTMENT MANAGEMENT COMPANY LIMITED—See China CITIC Financial Asset Management Co., Ltd.; *Int'l*, pg. 1489
HUARONG TIANZE INVESTMENT CO., LTD.—See China CITIC Financial Asset Management Co., Ltd.; *Int'l*, pg. 1489
HUARONG XIANGJIANG BANK CO., LTD.—See China CITIC Financial Asset Management Co., Ltd.; *Int'l*, pg. 1489
HUARONG YUFU EQUITY INVESTMENT FUND MANAGEMENT CO., LTD.—See China CITIC Financial Asset Management Co., Ltd.; *Int'l*, pg. 1489
HUARONG ZHIYUAN INVESTMENT & MANAGEMENT CO., LTD.—See China CITIC Financial Asset Management Co., Ltd.; *Int'l*, pg. 1489
HUARONG ZHONGGUANCUN DISTRESSED ASSET EXCHANGE CO., LTD.—See China CITIC Financial Asset Management Co., Ltd.; *Int'l*, pg. 1489
HUARUI ELECTRICAL APPLIANCE CO., LTD; *Int'l*, pg. 3514
HUARUI INTERNATIONAL NEW MATERIAL LIMITED; *Int'l*, pg. 3514
HUASHENG FUJITEC ELEVATOR CO. LTD.—See Fujitec Co., Ltd.; *Int'l*, pg. 2831
HUASHENG INTERNATIONAL HOLDING LIMITED; *Int'l*, pg. 3514
HUASU HOLDINGS CO., LTD.; *Int'l*, pg. 3514
HUATAI FINANCIAL HOLDINGS (HONG KONG) LIMITED—See Huatai Securities Co., Ltd.; *Int'l*, pg. 3514
HUATAI FINANCIAL USA INC—See Huatai Securities Co., Ltd.; *Int'l*, pg. 3514
HUATAI INSURANCE AGENCY & CONSULTANT SERVICE LIMITED—See China Reinsurance (Group) Corporation; *Int'l*, pg. 1547
HUATAI PURPLE GOLD INVESTMENT CO., LTD.—See Huatai Securities Co., Ltd.; *Int'l*, pg. 3514
HUATAI SECURITIES CO., LTD.; *Int'l*, pg. 3514
HUATAI SECURITIES (SHANGHAI) ASSET MANAGEMENT CO., LTD.—See Huatai Securities Co., Ltd.; *Int'l*, pg. 3514
HUATAI SECURITIES (SHANGHAI) ASSETS MANAGEMENT CO., LTD.—See Huatai Securities Co., Ltd.; *Int'l*, pg. 3514
HUATAI SURVEYORS & ADJUSTERS COMPANY LIMITED—See China Reinsurance (Group) Corporation; *Int'l*, pg. 1547
HUATAI UNITED SECURITIES CO., LTD.—See Huatai Securities Co., Ltd.; *Int'l*, pg. 3514
HUA TANG YOKADO COMMERCIAL CO., LTD.—See Seven & i Holdings Co., Ltd.; *Int'l*, pg. 6731
HUATIAN HOTEL GROUP CO., LTD.; *Int'l*, pg. 3514
HUATIONG GLOBAL LIMITED; *Int'l*, pg. 3514
HUAT LAI PAPER PRODUCTS SDN. BHD.—See Huat Lai Resources Berhad; *Int'l*, pg. 3514
HUAT LAI RESOURCES BERHAD; *Int'l*, pg. 3514
HUATONG UNITED (NANTONG) PLASTIC INDUSTRY CO., LTD.—See Great China Metal Ind. Co., Ltd.; *Int'l*, pg. 3064
HUATRACO INDUSTRIES SDN BHD—See Hiap Teck Venture Berhad; *Int'l*, pg. 3382
HUATRACO SCAFFOLD SDN BHD—See Hiap Teck Venture Berhad; *Int'l*, pg. 3382
HUATRACO SCAFFOLD SYSTEM SDN BHD—See Hiap Teck Venture Berhad; *Int'l*, pg. 3382
HUATU CENDES CO., LTD.; *Int'l*, pg. 3514
HUAWEI CHEMICAL & BIOLOGIC ENGINEERING CO., LTD.—See Shaanxi Aerospace Power High-tech Co., Ltd.; *Int'l*, pg. 6746
HUAWEI DEL PER S.A.C.—See Huawei Investment & Holding Co., Ltd.; *Int'l*, pg. 3515
HUAWEI INVESTMENT & HOLDING CO., LTD.; *Int'l*, pg. 3514

HUAWEI TECH. INVESTMENT CO., LTD—See Huawei Investment & Holding Co., Ltd.; *Int'l*, pg. 3515
HUAWEI TECH INVESTMENT TASHKENT MCHJ—See Huawei Investment & Holding Co., Ltd.; *Int'l*, pg. 3515
HUAWEI TECHNOLOGIES (BOLIVIA) S.R.L.—See Huawei Investment & Holding Co., Ltd.; *Int'l*, pg. 3515
HUAWEI TECHNOLOGIES CO., LTD.—See Huawei Investment & Holding Co., Ltd.; *Int'l*, pg. 3515
HUAWEI TECHNOLOGIES CO. LTD—See Huawei Investment & Holding Co., Ltd.; *Int'l*, pg. 3515
HUAWEI TECHNOLOGIES DE MEXICO, S.A. DE C.V.—See Huawei Investment & Holding Co., Ltd.; *Int'l*, pg. 3515
HUAWEI TECHNOLOGIES DUESSELDORF GMBH—See Huawei Investment & Holding Co., Ltd.; *Int'l*, pg. 3515
HUAWEI TECHNOLOGIES INDIA PVT. LTD.—See Huawei Investment & Holding Co., Ltd.; *Int'l*, pg. 3515
HUAWEI TECHNOLOGIES PHILS., INC.—See Huawei Investment & Holding Co., Ltd.; *Int'l*, pg. 3515
HUAWEI TECHNOLOGIES SWEDEN AB—See Huawei Investment & Holding Co., Ltd.; *Int'l*, pg. 3515
HUAWEI TECHNOLOGIES TANZANIA CO., LTD—See Huawei Investment & Holding Co., Ltd.; *Int'l*, pg. 3515
HUAWEI TECHNOLOGIES- (U) CO., LTD—See Huawei Investment & Holding Co., Ltd.; *Int'l*, pg. 3515
HUAWEI TECHNOLOGIES (UK) CO LTD—See Huawei Investment & Holding Co., Ltd.; *Int'l*, pg. 3515
HUAWEI TELECOMMUNICATIONS (INDIA) COMPANY PRIVATE LIMITED—See Huawei Investment & Holding Co., Ltd.; *Int'l*, pg. 3515
HUA XIA BANK CO., LIMITED; *Int'l*, pg. 3510
HUAXIA EYE HOSPITAL GROUP CO., LTD.; *Int'l*, pg. 3515
HUAXIA LIFE INSURANCE CO., LTD.; *Int'l*, pg. 3515
HUAXIAO PRECISION INDUSTRY (SUZHOU) CO., LTD.—See CSG Smart Science & Technology Co., Ltd.; *Int'l*, pg. 1864
HUAXIAO PRECISION (SUZHOU) CO., LTD.—See CSG Smart Science & Technology Co., Ltd.; *Int'l*, pg. 1864
HUAXI HOLDINGS COMPANY LIMITED; *Int'l*, pg. 3515
HUAXIN CEMENT CO., LTD.; *Int'l*, pg. 3515
HUAXIN TETRA PAK (FOSHAN) PACKAGING CO., LTD.—See Tetra Laval International S.A.; *Int'l*, pg. 7577
HUAXI SECURITIES CO., LTD.; *Int'l*, pg. 3515
HUAXUN FANGZHOU CO., LTD.; *Int'l*, pg. 3515
HUA YANG BERHAD; *Int'l*, pg. 3510
HUAYI BROTHERS MEDIA CORP.; *Int'l*, pg. 3515
HUAYI COMPRESSOR BARCELONA, S.L.—See Changhong Huayi Compressor Co., Ltd.; *Int'l*, pg. 1443
HUA YI COPPER PRODUCTS COMPANY LIMITED—See Solartech International Holdings Limited; *Int'l*, pg. 7070
HUAYI ELECTRIC COMPANY LIMITED; *Int'l*, pg. 3516
HUA YING SECURITIES CO., LTD.—See Guolian Securities Co., Ltd; *Int'l*, pg. 3186
HUA YIN INTERNATIONAL HOLDINGS LTD.; *Int'l*, pg. 3510
HUA YI PLASTIC PRODUCTS (SHENZHEN) CO., LTD.—See Mazzucchelli 1849 S.p.a.; *Int'l*, pg. 4750
HUAYI TENCENT ENTERTAINMENT COMPANY LIMITED; *Int'l*, pg. 3516
HUAYOU COBALT CO., LTD.; *Int'l*, pg. 3516
HUA YUAN PROPERTY CO., LTD.; *Int'l*, pg. 3510
HUAYUAN (VIETNAM) MACHINERY CO., LTD.—See Haitian International Holdings Ltd.; *Int'l*, pg. 3217
HUAYU AUTOMOTIVE SYSTEMS COMPANY LIMITED—See Shanghai Automotive Industry Corporation; *Int'l*, pg. 6761
HUAYU-COOPER STANDARD SEALING SYSTEMS CO., LTD.—See Cooper-Standard Holdings Inc.; *U.S. Public*, pg. 574
HUAYU EXPRESSWAY GROUP LIMITED; *Int'l*, pg. 3516
HUA YU LIEN DEVELOPMENT CO., LTD.; *Int'l*, pg. 3510
HUAYU VISION TECHNOLOGY (SHANGHAI) CO., LTD.—See Shanghai Automotive Industry Corporation; *Int'l*, pg. 6761
HUAZHANG TECHNOLOGY HOLDING LIMITED; *Int'l*, pg. 3516
HUAZHONG IN-VEHICLE HOLDINGS COMPANY LIMITED; *Int'l*, pg. 3516
HUB24 LIMITED; *Int'l*, pg. 3516
HUB30.COM SP. Z.O.O.—See IQ Partners S.A.; *Int'l*, pg. 3803
HUBA CONTROL AG—See Siemens Aktiengesellschaft; *Int'l*, pg. 6887
HUB ACQUISITION TRUST—See Equity CommonWealth; *U.S. Public*, pg. 790
HUBAU—See Tereos; *Int'l*, pg. 7564
HUBBARD BROADCASTING, INC.; *U.S. Private*, pg. 2000
HUBBARD CHEVROLET; *U.S. Private*, pg. 2000
THE HUBBARD COMPANY—See Individualized Apparel Group; *U.S. Private*, pg. 2064
HUBBARD CONSTRUCTION CO. - ATLANTIC COAST ASPHALT DIVISION—See VINCI S.A.; *Int'l*, pg. 8220
HUBBARD CONSTRUCTION CO. - EAST COAST PAVING DIVISION—See VINCI S.A.; *Int'l*, pg. 8220
HUBBARD CONSTRUCTION COMPANY—See VINCI S.A.; *Int'l*, pg. 8220

HUBBARD CONSTRUCTION CO. - ORLANDO PAVING DIVISION—See VINCI S.A.; *Int'l*, pg. 8220
HUBBARD & DRAKE GENERAL CONTRACTOR; *U.S. Private*, pg. 2000
HUBBARD-HALL, INC.; *U.S. Private*, pg. 2000
HUBBARD LLC—See Groupe Grimaud La Corbiere SA; *Int'l*, pg. 3103
HUBBARD PAVING & GRADING, INC.—See Construction Partners, Inc.; *U.S. Public*, pg. 572
HUBBARD RADIO CINCINNATI, LLC—See Hubbard Broadcasting, Inc.; *U.S. Private*, pg. 2000
HUBBARD RADIO, LLC—See Hubbard Broadcasting, Inc.; *U.S. Private*, pg. 2000
HUBBARD RADIO ST. LOUIS, LLC—See Hubbard Broadcasting, Inc.; *U.S. Private*, pg. 2000
HUBBARD SAS—See Groupe Grimaud La Corbiere SA; *Int'l*, pg. 3103
HUBBARD SCIENTIFIC—See Geneve Holdings Corp.; *U.S. Private*, pg. 1671
HUBBARDS; *U.S. Private*, pg. 2000
HUBBARD SUPPLY CO.; *U.S. Private*, pg. 2000
HUBBELL BUILDING AUTOMATION—See Hubbell Incorporated; *U.S. Public*, pg. 1066
HUBBELL CANADA, INC.—See Hubbell Incorporated; *U.S. Public*, pg. 1066
HUBBELL CANADA—See Hubbell Incorporated; *U.S. Public*, pg. 1066
HUBBELL CARIBE LTD—See Hubbell Incorporated; *U.S. Public*, pg. 1066
HUBBELL DE MEXICO, S.A. DE C.V.—See Hubbell Incorporated; *U.S. Public*, pg. 1067
HUBBELL DISTRIBUTION, INC.—See Hubbell Incorporated; *U.S. Public*, pg. 1066
HUBBELL ELECTRICAL PRODUCTS—See AIP, LLC; *U.S. Private*, pg. 134
HUBBELL INCORPORATED; *U.S. Public*, pg. 1066
HUBBELL INDUSTRIAL CONTROLS, INC.—See Hubbell Incorporated; *U.S. Public*, pg. 1066
HUBBELL KOREA, LTD.—See Hubbell Incorporated; *U.S. Public*, pg. 1066
HUBBELL LIGHTING - PROGRESS LIGHTING DIVISION—See Hubbell Incorporated; *U.S. Public*, pg. 1066
HUBBELL LIMITED—See Hubbell Incorporated; *U.S. Public*, pg. 1066
HUBBELL PICKERING LP—See Hubbell Incorporated; *U.S. Public*, pg. 1066
HUBBELL POWER SYSTEMS, INC. - CENTRALIA—See Hubbell Incorporated; *U.S. Public*, pg. 1067
HUBBELL POWER SYSTEMS, INC.—See Hubbell Incorporated; *U.S. Public*, pg. 1067
HUBBELL POWER SYSTEMS, INC. - WADSWORTH—See Hubbell Incorporated; *U.S. Public*, pg. 1067
HUBBELL PREMISE WIRING—See Hubbell Incorporated; *U.S. Public*, pg. 1067
HUBBELL PRODUCTS MEXICO S. DE R.L. DE C.V.—See Hubbell Incorporated; *U.S. Public*, pg. 1067
HUBBELL-TAIAN CO., LTD.—See Hubbell Incorporated; *U.S. Public*, pg. 1067
HUBBELL WIRING DEVICE-KELLEMS—See Hubbell Incorporated; *U.S. Public*, pg. 1067
HUBBELL WIRING SYSTEMS—See Hubbell Incorporated; *U.S. Public*, pg. 1067
HUBB, INC.—See Apollo Global Management, Inc.; *U.S. Public*, pg. 152
HUBB SYSTEMS LLC—See Vislink Technologies, Inc.; *U.S. Public*, pg. 2304
HUB BUICK INC; *U.S. Private*, pg. 1999
HUBCAST, INC.—See mimeo.com, Inc.; *U.S. Private*, pg. 2740
HUB CITY FORD INC.; *U.S. Private*, pg. 2000
HUB CITY FORD, INC.; *U.S. Private*, pg. 2000
HUB CITY, INC.—See Regal Rexnord Corporation; *U.S. Public*, pg. 1773
HUB CO., LTD.; *Int'l*, pg. 3516
HUBCONNECT PTY LTD—See HUB24 Limited; *Int'l*, pg. 3517
HUB CONSTRUCTION SPECIALTIES, INC.—See The Sterling Group, L.P.; *U.S. Private*, pg. 4122
HUB CYBER SECURITY LTD.; *Int'l*, pg. 3516
HUB DACIA S.R.L.—See Albert Ballin KG; *Int'l*, pg. 295
HUB DEALS CORP.; *U.S. Public*, pg. 1065
HUB DUNAV D.O.O.—See Albert Ballin KG; *Int'l*, pg. 295
HUBEI AOZE AUTOMOBILE SALES SERVICES CO., LTD.—See China ZhengTong Auto Services Holdings Limited; *Int'l*, pg. 1566
HUBEI BIOCAUSE PHARMACEUTICAL CO., LTD.; *Int'l*, pg. 3517
HUBEI BROADCASTING & TELEVISION INFORMATION NETWORK CO., LTD.; *Int'l*, pg. 3517
HUBEI CAMEL SPECIAL POWER SUPPLY COMPANY—See Camel Group Co., Ltd.; *Int'l*, pg. 1270
HUBEI CENTURY NETWORK TECHNOLOGY INC; *Int'l*, pg. 3517
HUBEI CHANGZE AUTOMOBILE SALES SERVICES CO., LTD.—See China ZhengTong Auto Services Holdings Limited; *Int'l*, pg. 1566

HUBEI CHUTIAN SMART COMMUNICATION CO., LTD.; *Int'l*, pg. 3517
HUBEI CUBIC-RUIYI INSTRUMENT CO., LTD.—See Cubic Sensor & Instrument Co., Ltd.; *Int'l*, pg. 1875
HUBEI DINGLONG CO., LTD.; *Int'l*, pg. 3517
HUBEI DONPER ELECTROMECHANICAL GROUP CO., LTD.; *Int'l*, pg. 3517
HUBEI DOTI-MICRO TECHNOLOGY CO., LTD.; *Int'l*, pg. 3517
HUBEI ELECTRIC POWER COMPANY—See State Grid Corporation of China; *Int'l*, pg. 5440
HUBEI ENERGY GROUP CO., LTD.; *Int'l*, pg. 3517
HUBEI ERZHONG RENEWABLE RESOURCES MARKET DEVELOPMENT CO., LTD.—See GEM Co., Ltd.; *Int'l*, pg. 2914
HUBEI FEILIHUA QUARTZ GLASS CO., LTD.; *Int'l*, pg. 3517
HUBEI FORBON TECHNOLOGY CO., LTD.; *Int'l*, pg. 3517
HUBEI FUXING SCIENCE & TECHNOLOGY CO., LTD.; *Int'l*, pg. 3517
HUBEI GEOWAY INVESTMENT CO., LTD.; *Int'l*, pg. 3517
HUBEI GOTO BIOPHARM CO., LTD.; *Int'l*, pg. 3517
HUBEI GRAND FUCHI PHARMACEUTICAL & CHEMICAL COMPANY LIMITED—See Grand Pharmaceutical Group Limited; *Int'l*, pg. 3056
HUBEI GUANGJI PHARMACEUTICAL CO., LTD.; *Int'l*, pg. 3517
HUBEI GUOCHUANG HI-TECH MATERIAL CO., LTD.; *Int'l*, pg. 3517
HUBEI HEYUAN GAS CO., LTD.; *Int'l*, pg. 3517
HUBEI HUARONG HOLDING CO., LTD.; *Int'l*, pg. 3517
HUBEI HUITIAN NEW MATERIALS CO., LTD.; *Int'l*, pg. 3518
HUBEI JIANGSHAN HEAVY INDUSTRIES CO., LTD.—See China North Industries Group Corporation; *Int'l*, pg. 1535
HUBEI JIUZHIYANG INFRARED SYSTEM CO., LTD; *Int'l*, pg. 3518
HUBEI JUMPCAN PHARMACEUTICAL CO., LTD.; *Int'l*, pg. 3518
HUBEI JUNEYAO GREAT HEALTH DAIRY CO., LTD.; *Int'l*, pg. 3518
HUBEI KAGA ELECTRONICS LIMITED—See Kaga Electronics Co., Ltd.; *Int'l*, pg. 4048
HUBEI KAILE SCIENCE & TECHNOLOGY CO., LTD.; *Int'l*, pg. 3518
HUBEI KAILONG CHEMICAL GROUP CO., LTD.; *Int'l*, pg. 3518
HUBEI KEYI PHARMACEUTICAL CO., LTD.—See China Meheco Group Co., Ltd.; *Int'l*, pg. 1519
HUBEI KOITO AUTOMOTIVE LAMP CO., LTD.—See Koito Manufacturing Co., Ltd.; *Int'l*, pg. 4230
HUBEI LIDI MACHINE TOOL CO. LTD.—See Miracle Automation Engineering Co., Ltd.; *Int'l*, pg. 4915
HUBEI LINGYONG ELECTRONIC MATERIALS CO., LTD.—See Mitsubishi Gas Chemical Company, Inc.; *Int'l*, pg. 4948
HUBEI MAILYARD SHARE CO., LTD.; *Int'l*, pg. 3518
HUBEI MINKANG PHARMACEUTICAL LTD.; *Int'l*, pg. 3518
HUBEI NEW HUAGUANG INFORMATION MATERIALS CO., LTD.—See North Electro-Optic Co., Ltd.; *Int'l*, pg. 5440
HUBEI O.R.G BEVERAGE INDUSTRY CO., LTD.—See ORG Technology Co., Ltd.; *Int'l*, pg. 5617
HUBEI ORG CAN MAKING CO., LTD.—See ORG Technology Co., Ltd.; *Int'l*, pg. 5617
HUBEI O.R.G PACKAGING CO., LTD.—See ORG Technology Co., Ltd.; *Int'l*, pg. 5617
HUBEI O.R.G TECHNOLOGY CO., LTD.—See ORG Technology Co., Ltd.; *Int'l*, pg. 5617
HUBEI RONBAY LITHIUM BATTERY MATERIALS CO., LTD.—See Ningbo Ronbay New Energy Technology Co., Ltd.; *Int'l*, pg. 5305
HUBEI RUNSHENG ELECTRONICS INDUSTRIAL CO., LTD.—See Shenzhen JingQuanHua Electronics Co., Ltd.; *Int'l*, pg. 6814
HUBEI SANXIA NEW BUILDING MATERIALS CO., LTD.; *Int'l*, pg. 3518
HUBEI SANYANG PETROCHEMICAL CO., LTD.—See SanFeng Intelligent Equipment Group Co., Ltd.; *Int'l*, pg. 6536
HUBEI SHUANGHUAN SCIENCE & TECHNOLOGY STOCK CO., LTD.; *Int'l*, pg. 3518
HUBEI SUNSMILE FOOTWEAR CO., LTD.—See Fulgent Sun International (Holding) Co., Ltd.; *Int'l*, pg. 2842
HUBEI SUPER-ELEC AUTO ELECTRIC MOTOR LTD., LIABILITY CO.—See Bain Capital, LP; *U.S. Private*, pg. 428
HUBEI THREE GORGES TOURISM GROUP CO., LTD.; *Int'l*, pg. 3518
HUBEI VALEO AUTOLIGHTING COMPANY LTD—See Valeo S.A.; *Int'l*, pg. 8112
HUBEI WOLF PHOTOELECTRIC TECHNOLOGY CO., LTD.; *Int'l*, pg. 3518
HUBEI WUCHANGYU CO., LTD.; *Int'l*, pg. 3518
HUBEI XIANGYUAN NEW MATERIAL TECHNOLOGY, INC.; *Int'l*, pg. 3518

HUBEI XINGFA CHEMICALS GROUP CO., LTD.; *Int'l*, pg. 3518
HUBEI YIHUA CHEMICAL INDUSTRY CO., LTD.; *Int'l*, pg. 3518
HUBEI YINGTONG ELECTRONICS CO., LTD.—See YingTong Telecommunication Co., Ltd.; *Int'l*, pg. 8584
HUBEI ZHENHUA CHEMICAL CO., LTD.; *Int'l*, pg. 3518
HUBEI ZHONGDA INTELLIGENT PARKING EQUIPMENT CO., LTD.—See SanFeng Intelligent Equipment Group Co., Ltd.; *Int'l*, pg. 6536
HUBEI ZHONGYI TECHNOLOGY INC.; *Int'l*, pg. 3519
HUBER & ASSOCIATES INC.; *U.S. Private*, pg. 2000
HUBERATOR SA—See Publigas; *Int'l*, pg. 6115
HUBER ENGINEERED MATERIALS, LLC - HAVRE DE GRACE—See J.M. Huber Corporation; *U.S. Private*, pg. 2168
HUBER ENGINEERED MATERIALS, LLC - QUINCY—See J.M. Huber Corporation; *U.S. Private*, pg. 2168
HUBER ENGINEERED MATERIALS, LLC—See J.M. Huber Corporation; *U.S. Private*, pg. 2168
HUBER ENGINEERED WOODS LLC—See J.M. Huber Corporation; *U.S. Private*, pg. 2168
HUBERGROUP DEUTSCHLAND GMBH; *Int'l*, pg. 3519
HUBERGROUP USA, INC. - ARLINGTON HEIGHTS—See Hubergroup Deutschland GmbH; *Int'l*, pg. 3519
HUBERGROUP USA, INC.—See Hubergroup Deutschland GmbH; *Int'l*, pg. 3519
HUBER INVESTMENT CORPORATION; *U.S. Private*, pg. 2000
HUBER RESOURCES CORPORATION—See J.M. Huber Corporation; *U.S. Private*, pg. 2168
HUBERS INC.; *U.S. Private*, pg. 2001
HUBER SPECIALTY HYDRATES, LLC—See J.M. Huber Corporation; *U.S. Private*, pg. 2168
HUBER+SUHNER AB—See Huber + Suhner AG; *Int'l*, pg. 3519
HUBER + SUHNER AG; *Int'l*, pg. 3519
HUBER+SUHNER AMERICA LATINA LTDA—See Huber + Suhner AG; *Int'l*, pg. 3519
HUBER+SUHNER A/S—See Huber + Suhner AG; *Int'l*, pg. 3519
HUBER + SUHNER (AUSTRALIA) PTY. LTD.—See Huber + Suhner AG; *Int'l*, pg. 3519
HUBER+SUHNER CUBE OPTICS AG—See Huber + Suhner AG; *Int'l*, pg. 3519
HUBER+SUHNER ELECTRONICS PRIVATE LIMITED—See Huber + Suhner AG; *Int'l*, pg. 3519
HUBER + SUHNER FRANCE—See Huber + Suhner AG; *Int'l*, pg. 3519
HUBER + SUHNER GMBH—See Huber + Suhner AG; *Int'l*, pg. 3519
HUBER + SUHNER (HONG KONG) LTD.—See Huber + Suhner AG; *Int'l*, pg. 3519
HUBER + SUHNER INC.—See Huber + Suhner AG; *Int'l*, pg. 3519
HUBER+SUHNER (MALAYSIA) SDN. BHD—See Huber + Suhner AG; *Int'l*, pg. 3519
HUBER + SUHNER (SINGAPORE) PTE. LTD.—See Huber + Suhner AG; *Int'l*, pg. 3519
HUBER+SUHNER (THAILAND) CO., LTD—See Huber + Suhner AG; *Int'l*, pg. 3519
HUBER + SUHNER (UK) LTD.—See Huber + Suhner AG; *Int'l*, pg. 3519
HUBER SUPPLY CO. INC.; *U.S. Private*, pg. 2000
HUBERT BURDA MEDIA HOLDING KOMMANDITGESELLSCHAFT; *Int'l*, pg. 3519
HUBERT BURDA MEDIA HONG KONG LIMITED—See Hubert Burda Media Holding Kommanditgesellschaft; *Int'l*, pg. 3520
HUBERT COMPANY—See Franz Haniel & Cie. GmbH; *Int'l*, pg. 2763
HUBERT CONSTRUCTION; *U.S. Private*, pg. 2001
HUBER TIRE CO.; *U.S. Private*, pg. 2001
HUBERT VESTER CHEVROLET; *U.S. Private*, pg. 2001
HUBERTY & ASSOCIATES, S.C.; *U.S. Private*, pg. 2001
HUB GIRISIM SERMAYESI YATIRIM ORTAKLIGI A.S.; *Int'l*, pg. 3516
HUB GROUP CANADA, L.P.—See Hub Group, Inc.; *U.S. Public*, pg. 1065
HUB GROUP, INC.; *U.S. Public*, pg. 1065
HUB GROUP TRUCKING, INC.—See Hub Group, Inc.; *U.S. Public*, pg. 1065
HUB GROUP TRUCKING—See Hub Group, Inc.; *U.S. Public*, pg. 1065
HUBIFY COMMUNICATIONS PTY LIMITED—See Hubify Limited; *Int'l*, pg. 3520
HUBIFY LIMITED; *Int'l*, pg. 3520
HUBILU VENTURE CORPORATION; *U.S. Public*, pg. 1067
HUB INTERNATIONAL GREAT PLAINS, LLC—See Hellman & Friedman LLC; *U.S. Private*, pg. 1909
HUB INTERNATIONAL INSURANCE SERVICES, INC.—See Hellman & Friedman LLC; *U.S. Private*, pg. 1909
HUB INTERNATIONAL LIMITED—See Hellman & Friedman LLC; *U.S. Private*, pg. 1908
HUB INTERNATIONAL MIDWEST LIMITED—See Hellman & Friedman LLC; *U.S. Private*, pg. 1909

COMPANY NAME INDEX

HUB INTERNATIONAL MOUNTAIN STATES LIMITED—See Hellman & Friedman LLC; *U.S. Private*, pg. 1909
HUB INTERNATIONAL NEW ENGLAND, LLC—See Hellman & Friedman LLC; *U.S. Private*, pg. 1909
HUB INTERNATIONAL NORTHEAST LIMITED—See Hellman & Friedman LLC; *U.S. Private*, pg. 1909
HUB INTERNATIONAL ONTARIO LIMITED—See Hellman & Friedman LLC; *U.S. Private*, pg. 1909
HUB INTERNATIONAL QUEBEC LIMITED—See Hellman & Friedman LLC; *U.S. Private*, pg. 1909
HUB INTERNATIONAL SOUTHEAST LIMITED—See Hellman & Friedman LLC; *U.S. Private*, pg. 1909
HUB INTERNATIONAL TEXAS, INC. - DALLAS; *U.S. Private*, pg. 2000
HUB INTERNATIONAL TEXAS, INC.—See Hellman & Friedman LLC; *U.S. Private*, pg. 1909
HUBLER CHEVROLET INC.; *U.S. Private*, pg. 2001
HUB LEVANT LIMITED—See Albert Ballin KG; *Int'l*, pg. 295
HUBL GMBH—See Gesco AG; *Int'l*, pg. 2945
HUBLINE BERHAD; *Int'l*, pg. 3520
HUBLOT JAPAN KK LTD—See LVMH Moet Hennessy Louis Vuitton SE; *Int'l*, pg. 4601
HUBLOT OF AMERICA, INC—See LVMH Moet Hennessy Louis Vuitton SE; *Int'l*, pg. 4601
HUBLOT SA GENEVE—See LVMH Moet Hennessy Louis Vuitton SE; *Int'l*, pg. 4601
HUBLOT SA—See LVMH Moet Hennessy Louis Vuitton SE; *Int'l*, pg. 4601
HUB MARINE PTE. LTD.—See Hubline Berhad; *Int'l*, pg. 3520
HUBNER NATURARZNEIMITTEL GMBH—See Dermapharm Holding SE; *Int'l*, pg. 2043
HUB ONLINE GLOBAL PTY. LTD—See News Corporation; *U.S. Public*, pg. 1520
HUBPER GROUP INC.; *U.S. Private*, pg. 2001
HUB & PORT SERVICES PTE. LTD.—See Vibrant Group Limited; *Int'l*, pg. 8184
THE HUB POWER COMPANY LIMITED; *Int'l*, pg. 7653
HUB SHIPPING SDN. BHD.—See Hubline Berhad; *Int'l*, pg. 3520
HUBSHOUT, LLC; *U.S. Private*, pg. 2001
HUBSPOT ASIA PTE, LTD.—See HubSpot, Inc.; *U.S. Public*, pg. 1068
HUBSPOT AUSTRALIA PTY. LTD.—See HubSpot, Inc.; *U.S. Public*, pg. 1068
HUBSPOT, INC.; *U.S. Public*, pg. 1067
HUBSPOT IRELAND LIMITED—See HubSpot, Inc.; *U.S. Public*, pg. 1068
HUBSPOT JAPAN K.K.—See HubSpot, Inc.; *U.S. Public*, pg. 1068
HUBSPOT LATIN AMERICA S.A.S.—See HubSpot, Inc.; *U.S. Public*, pg. 1068
HUB SUPPLY COMPANY—See Genuine Parts Company; *U.S. Public*, pg. 933
HUB TECHNICAL SERVICES; *U.S. Private*, pg. 2000
HUB TELECOM—See Aeroports de Paris S.A.; *Int'l*, pg. 181
HUBTOWN LIMITED; *Int'l*, pg. 3520
HUB TRUCK RENTAL CORP.; *U.S. Private*, pg. 2000
HUB WEST SCOTLAND LIMITED—See Morgan Sindall Group Plc; *Int'l*, pg. 5045
HUBWOO S.A.—See Perfect Commerce Holdings, LLC.; *U.S. Private*, pg. 3148
H.U. CELLS, INC.—See H.U. Group Holdings, Inc.; *Int'l*, pg. 3197
HUCENTECH CO., LTD.; *Int'l*, pg. 3521
HUCHEMS FINE CHEMICAL CORPORATION - YEOSU PLANT—See TKG Huchems Co.,Ltd; *Int'l*, pg. 7763
HUCHTEMEIER PAPIER GMBH—See MBB SE; *Int'l*, pg. 4751
HUCHTEMEIER PAPIER GMBH—See MBB SE; *Int'l*, pg. 4751
HUCKABEE ARCHITECTS LP—See Godspeed Capital Management LP; *U.S. Private*, pg. 1725
HUCKESTEIN MECHANICAL SERVICES, INC.—See Leonard Green & Partners, L.P.; *U.S. Private*, pg. 2426
HUCK FINN GMBH—See Ekosem-Agrar GmbH; *Int'l*, pg. 2339
HUCKLEBERRY MINES LTD.—See Imperial Metals Corporation; *Int'l*, pg. 3635
HUCKLE MEDIA, LLC.; *U.S. Private*, pg. 2001
HUCO CONSULTING INC.—See Montrose Environmental Group, Inc.; *U.S. Public*, pg. 1466
HUCO ELECTRONIC GMBH—See Landesbank Baden-Wurttemberg; *Int'l*, pg. 4405
HUCOSS CO., LTD.—See Takasago Thermal Engineering Co., Ltd.; *Int'l*, pg. 7434
HUDACO INDUSTRIES LIMITED - ANGUS HAWKEN DIVISION—See Hudaco Industries Limited; *Int'l*, pg. 3521
HUDACO INDUSTRIES LIMITED - ASTORE KEYMAK—See Hudaco Industries Limited; *Int'l*, pg. 3521
HUDACO INDUSTRIES LIMITED - BAUER GEARED MOTORS DIVISION—See Hudaco Industries Limited; *Int'l*, pg. 3521

HUDACO INDUSTRIES LIMITED - BEARINGS INTERNATIONAL DIVISION—See Hudaco Industries Limited; *Int'l*, pg. 3521
HUDACO INDUSTRIES LIMITED - BOSWORTH DIVISION—See Hudaco Industries Limited; *Int'l*, pg. 3521
HUDACO INDUSTRIES LIMITED; *Int'l*, pg. 3521
HUDACO INDUSTRIES PTY LTD.—See Hudaco Industries Limited; *Int'l*, pg. 3521
HUDACO INVESTMENT COMPANY LIMITED—See Hudaco Industries Limited; *Int'l*, pg. 3521
HUDACO TRADING LTD—See Hudaco Industries Limited; *Int'l*, pg. 3521
HUDACO TRANSMISSION (PTY) LTD—See Hudaco Industries Limited; *Int'l*, pg. 3521
HUDAK INSULATION, INC.; *U.S. Private*, pg. 2001
HUDBAY MARKETING AND SALES INC.—See HudBay Minerals Inc.; *Int'l*, pg. 3521
HUDBAY MINERALS INC.; *Int'l*, pg. 3521
HUDBAY PERU S.A.C.—See HudBay Minerals Inc.; *Int'l*, pg. 3521
HUDDERSFIELD VETS4PETS LIMITED—See Pets at Home Group Plc; *Int'l*, pg. 5834
HUDDLE HOUSE, INC.; *U.S. Private*, pg. 2001
HUDDLESTOCK FINTECH AS; *Int'l*, pg. 3521
HUDDLY AS; *Int'l*, pg. 3522
HUD GROUP—See CK Hutchison Holdings Limited; *Int'l*, pg. 1637
HUD GROUP—See John Swire & Sons Limited; *Int'l*, pg. 3980
HUDIBURG CHEVROLET BUICK GMC; *U.S. Private*, pg. 2001
HUDIKSHUS AB—See Storskogen Group AB; *Int'l*, pg. 7227
HUDLAND REAL ESTATE INVESTMENT AND DEVELOPMENT JSC; *Int'l*, pg. 3522
HUDSON 1099 STEWART REIT, LLC—See Hudson Pacific Properties, Inc.; *U.S. Public*, pg. 1068
HUDSON 1455 MARKET STREET, LLC—See Hudson Pacific Properties, Inc.; *U.S. Public*, pg. 1068
HUDSON 6922 HOLLYWOOD, LLC—See Hudson Pacific Properties, Inc.; *U.S. Public*, pg. 1068
HUDSON 901 MARKET, LLC—See Hudson Pacific Properties, Inc.; *U.S. Public*, pg. 1068
HUDSON ADVISORS LLC; *U.S. Private*, pg. 2001
HUDSON AND SUNSET MEDIA LLC—See Stagwell, Inc.; *U.S. Private*, pg. 1927
HUDSON AUTO SOURCE; *U.S. Private*, pg. 2001
HUDSON BAKING COMPANY LLC—See Arbor Investment Group; *U.S. Private*, pg. 308
HUDSON BAY PORT COMPANY—See The Broe Companies, Inc.; *U.S. Private*, pg. 4001
HUDSON BAY RAILWAY COMPANY—See The Broe Companies, Inc.; *U.S. Private*, pg. 4001
HUDSON BELGIUM SA/NV; *Int'l*, pg. 3522
HUDSON BLVD. GROUP LLC; *U.S. Private*, pg. 2001
HUDSON BUILDING SUPPLIES PTY LIMITED—See Woolworths Group Limited; *Int'l*, pg. 8452
HUDSON CLEAN ENERGY PARTNERS; *U.S. Private*, pg. 2001
HUDSON COMMUNITY ENTERPRISES; *U.S. Private*, pg. 2001
HUDSON CONSTRUCTION COMPANY; *U.S. Private*, pg. 2001
HUDSON CROSSING SURGERY CENTER, LLC—See KKR & Co. Inc.; *U.S. Public*, pg. 1245
HUDSON EUROPE BV—See Hudson Global, Inc; *U.S. Public*, pg. 1068
HUDSON EXECUTIVE CAPITATL LP; *U.S. Public*, pg. 1068
HUDSON FIBER NETWORK—See Stonepeak Partners L.P.; *U.S. Private*, pg. 3829
HUDSON FOOD STORES INCORPORATED; *U.S. Private*, pg. 2001
HUDSON GLOBAL, INC; *U.S. Public*, pg. 1068
HUDSON GLOBAL RESOURCES (AUSTRALIA) PTY LIMITED—See Hudson Highland (APAC) Pty. Limited; *Int'l*, pg. 3522
HUDSON GLOBAL RESOURCES HONG KONG LTD.—See Hudson Highland (APAC) Pty. Limited; *Int'l*, pg. 3522
HUDSON GLOBAL RESOURCES LLC—See Morgan Philips Group; *Int'l*, pg. 5044
HUDSON GLOBAL RESOURCES MANAGEMENT, INC.—See Hudson Global, Inc; *U.S. Public*, pg. 1068
HUDSON GLOBAL RESOURCES (NZ) LTD.—See Hudson Highland (APAC) Pty. Limited; *Int'l*, pg. 3522
HUDSON HEADWATERS HEALTH NETWORK; *U.S. Private*, pg. 2001
HUDSON HIGHLAND (APAC) PTY. LIMITED; *Int'l*, pg. 3522
HUDSON HILL CAPITAL LLC; *U.S. Private*, pg. 2002
HUDSON HOME HEALTH CARE INC.; *U.S. Private*, pg. 2002
HUDSON HORIZONS, INC.; *U.S. Private*, pg. 2002
HUDSON INC.; *U.S. Private*, pg. 2002
HUDSON INDUSTRIES INC.; *U.S. Private*, pg. 2002
HUDSON INDUSTRIES, INC.—See Midway Products Group, Inc.; *U.S. Private*, pg. 2719

HUDSONYARDS

HUDSON INSURANCE GROUP—See Fairfax Financial Holdings Limited; *Int'l*, pg. 2607
HUDSON INVESTMENT GROUP LIMITED; *Int'l*, pg. 3522
HUDSON & KEYSE, LLC; *U.S. Private*, pg. 2001
HUDSON & KNIGHT (PROPRIETARY) LIMITED—See Sime Darby Berhad; *Int'l*, pg. 6929
HUDSON LEASECO LLC—See SBEEG Holdings, LLC; *U.S. Private*, pg. 3559
HUDSON LOCK, LLC—See Dominus Capital, L.P.; *U.S. Private*, pg. 1256
HUDSON LTD.—See Avolta AG; *Int'l*, pg. 749
HUDSON LUXEMBOURG S.A.—See Hudson Belgium SA/NV; *Int'l*, pg. 3522
HUDSON MARKETING PTY LTD.—See Hudson Investment Group Limited; *Int'l*, pg. 3522
HUDSON MEDIA SERVICES LLC; *U.S. Private*, pg. 2002
HUDSON MET PARK NORTH, LLC—See Hudson Pacific Properties, Inc.; *U.S. Public*, pg. 1068
HUDSON NEWS COMPANY—See Avolta AG; *Int'l*, pg. 749
HUDSON PACIFIC GROUP LIMITED—See Retail Food Group Limited; *Int'l*, pg. 6305
HUDSON PACIFIC PROPERTIES, INC.; *U.S. Public*, pg. 1068
HUDSON PACIFIC PROPERTIES, L.P.—See Hudson Pacific Properties, Inc.; *U.S. Public*, pg. 1068
HUDSON PONTIAC BUICK GMC TRUCK INC.; *U.S. Private*, pg. 2002
HUDSON PRODUCTS CORPORATION—See Chart Industries, Inc.; *U.S. Public*, pg. 482
HUDSON RECRUITMENT SHANGHAI LIMITED—See Hudson Highland (APAC) Pty. Limited; *Int'l*, pg. 3522
HUDSON RESOURCES INC.; *Int'l*, pg. 3522
HUDSON RESOURCES LIMITED; *Int'l*, pg. 3522
HUDSON RESPIRATORY CARE TECATE, S. DE R.L. DE C.V.—See Teleflex Incorporated; *U.S. Public*, pg. 1996
HUDSON RIVER HEALTHCARE, INC.; *U.S. Private*, pg. 2002
HUDSON RIVER INLAY INC.—See United Vision Group Inc.; *U.S. Private*, pg. 4301
HUDSON RIVER MINERALS LTD.; *Int'l*, pg. 3522
HUDSON ROBOTICS, INC.—See Argosy Capital Group, LLC; *U.S. Private*, pg. 321
HUDSON SALVAGE INC.; *U.S. Private*, pg. 2002
HUDSON'S BAY COMPANY—See Abrams Capital, LLC; *U.S. Private*, pg. 40
HUDSON'S BAY COMPANY—See Rhone Group, LLC; *U.S. Private*, pg. 3423
HUDSON'S BAY COMPANY—See WeWork Inc.; *U.S. Public*, pg. 2364
THE HUDSON-SHARP MACHINE COMPANY—See Barry-Wehmiller Companies, Inc.; *U.S. Private*, pg. 482
HUDSON SOFT COMPANY, LIMITED—See Konami Group Corporation; *Int'l*, pg. 4245
HUDSON'S SUPER MARKETS, INC.—See GW Foods Inc.; *U.S. Private*, pg. 1821
HUDSON SUN—See Gannett Co., Inc.; *U.S. Public*, pg. 902
HUDSON TANK TERMINALS CORPORATION; *U.S. Private*, pg. 2002
HUDSON TECHNOLOGIES, INC.; *U.S. Public*, pg. 1068
HUDSON TECHNOLOGIES—See JSJ Corporation; *U.S. Private*, pg. 2241
HUDSON TOOL STEEL CORPORATION—See Ryerson Holding Corporation; *U.S. Public*, pg. 1829
HUDSON TRAIL OUTFITTERS LTD.; *U.S. Private*, pg. 2002
HUDSON VALLEY CREDIT UNION; *U.S. Private*, pg. 2002
HUDSON VALLEY ECONOMIC DEVELOPMENT CORPORATION; *U.S. Private*, pg. 2002
HUDSON VALLEY INSURANCE COMPANY—See PepsiCo, Inc.; *U.S. Public*, pg. 1669
HUDSON VALLEY ROOFING & SHEETMETAL, INC.—See Greenwood Industries; *U.S. Private*, pg. 1782
HUDSONYARDS; *U.S. Private*, pg. 2002
HUE BREWERY LTD.—See Carlsberg A/S; *Int'l*, pg. 1340
HUECK ALUMINIUM GMBH—See Norsk Hydro ASA; *Int'l*, pg. 5432
HUECK ALUMINIUM PROFIELTECHNIEK BENELUX B.V.—See Norsk Hydro ASA; *Int'l*, pg. 5432
HUECK RHEINISCHE GMBH—See Berndorf AG; *Int'l*, pg. 987
HUECK S.R.O.—See Norsk Hydro ASA; *Int'l*, pg. 5432
HUECK SYSTEM GMBH & CO. KG—See Norsk Hydro ASA; *Int'l*, pg. 5432
HUEGLI HOLDING AG—See Coop-Gruppe Genossenschaft; *Int'l*, pg. 1789
HUEGLI UK LTD.—See Coop-Gruppe Genossenschaft; *Int'l*, pg. 1790
HUELLA PUBLICIDAD—See Publicis Groupe S.A.; *Int'l*, pg. 6100
HUEN ELECTRIC INC.—See MYR Group Inc.; *U.S. Public*, pg. 1489
HUENEME HEALTHCARE, INC.—See The Ensign Group, Inc.; *U.S. Public*, pg. 2071
HUENNEBECK DEUTSCHLAND GMBH—See Brand Industrial Services, Inc.; *U.S. Private*, pg. 636

1279

HUDSONYARDS / CORPORATE AFFILIATIONS

HUENNEBECK GMBH—See Brand Industrial Services, Inc.; *U.S. Private*, pg. 636
HUESKER ASIA PACIFIC PTE. LTD.—See HUESKER Synthetic GmbH; *Int'l*, pg. 3522
HUESKER INC.—See HUESKER Synthetic GmbH; *Int'l*, pg. 3522
HUESKER LTDA.—See HUESKER Synthetic GmbH; *Int'l*, pg. 3522
HUESKER LTD.—See HUESKER Synthetic GmbH; *Int'l*, pg. 3522
HUESKER OOO—See HUESKER Synthetic GmbH; *Int'l*, pg. 3522
HUESKER S.A—See HUESKER Synthetic GmbH; *Int'l*, pg. 3522
HUESKER SAS—See HUESKER Synthetic GmbH; *Int'l*, pg. 3522
HUESKER S.R.L.—See HUESKER Synthetic GmbH; *Int'l*, pg. 3522
HUESKER SYNTHETIC B.V.—See HUESKER Synthetic GmbH; *Int'l*, pg. 3522
HUESKER SYNTHETIC GMBH; *Int'l*, pg. 3522
HUESTIS MACHINE CORP.—See Best Medical International, Inc.; *U.S. Private*, pg. 543
HUETTENES-ALBERTUS AUSTRALIA PTY. LTD.—See Huettenes-Albertus Chemische Werke GmbH; *Int'l*, pg. 3523
HUETTENES-ALBERTUS CHEMISCHE WERKE GMBH; *Int'l*, pg. 3522
HUETTENES-ALBERTUS CHINA (HONGKONG) CO., LIMITED—See Huettenes-Albertus Chemische Werke GmbH; *Int'l*, pg. 3523
HUETTENES-ALBERTUS KOREA CO., LTD.—See Huettenes-Albertus Chemische Werke GmbH; *Int'l*, pg. 3523
HUETTINGER ELECTRONIC GMBH & CO. KG—See TRUMPF SE + Co. KG; *Int'l*, pg. 7942
HUEY STOCKSTILL, INC.; *U.S. Private*, pg. 2002
HUFA SEAL GMBH—See Krupke Holding GmbH; *Int'l*, pg. 4309
HUFCOR INCORPORATED—See OpenGate Capital Management, LLC; *U.S. Private*, pg. 3030
HUF DO BRASIL LTDA.—See Huf Hulsbeck & Furst GmbH & Co. KG; *Int'l*, pg. 3523
HUF ELECTRONICS BRETTEN GMBH—See Huf Hulsbeck & Furst GmbH & Co. KG; *Int'l*, pg. 3523
HUF ELECTRONICS DUSSELDORF GMBH—See Huf Hulsbeck & Furst GmbH & Co. KG; *Int'l*, pg. 3523
HUF ESPANA S.A—See Huf Hulsbeck & Furst GmbH & Co. KG; *Int'l*, pg. 3523
HUFFINES AUTO GROUP; *U.S. Private*, pg. 2002
HUFFINES CHEVROLET LEWISVILLE—See Huffines Auto Group; *U.S. Private*, pg. 2003
HUFFINES CHRYSLER JEEP KIA DENTON—See Huffines Auto Group; *U.S. Private*, pg. 2003
HUFFINES CHRYSLER PLYMOUTH, INC.—See Huffines Auto Group; *U.S. Private*, pg. 2003
HUFFINES DODGE PLANO, L.P.—See Huffines Auto Group; *U.S. Private*, pg. 2003
HUFFINES HYUNDAI MCKINNEY, LP—See Huffines Auto Group; *U.S. Private*, pg. 2003
HUFFMAN OIL CO., INC.; *U.S. Private*, pg. 2003
HUFFMAN & WRIGHT LOGGING INC.; *U.S. Private*, pg. 2003
HUFF PAPER COMPANY INC.; *U.S. Private*, pg. 2002
HUFFY BICYCLE COMPANY—See Huffy Corporation; *U.S. Private*, pg. 2003
HUFFY CORPORATION; *U.S. Private*, pg. 2003
HUF HULSBECK & FURST GMBH & CO. KG; *Int'l*, pg. 3523
HUF INDIA PRIVATE LIMITED—See Huf Hulsbeck & Furst GmbH & Co. KG; *Int'l*, pg. 3523
HUF JAPAN CO., LTD.—See Huf Hulsbeck & Furst GmbH & Co. KG; *Int'l*, pg. 3523
HUF KOREA LIMITED—See Huf Hulsbeck & Furst GmbH & Co. KG; *Int'l*, pg. 3523
HUF MEXICO S. DE R.L. DE C.V.—See Huf Hulsbeck & Furst GmbH & Co. KG; *Int'l*, pg. 3523
HUF NORTH AMERICA AUTOMOTIVE PARTS MANUFACTURING CORP.; *U.S. Private*, pg. 2002
HUF POLSKA SP. Z.O.O.—See Huf Hulsbeck & Furst GmbH & Co. KG; *Int'l*, pg. 3523
HUF PORTUGUESA, LDA.—See Huf Hulsbeck & Furst GmbH & Co. KG; *Int'l*, pg. 3523
HU-FRIEDY ITALY SRL—See STERIS plc; *Int'l*, pg. 7209
HU-FRIEDY JAPAN GK—See STERIS plc; *Int'l*, pg. 7209
HU-FRIEDY MEDICAL INSTRUMENT (SHANGHAI) CHINA CO. LTD.—See STERIS plc; *Int'l*, pg. 7209
HU-FRIEDY MFG. CO., LLC—See Peak Rock Capital LLC; *U.S. Private*, pg. 3124
HUF ROMANIA S.R.L.—See Huf Hulsbeck & Furst GmbH & Co. KG; *Int'l*, pg. 3523
H.U. FRONTIER, INC.—See H.U. Group Holdings, Inc.; *Int'l*, pg. 3197
HUF SECURE MOBILE GMBH—See Huf Hulsbeck & Furst GmbH & Co. KG; *Int'l*, pg. 3523
HUF TOOLS GMBH—See Huf Hulsbeck & Furst GmbH & Co. KG; *Int'l*, pg. 3523
HUF U.K. LTD.—See Huf Hulsbeck & Furst GmbH & Co. KG; *Int'l*, pg. 3523

HUFVUDSTADEN AB—See L. E. Lundbergforetagen AB; *Int'l*, pg. 4381
HUGA KG—See Hormann KG Verkaufsgesellschaf; *Int'l*, pg. 3481
HUGA OPTOTECH INC.—See Ennostar Inc.; *Int'l*, pg. 2443
HUGE CONNECT PROPRIETARY LIMITED—See Huge Group Limited; *Int'l*, pg. 3524
HUGE DISTRIBUTION PROPRIETARY LIMITED—See Huge Group Limited; *Int'l*, pg. 3524
HUGE GROUP LIMITED; *Int'l*, pg. 3523
HUGE HILL BEIJING TECHNOLOGY DEVELOPMENT CO., LTD—See NutryFarm International Limited; *Int'l*, pg. 5494
HUGEL, INC.; *Int'l*, pg. 3524
HUGE, LLC—See The Interpublic Group of Companies, Inc.; *U.S. Public*, pg. 2094
HUGE NETWORKS PROPRIETARY LIMITED—See Huge Group Limited; *Int'l*, pg. 3524
HUGE—See The Interpublic Group of Companies, Inc.; *U.S. Public*, pg. 2091
HUGE TELECOM PROPRIETARY LIMITED—See Huge Group Limited; *Int'l*, pg. 3524
HUGGER MUGGER YOGA PRODUCTS LLC; *U.S. Private*, pg. 2003
HUGG & HALL EQUIPMENT COMPANY; *U.S. Private*, pg. 2003
HUGGINS SHIPPING & CUSTOMS BROKERAGE LIMITED—See Massy Holdings Ltd.; *Int'l*, pg. 4723
HUGHES-ANDERSON HEAT EXCHANGERS; *U.S. Private*, pg. 2004
HUGHES CASTELL (HONG KONG) LTD.; *Int'l*, pg. 3524
HUGHES CENTER, LLC—See Universal Health Services, Inc.; *U.S. Public*, pg. 2258
HUGHES CHRISTENSEN—See Baker Hughes Company; *U.S. Public*, pg. 264
HUGHES COMMUNICATIONS, INC.—See EchoStar Corporation; *U.S. Public*, pg. 711
HUGHES COMMUNICATIONS INDIA PRIVATE LTD.—See EchoStar Corporation; *U.S. Public*, pg. 711
HUGHES ENTERPRISES INC.; *U.S. Private*, pg. 2003
HUGHES EXTERMINATORS, INC.—See Arrow Exterminators Inc.; *U.S. Private*, pg. 335
HUGHES FURNITURE INDUSTRIES INC.; *U.S. Private*, pg. 2003
HUGHES GROUP ARCHITECTS, INC.—See Little Diversified Architectural Consulting, Inc.; *U.S. Private*, pg. 2468
HUGHES GROUP, INC.; *U.S. Private*, pg. 2003
HUGHES GROUP LLC; *U.S. Private*, pg. 2003
HUGHES HUBBARD & REED LLP; *U.S. Private*, pg. 2003
HUGHES INSURANCE AGENCY, INC.—See Arthur J. Gallagher & Co.; *U.S. Public*, pg. 206
HUGHESLEAHYKARLOVIC, INC.; *U.S. Private*, pg. 2004
HUGHES LUMBER COMPANY; *U.S. Private*, pg. 2003
HUGHES MACHINERY COMPANY; *U.S. Private*, pg. 2003
HUGHES MOTORS INC.; *U.S. Private*, pg. 2003
HUGHES NETWORK SYSTEMS EUROPE, LTD.—See EchoStar Corporation; *U.S. Public*, pg. 711
HUGHES NETWORK SYSTEMS INDIA, LTD.—See EchoStar Corporation; *U.S. Public*, pg. 711
HUGHES NETWORK SYSTEMS, LLC—See EchoStar Corporation; *U.S. Public*, pg. 711
HUGHES OIL CO. INC.; *U.S. Private*, pg. 2003
HUGHES PARKER INDUSTRIES LLC—See JMAC Inc.; *U.S. Private*, pg. 2214
HUGHES POOLS INC.; *U.S. Private*, pg. 2003
HUGHES RELOCATION SERVICE INC.; *U.S. Private*, pg. 2004
HUGHES SATELLITE SYSTEMS CORPORATION—See EchoStar Corporation; *U.S. Public*, pg. 711
HUGHEY & PHILLIPS, LLC; *U.S. Private*, pg. 2004
HUGHSON NUT, INCORPORATED; *U.S. Private*, pg. 2004
HUGH WOOD, INC.—See Kelso & Company, L.P.; *U.S. Private*, pg. 2280
HUGLI FOOD ELELMISZERIPARI KFT.—See Coop-Gruppe Genossenschaft; *Int'l*, pg. 1790
HUGLI FOOD POLSKA SP.Z O.O.—See Coop-Gruppe Genossenschaft; *Int'l*, pg. 1790
HUGLI FOOD SLOVAKIA S.R.O.—See Coop-Gruppe Genossenschaft; *Int'l*, pg. 1790
HUGLI NAHRMITTEL-ERZEUGUNG GES.M.B.H—See Coop-Gruppe Genossenschaft; *Int'l*, pg. 1790
HUGLI NAHRUNGSMITTEL GMBH—See Coop-Gruppe Genossenschaft; *Int'l*, pg. 1790
HUGO BOSCA COMPANY, INC.; *U.S. Private*, pg. 2004
HUGO BOSS AG—See Permira Advisers LLP; *Int'l*, pg. 5805
HUGO BOSS AUSTRALIA PTY. LTD.—See Permira Advisers LLP; *Int'l*, pg. 5805
HUGO BOSS BENELUX B.V.—See Permira Advisers LLP; *Int'l*, pg. 5805
HUGO BOSS CANADA INC.—See Permira Advisers LLP; *Int'l*, pg. 5805
HUGO BOSS DO BRASIL LTDA.—See Permira Advisers LLP; *Int'l*, pg. 5805
HUGO BOSS ESPANA S.A.—See Permira Advisers LLP; *Int'l*, pg. 5805

HUGO BOSS FASHIONS INC.—See Permira Advisers LLP; *Int'l*, pg. 5805
HUGO BOSS FRANCE S.A.S.—See Permira Advisers LLP; *Int'l*, pg. 5805
HUGO BOSS HONG KONG LTD.—See Permira Advisers LLP; *Int'l*, pg. 5805
HUGO BOSS ITALIA S.P.A.—See Permira Advisers LLP; *Int'l*, pg. 5805
HUGO BOSS JAPAN K.K.—See Permira Advisers LLP; *Int'l*, pg. 5805
HUGO BOSS MEXICO S.A. DE C.V.—See Permira Advisers LLP; *Int'l*, pg. 5805
HUGO BOSS (SCHWEIZ) AG—See Permira Advisers LLP; *Int'l*, pg. 5805
HUGO BOSS TEXTILE INDUSTRY LTD.—See Permira Advisers LLP; *Int'l*, pg. 5805
HUGO BOSS UK LTD.—See Permira Advisers LLP; *Int'l*, pg. 5805
HUGO BOSS USA INC.—See Permira Advisers LLP; *Int'l*, pg. 5805
HUGO DUNHILL MAILING LISTS, INC.; *U.S. Private*, pg. 2004
HUGO NEU CORPORATION; *U.S. Private*, pg. 2004
HUGO NEU-PROLER CO.—See Hugo Neu Corporation; *U.S. Private*, pg. 2004
HUGO NEU RECYCLING, LLC—See Closed Loop Partners LLC; *U.S. Private*, pg. 946
HUGO SACHS ELEKTRONIK-HARVARD APPARATUS GMBH—See Harvard Bioscience, Inc.; *U.S. Public*, pg. 987
HUGO'S FAMILY MARKETPLACE—See Valley Markets, Incorporated; *U.S. Private*, pg. 4334
HUGOTON ROYALTY TRUST; *U.S. Public*, pg. 1068
H.U. GROUP HOLDINGS, INC.; *Int'l*, pg. 3196
H.U. GROUP RESEARCH INSTITUTE G.K.—See H.U. Group Holdings, Inc.; *Int'l*, pg. 3197
HUGUAN GAOCE NEW MATERIAL TECHNOLOGY CO., LTD.—See Qingdao GaoCe Technology Co., Ltd.; *Int'l*, pg. 6143
HUHEHAOTE JIHONG PACKAGE CO., LTD—See Xiamen Jihong Technology Co., Ltd.; *Int'l*, pg. 8525
HUHN PRESSTECH, SPOL. S. R. O.—See HEINRICH HUHN GmbH + Co.KG; *Int'l*, pg. 3324
HUHOT MONGOLIAN GRILLS, LLC; *U.S. Private*, pg. 2004
HUHTALA OIL & TEMPLETON GARAGE; *U.S. Private*, pg. 2004
HUHTAMAKI ALF ZWEIGNIEDERLASSUNG DER HUHTAMAKI DEUTSCHLAND GMBH & CO KG—See Huhtamaki Oyj; *Int'l*, pg. 3525
HUHTAMAKI AUSTRALIA PTY LTD - FLEXIBLE PACKAGING SALES UNIT—See Huhtamaki Oyj; *Int'l*, pg. 3524
HUHTAMAKI AUSTRALIA PTY LTD - FOOD SERVICE BUSINESS UNIT—See Huhtamaki Oyj; *Int'l*, pg. 3524
HUHTAMAKI AUSTRALIA PTY. LTD.—See Huhtamaki Oyj; *Int'l*, pg. 3524
HUHTAMAKI AUSTRALIA PTY LTD.—See Huhtamaki Oyj; *Int'l*, pg. 3524
HUHTAMAKI AUSTRALIA PTY LTD.—See Huhtamaki Oyj; *Int'l*, pg. 3524
HUHTAMAKI CESKA REPUBLIKA A/S—See Huhtamaki Oyj; *Int'l*, pg. 3524
HUHTAMAKI CONSORCIO MEXICANA S.A. DE C.V.—See Huhtamaki Oyj; *Int'l*, pg. 3524
HUHTAMAKI CONSUMER PACKAGING INC.—See Huhtamaki Oyj; *Int'l*, pg. 3526
HUHTAMAKI CONSUMER PACKAGING—See Huhtamaki Oyj; *Int'l*, pg. 3526
HUHTAMAKI CONSUMER PACKAGING—See Huhtamaki Oyj; *Int'l*, pg. 3526
HUHTAMAKI DO BRASIL LTDA.—See Huhtamaki Oyj; *Int'l*, pg. 3526
HUHTAMAKI EGYPT—See Huhtamaki Oyj; *Int'l*, pg. 3524
HUHTAMAKI ESTONIA LTD.—See Huhtamaki Oyj; *Int'l*, pg. 3524
HUHTAMAKI FINANCE BV—See Huhtamaki Oyj; *Int'l*, pg. 3524
HUHTAMAKI FLEXIBLE PACKAGING GERMANY GMBH & CO. KG—See Huhtamaki Oyj; *Int'l*, pg. 3524
HUHTAMAKI FLEXIBLES ITALY S.R.L.—See Huhtamaki Oyj; *Int'l*, pg. 3525
HUHTAMAKI FOODSERVICE FINLAND OY—See Huhtamaki Oyj; *Int'l*, pg. 3525
HUHTAMAKI FOODSERVICE FRANCE S.A.S.—See Huhtamaki Oyj; *Int'l*, pg. 3525
HUHTAMAKI FOODSERVICE GERMANY GMBH & CO. KG—See Huhtamaki Oyj; *Int'l*, pg. 3525
HUHTAMAKI FOODSERVICE GERMANY SALES GMBH & CO. KG—See Huhtamaki Oyj; *Int'l*, pg. 3525
HUHTAMAKI FOODSERVICE GLIWICE SP. Z O.O.—See Huhtamaki Oyj; *Int'l*, pg. 3525
HUHTAMAKI FOODSERVICE POLAND SP. Z.O.O.—See Huhtamaki Oyj; *Int'l*, pg. 3525
HUHTAMAKI FOODSERVICE POLAND SP. Z.O.O. - XPS PLANT—See Huhtamaki Oyj; *Int'l*, pg. 3525
HUHTAMAKI FOODSERVICE (SHANGHAI) LIMITED—See Huhtamaki Oyj; *Int'l*, pg. 3525
HUHTAMAKI FOODSERVICE (TIANJIN) LTD.—See Huhtamaki Oyj; *Int'l*, pg. 3525

COMPANY NAME INDEX

HUHTAMAKI FOODSERVICE UKRAINE LLC—See Huhtamaki Oyj; *Int'l*, pg. 3525
HUHTAMAKI FORCHHEIM ZWEIGNIEDERLASSUNG DER HUHTAMAKI DEUTSCHLAND GMBH & CO KG—See Huhtamaki Oyj; *Int'l*, pg. 3525
HUHTAMAKI (GUANGZHOU) LIMITED—See Huhtamaki Oyj; *Int'l*, pg. 3524
HUHTAMAKI HENDERSON LIMITED - FOOD SERVICE BUSINESS UNIT—See Huhtamaki Oyj; *Int'l*, pg. 3525
HUHTAMAKI HENDERSON LTD.—See Huhtamaki Oyj; *Int'l*, pg. 3525
HUHTAMAKI HONG KONG LIMITED—See Huhtamaki Oyj; *Int'l*, pg. 3525
HUHTAMAKI HONG KONG LIMITED TAIWAN BRANCH OFFICE—See Huhtamaki Oyj; *Int'l*, pg. 3525
HUHTAMAKI HUNGARY KFT—See Huhtamaki Oyj; *Int'l*, pg. 3526
HUHTAMAKI, INC. - OHIO—See Huhtamaki Oyj; *Int'l*, pg. 3526
HUHTAMAKI, INC.—See Huhtamaki Oyj; *Int'l*, pg. 3526
HUHTAMAKI INDIA LIMITED; *Int'l*, pg. 3525
HUHTAMAKI ISTANBUL AMBALAJ SANAYI A.S.—See Huhtamaki Oyj; *Int'l*, pg. 3525
HUHTAMAKI LA ROCHELLE S.A.S.—See Huhtamaki Oyj; *Int'l*, pg. 3525
HUHTAMAKI LA ROCHELLE SNC—See Huhtamaki Oyj; *Int'l*, pg. 3525
HUHTAMAKI (LISBURN) LTD—See Huhtamaki Oyj; *Int'l*, pg. 3525
HUHTAMAKI LTD.—See Huhtamaki Oyj; *Int'l*, pg. 3525
HUHTAMAKI (LURGAN) LIMITED—See Huhtamaki Oyj; *Int'l*, pg. 3525
HUHTAMAKI MALAYSIA SDN BHD—See Huhtamaki Oyj; *Int'l*, pg. 3525
HUHTAMAKI MEXICANA S.A. DE C.V.—See Huhtamaki Oyj; *Int'l*, pg. 3525
HUHTAMAKI MOLDED FIBER TECHNOLOGY B.V.—See Huhtamaki Oyj; *Int'l*, pg. 3525
HUHTAMAKI MOULDED FIBRE DO BRASIL LTDA.—See Huhtamaki Oyj; *Int'l*, pg. 3525
HUHTAMAKI NEDERLAND B.V.—See Huhtamaki Oyj; *Int'l*, pg. 3525
HUHTAMAKI NEW ZEALAND LIMITED - FLEXIBLE FOOD PACKAGING BUSINESS UNIT—See Huhtamaki Oyj; *Int'l*, pg. 3524
HUHTAMAKI NEW ZEALAND LIMITED - MOLDED FIBER BUSINESS UNIT—See Huhtamaki Oyj; *Int'l*, pg. 3524
HUHTAMAKI NEW ZEALAND LIMITED—See Huhtamaki Oyj; *Int'l*, pg. 3525
HUHTAMAKI NORWAY A/S—See Huhtamaki Oyj; *Int'l*, pg. 3525
HUHTAMAKI (NZ) HOLDINGS LTD—See Huhtamaki Oyj; *Int'l*, pg. 3524
HUHTAMAKI OYJ; *Int'l*, pg. 3524
HUHTAMAKI PAPER RECYCLING B.V.—See Huhtamaki Oyj; *Int'l*, pg. 3525
HUHTAMAKI PHILIPPINES, INC.—See Huhtamaki Oyj; *Int'l*, pg. 3525
HUHTAMAKI PROTECTIVE PACKAGING B.V.—See Huhtamaki Oyj; *Int'l*, pg. 3525
HUHTAMAKI RONSBERG - ZWEIGNIEDERLASSUNG DER HUHTAMAKI DEUTSCHLAND GMBH & CO KG—See Huhtamaki Oyj; *Int'l*, pg. 3525
HUHTAMAKI RUSSIA—See Huhtamaki Oyj; *Int'l*, pg. 3525
HUHTAMAKI SINGAPORE PTE. LTD.—See Huhtamaki Oyj; *Int'l*, pg. 3525
HUHTAMAKI SOUTH AFRICA (PTY) LTD.—See Huhtamaki Oyj; *Int'l*, pg. 3525
HUHTAMAKI SOUTH AFRICA (PTY) LTD.—See Huhtamaki Oyj; *Int'l*, pg. 3526
HUHTAMAKI SOUTH AFRICA (PTY) LTD.—See Huhtamaki Oyj; *Int'l*, pg. 3525
HUHTAMAKI SPAIN S.L.—See Huhtamaki Oyj; *Int'l*, pg. 3526
HUHTAMAKI SVENSKA AB—See Huhtamaki Oyj; *Int'l*, pg. 3526
HUHTAMAKI SWEDEN AB—See Huhtamaki Oyj; *Int'l*, pg. 3526
HUHTAMAKI TAILORED PACKAGING PTY. LTD.—See Huhtamaki Oyj; *Int'l*, pg. 3526
HUHTAMAKI (THAILAND) LIMITED - PLANT 1—See Huhtamaki Oyj; *Int'l*, pg. 3524
HUHTAMAKI (THAILAND) LIMITED - PLANT 2—See Huhtamaki Oyj; *Int'l*, pg. 3524
HUHTAMAKI (THAILAND) LIMITED—See Huhtamaki Oyj; *Int'l*, pg. 3524
HUHTAMAKI (TIANJIN) LTD.—See Huhtamaki Oyj; *Int'l*, pg. 3524
HUHTAMAKI TURKEY GIDA SERVISI AMBALAJI A.S.—See Huhtamaki Oyj; *Int'l*, pg. 3526
HUHTAMAKI (UK) LTD.—See Huhtamaki Oyj; *Int'l*, pg. 3524
HUHTAMAKI (UK) LTD.—See Huhtamaki Oyj; *Int'l*, pg. 3524
HUHTAMAKI (VIETNAM) LTD—See Huhtamaki Oyj; *Int'l*, pg. 3524
HUIDA SANITARY WARE CO., LTD.; *Int'l*, pg. 3526
HUIFU PAYMENT LIMITED; *Int'l*, pg. 3526
HUIHENG MEDICAL, INC.; *Int'l*, pg. 3526

HUI HULIAU; *U.S. Private*, pg. 2004
HUIJING HOLDINGS COMPANY LIMITED; *Int'l*, pg. 3526
HUIJSMANS EN KUIJPERS AUTOMATISERING BV—See Online Computer Library Center, Inc.; *U.S. Private*, pg. 3026
HUIKWANG CORP.; *Int'l*, pg. 3526
HUI KWANG (THAILAND) CO., LTD.—See Huikwang Corp.; *Int'l*, pg. 3526
HUILI RESOURCES (GROUP) LIMITED; *Int'l*, pg. 3526
HUI LYU ECOLOGICAL TECHNOLOGY GROUPS CO., LTD.; *Int'l*, pg. 3526
HUIS CLOS SA; *Int'l*, pg. 3526
HUISEN HOUSEHOLD INTERNATIONAL GROUP LIMITED; *Int'l*, pg. 3526
HUISHANG BANK CORPORATION LIMITED; *Int'l*, pg. 3527
HUISHANGGULI HOTEL OF HUANGSHAN TOURISM DEVELOPMENT CO., LTD.—See Huangshan Tourism Development Co., Ltd.; *Int'l*, pg. 3513
HUISHENG INTERNATIONAL HOLDINGS LIMITED; *Int'l*, pg. 3527
HUISHENG PLASTICS (SHEN ZHEN) CO LTD—See Co-partner Technology Corporation; *Int'l*, pg. 1793
HUIS TEN BOSCH CO., LTD.—See H.I.S. Co., Ltd.; *Int'l*, pg. 3195
HUITEX LIMITED—See Huikwang Corp.; *Int'l*, pg. 3526
HUITONGDA NETWORK CO., LTD.; *Int'l*, pg. 3527
HUITONG INTELLIGENCE CO., LTD.—See Silicon Integrated Systems Corp.; *Int'l*, pg. 6920
HUITT-ZOLLARS, INC.; *U.S. Private*, pg. 2004
HUI XIAN ASSET MANAGEMENT LIMITED; *Int'l*, pg. 3526
HUIXINJIA CAPITAL GROUP, INC.; *U.S. Private*, pg. 2004
HUIXINTONG (TIANJIN) INFORMATION-ENTERPRISE CO., LTD.—See JTP Co., Ltd.; *Int'l*, pg. 4020
HUIXIN WASTE WATER SOLUTIONS, INC.; *Int'l*, pg. 3527
HUIYANG CCT PLASTIC PRODUCTS CO.,LTD—See CCT Fortis Holdings Limited; *Int'l*, pg. 1370
HUIYANG CCT TELECOMMUNICATIONS PRODUCTS CO., LTD—See CCT Fortis Holdings Limited; *Int'l*, pg. 1370
HUIYANG TECHWISE INDUSTRIAL TECHNOLOGY CO. LTD—See Kingboard Holdings Limited; *Int'l*, pg. 4171
HUIYE (VIETNAM) PLASTIC CO., LTD.—See Dynamic Colours Limited; *Int'l*, pg. 2240
HUI YING FINANCIAL HOLDINGS CORPORATION; *Int'l*, pg. 3526
HUIYIN HOLDINGS GROUP LIMITED; *Int'l*, pg. 3527
HUIYIN SMART COMMUNITY CO., LTD.; *Int'l*, pg. 3527
HUIZE HOLDING LIMITED; *Int'l*, pg. 3527
HUIZENGA HOLDINGS, INC.; *U.S. Private*, pg. 2004
HUIZENGA MANUFACTURING GROUP, INC.; *U.S. Private*, pg. 2004
HUIZE PHILEMON & BAUCIS WZC—See Ackermans & van Haaren NV; *Int'l*, pg. 106
HUIZHONG INSTRUMENTATION CO., LTD.; *Int'l*, pg. 3527
HUIZHOU CHINA EAGLE ELECTRONIC TECHNOLOGY CO., LTD.; *Int'l*, pg. 3527
HUIZHOU CHUNG SHUN CHEMICAL COMPANY LIMITED—See Kingboard Holdings Limited; *Int'l*, pg. 4171
HUIZHOU CITY GAS DEVELOPMENT CO., LTD.—See Shenzhen Energy Group Co., Ltd.; *Int'l*, pg. 6808
HUIZHOU DESAY SV AUTOMOTIVE CO., LTD.; *Int'l*, pg. 3527
HUIZHOU DONGJIANG ENVIRONMENT TECHNOLOGY CO. LIMITED—See Dongjiang Environmental Company Limited; *Int'l*, pg. 2168
HUIZHOU FOOK WOO PAPER COMPANY LIMITED—See Integrated Waste Solutions Group Holdings Limited; *Int'l*, pg. 3731
HUIZHOU FORYOU INDUSTRIES CO., LTD.—See Foryou Corporation; *Int'l*, pg. 2747
HUIZHOU FUSHENG INSULATION MATERIALS LTD, INC.—See Auxo Investment Partners, LLC; *U.S. Private*, pg. 402
HUIZHOU GOLF & RESORT CO., LTD.—See Okabe Co., Ltd.; *Int'l*, pg. 5544
HUIZHOU GP WIRING TECHNOLOGY LTD.—See Gold Peak Technology Group Limited; *Int'l*, pg. 3025
HUIZHOU HENGMINGDA ELECTRONIC TECHNOLOGY CO., LTD.—See Suzhou Hengmingda Electronic Technology Co., Ltd.; *Int'l*, pg. 7350
HUIZHOU HENGYI WUJIN ZHIPIN LIMITED—See Hang Yick Holdings Company Limited; *Int'l*, pg. 3245
HUIZHOU HONGLIN TECHNOLOGY CO., LTD.—See InvesTech Holdings Limited; *Int'l*, pg. 3778
HUIZHOU HUALI PACKAGING CO., LTD.—See Overseas Chinese Town (Asia) Holdings Limited; *Int'l*, pg. 5672
HUIZHOU INTERPLEX TECHNOLOGY, LTD.—See Blackstone Inc.; *U.S. Public*, pg. 354
HUIZHOU JECKSON ELECTRIC COMPANY LIMITED—See China Aerospace International Holdings Limited; *Int'l*, pg. 1481
HUIZHOU JUNYANG PLASTIC CO., LTD.—See Huasheng International Holding Co., Ltd.; *Int'l*, pg. 3514

HUIZHOU KEEN POINT PRECISION PLASTIC CO., LTD.—See Xin Point Holdings Limited; *Int'l*, pg. 8528
HUIZHOU KEEN POINT SURFACE DECORATION CO., LTD.—See Xin Point Holdings Limited; *Int'l*, pg. 8528
HUIZHOU LCY ELASTOMERS CORP.—See KKR & Co. Inc.; *U.S. Public*, pg. 1258
HUIZHOU LIEN SHUN ELECTRONICS CO., LTD.—See Brightking Holdings Limited; *Int'l*, pg. 1162
HUIZHOU LI SHIN ELECTRONIC CO., LTD.—See Lite-On Technology Corporation; *Int'l*, pg. 4525
HUIZHOU LONGLI TECHNOLOGY DEVELOPMENT CO., LTD.—See Shenzhen Longli Technology Co., Ltd.; *Int'l*, pg. 6817
HUIZHOU MMA CO., LTD.—See Mitsubishi Chemical Group Corporation; *Int'l*, pg. 4931
HUIZHOU NANXUAN KNITTING FACTORY LIMITED—See Nameson Holdings Limited; *Int'l*, pg. 5135
HUIZHOU NANYOU FOREST DEVELOPMENT CO., LTD.—See Oji Holdings Corporation; *Int'l*, pg. 5536
HUIZHOU PACIFIC CONTAINER CO., LTD—See Singamas Container Holdings Limited; *Int'l*, pg. 6939
HUIZHOU POLY CULTURE & ARTS CENTER MANAGEMENT CORPORATION LIMITED—See Poly Culture Group Corporation Limited; *Int'l*, pg. 5914
HUIZHOU RONGDA INK CO., LTD.—See ShenZhen RongDa Photosensitive Science & Technology Co., Ltd.; *Int'l*, pg. 6820
HUIZHOU SANLI THREE SYNERGY PRECISION CO., LTD.—See Nagase & Co., Ltd.; *Int'l*, pg. 5126
HUIZHOU SEKONIC TECHNOLOGIES CO., LTD.—See Sekonic Corporation; *Int'l*, pg. 6698
HUIZHOU SHENGHUA SCIENCE&TECHNOLOGY CO., LTD.—See Shenzhen Deren Electronic Co., Ltd.; *Int'l*, pg. 6808
HUIZHOU SHENTIAN PRECISION MACHINES CO. LTD.—See Tajima Industries Ltd.; *Int'l*, pg. 7428
HUIZHOU SHENZHEN ENERGY FENGDA POWER CO., LTD.—See Shenzhen Energy Group Co., Ltd.; *Int'l*, pg. 6808
HUIZHOU SINGAMAS ENERGY EQUIPMENT CO., LTD.—See Singamas Container Holdings Limited; *Int'l*, pg. 6939
HUIZHOU SPEED WIRELESS TECHNOLOGY CO., LTD.; *Int'l*, pg. 3527
HUIZHOU SPEED WIRELESS TECHNOLOGY - SAN JOSE BRANCH—See Huizhou Speed Wireless Technology Co., Ltd.; *Int'l*, pg. 3527
HUIZHOU SUMIDEN WIRING SYSTEMS CO., LTD.—See Sumitomo Electric Industries, Ltd.; *Int'l*, pg. 7278
HUIZHOU TIANXIN PETROCHEMICAL ENGINEERING CO., LTD.—See PEC Ltd.; *Int'l*, pg. 5778
HUIZHOU TON YI INDUSTRIAL CO., LTD.—See Uni-President Enterprises Corporation; *Int'l*, pg. 8028
HUIZHOU UNIPLUS ELECTRONICS CO., LTD.—See Guangdong Chaohua Technology Co., Ltd.; *Int'l*, pg. 3153
HUIZHOU WAI CHI ELECTRONICS COMPANY LIMITED—See Wai Chi Holdings Company Limited; *Int'l*, pg. 8330
HUIZHOU WEIBO (WEIBRASS) PRECISION TECHNOLOGY CO., LTD.—See Suzhou Anjie Technology Co., Ltd.; *Int'l*, pg. 7349
HUIZHOU WING YU METAL & PLASTIC MANUFACTORY COMPANY LIMITED—See Ka Shui International Holdings Limited; *Int'l*, pg. 4045
HUIZHOU WINONE PRECISION TECHNOLOGY CO., LTD.—See SUNWODA Electronics Co., Ltd.; *Int'l*, pg. 7333
HUIZHOU XIN POINT SURFACE DECORATION CO., LTD.—See Xin Point Holdings Limited; *Int'l*, pg. 8528
HUIZHOU XINSHENG TECHNOLOGY CO., LTD.—See Xin Point Holdings Limited; *Int'l*, pg. 8529
HUIZHOU YOUTE ELECTRONIC CO., LTD.—See InvesTech Holdings Limited; *Int'l*, pg. 3778
HUIZHOU ZHUCHENG WIRING SYSTEMS, CO., LTD.—See Sumitomo Electric Industries, Ltd.; *Int'l*, pg. 7278
HUIZHOU ZHU GUANG AUTO WIRING SYSTEMS CO., LTD.—See Sumitomo Electric Industries, Ltd.; *Int'l*, pg. 7278
HUIZHOU ZHURUN AUTOMOTIVE WIRE CO., LTD.—See Sumitomo Electric Industries, Ltd.; *Int'l*, pg. 7278
HUIZHOU ZHURUN WIRING SYSTEMS CO. LTD.—See Sumitomo Electric Industries, Ltd.; *Int'l*, pg. 7284
HUKA B.V.—See AdderaCare AB; *Int'l*, pg. 128
HULAMIN EXTRUSIONS (PTY) LIMITED - CAPE TOWN PLANT—See Hulamin Limited; *Int'l*, pg. 3527
HULAMIN EXTRUSIONS (PTY) LIMITED - PIETERMARITZBURG PLANT—See Hulamin Limited; *Int'l*, pg. 3527
HULAMIN EXTRUSIONS (PTY) LIMITED—See Hulamin Limited; *Int'l*, pg. 3527
HULAMIN LIMITED; *Int'l*, pg. 3527
HULAMIN NORTH AMERICA LLC—See Hulamin Limited; *Int'l*, pg. 3527
HULAMIN OPERATIONS (PTY) LIMITED—See Hulamin Limited; *Int'l*, pg. 3527
HULAMIN ROLLED PRODUCTS (PTY) LIMITED—See Hulamin Limited; *Int'l*, pg. 3528

HULAMIN LIMITED

HULAMIN SYSTEMS (PTY) LIMITED—See Hulamin Limited; *Int'l*, pg. 3528
HU LANE ASSOCIATE, INC.; *Int'l*, pg. 3509
HULBEE AG; *Int'l*, pg. 3528
HULETT BANCORP; *U.S. Private*, pg. 2005
HULIC CO., LTD.; *Int'l*, pg. 3528
HULIC HOTEL MANAGEMENT CO., LTD.—See Hulic Co., Ltd.; *Int'l*, pg. 3528
HULIC REIT MANAGEMENT CO., LTD.—See Hulic Co., Ltd.; *Int'l*, pg. 3528
HULINKS INC.—See Argo Graphics Inc.; *Int'l*, pg. 562
HULISANI LTD.; *Int'l*, pg. 3528
HULL & ASSOCIATES, INC. - BROWNFIELDS DIVISION—See Sterling Investment Partners, L.P.; *U.S. Private*, pg. 3806
HULL BLYTH & CO LTD—See Deutsche Post AG; *Int'l*, pg. 2080
HULL BLYTH GHANA LTD—See Deutsche Post AG; *Int'l*, pg. 2080
HULL BLYTH NIGERIA LTD—See Deutsche Post AG; *Int'l*, pg. 2080
HULL BLYTH SOUTH AFRICA PTY LTD—See Deutsche Post AG; *Int'l*, pg. 2081
HULL & COMPANY, INC. - TAMPA—See Brown & Brown, Inc.; *U.S. Public*, pg. 401
HULL & COMPANY, LLC—See Brown & Brown, Inc.; *U.S. Public*, pg. 401
HULL COOPERATIVE ASSOCIATION INC.; *U.S. Private*, pg. 2005
HULLERAS DEL NORTE, S.A.; *Int'l*, pg. 3528
HULLERA VASCO LEONESA S.A.; *Int'l*, pg. 3528
HULLER HILLE GMBH—See Fair Friend Group; *Int'l*, pg. 2604
HULLEY & KIRKWOOD CONSULTING ENGINEERS LTD; *Int'l*, pg. 3528
HULL LIFT TRUCK INC.; *U.S. Private*, pg. 2005
HULL STREET ENERGY, LLC; *U.S. Private*, pg. 2005
HULL TRAINS COMPANY LIMITED—See FirstGroup plc; *Int'l*, pg. 2689
HULMAN & COMPANY; *U.S. Private*, pg. 2005
HULME SUPERCARS LIMITED; *Int'l*, pg. 3528
HULTAFORS AB—See Investment AB Latour; *Int'l*, pg. 3781
HULTAFORS GROUP AB—See Investment AB Latour; *Int'l*, pg. 3781
HULTAFORS GROUP AUSTRIA GMBH—See Investment AB Latour; *Int'l*, pg. 3781
HULTAFORS GROUP BELGIUM NV—See Investment AB Latour; *Int'l*, pg. 3781
HULTAFORS GROUP DANMARK AS—See Investment AB Latour; *Int'l*, pg. 3781
HULTAFORS GROUP FINLAND OY—See Investment AB Latour; *Int'l*, pg. 3781
HULTAFORS GROUP FRANCE SARL—See Investment AB Latour; *Int'l*, pg. 3781
HULTAFORS GROUP GERMANY GMBH—See Investment AB Latour; *Int'l*, pg. 3781
HULTAFORS GROUP IRELAND LTD.—See Investment AB Latour; *Int'l*, pg. 3781
HULTAFORS GROUP ITALY S.R.L.—See Investment AB Latour; *Int'l*, pg. 3781
HULTAFORS GROUP LOGISTICS SP. Z O.O.—See Investment AB Latour; *Int'l*, pg. 3781
HULTAFORS GROUP NL BV—See Investment AB Latour; *Int'l*, pg. 3781
HULTAFORS GROUP NORGE AS—See Investment AB Latour; *Int'l*, pg. 3781
HULTAFORS GROUP POLAND SP. Z O.O.—See Investment AB Latour; *Int'l*, pg. 3781
HULTAFORS GROUP SVERIGE AB—See Investment AB Latour; *Int'l*, pg. 3781
HULTAFORS GROUP SWITZERLAND AG—See Investment AB Latour; *Int'l*, pg. 3781
HULTAFORS GROUP UK LTD.—See Investment AB Latour; *Int'l*, pg. 3781
HULTAFORS NORGE AS—See Investment AB Latour; *Int'l*, pg. 3781
HULTAFORS OY—See Investment AB Latour; *Int'l*, pg. 3781
HULTAFORS PRASIDENT GMBH—See Investment AB Latour; *Int'l*, pg. 3782
HULTAFORS U.M.I. S.R.L.—See Investment AB Latour; *Int'l*, pg. 3782
HULTBERG INRIKES TRANSPORTER AB—See PostNord AB; *Int'l*, pg. 5940
HULT FRITZ MATUSZAK; *U.S. Private*, pg. 2005
HULUDAO AOXIN Q & M STOMATOLOGY HOSPITAL CO., LTD.—See Aoxin Q & M Dental Group Limited; *Int'l*, pg. 498
HULUDAO CITY AOXIN STOMATOLOGY POLYCLINIC CO., LTD.—See Aoxin Q & M Dental Group Limited; *Int'l*, pg. 498
HULUDAO LONGGANG DISTRICT AOXIN STOMATOLOGY POLYCLINIC CO., LTD.—See Aoxin Q & M Dental Group Limited; *Int'l*, pg. 498
HULUDAO ZINC INDUSTRY CO., LTD.; *Int'l*, pg. 3528
HULUL BUSINESS SOLUTIONS LTD.—See Palestine Telecommunications Company P.L.C.; *Int'l*, pg. 5707

HULU, LLC—See The Walt Disney Company; *U.S. Public*, pg. 2139
HULUNBEIER NORTH EAST FUFENG BIOTECHNOLOGIES CO., LTD.—See Fufeng Group Limited; *Int'l*, pg. 2804
HUMACYTE GLOBAL, INC.—See Humacyte, Inc.; *U.S. Public*, pg. 1069
HUMACYTE, INC.; *U.S. Public*, pg. 1068
HUMAK ENGINEERING (PVT) LTD.—See Daikin Industries, Ltd.; *Int'l*, pg. 1935
HUMANA AB; *Int'l*, pg. 3529
HUMANA ASSISTANS AB—See Humana AB; *Int'l*, pg. 3530
HUMANA AT HOME (DALLAS), INC.—See Humana, Inc.; *U.S. Public*, pg. 1069
HUMANA AT HOME (HOUSTON), INC.—See Humana, Inc.; *U.S. Public*, pg. 1069
HUMANA AT HOME, INC.—See Humana, Inc.; *U.S. Public*, pg. 1070
HUMANA BEHAVIORAL HEALTH, INC.—See Humana, Inc.; *U.S. Public*, pg. 1069
HUMAN ACADEMY CO., LTD.—See Human Holdings Co., Ltd.; *Int'l*, pg. 3529
HUMAN ACADEMY HIGH SCHOOL CO., LTD.—See Human Holdings Co., Ltd.; *Int'l*, pg. 3529
HUMAN ACADEMY SHANGHAI CO., LTD.—See Human Holdings Co., Ltd.; *Int'l*, pg. 3529
HUMANA DANMARK APS—See Humana AB; *Int'l*, pg. 3530
HUMANA EMPLOYERS HEALTH PLAN OF GEORGIA, INC.—See Humana, Inc.; *U.S. Public*, pg. 1069
HUMANAGEMENT PTY. LIMITED—See Academies Australasia Group Limited; *Int'l*, pg. 77
HUMANA GMBH—See DMK Deutsches Milchkontor GmbH; *Int'l*, pg. 2146
HUMANA GOVERNMENT BUSINESS, INC.—See Humana, Inc.; *U.S. Public*, pg. 1070
HUMANA HEALTH BENEFIT PLAN OF LOUISIANA, INC.—See Humana, Inc.; *U.S. Public*, pg. 1070
HUMANA HEALTH INSURANCE COMPANY OF FLORIDA, INC.—See Humana, Inc.; *U.S. Public*, pg. 1070
HUMANA HEALTH PLAN, INC.—See Humana, Inc.; *U.S. Public*, pg. 1070
HUMANA HEALTH PLAN OF OHIO, INC.—See Humana, Inc.; *U.S. Public*, pg. 1070
HUMANA HEALTH PLAN OF TEXAS, INC.—See Humana, Inc.; *U.S. Public*, pg. 1070
HUMANA HEALTH PLANS OF PUERTO RICO, INC.—See Humana, Inc.; *U.S. Public*, pg. 1070
HUMANA, INC.; *U.S. Public*, pg. 1069
HUMANA INSURANCE OF PUERTO RICO, INC.—See Humana, Inc.; *U.S. Public*, pg. 1070
HUMANA ITALIA S.P.A.—See DMK Deutsches Milchkontor GmbH; *Int'l*, pg. 2146
HUMANA MEDICAL PLAN, INC.—See Humana, Inc.; *U.S. Public*, pg. 1070
HUMANAN KALLIO OY—See Humana AB; *Int'l*, pg. 3530
HUMANA PHARMA INTERNATIONAL SPA—See DMK Deutsches Milchkontor GmbH; *Int'l*, pg. 2146
HUMAN ARC CORPORATION—See ABRY Partners, LLC; *U.S. Public*, pg. 41
HUMANA SPAIN S.L.—See DMK Deutsches Milchkontor GmbH; *Int'l*, pg. 2146
HUMAN ASSET DEVELOPMENT INTERNATIONAL LIMITED—See Norman Broadbent Plc; *Int'l*, pg. 5431
HUMAN ASSOCIATES HOLDINGS, INC.—See Mitsui & Co., Ltd.; *Int'l*, pg. 4973
HUMANA VENTURES—See Humana, Inc.; *U.S. Public*, pg. 1070
HUMANA WISCONSIN HEALTH ORGANIZATION INSURANCE CORPORATION—See Humana, Inc.; *U.S. Public*, pg. 1070
HUMAN CAPITAL GROUP HCG AB—See NGS Group AB; *Int'l*, pg. 5255
THE HUMAN CAPITAL GROUP, INC.—See Arthur J. Gallagher & Co.; *U.S. Public*, pg. 207
HUMAN CAPITAL STAFFING, L.L.C.; *U.S. Private*, pg. 2005
HUMAN CARE BO AS—See Humana AB; *Int'l*, pg. 3530
HUMAN CARE HOLDING AS—See Humana AB; *Int'l*, pg. 3530
HUMAN CARE SERVICES FOR FAMILIES AND CHILDREN, INC.; *U.S. Private*, pg. 2005
HUMANCENTRIC; *U.S. Private*, pg. 2006
HUMANCO ACQUISITION CORP.; *U.S. Public*, pg. 1070
HUMANCO KFT—See Gedeon Richter Plc.; *Int'l*, pg. 2910
HUMANCO LLC; *U.S. Private*, pg. 2006
HUMAN CREATE CO., LTD.—See Shin-Etsu Chemical Co. Ltd.; *Int'l*, pg. 6838
HUMAN CREATION HOLDINGS, INC.; *Int'l*, pg. 3528
HUMAN DESIGN MEDICAL LLC—See Shanghai Fosun Pharmaceutical (Group) Co., Ltd.; *Int'l*, pg. 6767
HUMAN DEVELOPMENT ASSOCIATION; *U.S. Private*, pg. 2005
HUMAN DEVELOPMENT CENTER; *U.S. Private*, pg. 2005
HUMAN DIGICRAFTS (THAILAND) CO., LTD.—See Human Holdings Co., Ltd.; *Int'l*, pg. 3529

CORPORATE AFFILIATIONS

HUMAN DIGITAL CONSULTANTS CO., LTD.—See Human Holdings Co., Ltd.; *Int'l*, pg. 3529
HUMAN DIMENSIONS COMPANY (W.L.L)—See Lamar Holding Corp.; *Int'l*, pg. 4400
HUMANE MANUFACTURING COMPANY, LLC—See Hendricks Holding Company, Inc.; *U.S. Private*, pg. 1915
HUMANE SOCIETY CALUMET AREA; *U.S. Private*, pg. 2006
HUMANE SOCIETY OF MISSOURI; *U.S. Private*, pg. 2006
THE HUMANE SOCIETY OF THE UNITED STATES; *U.S. Private*, pg. 4054
HUMANETICS INNOVATIVE SOLUTIONS, INC.—See Bridgepoint Group Plc; *Int'l*, pg. 1155
HUMAN FACTORS INTERNATIONAL, INC.; *U.S. Private*, pg. 2005
THE HUMAN GEO GROUP LLC—See Advent International Corporation; *U.S. Private*, pg. 104
HUMAN GLOBAL COMMUNICATIONS CO., LTD.—See Human Holdings Co., Ltd.; *Int'l*, pg. 3529
HUMAN GLOBAL TALENT CO., LTD.—See Human Holdings Co., Ltd.; *Int'l*, pg. 3529
HUMAN HEALTH HOLDINGS LIMITED; *Int'l*, pg. 3528
HUMAN HOLDINGS CO., LTD.; *Int'l*, pg. 3529
HUMANICA ASIA PTE. LTD.—See Humanica Public Company Limited; *Int'l*, pg. 3530
HUMANICA PUBLIC COMPANY LIMITED; *Int'l*, pg. 3530
HUMANICA SDN. BHD.—See Humanica Public Company Limited; *Int'l*, pg. 3530
HUMANIFY, INC.—See TTEC Holdings, Inc.; *U.S. Public*, pg. 2202
HUMANIGEN, INC.; *U.S. Public*, pg. 1070
HUMANIM, INC.; *U.S. Private*, pg. 2006
HUMAN INTERNATIONAL CO., LTD.—See Human Holdings Co., Ltd.; *Int'l*, pg. 3529
HUMAN INVESTMENT CORPORATION—See Kuwait Finance House K.S.C.; *Int'l*, pg. 4344
HUMANITAS FOUNDATION FOR RESEARCH—See Techint S.p.A.; *Int'l*, pg. 7503
HUMANITAS MATER DOMINI - CASTELLANZA—See Techint S.p.A.; *Int'l*, pg. 7503
HUMANIX CORP.; *U.S. Private*, pg. 2006
HUMANKIND; *U.S. Private*, pg. 2006
HUMAN KINETICS AUSTRALIA—See Human Kinetics Publishers Inc.; *U.S. Private*, pg. 2005
HUMAN KINETICS CANADA—See Human Kinetics Publishers Inc.; *U.S. Private*, pg. 2005
HUMAN KINETICS EUROPE—See Human Kinetics Publishers Inc.; *U.S. Private*, pg. 2005
HUMAN KINETICS NEW ZEALAND—See Human Kinetics Publishers Inc.; *U.S. Private*, pg. 2005
HUMAN KINETICS PUBLISHERS INC.; *U.S. Private*, pg. 2005
HUMAN LIFE CARE CO., LTD.—See Human Holdings Co., Ltd.; *Int'l*, pg. 3529
HUMAN LINK CORPORATION—See Mitsubishi Corporation; *Int'l*, pg. 4938
HUMAN LONGEVITY, INC.; *U.S. Private*, pg. 2005
HUMAN MEDICS CO., LTD.—See Teleflex Incorporated; *U.S. Public*, pg. 1995
HUMAN METABOLOME TECHNOLOGIES AMERICA, INC.—See Human Metabolome Technologies Inc.; *Int'l*, pg. 3529
HUMAN METABOLOME TECHNOLOGIES EUROPE B.V.—See Human Metabolome Technologies Inc.; *Int'l*, pg. 3529
HUMAN METABOLOME TECHNOLOGIES INC.; *Int'l*, pg. 3529
HUMAN ND CO., LTD.—See Human Holdings Co., Ltd.; *Int'l*, pg. 3529
HUMAN N, INC; *Int'l*, pg. 3529
HUMANOPTICS AG; *Int'l*, pg. 3530
HUMANOPTICS DEUTSCHLAND VERWALTUNGS GMBH—See HumanOptics AG; *Int'l*, pg. 3530
HUMAN PLANNING CO., LTD.—See Human Holdings Co., Ltd.; *Int'l*, pg. 3529
HUMANPROTECT CONSULTING GMBH—See DZ BANK AG Deutsche Zentral-Genossenschaftsbank; *Int'l*, pg. 2244
HUMAN RESOCIA CO., LTD.—See Human Holdings Co., Ltd.; *Int'l*, pg. 3529
HUMAN RESOURCES AGENCY OF NEW BRITAIN, INC.; *U.S. Private*, pg. 2006
HUMAN RESOURCES INCORPORATED; *U.S. Private*, pg. 2006
HUMAN RESOURCE SPECIALTIES INC.—See DCI Consulting Group, Inc.; *U.S. Private*, pg. 1180
HUMAN RESOURCES PLUS INC.—See JER HR Group LLC; *U.S. Private*, pg. 2201
HUMAN RESOURCES RESEARCH ORGANIZATION; *U.S. Private*, pg. 2006
HUMAN RESOURCES SERVICES S.P.A.—See Stellantis N.V.; *Int'l*, pg. 7197
HUMAN RESOURCE STAFFING, LLC; *U.S. Private*, pg. 2005
HUMAN RESOURCE TRAINING, INC.—See ATAR Capital, LLC; *U.S. Private*, pg. 364
HUMAN RIGHTS DEFENSE; *U.S. Private*, pg. 2006
HUMAN RIGHTS FIRST; *U.S. Private*, pg. 2006

HUMAN RIGHTS WATCH; U.S. Private, pg. 2006
HUMANSCALE CORPORATION; U.S. Private, pg. 2006
HUMAN SERVICES CENTER; U.S. Private, pg. 2006
HUMAN (SHANGHAI) COMMERCE CONSULTANTS CO., LTD.—See Human Holdings Co., Ltd.; Int'l, pg. 3529
HUMAN SOFT HOLDING K.S.C.C.; Int'l, pg. 3529
HUMANSOFT KFT.—See 4iG Nyrt.; Int'l, pg. 12
HUMANSOFT SZERVIZ KFT.—See 4iG Nyrt.; Int'l, pg. 12
HUMAN SOLUTIONS, INC.—See Oasis Systems, LLC; U.S. Private, pg. 2986
HUMAN SOLUTIONS S.A.—See Randstad N.V.; Int'l, pg. 6201
HUMANTECH, INC.—See CVC Capital Partners SICAV-FIS S.A.; Int'l, pg. 1885
HUMAN TECHNOLOGIES, INC.; U.S. Private, pg. 2006
HUMAN TECHNOLOGY CO., LTD.; Int'l, pg. 3529
HUMAN TOUCH, LLC; U.S. Private, pg. 2006
HUMANTOUCH, LLC; U.S. Private, pg. 2006
HUMAN UNITEC INTERNATIONAL INC.; U.S. Public, pg. 1069
HUMANWELL HEALTHCARE (GROUP) CO., LTD.; Int'l, pg. 3530
HUMAN XTENSIONS LTD.; Int'l, pg. 3529
HUMANZYME, INC.—See Proteintech Group, Inc.; U.S. Private, pg. 3290
HUMAP JAPAN CO., LTD.—See Dynam Japan Holdings, Co., Ltd.; Int'l, pg. 2239
HUMAX CO., LTD.—See Humax Holdings Co., Ltd.; Int'l, pg. 3530
HUMAX HOLDINGS CO., LTD.; Int'l, pg. 3530
HUMAX PHARMACEUTICAL S.A.—See Bausch Health Companies Inc.; Int'l, pg. 897
HUMBERCLYDE COMMERCIAL INVESTMENTS LTD.—See BNP Paribas SA; Int'l, pg. 1091
HUMBER SEA TERMINAL LTD—See Simon Group plc; Int'l, pg. 6931
THE HUMBERSIDE LINCOLNSHIRE & NORTH YORKSHIRE COMMUNITY REHABILITATION COMPANY LTD.—See Interserve Plc; Int'l, pg. 3760
HUMBERTO ALVAREZ SUCESORES DE NICARAGUA S.A.—See Albert Ballin KG; Int'l, pg. 295
HUMBLE ABODE, INC.; U.S. Private, pg. 2007
HUMBLE CONSTRUCTION CO.; U.S. Private, pg. 2007
HUMBLE ENERGY, INC.; U.S. Public, pg. 1071
HUMBLE JUICE CO., LLC—See Pyxus International, Inc.; U.S. Public, pg. 1740
HUMBLE KINGWOOD ENDOSCOPY CENTER—See HCA Healthcare, Inc.; U.S. Public, pg. 1000
HUMBL, INC.; U.S. Public, pg. 1071
HUMBOLDT BEACON—See Alden Global Capital LLC; U.S. Private, pg. 156
HUMBOLDT DIALYSIS, LLC—See DaVita Inc.; U.S. Public, pg. 639
HUMBOLDT ELECTRIC LIMITED; Int'l, pg. 3530
HUMBOLDT MANUFACTURING CO. INC.; U.S. Private, pg. 2007
HUMBOLDT MARINE TRAINING LTDA.—See Ultramar Ltda.; Int'l, pg. 8018
HUMBOLDT SHIPMANAGEMENT CO.—See Ultramar Ltda.; Int'l, pg. 8018
HUMBOLDT STATE UNIVERSITY CENTER; U.S. Private, pg. 2007
HUMBOLDT WEDAG AUSTRALIA PTY. LTD.—See KHD Humboldt Wedag International AG; Int'l, pg. 4154
HUMBOLDT WEDAG GMBH—See KHD Humboldt Wedag International AG; Int'l, pg. 4154
HUMBOLDT WEDAG, INC.—See KHD Humboldt Wedag International AG; Int'l, pg. 4154
HUMBOLDT WEDAG INDIA PVT. LTD.—See KHD Humboldt Wedag International AG; Int'l, pg. 4154
HUMBOLDT WEDAG (S.A.) (PTY) LTD.—See KHD Humboldt Wedag International AG; Int'l, pg. 4154
HUMCAP LP; U.S. Private, pg. 2007
HUM&C CO., LTD.; Int'l, pg. 3528
HUMCO HOLDING GROUP, INC.—See Fagron NV; Int'l, pg. 2603
HUMCO, INC.—See Humana, Inc.; U.S. Public, pg. 1070
HUMDINGER LIMITED—See Zertus GmbH; Int'l, pg. 8639
HUME BROPHY COMMUNICATIONS; U.S. Private, pg. 2007
HUME CEMENT INDUSTRIES BERHAD; Int'l, pg. 3530
HUME CEMENT SDN. BHD.—See Hume Cement Industries Berhad; Int'l, pg. 3530
HUME CONCRETE SDN. BHD.—See Hume Cement Industries Berhad; Int'l, pg. 3530
HUMEDICA, INC.—See UnitedHealth Group Incorporated; U.S. Public, pg. 2241
HUMEDIQ GLOBAL GMBH—See Siemens Aktiengesellschaft; Int'l, pg. 6895
HUMEDIX CO., LTD.; Int'l, pg. 3530
HUMICLIMA CENTRO, S.A.—See ACS, Actividades de Construccion y Servicios, S.A.; Int'l, pg. 114
HUMICLIMA EST CATALUNYA, S.L.—See ACS, Actividades de Construccion y Servicios, S.A.; Int'l, pg. 114
HUMICLIMA EST, S.A.—See ACS, Actividades de Construccion y Servicios, S.A.; Int'l, pg. 114
HUMICLIMA SAC, S.A.—See ACS, Actividades de Construccion y Servicios, S.A.; Int'l, pg. 114

HUMICLIMA SUR, S.L.—See ACS, Actividades de Construccion y Servicios, S.A.; Int'l, pg. 114
HUMICLIMA VALLADOLID, S.L.—See ACS, Actividades de Construccion y Servicios, S.A.; Int'l, pg. 114
HUMILIS HOLDINGS CAPITAL MANAGEMENT COMPANY LLC; U.S. Private, pg. 2007
HUMILITY HOUSE—See Catholic Healthcare Partners; U.S. Private, pg. 792
HUMISEAL INDIA PRIVATE LIMITED—See KKR & Co. Inc.; U.S. Public, pg. 1243
HUMMEL A. LLC—See Thornico A/S; Int'l, pg. 7720
HUMMEL INTERNATIONAL SPORT & LEISURE A/S—See Thornico A/S; Int'l, pg. 7720
HUMMELS OFFICE EQUIPMENT CO.; U.S. Private, pg. 2007
HUMMEL SYSTEMHAUS GMBH & CO. KG—See STRABAG SE; Int'l, pg. 7230
HUMMEL UK LTD—See Thornico A/S; Int'l, pg. 7720
HUMMER DIALYSIS, LLC—See DaVita Inc.; U.S. Public, pg. 639
HUMMERT INTERNATIONAL INC.; U.S. Private, pg. 2007
HUMMERVOLL INDUSTRIBELEGG AS—See RPM International Inc.; U.S. Public, pg. 1818
HUMMER WINBLAD OPERATING CO., LLC; U.S. Private, pg. 2007
HUMM GROUP LIMITED—See Humm Group Limited; Int'l, pg. 3531
HUMM GROUP LIMITED; Int'l, pg. 3531
HUMMINBIRD—See Johnson Outdoors Inc.; U.S. Public, pg. 1200
HUMMINGBIRD COACHING SYSTEMS LLC—See Humana, Inc.; U.S. Public, pg. 1070
HUMMING BIRD EDUCATION LTD.; Int'l, pg. 3531
HUMMINGBIRD RESOURCES PLC; Int'l, pg. 3531
HUMMINGBIRD SYSTEMS GMBH—See Mensch und Maschine Software SE; Int'l, pg. 4817
HUMM KOMBUCHA, LLC—See SYSTM Brands, LLC; U.S. Private, pg. 3908
HUM NETWORK LIMITED; Int'l, pg. 3528
HUMONGO—See Stagwell, Inc.; U.S. Public, pg. 1928
HUMOR RAINBOW, INC.—See IAC Inc.; U.S. Public, pg. 1082
HUMPERDINK'S TEXAS LLC.; U.S. Private, pg. 2007
HUMPHREY & ASSOCIATES INC.; U.S. Private, pg. 2007
HUMPHREY AUTOMATION—See Humphrey Products Corporation; U.S. Private, pg. 2007
HUMPHREY COMPANIES LLC.; U.S. Private, pg. 2007
THE HUMPHREY COMPANY—See b.a. Sweetie Candy Company; U.S. Private, pg. 420
HUMPHREY LUMBER CORPORATION; U.S. Private, pg. 2007
HUMPHREY & PARTNERS MEDICAL SERVICES MANAGEMENT LIMITED—See HKR International Limited; Int'l, pg. 3429
HUMPHREY PRODUCTS CORPORATION; U.S. Private, pg. 2007
HUMPHREYS & PARTNERS ARCHITECTS, L.P.; U.S. Private, pg. 2007
HUMPHRIES & COMPANY, LLC.; U.S. Private, pg. 2007
HUMPTY DUMPTY SNACK FOODS, INC.—See Old Dutch Foods, Inc.; U.S. Private, pg. 3008
HUMULANI INVESTMENTS (PTY) LTD.—See Invicta Holdings Limited; Int'l, pg. 3788
HUM WORLD INC.—See Hum Network Limited; Int'l, pg. 3528
HUNAN AIHUA GROUP CO., LTD.; Int'l, pg. 3531
HUNAN AIRBLUER ENVIRONMENTAL PROTECTION TECHNOLOGY CO., LTD.; Int'l, pg. 3531
HUNAN APT MEDICAL INC.—See APT Medical, Inc.; Int'l, pg. 523
HUNAN BAILI ENGINEERING SCI & TECH CO.,LTD; Int'l, pg. 3531
HUNAN BOSSCO HUAYI ENVIRONMENT ENGINEERING CO., LTD—See Guangxi Bossco Environmental Protection Technology Co., Ltd.; Int'l, pg. 3163
HUNAN BOYUN NEW MATERIALS CO., LTD.; Int'l, pg. 3531
HUNAN BYNAV TECHNOLOGY CO., LTD.—See Duolun Technology Co., Ltd.; Int'l, pg. 2227
HUNAN CHENDIAN INTERNATIONAL DEVELOPMENT CO., LTD.; Int'l, pg. 3531
HUNAN CHILDREN & JUVENILE'S PUBLISHING HOUSE CO., LTD.—See China South Publishing & Media Group Co., Ltd.; Int'l, pg. 1552
HUNAN CHINA SUN PHARMACEUTICAL MACHINERY CO., LTD.; Int'l, pg. 3531
HUNAN COPOTE SCIENCE & TECHNOLOGY CO., LTD.; Int'l, pg. 3531
HUNAN CORUN NEW ENERGY CO., LTD.; Int'l, pg. 3531
HUNAN CREATOR INFORMATION TECHNOLOGIES CO., LTD.; Int'l, pg. 3532
HUNAN DAJIAWEIKANG PHARMACEUTICAL INDUSTRY CO., LTD.; Int'l, pg. 3532
HUNAN DEHAI PHARMACEUTICAL CO., LTD.—See Dahu Aquaculture Company Limited; Int'l, pg. 1913
HUNAN DEVELOPMENT GROUP CO., LTD.; Int'l, pg. 3532

HUNAN DONGTING CITRIC ACID CHEMICAL CO., LIMITED—See Hunan Er-Kang Pharmaceutical Co., Ltd.; Int'l, pg. 3532
HUNAN EDUCATION TELEVISION MEDIA CO., LTD.—See China South Publishing & Media Group Co., Ltd.; Int'l, pg. 1553
HUNAN ELECTRIC POWER COMPANY—See State Grid Corporation of China; Int'l, pg. 7182
HUNAN ELECTRONIC & AUDIO-VISUAL PUBLISHING HOUSE CO., LTD.—See China South Publishing & Media Group Co., Ltd.; Int'l, pg. 1553
HUNAN ER-KANG PHARMACEUTICAL CO., LTD.; Int'l, pg. 3532
HUNAN FANGSHENG PHARMACEUTICAL CO., LTD.; Int'l, pg. 3532
HUNAN FRIENDSHIP & APOLLO COMMERCIAL CO., LTD.; Int'l, pg. 3532
HUNAN GEM YINGHONG RESOURCE RECYCLING CO., LTD.—See GEM Co., Ltd.; Int'l, pg. 2914
HUNAN GOLD CORPORATION LIMITED; Int'l, pg. 3532
HUNAN HAILI CHEMICAL INDUSTRY CO., LTD.; Int'l, pg. 3532
HUNAN HAILI CHEMICAL INDUSTRY STOCK CO., LTD.—See Hunan Haili Chemical Industry Co., Ltd.; Int'l, pg. 3532
HUNAN HANSEN PHARMACEUTICAL CO., LTD.; Int'l, pg. 3532
HUNAN HAOHUA CHEMICAL CO LTD.—See China National Chemical Corporation; Int'l, pg. 1528
HUNAN HENGGUANG CHEMICAL CO., LTD.—See Hunan Hengguang Technology Co., Ltd.; Int'l, pg. 3532
HUNAN HENGGUANG TECHNOLOGY CO., LTD.; Int'l, pg. 3532
HUNAN HESHUN PETROLEUM CO., LTD.; Int'l, pg. 3532
HUNAN HONG YING BIOTECH CO., LTD.—See Guangdong VTR Bio-Tech Co., Ltd.; Int'l, pg. 3161
HUNAN HUAKAI CULTURAL AND CREATIVE CO., LTD; Int'l, pg. 3532
HUNAN HUALIAN CHINA INDUSTRY CO., LTD.; Int'l, pg. 3532
HUNAN HUAMIN HOLDINGS CO., LTD.; Int'l, pg. 3532
HUNAN HUASHENG CO., LTD.; Int'l, pg. 3532
HUNAN INVESTMENT GROUP CO., LTD.; Int'l, pg. 3532
HUNAN JIALI MACHINERY CO., LTD—See Hunan Oil Pump Co., Ltd.; Int'l, pg. 3533
HUNAN JINGFENG PHARMACEUTICAL CO., LTD.; Int'l, pg. 3533
HUNAN JINJIAN IMPORT & EXPORT CO., LTD.—See Jinjian Cereals Industry Co., Ltd.; Int'l, pg. 3968
HUNAN JIUDIAN PHARMACEUTICAL CO., LTD.; Int'l, pg. 3533
HUNAN JUNXIN ENVIRONMENTAL PROTECTION CO., LTD.; Int'l, pg. 3533
HUNAN KAIMEITE GASES CO., LTD.; Int'l, pg. 3533
HUNAN KELI MOTOR CO., LTD. - FAIRPORT BRANCH—See Keli Motor Group Co., Ltd.; Int'l, pg. 4119
HUNAN KIBING SOLAR TECHNOLOGY CO., LTD.—See Zhuzhou Kibing Group Co., Ltd.; Int'l, pg. 8680
HUNAN LEAD POWER TECHNOLOGY GROUP CO., LTD.; Int'l, pg. 3533
HUNAN LICHEN INDUSTRIAL CO., LTD.; Int'l, pg. 3533
HUNAN LITERATURE & ART PUBLISHING HOUSE CO., LTD.—See China South Publishing & Media Group Co., Ltd.; Int'l, pg. 1553
HUNAN MENDALE HOMETEXTILE CO., LTD.; Int'l, pg. 3533
HUNAN NEW WELLFUL CO., LTD.; Int'l, pg. 3533
HUNAN NINGXIANG JIWEIXIN METAL POWDER CO., LTD.—See Nippon Light Metal Holdings Company, Ltd.; Int'l, pg. 5323
HUNAN NONFERROUS METALS CORPORATION LTD.; Int'l, pg. 3533
HUNAN NUCIEN PHARMACEUTICAL CO., LTD.; Int'l, pg. 3533
HUNAN OIL PUMP CO., LTD.; Int'l, pg. 3533
HUNAN PEOPLE'S PUBLISHING HOUSE CO., LTD.—See China South Publishing & Media Group Co., Ltd.; Int'l, pg. 1553
HUNAN PETROCHEMICAL SUPPLY & MARKETING CORPORATION—See China National Chemical Corporation; Int'l, pg. 1528
HUNAN PUBLISHING INVESTMENT HOLDING GROUP FINANCIAL CO., LTD.—See China South Publishing & Media Group Co., Ltd.; Int'l, pg. 1553
HUNAN SCAS AUTOMOBILE SALES SERVICES CO., LTD.—See China ZhengTong Auto Services Holdings Limited; Int'l, pg. 1566
HUNAN SCIENCE & TECHNOLOGY PRESS CO., LTD.—See China South Publishing & Media Group Co., Ltd.; Int'l, pg. 1553
HUNAN SHENGLI XIANGGANG STEEL PIPE CO., LTD.—See Shengli Oil & Gas Pipe Holdings Limited; Int'l, pg. 6802
HUNAN SOKAN NEW MATERIALS CO., LTD.; Int'l, pg. 3533
HUNAN SUNDY SCIENCE AND TECHNOLOGY CO.,LTD; Int'l, pg. 3533

HUNAN SWITCHGEAR CO. LTD.—See Wasion Holdings Limited; *Int'l*, pg. 8352
HUNAN TIANQIAO JIACHENG INTELLIGENT TECHNOLOGY CO., LTD.—See Zhuzhou Tianqiao Crane Co., Ltd.; *Int'l*, pg. 8680
HUNAN TIANQIAO LIHENG PARKING EQUIPMENT CO., LTD.—See Zhuzhou Tianqiao Crane Co., Ltd.; *Int'l*, pg. 8680
HUNAN TIANRUN DIGITAL ENTERTAINMENT & CULTURAL MEDIA CO., LTD.; *Int'l*, pg. 3534
HUNAN TIANWEN XINHUA PRINTING CO., LTD.—See China South Publishing & Media Group Co., Ltd.; *Int'l*, pg. 1553
HUNAN TV & BROADCAST INTERMEDIARY CO., LTD.; *Int'l*, pg. 3534
HUNAN TYEN MACHINERY CO., LTD.; *Int'l*, pg. 3534
HUNAN VALIN CABLE CO., LTD.; *Int'l*, pg. 3534
HUNAN VALIN STEEL CO., LTD.; *Int'l*, pg. 3534
HUNAN XIANGJIA ANIMAL HUSBANDRY CO., LTD.; *Int'l*, pg. 3534
HUNAN XIANGJIANG KANSAI PAINT CO., LTD.—See Kansai Paint Co., Ltd.; *Int'l*, pg. 4072
HUNAN XIANGYUN BIOTECHNOLOGY CO., LTD.—See Dahu Aquaculture Company Limited; *Int'l*, pg. 1913
HUNAN XIAOXIANG MORNING HERALD MEDIA MANAGEMENT CO., LTD.—See China South Publishing & Media Group Co., Ltd.; *Int'l*, pg. 1553
HUNAN YONKER INVESTMENT GROUP CO., LTD.; *Int'l*, pg. 3534
HUNAN YUELU PUBLISHING HOUSE CO., LTD.—See China South Publishing & Media Group Co., Ltd.; *Int'l*, pg. 1553
HUNAN YUJING MACHINERY CO., LTD.; *Int'l*, pg. 3534
HUNAN YUNENG NEW ENERGY BATTERY MATERIAL CO., LTD.; *Int'l*, pg. 3534
HUNAN YUSSEN ENERGY TECHNOLOGY CO., LTD.; *Int'l*, pg. 3534
HUNAN ZHENGHONG SCIENCE AND TECHNOLOGY DEVELOP CO., LTD.; *Int'l*, pg. 3534
HUNAN ZHONGKE ELECTRIC CO., LTD.; *Int'l*, pg. 3534
HUNAN ZOOMLION INTERNATIONAL TRADE CO., LTD.—See Zoomlion Heavy Industry Science & Technology Co., Ltd.; *Int'l*, pg. 8690
HUNAS HOLDINGS PLC; *Int'l*, pg. 3534
HUNDLEY FARM INC.; *U.S. Private*, pg. 2007
HUNDLOKAN 10 I MALMO AB—See Wihlborgs Fastigheter AB; *Int'l*, pg. 8407
HUNDRED SYSTEM CO., LTD.—See Uchida Yoko Co., Ltd.; *Int'l*, pg. 8012
HUNDREDYEARS CO., LTD.—See Fantasista Co., Ltd.; *Int'l*, pg. 2613
HUNDSUN.COM CO., LTD.—See Hundsun Technologies Inc.; *Int'l*, pg. 3534
HUNDSUN TECHNOLOGIES INC.; *Int'l*, pg. 3534
HUNDT & PARTNER INGENIEURGESELLSCHAFT MBH & CO. KG—See TUV NORD AG; *Int'l*, pg. 7980
HUNEED TECHNOLOGIES; *Int'l*, pg. 3534
HUNESION CO., LTD.; *Int'l*, pg. 3535
HUNGAMA TV—See The Walt Disney Company; *U.S. Public*, pg. 2139
HUNGARIAN INTERNATIONAL FINANCE LTD.—See OTP Bank Plc; *Int'l*, pg. 5657
HUNGAROCORK, AMORIM, RT—See CORTICEIRA AMORIM, S.G.P.S., S.A.; *Int'l*, pg. 1808
HUNGAROPEC LTD.—See Groupe Seche SAS; *Int'l*, pg. 3110
HUNGAROPHARMA TRADING CO—See Les Laboratoires Servier SAS; *Int'l*, pg. 4468
HUNGAROPRESS KFT—See Vivendi SE; *Int'l*, pg. 8276
HUNGAROTON RECORDS KFT.—See Fotex Holding SE; *Int'l*, pg. 2752
HUNGARY CURT GEORGI KFT—See Curt Georgi GmbH & Co. KG; *Int'l*, pg. 1880
HUNGARY ENBI KFT.—See Platinum Equity, LLC; *U.S. Private*, pg. 3203
THE HUNGARY INITIATIVES FOUNDATION; *U.S. Private*, pg. 4054
HUNG CHING DEVELOPMENT & CONSTRUCTION CO., LTD.; *Int'l*, pg. 3535
HUNG CHOU FIBER IND. CO., LTD.; *Int'l*, pg. 3535
HUNG DAO CONTAINER JOINT STOCK COMPANY; *Int'l*, pg. 3535
HUNG DUN ELECTRONICS CO., LTD.—See Jess-Link Products Co., Ltd.; *Int'l*, pg. 3932
HUNGER DFE GMBH DICHTUNGS- UND FUHRUNGSELEMENTE—See Walter Hunger KG Hydraulics; *Int'l*, pg. 8336
HUNGERFORD & TERRY INC.; *U.S. Private*, pg. 2007
HUNGER GMBH & CO. KG—See Walter Hunger KG Hydraulics; *Int'l*, pg. 8336
HUNGER HYDRAULICS C.C. LIMITED—See Walter Hunger KG Hydraulics; *Int'l*, pg. 8336
HUNGER HYDRAULIC UK LTD.—See Walter Hunger KG Hydraulics; *Int'l*, pg. 8336
HUNGER MASCHINEN GMBH—See Walter Hunger KG Hydraulics; *Int'l*, pg. 8336
HUNGERRUSH—See The CapStreet Group LLC; *U.S. Private*, pg. 4004

HUNGER SCHLEIFMITTEL GMBH—See Walter Hunger KG Hydraulics; *Int'l*, pg. 8336
HUNGER (TIANJIN) HYDRAULIC ENGINEERING CO., LIMITED—See Walter Hunger KG Hydraulics; *Int'l*, pg. 8336
HUNG FOOK TONG GROUP HOLDINGS LTD; *Int'l*, pg. 3535
HUNG FU ELECTRONICS CO., LTD.—See Jess-Link Products Co., Ltd.; *Int'l*, pg. 3932
HUNG FU(SAMOA) INTERNATIONAL CO.,LTD—See Jess-Link Products Co., Ltd.; *Int'l*, pg. 3932
HUNG-GU OIL CO., LTD.; *Int'l*, pg. 3535
HUNGHAU HOLDINGS; *Int'l*, pg. 3535
HUNG HING OFF-SET PRINTING COMPANY, LIMITED—See Hung Hing Printing Group Limited; *Int'l*, pg. 3535
HUNG HING PRINTING (CHINA) COMPANY LIMITED—See Hung Hing Printing Group Limited; *Int'l*, pg. 3535
HUNG HING PRINTING GROUP LIMITED; *Int'l*, pg. 3535
HUNG HING PRINTING (HESHAN) COMPANY LIMITED—See Hung Hing Printing Group Limited; *Int'l*, pg. 3535
HUNG LONG MINERAL & BUILDING MATERIALS JSC; *Int'l*, pg. 3535
HUNG POO REAL ESTATE DEVELOPMENT CO., LTD.; *Int'l*, pg. 3535
HUNGRY HOWIE'S PIZZA & SUBS INC.; *U.S. Private*, pg. 2007
HUNGRY MAN LLC; *U.S. Private*, pg. 2008
HUNG SAN FOODS, INC.—See GrubMarket, Inc.; *U.S. Private*, pg. 1797
HUNGSEO INDUSTRIAL CO., LTD.—See Foga System International AB; *Int'l*, pg. 2721
HUNG SHENG CONSTRUCTION CO., LTD.; *Int'l*, pg. 3535
HUNG THINH INCONS JSC; *Int'l*, pg. 3535
HUNG VUONG CORPORATION; *Int'l*, pg. 3535
HUNG YEN BOOK PUBLISHING & EDUCATIONAL EQUIPMENT JSC; *Int'l*, pg. 3535
HUNNEBECK ROMANIA SRL—See Brand Industrial Services, Inc.; *U.S. Private*, pg. 636
HUNNIWELL LAKE VENTURES LLC; *U.S. Private*, pg. 2008
HUNNU COAL LIMITED—See Banpu Public Company Limited; *Int'l*, pg. 852
THE HUNSLET ENGINE COMPANY LIMITED—See Westinghouse Air Brake Technologies Corporation; *U.S. Public*, pg. 2359
HUNT ADKINS; *U.S. Private*, pg. 2008
HUNTAIR INC.; *U.S. Private*, pg. 2009
HUNTAVEN PROPERTIES LIMITED—See Hunting Plc; *Int'l*, pg. 3536
HUNT BROADCASTING, LLC; *U.S. Private*, pg. 2008
HUNT BUILDING COMPANY, LTD.—See Hunt Companies, Inc.; *U.S. Private*, pg. 2008
HUNT CLUB FORD LINCOLN SALES LIMITED; *Int'l*, pg. 3536
HUNT CLUB MHP LLC—See Manufactured Housing Properties Inc.; *U.S. Public*, pg. 1362
HUNT CLUB NISSAN LTD.—See AutoCanada Inc.; *Int'l*, pg. 726
HUNT COMMERCIAL REAL ESTATE CORP.—See Hastings + Cohn Real Estate, LLC; *U.S. Private*, pg. 1879
HUNT COMPANIES, INC.; *U.S. Private*, pg. 2008
HUNT CONSOLIDATED, INC.; *U.S. Private*, pg. 2008
HUNT CONSTRUCTION GROUP, INC. - EAST DIVISION—See AECOM; *U.S. Public*, pg. 51
HUNT CONSTRUCTION GROUP, INC. - ORLANDO—See AECOM; *U.S. Public*, pg. 51
HUNT CONSTRUCTION GROUP, INC. - SAN FRANCISCO—See AECOM; *U.S. Public*, pg. 51
HUNT CONSTRUCTION GROUP, INC.—See AECOM; *U.S. Public*, pg. 51
HUNT CONSTRUCTION GROUP, INC. - SOUTH DIVISION—See AECOM; *U.S. Public*, pg. 51
HUNT CONSTRUCTION GROUP, INC. - WEST DIVISION—See AECOM; *U.S. Public*, pg. 51
THE HUNT CORPORATION; *U.S. Private*, pg. 4054
HUNT COUNTRY FURNITURE INC.; *U.S. Private*, pg. 2009
HUNT COUNTY REGIONAL DIALYSIS CENTER LLC—See Nautic Partners, LLC; *U.S. Private*, pg. 2870
HUNT DEVELOPMENT GROUP, LLC—See Hunt Companies, Inc.; *U.S. Private*, pg. 2008
THE HUNTE CORPORATION; *U.S. Private*, pg. 4054
HUNT ELECTRIC SUPPLY COMPANY INC.; *U.S. Private*, pg. 2009
HUNT ENGINE INCORPORATED; *U.S. Private*, pg. 2009
HUNT ENTERPRISES INC.; *U.S. Private*, pg. 2009
HUNTER AEROSPACE CORPORATION PTY LIMITED—See BAE Systems plc; *Int'l*, pg. 798
HUNTER ASSOCIATES LABORATORY; *U.S. Private*, pg. 2009
HUNTER CANADA—See Hunter Engineering Company; *U.S. Private*, pg. 2009
HUNTER CAPITAL GROUP, LLC—See Kuwait Projects Company (Holding) K.S.C.P.; *Int'l*, pg. 4346

HUNTER CHEVROLET COMPANY INC.; *U.S. Private*, pg. 2009
HUNTER & COMPANY PLC; *Int'l*, pg. 3536
HUNTER CONTRACTING COMPANY; *U.S. Private*, pg. 2009
HUNTER CREEK MINING CO.; *U.S. Public*, pg. 1071
HUNTER DEUTSCHLAND GMBH—See Hunter Engineering Company; *U.S. Private*, pg. 2010
HUNTER DICKINSON INC.; *Int'l*, pg. 3536
HUNTER DISPOSAL, LLC—See GreenHunter Resources, Inc.; *U.S. Private*, pg. 1778
HUNTER DISTRIBUTION NETWORK PTY LTD—See Nine Entertainment Co. Holdings Limited; *Int'l*, pg. 5298
HUNTERDON TRANSFORMER CO. INC.; *U.S. Private*, pg. 2010
HUNTER DOUGLAS ALU - COIL OPERATIONS—See 3G Capital Partners L.P.; *U.S. Private*, pg. 11
HUNTER DOUGLAS ARCHITECTURAL PRODUCTS (BEIJING) CO., LTD.—See 3G Capital Partners L.P.; *U.S. Private*, pg. 11
HUNTER DOUGLAS ARCHITECTURAL PRODUCTS (CHINA) CO., LTD.—See 3G Capital Partners L.P.; *U.S. Private*, pg. 11
HUNTER DOUGLAS ARCHITECTURAL PRODUCTS INC.—See 3G Capital Partners L.P.; *U.S. Private*, pg. 13
HUNTER DOUGLAS ARCHITECTURAL PRODUCTS (SHENZHEN) CO.—See 3G Capital Partners L.P.; *U.S. Private*, pg. 11
HUNTER DOUGLAS ARCHITECTURAL PRODUCTS XIAMEN—See 3G Capital Partners L.P.; *U.S. Private*, pg. 11
HUNTER DOUGLAS ARCHITECTURAL PROJECTS NL—See 3G Capital Partners L.P.; *U.S. Private*, pg. 11
HUNTER DOUGLAS ARCHITEKTUR-SYSTEME GMBH—See 3G Capital Partners L.P.; *U.S. Private*, pg. 11
HUNTER DOUGLAS ARGENTINA SA—See 3G Capital Partners L.P.; *U.S. Private*, pg. 11
HUNTER DOUGLAS ASSEMBLY AUTOMATION AB—See 3G Capital Partners L.P.; *U.S. Private*, pg. 11
HUNTER DOUGLAS BELGIUM ARCHITECTURAL PRODUCTS—See 3G Capital Partners L.P.; *U.S. Private*, pg. 11
HUNTER DOUGLAS BELGIUM - HELIOSCREEN PROJECTS DIVISION—See 3G Capital Partners L.P.; *U.S. Private*, pg. 11
HUNTER DOUGLAS BELGIUM N.V. - HELIOSCREEN FABRICS DIVISION—See 3G Capital Partners L.P.; *U.S. Private*, pg. 11
HUNTER DOUGLAS BELGIUM N.V.—See 3G Capital Partners L.P.; *U.S. Private*, pg. 11
HUNTER DOUGLAS BENELUX—See 3G Capital Partners L.P.; *U.S. Private*, pg. 11
HUNTER DOUGLAS BULGARIA LTD—See 3G Capital Partners L.P.; *U.S. Private*, pg. 11
HUNTER DOUGLAS CANADA, INC.—See 3G Capital Partners L.P.; *U.S. Private*, pg. 11
HUNTER DOUGLAS CATALUNA SL—See 3G Capital Partners L.P.; *U.S. Private*, pg. 12
HUNTER DOUGLAS CHINA/HONG KONG LIMITED—See 3G Capital Partners L.P.; *U.S. Private*, pg. 12
HUNTER DOUGLAS C.I.S.—See 3G Capital Partners L.P.; *U.S. Private*, pg. 11
HUNTER DOUGLAS COMPONENTS—See 3G Capital Partners L.P.; *U.S. Private*, pg. 12
HUNTER DOUGLAS COMPONENTS—See 3G Capital Partners L.P.; *U.S. Private*, pg. 12
HUNTER DOUGLAS CROATIA—See 3G Capital Partners L.P.; *U.S. Private*, pg. 12
HUNTER DOUGLAS - CUSTOM SHUTTER DIVISION—See 3G Capital Partners L.P.; *U.S. Private*, pg. 13
HUNTER DOUGLAS CZECHIA NA—See 3G Capital Partners L.P.; *U.S. Private*, pg. 12
HUNTER DOUGLAS CZECHIA (SLOVAKIA) S.R.O.—See 3G Capital Partners L.P.; *U.S. Private*, pg. 12
HUNTER DOUGLAS DO BRAZIL LTDA.—See 3G Capital Partners L.P.; *U.S. Private*, pg. 12
HUNTER DOUGLAS ENTWICKLUNGSGESELLSCHAFT MBH—See 3G Capital Partners L.P.; *U.S. Private*, pg. 12
HUNTER DOUGLAS ESPANA S.A—See 3G Capital Partners L.P.; *U.S. Private*, pg. 12
HUNTER DOUGLAS EUROPE B.V.—See 3G Capital Partners L.P.; *U.S. Private*, pg. 12
HUNTER DOUGLAS EUROPE—See 3G Capital Partners L.P.; *U.S. Private*, pg. 12
HUNTER DOUGLAS FABRICATION CO.—See 3G Capital Partners L.P.; *U.S. Private*, pg. 13
HUNTER DOUGLAS FABRICATION—See 3G Capital Partners L.P.; *U.S. Private*, pg. 13
HUNTER DOUGLAS FABRICATION SP. Z.O.O.—See 3G Capital Partners L.P.; *U.S. Private*, pg. 12
HUNTER DOUGLAS FASHIONS INC.—See 3G Capital Partners L.P.; *U.S. Private*, pg. 13
HUNTER DOUGLAS HOLDINGS LTD.—See 3G Capital Partners L.P.; *U.S. Private*, pg. 12

COMPANY NAME INDEX

HUNTER DOUGLAS - HORIZONTAL BLINDS DIVISION—See 3G Capital Partners L.P.; *U.S. Private*, pg. 13
HUNTER DOUGLAS HOSPITALITY, INC—See 3G Capital Partners L.P.; *U.S. Private*, pg. 13
HUNTER DOUGLAS HUNGARY LTD—See 3G Capital Partners L.P.; *U.S. Private*, pg. 12
HUNTER DOUGLAS, INC.—See 3G Capital Partners L.P.; *U.S. Private*, pg. 13
HUNTER DOUGLAS INDIA PVT LTD.—See 3G Capital Partners L.P.; *U.S. Private*, pg. 12
HUNTER DOUGLAS ITALY—See 3G Capital Partners L.P.; *U.S. Private*, pg. 12
HUNTER DOUGLAS KADAN S.R.O.—See 3G Capital Partners L.P.; *U.S. Private*, pg. 12
HUNTER DOUGLAS KOREA LIMITED—See 3G Capital Partners L.P.; *U.S. Private*, pg. 12
HUNTER DOUGLAS LATINA AMERICA—See 3G Capital Partners L.P.; *U.S. Private*, pg. 12
HUNTER DOUGLAS LIMITED—See 3G Capital Partners L.P.; *U.S. Private*, pg. 12
HUNTER DOUGLAS (MALAYSIA) SDN. BHD.—See 3G Capital Partners L.P.; *U.S. Private*, pg. 11
HUNTER DOUGLAS MANAGEMENT AG—See 3G Capital Partners L.P.; *U.S. Private*, pg. 12
HUNTER DOUGLAS METALS—See 3G Capital Partners L.P.; *U.S. Private*, pg. 13
HUNTER DOUGLAS MEXICO S.A. DE C.V.—See 3G Capital Partners L.P.; *U.S. Private*, pg. 12
HUNTER DOUGLAS MIDDLE EAST FZE—See 3G Capital Partners L.P.; *U.S. Private*, pg. 12
HUNTER DOUGLAS N.V.—See 3G Capital Partners L.P.; *U.S. Private*, pg. 11
HUNTER DOUGLAS PANAMA SA—See 3G Capital Partners L.P.; *U.S. Private*, pg. 12
HUNTER DOUGLAS PERU S.A.C—See 3G Capital Partners L.P.; *U.S. Private*, pg. 12
HUNTER DOUGLAS PHILIPPINES INC—See 3G Capital Partners L.P.; *U.S. Private*, pg. 12
HUNTER DOUGLAS POLSKA SP. Z.O.O.—See 3G Capital Partners L.P.; *U.S. Private*, pg. 12
HUNTER DOUGLAS PRODUKTION GMBH—See 3G Capital Partners L.P.; *U.S. Private*, pg. 12
HUNTER DOUGLAS ROMANIA SRL—See 3G Capital Partners L.P.; *U.S. Private*, pg. 12
HUNTER DOUGLAS SCANDINAVIA AB—See 3G Capital Partners L.P.; *U.S. Private*, pg. 12
HUNTER DOUGLAS (SCHWEIZ) GMBH—See 3G Capital Partners L.P.; *U.S. Private*, pg. 12
HUNTER DOUGLAS SERBIA—See 3G Capital Partners L.P.; *U.S. Private*, pg. 12
HUNTER DOUGLAS SINGAPORE PTE. LTD.—See 3G Capital Partners L.P.; *U.S. Private*, pg. 12
HUNTER DOUGLAS SOUTH AFRICA PTY LTD—See 3G Capital Partners L.P.; *U.S. Private*, pg. 12
HUNTER DOUGLAS TAIWAN LTD.—See 3G Capital Partners L.P.; *U.S. Private*, pg. 12
HUNTER DOUGLAS (THAILAND) CO LTD.—See 3G Capital Partners L.P.; *U.S. Private*, pg. 11
HUNTER DOUGLAS TURKEY—See 3G Capital Partners L.P.; *U.S. Private*, pg. 12
HUNTER DOUGLAS VENEZUELA SA—See 3G Capital Partners L.P.; *U.S. Private*, pg. 12
HUNTER DOUGLAS VERTICALS—See 3G Capital Partners L.P.; *U.S. Private*, pg. 13
HUNTER DOUGLAS VIETNAM LTD—See 3G Capital Partners L.P.; *U.S. Private*, pg. 12
HUNTER DOUGLAS WINDOW COVERING PRODUCTS (BEIJING) CO., LTD.—See 3G Capital Partners L.P.; *U.S. Private*, pg. 13
HUNTER DOUGLAS WINDOW COVERING PRODUCTS (CHINA) CO., LTD.—See 3G Capital Partners L.P.; *U.S. Private*, pg. 13
HUNTER DOUGLAS WINDOW COVERING PRODUCTS (SHANGHAI) CO., LTD.—See 3G Capital Partners L.P.; *U.S. Private*, pg. 13
HUNTER DOUGLAS WINDOW COVERING PRODUCTS (SHENZHEN) CO., LTD.—See 3G Capital Partners L.P.; *U.S. Private*, pg. 13
HUNTER DOUGLAS - WINDOW DESIGNS DIVISION—See 3G Capital Partners L.P.; *U.S. Private*, pg. 13
HUNTER DOUGLAS WINDOW FASHIONS, INC.—See 3G Capital Partners L.P.; *U.S. Private*, pg. 13
HUNTER ENGINEERING COMPANY; *U.S. Private*, pg. 2009
HUNTER EQUIPMENT INC—See Brandt Holdings Company; *U.S. Private*, pg. 638
HUNTER EQUIPMENT—See Brandt Holdings Company; *U.S. Private*, pg. 638
HUNTER FAN COMPANY—See Griffon Corporation; *U.S. Public*, pg. 969
HUNTER GRAIN COMPANY; *U.S. Private*, pg. 2010
HUNTER GROUP ASA; *Int'l*, pg. 3536
HUNTER HALL INVESTMENT MANAGEMENT LTD—See Pengana Capital Group Limited; *Int'l*, pg. 5785
HUNTER & HARP HOLDINGS, LLC; *U.S. Private*, pg. 2009

HUNTER IMAGING GROUP PTY LIMITED—See Sonic Healthcare Limited; *Int'l*, pg. 7097
HUNTER INDUSTRIES INCORPORATED; *U.S. Private*, pg. 2010
HUNTER INDUSTRIES INC.—See American Superconductor Corporation; *U.S. Public*, pg. 110
HUNTER INDUSTRIES LTD.; *U.S. Private*, pg. 2010
HUNTER LANE, LLC—See New Rite Aid, LLC; *U.S. Private*, pg. 2905
HUNTER MANUFACTURING COMPANY—See Metalmark Capital Holdings LLC; *U.S. Private*, pg. 2681
HUNTER MARITIME ACQUISITION CORP.; *Int'l*, pg. 3536
HUNTER MOUNTAIN SHIOBARA CO., LTD.—See Tokyu Fudosan Holdings Corporation; *Int'l*, pg. 7798
HUNTER MOUNTAIN SKI BOWL, INC.—See Vail Resorts, Inc.; *U.S. Public*, pg. 2271
HUNTER OIL CO. INC.; *U.S. Private*, pg. 2010
HUNTER PANELS, LLC—See Carlisle Companies Incorporated; *U.S. Public*, pg. 436
HUNTER PIPE LINE COMPANY PTY LTD—See Ampol Limited; *Int'l*, pg. 436
HUNTER PLASTICS LTD.—See Aliaxis S.A./N.V.; *Int'l*, pg. 324
HUNTER PREMIUM FUNDING LTD.—See Allianz SE; *Int'l*, pg. 342
HUNTER PUBLIC RELATIONS, LLC—See Stagwell, Inc.; *U.S. Public*, pg. 1927
HUNTER RESORT VACATIONS, INC.—See Vail Resorts, Inc.; *U.S. Public*, pg. 2271
THE HUNTER RIVER COMPANY PTY LTD—See Elders Limited; *Int'l*, pg. 2346
HUNTERS FRANCHISING LIMITED—See The Property Franchise Group PLC; *Int'l*, pg. 7677
HUNTER'S GREEN COUNTRY CLUB—See Apollo Global Management, Inc.; *U.S. Public*, pg. 149
HUNTER; *U.S. Private*, pg. 2009
HUNTERS PARTNERS LIMITED—See The Property Franchise Group PLC; *Int'l*, pg. 7677
HUNTERS PROPERTY PLC—See The Property Franchise Group PLC; *Int'l*, pg. 7677
HUNTERS SPECIALTIES, INC.—See Peak Rock Capital LLC; *U.S. Private*, pg. 3124
HUNTERS TRUCK SALES & SERVICE; *U.S. Private*, pg. 2010
HUNTER TECHNICAL RESOURCES LLC.—See Cognizant Technology Solutions Corporation; *U.S. Public*, pg. 524
HUNTER TECHNOLOGY CORP.; *Int'l*, pg. 3536
HUNTER VENTILADORES DE MEXICO S.A. DE C.V.—See Griffon Corporation; *U.S. Public*, pg. 969
HUNTER WARFIELD; *U.S. Private*, pg. 2010
HUNTER WEST LEGAL RECRUITMENT LTD.; *Int'l*, pg. 3536
HUNT FOREST PRODUCTS INC.; *U.S. Private*, pg. 2009
HUNT, GUILLOT & ASSOCIATES, LLC.; *U.S. Private*, pg. 2009
HUNTING ALPHA (EPZ) LIMITED—See Hunting Plc; *Int'l*, pg. 3536
HUNTING COMPANY, US OFFICE—See Hunting Plc; *Int'l*, pg. 3537
HUNTING DOG CAPITAL CORP.; *U.S. Private*, pg. 2010
HUNTINGDON LIFE SCIENCES GROUP PLC—See Life Sciences Research, Inc.; *U.S. Public*, pg. 2449
HUNTING ENERGY DE MEXICO S. DE R.L. DE C.V—See Hunting Plc; *Int'l*, pg. 3536
HUNTING ENERGY SAUDI ARABIA LLC—See Hunting Plc; *Int'l*, pg. 3536
HUNTING ENERGY SERVICES (AUSTRALIA) PTY. LTD.—See Hunting Plc; *Int'l*, pg. 3536
HUNTING ENERGY SERVICES (CANADA) LIMITED—See Hunting Plc; *Int'l*, pg. 3536
HUNTING ENERGY SERVICES - DOFFING DIV—See Hunting Plc; *Int'l*, pg. 3537
HUNTING ENERGY SERVICES (DRILLING TOOLS) INC.—See Hunting Plc; *Int'l*, pg. 3537
HUNTING ENERGY SERVICES (DRILLING TOOLS) LIMITED—See Hunting Plc; *Int'l*, pg. 3536
HUNTING ENERGY SERVICES INC—See Hunting Plc; *Int'l*, pg. 3537
HUNTING ENERGY SERVICES (INTERNATIONAL) LIMITED—See Hunting Plc; *Int'l*, pg. 3536
HUNTING ENERGY SERVICES (INTERNATIONAL) PTE LIMITED—See Hunting Plc; *Int'l*, pg. 3536
HUNTING ENERGY SERVICES LLC—See Hunting Plc; *Int'l*, pg. 3537
HUNTING ENERGY SERVICES L.P.—See Hunting Plc; *Int'l*, pg. 3537
HUNTING ENERGY SERVICES (NORWAY) AS—See Hunting Plc; *Int'l*, pg. 3536
HUNTING ENERGY SERVICES PTE. LTD.—See Hunting Plc; *Int'l*, pg. 3537
HUNTING ENERGY SERVICES (SOUTH AFRICA) PTY. LTD.—See Hunting Plc; *Int'l*, pg. 3536
HUNTING ENERGY SERVICES (UK) LIMITED—See Hunting Plc; *Int'l*, pg. 3536
HUNTING ENERGY SERVICES (WELL INTERVENTION) LIMITED—See Hunting Plc; *Int'l*, pg. 3536
HUNTING ENERGY SERVICES (WELL INTERVENTION) PTE. LTD.—See Hunting Plc; *Int'l*, pg. 3536

HUNTLEY OIL & GAS COMPANY

HUNTING ENERGY SERVICES (WUXI) CO., LTD.—See Hunting Plc; *Int'l*, pg. 3536
HUNTING PLC; *Int'l*, pg. 3536
HUNTING SUBSEA TECHNOLOGIES—See Hunting Plc; *Int'l*, pg. 3537
HUNTING TITAN—See Hunting Plc; *Int'l*, pg. 3537
HUNTINGTON ARTIFICIAL KIDNEY CENTER, LTD.—See DaVita Inc.; *U.S. Public*, pg. 639
HUNTINGTON BANCSHARES INCORPORATED; *U.S. Public*, pg. 1071
HUNTINGTON BANCSHARES INC.; *U.S. Private*, pg. 2010
HUNTINGTON BEACH INDEPENDENT—See Los Angeles Times Communications, LLC; *U.S. Private*, pg. 2497
HUNTINGTON BUSINESS SYSTEMS INC.; *U.S. Private*, pg. 2010
HUNTINGTON DISTRIBUTION FINANCE, INC.—See Huntington Bancshares Incorporated; *U.S. Public*, pg. 1071
HUNTINGTON EXPLORATION INC.; *U.S. Private*, pg. 3537
HUNTINGTON FEDERAL SAVINGS BANK; *U.S. Private*, pg. 2010
HUNTINGTON FOAM, LLC—See Wynnchurch Capital, L.P.; *U.S. Private*, pg. 4577
HUNTINGTON FORD INC.; *U.S. Private*, pg. 2010
HUNTINGTON HOMES INC.; *U.S. Private*, pg. 2010
HUNTINGTON INGALLS INCORPORATED—See Huntington Ingalls Industries, Inc.; *U.S. Public*, pg. 1072
HUNTINGTON INGALLS INDUSTRIES, INC.; *U.S. Public*, pg. 1071
HUNTINGTON INSURANCE, INC.—See Huntington Bancshares Incorporated; *U.S. Public*, pg. 1071
THE HUNTINGTON INVESTMENT COMPANY—See Huntington Bancshares Incorporated; *U.S. Public*, pg. 1071
THE HUNTINGTON LIBRARY, ART COLLECTIONS, AND BOTANICAL GARDENS; *U.S. Private*, pg. 4054
THE HUNTINGTON MORTGAGE GROUP—See Huntington Bancshares Incorporated; *U.S. Public*, pg. 1071
HUNTINGTON MUNICIPAL SECURITIES, INC.—See Huntington Bancshares Incorporated; *U.S. Public*, pg. 1071
THE HUNTINGTON NATIONAL BANK—See Huntington Bancshares Incorporated; *U.S. Public*, pg. 1071
HUNTINGTON PACIFIC INSURANCE AGENCY, INC.—See Inszone Insurance Services, LLC; *U.S. Private*, pg. 2096
HUNTINGTON PARK DIALYSIS, LLC—See DaVita Inc.; *U.S. Public*, pg. 639
HUNTINGTON PLACE LIMITED PARTNERSHIP—See Formation Capital, LLC; *U.S. Private*, pg. 1571
HUNTINGTON PREFERRED CAPITAL, INC.—See Huntington Bancshares Incorporated; *U.S. Public*, pg. 1071
HUNTINGTON PUBLIC CAPITAL CORPORATION—See Huntington Bancshares Incorporated; *U.S. Public*, pg. 1071
HUNTINGTON SANITARY BOARD; *U.S. Private*, pg. 2010
HUNTINGTON SHEET METAL, INC.; *U.S. Private*, pg. 2010
HUNTINGTON STEEL & SUPPLY CO.; *U.S. Private*, pg. 2010
HUNTINGTON TECHNOLOGY FINANCE, INC.—See Huntington Bancshares Incorporated; *U.S. Public*, pg. 1071
HUNTINGTON TILE, INC.—See PGM Products, LLC; *U.S. Private*, pg. 3165
HUNTINGTON TREATMENT CENTER, LLC—See Acadia Healthcare Company, Inc.; *U.S. Public*, pg. 29
HUNTING WELLTONIC LLC—See Hunting Plc; *Int'l*, pg. 3537
HUNTING WELLTONIC LTD.—See Hunting Plc; *Int'l*, pg. 3537
HUNT INSURANCE GROUP, LLC; *U.S. Private*, pg. 2009
HUNT INVESTMENT GROUP, L.P.—See Hunt Consolidated, Inc.; *U.S. Private*, pg. 2008
HUNT INVESTMENT MANAGEMENT, LLC—See Hunt Companies, Inc.; *U.S. Private*, pg. 2008
HUNTLEIGH CORPORATION—See ICTS International, N.V.; *Int'l*, pg. 3587
HUNTLEIGH DIAGNOSTICS LTD—See Getinge AB; *Int'l*, pg. 2949
HUNTLEIGH HEALTHCARE A/S—See Getinge AB; *Int'l*, pg. 2948
HUNTLEIGH HEALTHCARE LLC—See Getinge AB; *Int'l*, pg. 2948
HUNTLEIGH HEALTHCARE PTE LTD—See Getinge AB; *Int'l*, pg. 2948
HUNTLEIGH HOLDINGS BV.—See Getinge AB; *Int'l*, pg. 2949
HUNTLEIGH INTERNATIONAL HOLDINGS LTD.—See Getinge AB; *Int'l*, pg. 2949
HUNTLEIGH NESBIT EVANS HEALTHCARE GMBH—See Getinge AB; *Int'l*, pg. 2949
HUNTLEIGH RENRAY LTD.—See Getinge AB; *Int'l*, pg. 2949
HUNTLEIGH SECURITIES CORP.; *U.S. Private*, pg. 2010
HUNTLEIGH (SST) LTD—See Getinge AB; *Int'l*, pg. 2949
HUNTLEIGH TECHNOLOGY (ENGINEERING) LTD—See Getinge AB; *Int'l*, pg. 2949
HUNTLEIGH TECHNOLOGY LTD—See Getinge AB; *Int'l*, pg. 2949
HUNTLEY OIL & GAS COMPANY; *U.S. Private*, pg. 2010

HUNTLEY OIL & GAS COMPANY

HUNTLEY POWER LLC—See NRG Energy, Inc.; *U.S. Public*, pg. 1550
HUNT MIDWEST ENTERPRISES INC.; *U.S. Private*, pg. 2009
HUNT MILITARY COMMUNITIES MGMT., LLC—See Hunt Companies, Inc.; *U.S. Private*, pg. 2008
HUNT MORTGAGE GROUP, LLC—See Hunt Companies, Inc.; *U.S. Private*, pg. 2008
HUNTMOUNTAIN RESOURCES LTD.; *U.S. Private*, pg. 2010
HUNTMOUNTAIN RESOURCES LTD.; *U.S. Private*, pg. 2010
HUNT OIL COMPANY OF CANADA, INC.—See Hunt Consolidated, Inc.; *U.S. Private*, pg. 2008
HUNT OIL COMPANY—See Hunt Consolidated, Inc.; *U.S. Private*, pg. 2008
THE HUNTON GROUP; *U.S. Private*, pg. 4055
HUNTONIT AS—See Byggma ASA; *Int'l*, pg. 1235
HUNT OVERSEAS OIL COMPANY—See Hunt Consolidated, Inc.; *U.S. Private*, pg. 2008
HUNT & PALMER AIR CHARTER INDIA PVT. LTD.—See Hunt & Palmer plc.; *Int'l*, pg. 3536
HUNT & PALMER GERMANY GMBH—See Hunt & Palmer plc.; *Int'l*, pg. 3536
HUNT & PALMER HONG KONG LTD.—See Hunt & Palmer plc.; *Int'l*, pg. 3536
HUNT & PALMER PLC.; *Int'l*, pg. 3536
HUNT & PALMER (PTY) LTD.—See Hunt & Palmer plc.; *Int'l*, pg. 3536
THE HUNT PAVING COMPANY, INC.—See AECOM; *U.S. Public*, pg. 51
HUNT REAL ESTATE CORPORATION; *U.S. Private*, pg. 2009
HUNT REALTY CORPORATION—See Hunt Consolidated, Inc.; *U.S. Private*, pg. 2009
HUNT REFINING COMPANY INC.—See Hunt Consolidated, Inc.; *U.S. Private*, pg. 2008
HUNTSINGER FARMS INC.; *U.S. Private*, pg. 2010
HUNTSMAN ADVANCED MATERIALS (AUSTRIA) GMBH—See Huntsman Corporation; *U.S. Public*, pg. 1073
HUNTSMAN ADVANCED MATERIALS (DEUTSCHLAND) GMBH—See Huntsman Corporation; *U.S. Public*, pg. 1072
HUNTSMAN ADVANCED MATERIALS (EUROPE) BVBA—See Huntsman Corporation; *U.S. Public*, pg. 1073
HUNTSMAN ADVANCED MATERIALS (HONG KONG) LTD—See Huntsman Corporation; *U.S. Public*, pg. 1073
HUNTSMAN ADVANCED MATERIALS (INDIA) PRIVATE LIMITED—See Huntsman Corporation; *U.S. Public*, pg. 1073
HUNTSMAN ADVANCED MATERIALS (ITALY) SRL—See Huntsman Corporation; *U.S. Public*, pg. 1073
HUNTSMAN ADVANCED MATERIALS LLC—See Huntsman Corporation; *U.S. Public*, pg. 1073
HUNTSMAN ADVANCED MATERIALS (NANJING) COMPANY LIMITED.—See Huntsman Corporation; *U.S. Public*, pg. 1073
HUNTSMAN ADVANCED MATERIALS (TAIWAN) CORPORATION—See Huntsman Corporation; *U.S. Public*, pg. 1073
HUNTSMAN ADVANCED MATERIALS (UAE) FZE—See Huntsman Corporation; *U.S. Public*, pg. 1073
HUNTSMAN ADVANCED MATERIALS (UK) LIMITED—See Huntsman Corporation; *U.S. Public*, pg. 1073
HUNTSMAN (ARGENTINA) S.R.L.—See Huntsman Corporation; *U.S. Public*, pg. 1073
HUNTSMAN (BELGIUM) BVBA—See Huntsman Corporation; *U.S. Public*, pg. 1073
HUNTSMAN BUILDING SOLUTIONS (CENTRAL EUROPE) A.S.—See Huntsman Corporation; *U.S. Public*, pg. 1072
HUNTSMAN BUILDING SOLUTIONS (EUROPE) BV—See Huntsman Corporation; *U.S. Public*, pg. 1072
HUNTSMAN BUILDING SOLUTIONS (FRANCE) SAS—See Huntsman Corporation; *U.S. Public*, pg. 1072
HUNTSMAN BUILDING SOLUTIONS (USA) LLC—See Huntsman Corporation; *U.S. Public*, pg. 1072
HUNTSMAN CHEMICAL TRADING (SHANGHAI) LTD.—See Huntsman Corporation; *U.S. Public*, pg. 1073
HUNTSMAN (COLOMBIA) LIMITADA—See Huntsman Corporation; *U.S. Public*, pg. 1073
HUNTSMAN CORPORATION CANADA INC.—See Huntsman Corporation; *U.S. Public*, pg. 1074
HUNTSMAN CORPORATION HUNGARY RT.—See Huntsman Corporation; *U.S. Public*, pg. 1074
HUNTSMAN CORPORATION; *U.S. Public*, pg. 1072
HUNTSMAN CORPORATION UK LIMITED—See Huntsman Corporation; *U.S. Public*, pg. 1074
HUNTSMAN (CZECH REPUBLIC) SPOL.SR.O—See Huntsman Corporation; *U.S. Public*, pg. 1073
HUNTSMAN DE MEXICO, S.A. DE C.V.—See Huntsman Corporation; *U.S. Public*, pg. 1074

HUNTSMAN (EUROPE) BVBA—See Huntsman Corporation; *U.S. Public*, pg. 1073
HUNTSMAN EXPLORATION INC.; *Int'l*, pg. 3537
HUNTSMAN FAMILY HOLDINGS COMPANY LLC—See Huntsman Family Investments, LLC; *U.S. Private*, pg. 2011
HUNTSMAN FAMILY INVESTMENTS, LLC; *U.S. Private*, pg. 2010
HUNTSMAN (GERMANY) GMBH—See Huntsman Corporation; *U.S. Public*, pg. 1073
HUNTSMAN GOMET S.R.L.—See Huntsman Corporation; *U.S. Public*, pg. 1072
HUNTSMAN (HOLDINGS) NETHERLANDS B.V.—See Huntsman Corporation; *U.S. Public*, pg. 1073
HUNTSMAN HOLLAND B.V.—See Huntsman Corporation; *U.S. Public*, pg. 1074
HUNTSMAN IFS POLYURETHANES LIMITED—See Huntsman Corporation; *U.S. Public*, pg. 1072
HUNTSMAN INTERNATIONAL (CANADA) CORPORATION—See Huntsman Corporation; *U.S. Public*, pg. 1074
HUNTSMAN INTERNATIONAL (INDIA) PRIVATE LIMITED—See Huntsman Corporation; *U.S. Public*, pg. 1074
HUNTSMAN INTERNATIONAL LLC—See Huntsman Corporation; *U.S. Public*, pg. 1073
HUNTSMAN (KOREA) LIMITED—See Huntsman Corporation; *U.S. Public*, pg. 1073
HUNTSMAN MA INVESTMENTS (NETHERLANDS) CV—See Huntsman Corporation; *U.S. Public*, pg. 1074
HUNTSMAN MEXICO S. DE R.L. DE C.V.—See Huntsman Corporation; *U.S. Public*, pg. 1075
HUNTSMAN (NETHERLANDS) BV—See Huntsman Corporation; *U.S. Public*, pg. 1073
HUNTSMAN NORDEN AB—See Huntsman Corporation; *U.S. Public*, pg. 1074
HUNTSMAN P&A AMERICAS LLC—See Huntsman Corporation; *U.S. Public*, pg. 1075
HUNTSMAN P&A FINLAND OY—See Huntsman Corporation; *U.S. Public*, pg. 1073
HUNTSMAN P&A GERMANY GMBH—See Huntsman Corporation; *U.S. Public*, pg. 1073
HUNTSMAN P&A UERDINGEN GMBH—See Huntsman Corporation; *U.S. Public*, pg. 1073
HUNTSMAN P&A WASSERCHEMIE GMBH—See Huntsman Corporation; *U.S. Public*, pg. 1073
HUNTSMAN PETROCHEMICAL LLC—See Huntsman Corporation; *U.S. Public*, pg. 1074
HUNTSMAN PIGMENTS & ADDITIVES—See Huntsman Corporation; *U.S. Public*, pg. 1074
HUNTSMAN PIGMENTS AMERICAS LLC—See Huntsman Corporation; *U.S. Public*, pg. 1074
HUNTSMAN PIGMENTS HOLDING GMBH—See Huntsman Corporation; *U.S. Public*, pg. 1073
HUNTSMAN PIGMENTS HONG KONG LIMITED—See Huntsman Corporation; *U.S. Public*, pg. 1074
HUNTSMAN PIGMENTS S.P.A.—See Huntsman Corporation; *U.S. Public*, pg. 1074
HUNTSMAN PIGMENTS & TRADING PTY. LTD.—See Huntsman Corporation; *U.S. Public*, pg. 1074
HUNTSMAN PIGMENTS (UK) LIMITED—See Huntsman Corporation; *U.S. Public*, pg. 1074
HUNTSMAN (POLAND) SP. Z O.O.—See Huntsman Corporation; *U.S. Public*, pg. 1073
HUNTSMAN POLYURETHANES (AUSTRALIA) PTY LTD.—See Huntsman Corporation; *U.S. Public*, pg. 1074
HUNTSMAN POLYURETHANES (CHINA) LIMITED—See Huntsman Corporation; *U.S. Public*, pg. 1074
HUNTSMAN - POLYURETHANES DIVISION—See Huntsman Corporation; *U.S. Public*, pg. 1074
HUNTSMAN POLYURETHANES SHANGHAI LTD.—See Huntsman Corporation; *U.S. Public*, pg. 1074
HUNTSMAN POLYURETHANES—See Huntsman Corporation; *U.S. Public*, pg. 1074
HUNTSMAN POLYURETHANES—See Huntsman Corporation; *U.S. Public*, pg. 1074
HUNTSMAN POLYURETHANES—See Huntsman Corporation; *U.S. Public*, pg. 1074
HUNTSMAN POLYURETHANES (UK) LTD.—See Huntsman Corporation; *U.S. Public*, pg. 1074
HUNTSMAN PRODUCTS GMBH—See Huntsman Corporation; *U.S. Public*, pg. 1075
HUNTSMAN PURSAN CHEMICALS KIMYA SANAYI VE TICARET LIMITED SIRKETI—See Huntsman Corporation; *U.S. Public*, pg. 1074
HUNTSMAN QUIMICA BRASIL LTDA.—See Huntsman Corporation; *U.S. Public*, pg. 1074
HUNTSMAN (RUSSIA INVESTMENTS) B.V.—See Huntsman Corporation; *U.S. Public*, pg. 1073
HUNTSMAN SAINT-MIHIEL SAS—See Huntsman Corporation; *U.S. Public*, pg. 1074
HUNTSMANS LODGE LIMITED—See Sheikh Holdings Group (Investments) Limited; *Int'l*, pg. 6793
HUNTSMAN SOLUTIONS INDIA PRIVATE LIMITED—See Huntsman Corporation; *U.S. Public*, pg. 1075
HUNTSMAN SPECIALTY CHEMICALS KIMYA SANAYI VE TICARET ANONIM SIRKETI—See Huntsman Corporation; *U.S. Public*, pg. 1075

CORPORATE AFFILIATIONS

HUNTSMAN SURFACE SCIENCES FRANCE SAS—See Huntsman Corporation; *U.S. Public*, pg. 1074
HUNTSMAN SURFACE SCIENCES ITALIA S.R.L.—See Huntsman Corporation; *U.S. Public*, pg. 1074
HUNTSMAN TEXTILE EFFECTS (BELGIUM) BVBA—See Huntsman Corporation; *U.S. Public*, pg. 1073
HUNTSMAN TEXTILE EFFECTS - CHARLOTTE PLANT—See Huntsman Corporation; *U.S. Public*, pg. 1074
HUNTSMAN TEXTILE EFFECTS DIVISION—See Huntsman Corporation; *U.S. Public*, pg. 1074
HUNTSMAN TEXTILE EFFECTS (GERMANY) GMBH—See Huntsman Corporation; *U.S. Public*, pg. 1074
HUNTSMAN TEXTILE EFFECTS - HIGH POINT PLANT—See Huntsman Corporation; *U.S. Public*, pg. 1074
HUNTSMAN TEXTILE EFFECTS (MEXICO) S. DE R.L. DE C.V.—See Huntsman Corporation; *U.S. Public*, pg. 1074
HUNTSMAN TEXTILE EFFECTS (QINGDAO) CO., LTD—See Huntsman Corporation; *U.S. Public*, pg. 1074
HUNTSMAN TEXTILE EFFECTS (SWITZERLAND) GMBH—See Huntsman Corporation; *U.S. Public*, pg. 1075
HUNTSMAN (UAE) FZE—See Huntsman Corporation; *U.S. Public*, pg. 1072
HUNTSMAN VERWALTUNGS GMBH—See Huntsman Corporation; *U.S. Public*, pg. 1073
HUNT & SONS, INC.; *U.S. Private*, pg. 2008
HUNT'S TRANSPORT LTD.; *Int'l*, pg. 3536
HUNTSVILLE EMERGENCY MEDICAL SERVICES INC; *U.S. Private*, pg. 2011
HUNTSVILLE FASTENER & SUPPLY INC.—See Birmingham Fastener & Supply Inc.; *U.S. Private*, pg. 564
HUNTSVILLE HOUSING AUTHORITY; *U.S. Private*, pg. 2011
HUNTSVILLE-MADISON COUNTY AIRPORT AUTHORITY; *U.S. Private*, pg. 2011
HUNTSVILLE TIMES—See Advance Publications, Inc.; *U.S. Private*, pg. 86
HUNTSWOOD CTC LIMITED—See ResultsCX; *U.S. Private*, pg. 3410
HUNTSWORTH HEALTH—See Clayton, Dubilier & Rice, LLC; *U.S. Private*, pg. 925
HUNTSWORTH LIMITED—See Clayton, Dubilier & Rice, LLC; *U.S. Private*, pg. 924
HUNT TELECOMMUNICATIONS LLC—See Uniti Group Inc.; *U.S. Public*, pg. 2253
HUNT TRANSPORTATION, INC.—See Crete Carrier Corp.; *U.S. Private*, pg. 1099
HUNT VALLEY COURTYARD, INC.—See Marriott International, Inc.; *U.S. Public*, pg. 1370
HUNT VALLEY PHARMACY, LLC—See Bond Pharmacy, Inc.; *U.S. Private*, pg. 613
HUNT VALVE - ACTUATOR DIVISION—See Arcline Investment Management LP; *U.S. Private*, pg. 313
HUNT VALVE COMPANY, INC.—See Arcline Investment Management LP; *U.S. Private*, pg. 313
HUNTWICKE CAPITAL GROUP INC.; *U.S. Public*, pg. 1075
HUNYADY AUCTION COMPANY; *U.S. Private*, pg. 2011
HUNYA FOODS CO., LTD.; *Int'l*, pg. 3537
HUNYVERS SA; *Int'l*, pg. 3537
HUNZA-LAND CORPORATION SDN. BHD.—See Hunza Properties Berhad; *Int'l*, pg. 3537
HUNZA PARADE DEVELOPMENT SDN. BHD.—See Hunza Properties Berhad; *Int'l*, pg. 3537
HUNZA PROPERTIES BERHAD; *Int'l*, pg. 3537
HUNZA PROPERTIES (GURNEY) SDN. BHD.—See Hunza Properties Berhad; *Int'l*, pg. 3537
HUNZA PROPERTIES (WILAYAH) SDN. BHD.—See Hunza Properties Berhad; *Int'l*, pg. 3537
HUNZA TRADING SDN. BHD.—See Hunza Properties Berhad; *Int'l*, pg. 3537
HUNZICKER BROTHERS INC.; *U.S. Private*, pg. 2011
HUNZIKER KALKSANDSTEIN AG—See H+H International A/S; *Int'l*, pg. 3194
HUNZINGER CONSTRUCTION COMPANY; *U.S. Private*, pg. 2011
HUOBI GLOBAL LTD.; *Int'l*, pg. 3537
HUON AQUACULTURE COMPANY PTY. LTD.—See JBS S.A.; *Int'l*, pg. 3918
HUON AQUACULTURE GROUP LIMITED—See JBS S.A.; *Int'l*, pg. 3918
HUON FERS SOUDAGE; *Int'l*, pg. 3537
HUONG VIET REAL ESTATE INVESTMENT JOINT STOCK COMPANY; *Int'l*, pg. 3537
HUONS GLOBAL CO., LTD.; *Int'l*, pg. 3537
HUP BALKAN A.D.; *Int'l*, pg. 3537
HUPER OPTIK INTERNATIONAL PTE. LTD.—See Eastman Chemical Company; *U.S. Public*, pg. 705
HUPER OPTIK U.S.A., L.P.—See Eastman Chemical Company; *U.S. Public*, pg. 705
HUP HENG POULTRY INDUSTRIES PTE. LTD.—See Leong Hup International Berhad; *Int'l*, pg. 4461
HUP-HOE CREDIT PTE. LTD.—See Credit Intelligence Limited; *Int'l*, pg. 1835

HUP LIAN ENGINEERING PTE LTD—See Chasen Holdings Limited; *Int'l*, pg. 1457
HUPPE BELGIUM N.V./S.A.—See Masco Corporation; *U.S. Public*, pg. 1391
HUPPE B.V.—See Masco Corporation; *U.S. Public*, pg. 1391
HUPPE GMBH—See Masco Corporation; *U.S. Public*, pg. 1391
HUPPE INSAAT SANAYI VE TICARET A.S.—See Masco Corporation; *U.S. Public*, pg. 1391
HUPP ELECTRIC MOTORS INC.; *U.S. Private*, pg. 2011
HUPPE SARL—See Masco Corporation; *U.S. Public*, pg. 1391
HUPPE (SHANGHAI) CO., LTD.—See Masco Corporation; *U.S. Public*, pg. 1391
HUPPE S.L.—See Masco Corporation; *U.S. Public*, pg. 1390
HUPPE SPAIN, S.L.U.—See Masco Corporation; *U.S. Public*, pg. 1391
HUPPE SP. Z.O.O.—See Masco Corporation; *U.S. Public*, pg. 1391
HUPPIN'S HI-FI, PHOTO & VIDEO INC.—See Wipliance, LLC; *U.S. Private*, pg. 4546
HUPP REALTY ADVISORS, INC.; *U.S. Private*, pg. 2011
HUP SENG HUAT LAND PTE LTD—See HupSteel Limited; *Int'l*, pg. 3538
HUP SENG INDUSTRIES BERHAD; *Int'l*, pg. 3537
HUP SENG PERUSAHAAN MAKANAN (M) SDN. BHD.—See Hup Seng Industries Berhad; *Int'l*, pg. 3538
HUP SOON GLOBAL CORPORATION LIMITED; *Int'l*, pg. 3538
HUP SRL—See Mondelez International, Inc.; *U.S. Public*, pg. 1461
HUPSTEEL LIMITED; *Int'l*, pg. 3538
HUP-ZAGREB INC; *Int'l*, pg. 3538
HURAY AUTOMOBILES SAS—See Groupe Dubreuil SA; *Int'l*, pg. 3102
HURCKMAN MECHANICAL INDUSTRIES; *U.S. Private*, pg. 2011
HURCO COMPANIES, INC.; *U.S. Public*, pg. 1075
HURCO EUROPE LIMITED—See Hurco Companies, Inc.; *U.S. Public*, pg. 1076
HURCO GMBH—See Hurco Companies, Inc.; *U.S. Public*, pg. 1076
HURCO INDIA PTE. LTD.—See Hurco Companies, Inc.; *U.S. Public*, pg. 1076
HURCO MACHINE TOOL PRODUCTION COMPANY—See Hurco Companies, Inc.; *U.S. Public*, pg. 1076
HURCO MANUFACTURING LTD.—See Hurco Companies, Inc.; *U.S. Public*, pg. 1076
HURCO S.A.R.L.—See Hurco Companies, Inc.; *U.S. Public*, pg. 1076
HURCO (S.E. ASIA) PTE LTD—See Hurco Companies, Inc.; *U.S. Public*, pg. 1075
HURCO S.R.L.—See Hurco Companies, Inc.; *U.S. Public*, pg. 1076
HURD HAULAGE PTY. LTD.—See CRH plc; *Int'l*, pg. 1842
HURIX SYSTEMS PVT. LTD.; *Int'l*, pg. 3538
HURLETRON INC.—See Altair Corporation; *U.S. Private*, pg. 86
HURLEY AUSTRALIA PTY. LTD.—See Bluestar Alliance LLC; *U.S. Private*, pg. 598
HURLEY CHANDLER & CHAFFER; *U.S. Private*, pg. 2011
HURLEY CHRYSLER PLYMOUTH; *U.S. Private*, pg. 2011
HURLEY INTERNATIONAL LLC—See Bluestar Alliance LLC; *U.S. Private*, pg. 598
HURLEY LIMOUSINE INC.; *U.S. Private*, pg. 2011
HURON CAPITAL PARTNERS LLC; *U.S. Private*, pg. 2011
HURON CASTING, INC.; *U.S. Private*, pg. 2012
HURON CENTRAL RAILWAY INC.—See Brookfield Infrastructure Partners L.P.; *Int'l*, pg. 1191
HURON CENTRAL RAILWAY INC.—See GIC Pte. Ltd.; *Int'l*, pg. 2966
HURON CONSULTING GROUP INC.; *U.S. Public*, pg. 1076
HURON CONSULTING SERVICES LLC—See Huron Consulting Group Inc.; *U.S. Public*, pg. 1076
HURON DAILY TRIBUNE—See The Hearst Corporation; *U.S. Private*, pg. 4047
HURON DISTRIBUTORS INC.; *U.S. Private*, pg. 2012
HURON & EASTERN RAILWAY COMPANY, INC.—See Brookfield Infrastructure Partners L.P.; *Int'l*, pg. 1191
HURON & EASTERN RAILWAY COMPANY, INC.—See GIC Pte. Ltd.; *Int'l*, pg. 2966
HURON GAS LLC—See Zimi Limited; *Int'l*, pg. 8684
HURONIA ALARM & FIRE SECURITY INC.; *Int'l*, pg. 3538
HURON INC.—See Seven Mile Capital Partners, LLC; *U.S. Private*, pg. 3618
HURON MOTOR PRODUCTS LTD.; *Int'l*, pg. 3538
HURON NEWSPAPERS LLC—See News Media Corporation; *U.S. Private*, pg. 2916
HURON SMITH OIL CO. INC.; *U.S. Private*, pg. 2012
HURON TRANSACTION ADVISORY LLC—See Huron Consulting Group Inc.; *U.S. Public*, pg. 1076
HURON VALLEY BANCORP, INC.; *U.S. Public*, pg. 1076

HURON VALLEY ELECTRIC, INC.—See Motor City Electric Co., Inc.; *U.S. Private*, pg. 2796
HURON VALLEY GLASS COMPANY LLC—See National Construction Enterprises Inc.; *U.S. Private*, pg. 2851
HURON VALLEY STEEL CORP. - MAGNETICS DIVISION—See Huron Valley Steel Corp.; *U.S. Private*, pg. 2012
HURON VALLEY STEEL CORP.; *U.S. Private*, pg. 2012
HURO NV—See Koninklijke Ahold Delhaize N.V.; *Int'l*, pg. 4261
HURRICANE AMT, LLC—See Fog Cutter Capital Group Inc.; *U.S. Private*, pg. 1557
HURRICANE ENERGY PLC—See State Oil Limited; *Int'l*, pg. 7184
HURRICANE FOODS INC.; *U.S. Private*, pg. 2012
HURRICANE HARBOR GP LLC—See Six Flags Entertainment Corp.; *U.S. Public*, pg. 1890
HURRICANE PURCHASE A/S—See New Wave Group AB; *Int'l*, pg. 5229
HURRICANE SANDY NEW JERSEY RELIEF FUND INC.; *U.S. Private*, pg. 2012
HURRICANES HOCKEY LIMITED PARTNERSHIP—See Hurricanes Holdings, LLC; *U.S. Private*, pg. 2013
HURRICANES HOLDINGS, LLC; *U.S. Private*, pg. 2013
HURRIYET GAZETECILIK VE MATBAACILIK A.S.—See Adil Bey Holding A.S.; *Int'l*, pg. 148
HURR.TV SDN. BHD.—See MY E.G. Services Berhad; *Int'l*, pg. 5111
HURST FARM SUPPLY INC.; *U.S. Private*, pg. 2013
HURST HARVEY OIL INC.; *U.S. Private*, pg. 2013
HURST JAWS OF LIFE, INC—See IDEX Corp; *U.S. Public*, pg. 1090
HURST STORES INCORPORATED; *U.S. Private*, pg. 2013
HURTIGRUTEN AS—See TDR Capital LLP; *Int'l*, pg. 7494
HURTIGRUTEN INC.—See TDR Capital LLP; *Int'l*, pg. 7494
HURTOPON.PL SP. Z O.O—See OPONEO.PL S.A.; *Int'l*, pg. 5600
HURTT FABRICATING CORP.; *U.S. Private*, pg. 2013
HURUM CO., LTD.; *Int'l*, pg. 3538
HURWITZ GELLER PTY. LTD.—See Azimut Holding SpA; *Int'l*, pg. 779
HURWITZ-MINTZ FINEST FURNITURE STORE SOUTH LLC; *U.S. Private*, pg. 2013
HURXLEY CORPORATION; *Int'l*, pg. 3538
HUSCH BLACKWELL LLP; *U.S. Private*, pg. 2013
HUSCO AUTOMOTIVE HOLDINGS, LLC.—See HUSCO International, Inc.; *U.S. Private*, pg. 2013
HUSCO HYDRAULICS PRIVATE LTD.—See HUSCO International, Inc.; *U.S. Private*, pg. 2013
HUSCO INTERNATIONAL, INC.; *U.S. Private*, pg. 2013
HUSCO INTERNATIONAL, LTD.—See HUSCO International, Inc.; *U.S. Private*, pg. 2013
HUSCO-KAYABA HYDRAULICS (SHANGHAI) LTD.—See HUSCO International, Inc.; *U.S. Private*, pg. 2013
HUSCOKE HOLDINGS LIMITED; *Int'l*, pg. 3538
HUSCOKE INTERNATIONAL GROUP LIMITED—See Huscoke Holdings Limited; *Int'l*, pg. 3538
HUSCOMPAGNIET A/S; *Int'l*, pg. 3538
HUSEBY, LLC; *U.S. Private*, pg. 2013
HUSEIN INDUSTRIES LIMITED; *Int'l*, pg. 3538
HUSER & CO GMBH—See Bilfinger SE; *Int'l*, pg. 1028
HUSH CRAFT LTD.—See Fugro N.V.; *Int'l*, pg. 2808
HUSH PUPPIES RETAIL, LLC—See Wolverine World Wide, Inc.; *U.S. Public*, pg. 2377
HUSKER AG, LLC; *U.S. Private*, pg. 2013
HUSKER COOP; *U.S. Private*, pg. 2013
HUSKY ADVERTISING, INC.; *U.S. Private*, pg. 2013
HUSKY CIS LLC—See Platinum Equity, LLC; *U.S. Private*, pg. 3203
HUSKY DO BRASIL SISTEMAS DE INJECAO LTDA.—See Platinum Equity, LLC; *U.S. Private*, pg. 3204
HUSKY ENVELOPE PRODUCTS INCORPORATED; *U.S. Private*, pg. 2013
HUSKY INJECTION MOLDING SYSTEMS ARGENTINA S.A.—See Platinum Equity, LLC; *U.S. Private*, pg. 3204
HUSKY INJECTION MOLDING SYSTEMS COLOMBIA LTD.—See Platinum Equity, LLC; *U.S. Private*, pg. 3204
HUSKY INJECTION MOLDING SYSTEMS IBERIA S.L.U.—See Platinum Equity, LLC; *U.S. Private*, pg. 3204
HUSKY INJECTION MOLDING SYSTEMS, INC.—See Platinum Equity, LLC; *U.S. Private*, pg. 3204
HUSKY INJECTION MOLDING SYSTEMS (INDIA) PRIVATE LIMITED—See Platinum Equity, LLC; *U.S. Private*, pg. 3203
HUSKY INJECTION MOLDING SYSTEMS (ISRAEL) LTD.—See Platinum Equity, LLC; *U.S. Private*, pg. 3203
HUSKY INJECTION MOLDING SYSTEMS KOREA INC—See Platinum Equity, LLC; *U.S. Private*, pg. 3204
HUSKY INJECTION MOLDING SYSTEMS LTD.—See Platinum Equity, LLC; *U.S. Private*, pg. 3203
HUSKY INJECTION MOLDING SYSTEMS (NORDIC) A/S—See Platinum Equity, LLC; *U.S. Private*, pg. 3203

HUSKY INJECTION MOLDING SYSTEMS S.A.—See Platinum Equity, LLC; *U.S. Private*, pg. 3204
HUSKY INJECTION MOLDING SYSTEMS (SHANGHAI) LTD.—See Platinum Equity, LLC; *U.S. Private*, pg. 3203
HUSKY INJECTION MOLDING SYSTEMS SINGAPORE PTE. LTD.—See Platinum Equity, LLC; *U.S. Private*, pg. 3204
HUSKY INJECTION MOLDING SYSTEMS (SOUTH AFRICA) PTY. LTD.—See Platinum Equity, LLC; *U.S. Private*, pg. 3203
HUSKY INJECTION MOLDING SYSTEMS (THAILAND) LTD.—See Platinum Equity, LLC; *U.S. Private*, pg. 3204
HUSKY INTERNATIONAL TRUCKS INC.; *U.S. Private*, pg. 2014
HUSKY SPRING; *U.S. Private*, pg. 2014
HUSKY TERMINAL & STEVEDORING, INC.—See Kawasaki Kisen Kaisha, Ltd.; *Int'l*, pg. 4099
HUSQVARNA AB; *Int'l*, pg. 3538
HUSQVARNA AUSTRIA GMBH—See Husqvarna AB; *Int'l*, pg. 3539
HUSQVARNA BELGIUM SA—See Husqvarna AB; *Int'l*, pg. 3539
HUSQVARNA CANADA CORP.—See Husqvarna AB; *Int'l*, pg. 3539
HUSQVARNA COLOMBIA S.A.—See Husqvarna AB; *Int'l*, pg. 3539
HUSQVARNA COMMERCIAL SOLUTIONS AUSTRIA GMBH—See Husqvarna AB; *Int'l*, pg. 3539
HUSQVARNA COMMERCIAL SOLUTIONS NORGE AS—See Husqvarna AB; *Int'l*, pg. 3539
HUSQVARNA CONSTRUCTION PRODUCTS NORTH AMERICA, INC. - CORONA—See Husqvarna AB; *Int'l*, pg. 3539
HUSQVARNA CONSTRUCTION PRODUCTS NORTH AMERICA, INC.—See Husqvarna AB; *Int'l*, pg. 3539
HUSQVARNA CONSUMER OUTDOOR PRODUCTS N.A., INC.—See Husqvarna AB; *Int'l*, pg. 3539
HUSQVARNA DANMARK A/S—See Husqvarna AB; *Int'l*, pg. 3539
HUSQVARNA DEUTSCHLAND GMBH—See Husqvarna AB; *Int'l*, pg. 3539
HUSQVARNA DIRECT AB—See Husqvarna AB; *Int'l*, pg. 3539
HUSQVARNA EESTI OSAUHING—See Husqvarna AB; *Int'l*, pg. 3539
HUSQVARNA FINANCE IRELAND LTD.—See Husqvarna AB; *Int'l*, pg. 3539
HUSQVARNA FORESTRY PRODUCTS NA INC.—See Husqvarna AB; *Int'l*, pg. 3539
HUSQVARNA FRANCE SAS—See Husqvarna AB; *Int'l*, pg. 3539
HUSQVARNA HOLDING AB—See Husqvarna AB; *Int'l*, pg. 3539
HUSQVARNA (INDIA) PRODUCTS PRIVATE LIMITED—See Husqvarna AB; *Int'l*, pg. 3539
HUSQVARNA LLC—See Husqvarna AB; *Int'l*, pg. 3539
HUSQVARNA MAGYARORSZAG KFT—See Husqvarna AB; *Int'l*, pg. 3539
HUSQVARNA OUTDOOR PRODUCTS - MCRAE—See Husqvarna AB; *Int'l*, pg. 3539
HUSQVARNA OUTDOOR PRODUCTS - NASHVILLE—See Husqvarna AB; *Int'l*, pg. 3539
HUSQVARNA OUTDOOR PRODUCTS - ORANGEBURG—See Husqvarna AB; *Int'l*, pg. 3539
HUSQVARNA OUTDOOR PRODUCTS - SWAINSBORO—See Husqvarna AB; *Int'l*, pg. 3539
HUSQVARNA POLAND SP. Z O.O.—See Husqvarna AB; *Int'l*, pg. 3539
HUSQVARNA POLSKA SP.Z.O.O.—See Husqvarna AB; *Int'l*, pg. 3539
HUSQVARNA PROFESSIONAL PRODUCTS, INC.—See Husqvarna AB; *Int'l*, pg. 3539
HUSQVARNA SLOVENSKO S.R.O.—See Husqvarna AB; *Int'l*, pg. 3539
HUSQVARNA SOUTH AFRICA (PROPRIETARY) LIMITED—See Husqvarna AB; *Int'l*, pg. 3539
HUSQVARNA TURF CARE—See Husqvarna AB; *Int'l*, pg. 3539
HUSQVARNA UK LTD.—See Husqvarna AB; *Int'l*, pg. 3539
HUSQVARNA ZENOAH CO., LTD—See Husqvarna AB; *Int'l*, pg. 3539
THE HUSSAR GRILL ADVERTISING (PTY) LTD.—See Spur Corporation; *Int'l*, pg. 7146
HUSS BREWING CO. LLC; *U.S. Private*, pg. 2014
HUSSEL GESCHENKSTUDIO GMBH—See EMERAM Capital Partners GmbH; *Int'l*, pg. 2378
HUSSEL IBERIA-CHOCOLATES E CONFEITARIA, S.A.—See Jeronimo Martins SGPS SA; *Int'l*, pg. 3931
HUSSEL SUSSWARENFACHGESCHAFTE GMBH—See EMERAM Capital Partners GmbH; *Int'l*, pg. 2378
HUSSEY SEATING CO.; *U.S. Private*, pg. 2014
HUSSMANN CANADA INC.—See Panasonic Holdings Corporation; *Int'l*, pg. 5720
HUSSMANN CORPORATION—See Panasonic Holdings Corporation; *Int'l*, pg. 5720
HUSSMANN INTERNATIONAL, INC.—See Clayton, Dubilier & Rice, LLC; *U.S. Private*, pg. 924

HUSSMANN SERVICE DO BRASIL LTDA.—See Ingersoll Rand Inc.; *U.S. Public*, pg. 1120
HUSSMANN (THAILAND) COMPANY LIMITED—See Ingersoll Rand Inc.; *U.S. Public*, pg. 1120
HUSSOR ERECTA SOC; *Int'l*, pg. 3540
HUSSUNG MECHANICAL CONTRACTORS, INC.; *U.S. Private*, pg. 2014
HUSTAL UAB—See Panevezio statybos trestas AB; *Int'l*, pg. 5727
HUSTEEL CO., LTD. - DANGJIN PLANT—See HUSTEEL CO., Ltd.; *Int'l*, pg. 3540
HUSTEEL CO., LTD.; *Int'l*, pg. 3540
HUSTEEL USA, INC.—See HUSTEEL CO., Ltd.; *Int'l*, pg. 3540
HUSTON ELECTRIC INC.; *U.S. Private*, pg. 2014
HUSTON-PATTERSON CORPORATION—See Radial Equity Partners LP; *U.S. Private*, pg. 3343
HUSTON SUPPLY CO. INC.; *U.S. Private*, pg. 2014
HUSYS CONSULTING LTD.—See TPG Capital, L.P.; *U.S. Public*, pg. 2177
HUT 8 CORP.; *U.S. Public*, pg. 1076
HUT 8 MINING CORP.—See Hut 8 Corp.; *U.S. Public*, pg. 1076
HUTAC SARL—See Randstad N.V.; *Int'l*, pg. 6202
HUTA CYNKU MIASTECZKO SLASKIE S.A.—See Stalprodukt S.A.; *Int'l*, pg. 7164
HUT ADUNA D.D.; *Int'l*, pg. 3540
HUTA POKOJ S.A.; *Int'l*, pg. 3540
HUTA SZKLA CZECHY S.A.—See Zignago Vetro S.p.A.; *Int'l*, pg. 8682
HUTA SZKLA GOSPODARCZEGO IRENA S.A.; *Int'l*, pg. 3540
HUTCHCRAFT VAN SERVICE, INC.; *U.S. Private*, pg. 2014
HUTCHENS CHEVROLET; *U.S. Private*, pg. 2014
HUTCHENS INDUSTRIES INC.; *U.S. Private*, pg. 2014
HUTCHERSON TILE COMPANY; *U.S. Private*, pg. 2014
HUTCHESON & COMPANY INC.; *U.S. Private*, pg. 2014
HUTCHINS EUGENE NISSAN, INC.—See Lithia Motors, Inc.; *U.S. Public*, pg. 1323
HUTCHINS IMPORTED MOTORS, INC.—See Lithia Motors, Inc.; *U.S. Public*, pg. 1323
HUTCHINSON (ANTIGUA) LIMITED—See Goddard Enterprises Limited; *Int'l*, pg. 3019
HUTCHINSON ANTIVIBRATION SYSTEMS, INC.—See TotalEnergies SE; *Int'l*, pg. 7837
HUTCHINSON & BLOODGOOD LLP; *U.S. Private*, pg. 2014
HUTCHINSON BRASIL AUTOMOTIVE LTDA—See TotalEnergies SE; *Int'l*, pg. 7837
HUTCHINSON CORPORATION—See TotalEnergies SE; *Int'l*, pg. 7836
HUTCHINSON FTS INC.—See TotalEnergies SE; *Int'l*, pg. 7837
HUTCHINSON FTS, INC.—See TotalEnergies SE; *Int'l*, pg. 7837
HUTCHINSON FTS INC.—See TotalEnergies SE; *Int'l*, pg. 7837
HUTCHINSON GMBH—See TotalEnergies SE; *Int'l*, pg. 7836
HUTCHINSON HEALTH; *U.S. Private*, pg. 2014
HUTCHINSON INDUSTRIAL RUBBER PRODUCTS (SUZHOU) COMPANY, LIMITED—See TotalEnergies SE; *Int'l*, pg. 7836
HUTCHINSON INDUSTRIES, INC.—See TotalEnergies SE; *Int'l*, pg. 7837
HUTCHINSON JAPAN COMPANY LIMITED—See TotalEnergies SE; *Int'l*, pg. 7836
HUTCHINSON KOREA LIMITED—See TotalEnergies SE; *Int'l*, pg. 7836
HUTCHINSON MANUFACTURING, INC.—See Daggett Ventures, LLC; *U.S. Private*, pg. 1144
HUTCHINSON MOTORS LTD—See The Colonial Motor Company Limited; *Int'l*, pg. 7634
HUTCHINSON NICHIRIN BRAKE HOSES, S.L.—See Nichirin Co., Ltd.; *Int'l*, pg. 5271
HUTCHINSON POLAND SP ZO,O.—See TotalEnergies SE; *Int'l*, pg. 7836
HUTCHINSON PORTO LDA.—See TotalEnergies SE; *Int'l*, pg. 7836
HUTCHINSON PRECISION SEALING SYSTEMS, INC.—See TotalEnergies SE; *Int'l*, pg. 7837
HUTCHINSON S.A - CENTRE DE RECHERCHE—See TotalEnergies SE; *Int'l*, pg. 7837
HUTCHINSON S.A.—See TotalEnergies SE; *Int'l*, pg. 7836
HUTCHINSON SEALING SYSTEMS INC.—See TotalEnergies SE; *Int'l*, pg. 7837
HUTCHINSON SEALING SYSTEMS, INC.—See TotalEnergies SE; *Int'l*, pg. 7837
HUTCHINSON SEALING SYSTEMS, INC.—See TotalEnergies SE; *Int'l*, pg. 7837
HUTCHINSON SEALING SYSTEMS NORTH AMERICA, INC.—See TotalEnergies SE; *Int'l*, pg. 7837
HUTCHINSON SHOCKEY ERLEY & CO.; *U.S. Private*, pg. 2014
HUTCHINSON STOP,- CHOC GMBH & CO. KG—See TotalEnergies SE; *Int'l*, pg. 7837
HUTCHINSON TECHNOLOGY INC. - EAU CLAIRE—See TDK Corporation; *Int'l*, pg. 7488
HUTCHINSON TECHNOLOGY INCORPORATED—See TDK Corporation; *Int'l*, pg. 7488
HUTCHINSON TECHNOLOGY OPERATIONS (THAILAND) CO., LTD.—See TDK Corporation; *Int'l*, pg. 7489
HUTCHINSON TELEPHONE COMPANY—See Nuvera Communications, Inc.; *U.S. Public*, pg. 1556
HUTCHINSON (WUHAN) AUTOMOTIVE RUBBER PRODUCTS COMPANY LIMITED—See TotalEnergies SE; *Int'l*, pg. 7836
HUTCHISON 3G AUSTRIA GMBH—See CK Hutchison Holdings Limited; *Int'l*, pg. 1637
HUTCHISON AJMAN INTERNATIONAL TERMINALS LIMITED - F.Z.E—See CK Hutchison Holdings Limited; *Int'l*, pg. 1637
HUTCHISON ESSAR LIMITED—See CK Hutchison Holdings Limited; *Int'l*, pg. 1638
HUTCHISON ESSAR LIMITED—See Essar Global Limited; *Int'l*, pg. 2508
HUTCHISON HAYES SEPARATION INC.—See Alfa Laval AB; *Int'l*, pg. 309
HUTCHISON HOTEL HONG KONG LIMITED—See CK Asset Holdings Limited; *Int'l*, pg. 1635
HUTCHISON INCORPORATED; *U.S. Private*, pg. 2014
HUTCHISON KOREA TERMINALS LIMITED—See CK Hutchison Holdings Limited; *Int'l*, pg. 1637
HUTCHISON LAEMCHABANG TERMINAL LIMITED—See CK Hutchison Holdings Limited; *Int'l*, pg. 1637
HUTCHISON MINERALS COMPANY LTD.; *Int'l*, pg. 3540
HUTCHISON PORT HOLDINGS LIMITED—See CK Hutchison Holdings Limited; *Int'l*, pg. 1637
HUTCHISON PORT HOLDINGS TRUST; *Int'l*, pg. 3540
HUTCHISON PORTS SWEDEN AB—See CK Hutchison Holdings Limited; *Int'l*, pg. 1637
HUTCHISON TELECOMMUNICATIONS (AUSTRALIA) LIMITED—See CK Hutchison Holdings Limited; *Int'l*, pg. 1637
HUTCHISON TELECOMMUNICATIONS HONG KONG HOLDINGS LIMITED—See CK Hutchison Holdings Limited; *Int'l*, pg. 1638
HUTCHISON TELECOMMUNICATIONS INTERNATIONAL LTD.—See CK Hutchison Holdings Limited; *Int'l*, pg. 1638
HUTCHISON WHAMPOA PROPERTIES (CHENGDU) LIMITED—See CK Asset Holdings Limited; *Int'l*, pg. 1635
HUTCHISON WHAMPOA PROPERTIES (CHONGQING NANAN) LIMITED—See CK Asset Holdings Limited; *Int'l*, pg. 1635
HUTCHISON WHAMPOA PROPERTIES (QINGDAO) LIMITED—See CK Asset Holdings Limited; *Int'l*, pg. 1635
HUTCHISON WHAMPOA PROPERTIES (WUHAN JIANGHAN SOUTH) LIMITED—See CK Asset Holdings Limited; *Int'l*, pg. 1635
HUTCHMED (CHINA) LIMITED—See CK Hutchison Holdings Limited; *Int'l*, pg. 1637
HUTCO INC.; *U.S. Private*, pg. 2014
HUTECH NORIN CO., LTD.—See Chilled & Frozen Logis; *Int'l*, pg. 1479
HUTHWAITE INC.—See Providence Equity Partners L.L.C.; *U.S. Private*, pg. 3292
HUTMEN S.A.—See Boryszew S.A.; *Int'l*, pg. 1115
HUTS/JWT—See WPP plc; *Int'l*, pg. 8479
HUTSON, INC. - JASPER—See Hutson, Inc.; *U.S. Private*, pg. 2014
HUTSON, INC.; *U.S. Private*, pg. 2014
HUTSONS AG EQUIPMENT INCORPORATED; *U.S. Private*, pg. 2014
HUTTENBAU GESELLSCHAFT PEUTE MBH—See Aurubis AG; *Int'l*, pg. 715
HUTTENES ALBERTUS BELGIE N.V.—See Huettenes-Albertus Chemische Werke GmbH; *Int'l*, pg. 3523
HUTTENES ALBERTUS NEDERLAND B.V.—See Huettenes-Albertus Chemische Werke GmbH; *Int'l*, pg. 3523
HUTTENES-ALBERTUS POLSKA SP. Z.O.O.—See Huettenes-Albertus Chemische Werke GmbH; *Int'l*, pg. 3523
HUTTENES-ALBERTUS (UK) LTD.—See Huettenes-Albertus Chemische Werke GmbH; *Int'l*, pg. 3523
HUTTER AUFZUGE GMBH—See Otis Worldwide Corporation; *U.S. Public*, pg. 1623
HUTTER & SCHRANTZ AG—See Hutter & Schrantz PMS Ges.m.b.H; *Int'l*, pg. 3540
HUTTER & SCHRANTZ PMS GES.M.B.H; *Int'l*, pg. 3540
HUTTIG BUILDING PRODUCTS, INC.—See Woodgrain, Inc.; *U.S. Private*, pg. 4558
HUTTIG, INC.—See Woodgrain, Inc.; *U.S. Private*, pg. 4558
HUTTIG TEXAS LIMITED PARTNERSHIP—See Woodgrain, Inc.; *U.S. Private*, pg. 4558
HUTTLIN GMBH—See Robert Bosch GmbH; *Int'l*, pg. 6361
HUTTON COMMUNICATIONS INC.—See Rupe Investment Corporation; *U.S. Private*, pg. 3504
HUTTON CONSTRUCTION CORP.; *U.S. Private*, pg. 2015
HUTTO REFRIGERATION SALES & SERVICE, LLC.—See Freeman Spogli & Co. Incorporated; *U.S. Private*, pg. 1606
HUTZEL WOMEN'S HOSPITAL—See Tenet Healthcare Corporation; *U.S. Public*, pg. 2015
HUUKED LABS OY—See Telenor ASA; *Int'l*, pg. 7538
HUU LIEN ASIA CORPORATION; *Int'l*, pg. 3540
HUU NGHI VINH SINH MINING & MECHANIC JSC; *Int'l*, pg. 3540
HUVEPHARMA EOOD; *Int'l*, pg. 3540
HUVEPHARMA, INC.—See Huvepharma EOOD; *Int'l*, pg. 3540
HUVEPHARMA NV—See Huvepharma EOOD; *Int'l*, pg. 3540
HUVEXEL CO LTD; *Int'l*, pg. 3540
HUVIS CORPORATION; *Int'l*, pg. 3540
HUVITZ CO., LTD.; *Int'l*, pg. 3540
HUVUDKONTOR PEAB AB—See Peab AB; *Int'l*, pg. 5771
H.U. WELLNESS, INC.—See H.U. Group Holdings, Inc.; *Int'l*, pg. 3197
HUXEN CORPORATION; *Int'l*, pg. 3541
HUXLEY ASSOCIATES BELGIUM NV—See SThree Plc; *Int'l*, pg. 7214
HUXLEY ASSOCIATES LIMITED—See SThree Plc.; *Int'l*, pg. 7214
HUXLEY BV—See SThree Plc.; *Int'l*, pg. 7214
HUXLEY QUAYLE VON BISMARK, INC.; *Int'l*, pg. 3541
HUYA, INC.—See Tencent Holdings Limited; *Int'l*, pg. 7558
HUYCK ARGENTINA SA—See ANDRITZ AG; *Int'l*, pg. 457
HUYCK.WANGNER AUSTRALIA PTY. LIMITED—See ANDRITZ AG; *Int'l*, pg. 457
HUYCK.WANGNER AUSTRIA GMBH—See ANDRITZ AG; *Int'l*, pg. 457
HUYCK.WANGNER GERMANY GMBH—See ANDRITZ AG; *Int'l*, pg. 457
HUYCK.WANGNER ITALIA S.P.A—See ANDRITZ AG; *Int'l*, pg. 457
HUYCK.WANGNER JAPAN LIMITED - ASAHI PLANT—See ANDRITZ AG; *Int'l*, pg. 455
HUYCK.WANGNER JAPAN LIMITED—See ANDRITZ AG; *Int'l*, pg. 457
HUYCK.WANGNER UK LTD.—See ANDRITZ AG; *Int'l*, pg. 457
HUYNH BANG TRADING & ENGINEERING SERVICE CO., LTD.—See Max Weishaupt GmbH; *Int'l*, pg. 4735
HUY PLC; *Int'l*, pg. 3541
HUYSE ELCKERLYC NV—See Clariane SE; *Int'l*, pg. 1643
HUY THANG CONSTRUCTION JSC; *Int'l*, pg. 3541
HUZHOU AUCHAN HYPERMARKETS CO., LTD.—See Alibaba Group Holding Limited; *Int'l*, pg. 326
HUZHOU DIXI GENGDU ECOLOGICAL AGRICULTURE DEVELOPMENT CO., LTD.—See Asia-Pacific Strategic Investments Limited; *Int'l*, pg. 616
HUZHOU ENCHI AUTOMOTIVE CO., LTD.—See Minth Group Limited; *Int'l*, pg. 4914
HUZHOU IRON FORCE METAL PRODUCTS CO., LTD—See Iron Force Industrial Co., Ltd.; *Int'l*, pg. 3810
HUZHOU MEMTECH ELECTRONIC INDUSTRIES CO., LTD.—See Memtech International Ltd; *Int'l*, pg. 4814
HUZHOU SHANSHAN NEW ENERGY TECHNOLOGY CO., LTD.—See Ningbo Shanshan Co., Ltd.; *Int'l*, pg. 5305
HUZHOU SHIKIBO HAPPINESS TEXTILES CO., LTD.—See Shikibo Ltd.; *Int'l*, pg. 6829
HUZHOU XINFU NEW MATERIALS CO., LTD—See Yifan Pharmaceutical Co., Ltd.; *Int'l*, pg. 8582
HUZHOU YONGDA AOCHENG AUTOMOBILE SALES AND SERVICES CO., LTD.—See China Yongda Automobiles Services Holdings Limited; *Int'l*, pg. 1564
HUZHOU YONGDA AUTOMOBILE SALES AND SERVICES CO., LTD.—See China Yongda Automobiles Services Holdings Limited; *Int'l*, pg. 1564
HUZHOU YONGDA LUBAO AUTOMOBILE SALES AND SERVICES CO., LTD.—See China Yongda Automobiles Services Holdings Limited; *Int'l*, pg. 1564
HUZUR FAKTORING A.S.; *Int'l*, pg. 3541
HUZUR RADYO TELEVIZYON AS—See The Walt Disney Company; *U.S. Public*, pg. 2140
HVAC CONSOLIDATED PTY. LTD.—See Beijer Ref AB; *Int'l*, pg. 944
HVAC DISTRIBUTORS, INC.; *U.S. Private*, pg. 2015
HVAC ENGINEERING LIMITED—See Daikin Industries, Ltd.; *Int'l*, pg. 1935
HVAC SALES AND SUPPLY CO. INC.; *U.S. Private*, pg. 2015
HVAC STORES; *U.S. Private*, pg. 2015
HVAC SUPPLY—See Geary Pacific Corporation; *U.S. Private*, pg. 1655
HVAC TECHNOLOGIES, INC.; *U.S. Private*, pg. 2015
HVAC TECHNOLOGIES, INC.; *U.S. Private*, pg. 2015
HVA FOODS PLC—See Citrus Leisure PLC; *Int'l*, pg. 1626
HVA IMPORTS, LLC—See AutoNation, Inc.; *U.S. Public*, pg. 235
HVB AUTO LEASING EOOD—See UniCredit S.p.A.; *Int'l*, pg. 8038
HVB CAPITAL MARKETS, INC.—See UniCredit S.p.A.; *Int'l*, pg. 8038
HVB EXPORT LEASING GMBH—See UniCredit S.p.A.; *Int'l*, pg. 8038

HVB GESELLSCHAFT FUR GEBAUDE BETEILIGUNGS GMBH—See UniCredit S.p.A.; *Int'l*, pg. 8038
HVB IMMOBILIEN AG—See UniCredit S.p.A.; *Int'l*, pg. 8038
HVB-LEASING ATLANTIS INGATLANHASZNOSITO KORLATOLT FELELOSSEGU TARSASAG—See UniCredit S.p.A.; *Int'l*, pg. 8034
HVB LEASING GMBH—See UniCredit S.p.A.; *Int'l*, pg. 8038
HVB-LEASING SPORT INGATLANHASZNOSITO KOLATPOT FEOEOASSEGU TARSASAG—See UniCredit S.p.A.; *Int'l*, pg. 8036
H.V. BOWEN & SONS (QUARRY) LTD.—See Breedon Group plc; *Int'l*, pg. 1144
HVB PROFIL GESELLSCHAFT FUR PERSONALMANAGEMENT MBH—See UniCredit S.p.A.; *Int'l*, pg. 8039
HVB PROFIL GMBH—See UniCredit S.p.A.; *Int'l*, pg. 8034
HVB TECTA GMBH—See UniCredit S.p.A.; *Int'l*, pg. 8038
HVB TRUST PENSIONSFONDS AG—See UniCredit S.p.A.; *Int'l*, pg. 8039
H&V CARPETS B.V.B.A.—See Likewise Group Plc; *Int'l*, pg. 4478
HVCC HAMBURG VESSEL COORDINATION CENTER GMBH—See Hamburger Hafen und Logistik AG; *Int'l*, pg. 3236
HVC INVESTMENT & TECHNOLOGY JSC; *Int'l*, pg. 3541
H&V COLLISION CENTER - CLIFTON PARK—See H&V Collision Center; *U.S. Private*, pg. 1824
H&V COLLISION CENTER; *U.S. Private*, pg. 1824
HVD MEDICAL GMBH—See Medios AG; *Int'l*, pg. 4778
HV FOOD PRODUCTS COMPANY—See The Clorox Company; *U.S. Public*, pg. 2062
HV GLOBAL GROUP, INC.—See Marriott Vacations Worldwide Corporation; *U.S. Public*, pg. 1373
HVH PRECISION ANALYTICS LLC—See JLL Partners, LLC; *U.S. Private*, pg. 2212
HVH PRECISION ANALYTICS LLC—See Water Street Healthcare Partners, LLC; *U.S. Private*, pg. 4452
HVH TRANSPORTATION INC.; *U.S. Private*, pg. 2015
HVIDBJERG BANK A/S; *Int'l*, pg. 3541
HVI HANDELS- UND VERWERTUNGSGESELLSCHAFT FUR IMMOBILIEN MBH—See Commerzbank AG; *Int'l*, pg. 1718
HVIVO SERVICES LIMITED—See Open Orphan plc; *Int'l*, pg. 5596
HVL INC.; *U.S. Private*, pg. 2015
HV MANUFACTURING COMPANY—See The Clorox Company; *U.S. Public*, pg. 2062
HVM IMPORTS, LLC—See AutoNation, Inc.; *U.S. Public*, pg. 235
HVPH MOTOR CORPORATION—See Penske Automotive Group, Inc.; *U.S. Public*, pg. 1665
HVR CONSULTING SERVICES LIMITED—See QinetiQ Group plc; *Int'l*, pg. 6141
HVR GROUP—See Omnicom Group Inc.; *U.S. Public*, pg. 1596
HVS MOTORS, LLC—See AutoNation, Inc.; *U.S. Public*, pg. 235
HVT HANDEL VERTRIEB TRANSPORT GMBH—See Veolia Environnement S.A.; *Int'l*, pg. 8153
HV-TURBO ITALIA S.R.L.—See Siemens Aktiengesellschaft; *Int'l*, pg. 6887
HV YORK ROAD IMPORTS, LLC—See AutoNation, Inc.; *U.S. Public*, pg. 235
HVZ GMBH & CO. OBJEKT KG—See UniCredit S.p.A.; *Int'l*, pg. 8034
HWA AG; *Int'l*, pg. 3541
HWACHEON ASIA PACIFIC PTE LTD—See Hwacheon Machine Tool Co., Ltd.; *Int'l*, pg. 3541
HWACHEON MACHINERY AMERICA, INC.—See Hwacheon Machine Tool Co., Ltd.; *Int'l*, pg. 3542
HWACHEON MACHINERY CO., LTD.; *Int'l*, pg. 3542
HWACHEON MACHINERY EUROPE GMBH—See Hwacheon Machine Tool Co., Ltd.; *Int'l*, pg. 3542
HWACHEON MACHINE TOOL CO., LTD.; *Int'l*, pg. 3541
HWACHEON MACHINE TOOL VIETNAM CO., LTD.—See Hwacheon Machine Tool Co., Ltd.; *Int'l*, pg. 3541
HWACOM SYSTEMS, INC.; *Int'l*, pg. 3542
HWA CREATE CORPORATION LTD.; *Int'l*, pg. 3541
HWA FONG RUBBER (CHINA) CO., LTD.—See Hwa Fong Rubber Industry Co., Ltd.; *Int'l*, pg. 3541
HWA FONG RUBBER INDUSTRY CO., LTD.; *Int'l*, pg. 3541
HWA FONG RUBBER (SUZHOU) CO., LTD.—See Hwa Fong Rubber Industry Co., Ltd.; *Int'l*, pg. 3541
HWA FONG RUBBER (THAILAND) PUBLIC COMPANY LIMITED—See Hwa Fong Rubber Industry Co., Ltd.; *Int'l*, pg. 3541
HWA FONG RUBBER (U.S.A.) INC.—See Hwa Fong Rubber Industry Co., Ltd.; *Int'l*, pg. 3541
HWA HONG CORPORATION LIMITED; *Int'l*, pg. 3541
HWA HONG EDIBLE OIL INDUSTRIES PTE. LTD.—See Hwa Hong Corporation Limited; *Int'l*, pg. 3541
HWA HSIA COMPANY LTD.—See China Airlines Ltd.; *Int'l*, pg. 1482
HWAIL PHARMACEUTICAL CO.,LTD.; *Int'l*, pg. 3542
HWA INTERNATIONAL, INC.—See Banyan Software, Inc.; *U.S. Private*, pg. 470
HWAJIN CO., LTD.; *Int'l*, pg. 3542

HWA KOON ENGINEERING PTE. LTD.—See Hke Holdings Ltd.; *Int'l*, pg. 3428
HWANG CAPITAL (MALAYSIA) BERHAD; *Int'l*, pg. 3542
HWANG CHANG GENERAL CONTRACTOR CO., LTD.; *Int'l*, pg. 3542
HWANGDBS VICKERS RESEARCH SDN. BHD.—See Alliance Financial Group Berhad; *Int'l*, pg. 339
HWANGE COLLIERY COMPANY LIMITED; *Int'l*, pg. 3542
HWANG KUM STEEL & TECHNOLOGY CO., LTD.; *Int'l*, pg. 3542
HWAN YOUNG STEEL IND, CO., LTD.—See KISCO Holdings Corp.; *Int'l*, pg. 4192
HWASEUNG AMERICA CORP.—See Hwaseung Industries Co., Ltd.; *Int'l*, pg. 3542
HWASEUNG CLIMATE CONTROL INDUSTRIES CO., LTD.—See Hwaseung Industries Co., Ltd.; *Int'l*, pg. 3542
HWASEUNG ENTERPRISE CO., LTD—See Hwaseung Industries Co., Ltd.; *Int'l*, pg. 3542
HWASEUNG EXWILL—See Hwaseung Industries Co., Ltd.; *Int'l*, pg. 3542
HWASEUNG (H.K) LTD.—See Hwaseung Industries Co., Ltd.; *Int'l*, pg. 3542
HWASEUNG INDUSTRIES CO., LTD. - DONGGUAN FACTORY—See Hwaseung Industries Co., Ltd.; *Int'l*, pg. 3542
HWASEUNG INDUSTRIES CO., LTD.; *Int'l*, pg. 3542
HWASEUNG MATERIAL CO., LTD.—See Hwaseung Industries Co., Ltd.; *Int'l*, pg. 3542
HWASEUNG NETWORKS CO., LTD.—See Hwaseung Industries Co., Ltd.; *Int'l*, pg. 3542
HWASEUNG R&A CO., LTD.; *Int'l*, pg. 3542
HWASEUNG SAVINGS BANK—See DHSteel; *Int'l*, pg. 2100
HWASEUNG (SHANGHAI) INT'L TRADE CO., LTD.—See Hwaseung Industries Co., Ltd.; *Int'l*, pg. 3542
HWASEUNG T&C CO., LTD.—See Hwaseung Industries Co., Ltd.; *Int'l*, pg. 3542
HWASHIN AMERICA CORP.—See Hwashin Co., Ltd.; *Int'l*, pg. 3543
HWASHIN AUTOMOTIVE INDIA PVT., LTD.—See Hwashin Co., Ltd.; *Int'l*, pg. 3543
HWASHIN BRASIL CORP.—See Hwashin Co., Ltd.; *Int'l*, pg. 3543
HWASHIN CHEMICAL CO., LTD—See Pungguk Alcohol Industrial Co., Ltd; *Int'l*, pg. 6119
HWASHIN CO., LTD.; *Int'l*, pg. 3542
HWASHIN CO., LTD.—See Hwashin Co., Ltd.; *Int'l*, pg. 3543
HWASHIN PRECISION INDUSTRY CO., LTD.—See Hwashin Co., Ltd.; *Int'l*, pg. 3543
HWASHIN TECH CO., LTD.; *Int'l*, pg. 3543
HWASUNG INDUSTRIAL CO., LTD.; *Int'l*, pg. 3543
HWA TAI DISTRIBUTION SDN. BHD.—See Hwa Tai Industries Berhad; *Int'l*, pg. 3541
HWA TAI FOOD INDUSTRIES (SABAH) SDN.BHD.—See Hwa Tai Industries Berhad; *Int'l*, pg. 3541
HWA TAI INDUSTRIES BERHAD - BATU PAHAT FACTORY—See Hwa Tai Industries Berhad; *Int'l*, pg. 3541
HWA TAI INDUSTRIES BERHAD; *Int'l*, pg. 3541
HWATALEE G.M. (TAIWAN) CO., LTD.—See Yihua Lifestyle Technology Co., Ltd.; *Int'l*, pg. 8582
HWA TAT LEE JAPAN CO., LTD.—See Yihua Lifestyle Technology Co., Ltd.; *Int'l*, pg. 8582
HWA WELL TEXTILES (BD) LTD.; *Int'l*, pg. 3541
HWAXIN ENVIRONMENTAL CO., LTD.; *Int'l*, pg. 3543
HWB KUNSTSTOFFWERKE AG—See Ring International Holding AG; *Int'l*, pg. 6343
HWCA, PLLC—See HCA Healthcare, Inc.; *U.S. Public*, pg. 998
HWCC-TUNICA, LLC—See PENN Entertainment, Inc.; *U.S. Public*, pg. 1662
HW CREATIVE—See HW Publishing, LLC; *U.S. Private*, pg. 2015
H.W. DRUMMOND INC.; *U.S. Private*, pg. 1836
HWEECHAN CO., LTD.—See SK Inc.; *Int'l*, pg. 6971
H.WESTON & SONS LTD; *Int'l*, pg. 3199
H. WETERINGS-PLASTICS B.V.—See Hexatronic Group AB; *Int'l*, pg. 3370
HWGB BIOTECH SDN. BHD.—See Ho Wah Genting Berhad; *Int'l*, pg. 3435
HWGB EV SDN. BHD.—See Ho Wah Genting Berhad; *Int'l*, pg. 3435
HWGG ENTERTAINMENT LIMITED; *Int'l*, pg. 3543
HWH CORP.; *U.S. Private*, pg. 2015
H. W. HERRELL DISTRIBUTING COMPANY; *U.S. Private*, pg. 1825
HWH INVESTMENTS LIMITED; *Int'l*, pg. 3543
HW HOLDINGS, INC.; *U.S. Private*, pg. 2015
HWH PUBLIC RELATIONS; *U.S. Private*, pg. 2015
HWH PUBLIC RELATIONS—See HWH Public Relations; *U.S. Private*, pg. 2015
H.W. HUNTER INC.; *U.S. Private*, pg. 1836
H. WILSON COMPANY—See EBSCO Industries, Inc.; *U.S. Private*, pg. 1325
H. WILSON INDUSTRIES LTD; *Int'l*, pg. 3195
HWI PARTNERS, LLC; *U.S. Private*, pg. 2015
H.W. JENKINS COMPANY; *U.S. Private*, pg. 1836

H.W. KAUFMAN FINANCIAL GROUP, INC.; *U.S. Private*, pg. 1836
H.W. LOCHNER, INC.; *U.S. Private*, pg. 1836
H.W. MCKEVITT CO. INC.—See US Auto Group Limited; *U.S. Private*, pg. 4317
HW MCKEVITT CO. INC.—See US Auto Group Limited; *U.S. Private*, pg. 4317
HW MEDIA, LLC; *U.S. Private*, pg. 2015
HWM-WATER LIMITED—See Halma plc; *Int'l*, pg. 3231
H WORLD GROUP LIMITED; *Int'l*, pg. 3191
HWP CAIRO PLANNING & ENGINEERING CONSULTANT LTD.—See HWP Planungs GmbH; *Int'l*, pg. 3543
HWP ISTANBUL MIMARLIK MUHENDISLIK VE DANISMANLIK LTD. SIRKETI—See HWP Planungs GmbH; *Int'l*, pg. 3543
HWP PLANUNGS GMBH; *Int'l*, pg. 3543
HW PUBLISHING, LLC; *U.S. Private*, pg. 2015
HWRT OIL COMPANY, LLC.—See Piasa Motor Fuels LLC; *U.S. Private*, pg. 3175
HWS COMPANY INC.—See Sherrill Furniture Company Inc.; *U.S. Private*, pg. 3634
HWT, INC.—See UnitedHealth Group Incorporated; *U.S. Public*, pg. 2248
THE H.W. WILSON CO.—See EBSCO Industries, Inc.; *U.S. Private*, pg. 1325
HWW WIENBERG WILHELM RECHTSANWALTE PARTNERSCHAFT; *Int'l*, pg. 3543
HXF SAW CO., LTD.—See Advanced Technology & Materials Co., Ltd.; *Int'l*, pg. 162
HXMTD, S.A. DE C.V.—See Desarrolladora Homex, S.A. de C.V.; *Int'l*, pg. 2044
HYAC CORPORATION—See Y.A.C. HOLDINGS CO., LTD.; *Int'l*, pg. 8543
THE HYAKUGO BANK, LTD.; *Int'l*, pg. 7653
THE HYAKUJUSHI BANK, LTD.; *Int'l*, pg. 7653
HYAKUJUSHI DC CARD, K.K.—See The Hyakujushi Bank, Ltd.; *Int'l*, pg. 7654
HYAKUJUSHI GINKO KENKO HOKEN KUMIAI K.K.—See The Hyakujushi Bank, Ltd.; *Int'l*, pg. 7654
HYAKUJUSHI JINZAI CENTER, K.K.—See The Hyakujushi Bank, Ltd.; *Int'l*, pg. 7654
HYAKUJUSHI SOGO HOSHO K.K.—See The Hyakujushi Bank, Ltd.; *Int'l*, pg. 7654
HYALTECH LTD.—See Carl-Zeiss-Stiftung; *Int'l*, pg. 1336
HYAS & CO., INC.; *Int'l*, pg. 3544
HYAS GROUP—See Morgan Stanley; *U.S. Public*, pg. 1472
HYATT ARCADE, L.L.C.—See Hyatt Hotels Corporation; *U.S. Public*, pg. 1077
HYATT AUTOMOTIVE LLC; *U.S. Private*, pg. 2016
HYATT CHAIN SERVICES LIMITED—See Hyatt Hotels Corporation; *U.S. Public*, pg. 1077
HYATT CRYSTAL CITY, L.L.C.—See Hyatt Hotels Corporation; *U.S. Public*, pg. 1077
HYATT DIE CAST & ENGINEERING CORP.; *U.S. Private*, pg. 2016
HYATT GTLD, L.L.C.—See Hyatt Hotels Corporation; *U.S. Public*, pg. 1077
HYATT HOTELS CORPORATION OF MARYLAND—See Hyatt Hotels Corporation; *U.S. Public*, pg. 1077
HYATT HOTELS CORPORATION; *U.S. Public*, pg. 1076
HYATT HOTELS OF CANADA, INC.—See Hyatt Hotels Corporation; *U.S. Public*, pg. 1077
HYATT HOTELS OF FLORIDA, INC.—See Hyatt Hotels Corporation; *U.S. Public*, pg. 1077
HYATT INTERNATIONAL (EUROPE AFRICA MIDDLE EAST) LLC—See Hyatt Hotels Corporation; *U.S. Public*, pg. 1078
HYATT INTERNATIONAL (OSAKA) CORPORATION—See Hyatt Hotels Corporation; *U.S. Public*, pg. 1078
HYATT INTERNATIONAL - SOUTHWEST ASIA, LIMITED—See Hyatt Hotels Corporation; *U.S. Public*, pg. 1078
HYATT LEGAL PLANS, INC.—See MetLife, Inc.; *U.S. Public*, pg. 1430
HYATT MINNEAPOLIS, LLC—See Hyatt Hotels Corporation; *U.S. Public*, pg. 1078
HYATT REGENCY CAMBRIDGE—See Hyatt Hotels Corporation; *U.S. Public*, pg. 1078
HYATT REGENCY COLOGNE GMBH—See Hyatt Hotels Corporation; *U.S. Public*, pg. 1078
HYATT REGENCY COLUMBUS; *U.S. Private*, pg. 2016
HYATT REGENCY LAKE TAHOE RESORT & CASINO—See Hyatt Hotels Corporation; *U.S. Public*, pg. 1078
HYATT REGENCY ORLANDO—See Ares Management Corporation; *U.S. Public*, pg. 191
HYATT REGENCY ORLANDO—See RIDA Development Corp.; *U.S. Private*, pg. 3431
HYATT REGENCY OSAKA—See Hoshino Resorts Inc.; *Int'l*, pg. 3483
HYATT SERVICES GMBH—See Hyatt Hotels Corporation; *U.S. Public*, pg. 1078
HYATTSVILLE LAND CO., INC.—See The Hillman Company; *U.S. Private*, pg. 4053
HYBE CO., LTD.; *Int'l*, pg. 3544
HYBIO PHARMACEUTICAL CO., LTD.; *Int'l*, pg. 3544
HYBMM OVERSEAS, INC.; *U.S. Private*, pg. 2016

HY-BON ENGINEERING COMPANY, INC.—See Turnbridge Capital, LLC; *U.S. Private*, pg. 4260
HYBRICON CORPORATION—See ACS Integrated Systems, Inc.; *U.S. Private*, pg. 66
HYBRID ANALYSIS GMBH—See CrowdStrike Holdings, Inc.; *U.S. Public*, pg. 596
HYBRID BROADCAST BROADBAND TV—See Institut fur Rundfunktechnik GMBH; *Int'l*, pg. 3723
HYBRID COATING TECHNOLOGIES INC.; *U.S. Public*, pg. 1078
THE HYBRID CREATIVE LLC—See Greenlane Holdings, Inc.; *U.S. Public*, pg. 965
HYBRID ENERGY HOLDINGS, INC.; *U.S. Public*, pg. 1078
HYBRIDE TECHNOLOGIES INC.—See Ubisoft Entertainment S.A.; *Int'l*, pg. 8003
HYBRID FINANCIAL SERVICES LIMITED; *Int'l*, pg. 3544
HYBRIDGE COMMERCIAL REAL ESTATE; *U.S. Private*, pg. 2016
HYBRID (HONGKONG) CO., LTD.—See Pixel Companyz Inc.; *Int'l*, pg. 5877
HYBRID INTERNATIONAL TRADING (SHANGHAI) CO., LTD.—See Pixel Companyz Inc.; *Int'l*, pg. 5877
HYBRID KINETIC GROUP LIMITED; *Int'l*, pg. 3544
HYBRID LOGISTICS, INC.—See CAI International, Inc.; *U.S. Public*, pg. 421
HYBRID SOFTWARE GROUP PLC; *Int'l*, pg. 3544
HYBRID TRANSIT SYSTEMS, INC.; *U.S. Private*, pg. 2016
HYBRIGENICS PHARMA—See Diagnostic Medical Systems S.A.; *Int'l*, pg. 2103
HYBRIGENICS S.A.—See Diagnostic Medical Systems S.A.; *Int'l*, pg. 2103
HYBRIGENICS SERVICES—See Diagnostic Medical Systems S.A.; *Int'l*, pg. 2103
HYBTRONICS MICROSYSTEMS, S.A.; *Int'l*, pg. 3544
HYCAST AS—See Norsk Hydro ASA; *Int'l*, pg. 5432
HY CITE CORPORATION; *U.S. Private*, pg. 2015
HYCLONE UK LIMITED—See Thermo Fisher Scientific Inc.; *U.S. Public*, pg. 2148
HYCO INDUSTRIAL SALES CORP.—See Hyundai Group; *Int'l*, pg. 3557
HYCOMP, INC.; *U.S. Private*, pg. 2016
HYCOMP, LLC—See Compagnie de Saint-Gobain SA; *Int'l*, pg. 1731
HY CONNECT—See Myelin Health Communications, Inc.; *U.S. Private*, pg. 2824
HYCOR BIOMEDICAL GMBH—See Linden LLC; *U.S. Private*, pg. 2460
HYCOR BIOMEDICAL, INC.—See Linden LLC; *U.S. Private*, pg. 2460
HYCROFT MINING CORPORATION—See Hycroft Mining Holding Corporation; *U.S. Public*, pg. 1079
HYCROFT MINING HOLDING CORPORATION; *U.S. Public*, pg. 1078
HYCROFT RESOURCES & DEVELOPMENT, INC.—See Hycroft Mining Holding Corporation; *U.S. Public*, pg. 1079
HYDAC ACCESSORIES GMBH—See Hydac International GmbH; *Int'l*, pg. 3544
HYDAC AG—See Hydac International GmbH; *Int'l*, pg. 3544
HYDAC AS—See Hydac International GmbH; *Int'l*, pg. 3544
HYDAC A/S—See Hydac International GmbH; *Int'l*, pg. 3544
HYDAC BELARUS—See Hydac International GmbH; *Int'l*, pg. 3544
HYDAC B.V.—See Hydac International GmbH; *Int'l*, pg. 3544
HYDAC CO., LTD.—See Hydac International GmbH; *Int'l*, pg. 3545
HYDAC COOLING GMBH—See Hydac International GmbH; *Int'l*, pg. 3545
HYDAC CORPORATION, ACCUMULATOR DIVISION—See Hydac Technology Corporation; *U.S. Private*, pg. 2016
HYDAC CORPORATION—See Hydac International GmbH; *Int'l*, pg. 3544
HYDAC D.O.O.—See Hydac International GmbH; *Int'l*, pg. 3545
HYDAC D.O.O.—See Hydac International GmbH; *Int'l*, pg. 3545
HYDAC DRIVE CENTER GMBH—See Hydac International GmbH; *Int'l*, pg. 3545
HYDAC ELECTRONIC GMBH—See Hydac International GmbH; *Int'l*, pg. 3545
HYDAC ELECTRONIC, S.R.O.—See Hydac International GmbH; *Int'l*, pg. 3545
HYDAC ENGINEERING AG—See Hydac International GmbH; *Int'l*, pg. 3545
HYDAC EOOD—See Hydac International GmbH; *Int'l*, pg. 3544
HYDAC FILTERTECHNIK GMBH—See Hydac International GmbH; *Int'l*, pg. 3545
HYDAC FLUIDTECHNIK GMBH—See Hydac International GmbH; *Int'l*, pg. 3545
HYDAC FLUIDTEKNIK AB—See Hydac International GmbH; *Int'l*, pg. 3545
HYDAC HIDRAULIKA ES SZURESTSCHNIKA KFT.—See Hydac International GmbH; *Int'l*, pg. 3545
HYDAC HYDRAULIK GES.M.B.H.—See Hydac International GmbH; *Int'l*, pg. 3545
HYDAC (INDIA) PVT. LTD.—See Hydac International GmbH; *Int'l*, pg. 3544
HYDAC INTERNATIONAL GMBH; *Int'l*, pg. 3544
HYDAC INTERNATIONAL SA DE CV—See Hydac International GmbH; *Int'l*, pg. 3545
HYDAC KOREA CO. LTD.—See Hydac International GmbH; *Int'l*, pg. 3545
HYDAC LTD.—See Hydac International GmbH; *Int'l*, pg. 3545
HYDAC LTD. STI.—See Hydac International GmbH; *Int'l*, pg. 3545
HYDAC N.V.—See Hydac International GmbH; *Int'l*, pg. 3545
HYDAC OY—See Hydac International GmbH; *Int'l*, pg. 3545
HYDAC PROCESS TECHNOLOGY GMBH—See Hydac International GmbH; *Int'l*, pg. 3545
HYDAC PTY. LTD.—See Hydac International GmbH; *Int'l*, pg. 3545
HYDAC S.A.R.L.—See Hydac International GmbH; *Int'l*, pg. 3545
HYDAC SOFTWARE GMBH—See Hydac International GmbH; *Int'l*, pg. 3545
HYDAC S.P.A.—See Hydac International GmbH; *Int'l*, pg. 3545
HYDAC SPOL. S R.O.—See Hydac International GmbH; *Int'l*, pg. 3545
HYDAC SP. Z O.O.—See Hydac International GmbH; *Int'l*, pg. 3545
HYDAC S.R.O.—See Hydac International GmbH; *Int'l*, pg. 3545
HYDAC SYSTEMS & SERVICES GMBH—See Hydac International GmbH; *Int'l*, pg. 3545
HYDAC TECHNOLOGY ARGENTINA S.R.L.—See Hydac International GmbH; *Int'l*, pg. 3545
HYDAC TECHNOLOGY CORPORATION, ELECTRONIC DIVISION—See Hydac Technology Corporation; *U.S. Private*, pg. 2016
HYDAC TECHNOLOGY CORPORATION, HYCON DIVISION—See Hydac Technology Corporation; *U.S. Private*, pg. 2016
HYDAC TECHNOLOGY CORPORATION, HYDRAULIC DIVISION—See Hydac Technology Corporation; *U.S. Private*, pg. 2016
HYDAC TECHNOLOGY CORPORATION; *U.S. Private*, pg. 2016
HYDAC TECHNOLOGY GMBH—See Hydac International GmbH; *Int'l*, pg. 3545
HYDAC TECHNOLOGY (HONGKONG) LTD.—See Hydac International GmbH; *Int'l*, pg. 3545
HYDAC TECHNOLOGY LIMITED—See Hydac International GmbH; *Int'l*, pg. 3545
HYDAC TECHNOLOGY LTD.—See Hydac International GmbH; *Int'l*, pg. 3545
HYDAC TECHNOLOGY PTE. LTD.—See Hydac International GmbH; *Int'l*, pg. 3545
HYDAC TECHNOLOGY PTE. LTD.—See Hydac International GmbH; *Int'l*, pg. 3545
HYDAC TECHNOLOGY PTY LTD—See Hydac International GmbH; *Int'l*, pg. 3545
HYDAC TECHNOLOGY SDN. BHD.—See Hydac International GmbH; *Int'l*, pg. 3545
HYDAC TECHNOLOGY (SHANGHAI) LTD.—See Hydac International GmbH; *Int'l*, pg. 3545
HYDAC TECHNOLOGY SL—See Hydac International GmbH; *Int'l*, pg. 3545
HYDAC TECNOLOGIA CHILE LTDA—See Hydac International GmbH; *Int'l*, pg. 3545
HYDAC TECNOLOGIA LTDA—See Hydac International GmbH; *Int'l*, pg. 3545
HYDAC TECNOLOGIA, UNIPESSOAL, LDA.—See Hydac International GmbH; *Int'l*, pg. 3545
HYDAC UKRAINE—See Hydac International GmbH; *Int'l*, pg. 3545
HYDAL TRANSPORTSYSTEMER AS—See SKA Invest AS; *Int'l*, pg. 6976
HYDE DIALYSIS, LLC—See DaVita Inc.; *U.S. Public*, pg. 639
HYDE & HYDE INC.; *U.S. Private*, pg. 2016
HYDEL INC.—See Equistone Partners Europe Limited; *Int'l*, pg. 2487
HYDE MANUFACTURING COMPANY; *U.S. Private*, pg. 2016
HYDE PARK CAPITAL PARTNERS, LLC; *U.S. Private*, pg. 2016
HYDE PARK COMMUNICATIONS; *U.S. Private*, pg. 2017
HYDE PARK FACILITIES, INC.—See Wintrust Financial Corporation; *U.S. Public*, pg. 2375
HYDE PARK HOLDINGS LLC; *U.S. Private*, pg. 2017
HYDE PARK INC.; *U.S. Private*, pg. 2016
HYDE PARK SHOPPING CENTRE—See Hyprop Investments Limited; *Int'l*, pg. 3554
HYDE PARK SURGERY CENTER, LLC—See Tenet Healthcare Corporation; *U.S. Public*, pg. 2005
HYDERABAD STOCK EXCHANGE LIMITED; *Int'l*, pg. 3546
HYDER CONSULTING GMBH DEUTSCHLAND—See ARCADIS N.V.; *Int'l*, pg. 541
HYDER CONSULTING INDIA PVT LTD—See ARCADIS N.V.; *Int'l*, pg. 541
HYDE'S DISTRIBUTION; *Int'l*, pg. 3546
HYDE TOOLS, INC.; *U.S. Private*, pg. 2017
HYDINA ZK AS—See Agrofert Holding, a.s.; *Int'l*, pg. 219
HYDNET AB—See Indutrade AB; *Int'l*, pg. 3679
HYDOR-TECH LIMITED—See Pic Investment Group Inc.; *Int'l*, pg. 5859
HYDR8 WATER—See Eneco Refresh Limited; *Int'l*, pg. 2411
HYDRACO INDUSTRIES INC.; *Int'l*, pg. 3546
HYDRACT A/S; *Int'l*, pg. 3546
HYDRADYNE, LLC—See Applied Industrial Technologies, Inc.; *U.S. Public*, pg. 171
HYDRA DYNE TECHNOLOGY INC.—See Interpump Group S.p.A.; *Int'l*, pg. 3756
HYDRA-ELECTRIC COMPANY—See Loar Group, Inc.; *U.S. Private*, pg. 2477
THE HYDRAFACIAL COMPANY IBERIA, S.L.U.—See The Beauty Health Company; *U.S. Public*, pg. 2038
THE HYDRAFACIAL COMPANY JAPAN K.K.—See The Beauty Health Company; *U.S. Public*, pg. 2038
THE HYDRAFACIAL COMPANY MX, S. DE R.L. DE C.V.—See The Beauty Health Company; *U.S. Public*, pg. 2038
HYDRAFACIAL UK LIMITED—See The Beauty Health Company; *U.S. Public*, pg. 2038
HYDRAFLOW EQUIPMENT CO.; *U.S. Private*, pg. 2017
HYDRAFLOW INC.; *U.S. Private*, pg. 2017
HYDRA FLOW WEST INC.—See Atlas Copco AB; *Int'l*, pg. 682
HYDRAFORCE INC.; *U.S. Private*, pg. 2017
HYDRA-GRENE A/S—See Aktieselskabet Schouw & Co.; *Int'l*, pg. 266
HYDRA GRENE HYDRAULICS EQUIPMENT ACCESSORY (TIANJIN) CO. LTD—See Aktieselskabet Schouw & Co.; *Int'l*, pg. 266
HYDRA GRENE INDIA PRIVATE LIMITED—See Aktieselskabet Schouw & Co.; *Int'l*, pg. 266
HYDRA GROUP, INC.—See Adknowledge, Inc.; *U.S. Private*, pg. 80
HYDRALIFT AS—See NOV, Inc.; *U.S. Public*, pg. 1545
HYDRALIFT FRANCE SAS—See NOV, Inc.; *U.S. Public*, pg. 1545
HYDRALIGN—See Butler Automatic, Inc.; *U.S. Private*, pg. 696
HYDRA MANAGEMENT LIMITED—See eTask Technologies Limited; *Int'l*, pg. 2520
HYDRA-MATIC PACKING COMPANY; *U.S. Private*, pg. 2017
HYDRANAUTICS—See Nitto Denko Corporation; *Int'l*, pg. 5387
HYDRA PLATFORMS MFG. INC.—See Terex Corporation; *U.S. Public*, pg. 2019
HYDRAPOWER DYNAMICS LIMITED—See Park-Ohio Holdings Corp.; *U.S. Public*, pg. 1639
HYDRA-POWER SYSTEMS INC.; *U.S. Private*, pg. 2017
HYDRAQUIP CUSTOM SYSTEMS, INC.—See Employee Owned Holdings, Inc.; *U.S. Private*, pg. 1386
HYDRAQUIP DISTRIBUTION, INC.—See Employee Owned Holdings, Inc.; *U.S. Private*, pg. 1386
HYDRASEARCH COMPANY, INC.—See Dixon Valve & Coupling Company; *U.S. Private*, pg. 1246
HYDRASPECMA COMPONENTS AB—See Aktieselskabet Schouw & Co.; *Int'l*, pg. 266
HYDRASPECMA DO BRAZIL LTDA.—See Aktieselskabet Schouw & Co.; *Int'l*, pg. 266
HYDRASPECMA HYDRAULIC SYSTEMS (TIANJIN) CO., LTD.—See Aktieselskabet Schouw & Co.; *Int'l*, pg. 266
HYDRASPECMA HYDRAULIKHUSET AB—See Aktieselskabet Schouw & Co.; *Int'l*, pg. 266
HYDRASPECMA INDIA PRIVATE LTD.—See Aktieselskabet Schouw & Co.; *Int'l*, pg. 266
HYDRASPECMA NORGE AS—See Aktieselskabet Schouw & Co.; *Int'l*, pg. 266
HYDRASPECMA OY—See Aktieselskabet Schouw & Co.; *Int'l*, pg. 266
HYDRASPECMA SAMWON LTD.—See Aktieselskabet Schouw & Co.; *Int'l*, pg. 266
HYDRASPECMA USA INC.—See Aktieselskabet Schouw & Co.; *Int'l*, pg. 266
HYDRASPECMA WIRO AB—See Aktieselskabet Schouw & Co.; *Int'l*, pg. 266
HYDRA-STOP, INC.—See IDEX Corp; *U.S. Public*, pg. 1089
HYDRATANE OF ATHENS—See UGI Corporation; *U.S. Public*, pg. 2221
HYDRA TECH A/S—See BWB Partners P/S; *Int'l*, pg. 1232
HYDRATECH, LLC—See Ligon Industries LLC; *U.S. Private*, pg. 2455
HYDRATEC INDUSTRIES NV; *Int'l*, pg. 3546
HYDRATIGHT BV—See Enerpac Tool Group Corp.; *U.S. Public*, pg. 766

HYDRATIGHT EQUIPAMENTOS SERVICOS E INDUSTRIA LTDA.—See Enerpac Tool Group Corp.; *U.S. Public*, pg. 766
HYDRATIGHT FZE—See Enerpac Tool Group Corp.; *U.S. Public*, pg. 766
HYDRATIGHT INJECTASEAL DEUTSCHLAND GMBH—See Enerpac Tool Group Corp.; *U.S. Public*, pg. 766
HYDRATIGHT LTD.—See Enerpac Tool Group Corp.; *U.S. Public*, pg. 766
HYDRATIGHT NORGE AS—See Enerpac Tool Group Corp.; *U.S. Public*, pg. 766
HYDRATIGHT OPERATIONS, INC.—See Enerpac Tool Group Corp.; *U.S. Public*, pg. 766
HYDRATIGHT PTE. LTD.—See Enerpac Tool Group Corp.; *U.S. Public*, pg. 766
HYDRAULEX INTERNATIONAL HOLDINGS LTD.—See Clearlake Capital Group, L.P.; *U.S. Private*, pg. 933
HYDRAULIC CONTROLS, INC.; *U.S. Private*, pg. 2017
HYDRAULIC ELEMENTS & SYSTEMS PLC; *Int'l*, pg. 3546
HYDRAULIC REPAIR AND DESIGN, INC.—See Clearlake Capital Group, L.P.; *U.S. Private*, pg. 933
HYDRAULICS INTERNATIONAL, INC. - PUMPS DIVISION—See Hydraulics International, Inc.; *U.S. Private*, pg. 2017
HYDRAULICS INTERNATIONAL, INC.; *U.S. Private*, pg. 2017
HYDRAULIC SPECIALISTS AUSTRALIA PTY. LTD.; *Int'l*, pg. 3546
HYDRAULICS & TRANSMISSIONS LIMITED—See Flowtech Fluidpower plc; *Int'l*, pg. 2709
HYDRAULIKSERVICE I MARKARYD AB—See NIBE Industrier AB; *Int'l*, pg. 5261
HYDRA-ZORB CO.—See TruArc Partners, L.P.; *U.S. Private*, pg. 4245
HYDREKA ENOVEO SAS—See Halma plc; *Int'l*, pg. 3232
HYDREKA S.A.—See Halma plc; *Int'l*, pg. 3232
HYDREL GMBH—See INA-Holding Schaeffler GmbH & Co. KG; *Int'l*, pg. 3640
HYDREUTES, S.A.U.—See Seika Corporation; *Int'l*, pg. 6685
HYDRIL PRIVATE LTD—See General Electric Company; *U.S. Public*, pg. 919
HYDRITE CHEMICAL COMPANY - COTTAGE GROVE PLANT—See Hydrite Chemical Company; *U.S. Private*, pg. 2017
HYDRITE CHEMICAL COMPANY - LACROSSE PLANT—See Hydrite Chemical Company; *U.S. Private*, pg. 2017
HYDRITE CHEMICAL COMPANY - MILWAUKEE PLANT—See Hydrite Chemical Company; *U.S. Private*, pg. 2017
HYDRITE CHEMICAL COMPANY - OSHKOSH PLANT—See Hydrite Chemical Company; *U.S. Private*, pg. 2017
HYDRITE CHEMICAL COMPANY; *U.S. Private*, pg. 2017
HYDRITE CHEMICAL COMPANY - TERRE HAUTE PLANT—See Hydrite Chemical Company; *U.S. Private*, pg. 2017
HYDRITE CHEMICAL COMPANY - WATERLOO PLANT—See Hydrite Chemical Company; *U.S. Private*, pg. 2017
HYDRITE CHEMICAL COMPANY - WAUSAU PLANT—See Hydrite Chemical Company; *U.S. Private*, pg. 2017
HYDRIX LIMITED; *Int'l*, pg. 3546
HYDRO-AIR COMPONENTS, INC.—See Zehnder Group AG; *Int'l*, pg. 8630
HYDRO-AIRE INC.—See Crane NXT, Co.; *U.S. Public*, pg. 589
HYDROAIR HUGHES, LLC—See Applied Industrial Technologies, Inc.; *U.S. Public*, pg. 171
HYDROAIR INTERNATIONAL A/S—See AEA Investors LP; *U.S. Private*, pg. 113
HYDRO AIR LLC—See Applied Industrial Technologies, Inc.; *U.S. Public*, pg. 171
HYDRO ALLUMINIO ATESSA S.P.A.—See Norsk Hydro ASA; *Int'l*, pg. 5432
HYDRO ALLUMINIO LA ROCA S.A.—See Norsk Hydro ASA; *Int'l*, pg. 5432
HYDRO ALLUMINIO ORNAGO S.P.A.—See Norsk Hydro ASA; *Int'l*, pg. 5432
HYDRO ALUMINIO AZUQUECA S.A.—See Norsk Hydro ASA; *Int'l*, pg. 5432
HYDRO ALUMINIO LA ROCA S.A.—See Norsk Hydro ASA; *Int'l*, pg. 5433
HYDRO ALUMINIUM ARDAL—See Norsk Hydro ASA; *Int'l*, pg. 5433
HYDRO ALUMINIUM ARGENTINA S.A.—See Norsk Hydro ASA; *Int'l*, pg. 5433
HYDRO ALUMINIUM AS KARMOY CARBON—See Norsk Hydro ASA; *Int'l*, pg. 5433
HYDRO ALUMINIUM AS—See Norsk Hydro ASA; *Int'l*, pg. 5433
HYDRO ALUMINIUM AS SUNNDAL CARBON—See Norsk Hydro ASA; *Int'l*, pg. 5433
HYDRO ALUMINIUM AUSTRALIA PTY. LTD.—See Norsk Hydro ASA; *Int'l*, pg. 5433
HYDRO ALUMINIUM BELLENBERG GMBH—See Norsk Hydro ASA; *Int'l*, pg. 5433
HYDRO ALUMINIUM CANADA, INC.—See Norsk Hydro ASA; *Int'l*, pg. 5433
HYDRO ALUMINIUM CHATEAUROUX S.N.C.—See Norsk Hydro ASA; *Int'l*, pg. 5433
HYDRO ALUMINIUM CHRZANOW SP. Z. O.O.—See Norsk Hydro ASA; *Int'l*, pg. 5433
HYDRO ALUMINIUM CLERVAUX S.A.—See Norsk Hydro ASA; *Int'l*, pg. 5433
HYDRO ALUMINIUM COLORS SRL—See Norsk Hydro ASA; *Int'l*, pg. 5433
HYDRO ALUMINIUM DEESIDE LTD.—See Norsk Hydro ASA; *Int'l*, pg. 5433
HYDRO ALUMINIUM DEUTSCHLAND GMBH—See Norsk Hydro ASA; *Int'l*, pg. 5433
HYDRO ALUMINIUM DEUTSCHLAND GMBH—See Norsk Hydro ASA; *Int'l*, pg. 5433
HYDRO ALUMINIUM DORMAGEN GMBH—See Norsk Hydro ASA; *Int'l*, pg. 5433
HYDRO ALUMINIUM EXPA SA—See Norsk Hydro ASA; *Int'l*, pg. 5435
HYDRO ALUMINIUM EXTRUSION DEUTSCHLAND GMBH—See Norsk Hydro ASA; *Int'l*, pg. 5433
HYDRO ALUMINIUM FABRICATION (TAICANG) CO. LTD.—See Norsk Hydro ASA; *Int'l*, pg. 5433
HYDRO ALUMINIUM FRANCE S.A.S.—See Norsk Hydro ASA; *Int'l*, pg. 5433
HYDRO ALUMINIUM GIESSEREI RACKWITZ GMBH—See Norsk Hydro ASA; *Int'l*, pg. 5433
HYDRO ALUMINIUM HIGH PURITY GMBH—See Norsk Hydro ASA; *Int'l*, pg. 5433
HYDRO ALUMINIUM HOYANGER VERK—See Norsk Hydro ASA; *Int'l*, pg. 5433
HYDRO ALUMINIUM INTERNATIONAL S.A.—See Norsk Hydro ASA; *Int'l*, pg. 5433
HYDRO ALUMINIUM ITC S.N.C.—See Norsk Hydro ASA; *Int'l*, pg. 5433
HYDRO ALUMINIUM KURRI KURRI PTY LTD.—See Norsk Hydro ASA; *Int'l*, pg. 5433
HYDRO ALUMINIUM MALAYSIA SDN. BHD.—See Norsk Hydro ASA; *Int'l*, pg. 5433
HYDRO ALUMINIUM METAL PRODUCTS S.R.L.—See Norsk Hydro ASA; *Int'l*, pg. 5433
HYDRO ALUMINIUM NENZING GMBH—See Norsk Hydro ASA; *Int'l*, pg. 5433
HYDRO ALUMINIUM PROFILER AS KARMOY—See Norsk Hydro ASA; *Int'l*, pg. 5433
HYDRO ALUMINIUM PROFILER AS—See Norsk Hydro ASA; *Int'l*, pg. 5433
HYDRO ALUMINIUM RAEREN SA - NV—See Norsk Hydro ASA; *Int'l*, pg. 5433
HYDRO ALUMINIUM ROLLED PRODUCTS AS HOLMESTRAND—See Norsk Hydro ASA; *Int'l*, pg. 5433
HYDRO ALUMINIUM ROLLED PRODUCTS AS KARMOY—See Norsk Hydro ASA; *Int'l*, pg. 5433
HYDRO ALUMINIUM ROLLED PRODUCTS BENELUX BV—See Norsk Hydro ASA; *Int'l*, pg. 5433
HYDRO ALUMINIUM ROLLED PRODUCTS DENMARK A.S—See Norsk Hydro ASA; *Int'l*, pg. 5434
HYDRO ALUMINIUM ROLLED PRODUCTS GMBH—See Norsk Hydro ASA; *Int'l*, pg. 5434
HYDRO ALUMINIUM ROLLED PRODUCTS IBERIA S.L.U.—See Norsk Hydro ASA; *Int'l*, pg. 5434
HYDRO ALUMINIUM ROLLED PRODUCTS LTD.—See Norsk Hydro ASA; *Int'l*, pg. 5434
HYDRO ALUMINIUM ROLLED PRODUCTS POLSKA SP. Z O.O.—See Norsk Hydro ASA; *Int'l*, pg. 5434
HYDRO ALUMINIUM SALES AND TRADING S.N.C.—See Norsk Hydro ASA; *Int'l*, pg. 5434
HYDRO ALUMINIUM SALES AND TRADING UK—See Norsk Hydro ASA; *Int'l*, pg. 5434
HYDRO ALUMINIUM SALKO OY—See Norsk Hydro ASA; *Int'l*, pg. 5434
HYDRO ALUMINIUM S.A.—See Norsk Hydro ASA; *Int'l*, pg. 5434
HYDRO ALUMINIUM SENEFFE S.A.—See Norsk Hydro ASA; *Int'l*, pg. 5434
HYDRO ALUMINIUM SUOMI OY—See Norsk Hydro ASA; *Int'l*, pg. 5434
HYDRO ALUMINIUM (SUZHOU) CO. LTD.—See Norsk Hydro ASA; *Int'l*, pg. 5433
HYDRO ALUMINIUM SVERIGE AB (TYRESO)—See Norsk Hydro ASA; *Int'l*, pg. 5434
HYDRO ALUMINIUM SYSTEMS HELLAS S.A.—See Norsk Hydro ASA; *Int'l*, pg. 5434
HYDRO ALUMINIUM TAIWAN CO LTD—See Norsk Hydro ASA; *Int'l*, pg. 5434
HYDRO ALUMINIUM UK LTD—See Norsk Hydro ASA; *Int'l*, pg. 5434
HYDRO ALUMINIUM VEKST—See Norsk Hydro ASA; *Int'l*, pg. 5434
HYDRO ALUMINIUM WALZPRODUKTE AG—See Norsk Hydro ASA; *Int'l*, pg. 5434
HYDRO ALUMINIUM AS—See Norsk Hydro ASA; *Int'l*, pg. 5434
HYDRO ALUMINUM CIS A.S. MOSCOW—See Norsk Hydro ASA; *Int'l*, pg. 5434
HYDRO ALUMINUM JAPAN KK—See Norsk Hydro ASA; *Int'l*, pg. 5434
HYDRO ALUMINUM LUCE S.N.C.—See Norsk Hydro ASA; *Int'l*, pg. 5434
HYDRO ALUMINUM MALAYSIA SDN. BHD.—See Norsk Hydro ASA; *Int'l*, pg. 5434
HYDRO ALUMINUM METAL PRODUCTS NORTH AMERICA INC.—See Norsk Hydro ASA; *Int'l*, pg. 5434
HYDRO ALUMINUM NORTH AMERICA INC.—See Norsk Hydro ASA; *Int'l*, pg. 5434
HYDRO ALUMINUM REYNOSA, S. DE R.L. DE C.V.—See Norsk Hydro ASA; *Int'l*, pg. 5434
HYDRO ALUMINUM USA, INC.—See Norsk Hydro ASA; *Int'l*, pg. 5434
HYDRO ALUNOVA LOGUMKLOSTER A/S—See Norsk Hydro ASA; *Int'l*, pg. 5434
HYDRO AUTOMOTIVE STRUCTURES ALUNORD SARL—See Norsk Hydro ASA; *Int'l*, pg. 5434
HYDRO AUTOMOTIVE STRUCTURES NORTH AMERICA, INC.—See Norsk Hydro ASA; *Int'l*, pg. 5434
HYDRO BELEM—See Norsk Hydro ASA; *Int'l*, pg. 5434
HYDROBUDOWA-6 S.A.—See Bilfinger SE; *Int'l*, pg. 1026
HYDROBUDOWA 9 S.A.—See PBG S.A.; *Int'l*, pg. 5765
HYDRO BUILDING SYSTEMS (BEIJING) CO. LTD.—See Norsk Hydro ASA; *Int'l*, pg. 5434
HYDRO BUILDING SYSTEMS CO. LTD—See Norsk Hydro ASA; *Int'l*, pg. 5434
HYDRO BUILDING SYSTEMS GMBH—See Norsk Hydro ASA; *Int'l*, pg. 5434
HYDRO BUILDING SYSTEMS GMBH—See Norsk Hydro ASA; *Int'l*, pg. 5434
HYDRO BUILDING SYSTEMS IBERIA—See Norsk Hydro ASA; *Int'l*, pg. 5434
HYDRO BUILDING SYSTEMS KFT.—See Norsk Hydro ASA; *Int'l*, pg. 5434
HYDRO BUILDING SYSTEMS LTD.—See Norsk Hydro ASA; *Int'l*, pg. 5434
HYDRO BUILDING SYSTEMS N.V.—See Norsk Hydro ASA; *Int'l*, pg. 5434
HYDRO BUILDING SYSTEMS OU—See Norsk Hydro ASA; *Int'l*, pg. 5434
HYDRO BUILDING SYSTEMS PRIVATE LIMITED—See Norsk Hydro ASA; *Int'l*, pg. 5434
HYDRO BUILDING SYSTEMS SA—See Norsk Hydro ASA; *Int'l*, pg. 5435
HYDRO BUILDING SYSTEMS S.L.—See Norsk Hydro ASA; *Int'l*, pg. 5434
HYDRO BUILDING SYSTEMS SLU—See Norsk Hydro ASA; *Int'l*, pg. 5435
HYDRO BUILDING SYSTEMS—See Norsk Hydro ASA; *Int'l*, pg. 5434
HYDRO BUILDING SYSTEMS SOUTH EAST ASIA—See Norsk Hydro ASA; *Int'l*, pg. 5434
HYDRO BUILDING SYSTEMS SOUTHWEST, S.L.U.—See Norsk Hydro ASA; *Int'l*, pg. 5435
HYDRO BUILDING SYSTEMS SPA—See Norsk Hydro ASA; *Int'l*, pg. 5435
HYDRO BUILDING SYSTEMS SP. Z. O. O.—See Norsk Hydro ASA; *Int'l*, pg. 5435
HYDRO CAPITAL CORPORATION—See Mitsui & Co., Ltd.; *Int'l*, pg. 4975
HYDRO CARBIDE, INC. - GULFPORT FACILITY—See HBD Industries, Inc.; *U.S. Private*, pg. 1887
HYDRO CARBIDE, INC. - LATROBE FACILITY—See HBD Industries, Inc.; *U.S. Private*, pg. 1887
HYDRO CARBIDE INC.—See HBD Industries, Inc.; *U.S. Private*, pg. 1887
HYDROCARBON DYNAMICS LIMITED; *Int'l*, pg. 3547
HYDROCARBURE TUNISIE CORP.—See PA Resources AB; *Int'l*, pg. 5684
HYDROCAR CHILE S.A.—See Interpump Group S.p.A.; *Int'l*, pg. 3756
HYDROCAR INDUSTRIE NV—See VINCI S.A.; *Int'l*, pg. 8222
HYDROCAR MODERNA S.P.A.—See Interpump Group S.p.A.; *Int'l*, pg. 3756
HYDROCAR ROMA S.R.L.—See Interpump Group S.p.A.; *Int'l*, pg. 3756
HYDROCHEM ENGINEERING (SHANGHAI) CO., LTD.—See Hyflux Ltd; *Int'l*, pg. 3548
HYDROCHEM ENGINEERING (S) PTE LTD—See Hyflux Ltd; *Int'l*, pg. 3548
HYDROCHEM ITALIA S.R.L.—See International Chemical Investors S.E.; *Int'l*, pg. 3745
HYDROCHEM (S) PTE LTD—See Hyflux Ltd; *Int'l*, pg. 3548
HYDROCHINA CORPORATION—See Power Construction Corporation of China; *Int'l*, pg. 5943
HYDRO CONSULTANTS INC.—See Atwell, LLC; *U.S. Private*, pg. 384
HYDROCONSULT GMBH—See BKW AG; *Int'l*, pg. 1055
HYDRO CONSULTING & MAINTENANCE SERVICES, INC.; *U.S. Private*, pg. 2017
HYDROCOOP, SPOL. S R.O.—See Sweco AB; *Int'l*, pg. 7363
HYDRODEC AUSTRALIA PTY. LTD.—See Hydrodec Group plc; *Int'l*, pg. 3547
HYDRODEC DEVELOPMENT CORPORATION PTY LIMITED—See Hydrodec Group plc; *Int'l*, pg. 3547

HYDRODEC GROUP PLC

HYDRODEC GROUP PLC; *Int'l*, pg. 3547
HYDRODEC NORTH AMERICA LLP—See Hydrodec Group plc; *Int'l*, pg. 3547
HYDRODEC NORTH AMERICAN HOLDINGS INC—See Hydrodec Group plc; *Int'l*, pg. 3547
HYDRO DEVELOPMENT GROUP INC.—See Enel S.p.A.; *Int'l*, pg. 2411
HYDROELECTRICITY INVESTMENT & DEVELOPMENT COMPANY LTD.; *Int'l*, pg. 3547
HYDRO ELLAY ENFIELD LTD.—See Norsk Hydro ASA; *Int'l*, pg. 5435
HYDRO ENERGI ARDAL—See Norsk Hydro ASA; *Int'l*, pg. 5435
HYDRO ENERGIES CORPORATION—See Enel S.p.A.; *Int'l*, pg. 2414
HYDRO ENERGI ROLDAL-SULDAL—See Norsk Hydro ASA; *Int'l*, pg. 5435
HYDRO ENERGI SOGN—See Norsk Hydro ASA; *Int'l*, pg. 5435
HYDRO ENERGY A.S.—See Norsk Hydro ASA; *Int'l*, pg. 5435
HYDRO EXPLOITATION SA; *Int'l*, pg. 3546
HYDRO EXTRUSION DENMARK A/S—See Norsk Hydro ASA; *Int'l*, pg. 5435
HYDRO EXTRUSION RAEREN SA—See Norsk Hydro ASA; *Int'l*, pg. 5435
HYDROFARM HOLDINGS GROUP, INC.; *U.S. Public*, pg. 1079
HYDRO FITTING MANUFACTURING CORP.—See KKR & Co. Inc.; *U.S. Public*, pg. 1262
HYDROFLEX-HYDRAULICS BELGIUM NV—See Flowtech Fluidpower plc; *Int'l*, pg. 2709
HYDROFLEX-HYDRAULICS BV—See Flowtech Fluidpower plc; *Int'l*, pg. 2709
HYDROFLEX-HYDRAULICS ROTTERDAM BV—See Flowtech Fluidpower plc; *Int'l*, pg. 2709
HYDRO GATE, LLC—See Mueller Water Products, Inc.; *U.S. Public*, pg. 1485
HYDRO-GEAR EUROPE BVBA—See Danfoss A/S; *Int'l*, pg. 1960
HYDRO-GEAR, INC.—See Danfoss A/S; *Int'l*, pg. 1960
HYDROGEL VISION CORP.—See Clerio Vision Inc.; *U.S. Private*, pg. 940
HYDROGENE DE FRANCE SA; *Int'l*, pg. 3547
HYDROGEN ENERGY CO., LTD.—See Fujian Snowman Co., Ltd.; *Int'l*, pg. 2819
HYDROGEN ENGINEERING AUSTRALIA PTY LTD—See Kawasaki Heavy Industries, Ltd.; *Int'l*, pg. 4095
HYDROGEN FUTURE CORPORATION; *U.S. Private*, pg. 2017
HYDROGEN GROUP PLC; *Int'l*, pg. 3547
HYDROGEN GROUP PTY. LIMITED—See Hydrogen Group Plc; *Int'l*, pg. 3547
HYDROGEN GROUP SDN. BHD.—See Hydrogen Group Plc; *Int'l*, pg. 3547
HYDROGENICS CORPORATION—See Cummins Inc.; *U.S. Public*, pg. 607
HYDROGENICS EUROPE N.V.—See Cummins Inc.; *U.S. Public*, pg. 607
HYDROGENICS TEST SYSTEMS—See Cummins Inc.; *U.S. Public*, pg. 607
HYDROGENICS USA, INC.—See Cummins Inc.; *U.S. Public*, pg. 607
HYDROGEN INTERNATIONAL LIMITED—See Hydrogen Group Plc; *Int'l*, pg. 3547
HYDROGENONE CAPITAL GROWTH PLC; *Int'l*, pg. 3547
HYDROGEN PARK MARGHERA PER L'IDROGENO SCRL—See Enel S.p.A.; *Int'l*, pg. 2414
HYDROGENPRO A.S.; *Int'l*, pg. 3547
HYDROGEN REFUELING SOLUTIONS SA; *Int'l*, pg. 3547
HYDROGEN UK LIMITED—See Hydrogen Group Plc; *Int'l*, pg. 3547
HYDROGEN UTOPIA INTERNATIONAL PLC; *Int'l*, pg. 3547
HYDROGEOPHYSICS, INC.; *U.S. Private*, pg. 2017
HYDROGEO SRL—See Societa Esercizi Commerciali Industriali; *Int'l*, pg. 7034
HYDROGRAPH CLEAN POWER INC.; *Int'l*, pg. 3547
HYDROGREEN INC.—See CubicFarm Systems Corp.; *Int'l*, pg. 1875
HYDROID EUROPE—See Huntington Ingalls Industries, Inc.; *U.S. Public*, pg. 1072
HYDROID, INC.—See Huntington Ingalls Industries, Inc.; *U.S. Public*, pg. 1072
HYDRO INNOVATIONS, LLC—See CEA Industries Inc.; *U.S. Public*, pg. 463
HYDRO INTERNATIONAL LIMITED—See CRH plc; *Int'l*, pg. 1846
HYDRO KAPITALFORVALTNING AS—See Norsk Hydro ASA; *Int'l*, pg. 5435
HYDROKIT; *Int'l*, pg. 3548
HYDROKIT UK LTD—See Hydrokit; *Int'l*, pg. 3548
HYDROLEVEL COMPANY—See C. Cowles & Co.; *U.S. Private*, pg. 705
HYDRO LITHIUM INC; *Int'l*, pg. 3546
HYDRO-LOGIC ASSOCIATES, INC.; *U.S. Private*, pg. 2017
HYDROLOGIC DISTRIBUTION COMPANY—See Winsupply, Inc.; *U.S. Private*, pg. 4545

HYDROMAC ENERGY BV—See Enel S.p.A.; *Int'l*, pg. 2414
HYDRO MAGUS PRIVATE LIMITED—See Power Mech Projects Ltd.; *Int'l*, pg. 5946
HYDROMASHSERVICE JSC—See HMS Hydraulic Machines & Systems Group plc; *Int'l*, pg. 3432
HYDRO MATERIAL OY—See Addtech AB; *Int'l*, pg. 133
HYDROMATIC PENTAIR—See Pentair plc; *Int'l*, pg. 5790
HYDROMAT INC.; *U.S. Private*, pg. 2018
HYDROMATION FRANCE S.A.R.L.—See Mann+Hummel GmbH; *Int'l*, pg. 4673
HYDROMAX PLUMBING, INC.—See Gallant Capital Partners, LLC; *U.S. Private*, pg. 1639
HYDROMAX USA, LLC—See Gallant Capital Partners, LLC; *U.S. Private*, pg. 1639
HYDROMELIORACIE AS; *Int'l*, pg. 3548
HYDROMER, INC.; *U.S. Public*, pg. 1079
HYDROMETAL S.R.L.—See Interpump Group S.p.A.; *Int'l*, pg. 3756
HYDROMET CORPORATION LIMITED; *Int'l*, pg. 3548
HYDROMET CORPORATION PTY LIMITED - SOUTHERN, NSW—See Hydromet Corporation Limited; *Int'l*, pg. 3548
HYDROMET OPERATIONS LIMITED—See Hydromet Corporation Limited; *Int'l*, pg. 3548
HYDROMETRICS, INC.; *U.S. Private*, pg. 2018
HYDRO MOBILE INC.; *Int'l*, pg. 3546
HYDROMOTION, INC.—See Dover Corporation; *U.S. Public*, pg. 681
HYDRONAMIC B.V.—See HAL Trust N.V.; *Int'l*, pg. 3226
HYDRONEXT SAS—See BKW AG; *Int'l*, pg. 1055
HYDRONIC & STEAM EQUIPMENT CO., INC.; *U.S. Private*, pg. 2018
HYDRONOVA AUSTRALIA-NZ PTY LTD—See Dover Corporation; *U.S. Public*, pg. 681
HYDRO NOVA EUROPE, LTD.—See Dover Corporation; *U.S. Public*, pg. 681
HYDRO ONE INC.—See Hydro One Limited; *Int'l*, pg. 3546
HYDRO ONE LIMITED; *Int'l*, pg. 3546
HYDRO ONE NETWORKS, INC.—See Hydro One Limited; *Int'l*, pg. 3546
HYDRO ONE REMOTE COMMUNITIES INC.—See Hydro One Limited; *Int'l*, pg. 3546
HYDRO ONE TELECOM INC.—See Hydro One Limited; *Int'l*, pg. 3546
HYDRO OTTAWA HOLDING INC.; *Int'l*, pg. 3546
HYDRO OTTAWA LIMITED—See Hydro Ottawa Holding Inc.; *Int'l*, pg. 3546
HYDROPHI TECHNOLOGIES GROUP, INC.; *U.S. Private*, pg. 2018
HYDROPLUS INC.—See VINCI S.A.; *Int'l*, pg. 8222
HYDROPLUS SA—See VINCI S.A.; *Int'l*, pg. 8235
HYDROPOWER EVOLUTIONS GMBH—See Fortum Oyj; *Int'l*, pg. 2742
HYDRO POWER JOINT STOCK COMPANY; *Int'l*, pg. 3547
HYDRO PRECISION TUBING TONDER A/S—See Norsk Hydro ASA; *Int'l*, pg. 5435
HYDRO PRODUITS CHIMIQUES—See Norsk Hydro ASA; *Int'l*, pg. 5435
HYDROPROJEKT SP. Z O.O.—See Koninklijke HaskoningDHV Groep B.V.; *Int'l*, pg. 4266
HYDRO-QUEBEC INDUSTECH INC—See Hydro-Quebec; *Int'l*, pg. 3547
HYDRO-QUEBEC INTERNATIONAL—See Hydro-Quebec; *Int'l*, pg. 3547
HYDRO-QUEBEC; *Int'l*, pg. 3547
HYDRO RESOURCES, INC.—See Laramide Resources Ltd.; *Int'l*, pg. 4418
HYDROSAAR GMBH—See Hydac International GmbH; *Int'l*, pg. 3545
HYDRO+ SA—See The Gorman-Rupp Company; *U.S. Public*, pg. 2085
HYDRO-SCAPE PRODUCTS, INC.—See SiteOne Landscape Supply, Inc.; *U.S. Public*, pg. 1889
HYDROSCIENCE TECHNOLOGIES, INC.; *U.S. Private*, pg. 2018
HYDR-O-SEAL, INC.; *U.S. Private*, pg. 2017
HYDRO SERVICE A/S—See Addtech AB; *Int'l*, pg. 133
HYDRO SERVICE PENTA S.P.A—See Interpump Group S.p.A.; *Int'l*, pg. 3755
HYDRO-SOLAR ENERGIE AG—See Alpiq Holding AG; *Int'l*, pg. 373
HYDRO SOLUTIONS CONSULTING LLC—See The Dewberry Companies Inc.; *U.S. Private*, pg. 4021
HYDROSTANDARD MATTEKNIK NORDIC AB—See Sdiptech AB; *Int'l*, pg. 6658
HYDROSTATIC EXTRUSIONS LTD.—See Bruker Corporation; *U.S. Public*, pg. 406
HYDRO SUPRA KEMISERVICE AB—See Norsk Hydro ASA; *Int'l*, pg. 5435
HYDRO SYSTEMS COMPANY—See Dover Corporation; *U.S. Public*, pg. 679
HYDRO SYSTEMS EUROPE, LTD.—See Dover Corporation; *U.S. Public*, pg. 681
HYDROTECH AB—See Veolia Environnement S.A.; *Int'l*, pg. 8161
HYDROTECH COMPANY LTD.; *Int'l*, pg. 3548

CORPORATE AFFILIATIONS

HYDROTECH INC.—See Fluid System Components Inc.; *U.S. Private*, pg. 1552
HYDROTECH MEMBRANE CORPORATION—See Sika AG; *Int'l*, pg. 6914
HYDRO TECHNOLOGIES, INC.—See Hughes Group, Inc.; *U.S. Private*, pg. 2003
HYDROTEK ENGINEERING CO.—See SMC Corporation; *Int'l*, pg. 7003
HYDROTEK PUBLIC COMPANY LIMITED; *Int'l*, pg. 3548
HYDRO TEK SYSTEMS, INC.—See Nilfisk Holding A/S; *Int'l*, pg. 5295
HYDROTEX PARTNERS LTD.; *U.S. Private*, pg. 2018
HYDRO TUBE ENTERPRISES, INC.; *U.S. Private*, pg. 2017
HYDROVEN S.R.L.—See Interpump Group S.p.A.; *Int'l*, pg. 3756
HYDROVEST SDN BHD—See Kumpulan Darul Ehsan Berhad; *Int'l*, pg. 4331
HYDSOFT TECHNOLOGY CO., LTD.; *Int'l*, pg. 3548
HYDUKE BUILDING SOLUTIONS—See Hyduke Energy Services Inc.; *Int'l*, pg. 3548
HYDUKE DRILLING SOLUTIONS INC—See Hyduke Energy Services Inc.; *Int'l*, pg. 3548
HYDUKE ENERGY SERVICES INC. - BIG RIG SANDBLASTING, PAINTING AND REPAIR DIVISION—See Hyduke Energy Services Inc.; *Int'l*, pg. 3548
HYDUKE ENERGY SERVICES INC. - HYDUKE DESIGN & ENGINEERING DIVISION—See Hyduke Energy Services Inc.; *Int'l*, pg. 3548
HYDUKE ENERGY SERVICES INC. - HYDUKE MECHANICAL & MACHINING DIVISION—See Hyduke Energy Services Inc.; *Int'l*, pg. 3548
HYDUKE ENERGY SERVICES INC.; *Int'l*, pg. 3548
HYDUKE MACHINING SOLUTIONS INC.—See Hyduke Energy Services Inc.; *Int'l*, pg. 3548
HY ENERGY GROUP CO., LTD.; *Int'l*, pg. 3543
HYER INDUSTRIES INC.; *U.S. Private*, pg. 2018
HYET SWEET S.A.S.—See Standard Investment Management B.V.; *Int'l*, pg. 7169
HYFCO DEVELOPMENT COMPANY LIMITED—See Henderson Land Development Co. Ltd.; *Int'l*, pg. 3344
HYFCO ESTATE MANAGEMENT AND AGENCY LIMITED—See Henderson Land Development Co. Ltd.; *Int'l*, pg. 3344
HYFCO TRADING AND INVESTMENTS COMPANY LIMITED—See Henderson Land Development Co. Ltd.; *Int'l*, pg. 3345
HYFIRE WIRELESS FIRE SOLUTIONS LTD.—See Halma plc; *Int'l*, pg. 3232
HYFLUX CONSUMER PRODUCTS PTE. LTD.—See Hyflux Ltd; *Int'l*, pg. 3548
HYFLUX ENGINEERING (INDIA) PVT LTD—See Hyflux Ltd; *Int'l*, pg. 3548
HYFLUX LIFESTYLE PRODUCTS (INDIA) PVT LTD—See Hyflux Ltd; *Int'l*, pg. 3548
HYFLUX LTD; *Int'l*, pg. 3548
HYFLUX (MALAYSIA) SDN BHD—See Hyflux Ltd; *Int'l*, pg. 3548
HYFLUX MEMBRANE MANUFACTURING (S) PTE.LTD—See Hyflux Ltd; *Int'l*, pg. 3548
HYFLUX NEWSPRING CONSTRUCTION ENGINEERING (SHANGHAI) CO., LTD—See Hyflux Ltd; *Int'l*, pg. 3548
HYFLUX WATER TRUST MANAGEMENT PTE LTD—See Hyflux Ltd; *Int'l*, pg. 3548
HYFN; *U.S. Private*, pg. 2018
HYFUSIN GROUP HOLDINGS LTD.; *Int'l*, pg. 3549
HYGEA HOLDINGS CORP.; *U.S. Private*, pg. 2018
HYGEAR B.V.—See Xebec Adsorption Inc.; *Int'l*, pg. 8520
HYGEIA CORPORATION—See UnitedHealth Group Incorporated; *U.S. Public*, pg. 2241
HYGEIA CORPORATION—See UnitedHealth Group Incorporated; *U.S. Public*, pg. 2241
HYGEIA HEALTHCARE HOLDINGS COMPANY LIMITED; *Int'l*, pg. 3549
THE HYGENIC CORPORATION—See Madison Dearborn Partners, LLC; *U.S. Private*, pg. 2542
HYGEN PHARMACEUTICALS, INC.; *U.S. Private*, pg. 2018
HYGGE INTEGRATED BRANDS CORP.; *Int'l*, pg. 3549
HYGGLO AB—See Schibsted ASA; *Int'l*, pg. 6616
HYGIANIS SPA; *Int'l*, pg. 3549
HYGIEIA GROUP LIMITED; *Int'l*, pg. 3549
HYGIENE COTTON INDUSTRIES PAMUK SANAYI VE TICARET LIMITED SIRKETI—See PAUL HARTMANN AG; *Int'l*, pg. 5760
HYGIENE PARTNERS S.A.R.L.—See PAUL HARTMANN AG; *Int'l*, pg. 5760
HYGINETT KFT—See The Procter & Gamble Company; *U.S. Public*, pg. 2120
HYGON INFORMATION TECHNOLOGY CO. LTD.; *Int'l*, pg. 3549
HYGRADE ACQUISITION METAL MOLDING; *U.S. Private*, pg. 2018
HYGRADE BUSINESS GROUP INC.; *U.S. Private*, pg. 2018
HYGRADE BUSINESS GROUP—See Hygrade Business Group Inc.; *U.S. Private*, pg. 2018
HYGRADE DISTRIBUTION & DELIVERY SYSTEMS; *U.S. Private*, pg. 2018

COMPANY NAME INDEX

HYGRADE METAL MOULDING MANUFACTURING CORP.—See Hygrade Acquisition Metal Molding; *U.S. Private*, pg. 2018
HYGROMATIK GMBH—See Carel Industries S.p.A.; *Int'l*, pg. 1324
HYGROVEST LIMITED; *Int'l*, pg. 3549
HY LABONNE & SONS INC.; *U.S. Private*, pg. 2015
HYLA MOBILE, INC.—See Assurant, Inc.; *U.S. Public*, pg. 215
HYLAN DATACOM & ELECTRICAL, LLC; *U.S. Private*, pg. 2018
THE HYLAND COMPANY; *U.S. Private*, pg. 4055
HYLAND LLC—See Thoma Bravo, L.P.; *U.S. Private*, pg. 4148
HYLANDS INTERNATIONAL HOLDINGS INC.; *Int'l*, pg. 3549
HYLAND SOFTWARE GERMANY GMBH—See Thoma Bravo, L.P.; *U.S. Private*, pg. 4148
HYLAND SOFTWARE, INC.—See Thoma Bravo, L.P.; *U.S. Private*, pg. 4148
HYLAN ELECTRICAL CONTRACTING; *U.S. Private*, pg. 2018
HYLANT GROUP - ANN ARBOR—See Hylant Group Inc.; *U.S. Private*, pg. 2019
HYLANT GROUP INC.; *U.S. Private*, pg. 2018
HYLANT GROUP - INDIANAPOLIS—See Hylant Group Inc.; *U.S. Private*, pg. 2019
HYLANT—See Hylant Group Inc.; *U.S. Private*, pg. 2019
HYLAR METAL PRODUCTS—See Degelman Industries Ltd.; *Int'l*, pg. 2004
HYLAS B.V.—See CRH plc; *Int'l*, pg. 1844
HYLAS YACHTS INC.; *U.S. Private*, pg. 2019
HYLETE, INC.; *U.S. Private*, pg. 2019
HYLIION HOLDINGS CORP.; *U.S. Public*, pg. 1079
HY-LINE AG—See Blue Cap AG; *Int'l*, pg. 1067
HY-LINE COMMUNICATION PRODUCTS VERTRIEBS GMBH—See Blue Cap AG; *Int'l*, pg. 1067
HY-LINE COMPUTER COMPONENTS VERTRIEBS GMBH—See Blue Cap AG; *Int'l*, pg. 1067
HY-LINE HOLDING GMBH—See Blue Cap AG; *Int'l*, pg. 1067
HY-LINE INTERNATIONAL; *U.S. Private*, pg. 2015
HY-LINE POWER COMPONENTS VERTRIEBS GMBH—See Blue Cap AG; *Int'l*, pg. 1067
HYLINK DIGITAL SOLUTION CO., LTD.; *Int'l*, pg. 3549
HY-LINK SCIENCE & TECHNOLOGY CO., LTD.—See Litu Holdings Limited; *Int'l*, pg. 4528
HYLOAD, INC.—See IKO Enterprises Ltd.; *Int'l*, pg. 3612
HY-LOK ASIA VALVES & FITTINGS PTE LTD.—See Hy-Lok Corporation; *Int'l*, pg. 3543
HY-LOK CANADA INC.—See Hy-Lok Corporation; *Int'l*, pg. 3543
HY-LOK CHINA—See Hy-Lok Corporation; *Int'l*, pg. 3543
HY-LOK CORPORATION; *Int'l*, pg. 3543
HY-LOK EUROPE B.V.—See Hy-Lok Corporation; *Int'l*, pg. 3543
HY-LOK OCEANIA PTY. LTD.—See Hy-Lok Corporation; *Int'l*, pg. 3544
HY-LOK USA—See Hy-Lok Corporation; *Int'l*, pg. 3544
HYLORIS PHARMACEUTICALS SA; *Int'l*, pg. 3549
HYLSA S.A.-BAR & ROD DIVISION—See Techint S.p.A.; *Int'l*, pg. 7505
HYLSA S.A. DE C.V.-TECHNOLOGY DIVISION—See Techint S.p.A.; *Int'l*, pg. 7505
HYLSA S.A.-FLAT STEEL DIVISION—See Techint S.p.A.; *Int'l*, pg. 7505
HYLTE JAKT & LANTMAN AB—See BHG Group AB; *Int'l*, pg. 1015
HYLTON CHELTENHAM—See Hylton Group Ltd.; *Int'l*, pg. 3549
HYLTON GROUP LTD.; *Int'l*, pg. 3549
HYLTON OF WORCESTER—See Hylton Group Ltd.; *Int'l*, pg. 3549
HYLTON ROSS TOURS (PTY) LTD—See Cullinan Holdings Limited; *Int'l*, pg. 1877
HYMAN BRICKLE & SON, INC. - BRANCH RIVER FACILITY—See Hyman Brickle & Son, Inc.; *U.S. Private*, pg. 2019
HYMAN BRICKLE & SON, INC. - BRICKLE FIBER TRADING DIVISION—See Hyman Brickle & Son, Inc.; *U.S. Private*, pg. 2019
HYMAN BRICKLE & SON, INC.; *U.S. Private*, pg. 2019
HYMAN LTD.; *U.S. Private*, pg. 2019
HYMAX, INC.—See Ship Supply of Florida, Inc.; *U.S. Private*, pg. 3637
HYMER GMBH & CO. KG—See Thor Industries, Inc.; *U.S. Public*, pg. 2156
HYMETAL CONSTRUCTION PRODUCTS CO., LTD.; *Int'l*, pg. 3549
HYMIX AUSTRALIA PTY. LTD.—See Heidelberg Materials AG; *Int'l*, pg. 3311
HYMNARIO - EAW (HK) LIMITED—See Tymphany Corp.; *U.S. Private*, pg. 4268
HYMNARIO-EAW (HUIYANG) CO., LTD.—See Eastern Holding Limited; *Int'l*, pg. 2272
HYMSON (JIANGMEN) LASER INTELLIGENT EQUIPMENTS CO., LTD.—See Hymson Laser Technology Group Co Ltd; *Int'l*, pg. 3549

HYMSON LASER INTELLIGENT EQUIPMENTS (JIANGSU) CO., LTD.—See Hymson Laser Technology Group Co Ltd; *Int'l*, pg. 3550
HYMSON LASER TECHNOLOGY GROUP CO LTD; *Int'l*, pg. 3549
HYNAR WATER GROUP CO., LTD.; *Int'l*, pg. 3550
HYNDMAN TRANSPORT (1972) LIMITED—See Celadon Group, Inc.; *U.S. Public*, pg. 464
HYNES INDUSTRIES INC.—See Crossplane Capital Management LP; *U.S. Private*, pg. 1107
HYNION AS; *Int'l*, pg. 3550
HYNIX SEMICONDUCTOR EUROPE HOLDING LTD—See SK hynix Inc.; *Int'l*, pg. 6970
HYNIX SEMICONDUCTOR (WUXI) LTD.—See SK hynix Inc.; *Int'l*, pg. 6970
HYOGO GUNZE CO., LTD.—See Gunze Limited; *Int'l*, pg. 3186
HYOGO KONO CO., LTD.—See Kato Sangyo Co., Ltd.; *Int'l*, pg. 4090
HYOKI KAIUN KAISHA LTD.; *Int'l*, pg. 3550
HYON AS; *Int'l*, pg. 3550
HYORIM INDUSTRIES INC.—See Kukje Pharma Co., Ltd.; *Int'l*, pg. 4327
HYOSUNG ADVANCED MATERIALS CO., LTD.; *Int'l*, pg. 3550
HYOSUNG (AMERICA), INC.—See Hyosung Corporation; *Int'l*, pg. 3550
HYOSUNG BRASIL INDUSTRIA E COMERCIO DE FIBRAS LTDA.—See Hyosung TNC Co. Ltd.; *Int'l*, pg. 3552
HYOSUNG CAPITAL CO., LTD.; *Int'l*, pg. 3550
HYOSUNG CHEMICALS GUMI PLANT I—See Hyosung Corporation; *Int'l*, pg. 3550
HYOSUNG CHEMICALS (JIAXING) CO., LTD.—See Hyosung Corporation; *Int'l*, pg. 3550
HYOSUNG COMPUTER PERFORMANCE UNIT—See Hyosung Corporation; *Int'l*, pg. 3550
HYOSUNG CONSTRUCTION PERFORMANCE UNIT—See Hyosung Corporation; *Int'l*, pg. 3550
HYOSUNG CORPORATION - ANYANG PLANT—See Hyosung Corporation; *Int'l*, pg. 3550
HYOSUNG CORPORATION BANGKOK—See Hyosung Corporation; *Int'l*, pg. 3550
HYOSUNG CORPORATION BEIJING—See Hyosung Corporation; *Int'l*, pg. 3550
HYOSUNG CORPORATION - DAEGU PLANT—See Hyosung Corporation; *Int'l*, pg. 3550
HYOSUNG CORPORATION - DAEJEON PLANT—See Hyosung Corporation; *Int'l*, pg. 3550
HYOSUNG CORPORATION DUBAI—See Hyosung Corporation; *Int'l*, pg. 3551
HYOSUNG CORPORATION EDUCATION CENTER—See Hyosung Corporation; *Int'l*, pg. 3551
HYOSUNG CORPORATION GUANGZHOU—See Hyosung Corporation; *Int'l*, pg. 3551
HYOSUNG CORPORATION - GWANGHYEWON PLANT—See Hyosung Corporation; *Int'l*, pg. 3550
HYOSUNG CORPORATION HO CHI MINH—See Hyosung Corporation; *Int'l*, pg. 3551
HYOSUNG CORPORATION - ICHEON PLANT—See Hyosung Corporation; *Int'l*, pg. 3550
HYOSUNG CORPORATION ISTANBUL—See Hyosung Corporation; *Int'l*, pg. 3551
HYOSUNG CORPORATION - JINCHEON PLANT—See Hyosung Corporation; *Int'l*, pg. 3550
HYOSUNG CORPORATION - JOCHIWON PLANT—See Hyosung Corporation; *Int'l*, pg. 3550
HYOSUNG CORPORATION KAOHSIUNG—See Hyosung Corporation; *Int'l*, pg. 3551
HYOSUNG CORPORATION KUALA LUMPUR—See Hyosung Corporation; *Int'l*, pg. 3551
HYOSUNG CORPORATION - KWANGHAEWON PLANT—See Hyosung Corporation; *Int'l*, pg. 3550
HYOSUNG CORPORATION MANILA—See Hyosung Corporation; *Int'l*, pg. 3551
HYOSUNG CORPORATION MEXICO—See Hyosung Corporation; *Int'l*, pg. 3551
HYOSUNG CORPORATION MOSCOW—See Hyosung Corporation; *Int'l*, pg. 3551
HYOSUNG CORPORATION PANAMA—See Hyosung Corporation; *Int'l*, pg. 3551
HYOSUNG CORPORATION SHANGHAI—See Hyosung Corporation; *Int'l*, pg. 3551
HYOSUNG CORPORATION; *Int'l*, pg. 3550
HYOSUNG CORPORATION TAIPEI—See Hyosung Corporation; *Int'l*, pg. 3551
HYOSUNG CORPORATION TEHRAN LIAISON OFFICE—See Hyosung Corporation; *Int'l*, pg. 3551
HYOSUNG CORPORATION - ULSAN PLANT—See Hyosung Corporation; *Int'l*, pg. 3550
HYOSUNG CORPORATION - YANGSAN PLANT—See Hyosung Corporation; *Int'l*, pg. 3550
HYOSUNG CORPORATION - YONGYEON PLANT 1—See Hyosung Corporation; *Int'l*, pg. 3550
HYOSUNG CORPORATION - YONGYEON PLANT 3—See Hyosung Corporation; *Int'l*, pg. 3550
HYOSUNG DO BRAZIL—See Hyosung Corporation; *Int'l*, pg. 3551

HYPEBEAST LIMITED

HYOSUNG DONG NAI CO., LTD.—See Hyosung TNC Co. Ltd.; *Int'l*, pg. 3552
HYOSUNG EBARA CO., LTD.—See Ebara Corporation; *Int'l*, pg. 2284
HYOSUNG EBARA CO., LTD.—See Flowserve Corporation; *U.S. Public*, pg. 856
HYOSUNG EBARA CO., LTD.—See Hyosung Corporation; *Int'l*, pg. 3550
HYOSUNG EBARA ENGINEERING CO., LTD.—See Hyosung Corporation; *Int'l*, pg. 3551
HYOSUNG EBARA ENVIRONMENTAL ENGINEERING CO. LTD.—See Hyosung Corporation; *Int'l*, pg. 3551
HYOSUNG EUROPE S.R.L.—See Hyosung Corporation; *Int'l*, pg. 3551
HYOSUNG GOODSPRINGS, INC.—See Hyosung Advanced Materials Co., Ltd.; *Int'l*, pg. 3550
HYOSUNG HEAVY INDUSTRIES CORP.; *Int'l*, pg. 3552
HYOSUNG (H.K.) LTD.—See Hyosung Corporation; *Int'l*, pg. 3550
HYOSUNG HOLDINGS USA, INC.—See Hyosung Corporation; *Int'l*, pg. 3551
HYOSUNG INDIA PVT. LTD.—See Hyosung TNC Co. Ltd.; *Int'l*, pg. 3552
HYOSUNG INDUSTRIAL PG—See Hyosung Corporation; *Int'l*, pg. 3551
HYOSUNG INFORMATION SYSTEMS CO., LTD.—See Hyosung Corporation; *Int'l*, pg. 3551
HYOSUNG INTERNATIONAL (HK) LTD.—See Hyosung Corporation; *Int'l*, pg. 3551
HYOSUNG INTERNATIONAL TRADE (JIAXING) CO., LTD.—See Hyosung Corporation; *Int'l*, pg. 3551
HYOSUNG ITX CO., LTD.; *Int'l*, pg. 3552
HYOSUNG JAPAN OSAKA—See Hyosung Corporation; *Int'l*, pg. 3551
HYOSUNG JAPAN—See Hyosung Corporation; *Int'l*, pg. 3551
HYOSUNG LUXEMBOURG S.A.—See Hyosung Corporation; *Int'l*, pg. 3551
HYOSUNG MEDIA CO., LTD.—See Hyosung Corporation; *Int'l*, pg. 3551
HYOSUNG MEXICO CITY S.A. DE C.V.—See Hyosung TNC Co. Ltd.; *Int'l*, pg. 3552
HYOSUNG NEW MATERIAL & HIGHTECH (QUZHOU) CO., LTD.—See Hyosung TNC Co. Ltd.; *Int'l*, pg. 3552
HYOSUNG ONB CO, LTD - ASAN FACTORY—See Hyosung ONB Co, Ltd; *Int'l*, pg. 3552
HYOSUNG ONB CO, LTD - CHEONGDO FACTORY—See Hyosung ONB Co, Ltd; *Int'l*, pg. 3552
HYOSUNG ONB CO, LTD - EUISUNG FACTORY—See Hyosung ONB Co, Ltd; *Int'l*, pg. 3552
HYOSUNG ONB CO, LTD - HAMPYEONG FACTORY—See Hyosung ONB Co, Ltd; *Int'l*, pg. 3552
HYOSUNG ONB CO, LTD; *Int'l*, pg. 3552
HYOSUNG ONB CO, LTD - SRI LANKA FACTORY—See Hyosung ONB Co, Ltd; *Int'l*, pg. 3552
HYOSUNG R&DB LABS—See Hyosung Corporation; *Int'l*, pg. 3551
HYOSUNG SINGAPORE PTE. LTD.—See Hyosung Corporation; *Int'l*, pg. 3551
HYOSUNG SPANDEX (GUANGDONG) CO., LTD.—See Hyosung Corporation; *Int'l*, pg. 3551
HYOSUNG SPANDEX (JIAXING) CO., LTD.—See Hyosung Corporation; *Int'l*, pg. 3551
HYOSUNG SPANDEX (QUZHOU) CO., LTD.—See Hyosung TNC Co. Ltd.; *Int'l*, pg. 3552
HYOSUNG SPANDEX (ZHUHAI) CO., LTD.—See Hyosung TNC Co. Ltd.; *Int'l*, pg. 3552
HYOSUNG STEEL CORD (QINGDAO) CO., LTD.—See Hyosung Corporation; *Int'l*, pg. 3551
HYOSUNG TAEGU BUSINESS CENTER—See Hyosung Corporation; *Int'l*, pg. 3551
HYOSUNG TECHNICAL RESEARCH INSTITUTE—See Hyosung Corporation; *Int'l*, pg. 3551
HYOSUNG TNC CO. LTD.; *Int'l*, pg. 3552
HYOSUNG TNC (TAIWAN) CORPORATION—See Hyosung TNC Co. Ltd.; *Int'l*, pg. 3552
HYOSUNG TNS INC.—See Hyosung Advanced Materials Co., Ltd.; *Int'l*, pg. 3550
HYOSUNG TRADING PERFORMANCE GROUP—See Hyosung Corporation; *Int'l*, pg. 3551
HYOSUNG TRANS-WORLD CO., LTD.—See Hyosung Corporation; *Int'l*, pg. 3552
HYOSUNG USA, INC. - DECATUR PLANT—See Hyosung Corporation; *Int'l*, pg. 3551
HYOSUNG USA, INC. - LOS ANGELES OFFICE—See Hyosung Corporation; *Int'l*, pg. 3551
HYOSUNG USA, INC.—See Hyosung Corporation; *Int'l*, pg. 3551
HYOSUNG WIRE LUXEMBOURG S.A.—See Hyosung Corporation; *Int'l*, pg. 3552
HY-PAC SELF STORAGE—See Yamada Group USA Ltd.; *U.S. Private*, pg. 4585
HYPAK SDN. BERHAD—See Tuan Sing Holdings Limited; *Int'l*, pg. 7962
HYPARLO S.A.—See Carrefour SA; *Int'l*, pg. 1345
HYPATIA GNC ACCESORIOS S.A.—See Nicolas Correa S.A.; *Int'l*, pg. 5273
HYPCO; *Int'l*, pg. 3552
HYPEBEAST LIMITED; *Int'l*, pg. 3552

HYPEFACTORS A/S

HYPEFACTORS A/S; *Int'l*, pg. 3552
HYPEMARKS, INC.; *U.S. Private*, pg. 2019
HYPERACTIVE TECHNOLOGIES, INC.—See GLORY Ltd.; *Int'l*, pg. 3009
HYPER ADVANCE SDN. BHD.—See Aiphone Co., Ltd.; *Int'l*, pg. 235
HYPERA PHARMA S.A.; *Int'l*, pg. 3553
HYPERBLOCK, INC.; *Int'l*, pg. 3553
HYPERBRANCH MEDICAL TECHNOLOGY, INC.—See Stryker Corporation; *U.S. Public*, pg. 1955
HYPERCHARGE NETWORKS CORP.; *Int'l*, pg. 3553
HYPERCOM CORPORATION—See British Columbia Investment Management Corp.; *Int'l*, pg. 1170
HYPERCOM CORPORATION—See Francisco Partners Management, LP; *U.S. Private*, pg. 1592
HYPERCOM FINANCIAL TERMINALS AB—See British Columbia Investment Management Corp.; *Int'l*, pg. 1170
HYPERCOM FINANCIAL TERMINALS AB—See Francisco Partners Management, LP; *U.S. Private*, pg. 1592
HYPER CORPORATION; *Int'l*, pg. 3552
HYPERDEMA SA—See Carrefour SA; *Int'l*, pg. 1345
HYPERDRIVE; *U.S. Private*, pg. 2019
HYPER ENGINEERING PTY. LTD.—See NIBE Industrier AB; *Int'l*, pg. 5261
HYPERFINE, INC.; *U.S. Public*, pg. 1079
HYPERFORM, INC.—See Patrick Industries, Inc.; *U.S. Public*, pg. 1652
HYPERICE, INC.; *U.S. Private*, pg. 2019
HYPER INC.; *Int'l*, pg. 3553
HYPERION ASSET MANAGEMENT LIMITED; *Int'l*, pg. 3553
HYPERION BOOKS—See Vivendi SE; *Int'l*, pg. 8273
HYPERION ENERGY LP; *U.S. Private*, pg. 2019
HYPERION INMOBILARIA S.A. DE C.V.—See Deutsche Post AG; *Int'l*, pg. 2081
HYPERION MATERIALS & TECHNOLOGIES DE MEXICO S.A. DE C.V.—See KKR & Co. Inc.; *U.S. Public*, pg. 1253
HYPERION MATERIALS & TECHNOLOGIES (FRANCE) S.A.S.—See KKR & Co. Inc.; *U.S. Public*, pg. 1253
HYPERION MATERIALS & TECHNOLOGIES GERMANY GMBH—See KKR & Co. Inc.; *U.S. Public*, pg. 1253
HYPERION MATERIALS & TECHNOLOGIES, INC.—See KKR & Co. Inc.; *U.S. Public*, pg. 1252
HYPERION MATERIALS & TECHNOLOGIES (SWEDEN) AB—See KKR & Co. Inc.; *U.S. Public*, pg. 1252
HYPERION PARTNERS LP; *U.S. Private*, pg. 2019
HYPERION S.A.; *Int'l*, pg. 3553
HYPERLAST LIMITED—See Dow Inc.; *U.S. Public*, pg. 686
HYPERLOCAL INDUSTRIES LLC—See SOCi, Inc.; *U.S. Private*, pg. 3702
HY-PER LUBE CORP.—See Bar's Products, Inc.; *U.S. Private*, pg. 471
HYPERNETICS LTD.—See Plaintree Systems Inc.; *Int'l*, pg. 5888
HYPER PET, LLC; *U.S. Private*, pg. 2019
HYPER-REGION LABELS SDN. BHD.—See Oji Holdings Corporation; *Int'l*, pg. 5536
HYPERSOFT TECHNOLOGIES LIMITED; *Int'l*, pg. 3553
HYPERSPRING, LLC—See GSE Systems, Inc.; *U.S. Public*, pg. 973
HYPERSTONE ASIA PACIFIC LTD.—See Swissbit AG; *Int'l*, pg. 7373
HYPERSTONE GMBH—See Swissbit AG; *Int'l*, pg. 7373
HYPERSTONE INC.—See Swissbit AG; *Int'l*, pg. 7373
HYPERTAC GMBH—See Smiths Group plc; *Int'l*, pg. 7012
HYPERTAC LIMITED—See Smiths Group plc; *Int'l*, pg. 7012
HYPERTAC SPA—See Smiths Group plc; *Int'l*, pg. 7009
HYPER-TECHNOLOGIES SAS—See Advent International Corporation; *U.S. Private*, pg. 99
HYPERTEC LIMITED—See DCC plc; *Int'l*, pg. 1991
HYPERTENSION DIAGNOSTICS, INC.; *U.S. Public*, pg. 1079
HYPERTHERM INC.; *U.S. Private*, pg. 2019
HYPERTRONICS CORPORATION—See Smiths Group plc; *Int'l*, pg. 7010
HYPERVIEW INC.; *Int'l*, pg. 3553
HYPERWALLET SYSTEMS INC.—See PayPal Holdings, Inc.; *U.S. Public*, pg. 1656
HYPE SOFTWARETECHNIK GMBH—See Main Capital Partners B.V.; *Int'l*, pg. 4650
HYPEX BIO EXPLOSIVES TECHNOLOGY AB; *Int'l*, pg. 3553
HYPEX INC.; *U.S. Private*, pg. 2019
HYPGEN INC.; *U.S. Private*, pg. 2020
HYPHA LABS, INC.; *U.S. Public*, pg. 1079
HYPHEN BIOMED, SAS—See Sysmex Corporation; *Int'l*, pg. 7388
HY-PHEN.COM LIMITED—See Adecco Group AG; *Int'l*, pg. 138
HYPHEN DIGITAL—See Omnicom Group Inc.; *U.S. Public*, pg. 1586
HYPHEN SOLUTIONS, LLC; *U.S. Private*, pg. 2020
HYPHENS PHARMA INTERNATIONAL LIMITED; *Int'l*, pg. 3553

HYPHENS PHARMA PHILIPPINES, INC.—See Hyphens Pharma International Limited; *Int'l*, pg. 3553
HYPHENS PHARMA PTE. LTD.—See Hyphens Pharma International Limited; *Int'l*, pg. 3553
HYPHENS PHARMA SDN. BHD.—See Hyphens Pharma International Limited; *Int'l*, pg. 3553
HYPOCASSO B.V.—See Infosys Limited; *Int'l*, pg. 3696
HYPO HOLDING GMBH—See Raiffeisenlandesbank Oberosterreich Aktiengesellschaft; *Int'l*, pg. 6187
HYPO-LEASING STEIERMARK D.O.O.—See Raiffeisen-Landesbank Steiermark AG; *Int'l*, pg. 6186
HYPONEX CORPORATION—See The Scotts Miracle-Gro Company; *U.S. Public*, pg. 2127
HYPO OBEROSTERREICH—See OO. Landesholding GmbH; *Int'l*, pg. 5593
HYPO OBEROSTERREICH—See Raiffeisenlandesbank Oberosterreich Aktiengesellschaft; *Int'l*, pg. 6187
HYPO PFANDBRIEF BANK INTERNATIONAL S.A.—See Hypo Real Estate Holding AG; *Int'l*, pg. 3553
HYPOPORT SE; *Int'l*, pg. 3554
HYPO PUBLIC FINANCE BANK—See Hypo Real Estate Holding AG; *Int'l*, pg. 3553
HYPO REAL ESTATE CAPITAL HONG KONG CORPORATION LIMITED—See Hypo Real Estate Holding AG; *Int'l*, pg. 3553
HYPO REAL ESTATE CAPITAL INDIA CORPORATION PRIVATE LIMITED—See Hypo Real Estate Holding AG; *Int'l*, pg. 3553
HYPO REAL ESTATE CAPITAL JAPAN CORPORATION—See Hypo Real Estate Holding AG; *Int'l*, pg. 3554
HYPO REAL ESTATE CAPITAL SINGAPORE CORPORATION PRIVATE LIMITED—See Hypo Real Estate Holding AG; *Int'l*, pg. 3554
HYPO REAL ESTATE HOLDING AG; *Int'l*, pg. 3553
HYPORE HONG KONG LTD.—See KISWIRE LTD; *Int'l*, pg. 4193
HYPO STEIERMARK LEASING - HOLDING GMBH—See Raiffeisen-Landesbank Steiermark AG; *Int'l*, pg. 6186
HYPOSWISS PRIVATE BANK GENEVE SA—See Mirelis Holding SA; *Int'l*, pg. 4919
HYPOTEKET BOLAN SVERIGE AB—See Schibsted ASA; *Int'l*, pg. 6616
HYPOTHEEKFONDS VOOR OVERHEIDSPERSONEEL B.V.—See BNG Bank N.V.; *Int'l*, pg. 1079
HYPOTHEKARBANK LENZBURG AG; *Int'l*, pg. 3554
HYPOTHEKEN MANAGEMENT GMBH—See Loancos GmbH; *Int'l*, pg. 4539
HYPOTHEKENZENTRUM LTD.—See VZ Holding AG; *Int'l*, pg. 8319
HYPOVEREINS IMMOBILIEN EOOD—See UniCredit S.p.A.; *Int'l*, pg. 8041
HYPOWER FUEL, INC.; *U.S. Private*, pg. 2020
HYPOWER INC.; *U.S. Private*, pg. 2020
HY-PRO CORPORATION—See Donaldson Company, Inc.; *U.S. Public*, pg. 676
HYPROC SC—See Sonatrach International Holding Corporation; *Int'l*, pg. 7089
HYPRO EU LIMITED—See Pentair plc; *Int'l*, pg. 5789
HYPRO INC.; *U.S. Private*, pg. 2020
HYPROMAG GMBH—See Mkango Resources Ltd.; *Int'l*, pg. 5002
HYPROP INVESTMENTS LIMITED; *Int'l*, pg. 3554
HYPRO—See Pentair plc; *Int'l*, pg. 5790
HYQUIP, LLC—See Applied Industrial Technologies, Inc.; *U.S. Public*, pg. 171
HYRECAR, INC.; *U.S. Public*, pg. 1079
HYRE ELECTRIC COMPANY OF INDIANA, INC.—See EMCOR Group, Inc.; *U.S. Public*, pg. 737
HYROPE (THAILAND) CO., LTD.—See KISWIRE LTD; *Int'l*, pg. 4193
HYSAN DEVELOPMENT COMPANY LIMITED; *Int'l*, pg. 3554
HYSAN LEASING COMPANY LIMITED—See Hysan Development Company Limited; *Int'l*, pg. 3554
HYSAN PROPERTY MANAGEMENT LIMITED—See Hysan Development Company Limited; *Int'l*, pg. 3554
HYSCO STEEL INDIA, LTD.—See Hyundai Motor Company; *Int'l*, pg. 3558
HY-SECURITY GATE, INC.—See Nice Group S.p.A.; *Int'l*, pg. 5264
HYS ENGINEERING SERVICE INC.—See Nisshinbo Holdings Inc.; *Int'l*, pg. 5373
HYSER C.A.—See Hydac International GmbH; *Int'l*, pg. 3545
HYSITRON, INC.—See Bruker Corporation; *U.S. Public*, pg. 406
HYSONIC CO., LTD.; *Int'l*, pg. 3554
HYSONIC PHILIPPINES INC.—See HYSONIC Co., Ltd.; *Int'l*, pg. 3554
HYSON INTERNATIONAL CORP.—See Edge Centres Pty Ltd; *Int'l*, pg. 2309
HYSOUNG INVESTMENT & DEVELOPMENT—See Hyosung Corporation; *Int'l*, pg. 3552
HYSPAN PRECISION PRODUCTS, INC.; *U.S. Private*, pg. 2020
HYSPEC ENGINEERING LTD—See MB Holding Company LLC; *Int'l*, pg. 4750

CORPORATE AFFILIATIONS

HYSPECO INC.; *U.S. Private*, pg. 2020
HYSTER FRANCE S.A.R.L.—See Hyster-Yale Materials Handling, Inc.; *U.S. Public*, pg. 1080
HYSTER-YALE AUSTRALIA HOLDING PTY LTD.—See Hyster-Yale Materials Handling, Inc.; *U.S. Public*, pg. 1080
HYSTER-YALE DEUTSCHLAND GMBH—See Hyster-Yale Materials Handling, Inc.; *U.S. Public*, pg. 1080
HYSTER-YALE GROUP, INC.—See Hyster-Yale Materials Handling, Inc.; *U.S. Public*, pg. 1080
HYSTER-YALE GROUP, INC.—See Hyster-Yale Materials Handling, Inc.; *U.S. Public*, pg. 1080
HYSTER-YALE ITALIA SPA—See Hyster-Yale Materials Handling, Inc.; *U.S. Public*, pg. 1080
HYSTER-YALE MATERIALS HANDLING GMBH—See Hyster-Yale Materials Handling, Inc.; *U.S. Public*, pg. 1080
HYSTER-YALE MATERIALS HANDLING, INC.; *U.S. Public*, pg. 1079
HYSTER-YALE MAXIMAL FORKLIFT (ZHEJIANG) CO., LTD.—See Hyster-Yale Materials Handling, Inc.; *U.S. Public*, pg. 1080
HYSTER-YALE UK PENSION CO. LIMITED—See Hyster-Yale Materials Handling, Inc.; *U.S. Public*, pg. 1080
HYT AMERICA, INC.—See Hytera Communications Corporation Limited; *Int'l*, pg. 3554
HYTEC ABU DHABI L.L.C.—See Al Jaber Group; *Int'l*, pg. 280
HYTEC AUTOMOTIVE—See DeBartolo Holdings, LLC; *U.S. Private*, pg. 1186
HYTEC GERATEBAU GMBH—See DZS Inc.; *U.S. Public*, pg. 701
HY-TECH MACHINE, INC.—See ShoreView Industries, LLC; *U.S. Private*, pg. 3642
HYTEC HYDRAULICS MOCAMBIQUE LDA.—See Robert Bosch GmbH; *Int'l*, pg. 6361
HY-TEC INDUSTRIES (QUEENSLAND) PTY. LTD.—See CRH plc; *Int'l*, pg. 1842
HYTEC NAMIBIA PTY. LTD.—See Robert Bosch GmbH; *Int'l*, pg. 6361
HYTEC ZAMBIA LTD.—See Robert Bosch GmbH; *Int'l*, pg. 6361
HYTEK FINISHES INC.—See TransDigm Group Incorporated; *U.S. Public*, pg. 2181
HY-TEK MATERIAL HANDLING, INC.—See Dunes Point Capital, LLC; *U.S. Private*, pg. 1288
HYTEK MICROSYSTEMS, INC.—See Natel Engineering Company, Inc.; *U.S. Private*, pg. 2838
HYTERA COMMUNICATIONS (AUSTRALIA) PTY LTD—See Hytera Communications Corporation Limited; *Int'l*, pg. 3554
HYTERA COMMUNICATIONS (CANADA) INC.—See Hytera Communications Corporation Limited; *Int'l*, pg. 3555
HYTERA COMMUNICATIONS CORPORATION LIMITED; *Int'l*, pg. 3554
HYTERA COMMUNICATIONS FZCO—See Hytera Communications Corporation Limited; *Int'l*, pg. 3555
HYTERA COMMUNICATIONS (HONG KONG) COMPANY LIMITED—See Hytera Communications Corporation Limited; *Int'l*, pg. 3555
HYTERA COMMUNICATIONS (UK) CO., LTD.—See Hytera Communications Corporation Limited; *Int'l*, pg. 3555
HYTERA COMUNICACOES DO BRASIL LTDA.—See Hytera Communications Corporation Limited; *Int'l*, pg. 3555
HYTERA MOBILFUNK GMBH—See Hytera Communications Corporation Limited; *Int'l*, pg. 3555
HYTERA US INC.—See Hytera Communications Corporation Limited; *Int'l*, pg. 3555
HY-TEST PACKAGING CORP.; *U.S. Private*, pg. 2015
HYTEXTS INTERACTIVE CO., LTD.—See COL Public Company Limited; *Int'l*, pg. 1697
HYTHANE COMPANY LLC.—See Eden Innovations Ltd.; *Int'l*, pg. 2306
HYTROL CONVEYOR CO., INC.; *U.S. Private*, pg. 2020
HYTRONICS CORP.—See Electro Technik Industries; *U.S. Private*, pg. 1354
HYTRUST, INC.—See DataCard Corporation; *U.S. Private*, pg. 1165
HYT TELECOMUNICATION (UK) CO., LTD.—See Hytera Communications Corporation Limited; *Int'l*, pg. 3555
HYUGA SMELTING CO., LTD.—See Sumitomo Metal Mining Co., Ltd.; *Int'l*, pg. 7291
HYUGA UNYU CO., LTD.—See Tosoh Corporation; *Int'l*, pg. 7832
HYULIM A-TECH CO. LTD; *Int'l*, pg. 3555
HYULIM NETWORKS CO., LTD.; *Int'l*, pg. 3555
HYULIM ROBOT CO., LTD.—See Dongbu Group; *Int'l*, pg. 2166
HYUNDAI ABLE 1ST SPECIAL PURPOSE ACQUISITION COMPANY; *Int'l*, pg. 3555
HYUNDAI ADM BIO INC; *Int'l*, pg. 3555
HYUNDAI AMERICA TECHNICAL CENTER, INC.—See Hyundai Motor Company; *Int'l*, pg. 3559
HYUNDAI ARCHITECTS & ENGINEERS ASSOCIATES CO., LTD.—See Hyundai Motor Company; *Int'l*, pg. 3558

COMPANY NAME INDEX

HYUNDAI ASAN CORPORATION—See Hyundai Group; *Int'l*, pg. 3557
HYUNDAI ASSAN OTOMOTIV SANAYI VE TICARET A.S.—See Hyundai Motor Company; *Int'l*, pg. 3558
HYUNDAI AUTO CANADA—See Hyundai Motor Company; *Int'l*, pg. 3559
HYUNDAI AUTOEVER CORP.—See Hyundai Motor Company; *Int'l*, pg. 3559
HYUNDAI AUTOMOTIVE SOUTH AFRICA PROPRIETARY LIMITED—See Motus Holdings Limited; *Int'l*, pg. 5056
HYUNDAI BEIJING STEEL PROCESS CO., LTD. (CHINA)—See Hyundai Steel Company; *Int'l*, pg. 3560
HYUNDAI BIOLAND CO., LTD.; *Int'l*, pg. 3555
HYUNDAI BIOSCIENCE CO., LTD.; *Int'l*, pg. 3555
HYUNDAI BNG STEEL CO., LTD.—See Hyundai Motor Company; *Int'l*, pg. 3559
HYUNDAI CAPITAL AMERICA, INC.—See Hyundai Motor Company; *Int'l*, pg. 3559
HYUNDAI CAPITAL BANK EUROPE GMBH—See Banco Santander, S.A.; *Int'l*, pg. 826
HYUNDAI CAPITAL BANK EUROPE GMBH—See Hyundai Motor Company; *Int'l*, pg. 3559
HYUNDAI CAPITAL CORPORATION—See Hyundai Motor Company; *Int'l*, pg. 3559
HYUNDAI CAPITAL EUROPE GMBH—See Hyundai Motor Company; *Int'l*, pg. 3559
HYUNDAI CAPITAL SERVICES, INC.—See Hyundai Motor Company; *Int'l*, pg. 3559
HYUNDAI CARD CO., LTD.—See Hyundai Motor Company; *Int'l*, pg. 3559
HYUNDAI COMMERCIAL INC.—See Hyundai Motor Company; *Int'l*, pg. 3559
HYUNDAI CONSTRUCTION EQUIPMENT INDUSTRIAL CO., LTD.—See Hyundai Heavy Industries Co., Ltd.; *Int'l*, pg. 3557
HYUNDAI CONSTRUCTION EQUIPMENT SERVICE CO., LTD.—See Hyundai Heavy Industries Co., Ltd.; *Int'l*, pg. 3557
HYUNDAI CONSTRUCTION EQUIPMENT U.S.A., INC.—See Hyundai Heavy Industries Co., Ltd.; *Int'l*, pg. 3557
HYUNDAI CORPORATION (CAMBODIA) CO., LTD.—See Hyundai Corporation; *Int'l*, pg. 3555
HYUNDAI CORPORATION EUROPE GMBH—See Hyundai Corporation; *Int'l*, pg. 3555
HYUNDAI CORPORATION HOLDINGS CO., LTD.—See Hyundai Corporation; *Int'l*, pg. 3555
HYUNDAI CORPORATION (SHANGHAI) CO., LTD.—See Hyundai Corporation; *Int'l*, pg. 3555
HYUNDAI CORPORATION; *Int'l*, pg. 3555
HYUNDAI COSMO PETROCHEMICAL CO., LTD.—See Cosmo Energy Holdings Co., Ltd.; *Int'l*, pg. 1812
HYUNDAI DEPARTMENT STORE CO., LTD.; *Int'l*, pg. 3555
HYUNDAI DE PUERTO RICO—See Sojitz Corporation; *Int'l*, pg. 7061
HYUNDAI DISPLAY TECHNOLOGY INC.—See SK hynix Inc.; *Int'l*, pg. 6971
HYUNDAI DREAM TOUR CO., LTD.—See Hyundai GF Holdings Co., Ltd.; *Int'l*, pg. 3556
HYUNDAI ELECTRIC & ENERGY SYSTEMS CO., LTD.; *Int'l*, pg. 3556
HYUNDAI ELEVATOR CO., LTD.—See Hyundai Group; *Int'l*, pg. 3557
HYUNDAI ELEVATOR CO., LTD.—See Hyundai Group; *Int'l*, pg. 3557
HYUNDAI ENGINEERING CO., LTD.—See Hyundai Engineering & Construction Co., Ltd.; *Int'l*, pg. 3556
HYUNDAI ENGINEERING & CONSTRUCTION CO., LTD.; *Int'l*, pg. 3556
HYUNDAI ENGINEERING & STEEL INDUSTRIES CO., LTD.—See Hyundai Engineering & Construction Co., Ltd.; *Int'l*, pg. 3556
HYUNDAI EVERDIGM AMERICA INC.—See Hyundai Everdigm Corp; *Int'l*, pg. 3556
HYUNDAI EVERDIGM CORP; *Int'l*, pg. 3556
HYUNDAI EZWEL CO.,LTD; *Int'l*, pg. 3556
HYUNDAI FARM LAND & DEVELOPMENT COMPANY—See Hyundai Motor Company; *Int'l*, pg. 3559
HYUNDAI FINANCIAL LEASING CO., LTD.—See Hyundai Heavy Industries Co., Ltd.; *Int'l*, pg. 3557
HYUNDAI FUTURENET CO., LTD—See Hyundai Department Store Co., Ltd.; *Int'l*, pg. 3556
HYUNDAI GF HOLDINGS CO., LTD.; *Int'l*, pg. 3556
HYUNDAI GLOVIS CO., LTD.; *Int'l*, pg. 3556
HYUNDAI GROUP; *Int'l*, pg. 3557
HYUNDAI HEAVY INDUSTRIES CO., LTD.—See Hyundai Electric & Energy Systems Co., Ltd.; *Int'l*, pg. 3556
HYUNDAI HEAVY INDUSTRIES CO., LTD.; *Int'l*, pg. 3557
HYUNDAI HEAVY INDUSTRIES FRANCE SAS—See Hyundai Heavy Industries Co., Ltd.; *Int'l*, pg. 3557
HYUNDAI HELLAS S.A.—See AUTOHELLAS S.A.; *Int'l*, pg. 727
HYUNDAI HOME SHOPPING NETWORK CORPORATION—See Hyundai Department Store Co., Ltd.; *Int'l*, pg. 3556
HYUNDAI H&S CO., LTD.—See Hyundai Department Store Co., Ltd.; *Int'l*, pg. 3556

HYUNDAI HT CO., LTD; *Int'l*, pg. 3557
HYUNDAI HYSCO RUS LLC—See Hyundai Motor Company; *Int'l*, pg. 3559
HYUNDAI IHL CO., LTD.—See Hyundai MOBIS Co., Ltd.; *Int'l*, pg. 3558
HYUNDAI INDUSTRIAL CO., LTD. - ASAN PLANT—See Hyundai Industrial Co., Ltd.; *Int'l*, pg. 3557
HYUNDAI INDUSTRIAL CO., LTD. - BEIJING PLANT—See Hyundai Industrial Co., Ltd.; *Int'l*, pg. 3557
HYUNDAI INDUSTRIAL CO., LTD.; *Int'l*, pg. 3557
HYUNDAI INFORMATION TECHNOLOGY CO., LTD.—See Lotte Co., Ltd.; *Int'l*, pg. 4559
HYUNDAI INSURANCE BROKERS PTE. LTD.—See Hyundai Marine & Fire Insurance Co., Ltd.; *Int'l*, pg. 3558
HYUNDAI INSURANCE (CHINA) COMPANY LTD.—See Hyundai Marine & Fire Insurance Co., Ltd.; *Int'l*, pg. 3558
HYUNDAI INVESTMENT (AMERICA) LTD.—See Hyundai Marine & Fire Insurance Co., Ltd.; *Int'l*, pg. 3558
HYUNDAI INVESTMENTS CO., LTD.—See Hyundai Marine & Fire Insurance Co., Ltd.; *Int'l*, pg. 3558
HYUNDAI KEFICO CORPORATION—See Hyundai Motor Company; *Int'l*, pg. 3559
HYUNDAI KHOROL AGRO LTD.—See Hyundai Heavy Industries Co., Ltd.; *Int'l*, pg. 3557
HYUNDAI L&C CO., LTD.—See Hyundai Department Store Co., Ltd.; *Int'l*, pg. 3556
HYUNDAI LIVART CO., LTD.—See Hyundai Department Store Co., Ltd.; *Int'l*, pg. 3556
HYUNDAI MARINE & FIRE INSURANCE CO., LTD.; *Int'l*, pg. 3557
HYUNDAI MERCHANT MARINE (AMERICA), INC.—See HMM Co., Ltd.; *Int'l*, pg. 3432
HYUNDAI MERCHANT MARINE (CHINA) CO., LTD.—See HMM Co., Ltd.; *Int'l*, pg. 3432
HYUNDAI MERCHANT MARINE (EUROPE) LTD.—See HMM Co., Ltd.; *Int'l*, pg. 3432
HYUNDAI MERCHANT MARINE (HONG KONG) LTD.—See HMM Co., Ltd.; *Int'l*, pg. 3432
HYUNDAI MERCHANT MARINE (JAPAN) LTD.—See HMM Co., Ltd.; *Int'l*, pg. 3432
HYUNDAI MERCHANT MARINE (SINGAPORE) PTE. LTD.—See HMM Co., Ltd.; *Int'l*, pg. 3432
HYUNDAI MIPO DOCKYARD CO., LTD.—See Hyundai Heavy Industries Co., Ltd.; *Int'l*, pg. 3557
HYUNDAI MNSOFT, INC.—See Hyundai Motor Company; *Int'l*, pg. 3559
HYUNDAI MOBIS CO., LTD. - ANYANG FACTORY—See Hyundai MOBIS Co., Ltd.; *Int'l*, pg. 3558
HYUNDAI MOBIS CO., LTD. - ASAN FACTORY—See Hyundai MOBIS Co., Ltd.; *Int'l*, pg. 3558
HYUNDAI MOBIS CO., LTD. - CHANGWON FACTORY—See Hyundai MOBIS Co., Ltd.; *Int'l*, pg. 3558
HYUNDAI MOBIS CO., LTD. - CHEONAN IP FACTORY—See Hyundai MOBIS Co., Ltd.; *Int'l*, pg. 3558
HYUNDAI MOBIS CO., LTD. - CHUNGJU FACTORY—See Hyundai MOBIS Co., Ltd.; *Int'l*, pg. 3558
HYUNDAI MOBIS CO., LTD. - GIMCHEON FACTORY—See Hyundai MOBIS Co., Ltd.; *Int'l*, pg. 3558
HYUNDAI MOBIS CO., LTD. - GWANGJU FACTORY—See Hyundai MOBIS Co., Ltd.; *Int'l*, pg. 3558
HYUNDAI MOBIS CO., LTD. - IHWA FACTORY—See Hyundai MOBIS Co., Ltd.; *Int'l*, pg. 3558
HYUNDAI MOBIS CO., LTD. - JINCHEON FACTORY—See Hyundai MOBIS Co., Ltd.; *Int'l*, pg. 3558
HYUNDAI MOBIS CO., LTD. - POSEUNG FACTORY—See Hyundai MOBIS Co., Ltd.; *Int'l*, pg. 3558
HYUNDAI MOBIS CO., LTD. - SEOSAN FACTORY—See Hyundai MOBIS Co., Ltd.; *Int'l*, pg. 3558
HYUNDAI MOBIS CO., LTD.; *Int'l*, pg. 3558
HYUNDAI MOBIS CO., LTD. - YEOMPO-DONG FACTORY—See Hyundai MOBIS Co., Ltd.; *Int'l*, pg. 3558
HYUNDAI MOTOR AMERICA—See Hyundai Motor Company; *Int'l*, pg. 3559
HYUNDAI MOTOR ARGENTINA S.A.—See Sojitz Corporation; *Int'l*, pg. 7061
HYUNDAI MOTOR COMPANY ITALY S.R.L.—See Hyundai Motor Company; *Int'l*, pg. 3559
HYUNDAI MOTOR COMPANY; *Int'l*, pg. 3558
HYUNDAI MOTOR DETROIT—See Hyundai Motor Company; *Int'l*, pg. 3559
HYUNDAI MOTOR ESPANA, S.L.U.—See Hyundai Motor Company; *Int'l*, pg. 3559
HYUNDAI MOTOR EUROPE GMBH—See Hyundai Motor Company; *Int'l*, pg. 3559
HYUNDAI MOTOR GROUP (CHINA) LTD.—See Hyundai Motor Company; *Int'l*, pg. 3559
HYUNDAI MOTOR INDIA LTD.—See Hyundai Motor Company; *Int'l*, pg. 3559
HYUNDAI MOTOR JAPAN CO.—See Hyundai Motor Company; *Int'l*, pg. 3559

HYUNDAI MOTOR JAPAN R&D CENTER INC.—See Hyundai Motor Company; *Int'l*, pg. 3559
HYUNDAI MOTOR MANUFACTURING ALABAMA, LLC—See Hyundai Motor Company; *Int'l*, pg. 3559
HYUNDAI MOTOR NORWAY AS—See Hyundai Motor Company; *Int'l*, pg. 3559
HYUNDAI MOTOR POLAND SP. Z.O.O—See Hyundai Motor Company; *Int'l*, pg. 3559
HYUNDAI MOTOR SECURITIES CO. LTD.; *Int'l*, pg. 3560
HYUNDAI MOTOR (SHANGHAI) CO., LTD.—See Hyundai MOBIS Co., Ltd.; *Int'l*, pg. 3558
HYUNDAI MOTOR (THAILAND) CO., LTD.—See Sojitz Corporation; *Int'l*, pg. 7061
HYUNDAI MOTOR TOKYO—See Hyundai Motor Company; *Int'l*, pg. 3559
HYUNDAI MOTOR U.K. LTD—See Hyundai Motor Company; *Int'l*, pg. 3559
HYUNDAI MOVEX CO., LTD.; *Int'l*, pg. 3560
HYUNDAI MSEAT CO., LTD.—See Hyundai Motor Company; *Int'l*, pg. 3559
HYUNDAI NISHAT MOTOR (PRIVATE) LIMITED—See Sojitz Corporation; *Int'l*, pg. 7061
HYUNDAI OF WESLEY CHAPEL, LLC.; *U.S. Private*, pg. 2020
HYUNDAI OILBANK CO., LTD. - DAESAN REFINERY PLANT—See Hyundai Oilbank Co., Ltd.; *Int'l*, pg. 3560
HYUNDAI OILBANK CO., LTD.; *Int'l*, pg. 3560
HYUNDAI OILBANK SINGAPORE PTE LTD.—See Hyundai Oilbank Co., Ltd.; *Int'l*, pg. 3560
HYUNDAI ONE ASIA PTE. LTD.—See Hyundai Corporation; *Int'l*, pg. 3555
HYUNDAI PARTECS INC.—See Hyundai Motor Company; *Int'l*, pg. 3559
HYUNDAI PETROCHEMICAL CO., LTD.—See LG Chem Ltd.; *Int'l*, pg. 4473
HYUNDAI PHARMACEUTICAL CO., LTD.; *Int'l*, pg. 3560
HYUNDAI PHARM CO., LTD.; *Int'l*, pg. 3560
HYUNDAI POWER TRANSFORMERS USA INC.—See Hyundai Electric & Energy Systems Co., Ltd.; *Int'l*, pg. 3556
HYUNDAI ROTEM COMPANY - CHANGWON PLANT—See Hyundai Motor Company; *Int'l*, pg. 3560
HYUNDAI ROTEM COMPANY - DANGJIN PLANT—See Hyundai Motor Company; *Int'l*, pg. 3560
HYUNDAI ROTEM COMPANY—See Hyundai Motor Company; *Int'l*, pg. 3559
HYUNDAI SHIPBUILDING—See Hyundai Heavy Industries Co., Ltd.; *Int'l*, pg. 3557
HYUNDAI SPECIAL STEEL CO., LTD.—See Hyundai Steel Company; *Int'l*, pg. 3560
HYUNDAI STEEL AMERICA, INC.—See Hyundai Steel Company; *Int'l*, pg. 3560
HYUNDAI STEEL CHONGQING CO., LTD.—See Hyundai Steel Company; *Int'l*, pg. 3560
HYUNDAI STEEL COMPANY; *Int'l*, pg. 3560
HYUNDAI STEEL COMPANY - ULSAN PLANT—See Hyundai Steel Company; *Int'l*, pg. 3560
HYUNDAI STEEL COMPANY - YESAN PLANT—See Hyundai Steel Company; *Int'l*, pg. 3560
HYUNDAI STEEL CZECH S.R.O—See Hyundai Steel Company; *Int'l*, pg. 3560
HYUNDAI STEEL INDIA PRIVATE, LTD.—See Hyundai Steel Company; *Int'l*, pg. 3560
HYUNDAI STEEL INDUSTRY & TRADE BRAZIL LLC—See Hyundai Steel Company; *Int'l*, pg. 3560
HYUNDAI STEEL INVESTMENT (CHINA) CO., LTD.—See Hyundai Steel Company; *Int'l*, pg. 3560
HYUNDAI STEEL JIANGSU PROCESS CO., LTD.—See Hyundai Steel Company; *Int'l*, pg. 3560
HYUNDAI STEEL MEXICO S DE R. L. DE C. V—See Hyundai Steel Company; *Int'l*, pg. 3560
HYUNDAI STEEL PIPE INDIA PRIVATE, LTD.—See Hyundai Steel Company; *Int'l*, pg. 3560
HYUNDAI STEEL RUS LLC—See Hyundai Steel Company; *Int'l*, pg. 3560
HYUNDAI STEEL SLOVAKIA S.R.O.—See Hyundai Steel Company; *Int'l*, pg. 3560
HYUNDAI STEEL SUZHOU PROCESS CO., LTD.—See Hyundai Steel Company; *Int'l*, pg. 3560
HYUNDAI STEEL TIANJIN CO., LTD.—See Hyundai Steel Company; *Int'l*, pg. 3561
HYUNDAI STEEL TR AUTOMOTIVE STEEL PARTS CO., LTD.—See Hyundai Steel Company; *Int'l*, pg. 3561
HYUNDAI STEEL USA, INC.—See Hyundai Steel Company; *Int'l*, pg. 3561
HYUNDAI TRANSLEAD, INC.—See Hyundai Motor Company; *Int'l*, pg. 3559
HYUNDAI TRANSYS—See Hyundai Motor Company; *Int'l*, pg. 3560
HYUNDAI U.K UNDERWRITING LTD.—See Hyundai Marine & Fire Insurance Co., Ltd.; *Int'l*, pg. 3558
HYUNDAI WEST-ISLAND; *Int'l*, pg. 3561
HYUNDAI WIA AUTOMOTIVE ENGINE (SHANDONG) COMPANY—See Hyundai Motor Company; *Int'l*, pg. 3560
HYUNDAI WIA CORPORATION—See Hyundai Motor Company; *Int'l*, pg. 3560
HYUNDAI WIA CORPORATION - ULSAN PLANT 2—See Hyundai Motor Company; *Int'l*, pg. 3560

HYUNDAI WEST-ISLAND

HYUNDAI-WIA INDIA PVT LTD—See Hyundai Motor Company; *Int'l*, pg. 3560
HYUNDAI-WIA MACHINE AMERICA CORP.—See Hyundai Motor Company; *Int'l*, pg. 3560
HYUNDAM INDUSTRIAL CO., LTD.—See Aisan Industry Co., Ltd.; *Int'l*, pg. 250
HYUNDAM SLOVAKIA S.R.O.—See Aisan Industry Co., Ltd.; *Int'l*, pg. 250
HYUNDAM TECH CO., LTD.—See Aisan Industry Co., Ltd.; *Int'l*, pg. 250
HYUNDAM (ZHANGJIAGANG) AUTOMOBILE PARTS CO., LTD.—See Aisan Industry Co., Ltd.; *Int'l*, pg. 250
HYUNGJI ELITE INC.; *Int'l*, pg. 3561
HYUNGJI INNOVATION AND CREATIVE COMPANY LIMITED; *Int'l*, pg. 3561
HYUNGKUK F&B CO.,LTD; *Int'l*, pg. 3561
HYUNION HOLDING CO., LTD.; *Int'l*, pg. 3561
HYUNJIN MATERIALS CO., LTD.—See IntroMedic Co., Ltd.; *Int'l*, pg. 3769
HYUN WOO INDUSTRIAL CO., LTD; *Int'l*, pg. 3555
HYUPJIN CO., LTD.; *Int'l*, pg. 3561
HYVE BEAUTY FUARCILIK AS—See Providence Equity Partners L.L.C.; *U.S. Private*, pg. 3292
HYVE BEAUTY FUARCILIK AS—See Searchlight Capital Partners, L.P.; *U.S. Private*, pg. 3587
HY-VEE CONSTRUCTION, L.C.—See Hy-Vee, Inc.; *U.S. Private*, pg. 2016
HY-VEE CONSTRUCTION LLC—See Hy-Vee, Inc.; *U.S. Private*, pg. 2016
HY-VEE, INC.; *U.S. Private*, pg. 2015
HYVE GROUP PLC—See Providence Equity Partners L.L.C.; *U.S. Private*, pg. 3292
HYVE GROUP PLC—See Searchlight Capital Partners, L.P.; *U.S. Private*, pg. 3587
HYVE INDIA PRIVATE LTD.—See Providence Equity Partners L.L.C.; *U.S. Private*, pg. 3292
HYVE INDIA PRIVATE LTD.—See Searchlight Capital Partners, L.P.; *U.S. Private*, pg. 3587
HYVE SOLUTIONS CORPORATION—See TD Synnex Corp; *U.S. Public*, pg. 1984
HYVE WORLDWIDE B.V.—See Providence Equity Partners L.L.C.; *U.S. Private*, pg. 3292
HYVE WORLDWIDE B.V.—See Searchlight Capital Partners, L.P.; *U.S. Private*, pg. 3587
HYVISION SYSTEM INC.; *Int'l*, pg. 3561
HYVISION TECHNOLOGY INC.—See HyVISION SYSTEM INC.; *Int'l*, pg. 3561
HYVISION VINA COMPANY LIMITED—See HyVISION SYSTEM INC.; *Int'l*, pg. 3561
HYWAX GMBH—See AWAX S.p.A.; *Int'l*, pg. 752
HYWAY TRUCKING COMPANY—See FST Logistics Inc.; *U.S. Private*, pg. 1618
HYWEB TECHNOLOGY CO., LTD.; *Int'l*, pg. 3561
HYWIN HOLDINGS LTD.; *Int'l*, pg. 3561
HYZA A.S.—See Agrofert Holding, a.s.; *Int'l*, pg. 219
HYZON MOTORS INC.; *U.S. Public*, pg. 1080
HZ FBZ FORMENBAU ZUTTLINGEN GMBH—See Huazhong In-Vehicle Holdings Company Limited; *Int'l*, pg. 3516
HZF SERVICES (MALAYSIA) SDN. BHD.—See Hitachi Zosen Corporation; *Int'l*, pg. 3412
HZ HRVATSKE ZELJEZNICE HOLDING D.O.O.; *Int'l*, pg. 3561
HZNP USA LLC—See Amgen Inc.; *U.S. Public*, pg. 123
HZO, INC.—See Evercel, Inc.; *U.S. Private*, pg. 1437
HZPC AMERICA LATINA S.A.—See HZPC Holland B.V.; *Int'l*, pg. 3561
HZPC DEUTSCHLAND GMBH—See HZPC Holland B.V.; *Int'l*, pg. 3561
HZPC FRANCE SAS—See HZPC Holland B.V.; *Int'l*, pg. 3561
HZPC HOLLAND B.V.; *Int'l*, pg. 3561
HZPC KANTAPERUNA OY—See HZPC Holland B.V.; *Int'l*, pg. 3561
HZPC PATATAS ESPANA S.L.—See HZPC Holland B.V.; *Int'l*, pg. 3561
HZPC POLSKA SP. Z.O.O—See HZPC Holland B.V.; *Int'l*, pg. 3561
HZPC PORTUGAL LDA—See HZPC Holland B.V.; *Int'l*, pg. 3561
HZPC SVERIGE AB—See HZPC Holland B.V.; *Int'l*, pg. 3561
HZPC UK LTD—See HZPC Holland B.V.; *Int'l*, pg. 3561

I

I12 GMBH—See ProSiebenSat.1 Media SE; *Int'l*, pg. 6001
I2 CAPITAL PARTNERS SGR SPA; *Int'l*, pg. 3566
I2 DEVELOPMENT SA; *Int'l*, pg. 3566
I2 ENERGY SDN BHD—See Protasco Berhad; *Int'l*, pg. 6003
I2 ENTERPRISE PUBLIC COMPANY LIMITED; *Int'l*, pg. 3566
I 2 I MUSIKPRODUKTIONS- UND MUSIKVERLAGSGESELLSCHAFT MBH—See Bertelsmann SE & Co. KGaA; *Int'l*, pg. 994
I2 INC.—See Constellation Software Inc.; *Int'l*, pg. 1774
I2LRESEARCH LIMITED—See IP Group plc; *Int'l*, pg. 3795

I2LRESEARCH USA, INC.—See IP Group plc; *Int'l*, pg. 3795
I2 LTD.—See Constellation Software Inc.; *Int'l*, pg. 1774
I2M GMBH—See Mann+Hummel GmbH; *Int'l*, pg. 4673
I2O WATER LTD.—See Mueller Water Products, Inc.; *U.S. Public*, pg. 1486
I2S LINESCAN IMAGING INC.—See i2S SA; *Int'l*, pg. 3566
I2S SA; *Int'l*, pg. 3566
I2TS, INC.—See Marubeni Corporation; *Int'l*, pg. 4710
I3-AXIA, LLC—See i3 Verticals, Inc.; *U.S. Public*, pg. 1081
I3D.NET BV—See Ubisoft Entertainment S.A.; *Int'l*, pg. 8004
I3D.NET LLC—See Ubisoft Entertainment S.A.; *Int'l*, pg. 8004
I3 ENERGY CANADA LIMITED—See i3 Energy Plc; *Int'l*, pg. 3566
I3 ENERGY PLC; *Int'l*, pg. 3566
I3-EZPAY, LLC—See i3 Verticals, Inc.; *U.S. Public*, pg. 1081
I3-INFIN, LLC—See i3 Verticals, Inc.; *U.S. Public*, pg. 1081
I3 INTERACTIVE, INC.; *Int'l*, pg. 3566
I3 INTERNATIONAL INC.; *Int'l*, pg. 3566
I3-LL, LLC—See i3 Verticals, Inc.; *U.S. Public*, pg. 1081
I3LOGIC; *U.S. Private*, pg. 2027
I3-ONE, LLC—See i3 Verticals, Inc.; *U.S. Public*, pg. 1081
I3-PBS, LLC—See i3 Verticals, Inc.; *U.S. Public*, pg. 1081
I3 PHARMACEUTICAL SERVICES, INC.—See Elliott Management Corporation; *U.S. Private*, pg. 1366
I3 PHARMACEUTICAL SERVICES, INC.—See Patient Square Capital; L.P.; *U.S. Private*, pg. 3108
I3 PHARMACEUTICAL SERVICES, INC.—See Veritas Capital Fund Management, LLC; *U.S. Private*, pg. 4365
I3-RANDALL, LLC—See i3 Verticals, Inc.; *U.S. Public*, pg. 1081
I3-RS, LLC—See i3 Verticals, Inc.; *U.S. Public*, pg. 1081
I3 SECURITY PRIVATE LIMITED—See Mercantile Ventures Limited; *Int'l*, pg. 4819
I3-SOFTWARE & SERVICES, LLC—See i3 Verticals, Inc.; *U.S. Public*, pg. 1081
I3SYSTEM INC.; *Int'l*, pg. 3567
I3 SYSTEMS, INC.; *Int'l*, pg. 3566
I3 VERTICALS, INC.; *U.S. Public*, pg. 1081
I3 VERTICALS, LLC—See i3 Verticals, Inc.; *U.S. Public*, pg. 1081
I4B SP. Z O.O.—See LKQ Corporation; *U.S. Public*, pg. 1336
I4C INNOVATIONS INC.—See General Catalyst Partners; *U.S. Private*, pg. 1664
I4C INNOVATIONS INC.—See iSubscribed Inc.; *U.S. Private*, pg. 2147
I4C INNOVATIONS INC.—See WndrCo Holdings, LLC; *U.S. Private*, pg. 4552
I4DM; *U.S. Private*, pg. 2027
I4TECH SP. Z O.O.—See Introl S.A.; *Int'l*, pg. 3769
I4VENTURES SP. Z O.O.; *Int'l*, pg. 3567
I 595 EXPRESS, LLC—See ACS, Actividades de Construccion y Servicios, S.A.; *Int'l*, pg. 114
I-77 MOBILITY PARTNERS LLC—See Ferrovial S.A.; *Int'l*, pg. 2644
I-80 GOLD CORP.; *U.S. Public*, pg. 1080
I95DEV; *U.S. Private*, pg. 2027
I-9 ADVANTAGE, LLC—See Equifax Inc.; *U.S. Public*, pg. 786
I9 SPORTS CORPORATION; *U.S. Private*, pg. 2027
IAA, INC.—See RB Global, Inc.; *Int'l*, pg. 6226
IA AMERICAN LIFE INSURANCE COMPANY—See iA Financial Corporation Inc.; *Int'l*, pg. 3567
IAA UK HOLDINGS LIMITED—See RB Global, Inc.; *Int'l*, pg. 6226
IA AUTO FINANCE INC.—See iA Financial Corporation Inc.; *Int'l*, pg. 3568
IAA VEHICLE SERVICES LIMITED—See RB Global, Inc.; *Int'l*, pg. 6226
IA BELL EQUIPMENT CO NAMIBIA (PROPRIETARY) LIMITED—See Bell Equipment Limited; *Int'l*, pg. 966
IAB HOLDINGS LIMITED; *Int'l*, pg. 3568
IAB IONENAUSTAUSCHER GMBH—See LANXESS AG; *Int'l*, pg. 4415
IAB SOLUTIONS, LLC; *U.S. Private*, pg. 2027
IAC ACOUSTICS AUSTRALIA—See AEA Investors LP; *U.S. Private*, pg. 114
IAC ACOUSTICS ITALIANA SPA—See AEA Investors LP; *U.S. Private*, pg. 114
IAC BOET STOPSON SAS—See AEA Investors LP; *U.S. Private*, pg. 114
IAC CANTON LLC—See Invesco Ltd.; *U.S. Public*, pg. 1164
IAC GROUP AB—See Invesco Ltd.; *U.S. Public*, pg. 1164
IAC GROUP B.V.B.A.—See Invesco Ltd.; *U.S. Public*, pg. 1164
IAC GROUP S.L.—See Invesco Ltd.; *U.S. Public*, pg. 1164
IAC INC.; *U.S. Public*, pg. 1081
IAC INDUSTRIES, INC.—See Treston Oy; *Int'l*, pg. 7916
IA CLARINGTON INVESTMENTS INC.—See iA Financial Corporation Inc.; *Int'l*, pg. 3567
IAC MENDON, LLC—See Invesco Ltd.; *U.S. Public*, pg. 1164

CORPORATE AFFILIATIONS

IAC NORDIC A/S—See AEA Investors LP; *U.S. Private*, pg. 114
IAC SEARCH & MEDIA, INC.—See IAC Inc.; *U.S. Public*, pg. 1082
IAC SIM ENGINEERING—See AEA Investors LP; *U.S. Private*, pg. 114
IAC STOPSON ESPANOLOA, SA—See AEA Investors LP; *U.S. Private*, pg. 114
IACT CORPORATION—See InfoNet inc.; *Int'l*, pg. 3690
IACX ENERGY LLC—See Glenfarne Group, LLC; *U.S. Private*, pg. 1710
IAD INDUSTRIEANLAGEN-DIENST GMBH—See Deufol SE; *Int'l*, pg. 2048
IAE INTERNATIONAL AERO ENGINES AG—See RTX Corporation; *U.S. Public*, pg. 1823
IA ENERGY CORP.; *U.S. Private*, pg. 2027
IAERO GROUP; *U.S. Private*, pg. 2027
IA FINANCIAL CORPORATION INC.; *Int'l*, pg. 3567
IAF LTD.; *U.S. Private*, pg. 2027
IAG CARGO LIMITED—See International Consolidated Airlines Group S.A.; *Int'l*, pg. 3745
IAG GLASS COMPANY LIMITED; *Int'l*, pg. 3568
IAG HOLDINGS INC.; *U.S. Private*, pg. 2027
IAG INDUSTRIE-ANLAGEN-BAU GEORGSMARIENHUETTE GMBH—See Georgsmarienhutte Holding GmbH; *Int'l*, pg. 2940
IAG MAGNUM GMBH—See Georgsmarienhutte Holding GmbH; *Int'l*, pg. 2940
IAG NEW ZEALAND LIMITED—See Insurance Australia Group Limited; *Int'l*, pg. 3725
I.A GROUP CORPORATION; *Int'l*, pg. 3565
I.A. HEDIN BIL AB; *Int'l*, pg. 3565
IAHGAMES HONG KONG LIMITED—See Shunten International (Holdings) Limited; *Int'l*, pg. 6870
IAHL CORP.; *U.S. Public*, pg. 1083
IAH OF FLORIDA, LLC—See Centene Corporation; *U.S. Public*, pg. 469
IAI AMERICA, INC.—See IAI Corporation; *Int'l*, pg. 3568
IAI ASIA PTE LTD—See Israel Aerospace Industries Ltd.; *Int'l*, pg. 3822
IAI CORPORATION; *Int'l*, pg. 3568
IAI DO BRASIL LTDA—See Israel Aerospace Industries Ltd.; *Int'l*, pg. 3822
IAI HOLDING A/S; *Int'l*, pg. 3568
IAI INDUSTRIAL SYSTEMS B.V.—See ASSA ABLOY AB; *Int'l*, pg. 636
IAI INDUSTRIEROBOTER GMBH—See IAI Corporation; *Int'l*, pg. 3568
IA INC.; *Int'l*, pg. 3568
IAI NORTH AMERICA, INC.—See Israel Aerospace Industries Ltd.; *Int'l*, pg. 3822
IAI ROBOT (THAILAND) CO., LTD.—See IAI Corporation; *Int'l*, pg. 3568
IAI (SHANGHAI) CO., LTD.—See IAI Corporation; *Int'l*, pg. 3568
IA KOREA CORP—See IAI Corporation; *Int'l*, pg. 3568
IA LODGING DENVER CITY CENTER, L.L.C.—See XENIA HOTELS & RESORTS, INC.; *U.S. Public*, pg. 2386
IA LODGING GARDEN GROVE HARBOR L.L.C.—See XENIA HOTELS & RESORTS, INC.; *U.S. Public*, pg. 2386
IA LODGING PITTSBURGH PENN TRS DST—See XENIA HOTELS & RESORTS, INC.; *U.S. Public*, pg. 2386
IAL SAATCHI & SAATCHI—See Publicis Groupe S.A.; *Int'l*, pg. 6108
IAMBA ARAD S.A.; *Int'l*, pg. 3568
I AM CONSULTING CO., LTD.—See TIS Inc.; *Int'l*, pg. 7757
IAMECH TECHNOLOGY INC.—See Contrel Technology Co., Ltd.; *Int'l*, pg. 1785
IAMGOLD CORPORATION; *Int'l*, pg. 3568
IAMGOLD ESSAKANE S.A.—See IAMGOLD Corporation; *Int'l*, pg. 3568
IAM REAL ESTATE GROUP—See Fiera Capital Corporation; *Int'l*, pg. 2660
IAMS EUROPE B.V.—See Spectrum Brands Holdings, Inc.; *U.S. Public*, pg. 1916
I AM SMART TECHNOLOGY, INC.; *U.S. Private*, pg. 2020
I.A.M.U. S.A.; *Int'l*, pg. 3565
IAN ALLAN LTD.—See Seera Group Holding Co.; *Int'l*, pg. 6679
IAN BANHAM & ASSOCIATES- CONSULTING ENGINEERS—See National Central Cooling Company PJSC; *Int'l*, pg. 5155
IAN BELL INSURANCE BROKERS PTY. LTD.—See Steadfast Group Limited; *Int'l*, pg. 7187
IAN BLACK REAL ESTATE; *U.S. Private*, pg. 2027
I AND I CO., LTD.—See SBS Holdings Inc.; *Int'l*, pg. 6607
IAN MACLEOD DISTILLERS & CO., LTD.; *Int'l*, pg. 3569
IAN MACLEOD DISTILLERS LTD.—See Ian Macleod Distillers & Co., Ltd.; *Int'l*, pg. 3569
IAN MOSEY LTD; *Int'l*, pg. 3569
I'ANSON BROTHERS LTD; *Int'l*, pg. 3562
IANTE INVESTMENTS SOCIMI, S.A.; *Int'l*, pg. 3569
IANTHUS CAPITAL HOLDINGS, INC.; *U.S. Public*, pg. 1083
IANYWHERE SOLUTIONS CANADA LTD.—See SAP SE; *Int'l*, pg. 6571

COMPANY NAME INDEX

IANYWHERE SOLUTIONS K. K.—See SAP SE; *Int'l*, pg. 6571
IAO PARTNERS—See D.R. Horton, Inc.; *U.S. Public*, pg. 620
IAP GROUP AUSTRALIA PTY. LTD.—See PTB Group Limited; *Int'l*, pg. 6090
IAPPSYS; *U.S. Private*, pg. 2028
IA PRIVATE WEALTH INC.—See iA Financial Corporation Inc.; *Int'l*, pg. 3568
IA PRIVATE WEALTH (USA) INC.—See iA Financial Corporation Inc.; *Int'l*, pg. 3568
IAP WORLD SERVICES INC.—See IAP Worldwide Services, Inc.; *U.S. Private*, pg. 2028
IAP WORLDWIDE SERVICES, INC.; *U.S. Private*, pg. 2027
IARGENTO HI TECH ASSETS LP; *Int'l*, pg. 3569
IAR SA; *Int'l*, pg. 3569
IAR SYSTEMS AB—See IAR Systems Group AB; *Int'l*, pg. 3569
IAR SYSTEMS AG—See IAR Systems Group AB; *Int'l*, pg. 3569
IAR SYSTEMS GMBH—See IAR Systems Group AB; *Int'l*, pg. 3569
IAR SYSTEMS GROUP AB; *Int'l*, pg. 3569
IAR SYSTEMS K.K.—See IAR Systems Group AB; *Int'l*, pg. 3569
IAR SYSTEMS LTD.—See IAR Systems Group AB; *Int'l*, pg. 3569
IAR SYSTEMS SOFTWARE INC.—See IAR Systems Group AB; *Int'l*, pg. 3569
IAR SYSTEMS SOFTWARE INC.—See IAR Systems Group AB; *Int'l*, pg. 3569
IAS CLAIM SERVICES—See IAS Services Group LLC; *U.S. Private*, pg. 2028
IAS GMBH—See SMS Holding GmbH; *Int'l*, pg. 7015
IASO BIOMED, INC.; *U.S. Private*, pg. 2028
IASOLUTION INC.—See Aplix Corporation; *Int'l*, pg. 516
IASON SA; *Int'l*, pg. 3569
IASO S.A.—See Brookfield Corporation; *Int'l*, pg. 1182
IAS SERVICES GROUP LLC; *U.S. Private*, pg. 2028
IAS SMARTS LIMITED—See Stein + Partners Brand Activation; *U.S. Private*, pg. 3797
IAS—See Shaw Electric Inc.; *U.S. Private*, pg. 3628
IAT DEUTSCHLAND GMBH—See PORR AG; *Int'l*, pg. 5923
IAT GMBH—See PORR AG; *Int'l*, pg. 5923
IAT IMPERMEABILIZZAZIONI SRL—See PORR AG; *Int'l*, pg. 5923
IAT LTDA—See CVC Capital Partners SICAV-FIS S.A.; *Int'l*, pg. 1887
IAT REINSURANCE COMPANY, LTD.; *U.S. Private*, pg. 2028
IATRIC SYSTEMS, INC.—See Constellation Software Inc.; *Int'l*, pg. 1774
IATRIKI TECHNIKI S.A.—See Athens Medical Centers SA; *Int'l*, pg. 670
IAT UK WATERPROOFING SYSTEMS LIMITED—See PORR AG; *Int'l*, pg. 5923
I-AUC INC.—See Aucnet Inc.; *Int'l*, pg. 700
IA URBAN HOTELS HOUSTON TRS LIMITED PARTNERSHIP—See XENIA HOTELS & RESORTS, INC.; *U.S. Public*, pg. 2386
IA URBAN HOTELS WASHINGTON DC FRANKLIN TRS, L.L.C.—See XENIA HOTELS & RESORTS, INC.; *U.S. Public*, pg. 2386
IAUTOMATION, INC.—See The Riverside Company; *U.S. Private*, pg. 4110
IAV AUTOMOTIVE ENGINEERING INC.—See Porsche Automobil Holding SE; *Int'l*, pg. 5929
IAV AUTOMOTIVE ENGINEERING (SHANGHAI) CO. LTD.—See Porsche Automobil Holding SE; *Int'l*, pg. 5929
IAV CO. LTD. JAPAN—See Porsche Automobil Holding SE; *Int'l*, pg. 5929
IAV FRANCE S.A.S.U.—See Porsche Automobil Holding SE; *Int'l*, pg. 5929
IAV KOREA CO., LTD.—See Porsche Automobil Holding SE; *Int'l*, pg. 5929
IAV U.K. LTD.—See Porsche Automobil Holding SE; *Int'l*, pg. 5929
IAW DE MEXICO, S.A. DE C.V.—See Atlantic China Welding Consumables, Inc.; *Int'l*, pg. 674
IBABS B.V.—See Euronext N.V.; *Int'l*, pg. 2554
IBA DOSIMETRY AMERICA INC.—See Ion Beam Applications, S.A.; *Int'l*, pg. 3793
IBA DOSIMETRY CO. LTD.—See Ion Beam Applications, S.A.; *Int'l*, pg. 3793
IBA DOSIMETRY GMBH—See Ion Beam Applications, S.A.; *Int'l*, pg. 3793
IBA DOSIMETRY LTD.—See Ion Beam Applications, S.A.; *Int'l*, pg. 3793
I. & B. AGISTRIOTIS SA—See A.A.G. STUCCHI s.r.l.; *Int'l*, pg. 23
IBA INC.; *U.S. Private*, pg. 2028
IBA INDUSTRIAL INC.—See Ion Beam Applications, S.A.; *Int'l*, pg. 3793
IBA JAPAN KK—See Ion Beam Applications, S.A.; *Int'l*, pg. 3793

IB ANDRESEN INDUSTRI A/S-FREDERICIA—See IAI Holding A/S; *Int'l*, pg. 3568
IB ANDRESEN INDUSTRI A/S—See IAI Holding A/S; *Int'l*, pg. 3568
IB ANDRESEN INDUSTRY (THAILAND) CO. LTD—See IAI Holding A/S; *Int'l*, pg. 3568
I-BANKERS SECURITIES, INC.; *U.S. Private*, pg. 2026
IBANK MARKETING CO., LTD.—See Fukuoka Financial Group, Inc.; *Int'l*, pg. 2840
IBA PROTON THERAPY—See Ion Beam Applications, S.A.; *Int'l*, pg. 3793
IBAR A.D.; *Int'l*, pg. 3569
IBARAKI DAIICHI TRAFFIC LTD.—See Daiichi Koutsu Sangyo Co., Ltd.; *Int'l*, pg. 1928
IBARAKI GRANDY HOUSE CO., LTD.—See Grandy House Corporation; *Int'l*, pg. 3058
IBARAKI GREEN CO., LTD.—See Obayashi Corporation; *Int'l*, pg. 5508
IBARAKI K-TECHNO CO., LTD—See Kandenko Co., Ltd.; *Int'l*, pg. 4065
IBARAKI TECHNOS LTD.—See Hitachi, Ltd.; *Int'l*, pg. 3423
IBASE SOLUTION CO., LTD; *Int'l*, pg. 3569
IBASE TECHNOLOGY INTERNATIONAL PTE. LTD.—See IBase Technology Pte. Ltd.; *Int'l*, pg. 3569
IBASE TECHNOLOGY PTE. LTD.; *Int'l*, pg. 3569
IBASE TECHNOLOGY (USA), INC.; *U.S. Private*, pg. 2028
IBASIS EUROPE LTD.—See Tofane Global SAS; *Int'l*, pg. 7774
IBASIS, INC.—See Tofane Global SAS; *Int'l*, pg. 7774
I BATT INC.; *U.S. Private*, pg. 2020
IBA USA INC.—See Ion Beam Applications, S.A.; *Int'l*, pg. 3793
IBB AMSTERDAM BV; *Int'l*, pg. 3569
IBB DUBLIN LTD—See IBB Amsterdam BV; *Int'l*, pg. 3569
IBBERSON ENGINEERING, INC.—See Peter Kiewit Sons', Inc.; *U.S. Private*, pg. 3158
IBBERSON, INC.—See Peter Kiewit Sons', Inc.; *U.S. Private*, pg. 3158
IBBERSON INTERNATIONAL, INC.—See Peter Kiewit Sons', Inc.; *U.S. Private*, pg. 3158
IBB PARIS SARL—See IBB Amsterdam BV; *Int'l*, pg. 3569
IBC ADVANCED ALLOYS CORP.; *U.S. Public*, pg. 1083
IBC ADVANCED TECHNOLOGIES, INC.; *U.S. Private*, pg. 2028
IBC ASIA (S) PTE LIMITED—See Informa plc; *Int'l*, pg. 3691
IBC GROUP INC.; *U.S. Private*, pg. 2028
IBC HOTELS, LLC—See InnSuites Hospitality Trust; *U.S. Public*, pg. 1127
I & B CLEANING EQUIPMENT LTD.—See L. Possehl & Co. mbH; *Int'l*, pg. 4383
IBC LIFE INSURANCE COMPANY—See International Bancshares Corporation; *Int'l*, pg. 1145
IBC MANAGEMENT, LLC; *U.S. Private*, pg. 2028
IBC NORTH AMERICA INC.; *U.S. Private*, pg. 2028
IBC PHARMACEUTICALS, INC.—See Gilead Sciences, Inc.; *U.S. Public*, pg. 937
IBC SHELL CONTAINERS INC.—See International Business Communications Inc.; *U.S. Private*, pg. 2115
IBC SOLAR A.E.—See IBC Solar AG; *Int'l*, pg. 3569
IBC SOLAR AG; *Int'l*, pg. 3569
IBC SOLAR AUSTRIA GMBH—See IBC Solar AG; *Int'l*, pg. 3569
IBC SOLAR B.V.—See IBC Solar AG; *Int'l*, pg. 3569
IBC SOLAR PROJECTS PRIVATE LIMITED—See IBC Solar AG; *Int'l*, pg. 3570
IBC SOLAR SRL—See IBC Solar AG; *Int'l*, pg. 3570
IBC SOLAR TEKNIK SDN BHD—See IBC Solar AG; *Int'l*, pg. 3570
IBC VEHICLES LIMITED—See Stellantis N.V.; *Int'l*, pg. 7203
IBD BIKES UK LIMITED—See Dorel Industries, Inc.; *Int'l*, pg. 2176
IBD INDIA—See Percept Holdings Pvt. Ltd.; *Int'l*, pg. 5796
IBEC BEARINGS AB—See OEM International AB; *Int'l*, pg. 5528
IBEC B.V.—See OEM International AB; *Int'l*, pg. 5528
I-BEHAVIOR, INC. - HARRISON—See WPP plc; *Int'l*, pg. 8491
I-BEHAVIOR, INC.—See WPP plc; *Int'l*, pg. 8491
I B E JUNUZOVIC D.O.O.—See Endress+Hauser (International) Holding AG; *Int'l*, pg. 2408
IBERA - INDUSTRIA DE BETAO S.A.—See Camargo Correa S.A.; *Int'l*, pg. 1268
IBERBANDA, S.A.—See Telefonica, S.A.; *Int'l*, pg. 7535
IBERBARNA PAPEL, S.A.—See Iberpapel Gestion SA; *Int'l*, pg. 3574
IBERCARRETILLAS OM ESPANA S.A.—See KKR & Co. Inc.; *U.S. Public*, pg. 1255
IBERCARRETILLAS OM ESPANA S.A.—See The Goldman Sachs Group, Inc.; *U.S. Public*, pg. 2079
IBERCHEM SOUTH AFRICA (PTY) LTD.—See Croda International plc; *Int'l*, pg. 1853
IBERDEFI—See DEFI Group SAS; *Int'l*, pg. 2004
IBERDROLA CANADA ENERGY SERVICES, LTD.—See Iberdrola, S.A.; *Int'l*, pg. 3573

IBERDROLA, S.A.

IBERDROLA CLIENTES PORTUGAL, UNIPESSOAL—See Iberdrola, S.A.; *Int'l*, pg. 3572
IBERDROLA CLIENTI ITALIA, S.R.L.—See Iberdrola, S.A.; *Int'l*, pg. 3572
IBERDROLA COGENERACION, S.L.U.—See Iberdrola, S.A.; *Int'l*, pg. 3572
IBERDROLA CONSULTORIA E SERVICOS DO BRASIL, LTD.—See Iberdrola, S.A.; *Int'l*, pg. 3572
IBERDROLA DISTRIBUCION DE GAS, S.A.U.—See Iberdrola, S.A.; *Int'l*, pg. 3572
IBERDROLA DISTRIBUCION ELECTRICA, S.A.U.—See Iberdrola, S.A.; *Int'l*, pg. 3572
IBERDROLA DIVERSIFICACION, S.A.U.—See Iberdrola, S.A.; *Int'l*, pg. 3572
IBERDROLA ENERGIA ALTAMIRA DE SERVICIOS, S.A. DE C.V.—See Iberdrola, S.A.; *Int'l*, pg. 3571
IBERDROLA ENERGIA ALTAMIRA, S.A. DE C.V.—See Iberdrola, S.A.; *Int'l*, pg. 3571
IBERDROLA ENERGIA DEL GOLFO, S.A. DE C.V.—See Iberdrola, S.A.; *Int'l*, pg. 3571
IBERDROLA ENERGIA DO BRASIL, LTDA.—See Iberdrola, S.A.; *Int'l*, pg. 3572
IBERDROLA ENERGIA LA LAGUNA, S.A. DE C.V.—See Iberdrola, S.A.; *Int'l*, pg. 3571
IBERDROLA ENERGIA MONTERREY, S.A. DE C.V.—See Iberdrola, S.A.; *Int'l*, pg. 3571
IBERDROLA ENERGIA, S.A.U.—See Iberdrola, S.A.; *Int'l*, pg. 3572
IBERDROLA ENERGIA SOLAR PUERTOLLANO, S.A.—See Iberdrola, S.A.; *Int'l*, pg. 3572
IBERDROLA ENERGIAS RENOVABLES, S.A.U.—See Iberdrola, S.A.; *Int'l*, pg. 3572
IBERDROLA ENERGIAS RENOVAVEIS DO BRASIL, S.A.—See Iberdrola, S.A.; *Int'l*, pg. 3572
IBERDROLA ENERGIAS RENOVAVEIS S.A.—See Iberdrola, S.A.; *Int'l*, pg. 3572
IBERDROLA ENERGIE FRANCE, S.A.S.—See Iberdrola, S.A.; *Int'l*, pg. 3572
IBERDROLA ENERGY SERVICE, LLC—See Iberdrola, S.A.; *Int'l*, pg. 3570
IBERDROLA ENGINEERING AND CONSTRUCTION BULGARIA—See Iberdrola, S.A.; *Int'l*, pg. 3572
IBERDROLA ENGINEERING AND CONSTRUCTION POLAND, SP. Z. O. O.—See Iberdrola, S.A.; *Int'l*, pg. 3572
IBERDROLA ENGINEERING AND CONSTRUCTION UK, LTD.—See Iberdrola, S.A.; *Int'l*, pg. 3572
IBERDROLA ESPANA, S.A.U.—See Iberdrola, S.A.; *Int'l*, pg. 3572
IBERDROLA FINANCIACION, S.A.—See Iberdrola, S.A.; *Int'l*, pg. 3572
IBERDROLA GENERACION, S.A.U.—See Iberdrola, S.A.; *Int'l*, pg. 3572
IBERDROLA INGENIERIA DE EXPLOTACION, S.A.U.—See Iberdrola, S.A.; *Int'l*, pg. 3572
IBERDROLA INGENIERIA Y CONSTRUCCION MEXICO, S.A. DE C.V.—See Iberdrola, S.A.; *Int'l*, pg. 3572
IBERDROLA INGENIERIA Y CONSTRUCCION, S.A.—See Iberdrola, S.A.; *Int'l*, pg. 3572
IBERDROLA INMOBILIARIA, S.A.—See Iberdrola, S.A.; *Int'l*, pg. 3572
IBERDROLA INTERNATIONAL, B.V.—See Iberdrola, S.A.; *Int'l*, pg. 3572
IBERDROLA IRELAND, LTD.—See Iberdrola, S.A.; *Int'l*, pg. 3572
IBERDROLA MAGYARORSZAG MERNOKI ES EPITO KORLATOLF—See Iberdrola, S.A.; *Int'l*, pg. 3572
IBERDROLA MEXICO, S.A. DE C.V.—See Iberdrola, S.A.; *Int'l*, pg. 3571
IBERDROLA QSTP, LLC—See Iberdrola, S.A.; *Int'l*, pg. 3572
IBERDROLA REDES, S.A.U.—See Iberdrola, S.A.; *Int'l*, pg. 3572
IBERDROLA RENEWABLES ROMANIA, S.R.L.—See Iberdrola, S.A.; *Int'l*, pg. 3572
IBERDROLA RENOVABLES ANDALUCIA, S.A.U.—See Iberdrola, S.A.; *Int'l*, pg. 3572
IBERDROLA RENOVABLES ARAGON, S.A.U.—See Iberdrola, S.A.; *Int'l*, pg. 3572
IBERDROLA RENOVABLES CASTILLA LA MANCHA, S.A.U.—See Iberdrola, S.A.; *Int'l*, pg. 3572
IBERDROLA RENOVABLES CASTILLA Y LEON, S.A.—See Iberdrola, S.A.; *Int'l*, pg. 3572
IBERDROLA RENOVABLES DEUTSCHLAND GMBH—See MVV Energie AG; *Int'l*, pg. 5109
IBERDROLA RENOVABLES DE VALENCIA, S.A.U.—See Iberdrola, S.A.; *Int'l*, pg. 3572
IBERDROLA RENOVABLES FRANCE, S.A.S.—See Iberdrola, S.A.; *Int'l*, pg. 3572
IBERDROLA RENOVABLES LA RIOJA, S.A.—See Iberdrola, S.A.; *Int'l*, pg. 3572
IBERDROLA RENOVABLES MAGYARORSZAG, KFT.—See Iberdrola, S.A.; *Int'l*, pg. 3572
IBERDROLA RENOVABLES MAGYARORSZAG MEGUJJULO—See Iberdrola, S.A.; *Int'l*, pg. 3572
IBERDROLA RE, S.A.—See Minor International PCL; *Int'l*, pg. 4911
IBERDROLA, S.A.; *Int'l*, pg. 3570

IBERDROLA, S.A.

IBERDROLA SERVICIOS ENERGETICOS, S.A.U.—See Iberdrola, S.A.; *Int'l*, pg. 3573
IBERDROLA SERVICIOS MONTERREY, S,A. DE C.V.—See Iberdrola, S.A.; *Int'l*, pg. 3572
IBERDROLA SISTEMAS, S.A.U.—See Iberdrola, S.A.; *Int'l*, pg. 3573
IBERDROLA USA ENTERPRISES, INC.—See Iberdrola, S.A.; *Int'l*, pg. 3570
IBERDROLA USA, INC.—See Iberdrola, S.A.; *Int'l*, pg. 3570
IBERDROLA USA, INC.—See Iberdrola, S.A.; *Int'l*, pg. 3570
IBERDROLA USA, INC.—See Iberdrola, S.A.; *Int'l*, pg. 3570
IBERDROLA USA, INC.—See Iberdrola, S.A.; *Int'l*, pg. 3570
IBERDROLA USA, INC.—See Iberdrola, S.A.; *Int'l*, pg. 3570
IBERDROLA USA, INC.—See Iberdrola, S.A.; *Int'l*, pg. 3570
IBERE PHARMACEUTICALS; *U.S. Public*, pg. 1083
IBEREUCALIPTOS, S.A.U.—See Iberpapel Gestion SA; *Int'l*, pg. 3574
IBERFLORESTAL - COMERCIO E SERVICOS FLORESTAIS, S A—See ENCE Energia y Celulosa, S.A.; *Int'l*, pg. 2401
IBERFOIL ARAGON S.L.U.—See Aliberico, S.L.; *Int'l*, pg. 326
IBERFRANCE POLAND—See Iberfrance; *Int'l*, pg. 3574
IBERFRANCE; *Int'l*, pg. 3574
I-BERHAD; *Int'l*, pg. 3562
IBERIA AIR LINES OF SPAIN—See International Consolidated Airlines Group S.A.; *Int'l*, pg. 3746
IBERIABANK CORPORATION—See First Horizon Corporation; *U.S. Public*, pg. 844
IBERIABANK MORTGAGE COMPANY—See First Horizon Corporation; *U.S. Public*, pg. 845
IBERIABANK—See First Horizon Corporation; *U.S. Public*, pg. 845
IBERIA FINANCIAL SERVICES, LLC—See First Horizon Corporation; *U.S. Public*, pg. 845
IBERIA INDUSTRY CAPITAL GROUP SARL; *Int'l*, pg. 3574
IBERIA LINEAS AEREAS DE ESPANA, S.A.—See International Consolidated Airlines Group S.A.; *Int'l*, pg. 3745
IBERIA, LINEAS AEREAS DE ESPANA, SOCIEDAD ANONIMA OPERADORA—See International Consolidated Airlines Group S.A.; *Int'l*, pg. 3746
IBERIAN LUBE BASE OILS COMPANY, S.A.—See SK Inc.; *Int'l*, pg. 6971
IBERIAN MINERALS CORP. PLC—See Trafigura Beheer B.V.; *Int'l*, pg. 7890
IBERIA TECNOLOGIA, S.A.—See International Consolidated Airlines Group S.A.; *Int'l*, pg. 3746
IBERIA TILE CORP.; *U.S. Private*, pg. 2028
IBERICA DE COMPRAS CORPORATIVAS, S.L.—See Banco Santander, S.A.; *Int'l*, pg. 826
IBERICA DE SUSPENSIONES, S.A.—See NHK Spring Co., Ltd.; *Int'l*, pg. 5257
IBEROALPLA PORTUGAL LDA—See Alpla-Werke Alwin Lehner GmbH & Co. KG; *Int'l*, pg. 374
IBEROAMERICANA DE HIDROCARBUROS, S.A. DE C.V.—See ACS, Actividades de Construccion y Servicios, S.A.; *Int'l*, pg. 114
IBEROASISTENCIA, S.A.—See MAPFRE S.A.; *Int'l*, pg. 4684
IBERO ASISTENCIA, S.A.—See MAPFRE S.A.; *Int'l*, pg. 4684
IBEROTEL OTELCILIK A.S—See TUI AG; *Int'l*, pg. 7965
IBERPAPEL ARGENTINA, S.A.—See Iberpapel Gestion SA; *Int'l*, pg. 3574
IBERPAPEL GESTION SA; *Int'l*, pg. 3574
IBERPAPEL ON LINE, S.L.U.—See Iberpapel Gestion SA; *Int'l*, pg. 3574
IBERPHONE SAU—See Teleperformance SE; *Int'l*, pg. 7540
IBERPOTASH S.A.—See Israel Corporation Ltd.; *Int'l*, pg. 3823
IBERSILVA, S.A.U.—See ENCE Energia y Celulosa, S.A.; *Int'l*, pg. 2401
IBERSOL S.G.P.S., S.A.; *Int'l*, pg. 3574
IBERTREDI MEDIOAMBIENTAL S.A.—See Groupe Seche SAS; *Int'l*, pg. 3110
IBERVILLE INSULATIONS INC.; *U.S. Private*, pg. 2028
IBETA QUALITY ASSURANCE LLC; *U.S. Private*, pg. 2028
IBEX CONSTRUCTION COMPANY, LLC; *U.S. Private*, pg. 2028
IBEX GLOBAL SOLUTIONS LIMITED—See The Resource Group International Ltd.; *U.S. Private*, pg. 4105
IBEX IT BUSINESS EXPERTS, LLC; *U.S. Private*, pg. 2028
IBEX LIMITED—See The Resource Group International Ltd.; *U.S. Private*, pg. 4105
IBEX MARITIME LTD—See Erria A/S; *Int'l*, pg. 2497
IBEX PRECLINICAL RESEARCH, INC.—See JP Lawrence Biomedical, Inc.; *U.S. Private*, pg. 2239

IBEX REINSURANCE COMPANY LIMITED—See Markel Group Inc.; *U.S. Public*, pg. 1367
IBEX TECHNOLOGIES INC.—See Novo Nordisk Fonden; *Int'l*, pg. 5463
IBF FINANCIAL HOLDINGS CO., LTD.; *Int'l*, pg. 3574
IBF SECURITIES CO., LTD.—See IBF Financial Holdings Co., Ltd.; *Int'l*, pg. 3574
IBF VENTURE CAPITAL CO., LTD.—See IBF Financial Holdings Co., Ltd.; *Int'l*, pg. 3574
IBG ADRIATICA HOLDINGS, INC.—See Independent Bank Group, Inc.; *U.S. Public*, pg. 1116
IBG IMMUCOR LTD.—See Werfen Life Group, S.A.U.; *Int'l*, pg. 8379
IBG LLC—See Interactive Brokers Group, Inc.; *U.S. Public*, pg. 1140
IBG REAL ESTATE HOLDINGS, INC.—See Independent Bank Group, Inc.; *U.S. Public*, pg. 1116
IBH BOOKS AND MAGAZINES DISTRIBUTORS LIMITED—See Future Corporate Resources Limited; *Int'l*, pg. 2853
IBH EHF.—See Interroll Holding AG; *Int'l*, pg. 3758
IBH ENGINEERING GMBH—See Enka Insaat ve Sanayi A.S.; *Int'l*, pg. 2440
IBIB GROUP CONSULTANTS (ISRAEL) LTD.—See ARCADIS N.V.; *Int'l*, pg. 542
IBI CORPORATE FINANCE LIMITED—See Daiwa Securities Group Inc.; *Int'l*, pg. 1948
IBIC—See SKion GmbH; *Int'l*, pg. 6987
IBIDEN ASIA HOLDINGS PTE. LTD.—See Ibiden Co., Ltd.; *Int'l*, pg. 3575
IBIDEN BUSSAN CO., LTD.—See Ibiden Co., Ltd.; *Int'l*, pg. 3575
IBIDEN CANADA INC.—See Ibiden Co., Ltd.; *Int'l*, pg. 3575
IBIDEN CAREER TECHNO CORP.—See Ibiden Co., Ltd.; *Int'l*, pg. 3575
IBIDEN CERAM ENVIRONMENTAL INC.—See Ibiden Co., Ltd.; *Int'l*, pg. 3575
IBIDEN CERAM GMBH—See Ibiden Co., Ltd.; *Int'l*, pg. 3575
IBIDEN CHEMICALS CO., LTD.—See Ibiden Co., Ltd.; *Int'l*, pg. 3575
IBIDEN CIRCUITS OF AMERICA CORP.—See Ibiden Co., Ltd.; *Int'l*, pg. 3575
IBIDEN CO., LTD. - AOYANAGI PLANT—See Ibiden Co., Ltd.; *Int'l*, pg. 3575
IBIDEN CO., LTD. - GAMA PLANT—See Ibiden Co., Ltd.; *Int'l*, pg. 3575
IBIDEN CO., LTD. - GODO PLANT—See Ibiden Co., Ltd.; *Int'l*, pg. 3575
IBIDEN CO., LTD. - KINUURA PLANT—See Ibiden Co., Ltd.; *Int'l*, pg. 3575
IBIDEN CO., LTD. - OGAKI CENTRAL PLANT—See Ibiden Co., Ltd.; *Int'l*, pg. 3575
IBIDEN CO., LTD. - OGAKI-KITA PLANT—See Ibiden Co., Ltd.; *Int'l*, pg. 3575
IBIDEN CO., LTD. - OGAKI PLANT—See Ibiden Co., Ltd.; *Int'l*, pg. 3575
IBIDEN CO., LTD.; *Int'l*, pg. 3575
IBIDEN DEUTSCHLAND GMBH—See Ibiden Co., Ltd.; *Int'l*, pg. 3575
IBIDEN DPF FRANCE S.A.S.—See Ibiden Co., Ltd.; *Int'l*, pg. 3575
IBIDEN ELECTRONICS (BEIJING) CO., LTD.—See Ibiden Co., Ltd.; *Int'l*, pg. 3575
IBIDEN ELECTRONICS INDUSTRIES CO., LTD.—See Ibiden Co., Ltd.; *Int'l*, pg. 3575
IBIDEN ELECTRONICS MALAYSIA SDN. BHD.—See Ibiden Co., Ltd.; *Int'l*, pg. 3575
IBIDEN ELECTRONICS (SHANGHAI) CO., LTD.—See Ibiden Co., Ltd.; *Int'l*, pg. 3575
IBIDEN ELECTRONICS TECHNOLOGY (SHANGHAI) CO., LTD.—See Ibiden Co., Ltd.; *Int'l*, pg. 3575
IBIDEN ENGINEERING CO., LTD.—See Ibiden Co., Ltd.; *Int'l*, pg. 3575
IBIDEN EUROPEAN HOLDINGS B.V.—See Ibiden Co., Ltd.; *Int'l*, pg. 3575
IBIDEN EUROPE B.V.—See Ibiden Co., Ltd.; *Int'l*, pg. 3575
IBIDEN FINE CERAMICS (SUZHOU) CO., LTD.—See Ibiden Co., Ltd.; *Int'l*, pg. 3575
IBIDEN FINLAND—See Ibiden Co., Ltd.; *Int'l*, pg. 3575
IBIDEN FRANCE S.A.S.—See Ibiden Co., Ltd.; *Int'l*, pg. 3575
IBIDEN GRAPHITE CO., LTD.—See Ibiden Co., Ltd.; *Int'l*, pg. 3575
IBIDEN GRAPHITE KOREA CO., LTD.—See Ibiden Co., Ltd.; *Int'l*, pg. 3575
IBIDEN GREENTEC CO., LTD.—See Ibiden Co., Ltd.; *Int'l*, pg. 3575
IBIDEN HUNGARY KFT.—See Ibiden Co., Ltd.; *Int'l*, pg. 3575
IBIDEN INDUSTRIES CO., LTD.—See Ibiden Co., Ltd.; *Int'l*, pg. 3575
IBIDEN INTERNATIONAL, INC.—See Ibiden Co., Ltd.; *Int'l*, pg. 3575
IBIDEN JUSHI CO., LTD.—See Ibiden Co., Ltd.; *Int'l*, pg. 3575

CORPORATE AFFILIATIONS

IBIDEN KOREA CO., LTD.—See Ibiden Co., Ltd.; *Int'l*, pg. 3575
IBIDEN MEXICO, S.A. DE C.V.—See Ibiden Co., Ltd.; *Int'l*, pg. 3575
IBIDEN PHILIPPINES, INC.—See Ibiden Co., Ltd.; *Int'l*, pg. 3575
IBIDEN PHILIPPINES LANDHOLDING, INC.—See Ibiden Co., Ltd.; *Int'l*, pg. 3575
IBIDEN PORZELLANFABRIK FRAUENTHAL GMBH—See Ibiden Co., Ltd.; *Int'l*, pg. 3575
IBIDEN SINGAPORE PTE. LTD.—See Ibiden Co., Ltd.; *Int'l*, pg. 3576
IBIDEN TAIWAN CO., LTD.—See Ibiden Co., Ltd.; *Int'l*, pg. 3576
IBIDEN U.S.A. CORP.—See Ibiden Co., Ltd.; *Int'l*, pg. 3575
IBIDEN U.S.A. R&D INC.—See Ibiden Co., Ltd.; *Int'l*, pg. 3576
IBI GROUP ARCHITECTS (USA) INC.—See ARCADIS N.V.; *Int'l*, pg. 542
IBI GROUP CONSULTANTS (IRELAND) LIMITED—See ARCADIS N.V.; *Int'l*, pg. 542
IBI GROUP GEOMATICS (CANADA) INC.—See ARCADIS N.V.; *Int'l*, pg. 542
IBI GROUP GREECE BUSINESS CONSULTANTS SINGLE MEMBER SOCIETE ANONYME IBI HELLAS S.A.—See ARCADIS N.V.; *Int'l*, pg. 542
IBI GROUP HOLDINGS LIMITED; *Int'l*, pg. 3574
IBI GROUP INC.—See ARCADIS N.V.; *Int'l*, pg. 541
IBI GROUP INDIA PRIVATE LIMITED—See ARCADIS N.V.; *Int'l*, pg. 542
IBI GROUP PROFESSIONAL SERVICES (USA) INC.—See ARCADIS N.V.; *Int'l*, pg. 542
IBI GROUP SAUDI LIMITED COMPANY—See ARCADIS N.V.; *Int'l*, pg. 542
IBI INVESTMENT HOUSE LTD.; *Int'l*, pg. 3574
IBIKEN CO., LTD.—See Ibiden Co., Ltd.; *Int'l*, pg. 3576
IBILLBOARD INTERNET REKLAM HIZMETLERI VE BILISIM TEKNOLOJILERI A.S.—See Stroer SE & Co. KGaA; *Int'l*, pg. 7243
IBILLBOARD POLAND SP. Z.O.O.—See Stroer SE & Co. KGaA; *Int'l*, pg. 7243
IBIL—See Ente Vasco de la Energia; *Int'l*, pg. 2450
IBI-MAAK CARIBBEAN LIMITED—See ARCADIS N.V.; *Int'l*, pg. 542
IBI-MAAK INC.—See ARCADIS N.V.; *Int'l*, pg. 542
IBI MACAU LIMITED—See IBI Group Holdings Limited; *Int'l*, pg. 3574
IB-IMRI—See Ipsos S.A.; *Int'l*, pg. 3801
I-BIMSA ULUSLARARASI IS BILGI VEYONETIM SISTEMLERI A.S.—See Haci Omer Sabanci Holding A.S.; *Int'l*, pg. 3204
I-BIMSA ULUSLARARASI IS BILGI VEYONETIM SISTEMLERI A.S.—See International Business Machines Corporation; *U.S. Public*, pg. 1145
IBIO, INC.; *U.S. Public*, pg. 1083
IBI PROMOTORA DE VENDAS LTDA—See Banco Bradesco S.A.; *Int'l*, pg. 819
IBIS BIOSCIENCES LLC—See Abbott Laboratories; *U.S. Public*, pg. 20
IBIS WEST PALM PARTNERS LP; *U.S. Private*, pg. 2028
IBISWORLD INC.—See IBISWorld Pty Ltd; *Int'l*, pg. 3576
IBISWORLD LTD—See IBISWorld Pty Ltd; *Int'l*, pg. 3576
IBISWORLD PTY LTD; *Int'l*, pg. 3576
IBI TAYLOR YOUNG LTD.—See ARCADIS N.V.; *Int'l*, pg. 542
IBITECH CO., LTD.—See Ibiden Co., Ltd.; *Int'l*, pg. 3576
IBIZ CONSULTANCY SERVICES INDIA PVT. LTD.—See Blackstone Inc.; *U.S. Public*, pg. 357
IBIZ CONSULTING SERVICES (SHANGHAI) CO., LTD.—See Blackstone Inc.; *U.S. Public*, pg. 357
IBJ AUTO LEASE COMPANY, LIMITED—See Mizuho Leasing Company, Limited; *Int'l*, pg. 4999
IBJ INC.; *Int'l*, pg. 3576
IBJ LEASING AMERICA CORP.—See Mizuho Leasing Company, Limited; *Int'l*, pg. 4999
IBJ LEASING (UK) LTD.—See Mizuho Leasing Company, Limited; *Int'l*, pg. 4999
IBK ASSET MANAGEMENT CO., LTD.—See Industrial Bank of Korea; *Int'l*, pg. 3671
IBK CAPITAL CORPORATION—See Industrial Bank of Korea; *Int'l*, pg. 3671
IBK CHINA LTD.—See Industrial Bank of Korea; *Int'l*, pg. 3671
IBKIMYOUNG CO., LTD.; *Int'l*, pg. 3576
IBK INSURANCE CO., LTD.—See Industrial Bank of Korea; *Int'l*, pg. 3671
IBK SECURITIES CO., LTD.—See Industrial Bank of Korea; *Int'l*, pg. 3671
IBKS NO. 14 SPECIAL PURPOSE ACQUISITION CO., LTD.; *Int'l*, pg. 3576
IBK SYSTEMS CO., LTD.—See Industrial Bank of Korea; *Int'l*, pg. 3671
IBL-AMERICA, INC.—See Level Biotechnology, Inc.; *Int'l*, pg. 4470
IBL CONSUMER HEALTH PRODUCTS LTD.—See Ireland Blyth Limited; *Int'l*, pg. 3807
IBL GESELLSCHAFT FUR IMMUNCHEMIE UND IMMUNBIOLOGIE M.B.H. I.L.—See november AG; *Int'l*, pg. 5462

COMPANY NAME INDEX IBRAHIM FIBRES LIMITED
Company Index

IBL HEALTHCARE LIMITED; *Int'l*, pg. 3576
IBL PROPERTIES LTD.—See Ireland Blyth Limited; *Int'l*, pg. 3807
IBL REUNION S.A.S.—See Ireland Blyth Limited; *Int'l*, pg. 3807
IBL SANTE S.A.R.L.—See Ireland Blyth Limited; *Int'l*, pg. 3807
IBL TRAVEL LIMITED—See Ireland Blyth Limited; *Int'l*, pg. 3807
IBL TREASURY LTD.—See Ireland Blyth Limited; *Int'l*, pg. 3807
IBL UNISYS LIMITED—See IBL HealthCare Limited; *Int'l*, pg. 3576
IBM APPLICATION SERVICES—See International Business Machines Corporation; *U.S. Public*, pg. 1146
IBM ARGENTINA, S.A.—See International Business Machines Corporation; *U.S. Public*, pg. 1146
IBM ARGENTINA SOCIEDAD DE RESPONSABILIDAD LIMITADA—See International Business Machines Corporation; *U.S. Public*, pg. 1145
IB MAROC; *Int'l*, pg. 3569
IBM AUSTRALIA LIMITED—See International Business Machines Corporation; *U.S. Public*, pg. 1146
IBM BAHAMAS LIMITED—See International Business Machines Corporation; *U.S. Public*, pg. 1146
IBM BRASIL - INDUSTRIA, MAQUINAS E SERVICOS LIMITADA—See International Business Machines Corporation; *U.S. Public*, pg. 1146
IBM BRASIL-INDUSTRIA, MAQUINAS E SERVICOS LIMITADA—See International Business Machines Corporation; *U.S. Public*, pg. 1146
IBM BULGARIA LTD.—See International Business Machines Corporation; *U.S. Public*, pg. 1146
IBM BURKINA FASO SARL—See International Business Machines Corporation; *U.S. Public*, pg. 1146
IBM BUSINESS CONTINUITY & RESILIENCY SERVICES—See International Business Machines Corporation; *U.S. Public*, pg. 1147
IBM CANADA LIMITED—See International Business Machines Corporation; *U.S. Public*, pg. 1146
IBM CANADA LIMITED—See International Business Machines Corporation; *U.S. Public*, pg. 1146
IBM CANADA LIMITED—See International Business Machines Corporation; *U.S. Public*, pg. 1146
IBM CANADA LIMITED—See International Business Machines Corporation; *U.S. Public*, pg. 1146
IBM CESKA REPUBLIKA SPOL. SR.O.—See International Business Machines Corporation; *U.S. Public*, pg. 1146
IBM CHINA COMPANY LIMITED—See International Business Machines Corporation; *U.S. Public*, pg. 1146
IBM CHINA/HONG KONG LIMITED—See International Business Machines Corporation; *U.S. Public*, pg. 1146
IBM (CHINA) INVESTMENT COMPANY LIMITED—See International Business Machines Corporation; *U.S. Public*, pg. 1145
IBM CONGO SARL—See International Business Machines Corporation; *U.S. Public*, pg. 1146
IBM CREDIT LLC—See International Business Machines Corporation; *U.S. Public*, pg. 1146
IBM CROATIA LTD.—See International Business Machines Corporation; *U.S. Public*, pg. 1146
IBM DANMARK A/S—See International Business Machines Corporation; *U.S. Public*, pg. 1146
IBM DE CHILE, S.A.C—See International Business Machines Corporation; *U.S. Public*, pg. 1149
IBM DE COLOMBIA, S.A.—See International Business Machines Corporation; *U.S. Public*, pg. 1149
IBM DEL ECUADOR, C.A.—See International Business Machines Corporation; *U.S. Public*, pg. 1149
IBM DEL PERU, S.A.—See International Business Machines Corporation; *U.S. Public*, pg. 1149
IBM DEL URUGUAY, S.A.—See International Business Machines Corporation; *U.S. Public*, pg. 1149
IBM DE MEXICO, COMERCIALIZACION Y SERVICIOS S. DE R.L. DE C.V.—See International Business Machines Corporation; *U.S. Public*, pg. 1149
IBM DE MEXICO, S. DE R.L.—See International Business Machines Corporation; *U.S. Public*, pg. 1149
IBM DEUTSCHLAND GMBH—See International Business Machines Corporation; *U.S. Public*, pg. 1146
IBM DEUTSCHLAND KREDITBANK GMBH—See International Business Machines Corporation; *U.S. Public*, pg. 1146
IBM DE VENEZUELA, S.A—See International Business Machines Corporation; *U.S. Public*, pg. 1149
IBM EAST AFRICA LIMITED—See International Business Machines Corporation; *U.S. Public*, pg. 1146
IBM EAST EUROPE/ASIA LTD.—See International Business Machines Corporation; *U.S. Public*, pg. 1146
IBM EESTI OSAUHING—See International Business Machines Corporation; *U.S. Public*, pg. 1146
IBM ESTONIA OU—See International Business Machines Corporation; *U.S. Public*, pg. 1146
IBM FINANS NORGE AS—See International Business Machines Corporation; *U.S. Public*, pg. 1146
IBM FOREIGN SALES CORPORATION—See International Business Machines Corporation; *U.S. Public*, pg. 1146
IBM FRANCE FINANCEMENT, S.A.—See International Business Machines Corporation; *U.S. Public*, pg. 1146
IBM GLOBAL BUSINESS SERVICES—See International Business Machines Corporation; *U.S. Public*, pg. 1147
IBM GLOBAL FINANCING AUSTRALIA LIMITED—See International Business Machines Corporation; *U.S. Public*, pg. 1146
IBM GLOBAL FINANCING CANADA CORPORATION—See International Business Machines Corporation; *U.S. Public*, pg. 1147
IBM GLOBAL FINANCING DEUTSCHLAND GMBH—See International Business Machines Corporation; *U.S. Public*, pg. 1147
IBM GLOBAL FINANCING ESPANA, S.L.U.—See International Business Machines Corporation; *U.S. Public*, pg. 1147
IBM GLOBAL FINANCING FINLAND OY—See International Business Machines Corporation; *U.S. Public*, pg. 1147
IBM GLOBAL FINANCING SCHWEIZ GMBH—See International Business Machines Corporation; *U.S. Public*, pg. 1147
IBM GLOBAL FINANCING—See International Business Machines Corporation; *U.S. Public*, pg. 1146
IBM GLOBAL FINANCING SWEDEN AB—See International Business Machines Corporation; *U.S. Public*, pg. 1147
IBM GLOBAL SERVICES ESPANA, S.A.—See International Business Machines Corporation; *U.S. Public*, pg. 1147
IBM GLOBAL SERVICES—See International Business Machines Corporation; *U.S. Public*, pg. 1147
IBM GLOBAL TECHNOLOGY SERVICES—See International Business Machines Corporation; *U.S. Public*, pg. 1147
IBM HELLAS INFORMATION HANDLING SYSTEMS S.A.—See International Business Machines Corporation; *U.S. Public*, pg. 1147
IBM INDIA PRIVATE LIMITED—See International Business Machines Corporation; *U.S. Public*, pg. 1147
IBM-INTERNATIONAL BUSINESS MACHINES D.O.O., BELGRADE—See International Business Machines Corporation; *U.S. Public*, pg. 1149
IBM (INTERNATIONAL BUSINESS MACHINES) TURK LTD SIRKETI—See International Business Machines Corporation; *U.S. Public*, pg. 1145
IBM INTERNATIONAL GROUP CAPITAL LLC—See International Business Machines Corporation; *U.S. Public*, pg. 1147
IBM IRELAND LIMITED—See International Business Machines Corporation; *U.S. Public*, pg. 1147
IBM IRELAND PRODUCT DISTRIBUTION LIMITED—See International Business Machines Corporation; *U.S. Public*, pg. 1147
IBM ISRAEL LIMITED—See International Business Machines Corporation; *U.S. Public*, pg. 1147
IBM ITALIA S.P.A. - CYPRUS—See International Business Machines Corporation; *U.S. Public*, pg. 1147
IBM ITALIA S.P.A.—See International Business Machines Corporation; *U.S. Public*, pg. 1147
IBM JAMAICA—See International Business Machines Corporation; *U.S. Public*, pg. 1147
IBM JAPAN LTD—See International Business Machines Corporation; *U.S. Public*, pg. 1147
IBM KOREA, INC.—See International Business Machines Corporation; *U.S. Public*, pg. 1147
IBM KUWAIT SPC—See International Business Machines Corporation; *U.S. Public*, pg. 1147
IBM LIETUVA—See International Business Machines Corporation; *U.S. Public*, pg. 1147
IBM LUXEMBOURG SARL—See International Business Machines Corporation; *U.S. Public*, pg. 1147
IBM MAGYARORSZAGI KFT—See International Business Machines Corporation; *U.S. Public*, pg. 1147
IBM MALAYSIA SDN. BHD.—See International Business Machines Corporation; *U.S. Public*, pg. 1147
IBM MALTA LIMITED—See International Business Machines Corporation; *U.S. Public*, pg. 1147
IBM MAROC—See International Business Machines Corporation; *U.S. Public*, pg. 1147
IBM MAURITIUS—See International Business Machines Corporation; *U.S. Public*, pg. 1147
IBM MIDDLE EAST FZ-LLC—See International Business Machines Corporation; *U.S. Public*, pg. 1147
IBM NEDERLAND B.V.—See International Business Machines Corporation; *U.S. Public*, pg. 1147
IBM NEDERLAND FINANCIERINGEN B.V.—See International Business Machines Corporation; *U.S. Public*, pg. 1147
IBM NETHERLANDS ANTILLES—See International Business Machines Corporation; *U.S. Public*, pg. 1147
IBM NEW ZEALAND LIMITED—See International Business Machines Corporation; *U.S. Public*, pg. 1148
IBM OESTERREICH INTERNATIONALE BUEROMASCHINEN GESELLSCHAFT M.B.H.—See International Business Machines Corporation; *U.S. Public*, pg. 1146
IB MOTORS PTY. LTD.—See Eagers Automotive Limited; *Int'l*, pg. 2264
IBM PAKISTAN—See International Business Machines Corporation; *U.S. Public*, pg. 1148
IBM PHILIPPINES, INCORPORATED—See International Business Machines Corporation; *U.S. Public*, pg. 1148
IBM POLSKA SP.Z.O.O.—See International Business Machines Corporation; *U.S. Public*, pg. 1148
IBM QATAR SSC—See International Business Machines Corporation; *U.S. Public*, pg. 1148
IBM ROMANIA SRL—See International Business Machines Corporation; *U.S. Public*, pg. 1148
IBM SCHWEIZ AG—See International Business Machines Corporation; *U.S. Public*, pg. 1146
IBM SINGAPORE PTE. LTD.—See International Business Machines Corporation; *U.S. Public*, pg. 1148
IBM SLOVENIJA D.O.O.—See International Business Machines Corporation; *U.S. Public*, pg. 1148
IBM SLOVENSKO SPOL. S.R.O.—See International Business Machines Corporation; *U.S. Public*, pg. 1148
IBM SOFTWARE - ENTERPRISE CONTENT MANAGEMENT—See International Business Machines Corporation; *U.S. Public*, pg. 1148
IBM SOFTWARE GROUP—See International Business Machines Corporation; *U.S. Public*, pg. 1148
IBM SOUTH AFRICA (PTY) LTD.—See International Business Machines Corporation; *U.S. Public*, pg. 1148
IBM SOUTHEAST EMPLOYEES' CREDIT UNION; *U.S. Private*, pg. 2028
IBM SURINAME—See International Business Machines Corporation; *U.S. Public*, pg. 1148
IBM SYSTEMS & TECHNOLOGY—See International Business Machines Corporation; *U.S. Public*, pg. 1148
IBM TAIWAN CORPORATION—See International Business Machines Corporation; *U.S. Public*, pg. 1148
IBM TANZANIA LIMITED—See International Business Machines Corporation; *U.S. Public*, pg. 1148
IBM THAILAND COMPANY LTD.—See International Business Machines Corporation; *U.S. Public*, pg. 1148
IBM TRINIDAD & TOBAGO—See International Business Machines Corporation; *U.S. Public*, pg. 1148
IBM TUNISIE—See International Business Machines Corporation; *U.S. Public*, pg. 1145
IBM UKRAINE—See International Business Machines Corporation; *U.S. Public*, pg. 1148
IBM UNITED KINGDOM FINANCIAL SERVICES LIMITED—See International Business Machines Corporation; *U.S. Public*, pg. 1148
IBM UNITED KINGDOM HOLDINGS LIMITED—See International Business Machines Corporation; *U.S. Public*, pg. 1148
IBM UNITED KINGDOM LIMITED—See International Business Machines Corporation; *U.S. Public*, pg. 1148
IBM UNITED KINGDOM LTD. - GREENFORD—See International Business Machines Corporation; *U.S. Public*, pg. 1149
IBM VIETNAM COMPANY—See International Business Machines Corporation; *U.S. Public*, pg. 1149
IBN HAYYAN PLASTIC PRODUCTS CO.—See Saudi Basic Industries Corporation; *Int'l*, pg. 6590
IBN SINA NATIONAL METHANOL CO.—See Saudi Basic Industries Corporation; *Int'l*, pg. 6590
THE IBN SINA PHARMACEUTICAL INDUSTRY LTD.; *Int'l*, pg. 7654
IBNSINA PHARMA CO.; *Int'l*, pg. 3576
IBOCO; *Int'l*, pg. 3576
IBOKIN CO., LTD.; *Int'l*, pg. 3576
IBOL CO., LTD.—See Business Online Public Company Limited; *Int'l*, pg. 1229
IBOPE ERATINGS.COM DO BRASIL LTDA.—See Brookfield Corporation; *Int'l*, pg. 1178
IBOPE ERATINGS.COM DO BRASIL LTDA.—See Elliott Management Corporation; *U.S. Private*, pg. 1371
IBOPE ERATINGS.COM MEXICO—See Brookfield Corporation; *Int'l*, pg. 1178
IBOPE ERATINGS.COM MEXICO—See Elliott Management Corporation; *U.S. Private*, pg. 1371
IBO TECHNOLOGY COMPANY LIMITED; *Int'l*, pg. 3576
IBOX S.R.L.—See Giglio Group S.p.A.; *Int'l*, pg. 2972
IBP ASSET, LLC—See Installed Building Products, Inc.; *U.S. Public*, pg. 1132
IBP ATCOSA, S.L.—See International Building Products Ltd.; *Int'l*, pg. 3744
IBP BANNINGER ITALIA SRL—See International Building Products Ltd.; *Int'l*, pg. 3744
IBP GMBH—See International Building Products Ltd.; *Int'l*, pg. 3744
IBP HOLDINGS, LLC—See Installed Building Products, Inc.; *U.S. Public*, pg. 1132
IBP MEDICAL GMBH—See Mesa Laboratories, Inc.; *U.S. Public*, pg. 1426
IBQ SYSTEMS LLC—See Clearlake Capital Group, L.P.; *U.S. Private*, pg. 938
IBRACO BERHAD; *Int'l*, pg. 3576
IBRAHIM FIBRES LIMITED; *Int'l*, pg. 3576
IBRAHIM LEASING LTD.—See Ibrahim Fibres Limited; *Int'l*, pg. 3576
I-BRIDGE BV—See Randstad N.V.; *Int'l*, pg. 6202
I-BRIDGE SYSTEMS PHILIPPINES INC.—See Computer Institute of Japan Ltd.; *Int'l*, pg. 1759
IB ROOF SYSTEMS, INC.—See Kingspan Group PLC; *Int'l*, pg. 4176

IBRAHIM FIBRES LIMITED

CORPORATE AFFILIATIONS

IBS AB—See Marlin Equity Partners, LLC; *U.S. Private*, pg. 2584
IBS&D CORP.; *U.S. Private*, pg. 2028
IB SECURITIES JOINT STOCK COMPANY; *Int'l*, pg. 3569
IBSEN PHOTONICS A/S—See Foss A/S; *Int'l*, pg. 2749
IBS FILTRAN KUNSTOFF-/METALLERZEUGNISSE GMBH—See Madison Industries Holdings LLC; *U.S. Private*, pg. 2543
IBS GROUP HOLDING LTD.; *Int'l*, pg. 3576
IBS OPENSYSTEMS (UK) LIMITED—See Capita plc; *Int'l*, pg. 1309
IBS PARTNERS LTD.; *U.S. Private*, pg. 2028
IBSP PLC; *Int'l*, pg. 3577
IBS SOFTWARE PRIVATE LIMITED; *Int'l*, pg. 3576
IBS SOFTWARE SERVICES AMERICAS, INC.—See IBS Software Private Limited; *Int'l*, pg. 3577
IBS—See FAYAT SAS; *Int'l*, pg. 2625
IBS TECHNICS, INC.—See IBS Software Private Limited; *Int'l*, pg. 3577
IBSTOCK BRICK LIMITED—See Ibstock plc; *Int'l*, pg. 3577
IBSTOCK GROUP LIMITED—See Ibstock plc; *Int'l*, pg. 3577
IBSTOCK PLC; *Int'l*, pg. 3577
IB SYSTEMS SP. Z O.O.—See Introl S.A.; *Int'l*, pg. 3769
IBT CENTRAL DISTRIBUTION CENTER—See IBT, Inc.; *U.S. Private*, pg. 2029
IB TECH A.S.—See National Bank of Greece S.A.; *Int'l*, pg. 5153
IBTECH ULUSLARARASI BILISIM VE ILETISIM TEKNOLOJILERI ARASTIRMA, GELISTIRME DANIS- MANLIK DESTEK SAN VE TIC A.S.—See Qatar National Bank S.A.Q.; *Int'l*, pg. 6135
IBT, INC.; *U.S. Private*, pg. 2029
IBT MEDIA INC.; *U.S. Private*, pg. 2028
IBUKI KOSAN CO., LTD.—See Kuraray Co., Ltd.; *Int'l*, pg. 4336
I-BUS CORPORATION; *U.S. Private*, pg. 2026
IBUSUKI SHOKUHIN CO., LTD.—See Kyokuyo Co. Ltd.; *Int'l*, pg. 4363
IBU-TEC ADVANCED MATERIALS AG; *Int'l*, pg. 3577
IBUYNEW GROUP LIMITED; *Int'l*, pg. 3577
IBUYOFFICESUPPLY.COM; *U.S. Private*, pg. 2029
IBWAVE SOLUTIONS INC.—See Corning Incorporated; *U.S. Public*, pg. 579
IB WEALTH MANAGEMENT, INC.—See Independent Bank Corporation; *U.S. Public*, pg. 1116
IBW FINANCIAL CORPORATION; *U.S. Public*, pg. 1083
IBYKUS AG; *Int'l*, pg. 3577
ICA BANKEN AB—See ICA Gruppen AB; *Int'l*, pg. 3577
I-CABLE COMMUNICATIONS LIMITED—See Wheelock & Company Limited; *Int'l*, pg. 8397
ICABLE SERVICEGMBH—See Liberty Global plc; *Int'l*, pg. 4485
ICA CONSTRUCCION CIVIL, S.A. DE C.V.—See Empresas ICA S.A.B. de C.V.; *Int'l*, pg. 2390
ICADE CAPRI S.A—See Caisse des Depots et Consignations; *Int'l*, pg. 1258
ICADE S.A—See Caisse des Depots et Consignations; *Int'l*, pg. 1258
ICA DEUTSCHLAND LACKE GMBH—See The Sherwin-Williams Company; *U.S. Public*, pg. 2128
iCAD, INC.—See iCad, Inc.; *U.S. Public*, pg. 1083
ICAD, INC.; *U.S. Public*, pg. 1083
ICA FASTIGHETER AB—See ICA Gruppen AB; *Int'l*, pg. 3577
ICAFE, INC.; *U.S. Private*, pg. 2029
ICA FLUOR—See Fluor Corporation; *U.S. Public*, pg. 859
ICAGEN, INC.; *U.S. Private*, pg. 2029
ICAGEN-T, INC.—See Icagen, Inc.; *U.S. Private*, pg. 2029
ICA GRUPPEN AB; *Int'l*, pg. 3577
ICA HANDLARNAS AB—See ICA Gruppen AB; *Int'l*, pg. 3577
ICAHN AUTOMOTIVE GROUP LLC—See Icahn Enterprises L.P.; *U.S. Public*, pg. 1084
ICAHN CAPITAL MANAGEMENT LP—See Icahn Enterprises L.P.; *U.S. Public*, pg. 1084
ICAHN ENTERPRISES HOLDINGS L.P.—See Icahn Enterprises L.P.; *U.S. Public*, pg. 1084
ICAHN ENTERPRISES L.P.; *U.S. Public*, pg. 1083
ICAHN NEVADA MANAGEMENT CORP.—See Icahn Enterprises L.P.; *U.S. Public*, pg. 1084
ICAHN PARTNERS MASTER FUND LP—See Icahn Enterprises L.P.; *U.S. Public*, pg. 1084
ICA INFRAESTRUCTURA, S.A. DE C.V.—See Empresas ICA S.A.B. de C.V.; *Int'l*, pg. 2391
ICA INGENIERIA, S.A. DE C.V.—See Empresas ICA S.A.B. de C.V.; *Int'l*, pg. 2391
IC AK BARS FINANCE JSC—See OJSC AK BARS Bank; *Int'l*, pg. 5539
ICA MIDWEST, INC.—See Amphenol Corporation; *U.S. Public*, pg. 130
ICA- MIRAMAR CORPORATION—See Empresas ICA S.A.B. de C.V.; *Int'l*, pg. 2391
ICA- MIRAMAR METRO SAN JUAN CORP.—See Empresas ICA S.A.B. de C.V.; *Int'l*, pg. 2391
ICAM TECHNOLOGIES CORP.—See Sandvik AB; *Int'l*, pg. 6529
ICANA B.V.—See Hon Hai Precision Industry Co., Ltd.; *Int'l*, pg. 3457

ICANA INC.—See Hon Hai Precision Industry Co., Ltd.; *Int'l*, pg. 3457
ICANA LTD.—See Hon Hai Precision Industry Co., Ltd.; *Int'l*, pg. 3457
ICANDY INTERACTIVE LIMITED; *Int'l*, pg. 3578
ICAN ENERGY CO.; *U.S. Private*, pg. 2029
ICAP AMERICA INVESTMENTS LIMITED—See CME Group, Inc.; *U.S. Public*, pg. 516
ICAP AP (SINGAPORE) PTE LIMITED—See CME Group, Inc.; *U.S. Public*, pg. 516
ICAP-AP (THAILAND) CO. LTD.—See CME Group, Inc.; *U.S. Public*, pg. 517
ICAP AUSTRALIA PTY LIMITED—See CME Group, Inc.; *U.S. Public*, pg. 516
ICAP BROKERS PTY LIMITED—See CME Group, Inc.; *U.S. Public*, pg. 516
ICAP CAPITAL MARKETS LLC—See CME Group, Inc.; *U.S. Public*, pg. 517
ICAP COLOMBIA INVESTMENT CORPORATION—See CME Group, Inc.; *U.S. Public*, pg. 516
ICAP CORPORATES LLC—See CME Group, Inc.; *U.S. Public*, pg. 517
ICAP CURRENCY OPTIONS PTE LIMITED—See CME Group, Inc.; *U.S. Public*, pg. 516
ICAP DEL ECUADOR S.A.—See CME Group, Inc.; *U.S. Public*, pg. 517
ICAP DEUTSCHLAND GMBH—See CME Group, Inc.; *U.S. Public*, pg. 516
ICAP DO BRASIL CORRETORA DE TITULOS E VALORES MOBILIARIOS LTDA.—See TP ICAP Finance PLC; *Int'l*, pg. 7881
ICAPE GROUP S.A.; *Int'l*, pg. 3578
ICAP ELECTRONIC BROKING LIMITED—See CME Group, Inc.; *U.S. Public*, pg. 516
ICAP ELECTRONIC BROKING LLC—See CME Group, Inc.; *U.S. Public*, pg. 517
ICAP ENERGY AS—See CME Group, Inc.; *U.S. Public*, pg. 516
ICAP ENERGY LIMITED—See CME Group, Inc.; *U.S. Public*, pg. 516
ICAP ENERGY LLC—See CME Group, Inc.; *U.S. Public*, pg. 517
ICAP ENERGY PTE LIMITED—See CME Group, Inc.; *U.S. Public*, pg. 516
ICAP EQUITIES ASIA LIMITED—See CME Group, Inc.; *U.S. Public*, pg. 516
ICAP EUROPE LIMITED—See CME Group, Inc.; *U.S. Public*, pg. 516
ICAP FOREIGN EXCHANGE BROKERAGE LIMITED—See CME Group, Inc.; *U.S. Public*, pg. 516
ICAP FUTURES (AUSTRALIA) PTY LTD—See CME Group, Inc.; *U.S. Public*, pg. 516
ICAP FUTURES LLC—See CME Group, Inc.; *U.S. Public*, pg. 517
ICAP HOLDINGS (NEDERLAND) B.V.—See CME Group, Inc.; *U.S. Public*, pg. 516
ICAP (HONG KONG) LIMITED—See CME Group, Inc.; *U.S. Public*, pg. 516
ICAP INDIA PRIVATE LIMITED—See CME Group, Inc.; *U.S. Public*, pg. 516
ICAPITAL.BIZ BERHAD; *Int'l*, pg. 3578
ICAPITAL, S.A. DE C.V.—See Empresas ICA S.A.B. de C.V.; *Int'l*, pg. 2391
ICAP MANAGEMENT SERVICES LIMITED—See CME Group, Inc.; *U.S. Public*, pg. 516
ICAP NEW ZEALAND LIMITED—See CME Group, Inc.; *U.S. Public*, pg. 516
ICAP NORTH AMERICA, INC.—See CME Group, Inc.; *U.S. Public*, pg. 517
ICA POLSKA SP. Z O.O.—See The Sherwin-Williams Company; *U.S. Public*, pg. 2128
ICAP PHILIPPINES INC—See CME Group, Inc.; *U.S. Public*, pg. 517
ICA PROPIEDADES INMUEBLES, S.A. DE C.V.—See Empresas ICA S.A.B. de C.V.; *Int'l*, pg. 2391
ICAP SCANDINAVIA A/S—See CME Group, Inc.; *U.S. Public*, pg. 517
ICAP SCANDINAVIA FONDSMAEGLERSELSKAB A/S—See CME Group, Inc.; *U.S. Public*, pg. 517
ICAP SECURITIES ARGENTINA S.A.—See CME Group, Inc.; *U.S. Public*, pg. 517
ICAP SECURITIES COLOMBIA S.A.—See CME Group, Inc.; *U.S. Public*, pg. 517
ICAP SECURITIES LIMITED—See CME Group, Inc.; *U.S. Public*, pg. 517
ICAP SERVICES NORTH AMERICA LLC—See CME Group, Inc.; *U.S. Public*, pg. 517
ICAP SHIPPING DERIVATIVES LIMITED—See CME Group, Inc.; *U.S. Public*, pg. 517
ICAP SHIPPING (GERMANY) GMBH—See CME Group, Inc.; *U.S. Public*, pg. 517
ICAP SHIPPING (GIBRALTAR) LIMITED—See CME Group, Inc.; *U.S. Public*, pg. 517
ICAP SHIPPING (HONG KONG) LIMITED—See CME Group, Inc.; *U.S. Public*, pg. 517
ICAP SHIPPING INTERNATIONAL LIMITED—See CME Group, Inc.; *U.S. Public*, pg. 517
ICAP SHIPPING LIMITED—See CME Group, Inc.; *U.S. Public*, pg. 517

ICAP SHIPPING SINGAPORE PTE LIMITED—See CME Group, Inc.; *U.S. Public*, pg. 517
ICAP SHIPPING TANKER DERIVATIVES LIMITED—See CME Group, Inc.; *U.S. Public*, pg. 517
ICAP SHIPPING USA INC—See CME Group, Inc.; *U.S. Public*, pg. 517
ICAP (SINGAPORE) PTE LIMITED—See TP ICAP Finance PLC; *Int'l*, pg. 7881
ICAP TOTAN SECURITIES CO., LTD.; *Int'l*, pg. 3578
ICAP UNITED INC—See CME Group, Inc.; *U.S. Public*, pg. 517
ICAP WCLK LIMITED—See CME Group, Inc.; *U.S. Public*, pg. 517
ICAR ASIA LIMITED—See Carsome Sdn. Bhd.; *Int'l*, pg. 1347
ICARE ASSURANCE S.A.—See BNP Paribas SA; *Int'l*, pg. 1083
ICARE.COM LLC; *U.S. Private*, pg. 2029
ICARE FINLAND OY—See Revenio Group Oyj; *Int'l*, pg. 6312
ICARE INDUSTRIES, INC.; *U.S. Private*, pg. 2029
ICARE S.A.—See BNP Paribas SA; *Int'l*, pg. 1083
ICARES MEDICUS, INC.; *Int'l*, pg. 3578
ICARIO, INC.—See CVC Capital Partners SICAV-FIS S.A.; *Int'l*, pg. 1888
ICA RISK MANAGEMENT LIMITED—See Wilmington plc; *Int'l*, pg. 8422
ICAR; *Int'l*, pg. 3578
ICARUS WIND ENERGY, INC.; *U.S. Private*, pg. 2029
ICAR VISION SYSTEMS, S.L.—See Mitek Systems, Inc.; *U.S. Public*, pg. 1452
ICA SERVICIOS DE DIRECCION CORPORATIVA, S.A. DE C.V.—See Empresas ICA S.A.B. de C.V.; *Int'l*, pg. 2391
ICA SVERIGE AB—See ICA Gruppen AB; *Int'l*, pg. 3577
ICATCH TECHNOLOGY, INC.—See Sunplus Technology Co., Ltd.; *Int'l*, pg. 7320
ICAT LOGISTICS, INC.—See KCM Capital Partners, LLC; *U.S. Private*, pg. 2270
ICAT LOGISTICS, INC.—See MMF Capital Management LLC; *U.S. Private*, pg. 2754
I.C. AUTOHANDEL BETEILIGUNGEN GMBH—See ITO-CHU Corporation; *Int'l*, pg. 3836
ICBC ASSET MANAGEMENT (GLOBAL) COMPANY LIMITED—See Industrial & Commercial Bank of China Limited; *Int'l*, pg. 3670
ICBC AUSTRIA BANK GMBH—See Industrial & Commercial Bank of China Limited; *Int'l*, pg. 3669
ICBC-AXA ASSURANCE CO., LTD.—See Industrial & Commercial Bank of China Limited; *Int'l*, pg. 3669
ICBC-AXA LIFE ASSURANCE—See AXA S.A.; *Int'l*, pg. 759
ICBC-AXA LIFE ASSURANCE—See Industrial & Commercial Bank of China Limited; *Int'l*, pg. 3670
ICBC-AXA-MINMETALS ASSURANCE CO., LTD.—See AXA S.A.; *Int'l*, pg. 759
ICBC-AXA-MINMETALS ASSURANCE CO., LTD.—See China Rare Earth Resources And Technology Co., Ltd.; *Int'l*, pg. 1545
ICBC-AXA-MINMETALS ASSURANCE CO., LTD.—See Industrial & Commercial Bank of China Limited; *Int'l*, pg. 3670
ICBC CREDIT SUISSE ASSET MANAGEMENT CO., LTD—See Industrial & Commercial Bank of China Limited; *Int'l*, pg. 3669
ICBC (EUROPE) N.V.—See Mega Financial Holding Co., Ltd.; *Int'l*, pg. 4791
ICBC FINANCIAL ASSET INVESTMENT CO., LIMITED—See Industrial & Commercial Bank of China Limited; *Int'l*, pg. 3669
ICBC FINANCIAL LEASING CO., LTD.—See Industrial & Commercial Bank of China Limited; *Int'l*, pg. 3669
ICBC INTERNATIONAL HOLDINGS LIMITED—See Industrial & Commercial Bank of China Limited; *Int'l*, pg. 3669
ICBC (LONDON) PLC—See Industrial & Commercial Bank of China Limited; *Int'l*, pg. 3669
ICBC (MACAU) CAPITAL LIMITED—See Industrial & Commercial Bank of China Limited; *Int'l*, pg. 3669
ICBC (MACAU) PENSION FUND MANAGEMENT COMPANY LIMITED—See Industrial & Commercial Bank of China Limited; *Int'l*, pg. 3669
ICBC PERU BANK S.A.—See Industrial & Commercial Bank of China Limited; *Int'l*, pg. 3669
ICBC PORTFOY YONETIMI A.S.—See ICBC Turkey Bank A.S.; *Int'l*, pg. 3578
ICBC STANDARD BANK PLC—See Industrial & Commercial Bank of China Limited; *Int'l*, pg. 3669
ICBC TURKEY BANK A.S.; *Int'l*, pg. 3578
ICBC TURKEY YATIRIM MENKUL DEGERLER A.S.—See ICBC Turkey Bank A.S.; *Int'l*, pg. 3578
ICBC WEALTH MANAGEMENT CO., LTD.—See Industrial & Commercial Bank of China Limited; *Int'l*, pg. 3669
ICB FINANCIAL GROUP HOLDINGS AG; *Int'l*, pg. 3578
ICB GLOBAL MANAGEMENT SDN. BHD.—See ICB Financial Group Holdings AG; *Int'l*, pg. 3578
ICB ISLAMIC BANK LIMITED—See ICB Financial Group Holdings AG; *Int'l*, pg. 3578

COMPANY NAME INDEX

IC BUS, LLC—See FreightCar America, Inc.; *U.S. Public*, pg. 885
ICC BIG CONSTRUCTION INVESTMENT JOINT STOCK COMPANY; *Int'l*, pg. 3578
ICC CHEMICAL CORPORATION—See ICC Industries, Inc.; *U.S. Private*, pg. 2029
ICC CHEMICALS S.R.L.—See ICC Industries, Inc.; *U.S. Private*, pg. 2030
ICC CHEMICALS UK LTD.—See ICC Industries, Inc.; *U.S. Private*, pg. 2030
ICC CHEMICAL (UK) LIMITED—See ICC Industries, Inc.; *U.S. Public*, pg. 2029
ICC-CHEMOL KFT.—See ICC Industries, Inc.; *U.S. Private*, pg. 2030
ICC CHICAGO—See International Code Council, Inc.; *U.S. Private*, pg. 2115
ICC COMMONWEALTH CORPORATION—See Global Dominion Access SA; *Int'l*, pg. 2995
ICC/DECISION SERVICES—See Thoma Bravo, L.P.; *U.S. Private*, pg. 4149
ICC EVALUATION SERVICE—See International Code Council, Inc.; *U.S. Private*, pg. 2115
ICC EVALUATION SERVICE—See International Code Council, Inc.; *U.S. Private*, pg. 2115
ICC FINANCIAL LIMITED—See CSI Properties Limited; *Int'l*, pg. 1865
ICC FUNDING INC.; *U.S. Private*, pg. 2029
ICC HANDELS AG—See ICC Industries, Inc.; *U.S. Private*, pg. 2030
ICC HEALTHCARE, LLC—See HCA Healthcare, Inc.; *U.S. Public*, pg. 999
ICC HEALTH LIMITED—See The Interpublic Group of Companies, Inc.; *U.S. Public*, pg. 2093
ICC HOLDINGS, INC.; *U.S. Public*, pg. 1085
ICC (HONG KONG) LTD.—See ICC Industries, Inc.; *U.S. Private*, pg. 2029
ICCHOU INC.—See create restaurants holdings inc.; *Int'l*, pg. 1832
ICC IBERICA S.A.—See ICC Industries, Inc.; *U.S. Private*, pg. 2030
ICC INDUSTRIES B.V.—See ICC Industries, Inc.; *U.S. Private*, pg. 2030
ICC INDUSTRIES B.V.—See ICC Industries, Inc.; *U.S. Private*, pg. 2030
ICC INDUSTRIES, INC.; *U.S. Private*, pg. 2029
ICC INSURANCE AGENCY, INC.—See RCAP Holdings, LLC; *U.S. Private*, pg. 3361
ICC INTELLIGENT PLATFORMS GMBH—See Emerson Electric Co.; *U.S. Public*, pg. 749
I.C.C. INTERNATIONAL PUBLIC COMPANY, LIMITED—See Saha Pathana Inter-Holding Public Company Limited; *Int'l*, pg. 6478
ICC ITALIA S.R.L.—See ICC Industries, Inc.; *U.S. Private*, pg. 2030
ICC LABS INC.—See Aurora Cannabis Inc.; *Int'l*, pg. 713
ICCNEXERGY, INC. - ESCONDIDO—See KRG Capital Management, L.P.; *U.S. Private*, pg. 2351
ICCNEXERGY, INC.—See KRG Capital Management, L.P.; *U.S. Private*, pg. 2351
I & C CO., LTD.—See Ship Healthcare Holdings, Inc.; *Int'l*, pg. 6852
IC CO., LTD.; *Int'l*, pg. 3577
ICCO MARKETING (M) SDN. BHD.—See Thien Long Group Corporation; *Int'l*, pg. 7709
IC COMPANYS CANADA INC.—See Friheden Invest A/S; *Int'l*, pg. 2792
IC COMPANYS FINLAND OY—See Friheden Invest A/S; *Int'l*, pg. 2792
IC COMPANYS FRANCE SARL—See Friheden Invest A/S; *Int'l*, pg. 2792
IC COMPANYS HONG KONG LTD.—See Friheden Invest A/S; *Int'l*, pg. 2792
IC COMPANYS HUNGARY KFT.—See Friheden Invest A/S; *Int'l*, pg. 2792
IC COMPANYS NEDERLAND B.V.—See Friheden Invest A/S; *Int'l*, pg. 2792
IC COMPANYS POLAND SP. Z O.O.—See Friheden Invest A/S; *Int'l*, pg. 2792
IC COMPANYS ROMANIA SRL—See Friheden Invest A/S; *Int'l*, pg. 2792
IC COMPANYS (SHANGHAI) LTD.—See Friheden Invest A/S; *Int'l*, pg. 2792
IC CONSULT GROUP GMBH; *Int'l*, pg. 3577
ICCREA BANCA S.P.A.—See Iccrea Holding S.p.A.; *Int'l*, pg. 3578
ICCREA HOLDING S.P.A.; *Int'l*, pg. 3578
ICC REALTY, LLC—See ICC Holdings, Inc.; *U.S. Public*, pg. 1085
ICC TRADING, INC.—See ICC Industries, Inc.; *U.S. Private*, pg. 2030
ICC TRADING (TAIWAN) LTD.—See ICC Industries, Inc.; *U.S. Private*, pg. 2030
ICC UKRAINE LTD.—See Carl-Zeiss-Stiftung; *Int'l*, pg. 1336
ICD ALLOYS AND METALS, LLC—See ICD Group International Inc.; *U.S. Private*, pg. 2030
ICD AMERICA, LLC—See ICD Group International Inc.; *U.S. Private*, pg. 2030

ICD AMERICAS, INC.—See The Brink's Company; *U.S. Public*, pg. 2043
ICD (ASIA PACIFIC) PTY LIMITED—See Apollo Global Management, Inc.; *U.S. Public*, pg. 167
ICDC II, LLC—See National Storage Affiliates Trust; *U.S. Public*, pg. 1498
ICD CO., LTD.; *Int'l*, pg. 3579
ICD ENGINEERING (BEIJING) CO., LTD.—See The Brink's Company; *U.S. Public*, pg. 2043
ICD GROUP INTERNATIONAL INC.; *U.S. Private*, pg. 2030
ICD INSTITUTE FOR CAREER DEVELOPMENT; *U.S. Private*, pg. 2030
ICD / MBT GROUP—See REHAU Verwaltungszentrale AG; *Int'l*, pg. 6255
ICD METALS, LLC.—See ICD Group International Inc.; *U.S. Private*, pg. 2030
ICD SECURITY SOLUTIONS (HK) LIMITED—See The Brink's Company; *U.S. Public*, pg. 2043
ICD SECURITY SOLUTIONS (INDIA) PRIVATE LTD.—See The Brink's Company; *U.S. Public*, pg. 2043
ICD SECURITY SOLUTIONS PTE. LTD.—See The Brink's Company; *U.S. Public*, pg. 2043
ICDS LIMITED; *Int'l*, pg. 3579
ICE ANIMATIONS (PRIVATE) LIMITED—See COLGATE-PALMOLIVE (PAKISTAN) LTD; *Int'l*, pg. 1698
THE ICEBOX, LLC; *U.S. Private*, pg. 4055
ICEBREAKER CZECH REPUBLIC S.R.O.—See V. F. Corporation; *U.S. Public*, pg. 2268
ICEBREAKER MERINO CLOTHING INC.—See V. F. Corporation; *U.S. Public*, pg. 2268
ICEBREAKER NEW ZEALAND LIMITED—See V. F. Corporation; *U.S. Public*, pg. 2268
ICE CLEAR CANADA, INC.—See Intercontinental Exchange, Inc.; *U.S. Public*, pg. 1143
ICE CLEAR CREDIT LLC—See Intercontinental Exchange, Inc.; *U.S. Public*, pg. 1143
ICE CLEAR EUROPE, LTD.—See Intercontinental Exchange, Inc.; *U.S. Public*, pg. 1143
ICE CLEAR NETHERLANDS B.V.—See Intercontinental Exchange, Inc.; *U.S. Public*, pg. 1142
ICE CLEAR SINGAPORE PTE. LTD—See Intercontinental Exchange, Inc.; *U.S. Public*, pg. 1142
ICE CLEAR U.S.—See Intercontinental Exchange, Inc.; *U.S. Public*, pg. 1143
ICECO INC.; *Int'l*, pg. 3579
ICE CONCEPT S.A.; *Int'l*, pg. 3579
ICE CREAM SPECIALTIES, INC.—See Prairie Farms Dairy, Inc.; *U.S. Private*, pg. 3242
ICE CREAM SPECIALTIES, INC.—See Prairie Farms Dairy, Inc.; *U.S. Private*, pg. 3242
ICECURE MEDICAL INC.—See Icecure Medical Ltd.; *Int'l*, pg. 3579
ICECURE MEDICAL LTD.; *Int'l*, pg. 3579
ICE DATA INDICES, LLC—See Intercontinental Exchange, Inc.; *U.S. Public*, pg. 1142
ICE DATA SERVICES, INC.—See Intercontinental Exchange, Inc.; *U.S. Public*, pg. 1143
ICE DELIVERY SYSTEMS INC.; *U.S. Private*, pg. 2030
THE ICEE COMPANY—See J&J Snack Foods Corporation; *U.S. Public*, pg. 1180
ICEE DE MEXICO, S.A. DE C.V.—See J&J Snack Foods Corporation; *U.S. Public*, pg. 1179
ICE EDGE BUSINESS SOLUTIONS LTD.—See DIRTT Environmental Solutions Ltd.; *Int'l*, pg. 2130
ICE ENDEX MARKETS B.V.—See Intercontinental Exchange, Inc.; *U.S. Public*, pg. 1142
ICE ENERGY INC.; *U.S. Private*, pg. 2030
ICE ENGINEERING & CONSTRUCTION PTY. LTD.—See E&A Limited; *Int'l*, pg. 2247
ICEE OF HAWAII, INC.—See J&J Snack Foods Corporation; *U.S. Public*, pg. 1179
ICEE-USA CORP.—See J&J Snack Foods Corporation; *U.S. Public*, pg. 1179
ICE FAR EAST (HK) LIMITED—See CSC Holdings Limited; *Int'l*, pg. 1862
ICE FAR EAST PTE. LTD.—See CSC Holdings Limited; *Int'l*, pg. 1862
ICE FAR EAST SDN. BHD.—See CSC Holdings Limited; *Int'l*, pg. 1862
ICE FAR EAST (THAILAND) CO., LTD.—See CSC Holdings Limited; *Int'l*, pg. 1862
ICE FISH FARM AS; *Int'l*, pg. 3579
ICEFRESH GMBH—See Samherji hf; *Int'l*, pg. 6505
ICE FRESH SEAFOOD UK LTD—See Samherji hf; *Int'l*, pg. 6505
ICE FUTURES CANADA, INC.—See Intercontinental Exchange, Inc.; *U.S. Public*, pg. 1143
ICE FUTURES EUROPE—See Intercontinental Exchange, Inc.; *U.S. Public*, pg. 1143
ICE FUTURES SINGAPORE PTE. LTD.—See Intercontinental Exchange, Inc.; *U.S. Public*, pg. 1142
ICE FUTURES U.S., INC.—See Intercontinental Exchange, Inc.; *U.S. Public*, pg. 1143
ICE GROUP ASA—See Access Industries, Inc.; *U.S. Private*, pg. 51
ICE HOUSE AMERICA, LLC—See Ulysses Management, LLC; *U.S. Public*, pg. 4278
ICE INDUSTRIES INC.; *U.S. Private*, pg. 2030

ICF KURSMAKLER AG

ICELANDAIR GROUP HF; *Int'l*, pg. 3579
ICELANDAIR HOTELS EHF.—See Berjaya Corporation Berhad; *Int'l*, pg. 983
ICE LAND ASSOCIATES, LP—See Blackstreet Capital Holdings LLC; *U.S. Private*, pg. 576
ICELAND FOODS LTD.; *Int'l*, pg. 3579
THE ICELANDIC AD AGENCY—See Omnicom Group Inc.; *U.S. Public*, pg. 1577
ICELANDIC GERMANY GMBH—See Enterprise Investment Fund slhf.; *Int'l*, pg. 2451
ICELANDIC GROUP HF—See Enterprise Investment Fund slhf.; *Int'l*, pg. 2451
ICELANDIC IBERICA SA—See Enterprise Investment Fund slhf.; *Int'l*, pg. 2451
ICELANDIC JAPAN KK—See Enterprise Investment Fund slhf.; *Int'l*, pg. 2451
ICELANDIC UK LIMITED—See Enterprise Investment Fund slhf.; *Int'l*, pg. 2451
ICELAND RESOURCES EHF—See St-Georges Eco-Mining Corp.; *Int'l*, pg. 7158
ICELAND SEAFOOD ICELAND; *Int'l*, pg. 3579
ICELAND TRAVEL EHF.—See Nordic Visitor Hf; *Int'l*, pg. 5423
ICELOLLY MARKETING LIMITED—See Moneysupermarket.com Group PLC; *Int'l*, pg. 5033
ICE MAKE REFRIGERATION LTD.; *Int'l*, pg. 3579
ICE MARKETS LIMITED—See Intercontinental Exchange, Inc.; *U.S. Public*, pg. 1143
ICEMENERG SA—See CNTEE TRANSELECTRICA SA; *Int'l*, pg. 1678
ICEMENERG SERVICE SA—See CNTEE TRANSELECTRICA SA; *Int'l*, pg. 1678
ICE MESSAGING PTE. LTD.—See Touchpoint Group Holdings, Inc.; *U.S. Public*, pg. 2165
ICE MILLER LLP; *U.S. Private*, pg. 2030
ICEMOBILE AGENCY BV—See Bread Financial Holdings Inc.; *U.S. Public*, pg. 381
ICE MOUNTAIN SPRING WATER—See Metropoulos & Co.; *U.S. Private*, pg. 2690
ICE MOUNTAIN SPRING WATER—See One Rock Capital Partners, LLC; *U.S. Private*, pg. 3021
ICE NGX CANADA, INC.—See Intercontinental Exchange, Inc.; *U.S. Public*, pg. 1143
ICENI GOLD LIMITED; *Int'l*, pg. 3579
ICENI MARINE SERVICES LTD—See Turner & Co. (Glasgow) Limited; *Int'l*, pg. 7978
I.CENTURY HOLDING LIMITED; *Int'l*, pg. 3565
ICE PORTAL, INC.—See Beijing Shiji Information Technology Co., Ltd.; *Int'l*, pg. 956
ICERA INC.—See NVIDIA Corporation; *U.S. Public*, pg. 1558
ICERA INC.—See NVIDIA Corporation; *U.S. Public*, pg. 1558
ICERA LLC—See NVIDIA Corporation; *U.S. Public*, pg. 1558
I.CERAM; *Int'l*, pg. 3565
ICE RIVER SPRINGS WATER COMPANY INC.; *Int'l*, pg. 3579
ICER RAIL S.L.—See Knorr-Bremse AG; *Int'l*, pg. 4210
I.C.E. SERVICE GROUP, INC.; *U.S. Private*, pg. 2026
ICESOFT TECHNOLOGIES, INC.; *Int'l*, pg. 3579
ICE SPECIALTY ENTERTAINMENT INC.; *U.S. Private*, pg. 2031
ICETANA LIMITED; *Int'l*, pg. 3579
ICE TECHNOLOGIES, INC.; *U.S. Private*, pg. 2030
ICE TRADE VAULT EUROPE LIMITED—See Intercontinental Exchange, Inc.; *U.S. Public*, pg. 1143
ICE UK LP, LLC—See Intercontinental Exchange, Inc.; *U.S. Public*, pg. 1143
IC EUROINS-LIFE EAD—See Eurohold Bulgaria AD; *Int'l*, pg. 2553
ICF CONSULTING CANADA, INC.—See ICF International, Inc.; *U.S. Public*, pg. 1086
ICF CONSULTING GROUP, INC.—See ICF International, Inc.; *U.S. Public*, pg. 1086
ICF CONSULTING INDIA PRIVATE, LTD.—See ICF International, Inc.; *U.S. Public*, pg. 1086
ICF CONSULTING LIMITED—See ICF International, Inc.; *U.S. Public*, pg. 1086
ICF CONSULTING SERVICES, INDIA PRIVATE, LTD.—See ICF International, Inc.; *U.S. Public*, pg. 1086
ICF CONSULTING SERVICES, LTD.—See ICF International, Inc.; *U.S. Public*, pg. 1086
ICF CONSULTING—See ICF International, Inc.; *U.S. Public*, pg. 1086
ICF CONSULTING—See ICF International, Inc.; *U.S. Public*, pg. 1086
ICF GROUP; *U.S. Private*, pg. 2031
ICF INDUSTRIES, INC.; *U.S. Private*, pg. 2031
ICF INTERNATIONAL CONSULTING (BEIJING) COMPANY, LTD.—See ICF International, Inc.; *U.S. Public*, pg. 1086
ICF INTERNATIONAL, INC.; *U.S. Public*, pg. 1085
ICF JONES & STOKES, INC.—See ICF International, Inc.; *U.S. Public*, pg. 1086
ICF KURSMAKLER AG; *Int'l*, pg. 3579
ICF MACRO, INC.—See ICF International, Inc.; *U.S. Public*, pg. 1086

ICF KURSMAKLER AG

CORPORATE AFFILIATIONS

ICF OLSON—See ICF International, Inc.; *U.S. Public*, pg. 1086

IC FONDS GMBH—See IC Immobilien Holding AG; *Int'l*, pg. 3577

ICF SH&E, INC.—See ICF International, Inc.; *U.S. Public*, pg. 1086

ICF SH&E LIMITED—See ICF International, Inc.; *U.S. Public*, pg. 1086

ICF SOLUTIONS, LLC—See Ritchie Corporation; *U.S. Private*, pg. 3441

ICF SYSTEMS AG—See ICF Kursmakler AG; *Int'l*, pg. 3579

I.C.F.& WELKO S.P.A.—See Keda Industrial Group Co., Ltd.; *Int'l*, pg. 4114

ICG ENTERPRISE TRUST PLC—See Intermediate Capital Group plc; *Int'l*, pg. 3742

ICG HOLLISTON HOLDINGS CORPORATION; *U.S. Private*, pg. 2031

ICG/HOLLISTON—See ICG Holliston Holdings Corporation; *U.S. Private*, pg. 2031

ICG HYPERSONIC ACQUISITION CORP.; *U.S. Public*, pg. 1086

ICG LOGISTICS, LLC—See US 1 Industries, Inc.; *U.S. Private*, pg. 4317

ICG-LONGBOW SENIOR SECURED UK PROP DEBT INV LTD.; *Int'l*, pg. 3579

IC GREEN ENERGY LTD.—See Israel Corporation Ltd.; *Int'l*, pg. 3822

IC GROUP A/S—See Friheden Invest A/S; *Int'l*, pg. 2792

IC GROUP; *U.S. Private*, pg. 2029

IC GUARDIA—See American International Group, Inc.; *U.S. Public*, pg. 107

ICHEMCO S.R.L.; *Int'l*, pg. 3579

ICHIA RUBBER IND. (M) SDN. BHD.—See Ichia Technologies Inc.; *Int'l*, pg. 3580

ICHIA TECHNOLOGIES INC.; *Int'l*, pg. 3579

ICHIBANYA CO., LTD. - SAGA PLANT—See House Foods Group Inc.; *Int'l*, pg. 3490

ICHIBANYA CO., LTD.—See House Foods Group Inc.; *Int'l*, pg. 3490

ICHIBANYA CO., LTD. - TOCHIGI PLANT—See House Foods Group Inc.; *Int'l*, pg. 3490

ICHIBANYA HONG KONG LIMITED—See House Foods Group Inc.; *Int'l*, pg. 3490

ICHIBANYA USA—See House Foods Group Inc.; *Int'l*, pg. 3490

ICHIBOU CO., LTD.—See Nohmi Bosai Ltd.; *Int'l*, pg. 5400

ICHIEI KOGYO CO., LTD.—See Toyoda Gosei Co., Ltd.; *Int'l*, pg. 7861

ICHIGO ASSET MANAGEMENT, LTD.; *Int'l*, pg. 3580

ICHIGO ECO ENERGY CO., LTD.—See Ichigo, Inc.; *Int'l*, pg. 3580

ICHIGO ESTATE CO., LTD.—See Ichigo, Inc.; *Int'l*, pg. 3580

ICHIGO GREEN INFRASTRUCTURE INVESTMENT CORPORATION; *Int'l*, pg. 3580

ICHIGO HOTEL REIT INVESTMENT CORPORATION; *Int'l*, pg. 3580

ICHIGO, INC.; *Int'l*, pg. 3580

ICHIGO INVESTMENT ADVISORS CO., LTD.—See Ichigo, Inc.; *Int'l*, pg. 3580

ICHIGO LAND SHINCHIKU CO., LTD.—See Ichigo, Inc.; *Int'l*, pg. 3580

ICHIGO LLC—See TECHMATRIX CORPORATION; *Int'l*, pg. 7505

ICHIGO MARCHE CO., LTD.—See Ichigo, Inc.; *Int'l*, pg. 3580

ICHIGO OFFICE REIT INVESTMENT CORPORATION; *Int'l*, pg. 3580

ICHIGO OWNERS CO., LTD.—See Ichigo, Inc.; *Int'l*, pg. 3580

ICHIGO REAL ESTATE SERVICES FUKUOKA CO., LTD.—See Ichigo, Inc.; *Int'l*, pg. 3580

ICHIHARA CABLE TELEVISION CORPORATION—See TOKAI Holdings Corporation; *Int'l*, pg. 7779

ICHIHARA COMMUNITY NETWORK TELEVISION CORPORATION—See TOKAI Holdings Corporation; *Int'l*, pg. 7779

ICHIHARA ECOCEMENT CORPORATION—See Taiheiyo Cement Corporation; *Int'l*, pg. 7411

ICHIHARA NEW ENERGY CO., LTD.—See Takuma Co., Ltd.; *Int'l*, pg. 7442

ICHIHARA POWER CO., LTD.—See The Kansai Electric Power Co., Inc.; *Int'l*, pg. 7661

ICHIHIRO CO., LTD.; *Int'l*, pg. 3580

ICHIKAWA CHINA CO., LTD.—See ICHIKAWA CO. LTD.; *Int'l*, pg. 3580

ICHIKAWA CO. LTD.; *Int'l*, pg. 3580

ICHIKAWA EUROPA GMBH—See ICHIKAWA CO. LTD.; *Int'l*, pg. 3580

ICHIKEN CO., LTD.; *Int'l*, pg. 3580

ICHIKOH INDUSTRIES, LTD. - FUJIOKA PLANT—See Valeo S.A.; *Int'l*, pg. 8113

ICHIKOH INDUSTRIES, LTD. - ISEHARA PLANT—See Valeo S.A.; *Int'l*, pg. 8113

ICHIKOH INDUSTRIES, LTD - MIRROR PLANT—See Valeo S.A.; *Int'l*, pg. 8113

ICHIKOH INDUSTRIES, LTD.—See Valeo S.A.; *Int'l*, pg. 8113

ICHIKOH INDUSTRIES (THAILAND) CO. LTD.—See Valeo S.A.; *Int'l*, pg. 8113

ICHIKOH (MALAYSIA) SDN. BHD.—See Valeo S.A.; *Int'l*, pg. 8113

ICHIKOH (WUXI) AUTOMOTIVE PARTS CO., LTD.—See Valeo S.A.; *Int'l*, pg. 8113

ICHIKURA CO., LTD.; *Int'l*, pg. 3580

ICHIMASA KAMABOKO CO., LTD.; *Int'l*, pg. 3580

ICHIMURA SANGYO CO., LTD.—See Toray Industries, Inc.; *Int'l*, pg. 7823

ICHIMURA (SHANGHAI) TRADING CO.,LTD—See Toray Industries, Inc.; *Int'l*, pg. 7823

ICHINEN AUTOS (N.Z.) LTD—See Ichinen Holdings Co., Ltd.; *Int'l*, pg. 3580

ICHINEN HOLDINGS CO., LTD.; *Int'l*, pg. 3580

ICHINEN JIKCO CO., LTD.—See Ichinen Holdings Co., Ltd.; *Int'l*, pg. 3580

ICHINEN JIKCO POLYMER CO., LTD.—See Ichinen Holdings Co., Ltd.; *Int'l*, pg. 3580

ICHINEN JIKCO TEC CO., LTD.—See Ichinen Holdings Co., Ltd.; *Int'l*, pg. 3580

ICHINOMIYA ENVIRONMENT TECHNOLOGY CO., LTD.—See Hitachi Zosen Corporation; *Int'l*, pg. 3411

ICHINOSE EMICO VALVES (S) PTE LTD.—See AnnAik Limited; *Int'l*, pg. 473

ICHINOSEKI HIROSE ELECTRIC CO., LTD.—See Hirose Electric Co., Ltd.; *Int'l*, pg. 3405

ICHINOSEKI REMICON CO., LTD.—See UBE Corporation; *Int'l*, pg. 8001

ICHINOSE-TRADING CO., LTD.—See Toyo Seikan Group Holdings, Ltd.; *Int'l*, pg. 7856

I-CHIPS TECHNOLOGY INC.—See Imagica Group Inc.; *Int'l*, pg. 3619

ICHIROKUDO CO., LTD.; *Int'l*, pg. 3581

ICHISHIN HOLDINGS CO., LTD.; *Int'l*, pg. 3581

ICHITAN CO., LTD.—See Subaru Corporation; *Int'l*, pg. 7247

ICHITAN GROUP PUBLIC COMPANY LIMITED; *Int'l*, pg. 3581

I-CHIUN PRECISION ELECTRIC INDUSTRY (CHINA) CO., LTD.—See I-CHIUN PRECISION INDUSTRY CO., LTD.; *Int'l*, pg. 3562

I-CHIUN PRECISION ELECTRIC (NANJING) CO., LTD.—See I-CHIUN PRECISION INDUSTRY CO., LTD.; *Int'l*, pg. 3562

I-CHIUN PRECISION INDUSTRY CO., LTD. - NANJING PLANT—See I-CHIUN PRECISION INDUSTRY CO., LTD.; *Int'l*, pg. 3563

I-CHIUN PRECISION INDUSTRY CO., LTD.—See I-CHIUN PRECISION INDUSTRY CO., LTD.; *Int'l*, pg. 3562

I-CHIUN PRECISION INDUSTRY CO., LTD.; *Int'l*, pg. 3562

ICHIYOSHI ASSET MANAGEMENT CO., LTD.—See Ichiyoshi Securities Co., Ltd.; *Int'l*, pg. 3581

ICHIYOSHI BUSINESS SERVICE CO., LTD.—See Ichiyoshi Securities Co., Ltd.; *Int'l*, pg. 3581

ICHIYOSHI RESEARCH INSTITUTE INC—See Ichiyoshi Securities Co., Ltd.; *Int'l*, pg. 3581

ICHIYOSHI SECURITIES CO., LTD.; *Int'l*, pg. 3581

ICHNOS SCIENCES INC.—See Glenmark Pharmaceuticals Limited; *Int'l*, pg. 2992

ICHOR HOLDINGS, LTD.—See Francisco Partners Management, LP; *U.S. Private*, pg. 1590

ICHOR SYSTEMS, INC.—See Francisco Partners Management, LP; *U.S. Private*, pg. 1590

IC HOTELS MANAGEMENT (PORTUGAL) UNIPESSOAL, LDA—See InterContinental Hotels Group PLC; *Int'l*, pg. 3737

ICICI BANK CANADA LTD.—See ICICI Bank Limited; *Int'l*, pg. 3581

ICICI BANK LIMITED; *Int'l*, pg. 3581

ICICI BANK UK PLC—See ICICI Bank Limited; *Int'l*, pg. 3581

ICICI HOME FINANCE COMPANY LIMITED—See ICICI Bank Limited; *Int'l*, pg. 3581

ICICI LOMBARD GENERAL INSURANCE CO. LTD.—See Fairfax Financial Holdings Limited; *Int'l*, pg. 2607

ICICI LOMBARD GENERAL INSURANCE CO. LTD.—See ICICI Bank Limited; *Int'l*, pg. 3581

ICICI PRUDENTIAL ASSET MANAGEMENT COMPANY LIMITED—See ICICI Bank Limited; *Int'l*, pg. 3581

ICICI PRUDENTIAL ASSET MANAGEMENT COMPANY LIMITED—See Prudential plc; *Int'l*, pg. 6009

ICICI PRUDENTIAL LIFE INSURANCE COMPANY LTD.—See ICICI Bank Limited; *Int'l*, pg. 3581

ICICI PRUDENTIAL LIFE INSURANCE COMPANY LTD.—See Prudential plc; *Int'l*, pg. 6009

ICICI SECURITIES INC.—See ICICI Bank Limited; *Int'l*, pg. 3581

ICICI SECURITIES LIMITED—See ICICI Bank Limited; *Int'l*, pg. 3581

ICICI VENTURE FUNDS MANAGEMENT COMPANY LIMITED—See ICICI Bank Limited; *Int'l*, pg. 3581

ICICLE SEAFOODS, INC.—See Cooke, Inc.; *Int'l*, pg. 1788

ICI CONSTRUCTION INC.; *U.S. Private*, pg. 2031

ICIC S.P.A.—See RINA S.p.A.; *Int'l*, pg. 6342

IC ICTAS ELEKTRIK URETIM A.S.—See The AES Corporation; *U.S. Public*, pg. 2031

ICIG BUSINESS SERVICES GMBH & CO. KG—See International Chemical Investors S.E.; *Int'l*, pg. 3745

ICI HOLDINGS (AUSTRALIA) PTY LTD—See Akzo Nobel N.V.; *Int'l*, pg. 274

ICI INDIA LTD.-PAINTS DIVISION—See Akzo Nobel N.V.; *Int'l*, pg. 273

ICIMB (MALAYSIA) SDN. BHD.—See CIMB Group Holdings Berhad; *Int'l*, pg. 1607

ICIMB (MSC) SDN BHD—See CIMB Group Holdings Berhad; *Int'l*, pg. 1608

IC IMMOBILIEN HOLDING AG; *Int'l*, pg. 3577

ICIM SERVICES INC.—See ICI Mutual Insurance Company; *U.S. Private*, pg. 2031

ICIMS HOLDING CORP.; *U.S. Private*, pg. 2031

ICIMS, INC.; *U.S. Private*, pg. 2031

ICI MUTUAL INSURANCE BROKERS—See ICI Mutual Insurance Company; *U.S. Private*, pg. 2031

ICI MUTUAL INSURANCE COMPANY; *U.S. Private*, pg. 2031

ICIN CO., LTD.—See Current Motor Corporation; *Int'l*, pg. 1879

IC INTERNATIONAL HOTELS LIMITED LIABILITY COMPANY—See InterContinental Hotels Group PLC; *Int'l*, pg. 3737

IC INTRACOM USA, INC.—See Intracom Holdings S.A.; *Int'l*, pg. 3767

ICI OMICRON B.V.—See Akzo Nobel N.V.; *Int'l*, pg. 274

ICI PACKAGING COATINGS LTDA.—See Akzo Nobel N.V.; *Int'l*, pg. 274

ICI PAINTS CZ SPOL.S.R.O.—See Akzo Nobel N.V.; *Int'l*, pg. 274

ICI PAINTS DECO FRANCE SA—See Akzo Nobel N.V.; *Int'l*, pg. 274

ICI PAINTS MERCOSUR B.V.—See Akzo Nobel N.V.; *Int'l*, pg. 274

ICI PAKISTAN LTD.-SODA ASH WORKS—See Lucky Cement Limited; *Int'l*, pg. 4574

ICIS BENCHMARKING EUROPE B.V.—See RELX plc; *Int'l*, pg. 6266

ICIS CHEMICAL BUSINESS—See RELX plc; *Int'l*, pg. 6266

ICIS ITALIA S.R.L.—See RELX plc; *Int'l*, pg. 6266

ICI SOUTH PACIFIC HOLDINGS PTY LTD—See Akzo Nobel N.V.; *Int'l*, pg. 274

ICI SWIRE PAINTS (SHANGHAI) LTD.—See Akzo Nobel N.V.; *Int'l*, pg. 274

ICI THETA B.V.—See Akzo Nobel N.V.; *Int'l*, pg. 274

ICKENROTH GMBH—See K+S Aktiengesellschaft; *Int'l*, pg. 4040

THE ICLA DA SILVA FOUNDATION; *U.S. Private*, pg. 4055

ICL ASIA LTD.—See Israel Corporation Ltd.; *Int'l*, pg. 3823

ICL FINCORP LIMITED; *Int'l*, pg. 3581

ICL GROUP LTD.—See Israel Corporation Ltd.; *Int'l*, pg. 3822

ICLICK, INC.; *U.S. Private*, pg. 2031

ICLICK INTERACTIVE ASIA GROUP LIMITED; *Int'l*, pg. 3581

ICLICK INTERACTIVE (SINGAPORE) PTE. LTD.—See iClick Interactive Asia Group Limited; *Int'l*, pg. 3581

ICL INDUSTRIAL PRODUCTS—See Israel Corporation Ltd.; *Int'l*, pg. 3823

ICLINIC DESENVOLVIMENTO DE SOFTWARE LTDA.—See Afya Limited; *Int'l*, pg. 196

ICL IP AMERICA INC., USA—See Israel Corporation Ltd.; *Int'l*, pg. 3823

ICL ORGANIC DAIRY PRODUCTS LIMITED; *Int'l*, pg. 3581

ICL PERFORMANCE PRODUCTS INC.—See Israel Corporation Ltd.; *Int'l*, pg. 3823

ICL PERFORMANCE PRODUCTS LLC—See Israel Corporation Ltd.; *Int'l*, pg. 3823

ICL PERFORMANCE PRODUCTS LP—See Israel Corporation Ltd.; *Int'l*, pg. 3823

ICL SYSTEMS, INC.—See Valsef Group; *Int'l*, pg. 8123

ICL TRADING (HK) LTD., HONG KONG—See Israel Corporation Ltd.; *Int'l*, pg. 3823

ICL ZAMBIA LTD.—See RHT Holding Ltd.; *Int'l*, pg. 6327

ICM AIRPORT TECHNICS AUSTRALIA PTY. LTD.—See Amadeus IT Group, S.A.; *Int'l*, pg. 407

ICM AIRPORT TECHNICS LLC—See Amadeus IT Group, S.A.; *Int'l*, pg. 407

ICM AIRPORT TECHNICS SINGAPORE PTE. LTD.—See Amadeus IT Group, S.A.; *Int'l*, pg. 407

ICM AIRPORT TECHNICS UK LTD.—See Amadeus IT Group, S.A.; *Int'l*, pg. 407

ICMA RETIREMENT CORPORATION; *Int'l*, pg. 3582

ICMA S.A.; *Int'l*, pg. 3582

ICM CAPITAL RESEARCH LIMITED—See ICM Limited; *Int'l*, pg. 3581

ICM CORPORATE SERVICES (PTY) LTD—See ICM Limited; *Int'l*, pg. 3581

IC MECHANICAL, INC.; *U.S. Private*, pg. 2029

ICME ECAB SA—See Viohalco SA/NV; *Int'l*, pg. 8243

ICM GROUP S.A.—See Legrand S.A.; *Int'l*, pg. 4444

ICM HOLDINGS INC.; *U.S. Private*, pg. 2031

I&C MICROSYSTEMS CO., LTD.—See P-Duke Technology Co., Ltd.; *Int'l*, pg. 5681

1302

COMPANY NAME INDEX

ICM INVESTMENT MANAGEMENT LIMITED—See ICM Limited; *Int'l*, pg. 3581
ICM INVESTMENT RESEARCH LIMITED—See ICM Limited; *Int'l*, pg. 3581
ICM LIMITED; *Int'l*, pg. 3581
ICM NZ LIMITED—See ICM Limited; *Int'l*, pg. 3581
ICM PACHAPAQUI S.A.C.—See Korea Zinc Company, Ltd.; *Int'l*, pg. 4287
ICM PRODUCTS, INC.—See Akoya Capital LLC; *U.S. Private*, pg. 146
ICM PRODUCTS, INC.—See Century Park Capital Partners, LLC; *U.S. Private*, pg. 833
ICM RESEARCH PTE LTD—See ICM Limited; *Int'l*, pg. 3581
ICM SAS—See VINCI S.A.; *Int'l*, pg. 8222
ICM—See Dalian Tonghai Machinery & Electronic Equipment Co., Ltd.; *Int'l*, pg. 1952
ICNET CO., LTD.—See BELLUNA CO. LTD.; *Int'l*, pg. 967
IC NET LIMITED—See Gakken Holdings Co., Ltd.; *Int'l*, pg. 2869
ICN POLFA RZESZOW S.A.—See Bausch Health Companies Inc.; *Int'l*, pg. 897
ICOA, INC.; *U.S. Public*, pg. 1086
I.C.O.A. SRL—See SOL S.p.A.; *Int'l*, pg. 7067
ICOE (SHANGHAI) TECHNOLOGIES CO., LTD.—See Beijing BDstar Navigation Co., Ltd.; *Int'l*, pg. 946
ICO EUROPE B.V.—See LyondellBasell Industries N.V.; *Int'l*, pg. 4608
ICO GROUP LIMITED; *Int'l*, pg. 3582
ICOGUANTI S.P.A.—See Hayleys PLC; *Int'l*, pg. 3291
ICO INTERNATIONAL GMBH—See Motork Plc; *Int'l*, pg. 5054
ICO LIMITED—See ICO Group Limited; *Int'l*, pg. 3582
ICOLLECTOR.COM TECHNOLOGIES, INC.—See Hongli Clean Energy Technologies Corp.; *Int'l*, pg. 3471
ICOLLEGE LIMITED; *Int'l*, pg. 3582
ICOLO LIMITED—See Digital Realty Trust, Inc.; *U.S. Public*, pg. 663
ICOLO MOZAMBIQUE, LIMITADA—See Digital Realty Trust, Inc.; *U.S. Public*, pg. 663
ICOM AMERICA, INC.—See ICOM INCORPORATED; *Int'l*, pg. 3583
ICOM AMERICA LICENSE HOLDING LLC—See ICOM INCORPORATED; *Int'l*, pg. 3582
ICOMARCH24 SA—See ComArch S.A.; *Int'l*, pg. 1707
ICOM (AUSTRALIA) PTY. LTD.—See ICOM INCORPORATED; *Int'l*, pg. 3582
ICOM (EUROPE) GMBH—See ICOM INCORPORATED; *Int'l*, pg. 3582
ICOM FRANCE S.A.S.—See ICOM INCORPORATED; *Int'l*, pg. 3583
ICOM INCORPORATED; *Int'l*, pg. 3582
ICOM INFORMATION & COMMUNICATIONS L.P.—See Bread Financial Holdings Inc.; *U.S. Public*, pg. 381
ICOM INFORMATION PRODUCTS INC.—See ICOM INCORPORATED; *Int'l*, pg. 3583
ICOMM INTERNATIONAL LANKA (PVT) LTD—See ICOMM Tele Limited; *Int'l*, pg. 3583
ICOMM TELE LIMITED; *Int'l*, pg. 3583
ICOMM TELE LIMITED - TOWERS UNIT—See ICOMM Tele Limited; *Int'l*, pg. 3583
ICOMM TELE LIMITED - TURNKEY SERVICES DIVISION—See ICOMM Tele Limited; *Int'l*, pg. 3583
I-COMMUNICATIONS CORPORATION—See Mitsubishi Corporation; *Int'l*, pg. 4938
ICOM NEW ZEALAND—See ICOM INCORPORATED; *Int'l*, pg. 3583
I-COMPONENTS CO., LTD.; *Int'l*, pg. 3563
I-COM SOFTWARE—See Global Industrial Company; *U.S. Public*, pg. 942
ICOM SPAIN, S.L.—See ICOM INCORPORATED; *Int'l*, pg. 3583
ICOM (UK) LTD.—See ICOM INCORPORATED; *Int'l*, pg. 3582
ICON ANALYTICAL EQUIPMENT PVT. LTD.; *Int'l*, pg. 3583
ICON ANKARA KLINIK ARASTIRMA DIS TICARET ANONIM SIRKETI—See ICON plc; *Int'l*, pg. 3584
ICON AVIATION SA; *Int'l*, pg. 3583
ICON BIOSCIENCE INC.—See EyePoint Pharmaceuticals, Inc.; *Int'l*, pg. 817
ICON BOROVEC EOOD—See Gek Terna Societe Anonyme Holdings Real Estate Constructions; *Int'l*, pg. 2913
ICON BRAZIL—See Wasserman Media Group, LLC; *U.S. Private*, pg. 4450
ICON CAPITAL CORP.; *U.S. Private*, pg. 2031
ICON CENTRAL LABORATORIES INC.—See ICON plc; *Int'l*, pg. 3584
ICON CITY DEVELOPMENT SDN. BHD.—See Mah Sing Group Berhad; *Int'l*, pg. 4643
ICON CLINICAL INVESTMENTS, LLC—See ICON plc; *Int'l*, pg. 3584
ICON CLINICAL RESEARCH AUSTRIA GMBH—See ICON plc; *Int'l*, pg. 3584
ICON CLINICAL RESEARCH (BEIJING) CO. LIMITED—See ICON plc; *Int'l*, pg. 3584
ICON CLINICAL RESEARCH (CANADA) INC.—See ICON plc; *Int'l*, pg. 3584
ICON CLINICAL RESEARCH D.O.O.—See ICON plc; *Int'l*, pg. 3585
ICON CLINICAL RESEARCH EOOD—See ICON plc; *Int'l*, pg. 3584
ICON CLINICAL RESEARCH ESPANA S.L—See ICON plc; *Int'l*, pg. 3584
ICON CLINICAL RESEARCH GMBH—See ICON plc; *Int'l*, pg. 3584
ICON CLINICAL RESEARCH INC—See ICON plc; *Int'l*, pg. 3584
ICON CLINICAL RESEARCH INDIA PRIVATE LIMITED—See ICON plc; *Int'l*, pg. 3584
ICON CLINICAL RESEARCH ISRAEL LIMITED—See ICON plc; *Int'l*, pg. 3585
ICON CLINICAL RESEARCH LIMITED—See ICON plc; *Int'l*, pg. 3584
ICON CLINICAL RESEARCH LLC—See ICON plc; *Int'l*, pg. 3585
ICON CLINICAL RESEARCH MEXICO, S.A. DE C.V.—See ICON plc; *Int'l*, pg. 3585
ICON CLINICAL RESEARCH (NEW ZEALAND) LIMITED—See ICON plc; *Int'l*, pg. 3584
ICON CLINICAL RESEARCH PERU S.A.—See ICON plc; *Int'l*, pg. 3585
ICON CLINICAL RESEARCH PTE LTD—See ICON plc; *Int'l*, pg. 3585
ICON CLINICAL RESEARCH PTY LIMITED—See ICON plc; *Int'l*, pg. 3585
ICON CLINICAL RESEARCH (RUS) LLC—See ICON plc; *Int'l*, pg. 3584
ICON CLINICAL RESEARCH RUSSIA OOO—See ICON plc; *Int'l*, pg. 3585
ICON CLINICAL RESEARCH SARL—See ICON plc; *Int'l*, pg. 3585
ICON CLINICAL RESEARCH S.A.—See ICON plc; *Int'l*, pg. 3585
ICON CLINICAL RESEARCH SERVICES PHILIPPINES, INC.—See ICON plc; *Int'l*, pg. 3585
ICON CLINICAL RESEARCH SLOVAKIA, S.R.O.—See ICON plc; *Int'l*, pg. 3585
ICON CLINICAL RESEARCH—See ICON plc; *Int'l*, pg. 3584
ICON CLINICAL RESEARCH—See ICON plc; *Int'l*, pg. 3584
ICON CLINICAL RESEARCH S.R.L.—See ICON plc; *Int'l*, pg. 3585
ICON CLINICAL RESEARCH S.R.O—See ICON plc; *Int'l*, pg. 3585
ICON CLINICAL RESEARCH (SWITZERLAND) GMBH—See ICON plc; *Int'l*, pg. 3584
ICON CLINICAL RESEARCH TAIWAN LIMITED—See ICON plc; *Int'l*, pg. 3585
ICON CLINICAL RESEARCH (THAILAND) LIMITED—See ICON plc; *Int'l*, pg. 3584
ICON CLINICAL RESEARCH (UK) LIMITED—See ICON plc; *Int'l*, pg. 3584
ICON COMMUNICATIONS CJSC; *Int'l*, pg. 3583
ICON CONTRACTING SOLUTIONS HOLDINGS B.V.—See ICON plc; *Int'l*, pg. 3585
ICON CO PTY LTD—See Kajima Corporation; *Int'l*, pg. 4054
ICON CREDIT UNION; *U.S. Private*, pg. 2032
ICON CULTURE GLOBAL COMPANY LIMITED; *Int'l*, pg. 3583
ICON DEVELOPMENTS AUTRATLIA PTY LTD—See Kajima Corporation; *Int'l*, pg. 4054
ICON DEVELOPMENT SOLUTIONS LIMITED—See ICON plc; *Int'l*, pg. 3585
ICON DUBAI—See Wasserman Media Group, LLC; *U.S. Private*, pg. 4450
ICON EARLY PHASE SERVICES, LLC—See ICON plc; *Int'l*, pg. 3585
ICON ECI FUND FIFTEEN, L.P.; *U.S. Private*, pg. 2032
ICON ECI FUND SIXTEEN; *U.S. Private*, pg. 2032
ICONECTIV, LLC; *U.S. Private*, pg. 2032
ICON ENERGY LIMITED; *Int'l*, pg. 3583
ICON ENERGY SYSTEM (SHENZHEN) CO., LTD.—See Highpower International, Inc.; *Int'l*, pg. 3388
ICON EOOD—See Gek Terna Societe Anonyme Holdings Real Estate Constructions; *Int'l*, pg. 2913
ICONEX LLC—See PT Sinar Mas Group; *Int'l*, pg. 6073
ICONEX SP. Z O.O.—See Amplex AB; *Int'l*, pg. 433
ICON FASHION HOLDING AG; *Int'l*, pg. 3583
ICON FINE WINE & SPIRITS LTD.; *Int'l*, pg. 3583
ICON FREIGHT SERVICES CO. LTD.—See FM Global Logistics Holdings Berhad; *Int'l*, pg. 2717
ICON GROUP LTD.; *Int'l*, pg. 3583
ICON HEALTH & FITNESS, INC.; *U.S. Private*, pg. 2032
ICONIC BRANDS, INC.; *U.S. Public*, pg. 1086
ICONIC DEVELOPMENT LLC; *U.S. Private*, pg. 2032
ICONIC IT, LLC—See Frontenac Company LLC; *U.S. Private*, pg. 1613
ICONIC MINERALS LTD.; *Int'l*, pg. 3586
ICONICS, INC.—See Mitsubishi Electric Corporation; *Int'l*, pg. 4944
ICONIC SPORTS ACQUISITION CORP.; *Int'l*, pg. 3586
ICONIC TRANSLATION MACHINES LTD.—See RWS Holdings plc; *Int'l*, pg. 6437

ICON UTILITY SERVICES, INC.

ICONIC WINES AB—See Viva Wine Group AB; *Int'l*, pg. 8264
ICONIC WORLDWIDE BHD; *Int'l*, pg. 3586
ICON IDENTITY SOLUTIONS, INC.—See MC Group; *U.S. Private*, pg. 2625
ICON IMMOBILIEN GMBH & CO. KG—See Allianz SE; *Int'l*, pg. 353
ICON INFORMATION CONSULTANTS, L.P.; *U.S. Private*, pg. 2032
ICON INFRASTRUCTURE LLP; *Int'l*, pg. 3583
ICON INTERNATIONAL COMMUNICATIONS PTY. LTD.; *Int'l*, pg. 3583
ICON INTERNATIONAL COMMUNICATIONS SINGAPORE PTE. LTD.—See Omnicom Group Inc.; *U.S. Public*, pg. 1586
ICON INTERNATIONAL INC.; *U.S. Private*, pg. 2032
ICON INTERNATIONAL INC.—See Omnicom Group Inc.; *U.S. Public*, pg. 1586
ICON INTERNATIONAL MODEL MANAGEMENT LIMITED—See Emperor Culture Group Limited; *Int'l*, pg. 2386
ICONIQ CAPITAL, LLC; *U.S. Private*, pg. 2032
ICONIX ACQUISITION LLC; *U.S. Private*, pg. 2032
ICONIX CHINA LIMITED—See Iconix Acquisition LLC; *U.S. Private*, pg. 2033
ICONIX INTERNATIONAL INC.—See Iconix Acquisition LLC; *U.S. Private*, pg. 2032
ICONIX LATIN AMERICA LLC—See Iconix Acquisition LLC; *U.S. Private*, pg. 2033
ICON JAPAN K.K.—See ICON plc; *Int'l*, pg. 3585
ICON KLINIKAI KUTATO KORLATOLT FELELOSSEGU TARSASAG—See ICON plc; *Int'l*, pg. 3585
ICONKRISHI INSTITUTE OF MEDICAL SCIENCES PRIVATE LIMITED—See Krishna Institute of Medical Sciences Limited; *Int'l*, pg. 4302
ICON LABORATORIES, INC.—See Francisco Partners Management, LP; *U.S. Private*, pg. 1591
ICON LABORATORY SERVICES, INC.—See ICON plc; *Int'l*, pg. 3585
ICON LIFE SCIENCES CANADA INC.—See ICON plc; *Int'l*, pg. 3585
ICONMA, LLC.; *U.S. Private*, pg. 2033
ICON MECHANICAL CONSTRUCTION & ENGINEERING LLC.; *U.S. Private*, pg. 2032
ICON MEDIA HOLDINGS, INC.; *U.S. Public*, pg. 1086
ICON MEDICAL NETWORK LLC; *U.S. Private*, pg. 2032
ICON METAL PTY. LTD.—See Teaminvest Private Group Limited; *Int'l*, pg. 7501
ICON NORTH AMERICA—See Wasserman Media Group, LLC; *U.S. Private*, pg. 4450
ICON NY HOLDINGS LLC—See Iconix Acquisition LLC; *U.S. Private*, pg. 2033
ICONOCULTURE, INC.—See Gartner, Inc.; *U.S. Public*, pg. 906
ICON OFFSHORE BERHAD—See Liannex Corporation (S) Pte. Ltd.; *Int'l*, pg. 4482
ICON OMAN—See Wasserman Media Group, LLC; *U.S. Private*, pg. 4450
ICON OVERLAY AND FITOUT—See Wasserman Media Group, LLC; *U.S. Private*, pg. 4450
ICONOVO AB; *Int'l*, pg. 3586
ICON PLC; *Int'l*, pg. 3583
ICON POLYMER GROUP, LTD.; *Int'l*, pg. 3586
ICON PROFESSIONAL SERVICES LLC—See Serent Capital Management Company, LLC; *U.S. Private*, pg. 3613
ICON QATAR—See Wasserman Media Group, LLC; *U.S. Private*, pg. 4450
ICON RECRUITMENT LIMITED—See Adecco Group AG; *Int'l*, pg. 136
ICON RECRUITMENT LTD.—See Adecco Group AG; *Int'l*, pg. 136
ICON RUSSIA—See Wasserman Media Group, LLC; *U.S. Private*, pg. 4450
ICONSOFT INC.; *U.S. Private*, pg. 2033
ICON—See Wasserman Media Group, LLC; *U.S. Private*, pg. 4450
ICONSTRUCTORS, LLC; *U.S. Private*, pg. 2033
ICONSUMER CORP.; *U.S. Public*, pg. 1086
ICON SYSTEMHAUS GMBH—See Quadient SA; *Int'l*, pg. 6149
ICONTACT LLC—See Ziff Davis, Inc.; *U.S. Public*, pg. 2404
ICONTACT MARKETING CORP.—See Ziff Davis, Inc.; *U.S. Public*, pg. 2404
I-CONTACTS CORPORATION—See PLDT Inc.; *Int'l*, pg. 5896
ICONTRACTS, INC.—See Rothschild & Co SCA; *Int'l*, pg. 6403
ICONTRACTS, INC.—See TA Associates, Inc.; *U.S. Private*, pg. 3918
I-CONTROL HOLDINGS LIMITED; *Int'l*, pg. 3563
ICONTROL NETWORKS, INC.; *U.S. Private*, pg. 2033
ICONTRONIC SDN. BHD.; *Int'l*, pg. 3586
ICONTRONIC TECHNOLOGY SDN. BHD.—See UNIMECH Group Berhad; *Int'l*, pg. 8049
ICON UTILITY SERVICES, INC.; *U.S. Private*, pg. 2032
ICON VENUE GROUP, LLC—See TPG Capital, L.P.; *U.S. Public*, pg. 2170

ICOPAL AB—See GAF Materials Corporation; *U.S. Private*, pg. 1633
ICOPAL APS—See GAF Materials Corporation; *U.S. Private*, pg. 1633
ICOPAL AS—See GAF Materials Corporation; *U.S. Private*, pg. 1633
ICOPAL DANMARK APS—See GAF Materials Corporation; *U.S. Private*, pg. 1633
ICOPAL ENTREPRENAD AB—See GAF Materials Corporation; *U.S. Private*, pg. 1633
ICOPAL GMBH—See GAF Materials Corporation; *U.S. Private*, pg. 1633
ICOPAL HISPANIA S.L.—See Siris Capital Group, LLC; *U.S. Private*, pg. 3674
ICOPAL KFT.—See GAF Materials Corporation; *U.S. Private*, pg. 1633
ICOPAL LTD—See GAF Materials Corporation; *U.S. Private*, pg. 1633
ICOPAL OY—See GAF Materials Corporation; *U.S. Private*, pg. 1634
ICOPAL S.A.—See GAF Materials Corporation; *U.S. Private*, pg. 1634
ICOPAL SIPLAST SAS—See GAF Materials Corporation; *U.S. Private*, pg. 1634
ICOPAL SP. Z O.O.—See GAF Materials Corporation; *U.S. Private*, pg. 1634
ICOPAL S.R.L.—See GAF Materials Corporation; *U.S. Private*, pg. 1634
ICOP DIGITAL, INC.—See Safety Vision, LLC; *U.S. Private*, pg. 3525
ICOR AB—See Teleflex Incorporated; *U.S. Public*, pg. 1995
ICORDA NV—See VINCI S.A.; *Int'l*, pg. 8222
ICORECONNECT INC.—See iCoreConnect Inc.; *U.S. Public*, pg. 1086
ICORECONNECT INC.; *U.S. Public*, pg. 1086
ICORE HEALTHCARE LLC—See Centene Corporation; *U.S. Public*, pg. 469
ICOR PARTNERS, LLC; *U.S. Private*, pg. 2033
ICORR PROPERTIES INTERNATIONAL; *Int'l*, pg. 3586
ICOSAVAX, INC.—See AstraZeneca PLC; *Int'l*, pg. 1086
ICOS DEUTSCHLAND GMBH—See Sesa S.p.A.; *Int'l*, pg. 6728
ICOS VISION SYSTEMS CORPORATION N.V.—See KLA Corporation; *U.S. Public*, pg. 1267
ICOS VISION SYSTEMS LTD.—See KLA Corporation; *U.S. Public*, pg. 1268
ICOS VISION SYSTEMS NV—See KLA Corporation; *U.S. Public*, pg. 1268
ICOS VISION SYSTEMS (SHENZHEN) CO. LTD.—See KLA Corporation; *U.S. Public*, pg. 1267
ICOT HONG KONG LTD.—See Toto Ltd.; *Int'l*, pg. 7845
ICOTTON SIA; *Int'l*, pg. 3586
ICOVA B.V.—See Renewi plc; *Int'l*, pg. 6279
ICP ADHESIVES & SEALANTS, INC.—See Audax Group, Limited Partnership; *U.S. Private*, pg. 388
ICP BUILDING SOLUTIONS GROUP—See Audax Group, Limited Partnership; *U.S. Private*, pg. 388
ICP CONSTRUCTION, INC.—See Audax Group, Limited Partnership; *U.S. Private*, pg. 388
ICPEI HOLDINGS INC.; *Int'l*, pg. 3586
ICPE S.A.—See SIF Muntenia S.A.; *Int'l*, pg. 6905
ICP INC.—See Island Computer Products, Inc.; *U.S. Private*, pg. 2145
ICP JIANGMEN CO. LTD.—See IJM Corporation Berhad; *Int'l*, pg. 3609
ICP LTD.; *Int'l*, pg. 3586
IC PLUS CORP.; *Int'l*, pg. 3577
ICP MARKETING SDN BHD—See IJM Corporation Berhad; *Int'l*, pg. 3608
ICPROA SA; *Int'l*, pg. 3586
ICPV SA; *Int'l*, pg. 3586
ICQ INC.—See VK Company; *Int'l*, pg. 8281
ICRAFT CO., LTD.; *Int'l*, pg. 3586
ICRA GLOBAL CAPITAL, INC.—See Moody's Corporation; *U.S. Public*, pg. 1467
ICRA LANKA LIMITED—See Moody's Corporation; *U.S. Public*, pg. 1467
ICRA LIMITED—See Moody's Corporation; *U.S. Public*, pg. 1467
ICRA MANAGEMENT CONSULTING SERVICES LIMITED—See Moody's Corporation; *U.S. Public*, pg. 1467
ICRA NEPAL LIMITED—See Moody's Corporation; *U.S. Public*, pg. 1467
ICRA ONLINE LIMITED—See Moody's Corporation; *U.S. Public*, pg. 1467
ICRA SAPPHIRE INC.—See Moody's Corporation; *U.S. Public*, pg. 1467
IC REALTIME, LLC; *U.S. Private*, pg. 2029
ICREATE LIMITED—See CN Innovations Holdings Limited; *Int'l*, pg. 1673
ICREO CO., LTD.—See Ezaki Glico Co., Ltd.; *Int'l*, pg. 2593
ICR, LLC; *U.S. Private*, pg. 2033
ICRON TECHNOLOGIES CORPORATION—See Analog Devices, Inc.; *U.S. Public*, pg. 135
ICROSSING BRIGHTON—See The Hearst Corporation; *U.S. Private*, pg. 4049

ICROSSING CHICAGO—See The Hearst Corporation; *U.S. Private*, pg. 4049
ICROSSING DALLAS—See The Hearst Corporation; *U.S. Private*, pg. 4049
ICROSSING, INC.—See The Hearst Corporation; *U.S. Private*, pg. 4049
ICROSSING IRVINE—See The Hearst Corporation; *U.S. Private*, pg. 4049
ICROSSING LONDON—See The Hearst Corporation; *U.S. Private*, pg. 4049
ICROSSING LOS ANGELES—See The Hearst Corporation; *U.S. Private*, pg. 4049
ICROSSING RESTON—See The Hearst Corporation; *U.S. Private*, pg. 4049
ICROSSING SALT LAKE CITY—See The Hearst Corporation; *U.S. Private*, pg. 4049
ICROSSING SAN FRANCISCO—See The Hearst Corporation; *U.S. Private*, pg. 4049
ICROSSING SCOTTSDALE—See The Hearst Corporation; *U.S. Private*, pg. 4049
ICSA (INDIA) LTD.; *Int'l*, pg. 3586
ICSA (INGENIERIA Y COMPUTACION, S.A.)—See Hexagon AB; *Int'l*, pg. 3369
ICS BUILDERS INC.; *U.S. Private*, pg. 2033
ICS BUNKERING SERVICES LTD.—See Minerva Bunkering; *Int'l*, pg. 4907
ICS CARGO CLEAN—See Stone Canyon Industries, LLC; *U.S. Private*, pg. 3817
ICS CUSTOMS SERVICE INC.; *U.S. Private*, pg. 2033
I.C.S. DRY-ICE EXPRESS B.V.—See Cryoport, Inc.; *U.S. Public*, pg. 600
ICS ENDAVA SRL—See Endava plc; *Int'l*, pg. 2402
ICSENSE NV—See TDK Corporation; *Int'l*, pg. 7487
ICS FUNDING PTE. LTD.—See Credit Intelligence Limited; *Int'l*, pg. 1835
ICSGLOBAL LIMITED - CYBRAND—See ICSGlobal Limited; *Int'l*, pg. 3586
ICSGLOBAL LIMITED; *Int'l*, pg. 3586
ICS GROUP HOLDINGS INC.—See INNOVATE Corp.; *U.S. Public*, pg. 1126
I.C.S. HERBALIFE MA, S.R.L.—See Herbalife Nutrition Ltd.; *U.S. Public*, pg. 3360
ICSH S.A; *Int'l*, pg. 3586
ICS, INC.; *U.S. Public*, pg. 2033
ICS INDUSTRIES PTY LTD—See EnerSys; *U.S. Public*, pg. 767
I.C.S INTERNATIONAL COLLECTIONS SERVICES BV—See Intrum AB; *Int'l*, pg. 3770
ICS KNAUF GIPS SRL—See Gebr. Knauf KG; *Int'l*, pg. 2906
ICS LOGISTICS, INC.; *U.S. Private*, pg. 2033
ICS METRO CASH & CARRY MOLDOVA S.R.L.—See Metro AG; *Int'l*, pg. 4857
ICS NETT INC.; *U.S. Private*, pg. 2033
ICSN INC.; *U.S. Private*, pg. 2033
IC SOLUTIONS, INC.; *U.S. Private*, pg. 2029
ICSOLUTIONS, LLC.—See Centric Group LLC; *U.S. Private*, pg. 830
ICS PENETRON INTERNATIONAL LTD.; *U.S. Private*, pg. 2033
ICS PETROLEUM LTD.—See Minerva Bunkering; *Int'l*, pg. 4907
ICS PETROLEUM (MONTREAL) LTD.—See Minerva Bunkering; *Int'l*, pg. 4907
ICS PETROM MOLDOVA SA—See OMV Aktiengesellschaft; *Int'l*, pg. 5567
ICS PETRUZALEK SRL—See Zeus Packaging Group Ltd.; *Int'l*, pg. 8640
ICS POLAND SP. Z O.O.—See Seri Industrial SpA; *Int'l*, pg. 6722
ICS RAIFFEISEN LEASING S.R.L—See Raiffeisen Bank International AG; *Int'l*, pg. 6182
ICS SOLUTIONS GROUP—See SECOM Co., Ltd.; *Int'l*, pg. 6671
ICS TERMINALS (UK) LIMITED—See Brookfield Infrastructure Partners L.P.; *Int'l*, pg. 1190
ICS TRIPLEX ISAGRAF INC.—See Rockwell Automation, Inc.; *U.S. Public*, pg. 1805
ICSYNERGY INTERNATIONAL, LLC—See iC Consult Group GmbH; *Int'l*, pg. 3577
I.C. SYSTEM, INC.; *U.S. Private*, pg. 2026
ICTA AB; *Int'l*, pg. 3587
I.C.T.C. HOLDINGS CORPORATION; *Int'l*, pg. 3565
I&C TECHNOLOGY CO., LTD.; *Int'l*, pg. 3562
ICT EUROPE GMBH—See Dentium Co., Ltd; *Int'l*, pg. 2033
ICT FZCO—See Dentium Co., Ltd; *Int'l*, pg. 2034
ICT GROUP N.V.—See La Cooperative WELCOOP SA; *Int'l*, pg. 4387
ICT HOLDING A/S—See DFDS A/S; *Int'l*, pg. 2095
ICT HOLDINGS INC.; *U.S. Private*, pg. 2033
I.C. THOMASSON ASSOCIATES, INC.—See Salas O'Brien Engineers, Inc.; *U.S. Private*, pg. 3530
I.C. THOMASSON ASSOCIATES—See Salas O'Brien Engineers, Inc.; *U.S. Private*, pg. 3530
I.C. THOMASSON ASSOCIATES—See Salas O'Brien Engineers, Inc.; *U.S. Private*, pg. 3530
I.C. THOMASSON ASSOCIATES—See Salas O'Brien Engineers, Inc.; *U.S. Private*, pg. 3530

ICT INTEGRATED CIRCUIT TESTING GMBH—See Applied Materials, Inc.; *U.S. Public*, pg. 172
ICT LOGICOM SOLUTIONS S.A.—See Logicom Public Ltd; *Int'l*, pg. 4542
ICT LOGISTICS GMBH—See DFDS A/S; *Int'l*, pg. 2095
ICT LOGISTICS UAB—See DFDS A/S; *Int'l*, pg. 2095
ICT MEDIA LTD.—See Economedia; *Int'l*, pg. 2298
ICT SERVICE MANAGEMENT SOLUTIONS (INDIA) PRIVATE LIMITED—See Wistron Corporation; *Int'l*, pg. 8438
ICTS HUNGARY KFT—See Proximus PLC; *Int'l*, pg. 6008
ICTSI DR CONGO S.A.—See International Container Terminal Services, Inc.; *Int'l*, pg. 3746
ICTS INTERNATIONAL, N.V.; *Int'l*, pg. 3587
ICTSI RIO BRASIL TERMINAL 1 S.A.—See LATAM Airlines Group S.A.; *Int'l*, pg. 4422
ICTSI SOUTH PACIFIC LIMITED—See International Container Terminal Services, Inc.; *Int'l*, pg. 3746
ICTSI WAREHOUSING, INC.—See International Container Terminal Services, Inc.; *Int'l*, pg. 3746
ICTS TECHNOLOGIES USA, INC.—See ICTS International, N.V.; *Int'l*, pg. 3587
ICTV BRANDS INC.; *U.S. Public*, pg. 1086
ICT WATCHER SH.P.K.—See WIIT SpA; *Int'l*, pg. 8408
I-CUBED, LLC.—See Airbus SE; *Int'l*, pg. 243
I-CUBE GMBH—See ecotel communication ag; *Int'l*, pg. 2300
ICU EYEWEAR, INC.—See 1847 Holdings LLC; *U.S. Public*, pg. 2
ICU MEDICAL AUSTRALIA PTY LIMITED—See ICU Medical, Inc.; *U.S. Public*, pg. 1087
ICU MEDICAL FLEET SERVICES, LLC—See ICU Medical, Inc.; *U.S. Public*, pg. 1087
ICU MEDICAL GERMANY GMBH—See ICU Medical, Inc.; *U.S. Public*, pg. 1087
ICU MEDICAL, INC.; *U.S. Public*, pg. 1086
ICU MEDICAL (UTAH), INC.—See ICU Medical, Inc.; *U.S. Public*, pg. 1087
ICURE PHARMACEUTICAL, INC.; *Int'l*, pg. 3587
ICV - INERTES DE CABO VERDE, LDA.—See SODIM, SGPS, SA; *Int'l*, pg. 7049
ICV PARTNERS, LLC; *U.S. Private*, pg. 2033
ICX GROUP INC.; *U.S. Private*, pg. 2034
ICX PLATFORM (PTY) LTD.—See 63 moons technologies limited; *Int'l*, pg. 14
ICYBREEZE COOLING LLC—See Solo Brands, Inc.; *U.S. Public*, pg. 1901
ICYNENE ASIA PACIFIC INC.—See Huntsman Corporation; *U.S. Public*, pg. 1075
ICYNENE, INC.—See Huntsman Corporation; *U.S. Public*, pg. 1075
ICYNENE LAPOLLA FRANCE SAS—See Huntsman Corporation; *U.S. Public*, pg. 1075
IC ZERICH CAPITAL MANAGEMENT JSC; *Int'l*, pg. 3577
ICZOOM GROUP INC.; *Int'l*, pg. 3587
ID4 AG—See Anemoi International Ltd; *Int'l*, pg. 458
IDA CASON CALLAWAY FOUNDATION; *U.S. Private*, pg. 2034
IDACORP FINANCIAL SERVICES, INC.—See IDACORP, Inc.; *U.S. Public*, pg. 1088
IDACORP, INC.; *U.S. Public*, pg. 1087
IDA COUNTY, IOWA COMMUNITY HOSPITAL; *U.S. Private*, pg. 2034
IDAC (PRIVATE) LIMITED—See Daikin Industries, Ltd.; *Int'l*, pg. 1935
ID ADDITIVES, INC.; *U.S. Private*, pg. 2034
IDA GROVE BANCSHARES, INC.; *U.S. Private*, pg. 2034
IDAHO AGRICULTURAL CREDIT ASSOCIATION; *U.S. Private*, pg. 2034
IDAHO ASPHALT SUPPLY INC.; *U.S. Private*, pg. 2034
IDAHO ATHLETIC CLUB, INC.—See TPG Capital, L.P.; *U.S. Public*, pg. 2176
IDAHO BEVERAGES INC.; *U.S. Private*, pg. 2034
IDAHO BUSINESS REVIEW, LLC—See The Dolan Company; *U.S. Private*, pg. 4022
IDAHO CENTRAL CREDIT UNION; *U.S. Private*, pg. 2034
IDAHO COMMUNITY FOUNDATION, INC.; *U.S. Private*, pg. 2034
IDAHO COPPER CORPORATION; *U.S. Public*, pg. 1088
IDAHO DEPARTMENT OF COMMERCE; *U.S. Private*, pg. 2034
IDAHO DIVISION OF TOURISM DEVELOPMENT—See Idaho Department of Commerce; *U.S. Private*, pg. 2034
IDAHO ENERGY RESOURCES COMPANY—See IDACORP, Inc.; *U.S. Public*, pg. 1088
IDAHO FIRST BANK; *U.S. Private*, pg. 2034
IDAHO FOREST GROUP, LLC; *U.S. Private*, pg. 2035
IDAHO FRESH-PAK INC.; *U.S. Private*, pg. 2035
IDAHO HOME HEALTH AND HOSPICE INC.—See UnitedHealth Group Incorporated; *U.S. Public*, pg. 2245
IDAHO INDEPENDENT TELEVISION, INC.—See Block Communications, Inc.; *U.S. Private*, pg. 582
IDAHO-MARYLAND MINING CORPORATION—See Emergent Metals Corp.; *Int'l*, pg. 2378
IDAHO MATERIAL HANDLING INC.—See Hoj Engineering & Sales Co., LLC; *U.S. Private*, pg. 1961
IDAHO MATERIAL HANDLING INC.—See Hoj Engineering & Sales Co., LLC; *U.S. Private*, pg. 1961

COMPANY NAME INDEX

IDAHO MILK TRANSPORT, INC.—See Ontario Municipal Employees Retirement System; *Int'l*, pg. 5584
IDAHO NORTH RESOURCES CORP.; *U.S. Private*, pg. 2035
IDAHO PACIFIC CORPORATION—See Continental Grain Company; *U.S. Private*, pg. 1029
IDAHO PACIFIC LUMBER COMPANY INC.; *U.S. Private*, pg. 2035
IDAHO PACKAGE COMPANY—See Kelso & Company, L.P.; *U.S. Private*, pg. 2279
IDAHO PACKAGE COMPANY—See Warburg Pincus LLC; *U.S. Private*, pg. 4437
IDAHO POTATO PACKERS CORPORATION—See Nonpareil Corporation; *U.S. Private*, pg. 2934
IDAHO POWER COMPANY—See IDACORP, Inc.; *U.S. Public*, pg. 1088
IDAHO PRESS-TRIBUNE INC.—See Pioneer Newspapers Inc.; *U.S. Private*, pg. 3187
IDAHO STATESMAN—See Chatham Asset Management, LLC; *U.S. Private*, pg. 866
IDAHO STEEL PRODUCTS INC.; *U.S. Private*, pg. 2035
IDAHO STRATEGIC RESOURCES, INC.; *U.S. Public*, pg. 1088
IDAHO SUPREME POTATOES, INC.; *U.S. Private*, pg. 2035
IDAHO TIMBER CORPORATION—See Jefferies Financial Group Inc.; *U.S. Public*, pg. 1188
IDAHO TROUT PROCESSORS COMPANY; *U.S. Private*, pg. 2035
IDAHO TRUST BANCORP; *U.S. Private*, pg. 2035
IDAHO TRUST BANK—See Idaho Trust Bancorp; *U.S. Private*, pg. 2035
IDAHO VENEER COMPANY; *U.S. Private*, pg. 2035
IDAHO VENEER CO.—See Idaho Veneer Company; *U.S. Private*, pg. 2035
IDAHO WESTERN, INC.—See UFP Industries, Inc.; *U.S. Public*, pg. 2219
IDA INFRONT AB—See Addnode Group AB; *Int'l*, pg. 130
IDA IRELAND USA OFFICE—See Investment & Development Agency-Ireland; *Int'l*, pg. 3780
ID-ALL BV—See Panasonic Holdings Corporation; *Int'l*, pg. 5725
IDAMAN HARMONI SDN. BHD.—See Mega First Corporation Berhad; *Int'l*, pg. 4792
ID ANALYTICS, LLC—See RELX plc; *Int'l*, pg. 6267
IDANT LABORATORY—See Daxor Corporation; *U.S. Public*, pg. 644
IDARTS AUSTRALIA PTY LTD.—See ST Group Food Industries Holdings Limited; *Int'l*, pg. 7158
IDA SERVICES, INC.—See Crossroads of Western Iowa, Inc.; *U.S. Private*, pg. 1108
IDATA TECHNOLOGIES INC; *U.S. Private*, pg. 2035
IDA-WEST ENERGY COMPANY—See IDACORP, Inc.; *U.S. Public*, pg. 1088
IDB DEUTSCHLAND GMBH—See Ornua Co-operative Limited; *Int'l*, pg. 5642
IDB DEVELOPMENT CORPORATION LTD.; *Int'l*, pg. 3588
IDB GLOBAL BV—See Ornua Co-operative Limited; *Int'l*, pg. 5642
IDBI HOMEFINANCE LTD.; *Int'l*, pg. 3588
I.D. BOOTH INC.; *U.S. Private*, pg. 2027
IDB TOURISM (2009) LTD.—See IDB Development Corporation Ltd.; *Int'l*, pg. 3588
ID BUSINESS SOLUTIONS LTD.; *Int'l*, pg. 3587
IDBYDNA INC.—See Illumina, Inc.; *U.S. Public*, pg. 1112
ID CABLES SAS—See TKH Group N.V.; *Int'l*, pg. 7764
IDC ASEAN—See China Oceanwide Holdings Group Co., Ltd.; *Int'l*, pg. 1536
IDC ASEAN—See IDG Capital; *Int'l*, pg. 3593
IDC ASIA PACIFIC (SINGAPORE)—See China Oceanwide Holdings Group Co., Ltd.; *Int'l*, pg. 1536
IDC ASIA PACIFIC (SINGAPORE)—See IDG Capital; *Int'l*, pg. 3593
IDC ASIA & PACIFIC—See China Oceanwide Holdings Group Co., Ltd.; *Int'l*, pg. 1536
IDC ASIA & PACIFIC—See IDG Capital; *Int'l*, pg. 3593
IDC AUSTRALIA—See China Oceanwide Holdings Group Co., Ltd.; *Int'l*, pg. 1536
IDC AUSTRALIA—See IDG Capital; *Int'l*, pg. 3593
IDC BENELUX—See China Oceanwide Holdings Group Co., Ltd.; *Int'l*, pg. 1536
IDC BENELUX—See IDG Capital; *Int'l*, pg. 3593
IDC BRAZIL—See China Oceanwide Holdings Group Co., Ltd.; *Int'l*, pg. 1536
IDC BRAZIL—See IDG Capital; *Int'l*, pg. 3593
IDC CENTRAL EUROPE GMBH—See China Oceanwide Holdings Group Co., Ltd.; *Int'l*, pg. 1537
IDC CENTRAL EUROPE GMBH—See IDG Capital; *Int'l*, pg. 3593
IDC CENTRAL EUROPE GMBH—See China Oceanwide Holdings Group Co., Ltd.; *Int'l*, pg. 1537
IDC CENTRAL EUROPE GMBH—See IDG Capital; *Int'l*, pg. 3593
IDC CHINA—See China Oceanwide Holdings Group Co., Ltd.; *Int'l*, pg. 1537
IDC CHINA—See IDG Capital; *Int'l*, pg. 3593
IDC COLUMBIA—See China Oceanwide Holdings Group Co., Ltd.; *Int'l*, pg. 1537

IDC COLUMBIA—See IDG Capital; *Int'l*, pg. 3593
IDC FRANCE—See China Oceanwide Holdings Group Co., Ltd.; *Int'l*, pg. 1537
IDC FRANCE—See IDG Capital; *Int'l*, pg. 3593
IDC FRONTIER INC.—See SoftBank Group Corp.; *Int'l*, pg. 7051
IDC GLOBAL, INC.—See GTT Communications, Inc.; *U.S. Private*, pg. 1808
IDC INDIA LTD.—See China Oceanwide Holdings Group Co., Ltd.; *Int'l*, pg. 1537
IDC INDIA LTD.—See IDG Capital; *Int'l*, pg. 3593
IDC ISRAEL—See China Oceanwide Holdings Group Co., Ltd.; *Int'l*, pg. 1537
IDC ISRAEL—See IDG Capital; *Int'l*, pg. 3593
IDC ITALY—See China Oceanwide Holdings Group Co., Ltd.; *Int'l*, pg. 1537
IDC ITALY—See IDG Capital; *Int'l*, pg. 3593
IDC JAPAN CO., LTD.—See China Oceanwide Holdings Group Co., Ltd.; *Int'l*, pg. 1537
IDC JAPAN CO., LTD.—See IDG Capital; *Int'l*, pg. 3593
IDC KOREA LTD.—See China Oceanwide Holdings Group Co., Ltd.; *Int'l*, pg. 1537
IDC KOREA LTD.—See IDG Capital; *Int'l*, pg. 3593
IDC LATIN AMERICA—See China Oceanwide Holdings Group Co., Ltd.; *Int'l*, pg. 1537
IDC LATIN AMERICA—See IDG Capital; *Int'l*, pg. 3593
IDC LIMAN ISLETMELERI A.S.—See Izmir Demir Celik Sanayi AS; *Int'l*, pg. 3851
IDC MEXICO—See China Oceanwide Holdings Group Co., Ltd.; *Int'l*, pg. 1537
IDC MEXICO—See IDG Capital; *Int'l*, pg. 3593
IDC NORDIC (DENMARK) A/S—See China Oceanwide Holdings Group Co., Ltd.; *Int'l*, pg. 1537
IDC NORDIC (DENMARK) A/S—See IDG Capital; *Int'l*, pg. 3593
IDC NORDIC (SWEDEN)—See China Oceanwide Holdings Group Co., Ltd.; *Int'l*, pg. 1537
IDC NORDIC (SWEDEN)—See IDG Capital; *Int'l*, pg. 3593
ID COMMERCE + LOGISTICS—See Inktel Direct Inc.; *U.S. Private*, pg. 2078
IDCON INCORPORATED—See Total Resource Management, Inc.; *U.S. Private*, pg. 4191
ID CONSEIL—See Jones Lang LaSalle Incorporated; *U.S. Public*, pg. 1202
IDC PHILIPPINES—See China Oceanwide Holdings Group Co., Ltd.; *Int'l*, pg. 1537
IDC PHILIPPINES—See IDG Capital; *Int'l*, pg. 3593
IDC POLSKA—See China Oceanwide Holdings Group Co., Ltd.; *Int'l*, pg. 1537
IDC POLSKA—See IDG Capital; *Int'l*, pg. 3594
IDC PORTUGAL—See China Oceanwide Holdings Group Co., Ltd.; *Int'l*, pg. 1537
IDC PORTUGAL—See IDG Capital; *Int'l*, pg. 3594
IDC PROPERTY MANAGEMENT—See Inuvialuit Regional Corporation; *Int'l*, pg. 3772
IDC RESEARCH, INC.—See China Oceanwide Holdings Group Co., Ltd.; *Int'l*, pg. 1537
IDC RESEARCH, INC.—See IDG Capital; *Int'l*, pg. 3594
IDC RUSSIA—See China Oceanwide Holdings Group Co., Ltd.; *Int'l*, pg. 1537
IDC RUSSIA—See IDG Capital; *Int'l*, pg. 3594
IDC SPAIN—See China Oceanwide Holdings Group Co., Ltd.; *Int'l*, pg. 1537
IDC SPAIN—See IDG Capital; *Int'l*, pg. 3594
IDC TAIWAN—See China Oceanwide Holdings Group Co., Ltd.; *Int'l*, pg. 1537
IDC TAIWAN—See IDG Capital; *Int'l*, pg. 3594
IDC TECHNOLOGIES, INC.; *U.S. Private*, pg. 2035
IDC TURKEY—See China Oceanwide Holdings Group Co., Ltd.; *Int'l*, pg. 1537
IDC TURKEY—See IDG Capital; *Int'l*, pg. 3594
IDC UK LTD.—See China Oceanwide Holdings Group Co., Ltd.; *Int'l*, pg. 1537
IDC UK LTD.—See IDG Capital; *Int'l*, pg. 3594
IDC USA, INC.—See Imaging Dynamics Company Ltd.; *Int'l*, pg. 3619
IDC VENEZUELA—See China Oceanwide Holdings Group Co., Ltd.; *Int'l*, pg. 1537
IDC VENEZUELA—See IDG Capital; *Int'l*, pg. 3594
IDC WORLDSOURCE INSURANCE NETWORK INC.—See Guardian Capital Group Limited; *Int'l*, pg. 3170
IDD AEROSPACE CORP.; *U.S. Private*, pg. 2035
IDDINGS TRUCKING, INC.; *U.S. Private*, pg. 2035
IDDINK SPAIN S.L.U.—See Sanoma Oyj; *Int'l*, pg. 6553
ID DO BRASIL LOGISTICA LTDA—See ID Logistics SAS; *Int'l*, pg. 3587
IDD PARTS B.V.—See ASSA ABLOY AB; *Int'l*, pg. 639
IDDRIVEN, INC.; *U.S. Public*, pg. 1088
IDEA BANK MARKETING; *U.S. Private*, pg. 2035
IDEA BANK S.A.—See Getin Holding S.A.; *Int'l*, pg. 2947
IDEA BANK S.A.—See Getin Holding S.A.; *Int'l*, pg. 2947
IDEA BANK SA—See Getin Holding S.A.; *Int'l*, pg. 2947
IDEA CAPITAL FUNDS SGR—See De Agostini S.p.A.; *Int'l*, pg. 1995
IDEA CONSULTANTS, INC.; *Int'l*, pg. 3588
IDEA CONSULTING INC.—See FUJISOFT INCORPORATED; *Int'l*, pg. 2831

IDEAL GROUP S.A.

IDEA CORPORATION—See SEMBA Corporation; *Int'l*, pg. 6702
IDEA COUTURE LATIN AMERICA, S.A.P.I. DE C.V.—See Cognizant Technology Solutions Corporation; *U.S. Public*, pg. 524
IDEA CUBE CORPORATION—See Nexyz.Group Corporation; *Int'l*, pg. 5252
IDEA ESTONIA—See The Interpublic Group of Companies, Inc.; *U.S. Public*, pg. 2093
IDEA FARMER LLC—See Zealot Networks, Inc.; *U.S. Private*, pg. 4599
IDEA FIMIT SGR—See De Agostini S.p.A.; *Int'l*, pg. 1995
IDEA FLEET S.A.—See Getin Holding S.A.; *Int'l*, pg. 2947
IDEAFORGE TECHNOLOGY LIMITED; *Int'l*, pg. 3588
IDEAGEN CAPTURE LIMITED—See HgCapital Trust plc; *Int'l*, pg. 3377
IDEAGEN PLC—See HgCapital Trust plc; *Int'l*, pg. 3377
IDEA GLOBAL LLC—See Expolanka Holdings PLC; *Int'l*, pg. 2589
I/D/E/A/ INC.; *U.S. Private*, pg. 2027
IDEA INTEGRATION CORP.—See The Gores Group, LLC; *U.S. Private*, pg. 4034
IDEA ISITME SISTEMLERI SANAYI VE TICARET A.S.—See Demant A/S; *Int'l*, pg. 2024
IDEALAB HOLDINGS, LLC; *U.S. Private*, pg. 2036
IDEALAB, INC.—See Idealab Holdings, LLC; *U.S. Private*, pg. 2036
IDEAL ALAMBREC SA—See NV Bekaert SA; *Int'l*, pg. 5496
IDEAL ANDERSON ASIA PACIFIC LTD.—See IDEAL Industries Inc; *U.S. Private*, pg. 2036
IDEAL ANDERSON TECHNOLOGIES (SHENZHEN) LTD.—See IDEAL Industries Inc; *U.S. Private*, pg. 2036
IDEALBASE SDN. BHD.—See Gromutual Berhad; *Int'l*, pg. 3087
IDEAL BOX CO.; *U.S. Private*, pg. 2035
IDEAL CAPITAL BERHAD; *Int'l*, pg. 3588
IDEAL CHEMICAL & SUPPLY COMPANY; *U.S. Private*, pg. 2035
IDEAL CHEMI PLAST PRIVATE LIMITED—See DIC Corporation; *Int'l*, pg. 2109
IDEAL CLAMP PRODUCTS, INC.-BROWNSVILLE—See TruArc Partners, L.P.; *U.S. Private*, pg. 4245
IDEAL CLAMP PRODUCTS, INC.—See TruArc Partners, L.P.; *U.S. Private*, pg. 4245
IDEAL CLASSIC CARS LLC; *U.S. Private*, pg. 2035
THE IDEAL COMPANY INC.; *U.S. Private*, pg. 4055
IDEAL CONTRACTING L.L.C.—See The Ideal Group, Inc.; *U.S. Private*, pg. 4055
IDEAL CORP.; *U.S. Private*, pg. 2035
IDEAL CREDIT UNION; *U.S. Private*, pg. 2035
IDEAL DEALS, LLC; *U.S. Private*, pg. 2036
IDEAL DISTRIBUTING CO. INC.; *U.S. Private*, pg. 2036
IDEALEASE DE MEXICO SA DE CV—See Idealease, Inc.; *U.S. Private*, pg. 2037
IDEALEASE, INC.; *U.S. Private*, pg. 2037
IDEALEASE OF ATLANTA, L.L.C.—See Idealease, Inc.; *U.S. Private*, pg. 2037
IDEALEASE OF CHICAGO LLC—See Rush Enterprises, Inc.; *U.S. Public*, pg. 1826
IDEALEASE OF FLINT INC.—See C&S Motors, Inc.; *U.S. Private*, pg. 704
IDEALEASE OF HOUSTON, L.L.C.—See Idealease, Inc.; *U.S. Private*, pg. 2037
IDEALEASE RISK SERVICES, INC.—See Idealease, Inc.; *U.S. Private*, pg. 2037
IDEALEASE SERVICES, INC.—See Idealease, Inc.; *U.S. Private*, pg. 2037
IDEAL ELECTRIC COMPANY—See Gulf Electroquip Ltd.; *U.S. Private*, pg. 1816
IDEAL ELECTRIC SUPPLY CORPORATION; *U.S. Private*, pg. 2036
IDEAL FENCING CORP.; *U.S. Private*, pg. 2036
IDEAL FIBRES & FABRICS COMINES SAS—See Beaulieu International Group NV; *Int'l*, pg. 934
IDEAL FIBRES & FABRICS WIELSBEKE NV—See Beaulieu International Group NV; *Int'l*, pg. 934
IDEAL FLOORCOVERINGS NV—See Beaulieu International Group NV; *Int'l*, pg. 934
THE IDEAL GROUP, INC.; *U.S. Private*, pg. 4055
IDEAL GROUP S.A.; *Int'l*, pg. 3589
IDEAL HEIGHTS PROPERTIES SDN. BHD.—See Bina Puri Holdings Bhd; *Int'l*, pg. 1032
IDEAL IMAGE DEVELOPMENT, INC.—See Catterton Management Company, LLC; *U.S. Private*, pg. 794
IDEAL IMPLANT, INC.—See Bimini Technologies, LLC; *U.S. Private*, pg. 560
IDEAL INDUSTRIES AUSTRALIA—See IDEAL Industries Inc; *U.S. Private*, pg. 2036
IDEAL INDUSTRIES BRASIL LTDA.—See IDEAL Industries Inc; *U.S. Private*, pg. 2036
IDEAL INDUSTRIES (CANADA) CORP.—See IDEAL Industries Inc; *U.S. Private*, pg. 2036
IDEAL INDUSTRIES CHINA L.L.C.—See IDEAL Industries Inc; *U.S. Private*, pg. 2036
IDEAL INDUSTRIES GMBH—See IDEAL Industries Inc; *U.S. Private*, pg. 2036

IDEAL GROUP S.A.   CORPORATE AFFILIATIONS

IDEAL INDUSTRIES, INC. - CASELLA MEASUREMENT DIVISION—See IDEAL Industries Inc; *U.S. Private*, pg. 2036
IDEAL INDUSTRIES INC; *U.S. Private*, pg. 2036
IDEAL INDUSTRIES INDIA PRIVATE LIMITED.—See IDEAL Industries Inc; *U.S. Private*, pg. 2036
IDEAL INDUSTRIES MEXICO—See IDEAL Industries Inc; *U.S. Private*, pg. 2036
IDEAL INDUSTRIES SAS.—See IDEAL Industries Inc; *U.S. Private*, pg. 2036
IDEAL INDUSTRIES (U.K.) LIMITED—See IDEAL Industries Inc; *U.S. Private*, pg. 2036
IDEAL INNOVATIONS, INC.; *U.S. Private*, pg. 2036
IDEAL INTEGRATIONS, INC.; *U.S. Private*, pg. 2036
IDEALIST GAYRIMENKUL YATIRIM ORTAKLIGI A.S.; *Int'l*, pg. 3589
IDEAL JACOBS (XIAMEN) CORPORATION; *Int'l*, pg. 3589
IDEAL MACHINING & SUPPLY INC.; *U.S. Private*, pg. 2036
IDEAL MEDIA LLC—See Schofield Media Ltd.; *U.S. Private*, pg. 3567
IDEAL MULTIFEED (MALAYSIA) SDN BERHAD—See Emivest Berhad; *Int'l*, pg. 2383
IDEAL PIPE—See Advanced Drainage Systems, Inc.; *U.S. Public*, pg. 46
IDEAL POWER INC.; *U.S. Public*, pg. 1088
I-DEAL PRINT LTD.—See Pabrik Kertas Tjiwi Kimia Tbk; *Int'l*, pg. 5684
IDEAL PRODUCTS OF CANADA LTD.—See TopBuild Corp.; *U.S. Public*, pg. 2163
IDEAL PRODUCTS OF DONGGUAN LTD.—See TopBuild Corp.; *U.S. Public*, pg. 2163
IDEAL READY-MIX COMPANY INC.—See Rasmussen Group Inc.; *U.S. Private*, pg. 3357
IDEAL RESTAURANT GROUP, INC.; *U.S. Private*, pg. 2036
IDEAL RICE INDUSTRIES (PVT) LTD.—See Ideal Spinning Mills Ltd; *Int'l*, pg. 3589
IDEAL ROAD BUILDERS PVT. LTD—See IRB Infrastructure Developers Ltd.; *Int'l*, pg. 3805
IDEAL ROOFING COMPANY LTD.; *Int'l*, pg. 3589
IDEALSEED RESOURCES SDN. BHD.—See TechnoDex Berhad; *Int'l*, pg. 7510
IDEAL SETECH HOLDCO, INC.—See The Ideal Group, Inc.; *U.S. Private*, pg. 4055
IDEAL SETECH, L.L.C.—See The Ideal Group, Inc.; *U.S. Private*, pg. 4055
IDEAL SETECH SHARE-THE-SPARE LLC—See The Ideal Group, Inc.; *U.S. Private*, pg. 4055
IDEAL SHIELD, L.L.C.—See The Ideal Group, Inc.; *U.S. Private*, pg. 4055
IDEAL SHOPPING DIRECT LTD.—See Aurelius Equity Opportunities SE & Co. KGaA; *Int'l*, pg. 708
IDEAL SNACKS CORPORATION—See Permira Advisers LLP; *Int'l*, pg. 5805
IDEAL SPINNING MILLS LTD; *Int'l*, pg. 3589
IDEAL STANDARD FRANCE—See Anchorage Capital Group, L.L.C.; *U.S. Private*, pg. 274
IDEAL STANDARD FRANCE—See CVC Capital Partners SICAV-FIS S.A.; *Int'l*, pg. 1888
IDEAL STANDARD GMBH—See Anchorage Capital Group, L.L.C.; *U.S. Private*, pg. 274
IDEAL STANDARD GMBH—See CVC Capital Partners SICAV-FIS S.A.; *Int'l*, pg. 1888
IDEAL STANDARD GMBH ZWEIGNIEDERLASSUNG OSTERREICH—See Anchorage Capital Group, L.L.C.; *U.S. Private*, pg. 274
IDEAL STANDARD GMBH ZWEIGNIEDERLASSUNG OSTERREICH—See CVC Capital Partners SICAV-FIS S.A.; *Int'l*, pg. 1888
IDEAL STANDARD INTERNATIONAL NV—See Anchorage Capital Group, L.L.C.; *U.S. Private*, pg. 274
IDEAL STANDARD INTERNATIONAL NV—See CVC Capital Partners SICAV-FIS S.A.; *Int'l*, pg. 1888
IDEAL STANDARD ITALIA S.R.L.—See Anchorage Capital Group, L.L.C.; *U.S. Private*, pg. 274
IDEAL STANDARD ITALIA S.R.L.—See CVC Capital Partners SICAV-FIS S.A.; *Int'l*, pg. 1888
IDEAL STANDARD S.A.I.—See Anchorage Capital Group, L.L.C.; *U.S. Private*, pg. 274
IDEAL STANDARD S.A.I.—See CVC Capital Partners SICAV-FIS S.A.; *Int'l*, pg. 1888
IDEAL STANDARD S.R.O.—See Anchorage Capital Group, L.L.C.; *U.S. Private*, pg. 274
IDEAL STANDARD S.R.O.—See CVC Capital Partners SICAV-FIS S.A.; *Int'l*, pg. 1888
IDEAL STANDARD (UK) LTD.—See Anchorage Capital Group, L.L.C.; *U.S. Private*, pg. 274
IDEAL STANDARD (UK) LTD.—See CVC Capital Partners SICAV-FIS S.A.; *Int'l*, pg. 1888
IDEAL STEEL & BUILDERS' SUPPLIES, LLC—See The Ideal Group, Inc.; *U.S. Private*, pg. 4055
IDEAL SUPPLY COMPANY LIMITED—See Groupe Deschenes Inc.; *Int'l*, pg. 3102
IDEAL SUPPLY CO.; *U.S. Private*, pg. 2036
IDEAL TAPE-BELGIUM—See American Biltrite Inc.; *U.S. Public*, pg. 97

IDEAL TAPE COMPANY—See American Biltrite Inc.; *U.S. Public*, pg. 97
IDEAL UNITED BINTANG BERHAD; *Int'l*, pg. 3589
IDEAL WELDERS LTD.; *Int'l*, pg. 3589
IDEAL WINDOW MANUFACTURING; *U.S. Private*, pg. 2036
IDEAL WOOD PRODUCTS, INC.—See Prophet Equity L.P.; *U.S. Private*, pg. 3286
IDEALWORKS GMBH—See Bayerische Motoren Werke Aktiengesellschaft; *Int'l*, pg. 912
IDEAL WORLD HOME SHOPPING LTD.—See Aurelius Equity Opportunities SE & Co. KGaA; *Int'l*, pg. 708
IDEA MONEY S.A.—See Getin Holding S.A.; *Int'l*, pg. 2947
IDEANOMICS, INC.; *U.S. Public*, pg. 1088
IDEA NUOVA INC.; *U.S. Private*, pg. 2035
IDEAOVERTEN, LLC; *U.S. Private*, pg. 2037
IDEAPAINT, INC.—See Audax Group, Limited Partnership; *U.S. Private*, pg. 388
IDEA PLUS COMMUNICATIONS DOO—See Pristop d.o.o.; *Int'l*, pg. 5983
IDEA POWER LIMITED—See Eveready Industries India Ltd; *Int'l*, pg. 2563
IDEAS BOX ENTERTAINMENT LIMITED—See Future Corporate Resources Limited; *Int'l*, pg. 2853
IDEAS, INC.; *U.S. Private*, pg. 2037
IDEAS INTERNATIONAL LIMITED—See Gartner, Inc.; *U.S. Public*, pg. 907
IDEA SPA; *Int'l*, pg. 3588
IDEAS THAT DELIVER; *U.S. Private*, pg. 2037
IDEASTREAM CONSUMER PRODUCTS, LLC; *U.S. Private*, pg. 2037
IDEASTREAM; *U.S. Private*, pg. 2037
IDEATEK SYSTEMS, INC.—See DigitalBridge Group, Inc.; *U.S. Public*, pg. 665
IDEATEK SYSTEMS, INC.—See EQT AB; *Int'l*, pg. 2482
IDEATEK TELECOM, LLC—See DigitalBridge Group, Inc.; *U.S. Public*, pg. 665
IDEATEK TELECOM, LLC—See EQT AB; *Int'l*, pg. 2482
IDEATION TRAINING PTY LTD.; *Int'l*, pg. 3589
IDEAWORKS, INC.; *U.S. Private*, pg. 2037
IDEAWORKS, INC.; *U.S. Private*, pg. 2037
IDEAWORKS—See WPP plc; *Int'l*, pg. 8491
IDEAWORK STUDIOS, INC.—See Once Upon A Time London Ltd.; *Int'l*, pg. 5574
IDEAYA BIOSCIENCES, INC.; *U.S. Public*, pg. 1088
IDEC AUSTRALIA PTY. LTD.—See IDEC Corporation; *Int'l*, pg. 3589
IDEC (BEIJING) CORPORATION—See IDEC Corporation; *Int'l*, pg. 3589
IDEC CANADA LTD.—See IDEC Corporation; *Int'l*, pg. 3589
IDEC CORPORATION - FUKUSAKI PLANT—See IDEC Corporation; *Int'l*, pg. 3589
IDEC CORPORATION - KYOTO PLANT—See IDEC Corporation; *Int'l*, pg. 3589
IDEC CORPORATION; *Int'l*, pg. 3589
IDEC CORPORATION—See IDEC Corporation; *Int'l*, pg. 3589
IDEC CORPORATION - TAKINO PLANT—See IDEC Corporation; *Int'l*, pg. 3589
IDEC CORPORATION - TSUKUBA PLANT—See IDEC Corporation; *Int'l*, pg. 3589
IDEC ENGINEERING SERVICE CORPORATION—See IDEC Corporation; *Int'l*, pg. 3590
IDEC IZUMI ASIA PTE. LTD.—See IDEC Corporation; *Int'l*, pg. 3590
IDEC IZUMI (H.K.) CO., LTD.—See IDEC Corporation; *Int'l*, pg. 3590
IDEC IZUMI SUZHOU CO., LTD.—See IDEC Corporation; *Int'l*, pg. 3590
IDEC IZUMI TAIWAN CORPORATION—See IDEC Corporation; *Int'l*, pg. 3590
IDEC LOGISTICS SERVICE CORPORATION—See IDEC Corporation; *Int'l*, pg. 3590
IDEC (SHANGHAI) CORPORATION—See IDEC Corporation; *Int'l*, pg. 3589
IDEC (SHENZHEN) CORPORATION—See IDEC Corporation; *Int'l*, pg. 3589
IDEC TAIWAN CORPORATION—See IDEC Corporation; *Int'l*, pg. 3590
IDEELI INC.—See Groupon Inc.; *U.S. Public*, pg. 972
IDEENION AUTOMOBIL AG—See Apollo Future Mobility Group Limited; *Int'l*, pg. 517
IDEENKAPITAL ANLAGEBETREUUNGS GMBH—See Munchener Ruckversicherungs AG; *Int'l*, pg. 5089
IDEENKAPITAL CLIENT SERVICE GMBH—See Munchener Ruckversicherungs AG; *Int'l*, pg. 5089
IDEENKAPITAL ERSTE INVESTOREN SERVICE GMBH—See Munchener Ruckversicherungs AG; *Int'l*, pg. 5089
IDEENKAPITAL FINANCIAL ENGINEERING GMBH—See Munchener Ruckversicherungs AG; *Int'l*, pg. 5089
IDEENKAPITAL FINANCIAL SERVICE GMBH—See Munchener Ruckversicherungs AG; *Int'l*, pg. 5089
IDEENKAPITAL FONDS TREUHAND GMBH—See Munchener Ruckversicherungs AG; *Int'l*, pg. 5089
IDEENKAPITAL GMBH—See Munchener Ruckversicherungs AG; *Int'l*, pg. 5089

IDEENKAPITAL MEDIA FINANCE GMBH—See Munchener Ruckversicherungs AG; *Int'l*, pg. 5089
IDEENKAPITAL METROPOLEN EUROPA GMBH & CO. KG—See Munchener Ruckversicherungs AG; *Int'l*, pg. 5089
IDEENKAPITAL SCHIFFSFONDS TREUHAND GMBH—See Munchener Ruckversicherungs AG; *Int'l*, pg. 5089
IDEE PARTNERS S.R.L.—See Pattern SpA; *Int'l*, pg. 5760
IDE GROUP LIMITED—See Tialis Essential IT PLC; *Int'l*, pg. 7737
I.D. ELECTROQUIMICA, S.L.—See Fluidra SA; *Int'l*, pg. 2714
IDELIK FOOTWEAR, INC.; *U.S. Private*, pg. 2037
IDELLE LABS, LTD.—See Helen of Troy Limited; *Int'l*, pg. 3329
IDEM CAPITAL SECURITIES LIMITED—See Paragon Banking Group PLC; *Int'l*, pg. 5735
IDEMIA AUSTRALASIA PTY. LTD.—See Advent International Corporation; *U.S. Private*, pg. 102
IDEMIA FRANCE SAS—See Advent International Corporation; *U.S. Private*, pg. 102
IDEMIA GERMANY GMBH—See Advent International Corporation; *U.S. Private*, pg. 102
IDEMIA IDENTITY & SECURITY CANADA, INC.—See Advent International Corporation; *U.S. Private*, pg. 102
IDEMIA IDENTITY & SECURITY FRANCE SAS—See Advent International Corporation; *U.S. Private*, pg. 102
IDEMIA IDENTITY & SECURITY GERMANY AG—See Advent International Corporation; *U.S. Private*, pg. 102
IDEMIA IDENTITY & SECURITY SUCURSAL COLOMBIA—See Advent International Corporation; *U.S. Private*, pg. 102
IDEMIA IDENTITY & SECURITY UK LIMITED—See Advent International Corporation; *U.S. Private*, pg. 102
IDEMIA IDENTITY & SECURITY USA, LLC—See Advent International Corporation; *U.S. Private*, pg. 102
IDEMIA IDENTITY & SECURITY USA, LLC—See Advent International Corporation; *U.S. Private*, pg. 102
IDEMIA SINGAPORE PTE LTD—See Advent International Corporation; *U.S. Private*, pg. 102
IDEMIA THE NETHERLANDS B.V.—See Advent International Corporation; *U.S. Private*, pg. 102
IDEMITSU APOLLO CORPORATION—See Idemitsu Kosan Co., Ltd.; *Int'l*, pg. 3590
IDEMITSU AUSTRALIA RESOURCES PTY. LTD.—See Idemitsu Kosan Co., Ltd.; *Int'l*, pg. 3590
IDEMITSU CANADA RESOURCES LTD.—See Idemitsu Kosan Co., Ltd.; *Int'l*, pg. 3590
IDEMITSU CHEMICALS EUROPE PLC—See Idemitsu Kosan Co., Ltd.; *Int'l*, pg. 3590
IDEMITSU CHEMICALS (HONG KONG) CO., LTD.—See Idemitsu Kosan Co., Ltd.; *Int'l*, pg. 3590
IDEMITSU CHEMICALS (M) SDN. BHD.—See Idemitsu Kosan Co., Ltd.; *Int'l*, pg. 3590
IDEMITSU CHEMICALS (SHANGHAI) CO., LTD.—See Idemitsu Kosan Co., Ltd.; *Int'l*, pg. 3590
IDEMITSU CHEMICALS SOUTHEAST ASIA PTE. LTD.—See Idemitsu Kosan Co., Ltd.; *Int'l*, pg. 3590
IDEMITSU CHEMICALS TAIWAN CORP.—See Idemitsu Kosan Co., Ltd.; *Int'l*, pg. 3590
IDEMITSU CHEMICALS U.S.A. CORPORATION—See Idemitsu Kosan Co., Ltd.; *Int'l*, pg. 3590
IDEMITSU CLEAN ENERGY (YANTAI) CO., LTD.—See Idemitsu Kosan Co., Ltd.; *Int'l*, pg. 3590
IDEMITSU COAL MARKETING AUSTRALIA PTY. LTD.—See Idemitsu Kosan Co., Ltd.; *Int'l*, pg. 3590
IDEMITSU CREDIT CO., LTD.—See Credit Saison Co., Ltd.; *Int'l*, pg. 1836
IDEMITSU ELECTRONIC MATERIALS (CHINA) CO., LTD.—See Idemitsu Kosan Co., Ltd.; *Int'l*, pg. 3590
IDEMITSU ELECTRONIC MATERIALS KOREA CO., LTD.—See Idemitsu Kosan Co., Ltd.; *Int'l*, pg. 3590
IDEMITSU ELECTRONIC MATERIALS (SHANGHAI) CO., LTD.—See Idemitsu Kosan Co., Ltd.; *Int'l*, pg. 3590
IDEMITSU ENERGY CONSULTING (BEIJING) CO., LTD.—See Idemitsu Kosan Co., Ltd.; *Int'l*, pg. 3590
IDEMITSU ENGINEERING CO., LTD.—See Idemitsu Kosan Co., Ltd.; *Int'l*, pg. 3590
IDEMITSU ENGINEERING VIETNAM CO., LTD.—See Idemitsu Kosan Co., Ltd.; *Int'l*, pg. 3591
IDEMITSU FINE COMPOSITES CO., LTD.—See Idemitsu Kosan Co., Ltd.; *Int'l*, pg. 3591
IDEMITSU GAS PRODUCTION (VIETNAM) CO., LTD.—See Idemitsu Kosan Co., Ltd.; *Int'l*, pg. 3591
IDEMITSU INTERNATIONAL (ASIA) PTE. LTD.—See Idemitsu Kosan Co., Ltd.; *Int'l*, pg. 3591
IDEMITSU KOSAN CO., LTD.; *Int'l*, pg. 3590
IDEMITSU LUBE ASIA PACIFIC PTE. LTD.—See Idemitsu Kosan Co., Ltd.; *Int'l*, pg. 3591
IDEMITSU LUBE (CHINA) CO., LTD.—See Idemitsu Kosan Co., Ltd.; *Int'l*, pg. 3591
IDEMITSU LUBE EUROPE GMBH—See Idemitsu Kosan Co., Ltd.; *Int'l*, pg. 3591
IDEMITSU LUBE INDIA PVT LTD.—See Idemitsu Kosan Co., Ltd.; *Int'l*, pg. 3591
IDEMITSU LUBE (MALAYSIA) SDN. BHD.—See Idemitsu Kosan Co., Ltd.; *Int'l*, pg. 3591

COMPANY NAME INDEX

IDEMITSU LUBE MIDDLE EAST & AFRICA FZE—See Idemitsu Kosan Co., Ltd.; *Int'l*, pg. 3591
IDEMITSU LUBE PAKISTAN (PRIVATE) LIMITED—See Idemitsu Kosan Co., Ltd., *Int'l*, pg. 3591
IDEMITSU LUBE (SINGAPORE) PTE.LTD.—See Idemitsu Kosan Co., Ltd.; *Int'l*, pg. 3591
IDEMITSU LUBE SOUTH AMERICA LTDA.—See Idemitsu Kosan Co., Ltd.; *Int'l*, pg. 3591
IDEMITSU LUBE VIETNAM CO., LTD.—See Idemitsu Kosan Co., Ltd.; *Int'l*, pg. 3591
IDEMITSU LUBRICANTS AMERICA CORPORATION—See Idemitsu Kosan Co., Ltd.; *Int'l*, pg. 3591
IDEMITSU LUBRICANTS MEXICO S.A. DE C.V.—See Idemitsu Kosan Co., Ltd.; *Int'l*, pg. 3591
IDEMITSU LUBRICANTS PHILIPPINES INC.—See Idemitsu Kosan Co., Ltd.; *Int'l*, pg. 3591
IDEMITSU LUBRICANTS RUS LLC—See Idemitsu Kosan Co., Ltd.; *Int'l*, pg. 3591
IDEMITSU LUBRICANTS (THAILAND) CO., LTD.—See Idemitsu Kosan Co., Ltd.; *Int'l*, pg. 3591
IDEMITSU OIL & GAS CO., LTD.—See Idemitsu Kosan Co., Ltd.; *Int'l*, pg. 3591
IDEMITSU OLED MATERIALS EUROPE AG—See Idemitsu Kosan Co., Ltd.; *Int'l*, pg. 3591
IDEMITSU PETROCHEMICAL CO., LTD.—See Idemitsu Kosan Co., Ltd.; *Int'l*, pg. 3591
IDEMITSU PETROLEUM NORGE AS—See Idemitsu Kosan Co., Ltd.; *Int'l*, pg. 3591
IDEMITSU SM (MALAYSIA) SDN. BHD.—See Idemitsu Kosan Co., Ltd.; *Int'l*, pg. 3591
IDEMITSU TANKER CO., LTD.—See Idemitsu Kosan Co., Ltd.; *Int'l*, pg. 3591
IDEMITSU TECHNOFINE CO., LTD.—See Idemitsu Kosan Co., Ltd.; *Int'l*, pg. 3591
IDEMITSU UNITECH CO., LTD. - CHIBA PLANT—See Idemitsu Kosan Co., Ltd.; *Int'l*, pg. 3591
IDEMITSU UNITECH CO., LTD. - ENGINEERING MATERIAL PLANT—See Idemitsu Kosan Co., Ltd.; *Int'l*, pg. 3591
IDEMITSU UNITECH CO., LTD. - HYOGO PLANT—See Idemitsu Kosan Co., Ltd.; *Int'l*, pg. 3591
IDEMITSU UNITECH CO., LTD.—See Idemitsu Kosan Co., Ltd.; *Int'l*, pg. 3591
IDEMITSU UNITECH CO., LTD. - SYIZUOKA PLANT—See Idemitsu Kosan Co., Ltd.; *Int'l*, pg. 3591
ID ENERGIES SAS—See Brookfield Corporation; *Int'l*, pg. 1188
IDENIX PHARMACEUTICALS, INC.—See Merck & Co., Inc.; *U.S. Public*, pg. 1416
IDENS DETAILING INC—See Pacific Northwest Capital Corp.; *U.S. Private*, pg. 3069
IDENTA CORP.; *Int'l*, pg. 3592
IDENTCO IDENTIFICATION CORP.; *U.S. Private*, pg. 2037
IDENTICA LIMITED—See Writtle Holdings Limited; *Int'l*, pg. 8495
IDENTICARD SYSTEMS CANADA LTD.—See Brady Corporation; *U.S. Public*, pg. 379
IDENTICARD SYSTEMS, INC.—See Brady Corporation; *U.S. Public*, pg. 379
IDENTICARE LIMITED—See Animalcare Group plc; *Int'l*, pg. 471
IDENTIFIED TECHNOLOGIES, CORP—See Alpine 4 Holdings, Inc.; *U.S. Public*, pg. 85
IDENTIFIX, INC.—See Vista Equity Partners, LLC; *U.S. Private*, pg. 4400
IDENTIGEN LIMITED—See Merck & Co., Inc.; *U.S. Public*, pg. 1416
IDENTIGEN NORTH AMERICA INC.—See Merck & Co., Inc.; *U.S. Public*, pg. 1416
IDENTIGEN SWITZERLAND AG—See Merck & Co., Inc.; *U.S. Public*, pg. 1416
IDENTILLECT TECHNOLOGIES CORP.; *U.S. Public*, pg. 1088
IDENTISYS, INC.; *U.S. Private*, pg. 2037
IDENTITII LIMITED; *Int'l*, pg. 3592
IDENTITY AUTOMATION, LP; *U.S. Private*, pg. 2037
IDENTITY GROUP HOLDINGS CORP.—See Ancor Holdings, L.P.; *U.S. Private*, pg. 275
IDENTITY GROUP HOLDINGS CORP.—See Merit Capital Partners; *U.S. Private*, pg. 2674
IDENTITY GROUP HOLDINGS CORP.—See The PNC Financial Services Group, Inc.; *U.S. Public*, pg. 2119
IDENTITY HEALTHCARE LTD.; *Int'l*, pg. 3592
IDENTITY REHAB CORPORATION—See Equifax Inc.; *U.S. Public*, pg. 786
IDENTITY RETAILING (PTY) LIMITED—See Truworths International Limited; *Int'l*, pg. 7946
IDENTITY; *U.S. Private*, pg. 2037
IDENTITY STRONGHOLD, LLC; *U.S. Private*, pg. 2037
IDENTITY THEFT GUARD SOLUTIONS, INC.—See Whanau Interests LLC.; *U.S. Private*, pg. 4504
IDENTIV AUSTRALIA PTY LTD—See Identiv, Inc.; *U.S. Public*, pg. 1089
IDENTIVE (JAPAN) KK—See Identiv, Inc.; *U.S. Public*, pg. 1089
IDENTIV GMBH—See Identiv, Inc.; *U.S. Public*, pg. 1089
IDENTIV GMBH—See Identiv, Inc.; *U.S. Public*, pg. 1089

IDENTIV, INC.; *U.S. Public*, pg. 1088
IDENTIV KK—See Identiv, Inc.; *U.S. Public*, pg. 1089
IDENTIV PTE. LTD.—See Identiv, Inc.; *U.S. Public*, pg. 1089
IDENTIV PVT. LTD.—See Identiv, Inc.; *U.S. Public*, pg. 1089
IDENTOGO—See Advent International Corporation; *U.S. Private*, pg. 102
IDENTROPY, INC.—See Robert Half Inc.; *U.S. Public*, pg. 1803
IDENTRUST, INC.—See ASSA ABLOY AB; *Int'l*, pg. 637
IDEO, LLC; *U.S. Private*, pg. 2037
IDEON S.A.; *Int'l*, pg. 3592
IDEO SAATCHI & SAATCHI—See Publicis Groupe S.A.; *Int'l*, pg. 6108
IDERA, INC.—See HGGC, LLC; *U.S. Private*, pg. 1929
IDESCO OY—See Lagercrantz Group AB; *Int'l*, pg. 4394
I-DESIGN GROUP LTD—See NCR Voyix Corporation.; *U.S. Public*, pg. 1502
IDESIGN INC.—See Phase 3 Media, LLC; *U.S. Private*, pg. 3166
I-DESIGN MULTIMEDIA LTD.—See NCR Voyix Corporation.; *U.S. Public*, pg. 1502
IDEST COMMUNICATION S.A.—See Straker Limited; *Int'l*, pg. 7235
IDE SYSTEMS LTD.—See Sdiptech AB; *Int'l*, pg. 6658
IDEVICES, LLC—See Hubbell Incorporated; *U.S. Public*, pg. 1067
IDEV TECHNOLOGIES B.V.—See Abbott Laboratories; *U.S. Public*, pg. 20
IDEV TECHNOLOGIES, INC.—See Abbott Laboratories; *U.S. Public*, pg. 20
IDEX AMERICA INC.—See IDEX Biometrics ASA; *Int'l*, pg. 3592
IDEX ASIA PACIFIC PTE. LTD.—See IDEX Corp; *U.S. Public*, pg. 1090
IDEX BIOMETRICS AMERICA INC.—See IDEX Biometrics ASA; *Int'l*, pg. 3592
IDEX BIOMETRICS ASA; *Int'l*, pg. 3592
IDEX BIOMETRICS UK LTD.—See IDEX Biometrics ASA; *Int'l*, pg. 3592
IDEX CORP; *U.S. Public*, pg. 1089
IDEX DO BRASIL SERVICOS E VENDAS LTDA.—See IDEX Corp; *U.S. Public*, pg. 1091
IDEX FLUID & METERING PVT. LTD.—See IDEX Corp; *U.S. Public*, pg. 1090
IDEX HEALTH & SCIENCE GMBH—See IDEX Corp; *U.S. Public*, pg. 1092
IDEX HEALTH & SCIENCE GMBH—See IDEX Corp; *U.S. Public*, pg. 1090
IDEX HEALTH & SCIENCE KK—See IDEX Corp; *U.S. Public*, pg. 1090
IDEX HEALTH & SCIENCE LLC—See IDEX Corp; *U.S. Public*, pg. 1090
IDEX HEALTH & SCIENCE LLC—See IDEX Corp; *U.S. Public*, pg. 1090
IDEX HEATH & SCIENCE GMBH—See IDEX Corp; *U.S. Public*, pg. 1090
IDEX HOLDINGS GMBH—See IDEX Corp; *U.S. Public*, pg. 1090
IDEX HOLDINGS, INC.—See IDEX Corp; *U.S. Public*, pg. 1091
IDEX INDIA PRIVATE LTD.—See IDEX Corp; *U.S. Public*, pg. 1091
IDEX MPT INC.; *U.S. Private*, pg. 2038
IDEX OPTICAL TECHNOLOGIES B.V.—See IDEX Corp; *U.S. Public*, pg. 1091
IDEX PUMP TECHNOLOGIES (IRELAND) LIMITED—See IDEX Corp; *U.S. Public*, pg. 1091
IDEX SAS—See IDEX Corp; *U.S. Public*, pg. 1091
IDEX TECHNOLOGY (SUZHOU) CO., LTD.—See IDEX Corp; *U.S. Public*, pg. 1091
IDEXX B.V.—See IDEXX Laboratories, Inc.; *U.S. Public*, pg. 1092
IDEXX COMPUTER SYSTEMS—See IDEXX Laboratories, Inc.; *U.S. Public*, pg. 1092
IDEXX DIAVET AG—See IDEXX Laboratories, Inc.; *U.S. Public*, pg. 1092
IDEXX EUROPE B.V.—See IDEXX Laboratories, Inc.; *U.S. Public*, pg. 1092
IDEXX GMBH—See IDEXX Laboratories, Inc.; *U.S. Public*, pg. 1092
IDEXX HOLDING B.V.—See IDEXX Laboratories, Inc.; *U.S. Public*, pg. 1092
IDEXX LABORATORIES INC.—See IDEXX Laboratories, Inc.; *U.S. Public*, pg. 1092
IDEXX LABORATORIES, INC.; *U.S. Public*, pg. 1092
IDEXX LABORATORIES ITALIA S.R.L.—See IDEXX Laboratories, Inc.; *U.S. Public*, pg. 1092
IDEXX LABORATORIES, KK—See IDEXX Laboratories, Inc.; *U.S. Public*, pg. 1093
IDEXX LABORATORIES LIMITED—See IDEXX Laboratories, Inc.; *U.S. Public*, pg. 1092
IDEXX LABORATORIES LIMITED—See IDEXX Laboratories, Inc.; *U.S. Public*, pg. 1092
IDEXX LABORATORIES NORGE AS—See IDEXX Laboratories, Inc.; *U.S. Public*, pg. 1092
IDEXX LABORATORIES PRIVATE LIMITED—See IDEXX Laboratories, Inc.; *U.S. Public*, pg. 1092

IDG CAPITAL

IDEXX LABORATORIES PTY. LTD.—See IDEXX Laboratories, Inc.; *U.S. Public*, pg. 1093
IDEXX LABORATORIES PTY. LTD.—See IDEXX Laboratories, Inc.; *U.S. Public*, pg. 1093
IDEXX LABORATORIES SINGAPORE PTE. LTD.—See IDEXX Laboratories, Inc.; *U.S. Public*, pg. 1093
IDEXX LABORATORIES SP. Z O.O.—See IDEXX Laboratories, Inc.; *U.S. Public*, pg. 1093
IDEXX LABORATORIOS, S.L.—See IDEXX Laboratories, Inc.; *U.S. Public*, pg. 1093
IDEXX OPERATIONS, INC.—See IDEXX Laboratories, Inc.; *U.S. Public*, pg. 1093
IDEXX PHARMACEUTICALS, INC.—See IDEXX Laboratories, Inc.; *U.S. Public*, pg. 1093
IDEXX REFERENCE LABORATORIES - DALLAS—See IDEXX Laboratories, Inc.; *U.S. Public*, pg. 1093
IDEXX REFERENCE LABORATORIES - DENVER—See IDEXX Laboratories, Inc.; *U.S. Public*, pg. 1093
IDEXX REFERENCE LABORATORIES - ELMHURST—See IDEXX Laboratories, Inc.; *U.S. Public*, pg. 1093
IDEXX REFERENCE LABORATORIES, INC.—See IDEXX Laboratories, Inc.; *U.S. Public*, pg. 1093
IDEXX REFERENCE LABORATORIES - IRVINE—See IDEXX Laboratories, Inc.; *U.S. Public*, pg. 1093
IDEXX REFERENCE LABORATORIES LTD.—See IDEXX Laboratories, Inc.; *U.S. Public*, pg. 1093
IDEXX REFERENCE LABORATORIES - PHOENIX—See IDEXX Laboratories, Inc.; *U.S. Public*, pg. 1093
IDEXX REFERENCE LABORATORIES - SACRAMENTO—See IDEXX Laboratories, Inc.; *U.S. Public*, pg. 1093
IDEXX REFERENCE LABORATORIES - TOTOWA—See IDEXX Laboratories, Inc.; *U.S. Public*, pg. 1093
IDEXX S.A.R.L.—See IDEXX Laboratories, Inc.; *U.S. Public*, pg. 1093
IDEXX TECHNOLOGIES LIMITED—See IDEXX Laboratories, Inc.; *U.S. Public*, pg. 1093
IDEXX TELEMEDICINE CONSULTANTS—See IDEXX Laboratories, Inc.; *U.S. Public*, pg. 1093
IDEYCO, S.A.U.—See Sacyr, S.A.; *Int'l*, pg. 6466
ID FACTOR LIMITED—See GlobalData Plc; *Int'l*, pg. 3003
IDFC AMC TRUSTEE COMPANY LIMITED—See IDFC Limited; *Int'l*, pg. 3593
IDFC CAPITAL LIMITED—See IDFC Limited; *Int'l*, pg. 3593
IDFC FIRST BANK LIMITED; *Int'l*, pg. 3592
IDFC INVESTMENT ADVISORS LIMITED—See IDFC Limited; *Int'l*, pg. 3593
IDFC LIMITED; *Int'l*, pg. 3593
IDFC PENSION FUND MANAGEMENT COMPANY LIMITED—See IDFC Limited; *Int'l*, pg. 3593
IDFC PRIVATE EQUITY (IDFC PE)—See IDFC Limited; *Int'l*, pg. 3593
IDFC PROJECT EQUITY COMPANY LIMITED—See IDFC Limited; *Int'l*, pg. 3593
IDFC PROJECT FINANCE—See IDFC Limited; *Int'l*, pg. 3593
IDFC PROJECTS LIMITED—See IDFC Limited; *Int'l*, pg. 3593
IDFC SECURITIES LIMITED; *Int'l*, pg. 3593
IDF THERMIC SA—See VINCI S.A.; *Int'l*, pg. 8237
IDG BUSINESS VERLAG GMBH—See China Oceanwide Holdings Group Co., Ltd.; *Int'l*, pg. 1537
IDG BUSINESS VERLAG GMBH—See IDG Capital; *Int'l*, pg. 3594
IDG CAPITAL; *Int'l*, pg. 3593
IDG CHINA CO., LTD.—See China Oceanwide Holdings Group Co., Ltd.; *Int'l*, pg. 1537
IDG CHINA CO., LTD.—See IDG Capital; *Int'l*, pg. 3594
IDG COMMUNICATIONS, INC.—See Eagle Publishing Inc.; *U.S. Private*, pg. 1310
IDG COMMUNICATIONS ITALIA SRL—See China Oceanwide Holdings Group Co., Ltd.; *Int'l*, pg. 1537
IDG COMMUNICATIONS ITALIA SRL—See IDG Capital; *Int'l*, pg. 3594
IDG COMMUNICATIONS MEDIA AG—See China Oceanwide Holdings Group Co., Ltd.; *Int'l*, pg. 1537
IDG COMMUNICATIONS MEDIA AG—See IDG Capital; *Int'l*, pg. 3594
IDG COMMUNICATIONS MEDIA AG—See China Oceanwide Holdings Group Co., Ltd.; *Int'l*, pg. 1537
IDG COMMUNICATIONS MEDIA AG—See IDG Capital; *Int'l*, pg. 3594
IDG COMMUNICATIONS NORGE AS—See China Oceanwide Holdings Group Co., Ltd.; *Int'l*, pg. 1537
IDG COMMUNICATIONS NORGE AS—See IDG Capital; *Int'l*, pg. 3594
IDG COMMUNICATIONS PTY. LTD.—See China Oceanwide Holdings Group Co., Ltd.; *Int'l*, pg. 1537
IDG COMMUNICATIONS PTY. LTD.—See IDG Capital; *Int'l*, pg. 3594
IDG COMMUNICATIONS PUBLISHING GROUP SRL—See China Oceanwide Holdings Group Co., Ltd.; *Int'l*, pg. 1537
IDG COMMUNICATIONS PUBLISHING GROUP SRL—See IDG Capital; *Int'l*, pg. 3594
IDG COMMUNICATIONS, S.A.U.—See China Oceanwide Holdings Group Co., Ltd.; *Int'l*, pg. 1537

IDG CAPITAL

CORPORATE AFFILIATIONS

IDG COMMUNICATIONS, S.A.U.—See IDG Capital; *Int'l*, pg. 3594
IDG COMMUNICATIONS UK, LTD.—See China Oceanwide Holdings Group Co., Ltd.; *Int'l*, pg. 1537
IDG COMMUNICATIONS UK, LTD.—See IDG Capital; *Int'l*, pg. 3594
IDG COMPUTERWORLD DO BRAZIL—See China Oceanwide Holdings Group Co., Ltd.; *Int'l*, pg. 1537
IDG COMPUTERWORLD DO BRAZIL—See IDG Capital; *Int'l*, pg. 3594
IDG CZECH REPUBLIC, A.S.—See China Oceanwide Holdings Group Co., Ltd.; *Int'l*, pg. 1537
IDG CZECH REPUBLIC, A.S.—See IDG Capital; *Int'l*, pg. 3594
IDG DENMARK A/S—See China Oceanwide Holdings Group Co., Ltd.; *Int'l*, pg. 1537
IDG DENMARK A/S—See IDG Capital; *Int'l*, pg. 3594
IDG ENTERPRISE—See China Oceanwide Holdings Group Co., Ltd.; *Int'l*, pg. 1536
IDG ENTERPRISE—See IDG Capital; *Int'l*, pg. 3593
IDG ENTERTAINMENT MEDIA GMBH—See China Oceanwide Holdings Group Co., Ltd.; *Int'l*, pg. 1537
IDG ENTERTAINMENT MEDIA GMBH—See IDG Capital; *Int'l*, pg. 3594
IDG ENTERTAINMENT VERLAG GMBH—See China Oceanwide Holdings Group Co., Ltd.; *Int'l*, pg. 1537
IDG ENTERTAINMENT VERLAG GMBH—See IDG Capital; *Int'l*, pg. 3594
IDG GLOBAL SOLUTIONS APAC—See China Oceanwide Holdings Group Co., Ltd.; *Int'l*, pg. 1537
IDG GLOBAL SOLUTIONS APAC—See IDG Capital; *Int'l*, pg. 3594
IDG GLOBAL SOLUTIONS—See China Oceanwide Holdings Group Co., Ltd.; *Int'l*, pg. 1537
IDG GLOBAL SOLUTIONS—See IDG Capital; *Int'l*, pg. 3594
IDG JAPAN, INC.—See China Oceanwide Holdings Group Co., Ltd.; *Int'l*, pg. 1537
IDG JAPAN, INC.—See IDG Capital; *Int'l*, pg. 3594
IDG MAGAZINES NORGE AS—See China Oceanwide Holdings Group Co., Ltd.; *Int'l*, pg. 1537
IDG MAGAZINES NORGE AS—See IDG Capital; *Int'l*, pg. 3594
IDG MEDIA PRIVATE LIMITED—See China Oceanwide Holdings Group Co., Ltd.; *Int'l*, pg. 1537
IDG MEDIA PRIVATE LIMITED—See IDG Capital; *Int'l*, pg. 3594
IDG NETHERLANDS—See China Oceanwide Holdings Group Co., Ltd.; *Int'l*, pg. 1538
IDG NETHERLANDS—See IDG Capital; *Int'l*, pg. 3594
IDG POLAND S.A.—See China Oceanwide Holdings Group Co., Ltd.; *Int'l*, pg. 1538
IDG POLAND S.A.—See IDG Capital; *Int'l*, pg. 3594
I.D. GRIFFITH, INC.; *U.S. Private*, pg. 2027
ID GROUP, INC.; *U.S. Private*, pg. 2034
IDG SWEDEN AB—See China Oceanwide Holdings Group Co., Ltd.; *Int'l*, pg. 1538
IDG SWEDEN AB—See IDG Capital; *Int'l*, pg. 3594
IDG TAIWAN—See China Oceanwide Holdings Group Co., Ltd.; *Int'l*, pg. 1538
IDG TAIWAN—See IDG Capital; *Int'l*, pg. 3594
IDG WORLD EXPO CORPORATION—See China Oceanwide Holdings Group Co., Ltd.; *Int'l*, pg. 1538
IDG WORLD EXPO CORPORATION—See IDG Capital; *Int'l*, pg. 3594
IDH DEVELOPMENT SA; *Int'l*, pg. 3594
ID HOLDINGS CORPORATION; *Int'l*, pg. 3587
ID HOME CO., LTD.—See Iida Group Holdings Co., Ltd.; *Int'l*, pg. 3607
IDIADA AUTOMOTIVE TECHNOLOGY INDIA PVT, LTD.—See I Squared Capital Advisors (US) LLC; *U.S. Private*, pg. 2022
IDIADA AUTOMOTIVE TECHNOLOGY INDIA PVT, LTD.—See TDR Capital LLP; *Int'l*, pg. 7492
IDIADA AUTOMOTIVE TECHNOLOGY MEXICO S DE RL DE CV.—See I Squared Capital Advisors (US) LLC; *U.S. Private*, pg. 2022
IDIADA AUTOMOTIVE TECHNOLOGY MEXICO S DE RL DE CV.—See TDR Capital LLP; *Int'l*, pg. 7492
IDIADA AUTOMOTIVE TECHNOLOGY RUS, LLC—See I Squared Capital Advisors (US) LLC; *U.S. Private*, pg. 2022
IDIADA AUTOMOTIVE TECHNOLOGY RUS, LLC—See TDR Capital LLP; *Int'l*, pg. 7492
IDIADA AUTOMOTIVE TECHNOLOGY, S.A.—See I Squared Capital Advisors (US) LLC; *U.S. Private*, pg. 2022
IDIADA AUTOMOTIVE TECHNOLOGY, S.A.—See TDR Capital LLP; *Int'l*, pg. 7492
IDIADA AUTOMOTIVE TECHNOLOGY UK, LTD.—See I Squared Capital Advisors (US) LLC; *U.S. Private*, pg. 2022
IDIADA AUTOMOTIVE TECHNOLOGY UK, LTD.—See TDR Capital LLP; *Int'l*, pg. 7492
IDIADA CZ, A.S.—See I Squared Capital Advisors (US) LLC; *U.S. Private*, pg. 2022
IDIADA CZ, A.S.—See TDR Capital LLP; *Int'l*, pg. 7492
IDIADA FAHRZEUGTECHNIK, GMBH—See I Squared Capital Advisors (US) LLC; *U.S. Private*, pg. 2022

IDIADA FAHRZEUGTECHNIK, GMBH—See TDR Capital LLP; *Int'l*, pg. 7492
IDI ASSET MANAGEMENT SA—See IDI SCA; *Int'l*, pg. 3595
IDI CARIBE, INC.—See Industrial Dielectrics Holdings, Inc.; *U.S. Private*, pg. 2065
IDICO CONSTRUCTUION COMPANY LIMITED—See Vietnam Urban Development Investment Corporation; *Int'l*, pg. 8204
IDICO INFRASTRUCTURE DEVELOPMENT INVESTMENT JSC—See Vietnam Urban Development Investment Corporation; *Int'l*, pg. 8204
IDICO INVESTMENT CONSTRUCTION OIL & NATURAL GAS JSC—See Vietnam Urban Development Investment Corporation; *Int'l*, pg. 8204
IDICO INVESTMENT CONSULTANCY JSC—See Vietnam Urban Development Investment Corporation; *Int'l*, pg. 8204
IDICO INVESTMENT CONSULTANT JSC; *Int'l*, pg. 3595
IDICO LONG AN INVESTMENT CONSTRUCTION JSC—See Vietnam Urban Development Investment Corporation; *Int'l*, pg. 8204
IDICO MACHINERY ERECTION CONSTRUCTION INVESTMENT JSC—See Vietnam Urban Development Investment Corporation; *Int'l*, pg. 8204
IDICO MATERIAL DEVELOPMENT & CONSTRUCTION INVESMENT JSC—See Vietnam Urban Development Investment Corporation; *Int'l*, pg. 8204
IDI COMPOSITE MATERIAL (SHANGHAI) CO., LTD—See Industrial Dielectrics Holdings, Inc.; *U.S. Private*, pg. 2065
IDI COMPOSITES INTERNATIONAL EUROPE (FR) SAS—See Industrial Dielectrics Holdings, Inc.; *U.S. Private*, pg. 2065
IDICO NO.10 INVESTMENT CONSTRUCTION JSC—See Vietnam Urban Development Investment Corporation; *Int'l*, pg. 8204
IDICO URBAN AND INDUSTRIAL ZONE DEVELOPMENT CO., LTD.—See Vietnam Urban Development Investment Corporation; *Int'l*, pg. 8204
IDICO URBAN & HOUSE DEVELOPMENT INVESTMENT JSC—See Vietnam Urban Development Investment Corporation; *Int'l*, pg. 8204
IDI EMERGING MARKETS S.A.—See IDI SCA; *Int'l*, pg. 3595
IDI FABRICATION, INC.—See Industrial Dielectrics Holdings, Inc.; *U.S. Private*, pg. 2065
THE IDI GROUP COMPANIES; *U.S. Private*, pg. 4055
IDI HOLDINGS, LLC—See Red Violet, Inc.; *U.S. Public*, pg. 1770
I.D.I. INFORMATICA DATA INTEGRATION LTD.—See Canada Pension Plan Investment Board; *Int'l*, pg. 1279
I.D.I. INFORMATICA DATA INTEGRATION LTD.—See Permira Advisers LLP; *Int'l*, pg. 5805
IDI LOGISTICS, LLC—See Brookfield Corporation; *Int'l*, pg. 1184
I.D. IMAGES LLC; *U.S. Private*, pg. 2027
IDIMENSION MSC PTE LTD—See Evd Berhad; *Int'l*, pg. 2561
IDIMENSION MSC SDN. BHD.—See Evd Berhad; *Int'l*, pg. 2561
IDINE—See TowerBrook Capital Partners, L.P.; *U.S. Private*, pg. 4195
ID INFO BUSINESS SERVICES LTD.; *Int'l*, pg. 3587
I.D. (INFORMED DECISIONS) PTY. LTD.—See PEXA Group Limited; *Int'l*, pg. 5835
ID INSIGHT, INC.; *U.S. Private*, pg. 2034
IDINVEST PARTNERS SA—See Eurazeo SE; *Int'l*, pg. 2529
IDIRECT GOVERNMENT, LLC—See Temasek Holdings (Private) Limited; *Int'l*, pg. 7552
IDIS AMERICA CO., LTD.—See IDIS Co., Ltd.; *Int'l*, pg. 3595
IDIS BENELUX BV—See IDIS Co., Ltd.; *Int'l*, pg. 3595
IDI SCA; *Int'l*, pg. 3594
IDIS CO., LTD.; *Int'l*, pg. 3595
IDISCOVERY SOLUTIONS, INC.; *U.S. Private*, pg. 2038
IDI SERVICES GROUP, LLC—See Brookfield Corporation; *Int'l*, pg. 1184
IDIS EUROPE LIMITED—See IDIS Co., Ltd.; *Int'l*, pg. 3595
IDIS HOLDINGS CO., LTD.; *Int'l*, pg. 3595
IDI THERMOSET MOLDING COMPOUNDS SHENZHEN COMPANY, LTD.—See Hidden Harbor Capital Partners; *U.S. Private*, pg. 1934
IDJ VIETNAM INVESTMENT JOINT STOCK COMPANY; *Int'l*, pg. 3595
ID KOMMUNIKATION AB; *Int'l*, pg. 3587
IDLC FINANCE LIMITED - MERCHANT BANKING DIVISON—See IDLC Finance PLC.; *Int'l*, pg. 3595
IDLC FINANCE PLC.; *Int'l*, pg. 3595
IDLC SECURITIES LIMITED—See IDLC Finance PLC.; *Int'l*, pg. 3595
IDLE MEDIA, INC.; *U.S. Public*, pg. 1093
IDLEWOOD ELECTRIC SUPPLY INC.; *U.S. Private*, pg. 2038
ID LOGISTICS BENELUX B.V.—See ID Logistics SAS; *Int'l*, pg. 3587

ID LOGISTICS ESPANA—See ID Logistics SAS; *Int'l*, pg. 3587
ID LOGISTICS POLSKA S.A.—See ID Logistics SAS; *Int'l*, pg. 3587
ID LOGISTICS RUS OOO—See ID Logistics SAS; *Int'l*, pg. 3587
ID LOGISTICS SAS; *Int'l*, pg. 3587
ID LOGISTICS TAIWAN CO., LTD.—See ID Logistics SAS; *Int'l*, pg. 3587
ID LOGISTICS US, INC.—See ID Logistics SAS; *Int'l*, pg. 3587
I.D. LOOK LTD.—See LOOK INCORPORATED; *Int'l*, pg. 4554
IDL PRECISION MACHINING, INC.—See CORE Industrial Partners, LLC; *U.S. Private*, pg. 1048
IDL SOLUTIONS, INC.—See CACI International Inc.; *U.S. Public*, pg. 418
IDL WORLDWIDE, INC.—See Matthews International Corporation; *U.S. Public*, pg. 1399
IDL WORLDWIDE, INC.—See Matthews International Corporation; *U.S. Public*, pg. 1399
I.D. MAGAZINE—See Tinicum Enterprises, Inc.; *U.S. Private*, pg. 4174
ID MEDIA-CHICAGO—See The Interpublic Group of Companies, Inc.; *U.S. Public*, pg. 2094
ID MEDIA-LOS ANGELES—See The Interpublic Group of Companies, Inc.; *U.S. Public*, pg. 2094
ID MEDIA—See The Interpublic Group of Companies, Inc.; *U.S. Public*, pg. 2094
IDM HOME FURNISHINGS, INC.; *U.S. Private*, pg. 2038
IDM PHARMA, S.A.S.—See Takeda Pharmaceutical Company Limited; *Int'l*, pg. 7439
IDM S.A.; *Int'l*, pg. 3595
I-DNA BIOTECHNOLOGY (M) SDN BHD—See BioLASCO Taiwan Co., Ltd.; *Int'l*, pg. 1038
IDN-ACME INC.—See IDN Inc.; *U.S. Private*, pg. 2038
IDN-H.HOFFMAN INC.; *U.S. Private*, pg. 2038
IDN INC.; *U.S. Private*, pg. 2038
IDNNT SA; *Int'l*, pg. 3595
IDNOW GMBH; *Int'l*, pg. 3595
I DO FLOWERS & GIFTS PTE, LTD.—See Neo Group Limited; *Int'l*, pg. 5196
IDO HUTNY PROJEKT A.S.—See Safichem Group AG; *Int'l*, pg. 6471
IDOLOGY INC.—See GB Group plc; *Int'l*, pg. 2892
IDOM, INC.; *Int'l*, pg. 3595
IDOMOO LTD.; *Int'l*, pg. 3595
IDORSIA LTD.; *Int'l*, pg. 3595
IDORSIA PHARMACEUTICALS JAPAN LTD.—See Idorsia Ltd.; *Int'l*, pg. 3595
IDORSIA PHARMACEUTICALS LTD.—See Idorsia Ltd.; *Int'l*, pg. 3595
IDO SECURITY INC.; *U.S. Private*, pg. 2038
IDOX BELGIUM NV—See IDOX PLC; *Int'l*, pg. 3595
IDOX FRANCE SARL—See IDOX PLC; *Int'l*, pg. 3595
IDOX GERMANY GMBH—See IDOX PLC; *Int'l*, pg. 3595
IDOX PLC - SOFTWARE DIVISION—See IDOX PLC; *Int'l*, pg. 3595
IDOX PLC; *Int'l*, pg. 3595
IDOX SOFTWARE LIMITED—See IDOX PLC; *Int'l*, pg. 3595
IDOXSOLUTIONS, INC.—See Bart & Associates Inc.; *U.S. Private*, pg. 482
IDP AMERICAS, INC.—See IDP Corp., Ltd.; *Int'l*, pg. 3596
IDP CORP., LTD.; *Int'l*, pg. 3596
IDP EDUCATION AUSTRALIA LIMITED; *Int'l*, pg. 3596
ID PROPERTY CO., LTD.—See Dear Life Co., Ltd.; *Int'l*, pg. 1998
I.D.Q. CANADA, INC.—See Berkshire Hathaway Inc.; *U.S. Public*, pg. 308
IDQ HOLDINGS, INC.—See Spectrum Brands Holdings, Inc.; *U.S. Public*, pg. 1915
ID QUANTIQUE S.A.—See SK Inc.; *Int'l*, pg. 6971
IDRA CHINA LTD—See Idra s.r.l.; *Int'l*, pg. 3596
IDRA LIMITED—See Idra s.r.l.; *Int'l*, pg. 3596
IDRA NORTH AMERICA—See Idra s.r.l.; *Int'l*, pg. 3596
IDRA PRESSEN GMBH—See Idra s.r.l.; *Int'l*, pg. 3596
IDRAPRINCE, INC.—See Buhler AG; *Int'l*, pg. 1212
IDRA S.R.L.; *Int'l*, pg. 3596
IDREAM FILM INFRASTRUCTURE COMPANY LIMITED; *Int'l*, pg. 3596
IDREAM MEDIA SERVICES GMBH—See A-TEC Industries AG; *Int'l*, pg. 21
IDREAMSKY TECHNOLOGY LIMITED; *Int'l*, pg. 3596
IDRECO B.V.—See Markel Group Inc.; *U.S. Public*, pg. 1368
IDREES TEXTILE MILLS LIMITED; *Int'l*, pg. 3596
IDROVALSESIA S.R.L.—See Alpiq Holding AG; *Int'l*, pg. 373
IDS AIRNAV S.R.L.—See ENAV S.p.A.; *Int'l*, pg. 2396
IDS AUSTRALASIA PTY. LTD.—See Fincantieri S.p.A.; *Int'l*, pg. 2671
IDS GMBH-ANALYSIS AND REPORTING SERVICES—See Allianz SE; *Int'l*, pg. 353
IDS GMBH—See Immunodiagnostic Systems Holdings plc; *Int'l*, pg. 3629
IDS INGEGNERIA DEI SISTEMI S.P.A.—See Fincantieri S.p.A.; *Int'l*, pg. 2671

COMPANY NAME INDEX

IDS INGEGNERIA DEI SISTEMI (UK) LTD.—See Fincantieri S.p.A.; *Int'l*, pg. 2671
IDS INTERNATIONAL GOVERNMENT SERVICES LLC; *U.S. Private*, pg. 2038
IDS KOREA CO. LTD.—See Fincantieri S.p.A.; *Int'l*, pg. 2671
IDS MANAGEMENT CORPORATION—See Ameriprise Financial, Inc.; *U.S. Public*, pg. 114
IDS MANUFACTURING SDN. BHD.—See Li & Fung Limited; *Int'l*, pg. 4479
IDS NORTH AMERICA LTD.—See Fincantieri S.p.A.; *Int'l*, pg. 2671
ID SOFTWARE, INC.—See Microsoft Corporation; *U.S. Public*, pg. 1443
IDS PROPERTY CASUALTY INSURANCE COMPANY—See Ameriprise Financial, Inc.; *U.S. Public*, pg. 114
IDS SA; *Int'l*, pg. 3596
IDS SCHEER AG—See Silver Lake Group, LLC; *U.S. Private*, pg. 3658
IDS SCHEER AMERICAS, INC.—See Silver Lake Group, LLC; *U.S. Private*, pg. 3658
IDS SCHEER AUSTRIA GMBH—See Silver Lake Group, LLC; *U.S. Private*, pg. 3658
IDS SCHEER CANADA—See Silver Lake Group, LLC; *U.S. Private*, pg. 3658
IDS SCHEER CHINA LTD.—See Silver Lake Group, LLC; *U.S. Private*, pg. 3658
IDS SCHEER CONSULTING AUSTRIA GMBH—See Scheer Group GmbH; *Int'l*, pg. 6615
IDS SCHEER, D.O.O.—See Silver Lake Group, LLC; *U.S. Private*, pg. 3658
IDS SCHEER D.O.O.—See Silver Lake Group, LLC; *U.S. Private*, pg. 3658
IDS SCHEER INDIA PVT. LTD.—See Silver Lake Group, LLC; *U.S. Private*, pg. 3658
IDS SCHEER RUSSIA—See Silver Lake Group, LLC; *U.S. Private*, pg. 3658
IDS SCHEER SAUDI ARABIA LLC.—See Silver Lake Group, LLC; *U.S. Private*, pg. 3658
IDS SCHEER SCHWEIZ AG—See Silver Lake Group, LLC; *U.S. Private*, pg. 3658
IDS SCHEER SDC S.R.O.—See Silver Lake Group, LLC; *U.S. Private*, pg. 3658
IDS SCHEER SINGAPORE PTE. LTD.—See Silver Lake Group, LLC; *U.S. Private*, pg. 3658
IDS SCHEER SISTEMAS DE PROCESSAMENTO DE DADOS LTDA.—See Silver Lake Group, LLC; *U.S. Private*, pg. 3658
IDSUD SA; *Int'l*, pg. 3596
IDSUMO DAIICHI TRAFFIC CO., LTD.—See Daiichi Koutsu Sangyo Co., Ltd.; *Int'l*, pg. 1928
ID SUPPLY CHAIN S.A.—See ID Logistics SAS; *Int'l*, pg. 3587
IDS USA INC.—See Li & Fung Limited; *Int'l*, pg. 4480
IDS USA WEST INC.—See Li & Fung Limited; *Int'l*, pg. 4480
I.D. SYSTEMS (UK) LTD—See PowerFleet, Inc.; *U.S. Public*, pg. 1706
IDT AUSTRALIA LIMITED; *Int'l*, pg. 3596
IDT CANADA INC.—See Renesas Electronics Corporation; *Int'l*, pg. 6276
IDT CARD SERVICES IRELAND LIMITED—See IDT Corporation; *U.S. Public*, pg. 1093
IDT COMMUNICATION TECHNOLOGY LIMITED—See IDT International Limited; *Int'l*, pg. 3596
IDT CORPORATION DE ARGENTINA S.A.—See IDT Corporation; *U.S. Public*, pg. 1093
IDT CORPORATION; *U.S. Public*, pg. 1093
IDT DATA SYSTEM LIMITED—See IDT International Limited; *Int'l*, pg. 3596
ID TECHNOLOGIES, LLC—See Acacia Capital NL LLC; *U.S. Private*, pg. 46
ID TECHNOLOGY LLC—See Leonard Green & Partners, L.P.; *U.S. Private*, pg. 2427
ID TECHNOLOGY LLC - UPPER MIDWEST OFFICE—See Leonard Green & Partners, L.P.; *U.S. Private*, pg. 2427
IDTEK IDENTIFIKATIONSLOSUNGEN GMBH—See STERIS plc; *Int'l*, pg. 7209
IDT ELECTRONIC PRODUCTS LIMITED—See IDT International Limited; *Int'l*, pg. 3596
IDT EUROPE BVBA—See IDT Corporation; *U.S. Public*, pg. 1093
IDT EUROPE GMBH—See Renesas Electronics Corporation; *Int'l*, pg. 6276
IDT FRANCE SARL—See IDT Corporation; *U.S. Public*, pg. 1093
IDT FZCO—See Trevi Finanziaria Industriale SpA.; *Int'l*, pg. 7916
IDT GLOBAL LIMITED—See IDT Corporation; *U.S. Public*, pg. 1093
IDT INTER DIRECT TEL SWEDEN AB—See IDT Corporation; *U.S. Public*, pg. 1093
IDT INTERNATIONAL LIMITED; *Int'l*, pg. 3596
IDT ITALIA S.R.L.—See IDT Corporation; *U.S. Public*, pg. 1093
IDT (JAPAN) LIMITED—See IDT International Limited; *Int'l*, pg. 3596

IDT NETHERLANDS BV—See IDT Corporation; *U.S. Public*, pg. 1093
IDT RETAIL EUROPE LIMITED—See IDT Corporation; *U.S. Public*, pg. 1093
IDT SINGAPORE PTE. LTD.—See Renesas Electronics Corporation; *Int'l*, pg. 6276
IDT SONICVISION LIMITED—See IDT International Limited; *Int'l*, pg. 3596
IDT SPAIN S.L.—See IDT Corporation; *U.S. Public*, pg. 1093
IDT TECHNOLOGY LIMITED—See IDT International Limited; *Int'l*, pg. 3596
IDT TELECOM ASIA PACIFIC (AUSTRALIA) PTY. LTD.—See IDT Corporation; *U.S. Public*, pg. 1094
IDUN INDUSTRI AS—See Orkla ASA; *Int'l*, pg. 5638
IDVATION GMBH—See H2APEX Group SCA; *Int'l*, pg. 3200
IDVERDE UK LTD.; *Int'l*, pg. 3597
IDVERIFACT INC.—See Prodigy Ventures, Inc.; *Int'l*, pg. 5988
IDW MEDIA HOLDINGS, INC.; *U.S. Public*, pg. 1094
IDX CORPORATION—See UFP Industries, Inc.; *U.S. Public*, pg. 2221
IDX INC.—See Adtec Plasma Technology Co., Ltd.; *Int'l*, pg. 154
IDX PATHOLOGY, INC.—See Laboratory Corporation of America Holdings; *U.S. Public*, pg. 1287
IDY CORPORATION—See Systena Corporation; *Int'l*, pg. 7393
IEA INCORPORATED; *U.S. Private*, pg. 2038
IEC EDUCATION LTD.; *Int'l*, pg. 3597
IEC ELECTRONICS - ALBUQUERQUE—See Goldberg Lindsay & Co., LLC; *U.S. Private*, pg. 1729
IEC ELECTRONICS CORP.—See Goldberg Lindsay & Co., LLC; *U.S. Private*, pg. 1729
IEC GROUP, INC.—See Elevance Health, Inc.; *U.S. Public*, pg. 730
IEC HOLDING AB—See Vivendi SE; *Int'l*, pg. 8276
IECL PTY. LTD.—See GrowthOps Limited; *Int'l*, pg. 3113
IE CONNECT LLC—See Interior Environments, Inc.; *U.S. Private*, pg. 2111
I & E CONSTRUCTION, INC.; *U.S. Private*, pg. 2020
I & E CONSULTANTS; *Int'l*, pg. 3561
IEC REAL ESTATE PTY LTD—See International Equities Corporation Limited; *Int'l*, pg. 3748
IEDUCNADO MEXICO S.A.P.I DE C.V.—See Scientia School, S.A.; *Int'l*, pg. 6648
IEEE GLOBALSPEC, INC.—See Institute of Electrical and Electronics Engineers, Inc.; *U.S. Private*, pg. 2093
IEF-WERNER GMBH—See INDUS Holding AG; *Int'l*, pg. 3663
IEF-WERNER (TAIWAN) LIMITED—See INDUS Holding AG; *Int'l*, pg. 3663
IEG INC.—See Inuvialuit Regional Corporation; *Int'l*, pg. 3772
IEG LLC—See WPP plc; *Int'l*, pg. 8474
IEG MALTA LIMITED—See New Silkroutes Group Limited; *Int'l*, pg. 5227
IE GROUP, INC.—See Hikari Tsushin, Inc.; *Int'l*, pg. 3390
IEH ARI HOLDINGS LLC—See Icahn Enterprises L.P.; *U.S. Public*, pg. 1084
IEH AUTO PARTS LLC—See Icahn Enterprises L.P.; *U.S. Public*, pg. 1084
IEH CORPORATION; *U.S. Public*, pg. 1094
IEH GH MANAGEMENT LLC—See Icahn Enterprises L.P.; *U.S. Public*, pg. 1084
IEI INTEGRATION CORP.; *Int'l*, pg. 3597
IEI TECHNOLOGY USA CORP.—See IEI Integration Corp.; *Int'l*, pg. 3597
IE LIMITED; *Int'l*, pg. 3597
IEMOLI TRASPORTI SA—See Die Schweizerische Post AG; *Int'l*, pg. 2113
IEMOLI TRASPORTI S.R.L.—See Die Schweizerische Post AG; *Int'l*, pg. 2113
IEMR RESOURCES INC.; *Int'l*, pg. 3597
IENERGIZER LIMITED; *Int'l*, pg. 3597
IENJOY HOME LLC; *U.S. Private*, pg. 2038
IENONAKA COMPANY, LTD.—See Senko Group Holdings Co., Ltd.; *Int'l*, pg. 6709
IENTERPRISE ONLINE SDN. BHD.—See Ancom Nylex Berhad; *Int'l*, pg. 449
IENTERTAINMENT NETWORK, INC.; *U.S. Private*, pg. 2038
IENTRY, INC.; *U.S. Private*, pg. 2038
IEOC PRODUCTION BV—See Eni S.p.A.; *Int'l*, pg. 2437
IEP INNOVATIVE ENERGIEN POTSDAM GMBH—See Stadtwerke Hannover AG; *Int'l*, pg. 7161
IEP INVEST SA; *Int'l*, pg. 3597
IEP TECHNOLOGIES GMBH—See Sentinel Capital Partners, L.L.C.; *U.S. Private*, pg. 3609
IEP TECHNOLOGIES, LLC—See Sentinel Capital Partners, L.L.C.; *U.S. Private*, pg. 3609
IER FUJIKURA INC.—See Fujikura Ltd.; *Int'l*, pg. 2829
IER—See Financiere de L'Odet; *Int'l*, pg. 2667
IERVOLINO & LADY BACARDI ENTERTAINMENT S.P.A.; *Int'l*, pg. 3597
IESA INC.—See IESA Pty Ltd; *Int'l*, pg. 3598
IESA INC.—See IESA Pty Ltd; *Int'l*, pg. 3598
IESA PTY LTD; *Int'l*, pg. 3598

IESA—See Sonepar S.A.; *Int'l*, pg. 7091
IES COMMERCIAL & INDUSTRIAL, LLC - GREENVILLE—See IES Holdings, Inc.; *U.S. Public*, pg. 1094
IES COMMERCIAL & INDUSTRIAL, LLC—See IES Holdings, Inc.; *U.S. Public*, pg. 1094
IES COMMUNICATIONS, LLC—See IES Holdings, Inc.; *U.S. Public*, pg. 1094
IES ENGINEERING SYSTEMS SDN. BHD.—See Annica Holdings Limited; *Int'l*, pg. 474
IES HOLDINGS, INC.; *U.S. Public*, pg. 1094
IES HOLDINGS LTD.; *Int'l*, pg. 3597
IESI-BFC HOLDINGS, INC.—See Waste Connections, Inc.; *Int'l*, pg. 8352
IES INFRASTRUCTURE SOLUTIONS, LLC—See IES Holdings, Inc.; *U.S. Public*, pg. 1094
IES - ITALIANA ENERGIA E SERVIZI SPA—See MOL Magyar Olaj- es Gazipari Nyrt.; *Int'l*, pg. 5020
IE SOLUTION SERVICE CO., LTD.—See Hitachi, Ltd.; *Int'l*, pg. 3423
IES RENEWABLE ENERGY, LLC—See IES Holdings, Inc.; *U.S. Public*, pg. 1094
IES RESIDENTIAL, INC.—See IES Holdings, Inc.; *U.S. Public*, pg. 1094
IES SUBSIDIARY HOLDINGS, INC.—See IES Holdings, Inc.; *U.S. Public*, pg. 1094
IE TECHNOLOGIES PTE LTD—See EnerSys; *U.S. Public*, pg. 767
IETG LTD.; *Int'l*, pg. 3598
I&E TIRE CORP.; *U.S. Private*, pg. 2026
IET SOLUTIONS, LLC—See UNICOM Global, Inc.; *U.S. Private*, pg. 4282
IETV ELEKTROTEKNIK AB—See Addtech AB; *Int'l*, pg. 133
IEV ENERGY SDN. BHD.—See Medi Lifestyle Limited; *Int'l*, pg. 4769
IEV INTERNATIONAL LIMITED—See Medi Lifestyle Limited; *Int'l*, pg. 4769
IEV MANUFACTURING SDN. BHD.—See Medi Lifestyle Limited; *Int'l*, pg. 4770
IEV OIL & GAS TECHNOLOGIES CO., LTD.—See Medi Lifestyle Limited; *Int'l*, pg. 4770
IEWC BRAZIL—See Industrial Electric Wire & Cable Inc.; *U.S. Private*, pg. 2066
IEWC GERMANY GMBH—See Industrial Electric Wire & Cable Inc.; *U.S. Private*, pg. 2066
IEWC MEXICO, S. DE R.L. DE C.V.—See Industrial Electric Wire & Cable Inc.; *U.S. Private*, pg. 2066
IEWC ONTARIO—See Industrial Electric Wire & Cable Inc.; *U.S. Private*, pg. 2066
IEWC SUZHOU—See Industrial Electric Wire & Cable Inc.; *U.S. Private*, pg. 2066
IEWC UK & IRELAND LTD.—See Industrial Electric Wire & Cable Inc.; *U.S. Private*, pg. 2066
IEW INNOVATIVE ENERGIEN WOLGAST GMBH—See Stadtwerke Hannover AG; *Int'l*, pg. 7161
IEXALT, INC.; *U.S. Public*, pg. 1094
IEX GROUP, INC.; *U.S. Private*, pg. 2038
IEX GROUP N.V.; *Int'l*, pg. 3598
I-FABER SPA—See UniCredit S.p.A.; *Int'l*, pg. 8034
IFABRIC CORP.; *Int'l*, pg. 3598
IFA CO., LTD.—See ITOCHU Corporation; *Int'l*, pg. 3836
IFACTOR CONSULTING, INC.—See The Hearst Corporation; *U.S. Private*, pg. 4049
I-FACTORY CO., LTD.; *Int'l*, pg. 3563
IFAD AUTOS LTD.; *Int'l*, pg. 3598
IFA HOTELS & RESORTS CO. K.S.C.C.—See International Financial Advisors K.S.C.C.; *Int'l*, pg. 3748
IFA HOTEL & TOURISTIK AG; *Int'l*, pg. 3598
IFAMIYSC CO., LTD.; *Int'l*, pg. 3598
IFAN FINANCIAL, INC.; *U.S. Public*, pg. 1095
I:FAO AG—See Amadeus IT Group, S.A.; *Int'l*, pg. 407
IFAP SERVICE-INSTITUT FUR ARZTE UND APOTHEKER GMBH—See CompuGroup Medical SE & Co. KGaA; *Int'l*, pg. 1757
I-FAST AUTOMOTIVE LOGISTICS S.R.L.—See Stellantis N.V.; *Int'l*, pg. 7200
IFAST CAPITAL SDN. BHD.—See iFAST Corporation Limited; *Int'l*, pg. 3598
IFAST CORPORATION LIMITED; *Int'l*, pg. 3598
IFAST FINANCIAL (HK) LIMITED—See iFAST Corporation Limited; *Int'l*, pg. 3598
IFAST FINANCIAL LIMITED—See iFAST Corporation Limited; *Int'l*, pg. 3598
IFAST FINANCIAL PTE. LTD.—See iFAST Corporation Limited; *Int'l*, pg. 3598
IFASTGROUPE AND COMPANY, LIMITED PARTNERSHIP—See The Heico Companies, L.L.C.; *U.S. Private*, pg. 4050
IFAST PLATFORM SERVICES (HK) LIMITED—See iFAST Corporation Limited; *Int'l*, pg. 3598
IFA SYSTEMS AG—See NEXUS AG; *Int'l*, pg. 5250
IFA TAGDAEKNING A/S—See Kingspan Group PLC; *Int'l*, pg. 4178
IFAT SAS—See VINCI S.A.; *Int'l*, pg. 8222
IFA UNITED I-TECH, INC.—See NEXUS AG; *Int'l*, pg. 5251
IFAX SOLUTIONS, INC.; *U.S. Private*, pg. 2038
IFB AGRO INDUSTRIES LIMITED; *Int'l*, pg. 3598

IF BANCORP, INC. CORPORATE AFFILIATIONS

IF BANCORP, INC.; *U.S. Public*, pg. 1095
IFB AUTOMOTIVE PRIVATE LIMITED—See IFB Industries Limited; *Int'l*, pg. 3598
IFB HOLDINGS, INC.; *U.S. Public*, pg. 1095
IFB INDUSTRIES LIMITED; *Int'l*, pg. 3598
IFB INSTITUT FUR BAHNTECHNIK GMBH—See Knorr-Bremse AG; *Int'l*, pg. 4210
IFB INSTITUT FUR BLUTGRUPPENFORSCHUNG GMBH—See Eurofins Scientific S.E.; *Int'l*, pg. 2550
IFBYPHONE; *U.S. Private*, pg. 2038
IFCA CONSULTING PRIVATE LIMITED—See IFCA MSC Berhad; *Int'l*, pg. 3598
IFCA CONSULTING (SABAH) SDN BHD—See IFCA MSC Berhad; *Int'l*, pg. 3598
IFCA CONSULTING (SARAWAK) SDN BHD—See IFCA MSC Berhad; *Int'l*, pg. 3598
IFCA (GUANGZHOU) TECHNOLOGY COMPANY LIMITED—See IFCA MSC Berhad; *Int'l*, pg. 3598
IFCA MSC BERHAD; *Int'l*, pg. 3598
IFCA SOFTWARE (GUANGZHOU) CO., LTD.—See IFCA MSC Berhad; *Int'l*, pg. 3598
IFC ASSET MANAGEMENT COMPANY—See The World Bank Group; *U.S. Private*, pg. 4139
IFCA SYSTEMS (JB) SDN BHD—See IFCA MSC Berhad; *Int'l*, pg. 3598
IFCA SYSTEMS (PENANG) SDN BHD—See IFCA MSC Berhad; *Int'l*, pg. 3598
IFCA (WUHAN) TECHNOLOGY COMPANY LIMITED—See IFCA MSC Berhad; *Int'l*, pg. 3598
IFC COMPANIES—See AMC Networks Inc.; *U.S. Public*, pg. 92
IFC CORP.—See Nippon Steel Corporation; *Int'l*, pg. 5337
IFC DISPOSABLES INC.—See Cascades Inc.; *Int'l*, pg. 1351
I.F.C.E.N. SAS—See VINCI S.A.; *Int'l*, pg. 8222
IFCI FACTORS LTD—See IFCI Limited; *Int'l*, pg. 3599
IFCI FINANCIAL SERVICES LTD—See IFCI Limited; *Int'l*, pg. 3599
IFCI LIMITED; *Int'l*, pg. 3599
IFCI VENTURE CAPITAL FUNDS LTD—See IFCI Limited; *Int'l*, pg. 3599
IFC NATIONAL MARKETING INC.—See Integrity Marketing Group LLC; *U.S. Private*, pg. 2103
IFCO JAPAN INC.—See Mitsubishi Chemical Group Corporation; *Int'l*, pg. 4931
IFCO SYSTEMS N.V.—See Triton Advisers Limited; *Int'l*, pg. 7931
IFCO SYSTEMS US, LLC—See Audax Group, Limited Partnership; *U.S. Private*, pg. 386
IFC SOLID CJSC; *Int'l*, pg. 3598
IFDS LUXEMBOURG S.A.—See SS&C Technologies Holdings, Inc.; *U.S. Public*, pg. 1923
IFEC INGEGNERIA SA—See AFRY AB; *Int'l*, pg. 194
IFE-CR A.S.—See Knorr-Bremse AG; *Int'l*, pg. 4210
IFE ELEVATORS CO., LTD; *Int'l*, pg. 3599
IFEG SAS—See Eurofins Scientific S.E.; *Int'l*, pg. 2543
IFE NORTH AMERICA LLC—See Knorr-Bremse AG; *Int'l*, pg. 4210
IFES GMBH—See TUV Rheinland Berlin-Brandenburg Pfalz e.V.; *Int'l*, pg. 7984
IFE TEBEL TECHNOLOGIES B.V.—See Knorr-Bremse AG; *Int'l*, pg. 4210
IFE-TEBEL TECHNOLOGIES B.V.—See Knorr-Bremse AG; *Int'l*, pg. 4210
IFE-VICTALL RAILWAY VEHICLE DOOR SYSTEMS (QINGDAO) CO., LTD.—See Knorr-Bremse AG; *Int'l*, pg. 4210
IFF AROMA ESANS SANAYI VE TICARET A.S.—See International Flavors & Fragrances Inc.; *U.S. Public*, pg. 1152
IFF BENICARLO, S.A.—See International Flavors & Fragrances Inc.; *U.S. Public*, pg. 1153
IFFCO-TOKIO GENERAL INSURANCE CO., LTD.—See Indian Farmers Fertiliser; *Int'l*, pg. 3654
IFFCO-TOKIO GENERAL INSURANCE CO., LTD.—See Tokio Marine Holdings, Inc.; *Int'l*, pg. 7784
IFF FRAGRANCE GMBH—See International Flavors & Fragrances Inc.; *U.S. Public*, pg. 1152
IFF INTERNATIONAL FLAVORS & FRAGRANCES INC.—See International Flavors & Fragrances Inc.; *U.S. Public*, pg. 1152
IFF (KOREA) INC.—See International Flavors & Fragrances Inc.; *U.S. Public*, pg. 1152
IFFLAND KAVANAGH WATERBURY, P.L.L.C.—See Jacobs Engineering Group, Inc.; *U.S. Public*, pg. 1184
IFF LATIN AMERICAN HOLDINGS (ESPANA), S.L.—See International Flavors & Fragrances Inc.; *U.S. Public*, pg. 1152
IFF TURKEY AROMA VE ESANS URUNLERI SATIS TICARET ANONIM SIRKETI—See International Flavors & Fragrances Inc.; *U.S. Public*, pg. 1152
IFG ASIA LIMITED—See Epiris Managers LLP; *Int'l*, pg. 2461
IFG ASOTA GMBH—See Duc Long Gia Lai Group JSC; *Int'l*, pg. 2222
IFG COMPANIES; *U.S. Private*, pg. 2038
IFG CORP.; *U.S. Private*, pg. 2038
IFG DRAKE LTD.—See Duroc AB; *Int'l*, pg. 2230

IFG EXELTO NV—See Duc Long Gia Lai Group JSC; *Int'l*, pg. 2222
IFG GROUP PLC—See Epiris Managers LLP; *Int'l*, pg. 2461
IFGL REFRACTORIES LTD.—See S K Bajoria Group; *Int'l*, pg. 6442
IFG QUIGLEY LIMITED—See Epiris Managers LLP; *Int'l*, pg. 2461
IFH GROUP INC.; *U.S. Private*, pg. 2039
IFIC BANK PLC; *Int'l*, pg. 3599
IFI CLAIMS PATENT SERVICES—See Wolters Kluwer n.v.; *Int'l*, pg. 8444
IFIC MONEY TRANSFER (UK) LIMITED—See IFIC Bank PLC; *Int'l*, pg. 3599
IFILM CORP.—See National Amusements, Inc.; *U.S. Private*, pg. 2842
IFINA BETEILIGUNGSGESELLSCHAFT MBH—See Phoenix Mecano AG; *Int'l*, pg. 5852
I-FINANCE LEASING PLC—See KB Financial Group Inc.; *Int'l*, pg. 4104
IFIRE GROUP LTD.—See CTS Corporation; *U.S. Public*, pg. 603
IFIRMA S.A.; *Int'l*, pg. 3599
IFIS FINANCE I.F.N. S.A.—See Banca IFIS S.p.A.; *Int'l*, pg. 815
IFIS FINANCE SP. Z O.O.—See Banca IFIS S.p.A.; *Int'l*, pg. 815
IFIS JAPAN LTD.—See Daiwa Securities Group Inc.; *Int'l*, pg. 1949
IFIS NPL INVESTING S.P.A.—See Banca IFIS S.p.A.; *Int'l*, pg. 815
IFIS NPL SERVICING S.P.A.—See Banca IFIS S.p.A.; *Int'l*, pg. 815
IFIS RENTAL SERVICES S.R.L.—See Banca IFIS S.p.A.; *Int'l*, pg. 815
IFIT HEALTH & FITNESS INC.; *U.S. Private*, pg. 2039
IF IT SERVICES A/S—See Sampo plc; *Int'l*, pg. 6507
IF IT'S PAPER (2) LLC; *U.S. Private*, pg. 2038
IF IT'S PAPER - GREENVILLE—See If It's Paper (2) LLC; *U.S. Private*, pg. 2038
IFIXIT, INC.—See Apple Inc.; *U.S. Public*, pg. 169
IFLAG CO., LTD.; *Int'l*, pg. 3599
IFLEET SOLUTIONS & SERVICES PVT. LTD.—See STRABAG SE; *Int'l*, pg. 7230
IFL ENTERPRISES LTD.; *Int'l*, pg. 3599
IF LIVFORSAKRING AB—See Sampo plc; *Int'l*, pg. 6507
I-FLOW, LLC—See Kimberly-Clark Corporation; *U.S. Public*, pg. 1229
IFL PROMOTERS LIMITED; *Int'l*, pg. 3599
IFLY HOLDINGS, LLC; *U.S. Private*, pg. 2039
IFLYTEK CO., LTD.; *Int'l*, pg. 3599
IFM AMERICAS INC.—See Infomedia Ltd; *Int'l*, pg. 3690
IFMA SA; *Int'l*, pg. 3599
IFM DEUTSCHLAND GMBH—See Infomedia Ltd; *Int'l*, pg. 3690
IFM EUROPE LTD—See Infomedia Ltd; *Int'l*, pg. 3690
IFM IMMOBILIEN AG; *Int'l*, pg. 3599
IFM INFOMASTER S.P.A.—See Sesa S.p.A.; *Int'l*, pg. 6728
IFM INVESTMENTS LIMITED; *Int'l*, pg. 3599
IFM INVESTORS PTY. LTD.—See Industry Super Holdings Pty. Ltd.; *Int'l*, pg. 3675
IFNET INC.—See FTGroup Co Ltd.; *Int'l*, pg. 2800
IFOCUS PTE. LTD.—See Natural Cool Holdings Limited; *Int'l*, pg. 5168
IFOLOR AG; *Int'l*, pg. 3599
IFOLOR GMBH—See Ifolor AG; *Int'l*, pg. 3599
IFOLOR OY—See Ifolor AG; *Int'l*, pg. 3599
IF ONLY HOLIDAYS LTD.—See Seera Group Holding Co.; *Int'l*, pg. 6679
IFOS INTERNATIONALE FONDS SERVICE AG—See VP Bank AG; *Int'l*, pg. 8311
IFOTEC SA—See BNP Paribas SA; *Int'l*, pg. 1089
IFP CANADA CORPORATION—See The Kraft Group LLC; *U.S. Private*, pg. 4065
IF P&C INSURANCE AB—See Sampo plc; *Int'l*, pg. 6507
IF P&C INSURANCE AS—See Sampo plc; *Int'l*, pg. 6508
IF P & C INSURANCE COMPANY LTD.—See Sampo plc; *Int'l*, pg. 6507
IF P&C INSURANCE HOLDING LTD.—See Sampo plc; *Int'l*, pg. 6507
IFP CORPORATE SERVICES SDN. BHD.—See The Kraft Group LLC; *U.S. Private*, pg. 4065
IF P&C—See Sampo plc; *Int'l*, pg. 6507
IFP ENERGIES NOUVELLES - LYON SITE—See IFP Energies Nouvelles; *Int'l*, pg. 3599
IFP ENERGIES NOUVELLES; *Int'l*, pg. 3599
IF&P FOODS LLC—See Wind Point Advisors LLC; *U.S. Private*, pg. 4534
IFP, INC.; *U.S. Private*, pg. 2039
IFP TRADING LTD.—See Enterprise Investment Fund slhf.; *Int'l*, pg. 2451
IFREEDOM DIRECT CORPORATION—See Wintrust Financial Corporation; *U.S. Public*, pg. 2374
I-FREEK MOBILE INC.; *Int'l*, pg. 3563
IFRESH INC.; *U.S. Public*, pg. 1095
IFR FRANCE S.A.S.—See Airbus SE; *Int'l*, pg. 246
IFS AMERICAS, INC.—See EQT AB; *Int'l*, pg. 2477

IFS APPLICATIONS IBERICA, S.A.—See EQT AB; *Int'l*, pg. 2477
IFSAR S.A.—See EQT AB; *Int'l*, pg. 2478
IFS BENELUX B.V.—See EQT AB; *Int'l*, pg. 2477
IFS BETEILIGUNGSGES MBH—See EQT AB; *Int'l*, pg. 2477
IFS CAPITAL ASSETS PTE. LTD.—See IFS Capital Limited; *Int'l*, pg. 3600
IFS CAPITAL HOLDINGS (THAILAND) LIMITED—See IFS Capital Limited; *Int'l*, pg. 3600
IFS CAPITAL LIMITED; *Int'l*, pg. 3599
IFS CAPITAL (MALAYSIA) SDN. BHD.—See IFS Capital Limited; *Int'l*, pg. 3600
IFS CAPITAL (THAILAND) PCL—See IFS Capital Limited; *Int'l*, pg. 3600
IFS CENTRAL & EASTERN EUROPE SP. Z.O.O.—See EQT AB; *Int'l*, pg. 2477
IFS COATINGS, INC.—See CFS Group, Inc.; *Int'l*, pg. 1430
IFS CZECH S.R.O.—See EQT AB; *Int'l*, pg. 2477
IFS DANMARK A/S—See EQT AB; *Int'l*, pg. 2477
IFS DEUTSCHLAND GMBH & CO KG—See EQT AB; *Int'l*, pg. 2477
IFS FINANCIAL SERVICES, INC.—See Western & Southern Financial Group, Inc.; *U.S. Private*, pg. 4490
IFS FINLAND OY AB—See EQT AB; *Int'l*, pg. 2477
IFS FRANCE SA—See EQT AB; *Int'l*, pg. 2477
IFS HOLDINGS, LLC; *U.S. Private*, pg. 2039
IFS HUNGARY KFT.—See EQT AB; *Int'l*, pg. 2477
IFS INDEPENDENT FINANCIAL SERVICES AG—See Mubadala Investment Company PJSC; *Int'l*, pg. 5074
IFS INDUSTRIAL FINANCIAL SYSTEMS CANADA, INC—See EQT AB; *Int'l*, pg. 2477
IFS INDUSTRIES, INC.—See CFS Group, Inc.; *Int'l*, pg. 1430
IFS INDUSTRIES, INC.—See CFS Group, Inc.; *Int'l*, pg. 1430
IFS ITALIA S.R.L.—See EQT AB; *Int'l*, pg. 2477
IFS JAPAN K.K.—See EQT AB; *Int'l*, pg. 2477
IFS MIDDLE EAST FZ-LLC—See EQT AB; *Int'l*, pg. 2478
IFS NEW ZEALAND PTY LTD—See EQT AB; *Int'l*, pg. 2478
IFS NORGE AS—See EQT AB; *Int'l*, pg. 2478
IFS NORTH AMERICA INC.—See EQT AB; *Int'l*, pg. 2478
IFS PHILIPPINES INC.—See EQT AB; *Int'l*, pg. 2478
IFS PROBITY B.V.—See Sopra Steria Group S.A.; *Int'l*, pg. 7109
IFS SCHWEIZ AG—See EQT AB; *Int'l*, pg. 2478
IFS SLOVAKIA, SPOL. S.R.O.—See EQT AB; *Int'l*, pg. 2477
IFS SOLUTION INDIA PVT LTD—See EQT AB; *Int'l*, pg. 2478
IFS SOLUTIONS ASIA PACIFIC PTE LTD—See EQT AB; *Int'l*, pg. 2478
IFS SOLUTIONS MALAYSIA SDN BHD—See EQT AB; *Int'l*, pg. 2478
IFS SOLUTIONS (SHANGHAI) CO LTD—See EQT AB; *Int'l*, pg. 2478
IFS SOLUTIONS (THAI) LTD.—See EQT AB; *Int'l*, pg. 2478
IFS SRI LANKA LTD—See EQT AB; *Int'l*, pg. 2478
IFS SVERIGE AB—See EQT AB; *Int'l*, pg. 2478
IFS UK LTD.—See EQT AB; *Int'l*, pg. 2478
IFS VENTURES PRIVATE LIMITED—See IFS Capital Limited; *Int'l*, pg. 3600
IFTG SVERIGE AB—See Indutrade AB; *Int'l*, pg. 3679
IFTHEN, LLC; *U.S. Private*, pg. 2039
IFT INGENIEURGESELLSCHAFT FUR TRIEBWERKSTECHNIK MBH—See INA-Holding Schaeffler GmbH & Co. KG; *Int'l*, pg. 3639
IFUJI SANGYO CO., LTD.; *Int'l*, pg. 3600
IFX NETWORKS ARGENTINA SRL—See Enel S.p.A.; *Int'l*, pg. 2414
IFX NETWORKS CHILE SA—See Enel S.p.A.; *Int'l*, pg. 2414
IFX NETWORKS LLC—See Enel S.p.A.; *Int'l*, pg. 2415
IG ACQUISITION CORP.; *U.S. Public*, pg. 1095
IGA DISTRIBUTION PTY LIMITED—See Metcash Limited; *Int'l*, pg. 4852
IGA DISTRIBUTION (VIC) PTY LIMITED—See Metcash Limited; *Int'l*, pg. 4852
IGA DISTRIBUTION (WA) PTY LIMITED—See Metcash Limited; *Int'l*, pg. 4852
IGA, INC.; *U.S. Private*, pg. 2039
IGA MACHINERY CO., LTD.—See TOKYO KIKAI SEISAKUSHO LTD.; *Int'l*, pg. 7793
IGAMING BUSINESS LIMITED—See Blackstone Inc.; *U.S. Public*, pg. 360
IGAM LLC—See Grupo Financiero Galicia S.A.; *Int'l*, pg. 3129
IGARASHI ELECTRIC WORKS (ZHUHAI) LTD.—See Igarashi Motors India Limited; *Int'l*, pg. 3601
IGARASHI MOTOREN GMBH—See Igarashi Motors India Limited; *Int'l*, pg. 3601
IGARASHI MOTORS INDIA LIMITED; *Int'l*, pg. 3601
IGARASHI SUISAN CO., LTD.—See Zensho Holdings Co., Ltd.; *Int'l*, pg. 8634
I-GARD CORPORATION—See Telema S.p.A; *Int'l*, pg. 7538

COMPANY NAME INDEX

IG ASIA PTE LIMITED—See IG Group Holdings plc; *Int'l*, pg. 3601
IGAS, INC.; *U.S. Private*, pg. 2039
IGATE COMPUTER SYSTEMS (SUZHOU) CO., LTD.—See Capgemini SE; *Int'l*, pg. 1306
IGATE SINGAPORE PTE LTD.—See Capgemini SE; *Int'l*, pg. 1306
IG BANK S.A.—See IG Group Holdings plc; *Int'l*, pg. 3601
IGB AUTOMOTIVE LTD.—See Lear Corporation; *U.S. Public*, pg. 1297
IGB AUTOMOTIVE VIETNAM CO., LTD.—See Lear Corporation; *U.S. Public*, pg. 1297
IGB AUTOMOTRIZ S. DE R.L. DE C.V.—See Lear Corporation; *U.S. Public*, pg. 1297
IGB BERHAD; *Int'l*, pg. 3601
IGB CORPORATION BERHAD—See IGB Berhad; *Int'l*, pg. 3601
IGB DIGITAL SDN. BHD.—See IGB Berhad; *Int'l*, pg. 3601
IGB INTEGRATIVES GESUNDHEITSZENTRUM BOIZENBURG GMBH—See Asklepios Kliniken GmbH & Co. KGaA; *Int'l*, pg. 624
IGB INTERNATIONAL SCHOOL SDN. BHD.—See IGB Berhad; *Int'l*, pg. 3601
IGB REAL ESTATE INVESTMENT TRUST; *Int'l*, pg. 3602
I.G. BURTON & CO. INC.; *U.S. Private*, pg. 2027
IGC-INDUSTRIAL GALVANIZERS CORPORATION (M) SDN. BHD.—See Valmont Industries, Inc.; *U.S. Public*, pg. 2273
IGC INDUSTRIES LIMITED; *Int'l*, pg. 3602
IG CONSULTING S.R.L.—See Maps SpA; *Int'l*, pg. 4687
IGC PHARMA, INC.; *U.S. Public*, pg. 1095
IGC PHARMA LLC—See IGC Pharma, Inc.; *U.S. Public*, pg. 1095
IG DESIGN GROUP AMERICAS, INC.—See IG Design Group Plc; *Int'l*, pg. 3600
IG DESIGN GROUP BV—See IG Design Group Plc; *Int'l*, pg. 3600
IG DESIGN GROUP PLC; *Int'l*, pg. 3600
IGD INDUSTRIES INC.; *U.S. Private*, pg. 2039
IG DOBLING HERRENHAUS-BAUTRAGER GMBH—See Oesterreichische Nationalbank; *Int'l*, pg. 5529
IG DOORS LTD.—See Hormann KG Verkaufsgesellschaf; *Int'l*, pg. 3481
IGD SIIQ S.P.A; *Int'l*, pg. 3002
IGEAMED SPA; *Int'l*, pg. 3602
IGEA PHARMA N.V.; *Int'l*, pg. 3602
IGE CO., LTD.—See SK Inc.; *Int'l*, pg. 6971
IGE-CZ S.R.O.—See Knorr-Bremse AG; *Int'l*, pg. 4210
IGE ENERGY SERVICES (UK) LTD—See General Electric Company; *U.S. Public*, pg. 919
IGEFI IRELAND LIMITED—See Temenos AG; *Int'l*, pg. 7554
I+G ELECTRICAL SERVICES CO. LTD.—See Endress+Hauser (International) Holding AG; *Int'l*, pg. 2408
IGENE BIOTECHNOLOGY, INC.; *U.S. Public*, pg. 1095
IGENII, INC.; *U.S. Private*, pg. 2039
IGEN NETWORKS CORP.; *U.S. Public*, pg. 1095
IGEPA BELUX N.V.—See Printers' Service, Inc.; *U.S. Private*, pg. 3265
IGES D.O.O.—See Petrol, Slovenska energetska druzba, d.d.; *Int'l*, pg. 5827
IGETA HEIM CO., LTD.—See Sumitomo Metal Mining Co., Ltd.; *Int'l*, pg. 7291
IGETA SUNRISE PIPE CORP.—See Nippon Steel Corporation; *Int'l*, pg. 5337
IGETO CO. LTD.—See Sumitomo Forestry Co., Ltd.; *Int'l*, pg. 7285
IGE XAO A/S—See Schneider Electric SE; *Int'l*, pg. 6624
IGE+XAO BV—See Schneider Electric SE; *Int'l*, pg. 6623
IGE XAO CHINA, INC.—See Schneider Electric SE; *Int'l*, pg. 6624
IGE+XAO ESPANA—See Schneider Electric SE; *Int'l*, pg. 6623
IGE XAO GROUP INC.—See Schneider Electric SE; *Int'l*, pg. 6624
IGE XAO, INC.—See Schneider Electric SE; *Int'l*, pg. 6624
IGE XAO, INC.—See Schneider Electric SE; *Int'l*, pg. 6624
IGE+XAO, INC.—See Schneider Electric SE; *Int'l*, pg. 6624
IGE XAO, INC.—See Schneider Electric SE; *Int'l*, pg. 6624
IGE XAO, INC.—See Schneider Electric SE; *Int'l*, pg. 6624
IGE XAO, INC.—See Schneider Electric SE; *Int'l*, pg. 6624
IGE XAO, INC.—See Schneider Electric SE; *Int'l*, pg. 6624
IGE XAO, INC.—See Schneider Electric SE; *Int'l*, pg. 6624
IGE+XAO LILLE—See Schneider Electric SE; *Int'l*, pg. 6623
IGE+XAO LTD—See Schneider Electric SE; *Int'l*, pg. 6623
IGE+XAO MADAGASCAR SARL—See Schneider Electric SE; *Int'l*, pg. 6623
IGE+XAO MARSEILLE—See Schneider Electric SE; *Int'l*, pg. 6623
IGE+XAO NANTES—See Schneider Electric SE; *Int'l*, pg. 6624
IGE-XAO NANTES—See Schneider Electric SE; *Int'l*, pg. 6624
IGE XAO NORTH AMERICA, INC.—See Schneider Electric SE; *Int'l*, pg. 6624

IGE XAO NORTH AMERICA, INC.—See Schneider Electric SE; *Int'l*, pg. 6624
IGE+XAO POLSKA SP. Z O.O.—See Schneider Electric SE; *Int'l*, pg. 6624
IGE+XAO SA—See Schneider Electric SE; *Int'l*, pg. 6623
IGE+XAO SOFTWARE VERTRIEBS GMBH—See Schneider Electric SE; *Int'l*, pg. 6624
IGE-XAO SRL—See Schneider Electric SE; *Int'l*, pg. 6624
IGE+XAO SWITZERLAND GMBH—See Schneider Electric SE; *Int'l*, pg. 6624
IGG ASELSAN INTEGRATED SYSTEMS LLC—See International Golden Group PJSC; *Int'l*, pg. 3749
IGGESUND PAPERBOARD AB—See Holmen AB; *Int'l*, pg. 3453
IGGESUND PAPERBOARD ASIA PTE LTD—See Holmen AB; *Int'l*, pg. 3453
IGGESUND PAPERBOARD EUROPE B.V.—See Holmen AB; *Int'l*, pg. 3453
IGGESUND PAPERBOARD INC.—See Holmen AB; *Int'l*, pg. 3453
IGGESUND PAPER & BOARD SERVICE B.V.—See Holmen AB; *Int'l*, pg. 3453
IGGESUND PAPER BOARD—See Holmen AB; *Int'l*, pg. 3453
IGGESUND PAPERBOARD (WORKINGTON) LTD.—See Holmen AB; *Int'l*, pg. 3453
IGGESUND PAPER LTD—See Holmen AB; *Int'l*, pg. 3453
IGGESUNDS BRUK—See Holmen AB; *Int'l*, pg. 3453
IGG INC.; *Int'l*, pg. 3602
IG GROUP HOLDINGS PLC; *Int'l*, pg. 3601
IGH MOSTAR D.O.O.—See INSTITUT IGH d.d.; *Int'l*, pg. 3723
IGI GAMSTAR INSURANCE COMPANY—See Industrial & General Insurance Plc; *Int'l*, pg. 3670
IGI HOLDINGS LIMITED; *Int'l*, pg. 3602
IGI LIFE ASSURANCE COMPANY LTD—See Industrial & General Insurance Plc; *Int'l*, pg. 3670
IGI LIFE INSURANCE LIMITED—See IGI Holdings Limited; *Int'l*, pg. 3602
IG IMMOBILIEN INVEST GMBH—See Oesterreichische Nationalbank; *Int'l*, pg. 5529
IG INDEX PLC—See IG Group Holdings plc; *Int'l*, pg. 3601
IG INNOVATIONS LIMITED—See Abbott Laboratories; *U.S. Public*, pg. 19
IGI PENSION FUND MANAGERS LIMITED—See Industrial & General Insurance Plc; *Int'l*, pg. 3671
IGI PRUDENTIAL INSURANCE LIMITED; *Int'l*, pg. 3602
IGIS NEPTUNE BARCELONA HOLDCO SOCIMI, S.A.; *Int'l*, pg. 3602
IGIS RESIDENCE REIT CO., LTD.; *Int'l*, pg. 3602
IGIS VALUE PLUS REIT CO., LTD.; *Int'l*, pg. 3602
I.G.I. UNDERWRITING AGENCY, INC.—See Stone Point Capital LLC; *U.S. Private*, pg. 3821
IG KOGYO CO., LTD.—See Sumitomo Corporation; *Int'l*, pg. 7268
IGL CHEM INTERNATIONAL PTE LTD.—See India Glycols Limited; *Int'l*, pg. 3651
IGL CHEM INTERNATIONAL USA LLC—See India Glycols Limited; *Int'l*, pg. 3651
IG LIMITED—See IG Group Holdings plc; *Int'l*, pg. 3601
IGLO AUSTRIA GMBH—See Nomad Foods Limited; *Int'l*, pg. 5408
IGLO BELGIUM S.A—See Nomad Foods Limited; *Int'l*, pg. 5408
IGLO GMBH—See Nomad Foods Limited; *Int'l*, pg. 5408
IGLO (M) SDN. BHD.—See Haisan Resources Berhad; *Int'l*, pg. 3217
IGLO NEDERLAND B.V.—See Nomad Foods Limited; *Int'l*, pg. 5408
IGLO NETHERLANDS B.V.—See Nomad Foods Limited; *Int'l*, pg. 5408
IGLOO CORPORATION; *Int'l*, pg. 3602
IGLOO PRODUCTS CORPORATION—See Dometic Group AB; *Int'l*, pg. 2160
IGLOO SUPPLY CHAIN PHILIPPINES, INC.—See YCH Group Pte. Ltd.; *Int'l*, pg. 8574
IGLO (SHANGHAI) CO., LTD.—See Haisan Resources Berhad; *Int'l*, pg. 3217
IGL (PTY) LIMITED—See Linde plc; *Int'l*, pg. 4505
IGLUE; *Int'l*, pg. 3602
IGMA D.O.O.—See Nexe Grupa d.d.; *Int'l*, pg. 5243
IGMAN D.D. KONJIC; *Int'l*, pg. 3602
IGM BIOSCIENCES, INC.; *U.S. Public*, pg. 1095
IGM CREATIVE GROUP; *U.S. Private*, pg. 2039
IGM DRINA AD; *Int'l*, pg. 3602
IG-MEX, S. DE R.L. DE C.V.—See Regal Rexnord Corporation; *U.S. Public*, pg. 1773
IGM FINANCIAL INC.—See Power Corporation of Canada; *Int'l*, pg. 5944
IGM RESINS B.V.—See Astorg Partners S.A.S.; *Int'l*, pg. 656
IGM RESINS USA INC.—See Astorg Partners S.A.S.; *Int'l*, pg. 656
IGM STRAZILOVO D.O.O.—See Nexe Grupa d.d.; *Int'l*, pg. 5243
IGN ENTERTAINMENT, INC.—See Ziff Davis, Inc.; *U.S. Public*, pg. 2404
IGNEO INFRASTRUCTURE PARTNERS—See Mitsubishi UFJ Financial Group, Inc.; *Int'l*, pg. 4971

IGN INGENIEURGESELLSCHAFT NORD MBH & CO. KG—See TUV NORD AG; *Int'l*, pg. 7980
IGNIS ASSET MANAGEMENT LIMITED—See Phoenix Group Holdings PLC; *Int'l*, pg. 5851
IGNIS IMAGEWORKS CORP.—See Silicon Studio Corp.; *Int'l*, pg. 6920
IGNIS LTD; *Int'l*, pg. 3602
IGNITE ACQUISITION, INC.—See PepsiCo, Inc.; *U.S. Public*, pg. 1669
IGNITED; *U.S. Private*, pg. 2039
IGNITE ENERGY LTD.—See Inspired PLC; *Int'l*, pg. 3720
IGNITE LIMITED; *Int'l*, pg. 3602
IGNITE MEDIA SOLUTIONS LLC; *U.S. Private*, pg. 2039
IGNITE RESTAURANT GROUP, INC.—See J.H. Whitney & Co., LLC; *U.S. Private*, pg. 2166
IGNITE RESTAURANTS-NEW JERSEY, INC.—See J.H. Whitney & Co., LLC; *U.S. Private*, pg. 2166
IGNITE RMSA RETAIL SOLUTIONS, LLC—See ESW Capital, LLC; *U.S. Private*, pg. 1430
IGNITE SCALEARC SOLUTIONS, INC.—See ESW Capital, LLC; *U.S. Private*, pg. 1430
IGNITE SOCIAL MEDIA LLC; *U.S. Private*, pg. 2039
IGNITE TECHNOLOGIES, INC.—See ESW Capital, LLC; *U.S. Private*, pg. 1430
IGNITE TRAVEL GROUP—See Flight Centre Travel Group Limited; *Int'l*, pg. 2706
IGNITE USA, LLC—See Newell Brands Inc.; *U.S. Public*, pg. 1514
IGNITION BRANDING; *U.S. Private*, pg. 2039
IGNITIONONE, INC. - AKRON—See IgnitionOne, Inc.; *U.S. Private*, pg. 2039
IGNITIONONE, INC.; *U.S. Private*, pg. 2039
IGNITION PARTNERS LLC; *U.S. Private*, pg. 2039
IGNITION TECHNOLOGY GROUP LIMITED—See Permira Advisers LLP; *Int'l*, pg. 5804
IGNITION TECHNOLOGY LTD.—See Permira Advisers LLP; *Int'l*, pg. 5804
IGNYTA, INC.—See Roche Holding AG; *Int'l*, pg. 6373
IGO, INC.—See Steel Partners Holdings L.P.; *U.S. Public*, pg. 1943
IGO LIMITED; *Int'l*, pg. 3603
IGORIA TRADE SA; *Int'l*, pg. 3603
IGO & SHOGI CHANNEL INC.—See Tohokushinsha Film Corporation; *Int'l*, pg. 7777
IGP ADVANTAG AG; *Int'l*, pg. 3603
IGPDECAUX SPA—See JCDecaux S.A.; *Int'l*, pg. 3920
IG PETROCHEMICALS LTD.; *Int'l*, pg. 3601
IGP INDUSTRIES, LLC; *U.S. Private*, pg. 2039
IGPI (SHANGHAI) LIMITED—See Industrial Growth Platform, Inc.; *Int'l*, pg. 3672
IG PORT, INC.; *Int'l*, pg. 3601
I GRANDI VIAGGI S.P.A.; *Int'l*, pg. 3561
IGS CAPITAL GROUP LTD.; *Int'l*, pg. 3603
IG SECURITIES LIMITED—See IG Group Holdings plc; *Int'l*, pg. 3601
IGS EHF.—See Icelandair Group hf.; *Int'l*, pg. 3579
IGS NETZE GMBH—See MVV Energie AG; *Int'l*, pg. 5108
IGS STORE FIXTURES INC.; *U.S. Private*, pg. 2064
I.G.T. - ARGENTINA S.A.—See International Game Technology PLC; *Int'l*, pg. 3749
IGT ASIA - MACAU, S.A.—See International Game Technology PLC; *Int'l*, pg. 3749
IGT ASIA PTE. LTD.—See International Game Technology PLC; *Int'l*, pg. 3749
I.G.T. (AUSTRALIA) PTY LIMITED—See International Game Technology PLC; *Int'l*, pg. 3749
IGT-CANADA INC.—See International Game Technology PLC; *Int'l*, pg. 3749
IGT-CHINA, INC.—See International Game Technology PLC; *Int'l*, pg. 3749
IGT DO BRASIL LTDA.—See International Game Technology PLC; *Int'l*, pg. 3749
IGT-EUROPE B.V.—See International Game Technology PLC; *Int'l*, pg. 3749
IGT GERMANY GAMING GMBH—See International Game Technology PLC; *Int'l*, pg. 3749
IGT GLOBAL SOLUTIONS CORPORATION—See International Game Technology PLC; *Int'l*, pg. 3749
IGT INDIANA, LLC—See International Game Technology PLC; *Int'l*, pg. 3749
IGT INTERACTIVE, INC.—See International Game Technology PLC; *Int'l*, pg. 3749
IGT INTERGESTIONS TRUST REG.—See VP Bank AG; *Int'l*, pg. 8311
IGT-MEXICANA DE JUEGOS, S. DE R.L. DE C.V.—See International Game Technology PLC; *Int'l*, pg. 3749
IGT—See International Game Technology PLC; *Int'l*, pg. 3749
IGT TECHNOLOGY DEVELOPMENT (BEIJING) CO. LTD.—See International Game Technology PLC; *Int'l*, pg. 3749
IGT U.K. LIMITED—See International Game Technology PLC; *Int'l*, pg. 3749
IGUANAMED LLC; *U.S. Private*, pg. 2040
IGUA SANEAMENTO SA; *Int'l*, pg. 3603
IGUATEMI EMPRESA DE SHOPPING CENTERS S.A.—See Iguatemi S.A.; *Int'l*, pg. 3603
IGUATEMI S.A.; *Int'l*, pg. 3603

IGUATEMI S.A.
CORPORATE AFFILIATIONS
Company Index

IGUAZU CORPORATION—See JBCC Holdings Inc.; *Int'l*, pg. 3918
IG US HOLDINGS INC.—See IG Group Holdings plc; *Int'l*, pg. 3601
IGUZZINI ILLUMINAZIONE SCHWEIZ AG—See Fagerhult Group AB; *Int'l*, pg. 2602
IGUZZINI ILLUMINAZIONE UK LTD.—See Fagerhult Group AB; *Int'l*, pg. 2602
IGUZZINI LIGHTING USA, LTD.—See Fagerhult Group AB; *Int'l*, pg. 2602
IGUZZINI LIGHTING WLL—See Fagerhult Group AB; *Int'l*, pg. 2602
IGUZZINI MIDDLE EAST FZE—See Fagerhult Group AB; *Int'l*, pg. 2602
IGUZZINI S.E.A. PTE. LTD.—See Fagerhult Group AB; *Int'l*, pg. 2602
IG WINDOWS CO., LTD.—See Iida Group Holdings Co., Ltd.; *Int'l*, pg. 3607
IGXGLOBAL, INC; *U.S. Private*, pg. 2040
IGXGLOBAL UK, LIMITED—See ePlus Inc.; *U.S. Public*, pg. 784
IGY MALAGA MARINA—See MarineMax, Inc.; *U.S. Public*, pg. 1366
IHAG HOLDING AG; *Int'l*, pg. 3603
IHA HEALTH SERVICES CORPORATION; *U.S. Private*, pg. 2040
IHARABRAS S.A. INDUSTRIAS QUIMICAS—See Kumiai Chemical Industry Co., Ltd.; *Int'l*, pg. 4330
IHARA NIKKEI CHEMICAL INDUSTRY CO., LTD.—See Kumiai Chemical Industry Co., Ltd.; *Int'l*, pg. 4330
IHARA SCIENCE CORPORATION - GIFU PLANT—See IHARA SCIENCE CORPORATION; *Int'l*, pg. 3603
IHARA SCIENCE CORPORATION - SHIZUOKA PLANT—See IHARA SCIENCE CORPORATION; *Int'l*, pg. 3603
IHARA SCIENCE CORPORATION; *Int'l*, pg. 3603
IHARA SHIKI CO., LTD.—See Rengo Co., Ltd.; *Int'l*, pg. 6280
IHATOV TOUHOKU INC.—See Pasona Group Inc.; *Int'l*, pg. 5753
IHB ELECTRIC AD—See Industrial Holding Bulgaria AD; *Int'l*, pg. 3672
IHB METAL CASTINGS EAD—See Industrial Holding Bulgaria AD; *Int'l*, pg. 3672
IHB SHIPDESIGN AD—See Industrial Holding Bulgaria AD; *Int'l*, pg. 3672
IHB SHIPPING CO EAD—See Industrial Holding Bulgaria AD; *Int'l*, pg. 3672
IHC ADMINISTRATIVE SERVICES, INC.—See Geneve Holdings Corp.; *U.S. Private*, pg. 1670
I.H. CAFFEY DISTRIBUTING CO.; *U.S. Private*, pg. 2027
IHC BUCKHEAD LLC—See InterContinental Hotels Group PLC; *Int'l*, pg. 3738
IHC FINANCIAL GROUP, INC.—See Geneve Holdings Corp.; *U.S. Private*, pg. 1670
IHC GROUP, INC.; *U.S. Private*, pg. 2040
IHC HOPKINS (HOLDINGS) CORP.—See InterContinental Hotels Group PLC; *Int'l*, pg. 3738
IHC HYDROHAMMER BV—See IHC Merwede Holding B.V.; *Int'l*, pg. 3603
IHC LONDON (HOLDINGS) LTD.—See InterContinental Hotels Group PLC; *Int'l*, pg. 3737
IHC MERWEDE HOLDING B.V.; *Int'l*, pg. 3603
IHC M-H (HOLDINGS) CORP.—See InterContinental Hotels Group PLC; *Int'l*, pg. 3738
IHC SPECIALTY BENEFITS, INC.—See JAB Holding Company S.a.r.l.; *Int'l*, pg. 3861
I.H.C. (THAILAND) LTD—See InterContinental Hotels Group PLC; *Int'l*, pg. 3737
IHC UNITED STATES (HOLDINGS) CORP.—See InterContinental Hotels Group PLC; *Int'l*, pg. 3738
IHDATHIAT CO-ORDINATES; *Int'l*, pg. 3603
IHD INDUSTRIES PVT. LTD.—See Aisan Industry Co., Ltd.; *Int'l*, pg. 251
IHEALTHCARE, INC.; *U.S. Private*, pg. 2040
I-HEALTH, INC.—See Koninklijke DSM N.V.; *Int'l*, pg. 4265
IHEARTCOMMUNICATIONS, INC.—See iHeartMedia, Inc.; *U.S. Public*, pg. 1096
IHEARTMEDIA + ENTERTAINMENT, INC. - ALBANY, GA—See iHeartMedia, Inc.; *U.S. Public*, pg. 1097
IHEARTMEDIA + ENTERTAINMENT, INC. - ALBANY, NY—See iHeartMedia, Inc.; *U.S. Public*, pg. 1097
IHEARTMEDIA + ENTERTAINMENT, INC. - ALBUQUERQUE, NM—See iHeartMedia, Inc.; *U.S. Public*, pg. 1097
IHEARTMEDIA + ENTERTAINMENT, INC. - AMES, IA—See iHeartMedia, Inc.; *U.S. Public*, pg. 1098
IHEARTMEDIA + ENTERTAINMENT, INC. - ANCHORAGE, AK—See iHeartMedia, Inc.; *U.S. Public*, pg. 1097
IHEARTMEDIA + ENTERTAINMENT, INC. - ASHLAND, OH—See iHeartMedia, Inc.; *U.S. Public*, pg. 1097
IHEARTMEDIA + ENTERTAINMENT, INC. - ATLANTA, GA—See iHeartMedia, Inc.; *U.S. Public*, pg. 1097
IHEARTMEDIA + ENTERTAINMENT, INC. - AUGUSTA, GA—See iHeartMedia, Inc.; *U.S. Public*, pg. 1097
IHEARTMEDIA + ENTERTAINMENT, INC. - BALTIMORE, MD—See iHeartMedia, Inc.; *U.S. Public*, pg. 1100
IHEARTMEDIA + ENTERTAINMENT, INC. - BATON ROUGE, LA—See iHeartMedia, Inc.; *U.S. Public*, pg. 1097
IHEARTMEDIA + ENTERTAINMENT, INC. - BEAUMONT, TX—See iHeartMedia, Inc.; *U.S. Public*, pg. 1097
IHEARTMEDIA + ENTERTAINMENT, INC. - BILOXI, MS—See iHeartMedia, Inc.; *U.S. Public*, pg. 1097
IHEARTMEDIA + ENTERTAINMENT, INC. - BINGHAMTON, NY—See iHeartMedia, Inc.; *U.S. Public*, pg. 1097
IHEARTMEDIA + ENTERTAINMENT, INC. - BIRMINGHAM, AL—See iHeartMedia, Inc.; *U.S. Public*, pg. 1097
IHEARTMEDIA + ENTERTAINMENT, INC. - BISMARCK, ND—See iHeartMedia, Inc.; *U.S. Public*, pg. 1097
IHEARTMEDIA + ENTERTAINMENT, INC. - BOSTON, MA—See iHeartMedia, Inc.; *U.S. Public*, pg. 1097
IHEARTMEDIA + ENTERTAINMENT, INC. - CEDAR RAPIDS, IA—See iHeartMedia, Inc.; *U.S. Public*, pg. 1097
IHEARTMEDIA + ENTERTAINMENT, INC. - CHARLESTON, SC—See iHeartMedia, Inc.; *U.S. Public*, pg. 1097
IHEARTMEDIA + ENTERTAINMENT, INC. - CHICAGO, IL—See iHeartMedia, Inc.; *U.S. Public*, pg. 1097
IHEARTMEDIA + ENTERTAINMENT, INC. - CHILLICOTHE, OH—See iHeartMedia, Inc.; *U.S. Public*, pg. 1097
IHEARTMEDIA + ENTERTAINMENT, INC. - CINCINNATI, OH—See iHeartMedia, Inc.; *U.S. Public*, pg. 1097
IHEARTMEDIA + ENTERTAINMENT, INC. - CLEVELAND, OH—See iHeartMedia, Inc.; *U.S. Public*, pg. 1097
IHEARTMEDIA + ENTERTAINMENT, INC. - COLUMBIA, SC—See iHeartMedia, Inc.; *U.S. Public*, pg. 1097
IHEARTMEDIA + ENTERTAINMENT, INC. - COLUMBUS, GA—See iHeartMedia, Inc.; *U.S. Public*, pg. 1097
IHEARTMEDIA + ENTERTAINMENT, INC. - COLUMBUS, OH—See iHeartMedia, Inc.; *U.S. Public*, pg. 1097
IHEARTMEDIA + ENTERTAINMENT, INC. - CORPUS CHRISTI, TX—See iHeartMedia, Inc.; *U.S. Public*, pg. 1098
IHEARTMEDIA + ENTERTAINMENT, INC. - DALLAS, TX—See iHeartMedia, Inc.; *U.S. Public*, pg. 1098
IHEARTMEDIA + ENTERTAINMENT, INC. - DAYTON, OH—See iHeartMedia, Inc.; *U.S. Public*, pg. 1098
IHEARTMEDIA + ENTERTAINMENT, INC. - DENVER, CO—See iHeartMedia, Inc.; *U.S. Public*, pg. 1098
IHEARTMEDIA + ENTERTAINMENT, INC. - DES MOINES, IA—See iHeartMedia, Inc.; *U.S. Public*, pg. 1098
IHEARTMEDIA + ENTERTAINMENT, INC. - DETROIT, MI—See iHeartMedia, Inc.; *U.S. Public*, pg. 1098
IHEARTMEDIA + ENTERTAINMENT, INC. - DICKINSON, ND—See iHeartMedia, Inc.; *U.S. Public*, pg. 1098
IHEARTMEDIA + ENTERTAINMENT, INC. - EL PASO, TX—See iHeartMedia, Inc.; *U.S. Public*, pg. 1098
IHEARTMEDIA + ENTERTAINMENT, INC. - FAIRBANKS, AK—See iHeartMedia, Inc.; *U.S. Public*, pg. 1098
IHEARTMEDIA + ENTERTAINMENT, INC. - FARMINGTON, NM—See iHeartMedia, Inc.; *U.S. Public*, pg. 1098
IHEARTMEDIA + ENTERTAINMENT, INC. - FAYETTEVILLE, AR—See iHeartMedia, Inc.; *U.S. Public*, pg. 1098
IHEARTMEDIA + ENTERTAINMENT, INC. - FLORIDA KEYS (KEY WEST), FL—See iHeartMedia, Inc.; *U.S. Public*, pg. 1098
IHEARTMEDIA + ENTERTAINMENT, INC. - FLORIDA KEYS (TAVERNIER), FL—See iHeartMedia, Inc.; *U.S. Public*, pg. 1098
IHEARTMEDIA + ENTERTAINMENT, INC. - FORT MYERS, FL—See iHeartMedia, Inc.; *U.S. Public*, pg. 1098
IHEARTMEDIA + ENTERTAINMENT, INC. - FORT SMITH, AR—See iHeartMedia, Inc.; *U.S. Public*, pg. 1098
IHEARTMEDIA + ENTERTAINMENT, INC. - GADSDEN, AL—See iHeartMedia, Inc.; *U.S. Public*, pg. 1098
IHEARTMEDIA + ENTERTAINMENT, INC. - GRAND FORKS, ND—See iHeartMedia, Inc.; *U.S. Public*, pg. 1098
IHEARTMEDIA + ENTERTAINMENT, INC. - GRAND RAPIDS, MI—See iHeartMedia, Inc.; *U.S. Public*, pg. 1098
IHEARTMEDIA + ENTERTAINMENT, INC. - GREENVILLE, SC—See iHeartMedia, Inc.; *U.S. Public*, pg. 1098
IHEARTMEDIA + ENTERTAINMENT, INC. - HARRISBURG, PA—See iHeartMedia, Inc.; *U.S. Public*, pg. 1098
IHEARTMEDIA + ENTERTAINMENT, INC. - HARTFORD, CT—See iHeartMedia, Inc.; *U.S. Public*, pg. 1098
IHEARTMEDIA + ENTERTAINMENT, INC. - HONOLULU, HI—See iHeartMedia, Inc.; *U.S. Public*, pg. 1098
IHEARTMEDIA + ENTERTAINMENT, INC. - HOUSTON, TX—See iHeartMedia, Inc.; *U.S. Public*, pg. 1098
IHEARTMEDIA + ENTERTAINMENT, INC. - HUNTSVILLE, AL—See iHeartMedia, Inc.; *U.S. Public*, pg. 1098
IHEARTMEDIA + ENTERTAINMENT, INC. - INDIANAPOLIS, IN—See iHeartMedia, Inc.; *U.S. Public*, pg. 1098
IHEARTMEDIA + ENTERTAINMENT, INC. - IOWA CITY, IA—See iHeartMedia, Inc.; *U.S. Public*, pg. 1098
IHEARTMEDIA + ENTERTAINMENT, INC. - JACKSON, MS—See iHeartMedia, Inc.; *U.S. Public*, pg. 1098
IHEARTMEDIA + ENTERTAINMENT, INC. - JACKSONVILLE, FL—See iHeartMedia, Inc.; *U.S. Public*, pg. 1098
IHEARTMEDIA + ENTERTAINMENT, INC. - LAGRANGE-NEWNAN, GA—See iHeartMedia, Inc.; *U.S. Public*, pg. 1097
IHEARTMEDIA + ENTERTAINMENT, INC. - LANCASTER/ANTELOPE, CA—See iHeartMedia, Inc.; *U.S. Public*, pg. 1098
IHEARTMEDIA + ENTERTAINMENT, INC. - LANCASTER, PA—See iHeartMedia, Inc.; *U.S. Public*, pg. 1098
IHEARTMEDIA + ENTERTAINMENT, INC. - LAS VEGAS, NV—See iHeartMedia, Inc.; *U.S. Public*, pg. 1098
IHEARTMEDIA + ENTERTAINMENT, INC. - LEXINGTON, KY—See iHeartMedia, Inc.; *U.S. Public*, pg. 1098
IHEARTMEDIA + ENTERTAINMENT, INC. - LIMA, OH—See iHeartMedia, Inc.; *U.S. Public*, pg. 1098
IHEARTMEDIA + ENTERTAINMENT, INC. - LITTLE ROCK, AR—See iHeartMedia, Inc.; *U.S. Public*, pg. 1099
IHEARTMEDIA + ENTERTAINMENT, INC. - LOS ANGELES, CA—See iHeartMedia, Inc.; *U.S. Public*, pg. 1099
IHEARTMEDIA + ENTERTAINMENT, INC. - LOUISVILLE, KY—See iHeartMedia, Inc.; *U.S. Public*, pg. 1099
IHEARTMEDIA + ENTERTAINMENT, INC. - MACON, GA—See iHeartMedia, Inc.; *U.S. Public*, pg. 1099
IHEARTMEDIA + ENTERTAINMENT, INC. - MADISON, WI—See iHeartMedia, Inc.; *U.S. Public*, pg. 1099
IHEARTMEDIA + ENTERTAINMENT, INC. - MANSFIELD, OH—See iHeartMedia, Inc.; *U.S. Public*, pg. 1097
IHEARTMEDIA + ENTERTAINMENT, INC. - MARION, OH—See iHeartMedia, Inc.; *U.S. Public*, pg. 1099
IHEARTMEDIA + ENTERTAINMENT, INC. - MEMPHIS, TN—See iHeartMedia, Inc.; *U.S. Public*, pg. 1099
IHEARTMEDIA + ENTERTAINMENT, INC. - MIAMI/FORT LAUDERDALE, FL—See iHeartMedia, Inc.; *U.S. Public*, pg. 1099
IHEARTMEDIA + ENTERTAINMENT, INC. - MILWAUKEE, WI—See iHeartMedia, Inc.; *U.S. Public*, pg. 1099
IHEARTMEDIA + ENTERTAINMENT, INC. - MINNEAPOLIS, MN—See iHeartMedia, Inc.; *U.S. Public*, pg. 1099
IHEARTMEDIA + ENTERTAINMENT, INC. - MINOT, ND—See iHeartMedia, Inc.; *U.S. Public*, pg. 1099
IHEARTMEDIA + ENTERTAINMENT, INC. - MOBILE, AL—See iHeartMedia, Inc.; *U.S. Public*, pg. 1099
IHEARTMEDIA + ENTERTAINMENT, INC. - MODESTO/STOCKTON, CA—See iHeartMedia, Inc.; *U.S. Public*, pg. 1099
IHEARTMEDIA + ENTERTAINMENT, INC. - MONTEREY, CA—See iHeartMedia, Inc.; *U.S. Public*, pg. 1099
IHEARTMEDIA + ENTERTAINMENT, INC. - MONTGOMERY, AL—See iHeartMedia, Inc.; *U.S. Public*, pg. 1099
IHEARTMEDIA + ENTERTAINMENT, INC. - NASHVILLE, TN—See iHeartMedia, Inc.; *U.S. Public*, pg. 1099
IHEARTMEDIA + ENTERTAINMENT, INC. - NASSAU/SUFFOLK, NY—See iHeartMedia, Inc.; *U.S. Public*, pg. 1099
IHEARTMEDIA + ENTERTAINMENT, INC. - NEW ORLEANS, LA—See iHeartMedia, Inc.; *U.S. Public*, pg. 1099
IHEARTMEDIA + ENTERTAINMENT, INC. - NEW YORK CITY, NY—See iHeartMedia, Inc.; *U.S. Public*, pg. 1099
IHEARTMEDIA + ENTERTAINMENT, INC. - NORFOLK, VA—See iHeartMedia, Inc.; *U.S. Public*, pg. 1099
IHEARTMEDIA + ENTERTAINMENT, INC. - OMAHA, NE—See iHeartMedia, Inc.; *U.S. Public*, pg. 1099
IHEARTMEDIA + ENTERTAINMENT, INC. - ORLANDO, FL—See iHeartMedia, Inc.; *U.S. Public*, pg. 1099
IHEARTMEDIA + ENTERTAINMENT, INC. - PANAMA CITY, FL—See iHeartMedia, Inc.; *U.S. Public*, pg. 1099
IHEARTMEDIA + ENTERTAINMENT, INC. - PARKERSBURG, WV—See iHeartMedia, Inc.; *U.S. Public*, pg. 1099
IHEARTMEDIA + ENTERTAINMENT, INC. - PENSACOLA, FL—See iHeartMedia, Inc.; *U.S. Public*, pg. 1099
IHEARTMEDIA + ENTERTAINMENT, INC. - PHILADELPHIA, PA—See iHeartMedia, Inc.; *U.S. Public*, pg. 1099
IHEARTMEDIA + ENTERTAINMENT, INC. - PHOENIX, AZ—See iHeartMedia, Inc.; *U.S. Public*, pg. 1099
IHEARTMEDIA + ENTERTAINMENT, INC. - PITTSBURGH, PA—See iHeartMedia, Inc.; *U.S. Public*, pg. 1099
IHEARTMEDIA + ENTERTAINMENT, INC. - PORTLAND, OR—See iHeartMedia, Inc.; *U.S. Public*, pg. 1099
IHEARTMEDIA + ENTERTAINMENT, INC. - PORTSMOUTH, NH—See iHeartMedia, Inc.; *U.S. Public*, pg. 1099
IHEARTMEDIA + ENTERTAINMENT, INC. - PUNTA GORDA, FL—See iHeartMedia, Inc.; *U.S. Public*, pg. 1098
IHEARTMEDIA + ENTERTAINMENT, INC. - RALEIGH, NC—See iHeartMedia, Inc.; *U.S. Public*, pg. 1099
IHEARTMEDIA + ENTERTAINMENT, INC. - RICHMOND, VA—See iHeartMedia, Inc.; *U.S. Public*, pg. 1099
IHEARTMEDIA + ENTERTAINMENT, INC. - RIVERSIDE/SAN BERNARDINO, CA—See iHeartMedia, Inc.; *U.S. Public*, pg. 1099
IHEARTMEDIA + ENTERTAINMENT, INC. - ROCHESTER, MN—See iHeartMedia, Inc.; *U.S. Public*, pg. 1099
IHEARTMEDIA + ENTERTAINMENT, INC. - ROCHESTER, NY—See iHeartMedia, Inc.; *U.S. Public*, pg. 1100

COMPANY NAME INDEX

IHEARTMEDIA + ENTERTAINMENT, INC. - SACRAMENTO, CA—See iHeartMedia, Inc.; *U.S. Public*, pg. 1100
IHEARTMEDIA + ENTERTAINMENT, INC. - SAINT LOUIS, MO—See iHeartMedia, Inc.; *U.S. Public*, pg. 1100
IHEARTMEDIA + ENTERTAINMENT, INC. - SALISBURY/OCEAN CITY, MD—See iHeartMedia, Inc.; *U.S. Public*, pg. 1100
IHEARTMEDIA + ENTERTAINMENT, INC. - SALT LAKE CITY, UT—See iHeartMedia, Inc.; *U.S. Public*, pg. 1100
IHEARTMEDIA + ENTERTAINMENT, INC. - SAN ANTONIO, TX—See iHeartMedia, Inc.; *U.S. Public*, pg. 1100
IHEARTMEDIA + ENTERTAINMENT, INC. - SAN DIEGO, CA—See iHeartMedia, Inc.; *U.S. Public*, pg. 1100
IHEARTMEDIA + ENTERTAINMENT, INC. - SAN FRANCISCO, CA—See iHeartMedia, Inc.; *U.S. Public*, pg. 1100
IHEARTMEDIA + ENTERTAINMENT, INC. - SAN JOSE, CA—See iHeartMedia, Inc.; *U.S. Public*, pg. 1100
IHEARTMEDIA + ENTERTAINMENT, INC. - SARASOTA, FL—See iHeartMedia, Inc.; *U.S. Public*, pg. 1100
IHEARTMEDIA + ENTERTAINMENT, INC. - SAVANNAH, GA—See iHeartMedia, Inc.; *U.S. Public*, pg. 1100
IHEARTMEDIA + ENTERTAINMENT, INC. - SEATTLE, WA—See iHeartMedia, Inc.; *U.S. Public*, pg. 1100
IHEARTMEDIA + ENTERTAINMENT, INC.—See iHeartMedia, Inc.; *U.S. Public*, pg. 1096
IHEARTMEDIA + ENTERTAINMENT, INC. - SPOKANE, WA—See iHeartMedia, Inc.; *U.S. Public*, pg. 1100
IHEARTMEDIA + ENTERTAINMENT, INC. - SPRINGFIELD, MA—See iHeartMedia, Inc.; *U.S. Public*, pg. 1100
IHEARTMEDIA + ENTERTAINMENT, INC. - SUSSEX, NJ—See iHeartMedia, Inc.; *U.S. Public*, pg. 1100
IHEARTMEDIA + ENTERTAINMENT, INC. - SYRACUSE, NY—See iHeartMedia, Inc.; *U.S. Public*, pg. 1100
IHEARTMEDIA + ENTERTAINMENT, INC. - TALLAHASSEE, FL—See iHeartMedia, Inc.; *U.S. Public*, pg. 1100
IHEARTMEDIA + ENTERTAINMENT, INC. - TAMPA, FL—See iHeartMedia, Inc.; *U.S. Public*, pg. 1100
IHEARTMEDIA + ENTERTAINMENT, INC. - TOLEDO, OH—See iHeartMedia, Inc.; *U.S. Public*, pg. 1100
IHEARTMEDIA + ENTERTAINMENT, INC. - TUCSON, AZ—See iHeartMedia, Inc.; *U.S. Public*, pg. 1100
IHEARTMEDIA + ENTERTAINMENT, INC. - TULSA CORPORATE OFFICE—See iHeartMedia, Inc.; *U.S. Public*, pg. 1100
IHEARTMEDIA + ENTERTAINMENT, INC. - TULSA, OK—See iHeartMedia, Inc.; *U.S. Public*, pg. 1100
IHEARTMEDIA + ENTERTAINMENT, INC. - TUPELO, MS—See iHeartMedia, Inc.; *U.S. Public*, pg. 1100
IHEARTMEDIA + ENTERTAINMENT, INC. - WACO, TX—See iHeartMedia, Inc.; *U.S. Public*, pg. 1100
IHEARTMEDIA + ENTERTAINMENT, INC. - WASHINGTON, DC—See iHeartMedia, Inc.; *U.S. Public*, pg. 1100
IHEARTMEDIA + ENTERTAINMENT, INC. - WEST PALM BEACH, FL—See iHeartMedia, Inc.; *U.S. Public*, pg. 1100
IHEARTMEDIA + ENTERTAINMENT, INC. - WICHITA, KS—See iHeartMedia, Inc.; *U.S. Public*, pg. 1100
IHEARTMEDIA + ENTERTAINMENT, INC. - WILLIAMSPORT, PA—See iHeartMedia, Inc.; *U.S. Public*, pg. 1100
IHEARTMEDIA + ENTERTAINMENT, INC. - WILMINGTON, DE—See iHeartMedia, Inc.; *U.S. Public*, pg. 1100
IHEARTMEDIA + ENTERTAINMENT, INC. - YOUNGSTOWN, OH—See iHeartMedia, Inc.; *U.S. Public*, pg. 1100
IHEARTMEDIA, INC.; *U.S. Public*, pg. 1095
IHEARTRAVES, LLC; *U.S. Private*, pg. 2040
I&H ENGINEERING CO., LTD.—See IHI Corporation; *Int'l*, pg. 3604
IHG ANA HOTELS HOLDINGS CO., LTD—See InterContinental Hotels Group PLC; *Int'l*, pg. 3737
IHG (AUSTRALASIA) LIMITED — See InterContinental Hotels Group PLC; *Int'l*, pg. 3737
IHG FRANCHISING BRASIL LTDA—See InterContinental Hotels Group PLC; *Int'l*, pg. 3737
IHG FRANCHISING LLC—See InterContinental Hotels Group PLC; *Int'l*, pg. 3738
IHG HOTELS MANAGEMENT (AUSTRALIA) PTY LIMITED—See InterContinental Hotels Group PLC; *Int'l*, pg. 3737
IHG IT SERVICES (INDIA) PRIVATE LIMITED—See InterContinental Hotels Group PLC; *Int'l*, pg. 3737
IHG JAPAN (OSAKA) LLC—See InterContinental Hotels Group PLC; *Int'l*, pg. 3737
IHG (MARSEILLE) SAS—See InterContinental Hotels Group PLC; *Int'l*, pg. 3737
IHG ORCHARD STREET MEMBER, LLC—See InterContinental Hotels Group PLC; *Int'l*, pg. 3738
IHG PS NOMINEES LIMITED—See InterContinental Hotels Group PLC; *Int'l*, pg. 3737
IHG SZALLODA BUDAPEST SZOLGALTATO KFT—See InterContinental Hotels Group PLC; *Int'l*, pg. 3737
IHG (THAILAND) LIMITED—See InterContinental Hotels Group PLC; *Int'l*, pg. 3737
IHH HEALTHCARE BERHAD—See Khazanah Nasional Berhad; *Int'l*, pg. 4152

IHI AEROSPACE CO., LTD.—See IHI Corporation; *Int'l*, pg. 3604
IHI ASIA PACIFIC PTE. LTD.—See IHI Corporation; *Int'l*, pg. 3604
IHI ASIA PACIFIC (THAILAND) CO., LTD.—See IHI Corporation; *Int'l*, pg. 3604
IHI CANADA PROJECTS INC.—See IHI Corporation; *Int'l*, pg. 3604
IHI CHARGING SYSTEMS INTERNATIONAL GMBH—See IHI Corporation; *Int'l*, pg. 3604
IHI CHARGING SYSTEMS INTERNATIONAL S.P.A.—See IHI Corporation; *Int'l*, pg. 3604
IHI CONSTRUCTION MATERIALS CO., LTD.—See IHI Corporation; *Int'l*, pg. 3604
IHI CONSTRUCTION SERVICE CO., LTD.—See IHI Corporation; *Int'l*, pg. 3604
IHI CORPORATION; *Int'l*, pg. 3603
IHI CORPORATION—See Nordex SE; *Int'l*, pg. 5418
IHI DALGAKIRAN MAKINA SANAYI VE TICARET A.S.—See IHI Corporation; *Int'l*, pg. 3604
IHI DO BRASIL REPRESENTACOES LTDA.—See IHI Corporation; *Int'l*, pg. 3604
IHI E&C INTERNATIONAL CORPORATION—See IHI Corporation; *Int'l*, pg. 3604
IHI ENGINEERING AUSTRALIA PTY. LTD.—See IHI Corporation; *Int'l*, pg. 3604
IHI ENVIRONMENTAL INC—See Terracon Consultants, Inc.; *U.S. Private*, pg. 3971
IHI EUROPE LTD.—See IHI Corporation; *Int'l*, pg. 3604
IHI FINANCE SUPPORT CORPORATION—See Tokyo Century Corporation; *Int'l*, pg. 7789
IHI FUSO ENGINEERING CO., LTD.—See IHI Corporation; *Int'l*, pg. 3605
IHI (HK) LTD.—See IHI Corporation; *Int'l*, pg. 3604
IHI-ICR, LLC.—See IHI Corporation; *Int'l*, pg. 3605
IHI INC.—See IHI Corporation; *Int'l*, pg. 3604
IHI INFRASTRUCTURE ASIA CO., LTD.—See IHI Corporation; *Int'l*, pg. 3604
IHI INFRASTRUCTURE SYSTEMS CO., LTD.—See IHI Corporation; *Int'l*, pg. 3605
IHI INSPECTION & INSTRUMENTATION CO., LTD.—See IHI Corporation; *Int'l*, pg. 3604
IHI JET SERVICE CO., LTD.—See IHI Corporation; *Int'l*, pg. 3605
IHI LOGISTICS & MACHINERY CORPORATION—See IHI Corporation; *Int'l*, pg. 3605
IHI LOGISTICS SYSTEM TECHNOLOGY SHANGHAI CO., LTD.—See IHI Corporation; *Int'l*, pg. 3604
IHI MASTER METAL CO., LTD.—See IHI Corporation; *Int'l*, pg. 3605
IHIMER S.P.A.—See IMER International S.p.A.; *Int'l*, pg. 3623
IHI METALTECH CO., LTD.—See IHI Corporation; *Int'l*, pg. 3604
IHI OXYFUEL AUSTRALIA PTY.LTD.—See IHI Corporation; *Int'l*, pg. 3604
IHI PACKAGED BOILER CO., LTD.—See IHI Corporation; *Int'l*, pg. 3605
IHI PHILIPPINES, INC.—See IHI Corporation; *Int'l*, pg. 3604
IHI PLANT SERVICES CORPORATION—See IHI Corporation; *Int'l*, pg. 3605
IHI POWER GENERATION CORP.—See IHI Corporation; *Int'l*, pg. 3605
IHI POWER SYSTEM MALAYSIA SDN. BHD.—See IHI Corporation; *Int'l*, pg. 3604
IHI POWER SYSTEMS CO., LTD.—See IHI Corporation; *Int'l*, pg. 3605
IHI POWER SYSTEM (THAILAND) CO., LTD.—See IHI Corporation; *Int'l*, pg. 3605
IHI PRESS TECHNOLOGY AMERICA, INC.—See IHI Corporation; *Int'l*, pg. 3604
IHI SCUBE CO., LTD.—See IHI Corporation; *Int'l*, pg. 3605
IHI (SHANGHAI) MANAGEMENT CO., LTD.—See IHI Corporation; *Int'l*, pg. 3604
IHI SOLID BIOMASS MALAYSIA SDN. BHD.—See IHI Corporation; *Int'l*, pg. 3605
IHI SOUTHWEST TECHNOLOGIES INC.—See IHI Corporation; *Int'l*, pg. 3605
IHI-SULLAIR COMPRESSION TECHNOLOGY (SUZHOU) CO., LTD.—See IHI Corporation; *Int'l*, pg. 3605
IHI SYSTEM TECHNOLOGY TAIWAN CO., LTD.—See IHI Corporation; *Int'l*, pg. 3605
IHI TAIWAN CORPORATION—See IHI Corporation; *Int'l*, pg. 3605
IHI TERRASUN SOLUTIONS INC.—See IHI Corporation; *Int'l*, pg. 3605
IHI TRANSPORT MACHINERY CO., LTD.—See IHI Corporation; *Int'l*, pg. 3604
IHI TURBO AMERICA CO.—See IHI Corporation; *Int'l*, pg. 3604
IHI TURBO KOREA CO., LTD.—See IHI Corporation; *Int'l*, pg. 3605
IHI TURBO (THAILAND) CO., LTD.—See IHI Corporation; *Int'l*, pg. 3605
IHI VTN GMBH—See IHI Corporation; *Int'l*, pg. 3605
IHLAS EV ALETLERI IMALAT SANAYI VE TICARET A.S.; *Int'l*, pg. 3606

IHLAS GAYRIMENKUL PROJE GELISTIRME VE TICARET A.S.—See Ihlas Holding A.S.; *Int'l*, pg. 3606
IHLAS GAZETECILIK A.S.—See Ihlas Holding A.S.; *Int'l*, pg. 3606
IHLAS GIRISIM SERMAYESI YATIRIM ORTAKLIGI A.S.—See Ihlas Holding A.S.; *Int'l*, pg. 3606
IHLAS HABER AJANSI A.S—See Ihlas Holding A.S.; *Int'l*, pg. 3606
IHLAS HOLDING A.S.; *Int'l*, pg. 3606
IHLAS MOTOR A.S.—See Ihlas Holding A.S.; *Int'l*, pg. 3606
IHLAS NET A.S.—See Ihlas Holding A.S.; *Int'l*, pg. 3606
IHLAS PAZARLAMA A.S—See Ihlas Holding A.S.; *Int'l*, pg. 3606
IHLAS YAPI TURIZM VE SAGLIK A.S.—See Ihlas Holding A.S.; *Int'l*, pg. 3606
IHLAS YAYIN HOLDING A.S.; *Int'l*, pg. 3606
IHLE ANVELOPE SRL—See Compagnie Generale des Etablissements Michelin SCA; *Int'l*, pg. 1742
IHLE CZECH, S.R.O.—See Compagnie Generale des Etablissements Michelin SCA; *Int'l*, pg. 1742
IHLE MAGYARORSZAG KFT.—See Compagnie Generale des Etablissements Michelin SCA; *Int'l*, pg. 1742
IHLE PNEVMATIKE, D.O.O.—See Compagnie Generale des Etablissements Michelin SCA; *Int'l*, pg. 1743
IHLE SLOVAKIA S.R.O.—See Compagnie Generale des Etablissements Michelin SCA; *Int'l*, pg. 1742
IHLE TIRES GMBH—See Compagnie Generale des Etablissements Michelin SCA; *Int'l*, pg. 1742
IHL HOME INSURANCE AGENCY, LLC—See Century Communities, Inc.; *U.S. Public*, pg. 475
IHLO SALES & IMPORT CO.; *U.S. Private*, pg. 2040
IH MEAT SOLUTIONS CO.,LTD.—See Itoham Yonekyu Holdings Inc.; *Int'l*, pg. 3842
IH MISSISSIPPI VALLEY CREDIT UNION; *U.S. Private*, pg. 2040
IHM SERVICES COMPANY—See Persivia, Inc.; *U.S. Private*, pg. 3155
IHO-AGRO INTERNATIONAL, INC.; *Int'l*, pg. 3607
IHOMEFINDER, INC.—See Community Investors, Inc.; *U.S. Public*, pg. 995
I HOMES PROPERTIES SDN. BHD.—See Ideal Capital Berhad; *Int'l*, pg. 3589
IHOP FRANCHISOR, LLC—See Dine Brands Global, Inc.; *U.S. Public*, pg. 667
IHOP PROPERTY LEASING, LLC—See Dine Brands Global, Inc.; *U.S. Public*, pg. 667
IHOP RESTAURANTS, LLC—See Dine Brands Global, Inc.; *U.S. Public*, pg. 667
IHP CAPITAL PARTNERS INC.; *U.S. Private*, pg. 2040
IHP INDUSTRIAL INC.; *U.S. Private*, pg. 2040
IHQ, INC.; *Int'l*, pg. 3607
IHRIE SUPPLY CO. INC.; *U.S. Private*, pg. 2040
IHS ACQUISITION XXX, INC.—See Cencora, Inc.; *U.S. Public*, pg. 467
I.H. SCHLEZINGER, INC.—See Cohen Brothers, Inc.; *U.S. Private*, pg. 962
IHS DISTRIBUTING CO. INC.; *U.S. Private*, pg. 2040
IHSEDU AGROCHEM PVT. LTD.—See Jayant Agro Organics Ltd; *Int'l*, pg. 3915
IHSE GMBH ASIA PACIFIC PTE. LTD.—See Brockhaus Private Equity GmbH; *Int'l*, pg. 1172
IHSE GMBH—See Brockhaus Private Equity GmbH; *Int'l*, pg. 1172
IH SERVICES, INC.—See GDI Integrated Facility Services Inc.; *Int'l*, pg. 2896
IHSE USA LLC—See Brockhaus Private Equity GmbH; *Int'l*, pg. 1172
IHS GMBH—See Sabre Corporation; *U.S. Public*, pg. 1833
IHS HOLDING LIMITED; *Int'l*, pg. 3607
IHS INC.—See S&P Global Inc.; *U.S. Public*, pg. 1830
IHS MARKIT LTD.—See S&P Global Inc.; *U.S. Public*, pg. 1830
IHSM B.V.—See Merck & Co., Inc.; *U.S. Public*, pg. 1416
IHS NIGERIA PLC; *Int'l*, pg. 3607
IHT HEALTH PRODUCTS, INC.—See Integrated Biopharma, Inc.; *U.S. Public*, pg. 1136
IHUD DAVID BERMAN INSURANCE AGENCY LTD.—See Shlomo Eliahu Holdings Ltd.; *Int'l*, pg. 6857
IHUD PELTOURS DIAMONDS INSURANCE AGENCY (2002) LTD.—See Shlomo Eliahu Holdings Ltd.; *Int'l*, pg. 6857
IHUMAN INC.; *Int'l*, pg. 3607
I-HUMAN PATIENTS, INC.—See Graham Holdings Company; *U.S. Public*, pg. 956
IHUNT TECHNOLOGY IMPORT-EXPORT S.A.; *Int'l*, pg. 3607
I-HWA INDUSTRIAL CO., LTD.; *Int'l*, pg. 3563
I-HWA INDUSTRIAL CO., LTD. - TEXTILE DIVISION—See I-Hwa Industrial Co., Ltd.; *Int'l*, pg. 3563
IHY IZMIR HAVAYOLLARI A.S.—See ESAS Holding A.S.; *Int'l*, pg. 2501
IIAA AGENCY ADMINISTRATIVE SERVICES, INC.—See Independent Insurance Agents & Brokers of America, Inc.; *U.S. Private*, pg. 2059
IIAA MEMBERSHIP SERVICES, INC.—See Independent Insurance Agents & Brokers of America, Inc.; *U.S. Private*, pg. 2059
IIDA GROUP HOLDINGS CO., LTD.; *Int'l*, pg. 3607

IIDA GROUP HOLDINGS CO., LTD.

CORPORATE AFFILIATIONS

IIDA HOME MAX CO., LTD.—See Iida Group Holdings Co., Ltd.; *Int'l*, pg. 3607
IIDA SANGYO CO., LTD.—See Iida Group Holdings Co., Ltd.; *Int'l*, pg. 3607
IIDGR (UK) LIMITED—See Anglo American PLC; *Int'l*, pg. 462
IID INC.; *Int'l*, pg. 3607
IIFCL ASSET MANAGEMENT COMPANY LTD.—See India Infrastructure Finance Company Limited; *Int'l*, pg. 3652
IIFCL PROJECTS LTD.—See India Infrastructure Finance Company Limited; *Int'l*, pg. 3652
IIFL (ASIA) PTE LTD.—See International Conveyors Limited; *Int'l*, pg. 3747
IIFL ASSET MANAGEMENT LTD.—See 360 ONE WAM Limited; *Int'l*, pg. 6
IIFL ASSET MANAGEMENT (MAURITIUS) LTD.—See 360 ONE WAM Limited; *Int'l*, pg. 6
IIFL CAPITAL (CANADA) LIMITED—See 360 ONE WAM Limited; *Int'l*, pg. 6
IIFL CAPITAL PTE. LTD.—See 360 ONE WAM Limited; *Int'l*, pg. 6
IIFL FINANCE LTD.—See International Conveyors Limited; *Int'l*, pg. 3747
IIFL HOME FINANCE LIMITED—See International Conveyors Limited; *Int'l*, pg. 3747
IIFL PRIVATE WEALTH MANAGEMENT (DUBAI) LTD.—See 360 ONE WAM Limited; *Int'l*, pg. 6
IIFL SAMASTA FINANCE LIMITED—See International Conveyors Limited; *Int'l*, pg. 3747
IIFL SECURITIES PTE LTD.—See International Conveyors Limited; *Int'l*, pg. 3747
I&I GROUP PUBLIC COMPANY LIMITED; *Int'l*, pg. 3562
III EXPLORATION COMPANY—See Intermountain Industries, Inc.; *U.S. Private*, pg. 2113
III SERVICIOS, S.A. DE C.V.—See Petroleos Mexicanos; *Int'l*, pg. 5828
IIJ AMERICA, INC.—See Internet Initiative Japan Inc.; *Int'l*, pg. 3753
IIJ DEUTSCHLAND GMBH—See Internet Initiative Japan Inc.; *Int'l*, pg. 3753
IIJ EUROPE LIMITED—See Internet Initiative Japan Inc.; *Int'l*, pg. 3753
IIJ EXLAYER INC.—See Internet Initiative Japan Inc.; *Int'l*, pg. 3753
IIJ EXLAYER SINGAPORE PTE. LTD—See Internet Initiative Japan Inc.; *Int'l*, pg. 3753
IIJ EXLAYER USA LLC—See Internet Initiative Japan Inc.; *Int'l*, pg. 3753
IIJ GLOBAL SOLUTIONS INC.—See Internet Initiative Japan Inc.; *Int'l*, pg. 3753
IIJ INNOVATION INSTITUTE INC.—See Internet Initiative Japan Inc.; *Int'l*, pg. 3753
IIJ MEDIA COMMUNICATIONS, INC.—See Internet Initiative Japan Inc.; *Int'l*, pg. 3753
IIMAGEMORE CO., LTD.—See Fullerton Technology Co., Ltd.; *Int'l*, pg. 2842
IIM CORPORATION—See Seiko Group Corporation; *Int'l*, pg. 6688
IIMI (AUSTRALIA) PTY LTD.—See Suncorp Group Limited; *Int'l*, pg. 7311
IINA DINING CO., LTD.—See Hankyu Hanshin Holdings Inc.; *Int'l*, pg. 3255
IINET LIMITED—See CK Hutchison Holdings Limited; *Int'l*, pg. 1638
IINET LIMITED—See Vodafone Group Plc; *Int'l*, pg. 8285
IINO BUILDING TECHNOLOGY CO., LTD.—See Iino Kaiun Kaisha Ltd.; *Int'l*, pg. 3608
IINO BUSINESS SERVICE CO., LTD.—See Iino Kaiun Kaisha Ltd.; *Int'l*, pg. 3608
IINO ENTERPRISE CO., LTD.—See Iino Kaiun Kaisha Ltd.; *Int'l*, pg. 3608
IINO (FOSHAN) TECHNOLOGY CO., LTD.—See Daido Metal Corporation; *Int'l*, pg. 1921
IINO GAS TRANSPORT CO., LTD.—See Iino Kaiun Kaisha Ltd.; *Int'l*, pg. 3608
IINO KAIUN KAISHA LTD.; *Int'l*, pg. 3607
IINO MANAGEMENT DATA PROCESSING CO., LTD.—See Iino Kaiun Kaisha Ltd.; *Int'l*, pg. 3608
IINO MANUFACTURING CO.—See Daido Metal Corporation; *Int'l*, pg. 1922
IINO MARINE SERVICE CO., LTD.—See Iino Kaiun Kaisha Ltd.; *Int'l*, pg. 3608
IINO MEDIA PRO CO., LTD.—See Iino Kaiun Kaisha Ltd.; *Int'l*, pg. 3608
IINO SHIPPING ASIA PTE. LTD.—See Iino Kaiun Kaisha Ltd.; *Int'l*, pg. 3608
IINO SINGAPORE PTE. LTD.—See Iino Kaiun Kaisha Ltd.; *Int'l*, pg. 3608
IINO UK LTD.—See Iino Kaiun Kaisha Ltd.; *Int'l*, pg. 3608
IIOT-OXYS, INC.; *U.S. Public*, pg. 1100
IIR EXHIBITIONS LIMITED—See Informa plc; *Int'l*, pg. 3691
IIR HOLDINGS LTD.—See Informa plc; *Int'l*, pg. 3692
IIR HUNGARY LIMITED—See Informa plc; *Int'l*, pg. 3691
IISAAK FOREST RESOURCE LTD.—See Weyerhaeuser Company; *U.S. Public*, pg. 2365
I&I SLING INC.; *U.S. Private*, pg. 2026
I&I SOFTWARE, INC.; *U.S. Private*, pg. 2026

I I STANLEY CO., INC.—See Stanley Electric Co., Ltd.; *Int'l*, pg. 7170
IIT INSURANCE BROKING AND RISK MANAGEMENT PRIVATE LIMITED—See Industrial Investment Trust Limited; *Int'l*, pg. 3672
IIT INVESTRUST LIMITED—See Industrial Investment Trust Limited; *Int'l*, pg. 3672
IITL PROJECTS LIMITED—See Industrial Investment Trust Limited; *Int'l*, pg. 3672
IITS LLC; *U.S. Private*, pg. 2040
IITTALA BVBA—See Fiskars Oyj Abp; *Int'l*, pg. 2695
IITTALA BV—See Fiskars Oyj Abp; *Int'l*, pg. 2695
IITTALA GMBH—See Fiskars Oyj Abp; *Int'l*, pg. 2695
IITTALA GROUP OY AB—See Fiskars Oyj Abp; *Int'l*, pg. 2694
IIVARI MONONEN OY; *Int'l*, pg. 3608
II-VI ADVANCED MATERIALS DEVELOPMENT CENTER—See Coherent Corp.; *U.S. Public*, pg. 528
II-VI BENELUX N.V.—See Coherent Corp.; *U.S. Public*, pg. 528
II-VI DEUTSCHLAND GMBH—See Coherent Corp.; *U.S. Public*, pg. 528
II-VI GMBH—See Coherent Corp.; *U.S. Public*, pg. 528
II-VI INFRARED LASER (SUZHOU) CO., LTD.—See Coherent Corp.; *U.S. Public*, pg. 528
II-VI INFRARED—See Coherent Corp.; *U.S. Public*, pg. 528
II-VI ITALIA S.R.L.—See Coherent Corp.; *U.S. Public*, pg. 528
II-VI JAPAN INCORPORATED—See Coherent Corp.; *U.S. Public*, pg. 528
II-VI LASER ENTERPRISE GMBH—See Coherent Corp.; *U.S. Public*, pg. 528
II-VI OPTICS (SUZHOU) CO., LTD.—See Coherent Corp.; *U.S. Public*, pg. 528
II-VI SINGAPORE PTE., LTD.—See Coherent Corp.; *U.S. Public*, pg. 528
II-VI SUISSE S.A.R.L.—See Coherent Corp.; *U.S. Public*, pg. 529
II-VI SUWTECH, INC.—See Coherent Corp.; *U.S. Public*, pg. 529
II-VI TAIWAN—See Coherent Corp.; *U.S. Public*, pg. 529
II-VI TECHNOLOGIES (BEIJING) CO., LTD.—See Coherent Corp.; *U.S. Public*, pg. 529
II-VI U.K. LTD.—See Coherent Corp.; *U.S. Public*, pg. 529
II-VI WIDE BAND GAP, INC.—See Coherent Corp.; *U.S. Public*, pg. 529
IIW SINGAPORE PTE. LTD.—See Ishii Iron Works Co., Ltd.; *Int'l*, pg. 3818
IIYAMA BENELUX B.V.—See MCJ Co., Ltd.; *Int'l*, pg. 4759
THE IJ COMPANY—See Performance Food Group Company; *U.S. Public*, pg. 1676
IJET INTERNATIONAL, INC.; *U.S. Private*, pg. 2040
I JIANG INDUSTRIAL CO., LTD.; *Int'l*, pg. 3562
IJJ CORP.; *U.S. Public*, pg. 1100
IJM BUILDING SYSTEMS SDN BHD—See IJM Corporation Berhad; *Int'l*, pg. 3608
I J MCGILL TRANSPORT LTD; *Int'l*, pg. 3561
IJM CONSTRUCTION (MIDDLE EAST) LIMITED LIABILITY COMPANY—See IJM Corporation Berhad; *Int'l*, pg. 3608
IJM CONSTRUCTION SDN BHD—See IJM Corporation Berhad; *Int'l*, pg. 3608
IJM CORPORATION BERHAD; *Int'l*, pg. 3608
IJM EDIBLE OILS SDN BHD—See IJM Corporation Berhad; *Int'l*, pg. 3608
IJM (INDIA) INFRASTRUCTURE LIMITED—See IJM Corporation Berhad; *Int'l*, pg. 3608
IJM LAND BERHAD—See IJM Corporation Berhad; *Int'l*, pg. 3608
IJM MANAGEMENT SERVICES SDN BHD—See IJM Corporation Berhad; *Int'l*, pg. 3609
I. J. MORRIS, LLC—See Service Corporation International; *U.S. Public*, pg. 1869
IJM OVERSEAS VENTURES SDN BHD—See IJM Corporation Berhad; *Int'l*, pg. 3609
IJM PLANTATIONS BERHAD—See Kuala Lumpur Kepong Berhad; *Int'l*, pg. 4318
IJM PROPERTIES SDN BHD—See IJM Corporation Berhad; *Int'l*, pg. 3608
IJOBS B.V.—See ManpowerGroup Inc.; *U.S. Public*, pg. 1362
IJTT CO., LTD.—See SPARX Group Co., Ltd.; *Int'l*, pg. 7127
IJUS, LLC—See TRC Companies, Inc.; *U.S. Private*, pg. 4215
IK4-IKERLAN—See Mondragon Corporation; *Int'l*, pg. 5030
IKA GMBH & CO.KG—See Floridienne SA; *Int'l*, pg. 2708
IKA LOGISTICS, INC.—See Inabata & Co. Ltd.; *Int'l*, pg. 3643
IKANG HEALTHCARE GROUP, INC.; *Int'l*, pg. 3610
IKANO COMMUNICATIONS INC.—See Ikano Communications, Inc.; *U.S. Private*, pg. 2040
IKANO COMMUNICATIONS, INC.; *U.S. Private*, pg. 2040
IKAN PAPER CRAFTS LTD.—See Aurelius Equity Opportunities SE & Co. KGaA; *Int'l*, pg. 710
IKAPA COACH CHARTERS—See Cullinan Holdings Limited; *Int'l*, pg. 1877

IKAPA TOURS & TRAVEL (PTY) LTD.—See Cullinan Holdings Limited; *Int'l*, pg. 1877
IKARBUS A.D.; *Int'l*, pg. 3610
IKARIA AUSTRALIA PTY. LTD.—See Mallinckrodt Public Limited Company; *Int'l*, pg. 4663
IKARIA CANADA INC.—See Mallinckrodt Public Limited Company; *Int'l*, pg. 4663
IKAR-IMPULSE LTD.—See Disco Corporation; *Int'l*, pg. 2132
IKAROS CLEANTECH AB—See Manutan International SA; *Int'l*, pg. 4679
IKAROS CO., LTD.—See Nippon Television Holdings Inc.; *Int'l*, pg. 5356
IKAROS FINLAND OY—See Manutan International SA; *Int'l*, pg. 4679
IKARUS PETROLEUM INDUSTRIES COMPANY K.S.C.C.—See National Industries Group Holding S.A.K.; *Int'l*, pg. 5159
IKASSA FINLAND OY—See Lone Star Global Acquisitions, LLC; *U.S. Private*, pg. 2487
IKASYSTEMS CORPORATION; *U.S. Private*, pg. 2040
IKATAN FLORA SDN BHD—See IJM Corporation Berhad; *Int'l*, pg. 3609
IKB CAPITAL CORPORATION—See Lone Star Global Acquisitions, LLC; *U.S. Private*, pg. 2488
IKB DEUTSCHE INDUSTRIEBANK AG—See Lone Star Global Acquisitions, LLC; *U.S. Private*, pg. 2488
IKB EQUITY FINANCE GMBH—See Lone Star Global Acquisitions, LLC; *U.S. Private*, pg. 2488
IKB IMMOBILIEN MANAGEMENT GMBH—See Lone Star Global Acquisitions, LLC; *U.S. Private*, pg. 2489
IKB LEASING GMBH—See Lone Star Global Acquisitions, LLC; *U.S. Private*, pg. 2489
IKB PRIVATE EQUITY GMBH—See Lone Star Global Acquisitions, LLC; *U.S. Private*, pg. 2489
IKD CO., LTD.; *Int'l*, pg. 3610
IKD FAEZA S.A. DE C.V.—See IKD Co., Ltd.; *Int'l*, pg. 3610
IKEA INDASTRI NOVGOROD, OOO—See Stichting INGKA Foundation; *Int'l*, pg. 7214
IKEA INDUSTRY AB—See Stichting INGKA Foundation; *Int'l*, pg. 7214
IKEA INTERNATIONAL A/S—See Stichting INGKA Foundation; *Int'l*, pg. 7214
IKEA NORTH AMERICA SERVICES LLC—See Stichting INGKA Foundation; *Int'l*, pg. 7214
IKEA SVENSKA AB—See Stichting INGKA Foundation; *Int'l*, pg. 7214
IKEA SVENSKA FORSALJNINGS AB—See Stichting INGKA Foundation; *Int'l*, pg. 7214
I. KEATING FURNITURE INC.; *U.S. Private*, pg. 2026
IKEBANA ENGINEERING LTD.—See Knill Holding GmbH; *Int'l*, pg. 4208
IKE BEHAR APPAREL & DESIGN LTD.; *U.S. Private*, pg. 2041
IKEBUKURO HORO KOGYO CO., LTD.—See NGK Insulators, Ltd.; *Int'l*, pg. 5254
IKEBUKURO SHOPPING PARK CO., LTD.—See Seven & i Holdings Co., Ltd.; *Int'l*, pg. 6730
IKEDA BAKERY CO., LTD.—See Yamazaki Baking Co., Ltd.; *Int'l*, pg. 8556
IKEDA BANK LEASE CO., LTD.—See Senshu Ikeda Holdings, Inc.; *Int'l*, pg. 6713
IKEDA INVESTMENT MANAGEMENT CO., LTD.—See Senshu Ikeda Holdings, Inc.; *Int'l*, pg. 6713
IKEDA KIKO CO., LTD.—See RAIZNEXT Corporation; *Int'l*, pg. 6192
IKEDA UNYU COMPANY LIMITED—See KKR & Co. Inc.; *U.S. Public*, pg. 1259
IKEDDI ENTERPRISES INC.; *U.S. Private*, pg. 2041
IKEGAI CORP—See Fair Friend Group; *Int'l*, pg. 2604
IKEGAI METAL CORP—See Fair Friend Group; *Int'l*, pg. 2604
IKEGAI (SHANGHAI) MACHINERY COMPANY—See Fair Friend Group; *Int'l*, pg. 2604
IKEGAMI ELECTRONICS ASIA PSIFIC PTE. LTD.—See Ikegami Tsushinki Co., Ltd.; *Int'l*, pg. 3610
IKEGAMI ELECTRONICS (EUROPE) GMBH—See Ikegami Tsushinki Co., Ltd.; *Int'l*, pg. 3610
IKEGAMI ELECTRONICS (U.S.A.), INC.—See Ikegami Tsushinki Co., Ltd.; *Int'l*, pg. 3610
IKE GAMING, INC.; *U.S. Private*, pg. 2041
IKEGAMI TSUSHINKI CO., LTD.-OVERSEAS SALES DIVISION—See Ikegami Tsushinki Co., Ltd.; *Int'l*, pg. 3610
IKEGAMI TSUSHINKI CO., LTD.; *Int'l*, pg. 3610
IKEGIN CAPITAL CO., LTD.—See Senshu Ikeda Holdings, Inc.; *Int'l*, pg. 6713
IKEGIN OFFICE SERVICE CO., LTD.—See Senshu Ikeda Holdings, Inc.; *Int'l*, pg. 6713
IKEGPS GROUP LIMITED; *Int'l*, pg. 3610
IKEGPS INC.—See ikeGPS Group Limited; *Int'l*, pg. 3610
IK EINKAUFSMARKTE DEUTSCHLAND VERWALTUNGSGESELLSCHAFT MBH—See Munchener Ruckversicherungs AG; *Int'l*, pg. 5089
IKE INTERNATIONAL CORPORATION—See Ike Trading Co. Ltd. Inc.; *U.S. Private*, pg. 2041
IKEJA HOTEL PLC; *Int'l*, pg. 3610

COMPANY NAME INDEX

I.KELA COMPANY—See Illinois Tool Works Inc.; *U.S. Public*, pg. 1104
IKEMITSU ENTERPRISES CO., LTD.—See Kamei Corporation; *Int'l*, pg. 4061
IKENA ONCOLOGY, INC.; *U.S. Public*, pg. 1101
IKESHITA SEKKEI CO. LTD.; *Int'l*, pg. 3610
IKE TRADING CO. LTD. INC.; *U.S. Private*, pg. 2041
IK FE FONDS MANAGEMENT GMBH—See Munchener Ruckversicherungs AG; *Int'l*, pg. 5089
IKFE PROPERTIES I AG—See Munchener Ruckversicherungs AG; *Int'l*, pg. 5089
IKF FINANCE LIMITED; *Int'l*, pg. 3610
IKF S.P.A.; *Int'l*, pg. 3610
IKF TECHNOLOGIES LIMITED; *Int'l*, pg. 3610
IKHAIRI & ALJENABI TRADING CO.—See Einhell Germany AG; *Int'l*, pg. 2333
IKHLAS AL DAIN SDN. BHD.—See MLABS Systems Berhad; *Int'l*, pg. 5003
IK HOLDINGS CO., LTD.; *Int'l*, pg. 3609
IKIGAI VENTURES LTD.; *Int'l*, pg. 3610
IKIKEN CO., LTD.—See Terumo Corporation; *Int'l*, pg. 7569
I-K-I MANUFACTURING CO. INC.; *U.S. Private*, pg. 2026
IK INVESTMENT PARTNERS AB—See IK Investment Partners Limited; *Int'l*, pg. 3609
IK INVESTMENT PARTNERS GMBH—See IK Investment Partners Limited; *Int'l*, pg. 3609
IK INVESTMENT PARTNERS LIMITED; *Int'l*, pg. 3609
IKIO LIGHTING LIMITED; *Int'l*, pg. 3610
IKKA DINING PROJECT CO., LTD.; *Int'l*, pg. 3611
IKKA (HONG KONG) CO., LIMITED—See Abico Group; *Int'l*, pg. 61
IKKA TECHNOLOGY DONGGUAN CO., LTD.—See Abico Group; *Int'l*, pg. 61
IKKA TECHNOLOGY (VIETNAM) CO., LTD.—See Abico Group; *Int'l*, pg. 61
IKK CO., LTD.—See SANKO TECHNO CO., LTD.; *Int'l*, pg. 6542
IKK ENGINEERING GMBH—See BKW AG; *Int'l*, pg. 1055
IKK HOLDINGS INC; *Int'l*, pg. 3611
IKKOEN CO., LTD.—See Inabata & Co. Ltd.; *Int'l*, pg. 3643
IKKUMA RESOURCES CORP.—See Pieridae Energy (Canada) Limited; *Int'l*, pg. 5864
IK LEASE & INSURANCE CO., LTD.—See Inabata & Co Ltd.; *Int'l*, pg. 3643
I. KLOUKINAS - I. LAPPAS CONSTRUCTION & COMMERCE S.A.; *Int'l*, pg. 3565
IKM ACONA AS—See IKM Gruppen AS; *Int'l*, pg. 3611
IKM ALFA SOLUTION AS—See IKM Gruppen AS; *Int'l*, pg. 3611
IKM CLEANDRILL AS—See EV Private Equity; *Int'l*, pg. 2560
IKM CLEANDRILL AS—See Shell plc; *Int'l*, pg. 6795
IKM CONSULTANTS A/S—See IKM Gruppen AS; *Int'l*, pg. 3611
IKM CONSULTANTS UK LTD.—See IKM Gruppen AS; *Int'l*, pg. 3611
IKM DSC ENGINEERING AS—See IKM Gruppen AS; *Int'l*, pg. 3611
IKM ELEKTRO AS—See IKM Gruppen AS; *Int'l*, pg. 3611
IKM GRUPPEN AS; *Int'l*, pg. 3611
IKM HAALAND AS—See IKM Gruppen AS; *Int'l*, pg. 3611
IKM HVAC AS—See IKM Gruppen AS; *Int'l*, pg. 3611
IKM HVAC PRODUCTION SP. Z.O.O.—See IKM Gruppen AS; *Int'l*, pg. 3611
IKM HYDRAULIC SERVICES AS—See IKM Gruppen AS; *Int'l*, pg. 3611
IKM INDUSTRIGRAVOREN AS—See IKM Gruppen AS; *Int'l*, pg. 3611
IKM INSPECTION AS—See IKM Gruppen AS; *Int'l*, pg. 3611
IKM INSTRUTEK AS—See IKM Gruppen AS; *Int'l*, pg. 3611
IKM INVEST AS—See IKM Gruppen AS; *Int'l*, pg. 3611
IKM KRAN & LOFTETEKNIKK AS—See IKM Gruppen AS; *Int'l*, pg. 3611
IKM LABORATORIUM AS—See IKM Gruppen AS; *Int'l*, pg. 3611
IKM MASKINERING AS—See IKM Gruppen AS; *Int'l*, pg. 3611
IKM MEASUREMENT SERVICES AUSTRALIA PTY. LTD.—See IKM Gruppen AS; *Int'l*, pg. 3611
IKM MEASUREMENT SERVICES LTD.—See IKM Gruppen AS; *Int'l*, pg. 3611
IKM MEKANISKE AS—See IKM Gruppen AS; *Int'l*, pg. 3611
IKM MEKANISKE KRISTIANSUND AS—See IKM Gruppen AS; *Int'l*, pg. 3611
IKM MOORING SERVICES AS—See IKM Gruppen AS; *Int'l*, pg. 3611
IKM NORWEGIAN TECHNOLOGY SOLUTIONS AS—See IKM Gruppen AS; *Int'l*, pg. 3611
IKM OCEAN DESIGN AS—See IKM Gruppen AS; *Int'l*, pg. 3611
IKM OPERATIONS AS—See IKM Gruppen AS; *Int'l*, pg. 3611
IKM PRODUCTION TECHNOLOGY AS—See IKM Gruppen AS; *Int'l*, pg. 3611

IKM PRODUCTION TECHNOLOGY UK LTD.—See IKM Gruppen AS; *Int'l*, pg. 3611
IKM PROMECH AS—See IKM Gruppen AS; *Int'l*, pg. 3611
IKM RADA AS—See IKM Gruppen AS; *Int'l*, pg. 3611
IKM RONTGENKONTROLLEN AS—See IKM Gruppen AS; *Int'l*, pg. 3611
IKM SOLIDTECH AS—See IKM Gruppen AS; *Int'l*, pg. 3611
IKM STAINLESS TECHNOLOGY AS—See IKM Gruppen AS; *Int'l*, pg. 3611
IKM SUBSEA AS—See IKM Gruppen AS; *Int'l*, pg. 3611
IKM SUBSEA BRASIL LTDA—See IKM Gruppen AS; *Int'l*, pg. 3611
IKM SUBSEA MALAYSIA SDN. BHD.—See IKM Gruppen AS; *Int'l*, pg. 3611
IKM SUBSEA MIDDLE EAST FZE—See IKM Gruppen AS; *Int'l*, pg. 3611
IKM SUBSEA MOTOR SOLUTIONS AS—See IKM Gruppen AS; *Int'l*, pg. 3611
IKM SUBSEA SINGAPORE PTE LTD—See IKM Gruppen AS; *Int'l*, pg. 3611
IKM SUBSEA UK LTD—See IKM Gruppen AS; *Int'l*, pg. 3611
IKM TECHNIQUE AS—See IKM Gruppen AS; *Int'l*, pg. 3612
IKM TECH TEAM SOLUTIONS AS—See IKM Gruppen AS; *Int'l*, pg. 3611
IKM TESTING ASIA PTE. LTD.—See IKM Gruppen AS; *Int'l*, pg. 3612
IKM TESTING AS—See IKM Gruppen AS; *Int'l*, pg. 3612
IKM TESTING AUSTRALIA PTY. LTD.—See IKM Gruppen AS; *Int'l*, pg. 3612
IKM TESTING BRASIL LTDA—See IKM Gruppen AS; *Int'l*, pg. 3612
IKM TESTING CANADA LTD—See IKM Gruppen AS; *Int'l*, pg. 3612
IKM TESTING KAZAKSTHAN—See IKM Gruppen AS; *Int'l*, pg. 3612
IKM TESTING KOREA LLC—See IKM Gruppen AS; *Int'l*, pg. 3612
IKM TESTING MALAYSIA SDN. BHD.—See IKM Gruppen AS; *Int'l*, pg. 3612
IKM TESTING MEXICO S DE RL DE CV—See IKM Gruppen AS; *Int'l*, pg. 3612
IKM TESTING POLAND SP. Z.O.O—See IKM Gruppen AS; *Int'l*, pg. 3612
IKM TESTING (THAILAND) CO. LTD.—See IKM Gruppen AS; *Int'l*, pg. 3612
IKM TESTING UK LIMITED—See IKM Gruppen AS; *Int'l*, pg. 3612
IKM WELLDRONE TECHNOLOGY AS—See IKM Gruppen AS; *Int'l*, pg. 3612
I KNOW PARTS & WRECKING PTY LTD—See Bapcor Limited; *Int'l*, pg. 857
IKNOWTION, LLC—See TTEC Holdings, Inc.; *U.S. Public*, pg. 2203
IKO ENTERPRISES LTD.; *Int'l*, pg. 3612
IKO INDUSTRIES LTD.—See IKO Enterprises Ltd.; *Int'l*, pg. 3612
IKO INTERNATIONAL, INC.—See Nippon Thompson Co., Ltd.; *Int'l*, pg. 5356
IKO MANUFACTURING INC.—See IKO Enterprises Ltd.; *Int'l*, pg. 3612
IKO MIDWEST INC.—See IKO Enterprises Ltd.; *Int'l*, pg. 3612
IKON COMMUNICATIONS (MELBOURNE) PTY LIMITED—See WPP plc; *Int'l*, pg. 8462
IKON COMMUNICATIONS; *Int'l*, pg. 3612
IKON CONSULTANCY LIMITED—See The Skipton Building Society; *Int'l*, pg. 7686
IKON FINANCIAL GROUP; *U.S. Private*, pg. 2041
IKONICS CORPORATION—See Terawulf Inc.; *U.S. Public*, pg. 2018
IKONIX GROUP, INC.; *U.S. Private*, pg. 2041
IKON OFFICE SOLUTIONS, INC.—See Ricoh Company, Ltd.; *Int'l*, pg. 6336
IKON PORTER NOVELLI—See Omnicom Group Inc.; *U.S. Public*, pg. 1590
IKON SCIENCE LIMITED; *Int'l*, pg. 3612
IKONSIGN ETCH—See Terawulf Inc.; *U.S. Public*, pg. 2018
IKO PLC—See IKO Enterprises Ltd.; *Int'l*, pg. 3612
IKO PRODUCTION INC.—See IKO Enterprises Ltd.; *Int'l*, pg. 3612
IKO THOMPSON ASIA CO., LTD.—See Nippon Thompson Co., Ltd.; *Int'l*, pg. 5356
IKO THOMPSON BEARINGS CANADA, INC.—See Nippon Thompson Co., Ltd.; *Int'l*, pg. 5356
IKO THOMPSON KOREA CO., LTD.—See Nippon Thompson Co., Ltd.; *Int'l*, pg. 5357
IKO-THOMPSON (SHANGHAI) LTD.—See Nippon Thompson Co., Ltd.; *Int'l*, pg. 5357
IKO THOMPSON VIETNAM CO., LTD.—See Nippon Thompson Co., Ltd.; *Int'l*, pg. 5357
IK PARTNERS; *Int'l*, pg. 3610
IK PLASTIC COMPOUND MEXICO, S.A. DE C.V.—See Inabata & Co. Ltd.; *Int'l*, pg. 3643
IK PLASTIC COMPOUND PHILS. INC.—See Inabata & Co. Ltd.; *Int'l*, pg. 3643

IKRAM QA SERVICES SDN BHD—See Protasco Berhad; *Int'l*, pg. 6003
IKRAM WORKS SDN. BHD.—See Protasco Berhad; *Int'l*, pg. 6003
IK SEMICON CO., LTD.; *Int'l*, pg. 3610
IKSPIARI CO. LTD.—See Oriental Land Co., Ltd.; *Int'l*, pg. 5625
IKS SOLINO S.A.—See Orlen S.A.; *Int'l*, pg. 5640
I & K SYSTEME GMBH—See Frankfurter Sparkasse; *Int'l*, pg. 2761
IKT GRUPPEN AS—See Dustin Group AB; *Int'l*, pg. 2235
IKTINOS HELLAS SA; *Int'l*, pg. 3612
IKTINOS MARMARON S.A.—See Iktinos Hellas SA; *Int'l*, pg. 3612
I. KUNIK COMPANY—See The Wonderful Company LLC; *U.S. Private*, pg. 4138
IKUNO CO.—See Ryobi Limited; *Int'l*, pg. 6440
IKUSASA RAIL (PTY) LTD.—See Wilson Bayly Holmes-Ovcon Limited; *Int'l*, pg. 8423
IK US PORTFOLIO INVEST DREI VERWALTUNGS- GMBH—See Munchener Ruckversicherungs AG; *Int'l*, pg. 5089
IKUTA & MARINE CO., LTD.—See Mitsui O.S.K. Lines, Ltd.; *Int'l*, pg. 4989
IKUYO CO., LTD.; *Int'l*, pg. 3612
IKWEZI MINING LIMITED; *Int'l*, pg. 3612
IKYU CORPORATION—See SoftBank Group Corp.; *Int'l*, pg. 7052
ILAB SOLUTIONS, LLC—See Agilent Technologies, Inc.; *U.S. Public*, pg. 62
ILAM CEMENT CO.; *Int'l*, pg. 3613
I-LAND INTERNET SERVICES LLC—See Keystone Group, L.P.; *U.S. Private*, pg. 2299
I LAN FOODS INDUSTRIAL CO., LTD.—See Want Want China Holdings Ltd.; *Int'l*, pg. 8342
ILANS S.A.S.—See Khiron Life Sciences Corp.; *Int'l*, pg. 4155
ILAPAK ASIA—See ILAPAK S.A.; *Int'l*, pg. 3613
ILAPAK (BEIJING) PACKAGING MACHINERY CO. LTD.—See I.M.A. Industria Macchine Automatiche S.p.A.; *Int'l*, pg. 3566
ILAPAK DO BRASIL LTDA—See ILAPAK S.A.; *Int'l*, pg. 3613
ILAPAK FRANCE S.A.—See ILAPAK S.A.; *Int'l*, pg. 3613
ILAPAK HUNGARY—See ILAPAK S.A.; *Int'l*, pg. 3613
ILAPAK INC.—See ILAPAK S.A.; *Int'l*, pg. 3613
ILAPAK INTERNATIONAL SA—See I.M.A. Industria Macchine Automatiche S.p.A.; *Int'l*, pg. 3566
ILAPAK ISRAEL LTD.—See ILAPAK S.A.; *Int'l*, pg. 3613
ILAPAK ITALIA S.P.A. - FILLDOSE DIVISION—See ILAPAK S.A.; *Int'l*, pg. 3613
ILAPAK ITALIA S.P.A.—See ILAPAK S.A.; *Int'l*, pg. 3613
ILAPAK (LANGFANG) PACKAGING MACHINERY CO.—See ILAPAK S.A.; *Int'l*, pg. 3613
ILAPAK LTD—See ILAPAK S.A.; *Int'l*, pg. 3613
ILAPAK S.A.; *Int'l*, pg. 3613
ILAPAK SNG—See ILAPAK S.A.; *Int'l*, pg. 3613
ILAPAK SP. Z O.O.—See ILAPAK S.A.; *Int'l*, pg. 3613
ILAPAK VERPACKUNGSMASCHINEN GMBH—See ILAPAK S.A.; *Int'l*, pg. 3613
ILARDUYA PRODUCTOS DE FUNDICION—See Huettenes-Albertus Chemische Werke GmbH; *Int'l*, pg. 3523
ILA SOUTH PACIFIC LIMITED—See Graham Holdings Company; *U.S. Public*, pg. 955
ILBAU GMBH DEUTSCHLAND—See STRABAG SE; *Int'l*, pg. 7230
ILBAU LIEGENSCHAFTSVERWALTUNG GMBH—See STRABAG SE; *Int'l*, pg. 7230
ILB GROUP BERHAD; *Int'l*, pg. 3613
ILB PTY. LTD.—See Experience Co Limited; *Int'l*, pg. 2588
ILCC CO., LTD; *Int'l*, pg. 3613
ILC DOVER LP—See New Mountain Capital, LLC; *U.S. Private*, pg. 2902
ILCHESTER CHEESE COMPANY—See TINE SA; *Int'l*, pg. 7753
ILD CORP.; *U.S. Private*, pg. 2041
ILD CORP.—See ILD Corp.; *U.S. Private*, pg. 2041
ILD HOTELS—See The Israel Land Development Co., Ltd.; *Int'l*, pg. 7657
I.L. DIAGNOSTICS, S.A. DE C.V.—See Werfen Life Group, S.A.U.; *Int'l*, pg. 8379
I.L.D. INSURANCE CO. LTD.—See The Israel Land Development Co., Ltd.; *Int'l*, pg. 7657
ILDONG HOLDINGS CO., LTD.; *Int'l*, pg. 3613
ILDONG PHARMACEUTICAL CO., LTD. - CHEONGJU PLANT—See Ildong Pharmaceutical Co., Ltd.; *Int'l*, pg. 3613
ILDONG PHARMACEUTICAL CO., LTD.; *Int'l*, pg. 3613
ILEARNINGENGINES HOLDINGS, INC.—See iLearningEngines, Inc.; *U.S. Public*, pg. 1101
ILEARNINGENGINES, INC.; *U.S. Public*, pg. 1101
THE ILE CAMERA—See Alden Global Capital LLC; *U.S. Private*, pg. 158
I.L.E.E. AG—See Rheinmetall AG; *Int'l*, pg. 6321
ILEMO HARDI, S.A.U.—See Exel Industries SA; *Int'l*, pg. 2582
ILENE INC.—See PT Indopoly Swakarsa Industry Tbk; *Int'l*, pg. 6046

ILEARNINGENGINES, INC.

CORPORATE AFFILIATIONS

ILENS SDN BHD—See Hoya Corporation; *Int'l*, pg. 3496
ILEX BIOTECH LTD.—See Ilex Medical Ltd.; *Int'l*, pg. 3614
ILEX MEDICAL LTD.; *Int'l*, pg. 3613
ILEX SOUTH AFRICA (PTY) LTD.—See Ilex Medical Ltd.; *Int'l*, pg. 3614
ILFA FEINSTLEITERTECHNIK GMBH; *Int'l*, pg. 3614
ILFC HOLDINGS, INC.—See American International Group, Inc.; *U.S. Public*, pg. 107
ILFORD IMAGING SWITZERLAND GMBH; *Int'l*, pg. 3614
IL FORNAIO (AMERICA) CORPORATION—See create restaurants holdings inc.; *Int'l*, pg. 1832
IL&FS CLUSTER DEVELOPMENT INITIATIVE LIMITED—See Schoolnet India Limited; *Int'l*, pg. 6638
IL&FS ENERGY DEVELOPMENT COMPANY LIMITED—See Infrastructure Leasing & Financial Services Limited; *Int'l*, pg. 3698
IL&FS ENGINEERING & CONSTRUCTION COMPANY LTD.; *Int'l*, pg. 3613
IL&FS ENVIRONMENTAL INFRASTRUCTURE & SERVICE LIMITED—See Everstone Capital Advisors Pvt. Ltd.; *Int'l*, pg. 2569
IL&FS FINANCIAL SERVICES LIMITED—See Infrastructure Leasing & Financial Services Limited; *Int'l*, pg. 3698
IL&FS GLOBAL FINANCIAL SERVICES (HK) LIMITED—See Infrastructure Leasing & Financial Services Limited; *Int'l*, pg. 3698
IL&FS GLOBAL FINANCIAL SERVICES (ME) LIMITED—See Infrastructure Leasing & Financial Services Limited; *Int'l*, pg. 3698
IL&FS GLOBAL FINANCIAL SERVICES (UK) LIMITED—See Infrastructure Leasing & Financial Services Limited; *Int'l*, pg. 3698
IL&FS INVESTMENT ADVISOR LLC—See Infrastructure Leasing & Financial Services Limited; *Int'l*, pg. 3698
IL&FS INVESTMENT MANAGERS LIMITED—See Infrastructure Leasing & Financial Services Limited; *Int'l*, pg. 3698
IL&FS RAIL LIMITED—See Infrastructure Leasing & Financial Services Limited; *Int'l*, pg. 3698
IL&FS SECURITIES SERVICES LIMITED—See Infrastructure Leasing & Financial Services Limited; *Int'l*, pg. 3698
IL&FS TRANSPORTATION NETWORKS LIMITED—See Infrastructure Leasing & Financial Services Limited; *Int'l*, pg. 3698
IL&FS URBAN INFRASTRUCTURE MANGAERS LIMITED—See Infrastructure Leasing & Financial Services Limited; *Int'l*, pg. 3698
IL&FS WATER LIMITED—See Infrastructure Leasing & Financial Services Limited; *Int'l*, pg. 3698
IL GAZZETTINO SPA—See Caltagirone Editore S.p.A.; *Int'l*, pg. 1265
ILG, LLC—See Marriott Vacations Worldwide Corporation; *U.S. Public*, pg. 1373
ILHWA AMERICAN CORPORATION—See Family Federation for World Peace & Unification; *U.S. Private*, pg. 1469
ILIAD S.A.; *Int'l*, pg. 3614
ILIASI LTD.—See Elco Limited; *Int'l*, pg. 2345
ILIGHT TECHNOLOGIES; *U.S. Private*, pg. 2041
ILIKA PLC; *Int'l*, pg. 3614
ILIKA TECHNOLOGIES LIMITED—See Ilika PLC; *Int'l*, pg. 3614
ILIM TIMBER EUROPE GMBH—See Ilim Timber Indastri OOO; *Int'l*, pg. 3614
ILIM TIMBER INDASTRI OOO; *Int'l*, pg. 3614
I.LINK GROUP LIMITED—See HM International Holdings Limited; *Int'l*, pg. 3431
ILINK SYSTEMS, INC.; *U.S. Private*, pg. 2041
ILIOHORA S.A.—See Gek Terna Societe Anonyme Holdings Real Estate Constructions; *Int'l*, pg. 2913
ILION CAPITAL PARTNERS; *U.S. Private*, pg. 2041
ILIRIJA D.D.; *Int'l*, pg. 3614
ILITCH HOLDINGS, INC.; *U.S. Private*, pg. 2041
ILI TECHNOLOGIES (2002) USA CORP.—See Divergent Energy Services Corp.; *Int'l*, pg. 2137
ILI TECHNOLOGY CORP.—See MediaTek Inc.; *Int'l*, pg. 4773
I.L. JAPAN CO. LTD.—See Werfen Life Group, S.A.U.; *Int'l*, pg. 8379
IL JEONG INDUSTRIAL CO., LTD; *Int'l*, pg. 3612
ILJIN DIAMOND CO LTD - ANSAN PLANT—See Iljin Diamond Co Ltd; *Int'l*, pg. 3614
ILJIN DIAMOND CO LTD - EUMSEONG PLANT—See Iljin Diamond Co Ltd; *Int'l*, pg. 3614
ILJIN DIAMOND CO LTD; *Int'l*, pg. 3614
ILJIN DISPLAY CO., LTD.; *Int'l*, pg. 3614
ILJIN ELECTRIC CO., LTD.—See Iljin Display Co., Ltd.; *Int'l*, pg. 3614
IL JIN ELECTRONICS (INDIA) PRIVATE LIMITED—See Amber Enterprises India Limited; *Int'l*, pg. 414
ILJINENERGY CO., LTD. - PLANT 2—See Iljin Power Co., Ltd.; *Int'l*, pg. 3615
ILJIN HOLDINGS CO., LTD.; *Int'l*, pg. 3614
ILJIN HYSOLUS CO., LTD.; *Int'l*, pg. 3615
ILJIN MATERIALS CO., LTD.—See Lotte Co., Ltd.; *Int'l*, pg. 4559
ILJIN POWER CO., LTD.; *Int'l*, pg. 3615

ILJIN SEMICONDUCTOR CO., LTD.—See Iljin Display Co., Ltd.; *Int'l*, pg. 3614
ILJIN STEEL CORPORATION—See Iljin Display Co., Ltd.; *Int'l*, pg. 3614
ILJI TECHNOLOGY CO., LTD.; *Int'l*, pg. 3614
ILKKA YHTYMAE OYJ; *Int'l*, pg. 3615
ILKNAK SU URUNLERI SAN VE TIC A.S.—See AMERRA Capital Management LLC; *Int'l*, pg. 424
ILKNAK SU URUNLERI SAN VE TIC A.S.—See Mubadala Investment Company PJSC; *Int'l*, pg. 5076
ILLA S.P.A.; *Int'l*, pg. 3615
ILLAWARRA NEWSPAPER HOLDINGS PTY. LIMITED—See Rural Press Pty Limited; *Int'l*, pg. 6429
ILLAWARRA X-RAY PTY LIMITED—See Sonic Healthcare Limited; *Int'l*, pg. 7097
ILLBRUCK FOAM TEC—See Illbruck GmbH; *Int'l*, pg. 3615
ILLBRUCK GMBH; *Int'l*, pg. 3615
ILLE ROUSSILLON; *Int'l*, pg. 3615
ILLIANA DISPOSAL PARTNERSHIP—See Republic Services, Inc.; *U.S. Public*, pg. 1786
ILLICHMANN CASTALLOY GMBH—See Alicon Castalloy Limited; *Int'l*, pg. 327
ILLICHMANN CASTALLOY S.R.O—See Alicon Castalloy Limited; *Int'l*, pg. 327
ILLIG MASCHINENBAU GMBH & CO. KG; *Int'l*, pg. 3615
ILLIMITY BANK S.P.A.; *Int'l*, pg. 3615
ILLIMITY SGR S.P.A.—See illimity Bank S.p.A.; *Int'l*, pg. 3615
I'LL INC.; *Int'l*, pg. 3562
ILLINGWORTH CORPORATION—See EMCOR Group, Inc.; *U.S. Public*, pg. 738
ILLINI FS INC.; *U.S. Private*, pg. 2042
ILLINI INC.—See Neil International Inc.; *U.S. Private*, pg. 2882
ILLINOIS ACTION FOR CHILDREN; *U.S. Private*, pg. 2042
ILLINOIS AMERICAN WATER—See American Water Works Company, Inc.; *U.S. Public*, pg. 112
ILLINOIS ASSOCIATION OF SCHOOL BOARDS; *U.S. Private*, pg. 2042
ILLINOIS AUTO CENTRAL DIVISION—See Illinois Auto Electric Co.; *U.S. Private*, pg. 2042
ILLINOIS AUTO ELECTRIC CO. - MIDWEST ENGINE WAREHOUSE DIVISION—See Illinois Auto Electric Co.; *U.S. Private*, pg. 2042
ILLINOIS AUTO ELECTRIC CO.; *U.S. Private*, pg. 2042
ILLINOIS BANK & TRUST—See Heartland Financial USA, Inc.; *U.S. Public*, pg. 1018
ILLINOIS CEMENT COMPANY LLC—See Eagle Materials Inc.; *U.S. Public*, pg. 702
ILLINOIS COMMUNITY BANCORP, INC.; *U.S. Public*, pg. 1101
ILLINOIS CONSOLIDATED TELEPHONE COMPANY—See Consolidated Communications Holdings, Inc.; *U.S. Public*, pg. 570
ILLINOIS CORN PROCESSING HOLDINGS INC.—See Alto Ingredients, Inc.; *U.S. Public*, pg. 88
ILLINOIS CORN PROCESSING, LLC—See Alto Ingredients, Inc.; *U.S. Public*, pg. 88
ILLINOIS CYBERKNIFE, LLC—See Akumin, Inc.; *U.S. Public*, pg. 70
ILLINOIS DISTRIBUTING CO.—See Grey Eagle Distributors Inc.; *U.S. Private*, pg. 1784
ILLINOIS ENERGY SOLUTIONS, USA, LLC—See The Southern Company; *U.S. Public*, pg. 2131
ILLINOIS FIBER RESOURCES GROUP; *U.S. Private*, pg. 2042
ILLINOIS FOUNDATION SEEDS INC.; *U.S. Private*, pg. 2042
ILLINOIS GAS CO.; *U.S. Private*, pg. 2042
ILLINOIS HEALTH & SCIENCE; *U.S. Private*, pg. 2042
ILLINOIS HIGH SCHOOL ASSOCIATION; *U.S. Private*, pg. 2042
ILLINOIS INDUSTRIAL TOOL INC.; *U.S. Private*, pg. 2042
THE ILLINOIS INSTITUTE OF ART AT SCHAUMBURG, INC.—See Dream Center Foundation, a California Nonprofit Corp.; *U.S. Private*, pg. 1275
THE ILLINOIS INSTITUTE OF ART, INC.—See Dream Center Foundation, a California Nonprofit Corp.; *U.S. Private*, pg. 1275
THE ILLINOIS INSTITUTE OF ART - TINLEY PARK LLC—See Dream Center Foundation, a California Nonprofit Corp.; *U.S. Private*, pg. 1275
ILLINOIS INSURANCE GUARANTY FUND; *U.S. Private*, pg. 2042
ILLINOIS J. LIVINGSTON COMPANY; *U.S. Private*, pg. 2042
ILLINOIS LANDFILL, INC.—See Republic Services, Inc.; *U.S. Public*, pg. 1786
ILLINOIS LIFE & HEALTH INSURANCE GUARANTY ASSOCIATION; *U.S. Private*, pg. 2042
ILLINOIS LIV, LLC—See UnitedHealth Group Incorporated; *U.S. Public*, pg. 2245
THE ILLINOIS LOCK COMPANY—See The Eastern Company; *U.S. Public*, pg. 2069
ILLINOIS MENTOR, INC.—See Centerbridge Partners, L.P.; *U.S. Private*, pg. 813
ILLINOIS & MIDLAND RAILROAD, INC.—See Brookfield Infrastructure Partners L.P.; *Int'l*, pg. 1192

ILLINOIS & MIDLAND RAILROAD, INC.—See GIC Pte. Ltd.; *Int'l*, pg. 2966
ILLINOIS MUTUAL LIFE INSURANCE COMPANY; *U.S. Private*, pg. 2042
ILLINOIS RAILWAY, LLC—See The Broe Companies, Inc.; *U.S. Private*, pg. 4001
ILLINOIS RIVER ENERGY, LLC—See CHS INC.; *U.S. Public*, pg. 492
ILLINOIS ROAD CONTRACTORS; *U.S. Private*, pg. 2042
ILLINOIS RURAL ELECTRIC COOPERATIVE; *U.S. Private*, pg. 2042
ILLINOIS SCHOOL BUS CO. INC.—See Cook-Illinois Corp.; *U.S. Private*, pg. 1038
ILLINOIS TECHNOLOGY ASSOCIATION—See Chicagoland Entrepreneurial Center; *U.S. Private*, pg. 879
ILLINOIS TOOL WORKS INC.; *U.S. Public*, pg. 1101
ILLINOIS UNION INSURANCE COMPANY—See Chubb Limited; *Int'l*, pg. 1593
ILLINOIS VALLEY COMMUNITY HOSPITAL; *U.S. Private*, pg. 2042
ILLINOVA CORPORATION—See Vistra Corp.; *U.S. Public*, pg. 2306
ILLIT GRUNDSTUCKSVERWALTUNGS-MANAGEMENT GMBH—See Siemens Aktiengesellschaft; *Int'l*, pg. 6887
I L LONG CONSTRUCTION COMPANY, INC.; *U.S. Private*, pg. 2020
ILLOVO SUGAR (MALAWI) LIMITED—See The Garfield Weston Foundation; *Int'l*, pg. 7648
ILLOVO SUGAR (PTY) LTD—See The Garfield Weston Foundation; *Int'l*, pg. 7648
ILLOVO SUGAR (SOUTH AFRICA) LIMITED—See The Garfield Weston Foundation; *Int'l*, pg. 7648
ILLOVO TANZANIA LIMITED—See The Garfield Weston Foundation; *Int'l*, pg. 7648
ILLUMA LIGHTING LIMITED—See Searchlight Electric Ltd.; *Int'l*, pg. 6666
ILLUMINA AUSTRALIA PTY. LTD.—See Illumina, Inc.; *U.S. Public*, pg. 1112
ILLUMINA BRASIL PRODUTOS DE BIOTECNOLOGIA LTDA.—See Illumina, Inc.; *U.S. Public*, pg. 1112
ILLUMINA CAMBRIDGE, LTD.—See Illumina, Inc.; *U.S. Public*, pg. 1112
ILLUMINA, INC.-HAYWARD—See Illumina, Inc.; *U.S. Public*, pg. 1112
ILLUMINA, INC.; *U.S. Public*, pg. 1111
ILLUMINA K.K.—See Illumina, Inc.; *U.S. Public*, pg. 1112
ILLUMINA KOREA LTD.—See Illumina, Inc.; *U.S. Public*, pg. 1112
ILLUMINA MIDDLE EAST FZE—See Illumina, Inc.; *U.S. Public*, pg. 1112
ILLUMINA SHANGHAI (TRADING) CO., LTD.—See Illumina, Inc.; *U.S. Public*, pg. 1112
ILLUMINA SINGAPORE PTE. LTD.—See Illumina, Inc.; *U.S. Public*, pg. 1112
ILLUMINAT (BARBADOS) LIMITED—See Massy Holdings Ltd.; *Int'l*, pg. 4723
ILLUMINATE OPERATIONS LLC; *U.S. Private*, pg. 2042
ILLUMINATE SEARCH & CONSULTING PTY. LTD.—See PeopleIn Limited; *Int'l*, pg. 5794
ILLUMINATI STUDIOS INC.; *U.S. Private*, pg. 2043
ILLUMINAT (JAMAICA) LIMITED—See Massy Holdings Ltd.; *Int'l*, pg. 4723
ILLUMINATOR INVESTMENT COMPANY LIMITED; *Int'l*, pg. 3615
ILLUMINA TRADING (SHANGHAI) CO., LTD.—See Illumina, Inc.; *U.S. Public*, pg. 1112
ILLUMINAT (TRINIDAD & TOBAGO) LIMITED—See Massy Holdings Ltd.; *Int'l*, pg. 4723
ILLUMIN HOLDINGS INC.; *Int'l*, pg. 3615
ILLUMINOSS MEDICAL, INC.—See HealthpointCapital, LLC; *U.S. Private*, pg. 1897
ILLUMIS, INC.; *U.S. Private*, pg. 2043
ILLUMS BOLIGHUS A/S—See Axcel Management A/S; *Int'l*, pg. 762
ILLUSTRATED PROPERTIES REAL ESTATE, INC.—See The Keyes Company; *U.S. Private*, pg. 4065
ILLUSTRO SYSTEMS INTERNATIONAL, LLC—See UNICOM Global, Inc.; *U.S. Private*, pg. 4282
ILLYCAFFE FRANCE BELUX SARL—See illycaffe S.p.A.; *Int'l*, pg. 3615
ILLYCAFFE FRANCE SAS—See illycaffe S.p.A.; *Int'l*, pg. 3615
ILLYCAFFE KOREA CO. LTD.—See illycaffe S.p.A.; *Int'l*, pg. 3615
ILLYCAFFE NEDERLAND B.V.—See illycaffe S.p.A.; *Int'l*, pg. 3615
ILLYCAFFE NORTH AMERICA INC.—See illycaffe S.p.A.; *Int'l*, pg. 3615
ILLYCAFFE SHANGHAI CO. LTD.—See illycaffe S.p.A.; *Int'l*, pg. 3615
ILLYCAFFE SHANGHAI CO. LTD.—See illycaffe S.p.A.; *Int'l*, pg. 3615
ILLYCAFFE S.P.A. NIEDERLASSUNG DEUTSCHLAND—See illycaffe S.p.A.; *Int'l*, pg. 3615
ILLYCAFFE S.P.A.; *Int'l*, pg. 3615
ILLYCAFFE' SUD AMERICA COM. IMP. EXP. LTD.—See illycaffe S.p.A.; *Int'l*, pg. 3615

COMPANY NAME INDEX

ILLY ESPRESSO CANADA—See illycaffe S.p.A.; *Int'l*, pg. 3615
ILLYRIA (PTY) LTD.; *Int'l*, pg. 3615
ILMARINEN MUTUAL PENSION INSURANCE COMPANY; *Int'l*, pg. 3615
IL MATTINO SPA—See Caltagirone Editore S.p.A.; *Int'l*, pg. 1266
IL MESSAGGERO SPA—See Caltagirone Editore S.p.A.; *Int'l*, pg. 1266
ILMO PRODUCTS COMPANY; *U.S. Private*, pg. 2043
ILMORE ENGINEERING LTD.—See Mercedes-Benz Group AG; *Int'l*, pg. 4825
ILMVAC GMBH; *Int'l*, pg. 3615
ILMVAC TRADING (SHANGHAI) CO. LTD.—See Ingersoll Rand Inc.; *U.S. Public*, pg. 1119
I LOAN INC.; *U.S. Private*, pg. 2020
ILOCAL INTERNATIONAL BV—See TomTom N.V.; *Int'l*, pg. 7804
I-LOGIC CO., LTD.—See FP Corporation; *Int'l*, pg. 2756
I-LOGISTICS (GUANGZHOU) LTD.—See ITOCHU Corporation; *Int'l*, pg. 3839
I-LOGISTICS (HK) LTD.—See ITOCHU Corporation; *Int'l*, pg. 3838
I-LOGISTICS (SHANGHAI) CORP.—See ITOCHU Corporation; *Int'l*, pg. 3839
I-LOGISTICS (SHANGHAI) FORWARDING CORP.—See ITOCHU Corporation; *Int'l*, pg. 3839
I-LOGISTICS (SHENZHEN) CORP.—See ITOCHU Corporation; *Int'l*, pg. 3839
ILOKA, INC.—See Schurz Communications, Inc.; *U.S. Private*, pg. 3571
ILOMAR HOLDING N.V.—See Louis Dreyfus Company B.V.; *Int'l*, pg. 4562
ILOODA CO., LTD.; *Int'l*, pg. 3616
ILOOKABOUT INC.—See Voxtur Analytics Corp.; *Int'l*, pg. 8311
ILOOP MOBILE, INC.—See LENCO MOBILE INC.; *U.S. Private*, pg. 2421
ILOVE GMBH—See freenet AG; *Int'l*, pg. 2770
I LOVE TOUR LIMITED—See TUI AG; *Int'l*, pg. 7968
ILPEA INC.; *U.S. Private*, pg. 2043
ILPEA INDUSTRIES, INC.—See Ilpea Inc.; *U.S. Private*, pg. 2043
ILP FUNDS; *Int'l*, pg. 3616
IL PHARMA INC.—See MEDInx Co., Ltd.; *Int'l*, pg. 1786
IL POINT SRL—See SOL S.p.A.; *Int'l*, pg. 7067
ILPRA BENELUX BV—See Ilpra SpA; *Int'l*, pg. 3616
ILPRA DEUTSCHLAND GMBH—See Ilpra SpA; *Int'l*, pg. 3616
ILPRA HONG KONG LTD.—See Ilpra SpA; *Int'l*, pg. 3616
ILPRA SPA; *Int'l*, pg. 3616
ILPRA SYSTEMS ESPANA SL—See Ilpra SpA; *Int'l*, pg. 3616
ILPRA SYSTEMS UK LTD.—See Ilpra SpA; *Int'l*, pg. 3616
IL RECYCLING AB—See STENA AB; *Int'l*, pg. 7207
THE ILSC EDUCATION GROUP, INC.—See Quad Partners, LLC; *U.S. Private*, pg. 3314
IL SCIENCE CO., LTD.; *Int'l*, pg. 3613
ILSCO CORPORATION—See nVent Electric plc; *Int'l*, pg. 5498
ILSE BERGBAU-GMBH—See E.ON SE; *Int'l*, pg. 2258
ILSENBURGER GROBBLECH GMBH—See Salzgitter AG; *Int'l*, pg. 6499
ILSERV S.R.L.—See Enviri Corporation; *U.S. Public*, pg. 781
IL SEUNG CO., LTD.; *Int'l*, pg. 3613
ILSHINBIOBASE CO., LTD.; *Int'l*, pg. 3616
ILSHIN INVESTMENT CO., LTD.—See Ilshin Spinning Co., Ltd.; *Int'l*, pg. 3616
ILSHIN SPINNING CO., LTD.; *Int'l*, pg. 3616
ILSHIN STONE CO., LTD; *Int'l*, pg. 3616
ILSHINWELLS CO., LTD; *Int'l*, pg. 3616
ILSI AMERICA LLC; *U.S. Private*, pg. 2043
ILS INC.—See Otsuka Holdings Co., Ltd.; *Int'l*, pg. 5659
ILS INOVATIVE LABORSYSTEME GMBH—See Ingersoll Rand Inc.; *U.S. Public*, pg. 1120
ILS LABORATORIES SCANDINAVIA A/S; *Int'l*, pg. 3616
ILS NORDIC AB—See Aspo Oyj; *Int'l*, pg. 631
IL SOLE 24 ORE SPA; *Int'l*, pg. 3613
ILS SERVICES SWITZERLAND LTD.—See Integra Life-Sciences Holdings Corporation; *U.S. Public*, pg. 1135
ILS SPETH GMBH—See EMKA-Beschlagteile GmbH & Co. KG; *Int'l*, pg. 2383
ILS SUPPLY TECHNOLOGIES SA DE CV—See Park-Ohio Holdings Corp.; *U.S. Public*, pg. 1639
ILS TECHNOLOGY LLC—See DBAY Advisors Limited; *Int'l*, pg. 1988
ILSUNG CONSTRUCTION CO., LTD.; *Int'l*, pg. 3616
ILSUNG PHARMACEUTICALS CO., LTD.; *Int'l*, pg. 3616
IL TIGLIO - SOCIETA' AGRICOLA S.R.L.—See Assicurazioni Generali S.p.A.; *Int'l*, pg. 647
ILTI LUCE S.R.L.—See Nemo S.r.l.; *Int'l*, pg. 5195
IL TROVATORE SRL—See Cairo Communication S.p.A.; *Int'l*, pg. 1253
ILUKA RESOURCES INC.—See Iluka Resources Limited; *Int'l*, pg. 3616
ILUKA RESOURCES LIMITED; *Int'l*, pg. 3616
ILUKA TRADING (SHANGHAI) CO., LTD.—See Iluka Resources Limited; *Int'l*, pg. 3616

ILUMARK GMBH—See Fortive Corporation; *U.S. Public*, pg. 871
ILUMINACION COOPER DE LAS CALIFORNIAS S. DE R.L. DE C.V.—See Signify N.V.; *Int'l*, pg. 6912
ILUNA USA INC.—See Sherpa Capital SL; *Int'l*, pg. 6826
ILUSTRATO PICTURES INTERNATIONAL INC.; *Int'l*, pg. 3616
ILVA S.P.A. IN AS—See Riva Forni Elettrici; *Int'l*, pg. 6352
ILVA (UK) LTD.—See Riva Forni Elettrici; *Int'l*, pg. 6352
ILWOUL GML CO.,LTD; *Int'l*, pg. 3617
ILWU CREDIT UNION; *U.S. Private*, pg. 2043
ILX LIGHTWAVE CORPORATION—See MKS Instruments, Inc.; *U.S. Public*, pg. 1453
ILYA CO., LTD. - PYEONGTAEK FACTORY—See Enterpartners Co., LTD; *Int'l*, pg. 2451
ILYA CO., LTD. - WEIHAI FACTORY—See Enterpartners Co., LTD; *Int'l*, pg. 2451
ILYA CORPORATION—See Kajima Corporation; *Int'l*, pg. 4054
ILYANG PHARMACEUTICAL CO., LTD.; *Int'l*, pg. 3617
ILYDA SA; *Int'l*, pg. 3617
ILYUSHIN FINANCE CO.; *Int'l*, pg. 3617
IM360 ENTERTAINMENT INC.—See Digital Domain Holdings Limited; *Int'l*, pg. 2121
IM 40 SP. Z O.O—See Agora S.A.; *Int'l*, pg. 212
IMA AMERICA CORPORATION—See Schelling Anlagenbau GmbH; *Int'l*, pg. 6615
IMA ASIA PACIFIC PTE. LTD.—See ADCURAM Group AG; *Int'l*, pg. 128
IMA AUSTRIA GMBH—See Schelling Anlagenbau GmbH; *Int'l*, pg. 6616
IMA AUTOMATION AMBERG GMBH—See Ningbo Joyson Electronic Corp.; *Int'l*, pg. 5304
IMA AUTOMATION MALAYSIA SDN. BHD.—See I.M.A. Industria Macchine Automatiche S.p.A.; *Int'l*, pg. 3565
IMA AUTOMATION USA, INC.—See I.M.A. Industria Macchine Automatiche S.p.A.; *Int'l*, pg. 3565
IMABARI HIGH TRUST CO., LTD.—See Takuma Co., Ltd.; *Int'l*, pg. 7442
I-MAB; *Int'l*, pg. 3563
IMA CANADA CORPORATION—See Schelling Anlagenbau GmbH; *Int'l*, pg. 6616
I MACHINE TECHNOLOGY LLC—See Chien Wei Precise Technology Co., Ltd.; *Int'l*, pg. 1477
IMAC HOLDINGS, INC.; *U.S. Public*, pg. 1112
IMACON, INC.—See Glunz & Jensen Holding A/S; *Int'l*, pg. 3011
IMA (DONGGUAN) INT'L TRADING CO., LTD.—See Schelling Anlagenbau GmbH; *Int'l*, pg. 6615
IM ADVERTISING PTY LIMITED—See WPP plc; *Int'l*, pg. 8462
IMA ESPANA, S.L.—See Schelling Anlagenbau GmbH; *Int'l*, pg. 6616
IMA EST VERPACKUNGSSYSTEME HANDELSGESELL-SCHAFT GM.BH.—See I.M.A. Industria Macchine Automatiche S.p.A.; *Int'l*, pg. 3565
IMA FINANCIAL GROUP, INC.; *U.S. Private*, pg. 2043
IMAFLEX INC.; *Int'l*, pg. 3617
IMAFLEX USA INC.—See Imaflex Inc.; *Int'l*, pg. 3617
IMA FRANCE—See Schelling Anlagenbau GmbH; *Int'l*, pg. 6616
IMAGE ADVERTISING, INC.; *U.S. Private*, pg. 2044
IMAGE API INC.; *U.S. Private*, pg. 2044
IMAGE APPAREL FOR BUSINESS INC.; *U.S. Private*, pg. 2044
IMAGEBOX GROUP PTY LIMITED—See Enero Group Limited; *Int'l*, pg. 2424
IMAGE BUSINESS INTERIORS; *U.S. Private*, pg. 2044
IMAGE CHAIN GROUP LIMITED, INC.; *Int'l*, pg. 3617
IMAGE COMICS INC.; *U.S. Private*, pg. 2044
IMAGE & COMPAGNIE SA—See Vivendi SE; *Int'l*, pg. 8271
IMAGE DESIGN, INC.; *U.S. Private*, pg. 2044
IMAGE ENGINEERING GROUP, LTD.—See Godspeed Capital Management LP; *U.S. Private*, pg. 1725
IMAGE ENTERTAINMENT, INC.—See AMC Networks Inc.; *U.S. Public*, pg. 92
IMAGE FACTORY LTD—See The Quarto Group, Inc.; *Int'l*, pg. 7677
IMAGEFIRST HEALTHCARE LAUNDRY SPECIALISTS; *U.S. Private*, pg. 2045
IMAGE FIRST PROFESSIONAL AP; *U.S. Private*, pg. 2044
THE IMAGE GROUP; *U.S. Private*, pg. 4055
IMAGEHAUS; *U.S. Private*, pg. 2045
IMAGE HOLDINGS CORPORATION; *U.S. Private*, pg. 2044
IMAGE INFORMATION INC.; *Int'l*, pg. 3617
IMAGE INTERGRATION SYSTEMS, INC.—See Clearlake Capital Group, L.P.; *U.S. Private*, pg. 936
IMAGE INTERGRATION SYSTEMS, INC.—See TA Associates, Inc.; *U.S. Private*, pg. 3916
IMAGE INTERNATIONAL GROUP, INC.; *U.S. Public*, pg. 1112
IMAGE IV SYSTEMS INC.; *U.S. Private*, pg. 2044
IMAGELINX MILTON KEYNES LTD—See Imagelinx Plc; *Int'l*, pg. 3618
IMAGELINX PLC; *Int'l*, pg. 3618

IMAGICA GROUP INC.

IMAGELINX SCOTLAND LTD—See Imagelinx Plc; *Int'l*, pg. 3618
IMAGELINX USA INC—See Imagelinx Plc; *Int'l*, pg. 3618
IMAGE LOCATIONS INC.; *U.S. Private*, pg. 2044
IMAGEMARK BUSINESS SERVICES; *U.S. Private*, pg. 2045
IMAGEMARK, INC.; *U.S. Private*, pg. 2045
IMAGE METRICS, INC.; *U.S. Public*, pg. 1112
IMAGEM GLOBAL MAPUTO—See WPP plc; *Int'l*, pg. 8479
IMAGE MICROSYSTEMS - COMMERCE—See Image Microsystems, Inc.; *U.S. Private*, pg. 2044
IMAGE MICROSYSTEMS, INC.; *U.S. Private*, pg. 2044
IMAGENET CONSULTING, LLC—See BMI Systems Corporation; *U.S. Private*, pg. 601
IMAGENET, LLC; *U.S. Private*, pg. 2045
IMAGEN PUBLICIDAD S.A.—See WPP plc; *Int'l*, pg. 8472
IMAGE OFFICE SERVICES—See Arvig Enterprises, Inc.; *U.S. Private*, pg. 345
IMAGEONE CO., LTD.; *Int'l*, pg. 3618
IMAGE ONE CORP.; *U.S. Private*, pg. 2044
IMAGE PAKISTAN LIMITED; *Int'l*, pg. 3617
IMAGE POLYMERS COMPANY—See Mitsui Chemicals, Inc.; *Int'l*, pg. 4981
IMAGE POWER S.A.; *Int'l*, pg. 3617
IMAGE PROCESSING SYSTEMS, INC.—See Edenred S.A.; *Int'l*, pg. 2307
IMAGE PROJECT, INC.; *U.S. Private*, pg. 2044
IMAGE PROJECTIONS WEST, INC.; *U.S. Private*, pg. 2045
IMAGE PROTECT, INC.; *U.S. Public*, pg. 1112
IMAGE PUBLISHING CO. LTD.—See GMM Grammy Public Company Limited; *Int'l*, pg. 3012
IMAGEQUEST, INC.—See Xerox Holdings Corporation; *U.S. Public*, pg. 2387
IMAGE RESOURCES NL; *Int'l*, pg. 3617
IMAGERIE DU FLON S.A.—See Sonic Healthcare Limited; *Int'l*, pg. 7097
IMA GERMANY GMBH—See I.M.A. Industria Macchine Automatiche S.p.A.; *Int'l*, pg. 3565
IMAGESAT INTERNATIONAL (ISI) LTD.; *Int'l*, pg. 3618
IMAGESCAN CREATIVE SDN. BHD.—See Versatile Creative Berhad; *Int'l*, pg. 8174
IMAGE SCAN HOLDINGS PLC; *Int'l*, pg. 3617
IMAGE SCAN LLC—See TE Connectivity Ltd.; *Int'l*, pg. 7497
IMAGE SENSING SYSTEMS EUROPE LIMITED—See Autoscope Technologies Corporation; *U.S. Public*, pg. 238
IMAGE SENSING SYSTEMS GERMANY, GMBH—See Autoscope Technologies Corporation; *U.S. Public*, pg. 238
IMAGE SENSING SYSTEMS HK LIMITED—See Autoscope Technologies Corporation; *U.S. Public*, pg. 239
IMAGE SENSING SYSTEMS UK LIMITED—See Autoscope Technologies Corporation; *U.S. Public*, pg. 239
IMAGES FLOORING, INC.—See The Sterling Group, L.P.; *U.S. Private*, pg. 4122
IMAGESOFT, INC.—See i3 Verticals, Inc.; *U.S. Public*, pg. 1081
IMAGE SOLUTIONS APPAREL, INC.; *U.S. Private*, pg. 2045
IMAGESTOCKHOUSE INC.; *U.S. Private*, pg. 2045
IMAGE STREAM MEDICAL, INC.—See Olympus Corporation; *Int'l*, pg. 5556
IMAGES USA; *U.S. Private*, pg. 2045
IMAGE SYSTEMS AB; *Int'l*, pg. 3618
IMAGE SYSTEMS NORDIC AB—See Image Systems AB; *Int'l*, pg. 3618
IMAGETAG, INC.—See Aldrich Capital Partners, LLC; *U.S. Private*, pg. 160
IMAGE TECHNOLOGY SPECIALISTS, INC.—See Xerox Holdings Corporation; *U.S. Public*, pg. 2387
IMAGETECH SYSTEMS INC.—See Black Belt Solutions LLC; *U.S. Private*, pg. 569
IMAGETEC L.P.; *U.S. Private*, pg. 2045
IMAGETREND, INC.; *U.S. Private*, pg. 2045
IMAGE WATCHES, INC.; *U.S. Private*, pg. 2045
IMAGEX, INC.—See Hits, Inc; *U.S. Private*, pg. 1953
IMAG GROUP, INC.; *U.S. Private*, pg. 2044
IMAGICA ALOBASE CO., LTD.—See Imagica Group Inc.; *Int'l*, pg. 3618
IMAGICAAWORLD ENTERTAINMENT LTD.; *Int'l*, pg. 3619
IMAGICA CORP. OF AMERICA—See IMAGICA Corp.; *Int'l*, pg. 3618
IMAGICA CORP.; *Int'l*, pg. 3618
IMAGICA DIGITAL SCAPE CO., LTD.—See Imagica Group Inc.; *Int'l*, pg. 3618
IMAGICA GROUP INC.; *Int'l*, pg. 3618
IMAGICA KADOKAWA EDITORIAL CO., LTD.—See Imagica Group Inc.; *Int'l*, pg. 3618
IMAGICA LAB. INC.—See Imagica Group Inc.; *Int'l*, pg. 3618
IMAGICA LIVE CORP.—See Imagica Group Inc.; *Int'l*, pg. 3618
IMAGICA TOTAL SERVICE CORP.—See Imagica Group Inc.; *Int'l*, pg. 3618
IMAGICA TV CORP.—See Imagica Group Inc.; *Int'l*, pg. 3618

IMAGICA GROUP INC.
CORPORATE AFFILIATIONS

IMAGIC—See H.I.G. Capital, LLC; *U.S. Private*, pg. 1827
IMAGI INTERNATIONAL HOLDINGS LTD.; *Int'l*, pg. 3618
IMAGINA INTERNATIONAL SALES, S.L.U.—See WPP plc; *Int'l*, pg. 8474
IMAGINA MEDIA AUDIOVISUAL, S.L.—See Orient Securities Company Limited; *Int'l*, pg. 5622
IMAGINARY FORCES LLC; *U.S. Private*, pg. 2045
IMAGINATION (ASIA) LTD.—See The Imagination Group Limited; *Int'l*, pg. 7654
IMAGINATION AUSTRALIA PTY LIMITED—See The Imagination Group Limited; *Int'l*, pg. 7654
IMAGINATION (DEUTSCHLAND) GMBH—See The Imagination Group Limited; *Int'l*, pg. 7654
THE IMAGINATION FACTORY; *U.S. Private*, pg. 4055
THE IMAGINATION GROUP LIMITED; *Int'l*, pg. 7654
IMAGINATION PUBLISHING, LLC; *U.S. Private*, pg. 2045
IMAGINATION (SCANDINAVIA) AB—See The Imagination Group Limited; *Int'l*, pg. 7654
IMAGINATION SPECIALTIES, INC.; *U.S. Private*, pg. 2045
IMAGINATION TECHNOLOGIES GROUP LIMITED—See Canyon Bridge Capital Partners, Inc.; *Int'l*, pg. 1300
IMAGINATION TECHNOLOGIES HYDERABAD PVT, LTD.—See Nordic Semiconductor ASA; *Int'l*, pg. 5423
IMAGINATION TECHNOLOGIES INDIA PVT. LTD.—See Canyon Bridge Capital Partners, Inc.; *Int'l*, pg. 1300
IMAGINATION TECHNOLOGIES KK—See Canyon Bridge Capital Partners, Inc.; *Int'l*, pg. 1300
IMAGINATION TECHNOLOGIES LTD.—See Canyon Bridge Capital Partners, Inc.; *Int'l*, pg. 1300
IMAGINATION (USA) INC. - DETROIT—See The Imagination Group Limited; *Int'l*, pg. 7654
IMAGINATION (USA) INC. - LOS ANGELES—See The Imagination Group Limited; *Int'l*, pg. 7654
IMAGINATION (USA) INC. - NEW YORK—See The Imagination Group Limited; *Int'l*, pg. 7654
IMAGINEAR INC.; *Int'l*, pg. 3619
IMAGINE ASIA CO., LTD.—See Ascendio Co., Ltd.; *Int'l*, pg. 601
IMAGINE COMMUNICATIONS - ARGENTINA—See The Gores Group, LLC; *U.S. Private*, pg. 4035
IMAGINE COMMUNICATIONS - AUSTRALIA—See The Gores Group, LLC; *U.S. Private*, pg. 4035
IMAGINE COMMUNICATIONS - AUSTRIA—See The Gores Group, LLC; *U.S. Private*, pg. 4035
IMAGINE COMMUNICATIONS - BRAZIL—See The Gores Group, LLC; *U.S. Private*, pg. 4035
IMAGINE COMMUNICATIONS CANADA LTD.—See The Gores Group, LLC; *U.S. Private*, pg. 4035
IMAGINE COMMUNICATIONS - CHINA—See The Gores Group, LLC; *U.S. Private*, pg. 4035
IMAGINE COMMUNICATIONS CORP. - CHESAPEAKE—See The Gores Group, LLC; *U.S. Private*, pg. 4035
IMAGINE COMMUNICATIONS CORP. - GERMANY—See L3Harris Technologies, Inc.; *U.S. Public*, pg. 1280
IMAGINE COMMUNICATIONS CORP. - NORTHRIDGE—See The Gores Group, LLC; *U.S. Private*, pg. 4035
IMAGINE COMMUNICATIONS CORP.—See The Gores Group, LLC; *U.S. Private*, pg. 4034
IMAGINE COMMUNICATIONS - FRANCE—See The Gores Group, LLC; *U.S. Private*, pg. 4035
IMAGINE COMMUNICATIONS - GERMANY—See The Gores Group, LLC; *U.S. Private*, pg. 4035
IMAGINE COMMUNICATIONS - HONG KONG—See The Gores Group, LLC; *U.S. Private*, pg. 4035
IMAGINE COMMUNICATIONS - HUNGARY—See The Gores Group, LLC; *U.S. Private*, pg. 4035
IMAGINE COMMUNICATIONS - INDIA—See The Gores Group, LLC; *U.S. Private*, pg. 4035
IMAGINE COMMUNICATIONS - JAPAN—See The Gores Group, LLC; *U.S. Private*, pg. 4035
IMAGINE COMMUNICATIONS - MEXICO—See The Gores Group, LLC; *U.S. Private*, pg. 4035
IMAGINE COMMUNICATIONS - SINGAPORE—See The Gores Group, LLC; *U.S. Private*, pg. 4035
IMAGINE CRUISING LIMITED—See The Emirates Group; *Int'l*, pg. 7639
IMAGINE CRUISING (PTY) LTD.—See The Emirates Group; *Int'l*, pg. 7639
IMAGINE CRUISING PTY LTD—See The Emirates Group; *Int'l*, pg. 7639
IMAGINEEASY SOLUTIONS, LLC; *U.S. Private*, pg. 2045
IMAGINE EDITIONS SAS—See CompuGroup Medical SE & Co. KGaA; *Int'l*, pg. 1757
IMAGINEENGINE—See Foundation 9 Entertainment, Inc.; *U.S. Private*, pg. 1579
IMAGINE ENTERTAINMENT; *U.S. Private*, pg. 2045
IMAGINEER CO., LTD.; *Int'l*, pg. 3619
IMAGINE LEARNING, LLC—See Silver Lake Group, LLC; *U.S. Private*, pg. 3661
IMAGINE LITHIUM INC.; *Int'l*, pg. 3619
IMAGINE NATION BOOKS, LTD.; *U.S. Private*, pg. 2045
IMAGINE POS LIMITED—See Li & Fung Limited; *Int'l*, pg. 4479
IMAGINE! PRINT SOLUTIONS, INC.—See Keystone Group, L.P.; *U.S. Private*, pg. 2298
IMAGINE SOFTWARE INC.; *U.S. Private*, pg. 2045

IMAGINE STAFFING TECHNOLOGY, INC.; *U.S. Private*, pg. 2045
IMAGINE SWIMMING, INC.; *U.S. Private*, pg. 2045
IMAGINE THAT, INC.—See ANDRITZ AG; *Int'l*, pg. 453
IMAGINE THIS, INC.; *U.S. Private*, pg. 2045
IMAGINETICS LLC—See Centerfield Capital Partners, LLC; *U.S. Private*, pg. 816
IMAGINETICS LLC—See Kidd & Company LLC; *U.S. Private*, pg. 2302
IMAGING ALLIANCE GROUP, LLC; *U.S. Private*, pg. 2046
IMAGING ASSOCIATES INC.; *U.S. Private*, pg. 2046
IMAGING BUSINESS MACHINES LLC; *U.S. Private*, pg. 2046
IMAGING BUSINESS SYSTEMS (N.I.) LIMITED—See Xerox Holdings Corporation; *U.S. Public*, pg. 2387
IMAGING CENTER AT BAXTER VILLAGE, L.L.C.—See Tenet Healthcare Corporation; *U.S. Public*, pg. 2008
IMAGING CONCEPTS OF NEW MEXICO, INC.—See Xerox Holdings Corporation; *U.S. Public*, pg. 2387
IMAGING CORE LAB LLC—See Cinven Limited; *Int'l*, pg. 1612
IMAGING DYNAMICS COMPANY LTD.; *Int'l*, pg. 3619
IMAGING EXPERTS & HEALTHCARE SERVICES S.A.S.—See IMEXHS Limited; *Int'l*, pg. 3624
IMAGING SCIENCES INTERNATIONAL LLC—See Danaher Corporation; *U.S. Public*, pg. 627
IMAGING SERVICES OF LOUISIANA, LLC—See HCA Healthcare, Inc.; *U.S. Public*, pg. 999
IMAGING SPECTRUM INC.—See Photoreflect, LLC; *U.S. Private*, pg. 3174
IMAGING SUPPLIES & EQUIPMENT; *U.S. Private*, pg. 2046
IMAGINIT TECHNOLOGIES—See Rand Worldwide, Inc.; *U.S. Public*, pg. 1762
IMAGIN MEDICAL INC.; *Int'l*, pg. 3619
IMAG - INTERNATIONALER MESSEUND AUSSTELLUNGSDIENST GMBH—See Messe Munchen GmbH; *Int'l*, pg. 4841
IMAGINUITY INTERACTIVE, INC.—See Calise Partners, LLC; *U.S. Private*, pg. 721
IMAGION BIOSYSTEMS LIMITED; *Int'l*, pg. 3619
IMAGIS CO., LTD.; *Int'l*, pg. 3619
IMAGITAS, INC.—See Red Ventures, LLC; *U.S. Private*, pg. 3376
IMAGN CONTENT SERVICES, LLC—See Gannett Co., Inc.; *U.S. Public*, pg. 906
IMAGO BIOSCIENCES, INC.—See Merck & Co., Inc.; *U.S. Public*, pg. 1416
IMAGO GROUP; *Int'l*, pg. 3619
IMAGO NORTH AMERICA—See IMAGO Group; *Int'l*, pg. 3619
IMA GROUP MANAGEMENT COMPANY, LLC; *U.S. Private*, pg. 2044
IMA INC.—See IMA Financial Group, Inc.; *U.S. Private*, pg. 2043
I.M.A. INDUSTRIA MACCHINE AUTOMATICHE S.P.A.; *Int'l*, pg. 3565
IMAJE NORDIC AB—See Dover Corporation; *U.S. Public*, pg. 680
IMA, KANSAS INC.—See IMA Financial Group, Inc.; *U.S. Private*, pg. 2043
IMAKENEWS, INC.—See The Reynolds & Reynolds Company; *U.S. Private*, pg. 4106
IMA KILIAN VERWALTUNGS GMBH—See I.M.A. Industria Macchine Automatiche S.p.A.; *Int'l*, pg. 3565
IMA KLESSMANN GMBH—See Schelling Anlagenbau GmbH; *Int'l*, pg. 6615
IMA (KLESSMANN) UK LTD.—See Schelling Anlagenbau GmbH; *Int'l*, pg. 6615
IMAKO A.D.; *Int'l*, pg. 3619
IMA LIFE (BEIJING) PHARMACEUTICAL SYSTEMS CO. LTD.—See I.M.A. Industria Macchine Automatiche S.p.A.; *Int'l*, pg. 3565
IMA LIFE NORTH AMERICA INC.—See I.M.A. Industria Macchine Automatiche S.p.A.; *Int'l*, pg. 3565
IMA LIFE THE NETHERLANDS B.V.—See I.M.A. Industria Macchine Automatiche S.p.A.; *Int'l*, pg. 3565
IMA MATERIALFORSCHUNG UND ANWENDUNGSTECHNIK GMBH—See I Squared Capital Advisors (US) LLC; *U.S. Private*, pg. 2022
IMA MATERIALFORSCHUNG UND ANWENDUNGSTECHNIK GMBH—See TDR Capital LLP; *Int'l*, pg. 7492
IMAM BUTTON INDUSTRIES LTD.; *Int'l*, pg. 3619
IMA MEDTECH SWITZERLAND SA—See I.M.A. Industria Macchine Automatiche S.p.A.; *Int'l*, pg. 3565
THE IMAMURA SECURITIES CO., LTD.; *Int'l*, pg. 7654
IMANAGE LLC; *U.S. Private*, pg. 2046
IMA NORTH AMERICA INC.—See I.M.A. Industria Macchine Automatiche S.p.A.; *Int'l*, pg. 3565
IMA OF COLORADO, INC.—See IMA Financial Group, Inc.; *U.S. Private*, pg. 2043
IMA OF TOPEKA INC.—See IMA Financial Group, Inc.; *U.S. Private*, pg. 2043
IMA PACIFIC CO. LTD.—See I.M.A. Industria Macchine Automatiche S.p.A.; *Int'l*, pg. 3565
IMA PACKAGING & PROCESSING EQUIPMENT CO. LTD.—See I.M.A. Industria Macchine Automatiche S.p.A.; *Int'l*, pg. 3566

IMA-PG INDIA PVT. LTD.—See I.M.A. Industria Macchine Automatiche S.p.A.; *Int'l*, pg. 3566
IMA POLSKA SP. Z O.O.—See Schelling Anlagenbau GmbH; *Int'l*, pg. 6616
IMAQLIQ SERVICE LTD.; *Int'l*, pg. 3619
IMARC LLC; *U.S. Private*, pg. 2046
IMAREX ASA; *Int'l*, pg. 3619
IMAREX, INC.—See IMAREX ASA; *Int'l*, pg. 3619
IMARI STEEL CENTER CO., LTD.—See Namura Shipbuilding Co., Ltd.; *Int'l*, pg. 5136
IMARI TOYO CO., LTD.—See Toyo Suisan Kaisha, Ltd.; *Int'l*, pg. 7858
IMARKET COMMUNICATIONS INC.—See Speakerbus, Inc.; *U.S. Private*, pg. 3747
IMARKETEUROPE KFT.—See iMarketKorea, Inc.; *Int'l*, pg. 3620
IMARKETING SOLUTIONS GROUP INC.; *Int'l*, pg. 3619
IMARKETKOREA, INC.; *Int'l*, pg. 3620
IMARKETS LIMITED—See CK Hutchison Holdings Limited; *Int'l*, pg. 1638
IMARK INTEGRATED MARKETING SERVICES; *U.S. Private*, pg. 2046
IMARK MOLDING, INC.—See Comar, LLC; *U.S. Private*, pg. 980
IMARLIN—See The Marlin Network, Inc.; *U.S. Private*, pg. 4075
IMA RUS—See Schelling Anlagenbau GmbH; *Int'l*, pg. 6616
IMAS A.E.—See Continental Aktiengesellschaft; *Int'l*, pg. 1781
IMASA S.A.; *Int'l*, pg. 3620
IMASBLUE—See WPP plc; *Int'l*, pg. 8474
IMASCAP SAS—See Wright Medical Group N.V.; *Int'l*, pg. 8494
IMASEN BUCYRUS TECHNOLOGY INC.—See Imasen Electric Industrial Co., Ltd.; *Int'l*, pg. 3620
IMASEN ELECTRIC INDUSTRIAL CO., LTD.; *Int'l*, pg. 3620
IMASEN ELECTRIC & MACHINERY CO., LTD.—See Imasen Electric Industrial Co., Ltd.; *Int'l*, pg. 3620
IMASEN ENGINEERING CORPORATION—See Imasen Electric Industrial Co., Ltd.; *Int'l*, pg. 3620
IMASEN MANUFACTURING (THAILAND) CO., LTD.—See Imasen Electric Industrial Co., Ltd.; *Int'l*, pg. 3620
IMASEN PHILIPPINE MANUFACTURING CORPORATION—See Imasen Electric Industrial Co., Ltd.; *Int'l*, pg. 3620
IMAS MAKINE SANAYI A.S.—See Loras Holding A.S.; *Int'l*, pg. 4557
IMASPRO CORPORATION BERHAD; *Int'l*, pg. 3620
IMASPRO RESOURCES SDN. BHD.—See IMASPRO Corporation Berhad; *Int'l*, pg. 3620
I.M.A. S.R.L.—See Koch Industries, Inc.; *U.S. Private*, pg. 2335
IM ASSOCIATES BV—See IQVIA Holdings Inc.; *U.S. Public*, pg. 1168
IMASTE-IPS S.L.—See ON24, Inc.; *U.S. Public*, pg. 1601
IMAT AUTOMOTIVE TECHNOLOGY SERVICES INC.—See Centre Testing International Corporation; *Int'l*, pg. 1411
IMAT AUTOMOTIVE TECHNOLOGY SERVICES MEXICO S. DE R.L. DE C.V.—See Centre Testing International Corporation; *Int'l*, pg. 1411
IMATEQ ITALIA S.R.L.—See Vossloh AG; *Int'l*, pg. 8308
IMATEQ SAS—See Vossloh AG; *Int'l*, pg. 8308
IMATRA BV—See DPG Media Group NV; *Int'l*, pg. 2189
IMATRA PAPERBOARDS—See Stora Enso Oyj; *Int'l*, pg. 7224
IMAT (SHENYANG) AUTOMOTIVE TECHNOLOGY CO., LTD.—See Centre Testing International Corporation; *Int'l*, pg. 1411
IMAT—See Marcegaglia S.p.A.; *Int'l*, pg. 4688
IMAT-UVE AUTOMOTIVE TESTING CENTER (PTY.) LTD.—See Centre Testing International Corporation; *Int'l*, pg. 1411
IMATX, INC.—See restor3d, Inc.; *U.S. Private*, pg. 3409
IMA UK LTD.—See I.M.A. Industria Macchine Automatiche S.p.A.; *Int'l*, pg. 3566
IM AUTOTRADE HOLDING G.M.B.H—See ITOCHU Corporation; *Int'l*, pg. 3836
IMAVEN IMOVEIS LTDA.—See Ultrapar Participacoes S.A.; *Int'l*, pg. 8019
IMA WORLD HEALTH; *U.S. Private*, pg. 2044
IMAX CHINA HOLDING, INC.—See Imax Corporation; *Int'l*, pg. 3620
IMAX CORPORATION; *Int'l*, pg. 3620
IMAX CORPORATION—See Imax Corporation; *Int'l*, pg. 3620
IMAX DIAGNOSTIC IMAGING LIMITED—See Zhejiang Starry Pharmaceutical Co., Ltd.; *Int'l*, pg. 8663
IMAX (SHANGHAI) MULTIMEDIA TECHNOLOGY CO., LTD.—See Imax Corporation; *Int'l*, pg. 3620
IMAXSHIFT, LLC—See Imax Corporation; *Int'l*, pg. 3620
IMAX VR, LLC—See Imax Corporation; *Int'l*, pg. 3620
IMAZINS CO., LTD.—See Saramin Co.; *Int'l*, pg. 6576
IMAZO AB—See Storskogen Group AB; *Int'l*, pg. 7227
IMBC CO., LTD.; *Int'l*, pg. 3620
IMBER COURT REPORTERS INC.—See Apax Partners LLP; *Int'l*, pg. 503

COMPANY NAME INDEX

IMB INDUSTRIE MONTAGE GMBH—See Pirson Montage SA; *Int'l*, pg. 5875
IMB PARTNERS; *U.S. Private*, pg. 2046
I&M BURBIDGE CAPITAL LIMITED—See I&M Group Plc; *Int'l*, pg. 3562
IMBV B.V.—See IHI Corporation; *Int'l*, pg. 3605
IMBV B.V.—See JFE Holdings, Inc.; *Int'l*, pg. 3938
IM CANNABIS CORP.; *Int'l*, pg. 3617
IM+ CAPITALS LIMITED; *Int'l*, pg. 3617
IMCAP PARTNERS AG; *Int'l*, pg. 3621
IMC ASSET MANAGEMENT B.V.—See IMC International Marketmakers Combination B.V.; *Int'l*, pg. 3620
IMC CONSULTING; *U.S. Private*, pg. 2046
IMCD ALGERIA—See IMCD N.V.; *Int'l*, pg. 3621
IMCD ASIA PTE. LTD.—See IMCD N.V.; *Int'l*, pg. 3621
IMCD AUSTRALIA LIMITED—See IMCD N.V.; *Int'l*, pg. 3621
IMCD BALTICS UAB—See IMCD N.V.; *Int'l*, pg. 3621
IMCD BENELUX BV—See IMCD N.V.; *Int'l*, pg. 3621
IMCD BENELUX B.V.—See IMCD N.V.; *Int'l*, pg. 3621
IMCD BENELUX N.V.—See IMCD N.V.; *Int'l*, pg. 3621
IMCD BRASIL COMERCIO E INDUSTRIA DE PRODUTOS QUIMICOS LTDA.—See IMCD N.V.; *Int'l*, pg. 3621
IMCD CANADA LIMITED—See IMCD N.V.; *Int'l*, pg. 3621
IMCD CZECH REPUBLIC A.S.—See IMCD N.V.; *Int'l*, pg. 3621
IMCD DANMARK A/S—See IMCD N.V.; *Int'l*, pg. 3622
IMCD DEUTSCHLAND GMBH & CO. KG—See IMCD N.V.; *Int'l*, pg. 3621
IMCD EGYPT LLC—See IMCD N.V.; *Int'l*, pg. 3621
IMCD ESPANA ESPECIALIDADES QUIMICAS, S.A.—See IMCD N.V.; *Int'l*, pg. 3621
IMCD FINLAND OY—See IMCD N.V.; *Int'l*, pg. 3622
IMCD FRANCE S.A.S.—See IMCD N.V.; *Int'l*, pg. 3622
IMCD GROUP B.V.—See IMCD N.V.; *Int'l*, pg. 3621
IMCD INDIA—See IMCD N.V.; *Int'l*, pg. 3622
IMCD IRELAND LTD—See IMCD N.V.; *Int'l*, pg. 3622
IMCD ITALIA S.P.A.—See IMCD N.V.; *Int'l*, pg. 3622
IMCD KENYA LTD.—See IMCD N.V.; *Int'l*, pg. 3622
IMCD MALAYSIA SDN BHD—See IMCD N.V.; *Int'l*, pg. 3622
IMCD MAROC S.A.R.L.—See IMCD N.V.; *Int'l*, pg. 3621
IMCD MEXICO S.A. DE C.V.—See IMCD N.V.; *Int'l*, pg. 3622
IMCD MIDDLE EAST ZFCO—See IMCD N.V.; *Int'l*, pg. 3622
IMCD NEW ZEALAND LTD.—See IMCD N.V.; *Int'l*, pg. 3622
IMCD NORWAY AS—See IMCD N.V.; *Int'l*, pg. 3622
IMCD N.V.; *Int'l*, pg. 3621
IMCD PHILIPPINES CORPORATION—See IMCD N.V.; *Int'l*, pg. 3622
IMCD PLASTICS (SHANGHAI) CO., LTD.—See IMCD N.V.; *Int'l*, pg. 3622
IMCD POLSKA SP. Z.O.O.—See IMCD N.V.; *Int'l*, pg. 3622
IMCD PORTUGAL PRODUTOS QUIMICOS, LDA.—See IMCD N.V.; *Int'l*, pg. 3621
IMCD RUS LLC—See IMCD N.V.; *Int'l*, pg. 3622
IMCD (SHANGHAI) TRADING CO. LTD.—See IMCD N.V.; *Int'l*, pg. 3622
IMCD SINGAPORE PTE. LTD.—See IMCD N.V.; *Int'l*, pg. 3622
IMCD SOUTH AFRICA (PTY) LTD.—See IMCD N.V.; *Int'l*, pg. 3622
IMCD SOUTH EAST EUROPE GMBH—See IMCD N.V.; *Int'l*, pg. 3622
IMCD SWEDEN AB—See IMCD N.V.; *Int'l*, pg. 3622
IMCD SWITZERLAND AG—See IMCD N.V.; *Int'l*, pg. 3622
IMCD (THAILAND) CO.—See IMCD N.V.; *Int'l*, pg. 3621
IMCD TICARET PAZARLAMA VE DANISMANLIK LIMITED SIRKETI—See IMCD N.V.; *Int'l*, pg. 3622
IMCD TUNISIA S.A.R.L.—See IMCD N.V.; *Int'l*, pg. 3622
IMCD UK LTD.—See IMCD N.V.; *Int'l*, pg. 3622
IMCD UKRAINE LLC—See IMCD N.V.; *Int'l*, pg. 3622
IMCD US—See IMCD N.V.; *Int'l*, pg. 3622
IMCD VIETNAM COMPANY LTD.—See IMCD N.V.; *Int'l*, pg. 3622
IMC EXPLORATION GROUP PLC; *Int'l*, pg. 3620
IMC (GERMANY) HOLDINGS GMBH—See Berkshire Hathaway Inc.; *U.S. Public*, pg. 307
IMC GLOBAL SERVICES—See Calibre Systems Inc.; *U.S. Private*, pg. 717
IMC GROUP USA HOLDINGS, INC.—See Berkshire Hathaway Inc.; *U.S. Public*, pg. 307
IMC HOLDING, LLC; *U.S. Private*, pg. 2046
IMC HOLDINGS GMBH—See Berkshire Hathaway Inc.; *U.S. Public*, pg. 307
IMC HOLDINGS, INC.; *U.S. Private*, pg. 2046
IMC INC.—See International Management Consultants Inc.; *U.S. Private*, pg. 2118
IMC INC.; *U.S. Private*, pg. 2046
IMC INDUSTRIAL PTE. LTD.—See IMC Pan Asia Alliance Pte. Ltd.; *Int'l*, pg. 3621
IMC INTERNATIONAL MARKETMAKERS COMBINATION B.V.; *Int'l*, pg. 3620
IMC INTERNATIONAL METALWORKING COMPANIES B.V.—See Berkshire Hathaway Inc.; *U.S. Public*, pg. 307
IMC INVESTMENTS PTE. LTD.—See IMC Pan Asia Alliance Pte. Ltd.; *Int'l*, pg. 3621
IMC LTD—See The Middleby Corporation; *U.S. Public*, pg. 2114
IMC MAGNETICS CORP.—See Curtiss-Wright Corporation; *U.S. Public*, pg. 611
IMC MP D.O.O—See Universal Music Group N.V.; *Int'l*, pg. 8079
IMCO CARBIDE TOOL INC.; *U.S. Private*, pg. 2046
IMCO INDUSTRIES LTD.; *Int'l*, pg. 3623
IM CO., LTD.; *Int'l*, pg. 3617
IMCORP; *U.S. Private*, pg. 2046
IMC PAN ASIA ALLIANCE PTE. LTD.; *Int'l*, pg. 3621
IMC RESOURCES (AUSTRALIA) PTY LTD—See IMC Pan Asia Alliance Pte. Ltd.; *Int'l*, pg. 3621
IMC RESOURCES (CHINA) LTD—See IMC Pan Asia Alliance Pte. Ltd.; *Int'l*, pg. 3621
IMC RETAIL, LLC—See Starwood Property Trust, Inc.; *U.S. Public*, pg. 1939
IMC SHIPPING (CHINA) COMPANY LIMITED—See IMC Pan Asia Alliance Pte. Ltd.; *Int'l*, pg. 3621
IMC SHIPPING SERVICES CO. PTE. LTD.—See IMC Pan Asia Alliance Pte. Ltd.; *Int'l*, pg. 3621
IMCS MARINE (SHANGHAI) CO., LTD.—See IHI Corporation; *Int'l*, pg. 3605
IMCS MARINE (SHANGHAI) CO., LTD.—See JFE Holdings, Inc.; *Int'l*, pg. 3938
IMC; *Int'l*, pg. 3620
IMC SUPPLY COMPANY—See Stellar Industrial Supply LLC; *U.S. Private*, pg. 3799
IMC TRADING B.V.—See IMC International Marketmakers Combination B.V.; *Int'l*, pg. 3620
IMDAD MEDICAL BUSINESS COMPANY LTD.—See Xenel Industries Ltd.; *Int'l*, pg. 8521
IMD ADSAT LIMITED—See Vitruvian Partners LLP; *Int'l*, pg. 8263
IMDEX LIMITED; *Int'l*, pg. 3623
IMDEX TECHNOLOGY GERMANY GMBH—See Imdex Limited; *Int'l*, pg. 3623
IMDEX TECHNOLOGY UK LTD—See Imdex Limited; *Int'l*, pg. 3623
I.M.D. INTERNATIONAL MEDICAL DEVICES S.P.A.; *Int'l*, pg. 3566
IMD INTERNATIONAL; *Int'l*, pg. 3623
IMDSOFT—See TPG Capital, L.P.; *U.S. Public*, pg. 2177
IMD SOFT—See Constellation Software Inc.; *Int'l*, pg. 1774
I.M.E. 2016 B.V—See Asahi Kasei Corporation; *Int'l*, pg. 597
IMECO EINWEGPRODUKTE GMBH & CO. KG VLIESSTOFFVERTRIEB—See INDUS Holding AG; *Int'l*, pg. 3663
IMECO GMBH & CO. KG—See INDUS Holding AG; *Int'l*, pg. 3663
IMECO, INC.—See J.F. Lehman & Company, Inc.; *U.S. Private*, pg. 2163
IMECS CO., LTD.—See ITOCHU Corporation; *Int'l*, pg. 3836
IMEC SERVICES LIMITED; *Int'l*, pg. 3623
I.MEC S.R.L.—See Interpump Group S.p.A.; *Int'l*, pg. 3755
IMECS (SHANGHAI) CO., LTD.—See ITOCHU Corporation; *Int'l*, pg. 3837
IMEDEX S.R.O.—See Mauna Kea Technologies SA; *Int'l*, pg. 4732
I MEDIA CORP LTD.—See DB Corp Limited; *Int'l*, pg. 1986
I-MEDI ASIA LIMITED—See Perfect Medical Health Management Limited; *Int'l*, pg. 5798
IMEDICAL EQUIPMENT & SERVICES LLC; *U.S. Private*, pg. 2046
IMEDICARE CO., LTD.—See Zensho Holdings Co., Ltd.; *Int'l*, pg. 8634
I-MED RADIOLOGY NETWORK LTD.—See Permira Advisers LLP; *Int'l*, pg. 5805
IMED STAR SERVICOS DE DESEMPENHO ORGANIZACIONAL LTDA.—See UnitedHealth Group Incorporated; *U.S. Public*, pg. 2241
IMEDX, INC.; *U.S. Private*, pg. 2046
IMEET CENTRAL—See Siris Capital Group, LLC; *U.S. Private*, pg. 3674
IMEG CORP.; *U.S. Private*, pg. 2046
IMEIK TECHNOLOGY DEVELOPMENT CO., LTD.; *Int'l*, pg. 3623
IME INTERMOUNTAIN ELECTRIC, INC.—See Quanta Services, Inc.; *U.S. Public*, pg. 1751
IM ELECTRIC, INC.—See Quanta Services, Inc.; *U.S. Public*, pg. 1751
IMENTI TEA FACTORY COMPANY LIMITED—See Kenya Tea Development Agency Limited; *Int'l*, pg. 4129
IMER FRANCE—See IMER International S.p.A.; *Int'l*, pg. 3623
IMERI JOINT STOCK COMPANY; *Int'l*, pg. 3624
IMER INTERNATIONAL S.P.A.; *Int'l*, pg. 3623
IMERITI, INC.—See Simplicity Financial Marketing Holdings, Inc.; *U.S. Private*, pg. 3667
IMER USA, INC.—See IMER International S.p.A.; *Int'l*, pg. 3623
IMERYS ALUMINATES S.A.—See Groupe Bruxelles Lambert SA; *Int'l*, pg. 3100
IMERYS CERAMICS FRANCE—See Groupe Bruxelles Lambert SA; *Int'l*, pg. 3100
IMERYS KILN FURNITURE ESPANA, S.A.—See Groupe Bruxelles Lambert SA; *Int'l*, pg. 3100
IMERYS KILN FURNITURE FRANCE—See Groupe Bruxelles Lambert SA; *Int'l*, pg. 3100
IMERYS KILN FURNITURE HUNGARY KFT—See Groupe Bruxelles Lambert SA; *Int'l*, pg. 3100
IMERYS KILN FURNITURE THAILAND LTD.—See Groupe Bruxelles Lambert SA; *Int'l*, pg. 3100
IMERYS MARBLE INC.—See Groupe Bruxelles Lambert SA; *Int'l*, pg. 3100
IMERYS MINERALI S.P.A.—See Groupe Bruxelles Lambert SA; *Int'l*, pg. 3100
IMERYS MINERALS AB—See Groupe Bruxelles Lambert SA; *Int'l*, pg. 3100
IMERYS MINERAUX BELGIQUE S.A./NV—See Groupe Bruxelles Lambert SA; *Int'l*, pg. 3100
IMERYS MINERAUX FRANCE SA—See Groupe Bruxelles Lambert SA; *Int'l*, pg. 3100
IMERYS REFRACTORY MINERALS GLOMEL SAS—See Groupe Bruxelles Lambert SA; *Int'l*, pg. 3100
IMERYS SA—See Groupe Bruxelles Lambert SA; *Int'l*, pg. 3099
IMERYS SERVICES SAS—See Groupe Bruxelles Lambert SA; *Int'l*, pg. 3100
IMERYS TABLEWARE—See Groupe Bruxelles Lambert SA; *Int'l*, pg. 3100
IMERYS TILES MINERALS ITALIA SRL—See Groupe Bruxelles Lambert SA; *Int'l*, pg. 3100
IMERYS USA, INC.—See Groupe Bruxelles Lambert SA; *Int'l*, pg. 3100
IMESAPI, S.A.—See ACS, Actividades de Construccion y Servicios, S.A.; *Int'l*, pg. 114
IMES AS—See Instalco AB; *Int'l*, pg. 3721
IMES DEXIS—See Descours & Cabaud SA; *Int'l*, pg. 2044
I.M.E.S. - INDUSTRIA MECCANICA E STAMPAGGIO SPA—See UniCredit S.p.A.; *Int'l*, pg. 8034
IMES PTE. LTD.—See IHI Corporation; *Int'l*, pg. 3606
IMES PTE. LTD.—See JFE Holdings, Inc.; *Int'l*, pg. 3938
IMES S.R.L.—See Heidelberg Materials AG; *Int'l*, pg. 3316
IMETAL RESOURCES INC.; *Int'l*, pg. 3624
I METAL TECHNOLOGY CO., LTD. - KITAIBARAKI MATERIALS PROCESSING FACTORY—See SPARX Group Co., Ltd.; *Int'l*, pg. 7127
I METAL TECHNOLOGY CO., LTD. - KITAKAMI-KITA FACTORY—See SPARX Group Co., Ltd.; *Int'l*, pg. 7127
I METAL TECHNOLOGY CO., LTD.—See SPARX Group Co., Ltd.; *Int'l*, pg. 7127
IMETHODS, LLC; *U.S. Private*, pg. 2046
IMETREX TECHNOLOGIES LIMITED—See Siemens Aktiengesellschaft; *Int'l*, pg. 6901
IMEX CO., LTD.—See Hitachi Zosen Corporation; *Int'l*, pg. 3411
IMEX GLOBAL SOLUTIONS LLC—See bpost NV/SA; *Int'l*, pg. 1133
IMEX GROUP CO. LTD.—See Gree Electric Appliances, Inc. of Zhuhai; *Int'l*, pg. 3069
IMEXHS LIMITED; *Int'l*, pg. 3624
IMEX INTERNATIONAL CORP.; *U.S. Private*, pg. 2047
IMEX INTERNATIONAL INC.; *U.S. Private*, pg. 2047
IMEXPHARM CORPORATION; *Int'l*, pg. 3624
IM EXPRESS CO., LTD.—See Mitsui-Soko Holdings Co., Ltd.; *Int'l*, pg. 4992
IME YOUNYI CO., LTD.; *Int'l*, pg. 3623
IMF BENTHAM LIMITED; *Int'l*, pg. 3624
IM FLASH TECHNOLOGIES, LLC—See Micron Technology, Inc.; *U.S. Public*, pg. 1437
IM FOOD STYLE LTD.—See Isetan Mitsukoshi Holdings Ltd.; *Int'l*, pg. 3814
I.M.G. 2 S.R.L.; *Int'l*, pg. 3566
IMG ACADEMY, LLC—See Canada Pension Plan Investment Board; *Int'l*, pg. 1281
IMG ACADEMY, LLC—See EQT AB; *Int'l*, pg. 2470
IMG BARCELONA—See Silver Lake Group, LLC; *U.S. Private*, pg. 3657
IMG BARCELONA—See William Morris Endeavor Entertainment, LLC; *U.S. Private*, pg. 4524
IMG COLLEGE—See Silver Lake Group, LLC; *U.S. Private*, pg. 3657
IMG COLLEGE—See William Morris Endeavor Entertainment, LLC; *U.S. Private*, pg. 4524
IMG COMPANIES, LLC—See Francisco Partners Management, LP; *U.S. Private*, pg. 1590
IMG CORPORATION LTD.—See Kontron AG; *Int'l*, pg. 4276
IMG D.O.O.—See SOL S.p.A.; *Int'l*, pg. 7067
IMG HUNGARY—See Silver Lake Group, LLC; *U.S. Private*, pg. 3657
IMG HUNGARY—See William Morris Endeavor Entertainment, LLC; *U.S. Private*, pg. 4524
IM GLOBAL, LLC—See Reliance - ADA Group Limited; *Int'l*, pg. 6261
IM GLOBAL PARTNER SAS—See Eurazeo SE; *Int'l*, pg. 2530
IMG MEDIA LIMITED—See Silver Lake Group, LLC; *U.S. Private*, pg. 3654
IMG MIDDLE EAST - DUBAI—See Silver Lake Group, LLC; *U.S. Private*, pg. 3657

I.M.G. 2 S.R.L.

CORPORATE AFFILIATIONS

IMG MIDDLE EAST - DUBAI—See William Morris Endeavor Entertainment, LLC; *U.S. Private*, pg. 4524
IMG MUMBAI—See Silver Lake Group, LLC; *U.S. Private*, pg. 3657
IMG MUMBAI—See William Morris Endeavor Entertainment, LLC; *U.S. Private*, pg. 4524
I&M GROUP PLC; *Int'l*, pg. 3562
IMG SRC INC.—See Nippon Telegraph & Telephone Corporation; *Int'l*, pg. 5343
IMGT CO., LTD.; *Int'l*, pg. 3624
IMG TORONTO—See Silver Lake Group, LLC; *U.S. Private*, pg. 3657
IMG TORONTO—See William Morris Endeavor Entertainment, LLC; *U.S. Private*, pg. 4524
IMG UNIVERSE LLC—See Silver Lake Group, LLC; *U.S. Private*, pg. 3657
IMG UNIVERSE LLC—See William Morris Endeavor Entertainment, LLC; *U.S. Private*, pg. 4524
IMG WORLDWIDE - ASIA-PACIFIC HEADQUARTERS—See Silver Lake Group, LLC; *U.S. Private*, pg. 3657
IMG WORLDWIDE - ASIA-PACIFIC HEADQUARTERS—See William Morris Endeavor Entertainment, LLC; *U.S. Private*, pg. 4524
IMG WORLDWIDE - EMEA HEADQUARTERS—See Silver Lake Group, LLC; *U.S. Private*, pg. 3657
IMG WORLDWIDE - EMEA HEADQUARTERS—See William Morris Endeavor Entertainment, LLC; *U.S. Private*, pg. 4524
IMG WORLDWIDE, INC. - CLEVELAND—See Silver Lake Group, LLC; *U.S. Private*, pg. 3657
IMG WORLDWIDE, INC. - CLEVELAND—See William Morris Endeavor Entertainment, LLC; *U.S. Private*, pg. 4524
IMG WORLDWIDE, INC.—See Silver Lake Group, LLC; *U.S. Private*, pg. 3657
IMG WORLDWIDE, INC.—See William Morris Endeavor Entertainment, LLC; *U.S. Private*, pg. 4523
IMH FINANCIAL CORPORATION; *U.S. Private*, pg. 2047
IMH HOLDINGS, LLC—See IMH Financial Corporation; *U.S. Private*, pg. 2047
IM (HK) CO., LTD.—See IM Co., Ltd.; *Int'l*, pg. 3617
IMHOFF SAS—See VINCI S.A.; *Int'l*, pg. 8222
IMI AERO-DYNAMIEK BVBA—See IMI plc; *Int'l*, pg. 3625
IMI CCI SOUTH AFRICA (PTY) LTD—See IMI plc; *Int'l*, pg. 3625
IMI CO., LTD.; *Int'l*, pg. 3624
IMI COMPONENTS LTD—See IMI plc; *Int'l*, pg. 3625
IMI CORNELIUS HELLAS S.A.—See Berkshire Hathaway Inc.; *U.S. Public*, pg. 309
IMI ELEKTROMOS GEPEKET GYARTO KFT—See Nidec Corporation; *Int'l*, pg. 5277
IMI FONDI CHIUSI S.G.R. S.P.A.—See Intesa Sanpaolo S.p.A.; *Int'l*, pg. 3765
IMI HYDRONIC ENGINEERING AB—See IMI plc; *Int'l*, pg. 3625
IMI HYDRONIC ENGINEERING A/S—See IMI plc; *Int'l*, pg. 3625
IMI HYDRONIC ENGINEERING AS—See IMI plc; *Int'l*, pg. 3625
IMI HYDRONIC ENGINEERING BV—See IMI plc; *Int'l*, pg. 3625
IMI HYDRONIC ENGINEERING DEUTSCHLAND GMBH—See IMI plc; *Int'l*, pg. 3625
IMI HYDRONIC ENGINEERING FRANCE S.A.—See IMI plc; *Int'l*, pg. 3625
IMI HYDRONIC ENGINEERING FZE—See IMI plc; *Int'l*, pg. 3625
IMI HYDRONIC ENGINEERING GESMBH—See IMI plc; *Int'l*, pg. 3625
IMI HYDRONIC ENGINEERING INC—See IMI plc; *Int'l*, pg. 3625
IMI HYDRONIC ENGINEERING INTERNATIONAL SA—See IMI plc; *Int'l*, pg. 3625
IMI HYDRONIC ENGINEERING LIMITED—See IMI plc; *Int'l*, pg. 3625
IMI HYDRONIC ENGINEERING LTDA.—See IMI plc; *Int'l*, pg. 3625
IMI HYDRONIC ENGINEERING NV—See IMI plc; *Int'l*, pg. 3625
IMI HYDRONIC ENGINEERING OY—See IMI plc; *Int'l*, pg. 3625
IMI HYDRONIC ENGINEERING S.A.—See IMI plc; *Int'l*, pg. 3625
IMI HYDRONIC ENGINEERING (SPAIN) SAU—See IMI plc; *Int'l*, pg. 3625
IMI HYDRONIC ENGINEERING S.R.L.—See IMI plc; *Int'l*, pg. 3625
IMI HYDRONIC ENGINEERING SWITZERLAND AG—See IMI plc; *Int'l*, pg. 3625
IMI INC.—See Firan Technology Group Corporation; *Int'l*, pg. 2678
IMI INDOOR CLIMATE TRADING (SHANGHAI) CO LTD—See IMI plc; *Int'l*, pg. 3625
IMI INTERNATIONAL CO SRL—See IMI plc; *Int'l*, pg. 3625
IMI INTERNATIONAL D.O.O.—See IMI plc; *Int'l*, pg. 3625
IMI INTERNATIONAL KFT—See IMI plc; *Int'l*, pg. 3625
IMI INTERNATIONAL LLC—See IMI plc; *Int'l*, pg. 3625
IMI INTERNATIONAL SP ZOO—See IMI plc; *Int'l*, pg. 3625

IMI INTERNATIONAL S.R.O.—See IMI plc; *Int'l*, pg. 3625
IMI INVESTIMENTI S.P.A.—See Intesa Sanpaolo S.p.A.; *Int'l*, pg. 3765
IMI KABEL PTE. LTD.—See Karin Technology Holdings Limited; *Int'l*, pg. 4081
IMI KYNOCH LTD—See IMI plc; *Int'l*, pg. 3625
IMI MANUFACTURING DE MEXICO, SA DE CV—See IMI plc; *Int'l*, pg. 3625
IMIMOBILE INTELLIGENT NETWORKS LIMITED—See Cisco Systems, Inc.; *U.S. Public*, pg. 499
IMIMOBILE PLC—See Cisco Systems, Inc.; *U.S. Public*, pg. 499
IMIMOBILE PVT. LTD.—See Cisco Systems, Inc.; *U.S. Public*, pg. 499
IMINDS INTERACTIVE LIMITED—See Guoen Holdings Limited; *Int'l*, pg. 3186
IMING CORP.; *Int'l*, pg. 3627
IMINING TECHNOLOGIES INC.; *Int'l*, pg. 3627
IMI NORGREN HERION PVT. LIMITED—See IMI plc; *Int'l*, pg. 3625
IMI NORGREN LOS ANGELES—See IMI plc; *Int'l*, pg. 3625
IMI NORGREN LTD—See IMI plc; *Int'l*, pg. 3625
IMI NORGREN OY—See IMI plc; *Int'l*, pg. 3625
IMI NORGREN SA—See IMI plc; *Int'l*, pg. 3625
IMI NORGREN—See IMI plc; *Int'l*, pg. 3625
IMIN PARTNERS, L.P.; *U.S. Private*, pg. 2047
IMI OVERSEAS INVESTMENTS LTD—See IMI plc; *Int'l*, pg. 3625
IMI PLC; *Int'l*, pg. 3624
IMI PROPERTY INVESTMENTS LTD—See IMI plc; *Int'l*, pg. 3625
IMI SCOTT LTD—See IMI plc; *Int'l*, pg. 3626
IMI SOFTWARE LTD.; *Int'l*, pg. 3627
IMI WEBBER LTD—See IMI plc; *Int'l*, pg. 3626
IMJACK PLC; *Int'l*, pg. 3627
IMJ CORPORATION—See Accenture plc; *Int'l*, pg. 86
I&MJ GROSS COMPANY; *U.S. Private*, pg. 2026
IMLACH MOVERS INC.; *U.S. Private*, pg. 2047
IMLAY CITY FORD; *U.S. Private*, pg. 2047
IML CORPORATION—See ITOCHU Corporation; *Int'l*, pg. 3836
IMLERS POULTRY; *U.S. Private*, pg. 2047
I.M. MATERIAL CORPORATION—See Moriroku Holdings Company, Ltd.; *Int'l*, pg. 5047
I.M. MATERIALS CO., LTD.—See Moriroku Holdings Company, Ltd.; *Int'l*, pg. 5047
IMMATICS BIOTECHNOLOGIES GMBH—See Immatics N.V.; *Int'l*, pg. 3627
IMMATICS N.V.; *Int'l*, pg. 3627
IMMATICS US, INC.—See Immatics N.V.; *Int'l*, pg. 3627
IMMCO DIAGNOSTICS, INC.—See Trinity Biotech Plc; *Int'l*, pg. 7924
IMMEDIA BROADCASTING TRUSTEES LIMITED—See Immedia Group Plc; *Int'l*, pg. 3627
IMMEDIA BROADCAST LIMITED—See AVC Immedia Limited; *Int'l*, pg. 737
IMMEDIA GROUP PLC; *Int'l*, pg. 3627
IMMEDIA, INC.—See Liberty Diversified International Inc.; *U.S. Private*, pg. 2443
IMMEDIA, LLC; *U.S. Private*, pg. 2047
IMMEDIA SEMICONDUCTOR, INC.—See Amazon.com, Inc.; *U.S. Public*, pg. 90
IMMEDIATE CARE, INC.; *U.S. Private*, pg. 2047
IMMEDIATEK INC.; *U.S. Public*, pg. 1112
IM-MEDICO SVENSKA AB—See ADDvise Group AB; *Int'l*, pg. 136
IMMEDIENT CORPORATION; *U.S. Private*, pg. 2047
IMMEDIENT CORPORATION—See Immedient Corporation; *U.S. Private*, pg. 2047
IMMEDION LLC; *U.S. Private*, pg. 2047
IMMEDIS, LTD—See Clune Technology Group; *Int'l*, pg. 1664
IMMERGUT GMBH & CO. KG—See J. Bauer GmbH & Co. KG; *Int'l*, pg. 3854
IMMERSION CANADA, INC.—See Immersion Corporation; *U.S. Public*, pg. 1112
IMMERSION CORPORATION; *U.S. Public*, pg. 1112
IMMERSION GAMES SA; *Int'l*, pg. 3627
IMMERSION JAPAN K.K.—See Immersion Corporation; *U.S. Public*, pg. 1112
IMMERSION LIMITED—See Immersion Corporation; *U.S. Public*, pg. 1112
IMMERSION MEDIA, INC.—See Clubessential Holdings, LLC; *U.S. Private*, pg. 949
IMMERSION SA; *Int'l*, pg. 3627
IMMERSION (SHANGHAI) SCIENCE & TECHNOLOGY CO., LTD.—See Immersion Corporation; *U.S. Public*, pg. 1112
IMMERSIVE MEDIA COMPANY—See Digital Domain Holdings Limited; *Int'l*, pg. 2121
IMMERSIVE VENTURES INC.—See Digital Domain Holdings Limited; *Int'l*, pg. 2121
IMMEUBLE JAZZ LONGUEUIL, SOCIETE EN COMMANDITE—See Welltower Inc.; *U.S. Public*, pg. 2348
IMM HYDRO EST—See Interpump Group S.p.A.; *Int'l*, pg. 3755
IMMI AD; *Int'l*, pg. 3627

IMMIGRANT AND REFUGEE COMMUNITY ORGANIZATION; *U.S. Private*, pg. 2047
IMMIGRANT LEGAL RESOURCE CENTER; *U.S. Private*, pg. 2047
IMMINGHAM STORAGE CO. LTD.—See Simon Group plc; *Int'l*, pg. 6931
IMM INVESTMENT CORP; *Int'l*, pg. 3627
IMMIX BIOPHARMA, INC.; *U.S. Public*, pg. 1112
IMMIXGROUP, INC.—See Arrow Electronics, Inc.; *U.S. Public*, pg. 200
IMMIXSOLUTIONS, INC.—See Arrow Electronics, Inc.; *U.S. Public*, pg. 200
IMMIXTECHNOLOGY, INC.—See Arrow Electronics, Inc.; *U.S. Public*, pg. 200
IMMO-BEAULIEU NV; *Int'l*, pg. 3627
IMMOBEL SA; *Int'l*, pg. 3627
IMMOBILIARE ARNO S.R.L.—See Kering S.A.; *Int'l*, pg. 4134
IMMOBILIARE GLOBAL INVESTMENTS, INC.; *U.S. Private*, pg. 2047
IMMOBILIARE MABETEX S.A.—See The Mabetex Group; *Int'l*, pg. 7665
IMMOBILIARE MARAM S.R.L.—See Intesa Sanpaolo S.p.A.; *Int'l*, pg. 3765
IMMOBILIARE METANOPOLI S.P.A.—See Eni S.p.A.; *Int'l*, pg. 2437
IMMOBILIENINVEST UND BETRIEBSGESELLSCHAFT HERZO-BASE GMBH & CO. KG—See adidas AG; *Int'l*, pg. 146
IMMOBILIENINVEST UND BETRIEBSGESELLSCHAFT HERZO-BASE VERWALTUNGS GMBH—See adidas AG; *Int'l*, pg. 146
IMMOBILIEN SCOUT OSTERREICH GMBH—See Scout24 SE; *Int'l*, pg. 6654
IMMOBILIEN VENNOOTSCHAP VAN VLAANDEREN (INVESTIMMO)—See Immobel SA; *Int'l*, pg. 3627
IMMOBILIENVERMIETUNG GESELLSCHAFT M.B.H.—See BayWa AG; *Int'l*, pg. 918
IMMOBILIEN-VERMIETUNGSGESELLSCHAFT REEDER & CO, OBJEKT AIRPORT BUROCENTER DRESDEN KG—See Commerzbank AG; *Int'l*, pg. 1718
IMMOBILIEN-VERMIETUNGSGESELLSCHAFT SCHUMACHER&CO OBJEKT BAHNHOFE DEUTSCHLAND KG—See Deutsche Bahn AG; *Int'l*, pg. 2052
IMMOBILIENVERMITTLUNG BW GMBH—See Landesbank Baden-Wurttemberg; *Int'l*, pg. 4405
IMMOBILIENVERWALTUNG AB GMBH—See United Internet AG; *Int'l*, pg. 8069
IMMOBILIENVERWALTUNGSGESELLSCHAFT GRAMMOPHON BUROPARK MBH—See Commerzbank AG; *Int'l*, pg. 1718
IMMOBILIENVERWALTUNGSGESELLSCHAFT SCHLACHTHOF OFFENBACH MBH—See Commerzbank AG; *Int'l*, pg. 1718
IMMOBILIENVERWALTUNGS- UND VERTRIEBSGESELLSCHAFT VILLEN AM GLIENICKER HORN MBH—See Commerzbank AG; *Int'l*, pg. 1718
IMMOBILIERE CARREFOUR S.A.S.—See Carrefour SA; *Int'l*, pg. 1345
IMMOBILIERE DASSAULT SA—See Groupe Industriel Marcel Dassault S.A.; *Int'l*, pg. 3105
IMMOBILIERE DEKA—See Immobel SA; *Int'l*, pg. 3627
IMMOBILIERE DES TECHNODES—See Heidelberg Materials AG; *Int'l*, pg. 3316
IMMOBILIERE DISTRI-LAND NV; *Int'l*, pg. 3628
IMMOBILIERE HOTELIERE SA; *Int'l*, pg. 3628
IMMOBILIERE LES FONTAINES S.A.R.L.—See Capgemini SE; *Int'l*, pg. 1306
IMMOBILIERE PARISIENNE DE LA PERLE ET DES PIERRES PRECIEUSES SA; *Int'l*, pg. 3628
IMMOBILIER S.A.—See Unibank S.A.; *Int'l*, pg. 8030
IMMOBURG N.V.—See China International Marine Containers (Group) Co., Ltd.; *Int'l*, pg. 1511
IMMOCHAN MAGYARORSZAG KFT.—See Auchan Holding S.A.; *Int'l*, pg. 699
IMMO CONSULTING S.P.A.—See Advent International Corporation; *U.S. Private*, pg. 96
IMMO CONSULTING S.P.A.—See Centerbridge Partners, L.P.; *U.S. Private*, pg. 813
IMMOCO S.A.S.—See Colruyt Group N.V.; *Int'l*, pg. 1705
IMMODIS—See Carrefour SA; *Int'l*, pg. 1345
IMMOEAST ACQUISITION & MANAGEMENT GMBH—See Immofinanz AG; *Int'l*, pg. 3628
IMMOEAST AG—See Immofinanz AG; *Int'l*, pg. 3628
IMMOEAST GMBH—See Immofinanz AG; *Int'l*, pg. 3628
IMMOEAST NETHERLANDS II B.V—See Immofinanz AG; *Int'l*, pg. 3628
IMMOFINANZ AG; *Int'l*, pg. 3628
IMMOFINANZ DEUTSCHLAND GMBH—See Immofinanz AG; *Int'l*, pg. 3628
IMMOFINANZ SERVICES CZECH REPUBLIC, S.R.O—See Immofinanz AG; *Int'l*, pg. 3628
IMMOFINANZ SERVICES HUNGARY KFT—See Immofinanz AG; *Int'l*, pg. 3628
IMMOFINANZ SERVICES POLAND SP. Z O.O—See Immofinanz AG; *Int'l*, pg. 3628
IMMOFINANZ SERVICES SLOVAK REPUBLIC, S.R.O—See Immofinanz AG; *Int'l*, pg. 3628

COMPANY NAME INDEX

IMMOKALEE BULLETIN—See Independent Newspapers, Inc.; *U.S. Private*, pg. 2060
IMMO KONINGSLO NV—See Patronale Life NV; *Int'l*, pg. 5759
IMMO MECHELEN CITY CENTER S.A.; *Int'l*, pg. 3627
IMMO MOURY SCA; *Int'l*, pg. 3627
IMMOPARIBAS ROYALE-NEUVE SA—See BNP Paribas SA; *Int'l*, pg. 1091
IMMORENT AKTIENGESELLSCHAFT—See Erste Group Bank AG; *Int'l*, pg. 2499
IMMORENT BETA, LEASING DRUZBA, D.O.O.—See Erste Group Bank AG; *Int'l*, pg. 2499
IMMORENT-MOBILIENVERMIETUNGSGESELLSCHAFT M.B.H. & CO LEASING 89 KG—See Erste Group Bank AG; *Int'l*, pg. 2499
IMMORENT-RAMON GRUNDVERWERTUNGSGESELLSCHAFT M.B.H.—See Erste Group Bank AG; *Int'l*, pg. 2499
IMMORENT S-IMMOBILIENMANAGEMENT GESMBH—See Erste Group Bank AG; *Int'l*, pg. 2499
IMMORTAL PART COMPANY LIMITED—See SNC Holding Company Limited; *Int'l*, pg. 7025
IM MORTGAGE SOLUTIONS, LLC—See Iron Mountain Incorporated; *U.S. Public*, pg. 1172
IMMO SERVICE DRESDEN GMBH—See Vonovia SE; *Int'l*, pg. 8305
IMMOSOLVE GMBH—See Axel Springer SE; *Int'l*, pg. 766
IMMOSTREET.CH SA—See TX Group AG; *Int'l*, pg. 7992
IMMOVALOR GESTION S.A.—See Allianz SE; *Int'l*, pg. 353
IMMO WAUTERS BVBA—See ADGAR INVESTMENTS AND DEVELOPMENT LIMITED; *Int'l*, pg. 145
IMMOWELT AG—See Axel Springer SE; *Int'l*, pg. 766
IMMOWELT HAMBURG GMBH—See Axel Springer SE; *Int'l*, pg. 766
IMMOWELT HOLDING AG—See Axel Springer SE; *Int'l*, pg. 766
IMMSI S.P.A.; *Int'l*, pg. 3628
IMMTECH PHARMACEUTICALS, INC.; *U.S. Private*, pg. 2047
IMMUCELL CORPORATION; *U.S. Public*, pg. 1112
IMMUCOR, INC.—See Werfen Life Group, S.A.U.; *Int'l*, pg. 8379
IMMUCOR MEDIZINISCHE DIAGNOSTIK GMBH—See Werfen Life Group, S.A.U.; *Int'l*, pg. 8379
IMMUCOR (PORTUGAL) DIAGNOSTICOS MEDICOS, LDA.—See Werfen Life Group, S.A.U.; *Int'l*, pg. 8379
IMMUNE DESIGN CORP.—See Merck & Co., Inc.; *U.S. Public*, pg. 1416
IMMUNEERING CORP.; *U.S. Public*, pg. 1113
IMMUNE PHARMACEUTICALS INC.; *U.S. Public*, pg. 1113
IMMUNE PHARMACEUTICALS LTD.—See Immune Pharmaceuticals Inc.; *U.S. Public*, pg. 1113
IMMUNE THERAPEUTICS, INC.; *U.S. Public*, pg. 1113
IMMUNETICS, INC.—See Revvity, Inc.; *U.S. Public*, pg. 1794
IMMUNETRICS INC.—See Simulations Plus, Inc.; *U.S. Public*, pg. 1884
IMMUNIC AG—See Immunic, Inc.; *U.S. Public*, pg. 1113
IMMUNIC, INC.; *U.S. Public*, pg. 1113
IMMUNITYBIO, INC.—See NantWorks, LLC; *U.S. Private*, pg. 2833
IMMUNITY, INC.—See Cyxtera Technologies, Inc.; *U.S. Public*, pg. 619
IMMUNKEMI F&D AB—See Addtech AB; *Int'l*, pg. 133
IMMUNO-BIOLOGICAL LABORATORIES CO., LTD.; *Int'l*, pg. 3629
IMMUNOCHEMISTRY TECHNOLOGIES, LLC—See Janel Corporation; *U.S. Public*, pg. 1187
IMMUNOCLIN CORPORATION; *U.S. Private*, pg. 2047
IMMUNOCORE COMMERCIAL LLC—See Immunocore Holdings plc; *Int'l*, pg. 3629
IMMUNOCORE HOLDINGS PLC; *Int'l*, pg. 3629
IMMUNO DIAGNOSTIC OY—See Addtech AB; *Int'l*, pg. 134
IMMUNO DIAGNOSTICS OY—See AddLife AB; *Int'l*, pg. 129
IMMUNODIAGNOSTIC SYSTEMS FRANCE SAS—See Immunodiagnostic Systems Holdings plc; *Int'l*, pg. 3629
IMMUNODIAGNOSTIC SYSTEMS HOLDINGS PLC; *Int'l*, pg. 3629
IMMUNODIAGNOSTIC SYSTEMS, INC.—See Immunodiagnostic Systems Holdings plc; *Int'l*, pg. 3629
IMMUNODIAGNOSTIC SYSTEMS LIMITED—See Immunodiagnostic Systems Holdings plc; *Int'l*, pg. 3629
IMMUNODIAGNOSTIC SYSTEMS NORDIC A/S—See Immunodiagnostic Systems Holdings plc; *Int'l*, pg. 3629
IMMUNOGEN EUROPE LIMITED—See AbbVie Inc.; *U.S. Public*, pg. 24
IMMUNOGEN, INC.—See AbbVie Inc.; *U.S. Public*, pg. 24
IMMUNOGEN SECURITIES CORP—See AbbVie Inc.; *U.S. Public*, pg. 24
IMMUNOLAB CLINICAL DIAGNOSTICS GMBH—See Eurofins Scientific S.E.; *Int'l*, pg. 2550
IMMUNOLAB GMBH—See Eurofins Scientific S.E.; *Int'l*, pg. 2550
IMMUNOMEDICS, B.V.—See Gilead Sciences, Inc.; *U.S. Public*, pg. 938

IMMUNOMEDICS GMBH—See Gilead Sciences, Inc.; *U.S. Public*, pg. 938
IMMUNOMEDICS, INC.—See Gilead Sciences, Inc.; *U.S. Public*, pg. 937
IMMUNOME, INC.; *U.S. Public*, pg. 1113
IMMUNOPRECISE ANTIBODIES LTD.; *Int'l*, pg. 3629
IMMUNO PTY. LTD.—See Paragon Care Limited; *Int'l*, pg. 5736
IMMUNOSTICS, INC.—See Boditech Med, Inc.; *Int'l*, pg. 1097
IMMUNOTECH BIOPHARM LTD.; *Int'l*, pg. 3629
IMMUNOTECH LABORATORIES, INC.—See Enzolytics, Inc.; *U.S. Public*, pg. 782
IMMUNOTECH SAS—See Danaher Corporation; *U.S. Public*, pg. 627
IMMUNOTECH SRO—See Danaher Corporation; *U.S. Public*, pg. 627
IMMUNOTEC INC.; *Int'l*, pg. 3629
IMMUNOTEC MEDICAL CORP.—See Immunotec Inc.; *Int'l*, pg. 3629
IMMUNOVANT, INC.—See Roivant Sciences Ltd.; *Int'l*, pg. 6388
IMMUNO-VET SERVICES (PTY) LTD. SOUTH AFRICA—See Eli Lilly & Company; *U.S. Public*, pg. 733
IMMUNOVIA AB; *Int'l*, pg. 3629
IMMUNOVIA GMBH—See Immunovia AB; *Int'l*, pg. 3629
IMMUNOVISION, INC.—See Transasia Bio-Medicals Ltd.; *Int'l*, pg. 7896
IMMUNXPERTS BV—See IQVIA Holdings Inc.; *U.S. Public*, pg. 1169
IMMUPHARMA FRANCE S.A.—See ImmuPharma plc; *Int'l*, pg. 3629
IMMUPHARMA PLC; *Int'l*, pg. 3629
IMMURON LIMITED; *Int'l*, pg. 3629
IMMUTEP LIMITED; *Int'l*, pg. 3629
IMO AUTOPFLEGE GMBH—See Roark Capital Group Inc.; *U.S. Private*, pg. 3455
I-MOBILE CO., LTD.; *Int'l*, pg. 3563
I-MOBILE INTERNATIONAL CO., LTD.—See Samart Corporation Public Company Limited; *Int'l*, pg. 6501
IMOBILE SOLUTIONS, INC.—See SPARTA COMMERCIAL SERVICES, INC.; *U.S. Public*, pg. 1914
IMOBILIARIA CONSTRUTORA GRAO-PARA, S.A.; *Int'l*, pg. 3630
IMOCAIXA - GESTAO IMOBILIARIA, S.A.—See Caixa Geral de Depositos S.A.; *Int'l*, pg. 1260
IMO CANADA—See IMO Precision Controls Ltd; *Int'l*, pg. 3629
IMO CAR WASH GROUP LTD.—See Roark Capital Group Inc.; *U.S. Private*, pg. 3455
IMOCO, INC.; *U.S. Private*, pg. 2047
IMODERATE LLC; *U.S. Private*, pg. 2047
IMODULES SOFTWARE, INC.—See Leeds Equity Partners, LLC; *U.S. Private*, pg. 2414
IMODULES SOFTWARE, INC.—See Veritas Capital Fund Management, LLC; *U.S. Private*, pg. 4360
IMO INDUSTRIES INC.—See KKR & Co. Inc.; *U.S. Public*, pg. 1242
IMOINVESTIMENTO - FUNDO ESPECIAL DE INVESTIMENTO IMOBILIARIO FECHADO—See Novo Banco, S.A.; *Int'l*, pg. 5462
IMO JEAMBRUN AUTOMATION SAS—See IMO Precision Controls Ltd; *Int'l*, pg. 3629
IMO LAVAGE—See Roark Capital Group Inc.; *U.S. Private*, pg. 3455
IMOLEASING-SOCCIEDADE DE LOCACAO FINANCIERA IMOBILIARIA SA—See Caixa Geral de Depositos S.A.; *Int'l*, pg. 1260
IMONEY TOOLS LLC; *U.S. Private*, pg. 2048
IMO PACIFIC PTY LTD—See IMO Precision Controls Ltd; *Int'l*, pg. 3629
IMOPAC LTDA.—See CAP S.A.; *Int'l*, pg. 1300
IMO PRECISION CONTROLS LTD; *Int'l*, pg. 3629
IMO PROPERTY INVESTMENTS A.D.—See Eurobank Ergasias Services and Holdings S.A.; *Int'l*, pg. 2533
IMOPTEL SAS—See VINCI S.A.; *Int'l*, pg. 8222
IMOREAL—See Carrefour SA; *Int'l*, pg. 1345
IMORTGAGE SERVICES, LLC; *U.S. Private*, pg. 2048
IMO RUSSIA—See IMO Precision Controls Ltd; *Int'l*, pg. 3629
IMOS A.D.; *Int'l*, pg. 3630
IMO SOUTH AFRICA (PTY) LTD—See IMO Precision Controls Ltd; *Int'l*, pg. 3630
IMOS-SYSTEMAIR SPOL. S.R.O.—See Systemair AB; *Int'l*, pg. 7391
I-MOTION GMBH EVENTS & COMMUNICATION—See DEAG Deutsche Entertainment AG; *Int'l*, pg. 1998
I-MOTION GMBH—See DEAG Deutsche Entertainment AG; *Int'l*, pg. 1998
I-MOTION GMBH—See LiveStyle, Inc.; *U.S. Private*, pg. 2473
IMOTIONS A/S—See Smart Eye AB; *Int'l*, pg. 7000
IMPAC COMMERCIAL ASSETS CORPORATION—See Drive Shack Inc.; *U.S. Public*, pg. 688
IMPAC FUNDING CORPORATION—See Impac Mortgage Holdings, Inc.; *U.S. Public*, pg. 1113
IMPAC GLOBAL SYSTEMS—See Elekta AB; *Int'l*, pg. 2356

IMPACKONE SDN BHD—See PT Impack Pratama Industri Tbk; *Int'l*, pg. 6044
IMPACK VIETNAM CO. LTD.—See PT Impack Pratama Industri Tbk; *Int'l*, pg. 6044
IMPAC MEDICAL SYSTEMS, INC.—See Elekta AB; *Int'l*, pg. 2356
IMPAC MORTGAGE HOLDINGS, INC.; *U.S. Public*, pg. 1113
IMPACT 21 GROUP LLC—See W. Capra Consulting Group, Inc.; *U.S. Private*, pg. 4417
IMPACT ADVISORS LLC; *U.S. Private*, pg. 2048
IMPACT AIR SYSTEMS LTD.—See Addtech AB; *Int'l*, pg. 134
IMPACT ALAPKEZELO ZRT.—See Duna House Holding Public Company Limited; *Int'l*, pg. 2225
IMPACT AUTO AUCTIONS LTD.—See RB Global, Inc.; *Int'l*, pg. 6226
IMPACT AUTO AUCTIONS SUDBURY LTD.—See RB Global, Inc.; *Int'l*, pg. 6226
IMPACT BBDO—See Omnicom Group Inc.; *U.S. Public*, pg. 1576
IMPACT BBDO—See Omnicom Group Inc.; *U.S. Public*, pg. 1576
IMPACT BBDO—See Omnicom Group Inc.; *U.S. Public*, pg. 1576
IMPACT BBDO—See Omnicom Group Inc.; *U.S. Public*, pg. 1576
IMPACT BBDO—See Omnicom Group Inc.; *U.S. Public*, pg. 1576
IMPACT BBDO—See Omnicom Group Inc.; *U.S. Public*, pg. 1576
IMPACT BBDO—See Omnicom Group Inc.; *U.S. Public*, pg. 1576
IMPACT BRIDGING SOLUTIONS LIMITED—See Impact Holdings (UK) Plc; *Int'l*, pg. 3630
IMPACT BUSINESS GROUP INC.; *U.S. Private*, pg. 2048
IMPACT! CHEMICAL TECHNOLOGIES, INC.—See Hastings Equity Partners, LLC; *U.S. Private*, pg. 1879
IMPACT COAL SUBTRUST; *U.S. Private*, pg. 2048
IMPACT COATINGS AB—See Duroc AB; *Int'l*, pg. 2229
IMPACT CONFECTIONS, INC.; *U.S. Private*, pg. 2048
IMPACT DATA SOLUTIONS LIMITED—See Hexatronic Group AB; *Int'l*, pg. 3371
IMPACT DEVELOPER & CONTRACTOR S.A.; *Int'l*, pg. 3630
IMPACT ENGINEERING, INC.—See urban-gro, inc.; *U.S. Public*, pg. 2266
IMPACT EXECUTIVES LTD—See DBAY Advisors Limited; *Int'l*, pg. 1987
IMPACT EXHIBITION MANAGEMENT COMPANY LIMITED—See Bangkok Land Public Company Limited; *Int'l*, pg. 835
IMPACT FERTILISERS PTY LTD—See Ameropa AG; *Int'l*, pg. 424
IMPACT FINANCIAL SYSTEMS—See Roper Technologies, Inc.; *U.S. Public*, pg. 1812
IMPACT FIRE SERVICES, LLC—See TruArc Partners, L.P.; *U.S. Private*, pg. 4244
IMPACT FITNESS—See Morgan Stanley; *U.S. Public*, pg. 1474
IMPACT FLOORD OF TEXAS, LLC—See Blue Sage Capital, L.P.; *U.S. Private*, pg. 592
IMPACT FORECASTING, L.L.C.—See Aon plc; *Int'l*, pg. 494
IMPACT FORGE GROUP, LLC—See American Axle & Manufacturing Holdings, Inc.; *U.S. Public*, pg. 96
IMPACT FORK TRUCKS LIMITED—See Monnoyeur SAS; *Int'l*, pg. 5034
IMPACT FULFILLMENT SERVICES, LLC—See IFS Holdings, LLC; *U.S. Private*, pg. 2039
IMPACT FUNDING (UK) LIMITED—See Impact Holdings (UK) Plc; *Int'l*, pg. 3630
IMPACT FUSION INTERNATIONAL, INC.; *U.S. Public*, pg. 1113
IMPACT GENETICS CORPORATION—See Laboratory Corporation of America Holdings; *U.S. Public*, pg. 1287
IMPACT GENETICS, INC.—See Laboratory Corporation of America Holdings; *U.S. Public*, pg. 1287
IMPACT GROUP INTERNATIONAL, LLC; *U.S. Private*, pg. 2048
IMPACT GROUP, LLC—See CI Capital Partners LLC; *U.S. Private*, pg. 895
IMPACT GROWTH REAL ESTATE INVESTMENT TRUST; *Int'l*, pg. 3630
IMPACT HD INC.—See Bain Capital, LP; *U.S. Private*, pg. 433
IMPACT HEALTHCARE REIT PLC; *Int'l*, pg. 3630
IMPACT HOLDINGS (UK) PLC; *Int'l*, pg. 3630
IMPACT HUMAN RESOURCES—See Impact Logistics, Inc.; *U.S. Private*, pg. 2048
IMPACT INDUSTRIAL SUPPLIES INC.; *U.S. Private*, pg. 2048
IMPACT INNOVATIONS, INC.—See IG Design Group Plc; *Int'l*, pg. 3600
IMPACT INSURANCE BROKERS, INC.; *Int'l*, pg. 3630
IMPACT INTERACTIVE, LLC—See AmWINS Group, Inc.; *U.S. Private*, pg. 269
IMPACT INVESTMENT GROUP PTY. LTD.; *Int'l*, pg. 3630
IMPACT LOGISTICS, INC.; *U.S. Private*, pg. 2048

IMPACT MAILING OF MINNESOTA, INC. CORPORATE AFFILIATIONS

IMPACT MAILING OF MINNESOTA, INC.; *U.S. Private,* pg. 2048
IMPACT MAKERS, INC.; *U.S. Private,* pg. 2048
IMPACT MANAGEMENT SERVICES LLC; *U.S. Private,* pg. 2048
IMPACT MEDICAL IMAGING CENTRE COMPANY LIMITED—See Human Health Holdings Limited; *Int'l,* pg. 3529
IMPACT MERCHANDISING CORP.—See Vista West, Inc.; *U.S. Private,* pg. 4403
IMPACT MINERALS LIMITED; *Int'l,* pg. 3630
IMPACT MOBILE INC.—See Cisco Systems, Inc.; *U.S. Public,* pg. 499
IMPACT NETWORKING, LLC; *U.S. Private,* pg. 2048
IMPACTO USA—See Alden Global Capital LLC; *U.S. Private,* pg. 158
THE IMPACT PARTNERSHIP (ROCHDALE BOROUGH) LIMITED—See Kier Group plc; *Int'l,* pg. 4159
IMPACT PORTER NOVELLI DUBAI—See Omnicom Group Inc.; *U.S. Public,* pg. 1590
IMPACT PORTER NOVELLI—See Omnicom Group Inc.; *U.S. Public,* pg. 1590
IMPACT PORTER NOVELLI—See Omnicom Group Inc.; *U.S. Public,* pg. 1590
IMPACT POWER, INC.—See Allis Electric Co., Ltd.; *Int'l,* pg. 359
IMPACT POWER SOLUTIONS, LLC—See Smartpitch Ventures, LLC; *U.S. Private,* pg. 3692
IMPACT PRODUCTS, LLC—See Genuine Parts Company; *U.S. Public,* pg. 932
IMPACT RADIUS, INC.—See Silversmith Management, L.P.; *U.S. Private,* pg. 3664
IMPACT RECHERCHE—See Bluefocus Intelligent Communications Group Co., Ltd.; *Int'l,* pg. 1071
IMPACT RESOURCES, LLC—See National Product Services; *U.S. Private,* pg. 2861
IMPACTRX, INC.—See IQVIA Holdings Inc.; *U.S. Public,* pg. 1169
IMPACT SALES & MARKETING SAS—See 21 Investimenti Societa' di Gestione del Risparmio S.p.A.; *Int'l,* pg. 4
IMPACT SCIENCE & TECHNOLOGY, INC.—See L3Harris Technologies, Inc.; *U.S. Public,* pg. 1280
IMPACT SILVER CORP.; *Int'l,* pg. 3630
IMPACT—See Publicis Groupe S.A.; *Int'l,* pg. 6099
IMPACT SPECIALTIES, INC.—See Construction Specialties, Inc.; *U.S. Public,* pg. 1024
IMPACT STAFFING SOLUTIONS—See Impact Logistics, Inc.; *U.S. Private,* pg. 2048
IMPACT TECHNICAL SERVICES LTD.—See Addtech AB; *Int'l,* pg. 134
IMPACT TECHNOLOGIES, LLC; *U.S. Private,* pg. 2048
IMPACT TECHNOLOGY SOLUTIONS—See Impact Logistics, Inc.; *U.S. Private,* pg. 2048
IMPACT TELECOM, INC.—See Blue Casa Communications, Inc.; *U.S. Private,* pg. 586
IMPACT TELECOM, INC.—See Garrison Investment Group LP; *U.S. Private,* pg. 1646
IMPACT UNLIMITED GMBH—See asm Messeprofis AG; *Int'l,* pg. 626
IMPACT UNLIMITED INC.; *U.S. Private,* pg. 2048
IMPACT UNLIMITED LTDA.—See Impact Unlimited Inc.; *U.S. Private,* pg. 2048
IMPACT XM—See Riverside Partners, LLC; *U.S. Private,* pg. 3446
I.M.P. AEROSPACE DIVISION—See I.M.P. Group International Inc.; *Int'l,* pg. 3566
IMPAG GMBH—See Sunjin Beauty Science Co., Ltd.; *Int'l,* pg. 7316
IMPALA CANADA LTD.—See Impala Platinum Holdings Limited; *Int'l,* pg. 3630
IMPALA DIGITAL LIMITED—See Entain PLC; *Int'l,* pg. 2450
IMPALA PLATINUM HOLDINGS LIMITED; *Int'l,* pg. 3630
IMPALA PLATINUM JAPAN LIMITED—See Impala Platinum Holdings Limited; *Int'l,* pg. 3630
IMPALA PLATINUM LIMITED—See Impala Platinum Holdings Limited; *Int'l,* pg. 3630
IMPALA REFINING SERVICES LIMITED—See Impala Platinum Holdings Limited; *Int'l,* pg. 3630
IMPALA SAS; *Int'l,* pg. 3631
IMPALA TERMINALS BURNSIDE LLC—See Trafigura Beheer B.V.; *Int'l,* pg. 7890
IMPALA USA INC—See Trafigura Beheer B.V.; *Int'l,* pg. 7890
IMPAR COMERCIO E REPRESENTACOES LTDA.—See Illinois Tool Works Inc.; *U.S. Public,* pg. 1108
IMPARTS AUTOMOTIVE PTY LTD—See Tye Soon Limited; *Int'l,* pg. 7994
IMPART SPECIAL PRODUCTS PTY LIMITED—See Inventis Limited; *Int'l,* pg. 3773
IMPAVIDI GMBH—See msg group GmbH; *Int'l,* pg. 5067
IMPAX ASSET MANAGEMENT GROUP PLC; *Int'l,* pg. 3631
IMPAX ASSET MANAGEMENT IRELAND LIMITED—See Impax Asset Management Group plc; *Int'l,* pg. 3631
IMPAX ENVIRONMENTAL MARKET PLC; *Int'l,* pg. 3631
IMPAX LABORATORIES, INC.—See Amneal Pharmaceuticals, Inc.; *U.S. Public,* pg. 125

IMPAX NEW ENERGY INVESTORS (GP) LIMITED—See Impax Asset Management Group plc; *Int'l,* pg. 3631
IMPAXX, INC.; *U.S. Private,* pg. 2049
IMPCO TECHNOLOGIES B.V.—See Genisys Controls, LLC; *U.S. Private,* pg. 1671
IMPCO TECHNOLOGIES, INC.—See Genisys Controls, LLC; *U.S. Private,* pg. 1671
IMPCO TECHNOLOGIES (JAPAN) CO, LTD.—See Genisys Controls, LLC; *U.S. Private,* pg. 1671
IMPEC MARTINIQUE S.A.—See Royal Unibrew A/S; *Int'l,* pg. 6414
IMPEDIMED INC.—See ImpediMed Limited; *Int'l,* pg. 3631
IMPEDIMED LIMITED; *Int'l,* pg. 3631
I.M.P.E.-INDUSTRIA MERIDIONALE POLIURETANI ESPANSI S.P.A.—See Natuzzi S.p.A.; *Int'l,* pg. 5170
IMPEL ACCOUNTING SP. Z.O.O.—See Impel S.A.; *Int'l,* pg. 3631
IMPEL AIRPORT PARTNER SP. Z.O.O.—See Impel S.A.; *Int'l,* pg. 3631
IMPEL CASH HANDLING SP. Z O.O.—See Impel S.A.; *Int'l,* pg. 3631
IMPEL CATERING SP. Z O.O.—See Impel S.A.; *Int'l,* pg. 3631
IMPEL CLEANING SP. Z.O.O.—See Impel S.A.; *Int'l,* pg. 3631
IMPEL FOOD HYGIENE SP. Z.O.O.—See Impel S.A.; *Int'l,* pg. 3632
IMPEL HR SERVICE SP. Z.O.O.—See Impel S.A.; *Int'l,* pg. 3632
IMPEL IT SP. Z O.O.—See Impel S.A.; *Int'l,* pg. 3632
IMPELLAM GROUP PLC—See HFBG Holding B.V.; *Int'l,* pg. 3374
IMPELLER REPAIR SERVICE—See ITT Inc.; *U.S. Public,* pg. 1178
IMPEL LOGISTICS SP. Z.O.O.—See Impel S.A.; *Int'l,* pg. 3632
IMPEL PERFEKTA SP. Z O.O.—See Impel S.A.; *Int'l,* pg. 3632
IMPEL PHARMACEUTICALS INC.; *U.S. Public,* pg. 1113
IMPEL REAL ESTATE SP. Z O.O.—See Impel S.A.; *Int'l,* pg. 3632
IMPEL RENTAL SP. Z O.O.—See Impel S.A.; *Int'l,* pg. 3632
IMPEL S.A.; *Int'l,* pg. 3631
IMPEL SA-WROCLAW—See Impel S.A.; *Int'l,* pg. 3632
IMPEL SECURITY POLSKA SP. Z O.O.—See Impel S.A.; *Int'l,* pg. 3632
IMPEL SECURITY PROVIDER SP. Z O.O.—See Impel S.A.; *Int'l,* pg. 3632
IMPEL SECURITY TECHNOLOGIES SP. Z O.O.—See Impel S.A.; *Int'l,* pg. 3632
IMPEL SERVIKS SIA—See Impel S.A.; *Int'l,* pg. 3632
IMPELSYS INC.; *U.S. Private,* pg. 2049
IMPELUS LIMITED; *Int'l,* pg. 3632
IMPENDULO LIMITED—See Vista Equity Partners, LLC; *U.S. Private,* pg. 4395
IMPERA CAPITAL SA; *Int'l,* pg. 3632
IMPERATIVE LOGISTICS GROUP—See Littlejohn & Co., LLC; *U.S. Private,* pg. 2470
IMPERIAL AUTO INDUSTRIES LTD.; *Int'l,* pg. 3632
IMPERIAL BANK LIMITED—See Dubai World Corporation; *Int'l,* pg. 2221
IMPERIAL BLADES LLC—See Techtronic Industries Co., Ltd.; *Int'l,* pg. 7513
IMPERIAL BRANDS, INC.—See Marie Brizard Wine & Spirits S.A.; *Int'l,* pg. 4693
IMPERIAL BRANDS PLC; *Int'l,* pg. 3632
IMPERIAL BROWN INC.; *U.S. Private,* pg. 2049
IMPERIAL CAPITAL GROUP, INC.; *U.S. Private,* pg. 2049
IMPERIAL CAPITAL GROUP LTD.; *Int'l,* pg. 3634
IMPERIAL CAPITAL LIMITED—See Dubai World Corporation; *Int'l,* pg. 2221
IMPERIAL CHEMICAL INDUSTRIES PLC—See Akzo Nobel N.V.; *Int'l,* pg. 274
IMPERIAL COFFEE & SERVICES, INC.; *Int'l,* pg. 3634
IMPERIAL COMMERCIALS LTD—See Dubai World Corporation; *Int'l,* pg. 2222
IMPERIAL COMMODITIES CORP.; *U.S. Private,* pg. 2049
IMPERIAL CRANE SERVICES INC.; *U.S. Private,* pg. 2049
IMPERIAL DADE, LLC—See Bain Capital, LP; *U.S. Private,* pg. 440
IMPERIAL DAIHATSU (PTY) LIMITED—See Dubai World Corporation; *Int'l,* pg. 2221
IMPERIAL-DELTAH, INC.; *U.S. Private,* pg. 2050
IMPERIAL DIE CASTING—See RCM Industries, Inc.; *U.S. Private,* pg. 3362
IMPERIAL DISTRIBUTORS CANADA INC—See Imperial Equities Inc.; *Int'l,* pg. 3634
IMPERIAL DISTRIBUTORS, INC.; *U.S. Private,* pg. 2049
THE IMPERIAL ELECTRIC COMPANY—See Nidec Corporation; *Int'l,* pg. 5280
IMPERIAL ENERGY CORPORATION PLC—See Oil & Natural Gas Corporation Limited; *Int'l,* pg. 5534
IMPERIAL EQUITIES INC. - PHARMACEUTICAL DIVISION—See Imperial Equities Inc.; *Int'l,* pg. 3634
IMPERIAL EQUITIES INC. - REAL ESTATE DIVISION—See Imperial Equities Inc.; *Int'l,* pg. 3634
IMPERIAL EQUITIES INC.; *Int'l,* pg. 3634

IMPERIAL FINANCE & TRADING LLC—See Emergent Capital, Inc.; *U.S. Private,* pg. 1381
IMPERIAL GARDEN & RESORT, INC.; *Int'l,* pg. 3634
IMPERIAL GINSENG DISTRIBUTORS LTD.—See Imperial Ginseng Products Ltd.; *Int'l,* pg. 3634
IMPERIAL GINSENG PRODUCTS LTD.; *Int'l,* pg. 3634
IMPERIAL GROUP (PTY) LIMITED—See Dubai World Corporation; *Int'l,* pg. 2221
IMPERIAL HARDWARE COMPANY INC.; *U.S. Private,* pg. 2049
IMPERIAL HEALTH CARE CENTER—See Sava Senior Care LLC; *U.S. Private,* pg. 3555
IMPERIAL HELIUM CORP.—See Royal Helium Ltd.; *Int'l,* pg. 6413
IMPERIAL HOMES MORTGAGE BANK LIMITED—See Guaranty Trust Bank plc; *Int'l,* pg. 3169
IMPERIAL HOSPITAL & RESEARCH CENTRE LIMITED—See Apollo Hospitals Enterprise Limited; *Int'l,* pg. 518
IMPERIAL HOTEL, LTD.; *Int'l,* pg. 3635
IMPERIAL HOTELS AUSTRIA AG—See Marriott International, Inc.; *U.S. Public,* pg. 1371
IMPERIAL, INC.; *U.S. Private,* pg. 2050
IMPERIAL INDUSTRIES, INC.—See Q.E.P. Co., Inc.; *U.S. Public,* pg. 1741
IMPERIAL INDUSTRIES, INC.—See Wausau Tile, Inc.; *U.S. Private,* pg. 4457
IMPERIAL INNOVATIONS GROUP PLC; *Int'l,* pg. 3635
IMPERIAL INSURANCE MANAGERS, LLC—See The Allstate Corporation; *U.S. Public,* pg. 2033
IMPERIAL INTERNATIONAL—See H. Betti Industries, Inc.; *U.S. Private,* pg. 1824
IMPERIAL INVESTMENT COMPANY INC.; *U.S. Private,* pg. 2049
IMPERIAL IRRIGATION SUPPLY, INC.; *U.S. Private,* pg. 2049
IMPERIAL LANDFILL, INC.—See Republic Services, Inc.; *U.S. Public,* pg. 1786
IMPERIAL LIFE SETTLEMENTS, LLC—See Emergent Capital, Inc.; *U.S. Private,* pg. 1381
IMPERIAL LOGISTICS INTERNATIONAL B.V. & CO. KG—See Dubai World Corporation; *Int'l,* pg. 2221
IMPERIAL LOGISTICS LIMITED—See Dubai World Corporation; *Int'l,* pg. 2221
IMPERIAL LOGISTICS & TRANSPORT—See Dubai World Corporation; *Int'l,* pg. 2221
IMPERIAL MACHINE COMPANY LIMITED—See The Middleby Corporation; *U.S. Public,* pg. 2115
IMPERIAL MACHINE & TOOL CO.—See Kaiser Aluminum Corporation; *U.S. Public,* pg. 1213
IMPERIAL MARKETING CORPORATION—See The Allstate Corporation; *U.S. Public,* pg. 2033
IMPERIAL MEAT PRODUCTS N.V.—See ALFA, S.A.B. de C.V.; *Int'l,* pg. 314
IMPERIAL METALS CORPORATION; *Int'l,* pg. 3635
IMPERIAL MINING GROUP LTD.; *Int'l,* pg. 3635
IMPERIAL MOBILITY DEUTSCHLAND BETEILIGUNGS GMBH—See Dubai World Corporation; *Int'l,* pg. 2221
IMPERIAL MOBILITY INTERNATIONAL BV—See Dubai World Corporation; *Int'l,* pg. 2221
IMPERIAL MUSIC & MEDIA PLC; *Int'l,* pg. 3635
IMPERIAL OIL COMPANY INC.—See Supertest Oil Company Inc.; *U.S. Private,* pg. 3881
IMPERIAL OIL LIMITED PRODUCTS & CHEMICALS DIVISION—See Exxon Mobil Corporation; *U.S. Public,* pg. 816
IMPERIAL OIL LIMITED—See Exxon Mobil Corporation; *U.S. Public,* pg. 816
IMPERIAL OIL LIMITED—See Exxon Mobil Corporation; *U.S. Public,* pg. 816
IMPERIAL OIL LIMITED—See Exxon Mobil Corporation; *U.S. Public,* pg. 816
IMPERIAL OIL LIMITED—See Exxon Mobil Corporation; *U.S. Public,* pg. 816
IMPERIAL OIL LIMITED—See Exxon Mobil Corporation; *U.S. Public,* pg. 816
IMPERIAL OIL LIMITED—See Exxon Mobil Corporation; *U.S. Public,* pg. 816
IMPERIAL OIL LIMITED—See Exxon Mobil Corporation; *U.S. Public,* pg. 816
IMPERIAL OIL LIMITED—See Exxon Mobil Corporation; *U.S. Public,* pg. 816
IMPERIAL OIL LIMITED—See Exxon Mobil Corporation; *U.S. Public,* pg. 816
IMPERIAL PACIFIC INTERNATIONAL HOLDINGS LIMITED; *Int'l,* pg. 3635
IMPERIAL PACIFIC LIMITED; *Int'l,* pg. 3635
IMPERIAL PARKING INDUSTRIES, INC.—See Propark, Inc.; *U.S. Private,* pg. 3284
IMPERIAL PFS—See IPFS Corporation; *U.S. Private,* pg. 2136
IMPERIAL PLASTICS, INC.; *U.S. Private,* pg. 2049
IMPERIAL POOLS, INC.; *U.S. Private,* pg. 2049
IMPERIAL PREMIUM FINANCE, LLC—See Emergent Capital, Inc.; *U.S. Private,* pg. 1381
IMPERIAL PRINTING PRODUCTS CO., INC.—See Imagemark Business Services; *U.S. Private,* pg. 2045
IMPERIAL REALTY COMPANY INC.; *U.S. Private,* pg. 2049

1322

COMPANY NAME INDEX

IMPERIAL RESOURCES INC.; *Int'l*, pg. 3635
IMPERIAL RESOURCES, LLC—See Empire Energy Group Limited; *Int'l*, pg. 2387
IMPERIAL SASFIN LOGISTICS—See Dubai World Corporation; *Int'l*, pg. 2221
IMPERIAL SELECT ALBERTON—See Dubai World Corporation; *Int'l*, pg. 2221
IMPERIAL SHIPPING ROTTERDAM B.V.—See Dubai World Corporation; *Int'l*, pg. 2221
IMPERIAL SUGAR COMPANY—See Louis Dreyfus S.A.S.; *Int'l*, pg. 4562
IMPERIAL SUGAR COMPANY—See Louis Dreyfus S.A.S.; *Int'l*, pg. 4562
IMPERIAL SUPPLIES LLC—See W.W. Grainger, Inc.; *U.S. Public*, pg. 2320
IMPERIAL TOBACCO (ASIA) PTE LTD—See Imperial Brands PLC; *Int'l*, pg. 3633
IMPERIAL TOBACCO AUSTRALIA LTD—See Imperial Brands PLC; *Int'l*, pg. 3633
IMPERIAL TOBACCO BELGIUM—See Imperial Brands PLC; *Int'l*, pg. 3633
IMPERIAL TOBACCO CANADA LIMITED—See British American Tobacco plc; *Int'l*, pg. 1167
IMPERIAL TOBACCO CR, S.R.O.—See Imperial Brands PLC; *Int'l*, pg. 3633
IMPERIAL TOBACCO (EFKA) GMBH & CO KG—See Imperial Brands PLC; *Int'l*, pg. 3633
IMPERIAL TOBACCO FINANCE PLC—See Imperial Brands PLC; *Int'l*, pg. 3633
IMPERIAL TOBACCO FINLAND OY—See Imperial Brands PLC; *Int'l*, pg. 3633
IMPERIAL TOBACCO FRANCE S.A.—See Imperial Brands PLC; *Int'l*, pg. 3633
IMPERIAL TOBACCO HELLAS S.A.—See Imperial Brands PLC; *Int'l*, pg. 3633
IMPERIAL TOBACCO INTERNATIONAL LTD.—See Imperial Brands PLC; *Int'l*, pg. 3633
IMPERIAL TOBACCO ITALY S.R.L.—See Imperial Brands PLC; *Int'l*, pg. 3633
IMPERIAL TOBACCO LIMITED—See Imperial Brands PLC; *Int'l*, pg. 3633
IMPERIAL TOBACCO LTD. - NORTHERN TRADING DIVISION—See Imperial Brands PLC; *Int'l*, pg. 3633
IMPERIAL TOBACCO MAGYARORSZAG DOHANYFORGALMAZO KFT—See Imperial Brands PLC; *Int'l*, pg. 3633
IMPERIAL TOBACCO MULLINGAR—See Imperial Brands PLC; *Int'l*, pg. 3633
IMPERIAL TOBACCO NETHERLANDS—See Imperial Brands PLC; *Int'l*, pg. 3633
IMPERIAL TOBACCO NEW ZEALAND LIMITED—See Imperial Brands PLC; *Int'l*, pg. 3633
IMPERIAL TOBACCO NORWAY A.S.—See Imperial Brands PLC; *Int'l*, pg. 3633
IMPERIAL TOBACCO POLSKA MANUFACTURING SA—See Imperial Brands PLC; *Int'l*, pg. 3633
IMPERIAL TOBACCO POLSKA S.A.—See Imperial Brands PLC; *Int'l*, pg. 3633
IMPERIAL TOBACCO PORTUGAL SSPLC—See Imperial Brands PLC; *Int'l*, pg. 3633
IMPERIAL TOBACCO PRODUCTION UKRAINE CJSC—See Imperial Brands PLC; *Int'l*, pg. 3633
IMPERIAL TOBACCO SALES & MARKETING LLC—See Imperial Brands PLC; *Int'l*, pg. 3634
IMPERIAL TOBACCO SIGARA VE TUTUNCULUK SANAYI VE TICARET A.S.—See Imperial Brands PLC; *Int'l*, pg. 3633
IMPERIAL TOBACCO SLOVAKIA—See Imperial Brands PLC; *Int'l*, pg. 3633
IMPERIAL TOBACCO TAIWAN CO. LIMITED—See Imperial Brands PLC; *Int'l*, pg. 3633
IMPERIAL TOBACCO TKS A.D.—See Imperial Brands PLC; *Int'l*, pg. 3633
IMPERIAL TOBACCO TUTUN URUNLERI SATIS VE PAZARLAMA A.S.—See Imperial Brands PLC; *Int'l*, pg. 3633
IMPERIAL TOBACCO UKRAINE—See Imperial Brands PLC; *Int'l*, pg. 3634
IMPERIAL TOY CORPORATION; *U.S. Private*, pg. 2049
IMPERIAL TRADING CO, INC.; *U.S. Private*, pg. 2049
IMPERIAL VALLEY FOODS INC.; *U.S. Private*, pg. 2049
IMPERIAL VALLEY MALL, L.P.—See CBL & Associates Properties, Inc.; *U.S. Public*, pg. 458
IMPERIAL WOODWORKING COMPANY; *U.S. Private*, pg. 2049
IMPERIAL WOODWORKS, INC.; *U.S. Private*, pg. 2049
IMPERIAL ZINC CORP.; *U.S. Private*, pg. 2050
IMPERILOG LIMITED—See Dubai World Corporation; *Int'l*, pg. 2221
IMPERIO ARGO GROUP S.A.; *Int'l*, pg. 3635
IMPERIUM CROWN LIMITED; *Int'l*, pg. 3635
IMPERIUM FINANCIAL GROUP LIMITED; *Int'l*, pg. 3635
IMPERIUM HEALTH MANAGEMENT, LLC—See UnitedHealth Group Incorporated; *U.S. Public*, pg. 2244
IMPERIUM INSURANCE COMPANY—See SKYWARD SPECIALTY INSURANCE GROUP, INC.; *U.S. Public*, pg. 1893
IMPERIUM PARTNERS GROUP, LLC; *U.S. Private*, pg. 2050

IMPERIUM TECHNOLOGY GROUP LIMITED; *Int'l*, pg. 3635
IMPERO A/S; *Int'l*, pg. 3635
IMPERO ELECTRONICS, INC.; *U.S. Private*, pg. 2050
IMPERO SOLUTIONS LIMITED—See Investcorp Holdings B.S.C.; *Int'l*, pg. 3776
IMPERVA AUSTRALIA PTY. LTD.—See Thales S.A.; *Int'l*, pg. 7600
IMPERVA B.V.—See Thales S.A.; *Int'l*, pg. 7600
IMPERVA FRANCE SARL—See Thales S.A.; *Int'l*, pg. 7600
IMPERVA, INC.—See Thales S.A.; *Int'l*, pg. 7600
IMPERVA ITALY SRL—See Thales S.A.; *Int'l*, pg. 7600
IMPERVA JAPAN K.K.—See Thales S.A.; *Int'l*, pg. 7600
IMPERVA LTD.—See Thales S.A.; *Int'l*, pg. 7600
IMPERVA SINGAPORE PTE.—See Thales S.A.; *Int'l*, pg. 7600
IMPERVA UK LTD.—See Thales S.A.; *Int'l*, pg. 7600
IMPET SP. Z O.O.—See Grupa Kety S.A.; *Int'l*, pg. 3117
IMPETUS AGRICULTURE INC.—See KWS SAAT SE & Co. KGaA; *Int'l*, pg. 4352
IMPEX ELECTRO LLC; *Int'l*, pg. 3635
IMPEX FERRO TECH LIMITED; *Int'l*, pg. 3635
IMPEX GLOBAL, LLC—See LSCG Management, Inc.; *U.S. Private*, pg. 2508
THE IMPEX GROUP OF COMPANIES; *U.S. Private*, pg. 4055
IMPEXMETAL S.A.—See Boryszew S.A.; *Int'l*, pg. 1115
IMPEX SERVICES INC.; *U.S. Private*, pg. 2050
IMPEX TECH LAB INC.; *U.S. Private*, pg. 2050
I.M.P. GROUP INTERNATIONAL INC. - IMP AEROSPACE & DEFENCE UNIT—See I.M.P. Group International Inc.; *Int'l*, pg. 3566
I.M.P. GROUP INTERNATIONAL INC. - PACIFIC AVIONICS & INSTRUMENTS DIVISION—See I.M.P. Group International Inc.; *Int'l*, pg. 3566
I.M.P. GROUP INTERNATIONAL INC.; *Int'l*, pg. 3566
IMP HOLDINGS LLC—See Patrick Industries, Inc.; *U.S. Public*, pg. 1652
IMPIANA HOTELS & RESORTS MANAGEMENT SDN BHD; *Int'l*, pg. 3636
IMPIAN GOLF RESORT BERHAD—See Sime Darby Berhad; *Int'l*, pg. 6929
IMPIANTI S.P.A.; *Int'l*, pg. 3636
IMPIKA SA—See Xerox Holdings Corporation; *U.S. Public*, pg. 2387
IMPINJ, INC.; *U.S. Public*, pg. 1113
IMPINJ RFID TECHNOLOGY (SHANGHAI) CO., LTD.—See Impinj, Inc.; *U.S. Public*, pg. 1113
IMPLADENT, LTD.—See Avista Capital Partners, L.P.; *U.S. Private*, pg. 409
IMPLANET SA; *Int'l*, pg. 3636
IMPLANTABLE PROVIDER GROUP—See TPG Capital, L.P.; *U.S. Public*, pg. 2176
IMPLANT CONCIERGE, LLC—See Zimmer Biomet Holdings, Inc.; *U.S. Public*, pg. 2406
IMPLANT DIRECT SYBRON INTERNATIONAL LLC—See Danaher Corporation; *U.S. Public*, pg. 627
IMPLANT DIRECT SYBRON MANUFACTUING LLC—See Danaher Corporation; *U.S. Public*, pg. 627
IMPLANTES Y SISTEMAS MEDICOS, INC.—See Orthofix Medical Inc.; *U.S. Public*, pg. 1619
IMPLANT & GENERAL DENTISTRY OF NORTHERN COLORADO; *U.S. Private*, pg. 2050
IMPLANTIUM CO..LTD—See Dentium Co., Ltd; *Int'l*, pg. 2033
IMPLANTIUM DE MEXICO SA DE CV—See Dentium Co., Ltd; *Int'l*, pg. 2034
IMPLANTIUM HONGKONG LTD—See Dentium Co., Ltd; *Int'l*, pg. 2033
IMPLANTIUM INDIA PVT. LTD.—See Dentium Co., Ltd; *Int'l*, pg. 2033
IMPLANTIUM MALAYSIA SDN. BHD.—See Dentium Co., Ltd; *Int'l*, pg. 2033
IMPLANTIUM & MEDICAL COMPANY SRL—See Dentium Co., Ltd; *Int'l*, pg. 2033
IMPLANTIUM UK LTD.—See Dentium Co., Ltd; *Int'l*, pg. 2033
IMPLANT SOLUTIONS, LLC—See Tenet Healthcare Corporation; *U.S. Public*, pg. 2010
IMPLENIA AG; *Int'l*, pg. 3636
IMPLENIA BAU AG—See Implenia AG; *Int'l*, pg. 3636
IMPLENIA BAU AG - TUNNEL + TU DIVISION—See Implenia AG; *Int'l*, pg. 3636
IMPLENIA CONSTRUCTION GMBH—See Implenia AG; *Int'l*, pg. 3636
IMPLENIA FASSADENTECHNIK GMBH—See Implenia AG; *Int'l*, pg. 3636
IMPLENIA FRANCE SA—See Implenia AG; *Int'l*, pg. 3636
IMPLENIA GENERALUNTERNEHMUNG AG—See Implenia AG; *Int'l*, pg. 3636
IMPLENIA GLOBAL SOLUTIONS AG—See Implenia AG; *Int'l*, pg. 3636
IMPLENIA HOLDING GMBH—See Implenia AG; *Int'l*, pg. 3636
IMPLENIA IMMOBILIEN AG—See Implenia AG; *Int'l*, pg. 3636
IMPLENIA MANAGEMENT AG—See Implenia AG; *Int'l*, pg. 3636

IMPLENIA NORGE AS—See Implenia AG; *Int'l*, pg. 3636
IMPLENIA OSTERREICH GMBH—See Implenia AG; *Int'l*, pg. 3636
IMPLENIA REAL ESTATE DIVISION—See Implenia AG; *Int'l*, pg. 3636
IMPLENIA SCHALUNGSBAU GMBH—See Implenia AG; *Int'l*, pg. 3636
IMPLENIA SPEZIALTIEFBAU GMBH—See Implenia AG; *Int'l*, pg. 3636
IMPLENIA SWITZERLAND LTD.—See Implenia AG; *Int'l*, pg. 3636
IMPLENIA TESCH GMBH—See Bilfinger SE; *Int'l*, pg. 1024
IMPLICO AG—See Implico GmbH; *Int'l*, pg. 3636
IMPLICO CONSULTING S.R.L.—See Implico GmbH; *Int'l*, pg. 3636
IMPLICO GMBH; *Int'l*, pg. 3636
IMPLICO, INC.—See Implico GmbH; *Int'l*, pg. 3636
IMPLICO (M) SDN BHD—See Implico GmbH; *Int'l*, pg. 3636
IMPLIX SP. Z O.O.; *Int'l*, pg. 3636
IMPLUS FOOTCARE, LLC—See Berkshire Partners LLC; *U.S. Private*, pg. 534
IMPOL ALUMINUM CORPORATION—See Impol d.d.; *Int'l*, pg. 3636
IMPOL D.D.; *Int'l*, pg. 3636
IMPOLIN AB—See Navamedic ASA; *Int'l*, pg. 5173
IMPOL MONTAL, D.O.O.—See Impol d.d.; *Int'l*, pg. 3636
IMPOL SEVAL, A.D.—See Impol d.d.; *Int'l*, pg. 3636
IMPOL SEVAL FINAL, D. O. O.—See Impol d.d.; *Int'l*, pg. 3636
IMPOL SEVAL PRESIDENT, D. O. O.—See Impol d.d.; *Int'l*, pg. 3636
IMPOL SEVAL TEHNIKA, D. O. O.—See Impol d.d.; *Int'l*, pg. 3636
IMPOL STANOVANJA, D.O.O.—See Impol d.d.; *Int'l*, pg. 3636
IMPO MOTOR POMPA SANAYI VE TICARET A.S.—See Franklin Electric Co., Inc.; *U.S. Public*, pg. 878
IMPORT, BUILDING & TRADING CO., LTD.—See CHINO Corporation; *Int'l*, pg. 1571
IMPORTED CARS OF MARYLAND; *U.S. Private*, pg. 2050
IMPORT-EXPORT COMPAGNIE S.A.—See Royal Unibrew A/S; *Int'l*, pg. 6414
IMPORTEX SA—See London Security PLC; *Int'l*, pg. 4547
IMPORTHAUS WILMS/IMPULS GMBH & CO. KG—See Zertus GmbH; *Int'l*, pg. 8639
IMPORT-IO CORPORATION; *U.S. Private*, pg. 2050
IMPORTLA, INC.—See Bunker Hill Capital LP; *U.S. Private*, pg. 685
IMPORT MOTORS II, INC.—See Sojitz Corporation; *Int'l*, pg. 7061
IMPORT MOTORS INC.; *U.S. Private*, pg. 2050
IMPORT PARFUMERIEN AG—See Coop-Gruppe Genossenschaft; *Int'l*, pg. 1790
IMPORT PRODUCTS CO. INC.; *U.S. Private*, pg. 2050
IMPORT TOOL CORP. LTD.; *Int'l*, pg. 3637
IMPORT VOLKSWAGEN GROUP S.R.O.—See Porsche Automobil Holding SE; *Int'l*, pg. 5929
IMPORT WAREHOUSE INC.; *U.S. Private*, pg. 2050
IMP POLAND SP. Z O.O.—See Alten S.A.; *Int'l*, pg. 390
IMP POWERS LTD; *Int'l*, pg. 3630
IMP POWERS LTD. - UNIT 1—See IMP Powers Ltd; *Int'l*, pg. 3630
IMPRA WOOD PROTECTION LIMITED—See International Chemical Investors S.E.; *Int'l*, pg. 3745
IMPREGILO COLOMBIA SAS—See Salini Costruttori S.p.A.; *Int'l*, pg. 6493
IMPREGILO INTERNATIONAL INFRASTRUCTURES N.V.—See Salini Costruttori S.p.A.; *Int'l*, pg. 6493
IMPREGILO NEW CROSS LTD.—See Salini Costruttori S.p.A.; *Int'l*, pg. 6493
IMPREGLON CELLRAMIC—See Aalberts N.V.; *Int'l*, pg. 34
IMPREGLON GMBH—See Aalberts N.V.; *Int'l*, pg. 34
IMPREGLON, INC.—See Aalberts N.V.; *Int'l*, pg. 34
IMPREGLON, INC. - WOONSOCKET—See Aalberts N.V.; *Int'l*, pg. 34
IMPREGLON OBERFLACHENTECHNIK GMBH—See Westland Gummiwerke GmbH & Co. KG; *Int'l*, pg. 8390
IMPREMEDIA LLC—See S.A. La Nacion; *Int'l*, pg. 6448
IMPRESA AEROSPACE, LLC—See Graycliff Partners LP; *U.S. Private*, pg. 1761
IMPRESA MEDIA SOLUTIONS - SOCIEDADE UNIPESSOAL, LDA.—See Impresa SGPS S.A.; *Int'l*, pg. 3637
IMPRESA PIZZAROTTI & C. S.P.A.—See Mipien S.p.A; *Int'l*, pg. 4915
IMPRESA PUBLISHING S.A.—See Impresa SGPS S.A.; *Int'l*, pg. 3637
IMPRESA SGPS S.A.; *Int'l*, pg. 3637
I.M.P. RESEARCH INSTITUTE OF MOLECULAR PATHOLOGY—See C.H. Boehringer Sohn AG & Co. KG; *Int'l*, pg. 1241
IMPRESE TIPOGRAFICHE VENETE SPA—See Caltagirone Editore S.p.A.; *Int'l*, pg. 1266
IMPRESO, INC.; *U.S. Public*, pg. 1114
IMPRESS ETHANOL CO., LTD.—See KNM Group Berhad; *Int'l*, pg. 4209

IMPRESO, INC.

CORPORATE AFFILIATIONS

IMPRESS GROUP SINGAPORE PTE. LTD.—See Impress Holdings Inc.; *Int'l*, pg. 3637
IMPRESS HOLDINGS INC.; *Int'l*, pg. 3637
IMPRESSION HOMES LLC—See Toyota Motor Corporation; *Int'l*, pg. 7873
IMPRESSIONS-A.B.A. INDUSTRIES, INC.; *U.S. Private*, pg. 2051
IMPRESSIONS DIRECT, INC.—See Ennis, Inc.; *U.S. Public*, pg. 769
IMPRESSIONS INCORPORATED—See Great Mill Rock LLC; *U.S. Private*, pg. 1766
IMPRESSIONS INCORPORATED—See Vivid Impact Corporation; *U.S. Private*, pg. 4406
IMPRESSIONS IN PRINT, INC.; *U.S. Private*, pg. 2050
IMPRESSIONS MARKETING GROUP INC; *U.S. Private*, pg. 2050
IMPRESSIONS MEDIA SERVICES, INC.; *U.S. Private*, pg. 2050
IMPRESSIONS PRESSES DE BRETAGNE; *Int'l*, pg. 3637
IMPRESSIONS PRINTING & COPYING SERVICES; *U.S. Private*, pg. 2051
IMPRESS PUBLIC RELATIONS, INC.; *U.S. Private*, pg. 2050
IMPRESS PUBLIC RELATIONS, INC.—See Impress Public Relations, Inc.; *U.S. Private*, pg. 2050
IMPRESS PUBLIC RELATIONS, INC.—See Impress Public Relations, Inc.; *U.S. Private*, pg. 2050
IMPRESS SENSORS & SYSTEMS LIMITED—See Sensata Technologies Holding plc; *U.S. Public*, pg. 1865
IMPRESS TECHNOLOGY (BEIJING) CO., LTD.—See Impress Holdings Inc.; *Int'l*, pg. 3637
IMPRESSUM S.A.—See Windmoeller & Hoelscher KG; *Int'l*, pg. 8426
IMPRESSU PRINT GROUP PTY. LTD.—See Domino's Pizza Enterprises Ltd.; *Int'l*, pg. 2162
IMPRES TECHNOLOGY SOLUTIONS, INC.; *U.S. Private*, pg. 2050
IMPREV, INC.—See Vector Capital Management, L.P.; *U.S. Private*, pg. 4351
IMPRIMA (DEUTSCHLAND) GMBH—See HAL Trust N.V.; *Int'l*, pg. 3224
IMPRIMA (FRANCE) SARL—See HAL Trust N.V.; *Int'l*, pg. 3224
IMPRIMA IROOMS LIMITED—See HAL Trust N.V.; *Int'l*, pg. 3224
IMPRIMA (NEDERLAND) B.V.—See HAL Trust N.V.; *Int'l*, pg. 3224
IMPRIMERIE BILLET S.A.S.; *Int'l*, pg. 3637
IMPRIMERIE CHIRAT SA; *Int'l*, pg. 3637
IMPRIMERIE HENRI DRIDE; *Int'l*, pg. 3637
IMPRIMERIE LEBONFON INC.; *Int'l*, pg. 3637
IMPRIMERIE LEFRANCQ & CIE; *Int'l*, pg. 3637
IMPRIMERIE RAULT SA; *Int'l*, pg. 3637
IMPRIMERIE SAVOY OFFSET; *Int'l*, pg. 3637
IMPRIMERIE TONNELLIER; *Int'l*, pg. 3637
IMPRIMIS GROUP; *U.S. Private*, pg. 2051
IMPRINT ENTERPRISES INC.; *U.S. Private*, pg. 2051
IMPRIPOST TECNOLOGIAS S.A—See Grupo Clarin S.A.; *Int'l*, pg. 3124
IMPRIPOST TECNOLOGIAS S.A—See Techint S.p.A.; *Int'l*, pg. 7503
IMPRIVATA, INC.—See Thoma Bravo, L.P.; *U.S. Private*, pg. 4148
IMPROCHEM (PTY) LIMITED—See AECI Limited; *Int'l*, pg. 171
IMPROMED, LLC—See Clayton, Dubilier & Rice, LLC; *U.S. Private*, pg. 921
IMPROMED, LLC—See TPG Capital, L.P.; *U.S. Public*, pg. 2170
IM PROMOS PTY LTD—See WPP plc; *Int'l*, pg. 8462
IMPRO PRECISION INDUSTRIES LIMITED; *Int'l*, pg. 3637
IMPROTECH LTD.—See Ag Growth International Inc.; *Int'l*, pg. 198
IMPROVED CONSTRUCTION METHODS INC.; *U.S. Private*, pg. 2051
IMPROVED MACHINERY INC.—See Ingersoll Rand Inc.; *U.S. Public*, pg. 1120
IMPROVED SOLUTIONS PORTUGAL UNIPESSOAL LTDA.—See Interpump Group S.p.A.; *Int'l*, pg. 3755
IMPROVED SOLUTIONS UNIPESSOAL LTDA.—See Interpump Group S.p.A.; *Int'l*, pg. 3755
IMPROVEIT; *U.S. Private*, pg. 2051
IMPROVE MEDICAL INSTRUMENTS CO., LTD; *Int'l*, pg. 3637
IMPROVING HOLDINGS, LLC—See Trinity Hunt Management, L.P.; *U.S. Private*, pg. 4234
IMP SOLUTIONS INC.—See I.M.P. Group International Inc.; *Int'l*, pg. 3566
IMPULSA SOLUCIONES TECNOLOGICAS, S.L.—See AZKOYEN S.A.; *Int'l*, pg. 780
IMPULSE FITNESS SOLUTIONS, S.A.; *Int'l*, pg. 3638
IMPULSE HOTEL DEVELOPMENT BV—See Melia Hotels International, S.A.; *Int'l*, pg. 4809
IMPULSE MONITORING, INC.—See Globus Medical, Inc.; *U.S. Public*, pg. 947
IMPULSE NC, LLC—See Berkshire Hathaway Inc.; *U.S. Public*, pg. 310
IMPULSE NOVELTIES INC.; *U.S. Private*, pg. 2051

IMPULSE (QINGDAO) HEALTH TECH CO., LTD.; *Int'l*, pg. 3638
IMPULSERADAR SWEDEN AB—See Addtech AB; *Int'l*, pg. 134
IMPULS GMBH—See H&M Hennes & Mauritz AB; *Int'l*, pg. 3192
IMPULS-LEASING-AUSTRIA S.R.O.—See Raiffeisenlandesbank Oberosterreich Aktiengesellschaft; *Int'l*, pg. 6187
IMPULSORA DEL DEPORTIVO NECAXA, S.A. DE C.V.—See Grupo Televisa, S.A.B.; *Int'l*, pg. 3136
IMPULSORA DEL DESARROLLO Y EL EMPLEO EN AMERICA LATINA S.A. DE C.V.; *Int'l*, pg. 3638
IMPULSYON—See Regie Autonome des Transports Parisiens; *Int'l*, pg. 6253
I M QUARRIES LIMITED; *Int'l*, pg. 3562
IMQUEST BIOSCIENCES INC.; *U.S. Private*, pg. 2051
IMRA AMERICA, INC.—See AISIN Corporation; *Int'l*, pg. 252
IMRA EUROPE S.A.—See AISIN Corporation; *Int'l*, pg. 253
IM RAKOVICA U RESTRUKTURIRANJU A.D.; *Int'l*, pg. 3617
IMRA MATERIAL R&D CO., LTD.—See AISIN Corporation; *Int'l*, pg. 253
IMRB INTERNATIONAL LTD.—See WPP plc; *Int'l*, pg. 8465
IMRE, LLC; *U.S. Private*, pg. 2051
IMRES B.V.—See Dubai World Corporation; *Int'l*, pg. 2221
IMRICOR MEDICAL SYSTEMS, INC.; *U.S. Private*, pg. 2051
IMRIS (EUROPE) SPRL—See IMRIS Inc.; *U.S. Public*, pg. 1114
IMRIS INC.; *U.S. Public*, pg. 1114
IMRIS SINGAPORE PTE. LTD.—See IMRIS Inc.; *U.S. Public*, pg. 1114
IMR TEST LABS INC.—See Curtiss-Wright Corporation; *U.S. Public*, pg. 612
IMSAUM SCI—See Thai Union Group Public Company Limited; *Int'l*, pg. 7596
IMS AUSTRIA GMBH—See Jacquet Metal Service SA; *Int'l*, pg. 3866
IMS BELGIUM S.A./N.V.—See Jacquet Metal Service SA; *Int'l*, pg. 3866
IMS BUHRKE-OLSON—See Innovative Manufacturing Solutions Corp.; *U.S. Private*, pg. 2083
IMS CO., LTD.—See Mitsubishi Estate Co., Ltd.; *Int'l*, pg. 4946
IMS CONCEPTS S.A./N.V.—See DIC Corporation; *Int'l*, pg. 2109
IMS CONSULTING & EXPERT SERVICES, LLC—See Trinity Hunt Management, L.P.; *U.S. Private*, pg. 4234
IMS CONSULTING & EXPERT SERVICES; *U.S. Private*, pg. 2051
IMS ENGINEERS, PA—See Integrated Management Services, PA; *U.S. Private*, pg. 2100
IMSERV EUROPE LIMITED—See Blue Water Energy LLP; *Int'l*, pg. 1070
IMS FRANCE SAS—See Jacquet Metal Service SA; *Int'l*, pg. 3866
IMS GESELLSCHAFT FUR INFORMATIONS-UND MANAGEMENTSYSTEME MBH—See Schneider Electric SE; *Int'l*, pg. 6624
IMS GROUP HOLDINGS LTD.; *Int'l*, pg. 3638
IMS HEALTH ANALYTICS SERVICES PRIVATE LIMITED—See IQVIA Holdings Inc.; *U.S. Public*, pg. 1168
IMS HEALTH HOLDINGS, INC.—See IQVIA Holdings Inc.; *U.S. Public*, pg. 1168
IMS HEALTH INFORMATION SOLUTIONS INDIA PRIVATE LTD.—See IQVIA Holdings Inc.; *U.S. Public*, pg. 1169
IMS HEALTH KOREA LTD.—See IQVIA Holdings Inc.; *U.S. Public*, pg. 1168
IMS HEALTH MARKET RESEARCH CONSULTING (SHANGHAI) CO. LTD.—See IQVIA Holdings Inc.; *U.S. Public*, pg. 1168
IMS HEALTH PAKISTAN (PRIVATE) LIMITED—See IQVIA Holdings Inc.; *U.S. Public*, pg. 1169
IMS HEALTH TECHNOLOGY SOLUTIONS INDIA PRIVATE LTD.—See IQVIA Holdings Inc.; *U.S. Public*, pg. 1169
IMS INTERNATIONAL MARKING SYSTEMS, GMBH—See SWARCO AG; *Int'l*, pg. 7360
IMS INTERNET MEDIA SERVICES, INC.; *U.S. Private*, pg. 2051
I.M.S.I STAFFING PRIVATE LIMITED—See TeamLease Services Ltd.; *Int'l*, pg. 7501
IMS MASKINTEKNIK AB—See Storskogen Group AB; *Int'l*, pg. 7227
IMS MAXIMS PLC; *Int'l*, pg. 3638
IMS NEDERLAND BV—See Jacquet Metal Service SA; *Int'l*, pg. 3866
IMS OZEL CELIK TICARET LTD SIRKETI—See Jacquet Metal Service SA; *Int'l*, pg. 3866
IMS PORTUGAL SA—See Jacquet Metal Service SA; *Int'l*, pg. 3866
IMS RECYCLING SERVICE INC.; *U.S. Private*, pg. 2051
IMS RHEIN-MAIN GMBH—See Jacquet Metal Service SA; *Int'l*, pg. 3866

IMS S.A.; *Int'l*, pg. 3638
IMS SPA—See Jacquet Metal Service SA; *Int'l*, pg. 3866
IMSTALCON JSC; *Int'l*, pg. 3638
IMS TECHNOLOGY SERVICES; *U.S. Private*, pg. 2051
IMS UK LIMITED—See Jacquet Metal Service SA; *Int'l*, pg. 3866
IMS-VERBINDUNGSTECHNIK GMBH & CO. KG—See Wurth Verwaltungsgesellschaft mbH; *Int'l*, pg. 8505
IMTAC TECHNOLOGIES LLC—See Sobha Limited; *Int'l*, pg. 7030
IMTAC YEMEN LTD.—See Sobha Limited; *Int'l*, pg. 7030
IM TAPE STORAGE OY—See Iron Mountain Incorporated; *U.S. Public*, pg. 1172
IMT B.V.—See Xylem Inc.; *U.S. Public*, pg. 2394
IMTC, INC.; *U.S. Private*, pg. 2051
IMT CO., LTD.; *Int'l*, pg. 3638
IMT CORPORATION—See Mission Essential Personnel, LLC; *U.S. Private*, pg. 2747
IMT CORPORATION—See Marubeni Corporation; *Int'l*, pg. 4705
IMT DEFENCE CORP—See Mission Essential Personnel, LLC; *U.S. Private*, pg. 2747
IMTECH AQUA LTD.—See Electricite de France S.A.; *Int'l*, pg. 2351
IMTECH BELGIUM N.V.—See Electricite de France S.A.; *Int'l*, pg. 2351
IMTECH CO., LTD.—See Wooree E&L Co., Ltd.; *Int'l*, pg. 8453
IMTECH ENGINEERING SERVICES LONDON AND SOUTH LTD.—See Electricite de France S.A.; *Int'l*, pg. 2351
IMTECH ENGINEERING SERVICES LTD.—See Electricite de France S.A.; *Int'l*, pg. 2351
IMTECH HUNGARY KFT—See Electricite de France S.A.; *Int'l*, pg. 2351
IM TECH INC; *Int'l*, pg. 3617
IMTECH INVIRON LTD.—See Electricite de France S.A.; *Int'l*, pg. 2351
IMTECH MAINTENANCE N.V.—See Electricite de France S.A.; *Int'l*, pg. 2351
IMTECH PROJECTS N.V.—See Electricite de France S.A.; *Int'l*, pg. 2351
IMTECH PROJECTS N.V.—See Electricite de France S.A.; *Int'l*, pg. 2351
IMTECH PROJECTS N.V.—See Electricite de France S.A.; *Int'l*, pg. 2351
IMTECH SPAIN S.L.—See Electricite de France S.A.; *Int'l*, pg. 2351
IMTECH TECHNOLOGY SRL—See Electricite de France S.A.; *Int'l*, pg. 2351
IM TELECOM, LLC—See KonaTel, Inc.; *U.S. Public*, pg. 1271
IMTEL KOMUNIKACIJE A.D.; *Int'l*, pg. 3638
IMTEL RTV A.D.; *Int'l*, pg. 3638
IMT FORGE GROUP—See Mission Essential Personnel, LLC; *U.S. Private*, pg. 2747
IMT INSURANCE COMPANY; *U.S. Private*, pg. 2051
IMTRA CORPORATION; *U.S. Private*, pg. 2051
IMTRON GMBH—See Ceconomy AG; *Int'l*, pg. 1373
IMTT-BAYONNE—See Riverstone Holdings LLC; *U.S. Private*, pg. 3447
IMTT-GEISMAR—See Riverstone Holdings LLC; *U.S. Private*, pg. 3447
IMTT-GRETNA—See BWC Terminals LLC; *U.S. Private*, pg. 700
IMT-THL INDIA PRIVATE LIMITED—See CSC Holdings Limited; *Int'l*, pg. 1862
IMTT HOLDINGS LLC—See Riverstone Holdings LLC; *U.S. Private*, pg. 3447
IMTT-ILLINOIS—See Riverstone Holdings LLC; *U.S. Private*, pg. 3447
IMTT-NTL, LTD.—See Riverstone Holdings LLC; *U.S. Private*, pg. 3447
IMTT QUEBEC INC.—See Riverstone Holdings LLC; *U.S. Private*, pg. 3447
IMTT-RICHMOND-CA—See Riverstone Holdings LLC; *U.S. Private*, pg. 3447
IMTT-VIRGINIA—See Riverstone Holdings LLC; *U.S. Private*, pg. 3447
IMUGENE LIMITED; *Int'l*, pg. 3638
IMUGEN, INC.—See Revvity, Inc.; *U.S. Public*, pg. 1794
IMULUS, LLC; *U.S. Private*, pg. 2051
IMUNON, INC.; *U.S. Public*, pg. 1114
IMURA CO., LTD.; *Int'l*, pg. 3638
IMURAYA FOODS CO., LTD.—See Imuraya Group Co., Ltd.; *Int'l*, pg. 3638
IMURAYA GROUP CO., LTD.; *Int'l*, pg. 3638
IMURAYA USA, INC.—See Imuraya Group Co., Ltd.; *Int'l*, pg. 3638
IMV CORPORATION; *Int'l*, pg. 3638
IMVEST S.P.A.; *Int'l*, pg. 3639
IMV EUROPE LIMITED—See IMV CORPORATION; *Int'l*, pg. 3638
IMV HUNGARIA KFT—See Immofinanz AG; *Int'l*, pg. 3628
IMV INC.; *Int'l*, pg. 3638
IMV MEDICAL INFORMATION DIVISION, INC.—See Bio-Rad Laboratories, Inc.; *U.S. Public*, pg. 334
IMV (THAILAND) CO., LTD.—See IMV CORPORATION; *Int'l*, pg. 3638

COMPANY NAME INDEX

IMVU INC.; *U.S. Private,* pg. 2051
IMWAVE, INC.; *U.S. Private,* pg. 2052
I.M.W. CNG BANGLADESH LTD.—See Clean Energy Fuels Corp.; *U.S. Public,* pg. 508
IMW COLOMBIA LTD.—See Clean Energy Fuels Corp.; *U.S. Public,* pg. 508
IMWELL HEALTH, LLC—See Ontario Municipal Employees Retirement System; *Int'l,* pg. 5584
IMW IMMOBILIEN SE; *Int'l,* pg. 3639
IMW INDUSTRIES LTD.—See Clean Energy Fuels Corp.; *U.S. Public,* pg. 508
IMW INDUSTRIES LTD.—See Landi Renzo S.p.a.; *Int'l,* pg. 4406
IMWINKELRIED LUFTUNG UND KLIMA AG—See Burkhalter Holding AG; *Int'l,* pg. 1225
IMWOO TECHNOLOGIES, LLC; *U.S. Private,* pg. 2052
IMX HOLDINGS, LLC—See HCA Healthcare, Inc.; *U.S. Public,* pg. 999
IMX SOFTWARE GROUP LIMITED—See Holley Holland Limited; *Int'l,* pg. 3451
IMX SOFTWARE GROUP PTY. LTD.—See Holley Holland Limited; *Int'l,* pg. 3451
IMX SOFTWARE SOUTH AFRICA—See Holley Holland Limited; *Int'l,* pg. 3451
IMX SOFTWARE UK LIMITED—See Holley Holland Limited; *Int'l,* pg. 3451
IMX UK LIMITED—See Indiana Resources Limited; *Int'l,* pg. 3655
IN2VATE, LLC.—See iLearningEngines, Inc.; *U.S. Public,* pg. 1101
IN8BIO, INC.; *U.S. Public,* pg. 1114
INABA DENKI SANGYO CO., LTD.; *Int'l,* pg. 3643
INABA SEISAKUSHO CO., LTD.; *Int'l,* pg. 3643
INABATA AMERICA CORPORATION—See Inabata & Co. Ltd.; *Int'l,* pg. 3643
INABATA BRAZIL IMPORT & EXPORT LTD.—See Inabata & Co. Ltd.; *Int'l,* pg. 3643
INABATA & CO. LTD.; *Int'l,* pg. 3643
INABATA EUROPE GMBH—See Inabata & Co. Ltd.; *Int'l,* pg. 3643
INABATA EUROPE S.A.—See Inabata & Co. Ltd.; *Int'l,* pg. 3643
INABATA FINE TECH CO., LTD.—See Inabata & Co. Ltd.; *Int'l,* pg. 3643
INABATA FRANCE S.A.S.—See Inabata & Co. Ltd.; *Int'l,* pg. 3643
INABATA INDIA PRIVATE LTD.—See Inabata & Co. Ltd.; *Int'l,* pg. 3643
INABATA INDUSTRY & TRADE (DALIAN F.T.Z.) CO., LTD.—See Inabata & Co. Ltd.; *Int'l,* pg. 3643
INABATA KOREA & CO., LTD.—See Inabata & Co. Ltd.; *Int'l,* pg. 3643
INABATA MALAYSIA SDN. BHD.—See Inabata & Co. Ltd.; *Int'l,* pg. 3643
INABATA MEXICO, S.A. DE C.V.—See Inabata & Co. Ltd.; *Int'l,* pg. 3643
INABATA NANODAX CO., LTD.—See Inabata & Co. Ltd.; *Int'l,* pg. 3644
INABATA OPTECH CO., LTD.—See Inabata & Co. Ltd.; *Int'l,* pg. 3644
INABATA PHILIPPINES, INC.—See Inabata & Co. Ltd.; *Int'l,* pg. 3644
INABATA SANGYO (H.K.) LTD.—See Inabata & Co. Ltd.; *Int'l,* pg. 3644
INABATA SINGAPORE (PTE.) LTD.—See Inabata & Co. Ltd.; *Int'l,* pg. 3644
INABATA SINGAPORE (PTE.) LTD.—See Inabata & Co. Ltd.; *Int'l,* pg. 3644
INABATA THAI CO., LTD.—See Inabata & Co. Ltd.; *Int'l,* pg. 3644
INABATA THAI CO., LTD.—See Inabata & Co. Ltd.; *Int'l,* pg. 3644
INABATA UK LIMITED—See Inabata & Co. Ltd.; *Int'l,* pg. 3644
INABATA VIETNAM CO., LTD.—See Inabata & Co. Ltd.; *Int'l,* pg. 3644
INA BEARING (PTY) LTD.—See INA-Holding Schaeffler GmbH & Co. KG; *Int'l,* pg. 3640
INA BEARINGS INDIA PRIVATE LIMITED—See INA-Holding Schaeffler GmbH & Co. KG; *Int'l,* pg. 3640
INA BH D.D.—See INA-Industrija Nafte, d.d.; *Int'l,* pg. 3642
INACOMP TECHNICAL SERVICES GROUP; *U.S. Private,* pg. 2052
INAC PROCESS AB—See VINCI S.A.; *Int'l,* pg. 8222
INA CRNA GORA D.O.O.—See INA-Industrija Nafte, d.d.; *Int'l,* pg. 3642
INACUI S.A.—See Air Products & Chemicals, Inc.; *U.S. Public,* pg. 66
INADALE WF HOLDCO, LLC—See E.ON SE; *Int'l,* pg. 2258
INADALE WIND FARM, LLC—See E.ON SE; *Int'l,* pg. 2258
INADI S.A.—See Bertelsmann SE & Co. KGaA; *Int'l,* pg. 994
INA D.O.O.—See INA-Industrija Nafte, d.d.; *Int'l,* pg. 3642
INA - DRIVES & MECHATRONICS AG & CO. KG—See INA-Holding Schaeffler GmbH & Co. KG; *Int'l,* pg. 3640
INAER HELICOPTER FRANCE SA—See Inversiones Aereas S.L.; *Int'l,* pg. 3774

INAER HELICOPTER ITALIA S.P.A.—See Inversiones Aereas S.L.; *Int'l,* pg. 3774
INAER-HELICOPTER PORTUGAL LDA—See Inversiones Aereas S.L.; *Int'l,* pg. 3774
INAGEYA CO., LTD.; *Int'l,* pg. 3644
INAGIP D.O.O.—See INA-Industrija Nafte, d.d.; *Int'l,* pg. 3642
INAG-NIEVERGELT AG—See BKW AG; *Int'l,* pg. 1055
INAGRA, S.A.—See Ferrovial S.A.; *Int'l,* pg. 2644
INAGRO SDN. BHD.—See Analabs Resources Berhad; *Int'l,* pg. 446
INA GROUP LTD OY; *Int'l,* pg. 3639
INAGUA GENERAL STORE, LTD.—See K+S Aktiengesellschaft; *Int'l,* pg. 4040
INA-HOLDING SCHAEFFLER GMBH & CO. KG; *Int'l,* pg. 3639
INA HUNGARY KFT.—See INA-Industrija Nafte, d.d.; *Int'l,* pg. 3642
INAI BENUA SDN. BHD.—See MBM Resources Berhad; *Int'l,* pg. 4754
INA-INDUSTRIJA NAFTE, D.D.; *Int'l,* pg. 3642
INAIRE (PVT) LTD.—See Daikin Industries, Ltd.; *Int'l,* pg. 1935
INAKAYA NEW YORK, L.L.C.—See WDI Corporation; *Int'l,* pg. 8362
INA KOSOVO D.O.O.—See INA-Industrija Nafte, d.d.; *Int'l,* pg. 3642
INALAB, INC.—See SGS SA; *Int'l,* pg. 6744
INA LANSKROUN, S.R.O.—See INA-Holding Schaeffler GmbH & Co. KG; *Int'l,* pg. 3640
INALCA ALGERIE S.A.R.L.—See Cremonini S.p.A.; *Int'l,* pg. 1838
INALCA ANGOLA L.T.D.A.—See Cremonini S.p.A.; *Int'l,* pg. 1838
INALCA KINSHASA S.P.R.L.—See Cremonini S.p.A.; *Int'l,* pg. 1838
INALCA S.P.A.—See Cremonini S.p.A.; *Int'l,* pg. 1838
INALIA CAP DJINET, S.L.—See GS Holdings Corp.; *Int'l,* pg. 3142
INAL NORDESTE S.A.—See Companhia Siderurgica Nacional; *Int'l,* pg. 1748
INALWAYS CORP.; *Int'l,* pg. 3645
INALWAYS ELECTRONICS (DONGGUAN) CO., LTD.—See Inalways Corp.; *Int'l,* pg. 3645
INALWAYS ELECTRONICS INC.—See Inalways Corp.; *Int'l,* pg. 3645
INA MAZIVA D.O.O.—See INA-Industrija Nafte, d.d.; *Int'l,* pg. 3642
INAMI DAIKEN CORPORATION—See Daiken Corporation; *Int'l,* pg. 1931
INAMI DAIKEN PRODUCTS CORPORATION—See Daiken Corporation; *Int'l,* pg. 1931
INAMOTO MANUFACTURING CO., LTD.—See Sumitomo Corporation; *Int'l,* pg. 7268
INANI MARBLES & INDUSTRIES LTD.; *Int'l,* pg. 3645
INANI SECURITIES LTD.; *Int'l,* pg. 3645
INA ORIENTAL MOTOR CO., LTD.—See Oriental Motor Co., Ltd.; *Int'l,* pg. 5626
INA-OSIJEK - PETROL D.D.—See INA-Industrija Nafte, d.d.; *Int'l,* pg. 3642
INAPA ANGOLA DISTRIBUICAO DE PAPEL, SA—See Inapa - Investimentos, Participacoes e Gestao, SA; *Int'l,* pg. 3645
INAPA BELGIQUE, SA—See Inapa - Investimentos, Participacoes e Gestao, SA; *Int'l,* pg. 3645
INAPA DEUTSCHLAND, GMBH—See Inapa - Investimentos, Participacoes e Gestao, SA; *Int'l,* pg. 3645
INAPA ESPANA DISTRIBUICION DE PAPEL, SA—See Inapa - Investimentos, Participacoes e Gestao, SA; *Int'l,* pg. 3645
INAPA FRANCE, SA—See Inapa - Investimentos, Participacoes e Gestao, SA; *Int'l,* pg. 3645
INAPA - INVESTIMENTOS, PARTICIPACOES E GESTAO, SA; *Int'l,* pg. 3645
INAPA LUXEMBOURG, SA—See Inapa - Investimentos, Participacoes e Gestao, SA; *Int'l,* pg. 3645
INAPA PACKAGING, LDA.—See Inapa - Investimentos, Participacoes e Gestao, SA; *Int'l,* pg. 3645
INAPA PORTUGAL DISTRIBUICAO DE PAPEL, SA—See Inapa - Investimentos, Participacoes e Gestao, SA; *Int'l,* pg. 3645
INAPA SUISSE, SA—See Inapa - Investimentos, Participacoes e Gestao, SA; *Int'l,* pg. 3645
INAPEL EMBALAGENS LTDA.—See Sonoco Products Company; *U.S. Public,* pg. 1904
INA RESEARCH, INC.—See Shin Nippon Biomedical Laboratories, Ltd.; *Int'l,* pg. 6837
INA RESEARCH PHILIPPINES, INC.—See Shin Nippon Biomedical Laboratories, Ltd.; *Int'l,* pg. 6837
INARIA INTERNATIONAL INC.—See Fairfax Financial Holdings Limited; *Int'l,* pg. 2605
INARIA INTERNATIONAL INC.—See Power Corporation of Canada; *Int'l,* pg. 5944
INARI AMERTRON BERHAD; *Int'l,* pg. 3645
INARI BERHAD - PLANT 8—See Inari Amertron Berhad; *Int'l,* pg. 3645
INARI INTEGRATED SYSTEMS SDN. BHD.—See Inari Amertron Berhad; *Int'l,* pg. 3645
INARI MEDICAL, INC.; *U.S. Public,* pg. 1114

INARI SEMICONDUCTOR LABS SDN. BHD.—See Inari Amertron Berhad; *Int'l,* pg. 3645
INA ROLAMENTOS LDA.—See INA-Holding Schaeffler GmbH & Co. KG; *Int'l,* pg. 3640
INA SKALICA SPOL. S.R.O.—See INA-Holding Schaeffler GmbH & Co. KG; *Int'l,* pg. 3640
INASSET S.R.L.—See Retelit S.p.A.; *Int'l,* pg. 6306
INAUTH, INC.—See American Express Company; *U.S. Public,* pg. 102
INAVI MOBILITY INC.—See UbiVelox Co., Ltd.; *Int'l,* pg. 8004
INAVI SYSTEMS INC.—See UbiVelox Co., Ltd.; *Int'l,* pg. 8004
INAWISDOM LTD.—See Cognizant Technology Solutions Corporation; *U.S. Public,* pg. 524
INAX (CHINA) INVESTMENT CO., LTD.—See LIXIL Group Corporation; *Int'l,* pg. 4534
INAX ENGINEERING CORPORATION—See LIXIL Group Corporation; *Int'l,* pg. 4534
INAX ITALIA S.R.L.—See LIXIL Group Corporation; *Int'l,* pg. 4534
INAX MAINTENANCE CORPORATION—See LIXIL Group Corporation; *Int'l,* pg. 4534
INAX MALAYSIA SDN. BHD.—See LIXIL Group Corporation; *Int'l,* pg. 4534
INAX VIETNAM CO., LTD.—See LIXIL Group Corporation; *Int'l,* pg. 4534
INAX VIETNAM PLUMBING FIXTURES CO., LTD.—See LIXIL Group Corporation; *Int'l,* pg. 4534
INAX VIETNAM SANITARY WARE CO., LTD.—See LIXIL Group Corporation; *Int'l,* pg. 4534
INAYA FACILITIES MANAGEMENT SERVICES—See Belhasa Group of Companies; *Int'l,* pg. 964
INBANKSHARES CORP.; *U.S. Public,* pg. 1114
INBAR GROUP FINANCE LTD; *Int'l,* pg. 3645
INBEGO AB—See Storskogen Group AB; *Int'l,* pg. 7227
INBENTA TECHNOLOGIES INC.; *U.S. Private,* pg. 2052
INB ENTERPRISE COMPANY LIMITED—See THK CO., LTD.; *Int'l,* pg. 7711
INBET SP. Z O.O.—See INPRO S.A.; *Int'l,* pg. 3717
INBEV N.V.—See Anheuser-Busch InBev SA/NV; *Int'l,* pg. 466
INBEV SEDRIN BREWERY CO, LTD—See Anheuser-Busch InBev SA/NV; *Int'l,* pg. 466
INBEV UK LTD.—See Anheuser-Busch InBev SA/NV; *Int'l,* pg. 466
INBICON A/S—See Orsted AS; *Int'l,* pg. 5644
INBIOGEN CO., LTD; *Int'l,* pg. 3645
INBIOPRO SOLUTIONS PRIVATE LIMITED—See Strides Pharma Science Limited; *Int'l,* pg. 7240
INBIT CORP.; *Int'l,* pg. 3645
IN BLOOM, INC.; *U.S. Private,* pg. 2052
INBODY CO., LTD.; *Int'l,* pg. 3646
INBODY EUROPE B.V.—See Inbody Co., Ltd.; *Int'l,* pg. 3646
INBODY INDIA PVT LTD—See Inbody Co., Ltd.; *Int'l,* pg. 3646
INBODY JAPAN INC.—See Inbody Co., Ltd.; *Int'l,* pg. 3646
INBOUND PLATFORM CORP.—See AirTrip Corp.; *Int'l,* pg. 250
INBOUND TECH, INC.—See Link & Motivation Inc.; *Int'l,* pg. 4513
INCA BRONZE POWDERS LTD.—See BASF SE; *Int'l,* pg. 884
INCAB S.P.A.—See Julius Meinl Industrieholding GmbH; *Int'l,* pg. 4025
INCADEA (BEIJING) ITC LTD.—See Cox Enterprises, Inc.; *U.S. Private,* pg. 1078
INCADEA GMBH—See Cox Enterprises, Inc.; *U.S. Private,* pg. 1077
INCADEA GMBH—See Cox Enterprises, Inc.; *U.S. Private,* pg. 1077
INCADEA GREECE INFORMATICS SYSTEMS S.A.—See Cox Enterprises, Inc.; *U.S. Private,* pg. 1078
INCADEA INDIA PRIVATE LIMITED—See Cox Enterprises, Inc.; *U.S. Private,* pg. 1078
INCADEA NEW ZEALAND LIMITED—See Cox Enterprises, Inc.; *U.S. Private,* pg. 1078
INCADEA SL—See Cox Enterprises, Inc.; *U.S. Private,* pg. 1078
INCADEA TAIWAN—See Cox Enterprises, Inc.; *U.S. Private,* pg. 1078
INCA DIGITAL PRINTERS LTD—See Screen Holdings Co., Ltd.; *Int'l,* pg. 6655
INCALL SYSTEMS PTE. LTD.—See Challenger Technologies Ltd.; *Int'l,* pg. 1438
INCAM AG; *Int'l,* pg. 3646
INCA MINERALS LTD.; *Int'l,* pg. 3646
INCANNEX HEALTHCARE LIMITED; *Int'l,* pg. 3646
INCA ONE GOLD CORP.; *Int'l,* pg. 3646
INCAP ELECTRONICS ESTONIA OU - KURESSAARE FACTORY—See InCap Oyj; *Int'l,* pg. 3646
INCAP ELECTRONICS ESTONIA OU—See InCap Oyj; *Int'l,* pg. 3646
INCAPITAL HOLDINGS, LLC—See Bank of America Corporation; *U.S. Public,* pg. 272
INCAPITAL LLC; *U.S. Private,* pg. 2052
INCAP LTD.; *Int'l,* pg. 3646

INCAP OYJ - HELSINKI FACTORY—See InCap Oyj; *Int'l*, pg. 3646
INCAP OYJ; *Int'l*, pg. 3646
INCA PRODUCTS ACQUISITION CORP.—See Dometic Group AB; *Int'l*, pg. 2160
INCAPSULA, INC.—See Thales S.A.; *Int'l*, pg. 7600
INCAPSULATE, LLC—See Accenture plc; *Int'l*, pg. 87
INCAPTA, INC.; *U.S. Public*, pg. 1114
INCAR FINANCIAL SERVICE CO LTD; *Int'l*, pg. 3646
INCARNUS MALAYSIA SDN. BHD.—See IQVIA Holdings Inc.; *U.S. Public*, pg. 1169
INCASEC AB—See Peab AB; *Int'l*, pg. 5772
INCA SOFTWARE LIMITED—See Datatec Limited; *Int'l*, pg. 1980
INCAUCA S.A.—See Organizacion Cultiba, S.A.B. de C.V.; *Int'l*, pg. 5618
INC.COM LLC—See Mansueto Ventures LLC; *U.S. Private*, pg. 2567
INCE & CO MIDDLE EAST LLP—See The Ince Group Plc; *Int'l*, pg. 7654
INCE CONSULTANCY CYPRUS LIMITED—See The Ince Group Plc; *Int'l*, pg. 7654
INCE CONSULTANCY UG—See The Ince Group Plc; *Int'l*, pg. 7654
INCE CONSULTING MIDDLE EAST LIMITED—See The Ince Group Plc; *Int'l*, pg. 7654
INCE DISTRIBUTING INCORPORATED; *U.S. Private*, pg. 2053
INCEDO, INC.; *U.S. Private*, pg. 2053
INCE GERMANY RECHTSANWALTSGESELLSCHAFT MBH—See The Ince Group Plc; *Int'l*, pg. 7654
INCE (GIBRALTAR) LIMITED—See The Ince Group Plc; *Int'l*, pg. 7654
INCE GORDON DADDS LLP—See The Ince Group Plc; *Int'l*, pg. 7654
THE INCE GROUP PLC; *Int'l*, pg. 7654
INCEKARALAR A.S.; *Int'l*, pg. 3646
INCEKARA TEKNIK CIHAZLAR ENDUSTRI VE TICARET A.S.—See Incekaralar A.S.; *Int'l*, pg. 3646
INCENDIA PARTNERS, INC.; *U.S. Private*, pg. 2053
INC ENGINEERING CO., LTD.—See IHI Corporation; *Int'l*, pg. 3604
INCENTER, LLC; *U.S. Private*, pg. 2053
INCENTIAPAY LIMITED; *Int'l*, pg. 3646
INCENTIVE MAGAZINE—See EagleTree Capital, LP; *U.S. Private*, pg. 1312
INCENTIVE SOLUTIONS; *U.S. Private*, pg. 2053
INCENTIVE TECHNOLOGY GROUP, LLC—See ICF International, Inc.; *U.S. Public*, pg. 1086
INCENTRA SOLUTIONS NW—See Presilient, LLC; *U.S. Private*, pg. 3255
INCEPTION GROWTH ACQUISITION LIMITED; *U.S. Public*, pg. 1114
INCEPTION MEDIA GROUP, LLC; *U.S. Private*, pg. 2053
INCEPTION MINING, INC.; *U.S. Public*, pg. 1114
INCEPTUM ENTERPRISES LIMITED; *Int'l*, pg. 3646
INCEPTURE INC.—See GuideWell Mutual Holding Corporation; *U.S. Private*, pg. 1814
INCEPTUS MEDIA GP INC—See GVIC Communications Corp.; *Int'l*, pg. 3189
INCERTEC PLATING CORP.; *U.S. Private*, pg. 2053
INCHARGE INSTITUTE OF AMERICA, INC.; *U.S. Private*, pg. 2053
INCHCAPE ARGENTINA SA—See Inchcape plc; *Int'l*, pg. 3647
INCHCAPE AUSTRALIA LIMITED—See Inchcape plc; *Int'l*, pg. 3647
INCHCAPE FINANCE PLC—See Inchcape plc; *Int'l*, pg. 3647
INCHCAPE FLEET SOLUTIONS LIMITED—See Inchcape plc; *Int'l*, pg. 3647
INCHCAPE INTERNATIONAL HOLDINGS LIMITED—See Inchcape plc; *Int'l*, pg. 3647
INCHCAPE LATAM PERU SA—See Inchcape plc; *Int'l*, pg. 3647
INCHCAPE MANAGEMENT SERVICES LTD.—See Inchcape plc; *Int'l*, pg. 3647
INCHCAPE MOTORS FINLAND OY—See Inchcape plc; *Int'l*, pg. 3647
INCHCAPE PARK LANE LTD.—See Inchcape plc; *Int'l*, pg. 3647
INCHCAPE PLC; *Int'l*, pg. 3646
INCHCAPE RETAIL LIMITED—See Inchcape plc; *Int'l*, pg. 3647
INCHCAPE SHIPPING SERVICES (CAMBODIA) LTD.—See Albert Ballin KG; *Int'l*, pg. 295
INCHCAPE SHIPPING SERVICES LLC—See Albert Ballin KG; *Int'l*, pg. 295
INCHCAPE SHIPPING SERVICES LTD.; *Int'l*, pg. 3647
INCHCAPE SHIPPING SERVICES WLL—See Albert Ballin KG; *Int'l*, pg. 295
INCHEON CITY GAS CO., LTD.; *Int'l*, pg. 3647
INCHEON TOTAL ENERGY COMPANY—See GS Holdings Corp.; *Int'l*, pg. 3142
INCHES FITNESS; *U.S. Private*, pg. 2053
INCHIARO LIFE DESIGNATED ACTIVITY COMPANY—See Talanx AG; *Int'l*, pg. 7445

INCH KENNETH DEVELOPMENT (M) SDN. BHD.—See Inch Kenneth Kajang Rubber Public Limited Company; *Int'l*, pg. 3646
INCH KENNETH KAJANG RUBBER PLC - MALAYSIA PRINCIPAL OFFICE—See Inch Kenneth Kajang Rubber Public Limited Company; *Int'l*, pg. 3646
INCH KENNETH KAJANG RUBBER PUBLIC LIMITED COMPANY; *Int'l*, pg. 3646
INCIDENT RESPONSE TECHNOLOGIES, INC.—See The Riverside Company; *U.S. Private*, pg. 4109
INCIPE, LLC—See Hawk Auto Group; *U.S. Private*, pg. 1882
INCIPIO, LLC; *U.S. Private*, pg. 2053
INCIPIO TECHNOLOGIES, INC.—See Incipio, LLC; *U.S. Private*, pg. 2053
INCISIVE FINANCIAL PUBLISHING LIMITED—See Apax Partners LLP; *Int'l*, pg. 504
INCISIVE LAW LLC—See The Ince Group Plc; *Int'l*, pg. 7654
INCISIVE MEDIA INVESTMENT LIMITED—See Apax Partners LLP; *Int'l*, pg. 504
INCISIVE MEDIA LIMITED—See Apax Partners LLP; *Int'l*, pg. 504
INCISIVE MEDIA—See Apax Partners LLP; *Int'l*, pg. 504
INCISIVE RWG LIMITED—See Apax Partners LLP; *Int'l*, pg. 504
INCITEC PIVOT EXPLOSIVES HOLDINGS PTY LIMITED—See Incitec Pivot Limited; *Int'l*, pg. 3648
INCITEC PIVOT FERTILIZERS LIMITED—See Incitec Pivot Limited; *Int'l*, pg. 3648
INCITEC PIVOT FINANCE AUSTRALIA PTY LTD—See Incitec Pivot Limited; *Int'l*, pg. 3648
INCITEC PIVOT LIMITED; *Int'l*, pg. 3647
INCITEC PIVOT US HOLDINGS PTY LTD—See Incitec Pivot Limited; *Int'l*, pg. 3648
INCITY IMMOBILIEN AG; *Int'l*, pg. 3648
INC.JET, INC.—See Norwix Inc.; *U.S. Public*, pg. 1543
INCJ, LTD.—See Japan Investment Corporation; *Int'l*, pg. 3898
INCKA; *Int'l*, pg. 3648
INCLAM SA; *Int'l*, pg. 3648
INCLARITY PLC; *Int'l*, pg. 3648
INCLINATOR COMPANY OF AMERICA, INC.; *U.S. Private*, pg. 2053
INCLINE MGMT CORP.; *U.S. Private*, pg. 2053
IN CLOUD CO., LTD.—See Jasmine International Public Company Limited; *Int'l*, pg. 3912
INCLUSIO SA; *Int'l*, pg. 3648
INCLUSIVE, INC.; *Int'l*, pg. 3648
INC. MAGAZINE—See Mansueto Ventures LLC; *U.S. Private*, pg. 2566
INC NAVIGATION COMPANY PHILIPPINES INC—See Interorient Navigation Company Ltd.; *Int'l*, pg. 3754
INCOATEC GMBH—See Bruker Corporation; *U.S. Public*, pg. 404
INCOAX NETWORKS AB; *Int'l*, pg. 3648
INCODE COMPUTER MANAGEMENT SERVICES—See Tyler Technologies, Inc.; *U.S. Public*, pg. 2208
INCODEMA HOLDINGS LLC—See CORE Industrial Partners, LLC; *U.S. Private*, pg. 1048
INCODE TECHNOLOGIES, INC.; *U.S. Private*, pg. 2054
INCODE TELECOM GROUP, INC.; *U.S. Private*, pg. 2054
INCODE TELECOM GROUP—See inCode Telecom Group, Inc.; *U.S. Private*, pg. 2054
INCOE CORPORATION; *U.S. Private*, pg. 2054
INCOFARMING AGRARPRODUKTE UND SERVICE GMBH—See KTG Agrar SE; *Int'l*, pg. 4316
INCOGNITO SOFTWARE SYSTEMS INC.—See Constellation Software Inc.; *Int'l*, pg. 1775
INCO INDUSTRIAL COMPONENTS 'S-GRAVENHAGE B.V.—See ION Geophysical Corporation; *U.S. Public*, pg. 1166
INCOMA SAL—See Holdal s.a.l.; *Int'l*, pg. 3449
INCOM CO., LTD.—See Japan Communications, Inc.; *Int'l*, pg. 3887
INCOM CO., LTD.—See Thomas Publishing Company LLC; *U.S. Private*, pg. 4157
INCOME ASSET MANAGEMENT GROUP LIMITED; *Int'l*, pg. 3648
INCOME FINANCIAL TRUST—See Quadravest Capital Management Inc.; *Int'l*, pg. 6150
THE INCOME & GROWTH VCT PLC; *Int'l*, pg. 7654
INCOME OPPORTUNITY REALTY INVESTORS, INC.; *U.S. Public*, pg. 1114
INCOME; *Int'l*, pg. 3648
IN-COMIX FOOD INDUSTRIES SDN. BHD.—See Hup Seng Industries Berhad; *Int'l*, pg. 3538
INCOMM BRODEUR—See Omnicom Group Inc.; *U.S. Public*, pg. 1578
INCOMM CANADA LLC—See Interactive Communications Inc; *U.S. Private*, pg. 2108
INCOMM EUROPE LIMITED—See Interactive Communications Inc; *U.S. Private*, pg. 2108
INCOMM JAPAN KK—See Interactive Communications Inc; *U.S. Private*, pg. 2108
INCOMM LTD.—See Interactive Communications Inc; *U.S. Private*, pg. 2108
INCOMM MEXICO, LLC—See Interactive Communications Inc; *U.S. Private*, pg. 2108

INCOMM PUERTO RICO LLC—See Interactive Communications Inc; *U.S. Private*, pg. 2108
INCOMM S.A.S.—See StoneX Group Inc.; *U.S. Public*, pg. 1952
INCOMM SOLUTIONS, INC.—See Chorus Call, Inc.; *U.S. Private*, pg. 889
INCOMPASS LLC; *U.S. Private*, pg. 2054
INCOMTECH-PROJECT LTD.—See SEMIKRON International GmbH; *Int'l*, pg. 6705
INCON CO., LTD.; *Int'l*, pg. 3649
INCONEN CORPORATION; *U.S. Private*, pg. 2054
INCON ENGINEERS LIMITED; *Int'l*, pg. 3649
INCON PROCESSING SYSTEMS, INC.—See Cooke, Inc.; *Int'l*, pg. 1788
INCONSO AG—See Korber AG; *Int'l*, pg. 4281
IN CONSTRUCTION HOLDINGS LIMITED; *Int'l*, pg. 3639
INCONTACT, INC.—See NICE Ltd.; *Int'l*, pg. 5265
INCONTROL TECH CO. LTD—See PSI Software SE; *Int'l*, pg. 6017
INCONTROL TECHNOLOGIES, INC.—See Universal Engineering Sciences, LLC; *U.S. Private*, pg. 4304
INCORDEX CORP.; *Int'l*, pg. 3649
INCOREZ LTD.—See Sika AG; *Int'l*, pg. 6917
INCORP HOLDINGS, LLC; *U.S. Private*, pg. 2054
INCORPORATE MASSAGE CO.; *U.S. Private*, pg. 2054
INCORPORATING SERVICES, LTD; *U.S. Private*, pg. 2054
INCORR ENERGY GROUP LLC—See ARB Midstream, LLC; *U.S. Private*, pg. 308
INCOR S.R.L.—See THK CO., LTD.; *Int'l*, pg. 7711
INCO SERVICES, INC.—See INNOVATE Corp.; *U.S. Public*, pg. 1126
INCOS ITALIA SRL—See Sesa S.p.A.; *Int'l*, pg. 6728
INCO SPOLKA Z O.O.—See Bundesdruckerei GmbH; *Int'l*, pg. 1216
INCOTEC AMERICA DO SUL TECNOLOGIA EM SEMENTES LTDA.—See Croda International plc; *Int'l*, pg. 1853
INCOTEC ARGENTINA S.A—See Croda International plc; *Int'l*, pg. 1853
INCOTEC (BEIJING) AGRICULTURAL TECHNOLOGY CO., LTD.—See Croda International plc; *Int'l*, pg. 1853
INCOTEC GROUP B.V.—See Croda International plc; *Int'l*, pg. 1852
INCOTEC INTEGRATED COATING & SEED TECHNOLOGY, INC.—See Croda International plc; *Int'l*, pg. 1852
INCOTEC MALAYSIA SDN. BHD.—See Croda International plc; *Int'l*, pg. 1853
INCOTECNICA S.A. DE C.V.—See Windmoeller & Hoelscher KG; *Int'l*, pg. 8426
INCOTEC (TIANJIN) AGRICULTURAL TECHNOLOGY CO., LTD.—See Croda International plc; *Int'l*, pg. 1853
INCOTRA N.V.—See Vandemoortele N.V.; *Int'l*, pg. 8128
INCOVA TECHNOLOGIES, INC.—See HUSCO International, Inc.; *U.S. Private*, pg. 2013
INCREASE VISIBILITY, INC.; *U.S. Private*, pg. 2054
THE INCREDIBLE CHRISTMAS PLACE; *U.S. Private*, pg. 4055
INCREDIBLE HOLDINGS LTD.; *Int'l*, pg. 3649
INCREDIBLE INDUSTRIES LIMITED; *Int'l*, pg. 3649
INCREDIBLE TECHNOLOGIES, INC.; *U.S. Private*, pg. 2054
INCREDIMAIL USA—See Perion Network Ltd.; *Int'l*, pg. 5801
INCREMENT P CORP—See EQT AB; *Int'l*, pg. 2470
INCREMENT P SHANGHAI CO.,LTD—See EQT AB; *Int'l*, pg. 2470
INC RESEARCH - GLOBAL CLINICAL DEVELOPMENT—See Elliott Management Corporation; *U.S. Private*, pg. 1365
INC RESEARCH - GLOBAL CLINICAL DEVELOPMENT—See Patient Square Capital, L.P.; *U.S. Private*, pg. 3108
INC RESEARCH - GLOBAL CLINICAL DEVELOPMENT—See Veritas Capital Fund Management, LLC; *U.S. Private*, pg. 4365
INC RESEARCH, LLC—See Elliott Management Corporation; *U.S. Private*, pg. 1365
INC RESEARCH, LLC—See Patient Square Capital, L.P.; *U.S. Private*, pg. 3108
INC RESEARCH, LLC—See Veritas Capital Fund Management, LLC; *U.S. Private*, pg. 4364
INC RESEARCH - MUNICH—See Elliott Management Corporation; *U.S. Private*, pg. 1365
INC RESEARCH - MUNICH—See Patient Square Capital, L.P.; *U.S. Private*, pg. 3108
INC RESEARCH - MUNICH—See Veritas Capital Fund Management, LLC; *U.S. Private*, pg. 4365
INC RESEARCH - SARONNO—See Elliott Management Corporation; *U.S. Private*, pg. 1365
INC RESEARCH - SARONNO—See Patient Square Capital, L.P.; *U.S. Private*, pg. 3108
INC RESEARCH - SARONNO—See Veritas Capital Fund Management, LLC; *U.S. Private*, pg. 4365
INC RESEARCH—See Elliott Management Corporation; *U.S. Private*, pg. 1365
INC RESEARCH—See Patient Square Capital, L.P.; *U.S. Private*, pg. 3108

COMPANY NAME INDEX

INC RESEARCH—See Veritas Capital Fund Management, LLC; *U.S. Private*, pg. 4364
INC RESEARCH—See Elliott Management Corporation; *U.S. Private*, pg. 1365
INC RESEARCH—See Elliott Management Corporation; *U.S. Private*, pg. 1365
INC RESEARCH—See Elliott Management Corporation; *U.S. Private*, pg. 1365
INC RESEARCH—See Patient Square Capital, L.P.; *U.S. Private*, pg. 3108
INC RESEARCH—See Patient Square Capital, L.P.; *U.S. Private*, pg. 3108
INC RESEARCH—See Patient Square Capital, L.P.; *U.S. Private*, pg. 3108
INC RESEARCH—See Veritas Capital Fund Management, LLC; *U.S. Private*, pg. 4364
INC RESEARCH—See Veritas Capital Fund Management, LLC; *U.S. Private*, pg. 4365
INC RESEARCH—See Veritas Capital Fund Management, LLC; *U.S. Private*, pg. 4365
INCRETE SYSTEMS INC.—See RPM International Inc.; *U.S. Public*, pg. 1818
INCROSS CO., LTD.; *Int'l*, pg. 3649
INC S.A.; *Int'l*, pg. 3646
INCUBADORA HIDALGO S. DE R.L. DE C.V.—See JBS S.A.; *Int'l*, pg. 3919
INCUBE NISHITETSU CO., LTD.—See Nishi-Nippon Railroad Co., Ltd.; *Int'l*, pg. 5364
INCYTE BIOSCIENCES AUSTRIA GMBH—See Incyte Corporation; *U.S. Public*, pg. 1115
INCYTE BIOSCIENCES BENELUX B.V.—See Incyte Corporation; *U.S. Public*, pg. 1115
INCYTE BIOSCIENCES FRANCE—See Incyte Corporation; *U.S. Public*, pg. 1115
INCYTE BIOSCIENCES GERMANY GMBH—See Incyte Corporation; *U.S. Public*, pg. 1115
INCYTE BIOSCIENCES IBERIA S.L.—See Incyte Corporation; *U.S. Public*, pg. 1115
INCYTE BIOSCIENCES INTERNATIONAL S.A R.L.—See Incyte Corporation; *U.S. Public*, pg. 1115
INCYTE BIOSCIENCES ITALY S.R.L.—See Incyte Corporation; *U.S. Public*, pg. 1115
INCYTE BIOSCIENCES JAPAN G.K.—See Incyte Corporation; *U.S. Public*, pg. 1115
INCYTE BIOSCIENCES NORDIC AB—See Incyte Corporation; *U.S. Public*, pg. 1115
INCYTE BIOSCIENCES TECHNICAL OPERATIONS S.A R.L.—See Incyte Corporation; *U.S. Public*, pg. 1115
INCYTE BIOSCIENCES UK LTD—See Incyte Corporation; *U.S. Public*, pg. 1115
INCYTE CORPORATION; *U.S. Public*, pg. 1114
INDACO METALS, LLC.; *U.S. Private*, pg. 2054
INDAG GMBH & CO. BETRIEBS KG—See Rudolf Wild GmbH & Co. KG; *Int'l*, pg. 6425
IND-AGIV COMMERCE LTD.; *Int'l*, pg. 3649
INDAG RUBBER LTD.; *Int'l*, pg. 3649
INDAH CORPORATION BERHAD—See Berjaya Corporation Berhad; *Int'l*, pg. 983
INDAH PAPER INDUSTRIES SDN. BHD.—See Minho (M) Berhad; *Int'l*, pg. 4910
INDAH SPECIALIST EYE CENTRE SDN. BHD.—See ISEC Healthcare Limited; *Int'l*, pg. 3813
INDAH WOOD PRODUCTS SDN. BHD.—See Minho (M) Berhad; *Int'l*, pg. 4910
INDAK MANUFACTURING CORP.; *U.S. Private*, pg. 2054
INDAL BELGIE S.A.—See Koninklijke Philips N.V.; *Int'l*, pg. 4268
INDAL C&EE, S.R.O.—See Koninklijke Philips N.V.; *Int'l*, pg. 4268
INDAL TECHNOLOGIES INC.—See Curtiss-Wright Corporation; *U.S. Public*, pg. 611
INDALUM S.A.—See Quinenco S.A.; *Int'l*, pg. 6164
INDALUX ILUMINACION TECNICA, S.L.—See Koninklijke Philips N.V.; *Int'l*, pg. 4268
INDAMIN COMPANY; *Int'l*, pg. 3649
INDAPTUS THERAPEUTICS, INC.; *U.S. Public*, pg. 1115
INDAS EURL—See PT Sinar Mas Group; *Int'l*, pg. 6073
INDASTRI KIAN JOO SDN. BHD.—See Can-One Berhad; *Int'l*, pg. 1276
INDAT ROBOTICS GMBH—See MAX Automation SE; *Int'l*, pg. 4734
INDAVER NEDERLAND B.V.—See Delta N.V.; *Int'l*, pg. 2019
INDAVER N.V.—See Katoen Natie N.V.; *Int'l*, pg. 4090
IND BANK HOUSING LTD; *Int'l*, pg. 3649
INDBANK MERCHANT BANKING SERVICES LTD.—See Indian Bank; *Int'l*, pg. 3653
INDCHEMIE HEALTH SPECIALITIES PRIVATE LIMITED—See Alkem Laboratories Ltd.; *Int'l*, pg. 330
INDCHEM INTERNATIONAL—See IMCD N.V.; *Int'l*, pg. 3622
INDCO, INC.—See Janel Corporation; *U.S. Public*, pg. 1187
IND EAST VILLAGE SD HOLDINGS LLC—See InterContinental Hotels Group PLC; *Int'l*, pg. 3738
INDECK-CORINTH LIMITED PARTNERSHIP—See Indeck Power Equipment Company; *U.S. Private*, pg. 2055
INDECK ENERGY SERVICES, INC.—See Indeck Power Equipment Company; *U.S. Private*, pg. 2055

INDECK ENERGY SERVICES OF ILION INC.—See Indeck Power Equipment Company; *U.S. Private*, pg. 2055
INDECK ENERGY SERVICES OF OLEAN INC.—See Indeck Power Equipment Company; *U.S. Private*, pg. 2055
INDECK ENERGY SERVICES OF OSWEGO INC.—See Indeck Power Equipment Company; *U.S. Private*, pg. 2055
INDECK ENERGY SERVICES OF SILVER SPRINGS INC.—See Indeck Power Equipment Company; *U.S. Private*, pg. 2055
INDECK POWER EQUIPMENT COMPANY; *U.S. Private*, pg. 2054
INDECK-YERKES ENERGY SERVICES INC.—See Indeck Power Equipment Company; *U.S. Private*, pg. 2055
INDECON INC.; *U.S. Private*, pg. 2055
IND.ECO S.R.L.—See Green Holding S.p.A.; *Int'l*, pg. 3071
INDEED, INC.—See Recruit Holdings Co., Ltd.; *Int'l*, pg. 6240
INDEGENE ENCIMA, INC.—See Indegene Lifesystems Pvt. Ltd.; *Int'l*, pg. 3649
INDEGENE LIFESYSTEMS PVT. LTD.; *Int'l*, pg. 3649
INDEKS BILGISAYAR SISTEMLERI MUHENDISLIK SANAYI VE TICARET A.S.; *Int'l*, pg. 3649
INDEL B S.P.A.; *Int'l*, pg. 3649
INDEL, INC.; *U.S. Private*, pg. 2055
INDELPRO, S.A. DE C.V.—See ALFA, S.A.B. de C.V.; *Int'l*, pg. 313
IN DEMAND L.L.C.—See Comcast Corporation; *U.S. Public*, pg. 538
INDENA BIOTECHNOLOGY CO. LTD.—See Indena S.p.A.; *Int'l*, pg. 3650
INDENA BRASIL LTDA—See Indena S.p.A.; *Int'l*, pg. 3650
INDENA FRANCE S.A.S.—See Indena S.p.A.; *Int'l*, pg. 3650
INDENA INDIA PVT. LTD—See Indena S.p.A.; *Int'l*, pg. 3650
INDENA JAPAN CO. LTD—See Indena S.p.A.; *Int'l*, pg. 3650
INDENA S.P.A.; *Int'l*, pg. 3649
INDENA USA INC—See Indena S.p.A.; *Int'l*, pg. 3650
INDENOVA, S.L.—See Liquidanetworks Serveis Telematics SA; *Int'l*, pg. 4535
INDEPAK, INC.—See Cameron Holdings Corporation; *U.S. Private*, pg. 729
INDEPENDENCE AMERICAN HOLDINGS CORP.—See JAB Holding Company S.a.r.l.; *Int'l*, pg. 3861
INDEPENDENCE AMERICAN INSURANCE COMPANY—See JAB Holding Company S.a.r.l.; *Int'l*, pg. 3861
INDEPENDENCE ANESTHESIA SERVICES—See ICON Medical Network LLC; *U.S. Private*, pg. 2032
INDEPENDENCE BANCSHARES, INC.; *U.S. Private*, pg. 2055
INDEPENDENCE BANK; *U.S. Private*, pg. 2055
INDEPENDENCE CAPITAL COMPANY; *U.S. Private*, pg. 2055
INDEPENDENCE CAPITAL PARTNERS, LLC; *U.S. Private*, pg. 2055
INDEPENDENCE CARE SYSTEM; *U.S. Private*, pg. 2058
INDEPENDENCE COAL COMPANY, INC.—See Alpha Natural Resources, Inc.; *U.S. Public*, pg. 198
INDEPENDENCE COMMUNITY COMMERCIAL REINVESTMENT CORP.—See Banco Santander, S.A.; *Int'l*, pg. 827
INDEPENDENCE CONTRACT DRILLING, INC.; *U.S. Public*, pg. 1115
INDEPENDENCE ENERGY GROUP LLC—See NRG Energy, Inc.; *U.S. Public*, pg. 1550
INDEPENDENCE EXCAVATING, INC.; *U.S. Private*, pg. 2058
INDEPENDENCEFIRST; *U.S. Private*, pg. 2058
INDEPENDENCE FISH COMPANY; *U.S. Private*, pg. 2058
INDEPENDENCE FUND, INC.; *U.S. Private*, pg. 2058
INDEPENDENCE GOLD CORP.; *Int'l*, pg. 3650
INDEPENDENCE HEALTHCARE CORPORATION—See ModivCare, Inc.; *U.S. Public*, pg. 1455
INDEPENDENCE HOLDING COMPANY—See Geneve Holdings Corp.; *U.S. Private*, pg. 1670
INDEPENDENCE HOLDINGS CORP.; *U.S. Public*, pg. 1115
INDEPENDENCE MATERIAL HANDLING, LLC—See Peabody Energy Corporation; *U.S. Public*, pg. 1659
INDEPENDENCE MORTGAGE TRUST, INC.; *U.S. Private*, pg. 2058
INDEPENDENCE OILFIELD CHEMICALS LLC—See Innospec Inc.; *U.S. Public*, pg. 1125
INDEPENDENCE PET HOLDINGS, INC.—See JAB Holding Company S.a.r.l.; *Int'l*, pg. 3861
INDEPENDENCE REALTY, LLC; *U.S. Private*, pg. 2058
INDEPENDENCE REALTY TRUST, INC.; *U.S. Public*, pg. 1115
INDEPENDENCE RECYCLING DIVISION—See Independence Excavating, Inc.; *U.S. Private*, pg. 2058
INDEPENDENCE REGIONAL MEDICAL GROUP, LLC—See HCA Healthcare, Inc.; *U.S. Public*, pg. 999

INDEPENDENT INVESTMENT TRUST PLC

INDEPENDENCE RESIDENCES, INC.; *U.S. Private*, pg. 2058
INDEPENDENCE RV SALES & SERVICES, INC—See General RV Center Inc.; *U.S. Private*, pg. 1667
INDEPENDENCE TECHNOLOGY, LLC—See Johnson & Johnson; *U.S. Public*, pg. 1196
INDEPENDENCE TELEVISION CO.—See Block Communications, Inc.; *U.S. Private*, pg. 582
INDEPENDENCE TUBE CORPORATION—See Nucor Corporation; *U.S. Public*, pg. 1553
INDEPENDENTA S.A.; *Int'l*, pg. 3650
INDEPENDENT BANCORP., LIMITED; *U.S. Private*, pg. 2058
INDEPENDENT BANCSHARES, INC.; *U.S. Private*, pg. 2058
INDEPENDENT BANK CORPORATION; *U.S. Public*, pg. 1116
INDEPENDENT BANK CORP.; *U.S. Public*, pg. 1116
INDEPENDENT BANKERS FINANCIAL CORPORATION; *U.S. Private*, pg. 2058
INDEPENDENT BANK GROUP, INC.; *U.S. Public*, pg. 1116
INDEPENDENT BANK; *U.S. Private*, pg. 2058
INDEPENDENT BANK—See Independent Bank Corporation; *U.S. Public*, pg. 1116
INDEPENDENT BANK—See Independent Bank Group, Inc.; *U.S. Public*, pg. 1116
INDEPENDENT BELGIAN REFINERY N.V.—See Gunvor Group Ltd.; *Int'l*, pg. 3185
INDEPENDENT BEVERAGE COMPANY, LLC; *U.S. Private*, pg. 2058
INDEPENDENT BRANDS AUSTRALIA PTY LIMITED—See Metcash Limited; *Int'l*, pg. 4852
INDEPENDENT BREWERS UNITED, INC.—See Florida Ice and Farm Co. S.A.; *Int'l*, pg. 2707
INDEPENDENT CAN COMPANY - DISTRIBUTION DIV—See Independent Can Company; *U.S. Private*, pg. 2058
INDEPENDENT CAN COMPANY; *U.S. Private*, pg. 2058
INDEPENDENT CAPITAL MANAGEMENT; *U.S. Private*, pg. 2058
INDEPENDENT CARE HEALTH PLAN, INC.—See Humana, Inc.; *U.S. Public*, pg. 1070
INDEPENDENT CARE HEALTH PLAN, INC.—See Milwaukee Center for Independence, Inc.; *U.S. Private*, pg. 2739
INDEPENDENT CHEMICAL CORP.; *U.S. Private*, pg. 2058
INDEPENDENT COLLEGES LIMITED—See Mediahuis Partners NV; *Int'l*, pg. 4772
INDEPENDENT COLLEGES LIMITED—See VP Exploitatie N.V.; *Int'l*, pg. 8311
INDEPENDENT COMMUNICATIONS (IRELAND) LIMITED—See Mediahuis Partners NV; *Int'l*, pg. 4772
INDEPENDENT COMMUNICATIONS (IRELAND) LIMITED—See VP Exploitatie N.V.; *Int'l*, pg. 8311
INDEPENDENT COMMUNICATIONS LIMITED—See Mediahuis Partners NV; *Int'l*, pg. 4772
INDEPENDENT COMMUNICATIONS LIMITED—See VP Exploitatie N.V.; *Int'l*, pg. 8311
INDEPENDENT COMMUNITY BANKERS OF AMERICA; *U.S. Private*, pg. 2058
INDEPENDENT DIGITAL LIMITED—See Mediahuis Partners NV; *Int'l*, pg. 4772
INDEPENDENT DIGITAL LIMITED—See VP Exploitatie N.V.; *Int'l*, pg. 8311
INDEPENDENT DIGITAL NEWS & MEDIA LIMITED; *Int'l*, pg. 3650
INDEPENDENT DISTRIBUTORS, INC.—See Affiliated Distributors Inc.; *U.S. Private*, pg. 121
INDEPENDENT DRAFT GEAR CO.—See Stone Canyon Industries, LLC; *U.S. Private*, pg. 3817
INDEPENDENT ELECTRICAL CONTRACTORS, INC.; *U.S. Private*, pg. 2059
INDEPENDENT ELECTRIC SUPPLY; *U.S. Private*, pg. 2059
INDEPENDENT EXECUTOR & TRUST (PTY) LIMITED—See NVest Financial Holdings Limited; *Int'l*, pg. 5498
INDEPENDENT FINANCIAL AGENTS; *U.S. Private*, pg. 2059
INDEPENDENT FINANCIAL GROUP, LLC; *U.S. Private*, pg. 2059
INDEPENDENT FINANCIAL PARTNERS; *U.S. Private*, pg. 2059
INDEPENDENT FINANCIAL SYSTEMS, INC.; *U.S. Private*, pg. 2059
INDEPENDENT GROUP HOME LIVING PROGRAM INC.; *U.S. Private*, pg. 2059
INDEPENDENT II, LLC; *U.S. Private*, pg. 2059
THE INDEPENDENT INSTITUTE OF EDUCATION (PTY) LTD—See ADvTECH Limited; *Int'l*, pg. 169
INDEPENDENT INSURANCE AGENTS & BROKERS OF AMERICA, INC.; *U.S. Private*, pg. 2059
INDEPENDENT INSURANCE CENTER, INC.; *U.S. Private*, pg. 2059
INDEPENDENT INVESTMENT TRUST PLC; *Int'l*, pg. 3650

INDEPENDENT INVESTMENT TRUST PLC / CORPORATE AFFILIATIONS

INDEPENDENT LIQUOR (NZ) LTD.—See Asahi Group Holdings Ltd.; *Int'l*, pg. 593
INDEPENDENT LIVING, INC.; *U.S. Private*, pg. 2059
INDEPENDENT LIVING SYSTEMS, LLC.; *U.S. Private*, pg. 2059
INDEPENDENT MEDIA DISTRIBUTION PLC—See Vitruvian Partners LLP; *Int'l*, pg. 8263
INDEPENDENT MEDIA; *U.S. Private*, pg. 2060
INDEPENDENT MEDIA—See Novamedia Group; *Int'l*, pg. 5455
INDEPENDENT MEDICAL EXPERT CONSULTING SERVICES, INC.—See Apax Partners LLP; *Int'l*, pg. 504
INDEPENDENT NAIL COMPANY—See W.H. Maze Company; *U.S. Private*, pg. 4420
INDEPENDENT NEWS & MEDIA PLC—See Mediahuis Partners NV; *Int'l*, pg. 4772
INDEPENDENT NEWS & MEDIA PLC—See VP Exploitatie N.V.; *Int'l*, pg. 8311
INDEPENDENT NEWS & MEDIA (SOUTH AFRICA) (PTY) LIMITED; *Int'l*, pg. 3650
INDEPENDENT NEWSPAPERS, INC. - ARIZONA—See Independent Newspapers, Inc.; *U.S. Private*, pg. 2060
INDEPENDENT NEWSPAPERS, INC.; *U.S. Private*, pg. 2060
INDEPENDENT NEWSPAPERS (IRELAND) LIMITED—See Mediahuis Partners NV; *Int'l*, pg. 4772
INDEPENDENT NEWSPAPERS (IRELAND) LIMITED—See VP Exploitatie N.V.; *Int'l*, pg. 8311
INDEPENDENT NEWSPAPERS MANAGEMENT SERVICES LIMITED—See Mediahuis Partners NV; *Int'l*, pg. 4772
INDEPENDENT NEWSPAPERS MANAGEMENT SERVICES LIMITED—See VP Exploitatie N.V.; *Int'l*, pg. 8311
INDEPENDENT OIL & COAL COMPANY; *U.S. Private*, pg. 2060
THE INDEPENDENT OIL CORPORATION—See Molo Oil Company Inc.; *U.S. Private*, pg. 2767
INDEPENDENT OIL TOOLS AS—See Petrolia SE; *Int'l*, pg. 5829
INDEPENDENT OIL TOOLS SRL—See Petrolia SE; *Int'l*, pg. 5829
THE INDEPENDENT ORDER OF FORESTERS; *Int'l*, pg. 7654
INDEPENDENT PAPERBOARD MARKETING INC.; *U.S. Private*, pg. 2060
INDEPENDENT PETROLEUM GROUP (ASIA) PTE. LIMITED—See Independent Petroleum Group Company S.A.K.; *Int'l*, pg. 3650
INDEPENDENT PETROLEUM GROUP COMPANY S.A.K.; *Int'l*, pg. 3650
INDEPENDENT PETROLEUM GROUP KENYA LIMITED—See Independent Petroleum Group Company S.A.K.; *Int'l*, pg. 3650
INDEPENDENT PETROLEUM GROUP OF KUWAIT LIMITED—See Independent Petroleum Group Company S.A.K.; *Int'l*, pg. 3650
INDEPENDENT PETROLEUM GROUP SA—See Independent Petroleum Group Company S.A.K.; *Int'l*, pg. 3650
INDEPENDENT PETROLEUM GROUP (SOUTHERN AFRICA) (PTY) LIMITED—See Independent Petroleum Group Company S.A.K.; *Int'l*, pg. 3650
INDEPENDENT PETROLEUM LABORATORY LIMITED—See Channel Infrastructure NZ Limited; *Int'l*, pg. 1446
INDEPENDENT PHARMACEUTICAL CONSULTANTS, INC.—See Aquiline Capital Partners LLC; *U.S. Private*, pg. 304
INDEPENDENT PIPE PRODUCTS INC.—See Georg Fischer AG; *Int'l*, pg. 2936
INDEPENDENT PIPE & SUPPLY CORPORATION; *U.S. Private*, pg. 2060
INDEPENDENT PLASTIC INC.; *U.S. Private*, pg. 2060
INDEPENDENT POWER CO., LTD.—See Thai Oil Public Company Limited; *Int'l*, pg. 7594
INDEPENDENT POWER TANZANIA LIMITED—See Mechmar Corporation (Malaysia) Berhad; *Int'l*, pg. 4766
INDEPENDENT POWER TRANSMISSION OPERATOR S.A.—See Holding Co ADMIE (IPTO) SA; *Int'l*, pg. 3450
INDEPENDENT PRACTITIONER NETWORK LIMITED—See Sonic Healthcare Limited; *Int'l*, pg. 7097
INDEPENDENT PRINTING CO., INC.—See Independent Printing; *U.S. Private*, pg. 2061
INDEPENDENT PRINTING COMPANY, INC.; *U.S. Private*, pg. 2060
INDEPENDENT PRINTING COMPANY, INC.—See Ennis, Inc.; *U.S. Public*, pg. 769
INDEPENDENT PRINT LIMITED—See Evening Standard Ltd.; *Int'l*, pg. 2562
INDEPENDENT PROPANE COMPANY—See Suburban Propane Partners, L.P.; *U.S. Public*, pg. 1958
INDEPENDENT PROTECTION COMPANY; *U.S. Private*, pg. 2061
INDEPENDENT PUBLICATIONS, INC.; *U.S. Private*, pg. 2061
INDEPENDENT PUBLISHER ONLINE—See Jenkins Group, Inc.; *U.S. Private*, pg. 2199

THE INDEPENDENT RECORD—See Lee Enterprises, Incorporated; *U.S. Public*, pg. 1300
INDEPENDENT RESOURCES, INC.; *U.S. Private*, pg. 2061
INDEPENDENT ROUGH TERRAIN CENTER LLC—See Congruent Investment Partners, LLC; *U.S. Private*, pg. 1014
INDEPENDENT ROUGH TERRAIN CENTER LLC—See IBC Management, LLC; *U.S. Private*, pg. 2028
INDEPENDENT SETTLEMENT SERVICES, LLC—See Radian Group, Inc.; *U.S. Public*, pg. 1759
THE INDEPENDENT—See Gannett Co., Inc.; *U.S. Public*, pg. 904
INDEPENDENT SOUTHERN BANCSHARES, INC.; *U.S. Private*, pg. 2061
INDEPENDENT SPECIALTY INSURANCE COMPANY—See Markel Group Inc.; *U.S. Public*, pg. 1369
INDEPENDENT STAR LIMITED—See Mediahuis Partners NV; *Int'l*, pg. 4772
INDEPENDENT STAR LIMITED—See VP Exploitatie N.V.; *Int'l*, pg. 8311
INDEPENDENT STAVE CO. INC.—See Isco Holding Company Inc.; *U.S. Private*, pg. 2143
INDEPENDENT STEEL—See Esmark Incorporated; *U.S. Private*, pg. 1426
INDEPENDENT SUPPLY COMPANY INC.—See Blackfriars Corp.; *U.S. Private*, pg. 575
INDEPENDENT SUPPORT SERVICES INC.; *U.S. Private*, pg. 2061
INDEPENDENT TALENT GROUP LTD.—See The Yucaipa Companies LLC; *U.S. Private*, pg. 4140
INDEPENDENT TANKERS CORPORATION LIMITED; *Int'l*, pg. 3650
INDEPENDENT TELECOM SYSTEMS; *U.S. Private*, pg. 2061
INDEPENDENT TELEVISION NETWORK; *U.S. Private*, pg. 2061
INDEPENDENT TELEVISION NEWS LTD.—See ITV plc; *Int'l*, pg. 3845
INDEPENDENT TITLE SERVICES, INC.—See Independent Bank Corporation; *U.S. Public*, pg. 1116
INDEPENDENT TRANSPORTATION COMPANY LLC—See Universal Cargo Logistics Holding B.V.; *Int'l*, pg. 8077
INDEPENDENT TRANSPORT COMPANY—See Novolipetski Metallurgicheski Komb OAO; *Int'l*, pg. 5466
INDEPENDENT TRIBUNE—See Lee Enterprises, Incorporated; *U.S. Public*, pg. 1299
INDEPENDENT TRUST COMPANY OF AMERICA, LLC; *U.S. Private*, pg. 2061
INDEPENDENT TUBULAR CORP.; *U.S. Private*, pg. 2061
INDEPENDENT VETS OF AUSTRALIA (IVA) PTY. LTD.—See Vimian Group AB; *Int'l*, pg. 8208
INDEPENDENZIA COMPANY OF LIFE INSURANCE—See W.R. Berkley Corporation; *U.S. Public*, pg. 2316
INDEPENDER.NL N.V.—See DPG Media Group NV; *Int'l*, pg. 2188
INDEPENDER SERVICES B.V.—See DPG Media Group NV; *Int'l*, pg. 2188
INDEQUITY GROUP LIMITED; *Int'l*, pg. 3650
INDERA MILLS COMPANY—See Intradeco, Inc.; *U.S. Private*, pg. 2129
INDERGIRI FINANCE LIMITED; *Int'l*, pg. 3650
INDESA CAPITAL, INC.—See Indesa Holdings Corp.; *Int'l*, pg. 3650
INDESA HOLDINGS CORP.; *Int'l*, pg. 3650
INDES FUGGERHAUS TEXTIL GMBH—See A.S. Creation Tapeten AG; *Int'l*, pg. 28
INDESIGN GROUP; *Int'l*, pg. 3650
INDESIT COMPANY BEYAZ ESYA PAZARLAMA A.S.—See Whirlpool Corporation; *U.S. Public*, pg. 2367
INDESIT COMPANY BULGARIA LTD.—See Whirlpool Corporation; *U.S. Public*, pg. 2367
INDESIT COMPANY MAGYARORSZAG KFT—See Whirlpool Corporation; *U.S. Public*, pg. 2367
INDESIT COMPANY OSTERREICH GES. M.B.H—See Whirlpool Corporation; *U.S. Public*, pg. 2367
INDESIT COMPANY POLSKA SP. Z O.O.—See Whirlpool Corporation; *U.S. Public*, pg. 2367
INDESIT COMPANY S.P.A—See Whirlpool Corporation; *U.S. Public*, pg. 2367
INDESS CO., LTD.—See Sinanen Holdings Co., Ltd.; *Int'l*, pg. 6936
INDES WONTEXTIL GMBH—See A.S. Creation Tapeten AG; *Int'l*, pg. 28
INDET SAFETY SYSTEMS A.S.—See Nippon Kayaku Co., Ltd.; *Int'l*, pg. 5320
INDEVCO NORTH AMERICA, INC.—See Industrial Development Company sal; *Int'l*, pg. 3671
INDEV GAUGING SYSTEMS, INC.—See Numina Group, Incorporated; *U.S. Private*, pg. 2973
INDEXABLE CUTTING TOOLS OF CANADA LIMITED—See Sandvik AB; *Int'l*, pg. 6529
INDEX ASIA LTD—See HS Holdings Co., Ltd.; *Int'l*, pg. 3503
INDEX BROOK LIMITED—See Index Brook Limited; *Int'l*, pg. 3650
INDEX BROOK LIMITED; *Int'l*, pg. 3650

INDEXCOMPUTER.COM; *U.S. Private*, pg. 2061
INDEX CONSULTANTS PTY. LTD.—See Bain Capital, LP; *U.S. Private*, pg. 435
INDEX CORPORATION—See INDEX-Werke GmbH & Co. KG; *Int'l*, pg. 3651
INDEX CREDIT PTE LTD—See JACKSPEED CORPORATION LIMITED; *Int'l*, pg. 3865
INDEX DALIAN MACHINE TOOL LTD.—See INDEX-Werke GmbH & Co. KG; *Int'l*, pg. 3651
INDEX EXCHANGE, INC.; *U.S. Private*, pg. 2061
INDEX-FRANCE S.A.R.L.—See INDEX-Werke GmbH & Co. KG; *Int'l*, pg. 3651
INDEX INTERFURN COMPANY LIMITED—See Index Living Mall Public Company Limited; *Int'l*, pg. 3651
INDEX INTERNATIONAL GROUP PUBLIC COMPANY LIMITED; *Int'l*, pg. 3650
INDEX INTERNATIONAL GROUP; *Int'l*, pg. 3650
INDEX INVESTMENT GROUP—See Index International Group; *Int'l*, pg. 3650
INDEXIUM AG—See Deutsche Borse AG; *Int'l*, pg. 2064
INDEX LIVING MALL PUBLIC COMPANY LIMITED; *Int'l*, pg. 3651
INDEX MACHINE TOOLS (TAICANG) CO., LTD.—See INDEX-Werke GmbH & Co. KG; *Int'l*, pg. 3651
INDEX NOTION COMPANY INC.; *U.S. Private*, pg. 2061
INDEXPLUS INCOME FUND—See Middlefield Group Limited; *Int'l*, pg. 4884
INDEX PUBLISHING AS—See Eniro Group AB; *Int'l*, pg. 2439
INDEX ROOT CO., LTD.—See MAXIMUS, Inc.; *U.S. Public*, pg. 1402
INDEX RUS—See INDEX-Werke GmbH & Co. KG; *Int'l*, pg. 3651
INDEX SLOVAKIA S.R.O.—See INDEX-Werke GmbH & Co. KG; *Int'l*, pg. 3651
INDEX-TORNOS AUTOMATICOS INDUSTRIA E COMERCIO LTDA.—See INDEX-Werke GmbH & Co. KG; *Int'l*, pg. 3651
INDEX TRADING (SHANGHAI) CO., LTD.—See INDEX-Werke GmbH & Co. KG; *Int'l*, pg. 3651
INDEX-TRAUB AB—See INDEX-Werke GmbH & Co. KG; *Int'l*, pg. 3651
INDEX-TRAUB AB—See INDEX-Werke GmbH & Co. KG; *Int'l*, pg. 3651
INDEX-TRAUB DENMARK—See INDEX-Werke GmbH & Co. KG; *Int'l*, pg. 3651
INDEX VENTURES SA; *Int'l*, pg. 3651
INDEX-WERKE GMBH & CO. KG; *Int'l*, pg. 3651
INDEX WERKZEUGMASCHINEN SCHWEIZ AG—See INDEX-Werke GmbH & Co. KG; *Int'l*, pg. 3651
INDIA ABROAD PUBLICATIONS INC.—See Rediff.com India Limited; *Int'l*, pg. 6247
INDIABULLS ASSET MANAGEMENT COMPANY LIMITED—See Nextbillion Technology Private Limited; *Int'l*, pg. 5248
INDIABULLS GROUP; *Int'l*, pg. 3653
INDIABULLS HOUSING FINANCE LTD.—See Indiabulls Group; *Int'l*, pg. 3653
INDIABULLS INFRASTRUCTURE CREDIT LIMITED—See Indiabulls Group; *Int'l*, pg. 3653
INDIABULLS REAL ESTATE LIMITED—See Indiabulls Group; *Int'l*, pg. 3653
INDIABULLS RURAL FINANCE PRIVATE LIMITED—See SORIL Infra Resources Limited; *Int'l*, pg. 7112
INDIABULLS SECURITIES LIMITED—See Indiabulls Group; *Int'l*, pg. 3653
INDIABULLS TRUSTEE COMPANY LIMITED—See Indiabulls Group; *Int'l*, pg. 3653
INDIA BUSINESS EXCELLENCE MANAGEMENT COMPANY—See Motilal Oswal Financial Services Ltd.; *Int'l*, pg. 5053
INDIA CAPITAL GROWTH FUND LIMITED; *Int'l*, pg. 3651
INDIA CEMENTS CAPITAL LIMITED—See The India Cements Limited; *Int'l*, pg. 7654
THE INDIA CEMENTS LIMITED - CHILAMKUR PLANT—See The India Cements Limited; *Int'l*, pg. 7654
THE INDIA CEMENTS LIMITED - DALAVOI PLANT—See The India Cements Limited; *Int'l*, pg. 7655
THE INDIA CEMENTS LIMITED; *Int'l*, pg. 7654
THE INDIA CEMENTS LIMITED - VISHNUPURAM PLANT—See The India Cements Limited; *Int'l*, pg. 7655
THE INDIA CEMENTS LIMITED - YERRAGUNTLA PLANT—See The India Cements Limited; *Int'l*, pg. 7655
INDIA COMNET INTERNATIONAL PVT LTD—See Infinite Computer Solutions (India) Ltd.; *Int'l*, pg. 3687
INDIA CORPORATION—See UIL Co., Ltd.; *Int'l*, pg. 8016
INDIA FIBC CUSTOMER SERVICE CENTER—See Greif Inc.; *U.S. Public*, pg. 967
INDIA FINSEC LIMITED; *Int'l*, pg. 3651
INDIAGAMES LTD.—See UTV Software Communications Limited; *Int'l*, pg. 8102
INDIA GATEWAY TERMINAL PVT. LTD.—See Dubai World Corporation; *Int'l*, pg. 2221
INDIA GELATINE & CHEMICALS LTD.; *Int'l*, pg. 3651
INDIA GLYCOLS LIMITED; *Int'l*, pg. 3651
INDIA GREEN REALITY LIMITED; *Int'l*, pg. 3651

COMPANY NAME INDEX

INDIA GRID TRUST; *Int'l*, pg. 3651
INDIA HOME LOAN LIMITED; *Int'l*, pg. 3651
INDIA IMPORTS INC.; *U.S. Private*, pg. 2061
INDIA INDEX SERVICES AND PRODUCTS LIMITED—See National Stock Exchange of India Limited; *Int'l*, pg. 5163
INDIA INDEX SERVICES AND PRODUCTS LIMITED—See S&P Global Inc.; *U.S. Public*, pg. 1831
INDIA INFOLINE FINANCE LIMITED—See International Conveyors Limited; *Int'l*, pg. 3747
INDIA INFRADEBT LTD.—See Bank of Baroda; *Int'l*, pg. 840
INDIA INFRASPACE LIMITED; *Int'l*, pg. 3652
INDIA INFRASTRUCTURE FINANCE COMPANY LIMITED; *Int'l*, pg. 3652
INDIA INFRASTRUCTURE FINANCE COMPANY (UK) LIMITED—See India Infrastructure Finance Company Limited; *Int'l*, pg. 3652
INDIA INFRASTRUCTURE TRUST; *Int'l*, pg. 3652
INDIA JAPAN LIGHTING PRIVATE LIMITED—See Koito Manufacturing Co., Ltd.; *Int'l*, pg. 4230
INDIA KAWASAKI MOTORS PVT. LTD.—See Kawasaki Heavy Industries, Ltd.; *Int'l*, pg. 4095
INDIA LEASE DEVELOPMENT LTD.; *Int'l*, pg. 3652
INDIAMART INTERMESH LIMITED; *Int'l*, pg. 3653
INDIA MEDTRONIC PRIVATE LIMITED—See Medtronic plc; *Int'l*, pg. 4788
INDIA MOTOR PARTS & ACCESSORIES LTD; *Int'l*, pg. 3652
INDIANA-AMERICAN WATER COMPANY, INC.—See American Water Works Company, Inc.; *U.S. Public*, pg. 112
INDIANA AMERICAN WATER—See American Water Works Company, Inc.; *U.S. Public*, pg. 112
INDIANA BENEFITS INC.—See Blue Benefits Consulting Inc.; *U.S. Private*, pg. 585
INDIANA BOX CORP.—See Royal Continental Box Company Inc.; *U.S. Private*, pg. 3491
INDIANA BUILDING SYSTEMS LLC—See Pleasant Street Homes LLC; *U.S. Private*, pg. 3213
INDIANA BUSINESS EQUIPMENT, LLC—See Gordon Flesch Company, Inc.; *U.S. Private*, pg. 1743
INDIANA CHAIR FRAME—See Leggett & Platt, Incorporated; *U.S. Public*, pg. 1302
INDIANA COMPREHENSIVE HEALTH INSURANCE ASSOCIATION; *U.S. Private*, pg. 2062
INDIAN ACRYLICS LIMITED; *Int'l*, pg. 3653
INDIANA DONOR NETWORK; *U.S. Private*, pg. 2062
INDIANA ENDOWMENT FUND, INC.; *U.S. Private*, pg. 2062
INDIANA ENGINEERING AND TEST CENTER—See Resilience Capital Partners, LLC; *U.S. Private*, pg. 3405
INDIANA FARM BUREAU INC.; *U.S. Private*, pg. 2062
INDIANA FARM BUREAU INSURANCE—See Indiana Farm Bureau Inc.; *U.S. Private*, pg. 2062
INDIANA FIBER NETWORK, LLC—See DigitalBridge Group, Inc.; *U.S. Public*, pg. 665
INDIANA FIBER NETWORK, LLC—See EQT AB; *Int'l*, pg. 2481
INDIANA FIRST SAVINGS BANK; *U.S. Private*, pg. 2062
INDIANA FURNITURE INDUSTRIES, INC.; *U.S. Private*, pg. 2062
INDIANA GAMING COMPANY, LLC—See PENN Entertainment, Inc.; *U.S. Public*, pg. 1662
INDIANA HARBOR BELT RAILROAD CO.—See CSX Corporation; *U.S. Public*, pg. 602
INDIANA HARBOR BELT RAILROAD CO.—See Norfolk Southern Corporation; *U.S. Public*, pg. 1535
INDIANA HARBOR COKE CORPORATION—See Energy Transfer LP; *U.S. Public*, pg. 764
THE INDIANA HEMOPHILIA & THROMBOSIS CENTER, INC.; *U.S. Private*, pg. 4055
INDIANA HISTORICAL SOCIETY; *U.S. Private*, pg. 2062
INDIANA HYDRAULIC EQUIPMENT CORP.—See Toyota Industries Corporation; *Int'l*, pg. 7869
INDIANA INSURANCE COMPANY—See Liberty Mutual Holding Company Inc.; *U.S. Private*, pg. 2445
INDIANA INTERACTIVE, LLC—See Tyler Technologies, Inc.; *U.S. Public*, pg. 2208
INDIANA-KENTUCKY ELECTRIC CORPORATION—See American Electric Power Company, Inc.; *U.S. Public*, pg. 99
INDIANA LIMESTONE COMPANY, INC.—See TorQuest Partners Inc.; *Int'l*, pg. 7830
INDIANA LUMBERMENS MUTUAL INSURANCE CO.—See Talanx AG; *Int'l*, pg. 7444
INDIANA MASONIC HOME, INC.; *U.S. Private*, pg. 2062
INDIANA MEMBERS CREDIT UNION; *U.S. Private*, pg. 2062
INDIANA MICHIGAN POWER COMPANY—See American Electric Power Company, Inc.; *U.S. Public*, pg. 99
INDIANA MILLS & MANUFACTURING, INC.; *U.S. Private*, pg. 2062
INDIANA MUNICIPAL POWER AGENCY; *U.S. Private*, pg. 2062
INDIANA NATURAL GAS CORP.—See Midwest Natural Gas Corp.; *U.S. Private*, pg. 2722
INDIANA NEWSPAPERS, LLC—See Gannett Co., Inc.; *U.S. Public*, pg. 898

THE INDIANA & OHIO RAILWAY COMPANY—See Brookfield Infrastructure Partners L.P.; *Int'l*, pg. 1192
THE INDIANA & OHIO RAILWAY COMPANY—See GIC Pte. Ltd.; *Int'l*, pg. 2967
INDIANA OXYGEN COMPANY INCORPORATED; *U.S. Private*, pg. 2062
INDIANA PACKERS CORPORATION—See Mitsubishi Corporation; *Int'l*, pg. 4938
INDIANA PICKLING & PROCESSING COMPANY—See Reliance Steel & Aluminum Co.; *U.S. Public*, pg. 1780
INDIANAPOLIS AIRPORT AUTHORITY; *U.S. Private*, pg. 2063
INDIANAPOLIS CHAMBER ORCHESTRA; *U.S. Private*, pg. 2063
INDIANAPOLIS COLTS, INC.; *U.S. Private*, pg. 2063
INDIANAPOLIS ELECTRIC COMPANY, INC.; *U.S. Private*, pg. 2063
INDIANAPOLIS JEWISH HOME, INC.; *U.S. Private*, pg. 2063
INDIANAPOLIS MOTOR SPEEDWAY CORPORATION—See Penske Corporation; *U.S. Private*, pg. 3138
INDIANAPOLIS MOTOR SPEEDWAY, LLC—See Penske Corporation; *U.S. Private*, pg. 3138
INDIANAPOLIS MUSEUM OF ART; *U.S. Private*, pg. 2063
INDIANAPOLIS PHYSICAL THERAPY AND SPORTS MEDICINE, INC.—See Select Medical Holdings Corporation; *U.S. Public*, pg. 1858
INDIANAPOLIS POWER & LIGHT COMPANY—See The AES Corporation; *U.S. Public*, pg. 2031
INDIANAPOLIS STAR—See Gannett Co., Inc.; *U.S. Public*, pg. 898
INDIANAPOLIS TREATMENT CENTER, LLC—See Acadia Healthcare Company, Inc.; *U.S. Public*, pg. 29
INDIANA PRINTING & PUBLISHING CO., INC.; *U.S. Private*, pg. 2062
INDIANA RECORDS MANAGERS, INC.; *U.S. Private*, pg. 2062
INDIANA REGIONAL MEDICAL CENTER; *U.S. Private*, pg. 2063
INDIANA RESOURCES LIMITED; *Int'l*, pg. 3655
INDIANA SOUTHERN RAILROAD, LLC—See Brookfield Infrastructure Partners L.P.; *Int'l*, pg. 1192
INDIANA SOUTHERN RAILROAD, LLC—See GIC Pte. Ltd.; *Int'l*, pg. 2966
INDIANA SOYBEAN ALLIANCE; *U.S. Private*, pg. 2063
INDIANA STATE TEACHERS ASSOCIATION; *U.S. Private*, pg. 2063
INDIANA STEEL FABRICATING INC.; *U.S. Private*, pg. 2063
INDIANA SUGARS, INC.; *U.S. Private*, pg. 2063
INDIANA TOOL & DIE CO. INC.—See Jasper Engine & Transmission Exchange Inc.; *U.S. Private*, pg. 2190
INDIANA TRANSPORT, INC.—See Patrick Industries, Inc.; *U.S. Public*, pg. 1652
INDIANA TUBE CORP.—See Steel Partners Holdings L.P.; *U.S. Public*, pg. 1943
INDIANA VENEERS CORP.; *U.S. Private*, pg. 2063
INDIANA WESTERN EXPRESS INC.; *U.S. Private*, pg. 2063
INDIANA WHOLESALE WINE & LIQUOR CO.—See Johnson Brothers Liquor Company; *U.S. Private*, pg. 2227
INDIAN BANK; *Int'l*, pg. 3653
INDIAN BRIGHT STEEL COMPANY LIMITED; *Int'l*, pg. 3653
INDIAN BULLION MARKET ASSOCIATION LIMITED—See 63 moons technologies limited; *Int'l*, pg. 14
INDIAN CABLE NET COMPANY LIMITED—See Essel Corporate Resources Pvt. Ltd.; *Int'l*, pg. 2509
THE INDIAN CARD CLOTHING COMPANY LIMITED; *Int'l*, pg. 7655
INDIAN COMMODITY EXCHANGE LTD.—See MMTC Limited; *Int'l*, pg. 5006
INDIAN COUNTRY BLUESTONE, LLC—See Indian Country Inc.; *U.S. Private*, pg. 2061
INDIAN COUNTRY INC.; *U.S. Private*, pg. 2061
INDIAN ELECTRIC COOPERATIVE; *U.S. Private*, pg. 2061
INDIAN ENERGY EXCHANGE LIMITED; *Int'l*, pg. 3653
INDIAN ENERGY LIMITED—See Infrastructure India plc; *Int'l*, pg. 3697
INDIAN EXTRACTION LTD.; *Int'l*, pg. 3653
INDIAN EXTRACTIONS LIMITED; *Int'l*, pg. 3653
INDIAN FARMERS FERTILISER COOPERATIVE LIMITED; *Int'l*, pg. 3653
INDIAN HARBOR INSURANCE COMPANY—See AXA S.A.; *Int'l*, pg. 761
INDIANHEAD COMMUNITY ACTION AGENCY, INC.; *U.S. Private*, pg. 2063
INDIAN HEAD INDUSTRIES, INC.; *U.S. Private*, pg. 2061
INDIANHEAD PLATING, INC.—See Aterian Investment Management, L.P.; *U.S. Private*, pg. 366
INDIAN HEALTH COUNCIL, INC.; *U.S. Private*, pg. 2061
INDIAN HEALTH ORGANISATION PRIVATE LIMITED—See Medi Assist Healthcare Services Private Limited; *Int'l*, pg. 4769
THE INDIAN HOTELS COMPANY LIMITED—See Tata Sons Limited; *Int'l*, pg. 7473
INDIAN HUME PIPE COMPANY LTD.; *Int'l*, pg. 3654

INDICAR OF DAYTONA INC.

INDIAN INDUSTRIES, INC.—See Escalade, Incorporated; *U.S. Public*, pg. 793
INDIAN INFOTECH & SOFTWARE LIMITED; *Int'l*, pg. 3654
INDIAN INSTITUTE OF JEWELLERY LIMITED—See Modern India Ltd; *Int'l*, pg. 5013
INDIA NIPPON ELECTRICALS LIMITED; *Int'l*, pg. 3652
INDIAN IRON & STEEL COMPANY—See Steel Authority of India Limited; *Int'l*, pg. 7189
INDIANIVESH LTD.; *Int'l*, pg. 3655
INDIANIVESH SECURITIES PVT. LTD.—See IndiaNivesh Ltd.; *Int'l*, pg. 3655
INDIAN JEWELERS SUPPLY CO.; *U.S. Private*, pg. 2061
INDIAN LAKES WILDERNESS PRESERVE CORPORATION—See Equity LifeStyle Properties, Inc.; *U.S. Public*, pg. 790
THE INDIAN LINK CHAIN MANUFACTURES LIMITED; *Int'l*, pg. 7655
INDIAN METALS & FERRO ALLOYS LIMITED; *Int'l*, pg. 3654
INDIAN NATIONS FIBER OPTICS, INC.—See Chickasaw Holding Company; *U.S. Private*, pg. 880
INDIAN OCEAN LOGISTICS LTD.—See Ireland Blyth Limited; *Int'l*, pg. 3807
INDIAN OCEAN TUNA LIMITED—See Thai Union Group Public Company Limited; *Int'l*, pg. 7596
INDIAN OIL CORPORATION LIMITED - GUWAHATI REFINERY DIVISION—See Indian Oil Corporation Limited; *Int'l*, pg. 3654
INDIAN OIL CORPORATION LIMITED - IBP DIVISION—See Indian Oil Corporation Limited; *Int'l*, pg. 3654
INDIAN OIL CORPORATION LIMITED; *Int'l*, pg. 3654
INDIANOIL (MAURITIUS) LIMITED—See Indian Oil Corporation Limited; *Int'l*, pg. 3654
INDIANOIL MIDDLE EAST FZE—See Indian Oil Corporation Limited; *Int'l*, pg. 3654
INDIANOIL SKYTANKING DELHI LTD.—See Marquard & Bahls AG; *Int'l*, pg. 4700
INDIAN OVERSEAS BANK; *Int'l*, pg. 3654
INDIAN OVERSEAS BANK—See Indian Overseas Bank; *Int'l*, pg. 3654
INDIAN PATH HOSPITAL, INC.—See HCA Healthcare, Inc.; *U.S. Public*, pg. 999
INDIAN QUEENS POWER LTD.—See ENGIE SA; *Int'l*, pg. 2433
INDIAN RAILWAY CATERING & TOURISM CORPORATION LIMITED; *Int'l*, pg. 3654
INDIAN RAILWAY CATERING & TOURISM CORPORATION LTD.; *Int'l*, pg. 3654
INDIAN RAILWAY FINANCE CORPORATION LTD.; *Int'l*, pg. 3654
INDIAN RESTAURANTS GROUP PLC; *Int'l*, pg. 3654
INDIAN RIVER BEHAVIORAL HEALTH, LLC—See Universal Health Services, Inc.; *U.S. Public*, pg. 2258
INDIAN RIVER BEVERAGE CORPORATION—See ANSA McAL Limited; *Int'l*, pg. 477
INDIAN RIVER DIALYSIS CENTER, LLC—See DaVita Inc.; *U.S. Public*, pg. 639
INDIAN RIVER PRESS JOURNAL—See Gannett Co., Inc.; *U.S. Public*, pg. 898
INDIAN RIVER TRANSPORT CO.; *U.S. Private*, pg. 2061
INDIAN SUCROSE LIMITED; *Int'l*, pg. 3654
INDIAN SUMMER CARPET MILLS, INC.; *U.S. Private*, pg. 2061
INDIAN SUMMER CO-OP, INC.; *U.S. Private*, pg. 2062
INDIAN TERRAIN FASHIONS LIMITED; *Int'l*, pg. 3654
INDIAN TONERS & DEVELOPERS LTD.; *Int'l*, pg. 3654
INDIAN TOOL MANUFACTURERS LTD. - NASHIK UNIT—See The Yash Birla Group; *Int'l*, pg. 7702
INDIAN TOOL MANUFACTURERS LTD.—See The Yash Birla Group; *Int'l*, pg. 7702
INDIAN VALLEY RECORD—See Feather Publishing Co., Inc.; *U.S. Private*, pg. 1486
THE INDIAN WOOD PRODUCTS CO. LTD.; *Int'l*, pg. 7655
INDIA PESTICIDES LIMITED; *Int'l*, pg. 3652
INDIA POWER CORPORATION LIMITED; *Int'l*, pg. 3652
INDIA RADIATORS LIMITED; *Int'l*, pg. 3652
INDIA SEAH PRECISION METAL PVT. LTD.—See SeAH Holdings Corp.; *Int'l*, pg. 6664
INDIA SHELTER FINANCE CORPORATION LIMITED; *Int'l*, pg. 3652
INDIA STEEL SUMMIT PRIVATE LIMITED—See Sumitomo Corporation; *Int'l*, pg. 7268
INDIA STEEL WORKS LTD.; *Int'l*, pg. 3652
INDIA SUGARS & REFINERIES LIMITED; *Int'l*, pg. 3652
INDIA TOURISM DEVELOPMENT CORPORATION LTD - CATERING UNITS—See India Tourism Development Corporation Ltd; *Int'l*, pg. 3652
INDIA TOURISM DEVELOPMENT CORPORATION LTD; *Int'l*, pg. 3652
INDIA TRIMMINGS PRIVATE LIMITED—See IG Design Group Plc; *Int'l*, pg. 3600
INDIA TYRE & RUBBER CO. (INDIA) LTD.—See Ruia Group; *Int'l*, pg. 6426
INDIA VALUE FUND ADVISORS PVT LTD.; *Int'l*, pg. 3652
INDICAL BIOSCIENCE GMBH—See Vimian Group AB; *Int'l*, pg. 8208
INDICAR OF DAYTONA INC.; *U.S. Private*, pg. 2063

INDICATOR - FL MEMO LTD.—See Editions Lefebvre Sarrut SA; *Int'l*, pg. 2311
INDICON CORP.; *U.S. Private*, pg. 2063
INDICO RESOURCES LIMITED; *Int'l*, pg. 3655
INDICOR OF NC, LLC—See Clayton, Dubilier & Rice, LLC; *U.S. Private*, pg. 924
INDICUS ANALYTICS PRIVATE LIMITED—See Brookfield Corporation; *Int'l*, pg. 1179
INDICUS ANALYTICS PRIVATE LIMITED—See Elliott Management Corporation; *U.S. Private*, pg. 1371
INDIEFLIX GROUP, INC.—See Liquid Media Group Ltd.; *Int'l*, pg. 4523
INDI ENERGIE B.V.—See RWE AG; *Int'l*, pg. 6434
INDIE SEMICONDUCTOR, INC.; *U.S. Public*, pg. 1116
INDIES PHARMA JAMAICA LTD.; *Int'l*, pg. 3655
INDIFRA LIMITED; *Int'l*, pg. 3655
INDIGEN ARMOR, INC.—See J.F. Lehman & Company, Inc.; *U.S. Private*, pg. 2163
INDIGIO GROUP, INC.—See Bridgeline Digital, Inc.; *U.S. Public*, pg. 382
INDIGO BOOKS & MUSIC, INC.—See Trilogy Retail Enterprises L.P.; *Int'l*, pg. 7923
INDIGO BRANDS—See AVI Limited; *Int'l*, pg. 740
INDIGO CAPITAL FRANCE SAS—See Indigo Capital LLP; *Int'l*, pg. 3655
INDIGO CAPITAL LLP; *Int'l*, pg. 3655
INDIGO DEVELOPMENT INC.—See CTO Realty Growth, Inc.; *U.S. Public*, pg. 602
INDIGO EXPLORATION INC.; *Int'l*, pg. 3655
INDIGO GOLF PARTNERS, LLC—See Troon Golf L.L.C.; *U.S. Private*, pg. 4242
INDIGO GROUP INC.—See CTO Realty Growth, Inc.; *U.S. Public*, pg. 602
INDIGO GROUP S.A.S.; *Int'l*, pg. 3655
INDIGO INFRA BELGIUM N.V.—See Indigo Group S.A.S.; *Int'l*, pg. 3655
INDIGO INFRA CGST S.A.—See Indigo Group S.A.S.; *Int'l*, pg. 3655
INDIGO INFRA ESPANA S.A.—See Indigo Group S.A.S.; *Int'l*, pg. 3655
INDIGO INFRA NEUILLY SAS—See Indigo Group S.A.S.; *Int'l*, pg. 3655
INDIGO INFRA NOISY-LE-GRAND SA—See Indigo Group S.A.S.; *Int'l*, pg. 3655
INDIGO INFRA RUSSIE—See Indigo Group S.A.S.; *Int'l*, pg. 3655
INDIGO INSURANCE (CAYMAN) LIMITED—See Colina Holdings Bahamas Limited; *Int'l*, pg. 1698
INDIGO INTERNATIONAL INC.—See CTO Realty Growth, Inc.; *U.S. Public*, pg. 602
INDIGO LIVING LIMITED—See Pacific Legend Group Ltd.; *Int'l*, pg. 5690
INDIGO PACIFIC CORPORATION—See PT Berlian Laju Tanker Tbk; *Int'l*, pg. 6029
INDIGO PAINTS LIMITED; *Int'l*, pg. 3656
INDIGO PARK CANADA INC.—See Indigo Group S.A.S.; *Int'l*, pg. 3655
INDIGO PARK DEUTSCHLAND GMBH—See Fundacion Bancaria Caixa d'Estalvis i Pensions de Barcelona, la Caixa; *Int'l*, pg. 2845
INDIGO PARK LUXEMBOURG S.A.—See Indigo Group S.A.S.; *Int'l*, pg. 3655
INDIGO PARK S.A.—See Indigo Group S.A.S.; *Int'l*, pg. 3655
INDIGO PARK SERVICES UK LTD.—See Fundacion Bancaria Caixa d'Estalvis i Pensions de Barcelona, la Caixa; *Int'l*, pg. 2845
INDIGO PARK SLOVAKIA, S.R.O.—See Fundacion Bancaria Caixa d'Estalvis i Pensions de Barcelona, la Caixa; *Int'l*, pg. 2845
INDIGO PARTNERS LLC; *U.S. Private*, pg. 2063
INDIGO PEARL LIMITED—See Canada Pension Plan Investment Board; *Int'l*, pg. 1280
INDIGO PEARL LIMITED—See EQT AB; *Int'l*, pg. 2482
INDIGO PEARL LIMITED—See Temasek Holdings (Private) Limited; *Int'l*, pg. 7548
INDIGO PROPERTIES AUSTRALIA LIMITED; *Int'l*, pg. 3656
THE INDIGO ROAD HOSPITALITY GROUP, LLC; *U.S. Private*, pg. 4055
INDIGO SLATE, INC.—See RPG Group; *Int'l*, pg. 6415
INDIGO SOUTH CAPITAL, INC.; *U.S. Private*, pg. 2063
INDIGO STAR HOLDINGS LIMITED; *Int'l*, pg. 3656
INDIGO TELECOM GROUP LIMITED—See Pollen Street Limited; *Int'l*, pg. 5910
INDIGO TELECOM GROUP LIMITED—See YFM Equity Partners LLP; *Int'l*, pg. 8579
INDIGOVISION GROUP PLC—See Motorola Solutions, Inc.; *U.S. Public*, pg. 1477
INDIGOVISION INC.—See Motorola Solutions, Inc.; *U.S. Public*, pg. 1478
INDIGOVISION LIMITED—See Motorola Solutions, Inc.; *U.S. Public*, pg. 1477
INDIGO WERBEAGENTUR GMBH—See Dentsu Group Inc.; *Int'l*, pg. 2037
INDIKA POWER INVESTMENTS PTE. LTD.—See PT Indika Energy Tbk; *Int'l*, pg. 6044
INDIKAR - INDIVIDUAL KAROSSERIEBAU GMBH—See Farmingtons Holding GmbH; *Int'l*, pg. 2619

INDILINX CO., LTD.—See Japan Industrial Partners, Inc.; *Int'l*, pg. 3891
INDINERO INC.; *U.S. Private*, pg. 2064
INDINFRAVIT TRUST; *Int'l*, pg. 3656
INDIPUNT DISENO, S.L.—See Industria de Diseno Textil, S.A.; *Int'l*, pg. 3666
INDIPUNT, S.L.—See Industria de Diseno Textil, S.A.; *Int'l*, pg. 3666
INDIQUE HAIR, LLC.; *U.S. Private*, pg. 2064
INDISOFT LLC; *U.S. Private*, pg. 2064
INDITEX LOGISTICA, S.A.—See Industria de Diseno Textil, S.A.; *Int'l*, pg. 3666
INDITRADE CAPITAL LIMITED; *Int'l*, pg. 3656
INDITRADE DERIVATIVES & COMMODITIES LIMITED—See Inditrade Capital Limited; *Int'l*, pg. 3656
INDIUM CORPORATION OF AMERICA; *U.S. Private*, pg. 2064
THE INDIUM DIVISION COMPANY S.L.—See Interserve Plc; *Int'l*, pg. 3760
INDIVA LIMITED—See SNDL Inc.; *Int'l*, pg. 7027
INDIVAL, INC.—See Tsunagu Group Holdings Inc.; *Int'l*, pg. 7957
INDIVER S.A.; *Int'l*, pg. 3656
INDIVIDUAL CENTRICITY CORPORATION; *U.S. Private*, pg. 2064
INDIVIDUALIZED APPAREL GROUP; *U.S. Private*, pg. 2064
INDIVIDUAL RESTAURANT CO. LTD.; *Int'l*, pg. 3656
INDIVIOR PLC; *Int'l*, pg. 3656
INDLON CHEMICALS LTD—See Indian Acrylics Limited; *Int'l*, pg. 3653
INDLUPLACE PROPERTIES LIMITED—See Fairvest Limited; *Int'l*, pg. 2609
INDO AMAN BINA SDN BHD—See TA Enterprise Berhad; *Int'l*, pg. 7399
INDO AMINES LTD; *Int'l*, pg. 3656
INDO ASIAN FUSEGEAR LTD - HARIDWAR LIGHTING PLANT—See EON Electric Ltd.; *Int'l*, pg. 2457
INDO ASIAN FUSEGEAR LTD - INDO SIMON PLANT HARIDWAR—See EON Electric Ltd.; *Int'l*, pg. 2458
INDO ASIAN FUSEGEAR LTD - JALANDHAR SWITCHGEAR PLANT—See EON Electric Ltd.; *Int'l*, pg. 2458
INDO ASIAN FUSEGEAR LTD - NOIDA LIGHTING PLANT—See EON Electric Ltd.; *Int'l*, pg. 2458
INDO-BANGLA PHARMACEUTICALS LTD.; *Int'l*, pg. 3657
INDO BORAX & CHEMICALS LTD.; *Int'l*, pg. 3656
INDO BRITISH GARMENTS (P) LTD.—See Allied Universal Manager LLC; *U.S. Private*, pg. 190
INDOCHINA KAJIMA DEVELOPMENT LTD.—See Kajima Corporation; *Int'l*, pg. 4054
INDOCHINE ENGINEERING LIMITED—See Tokyu Construction Co., Ltd.; *Int'l*, pg. 7797
INDOCHINE REAL ESTATE JOINT STOCK COMPANY—See Dat Xanh Group Joint Stock Company; *Int'l*, pg. 1975
INDO-CITY INFOTECH LTD.; *Int'l*, pg. 3657
INDOC MILK GMBH—See DMK Deutsches Milchkontor GmbH; *Int'l*, pg. 2146
INDOCO INTERNATIONAL B.V.—See Universal Corporation; *U.S. Public*, pg. 2254
INDOCO REMEDIES LTD; *Int'l*, pg. 3657
INDO COTSPIN LIMITED; *Int'l*, pg. 3656
INDO COUNT GLOBAL INC.—See Indo Count Industries Ltd.; *Int'l*, pg. 3656
INDO COUNT INDUSTRIES LTD.; *Int'l*, pg. 3656
INDO COUNT UK LIMITED—See Indo Count Industries Ltd.; *Int'l*, pg. 3656
INDO CREDIT CAPITAL LIMITED; *Int'l*, pg. 3656
INDO EURO INDCHEM LIMITED; *Int'l*, pg. 3656
INDO EUROPEAN FOODS LIMITED—See Kohinoor Foods Limited; *Int'l*, pg. 4229
INDOFF INC.—See Global Industrial Company; *U.S. Public*, pg. 942
INDOFOOD AGRI RESOURCES LTD.—See First Pacific Company Limited; *Int'l*, pg. 2686
INDOFOOD (M) FOOD INDUSTRIES SDN. BHD.—See PT Indofood CBP Sukses Makmur Tbk.; *Int'l*, pg. 6045
INDO-GLOBAL ENTERPRISES LIMITED; *Int'l*, pg. 3657
INDO GLOBAL EXCHANGES PTE LTD; *Int'l*, pg. 3656
INDO GULF FERTILISERS LIMITED—See The Aditya Birla Group; *Int'l*, pg. 7611
INDO GULF INDUSTRIES LTD.; *Int'l*, pg. 3657
INDOGUNA (CAMBODIA) COMPANY LIMITED—See C.P. All Public Company Limited; *Int'l*, pg. 1244
INDOGUNA DUBAI L.L.C.—See C.P. All Public Company Limited; *Int'l*, pg. 1244
INDOGUNA LORDLY COMPANY LIMITED—See C.P. All Public Company Limited; *Int'l*, pg. 1244
INDOGUNA (SINGAPORE) PTE. LTD.—See C.P. All Public Company Limited; *Int'l*, pg. 1244
INDOGUNA VINA FOOD SERVICE COMPANY LIMITED—See C.P. All Public Company Limited; *Int'l*, pg. 1244
INDO INTERNACIONAL S.A.; *Int'l*, pg. 3657
INDO-JORDAN CHEMICALS COMPANY LIMITED - MA'AN FACTORY—See Jordan Phosphate Mines Company Ltd.; *Int'l*, pg. 3999

INDO-JORDAN CHEMICALS COMPANY LIMITED—See Jordan Phosphate Mines Company Ltd.; *Int'l*, pg. 3999
INDOKEM LIMITED; *Int'l*, pg. 3657
INDOLA GMBH—See Henkel AG & Co. KGaA; *Int'l*, pg. 3354
INDOMA AB—See Nordstjernan AB; *Int'l*, pg. 5425
INDO-MALAY PLC—See Carson Cumberbatch PLC; *Int'l*, pg. 1347
INDO MAROC, S.A—See Indo Internacional S.A.; *Int'l*, pg. 3657
INDOMETAL (LONDON) LTD.—See PT Timah Tbk.; *Int'l*, pg. 6078
INDO-NATIONAL LIMITED; *Int'l*, pg. 3657
INDONESIA CORPORATION OF SHINSUNG DELTATECH CO., LTD.—See Shinsung Delta Tech Co., Ltd.; *Int'l*, pg. 6848
INDONESIA ENERGY CORPORATION LIMITED; *Int'l*, pg. 3657
INDONESIAN IMPORTS, INC.; *U.S. Private*, pg. 2064
INDONESIA WACOAL CO., LTD.—See Wacoal Holdings Corp.; *Int'l*, pg. 8325
INDON INTERNATIONAL, LLC; *U.S. Private*, pg. 2064
INDO NISSIN FOODS LIMITED—See Nissin Foods Holdings Co., Ltd.; *Int'l*, pg. 5376
INDO OPTICAL S.L.—See Indo Internacional S.A.; *Int'l*, pg. 3657
INDOOR CLIMATE MANAGEMENT S.L.—See I Squared Capital Advisors (US) LLC; *U.S. Private*, pg. 2022
INDOOR CLIMATE MANAGEMENT S.L.—See TDR Capital LLP; *Int'l*, pg. 7492
INDOOR CYCLING GROUP GMBH—See Brunswick Corporation; *U.S. Public*, pg. 408
INDOOR ENVIRONMENTAL TECHNOLOGY INC.—See Team Solutions Project Group, Inc.; *U.S. Private*, pg. 3950
INDOOR GARDEN & LIGHTING INC.—See GrowGeneration Corp.; *U.S. Public*, pg. 972
INDOOR GROUP OY—See Sievi Capital Oyj; *Int'l*, pg. 6905
INDOOR HARVEST, CORP.; *U.S. Public*, pg. 1116
INDOOR MEDIA; *Int'l*, pg. 3657
INDOOR & OUTDOOR COMMUNICATION HOLDING SA; *Int'l*, pg. 3657
INDOPACIFIC EDELMAN—See Daniel J. Edelman, Inc.; *U.S. Private*, pg. 1155
INDO PACIFIC PROJECTS LTD.; *Int'l*, pg. 3657
INDOP D.O.O.—See Hisense Co., Ltd.; *Int'l*, pg. 3407
INDOPHIL RESOURCES NL—See Alcantara Group; *Int'l*, pg. 300
INDORAMA CORPORATION PTE. LTD.; *Int'l*, pg. 3657
INDORAMA INDIA PVT. LTD.—See Indorama Corporation Pte. Ltd.; *Int'l*, pg. 3657
INDORAMA INDUSTRIES LIMITED—See Indorama Corporation Pte. Ltd.; *Int'l*, pg. 3657
INDORAMA IPLIK SANAYI VE TICARET A.S.—See Indorama Corporation Pte. Ltd.; *Int'l*, pg. 3658
INDORAMA IPLIK SANAYI VE TICARET A.S.—See Indorama Corporation Pte. Ltd.; *Int'l*, pg. 3658
INDORAMA NETHERLANDS B.V.—See Indorama Ventures Public Company Limited; *Int'l*, pg. 3658
INDORAMA PET (NIGERIA) LTD.—See Indorama Ventures Public Company Limited; *Int'l*, pg. 3658
INDORAMA POLYMERS PUBLIC COMPANY LIMITED—See Indorama Ventures Public Company Limited; *Int'l*, pg. 3658
INDO RAMA SYNTHETICS (INDIA) LTD.; *Int'l*, pg. 3657
INDORAMA VENTURES ADANA PET SANAYI ANONIM SIRKETI—See Indorama Ventures Public Company Limited; *Int'l*, pg. 3658
INDORAMA VENTURES CORLU PET SANAYI ANONIM SIRKETI—See Indorama Ventures Public Company Limited; *Int'l*, pg. 3658
INDORAMA VENTURES EUROPE B.V.—See Indorama Ventures Public Company Limited; *Int'l*, pg. 3658
INDORAMA VENTURES FIBRAS BRASIL LTDA.—See Indorama Ventures Public Company Limited; *Int'l*, pg. 3658
INDORAMA VENTURES OXIDES ANKLESHWAR PRIVATE LIMITED—See Indorama Ventures Public Company Limited; *Int'l*, pg. 3658
INDORAMA VENTURES PACKAGING (GHANA) LTD.—See Indorama Ventures Public Company Limited; *Int'l*, pg. 3658
INDORAMA VENTURES PACKAGING (MYNAMAR) LTD.—See Indorama Ventures Public Company Limited; *Int'l*, pg. 3658
INDORAMA VENTURES PACKAGING (NIGERIA) LTD.—See Indorama Ventures Public Company Limited; *Int'l*, pg. 3658
INDORAMA VENTURES POLAND SP.Z.O.O.—See Indorama Ventures Public Company Limited; *Int'l*, pg. 3658
INDORAMA VENTURES POLIMEROS S.A.—See Indorama Ventures Public Company Limited; *Int'l*, pg. 3658
INDORAMA VENTURES POLYMERS MEXICO, S.DE R.L. DE C.V.—See Indorama Ventures Public Company Limited; *Int'l*, pg. 3659

COMPANY NAME INDEX

INDORAMA VENTURES PORTUGAL PTA—See Indorama Ventures Public Company Limited; *Int'l*, pg. 3659
INDORAMA VENTURES PORTUGAL PTA-UNIPESSOAL, LDA.—See Indorama Ventures Public Company Limited; *Int'l*, pg. 3659
INDORAMA VENTURES PTA MONTREAL L.P.—See Indorama Ventures Public Company Limited; *Int'l*, pg. 3658
INDORAMA VENTURES PUBLIC COMPANY LIMITED; *Int'l*, pg. 3658
INDORAMA VENTURES QUIMICA S.L.U.—See Indorama Ventures Public Company Limited; *Int'l*, pg. 3659
INDORAMA VENTURES SUSTAINABLE SOLUTIONS FONTANA, INC.—See Indorama Ventures Public Company Limited; *Int'l*, pg. 3659
INDORAMA VENTURES SUSTAINABLE SOLUTIONS LLC—See Indorama Ventures Public Company Limited; *Int'l*, pg. 3659
INDORAMA VENTURES XYLENES & PTA, LLC—See Indorama Ventures Public Company Limited; *Int'l*, pg. 3659
INDORAMA YARNS PRIVATE LIMITED—See Indo Rama Synthetics (India) Ltd.; *Int'l*, pg. 3657
INDOSAT SINGAPORE PTE LTD—See Ooredoo Q.S.C.; *Int'l*, pg. 5595
INDOS FINANCIAL (IRELAND) LIMITED—See JTC PLC; *Int'l*, pg. 4016
INDOS FINANCIAL LIMITED—See JTC PLC; *Int'l*, pg. 4016
INDOSOLAR LIMITED; *Int'l*, pg. 3659
INDOSTAR CAPITAL FINANCE LIMITED; *Int'l*, pg. 3659
INDO SYNERGY PTE LTD—See KS Energy Limited; *Int'l*, pg. 4310
INDO TECH TRANSFORMERS LTD - PALAKKAD PLANT—See Shirdi Sai Electricals Ltd.; *Int'l*, pg. 6853
INDO TECH TRANSFORMERS LTD.—See Shirdi Sai Electricals Ltd.; *Int'l*, pg. 6853
INDO THAI SECURITIES LTD; *Int'l*, pg. 3657
INDO THAI SYNTHETICS COMPANY LIMITED - ITS FACTORY—See The Aditya Birla Group; *Int'l*, pg. 7612
INDO THAI SYNTHETICS COMPANY LIMITED—See The Aditya Birla Group; *Int'l*, pg. 7612
INDO TOOLINGS PRIVATE LIMITED—See JBM Auto Ltd.; *Int'l*, pg. 3918
INDOTRONIX INTERNATIONAL CORPORATION; *U.S. Private*, pg. 2064
INDO US BIO-TECH LTD.; *Int'l*, pg. 3657
INDOWIND ENERGY LTD; *Int'l*, pg. 3659
INDOWORTH HOLDING LIMITED; *Int'l*, pg. 3659
INDOX SERVICES INC.—See SBI Incorporated; *U.S. Private*, pg. 3560
INDOX SERVICES—See SBI Incorporated; *U.S. Private*, pg. 3560
INDO ZAMBIA BANK LTD.—See Bank of Baroda; *Int'l*, pg. 840
INDO ZAMBIA BANK LTD.—See Bank of India; *Int'l*, pg. 843
INDO ZAMBIA BANK LTD.—See Central Bank of India Limited; *Int'l*, pg. 1404
INDRA ATM, S.L.—See Indra Sistemas, S.A.; *Int'l*, pg. 3660
INDRA AUSTRALIA PTY LIMITED—See Indra Sistemas, S.A.; *Int'l*, pg. 3660
INDRA BAHRAIN CONSULTANCY SPC—See Indra Sistemas, S.A.; *Int'l*, pg. 3660
INDRA BEIJING INFORMATION TECHNOLOGY SYSTEMS CO.LTD.—See Indra Sistemas, S.A.; *Int'l*, pg. 3660
INDRA BMB SERVICIOS DIGITALES S.A.—See Indra Sistemas, S.A.; *Int'l*, pg. 3660
INDRA BMB S.L.—See Indra Sistemas, S.A.; *Int'l*, pg. 3660
INDRA BRASIL, LTDA.—See Indra Sistemas, S.A.; *Int'l*, pg. 3660
INDRA BUSINESS CONSULTING, S.L.U.—See Indra Sistemas, S.A.; *Int'l*, pg. 3660
INDRA COLOMBIA LTDA.—See Indra Sistemas, S.A.; *Int'l*, pg. 3660
INDRA CZECH REPUBLIC S.R.O.—See Indra Sistemas, S.A.; *Int'l*, pg. 3660
INDRA EHSAN SDN BHD—See Berjaya Corporation Berhad; *Int'l*, pg. 982
INDRA EMAC, S.A.—See Indra Sistemas, S.A.; *Int'l*, pg. 3660
INDRA ESLOVAKIA, A.S.—See Indra Sistemas, S.A.; *Int'l*, pg. 3660
INDRA ESPACIO, S.A.—See Indra Sistemas, S.A.; *Int'l*, pg. 3660
INDRA EWS, S.A.—See Indra Sistemas, S.A.; *Int'l*, pg. 3660
INDRA FRANCE S.A.S.—See Indra Sistemas, S.A.; *Int'l*, pg. 3660
INDRA HUNGARY L.L.C.—See Indra Sistemas, S.A.; *Int'l*, pg. 3660
INDRA INDUSTRIES LTD.; *Int'l*, pg. 3659
INDRAJIT PROPERTIES PRIVATE LIMITED—See Shree Global Tradefin Limited; *Int'l*, pg. 6863
INDRA LIMITED (KENYA)—See Indra Sistemas, S.A.; *Int'l*, pg. 3660

INDRA L.L.C.—See Indra Sistemas, S.A.; *Int'l*, pg. 3660
INDRA LTDA.—See Indra Sistemas, S.A.; *Int'l*, pg. 3660
INDRA PANAMA, S.A.—See Indra Sistemas, S.A.; *Int'l*, pg. 3660
INDRA PHILIPPINES, INC.—See Indra Sistemas, S.A.; *Int'l*, pg. 3660
INDRAPRASTHA GAS LIMITED; *Int'l*, pg. 3661
INDRAPRASTHA MEDICAL CORPORATION LIMITED; *Int'l*, pg. 3661
INDRA SISTEMAS CHILE S.A.—See Indra Sistemas, S.A.; *Int'l*, pg. 3660
INDRA SISTEMAS DE COMUNICACIONES SEGURAS S.L.—See Indra Sistemas, S.A.; *Int'l*, pg. 3660
INDRA SISTEMAS DE SEGURIDAD, S.A.—See Indra Sistemas, S.A.; *Int'l*, pg. 3660
INDRA SISTEMAS INDIA PRIVATE LTD.—See Indra Sistemas, S.A.; *Int'l*, pg. 3660
INDRA SISTEMAS MAGREB S.A.R.L.—See Indra Sistemas, S.A.; *Int'l*, pg. 3660
INDRA SISTEMAS MEXICO S.A. DE C.V.—See Indra Sistemas, S.A.; *Int'l*, pg. 3660
INDRA SISTEMAS MEXICO S.A. DE C.V.—See Synthomer plc; *Int'l*, pg. 7387
INDRA SISTEMAS PORTUGAL S.A.—See Indra Sistemas, S.A.; *Int'l*, pg. 3660
INDRA SISTEMAS, S.A.; *Int'l*, pg. 3659
INDRA SISTEME S.R.L.—See Indra Sistemas, S.A.; *Int'l*, pg. 3660
INDRA SLOVAKIA, A.S.—See Indra Sistemas, S.A.; *Int'l*, pg. 3660
INDRASOFT INC.—See ASGN Incorporated; *U.S. Public*, pg. 210
INDRA SOFTWARE LABS S.L.U.—See Indra Sistemas, S.A.; *Int'l*, pg. 3660
INDRA TECHNOLOGY SOLUTIONS MALASYA SDN. BHD.—See Indra Sistemas, S.A.; *Int'l*, pg. 3660
INDRA UCRANIA L.L.C.—See Indra Sistemas, S.A.; *Int'l*, pg. 3661
INDRA USA INC.—See Indra Sistemas, S.A.; *Int'l*, pg. 3660
INDRAYANI BIOTECH LIMITED; *Int'l*, pg. 3661
IND RENEWABLE ENERGY LIMITED; *Int'l*, pg. 3649
INDSIL HYDRO POWER AND MANGANESE LTD.; *Int'l*, pg. 3661
INDSOFT, INC.; *U.S. Private*, pg. 2064
INDSOYA LTD.; *Int'l*, pg. 3661
INDSPEC CHEMICAL CORPORATION—See Occidental Petroleum Corporation; *U.S. Public*, pg. 1561
INDSPEC CHEMICAL EXPORT SALES, LLC—See Occidental Petroleum Corporation; *U.S. Public*, pg. 1561
IND SWIFT LABORATORIES INC.—See Ind-Swift Laboratories Limited; *Int'l*, pg. 3649
IND-SWIFT LABORATORIES LIMITED; *Int'l*, pg. 3649
IND-SWIFT LTD.; *Int'l*, pg. 3649
INDTACT GMBH; *Int'l*, pg. 3661
INDTAI INC.; *U.S. Private*, pg. 2064
INDTRANS CONTAINER LINES PRIVATE LIMITED—See Mangal Credit & Fincorp Limited; *Int'l*, pg. 4669
INDUBODEN GMBH & CO. INDUSTRIEWERTE OHG—See E.ON SE; *Int'l*, pg. 2258
INDUCT AS; *Int'l*, pg. 3661
INDUCTION EQUIPMENT (INDIA) PRIVATE LIMITED—See Park-Ohio Holdings Corp.; *U.S. Public*, pg. 1639
INDUCTION HEALTHCARE GROUP PLC; *Int'l*, pg. 3661
INDUCTIVE TECHNOLOGIES, INC.—See Electro Technik Industries; *U.S. Private*, pg. 1354
INDUCTOHEAT, INC.—See Indel, Inc.; *U.S. Private*, pg. 2055
INDUCTORS INC.; *U.S. Private*, pg. 2064
INDUCTO STEEL LTD.; *Int'l*, pg. 3661
INDUCTOTHERM CORP.—See Indel, Inc.; *U.S. Private*, pg. 2055
INDUCTOTHERM EUROPE LIMITED—See Indel, Inc.; *U.S. Private*, pg. 2055
INDUCTOTHERM GROUP BRASIL LTDA—See Indel, Inc.; *U.S. Private*, pg. 2055
INDUCTOTHERM GROUP CANADA LTD.—See Indel, Inc.; *U.S. Private*, pg. 2055
INDUCTOTHERM GROUP FRANCE—See Indel, Inc.; *U.S. Private*, pg. 2055
INDUCTOTHERM HEATING & WELDING TECHNOLOGIES LTD—See Indel, Inc.; *U.S. Private*, pg. 2055
INDUCTOTHERM PTY., LTD.—See Indel, Inc.; *U.S. Private*, pg. 2055
INDUFLOW—See Indutrade AB; *Int'l*, pg. 3679
INDUFOR N.V.—See Scandinavian Investment Group A/S; *Int'l*, pg. 6612
INDUGA INDUSTRIEOFEN AND GIESSEREI-ANLAGEN GMBH & CO. KG—See Otto Junker GmbH; *Int'l*, pg. 5664
INDUKERN, S.A.; *Int'l*, pg. 3661
INDU-LIGHT AG—See ThyssenKrupp AG; *Int'l*, pg. 7724
INDUNORM BEWEGUNGSTECHNIK GMBH—See THK CO., LTD.; *Int'l*, pg. 7711
INDUNORM HYDRAULIK GMBH—See Wurth Verwaltungsgesellschaft mbH; *Int'l*, pg. 8506
INDUPIPE AB—See Bravida Holding AB; *Int'l*, pg. 1142

INDUPLATE, LLC—See Greystone Incorporated; *U.S. Private*, pg. 1786
INDUPLEX, INC.—See RGP Holding, Inc.; *U.S. Private*, pg. 3420
INDUQUIP, C.A.—See Nordson Corporation; *U.S. Public*, pg. 1533
INDURA ARGENTINA S.A.—See Air Products & Chemicals, Inc.; *U.S. Public*, pg. 66
INDURA ECUADOR S.A.—See Air Products & Chemicals, Inc.; *U.S. Public*, pg. 66
INDURA PERU S.A.—See Air Products & Chemicals, Inc.; *U.S. Public*, pg. 66
INDURA S.A.—See Air Products & Chemicals, Inc.; *U.S. Public*, pg. 66
INDURA URUGUAY S.A.—See Air Products & Chemicals, Inc.; *U.S. Public*, pg. 66
INDUS AUTOMOTIVES PVT LTD—See SINDHU TRADE LINKS LIMITED; *Int'l*, pg. 6938
INDUS COAL LIMITED; *Int'l*, pg. 3661
INDUS COAL SINGAPORE PTE LTD—See Indus Coal Limited; *Int'l*, pg. 3662
INDUS CORPORATION—See Tetra Tech, Inc.; *U.S. Public*, pg. 2023
INDUS DYEING & MANUFACTURING COMPANY LTD.; *Int'l*, pg. 3662
INDUS ENERGY NL; *Int'l*, pg. 3662
INDUSERVICES FR S.A.—See Socfinasia S.A.; *Int'l*, pg. 7031
INDUS FILA LIMITED; *Int'l*, pg. 3662
INDUS FILMS LIMITED—See Boomerang Plus plc; *Int'l*, pg. 1110
INDUS FINANCE LIMITED; *Int'l*, pg. 3662
INDUS GAS LIMITED; *Int'l*, pg. 3662
INDUS HOLDING AG; *Int'l*, pg. 3662
INDUSIND BANK LTD.; *Int'l*, pg. 3664
INDUSIND INTERNATIONAL HOLDINGS LIMITED—See Hinduja Group Ltd.; *Int'l*, pg. 3399
INDUSIND MEDIA & COMMUNICATIONS LIMITED—See Hinduja Global Solutions Ltd.; *Int'l*, pg. 3398
INDUS-LEAGUE CLOTHING LIMITED—See Future Corporate Resources Limited; *Int'l*, pg. 2853
INDUS MOTOR COMPANY LIMITED—See House of Habib; *Int'l*, pg. 3491
INDUS MOTOR COMPANY LIMITED—See Toyota Motor Corporation; *Int'l*, pg. 7872
INDUSOFT, INC.—See Schneider Electric SE; *Int'l*, pg. 6627
INDUS PETROCHEM LIMITED; *Int'l*, pg. 3664
INDUS REALTY TRUST, INC.—See Centerbridge Partners, L.P.; *U.S. Private*, pg. 815
INDUS REALTY TRUST, INC.—See GIC Pte. Ltd.; *Int'l*, pg. 2964
INDUS SURVEYORS (PVT.) LTD.—See First Elite Capital Modaraba; *Int'l*, pg. 2683
INDUS TECHNOLOGY, INC.; *U.S. Private*, pg. 2064
INDUSTEEL BELGIUM S.A.—See ArcelorMittal S.A.; *Int'l*, pg. 545
INDUS TOWERS LIMITED—See Bharti Enterprises Limited; *Int'l*, pg. 1013
INDUSTRA - COMERCIO DE EQUIPAMENTOS INDUSTRIAIS, S.A.—See Triton Advisers Limited; *Int'l*, pg. 7934
INDUSTREA MINING TECHNOLOGY PTY LTD—See General Electric Company; *U.S. Public*, pg. 920
INDUSTRIA AUTOMOTRIZ CIFUNSA, S.A. DE C.V.—See Grupo Industrial Saltillo S.A. de C.V.; *Int'l*, pg. 3130
INDUSTRIA AUTOMOTRIZ, S.A. DE C.V.; *Int'l*, pg. 3665
INDUSTRIA CARTONERA ASTURIANA, S.A.—See DS Smith Plc; *Int'l*, pg. 2209
INDUSTRIA CENTROAMERICANA DE SANITARIOS S.A.—See Organizacion Corona SA; *Int'l*, pg. 5618
INDUSTRIA CERAMICA CENTROAMERICANA S.A.—See Organizacion Corona SA; *Int'l*, pg. 5618
INDUSTRIA CERAMICA COSTARRICENSE, S.A.—See Organizacion Corona SA; *Int'l*, pg. 5618
INDUSTRIA CHIMICA REGGIANA I.C.R. SPA—See PPG Industries, Inc.; *U.S. Public*, pg. 1707
INDUSTRIA COLOMBIANA DE CAFE S.A.S.—See Grupo Nutresa S.A.; *Int'l*, pg. 3133
INDUSTRIA CORCHERA, S.A.—See CORTICEIRA AMORIM, S.G.P.S., S.A.; *Int'l*, pg. 1808
INDUSTRIA DE ALIMENTOS ZENU S.A.S.—See Grupo Nutresa S.A.; *Int'l*, pg. 3133
INDUSTRIA DE DISENO TEXTIL, S.A.; *Int'l*, pg. 3665
INDUSTRIA DE EJES Y TRANSMISSIONES S.A.—See Dana Incorporated; *U.S. Public*, pg. 623
INDUSTRIA DE PRODUTOS ALIMENTICIOS PIRAQUE S.A.—See M. Dias Branco S.A. Industria e Comercio de Alimentos; *Int'l*, pg. 4615
INDUSTRIA DE REFRESCOS DEL NORESTE, S.R.L. DE C.V.—See PepsiCo, Inc.; *U.S. Public*, pg. 1669
INDUSTRIA DE TURBO PROPULSORES S.A. - AJALVIR PLANT—See Bain Capital, LP; *U.S. Private*, pg. 433
INDUSTRIA DE TURBO PROPULSORES S.A. - SEVILLE PLANT—See Bain Capital, LP; *U.S. Private*, pg. 433
INDUSTRIA DE TURBO PROPULSORES S.A.—See Bain Capital, LP; *U.S. Private*, pg. 433

1331

INDUSTRIA DOS EN UNO DE COLOMBIA LTDA—See Arcor Sociedad Anonima, Industrial y Comercial; *Int'l*, pg. 550
INDUSTRIA E COMERCIO DE MAQUINAS PERFECTA CURITIBA LTDA.—See Illinois Tool Works Inc.; *U.S. Public*, pg. 1108
INDUSTRIA E COMERCIO METALURGICA ATLAS S.A.—See Votorantim S.A.; *Int'l*, pg. 8310
INDUSTRIA ELETROMECANICA BALESTRO LTDA.—See Hubbell Incorporated; *U.S. Public*, pg. 1067
INDUSTRIA FARMACEUTICA SERONO SPA—See Merck KGaA; *Int'l*, pg. 4831
INDUSTRIA ITALIANA INTEGRATORI TREI S.P.A.—See AGRAVIS Raiffeisen AG; *Int'l*, pg. 215
INDUSTRIAL ACOUSTICS COMPANY GMBH—See AEA Investors LP; *U.S. Private*, pg. 114
INDUSTRIAL ACOUSTICS COMPANY, INC.—See AEA Investors LP; *U.S. Private*, pg. 114
INDUSTRIAL ACOUSTICS COMPANY, LTD.—See AEA Investors LP; *U.S. Private*, pg. 114
INDUSTRIAL AGRICOLA FORTALEZA IMPORTACAO E EXPORTACAO LTDA—See AGCO Corporation; *U.S. Public*, pg. 59
INDUSTRIAL AIR INC.—See Limbach Holdings, Inc.; *U.S. Public*, pg. 1316
INDUSTRIAL ALLIANCE AUTO & HOME INSURANCE—See iA Financial Corporation Inc.; *Int'l*, pg. 3567
INDUSTRIAL ALLIANCE INSURANCE AND FINANCIAL SERVICES INC.—See iA Financial Corporation Inc.; *Int'l*, pg. 3567
INDUSTRIAL ALLIANCE PACIFIC GENERAL INSURANCE CORPORATION—See iA Financial Corporation Inc.; *Int'l*, pg. 3567
INDUSTRIAL ALLIANCE PACIFIC INSURANCE AND FINANCIAL SERVICES INC.—See iA Financial Corporation Inc.; *Int'l*, pg. 3567
INDUSTRIAL ALLIANCE PACIFIC LIFE INSURANCE COMPANY—See iA Financial Corporation Inc.; *Int'l*, pg. 3567
INDUSTRIAL ALLIANCE SECURITIES INC.—See iA Financial Corporation Inc.; *Int'l*, pg. 3567
INDUSTRIAL ALLIANCE TRUST INC.—See iA Financial Corporation Inc.; *Int'l*, pg. 3567
INDUSTRIAL AND COMMERCIAL BANK OF CHINA (ARGENTINA) S.A.—See Industrial & Commercial Bank of China Limited; *Int'l*, pg. 3670
INDUSTRIAL AND FINANCIAL SYSTEMS, IFS AB—See EQT AB; *Int'l*, pg. 2477
INDUSTRIAL AND FINANCIAL SYSTEMS, IFS UK LTD—See EQT AB; *Int'l*, pg. 2478
INDUSTRIAL AND MARINE ENGINEERING LTD.—See MBf Holdings Berhad; *Int'l*, pg. 4752
INDUSTRIAL AND WELDING MANAGEMENT LIMITED—See Linde plc; *Int'l*, pg. 4505
INDUSTRIAL ASPHALT, LLC—See Summit Materials, Inc.; *U.S. Public*, pg. 1960
INDUSTRIAL ASPHALTS (CEYLON) PLC; *Int'l*, pg. 3671
INDUSTRIAL ASSETS CORP.; *U.S. Private*, pg. 2064
INDUSTRIAL AUTOMATION CONTROLS; *U.S. Private*, pg. 2064
INDUSTRIAL BANK CO., LTD.; *Int'l*, pg. 3671
INDUSTRIAL BANK FINANCIAL LEASING CO., LTD.—See Industrial Bank Co., Ltd.; *Int'l*, pg. 3671
INDUSTRIAL BANK OF KOREA; *Int'l*, pg. 3671
INDUSTRIALBANK PJSC; *Int'l*, pg. 3673
INDUSTRIAL BANK—See IBW Financial Corporation; *U.S. Public*, pg. 1083
INDUSTRIAL BATTERY & CHARGER, INC.; *U.S. Private*, pg. 2064
INDUSTRIAL BELTING & TRANSMISSION, INC.; *U.S. Private*, pg. 2064
INDUSTRIAL BEREARBEITGSCENTER AG—See SKion GmbH; *Int'l*, pg. 6987
INDUSTRIAL CAPACITORS (WREXHAM) LIMITED—See BorgWarner Inc.; *U.S. Public*, pg. 369
INDUSTRIAL CAPITAL HOLDING AD-SOFIA; *Int'l*, pg. 3671
INDUSTRIAL CASTER & WHEEL CO.; *U.S. Private*, pg. 2065
INDUSTRIAL CHEMICALS CORP.; *U.S. Private*, pg. 2065
INDUSTRIAL CHEMICALS INC.; *U.S. Private*, pg. 2065
INDUSTRIAL CHEMICALS INC—See Industrial Chemicals Inc.; *U.S. Private*, pg. 2065
INDUSTRIAL COATINGS & FIREPROOFING—See North American Coatings, Inc.; *U.S. Private*, pg. 2940
INDUSTRIAL COATINGS GROUP, INC.—See ICG Holliston Holdings Corporation; *U.S. Private*, pg. 2031
INDUSTRIAL COIL INC.—See Jay Industrial Repair, Inc.; *U.S. Private*, pg. 2192
INDUSTRIAL COLD STORAGE INC.—See ICS Logistics, Inc.; *U.S. Private*, pg. 2033
INDUSTRIAL COLOR PRODUCTIONS, INC.—See Frontenac Company LLC; *U.S. Private*, pg. 1613
THE INDUSTRIAL COMMERCIAL & AGRICULTURAL CO. LTD.; *Int'l*, pg. 7655
INDUSTRIAL & COMMERCIAL BANK OF CHINA ALMATY JSC—See Industrial & Commercial Bank of China Limited; *Int'l*, pg. 3670

INDUSTRIAL & COMMERCIAL BANK OF CHINA (ASIA) LIMITED—See Industrial & Commercial Bank of China Limited; *Int'l*, pg. 3670
INDUSTRIAL & COMMERCIAL BANK OF CHINA (BRASIL) S.A.—See Industrial & Commercial Bank of China Limited; *Int'l*, pg. 3670
INDUSTRIAL & COMMERCIAL BANK OF CHINA (CANADA) LIMITED—See Industrial & Commercial Bank of China Limited; *Int'l*, pg. 3670
INDUSTRIAL & COMMERCIAL BANK OF CHINA (EUROPE) S.A.—See Industrial & Commercial Bank of China Limited; *Int'l*, pg. 3670
INDUSTRIAL & COMMERCIAL BANK OF CHINA FINANCIAL SERVICES LLC—See Industrial & Commercial Bank of China Limited; *Int'l*, pg. 3670
INDUSTRIAL & COMMERCIAL BANK OF CHINA LIMITED; *Int'l*, pg. 3669
INDUSTRIAL & COMMERCIAL BANK OF CHINA LUXEMBOURG S.A.—See Industrial & Commercial Bank of China Limited; *Int'l*, pg. 3670
INDUSTRIAL & COMMERCIAL BANK OF CHINA (MACAU) LIMITED—See Industrial & Commercial Bank of China Limited; *Int'l*, pg. 3670
INDUSTRIAL & COMMERCIAL BANK OF CHINA (MALAYSIA) BERHAD—See Industrial & Commercial Bank of China Limited; *Int'l*, pg. 3670
INDUSTRIAL & COMMERCIAL BANK OF CHINA MEXICO S.A.—See Industrial & Commercial Bank of China Limited; *Int'l*, pg. 3670
INDUSTRIAL & COMMERCIAL BANK OF CHINA (MIDDLE EAST) LIMITED—See Industrial & Commercial Bank of China Limited; *Int'l*, pg. 3670
INDUSTRIAL & COMMERCIAL BANK OF CHINA (NEW ZEALAND) LIMITED—See Industrial & Commercial Bank of China Limited; *Int'l*, pg. 3670
INDUSTRIAL & COMMERCIAL BANK OF CHINA (THAI) PUBLIC COMPANY LIMITED—See Industrial & Commercial Bank of China Limited; *Int'l*, pg. 3670
INDUSTRIAL & COMMERCIAL BANK OF CHINA (USA) NA - BROOKLYN BRANCH—See Industrial & Commercial Bank of China Limited; *Int'l*, pg. 3670
INDUSTRIAL & COMMERCIAL BANK OF CHINA (USA) NA - FLUSHING BRANCH—See Industrial & Commercial Bank of China Limited; *Int'l*, pg. 3670
INDUSTRIAL & COMMERCIAL BANK OF CHINA (USA) NA - HACIENDA HEIGHTS BRANCH—See Industrial & Commercial Bank of China Limited; *Int'l*, pg. 3670
INDUSTRIAL & COMMERCIAL BANK OF CHINA (USA) NA - NORIEGA BRANCH—See Industrial & Commercial Bank of China Limited; *Int'l*, pg. 3670
INDUSTRIAL & COMMERCIAL BANK OF CHINA (USA) NA - OAKLAND BRANCH—See Industrial & Commercial Bank of China Limited; *Int'l*, pg. 3670
INDUSTRIAL & COMMERCIAL BANK OF CHINA (USA) NA - SAN GABRIEL BRANCH—See Industrial & Commercial Bank of China Limited; *Int'l*, pg. 3670
INDUSTRIAL & COMMERCIAL BANK OF CHINA (USA) NA—See Industrial & Commercial Bank of China Limited; *Int'l*, pg. 3670
INDUSTRIAL & COMMERCIAL BANK OF CHINA (USA) NA—See Industrial & Commercial Bank of China Limited; *Int'l*, pg. 3670
INDUSTRIAL & COMMERCIAL BANK OF CHINA (USA) NA - SOUTH SAN FRANCISCO BRANCH—See Industrial & Commercial Bank of China Limited; *Int'l*, pg. 3670
INDUSTRIAL & COMMERCIAL BANK OF CHINA (USA) NA - TEMPLE CITY BRANCH—See Industrial & Commercial Bank of China Limited; *Int'l*, pg. 3670
INDUSTRIAL & COMMERCIAL BANK OF CHINA (USA) NA - TORRANCE BRANCH—See Industrial & Commercial Bank of China Limited; *Int'l*, pg. 3670
INDUSTRIAL COMMERCIAL EQUIPMENT MANUFACTURING LTD.; *Int'l*, pg. 3671
INDUSTRIAL COMMUNICATIONS AND ELECTRONICS, INC.; *U.S. Private*, pg. 2065
INDUSTRIAL COMPONENTS INC.; *U.S. Private*, pg. 2065
INDUSTRIAL CONCRETE PRODUCTS BERHAD—See IJM Corporation Berhad; *Int'l*, pg. 3609
INDUSTRIAL CONSTRUCTION COMPANY, INC.; *U.S. Private*, pg. 2065
INDUSTRIAL CONSTRUCTORS/MANAGERS, INC.; *U.S. Private*, pg. 2065
INDUSTRIAL CONSUMER FINANCE CO., LTD.—See Industrial Bank Co., Ltd.; *Int'l*, pg. 3671
INDUSTRIAL CONTAINER SERVICES, LLC - CINCINNATI 26—See Stone Canyon Industries, LLC; *U.S. Private*, pg. 3817
INDUSTRIAL CONTAINER SERVICES, LLC - COLUMBUS—See Stone Canyon Industries, LLC; *U.S. Private*, pg. 3817
INDUSTRIAL CONTAINER SERVICES, LLC - DENVER—See Stone Canyon Industries, LLC; *U.S. Private*, pg. 3817
INDUSTRIAL CONTAINER SERVICES, LLC - LOUISVILLE—See Stone Canyon Industries, LLC; *U.S. Private*, pg. 3817

INDUSTRIAL CONTAINER SERVICES, LLC - ORLANDO—See Stone Canyon Industries, LLC; *U.S. Private*, pg. 3817
INDUSTRIAL CONTAINER SERVICES, LLC—See Stone Canyon Industries, LLC; *U.S. Private*, pg. 3817
INDUSTRIAL CONTAINER & SUPPLY; *U.S. Private*, pg. 2065
INDUSTRIAL CONTRACTING OF FAIRMONT, INC.—See Victory of West Virginia, Inc.; *U.S. Private*, pg. 4379
INDUSTRIAL CONTRACTORS, INC.—See Skanska AB; *Int'l*, pg. 6979
INDUSTRIAL CONTRACTORS, INC.—See APi Group Corporation; *Int'l*, pg. 514
INDUSTRIAL CONTROL REPAIR, INC.; *U.S. Private*, pg. 2065
INDUSTRIAL CONTROLS DISTRIBUTORS LLC—See SHV Holdings N.V.; *Int'l*, pg. 6871
INDUSTRIAL CONTROLS DISTRIBUTORS—See SHV Holdings N.V.; *Int'l*, pg. 6871
INDUSTRIAL CONTROLS DISTRIBUTORS—See SHV Holdings N.V.; *Int'l*, pg. 6871
INDUSTRIAL CREDIT COMPANY AFRICA HOLDINGS LIMITED; *Int'l*, pg. 3671
INDUSTRIAL CUSTOM PRODUCTS, INC. - ROSEVILLE PLANT—See Industrial Custom Products, Inc.; *U.S. Private*, pg. 2065
INDUSTRIAL CUSTOM PRODUCTS, INC.; *U.S. Private*, pg. 2065
INDUSTRIAL DE CUAUTITLAN SA DE CV—See Societe BIC S.A.; *Int'l*, pg. 7037
INDUSTRIAL DEFENDER, INC.—See Teleo Capital Management, LLC; *U.S. Private*, pg. 3961
INDUSTRIAL DE PLASTICOS DE CHIHUAHUA, S.A. DE C.V.—See Northern Technologies International Corporation; *U.S. Public*, pg. 1538
INDUSTRIAL DESIGN & CONSTRUCTION, INC.; *U.S. Private*, pg. 2065
INDUSTRIAL DEVELOPMENT AND RENOVATION ORGANIZATION OF IRAN; *Int'l*, pg. 3671
INDUSTRIAL DEVELOPMENT COMPANY SAL; *Int'l*, pg. 3671
INDUSTRIAL DEVELOPMENT CORPORATION OF SOUTH AFRICA, LTD.; *Int'l*, pg. 3671
INDUSTRIAL DIELECTRICS HOLDINGS, INC.; *U.S. Private*, pg. 2065
INDUSTRIAL DIELECTRICS, INC.—See Industrial Dielectrics Holdings, Inc.; *U.S. Private*, pg. 2065
INDUSTRIAL DIELECTRICS (UK) LTD.—See Industrial Dielectrics Holdings, Inc.; *U.S. Private*, pg. 2065
INDUSTRIAL DIESEL INC.; *U.S. Private*, pg. 2065
INDUSTRIAL DISPOSAL SUPPLY COMPANY; *U.S. Private*, pg. 2065
INDUSTRIAL DISTRIBUTION GROUP, INC. - CINCINNATI—See Sonepar S.A.; *Int'l*, pg. 7093
INDUSTRIAL DISTRIBUTION GROUP, INC. - CONNECTICUT—See Sonepar S.A.; *Int'l*, pg. 7093
INDUSTRIAL DISTRIBUTION GROUP, INC. - KINGSFORD—See Sonepar S.A.; *Int'l*, pg. 7093
INDUSTRIAL DISTRIBUTION GROUP, INC. - MANITOWOC—See Sonepar S.A.; *Int'l*, pg. 7093
INDUSTRIAL DISTRIBUTION GROUP, INC. - NASHUA—See Sonepar S.A.; *Int'l*, pg. 7093
INDUSTRIAL DISTRIBUTION GROUP, INC. - NASHVILLE—See Sonepar S.A.; *Int'l*, pg. 7094
INDUSTRIAL DISTRIBUTION GROUP, INC. - ST. LOUIS—See Sonepar S.A.; *Int'l*, pg. 7094
INDUSTRIAL DISTRIBUTION GROUP, INC. - WICHITA—See Sonepar S.A.; *Int'l*, pg. 7094
INDUSTRIAL DISTRIBUTION GROUP, INC. - YORK—See Sonepar S.A.; *Int'l*, pg. 7094
INDUSTRIAL DISTRIBUTION RESOURCES, LLC; *U.S. Private*, pg. 2065
INDUSTRIAL DOOR CO. INC.; *U.S. Private*, pg. 2065
INDUSTRIAL DRIVE INC.—See Simona AG; *Int'l*, pg. 6932
INDUSTRIAL DRUG SERVICE DIV.—See General Scientific Safety Equipment Co.; *U.S. Private*, pg. 1667
INDUSTRIAL DYNAMICS CO. LTD.; *U.S. Private*, pg. 2066
INDUSTRIAL ELECTRIC COMPANY—See The Egan Companies; *U.S. Private*, pg. 4025
INDUSTRIAL ELECTRIC WIRE & CABLE INC.; *U.S. Private*, pg. 2066
INDUSTRIAL ELECTRIC WIRE & CABLE NORTHWEST—See Industrial Electric Wire & Cable Inc.; *U.S. Private*, pg. 2066
INDUSTRIAL ELECTRONIC ENGINEERS, INC.; *U.S. Private*, pg. 2066
INDUSTRIAL ELECTRONICS PTE. LTD.; *Int'l*, pg. 3672
INDUSTRIAL ELECTRONIC SUPPLY; *U.S. Private*, pg. 2066
INDUSTRIAL ENERGY INC.—See Russell Lands Inc.; *U.S. Private*, pg. 3506
INDUSTRIAL ENGINEERING COMPANY FOR CONSTRUCTION & DEVELOPMENT; *Int'l*, pg. 3672
INDUSTRIAL ENGINEERING & EQUIPMENT CO. INC.; *U.S. Private*, pg. 2066
INDUSTRIAL ENGINEERING SYSTEMS PTE. LTD.—See Annica Holdings Limited; *Int'l*, pg. 474

COMPANY NAME INDEX

INDUSTRIAL ENGRAVING & MANUFACTURING CORP.; U.S. Private, pg. 2066
INDUSTRIAL EQUIPMENT CO. OF HOUSTON; U.S. Private, pg. 2066
INDUSTRIAL EQUIPMENT & PARTS INC.—See Winsupply, Inc.; U.S. Private, pg. 4545
INDUSTRIAL FABRICATORS, INC.; U.S. Private, pg. 2066
INDUSTRIAL FABRICATORS, INC.—See APi Group Corporation; Int'l, pg. 514
INDUSTRIAL FABRICATORS INC.—See Williams Enterprises of Georgia, Inc.; U.S. Private, pg. 4525
INDUSTRIAL FABRICS CORP.—See Gilde Buy Out Partners B.V.; Int'l, pg. 2974
INDUSTRIAL FABRICS CORP.—See Parcom Capital Management B.V.; Int'l, pg. 5740
INDUSTRIAL FERRO DISTRIBUIDORA, S.A.—See Corporacion Gestamp SL; Int'l, pg. 1804
INDUSTRIAL FIBERGLASS CORP.; U.S. Private, pg. 2066
INDUSTRIAL FILTER PUMP MANUFACTURING CO; U.S. Private, pg. 2066
INDUSTRIAL FINANCE CO., INC.—See The Pape Group, Inc.; U.S. Private, pg. 4090
INDUSTRIAL FINISHES & SYSTEMS INC.; U.S. Private, pg. 2066
INDUSTRIAL FIRST INC.; U.S. Private, pg. 2066
INDUSTRIAL FUMIGANT COMPANY—See Rollins, Inc.; U.S. Public, pg. 1809
INDUSTRIAL FUND AD-SOFIA; Int'l, pg. 3672
INDUSTRIAL FUTURES CO., LTD.—See Industrial Bank Co., Ltd.; Int'l, pg. 3671
INDUSTRIAL GALVANIZERS AMERICA HOLDINGS, INC.—See Valmont Industries, Inc.; U.S. Public, pg. 2273
INDUSTRIAL GALVANIZERS AMERICA, INC—See Valmont Industries, Inc.; U.S. Public, pg. 2273
INDUSTRIAL GALVANIZERS CORPORATION OF THE PHILIPPINES INC.—See Valmont Industries, Inc.; U.S. Public, pg. 2273
INDUSTRIAL GALVANIZERS CORPORATION PTY. LTD.—See Valmont Industries, Inc.; U.S. Public, pg. 2273
INDUSTRIAL GAS DISTRIBUTORS—See Advance Auto Parts, Inc.; U.S. Public, pg. 46
INDUSTRIAL GASKET INC.; U.S. Private, pg. 2066
INDUSTRIAL GAS SPRINGS INC.—See Barnes Group Inc.; U.S. Public, pg. 277
INDUSTRIAL GAS SPRINGS LIMITED—See Barnes Group Inc.; U.S. Public, pg. 277
INDUSTRIAL & GENERAL INSURANCE PLC; Int'l, pg. 3670
THE INDUSTRIAL GROUP, LLC—See BWAB, Inc.; U.S. Private, pg. 700
INDUSTRIAL GROWTH PLATFORM, INC.; Int'l, pg. 3672
INDUSTRIAL GROWTH PLATFORM PTE. LTD.—See Industrial Growth Platform, Inc.; Int'l, pg. 3672
INDUSTRIAL HARNESS COMPANY; U.S. Private, pg. 2066
INDUSTRIAL HARNESS CO.—See Cerberus Capital Management, L.P.; U.S. Private, pg. 838
INDUSTRIAL HEAT TRANSFER INC.; U.S. Private, pg. 2066
INDUSTRIAL HOLDING BULGARIA AD; Int'l, pg. 3672
INDUSTRIAL HUMAN CAPITAL, INC.; U.S. Private, pg. 2066
INDUSTRIA LIBRARIA TIPOGRAFICA EDITRICE SPA—See UniCredit S.p.A.; Int'l, pg. 8034
INDUSTRIAL & INFRASTRUCTURE FUND INVESTMENT CORPORATION; Int'l, pg. 3671
INDUSTRIAL INNOVATIONS, INC.; U.S. Private, pg. 2066
INDUSTRIAL INSULATION GROUP, LLC—See Berkshire Hathaway Inc.; U.S. Public, pg. 308
INDUSTRIAL INTERFACE LIMITED—See Sensata Technologies Holding plc; U.S. Public, pg. 1865
INDUSTRIAL INTERNATIONAL TIRE COMPANY NV—See Compagnie Generale des Etablissements Michelin SCA; Int'l, pg. 1743
INDUSTRIAL INVESTMENT TRUST LIMITED; Int'l, pg. 3672
INDUSTRIAL INVESTORS LLC; Int'l, pg. 3672
INDUSTRIAL-IRRIGATION SERVICES; U.S. Private, pg. 2069
INDUSTRIAL LADDER & SUPPLY CO.; U.S. Private, pg. 2066
INDUSTRIAL LAMINATES/NORPLEX, INC.—See Hidden Harbor Capital Partners; U.S. Private, pg. 1934
INDUSTRIAL LASER SYSTEMS SARL—See Optoprim SAS; Int'l, pg. 5606
INDUSTRIAL LAUNDRY SERVICES, LLC—See EVI Industries, Inc.; U.S. Public, pg. 803
INDUSTRIAL LEVORIN S.A.—See Compagnie Generale des Etablissements Michelin SCA; Int'l, pg. 1743
INDUSTRIAL LIFT TRUCK & EQUIPMENT CO., INC.—See Gibson Energy Inc.; Int'l, pg. 2963
INDUSTRIAL LIGHTING PRODUCTS, LLC—See Harbour Group Industries, Inc.; U.S. Private, pg. 1860
INDUSTRIAL LOGISTICS PROPERTIES TRUST—See The RMR Group Inc.; U.S. Public, pg. 2126

INDUSTRIAL MACHINE & TOOL COMPANY INC.; U.S. Private, pg. 2066
INDUSTRIAL MACHINING SERVICES, INC.; U.S. Private, pg. 2066
INDUSTRIAL MAGNETICS, INC.—See DNS Capital, LLC; U.S. Private, pg. 1249
INDUSTRIAL MAINTENANCE CONTRACTORS, INC.; U.S. Private, pg. 2067
INDUSTRIAL MAINTENANCE, WELDING & MACHINING CO, INC.; U.S. Private, pg. 2067
INDUSTRIAL MANAGEMENT TECHNOLOGY & CONTRACTING LLC—See Sobha Limited; Int'l, pg. 7030
INDUSTRIAL MANUFACTURING SERVICES, LLC—See Klockner & Co, SE; Int'l, pg. 4203
INDUSTRIAL & MARINE EQUIPMENT CO., INC.—See AEA Investors LP; U.S. Private, pg. 115
INDUSTRIAL MARKETING INC.—See Slay Industries Inc.; U.S. Private, pg. 3687
INDUSTRIAL MECANICA AGRICOLA S. A.—See IMASA S.A.; Int'l, pg. 3620
INDUSTRIAL METAL PRODUCTS CORP.; U.S. Private, pg. 2067
INDUSTRIAL METAL SUPPLY COMPANY; U.S. Private, pg. 2067
INDUSTRIAL MILL & MAINTENANCE SUPPLY INC.; U.S. Private, pg. 2067
INDUSTRIAL MINERALS LTD.; Int'l, pg. 3672
INDUSTRIAL MODULES—See VDL Groep B.V.; Int'l, pg. 8140
INDUSTRIAL MOLDING CORPORATION—See Blackford Capital LLC; U.S. Private, pg. 574
INDUSTRIAL MOTION CONTROL, LLC—See Stabilus; U.S. Private, pg. 3774
INDUSTRIAL MOTOR POWER COPORATION; U.S. Private, pg. 2067
INDUSTRIAL NANOTECH, INC.; U.S. Public, pg. 1117
INDUSTRIAL NETTING, INC.—See Frandsen Corporation; U.S. Private, pg. 1593
INDUSTRIAL OILS UNLIMITED, LLC—See KFM Enterprises, LLC; U.S. Private, pg. 2301
INDUSTRIAL OLEOCHEMICAL PRODUCTS (PTY) LIMITED—See AECI Limited; Int'l, pg. 171
INDUSTRIAL OPPORTUNITY PARTNERS, LLC; U.S. Private, pg. 2067
INDUSTRIAL PACKAGING CORP.; U.S. Private, pg. 2067
INDUSTRIAL PALLET CORPORATION; U.S. Private, pg. 2067
INDUSTRIAL PALLET CORPORATION—See Industrial Pallet Corporation; U.S. Private, pg. 2067
INDUSTRIAL PALLET, LLC—See Audax Group, Limited Partnership; U.S. Private, pg. 386
INDUSTRIAL PARAMEDIC SERVICES, LTD.—See DXP Enterprises, Inc.; U.S. Public, pg. 697
INDUSTRIAL PARTS DEPOT INC.; U.S. Private, pg. 2067
INDUSTRIAL PINE PRODUCTS, INC.—See Oregon Canadian Forest Products Inc.; U.S. Private, pg. 3039
INDUSTRIAL PIPING SPECIALISTS INC.; U.S. Private, pg. 2067
INDUSTRIAL POWER ALLIANCE, LTD.—See Cummins Inc.; U.S. Public, pg. 607
INDUSTRIAL POWER ALLIANCE, LTD.—See Komatsu Ltd.; Int'l, pg. 4235
INDUSTRIAL POWER & LIGHTING CORP.; U.S. Private, pg. 2068
INDUSTRIAL POWER SYSTEMS INCORPORATED; U.S. Private, pg. 2068
INDUSTRIAL POWERTRAIN PTY. LTD.—See Engenco Limited; Int'l, pg. 2427
INDUSTRIAL PROCESS INSULATORS, INC.—See Thermon Group Holdings, Inc.; U.S. Public, pg. 2155
INDUSTRIAL PRODUCTS ENTERPISES LLC; U.S. Private, pg. 2068
INDUSTRIAL PROMOTION SERVICES LTD—See Aga Khan Development Network; Int'l, pg. 199
INDUSTRIAL PROMOTION SERVICES S.A.—See Aga Khan Development Network; Int'l, pg. 199
INDUSTRIAL PROMOTION SERVICES (WEST AFRICA) S.A.—See Aga Khan Development Network; Int'l, pg. 199
INDUSTRIAL PROPERTY TRUST INC.—See Prologis, Inc.; U.S. Public, pg. 1727
THE INDUSTRIAL & PRUDENTIAL INVESTMENT COMPANY LIMITED; Int'l, pg. 7655
INDUSTRIAL QUIMICA LASEM, S.A.U.—See The Nisshin OilliO Group, Ltd.; Int'l, pg. 7671
INDUSTRIAL REALTY SOLUTIONS, INC.; U.S. Private, pg. 2068
INDUSTRIAL RESIN RECYCLING, INC.—See Ravago Holding S.A.; Int'l, pg. 6222
INDUSTRIAL RESOURCES, INC.—See Victory of West Virginia, Inc.; U.S. Private, pg. 4379
INDUSTRIAL REVOLUTION, INC.; U.S. Private, pg. 2068
INDUSTRIAL RISKS PROTECTION CONSULTANTS—See Marsh & McLennan Companies, Inc.; U.S. Public, pg. 1376
INDUSTRIAL RUBBER APPLICATORS, INC.—See Lime Rock Partners, LLC; U.S. Private, pg. 2456

INDUSTRIAL TOWEL & UNIFORM

INDUSTRIAL RUBBER APPLICATORS, INC.—See Thompson Street Capital Manager LLC; U.S. Private, pg. 4161
INDUSTRIAL SALES COMPANY INC.; U.S. Private, pg. 2068
INDUSTRIAL SALES COMPANY INC.; U.S. Private, pg. 2068
INDUSTRIAL SALES & SERVICE-GC S.R.L.—See Endress+Hauser (International) Holding AG; Int'l, pg. 2408
INDUSTRIAL SANDS & GRAVELS PTY. LTD.—See GBM Gold Limited; Int'l, pg. 2893
INDUSTRIAL SAVINGS BANK JSC; Int'l, pg. 3672
INDUSTRIAL SCIENTIFIC ASIA-PACIFIC—See Fortive Corporation; U.S. Public, pg. 871
INDUSTRIAL SCIENTIFIC AUSTRALIA PTY LTD—See Fortive Corporation; U.S. Public, pg. 871
INDUSTRIAL SCIENTIFIC CANADA ULC—See Fortive Corporation; U.S. Public, pg. 870
INDUSTRIAL SCIENTIFIC CORPORATION PTE. LTD.—See Fortive Corporation; U.S. Public, pg. 871
INDUSTRIAL SCIENTIFIC CORPORATION—See Fortive Corporation; U.S. Public, pg. 871
INDUSTRIAL SCIENTIFIC DEUTSCHLAND GMBH—See Fortive Corporation; U.S. Public, pg. 871
INDUSTRIAL SCIENTIFIC FRANCE SAS—See Fortive Corporation; U.S. Public, pg. 871
INDUSTRIAL SCIENTIFIC FZCO—See Fortive Corporation; U.S. Public, pg. 871
INDUSTRIAL SCIENTIFIC INDIA PVT. LTD—See Fortive Corporation; U.S. Public, pg. 871
INDUSTRIAL SCIENTIFIC LTD—See Fortive Corporation; U.S. Public, pg. 871
INDUSTRIAL SECURITIES CO., LTD.; Int'l, pg. 3673
INDUSTRIAL SERVICE SOLUTIONS LLC—See Wynnchurch Capital, L.P.; U.S. Private, pg. 4577
INDUSTRIAL SERVICES PTE LTD—See Hai Leck Holdings Limited; Int'l, pg. 3208
INDUSTRIAL SOLUTIONS, INC.; U.S. Private, pg. 2068
INDUSTRIAL SOLUTIONS, INC.—See The Helm Group; U.S. Private, pg. 4051
INDUSTRIAL SPECIALITY CONTRACTOR LLC; U.S. Private, pg. 2068
INDUSTRIAL SPECIALTIES, LLC—See Aberdeen Dynamics Supply Inc.; U.S. Private, pg. 38
INDUSTRIAL SPECIALTY CHEMICALS, INC.—See Element Solutions Inc.; U.S. Public, pg. 726
INDUSTRIAL SPECIALTY CONTRACTORS INC.—See Industrial Speciality Contractor LLC; U.S. Private, pg. 2068
INDUSTRIALS REIT LIMITED—See Blackstone Inc.; U.S. Public, pg. 354
INDUSTRIAL STAFFING SERVICES, INC.; U.S. Private, pg. 2068
INDUSTRIAL STARS OF ITALY S.P.A.—See LU-VE SpA; Int'l, pg. 4572
INDUSTRIAL STEEL INC.; U.S. Private, pg. 2068
INDUSTRIAL STEEL & WIRE COMPANY; U.S. Private, pg. 2068
INDUSTRIAL SUPPLIES & SERVICES LIMITED—See Linde plc; Int'l, pg. 4505
INDUSTRIAL SUPPLY COMPANY INC.; U.S. Private, pg. 2068
INDUSTRIAL SUPPLY EXPORT CORPORATION; U.S. Private, pg. 2068
INDUSTRIAL SUPPLY SOLUTIONS, INC.; U.S. Private, pg. 2068
INDUSTRIAL SUPPLY SOLUTIONS, INC.—See Industrial Supply Solutions, Inc.; U.S. Private, pg. 2068
INDUSTRIAL SURINDU S.A.—See Nestle S.A.; Int'l, pg. 5203
INDUSTRIAL TECH ACQUISITIONS, INC.; U.S. Public, pg. 1117
INDUSTRIAL TECHNICAL HOLDINGS CORPORATION; Int'l, pg. 3673
INDUSTRIAL TECHNOLOGIES INC.; U.S. Private, pg. 2068
INDUSTRIAL TECH SERVICES, INC.—See Toyota Tsusho Corporation; Int'l, pg. 7879
INDUSTRIAL TECTONICS BEARING CORP.—See RBC Bearings Incorporated; U.S. Public, pg. 1766
INDUSTRIAL TECTONICS BEARINGS CORPORATION—See RBC Bearings Incorporated; U.S. Public, pg. 1766
INDUSTRIAL TECTONICS INC.—See SKF AB; Int'l, pg. 6985
INDUSTRIAL TERMINALS, L.P.—See Intermarine, Inc.; U.S. Private, pg. 2112
INDUSTRIAL THERMO POLYMERS LIMITED—See PAI Partners S.A.S.; Int'l, pg. 5700
INDUSTRIAL THREADED PRODUCTS; U.S. Private, pg. 2068
INDUSTRIAL TOOL, INC.—See Maruka Furusato Corporation; Int'l, pg. 4714
INDUSTRIAL TOWEL & UNIFORM - NEENAH PLANT—See Industrial Towel & Uniform; U.S. Private, pg. 2068
INDUSTRIAL TOWEL & UNIFORM; U.S. Private, pg. 2068

INDUSTRIAL TOWEL & UNIFORM — CORPORATE AFFILIATIONS

Company Index

INDUSTRIAL TRAINING INTERNATIONAL, INC.—See Interplay Learning Inc.; *U.S. Private*, pg. 2123
INDUSTRIAL TUBE COMPANY LLC—See ITT Inc.; *U.S. Public*, pg. 1178
INDUSTRIAL TUBE & STEEL CORPORATION; *U.S. Private*, pg. 2068
INDUSTRIAL TURNAROUND CORPORATION; *U.S. Private*, pg. 2069
INDUSTRIAL UNION OF DONBASS CORPORATION - ALCHEVSK COKING PLANT—See Industrial Union of Donbass Corporation; *Int'l*, pg. 3673
INDUSTRIAL UNION OF DONBASS CORPORATION; *Int'l*, pg. 3673
INDUSTRIAL - UNIROSS BATTERIES (PTY) LTD.—See Eveready Industries India Ltd; *Int'l*, pg. 2563
INDUSTRIAL VALUE PARTNERS, LLC; *U.S. Private*, pg. 2069
INDUSTRIAL VALVE SALES & SERVICE; *U.S. Private*, pg. 2069
INDUSTRIAL VENTILATION INC.; *U.S. Private*, pg. 2069
INDUSTRIAL VENTILATION, INC.; *U.S. Private*, pg. 2069
INDUSTRIAL VETERINARIA, S.A.—See Espiga Capital Gestion S.G.E.C.R, S.A.; *Int'l*, pg. 2506
INDUSTRIAL VIDEO & CONTROL CO.; *U.S. Private*, pg. 2069
INDUSTRIAL VIDEO CORPORATION; *U.S. Private*, pg. 2069
INDUSTRIAL WELDING SUPPLIES OF HATTIESBURG, INC.—See Tatum Development Corp.; *U.S. Private*, pg. 3936
INDUSTRIAL WELDING SUPPLY INC.; *U.S. Private*, pg. 2069
INDUSTRIAL YORKA DE TEPOTZOTLAN S.A. DE C.V.—See Stellantis N.V.; *Int'l*, pg. 7200
INDUSTRIA MAIMERI S.P.A.—See F.I.L.A. - Fabbrica Italiana Lapis ed Affini S.p.A.; *Int'l*, pg. 2597
INDUSTRIA MOLINERA MONTSERRAT, S.A. DE C.V.—See Bunge Limited; *U.S. Public*, pg. 412
INDUSTRIA ORTOPEDICA OTTO BOCK UNIP. LDA.—See Ottobock Holding GmbH & Co. KG; *Int'l*, pg. 5664
INDUSTRIA QUIMICA DEL ISTMO, S.A. DE C.V. - COATZACOALCOS PLANT—See Cydsa S.A.B. de C.V.; *Int'l*, pg. 1895
INDUSTRIA QUIMICA DEL ISTMO, S.A. DE C.V. - HERMOSILLO PLANT—See Cydsa S.A.B. de C.V.; *Int'l*, pg. 1895
INDUSTRIA QUIMICA DEL ISTMO, S.A. DE C.V.—See Cydsa S.A.B. de C.V.; *Int'l*, pg. 1895
INDUSTRIAS ALEN S.A. DE C.V.; *Int'l*, pg. 3673
INDUSTRIAS ALIADAS S.A.S.—See Grupo Nutresa S.A.; *Int'l*, pg. 3133
INDUSTRIAS ALIMENTARIAS DE NAVARRA S.A.U.—See Portobello Capital Advisors SL; *Int'l*, pg. 5935
INDUSTRIAS ALIMENTICIAS FAGAL S.R.L.—See Nestle S.A.; *Int'l*, pg. 5203
INDUSTRIAS AMAYA TELLERIA, S.A.U.—See Cie Automotive S.A.; *Int'l*, pg. 1604
INDUSTRIAS ARGA, S.A. DE C.V.—See Hillenbrand, Inc.; *U.S. Public*, pg. 1035
INDUSTRIA SARMEI CAMPIA TURZII S.A.—See Invest Nikarom Srl; *Int'l*, pg. 3775
INDUSTRIAS BACHOCO S.A.B. DE C.V.; *Int'l*, pg. 3673
INDUSTRIAS CHILENAS DE ALAMBRE - INCHALAM SA—See NV Bekaert SA; *Int'l*, pg. 5496
INDUSTRIAS CH, S.A.B. DE C.V.; *Int'l*, pg. 3674
INDUSTRIAS CYDSA BAYER, S.A. DE C.V.—See Cydsa S.A.B. de C.V.; *Int'l*, pg. 1895
INDUSTRIAS DE ACEITE S.A.—See Grupo Romero; *Int'l*, pg. 3134
INDUSTRIAS DE CARNES NOBRE S.A.—See ALFA, S.A.B. de C.V.; *Int'l*, pg. 314
INDUSTRIAS DE LINAMAR S.A. DE C.V.—See Linamar Corporation; *Int'l*, pg. 4501
INDUSTRIAS DEL MAIZ C.A.—See Ingredion Incorporated; *U.S. Public*, pg. 1123
INDUSTRIAS DEL MAIZ S.A.-CORN PRODUCTS ANDINA—See Ingredion Incorporated; *U.S. Public*, pg. 1123
INDUSTRIAS DEL TABACO, ALIMENTOS Y BEBIDAS S.A.—See Philip Morris International Inc.; *U.S. Public*, pg. 1685
INDUSTRIAS DEL UBIERNA, S.A.—See NV Bekaert SA; *Int'l*, pg. 5496
INDUSTRIAS DEL UBIERNA S.A.—See NV Bekaert SA; *Int'l*, pg. 5496
INDUSTRIAS ELECTRONICAS PACIFICO, S.A. DE C.V.—See Schneider Electric SE; *Int'l*, pg. 6627
INDUSTRIAS ELECTRO QUIMICAS SA; *Int'l*, pg. 3674
INDUSTRIAS ESTRA SA; *Int'l*, pg. 3674
INDUSTRIAS FORESTALES S.A.—See Empresas CMPC S.A.; *Int'l*, pg. 2390
INDUSTRIAS JOHN CRANE MEXICO S.A. DE C.V.—See Smiths Group plc; *Int'l*, pg. 7010
INDUSTRIAS JOHN DEERE ARGENTINA S.A.—See Deere & Company; *U.S. Public*, pg. 647
INDUSTRIAS JOHN DEERE S.A. DE C.V.—See Deere & Company; *U.S. Public*, pg. 646
INDUSTRIAS LA CONSTANCIA S.A.—See Anheuser-Busch InBev SA/NV; *Int'l*, pg. 464

INDUSTRIAS LAKELAND S.A. DE C.V.—See Lakeland Industries, Inc.; *U.S. Public*, pg. 1288
INDUSTRIAS MARTINREA, S.A DE C.V.—See Martinrea International, Inc.; *Int'l*, pg. 4704
INDUSTRIAS MECANICAS LAGO, S.A.U—See Fluidra SA; *Int'l*, pg. 2714
INDUSTRIAS NIASA, S.A. DE C.V.—See Grupo Lamosa S.A. de C.V.; *Int'l*, pg. 3132
INDUSTRIAS OXFORD DE MERIDA S.A. DE CV—See Oxford Industries, Inc.; *U.S. Public*, pg. 1629
INDUSTRIAS PENOLES, S.A. DE C.V.—See Grupo BAL; *Int'l*, pg. 3121
INDUSTRIAS P. KAY DE MEXICO—See P. Kay Metal Supply Inc.; *U.S. Private*, pg. 3060
INDUSTRIAS QUILMES S.A.—See Kuriyama Holdings Corporation; *Int'l*, pg. 4341
INDUSTRIAS QUIMICAS FALCON DE MEXICO, S.A. DE CV—See Dr. Reddy's Laboratories Limited; *Int'l*, pg. 2195
INDUSTRIAS ROMI S.A.; *Int'l*, pg. 3674
INDUSTRIAS ROTOR PUMP S.A.—See Franklin Electric Co., Inc.; *U.S. Public*, pg. 878
INDUSTRIAS STAHL S.A.—See R. STAHL AG; *Int'l*, pg. 6169
INDUSTRIAS TRATERH, S.A.—See Senior plc; *Int'l*, pg. 6708
INDUSTRIAS TRI-CON DE MEXICO S.A. DE C.V.—See TS Tech Co Ltd; *Int'l*, pg. 7947
INDUSTRIAS ULMA VENEZOLANA C.A.—See Mondragon Corporation; *Int'l*, pg. 5029
INDUSTRIAS UNIDAS, S.A.—See Toyobo Co., Ltd.; *Int'l*, pg. 7860
INDUSTRIAS W DE MEXICO, SA DE C.V.—See CSE Global Ltd.; *Int'l*, pg. 1864
INDUSTRIA TEXTIL PIURA S.A.—See Axxion Asset Management SAC; *Int'l*, pg. 773
INDUSTRIA VENEZOLANA DE GAS INVEGAS, S.C.A.—See Linde plc; *Int'l*, pg. 4508
INDUSTRIA VIDRIERA DE COAHUILA, S. DE R.L. DE C.V.—See Constellation Brands, Inc.; *U.S. Public*, pg. 571
INDUSTRIA Y TECNOLOGIA EN ACEROS S.A.—See Sophia Capital S.A.; *Int'l*, pg. 7108
INDUSTRI BELOS AB—See Indutrade AB; *Int'l*, pg. 3679
INDUSTRI BETON AS; *Int'l*, pg. 3665
INDUSTRIEALPINE BAUTRAGER GMBH—See ELMOS Semiconductor AG; *Int'l*, pg. 2368
INDUSTRIEBANK LIOF N.V.; *Int'l*, pg. 3675
INDUSTRIE CHIMICHE FORESTALI S.P.A.; *Int'l*, pg. 3674
INDUSTRIE-CONTACT AG; *Int'l*, pg. 3675
INDUSTRIE DE NORA S.P.A.; *Int'l*, pg. 3674
INDUSTRIE-ELECTRONIC GMBH & CO. KG; *Int'l*, pg. 3675
INDUSTRIE ELEKTRO HANDELSGESELLSCHAFT—See Sonepar S.A.; *Int'l*, pg. 7092
INDUSTRIEGRUNDSTUCKS-VERWALTUNGSGESELLSCHAFT M.B.H.—See Koninklijke Philips N.V.; *Int'l*, pg. 4268
INDUSTRIEHOF SCHERENBOSTEL HEINRICH RODENBOSTEL GMBH; *Int'l*, pg. 3675
INDUSTRIE-IMMOBILIEN-VERWALTUNG GMBH—See UniCredit S.p.A.; *Int'l*, pg. 8039
INDUSTRIELACK AG—See Resonac Holdings Corporation; *Int'l*, pg. 6298
INDUSTRIELLE BETEILIGUNG CO., LTD.—See Danieli & C. Officine Meccaniche S.p.A.; *Int'l*, pg. 1963
INDUSTRIELLE DE CHAUFFAGE ENTREPRISES SAS—See VINCI S.A.; *Int'l*, pg. 8222
INDUSTRIELLE DE CONTROLE ET D EQUIPEMENT; *Int'l*, pg. 3675
INDUSTRIELLE NALE REEMPLOIS AUTOMOBILES; *Int'l*, pg. 3675
INDUSTRIELLES BAUEN BETREUUNGSGESELLSCHAFT MBH—See STRABAG SE; *Int'l*, pg. 7230
INDUSTRIE MAGAZINE—See Saturday Group Ltd; *Int'l*, pg. 6588
INDUSTRIE MECCANICHE DI BAGNOLO S.R.L.—See Chart Industries, Inc.; *U.S. Public*, pg. 482
INDUSTRIENETZGESELLSCHAFT SCHKOPAU MBH—See Dow Inc.; *U.S. Public*, pg. 683
INDUSTRIEPARK GERSTHOFEN SERVICEGESELLSCHAFT MBH.—See MVV Energie AG; *Int'l*, pg. 5108
INDUSTRIEPARK MUNCHMUNSTER GMBH & CO. KG—See LyondellBasell Industries N.V.; *Int'l*, pg. 4608
INDUSTRIEPARK MUNCHMUNSTER VERWALTUNGSGESELLSCHAFT MBH—See LyondellBasell Industries N.V.; *Int'l*, pg. 4608
INDUSTRIEPARK NIENBURG GMBH—See Eastman Chemical Company; *U.S. Public*, pg. 705
INDUSTRIE PLASTIC ELSASSER GMBH—See Illinois Tool Works Inc.; *U.S. Public*, pg. 1108
INDUSTRIESCHUTZ ASSEKURANZ VERMITTLUNG GMBH—See Siemens Aktiengesellschaft; *Int'l*, pg. 6887
INDUSTRIES QATAR Q.S.C.—See Qatar Petroleum; *Int'l*, pg. 6135
INDUSTRIES S.P.A.—See Moncler S.p.A.; *Int'l*, pg. 5025
INDUSTRIEVERWALTUNGSGESELLSCHAFT CHAM AG—See Cham Group AG; *Int'l*, pg. 1439

INDUSTRIEWATER EERBEEK B.V.—See Mayr-Melnhof Karton AG; *Int'l*, pg. 4745
INDUSTRIE ZIGNAGO SANTA MARGHERITA SPA; *Int'l*, pg. 3674
INDUSTRIFORSIKRING A/S—See Norsk Hydro ASA; *Int'l*, pg. 5435
INDUSTRIJA BRUSNIH ALATA A.D., ADA; *Int'l*, pg. 3675
INDUSTRIJA NAMESTAJA BAJMOK A.D.; *Int'l*, pg. 3675
INDUSTRI-MATEMATIK, LIMITED—See TA Associates, Inc.; *U.S. Private*, pg. 3914
INDUSTRI-MATEMATIK NEDERLAND B.V.—See TA Associates, Inc.; *U.S. Private*, pg. 3914
INDUSTRIOUS GROUP INC.—See ITOCHU Corporation; *Int'l*, pg. 3838
INDUSTRIOUS NATIONAL MANAGEMENT COMPANY LLC; *U.S. Private*, pg. 2069
INDUSTRI TOOLS & EQUIPMENT (PTY.) LTD.—See Invicta Holdings Limited; *Int'l*, pg. 3788
INDUSTRIVARDEN SERVICE AB—See AB Industrivarden; *Int'l*, pg. 41
INDUSTRI VERKTOY AS—See Indutrade AB; *Int'l*, pg. 3679
INDUSTROCHEM D.O.O.—See Omya (Schweiz) AG; *Int'l*, pg. 5570
INDUSTRONIC, INC.—See Industrie-Electronic GmbH & Co. KG; *Int'l*, pg. 3675
INDUSTRONIC INDUSTRIE-ELECTRONIC EQUIPMENT CO. LTD.—See Industrie-Electronic GmbH & Co. KG; *Int'l*, pg. 3675
INDUSTRONICS BERHAD; *Int'l*, pg. 3675
INDUSTRONICS MANUFACTURING SDN. BHD.—See Industronics Berhad; *Int'l*, pg. 3675
INDUSTROPROJEKT A.D.—See Grupa Fortis d.o.o. Banja Luka; *Int'l*, pg. 3116
INDUSTRY CONSULTING GROUP, INC.—See Brown & Brown, Inc.; *U.S. Public*, pg. 401
INDUSTRY DATA EXCHANGE ASSOCIATION, INC.; *U.S. Private*, pg. 2069
INDUSTRY DIVE, LLC—See Falfurrias Capital Partners, LP; *U.S. Private*, pg. 1467
INDUSTRY FUND SERVICES PTY. LIMITED—See Industry Super Holdings Pty. Ltd.; *Int'l*, pg. 3675
INDUSTRY IDS, INC.; *U.S. Private*, pg. 2069
INDUSTRY IDS, INC.—See Industry IDS, Inc.; *U.S. Private*, pg. 2069
INDUSTRY-RAILWAY SUPPLIERS, INC.; *U.S. Private*, pg. 2069
INDUSTRY SERVICES CO INC.—See Osceola Capital Management, LLC; *U.S. Private*, pg. 3047
INDUSTRY SUPER HOLDINGS PTY. LTD.; *Int'l*, pg. 3675
INDUSTRY WEAPON, INC.—See The Jordan Company, L.P.; *U.S. Private*, pg. 4062
INDUSTYL SAS—See Sonepar S.A.; *Int'l*, pg. 7091
INDUSUL INDUSTRIA DE TRANSFORMADORES LTDA.—See Tamura Corporation; *Int'l*, pg. 7451
INDU-TOOLS B.V.—See United Rentals, Inc.; *U.S. Public*, pg. 2235
INDU-TOOLS N.V.—See United Rentals, Inc.; *U.S. Public*, pg. 2235
INDU-TOOLS SAS—See United Rentals, Inc.; *U.S. Public*, pg. 2235
INDUTRADE AB; *Int'l*, pg. 3676
INDUTRADE BENELUX B.V.—See Indutrade AB; *Int'l*, pg. 3679
INDUTRADE OY—See Indutrade AB; *Int'l*, pg. 3679
INDVA SVERIGE AB—See AVK Holding A/S; *Int'l*, pg. 748
INDVR BRANDS INC.; *Int'l*, pg. 3682
INDVR BRANDS, INC.; *U.S. Public*, pg. 1117
IND-X ADVISORS LIMITED—See Haitong Securities Co., Ltd.; *Int'l*, pg. 3218
INDY CONNECTION ELECTRICAL CONTRACTORS, INC.; *U.S. Private*, pg. 2069
INDYGOTECH MINERALS SA; *Int'l*, pg. 3682
INDYKPOL S.A.—See LDC SA; *Int'l*, pg. 4431
INDYNE INC.; *U.S. Private*, pg. 2069
IN DYNE INC.; *U.S. Private*, pg. 2052
INDY POWER GRID LLC—See Mitsubishi Heavy Industries, Ltd.; *Int'l*, pg. 4953
INDY ROHR MOTORS INC.; *U.S. Private*, pg. 2069
INDY TIRE CENTERS, INC.; *U.S. Private*, pg. 2069
INDY WALLS & CEILINGS INCORPORATED; *U.S. Private*, pg. 2069
INEC ENGINEERING CO. LTD.—See Energoprojekt Holding a.d.; *Int'l*, pg. 2422
INEC N.V.—See TKH Group N.V.; *Int'l*, pg. 7764
I-NE CO., LTD.; *Int'l*, pg. 3563
INEDA SYSTEMS INC.—See Intel Corporation; *U.S. Public*, pg. 1138
INEDA SYSTEMS PVT. LTD.—See Intel Corporation; *U.S. Public*, pg. 1138
INEDIT—See Agence France-Presse; *Int'l*, pg. 205
INEEDHITS.COM PTY LTD.; *Int'l*, pg. 3682
INEFI INCORPORATION—See Flytech Technology Co., Ltd.; *Int'l*, pg. 2716
INE, INC.; *U.S. Private*, pg. 2069
INELECTRO SA—See BKW AG; *Int'l*, pg. 1055
INEL INC.—See Thermo Fisher Scientific Inc.; *U.S. Public*, pg. 2148

INEL SAS—See Thermo Fisher Scientific Inc.; *U.S. Public*, pg. 2148
INENCO DIRECT—See Intermediate Capital Group plc; *Int'l*, pg. 3742
INENCO DIRECT—See Vitruvian Partners LLP; *Int'l*, pg. 8263
INENCO GROUP LIMITED—See Intermediate Capital Group plc; *Int'l*, pg. 3742
INENCO GROUP LIMITED—See Vitruvian Partners LLP; *Int'l*, pg. 8263
INENCO GROUP PTY LTD.—See Genuine Parts Company; *U.S. Public*, pg. 933
IN ENTERTAINMENT INDIA LTD.—See Hinduja Group Ltd.; *Int'l*, pg. 3399
INEO DEFENSE—See ENGIE SA; *Int'l*, pg. 2430
INEO MIDI PYRENEES LANGUEDOC ROUSSILLON; *Int'l*, pg. 3682
INEOQUEST TECHNOLOGIES DEUTSCHLAND GMBH—See Genstar Capital, LLC; *U.S. Private*, pg. 1679
INEOQUEST TECHNOLOGIES, INC.—See Genstar Capital, LLC; *U.S. Private*, pg. 1679
INEOQUEST TECHNOLOGIES LTD.—See Genstar Capital, LLC; *U.S. Private*, pg. 1679
INEOS ABS CORPORATION—See INEOS Limited; *Int'l*, pg. 3682
INEOS AG—See INEOS Limited; *Int'l*, pg. 3682
INEOS AMERICAS LLC—See INEOS Limited; *Int'l*, pg. 3682
INEOS BAMBLE AS—See INEOS Limited; *Int'l*, pg. 3682
INEOS BIO USA, LLC—See INEOS Limited; *Int'l*, pg. 3682
INEOS CALABRIAN—See One Rock Capital Partners, LLC; *U.S. Private*, pg. 3023
INEOS CHLOR AMERICAS INC.—See One Rock Capital Partners, LLC; *U.S. Private*, pg. 3023
INEOS CHLOR ATLANTIK GMBH—See One Rock Capital Partners, LLC; *U.S. Private*, pg. 3022
INEOS CHLOR QUIMICA, SA—See One Rock Capital Partners, LLC; *U.S. Private*, pg. 3023
INEOS CHLOR SALES INTERNATIONAL LIMITED—See One Rock Capital Partners, LLC; *U.S. Private*, pg. 3023
INEOS CHLORVINYLS BELGIUM NV—See One Rock Capital Partners, LLC; *U.S. Private*, pg. 3022
INEOS CHLORVINYLS LIMITED—See INEOS Limited; *Int'l*, pg. 3682
INEOS COLOGNE GMBH—See INEOS Limited; *Int'l*, pg. 3682
INEOS COMPOUNDS FRANCE SAS—See One Rock Capital Partners, LLC; *U.S. Private*, pg. 3022
INEOS COMPOUNDS ITALIA SRL—See One Rock Capital Partners, LLC; *U.S. Private*, pg. 3022
INEOS COMPOUNDS SWEDEN AB—See One Rock Capital Partners, LLC; *U.S. Private*, pg. 3022
INEOS COMPOUNDS SWITZERLAND AG—See One Rock Capital Partners, LLC; *U.S. Private*, pg. 3023
INEOS COMPOUNDS UK LTD.—See One Rock Capital Partners, LLC; *U.S. Private*, pg. 3023
INEOS ENTERPRISES FRANCE SAS—See One Rock Capital Partners, LLC; *U.S. Private*, pg. 3023
INEOS ENTERPRISES GROUP LIMITED—See One Rock Capital Partners, LLC; *U.S. Private*, pg. 3023
INEOS FELUY SPRL—See INEOS Limited; *Int'l*, pg. 3682
INEOS FILMS & COMPOUNDS—See One Rock Capital Partners, LLC; *U.S. Private*, pg. 3022
INEOS GROUP AG—See INEOS Limited; *Int'l*, pg. 3682
INEOS GROUP LIMITED—See INEOS Limited; *Int'l*, pg. 3682
INEOS ITALIA SRL—See One Rock Capital Partners, LLC; *U.S. Private*, pg. 3023
INEOS LIMITED; *Int'l*, pg. 3682
INEOS MANUFACTURING BELGIUM NV—See INEOS Limited; *Int'l*, pg. 3682
INEOS MANUFACTURING FRANCE SAS—See INEOS Limited; *Int'l*, pg. 3682
INEOS MANUFACTURING ITALIA SPA—See INEOS Limited; *Int'l*, pg. 3682
INEOS MELAMINES GMBH—See One Rock Capital Partners, LLC; *U.S. Private*, pg. 3022
INEOS NEWTON AYCLIFFE LIMITED—See One Rock Capital Partners, LLC; *U.S. Private*, pg. 3023
INEOS NITRILES - GREEN LAKE SITE—See INEOS Limited; *Int'l*, pg. 3683
INEOS NITRILES—See INEOS Limited; *Int'l*, pg. 3682
INEOS NITRILES—See INEOS Limited; *Int'l*, pg. 3682
INEOS NORGE AS—See One Rock Capital Partners, LLC; *U.S. Private*, pg. 3023
INEOS NV—See INEOS Limited; *Int'l*, pg. 3682
INEOS OLEFINS & POLYMERS USA—See INEOS Limited; *Int'l*, pg. 3683
INEOS OXIDE LTD.—See INEOS Limited; *Int'l*, pg. 3683
INEOS PARAFORM GMBH & CO. KG—See One Rock Capital Partners, LLC; *U.S. Private*, pg. 3022
INEOS PHENOL BELGIUM N.V.—See INEOS Limited; *Int'l*, pg. 3683
INEOS PHENOL GMBH & CO. KG—See INEOS Limited; *Int'l*, pg. 3683
INEOS PHENOL—See INEOS Limited; *Int'l*, pg. 3683

INEOS SOLVENTS GERMANY GMBH—See One Rock Capital Partners, LLC; *U.S. Private*, pg. 3023
INEOS STYRENICS NETHERLANDS B.V.—See INEOS Limited; *Int'l*, pg. 3683
INEOS STYRENICS RIBECOURT SAS—See INEOS Limited; *Int'l*, pg. 3683
INEOS STYRENICS WINGLES SAS—See INEOS Limited; *Int'l*, pg. 3683
INEOS STYROLUTION INDIA LIMITED—See INEOS Limited; *Int'l*, pg. 3683
INEOS VINYLS BELGIUM SA/NV—See INEOS Limited; *Int'l*, pg. 3683
INEO USA, INC.—See Xcelera Inc.; *Int'l*, pg. 8520
INEPAR S.A INDUSTRIA E CONSTRUCOES; *Int'l*, pg. 3683
INEPRO B.V.—See Nayax Ltd.; *Int'l*, pg. 5178
INERCO TRADE S.A.—See Kernel Holding S.A.; *Int'l*, pg. 4137
INERGETICS, INC.; *U.S. Private*, pg. 2069
INERGEX INC.; *U.S. Private*, pg. 2069
INERGI LP—See Capgemini SE; *Int'l*, pg. 1306
INERGIZE DIGITAL MEDIA—See Nexstar Media Group, Inc.; *U.S. Public*, pg. 1522
INERGY AUTOMOTIVE SYSTEMS ARGENTINA S.A.—See Burelle S.A.; *Int'l*, pg. 1222
INERGY AUTOMOTIVE SYSTEMS BELGIUM NV—See Burelle S.A.; *Int'l*, pg. 1222
INERGY AUTOMOTIVE SYSTEMS (BELGIUM) N.V.—See Burelle S.A.; *Int'l*, pg. 1222
INERGY AUTOMOTIVE SYSTEMS FRANCE—See Burelle S.A.; *Int'l*, pg. 1222
INERGY AUTOMOTIVE SYSTEMS GERMANY GMBH—See Burelle S.A.; *Int'l*, pg. 1222
INERGY AUTOMOTIVE SYSTEMS GERMANY GMBH—See Burelle S.A.; *Int'l*, pg. 1222
INERGY AUTOMOTIVE SYSTEMS GERMANY GMBH—See Burelle S.A.; *Int'l*, pg. 1222
INERGY AUTOMOTIVE SYSTEMS INC.—See Burelle S.A.; *Int'l*, pg. 1222
INERGY AUTOMOTIVE SYSTEMS MEXICO S.A. DE C.V.—See Burelle S.A.; *Int'l*, pg. 1222
INERGY AUTOMOTIVE SYSTEMS S.A.—See Burelle S.A.; *Int'l*, pg. 1222
INERGY AUTOMOTIVE SYSTEMS U.K. LTD.—See Burelle S A ; *Int'l*, pg. 1222
INERGY GAS MARKETING, LLC—See Crestwood Equity Partners LP; *U.S. Public*, pg. 594
INERTAM SAS—See Europlasma SA; *Int'l*, pg. 2557
INERTEC—See VINCI S.A.; *Int'l*, pg. 8234
INERTIA DYNAMICS, INC.—See Matrix International Ltd.; *U.S. Private*, pg. 2612
INERTIA ENGINEERING & MACHINE WORKS, INC.—See Centerbridge Partners, L.P.; *U.S. Private*, pg. 815
INERTIAL AEROSPACE SERVICES—See HEICO Corporation; *U.S. Public*, pg. 1020
INERTIA STEEL LIMITED; *Int'l*, pg. 3683
INESA EUROPA KFT.—See Shanghai Feilo Acoustics Co., Ltd.; *Int'l*, pg. 6766
INESA INTELLIGENT TECH INC.; *Int'l*, pg. 3683
INES CORPORATION; *Int'l*, pg. 3683
INEST, INC.; *Int'l*, pg. 3683
INET AIRPORT SYSTEMS, INC.—See Cavotec SA; *Int'l*, pg. 1363
I-NET CORPORATION; *Int'l*, pg. 3563
I-NET DATA SERVICE CORP.—See I-Net Corporation; *Int'l*, pg. 3563
INE TECHNOLOGIES SDN BHD—See Al Jaber Group; *Int'l*, pg. 280
INETEST MALAYSIA SDN. BHD.—See Ellipsiz Ltd.; *Int'l*, pg. 2366
INETEST (VIETNAM) CO. LTD.—See ViTrox Corporation Berhad; *Int'l*, pg. 8263
INETICO, INC.; *U.S. Private*, pg. 2070
I NET RELY CORPORATION—See LAC Co., Ltd.; *Int'l*, pg. 4391
INET SOLUTIONS GROUP, INC.—See Myriad Mobile LLC; *U.S. Private*, pg. 2825
INETUM SA—See Mannai Corporation QPSC; *Int'l*, pg. 4674
INETVIDEO.COM; *Int'l*, pg. 3683
INETVIDEO.COM—See iNetVideo.com; *Int'l*, pg. 3683
INETXPERTS, CORP.—See TruBridge, Inc.; *U.S. Public*, pg. 2198
INEVIDENCE LIMITED—See Providence Equity Partners L.L.C.; *U.S. Private*, pg. 3291
INEWA SRL—See CEZ, a.s.; *Int'l*, pg. 1428
I-NEW UNIFIED MOBILE SOLUTIONS AG—See cyan AG; *Int'l*, pg. 1891
INEX BAKAR AD; *Int'l*, pg. 3683
INEX BUDUCNOST A.D.; *Int'l*, pg. 3684
INEX CORPORATION INC.; *U.S. Private*, pg. 2070
INEX CORP.; *U.S. Private*, pg. 2070
INEX DIVCIBARE A.D.; *Int'l*, pg. 3684
INEX DRIM AD; *Int'l*, pg. 3684
INEX LORIS A.D.; *Int'l*, pg. 3684
INEX PARTNERS OY—See Suomen Osuuskauppojen Keskuskunta; *Int'l*, pg. 7333
INEX RADULASKA A.D.; *Int'l*, pg. 3684
INEX-SOLUTIONS GMBH—See Gesco AG; *Int'l*, pg. 2945

I NEXT GE INC.—See Rhythm Co., Ltd.; *Int'l*, pg. 6327
I-NEXUS (AMERICA) INC.—See i-nexus Global plc; *Int'l*, pg. 3563
I-NEXUS GLOBAL PLC; *Int'l*, pg. 3563
INEX-UZOR A.D.; *Int'l*, pg. 3684
INFABRA INDUSTRIA FARMACEUTICA LTD.—See Strides Pharma Science Limited; *Int'l*, pg. 7240
INFACARE PHARMACEUTICAL CORPORATION—See Mallinckrodt Public Limited Company; *Int'l*, pg. 4663
INFAC CABLE—See INFAC Corporation; *Int'l*, pg. 3684
INFAC CORPORATION - CHEONAN PLANT—See INFAC Corporation; *Int'l*, pg. 3684
INFAC CORPORATION; *Int'l*, pg. 3684
INFAC ELECS CO., LTD.—See INFAC Corporation; *Int'l*, pg. 3684
INFAC HORN SYSTEMS CO., LTD.—See INFAC Corporation; *Int'l*, pg. 3684
INFAC INDIA PVT LTD.—See INFAC Corporation; *Int'l*, pg. 3684
INFAC NORTH AMERICA INC.—See INFAC Corporation; *Int'l*, pg. 3684
INFACON GMBH—See Zech Group SE; *Int'l*, pg. 8629
INFAI CH GMBH—See INFAI GmbH; *Int'l*, pg. 3684
INFAI FRANCE SARL—See INFAI GmbH; *Int'l*, pg. 3684
INFAI GMBH; *Int'l*, pg. 3684
INFAIMON DO BRASIL VISAO ARTIFICIAL LTDA—See MiddleGround Management, LP; *U.S. Private*, pg. 2712
INFAIMON MEXICO S.A.DE C.V.—See MiddleGround Management, LP; *U.S. Private*, pg. 2712
INFAIMON S.L.U.—See MiddleGround Management, LP; *U.S. Private*, pg. 2712
INFAIMON UNIPESSOAL, LDA.—See MiddleGround Management, LP; *U.S. Private*, pg. 2712
INFAITH COMMUNITY FOUNDATION; *U.S. Private*, pg. 2070
INFAITH; *U.S. Private*, pg. 2070
INFAI TR GMBH—See INFAI GmbH; *Int'l*, pg. 3684
INFAI UK LTD—See INFAI GmbH; *Int'l*, pg. 3684
INFANT BACTERIAL THERAPEUTICS AB; *Int'l*, pg. 3684
INFANTE ASSOCIATES INC.; *U.S. Private*, pg. 2070
INFANTINE INSURANCE, INC.—See Cross Financial Corporation; *U.S. Private*, pg. 1105
INFANTINO, LLC—See Aterian Investment Management, L.P.; *U.S. Private*, pg. 367
INFARCO SA; *Int'l*, pg. 3684
INFASCO DIVISION—See The Heico Companies, L.L.C.; *U.S. Private*, pg. 4050
INFAS HOLDING AG; *Int'l*, pg. 3684
INFAST BROKERAGE LIMITED—See FDG Electric Vehicles Limited; *Int'l*, pg. 2629
INFASTECH (AUSTRALIA) PTY LIMITED—See Stanley Black & Decker, Inc.; *U.S. Public*, pg. 1934
INFASTECH CAMCAR MALAYSIA SBD. BHD—See Stanley Black & Decker, Inc.; *U.S. Public*, pg. 1932
INFASTECH (CHINA) LIMITED—See Stanley Black & Decker, Inc.; *U.S. Public*, pg. 1934
INFASTECH DECORAH, LLC—See Stanley Black & Decker, Inc.; *U.S. Public*, pg. 1932
INFASTECH FASTENING SYSTEMS (WUXI) LIMITED—See Stanley Black & Decker, Inc.; *U.S. Public*, pg. 1932
INFASTECH (GUANGZHOU) LIMITED—See Stanley Black & Decker, Inc.; *U.S. Public*, pg. 1932
INFASTECH KABUSHIKI KAISHA—See Stanley Black & Decker, Inc.; *U.S. Public*, pg. 1932
INFASTECH (KOREA) LIMITED—See Stanley Black & Decker, Inc.; *U.S. Public*, pg. 1932
INFASTECH (MALAYSIA) SDN BHD—See Stanley Black & Decker, Inc.; *U.S. Public*, pg. 1932
INFASTECH (SHENZHEN) LIMITED—See Stanley Black & Decker, Inc.; *U.S. Public*, pg. 1932
INFASTECH (SINGAPORE) PTE LTD—See Stanley Black & Decker, Inc.; *U.S. Public*, pg. 1934
INFASTECH THAI COMPANY LIMITED—See Stanley Black & Decker, Inc.; *U.S. Public*, pg. 1933
INFASTEHC (SINGAPORE) PTE. LTD.—See Stanley Black & Decker, Inc.; *U.S. Public*, pg. 1933
INFECTIOUS DISEASES SOCIETY OF AMERICA; *U.S. Private*, pg. 2070
INFECTIOUS MEDIA LTD.; *Int'l*, pg. 3684
INFEENY S.A.S.—See Econocom Group SA; *Int'l*, pg. 2298
INFERENCE TECHNOLOGIES GROUP, INC.—See Five9, Inc.; *U.S. Public*, pg. 852
INFERNO LLC; *U.S. Private*, pg. 2070
INFIANA GERMANY GMBH & CO. KG—See Deutsche Beteiligungs AG; *Int'l*, pg. 2063
INFIANA (THAILAND) LIMITED—See Deutsche Beteiligungs AG; *Int'l*, pg. 2063
INFIANA USA, INC.—See Deutsche Beteiligungs AG; *Int'l*, pg. 2063
INFIBEAM AVENUES LIMITED; *Int'l*, pg. 3684
INFICON AALAND AB.—See INFICON Holding AG; *Int'l*, pg. 3684
INFICON EDC, INC.—See INFICON Holding AG; *Int'l*, pg. 3684
INFICON HOLDING AG; *Int'l*, pg. 3684
INFICON INC.—See INFICON Holding AG; *Int'l*, pg. 3684

INFICON HOLDING AG CORPORATE AFFILIATIONS
Company Index

INFICON INSTRUTECH LLC—See INFICON Holding AG; *Int'l*, pg. 3685
INFICON PTE. LTD.—See INFICON Holding AG; *Int'l*, pg. 3685
INFICON S.A.R.L.—See INFICON Holding AG; *Int'l*, pg. 3685
INFIELD CO., LTD.—See Tokyu Fudosan Holdings Corporation; *Int'l*, pg. 7798
INFIELD MINERALS CORP.; *Int'l*, pg. 3685
INFIELD SAFETY GMBH—See EssilorLuxottica SA; *Int'l*, pg. 2515
INFIELD SAFETY UK, LTD.—See EssilorLuxottica SA; *Int'l*, pg. 2515
INFIFRESH FOODS PVT. LTD.; *Int'l*, pg. 3685
INFI GAMMA HOLDING SAL—See Bank Audi sal; *Int'l*, pg. 837
INFIGEN ENERGY LIMITED; *Int'l*, pg. 3685
INFIGEN ENERGY RE LIMITED—See Infigen Energy Limited; *Int'l*, pg. 3685
INFILL CO., LTD.—See Mitani Sangyo Co., Ltd.; *Int'l*, pg. 4924
INFILTRATOR SYSTEMS INC.—See The Graham Group, Inc.; *U.S. Private*, pg. 4037
INFILTRATOR WATER TECHNOLOGIES, LLC—See Advanced Drainage Systems, Inc.; *U.S. Public*, pg. 46
INFIMER LTD.; *Int'l*, pg. 3685
INFINATA, INC.—See GlobalData Plc; *Int'l*, pg. 3003
INFINCOM, INC.; *U.S. Private*, pg. 2070
INFINEDI PARTNERS LP; *U.S. Private*, pg. 2070
INFINEER, LTD.—See Chazak Value Corp.; *U.S. Private*, pg. 868
INFINEON INTEGRATED CIRCUIT (BEIJING) CO., LTD.—See Infineon Technologies AG; *Int'l*, pg. 3686
INFINEON TECHNOLOGIES (ADVANCED LOGIC) SDN. BHD.—See Infineon Technologies AG; *Int'l*, pg. 3686
INFINEON TECHNOLOGIES AG - DUISBURG—See Infineon Technologies AG; *Int'l*, pg. 3686
INFINEON TECHNOLOGIES AG; *Int'l*, pg. 3685
INFINEON TECHNOLOGIES AG - WARSTEIN—See Infineon Technologies AG; *Int'l*, pg. 3686
INFINEON TECHNOLOGIES AMERICAS CORP.—See Infineon Technologies AG; *Int'l*, pg. 3686
INFINEON TECHNOLOGIES ASIA PACIFIC PTE. LTD.—See Infineon Technologies AG; *Int'l*, pg. 3686
INFINEON TECHNOLOGIES AUSTRALIA PTY. LTD.—See Infineon Technologies AG; *Int'l*, pg. 3686
INFINEON TECHNOLOGIES AUSTRIA AG—See Infineon Technologies AG; *Int'l*, pg. 3686
INFINEON TECHNOLOGIES AUSTRIA PENSIONSKASSE AG—See Infineon Technologies AG; *Int'l*, pg. 3686
INFINEON TECHNOLOGIES BATAM P.T.—See Infineon Technologies AG; *Int'l*, pg. 3686
INFINEON TECHNOLOGIES BIPOLAR GMBH & CO. KG—See Infineon Technologies AG; *Int'l*, pg. 3686
INFINEON TECHNOLOGIES BIPOLAR VERWALTUNGS GMBH—See Infineon Technologies AG; *Int'l*, pg. 3686
INFINEON TECHNOLOGIES CEGLED KFT.—See Infineon Technologies AG; *Int'l*, pg. 3686
INFINEON TECHNOLOGIES CENTER OF COMPETENCE (SHANGHAI) CO., LTD.—See Infineon Technologies AG; *Int'l*, pg. 3686
INFINEON TECHNOLOGIES CHINA CO., LTD.—See Infineon Technologies AG; *Int'l*, pg. 3686
INFINEON TECHNOLOGIES DRESDEN GMBH & CO. KG—See Infineon Technologies AG; *Int'l*, pg. 3686
INFINEON TECHNOLOGIES FABRICO DE SEMICONDUTORES (PORTUGAL) S.A.—See Infineon Technologies AG; *Int'l*, pg. 3686
INFINEON TECHNOLOGIES FRANCE S.A.S.—See Infineon Technologies AG; *Int'l*, pg. 3686
INFINEON TECHNOLOGIES HOLDING B.V—See Infineon Technologies AG; *Int'l*, pg. 3686
INFINEON TECHNOLOGIES HONG KONG LTD.—See Infineon Technologies AG; *Int'l*, pg. 3686
INFINEON TECHNOLOGIES IBERIA S.L.U.—See Infineon Technologies AG; *Int'l*, pg. 3686
INFINEON TECHNOLOGIES INDIA PVT. LTD.—See Infineon Technologies AG; *Int'l*, pg. 3686
INFINEON TECHNOLOGIES INDUSTRIAL POWER, INC.—See Infineon Technologies AG; *Int'l*, pg. 3686
INFINEON TECHNOLOGIES (INTEGRATED CIRCUIT) SDN. BHD.—See Infineon Technologies AG; *Int'l*, pg. 3686
INFINEON TECHNOLOGIES INVESTMENT B.V.—See Infineon Technologies AG; *Int'l*, pg. 3686
INFINEON TECHNOLOGIES IRELAND LTD.—See Infineon Technologies AG; *Int'l*, pg. 3686
INFINEON TECHNOLOGIES ITALIA S.R.L—See Infineon Technologies AG; *Int'l*, pg. 3686
INFINEON TECHNOLOGIES IT-SERVICES GMBH—See Infineon Technologies AG; *Int'l*, pg. 3686
INFINEON TECHNOLOGIES JAPAN K.K.—See Infineon Technologies AG; *Int'l*, pg. 3686
INFINEON TECHNOLOGIES KOREA CO., LTD.—See Infineon Technologies AG; *Int'l*, pg. 3686
INFINEON TECHNOLOGIES (KULIM) SDN. BHD.—See Infineon Technologies AG; *Int'l*, pg. 3686
INFINEON TECHNOLOGIES (MALAYSIA) SDN BHD—See Infineon Technologies AG; *Int'l*, pg. 3686
INFINEON TECHNOLOGIES NORDIC AB—See Infineon Technologies AG; *Int'l*, pg. 3686
INFINEON TECHNOLOGIES NORDIC A/S—See Infineon Technologies AG; *Int'l*, pg. 3686
INFINEON TECHNOLOGIES NORDIC OY—See Infineon Technologies AG; *Int'l*, pg. 3686
INFINEON TECHNOLOGIES ROMANIA & CO. SOCIETATE IN COMANDITA—See Infineon Technologies AG; *Int'l*, pg. 3686
INFINEON TECHNOLOGIES RUS LLC—See Infineon Technologies AG; *Int'l*, pg. 3686
INFINEON TECHNOLOGIES SC 300 GMBH & CO. KG—See Infineon Technologies AG; *Int'l*, pg. 3686
INFINEON TECHNOLOGIES SOUTH AMERICA LTDA.—See Infineon Technologies AG; *Int'l*, pg. 3687
INFINEON TECHNOLOGIES SWEDEN AB—See Infineon Technologies AG; *Int'l*, pg. 3687
INFINEON TECHNOLOGIES TAIWAN COMPANY LTD.—See Infineon Technologies AG; *Int'l*, pg. 3687
INFINEON TECHNOLOGIES UK LTD.—See Infineon Technologies AG; *Int'l*, pg. 3687
INFINEON TECHNOLOGIES (WUXI) CO., LTD.—See Infineon Technologies AG; *Int'l*, pg. 3686
INFINERA ASIA LIMITED—See Infinera Corporation; *U.S. Public*, pg. 1117
INFINERA CORPORATION; *U.S. Public*, pg. 1117
INFINERA INDIA PVT. LTD—See Infinera Corporation; *U.S. Public*, pg. 1117
INFINERA JAPAN K.K.—See Infinera Corporation; *U.S. Public*, pg. 1117
INFINERA LIMITED—See Infinera Corporation; *U.S. Public*, pg. 1117
INFINEUM INTERNATIONAL LTD.—See Exxon Mobil Corporation; *U.S. Public*, pg. 814
INFINEUM INTERNATIONAL LTD.—See Shell plc; *Int'l*, pg. 6797
INFINEX FINANCIAL HOLDINGS, INC.; *U.S. Private*, pg. 2070
INFINEX INVESTMENTS, INC.—See Infinex Financial Holdings, Inc.; *U.S. Private*, pg. 2070
INFINIDAT INC.; *U.S. Private*, pg. 2070
INFINIDENT SERVICES GMBH—See DENTSPLY SIRONA Inc.; *U.S. Public*, pg. 655
INFINIGATE DANMARK A/S—See H.I.G. Capital, LLC; *U.S. Private*, pg. 1833
INFINIGATE DEUTSCHLAND GMBH—See H.I.G. Capital, LLC; *U.S. Private*, pg. 1833
INFINIGATE FRANCE SAS—See H.I.G. Capital, LLC; *U.S. Private*, pg. 1833
INFINIGATE HOLDING AG—See H.I.G. Capital, LLC; *U.S. Private*, pg. 1833
INFINIGATE NORGE AS—See H.I.G. Capital, LLC; *U.S. Private*, pg. 1833
INFINIGATE OSTERREICH GMBH—See H.I.G. Capital, LLC; *U.S. Private*, pg. 1833
INFINIGATE SVERIGE AB—See H.I.G. Capital, LLC; *U.S. Private*, pg. 1833
INFINIGATE UK LTD.—See H.I.G. Capital, LLC; *U.S. Private*, pg. 1833
INFINIGY ENGINEERING; *U.S. Private*, pg. 2070
INFINIS LIMITED—See 3i Group plc; *Int'l*, pg. 8
INFINISOURCE; *U.S. Private*, pg. 2070
INFINITAS LEARNING HOLDING B.V.—See Bridgepoint Group Plc; *Int'l*, pg. 1154
INFINITAS LEARNING NETHERLANDS B.V.—See SHV Holdings N.V.; *Int'l*, pg. 6871
INFINIT CODELAB SP. Z O.O.—See SPARTA AG; *Int'l*, pg. 7127
INFINITE ACQUISITION CORP.; *U.S. Public*, pg. 1117
INFINITE BLUE PLATFORM LLC; *U.S. Private*, pg. 2070
INFINITEC CO., LTD—See Restar Holdings Corporation; *Int'l*, pg. 6303
INFINITE COMPUTER SOLUTIONS INC.—See Infinite Computer Solutions (India) Ltd.; *Int'l*, pg. 3687
INFINITE COMPUTER SOLUTIONS (INDIA) LTD.; *Int'l*, pg. 3687
INFINITE COMPUTER SOLUTIONS LTD—See Infinite Computer Solutions (India) Ltd.; *Int'l*, pg. 3687
INFINITE COMPUTER SOLUTIONS PTE. LTD.—See Infinite Computer Solutions (India) Ltd.; *Int'l*, pg. 3687
INFINITE CONFERENCING, INC.—See Onstream Media Corporation; *U.S. Private*, pg. 3028
INFINITE CONSULTING CO., LTD.—See SOLXYZ Co., Ltd.; *Int'l*, pg. 7083
INFINITE DATA SYSTEMS PVT. LTD.—See Infinite Computer Solutions (India) Ltd.; *Int'l*, pg. 3687
INFINITE ENERGY INC.; *U.S. Private*, pg. 2071
INFINITE FINANCIAL SOLUTIONS LIMITED—See Shanghai Commercial Bank Limited; *Int'l*, pg. 6763
INFINITE GRAPHICS INCORPORATED; *U.S. Public*, pg. 1117
INFINITE GREEN CO., LTD.—See Premier Marketing Public Company Limited; *Int'l*, pg. 5960
INFINITE GROUP, INC.; *U.S. Public*, pg. 1117
INFINITE INFOSOFT SERVICES PVT. LTD.—See Infinite Computer Solutions (India) Ltd.; *Int'l*, pg. 3687
INFINITE LEAP, INC.—See Halma plc; *Int'l*, pg. 3232
INFINITE MATERIAL SOLUTIONS, LLC—See Nagase & Co., Ltd.; *Int'l*, pg. 5126
INFINITE NETWORKS CORPORATION; *U.S. Private*, pg. 2071
INFINITE POOL FINISHES, LLC; *U.S. Private*, pg. 2071
INFINITE QL SDN. BHD.—See AWC Berhad; *Int'l*, pg. 752
INFINITE REALTY; *U.S. Private*, pg. 2071
INFINITE RF HOLDINGS, INC.—See Genstar Capital, LLC; *U.S. Private*, pg. 1677
INFINITE SOFTWARE SOLUTIONS, INC.—See Fortive Corporation; *U.S. Public*, pg. 871
INFINITE SP.Z.O.O—See DialCom24 Sp. z o.o.; *Int'l*, pg. 2104
INFINITE TECHNOLOGY GROUP LTD.; *U.S. Private*, pg. 2071
INFINITE VELOCITY AUTOMOTIVE, INC.—See General Motors Company; *U.S. Public*, pg. 926
INFINITI HR, LLC.; *U.S. Private*, pg. 2071
INFINITII AI—See Carl Data Solutions, Inc.; *Int'l*, pg. 1332
INFINITI NORTH SHORE; *U.S. Private*, pg. 2071
INFINITI OF ARDMORE, INC.; *U.S. Private*, pg. 2071
INFINITI OF BLOOMINGTON INC.—See Luther Holding Company; *U.S. Private*, pg. 2517
INFINITI OF COCONUT CREEK INC.; *U.S. Private*, pg. 2071
INFINITI OF HONOLULU; *U.S. Private*, pg. 2071
INFINITI OF MELBOURNE—See Kelly Automotive Group; *U.S. Private*, pg. 2276
INFINITI OF MEMPHIS, INC.—See Gossett Motor Cars Inc.; *U.S. Private*, pg. 1744
INFINITI OF NORWOOD; *U.S. Private*, pg. 2071
INFINITI ON CAMELBACK; *U.S. Private*, pg. 2071
INFINITI RETAIL LIMITED—See Tata Sons Limited; *Int'l*, pg. 7468
INFINITI SOLUTIONS LTD.; *Int'l*, pg. 3687
INFINITI SOLUTIONS USA—See Infiniti Solutions Ltd.; *Int'l*, pg. 3687
INFINITI SOUTH BAY—See AutoNation, Inc.; *U.S. Public*, pg. 235
INFINITI SYSTEMS GROUP, INC.; *U.S. Private*, pg. 2071
INFINITI TUSTIN—See AutoNation, Inc.; *U.S. Public*, pg. 235
INFINITT BRASIL IMPORTADORA; *Int'l*, pg. 3687
INFINITT CHINA—See INFINITT Healthcare Co., Ltd.; *Int'l*, pg. 3687
INFINITT EUROPE GMBH—See INFINITT Healthcare Co., Ltd.; *Int'l*, pg. 3687
INFINITT HEALTHCARE CO., LTD.; *Int'l*, pg. 3687
INFINITT JAPAN CO., LTD.—See INFINITT Healthcare Co., Ltd.; *Int'l*, pg. 3687
INFINITT MEA DMCC; *Int'l*, pg. 3687
INFINITT NORTH AMERICA INC.—See INFINITT Healthcare Co., Ltd.; *Int'l*, pg. 3687
INFINITT SE ASIA SDN BHD; *Int'l*, pg. 3687
INFINITT UK LTD.; *Int'l*, pg. 3687
INFINITUM COPPER CORP.; *Int'l*, pg. 3687
INFINITUM ELECTRIC, INC.; *U.S. Private*, pg. 2071
INFINITY ASSOCIATES LLC; *U.S. Private*, pg. 2071
INFINITY AUTO INSURANCE COMPANY—See Kemper Corporation; *U.S. Public*, pg. 1220
INFINITY BANK; *U.S. Public*, pg. 1117
INFINITY BIO-ENERGY LTD.; *Int'l*, pg. 3687
INFINITY BULK LOGISTICS SDN. BHD.—See Infinity Logistics & Transport Ventures Limited; *Int'l*, pg. 3688
INFINITY CASUALTY INSURANCE COMPANY—See Kemper Corporation; *U.S. Public*, pg. 1220
INFINITY CLASSICS INTERNATIONAL; *U.S. Private*, pg. 2071
INFINITY.COM FINANCIAL SECURITIES LTD—See Pioneer Investcorp Ltd; *Int'l*, pg. 5872
INFINITY COMMUNICATION CO., LTD.—See T-Gaia Corp.; *Int'l*, pg. 7396
INFINITY COMPUTER SOLUTIONS LLC; *U.S. Private*, pg. 2071
INFINITY COMPUTER SYSTEMS, INC.—See Sourcepass, Inc.; *U.S. Private*, pg. 3719
INFINITY CONSTRUCTION SERVICES, LP—See John Wood Group PLC; *Int'l*, pg. 3984
INFINITY CONSULTING SOLUTIONS, INC.—See Korn Ferry; *U.S. Public*, pg. 1272
INFINITY CONTRACTORS, INC.—See Ontario Municipal Employees Retirement System; *Int'l*, pg. 5584
INFINITY DESIGN LLC—See CNC Associates NY Inc.; *U.S. Private*, pg. 952
INFINITY DEVELOPMENT HOLDINGS COMPANY LIMITED; *Int'l*, pg. 3687
INFINITY DIRECT, INC.—See Impact Mailing Of Minnesota, Inc.; *U.S. Private*, pg. 2048
INFINITY DISCOVERY, INC.—See Infinity Pharmaceuticals, Inc.; *U.S. Public*, pg. 1117
INFINITY DISTRIBUTION, INC.; *U.S. Private*, pg. 2071
INFINITY EQUITY; *Int'l*, pg. 3687
INFINITY GENERAL INSURANCE PLC—See Royal Group of Companies Ltd.; *Int'l*, pg. 6412
INFINITY GROUP, L.L.C.—See Kemper Corporation; *U.S. Public*, pg. 1220
INFINITY GROUP MANAGEMENT SERVICES, INC.; *U.S. Private*, pg. 2071
INFINITY HOLDING GROUP; *Int'l*, pg. 3688
INFINITY HOME CARE, L.L.C.—See Amedisys, Inc.; *U.S. Public*, pg. 94

COMPANY NAME INDEX

INFINITY HOME SERVICES; *U.S. Private,* pg. 2071
INFINITY INFORMATICA INC.—See STMicroelectronics N.V.; *Int'l,* pg. 7217
INFINITY INFO SYSTEMS CORP.—See Genesis Corp.; *U.S. Private,* pg. 1669
INFINITY INSURANCE AGENCY INC.—See Kemper Corporation; *U.S. Public,* pg. 1220
INFINITY INSURANCE AGENCY, INC.—See Kemper Corporation; *U.S. Public,* pg. 1220
INFINITY INTERNET, INC.—See Atmosera, Inc.; *U.S. Private,* pg. 381
INFINITY (INTL) TRAVEL HOLDINGS INC.; *Int'l,* pg. 3687
INFINITY LABORATORIES INC.—See Eurofins Scientific S.E.; *Int'l,* pg. 2550
INFINITY LITHIUM CORPORATION LIMITED; *Int'l,* pg. 3688
INFINITY LOGISTICS & TRANSPORT VENTURES LIMITED; *Int'l,* pg. 3688
INFINITY NETWORK SOLUTIONS, INC.; *U.S. Private,* pg. 2071
INFINITY OFFSHORE MARINE, LLC—See J.F. Lehman & Company, Inc.; *U.S. Private,* pg. 2164
INFINITY OIL AND GAS OF TEXAS, INC.—See American Noble Gas, Inc.; *U.S. Public,* pg. 108
INFINITY PART COMPANY LIMITED—See SNC Holding Company Limited; *Int'l,* pg. 7025
INFINITY PHARMA BV—See Fagron NV; *Int'l,* pg. 2603
INFINITY PHARMACEUTICALS, INC.; *U.S. Public,* pg. 1117
INFINITY PROPERTY & CASUALTY CORPORATION—See Kemper Corporation; *U.S. Public,* pg. 1220
INFINITY PROPERTY & CASUALTY SERVICES—See Kemper Corporation; *U.S. Public,* pg. 1220
INFINITY RESOURCES, INC.; *U.S. Private,* pg. 2071
INFINITY ROOFING & SIDING, INC.—See O2 Investment Partners, LLC; *U.S. Private,* pg. 2982
INFINITY SDC LIMITED; *Int'l,* pg. 3688
INFINITY SPECIALTY INSURANCE COMPANY—See Kemper Corporation; *U.S. Public,* pg. 1220
INFINITY SUPPORT SERVICES, INC.—See Sedulous Consulting Services, LLC; *U.S. Private,* pg. 3597
INFINITY SYSTEMS ENGINEERING, LLC; *U.S. Private,* pg. 2072
INFINITY SYSTEMS, INC.—See Samsung Group; *Int'l,* pg. 6512
INFINITY TECHNOLOGY, INC.; *U.S. Private,* pg. 2072
INFINITY TRADING & SOLUTIONS; *U.S. Private,* pg. 2072
INFINITY TRUST MORTGAGE BANK PLC; *Int'l,* pg. 3688
INFINITY WARD, INC.—See Microsoft Corporation; *U.S. Public,* pg. 1439
INFINITY WIRELESS, INC.—See OwnersEdge Inc.; *U.S. Private,* pg. 3055
INFINOVA CORPORATION—See Shenzhen Infinova Co., Ltd.; *Int'l,* pg. 6813
INFINYA LTD.—See Veridis Environment Ltd; *Int'l,* pg. 8168
INFIRMARY HOME HEALTH AGENCY, INC.—See UnitedHealth Group Incorporated; *U.S. Public,* pg. 2245
IN-FISHERMAN—See InterMedia Advisors, LLC; *U.S. Private,* pg. 2112
INFITECH, LLC—See Pro-Copy Technologies, Inc.; *U.S. Private,* pg. 3270
INFITECH VENTURES INC.; *Int'l,* pg. 3688
INFLAME APPLIANCES LTD.; *Int'l,* pg. 3688
INFLARX GMBH—See InflaRx N.V.; *Int'l,* pg. 3688
INFLARX N.V.; *Int'l,* pg. 3688
INFLECTION LLC; *U.S. Private,* pg. 2072
INFLECTION MANAGEMENT CORPORATION LIMITED; *Int'l,* pg. 3688
INFLECTION POINT SYSTEMS INC.—See EQT AB; *Int'l,* pg. 2483
INFLECTION RESOURCES LTD.; *Int'l,* pg. 3688
INFLEXION PRIVATE EQUITY PARTNERS LLP; *Int'l,* pg. 3688
INFLEXXION, INC.—See Integrated Behavioral Health, Inc.; *U.S. Private,* pg. 2099
INFLIGHT CATERING SERVICES LIMITED—See Deutsche Lufthansa AG; *Int'l,* pg. 2067
INFLIGHT SALES GROUP INC.; *U.S. Private,* pg. 2072
INFLOW TECHNOLOGIES PVT LIMITED—See Savex Technologies Pvt. Ltd.; *Int'l,* pg. 6597
INFLOW TECHNOLOGIES SINGAPORE PTE LIMITED—See Savex Technologies Pvt. Ltd.; *Int'l,* pg. 6597
INFLUENCE GRAPHICS; *U.S. Private,* pg. 2072
INFLUENCE HEALTH, INC.—See Vestar Capital Partners, LLC; *U.S. Private,* pg. 4372
INFLUENCER BANK,INC.—See Vector Inc.; *Int'l,* pg. 8144
INFLUENCE SPORTS LTD.—See The Mission Group Public Limited Company; *Int'l,* pg. 7667
INFO2CELL.COM—See Altruist Technologies Pvt. Ltd.; *Int'l,* pg. 399
INFOARMOR, INC.—See The Allstate Corporation; *U.S. Public,* pg. 2033
INFOAXIS INC; *U.S. Private,* pg. 2072
INFOBANK CORPORATION; *Int'l,* pg. 3689

INFOBASE HOLDINGS, LLC—See Centre Lane Partners, LLC; *U.S. Private,* pg. 827
INFOBEANS INC.—See InfoBeans Technologies Limited; *Int'l,* pg. 3690
INFOBEANS TECHNOLOGIES LIMITED; *Int'l,* pg. 3690
INFOBIP LTD.; *Int'l,* pg. 3690
INFOBIRD CO., LTD.; *Int'l,* pg. 3690
INFOBLOX INC.—See Vista Equity Partners, LLC; *U.S. Private,* pg. 4398
INFOBLU SPA—See Edizione S.r.l.; *Int'l,* pg. 2312
INFOBOLSA, S.A.—See SIX Group AG; *Int'l,* pg. 6966
INFOCANADA CORP.—See CCMP Capital Advisors, LP; *U.S. Private,* pg. 800
INFOCHAMP SYSTEMS CORPORATION—See China Steel Corporation; *Int'l,* pg. 1556
INFOCHOICE LTD—See iSelect Ltd.; *Int'l,* pg. 3814
INFOCISION MANAGEMENT CORP.; *U.S. Private,* pg. 2072
INFOCLIP SA; *Int'l,* pg. 3690
INFOCOM AMERICA, INC.—See Teijin Limited; *Int'l,* pg. 7522
INFOCOM CORPORATION—See Teijin Limited; *Int'l,* pg. 7522
INFOCOM RESEARCH, INC.—See Nippon Telegraph & Telephone Corporation; *Int'l,* pg. 5343
INFOCOM TECHNOLOGIES, INC.—See PLDT Inc.; *Int'l,* pg. 5896
INFOCORE, INC.; *U.S. Private,* pg. 2072
INFOCORP COMPUTER SOLUTIONS LTD.; *Int'l,* pg. 3690
INFOCRAFT LTD.—See Hayleys PLC; *Int'l,* pg. 3292
INFOCROSSING HEALTHCARE, INC.—See Verizon Communications Inc.; *U.S. Public,* pg. 2286
INFOCROSSING, INC.—See Wipro Limited; *Int'l,* pg. 8432
INFO CUBIC LLC—See Boathouse Capital Management, LLC; *U.S. Private,* pg. 603
INFOCUS CORPORATION—See Image Holdings Corporation; *U.S. Private,* pg. 2044
INFOCUS PARTNERS; *U.S. Private,* pg. 2072
INFODATA AB—See Ratos AB; *Int'l,* pg. 6217
INFODEMA S.A.; *Int'l,* pg. 3690
INFODESK, INC.—See Cuadrilla Capital LLC; *U.S. Private,* pg. 1119
INFODIREKT A/S—See Ratos AB; *Int'l,* pg. 6217
INFO EDGE INDIA LTD; *Int'l,* pg. 3689
INFOEMPLEO, S.L.—See Vocento, S.A.; *Int'l,* pg. 8284
INFOENGINE S.A.—See Gielda Papierow Wartosciowych w Warszawie S.A.; *Int'l,* pg. 2968
INFOFORT BAHRAIN CO.WLL—See Iron Mountain Incorporated; *U.S. Public,* pg. 1172
INFOFORT EGYPT S.A.E.—See Iron Mountain Incorporated; *U.S. Public,* pg. 1172
INFOFORT MUSCAT SPC—See Iron Mountain Incorporated; *U.S. Public,* pg. 1172
INFOGAIN CORPORATION—See ChrysCapital Investment Advisors (India) Private Limited; *Int'l,* pg. 1588
INFOGARD LABORATORIES—See Underwriters Laboratories Inc.; *U.S. Private,* pg. 4280
INFOGIX, INC.—See Clearlake Capital Group, L.P.; *U.S. Private,* pg. 936
INFOGIX, INC.—See TA Associates, Inc.; *U.S. Private,* pg. 3917
INFOGLIDE SOFTWARE CORPORATION—See Fair Isaac Corporation; *U.S. Public,* pg. 820
INFOGRESSIVE, INC.—See Ascend Technologies, LLC; *U.S. Private,* pg. 346
INFOGROUP DIRECT MARKETING SOLUTIONS—See CCMP Capital Advisors, LP; *U.S. Private,* pg. 800
INFOGROUP/EDITH ROMAN ASSOCIATES—See CCMP Capital Advisors, LP; *U.S. Private,* pg. 800
INFOGROUP INC.—See CCMP Capital Advisors, LP; *U.S. Private,* pg. 800
INFOGROUP INTERACTIVE—See CCMP Capital Advisors, LP; *U.S. Private,* pg. 800
INFOGROUP LICENSING—See CCMP Capital Advisors, LP; *U.S. Private,* pg. 800
INFOGROUP TARGETING SOLUTIONS—See CCMP Capital Advisors, LP; *U.S. Private,* pg. 800
INFOJINI INC; *U.S. Private,* pg. 2072
INFOJOBS S.A.—See Schibsted ASA; *Int'l,* pg. 6616
INFOLAB INC.; *U.S. Private,* pg. 2072
INFOLINE TEC GROUP BERHAD; *Int'l,* pg. 3690
INFO-LINK TECHNOLOGIES, INC.—See Tonka Bay Equity Partners LLC; *U.S. Private,* pg. 4185
INFOLLION RESEARCH SERVICES LIMITED; *Int'l,* pg. 3690
INFOLOB SOLUTIONS, INC.; *U.S. Private,* pg. 2072
INFOLOGIC PTE LTD—See Beijing E-Hualu Information Technology Co., Ltd.; *Int'l,* pg. 949
INFOLOG SOLUTIONS; *Int'l,* pg. 3690
INFOLOG S.P.A.—See Sesa S.p.A.; *Int'l,* pg. 6728
INFOLYNX SERVICES, INC.; *U.S. Private,* pg. 2072
INFOLYTX BANGLADESH LIMITED—See Advanced Chemical Industries Limited; *Int'l,* pg. 158
INFOMART CORPORATION; *Int'l,* pg. 3690
INFOMART DALLAS, LP—See Equinix, Inc.; *U.S. Public,* pg. 788
INFOMART INTERNATIONAL CORPORATION—See Infomart Corporation; *Int'l,* pg. 3690

INFO RETAIL COMPANY

INFOMATE (PVT) LTD.—See John Keells Holdings PLC; *Int'l,* pg. 3978
INFOMATICS, INC; *U.S. Private,* pg. 2072
INFOMATICS SOFTWARE SOLUTIONS INDIA—See Infomatics, Inc; *U.S. Private,* pg. 2072
INFOMAT N.V.—See KKR & Co. Inc.; *U.S. Public,* pg. 1257
INFOMAX COMMUNICATION CO., LTD.—See Macronix International Co., Ltd.; *Int'l,* pg. 4632
INFOMEDIA A/S—See DPG Media Group NV; *Int'l,* pg. 2188
INFOMEDIA A/S—See JP/Politiken Hus A/S; *Int'l,* pg. 4005
INFOMEDIA GROUP INC; *U.S. Private,* pg. 2072
INFOMEDIA INC.; *U.S. Private,* pg. 2072
INFOMEDIA LTD; *Int'l,* pg. 3690
INFOMEDIA PRESS LTD.; *Int'l,* pg. 3690
INFOMED SOFTWARE, S.L.—See Henry Schein, Inc.; *U.S. Public,* pg. 1027
INFOMINA BERHAD; *Int'l,* pg. 3690
INFONET INC.; *Int'l,* pg. 3690
INFONIQA HOLDING GMBH—See Warburg Pincus LLC; *U.S. Private,* pg. 4438
INFONOVA GMBH—See BearingPoint, Inc.; *U.S. Private,* pg. 507
INFOOBJECTS INC; *U.S. Private,* pg. 2072
INFOPIA CO., LTD.; *Int'l,* pg. 3690
INFOPLUS TECHNOLOGIES B.V.—See Infoplus Technologies Limited; *Int'l,* pg. 3691
INFOPLUS TECHNOLOGIES LIMITED; *Int'l,* pg. 3690
INFOPLUS TECHNOLOGIES SPRL—See Infoplus Technologies Limited; *Int'l,* pg. 3691
INFOPORTUGAL SISTEMAS DE INFORMACAO E CONTEUDOS S.A.—See Impresa SGPS S.A.; *Int'l,* pg. 3637
INFOPRO DIGITAL SAS—See Apax Partners LLP; *Int'l,* pg. 501
INFOPRO DIGITAL SAS—See TowerBrook Capital Partners, L.P.; *U.S. Private,* pg. 4195
INFOPULSE EUROPE GMBH—See TietoEVRY Oyj; *Int'l,* pg. 7745
INFOPULSE UKRAINE LLC—See TietoEVRY Oyj; *Int'l,* pg. 7745
INFOPULSE USA LLC—See TietoEVRY Oyj; *Int'l,* pg. 7745
INFORADIO SP. Z O. O.—See Agora S.A.; *Int'l,* pg. 212
INFOR BV—See Koch Industries, Inc.; *U.S. Private,* pg. 2330
INFORE ENVIRONMENT TECHNOLOGY GROUP CO., LTD.; *Int'l,* pg. 3691
INFORELAY ONLINE SYSTEMS, INC.—See Stonecourt Capital LP; *U.S. Private,* pg. 3828
INFOR ENTERPRISE ASSET MANAGEMENT—See Koch Industries, Inc.; *U.S. Private,* pg. 2330
INFO RETAIL COMPANY; *U.S. Private,* pg. 2072
INFOR GLOBAL SOLUTIONS - BANGKOK—See Koch Industries, Inc.; *U.S. Private,* pg. 2330
INFOR GLOBAL SOLUTIONS - BIRMINGHAM—See Koch Industries, Inc.; *U.S. Private,* pg. 2330
INFOR GLOBAL SOLUTIONS - BUENOS AIRES—See Koch Industries, Inc.; *U.S. Private,* pg. 2330
INFOR GLOBAL SOLUTIONS - CAPELLE AAN DEN IJSSEL—See Koch Industries, Inc.; *U.S. Private,* pg. 2330
INFOR GLOBAL SOLUTIONS - GUANGZHOU—See Koch Industries, Inc.; *U.S. Private,* pg. 2330
INFOR GLOBAL SOLUTIONS - HONG KONG—See Koch Industries, Inc.; *U.S. Private,* pg. 2330
INFOR GLOBAL SOLUTIONS, INC. - CHICAGO—See Koch Industries, Inc.; *U.S. Private,* pg. 2330
INFOR GLOBAL SOLUTIONS, INC. - COLORADO SPRINGS—See Koch Industries, Inc.; *U.S. Private,* pg. 2330
INFOR GLOBAL SOLUTIONS, INC. - DALLAS—See Koch Industries, Inc.; *U.S. Private,* pg. 2330
INFOR GLOBAL SOLUTIONS, INC. - EAST GREENWICH—See Koch Industries, Inc.; *U.S. Private,* pg. 2330
INFOR GLOBAL SOLUTIONS, INC. - GRAND RAPIDS—See Koch Industries, Inc.; *U.S. Private,* pg. 2331
INFOR GLOBAL SOLUTIONS, INC. - HAMPTON—See Koch Industries, Inc.; *U.S. Private,* pg. 2331
INFOR GLOBAL SOLUTIONS, INC. - OPERATIONS CENTER—See Koch Industries, Inc.; *U.S. Private,* pg. 2331
INFOR GLOBAL SOLUTIONS - MELBOURNE—See Koch Industries, Inc.; *U.S. Private,* pg. 2330
INFOR GLOBAL SOLUTIONS - MUNICH—See Koch Industries, Inc.; *U.S. Private,* pg. 2330
INFOR GLOBAL SOLUTIONS - PETALING JAYA—See Koch Industries, Inc.; *U.S. Private,* pg. 2330
INFOR GLOBAL SOLUTIONS - SANTIAGO—See Koch Industries, Inc.; *U.S. Private,* pg. 2330
INFOR GLOBAL SOLUTIONS - SAO PAOLO—See Koch Industries, Inc.; *U.S. Private,* pg. 2330
INFOR GLOBAL SOLUTIONS - SINGAPORE—See Koch Industries, Inc.; *U.S. Private,* pg. 2330
INFOR GLOBAL SOLUTIONS - SYDNEY—See Koch Industries, Inc.; *U.S. Private,* pg. 2330

INFO RETAIL COMPANY

INFOR GLOBAL SOLUTIONS - TORONTO—See Koch Industries, Inc.; *U.S. Private*, pg. 2330
INFORICA INDIA PVT. LTD.—See The Co-operators Group Limited; *Int'l*, pg. 7634
INFORICH INC.; *Int'l*, pg. 3691
INFOR, INC.—See Koch Industries, Inc.; *U.S. Private*, pg. 2330
INFOR JAPAN K.K.—See Koch Industries, Inc.; *U.S. Private*, pg. 2331
INFOR LIBRARY & INFORMATION SOLUTIONS—See Koch Industries, Inc.; *U.S. Private*, pg. 2331
INFOR LIBRARY & INFORMATION SOLUTIONS - USA—See Koch Industries, Inc.; *U.S. Private*, pg. 2331
INFORMA BUSINESS INFORMATION, INC. - PHARMA & MEDTECH BUSINESS INTELLIGENCE, ROCKVILLE EDITORIAL OFFICE—See Informa plc; *Int'l*, pg. 3692
INFORMA BUSINESS INFORMATION, INC. - PHARMA & MEDTECH BUSINESS INTELLIGENCE—See Informa plc; *Int'l*, pg. 3692
INFORMA BUSINESS INFORMATION, INC.—See Informa plc; *Int'l*, pg. 3692
INFORMA BUSINESS INFORMATION—See Informa plc; *Int'l*, pg. 3692
INFORMACION DE MEDIOS S.A.—See Brookfield Corporation; *Int'l*, pg. 1178
INFORMACION DE MEDIOS S.A.—See Elliott Management Corporation; *U.S. Private*, pg. 1371
INFORMACION ESTADIO DEPORTIVO S.A.—See RCS MediaGroup S.p.A.; *Int'l*, pg. 6230
INFORMACNI SLUZBY - ENERGETIKA, A.S.—See E.ON SE; *Int'l*, pg. 2258
INFORMA CONNECT LIMITED—See Informa plc; *Int'l*, pg. 3691
INFORMA DB LTD.—See Informa SA; *Int'l*, pg. 3694
INFORMA ECONOMICS FNP CONSULTORIA LTDA.—See Informa plc; *Int'l*, pg. 3691
INFORMA FINANCE GMBH—See Informa plc; *Int'l*, pg. 3692
INFORMA FINANCIAL INFORMATION, INC.—See Informa plc; *Int'l*, pg. 3692
INFORMA GLOBAL MARKETS (EUROPE) LIMITED—See Informa plc; *Int'l*, pg. 3692
INFORMA GROUP PLC—See Informa plc; *Int'l*, pg. 3691
INFORMA HEALTHCARE AB—See Informa plc; *Int'l*, pg. 3692
INFORMA HIS GMBH—See Bertelsmann SE & Co. KGaA; *Int'l*, pg. 997
INFORMA INVESTMENT SOLUTIONS, INC.—See Informa plc; *Int'l*, pg. 3692
INFORMA IP GMBH—See Informa plc; *Int'l*, pg. 3692
INFORMA MARKETS BN CO., LTD.—See Informa plc; *Int'l*, pg. 3693
INFORMA MARKETS B.V.—See Informa plc; *Int'l*, pg. 3693
INFORMA MARKETS JAPAN CO. LTD.—See Informa plc; *Int'l*, pg. 3693
INFORMA MARKETS LIMITED—See Informa plc; *Int'l*, pg. 3693
INFORMA MARKETS LTDA.—See Informa plc; *Int'l*, pg. 3693
INFORMA MARKETS MALAYSIA SDN BHD—See Informa plc; *Int'l*, pg. 3693
INFORMA MEDIA, INC.—See Informa plc; *Int'l*, pg. 3692
INFORMA PLC; *Int'l*, pg. 3691
INFORMA SA; *Int'l*, pg. 3694
INFORMASCOPE; *Int'l*, pg. 3694
INFORMA SWITZERLAND LIMITED—See Informa plc; *Int'l*, pg. 3692
INFORMA TIANYI EXHIBITIONS (CHENGDU) CO., LTD.—See Informa plc; *Int'l*, pg. 3693
INFORMATICA AUSTRALIA PTY. LTD. - ASIA/PACIFIC HEADQUARTERS—See Canada Pension Plan Investment Board; *Int'l*, pg. 1279
INFORMATICA AUSTRALIA PTY. LTD. - ASIA/PACIFIC HEADQUARTERS—See Permira Advisers LLP; *Int'l*, pg. 5806
INFORMATICA (BEIJING) INFORMATION TECHNOLOGY CO., LTD.—See Canada Pension Plan Investment Board; *Int'l*, pg. 1279
INFORMATICA (BEIJING) INFORMATION TECHNOLOGY CO., LTD.—See Permira Advisers LLP; *Int'l*, pg. 5806
INFORMATICA BUSINESS SOLUTIONS PVT. LTD.—See Canada Pension Plan Investment Board; *Int'l*, pg. 1279
INFORMATICA BUSINESS SOLUTIONS PVT. LTD.—See Permira Advisers LLP; *Int'l*, pg. 5806
INFORMATICA CORPORATION—See Canada Pension Plan Investment Board; *Int'l*, pg. 1279
INFORMATICA CORPORATION—See Permira Advisers LLP; *Int'l*, pg. 5805
INFORMATICA CZ, S.R.O.—See Canada Pension Plan Investment Board; *Int'l*, pg. 1279
INFORMATICA CZ, S.R.O.—See Permira Advisers LLP; *Int'l*, pg. 5806
INFORMATICA DE EUSKADI S.L—See Accenture plc; *Int'l*, pg. 87
INFORMATICA FRANCE S.A.S.—See Canada Pension Plan Investment Board; *Int'l*, pg. 1279
INFORMATICA FRANCE S.A.S.—See Permira Advisers LLP; *Int'l*, pg. 5806

INFORMATICA GMBH—See Canada Pension Plan Investment Board; *Int'l*, pg. 1280
INFORMATICA GMBH—See Permira Advisers LLP; *Int'l*, pg. 5806
INFORMATICA HONG KONG—See Canada Pension Plan Investment Board; *Int'l*, pg. 1279
INFORMATICA HONG KONG—See Permira Advisers LLP; *Int'l*, pg. 5806
INFORMATICA INC.; *U.S. Public*, pg. 1117
INFORMATICA INTERNATIONAL DO BRAZIL LTD. - LATIN AMERICA REGION HEADQUARTERS—See Canada Pension Plan Investment Board; *Int'l*, pg. 1279
INFORMATICA INTERNATIONAL DO BRAZIL LTD. - LATIN AMERICA REGION HEADQUARTERS—See Permira Advisers LLP; *Int'l*, pg. 5806
INFORMATICA IRELAND LIMITED—See Canada Pension Plan Investment Board; *Int'l*, pg. 1280
INFORMATICA IRELAND LIMITED—See Permira Advisers LLP; *Int'l*, pg. 5806
INFORMATICA JAPAN K.K.—See Canada Pension Plan Investment Board; *Int'l*, pg. 1279
INFORMATICA JAPAN K.K.—See Permira Advisers LLP; *Int'l*, pg. 5806
INFORMATICA KOREA CORPORATION—See Canada Pension Plan Investment Board; *Int'l*, pg. 1279
INFORMATICA KOREA CORPORATION—See Permira Advisers LLP; *Int'l*, pg. 5806
INFORMATICA MIDDLE EAST FZ-LLC—See Canada Pension Plan Investment Board; *Int'l*, pg. 1280
INFORMATICA MIDDLE EAST FZ-LLC—See Permira Advisers LLP; *Int'l*, pg. 5806
INFORMATICA NEDERLAND B.V. - EMEA HEADQUARTERS—See Canada Pension Plan Investment Board; *Int'l*, pg. 1279
INFORMATICA NEDERLAND B.V. - EMEA HEADQUARTERS—See Permira Advisers LLP; *Int'l*, pg. 5806
INFORMATICA RESEARCH AND DEVELOPMENT CENTER LLC—See Canada Pension Plan Investment Board; *Int'l*, pg. 1280
INFORMATICA RESEARCH AND DEVELOPMENT CENTER LLC—See Permira Advisers LLP; *Int'l*, pg. 5806
INFORMATICA - RIO DE JANEIRO—See Canada Pension Plan Investment Board; *Int'l*, pg. 1279
INFORMATICA - RIO DE JANEIRO—See Permira Advisers LLP; *Int'l*, pg. 5806
INFORMATICA S.E.A. PTE., LTD.—See Canada Pension Plan Investment Board; *Int'l*, pg. 1279
INFORMATICA S.E.A. PTE., LTD.—See Permira Advisers LLP; *Int'l*, pg. 5806
INFORMATICA SOFTWARE DE MEXICO S. DE R.L. DE C.V.—See Canada Pension Plan Investment Board; *Int'l*, pg. 1280
INFORMATICA SOFTWARE DE MEXICO S. DE R.L. DE C.V.—See Permira Advisers LLP; *Int'l*, pg. 5806
INFORMATICA SOFTWARE ITALIA S.R.L.—See Canada Pension Plan Investment Board; *Int'l*, pg. 1280
INFORMATICA SOFTWARE ITALIA S.R.L.—See Permira Advisers LLP; *Int'l*, pg. 5806
INFORMATICA SOFTWARE LIMITED—See Canada Pension Plan Investment Board; *Int'l*, pg. 1280
INFORMATICA SOFTWARE LIMITED—See Permira Advisers LLP; *Int'l*, pg. 5806
INFORMATICA SOFTWARE LTD.—See Canada Pension Plan Investment Board; *Int'l*, pg. 1280
INFORMATICA SOFTWARE LTD.—See Permira Advisers LLP; *Int'l*, pg. 5806
INFORMATICA SOFTWARE LTD.—See Canada Pension Plan Investment Board; *Int'l*, pg. 1280
INFORMATICA SOFTWARE LTD.—See Permira Advisers LLP; *Int'l*, pg. 5806
INFORMATICA SOFTWARE (SCHWEIZ) AG—See Canada Pension Plan Investment Board; *Int'l*, pg. 1280
INFORMATICA SOFTWARE (SCHWEIZ) AG—See Permira Advisers LLP; *Int'l*, pg. 5806
INFORMATICA SOFTWARE SERVICES DE MEXICO S.A. DE C.V.—See Canada Pension Plan Investment Board; *Int'l*, pg. 1279
INFORMATICA SOFTWARE SERVICES DE MEXICO S.A. DE C.V.—See Permira Advisers LLP; *Int'l*, pg. 5806
INFORMATICA SOUTH AFRICA—See Canada Pension Plan Investment Board; *Int'l*, pg. 1280
INFORMATICA SOUTH AFRICA—See Permira Advisers LLP; *Int'l*, pg. 5806
INFORMATICA TAIWAN CO. LTD.—See Canada Pension Plan Investment Board; *Int'l*, pg. 1279
INFORMATICA TAIWAN CO. LTD.—See Permira Advisers LLP; *Int'l*, pg. 5806
INFORMATICA TURKEY—See Canada Pension Plan Investment Board; *Int'l*, pg. 1280
INFORMATICA TURKEY—See Permira Advisers LLP; *Int'l*, pg. 5806
INFORMATICS ACADEMY PTE. LTD.—See Informatics Education Ltd; *Int'l*, pg. 3694
INFORMATICS EDUCATION (HK) LTD.—See Informatics Education Ltd; *Int'l*, pg. 3694
INFORMATICS EDUCATION LTD; *Int'l*, pg. 3694
INFORMATICS GLOBAL CAMPUS PTE LTD—See Informatics Education Ltd; *Int'l*, pg. 3694

CORPORATE AFFILIATIONS

INFORMATICS GROUP; *U.S. Private*, pg. 2073
INFORMATICS HOLDINGS, INC.—See Renovo Capital, LLC; *U.S. Private*, pg. 3399
INFORMATICS SERVICES CORPORATION; *Int'l*, pg. 3694
INFORMATIKA A.D.; *Int'l*, pg. 3694
INFORMATION ACCESS TECHNOLOGY, INC.—See Enghouse Systems Limited; *Int'l*, pg. 2427
INFORMATION AND TELECOMMUNICATION TECHNOLOGIES OJSC—See Russian Technologies State Corporation; *Int'l*, pg. 6431
INFORMATION BUILDERS BELGIUM—See Vista Equity Partners, LLC; *U.S. Private*, pg. 4401
INFORMATION BUILDERS (CANADA) - CALGARY—See Vista Equity Partners, LLC; *U.S. Private*, pg. 4401
INFORMATION BUILDERS (CANADA) INC.—See Vista Equity Partners, LLC; *U.S. Private*, pg. 4401
INFORMATION BUILDERS (CANADA) - VANCOUVER—See Vista Equity Partners, LLC; *U.S. Private*, pg. 4401
INFORMATION BUILDERS (DEUTSCHLAND) GMBH—See Vista Equity Partners, LLC; *U.S. Private*, pg. 4401
INFORMATION BUILDERS FRANCE—See Vista Equity Partners, LLC; *U.S. Private*, pg. 4401
INFORMATION BUILDERS INC.—See Vista Equity Partners, LLC; *U.S. Private*, pg. 4401
INFORMATION BUILDERS MEXICO—See Vista Equity Partners, LLC; *U.S. Private*, pg. 4401
INFORMATION BUILDERS NETHERLANDS—See Vista Equity Partners, LLC; *U.S. Private*, pg. 4401
INFORMATION BUILDERS PORTUGAL—See Vista Equity Partners, LLC; *U.S. Private*, pg. 4401
INFORMATION BUILDERS PTY., LTD.—See Vista Equity Partners, LLC; *U.S. Private*, pg. 4402
INFORMATION BUILDERS SPAIN—See Vista Equity Partners, LLC; *U.S. Private*, pg. 4402
INFORMATION BUILDERS SWITZERLAND—See Vista Equity Partners, LLC; *U.S. Private*, pg. 4402
INFORMATION BUILDERS UK—See Vista Equity Partners, LLC; *U.S. Private*, pg. 4402
INFORMATION & COMMUNICATION NETWORKS PCL; *Int'l*, pg. 3695
INFORMATION COMMUNICATION SERVICES INC.—See TFI International Inc.; *Int'l*, pg. 7586
INFORMATION & COMPUTING SERVICES, INC.; *U.S. Private*, pg. 2073
INFORMATION CONTROL CORPORATION; *U.S. Private*, pg. 2073
INFORMATION DEVELOPMENT AMERICA INC.—See ID Holdings Corporation; *Int'l*, pg. 3587
INFORMATION DEVELOPMENT SINGAPORE PTE. LTD.—See ID Holdings Corporation; *Int'l*, pg. 3587
INFORMATION DEVELOPMENT WUHAN CO., LTD.—See ID Holdings Corporation; *Int'l*, pg. 3587
INFORMATION DISPLAY COMPANY—See Carmanah Technologies Corporation; *Int'l*, pg. 1341
INFORMATION EXPERTS, INC.; *U.S. Private*, pg. 2073
THE INFORMATION EXPERTS LTD.—See Malam-Team Ltd.; *Int'l*, pg. 4659
INFORMATION GATEWAY INC.—See LaNetro Zed S.A.; *Int'l*, pg. 4408
INFORMATION, INC.—See SmithBucklin Corporation; *U.S. Private*, pg. 3697
THE INFORMATION MANAGEMENT GROUP (NZ) LIMITED—See Freightways Group Limited; *Int'l*, pg. 2772
THE INFORMATION MANAGEMENT GROUP PTY LIMITED—See Freightways Group Limited; *Int'l*, pg. 2772
INFORMATION MANAGEMENT RESOURCES, INC.; *U.S. Private*, pg. 2073
INFORMATION MANAGEMENT SERVICES; *U.S. Private*, pg. 2073
INFORMATION MANAGEMENT SOLUTIONS, LLC—See Usio Inc.; *U.S. Public*, pg. 2267
INFORMATION & NETWORKING TECHNOLOGY JOINT STOCK COMPANY; *Int'l*, pg. 3695
INFORMATION PLANNING CO., LTD.; *Int'l*, pg. 3695
INFORMATION PLANNING & MANAGEMENT SERVICE, INC.—See Court Square Capital Partners, L.P.; *U.S. Private*, pg. 1069
INFORMATION PORT CO., LTD.—See Yumeshin Holdings Co., Ltd.; *Int'l*, pg. 8613
INFORMATION RESOURCES, INC.—See Hellman & Friedman LLC; *U.S. Private*, pg. 1910
INFORMATION SECURITY ARCHITECTS PROPRIETARY LIMITED—See ISA Holdings Limited; *Int'l*, pg. 3812
INFORMATION SECURITY ONE (CHINA) LTD.; *Int'l*, pg. 3695
INFORMATION SERVICES CORPORATION; *Int'l*, pg. 3695
INFORMATION SERVICES GROUP DENMARK APS—See Information Services Group, Inc.; *U.S. Public*, pg. 1118
INFORMATION SERVICES GROUP EUROPE LIMITED—See Information Services Group, Inc.; *U.S. Public*, pg. 1118

INFORMATION SERVICES GROUP GERMANY GMBH—See Information Services Group, Inc.; *U.S. Public*, pg. 1118
INFORMATION SERVICES GROUP, INC.; *U.S. Public*, pg. 1117
INFORMATION SERVICES GROUP NETHERLANDS B.V.—See Information Services Group, Inc.; *U.S. Public*, pg. 1118
INFORMATION SERVICES GROUP OY—See Information Services Group, Inc.; *U.S. Public*, pg. 1118
INFORMATION SERVICES GROUP SA—See Information Services Group, Inc.; *U.S. Public*, pg. 1118
INFORMATION SERVICES GROUP SWEDEN AB—See Information Services Group, Inc.; *U.S. Public*, pg. 1118
INFORMATION SERVICES GROUP SWITZERLAND GMBH—See Information Services Group, Inc.; *U.S. Public*, pg. 1118
INFORMATION SERVICES NETWORK LIMITED; *Int'l*, pg. 3695
INFORMATIONS TECHNOLOGIE AUSTRIA SK SPOL. S R.O.—See Erste Group Bank AG; *Int'l*, pg. 2499
INFORMATION STRATEGIES, INC.—See Sylogist Ltd.; *Int'l*, pg. 7378
INFORMATION SYSTEM ASSOCIATES LIMITED—See SHAHTAJ SUGAR MILLS LIMITED; *Int'l*, pg. 6749
INFORMATION SYSTEMS AUDIT & CONTROL ASSOCIATION, INC.; *U.S. Private*, pg. 2073
INFORMATION SYSTEMS EXPERTS, LLC; *U.S. Private*, pg. 2073
INFORMATION SYSTEMS MANAGEMENT, INC.; *U.S. Private*, pg. 2073
INFORMATION SYSTEMS SOLUTIONS, INC.; *U.S. Private*, pg. 2073
INFORMATION TECHNOLOGY ENGINEERING CORP.—See Global Employment Holdings, Inc.; *U.S. Private*, pg. 1713
INFORMATION TECHNOLOGY EXPERTS, INC.; *U.S. Private*, pg. 2073
INFORMATION TECHNOLOGY GROUP COMPANY LIMITED—See Bliss Intelligence Public Company Limited; *Int'l*, pg. 1064
INFORMATION TECHNOLOGY PROFESSIONALS, LLC—See Gordon Flesch Company, Inc.; *U.S. Private*, pg. 1743
INFORMATION TECHNOLOGY SERVICES (ITS) LTD—See HgCapital Trust plc; *Int'l*, pg. 3376
INFORMATION TECHNOLOGY TOTAL SERVICES CO., LTD.—See Teco Electric & Machinery Co., Ltd.; *Int'l*, pg. 7518
INFORMATION TODAY INC.; *U.S. Private*, pg. 2073
INFORMATION TODAY, LTD—See Information Today Inc.; *U.S. Private*, pg. 2073
INFORMATION TRANSPORT SOLUTIONS, INC—See Uniti Group Inc.; *U.S. Public*, pg. 2253
INFORMATION VISUALIZATION AND INNOVATIVE RESEARCH INC.; *U.S. Private*, pg. 2073
INFORMATIQUE BANQUES POPULAIRES SA—See Groupe BPCE; *Int'l*, pg. 3098
INFORMATIVE GRAPHICS CORPORATION—See Open Text Corporation; *Int'l*, pg. 5597
INFORMATIVE, INC.—See Satmetrix Systems, Inc.; *U.S. Private*, pg. 3553
INFORMATIVE RESEARCH INC.; *U.S. Private*, pg. 2073
INFORMA UK LIMITED - BASKERVILLE—See Informa plc; *Int'l*, pg. 3692
INFORMA UK LIMITED—See Informa plc; *Int'l*, pg. 3692
INFORMA USA INC.—See Informa plc; *Int'l*, pg. 3692
INFORM DIAGNOSTICS, INC.—See Fulgent Genetics, Inc.; *U.S. Public*, pg. 892
INFORMED FAMILY FINANCIAL SERVICES, INC.; *U.S. Private*, pg. 2073
INFORMED TECHNOLOGIES INDIA LIMITED; *Int'l*, pg. 3695
INFORM ELEKTRONIK SAN. VE TIC. A.S.—See Legrand S.A.; *Int'l*, pg. 4444
INFORMER GROUP S.A.; *Int'l*, pg. 3695
INFORMEX MATSUMOTO CO., LTD.—See NAGOYA ELECTRIC WORKS CO., LTD.; *Int'l*, pg. 5129
INFORMEX S.A.—See Vista Equity Partners, LLC; *U.S. Private*, pg. 4400
INFORM, INC.; *U.S. Private*, pg. 2072
INFORM INFORMATION SYSTEMS LIMITED—See TA Associates, Inc.; *U.S. Private*, pg. 3917
INFORM LYKOS S.A.—See INFORM P. LYKOS S.A.; *Int'l*, pg. 3691
INFORM P. LYKOS S.A.; *Int'l*, pg. 3691
INFORM PRODUCT DEVELOPMENT, INC.; *U.S. Private*, pg. 2072
INFORMZ, LLC—See Higher Logic, LLC; *U.S. Private*, pg. 1937
INFORONICS, LLC; *U.S. Private*, pg. 2074
INFOR S.A.—See Koch Industries, Inc.; *U.S. Private*, pg. 2331
INFORTAL ASSOCIATES; *U.S. Private*, pg. 2074
INFORTE CORP.—See Orange S.A.; *Int'l*, pg. 5608
INFORTREND CORPORATION—See Infortrend Technology Inc.; *Int'l*, pg. 3695
INFORTREND DEUTSCHLAND GMBH—See Infortrend Technology Inc.; *Int'l*, pg. 3695

INFORTREND EUROPE LTD.—See Infortrend Technology Inc.; *Int'l*, pg. 3695
INFORTREND JAPAN, INC.—See Infortrend Technology Inc.; *Int'l*, pg. 3695
INFORTREND TECHNOLOGY INC.; *Int'l*, pg. 3695
INFORTREND TECHNOLOGY, LTD.—See Infortrend Technology Inc.; *Int'l*, pg. 3695
INFORUM NORGE AS—See Hafslund ASA; *Int'l*, pg. 3206
INFOSCITEX CORPORATION—See DCS Corporation; *U.S. Private*, pg. 1180
INFOSCORE AG—See Bertelsmann SE & Co. KGaA; *Int'l*, pg. 997
INFOSCORE NEDERLAND B.V.—See Bertelsmann SE & Co. KGaA; *Int'l*, pg. 992
INFOSCREEN AUSTRIA GMBH—See JCDecaux S.A.; *Int'l*, pg. 3921
INFOSCREEN GMBH—See Stroer SE & Co. KGaA; *Int'l*, pg. 7242
INFOSEAL, LLC—See Ennis, Inc.; *U.S. Public*, pg. 769
INFOSEMANTICS; *U.S. Private*, pg. 2074
INFOSERA, INC.—See SECOM Co., Ltd.; *Int'l*, pg. 6671
INFOSERVE GROUP PLC; *Int'l*, pg. 3695
INFOSERVE LIMITED—See Infoserve Group plc; *Int'l*, pg. 3695
INFOSERVICIOS S.A.—See Atos SE; *Int'l*, pg. 691
INFOSIGN INC.—See Uchida Yoko Co., Ltd.; *Int'l*, pg. 8012
INFOSKY TECHNOLOGY CO., LTD.—See TravelSky Technology Limited; *Int'l*, pg. 7907
INFOSMART GROUP LIMITED; *Int'l*, pg. 3695
INFOSMART SYSTEMS, INC.; *U.S. Private*, pg. 2074
THE INFOSOFT GROUP LLC—See Ontario Teachers' Pension Plan; *Int'l*, pg. 5586
INFOSONICS EL SALVADOR S.A. DE C.V.—See Simply, Inc.; *U.S. Public*, pg. 1882
INFOSONICS LATIN AMERICA, INC.—See Simply, Inc.; *U.S. Public*, pg. 1882
INFOSONICS S.A.—See Simply, Inc.; *U.S. Public*, pg. 1882
INFOSOURCE INC.—See Gauge Capital LLC; *U.S. Private*, pg. 1652
INFOSPACE HOLDINGS LLC—See OpenMail LLC; *U.S. Private*, pg. 3031
INFOSPECTRUM CONSULTING INC.—See GSS Infotech Limited; *Int'l*, pg. 3150
INFOSPECTRUM, INC.; *U.S. Private*, pg. 2074
INFOSTRADA CONCEPTS B.V.—See Nexstar Media Group, Inc.; *U.S. Public*, pg. 1524
INFOSTRETCH CORPORATION; *U.S. Private*, pg. 2074
INFOSURV, INC.; *U.S. Private*, pg. 2074
INFOSYNC SERVICES LLC; *U.S. Private*, pg. 2074
INFOSYS BPM LIMITED—See Infosys Limited; *Int'l*, pg. 3696
INFOSYS CONSULTING HOLDING AG—See Infosys Limited; *Int'l*, pg. 3696
INFOSYS CONSULTING, INC.—See Infosys Limited; *Int'l*, pg. 3696
INFOSYS CONSULTING PTE. LTD.—See Infosys Limited; *Int'l*, pg. 3696
INFOSYS CONSULTING SAS—See Infosys Limited; *Int'l*, pg. 3696
INFOSYS INFORMATIONSSYSTEME GMBH—See STRABAG SE; *Int'l*, pg. 7230
INFOSYS INTERNATIONAL, INC.; *U.S. Private*, pg. 2074
INFOSYS LIMITED; *Int'l*, pg. 3696
INFOSYS MANAGEMENT CONSULTING PTY. LIMITED—See Infosys Limited; *Int'l*, pg. 3696
INFOSYS MCCAMISH SYSTEMS LLC—See Infosys Limited; *Int'l*, pg. 3696
INFOSYS MIDDLE EAST FZ LLC—See Infosys Limited; *Int'l*, pg. 3696
INFOSYS NOVA HOLDINGS LLC—See Infosys Limited; *Int'l*, pg. 3696
INFOSYS POLAND SP. Z O.O.—See Infosys Limited; *Int'l*, pg. 3696
INFOSYS PUBLIC SERVICES, INC.—See Infosys Limited; *Int'l*, pg. 3696
INFOSYS SOUTH AFRICA (PTY.) LTD—See Infosys Limited; *Int'l*, pg. 3696
INFOSYS TECHNOLOGIES (AUSTRALIA) PTY. LIMITED—See Infosys Limited; *Int'l*, pg. 3696
INFOSYS TECHNOLOGIES (CHINA) CO. LTD.—See Infosys Limited; *Int'l*, pg. 3696
INFOSYS TECHNOLOGIES S. DE R. L. DE C. V.—See Infosys Limited; *Int'l*, pg. 3696
INFOSYS TECHNOLOGIES (SHANGHAI) CO. LIMITED—See Infosys Limited; *Int'l*, pg. 3696
INFOSYS TECHNOLOGIES (SWEDEN) AB—See Infosys Limited; *Int'l*, pg. 3696
INFOTECH ENTERPRISES AMERICA INC.—See Cyient Limited; *Int'l*, pg. 1896
INFOTECH ENTERPRISES AMERICA INC.—See Cyient Limited; *Int'l*, pg. 1896
INFOTECH ENTERPRISES EUROPE LTD—See Cyient Limited; *Int'l*, pg. 1896
INFOTECH ENTERPRISES EUROPE LTD.—See Cyient Limited; *Int'l*, pg. 1896
INFOTECH ENTERPRISES GMBH FRANCE—See Cyient Limited; *Int'l*, pg. 1896

INFOTECH ENTERPRISES JAPAN KK—See Cyient Limited; *Int'l*, pg. 1896
INFOTECH ENTERPRISES LTD - SOFTWARE & ENGINEERING DIVISIONS—See Cyient Limited; *Int'l*, pg. 1896
INFOTECH ENTERPRISES LTD.—See Cyient Limited; *Int'l*, pg. 1896
INFOTECH ENTERPRISES LTD—See Cyient Limited; *Int'l*, pg. 1896
INFOTECH ENTERPRISES LTD—See Cyient Limited; *Int'l*, pg. 1896
INFOTECH PRISM, LLC; *U.S. Private*, pg. 2074
INFO-TECH RESEARCH GROUP; *Int'l*, pg. 3689
INFOTECH SOFTWARE SOLUTIONS CANADA INC—See Cyient Limited; *Int'l*, pg. 1896
INFO-TEK CORPORATION; *Int'l*, pg. 3689
INFOTEL BUSINESS CONSULTING SAS—See Infotel SA; *Int'l*, pg. 3696
INFOTEL CORPORATION—See Infotel SA; *Int'l*, pg. 3696
INFOTEL GMBH—See Infotel SA; *Int'l*, pg. 3696
INFOTEL SA; *Int'l*, pg. 3696
INFOTERRA GMBH—See Airbus SE; *Int'l*, pg. 245
INFOTERRA LIMITED—See Airbus SE; *Int'l*, pg. 245
INFOTERRA MAGYARORSZAG KFT.—See Airbus SE; *Int'l*, pg. 245
INFOTERRA SERVICIOS DE GEOINFORMACION SA—See Airbus SE; *Int'l*, pg. 245
INFOTILITY, INC.—See Pacific Controls Inc.; *Int'l*, pg. 5687
INFOTMIC CO., LTD.; *Int'l*, pg. 3696
INFOTORG AB—See Ratos AB; *Int'l*, pg. 6217
INFOTRACK PTY LTD.; *Int'l*, pg. 3696
INFOTREE SERVICE INC.; *U.S. Private*, pg. 2074
INFOTRIEVE INC.; *U.S. Private*, pg. 2074
INFOTRUST GROUP, INC.; *U.S. Private*, pg. 2074
INFOVINE CO., LTD.; *Int'l*, pg. 3696
INFOVISA INC.—See Farmers & Merchants Investment Inc.; *U.S. Private*, pg. 1476
INFOVISION CONSULTANTS, INC.; *U.S. Private*, pg. 2074
INFOVISION OPTOELECTRONICS KUNSHN CO., LTD.; *Int'l*, pg. 3697
INFOVISION TECHNOLOGIES INC.; *U.S. Private*, pg. 2074
INFOVISION TECHNOLOGIES—See Infovision Technologies Inc.; *U.S. Private*, pg. 2074
INFOVISION TECHNOLOGIES—See Infovision Technologies Inc.; *U.S. Private*, pg. 2074
INFOVISION TECHNOLOGIES—See Infovision Technologies Inc.; *U.S. Private*, pg. 2074
INFOVISTA CORPORATION—See Apax Partners LLP; *Int'l*, pg. 504
INFOVISTA GMBH—See Apax Partners LLP; *Int'l*, pg. 504
INFOVISTA IBE SA—See Apax Partners LLP; *Int'l*, pg. 504
INFOVISTA PTE LTD—See Apax Partners LLP; *Int'l*, pg. 504
INFOVISTA S.A.S.—See Apax Partners LLP; *Int'l*, pg. 504
INFOVISTA UK LIMITED—See Apax Partners LLP; *Int'l*, pg. 504
INFOWAY SOFTWARE; *U.S. Private*, pg. 2074
INFO YATIRIM MENKUL DEGERLER A.S.; *Int'l*, pg. 3689
INFOYOGI LLC; *U.S. Private*, pg. 2074
INFOZEN, LLC—See The Carlyle Group Inc.; *U.S. Public*, pg. 2048
INFRAAVEST LIMITED; *Int'l*, pg. 3697
INFRABEL NV; *Int'l*, pg. 3697
INFRABUILD STEEL (MANUFACTURING) PTY LIMITED—See GFG Alliance Limited; *Int'l*, pg. 2956
INFRACAPITAL—See M&G Group Limited; *Int'l*, pg. 4612
INFRACOM GROUP AB; *Int'l*, pg. 3697
INFRA COMMERCE EOOD LTD.—See Trace Group Hold PLC; *Int'l*, pg. 7886
INFRACOMMERCE LTD.—See Transcosmos Inc.; *Int'l*, pg. 7898
INFRACON INFRASTRUKTUR SERVICE GMBH & CO. KG—See EnBW Energie Baden-Wurttemberg AG; *Int'l*, pg. 2400
INFRACORE SA—See AEVIS VICTORIA SA; *Int'l*, pg. 183
INFRA DEL SUR, S.A. DE C.V.—See Air Products & Chemicals, Inc.; *U.S. Public*, pg. 66
INFRAESTRUCTURA ENERGETICA NOVA, S.A.B. DE C.V.—See Sempra; *U.S. Public*, pg. 1863
INFRAESTRUCTURAS ENERGETICAS CASTELLANAS, S.L—See ACS, Actividades de Construccion y Servicios, S.A.; *Int'l*, pg. 114
INFRAESTRUCTURAS VIARIES DE CATALUNYA, S.A.—See ACS, Actividades de Construccion y Servicios, S.A.; *Int'l*, pg. 112
INFRAFLEGREA PROGETTO S.P.A.—See Salini Costruttori S.p.A.; *Int'l*, pg. 6493
INFRAHARTA BINA SDN. BHD.—See Infraharta Holdings Berhad; *Int'l*, pg. 3697
INFRAHARTA HOLDINGS BERHAD; *Int'l*, pg. 3697
INFRA HOLDING PLC; *Int'l*, pg. 3697
INFRA INDUSTRIES LTD.; *Int'l*, pg. 3697
INFRALINQ—See Koninklijke VolkerWessels N.V.; *Int'l*, pg. 4271
INFRA-METALS CO.—See Reliance Steel & Aluminum Co.; *U.S. Public*, pg. 1780

INFRA INDUSTRIES LTD.

CORPORATE AFFILIATIONS

INFRA-METALS CO.—See Reliance Steel & Aluminum Co.; *U.S. Public*, pg. 1780
INFRANET TECHNOLOGIES GROUP, INC.; *U.S. Private*, pg. 2074
INFRANODE HOLDING AB; *Int'l*, pg. 3697
INFRANOR B.V.—See Perrot Duval Holding S.A.; *Int'l*, pg. 5814
INFRANOR ELECTRONICS SAS—See Perrot Duval Holding S.A.; *Int'l*, pg. 5814
INFRANOR GMBH—See Perrot Duval Holding S.A.; *Int'l*, pg. 5814
INFRANOR GMBH—See Perrot Duval Holding S.A.; *Int'l*, pg. 5814
INFRANOR, INC.—See Perrot Duval Holding S.A.; *Int'l*, pg. 5814
INFRANOR INTER AG—See Perrot Duval Holding S.A.; *Int'l*, pg. 5814
INFRANOR LTD.—See Perrot Duval Holding S.A.; *Int'l*, pg. 5814
INFRANOR SA—See Perrot Duval Holding S.A.; *Int'l*, pg. 5814
INFRANOR SA—See Perrot Duval Holding S.A.; *Int'l*, pg. 5814
INFRANOR SAS—See Perrot Duval Holding S.A.; *Int'l*, pg. 5814
INFRAPLUS SAS—See Schneider Electric SE; *Int'l*, pg. 6627
INFRAPOST AG—See Die Schweizerische Post AG; *Int'l*, pg. 2113
INFRARAIL FIRENZE S.R.L.—See Ferrovie dello Stato Italiane S.p.A.; *Int'l*, pg. 2645
INFRARED INTEGRATED SYSTEMS LTD.—See Fortive Corporation; *U.S. Public*, pg. 871
INFRARED SYSTEMS GROUP, LLC—See Johnson Controls International plc; *Int'l*, pg. 3985
INFRARED SYSTEMS GROUP LTD.—See Johnson Controls International plc; *Int'l*, pg. 3985
INFRAREDX, INC.—See Nipro Corporation; *Int'l*, pg. 5361
INFRA, S.A. DE C.V.—See Air Products & Chemicals, Inc.; *U.S. Public*, pg. 66
INFRASAFE, INC.; *U.S. Private*, pg. 2074
INFRA SA—See PBG S.A.; *Int'l*, pg. 5765
INFRASERV GMBH & CO. HOCHST KG—See Lyondell-Basell Industries N.V.; *Int'l*, pg. 4608
INFRASERV US, LLC—See Brightstar Capital Partners, L.P.; *U.S. Private*, pg. 653
INFRASERV VAKUUMSERVICE GMBH—See Shimadzu Corporation; *Int'l*, pg. 6831
INFRASET PUBLIC COMPANY LIMITED; *Int'l*, pg. 3697
INFRA SILESIA S.A.—See Deutsche Bahn AG; *Int'l*, pg. 2051
INFRASOFT CORPORATION—See Bentley Systems, Inc.; *U.S. Public*, pg. 297
INFRASORS HOLDINGS LIMITED—See Afrimat Limited; *Int'l*, pg. 192
INFRASOURCE CONSTRUCTION, LLC—See Quanta Services, Inc.; *U.S. Public*, pg. 1751
INFRASOURCE INSTALLATION, LLC—See Quanta Services, Inc.; *U.S. Public*, pg. 1751
INFRASOURCE, LLC—See Quanta Services, Inc.; *U.S. Public*, pg. 1751
INFRASTROJ LTD.—See Trace Group Hold PLC; *Int'l*, pg. 7886
INFRASTRUCTURE ALTERNATIVES, INC.; *U.S. Private*, pg. 2075
INFRASTRUCTURE CAPITAL GROUP LTD.—See Foresight Group Holdings Limited; *Int'l*, pg. 2731
INFRASTRUCTURE DEVELOPMENT AND CONSTRUCTION CORPORATION; *Int'l*, pg. 3697
INFRASTRUCTURE DEVELOPMENTS CORP.; *U.S. Public*, pg. 1118
INFRASTRUCTURE & ENERGY ALTERNATIVES INC.—See MasTec, Inc.; *U.S. Public*, pg. 1393
INFRASTRUCTURE & ENERGY ALTERNATIVES, LLC—See MasTec, Inc.; *U.S. Public*, pg. 1393
INFRASTRUCTURE ENGINEERING CORP.—See Littlejohn & Co., LLC; *U.S. Private*, pg. 2469
INFRASTRUCTURE INDIA PLC; *Int'l*, pg. 3697
INFRASTRUCTURE LEASING & FINANCIAL SERVICES LIMITED; *Int'l*, pg. 3697
INFRASTRUCTURE MATERIALS CORP.; *U.S. Public*, pg. 1118
INFRASTRUCTURE PRODUCTS AUSTRALIA PTY. LTD.—See CRH plc; *Int'l*, pg. 1844
INFRASTRUCTURE SERVICES INC.; *U.S. Private*, pg. 2075
INFRASTRUCTURE SERVICES INC.—See Infrastructure Services Inc.; *U.S. Private*, pg. 2075
INFRASTRUCTURES URBAINES ET ROUTIERS SAS—See VINCI S.A.; *Int'l*, pg. 8222
INFRASYS (BEIJING) LTD.—See Beijing Shiji Information Technology Co., Ltd.; *Int'l*, pg. 956
INFRASYS INTERNATIONAL LIMITED—See Beijing Shiji Information Technology Co., Ltd.; *Int'l*, pg. 956
INFRASYS MALAYSIA SDN. BHD.—See Beijing Shiji Information Technology Co., Ltd.; *Int'l*, pg. 956
INFRATEC GMBH; *Int'l*, pg. 3698
INFRATEC INFRARED LLC—See InfraTec GmbH; *Int'l*, pg. 3698

INFRATEC INFRARED LTD.—See InfraTec GmbH; *Int'l*, pg. 3698
INFRATEK ASA—See Triton Advisers Limited; *Int'l*, pg. 7931
INFRATEK ELSIKKERHET AS—See Triton Advisers Limited; *Int'l*, pg. 7931
INFRATEK FINLAND OY—See Triton Advisers Limited; *Int'l*, pg. 7931
INFRATEK INSTALLASJON AS—See Triton Advisers Limited; *Int'l*, pg. 7931
INFRATEK NORGE AS—See VINCI S.A.; *Int'l*, pg. 8222
INFRATEK SECURITY FINLAND OY—See Triton Advisers Limited; *Int'l*, pg. 7931
INFRATEK SIKKERHET AS—See Triton Advisers Limited; *Int'l*, pg. 7931
INFRATEK SVERIGE AB—See Triton Advisers Limited; *Int'l*, pg. 7931
INFRATEL SERVICES SAS—See VINCI S.A.; *Int'l*, pg. 8223
INFRATIL LIMITED; *Int'l*, pg. 3698
INFRATOP INC.—See Vector Inc.; *Int'l*, pg. 8144
INFRAVIA CAPITAL PARTNERS SAS; *Int'l*, pg. 3699
INFRAWARE TECHNOLOGY, INC.—See Polaris Office Corp.; *Int'l*, pg. 5908
INFRAXIS AG—See Tas Tecnologia Avanzata Dei Sistemi Spa; *Int'l*, pg. 7464
INFRONEER HOLDINGS, INC.; *Int'l*, pg. 3699
INFRONT ASA; *Int'l*, pg. 3699
INFRONT AUSTRIA GMBH—See Dalian Wanda Group Corporation Ltd.; *Int'l*, pg. 1953
INFRONT CONSULTING GROUP (S) PTE LTD.—See Axiata Group Berhad; *Int'l*, pg. 768
INFRONT FINLAND OY—See Dalian Wanda Group Corporation Ltd.; *Int'l*, pg. 1953
INFRONT FRANCE SAS—See Dalian Wanda Group Corporation Ltd.; *Int'l*, pg. 1953
INFRONT GERMANY GMBH—See Dalian Wanda Group Corporation Ltd.; *Int'l*, pg. 1953
INFRONTIER LTD.—See First Pacific Company Limited; *Int'l*, pg. 2686
INFRONT ITALY S.R.L.—See Dalian Wanda Group Corporation Ltd.; *Int'l*, pg. 1953
INFRONT NETHERLANDS BV—See Dalian Wanda Group Corporation Ltd.; *Int'l*, pg. 1953
INFRONT PAN-ASIA PTE. LTD.—See Dalian Wanda Group Corporation Ltd.; *Int'l*, pg. 1953
INFRONT SPORTIF PAZARLAMA ANONIM SIRKETI—See Dalian Wanda Group Corporation Ltd.; *Int'l*, pg. 1953
INFRONT SPORTS & MEDIA AG—See Dalian Wanda Group Corporation Ltd.; *Int'l*, pg. 1953
INFRONT SPORTS & MEDIA (CHINA) CO., LTD—See Dalian Wanda Group Corporation Ltd.; *Int'l*, pg. 1953
INFSITRONIX TECHNOLOGY CORP.—See Sitronix Technology Corporation; *Int'l*, pg. 6965
INF - SOCIETA' AGRICOLA S.P.A.—See Assicurazioni Generali S.p.A.; *Int'l*, pg. 647
INFUND HOLDING CO., LTD.; *Int'l*, pg. 3699
INFURN (USA) LLC—See GI Ventures; *Int'l*, pg. 2960
INFUSCIENCE, INC.—See Option Care Health, Inc.; *U.S. Public*, pg. 1609
INFUSE MEDICAL; *U.S. Private*, pg. 2075
INFUSERVE AMERICA, INC.; *U.S. Private*, pg. 2075
INFUSIONCARE—See Option Care Health, Inc.; *U.S. Public*, pg. 1610
INFUSION DEVELOPMENT CORPORATION; *U.S. Private*, pg. 2075
INFUSION PARTNERS, LLC—See Option Care Health, Inc.; *U.S. Public*, pg. 1610
INFUSION PARTNERS OF BRUNSWICK, LLC—See Option Care Health, Inc.; *U.S. Public*, pg. 1610
INFUSION PARTNERS OF MELBOURNE, LLC—See Option Care Health, Inc.; *U.S. Public*, pg. 1610
INFUSIONSOFT, INC.; *U.S. Private*, pg. 2075
INFUSION SOFTWARE, INC.—See Thryv Holdings, Inc.; *U.S. Public*, pg. 2157
INFUSION SOLUTIONS OF PUERTO RICO, LLC—See The Kroger Co.; *U.S. Public*, pg. 2108
INFUSIONS SOLUTIONS CORP.—See Option Care Health, Inc.; *U.S. Public*, pg. 1610
INFUSYSTEM HOLDINGS, INC.; *U.S. Public*, pg. 1118
INFUSYSTEMS HOLDINGS, INC.; *U.S. Private*, pg. 2075
INFUTOR DATA SOLUTIONS, INC.; *U.S. Private*, pg. 2075
INFY CONSULTING B.V.—See Infosys Limited; *Int'l*, pg. 3696
ING3E GMBH—See VINCI S.A.; *Int'l*, pg. 8223
ING ADMINISTRADORA DE FONDOS DE INVERSIONES S.A.—See ING Groep N.V.; *Int'l*, pg. 3699
ING ADMINISTRADORA DE FONDOS DE PENSIONES Y CESANTIAS S.A.—See Grupo de Inversiones Suramericana S.A.; *Int'l*, pg. 3125
INGAGE NETWORKS, INC.; *U.S. Private*, pg. 2075
INGAL CIVIL PRODUCTS PTY LTD.—See Valmont Industries, Inc.; *U.S. Public*, pg. 2273
INGAL EPS—See Valmont Industries, Inc.; *U.S. Public*, pg. 2273
INGALLS DEVELOPMENT FOUNDATION INC.—See University of Chicago; *U.S. Public*, pg. 4308

INGALLS HEALTH SYSTEM INC.—See University of Chicago; *U.S. Private*, pg. 4308
INGALLS INFORMATION SECURITY LLC—See C3 Integrated Solutions Inc.; *U.S. Public*, pg. 710
INGALLS SHIPBUILDING, INC.—See Huntington Ingalls Industries, Inc.; *U.S. Public*, pg. 1072
INGASCO, INC.—See Mitsubishi Chemical Group Corporation; *Int'l*, pg. 4936
ING ASIA PACIFIC LTD.—See ING Groep N.V.; *Int'l*, pg. 3699
ING AUSTRALIA LTD.—See ING Groep N.V.; *Int'l*, pg. 3699
ING BANK A.S.—See ING Groep N.V.; *Int'l*, pg. 3700
ING BANK (AUSTRALIA) LIMITED—See ING Groep N.V.; *Int'l*, pg. 3700
ING BANK (EURASIA) ZAO—See ING Groep N.V.; *Int'l*, pg. 3700
ING BANK LUXEMBOURG SA—See ING Groep N.V.; *Int'l*, pg. 3700
ING BANK MAGYARORSZAG RT—See ING Groep N.V.; *Int'l*, pg. 3700
ING BANK N.V. - LONDON REPRESENTATIVE OFFICE—See ING Groep N.V.; *Int'l*, pg. 3700
ING BANK N.V.—See ING Groep N.V.; *Int'l*, pg. 3700
ING BANK OF CANADA—See The Bank of Nova Scotia; *Int'l*, pg. 7617
ING BANK SLASKI S.A.—See ING Groep N.V.; *Int'l*, pg. 3700
ING BELGIE N.V.—See ING Groep N.V.; *Int'l*, pg. 3700
ING BELGIUM SA/NV—See ING Groep N.V.; *Int'l*, pg. 3700
ING CAPITAL LLC—See ING Groep N.V.; *Int'l*, pg. 3700
ING COMMERCIAL BANKING—See ING Groep N.V.; *Int'l*, pg. 3700
ING COMMERCIAL FINANCE B.V.—See ING Groep N.V.; *Int'l*, pg. 3700
ING COMMUNICATIONS CORP.—See Aucnet Inc.; *Int'l*, pg. 700
ING COMPANIA DE INVERSIONES Y SERVICIOS LTDA—See Grupo de Inversiones Suramericana S.A.; *Int'l*, pg. 3125
ING CORPORATE INVESTMENTS B.V.—See ING Groep N.V.; *Int'l*, pg. 3700
INGDAN, INC.; *Int'l*, pg. 3701
ING-DIBA AG—See ING Groep N.V.; *Int'l*, pg. 3700
ING DUBLIN—See ING Groep N.V.; *Int'l*, pg. 3700
INGECAL S.A.S.—See Durr AG; *Int'l*, pg. 2233
INGECLEAN S.A.—See Rentokil Initial plc; *Int'l*, pg. 6287
INGE GMBH—See DuPont de Nemours, Inc.; *U.S. Public*, pg. 694
INGELEC S.A.—See Golden Minerals Company; *U.S. Public*, pg. 950
INGELHEIM PHARMACEUTICALS (PTY.) LTD.—See C.H. Boehringer Sohn AG & Co. KG; *Int'l*, pg. 1241
ING. EMIL NOVY—See Komax Holding AG; *Int'l*, pg. 4240
INGENERIA DE POLIURETANO FLEXIBLE S.L.—See Recticel S.A.; *Int'l*, pg. 6241
INGENESIS, INC.; *U.S. Private*, pg. 2075
INGENHOVEN ARCHITECTS INTERNATIONAL GMBH & CO. KG—See BKW AG; *Int'l*, pg. 1055
INGENIA-CAT S.L.—See Novanta Inc.; *U.S. Public*, pg. 1548
INGENIA COMMUNITIES GROUP; *Int'l*, pg. 8701
INGENICO ARGENTINA—See Apollo Global Management, Inc.; *U.S. Public*, pg. 151
INGENICO BUSINESS SUPPORT SAS—See Apollo Global Management, Inc.; *U.S. Public*, pg. 151
INGENICO CANADA LTD.—See Apollo Global Management, Inc.; *U.S. Public*, pg. 151
INGENICO CORP.—See Apollo Global Management, Inc.; *U.S. Public*, pg. 151
INGENICO OZ S.R.O.—See Apollo Global Management, Inc.; *U.S. Public*, pg. 151
INGENICO DO BRASIL LTDA.—See Apollo Global Management, Inc.; *U.S. Public*, pg. 152
INGENICO E-COMMERCE SOLUTIONS BVBA—See Apollo Global Management, Inc.; *U.S. Public*, pg. 152
INGENICO E-COMMERCE SOLUTIONS BV—See Apollo Global Management, Inc.; *U.S. Public*, pg. 152
INGENICO E-COMMERCE SOLUTIONS LTD.—See Apollo Global Management, Inc.; *U.S. Public*, pg. 152
INGENICO E-COMMERCE SOLUTIONS SAS—See Apollo Global Management, Inc.; *U.S. Public*, pg. 152
INGENICO FINANCIAL SOLUTIONS SA—See Apollo Global Management, Inc.; *U.S. Public*, pg. 151
INGENICO FRANCE SAS—See Apollo Global Management, Inc.; *U.S. Public*, pg. 151
INGENICO GMBH—See Apollo Global Management, Inc.; *U.S. Public*, pg. 151
INGENICO GROUP S.A.—See Apollo Global Management, Inc.; *U.S. Public*, pg. 151
INGENICO HEALTHCARE GMBH—See Apollo Global Management, Inc.; *U.S. Public*, pg. 151
INGENICO HUNGARY KFT.—See Apollo Global Management, Inc.; *U.S. Public*, pg. 151
INGENICO IBERIA, SL—See Apollo Global Management, Inc.; *U.S. Public*, pg. 151
INGENICO INTERNATIONAL (PACIFIC) PTY. LTD.—See Apollo Global Management, Inc.; *U.S. Public*, pg. 151

COMPANY NAME INDEX

INGENICO INTERNATIONAL (SINGAPORE) PTE. LTD.—See Apollo Global Management, Inc.; *U.S. Public*, pg. 151
INGENICO ITALIA SPA—See Apollo Global Management, Inc.; *U.S. Public*, pg. 151
INGENICO LLC—See Apollo Global Management, Inc.; *U.S. Public*, pg. 151
INGENICO MARKETING SOLUTIONS GMBH—See Apollo Global Management, Inc.; *U.S. Public*, pg. 151
INGENICO MEXICO S.A. DE C.V.—See Apollo Global Management, Inc.; *U.S. Public*, pg. 151
INGENICOMM, LLC—See Parsons Corporation; *U.S. Public*, pg. 1651
INGENICO ODEME SISTEM COZUMLERI A.S.—See Apollo Global Management, Inc.; *U.S. Public*, pg. 152
INGENICO POLSKA SP. Z O.O—See Apollo Global Management, Inc.; *U.S. Public*, pg. 152
INGENICO SOLUTIONS (MALAYSIA) SDN. BHD.—See Apollo Global Management, Inc.; *U.S. Public*, pg. 152
INGENICO SWITZERLAND SA—See Apollo Global Management, Inc.; *U.S. Public*, pg. 152
INGENICO TELESINCRO—See Apollo Global Management, Inc.; *U.S. Public*, pg. 151
INGENICO TERMINALS SAS—See Apollo Global Management, Inc.; *U.S. Public*, pg. 152
INGENICO (THAILAND) CO., LTD.—See Apollo Global Management, Inc.; *U.S. Public*, pg. 151
INGENICO (UK) LTD.—See Apollo Global Management, Inc.; *U.S. Public*, pg. 151
INGENICO VENTURES SAS—See Apollo Global Management, Inc.; *U.S. Public*, pg. 152
INGENICO VIETNAM CO., LTD.—See Apollo Global Management, Inc.; *U.S. Public*, pg. 152
INGENICS AG; *Int'l*, pg. 3701
INGENICS CONSULTING (SHANGHAI) CO., LTD.—See inGenics AG; *Int'l*, pg. 3701
INGENICS CORPORATION—See inGenics AG; *Int'l*, pg. 3701
INGENIC SEMICONDUCTOR CO., LTD.; *Int'l*, pg. 3701
INGENICS S.A. DE C.V.—See inGenics AG; *Int'l*, pg. 3701
INGENICS SAS—See inGenics AG; *Int'l*, pg. 3701
INGENICS S.R.O.—See inGenics AG; *Int'l*, pg. 3701
INGENIERIA DE LOS RECURSOS NATURALES, S.A.—See Grupo Villar Mir, S.A.U., *Int'l*, pg. 0100
INGENIERIA DE SOFTWARE BANCARIO, S.L.—See Banco Santander, S.A.; *Int'l*, pg. 826
INGENIERIA, ESTUDIOS Y CONSTRUCCIONES, S.A.—See Iberdrola, S.A.; *Int'l*, pg. 3573
INGENIERIAS Y BIOGAS, S.L.; *Int'l*, pg. 3701
INGENIERIA Y CONSTRUCCION DE MATRICES, S.A.—See Acek Desarrollo y Gestion Industrial SL; *Int'l*, pg. 98
INGENIERIA Y CONSTRUCCION SIGDO KOPPERS GROUP S.A.—See Sigdo Koppers S.A.; *Int'l*, pg. 6907
INGENIERIA Y CONSTRUCCION SIGDO KOPPERS S.A.—See Sigdo Koppers S.A.; *Int'l*, pg. 6907
INGENIERIA Y DESARROLLO TECNOLOGICO S.A.—See State Grid Corporation of China; *Int'l*, pg. 7183
INGENIERIA Y SERVICIOS METALCROM LTDA.—See Parker Hannifin Corporation; *U.S. Public*, pg. 1641
INGENIEROS ASESORES, S.A.; *Int'l*, pg. 3701
INGENIEROS CIVILES ASOCIADOS MEXICO, S.A.—See Empresas ICA S.A.B. de C.V.; *Int'l*, pg. 2391
INGENIEROS CIVILES ASOCIADOS, S. A. DE C. V.—See Empresas ICA S.A.B. de C.V.; *Int'l*, pg. 2391
INGENIEURBURO KIEFER & VOSS GMBH—See Alpiq Holding AG; *Int'l*, pg. 372
INGENIEURBURO OTTO KUEHNEN—See Nederman Holding AB; *Int'l*, pg. 5190
INGENIEURBURO PROF. DR.-ING. VOGT PLANUNGSGESELLSCHAFT MBH—See BKW AG; *Int'l*, pg. 1055
INGENIEURGESELLSCHAFT AUTO UND VERKEHR—See Porsche Automobil Holding SE; *Int'l*, pg. 5929
INGENIEURGESELLSCHAFT FUR ENERGIE UND KRAFTWERKSTECHNIK MBH—See VINCI S.A.; *Int'l*, pg. 8223
INGENIEUR GUDANG BERHAD; *Int'l*, pg. 3701
INGENIEURSBUREAU EBATECH B.V.—See Vattenfall AB; *Int'l*, pg. 8136
INGENIEURSBUREAU VOOR SYSTEMEN EN OCTROOIEN SPANSTAAL B.V.—See Ronesans Holding A.S.; *Int'l*, pg. 6396
INGENIO-FILIALE DE LOTO-QUEBEC, INC.—See Loto-Quebec; *Int'l*, pg. 4559
INGENIO, LLC—See Thryv Holdings, Inc.; *U.S. Public*, pg. 2157
INGENIOR IVAR PETTERSEN AS; *Int'l*, pg. 3701
INGENIOUS DESIGNS LLC—See Qurate Retail, Inc.; *U.S. Public*, pg. 1758
INGENIOUS ENE-CARBON NEW MATERIALS CO., LTD.; *Int'l*, pg. 3701
INGENIOUS INC.—See John Wood Group PLC; *Int'l*, pg. 3984
INGENIOUS MEDIA LIMITED; *Int'l*, pg. 3701
INGENIOUS MED, INC.—See Constellation Software Inc.; *Int'l*, pg. 1774

INGENIO Y REFINERIA SAN MARTIN DEL TABACAL S.A.—See Seaboard Corporation; *U.S. Public*, pg. 1850
INGENIUM ARCHIAL LTD.—See The Ingenium Group Inc.; *Int'l*, pg. 7655
THE INGENIUM GROUP INC.; *Int'l*, pg. 7655
INGENIUM PROFESSIONAL SERVICES INC; *U.S. Private*, pg. 2075
INGENIUM; *U.S. Private*, pg. 2075
INGENIUS, LLC; *U.S. Private*, pg. 2075
INGENIUX CORP.; *U.S. Private*, pg. 2075
INGENJORSFIRMAN GA LINDBERG AB—See Indutrade AB; *Int'l*, pg. 3679
INGENJORSFIRMAN GEOTECH AB—See Indutrade AB; *Int'l*, pg. 3679
INGENTA PLC; *Int'l*, pg. 3701
INGEN TECHNOLOGIES, INC.; *U.S. Public*, pg. 1118
INGENUITY ASSOCIATES, LLC; *U.S. Private*, pg. 2075
INGENUITY CONSULTING PARTNERS, INC.—See Speridian Technologies, LLC; *U.S. Private*, pg. 3756
INGENUITY, INC.; *U.S. Private*, pg. 2075
INGENUITY MEDIA GROUP AT THE MARTIN AGENCY—See The Interpublic Group of Companies, Inc.; *U.S. Public*, pg. 2102
INGENUITY PROPERTY INVESTMENTS LIMITED; *Int'l*, pg. 3702
INGEPAR SA—See Groupe BPCE; *Int'l*, pg. 3098
INGEROSEC CORPORATION—See SE Corporation; *Int'l*, pg. 6660
INGERSOLL CUTTING TOOL COMPANY—See Berkshire Hathaway Inc.; *U.S. Public*, pg. 307
INGERSOLL-DRESSER PUMPS S.R.L.—See Flowserve Corporation; *U.S. Public*, pg. 856
INGERSOLL MACHINES TOOLS, INC. (IMTA)—See Camozzi Group; *Int'l*, pg. 1274
INGERSOLL PAPER BOX CO LIMITED; *Int'l*, pg. 3702
INGERSOLL PRODUCTION SYSTEMS—See Dalian Tonghai Machinery & Electronic Equipment Co., Ltd.; *Int'l*, pg. 1952
INGERSOLL PRODUCTS COMPANY—See Amerop Products; *U.S. Private*, pg. 261
INGERSOLL-RAND AB—See Ingersoll Rand Inc.; *U.S. Public*, pg. 1121
INGERSOLL-RAND AIR SOLUTIONS HIBON SARL—See Ingersoll Rand Inc.; *U.S. Public*, pg. 1120
INGERSOLL-RAND ARCHITECTURAL HARDWARE (AUSTRALIA) PTY LIMITED—See Ingersoll Rand Inc.; *U.S. Public*, pg. 1120
INGERSOLL-RAND ARCHITECTURAL HARDWARE LIMITED—See Ingersoll Rand Inc.; *U.S. Public*, pg. 1121
INGERSOLL-RAND (AUSTRALIA) LTD.—See Ingersoll Rand Inc.; *U.S. Public*, pg. 1121
INGERSOLL-RAND BEST-MATIC AB—See Ingersoll Rand Inc.; *U.S. Public*, pg. 1121
INGERSOLL-RAND CHARITABLE FOUNDATION—See Ingersoll Rand Inc.; *U.S. Public*, pg. 1121
INGERSOLL-RAND (CHINA) INDUSTRIAL EQUIPMENT MANUFACTURING CO., LTD.—See Ingersoll Rand Inc.; *U.S. Public*, pg. 1120
INGERSOLL-RAND (CHINA) INVESTMENT COMPANY LIMITED—See Ingersoll Rand Inc.; *U.S. Public*, pg. 1120
INGERSOLL-RAND COLOMBIA S.A.S.—See Ingersoll Rand Inc.; *U.S. Public*, pg. 1120
INGERSOLL-RAND COMPANY (CHILE) Y CIA LTDA.—See Ingersoll Rand Inc.; *U.S. Public*, pg. 1121
INGERSOLL-RAND COMPANY LIMITED—See Ingersoll Rand Inc.; *U.S. Public*, pg. 1120
INGERSOLL-RAND COMPANY LIMITED (UK)—See Ingersoll Rand Inc.; *U.S. Public*, pg. 1121
INGERSOLL-RAND COMPANY SA (PTY) LTD.—See Ingersoll Rand Inc.; *U.S. Public*, pg. 1121
INGERSOLL-RAND COMPANY—See Ingersoll Rand Inc.; *U.S. Public*, pg. 1120
INGERSOLL-RAND DO BRASIL LTDA.—See Ingersoll Rand Inc.; *U.S. Public*, pg. 1122
INGERSOLL-RAND EQUIPEMENTS DE PRODUCTION S.A.S.—See Ingersoll Rand Inc.; *U.S. Public*, pg. 1121
INGERSOLL-RAND EQUIPMENT MANUFACTURING CZECH REPUBLIC LIMITED—See Trane Technologies Plc; *U.S. Public*, pg. 7892
INGERSOLL-RAND EQUIPMENT MANUFACTURING CZECH REPUBLIC S.R.O.—See Trane Technologies Plc; *U.S. Public*, pg. 7892
INGERSOLL-RAND EUROPEAN HOLDING COMPANY B.V.—See Ingersoll Rand Inc.; *U.S. Public*, pg. 1121
INGERSOLL-RAND EUROPEAN SALES LIMITED—See Ingersoll Rand Inc.; *U.S. Public*, pg. 1121
INGERSOLL-RAND FINLAND OY—See Ingersoll Rand Inc.; *U.S. Public*, pg. 1121
INGERSOLL-RAND GMBH—See Ingersoll Rand Inc.; *U.S. Public*, pg. 1121
INGERSOLL-RAND (GUILIN) TOOLS COMPANY LIMITED—See Ingersoll Rand Inc.; *U.S. Public*, pg. 1120
INGERSOLL-RAND HOLDINGS LTD.—See Ingersoll Rand Inc.; *U.S. Public*, pg. 1121

INGERSOLL-RAND (HONG KONG) LIMITED—See Ingersoll Rand Inc.; *U.S. Public*, pg. 1120
INGERSOLL RAND INC.; *U.S. Public*, pg. 1118
INGERSOLL RAND (INDIA) LIMITED; *Int'l*, pg. 3702
INGERSOLL-RAND (INDIA) PRIVATE LTD.—See Ingersoll Rand Inc.; *U.S. Public*, pg. 1121
INGERSOLL-RAND INDUSTRIAL TECHNOLOGIES - COMPRESSED AIR SOLUTIONS—See Ingersoll Rand Inc.; *U.S. Public*, pg. 1121
INGERSOLL-RAND INDUSTRIAL TECHNOLOGIES - TOOLS & LIFTING/MATERIAL HANDLING SOLUTIONS—See Ingersoll Rand Inc.; *U.S. Public*, pg. 1122
INGERSOLL-RAND INTERNATIONAL LIMITED—See Ingersoll Rand Inc.; *U.S. Public*, pg. 1121
INGERSOLL-RAND IRISH HOLDINGS—See Ingersoll Rand Inc.; *U.S. Public*, pg. 1121
INGERSOLL-RAND ITALIANA S.P.A.—See Ingersoll Rand Inc.; *U.S. Public*, pg. 1121
INGERSOLL-RAND ITALIA S.R.L.—See Ingersoll Rand Inc.; *U.S. Public*, pg. 1121
INGERSOLL-RAND ITS JAPAN LTD.—See Ingersoll Rand Inc.; *U.S. Public*, pg. 1121
INGERSOLL-RAND KOREA LIMITED—See Ingersoll Rand Inc.; *U.S. Public*, pg. 1121
INGERSOLL-RAND MACHINERY (SHANGHAI) COMPANY LIMITED—See Ingersoll Rand Inc.; *U.S. Public*, pg. 1121
INGERSOLL-RAND MALAYSIA CO. SDN. BHD.—See Ingersoll Rand Inc.; *U.S. Public*, pg. 1121
INGERSOLL-RAND NETHERLANDS B.V.—See Ingersoll Rand Inc.; *U.S. Public*, pg. 1121
INGERSOLL-RAND POLSKA SP.Z.O.O.—See Ingersoll Rand Inc.; *U.S. Public*, pg. 1121
INGERSOLL-RAND S.A. DE C.V.—See Ingersoll Rand Inc.; *U.S. Public*, pg. 1121
INGERSOLL RAND S.E. ASIA (PRIVATE) LIMITED—See Ingersoll Rand Inc.; *U.S. Public*, pg. 1121
INGERSOLL-RAND SECURITY TECHNOLOGIES CONSULTANTS—See Allegion Public Limited Company; *Int'l*, pg. 335
INGERSOLL-RAND SERVICES AND TRADING LIMITED LIABILITY COMPANY—See Ingersoll Rand Inc.; *U.S. Public*, pg. 1121
INGERSOLL-RAND SERVICIOS, S.A.—See Ingersoll Rand Inc.; *U.S. Public*, pg. 1121
INGERSOLL-RAND SOUTH EAST ASIA (PTE.) LTD.—See Ingersoll Rand Inc.; *U.S. Public*, pg. 1121
INGERSOLL-RAND US TRANE HOLDINGS CORPORATION—See Ingersoll Rand Inc.; *U.S. Public*, pg. 1121
INGERSOLL-RAND WORLDWIDE CAPITAL S.A.R.L.—See Ingersoll Rand Inc.; *U.S. Public*, pg. 1121
INGERSOLL TILLAGE GROUP, INC.; *Int'l*, pg. 3702
INGERSOLL WERKZEUGE GMBH—See Berkshire Hathaway Inc.; *U.S. Public*, pg. 307
INGESPORT—See Corpfin Capital SA; *Int'l*, pg. 1802
INGEST FACILITY S.P.A.—See Prelios S.p.A.; *Int'l*, pg. 5959
INGEUS AB—See ModivCare, Inc.; *U.S. Public*, pg. 1455
INGEUS AG—See ModivCare, Inc.; *U.S. Public*, pg. 1455
INGEUS GMBH—See ModivCare, Inc.; *U.S. Public*, pg. 1455
INGEUS LLC—See ModivCare, Inc.; *U.S. Public*, pg. 1455
INGEUS SP Z.O.O.—See ModivCare, Inc.; *U.S. Public*, pg. 1455
INGEUS UK LIMITED—See ModivCare, Inc.; *U.S. Public*, pg. 1455
INGEVEC S.A.; *Int'l*, pg. 3702
INGEVITY CORPORATION; *U.S. Public*, pg. 1122
INGEVITY GEORGIA, LLC—See Ingevity Corporation; *U.S. Public*, pg. 1122
INGEVITY HOLDINGS SPRL—See Ingevity Corporation; *U.S. Public*, pg. 1122
INGEVITY SOUTH CAROLINA, LLC—See Ingevity Corporation; *U.S. Public*, pg. 1122
ING FINANCIAL HOLDINGS CORPORATION—See ING Groep N.V.; *Int'l*, pg. 3700
ING FINANCIAL SERVICES LLC—See ING Groep N.V.; *Int'l*, pg. 3700
ING GROEP N.V.; *Int'l*, pg. 3699
INGHAM ENTERPRISES PTY LIMITED—See Inghams Group Limited; *Int'l*, pg. 3702
INGHAM FARM CENTRE PTY. LTD.—See Nutrien Ltd.; *Int'l*, pg. 5493
INGHAMS ENTERPRISES PTY LTD.—See TPG Capital, L.P.; *U.S. Public*, pg. 2174
INGHAMS GROUP LIMITED; *Int'l*, pg. 3702
ING INSURANCE INTERNATIONAL—See ING Groep N.V.; *Int'l*, pg. 3700
ING INVESTMENT MANAGEMENT—See Grupo de Inversiones Suramericana S.A.; *Int'l*, pg. 3125
INGKA HOLDING B.V.—See Stichting INGKA Foundation; *Int'l*, pg. 7214
ING. KARL VOITL GESELLSCHAFT M.B.H.—See Swietelsky Baugesellschaft m.b.H.; *Int'l*, pg. 7367
ING LEASE BELGIUM N.V.—See ING Groep N.V.; *Int'l*, pg. 3700

INGHAMS GROUP LIMITED

CORPORATE AFFILIATIONS

Company Index

ING LEASE (EURASIA) LLC—See ING Groep N.V.; *Int'l*, pg. 3700
ING LEASE (NEDERLAND) B.V.—See ING Groep N.V.; *Int'l*, pg. 3700
INGLE-BARR INC.; *U.S. Private*, pg. 2075
INGLEFIELD/OGILVY & MATHER CARIBBEAN LTD.—See WPP plc; *Int'l*, pg. 8484
INGLENOOK AT BRIGHTON; *U.S. Private*, pg. 2075
INGLESIDE AT ROCK CREEK; *U.S. Private*, pg. 2076
INGLESIDE CAPITAL CO., INC.—See A.C. Israel Enterprises, Inc.; *U.S. Private*, pg. 24
INGLESIDE COGENERATION LIMITED PARTNERSHIP—See Occidental Petroleum Corporation; *U.S. Public*, pg. 1561
INGLES MARKETS, INCORPORATED; *U.S. Public*, pg. 1122
INGLET BLAIR LLC—See QC Ally, LLC; *U.S. Private*, pg. 3312
INGLETT & STUBBS, LLC; *U.S. Private*, pg. 2076
INGLEWOOD DAY NURSERY AND COLLEGE LTD.—See Bain Capital, LP; *U.S. Private*, pg. 437
INGLEWOOD IMAGING CENTER LLC; *U.S. Private*, pg. 2076
INGLEWOOD PARK CEMETERY INC.; *U.S. Private*, pg. 2076
ING LUXEMBOURG S.A.—See ING Groep N.V.; *Int'l*, pg. 3700
ING MENKUL DEGERLER A.S.—See ING Groep N.V.; *Int'l*, pg. 3700
INGOLSTADTER ASPHALTMISCHWERKE GMBH & CO. KG—See H. Geiger GmbH; *Int'l*, pg. 3194
INGOMAR PACKING; *U.S. Private*, pg. 2076
INGO MAURER GMBH; *Int'l*, pg. 3702
INGO MAURER LLC—See Ingo Maurer GmbH; *Int'l*, pg. 3702
INGOSSTRAKH INSURANCE COMPANY; *Int'l*, pg. 3702
INGOSSTRAKH - INVESTMENTS ASSET MANAGEMENT, JSC—See Ingosstrakh Insurance Company; *Int'l*, pg. 3702
INGOT METAL COMPANY LIMITED; *Int'l*, pg. 3702
ING. OTTO RICHTER AND CO STRASSENMARKIERUNGEN GMBH—See PORR AG; *Int'l*, pg. 5923
ING PORTFOY YONETIMI A.S.—See ING Groep N.V.; *Int'l*, pg. 3700
INGRA D.D.; *Int'l*, pg. 3702
ING. RADL-BAU GMBH—See PORR AG; *Int'l*, pg. 5923
INGRADO S.R.L.—See Ariston Holding N.V.; *Int'l*, pg. 567
INGRAIN CONSTRUCTION, LLC; *U.S. Private*, pg. 2076
INGRAIN, INC.—See Halliburton Company; *U.S. Public*, pg. 981
INGRAM & ASSOCIATES, LLC—See UnitedHealth Group Incorporated; *U.S. Public*, pg. 2241
INGRAM BARGE COMPANY—See Ingram Industries, Inc.; *U.S. Private*, pg. 2076
INGRAM BOOK COMPANY—See Ingram Industries, Inc.; *U.S. Private*, pg. 2076
INGRAM BOOK GROUP INC.—See Ingram Industries, Inc.; *U.S. Private*, pg. 2076
INGRAM CONTENT GROUP INC.—See Ingram Industries, Inc.; *U.S. Private*, pg. 2076
INGRAM CUSTOMER SYSTEMS INC.—See Ingram Industries, Inc.; *U.S. Private*, pg. 2076
INGRAM D.D.; *Int'l*, pg. 3702
INGRAM DISTRIBUTION GROUP INC.—See Ingram Industries, Inc.; *U.S. Private*, pg. 2077
INGRAM ENTERPRISES INC.; *U.S. Private*, pg. 2076
INGRAM ENTERTAINMENT INC. - INDIANAPOLIS—See Ingram Entertainment Inc.; *U.S. Private*, pg. 2076
INGRAM ENTERTAINMENT INC.; *U.S. Private*, pg. 2076
INGRAM EQUIPMENT COMPANY, LLC.; *U.S. Private*, pg. 2076
INGRAM INDUSTRIES, INC.; *U.S. Private*, pg. 2076
INGRAM MACROTRON GMBH—See Hainan Traffic Administration Holding Co., Ltd.; *Int'l*, pg. 3214
INGRAM MARINE GROUP—See Ingram Industries, Inc.; *U.S. Private*, pg. 2077
INGRAM MATERIALS CO.—See Ingram Industries, Inc.; *U.S. Private*, pg. 2077
INGRAM MICRO AB—See Hainan Traffic Administration Holding Co., Ltd.; *Int'l*, pg. 3215
INGRAM MICRO AB—See Hainan Traffic Administration Holding Co., Ltd.; *Int'l*, pg. 3214
INGRAM MICRO AMERICAS INC.—See Hainan Traffic Administration Holding Co., Ltd.; *Int'l*, pg. 3214
INGRAM MICRO APS—See Hainan Traffic Administration Holding Co., Ltd.; *Int'l*, pg. 3214
INGRAM MICRO ARGENTINA, S.A.—See Hainan Traffic Administration Holding Co., Ltd.; *Int'l*, pg. 3214
INGRAM MICRO ASIA LTD.—See Hainan Traffic Administration Holding Co., Ltd.; *Int'l*, pg. 3214
INGRAM MICRO ASIA PACIFIC PTE. LTD—See Hainan Traffic Administration Holding Co., Ltd.; *Int'l*, pg. 3214
INGRAM MICRO A/S—See Hainan Traffic Administration Holding Co., Ltd.; *Int'l*, pg. 3215
INGRAM MICRO AUSTRALIA PTY LTD—See Hainan Traffic Administration Holding Co., Ltd.; *Int'l*, pg. 3214
INGRAM MICRO BILIIM SISTEMLERI A.S.—See Hainan Traffic Administration Holding Co., Ltd.; *Int'l*, pg. 3213
INGRAM MICRO BRASIL LTDA.—See Hainan Traffic Administration Holding Co., Ltd.; *Int'l*, pg. 3214
INGRAM MICRO BVBA—See Hainan Traffic Administration Holding Co., Ltd.; *Int'l*, pg. 3214
INGRAM MICRO BV—See Hainan Traffic Administration Holding Co., Ltd.; *Int'l*, pg. 3214
INGRAM MICRO CFS BENELUX B.V.—See Hainan Traffic Administration Holding Co., Ltd.; *Int'l*, pg. 3214
INGRAM MICRO CFS COMMERCE B.V.—See Hainan Traffic Administration Holding Co., Ltd.; *Int'l*, pg. 3214
INGRAM MICRO CFS E-BUSINESS GMBH—See Hainan Traffic Administration Holding Co., Ltd.; *Int'l*, pg. 3214
INGRAM MICRO CFS ESERVICES B.V.—See Hainan Traffic Administration Holding Co., Ltd.; *Int'l*, pg. 3214
INGRAM MICRO CFS FULFILMENT GMBH—See Hainan Traffic Administration Holding Co., Ltd.; *Int'l*, pg. 3214
INGRAM MICRO CFS FULFILMENT LTD—See Hainan Traffic Administration Holding Co., Ltd.; *Int'l*, pg. 3214
INGRAM MICRO CFS GERMANY GMBH—See Hainan Traffic Administration Holding Co., Ltd.; *Int'l*, pg. 3214
INGRAM MICRO CFS INTERNATIONAL B.V.—See Hainan Traffic Administration Holding Co., Ltd.; *Int'l*, pg. 3214
INGRAM MICRO (CHINA) LTD—See Hainan Traffic Administration Holding Co., Ltd.; *Int'l*, pg. 3214
INGRAM MICRO CONSUMER ELECTRONICS—See Hainan Traffic Administration Holding Co., Ltd.; *Int'l*, pg. 3214
INGRAM MICRO DATA CAPTURE/POS DIVISION—See Hainan Traffic Administration Holding Co., Ltd.; *Int'l*, pg. 3214
INGRAM MICRO DISTRIBUTION GMBH—See Hainan Traffic Administration Holding Co., Ltd.; *Int'l*, pg. 3214
INGRAM MICRO GMBH—See Hainan Traffic Administration Holding Co., Ltd.; *Int'l*, pg. 3214
INGRAM MICRO GMBH—See Hainan Traffic Administration Holding Co., Ltd.; *Int'l*, pg. 3214
INGRAM MICRO GMBH—See Hainan Traffic Administration Holding Co., Ltd.; *Int'l*, pg. 3215
INGRAM MICRO HOLDINGS (AUSTRALIA) PTY LTD—See Hainan Traffic Administration Holding Co., Ltd.; *Int'l*, pg. 3214
INGRAM MICRO HOLDINGS LIMITED—See Hainan Traffic Administration Holding Co., Ltd.; *Int'l*, pg. 3214
INGRAM MICRO HOSTING B.V.—See Hainan Traffic Administration Holding Co., Ltd.; *Int'l*, pg. 3214
INGRAM MICRO INC.—See Hainan Traffic Administration Holding Co., Ltd.; *Int'l*, pg. 3213
INGRAM MICRO (INDIA) EXPORTS PTE LTD—See Hainan Traffic Administration Holding Co., Ltd.; *Int'l*, pg. 3214
INGRAM MICRO INDIA PRIVATE LIMITED—See Hainan Traffic Administration Holding Co., Ltd.; *Int'l*, pg. 3214
INGRAM MICRO INDIA SSC PRIVATE LIMITED—See Hainan Traffic Administration Holding Co., Ltd.; *Int'l*, pg. 3214
INGRAM MICRO ISRAEL LTD—See Hainan Traffic Administration Holding Co., Ltd.; *Int'l*, pg. 3214
INGRAM MICRO ISTANBUL MERKEZ—See Hainan Traffic Administration Holding Co., Ltd.; *Int'l*, pg. 3214
INGRAM MICRO LEVANT S.A.L.—See Hainan Traffic Administration Holding Co., Ltd.; *Int'l*, pg. 3214
INGRAM MICRO LOGISTICS LP—See Hainan Traffic Administration Holding Co., Ltd.; *Int'l*, pg. 3214
INGRAM MICRO MALAYSIA SDN BHD—See Hainan Traffic Administration Holding Co., Ltd.; *Int'l*, pg. 3214
INGRAM MICRO MEXICO LLC—See Hainan Traffic Administration Holding Co., Ltd.; *Int'l*, pg. 3215
INGRAM MICRO MEXICO, S.A. DE C.V.—See Hainan Traffic Administration Holding Co., Ltd.; *Int'l*, pg. 3215
INGRAM MICRO - MIAMI—See Hainan Traffic Administration Holding Co., Ltd.; *Int'l*, pg. 3214
INGRAM MICRO MOBILITY AS—See Hainan Traffic Administration Holding Co., Ltd.; *Int'l*, pg. 3215
INGRAM MICRO MOBILITY FINLAND OY—See Hainan Traffic Administration Holding Co., Ltd.; *Int'l*, pg. 3215
INGRAM MICRO MOBILITY PHILIPPINES, INC.—See Hainan Traffic Administration Holding Co., Ltd.; *Int'l*, pg. 3215
INGRAM MICRO MOBILITY—See Hainan Traffic Administration Holding Co., Ltd.; *Int'l*, pg. 3215
INGRAM MICRO (NZ) LIMITED—See Hainan Traffic Administration Holding Co., Ltd.; *Int'l*, pg. 3214
INGRAM MICRO OY—See Hainan Traffic Administration Holding Co., Ltd.; *Int'l*, pg. 3215
INGRAM MICRO S.A.C.—See Hainan Traffic Administration Holding Co., Ltd.; *Int'l*, pg. 3215
INGRAM MICRO SERVICES GMBH—See Hainan Traffic Administration Holding Co., Ltd.; *Int'l*, pg. 3215
INGRAM MICRO SERVICES LTD.—See Hainan Traffic Administration Holding Co., Ltd.; *Int'l*, pg. 3215
INGRAM MICRO (SHANGHAI) COMMERCIAL FACTORING CO., LTD.—See Hainan Traffic Administration Holding Co., Ltd.; *Int'l*, pg. 3214
INGRAM MICRO SLOVAKIA, S. R. O—See Hainan Traffic Administration Holding Co., Ltd.; *Int'l*, pg. 3215
INGRAM MICRO SL—See Hainan Traffic Administration Holding Co., Ltd.; *Int'l*, pg. 3215
INGRAM MICRO SOUTHERN AFRICA (PROPRIETARY) LIMITED—See Hainan Traffic Administration Holding Co., Ltd.; *Int'l*, pg. 3215
INGRAM MICRO SP. Z O.O.—See Hainan Traffic Administration Holding Co., Ltd.; *Int'l*, pg. 3215
INGRAM MICRO SRL—See Hainan Traffic Administration Holding Co., Ltd.; *Int'l*, pg. 3215
INGRAM MICRO (THAILAND) LTD—See Hainan Traffic Administration Holding Co., Ltd.; *Int'l*, pg. 3214
INGRAM MICRO (UK) LIMITED—See Hainan Traffic Administration Holding Co., Ltd.; *Int'l*, pg. 3214
INGRAM MOTOR GROUP LIMITED; *Int'l*, pg. 3702
INGRAM PERIODICALS INC.—See Ingram Industries, Inc.; *U.S. Private*, pg. 2076
INGRAM READYMIX, INC.; *U.S. Private*, pg. 2077
INGRAM SQUARE PRESERVATION, L.P.—See Apartment Investment and Management Company; *U.S. Public*, pg. 144
INGRASYS TECHNOLOGY INC.—See Hon Hai Precision Industry Co., Ltd.; *Int'l*, pg. 3457
ING REAL ESTATE B.V.—See ING Groep N.V.; *Int'l*, pg. 3700
ING REAL ESTATE DEVELOPMENT ITALY S.R.L.—See ING Groep N.V.; *Int'l*, pg. 3700
INGREDIENTES NATURALES SELECCIONADOS S.L.—See International Flavors & Fragrances Inc.; *U.S. Public*, pg. 1152
INGREDIENTS, INC.—See Cinven Limited; *Int'l*, pg. 1611
INGREDIENTS SOLUTIONS INC.; *U.S. Private*, pg. 2077
INGREDIENTS UNLIMITED, INC.—See Arsenal Capital Management LP; *U.S. Private*, pg. 337
INGREDION ANZ PTY LTD—See Ingredion Incorporated; *U.S. Public*, pg. 1123
INGREDION ANZ PTY LTD.—See Ingredion Incorporated; *U.S. Public*, pg. 1123
INGREDION APAC EMEA SHARED SERVICES SDN. BHD.—See Ingredion Incorporated; *U.S. Public*, pg. 1123
INGREDION ARGENTINA S.A.—See Ingredion Incorporated; *U.S. Public*, pg. 1123
INGREDION BRASIL INGREDIENTES INDUSTRIAIS LTDA.—See Ingredion Incorporated; *U.S. Public*, pg. 1123
INGREDION CANADA CORPORATION—See Ingredion Incorporated; *U.S. Public*, pg. 1123
INGREDION CHILE S.A.—See Ingredion Incorporated; *U.S. Public*, pg. 1123
INGREDION CHINA LIMITED—See Ingredion Incorporated; *U.S. Public*, pg. 1123
INGREDION COLOMBIA S.A.—See Ingredion Incorporated; *U.S. Public*, pg. 1123
INGREDION INCORPORATED; *U.S. Public*, pg. 1122
INGREDION INDIA PRIVATE LIMITED—See Ingredion Incorporated; *U.S. Public*, pg. 1123
INGREDION JAPAN K.K.—See Ingredion Incorporated; *U.S. Public*, pg. 1123
INGREDION KOREA INCORPORATED—See Sajo Industry Co., Ltd.; *Int'l*, pg. 6485
INGREDION MALAYSIA SDN. BHD.—See Ingredion Incorporated; *U.S. Public*, pg. 1123
INGREDION MEXICO, S.A. DE C.V.—See Ingredion Incorporated; *U.S. Public*, pg. 1123
INGREDION PHILIPPINES, INC.—See Ingredion Incorporated; *U.S. Public*, pg. 1123
INGREDION SINGAPORE PTE. LTD.—See Ingredion Incorporated; *U.S. Public*, pg. 1123
INGREDION SOUTH AFRICA (PTY) LIMITED—See Ingredion Incorporated; *U.S. Public*, pg. 1123
INGREDION SOUTH AFRICA (PTY) LTD.—See Ingredion Incorporated; *U.S. Public*, pg. 1123
INGREDION SWEETENER & STARCH (THAILAND) CO., LTD.—See Ingredion Incorporated; *U.S. Public*, pg. 1123
INGREDION (THAILAND) LTD.—See Ingredion Incorporated; *U.S. Public*, pg. 1123
INGREDION UK LIMITED—See Ingredion Incorporated; *U.S. Public*, pg. 1123
INGREDION URUGUAY S.A.—See Ingredion Incorporated; *U.S. Public*, pg. 1123
INGREDION VIETNAM COMPANY LIMITED—See Ingredion Incorporated; *U.S. Public*, pg. 1123
INGRESS AOI TECHNOLOGIES SDN. BHD.—See Ingress Industrial (Thailand) Public Company Limited; *Int'l*, pg. 3703
INGRESS AUTO SDN. BHD.—See Ingress Corporation Berhad; *Int'l*, pg. 3702
INGRESS AUTOVENTURES CO., LTD. - RAYONG PLANT—See Ingress Corporation Berhad; *Int'l*, pg. 3703
INGRESS AUTOVENTURES CO., LTD.—See Ingress Corporation Berhad; *Int'l*, pg. 3703
INGRESS CORPORATION BERHAD; *Int'l*, pg. 3702
INGRESS ENERGY SDN. BHD.—See G Capital Berhad; *Int'l*, pg. 2861
INGRESS ENGINEERING SDN. BHD. (NILAI PLANT)—See Ingress Corporation Berhad; *Int'l*, pg. 3703

COMPANY NAME INDEX INJURED WORKERS' INSURANCE FUND
Company Index

INGRESS INDUSTRIAL (MALAYSIA) SDN. BHD.—See Ingress Industrial (Thailand) Public Company Limited; *Int'l*, pg. 3703
INGRESS INDUSTRIAL (THAILAND) PUBLIC COMPANY LIMITED; *Int'l*, pg. 3703
INGRESS KATAYAMA TECHNOLOGY CENTRE SDN. BHD.—See Ingress Corporation Berhad; *Int'l*, pg. 3703
INGRESS MOTORS CENTRE SDN. BHD.—See Ingress Corporation Berhad; *Int'l*, pg. 3703
INGRESS PRECISION SDN. BHD.—See Ingress Corporation Berhad; *Int'l*, pg. 3703
INGRESS SWEDE AUTOMOBILE SDN. BHD.—See Ingress Corporation Berhad; *Int'l*, pg. 3703
INGRESS TECHNOLOGIES SDN. BHD.—See Ingress Corporation Berhad; *Int'l*, pg. 3703
INGRETEC, LTD.; *U.S. Private*, pg. 2077
INGROUP ASSOCIATES, LLC—See Genstar Capital, LLC; *U.S. Private*, pg. 1674
ING RUGGERO VIO—See Coeclerici S.p.A.; *Int'l*, pg. 1689
ING SECURITIES (ANDEAN PACT)—See ING Groep N.V.; *Int'l*, pg. 3700
ING SOLUTIONS LLC; *U.S. Private*, pg. 2075
ING. TOMAS FRIED—See Doppelmayr Group; *Int'l*, pg. 2175
ING TRUST COMPANY (JERSEY) LTD.—See ING Groep N.V.; *Int'l*, pg. 3700
ING TRUST (HONG KONG)—See ING Groep N.V.; *Int'l*, pg. 3700
ING VASTGOED BELEGGING B.V.—See ING Groep N.V.; *Int'l*, pg. 3700
ING VYSYA LIFE INSURANCE COMPANY LTD.—See EXIDE INDUSTRIES LIMITED; *Int'l*, pg. 2585
INHALATION SCIENCES SWEDEN AB—See Karolinska Development AB; *Int'l*, pg. 4084
INHALERX LIMITED; *Int'l*, pg. 3703
INHAND ELECTRONICS, INC.—See SECO S.p.A.; *Int'l*, pg. 6670
INHA WORKS LTD.—See Yamaha Corporation; *Int'l*, pg. 8550
INHA WORKS LTD.—See Fiskars Oyj Abp; *Int'l*, pg. 2694
INHEALTHCARE LTD—See InTechnology Plc; *Int'l*, pg. 3729
INHEALTH TECHNOLOGIES—See Freudenberg SE; *Int'l*, pg. 2700
INHER S.A. (PTY) LTD.—See Sulzer Ltd.; *Int'l*, pg. 7256
INHIBIKASE THERAPEUTICS, INC.; *U.S. Public*, pg. 1124
INHIBITEX, L.L.C.—See Bristol-Myers Squibb Company; *U.S. Public*, pg. 386
INHIBITOR THERAPEUTICS, INC.; *U.S. Public*, pg. 1124
INHIBRX, INC.; *U.S. Private*, pg. 2077
INHOME THERAPY INC.; *U.S. Private*, pg. 2077
THE IN-HOUSE AGENCY, INC.; *U.S. Private*, pg. 4055
IN HOUSE—See PHSC plc; *Int'l*, pg. 5857
INHWA PRECISION CO., LTD.; *Int'l*, pg. 3703
INICIAL AUTOHAZ KFT.—See AutoWallis Public Limited Company; *Int'l*, pg. 732
INICIJAL A.D.; *Int'l*, pg. 3703
INIFY LABORATORIES AB—See Contextvision AB; *Int'l*, pg. 1780
INILEX, INC.—See Greenbriar Equity Group, L.P.; *U.S. Private*, pg. 1776
INIMA CHILE LTDA.—See GS Holdings Corp.; *Int'l*, pg. 3142
INIMA CVV, S.A.—See GS Holdings Corp.; *Int'l*, pg. 3142
ININ GROUP AS; *Int'l*, pg. 3703
ININ UK LIMITED—See Permira Advisers LLP; *Int'l*, pg. 5805
INI POWER SYSTEMS, INC.—See The Dewey Electronics Corporation; *U.S. Public*, pg. 2067
INIS INTERNATIONAL INSURANCE SERVICE S.R.O.—See Porsche Automobil Holding SE; *Int'l*, pg. 5929
INIS INTERNATIONAL INSURANCE SERVICES S.R.O.—See Porsche Automobil Holding SE; *Int'l*, pg. 5929
INISSION AB; *Int'l*, pg. 3703
INISSION MALMO AB—See Inission AB; *Int'l*, pg. 3703
INISSION MUNKFORS AB—See Inission AB; *Int'l*, pg. 3703
INISSION STOCKHOLM AB—See Inission AB; *Int'l*, pg. 3703
INISSION TALLINN OU—See Inission AB; *Int'l*, pg. 3704
INISSION VASTERAS AB—See Inission AB; *Int'l*, pg. 3704
INIT AG; *Int'l*, pg. 3704
INITEC ENERGIA, S.A.—See ACS, Actividades de Construccion y Servicios, S.A.; *Int'l*, pg. 114
INITECH CO., LTD.—See KT Corporation; *Int'l*, pg. 4315
INIT EUROPE—See init AG; *Int'l*, pg. 3704
INITIAL AUSTRIA GMBH—See Rentokil Initial plc; *Int'l*, pg. 6287
INITIAL BELUX N.V.—See Rentokil Initial plc; *Int'l*, pg. 6287
INITIAL BTB SA—See Rentokil Initial plc; *Int'l*, pg. 6287
INITIAL B.V.—See Rentokil Initial plc; *Int'l*, pg. 6287
INITIAL ECOTEX S.R.O.—See Rentokil Initial plc; *Int'l*, pg. 6287
INITIAL FACILITIES SERVICES - SPAIN—See Rentokil Initial plc; *Int'l*, pg. 6288
INITIAL FILM & TELEVISION LTD—See LOV Group Invest SAS; *Int'l*, pg. 4564
INITIAL HYGIENE CO LTD—See Rentokil Initial plc; *Int'l*, pg. 6287
INITIAL HYGOFORM—See Rentokil Initial plc; *Int'l*, pg. 6288
INITIAL ITALIA SRL—See Rentokil Initial plc; *Int'l*, pg. 6287
INITIAL MATADOR SP Z.O.O.—See Rentokil Initial plc; *Int'l*, pg. 6287
INITIAL MEDICAL SERVICES (IRELAND) LTD—See Rentokil Initial plc; *Int'l*, pg. 6287
INITIAL MEDICAL SERVICES LTD—See Rentokil Initial plc; *Int'l*, pg. 6287
INITIAL PORTUGAL - SERVICOS DE PROTECAO AMBIENTAL LDA—See Rentokil Initial plc; *Int'l*, pg. 6287
INITIAL SERVICES CO LTD—See Rentokil Initial plc; *Int'l*, pg. 6287
INITIALS, INC.; *U.S. Private*, pg. 2077
INITIAL SVERIGE AB—See Rentokil Initial plc; *Int'l*, pg. 6287
INITIAL TECHNOLOGY PTE LTD—See Compeq Manufacturing Co., Ltd.; *Int'l*, pg. 1753
INITIAL TEXTILE LUXEMBOURG SARL—See Rentokil Initial plc; *Int'l*, pg. 6287
INITIAL TEXTILES E HIGIENE SLU—See Rentokil Initial plc; *Int'l*, pg. 6287
INITIAL TEXTILE SERVICE GMBH & CO. KG—See Rentokil Initial plc; *Int'l*, pg. 6287
INITIAL TEXTILE SERVICES SRO—See Rentokil Initial plc; *Int'l*, pg. 6287
INITIAL TEXTILES NV/SA—See Rentokil Initial plc; *Int'l*, pg. 6287
INITIATE SYSTEMS, INC.—See International Business Machines Corporation; *U.S. Public*, pg. 1148
INITIATIVE ATHENS—See The Interpublic Group of Companies, Inc.; *U.S. Public*, pg. 2095
INITIATIVE ATLANTA—See The Interpublic Group of Companies, Inc.; *U.S. Public*, pg. 2095
INITIATIVE BANGKOK—See The Interpublic Group of Companies, Inc.; *U.S. Public*, pg. 2095
INITIATIVE BARCELONA—See The Interpublic Group of Companies, Inc.; *U.S. Public*, pg. 2095
INITIATIVE BEIRUT—See The Interpublic Group of Companies, Inc.; *U.S. Public*, pg. 2095
INITIATIVE BOGOTA—See The Interpublic Group of Companies, Inc.; *U.S. Public*, pg. 2095
INITIATIVE BRUSSELS—See The Interpublic Group of Companies, Inc.; *U.S. Public*, pg. 2095
INITIATIVE BUDAPEST—See The Interpublic Group of Companies, Inc.; *U.S. Public*, pg. 2095
INITIATIVE BUENOS AIRES—See The Interpublic Group of Companies, Inc.; *U.S. Public*, pg. 2095
INITIATIVE CARACAS—See The Interpublic Group of Companies, Inc.; *U.S. Public*, pg. 2095
INITIATIVE DUBAI—See The Interpublic Group of Companies, Inc.; *U.S. Public*, pg. 2095
INITIATIVE DUBLIN—See The Interpublic Group of Companies, Inc.; *U.S. Public*, pg. 2095
INITIATIVE & FINANCE—See Groupe BPCE; *Int'l*, pg. 3095
INITIATIVE GROUP B.V.—See The Interpublic Group of Companies, Inc.; *U.S. Public*, pg. 2095
INITIATIVE HAMBURG—See The Interpublic Group of Companies, Inc.; *U.S. Public*, pg. 2095
INITIATIVE HONG KONG—See The Interpublic Group of Companies, Inc.; *U.S. Public*, pg. 2095
INITIATIVE JAKARTA—See The Interpublic Group of Companies, Inc.; *U.S. Public*, pg. 2095
INITIATIVE LIMA—See The Interpublic Group of Companies, Inc.; *U.S. Public*, pg. 2095
INITIATIVE LISBON—See The Interpublic Group of Companies, Inc.; *U.S. Public*, pg. 2095
INITIATIVE LONDON—See The Interpublic Group of Companies, Inc.; *U.S. Public*, pg. 2095
INITIATIVE LOS ANGELES—See The Interpublic Group of Companies, Inc.; *U.S. Public*, pg. 2095
INITIATIVE MADRID—See The Interpublic Group of Companies, Inc.; *U.S. Public*, pg. 2095
INITIATIVE MEDIA AUSTRALIA PTY LTD—See The Interpublic Group of Companies, Inc.; *U.S. Public*, pg. 2095
INITIATIVE MELBOURNE—See The Interpublic Group of Companies, Inc.; *U.S. Public*, pg. 2095
INITIATIVE MEXICO CITY—See The Interpublic Group of Companies, Inc.; *U.S. Public*, pg. 2095
INITIATIVE MIAMI—See The Interpublic Group of Companies, Inc.; *U.S. Public*, pg. 2095
INITIATIVE MILAN—See The Interpublic Group of Companies, Inc.; *U.S. Public*, pg. 2095
INITIATIVE MOSCOW—See The Interpublic Group of Companies, Inc.; *U.S. Public*, pg. 2096
INITIATIVE MUMBAI—See The Interpublic Group of Companies, Inc.; *U.S. Public*, pg. 2096
INITIATIVE PARIS—See The Interpublic Group of Companies, Inc.; *U.S. Public*, pg. 2096
INITIATIVE PERTH—See The Interpublic Group of Companies, Inc.; *U.S. Public*, pg. 2096
INITIATIVE PRAGUE—See The Interpublic Group of Companies, Inc.; *U.S. Public*, pg. 2096
INITIATIVE SAN DIEGO—See The Interpublic Group of Companies, Inc.; *U.S. Public*, pg. 2096
INITIATIVE SANTIAGO—See The Interpublic Group of Companies, Inc.; *U.S. Public*, pg. 2096
INITIATIVE SINGAPORE—See The Interpublic Group of Companies, Inc.; *U.S. Public*, pg. 2096
INITIATIVE—See The Interpublic Group of Companies, Inc.; *U.S. Public*, pg. 2095
INITIATIVE—See The Interpublic Group of Companies, Inc.; *U.S. Public*, pg. 2095
INITIATIVE—See The Interpublic Group of Companies, Inc.; *U.S. Public*, pg. 2095
INITIATIVE SYDNEY—See The Interpublic Group of Companies, Inc.; *U.S. Public*, pg. 2096
INITIATIVE TAIPEI—See The Interpublic Group of Companies, Inc.; *U.S. Public*, pg. 2096
INITIATIVE TOKYO—See The Interpublic Group of Companies, Inc.; *U.S. Public*, pg. 2096
INITIATIVE TORONTO—See The Interpublic Group of Companies, Inc.; *U.S. Public*, pg. 2096
INITIATIVE UNIVERSAL COPENHAGEN—See The Interpublic Group of Companies, Inc.; *U.S. Public*, pg. 2096
INITIATIVE UNIVERSAL MEDIA—See The Interpublic Group of Companies, Inc.; *U.S. Public*, pg. 2096
INITIATIVE UNIVERSAL OSLO—See The Interpublic Group of Companies, Inc.; *U.S. Public*, pg. 2096
INITIATIVE UNIVERSAL WARSAW—See The Interpublic Group of Companies, Inc.; *U.S. Public*, pg. 2096
INITIATIVE VIENNA—See The Interpublic Group of Companies, Inc.; *U.S. Public*, pg. 2096
INITIATIVE WORLDWIDE—See The Interpublic Group of Companies, Inc.; *U.S. Public*, pg. 2095
INITIATIVE ZURICH—See The Interpublic Group of Companies, Inc.; *U.S. Public*, pg. 2096
INITIATOR PHARMA A/S; *Int'l*, pg. 3704
INIT INDIA—See init AG; *Int'l*, pg. 3704
INIT INNOVATION IN TRAFFIC SYSTEMS FZE—See init innovation in traffic systems SE; *Int'l*, pg. 3704
INIT INNOVATION IN TRAFFIC SYSTEMS SE; *Int'l*, pg. 3704
INIT INNOVATIONS IN TRANSPORTATION (EASTERN CANADA) INC.—See init innovation in traffic systems SE; *Int'l*, pg. 3704
INIT INNOVATIONS IN TRANSPORTATION INC.—See init innovation in traffic systems SE; *Int'l*, pg. 3704
INIT INNOVATIONS IN TRANSPORTATION LTD.—See init innovation in traffic systems SE; *Int'l*, pg. 3704
INIT INNOVATIONS IN TRANSPORTATIONS LTD.—See init innovation in traffic systems SE; *Int'l*, pg. 3704
INIT INNOVATIONS IN TRANSPORTATION (WESTERN CANADA) INC.—See init innovation in traffic systems SE; *Int'l*, pg. 3704
INIT INNOVATIVE INFORMATIKANWENDUNGEN IN TRANSPORT-, VERKEHRS- UND LEITSYSTEMEN GMBH—See init innovation in traffic systems SE; *Int'l*, pg. 3704
INITIO FOODS INC.—See Nisshin Seifun Group, Inc.; *Int'l*, pg. 5372
INITIO, INC.; *U.S. Private*, pg. 2077
INITIUM,INC. - CHIGASAKI FACTORY—See ULVAC, Inc.; *Int'l*, pg. 8020
INIT MIDDLE EAST—See init AG; *Int'l*, pg. 3704
INIT MOBILITY SOFTWARE SOLUTIONS GMBH—See init innovation in traffic systems SE; *Int'l*, pg. 3704
INITOUT JAPAN CO., LTD.—See Screen Holdings Co., Ltd.; *Int'l*, pg. 6655
INITPERDIS GMBH—See init innovation in traffic systems SE; *Int'l*, pg. 3704
INITPLAN GMBH—See init innovation in traffic systems SE; *Int'l*, pg. 3704
INIT POLYMERS B.V.—See Sun Capital Partners, Inc.; *U.S. Private*, pg. 3861
INIT PTY LTD—See init innovation in traffic systems SE; *Int'l*, pg. 3704
INIT.VOICE GMBH—See ecotel communication ag; *Int'l*, pg. 2300
INIVEN—See Conolog Corporation; *U.S. Private*, pg. 1018
INIZIATIVE BRESCIANE S.P.A.; *Int'l*, pg. 3704
INIZIO GROUP LIMITED—See Clayton, Dubilier & Rice, LLC; *U.S. Private*, pg. 924
INJAR, S.A.—See ACS, Actividades de Construccion y Servicios, S.A.; *Int'l*, pg. 114
INJAZAT DATA SYSTEMS—See Mubadala Investment Company PJSC; *Int'l*, pg. 5075
INJAZZAT REAL ESTATE DEVELOPMENT COMPANY K.S.C.C.; *Int'l*, pg. 3704
INJECTION MOLDERS SUPPLY COMPANY; *U.S. Private*, pg. 2077
INJECTION PLASTIQUES SYSTEMES—See Plastiques du Val de Loire S.A.; *Int'l*, pg. 5892
INJECTRON CORPORATION; *U.S. Private*, pg. 2077
INJECTRONICS INC.; *U.S. Private*, pg. 2077
INJIXO AG—See InVision AG; *Int'l*, pg. 3789
INJURED GADGETS LLC; *U.S. Private*, pg. 2077
INJURED WORKERS' INSURANCE FUND; *U.S. Private*, pg. 2077
INJURY NET AUSTRALIA PTY LTD—See MAXIMUS, Inc.; *U.S. Public*, pg. 1402

INJURED WORKERS' INSURANCE FUND — CORPORATE AFFILIATIONS

INJURY QED LIMITED—See AnaCap Financial Partners LLP; *Int'l*, pg. 445
INKAS FINANCIAL CORP. LTD.—See 3 Sixty Secure Corp.; *Int'l*, pg. 5
INKASSO MED AG—See Intrum AB; *Int'l*, pg. 3770
INKBOX INK INCORPORATED—See Societe BIC S.A.; *Int'l*, pg. 7037
INKD LLC—See IAC Inc.; *U.S. Public*, pg. 1082
INKED PRODUCTIONS, INC.—See The Walt Disney Company; *U.S. Public*, pg. 2140
INKEL CORPORATION - BU-PYEONG FACTORY—See INKEL Corporation; *Int'l*, pg. 3705
INKEL CORPORATION; *Int'l*, pg. 3704
INKEL VIETNAM CO LTD—See INKEL Corporation; *Int'l*, pg. 3705
INKEVERSE GROUP LIMITED; *Int'l*, pg. 3705
INKHEAD PROMOTIONAL PRODUCTS—See Deluxe Corporation; *U.S. Public*, pg. 653
INKHOUSE—See O2 Investment Partners, LLC; *U.S. Private*, pg. 2982
INK, INC. PR; *U.S. Private*, pg. 2077
INKJET INC.; *U.S. Private*, pg. 2077
INKJET INTERNATIONAL, LTD.; *U.S. Private*, pg. 2077
INKJETMADNESS.COM, INC.; *U.S. Private*, pg. 2077
INKLING SYSTEMS, INC.—See Marlin Equity Partners, LLC; *U.S. Private*, pg. 2584
INK MILL CORP.—See Avery Dennison Corporation; *U.S. Public*, pg. 244
INKOK INDUSTRIAL CO., LTD.—See Miki Pulley Co., Ltd.; *Int'l*, pg. 4891
INKON LIFE TECHNOLOGY CO., LTD.; *Int'l*, pg. 3705
INKO SPORTS AG—See B. Braun Melsungen AG; *Int'l*, pg. 787
INKO'S TEA, LLC; *U.S. Private*, pg. 2078
I/N KOTE L.P.—See Cleveland-Cliffs, Inc.; *U.S. Public*, pg. 514
INKOZELL ZELLSTOFF-VERTRIEB GMBH—See Bunzl plc; *Int'l*, pg. 1218
INKRON OY—See Nagase & Co., Ltd.; *Int'l*, pg. 5126
INKSOLUTIONS, LLC; *U.S. Private*, pg. 2078
INK; *U.S. Private*, pg. 2077
INKSTONE FEIBO ACQUISITION CORPORATION; *U.S. Private*, pg. 2078
INK SYSTEMS INC.; *U.S. Private*, pg. 2077
INKTEC AMERICA CORP.—See InkTec Co., Ltd.; *Int'l*, pg. 3705
INKTEC CO., LTD.; *Int'l*, pg. 3705
INKTEC (ZHUHAI) TRADING CO., LTD.—See InkTec Co., Ltd.; *Int'l*, pg. 3705
INKTEL CHICAGO—See Inktel Direct Inc.; *U.S. Private*, pg. 2078
INKTEL DIRECT INC.; *U.S. Private*, pg. 2078
INKWELL GLOBAL MARKETING; *U.S. Private*, pg. 2078
INKY; *Int'l*, pg. 3705
INLAB GMBH INSTITUT FUR LEBENSMITTELMIKROBIOLOGIE—See Eurofins Scientific S.E.; *Int'l*, pg. 2550
INLAD TRUCK & VAN EQUIPMENT COMPANY, INCORPORATED—See Driverge Vehicle Innovations, LLC; *U.S. Private*, pg. 1278
INLAND AMERICAN COMMUNITIES GROUP INC.; *U.S. Private*, pg. 2078
INLAND ASSOCIATES, INC.; *U.S. Private*, pg. 2078
INLAND AUTO CENTRE LTD; *Int'l*, pg. 3705
INLAND BANCORP, INC.—See Byline Bancorp, Inc.; *U.S. Public*, pg. 414
INLAND BANK & TRUST—See Byline Bancorp, Inc.; *U.S. Public*, pg. 414
INLAND BUSINESS MACHINES, INC.—See Xerox Holdings Corporation; *U.S. Public*, pg. 2387
INLAND CHEVROLET; *U.S. Private*, pg. 2078
INLAND COATINGS CORPORATION—See Midwest Growth Partners, LLLP; *U.S. Private*, pg. 2721
INLAND COMPANIES, INC.; *U.S. Private*, pg. 2078
INLAND CONCRETE CONSTRUCTORS—See J.D. Diffenbaugh, Inc.; *U.S. Private*, pg. 2160
INLAND CONSTRUCTION COMPANY; *U.S. Private*, pg. 2078
INLAND CORPORATION—See Energy Transfer LP; *U.S. Public*, pg. 764
INLAND DIE CASTING—See RCM Industries, Inc.; *U.S. Private*, pg. 3362
INLAND EMPIRE PAPER COMPANY INC.—See Cowles Company; *U.S. Private*, pg. 1073
INLAND EMPIRE UTILITIES AGENCY; *U.S. Private*, pg. 2078
INLAND ENVIRONMENTAL RESOURCES, INC.—See Calix Limited; *Int'l*, pg. 1265
INLAND FINANCE COMPANY—See The Wittern Group; *U.S. Private*, pg. 4138
INLAND FOREST MANAGEMENT, INC.—See F&W Forestry Services Inc.; *U.S. Private*, pg. 1455
INLAND FUEL TERMINALS, INC.—See Santa Energy Corporation; *U.S. Private*, pg. 3547
THE INLAND GROUP; *Int'l*, pg. 7655
INLAND HOMES LIMITED—See Inland Homes PLC; *Int'l*, pg. 3705
INLAND HOMES PLC; *Int'l*, pg. 3705

INLAND IMAGING ASSOCIATES, P.S.; *U.S. Private*, pg. 2078
INLAND INDUSTRIES, INC.; *U.S. Private*, pg. 2078
INLAND KENWORTH INC - ALBUQUERQUE FACILITY—See The Inland Group; *Int'l*, pg. 7655
INLAND KENWORTH INC - BURNABY FACILITY—See The Inland Group; *Int'l*, pg. 7655
INLAND KENWORTH INC - CAMPBELL RIVER FACILITY—See The Inland Group; *Int'l*, pg. 7655
INLAND KENWORTH INC - CARSON FACILITY—See The Inland Group; *Int'l*, pg. 7655
INLAND KENWORTH INC - CRANBROOK FACILITY—See The Inland Group; *Int'l*, pg. 7655
INLAND KENWORTH INC - EL CAJON FACILITY—See The Inland Group; *Int'l*, pg. 7655
INLAND KENWORTH INC - FARMINGTON FACILITY—See The Inland Group; *Int'l*, pg. 7655
INLAND KENWORTH INC - FONTANA FACILITY—See The Inland Group; *Int'l*, pg. 7655
INLAND KENWORTH INC - FORT ST JOHN FACILITY—See The Inland Group; *Int'l*, pg. 7655
INLAND KENWORTH INC - KAMLOOPS FACILITY—See The Inland Group; *Int'l*, pg. 7655
INLAND KENWORTH INC - KELOWNA FACILITY—See The Inland Group; *Int'l*, pg. 7655
INLAND KENWORTH INC - LANGLEY FACILITY—See The Inland Group; *Int'l*, pg. 7655
INLAND KENWORTH INC - NANAIMO FACILITY—See The Inland Group; *Int'l*, pg. 7655
INLAND KENWORTH INC - PENTICTON FACILITY—See The Inland Group; *Int'l*, pg. 7655
INLAND KENWORTH INC - PHOENIX FACILITY—See The Inland Group; *Int'l*, pg. 7656
INLAND KENWORTH INC - PRINCE GEORGE FACILITY—See The Inland Group; *Int'l*, pg. 7656
INLAND KENWORTH INC - QUESNEL FACILITY—See The Inland Group; *Int'l*, pg. 7656
INLAND KENWORTH INC.—See The Inland Group; *Int'l*, pg. 7656
INLAND KENWORTH INC - TUCSON FACILITY—See The Inland Group; *Int'l*, pg. 7656
INLAND KENWORTH INC - VERNON FACILITY—See The Inland Group; *Int'l*, pg. 7656
INLAND KENWORTH INC - WHITEHORSE FACILITY—See The Inland Group; *Int'l*, pg. 7656
INLAND KENWORTH INC - WILLIAMS LAKE FACILITY—See The Inland Group; *Int'l*, pg. 7656
INLAND LABEL & MARKETING SERVICES, LLC - IN*TECH DIVISION—See Inland Label & Marketing Services, LLC; *U.S. Private*, pg. 2078
INLAND LABEL & MARKETING SERVICES, LLC - LA CROSSE FACILITY—See Inland Label & Marketing Services, LLC; *U.S. Private*, pg. 2078
INLAND LABEL & MARKETING SERVICES, LLC; *U.S. Private*, pg. 2078
INLAND LABEL & MARKETING SERVICES, LLC - WINONA FACILITY—See Inland Label & Marketing Services, LLC; *U.S. Private*, pg. 2078
INLAND LAKES MANAGEMENT INC.; *U.S. Private*, pg. 2078
INLAND MARINE SERVICES, LLC; *U.S. Private*, pg. 2078
INLAND MEDIA COMPANY—See Inland Industries, Inc.; *U.S. Private*, pg. 2078
INLAND MORTGAGE CAPITAL, LLC—See The Inland Real Estate Group of Companies, Inc.; *U.S. Private*, pg. 4056
INLAND NETWORKS—See Western Elite Incorporated Services; *U.S. Private*, pg. 4492
INLAND NEWSPAPER MACHINERY LLC; *U.S. Private*, pg. 2078
INLAND NORTHWEST HEALTH SERVICES; *U.S. Private*, pg. 2078
INLAND OIL COMPANY INC.; *U.S. Private*, pg. 2079
INLAND PACLEASE—See The Inland Group; *Int'l*, pg. 7656
INLAND PIPE REHABILITATION LLC—See J.F. Lehman & Company, Inc.; *U.S. Private*, pg. 2163
INLAND PLYWOOD COMPANY—See Patrick Industries, Inc.; *U.S. Public*, pg. 1652
INLAND POWER GROUP, INC.; *U.S. Private*, pg. 2079
INLAND POWER & LIGHT COMPANY INC.; *U.S. Private*, pg. 2079
INLAND PRINTERS LIMITED; *Int'l*, pg. 3705
THE INLAND REAL ESTATE GROUP, LLC—See The Inland Real Estate Group of Companies, Inc.; *U.S. Private*, pg. 4056
THE INLAND REAL ESTATE GROUP OF COMPANIES, INC.; *U.S. Private*, pg. 4055
INLAND REAL ESTATE INCOME TRUST, INC.; *U.S. Public*, pg. 1124
INLAND REAL ESTATE INVESTMENT CORPORATION—See The Inland Real Estate Group of Companies, Inc.; *U.S. Private*, pg. 4056
INLAND REGIONAL CENTER; *U.S. Private*, pg. 2079
INLAND RESIDENTIAL PROPERTIES TRUST, INC.—See The Inland Real Estate Group of Companies, Inc.; *U.S. Private*, pg. 4056
INLAND SEAFOOD-CHARLOTTE—See Inland Seafood; *U.S. Private*, pg. 2079

INLAND SEAFOOD; *U.S. Private*, pg. 2079
INLAND SEAFOOD—See Inland Seafood; *U.S. Private*, pg. 2079
INLAND SEAFOOD—See Inland Seafood; *U.S. Private*, pg. 2079
INLAND SECURITIES CORPORATION—See The Inland Real Estate Group of Companies, Inc.; *U.S. Private*, pg. 4056
INLANDS LUFT AB—See Instalco AB; *Int'l*, pg. 3721
INLAND STAR DISTRIBUTION CENTERS; *U.S. Private*, pg. 2079
INLAND SUPPLY CO., INC.; *U.S. Private*, pg. 2079
INLAND SURGERY CENTER, L.P.—See UnitedHealth Group Incorporated; *U.S. Public*, pg. 2250
INLAND TECHNOLOGY—See Canon Inc.; *Int'l*, pg. 1293
INLAND TRUCK PARTS COMPANY; *U.S. Private*, pg. 2079
INLAND VALLEY DAILY BULLETIN—See Alden Global Capital LLC; *U.S. Private*, pg. 157
INLAND WATERS POLLUTION CONTROL INC.—See J.F. Lehman & Company, Inc.; *U.S. Private*, pg. 2163
INLAND WATER WORKS SUPPLY CO.—See Core & Main, Inc.; *U.S. Public*, pg. 576
INLAND ZDP PLC—See Inland Homes PLC; *Int'l*, pg. 3705
INLANTA MORTGAGE, INC.—See McCarthy Group, LLC; *U.S. Private*, pg. 2627
INLES CENTER MOZE D.O.O.—See Inles d.d.; *Int'l*, pg. 3705
INLES D.D. - LILI RUS—See Inles d.d.; *Int'l*, pg. 3705
INLES D.D.; *Int'l*, pg. 3705
INLES KOMERC A.D.; *Int'l*, pg. 3705
INLES KOMERC D.O.O.—See Inles d.d.; *Int'l*, pg. 3705
INLES RAZSTAVNO PRODAJNI SALON RIBNICA—See Inles d.d.; *Int'l*, pg. 3705
INLES USA, LLC—See Inles d.d.; *Int'l*, pg. 3705
INLES VINKOVCI D.O.O.—See Inles d.d.; *Int'l*, pg. 3705
INLET BAY AT GATEWAY, LLC—See UDR, Inc.; *U.S. Public*, pg. 2218
INLIGN CAPITAL PARTNERS, LLC; *U.S. Private*, pg. 2079
INLINEA S.P.A.—See Talanx AG; *Int'l*, pg. 7445
INLINE CONSULTING, LLC—See YOUNG & Associates; *U.S. Private*, pg. 4592
INLINE ELECTRIC SUPPLY CO., INC.; *U.S. Private*, pg. 2079
INLINE ELECTRIC SUPPLY CO., INC.—See Inline Electric Supply Co., Inc.; *U.S. Private*, pg. 2079
INLINE ELECTRIC SUPPLY CO., INC.—See Inline Electric Supply Co., Inc.; *U.S. Private*, pg. 2079
INLINE FILLING SYSTEMS, LLC—See The Middleby Corporation; *U.S. Public*, pg. 2114
INLINE HYDRAULIK GMBH—See Jiangsu Hengli Hydraulic Co., Ltd.; *Int'l*, pg. 3947
INLINE MANAGEMENT, LLC—See Accenture plc; *Int'l*, pg. 86
INLINE PLASTICS CORP. - SHUR-LOCK DIVISION—See Inline Plastics Corp.; *U.S. Private*, pg. 2079
INLINE PLASTICS CORP.; *U.S. Private*, pg. 2079
INLINE POLAND SP. Z O.O.—See Inline Plastics Corp.; *U.S. Private*, pg. 2079
INLINER TECHNOLOGIES, LLC—See J.F. Lehman & Company, Inc.; *U.S. Private*, pg. 2163
INLINE SERVICES, INC.; *U.S. Private*, pg. 2079
IN-LINE VALVE COMPANY LIMITED—See MTQ Corporation Limited; *Int'l*, pg. 5071
INLITE PTY LIMITED—See Bain Capital, LP; *U.S. Private*, pg. 439
INLITE PTY LIMITED—See Investec Limited; *Int'l*, pg. 3777
INLOG—See Haemonetics Corporation; *U.S. Public*, pg. 979
INLY MEDIA CO., LTD.; *Int'l*, pg. 3706
INMA CO. QATAR L.L.C.—See INMA Gulf Development & Construction L.L.C.; *Int'l*, pg. 3706
INMA GULF DEVELOPMENT & CONSTRUCTION L.L.C.; *Int'l*, pg. 3706
INMAN GROUP, LLC—See Beringer Capital; *Int'l*, pg. 981
INMAN HOLDING CO. INC.; *U.S. Private*, pg. 2079
INMAN MILLS INC.—See Inman Holding Co. Inc.; *U.S. Private*, pg. 2079
INMAPE ASCENSORES, S.L.—See KONE Oyj; *Int'l*, pg. 4247
INMAR, INC.—See Ontario Municipal Employees Retirement System; *Int'l*, pg. 5584
INMARKET MEDIA LLC; *U.S. Private*, pg. 2079
INMARK, LLC - BIOMEDICAL PACKAGING DIVISION—See Kelso & Company, L.P.; *U.S. Private*, pg. 2278
INMARK, LLC—See Kelso & Company, L.P.; *U.S. Private*, pg. 2278
INMARSAT AUSTRALIA PTY LIMITED—See ViaSat, Inc.; *U.S. Public*, pg. 2291
INMARSAT GLOBAL LIMITED—See ViaSat, Inc.; *U.S. Public*, pg. 2291
INMARSAT GROUP LIMITED—See ViaSat, Inc.; *U.S. Public*, pg. 2291
INMARSAT HONG KONG LIMITED—See ViaSat, Inc.; *U.S. Public*, pg. 2292
INMARSAT INC.—See ViaSat, Inc.; *U.S. Public*, pg. 2291

COMPANY NAME INDEX

INMARSAT INC.—See ViaSat, Inc.; *U.S. Public*, pg. 2292
INMARSAT KK—See ViaSat, Inc.; *U.S. Public*, pg. 2292
INMARSAT LEASING (TWO) LIMITED—See ViaSat, Inc.; *U.S. Public*, pg. 2292
INMARSAT PLC—See ViaSat, Inc.; *U.S. Public*, pg. 2291
INMARSAT SA—See ViaSat, Inc.; *U.S. Public*, pg. 2292
INMARSAT SOLUTIONS AS—See ViaSat, Inc.; *U.S. Public*, pg. 2292
INMARSAT SOLUTIONS B.V.—See ViaSat, Inc.; *U.S. Public*, pg. 2292
INMARSAT SOLUTIONS (CANADA) INC. - MOUNT PEARL—See ViaSat, Inc.; *U.S. Public*, pg. 2292
INMARSAT SOLUTIONS (CANADA) INC.—See ViaSat, Inc.; *U.S. Public*, pg. 2292
INMARSAT SOLUTIONS GLOBAL LIMITED—See ViaSat, Inc.; *U.S. Public*, pg. 2292
INMARSAT SOLUTIONS GLOBAL LTD. - ABERDEEN—See ViaSat, Inc.; *U.S. Public*, pg. 2292
INMARSAT SOLUTIONS PTE. LTD.—See ViaSat, Inc.; *U.S. Public*, pg. 2292
INMARSAT SOLUTIONS SA PTY LIMITED—See ViaSat, Inc.; *U.S. Public*, pg. 2292
INMARSAT SOLUTIONS SHANGHAI CO. LIMITED—See ViaSat, Inc.; *U.S. Public*, pg. 2292
INMARSAT SOLUTIONS (US) INC.—See ViaSat, Inc.; *U.S. Public*, pg. 2292
INMARSAT SPAIN S.A—See ViaSat, Inc.; *U.S. Public*, pg. 2292
INMAR SCANNER APPLICATIONS, LLC—See Ontario Municipal Employees Retirement System; *Int'l*, pg. 5584
INMAR SUPPLY CHAIN SOLUTIONS, LLC—See Ontario Municipal Employees Retirement System; *Int'l*, pg. 5584
INMATEC GASE TECHNOLOGIE GMBH & CO. KG—See Xebec Adsorption Inc.; *Int'l*, pg. 8520
INMATION BNX B.V.—See Emerson Electric Co.; *U.S. Public*, pg. 752
INMATION SOFTWARE GMBH—See Emerson Electric Co.; *U.S. Public*, pg. 752
INMATION UK LTD.—See Emerson Electric Co.; *U.S. Public*, pg. 752
INMAX HOLDING CO., LTD.; *Int'l*, pg. 3706
INMEDEA GMBH—See CompuGroup Medical SE & Co. KGaA; *Int'l*, pg. 1757
INMED GROUP, INC.—See All Things Mobile Analytic, Inc.; *U.S. Public*, pg. 78
IN-MEDIA AG—See Die Schweizerische Post AG; *Int'l*, pg. 2113
INMEDIA PUBLIC RELATIONS - GLASGOW—See inmedia Public Relations Inc; *Int'l*, pg. 3706
INMEDIA PUBLIC RELATIONS INC - BEDFORD—See inmedia Public Relations Inc; *Int'l*, pg. 3706
INMEDIA PUBLIC RELATIONS INC; *Int'l*, pg. 3706
INMEDIO SP. Z O.O.—See Eurocash S.A.; *Int'l*, pg. 2533
INMED PARTNERSHIPS FOR CHILDREN; *U.S. Private*, pg. 2080
INMED PHARMACEUTICALS INC.; *Int'l*, pg. 3706
INMED SP. Z O.O.—See Demant A/S; *Int'l*, pg. 2024
INMEX CORPORATION—See The Coca-Cola Company; *U.S. Public*, pg. 2065
INMINS LIMITED—See Winhold Limited; *Int'l*, pg. 8428
INMINS TRADING (PTY) LIMITED—See Winhold Limited; *Int'l*, pg. 8428
INMIZE CAPITAL S.L.—See Indra Sistemas, S.A.; *Int'l*, pg. 3661
INMIZE SISTEMAS S.L.—See Indra Sistemas, S.A.; *Int'l*, pg. 3661
INM NUVENT PAINTS PRIVATE LIMITED—See Shilpa Medicare Ltd; *Int'l*, pg. 6831
INMOBILIARIA BAJA, S.A. DE C.V.—See Empresas ICA S.A.B. de C.V.; *Int'l*, pg. 2391
INMOBILIARIA CIT., S.A. DE C.V.—See Illinois Tool Works Inc.; *U.S. Public*, pg. 1108
INMOBILIARIA CLUB DE CAMPO S.A.; *Int'l*, pg. 3706
INMOBILIARIA COLONIAL SOCIMI SA; *Int'l*, pg. 3706
INMOBILIARIA CORONEL S.A.—See State Grid Corporation of China; *Int'l*, pg. 7183
INMOBILIARIA CRAIGHOUSE SA; *Int'l*, pg. 3706
INMOBILIARIA DE DEPORTES LA DEHESA S.A.; *Int'l*, pg. 3706
INMOBILIARIA DEL SUR, S.A.; *Int'l*, pg. 3706
INMOBILIARIA ESPACIO, S.A; *Int'l*, pg. 3706
INMOBILIARIA GEU-GAMSA, S.A. DE C.V.—See Organizacion Cultiba, S.A.B. de C.V.; *Int'l*, pg. 5618
INMOBILIARIA GEUSA, S.A. DE C.V.—See Organizacion Cultiba, S.A.B. de C.V.; *Int'l*, pg. 5618
INMOBILIARIA HOTELERA DE TOLUCA, S.A. DE C.V.—See Grupo Posadas S.A.B. de C.V.; *Int'l*, pg. 3134
INMOBILIARIA HOTELERA POSADAS, S.A. DE C.V.—See Grupo Posadas S.A.B. de C.V.; *Int'l*, pg. 3134
INMOBILIARIA MANQUEHUE SA; *Int'l*, pg. 3706
INMOBILIARIA MANSO DE VELASCO LTDA—See Enel S.p.A.; *Int'l*, pg. 2414
INMOBILIARIA NORTE VERDE S.A.—See Quinenco S.A.; *Int'l*, pg. 6163
INMOBILIARIA RAPID S.A.C.; *Int'l*, pg. 3706

INMOBILIARIA SAN PATRICIO SA; *Int'l*, pg. 3706
INMOBILIARIA SIXTERRA S.A.; *Int'l*, pg. 3706
INMOBILIARIA STADIO ITALIANO S.A.; *Int'l*, pg. 3706
INMOBILIARIA TEPALCAPA SA DE CV—See Enovis Corporation; *U.S. Public*, pg. 773
INMOBILIARIA YUGOSLAVA S.A.; *Int'l*, pg. 3706
INMOBI PTE LTD.; *Int'l*, pg. 3706
IN MOCEAN GROUP LLC; *U.S. Private*, pg. 2052
INMODE LTD.; *Int'l*, pg. 3707
INMOMENT, INC.—See Madison Dearborn Partners, LLC; *U.S. Private*, pg. 2541
INMOMENT MISSISSAUGA—See Mindshare Technologies, Inc.; *U.S. Private*, pg. 2741
INMOSUPA, SOCIMI, S.A.; *Int'l*, pg. 3707
INMOTION ENTERTAINMENT GROUP, LLC—See W.H. Smith PLC; *Int'l*, pg. 8322
INM SECURITIES (IRELAND) LIMITED—See Mediahuis Partners NV; *Int'l*, pg. 4772
INM SECURITIES (IRELAND) LIMITED—See VP Exploitatie N.V.; *Int'l*, pg. 8311
INMUEBLES ONLINE SAPI DE CV—See MercadoLibre, Inc.; *Int'l*, pg. 4819
INMUNE BIO, INC.; *U.S. Public*, pg. 1125
INMUSIC GMBH—See inMusic, LLC; *U.S. Private*, pg. 2080
INMUSIC, LLC; *U.S. Private*, pg. 2080
INMYSHOW DIGITAL TECHNOLOGY (GROUP) CO., LTD.; *Int'l*, pg. 3707
INNATE PHARMA S.A.; *Int'l*, pg. 3707
INN AT PERRY CABIN CORPORATION—See LVMH Moet Hennessy Louis Vuitton SE; *Int'l*, pg. 4591
INNATURE BERHAD; *Int'l*, pg. 3707
THE INN AT WILDERNESS ROAD, LLC—See UTG, Inc.; *U.S. Public*, pg. 2267
INNCO MANAGEMENT CORP.—See Family Inns of America, Inc.; *U.S. Private*, pg. 1470
INNCOM INTERNATIONAL INC.—See Honeywell International Inc.; *U.S. Public*, pg. 1048
INNECTO PEOPLE CONSULTING LIMITED—See Personal Group Holdings plc; *Int'l*, pg. 5820
INNELEC MULTIMEDIA; *Int'l*, pg. 3707
INNEONUSA SDN. BHD.—See Telekom Malaysia Berhad; *Int'l*, pg. 7537
INNEOS LLC—See OMRON Corporation; *Int'l*, pg. 5564
INNERCEPT MANAGEMENT CORPORATION; *U.S. Private*, pg. 2080
INNER EAST COMMUNITY FINANCE LIMITED.; *Int'l*, pg. 3707
INNERFAX INC.; *U.S. Private*, pg. 2080
INNERGEX RENEWABLE ENERGY INC.; *Int'l*, pg. 3708
INNER HARMONY PTE LTD—See Fitgenes Australia Pty Ltd.; *Int'l*, pg. 2695
INNER MONGOLIA BAOTOU STEEL UNION COMPANY LIMITED—See Baotou Iron & Steel (Group) Company Limited; *Int'l*, pg. 857
INNER MONGOLIA DAZHONG MINING CO., LTD.; *Int'l*, pg. 3707
INNER MONGOLIA DIAN TOU ENERGY CORPORATION LIMITED; *Int'l*, pg. 3707
INNER MONGOLIA EERDUOSI RESOURCES CO., LTD.; *Int'l*, pg. 3707
INNER MONGOLIA ENERGY ENGINEERING CO., LTD.; *Int'l*, pg. 3707
INNER MONGOLIA ERDOS RESOURCES CO., LTD.; *Int'l*, pg. 3707
INNER MONGOLIA FIRST MACHINERY GROUP CO., LTD.; *Int'l*, pg. 3707
INNER MONGOLIA FURUI MEDICAL SCIENCE CO.,LTD.; *Int'l*, pg. 3707
INNER MONGOLIA JINGHUAN ELECTRONIC MATERIAL CO., LTD.—See Zhejiang Jingsheng Mechanical & Electrical Co., Ltd.; *Int'l*, pg. 8657
INNER MONGOLIA JUNZHENG ENERGY & CHEMICAL GROUP CO., LTD.; *Int'l*, pg. 3707
INNER MONGOLIA KING DEER CASHMERE GROUP CO.—See Suez Asia Holdings Pte. Ltd.; *Int'l*, pg. 7253
INNER MONGOLIA LIANFENG RARE EARTH CHEMICAL INSTITUTE CO., LTD.—See Hongda Xingye Co., Ltd.; *Int'l*, pg. 3470
INNER MONGOLIA LITTLE SHEEP CATERING CHAIN CO., LTD.; *Int'l*, pg. 3707
INNER MONGOLIA MENGDIAN HUANENG THERMAL POWER CORPORATION LIMITED; *Int'l*, pg. 3707
INNER MONGOLIA MENGHUA HAIBOWAN POWER GENERATION CO., LTD.—See Hongda Xingye Co., Ltd.; *Int'l*, pg. 3470
INNER MONGOLIA NORTH HAULER JOINT STOCK CO., LTD.; *Int'l*, pg. 3707
INNER MONGOLIA OJING SCIENCE & TECHNOLOGY CO., LTD.; *Int'l*, pg. 3707
INNER MONGOLIA PINGZHUANG ENERGY RESOURCES CO., LTD.; *Int'l*, pg. 3708
INNER MONGOLIA SHANSHAN NEW MATERIAL CO., LTD.—See Ningbo Shanshan Co., Ltd.; *Int'l*, pg. 5305
INNER MONGOLIA SHANSHAN TECHNOLOGY CO., LTD.—See Ningbo Shanshan Co., Ltd.; *Int'l*, pg. 5305
INNER MONGOLIA TIANSHOU TECHNOLOGY & DEVELOPMENT CO., LTD.; *Int'l*, pg. 3708

INNER MONGOLIA TONGWEI SILICON CO., LTD.—See Tongwei Co., Ltd.; *Int'l*, pg. 7808
INNER MONGOLIA WUHAI CHEMICAL INDUSTRY CO., LTD.—See Hongda Xingye Co., Ltd.; *Int'l*, pg. 3470
INNER MONGOLIA XINCHUANG RESOURCE RECYCLING CO., LTD.—See GEM Co., Ltd.; *Int'l*, pg. 2914
INNER MONGOLIA XINGYE MINING CO., LTD.; *Int'l*, pg. 3708
INNER MONGOLIA YILI INDUSTRIAL GROUP CO., LTD.; *Int'l*, pg. 3708
INNER MONGOLIA YITAI COAL COMPANY LIMITED; *Int'l*, pg. 3708
INNER MONGOLIA YUAN XING ENERGY CO., LTD.; *Int'l*, pg. 3708
INNER MONGOLIA ZHONGGU MINING INDUSTRY CO., LTD.—See Hongda Xingye Co., Ltd.; *Int'l*, pg. 3470
INNER MONGOLIA ZHONGHUAN SOLAR MATERIAL CO., LTD.—See TCL Zhonghuan Renewable Energy Technology Co.,Ltd.; *Int'l*, pg. 7484
INNER MONGOLIA ZHONGKE EQUIPMENT CO., LTD.—See Hongda Xingye Co., Ltd.; *Int'l*, pg. 3470
INNERPLAN; *U.S. Private*, pg. 2080
INNER RANGE PTY. LTD.—See WESCO International, Inc.; *U.S. Public*, pg. 2351
INNERSCOPE HEARING TECHNOLOGIES, INC.; *U.S. Public*, pg. 1125
INNERSCOPE RESEARCH, INC.—See Brookfield Corporation; *Int'l*, pg. 1179
INNERSCOPE RESEARCH, INC.—See Elliott Management Corporation; *U.S. Private*, pg. 1371
INNERSENSE—See KLA Corporation; *U.S. Public*, pg. 1268
INNERSPACE LUXURY PRODUCTS, LLC—See FirsTime Design Limited; *U.S. Public*, pg. 849
INNER SPIRIT HOLDINGS LTD.—See SNDL Inc.; *Int'l*, pg. 7027
INNER TRADITIONS INTERNATIONAL; *U.S. Private*, pg. 2080
INNERWIRELESS, INC.—See Black Box Limited; *Int'l*, pg. 1058
INNERWORKINGS ANDINA S.A.S.—See HH Global Group Limited; *Int'l*, pg. 3378
INNERWORKINGS ASIA PACIFIC—See HH Global Group Limited; *Int'l*, pg. 3378
INNERWORKINGS BELGIUM SPRL/BVBA—See HH Global Group Limited; *Int'l*, pg. 3378
INNERWORKINGS BRASIL GERENCIAMENTO DE IMPRESSOES—See HH Global Group Limited; *Int'l*, pg. 3378
INNERWORKINGS CANADA—See HH Global Group Limited; *Int'l*, pg. 3378
INNERWORKINGS COLOMBIA S.A.S.—See HH Global Group Limited; *Int'l*, pg. 3378
INNERWORKINGS DANMARK A/S—See HH Global Group Limited; *Int'l*, pg. 3378
INNERWORKINGS DEUTSCHLAND GMBH—See HH Global Group Limited; *Int'l*, pg. 3378
INNERWORKINGS DUBAI—See HH Global Group Limited; *Int'l*, pg. 3378
INNERWORKINGS EUROPE LIMITED—See HH Global Group Limited; *Int'l*, pg. 3378
INNERWORKINGS FRANCE—See HH Global Group Limited; *Int'l*, pg. 3378
INNERWORKINGS, INC. - CINCINNATI OFFICE—See HH Global Group Limited; *Int'l*, pg. 3378
INNERWORKINGS, INC. - EAST BRUNSWICK OFFICE—See HH Global Group Limited; *Int'l*, pg. 3379
INNERWORKINGS, INC. - NEW YORK CITY OFFICE—See HH Global Group Limited; *Int'l*, pg. 3379
INNERWORKINGS, INC.—See HH Global Group Limited; *Int'l*, pg. 3378
INNERWORKINGS INDIA PRIVATE LIMITED—See HH Global Group Limited; *Int'l*, pg. 3378
INNERWORKINGS NEDERLAND BV—See HH Global Group Limited; *Int'l*, pg. 3378
INNERWORKINGS PERU S.A.C.—See HH Global Group Limited; *Int'l*, pg. 3378
INNERWORKINGS RUS LLC—See HH Global Group Limited; *Int'l*, pg. 3378
INNERWORKINGS RUSSIA LLA—See HH Global Group Limited; *Int'l*, pg. 3378
INNERWORKINGS SINGAPORE PRIVATE LIMITED—See HH Global Group Limited; *Int'l*, pg. 3378
INNEVATION, LLC—See DigitalBridge Group, Inc.; *U.S. Public*, pg. 665
INNEVATION, LLC—See Industry Super Holdings Pty. Ltd.; *Int'l*, pg. 3676
INNEX, INC.; *U.S. Private*, pg. 2080
INNFLUX LLC—See TZP Group LLC; *U.S. Private*, pg. 4269
INNFOCUS, INC.—See Santen Pharmaceutical Co., Ltd.; *Int'l*, pg. 6557
INN FOODS INC.—See The VPS Companies Inc.; *U.S. Private*, pg. 4132
INN HOTEL MACAU LIMITED—See Emperor Entertainment Hotel Limited; *Int'l*, pg. 2386
INNIS ARDEN GOLF CLUB; *U.S. Private*, pg. 2080
INNISFREE COSMETICS INDIA PRIVATE LIMITED—See Amorepacific Corp.; *Int'l*, pg. 430

INNISFREE HOTELS, INC.

INNISFREE HOTELS, INC.; *U.S. Private*, pg. 2080
INNISKILLIN WINES, INC.—See Ontario Teachers' Pension Plan; *Int'l*, pg. 5587
INNIS MAGGIORE GROUP, INC.; *U.S. Private*, pg. 2080
INNITY CORPORATION BERHAD; *Int'l*, pg. 3708
INNITY DIGITAL MEDIA (THAILAND) CO. LTD.—See Innity Corporation Berhad; *Int'l*, pg. 3708
INNITY LIMITED—See Innity Corporation Berhad; *Int'l*, pg. 3708
INNITY PHILIPPINES, INC.—See Innity Corporation Berhad; *Int'l*, pg. 3708
INNITY SDN BHD—See Innity Corporation Berhad; *Int'l*, pg. 3708
INNITY SINGAPORE PTE LTD—See Innity Corporation Berhad; *Int'l*, pg. 3708
INNITY VIETNAM CO LTD—See Innity Corporation Berhad; *Int'l*, pg. 3708
INNKEEPERS USA TRUST; *U.S. Private*, pg. 2080
INNOAGE PEI S.A.M.—See Aliaxis S.A./N.V.; *Int'l*, pg. 324
INNOAUTO TECHNOLOGIES INC.—See Hitron Technologies Inc.; *Int'l*, pg. 3427
INNO-BAG LIMITED—See China Eco-Farming Limited; *Int'l*, pg. 1498
INNOBIC (ASIA) COMPANY LIMITED—See PTT Public Company Limited; *Int'l*, pg. 6092
INNOBIT GMBH—See L. Possehl & Co. mbH; *Int'l*, pg. 4383
INNOBYTE ZRT.—See 4iG Nyrt.; *Int'l*, pg. 12
INNOCAN PHARMA CORPORATION; *Int'l*, pg. 3709
INNOCAP INVESTMENT MANAGEMENT INC.—See National Bank of Canada; *Int'l*, pg. 5152
INNOCARE OPTOELECTRONICS CORPORATION; *Int'l*, pg. 3709
INNOCARE PHARMA LIMITED; *Int'l*, pg. 3709
INNOCEAN AMERICAS WORLDWIDE; *U.S. Private*, pg. 2080
INNOCEAN WORLDWIDE INC.; *Int'l*, pg. 3709
INNOCENTIVE, INC.—See Wazoku Limited; *Int'l*, pg. 8361
INNOCENT LTD.—See The Coca-Cola Company; *U.S. Public*, pg. 2065
INNOCERIA SDN. BHD.—See NCT Alliance Berhad; *Int'l*, pg. 5182
INNOCLEANING CONCEPTS HOLDING B.V.—See InnoConcepts N.V.; *Int'l*, pg. 3709
INNOCLEAN S.A.—See Compass Group PLC; *Int'l*, pg. 1752
INNOCOLL HOLDINGS PLC—See Gurnet Point Capital LLC; *U.S. Private*, pg. 1819
INNOCOM TECHNOLOGY HOLDINGS, INC.; *Int'l*, pg. 3709
INNOCONCEPTS N.V.; *Int'l*, pg. 3709
INNOCORP LTD.; *Int'l*, pg. 3709
INNO COSTEC CORPORATION—See KODI Co., Ltd.; *Int'l*, pg. 4226
INNOCV SOLUTIONS S.L.—See Alkemy SpA; *Int'l*, pg. 331
INNODATA, INC.; *U.S. Public*, pg. 1125
INNODATA KNOWLEDGE SERVICES, INC.—See Innodata, Inc.; *U.S. Public*, pg. 1125
INNODEP INC.; *Int'l*, pg. 3709
INNODISC AG—See OC Oerlikon Corporation AG; *Int'l*, pg. 5512
INNODISK CORP.; *Int'l*, pg. 3709
INNODISK EUROPE B.V.—See InnoDisk Corp.; *Int'l*, pg. 3709
INNODISK FRANCE S.A.S.—See InnoDisk Corp.; *Int'l*, pg. 3709
INNODISK JAPAN CORPORATION—See InnoDisk Corp.; *Int'l*, pg. 3710
INNODISK SHENZHEN CORPORATION—See InnoDisk Corp.; *Int'l*, pg. 3710
INNODISK USA CORPORATION—See InnoDisk Corp.; *Int'l*, pg. 3710
INNODIS LTD; *Int'l*, pg. 3709
INNOESSENTIALS INTERNATIONAL B.V.—See InnoConcepts N.V.; *Int'l*, pg. 3709
INNOFACTOR PLC—See CapMan PLC; *Int'l*, pg. 1315
INNOFACTOR PLC—See Osprey Capital LLC; *U.S. Private*, pg. 3048
INNOFIS ESGM S.L.—See Constellation Software Inc.; *Int'l*, pg. 1772
INN OF LAKE CITY INC.; *U.S. Private*, pg. 2080
INN OF NAPLES, LLC; *U.S. Private*, pg. 2080
INNOFORM ENTERTAINMENT PTE. LTD.—See PSC Corporation Ltd.; *Int'l*, pg. 6015
INNOFORM MEDIA (HK) LIMITED—See PSC Corporation Ltd.; *Int'l*, pg. 6015
INNOFORM MEDIA (M) SDN. BHD—See PSC Corporation Ltd.; *Int'l*, pg. 6015
INNOFORM MEDIA PTE LTD—See PSC Corporation Ltd.; *Int'l*, pg. 6015
INNOGAMES GMBH—See Modern Times Group MTG AB; *Int'l*, pg. 5014
INNOGENE CO., LTD.; *Int'l*, pg. 3710
INNOGENE KALBIOTECH PTE LTD—See PT Kalbe Farma Tbk.; *Int'l*, pg. 6050
INNO-GENE SA; *Int'l*, pg. 3709
INNOGENETICS DIAGNOSTICA IBERIA, S.L.—See H.U. Group Holdings, Inc.; *Int'l*, pg. 3196

INNOGENETICS, INC.—See H.U. Group Holdings, Inc.; *Int'l*, pg. 3196
INNOGENETICS SARL—See H.U. Group Holdings, Inc.; *Int'l*, pg. 3196
INNOGENETICS S.R.L.—See H.U. Group Holdings, Inc.; *Int'l*, pg. 3196
INNOGEO SAS—See ABO-Group NV/SA; *Int'l*, pg. 66
INNOGE PE INDUSTRIES S.A.M.—See Aliaxis S.A./N.V.; *Int'l*, pg. 324
INNOGY CONSULTING GMBH—See RWE AG; *Int'l*, pg. 6436
INNOGY DIREKT GMBH—See RWE AG; *Int'l*, pg. 6436
INNOGY GAS STORAGE NWE GMBH—See RWE AG; *Int'l*, pg. 6436
INNOGY INNOVATION GMBH—See RWE AG; *Int'l*, pg. 6436
INNOGY LIMITED; *Int'l*, pg. 3710
INNOGY METERING GMBH—See RWE AG; *Int'l*, pg. 6436
INNOGY POLSKA S.A.—See RWE AG; *Int'l*, pg. 6436
INNOGY RENEWABLES UK LIMITED—See RWE AG; *Int'l*, pg. 6434
INNOGY SE—See E.ON SE; *Int'l*, pg. 2258
INNOGY SLOVENSKO S.R.O.—See RWE AG; *Int'l*, pg. 6436
INNOGY STIFTUNG FUR ENERGIE UND GESELLSCHAFT GGMBH—See RWE AG; *Int'l*, pg. 6436
INNOGY STOEN OPERATOR SP. Z O.O.—See RWE AG; *Int'l*, pg. 6436
INNOGY VENTURES GMBH—See RWE AG; *Int'l*, pg. 6436
INNO HOLDINGS, INC.; *U.S. Public*, pg. 1125
INNO HUB CO., LTD.—See Samart Corporation Public Company Limited; *Int'l*, pg. 6501
INNOHUBS GMBH—See 3U Holding AG; *Int'l*, pg. 10
INNO INSTRUMENT AMERICA INC.—See INNO Instrument Inc.; *Int'l*, pg. 3708
INNO INSTRUMENT (CHINA) INC.—See INNO Instrument Inc.; *Int'l*, pg. 3708
INNO INSTRUMENT EUROPE GMBH—See INNO Instrument Inc.; *Int'l*, pg. 3709
INNO INSTRUMENT INC.; *Int'l*, pg. 3708
INNO INSTRUMENT INDIA PVT. LTD.—See INNO Instrument Inc.; *Int'l*, pg. 3709
INNO INSTRUMENT MALAYSIA INC.—See INNO Instrument Inc.; *Int'l*, pg. 3709
INNO INSTRUMENT MYANMAR INC.—See INNO Instrument Inc.; *Int'l*, pg. 3709
INNO INSTRUMENT PHILIPPINES INC.—See INNO Instrument Inc.; *Int'l*, pg. 3709
INNO INSTRUMENT VIETNAM INC.—See INNO Instrument Inc.; *Int'l*, pg. 3709
INNOKAIZ INDIA LIMITED; *Int'l*, pg. 3710
INNOLAB DO BRASIL LTDA.—See Eurofins Scientific S.E.; *Int'l*, pg. 2550
INNO LASER TECHNOLOGY CO., LTD.; *Int'l*, pg. 3709
INNOLATEX SDN. BHD.—See Karex Berhad; *Int'l*, pg. 4081
INNOLATION GMBH—See Sto SE & Co. KGaA; *Int'l*, pg. 7219
INNOLIGHT TECHNOLOGY (SUZHOU) LTD.—See Zhongji Innolight Co., Ltd.; *Int'l*, pg. 8673
INNOLUX CORPORATION - NINGBO—See Innolux Corporation; *Int'l*, pg. 3710
INNOLUX CORPORATION; *Int'l*, pg. 3710
INNOLUX EUROPE B.V.—See Innolux Corporation; *Int'l*, pg. 3710
INNOLUX GERMANY GMBH—See Innolux Corporation; *Int'l*, pg. 3710
INNOLUX USA, INC.—See Innolux Corporation; *Int'l*, pg. 3710
INNOMAR STRATEGIES, INC.—See Cencora, Inc.; *U.S. Public*, pg. 467
INNOMAX CORPORATION; *U.S. Private*, pg. 2080
INNOMED GESELLSCHAFT FUR MEDIZINISCHE SOFTWAREANWENDUNGEN GMBH—See CompuGroup Medical SE & Co. KGaA; *Int'l*, pg. 1757
INNOMETRY CO., LTD.; *Int'l*, pg. 3710
INNOMINATA—See Eurobio Scientific SA; *Int'l*, pg. 2533
INNOMINATE SECURITY TECHNOLOGIES AG—See PHOENIX CONTACT GmbH & Co. KG; *Int'l*, pg. 5849
INNOMOTICS GMBH—See Siemens Aktiengesellschaft; *Int'l*, pg. 6887
THE INN ON FIFTH—See Hybridge Commercial Real Estate; *U.S. Private*, pg. 2016
INNOPAC HOLDINGS LIMITED; *Int'l*, pg. 3710
INNO-PAK, LLC; *U.S. Private*, pg. 2080
INNOPARTNER PTE. LIMITED—See PC Partner Group Limited; *Int'l*, pg. 5766
INNOPATH SOFTWARE, INC.; *U.S. Private*, pg. 2080
INNOPHARMA, INC.—See Pfizer Inc.; *U.S. Public*, pg. 1680
INNOPHOS HOLDINGS, INC.—See One Rock Capital Partners, LLC; *U.S. Private*, pg. 3022
INNOPHOS MEXICANA S.A. DE C.V.—See One Rock Capital Partners, LLC; *U.S. Private*, pg. 3022
INNOPHOS NUTRITION, INC.—See One Rock Capital Partners, LLC; *U.S. Private*, pg. 3022

CORPORATE AFFILIATIONS

INNO POLYTECH CORPORATION—See GS Holdings Corp.; *Int'l*, pg. 3142
INNOPOWER TECHNOLOGY CORPORATION—See Faraday Technology Corporation; *Int'l*, pg. 2618
INNOPRISE PLANTATIONS BERHAD; *Int'l*, pg. 3710
INNOPRISE SOFTWARE, INC.—See Constellation Software, Inc.; *Int'l*, pg. 1774
INNOQOS CORPORATION—See J-Stream Inc.; *Int'l*, pg. 3854
INNORIID GMBH—See AMETEK, Inc.; *U.S. Public*, pg. 122
INNORULES CO., LTD.; *Int'l*, pg. 3710
INNOSIGHT CONSULTING ASIA PACIFIC PTE. LTD.—See Huron Consulting Group Inc.; *U.S. Public*, pg. 1076
INNOSIGHT CONSULTING, LLC—See Huron Consulting Group Inc.; *U.S. Public*, pg. 1076
INNOSIMULATION CO. LTD.; *Int'l*, pg. 3710
INNO SMART GROUP LIMITED; *Int'l*, pg. 3709
INNOSPEC ACTIVE CHEMICALS LLC—See Innospec Inc.; *U.S. Public*, pg. 1125
INNOSPEC DEUTSCHLAND GMBH—See Innospec Inc.; *U.S. Public*, pg. 1125
INNOSPEC DEVELOPMENTS LIMITED—See Innospec Inc.; *U.S. Public*, pg. 1125
INNOSPEC FRANCE S.A.—See Innospec Inc.; *U.S. Public*, pg. 1125
INNOSPEC FUEL SPECIALTIES LLC—See Innospec Inc.; *U.S. Public*, pg. 1125
INNOSPEC HELLAS LTD.—See Innospec Inc.; *U.S. Public*, pg. 1125
INNOSPEC INC.; *U.S. Public*, pg. 1125
INNOSPEC PERFORMANCE CHEMICALS ITALIA S.R.L.—See Innospec Inc.; *U.S. Public*, pg. 1125
INNOSPEC PERFORMANCE CHEMICALS SPAIN S.L.—See Innospec Inc.; *U.S. Public*, pg. 1125
INNOSPEC RUSS OOO—See Innospec Inc.; *U.S. Public*, pg. 1125
INNOSPEC SPECIALTY CHEMICALS—See Innospec Inc.; *U.S. Public*, pg. 1125
INNOSPEC SWEDEN AB—See Innospec Inc.; *U.S. Public*, pg. 1125
INNOSYS CORP.; *Int'l*, pg. 3710
INNOTAS, INC.—See TA Associates, Inc.; *U.S. Private*, pg. 3917
INNOTAS, INC.—See TPG Capital, L.P.; *U.S. Public*, pg. 2175
INNOTEC, CORP.; *U.S. Private*, pg. 2080
INNOTECH CORPORATION; *Int'l*, pg. 3710
INNOTECH GREEN ENERGY CO., LTD.—See PTG Energy Public Company Limited; *Int'l*, pg. 6090
INNO-TECH HOLDINGS LIMITED; *Int'l*, pg. 3709
INNOTECH LASER GMBH—See Wuhan Raycus Fiber Laser Technologies Co., Ltd.; *Int'l*, pg. 8501
INNOTEK CORPORATION; *U.S. Private*, pg. 2081
INNOTEK LIMITED; *Int'l*, pg. 3710
INNOTEQ, INC.—See Endo International plc; *Int'l*, pg. 2404
INNOTHERAPY AMERICA, INC.—See InnoTherapy, Inc.; *Int'l*, pg. 3711
INNOTHERAPY, INC.; *Int'l*, pg. 3711
INNOTHERA SA; *Int'l*, pg. 3711
INNOTION ENTERPRISES, INC.; *U.S. Private*, pg. 2081
IN-N-OUT BURGERS, INC.; *U.S. Private*, pg. 2052
INNOV8 SOLUTIONS USA LLC; *U.S. Private*, pg. 2081
INNOVA CAPITAL SP. Z O.O.; *Int'l*, pg. 3711
INNOVA CAPTAB LIMITED; *Int'l*, pg. 3711
INNOVACARE HEALTH, INC.—See UnitedHealth Group Incorporated; *U.S. Public*, pg. 2241
INNOVACOM, INC.; *U.S. Public*, pg. 1125
INNOVADERMA PLC—See Brand Architekts Group plc; *Int'l*, pg. 1139
INNOVA GLOBAL LIMITED—See TriWest Capital Management Corp.; *Int'l*, pg. 7937
INNOVA INTERNATIONAL CORP.—See Great Universal Incorporated; *U.S. Private*, pg. 1768
INNOVAL TECHNOLOGY LTD.—See Danieli & C. Officine Meccaniche S.p.A.; *Int'l*, pg. 1963
INNOVALUES PTE LTD—See Northstar Advisors Pte. Ltd.; *Int'l*, pg. 5446
INNOVANA FITNESS LABS LIMITED—See Innovana Thinklabs Ltd.; *Int'l*, pg. 3711
INNOVANA TECHLABS LIMITED—See Innovana Thinklabs Ltd.; *Int'l*, pg. 3711
INNOVANA THINKLABS LTD.; *Int'l*, pg. 3711
INNOVANCE, INC.; *U.S. Private*, pg. 2081
INNOVA PHARMA SPA—See Recordati S.p.A.; *Int'l*, pg. 6239
INNOVAPOST, INC.—See Canada Post Corporation; *Int'l*, pg. 1282
INNOVAPOST, INC.—See CGI Inc.; *Int'l*, pg. 1433
INNOVAR ENVIRONMENTAL, INC.; *U.S. Private*, pg. 2081
INNOVARO, INC.; *U.S. Private*, pg. 2081
INNOVA S.A.—See Petroleo Brasileiro S.A. - PETROBRAS; *Int'l*, pg. 5827
INNOVASCIENCE INC.—See Brand Architekts Group plc; *Int'l*, pg. 1139
INNOVAS GMBH—See msg group GmbH; *Int'l*, pg. 5067

COMPANY NAME INDEX

INNOVASIAN CUISINE ENTERPRISES, LLC—See Nichirei Corporation; *Int'l*, pg. 5270
INNOVASIC, INC.—See Analog Devices, Inc.; *U.S. Public*, pg. 135
INNOVASOURCE LLC—See Energizer Holdings, Inc.; *U.S. Public*, pg. 761
INNOVASSYNTH INVESTMENTS LIMITED; *Int'l*, pg. 3711
INNOVA SUPERCONDUCTOR TECHNOLOGY CO.,LTD.—See Tianjin Benefo Tejing Electric Co., Ltd.; *Int'l*, pg. 7738
INNOVA TAXFREE BELGIUM SPRL—See Euronet Worldwide, Inc.; *U.S. Public*, pg. 798
INNOVA TAX FREE FRANCE SAS—See Euronet Worldwide, Inc.; *U.S. Public*, pg. 798
INNOVA TAXFREE IRELAND LIMITED—See Euronet Worldwide, Inc.; *U.S. Public*, pg. 798
INNOVA TAXFREE ITALY S.R.L.—See Euronet Worldwide, Inc.; *U.S. Public*, pg. 798
INNOVA TAXFREE NETHERLANDS B.V.—See Euronet Worldwide, Inc.; *U.S. Public*, pg. 798
INNOVA TAXFREE PORTUGAL UNIPESSOAL LDA.—See Euronet Worldwide, Inc.; *U.S. Public*, pg. 798
INNOVA TAXFREE SPAIN S.L.—See Euronet Worldwide, Inc.; *U.S. Public*, pg. 798
INNOVA TAX FREE (UK) LIMITED—See Euronet Worldwide, Inc.; *U.S. Public*, pg. 798
INNOVATE360, INC.—See GTCR LLC; *U.S. Private*, pg. 1803
INNOVATE CORP.; *U.S. Public*, pg. 1125
INNOVATEC S.P.A.; *Int'l*, pg. 3712
INNOVATEK INNOVATION TECHNOLOGIES LTDA—See Abbott Laboratories; *U.S. Public*, pg. 20
INNOVA TELECOMMUNICATION COMPANY LIMITED—See ALT Telecom PCL; *Int'l*, pg. 383
INNOVATEMAP LLC; *U.S. Private*, pg. 2081
INNOVATIA INC.—See BCE Inc.; *Int'l*, pg. 926
INNOVATION1 BIOTECH INC.; *U.S. Public*, pg. 1126
INNOVATION ADS, INC.; *U.S. Private*, pg. 2081
INNOVATION ADS, INC.—See Innovation Ads, Inc.; *U.S. Private*, pg. 2081
INNOVATION CAPITAL SAS—See LBO France S.a.r.l.; *Int'l*, pg. 4429
INNOVATION CORE SEI, INC.—See Sumitomo Electric Industries, Ltd.; *Int'l*, pg. 7278
INNOVATION DIC CHIMITRONIQUES INC.—See DIC Corporation; *Int'l*, pg. 2109
INNOVATION DIGITAL, LLC—See COMSovereign Holding Corp.; *U.S. Public*, pg. 562
INNOVATION FOOTWEAR CO., LTD.—See Bangkok Rubber Public Co., Ltd.; *Int'l*, pg. 835
INNOVATION GRAPHICS; *U.S. Private*, pg. 2081
THE INNOVATION GROUP (EMEA) LIMITED—See The Innovation Group Ltd.; *Int'l*, pg. 7656
INNOVATION GROUP HOLDINGS GMBH—See The Innovation Group Ltd.; *Int'l*, pg. 7656
THE INNOVATION GROUP LTD.; *Int'l*, pg. 7656
INNOVATION GROUP PARTS GMBH—See The Innovation Group Ltd.; *Int'l*, pg. 7656
INNOVATION GROUP (PTY) LTD.—See The Innovation Group Ltd.; *Int'l*, pg. 7656
INNOVATION, INC.; *Int'l*, pg. 3712
THE INNOVATION INSTITUTE; *U.S. Public*, pg. 4056
INNOVATION LABORATORY, INC.—See Future Corporation; *Int'l*, pg. 2853
INNOVATION LEO BURNETT—See Publicis Groupe S.A.; *Int'l*, pg. 6100
INNOVATION MEDICAL MANAGEMENT CO., LTD.; *Int'l*, pg. 3712
INNOVATION NETWORK, INC.—See eTRANSERVICES, LLC; *U.S. Private*, pg. 1432
INNOVATION OF SOCIAL ENVIRONMENT CO., LTD.—See Tokyo Sangyo Co., Ltd.; *Int'l*, pg. 7795
INNOVATIONONE, LLC—See The Chickasaw Nation; *U.S. Private*, pg. 4008
INNOVATION PHARMACEUTICALS INC.; *U.S. Public*, pg. 1126
INNOVATION REAL ESTATE S.P.A.; *Int'l*, pg. 3712
INNOVATIONSFONDS HESSEN GMBH & CO. KG—See Helaba Landesbank Hessen-Thuringen; *Int'l*, pg. 3328
INNOVATIONS FOR POVERTY ACTION; *U.S. Private*, pg. 2081
INNOVATIONSKAPITAL NORDIC ADVISORS AB; *Int'l*, pg. 3712
INNOVATION SOFTWARE EXPORTS LIMITED; *Int'l*, pg. 3712
INNOVATIONS SURGERY CENTER, LLC—See Community Health Systems, Inc.; *U.S. Public*, pg. 553
INNOVATION TEAM SWEDEN AB—See Etteplan Oyj; *Int'l*, pg. 2525
INNOVATION TECHNOLOGY GROUP; *U.S. Private*, pg. 2081
INNOVATION VENTURES LLC; *U.S. Private*, pg. 2081
INNOVATIVE ADVERTISING, LLC.; *U.S. Private*, pg. 2081
INNOVATIVE AFTERMARKET SYSTEMS L.P.—See iA Financial Corporation Inc.; *U.S. Private*, pg. 3568
INNOVATIVE AG SERVICES CO.; *U.S. Private*, pg. 2081
INNOVATIVE ANALYTICS INC.; *U.S. Private*, pg. 2081
INNOVATIVE AUTOMATION AND CONTROLS, INC.—See Airline Hydraulics Corporation; *U.S. Private*, pg. 141

INNOVATIVE AUTOMATION, INC.—See Paragon Technologies, Inc.; *U.S. Public*, pg. 1637
INNOVATIVE BANKING SOLUTIONS AG—See DXC Technology Company; *U.S. Public*, pg. 695
INNOVATIVE BANKING SOLUTIONS AG—See DXC Technology Company; *U.S. Public*, pg. 695
INNOVATIVE BUILDING SYSTEMS LLC; *U.S. Private*, pg. 2081
INNOVATIVE CHEMICAL PRODUCTS GROUP, LLC—See Audax Group, Limited Partnership; *U.S. Private*, pg. 388
INNOVATIVE CLIMATIC TECHNOLOGIES CORP.; *U.S. Public*, pg. 1126
INNOVATIVE COLLABORATION, INC.; *U.S. Private*, pg. 2082
INNOVATIVE COMMUNICATION CONCEPTS, INC.; *U.S. Private*, pg. 2082
INNOVATIVE COMMUNICATIONS; *U.S. Private*, pg. 2082
INNOVATIVE COMPONENTS, INC.—See Essentra plc; *Int'l*, pg. 2511
INNOVATIVE COMPOSITES INTERNATIONAL, INC.; *Int'l*, pg. 3712
INNOVATIVE COMPUTER SOLUTIONS, INC.—See Constellation Software Inc.; *Int'l*, pg. 1773
INNOVATIVE COMPUTING & APPLIED TECHNOLOGY LLC; *U.S. Private*, pg. 2082
INNOVATIVE COMPUTING SYSTEMS, INC.; *U.S. Private*, pg. 2082
INNOVATIVE CONCEPT GROUP; *U.S. Private*, pg. 2082
INNOVATIVE CONCEPTS, INC.—See Elbit Systems Limited; *Int'l*, pg. 2344
INNOVATIVE CONCRETE TECHNOLOGY CORP.—See Elvisridge Capital, LLC; *U.S. Private*, pg. 1377
INNOVATIVE CONSTRUCTION GROUP, LLC—See PulteGroup, Inc.; *U.S. Public*, pg. 1737
INNOVATIVE CONSTRUCTION & ROOFING; *U.S. Private*, pg. 2082
INNOVATIVE CONSTRUCTION SERVICES—See P.J. Dick Incorporated; *U.S. Private*, pg. 3060
INNOVATIVE CONTROL SYSTEMS, INC.—See Dover Corporation; *U.S. Public*, pg. 681
INNOVATIVE CONTROL SYSTEMS LP; *U.S. Private*, pg. 2082
INNOVATIVE COURIER SOLUTIONS INC.; *U.S. Private*, pg. 2082
INNOVATIVE DESIGNS, INC.; *U.S. Public*, pg. 1126
INNOVATIVE DESIGN SOLUTIONS, INC.—See LCI Industries; *U.S. Public*, pg. 1295
INNOVATIVE DESIGNS—See Barco N.V.; *Int'l*, pg. 864
INNOVATIVE DISCOVERY, LLC—See Silver Oak Services Partners, LLC; *U.S. Private*, pg. 3661
INNOVATIVE DISPLAYWORKS, INC.—See Oxford Financial Group Ltd.; *U.S. Private*, pg. 3057
INNOVATIVE DIVERSIFIED TECHNOLOGIES INC.; *U.S. Private*, pg. 2082
INNOVATIVE ELASTOMERS, INC.—See AirBoss of America Corp.; *Int'l*, pg. 241
INNOVATIVE ELECTRIC, INC.—See Gryphon Investors, LLC; *U.S. Private*, pg. 1799
INNOVATIVE ELECTRONIC DESIGNS, INC.—See MiTek Corporation; *U.S. Private*, pg. 2751
INNOVATIVE ENERGY SYSTEMS, LLC—See BP plc; *Int'l*, pg. 1126
INNOVATIVE ENGINEERING, INC.—See OceanSound Partners, LP; *U.S. Private*, pg. 2991
INNOVATIVE EYEWEAR, INC.; *U.S. Public*, pg. 1126
INNOVATIVE FOOD HOLDINGS, INC.; *U.S. Public*, pg. 1126
INNOVATIVE FOOD PROCESSORS, INC.—See Balchem Corporation; *U.S. Public*, pg. 265
INNOVATIVE FOODS, INC.; *U.S. Private*, pg. 2082
INNOVATIVE GOURMET, LLC—See Innovative Food Holdings, Inc.; *U.S. Public*, pg. 1127
INNOVATIVE GROWERS EQUIPMENT CANADA, INC.—See Hydrofarm Holdings Group, Inc.; *U.S. Public*, pg. 1079
INNOVATIVE GROWERS EQUIPMENT, INC.—See Hydrofarm Holdings Group, Inc.; *U.S. Public*, pg. 1079
INNOVATIVE HEARTH PRODUCTS LLC—See TRM Equity LLC; *U.S. Private*, pg. 4241
INNOVATIVE HEARTH PRODUCTS—See TRM Equity LLC; *U.S. Private*, pg. 4241
INNOVATIVE HESS PRODUCTS, LLC.; *U.S. Private*, pg. 2082
INNOVATIVE HOLDINGS ALLIANCE, INC.; *U.S. Public*, pg. 1127
INNOVATIVE IDEALS & SERVICES (INDIA) LTD.; *Int'l*, pg. 3712
INNOVATIVE IDM LLC; *U.S. Private*, pg. 2082
INNOVATIVE, INC.; *U.S. Private*, pg. 2083
INNOVATIVE INDUSTRIAL PROPERTIES, INC.; *U.S. Public*, pg. 1127
INNOVATIVE INFORMATION SOLUTIONS; *U.S. Private*, pg. 2082
INNOVATIVE INTEGRATION, INC.; *U.S. Private*, pg. 2082
INNOVATIVE INTERFACES INC.—See HGGC, LLC; *U.S. Private*, pg. 1930
INNOVATIVE INTERFACES INC.—See JMI Services, Inc.; *U.S. Private*, pg. 2216

INNOVATIVE LASER TECHNOLOGIES, INC.—See IPG Photonics Corporation; *U.S. Public*, pg. 1167
INNOVATIVE LIGHTING, INC.; *U.S. Private*, pg. 2082
INNOVATIVE LOGISTICS UMEA AB—See Storskogen Group AB; *Int'l*, pg. 7227
INNOVATIVE MANUFACTURING SOLUTIONS CORP.; *U.S. Private*, pg. 2082
INNOVATIVE MATTRESS SOLUTIONS, LLC—See Tempur Sealy International, Inc.; *U.S. Public*, pg. 1999
INNOVATIVE MEDICAL SYSTEMS, INC.—See Ares Management Corporation; *U.S. Public*, pg. 189
INNOVATIVE MODULAR SOLUTIONS, INC.—See McGrath RentCorp.; *U.S. Public*, pg. 1407
INNOVATIVE MOLDING INC.—See TriMas Corporation; *U.S. Public*, pg. 2189
INNOVATIVE NANOTECH INCORPORATED—See Chroma ATE Inc.; *Int'l*, pg. 1588
INNOVATIVE NEUROTRONICS, INC.—See Patient Square Capital, L.P.; *U.S. Private*, pg. 3107
INNOVATIVE NOAH ELECTRONIC (SHENZHEN) CO., LTD—See Noah Education Holdings Ltd.; *Int'l*, pg. 5394
INNOVATIVE OFFICE SOLUTIONS LLC; *U.S. Private*, pg. 2083
INNOVATIVE PAYMENT SOLUTIONS, INC.; *U.S. Public*, pg. 1127
INNOVATIVE PEST MANAGEMENT, LLC—See EQT AB; *Int'l*, pg. 2467
INNOVATIVE PEST MANAGEMENT (PTY) LTD—See Ascendis Health Limited; *Int'l*, pg. 601
INNOVATIVE PHARMACEUTICAL BIOTECH LIMITED; *Int'l*, pg. 3712
INNOVATIVE PHOTONIC SOLUTIONS, INC.—See Metrohm AG; *Int'l*, pg. 4862
INNOVATIVE PICKING TECHNOLOGIES, INC.; *U.S. Private*, pg. 2083
INNOVATIVE PLASTICS CORPORATION—See Global Supply LLC; *U.S. Private*, pg. 1718
INNOVATIVE PLASTICS—See Global Supply LLC; *U.S. Private*, pg. 1718
INNOVATIVE PLASTICS WEST CORP.—See Global Supply LLC; *U.S. Private*, pg. 1718
INNOVATIVE POLYMERS, INC.—See Nimbus B.V.; *Int'l*, pg. 5296
INNOVATIVE POWER PRODUCTS, INC.; *U.S. Private*, pg. 2083
INNOVATIVE POWER SYSTEMS, INC.—See TSS, Inc.; *U.S. Public*, pg. 2202
INNOVATIVE PRINT & MEDIA GROUP, INC.—See Deluxe Corporation; *U.S. Public*, pg. 653
INNOVATIVE PRODUCT ACHIEVEMENTS LLC—See Roper Technologies, Inc.; *U.S. Public*, pg. 1811
INNOVATIVE RENAL CARE LLC—See Nautic Partners, LLC; *U.S. Private*, pg. 2868
INNOVATIVE-RFK S.P.A.; *Int'l*, pg. 3712
INNOVATIVE SCIENCE SOLUTIONS, LLP—See Arsenal Capital Management LP; *U.S. Private*, pg. 338
INNOVATIVE SENIOR CARE HOME HEALTH OF NASHVILLE LLC—See Brookdale Senior Living Inc.; *U.S. Public*, pg. 394
INNOVATIVE SENSOR TECHNOLOGY IST AG—See Endress+Hauser (International) Holding AG; *Int'l*, pg. 2408
INNOVATIVE SERVICES, INC.; *U.S. Private*, pg. 2083
INNOVATIVE SOFTWARE ENGINEERING, LLC—See Trimble, Inc.; *U.S. Public*, pg. 2190
INNOVATIVE SOFTWARE SOLUTIONS, INC.—See Advanced Solutions International Inc.; *U.S. Private*, pg. 92
INNOVATIVE SOLUTIONS AND SUPPORT, LLC—See Innovative Solutions & Support, Inc.; *U.S. Public*, pg. 1127
INNOVATIVE SOLUTIONS INSURANCE SERVICES, LLC.; *U.S. Private*, pg. 2083
INNOVATIVE SOLUTIONS & SUPPORT, INC.; *U.S. Public*, pg. 1127
INNOVATIVE SOLUTIONS UNLIMITED, LLC; *U.S. Private*, pg. 2083
INNOVATIVE SOLUTION SYSTEMS; *U.S. Private*, pg. 2083
INNOVATIVE STAFFING, INC.; *U.S. Private*, pg. 2083
INNOVATIVE STEAM TECHNOLOGIES—See Propak Systems Ltd.; *Int'l*, pg. 5997
INNOVATIVE SURFACES, LLC; *U.S. Private*, pg. 2083
INNOVATIVE SYSTEMS GROUP INC.; *U.S. Private*, pg. 2083
INNOVATIVE SYSTEMS, LLC—See TA Associates, Inc.; *U.S. Private*, pg. 3914
INNOVATIVE TECHNICAL SOLUTIONS, INC.—See Gilbane, Inc.; *U.S. Public*, pg. 1698
INNOVATIVE TECHNICAL SOLUTIONS, INC.—See Corning Incorporated; *U.S. Public*, pg. 579
INNOVATIVE TECHNOLOGIES IN PRINT—See Continental Press Inc.; *U.S. Private*, pg. 1030
INNOVATIVE TECHNOLOGY DEVELOPMENT CORPORATION; *Int'l*, pg. 3712
INNOVATIVE TECHNOLOGY, INC.—See Eaton Corporation plc; *Int'l*, pg. 2282
INNOVATIVE TECHNOLOGY PARTNERSHIPS, LLC; *U.S. Private*, pg. 2083

INNOVATIVE TECHNOLOGY PARTNERSHIPS, LLC

CORPORATE AFFILIATIONS

INNOVATIVE TECHNOLOGY SYSTEMS & SOLUTIONS INC.—See ePlus Inc.; *U.S. Public*, pg. 784
INNOVATIVE TECH PACK LIMITED; *Int'l*, pg. 3712
INNOVATIVE TEXTILES, INC.—See Shimano, Inc.; *Int'l*, pg. 6833
INNOVATIVE TRAINING & RECRUITMENT PTY LTD.—See Madison Dearborn Partners, LLC; *U.S. Private*, pg. 2540
INNOVATIVE TREK TECHNOLOGY PTE LTD—See Venture Corporation Limited; *Int'l*, pg. 8151
INNOVATIVE TYRES & TUBES LIMITED; *Int'l*, pg. 3712
INNOVATIVE UNDERWRITERS INC.—See The Guardian Life Insurance Company of America; *U.S. Private*, pg. 4040
INNOVATIVE USA, INC.; *U.S. Private*, pg. 2083
INNOVATIVE VACUUM SOLUTIONS, INC.—See Atlas Copco AB; *Int'l*, pg. 683
INNOVATIVE WATER CARE, LLC—See Platinum Equity, LLC; *U.S. Private*, pg. 3204
INNOVATIVE WEB LTD.—See Swisscom AG; *Int'l*, pg. 7373
INNOVATIX, LLC—See Premier, Inc.; *U.S. Public*, pg. 1715
INNOVATORS FACADE SYSTEMS LTD.; *Int'l*, pg. 3712
INNOVATUM, INC.—See Banyan Software, Inc; *U.S. Private*, pg. 470
INNOVATUS CAPITAL PARTNERS LLC; *U.S. Private*, pg. 2083
INNOVATUS LIFE SCIENCES ACQUISITION CORP.; *U.S. Private*, pg. 2083
INNOVATYS (FRANCE)—See SafeTIC S.A.; *Int'l*, pg. 6470
INNOVAVENT GMBH—See Jenoptik AG; *Int'l*, pg. 3928
INNOVAX HOLDINGS LTD.; *Int'l*, pg. 3712
INNOVAX SDN BHD—See Batu Kawan Berhad; *Int'l*, pg. 891
INNOVAZIONE ITALIA S.P.A.—See Agenzia Nazionale per l'Attrazione degli Investimenti e lo Sviluppo d'Impresa SpA; *Int'l*, pg. 206
INNOVE COMMUNICATIONS INC—See Globe Telecom, Inc.; *Int'l*, pg. 3006
INNOVEN CAPITAL INDIA PRIVATE LIMITED—See Temasek Holdings (Private) Limited; *Int'l*, pg. 7547
INNOVEN CAPITAL INDIA PRIVATE LIMITED—See United Overseas Bank Limited; *Int'l*, pg. 8071
INNOVEN CAPITAL SINGAPORE PTE. LTD.—See Temasek Holdings (Private) Limited; *Int'l*, pg. 7547
INNOVEN CAPITAL SINGAPORE PTE. LTD.—See United Overseas Bank Limited; *Int'l*, pg. 8071
INNOVENT BIOLOGICS (EUROPE) LIMITED—See Innovent Biologics, Inc.; *Int'l*, pg. 3712
INNOVENT BIOLOGICS, INC.; *Int'l*, pg. 3712
INNOVENT BIOLOGICS (SHANGHAI) CO., LTD.—See Innovent Biologics, Inc.; *Int'l*, pg. 3712
INNOVENTE INC.; *Int'l*, pg. 3712
INNOVENTE INC. - ST-PATRICE-DE-BEAURIVAGE FACTORY—See Innovente Inc.; *Int'l*, pg. 3713
INNOVENTIVE INDUSTRIES LIMITED; *Int'l*, pg. 3713
INNOVENTIVE VENTURE LIMITED; *Int'l*, pg. 3713
INNOVENT—See Standex International; *U.S. Public*, pg. 1930
INNOVEOX SA; *Int'l*, pg. 3713
INNOVEREN SCIENTIFIC, INC.; *U.S. Public*, pg. 1127
INNOVERSA MOBILE SOLUTIONS GP LTD.—See Quanta Services, Inc.; *U.S. Public*, pg. 1751
INNOVEST GLOBAL, INC.; *U.S. Public*, pg. 1127
INNOVEST INVESTMENT CORP—See CTCI Corporation; *Int'l*, pg. 1870
INNOVEST SYSTEMS, LLC—See SS&C Technologies Holdings, Inc.; *U.S. Public*, pg. 1923
INNOVESTX SECURITIES CO., LTD.—See SCB X Public Company Limited; *Int'l*, pg. 6614
INNOVETIVE PETCARE HOLDINGS LLC; *U.S. Private*, pg. 2083
INNOVEX CO., LTD.—See Wavelock Holdings Co., Ltd.; *Int'l*, pg. 8359
INNOVEX DOWNHOLE SOLUTIONS, INC.—See Intervale Capital, LLC; *U.S. Private*, pg. 2127
INNOVIA COMMUNITY MANAGEMENT COOPERATIVE—See CCA Global Partners, Inc.; *U.S. Private*, pg. 799
INNOVIA FILMS AMERICA, INC.—See CCL Industries Inc.; *Int'l*, pg. 1369
INNOVIA FILMS (ASIA PACIFIC) PTY. LTD.—See Newgate Private Equity LLP; *Int'l*, pg. 5234
INNOVIA FILMS BVBA—See Newgate Private Equity LLP; *Int'l*, pg. 5234
INNOVIA FILMS (COMMERCIAL) LTD.—See Newgate Private Equity LLP; *Int'l*, pg. 5234
INNOVIA FILMS, INC.—See Newgate Private Equity LLP; *Int'l*, pg. 5234
INNOVIA FILMS LIMITED—See Newgate Private Equity LLP; *Int'l*, pg. 5234
INNOVIA MEDICAL, INC.—See The Graham Group, Inc.; *U.S. Private*, pg. 4037
INNOVIA ST CO., LTD.—See Hoya Corporation; *Int'l*, pg. 3498
INNOVID CORP.; *Int'l*, pg. 3713
INNOVID, INC.—See Innovid Corp.; *Int'l*, pg. 3713
INNOVIM LLC; *U.S. Private*, pg. 2084

INNOVION CORPORATION—See Coherent Corp.; *U.S. Public*, pg. 528
INNOVIOPAPERS BV—See American Industrial Acquisition Corporation; *U.S. Private*, pg. 237
INNOVISE LTD.—See Accel Partners L.P.; *U.S. Private*, pg. 49
INNOVISE LTD.—See KKR & Co. Inc.; *U.S. Public*, pg. 1238
INNOVISION ARCHITECTS & ENGINEERS LIMITED—See Yau Lee Holdings Limited; *Int'l*, pg. 8571
INNOVISION MEDIA GROUP; *U.S. Private*, pg. 2084
INNOVISION MULTIMEDIA LIMITED—See PC Partner Group Limited; *Int'l*, pg. 5766
INNOVISTA SENSORS—See PAI Partners S.A.S.; *Int'l*, pg. 5700
INNOVISTA SENSORS—See The Carlyle Group Inc.; *U.S. Public*, pg. 2047
INNOVIUM MEDIA PROPERTIES CORP.-EXECUTIVE OFFICE—See Innovium Media Properties Corp.; *Int'l*, pg. 3713
INNOVIUM MEDIA PROPERTIES CORP.; *Int'l*, pg. 3713
INNOVIVA, INC.; *U.S. Public*, pg. 1127
INNOVIZANT, LLC—See Blackstone Inc.; *U.S. Public*, pg. 357
INNOVIZE, INC.—See Vance Street Capital LLC; *U.S. Private*, pg. 4342
INNOVIZ TECHNOLOGIES LTD.; *Int'l*, pg. 3713
INNOVO CLOUD GMBH—See Friedhelm Loh Stiftung & Co. KG; *Int'l*, pg. 2792
INNOVO INC.; *U.S. Private*, pg. 2084
INNOVOTECH INC.; *Int'l*, pg. 3713
INNOVUS PHARMACEUTICALS, INC.—See Aytu BioPharma, Inc.; *U.S. Public*, pg. 257
INNOVYX—See Omnicom Group Inc.; *U.S. Public*, pg. 1594
INNOVYX—See Omnicom Group Inc.; *U.S. Public*, pg. 1594
INNOVYX—See Omnicom Group Inc.; *U.S. Public*, pg. 1594
INNOVYX—See Omnicom Group Inc.; *U.S. Public*, pg. 1594
INNOVYZE, INC.—See Autodesk, Inc.; *U.S. Public*, pg. 229
INNOWACYJNA PLATFORMA HANDLU SP. Z O.O.—See Eurocash S.A.; *Int'l*, pg. 2533
INNOWATIO S.P.A.; *Int'l*, pg. 3713
INNOWATIE MARKETING GROUP, LLC; *U.S. Private*, pg. 2084
INNOWIRELESS CO., LTD.; *Int'l*, pg. 3713
INNOX ADVANCED MATERIALS CO., LTD.; *Int'l*, pg. 3713
INNOX CORPORATION; *Int'l*, pg. 3713
INN PARTNERS, L.C.—See Lee Enterprises, Incorporated; *U.S. Public*, pg. 1299
INNQUEST SOFTWARE CORP.—See Valsef Group; *Int'l*, pg. 8123
INNSBRUCKER NORDKETTENBAHNEN BETRIEBS GMBH—See STRABAG SE; *Int'l*, pg. 7230
INNSCOR AFRICA LTD.; *Int'l*, pg. 3713
INNSCOR (PVT) LTD—See Innscor Africa Ltd.; *Int'l*, pg. 3713
INNSE-BERARDI GMBH—See Camozzi Group; *Int'l*, pg. 1274
INNSE-BERARDI INC.—See Camozzi Group; *Int'l*, pg. 1274
INNSE-BERARDI SPA—See Camozzi Group; *Int'l*, pg. 1274
INNSE MILANO SPA—See Camozzi Group; *Int'l*, pg. 1274
INNSLAKE TITLE AGENCY, LLC—See Markel Group Inc.; *U.S. Public*, pg. 1368
INNS OF AMERICA; *U.S. Private*, pg. 2084
INNS OF UGANDA—See Alam Group of Companies; *Int'l*, pg. 289
INN SP Z O.O.—See Illinois Tool Works Inc.; *U.S. Public*, pg. 1104
INNSTAFF (PTY) LTD—See Adcorp Holdings Limited; *Int'l*, pg. 127
INNSUITES HOSPITALITY TRUST; *U.S. Public*, pg. 1127
INNSUITES HOTELS, INC.—See InnSuites Hospitality Trust; *U.S. Public*, pg. 1127
INNUA AMERICAS LTD—See The Normandy Group S.A.; *Int'l*, pg. 7671
INNUA CHINA LTD—See The Normandy Group S.A.; *Int'l*, pg. 7671
INNUA EUROPE LTD—See The Normandy Group S.A.; *Int'l*, pg. 7671
INNUA PETROCHEM LATIN AMERICA—See The Normandy Group S.A.; *Int'l*, pg. 7671
INNUA PETROCHEM LIMITED—See The Normandy Group S.A.; *Int'l*, pg. 7671
INNUA PETROCHEM LIMITED—See The Normandy Group S.A.; *Int'l*, pg. 7671
INNUOVO TECHNOLOGY CO., LTD.; *Int'l*, pg. 3713
INNVENTURES INC.; *U.S. Private*, pg. 2084
INO24 AG—See Hubert Burda Media Holding Kommanditgesellschaft; *Int'l*, pg. 3520
INOAC AUTOMOTIVE (THAILAND) LTD.—See INOAC Corporation; *Int'l*, pg. 3714

INOAC CORPORATION - ANJO PLANT—See INOAC Corporation; *Int'l*, pg. 3714
INOAC CORPORATION - KIKUCHI PLANT—See INOAC Corporation; *Int'l*, pg. 3714
INOAC CORPORATION - KIRA PLANT—See INOAC Corporation; *Int'l*, pg. 3714
INOAC CORPORATION - KITAKYUSHU PLANT—See INOAC Corporation; *Int'l*, pg. 3714
INOAC CORPORATION - NANNO PLANT—See INOAC Corporation; *Int'l*, pg. 3714
INOAC CORPORATION - SAKURAI PLANT—See INOAC Corporation; *Int'l*, pg. 3714
INOAC CORPORATION - SEINO PLANT—See INOAC Corporation; *Int'l*, pg. 3714
INOAC CORPORATION - SHINSHIRO PLANT—See INOAC Corporation; *Int'l*, pg. 3714
INOAC CORPORATION; *Int'l*, pg. 3713
INOAC CORPORATION - TAKETOYO PLANT—See INOAC Corporation; *Int'l*, pg. 3714
INOAC CORPORATION - TOYOHASHI PLANT—See INOAC Corporation; *Int'l*, pg. 3714
INOAC CORPORATION - UKIHA PLANT—See INOAC Corporation; *Int'l*, pg. 3714
INOAC CORPORATION - YANA PLANT—See INOAC Corporation; *Int'l*, pg. 3714
INOAC ELASTOMER CO., LTD.—See INOAC Corporation; *Int'l*, pg. 3714
INOAC ENGINEERING CO., LTD.—See INOAC Corporation; *Int'l*, pg. 3714
INOAC EUROPE GMBH—See INOAC Corporation; *Int'l*, pg. 3714
INOAC HONG KONG LIMITED—See INOAC Corporation; *Int'l*, pg. 3714
INOAC HOUSING & CONSTRUCTION MATERIALS CO., LTD.—See INOAC Corporation; *Int'l*, pg. 3714
INOAC INDUSTRIES (THAILAND) CO., LTD.—See INOAC Corporation; *Int'l*, pg. 3714
INOAC LIVING CO., LTD.—See INOAC Corporation; *Int'l*, pg. 3714
INOAC MALAYSIA SDN. BHD.—See INOAC Corporation; *Int'l*, pg. 3714
INOAC PACKAGING GROUP INC.—See INOAC Corporation; *Int'l*, pg. 3714
INOAC POLYMER LANKA (PVT) LTD.—See INOAC Corporation; *Int'l*, pg. 3714
INOAC POLYTEC DE MEXICO S.A DE C.V.—See INOAC Corporation; *Int'l*, pg. 3714
INOAC TECHNICAL CENTER, CO., LTD.—See INOAC Corporation; *Int'l*, pg. 3714
INOAC (THAILAND) CO., LTD.—See INOAC Corporation; *Int'l*, pg. 3714
INOAC TOKAI (THAILAND) COMPANY LIMITED—See INOAC Corporation; *Int'l*, pg. 3714
INOAC TRADING CO., LTD.—See INOAC Corporation; *Int'l*, pg. 3714
INOAC USA, INC.—See INOAC Corporation; *Int'l*, pg. 3714
INOAC VIETNAM CO., LTD.—See INOAC Corporation; *Int'l*, pg. 3714
INOAPPS LIMITED; *Int'l*, pg. 3715
INOAPPS SDN BHD—See Inoapps Limited; *Int'l*, pg. 3715
INOAPPS SINGAPORE PTE. LTD.—See Inoapps Limited; *Int'l*, pg. 3715
INOBIZ AB—See WiseTech Global Limited; *Int'l*, pg. 8437
INOC DEAD SEA LP; *Int'l*, pg. 3715
INOCEAN AB—See Technip Energies N.V.; *Int'l*, pg. 7506
INOCEAN AS—See Technip Energies N.V.; *Int'l*, pg. 7506
INOCEAN POLAND SP. Z O.O.—See Technip Energies N.V.; *Int'l*, pg. 7506
INOCHEM S.A. DE C.V.—See Revvity, Inc.; *U.S. Public*, pg. 1794
INOC LLC—See GenNx360 Capital Partners, L.P.; *U.S. Private*, pg. 1672
INO.COM; *U.S. Private*, pg. 2084
INOCRETE CO., LTD.—See Nichias Corporation; *Int'l*, pg. 5267
INOEX GMBH; *Int'l*, pg. 3715
INOEX LLC—See iNOEX GmbH; *Int'l*, pg. 3715
INOEX TRADING (BEIJING) CO. LTD.—See iNOEX GmbH; *Int'l*, pg. 3715
INO FITA GMBH—See General Mills, Inc.; *U.S. Public*, pg. 922
INOFORGES POLSKA SP. Z O.O.—See Inoforges; *Int'l*, pg. 3715
INOFORGES; *Int'l*, pg. 3715
INOGEN, INC.; *U.S. Public*, pg. 1128
INOKOM CORPORATION SDN. BHD.—See Sime Darby Berhad; *Int'l*, pg. 6929
INOLA GMBH—See init innovation in traffic systems SE; *Int'l*, pg. 3704
INOLEX CHEMICAL COMPANY—See Inolex Group Inc.; *U.S. Private*, pg. 2084
INOLEX GROUP INC.; *U.S. Private*, pg. 2084
INOLIFE TECHNOLOGIES INC.; *U.S. Private*, pg. 2084
INOMA CORPORATION—See USI Corporation; *Int'l*, pg. 8098
INONET COMPUTER GMBH—See Eurotech S.p.A.; *Int'l*, pg. 2558

COMPANY NAME INDEX

INONE TECHNOLOGY, LLC—See Nayax Ltd.; *Int'l*, pg. 5178
INORA LIFE DAC—See Enstar Group Limited; *Int'l*, pg. 2449
INOREC S.A.S.—See Derichebourg S.A.; *Int'l*, pg. 2041
INOREK & GREY—See WPP plc; *Int'l*, pg. 8472
INOR PROCESS AB—See Krohne International, Inc.; *Int'l*, pg. 4303
INOR TRANSMITTER GMBH—See Krohne International, Inc.; *Int'l*, pg. 4303
INOR TRANSMITTER OY—See Krohne International, Inc.; *Int'l*, pg. 4303
INOS AUTOMATIONSSOFTWARE GMBH—See Grenzebach Maschinenbau GmbH; *Int'l*, pg. 3082
INOS BALCAN DOO—See Viohalco SA/NV; *Int'l*, pg. 8243
INOS BALKAN DOO—See Viohalco SA/NV; *Int'l*, pg. 8243
INOS HELLAS S.A.—See Grenzebach Maschinenbau GmbH; *Int'l*, pg. 3082
INOS SINMA AD; *Int'l*, pg. 3715
INOTEC COATINGS & HYDRAULICS, INC.—See Corrosion & Abrasion Solutions Ltd.; *Int'l*, pg. 1806
INOTEC TAIWAN CO., LTD.—See Air Water Inc.; *Int'l*, pg. 240
INO THERAPEUTICS LLC—See Mallinckrodt Public Limited Company; *Int'l*, pg. 4663
INOTIV, INC.; *U.S. Public*, pg. 1128
INOUE JIKIUUKE KOGYO CO., LTD.—See NSK Ltd.; *Int'l*, pg. 5478
INOUEKI (MALAYSIA) SDN. BHD.—See Air Water Inc.; *Int'l*, pg. 240
INOUEKI PHILIPPINES, INC.—See Air Water Inc.; *Int'l*, pg. 240
INOUEKI SINGAPORE PTE. LTD.—See Air Water Inc.; *Int'l*, pg. 240
INOUEKI (THAILAND) CO., LTD.—See Air Water Inc.; *Int'l*, pg. 240
INOUE KOSAN CO., LTD.—See Cleanup Corporation; *Int'l*, pg. 1656
INOUE RUBBER CO., LTD.—See INOAC Corporation; *Int'l*, pg. 3714
INOUE RUBBER (THAILAND) PUBLIC COMPANY LIMITED; *Int'l*, pg. 3715
INOUE TECHNICA CO., LTD.—See TOKAI Holdings Corporation; *Int'l*, pg. 7779
INOUTIC DECEUNINCK GMBH—See Deceuninck NV; *Int'l*, pg. 2000
INOUTIC / DECEUNINCK, SPOL. S R.O.—See Deceuninck NV; *Int'l*, pg. 2000
INOUTIC D.O.O.—See Deceuninck NV; *Int'l*, pg. 2000
IN & OUT SPA—See Teleperformance SE; *Int'l*, pg. 7540
IN & OUT ST CO., LTD.—See INDUS Holding AG; *Int'l*, pg. 3664
INOV8 SURGICAL AT MEMORIAL CITY, LLC—See UnitedHealth Group Incorporated; *U.S. Public*, pg. 2241
INOVA ALEXANDRIA HOSPITAL—See Inova Health System; *U.S. Private*, pg. 2084
INOVA CENTRUM INNOWACJI TECHNICZNYCH SP. Z O.O.—See KGHM Polska Miedz S.A.; *Int'l*, pg. 4149
INOVACIA AB—See Kancera AB; *Int'l*, pg. 4064
INOVA DIAGNOSTICS, INC.—See Werfen Life Group, S.A.U.; *Int'l*, pg. 8379
INOVA GROUPE—See Altawest Group; *Int'l*, pg. 388
INOVA HEALTH SYSTEM FOUNDATION; *U.S. Private*, pg. 2084
INOVA HEALTH SYSTEM; *U.S. Private*, pg. 2084
INOVA LABS, INC.—See ResMed Inc.; *U.S. Public*, pg. 1790
INOVA LAB S.R.L.—See Park-Ohio Holdings Corp.; *U.S. Public*, pg. 1639
INOVALIS REAL ESTATE INVESTMENT TRUST; *Int'l*, pg. 3715
INOVALON HOLDINGS, INC.; *U.S. Public*, pg. 1128
INOVALON, INC.—See Inovalon Holdings, Inc.; *U.S. Public*, pg. 1128
INOVANCE TECHNOLOGY EUROPE GMBH—See Shenzhen Inovance Technology Co., Ltd.; *Int'l*, pg. 6813
INOVAN GMBH & CO KG—See William Prym GmbH & Co. KG; *Int'l*, pg. 8413
INOVANT, LLC—See Visa, Inc.; *U.S. Public*, pg. 2302
INOVA PAYROLL, INC.; *U.S. Private*, pg. 2084
INOVA PHARMACEUTICALS (AUSTRALIA) PTY LIMITED—See Pacific Equity Partners Pty. Limited; *Int'l*, pg. 5689
INOVA PHARMACEUTICALS (AUSTRALIA) PTY LIMITED—See The Carlyle Group Inc.; *U.S. Public*, pg. 2057
INOVA PHARMACEUTICALS (PTY) LIMITED—See Pacific Equity Partners Pty. Limited; *Int'l*, pg. 5689
INOVA PHARMACEUTICALS (PTY) LIMITED—See The Carlyle Group Inc.; *U.S. Public*, pg. 2057
INOVAR PACKAGING GROUP, LLC—See AEA Investors LP; *U.S. Private*, pg. 114
INOVATECH ENGINEERING CORPORATION—See Lincoln Electric Holdings, Inc.; *U.S. Public*, pg. 1317
IN-O-VATE TECHNOLOGIES, INC.—See Bee Street Holdings LLC; *U.S. Private*, pg. 513
INOVATIVNI TECHNOLOGIE S.R.O.—See CHINO Corporation; *Int'l*, pg. 1571

INOVATOOLS AUSTRIA GMBH—See Indutrade AB; *Int'l*, pg. 3679
INOVATOOLS ECKERLE & ERTÉL GMBH—See Indutrade AB; *Int'l*, pg. 3679
INOVATOOLS ITALY SRL—See Indutrade AB; *Int'l*, pg. 3679
INOVATOOLS PORTUGAL LDA—See Indutrade AB; *Int'l*, pg. 3679
INOVATOOLS SPAIN S.L.—See Indutrade AB; *Int'l*, pg. 3679
INOVATOOLS USA LLC—See Indutrade AB; *Int'l*, pg. 3679
INOVA VENTURE PTE. LTD.—See Green Packet Berhad; *Int'l*, pg. 3072
INOVEC INC.—See USNR; *U.S. Private*, pg. 4323
INOVELAN S.A.—See Agfa-Gevaert N.V.; *Int'l*, pg. 208
INOVEON CORP.—See NEXUS AG; *Int'l*, pg. 5250
INOVERIS, LLC—See Comvest Group Holdings LLC; *U.S. Private*, pg. 1007
INOVEST BSC; *Int'l*, pg. 3715
INOVEX INDUSTRIES INC.; *U.S. Private*, pg. 2084
INOVEX INFORMATION SYSTEMS, INC.; *U.S. Private*, pg. 2084
INOVINE BH D.O.O.—See British American Tobacco plc; *Int'l*, pg. 1168
INOVIO PHARMACEUTICALS, INC.; *U.S. Public*, pg. 1128
INOVIQ LTD; *Int'l*, pg. 3715
INOVIS EMPLOYMENT SERVICE; *U.S. Private*, pg. 2084
INOVITY, INC.—See Sole Source Capital LLC; *U.S. Private*, pg. 3708
INOVO, INC.—See Medical Depot, Inc.; *U.S. Private*, pg. 2655
INOVONICS CORPORATION—See Roper Technologies, Inc.; *U.S. Public*, pg. 1812
INOVRETAIL, S.A.—See Sonaecom SGPS SA; *Int'l*, pg. 7088
INOVUS SOLAR, INC.—See SolarOne Solutions, Inc.; *U.S. Private*, pg. 3708
INOVUUS TECHNOLOGIES PTE. LTD.; *Int'l*, pg. 3715
INOWROCLAWSKIE KOPALNIE SOLI SOLINO S.A.—See Orlen S.A.; *Int'l*, pg. 5640
INOX AIR PRODUCTS PVT. LTD.—See Air Products & Chemicals, Inc.; *U.S. Public*, pg. 66
INOXCENTER CANARIAS, S.A—See Acerinox, S.A.; *Int'l*, pg. 101
INOX EGE METAL URUNLERI DIS TICARET LIMITED SIRKETI—See Wurth Verwaltungsgesellschaft mbH; *Int'l*, pg. 8506
INOXFIL S.A.—See Acerinox, S.A.; *Int'l*, pg. 101
INOXIDABLES DE EUSKADI S.A.—See Acerinox, S.A.; *Int'l*, pg. 101
INOXIHP S.R.L.—See Interpump Group S.p.A.; *Int'l*, pg. 3755
INOX INDIA LIMITED; *Int'l*, pg. 3715
INOX LEASING & FINANCE LIMITED; *Int'l*, pg. 3715
INOX LEISURE LIMITED—See INOX Leasing & Finance Limited; *Int'l*, pg. 3716
INOX MARE HELLAS SA—See Wurth Verwaltungsgesellschaft mbH; *Int'l*, pg. 8512
INOX MARE S.R.L.—See Wurth Verwaltungsgesellschaft mbH; *Int'l*, pg. 8506
INOXPA AUSTRALIA PROPRIETARY LTD.—See Interpump Group S.p.A.; *Int'l*, pg. 3756
INOXPA COLOMBIA SAS—See Interpump Group S.p.A.; *Int'l*, pg. 3756
INOXPA INDIA PRIVATE LTD.—See Interpump Group S.p.A.; *Int'l*, pg. 3756
INOXPA ITALIA S.R.L.—See Interpump Group S.p.A.; *Int'l*, pg. 3756
INOXPA LTD.—See Interpump Group S.p.A.; *Int'l*, pg. 3755
INOXPA MEXICO S.A. DE C.V.—See Interpump Group S.p.A.; *Int'l*, pg. 3756
INOXPA MIDDLE EAST FZCO—See Interpump Group S.p.A.; *Int'l*, pg. 3756
INOXPA S.A.—See Interpump Group S.p.A.; *Int'l*, pg. 3756
INOXPA SKANDINAVIEN A/S—See Interpump Group S.p.A.; *Int'l*, pg. 3756
INOXPA SOLUTIONS FRANCE SAS—See Interpump Group S.p.A.; *Int'l*, pg. 3756
INOXPA SOLUTIONS SRL—See Interpump Group S.p.A.; *Int'l*, pg. 3756
INOXPA SOUTH AFRICA PROPRIETARY LTD.—See Interpump Group S.p.A.; *Int'l*, pg. 3756
INOXPA SPECIAL PROCESSING EQUIPMENT CO. LTD.—See Interpump Group S.p.A.; *Int'l*, pg. 3756
INOXPA (UK) LTD.—See Interpump Group S.p.A.; *Int'l*, pg. 3756
INOXPA UKRAINE S.L.—See Interpump Group S.p.A.; *Int'l*, pg. 3756
INOXPA USA INC.—See Interpump Group S.p.A.; *Int'l*, pg. 3756
INOXPLATE, LTDA.—See Acerinox, S.A.; *Int'l*, pg. 101
INOX SA; *Int'l*, pg. 3716
INOX TIRRENICA S.R.L.—See Wurth Verwaltungsgesellschaft mbH; *Int'l*, pg. 8506
INOX WIND INFRASTRUCTURE SERVICES LIMITED—See Inox Wind Energy Limited; *Int'l*, pg. 4539

INOX WIND LTD.—See INOX Leasing & Finance Limited; *Int'l*, pg. 3716
INOZYME PHARMA, INC.; *U.S. Public*, pg. 1128
IN-PACT, INC.; *U.S. Private*, pg. 2052
INPAKCENTRALE ICN B.V.—See Metro AG; *Int'l*, pg. 4857
INPAQ KOREA CO., LTD.—See Inpaq Technology Co., Ltd.; *Int'l*, pg. 3716
INPAQ TECHNOLOGY (CHINA) CO., LTD.—See Inpaq Technology Co., Ltd.; *Int'l*, pg. 3716
INPAQ TECHNOLOGY CO., LTD.; *Int'l*, pg. 3716
INPAQ TECHNOLOGY (SUZHOU) CO., LTD.—See Walsin Technology Corporation; *Int'l*, pg. 8335
INPAQ TRADING (SHANGHAI) CO., LTD.—See Inpaq Technology Co., Ltd.; *Int'l*, pg. 3716
INPARK DETACHERINGEN B.V.—See Fugro N.V.; *Int'l*, pg. 2807
INPATIENT MEDICAL SERVICES, INC.; *U.S. Private*, pg. 2084
INP CANADA INC.—See VINCI S.A.; *Int'l*, pg. 8222
INP DEUTSCHLAND GMBH; *Int'l*, pg. 3716
INPELLIS, INC.; *U.S. Private*, pg. 2084
INPEX ABK, LTD.—See INPEX CORPORATION; *Int'l*, pg. 3716
INPEX ALPHA, LTD.—See INPEX CORPORATION; *Int'l*, pg. 3716
INPEX BROWSE, LTD.—See INPEX CORPORATION; *Int'l*, pg. 3716
INPEX BUSINESS SERVICES, LTD.—See INPEX CORPORATION; *Int'l*, pg. 3716
INPEX CANADA, LTD.—See INPEX CORPORATION; *Int'l*, pg. 3716
INPEX CORPORATION; *Int'l*, pg. 3716
INPEX EAST ARGUNI, LTD.—See INPEX CORPORATION; *Int'l*, pg. 3716
INPEX ENGINEERING (JAPAN) CO., LTD.—See INPEX CORPORATION; *Int'l*, pg. 3716
INPEX IDEMITSU NORGE AS—See INPEX CORPORATION; *Int'l*, pg. 3716
INPEX JAWA, LTD.—See INPEX CORPORATION; *Int'l*, pg. 3716
INPEX LIBYA, LTD.—See INPEX CORPORATION; *Int'l*, pg. 3716
INPEX LOGISTICS (JAPAN) CO., LTD.—See INPEX CORPORATION; *Int'l*, pg. 3716
INPEX MASELA, LTD.—See INPEX CORPORATION; *Int'l*, pg. 3716
INPEX NORTH CASPIAN SEA, LTD.—See INPEX CORPORATION; *Int'l*, pg. 3716
INPEX OFFSHORE NORTHEAST JAVA, LTD.—See INPEX CORPORATION; *Int'l*, pg. 3716
INPEX OFFSHORE NORTHEAST MAHAKAM, LTD.—See INPEX CORPORATION; *Int'l*, pg. 3716
INPEX OFFSHORE NORTH MAHAKAM, LTD.—See INPEX CORPORATION; *Int'l*, pg. 3716
INPEX OFFSHORE SOUTH EAST MAHAKAM, LTD.—See INPEX CORPORATION; *Int'l*, pg. 3716
INPEX SAHUL, LTD.—See INPEX CORPORATION; *Int'l*, pg. 3716
INPEX SOLUTIONS, LTD.—See INPEX CORPORATION; *Int'l*, pg. 3716
INPEX SOUTHWEST CASPIAN SEA, LTD.—See INPEX CORPORATION; *Int'l*, pg. 3716
INPEX SUMATRA, LTD.—See INPEX CORPORATION; *Int'l*, pg. 3716
INPEX TENGAH, LTD.—See INPEX CORPORATION; *Int'l*, pg. 3716
INPEX TIMOR SEA, LTD.—See INPEX CORPORATION; *Int'l*, pg. 3717
INPEX TRADING, LTD.—See INPEX CORPORATION; *Int'l*, pg. 3717
INPEX WEST ARGUNI, LTD.—See INPEX CORPORATION; *Int'l*, pg. 3717
IN PHASE INTERNATIONAL LTD.; *Int'l*, pg. 3639
INPHASE TECHNOLOGIES, INC.—See Signal Lake Management LLC; *U.S. Private*, pg. 3649
INPHI CORPORATION—See Marvell Technology Group Ltd.; *Int'l*, pg. 4717
INPHOSOFT MALAYSIA SDN BHD—See GINSMS Inc.; *Int'l*, pg. 2977
INPHOSOFT SINGAPORE PTE LTD—See GINSMS Inc.; *Int'l*, pg. 2977
INPIPE GMBH—See Halma plc; *Int'l*, pg. 3232
INPIXON CANADA, INC.—See XTI Aerospace, Inc.; *U.S. Public*, pg. 2393
INPIXON FEDERAL, INC.—See XTI Aerospace, Inc.; *U.S. Public*, pg. 2393
INPLANTA INNOVATIONS INC.—See OAT Agrio Co., Ltd.; *Int'l*, pg. 5507
INPLASTOR AB; *Int'l*, pg. 3717
INPLASTOR GRAPHISCHE PRODUKTE GESELLSCHAFT M.B.H.—See H2APEX Group SCA; *Int'l*, pg. 3199
INPLAY OIL CORP.—See Freehold Royalties Ltd.; *Int'l*, pg. 2770
INP NORTH AMERICA, INC.—See INP Deutschland GmbH; *Int'l*, pg. 3716
INP NORTH AMERICA, INC.—See VINCI S.A.; *Int'l*, pg. 8238

INPLASTOR AB
CORPORATE AFFILIATIONS

INPOINT COMMERCIAL REAL ESTATE INCOME, INC.—See The Inland Real Estate Group of Companies, Inc.; *U.S. Private*, pg. 4056
INPOKOMERC D.D.; *Int'l*, pg. 3717
INPOST S.A.; *Int'l*, pg. 3717
INPOST UK LIMITED—See InPost S.A.; *Int'l*, pg. 3717
INPOWER LLC; *U.S. Private*, pg. 2084
IN PRACTICE SYSTEMS LTD.—See Cegedim S.A.; *Int'l*, pg. 1390
INPRESS PORTER NOVELLI-SAO PAULO—See Omnicom Group Inc.; *U.S. Public*, pg. 1590
IN PRESS PORTER NOVELLI—See Omnicom Group Inc.; *U.S. Public*, pg. 1590
INPRIA CORPORATION; *U.S. Private*, pg. 2084
INPRINT CORPORATION—See ARC DOCUMENT SOLUTIONS, INC.; *U.S. Public*, pg. 179
INPRINT PTY LTD—See IVE Group Limited; *Int'l*, pg. 3847
INPRO CORPORATION; *U.S. Private*, pg. 2084
INPROG AS—See SmartCraft ASA; *Int'l*, pg. 7002
INPRO INSURANCE GROUP, LLC—See ABRY Partners, LLC; *U.S. Private*, pg. 42
IN PROJEKT LOUNY ENGINEERING S.R.O.—See CEZ, a.s.; *Int'l*, pg. 1426
INPRO S.A.; *Int'l*, pg. 3717
INPRO/SEAL LLC—See Dover Corporation; *U.S. Public*, pg. 681
INPROVA ENERGY LIMITED—See Inspired PLC; *Int'l*, pg. 3720
IN PUBLISHING CO., LTD.—See GMM Grammy Public Company Limited; *Int'l*, pg. 3012
INPUT PROJEKTENTWICKLUNGS GMBH—See Doppelmayr Group; *Int'l*, pg. 2175
INQBE SP. Z.O.O.—See IQ Partners S.A.; *Int'l*, pg. 3803
INQBRANDS, INC.—See Focus Technology Co., Ltd.; *Int'l*, pg. 2720
IN-Q-TEL, INC.; *U.S. Private*, pg. 2052
INQUEST MARKETING; *U.S. Private*, pg. 2085
INQUIDE ITALIA SRL—See Fluidra SA; *Int'l*, pg. 2714
INQUIP ASSOCIATES INCORPORATED—See Forgen, LLC; *U.S. Private*, pg. 1568
INQUIP ASSOCIATES—See Forgen, LLC; *U.S. Private*, pg. 1568
INQUIRER & MIRROR, INC.—See Gannett Co., Inc.; *U.S. Public*, pg. 904
INQVENTURES GMBH—See adesso SE; *Int'l*, pg. 144
INRAD OPTICS, INC.—See Edgewater Capital Partners, L.P.; *U.S. Private*, pg. 1335
INRAD OPTICS, INC.—See Edgewater Capital Partners, L.P.; *U.S. Private*, pg. 1335
INRAD OPTICS, INC.—See SK Capital Partners, LP; *U.S. Private*, pg. 3679
INRAD OPTICS, INC.—See SK Capital Partners, LP; *U.S. Private*, pg. 3679
INRCORE, LLC—See The Jordan Company, L.P.; *U.S. Private*, pg. 4063
INREALITY, LLC—See The Jordan Company, L.P.; *U.S. Private*, pg. 4062
IN-REL PROPERTIES, INC.; *U.S. Private*, pg. 2052
INREOS SOLVENTS GERMANY GMBH—See One Rock Capital Partners, LLC; *U.S. Private*, pg. 3023
INRETAIL PERU CORP.; *Int'l*, pg. 3717
INRHYTHM; *U.S. Private*, pg. 2085
INRIX, INC.; *U.S. Private*, pg. 2085
INROCK DRILLING SYSTEMS, INC.—See Sandvik AB; *Int'l*, pg. 6529
INROM CONSTRUCTION INDUSTRIES LTD.; *Int'l*, pg. 3717
INRULE TECHNOLOGY INC.—See OpenGate Capital Management, LLC; *U.S. Private*, pg. 3030
INSA A.D.; *Int'l*, pg. 3717
INSA ALLIANCE SDN. BHD.—See Puncak Niaga Holdings Berhad; *Int'l*, pg. 6118
INSAGE (MSC) SDN BHD—See ExcelForce MSC Berhad; *Int'l*, pg. 2578
INSALA, LLC; *U.S. Private*, pg. 2085
INSALUTE SERVIZI S.P.A.—See Intesa Sanpaolo S.p.A.; *Int'l*, pg. 3765
INSAN INC - INSAN BAMBOO SALT FACTORY—See IN-SAN Inc; *Int'l*, pg. 3718
INSAN INC; *Int'l*, pg. 3718
INSAS BERHAD; *Int'l*, pg. 3718
INSAS PACIFIC RENT-A-CAR SDN. BHD.—See Insas Berhad; *Int'l*, pg. 3718
INSAS PROPERTIES SDN. BHD.—See Insas Berhad; *Int'l*, pg. 3718
INSAS TECHNOLOGY BERHAD—See Insas Berhad; *Int'l*, pg. 3718
INSAS TECHNOLOGY PTE. LTD.—See Insas Berhad; *Int'l*, pg. 3718
INSATECH A/S—See Addtech AB; *Int'l*, pg. 134
INSBANK—See InsCorp, Inc.; *U.S. Public*, pg. 1129
INSCAPE CORPORATION; *Int'l*, pg. 3718
INSCAPE (NEW YORK) INC—See Inscape Corporation; *Int'l*, pg. 3718
INSCEPTION BIOSCIENCES, INC.; *Int'l*, pg. 3718
INSCEPTION LIFEBANK CORD BLOOD PROGRAM—See Inscepton Biosciences, Inc.; *Int'l*, pg. 3718
INSCERCO MANUFACTURING INC.; *U.S. Private*, pg. 2085

INSCIENCE SDN BHD—See HORIBA Ltd; *Int'l*, pg. 3477
INSCLEAR AB—See Willis Towers Watson Public Limited Company; *Int'l*, pg. 8414
INSCOBEE INC.; *Int'l*, pg. 3718
INSCO DISTRIBUTING, INC.; *U.S. Private*, pg. 2085
INSCO, INC.; *U.S. Private*, pg. 2085
INS COMMUNICATIONS PTE. LTD.; *Int'l*, pg. 3717
INSCOPIX, INC.—See Bruker Corporation; *U.S. Public*, pg. 404
INSCORP, INC.; *U.S. Public*, pg. 1128
INSDATA SPOL S.R.O.—See UNIQA Insurance Group AG; *Int'l*, pg. 8057
INSEARCH WORLDWIDE CORPORATION; *U.S. Private*, pg. 2085
INSECTICIDES (INDIA) LIMITED; *Int'l*, pg. 3718
INSECT IQ, INC.—See Rentokil Initial plc; *Int'l*, pg. 6288
INSEEC EXECUTIVE EDUCATION SASU—See Cinven Limited; *Int'l*, pg. 1612
INSEE DIGITAL COMPANY LIMITED—See Siam City Cement Public Company Limited; *Int'l*, pg. 6874
INSEE ECOCYCLE COMPANY LIMITED—See Siam City Cement Public Company Limited; *Int'l*, pg. 6874
INSEE ECOCYCLE LANKA (PRIVATE) LIMITED—See Siam City Cement Public Company Limited; *Int'l*, pg. 6874
INSEEGO AUSTRALIA PTY LTD.—See Inseego Corp.; *U.S. Public*, pg. 1129
INSEEGO BELGIUM B.V.—See Inseego Corp.; *U.S. Public*, pg. 1129
INSEEGO BENELUX B.V.—See Inseego Corp.; *U.S. Public*, pg. 1129
INSEEGO CORP.; *U.S. Public*, pg. 1129
INSEEGO DEUTSCHLAND GMBH—See Inseego Corp.; *U.S. Public*, pg. 1129
INSEEGO INTERNATIONAL HOLDINGS LTD.—See Inseego Corp.; *U.S. Public*, pg. 1129
INSEEGO IRELAND LIMITED—See Inseego Corp.; *U.S. Public*, pg. 1129
INSEEGO NEW ZEALAND LTD.—See Inseego Corp.; *U.S. Public*, pg. 1129
INSEEGO NORTH AMERICA, LLC—See Inseego Corp.; *U.S. Public*, pg. 1129
INSEEV INTERACTIVE INC.; *U.S. Private*, pg. 2085
INSEL BELGIUM—See Randstad N.V.; *Int'l*, pg. 6202
INSELKO AS—See Bilfinger SE; *Int'l*, pg. 1028
INSENSYS HOLDINGS LTD.—See Moog Inc.; *U.S. Public*, pg. 1469
INSENSYS LIMITED—See Moog Inc.; *U.S. Public*, pg. 1469
INSENTIAL, INC.—See Hendricks Holding Company, Inc.; *U.S. Private*, pg. 1915
INSERCO BRASIL SERVICOS INDUSTRIAIS LTDA.—See Dieffenbacher Holding GmbH & Co. KG; *Int'l*, pg. 2114
INSERO & CO. CPAS, LLP; *U.S. Private*, pg. 2085
INSERRA SUPERMARKETS, INC.; *U.S. Private*, pg. 2085
INSERSO CORPORATION; *U.S. Private*, pg. 2085
INSERTECH, LLC; *U.S. Private*, pg. 2085
INSERT LTD.—See Taller GmbH; *Int'l*, pg. 7447
INSER-TRANSFIELD SERVICES S.A.—See Apollo Global Management, Inc.; *U.S. Public*, pg. 167
INSERVCO, INC.—See Centre Lane Partners, LLC; *U.S. Private*, pg. 827
INSERVCO INSURANCE SERVICES, INC.—See Pennsylvania National Mutual Casualty Insurance Company; *U.S. Private*, pg. 3137
INSERVICE AMERICA INCORPORATED; *U.S. Private*, pg. 2085
INSETCO PLC; *Int'l*, pg. 3718
INSGROUP, INC.—See The Baldwin Insurance Group, Inc.; *U.S. Public*, pg. 2036
INSHA'A HOLDING COMPANY K.S.C.—See Kuwait Projects Company (Holding) K.S.C.P.; *Int'l*, pg. 4346
INSHA GMBH—See Albaraka Turk Katilim Bankasi A.S.; *Int'l*, pg. 293
INSIA A.S.—See Marsh & McLennan Companies, Inc.; *U.S. Public*, pg. 1376
INSIA EUROPE SE—See Marsh & McLennan Companies, Inc.; *U.S. Public*, pg. 1376
INSIA SK S.R.O.—See Marsh & McLennan Companies, Inc.; *U.S. Public*, pg. 1376
INSIDE BUSINESS INC.—See Irish Times; *U.S. Private*, pg. 2138
INSIDE DATA INGENIOUS GLOBAL LIMITED—See Sarda Proteins Limited; *Int'l*, pg. 6577
INSIDE EDITION INC.—See National Amusements, Inc.; *U.S. Private*, pg. 2841
INSIDE IDEAS GROUP LTD.—See You & Mr Jones Inc.; *U.S. Private*, pg. 4591
INSIDEMETALS.COM—See Itronics Inc.; *U.S. Public*, pg. 1177
INSIDE OUT COMMUNICATIONS; *U.S. Private*, pg. 2085
INSIDER, INC.—See Axel Springer SE; *Int'l*, pg. 766
INSIDESALES.COM, INC.; *U.S. Private*, pg. 2085
INSIDE SOURCE INC.; *U.S. Private*, pg. 2085
INSIDETRACK, INC.; *U.S. Private*, pg. 2085
INSIDEVALUATION PARTNERS, LLC—See LRES Corp.; *U.S. Private*, pg. 2507
INSIDEVIEW TECHNOLOGIES, INC.—See Demandbase, Inc.; *U.S. Private*, pg. 1203

INSIDEVIEW TECHNOLOGIES (INDIA) PVT LTD.—See Demandbase, Inc.; *U.S. Private*, pg. 1203
INSIEL MERCATO S.P.A.—See GPI S.p.A.; *Int'l*, pg. 3046
INSIG AI PLC; *Int'l*, pg. 3718
INSIGHT ACQUISITION CORP.; *U.S. Public*, pg. 1129
INSIGHT AGENTS FRANCE S.R.L.—See Agfa-Gevaert N.V.; *Int'l*, pg. 208
INSIGHT BEVERAGES, INC.—See Kerry Group plc; *Int'l*, pg. 4138
INSIGHT COMMUNICATIONS—See WPP plc; *Int'l*, pg. 8472
IN:SIGHT CUSTOMER INFORMATION MANAGEMENT GMBH—See Plenum AG; *Int'l*, pg. 5897
INSIGHT DIRECT UK LIMITED—See Insight Enterprises, Inc.; *U.S. Public*, pg. 1129
INSIGHT DIRECT USA, INC.—See Insight Enterprises, Inc.; *U.S. Public*, pg. 1130
INSIGHT DIRECT WORLDWIDE, INC.—See Insight Enterprises, Inc.; *U.S. Public*, pg. 1130
INSIGHT DISTRIBUTING, INC.—See Bain Capital, LP; *U.S. Private*, pg. 441
INSIGHTEC LTD.—See Elbit Imaging Ltd.; *Int'l*, pg. 2344
INSIGHT EDITIONS, LP; *U.S. Private*, pg. 2085
INSIGHT ENTERPRISES BV—See Insight Enterprises, Inc.; *U.S. Public*, pg. 1130
INSIGHT ENTERPRISES HONG KONG—See Insight Enterprises, Inc.; *U.S. Public*, pg. 1130
INSIGHT ENTERPRISES, INC.—See Insight Enterprises, Inc.; *U.S. Public*, pg. 1130
INSIGHT ENTERPRISES, INC.—See Insight Enterprises, Inc.; *U.S. Public*, pg. 1130
INSIGHT ENTERPRISES, INC.; *U.S. Public*, pg. 1129
INSIGHT ENTERPRISES NETHERLANDS BV—See Insight Enterprises, Inc.; *U.S. Public*, pg. 1130
INSIGHT ENTERPRISES UK, LTD.—See Insight Enterprises, Inc.; *U.S. Public*, pg. 1130
INSIGHT EQUITY HOLDINGS LLC; *U.S. Private*, pg. 2086
INSIGHT GENETICS, INC.—See OncoCyte Corporation; *U.S. Public*, pg. 1601
INSIGHT GLOBAL, INC.—See Harvest Partners L.P.; *U.S. Private*, pg. 1876
INSIGHT HEALTH CORP.—See Black Diamond Capital Holdings, LLC; *U.S. Private*, pg. 570
INSIGHT HEALTH GMBH—See CompuGroup Medical SE & Co. KGaA; *Int'l*, pg. 1757
INSIGHT HEALTH SERVICES HOLDINGS CORP.—See Black Diamond Capital Holdings, LLC; *U.S. Private*, pg. 570
INSIGHT HUMAN SERVICES; *U.S. Private*, pg. 2086
INSIGHT INC.; *Int'l*, pg. 3718
INSIGHT INSURANCE SERVICES, INC.—See Brookfield Reinsurance Ltd.; *Int'l*, pg. 1194
INSIGHT INVESTMENT FUNDS MANAGEMENT LIMITED—See The Bank of New York Mellon Corporation; *U.S. Public*, pg. 2037
INSIGHT INVESTMENT MANAGEMENT (EUROPE) LIMITED—See The Bank of New York Mellon Corporation; *U.S. Public*, pg. 2037
INSIGHT INVESTMENT MANAGEMENT (GLOBAL) LIMITED—See The Bank of New York Mellon Corporation; *U.S. Public*, pg. 2037
INSIGHT INVESTMENT MANAGEMENT LIMITED—See The Bank of New York Mellon Corporation; *U.S. Public*, pg. 2037
INSIGHT INVESTMENTS LLC; *U.S. Private*, pg. 2086
INSIGHT MEDIA ADVERTISING LTD.—See WPP plc; *Int'l*, pg. 8472
INSIGHT MEDICAL SYSTEMS, INC.—See Envois Corporation; *U.S. Public*, pg. 773
INSIGHT MERCHANDISING, INC.; *U.S. Private*, pg. 2086
INSIGHT NORTH AMERICA, INC.—See Insight Enterprises, Inc.; *U.S. Public*, pg. 1130
INSIGHT OCEANIA PTY. LTD.—See Paragon Care Limited; *Int'l*, pg. 5736
INSIGHT OPTICAL MANUFACTURING CO.; *U.S. Private*, pg. 2086
INSIGHT PERFORMANCE, INC.—See New Mountain Capital, LLC; *U.S. Private*, pg. 2901
INSIGHT PEST SOLUTIONS, LLC—See Massey Services, Inc.; *U.S. Private*, pg. 2606
INSIGHT RADIOLOGY LIMITED—See BGH Capital Pty Ltd; *Int'l*, pg. 1008
INSIGHT RADIOLOGY LIMITED—See Ontario Teachers' Pension Plan; *Int'l*, pg. 5586
INSIGHT RESOURCE GROUP; *U.S. Private*, pg. 2086
INSIGHT SELECT INCOME FUND; *U.S. Public*, pg. 1130
INSIGHTSNOW, INC.; *U.S. Private*, pg. 2091
INSIGHT SOFTWARE, LLC; *U.S. Private*, pg. 2086
INSIGHT SOURCING GROUP, INC.; *U.S. Private*, pg. 2087
INSIGHT SURGICAL PTY. LTD.—See Paragon Care Limited; *Int'l*, pg. 5736
INSIGHT TECH INC.—See en-japan Inc.; *Int'l*, pg. 2395
INSIGHT TECHNOLOGY INCORPORATED—See L3Harris Technologies, Inc.; *U.S. Public*, pg. 1281
INSIGHT TECHNOLOGY SOLUTIONS AB—See Insight Enterprises, Inc.; *U.S. Public*, pg. 1130
INSIGHT TECHNOLOGY SOLUTIONS AG—See Insight Enterprises, Inc.; *U.S. Public*, pg. 1130

INSIGHT TECHNOLOGY SOLUTIONS GMBH—See Softline AG; *Int'l*, pg. 7055
INSIGHT TECHNOLOGY SOLUTIONS, INC.—See Insight Enterprises, Inc.; *U.S. Public*, pg. 1130
INSIGHT TECHNOLOGY SOLUTIONS N.U.F.—See Insight Enterprises, Inc.; *U.S. Public*, pg. 1130
INSIGHT TECHNOLOGY SOLUTIONS PTE LTD—See Insight Enterprises, Inc.; *U.S. Public*, pg. 1130
INSIGHT TECHNOLOGY SOLUTIONS SAS—See Insight Enterprises, Inc.; *U.S. Public*, pg. 1130
INSIGHT TECHNOLOGY SOLUTIONS, S.L.—See Insight Enterprises, Inc.; *U.S. Public*, pg. 1130
INSIGHT TECHNOLOGY SOLUTIONS S.R.L.—See Insight Enterprises, Inc.; *U.S. Public*, pg. 1130
INSIGHT TELEPSYCHIATRY LLC—See Harbour Point Management LLC; *U.S. Private*, pg. 1861
INSIGHT VENTURE MANAGEMENT, LLC; *U.S. Private*, pg. 2087
INSIGMA INC.—See Futuris Company; *U.S. Public*, pg. 893
INSIGMA TECHNOLOGY CO., LTD.—See Zhejiang Zheda Insigma Group Co., Ltd.; *Int'l*, pg. 8668
INSIGMA US, INC.—See Zhejiang Zheda Insigma Group Co., Ltd.; *Int'l*, pg. 8668
INSIGNIA CAPITAL GROUP, L.P.; *U.S. Private*, pg. 2091
INSIGNIA ENERGY LTD.—See Brookfield Corporation; *Int'l*, pg. 1189
INSIGNIA FINANCE LIMITED—See West Bromwich Building Society; *Int'l*, pg. 8383
INSIGNIA FINANCIAL LTD.; *Int'l*, pg. 3718
INSIGNIA HEALTH, LLC—See Phreesia, Inc.; *U.S. Public*, pg. 1689
INSIGNIAM PERFORMANCE, L.P.—See Elixirr International plc; *Int'l*, pg. 2363
INSIGNIA REAL ESTATE COMPANIES, LLC; *U.S. Private*, pg. 2091
INSIGNIA TECHNOLOGY SERVICES, LLC; *U.S. Private*, pg. 2091
INSIGNIS, INC.—See Resurgens Technology Partners, LLC; *U.S. Private*, pg. 3411
INSILICA, INC.; *U.S. Private*, pg. 2091
IN SILICO SOLUTIONS LLC—See Kiromic Biopharma, Inc.; *U.S. Public*, pg. 1236
INSIMBI ALUMINIUM ALLOYS PROPRIETARY LIMITED—See Insimbi Industrial Holdings Limited; *Int'l*, pg. 3719
INSIMBI INDUSTRIAL HOLDINGS LIMITED; *Int'l*, pg. 3719
INSINGER DE BEAUFORT ASSET MANAGEMENT NV—See BNP Paribas SA; *Int'l*, pg. 1091
INSINGER DE BEAUFORT ASSOCIATES BV—See BNP Paribas SA; *Int'l*, pg. 1091
INSINGER DE BEAUFORT BV—See BNP Paribas SA; *Int'l*, pg. 1091
INSINGERGILISSEN, N.V.—See KBL European Private Bankers S.A.; *Int'l*, pg. 4107
IN-SINK-ERATOR—See Whirlpool Corporation; *U.S. Public*, pg. 2367
INSITE CO., LTD.—See Actcall Inc.; *Int'l*, pg. 117
INSITE-INTERVENTIONS GMBH—See Asklepios Kliniken GmbH & Co. KGaA; *Int'l*, pg. 623
INSITE ONE, INC.—See Dell Technologies Inc.; *U.S. Public*, pg. 650
INSITE SOFTWARE SOLUTIONS, INC.—See Insight Venture Management, LLC; *U.S. Private*, pg. 2090
INSITE VISION INCORPORATED—See Sun Pharmaceutical Industries Ltd.; *Int'l*, pg. 7307
INSITE WIRELESS GROUP, LLC—See American Tower Corporation; *U.S. Public*, pg. 111
INSITU ENVIROTECH (S.E. ASIA) PTE. LTD.—See New Mountain Capital, LLC; *U.S. Private*, pg. 2899
INSITUFORM ASIA LIMITED—See New Mountain Capital, LLC; *U.S. Private*, pg. 2899
INSITUFORM A/S—See New Mountain Capital, LLC; *U.S. Private*, pg. 2899
INSITUFORM LININGS LIMITED—See New Mountain Capital, LLC; *U.S. Private*, pg. 2899
INSITUFORM LININGS PLC—See Per Aarsleff Holding A/S; *Int'l*, pg. 5795
INSITUFORM OF NEW ENGLAND, INC—See New Mountain Capital, LLC; *U.S. Private*, pg. 2900
INSITUFORM RIOOLRENOVATIETECHNIEKEN B.V.—See New Mountain Capital, LLC; *U.S. Private*, pg. 2899
INSITUFORM ROHRSANIERUNGSTECHNIKEN GMBH—See Per Aarsleff Holding A/S; *Int'l*, pg. 5796
INSITUFORM—See New Mountain Capital, LLC; *U.S. Private*, pg. 2900
INSITUFORM TECH, INC.—See New Mountain Capital, LLC; *U.S. Private*, pg. 2900
INSITUFORM TECHNOLOGIES IBERICA S.A.—See New Mountain Capital, LLC; *U.S. Private*, pg. 2899
INSITUFORM TECHNOLOGIES LIMITED—See New Mountain Capital, LLC; *U.S. Private*, pg. 2900
INSITUFORM TECHNOLOGIES LIMITED—See New Mountain Capital, LLC; *U.S. Private*, pg. 2900
INSITUFORM TECHNOLOGIES, LLC—See New Mountain Capital, LLC; *U.S. Private*, pg. 2900
INSITUFORM TECHNOLOGIES USA, INC.—See New Mountain Capital, LLC; *U.S. Private*, pg. 2900

IN-SITU GMBH—See INDUS Holding AG; *Int'l*, pg. 3664
IN-SITU, INC.; *U.S. Private*, pg. 2052
INSITU, INC.—See The Boeing Company; *U.S. Public*, pg. 2040
IN-SITU SARL—See VINCI S.A.; *Int'l*, pg. 8222
IN SITU SOLUTIONS CO., LTD.—See EnBio Holdings Inc.; *Int'l*, pg. 2396
INSKIP AUTO MALL—See Penske Automotive Group, Inc.; *U.S. Public*, pg. 1665
INSL-X PRODUCTS CORP.—See Berkshire Hathaway Inc.; *U.S. Public*, pg. 300
INSMARK COMPANY—See Maximum Corporation; *U.S. Private*, pg. 2618
INSMED GERMANY GMBH—See Insmed Incorporated; *U.S. Public*, pg. 1131
INSMED INCORPORATED; *U.S. Public*, pg. 1130
INSMED NETHERLANDS B.V.—See Insmed Incorporated; *U.S. Public*, pg. 1131
IN'S MERCATO S.P.A.—See GECOS S.p.A.; *Int'l*, pg. 2909
INSOFT INFOTEL SOFTWARE GMBH—See Infotel SA; *Int'l*, pg. 3696
INSOLATION ENERGY LTD.; *Int'l*, pg. 3719
INSOLUTIONS LIMITED—See Marsh & McLennan Companies, Inc.; *U.S. Public*, pg. 1377
INSOMNIAC HOLDINGS, LLC—See Live Nation Entertainment, Inc.; *U.S. Public*, pg. 1329
INSOURCE CO., LTD.; *Int'l*, pg. 3719
INSOURCE SOFTWARE SOLUTIONS LLC; *U.S. Private*, pg. 2092
INSOUTH BANK—See Independent Southern Bancshares, Inc.; *U.S. Private*, pg. 2061
INSPA INDUSTRIESERVICE FUR PUMPENANTRIEBE GMBH—See VINCI S.A.; *Int'l*, pg. 8223
INSPEARIT SAS; *Int'l*, pg. 3719
INSPEARIT S.R.L.—See Ardian SAS; *Int'l*, pg. 555
INSPECCIO TECNICA DE VEHICLES I SERVEIS, S.A.—See I Squared Capital Advisors (US) LLC; *U.S. Private*, pg. 2022
INSPECCIO TECNICA DE VEHICLES I SERVEIS, S.A.—See TDR Capital LLP; *Int'l*, pg. 7492
INSPEC INC.; *Int'l*, pg. 3719
INSPECS GROUP PLC; *Int'l*, pg. 3719
INSPEC TAIWAN INC.—See inspec Inc.; *Int'l*, pg. 3719
INSPEC TECH, INC.; *U.S. Private*, pg. 2092
THE INSPECTION COMPANY OF KOREA—See TUV NORD AG; *Int'l*, pg. 7980
INSPECTION SERVICES UK LIMITED—See PHSC plc; *Int'l*, pg. 5857
INSPECTIONXPERT CORPORATION—See HgCapital Trust plc; *Int'l*, pg. 3377
INSPECTMYRIDE LLC—See JM Family Enterprises Inc.; *U.S. Private*, pg. 2214
INSPECTORATE AMERICA CORPORATION—See Bureau Veritas S.A.; *Int'l*, pg. 1222
INSPECTORATE INTERNATIONAL LIMITED—See Bureau Veritas S.A.; *Int'l*, pg. 1222
INSPECTORATE SUISSE S.A.—See Bureau Veritas S.A.; *Int'l*, pg. 1222
INSPECTORES Y CONSULTORES IBERCAL S.L.U.—See Enel S.p.A.; *Int'l*, pg. 2414
INSPECTTECH SYSTEMS, INC.—See Bentley Systems, Inc.; *U.S. Public*, pg. 297
INSPERITY BUSINESS SERVICES, L.P.—See Insperity, Inc.; *U.S. Public*, pg. 1131
INSPERITY EMPLOYMENT SCREENING, L.L.C—See Insperity, Inc.; *U.S. Public*, pg. 1131
INSPERITY EXPENSE MANAGEMENT, INC.—See Insperity, Inc.; *U.S. Public*, pg. 1131
INSPERITY, INC.; *U.S. Public*, pg. 1131
INSPERITY PAYROLL SERVICES, L.L.C.—See Insperity, Inc.; *U.S. Public*, pg. 1131
INSPERITY TIME AND ATTENDANCE—See Insperity, Inc.; *U.S. Public*, pg. 1131
INSPHERE INSURANCE SOLUTIONS, INC.—See Blackstone Inc.; *U.S. Public*, pg. 354
INSPIRA FINANCIAL INC.; *Int'l*, pg. 3719
INSPIRAFS, INC.—See ABRY Partners, LLC; *U.S. Private*, pg. 42
INSPIRAGE, LLC—See Accenture plc; *Int'l*, pg. 87
INSPIRA MARKETING GROUP; *U.S. Private*, pg. 2092
INSPIRATA, INC.; *U.S. Private*, pg. 2092
INSPIRA TECHNOLOGIES OXY B.H.N. LTD.; *Int'l*, pg. 3719
INSPIRATION CO., LTD.; *Int'l*, pg. 3719
INSPIRATION HEALTHCARE GROUP PLC; *Int'l*, pg. 3720
INSPIRATION HEALTHCARE LIMITED—See Inspiration Healthcare Group Plc; *Int'l*, pg. 3720
INSPIRATION LEAD CO., INC.; *U.S. Public*, pg. 1131
THE INSPIRATION NETWORKS; *U.S. Private*, pg. 4056
THE INSPIRATION NETWORKS—See The Inspiration Networks; *U.S. Private*, pg. 4056
INSPIRATION SOFTWARE, INC.; *U.S. Private*, pg. 2092
INSPIRATO INCORPORATED; *U.S. Public*, pg. 1131
INSPIRE BRANDS, INC.—See Roark Capital Group Inc.; *U.S. Private*, pg. 3455
INSPIRE CREATIVE STUDIOS; *U.S. Private*, pg. 2092
INSPIRED BEAUTY BRANDS INC.; *U.S. Private*, pg. 2092

INSPIRED EDUCATION HOLDINGS LIMITED; *Int'l*, pg. 3720
INSPIRE DEFENCE LTD—See Jacobs Engineering Group, Inc.; *U.S. Public*, pg. 1186
INSPIRED ELEARNING, LLC—See Ziff Davis, Inc.; *U.S. Public*, pg. 2403
INSPIRED ENERGY SOLUTIONS LIMITED—See Inspired PLC; *Int'l*, pg. 3720
INSPIRED ENTERTAINMENT INC; *U.S. Public*, pg. 1131
INSPIRE DEVELOPMENT CENTERS; *U.S. Private*, pg. 2092
INSPIRED GAMING (GIBRALTAR) LIMITED—See Inspired Entertainment Inc; *U.S. Public*, pg. 1131
INSPIRED GAMING GROUP LIMITED—See Inspired Entertainment Inc; *U.S. Public*, pg. 1131
INSPIRED GAMING (ITALY) LIMITED—See Inspired Entertainment Inc; *U.S. Public*, pg. 1131
INSPIRED GAMING (UK) LIMITED—See Inspired Entertainment Inc; *U.S. Public*, pg. 1131
INSPIRED MEDICAL JAPAN CO., LTD.—See Vincent Medical Holdings Limited; *Int'l*, pg. 8211
INSPIRED PLC; *Int'l*, pg. 3720
INSPIRED TECHNOLOGY UK LIMITED—See Inspired Entertainment Inc; *U.S. Public*, pg. 1131
INSPIRE FILMS LIMITED; *Int'l*, pg. 3720
INSPIRE FITNESS—See HighPost Capital, LLC; *U.S. Private*, pg. 1941
INSPIRE HOME LOANS, INC.—See Century Communities, Inc.; *U.S. Public*, pg. 475
INSPIREMD, INC.; *Int'l*, pg. 3720
INSPIREMD LTD.—See InspireMD, Inc.; *Int'l*, pg. 3720
INSPIRE MEDICAL SYSTEMS, INC.; *U.S. Public*, pg. 1131
INSPIRE PHARMACEUTICALS, INC.—See Merck & Co., Inc.; *U.S. Public*, pg. 1419
INSPIRE TRAVEL MANAGEMENT PTY. LTD.—See Corporate Travel Management Limited; *Int'l*, pg. 1805
INSPIRE VETERINARY PARTNERS, INC.; *U.S. Public*, pg. 1131
INSPIRICA, INC.; *U.S. Private*, pg. 2092
INSPIRIS OF NEW YORK MANAGEMENT, INC.—See UnitedHealth Group Incorporated; *U.S. Public*, pg. 2241
INSPIRISYS SOLUTIONS LIMITED—See CAC Corporation; *Int'l*, pg. 1247
INSPIRIT ENERGY HOLDINGS PLC; *Int'l*, pg. 3720
INSPIRIT ENERGY LIMITED—See Inspirit Energy Holdings plc; *Int'l*, pg. 3720
INSPIRIT MANAGEMENT LTD.; *Int'l*, pg. 3720
INSPIRIX TECHNOLOGIES LLC; *U.S. Private*, pg. 2092
INSPIRO RELIA, INC.—See Relia, Inc.; *Int'l*, pg. 6260
INSPIRUS CREDIT UNION; *U.S. Private*, pg. 2092
INSPIRUS, LLC—See Sodexo S.A.; *Int'l*, pg. 7045
INSPLORION AB; *Int'l*, pg. 3720
INSPRO CORPORATION—See Tokio Marine Holdings, Inc.; *Int'l*, pg. 7784
INSPRO, INC.—See Marsh & McLennan Companies, Inc.; *U.S. Public*, pg. 1380
INSPRO TECHNOLOGIES CORPORATION—See Thoma Bravo, L.P.; *U.S. Private*, pg. 4149
INSPRO TECHNOLOGIES, LLC—See Thoma Bravo, L.P.; *U.S. Private*, pg. 4149
INSPUR BEIJING GENERSOFT TECHNOLOGY LIMITED—See Inspur Group Ltd.; *Int'l*, pg. 3720
INSPUR DIGITAL ENTERPRISE TECHNOLOGY LIMITED—See Inspur Group Ltd.; *Int'l*, pg. 3720
INSPUR ELECTRONIC INFORMATION INDUSTRY CO., LTD.—See Inspur Group Ltd.; *Int'l*, pg. 3721
INSPUR FINANCIAL INFORMATION SYSTEM CO., LTD.—See Diebold Nixdorf, Inc.; *U.S. Public*, pg. 661
INSPUR GROUP LTD.; *Int'l*, pg. 3720
INSPUR (HK) ELECTRONICS LIMITED—See Inspur Group Ltd.; *Int'l*, pg. 3720
INSPUR JAPAN CO. LTD—See Inspur Group Ltd.; *Int'l*, pg. 3720
INSPUR SOFTWARE CO., LTD.—See Inspur Group Ltd.; *Int'l*, pg. 3721
INSPUR WORLDWIDE SERVICES LIMITED—See Inspur Group Ltd.; *Int'l*, pg. 3720
INSPYRE SOLUTIONS INC.; *Int'l*, pg. 3721
INSTABANK ASA; *Int'l*, pg. 3721
INSTA-BED, INC.—See Exxel Outdoors, Inc.; *U.S. Private*, pg. 1453
INSTACLUSTR PTY. LTD.—See NetApp, Inc.; *U.S. Public*, pg. 1507
INSTACOM ENGINEERING SDN. BHD.—See Vinvest Capital Holdings Berhad; *Int'l*, pg. 8242
INSTA EL SYD AB—See Instalco AB; *Int'l*, pg. 3721
INSTA FINANCE LTD.; *Int'l*, pg. 3721
INSTAGRAM, INC.—See Meta Platforms, Inc.; *U.S. Public*, pg. 1427
INSTALACIONES Y MONTAJES DE AIRE CLIMATIZADO, S.L.—See ACS, Actividades de Construccion y Servicios, S.A.; *Int'l*, pg. 114
INSTALACIONES Y SERVICIOS CODEVEN, C.A.—See ACS, Actividades de Construccion y Servicios, S.A.; *Int'l*, pg. 115
INSTALARME INDUSTRIA E COMERCIO LTDA—See Allied Universal Manager LLC; *U.S. Private*, pg. 190

INSTALCO AB; *Int'l*, pg. 3721
INSTAL KRAKOW S.A.; *Int'l*, pg. 3721
INSTALLATIETECHNIEK BELGIE NV—See VINCI S.A.; *Int'l*, pg. 8223
INSTALLATIONS ELECTRIQUES PREFABRICATION; *Int'l*, pg. 3723
INSTALLATIONSSERVICE NICKLAS ERIKSSON AB—See Instalco AB; *Int'l*, pg. 3721
INSTALLED BUILDING PRODUCTS, INC.; *U.S. Public*, pg. 1131
INSTALLED BUILDING PRODUCTS, LLC—See Installed Building Products, Inc.; *U.S. Public*, pg. 1133
INSTALLED BUILDING PRODUCTS OF FORT MYERS, LLC—See Installed Building Products, Inc.; *U.S. Public*, pg. 1133
INSTALLED BUILDING PRODUCTS OF JACKSONVILLE, LLC—See Installed Building Products, Inc.; *U.S. Public*, pg. 1133
INSTALLED BUILDING PRODUCTS OF MAINE, LLC—See Installed Building Products, Inc.; *U.S. Public*, pg. 1133
INSTALLED BUILDING PRODUCTS OF MIAMI, LLC—See Installed Building Products, Inc.; *U.S. Public*, pg. 1133
INSTALLED BUILDING PRODUCTS OF TAMPA, LLC—See Installed Building Products, Inc.; *U.S. Public*, pg. 1133
INSTALLED BUILDING PRODUCTS OF WEST PALM, LLC—See Installed Building Products, Inc.; *U.S. Public*, pg. 1133
INSTALLED BUILDING PRODUCTS - PANHANDLE, LLC—See Installed Building Products, Inc.; *U.S. Public*, pg. 1132
INSTALLED BUILDING PRODUCTS - PORTLAND, LLC—See Installed Building Products, Inc.; *U.S. Public*, pg. 1133
INSTALLED BUILDING SOLUTIONS II, LLC—See Installed Building Products, Inc.; *U.S. Public*, pg. 1133
INSTALLER SALES & SERVICE INCORPORATED; *U.S. Private*, pg. 2092
INSTALLIT AS—See Endur ASA; *Int'l*, pg. 2410
INSTAL-LUBIN S.A.—See Polimex-Mostostal S.A.; *Int'l*, pg. 5909
INSTALLUX SA; *Int'l*, pg. 3723
INSTAMATIC AB—See Instalco AB; *Int'l*, pg. 3721
INSTAMED COMMUNICATIONS, LLC—See JPMorgan Chase & Co.; *U.S. Public*, pg. 1207
INSTAMED HOLDINGS, INC.—See JPMorgan Chase & Co.; *U.S. Public*, pg. 1207
INSTANATURAL, LLC; *U.S. Private*, pg. 2092
INSTANT CARE OF ARIZONA LLC—See Coltala Holdings, LLC; *U.S. Private*, pg. 976
INSTANT DIAGNOSTIC SYSTEMS, INC.—See Cardinal Health, Inc.; *U.S. Public*, pg. 434
INSTANTEL INC.—See Stanley Black & Decker, Inc.; *U.S. Public*, pg. 1935
INSTANT GROUP LIMITED; *Int'l*, pg. 3723
INSTANTINA NAHRUNGSMITTEL ENTWICKLUNGS- UND PRODUKTIONSGESELLSCHAFT M.B.H.—See AGRANA Beteiligungs-AG; *Int'l*, pg. 214
INSTANT KARMA FILMS, LLC—See Beijing Galloping Horse Film & TV Production Co., Ltd.; *Int'l*, pg. 950
INSTANT KARMA FILMS, LLC—See Reliance - ADA Group Limited; *Int'l*, pg. 6263
INSTANT OFFICES LIMITED—See Instant Group Limited; *Int'l*, pg. 3723
INSTANTRON CO., INC.; *U.S. Private*, pg. 2092
INSTANT TECHNOLOGY, LLC; *U.S. Private*, pg. 2092
THE INSTANT WEB COMPANIES - MAIL-GARD DIVISION—See The Instant Web Companies; *U.S. Private*, pg. 4056
THE INSTANT WEB COMPANIES; *U.S. Private*, pg. 4056
INSTANTWHIP-AKRON, INC.—See Instantwhip Foods, Inc.; *U.S. Private*, pg. 2092
INSTANTWHIP-BALTIMORE, INC.—See Instantwhip Foods, Inc.; *U.S. Private*, pg. 2092
INSTANTWHIP-BUFFALO, INC.—See Instantwhip Foods, Inc.; *U.S. Private*, pg. 2092
INSTANTWHIP-CHICAGO, INC.—See Instantwhip Foods, Inc.; *U.S. Private*, pg. 2092
INSTANTWHIP-CONNECTICUT, INC.—See Instantwhip Foods, Inc.; *U.S. Private*, pg. 2092
INSTANTWHIP-EASTERN NEW YORK, INC.—See Instantwhip Foods, Inc.; *U.S. Private*, pg. 2092
INSTANTWHIP FOODS, INC.; *U.S. Private*, pg. 2092
INSTANTWHIP-INDIANAPOLIS, INC.—See Instantwhip Foods, Inc.; *U.S. Private*, pg. 2092
INSTANTWHIP-MINNEAPOLIS, INC.—See Instantwhip Foods, Inc.; *U.S. Private*, pg. 2092
INSTANTWHIP OF PENNSYLVANIA, INC.—See Instantwhip Foods, Inc.; *U.S. Private*, pg. 2092
INSTANTWHIP-ROCHESTER, INC.—See Instantwhip Foods, Inc.; *U.S. Private*, pg. 2092
INSTARAGF ASSET MANAGEMENT INC.—See AGF Management Limited; *Int'l*, pg. 206
INSTARAGF ASSET MANAGEMENT INC.—See Instar Group Inc.; *Int'l*, pg. 3723
INSTAR GROUP INC.; *Int'l*, pg. 3723
INSTARMAC GROUP PLC; *Int'l*, pg. 3723

INSTAR SERVICES GROUP, LP—See BlackEagle Partners, LLC; *U.S. Private*, pg. 573
INSTASAFE INC.—See ABM Knowledgeware Ltd; *Int'l*, pg. 63
INSTASHOP DMCC—See Delivery Hero SE; *Int'l*, pg. 2013
INSTAWARES, LLC—See ITC Holding Company, LLC; *U.S. Private*, pg. 2149
INSTEEL INDUSTRIES, INC.; *U.S. Public*, pg. 1134
INSTEEL WIRE PRODUCTS COMPANY—See Insteel Industries, Inc.; *U.S. Public*, pg. 1134
INSTEK AMERICA CORP.—See Good Will Instrument Co., Ltd.; *Int'l*, pg. 3039
INSTEK ELECTRONIC (SHANGHAI) CO., LTD.—See Good Will Instrument Co., Ltd.; *Int'l*, pg. 3039
INSTEL AB OY—See YIT Corporation; *Int'l*, pg. 8586
INSTEM INFORMATION SYSTEMS (SHANGHAI) LIMITED—See ArchiMed SAS; *Int'l*, pg. 548
INSTEM LIFE SCIENCE SYSTEMS, LTD.—See ArchiMed SAS; *Int'l*, pg. 548
INSTEM PLC—See ArchiMed SAS; *Int'l*, pg. 548
INSTEP SOFTWARE LLC—See Schneider Electric SE; *Int'l*, pg. 6633
INSTIL BIO, INC.; *U.S. Public*, pg. 1134
INSTIL DRINKS LIMITED—See C&C Group Plc; *Int'l*, pg. 1238
INSTINCTIF PARTNERS HOLDINGS LTD—See Lloyds Banking Group plc; *Int'l*, pg. 4537
INSTINET CANADA LIMITED—See Nomura Holdings, Inc.; *Int'l*, pg. 5409
INSTINET EUROPE LTD.—See Nomura Holdings, Inc.; *Int'l*, pg. 5411
INSTINET INCORPORATED—See Nomura Holdings, Inc.; *Int'l*, pg. 5411
INSTINET, LLC—See Nomura Holdings, Inc.; *Int'l*, pg. 5411
INSTINET PACIFIC LTD.—See Nomura Holdings, Inc.; *Int'l*, pg. 5409
INSTINET SINGAPORE SERVICES PTE. LTD.—See Nomura Holdings, Inc.; *Int'l*, pg. 5409
INSTITUT DR. APPELT HILTER GMBH & CO. KG—See Eurofins Scientific S.E.; *Int'l*, pg. 2546
INSTITUT DR. APPELT THURINGEN GMBH & CO. KG—See Eurofins Scientific S.E.; *Int'l*, pg. 2546
INSTITUT DR.-ING. GAUER INGENIEURGESELLSCHAFT MBH—See BKW AG; *Int'l*, pg. 1055
INSTITUT DR. ROTHE GMBH—See Eurofins Scientific S.E.; *Int'l*, pg. 2550
INSTITUTE FOR BETTER EDUCATION; *U.S. Private*, pg. 2093
INSTITUTE FOR BUILDING TECHNOLOGY AND SAFETY; *U.S. Private*, pg. 2093
INSTITUTE FOR COMMUNITY LIVING; *U.S. Private*, pg. 2093
INSTITUTE FOR CORPORATE PRODUCTIVITY, INC.; *U.S. Private*, pg. 2093
INSTITUTE FOR FAMILY CENTERED SERVICES, INC.—See Centerbridge Partners, L.P.; *U.S. Private*, pg. 813
THE INSTITUTE FOR FAMILY HEALTH; *U.S. Private*, pg. 4056
INSTITUTE FOR HEALTHCARE COMMUNICATION, INC.; *U.S. Private*, pg. 2093
THE INSTITUTE FOR HEALTHCARE IMPROVEMENT; *U.S. Private*, pg. 4056
INSTITUTE FOR INTERNATIONAL PRODUCT SAFETY GMBH—See Eaton Corporation plc; *Int'l*, pg. 2282
INSTITUTE FOR INTERNATIONAL RESEARCH (IIR) BV—See Informa plc; *Int'l*, pg. 3692
INSTITUTE FOR INTERNATIONAL RESEARCH, INC.—See Informa plc; *Int'l*, pg. 3692
INSTITUTE FOR LANGUAGE STUDY—See Cortina Learning International, Inc.; *U.S. Private*, pg. 1061
INSTITUTE FOR PHYSICAL SCIENCE, INC.; *U.S. Private*, pg. 2093
INSTITUTE FOR POPULATION HEALTH; *U.S. Private*, pg. 2093
INSTITUTE FOR PROFESSIONAL DEVELOPMENT—See Apollo Global Management, Inc.; *U.S. Public*, pg. 146
INSTITUTE FOR PROFESSIONAL DEVELOPMENT—See The Vistria Group, LP; *U.S. Private*, pg. 4131
INSTITUTE FOR SUPPLY MANAGMENT; *U.S. Private*, pg. 2093
INSTITUTE FOR SYSTEMS BIOLOGY—See Providence St. Joseph Health; *U.S. Private*, pg. 3294
INSTITUTE FOR TRANSPORTATION & DEVELOPMENT POLICY; *U.S. Private*, pg. 2093
INSTITUTE FOR WOMEN'S HEALTH AND BODY, LLC—See HCA Healthcare, Inc.; *U.S. Public*, pg. 999
INSTITUTE OF ADVANCED ENT SURGERY, LLC—See HCA Healthcare, Inc.; *U.S. Public*, pg. 999
INSTITUTE OF BIO-MEDICAL AND WELFARE ENGINEERING CO., LTD—See Core Corporation; *Int'l*, pg. 1797
THE INSTITUTE OF CLASSICAL ARCHITECTURE; *U.S. Private*, pg. 4056
INSTITUTE OF COMMUNITY SERVICES, INC.; *U.S. Private*, pg. 2093
INSTITUTE OF DIGITAL MEDIA TECHNOLOGY (SHANGHAI) LIMITED—See Global Digital Creations Holdings Limited; *Int'l*, pg. 2994

INSTITUTE OF DIGITAL MEDIA TECHNOLOGY (SHENZHEN) LIMITED—See Global Digital Creations Holdings Limited; *Int'l*, pg. 2994
INSTITUTE OF ELECTRICAL AND ELECTRONICS ENGINEERS, INC.; *U.S. Private*, pg. 2093
THE INSTITUTE OF FINANCIAL OPERATIONS; *U.S. Private*, pg. 4056
INSTITUTE OF FOOD TECHNOLOGISTS; *U.S. Private*, pg. 2093
INSTITUTE OF NUCLEAR ENERGY RESEARCH; *Int'l*, pg. 3724
INSTITUTE OF NUCLEAR POWER OPERATIONS; *U.S. Private*, pg. 2093
THE INSTITUTE OF POST-SECONDARY EDUCATION, INC.—See Dream Center Foundation, a California Nonprofit Corp.; *U.S. Private*, pg. 1275
THE INSTITUTE OF PROFESSIONAL PRACTICE, INC.; *U.S. Private*, pg. 4056
INSTITUTE OF REAL ESTATE MANAGEMENT—See National Association of Realtors; *U.S. Private*, pg. 2847
INSTITUTE OF SCRAP RECYCLING INDUSTRIES, INC.; *U.S. Private*, pg. 2093
INSTITUTE OF ZOOLOGY—See The Zoological Society of London; *Int'l*, pg. 7705
INSTITUTE ROSTOVSKIY VODOKANALPROEKT JSC—See HMS Hydraulic Machines & Systems Group plc; *Int'l*, pg. 3432
INSTITUT FRANCAIS DES EMPREINTES GENETIQUES S.A.S.—See Eurofins Scientific S.E.; *Int'l*, pg. 2550
INSTITUT FUR LEBENSMITTEL-, WASSER- UND UMWELTANALYTIK NURNBERG GMBH—See Eurofins Scientific S.E.; *Int'l*, pg. 2544
INSTITUT FUR MEDIZINISCHE UND CHEMISCHE LABORDIAGNOSTIK GMBH—See Cinven Limited; *Int'l*, pg. 1614
INSTITUT FUR RUNDFUNKTECHNIK GMBH; *Int'l*, pg. 3723
INSTITUT GAUER GMBH—See BKW AG; *Int'l*, pg. 1055
INSTITUT IGH D.D.; *Int'l*, pg. 3723
INSTITUTIONAL CAPITAL NETWORK, INC.; *U.S. Private*, pg. 2094
INSTITUTIONAL CASEWORK INC.; *U.S. Private*, pg. 2094
INSTITUTIONAL CASH DISTRIBUTORS LLC—See PCP Enterprise, L.P.; *U.S. Private*, pg. 3121
INSTITUTIONAL INVESTOR, LLC—See Pageant Media Ltd.; *Int'l*, pg. 5697
INSTITUTIONAL LIFE SERVICES, LLC—See Aon plc; *Int'l*, pg. 496
INSTITUTIONAL PROCESSING SERVICES, LLC—See Aramark; *U.S. Public*, pg. 177
INSTITUTIONAL SHAREHOLDER SERVICES GERMANY AG—See Deutsche Borse AG; *Int'l*, pg. 2064
INSTITUTIONAL SHAREHOLDER SERVICES INC.—See Deutsche Borse AG; *Int'l*, pg. 2064
INSTITUTIONAL SHAREHOLDER SERVICES UK LIMITED—See Deutsche Borse AG; *Int'l*, pg. 2064
INSTITUTIONAL TRADING, MONEY MANAGEMENT OFFICE—See The Ziegler Companies, Inc.; *U.S. Private*, pg. 4140
INSTITUTIONAL VENTURE PARTNERS; *U.S. Private*, pg. 2094
INSTITUTION FOR A GLOBAL SOCIETY CORPORATION; *Int'l*, pg. 3724
INSTITUTION FOR SAVINGS IN NEWBURYPORT & ITS VICINITY; *U.S. Private*, pg. 2094
INSTITUT LORRAIN DE PARTICIPATION SA; *Int'l*, pg. 3723
INSTITUT MERIEUX; *Int'l*, pg. 3723
INSTITUT NATIONAL DE RECHERCHE POUR L'AGRICULTURE L'ALIMENTATION ET L'ENVIRONNEMENT; *Int'l*, pg. 3724
INSTITUTO AUDITIVO WIDEX S.A.—See EQT AB; *Int'l*, pg. 2480
INSTITUTO DE CREDITO OFICIAL; *Int'l*, pg. 3724
INSTITUTO DE DIAGNOSTICO S.A.; *Int'l*, pg. 3724
INSTITUTO DE GESTION SANITARIA, S.A.U.—See Grupo Villar Mir, S.A.U.; *Int'l*, pg. 3138
INSTITUTO DE HOSPITALIDADE—See Novonor S.A.; *Int'l*, pg. 5470
INSTITUTO DO RADIUM DE CAMMPINAS LTDA—See UnitedHealth Group Incorporated; *U.S. Public*, pg. 2241
INSTITUTO EDUCACIONAL SANTO AGOSTINHO S.A.—See Afya Limited; *Int'l*, pg. 196
INSTITUTO EM DIAGNOSTICO MOLECULAR THERANOSTICA LTDA—See H.U. Group Holdings, Inc.; *Int'l*, pg. 3196
INSTITUTO GRIFOLS, S.A.—See Grifols, S.A.; *Int'l*, pg. 3085
INSTITUTO HERMES PARDINI S.A.—See Fleury S.A.; *Int'l*, pg. 2701
INSTITUTO INTERNATIONAL PAPER—See International Paper Company; *U.S. Public*, pg. 1155
INSTITUTO MOVILIZADOR DE FONDOS COOPERATIVOS; *Int'l*, pg. 3724
INSTITUT PROF. DR. JAGER GMBH—See Eurofins Scientific S.E.; *Int'l*, pg. 2550

COMPANY NAME INDEX

INSTITUT REGIONAL DE DEVELOPPEMENT INDUSTRIEL DE MIDI-PYRENEES; *Int'l*, pg. 3724
INSTITUT STRAUMANN AG—See Straumann Holding AG; *Int'l*, pg. 7237
INSTITUT ZA ISPITIVANJE MATERIJALA A.D.; *Int'l*, pg. 3724
INSTITUT ZA TRZISNA ISTRAZIVANJA A.D.; *Int'l*, pg. 3724
INSTONE REAL ESTATE GROUP SE; *Int'l*, pg. 3724
INSTRAT INSURANCE BROKERS LTD—See Arthur J. Gallagher & Co.; *U.S. Public*, pg. 203
INSTREAM, LLC; *U.S. Private*, pg. 2094
INSTREET INVESTMENT LIMITED—See Raiz Invest Limited; *Int'l*, pg. 6191
INSTRON BRASIL EQUIPAMENTOS CIENTIFICOS LTDA.—See Illinois Tool Works Inc.; *U.S. Public*, pg. 1108
INSTRON CORPORATION—See Illinois Tool Works Inc.; *U.S. Public*, pg. 1108
INSTRON DEUTSCHLAND GMBH—See Illinois Tool Works Inc.; *U.S. Public*, pg. 1108
INSTRON FRANCE S.A.S.—See Illinois Tool Works Inc.; *U.S. Public*, pg. 1108
INSTRON GMBH—See Illinois Tool Works Inc.; *U.S. Public*, pg. 1108
INSTRON INDUSTRIAL PRODUCTS GROUP—See Illinois Tool Works Inc.; *U.S. Public*, pg. 1108
INSTRON JAPAN CO. LTD.—See Illinois Tool Works Inc.; *U.S. Public*, pg. 1108
INSTRON KOREA LLC—See Illinois Tool Works Inc.; *U.S. Public*, pg. 1108
INSTRON LIMITED—See Illinois Tool Works Inc.; *U.S. Public*, pg. 1108
INSTRON PTY. LTD.—See Illinois Tool Works Inc.; *U.S. Public*, pg. 1108
INSTRON S.A.S.—See Illinois Tool Works Inc.; *U.S. Public*, pg. 1108
INSTRON (SHANGHAI) LTD.—See Illinois Tool Works Inc.; *U.S. Public*, pg. 1108
INSTRON SINGAPORE PTE LIMITED—See Illinois Tool Works Inc.; *U.S. Public*, pg. 1108
INSTRON STRUCTURAL TESTING SYSTEMS GMBH—See Illinois Tool Works Inc.; *U.S. Public*, pg. 1108
INSTRUCLEAN GMBH—See Fresenius SE & Co. KGaA; *Int'l*, pg. 2780
INSTRUCTIVISION, INC.; *U.S. Public*, pg. 1134
INSTRUCTURE GLOBAL LIMITED—See Thoma Bravo, L.P.; *U.S. Private*, pg. 4148
INSTRUCTURE HOLDINGS, INC.—See KKR & Co. Inc.; *U.S. Public*, pg. 1253
INSTRUCTURE, INC.—See Thoma Bravo, L.P.; *U.S. Private*, pg. 4148
INSTRULABQ CIA. LTDA.—See HORIBA Ltd; *Int'l*, pg. 3477
INSTRUMART; *U.S. Private*, pg. 2094
INSTRUMATIC, S.A. DE C.V.; *Int'l*, pg. 3724
INSTRUMEDICS, LLC—See Stryker Corporation; *U.S. Public*, pg. 1955
INSTRUMED INTERNATIONAL, INC.—See Arlington Capital Partners LLC; *U.S. Private*, pg. 327
INSTRUMED PANAMA, S.A.—See HORIBA Ltd; *Int'l*, pg. 3477
INSTRUMENTARIUM DENTAL INC.—See Danaher Corporation; *U.S. Public*, pg. 630
INSTRUMENTARIUM DENTAL S.A.R.L.—See Danaher Corporation; *U.S. Public*, pg. 630
INSTRUMENT ASSOCIATES INC.; *U.S. Private*, pg. 2094
INSTRUMENTATION LAB. (LIETUVA) B.I.—See Werfen Life Group, S.A.U.; *Int'l*, pg. 8379
INSTRUMENTATION LABORATORY, B.V.—See Werfen Life Group, S.A.U.; *Int'l*, pg. 8379
INSTRUMENTATION LABORATORY (CANADA) LTD.—See Werfen Life Group, S.A.U.; *Int'l*, pg. 8379
INSTRUMENTATION LABORATORY GMBH—See Werfen Life Group, S.A.U.; *Int'l*, pg. 8379
INSTRUMENTATION LABORATORY S.A.—See Werfen Life Group, S.A.U.; *Int'l*, pg. 8379
INSTRUMENTATION LABORATORY—See Werfen Life Group, S.A.U.; *Int'l*, pg. 8379
INSTRUMENT CASES LLC—See Reliance Steel & Aluminum Co.; *U.S. Public*, pg. 1780
INSTRUMENTOS WIKA COLOMBIA S.A.S.—See WIKA Alexander-Wiegand GmbH & Co. KG; *Int'l*, pg. 8408
INSTRUMENTOS WIKA MEXICO S.A. DE C.V.—See WIKA Alexander-Wiegand GmbH & Co. KG; *Int'l*, pg. 8408
INSTRUMENTOS WIKA, S.A.U.—See WIKA Alexander-Wiegand GmbH & Co. KG; *Int'l*, pg. 8408
INSTRUMENT SALES AND SERVICE; *U.S. Private*, pg. 2094
INSTRUMENTS FOR INDUSTRIES, INC.—See AMETEK, Inc.; *U.S. Public*, pg. 119
INSTRUMENTS FOR INDUSTRY, INC.—See AMETEK, Inc.; *U.S. Public*, pg. 120
INSTRUMENTS NANOTECH SA. DE CV.; *Int'l*, pg. 3724
INSTRUMENTS TECHNOLOGY (JOHOR) SDN. BHD.—See Seiko Group Corporation; *Int'l*, pg. 6689

INSTRUMENT TRANSFORMER EQUIPMENT CORPORATION—See Falfurrias Capital Partners, LP; *U.S. Private*, pg. 1467
INSTRUMENT & VALVE SERVICES COMPANY—See Emerson Electric Co.; *U.S. Public*, pg. 748
INSTRUMETRICS INDUSTRIAL CONTROL LTD.—See Endress+Hauser (International) Holding AG; *Int'l*, pg. 2408
INSTRUTECH, INC.—See INFICON Holding AG; *Int'l*, pg. 3684
INSTRUTECH LTDA—See WEG S.A.; *Int'l*, pg. 8367
INSTYLE MAGAZINE—See Meredith Corporation; *U.S. Public*, pg. 1423
INSUD PHARMA, S.L.; *Int'l*, pg. 3724
INSULA COMPANIES; *U.S. Private*, pg. 2094
INSULAIR, INC.—See Koch Industries, Inc.; *U.S. Private*, pg. 2327
INSULA PROPERTIES, LLC; *U.S. Private*, pg. 2094
INSULATED STRUCTURES (1989) (PTY) LIMITED—See TRG Management LP; *U.S. Private*, pg. 4220
INSULATING SERVICES INC.; *U.S. Private*, pg. 2094
INSULATION CONTRACTORS INC.—See Installed Building Products, Inc.; *U.S. Public*, pg. 1133
INSULATION DEALERS & SUPPLY CO.; *U.S. Private*, pg. 2094
INSULATION DISTRIBUTORS, INC.—See MacArthur Co.; *U.S. Private*, pg. 2534
INSULATION HOLDINGS LNC.—See Bird Construction Inc.; *Int'l*, pg. 1047
INSULATION PLUS, LLC—See MacArthur Co.; *U.S. Private*, pg. 2534
INSULATIONS INCORPORATED; *U.S. Private*, pg. 2094
INSULATION SOLUTIONS HOLDINGS PTY LIMITED—See Fletcher Building Limited; *Int'l*, pg. 2700
INSULATION SUPPLY COMPANY INC.; *U.S. Private*, pg. 2094
INSULATION WHOLESALE SUPPLY, LLC—See Installed Building Products, Inc.; *U.S. Public*, pg. 1133
INSULECTRO; *U.S. Private*, pg. 2094
INSULET CORPORATION; *U.S. Public*, pg. 1134
INSULEX GMBH—See VINCI S.A.; *Int'l*, pg. 8223
INSULFOAM, LLC—See Carlisle Companies Incorporated; *U.S. Public*, pg. 436
INSULMAX CONSTRUCTION SERVICES—See Irex Corporation; *U.S. Private*, pg. 2138
INSULPANE OF CONNECTICUT, INC.—See Grey Mountain Partners, LLC; *U.S. Private*, pg. 1784
INSULSPAN, LLC - DELTA PLANT—See The Riverside Company; *U.S. Private*, pg. 4109
INSULSPAN, LLC—See The Riverside Company; *U.S. Private*, pg. 4109
INSULTAB, INC.—See Odyssey Investment Partners, LLC; *U.S. Private*, pg. 2995
INSULVAIL, LLC—See Installed Building Products, Inc.; *U.S. Public*, pg. 1133
INSUN ENVIRONMENTAL NEW TECHNOLOGY CO., LTD.; *Int'l*, pg. 3725
INSUNG DIGITAL CO., LTD.—See Insung Information Co., Ltd.; *Int'l*, pg. 3725
INSUNG INFORMATION CO., LTD.; *Int'l*, pg. 3725
INSURAGEST TECHNOLOGIES, INC.; *Int'l*, pg. 3725
INSURAGUEST TECHNOLOGIES, INC.; *U.S. Public*, pg. 1134
INSURAMATCH, LLC—See The Travelers Companies, Inc.; *U.S. Public*, pg. 2136
INSURANCE ADMINISTRATIVE SOLUTIONS, LLC—See Integrity Marketing Group LLC; *U.S. Private*, pg. 2103
INSURANCEAGENTS.COM; *U.S. Private*, pg. 2095
INSURANCE ANSWER CENTER, LLC—See The Allstate Corporation; *U.S. Public*, pg. 2033
INSURANCE APPLICATIONS GROUP, LLC; *U.S. Private*, pg. 2094
INSURANCE ASSOCIATES INC.; *U.S. Private*, pg. 2095
INSURANCE AUSTRALIA GROUP LIMITED; *Int'l*, pg. 3725
INSURANCE AUTO AUCTIONS, INC.—See RB Global, Inc.; *Int'l*, pg. 6226
INSURANCE AUTO AUCTIONS SPECIALTY SALVAGE DIVISION—See RB Global, Inc.; *Int'l*, pg. 6226
INSURANCE & BENEFITS GROUP LLC—See GTCR LLC; *U.S. Private*, pg. 1803
INSURANCE BROKERS & AGENTS OF THE WEST—See Independent Insurance Agents & Brokers of America, Inc.; *U.S. Private*, pg. 2059
INSURANCE BROKERS OF NIGERIA LIMITED—See Marsh & McLennan Companies, Inc.; *U.S. Public*, pg. 1376
INSURANCE BROKERS WEST INC.; *U.S. Private*, pg. 2095
INSURANCE BY KEN BROWN, INC.—See Arthur J. Gallagher & Co.; *U.S. Public*, pg. 206
INSURANCE CARE DIRECT INC; *U.S. Private*, pg. 2095
INSURANCE CENTER FOR EXCELLENCE, LLC—See Madison Dearborn Partners, LLC; *U.S. Private*, pg. 2540
INSURANCE CENTER, INC.; *U.S. Private*, pg. 2095
INSURANCE CLUB, INC.—See Unico American Corporation; *U.S. Public*, pg. 2225

INSURANCE SERVICES GROUP

T.H.E. INSURANCE CO. INC.—See AXA S.A.; *Int'l*, pg. 760
INSURANCE.COM, INC.; *U.S. Private*, pg. 2095
INSURANCE COMPANY AMANAT JSC; *Int'l*, pg. 3725
INSURANCE COMPANY EURASIA JSC—See Eurasian Bank JSC; *Int'l*, pg. 2527
INSURANCE COMPANY KOMMESK-OMIR JSC; *Int'l*, pg. 3725
INSURANCE COMPANY LONDON-ALMATY JSC; *Int'l*, pg. 3725
INSURANCE COMPANY MEDICO 21 AD—See Doverie United Holding AD; *Int'l*, pg. 2182
INSURANCE COMPANY NOVA INS EAD—See Vienna Insurance Group AG Wiener Versicherung Gruppe; *Int'l*, pg. 8194
INSURANCE COMPANY OF GREATER NEW YORK—See Greater New York Mutual Insurance Company; *U.S. Private*, pg. 1770
INSURANCE COMPANY OF THE BAHAMAS LIMITED—See Aon plc; *Int'l*, pg. 494
THE INSURANCE COMPANY OF THE STATE OF PENNSYLVANIA—See American International Group, Inc.; *U.S. Public*, pg. 107
INSURANCE COMPANY SBERBANK INSURANCE LIFE LLC—See OJSC Sberbank of Russia; *Int'l*, pg. 5541
INSURANCE COMPANY UNIQA—See UNIQA Insurance Group AG; *Int'l*, pg. 8057
INSURANCE COMPANY VIENNA OSIGURANJE D.D.—See Vienna Insurance Group AG Wiener Versicherung Gruppe; *Int'l*, pg. 8194
THE INSURANCE CORPORATION OF BRITISH COLUMBIA; *Int'l*, pg. 7656
INSURANCE CORPORATION OF THE CHANNEL ISLANDS LIMITED—See Intact Financial Corporation; *Int'l*, pg. 3725
INSURANCE CORPORATION OF THE CHANNEL ISLANDS LIMITED—See Tryg A/S; *Int'l*, pg. 7946
INSURANCE DIALOGUE LIMITED—See Arthur J. Gallagher & Co.; *U.S. Public*, pg. 203
THE INSURANCE EXCHANGE, INC.—See Cross Financial Corporation; *U.S. Private*, pg. 1105
INSURANCE FIRST BROKERS LTD.—See LSL Property Services plc; *Int'l*, pg. 4570
INSURANCE HOUSE P.S.C.; *Int'l*, pg. 3726
INSURANCE HOUSE; *U.S. Private*, pg. 2095
INSURANCE INCOME STRATEGIES LTD.; *Int'l*, pg. 3726
INSURANCE INSTITUTE FOR HIGHWAY SAFETY; *U.S. Private*, pg. 2095
INSURANCE LICENSING SERVICES-AMERICA—See ReSource Pro, LLC; *U.S. Private*, pg. 3407
INSURANCE MACEDONIA AD SKOPJE VIENNA INSURANCE GROUP—See Vienna Insurance Group AG Wiener Versicherung Gruppe; *Int'l*, pg. 8194
INSURANCE MANAGEMENT COMPANY—See Hellman & Friedman LLC; *U.S. Private*, pg. 1909
INSURANCE MARKETING AGENCIES, INC.; *U.S. Private*, pg. 2095
INSURANCE MARKETING CENTER, INC.—See GTCR LLC; *U.S. Private*, pg. 1803
INSURANCE MARKETING GROUP, LLC—See Integrity Marketing Group LLC; *U.S. Private*, pg. 2103
INSURANCE NETWORK, LC—See Gibson Insurance Agency Inc.; *U.S. Private*, pg. 1696
INSURANCE NETWORK OF TEXAS, INC.; *U.S. Private*, pg. 2095
INSURANCE NETWORKS ALLIANCE, LLC—See W.R. Berkley Corporation; *U.S. Public*, pg. 2317
INSURANCE NETWORK SERVICES, INC.—See The Seibels Bruce Group, Inc.; *U.S. Private*, pg. 4116
INSURANCENOODLE LLC—See Insureon; *U.S. Private*, pg. 2095
THE INSURANCENTER—See American International Group, Inc.; *U.S. Public*, pg. 107
INSURANCE OF AMERICA AGENCY; *U.S. Private*, pg. 2095
INSURANCE OFFICE OF AMERICA, INC.; *U.S. Private*, pg. 2095
INSURANCE OVERLOAD SERVICES, INC.; *U.S. Private*, pg. 2095
THE INSURANCE PARTNERSHIP HOLDINGS LIMITED—See Marsh & McLennan Companies, Inc.; *U.S. Public*, pg. 1388
INSURANCE PARTNERS OF TEXAS—See Marsh & McLennan Companies, Inc.; *U.S. Public*, pg. 1381
INSURANCE RESOURCE BROKERAGE GROUP; *U.S. Private*, pg. 2095
INSURANCE RESTORATION SPECIALISTS, INC.—See FirstService Corporation; *Int'l*, pg. 2691
INSURANCE RISK MANAGEMENT GROUP, INC.—See Williams Industries, Inc.; *U.S. Public*, pg. 4526
INSURANCE SERVICES GROUP; *U.S. Private*, pg. 2095
INSURANCE SERVICES OF AMERICA INC.—See Stone Point Capital LLC; *U.S. Private*, pg. 3819
INSURANCE SERVICES OFFICE, INC.—See Verisk Analytics, Inc.; *U.S. Public*, pg. 2282
INSURANCE SERVICES OFFICE, LTD.—See Verisk Analytics, Inc.; *U.S. Public*, pg. 2283
INSURANCE SPECIALISTS—See Houchens Industries, Inc.; *U.S. Private*, pg. 1990

INSURANCE SERVICES GROUP

INSURANCE SYSTEMS, INC.—See GTCR LLC; *U.S. Private*, pg. 1803
INSURANCE TECHNOLOGIES CORPORATION—See Clearlake Capital Group, L.P.; *U.S. Private*, pg. 938
INSURANCE TECHNOLOGIES CORP. - TURBORATER—See Clearlake Capital Group, L.P.; *U.S. Private*, pg. 938
INSURAPRISE INC.; *U.S. Private*, pg. 2095
INSURCOMM CONSTRUCTION, INC.; *U.S. Private*, pg. 2095
INSURED GROUP LIMITED; *Int'l*, pg. 3726
INSURE-LINK, INC.—See NSI Insurance Group; *U.S. Private*, pg. 2970
INSURE MY VILLA LIMITED—See Arthur J. Gallagher & Co.; *U.S. Public*, pg. 206
INSUREON; *U.S. Private*, pg. 2095
INSURERS ADMINISTRATIVE CORPORATION—See Geneve Holdings Corp.; *U.S. Private*, pg. 1670
INSURESUPERMARKET.COM LIMITED—See Moneysupermarket.com Group PLC; *Int'l*, pg. 5033
INSURE THE BOX LIMITED—See MS&AD Insurance Group Holdings, Inc.; *Int'l*, pg. 5066
INSURICA, INC.; *U.S. Private*, pg. 2095
INSURITY, INC.—See GI Manager L.P.; *U.S. Private*, pg. 1692
INSURMARK, INC.; *U.S. Private*, pg. 2096
INSWAVE SYSTEMS CO., LTD.; *Int'l*, pg. 3726
INSYDE SOFTWARE CO., LTD.—See Insyde Software Corporation; *Int'l*, pg. 3726
INSYDE SOFTWARE CORPORATION; *Int'l*, pg. 3726
INSYDE SOFTWARE, INC.—See Insyde Software Corporation; *Int'l*, pg. 3726
INSYDE SOFTWARE, LTD.—See Insyde Software Corporation; *Int'l*, pg. 3726
INSYDE TECHNOLOGY, INC.—See Insyde Software Corporation; *Int'l*, pg. 3726
INSYGHT; *U.S. Private*, pg. 2096
IN SYNC BEMIS BALKIND; *U.S. Private*, pg. 2052
INSYNC INFORMATION SYSTEMS, PVT. LTD.—See ORBCOMM, Inc.; *U.S. Public*, pg. 1614
INSYNC INSURANCE SOLUTIONS LIMITED—See Brown & Brown, Inc.; *U.S. Public*, pg. 401
INSYNC SOFTWARE, INC.—See ORBCOMM, Inc.; *U.S. Public*, pg. 1614
INSYNQ INC.—See Summit Hosting LLC; *U.S. Private*, pg. 3854
INSYSCO, INC.—See MAXIMUS, Inc.; *U.S. Public*, pg. 1402
INSYS GROUP, INC.—See DXC Technology Company; *U.S. Public*, pg. 696
INSYS MANUFACTURING, LLC—See Insys Therapeutics, Inc.; *U.S. Private*, pg. 2096
INSYS PHARMA, INC.—See Insys Therapeutics, Inc.; *U.S. Private*, pg. 2096
IN-SYSTCOM, INC.; *U.S. Public*, pg. 1114
INSYS THERAPEUTICS, INC.; *U.S. Private*, pg. 2096
INSZONE INSURANCE SERVICES, LLC; *U.S. Private*, pg. 2096
INTA BINA GROUP BERHAD; *Int'l*, pg. 3726
INTAC ACTUARIAL SERVICES, INC.—See Aquiline Capital Partners LLC; *U.S. Private*, pg. 303
INTAC ACTUARIAL SERVICES, INC.—See Genstar Capital, LLC; *U.S. Private*, pg. 1675
INTAC INTERNATIONAL, INC.—See Remark Holdings, Inc.; *U.S. Public*, pg. 1782
INTACT BUILDERS PRIVATE LIMITED—See Keystone Realtors Limited; *Int'l*, pg. 4147
INTACT FINANCIAL CORPORATION; *Int'l*, pg. 3726
INTACT FINANCIAL CORPORATION—See Intact Financial Corporation; *Int'l*, pg. 3726
INTACT FINANCIAL CORPORATION—See Intact Financial Corporation; *Int'l*, pg. 3726
INTACT GOLD CORPORATION; *Int'l*, pg. 3727
INTACT INFO SOLUTIONS LLC; *U.S. Private*, pg. 2097
INTACT INSURANCE CANADA—See Intact Financial Corporation; *Int'l*, pg. 3726
INTACT INVESTMENT MANAGEMENT INC.—See Intact Financial Corporation; *Int'l*, pg. 3726
INTACT TECHNOLOGY, INC.; *U.S. Private*, pg. 2097
INTAGE ASSOCIATES, INC.—See Nippon Telegraph & Telephone Corporation; *Int'l*, pg. 5350
INTAGE CHINA INC.—See Nippon Telegraph & Telephone Corporation; *Int'l*, pg. 5350
INTAGE HOLDINGS INC.—See Nippon Telegraph & Telephone Corporation; *Int'l*, pg. 5350
INTAGE INDIA PRIVATE LIMITED—See Nippon Telegraph & Telephone Corporation; *Int'l*, pg. 5350
INTAGE REAL WORLD INC—See Nippon Telegraph & Telephone Corporation; *Int'l*, pg. 5350
INTAGE RESEARCH INC.—See Nippon Telegraph & Telephone Corporation; *Int'l*, pg. 5350
INTAGE SINGAPORE PTE. LTD.—See Nippon Telegraph & Telephone Corporation; *Int'l*, pg. 5350
INTAGE TECHNOSPHERE INC.—See Nippon Telegraph & Telephone Corporation; *Int'l*, pg. 5350
INTAGE (THAILAND) CO., LTD.—See Nippon Telegraph & Telephone Corporation; *Int'l*, pg. 5350
INTAI TECHNOLOGY CORP.; *Int'l*, pg. 3727

INTAJ MARKETING & DISTRIBUTION CO. LTD.—See The Industrial Commercial & Agricultural Co. Ltd.; *Int'l*, pg. 7655
INTALEQ TECHNOLOGY CONSULTING & SERVICES W.L.L.—See Ooredoo Q.S.C.; *Int'l*, pg. 5594
INTALIO APAC—See Intalio, Inc.; *U.S. Private*, pg. 2097
INTALIO EMEA—See Intalio, Inc.; *U.S. Private*, pg. 2097
INTALIO, INC.; *U.S. Private*, pg. 2097
INTALIO INDIA—See Intalio, Inc.; *U.S. Private*, pg. 2097
INTALIO LATIN AMERICA—See Intalio, Inc.; *U.S. Private*, pg. 2097
INTALYSIS PTY LTD—See Thermo Fisher Scientific Inc.; *U.S. Public*, pg. 2154
INTALYTICS, INC.—See Hanover Investors Management LLP; *Int'l*, pg. 3258
INTANASIA DEVELOPMENT SDN BHD—See Tambun Indah Land Berhad; *Int'l*, pg. 7449
INTANDEM CAPITAL PARTNERS, LLC; *U.S. Private*, pg. 2097
INTAPP, INC.; *U.S. Public*, pg. 1134
INTARCIA THERAPEUTICS, INC.; *U.S. Private*, pg. 2097
INTARYA LIMITED—See SHUAA Capital psc; *Int'l*, pg. 6868
INTASA S.A.—See CAP S.A.; *Int'l*, pg. 1300
INTAS BIOPHARMACEUTICALS LTD.—See Intas Pharmaceuticals Ltd.; *Int'l*, pg. 3728
INTAS PHARMACEUTICALS LTD. - ANKLESHWAR PLANT—See Intas Pharmaceuticals Ltd.; *Int'l*, pg. 3728
INTAS PHARMACEUTICALS LTD. - DEHRADUN FACILITY—See Intas Pharmaceuticals Ltd.; *Int'l*, pg. 3728
INTAS PHARMACEUTICALS LTD. - MATODA FACILITY—See Intas Pharmaceuticals Ltd.; *Int'l*, pg. 3728
INTAS PHARMACEUTICALS LTD. - MORAIYA FACILITY—See Intas Pharmaceuticals Ltd.; *Int'l*, pg. 3728
INTAS PHARMACEUTICALS LTD. - PHARMEZ FACILITY—See Intas Pharmaceuticals Ltd.; *Int'l*, pg. 3728
INTAS PHARMACEUTICALS LTD. - SANAND FACILITY—See Intas Pharmaceuticals Ltd.; *Int'l*, pg. 3728
INTAS PHARMACEUTICALS LTD. - SIKKIM FACILITY—See Intas Pharmaceuticals Ltd.; *Int'l*, pg. 3728
INTAS PHARMACEUTICALS LTD.; *Int'l*, pg. 3727
INTAS PHARMACEUTICALS LTD. - VATVA FACILITY—See Intas Pharmaceuticals Ltd.; *Int'l*, pg. 3728
INTA TECHNOLOGIES CORPORATION—See Francisco Partners Management, LP; *U.S. Private*, pg. 1590
INTAT PRECISION, INC.—See AISIN Corporation; *Int'l*, pg. 253
INTC CO., LTD.—See Sebang Co., Ltd.; *Int'l*, pg. 6669
INTCHAINS GROUP LIMITED; *Int'l*, pg. 3728
I.N.T. CO., LTD.—See TOPPAN Holdings Inc.; *Int'l*, pg. 7816
INTCO MEDICAL TECHNOLOGY CO., LTD.; *Int'l*, pg. 3728
INTCOMEX, INC.; *U.S. Private*, pg. 2097
INTDEV INTERNET TECHNOLOGIES PROPRIETARY LIMITED—See Alviva Holdings Limited; *Int'l*, pg. 402
INTEA HOLDINGS INC.—See Hikari Tsushin, Inc.; *Int'l*, pg. 3390
INTECARE, INC.; *U.S. Private*, pg. 2097
INTEC BIELENBERG GMBH & CO. KG—See Eisenmann AG; *Int'l*, pg. 2336
INTEC BILLING IRELAND—See CSG Systems International, Inc.; *U.S. Public*, pg. 601
INTEC CAPITAL LIMITED; *Int'l*, pg. 3728
INTEC COMPANY, INC.; *U.S. Private*, pg. 2097
INTEC ENVIROMETALS PTY LTD—See SciDev Ltd; *Int'l*, pg. 6647
INTEC FRANCE S.A.S.—See Rheinmetall AG; *Int'l*, pg. 6321
THE INTEC GROUP INC.; *U.S. Private*, pg. 4056
INTECH BIOPHARM LTD.; *Int'l*, pg. 3728
INTECH, INC.—See Electricite de France S.A.; *Int'l*, pg. 2351
INTECH INTERNATIONAL INC.—See BWX Technologies, Inc.; *U.S. Public*, pg. 413
INTECH INVESTMENT MANAGEMENT LLC; *U.S. Private*, pg. 2097
INTECH LIMITED; *Int'l*, pg. 3728
INTECH MACHINES (SUZHOU) CO. LTD—See Manz AG; *Int'l*, pg. 4680
IN'TECH MEDICAL INC—See In'Tech Medical SAS; *Int'l*, pg. 3639
IN'TECH MEDICAL SAS; *Int'l*, pg. 3639
IN TECHNICAL PRODUCTIONS HOLDINGS LIMITED; *Int'l*, pg. 3639
INTECHNOLOGY PLC; *Int'l*, pg. 3729
INTECH PRINTING & DIRECT MAIL; *U.S. Private*, pg. 2097
INTECHSTRA CO., LTD.—See BIPROGY Inc.; *Int'l*, pg. 1045
INTECH TECHNICAL (SHENZHEN) CO., LTD.—See Manz AG; *Int'l*, pg. 4680

CORPORATE AFFILIATIONS

INTECH TRAILERS, INC.; *U.S. Private*, pg. 2097
INTEC INC.; *Int'l*, pg. 3728
INTEC IT CAPITAL, INC.—See TIS Inc.; *Int'l*, pg. 7757
INTEC KEISOKU CO., LTD.—See NIHON DENKEI CO., LTD.; *Int'l*, pg. 5284
INTEC LLC; *U.S. Private*, pg. 2097
INTEC MERNOKI KFT—See Nicolas Correa S.A.; *Int'l*, pg. 5273
INTEC NETCORE INC.—See Intec Inc.; *Int'l*, pg. 3728
INTECNO S.R.L.—See Interpump Group S.p.A.; *Int'l*, pg. 3756
INTEC PHARMA LTD.; *Int'l*, pg. 3728
INTECSA-INARSA, S.A.—See AtkinsRealis Group Inc.; *Int'l*, pg. 673
INTECSA INGENIERIA INDUSTRIAL, S.A.—See ACS, Actividades de Construccion y Servicios, S.A.; *Int'l*, pg. 115
INTEC SOLUTION POWER INC.—See TIS Inc.; *Int'l*, pg. 7757
INTEC SYSTEMS, INC.; *U.S. Private*, pg. 2097
INTECT APS—See TowerBrook Capital Partners, L.P.; *U.S. Private*, pg. 4195
INTEC TELECOM SYSTEMS LIMITED—See CSG Systems International, Inc.; *U.S. Public*, pg. 601
INTEC (UK) LIMITED—See NRL Group Ltd; *Int'l*, pg. 5475
INTEC WEB AND GENOME INFORMATICS CORPORATION—See Intec Inc.; *Int'l*, pg. 3728
INTEGA GMBH—See L'Air Liquide S.A.; *Int'l*, pg. 4370
INTEGBUSINESS SERVICES, INC.—See Berkshire Partners LLC; *U.S. Private*, pg. 534
INTEGENX INC.—See Thermo Fisher Scientific Inc.; *U.S. Public*, pg. 2148
THE INTEGER GROUP, LLC - DALLAS—See Omnicom Group Inc.; *U.S. Public*, pg. 1599
THE INTEGER GROUP, LLC - MIDWEST—See Omnicom Group Inc.; *U.S. Public*, pg. 1599
THE INTEGER GROUP, LLC—See Omnicom Group Inc.; *U.S. Public*, pg. 1599
INTEGER HOLDINGS CORPORATION; *U.S. Public*, pg. 1134
INTEGER PL S.A.—See Advent International Corporation; *U.S. Private*, pg. 103
INTEG GROUP PTY. LTD.—See DXC Technology Company; *U.S. Public*, pg. 696
INTEGON INDEMNITY CORPORATION—See The Allstate Corporation; *U.S. Public*, pg. 2033
INTEGON NATIONAL INSURANCE COMPANY—See The Allstate Corporation; *U.S. Public*, pg. 2033
INTEGON SERVICE CO, S.A. DE C.V.—See The Allstate Corporation; *U.S. Public*, pg. 2033
INTEG QUEENSLAND PTY LTD—See DXC Technology Company; *U.S. Public*, pg. 696
INTEGRA APPARELS AND TEXTILES PVT LTD—See Ashok Piramal Group; *Int'l*, pg. 608
INTEGRA BIOSCIENCES AG—See INTEGRA Holding AG; *Int'l*, pg. 3729
INTEGRA BIOSCIENCES CORP.—See INTEGRA Holding AG; *Int'l*, pg. 3729
INTEGRA BIOSCIENCES DEUTSCHLAND GMBH—See INTEGRA Holding AG; *Int'l*, pg. 3729
INTEGRA BIOSCIENCES LTD.—See INTEGRA Holding AG; *Int'l*, pg. 3729
INTEGRA BIOSCIENCES SAS—See INTEGRA Holding AG; *Int'l*, pg. 3729
INTEGRA BURLINGTON MA, INC.—See Integra LifeSciences Holdings Corporation; *U.S. Public*, pg. 1135
INTEGRA BUSINESS CENTER INC.; *U.S. Private*, pg. 2097
INTEGRA CAPITAL LIMITED—See Willis Towers Watson Public Limited Company; *Int'l*, pg. 8414
INTEGRA CAPITAL MANAGEMENT LIMITED; *Int'l*, pg. 3729
INTEGRACARE OF ABILENE, LLC—See Apollo Global Management, Inc.; *U.S. Public*, pg. 156
INTEGRACARE OF ALBANY, LLC—See Apollo Global Management, Inc.; *U.S. Public*, pg. 156
INTEGRACARE OF GRANBURY, LLC—See Apollo Global Management, Inc.; *U.S. Public*, pg. 156
INTEGRACARE OF OLNEY HOME HEALTH, LLC—See Apollo Global Management, Inc.; *U.S. Public*, pg. 156
INTEGRACARE OF WICHITA FALLS, LLC—See Apollo Global Management, Inc.; *U.S. Public*, pg. 156
INTEGRACLICK, LLC; *U.S. Private*, pg. 2098
INTEGRA COAL OPERATIONS PTY LTD—See Vale S.A.; *Int'l*, pg. 8111
INTEGRACOLOR LTD—See Orora Limited; *Int'l*, pg. 5642
INTEGRA CONSTRUCTION KZ LLP; *Int'l*, pg. 3729
INTEGRA CONSULTING & COMPUTER SERVICES; *U.S. Private*, pg. 2098
INTEGRACORE, INC.; *U.S. Private*, pg. 2098
INTEGRACORE, LLC—See A.P. Moller-Maersk A/S; *Int'l*, pg. 28
INTEGRA DATA & ANALYTIC SOLUTIONS CORP.—See NowVertical Group Inc.; *Int'l*, pg. 5471
INTEGRA DOCUMENT MANAGEMENT SRL; *Int'l*, pg. 3729
INTEGRA ENCLOSURES, INC.; *U.S. Private*, pg. 2098
INTEGRA ENGINEERING INDIA LTD.—See INTEGRA Holding AG; *Int'l*, pg. 3729

COMPANY NAME INDEX

INTEGRAFIN HOLDINGS PLC; *Int'l*, pg. 3730
INTEGRA GARMENTS & TEXTILES LTD.; *Int'l*, pg. 3729
INTEGRAGEN, INC.—See IntegraGen SA; *Int'l*, pg. 3730
INTEGRAGEN SA; *Int'l*, pg. 3730
INTEGRA GMBH—See Integra LifeSciences Holdings Corporation; *U.S. Public*, pg. 1135
INTEGRA HOLDING AG; *Int'l*, pg. 3729
INTEGRA IMMOBILIEN AG—See INTEGRA Holding AG; *Int'l*, pg. 3729
INTEGRA ITC; *Int'l*, pg. 3729
INTEGRAL ACCUMULATOR GMBH & CO. KG—See NOK Corporation; *Int'l*, pg. 5401
INTEGRAL AD SCIENCE HOLDING CORP.; *U.S. Public*, pg. 1136
INTEGRAL AD SCIENCE, INC.—See Vista Equity Partners, LLC; *U.S. Private*, pg. 4398
INTEGRAL ANALYTICS, INC.—See Willdan Group, Inc.; *U.S. Public*, pg. 2371
INTEGRAL AP TRZIC DD—See I Squared Capital Advisors (US) LLC; *U.S. Private*, pg. 2024
INTEGRAL AVTO D.O.O—See I Squared Capital Advisors (US) LLC; *U.S. Private*, pg. 2024
INTEGRAL BETONIRCI AD; *Int'l*, pg. 3730
THE INTEGRAL BUILDING GROUP LLC—See The Integral Group LLC; *U.S. Private*, pg. 4057
INTEGRAL CORPORATION; *Int'l*, pg. 3730
INTEGRAL DESIGNS—See Bantam Capital Corp.; *Int'l*, pg. 855
INTEGRAL DIAGNOSTICS LIMITED; *Int'l*, pg. 3730
INTEGRAL FACILITY SERVICES LIMITED—See Jones Lang LaSalle Incorporated; *U.S. Public*, pg. 1202
INTEGRAL GROUP, INC.; *U.S. Private*, pg. 2098
THE INTEGRAL GROUP LLC; *U.S. Private*, pg. 4056
INTEGRAL GVG A.D.; *Int'l*, pg. 3730
INTEGRAL HYDRAULIK GMBH & CO.—See Rupf Industries GmbH; *Int'l*, pg. 6428
INTEGRA LIFESCIENCES CORPORATION—See Integra LifeSciences Holdings Corporation; *U.S. Public*, pg. 1135
INTEGRA LIFESCIENCES HOLDINGS CORPORATION; *U.S. Public*, pg. 1135
INTEGRA LIFESCIENCES ITALY S.R.L.—See Integra LifeSciences Holdings Corporation; *U.S. Public*, pg. 1135
INTEGRA LIFESCIENCES SERVICES (FRANCE) SAS—See Integra LifeSciences Holdings Corporation; *U.S. Public*, pg. 1135
INTEGRA LIFESCIENCES (SHANGHAI) CO., LTD.—See Integra LifeSciences Holdings Corporation; *U.S. Public*, pg. 1135
INTEGRAL MARKETING, INC.; *U.S. Private*, pg. 2098
INTEGRAL MEDIA COMPANY; *U.S. Private*, pg. 2098
INTEGRAL PROPERTIES LLC—See The Integral Group LLC; *U.S. Private*, pg. 4057
INTEGRAL QUALITY CARE; *U.S. Private*, pg. 2098
INTEGRA LS (BENELUX) NV—See Integra LifeSciences Holdings Corporation; *U.S. Public*, pg. 1135
INTEGRAL SEARCH & SELECTION LIMITED—See ManpowerGroup Inc.; *U.S. Public*, pg. 1358
INTEGRA SHOPPER FZ LLC—See HighCo S.A.; *Int'l*, pg. 3387
INTEGRAL SOLUTIONS, LLC—See J.M. Smith Corporation; *U.S. Private*, pg. 2169
INTEGRAL SYSTEMS EUROPE LTD.—See Kratos Defense & Security Solutions, Inc.; *U.S. Public*, pg. 1276
INTEGRAL UK LTD—See Jones Lang LaSalle Incorporated; *U.S. Public*, pg. 1202
INTEGRA LUXTEC, INC.—See Integra LifeSciences Holdings Corporation; *U.S. Public*, pg. 1136
INTEGRA MANAGEMENT LLC; *Int'l*, pg. 3729
INTEGRA MANTENIMENT, GESTIO I SERVEIS INTEGRATS, CENTRE ESPECIAL DE TREBALL, CATALUNYA, S.L—See ACS, Actividades de Construccion y Servicios, S.A.; *Int'l*, pg. 115
INTEGRA MANTENIMIENTO, GESTION Y SERVICIOS INTEGRADOS CENTRO ESPECIAL DE EMPLEO GALICIA S.L.—See ACS, Actividades de Construccion y Servicios, S.A.; *Int'l*, pg. 115
INTEGRA MANTENIMIENTO, GESTION Y SERVICIOS INTEGRADOS CENTRO ESPECIAL DE EMPLEO, S.L.—See ACS, Actividades de Construccion y Servicios, S.A.; *Int'l*, pg. 115
INTEGRAMED AMERICA CONSUMER SERVICES DIVISION—See Power Corporation of Canada; *Int'l*, pg. 5944
INTEGRAMED AMERICA FERTILITY CENTERS—See Power Corporation of Canada; *Int'l*, pg. 5944
INTEGRAMED AMERICA, INC.—See Power Corporation of Canada; *Int'l*, pg. 5944
INTEGRAMED AMERICA VEIN CLINICS—See Power Corporation of Canada; *Int'l*, pg. 5944
INTEGRA MICROFRANCE SAS—See Integra LifeSciences Holdings Corporation; *U.S. Public*, pg. 1136
INTEGRA MICRO SYSTEMS (P) LTD.; *Int'l*, pg. 3730
INTEGRAND INSURANCE COMPANY; *U.S. Private*, pg. 2098
INTEGRA NETWORK CORPORATION—See Plurilock Security, Inc.; *Int'l*, pg. 5898
INTEGRA NETWORKS INC.; *U.S. Private*, pg. 2098

INTEGRA NEUROSCIENCES LIMITED—See Integra LifeSciences Holdings Corporation; *U.S. Public*, pg. 1136
INTEGRANT, INC.; *U.S. Private*, pg. 2098
INTEGRA ORTHOBIOLOGICS, INC.—See Integra LifeSciences Holdings Corporation; *U.S. Public*, pg. 1136
INTEGRA PACKAGING PTY LTD—See UFP Industries, Inc.; *U.S. Public*, pg. 2219
INTEGRA PARTNERS LLC; *U.S. Private*, pg. 2098
INTEGRA PORT SERVICES N.V.—See Dubai World Corporation; *Int'l*, pg. 2221
INTEGRA REALTY RESOURCES, INC.; *U.S. Private*, pg. 2098
INTEGRA RESOURCES CORP.; *Int'l*, pg. 3730
INTEGRA STAFFING & SEARCH; *U.S. Private*, pg. 2098
INTEGRA SWITCHGEAR LIMITED; *Int'l*, pg. 3730
INTEGRA TECHNOLOGIES LLC; *U.S. Private*, pg. 2098
INTEGRA TECHNOLOGY CONSULTING CORPORATION; *U.S. Private*, pg. 2098
INTEGRATEC—See Bread Financial Holdings Inc.; *U.S. Public*, pg. 381
INTEGRATED ACCESS CORP; *U.S. Private*, pg. 2098
INTEGRATED ACCESS SOLUTIONS, INC.—See TTEC Holdings, Inc.; *U.S. Public*, pg. 2203
INTEGRATED AIRLINE SERVICES, INC.; *U.S. Private*, pg. 2098
INTEGRATED ALTERNATIVE INVESTMENTS LIMITED—See Integrated Asset Management plc; *Int'l*, pg. 3730
INTEGRATED ALUMINIUM COMPONENTS LIMITED—See Lendlock Group Limited; *Int'l*, pg. 4453
INTEGRATED APPLICATION DEVELOPMENT PTY LTD—See IntegraFin Holdings plc; *Int'l*, pg. 3730
INTEGRATED ARCHIVE SYSTEMS INC.; *U.S. Private*, pg. 2098
INTEGRATED ASSET MANAGEMENT CORP.—See Fiera Capital Corporation; *Int'l*, pg. 2660
INTEGRATED ASSET MANAGEMENT PLC; *Int'l*, pg. 3730
INTEGRATED ASSET SERVICES, LLC; *U.S. Private*, pg. 2098
INTEGRATED A/V SYSTEMS LLC—See AEA Investors LP; *U.S. Private*, pg. 116
INTEGRATED BEHAVIORAL HEALTH, INC.; *U.S. Private*, pg 2099
INTEGRATED BIOMETRICS, INC.—See Reserve Group Management Company; *U.S. Private*, pg. 3404
INTEGRATED BIOMETRIC TECHNOLOGY SERVICES LLC—See Safran SA; *Int'l*, pg. 6473
INTEGRATED BIOPHARMA, INC.; *U.S. Public*, pg. 1136
INTEGRATED BROADCAST SERVICES LIMITED (IBIS)—See Symphony Technology Group, LLC; *U.S. Private*, pg. 3901
INTEGRATED BUSINESS SOLUTIONS, INC.—See Apollo Global Management, Inc.; *U.S. Public*, pg. 146
INTEGRATED BUSINESS SYSTEMS, INC.; *U.S. Private*, pg. 2099
INTEGRATED BUSINESS SYSTEMS INC.—See Comcast Corporation; *U.S. Public*, pg. 539
INTEGRATED BUSINESS SYSTEMS & SERVICES, INC.; *U.S. Public*, pg. 1136
INTEGRATED BUSINESS TECHNOLOGIES, LLC—See The 20 Msp Group LLC; *U.S. Private*, pg. 3980
INTEGRATED CANNABIS SOLUTIONS, INC.; *U.S. Public*, pg. 1136
INTEGRATED CAPITAL SERVICES LIMITED; *Int'l*, pg. 3731
INTEGRATED CARE PTY LTD.—See Madison Dearborn Partners, LLC; *U.S. Private*, pg. 2540
INTEGRATED CASETECH CONSULTANTS PVT LTD—See Simbhaoli Sugars Limited; *Int'l*, pg. 6928
INTEGRATED CIRCUIT PACKAGING CORPORATION; *U.S. Private*, pg. 2099
INTEGRATED CLEANROOM TECHNOLOGIES PVT. LTD.—See Takasago Thermal Engineering Co., Ltd.; *Int'l*, pg. 7434
INTEGRATED COATING & SEED TECHNOLOGY INDIA PVT. LTD.—See Croda International plc; *Int'l*, pg. 1853
INTEGRATED COIL COATING INDUSTRIES SDN. BHD.; *Int'l*, pg. 3731
INTEGRATED COMBAT SYSTEMS, INC.—See Orbit International Corp.; *U.S. Public*, pg. 1614
INTEGRATED COMMERCIALIZATION SOLUTIONS—See Cencora, Inc.; *U.S. Public*, pg. 467
INTEGRATED COMMUNICATIONS CORP.; *U.S. Private*, pg. 2099
INTEGRATED COMMUNICATIONS GROUP PTE LTD.—See Hakuhodo DY Holdings Incorporated; *Int'l*, pg. 3221
INTEGRATED COMMUNITY SOLUTIONS, INC.; *U.S. Private*, pg. 2099
INTEGRATED COMPUTER SYSTEMS, INC.—See Banneker Partners, LLC; *U.S. Private*, pg. 469
INTEGRATED CONSTRUCTION, LLC; *U.S. Private*, pg. 2099
INTEGRATED CONTROL SYSTEMS INC.; *U.S. Private*, pg. 2099
INTEGRATED CONTROL SYSTEMS INC.—See Integrated Control Systems Inc.; *U.S. Private*, pg. 2099

INTEGRATED CONTROL SYSTEMS INC.—See Integrated Control Systems Inc.; *U.S. Private*, pg. 2099
INTEGRATED CYBER SOLUTIONS INC.; *Int'l*, pg. 3731
INTEGRATED DATA SERVICES, INC.—See Arlington Capital Partners LLC; *U.S. Private*, pg. 328
INTEGRATED DATA SERVICES LIMITED—See Nigerian National Petroleum Corporation; *Int'l*, pg. 5282
INTEGRATED DATA STORAGE, LLC; *U.S. Private*, pg. 2099
INTEGRATED DEALER SYSTEMS, INC.—See Constellation Software Inc.; *Int'l*, pg. 1772
INTEGRATED DEICING SERVICES, LLC; *U.S. Private*, pg. 2099
INTEGRATED DENTAL HOLDINGS LTD.; *Int'l*, pg. 3731
INTEGRATED DERMATOLOGY GROUP; *U.S. Private*, pg. 2099
INTEGRATED DERMATOLOGY OF HICKORY PLLC—See Integrated Dermatology Group; *U.S. Private*, pg. 2099
INTEGRATED DERMATOLOGY OF PONCHATOULA LLC—See Integrated Dermatology Group; *U.S. Private*, pg. 2099
INTEGRATED DESIGN GROUP, INC.—See Harley Ellis Devereaux Corporation; *U.S. Private*, pg. 1865
INTEGRATED DESIGN, INC.; *U.S. Private*, pg. 2099
INTEGRATED DESIGNS L.P.—See Roper Technologies, Inc.; *U.S. Public*, pg. 1812
INTEGRATED DEVELOPMENT ASSOCIATES CO., LTD.—See Laboratory Corporation of America Holdings; *U.S. Public*, pg. 1287
INTEGRATED DEVELOPMENT ASSOCIATES PHILIPPINES, INC.—See Laboratory Corporation of America Holdings; *U.S. Public*, pg. 1287
INTEGRATED DEVICE TECHNOLOGY EUROPE LIMITED—See Renesas Electronics Corporation; *Int'l*, pg. 6276
INTEGRATED DEVICE TECHNOLOGY, INC.—See Renesas Electronics Corporation; *Int'l*, pg. 6276
INTEGRATED DEVICE TECHNOLOGY (ISRAEL) LTD.—See Renesas Electronics Corporation; *Int'l*, pg. 6276
INTEGRATED DEVICE TECHNOLOGY - LONGMONT—See Renesas Electronics Corporation; *Int'l*, pg. 6276
INTEGRATED DEVICE TECHNOLOGY (MALAYSIA) SDN. BHD—See Renesas Electronics Corporation; *Int'l*, pg. 6276
INTEGRATED DEVICE TECHNOLOGY UK LIMITED—See Renesas Electronics Corporation; *Int'l*, pg. 6276
INTEGRATED DIAGNOSTICS HOLDINGS PLC; *Int'l*, pg. 3731
INTEGRATED DIRECT MARKETING SOLUTIONS, INC.—See Arthur J. Gallagher & Co.; *U.S. Public*, pg. 206
INTEGRATED DISPENSE SOLUTIONS, LLC—See Carlisle Companies Incorporated; *U.S. Public*, pg. 436
INTEGRATED DISPLAY TECHNOLOGY LIMITED—See IDT International Limited; *Int'l*, pg. 3596
INTEGRATED DISTRIBUTION & LOGISTICS DIRECT LLC; *U.S. Private*, pg. 2099
INTEGRATED DNA TECHNOLOGIES BVBA—See Danaher Corporation; *U.S. Public*, pg. 627
INTEGRATED DNA TECHNOLOGIES, INC.—See Danaher Corporation; *U.S. Public*, pg. 627
INTEGRATED DNA TECHNOLOGIES PTE. LTD.—See Danaher Corporation; *U.S. Public*, pg. 627
INTEGRATED DYNAMIC ELECTRON SOLUTIONS, INC.—See JEOL Ltd.; *Int'l*, pg. 3930
INTEGRATED DYNAMICS ENGINEERING GMBH—See Aalberts N.V.; *Int'l*, pg. 34
INTEGRATED DYNAMICS ENGINEERING INC.—See Aalberts N.V.; *Int'l*, pg. 34
INTEGRATED DYNAMICS ENGINEERING LTD.—See Aalberts N.V.; *Int'l*, pg. 34
INTEGRATED ELECTRONIC SYSTEMS LAB CO., LTD.; *Int'l*, pg. 3731
INTEGRATED ENERGY SERVICES LLC—See Gainline Capital Partners LP; *U.S. Private*, pg. 1635
INTEGRATED ENERGY TECHNOLOGIES, INC.—See Dubai Holding LLC; *Int'l*, pg. 2218
INTEGRATED ENERGY TRANSITION ACQUISITION CORP.; *U.S. Public*, pg. 1136
INTEGRATED ENGINEERING, PLLC—See NewHold Enterprises LLC; *U.S. Private*, pg. 2915
INTEGRATED ENGINEERING SERVICES—See SSOE Group; *U.S. Private*, pg. 3769
INTEGRATED ENTERPRISE SOLUTIONS, INC.—See Cloud Equity Group, LLC; *U.S. Private*, pg. 946
INTEGRATED ENVIRONMENTAL TECHNOLOGIES, LTD.; *U.S. Public*, pg. 1136
INTEGRATED FACADE SOLUTIONS—See Orascom Construction PLC; *Int'l*, pg. 5613
INTEGRATED FINANCE & ACCOUNTING SOLUTIONS, LLC; *U.S. Private*, pg. 2099
INTEGRATED FINANCIAL ARRANGEMENTS LTD.—See IntegraFin Holdings plc; *Int'l*, pg. 3730
INTEGRATED FINANCIAL HOLDINGS, INC.—See Capital Bancorp, Inc.; *U.S. Public*, pg. 431
INTEGRATED FINANCIAL PARTNERS, INC.—See Integrated Wealth Concepts, LLC; *U.S. Private*, pg. 2101

INTEGRATED FINANCIAL PRODUCTS LIMITED—See Integrated Asset Management plc; *Int'l*, pg. 3731
INTEGRATED FINANCIAL SERVICES LIMITED; *Int'l*, pg. 3731
INTEGRATED FINANCIAL SETTLEMENTS, INC.; *U.S. Private*, pg. 2099
INTEGRATED FIRE PROTECTION LLC—See Blue Point Capital Partners, LLC; *U.S. Private*, pg. 590
INTEGRATED FIRE SYSTEMS, INC.—See Performance Systems Integration, LLC; *U.S. Private*, pg. 3150
INTEGRATED FLOW SOLUTIONS, LLC—See DXP Enterprises, Inc.; *U.S. Public*, pg. 697
INTEGRATED FORWARDING & SHIPPING BERHAD—See ILB Group Berhad; *Int'l*, pg. 3613
INTEGRATED FREIGHT CORPORATION; *U.S. Private*, pg. 2100
INTEGRATED FREIGHT SERVICES SDN. BHD.—See ILB Group Berhad; *Int'l*, pg. 3613
INTEGRATED GEOTECHNOLOGY INSTITUTE, LTD.—See TENOX CO., LTD; *Int'l*, pg. 7561
INTEGRATED GLOBAL LOW-TEMPERATURE OPERATIONS PHILS. INC.—See RFM Corporation; *Int'l*, pg. 6319
INTEGRATED GLOBAL SERVICES, INC.—See J.F. Lehman & Company, Inc.; *U.S. Private*, pg. 2163
INTEGRATED GREEN ENERGY SOLUTIONS LTD; *Int'l*, pg. 3731
INTEGRATED HEALTH 21 LLC—See Cardiac Imaging Solutions, LLC; *U.S. Private*, pg. 749
INTEGRATED HEALTHCARE COMMUNICATIONS, INC.—See Stagwell, Inc.; *U.S. Public*, pg. 1927
INTEGRATED HEALTHCARE STRATEGIES, LLC—See Arthur J. Gallagher & Co.; *U.S. Public*, pg. 205
INTEGRATED INDUSTRIAL INFORMATION, INC.—See KPIT Technologies Ltd; *Int'l*, pg. 4296
INTEGRATED IT SOLUTIONS, INC.; *U.S. Private*, pg. 2100
INTEGRATED LAB SYSTEMS INC.; *U.S. Private*, pg. 2100
INTEGRATED LENS TECHNOLOGY PTE LTD—See EssilorLuxottica SA; *Int'l*, pg. 2515
INTEGRATED, LLC; *U.S. Private*, pg. 2101
INTEGRATED LOGISTICS (H.K.) LIMITED—See Hovid Berhad; *Int'l*, pg. 3492
INTEGRATED LOGISTICS, LLC—See U.S. Bancorp; *U.S. Public*, pg. 2212
INTEGRATED MACHINERY SOLUTIONS, LLC—See DeSHAZO Service Company, LLC; *U.S. Private*, pg. 1213
INTEGRATED MAGNETICS; *U.S. Private*, pg. 2100
INTEGRATED MANAGEMENT RESOURCES GROUP INC.; *U.S. Private*, pg. 2100
INTEGRATED MANAGEMENT SERVICES, PA; *U.S. Private*, pg. 2100
INTEGRATED MANUFACTURING TECHNOLOGIES, INC.—See UMS Holdings Limited; *Int'l*, pg. 8026
INTEGRATED MARKETING GROUP; *U.S. Private*, pg. 2100
INTEGRATED MARKETING SERVICES; *U.S. Private*, pg. 2100
INTEGRATED MARKETING SYSTEMS, INC.—See Symphony Technology Group, LLC; *U.S. Private*, pg. 3900
INTEGRATED MARKETING WORKS; *U.S. Private*, pg. 2100
INTEGRATED MATERIALS, INC.—See Ferrotec Holdings Corporation; *Int'l*, pg. 2643
INTEGRATED MEDIA MANAGEMENT, INC.—See OceanSound Partners, LP; *U.S. Private*, pg. 2990
INTEGRATED MEDIA SOLUTIONS, LCC—See Stagwell, Inc.; *U.S. Public*, pg. 1927
INTEGRATED MEDIA SOLUTIONS; *U.S. Private*, pg. 2100
INTEGRATED MEDIA TECHNOLOGIES, INC.; *U.S. Private*, pg. 2100
INTEGRATED MEDIA TECHNOLOGY LIMITED; *Int'l*, pg. 3731
INTEGRATED MEDICAL SOLUTIONS LIMITED—See IMS MAXIMS plc; *Int'l*, pg. 3638
INTEGRATED MEDICAL SOLUTIONS, LLC; *U.S. Private*, pg. 2100
INTEGRATED MEDICAL SYSTEMS INTERNATIONAL, INC.—See STERIS plc; *Int'l*, pg. 7209
INTEGRATED MERCHANDISING SYSTEMS—See Omnicom Group Inc.; *U.S. Public*, pg. 1586
INTEGRATED MICROELECTRONICS, INC.—See Ayala Corporation; *Int'l*, pg. 774
INTEGRATED MICROWAVE CORPORATION—See Knowles Corporation; *U.S. Public*, pg. 1270
INTEGRATED MICROWAVE TECHNOLOGIES, LLC—See Vislink Technologies Inc.; *U.S. Public*, pg. 2304
INTEGRATED NEPHROLOGY NETWORK—See Cencora, Inc.; *U.S. Public*, pg. 467
INTEGRATED OE PTY. LTD.—See National Tyre & Wheel Limited; *Int'l*, pg. 5164
INTEGRATED ONCOLOGY NETWORK LLC—See Silver Oak Services Partners, LLC; *U.S. Private*, pg. 3661
INTEGRATED OPENINGS SOLUTIONS, LLC—See Frontenac Company LLC; *U.S. Private*, pg. 1613
INTEGRATED PACKAGING CORP.; *U.S. Private*, pg. 2100

INTEGRATED PACKAGING SYSTEMS INC.—See Krones AG; *Int'l*, pg. 4305
INTEGRATED PACKAGING SYSTEMS (IPS) FZCO—See Krones AG; *Int'l*, pg. 4305
INTEGRATED PAPER SERVICES, INC.—See SGS SA; *Int'l*, pg. 6744
INTEGRATED PARTNERS, INC.; *U.S. Private*, pg. 2100
INTEGRATED PETROLEUM EXPERTISE COMPANY - SERVICOS EM PETROLEO LTDA.—See Eurofins Scientific S.E.; *Int'l*, pg. 2550
INTEGRATED PETROLEUM TECHNOLOGIES, INC.; *U.S. Private*, pg. 2100
INTEGRATED PHOTONICS, INC.—See Coherent Corp.; *U.S. Public*, pg. 529
INTEGRATED PIPE INDUSTRIES SDN. BHD.—See JAKS Resources Berhad; *Int'l*, pg. 3873
INTEGRATED PIPELINE SERVICES, INC.—See Brookfield Corporation; *Int'l*, pg. 1181
INTEGRATED PLASTICS SYSTEMS AG—See Krones AG; *Int'l*, pg. 4305
INTEGRATED POLYMER SOLUTIONS, INC.—See Arcline Investment Management LP; *U.S. Private*, pg. 314
INTEGRATED POWER SERVICES LLC—See Odyssey Investment Partners, LLC; *U.S. Private*, pg. 2995
INTEGRATED PRACTICE SOLUTIONS, INC.—See Waud Capital Partners LLC; *U.S. Private*, pg. 4457
INTEGRATED PREMISES SERVICES PTY LIMITED—See OCS Group Limited; *Int'l*, pg. 5521
INTEGRATED PRINT & GRAPHICS—See Ennis, Inc.; *U.S. Public*, pg. 769
INTEGRATED PRIVATE DEBT CORP.—See Fiera Capital Corporation; *Int'l*, pg. 2660
INTEGRATED PROCESS TECHNOLOGIES, INC.; *U.S. Private*, pg. 2100
INTEGRATED PROCESS TECHNOLOGIES, INC.—See Integrated Process Technologies, Inc.; *U.S. Private*, pg. 2100
INTEGRATED PROCUREMENT TECHNOLOGIES, INC; *U.S. Private*, pg. 2100
INTEGRATED PRODUCTION SERVICES—See Superior Energy Services, Inc.; *U.S. Private*, pg. 3877
INTEGRATED PROJECT MANAGEMENT CO., INC.—See Integrated Project Management Company, Inc.; *U.S. Private*, pg. 2100
INTEGRATED PROJECT MANAGEMENT CO.—See Integrated Project Management Company, Inc.; *U.S. Private*, pg. 2100
INTEGRATED PROJECT MANAGEMENT CO., INC.—See Integrated Project Management Company, Inc.; *U.S. Private*, pg. 2100
INTEGRATED PROJECT MANAGEMENT COMPANY, INC.; *U.S. Private*, pg. 2100
INTEGRATED PROPERTIES, INC.—See Apartment Investment and Management Company; *U.S. Public*, pg. 144
INTEGRATED PROPERTY MANAGEMENT PTE LTD—See Bonvests Holdings Limited; *Int'l*, pg. 1110
INTEGRATED PROPERTY SYSTEMS; *U.S. Private*, pg. 2101
INTEGRATED PROTEINS LIMITED; *Int'l*, pg. 3731
INTEGRATED PUBLICATION SOLUTIONS PTY LTD—See Nine Entertainment Co. Holdings Limited; *Int'l*, pg. 5298
INTEGRATED PUBLISHING SYSTEMS LIMITED—See Onzima Ventures PLC; *Int'l*, pg. 5593
INTEGRATED RAIL & RESOURCES ACQUISITION CORP.; *U.S. Public*, pg. 1136
INTEGRATED RECYCLING PTY. LTD.—See Pro-Pac Packaging Limited; *Int'l*, pg. 5985
INTEGRATED REGIONAL LAB, LLC—See HCA Healthcare, Inc.; *U.S. Public*, pg. 999
INTEGRATED REGIONAL LABORATORIES PATHOLOGY SERVICES, LLC—See HCA Healthcare, Inc.; *U.S. Public*, pg. 999
INTEGRATED REGIONAL LABORATORIES; *U.S. Private*, pg. 2101
INTEGRATED REHAB GROUP, LIMITED PARTNERSHIP—See U.S. Physical Therapy, Inc.; *U.S. Public*, pg. 2214
INTEGRATED RESEARCH, INC.—See Integrated Research Ltd; *Int'l*, pg. 3731
INTEGRATED RESEARCH LTD; *Int'l*, pg. 3731
INTEGRATED RESEARCH UK LIMITED—See Integrated Research Ltd; *Int'l*, pg. 3731
INTEGRATED RESOURCES, INC.; *U.S. Private*, pg. 2101
INTEGRATED SCIENCE & TECHNOLOGY, INC.—See Hunan Yonker Investment Group Co., Ltd.; *Int'l*, pg. 3534
INTEGRATED SCM CO., LTD.—See FM Global Logistics Holdings Berhad; *Int'l*, pg. 2717
INTEGRATED SECURE, LLC; *U.S. Private*, pg. 2101
INTEGRATED SECURITY SYSTEMS—See Ares Management Corporation; *U.S. Public*, pg. 189
INTEGRATED SERVICES INC.—See Roadrunner Transportation Systems, Inc.; *U.S. Public*, pg. 1802
INTEGRATED SERVICES (INTL) LIMITED—See Expro Group Holdings N.V.; *Int'l*, pg. 2591
INTEGRATED SERVICE SOLUTIONS, INC.—See Ontario Municipal Employees Retirement System; *Int'l*, pg. 5585

INTEGRATED SHUN HING LOGISTICS (LINGANG) CO. LTD.—See ILB Group Berhad; *Int'l*, pg. 3613
INTEGRATED SHUN HING LOGISTICS (SHANGHAI) LTD.—See ILB Group Berhad; *Int'l*, pg. 3613
INTEGRATED SHUN HING LOGISTICS (SHENZHEN) CO. LTD.—See ILB Group Berhad; *Int'l*, pg. 3613
INTEGRATED SILICON SOLUTION, INC.—See SummitView Capital Management Ltd.; *Int'l*, pg. 7302
INTEGRATED SILICON SOLUTION ISRAEL LTD.—See SummitView Capital Management Ltd.; *Int'l*, pg. 7302
INTEGRATED SOFTWARE SOLUTIONS, INC.; *U.S. Private*, pg. 2101
INTEGRATED SOFTWARE SOLUTIONS LTD—See Integrated Software Solutions Pty. Ltd.; *Int'l*, pg. 3731
INTEGRATED SOFTWARE SOLUTIONS PTY. LTD.; *Int'l*, pg. 3731
INTEGRATED SOLUTIONS GROUP, INC.; *U.S. Private*, pg. 2101
INTEGRATED SUPPLY NETWORK, LLC—See Freeman Spogli & Co. Incorporated; *U.S. Private*, pg. 1606
INTEGRATED SYSTEM CREDIT CONSULTING FINTECH SPA; *Int'l*, pg. 3731
INTEGRATED SYSTEMS ANALYSTS, INC.; *U.S. Private*, pg. 2101
INTEGRATED SYSTEMS CO. LTD.—See Ali Zaid Al-Quraishi & Brothers Co.; *Int'l*, pg. 323
INTEGRATED SYSTEM SERVICES CO., LTD.—See Kyokuyo Co. Ltd.; *Int'l*, pg. 4363
INTEGRATED SYSTEMS IMPROVEMENT SERVICES, INC.—See KCB Management LLC; *U.S. Private*, pg. 2269
INTEGRATED TECHNICAL SYSTEMS, INC.; *U.S. Private*, pg. 2101
INTEGRATED TECHNOLOGIES LIMITED; *Int'l*, pg. 3731
INTEGRATED TELEMANAGEMENT SERVICES, INC.; *U.S. Private*, pg. 2101
INTEGRATED THERMOPLASTICS LIMITED; *Int'l*, pg. 3731
INTEGRATED TOWER SYSTEMS, INC.—See The Will-Burt Co., Inc.; *U.S. Private*, pg. 4136
INTEGRATED VENTURES, INC.; *U.S. Public*, pg. 1136
INTEGRATED VIDEO SUPPLY—See Integrated, LLC; *U.S. Private*, pg. 2101
INTEGRATED WASTE SOLUTIONS GROUP HOLDINGS LIMITED; *Int'l*, pg. 3731
INTEGRATED WASTE SOLUTIONS GROUP, LLC; *U.S. Private*, pg. 2101
INTEGRATED WATER SERVICES, INC.—See Sciens Capital Management LLC; *U.S. Private*, pg. 3574
INTEGRATED WATER SERVICES LTD. - PIPELINE SERVICES DIV—See Arjun Infrastructure Partners Limited; *Int'l*, pg. 568
INTEGRATED WATER SERVICES LTD—See Arjun Infrastructure Partners Limited; *Int'l*, pg. 568
INTEGRATED WEALTH CONCEPTS, LLC; *U.S. Private*, pg. 2101
INTEGRATED WELLNESS ACQUISITION CORP.; *U.S. Public*, pg. 1136
INTEGRATED WIND SOLUTIONS ASA; *Int'l*, pg. 3732
INTEGRATE IT—See Sterling Investment Partners, L.P.; *U.S. Private*, pg. 3806
INTEGRA TELECOM HOLDINGS, INC.—See Warburg Pincus LLC; *U.S. Private*, pg. 4438
INTEGRA TELECOM, INC.—See Warburg Pincus LLC; *U.S. Private*, pg. 4438
INTEGRA TELECOMMUNICATION & SOFTWARE LIMITED; *Int'l*, pg. 3730
INTEGRA TELECOM OF NORTH DAKOTA, INC.—See Warburg Pincus LLC; *U.S. Private*, pg. 4438
INTEGRA TELECOM OF OREGON INC.—See Warburg Pincus LLC; *U.S. Private*, pg. 4438
INTEGRA TELECOM OF WASHINGTON, INC.—See Warburg Pincus LLC; *U.S. Private*, pg. 4438
INTEGRATE MARKETING PTE LTD.—See Compact Metal Industries Ltd.; *Int'l*, pg. 1721
INTEGRATE PTE LTD—See Compact Metal Industries Ltd.; *Int'l*, pg. 1721
INTEGRATION INNOVATION, INC.; *U.S. Private*, pg. 2101
INTEGRATION MANAGEMENT, INC.—See ABRY Partners, LLC; *U.S. Private*, pg. 41
INTEGRATION PARTNERS CORP.—See InterCloud Systems, Inc.; *U.S. Public*, pg. 1141
INTEGRATION PARTNERS - NY CORPORATION—See InterCloud Systems, Inc.; *U.S. Public*, pg. 1141
INTEGRATION TECHNOLOGIES GROUP, INC.; *U.S. Private*, pg. 2101
INTEGRATION TECHNOLOGIES, INC.; *U.S. Private*, pg. 2101
INTEGRATIVE LOGIC LLC—See Luckie & Co. Ltd.; *U.S. Private*, pg. 2511
THE INTEGRATIVE MEDICAL CENTRE (PTY) LTD—See Ascendis Health Limited; *Int'l*, pg. 601
INTEGRATIVE SYSTEMS, INC.; *U.S. Private*, pg. 2101
INTEGRATOUCH, LLC; *U.S. Private*, pg. 2101
INTEGRAX BERHAD—See Tenaga Nasional Berhad; *Int'l*, pg. 7557
INTEGRA YORK PA, INC.—See Integra LifeSciences Holdings Corporation; *U.S. Public*, pg. 1136
INTEGREON GLOBAL; *U.S. Private*, pg. 2102

COMPANY NAME INDEX

INTEGREON MANAGED SOLUTIONS, INC.—See NewQuest Capital Advisors (HK) Ltd.; *Int'l*, pg. 5236
INTEGREVIEW, LLC—See Genstar Capital, LLC; *U.S. Private*, pg. 1673
INTEGRICHAIN INC.—See Nordic Capital AB; *Int'l*, pg. 5420
INTEGRIGUARD, LLC—See Veritas Capital Fund Management, LLC; *U.S. Private*, pg. 4362
INTEGRIS BASS BAPTIST HEALTH CENTER—See INTEGRIS Health, Inc.; *U.S. Private*, pg. 2102
INTEGRIS CARDIOVASCULAR PHYSICIANS LLC—See INTEGRIS Health, Inc.; *U.S. Private*, pg. 2102
INTEGRIS HEALTH, INC.; *U.S. Private*, pg. 2102
INTEGRIS JIM THORPE REHABILITATION CENTER—See INTEGRIS Health, Inc.; *U.S. Private*, pg. 2102
INTEGRIS MANAGEMENT SERVICES LIMITED—See OCS Group Limited; *Int'l*, pg. 5521
INTEGRIS REALTY CORPORATION—See INTEGRIS Health, Inc.; *U.S. Private*, pg. 2102
INTEGRIS RURAL HEALTHCARE OF OKLAHOMA, INC.—See INTEGRIS Health, Inc.; *U.S. Private*, pg. 2102
INTEGRIS SECURITISATION SERVICES PTY LIMITED—See Cuscal Ltd.; *Int'l*, pg. 1880
INTEGRIS—See Frontenac Company LLC; *U.S. Private*, pg. 1613
INTEGRIS SOUTHWEST MEDICAL CENTER—See INTEGRIS Health, Inc.; *U.S. Private*, pg. 2102
INTEGRITAS VIAGER SA; *Int'l*, pg. 3732
INTEGRITEK LLC; *U.S. Private*, pg. 2102
INTEGRITY CARGO SOLUTIONS, INC.; *U.S. Private*, pg. 2102
INTEGRITY COAL SALES INC.; *U.S. Private*, pg. 2102
INTEGRITY COAL SALES INTERNATIONAL, INC.—See Integrity Coal Sales Inc.; *U.S. Private*, pg. 2102
INTEGRITY COMMUNICATIONS; *U.S. Private*, pg. 2102
INTEGRITY DATA SOLUTIONS INC.; *U.S. Private*, pg. 2102
INTEGRITY ELECTRONICS INC.; *U.S. Private*, pg. 2102
INTEGRITY EMPLOYEE LEASING, INC.; *U.S. Private*, pg. 2102
INTEGRITY ENGINEERING & DESIGN SOLUTIONS; *U.S. Private*, pg. 2102
INTEGRITY EXPRESS LOGISTICS; *U.S. Private*, pg. 2102
INTEGRITY FEEDS; *U.S. Private*, pg. 2102
INTEGRITY FIRST FINANCIAL GROUP INC.; *U.S. Private*, pg. 2102
INTEGRITY FUNDING, LLC; *U.S. Private*, pg. 2103
INTEGRITY FUNERAL CARE—See Birch Hill Equity Partners Management Inc.; *Int'l*, pg. 1046
INTEGRITY FUNERAL CARE—See Homesteaders Life Co. Inc.; *U.S. Private*, pg. 1974
INTEGRITY FUNERAL SERVICES PTY LTD—See Propel Funeral Partners Limited; *Int'l*, pg. 5997
INTEGRITY GAMING ULC—See PlayAGS, Inc.; *U.S. Public*, pg. 1697
INTEGRITY GLOBAL SECURITY, LLC—See Green Hills Software Inc.; *U.S. Private*, pg. 1773
INTEGRITY HOUSE, INC.; *U.S. Private*, pg. 2103
INTEGRITY HR INC.—See Fifth Third Bancorp; *U.S. Public*, pg. 833
INTEGRITY HR, INC.—See Marsh & McLennan Companies, Inc.; *U.S. Public*, pg. 1381
INTEGRITY INTERNATIONAL CORP.—See Integrity Coal Sales Inc.; *U.S. Private*, pg. 2102
INTEGRITY JANITORIAL SERVICES, INC.; *U.S. Private*, pg. 2103
INTEGRITY LIFE INSURANCE COMPANY—See Western & Southern Financial Group, Inc.; *U.S. Private*, pg. 4490
INTEGRITY MANAGEMENT CONSULTING, INC.; *U.S. Private*, pg. 2103
INTEGRITY MARKETING GROUP LLC; *U.S. Private*, pg. 2103
INTEGRITY MOLD, INC.—See BlackBern Partners LLC; *U.S. Private*, pg. 573
INTEGRITY MOLD, INC.—See Lee Equity Partners LLC; *U.S. Private*, pg. 2413
INTEGRITY MUTUAL INSURANCE COMPANY—See Grange Mutual Casualty Company; *U.S. Private*, pg. 1754
INTEGRITY NETWORKING SYSTEMS; *U.S. Private*, pg. 2104
INTEGRITY ONE TECHNOLOGIES, INC.—See Xerox Holdings Corporation; *U.S. Public*, pg. 2387
INTEGRITY PHYSICAL THERAPY, INC.—See Select Medical Holdings Corporation; *U.S. Public*, pg. 1858
INTEGRITY STAFFING SOLUTIONS; *U.S. Private*, pg. 2104
INTEGRITY TEXTILES INC.; *U.S. Private*, pg. 2104
INTEGRITY URGENT CARE - EAST—See University of Colorado Health; *U.S. Private*, pg. 4308
INTEGRIUS, LLC—See U.S. Physical Therapy, Inc.; *U.S. Public*, pg. 2214
INTEGRO BUILDERS LLC; *U.S. Private*, pg. 2104
INTEGRO, INC.—See Silver Oak Services Partners, LLC; *U.S. Private*, pg. 3661

INTEGRO TECHNOLOGIES CO. LTD.—See Aurionpro Solutions Limited; *Int'l*, pg. 711
INTEGRO TECHNOLOGIES PTE LTD.—See Aurionpro Solutions Limited; *Int'l*, pg. 711
INTEGRO TECHNOLOGIES SDN. BHD.—See Aurionpro Solutions Limited; *Int'l*, pg. 711
INTEGRO TECHNOLOGIES (VIETNAM) LLC—See Aurionpro Solutions Limited; *Int'l*, pg. 711
INTEGRO USA INC.—See Keystone Group, L.P.; *U.S. Private*, pg. 2297
INTEGRUM AB; *Int'l*, pg. 3732
INTEGRUM HOLDINGS LP; *Int'l*, pg. 3732
INTEGRUM INC.—See Integrum AB; *Int'l*, pg. 3732
INTEGRYS HOLDING, INC.—See WEC Energy Group, Inc.; *U.S. Public*, pg. 2342
INTEGWARE, INC.; *U.S. Private*, pg. 2104
INTEK GROUP S.P.A.; *Int'l*, pg. 3732
INTEK HONDURAS, S.A. DE C.V.—See Endress+Hauser (International) Holding AG; *Int'l*, pg. 2408
I/N TEK L.P.—See Cleveland-Cliffs, Inc.; *U.S. Public*, pg. 514
INTEK NICARAGUA, S.A.—See Endress+Hauser (International) Holding AG; *Int'l*, pg. 2408
INTEK PLASTICS INC.; *U.S. Private*, pg. 2104
INTEKPLUS CO., LTD.; *Int'l*, pg. 3733
INTEKRAS, INC.; *U.S. Private*, pg. 2104
INTEK SP. Z O.O.—See Dekpol S.A.; *Int'l*, pg. 2006
INTEL-ASSESS, INC.—See News Corporation; *U.S. Public*, pg. 1519
INTEL AUSTRALIA PTY. LTD.—See Intel Corporation; *U.S. Public*, pg. 1138
INTEL CAPITAL CORPORATION—See Intel Corporation; *U.S. Public*, pg. 1138
INTEL CHINA LTD.—See Intel Corporation; *U.S. Public*, pg. 1138
INTEL CHINA LTD.—See Intel Corporation; *U.S. Public*, pg. 1138
INTELCOM EXPRESS INC.—See Canada Post Corporation; *Int'l*, pg. 1282
INTEL CORP. IBERIA, S.A.—See Intel Corporation; *U.S. Public*, pg. 1138
INTEL CORPORATION - CHANDLER OFFICE—See Intel Corporation; *U.S. Public*, pg. 1138
INTEL CORPORATION - PARSIPPANY OFFICE—See Intel Corporation; *U.S. Public*, pg. 1138
INTEL CORPORATION; *U.S. Public*, pg. 1136
INTEL CORPORATION U.K. LTD.—See Intel Corporation; *U.S. Public*, pg. 1138
INTEL CORP. S.A.R.L.—See Intel Corporation; *U.S. Public*, pg. 1138
INTEL CZECH TRADINGS, INC.—See Intel Corporation; *U.S. Public*, pg. 1138
INTEL DEUTSCHLAND GMBH—See Intel Corporation; *U.S. Public*, pg. 1138
INTELECOM DANMARK AS—See Herkules Capital AS; *Int'l*, pg. 3362
INTELECOM GROUP AS—See Herkules Capital AS; *Int'l*, pg. 3362
INTELECOM SWEDEN AB—See Herkules Capital AS; *Int'l*, pg. 3362
INTELECOM UK LTD.—See Herkules Capital AS; *Int'l*, pg. 3362
INTELECT CORPORATION; *U.S. Private*, pg. 2104
INTELECT RECRUITMENT PLC—See Interquest Group plc; *Int'l*, pg. 3757
INTELEK LIMITED—See Teledyne Technologies Incorporated; *U.S. Public*, pg. 1994
INTEL ELECTRONICS (MALAYSIA) SDN. BHD.—See Intel Corporation; *U.S. Public*, pg. 1138
INTELENET GLOBAL SERVICES PRIVATE LIMITED—See Teleperformance SE; *Int'l*, pg. 7540
INTELENET GLOBAL (UK) LIMITED—See Teleperformance SE; *Int'l*, pg. 7540
INTELEPEER, INC.; *U.S. Private*, pg. 2104
INTELERAD MEDICAL SYSTEMS INC.—See HgCapital Trust plc; *Int'l*, pg. 3376
INTELESYS CORPORATION—See Arlington Capital Partners LLC; *U.S. Private*, pg. 328
INTELETRAVEL.COM; *U.S. Private*, pg. 2104
INTELEX TECHNOLOGIES, ULC—See Fortive Corporation; *U.S. Public*, pg. 871
INTEL FINLAND OY—See Intel Corporation; *U.S. Public*, pg. 1138
INTELGENX CORP.—See IntelGenx Technologies Corp.; *Int'l*, pg. 3733
INTELGENX TECHNOLOGIES CORP.; *Int'l*, pg. 3733
INTEL GMBH—See Intel Corporation; *U.S. Public*, pg. 1138
INTEL HOLDINGS B.V.—See Intel Corporation; *U.S. Public*, pg. 1138
INTELICA COMMERCIAL REAL ESTATE COMPANY; *U.S. Private*, pg. 2104
INTELICARE HOLDINGS LIMITED; *Int'l*, pg. 3733
INTELICLEAR, LLC—See Prometheum, Inc.; *U.S. Private*, pg. 3283
INTELICOAT TECHNOLOGIES, LLC—See Sun Capital Partners, Inc.; *U.S. Private*, pg. 3859
INTELIE TECHNOLOGY LLC—See ViaSat, Inc.; *U.S. Public*, pg. 2292

INTELIG 23—See National Grid plc; *Int'l*, pg. 5157
INTELIG 23—See Orange S.A.; *Int'l*, pg. 5608
INTELIGO BANK LTD.—See Intercorp Financial Services Inc.; *Int'l*, pg. 3739
INTELIGO FINANCIAL SERVICES S.A.—See PKO Bank Polski SA; *Int'l*, pg. 5887
INTEL INDONESIA CORPORATION—See Intel Corporation; *U.S. Public*, pg. 1138
INTELIQUENT, INC.—See Sinch AB; *Int'l*, pg. 6937
INTEL IRELAND LTD.—See Intel Corporation; *U.S. Public*, pg. 1138
INTELISHIFT TECHNOLOGIES; *U.S. Private*, pg. 2104
INTEL ISRAEL (74) LIMITED—See Intel Corporation; *U.S. Public*, pg. 1138
INTELISYS COMMUNICATIONS, INC.—See ScanSource, Inc.; *U.S. Public*, pg. 1843
INTEL ITALIA, S.P.A.—See Intel Corporation; *U.S. Public*, pg. 1138
INTELITEK, INC.—See RoboGroup T.E.K. Ltd.; *Int'l*, pg. 6371
INTELITEK INC.—See RoboGroup T.E.K. Ltd.; *Int'l*, pg. 6371
INTELITOOL, INC.—See Phipps & Bird, Inc.; *U.S. Private*, pg. 3172
INTELIUS, INC.; *U.S. Private*, pg. 2104
INTEL KABUSHIKI KAISHA—See Intel Corporation; *U.S. Public*, pg. 1138
INTEL KABUSHIKI KAISHA—See Intel Corporation; *U.S. Public*, pg. 1138
INTEL KOREA LTD.—See Intel Corporation; *U.S. Public*, pg. 1138
INTELLABRIDGE TECHNOLOGY CORP.; *Int'l*, pg. 3733
INTELLA II, INC.—See Onstream Media Corporation; *U.S. Private*, pg. 3028
INTELLECT BIZWARE SERVICES PRIVATE LIMITED—See Nippon Telegraph & Telephone Corporation; *Int'l*, pg. 5343
INTELLECT DESIGN ARENA CO. LTD.—See Intellect Design Arena Limited; *Int'l*, pg. 3733
INTELLECT DESIGN ARENA FZ LLC—See Intellect Design Arena Limited; *Int'l*, pg. 3733
INTELLECT DESIGN ARENA, INC.—See Intellect Design Arena Limited; *Int'l*, pg. 3733
INTELLECT DESIGN ARENA INC.—See Intellect Design Arena Limited; *Int'l*, pg. 3733
INTELLECT DESIGN ARENA LIMITED; *Int'l*, pg. 3733
INTELLECT DESIGN ARENA LIMITED—See Intellect Design Arena Limited; *Int'l*, pg. 3733
INTELLECT DESIGN ARENA LTDA.—See Intellect Design Arena Limited; *Int'l*, pg. 3733
INTELLECT DESIGN ARENA LTD.—See Intellect Design Arena Limited; *Int'l*, pg. 3733
INTELLECT DESIGN ARENA PHILLIPINES, INC.—See Intellect Design Arena Limited; *Int'l*, pg. 3733
INTELLECT DESIGN ARENA PTE. LTD.—See Intellect Design Arena Limited; *Int'l*, pg. 3733
INTELLECT DESIGN ARENA PTE. LTD.—See Intellect Design Arena Limited; *Int'l*, pg. 3733
INTELLECT DESIGN ARENA, PT—See Intellect Design Arena Limited; *Int'l*, pg. 3733
INTELLECT DESIGN ARENA SA—See Intellect Design Arena Limited; *Int'l*, pg. 3733
INTELLECT NEUROSCIENCES, INC.; *U.S. Private*, pg. 2105
INTELLECT RESOURCES, INC.; *U.S. Private*, pg. 2105
INTELLECT TECHNICAL SOLUTIONS, INC.; *U.S. Private*, pg. 2105
INTELLECTUAL CAPITAL GROUP LTD.; *Int'l*, pg. 3733
INTELLECTUAL TECHNOLOGY, INC.—See Arlington Capital Partners LLC; *U.S. Private*, pg. 328
INTELLEGO TECHNOLOGIES AB; *Int'l*, pg. 3733
INTELLEX CO., LTD.; *Int'l*, pg. 3733
INTELLEX JYU-HAN CO., LTD.—See Intellex Co., Ltd.; *Int'l*, pg. 3733
INTELLEX SPACE PLAN CO., LTD.—See Intellex Co., Ltd.; *Int'l*, pg. 3733
INTELLIAN B.V.—See Intellian Technologies, Inc; *Int'l*, pg. 3733
INTELLIAN DO BRASIL TECNOLOGIA LTDA.—See Intellian Technologies, Inc; *Int'l*, pg. 3734
INTELLIAN LTD.—See Intellian Technologies, Inc; *Int'l*, pg. 3733
INTELLIAN SINGAPORE PTE LTD.—See Intellian Technologies, Inc; *Int'l*, pg. 3733
INTELLIAN TECHNOLOGIES, INC; *Int'l*, pg. 3733
INTELLIAN TECHNOLOGIES USA, INC.—See Intellian Technologies, Inc; *Int'l*, pg. 3734
INTELLIA THERAPEUTICS, INC.; *U.S. Public*, pg. 1139
INTELLIBED, LLC—See Purple Innovation, Inc.; *U.S. Public*, pg. 1738
INTELLIBRIDGE, LLC—See Enlightenment Capital LLC; *U.S. Private*, pg. 1400
INTELLIBRIGHT CORPORATION; *U.S. Private*, pg. 2105
INTELLICENTRICS GLOBAL HOLDINGS LTD.; *U.S. Public*, pg. 1139
INTELLI CENTRICS INC.; *U.S. Private*, pg. 2105
INTELLICENTS INC.; *U.S. Private*, pg. 2105
INTELLICHECK, INC.; *U.S. Public*, pg. 1139

INTELLICHECK, INC.
CORPORATE AFFILIATIONS

INTELLICHOICE SOURCE INTERLINK MEDIA, INC.—See TEN: The Enthusiast Network, Inc.; *U.S. Private*, pg. 3964
INTELLICOM INNOVATION AB—See HMS Networks AB; *Int'l*, pg. 3433
INTELLICORP, INC.; *U.S. Private*, pg. 2105
INTELLICORP RECORDS, INC.—See Verisk Analytics, Inc.; *U.S. Public*, pg. 2283
INTELLIDYN CORPORATION; *U.S. Private*, pg. 2105
INTELLIENT (PTY) LIMITED—See EOH HOLDINGS LIMITED; *Int'l*, pg. 2457
INTELLIFLO LIMITED—See HgCapital Trust plc; *Int'l*, pg. 3376
INTELLIFUEL SYSTEMS INC.—See TA Associates, Inc.; *U.S. Private*, pg. 3917
INTELLIFY TALENT SOLUTIONS, LLC—See Cross Country Healthcare, Inc.; *U.S. Public*, pg. 595
INTELLIGENCE ASIA PTE. LTD.—See Persol Holdings Co., Ltd.; *Int'l*, pg. 5819
INTELLIGENCE HOLDINGS, LTD.—See Persol Holdings Co., Ltd.; *Int'l*, pg. 5819
INTELLIGENCE PARTNERS SL—See SoftwareONE Holding AG; *Int'l*, pg. 7057
INTELLIGENCE PARTNER U.K. LIMITED—See SoftwareONE Holding AG; *Int'l*, pg. 7057
INTELLIGENCER PRINTING COMPANY INC.; *U.S. Private*, pg. 2105
INTELLIGENT ACCESS SYSTEMS OF NORTH CAROLINA LLC—See Allied Universal Manager LLC; *U.S. Private*, pg. 191
INTELLIGENT AUDIT; *U.S. Private*, pg. 2105
INTELLIGENT BEAUTY, LLC; *U.S. Private*, pg. 2105
INTELLIGENT BIO SOLUTIONS INC; *U.S. Public*, pg. 1139
INTELLIGENT CLAIMS MANAGEMENT LIMITED—See Watchstone Group plc; *Int'l*, pg. 8356
INTELLIGENT CLOUD RESOURCES, INC.; *Int'l*, pg. 3734
INTELLIGENT CONTENT CORP.; *U.S. Private*, pg. 2105
INTELLIGENT DEVICES, LLC—See HEICO Corporation; *U.S. Public*, pg. 1021
INTELLIGENT DIGITAL AVATARS, INC.; *U.S. Private*, pg. 2105
INTELLIGENT DIGITAL SERVICES GMBH—See Sandmartin International Holdings Limited; *Int'l*, pg. 6526
INTELLIGENT ENERGY, INC.—See Lb-shell plc; *Int'l*, pg. 4429
INTELLIGENT ENERGY LIMITED—See Lb-shell plc; *Int'l*, pg. 4429
INTELLIGENT ENERGY SAVING COMPANY LTD; *Int'l*, pg. 3734
INTELLIGENT ENVIRONMENTS EUROPE LIMITED—See Parseq plc; *Int'l*, pg. 5747
INTELLIGENTE SENSORSYSTEME DRESDEN GMBH—See Amphenol Corporation; *U.S. Public*, pg. 130
INTELLIGENT FINANCE—See Lloyds Banking Group plc; *Int'l*, pg. 4537
INTELLIGENT FINGERPRINTING LIMITED—See Intelligent Bio Solutions Inc.; *U.S. Public*, pg. 1140
INTELLIGENT HEARING SYSTEMS CORP.; *U.S. Private*, pg. 2105
INTELLIGENT HOSPITAL SYSTEMS INC.; *Int'l*, pg. 3734
INTELLIGENT HOSPITAL SYSTEMS, INC.—See Intelligent Hospital Systems Inc.; *Int'l*, pg. 3734
INTELLIGENT INSITES, INC.—See Koch Industries, Inc.; *U.S. Private*, pg. 2331
INTELLIGENT INSTRUMENTATION, INC.; *U.S. Private*, pg. 2105
INTELLIGENT INTEGRATION SYSTEMS, INC.; *U.S. Private*, pg. 2106
INTELLIGENT INTERIORS INC.; *U.S. Private*, pg. 2106
INTELLIGENT LIVING APPLICATION GROUP INC.; *Int'l*, pg. 3734
INTELLIGENT LOGISTICS, LLC—See AIT Worldwide Logistics, Inc.; *U.S. Private*, pg. 142
INTELLIGENT MEDICAL OBJECTS, INC.—See Thomas H. Lee Partners, L.P.; *U.S. Private*, pg. 4156
INTELLIGENT MEDICINE ACQUISITION CORP.; *U.S. Public*, pg. 1140
INTELLIGENT MICRO PATTERNING, LLC; *U.S. Private*, pg. 2106
INTELLIGENT MOBILE SOLUTIONS, INC.; *U.S. Private*, pg. 2106
INTELLIGENT MONITORING GROUP LIMITED; *Int'l*, pg. 3734
THE INTELLIGENT OFFICE, INC.—See MidOcean Partners, LLP; *U.S. Private*, pg. 2717
INTELLIGENT OPTICAL SYSTEMS—See Mercury Systems, Inc.; *U.S. Public*, pg. 1422
INTELLIGENT PAYMENTS GROUP LIMITED—See Global Payments Inc.; *U.S. Public*, pg. 943
INTELLIGENT PROCESSING SOLUTIONS LIMITED—See Unisys Corporation; *U.S. Public*, pg. 2228
INTELLIGENT PRODUCT SOLUTIONS, INC.—See Forward Industries, Inc.; *U.S. Public*, pg. 874
INTELLIGENT RESULTS, INC.—See Fiserv, Inc.; *U.S. Public*, pg. 851
INTELLIGENT RETAIL UK LIMITED—See 3Q Holdings Limited; *Int'l*, pg. 9

INTELLIGENTSIA COFFEE, INC.—See JAB Holding Company S.a.r.l.; *Int'l*, pg. 3863
INTELLIGENT SOFTWARE SOLUTIONS—See Intelligraphics Inc.; *U.S. Private*, pg. 2106
INTELLIGENT SOLAR SYSTEM CO., LTD.—See Onamba Co., Ltd.; *Int'l*, pg. 5573
INTELLIGENT SOLUTIONS, INC.; *U.S. Private*, pg. 2106
INTELLIGENT TECHNOLOGIES & SERVICES, INC.—See Fike Corporation; *U.S. Private*, pg. 1505
INTELLIGENT ULTRASOUND GROUP PLC; *Int'l*, pg. 3734
INTELLIGENT ULTRASOUND NORTH AMERICA INCORPORATED—See Intelligent Ultrasound Group plc; *Int'l*, pg. 3734
INTELLIGENT VAR TECHNOLOGY INC.; *U.S. Private*, pg. 2106
INTELLIGENT WAVE INC.; *Int'l*, pg. 3734
INTELLIGENT WAVE KOREA INC.—See Intelligent Wave Inc.; *Int'l*, pg. 3734
INTELLIGERE; *U.S. Private*, pg. 2106
INTELLIGIZE, INCORPORATED—See RELX plc; *Int'l*, pg. 6267
INTELLIGRAPHICS INC.; *U.S. Private*, pg. 2106
INTELLIGRATED, INC.—See Honeywell International Inc.; *U.S. Public*, pg. 1051
INTELLIGROUP ASIA PRIVATE, LTD.—See Nippon Telegraph & Telephone Corporation; *Int'l*, pg. 5348
INTELLIGROUP EUROPE LIMITED—See Nippon Telegraph & Telephone Corporation; *Int'l*, pg. 5346
INTELLIGROUP INC.—See Nippon Telegraph & Telephone Corporation; *Int'l*, pg. 5347
INTELLIHR LIMITED—See Accel Partners L.P.; *U.S. Private*, pg. 49
INTELLIHR LIMITED—See KKR & Co. Inc.; *U.S. Public*, pg. 1239
INTELLILIFT AS—See Nekkar ASA; *Int'l*, pg. 5192
INTELLIMAR, INC.; *U.S. Private*, pg. 2106
INTELLI-MARK TECHNOLOGIES, INC.; *U.S. Private*, pg. 2105
INTELLIMEDIA-DBC—See Diccicco Battista Communications; *U.S. Private*, pg. 1225
INTELLINET CONSULTING, LLC—See FPT Corporation; *Int'l*, pg. 2758
INTELLINETICS, INC.; *U.S. Public*, pg. 1140
INTELLIPHARMACEUTICS INTERNATIONAL INC.; *Int'l*, pg. 3734
INTELLIPHARMACEUTICS LTD.—See Intellipharmaceutics International Inc.; *Int'l*, pg. 3734
INTELLIPHARM PTY LTD—See EBOS Group Limited; *Int'l*, pg. 2285
INTELLIPOWER, INC.—See AMETEK, Inc.; *U.S. Public*, pg. 120
INTELLIQUIP, INC.—See FPX, LLC; *U.S. Private*, pg. 1586
INTELLISERV, INC.—See NOV, Inc.; *U.S. Public*, pg. 1545
INTELLISERV NORWAY AS—See NOV, Inc.; *U.S. Public*, pg. 1545
INTELLISITE CORPORATION; *U.S. Private*, pg. 2106
INTELLISTANCE, LLC—See Verisk Analytics, Inc.; *U.S. Public*, pg. 2283
INTELLISWIFT SOFTWARE INC.; *U.S. Private*, pg. 2106
INTELLISYNC CORPORATION—See Nokia Corporation; *Int'l*, pg. 5405
INTELLITRANS, LLC—See Roper Technologies, Inc.; *U.S. Public*, pg. 1813
INTELLITRON PTY. LTD.—See Jumbo Interactive Limited; *Int'l*, pg. 4026
INTELLIVATE CAPITAL VENTURES LIMITED; *Int'l*, pg. 3734
INTELLIVERSE—See The Gores Group, LLC; *U.S. Private*, pg. 4035
INTELLIVIEW TECHNOLOGIES INC.—See Enbridge Inc.; *Int'l*, pg. 2397
INTELLIVISION TECHNOLOGIES CORP.—See Melrose Industries PLC; *Int'l*, pg. 4813
INTEL MALAYSIA SDN. BERHAD—See Intel Corporation; *U.S. Public*, pg. 1138
INTEL MASSACHUSETTS, INC.—See Intel Corporation; *U.S. Public*, pg. 1138
INTEL MEDITERRANEAN TRADING COMPANY—See Intel Corporation; *U.S. Public*, pg. 1138
INTEL MICROELECTRONICS ASIA—See Intel Corporation; *U.S. Public*, pg. 1138
INTEL MOBILE COMMUNICATIONS GMBH—See Intel Corporation; *U.S. Public*, pg. 1138
INTEL SA CORP—See Intel Corporation; *U.S. Public*, pg. 1138
INTEL, INC. SA—See Aiphone Co., Ltd.; *Int'l*, pg. 235
INTELSAT S.A.—See BC Partners LLP; *Int'l*, pg. 924
INTELSAT S.A.—See Silver Lake Group, LLC; *U.S. Private*, pg. 3658
INTEL SEMICONDUCTOR (DALIAN) LTD.—See Intel Corporation; *U.S. Public*, pg. 1138
INTEL SEMICONDUCTOR LIMITED—See Intel Corporation; *U.S. Public*, pg. 1139
INTEL SEMICONDUCTOR LTD.—See Intel Corporation; *U.S. Public*, pg. 1139
INTEL SEMICONDUCTOR LTD.—See Intel Corporation; *U.S. Public*, pg. 1139

INTEL SEMICONDUCTOR LTD.—See Intel Corporation; *U.S. Public*, pg. 1139
INTEL SEMICONDUCTOR LTD.—See Intel Corporation; *U.S. Public*, pg. 1139
INTEL SEMICONDUTORES DO BRASIL LTDA.—See Intel Corporation; *U.S. Public*, pg. 1139
INTEL SWEDEN AB—See Intel Corporation; *U.S. Public*, pg. 1139
INTEL TECHNOLOGIES, INC.—See Intel Corporation; *U.S. Public*, pg. 1139
INTEL TECHNOLOGY ASIA PTE. LTD.—See Intel Corporation; *U.S. Public*, pg. 1139
INTEL TECHNOLOGY INDIA PVT. LTD.—See Intel Corporation; *U.S. Public*, pg. 1139
INTEL TECHNOLOGY PHILIPPINES, INC.—See Intel Corporation; *U.S. Public*, pg. 1139
INTEL TECHNOLOGY POLAND—See Intel Corporation; *U.S. Public*, pg. 1139
INTELTECH S.A. DE C.V.—See Intel Corporation; *U.S. Public*, pg. 1139
INTEL TECNOLOGIA DE ARGENTINA S.A.—See Intel Corporation; *U.S. Public*, pg. 1139
INTEL TECNOLOGIA DE COLOMBIA S.A.—See Intel Corporation; *U.S. Public*, pg. 1139
INTEL TECNOLOGIA DE MEXICO, S.A. DE C.V.—See Intel Corporation; *U.S. Public*, pg. 1139
INTEMA INSAAT VE TESISAT MALZEMELERI YATIRIM VE PAZARLAMA A.S; *Int'l*, pg. 3734
INTEMA SOLUTIONS INC.; *Int'l*, pg. 3734
INTENDIS DERMA, S.L.—See Bayer Aktiengesellschaft; *Int'l*, pg. 908
INTENDIS MANUFACTURING S.P.A.—See Bayer Aktiengesellschaft; *Int'l*, pg. 908
INTENO BROADBAND TECHNOLOGY AS—See Amplex AB; *Int'l*, pg. 434
INTENO BVBA—See Amplex AB; *Int'l*, pg. 433
INTENO DENMARK A/S—See Amplex AB; *Int'l*, pg. 434
INTENO NETMEDIA OY AB—See Amplex AB; *Int'l*, pg. 434
INTENSE LIGHTING, LLC—See Leviton Manufacturing Company, Inc.; *U.S. Private*, pg. 2436
INTENSE TECHNOLOGIES LIMITED; *Int'l*, pg. 3734
INTENSITY THERAPEUTICS, INC.; *U.S. Public*, pg. 1140
INTENSIVPFLEGEDIENST KOMPASS GMBH—See SOL S.p.A.; *Int'l*, pg. 7067
INTENSIVSERVICE WANNINGER GMBH—See SOL S.p.A.; *Int'l*, pg. 7067
INTENSUS ENGINEERING, INC, LLC—See Xuzhou Construction Machinery Group Co., Ltd.; *Int'l*, pg. 8540
INTENTIONAL SOFTWARE CORPORATION—See Microsoft Corporation; *U.S. Public*, pg. 1439
INTEPE ELEKTRIK URETIM VE TIC. A.S.—See EnBW Energie Baden-Wurttemberg AG; *Int'l*, pg. 2399
INTEPLAST GROUP, LTD. - INTEGRATED BAGGING SYSTEMS—See Inteplast Group, Ltd.; *U.S. Private*, pg. 2106
INTEPLAST GROUP, LTD.; *U.S. Private*, pg. 2106
INTEPLAST GROUP, LTD. - WORLD-PAK—See Inteplast Group, Ltd.; *U.S. Private*, pg. 2106
INTEPROD LLC; *U.S. Private*, pg. 2106
INTEPROS CONSULTING INC; *U.S. Private*, pg. 2106
INTERACID AUSTRALIA PTY LTD.—See Sumitomo Corporation; *Int'l*, pg. 7269
INTERACID TRADING (CHILE) S.A.—See Sumitomo Corporation; *Int'l*, pg. 7268
INTERACID TRADING S.A.—See Sumitomo Corporation; *Int'l*, pg. 7269
INTERACOUSTICS A/S—See Demant A/S; *Int'l*, pg. 2024
INTERACOUSTICS DO BRASIL. COM. DE EQUIP. MEDICOS LTDA.—See Demant A/S; *Int'l*, pg. 2024
INTERACOUSTICS PTY. LTD.—See Demant A/S; *Int'l*, pg. 2024
INTERACT BRANDING LTD.; *Int'l*, pg. 3735
INTERACT FOR HEALTH; *U.S. Private*, pg. 2107
INTER ACT GMBH—See Wienerberger AG; *Int'l*, pg. 8405
INTERACT HOLDINGS GROUP, INC.; *U.S. Public*, pg. 1140
INTERACT INCORPORATED; *U.S. Private*, pg. 2108
INTER ACTION CORPORATION; *Int'l*, pg. 3734
INTERACTIONS CONSUMER EXPERIENCE MARKETING INC.—See Bain Capital, LP; *U.S. Private*, pg. 439
INTERACTIVATION HEALTH NETWORKS LLC - OPERATIONS OFFICE—See Interactivation Health Networks LLC; *U.S. Private*, pg. 2108
INTERACTIVATION HEALTH NETWORKS LLC; *U.S. Private*, pg. 2108
INTERACTIVE BROADBAND CONSULTING GROUP LLC—See Accenture plc; *Int'l*, pg. 87
INTERACTIVE BROKERS AUSTRALIA NOMINEES PTY LIMITED—See Interactive Brokers Group, Inc.; *U.S. Public*, pg. 1140
INTERACTIVE BROKERS CANADA, INC.—See Interactive Brokers Group, Inc.; *U.S. Public*, pg. 1140
INTERACTIVE BROKERS CENTRAL EUROPE ZRT.—See Interactive Brokers Group, Inc.; *U.S. Public*, pg. 1140
INTERACTIVE BROKERS GROUP, INC.; *U.S. Public*, pg. 1140
INTERACTIVE BROKERS HONG KONG LIMITED—See Interactive Brokers Group, Inc.; *U.S. Public*, pg. 1140

INTERACTIVE BROKERS (INDIA) PRIVATE LIMITED—See Interactive Brokers Group, Inc.; *U.S. Public*, pg. 1140
INTERACTIVE BROKERS, LLC—See Interactive Brokers Group, Inc.; *U.S. Public*, pg. 1140
INTERACTIVE BROKERS (UK) LIMITED—See Interactive Brokers Group, Inc.; *U.S. Public*, pg. 1140
INTERACTIVE BUSINESS INFORMATION SYSTEMS, INC.—See Sonata Software Limited; *Int'l*, pg. 7089
INTERACTIVE BUSINESS SYSTEMS, INC.—See Odyssey Investment Partners, LLC; *U.S. Private*, pg. 2996
THE INTERACTIVE CIRCUIT IN STOCKHOLM AB—See Oniva Online Group Europe AB; *Int'l*, pg. 5581
INTERACTIVE COMMUNICATIONS INC; *U.S. Private*, pg. 2108
INTERACTIVE COMMUNICATIONS SOLUTIONS GROUP, INC.—See Strattam Capital, LLC; *U.S. Private*, pg. 3837
INTERACTIVE DATA, LLC—See Red Violet, Inc.; *U.S. Public*, pg. 1770
INTERACTIVE DATA VISUALIZATION, INC.—See Unity Software Inc.; *U.S. Public*, pg. 2254
INTERACTIVE DIGITAL SOLUTIONS, INC.—See Berenson & Company, Inc.; *U.S. Private*, pg. 530
INTERACTIVE DIGITAL TECHNOLOGIES INC.—See Hitron Technologies Inc.; *Int'l*, pg. 3427
INTERACTIVE ENERGY GROUP LLC—See Just Energy Group Inc.; *Int'l*, pg. 4031
INTER-ACTIVE ENTERTAINMENT SOLUTIONS TECHNOLOGIES, INC.—See DFNN, Inc.; *Int'l*, pg. 2096
INTERACTIVE FINANCIAL CORPORATION; *U.S. Private*, pg. 2108
INTERACTIVE FINANCIAL SERVICES LIMITED; *Int'l*, pg. 3736
INTERACTIVE FINANCIAL SOLUTIONS, INC.—See Sandata Holdings, Inc.; *U.S. Private*, pg. 3543
INTERACTIVE HEALTH, INC.—See CI Capital Partners LLC; *U.S. Private*, pg. 895
INTERACTIVE IDEAS, LLC—See Condeco Ltd.; *Int'l*, pg. 1766
INTERACTIVE INNOVATION GROUP, INC.; *U.S. Private*, pg. 2108
INTERACTIVE INTELLIGENCE GROUP, INC.—See Permira Advisers LLP; *Int'l*, pg. 5805
INTERACTIVE INTELLIGENCE, INC.—See Permira Advisers LLP; *Int'l*, pg. 5805
INTERACTIVE INTELLIGENCE (SOUTH AFRICA) (PTY) LTD—See Permira Advisers LLP; *Int'l*, pg. 5805
INTERACTIVE INVESTOR LIMITED—See abrdn PLC; *Int'l*, pg. 68
INTERACTIVE INVESTOR SERVICES LIMITED—See abrdn PLC; *Int'l*, pg. 69
INTERACTIVE LEISURE SYSTEMS, INC.; *U.S. Public*, pg. 1140
INTERACTIVE LIMITED—See News Group International Holding; *Int'l*, pg. 5237
INTERACTIVE LIQUID, LLC; *U.S. Private*, pg. 2108
INTERACTIVE LOGISTICS INC.—See NFI Industries, Inc.; *U.S. Private*, pg. 2923
INTERACTIVE MANPOWER SOLUTIONS PRIVATE LIMITED—See Empresaria Group Plc; *Int'l*, pg. 2389
INTERACTIVE MARKETING SERVICES, INC.; *U.S. Private*, pg. 2108
INTERACTIVE MEDIA GROUP INCORPORATED; *U.S. Private*, pg. 2108
INTERACTIVE MOTION TECHNOLOGIES, INC.—See Bionik Laboratories Corp.; *Int'l*, pg. 1040
INTERACTIVE NETWORK COMMUNICATIONS GMBH—See MEDIQON Group AG; *Int'l*, pg. 4780
INTERACTIVE ONE, INC.—See Urban One, Inc.; *U.S. Public*, pg. 2265
INTERACTIVE ONE, LLC—See Urban One, Inc.; *U.S. Public*, pg. 2265
INTERACTIVE PROSPECT TARGETING LIMITED; *Int'l*, pg. 3736
INTERACTIVE QUALITY SERVICES, INC.—See Integrated Research Ltd; *Int'l*, pg. 3731
INTERACTIVE RESPONSE TECHNOLOGIES; *U.S. Private*, pg. 2108
INTERACTIVE SERVICES NETWORK, INC.; *U.S. Private*, pg. 2108
INTERACTIVE SOLUTIONS, INC.; *U.S. Private*, pg. 2108
INTERACTIVE SOLUTIONS, LLC; *U.S. Private*, pg. 2108
INTERACTIVE SPORTS (CI) LIMITED—See Entain PLC; *Int'l*, pg. 2450
INTERACTIVE STRENGTH INC.; *U.S. Public*, pg. 1140
INTERACTIVE STUDY SYSTEMS, INC.; *U.S. Private*, pg. 2108
INTERACTIVE SYSTEMS, INC.—See Triple-S Management Corp.; *U.S. Public*, pg. 2195
INTERACTIVE TECHNOLOGIES—See Montage Partners, Inc.; *U.S. Private*, pg. 2774
INTERACTIVE TELEVISION PRIVATE LIMITED—See WPP plc; *Int'l*, pg. 8465
INTERACTIVE THERAPY GROUP CONSULTANTS, INC.—See American Learning Corporation; *U.S. Private*, pg. 239
INTERACTIVE ZENITHOPTIMEDIA—See Publicis Groupe S.A.; *Int'l*, pg. 6113

INTERACT PMTI, INC.—See Buckthorn Partners LLP; *Int'l*, pg. 1210
INTERACT PMTI, INC.—See OEP Capital Advisors, L.P.; *U.S. Private*, pg. 2997
INTERACT PUBLIC SAFETY SYSTEMS; *U.S. Private*, pg. 2108
INTERACT-TV, INCORPORATED; *U.S. Public*, pg. 1140
INTERACTYX LIMITED; *U.S. Private*, pg. 2109
INTERACTYX LIMITED—See Interactyx Limited; *U.S. Private*, pg. 2109
INTERA EQUITY PARTNERS OY; *Int'l*, pg. 3735
INTERAFRICA GRAINS (PROPRIETARY) LIMITED—See Seaboard Corporation; *U.S. Public*, pg. 1850
INTERAGENT D.O.O.—See Intereuropa d.d.; *Int'l*, pg. 3740
INTERALBANIAN SH.A—See Vienna Insurance Group AG Wiener Versicherung Gruppe; *Int'l*, pg. 8194
INTERALPEN-HOTEL TYROL GMBH—See Liebherr-International AG; *Int'l*, pg. 4488
INTERAMERICAN BANK FSB; *U.S. Private*, pg. 2109
INTER AMERICAN COSMETICS INC.; *U.S. Private*, pg. 2106
INTER-AMERICAN DEVELOPMENT BANK; *U.S. Private*, pg. 2107
INTER-AMERICAN FOODS, INC.—See The Kroger Co.; *U.S. Public*, pg. 2108
INTERAMERICAN GAMING, INC.; *Int'l*, pg. 3736
INTERAMERICAN HELLENIC LIFE INSURANCE COMPANY S.A.—See Achmea B.V.; *Int'l*, pg. 103
INTER-AMERICAN INVESTMENT CORPORATION—See Inter-American Development Bank; *U.S. Private*, pg. 2107
INTERAMERICAN MOTOR CORPORATION—See Parts Authority Inc.; *U.S. Private*, pg. 3103
INTER-AMERICAN OIL WORKS INC.; *U.S. Private*, pg. 2107
INTERAPP AG—See AVK Holding A/S; *Int'l*, pg. 748
INTERAPP DEUTSCHLAND GMBH—See AVK Holding A/S; *Int'l*, pg. 748
INTERAPP GES.M.B.H.—See AVK Holding A/S; *Int'l*, pg. 748
INTERAPPTIVE, INC.—See Thoma Bravo, L.P.; *U.S. Private*, pg. 4153
INTERAPP VALCOM S.A.—See AVK Holding A/S; *Int'l*, pg. 748
INTERAQT CORP.—See Aluf Holdings, Inc.; *U.S. Public*, pg. 89
INTERARGEM GMBH—See Stadtwerke Bielefeld GmbH; *Int'l*, pg. 7161
INTERART S.A.R.L—See Thames & Hudson Ltd; *Int'l*, pg. 7607
INTERASCO SOCIETE ANONYME GENERAL INSURANCE COMPANY—See Harel Insurance Investments & Financial Services Ltd.; *Int'l*, pg. 3274
INTERASPHALT SP. Z O.O.—See Dortmunder Gussasphalt GmbH & Co. KG; *Int'l*, pg. 2180
INTERAUTO SA; *Int'l*, pg. 3736
INTERBAKE FOODS LLC—See George Weston Limited; *Int'l*, pg. 2939
INTERBALANCE GROUP B.V.; *Int'l*, pg. 3736
INTERBANK—See Olney Bancshares of Texas, Inc.; *U.S. Private*, pg. 3011
INTERBANK—See ABN AMRO Group N.V.; *Int'l*, pg. 65
INTERBAY ASSET FINANCE LIMITED—See OneSavings Bank plc; *Int'l*, pg. 5577
INTERBAY COATINGS INC.—See Odyssey Investment Partners, LLC; *U.S. Private*, pg. 2995
INTERBETON CONSTRUCTION MATERIALS S.A.—See Titan Cement Company S.A.; *Int'l*, pg. 7759
INTER-BETON S.A.—See Heidelberg Materials AG; *Int'l*, pg. 3310
INTERBEV AS—See Altia Oyj; *Int'l*, pg. 392
INTERBEV (CAMBODIA) CO., LTD—See Thai Beverage Public Company Limited; *Int'l*, pg. 7590
INTERBEV MALAYSIA SDN. BHD.—See Thai Beverage Public Company Limited; *Int'l*, pg. 7590
INTERBEV (SINGAPORE) LIMITED—See Thai Beverage Public Company Limited; *Int'l*, pg. 7590
INTERBEV TRADING (CHINA) LIMITED—See Thai Beverage Public Company Limited; *Int'l*, pg. 7590
INTERBIT DATA, INC.; *U.S. Private*, pg. 2109
INTERBOLSA S.A.—See Euronext N.V.; *Int'l*, pg. 2554
INTERBORO INSURANCE COMPANY—See American Coastal Insurance Corporation; *U.S. Public*, pg. 98
INTERBORO SYSTEMS CORPORATION—See Hellman & Friedman LLC; *U.S. Private*, pg. 1910
INTERBOROUGH DEVELOPMENTAL AND CONSULTATION CENTER; *U.S. Private*, pg. 2109
INTERBRAND B.V.—See Interbrand Europe; *Int'l*, pg. 3736
INTERBRAND CORPORATION—See Omnicom Group Inc.; *U.S. Public*, pg. 1586
INTERBRAND DESIGN FORUM—See Omnicom Group Inc.; *U.S. Public*, pg. 1586
INTERBRAND EUROPE; *Int'l*, pg. 3736
INTERBRANDHEALTH—See Omnicom Group Inc.; *U.S. Public*, pg. 1586
INTERBRAND SAN FRANCISCO—See Omnicom Group Inc.; *U.S. Public*, pg. 1586

INTERBRAND—See Omnicom Group Inc.; *U.S. Public*, pg. 1585
INTERBRAND—See Interbrand Europe; *Int'l*, pg. 3736
INTERBRAND—See Interbrand Europe; *Int'l*, pg. 3736
INTERBRAND—See Interbrand Europe; *Int'l*, pg. 3736
INTERBRAND—See Omnicom Group Inc.; *U.S. Public*, pg. 1586
INTERBRAU GMBH—See Ameropa AG; *Int'l*, pg. 424
INTERBREW INTERNATIONAL B.V.—See Anheuser-Busch InBev SA/NV; *Int'l*, pg. 466
INTERBUD-LUBLIN S.A.; *Int'l*, pg. 3736
INTERBUILD A/S—See Maj Invest Holding A/S; *Int'l*, pg. 4653
INTERBUILD NV—See Koninklijke BAM Groep N.V.; *Int'l*, pg. 4261
INTERBULK GROUP LIMITED—See Den Hartogh Holding BV; *Int'l*, pg. 2026
INTERBULK TRADING S.A.—See Heidelberg Materials AG; *Int'l*, pg. 3316
INTER BUSINESS'91 LTD.—See HORIBA Ltd; *Int'l*, pg. 3477
INTERCALL ASIA PACIFIC HOLDINGS PTE. LTD.—See Apollo Global Management, Inc.; *U.S. Public*, pg. 152
INTERCALL DE MEXICO, S. DE R.L. DE C.V.—See Apollo Global Management, Inc.; *U.S. Public*, pg. 152
INTERCALL DE MEXICO S DE RL DE CV—See Apollo Global Management, Inc.; *U.S. Public*, pg. 152
INTERCAM BANCO, S.A.; *Int'l*, pg. 3736
INTERCAMBIADOR DE TRANSPORTES DE MONCLOA, S.A.—See Sacyr, S.A.; *Int'l*, pg. 6465
INTERCAMBIADOR DE TRANSPORTES DE PRINCIPE PIO, S.A.—See ACS, Actividades de Construccion y Servicios, S.A.; *Int'l*, pg. 115
INTERCAPITAL GROUP LTD.; *Int'l*, pg. 3736
INTERCAPITAL PROPERTY DEVELOPMENT REIT; *Int'l*, pg. 3736
INTER CAPITAL REALTY CORPORATION—See Old Republic International Corporation; *U.S. Public*, pg. 1567
INTERCARABAO LIMITED—See Carabao Group Public Company Limited; *Int'l*, pg. 1319
INTERCARE DX, INC.; *U.S. Public*, pg. 1141
INTER CARS S.A.; *Int'l*, pg. 3735
INTERCAST EUROPE S.R.L.—See EssilorLuxottica SA; *Int'l*, pg. 2515
INTERCAST SA—See American Cast Iron Pipe Company; *U.S. Private*, pg. 226
INTERCAT EQUIPMENT MUMBAI PVT LTD—See Johnson Matthey PLC; *Int'l*, pg. 3991
INTERCAT EUROPE B.V.—See Johnson Matthey PLC; *Int'l*, pg. 3991
INTERCAT INC.—See Johnson Matthey PLC; *Int'l*, pg. 3991
INTERCEDE GROUP PLC; *Int'l*, pg. 3736
INTERCEDE LIMITED—See Intercede Group plc; *Int'l*, pg. 3736
INTERCELL USA, INC.—See Valneva SE; *Int'l*, pg. 8121
INTERCEL TELECOMS GROUP, INC.; *U.S. Private*, pg. 2109
INTERCEMENT BRASIL S.A.—See Camargo Correa S.A.; *Int'l*, pg. 1268
INTER CENTRAL, INC.—See ARE Holdings, Inc.; *Int'l*, pg. 557
INTERCEPT CORPORATION; *U.S. Private*, pg. 2109
INTERCEPT ENERGY SERVICES INC.; *Int'l*, pg. 3736
INTERCEPT INTERACTIVE, INC.—See Perion Network Ltd.; *Int'l*, pg. 5801
INTERCEPT PHARMACEUTICALS, INC.—See Alfasigma S.p.A; *Int'l*, pg. 315
INTERCERAMIC DE OCCIDENTE, S.A. DE C.V.—See Internacional de Ceramica, S.A.B. de C.V.; *Int'l*, pg. 3743
INTERCERAMIC INC.—See Internacional de Ceramica, S.A.B. de C.V.; *Int'l*, pg. 3743
INTERCERAMIC TRADING CO. INC.—See Internacional de Ceramica, S.A.B. de C.V.; *Int'l*, pg. 3743
INTERCHANGE TECHNOLOGIES, INC.—See ePlus Inc.; *U.S. Public*, pg. 784
INTERCHEM CORPORATION; *U.S. Private*, pg. 2109
THE INTERCHURCH CENTER; *U.S. Private*, pg. 4057
INTER-CITIC MINERALS INC.—See Western Mining Co., Ltd.; *Int'l*, pg. 8389
INTERCITY HOTEL GMBH—See H World Group Limited; *Int'l*, pg. 3191
INTER-CITY MPC (M) SDN. BHD.—See HeiTech Padu Berhad; *Int'l*, pg. 3326
INTERCITY PRIVATE HIRE LIMITED—See MBH Corporation Plc; *Int'l*, pg. 4752
INTER CITY TIRE & AUTO CENTER; *U.S. Private*, pg. 2106
INTERCITY TRANSIT; *U.S. Private*, pg. 2109
INTERCLAD—See The Egan Companies; *U.S. Private*, pg. 4025
INTERCLEAN ASSISTANCE ICA S.A.—See Tennant Company; *U.S. Public*, pg. 2016
INTERCLEAN EQUIPMENT, LLC—See Oakland Standard Co., LLC; *U.S. Private*, pg. 2985
INTERCLOUD SYSTEMS, INC.; *U.S. Public*, pg. 1141
INTER-COASTAL ELECTRONICS, LLC—See Greenbriar Equity Group, L.P.; *U.S. Private*, pg. 1775

INTERCOASTAL, INC.—See HCI Equity Management, L.P.; *U.S. Private*, pg. 1889
INTERCOASTAL MEDICAL GROUP, INC.; *U.S. Private*, pg. 2109
INTERCOASTAL MORTGAGE, LLC; *U.S. Private*, pg. 2109
INTER & CO, INC.; *Int'l*, pg. 3734
INTERCOL CONTRACTING CO. LTD.—See International Agencies Company Ltd.; *Int'l*, pg. 3743
INTERCOM CONSULTING & FEDERAL SYSTEMS CORPORATION—See AE Industrial Partners, LP; *U.S. Private*, pg. 111
INTERCOM - KURZ LTD—See Leonhard Kurz GmbH & Co. KG; *Int'l*, pg. 4462
INTER-COMMERCIAL BUSINESS SYSTEMS; *U.S. Private*, pg. 2107
INTERCOMMUNICATIONS INC.; *U.S. Private*, pg. 2109
INTER-COMMUNITY TELEPHONE COMPANY—See LICT Corporation; *U.S. Public*, pg. 1312
INTERCOMPONENTWARE GMBH—See x-tention Informationstechnologie GmbH; *Int'l*, pg. 8518
INTERCOMPONENTWARE INC.—See x-tention Informationstechnologie GmbH; *Int'l*, pg. 8518
INTERCOMP U.S.A., INC.; *U.S. Private*, pg. 2109
INTERCOM S.R.L.—See Heidelberg Materials AG; *Int'l*, pg. 3316
INTERCON CHEMICAL COMPANY—See C&I Holdings Inc.; *U.S. Private*, pg. 703
INTERCOND SERVICES SPA—See Nexans S.A.; *Int'l*, pg. 5240
INTERCONEXION ELECTRICA ISA PERU S.A.—See Ecopetrol S.A.; *Int'l*, pg. 2299
INTERCONEXION ELECTRICA S.A. E.S.P.—See Ecopetrol S.A.; *Int'l*, pg. 2299
INTERCON INC.; *U.S. Private*, pg. 2109
INTERCONNECT CABLE TECHNOLOGIES CORP. - ASIA—See Interconnect Cable Technologies Corp.; *U.S. Private*, pg. 2109
INTERCONNECT CABLE TECHNOLOGIES CORP.; *U.S. Private*, pg. 2109
INTER-CONNECTED STOCK EXCHANGE OF INDIA LIMITED; *Int'l*, pg. 3735
THE INTERCONNECT GROUP; *U.S. Private*, pg. 4057
INTERCONNECTOR GMBH—See EnBW Energie Baden-Wurttemberg AG; *Int'l*, pg. 2399
INTERCONNECTOR (UK) LIMITED—See Publigas; *Int'l*, pg. 6115
INTERCONNECT PRODUCTS DIVISION—See Methode Electronics, Inc.; *U.S. Public*, pg. 1428
INTERCONNECT SERVICES GROUP; *U.S. Private*, pg. 2109
INTERCONNECT SOLUTIONS INC.; *U.S. Private*, pg. 2109
INTERCONNECT VENTURES CORPORATION; *Int'l*, pg. 3736
INTERCONN RESOURCES, LLC; *U.S. Private*, pg. 2109
INTER-CON SECURITY SYSTEMS, INC.; *U.S. Private*, pg. 2107
INTERCON SOLUTIONS, INC.; *U.S. Private*, pg. 2109
INTER CONSTRUTORA E INCORPORADORA S.A.; *Int'l*, pg. 3735
INTERCONSULT BULGARIA LTD.—See Kongsberg Gruppen ASA; *Int'l*, pg. 4255
INTERCONTINENTAL CHEMICAL CORP; *U.S. Private*, pg. 2109
INTERCONTINENTAL - CHICAGO MAGNIFICENT MILE—See InterContinental Hotels Group PLC; *Int'l*, pg. 3738
INTERCONTINENTAL D.C. OPERATING CORP.—See InterContinental Hotels Group PLC; *Int'l*, pg. 3738
INTERCONTINENTAL EXCHANGE HOLDINGS, INC.—See Intercontinental Exchange, Inc.; *U.S. Public*, pg. 1143
INTERCONTINENTAL EXCHANGE, INC.; *U.S. Public*, pg. 1141
INTERCONTINENTAL EXPORT IMPORT INC.; *U.S. Private*, pg. 2109
INTER-CONTINENTAL FLORIDA INVESTMENT CORP.—See InterContinental Hotels Group PLC; *Int'l*, pg. 3738
INTERCONTINENTAL GESTION HOTELERA S.L.—See InterContinental Hotels Group PLC; *Int'l*, pg. 3737
INTERCONTINENTAL GOLD AND METALS LTD; *Int'l*, pg. 3736
INTERCONTINENTAL GRAND STANFORD HONG KONG—See InterContinental Hotels Group PLC; *Int'l*, pg. 3737
INTERCONTINENTAL HIRE CARS LIMITED—See KWOON CHUNG BUS HOLDINGS LIMITED; *Int'l*, pg. 4351
INTERCONTINENTAL HOMES SAVINGS & LOANS LIMITED—See Access Corporation; *Int'l*, pg. 89
INTERCONTINENTAL HONG KONG—See Pioneer Global Group Limited; *Int'l*, pg. 5872
INTERCONTINENTAL HOTEL BERLIN GMBH—See InterContinental Hotels Group PLC; *Int'l*, pg. 3737
INTERCONTINENTAL HOTEL DUSSELDORF GMBH—See InterContinental Hotels Group PLC; *Int'l*, pg. 3737

INTERCONTINENTAL HOTELS CORPORATION DE VENEZUELA C.A.—See InterContinental Hotels Group PLC; *Int'l*, pg. 3738
INTERCONTINENTAL HOTELS CORPORATION—See InterContinental Hotels Group PLC; *Int'l*, pg. 3738
INTERCONTINENTAL HOTELS GROUP (ASIA PACIFIC) PTE. LTD.—See InterContinental Hotels Group PLC; *Int'l*, pg. 3738
INTERCONTINENTAL HOTELS GROUP (AUSTRALIA) PTY LIMITED—See InterContinental Hotels Group PLC; *Int'l*, pg. 3738
INTERCONTINENTAL HOTELS GROUP (CANADA) INC.—See InterContinental Hotels Group PLC; *Int'l*, pg. 3738
INTERCONTINENTAL HOTELS GROUP CUSTOMER SERVICES LTD.—See InterContinental Hotels Group PLC; *Int'l*, pg. 3738
INTERCONTINENTAL HOTELS GROUP (ESPANA) SA—See InterContinental Hotels Group PLC; *Int'l*, pg. 3738
INTERCONTINENTAL HOTELS GROUP (GREATER CHINA) LIMITED—See InterContinental Hotels Group PLC; *Int'l*, pg. 3738
INTERCONTINENTAL HOTELS GROUP HEALTHCARE TRUSTEE LTD—See InterContinental Hotels Group PLC; *Int'l*, pg. 3738
INTERCONTINENTAL HOTELS GROUP (NEW ZEALAND) LIMITED—See InterContinental Hotels Group PLC; *Int'l*, pg. 3738
INTERCONTINENTAL HOTELS GROUP PLC; *Int'l*, pg. 3736
INTERCONTINENTAL HOTELS GROUP RESOURCES INC—See InterContinental Hotels Group PLC; *Int'l*, pg. 3738
INTERCONTINENTAL HOTELS GROUP SERVICES COMPANY—See InterContinental Hotels Group PLC; *Int'l*, pg. 3738
INTERCONTINENTAL HOTELS GROUP (SHANGHAI) LTD—See InterContinental Hotels Group PLC; *Int'l*, pg. 3738
INTERCONTINENTAL HOTELS ITALIA, SRL—See InterContinental Hotels Group PLC; *Int'l*, pg. 3738
INTERCONTINENTAL HOTELS LIMITED—See InterContinental Hotels Group PLC; *Int'l*, pg. 3738
INTERCONTINENTAL HOTELS MANAGEMENT GMBH—See InterContinental Hotels Group PLC; *Int'l*, pg. 3738
INTER-CONTINENTAL HOTELS (MONTREAL) OPERATING CORP.—See InterContinental Hotels Group PLC; *Int'l*, pg. 3737
INTER-CONTINENTAL HOTELS (MONTREAL) OWNING CORP.—See InterContinental Hotels Group PLC; *Int'l*, pg. 3737
INTERCONTINENTAL HOTELS OF SAN FRANCISCO, INC.—See InterContinental Hotels Group PLC; *Int'l*, pg. 3738
INTERCONTINENTAL HOTELS (PUERTO RICO) INC—See InterContinental Hotels Group PLC; *Int'l*, pg. 3738
INTER-CONTINENTAL HOTELS (SINGAPORE) PTE LTD—See InterContinental Hotels Group PLC; *Int'l*, pg. 3737
INTERCONTINENTAL INTERNATIONAL REAL ESTATE INVESTMENT COMPANY; *Int'l*, pg. 3739
INTERCONTINENTAL JET SERVICE CORP.—See Mitsubishi Heavy Industries, Ltd.; *Int'l*, pg. 4956
INTERCONTINENTAL LIFE ASSURANCE COMPANY LIMITED—See Access Corporation; *Int'l*, pg. 89
INTERCONTINENTAL OVERSEAS HOLDING CORPORATION—See InterContinental Hotels Group PLC; *Int'l*, pg. 3738
INTERCONTINENTAL PROPERTIES LIMITED—See Access Corporation; *Int'l*, pg. 89
INTERCONTINENTAL SPECIALTY FATS SDN. BHD.—See The Nisshin OilliO Group, Ltd.; *Int'l*, pg. 7671
INTERCONTINENTAL TERMINALS COMPANY; *U.S. Private*, pg. 2109
INTERCONTINENTAL - THE BARCLAY NEW YORK—See InterContinental Hotels Group PLC; *Int'l*, pg. 3738
INTERCONTROLE SA—See Electricite de France S.A.; *Int'l*, pg. 2351
INTERCORE, INC.; *U.S. Private*, pg. 2110
INTERCORP FINANCIAL SERVICES INC.; *Int'l*, pg. 3739
INTERCORP GROUP; *Int'l*, pg. 3739
INTERCOS ASIA PACIFIC LTD.—See Intercos S.p.A.; *Int'l*, pg. 3739
INTERCOS COSMETICS (SUZHOU) CO., LTD.—See Intercos S.p.A.; *Int'l*, pg. 3739
INTERCOSME INC.—See KOSE Corporation; *Int'l*, pg. 4290
INTERCOSMOS MEDIA GROUP, INC.; *U.S. Private*, pg. 2110
INTERCOS PARIS S.A.R.L.—See Intercos S.p.A.; *Int'l*, pg. 3739
INTERCOS S.P.A.; *Int'l*, pg. 3739
INTERCOS TECHNOLOGY (SIP) CO., LTD.—See Intercos S.p.A.; *Int'l*, pg. 3739
INTER-COUNTY BAKERS, INC.; *U.S. Private*, pg. 2107

INTER-COUNTY ELECTRIC COOP ASSOCIATION; *U.S. Private*, pg. 2107
INTERCOUNTY ELECTRIC COOPERATIVE; *U.S. Private*, pg. 2110
INTER-COUNTY ENERGY COOP CORP.; *U.S. Private*, pg. 2107
INTERCOUNTY SUPPLY INC.; *U.S. Private*, pg. 2110
INTERCOVAMEX, S.A. DE C.V.—See HORIBA Ltd; *Int'l*, pg. 3477
INTERCREDIT BANK, N.A.; *U.S. Private*, pg. 2110
INTERCRUISES SHORESIDE & PORT SERVICES INC.—See Canada Pension Plan Investment Board; *Int'l*, pg. 1279
INTERCRUISES SHORESIDE & PORT SERVICES INC.—See Cinven Limited; *Int'l*, pg. 1612
INTERCRUISES SHORESIDE & PORT SERVICES PTY LTD.—See Canada Pension Plan Investment Board; *Int'l*, pg. 1279
INTERCRUISES SHORESIDE & PORT SERVICES PTY LTD.—See Cinven Limited; *Int'l*, pg. 1612
INTERCUBE CO., LTD.—See World Co., Ltd.; *Int'l*, pg. 8456
INTERCURE LTD.; *Int'l*, pg. 3739
INTERDEAN AUGUSTE DALEIDEN SARL—See EAC Invest AS; *Int'l*, pg. 2261
INTERDEAN BULGARIA EOOD—See EAC Invest AS; *Int'l*, pg. 2261
INTERDEAN B.V.—See EAC Invest AS; *Int'l*, pg. 2261
INTERDEAN CENTRAL ASIA LLC—See EAC Invest AS; *Int'l*, pg. 2261
INTERDEAN EASTERN EUROPE GES.M.B.H—See EAC Invest AS; *Int'l*, pg. 2261
INTERDEAN HOLDINGS LIMITED—See EAC Invest AS; *Int'l*, pg. 2261
INTERDEAN HUNGARIA NEMZETKOZI KOLTOZTETO KFT—See EAC Invest AS; *Int'l*, pg. 2261
INTERDEAN INTERNATIONALE SPEDITION GES.M.B.H—See EAC Invest AS; *Int'l*, pg. 2262
INTERDEAN INTERNATIONAL LTD.—See EAC Invest AS; *Int'l*, pg. 2262
INTERDEAN INTERNATIONAL RELOCATION SA—See EAC Invest AS; *Int'l*, pg. 2261
INTERDEAN INTERNATIONAL RELOCATION UKRAINE LLC—See EAC Invest AS; *Int'l*, pg. 2262
INTERDEAN INT' MOVERS S.R.L.—See EAC Invest AS; *Int'l*, pg. 2261
INTERDEAN LIMITED—See EAC Invest AS; *Int'l*, pg. 2262
INTERDEAN RELOCATION SERVICES GMBH—See EAC Invest AS; *Int'l*, pg. 2262
INTERDEAN RELOCATION SERVICES NV—See EAC Invest AS; *Int'l*, pg. 2262
INTERDEAN SA—See EAC Invest AS; *Int'l*, pg. 2262
INTERDEAN, SPOL S.R.O—See EAC Invest AS; *Int'l*, pg. 2262
INTERDEAN SP. Z.O.O—See EAC Invest AS; *Int'l*, pg. 2262
INTERDEAN SRL—See EAC Invest AS; *Int'l*, pg. 2262
INTERDECO ESPAGNE—See Vivendi SE; *Int'l*, pg. 8274
INTERDELTA S.A.—See Perrigo Company plc; *Int'l*, pg. 5813
INTER-DELTA TBK; *Int'l*, pg. 3735
INTERDENT, INC.—See H.I.G. Capital, LLC; *U.S. Private*, pg. 1829
INTERDESCO—See VINCI S.A.; *Int'l*, pg. 8220
INTERDIGITAL CANADA LTEE.—See InterDigital, Inc.; *U.S. Public*, pg. 1144
INTERDIGITAL FACILITY COMPANY—See InterDigital, Inc.; *U.S. Public*, pg. 1144
INTERDIGITAL, INC.; *U.S. Public*, pg. 1143
INTERDIGITAL INTERNATIONAL, INC.—See InterDigital, Inc.; *U.S. Public*, pg. 1144
INTERDIGITAL - MELVILLE—See InterDigital, Inc.; *U.S. Public*, pg. 1144
INTERDIN, S.A.—See Banca Privada D'Andorra, SA; *Int'l*, pg. 816
INTERDIRECT TEL LTD.—See IDT Corporation; *U.S. Public*, pg. 1093
INTERDIS SNC—See Carrefour SA; *Int'l*, pg. 1345
INTERDOM LLC—See Odyssey Logistics & Technology Corp.; *U.S. Private*, pg. 2996
INTERDYN BMI—See Columbus A/S; *Int'l*, pg. 1706
INTERDYNE COMPANY, INC.; *U.S. Public*, pg. 1144
INTER EDITION DIFFUS REVUE JOURN PERIOD; *Int'l*, pg. 3735
INTEREL ASSOCIATION MANAGEMENT SA—See Interel Holdings SA; *Int'l*, pg. 3740
INTEREL CONSULTING INC.—See Interel Holdings SA; *Int'l*, pg. 3739
INTEREL CONSULTING UK LIMITED—See Interel Holdings SA; *Int'l*, pg. 3739
INTEREL EUROPEAN AFFAIRS SA—See Interel Holdings SA; *Int'l*, pg. 3740
INTEREL HOLDINGS SA; *Int'l*, pg. 3739
INTEREL MANAGEMENT GROUP NV—See Interel Holdings SA; *Int'l*, pg. 3740
INTEREL SAS—See Interel Holdings SA; *Int'l*, pg. 3740
INTERENVASES, S.A.—See ACS, Actividades de Construccion y Servicios, S.A.; *Int'l*, pg. 115
INTEREUROPA D.D.; *Int'l*, pg. 3740

INTEREUROPA GLOBAL LOGISTICS SERVICE ALBANIA SHPK—See Intereuropa d.d.; *Int'l*, pg. 3740
INTEREUROPA KOSOVA L.L.C.—See Intereuropa d.d.; *Int'l*, pg. 3740
INTEREUROPA - LOGISTICKE USLUGE A.D.; *Int'l*, pg. 3740
INTEREUROPA LOGISTICKE USLUGE D.O.O—See Intereuropa d.d.; *Int'l*, pg. 3740
INTEREUROPA RTC D.D—See Intereuropa d.d.; *Int'l*, pg. 3740
INTEREUROPA SAJAM, D.O.O.—See Intereuropa d.d.; *Int'l*, pg. 3740
INTEREUROPA S.A.S.—See Intereuropa d.d.; *Int'l*, pg. 3740
INTEREUROPA SKOPJE, DOO—See Intereuropa d.d.; *Int'l*, pg. 3740
INTEREUROPA TRANSPORT, D.O.O.—See Intereuropa d.d.; *Int'l*, pg. 3740
INTEREVCO, LTD.; *U.S. Private*, pg. 2110
INTEREXPO COMMUNICATIONS; *U.S. Private*, pg. 2110
INTERFAB INC.; *U.S. Private*, pg. 2110
INTERFACE AMERICAS HOLDINGS, LLC—See Interface, Inc.; *U.S. Public*, pg. 1144
INTERFACE AMERICAS, INC.—See Interface, Inc.; *U.S. Public*, pg. 1144
INTERFACE AUST. HOLDINGS PTY LIMITED—See Interface, Inc.; *U.S. Public*, pg. 1144
INTERFACE AUST. PTY LIMITED—See Interface, Inc.; *U.S. Public*, pg. 1144
INTERFACE CABLE ASSEMBLIES & SERVICES CORP.; *U.S. Private*, pg. 2110
INTERFACE CLINICAL SERVICES LTD.—See IQVIA Holdings Inc.; *U.S. Public*, pg. 1169
INTERFACE COMMUNICATIONS LTD.—See The Interpublic Group of Companies, Inc.; *U.S. Public*, pg. 2093
INTERFACE CONTRACTS LIMITED; *Int'l*, pg. 3740
INTERFACE EUROPE B.V.—See Interface, Inc.; *U.S. Public*, pg. 1144
INTERFACE EUROPE, LTD.—See Interface, Inc.; *U.S. Public*, pg. 1144
INTERFACE, INC.; *U.S. Public*, pg. 1144
INTERFACE IN DESIGN, INC.—See IID Inc.; *Int'l*, pg. 3607
INTERFACE INTERNATIONAL B.V.—See Interface, Inc.; *U.S. Public*, pg. 1144
INTERFACE MANAGEMENT SERVICES LTD.—See Ireland Blyth Limited; *Int'l*, pg. 3807
INTERFACE NETWORK TECHNOLOGY (PTY) LTD—See Stellar Capital Partners Limited; *Int'l*, pg. 7204
INTERFACE OPTOELECTRONCIS (SHENZHEN) CO., LTD.—See General Interface Solution (GIS) Holding Ltd.; *Int'l*, pg. 2918
INTERFACE OPTOELECTRONCIS (WUXI) CO., LTD.—See General Interface Solution (GIS) Holding Ltd.; *Int'l*, pg. 2918
INTERFACE OPTOELECTRONICS (SHENZHEN) CO., LTD.—See General Interface Solution (GIS) Holding Ltd.; *Int'l*, pg. 2918
INTERFACE OPTOELECTRONICS (WUXI) CO., LTD.—See General Interface Solution (GIS) Holding Ltd.; *Int'l*, pg. 2918
INTERFACE OVERSEAS HOLDINGS, INC.—See Interface, Inc.; *U.S. Public*, pg. 1144
INTERFACE PERFORMANCE MATERIALS, INC.—See Lydall, Inc.; *U.S. Public*, pg. 1349
INTERFACE PERFORMANCE MATERIALS INDIA, LLP—See Lydall, Inc.; *U.S. Public*, pg. 1349
INTERFACE SEALING SOLUTIONS, EUROPE SARL—See Lydall, Inc.; *U.S. Public*, pg. 1349
INTERFACE SEALING SOLUTIONS—See Lydall, Inc.; *U.S. Public*, pg. 1349
INTERFACE SECURITY SYSTEMS, LLC; *U.S. Private*, pg. 2110
INTERFACE SINGAPORE PTE. LTD.—See Interface, Inc.; *U.S. Public*, pg. 1144
INTERFACE SOLUTIONS CO., LTD.—See Daido Kogyo Co., Ltd.; *Int'l*, pg. 1921
INTERFACE SYSTECH CO., LTD.—See Daido Kogyo Co., Ltd.; *Int'l*, pg. 1921
INTERFACE TECHNOLOGY (CHENGDU) CO., LTD.—See General Interface Solution (GIS) Holding Ltd.; *Int'l*, pg. 2918
INTERFACIAL CONSULTANTS LLC—See Nagase & Co., Ltd.; *Int'l*, pg. 5126
INTERFACING COMPANY OF TEXAS, LLC—See I Squared Capital Advisors (US) LLC; *U.S. Private*, pg. 2025
INTERFACTORY, INC.; *Int'l*, pg. 3740
INTERFAITH HOUSING FOUNDATION; *U.S. Private*, pg. 2110
INTERFAITH MEDICAL CENTER; *U.S. Private*, pg. 2110
INTER FAR EAST ENERGY CORPORATION PUBLIC COMPANY LIMITED; *Int'l*, pg. 3735
INTER FAR EAST (HONGKONG) COMPANY LIMITED—See Inter Far East Energy Corporation Public Company Limited; *Int'l*, pg. 3735
INTERFASHION S.P.A.—See Stefanel S.p.A.; *Int'l*, pg. 7192
INTERFAST AG—See Bossard Holding AG; *Int'l*, pg. 1117

INTERFAX AMERICA—See Interfax Information Service; *Int'l*, pg. 3740
INTERFAX AZERBAIJAN LLC—See Interfax Information Service; *Int'l*, pg. 3740
INTERFAX CHINA—See Interfax Information Service; *Int'l*, pg. 3740
INTERFAX COMMUNICATIONS LIMITED—See Upland Software, Inc.; *U.S. Public*, pg. 2264
INTERFAX EUROPE—See Interfax Information Service; *Int'l*, pg. 3740
INTERFAX GERMANY—See Interfax Information Service; *Int'l*, pg. 3740
INTERFAX INFORMATION SERVICE; *Int'l*, pg. 3740
INTERFAX KAZAKHSTAN—See Interfax Information Service; *Int'l*, pg. 3740
INTERFAX UKRAINE—See Interfax Information Service; *Int'l*, pg. 3740
INTERFAX WEST (BELARUS)—See Interfax Information Service; *Int'l*, pg. 3740
INTERFER ALUMINIUM GMBH—See Knauf Interfer SE; *Int'l*, pg. 4205
INTERFERIE S.A.—See KGHM Polska Miedz S.A.; *Int'l*, pg. 4149
INTERFERM BV—See Koninklijke DSM N.V.; *Int'l*, pg. 4266
INTERFER PRAZISROHR GMBH—See Knauf Interfer SE; *Int'l*, pg. 4205
INTERFER ROHRUNION GMBH—See Knauf Interfer SE; *Int'l*, pg. 4205
INTERFER STAAL—See Knauf Interfer SE; *Int'l*, pg. 4205
INTERFER STAHL GMBH - DORTMUND—See Knauf Interfer SE; *Int'l*, pg. 4205
INTERFER TECHNIK GMBH—See Knauf Interfer SE; *Int'l*, pg. 4205
INTERFIELD GLOBAL SOFTWARE INC.; *Int'l*, pg. 3740
INTERFILM HOLDINGS INC.—See Nicolet Capital Partners, LLC; *U.S. Private*, pg. 2926
INTERFIT LTD—See Trelleborg AB; *Int'l*, pg. 7910
INTERFIT SAS—See Trelleborg AB; *Int'l*, pg. 7910
INTERFLASH D.O.O.—See APG/SGA SA; *Int'l*, pg. 513
INTERFLEX ACQUISITION COMPANY, LLC—See Nicolet Capital Partners, LLC; *U.S. Private*, pg. 2926
INTERFLEX CO., LTD.; *Int'l*, pg. 3740
INTERFLEX DATENSYSTEME GESMBH—See Ingersoll Rand Inc.; *U.S. Public*, pg. 1121
INTERFLEX DATENSYSTEME GMBH & CO. KG—See Ingersoll Rand Inc.; *U.S. Public*, pg. 1121
INTERFLOOR LTD.—See Victoria Plc; *Int'l*, pg. 8188
INTERFLORA BRITISH UNIT—See The Wonderful Company LLC; *U.S. Private*, pg. 4138
INTERFLOUR VIETNAM LTD.—See Sojitz Corporation; *Int'l*, pg. 7061
INTERFOOD SHAREHOLDING COMPANY—See Kirin Holdings Company, Limited; *Int'l*, pg. 4187
INTERFOODS OF AMERICA, INC.; *U.S. Private*, pg. 2110
INTERFOR CEDARPRIME INC.—See Interfor Corporation; *Int'l*, pg. 3741
INTERFOR CORP. - CASTLEGAR DIVISION—See Interfor Corporation; *Int'l*, pg. 3741
INTERFOR CORP. - GRAND FORKS DIVISION—See Interfor Corporation; *Int'l*, pg. 3741
INTERFOR CORPORATION; *Int'l*, pg. 3740
INTERFOR JAPAN LTD.—See Interfor Corporation; *Int'l*, pg. 3741
INTERFORM CORPORATION—See Champion Industries, Inc.; *U.S. Public*, pg. 478
INTERFORM INC.—See Nakayamafuku Co., Ltd.; *Int'l*, pg. 5133
INTERFORM; *U.S. Private*, pg. 2110
INTERFORUM CANADA INC.—See Czech Media Invest as; *Int'l*, pg. 1898
INTERFORUM SAS—See Vivendi SE; *Int'l*, pg. 8271
INTERFOR U.S. INC. - EATONTON DIVISION—See Interfor Corporation; *Int'l*, pg. 3741
INTERFOR U.S. INC. - GEORGETOWN DIVISION—See Interfor Corporation; *Int'l*, pg. 3741
INTERFOR U.S. INC. - MELDRIM DIVISION—See Interfor Corporation; *Int'l*, pg. 3741
INTERFOR U.S. INC. - PERRY DIVISION—See Interfor Corporation; *Int'l*, pg. 3741
INTERFOR U.S. INC. - PRESTON DIVISION—See Interfor Corporation; *Int'l*, pg. 3741
INTERFOR U.S. INC.—See Interfor Corporation; *Int'l*, pg. 3741
INTERFOR U.S. INC. - TACOMA DIVISION—See Interfor Corporation; *Int'l*, pg. 3741
INTERFOUNDRY, INC.; *U.S. Public*, pg. 1144
INTERFRESH INC.; *U.S. Private*, pg. 2110
INTERFUND INVESTMENTS PLC; *Int'l*, pg. 3741
INTERGALACTIC INC.; *U.S. Private*, pg. 2110
INTER-GAMMA INVESTMENT COMPANY LTD.; *Int'l*, pg. 3735
INTERGEMAS MINERACAO E INDUSTRIALIZACAO LTDA—See Belo Sun Mining Corp.; *Int'l*, pg. 968
INTERGENERATIONAL LIVING AND HEALTH CARE, INC.; *U.S. Private*, pg. 2110
INTERGIS CO., LTD.—See Dongkuk Steel Mill Co., Ltd.; *Int'l*, pg. 2169
INTERGLASS CORP.; *U.S. Private*, pg. 2110

INTERGLOBE AIR TRANSPORT LTD.—See InterGlobe Enterprises Limited; *Int'l*, pg. 3741
INTERGLOBE AIR TRANSPORT LTD.—See InterGlobe Enterprises Limited; *Int'l*, pg. 3741
INTERGLOBE AIR TRANSPORT SOUTH AFRICA (PTY) LTD—See InterGlobe Enterprises Limited; *Int'l*, pg. 3741
INTERGLOBE AVIATION LIMITED—See InterGlobe Enterprises Limited; *Int'l*, pg. 3741
INTERGLOBE ENTERPRISES LIMITED; *Int'l*, pg. 3741
INTER GLOBE FINANCE LIMITED; *Int'l*, pg. 3735
INTERGLOBE PRINTING, INC.—See Transcontinental Inc.; *Int'l*, pg. 7897
INTERGLOBE TECHNOLOGY QUOTIENT PVT. LTD.—See InterGlobe Enterprises Limited; *Int'l*, pg. 3741
INTERGRAFICA PRINT & PACK GMBH DRUCKMASCHINENVERTRIEB—See MPC Munchmeyer Petersen & Co. GmbH; *Int'l*, pg. 5061
INTERGRAPH (AUSTRIA) GMBH—See Hexagon AB; *Int'l*, pg. 3368
INTERGRAPH BELGIUM NV/SA—See Hexagon AB; *Int'l*, pg. 3368
INTERGRAPH BENELUX B.V.—See Hexagon AB; *Int'l*, pg. 3368
INTERGRAPH CANADA LTD.—See Hexagon AB; *Int'l*, pg. 3368
INTERGRAPH CONSULTING PVT LTD.—See Hexagon AB; *Int'l*, pg. 3368
INTERGRAPH CORP. (N.Z.) LIMITED—See Hexagon AB; *Int'l*, pg. 3368
INTERGRAPH CORP. (NZ) LIMITED—See Hexagon AB; *Int'l*, pg. 3368
INTERGRAPH CORPORATION—See Hexagon AB; *Int'l*, pg. 3368
INTERGRAPH CORPORATION TAIWAN—See Hexagon AB; *Int'l*, pg. 3368
INTERGRAPH CORP. PTY. LTD.—See Hexagon AB; *Int'l*, pg. 3368
INTERGRAPH CORP. PTY. LTD.—See Hexagon AB; *Int'l*, pg. 3368
INTERGRAPH CR SPOL S.R.O.—See Hexagon AB; *Int'l*, pg. 3368
INTERGRAPH DANMARK A/S—See Hexagon AB; *Int'l*, pg. 3368
INTERGRAPH DE MEXICO S.A. DE C.V.—See Hexagon AB; *Int'l*, pg. 3369
INTERGRAPH DEUTSCHLAND GMBH—See Hexagon AB; *Int'l*, pg. 3368
INTERGRAPH (ESPANA) S.A.—See Hexagon AB; *Int'l*, pg. 3368
INTERGRAPH (ESPANA) S.A.—See Hexagon AB; *Int'l*, pg. 3368
INTERGRAPH EUROPEAN MANUFACTURING L.L.C.—See Hexagon AB; *Int'l*, pg. 3368
INTERGRAPH (FINLAND) OY—See Hexagon AB; *Int'l*, pg. 3368
INTERGRAPH FRANCE S.A.—See Hexagon AB; *Int'l*, pg. 3369
INTERGRAPH HONG KONG LIMITED—See Hexagon AB; *Int'l*, pg. 3369
INTERGRAPH (INDIA) PRIVATE LTD.—See Hexagon AB; *Int'l*, pg. 3368
INTERGRAPH ISRAEL SOFTWARE DEVELOPMENT CENTER LTD—See Hexagon AB; *Int'l*, pg. 3369
INTERGRAPH ITALIA LLC—See Hexagon AB; *Int'l*, pg. 3369
INTERGRAPH KOREA, LTD.—See Hexagon AB; *Int'l*, pg. 3369
INTERGRAPH NORGE AS—See Hexagon AB; *Int'l*, pg. 3369
INTERGRAPH POLSKA SP. Z O.O.—See Hexagon AB; *Int'l*, pg. 3369
INTERGRAPH SERVICIOS DE VENEZUELA, C.A.—See Hexagon AB; *Int'l*, pg. 3369
INTERGRAPH (SHENZHEN) COMPANY LTD.—See Hexagon AB; *Int'l*, pg. 3368
INTERGRAPH (SVERIGE) A.B.—See Hexagon AB; *Int'l*, pg. 3368
INTERGRAPH (SWITZERLAND) AG—See Hexagon AB; *Int'l*, pg. 3368
INTERGRAPH SYSTEMS (SHENZHEN) CO. LTD—See Hexagon AB; *Int'l*, pg. 3369
INTERGRAPH (UK) LIMITED—See Hexagon AB; *Int'l*, pg. 3368
INTER GREEN COMPANY LIMITED—See Interhides Public Company Limited; *Int'l*, pg. 3741
INTERGRID GROUP PTY. LTD.—See 5G Networks Limited; *Int'l*, pg. 13
INTERGROUP CORPORATION; *U.S. Public*, pg. 1144
INTERGROUP INTERNATIONAL, LTD.; *U.S. Private*, pg. 2110
INTERGROUP LIMITED; *Int'l*, pg. 3741
INTERGROUP MEADOWBROOK GARDENS, INC.—See InterGroup Corporation; *U.S. Public*, pg. 1144
INTERGROUP PINE LAKE, INC.—See InterGroup Corporation; *U.S. Public*, pg. 1144
INTERGUARD, LTD.—See Berkshire Hathaway Inc.; *U.S. Public*, pg. 302

Company Index
INTERGROUP LIMITED
CORPORATE AFFILIATIONS

INTERGULF CORPORATION—See EQT AB; *Int'l*, pg. 2473
INTERGY EMARKETING SOLUTIONS—See Pacrim International Capital Inc.; *Int'l*, pg. 5693
INTERHEALTH NUTRACEUTICALS, INC.—See Lonza Group AG; *Int'l*, pg. 4553
INTERHIDES PUBLIC COMPANY LIMITED; *Int'l*, pg. 3741
INTERHIGH EDUCATION LIMITED—See Inspired Education Holdings Limited; *Int'l*, pg. 3720
INTERHOUSE COMPANY; *Int'l*, pg. 3741
INTERHYDRAULIK ZEPRO GMBH—See Cargotec Corporation; *Int'l*, pg. 1328
INTERHYP AG—See ING Groep N.V.; *Int'l*, pg. 3700
INTERICA, INC.—See ALS Limited; *Int'l*, pg. 378
INTERICA LIMITED—See ALS Limited; *Int'l*, pg. 378
INTERICA LIMITED—See ALS Limited; *Int'l*, pg. 378
INTER IKEA CENTRE GROUP A/S—See Interogo Holding AG; *Int'l*, pg. 3754
INTER IKEA CENTRE GROUP A/S—See Stichting INGKA Foundation; *Int'l*, pg. 7214
INTER IKEA SYSTEMS B.V.—See Interogo Holding AG; *Int'l*, pg. 3754
INTER IMAGING PTE. LTD.—See Indian Toners & Developers Ltd.; *Int'l*, pg. 3654
INTERIM HEALTHCARE INC.—See The Halifax Group LLC; *U.S. Private*, pg. 4042
INTERIM HEALTHCARE OF HARTFORD, INC.; *U.S. Private*, pg. 2110
INTERIM HEALTHCARE OF WYOMING, INC.—See Natur International Corp.; *Int'l*, pg. 5166
INTERIM HOUSE INC.—See Public Health Management Corporation; *U.S. Private*, pg. 3299
INTERIM HOUSE WEST FACILITIES, INC.—See Public Health Management Corporation; *U.S. Private*, pg. 3299
INTERIMMOBILI SRL—See Vittoria Assicurazioni S.p.A.; *Int'l*, pg. 8264
INTERIM PHYSICIANS, LLC; *U.S. Private*, pg. 2110
INTERIM SOLUTIONS FOR GOVERNMENT, LLC; *U.S. Private*, pg. 2110
INTERIM STORAGE PARTNERS LLC—See Orano SA; *Int'l*, pg. 5611
INTERINA D.O.O.—See INA-Industrija Nafte, d.d.; *Int'l*, pg. 3643
INTERINA HOLDING LTD.—See INA-Industrija Nafte, d.d.; *Int'l*, pg. 3643
INTER INA LTD.—See INA-Industrija Nafte, d.d.; *Int'l*, pg. 3642
INTER INDUSTRIES PLUS LTD.; *Int'l*, pg. 3735
INTER-INDUSTRY CONFERENCE ON AUTO COLLISION REPAIR; *U.S. Private*, pg. 2107
INTER-INOX S.A.R.L.—See Wurth Verwaltungsgesellschaft mbH; *Int'l*, pg. 8511
INTERIOR ARCHITECTS, INC.; *U.S. Private*, pg. 2111
INTERIOR ARCHITECTS, INC .—See Interior Architects, Inc.; *U.S. Private*, pg. 2111
INTERIOR CONCEPTS, INC.—See Blue Sage Capital, L.P.; *U.S. Private*, pg. 592
INTERIOR CRAFTS INC.; *U.S. Private*, pg. 2111
INTERIOR DESIGN & ARCHITECTURE, INC.; *U.S. Private*, pg. 2111
INTERIOR DESIGN SERVICES, INC.; *U.S. Private*, pg. 2111
INTERIOR DISTRIBUTORS INC.; *U.S. Private*, pg. 2111
INTERIOR DYNAMICS INC.; *U.S. Private*, pg. 2111
INTERIOR ENVIRONMENTS, INC.; *U.S. Private*, pg. 2111
INTERIORES AEREOS S.A. DE C.V.—See General Dynamics Corporation; *U.S. Public*, pg. 916
INTERIOR FUSION, LLC; *U.S. Private*, pg. 2111
INTERIOR INVESTMENTS LLC; *U.S. Private*, pg. 2111
INTERIOR LOGIC GROUP HOLDINGS, LLC—See Littlejohn & Co., LLC; *U.S. Private*, pg. 2470
INTERIOR LOGIC GROUP HOLDINGS, LLC—See Platinum Equity, LLC; *U.S. Private*, pg. 3205
INTERIOR LOGIC GROUP, INC.—See Littlejohn & Co., LLC; *U.S. Private*, pg. 2470
INTERIOR LOGIC GROUP, INC.—See Platinum Equity, LLC; *U.S. Private*, pg. 3205
INTERIOR MANUFACTURING GROUP INC; *Int'l*, pg. 3741
INTERIOR ROADS LTD.; *Int'l*, pg. 3741
INTERIORS OF WINTER PARK, INC.; *U.S. Private*, pg. 2111
INTERIOR SPECIALISTS, INC.—See Littlejohn & Co., LLC; *U.S. Private*, pg. 2470
INTERIOR SPECIALISTS, INC.—See Platinum Equity, LLC; *U.S. Private*, pg. 3205
INTERIOR SPECIALTIES INC.; *U.S. Private*, pg. 2111
INTERIOR SYSTEMS INC.; *U.S. Private*, pg. 2111
INTERIOR SYSTEMS INC.; *U.S. Private*, pg. 2111
INTERIOR SYSTEMS INC.; *U.S. Private*, pg. 2111
INTERIOR TELEPHONE COMPANY—See Telalaska Inc.; *U.S. Private*, pg. 3959
INTERIOR WORKPLACE SOLUTIONS LLC; *U.S. Private*, pg. 2111
INTER ISLAND PETROLEUM, INC.—See Par Pacific Holdings, Inc.; *U.S. Public*, pg. 1636
INTERJET S.R.L.—See Cremonini S.p.A.; *Int'l*, pg. 1838
INTERKAL, LLC—See Kotobuki Corporation; *Int'l*, pg. 4292
INTERKAT KATALYSATOREN GMBH—See Baumot Group AG; *Int'l*, pg. 895
INTERKOS INC.; *Int'l*, pg. 3741
INTERKOV SPOL.S R.O.—See Ring International Holding AG; *Int'l*, pg. 6343
INTERKREDITT AS—See B2Holding AS; *Int'l*, pg. 790
INTERLAB SP. Z O.O.—See Yokogawa Electric Corporation; *Int'l*, pg. 8592
INTERLAB SUPPLY; *U.S. Private*, pg. 2111
INTERLAKE MECALUX, INC.—See Acerolux SL; *Int'l*, pg. 101
INTERLAKEN CAPITAL AVIATION SERVICES, INC.—See W.R. Berkley Corporation; *U.S. Public*, pg. 2318
INTERLAKEN CAPITAL, INC.; *U.S. Private*, pg. 2111
INTERLAKEN TECHNOLOGY CORPORATION—See Wind Point Advisors LLC; *U.S. Private*, pg. 4534
INTER-LAKES COMMUNITY ACTION PARTNERSHIP; *U.S. Private*, pg. 2107
INTERLAKE STEAMSHIP COMPANY INC.—See Mormac Marine Group, Inc.; *U.S. Private*, pg. 2785
INTERLANA S.R.O—See Chargeurs SA; *Int'l*, pg. 1449
INTERLAND TECHNIEK B.V.—See SIG plc; *Int'l*, pg. 6906
INTERLATES LTD.—See BASF SE; *Int'l*, pg. 884
INTERLEAF GMBH—See ESW Capital, LLC; *U.S. Private*, pg. 1430
INTERLEASE AUTO E.A.D.—See KBC Group NV; *Int'l*, pg. 4105
INTERLEASE E.A.D.—See KBC Group NV; *Int'l*, pg. 4105
INTERLEGO AG—See Kirkbi A/S; *Int'l*, pg. 4189
INTERLET PROPERTY MANAGEMENT LIMITED—See The Skipton Building Society; *Int'l*, pg. 7686
INTERLEX COMMUNICATIONS INC; *U.S. Private*, pg. 2111
INTERLIFE HOLDINGS CO., LTD.; *Int'l*, pg. 3741
INTERLIGACAO ELETRICA GARANHUNS S.A.—See Cia de Transmissao de Energia Eletrica Paulista; *Int'l*, pg. 1601
INTERLINC MORTGAGE SERVICES, LLC; *U.S. Private*, pg. 2111
INTERLINE BRANDS, INC.—See The Home Depot, Inc.; *U.S. Public*, pg. 2089
INTERLINE INSURANCE SERVICES, INC.—See Fosun International Limited; *Int'l*, pg. 2752
INTERLINK COMMUNICATION PUBLIC COMPANY LIMITED; *Int'l*, pg. 3741
INTERLINK COMMUNICATION SYSTEMS, INC.—See Global Convergence, Inc.; *U.S. Private*, pg. 1713
INTERLINK ELECTRONICS, INC.; *U.S. Public*, pg. 1144
INTERLINK ELECTRONICS, K.K.—See Interlink Electronics, Inc.; *U.S. Public*, pg. 1144
INTERLINK EXPRESS & INTERLINK IRELAND—See La Poste S.A.; *Int'l*, pg. 4388
INTERLINK HEALTHCARE COMMUNICATION—See Integrated Communications Corp.; *U.S. Private*, pg. 2099
INTERLINK INSURED SWEEP LLC—See Webster Financial Corporation; *U.S. Public*, pg. 2341
INTERLINK PRODUCTS INTERNATIONAL, INC.; *U.S. Public*, pg. 1144
INTERLINK ROADS PTY. LTD.; *Int'l*, pg. 3741
INTERLINK TELECOM PCL; *Int'l*, pg. 3741
INTERLITE AB; *Int'l*, pg. 3741
INTERLOAD SERVICES LTD.—See Caron Transportation Systems Partnership; *Int'l*, pg. 1342
INTERLOCK INDUSTRIES, INC.; *U.S. Private*, pg. 2111
INTERLOGIC-LEASING SA; *Int'l*, pg. 3742
INTERLOGIC REAL ESTATE JSC; *Int'l*, pg. 3742
INTERLOGICS, INC.—See Dentsu Group Inc.; *Int'l*, pg. 2039
INTERLUBES GMBH—See BayWa AG; *Int'l*, pg. 918
INTERLUBE USA INC.—See The Timken Company; *U.S. Public*, pg. 2132
INTERLUDE HOME, INC.; *U.S. Private*, pg. 2112
INTERMAC DO BRASIL COMERCIO DE MAQUINAS E EQUIPAMENTOS LTDA.—See Biesse S.p.A.; *Int'l*, pg. 1020
INTERMACO S.R.L.—See SED International Holdings, Inc.; *U.S. Private*, pg. 3597
INTERMAGNETICS SRL—See ABB Ltd.; *Int'l*, pg. 54
INTERMAIL A/S; *Int'l*, pg. 3742
INTERMAIL DANMARK A/S—See InterMail A/S; *Int'l*, pg. 3742
INTERMAIL SVERIGE AB—See InterMail A/S; *Int'l*, pg. 3742
INTERMALTA, S.A.—See Vivescia; *Int'l*, pg. 8279
INTERMAP TECHNOLOGIES CORPORATION; *U.S. Public*, pg. 1144
INTERMAP TECHNOLOGIES INC.—See Intermap Technologies Corporation; *U.S. Public*, pg. 1145
INTERMARINE DENMARK APS—See Intermarine, Inc.; *U.S. Private*, pg. 2112
INTERMARINE, INC.; *U.S. Private*, pg. 2112
INTERMARINE PROJECT SERVICES S.L.—See Intermarine, Inc.; *U.S. Private*, pg. 2112
INTERMARINE SERVICOS PETROLIFEROS LTDA.—See Transocean Ltd.; *Int'l*, pg. 7903
INTERMARINE S.P.A.—See Immsi S.p.a.; *Int'l*, pg. 3628
INTERMARKET CORP.; *U.S. Private*, pg. 2112
INTERMARKETS, INC.; *U.S. Private*, pg. 2112
INTERMARK FOODS, INC.; *U.S. Private*, pg. 2112
INTERMARK GROUP, INC.; *U.S. Private*, pg. 2112
INTERMARK (PRIVATE) LIMITED—See Pakistan Cables Limited; *Int'l*, pg. 5704
INTERMATE ELECTRONICS AB—See OEM International AB; *Int'l*, pg. 5528
INTERMATIC, INC.; *U.S. Private*, pg. 2112
INTERMAT—See Edgewater Capital Partners, L.P.; *U.S. Private*, pg. 1335
INTERMAT TRADING CORP.; *U.S. Private*, pg. 2112
INTER-M CO., LTD.; *Int'l*, pg. 3735
INTERMEC BY HONEYWELL—See Honeywell International Inc.; *U.S. Public*, pg. 1050
INTERMECH LTD—See Atlas Copco AB; *Int'l*, pg. 677
INTERMEC, INC.—See Honeywell International Inc.; *U.S. Public*, pg. 1050
INTERMEC MEDIA PRODUCTS—See Honeywell International Inc.; *U.S. Public*, pg. 1050
INTERMEC (SOUTH AMERICA) LTDA.—See Honeywell International Inc.; *U.S. Public*, pg. 1050
INTERMEC TECHNOLOGIES AB—See Honeywell International Inc.; *U.S. Public*, pg. 1050
INTERMEC TECHNOLOGIES AUSTRALIA PTY. LIMITED—See Honeywell International Inc.; *U.S. Public*, pg. 1050
INTERMEC TECHNOLOGIES CANADA ULC—See Honeywell International Inc.; *U.S. Public*, pg. 1050
INTERMEC TECHNOLOGIES CORPORATION—See Honeywell International Inc.; *U.S. Public*, pg. 1050
INTERMEC TECHNOLOGIES DE MEXICO, S. DE R.L. DE C.V.—See Honeywell International Inc.; *U.S. Public*, pg. 1050
INTERMEC TECHNOLOGIES GMBH—See Honeywell International Inc.; *U.S. Public*, pg. 1050
INTERMEC TECHNOLOGIES S.A.S.—See Honeywell International Inc.; *U.S. Public*, pg. 1050
INTERMEC TECHNOLOGIES, S.L.U.—See Honeywell International Inc.; *U.S. Public*, pg. 1050
INTERMEC TECHNOLOGIES (S) PTE LTD—See Honeywell International Inc.; *U.S. Public*, pg. 1050
INTERMEC TECHNOLOGIES S.R.L.—See Honeywell International Inc.; *U.S. Public*, pg. 1050
INTERMEC TECHNOLOGIES U.K. LIMITED—See Honeywell International Inc.; *U.S. Public*, pg. 1050
INTERMED EQUIPAMENTO MEDICO HOSPITALAR LTDA.—See Becton, Dickinson & Company; *U.S. Public*, pg. 292
INTERMEDES SAS; *Int'l*, pg. 3742
THE INTERMED GROUP, INC.—See Cressey & Company, LP; *U.S. Private*, pg. 1095
THE INTERMED GROUP, INC.—See Health Enterprise Partners LLC; *U.S. Private*, pg. 1893
INTERMEDIA ADVISORS, LLC; *U.S. Private*, pg. 2112
INTERMEDIA ESPANOL, INC.—See Hemisphere Media Group, Inc.; *U.S. Private*, pg. 1913
INTER-MEDIA MARKETING, LLC—See Qualfon SA de CV; *Int'l*, pg. 6150
INTERMEDIA.NET, INC.—See Madison Dearborn Partners, LLC; *U.S. Private*, pg. 2541
INTERMEDIA OUTDOORS, INC.—See InterMedia Advisors, LLC; *U.S. Private*, pg. 2112
INTERMEDIA PARTNERS, L.P.—See InterMedia Advisors, LLC; *U.S. Private*, pg. 2112
INTERMEDIATE CAPITAL ASIA PACIFIC LIMITED—See Intermediate Capital Group plc; *Int'l*, pg. 3742
INTERMEDIATE CAPITAL AUSTRALIA PTY. LIMITED—See Intermediate Capital Group plc; *Int'l*, pg. 3742
INTERMEDIATE CAPITAL BERATUNGSGESELLSCHAFT MBH—See Intermediate Capital Group plc; *Int'l*, pg. 3742
INTERMEDIATE CAPITAL GROUP BENELUX B.V.—See Intermediate Capital Group plc; *Int'l*, pg. 3742
INTERMEDIATE CAPITAL GROUP ESPANA S.L.U.—See Intermediate Capital Group plc; *Int'l*, pg. 3742
INTERMEDIATE CAPITAL GROUP, INC.—See Intermediate Capital Group plc; *Int'l*, pg. 3742
INTERMEDIATE CAPITAL GROUP PLC; *Int'l*, pg. 3742
INTERMEDIATE CAPITAL GROUP SAS—See Intermediate Capital Group plc; *Int'l*, pg. 3742
INTERMEDIATE CAPITAL GROUP (SINGAPORE) PTE. LIMITED—See Intermediate Capital Group plc; *Int'l*, pg. 3742
INTERMEDIATE CAPITAL INVESTMENTS LIMITED—See Intermediate Capital Group plc; *Int'l*, pg. 3742
INTERMEDIATE CAPITAL MANAGERS LIMITED—See Intermediate Capital Group plc; *Int'l*, pg. 3742
INTERMEDIATE CAPITAL NORDIC AB—See Intermediate Capital Group plc; *Int'l*, pg. 3742
INTERMEDIATE PETROCHEMICALS INDUSTRIES COMPANY LIMITED; *Int'l*, pg. 3743
INTERMEDICAL CARE & LAB HOSPITAL PUBLIC COMPANY LIMITED; *Int'l*, pg. 3743
INTER-MED, INC.—See Behrman Brothers Management Corp.; *U.S. Private*, pg. 515
INTERMEDIX CESKA REPUBLIKA S.R.O.—See CompuGroup Medical SE & Co. KGaA; *Int'l*, pg. 1757
INTERMEDIX DEUTSCHLAND GMBH—See CompuGroup Medical SE & Co. KGaA; *Int'l*, pg. 1755

COMPANY NAME INDEX

INTERMEDIX FRANCE S.A.R.L.—See CompuGroup Medical SE & Co. KGaA; *Int'l*, pg. 1755
INTERMEDIX OSTERREICH GMBH—See CompuGroup Medical SE & Co. KGaA; *Int'l*, pg. 1755
INTERMEDIX SA (PTY) LTD.—See CompuGroup Medical SE & Co. KGaA; *Int'l*, pg. 1756
INTERMED NUCLEAR MEDICINE, INC.—See Cressey & Company, LP; *U.S. Private*, pg. 1095
INTERMED NUCLEAR MEDICINE, INC.—See Health Enterprise Partners LLC; *U.S. Private*, pg. 1893
INTERMED ULTRASOUND—See Cressey & Company, LP; *U.S. Private*, pg. 1095
INTERMED ULTRASOUND—See Health Enterprise Partners LLC; *U.S. Private*, pg. 1893
INTERMED X-RAY, INC.—See Cressey & Company, LP; *U.S. Private*, pg. 1095
INTERMED X-RAY, INC.—See Health Enterprise Partners LLC; *U.S. Private*, pg. 1893
INTERMERKUR , D.O.O.—See Merkur, d.d.; *Int'l*, pg. 4837
INTERMESS DORGELOH AG—See Messe Munchen GmbH; *Int'l*, pg. 4841
INTERMESTIC INC.; *Int'l*, pg. 3743
INTERMETAL ENGINEERS PRIVATE LIMITED—See RHI Magnesita N.V.; *Int'l*, pg. 6325
INTERMETRO COMMUNICATIONS, INC.; *U.S. Private*, pg. 2112
INTERMETRO DE MEXICO, S. DE R.L. DE C.V.—See Emerson Electric Co.; *U.S. Public*, pg. 750
INTERMETRO INDUSTRIES B.V.—See Emerson Electric Co.; *U.S. Public*, pg. 750
INTERMETRO INDUSTRIES CORPORATION—See Emerson Electric Co.; *U.S. Public*, pg. 750
INTERMETRO INDUSTRIES CORPORATION—See Emerson Electric Co.; *U.S. Public*, pg. 750
INTERMETRO INDUSTRIES CORPORATION—See Emerson Electric Co.; *U.S. Public*, pg. 750
INTERMETRO INDUSTRIES CORPORATION—See Emerson Electric Co.; *U.S. Public*, pg. 750
INTERMEX WIRE TRANSFER, LLC—See International Money Express Inc.; *U.S. Public*, pg. 1154
INTERMEX WIRE TRANSFERS DE GUATEMALA S.A.—See International Money Express Inc.; *U.S. Public*, pg. 1155
INTERMIX, A.E.—See Titan Cement Company S.A.; *Int'l*, pg. 7759
INTERMIX (ITM) INC.—See Altamont Capital Partners; *U.S. Private*, pg. 205
INTERMOBILIARIA, S.A.—See Bankinter, S.A.; *Int'l*, pg. 850
INTERMOBIL OTOMOTIV MUMESSILLIK VE TICARET A.S.—See Hella GmbH & Co. KGaA; *Int'l*, pg. 3332
INTER-MODA GMBH—See CVC Capital Partners SICAV-FIS S.A.; *Int'l*, pg. 1883
INTERMODAL CARTAGE CO. INC.; *U.S. Private*, pg. 2112
INTERMODAL ENGINEERING CO., LTD.—See Kawasaki Kisen Kaisha, Ltd.; *Int'l*, pg. 4099
INTERMODAL MEXICO, S.A. DE C.V.—See Grupo Mexico, S.A.B. de C.V.; *Int'l*, pg. 3132
INTERMODAL SALES CORPORATION; *U.S. Private*, pg. 2112
INTERMODAL TRANSPORTATION CENTER, INC.—See Central New York Regional Transportation Authority; *U.S. Private*, pg. 824
INTERMOLECULAR, INC.—See Merck KGaA; *Int'l*, pg. 4831
INTERMONTE PARTNERS SIM S.P.A.; *Int'l*, pg. 3743
INTERMOOR INC.—See Buckthorn Partners LLP; *Int'l*, pg. 1210
INTERMOOR INC.—See OEP Capital Advisors, L.P.; *U.S. Private*, pg. 2997
INTERMOOR PTE. LTD.—See Buckthorn Partners LLP; *Int'l*, pg. 1210
INTERMOOR PTE. LTD.—See OEP Capital Advisors, L.P.; *U.S. Private*, pg. 2997
INTERMOOR—See Buckthorn Partners LLP; *Int'l*, pg. 1210
INTERMOOR—See OEP Capital Advisors, L.P.; *U.S. Private*, pg. 2997
INTERMOTEL LEASING, INC.—See Corpay, Inc.; *U.S. Public*, pg. 580
INTERMOUNTAIN AUTO GLASS—See s.a. D'Ieteren n.v.; *Int'l*, pg. 6448
INTER MOUNTAIN CABLE INC.—See Gearheart Communications Company, Inc.; *U.S. Private*, pg. 1655
INTERMOUNTAIN CONCRETE SPCECIALTY; *U.S. Private*, pg. 2112
INTERMOUNTAIN DONOR SERVICES; *U.S. Private*, pg. 2113
INTERMOUNTAIN ELECTRIC, INC.; *U.S. Private*, pg. 2113
INTERMOUNTAIN ELECTRIC, INC.—See Quanta Services, Inc.; *U.S. Public*, pg. 1751
INTERMOUNTAIN ELECTRIC SERVICE INC.; *U.S. Private*, pg. 2113
INTERMOUNTAIN FARMERS ASSOCIATION - DRAPER FEED MILL—See Intermountain Farmers Association; *U.S. Private*, pg. 2113

INTERMOUNTAIN FARMERS ASSOCIATION - NORTH REGION FEED MILL—See Intermountain Farmers Association; *U.S. Private*, pg. 2113
INTERMOUNTAIN FARMERS ASSOCIATION; *U.S. Private*, pg. 2113
INTERMOUNTAIN FARMERS ASSOCIATION - SOUTH REGION FEED MILL—See Intermountain Farmers Association; *U.S. Private*, pg. 2113
INTERMOUNTAIN GAS COMPANY—See MDU Resources Group, Inc.; *U.S. Public*, pg. 1410
INTERMOUNTAIN HEALTHCARE INC.; *U.S. Private*, pg. 2113
INTERMOUNTAIN INDUSTRIES, INC.; *U.S. Private*, pg. 2113
INTERMOUNTAIN MEDICAL GROUP, INC.—See Community Health Systems, Inc.; *U.S. Public*, pg. 553
INTERMOUNTAIN PHYSICAL THERAPY, LIMITED PARTNERSHIP—See U.S. Physical Therapy, Inc.; *U.S. Public*, pg. 2214
INTERMOUNTAIN PLANTINGS INC.—See BrightView Holdings, Inc.; *U.S. Public*, pg. 384
INTERMOUNTAIN POWER AGENCY; *U.S. Private*, pg. 2113
INTERMOUNTAIN RURAL ELECTRIC ASSOCIATION; *U.S. Private*, pg. 2113
INTERMOUNTAIN VALVE & CONTROLS INC.—See Bray International, Inc.; *U.S. Private*, pg. 642
INTERMOUNTAIN WEST COMMUNICATIONS COMPANY; *U.S. Private*, pg. 2113
INTERMOUNTAIN WOOD PRODUCTS INC.; *U.S. Private*, pg. 2113
INTERNACIONAL DE CERAMICA, S.A.B. DE C.V.; *Int'l*, pg. 3743
INTERNACIONAL DE ELEVADORES, S.A. DE C.V.—See Mitsubishi Electric Corporation; *Int'l*, pg. 4944
INTERNACIONAL NEGOCIO ELECTRONICA Y COMPONENTES ESPANA SAU—See TKH Group N.V.; *Int'l*, pg. 7764
INTERNAL ENGINE PARTS GROUP INC.; *U.S. Private*, pg. 2113
INTERNAL MEDIA SERVICES—See Qatar Investment Authority; *Int'l*, pg. 6134
INTERNAL MEDICINE ASSOCIATES OF SOUTHERN HILLS, LLC—See HCA Healthcare, Inc.; *U.S. Public*, pg. 999
INTERNAL MEDICINE OF BLACKSBURG, LLC—See HCA Healthcare, Inc.; *U.S. Public*, pg. 999
INTERNAL MEDICINE OF PASADENA, PLLC—See HCA Healthcare, Inc.; *U.S. Public*, pg. 999
INTERNAP CONNECTIVITY LLC—See Internap Holding LLC; *U.S. Private*, pg. 2113
INTERNAP HOLDING LLC; *U.S. Private*, pg. 2113
INTERNAP JAPAN CO., LTD.—See Internap Holding LLC; *U.S. Private*, pg. 2113
INTERNAP NETWORK SERVICES (AUSTRALIA) LTD.—See Internap Holding LLC; *U.S. Private*, pg. 2113
INTERNAP NETWORK SERVICES UK LTD.—See Internap Holding LLC; *U.S. Private*, pg. 2113
INTERNATIONAAL HANDELSKANTOOR B.V.—See Aiphone Co., Ltd.; *Int'l*, pg. 235
INTERNATIONAL ACADEMY OF DESIGN AND TECHNOLOGY—See Perdoceo Education Corporation; *U.S. Public*, pg. 1673
INTERNATIONAL ACADEMY OF DESIGN & TECHNOLOGY DETROIT, INC.—See Perdoceo Education Corporation; *U.S. Public*, pg. 1673
INTERNATIONAL ACADEMY OF DESIGN & TECHNOLOGY-NASHVILLE, LLC—See Perdoceo Education Corporation; *U.S. Public*, pg. 1673
INTERNATIONAL ACADEMY OF DESIGN & TECHNOLOGY—See Perdoceo Education Corporation; *U.S. Public*, pg. 1673
INTERNATIONAL ACCOUNTS PAYABLE PROFESSIONALS—See The Institute of Financial Operations; *U.S. Private*, pg. 4056
INTERNATIONAL ADVERTISING AGENCY—See International Agencies Company Ltd.; *Int'l*, pg. 3743
INTERNATIONAL AERO ENGINES AG—See MTU Aero Engines AG; *Int'l*, pg. 5072
INTERNATIONAL AERO ENGINES AG—See Rolls-Royce Holdings plc; *Int'l*, pg. 6393
INTERNATIONAL AERO ENGINES AG—See RTX Corporation; *U.S. Public*, pg. 1823
INTERNATIONAL AGENCIES COMPANY LTD.; *Int'l*, pg. 3743
INTERNATIONAL AGRICULTURAL PRODUCTS; *Int'l*, pg. 3743
INTERNATIONAL AIR CONSOLIDATORS; *U.S. Private*, pg. 2114
INTERNATIONAL AIRLINE SERVICES AMERICAS L.P.—See Air France-KLM S.A.; *Int'l*, pg. 237
INTERNATIONAL AIRLINE SERVICES EUROPE LIMITED—See Air France-KLM S.A.; *Int'l*, pg. 237
INTERNATIONAL AIRLINE SERVICES LIMITED—See Air France-KLM S.A.; *Int'l*, pg. 237
INTERNATIONAL AIRPORT UTILITY CO., LTD—See ANA Holdings Inc.; *Int'l*, pg. 444

INTERNATIONAL AIR TRANSPORT ASSOCIATION; *Int'l*, pg. 3743
INTERNATIONAL APPLICATIONS LIMITED; *Int'l*, pg. 3743
INTERNATIONAL ARABIAN DEVELOPMENT & INVESTMENT TRADING CO.; *Int'l*, pg. 3743
INTERNATIONAL ARMORING CORP.—See IAG Holdings Inc.; *U.S. Private*, pg. 2027
INTERNATIONAL ASSEMBLY SOLUTIONS, LIMITED—See SPI Energy Co., Ltd.; *Int'l*, pg. 7135
INTERNATIONAL ASSEMBLY SPECIALISTS S.A. DE C.V.—See Shugart Corporation; *U.S. Private*, pg. 3644
INTERNATIONAL ASSET MANAGEMENT LIMITED, LLC—See International Asset Management Ltd.; *Int'l*, pg. 3743
INTERNATIONAL ASSET MANAGEMENT LTD.; *Int'l*, pg. 3743
INTERNATIONAL ASSET RECONSTRUCTION COMPANY PRIVATE LIMITED; *Int'l*, pg. 3743
INTERNATIONAL ASSOCIATED CARGO CARRIER S.A.E.—See Abu Dhabi Developmental Holding Company PJSC; *Int'l*, pg. 71
INTERNATIONAL ASSOCIATION FOR K-12 ONLINE LEARNING; *U.S. Private*, pg. 2114
INTERNATIONAL ASSOCIATION OF AMUSEMENT PARKS & ATTRACTIONS; *U.S. Private*, pg. 2114
INTERNATIONAL ASSOCIATION OF BRIDGE, STRUCTURAL, ORNAMENTAL, AND REINFORCING IRON WORKERS; *U.S. Private*, pg. 2114
INTERNATIONAL ASSOCIATION OF CHIEFS OF POLICE; *U.S. Private*, pg. 2114
THE INTERNATIONAL ASSOCIATION OF FIRE CHIEFS; *U.S. Private*, pg. 4057
INTERNATIONAL ASSOCIATION OF FIRE FIGHTERS; *U.S. Private*, pg. 2114
INTERNATIONAL AUTOMATED SYSTEMS, INC.; *U.S. Private*, pg. 2114
INTERNATIONAL AUTOMOTIVE COMPONENTS GROUP EUROPE—See Invesco Ltd.; *U.S. Public*, pg. 1164
INTERNATIONAL AUTOMOTIVE COMPONENTS GROUP, LLC—See Invesco Ltd.; *U.S. Public*, pg. 1164
INTERNATIONAL AUTOMOTIVE COMPONENTS GROUP NORTH AMERICA INC.—See Invesco Ltd.; *U.S. Public*, pg. 1164
INTERNATIONAL AUTOMOTIVE COMPONENTS GROUP, S.A.—See Invesco Ltd.; *U.S. Public*, pg. 1164
INTERNATIONAL AUTOMOTIVE TECHNICIANS' NETWORK, INC.—See Vista Equity Partners, LLC; *U.S. Private*, pg. 4400
INTERNATIONAL AUTOPARTS, INC.; *U.S. Private*, pg. 2114
INTERNATIONAL BACCALAUREATE; *U.S. Private*, pg. 2114
INTERNATIONAL BALER CORP.; *U.S. Public*, pg. 1145
INTERNATIONAL BANCSHARES CORPORATION; *U.S. Public*, pg. 1145
INTERNATIONAL BANCSHARES OF OKLAHOMA, INC.; *U.S. Private*, pg. 2114
INTERNATIONAL BANK FOR ECONOMIC CO-OPERATION; *Int'l*, pg. 3743
THE INTERNATIONAL BANK FOR TRADE & FINANCE; *Int'l*, pg. 7656
INTERNATIONAL BANK OF AZERBAIJAN-MOSCOW—See International Bank of Azerbaijan; *Int'l*, pg. 3744
INTERNATIONAL BANK OF AZERBAIJAN; *Int'l*, pg. 3743
INTERNATIONAL BANK OF COMMERCE, BROWNSVILLE—See International Bancshares Corporation; *U.S. Public*, pg. 1145
INTERNATIONAL BANK OF COMMERCE, OKLAHOMA—See International Bancshares Corporation; *U.S. Public*, pg. 1145
INTERNATIONAL BANK OF COMMERCE—See International Bancshares Corporation; *U.S. Public*, pg. 1145
INTERNATIONAL BANK OF COMMERCE, ZAPATA—See International Bancshares Corporation; *U.S. Public*, pg. 1145
THE INTERNATIONAL BANK OF NEVIS—See The Bank of Nevis Ltd.; *Int'l*, pg. 7616
THE INTERNATIONAL BANK OF QATAR (Q.S.C); *Int'l*, pg. 7656
INTERNATIONAL BASE METALS LIMITED; *Int'l*, pg. 3744
INTERNATIONAL BATTERY METALS LTD.; *Int'l*, pg. 3744
INTERNATIONAL BEDDING CORP.—See IBC Group Inc.; *U.S. Private*, pg. 2028
INTERNATIONAL BEDDING CORP.—See IBC Group Inc.; *U.S. Private*, pg. 2028
INTERNATIONAL BEDDING CORP.—See IBC Group Inc.; *U.S. Private*, pg. 2028
INTERNATIONAL BEDDING CORP.—See IBC Group Inc.; *U.S. Private*, pg. 2028
INTERNATIONAL BETHLEHEM MINING CORP.; *Int'l*, pg. 3744
INTERNATIONAL BEVERAGE COMPANY, INC.—See L'Arche Green N.V.; *Int'l*, pg. 4376
INTERNATIONAL BEVERAGE HOLDINGS (CHINA) LIMITED—See Thai Beverage Public Company Limited; *Int'l*, pg. 7590

1363

INTERNATIONAL BEVERAGE HOLDINGS LIMITED USA, INC.—See Thai Beverage Public Company Limited; *Int'l*, pg. 7591

INTERNATIONAL BEVERAGE HOLDINGS (SINGAPORE) PTE. LIMITED—See Thai Beverage Public Company Limited; *Int'l*, pg. 7590

INTERNATIONAL BEVERAGE HOLDINGS (UK) LIMITED—See Thai Beverage Public Company Limited; *Int'l*, pg. 7590

INTERNATIONAL BEVERAGES INC.—See Brooklyn Brewery Corporation; *U.S. Private*, pg. 663

INTERNATIONAL BEVERAGE VIETNAM COMPANY LIMITED—See Thai Beverage Public Company Limited; *Int'l*, pg. 7591

INTERNATIONAL BILLS FINANCE CORP.—See IBF Financial Holdings Co., Ltd.; *Int'l*, pg. 3574

INTERNATIONAL BIOTECHNOLOGY TRUST PLC; *Int'l*, pg. 3744

INTERNATIONAL BISCUITS LIMITED—See Seprod Limited; *Int'l*, pg. 6718

INTERNATIONAL BLENDS COFFEE CO—See Huron Capital Partners LLC; *U.S. Private*, pg. 2012

INTERNATIONAL BONDED COURIERS INC.; *U.S. Private*, pg. 2114

INTERNATIONAL BRAKE INDUSTRIES, INC.—See Wellspring Capital Management LLC; *U.S. Private*, pg. 4477

INTERNATIONAL BRAND MANAGEMENT LIMITED—See Frasers Group plc; *Int'l*, pg. 2765

INTERNATIONAL BRANDS PRIVATE LIMITED; *Int'l*, pg. 3744

INTERNATIONAL BRICK & TILE PTY LTD—See Brickworks Limited; *Int'l*, pg. 1152

INTERNATIONAL BRIQUETTES HOLDING—See Siderurgica Venezolana Sivensa S.A.; *Int'l*, pg. 6883

INTERNATIONAL BROKERAGE & FINANCIAL MARKETS CO.; *Int'l*, pg. 3744

INTERNATIONAL BROTHERHOOD OF ELECTRICAL WORKERS; *U.S. Private*, pg. 2114

INTERNATIONAL BROTHERHOOD OF TEAMSTERS; *U.S. Private*, pg. 2114

INTERNATIONAL BUILDING MATERIALS LLC; *U.S. Private*, pg. 2114

INTERNATIONAL BUILDING PRODUCTS LTD; *Int'l*, pg. 3744

INTERNATIONAL BUILDING SYSTEMS FACTORY CO. LTD.—See ASTRA INDUSTRIAL GROUP COMPANY; *Int'l*, pg. 657

INTERNATIONAL BUSINESS COMMUNICATIONS INC.; *U.S. Private*, pg. 2114

INTERNATIONAL BUSINESS DIGITAL TECHNOLOGY LIMITED; *Int'l*, pg. 3744

INTERNATIONAL BUSINESS EXCHANGE CORPORATION; *U.S. Private*, pg. 2115

INTERNATIONAL BUSINESS MACHINES A/S—See International Business Machines Corporation; *U.S. Public*, pg. 1149

INTERNATIONAL BUSINESS MACHINES AS—See International Business Machines Corporation; *U.S. Public*, pg. 1149

INTERNATIONAL BUSINESS MACHINES CORPORATION MAGYSRORSSYAGI KFT.—See International Business Machines Corporation; *U.S. Public*, pg. 1149

INTERNATIONAL BUSINESS MACHINES CORPORATION; *U.S. Public*, pg. 1145

INTERNATIONAL BUSINESS MACHINES, S.A.—See International Business Machines Corporation; *U.S. Public*, pg. 1149

INTERNATIONAL BUSINESS MACHINES SENEGAL—See International Business Machines Corporation; *U.S. Public*, pg. 1149

INTERNATIONAL BUSINESS MACHINES SVENSKA AB—See International Business Machines Corporation; *U.S. Public*, pg. 1149

INTERNATIONAL BUSINESS MACHINES WEST AFRICA LIMITED—See International Business Machines Corporation; *U.S. Public*, pg. 1149

INTERNATIONAL BUSINESS SETTLEMENT HOLDINGS LIMITED; *Int'l*, pg. 3744

INTERNATIONAL BUSINESS SYSTEMS, INC.—See Maestro Print Management LLC; *U.S. Private*, pg. 2545

INTERNATIONAL CARD ESTABLISHMENT, INC.; *U.S. Public*, pg. 1151

INTERNATIONAL CARD PROCESSING SERVICES LTD—See The Mauritius Commercial Bank Ltd.; *Int'l*, pg. 7665

INTERNATIONAL CARDS COMPANY; *Int'l*, pg. 3744

INTERNATIONAL CARD SERVICES B.V.—See ABN AMRO Group N.V.; *Int'l*, pg. 65

INTERNATIONAL CARE COMPANY S.P.A.; *Int'l*, pg. 3744

INTERNATIONAL CARGO MARKETING CONSULTANTS, INC.—See Alliance Ground International, LLC; *U.S. Private*, pg. 182

INTERNATIONAL CARGO SERVICE CO., LTD.—See ANA Holdings Inc.; *Int'l*, pg. 444

INTERNATIONAL CAR OPERATORS N.V.—See Nippon Yusen Kabushiki Kaisha; *Int'l*, pg. 5358

INTERNATIONAL CARS LTD.; *U.S. Private*, pg. 2115

INTERNATIONAL CASINGS GROUP, INC.; *U.S. Private*, pg. 2115

INTERNATIONAL CATERING LTD.—See Japan Airlines Co., Ltd.; *Int'l*, pg. 3881

INTERNATIONAL CAVIAR CORPORATION SA; *Int'l*, pg. 3744

INTERNATIONAL CELLULOSE CORP.—See Compagnie de Saint-Gobain SA; *Int'l*, pg. 1730

INTERNATIONAL CENTER FOR ENTREPRENEURIAL DEVELOPMENT, INC.; *U.S. Private*, pg. 2115

INTERNATIONAL CENTER FOR ENVIROMENTAL ARTS; *U.S. Private*, pg. 2115

INTERNATIONAL CENTER FOR JOURNALISTS; *U.S. Private*, pg. 2115

INTERNATIONAL CENTER FOR LEADERSHIP IN EDUCATION, INC.—See Veritas Capital Fund Management, LLC; *U.S. Private*, pg. 4363

INTERNATIONAL CENTER FOR NOT-FOR-PROFIT LAW; *U.S. Private*, pg. 2115

INTERNATIONAL CENTER FOR POSTGRADUATE MEDICAL EDUCATION, LLC—See The Wicks Group of Companies, LLC; *U.S. Private*, pg. 4135

INTERNATIONAL CERAMIC CONSTRUCTION, LLC; *U.S. Private*, pg. 2115

INTERNATIONAL CERAMIC INDUSTRIES CO. LTD.; *Int'l*, pg. 3744

INTERNATIONAL CERAMICS S.A.E.—See Lecico Egypt S.A.E.; *Int'l*, pg. 4437

INTERNATIONAL CERTIFICATION SERVICES, INC.—See Where Food Comes From, Inc.; *U.S. Public*, pg. 2366

INTERNATIONAL CHECKOUT, INC.; *U.S. Private*, pg. 2115

INTERNATIONAL CHEMICAL COMPANY; *U.S. Private*, pg. 2115

INTERNATIONAL CHEMICAL CORP.; *U.S. Private*, pg. 2115

INTERNATIONAL CHEMICAL INVESTORS S.E.; *Int'l*, pg. 3744

INTERNATIONAL CHEMICALS ENGINEERING PTY. LTD.—See ENRA Group Berhad; *Int'l*, pg. 2445

INTERNATIONAL CITY/COUNTY MANAGEMENT ASSOCIATION; *U.S. Private*, pg. 2115

INTERNATIONAL CLAIMS HANDLING SERVICES INC.—See DSV A/S; *Int'l*, pg. 2214

INTERNATIONAL CLAIMS HANDLING SERVICES LTD.—See DSV A/S; *Int'l*, pg. 2214

INTERNATIONAL CMA RETIREMENT CORP.; *U.S. Private*, pg. 2115

INTERNATIONAL COAL HOLDINGS LIMITED—See PTT Public Company Limited; *Int'l*, pg. 6092

INTERNATIONAL COATINGS LTD—See Akzo Nobel N.V.; *Int'l*, pg. 274

INTERNATIONAL COATINGS PTE LTD—See Akzo Nobel N.V.; *Int'l*, pg. 274

INTERNATIONAL CODE COUNCIL, INC.; *U.S. Private*, pg. 2115

INTERNATIONAL COFFEE & TEA, LLC—See Jollibee Foods Corporation; *Int'l*, pg. 3996

INTERNATIONAL COLLEGE OF CAPOEIRA PTY. LIMITED—See Academies Australasia Group Limited; *Int'l*, pg. 77

INTERNATIONAL COLLEGE WALES LTD.—See Navitas Limited; *Int'l*, pg. 5176

INTERNATIONAL COLOUR CORPORATION (PTY) LIMITED—See Kansai Paint Co., Ltd.; *Int'l*, pg. 4072

INTERNATIONAL COMBUSTION (INDIA) LTD.; *Int'l*, pg. 3745

INTERNATIONAL COMFORT PRODUCTS CORPORATION (CANADA)—See Carrier Global Corporation; *U.S. Public*, pg. 442

INTERNATIONAL COMFORT PRODUCTS CORPORATION—See Carrier Global Corporation; *U.S. Public*, pg. 442

INTERNATIONAL COMMERCIAL BANK LAO LTD—See ICB Financial Group Holdings AG; *Int'l*, pg. 3578

INTERNATIONAL COMMERCIAL BANK LIMITED—See FBN Holdings PLC; *Int'l*, pg. 2627

INTERNATIONAL COMMERCIAL BANK LIMITED—See ICB Financial Group Holdings AG; *Int'l*, pg. 3578

INTERNATIONAL COMMERCIAL BANK (MOZAMBIQUE), S.A.—See ICB Financial Group Holdings AG; *Int'l*, pg. 3578

INTERNATIONAL COMMERCIAL BANK SH.A.—See ICB Financial Group Holdings AG; *Int'l*, pg. 3578

INTERNATIONAL COMMERCIAL BANK ZAMBIA LTD—See ICB Financial Group Holdings AG; *Int'l*, pg. 3578

INTERNATIONAL COMMUNICATION SERVICES LIMITED—See Belize Telecommunications Limited; *Int'l*, pg. 965

INTERNATIONAL COMMUNITY HEALTH SERVICES; *U.S. Private*, pg. 2115

INTERNATIONAL COMPANY FOR AGRICULTURAL INDUSTRIES PROJECTS (BEYTI) (SAE)—See Almarai Company Ltd.; *Int'l*, pg. 363

INTERNATIONAL COMPANY FOR LEASING S.A.E.; *Int'l*, pg. 3745

INTERNATIONAL COMPANY PROFILE FZ LLC—See Wilmington plc; *Int'l*, pg. 8422

INTERNATIONAL COMPLIANCE TRAINING ACADEMY PTE LIMITED—See Wilmington plc; *Int'l*, pg. 8422

INTERNATIONAL COMPLIANCE TRAINING LIMITED—See Wilmington plc; *Int'l*, pg. 8422

INTERNATIONAL COMPLIANCE TRAINING SDN. BHD.—See Wilmington plc; *Int'l*, pg. 8422

INTERNATIONAL COMPONENTS CORPORATION; *U.S. Private*, pg. 2116

INTERNATIONAL COMPRESSOR DISTRIBUTION N.V.—See Atlas Copco AB; *Int'l*, pg. 678

INTERNATIONAL COMPUTER MARKETING CORPORATION (ICM); *U.S. Private*, pg. 2116

INTERNATIONAL COMPUTER SOLUTIONS INC.; *U.S. Private*, pg. 2116

INTERNATIONAL CONGLOMERATE OF DISTRIBUTION FOR AUTOMOBILE HOLDINGS CO., LTD.; *Int'l*, pg. 3745

INTERNATIONAL CONSOLIDATED AIRLINES GROUP S.A.; *Int'l*, pg. 3745

INTERNATIONAL CONSOLIDATED BUSINESS GROUP PTY LTD.; *Int'l*, pg. 3746

INTERNATIONAL CONSTRUCTION DEVELOPMENT COMPANY; *Int'l*, pg. 3746

INTERNATIONAL CONSTRUCTION EQUIPMENT; *U.S. Private*, pg. 2116

INTERNATIONAL CONSTRUCTIONS LIMITED; *Int'l*, pg. 3746

INTERNATIONAL CONSTRUCTION TECHNOLOGY CO., LTD.; *Int'l*, pg. 3746

INTERNATIONAL CONTAINER TERMINAL SERVICES, INC.; *Int'l*, pg. 3746

INTERNATIONAL CONTAINER TRANSPORT CO., LTD.—See Mitsui O.S.K. Lines, Ltd.; *Int'l*, pg. 4989

INTERNATIONAL CONTRACT FURNITURE; *U.S. Private*, pg. 2116

INTERNATIONAL CONTROLS & MEASUREMENTS CORP.; *U.S. Private*, pg. 2116

INTERNATIONAL CONVERTER LLC—See Apollo Global Management, Inc.; *U.S. Public*, pg. 154

INTERNATIONAL CONVEYORS AUSTRALIA PTY LIMITED—See International Conveyors Limited; *Int'l*, pg. 3747

INTERNATIONAL CONVEYORS LIMITED; *Int'l*, pg. 3747

INTERNATIONAL COOPERATING MINISTRIES; *U.S. Private*, pg. 2116

INTERNATIONAL CORONA CAPITAL CORP.; *Int'l*, pg. 3747

INTERNATIONAL COSMETICS AND PERFUMES, INC.—See Kering S.A.; *Int'l*, pg. 4134

INTERNATIONAL CREATIVE MANAGEMENT, INC. - NEW YORK—See TPG Capital, L.P.; *U.S. Public*, pg. 2170

INTERNATIONAL CREATIVE MANAGEMENT, INC.—See TPG Capital, L.P.; *U.S. Public*, pg. 2170

INTERNATIONAL CRYSTAL MANUFACTURING, INC.; *U.S. Private*, pg. 2116

INTERNATIONAL CSRC INVESTMENT HOLDINGS CO., LTD.; *Int'l*, pg. 3747

INTERNATIONAL CUMO MINING CORPORATION—See Idaho Copper Corporation; *U.S. Public*, pg. 1088

INTERNATIONAL DAIRY QUEEN, INC.—See Berkshire Hathaway Inc.; *U.S. Public*, pg. 308

INTERNATIONAL DALECO CORPORATION; *U.S. Public*, pg. 1151

INTERNATIONAL DATACASTING CORPORATION—See Novra Technologies Inc.; *Int'l*, pg. 5471

INTERNATIONAL DATA CORPORATION (CANADA) LTD—See China Oceanwide Holdings Group Co., Ltd.; *Int'l*, pg. 1538

INTERNATIONAL DATA CORPORATION (CANADA) LTD—See IDG Capital; *Int'l*, pg. 3594

INTERNATIONAL DATA DEPOSITORY—See Berkshire Partners LLC; *U.S. Private*, pg. 534

INTERNATIONAL DATA GROUP, INC.—See China Oceanwide Holdings Group Co., Ltd.; *Int'l*, pg. 1536

INTERNATIONAL DATA GROUP, INC.—See IDG Capital; *Int'l*, pg. 3593

INTERNATIONAL DATA MANAGEMENT LIMITED; *Int'l*, pg. 3747

INTERNATIONAL DECISION SYSTEMS, INC.—See TA Associates, Inc.; *U.S. Private*, pg. 3916

INTERNATIONAL DEHYDRATED FOODS, INC.—See Symrise AG; *Int'l*, pg. 7380

INTERNATIONAL DELIGHTS, LLC; *U.S. Private*, pg. 2116

INTERNATIONAL DELIVERY SOLUTIONS; *U.S. Private*, pg. 2116

INTERNATIONAL DESIGN GUILD—See CCA Global Partners, Inc.; *U.S. Private*, pg. 799

INTERNATIONAL DEVELOPMENT GROUP LIMITED—See XWELL, Inc.; *U.S. Public*, pg. 2393

INTERNATIONAL DEVELOPMENT & INVESTMENT CORPORATION; *Int'l*, pg. 3747

INTERNATIONAL DEVELOPMENT, LLC; *U.S. Private*, pg. 2116

INTERNATIONAL DIAGNOSTIC SYSTEMS INC.—See Neogen Corporation; *U.S. Public*, pg. 1505

INTERNATIONAL DIRECTIONAL SERVICES, L.L.C.—See Granite Construction Incorporated; *U.S. Public*, pg. 957

COMPANY NAME INDEX

INTERNATIONAL DIRECTIONAL SERVICES OF CANADA, LTD.—See Granite Construction Incorporated; *U.S. Public*, pg. 957
INTERNATIONAL DIRECT SELLING TECHNOLOGY CORP.; *U.S. Private*, pg. 2116
INTERNATIONAL DISPENSING CORPORATION; *U.S. Public*, pg. 1151
INTERNATIONAL DISPLAY ADVERTISING, INC., *U.S. Public*, pg. 1151
INTERNATIONAL DISTILLERS SOUTH ASIA—See Diageo plc; *Int'l*, pg. 2102
INTERNATIONAL DISTRIBUTIONS SERVICES PLC; *Int'l*, pg. 3747
INTERNATIONAL DRILLING FLUIDS AND ENGINEERING SERVICES (IDEC) LTD—See Palladium Equity Partners, LLC; *U.S. Private*, pg. 3078
INTERNATIONAL DUTY FREE SA—See Vivendi SE; *Int'l*, pg. 8271
INTERNATIONALE FRUCHTIMPORT GESELLSCHAFT WEICHERT & CO. KG—See Sumitomo Corporation; *Int'l*, pg. 7268
THE INTERNATIONAL ELECTRICAL PRODUCTS COMPANY (TIEPCO)—See Al-Tuwairqi Group; *Int'l*, pg. 289
INTERNATIONAL ELECTRICAL SALES CORPORATION; *U.S. Private*, pg. 2116
INTERNATIONAL ELECTRIC WIRES PHILS. CORP.—See Sumitomo Electric Industries, Ltd.; *Int'l*, pg. 7278
INTERNATIONAL ELECTRO-MECHANICAL SERVICES CO.—See Kinden Corporation; *Int'l*, pg. 4165
INTERNATIONAL ELECTRONIC RESEARCH CORP.—See CTS Corporation; *U.S. Public*, pg. 603
INTERNATIONALE METALL IMPRAGNIER GMBH—See Quaker Chemical Corporation; *U.S. Public*, pg. 1746
INTERNATIONAL ENDEAVORS CORPORATION; *U.S. Public*, pg. 1151
INTERNATIONAL ENDESA BV—See Enel S.p.A.; *Int'l*, pg. 2412
INTERNATIONAL ENERGY GROUP PTE. LTD.—See New Silkroutes Group Limited; *Int'l*, pg. 5227
INTERNATIONAL ENERGY INSURANCE PLC; *Int'l*, pg. 3748
INTERNATIONAL ENERGY SERVICES, INC.; *U.S. Private*, pg. 2116
INTERNATIONAL ENERGY TRADING LLC—See Osyka Corporation; *U.S. Public*, pg. 1022
INTERNATIONAL ENGINEERING PUBLIC COMPANY LIMITED; *Int'l*, pg. 3748
INTERNATIONAL ENTERPRISES, INC.—See Elbit Systems Limited; *Int'l*, pg. 2344
INTERNATIONAL ENTERTAINMENT CORPORATION; *Int'l*, pg. 3748
INTERNATIONAL ENVIRONMENTAL CORPORATION—See NIBE Industrier AB; *Int'l*, pg. 5263
INTERNATIONAL EQUIPMENT SOLUTIONS, LLC—See KPS Capital Partners, LP; *U.S. Private*, pg. 2347
INTERNATIONAL EQUITIES CORPORATION LIMITED; *Int'l*, pg. 3748
INTERNATIONALES BANKHAUS BODENSEE AG—See Wurth Verwaltungsgesellschaft mbH; *Int'l*, pg. 8506
INTERNATIONAL EXCESS PROGRAMS MANAGERS—See One80 Intermediaries LLC; *U.S. Private*, pg. 3024
INTERNATIONAL EXHIBITIONS, INC.; *U.S. Private*, pg. 2116
INTERNATIONAL EXPEDITIONS, INC.—See TUI AG; *Int'l*, pg. 7965
INTERNATIONAL EXPRESS TRUCKING, INC.—See Bluejay Capital Partners, LLC; *U.S. Private*, pg. 597
INTERNATIONAL EXTRUSION CORP.—See UMC Acquisition Corp.; *U.S. Private*, pg. 4278
INTERNATIONAL EXTRUSIONS, INC.; *U.S. Private*, pg. 2116
INTERNATIONAL EYEWEAR LTD.—See Equistone Partners Europe Limited; *Int'l*, pg. 2486
INTERNATIONAL FACTORS ITALIA SPA—See BNP Paribas SA; *Int'l*, pg. 1091
INTERNATIONAL FALLS MEMORIAL HOSPITAL ASSOCIATION; *U.S. Private*, pg. 2116
INTERNATIONAL FARBENWERKE GMBH—See Akzo Nobel N.V.; *Int'l*, pg. 274
INTERNATIONAL FAR EASTERN LEASING CO., LTD.—See Sinochem Corporation; *Int'l*, pg. 6949
INTERNATIONAL FARG AB—See Akzo Nobel N.V.; *Int'l*, pg. 274
INTERNATIONAL FASHION CONCEPTS, INC.; *U.S. Private*, pg. 2116
INTERNATIONAL FERRO METALS LIMITED; *Int'l*, pg. 3748
INTERNATIONAL FERTILIZER DEVELOPMENT CENTER; *U.S. Private*, pg. 2116
INTERNATIONAL FIBER CORP.—See Arsenal Capital Management LP; *U.S. Private*, pg. 338
INTERNATIONAL FIBRES GROUP (HOLDINGS) LIMITED—See Duroc AB; *Int'l*, pg. 2230
INTERNATIONAL FIDELITY INSURANCE COMPANY; *U.S. Private*, pg. 2116
INTERNATIONAL FILM GUARANTORS LLC—See Allianz SE; *Int'l*, pg. 347

INTERNATIONAL FILM GUARANTORS LTD.—See Allianz SE; *Int'l*, pg. 353
INTERNATIONAL FINAF 2000 S.A.—See Angelini ACRAF S.p.A.; *Int'l*, pg. 460
INTERNATIONAL FINANCE COMPANY - SAL—See Arzan Financial Group for Financing & Investment K.S.P.C.; *Int'l*, pg. 589
INTERNATIONAL FINANCE CORPORATION—See The World Bank Group; *U.S. Private*, pg. 4139
INTERNATIONAL FINANCIAL ADVISORS K.S.C.C.; *Int'l*, pg. 3748
INTERNATIONAL FINANCIAL DATA SERVICES (CANADA) LIMITED—See SS&C Technologies Holdings, Inc.; *U.S. Public*, pg. 1923
INTERNATIONAL FINANCIAL DATA SERVICES (IRELAND) LIMITED—See SS&C Technologies Holdings, Inc.; *U.S. Public*, pg. 1923
INTERNATIONAL FINANCIAL GROUP, INC.—See Assurant, Inc.; *U.S. Public*, pg. 215
INTERNATIONAL FINANCIAL GROUP LTD.; *Int'l*, pg. 3748
INTERNATIONAL FIRE PROTECTION, INC.—See APi Group Corporation; *Int'l*, pg. 514
INTERNATIONAL FLAVORS E FRAGRANCES IFF (ITALIA) S.R.L.—See International Flavors & Fragrances Inc.; *U.S. Public*, pg. 1153
INTERNATIONAL FLAVORS & FRAGRANCES (ASIA PACIFIC) PTE. LTD.—See International Flavors & Fragrances Inc.; *U.S. Public*, pg. 1152
INTERNATIONAL FLAVORS & FRAGRANCES (CHINA) LTD. - BEIJING OFFICE—See International Flavors & Fragrances Inc.; *U.S. Public*, pg. 1152
INTERNATIONAL FLAVORS & FRAGRANCES (CHINA) LTD. - SHANGHAI OFFICE—See International Flavors & Fragrances Inc.; *U.S. Public*, pg. 1152
INTERNATIONAL FLAVORS & FRAGRANCES (CHINA) LTD.—See International Flavors & Fragrances Inc.; *U.S. Public*, pg. 1152
INTERNATIONAL FLAVORS & FRAGRANCES (HANGZHOU) CO. LTD—See International Flavors & Fragrances Inc.; *U.S. Public*, pg. 1152
INTERNATIONAL FLAVORS & FRAGRANCES (HANGZHOU) CO., LTD.—See International Flavors & Fragrances Inc.; *U.S. Public*, pg. 1152
INTERNATIONAL FLAVORS & FRAGRANCES I.F.F. (DEUTSCHLAND) GMBH—See International Flavors & Fragrances Inc.; *U.S. Public*, pg. 1153
INTERNATIONAL FLAVORS & FRAGRANCES I.F.F. (ESPANA) S.A. - BARCELONA—See International Flavors & Fragrances Inc.; *U.S. Public*, pg. 1153
INTERNATIONAL FLAVORS & FRAGRANCES I.F.F. (ESPANA) S.A.—See International Flavors & Fragrances Inc.; *U.S. Public*, pg. 1153
INTERNATIONAL FLAVORS & FRAGRANCES I.F.F. (FRANCE) S.A.R.L.—See International Flavors & Fragrances Inc.; *U.S. Public*, pg. 1153
INTERNATIONAL FLAVORS & FRAGRANCES I.F.F. (FRANCE) S.A.S.—See International Flavors & Fragrances Inc.; *U.S. Public*, pg. 1153
INTERNATIONAL FLAVORS & FRAGRANCES I.F.F. (ISRAEL) LTD.—See International Flavors & Fragrances Inc.; *U.S. Public*, pg. 1153
INTERNATIONAL FLAVORS & FRAGRANCES I.F.F. (ITALIA) S.R.L.—See International Flavors & Fragrances Inc.; *U.S. Public*, pg. 1153
INTERNATIONAL FLAVORS & FRAGRANCES I.F.F. (MIDDLE EAST) FZE—See International Flavors & Fragrances Inc.; *U.S. Public*, pg. 1153
INTERNATIONAL FLAVORS & FRAGRANCES I.F.F. (NEDERLAND) B.V.—See International Flavors & Fragrances Inc.; *U.S. Public*, pg. 1153
INTERNATIONAL FLAVORS & FRAGRANCES I.F.F. (NEDERLAND) B.V. - TILBURG PLANT—See International Flavors & Fragrances Inc.; *U.S. Public*, pg. 1153
INTERNATIONAL FLAVORS & FRAGRANCES I.F.F. (NORDEN) AB—See International Flavors & Fragrances Inc.; *U.S. Public*, pg. 1153
INTERNATIONAL FLAVORS & FRAGRANCES I.F.F. (S.A.) (PTY) LTD.—See International Flavors & Fragrances Inc.; *U.S. Public*, pg. 1153
INTERNATIONAL FLAVORS & FRAGRANCES INC.; *U.S. Public*, pg. 1151
INTERNATIONAL FLAVORS & FRAGRANCES (JAPAN) LTD. - GOTEMBA PLANT—See International Flavors & Fragrances Inc.; *U.S. Public*, pg. 1152
INTERNATIONAL FLAVORS & FRAGRANCES (JAPAN) LTD.—See International Flavors & Fragrances Inc.; *U.S. Public*, pg. 1152
INTERNATIONAL FLAVORS & FRAGRANCES (KOREA), INC.—See International Flavors & Fragrances Inc.; *U.S. Public*, pg. 1152
INTERNATIONAL FLAVORS & FRAGRANCES (LUXEMBOURG) S.A.R.L.—See International Flavors & Fragrances Inc.; *U.S. Public*, pg. 1152
INTERNATIONAL FLAVORS & FRAGRANCES (MEXICO) S.A. DE C.V.—See International Flavors & Fragrances Inc.; *U.S. Public*, pg. 1152

INTERNATIONAL FLAVORS & FRAGRANCES (MEXICO), S. DE R.L. DE C.V.—See International Flavors & Fragrances Inc.; *U.S. Public*, pg. 1152
INTERNATIONAL FLAVORS & FRAGRANCES (MIDDLE EAST) FZ-LLC—See International Flavors & Fragrances Inc.; *U.S. Public*, pg. 1152
INTERNATIONAL FLAVORS & FRAGRANCES (NEDERLAND) HOLDING B.V.—See International Flavors & Fragrances Inc.; *U.S. Public*, pg. 1153
INTERNATIONAL FLAVORS & FRAGRANCES (PHILIPPINES), INC.—See International Flavors & Fragrances Inc.; *U.S. Public*, pg. 1153
INTERNATIONAL FLAVORS & FRAGRANCES (POLAND) SP.Z.O.O.—See International Flavors & Fragrances Inc.; *U.S. Public*, pg. 1153
INTERNATIONAL FLAVORS & FRAGRANCES S.R.L.—See International Flavors & Fragrances Inc.; *U.S. Public*, pg. 1153
INTERNATIONAL FLAVORS & FRAGRANCES S.R.L.—See International Flavors & Fragrances Inc.; *U.S. Public*, pg. 1153
INTERNATIONAL FLAVORS & FRAGRANCES (THAILAND) LTD.—See International Flavors & Fragrances Inc.; *U.S. Public*, pg. 1153
INTERNATIONAL FLAVORS & FRAGRANCES (ZHEJIANG) CO., LTD.—See International Flavors & Fragrances Inc.; *U.S. Public*, pg. 1152
INTERNATIONAL FLAVOURS & FRAGRANCES (AUSTRALIA) PTY. LTD.—See International Flavors & Fragrances Inc.; *U.S. Public*, pg. 1153
INTERNATIONAL FLAVOURS & FRAGRANCES (CIL) LIMITED—See International Flavors & Fragrances Inc.; *U.S. Public*, pg. 1153
INTERNATIONAL FLAVOURS & FRAGRANCES I.F.F. (GREAT BRITAIN) LTD.—See International Flavors & Fragrances Inc.; *U.S. Public*, pg. 1153
INTERNATIONAL FLAVOURS & FRAGRANCES (INDIA) LTD.—See International Flavors & Fragrances Inc.; *U.S. Public*, pg. 1153
INTERNATIONAL FLAVOURS & FRAGRANCES INDIA PRIVATE LIMITED—See International Flavors & Fragrances Inc.; *U.S. Public*, pg. 1153
INTERNATIONAL FLAVOURS & FRAGRANCES (NEW ZEALAND) LTD.—See International Flavors & Fragrances Inc.; *U.S. Public*, pg. 1153
INTERNATIONAL FLAVOURS & FRAGRANCES (NZ) LIMITED—See International Flavors & Fragrances Inc.; *U.S. Public*, pg. 1153
INTERNATIONAL FLAVOURS & FRAGRANCES (NZ) LTD—See International Flavors & Fragrances Inc.; *U.S. Public*, pg. 1153
INTERNATIONAL FLAVOURS & FRAGRANCES (THAILAND) LIMITED—See International Flavors & Fragrances Inc.; *U.S. Public*, pg. 1153
INTERNATIONAL FLAVOURS & FRAGRANCES (VIETNAM) LIMITED LIABILITY COMPANY—See International Flavors & Fragrances Inc.; *U.S. Public*, pg. 1153
INTERNATIONAL FOOD CONSULTANTS, LLC—See Rollins, Inc.; *U.S. Public*, pg. 1809
INTERNATIONAL FOOD CORPORATION LIMITED—See Kumpulan Fima Berhad; *Int'l*, pg. 4331
INTERNATIONAL FOOD NETWORK LTD.—See Laboratory Corporation of America Holdings; *U.S. Public*, pg. 1286
INTERNATIONAL FOOD POLICY RESEARCH INSTITUTE; *U.S. Private*, pg. 2116
INTERNATIONAL FOODSOURCE LLC; *U.S. Private*, pg. 2117
INTERNATIONAL FOOD SUPPLY COMPANY LIMITED—See MK Restaurant Group Public Company Limited; *Int'l*, pg. 5000
INTERNATIONAL FOREST PRODUCTS CORPORATION—See The Kraft Group LLC; *U.S. Private*, pg. 4065
INTERNATIONAL FOREST PRODUCTS (H.K.) LTD.—See The Kraft Group LLC; *U.S. Private*, pg. 4065
INTERNATIONAL FOREST PRODUCTS (SHANGHAI)—See The Kraft Group LLC; *U.S. Private*, pg. 4065
INTERNATIONAL FOREST PRODUCTS—See Norske Skog ASA; *Int'l*, pg. 5437
INTERNATIONAL FOREST PRODUCTS SVENSKA KB—See The Kraft Group LLC; *U.S. Private*, pg. 4066
INTERNATIONAL FOREST PRODUCTS (UK)—See The Kraft Group LLC; *U.S. Private*, pg. 4066
INTERNATIONAL FOR MEDICAL INVESTMENT PLC; *Int'l*, pg. 3748
INTERNATIONAL FORWARDERS, INC.—See Odyssey Logistics & Technology Corp.; *U.S. Private*, pg. 2996
INTERNATIONAL FOUNDATION FOR ELECTION SYSTEMS; *U.S. Private*, pg. 2117
INTERNATIONAL FOUNDATION OF EMPLOYEE BENEFIT PLANS; *U.S. Private*, pg. 2117
INTERNATIONAL FRAGRANCE & TECHNOLOGY; *U.S. Private*, pg. 2117
INTERNATIONAL FREIGHT FORWARDING, INC.; *U.S. Private*, pg. 2117
INTERNATIONAL FREIGHT LOGISTICS—See DSV A/S; *Int'l*, pg. 2214

INTERNATIONAL FREIGHT FORWARDING, INC.

INTERNATIONAL FREIGHT SERVICES, INC.—See Deutsche Bahn AG; *Int'l*, pg. 2054
INTERNATIONAL FREIGHT SYSTEMS LLC.; *U.S. Private*, pg. 2117
INTERNATIONAL FREIGHT SYSTEMS (OF OREGON), INC.—See Radiant Logistics, Inc.; *U.S. Public*, pg. 1759
INTERNATIONAL FRONTIER RESOURCES CORPORATION; *Int'l*, pg. 3748
INTERNATIONAL FUND FOR ANIMAL WELFARE; *U.S. Private*, pg. 2117
INTERNATIONAL FUND SERVICES (IRELAND) LIMITED—See State Street Corporation; *U.S. Public*, pg. 1941
INTERNATIONAL FUND SERVICES (N.A.), L.L.C.—See State Street Corporation; *U.S. Public*, pg. 1940
INTERNATIONAL GALVANIZERS LP—See AZZ, Inc.; *U.S. Public*, pg. 259
INTERNATIONAL GAMCO INC.; *U.S. Private*, pg. 2117
INTERNATIONAL GAMES SYSTEM CO., LTD.; *Int'l*, pg. 3749
INTERNATIONAL GAME TECHNOLOGY-AFRICA (PTY) LTD.—See International Game Technology PLC; *Int'l*, pg. 3749
INTERNATIONAL GAME TECHNOLOGY PLC; *Int'l*, pg. 3748
INTERNATIONAL GAME TECHNOLOGY - RENO—See International Game Technology PLC; *Int'l*, pg. 3749
INTERNATIONAL GAME TECHNOLOGY—See International Game Technology PLC; *Int'l*, pg. 3749
INTERNATIONAL GAMING TECHNOLOGY (NZ) LTD.—See International Game Technology PLC; *Int'l*, pg. 3749
INTERNATIONAL GARDEN HOTEL NARITA—See Alpine Grove Partners LLP; *U.S. Private*, pg. 201
INTERNATIONAL GARDEN HOTEL NARITA—See Hoshino Resorts Inc.; *Int'l*, pg. 3483
INTERNATIONAL GASES INC—See StealthGas Inc.; *Int'l*, pg. 7188
INTERNATIONAL GAS PRODUCT SHIPPING JOINT STOCK COMPANY; *Int'l*, pg. 3749
INTERNATIONAL GENERAL INSURANCE HOLDINGS LTD.; *Int'l*, pg. 3749
INTERNATIONAL GOLDEN GROUP PJSC; *Int'l*, pg. 3749
INTERNATIONAL GOLDFIELDS LIMITED; *Int'l*, pg. 3750
INTERNATIONAL GOLF RESORT KYOCERA CO., LTD.—See KYOCERA Corporation; *Int'l*, pg. 4356
INTERNATIONAL GOURMET FOODS INC.; *U.S. Private*, pg. 2117
INTERNATIONAL GOVERNOR SERVICES, LLC—See BlackRock, Inc.; *U.S. Public*, pg. 346
INTERNATIONAL GOVERNOR SERVICES, LLC—See Blackstone Inc.; *U.S. Public*, pg. 358
INTERNATIONAL GOVERNOR SERVICES, LLC—See Cascade Investment LLC; *U.S. Private*, pg. 780
INTERNATIONAL GRADUATE INSIGHT GROUP LIMITED—See Tribal Group plc; *Int'l*, pg. 7919
INTERNATIONAL GRANITE & MARBLE; *U.S. Private*, pg. 2117
INTERNATIONAL GRAPHICS ULC—See Taylor Corporation; *U.S. Private*, pg. 3938
INTERNATIONAL GRAPHITE LIMITED; *Int'l*, pg. 3750
INTERNATIONAL GREETINGS ASIA LIMITED—See IG Design Group Plc; *Int'l*, pg. 3600
INTERNATIONAL GREETINGS (UK) LIMITED—See IG Design Group Plc; *Int'l*, pg. 3600
INTERNATIONAL GROUND SERVICES, S.A. DE C.V.—See American Airlines Group Inc.; *U.S. Public*, pg. 96
INTERNATIONAL HAIRGOODS INC—See Aderans Co., Ltd.; *Int'l*, pg. 143
INTERNATIONAL HARDCOAT, INC.; *U.S. Private*, pg. 2117
INTERNATIONAL HARVESTER EMPLOYEE CREDIT UNION, INC.; *U.S. Private*, pg. 2117
INTERNATIONAL HEALTH GROUP INC—See Dalrada Financial Corporation; *U.S. Public*, pg. 621
INTERNATIONAL HEALTH MANAGEMENT SERVICES LTD.—See Industrial & General Insurance Plc; *Int'l*, pg. 3671
INTERNATIONAL HEARTH MELTING, LLC—See ATI Inc.; *U.S. Public*, pg. 222
INTERNATIONAL HERALD TRIBUNE LTD.—See The New York Times Company; *U.S. Public*, pg. 2116
INTERNATIONAL HERALD TRIBUNE S.A.S.—See The New York Times Company; *U.S. Public*, pg. 2116
INTERNATIONAL HERALD TRIBUNE U.S. INC—See The New York Times Company; *U.S. Public*, pg. 2116
INTERNATIONAL HOLDING COMPANY PJSC; *Int'l*, pg. 3750
INTERNATIONAL HOLDINGS COMPANY PJSC; *Int'l*, pg. 3750
INTERNATIONAL HOME SHOPPING—See Suarez Corporation Industries; *U.S. Private*, pg. 3847
INTERNATIONAL HOTEL INVESTMENTS P.L.C.—See Corinthia Palace Hotel Company Limited; *Int'l*, pg. 1801
INTERNATIONAL HOTEL LICENSING COMPANY S.A.R.L. LUXEMBOURG—See Marriott International, Inc.; *U.S. Public*, pg. 1370
INTERNATIONAL HOT ROD ASSOCIATION—See Feld Entertainment, Inc.; *U.S. Private*, pg. 1493
INTERNATIONAL HOUSE OF PANCAKES, INC.—See Dine Brands Global, Inc.; *U.S. Public*, pg. 667
INTERNATIONAL HOUSE PHILADELPHIA; *U.S. Private*, pg. 2117
INTERNATIONAL HOUSE; *U.S. Private*, pg. 2117
INTERNATIONAL HOUSEWARES RETAIL COMPANY LIMITED; *Int'l*, pg. 3750
INTERNATIONAL HOUSING FINANCE COMPANY LIMITED; *Int'l*, pg. 3750
INTERNATIONAL HOUSING SOLUTIONS S.A.R.L.—See Fundamental Advisors LP; *U.S. Private*, pg. 1622
INTERNATIONAL HUMAN RESOURCES COMPANY; *Int'l*, pg. 3750
INTERNATIONAL ICONIC GOLD EXPLORATION CORP.; *Int'l*, pg. 3750
INTERNATIONAL IMAGE SERVICES INC.—See Sonic Foundry, Inc.; *U.S. Public*, pg. 1903
INTERNATIONAL IMAGING MATERIALS, INC.—See ACON Investments, LLC; *U.S. Private*, pg. 62
INTERNATIONAL IMPACT BUILDING PRODUCTS, LLC.; *U.S. Private*, pg. 2117
INTERNATIONAL INDEMNITY LTD.—See Merck & Co., Inc.; *U.S. Public*, pg. 1416
INTERNATIONAL INDUSTRIES, INC.; *U.S. Private*, pg. 2117
INTERNATIONAL INDUSTRIES LIMITED; *Int'l*, pg. 3750
INTERNATIONAL IN-FLIGHT CATERING CO., LTD.—See Japan Airlines Co., Ltd.; *Int'l*, pg. 3882
INTERNATIONAL INFORMATION SYSTEMS CONSORTIUM INC.; *U.S. Private*, pg. 2117
INTERNATIONAL INFORMATION TECHNOLOGY CO. LLC—See Oman Holdings International Company SAOG; *Int'l*, pg. 5560
INTERNATIONAL INGREDIENT CORP.; *U.S. Private*, pg. 2118
INTERNATIONAL INSPECTION SERVICES LIMITED—See Intertek Group plc; *Int'l*, pg. 3762
INTERNATIONAL INSPIRATIONS; *U.S. Private*, pg. 2118
INTERNATIONAL INSTITUTE FOR LEARNING, INC.; *U.S. Private*, pg. 2118
INTERNATIONAL INSTITUTE FOR TRAUMA AND ADDICTION PROFESSIONALS; *U.S. Private*, pg. 2118
INTERNATIONAL INSURANCE BROKERS, LTD.—See Kelso & Company, L.P.; *U.S. Private*, pg. 2280
INTERNATIONAL INSURANCE COMPANY IRAQ LTD.—See Vienna Insurance Group AG Wiener Versicherung Gruppe; *Int'l*, pg. 8194
INTERNATIONAL INSURANCE COMPANY OF HANNOVER LTD.-LONDON—See Talanx AG; *Int'l*, pg. 7444
INTERNATIONAL INSURANCE COMPANY OF HANNOVER LTD.—See Talanx AG; *Int'l*, pg. 7444
INTERNATIONAL INSURANCE COMPANY OF HANNOVER LTD.-STOCKHOLM—See Talanx AG; *Int'l*, pg. 7445
INTERNATIONAL INSURANCE COMPANY—See International Bank of Azerbaijan; *Int'l*, pg. 3744
INTERNATIONAL INSURANCE GROUP, INC.—See Aon plc; *Int'l*, pg. 496
INTERNATIONAL INTEGRATED SOLUTIONS, LTD.; *U.S. Private*, pg. 2118
INTERNATIONAL INTIMATES, INC.; *U.S. Private*, pg. 2118
INTERNATIONAL INVESTMENT GROUP K.S.C.C.; *Int'l*, pg. 3750
THE INTERNATIONAL INVESTOR COMPANY K.S.C.C.; *Int'l*, pg. 7656
INTERNATIONAL ISOTOPES INC.; *U.S. Public*, pg. 1154
INTERNATIONAL JUSTICE MISSION; *U.S. Private*, pg. 2118
INTERNATIONAL KNITWEAR LIMITED; *Int'l*, pg. 3750
INTERNATIONAL LABORATORIES CORP., LTD.—See Saha Pathanapibul Public Company Limited; *Int'l*, pg. 6479
INTERNATIONAL LAND ALLIANCE, INC.; *U.S. Public*, pg. 1154
INTERNATIONAL LAUNCH SERVICES—See The Khrunichev State Research & Production Space Centre; *Int'l*, pg. 7662
INTERNATIONAL LAZAR COMPANY; *Int'l*, pg. 3750
INTERNATIONAL LEASE FINANCE CORPORATION—See AerCap Holdings N.V.; *Int'l*, pg. 179
INTERNATIONAL LEASING COMPANY LLC—See Illinois Tool Works Inc.; *U.S. Public*, pg. 1108
INTERNATIONAL LEASING & FINANCIAL SERVICES LIMITED; *Int'l*, pg. 3751
INTERNATIONAL LEASING & INVESTMENT COMPANY K.S.C.C.; *Int'l*, pg. 3751
INTERNATIONAL LEASING SECURITIES LIMITED—See International Leasing & Financial Services Limited; *Int'l*, pg. 3751
INTERNATIONAL LIFE INVESTORS INSURANCE COMPANY—See Aegon N.V.; *Int'l*, pg. 174
INTERNATIONAL LIFE SCIENCES LLC; *U.S. Private*, pg. 2118
INTERNATIONAL LIFE SUPPORT, INC.—See KKR & Co. Inc.; *U.S. Public*, pg. 1251
INTERNATIONAL LIFT SYSTEMS, LLC—See KPS Capital Partners, LP; *U.S. Private*, pg. 2347
INTERNATIONAL LIGHT TECHNOLOGIES, INC.—See Halma plc; *Int'l*, pg. 3232
INTERNATIONAL LIMOUSINE SERVICE, INC.—See Errands Plus, Inc.; *U.S. Private*, pg. 1423
INTERNATIONAL LINE BUILDERS, INC.—See MDU Resources Group, Inc.; *U.S. Public*, pg. 1410
INTERNATIONAL LITHIUM CORP.—See TNR Gold Corp.; *Int'l*, pg. 7768
INTERNATIONAL LOGGING NETHERLANDS B.V.—See Weatherford International plc; *U.S. Public*, pg. 2339
INTERNATIONAL LOGISTICS COMPANY, INC.—See Cooper/T. Smith Corporation; *U.S. Private*, pg. 1042
INTERNATIONAL LONGSHOREMEN'S ASSOCIATION, AFL-CIO; *U.S. Private*, pg. 2118
INTERNATIONAL LOTTERY & TOTALIZATOR SYSTEMS, INC.—See Berjaya Corporation Berhad; *Int'l*, pg. 983
INTERNATIONAL LUXURY PRODUCTS, INC.; *U.S. Public*, pg. 1154
INTERNATIONAL MACGREGOR-NAVIRE HOLDING BV—See Cargotec Corporation; *Int'l*, pg. 1328
INTERNATIONAL MAGNESIUM GROUP, INC.—See CD International Enterprises, Inc.; *U.S. Public*, pg. 461
INTERNATIONAL MALING A/S—See Akzo Nobel N.V.; *Int'l*, pg. 274
INTERNATIONAL MANAGEMENT CONSULTANTS INC.; *U.S. Private*, pg. 2118
INTERNATIONAL MANAGEMENT CONSULTING INC.; *U.S. Private*, pg. 2118
INTERNATIONAL MANAGEMENT (MAURITIUS) LIMITED—See Cim Financial Services Limited; *Int'l*, pg. 1607
INTERNATIONAL MANAGEMENT SERVICES COMPANY; *U.S. Private*, pg. 2118
INTERNATIONAL MANAGEMENT SERVICES GROUP, INC.; *U.S. Private*, pg. 2118
INTERNATIONAL MANUFACTURING COMPANY LLC—See Summa Holdings, Inc.; *U.S. Private*, pg. 3852
INTERNATIONAL MARCH OF THE LIVING; *U.S. Private*, pg. 2118
INTERNATIONAL MARINA GROUP, LP; *U.S. Private*, pg. 2118
INTERNATIONAL MARINE AIRLINE SERVICES LIMITED—See Air France-KLM S.A.; *Int'l*, pg. 237
INTERNATIONAL MARINE CONSULTING CO., LTD.—See NS United Kaiun Kaisha, Ltd.; *Int'l*, pg. 5475
INTERNATIONAL MARINE & INDUSTRIAL APPLICATORS, LLC—See Stellex Capital Management LP; *U.S. Private*, pg. 3800
INTERNATIONAL MARINE PRODUCTS INC.—See Eiwa International Inc.; *U.S. Private*, pg. 1348
INTERNATIONAL MARINE PRODUCTS NEVADA INC.—See Eiwa International Inc.; *U.S. Private*, pg. 1348
INTERNATIONAL MARITIME INDUSTRIES COMPANY—See Saudi Arabian Oil Company; *Int'l*, pg. 6590
INTERNATIONAL MARKET CENTERS, INC.—See Blackstone Inc.; *U.S. Public*, pg. 350
INTERNATIONAL MARKETING VENTURES, LIMITED—See Bio-Rad Laboratories, Inc.; *U.S. Public*, pg. 334
INTERNATIONAL MASONRY INSTITUTE; *U.S. Private*, pg. 2118
INTERNATIONAL MATERIALS INC.; *U.S. Private*, pg. 2119
INTERNATIONAL-MATEX TANK TERMINALS, INC.—See Riverstone Holdings LLC; *U.S. Private*, pg. 3447
INTERNATIONAL MEAL COMPANY ALIMENTACAO S.A.; *Int'l*, pg. 3751
INTERNATIONAL MEAL COMPANY HOLDINGS S.A.; *Int'l*, pg. 3751
INTERNATIONAL MEDIA ACQUISITION CORP.; *U.S. Public*, pg. 1154
INTERNATIONAL MEDIA CONCEPTS, INC.—See The New York Times Company; *U.S. Public*, pg. 2117
INTERNATIONAL MEDIA DISTRIBUTION, LLC—See Comcast Corporation; *U.S. Public*, pg. 538
INTERNATIONAL MEDIA PARTNERS, INC.; *U.S. Private*, pg. 2119
INTERNATIONAL MEDICAL CENTRE (HONG KONG) LIMITED—See First Shanghai Investments Limited; *Int'l*, pg. 2687
INTERNATIONAL MEDICAL CENTRES LIMITED—See CIEL Ltd.; *Int'l*, pg. 1605
INTERNATIONAL MEDICAL EQUIPMENT COLLABORATIVE; *U.S. Private*, pg. 2119
INTERNATIONAL MEDICAL EQUIPMENT & SERVICE, INC.—See Richardson Electronics, Ltd.; *U.S. Public*, pg. 1797
INTERNATIONAL MEDICAL INSURERS PTE LTD—See Raffles Medical Group Ltd; *Int'l*, pg. 6177
INTERNATIONAL MEDICATION SYSTEMS, LIMITED—See Amphastar Pharmaceuticals, Inc.; *U.S. Public*, pg. 126
INTERNATIONAL MESH PRODUCTS PTE. LTD.—See Nippon Filcon Co., Ltd.; *Int'l*, pg. 5317

COMPANY NAME INDEX

INTERNATIONAL METALS & CHEMICALS GROUP; *U.S. Private*, pg. 2119
INTERNATIONAL METALS EKCO LTD.; *U.S. Private*, pg. 2119
INTERNATIONAL METAL SERVICE NORD GMBH—See Jacquet Metal Service SA; *Int'l*, pg. 3866
INTERNATIONAL METAL SERVICE TRADE GMBH—See Jacquet Metal Service SA; *Int'l*, pg. 3866
INTERNATIONAL METALS MINING CORP; *Int'l*, pg. 3751
THE INTERNATIONAL METALS RECLAMATION COMPANY, INC.—See Befesa S.A.; *Int'l*, pg. 939
INTERNATIONAL METHANOL COMPANY—See Sahara International Petrochemical Company; *Int'l*, pg. 6481
INTERNATIONAL METROPOLIS MEDIA D.O.O.—See APG/SGA SA; *Int'l*, pg. 513
INTERNATIONAL METROPOLITAN AUTOMOTIVE PROMOTION (FRANCE) S.A.—See Stellantis N.V.; *Int'l*, pg. 7200
INTERNATIONAL MEZZO TECHNOLOGIES, INC.—See Arcline Investment Management LP; *U.S. Private*, pg. 314
INTERNATIONAL MINING & INFRASTRUCTURE CORPORATION PLC; *Int'l*, pg. 3751
INTERNATIONAL MISSING PERSONS FOUNDATION; *U.S. Private*, pg. 2119
INTERNATIONAL MOLD STEEL, INC.—See Okaya & Co., Ltd.; *Int'l*, pg. 5546
INTERNATIONAL MONETARY SYSTEMS, LTD.; *U.S. Public*, pg. 1154
INTERNATIONAL MONEY EXPRESS INC.; *U.S. Public*, pg. 1154
INTERNATIONAL MONEY MATTERS PVT LTD—See TVS Electronics Limited; *Int'l*, pg. 7989
INTERNATIONAL MOTION CONTROL, INC.—See ITT Inc.; *U.S. Public*, pg. 1178
INTERNATIONAL MOTOR CARS; *U.S. Private*, pg. 2119
INTERNATIONAL NETWORKS, LLC—See Comcast Corporation; *U.S. Public*, pg. 538
INTERNATIONAL NETWORK SYSTEM PUBLIC COMPANY LIMITED; *Int'l*, pg. 3751
INTERNATIONAL NEW YORK TIMES—See The New York Times Company; *U.S. Public*, pg. 2116
INTERNATIONAL OCD FOUNDATION; *U.S. Private*, pg. 2119
INTERNATIONAL OFFICE SUPPLY, *U.S. Private*, pg. 2119
INTERNATIONAL OLYMPIC COMMITTEE; *Int'l*, pg. 3751
INTERNATIONAL ONCOLOGY NETWORK, LLC—See Cencora, Inc.; *U.S. Public*, pg. 467
INTERNATIONAL OPERATIONS DIVISION—See Kikkoman Corporation; *Int'l*, pg. 4160
INTERNATIONAL PACKAGING CORP.; *U.S. Private*, pg. 2119
INTERNATIONAL PACKAGING PRODUCTS PVT. LTD.—See Owens Corning; *U.S. Public*, pg. 1626
INTERNATIONAL PAINT (AKZO NOBEL CHILE) LTDA—See Akzo Nobel N.V.; *Int'l*, pg. 270
INTERNATIONAL PAINT (BELGIUM) NV—See Akzo Nobel N.V.; *Int'l*, pg. 270
INTERNATIONAL PAINT (EAST RUSSIA) LTD—See Akzo Nobel N.V.; *Int'l*, pg. 270
INTERNATIONAL PAINT FRANCE S.A.—See Akzo Nobel N.V.; *Int'l*, pg. 270
INTERNATIONAL PAINT (HELLAS) S.A.—See Akzo Nobel N.V.; *Int'l*, pg. 270
INTERNATIONAL PAINT (HONG KONG) LIMITED—See Akzo Nobel N.V.; *Int'l*, pg. 270
INTERNATIONAL PAINT INC.—See Akzo Nobel N.V.; *Int'l*, pg. 274
INTERNATIONAL PAINT ITALIA SPA—See Akzo Nobel N.V.; *Int'l*, pg. 270
INTERNATIONAL PAINT JAPAN K.K.—See Akzo Nobel N.V.; *Int'l*, pg. 270
INTERNATIONAL PAINT (KOREA) LTD - CHILSEO FACTORY—See Akzo Nobel N.V.; *Int'l*, pg. 270
INTERNATIONAL PAINT (KOREA) LTD—See Akzo Nobel N.V.; *Int'l*, pg. 270
INTERNATIONAL PAINT LBERIA, LDA—See Akzo Nobel N.V.; *Int'l*, pg. 271
INTERNATIONAL PAINT LLC—See Akzo Nobel N.V.; *Int'l*, pg. 271
INTERNATIONAL PAINT LTD—See Akzo Nobel N.V.; *Int'l*, pg. 270
INTERNATIONAL PAINT (NEDERLAND) B.V.—See Akzo Nobel N.V.; *Int'l*, pg. 274
INTERNATIONAL PAINT OF SHANGHAI CO LTD—See Akzo Nobel N.V.; *Int'l*, pg. 271
INTERNATIONAL PAINT PAZARLAMA LIMITED SIRKETI—See Akzo Nobel N.V.; *Int'l*, pg. 271
INTERNATIONAL PAINT (RESEARCH) LTD—See Akzo Nobel N.V.; *Int'l*, pg. 270
INTERNATIONAL PAINTS (CANADA) LTD—See Akzo Nobel N.V.; *Int'l*, pg. 271
INTERNATIONAL PAINT SDN BHD—See Akzo Nobel N.V.; *Int'l*, pg. 271
INTERNATIONAL PAINT SINGAPORE PTE LTD—See Akzo Nobel N.V.; *Int'l*, pg. 271
INTERNATIONAL PAINT (TAIWAN) LTD—See Akzo Nobel N.V.; *Int'l*, pg. 270

INTERNATIONAL PAPER AGROFLORESTAL LTDA.—See International Paper Company; *U.S. Public*, pg. 1155
INTERNATIONAL PAPER APPM LIMITED—See International Paper Company; *U.S. Public*, pg. 1155
INTERNATIONAL PAPER ASIA LIMITED—See International Paper Company; *U.S. Public*, pg. 1155
INTERNATIONAL PAPER CABOURG SAS—See International Paper Company; *U.S. Public*, pg. 1155
INTERNATIONAL PAPER CANADA, INC.—See International Paper Company; *U.S. Public*, pg. 1155
INTERNATIONAL PAPER CARTONES LTDA.—See International Paper Company; *U.S. Public*, pg. 1156
INTERNATIONAL PAPER CARTOVAR, S.A.—See International Paper Company; *U.S. Public*, pg. 1156
INTERNATIONAL PAPER CELLULOSE FIBERS (POLAND) SP. Z O.O.—See International Paper Company; *U.S. Public*, pg. 1156
INTERNATIONAL PAPER CELLULOSE FIBERS SALES SARL—See International Paper Company; *U.S. Public*, pg. 1156
INTERNATIONAL PAPER CHALON SAS—See International Paper Company; *U.S. Public*, pg. 1156
INTERNATIONAL PAPER (CHONGQING) PACKAGING CO., LTD—See International Paper Company; *U.S. Public*, pg. 1155
INTERNATIONAL PAPER CO. - GEORGETOWN CONTAINER—See International Paper Company; *U.S. Public*, pg. 1156
INTERNATIONAL PAPER CO. - MANSFIELD MILL—See International Paper Company; *U.S. Public*, pg. 1156
INTERNATIONAL PAPER COMPANY - AUGUSTA LUMBER MILL—See International Paper Company; *U.S. Public*, pg. 1157
INTERNATIONAL PAPER COMPANY - COURTLAND—See International Paper Company; *U.S. Public*, pg. 1157
INTERNATIONAL PAPER COMPANY (EUROPE) LIMITED—See International Paper Company; *U.S. Public*, pg. 1157
INTERNATIONAL PAPER COMPANY - FORT WAYNE—See International Paper Company; *U.S. Public*, pg. 1157
INTERNATIONAL PAPER COMPANY - FORT WORTH CONTAINER—See International Paper Company; *U.S. Public*, pg. 1157
INTERNATIONAL PAPER COMPANY (JAPAN) LTD.—See International Paper Company; *U.S. Public*, pg. 1157
INTERNATIONAL PAPER COMPANY - LOVELAND—See International Paper Company; *U.S. Public*, pg. 1157
INTERNATIONAL PAPER COMPANY - MEMPHIS SOUTHWIND INFORMATION TECHNOLOGY CENTER—See International Paper Company; *U.S. Public*, pg. 1157
INTERNATIONAL PAPER COMPANY - MOUNT CARMEL CONTAINER—See International Paper Company; *U.S. Public*, pg. 1157
INTERNATIONAL PAPER COMPANY - MURFREESBORO—See International Paper Company; *U.S. Public*, pg. 1157
INTERNATIONAL PAPER COMPANY - RIEGELWOOD MILL—See International Paper Company; *U.S. Public*, pg. 1157
INTERNATIONAL PAPER COMPANY - SAN ANTONIO—See International Paper Company; *U.S. Public*, pg. 1157
INTERNATIONAL PAPER COMPANY—See International Paper Company; *U.S. Public*, pg. 1157
INTERNATIONAL PAPER COMPANY; *U.S. Public*, pg. 1155
INTERNATIONAL PAPER COMPANY—See International Paper Company; *U.S. Public*, pg. 1156
INTERNATIONAL PAPER COMPANY—See International Paper Company; *U.S. Public*, pg. 1156
INTERNATIONAL PAPER COMPANY—See International Paper Company; *U.S. Public*, pg. 1156
INTERNATIONAL PAPER COMPANY—See International Paper Company; *U.S. Public*, pg. 1156
INTERNATIONAL PAPER COMPANY—See International Paper Company; *U.S. Public*, pg. 1156
INTERNATIONAL PAPER COMPANY—See International Paper Company; *U.S. Public*, pg. 1156
INTERNATIONAL PAPER COMPANY—See International Paper Company; *U.S. Public*, pg. 1156
INTERNATIONAL PAPER COMPANY—See International Paper Company; *U.S. Public*, pg. 1156
INTERNATIONAL PAPER COMPANY—See International Paper Company; *U.S. Public*, pg. 1156
INTERNATIONAL PAPER COMPANY—See International Paper Company; *U.S. Public*, pg. 1156
INTERNATIONAL PAPER COMPANY—See International Paper Company; *U.S. Public*, pg. 1156
INTERNATIONAL PAPER COMPANY—See International Paper Company; *U.S. Public*, pg. 1156
INTERNATIONAL PAPER COMPANY—See International Paper Company; *U.S. Public*, pg. 1156
INTERNATIONAL PAPER COMPANY—See International Paper Company; *U.S. Public*, pg. 1156
INTERNATIONAL PAPER COMPANY—See International Paper Company; *U.S. Public*, pg. 1156

INTERNATIONAL PAPER COMPANY—See International Paper Company; *U.S. Public*, pg. 1156
INTERNATIONAL PAPER COMPANY—See International Paper Company; *U.S. Public*, pg. 1156
INTERNATIONAL PAPER COMPANY—See International Paper Company; *U.S. Public*, pg. 1156
INTERNATIONAL PAPER COMPANY—See International Paper Company; *U.S. Public*, pg. 1156
INTERNATIONAL PAPER COMPANY—See International Paper Company; *U.S. Public*, pg. 1156
INTERNATIONAL PAPER COMPANY—See International Paper Company; *U.S. Public*, pg. 1156
INTERNATIONAL PAPER COMPANY—See International Paper Company; *U.S. Public*, pg. 1156
INTERNATIONAL PAPER COMPANY—See International Paper Company; *U.S. Public*, pg. 1156
INTERNATIONAL PAPER COMPANY—See International Paper Company; *U.S. Public*, pg. 1156
INTERNATIONAL PAPER COMPANY—See International Paper Company; *U.S. Public*, pg. 1156
INTERNATIONAL PAPER COMPANY—See International Paper Company; *U.S. Public*, pg. 1156
INTERNATIONAL PAPER COMPANY—See International Paper Company; *U.S. Public*, pg. 1156
INTERNATIONAL PAPER COMPANY—See International Paper Company; *U.S. Public*, pg. 1156
INTERNATIONAL PAPER COMPANY—See International Paper Company; *U.S. Public*, pg. 1156
INTERNATIONAL PAPER COMPANY—See International Paper Company; *U.S. Public*, pg. 1156
INTERNATIONAL PAPER COMPANY - SPRINGHILL CONTAINER—See International Paper Company; *U.S. Public*, pg. 1157
INTERNATIONAL PAPER COMPANY - STAMFORD—See International Paper Company; *U.S. Public*, pg. 1157
INTERNATIONAL PAPER COMPANY - WOOSTER CONTAINER PLANT—See International Paper Company; *U.S. Public*, pg. 1157
INTERNATIONAL PAPER CO. - PHOENIX—See International Paper Company; *U.S. Public*, pg. 1156
INTERNATIONAL PAPER CO. - SNOW HILL CHIP MILL—See International Paper Company; *U.S. Public*, pg. 1156
INTERNATIONAL PAPER CO. - STATESVILLE CONTAINER MILL—See International Paper Company; *U.S. Public*, pg. 1156
INTERNATIONAL PAPER CO. - TICONDEROGA MILL—See International Paper Company; *U.S. Public*, pg. 1156
INTERNATIONAL PAPER CO. - WOOD PRODUCTS—See International Paper Company; *U.S. Public*, pg. 1156
INTERNATIONAL PAPER CTA (MEXICO), S. DE R.L. DE C.V.—See International Paper Company; *U.S. Public*, pg. 1155
INTERNATIONAL PAPER CZECH REPUBLIC, S.R.O.—See International Paper Company; *U.S. Public*, pg. 1157
INTERNATIONAL PAPER (DEUTSCHLAND)GMBH—See International Paper Company; *U.S. Public*, pg. 1155
INTERNATIONAL PAPER DISTRIBUTION GROUP (TAIWAN) LIMITED—See International Paper Company; *U.S. Public*, pg. 1157
INTERNATIONAL PAPER DISTRIBUTION (SHANGHAI) LIMITED—See International Paper Company; *U.S. Public*, pg. 1157
INTERNATIONAL PAPER DO BRASIL LTDA.—See International Paper Company; *U.S. Public*, pg. 1157
INTERNATIONAL PAPER EMPAQUES INDUSTRIALES DE MEXICO S. DE R.L. DE C.V.—See International Paper Company; *U.S. Public*, pg. 1157
INTERNATIONAL PAPER ESPALY SAS—See International Paper Company; *U.S. Public*, pg. 1157
INTERNATIONAL PAPER (ESPANA), S. L.—See International Paper Company; *U.S. Public*, pg. 1155
INTERNATIONAL PAPER (EUROPE) S.A.—See International Paper Company; *U.S. Public*, pg. 1155
INTERNATIONAL PAPER FOODSERVICE EUROPE LIMITED—See International Paper Company; *U.S. Public*, pg. 1157
INTERNATIONAL PAPER FOODSERVICE (SHANGHAI) CO., LTD.—See Huhtamaki Oyj; *Int'l*, pg. 3526
INTERNATIONAL PAPER GRINON, S.L.—See International Paper Company; *U.S. Public*, pg. 1157
INTERNATIONAL PAPER GROUP, S. DE R.L. DE C.V.—See International Paper Company; *U.S. Public*, pg. 1157
INTERNATIONAL PAPER-HUNGARY KEREKEDELMI KFT.—See International Paper Company; *U.S. Public*, pg. 1157
INTERNATIONAL PAPER (INDIA) PRIVATE LIMITED—See International Paper Company; *U.S. Public*, pg. 1155
INTERNATIONAL PAPER INVESTMENTS FRANCE S.A.—See International Paper Company; *U.S. Public*, pg. 1157
INTERNATIONAL PAPER ITALIA S.P.A.—See International Paper Company; *U.S. Public*, pg. 1157

INTERNATIONAL PAPER COMPANY — CORPORATE AFFILIATIONS

INTERNATIONAL PAPER - KWIDZYN SP. Z O.O.—See International Paper Company; *U.S. Public,* pg. 1155

INTERNATIONAL PAPER MADRID MILL, S.L.—See International Paper Company; *U.S. Public,* pg. 1157

INTERNATIONAL PAPER (MALAYSIA) SDN BHD—See International Paper Company; *U.S. Public,* pg. 1155

INTERNATIONAL PAPER MANUFACTURING AND DISTRIBUTION LTD.—See International Paper Company; *U.S. Public,* pg. 1157

INTERNATIONAL PAPER MONTBLANC, S.L.—See International Paper Company; *U.S. Public,* pg. 1157

INTERNATIONAL PAPER MONTERREY, S. DE R.L. DE C.V.—See International Paper Company; *U.S. Public,* pg. 1157

INTERNATIONAL PAPER MORTAGNE S.A.S.—See International Paper Company; *U.S. Public,* pg. 1157

INTERNATIONAL PAPER PACKAGING MALAYSIA (KUALA LUMPUR) SDN. BHD.—See International Paper Company; *U.S. Public,* pg. 1157

INTERNATIONAL PAPER POLSKA SP. Z O.O.—See International Paper Company; *U.S. Public,* pg. 1157

INTERNATIONAL PAPER REALTY CORP. - SAVANNAH OFFICE—See International Paper Company; *U.S. Public,* pg. 1155

INTERNATIONAL PAPER RETAIL DISPLAY & PACKAGING—See International Paper Company; *U.S. Public,* pg. 1157

INTERNATIONAL PAPER SAINT-AMAND—See International Paper Company; *U.S. Public,* pg. 1157

INTERNATIONAL PAPER S.A.—See International Paper Company; *U.S. Public,* pg. 1157

INTERNATIONAL PAPER SINGAPORE—See International Paper Company; *U.S. Public,* pg. 1155

INTERNATIONAL PAPER—See International Paper Company; *U.S. Public,* pg. 1155

INTERNATIONAL PAPER & SUN CARTONBOARD CO., LTD.—See International Paper Company; *U.S. Public,* pg. 1155

INTERNATIONAL PAPER SWITZERLAND GMBH—See International Paper Company; *U.S. Public,* pg. 1157

INTERNATIONAL PAPER TAIWAN LTD.—See International Paper Company; *U.S. Public,* pg. 1157

INTERNATIONAL PAPER (UK) LIMITED—See International Paper Company; *U.S. Public,* pg. 1155

INTERNATIONAL PAPER VALLS, S.A.—See International Paper Company; *U.S. Public,* pg. 1157

INTERNATIONAL PARKING MANAGEMENT, INC.—See LAZ Parking Ltd, LLC; *U.S. Private,* pg. 2402

INTERNATIONAL PARKSIDE PRODUCTS INC.; *Int'l,* pg. 3751

INTERNATIONAL PARTNERSHIP FOR HUMAN DEVELOPMENT; *U.S. Private,* pg. 2119

INTERNATIONAL PAYMENT SOLUTIONS HOLDINGS LIMITED; *Int'l,* pg. 3751

INTERNATIONAL PAYMENT SOLUTIONS (HONG KONG) LIMITED—See Universal Technologies Holdings Limited; *Int'l,* pg. 8082

INTERNATIONAL PEINTURE S.A.—See Akzo Nobel N.V.; *Int'l,* pg. 271

THE INTERNATIONAL PEN SHOP—See Arthur Brown & Bro., Inc.; *U.S. Private,* pg. 341

INTERNATIONAL PERSONAL FINANCE DIGITAL SPAIN S.A.U—See International Personal Finance plc; *Int'l,* pg. 3751

INTERNATIONAL PERSONAL FINANCE PLC; *Int'l,* pg. 3751

INTERNATIONAL PET FOOD CO., LTD.—See Charoen Pokphand Foods Public Company Limited; *Int'l,* pg. 1452

INTERNATIONAL PETROLEUM CORPORATION OF DELAWARE—See J.F. Lehman & Company, Inc.; *U.S. Private,* pg. 2163

INTERNATIONAL PETROLEUM CORPORATION—See Lundin Group of Companies; *Int'l,* pg. 4583

INTERNATIONAL PETROLEUM INVESTMENT COMPANY PJSC—See Mubadala Investment Company PJSC; *Int'l,* pg. 5074

INTERNATIONAL PETROLEUM LIMITED; *Int'l,* pg. 3751

INTERNATIONAL PHYSICIANS NETWORK, L.L.C.—See Cencora, Inc.; *U.S. Public,* pg. 467

INTERNATIONAL PICTURES CORP.; *U.S. Private,* pg. 2119

INTERNATIONAL PIPE MACHINERY CORP.—See Besser Company; *U.S. Private,* pg. 542

INTERNATIONAL PLANNING ALLIANCE, LLC; *U.S. Private,* pg. 2119

INTERNATIONAL PLANTATION SERVICES LIMITED—See UIE Plc; *Int'l,* pg. 8016

INTERNATIONAL PLANT NUTRITION INSTITUTE; *U.S. Private,* pg. 2119

INTERNATIONAL PLASTIC SYSTEMS LTD—See Indutrade AB; *Int'l,* pg. 3679

INTERNATIONAL PLAY COMPANY INC—See Iplayco Corporation Ltd.; *Int'l,* pg. 3797

INTERNATIONAL PLAYTHINGS, LLC—See Epoch Co. Ltd.; *Int'l,* pg. 2463

INTERNATIONAL PLAZA & BAY STREET—See Simon Property Group, Inc.; *U.S. Public,* pg. 1881

INTERNATIONAL PLYWOOD (IMPORTERS) LTD.; *Int'l,* pg. 3751

INTERNATIONAL POLO CLUB PALM BEACH—See Wellington Equestrian Partners, LLC; *U.S. Private,* pg. 4475

INTERNATIONAL POLYMER SOLUTIONS INC.—See Graco, Inc.; *U.S. Public,* pg. 954

INTERNATIONAL POLYURETHANE INVESTMENTS B.V.—See Huntsman Corporation; *U.S. Public,* pg. 1074

INTERNATIONAL PORT HOLDINGS LTD.—See BlackRock, Inc.; *U.S. Public,* pg. 346

INTERNATIONAL PORT SERVICES, INC.; *U.S. Private,* pg. 2119

INTERNATIONAL POULTRY BREEDERS LLC—See Jamaica Broilers Group Limited; *Int'l,* pg. 3874

INTERNATIONAL POWER AMERICA, INC.—See ENGIE SA; *Int'l,* pg. 2433

INTERNATIONAL POWER AUSTRALIA FINANCE—See ENGIE SA; *Int'l,* pg. 2434

INTERNATIONAL POWER AUSTRALIA PTY LTD.—See ENGIE SA; *Int'l,* pg. 2433

INTERNATIONAL POWER CONSOLIDATED HOLDINGS LIMITED—See ENGIE SA; *Int'l,* pg. 2434

INTERNATIONAL POWER GROUP LTD.; *U.S. Public,* pg. 1158

INTERNATIONAL POWER PLC—See ENGIE SA; *Int'l,* pg. 2432

INTERNATIONAL PRECIOUS METALS INCORPORATED; *U.S. Private,* pg. 2119

INTERNATIONAL PRECISION COMPONENTS CORPORATION; *U.S. Private,* pg. 2119

INTERNATIONAL PRESS SOFTCOM LIMITED; *Int'l,* pg. 3752

INTERNATIONAL PRESS SOFTCOM (VIETNAM) CO., LTD.—See International Press Softcom Limited; *Int'l,* pg. 3752

INTERNATIONAL PROCESSING CORP—See ReConserve, Inc.; *U.S. Private,* pg. 3371

INTERNATIONAL PROCESS TECHNOLOGIES LIMITED; *Int'l,* pg. 3752

INTERNATIONAL PRODUCE HOLDING COMPANY—See Pulsar Internacional S.A. de C.V.; *Int'l,* pg. 6117

INTERNATIONAL PRODUCE LTD.—See Bunge Limited; *U.S. Public,* pg. 412

INTERNATIONAL PRODUCE LTD.—See Bakkavor Group plc; *Int'l,* pg. 806

INTERNATIONAL PRODUCT DEVELOPMENT CO., INC.; *U.S. Private,* pg. 2119

INTERNATIONAL PROJECT DEVELOPERS LTD.—See Dabbagh Group Holding Company Ltd.; *Int'l,* pg. 1902

INTERNATIONAL PROJECT DEVELOPERS LTD.—See Renaissance United Limited; *Int'l,* pg. 6273

INTERNATIONAL PROSPECT VENTURES LTD.; *Int'l,* pg. 3752

INTERNATIONAL PROTECTION GROUP, INC.—See Allied Universal Manager LLC; *U.S. Private,* pg. 190

INTERNATIONAL PUBLIC PARTNERSHIPS LIMITED; *Int'l,* pg. 3752

INTERNATIONAL PULP SALES COMPANY—See International Paper Company; *U.S. Public,* pg. 1157

INTERNATIONAL PURCHASE SYSTEMS, INC.; *U.S. Private,* pg. 2119

INTERNATIONAL READING ASSOCIATION, INC.; *U.S. Private,* pg. 2119

INTERNATIONAL REMITTANCE (CANADA) LTD.—See I-Remit, Inc.; *Int'l,* pg. 3564

INTERNATIONAL RESCUE COMMITTEE, INC.; *U.S. Private,* pg. 2119

INTERNATIONAL RESEARCH AND EXCHANGES BOARD; *U.S. Private,* pg. 2120

INTERNATIONAL RESEARCH & ASSET MANAGEMENT, INC.—See EP Wealth Advisors, LLC; *U.S. Private,* pg. 1411

INTERNATIONAL RESEARCH CORPORATION PUBLIC COMPANY LIMITED; *Int'l,* pg. 3752

INTERNATIONAL RESERVATIONS LIMITED—See Hyatt Hotels Corporation; *U.S. Public,* pg. 1078

INTERNATIONAL RESISTIVE COMPANY, INC.—See TT Electronics plc; *Int'l,* pg. 7959

INTERNATIONAL RESORTS COMPANY - KPSC; *Int'l,* pg. 3752

INTERNATIONAL RESOURCES GROUP LTD.; *Int'l,* pg. 3752

INTERNATIONAL RESOURCE STRATEGIES LIBERIA ENERGY, INC.—See Simba Essel Energy Inc.; *Int'l,* pg. 6927

INTERNATIONAL RESTAURANT DISTRIBUTORS, INC.; *U.S. Private,* pg. 2120

INTERNATIONAL RESTAURANT SERVICES; *U.S. Private,* pg. 2120

INTERNATIONAL REVOLVING DOOR COMPANY; *U.S. Private,* pg. 2120

INTERNATIONAL RISK - IRC, INC.—See Aon plc; *Int'l,* pg. 496

INTERNATIONAL ROAD DYNAMICS CORP—See Quarterhill Inc.; *Int'l,* pg. 6155

INTERNATIONAL ROAD DYNAMICS INC.—See Quarterhill Inc.; *Int'l,* pg. 6155

INTERNATIONAL ROBOTICS, INC.; *U.S. Private,* pg. 2120

INTERNATIONAL ROLLFORMS INC.; *U.S. Private,* pg. 2120

INTERNATIONAL ROYALTY CORPORATION—See Royal Gold, Inc.; *U.S. Public,* pg. 1815

INTERNATIONAL RUBBER CO. LLC—See Dubai Investments PJSC; *Int'l,* pg. 2219

INTERNATIONAL SAINT-GOBAIN—See Compagnie de Saint-Gobain SA; *Int'l,* pg. 1723

INTERNATIONAL SALT COMPANY LLC—See K+S Aktiengesellschaft; *Int'l,* pg. 4040

INTERNATIONAL SANITARY SUPPLY ASSOCIATION, INC.—See Specialised Cleaning & Restoration Industry Association, Inc.; *Int'l,* pg. 7128

INTERNATIONAL SCHOOL AUGSBURG ISA GAG; *Int'l,* pg. 3752

INTERNATIONAL SCHOOL OF BERNE AG—See Stride, Inc.; *U.S. Public,* pg. 1955

INTERNATIONAL SCHOOL OF COLOUR & DESIGN PTY LTD—See iCollege Limited; *Int'l,* pg. 3582

INTERNATIONAL SEA DRILLING LTD.—See Nabors Industries Ltd.; *Int'l,* pg. 5119

INTERNATIONAL SEAWAYS, INC.; *U.S. Public,* pg. 1158

INTERNATIONAL SEAWAY TRADING CORPORATION; *U.S. Private,* pg. 2120

INTERNATIONAL SECURITIES EXCHANGE HOLDINGS, INC.—See Nasdaq, Inc.; *U.S. Public,* pg. 1491

INTERNATIONAL SECURITIES EXCHANGE LLC—See Nasdaq, Inc.; *U.S. Public,* pg. 1491

INTERNATIONAL SHAKESPEARE GLOBE CENTRE LTD.; *Int'l,* pg. 3752

INTERNATIONAL SHARED SERVICES, INC.—See Geisinger Health System; *U.S. Private,* pg. 1656

INTERNATIONAL SHIPHOLDING CORPORATION—See AIP, LLC; *U.S. Private,* pg. 136

INTERNATIONAL SILICA INDUSTRIES CO.; *Int'l,* pg. 3752

INTERNATIONAL SILVER, INC.; *U.S. Public,* pg. 1158

INTERNATIONAL SINAIA; *Int'l,* pg. 3752

INTERNATIONAL SNUBBING SERVICES—See Superior Energy Services, Inc.; *U.S. Private,* pg. 3877

INTERNATIONAL SOCIETY FOR PHARMACEUTICAL ENGINEERING INC.; *U.S. Private,* pg. 2120

INTERNATIONAL SOCIETY FOR THE STUDY OF XENOBIOTICS; *U.S. Private,* pg. 2120

INTERNATIONAL SOCIETY OF AUTOMATION; *U.S. Private,* pg. 2120

INTERNATIONAL SOCIETY ON THROMBOSIS AND HAEMOSTASIS, INC.; *U.S. Private,* pg. 2120

INTERNATIONAL SOFTWARE SYSTEMS, INC.; *U.S. Private,* pg. 2120

INTERNATIONAL SOLUTIONS GROUP, INC.; *U.S. Private,* pg. 2121

INTERNATIONAL SOS ASSISTANCE, INC.—See AEA International Holdings Pte. Ltd.; *Int'l,* pg. 170

INTERNATIONAL SOS ASSISTANCE UK LIMITED—See TAC Healthcare Group Ltd.; *Int'l,* pg. 7402

INTERNATIONAL SOS (FRANCE) S.A.—See AEA International Holdings Pte. Ltd.; *Int'l,* pg. 170

INTERNATIONAL SOS PTE. LTD.—See AEA International Holdings Pte. Ltd.; *Int'l,* pg. 170

INTERNATIONAL SOURCING COMPANY INC.—See Bunzl plc; *Int'l,* pg. 1217

INTERNATIONAL SPECIAL RISKS; *U.S. Private,* pg. 2121

INTERNATIONAL SPECIALTY INSURANCE—See Ryan Specialty Holdings, Inc.; *U.S. Public,* pg. 1828

INTERNATIONAL SPECIALTY PRODUCTS, INC.—See Ashland Inc.; *U.S. Public,* pg. 212

INTERNATIONAL SPEEDWAY CORPORATION—See National Association for Stock Car Auto Racing, Inc.; *U.S. Private,* pg. 2845

THE INTERNATIONAL SPY MUSEUM; *U.S. Private,* pg. 4057

INTERNATIONAL STANDARD RESOURCES SECURITIES LIMITED—See Golden Century International Holdings Group Limited; *Int'l,* pg. 3028

INTERNATIONAL STANDARDS LABORATORY CORP.—See Wistron Corporation; *Int'l,* pg. 8438

INTER-NATIONAL STARCH & CHEMICAL CO., INC.—See Ingredion Incorporated; *U.S. Public,* pg. 1123

INTER-NATIONAL STARCH INC.—See Ingredion Incorporated; *U.S. Public,* pg. 1124

INTERNATIONAL STEEL SERVICES, INC.; *U.S. Private,* pg. 2121

INTERNATIONAL STEELS LIMITED—See International Industries Limited; *Int'l,* pg. 3750

INTERNATIONAL STEEL WOOL CORPORATION—See F.H. Bonn Company; *U.S. Private,* pg. 1456

INTERNATIONAL STEM CELL CORPORATION; *U.S. Public,* pg. 1158

INTERNATIONAL STRATEGY & INVESTMENT GROUP L.L.C.—See Evercore, Inc.; *U.S. Public,* pg. 800

INTERNATIONAL STUDENT VOLUNTEERS; *U.S. Private,* pg. 2121

INTERNATIONAL STUDIES ABROAD, INC.; *U.S. Private,* pg. 2121

INTERNATIONAL SUN GROUP FZCO; *Int'l,* pg. 3752

INTERNATIONAL SUNRISE PARTNERS LLC—See Unibank S.A.; *Int'l*, pg. 8030
INTERNATIONAL SYSTEMS DEVELOPMENT CO., LTD.—See BIPROGY Inc.; *Int'l*, pg. 1045
INTERNATIONAL TAIYO TRADING PTE LTD—See Taiyo Kogyo Corporation; *Int'l*, pg. 7425
INTERNATIONAL TANK TERMINALS, LLC—See Macquarie Group Limited; *Int'l*, pg. 4624
INTERNATIONAL TECHNEGROUP INC.—See Wipro Limited; *Int'l*, pg. 8432
INTERNATIONAL TECHNEGROUP LTD.—See Wipro Limited; *Int'l*, pg. 8432
INTERNATIONAL TECHNOLOGIES, LLC—See Rennova Health, Inc.; *U.S. Public*, pg. 1783
INTERNATIONAL TECHNOLOGY EXHIBITION AND EVENTS JOINT STOCK COMPANY—See Messe Munchen GmbH; *Int'l*, pg. 4841
INTERNATIONAL TECHNOLOGY PRODUCTS GMBH—See Restore plc; *Int'l*, pg. 6304
INTERNATIONAL TEFL ACADEMY, INC.; *U.S. Private*, pg. 2121
INTERNATIONAL TEST SOLUTIONS KOREA LIMITED—See Entegris, Inc.; *U.S. Public*, pg. 776
INTERNATIONAL TEST SOLUTIONS, LLC—See Entegris, Inc.; *U.S. Public*, pg. 776
INTERNATIONAL THERMAL SYSTEMS, LLC; *U.S. Private*, pg. 2121
INTERNATIONAL TOBACCO COMPANY LIMITED—See Godfrey Phillips India Ltd.; *Int'l*, pg. 3019
INTERNATIONAL TOOLING SOLUTIONS LLC; *U.S. Private*, pg. 2121
INTERNATIONAL TOOL MANUFACTURING; *U.S. Private*, pg. 2121
INTERNATIONAL TOURISTIC PROJECTS LEBANESE COMPANY—See Adeptio LLC; *Int'l*, pg. 143
INTERNATIONAL TOWER HILL MINES LTD.; *Int'l*, pg. 3753
INTERNATIONAL TRADE AGENCIES AND MARKETING CO. S.A.E.—See Ghabbour Auto S.A.E.; *Int'l*, pg. 2958
INTERNATIONAL TRADEMART COMPANY LIMITED—See Hopewell Holdings Limited; *Int'l*, pg. 3473
INTERNATIONAL TRADE S.A.—See Viohalco SA/NV; *Int'l*, pg. 8243
INTERNATIONAL TRADING AND FINANCE (ITF) B.V.—See Heidelberg Materials AG; *Int'l*, pg. 3316
INTERNATIONAL TRANSMISSION COMPANY—See Fortis Inc.; *Int'l*, pg. 2739
INTERNATIONAL TRANSPORTATION CORP.; *U.S. Private*, pg. 2121
INTERNATIONAL TRANSPORTATION SERVICE, INC.—See Kawasaki Kisen Kaisha, Ltd.; *Int'l*, pg. 4099
INTERNATIONAL TRAVEL ASSOCIATES CORP—See ITAGroup, Inc.; *U.S. Private*, pg. 2148
INTERNATIONAL TRAVEL BUREAU—See International Agencies Company Ltd.; *Int'l*, pg. 3743
INTERNATIONAL TRAVEL HOUSE LTD; *Int'l*, pg. 3753
INTERNATIONAL TRAY PADS & PACKAGING, INC.—See Pactiv Evergreen Inc.; *U.S. Public*, pg. 1633
INTERNATIONAL TRUCKS OF HOUSTON; *U.S. Private*, pg. 2121
INTERNATIONAL TRUSS SYSTEMS PROPRIETARY LIMITED—See Illinois Tool Works Inc.; *U.S. Public*, pg. 1108
INTERNATIONAL TUBE TECHNOLOGY (PTY) LTD—See Berry Global Group, Inc; *U.S. Public*, pg. 324
INTERNATIONAL TUBULAR SERVICES DE MEXICO, S. DE R.I. DE C.V.—See Parker Wellbore Company; *U.S. Public*, pg. 1650
INTERNATIONAL TUBULARS FZE—See Parker Wellbore Company; *U.S. Public*, pg. 1650
INTERNATIONAL TURF INVESTMENT CO., INC.; *U.S. Private*, pg. 2121
INTERNATIONAL TURNKEY SYSTEMS; *Int'l*, pg. 3753
INTERNATIONAL UNION OF PAINTERS AND ALLIED TRADES; *U.S. Private*, pg. 2121
INTERNATIONAL UNITED TECHNOLOGY CO., LTD.—See ASUSTeK Computer Inc.; *Int'l*, pg. 664
INTERNATIONAL UNIVERSITY OF MONACO, SAM—See Perdoceo Education Corporation; *U.S. Public*, pg. 1673
INTERNATIONAL VALUERS LTD.—See ENL Limited; *Int'l*, pg. 2441
INTERNATIONAL VENEER COMPANY—See IVC-USA Inc.; *U.S. Private*, pg. 2151
INTERNATIONAL VIDEO-CONFERENCING, INC.; *U.S. Private*, pg. 2121
INTERNATIONAL VOYAGER HOLDINGS, INC.; *U.S. Private*, pg. 2121
INTERNATIONAL WAREHOUSING & DISTRIBUTION INC.—See Mullen Group Ltd.; *Int'l*, pg. 5080
INTERNATIONAL WATCH CO. AG—See Compagnie Financiere Richemont S.A.; *Int'l*, pg. 1741
INTERNATIONAL WATER-GUARD INDUSTRIES INC.—See Arcline Investment Management LP; *U.S. Private*, pg. 314
INTERNATIONAL WATERJET PARTS, INC.; *U.S. Private*, pg. 2121
INTERNATIONAL WHOLESALE SUPPLY, INC.; *U.S. Private*, pg. 2122

INTERNATIONAL WHOLESALE TILE, LLC—See Victoria Plc; *Int'l*, pg. 8189
INTERNATIONAL WINDOW CORP. - NORTHERN CALIFORNIA—See UMC Acquisition Corp.; *U.S. Private*, pg. 4278
INTERNATIONAL WINDOW CORP.—See UMC Acquisition Corp.; *U.S. Private*, pg. 4278
INTERNATIONAL WINE ACCESSORIES, INC.—See Vintage Wine Estates, Inc.; *U.S. Public*, pg. 2298
INTERNATIONAL WINE & SPIRITS LTD.—See Altria Group, Inc.; *U.S. Public*, pg. 89
INTERNATIONAL WINE & SPIRITS OF LOUISIANA, INC.; *U.S. Private*, pg. 2122
INTERNATIONAL WIRE CO.—See Atlas Holdings, LLC; *U.S. Private*, pg. 376
INTERNATIONAL WIRE GROUP-HIGH PERFORMANCE CONDUCTORS—See Atlas Holdings, LLC; *U.S. Private*, pg. 376
INTERNATIONAL WIRE GROUP, INC.—See Atlas Holdings, LLC; *U.S. Private*, pg. 376
INTERNATIONAL WIRE GROUP - INSULATED DIVISION—See Atlas Holdings, LLC; *U.S. Private*, pg. 376
INTERNATIONAL WIRE GROUP-WYRE WYND—See Atlas Holdings, LLC; *U.S. Private*, pg. 376
INTERNATIONAL WIRING SYSTEMS (PHILS.) CORPORATION—See Sumitomo Electric Industries, Ltd.; *Int'l*, pg. 7284
INTERNATIONAL WOOD INDUSTRIES, INC.—See UFP Industries, Inc.; *U.S. Public*, pg. 2219
INTERNATIONAL YOUTH FOUNDATION; *U.S. Private*, pg. 2122
INTERNATIONAL ZEOLITE CORP.; *Int'l*, pg. 3753
INTERNATIONELLA ENGELSKA SKOLAN I SVERIGE HOLDINGS II AB; *Int'l*, pg. 3753
INTERNATIONELLA HOTELL- OCH RESTAURANGSKOLAN IHR AB—See AcadeMedia AB; *Int'l*, pg. 76
INTERNATIONAL BULLION & METAL BROKERS—See IBB Amsterdam BV; *Int'l*, pg. 3569
INTERNATURAL FOODS LLC—See World Finer Foods, Inc.; *U.S. Private*, pg. 4565
INTERNESENAL HOTELS AD; *Int'l*, pg. 3753
INTERNET ACCESS GMBH LILIBIT BERLIN GESELLSCHAFT FUR KOMMUNIKATION UND DIGITALTECHNIK—See Francotyp-Postalia Holding AG; *Int'l*, pg. 2761
INTERNETARRAY, INC.; *U.S. Public*, pg. 1158
INTERNET AUTOPARTS, INC.—See Clayton, Dubilier & Rice, LLC; *U.S. Private*, pg. 923
INTERNET BILLBOARD A.S.—See Stroer SE & Co. KGaA; *Int'l*, pg. 7242
INTERNET BRANDS, INC.—See KKR & Co. Inc.; *U.S. Public*, pg. 1253
INTERNET BROADCASTING SYSTEMS—See Nexstar Media Group, Inc.; *U.S. Public*, pg. 1522
THE INTERNET BUSINESS LIMITED—See News Corporation; *U.S. Public*, pg. 1520
INTERNET CENTRAL LTD.—See Goodwin PLC; *Int'l*, pg. 3042
INTERNET CORPORATION FOR ASSIGNED NAMES & NUMBERS; *U.S. Private*, pg. 2122
INTERNET COWBOY VENTURES LLC; *U.S. Private*, pg. 2122
INTERNET DISCLOSURE CO., LTD.—See Avant Corporation; *Int'l*, pg. 735
INTERNETDOM LLC—See TCS TurControlSysteme AG; *Int'l*, pg. 7485
INTERNETFITNESS.COM, INC.; *U.S. Private*, pg. 2122
INTERNET FOR CONTINUING EDUCATION INC.; *U.S. Private*, pg. 2122
INTERNET INFINITY, INC.; *Int'l*, pg. 3753
INTERNET INITIATIVE JAPAN INC.; *Int'l*, pg. 3753
INTERNET INTERACTION LIMITED—See Mediahuis Partners NV; *Int'l*, pg. 4772
INTERNET INTERACTION LIMITED—See VP Exploitatie N.V.; *Int'l*, pg. 8311
THE INTERNET LANGUAGE COMPANY; *U.S. Private*, pg. 4057
INTERNET MARKETING INC.—See Trinity Hunt Management, L.P.; *U.S. Private*, pg. 4235
INTERNET MARKETING INC.—See Trinity Hunt Management, L.P.; *U.S. Private*, pg. 4235
INTERNET MULTIFEED CO.—See Internet Initiative Japan Inc.; *Int'l*, pg. 3753
INTERNET NAMES WORDWIDE ESPANA SL—See Corporation Service Company; *U.S. Private*, pg. 1057
INTERNET NUMBER CORPORATION—See GMO Internet Group, Inc.; *Int'l*, pg. 3014
INTERNET PARA TODOS S.A.C.—See Telefonica, S.A.; *Int'l*, pg. 7535
INTERNET PIPELINE, INC.—See Roper Technologies, Inc.; *U.S. Public*, pg. 1812
INTERNETPLATFORM ZEELAND B.V.—See Delta N.V.; *Int'l*, pg. 2019
INTERNET PRODUCTION INC.; *U.S. Private*, pg. 2122
INTERNETQ PLC; *Int'l*, pg. 3754
INTERNETQ POLAND SP. Z O.O.—See InternetQ plc; *Int'l*, pg. 3754

INTERNET REVOLUTION, INC.—See Konami Group Corporation; *Int'l*, pg. 4245
INTERNET SCIENCES, INC.; *U.S. Private*, pg. 2122
INTERNET SERVICES CORPORATION; *U.S. Private*, pg. 2122
INTERNET SERVICES FIJI LIMITED—See Fiji National Provident Fund; *Int'l*, pg. 2661
INTERNET SERVICES POLEN SP. Z O.O.—See Rocket Internet SE; *Int'l*, pg. 6379
INTERNET SOLUTIONS PTY LIMITED—See Nippon Telegraph & Telephone Corporation; *Int'l*, pg. 5342
INTERNET SOLUTIONS—See Nippon Telegraph & Telephone Corporation; *Int'l*, pg. 5342
INTERNET SOLUTIONS—See Nippon Telegraph & Telephone Corporation; *Int'l*, pg. 5342
INTERNET SPORTS MARKETING LIMITED—See AsianLogic Limited; *Int'l*, pg. 620
INTERNET TECHNOLOGY GROUP LTD.; *Int'l*, pg. 3753
INTERNETTERS LIMITED—See iomart Group plc; *Int'l*, pg. 3792
INTERNET THAILAND PUBLIC COMPANY LIMITED; *Int'l*, pg. 3754
INTERNET TRUCKSTOP GROUP, LLC; *U.S. Private*, pg. 2122
INTERNET VIDEO ARCHIVE LLC—See Meta Data Software, Inc.; *U.S. Private*, pg. 2679
INTERNETWORK ENGINEERING—See BC Partners LLP; *Int'l*, pg. 925
INTERNETWORKING & BROADBAND CONSULTING CO., LTD.; *Int'l*, pg. 3754
INTERNETX CORP.—See United Internet AG; *Int'l*, pg. 8069
INTERNETX GMBH—See United Internet AG; *Int'l*, pg. 8069
INTERNEWS NETWORK; *U.S. Private*, pg. 2122
INTERNEWS NETWORK; *U.S. Private*, pg. 2122
INTERNEXA S.A.—See Ecopetrol S.A.; *Int'l*, pg. 2299
INTERNEXUM GMBH—See Team Internet Group plc; *Int'l*, pg. 7500
INTERNICKEL AUSTRALIA PTY LTD—See Macarthur Minerals Limited; *Int'l*, pg. 4620
INTERNIST ASSOCIATES OF HOUSTON, PLLC—See HCA Healthcare, Inc.; *U.S. Public*, pg. 999
INTERNO ENGINEERING (1996) PTE. LTD.—See Indigo Star Holdings Limited; *Int'l*, pg. 3656
INTERNORDIC BEARINGS AB—See OEM International AB; *Int'l*, pg. 5528
INTERNOS GLOBAL INVESTORS KAPITALVERWALTUNGSGESELLSCHAFT MBH—See Internos Real Ltd.; *Int'l*, pg. 3754
INTERNOS REAL LTD.; *Int'l*, pg. 3754
INTERNSHIPS.COM, LLC—See Chegg Inc.; *U.S. Public*, pg. 483
INTEROC AB—See Peab AB; *Int'l*, pg. 5772
INTEROCEANIC CORPORATION; *U.S. Private*, pg. 2122
INTEROGO HOLDING AG; *Int'l*, pg. 3754
INTEROIL EXPLORATION & PRODUCTION ASA; *Int'l*, pg. 3754
INTEROJO CO., LTD.; *Int'l*, pg. 3754
INTERONE COLOGNE—See Omnicom Group Inc.; *U.S. Public*, pg. 1576
INTERONE HAMBURG—See Omnicom Group Inc.; *U.S. Public*, pg. 1576
INTERONE WORLDWIDE—See Omnicom Group Inc.; *U.S. Public*, pg. 1576
INTEROP TECHNOLOGIES, LLC; *U.S. Private*, pg. 2122
INTERO REAL ESTATE SERVICES, INC.—See Berkshire Hathaway Inc.; *U.S. Public*, pg. 306
INTERORIENT MARINE SERVICES (GERMANY) GMBH & CO. KG—See Interorient Navigation Company Ltd.; *Int'l*, pg. 3754
INTERORIENT NAVIGATION COMPANY LTD.; *Int'l*, pg. 3754
INTERORIENT NAVIGATION (LATVIA) CO. LTD—See Interorient Navigation Company Ltd.; *Int'l*, pg. 3755
INTERORIENT NAVIGATION (ST. PETERSBURG) INC.—See Interorient Navigation Company Ltd.; *Int'l*, pg. 3755
INTEROUTE AUSTRIA GMBH—See GTT Communications, Inc.; *U.S. Private*, pg. 1808
INTEROUTE BULGARIA JSCO—See GTT Communications, Inc.; *U.S. Private*, pg. 1808
INTEROUTE COMMUNICATIONS LIMITED—See GTT Communications, Inc.; *U.S. Private*, pg. 1808
INTEROUTE CZECH S.R.O—See GTT Communications, Inc.; *U.S. Private*, pg. 1808
INTEROUTE FINLAND OY—See GTT Communications, Inc.; *U.S. Private*, pg. 1808
INTEROUTE FRANCE SAS—See GTT Communications, Inc.; *U.S. Private*, pg. 1808
INTEROUTE IBERIA S.A.U.—See GTT Communications, Inc.; *U.S. Private*, pg. 1808
INTEROUTE MAGYARORSZAG TAVKOZLESI KFT—See GTT Communications, Inc.; *U.S. Private*, pg. 1808
INTEROUTE MANAGED SERVICES DENMARK A/S—See GTT Communications, Inc.; *U.S. Private*, pg. 1808
INTEROUTE MANAGED SERVICES SWEDEN AB—See GTT Communications, Inc.; *U.S. Private*, pg. 1808

INTERORIENT NAVIGATION COMPANY LTD.
CORPORATE AFFILIATIONS

INTEROUTE MANAGED SERVICES SWITZERLAND SARL—See GTT Communications, Inc.; *U.S. Private*, pg. 1808
INTEROUTE SLOVAKIA S.R.O.—See GTT Communications, Inc.; *U.S. Private*, pg. 1808
INTEROUTE S.R.L—See GTT Communications, Inc.; *U.S. Private*, pg. 1808
INTEROUTE USA INC.—See GTT Communications, Inc.; *U.S. Private*, pg. 1808
INTERPACE BIOPHARMA, LLC—See Flagship Biosciences, Inc.; *U.S. Private*, pg. 1539
INTERPACE BIOSCIENCES, INC.; *U.S. Public*, pg. 1158
INTERPACE DIAGNOSTICS CORPORATION—See Interpace Biosciences, Inc.; *U.S. Public*, pg. 1158
INTERPACE DIAGNOSTICS, LLC—See Interpace Biosciences, Inc.; *U.S. Public*, pg. 1158
INTER-PACIFIC ASSET MANAGEMENT SDN BHD—See Berjaya Corporation Berhad; *Int'l*, pg. 982
INTER-PACIFIC CAPITAL SDN BHD—See Berjaya Corporation Berhad; *Int'l*, pg. 982
INTER-PACIFIC CORPORATION; *U.S. Private*, pg. 2107
INTER-PACIFIC EQUITY NOMINEES (ASING) SDN BHD—See Berjaya Corporation Berhad; *Int'l*, pg. 984
INTERPACIFIC GROUP INC.; *U.S. Private*, pg. 2122
INTERPACIFIC INVESTORS SERVICES, INC.; *U.S. Private*, pg. 2122
INTER-PACIFIC MOTORS INC.—See Steve Marshall Group Ltd.; *Int'l*, pg. 7213
INTER-PACIFIC PACKAGING SDN. BHD.—See Magni-Tech Industries Berhad; *Int'l*, pg. 4640
INTER-PACIFIC RESEARCH SDN BHD—See Berjaya Corporation Berhad; *Int'l*, pg. 982
INTER-PACIFIC SECURITIES SDN BHD—See Berjaya Corporation Berhad; *Int'l*, pg. 982
INTER-PACIFIC TRADING SDN BHD—See Berjaya Corporation Berhad; *Int'l*, pg. 982
INTERPACK LIMITED—See Coral Products PLC; *Int'l*, pg. 1795
INTERPAK SN SA—See BERICAP GmbH & Co. KG; *Int'l*, pg. 981
INTER PARFUMS GRAND PUBLIC, S.A.—See Inter Parfums, Inc.; *U.S. Public*, pg. 1140
INTER PARFUMS HOLDINGS, S.A.—See Inter Parfums, Inc.; *U.S. Public*, pg. 1140
INTER PARFUMS, INC.; *U.S. Public*, pg. 1140
INTERPARFUMS SA—See Inter Parfums, Inc.; *U.S. Public*, pg. 1140
INTERPARFUMS SINGAPORE PTE.—See Inter Parfums, Inc.; *U.S. Public*, pg. 1140
INTERPARK IMMOBILIEN GMBH—See VIB Vermogen AG; *Int'l*, pg. 8184
INTERPARKING FRANCE SA—See Ageas SA/NV; *Int'l*, pg. 204
INTERPARKING HISPANIA, S.A.—See Ageas SA/NV; *Int'l*, pg. 204
INTERPARKING NEDERLAND B.V.—See Ageas SA/NV; *Int'l*, pg. 204
INTERPARKING SA—See Ageas SA/NV; *Int'l*, pg. 204
INTERPARK LLC; *U.S. Private*, pg. 2122
INTERPARK PITTSBURGH, LLC—See Brookfield Corporation; *Int'l*, pg. 1174
INTERPARK (SOUTH AFRICA) (PTY) LTD.—See Excellerate Holdings Ltd.; *Int'l*, pg. 2578
INTER PARTNER ASISTENCIA SERVICIOS ESPANA SA—See AXA S.A.; *Int'l*, pg. 754
INTER PARTNER ASSISTANCE ALGERIE SPA—See AXA S.A.; *Int'l*, pg. 754
INTER PARTNER ASSISTANCE CO., LTD.—See AXA S.A.; *Int'l*, pg. 755
INTER PARTNER ASSISTANCE GREECE—See AXA S.A.; *Int'l*, pg. 755
INTER PARTNER ASSISTANCE HONG-KONG LTD—See AXA S.A.; *Int'l*, pg. 755
INTER PARTNER ASSISTANCE LTD—See AXA S.A.; *Int'l*, pg. 755
INTER PARTNER ASSISTANCE POLSKA S.A.—See AXA S.A.; *Int'l*, pg. 755
INTER PARTNER ASSISTANCE S.A.—See AXA S.A.; *Int'l*, pg. 754
INTER PARTNER ASSISTANCE S.A.—See AXA S.A.; *Int'l*, pg. 755
INTER PARTNER ASSISTANCE S/C LTDA—See AXA S.A.; *Int'l*, pg. 755
INTER PARTNER ASSISTANCE TURKEY—See AXA S.A.; *Int'l*, pg. 755
INTER PARTNER ASSISTENZA SERVIZI SPA—See AXA S.A.; *Int'l*, pg. 755
INTERPATH SERVICES PTY. LTD.—See Bunzl plc; *Int'l*, pg. 1218
INTERPEC IBERICA S.A.—See Sapec S.A.; *Int'l*, pg. 6571
INTERPEX SERVICES PRIVATE LIMITED—See Singapore Land Group Limited; *Int'l*, pg. 6940
INTERPHARMA PUBLIC COMPANY LIMITED; *Int'l*, pg. 3755
INTERPHASE SYSTEMS, INC.—See NewSpring Capital LLC; *U.S. Private*, pg. 2918
INTER PIPELINE LTD. - COCHRANE EXTRACTION PLANT—See Brookfield Infrastructure Partners L.P.; *Int'l*, pg. 1193

INTER PIPELINE LTD.—See Brookfield Infrastructure Partners L.P.; *Int'l*, pg. 1193
INTERPIPE NYZHNODNIPROVSKY TUBE-ROLLING PLANT PJSC; *Int'l*, pg. 3755
INTERPLAN GROUP—See Hakuhodo DY Holdings Incorporated; *Int'l*, pg. 3221
INTER - PLANING GMBH—See Coop-Gruppe Genossenschaft; *Int'l*, pg. 1790
INTERPLASP S.L.—See Sheela Foam Limited; *Int'l*, pg. 6792
INTERPLASTIC CORPORATION MOLDING PRODUCTS DIV.—See Interplastic Corporation; *U.S. Private*, pg. 2123
INTERPLASTIC CORPORATION; *U.S. Private*, pg. 2122
INTERPLASTIC CORPORATION—See Interplastic Corporation; *U.S. Private*, pg. 2123
INTERPLASTIC CORPORATION—See Interplastic Corporation; *U.S. Private*, pg. 2123
INTERPLAY ENTERTAINMENT CORP.; *U.S. Public*, pg. 1158
INTERPLAY LEARNING INC.; *U.S. Private*, pg. 2123
INTERPLAY OEM, INC.—See Interplay Entertainment Corp.; *U.S. Public*, pg. 1158
INTERPLEX AUTOMATION, INC.—See Blackstone Inc.; *U.S. Public*, pg. 355
INTERPLEX DAYSTAR, INC.—See Blackstone Inc.; *U.S. Public*, pg. 355
INTERPLEX ELECTRONIC (DALIAN) CO., LTD.—See Blackstone Inc.; *U.S. Public*, pg. 354
INTERPLEX ELECTRONIC HANGZHOU CO., LTD.—See Blackstone Inc.; *U.S. Public*, pg. 355
INTERPLEX ELECTRONICS INDIA PVT LIMITED—See Blackstone Inc.; *U.S. Public*, pg. 355
INTERPLEX ELECTRONICS MALAYSIA SDN. BHD.—See Blackstone Inc.; *U.S. Public*, pg. 355
INTERPLEX ENGINEERED PRODUCTS, INC.—See Blackstone Inc.; *U.S. Public*, pg. 355
INTERPLEX HOLDINGS PTE. LTD.—See Blackstone Inc.; *U.S. Public*, pg. 354
INTERPLEX HUIZHOU (HK) INDUSTRIES LTD.—See Blackstone Inc.; *U.S. Public*, pg. 355
INTERPLEX (HUIZHOU) INDUSTRIES LTD.—See Blackstone Inc.; *U.S. Public*, pg. 354
INTERPLEX HUNGARY, KFT.—See Blackstone Inc.; *U.S. Public*, pg. 355
INTERPLEXICO MANUFACTURING COMPANY, S.A. DE C.V.—See Blackstone Inc.; *U.S. Public*, pg. 355
INTERPLEX INDUSTRIES INC.—See Blackstone Inc.; *U.S. Public*, pg. 355
INTERPLEX MEDICAL, LLC—See Blackstone Inc.; *U.S. Public*, pg. 355
INTERPLEX METALFORMING (SHANGHAI) LTD.—See Blackstone Inc.; *U.S. Public*, pg. 355
INTERPLEX NASCAL, INC.—See Blackstone Inc.; *U.S. Public*, pg. 355
INTERPLEX NAS ELECTRONICS GMBH—See Blackstone Inc.; *U.S. Public*, pg. 355
INTERPLEX NAS INC.—See Blackstone Inc.; *U.S. Public*, pg. 355
INTERPLEX PMP LIMITED—See Blackstone Inc.; *U.S. Public*, pg. 355
INTERPLEX PRECISION ENGINEERING CZECH REPUBLIC S.R.O—See Blackstone Inc.; *U.S. Public*, pg. 355
INTERPLEX PRECISION TECHNOLOGY (HANOI) CO., LTD.—See Blackstone Inc.; *U.S. Public*, pg. 355
INTERPLEX PRECISION TECHNOLOGY (SINGAPORE) PTE. LTD.—See Blackstone Inc.; *U.S. Public*, pg. 355
INTERPLEX SINGAPORE PTE. LTD.—See Blackstone Inc.; *U.S. Public*, pg. 355
INTERPLEX SOPREC SAS—See Blackstone Inc.; *U.S. Public*, pg. 355
INTERPLEX SUNBELT, INC.—See Blackstone Inc.; *U.S. Public*, pg. 355
INTERPLEX (SUZHOU) PRECISION ENGINEERING LTD.—See Blackstone Inc.; *U.S. Public*, pg. 354
INTERPLEX TECHNOLOGY (H.K.) LIMITED—See Blackstone Inc.; *U.S. Public*, pg. 355
INTERPLEX TECHNOLOGY PTE. LTD.—See Blackstone Inc.; *U.S. Public*, pg. 355
INTERPOINT U.K. LTD.—See Crane NXT, Co.; *U.S. Public*, pg. 589
INTERPOOL, INC.—See SoftBank Group Corp.; *Int'l*, pg. 7053
INTERPORE CROSS INTERNATIONAL, LLC—See Zimmer Biomet Holdings, Inc.; *U.S. Public*, pg. 2406
INTERPORT LIMITED; *Int'l*, pg. 3755
INTERPORTO DI VADO I.O.S.C.P.A.—See B. Pacorini S.p.A.; *Int'l*, pg. 789
INTER-POWER /AHLCON PARTNERS LP; *U.S. Private*, pg. 2107
INTERPOWER CORPORATION; *U.S. Private*, pg. 2123
INTERPRAC FINANCIAL PLANNING PTY LTD—See Sequoia Financial Group Limited; *Int'l*, pg. 6719
INTERPRESS PRINTERS SENDIRIAN BERHAD—See The Siam Cement Public Company Limited; *Int'l*, pg. 7682
INTERPRESS SLOVAKIA, SPOL. S.R.O.—See Vivendi SE; *Int'l*, pg. 8276

INTERPRETA, INC.—See Centene Corporation; *U.S. Public*, pg. 469
INTERPRETERS UNLIMITED, INC.; *U.S. Private*, pg. 2123
INTERPRINT GMBH—See TOPPAN Holdings Inc.; *Int'l*, pg. 7816
INTERPRINT INCORPORATED—See Morten Enterprises Inc.; *U.S. Private*, pg. 2791
INTERPRINT INC.; *U.S. Private*, pg. 2123
INTERPRINT S.A.—See Valid Solucoes S.A.; *Int'l*, pg. 8116
INTERPRISE/SOUTHWEST INTERIOR & SPACE DESIGN, INC.; *U.S. Private*, pg. 2123
INTERPROGRESSBANK JSC; *Int'l*, pg. 3755
INTERPROMBANK JSCB; *Int'l*, pg. 3755
INTERPROMET AD; *Int'l*, pg. 3755
INTERPROSE INC.; *U.S. Private*, pg. 2123
INTER PROTECT RE AG—See International Bank of Azerbaijan; *Int'l*, pg. 3743
INTERPROVINCIAL COOPERATIVE LIMITED—See Federated Co-operatives Limited; *Int'l*, pg. 2631
INTERPROVINCIAL COOPERATIVE LIMITED—See Growmark, Inc.; *U.S. Private*, pg. 1795
INTERPROVINCIAL COOPERATIVE LIMITED—See Nutrien Ltd.; *Int'l*, pg. 5492
INTERPROVINCIAL COOPERATIVE LIMITED—See Sollio Cooperative Group; *Int'l*, pg. 7074
INTERPUBLIC GROUP DEUTSCHLAND GMBH—See The Interpublic Group of Companies, Inc.; *U.S. Public*, pg. 2096
THE INTERPUBLIC GROUP OF COMPANIES, INC.; *U.S. Public*, pg. 2089
INTERPUBLIC LIMITED—See The Interpublic Group of Companies, Inc.; *U.S. Public*, pg. 2096
INTERPUMP ENGINEERING S.R.L.—See Interpump Group S.p.A.; *Int'l*, pg. 3756
INTERPUMP FLUID SOLUTIONS GERMANY GMBH—See Interpump Group S.p.A.; *Int'l*, pg. 3756
INTERPUMP GROUP S.P.A.; *Int'l*, pg. 3755
INTERPUMP HYDRAULICS BRASIL LTDA—See Interpump Group S.p.A.; *Int'l*, pg. 3756
INTERPUMP HYDRAULICS FRANCE S.A.R.L.—See Interpump Group S.p.A.; *Int'l*, pg. 3756
INTERPUMP HYDRAULICS INDIA PRIVATE LTD—See Interpump Group S.p.A.; *Int'l*, pg. 3756
INTERPUMP HYDRAULICS INTERNATIONAL S.P.A.—See Interpump Group S.p.A.; *Int'l*, pg. 3756
INTERPUMP HYDRAULICS MIDDLE EAST FZE—See Interpump Group S.p.A.; *Int'l*, pg. 3756
INTERPUMP HYDRAULICS RUS LLC—See Interpump Group S.p.A.; *Int'l*, pg. 3756
INTERPUMP HYDRAULICS S.P.A.—See Interpump Group S.p.A.; *Int'l*, pg. 3756
INTERPUMP HYDRAULICS (UK) LTD.—See Interpump Group S.p.A.; *Int'l*, pg. 3756
INTERPUMP PIPING GS S.R.L.—See Interpump Group S.p.A.; *Int'l*, pg. 3756
INTERPUMP SOUTH AFRICA PTY. LTD.—See Interpump Group S.p.A.; *Int'l*, pg. 3756
INTERQUEST GROUP PLC; *Int'l*, pg. 3757
INTERQUEST GROUP (UK) LIMITED—See Interquest Group plc; *Int'l*, pg. 3757
INTERRA ACQUISITION CORPORATION; *Int'l*, pg. 3757
INTERRA BRONZ (SHANGHAI) BUILDING MATERIALS CO., LTD.—See JK Holdings Co., Ltd.; *Int'l*, pg. 3972
INTERRA COPPER CORP.; *Int'l*, pg. 3757
INTERRA CREDIT UNION; *U.S. Private*, pg. 2123
INTERRA HEALTH, INC.; *U.S. Private*, pg. 2123
INTERRA INTERNATIONAL MEXICO, S. DE R.L. DE C.V.—See Seaboard Corporation; *U.S. Public*, pg. 1850
INTERRA JK SINGAPORE PTE., LTD.—See JK Holdings Co., Ltd.; *Int'l*, pg. 3972
INTER RAO EESTI OU—See JSC INTER RAO UES; *Int'l*, pg. 4009
INTERRA RESOURCES LIMITED; *Int'l*, pg. 3757
INTERRA USA, INC.—See JK Holdings Co., Ltd.; *Int'l*, pg. 3972
INTERREL CONSULTING PARTNERS; *U.S. Private*, pg. 2123
INTERRENT NO.1 LIMITED PARTNERSHIP—See Inter-Rent Real Estate Investment Trust; *Int'l*, pg. 3757
INTERRENT REAL ESTATE INVESTMENT TRUST; *Int'l*, pg. 3757
INTER-RISCO - SOCIEDADE DE CAPITAL DE RISCO, S.A.—See Lone Star Funds; *U.S. Private*, pg. 2484
INTERRISK ASIA (THAILAND) CO., LTD.—See MS&AD Insurance Group Holdings, Inc.; *Int'l*, pg. 5066
INTERRISK CONSULTING (SHANGHAI) CO., LTD.—See MS&AD Insurance Group Holdings, Inc.; *Int'l*, pg. 5066
INTERRISK LEBENSVERSICHERUNGS AG—See Vienna Insurance Group AG Wiener Versicherung Gruppe; *Int'l*, pg. 8194
INTERRISK TOWARZYSTWO UBEZPIECZEN S.A.—See Vienna Insurance Group AG Wiener Versicherung Gruppe; *Int'l*, pg. 8194
INTERRISK VERSICHERUNGS AG—See Vienna Insurance Group AG Wiener Versicherung Gruppe; *Int'l*, pg. 8194

COMPANY NAME INDEX

INTER-ROCK MINERALS INC.; *Int'l*, pg. 3735
INTERROLL (ASIA) PTE. LTD—See Interroll Holding AG; *Int'l*, pg. 3758
INTERROLL ATLANTA, LLC—See Interroll Holding AG; *Int'l*, pg. 3758
INTERROLL AUSTRALIA PTY. LTD.—See Interroll Holding AG; *Int'l*, pg. 3758
INTERROLL AUTOMATION GMBH—See Interroll Holding AG; *Int'l*, pg. 3758
INTERROLL AUTOMATION LTD.—See Interroll Holding AG; *Int'l*, pg. 3758
INTERROLL CANADA LTD.—See Interroll Holding AG; *Int'l*, pg. 3758
INTERROLL COMPONENTS CANADA LTD—See Interroll Holding AG; *Int'l*, pg. 3758
INTERROLL CORPORATION—See Interroll Holding AG; *Int'l*, pg. 3758
INTERROLL CZ SRO—See Interroll Holding AG; *Int'l*, pg. 3758
INTERROLL DYNAMIC STORAGE, INC.—See Interroll Holding AG; *Int'l*, pg. 3758
INTERROLL ENGINEERING GMBH—See Interroll Holding AG; *Int'l*, pg. 3758
INTERROLL ENGINEERING LTD.—See Interroll Holding AG; *Int'l*, pg. 3758
INTERROLL ENGINEERING WEST INC.—See Interroll Holding AG; *Int'l*, pg. 3758
INTERROLL ESPANA S.A.—See Interroll Holding AG; *Int'l*, pg. 3758
INTERROLL FORDERTECHNIK GMBH—See Interroll Holding AG; *Int'l*, pg. 3758
INTERROLL GMBH—See Interroll Holding AG; *Int'l*, pg. 3758
INTERROLL HOLDING AG; *Int'l*, pg. 3758
INTERROLL HOLDING GMBH—See Interroll Holding AG; *Int'l*, pg. 3758
INTERROLL HOLDING MANAGEMENT (SHANGHAI) CO., LTD.—See Interroll Holding AG; *Int'l*, pg. 3758
INTERROLL ITALIA S.R.L—See Interroll Holding AG; *Int'l*, pg. 3758
INTERROLL JAPAN CO. LTD—See Interroll Holding AG; *Int'l*, pg. 3758
INTERROLL JOKI AS—See Interroll Holding AG; *Int'l*, pg. 3758
INTERROLL (KOREA) CORPORATION—See Interroll Holding AG; *Int'l*, pg. 3758
INTERROLL LOGISTICA LTDA.—See Interroll Holding AG; *Int'l*, pg. 3758
INTERROLL LOJISTIK SISTEMLERI TIC. LTD.—See Interroll Holding AG; *Int'l*, pg. 3758
INTERROLL LTD.—See Interroll Holding AG; *Int'l*, pg. 3758
INTERROLL MANAGEMENT AG—See Interroll Holding AG; *Int'l*, pg. 3758
INTERROLL MANUFACTURING LLC—See Interroll Holding AG; *Int'l*, pg. 3758
INTERROLL MEXICO S. DE R.L. DE C.V.—See Interroll Holding AG; *Int'l*, pg. 3758
INTERROLL NORDIC AS—See Interroll Holding AG; *Int'l*, pg. 3758
INTERROLL POLSKA SP.Z.O.O.—See Interroll Holding AG; *Int'l*, pg. 3758
INTERROLL SA (PROPRIETARY) LTD.—See Interroll Holding AG; *Int'l*, pg. 3758
INTERROLL SA—See Interroll Holding AG; *Int'l*, pg. 3758
INTERROLL SAS—See Interroll Holding AG; *Int'l*, pg. 3758
INTERROLL (SCHWEIZ) AG—See Interroll Holding AG; *Int'l*, pg. 3758
INTERROLL SHENZHEN CO., LTD.—See Interroll Holding AG; *Int'l*, pg. 3758
INTERROLL SUZHOU CO. LTD.—See Interroll Holding AG; *Int'l*, pg. 3758
INTERROLL (THAILAND) CO. LTD—See Interroll Holding AG; *Int'l*, pg. 3758
INTERROLL TROMMELMOTOREN GMBH—See Interroll Holding AG; *Int'l*, pg. 3758
INTERROS HOLDING COMPANY; *Int'l*, pg. 3759
INTERSAATZUCHT GMBH—See BayWa AG; *Int'l*, pg. 918
INTERSARE S.A.—See Codere S.A.; *Int'l*, pg. 1688
INTER-SCAN SEA & AIR A/S; *Int'l*, pg. 3735
INTERSCHOLASTIC TRADING COMPANY LLC; *U.S. Private*, pg. 2123
INTER SCIENCE LTDA.—See HORIBA Ltd; *Int'l*, pg. 3477
INTERSCOPE GEFFEN & A&M RECORDS—See Universal Music Group N.V.; *Int'l*, pg. 8079
INTERSCOPE RECORDS—See Universal Music Group N.V.; *Int'l*, pg. 8079
INTERSEA FISHERIES LTD.; *U.S. Private*, pg. 2123
INTERSEAS SHIPPING (PRIVATE) LIMITED—See Baker Technology Limited; *Int'l*, pg. 805
INTERSECT ENT, INC.—See Medtronic plc; *Int'l*, pg. 4787
INTERSECT GROUP; *U.S. Private*, pg. 2123
INTERSECTIONS INC.—See General Catalyst Partners; *U.S. Private*, pg. 1664
INTERSECTIONS INC.—See iSubscribed Inc.; *U.S. Private*, pg. 2147
INTERSECTIONS INC.—See WndrCo Holdings, LLC; *U.S. Private*, pg. 4552
INTERSECTIONS INSURANCE SERVICES INC.—See General Catalyst Partners; *U.S. Private*, pg. 1664

INTERSECTIONS INSURANCE SERVICES INC.—See iSubscribed Inc.; *U.S. Private*, pg. 2147
INTERSECTIONS INSURANCE SERVICES INC.—See WndrCo Holdings, LLC; *U.S. Private*, pg. 4552
INTERSECT MEDIA SOLUTIONS—See Florida Press Association Inc.; *U.S. Private*, pg. 1550
INTERSECT—See Insight Venture Management, LLC; *U.S. Private*, pg. 2089
INTERSECT—See Stone Point Capital LLC; *U.S. Private*, pg. 3822
INTERSEGURO COMPANIA DE SEGUROS S.A.—See Intercorp Financial Services Inc.; *Int'l*, pg. 3739
INTERSENTIA LTD.—See Editions Lefebvre Sarrut SA; *Int'l*, pg. 2311
INTERSEQT, LLC—See Occidental Petroleum Corporation; *U.S. Public*, pg. 1561
INTERSEROH AUSTRIA GMBH—See Alba SE; *Int'l*, pg. 293
INTERSEROH ORGANIZACJA ODZYSKU OPAKOWAN S.A.—See Alba SE; *Int'l*, pg. 293
INTERSEROH PRODUCT CYCLE GMBH—See Alba SE; *Int'l*, pg. 293
INTERSEROH SERVICE ITALIA S.R.L.—See Alba SE; *Int'l*, pg. 293
INTERSEROH SERVICES D. O. O.—See Alba SE; *Int'l*, pg. 293
INTERSERVE CATERING SERVICES LIMITED—See MITIE Group Plc; *Int'l*, pg. 4926
INTERSERVE (DEFENCE) LTD.—See Interserve Plc; *Int'l*, pg. 3759
INTERSERVE ENGINEERING SERVICES LTD.—See Interserve Plc; *Int'l*, pg. 3759
INTERSERVE ENVIRONMENTAL SERVICES LTD.—See Interserve Plc; *Int'l*, pg. 3759
INTERSERVE (FACILITIES MANAGEMENT) LTD.—See MITIE Group Plc; *Int'l*, pg. 4926
INTERSERVE (FACILITIES SERVICES SLOUGH) LTD.—See MITIE Group Plc; *Int'l*, pg. 4926
INTERSERVE FS (UK) LTD.—See MITIE Group Plc; *Int'l*, pg. 4926
INTERSERVE GROUP HOLDINGS LTD.—See Interserve Plc; *Int'l*, pg. 3759
INTERSERVE HEALTHCARE LTD.—See Interserve Plc; *Int'l*, pg. 3759
INTERSERVE INDUSTRIAL SERVICES LTD—See Interserve Plc; *Int'l*, pg. 3759
INTERSERVE INVESTMENTS PLC—See Interserve Plc; *Int'l*, pg. 3759
INTERSERVE LEARNING EMPLOYMENT SERVICES LTD.—See Endless LLP; *Int'l*, pg. 2403
INTERSERVE PFI 2005 LTD.—See Interserve Plc; *Int'l*, pg. 3759
INTERSERVE PLC; *Int'l*, pg. 3759
INTERSERVE PROJECT SERVICES LTD.—See Interserve Plc; *Int'l*, pg. 3759
INTERSERVE SECURITY (FIRE & ELECTRONICS) LTD.—See Interserve Plc; *Int'l*, pg. 3759
INTERSERVE SECURITY LTD.—See Interserve Plc; *Int'l*, pg. 3759
INTERSERVE SPECIALIST SERVICES (HOLDINGS) LTD.—See Interserve Plc; *Int'l*, pg. 3759
INTERSERVE TECHNICAL SERVICES LTD.—See Interserve Plc; *Int'l*, pg. 3759
INTERSERV GESELLSCHAFT FUR PERSONALUND BERATERDIENSTLEISTUNGEN MBH—See Deutsche Post AG; *Int'l*, pg. 2083
INTERSERVICES & TRADING SA—See LVMH Moet Hennessy Louis Vuitton SE; *Int'l*, pg. 4594
INTERSERV INTERNATIONAL INC.; *Int'l*, pg. 3759
INTERSERVIS A.D.; *Int'l*, pg. 3760
INTERSHOP COMMUNICATIONS AB—See Intershop Communications AG; *Int'l*, pg. 3760
INTERSHOP COMMUNICATIONS AG; *Int'l*, pg. 3760
INTERSHOP COMMUNICATIONS AG—See Intershop Communications AG; *Int'l*, pg. 3760
INTERSHOP COMMUNICATIONS ASIA LIMITED—See Intershop Communications AG; *Int'l*, pg. 3760
INTERSHOP COMMUNICATIONS AUSTRALIA PTY LIMITED—See Intershop Communications AG; *Int'l*, pg. 3760
INTERSHOP COMMUNICATIONS, INC.—See Intershop Communications AG; *Int'l*, pg. 3760
INTERSHOP COMMUNICATIONS LTD.—See Intershop Communications AG; *Int'l*, pg. 3760
INTERSHOP COMMUNICATIONS SARL—See Intershop Communications AG; *Int'l*, pg. 3760
INTERSHOP COMMUNICATIONS SINGAPORE PTE LTD.—See Intershop Communications AG; *Int'l*, pg. 3760
INTERSHOP HOLDING AG—See BZ Bank Aktiengesellschaft; *Int'l*, pg. 1237
INTERSIL CORPORATION - DESIGN CENTER—See Renesas Electronics Corporation; *Int'l*, pg. 6276
INTERSIL CORPORATION—See Renesas Electronics Corporation; *Int'l*, pg. 6276
INTERSILESIA MCBRIDE POLSKA SP. Z.O.O.—See McBride plc; *Int'l*, pg. 4755
INTERSIL GMBH—See Renesas Electronics Corporation; *Int'l*, pg. 6276

INTERSIL (WUHAN) COMPANY LTD.—See Renesas Electronics Corporation; *Int'l*, pg. 6276
INTERSNACK ADRIA D.O.O.—See Intersnack Group GmbH & Co. KG; *Int'l*, pg. 3760
INTERSNACK, A.S.—See Intersnack Group GmbH & Co. KG; *Int'l*, pg. 3760
INTERSNACK BULGARIA EOOD—See Intersnack Group GmbH & Co. KG; *Int'l*, pg. 3760
INTERSNACK CASHEW COMPANY PTE. LTD.—See Intersnack Group GmbH & Co. KG; *Int'l*, pg. 3760
INTERSNACK D.O.O.—See Intersnack Group GmbH & Co. KG; *Int'l*, pg. 3760
INTERSNACK FRANCE S.A.S.—See Intersnack Group GmbH & Co. KG; *Int'l*, pg. 3760
INTERSNACK GROUP GMBH & CO. KG; *Int'l*, pg. 3760
INTERSNACK KNABBER-GEBACK GMBH & CO. KG—See Intersnack Group GmbH & Co. KG; *Int'l*, pg. 3760
INTERSNACK MAGYARORSZAG KFT.—See Intersnack Group GmbH & Co. KG; *Int'l*, pg. 3760
INTERSNACK NEDERLAND BV—See Intersnack Group GmbH & Co. KG; *Int'l*, pg. 3760
INTERSNACK POLAND SP. Z O.O.—See Intersnack Group GmbH & Co. KG; *Int'l*, pg. 3760
INTERSNACK ROMANIA S.R.L.—See Intersnack Group GmbH & Co. KG; *Int'l*, pg. 3760
INTERSNACK SLOVENSKO, A.S.—See Intersnack Group GmbH & Co. KG; *Int'l*, pg. 3760
INTERSNACK SWITZERLAND LTD.—See Intersnack Group GmbH & Co. KG; *Int'l*, pg. 3760
INTERSNACK UKRAINE LTD.—See Intersnack Group GmbH & Co. KG; *Int'l*, pg. 3760
INTERSOCIETAL ACCREDITATION COMMISSION; *U.S. Private*, pg. 2123
INTERSONO LTD.—See Medicover Holding S.A.; *Int'l*, pg. 4776
INTERSOURCE INSURANCE COMPANY—See MDU Resources Group, Inc.; *U.S. Public*, pg. 1410
INTERSOURCE TECHNOLOGY LIMITED—See Inspur Group Ltd.; *Int'l*, pg. 3720
INTERSOUTH PARTNERS; *U.S. Private*, pg. 2123
INTERSPACE CO., LTD.; *Int'l*, pg. 3761
IN-TER-SPACE SERVICES, INC.—See iHeartMedia, Inc.; *U.S. Public*, pg. 1095
INTERSPACE (THAILAND) CO., LTD.—See Interspace Co., Ltd.; *Int'l*, pg. 3761
INTERSPED A.D.; *Int'l*, pg. 3761
INTERSPED D.D.; *Int'l*, pg. 3761
INTERSPED D.D. TUZLA; *Int'l*, pg. 3761
INTERSPIRO INC.; *U.S. Private*, pg. 2123
INTERSPORT ATHLETICS AE—See FOURLIS HOLDINGS S.A.; *Int'l*, pg. 2755
INTERSPORT ATHLETICS (CYPRUS) LTD.—See FOURLIS HOLDINGS S.A.; *Int'l*, pg. 2755
INTERSPORT AUSTRALIA LIMITED—See INTERSPORT International Corporation; *Int'l*, pg. 3761
INTERSPORT AUSTRIA GES. M.B.H.—See INTERSPORT International Corporation; *Int'l*, pg. 3761
INTERSPORT BELARUS—See INTERSPORT International Corporation; *Int'l*, pg. 3761
INTERSPORT BELGIUM CVBA—See INTERSPORT International Corporation; *Int'l*, pg. 3761
INTERSPORT CCS, S.A.—See INTERSPORT International Corporation; *Int'l*, pg. 3761
INTERSPORT CHINA—See INTERSPORT International Corporation; *Int'l*, pg. 3761
INTERSPORT CR S.R.O.—See INTERSPORT International Corporation; *Int'l*, pg. 3761
INTERSPORT DENMARK AS—See INTERSPORT International Corporation; *Int'l*, pg. 3761
INTERSPORT DEUTSCHLAND EG—See INTERSPORT International Corporation; *Int'l*, pg. 3761
INTERSPORT EGYPT—See INTERSPORT International Corporation; *Int'l*, pg. 3761
INTERSPORT FINLAND LTD—See Kesko Corporation; *Int'l*, pg. 4141
INTERSPORT FRANCE SA—See INTERSPORT International Corporation; *Int'l*, pg. 3761
INTERSPORT HOLLAND—See INTERSPORT International Corporation; *Int'l*, pg. 3761
INTERSPORT ICELAND—See INTERSPORT International Corporation; *Int'l*, pg. 3761
INTERSPORT INTERNATIONAL CORPORATION; *Int'l*, pg. 3761
INTERSPORT ISI, D.O.O.—See Enterprise Investors Sp. z o.o.; *Int'l*, pg. 2452
INTERSPORT ITALIA SPA—See INTERSPORT International Corporation; *Int'l*, pg. 3761
INTERSPORT MOROCCO—See INTERSPORT International Corporation; *Int'l*, pg. 3761
INTERSPORT NORTH AMERICA LTD.—See INTERSPORT International Corporation; *Int'l*, pg. 3761
INTERSPORT NORWAY/GRESVIG AS—See INTERSPORT International Corporation; *Int'l*, pg. 3761
INTERSPORT POLSKA SP Z O O—See INTERSPORT International Corporation; *Int'l*, pg. 3761
INTERSPORT PSC HOLDING AG; *Int'l*, pg. 3761
INTERSPORT RUSSIA—See INTERSPORT International Corporation; *Int'l*, pg. 3761

INTERSPORT PSC HOLDING AG

INTERSPORT SCHWEIZ AG—See INTERSPORT International Corporation; *Int'l*, pg. 3761
INTERSPORT SK S.R.O.—See INTERSPORT International Corporation; *Int'l*, pg. 3761
INTERSPORT SVERIGE AB—See INTERSPORT International Corporation; *Int'l*, pg. 3761
INTERSPORT TURKEY—See INTERSPORT International Corporation; *Int'l*, pg. 3761
INTERSPORT UK LTD.—See INTERSPORT International Corporation; *Int'l*, pg. 3761
INTERSTAB ENGINEERING D.O.O.E.L.—See SMC Corporation; *Int'l*, pg. 7003
INTERSTAHL SERVICE GMBH & CO.KG; *Int'l*, pg. 3761
INTERSTAHL SUD GMBH—See INTERSTAHL Service GmbH & Co.KG; *Int'l*, pg. 3761
INTERSTANDARTS AD; *Int'l*, pg. 3762
INTERSTAR COMMUNICATIONS, INC.—See Star Telephone Membership Corp.; *U.S. Private*, pg. 3785
INTERSTAR MARKETING & PUBLIC RELATIONS; *U.S. Private*, pg. 2123
INTERSTATE BANK; *Int'l*, pg. 3762
INTERSTATE BATTERY SYSTEM OF AMERICA INC.; *U.S. Private*, pg. 2123
INTERSTATE BATTERY SYSTEM OF AMERICA INC.—See Interstate Battery System of America Inc.; *U.S. Private*, pg. 2124
INTERSTATE BATTERY SYSTEM OF HAWAII INC.—See Interstate Battery System of America Inc.; *U.S. Private*, pg. 2124
INTERSTATE BILLING SERVICE INC.—See BancIndependent Inc.; *U.S. Private*, pg. 464
INTERSTATE BIOLOGIC SERVICES, LLC—See Grifols, S.A.; *Int'l*, pg. 3085
INTERSTATE BLOOD BANK, INC.—See Grifols, S.A.; *Int'l*, pg. 3085
INTERSTATE BRICK COMPANY—See Pacific Coast Building Products, Inc.; *U.S. Private*, pg. 3065
INTERSTATE CATERERS; *U.S. Private*, pg. 2124
INTERSTATE CHEMICAL CO., INC.; *U.S. Private*, pg. 2124
INTERSTATE CHEMICAL—See Interstate Chemical Co., Inc.; *U.S. Private*, pg. 2124
INTERSTATE COMMODITIES INC.; *U.S. Private*, pg. 2124
INTERSTATE COMPANIES, INC.; *U.S. Private*, pg. 2124
INTERSTATE CONNECTING COMPONENTS—See Heilind Electronics, Inc.; *U.S. Private*, pg. 1904
INTERSTATE CONSTRUCTION CO.; *U.S. Private*, pg. 2124
INTERSTATE CONTAINER - CAMBRIDGE—See Interstate Resources, Inc.; *U.S. Private*, pg. 2125
INTERSTATE CONTAINER LOWELL, LLC—See Interstate Resources, Inc.; *U.S. Private*, pg. 2125
INTERSTATE CONTAINER READING LLC—See Interstate Resources, Inc.; *U.S. Private*, pg. 2125
INTERSTATE CONTAINER—See Interstate Resources, Inc.; *U.S. Private*, pg. 2125
INTERSTATE DIESEL SERVICE, INC.; *U.S. Private*, pg. 2124
INTERSTATE ELECTRICAL SERVICES CORP.; *U.S. Private*, pg. 2124
INTERSTATE ELECTRICAL SUPPLY, INC.; *U.S. Private*, pg. 2124
INTERSTATE ELECTRIC COMPANY INCORPORATED; *U.S. Private*, pg. 2124
INTERSTATE ELECTRONICS CORPORATION—See L3Harris Technologies, Inc.; *U.S. Public*, pg. 1281
INTERSTATE ENERGY LLC; *U.S. Private*, pg. 2124
INTERSTATE ENGINEERING CORP.; *U.S. Private*, pg. 2124
INTERSTATE EQUIPMENT COMPANY; *U.S. Private*, pg. 2124
INTERSTATE FEEDERS, LLC—See Pinnacle Asset Management, L.P.; *U.S. Private*, pg. 3184
INTERSTATE FIRE & CASUALTY COMPANY—See Allianz SE; *Int'l*, pg. 347
INTERSTATE FOOD PROCESSING CORPORATION—See Oppenheimer Companies, Inc.; *U.S. Private*, pg. 3033
INTER-STATE FORD TRUCK SALES, INC.; *U.S. Private*, pg. 2107
INTERSTATE FUEL SYSTEMS, INC.; *U.S. Private*, pg. 2124
INTERSTATE GAS SUPPLY INC.; *U.S. Private*, pg. 2124
INTER STATE GAS SYSTEMS (PVT) LTD.—See Sui Southern Gas Company Limited; *Int'l*, pg. 7255
INTERSTATE GROUP HOLDINGS, INC.; *U.S. Private*, pg. 2124
INTER-STATE HARDWOODS COMPANY, INC.; *U.S. Private*, pg. 2107
INTERSTATE HIGHWAY CONSTRUCTION; *U.S. Private*, pg. 2125
INTERSTATE HIGHWAY SIGN CORP.; *U.S. Private*, pg. 2125
INTERSTATE HOME LOAN CENTER; *U.S. Private*, pg. 2125
INTERSTATE HOTELS & RESORTS, INC.—See Advent International Corporation; *U.S. Private*, pg. 97
INTERSTATE INSURANCE GROUP—See Allianz SE; *Int'l*, pg. 347

INTERSTATE INSURANCE MANAGEMENT, INC.—See Ryan Specialty Holdings, Inc.; *U.S. Public*, pg. 1828
INTERSTATE INTERNATIONAL, INC.—See Interstate Group Holdings, Inc.; *U.S. Private*, pg. 2125
INTERSTATE INTERNATIONAL, INC.; *U.S. Private*, pg. 2125
INTERSTATE LOGISTICS GROUP, INC.; *U.S. Private*, pg. 2125
INTERSTATE LOGOS, L.L.C.—See Lamar Advertising Company; *U.S. Public*, pg. 1290
INTERSTATE LUMBER & MILL CORP.; *U.S. Private*, pg. 2125
INTERSTATE MECHANICAL CONTRACTORS, INC.; *U.S. Private*, pg. 2125
INTERSTATE MOTOR TRUCKS INC.; *U.S. Private*, pg. 2125
INTERSTATE MOVING SYSTEMS, INC.—See Interstate Group Holdings, Inc.; *U.S. Private*, pg. 2125
INTERSTATE NATIONAL CORPORATION—See Dai-ichi Life Holdings, Inc.; *Int'l*, pg. 1917
INTERSTATE NATIONAL DEALER SERVICES, INC.—See Dai-ichi Life Holdings, Inc.; *Int'l*, pg. 1917
INTER-STATE NURSERIES, INC.—See Plantron, Inc.; *U.S. Private*, pg. 3198
INTER STATE OIL CARRIER LTD; *Int'l*, pg. 3735
INTERSTATE OIL COMPANY; *U.S. Private*, pg. 2125
INTERSTATE OPTICAL CO INC—See EssilorLuxottica SA; *Int'l*, pg. 2513
INTERSTATE PAPER LLC—See Interstate Resources, Inc.; *U.S. Private*, pg. 2125
INTERSTATE PERSONNEL SERVICES, INC.; *U.S. Private*, pg. 2125
INTERSTATE POTATO PACKERS CORP.—See Oppenheimer Companies, Inc.; *U.S. Private*, pg. 3033
INTERSTATE PRODUCTS, INC.; *U.S. Private*, pg. 2125
INTERSTATE REALTY MANAGEMENT CO.; *U.S. Private*, pg. 2125
INTERSTATE RELOCATION SERVICES, INC.—See Interstate Group Holdings, Inc.; *U.S. Private*, pg. 2125
INTERSTATE RESOURCES, INC.; *U.S. Private*, pg. 2125
INTERSTATE RESTORATION GROUP, INC.; *U.S. Private*, pg. 2125
INTERSTATE RESTORATION HAWAII LLC—See Interstate Restoration Group, Inc.; *U.S. Private*, pg. 2126
INTERSTATE ROCK PRODUCTS INC.; *U.S. Private*, pg. 2126
INTERSTATES CONSTRUCTION SERVICES INC—See Harbor Group Inc; *U.S. Private*, pg. 1859
INTERSTATES CONTROL SYSTEMS, INC.—See Harbor Group Inc; *U.S. Private*, pg. 1859
INTERSTATES ENGINEERING—See Harbor Group Inc; *U.S. Private*, pg. 1859
INTERSTATES MARKET (2007) PTE LTD—See NTUC Fairprice Co-operative Ltd.; *Int'l*, pg. 5485
INTERSTATE STEEL CO. INC.—See Tang Industries Inc.; *U.S. Private*, pg. 3930
INTERSTATE TELECOM COOPERATIVE, INC.; *U.S. Private*, pg. 2126
INTERSTATE TRANSPORT, INC.—See Dupre Logistics, LLC; *U.S. Private*, pg. 1291
INTERSTATE TRUCK CENTER, LLC—See Interstate International, Inc.; *U.S. Private*, pg. 2125
INTERSTATE VAN LINES, INC.—See Interstate Group Holdings, Inc.; *U.S. Private*, pg. 2125
INTERSTATE WAREHOUSING INC.; *U.S. Private*, pg. 2126
INTERSTATE WASTE SERVICES, INC.; *U.S. Private*, pg. 2126
INTERSTEEL INC.; *U.S. Private*, pg. 2126
INTERSTEEL STAHLHANDEL GMBH—See voestalpine AG; *Int'l*, pg. 8289
INTERSTELLA PLASTICS (SHENZHEN) CO., LTD.—See TOMOE Engineering Co., Ltd.; *Int'l*, pg. 7800
INTERSTELLAR, INC.—See Stellar Development, Inc.; *U.S. Private*, pg. 3799
INTERSTEM CO., LTD.—See Rohto Pharmaceutical Co. Ltd.; *Int'l*, pg. 6387
INTERSTROY OOO—See Kesko Corporation; *Int'l*, pg. 4141
INTERSTUDIO INC.—See K&L Inc.; *Int'l*, pg. 4038
INTERSYS CONSULTING, INC.—See ASGN Incorporated; *U.S. Public*, pg. 210
INTERSYSTEMS (ASIA PACIFIC) PTY. LTD.—See Daifuku Co., Ltd.; *Int'l*, pg. 1926
INTERSYSTEMS AUSTRALIA PTY LIMITED—See InterSystems Corporation; *U.S. Private*, pg. 2126
INTERSYSTEMS AUSTRALIA PTY LIMITED—See InterSystems Corporation; *U.S. Private*, pg. 2126
INTERSYSTEMS B.V. - BELGIUM BRANCH—See InterSystems Corporation; *U.S. Private*, pg. 2126
INTERSYSTEMS B.V. - CZECH REPUBLIC BRANCH—See InterSystems Corporation; *U.S. Private*, pg. 2126
INTERSYSTEMS B.V. - FINLAND BRANCH—See InterSystems Corporation; *U.S. Private*, pg. 2126
INTERSYSTEMS B.V. - ISRAEL BRANCH—See InterSystems Corporation; *U.S. Private*, pg. 2126
INTERSYSTEMS B.V. - SAUDI ARABIA BRANCH—See InterSystems Corporation; *U.S. Private*, pg. 2126

CORPORATE AFFILIATIONS

INTERSYSTEMS B.V.—See InterSystems Corporation; *U.S. Private*, pg. 2126
INTERSYSTEMS CHILE—See InterSystems Corporation; *U.S. Private*, pg. 2126
INTERSYSTEMS CHILE—See InterSystems Corporation; *U.S. Private*, pg. 2126
INTERSYSTEMS CORPORATION - NEW YORK—See InterSystems Corporation; *U.S. Private*, pg. 2126
INTERSYSTEMS CORPORATION; *U.S. Private*, pg. 2126
INTERSYSTEMS DO BRASIL LTDA.—See InterSystems Corporation; *U.S. Private*, pg. 2127
INTERSYSTEMS DO BRASIL LTDA.—See InterSystems Corporation; *U.S. Private*, pg. 2127
INTERSYSTEMS DUBAI—See InterSystems Corporation; *U.S. Private*, pg. 2126
INTERSYSTEMS GMBH—See InterSystems Corporation; *U.S. Private*, pg. 2126
INTERSYSTEMS IBERIA, S.L.—See InterSystems Corporation; *U.S. Private*, pg. 2126
INTERSYSTEMS IBERIA, S.L.—See InterSystems Corporation; *U.S. Private*, pg. 2126
INTERSYSTEMS INTERNATIONAL, LLC—See AGCO Corporation; *U.S. Public*, pg. 58
INTERSYSTEMS ITALIA S.R.L.—See InterSystems Corporation; *U.S. Private*, pg. 2126
INTERSYSTEMS ITALIA S.R.L.—See InterSystems Corporation; *U.S. Private*, pg. 2126
INTERSYSTEMS JAPAN KK—See InterSystems Corporation; *U.S. Private*, pg. 2126
INTERSYSTEMS JAPAN KK—See InterSystems Corporation; *U.S. Private*, pg. 2126
INTERSYSTEMS KOREA—See InterSystems Corporation; *U.S. Private*, pg. 2126
INTERSYSTEMS RUSSIA—See InterSystems Corporation; *U.S. Private*, pg. 2126
INTERSYSTEMS SA—See InterSystems Corporation; *U.S. Private*, pg. 2126
INTERSYSTEMS SAS—See InterSystems Corporation; *U.S. Private*, pg. 2127
INTERSYSTEMS SHANGHAI—See InterSystems Corporation; *U.S. Private*, pg. 2127
INTERSYSTEMS SOFTWARE (BEIJING) CO., LTD.—See InterSystems Corporation; *U.S. Private*, pg. 2127
INTERSYSTEMS SOFTWARE (THAILAND) LTD.—See InterSystems Corporation; *U.S. Private*, pg. 2127
INTERSYSTEMS UK—See InterSystems Corporation; *U.S. Private*, pg. 2127
INTERSYSTEMS UK—See InterSystems Corporation; *U.S. Private*, pg. 2127
INTERTABA S.P.A.—See Philip Morris International Inc.; *U.S. Public*, pg. 1685
THE INTERTAIN GROUP LIMITED; *Int'l*, pg. 7656
INTERTAINMENT AG; *Int'l*, pg. 3762
INTERTAINMENT MEDIA INC.; *Int'l*, pg. 3762
INTERTAPE POLYMER CORP.—See Clearlake Capital Group, L.P.; *U.S. Private*, pg. 935
INTERTAPE POLYMER EUROPE GMBH—See Clearlake Capital Group, L.P.; *U.S. Private*, pg. 935
INTERTAPE POLYMER GROUP INC.—See Clearlake Capital Group, L.P.; *U.S. Private*, pg. 935
INTERTAPE POLYMER INC.—See Clearlake Capital Group, L.P.; *U.S. Private*, pg. 935
INTER-TEAM SP. Z O.O.—See MEKO AB; *Int'l*, pg. 4805
INTERTECH BILGI ISLEM VE PAZARLAMA TICARET AS—See OJSC Sberbank of Russia; *Int'l*, pg. 5542
INTERTECH COMPUTER PRODUCTS INC.; *U.S. Private*, pg. 2127
THE INTERTECH GROUP, INC.; *U.S. Private*, pg. 4057
INTERTECH INC.; *U.S. Private*, pg. 2127
INTER TECHNOLOGIES CORPORATION (ITC); *U.S. Private*, pg. 2106
INTERTECH PLASTICS INC.—See TriMas Corporation; *U.S. Public*, pg. 2189
INTERTECH S.A.; *Int'l*, pg. 3762
INTERTECH SECURITY, LLC; *U.S. Private*, pg. 2127
INTERTECHSERVICE LTD.—See Herti AD; *Int'l*, pg. 3365
INTERTECH WORLDWIDE CORPORATION; *U.S. Private*, pg. 2127
INTERTEC POLSKA SP.Z.O.O.—See Deutsche Bahn AG; *Int'l*, pg. 2052
INTERTEC SPOL. S R.O.—See Agrofert Holding, a.s.; *Int'l*, pg. 219
INTERTEC SYSTEMS, LLC—See Adient Inc.; *Int'l*, pg. 148
INTERTEC SYSTEMS, LLC—See INOAC Corporation; *Int'l*, pg. 3714
INTERTEK ALCHEMY—See Intertek Group plc; *Int'l*, pg. 3762
INTERTEK ANGOLA LDA—See Intertek Group plc; *Int'l*, pg. 3762
INTERTEK ARUBA N.V.—See Intertek Group plc; *Int'l*, pg. 3762
INTERTEK ASSET INTEGRITY MANAGEMENT, INC.—See Intertek Group plc; *Int'l*, pg. 3762
INTERTEK ATI SRL—See Intertek Group plc; *Int'l*, pg. 3762
INTERTEK CALEB BRETT CHILE S.A.—See Intertek Group plc; *Int'l*, pg. 3762
INTERTEK CALEB BRETT EL SALVADOR S.A. DE C.V.—See Intertek Group plc; *Int'l*, pg. 3762

INTERTEK CALEB BRETT PANAMA, INC.—See Intertek Group plc; *Int'l*, pg. 3762
INTERTEK CALEB BRETT (URUGUAY) S.A.—See Intertek Group plc; *Int'l*, pg. 3762
INTERTEK CALEB BRETT VENEZUELA C.A.—See Intertek Group plc; *Int'l*, pg. 3762
INTERTEK CERTIFICATION AB—See Intertek Group plc; *Int'l*, pg. 3762
INTERTEK CERTIFICATION AS—See Intertek Group plc; *Int'l*, pg. 3762
INTERTEK CERTIFICATION GMBH—See Intertek Group plc; *Int'l*, pg. 3762
INTERTEK CERTIFICATION JAPAN LIMITED—See Intertek Group plc; *Int'l*, pg. 3762
INTERTEK CONSULTING & TRAINING COLOMBIA LIMITADA—See Intertek Group plc; *Int'l*, pg. 3762
INTERTEK CONSULTING & TRAINING (UK) LIMITED—See Intertek Group plc; *Int'l*, pg. 3762
INTERTEK CONSUMER GOODS GMBH—See Intertek Group plc; *Int'l*, pg. 3762
INTERTEK DENMARK A/S—See Intertek Group plc; *Int'l*, pg. 3763
INTERTEK DEUTSCHLAND GMBH—See Intertek Group plc; *Int'l*, pg. 3763
INTERTEK ETL SEMKO OY—See Intertek Group plc; *Int'l*, pg. 3763
INTERTEK FINANCE PLC—See Intertek Group plc; *Int'l*, pg. 3763
INTERTEK FRANCE SAS—See Intertek Group plc; *Int'l*, pg. 3763
INTERTEK GROUP PLC; *Int'l*, pg. 3762
INTERTEK HOLDINGS LIMITED—See Intertek Group plc; *Int'l*, pg. 3763
INTERTEK HOLDINGS NEDERLAND BV—See Intertek Group plc; *Int'l*, pg. 3763
INTERTEK IBERICA SPAIN, S.L.—See Intertek Group plc; *Int'l*, pg. 3763
INTERTEK INDIA PRIVATE LIMITED—See Intertek Group plc; *Int'l*, pg. 3763
INTERTEK INDUSTRIAL SERVICES GMBH—See Intertek Group plc; *Int'l*, pg. 3763
INTERTEK INDUSTRY & CERTIFICATION SERVICES (THAILAND) LIMITED—See Intertek Group plc; *Int'l*, pg. 3763
INTERTEK INDUSTRY SERVICES BRASIL LTDA.—See Intertek Group plc; *Int'l*, pg. 3763
INTERTEK INDUSTRY SERVICES COLOMBIA LIMITED—See Intertek Group plc; *Int'l*, pg. 3763
INTERTEK INDUSTRY SERVICES JAPAN LIMITED—See Intertek Group plc; *Int'l*, pg. 3763
INTERTEK INDUSTRY SERVICES (S) PTE LTD.—See Intertek Group plc; *Int'l*, pg. 3763
INTERTEK INDUSTRY WLL—See Intertek Group plc; *Int'l*, pg. 3763
INTERTEK INSPECTION SERVICES SCANDINAVIA AS—See Intertek Group plc; *Int'l*, pg. 3763
INTERTEK INTERNATIONAL FRANCE SAS—See Intertek Group plc; *Int'l*, pg. 3763
INTERTEK INTERNATIONAL GABON SARL—See Intertek Group plc; *Int'l*, pg. 3763
INTERTEK INTERNATIONAL INC.—See Intertek Group plc; *Int'l*, pg. 3763
INTERTEK INTERNATIONAL LIMITED—See Intertek Group plc; *Int'l*, pg. 3763
INTERTEK KALITE SERVISLERI LIMITED SIRKETI—See Intertek Group plc; *Int'l*, pg. 3763
INTERTEK KOREA INDUSTRY SERVICE LTD.—See Intertek Group plc; *Int'l*, pg. 3763
INTERTEK LIBYA TECHNICAL SERVICES & CONSULTATIONS COMPANY SPA—See Intertek Group plc; *Int'l*, pg. 3763
INTERTEK OVERSEAS HOLDINGS LIMITED—See Intertek Group plc; *Int'l*, pg. 3763
INTERTEK PHARMACEUTICAL SERVICES IMMUNOCHEMISTRY—See Intertek Group plc; *Int'l*, pg. 3763
INTERTEK PHARMACEUTICAL SERVICES LCMS—See Intertek Group plc; *Int'l*, pg. 3763
INTERTEK PHARMACEUTICAL SERVICES—See Intertek Group plc; *Int'l*, pg. 3763
INTERTEK PLASTICS TECHNOLOGY LABORATORIES—See Intertek Group plc; *Int'l*, pg. 3763
INTERTEK POLAND SP. Z O.O.—See Intertek Group plc; *Int'l*, pg. 3763
INTERTEK POLYCHEMLAB B.V.—See Intertek Group plc; *Int'l*, pg. 3763
INTERTEK RUS JSC—See Intertek Group plc; *Int'l*, pg. 3763
INTERTEK (SCHWEIZ) AG—See Intertek Group plc; *Int'l*, pg. 3762
INTERTEK SEMKO AB—See Intertek Group plc; *Int'l*, pg. 3763
INTERTEK TESTING MANAGEMENT LIMITED—See Intertek Group plc; *Int'l*, pg. 3763
INTERTEK TESTING SERVICES (FRANCE) SARL—See Intertek Group plc; *Int'l*, pg. 3763
INTERTEK TESTING SERVICES HOLDINGS LIMITED—See Intertek Group plc; *Int'l*, pg. 3763

INTERTEK TESTING SERVICES HONG KONG LTD.—See Intertek Group plc; *Int'l*, pg. 3763
INTERTEK TESTING SERVICES (ITS) CANADA LIMITED—See Intertek Group plc; *Int'l*, pg. 3763
INTERTEK TESTING SERVICES NA, INC. - COMMERCIAL & ELECTRICAL—See Intertek Group plc; *Int'l*, pg. 3763
INTERTEK TESTING SERVICES NA, INC. - RAM CONSULTING—See Intertek Group plc; *Int'l*, pg. 3763
INTERTEK TESTING SERVICES NA, INC.—See Intertek Group plc; *Int'l*, pg. 3763
INTERTEK TESTING SERVICES NA, INC. - SYSTEMS CERTIFICATION, KENTWOOD—See Intertek Group plc; *Int'l*, pg. 3763
INTERTEK TESTING SERVICES PHILIPPINES, INC.—See Intertek Group plc; *Int'l*, pg. 3763
INTERTEK TESTING SERVICES SHENZHEN LIMITED—See Intertek Group plc; *Int'l*, pg. 3764
INTERTEK TESTING SERVICES (SINGAPORE) PTE LIMITED—See Intertek Group plc; *Int'l*, pg. 3763
INTERTEK TESTING SERVICES UK LIMITED—See Intertek Group plc; *Int'l*, pg. 3764
INTERTEK TRINIDAD LIMITED—See Intertek Group plc; *Int'l*, pg. 3764
INTERTEK UK HOLDINGS LIMITED—See Intertek Group plc; *Int'l*, pg. 3764
INTERTEK UK—See Intertek Group plc; *Int'l*, pg. 3764
INTERTEK USA INC.—See Intertek Group plc; *Int'l*, pg. 3764
INTERTEK VIETNAM LIMITED—See Intertek Group plc; *Int'l*, pg. 3764
INTERTEK WEST LAB AS—See Intertek Group plc; *Int'l*, pg. 3764
INTER TERMINALS SWEDEN AB—See Brookfield Infrastructure Partners L.P.; *Int'l*, pg. 1193
INTERTEX GENERAL CONTRACTORS, INC.; *U.S. Private*, pg. 2127
INTERTEX, INC.—See Lasko Products, LLC; *U.S. Private*, pg. 2395
INTERTHOR INC.—See Logitrans A/S; *Int'l*, pg. 4542
INTER-TRACK PARTNERS LLC; *U.S. Private*, pg. 2107
INTERTRACTOR AMERICA, CORP.—See Titan International, Inc.; *U.S. Public*, pg. 2160
INTERTRADE CO., LTD.; *Int'l*, pg. 3764
INTERTRADE INDUSTRIES LTD.; *U.S. Private*, pg. 2127
INTERTRADE LIMITED—See RTX Corporation; *U.S. Public*, pg. 1823
INTERTRADE SYSTEMS INC.—See KKR & Co. Inc.; *U.S. Public*, pg. 1267
INTERTRADING S.R.L.—See Heidelberg Materials AG; *Int'l*, pg. 3316
INTERTRAFO OY—See Addtech AB; *Int'l*, pg. 134
INTERTREND COMMUNICATIONS, INC.; *U.S. Private*, pg. 2127
INTER TRIBAL COUNCIL OF ARIZONA, INC.; *U.S. Private*, pg. 2106
INTERTRIM, LTDA.—See Grupo Antolin-Irausa, S.A.; *Int'l*, pg. 3120
INTERTRONIC LIMITED—See Entain PLC; *Int'l*, pg. 2450
INTERTRONIC SOLUTIONS INC.—See Calian Group Ltd.; *Int'l*, pg. 1264
INTERTRUCK BENELUX B.V.—See Unipart Group of Companies Limited; *Int'l*, pg. 8055
INTERTRUCK DEUTSCHLAND GMBH—See Unipart Group of Companies Limited; *Int'l*, pg. 8055
INTERTRUST (BELGIUM) NV/SA—See Corporation Service Company; *U.S. Private*, pg. 1057
INTERTRUST B.V.—See Corporation Service Company; *U.S. Private*, pg. 1057
INTERTRUST CAYMAN ISLANDS—See Corporation Service Company; *U.S. Private*, pg. 1057
INTERTRUST CHINA - GUANGZHOU OFFICE—See Corporation Service Company; *U.S. Private*, pg. 1058
INTERTRUST (CURACAO) BV—See Corporation Service Company; *U.S. Private*, pg. 1057
INTERTRUST DANISMANLIK AS—See Corporation Service Company; *U.S. Private*, pg. 1057
INTERTRUST (DENMARK) A/S—See Corporation Service Company; *U.S. Private*, pg. 1057
INTERTRUST (DUBAI) LIMITED—See Corporation Service Company; *U.S. Private*, pg. 1057
INTERTRUST FIDUCIARY SERVICES (JERSEY) LIMITED—See Corporation Service Company; *U.S. Private*, pg. 1057
INTERTRUST GROUP B.V.—See Corporation Service Company; *U.S. Private*, pg. 1057
INTERTRUST GROUP HOLDING S.A.—See Corporation Service Company; *U.S. Private*, pg. 1057
INTERTRUST (GUERNSEY) LIMITED—See Corporation Service Company; *U.S. Private*, pg. 1057
INTERTRUST HOLDINGS (UK) LIMITED—See Corporation Service Company; *U.S. Private*, pg. 1057
INTERTRUST HONG KONG LIMITED—See Corporation Service Company; *U.S. Private*, pg. 1057
INTERTRUST (LUXEMBOURG) S.A.R.L.—See Corporation Service Company; *U.S. Private*, pg. 1057
INTERTRUST MANAGEMENT IRELAND LIMITED—See Corporation Service Company; *U.S. Private*, pg. 1057

INTERTRUST (NETHERLANDS) B.V.—See Corporation Service Company; *U.S. Private*, pg. 1057
INTERTRUST SERVICES (SCHWEIZ) AG—See Corporation Service Company; *U.S. Private*, pg. 1057
INTERTRUST (SHANGHAI) CONSULTANTS LIMITED—See Corporation Service Company; *U.S. Private*, pg. 1058
INTERTRUST (SINGAPORE) LTD.—See Corporation Service Company; *U.S. Private*, pg. 1058
INTERTRUST (SPAIN) S.L.—See Corporation Service Company; *U.S. Private*, pg. 1057
INTERTRUST (SUISSE) S.A.—See Corporation Service Company; *U.S. Private*, pg. 1057
INTERTRUST (SWEDEN) AB—See Corporation Service Company; *U.S. Private*, pg. 1057
INTERTRUST TECHNOLOGIES CORPORATION—See Koninklijke Philips N.V.; *Int'l*, pg. 4268
INTERTRUST TECHNOLOGIES CORPORATION—See Sony Group Corporation; *Int'l*, pg. 7102
INTER TURIZM VE SEYAHAT A.S.—See Net Holding A.S.; *Int'l*, pg. 5211
INTER-UNION TECHNOHANDEL GESELLSCHAFT M.B.H.—See Deutsche Bahn AG; *Int'l*, pg. 2052
INTERUPS INC.; *U.S. Public*, pg. 1158
INTER-URBAN DELIVERY SERVICE, LTD.—See Mullen Group Ltd.; *Int'l*, pg. 5080
INTERVACC AB; *Int'l*, pg. 3764
INTERVALA, LLC; *U.S. Private*, pg. 2127
INTERVALE CAPITAL, LLC - HOUSTON—See Intervale Capital, LLC; *U.S. Private*, pg. 2127
INTERVALE CAPITAL, LLC; *U.S. Private*, pg. 2127
INTERVAL INTERNATIONAL ARGENTINA S.A.—See Marriott Vacations Worldwide Corporation; *U.S. Public*, pg. 1373
INTERVAL INTERNATIONAL EGYPT LTD.—See Marriott Vacations Worldwide Corporation; *U.S. Public*, pg. 1373
INTERVAL INTERNATIONAL FINLAND OY—See Marriott Vacations Worldwide Corporation; *U.S. Public*, pg. 1373
INTERVAL INTERNATIONAL GMBH—See Marriott Vacations Worldwide Corporation; *U.S. Public*, pg. 1373
INTERVAL INTERNATIONAL ITALIA SRL—See Marriott Vacations Worldwide Corporation; *U.S. Public*, pg. 1373
INTERVAL INTERNATIONAL LIMITED—See Marriott Vacations Worldwide Corporation; *U.S. Public*, pg. 1373
INTERVAL INTERNATIONAL SINGAPORE (PTE) LTD.—See Marriott Vacations Worldwide Corporation; *U.S. Public*, pg. 1373
INTER VALLEY POOL SUPPLY, INC.—See GHK Capital Partners LP; *U.S. Private*, pg. 1690
INTERVAL MANAGEMENT INC.—See QM Corporation; *U.S. Private*, pg. 3313
INTERVAL SOFTWARE SERVICES, LLC—See Marriott Vacations Worldwide Corporation; *U.S. Public*, pg. 1373
INTERVALVE INC.—See Venus MedTech (HangZhou) Inc.; *Int'l*, pg. 8152
INTERVALZERO INC.; *U.S. Private*, pg. 2128
INTERVASCULAR SARL.—See Getinge AB; *Int'l*, pg. 2951
INTERVEST MORTGAGE INVESTMENT COMPANY—See Columbia Banking System, Inc.; *U.S. Public*, pg. 534
INTERVEST MORTGAGE INVESTMENT COMPANY—See Columbia Banking System, Inc.; *U.S. Public*, pg. 534
INTERVEST OFFICES & WAREHOUSES N.V.—See TPG Capital, L.P.; *U.S. Public*, pg. 2174
INTERVET AB—See Merck & Co., Inc.; *U.S. Public*, pg. 1416
INTERVET AGENCIES B.V.—See Merck & Co., Inc.; *U.S. Public*, pg. 1416
INTERVET ARGENTINA S.A.—See Merck & Co., Inc.; *U.S. Public*, pg. 1416
INTERVET AUSTRALIA PTY LTD—See Merck & Co., Inc.; *U.S. Public*, pg. 1416
INTERVET CANADA CORP.—See Merck & Co., Inc.; *U.S. Public*, pg. 1416
INTERVET COLOMBIA LTDA—See Merck & Co., Inc.; *U.S. Public*, pg. 1416
INTERVET DENMARK A/S—See Merck & Co., Inc.; *U.S. Public*, pg. 1416
INTERVET DEUTSCHLAND GMBH—See Merck & Co., Inc.; *U.S. Public*, pg. 1416
INTERVET EGYPT FOR ANIMAL HEALTH SAE—See Merck & Co., Inc.; *U.S. Public*, pg. 1416
INTERVET GES MBH—See Merck & Co., Inc.; *U.S. Public*, pg. 1416
INTERVET HELLAS A.E.—See Merck & Co., Inc.; *U.S. Public*, pg. 1416
INTERVET HUNGARIA KFT—See Merck & Co., Inc.; *U.S. Public*, pg. 1416
INTERVET INC. - ELKHORN—See Merck & Co., Inc.; *U.S. Public*, pg. 1416
INTERVET INC. - MILLSBORO—See Merck & Co., Inc.; *U.S. Public*, pg. 1416
INTERVET INC.—See Merck & Co., Inc.; *U.S. Public*, pg. 1416
INTERVET INDIA PVT. LTD—See Merck & Co., Inc.; *U.S. Public*, pg. 1417

INTERVALZERO INC.

CORPORATE AFFILIATIONS

INTERVET INDIA PVT. LTD.—See Merck & Co., Inc.; *U.S. Public*, pg. 1417
INTERVET (IRELAND) LIMITED—See Merck & Co., Inc.; *U.S. Public*, pg. 1416
INTERVET K.K.—See Merck & Co., Inc.; *U.S. Public*, pg. 1416
INTERVET LLC—See Merck & Co., Inc.; *U.S. Public*, pg. 1417
INTERVET MEXICO S.A. DE C.V.—See Merck & Co., Inc.; *U.S. Public*, pg. 1417
INTERVET MIDDLE EAST LTD—See Merck & Co., Inc.; *U.S. Public*, pg. 1417
INTERVET (M) SDN BHD—See Merck & Co., Inc.; *U.S. Public*, pg. 1416
INTERVET NEDERLAND B.V.—See Merck & Co., Inc.; *U.S. Public*, pg. 1417
INTERVET NORBIO A.S.—See Merck & Co., Inc.; *U.S. Public*, pg. 1417
INTERVET NORBIO SINGAPORE PTE LTD—See Merck & Co., Inc.; *U.S. Public*, pg. 1417
INTERVET NORGE AS—See Merck & Co., Inc.; *U.S. Public*, pg. 1417
INTERVET OY—See Merck & Co., Inc.; *U.S. Public*, pg. 1417
INTERVET PHILIPPINES, INC.—See Merck & Co., Inc.; *U.S. Public*, pg. 1417
INTERVET (PROPRIETARY) LIMITED—See Merck & Co., Inc.; *U.S. Public*, pg. 1416
INTERVET ROMANIA SRL—See Merck & Co., Inc.; *U.S. Public*, pg. 1417
INTERVET S.A.S—See Merck & Co., Inc.; *U.S. Public*, pg. 1417
INTERVET SCHERING-PLOUGH ANIMAL HEALTH PTY LTD—See Merck & Co., Inc.; *U.S. Public*, pg. 1417
INTERVET SOUTH AFRICA (PROPRIETARY) LIMITED—See Merck & Co., Inc.; *U.S. Public*, pg. 1417
INTERVET SP. Z O.O.—See Merck & Co., Inc.; *U.S. Public*, pg. 1417
INTERVET SP. Z.O.O.—See Merck & Co., Inc.; *U.S. Public*, pg. 1417
INTERVET, S.R.O.—See Merck & Co., Inc.; *U.S. Public*, pg. 1417
INTER VETTA CO., LTD.—See Interpharma Public Company Limited; *Int'l*, pg. 3755
INTERVET (THAILAND) LTD.—See Merck & Co., Inc.; *U.S. Public*, pg. 1416
INTERVET U.K. LTD.—See Merck & Co., Inc.; *U.S. Public*, pg. 1417
INTERVET VENEZOLANA SA—See Merck & Co., Inc.; *U.S. Public*, pg. 1417
INTERVET VETERINARIA CHILE LTDA—See Merck & Co., Inc.; *U.S. Public*, pg. 1417
INTERVET VIETNAM CO., LTD.—See Merck & Co., Inc.; *U.S. Public*, pg. 1417
INTERVIAL CHILE SA—See Ecopetrol S.A.; *Int'l*, pg. 2299
INTERVIEWING SERVICE OF AMERICA; *U.S. Private*, pg. 2128
INTERVISE CONSULTANTS INC.; *U.S. Private*, pg. 2128
INTERVISION SYSTEMS, LLC—See Huron Capital Partners LLC; *U.S. Private*, pg. 2012
INTERVISION SYSTEMS, LLC—See MidOcean Partners, LLP; *U.S. Private*, pg. 2716
INTERVISTAS—See Koninklijke HaskoningDHV Groep B.V.; *Int'l*, pg. 4266
INTERWARE DEVELOPMENT COMPANY, INC.—See Arlington Capital Partners LLC; *U.S. Private*, pg. 327
INTERWASTE HOLDINGS LIMITED—See Groupe Seche SAS; *Int'l*, pg. 3110
INTER-WASTE PROPRIETARY LIMITED—See Groupe Seche SAS; *Int'l*, pg. 3110
INTERWELL AS—See Ferd AS; *Int'l*, pg. 2636
INTERWELL AUSTRALIA PTY LTD—See Ferd AS; *Int'l*, pg. 2636
INTERWELL LLC—See Ferd AS; *Int'l*, pg. 2636
INTERWELL QATAR PETROLEUM TECHNOLOGY CO. W.L.L.—See Ferd AS; *Int'l*, pg. 2636
INTERWELL SAUDI ARABIA GAS & OIL TECHNOLOGIES L.L.C.—See Ferd AS; *Int'l*, pg. 2636
INTERWELL UK LTD—See Ferd AS; *Int'l*, pg. 2636
INTERWELL US LLC—See Ferd AS; *Int'l*, pg. 2636
INTERWEST CONSTRUCTION COMPANY, INC.—See Interwest Corporation; *U.S. Private*, pg. 2128
INTERWEST CONSTRUCTION, INC.; *U.S. Private*, pg. 2128
INTERWEST CORPORATION; *U.S. Private*, pg. 2128
INTERWEST INSURANCE SERVICES, INC.; *U.S. Private*, pg. 2128
INTERWEST SAFETY SUPPLY INC.; *U.S. Private*, pg. 2128
INTER-WIRE PRODUCTS INC.; *U.S. Private*, pg. 2107
INTERWOOD DIRECT; *Int'l*, pg. 3764
INTERWOOD MARKETING LIMITED—See Interwood Direct; *Int'l*, pg. 3764
INTERWOOD-XYLEMPORIA A.T.E.N.E.; *Int'l*, pg. 3764
INTERWORKS, INC.; *U.S. Private*, pg. 2128
INTERWORKS, INC.; *Int'l*, pg. 3764
INTERWORLD DIGITAL LTD.; *Int'l*, pg. 3764

INTERWORLD HIGHWAY, LLC—See Distribution Solutions Group, Inc.; *U.S. Public*, pg. 669
INTER-WORLD PAPER OVERSEAS LTD.; *Int'l*, pg. 3735
INTERWRAP CORP. PVT. LTD.—See Owens Corning; *U.S. Public*, pg. 1626
INTERWRAP CORP.—See Owens Corning; *U.S. Public*, pg. 1628
INTERWRAP, INC.—See Owens Corning; *U.S. Public*, pg. 1628
INTERXION BELGIUM N.V.—See Digital Realty Trust, Inc.; *U.S. Public*, pg. 663
INTERXION DANMARK APS—See Digital Realty Trust, Inc.; *U.S. Public*, pg. 663
INTERXION DEUTSCHLAND GMBH—See Digital Realty Trust, Inc.; *U.S. Public*, pg. 663
INTERXION ESPANA SA—See Digital Realty Trust, Inc.; *U.S. Public*, pg. 663
INTERXION EUROPE LTD.—See Digital Realty Trust, Inc.; *U.S. Public*, pg. 663
INTERXION FRANCE SAS—See Digital Realty Trust, Inc.; *U.S. Public*, pg. 663
INTERXION HOLDING N.V.—See Digital Realty Trust, Inc.; *U.S. Public*, pg. 663
INTERXION IRELAND LTD.—See Digital Realty Trust, Inc.; *U.S. Public*, pg. 663
INTERXION N.V.—See Digital Realty Trust, Inc.; *U.S. Public*, pg. 663
INTERXION OSTERREICH GMBH—See Digital Realty Trust, Inc.; *U.S. Public*, pg. 663
INTERXION (SCHWEIZ) AG—See Digital Realty Trust, Inc.; *U.S. Public*, pg. 663
INTERXION SVERIGE AB—See Digital Realty Trust, Inc.; *U.S. Public*, pg. 663
INTERYACHTING—See Francoudi & Stephanou Ltd.; *Int'l*, pg. 2761
INTER YEAST SP. Z OO—See Leiber GmbH; *Int'l*, pg. 4446
INTERZAV, D.O.O.—See Intereuropa d.d.; *Int'l*, pg. 3740
INTERZERO D.O.O—See Alba SE; *Int'l*, pg. 293
INTERZON AB—See Absolent Air Care Group AB; *Int'l*, pg. 70
INTESA HOLDING INTERNATIONAL SA—See Intesa Sanpaolo S.p.A.; *Int'l*, pg. 3765
INTESA LEASING SPA—See Intesa Sanpaolo S.p.A.; *Int'l*, pg. 3765
INTESA SANPAOLO BANKA D.D. BOSNA I HERCEGOVINA—See Intesa Sanpaolo S.p.A.; *Int'l*, pg. 3766
INTESA SANPAOLO BANK ALBANIA—See Intesa Sanpaolo S.p.A.; *Int'l*, pg. 3765
INTESA SANPAOLO BANK IRELAND PLC—See Intesa Sanpaolo S.p.A.; *Int'l*, pg. 3765
INTESA SANPAOLO BANK LUXEMBOURG S.A.—See Intesa Sanpaolo S.p.A.; *Int'l*, pg. 3765
INTESA SANPAOLO BANQUE—See Intesa Sanpaolo S.p.A.; *Int'l*, pg. 3765
INTESA SANPAOLO BRASIL S.A. - BANCO MULTIPLO—See Intesa Sanpaolo S.p.A.; *Int'l*, pg. 3765
INTESA SANPAOLO GROUP SERVICES S.C.P.A.—See Intesa Sanpaolo S.p.A.; *Int'l*, pg. 3765
INTESA SANPAOLO HOLDING INTERNATIONAL S.A.—See Intesa Sanpaolo S.p.A.; *Int'l*, pg. 3765
INTESA SANPAOLO INTERNATIONAL VALUE SERVICES D.O.O.—See Intesa Sanpaolo S.p.A.; *Int'l*, pg. 3765
INTESA SANPAOLO LIFE DESIGNED ACTIVITY COMPANY—See Intesa Sanpaolo S.p.A.; *Int'l*, pg. 3765
INTESA SANPAOLO LIFE LIMITED—See Intesa Sanpaolo S.p.A.; *Int'l*, pg. 3766
INTESA SANPAOLO PREVIDENZA - SOCIETA DI INTERMEDIAZIONE MOBILIARE S.P.A.—See Intesa Sanpaolo S.p.A.; *Int'l*, pg. 3765
INTESA SANPAOLO PRIVATE BANKING S.P.A.—See Intesa Sanpaolo S.p.A.; *Int'l*, pg. 3765
INTESA SANPAOLO RBM SALUTE S.P.A.—See Intesa Sanpaolo S.p.A.; *Int'l*, pg. 3765
INTESA SANPAOLO RENT FORYOU S.P.A.—See Intesa Sanpaolo S.p.A.; *Int'l*, pg. 3766
INTESA SANPAOLO ROMANIA S.A.—See Intesa Sanpaolo S.p.A.; *Int'l*, pg. 3766
INTESA SANPAOLO SERVITIA S.A.—See Intesa Sanpaolo S.p.A.; *Int'l*, pg. 3765
INTESA SANPAOLO S.P.A.; *Int'l*, pg. 3764
INTESA SANPAOLO VITA S.P.A.—See Intesa Sanpaolo S.p.A.; *Int'l*, pg. 3766
INTESA SEC. S.P.A.—See Intesa Sanpaolo S.p.A.; *Int'l*, pg. 3766
IN.TE.SA S.P.A.—See Sacmi Imola S.C.A.R.L.; *Int'l*, pg. 6463
INTESCIA GROUP SAS—See Andera Partners SCA; *Int'l*, pg. 450
INTESOURCE, INC.—See Pollen Street Limited; *Int'l*, pg. 5910
INTESSA PREFERRED CAPITAL CORPORATION LLC—See Intesa Sanpaolo S.p.A.; *Int'l*, pg. 3766
INTES STORITVE, D.O.O.—See Podravka d.d.; *Int'l*, pg. 5903
IN TESTA HQ—See Armando Testa S.p.A.; *Int'l*, pg. 574

INTEST CORPORATION; *U.S. Public*, pg. 1158
INTEST PTE, LTD.—See inTEST Corporation; *U.S. Public*, pg. 1159
INTEST SILICON VALLEY CORPORATION—See inTEST Corporation; *U.S. Public*, pg. 1159
INTEST THERMAL SOLUTIONS GMBH—See inTEST Corporation; *U.S. Public*, pg. 1159
INTESYS NETWORKING S.R.L.—See Intesys S.r.l.; *Int'l*, pg. 3767
INTESYS S.R.L.; *Int'l*, pg. 3767
INTETICS CO.; *U.S. Private*, pg. 2128
INTEVAC ASIA PRIVATE LIMITED—See Intevac, Inc.; *U.S. Public*, pg. 1159
INTEVAC, INC.; *U.S. Public*, pg. 1159
INTEVAC (SHENZHEN) CO. LTD.—See Intevac, Inc.; *U.S. Public*, pg. 1159
INTEVEP, S.A.—See Petroleos de Venezuela S.A.; *Int'l*, pg. 5828
INTEVIAL-GAESTO INTEGRAL RODOVIARIA S.A.—See Infrastructure Leasing & Financial Services Limited; *Int'l*, pg. 3698
INTEX DEVELOPMENT COMPANY LTD.—See Intex Recreation Corp.; *U.S. Private*, pg. 2128
INTEX ENVIRONMENTAL GROUP, INC.; *U.S. Private*, pg. 2128
INTEX RECREATION CORP.; *U.S. Private*, pg. 2128
INTEX RESOURCES PHILIPPINES, INC.—See DLT ASA; *Int'l*, pg. 2142
INTEXT CO., LTD.—See Naigai Co., Ltd.; *Int'l*, pg. 5130
INT/EXT COMMUNICATIONS AG; *Int'l*, pg. 3726
INTEX TRADING B. V.—See Intex Recreation Corp.; *U.S. Private*, pg. 2128
INTEX TRADING S.R.O.—See Intex Recreation Corp.; *U.S. Private*, pg. 2128
INTEZYNE TECHNOLOGIES, INC.; *U.S. Private*, pg. 2128
IN THE F CO.,LTD.; *Int'l*, pg. 3639
IN THE KNOW EXPERIENCES; *U.S. Private*, pg. 2052
IN THE KNOW, INC.; *U.S. Private*, pg. 2052
IN THE STYLE GROUP PLC; *Int'l*, pg. 3639
INTHINC, INC.—See ORBCOMM, Inc.; *U.S. Public*, pg. 1614
INTHINC; *U.S. Private*, pg. 2128
INTHINC TECHNOLOGY SOLUTIONS, INC; *U.S. Private*, pg. 2128
INTICA SYSTEMS SE; *Int'l*, pg. 3767
INTICA SYSTEMS S.R.O.—See InTiCa Systems SE; *Int'l*, pg. 3767
INTIFIC, INC—See Elliott Management Corporation; *U.S. Private*, pg. 1368
INTIFIC, INC—See Veritas Capital Fund Management, LLC; *U.S. Private*, pg. 4362
INTIGER GROUP LIMITED; *Int'l*, pg. 3767
INTIGRAL INC; *U.S. Private*, pg. 2128
INTIMACY MANAGEMENT COMPANY LLC—See Van de Velde N.V.; *Int'l*, pg. 8125
INTIMATE MERGER, INC.—See FreakOut Holdings, Inc.; *Int'l*, pg. 2767
INTIMATES CO., LTD.—See Onward Holdings Co., Ltd.; *Int'l*, pg. 5592
INTIMATES ONLINE, INC.—See Wacoal Holdings Corp.; *Int'l*, pg. 8325
IN TIME EXPRESS LOGISTIK GMBH—See Super Group Limited; *Int'l*, pg. 7334
INTIME MEDIA SERVICES GMBH—See Hubert Burda Media Holding Kommanditgesellschaft; *Int'l*, pg. 3520
INTIME RETAIL (GROUP) COMPANY LIMITED—See Alibaba Group Holding Limited; *Int'l*, pg. 326
IN TIME S.R.O.—See Osterreichische Post AG; *Int'l*, pg. 5653
INTIMO INC.; *U.S. Private*, pg. 2128
INTIMUS INTERNATIONAL AUSTRIA GES.M.B.H.—See PHI Asset Management Partners SGEIC S.A.; *Int'l*, pg. 5843
INTIMUS INTERNATIONAL BELGIUM—See PHI Asset Management Partners SGEIC S.A.; *Int'l*, pg. 5843
INTIMUS INTERNATIONAL GMBH—See PHI Asset Management Partners SGEIC S.A.; *Int'l*, pg. 5843
INTIMUS INTERNATIONAL IBERICA, S.A.U.—See PHI Asset Management Partners SGEIC S.A.; *Int'l*, pg. 5843
INTIMUS INTERNATIONAL LIMITED—See PHI Asset Management Partners SGEIC S.A.; *Int'l*, pg. 5843
INTIMUS INTERNATIONAL LUXEMBOURG S.A.R.L.—See PHI Asset Management Partners SGEIC S.A.; *Int'l*, pg. 5843
INTIMUS INTERNATIONAL NETHERLANDS B.V.—See PHI Asset Management Partners SGEIC S.A.; *Int'l*, pg. 5843
INTIMUS INTERNATIONAL NORTH AMERICA, INC.—See PHI Asset Management Partners SGEIC S.A.; *Int'l*, pg. 5844
INTIRION CORP.—See Danby Products Ltd.; *Int'l*, pg. 1958
INTISSEL SAS—See Chargeurs SA; *Int'l*, pg. 1450
INTIVA INC.; *U.S. Private*, pg. 2128
INTL ADVISORY CONSULTANTS INC.—See StoneX Group Inc.; *U.S. Public*, pg. 1952
INTL ASIA PTE. LTD.—See StoneX Group Inc.; *U.S. Public*, pg. 1952

COMPANY NAME INDEX

INTL CAPITAL LIMITED—See StoneX Group Inc.; *U.S. Public*, pg. 1952
INTL CAPITAL S.A.—See StoneX Group Inc.; *U.S. Public*, pg. 1952
INTL CIBSA S.A.—See StoneX Group Inc.; *U.S. Public*, pg. 1952
INTL CUSTODY & CLEARING SOLUTIONS INC.—See StoneX Group Inc.; *U.S. Public*, pg. 1952
INTL FCSTONE BANCO DE CAMBIO S.A.—See StoneX Group Inc.; *U.S. Public*, pg. 1952
INTL FCSTONE CAPITAL ASSESSORIA FINANCEIRA LTDA.—See StoneX Group Inc.; *U.S. Public*, pg. 1952
INTL FCSTONE COMMODITIES DMCC—See StoneX Group Inc.; *U.S. Public*, pg. 1952
INTL FCSTONE DE MEXICO, S. DE R.L. DE C.V.—See StoneX Group Inc.; *U.S. Public*, pg. 1952
INTL FCSTONE DTVM LTDA.—See StoneX Group Inc.; *U.S. Public*, pg. 1952
INTL FCSTONE EUROPE S.A.—See StoneX Group Inc.; *U.S. Public*, pg. 1952
INTL FCSTONE FINANCIAL (CANADA) INC.—See StoneX Group Inc.; *U.S. Public*, pg. 1952
INTL FCSTONE FINANCIAL INC.—See StoneX Group Inc.; *U.S. Public*, pg. 1952
INTL FCSTONE (HK) LTD.—See StoneX Group Inc.; *U.S. Public*, pg. 1952
INTL FCSTONE PTE. LTD.—See StoneX Group Inc.; *U.S. Public*, pg. 1952
INTL FCSTONE PTY. LTD.—See StoneX Group Inc.; *U.S. Public*, pg. 1952
INTL FCSTONE (SHANGHAI) TRADING CO., LTD—See StoneX Group Inc.; *U.S. Public*, pg. 1952
INTL GAINVEST S.A.—See StoneX Group Inc.; *U.S. Public*, pg. 1952
INTL GLOBAL CURRENCIES LIMITED—See StoneX Group Inc.; *U.S. Public*, pg. 1952
INTL KOREA LIMITED—See StoneX Group Inc.; *U.S. Public*, pg. 1952
INTL NETHERLANDS B.V.—See StoneX Group Inc.; *U.S. Public*, pg. 1952
INTLX SOLUTIONS, LLC; *U.S. Private*, pg. 2129
THE INTOLLIGENT LTD—See STRABAG SE; *Int'l*, pg. 7233
INTO METAL INC.; *U.S. Private*, pg. 2129
INTONE NETWORKS INC.; *U.S. Private*, pg. 2129
INTOPS CO., LTD.; *Int'l*, pg. 3767
INTORQ INDIA PVT. LTD.—See Kendrion N.V.; *Int'l*, pg. 4126
INTORQ (SHANGHAI) CO., LTD.—See Kendrion N.V.; *Int'l*, pg. 4126
INTORQ US INC.—See Kendrion N.V.; *Int'l*, pg. 4126
INTOS ELECTRONIC AG; *Int'l*, pg. 3767
INTOS S.A.U.—See Indra Sistemas, S.A.; *Int'l*, pg. 3661
INTOTAL HEALTH—See Inova Health System; *U.S. Private*, pg. 2084
INTOUCH AUTOMATION, INC.—See Lear Corporation; *U.S. Public*, pg. 1297
INTOUCH CREDIT UNION; *U.S. Private*, pg. 2129
THE INTOUCH GROUP LTD—See Matthews International Corporation; *U.S. Public*, pg. 1401
INTOUCH HOLDINGS PLC; *Int'l*, pg. 3767
INTOUCH INSIGHT LTD.; *Int'l*, pg. 3767
IN-TOUCH INSIGHT SYSTEMS CORP.—See Intouch Insight Ltd.; *Int'l*, pg. 3767
IN-TOUCH INSIGHT SYSTEMS INC.—See Intouch Insight Ltd.; *Int'l*, pg. 3767
INTOUCH PLC—See Temasek Holdings (Private) Limited; *Int'l*, pg. 7547
INTOUCH TECHNOLOGIES, INC.; *U.S. Private*, pg. 2129
IN TOUCH WEEKLY—See Heinrich Bauer Verlag KG; *Int'l*, pg. 3324
INTOUCH WITH HEALTH LIMITED—See Vitalhub Corp.; *Int'l*, pg. 8258
INTOWARE LTD.—See Kopin Corporation; *U.S. Public*, pg. 1271
INTOWN DESIGN, INC.—See Littlejohn & Co., LLC; *U.S. Private*, pg. 2470
INTOWN DESIGN, INC.—See Platinum Equity, LLC; *U.S. Private*, pg. 3205
INTOXIMETERS INC.; *U.S. Private*, pg. 2129
INTPROPCO S.A.—See The Procter & Gamble Company; *U.S. Public*, pg. 2120
INTRA-CELLULAR THERAPIES, INC.; *U.S. Public*, pg. 1159
INTRACOASTAL SURGERY CENTER, LLC—See Tenet Healthcare Corporation; *U.S. Public*, pg. 2004
INTRACO HOLDING B.V.—See New Wave Group AB; *Int'l*, pg. 5229
INTRACO HONG KONG LTD.—See New Wave Group AB; *Int'l*, pg. 5229
INTRACO INTERNATIONAL PTE LTD—See INTRACO Limited; *Int'l*, pg. 3767
INTRACO LIMITED; *Int'l*, pg. 3767
INTRACOM CONSTRUCTIONS SOCIETE ANONYME TECHNICAL & STEEL CONSTRUCTIONS—See Intracom Holdings S.A.; *Int'l*, pg. 3768
INTRACOM CONSTRUCT SA—See Intracom Holdings S.A.; *Int'l*, pg. 3768
INTRACOM CYPRUS LTD—See Netcompany Group AS; *Int'l*, pg. 5213
INTRACOM HOLDINGS S.A.; *Int'l*, pg. 3767
INTRACOM IT SERVICES DENMARK A/S—See Netcompany Group AS; *Int'l*, pg. 5213
INTRACOM IT SERVICES—See Intracom Holdings S.A.; *Int'l*, pg. 3768
INTRACOM IT SERVICES—See Netcompany Group AS; *Int'l*, pg. 5213
INTRACOM S.A.—See Intracom Holdings S.A.; *Int'l*, pg. 3768
INTRACO REFUELING STATON LTD.; *Int'l*, pg. 3767
INTRACORP (B) SDN. BHD.—See TT International Limited; *Int'l*, pg. 7960
INTRACORP COMPANIES; *U.S. Private*, pg. 2129
INTRACORP PROJECTS LTD.; *Int'l*, pg. 3768
INTRA, CORP.; *U.S. Private*, pg. 2129
INTRACO SHENZHEN LTD—See New Wave Group AB; *Int'l*, pg. 5229
INTRACO TRADING B.V.—See New Wave Group AB; *Int'l*, pg. 5229
INTRADECO APPAREL, INC.—See Intradeco, Inc.; *U.S. Private*, pg. 2129
INTRADECO, INC.; *U.S. Private*, pg. 2129
INTRADEVELOPMENT SA—See Intracom Holdings S.A.; *Int'l*, pg. 3768
INTRADO BELGIUM—See Apollo Global Management, Inc.; *U.S. Public*, pg. 152
INTRADO COMMUNICATIONS LLC—See Apollo Global Management, Inc.; *U.S. Public*, pg. 152
INTRADO CORPORATION—See Apollo Global Management, Inc.; *U.S. Public*, pg. 152
INTRADO EC INDIA PRIVATE LIMITED—See Apollo Global Management, Inc.; *U.S. Public*, pg. 152
INTRADO EC SERVICES SPAIN SA—See Apollo Global Management, Inc.; *U.S. Public*, pg. 152
INTRADO EC SINGAPORE PRIVATE LIMITED—See Apollo Global Management, Inc.; *U.S. Public*, pg. 152
INTRADO HONG KONG LIMITED—See Apollo Global Management, Inc.; *U.S. Public*, pg. 152
INTRADO ITALY S.R.L.—See Apollo Global Management, Inc.; *U.S. Public*, pg. 152
INTRADO JAPAN K.K.—See Apollo Global Management, Inc.; *U.S. Public*, pg. 152
INTRA ENERGY CORPORATION LIMITED; *Int'l*, pg. 3767
INTRAFISH MEDIA AS—See Fred. Olsen & Co.; *Int'l*, pg. 2768
INTRAFRICAN RESOURCES LIMITED—See Intra Energy Corporation Limited; *Int'l*, pg. 3767
INTRAGRAIN TECHNOLOGIES INC.—See Calian Group Ltd.; *Int'l*, pg. 1264
INTRAGRATED RESOURCES HOLDINGS, INC.—See Marubeni Corporation; *Int'l*, pg. 4706
INTRAHEALTH SYSTEMS LIMITED—See HEALWELL AI Inc.; *Int'l*, pg. 3304
INTRAKAT INTERNATIONAL LTD—See Intracom Holdings S.A.; *Int'l*, pg. 3768
INTRALINKS ASIA PACIFIC PTE. LTD.—See SS&C Technologies Holdings, Inc.; *U.S. Public*, pg. 1923
INTRALINKS EMEA HOLDINGS B.V.—See SS&C Technologies Holdings, Inc.; *U.S. Public*, pg. 1923
INTRALINKS HOLDINGS, INC.—See SS&C Technologies Holdings, Inc.; *U.S. Public*, pg. 1923
INTRALINKS INC.—See SS&C Technologies Holdings, Inc.; *U.S. Public*, pg. 1923
INTRALINKS INDIA SOLUTIONS PVT. LIMITED—See SS&C Technologies Holdings, Inc.; *U.S. Public*, pg. 1923
INTRALINKS PTY LIMITED—See SS&C Technologies Holdings, Inc.; *U.S. Public*, pg. 1923
INTRALINKS SERVICIOS DE TECNOLOGIA DE MEXICO, S DE R.L. DE C.V.—See SS&C Technologies Holdings, Inc.; *U.S. Public*, pg. 1923
INTRALINKS SERVICOS DE INFORMATICA LTDA.—See SS&C Technologies Holdings, Inc.; *U.S. Public*, pg. 1923
INTRALINKS SRL—See SS&C Technologies Holdings, Inc.; *U.S. Public*, pg. 1923
INTRALOG HERMES AG—See Die Schweizerische Post AG; *Int'l*, pg. 2113
INTRALOGIC SOLUTIONS INC.; *U.S. Private*, pg. 2129
INTRALOG OVERSEAS AG—See Die Schweizerische Post AG; *Int'l*, pg. 2113
INTRALOT ASIA PACIFIC LTD.—See INTRALOT S.A.; *Int'l*, pg. 3768
INTRALOT AUSTRALIA PTY LTD.—See INTRALOT S.A.; *Int'l*, pg. 3768
INTRALOT BEIJING CO., LTD.—See INTRALOT S.A.; *Int'l*, pg. 3768
INTRALOT DE CHILE S.A.—See INTRALOT S.A.; *Int'l*, pg. 3768
INTRALOT DE PERU S.A.; *Int'l*, pg. 3768
INTRALOT DO BRAZIL LTDA—See INTRALOT S.A.; *Int'l*, pg. 3768
INTRALOT GAMING SERVICES PTY. LTD.—See INTRALOT S.A.; *Int'l*, pg. 3768
INTRALOT INC.—See INTRALOT S.A.; *Int'l*, pg. 3768
INTRALOT S.A.; *Int'l*, pg. 3768

INTREPID CAPITAL CORP.

INTRALOT SOUTH AFRICA LTD.—See INTRALOT S.A.; *Int'l*, pg. 3768
INTRALOX (INDIA) PRIVATE LTD.—See The Laitram LLC; *U.S. Private*, pg. 4067
INTRALOX LLC—See The Laitram LLC; *U.S. Private*, pg. 4067
INTRALOX LLC—See The Laitram LLC; *U.S. Private*, pg. 4067
INTRALOX LTD.—See The Laitram LLC; *U.S. Private*, pg. 4067
INTRALOX SHANGHAI LTD.—See The Laitram LLC; *U.S. Private*, pg. 4067
INTRA-MART CSI—See Nippon Telegraph & Telephone Corporation; *Int'l*, pg. 5346
INTRAMED COMMUNICATIONS MILAN—See WPP plc; *Int'l*, pg. 8492
INTRAMEDICAL HEALTH SERVICES PARIS—See WPP plc; *Int'l*, pg. 8492
INTRAMEDIC GMBH—See WPP plc; *Int'l*, pg. 8492
INTRAMED—See WPP plc; *Int'l*, pg. 8492
INTRAMED WEST EDUCATIONAL GROUP—See WPP plc; *Int'l*, pg. 8492
INTRAMERICA LIFE INSURANCE COMPANY—See The Allstate Corporation; *U.S. Public*, pg. 2033
INTRA METALS BV—See Jacquet Metal Service SA; *Int'l*, pg. 3866
INTRA METAL TRADING LLC—See NHC Foods Limited; *Int'l*, pg. 5257
INTRANCE CO., LTD.; *Int'l*, pg. 3768
INTRANS ENGINEERING LIMITED—See Westinghouse Air Brake Technologies Corporation; *U.S. Public*, pg. 2358
INTRANSIT INC.; *U.S. Private*, pg. 2129
INTRA OIL SERVICES BERHAD—See Dayang Enterprise Holdings Berhad; *Int'l*, pg. 1985
INTRAOP MEDICAL CORP.—See Firsthand Capital Management, Inc.; *U.S. Private*, pg. 1532
INTRA-OP MONITORING SERVICES, LLC—See HealthEdge Investment Partners, LLC; *U.S. Private*, pg. 1896
INTRAPAC (AUSTRALIA) PTY. LTD.—See Muda Holdings Berhad; *Int'l*, pg. 5076
INTRAPAC CANADA CORPORATION—See IntraPac Corporation; *Int'l*, pg. 3768
INTRAPAC CORPORATION - ENVASA DIVISION—See IntraPac Corporation; *Int'l*, pg. 3768
INTRAPAC CORPORATION; *Int'l*, pg. 3768
INTRAPAC CORPORATION—See IntraPac Corporation; *Int'l*, pg. 3768
INTRAPAC GROUP—See CI Capital Partners LLC; *U.S. Private*, pg. 895
INTRAPAC (SINGAPORE) PTE. LTD.—See Muda Holdings Berhad; *Int'l*, pg. 5076
INTRAPAC TRADING (M) SDN. BHD.—See Muda Holdings Berhad; *Int'l*, pg. 5076
INTRAPAC (UK) LTD.—See K.L. Resources Pte. Ltd.; *Int'l*, pg. 4044
INTRAPHONE SOLUTIONS AB—See Addnode Group AB; *Int'l*, pg. 130
INTRAPOWER S.A. ENERGY PROJECTS COMPANY—See Intracom Holdings S.A.; *Int'l*, pg. 3768
INTRASENSE SAS - INTERNATIONAL DIVISION—See Intrasense SAS; *Int'l*, pg. 3768
INTRASENSE SAS; *Int'l*, pg. 3768
INTRASOFT INTERNATIONAL BELGIUM SA—See Netcompany Group AS; *Int'l*, pg. 5213
INTRASOFT INTERNATIONAL BULGARIA LTD.—See Netcompany Group AS; *Int'l*, pg. 5213
INTRASOFT INTERNATIONAL EAST AFRICA LTD.—See Netcompany Group AS; *Int'l*, pg. 5213
INTRASOFT INTERNATIONAL ME FZC—See Netcompany Group AS; *Int'l*, pg. 5213
INTRASOFT INTERNATIONAL SA—See Netcompany Group AS; *Int'l*, pg. 5213
INTRASOFT INTERNATIONAL SCANDINAVIA A/S—See Netcompany Group AS; *Int'l*, pg. 5213
INTRASOFT INTERNATIONAL SOUTH AFRICA (PTY). LTD.—See Netcompany Group AS; *Int'l*, pg. 5213
INTRASOFT INTERNATIONAL USA INC.—See Netcompany Group AS; *Int'l*, pg. 5213
INTRASOFT JORDAN LTD.—See Netcompany Group AS; *Int'l*, pg. 5213
INTRASOFT TECHNOLOGIES LIMITED; *Int'l*, pg. 3769
INTRASONICS LIMITED—See Ipsos S.A.; *Int'l*, pg. 3799
INTRATONE UK LTD—See Cogelec SA; *Int'l*, pg. 1694
INTRAVENOUS INFUSIONS PLC; *Int'l*, pg. 3769
INTRAWARE INVESTMENTS PUBLIC LTD.; *Int'l*, pg. 3769
INTRAWEST HOSPITALITY MANAGEMENT, LLC—See KSL Capital Partners, LLC; *U.S. Private*, pg. 2354
INTRAWEST/WINTER PARK OPERATIONS CORPORATION—See KSL Capital Partners, LLC; *U.S. Private*, pg. 2354
INTR. B.V.—See Uzin Utz AG; *Int'l*, pg. 8103
INTRED S.P.A.; *Int'l*, pg. 3769
INTREN, INC.—See MasTec, Inc.; *U.S. Public*, pg. 1393
INTREORG SYSTEMS, INC.; *U.S. Private*, pg. 2129
INTREPID CAPITAL CORP.; *U.S. Public*, pg. 1159

1375

INTREPID CAPITAL MANAGEMENT, INC.

INTREPID CAPITAL MANAGEMENT, INC.; *U.S. Private*, pg. 2129
INTREPID CONSULTANTS INC—See RWS Holdings plc; *Int'l*, pg. 6437
INTREPID CONSULTANTS LIMITED—See RWS Holdings plc; *Int'l*, pg. 6437
INTREPID DIRECT INSURANCE AGENCY, LLC—See W.R. Berkley Corporation; *U.S. Public*, pg. 2317
INTREPID ENTERPRISES, INC.; *U.S. Private*, pg. 2129
INTREPID GEOPHYSICS PTY. LTD.—See Premier1 Lithium Ltd.; *Int'l*, pg. 5962
INTREPID LEARNING, INC.—See Ingram Industries, Inc.; *U.S. Private*, pg. 2076
INTREPID METALS CORP.; *Int'l*, pg. 3769
INTREPID POTASH, INC.; *U.S. Public*, pg. 1159
INTREPID POTASH-MOAB, LLC—See Intrepid Potash, Inc.; *U.S. Public*, pg. 1159
INTREPID POTASH-NEW MEXICO, LLC—See Intrepid Potash, Inc.; *U.S. Public*, pg. 1159
INTREPID SOLUTIONS AND SERVICES, LLC—See Hammond, Kennedy, Whitney & Company, Inc.; *U.S. Private*, pg. 1850
INTREPID SOUTHEAST INC.; *U.S. Private*, pg. 2129
INTREPID USA HEALTHCARE SERVICES—See Patriarch Partners, LLC; *U.S. Private*, pg. 3109
INTREXON BIOINFORMATICS GERMANY GMBH—See Precigen, Inc.; *U.S. Public*, pg. 1713
INTRIA ITEMS INC.—See Canadian Imperial Bank of Commerce; *Int'l*, pg. 1283
INTRICITY, LLC—See KKR & Co. Inc.; *U.S. Public*, pg. 1261
INTRICON CORPORATION; *U.S. Public*, pg. 1159
INTRICON DATRIX CORPORATION—See IntriCon Corporation; *U.S. Public*, pg. 1159
INTRICON GMBH—See IntriCon Corporation; *U.S. Public*, pg. 1159
INTRICON PTE. LTD.—See IntriCon Corporation; *U.S. Public*, pg. 1159
INTRIDEA INC.; *U.S. Private*, pg. 2129
INTRIGO SYSTEMS, INC.—See Accenture plc; *Int'l*, pg. 87
INTRINIUM, INC.; *U.S. Private*, pg. 2129
INTRINSEC SARL—See Neurones S.A.; *Int'l*, pg. 5219
INTRINSIC4D LLC—See Must Capital Inc.; *Int'l*, pg. 5103
INTRINSIC FINANCIAL SERVICES LIMITED—See Quilter plc; *Int'l*, pg. 6162
INTRINSIC MEDICINE, INC.; *U.S. Private*, pg. 2129
INTRINSIC SAFETY EQUIPMENT OF TEXAS, INC.—See Emerson Electric Co.; *U.S. Public*, pg. 750
INTRINSICS—See Barnhardt Manufacturing Company; *U.S. Private*, pg. 478
INTRINSIC TECHNOLOGY, LTD.; *Int'l*, pg. 3769
INTRINSIQ, LLC—See Cencora, Inc.; *U.S. Public*, pg. 467
INTRINSYC SOFTWARE (BARBADOS) INC.—See Lantronix, Inc.; *U.S. Public*, pg. 1293
INTRINSYC TECHNOLOGIES CORPORATION—See Lantronix, Inc.; *U.S. Public*, pg. 1293
INTRI-PLEX TECHNOLOGIES INC.; *U.S. Private*, pg. 2129
INTRIS N.V.—See WiseTech Global Limited; *Int'l*, pg. 8437
INTRIX TECHNOLOGIES INC.—See SunChase Holdings, Inc.; *U.S. Private*, pg. 3865
INTRO AVIATION GMBH—See INTRO-Verwaltungs GmbH; *Int'l*, pg. 3769
INTRO CORP.—See Audax Group, Limited Partnership; *U.S. Private*, pg. 388
INTROL AUTOMATION S.R.O.—See Introl S.A.; *Int'l*, pg. 3769
INTROL AUTOMATYKA SP. Z O.O. SP.K.—See Introl S.A.; *Int'l*, pg. 3769
INTRO LEASING GESELLSCHAFT M.B.H.—See UniCredit S.p.A.; *Int'l*, pg. 8034
INTROL-ENERGOMONTAZ SP. Z O.O.—See Introl S.A.; *Int'l*, pg. 3769
INTROL PRO-ZAP SP. Z O.O.—See Introl S.A.; *Int'l*, pg. 3769
INTROL S.A.; *Int'l*, pg. 3769
INTROMARK, INC.—See Technosystems Consolidated Corporation; *U.S. Private*, pg. 3956
INTROMEDIC CO., LTD.; *Int'l*, pg. 3769
INTRON BIOTECHNOLOGY INC - REAGENT BUSINESS DIVISION—See iNtRON Biotechnology, Inc.; *Int'l*, pg. 3769
INTRON BIOTECHNOLOGY, INC.; *Int'l*, pg. 3769
INTRONICS B.V.—See TKH Group N.V.; *Int'l*, pg. 7764
INTRON TECHNOLOGY (CHINA) LIMITED—See Intron Technology Holdings Limited; *Int'l*, pg. 3769
INTRON TECHNOLOGY HOLDINGS LIMITED; *Int'l*, pg. 3769
INTROTEC SCHWARZA GMBH—See Veolia Environnement S.A.; *Int'l*, pg. 8153
INTROTEK INTERNATIONAL—See AMETEK, Inc.; *U.S. Public*, pg. 121
INTRO-VERWALTUNGS GMBH; *Int'l*, pg. 3769
INTRUM AB; *Int'l*, pg. 3770
INTRUM AG—See Intrum AB; *Int'l*, pg. 3770
INTRUM A/S—See Intrum AB; *Int'l*, pg. 3770
INTRUM AUSTRIA GMBH—See Intrum AB; *Int'l*, pg. 3770
INTRUM BRASIL CONSULTORIA E PARTICIPACOES, S.A.—See Intrum AB; *Int'l*, pg. 3770

INTRUM CORPORATE SAS—See Intrum AB; *Int'l*, pg. 3770
INTRUM DATA SYSTEMS (DEUTSCHLAND) GMBH—See Intrum AB; *Int'l*, pg. 3770
INTRUM DELGIVNINGSSERVICE AB—See Intrum AB; *Int'l*, pg. 3770
INTRUM DEUTSCHLAND GMBH—See Intrum AB; *Int'l*, pg. 3770
INTRUM FINANCIAL SERVICES GMBH—See Intrum AB; *Int'l*, pg. 3770
INTRUM GLOBAL BUSINESS SERVICES UAB—See Intrum AB; *Int'l*, pg. 3770
INTRUM HANSEATISCHE INKASSOTREUHAND GMBH—See Intrum AB; *Int'l*, pg. 3770
INTRUM HELLAS A.E.D.A.D.P.—See Intrum AB; *Int'l*, pg. 3770
INTRUM INFORMATION SERVICES DEUTSCHLAND GMBH—See Intrum AB; *Int'l*, pg. 3770
INTRUM INTERNATIONAL S.A.—See Intrum AB; *Int'l*, pg. 3770
INTRUM IRELAND LTD.—See Intrum AB; *Int'l*, pg. 3770
INTRUM JUSTITIA AG—See Intrum AB; *Int'l*, pg. 3770
INTRUM JUSTITIA A/S—See Intrum AB; *Int'l*, pg. 3770
INTRUM JUSTITIA A/S—See Intrum AB; *Int'l*, pg. 3770
INTRUM JUSTITIA AS—See Intrum AB; *Int'l*, pg. 3770
INTRUM JUSTITIA BV—See Intrum AB; *Int'l*, pg. 3770
INTRUM JUSTITIA CENTRAL EUROPE BV—See Intrum AB; *Int'l*, pg. 3770
INTRUM JUSTITIA DATA CENTRE BV—See Intrum AB; *Int'l*, pg. 3770
INTRUM JUSTITIA DEBT FINANCE DOMESTIC AG—See Intrum AB; *Int'l*, pg. 3770
INTRUM JUSTITIA DEBT FINANCE POLAND SP. Z. O. O—See Intrum AB; *Int'l*, pg. 3770
INTRUM JUSTITIA DEBT FUND 1 FUNDUSZ IN-WESTYCYJNY ZAMKNIETY NIESTANDARYZOWANY FUNDUSZ SEKURYTYZACYJNY—See Intrum AB; *Int'l*, pg. 3770
INTRUM JUSTITIA DEBT SURVEILLANCE SP. Z.O.O—See Intrum AB; *Int'l*, pg. 3770
INTRUM JUSTITIA FINANCE SERVICE AG—See Intrum AB; *Int'l*, pg. 3770
INTRUM JUSTITIA FINLAND OY—See Intrum AB; *Int'l*, pg. 3770
INTRUM JUSTITIA GMBH—See Intrum AB; *Int'l*, pg. 3770
INTRUM JUSTITIA GMBH—See Intrum AB; *Int'l*, pg. 3770
INTRUM JUSTITIA HITEL UGYINTEZO SZOLGALTATAS KFT—See Intrum AB; *Int'l*, pg. 3770
INTRUM JUSTITIA HOLDING GMBH—See Intrum AB; *Int'l*, pg. 3770
INTRUM JUSTITIA (HOLDINGS) LTD—See Intrum AB; *Int'l*, pg. 3770
INTRUM JUSTITIA IBERICA S.A.U.—See Intrum AB; *Int'l*, pg. 3770
INTRUM JUSTITIA INKASSO GESELLSCHAFT M. B. H.—See Intrum AB; *Int'l*, pg. 3770
INTRUM JUSTITIA INKASSO GMBH—See Intrum AB; *Int'l*, pg. 3770
INTRUM JUSTITIA INKASSOSYSTEM AB—See Intrum AB; *Int'l*, pg. 3770
INTRUM JUSTITIA IRELAND LTD—See Intrum AB; *Int'l*, pg. 3770
INTRUM JUSTITIA KOVETELESKEZELO ZRT.—See Intrum AB; *Int'l*, pg. 3771
INTRUM JUSTITIA LICENSING AG—See Intrum AB; *Int'l*, pg. 3771
INTRUM JUSTITIA LTD—See Intrum AB; *Int'l*, pg. 3771
INTRUM JUSTITIA NEDERLAND BV—See Intrum AB; *Int'l*, pg. 3771
INTRUM JUSTITIA NORGE AS—See Intrum AB; *Int'l*, pg. 3771
INTRUM JUSTITIA OY—See Intrum AB; *Int'l*, pg. 3771
INTRUM JUSTITIA PORTUGAL UNIPESSOAL LDA.—See Intrum AB; *Int'l*, pg. 3771
INTRUM JUSTITIA SAS—See Intrum AB; *Int'l*, pg. 3771
INTRUM JUSTITIA SIA—See Intrum AB; *Int'l*, pg. 3771
INTRUM JUSTITIA SLOVAKIA S. R. O.—See Intrum AB; *Int'l*, pg. 3771
INTRUM JUSTITIA SPA—See Intrum AB; *Int'l*, pg. 3771
INTRUM JUSTITIA SP.ZO.O.—See Intrum AB; *Int'l*, pg. 3771
INTRUM JUSTITIA S.R.O.—See Intrum AB; *Int'l*, pg. 3771
INTRUM JUSTITIA SVERIGE AB—See Intrum AB; *Int'l*, pg. 3771
INTRUM JUSTITIA SWEDEN HOLDING AB—See Intrum AB; *Int'l*, pg. 3771
INTRUM JUSTITIA TOWARZYSTWO FUNDUSZY IN-WESTYCYJNYCH S.A—See Intrum AB; *Int'l*, pg. 3771
INTRUM LIETUVA UAB—See Intrum AB; *Int'l*, pg. 3771
INTRUM OY—See Intrum AB; *Int'l*, pg. 3771
INTRUM ROMANIA SA—See Intrum AB; *Int'l*, pg. 3771
INTRUM SLOVAKIA S.R.O.—See Intrum AB; *Int'l*, pg. 3771
INTRUM SP. Z O.O.—See Intrum AB; *Int'l*, pg. 3771
INTRUM ZRT.—See Intrum AB; *Int'l*, pg. 3771
INTRUSION INC.; *U.S. Public*, pg. 1159
INTRUST ADVISORS MANAGEMENT CONSULTANCIES LLC—See inTrust Group of Companies; *Int'l*, pg. 3771
INTRUST BANK, N.A.—See Intrust Financial Corporation; *U.S. Private*, pg. 2130

CORPORATE AFFILIATIONS

INTRUST FINANCIAL CORPORATION; *U.S. Private*, pg. 2130
THE INTRUST GROUP, INC.; *U.S. Private*, pg. 4057
INTRUST GROUP OF COMPANIES; *Int'l*, pg. 3771
INTRUST LIMITED—See inTrust Group of Companies; *Int'l*, pg. 3771
INTRUST (MANX) LIMITED—See inTrust Group of Companies; *Int'l*, pg. 3771
INTRUST MIDEAST LIMITED—See inTrust Group of Companies; *Int'l*, pg. 3771
INTSEL STEEL—See Triple-S Steel Holdings Inc.; *U.S. Private*, pg. 4237
INT TECHNOLOGIES LLC—See ManpowerGroup Inc.; *U.S. Public*, pg. 1362
INTTRA, INC.—See Insight Venture Management, LLC; *U.S. Private*, pg. 2090
INTUEOR CONSULTING INC.; *U.S. Private*, pg. 2130
INTUIT CANADA LIMITED—See Intuit Inc.; *U.S. Public*, pg. 1160
INTUIT GREENPOINT—See Intuit Inc.; *U.S. Public*, pg. 1160
INTUIT INC.-CONSUMER TAX GROUP—See Intuit Inc.; *U.S. Public*, pg. 1160
INTUIT INC.-CUSTOMER CONTACT CENTER—See Intuit Inc.; *U.S. Public*, pg. 1160
INTUIT INC.; *U.S. Public*, pg. 1159
INTUITION IT SOLUTIONS; *Int'l*, pg. 3771
INTUITIVE INVESTMENTS GROUP PLC; *Int'l*, pg. 3771
INTUITIVE MACHINES, INC.; *U.S. Public*, pg. 1160
INTUITIVE MACHINES, LLC—See Intuitive Machines, Inc.; *U.S. Public*, pg. 1160
INTUITIVE RESEARCH & TECHNOLOGY CORPORATION; *U.S. Private*, pg. 2130
INTUITIVE SURGICAL DEUTSCHLAND GMBH—See Intuitive Surgical, Inc.; *U.S. Public*, pg. 1160
INTUITIVE SURGICAL GK—See Intuitive Surgical, Inc.; *U.S. Public*, pg. 1160
INTUITIVE SURGICAL HOLDINGS, INC.—See Intuitive Surgical, Inc.; *U.S. Public*, pg. 1160
INTUITIVE SURGICAL, INC.; *U.S. Public*, pg. 1160
INTUITIVE SURGICAL KOREA LIMITED—See Intuitive Surgical, Inc.; *U.S. Public*, pg. 1160
INTUITIVE SURGICAL MEDICAL DEVICE SCIENCE & TECHNOLOGY (SHANGHAI) CO., LTD.—See Intuitive Surgical, Inc.; *U.S. Public*, pg. 1160
INTUITIVE SURGICAL, SARL—See Intuitive Surgical, Inc.; *U.S. Public*, pg. 1160
INTUITIVE TECHNOLOGIES, LLC—See Kainos Group plc; *Int'l*, pg. 4051
INTUITIVE TECHNOLOGY GROUP LLC; *U.S. Private*, pg. 2130
INTUITIVE WEB SOLUTIONS, L.L.C.; *U.S. Private*, pg. 2130
INTUIT LIMITED—See Intuit Inc.; *U.S. Public*, pg. 1160
INTUIT TECHNOLOGY SERVICES PRIVATE LIMITED—See Intuit Inc.; *U.S. Public*, pg. 1160
INTUMESCENT PROTECTIVE COATINGS LIMITED—See Fieldway Group Limited; *Int'l*, pg. 2655
INTUMEX S.R.O.—See Etex SA/NV; *Int'l*, pg. 2522
INTY LTD.—See Giacom (Cloud) Holdings Limited; *Int'l*, pg. 2961
INUI GLOBAL LOGISTICS CO., LTD.; *Int'l*, pg. 3772
INUI TRANSPORT CO., LTD.—See Inui Global Logistics Co., Ltd.; *Int'l*, pg. 3772
INUVA INFO MANAGEMENT INC.—See K.K. Birla Group; *Int'l*, pg. 4044
INUVA INFO MANAGEMENT (PVT) LTD.—See K.K. Birla Group; *Int'l*, pg. 4044
INUVIALUIT DEVELOPMENT CORPORATION—See Inuvialuit Regional Corporation; *Int'l*, pg. 3772
INUVIALUIT INVESTMENT CORPORATION—See Inuvialuit Regional Corporation; *Int'l*, pg. 3772
INUVIALUIT PETROLEUM CORPORATION—See Inuvialuit Regional Corporation; *Int'l*, pg. 3772
INUVIALUIT REGIONAL CORPORATION; *Int'l*, pg. 3772
INUVO, INC.; *U.S. Public*, pg. 1161
INVACARE AG—See Invacare Corporation; *U.S. Private*, pg. 2130
INVACARE A/S—See Invacare Corporation; *U.S. Private*, pg. 2130
INVACARE AUSTRALIA PTY LIMITED—See Invacare Corporation; *U.S. Private*, pg. 2130
INVACARE AUSTRIA GMBH—See Invacare Corporation; *U.S. Private*, pg. 2130
INVACARE B.V.—See Invacare Corporation; *U.S. Private*, pg. 2130
INVACARE CANADA LP—See Invacare Corporation; *U.S. Private*, pg. 2130
INVACARE CANADIAN HOLDINGS, INC.—See Invacare Corporation; *U.S. Private*, pg. 2130
INVACARE CONTINUING CARE, INC.—See Invacare Corporation; *U.S. Private*, pg. 2130
INVACARE CORPORATION; *U.S. Private*, pg. 2130
INVACARE DEUTSCHLAND GMBH—See Invacare Corporation; *U.S. Private*, pg. 2130
INVACARE DOLOMITE AB—See Invacare Corporation; *U.S. Private*, pg. 2130
INVACARE EC-HONG A/S—See Invacare Corporation; *U.S. Private*, pg. 2130

INVACARE FRANCE OPERATIONS SAS—See Invacare Corporation; *U.S. Private*, pg. 2130
INVACARE FRANCE—See Invacare Corporation; *U.S. Private*, pg. 2130
INVACARE GERMANY HOLDING GMBH—See Invacare Corporation; *U.S. Private*, pg. 2130
INVACARE GMBH—See Invacare Corporation; *U.S. Private*, pg. 2130
INVACARE HOLDINGS AS—See Invacare Corporation; *U.S. Private*, pg. 2131
INVACARE HOLDINGS C.V.—See Invacare Corporation; *U.S. Private*, pg. 2131
INVACARE HOLDING TWO AB—See Invacare Corporation; *U.S. Private*, pg. 2131
INVACARE INTERNATIONAL SARL—See Invacare Corporation; *U.S. Private*, pg. 2131
INVACARE IRELAND LTD.—See Invacare Corporation; *U.S. Private*, pg. 2131
INVACARE LDA.—See Invacare Corporation; *U.S. Private*, pg. 2131
INVACARE LTD.—See Invacare Corporation; *U.S. Private*, pg. 2131
INVACARE NV—See Invacare Corporation; *U.S. Private*, pg. 2131
INVACARE OUTCOMES MANAGEMENT LLC—See Invacare Corporation; *U.S. Private*, pg. 2131
INVACARE POIRIER SAS—See Invacare Corporation; *U.S. Private*, pg. 2131
INVACARE (PORTUGAL) II-MATERIAL ORTOPEDICO, LDA.—See Invacare Corporation; *U.S. Private*, pg. 2130
INVACARE REA AB—See Invacare Corporation; *U.S. Private*, pg. 2131
INVACARE, S.A.—See Invacare Corporation; *U.S. Private*, pg. 2131
INVACARE VERWALTUNGS GMBH—See Invacare Corporation; *U.S. Private*, pg. 2131
INVADO SP. Z.O.O.—See Arbonia AG; *Int'l*, pg. 538
INVA ENGINEERING AS—See Instalco AB; *Int'l*, pg. 3721
INVAGEN PHARMACEUTICALS INC.—See Cipla Ltd.; *Int'l*, pg. 1617
INVALANCE LTD.—See Daito Trust Construction Co., Ltd.; *Int'l*, pg. 1944
INVALDA INVL AB; *Int'l*, pg. 3772
INVALIFTS LTD.—See Investment AB Latour; *Int'l*, pg. 3781
INVAR BUILDING CORPORATION; *Int'l*, pg. 3772
INVAR MANUFACTURING, LTD.—See Linamar Corporation; *Int'l*, pg. 4500
INVAST CAPITAL MANAGEMENT CO., LTD.—See INV, Inc.; *Int'l*, pg. 3772
INVAST FINANCIAL SERVICES PTY LTD.—See INVAST SECURITIES CO., LTD.; *Int'l*, pg. 3772
INVAST SECURITIES CO., LTD.; *Int'l*, pg. 3772
INVATEC S.P.A.—See Medtronic plc; *Int'l*, pg. 4788
INVATEC TECHNOLOGY CENTER GMBH—See Medtronic plc; *Int'l*, pg. 4788
INVE AQUACULTURE, INC.—See Benchmark Holdings Plc; *Int'l*, pg. 970
INVE AQUACULTURE MEXICO, S.A. DE C.V.—See Benchmark Holdings Plc; *Int'l*, pg. 970
INVE ASIA SERVICES LTD.—See Benchmark Holdings Plc; *Int'l*, pg. 970
INVECH HOLDINGS, INC.; *U.S. Public*, pg. 1161
INVECTURE GROUP, S.A. DE C.V.; *Int'l*, pg. 3772
INVE DO BRASIL LTDA.—See Benchmark Holdings Plc; *Int'l*, pg. 970
INVE EURASIA SA—See Benchmark Holdings Plc; *Int'l*, pg. 970
INVE HELLAS S.A.—See Benchmark Holdings Plc; *Int'l*, pg. 970
INVEKRA S.A.P.I. DE C.V.; *Int'l*, pg. 3772
INVEL REAL ESTATE ADVISORS LLP; *Int'l*, pg. 3772
INVENCO I2 LLC—See Vontier Corporation; *U.S. Public*, pg. 2309
INVENDA CORPORATION; *U.S. Private*, pg. 2131
INVENFIN (PTY) LIMITED—See Remgro Limited; *Int'l*, pg. 6269
INVENGER TECHNOLOGIES, INC.—See Great Hill Partners, L.P.; *U.S. Private*, pg. 1763
INVENGO INFORMATION TECHNOLOGY CO., LTD.; *Int'l*, pg. 3772
INVENGO TECHNOLOGIES SARL—See Invengo Information Technology Co., Ltd.; *Int'l*, pg. 3772
INVENIA CO., LTD.; *Int'l*, pg. 3772
INVENIO BUSINESS SOLUTIONS DWC LLC—See BGF Group PLC; *Int'l*, pg. 1007
INVENIO BUSINESS SOLUTIONS GMBH—See BGF Group PLC; *Int'l*, pg. 1007
INVENIO BUSINESS SOLUTIONS INC.—See BGF Group PLC; *Int'l*, pg. 1007
INVENIO BUSINESS SOLUTIONS LIMITED—See BGF Group PLC; *Int'l*, pg. 1007
INVENIO BUSINESS SOLUTIONS LTD—See BGF Group PLC; *Int'l*, pg. 1007
INVENIO BUSINESS SOLUTIONS PVT LTD—See BGF Group PLC; *Int'l*, pg. 1007
INVENIOS, INC.; *U.S. Private*, pg. 2131
INVENIO SOLUTIONS; *U.S. Private*, pg. 2131
INVENIO SYSTEMS LIMITED—See Halma plc; *Int'l*, pg. 3232
INVENSAS CORPORATION—See Adeia Inc.; *U.S. Public*, pg. 41
INVENSENSE, INC.—See TDK Corporation; *Int'l*, pg. 7489
INVENSENSE JAPAN G.K.—See TDK Corporation; *Int'l*, pg. 7489
INVENSENSE KOREA LTD.—See TDK Corporation; *Int'l*, pg. 7489
INVENSENSE TAIWAN CO., LTD.—See TDK Corporation; *Int'l*, pg. 7489
INVENSENSE TAIWAN SALES CO., LTD.—See TDK Corporation; *Int'l*, pg. 7489
INVENSURE INSURANCE BROKERS, INC.—See Hellman & Friedman LLC; *U.S. Private*, pg. 1909
INVENSYS CONTROLS UK LIMITED—See Schneider Electric SE; *Int'l*, pg. 6627
INVENSYS EUROTHERM SP.Z O.O.—See Schneider Electric SE; *Int'l*, pg. 6627
INVENSYS LIMITED—See Schneider Electric SE; *Int'l*, pg. 6627
INVENSYS SAM—See Schneider Electric SE; *Int'l*, pg. 6627
INVENSYS SYSTEMS CANADA INC.—See Schneider Electric SE; *Int'l*, pg. 6627
INVENSYS SYSTEMS FRANCE SAS—See Schneider Electric SE; *Int'l*, pg. 6627
INVENSYS SYSTEMS, INC.—See Schneider Electric SE; *Int'l*, pg. 6627
INVENSYS SYSTEMS MEXICO SA—See Schneider Electric SE; *Int'l*, pg. 6627
INVENTABIOTECH INC.; *U.S. Private*, pg. 2131
INVENTA CPM S.R.L.—See Omnicom Group Inc.; *U.S. Public*, pg. 1578
INVENTA TECHNOLOGIES INC.—See ANTs Software Inc.; *U.S. Private*, pg. 289
INVENTCOMMERCE LTD.—See DBAY Advisors Limited; *Int'l*, pg. 1987
INVENTCOMMERCE PROPRIETARY LTD.—See DBAY Advisors Limited; *Int'l*, pg. 1987
INVENTEC APPLIANCES CORPORATION—See Inventec Corporation; *Int'l*, pg. 3773
INVENTEC APPLIANCES (JIANGNING) CORP.—See Inventec Corporation; *Int'l*, pg. 3773
INVENTEC APPLIANCES (NANCHANG) CORPORATION—See Inventec Corporation; *Int'l*, pg. 3773
INVENTEC APPLIANCES (PUDONG) CORPORATION (IACP)—See Inventec Corporation; *Int'l*, pg. 3773
INVENTEC APPLIANCES (SHANGHAI) CO., LTD. (IACS)—See Inventec Corporation; *Int'l*, pg. 3773
INVENTEC APPLIANCES (XI AN) CORPORATION—See Inventec Corporation; *Int'l*, pg. 3773
INVENTEC (BEIJING) ELECTRONICS TECHNOLOGY CO., LTD.—See Inventec Corporation; *Int'l*, pg. 3773
INVENTEC BESTA CO., LTD.; *Int'l*, pg. 3773
INVENTEC (CHONGQING) CORP.—See Inventec Corporation; *Int'l*, pg. 3773
INVENTEC (CHONGQING) SERVICE CO., LTD.—See Inventec Corporation; *Int'l*, pg. 3773
INVENTEC CORPORATION; *Int'l*, pg. 3773
INVENTEC HI-TECH CORP.—See Inventec Corporation; *Int'l*, pg. 3773
INVENTEC HUAN HSIN (ZHEJIANG) TECHNOLOGY CO., LTD.—See Inventec Corporation; *Int'l*, pg. 3773
INVENTEC MULTIMEDIA & TELECOM CORPORATION—See Inventec Corporation; *Int'l*, pg. 3773
INVENTEC MULTIMEDIA & TELECOM (MALAYSIA) CO., LTD.—See Inventec Corporation; *Int'l*, pg. 3773
INVENTEC (PUDONG) CORP.—See Inventec Corporation; *Int'l*, pg. 3773
INVENTEC (PUDONG) TECHNOLOGY CORP.—See Inventec Corporation; *Int'l*, pg. 3773
INVENTEC (SHANGHAI) CORP.—See Inventec Corporation; *Int'l*, pg. 3773
INVENTEC (SHANGHAI) SERVICE CO., LTD.—See Inventec Corporation; *Int'l*, pg. 3773
INVENTEC (TIANJIN) ELECTRONICS CO. LTD.—See Inventec Corporation; *Int'l*, pg. 3773
INVENTERGY GLOBAL, INC.; *U.S. Public*, pg. 1161
INVENTERGY, INC.—See Inventergy Global, Inc.; *U.S. Public*, pg. 1161
INVENTI B.V.—See Nedap N.V.; *Int'l*, pg. 5187
INVENTIO AG—See Schindler Holding AG; *Int'l*, pg. 6619
INVENTIO IT A/S—See Dustin Group AB; *Int'l*, pg. 2235
INVENTION SUBMISSION CORPORATION—See Technosystems Consolidated Corporation; *U.S. Private*, pg. 3956
INVENTIS LIMITED; *Int'l*, pg. 3773
INVENTIS TECHNOLOGY PTY LIMITED—See Inventis Limited; *Int'l*, pg. 3773
INVENTIVA S.A; *Int'l*, pg. 3773
INVENTIVE FOOD TECHNOLOGY (ZQ) LTD.—See International Flavors & Fragrances Inc.; *U.S. Public*, pg. 1153
INVENTIVE POTENTIALS SDN. BHD.—See UNIMECH Group Berhad; *Int'l*, pg. 8049
INVENTIV MEDICAL COMMUNICATIONS, LLC—See Elliott Management Corporation; *U.S. Private*, pg. 1366
INVENTIV MEDICAL COMMUNICATIONS, LLC—See Patient Square Capital, L.P.; *U.S. Private*, pg. 3108
INVENTIV MEDICAL COMMUNICATIONS, LLC—See Veritas Capital Fund Management, LLC; *U.S. Private*, pg. 4365
INVENT MEDIC SWEDEN AB; *Int'l*, pg. 3772
INVENT NOW, INC.; *U.S. Private*, pg. 2131
INVENTOR A.G.S.A.—See Beijer Ref AB; *Int'l*, pg. 944
INVENTOR CONCEPT S.R.L.—See Beijer Ref AB; *Int'l*, pg. 944
THE INVENTORS SHOP LLC—See Sea Box, Inc.; *U.S. Private*, pg. 3582
INVENTORY LIQUIDATORS CORP.; *U.S. Private*, pg. 2131
INVENTORY LOCATOR SERVICE, LLC—See The Boeing Company; *U.S. Public*, pg. 2041
INVENTORY SALES CO., INC.; *U.S. Private*, pg. 2131
INVENTRONICS (HANGZHOU) CO LTD; *Int'l*, pg. 3773
INVENTRONICS LIMITED; *Int'l*, pg. 3773
INVENTRUST PROPERTIES CORP.; *U.S. Public*, pg. 1161
INVENT UMWELT- UND VERFAHRENSTECHNIK AG—See PINOVA Capital GmbH; *Int'l*, pg. 5870
INVENTURE FINANCE PRIVATE LIMITED—See Inventure Growth & Securities Ltd; *Int'l*, pg. 3774
INVENTURE FOODS, INC.—See Utz Brands, Inc.; *U.S. Public*, pg. 2268
INVENTURE GROWTH & SECURITIES LTD; *Int'l*, pg. 3773
INVENTURE INC.—See Zuken, Inc.; *Int'l*, pg. 8694
INVENTURE MERCHANT BANKER SERVICES PRIVATE LIMITED—See Inventure Growth & Securities Ltd; *Int'l*, pg. 3774
INVENTURE RESTAURANTES LTDA.—See Yum! Brands, Inc.; *U.S. Private*, pg. 2400
INVENTURUS KNOWLEDGE SOLUTIONS, INC.—See Rare Enterprises Ltd.; *Int'l*, pg. 6211
INVENTUS, LLC—See HGGC, LLC; *U.S. Private*, pg. 1930
INVENTUS MINING CORP.; *Int'l*, pg. 3774
INVENTUS POWER, INC.—See KRG Capital Management, L.P.; *U.S. Private*, pg. 2351
INVENT VENTURES, INC.; *U.S. Private*, pg. 2131
INVERAHORRO, S.L.—See Banco Bilbao Vizcaya Argentaria, S.A.; *Int'l*, pg. 818
INVERCAP S.A.; *Int'l*, pg. 3774
INVERCARPRO, S.A.—See Industria de Diseno Textil, S.A.; *Int'l*, pg. 3666
INVERCOLOR BOLOGNA SRL—See The Sherwin-Williams Company; *U.S. Public*, pg. 2128
INVERCOLOR TOSCANA SRL—See The Sherwin-Williams Company; *U.S. Public*, pg. 2128
INVER EAST MED S.A.—See The Sherwin-Williams Company; *U.S. Public*, pg. 2129
INVERFIATC S.A.—See FIATC Mutua de Seguros y de Reaseguros APF; *Int'l*, pg. 2651
INVER FRANE SAS—See The Sherwin-Williams Company; *U.S. Public*, pg. 2129
INVER GMBH—See The Sherwin-Williams Company; *U.S. Public*, pg. 2129
INVER HOUSE DISTILLERS LIMITED—See Thai Beverage Public Company Limited; *Int'l*, pg. 7591
INVER HOUSE DISTILLERS (ROI) LTD.—See Thai Beverage Public Company Limited; *Int'l*, pg. 7591
INVER INDUSTRIAL COATINGS SRL—See The Sherwin-Williams Company; *U.S. Public*, pg. 2128
INVERIS TRAINING SOLUTIONS, INC.—See Parker Hannifin Corporation; *U.S. Public*, pg. 1642
INVERITE INSIGHTS INC.; *Int'l*, pg. 3774
INVERITE VERIFICATION INC.—See Inverite Insights Inc.; *Int'l*, pg. 3774
INVERLOCH & DISTRICT FINANCIAL ENTERPRISES LIMITED—See Bendigo & Adelaide Bank Ltd.; *Int'l*, pg. 971
INVERNESS CORPORATION—See Berkshire Hathaway Inc.; *U.S. Public*, pg. 316
INVERNESS GRAHAM INVESTMENTS, INC.—See The Graham Group, Inc.; *U.S. Private*, pg. 4037
INVERNESS MANAGEMENT, LLC; *U.S. Private*, pg. 2131
INVERNESS UK—See Berkshire Hathaway Inc.; *U.S. Public*, pg. 316
INVERNOVA SA; *Int'l*, pg. 3774
INVER POLSKA SPOLKA Z O.O.—See The Sherwin-Williams Company; *U.S. Public*, pg. 2128
INVER POLSKA SP.Z.O.O.—See The Sherwin-Williams Company; *U.S. Public*, pg. 2129
INVER PORT SERVICES PTY. LTD.—See Cargotec Corporation; *Int'l*, pg. 1328
INVERSE GROUP PTY. LTD.—See Hiremii Limited; *Int'l*, pg. 3404
INVERSENET CO LTD—See Yamada Holdings Co., Ltd.; *Int'l*, pg. 8548
INVERSE—See Omnicom Group Inc.; *U.S. Public*, pg. 1594
INVERSIONES AEREAS S.L.; *Int'l*, pg. 3774
INVERSIONES AGRICOLAS Y COMERCIALES SA; *Int'l*, pg. 3774

INVERSIONES AGUAS METROPOLITANAS S.A.—See Veolia Environnement S.A.; *Int'l*, pg. 8155
INVERSIONES ASTRAU SL; *Int'l*, pg. 3774
INVERSIONES BORNEO S.R.L.—See PepsiCo, Inc.; *U.S. Public*, pg. 1669
INVERSIONES BRECA SA; *Int'l*, pg. 3774
INVERSIONES CENTENARIO SA; *Int'l*, pg. 3774
INVERSIONES COLQUIJIRCA S.A.—See Compania de Minas Buenaventura SAA; *Int'l*, pg. 1748
INVERSIONES CONCHA Y TORO S.A.—See Vina Concha y Toro S.A.; *Int'l*, pg. 8209
INVERSIONES COVADONGA SA; *Int'l*, pg. 3774
INVERSIONES CRECE PYMES CA; *Int'l*, pg. 3774
INVERSIONES DEL SUR S.A.—See SMU S.A.; *Int'l*, pg. 7017
INVERSIONES DOPPELMAYR DE VENEZUELA C.A.—See Doppelmayr Group; *Int'l*, pg. 2175
INVERSIONES EN CONCESIONES FERROVIARIAS, S.A.—See Construcciones y Auxiliar de Ferrocarriles S.A.; *Int'l*, pg. 1777
INVERSIONES EQUIFAX DE CHILE LTDA.—See Equifax Inc.; *U.S. Public*, pg. 786
INVERSIONES EQUIPOS Y SERVICIOS SA; *Int'l*, pg. 3774
INVERSIONES HILTI DE VENEZUELA S.A.—See Hilti AG; *Int'l*, pg. 3395
INVERSIONES INIMA, S.A.—See GS Holdings Corp.; *Int'l*, pg. 3142
INVERSIONES K+S SAL DE CHILE LTDA.—See K+S Aktiengesellschaft; *Int'l*, pg. 4040
INVERSIONES LA CONSTRUCCION SA; *Int'l*, pg. 3774
INVERSIONES LA RIOJA S.A.—See Inversiones Breca SA; *Int'l*, pg. 3774
INVERSIONES MEXIMEX, S.A. DE C.V.—See Cydsa S.A.B. de C.V.; *Int'l*, pg. 1895
INVERSIONES NACIONALES DE TURISMO SA—See Inversiones Breca SA; *Int'l*, pg. 3774
INVERSIONES NELTUME LTDA.—See Ultramar Ltda.; *Int'l*, pg. 8018
INVERSIONES NUTRAVALOR SA; *Int'l*, pg. 3774
INVERSIONES PACUCHA S.A.—See SMU S.A.; *Int'l*, pg. 7017
INVERSIONES PCS CHILE S.A.—See GraceKennedy Limited; *Int'l*, pg. 3049
INVERSIONES PRYCA, S.A.—See Carrefour SA; *Int'l*, pg. 1345
INVERSIONES QUIMICAS S.A.—See BRENNTAG SE; *Int'l*, pg. 1149
INVERSIONES SCHNEIDER ELECTRIC UNO LIMITADA—See Schneider Electric SE; *Int'l*, pg. 6628
INVERSIONES SIEMEL SA; *Int'l*, pg. 3774
INVERSIONES SONOCO DO CHILE DO LTDA.—See Sonoco Products Company; *U.S. Public*, pg. 1905
INVERSIONES TRICAHUE S.A.; *Int'l*, pg. 3774
INVERSIONES UNESPA S.A.; *Int'l*, pg. 3774
INVERSIONES UNION ESPANOLA S.A.; *Int'l*, pg. 3774
INVERSIONES VENECIA SA; *Int'l*, pg. 3774
INVERSIONES Y RENTAS S.A.—See L'Arche Green N.V.; *Int'l*, pg. 4377
INVERSIONES Y RENTAS S.A.—See Quinenco S.A.; *Int'l*, pg. 6164
INVERSORA BURSATIL S.A. DE C.V.—See Grupo Financiero Inbursa, S.A. de C.V.; *Int'l*, pg. 3129
INVERSORA DE AUTOPISTAS DEL SUR, S.L.—See Sacyr, S.A.; *Int'l*, pg. 6465
INVERSORA LOCKEY DE VENEZUELA CA—See Ingersoll Rand Inc.; *U.S. Public*, pg. 1121
INVERSORA LOCKEY LTDA.—See Ingersoll Rand Inc.; *U.S. Public*, pg. 1121
INVERSORES Y GESTORES ASOCIADOS, S.A.—See Minor International PCL; *Int'l*, pg. 4911
INVER S.P.A.—See The Sherwin-Williams Company; *U.S. Public*, pg. 2129
INVERTEC FOODS S.A.; *Int'l*, pg. 3774
INVERTEK DRIVES LTD.—See Sumitomo Heavy Industries, Ltd.; *Int'l*, pg. 7286
INVERTIX COMMUNICATIONS MISSION SYSTEM OPERATIONS—See Altamira Technologies Corporation; *U.S. Private*, pg. 204
INVESCO ADMINISTRATION SERVICES LIMITED—See Invesco Ltd.; *U.S. Public*, pg. 1161
INVESCO ADVANTAGE MUNICIPAL INCOME TRUST II; *U.S. Public*, pg. 1161
INVESCO ADVISERS, INC.—See Invesco Ltd.; *U.S. Public*, pg. 1161
INVESCO ASIA TRUST PLC—See Invesco Ltd.; *U.S. Public*, pg. 1164
INVESCO ASSET MANAGEMENT ASIA LIMITED—See Invesco Ltd.; *U.S. Public*, pg. 1162
INVESCO ASSET MANAGEMENT DEUTSCHLAND GMBH—See Invesco Ltd.; *U.S. Public*, pg. 1163
INVESCO ASSET MANAGEMENT GMBH—See Invesco Ltd.; *U.S. Public*, pg. 1163
INVESCO ASSET MANAGEMENT (INDIA) PVT. LTD.—See Invesco Ltd.; *U.S. Public*, pg. 1162
INVESCO ASSET MANAGEMENT (JAPAN) LTD.—See Invesco Ltd.; *U.S. Public*, pg. 1161
INVESCO ASSET MANAGEMENT LIMITED—See Invesco Ltd.; *U.S. Public*, pg. 1162

INVESCO ASSET MANAGEMENT LTD.—See Invesco Ltd.; *U.S. Public*, pg. 1163
INVESCO ASSET MANAGEMENT OSTERREICH GMBH—See Invesco Ltd.; *U.S. Public*, pg. 1162
INVESCO ASSET MANAGEMENT S.A.—See Invesco Ltd.; *U.S. Public*, pg. 1162
INVESCO ASSET MANAGEMENT S.A.—See Invesco Ltd.; *U.S. Public*, pg. 1162
INVESCO ASSET MANAGEMENT S.A.—See Invesco Ltd.; *U.S. Public*, pg. 1162
INVESCO ASSET MANAGEMENT (SCHWEIZ) AG—See Invesco Ltd.; *U.S. Public*, pg. 1161
INVESCO ASSET MANAGEMENT SINGAPORE LTD.—See Invesco Ltd.; *U.S. Public*, pg. 1162
INVESCO ASSET MANAGEMENT (SWITZERLAND) LTD.—See Invesco Ltd.; *U.S. Public*, pg. 1162
INVESCO AUSTRALIA LTD—See Invesco Ltd.; *U.S. Public*, pg. 1162
INVESCO BOND FUND; *U.S. Public*, pg. 1161
INVESCO BOND INCOME PLUS LIMITED—See Invesco Ltd.; *U.S. Public*, pg. 1163
INVESCO CALIFORNIA VALUE MUNICIPAL INCOME TRUST; *U.S. Public*, pg. 1161
INVESCO CANADA LTD.—See Invesco Ltd.; *U.S. Public*, pg. 1162
INVESCO CAPITAL MARKETS, INC.—See Invesco Ltd.; *U.S. Public*, pg. 1162
INVESCO CONTINENTAL EUROPE SERVICES S.A.—See Invesco Ltd.; *U.S. Public*, pg. 1162
INVESCO CURRENCYSHARES AUSTRALIAN DOLLAR TRUST—See Invesco Ltd.; *U.S. Public*, pg. 1162
INVESCO CURRENCYSHARES BRITISH POUND STERLING TRUST—See Invesco Ltd.; *U.S. Public*, pg. 1162
INVESCO CURRENCYSHARES CANADIAN DOLLAR TRUST—See Invesco Ltd.; *U.S. Public*, pg. 1162
INVESCO CURRENCYSHARES EURO TRUST—See Invesco Ltd.; *U.S. Public*, pg. 1162
INVESCO CURRENCYSHARES JAPANESE YEN TRUST—See Invesco Ltd.; *U.S. Public*, pg. 1162
INVESCO CURRENCYSHARES SWISS FRANC TRUST—See Invesco Ltd.; *U.S. Public*, pg. 1162
INVESCO DUBLIN—See Invesco Ltd.; *U.S. Public*, pg. 1162
INVESCO DYNAMIC CREDIT OPPORTUNITIES FUND; *U.S. Public*, pg. 1161
INVESCO FAR EAST LIMITED—See Invesco Ltd.; *U.S. Public*, pg. 1162
INVESCO FUND MANAGERS LIMITED—See Invesco Ltd.; *U.S. Public*, pg. 1163
INVESCO GESTION S.A.—See Invesco Ltd.; *U.S. Public*, pg. 1162
INVESCO GLOBAL ADVISORS, INC.—See Invesco Ltd.; *U.S. Public*, pg. 1163
INVESCO GLOBAL ASSET MANAGEMENT LIMITED—See Invesco Ltd.; *U.S. Public*, pg. 1161
INVESCO GLOBAL REAL ESTATE ASIA PACIFIC INC.M—See Invesco Ltd.; *U.S. Public*, pg. 1162
INVESCO GREAT WALL FUND MANAGEMENT COMPANY LIMITED—See Invesco Ltd.; *U.S. Public*, pg. 1162
INVESCO HIGH INCOME 2023 TARGET TERM FUND; *U.S. Public*, pg. 1161
INVESCO HIGH INCOME 2024 TARGET TERM FUND; *U.S. Public*, pg. 1161
INVESCO HIGH INCOME TRUST II; *U.S. Public*, pg. 1161
INVESCO HONG KONG LIMITED—See Invesco Ltd.; *U.S. Public*, pg. 1162
INVESCO (HYDERABAD) PRIVATE LIMITED—See Invesco Ltd.; *U.S. Public*, pg. 1161
INVESCO INSTITUTIONAL (N.A.) INC.—See Invesco Ltd.; *U.S. Public*, pg. 1162
INVESCO INSTITUTIONAL—See Invesco Ltd.; *U.S. Public*, pg. 1162
INVESCO INSTITUTIONAL—See Invesco Ltd.; *U.S. Public*, pg. 1162
INVESCO INTERNATIONAL LTD.—See Invesco Ltd.; *U.S. Public*, pg. 1162
INVESCO INVESTMENT ADVISERS LLC—See Invesco Ltd.; *U.S. Public*, pg. 1162
INVESCO INVESTMENT MANAGEMENT (SHANGHAI) LIMITED—See Invesco Ltd.; *U.S. Public*, pg. 1162
INVESCO INVESTMENT SERVICES, INC.—See Invesco Ltd.; *U.S. Public*, pg. 1162
INVESCO INVESTMENT SERVICES, INC.—See Invesco Ltd.; *U.S. Public*, pg. 1162
INVESCO IP HOLDINGS (CANADA) LTD.—See Invesco Ltd.; *U.S. Public*, pg. 1162
INVESCO LTD.; *U.S. Public*, pg. 1161
INVESCO MANAGED ACCOUNTS, LLC—See Invesco Ltd.; *U.S. Public*, pg. 1163
INVESCO MORTGAGE CAPITAL, INC.—See Invesco Ltd.; *U.S. Public*, pg. 1163
INVESCO MUNICIPAL OPPORTUNITY TRUST; *U.S. Public*, pg. 1164
INVESCO MUNICIPAL TRUST; *U.S. Public*, pg. 1164
INVESCO MUNI INCOME OPPS TRUST; *U.S. Public*, pg. 1164
INVESCO NORTH AMERICAN HOLDINGS, INC.—See Invesco Ltd.; *U.S. Public*, pg. 1163

INVESCO NORTH AMERICA—See Invesco Ltd.; *U.S. Public*, pg. 1163
INVESCO (NY) INC.—See Invesco Ltd.; *U.S. Public*, pg. 1161
INVESCO OFFICE J-REIT, INC.; *Int'l*, pg. 3775
INVESCO PENNSYLVANIA VALUE MUNICIPAL INCOME TRUST; *U.S. Public*, pg. 1164
INVESCO PENSIONS LIMITED—See Invesco Ltd.; *U.S. Public*, pg. 1163
INVESCO PERPETUAL (NOMINEES) LIMITED—See Invesco Ltd.; *U.S. Public*, pg. 1163
INVESCO POWERSHARES CAPITAL MANAGEMENT LLC—See Invesco Ltd.; *U.S. Public*, pg. 1163
INVESCO PUERTO RICO—See Invesco Ltd.; *U.S. Public*, pg. 1163
INVESCO QUALITY MUNICIPAL INCOME TRUST; *U.S. Public*, pg. 1164
INVESCO REAL ESTATE ADVISORS (SHANGHAI) LIMITED—See Invesco Ltd.; *U.S. Public*, pg. 1163
INVESCO REAL ESTATE GMBH—See Invesco Ltd.; *U.S. Public*, pg. 1163
INVESCO REAL ESTATE KOREA—See Invesco Ltd.; *U.S. Public*, pg. 1163
INVESCO REAL ESTATE LTD.—See Invesco Ltd.; *U.S. Public*, pg. 1163
INVESCO REAL ESTATE MANAGEMENT S.A.R.L.—See Invesco Ltd.; *U.S. Public*, pg. 1163
INVESCO REAL ESTATE—See Invesco Ltd.; *U.S. Public*, pg. 1163
INVESCO REAL ESTATE S.R.O.—See Invesco Ltd.; *U.S. Public*, pg. 1161
INVESCO RUIHE (SHANGHAI) PRIVATE EQUITY INVESTMENT MANAGEMENT COMPANY LIMITED—See Invesco Ltd.; *U.S. Public*, pg. 1163
INVESCO SELECT TRUST PLC—See Invesco Ltd.; *U.S. Public*, pg. 1163
INVESCO SENIOR INCOME TRUST; *U.S. Public*, pg. 1164
INVESCO TAIWAN LTD.—See Invesco Ltd.; *U.S. Public*, pg. 1163
INVESCO TRIMARK LTD.—See Invesco Ltd.; *U.S. Public*, pg. 1163
INVESCO TRUSTEE PVT. LTD.—See Invesco Ltd.; *U.S. Public*, pg. 1162
INVESCO TRUST FOR INVESTMENT GRADE MUNICIPALS; *U.S. Public*, pg. 1164
INVESCO TRUST FOR INVESTMENT GRADE NEW YORK MUNICIPALS; *U.S. Public*, pg. 1164
INVESCO UK LTD.—See Invesco Ltd.; *U.S. Public*, pg. 1163
INVESCO VALUE MUNICIPAL INCOME TRUST; *U.S. Public*, pg. 1164
INVESCO VERWALTUNGSGESELLSCHAFT MBH—See Invesco Ltd.; *U.S. Public*, pg. 1163
INVESHARE INC.; *U.S. Private*, pg. 2131
INVESQUE INC.; *U.S. Public*, pg. 1164
INVESTACORP ADVISORY SERVICES INC.—See Reverence Capital Partners LLC; *U.S. Private*, pg. 3414
INVESTACORP, INC.—See Reverence Capital Partners LLC; *U.S. Private*, pg. 3414
INVESTACOR - SOCIEDADE GESTORA DE PARTICIPACOES SOCIAIS, S A—See Banco Santander, S.A.; *Int'l*, pg. 825
INVESTANCE CONSULTING; *Int'l*, pg. 3775
INVESTA PROPERTY GROUP; *Int'l*, pg. 3775
INVESTAR BANK, N.A.—See Investar Holding Corporation; *U.S. Public*, pg. 1164
INVESTAR HOLDING CORPORATION; *U.S. Public*, pg. 1164
INVESTAR HOLDINGS INC.; *U.S. Private*, pg. 2131
INVESTBANK AD—See Festa Holding Plc; *Int'l*, pg. 2646
INVEST BANK P.S.C.; *Int'l*, pg. 3775
INVEST BANK; *Int'l*, pg. 3775
INVEST CAPITAL INVESTMENT BANK LIMITED; *Int'l*, pg. 3775
INVESTCORP CREDIT MANAGEMENT BDC, INC.; *U.S. Public*, pg. 1165
INVESTCORP CREDIT MANAGEMENT EU LTD.—See Investcorp Holdings B.S.C.; *Int'l*, pg. 3775
INVESTCORP EUROPE ACQUISITION CORP I—See Investcorp Holdings B.S.C.; *Int'l*, pg. 3775
INVESTCORP HOLDINGS B.S.C.; *Int'l*, pg. 3775
INVESTCORP INDIA ACQUISITION CORP.; *Int'l*, pg. 3777
INVESTCORP INTERNATIONAL, INC.—See Investcorp Holdings B.S.C.; *Int'l*, pg. 3776
INVESTCORP INTERNATIONAL LTD.—See Investcorp Holdings B.S.C.; *Int'l*, pg. 3775
INVESTCORP TECHNOLOGY VENTURES, L.P.—See Investcorp Holdings B.S.C.; *Int'l*, pg. 3776
INVEST-DEVELOPMENT PJSC; *Int'l*, pg. 3775
INVESTEC ASSET FINANCE PLC—See Investec Limited; *Int'l*, pg. 3777
INVESTEC ASSET MANAGEMENT ASIA LTD—See Ninety One Plc; *Int'l*, pg. 5300
INVESTEC ASSET MANAGEMENT AUSTRALIA PTY LTD—See Ninety One Plc; *Int'l*, pg. 5300
INVESTEC ASSET MANAGEMENT GUERNSEY LIMITED—See Ninety One Plc; *Int'l*, pg. 5300

INVESTEC ASSET MANAGEMENT NAMIBIA (PTY) LTD—See Ninety One Plc; *Int'l*, pg. 5300
INVESTEC ASSET MANAGEMENT (PTY) LTD—See Investec Limited; *Int'l*, pg. 3777
INVESTEC ASSET MANAGEMENT TAIWAN LIMITED—See Investec Limited; *Int'l*, pg. 3777
INVESTEC ASSET MANAGEMENT US LIMITED—See Investec Limited; *Int'l*, pg. 3777
INVESTEC AUSTRALIA PROPERTY FUND; *Int'l*, pg. 3777
INVESTEC BANK (CHANNEL ISLANDS) LIMITED—See Investec Limited; *Int'l*, pg. 3777
INVESTEC BANK (MAURITIUS) LIMITED—See Investec Limited; *Int'l*, pg. 3777
INVESTEC BANK (SWITZERLAND) AG—See Investec Limited; *Int'l*, pg. 3777
INVESTEC CAPITAL ASIA LIMITED—See Investec Limited; *Int'l*, pg. 3777
INVESTEC EXPERIEN PTY LIMITED—See Investec Limited; *Int'l*, pg. 3777
INVESTEC FUND MANAGERS LIMITED—See Investec Limited; *Int'l*, pg. 3777
INVESTEC FUND MANAGERS SA LTD—See Investec Limited; *Int'l*, pg. 3777
INVESTEC GROUP INVESTMENTS (UK) LIMITED—See Investec Limited; *Int'l*, pg. 3778
INVESTEC GROUP (UK) PLC—See Investec Limited; *Int'l*, pg. 3777
INVESTECH HOLDINGS LIMITED; *Int'l*, pg. 3778
INVESTEC HOLDING COMPANY LIMITED—See Investec Limited; *Int'l*, pg. 3778
INVESTEC IRELAND LIMITED—See Investec Limited; *Int'l*, pg. 3778
INVESTEC LIMITED; *Int'l*, pg. 3777
INVESTEC PLC—See Investec Limited; *Int'l*, pg. 3777
INVESTEC PRIVATE TRUST LIMITED—See Investec Limited; *Int'l*, pg. 3777
INVESTEC PROPERTY GROUP HOLDINGS LTD—See Investec Limited; *Int'l*, pg. 3777
INVESTEC SECURITIES LTD—See Investec Limited; *Int'l*, pg. 3778
INVESTEC SECURITIES (US) LLC—See Investec Limited; *Int'l*, pg. 3778
INVESTEC TRUST (JERSEY) LIMITED—See Investec Limited; *Int'l*, pg. 3778
INVESTEC TRUST (MAURITIUS) LIMITED—See Investec Limited; *Int'l*, pg. 3777
INVESTEC TRUST (SWITZERLAND) S.A.—See Investec Limited; *Int'l*, pg. 3778
INVESTEC WEALTH & INVESTMENT LIMITED—See Rathbones Group Plc; *Int'l*, pg. 6214
INVESTEDGE, INC.—See Featheringill Capital, LLC; *U.S. Private*, pg. 1486
INVESTEKO SA; *Int'l*, pg. 3778
INVESTERINGSSELSKABET LUXOR A/S; *Int'l*, pg. 3778
INVESTIA FINANCIAL SERVICES INC.—See iA Financial Corporation Inc.; *Int'l*, pg. 3567
INVESTICNI KAPITALOVA SPOLECNOST—See Societe Generale S.A.; *Int'l*, pg. 7040
INVESTIGACION Y DESARROLLO DE EQUIPOS AVANZADOS, S.A.U.—See Iberdrola, S.A.; *Int'l*, pg. 3573
INVESTIGATOR RESOURCES LIMITED; *Int'l*, pg. 3778
INVESTIGO GUILDFORD—See Investigo Ltd; *Int'l*, pg. 3778
INVESTIGO LTD; *Int'l*, pg. 3778
INVESTIGO MILTON KEYNES—See Investigo Ltd; *Int'l*, pg. 3778
INVESTIGO READING—See Investigo Ltd; *Int'l*, pg. 3779
INVESTIGO ST ALBANS—See Investigo Ltd; *Int'l*, pg. 3779
INVESTIM CHILE S.A.—See Pentair plc; *Int'l*, pg. 5789
INVESTIMENTOS BEMGE S.A.—See Itau Unibanco Holding S.A.; *Int'l*, pg. 3830
INVESTIMENTOS E PARTICIPACOES EM INFRAESTRUTURA S.A.; *Int'l*, pg. 3779
INVESTIMENTOS E PARTICIPACOES & INFRAESTRUTURA SA- INVEPAR; *Int'l*, pg. 3779
INVEST-IMPORT A.D.; *Int'l*, pg. 3775
INVESTINDUSTRIAL ACQUISITION CORP.; *Int'l*, pg. 3779
INVESTINDUSTRIAL ADVISORS LTD.; *Int'l*, pg. 3779
INVESTINDUSTRIAL S.A.—See BI-Invest Advisors S.A.; *Int'l*, pg. 1016
INVESTING DAILY—See Capitol Information Group, Inc.; *U.S. Private*, pg. 744
INVESTING PROFIT WISELY, SL; *Int'l*, pg. 3780
INVESTIRE IMMOBILIARE SGR S.P.A.—See Banca Finnat Euramerica S.p.A.; *Int'l*, pg. 814
INVESTIRE SGR S.P.A.—See Banca Finnat Euramerica S.p.A.; *Int'l*, pg. 814
INVESTIS HOLDING SA; *Int'l*, pg. 3780
INVESTIS LIMITED; *Int'l*, pg. 3780
INVESTIS SA—See PHM Group Holding Oyj; *Int'l*, pg. 5848
INVESTISSEMENT QUEBEC; *Int'l*, pg. 3780
INVESTITORI ASSOCIATI SOCIETA DI GESTIONE DEL RISPARMIO (SGR) S.P.A.; *Int'l*, pg. 3780
INVESTITORI SGR S.P.A.—See Allianz SE; *Int'l*, pg. 350
INVESTKREDIT BANK AG—See Osterreichische Volksbanken AG; *Int'l*, pg. 5654

INVESTMENT AB LATOUR; *Int'l*, pg. 3780
INVESTMENT AB ORESUND; *Int'l*, pg. 3784
INVESTMENT & ALLIED ASSURANCE PLC; *Int'l*, pg. 3780
INVESTMENT AND DEVELOPMENT BREED PROCESSING COMPANY LIMITED—See DABACO Group Joint Stock Company; *Int'l*, pg. 1902
INVESTMENT BANK OF IRAQ - INTERNATIONAL DIVISION—See Investment Bank of Iraq; *Int'l*, pg. 3784
INVESTMENT BANK OF IRAQ; *Int'l*, pg. 3784
INVESTMENT COMMERCE FISHERIES CORPORATION; *Int'l*, pg. 3784
INVESTMENT COMPANY GRANDIS CAPITAL LLC; *Int'l*, pg. 3784
THE INVESTMENT COMPANY PLC; *Int'l*, pg. 7656
INVESTMENT & CONSTRUCTION JSC NO.18; *Int'l*, pg. 3780
INVESTMENT CORPORATION OF DUBAI; *Int'l*, pg. 3784
INVESTMENT COUNSELORS OF MARYLAND, LLC—See William Blair Investment Management LLC; *U.S. Private*, pg. 4522
INVESTMENT DAR COMPANY K.S.C.C.—See Efad Real Estate Company; *Int'l*, pg. 2318
INVESTMENT & DEVELOPMENT AGENCY-IRELAND; *Int'l*, pg. 3780
INVESTMENT DEVELOPMENT GROUP LLC (IDG)—See OJSC Rosneftegaz; *Int'l*, pg. 5541
INVESTMENT ENTERPRISES INC.; *U.S. Private*, pg. 2132
INVESTMENT FRIENDS CAPITAL S.A.; *Int'l*, pg. 3785
INVESTMENT FRIENDS SE; *Int'l*, pg. 3785
INVESTMENT FUND OF KAZAKHSTAN JOINT STOCK COMPANY—See National Managing Holding Baiterek JSC; *Int'l*, pg. 5161
INVESTMENT FUNDS DIRECT LIMITED—See M&G Plc; *Int'l*, pg. 4612
INVESTMENT HOLDING GROUP QPSC; *Int'l*, pg. 3785
INVESTMENT INTERNATIONAL, D.O.O.E.L—See Fortenova Group d.d.; *Int'l*, pg. 2738
INVESTMENT MANAGEMENT CORPORATION OF ONTARIO; *Int'l*, pg. 3785
INVESTMENT MANAGEMENT OF VIRGINIA, LLC—See Pinnacle Associates, Ltd.; *U.S. Private*, pg. 3184
INVESTMENT METRICS LLC—See Resurgens Technology Partners, LLC; *U.S. Private*, pg. 3411
INVESTMENTNEWS LLC—See Bonhill Group PLC; *Int'l*, pg. 1107
INVESTMENT ONE FINANCIAL SERVICES LIMITED; *Int'l*, pg. 3785
INVESTMENT ONE FUNDS MANAGEMENT LIMITED—See Investment One Financial Services Limited; *Int'l*, pg. 3785
INVESTMENT ONE PENSION MANAGERS LIMITED—See Investment One Financial Services Limited; *Int'l*, pg. 3785
INVESTMENT ONE STOCKBROKERS INT'L LIMITED—See Investment One Financial Services Limited; *Int'l*, pg. 3785
INVESTMENT PARTNERS ASSET MANAGEMENT, INC.—See Investment Partners Group, Inc.; *U.S. Private*, pg. 2132
INVESTMENT PARTNERS GROUP, INC.; *U.S. Private*, pg. 2132
INVESTMENT PLANNING COUNSEL INC.—See Power Corporation of Canada; *Int'l*, pg. 5943
INVESTMENT & PRECISION CASTINGS LTD.; *Int'l*, pg. 3780
INVESTMENT PROFESSIONALS, INC.—See Ameriprise Financial, Inc.; *U.S. Public*, pg. 114
INVESTMENT PROPERTIES AND MANAGEMENT—See Tutera Group Inc.; *U.S. Private*, pg. 4262
INVESTMENT PROPERTIES CORPORATION; *U.S. Private*, pg. 2132
INVESTMENT PROPERTY DATABANK LIMITED—See MSCI Inc.; *U.S. Public*, pg. 1483
INVESTMENT RARITIES INCORPORATED; *U.S. Private*, pg. 2132
INVESTMENT RESEARCH GROUP LIMITED; *Int'l*, pg. 3785
INVESTMENTS AFRICA ISRAEL S.R.O—See Africa Israel Investments Ltd.; *Int'l*, pg. 190
INVESTMENT SECURITY GROUP INC.—See HighTower Holding LLC; *U.S. Private*, pg. 1941
INVESTMENT SEMINARS, INC.; *U.S. Private*, pg. 2132
INVESTMENT TOOLING INTERNATIONAL LIMITED—See Valmont Industries, Inc.; *U.S. Public*, pg. 2273
INVESTMENT & TRADING OF REAL ESTATE JSC; *Int'l*, pg. 3780
INVESTMENT TRUST COMPANY; *U.S. Private*, pg. 2132
THE INVESTMENT TRUST OF INDIA LIMITED; *Int'l*, pg. 7656
INVESTNET ITALIA SRL—See Intesa Sanpaolo S.p.A.; *Int'l*, pg. 3766
INVEST NEXUS LIMITED; *Int'l*, pg. 3775
INVEST NIKAROM SRL; *Int'l*, pg. 3775
INVESTOPEDIA, LLC—See IAC Inc.; *U.S. Public*, pg. 1082
INVESTOPEDIA LLC—See IAC Inc.; *U.S. Public*, pg. 1082
INVESTOR AB; *Int'l*, pg. 3785

INVESTOR.BG AD; *Int'l*, pg. 3787
INVESTORCOM INC.; *U.S. Private*, pg. 2132
INVESTOR FINANCIAL SOLUTIONS, LLC—See Lee Equity Partners LLC; *U.S. Private*, pg. 2412
INVESTOR FORCE HOLDINGS, INC.—See Resurgens Technology Partners, LLC; *U.S. Private*, pg. 3411
INVESTOR FORCE, INC.—See Resurgens Technology Partners, LLC; *U.S. Private*, pg. 3411
THE INVESTOR FOR SECURITIES COMPANY S.S.C—See The International Investor Company K.S.C.C.; *Int'l*, pg. 7656
INVESTOR GROWTH CAPITAL AB—See Investor AB; *Int'l*, pg. 3785
INVESTOR GROWTH CAPITAL HOLDING BV—See Investor AB; *Int'l*, pg. 3785
INVESTOR GROWTH CAPITAL, INC—See Investor AB; *Int'l*, pg. 3786
INVESTOR MANAGEMENT SERVICES, LLC—See Thoma Bravo, L.P.; *U.S. Private*, pg. 4152
INVESTORPLACE MEDIA, LLC—See Avista Capital Partners, L.P.; *U.S. Private*, pg. 408
INVESTORS BANCORP, INC.—See Citizens Financial Group, Inc.; *U.S. Public*, pg. 505
INVESTORS BANK—See Citizens Financial Group, Inc.; *U.S. Public*, pg. 505
INVESTORS BROKERAGE SERVICES INC.—See Zurich Insurance Group Limited; *Int'l*, pg. 8698
INVESTORS CAPITAL CORPORATION—See RCAP Holdings, LLC; *U.S. Private*, pg. 3361
INVESTORS CAPITAL HOLDINGS, LTD.—See RCAP Holdings, LLC; *U.S. Private*, pg. 3361
INVESTORS CAPITAL MANAGEMENT COMPANY—See Investors Title Company; *U.S. Public*, pg. 1165
INVESTORS COMMUNITY BANK—See Nicolet Bankshares, Inc.; *U.S. Public*, pg. 1528
INVESTORS CONSOLIDATED INSURANCE COMPANY—See The Manhattan Insurance Group; *U.S. Private*, pg. 4074
INVESTORS CORPORATION OF VERMONT; *U.S. Private*, pg. 2132
THE INVESTORS & EASTERN ARAB FOR INDUSTRIAL & REAL ESTATE INVESTMENTS LTD.; *Int'l*, pg. 7656
INVESTORS' EXCHANGE LLC—See IEX Group, Inc.; *U.S. Private*, pg. 2038
INVESTORS FINANCIAL GROUP, INC.—See Citizens Financial Group, Inc.; *U.S. Public*, pg. 505
INVESTORS FINANCIAL SERVICES, INC.—See Citizens Financial Group, Inc.; *U.S. Public*, pg. 505
INVESTORS GROUP, INC.—See Power Corporation of Canada; *Int'l*, pg. 5944
INVESTORS HERITAGE CAPITAL CORP.; *U.S. Private*, pg. 2132
INVESTORS HERITAGE LIFE INSURANCE COMPANY—See Investors Heritage Capital Corp.; *U.S. Private*, pg. 2132
INVESTORS HOLDING GROUP CO. (K.P.S.C.); *Int'l*, pg. 3787
INVESTORS HOUSE OYJ; *Int'l*, pg. 3787
INVESTORSHUB.COM INC.—See ADVFN PLC; *Int'l*, pg. 168
INVESTORS IN PEOPLE (SCOTLAND) LIMITED—See Scottish Enterprise; *Int'l*, pg. 6652
INVESTORS LIFE INSURANCE COMPANY OF NORTH AMERICA—See Financial Holding Corp.; *U.S. Private*, pg. 1507
INVESTORS MANAGEMENT CORPORATION; *U.S. Private*, pg. 2132
INVESTORS MANAGEMENT TRUST REAL ESTATE GROUP INC.; *U.S. Private*, pg. 2132
INVESTORS MUTUAL LIMITED—See Groupe BPCE; *Int'l*, pg. 3098
INVESTOR SOLUTIONS INC.; *U.S. Private*, pg. 2132
INVESTORS' SECURITY TRUST COMPANY—See First Busey Corporation; *U.S. Public*, pg. 840
INVESTORS TITLE COMPANY—See FB Financial Corporation; *U.S. Public*, pg. 824
INVESTORS TITLE COMPANY; *U.S. Public*, pg. 1165
INVESTORS TITLE EXCHANGE CORPORATION—See Investors Title Company; *U.S. Public*, pg. 1165
INVESTORS TITLE INSURANCE COMPANY—See Investors Title Company; *U.S. Public*, pg. 1165
INVESTORS TRUST COMPANY—See Investors Title Company; *U.S. Public*, pg. 1165
INVESTORS UNDERWRITING MANAGERS, INC.—See Markel Group Inc.; *U.S. Public*, pg. 1368
INVESTORTOOLS INC.; *U.S. Private*, pg. 2132
INVEST PROPERTY REIT; *Int'l*, pg. 3775
INVESTRONICA, S.A.—See El Corte Ingles, S.A.; *Int'l*, pg. 2340
INVESTRUST BANK PLC—See ZCCM Investments Holdings Plc.; *Int'l*, pg. 8627
INVESTRUST, N.A.—See American Fidelity Corporation; *U.S. Private*, pg. 234
INVESTSMART FINANCIAL SERVICES PTY LTD—See Regal Partners Limited; *Int'l*, pg. 6251
INVESTSMART GROUP LTD.; *Int'l*, pg. 3787
INVEST TECH PARTICIPACOES E INVESTIMENTOS LTDA.; *Int'l*, pg. 3775

INVEST TECH PARTICIPACOES E INVESTIMENTOS LTDA.
CORPORATE AFFILIATIONS

INVEST UNTERNEHMENSBETEILIGUNGS AKTIENGESELLSCHAFT—See Raiffeisenlandesbank Oberosterreich Aktiengesellschaft; *Int'l*, pg. 6187
INVESTVIEW, INC.; *U.S. Public*, pg. 1165
INVEST WEST FINANCIAL CORPORATION; *U.S. Private*, pg. 2131
INVESTX CAPITAL LTD.; *Int'l*, pg. 3787
INVETECH, LLC; *U.S. Private*, pg. 2132
INVE TECHNOLOGIES NV—See Benchmark Holdings Plc; *Int'l*, pg. 970
INVETECH PTY. LTD.—See Fortive Corporation; *U.S. Public*, pg. 871
INVETEK, INC.; *U.S. Private*, pg. 2132
INVE (THAILAND) LTD.—See Benchmark Holdings Plc; *Int'l*, pg. 970
INVE VIETNAM COMPANY LTD.—See Benchmark Holdings Plc; *Int'l*, pg. 970
INVEXANS LIMITED—See Quinenco S.A.; *Int'l*, pg. 6164
INVEXANS S.A.—See Quinenco S.A.; *Int'l*, pg. 6164
INVEX CONTROLADORA, S.A.B. DE C.V.; *Int'l*, pg. 3788
INVEX THERAPEUTICS LIMITED; *Int'l*, pg. 3788
INVIARCO SAS—See China Oceanwide Holdings Group Co., Ltd.; *Int'l*, pg. 1538
INVIARCO SAS—See IDG Capital; *Int'l*, pg. 3594
INVIBE LABS, LLC—See JLL Partners, LLC; *U.S. Private*, pg. 2212
INVIBE LABS, LLC—See Water Street Healthcare Partners, LLC; *U.S. Private*, pg. 4452
INVIBES ADVERTISING NV; *Int'l*, pg. 3788
INVIBIO LIMITED—See Victrex plc; *Int'l*, pg. 8190
INVICRO LLC—See Konica Minolta, Inc.; *Int'l*, pg. 4257
INVICTA HOLDINGS LIMITED; *Int'l*, pg. 3788
INVICTA PUBLIC AFFAIRS LTD.; *Int'l*, pg. 3789
INVICTA VALVES LTD.—See AVK Holding A/S; *Int'l*, pg. 747
INVICTUS ENERGY LTD.; *Int'l*, pg. 3789
INVICTUS INTERNATIONAL CONSULTING, LLC; *U.S. Private*, pg. 2132
INVICTUS INTERNATIONAL SCHOOL (HONG KONG) LIMITED—See Chip Eng Seng Corporation Ltd.; *Int'l*, pg. 1572
INVICTUS INTERNATIONAL SCHOOL PTE. LTD.—See Chip Eng Seng Corporation Ltd.; *Int'l*, pg. 1572
INVICTUS JUNIOR SCHOOLS PTE. LTD.—See Chip Eng Seng Corporation Ltd.; *Int'l*, pg. 1572
INVICTUS MD STRATEGIES CORP.; *Int'l*, pg. 3789
INVICTUS SCHOOL (CHAI WAN) LIMITED—See Chip Eng Seng Corporation Ltd.; *Int'l*, pg. 1572
INVIDI TECHNOLOGIES CORPORATION—See AT&T Inc.; *U.S. Public*, pg. 220
INVIGOR GROUP LIMITED; *Int'l*, pg. 3789
INVIGORS EMEA LLP—See The Alta Group, LLC; *U.S. Private*, pg. 3984
INVINCEA, INC.—See Apax Partners LLP; *Int'l*, pg. 593
INVINCIBLE BOAT COMPANY—See EagleTree Capital, LP; *U.S. Private*, pg. 1311
INVINCIBLE INVESTMENT CORPORATION; *Int'l*, pg. 3789
INVINCIBLE OFFICE FURNITURE; *U.S. Private*, pg. 2133
INV, INC.; *Int'l*, pg. 3772
INVINITY ENERGY SYSTEMS PLC; *Int'l*, pg. 3789
IN VINO NATUKHAEVSKOE LLC—See PPF Group N.V.; *Int'l*, pg. 5950
INVION LIMITED; *Int'l*, pg. 3789
INVISAFLOW, LLC—See Omnimax Holdings, Inc.; *U.S. Private*, pg. 3017
INVISALIGN AUSTRALIA PTY LTD—See Align Technology, Inc.; *U.S. Public*, pg. 77
INVISIBLE CLOSE; *U.S. Private*, pg. 2133
INVISIBLE FENCE, INC.—See Radio Systems Corporation; *U.S. Private*, pg. 3344
INVISIBLE SENTINEL, INC.—See Institut Merieux; *Int'l*, pg. 3724
INVISIBLE WASTE SERVICES LLC—See GI Manager L.P.; *U.S. Private*, pg. 1694
INVISIO A/S; *Int'l*, pg. 3789
INVISION AG; *Int'l*, pg. 3789
INVISION AG; *Int'l*, pg. 3789
INVISION AUTOMOTIVE SYSTEMS, INC.—See VOXX International Corporation; *U.S. Public*, pg. 2311
INVISION BENEFIT, INC.—See Stone Point Capital LLC; *U.S. Private*, pg. 3819
INVISION COMMUNICATIONS, INC. - CHICAGO—See InVision Communications, Inc.; *U.S. Private*, pg. 2133
INVISION COMMUNICATIONS, INC.; *U.S. Private*, pg. 2133
INVISION COMMUNICATIONS, INC.—See InVision Communications, Inc.; *U.S. Private*, pg. 2133
INVISIONS HOLDING B.V.—See National Amusements, Inc.; *U.S. Private*, pg. 2841
INVISION SOFTWARE INC.—See InVision AG; *Int'l*, pg. 3789
INVISION SOFTWARE, INC.—See InVision AG; *Int'l*, pg. 3789
INVISION SOFTWARE LTD.—See InVision AG; *Int'l*, pg. 3789
INVISION SOFTWARE SAS—See InVision AG; *Int'l*, pg. 3789

INVISION UK LTD.—See Midwich Group Plc; *Int'l*, pg. 4887
INVISTA GMBH—See Koch Industries, Inc.; *U.S. Private*, pg. 2330
INVISTA REAL ESTATE INVESTMENT MANAGEMENT HOLDINGS LIMITED—See Fiera Capital Corporation; *Int'l*, pg. 2659
INVISTA REAL ESTATE INVESTMENT MANAGEMENT LIMITED—See Fiera Capital Corporation; *Int'l*, pg. 2659
INVISTA S.A.R.L.—See Koch Industries, Inc.; *U.S. Private*, pg. 2330
INVISTA S.A.; *Int'l*, pg. 3789
INVISTA—See Koch Industries, Inc.; *U.S. Private*, pg. 2330
INVISTICS CORPORATION—See Wolters Kluwer n.v.; *Int'l*, pg. 8444
INVITA AG; *Int'l*, pg. 3789
INVITA B.S.C.—See BBK B.S.C.; *Int'l*, pg. 920
INVITA DETAIL & PROJEKT A/S—See Nobia AB; *Int'l*, pg. 5395
INVITAE AUSTRALIA PTY. LTD.—See Invitae Corporation; *U.S. Public*, pg. 1165
INVITAE CORPORATION; *U.S. Public*, pg. 1165
INVITA KOKKENER A/S—See Nobia AB; *Int'l*, pg. 5395
INVITA KUWAIT K.S.C.C—See BBK B.S.C.; *Int'l*, pg. 920
INVITALIA PARTECIPAZIONI S.P.A.—See Agenzia Nazionale per l'Attrazione degli Investimenti e lo Sviluppo d'Impresa SpA; *Int'l*, pg. 206
INVITA RETAIL A/S—See Nobia AB; *Int'l*, pg. 5395
INVITATION CONSULTANTS, INC.; *U.S. Private*, pg. 2133
INVITATION HOMES, INC.; *U.S. Public*, pg. 1165
INVITATION HOMES L.P.—See Invitation Homes Inc.; *U.S. Public*, pg. 1165
INVITECH ICT SERVICES KFT. LTD.—See 4iG Nyrt.; *Int'l*, pg. 12
INVITEL HOLDINGS A/S—See Mid Europa Partners LLP; *Int'l*, pg. 4882
INVITEL HOLDINGS - U.S. EXECUTIVE OFFICE—See Mid Europa Partners LLP; *Int'l*, pg. 4882
INVITEL LEGACY S.A.; *Int'l*, pg. 3789
INVITEL TAVKOZLESI SZOLGALTATO ZRT.—See Mid Europa Partners LLP; *Int'l*, pg. 4882
INVITES BIOCORE CO., LTD.; *Int'l*, pg. 3790
INVITING FOODS LLC—See PepsiCo, Inc.; *U.S. Public*, pg. 1669
INVITO BV—See Macintosh Retail Group NV; *Int'l*, pg. 4622
INVITROCUE LIMITED; *Int'l*, pg. 3790
INVITROCUE PTE LTD.—See Invitrocue Limited; *Int'l*, pg. 3790
INVITROGEN BIOSERVICES INDIA PRIVATE LIMITED—See Thermo Fisher Scientific Inc.; *U.S. Public*, pg. 2149
INVITRO INTERNATIONAL; *U.S. Public*, pg. 1165
IN VITRO-LABOR FUR VETERINARMEDIZINISCHE DIAGNOSTIK UND HYGIENE GMBH—See IDEXX Laboratories, Inc.; *U.S. Public*, pg. 1093
IN VITRO TECHNOLOGIES PTY. LTD.—See HORIBA Ltd; *Int'l*, pg. 3477
INVIVO BIOTECH SVS GMBH.—See Bruker Corporation; *U.S. Public*, pg. 405
INVIVO BIOTECH SVX GMBH—See Bruker Corporation; *U.S. Public*, pg. 407
INVIVOLINK, INC.—See HCA Healthcare, Inc.; *U.S. Public*, pg. 999
INVIVO THERAPEUTICS HOLDINGS CORP.; *U.S. Public*, pg. 1166
INVIVYD, INC.; *U.S. Public*, pg. 1166
INVIZION, INC.; *U.S. Private*, pg. 2133
INVL ASSET MANAGEMENT UAB—See Invalda INVL AB; *Int'l*, pg. 3772
INVL BALTIC FARMLAND AB; *Int'l*, pg. 3790
INVL BALTIC REAL ESTATE AB; *Int'l*, pg. 3790
INVL TECHNOLOGY AB; *Int'l*, pg. 3790
INV METALS INC.—See Dundee Precious Metals Inc.; *Int'l*, pg. 2226
INVNT, LLC; *U.S. Private*, pg. 2133
INVO BIOSCIENCE, INC.; *U.S. Public*, pg. 1166
INVOCARE AUSTRALIA PTY LIMITED—See TPG Capital, L.P.; *U.S. Public*, pg. 2174
INVOCARE LIMITED—See TPG Capital, L.P.; *U.S. Public*, pg. 2174
INVOCAS BUSINESS RECOVERY AND INSOLVENCY LIMITED—See Invocas Group plc; *Int'l*, pg. 3790
INVOCAS FINANCIAL SOLUTIONS LIMITED—See Invocas Group plc; *Int'l*, pg. 3790
INVOCAS GROUP PLC; *Int'l*, pg. 3790
INVOCO COMMUNICATION CENTER GMBH—See Conduent Incorporated; *U.S. Public*, pg. 566
INVOCO CUSTOMER SERVICE GMBH—See Conduent Incorporated; *U.S. Public*, pg. 566
INVOCO HOLDING GMBH—See Conduent Incorporated; *U.S. Public*, pg. 566
INVO HEALTHCARE ASSOCIATES, INC.—See Golden Gate Capital Management II, LLC; *U.S. Private*, pg. 1731
INVOICE2GO, LLC—See BILL HOLDINGS, INC.; *U.S. Public*, pg. 331

INVOICE INC.—See Fuyo General Lease Co., Ltd.; *Int'l*, pg. 2859
INVOKE MEDIA; *Int'l*, pg. 3790
INVOKE MEDIA—See Invoke Media; *Int'l*, pg. 3790
INVOKE SOLUTIONS, INC.—See Kohlberg & Company, LLC; *U.S. Private*, pg. 2338
INVOLTA, LLC; *U.S. Private*, pg. 2133
INVOLVE! ADVERTISING AS; *Int'l*, pg. 3790
INVOLVIO LLC—See Cisco Systems, Inc.; *U.S. Public*, pg. 499
INVOLYS; *Int'l*, pg. 3790
INVOMO LTD.; *Int'l*, pg. 3790
INVOTECH SYSTEMS, INC.—See ASSA ABLOY AB; *Int'l*, pg. 637
INVOX PHARMA LIMITED—See Sino Biopharmaceutical Limited; *Int'l*, pg. 6946
INVOYENT, LLC—See West Monroe Partners, LLC; *U.S. Private*, pg. 4486
INVT ELECTRIC (INDIA) CO., LTD.—See Shenzhen INVT Electric Co., Ltd.; *Int'l*, pg. 6814
INVT ELECTRIC THAILAND CO., LTD.—See Shenzhen INVT Electric Co., Ltd.; *Int'l*, pg. 6814
INVT ELEVATOR CONTROL TECHNOLOGY (WUXI) CO., LTD.—See Shenzhen INVT Electric Co., Ltd.; *Int'l*, pg. 6814
INVT POWER SYSTEM (SHENZHEN) CO., LTD.—See Shenzhen INVT Electric Co., Ltd.; *Int'l*, pg. 6814
INVUE SECURITY PRODUCTS; *U.S. Private*, pg. 2133
INVUITY, INC.—See Stryker Corporation; *U.S. Public*, pg. 1955
INVU SERVICES LTD.; *Int'l*, pg. 3790
INVUS FINANCIAL ADVISORS, LLC—See The Invus Group, LLC; *U.S. Private*, pg. 4057
THE INVUS GROUP, LLC; *U.S. Private*, pg. 4057
INWARE TECHNOLOGIES, INC.; *U.S. Private*, pg. 2133
INWHATLANGUAGE, LLC—See TrustPoint International, LLC; *U.S. Private*, pg. 4251
INWIDO AB—See Ratos AB; *Int'l*, pg. 6219
INWIDO DENMARK A/S—See Ratos AB; *Int'l*, pg. 6219
INWIDO FINLAND OY—See Ratos AB; *Int'l*, pg. 6220
INWIDO IRELAND LTD.—See Ratos AB; *Int'l*, pg. 6220
INWIDO NORGE AS—See Ratos AB; *Int'l*, pg. 6220
INWIDO POLAND SA—See Ratos AB; *Int'l*, pg. 6220
INWIDO PRODUKTION AB—See Ratos AB; *Int'l*, pg. 6220
INWIDO PRODUKTION DORRAR AB—See Ratos AB; *Int'l*, pg. 6220
INWIDO PRODUKTION SYD A/S—See Ratos AB; *Int'l*, pg. 6220
INWIDO SUPPLY AB—See Ratos AB; *Int'l*, pg. 6220
INWIDO SVERIGE AB—See Ratos AB; *Int'l*, pg. 6220
INWIDO UK LTD—See Ratos AB; *Int'l*, pg. 6220
IN WIN DEVELOPMENT INC.; *Int'l*, pg. 3639
IN WIN DEVELOPMENT (N.L.) B.V.—See In Win Development Inc.; *Int'l*, pg. 3639
IN WIN DEVELOPMENT (UK) LTD.—See In Win Development Inc.; *Int'l*, pg. 3639
IN WIN DEVELOPMENT (U.S.A.) INC.—See In Win Development Inc.; *Int'l*, pg. 3639
INWINSTACK INC.—See In Win Development Inc.; *Int'l*, pg. 3639
INWIT SPA—See TIM S.p.A.; *Int'l*, pg. 7749
INWK MEXICO S DE R.L. DE C.V.—See HH Global Group Limited; *Int'l*, pg. 3378
INWK PANAMA S.A.—See HH Global Group Limited; *Int'l*, pg. 3378
INW MANUFACTURING LLC—See Cornell Capital LLC; *U.S. Private*, pg. 1051
INWOOD BANCSHARES INC.; *U.S. Private*, pg. 2133
INWOOD NATIONAL BANK INC.—See Inwood Bancshares Inc.; *U.S. Private*, pg. 2133
INX CORPORATION—See Sakata INX Corporation; *Int'l*, pg. 6487
THE INX DIGITAL COMPANY, INC; *Int'l*, pg. 7657
INX DIGITAL CZECH, A.S.—See Sakata INX Corporation; *Int'l*, pg. 6487
INX DIGITAL ITALY S.R.L.—See Sakata INX Corporation; *Int'l*, pg. 6487
INX EUROPE LTD.—See Sakata INX Corporation; *Int'l*, pg. 6487
INX GRAVURE CO., LTD.—See Sakata INX Corporation; *Int'l*, pg. 6487
THE INX GROUP LTD.—See Sakata INX Corporation; *Int'l*, pg. 6488
INXILE ENTERTAINMENT, INC.—See Microsoft Corporation; *U.S. Public*, pg. 1440
INX INTERNATIONAL FRANCE SAS—See Sakata INX Corporation; *Int'l*, pg. 6487
INX INTERNATIONAL INK CORP.—See Sakata INX Corporation; *Int'l*, pg. 6487
INX INTERNATIONAL INK CO.—See Sakata INX Corporation; *Int'l*, pg. 6487
INX INTERNATIONAL UK LTD.—See Sakata INX Corporation; *Int'l*, pg. 6487
INX LIMITED—See The INX Digital Company, Inc; *Int'l*, pg. 7657
INXPO INC.—See Apollo Global Management, Inc.; *U.S. Public*, pg. 152
INX TECHNO SERVICE CO., LTD.—See Sakata INX Corporation; *Int'l*, pg. 6487

COMPANY NAME INDEX

INYANDA COAL (PTY) LIMITED—See Exxaro Resources Ltd.; *Int'l*, pg. 2592
INYECTAMETAL, S.A.—See Cie Automotive S.A.; *Int'l*, pg. 1604
INYX, INC.; *U.S. Private*, pg. 2133
INZETBAAR BV—See Allied Universal Manager LLC; *U.S. Private*, pg. 190
INZHSYSTEMS LTD.; *Int'l*, pg. 3790
INZI AMT CO., LTD—See INZI Controls Co., Ltd; *Int'l*, pg. 3790
INZI CONTROLS CO., LTD; *Int'l*, pg. 3790
INZI DISPLAY CO., LTD. - ANSEONG PLANT—See INZI Controls Co., Ltd; *Int'l*, pg. 3790
INZI DISPLAY CO., LTD.—See INZI Controls Co., Ltd; *Int'l*, pg. 3790
INZI DISPLAY CO., LTD. - YESAN PLANT—See INZI Controls Co., Ltd; *Int'l*, pg. 3790
INZI MOBILE SOLUTION CO., LTD.—See INZI Controls Co., Ltd; *Int'l*, pg. 3790
INZINC MINING LTD.; *Int'l*, pg. 3790
INZISOFT CO., LTD.; *Int'l*, pg. 3791
INZONE GROUP CO., LTD.; *Int'l*, pg. 3791
IN ZONE, INC.; *U.S. Private*, pg. 2052
INZPIRE LIMITED—See QinetiQ Group plc; *Int'l*, pg. 6141
IOA RE, LLC—See ELMC Holdings, LLC; *U.S. Private*, pg. 1376
IO BIOTECH, INC.; *Int'l*, pg. 3791
IOC-CARUTHERSVILLE, LLC—See Century Casinos, Inc.; *U.S. Public*, pg. 474
IOCHEM CORPORATION; *U.S. Private*, pg. 2133
IOCHPE-MAXION S.A.; *Int'l*, pg. 3791
IOCHPE-MAXION—See Iochpe-Maxion S.A.; *Int'l*, pg. 3791
IOC-KANSAS CITY, INC.—See Bally's Corporation; *U.S. Public*, pg. 268
I-O DATA DEVICE, INC.; *Int'l*, pg. 3563
IODINE SOFTWARE, LLC; *U.S. Private*, pg. 2133
IODO-FINECHEM CORPORATION - CHIBA PLANT—See Manac Incorporated; *Int'l*, pg. 4666
IODO-FINECHEM CORPORATION—See Manac Incorporated; *Int'l*, pg. 4666
IOFFICE, LLC; *U.S. Private*, pg. 2133
IOFIL S.A.—See Vis Containers Manufacturing Co., Ltd.; *Int'l*, pg. 8249
IOFINA CHEMICAL INC—See Iofina plc; *Int'l*, pg. 3791
IOFINA INC.—See Iofina plc; *Int'l*, pg. 3791
IOFINA NATURAL GAS INC—See Iofina plc; *Int'l*, pg. 3791
IOFINA PLC; *Int'l*, pg. 3791
IOFINA RESOURCES, INC.—See Iofina plc; *Int'l*, pg. 3791
IOG PLC; *Int'l*, pg. 3791
IOI BIO-ENERGY SDN BHD—See IOI Corporation Berhad; *Int'l*, pg. 3792
IOI CITY MALL SDN. BHD.—See IOI Properties Group Berhad; *Int'l*, pg. 3792
IOI COMMODITY TRADING SDN BHD—See IOI Corporation Berhad; *Int'l*, pg. 3792
IOI CORPORATION BERHAD; *Int'l*, pg. 3791
IOI EDIBLE OILS SDN BHD—See IOI Corporation Berhad; *Int'l*, pg. 3792
IOI LANDSCAPE SERVICES SDN BHD—See IOI Corporation Berhad; *Int'l*, pg. 3792
IOI LODERS CROKLAAN OILS SDN BHD—See IOI Corporation Berhad; *Int'l*, pg. 3792
IOI LODERS CROKLAAN PROCUREMENT COMPANY SDN BHD—See IOI Corporation Berhad; *Int'l*, pg. 3792
I.O. INCORPORATED; *U.S. Private*, pg. 2027
IO INTERACTIVE A/S—See Square Enix Holdings Co. Ltd.; *Int'l*, pg. 7147
IOI OLEOCHEMICAL INDUSTRIES BERHAD—See IOI Corporation Berhad; *Int'l*, pg. 3792
IOI PROPERTIES GROUP BERHAD; *Int'l*, pg. 3792
IOI PROPERTIES (SINGAPORE) PTE. LTD.—See IOI Properties Group Berhad; *Int'l*, pg. 3792
IOI SPECIALITY FATS SDN BHD—See IOI Corporation Berhad; *Int'l*, pg. 3792
IOI VENTURES (L) BERHAD—See IOI Corporation Berhad; *Int'l*, pg. 3792
IOKI GMBH—See Deutsche Bahn AG; *Int'l*, pg. 2055
I. OLA LAHUI INC.; *U.S. Private*, pg. 2026
IOLAP, INC.—See Elixirr International plc; *Int'l*, pg. 2363
IOL CHEMICALS & PHARMACEUTICALS LTD - MANUFACTURING PLANT—See IOL Chemicals & Pharmaceuticals Ltd.; *Int'l*, pg. 3792
IOL CHEMICALS & PHARMACEUTICALS LTD.; *Int'l*, pg. 3792
IOLKOS S.A.—See Gek Terna Societe Anonyme Holdings Real Estate Constructions; *Int'l*, pg. 2913
I/OMAGIC CORPORATION; *U.S. Private*, pg. 2027
I/O MARINE SYSTEMS, INC.—See ION Geophysical Corporation; *U.S. Public*, pg. 1166
I/O MARINE SYSTEMS LIMITED—See ION Geophysical Corporation; *U.S. Public*, pg. 1166
IOMART GROUP PLC; *Int'l*, pg. 3792
IOMART HOSTING LIMITED—See iomart Group plc; *Int'l*, pg. 3793
IO MEDIA, INC.—See Live Nation Entertainment, Inc.; *U.S. Public*, pg. 1329
IOMEDIA; *U.S. Private*, pg. 2133
IOMNI PRECISION, INC.—See Ionics, Inc.; *Int'l*, pg. 3795

ION-3 CORPORATION; *U.S. Private*, pg. 2134
ION ACQUISITION CORP 1 LTD.—See Taboola.com Ltd.; *U.S. Public*, pg. 1978
IONA ENERGY COMPANY (UK) LIMITED—See Iona Energy Inc.; *Int'l*, pg. 3794
IONA ENERGY INC.; *Int'l*, pg. 3794
IONA INTERNATIONAL CORPORATION—See Zeria Pharmaceutical Co., Ltd.; *Int'l*, pg. 8638
IONA MEDICAL PRODUCTS PTY LTD—See Paragon Care Limited; *Int'l*, pg. 5736
ION AUDIO, LLC—See inMusic, LLC; *U.S. Private*, pg. 2080
ION BANK—See Ion Financial, MHC; *U.S. Private*, pg. 2133
ION BEAM APPLICATIONS CO. LTD.—See Ion Beam Applications, S.A.; *Int'l*, pg. 3793
ION BEAM APPLICATIONS, S.A.; *Int'l*, pg. 3793
ION BEAM MILLING, INC.—See Semi-General, Inc.; *U.S. Private*, pg. 3603
IONBOND AG - NUREMBERG—See IHI Corporation; *Int'l*, pg. 3605
IONBOND AG—See IHI Corporation; *Int'l*, pg. 3605
IONBOND AUSTRIA GMBH—See IHI Corporation; *Int'l*, pg. 3605
IONBOND CONSETT—See IHI Corporation; *Int'l*, pg. 3605
IONBOND CZECHCOATING CZECHCOATING S.R.O.—See IHI Corporation; *Int'l*, pg. 3605
IONBOND CZECHIA, S.R.O.—See IHI Corporation; *Int'l*, pg. 3605
IONBOND ICC PARIS INNOVATIVE COATING CO.—See IHI Corporation; *Int'l*, pg. 3605
IONBOND ITALIA SRL—See IHI Corporation; *Int'l*, pg. 3605
IONBOND LLC—See IHI Corporation; *Int'l*, pg. 3605
IONBOND (MALAYSIA) SDN. BHD.—See IHI Corporation; *Int'l*, pg. 3605
IONBOND MEXICO - TECATE—See IHI Corporation; *Int'l*, pg. 3605
IONBOND MULHOUSE—See IHI Corporation; *Int'l*, pg. 3605
IONBOND NETHERLANDS B.V.—See IHI Corporation; *Int'l*, pg. 3605
IONBOND SWEDEN AB—See IHI Corporation; *Int'l*, pg. 3605
IONBOND TINKAP ISTANBUL TINKAP VAKUM PLAZMA TEK. LTD.—See IHI Corporation; *Int'l*, pg. 3605
ION CORPORATION; *U.S. Private*, pg. 2133
I-ON DIGITAL CORP.; *Int'l*, pg. 3563
IONE CO., LTD—See NICE Holdings Co., Ltd.; *Int'l*, pg. 5264
IONEER LTD; *Int'l*, pg. 3794
IONEER RHYOLITE RIDGE LLC—See ioneer Ltd; *Int'l*, pg. 3794
IONE FINANCIAL PRESS LIMITED—See Huafa Property Services Group Company Limited; *Int'l*, pg. 3511
ION EQUITY LIMITED; *Int'l*, pg. 3793
ION EXCHANGE & COMPANY LLC OMAN—See Ion Exchange India Ltd; *Int'l*, pg. 3793
ION EXCHANGE INDIA LTD; *Int'l*, pg. 3793
ION EXCHANGE LIMITED (UAE)—See Ion Exchange India Ltd; *Int'l*, pg. 3793
ION EXCHANGE SOUTH AFRICA—See Ion Exchange India Ltd; *Int'l*, pg. 3793
ION EXPLORATION PRODUCTS (U.S.A.), INC.—See ION Geophysical Corporation; *U.S. Public*, pg. 1166
IONEX RESEARCH CORP.; *U.S. Private*, pg. 2134
ION FINANCIAL, MHC; *U.S. Private*, pg. 2133
ION GEOPHYSICAL CIS LLC—See ION Geophysical Corporation; *U.S. Public*, pg. 1166
ION GEOPHYSICAL CORPORATION; *U.S. Public*, pg. 1166
ION GROUP LLC—See ION Investment Group Ltd.; *Int'l*, pg. 3794
IONIA DIALYSIS, LLC—See DaVita Inc.; *U.S. Public*, pg. 639
IONIAN HOTEL ENTERPRISES S.A.—See Alpha Services and Holdings S.A.; *Int'l*, pg. 369
IONIA S.A.—See Titan Cement Company S.A.; *Int'l*, pg. 7759
IONIC BRANDS CORP.; *Int'l*, pg. 3794
IONIC MEDIA; *U.S. Private*, pg. 2134
IONIC RARE EARTHS LIMITED; *Int'l*, pg. 3794
IONICS EMS, INC.—See Ionics, Inc.; *Int'l*, pg. 3795
IONICS, INC.; *Int'l*, pg. 3795
IONICS PROPERTIES, INC.—See Ionics, Inc.; *Int'l*, pg. 3795
IONIC TECHNOLOGIES, INC.—See Aalberts N.V.; *Int'l*, pg. 34
IONIDEA, INC.; *U.S. Private*, pg. 2134
I-ON INTERACTIVE, INC.—See e.Bricks Ventures; *Int'l*, pg. 2251
ION INTERACTIVE, INC.; *U.S. Private*, pg. 2133
ION INVESTMENT GROUP LTD.; *Int'l*, pg. 3793
IONIQ SCIENCES, INC.; *U.S. Private*, pg. 2134
IONIS PHARMACEUTICALS, INC.; *U.S. Public*, pg. 1166
IONIX AEROSPACE LIMITED—See Amphenol Corporation; *U.S. Public*, pg. 130
IONIX SYSTEMS LTD.; *Int'l*, pg. 3795

IONIX TECHNOLOGY, INC.

IONIX SYSTEMS OU—See Amphenol Corporation; *U.S. Public*, pg. 130
IONIX TECHNOLOGY, INC.; *Int'l*, pg. 3795
ION LABS, INC.—See DCC plc; *Int'l*, pg. 1990
ION MEDIA HITS, INC.—See The E.W. Scripps Company; *U.S. Public*, pg. 2067
ION MEDIA NETWORKS, INC.—See The E.W. Scripps Company; *U.S. Public*, pg. 2067
ION MEDIA OF ALBANY, INC.—See The E.W. Scripps Company; *U.S. Public*, pg. 2067
ION MEDIA OF ATLANTA, INC.—See The E.W. Scripps Company; *U.S. Public*, pg. 2067
ION MEDIA OF BATTLE CREEK, INC.—See The E.W. Scripps Company; *U.S. Public*, pg. 2067
ION MEDIA OF BIRMINGHAM, INC.—See The E.W. Scripps Company; *U.S. Public*, pg. 2067
ION MEDIA OF BOSTON, INC.—See The E.W. Scripps Company; *U.S. Public*, pg. 2067
ION MEDIA OF BRUNSWICK, INC.—See The E.W. Scripps Company; *U.S. Public*, pg. 2067
ION MEDIA OF BUFFALO, INC.—See The E.W. Scripps Company; *U.S. Public*, pg. 2067
ION MEDIA OF CEDAR RAPIDS, INC.—See The E.W. Scripps Company; *U.S. Public*, pg. 2067
ION MEDIA OF CHICAGO, INC.—See The E.W. Scripps Company; *U.S. Public*, pg. 2067
ION MEDIA OF DALLAS, INC.—See The E.W. Scripps Company; *U.S. Public*, pg. 2067
ION MEDIA OF DENVER, INC.—See The E.W. Scripps Company; *U.S. Public*, pg. 2067
ION MEDIA OF DES MOINES, INC.—See The E.W. Scripps Company; *U.S. Public*, pg. 2067
ION MEDIA OF DETROIT, INC.—See The E.W. Scripps Company; *U.S. Public*, pg. 2067
ION MEDIA OF FAYETTEVILLE, INC.—See The E.W. Scripps Company; *U.S. Public*, pg. 2067
ION MEDIA OF GREENSBORO, INC.—See The E.W. Scripps Company; *U.S. Public*, pg. 2067
ION MEDIA OF GREENVILLE, INC.—See The E.W. Scripps Company; *U.S. Public*, pg. 2067
ION MEDIA OF HONOLULU, INC.—See The E.W. Scripps Company; *U.S. Public*, pg. 2067
ION MEDIA OF INDIANAPOLIS, INC.—See The E.W. Scripps Company; *U.S. Public*, pg. 2067
ION MEDIA OF KANSAS CITY, INC.—See The E.W. Scripps Company; *U.S. Public*, pg. 2067
ION MEDIA OF KNOXVILLE, INC.—See The E.W. Scripps Company; *U.S. Public*, pg. 2068
ION MEDIA OF LEXINGTON, INC.—See The E.W. Scripps Company; *U.S. Public*, pg. 2068
ION MEDIA OF LOS ANGELES, INC.—See The E.W. Scripps Company; *U.S. Public*, pg. 2068
ION MEDIA OF MEMPHIS, INC.—See The E.W. Scripps Company; *U.S. Public*, pg. 2068
ION MEDIA OF MILWAUKEE, INC.—See The E.W. Scripps Company; *U.S. Public*, pg. 2068
ION MEDIA OF MINNEAPOLIS, INC.—See The E.W. Scripps Company; *U.S. Public*, pg. 2068
ION MEDIA OF NASHVILLE, INC.—See The E.W. Scripps Company; *U.S. Public*, pg. 2068
ION MEDIA OF NEW ORLEANS, INC.—See The E.W. Scripps Company; *U.S. Public*, pg. 2068
ION MEDIA OF NEW YORK, INC.—See The E.W. Scripps Company; *U.S. Public*, pg. 2068
ION MEDIA OF NORFOLK, INC.—See The E.W. Scripps Company; *U.S. Public*, pg. 2068
ION MEDIA OF OKLAHOMA CITY, INC.—See The E.W. Scripps Company; *U.S. Public*, pg. 2068
ION MEDIA OF ORLANDO, INC.—See The E.W. Scripps Company; *U.S. Public*, pg. 2068
ION MEDIA OF PHILADELPHIA, INC.—See The E.W. Scripps Company; *U.S. Public*, pg. 2068
ION MEDIA OF PHOENIX, INC.—See The E.W. Scripps Company; *U.S. Public*, pg. 2068
ION MEDIA OF PORTLAND, INC.—See The E.W. Scripps Company; *U.S. Public*, pg. 2068
ION MEDIA OF PROVIDENCE, INC.—See The E.W. Scripps Company; *U.S. Public*, pg. 2068
ION MEDIA OF RALEIGH, INC.—See The E.W. Scripps Company; *U.S. Public*, pg. 2068
ION MEDIA OF ROANOKE, INC.—See The E.W. Scripps Company; *U.S. Public*, pg. 2068
ION MEDIA OF SACRAMENTO, INC.—See The E.W. Scripps Company; *U.S. Public*, pg. 2068
ION MEDIA OF SAN ANTONIO, INC.—See The E.W. Scripps Company; *U.S. Public*, pg. 2068
ION MEDIA OF SAN JOSE, INC.—See The E.W. Scripps Company; *U.S. Public*, pg. 2068
ION MEDIA OF SCRANTON, INC.—See The E.W. Scripps Company; *U.S. Public*, pg. 2068
ION MEDIA OF SEATTLE, INC.—See The E.W. Scripps Company; *U.S. Public*, pg. 2068
ION MEDIA OF SPOKANE, INC.—See The E.W. Scripps Company; *U.S. Public*, pg. 2068
ION MEDIA OF SYRACUSE, INC.—See The E.W. Scripps Company; *U.S. Public*, pg. 2068
ION MEDIA OF TULSA, INC.—See The E.W. Scripps Company; *U.S. Public*, pg. 2068

IONIX TECHNOLOGY, INC. | **CORPORATE AFFILIATIONS**

ION MEDIA OF WASHINGTON, INC.—See The E.W. Scripps Company; *U.S. Public*, pg. 2068
ION MEDIA OF WEST PALM BEACH, INC.—See The E.W. Scripps Company; *U.S. Public*, pg. 2068
ION MEDIA SONGS, INC.—See The E.W. Scripps Company; *U.S. Public*, pg. 2067
ION NETWORKS, INC.—See AEA Investors LP; *U.S. Private*, pg. 113
IONOS CLOUD LTD.—See IONOS Group SE; *Int'l*, pg. 3795
IONOS CLOUD S.L.U.—See IONOS Group SE; *Int'l*, pg. 3795
IONOS GROUP SE; *Int'l*, pg. 3795
IONOS—See United Internet AG; *Int'l*, pg. 8069
IONOTE ELECTRONICS (DONGGUAN) LTD—See Note AB; *Int'l*, pg. 5449
IONQ, INC.; *U.S. Public*, pg. 1166
IONSENSE, INC.—See Bruker Corporation; *U.S. Public*, pg. 407
ION TORRENT SYSTEMS, INC.—See Thermo Fisher Scientific Inc.; *U.S. Public*, pg. 2149
ION TRADING, INC. - NEW YORK OFFICE—See ION Investment Group Ltd.; *Int'l*, pg. 3794
ION TRADING, INC.—See ION Investment Group Ltd.; *Int'l*, pg. 3794
ION TRADING IRELAND LTD.—See ION Investment Group Ltd.; *Int'l*, pg. 3794
ION TRADING UK LIMITED—See ION Investment Group Ltd.; *Int'l*, pg. 3794
ION WAVE TECHNOLOGIES, INC.—See GI Manager L.P.; *U.S. Private*, pg. 1692
IOOF LTD—See Australian Unity Limited; *Int'l*, pg. 723
IOO KNAUF MARKETING—See Gebr. Knauf KG; *Int'l*, pg. 2906
IOOO ALGOL CHEMICALS—See Algol Oy; *Int'l*, pg. 318
IOOO EGGER DREVPLIT—See Fritz Egger GmbH & Co.; *Int'l*, pg. 2794
IOOO ERICPOL BREST—See Ericpol Sp. z o.o.; *Int'l*, pg. 2493
IOOO KSB BEL—See KSB SE & Co. KGaA; *Int'l*, pg. 4310
IOOO LENZE—See Lenze SE; *Int'l*, pg. 4454
IOOO RENOLIT TRADE—See RENOLIT SE; *Int'l*, pg. 6284
IOOO SIEMPELKAMP BEL—See G. Siempelkamp GmbH & Co. KG; *Int'l*, pg. 2864
IORA HEALTH, INC.—See Amazon.com, Inc.; *U.S. Public*, pg. 90
IOS ACQUISITIONS, INC.—See L.B. Foster Company; *U.S. Public*, pg. 1278
IOSAFE, INC.—See CRU Data Security Group, LLC; *U.S. Private*, pg. 1113
IOS CO., LTD.—See Cresco, Ltd.; *Int'l*, pg. 1840
IOS FINANCE EFC, S.A.—See Banca Farmafactoring S.p.A.; *Int'l*, pg. 814
IOS HOLDINGS, INC.—See L.B. Foster Company; *U.S. Public*, pg. 1278
IOS/PCI, LLC—See L.B. Foster Company; *U.S. Public*, pg. 1278
IOS TUBULAR MANAGEMENT AS—See DNB Bank ASA; *Int'l*, pg. 2148
IOSTUDIO; *U.S. Private*, pg. 2134
IOTA COMMUNICATIONS, INC.; *U.S. Public*, pg. 1167
IOTA ENGINEERING, L.L.C.—See Acuity Brands, Inc.; *U.S. Public*, pg. 37
IO-TAHOE LLC—See NRG Energy, Inc.; *U.S. Public*, pg. 1550
IOT ANWESHA ENGINEERING & CONSTRUCTION LIMITED—See Marquard & Bahls AG; *Int'l*, pg. 4700
IOT ANWESHA ENGINEERING & CONSTRUCTION LIMITED - STORAGE & MAINTENANCE UNIT—See Marquard & Bahls AG; *Int'l*, pg. 4700
IOT DEUTSCHLAND GMBH—See adesso SE; *Int'l*, pg. 144
IOT GROUP LIMITED—See Petrolia SE; *Int'l*, pg. 5829
IOT GROUP LIMITED; *Int'l*, pg. 3795
IOT INFRASTRUCTURE & ENERGY SERVICES LTD.—See Marquard & Bahls AG; *Int'l*, pg. 4700
IOU CENTRAL INC.—See Neuberger Berman Group LLC; *U.S. Private*, pg. 2890
IOU CENTRAL INC.—See Palos Capital Corporation; *Int'l*, pg. 5710
IOU FINANCIAL INC.—See Neuberger Berman Group LLC; *U.S. Private*, pg. 2890
IOU FINANCIAL INC.—See Palos Capital Corporation; *Int'l*, pg. 5710
IOUPAY LIMITED; *Int'l*, pg. 3795
IOVANCE BIOTHERAPEUTICS, INC.; *U.S. Public*, pg. 1167
IOVATION INC.—See TransUnion; *U.S. Public*, pg. 2185
IOWA 80.COM INC.—See Iowa 80 Group, Inc.; *U.S. Private*, pg. 2134
IOWA 80 GROUP, INC.; *U.S. Private*, pg. 2134
IOWA 80 TRUCKSTOP—See Iowa 80 Group, Inc.; *U.S. Private*, pg. 2134
IOWA BEER & BEVERAGE COMPANY—See Iowa Beverage Systems Inc.; *U.S. Private*, pg. 2134
IOWA BEER & BEVERAGE; *U.S. Private*, pg. 2134
IOWA BEVERAGE SYSTEMS INC.; *U.S. Private*, pg. 2134
IOWA BRIDGE & CULVERT LLC; *U.S. Private*, pg. 2134

IOWA CITY ELECTRIC COMPANY—See Motor City Electric Co., Inc.; *U.S. Private*, pg. 2796
THE IOWA CLINIC PC; *U.S. Private*, pg. 4057
IOWA COMPREHENSIVE HEALTH ASSOCIATION; *U.S. Private*, pg. 2134
IOWA CONTRACT FABRICATORS,INC.—See Oshkosh Corporation; *U.S. Public*, pg. 1620
IOWA DONOR NETWORK; *U.S. Private*, pg. 2134
IOWA EXPORT-IMPORT—See Ruan Transportation; *U.S. Private*, pg. 3499
IOWA FARM BUREAU FEDERATION; *U.S. Private*, pg. 2134
IOWA FARMER TODAY—See Lee Enterprises, Incorporated; *U.S. Public*, pg. 1299
IOWA FIRE EQUIPMENT COMPANY—See Pye-Barker Fire & Safety, LLC; *U.S. Private*, pg. 3309
IOWA FIRST BANCSHARES CORP.—See MidWestOne Financial Group, Inc.; *U.S. Public*, pg. 1446
IOWA HOSPICE, L.L.C.—See Humana, Inc.; *U.S. Public*, pg. 1070
IOWA INTERACTIVE, LLC—See Tyler Technologies, Inc.; *U.S. Public*, pg. 2208
IOWA INTERSTATE RAILROAD, LTD.—See Railroad Development Corp.; *U.S. Private*, pg. 3346
IOWA LABORERS DISTRICT COUNCIL HEALTH & WELFARE PLAN; *U.S. Private*, pg. 2134
IOWA LAKES ELECTRIC COOPERATIVE; *U.S. Private*, pg. 2134
IOWA LASER TECHNOLOGY INC.—See O'Neal Industries, Inc.; *U.S. Private*, pg. 2979
IOWA LIMESTONE COMPANY; *U.S. Private*, pg. 2135
IOWA LUTHERAN HOSPITAL MEDICAL EDUCATION FOUNDATION—See UnityPoint Health; *U.S. Private*, pg. 4303
IOWA MANAGEMENT SYSTEMS INC.; *U.S. Private*, pg. 2135
IOWA MOLD TOOLING CO., INC.—See Oshkosh Corporation; *U.S. Public*, pg. 1620
IOWA MUTUAL INSURANCE COMPANY; *U.S. Private*, pg. 2135
IOWA NATURAL HERITAGE FOUNDATION; *U.S. Private*, pg. 2135
IOWA NETWORK SERVICES INC.; *U.S. Private*, pg. 2135
IOWA NORTHERN RAILWAY CO., INC.; *U.S. Private*, pg. 2135
IOWA PACIFIC HOLDINGS, LLC; *U.S. Private*, pg. 2135
IOWA PACIFIC PROCESSORS INC.; *U.S. Private*, pg. 2135
IOWA PREMIUM, LLC—See Marfrig Global Foods S.A.; *Int'l*, pg. 4692
IOWA REALTY CO., INC.—See Berkshire Hathaway Inc.; *U.S. Public*, pg. 306
IOWA REBUILDERS, INC.—See Mestek, Inc.; *U.S. Public*, pg. 1426
IOWA REGIONAL UTILITIES ASSOCIATION; *U.S. Private*, pg. 2135
IOWA RENEWABLE ENERGY, LLC; *U.S. Private*, pg. 2135
IOWA RIVER BANCORP, INC.; *U.S. Private*, pg. 2135
IOWA SECURITIES INVESTMENT CORPORATION—See LLJ Inc.; *U.S. Private*, pg. 2475
IOWA SELECT FARMS, L.L.P.; *U.S. Private*, pg. 2135
IOWA SPEEDWAY, LLC; *U.S. Private*, pg. 2135
IOWA STATE BANK; *U.S. Private*, pg. 2135
IOWA STATE EDUCATION ASSOCIATION; *U.S. Private*, pg. 2136
IOWA STATE SAVINGS BANK—See Ames National Corporation; *U.S. Public*, pg. 115
IOWA STATE SAVINGS BANK—See Duclarkee, Inc.; *U.S. Private*, pg. 1284
IOWA STUDENT LOAN LIQUIDITY CORPORATION; *U.S. Private*, pg. 2136
IOWA TANKLINES INC.; *U.S. Private*, pg. 2136
IOWA TELECOMMUNICATIONS SERVICES, INC.—See Windstream Holdings, Inc.; *U.S. Public*, pg. 2373
IOWA TOTAL CARE, INC.—See Centene Corporation; *U.S. Public*, pg. 469
IOWA TRUST AND SAVINGS BANK—See Bradley Bancorp, Inc.; *U.S. Private*, pg. 632
IOWA TRUST & SAVINGS BANK—See Emmetsburg Bank Shares, Inc.; *U.S. Private*, pg. 1383
IOWA TURKEY GROWERS COOPERATIVE; *U.S. Private*, pg. 2136
IOWA WASTE SERVICES, LLC—See Waste Connections, Inc.; *Int'l*, pg. 8352
IOXP GMBH—See PTC Inc.; *U.S. Public*, pg. 1734
IOXUS, INC.—See Systematic Power Solutions, LLC; *U.S. Private*, pg. 3907
IP2IPO LIMITED—See IP Group plc; *Int'l*, pg. 3795
IP3 LYONS—See American Industrial Acquisition Corporation; *U.S. Private*, pg. 237
IPACESETTERS INDIA—See iPacesetters, LLC; *U.S. Private*, pg. 2136
IPACESETTERS, LLC; *U.S. Private*, pg. 2136
IPACKETS INTERNATIONAL, INC.; *Int'l*, pg. 3796
I-PAC TECHNOLOGIES N.V.—See InnoConcepts N.V.; *Int'l*, pg. 3709
IPA FAMILY, LLC—See JAB Holding Company S.a.r.l.; *Int'l*, pg. 3861

IP-AGENCY FINLAND OY—See BHG Group AB; *Int'l*, pg. 1015
IPAGSA TECHNOLOGIES S.L.U.—See Agfa-Gevaert N.V.; *Int'l*, pg. 208
IPA INVESTMENTS CORPORATION; *Int'l*, pg. 3795
IPALCO ENTERPRISES, INC.—See The AES Corporation; *U.S. Public*, pg. 2031
IPAL S.A.; *Int'l*, pg. 3796
IPANEMA SHOE CORPORATION—See Sumitomo Corporation; *Int'l*, pg. 7273
IPANEMA SOLUTIONS LLC—See Allbridge, LLC; *U.S. Private*, pg. 175
IPA PERSONNEL SERVICES PTY. LTD.—See Karingal St Laurence Limited; *Int'l*, pg. 4081
IPARADIGMS, LLC—See Insight Venture Management, LLC; *U.S. Private*, pg. 2091
IPARAN PROMOCIONES INMOBILIARIAS, S.L.—See Sacyr, S.A.; *Int'l*, pg. 6465
IPAR INDUSTRIAL PARTNERS B.V.—See LKQ Corporation; *U.S. Public*, pg. 1334
IPARK DEVELOPMENT SDN. BHD.—See AME Elite Consortium Berhad; *Int'l*, pg. 420
IPAS AS—See Addtech AB; *Int'l*, pg. 133
IPA SINGAPORE PTE LTD—See AXA S.A.; *Int'l*, pg. 759
IPASS ASIA PTE LTD.—See Pareteum Corporation; *U.S. Public*, pg. 1637
IPASS DEUTSCHLAND GMBH—See Pareteum Corporation; *U.S. Public*, pg. 1637
IPASS, INC.—See Pareteum Corporation; *U.S. Public*, pg. 1637
IPASS INDIA PRIVATE LIMITED—See Pareteum Corporation; *U.S. Public*, pg. 1637
IPASS JAPAN K.K.—See Pareteum Corporation; *U.S. Public*, pg. 1637
IPASS UK LTD—See Pareteum Corporation; *U.S. Public*, pg. 1637
IPA SYSTEMS LTD.; *Int'l*, pg. 3795
IPA SYSTEMS LTD. UK—See IPA Systems Ltd.; *Int'l*, pg. 3796
IPATH LLC—See Madison Parker Capital; *U.S. Private*, pg. 2544
IPAY88 HOLDING SDN. BHD.—See Nippon Telegraph & Telephone Corporation; *Int'l*, pg. 5356
IPAY88 (M) SDN. BHD.—See Nippon Telegraph & Telephone Corporation; *Int'l*, pg. 5356
IPAYABLES, INC.—See LoneTree Capital LLC; *U.S. Private*, pg. 2490
IPAY TECHNOLOGIES, LLC—See Jack Henry & Associates, Inc.; *U.S. Public*, pg. 1183
IP BEAUTY, INC.—See Inter Parfums, Inc.; *U.S. Public*, pg. 1140
IP BELGIAN SERVICES COMPANY SPRL—See International Paper Company; *U.S. Public*, pg. 1155
IP BELGIUM S.A.—See Bertelsmann SE & Co. KGaA; *Int'l*, pg. 992
IPB PETROLEUM LIMITED; *Int'l*, pg. 3796
IPCA LABORATORIES LTD.; *Int'l*, pg. 3796
I.P. CALLISON & SONS INC.; *U.S. Private*, pg. 2027
IP CANADIAN PACKAGING OPERATIONS INC.—See International Paper Company; *U.S. Public*, pg. 1155
IPCAS GMBH—See Adecco Group AG; *Int'l*, pg. 140
IPC CORPORATION LTD.; *Int'l*, pg. 3796
IPC DATA CENTER, INC.; *Int'l*, pg. 3796
IPC EAGLE CORPORATION—See Tennant Company; *U.S. Public*, pg. 2016
IPC HEALTHCARE, INC.—See Blackstone Inc.; *U.S. Public*, pg. 359
IPC INFORMATION SYSTEMS LTD.—See Strategic Value Partners, LLC; *U.S. Private*, pg. 3836
IPC INSPIRE—See Meredith Corporation; *U.S. Public*, pg. 1423
IPCITY CORPORATION—See Sojitz Corporation; *Int'l*, pg. 7063
IP CLEANING S.R.L.—See Tennant Company; *U.S. Public*, pg. 2016
IPC MEDIA LIMITED—See Meredith Corporation; *U.S. Public*, pg. 1423
IPCO AB—See FAM AB; *Int'l*, pg. 2611
IPCO CONSTRUCTORS PRIVATE LIMITED—See Renaissance United Limited; *Int'l*, pg. 6273
IPCO CONSTRUCTORS SDN. BHD.—See Renaissance United Limited; *Int'l*, pg. 6273
IPCO GERMANY GMBH—See FAM AB; *Int'l*, pg. 2611
I & P CO. LTD.—See Inabata & Co. Ltd.; *Int'l*, pg. 3643
IP COMMERCIAL PROPERTIES INC.—See International Paper Company; *U.S. Public*, pg. 1155
IP COMMUNICATIONS LLC; *U.S. Private*, pg. 2136
IPCONCEPT (LUXEMBURG) S.A.—See DZ BANK AG Deutsche Zentral-Genossenschaftsbank; *Int'l*, pg. 2244
IPCONCEPT (SCHWEIZ) AG—See DZ BANK AG Deutsche Zentral-Genossenschaftsbank; *Int'l*, pg. 2244
I.P. CONTAINER HOLDINGS (SPAIN) S.L.—See International Paper Company; *U.S. Public*, pg. 1155
IPCO PROCESS SYSTEMS B.V.—See FAM AB; *Int'l*, pg. 2611
IPCO PROCESS SYSTEM (SHANGHAI) LTD.—See FAM AB; *Int'l*, pg. 2611
IPCO RUS LTD—See FAM AB; *Int'l*, pg. 2611
IPCOS BV—See ATS Corporation; *Int'l*, pg. 695

COMPANY NAME INDEX

IPCOS ENGINEERING SOLUTIONS PVT. LTD.—See ATS Corporation; *Int'l*, pg. 695
IPCOS NV—See ATS Corporation; *Int'l*, pg. 695
IPCOS (UK) LTD.—See ATS Corporation; *Int'l*, pg. 695
IPCO US, LLC—See FAM AB; *Int'l*, pg. 2611
IPC PRINT SERVICES, INC.—See Walsworth Publishing Company, Inc.; *U.S. Private*, pg. 4433
IPCREATE INC.; *U.S. Private*, pg. 2136
IPC; *U.S. Private*, pg. 2136
IPC SYSTEMS, INC.—See Strategic Value Partners, LLC; *U.S. Private*, pg. 3836
IPC (USA) INC.—See Truman Arnold Companies; *U.S. Private*, pg. 4250
IPDC FINANCE LIMITED—See Aga Khan Development Network; *Int'l*, pg. 199
IPD DALIAN ENGINEERING LIMITED—See Japan Process Development Co., Ltd.; *Int'l*, pg. 3903
IPDECAUX INC.—See JCDecaux S.A.; *Int'l*, pg. 3921
IP DECORA EAST—See Decora S.A.; *Int'l*, pg. 2001
IPD GROUP LIMITED; *Int'l*, pg. 3796
IPD NEDERLAND B.V.—See MSCI Inc.; *U.S. Public*, pg. 1483
IPD PRINTING—See Chatham Asset Management, LLC; *U.S. Private*, pg. 863
IPE BV—See Aviva plc; *Int'l*, pg. 746
IPECO HOLDINGS LTD. - IPECO COMPOSITES DIVISION—See Ipeco Holdings Ltd.; *Int'l*, pg. 3796
IPECO HOLDINGS LTD.; *Int'l*, pg. 3796
IPECO INC.—See Ipeco Holdings Ltd.; *Int'l*, pg. 3796
IP E-GAME VENTURES INC.—See Millennium Global Holdings, Inc.; *Int'l*, pg. 4895
IPE GROUP LIMITED—See China Baoan Group Co., Ltd.; *Int'l*, pg. 1485
IPEK DOGAL ENERJI KAYNAKLARI ARASTIRMA VE URETIM AS; *Int'l*, pg. 3796
IPEK KAGIT KAZAKHSTAN LLP—See Eczacibasi Holding A.S.; *Int'l*, pg. 2302
IPEK KAGIT SAN. VE TIC. A.S.—See Eczacibasi Holding A.S.; *Int'l*, pg. 2301
IPE KRYVBASVYBUHPROM, PJSC; *Int'l*, pg. 3796
IPEK SPEZIAL-TV GMBH—See IDEX Corp; *U.S. Public*, pg. 1092
IP EMPAQUES DE MEXICO, S. DE R.L. DE C.V.—See International Paper Company; *U.S. Public*, pg. 1155
IPEOPLE INC.—See Yuchengco Group of Companies; *Int'l*, pg. 8609
IPERCEPTIONS INC.; *Int'l*, pg. 3796
IPERIONX LIMITED; *Int'l*, pg. 3796
IPERIONX TECHNOLOGY LLC—See Iperionx Limited; *Int'l*, pg. 3797
IPESA DE GUATEMALA—See Hewlett Packard Enterprise Company; *U.S. Public*, pg. 1032
IPET INSURANCE CO., LTD.—See Dream Incubator Inc.; *Int'l*, pg. 2202
IPETRONIK EICHSTATT GMBH—See INDUS Holding AG; *Int'l*, pg. 3663
IPETRONIK GMBH & CO. KG—See INDUS Holding AG; *Int'l*, pg. 3663
IPETRONIK INC.—See INDUS Holding AG; *Int'l*, pg. 3663
IPETRONIK INDIA PRIVATE LIMITED—See INDUS Holding AG; *Int'l*, pg. 3663
IPEX BRANDING INC—See Aliaxis S.A./N.V.; *Int'l*, pg. 324
IPEX CAPITAL, LTD.; *Int'l*, pg. 3797
I-PEX CO., LTD—See I-PEX Inc.; *Int'l*, pg. 3564
I-PEX ELECTRICAL INC—See Aliaxis S.A./N.V.; *Int'l*, pg. 325
I-PEX ELECTRONICS (H.K.) LTD.—See I-PEX Inc.; *Int'l*, pg. 3564
I-PEX EUROPE SARL—See I-PEX Inc.; *Int'l*, pg. 3564
I-PEX GLOBAL OPERATIONS, INC.—See I-PEX Inc.; *Int'l*, pg. 3564
IPEX, INC.—See Aliaxis S.A./N.V.; *Int'l*, pg. 324
I-PEX INC.; *Int'l*, pg. 3563
I-PEX KOREA CO., LTD.—See I-PEX Inc.; *Int'l*, pg. 3564
IPEX MANAGEMENT INC—See Aliaxis S.A./N.V.; *Int'l*, pg. 325
IPEXPERT, INC.; *U.S. Private*, pg. 2136
I-PEX (SHANGHAI) CO., LTD.—See I-PEX Inc.; *Int'l*, pg. 3564
I-PEX SINGAPORE PTE. LTD.—See I-PEX Inc.; *Int'l*, pg. 3564
IPEX USA LLC—See Aliaxis S.A./N.V.; *Int'l*, pg. 325
IPEX USA MANUFACTURING/DISTRIBUTION—See Aliaxis S.A./N.V.; *Int'l*, pg. 324
IPF DIGITAL AS—See International Personal Finance plc; *Int'l*, pg. 3751
IPF DIGITAL AUSTRALIA PTY. LIMITED—See International Personal Finance plc; *Int'l*, pg. 3751
IPF DIGITAL FINLAND OY—See International Personal Finance plc; *Int'l*, pg. 3751
IPF DIGITAL LATVIA, SIA—See International Personal Finance plc; *Int'l*, pg. 3751
IPF DIGITAL LIETUVA, UAB—See International Personal Finance plc; *Int'l*, pg. 3751
IPF DIGITAL MEXICO S.A DE C.V—See International Personal Finance plc; *Int'l*, pg. 3751
IPF ELECTRONIC GMBH; *Int'l*, pg. 3797
IPFOLIO CORPORATION; *U.S. Private*, pg. 2136

IPF POLSKA SP. Z O.O.—See International Personal Finance plc; *Int'l*, pg. 3751
IPFS CORPORATION; *U.S. Private*, pg. 2136
IP FUSION, INC.—See Access Co., Ltd.; *Int'l*, pg. 88
IP GANSOW GMBH—See Tennant Company; *U.S. Public*, pg. 2016
IPG (BEIJING) FIBER LASER TECHNOLOGY CO., LTD.—See IPG Photonics Corporation; *U.S. Public*, pg. 1167
IPG FIBERTECH S.R.L.—See IPG Photonics Corporation; *U.S. Public*, pg. 1167
IPG INC.—See Dentsu Group Inc.; *Int'l*, pg. 2039
IPG IRE-POLUS—See IPG Photonics Corporation; *U.S. Public*, pg. 1167
IPG LASER GMBH—See IPG Photonics Corporation; *U.S. Public*, pg. 1167
IPGL LIMITED; *Int'l*, pg. 3797
IPG MARKETING SOLUTIONS PTY LTD—See Domino's Pizza Enterprises Ltd.; *Int'l*, pg. 2162
IPG MEDIABRANDS—See The Interpublic Group of Companies, Inc.; *U.S. Public*, pg. 2094
IPG PHOTONICS CORPORATION; *U.S. Public*, pg. 1167
IPG PHOTONICS (INDIA) PVT. LTD.—See IPG Photonics Corporation; *U.S. Public*, pg. 1167
IPG PHOTONICS (JAPAN) LTD.—See IPG Photonics Corporation; *U.S. Public*, pg. 1167
IPG PHOTONICS (KOREA) LTD.—See IPG Photonics Corporation; *U.S. Public*, pg. 1167
IPG PHOTONICS (UK) LTD.—See IPG Photonics Corporation; *U.S. Public*, pg. 1167
IP GROUP PLC; *Int'l*, pg. 3795
I&P GROUP SDN. BERHAD—See S P Setia Berhad; *Int'l*, pg. 6443
IPG; *U.S. Private*, pg. 2136
IPG USA PLAN LLC—See IP Group plc; *Int'l*, pg. 3795
IPG (US) HOLDINGS INC.—See Clearlake Capital Group, L.P.; *U.S. Private*, pg. 935
IPH LIMITED; *Int'l*, pg. 3797
IP HOLDINGS AND MANAGEMENT CORPORATION—See Iconix Acquisition LLC; *U.S. Private*, pg. 2032
IP HOLDINGS UNLTD LLC—See Iconix Acquisition LLC; *U.S. Private*, pg. 2032
IPIC ENTERTAINMENT INC.; *U.S. Public*, pg. 1167
IPICO.—See Brookfield Corporation; *Int'l*, pg. 1189
IPICO SOUTH AFRICA (PTY) LTD.—See Brookfield Corporation; *Int'l*, pg. 1189
IPICS CORPORATION—See Denso Corporation; *Int'l*, 2032
IPI GRAMMTECH, INC.; *U.S. Private*, pg. 2136
I PINCO PALLINO S.P.A.—See Lunar Capital Management Ltd.; *Int'l*, pg. 4579
IP INDIA FOUNDATION—See International Paper Company; *U.S. Public*, pg. 1155
IP INFUSION SOFTWARE INDIA PVT. LTD.—See Access Co., Ltd.; *Int'l*, pg. 88
IPI PARTNERS, LLC—See ICONIQ Capital, LLC; *U.S. Private*, pg. 2032
IPI PARTNERS, LLC—See Iron Point Partners, LLC; *U.S. Private*, pg. 2139
IPIPELINE, INC.—See Roper Technologies, Inc.; *U.S. Public*, pg. 1814
IPIPELINE LIMITED—See Roper Technologies, Inc.; *U.S. Public*, pg. 1814
IPIRANGA IMOBILIARIA LTDA.—See Ultrapar Participacoes S.A.; *Int'l*, pg. 8019
IPIRANGA PRODUTOS DE PETROLEO S.A.—See Ultrapar Participacoes S.A.; *Int'l*, pg. 8019
IPIRANGA QUIMICA S.A.—See Novonor S.A.; *Int'l*, pg. 5469
IPI S.R.L.—See Coesia S.p.A.; *Int'l*, pg. 1690
IPITEK; *U.S. Private*, pg. 2136
IPK CO., LTD.—See NOROO Paint & Coatings Co., Ltd.; *Int'l*, pg. 5431
IPKEYS POWER PARTNERS, INC—See Parsons Corporation; *U.S. Public*, pg. 1651
IPKEYS TECHNOLOGIES LLC—See The Chickasaw Nation; *U.S. Private*, pg. 4008
I & P KOTA BAYUEMAS SDN BHD—See S P Setia Berhad; *Int'l*, pg. 6443
IP LABS GMBH—See FUJIFILM Holdings Corporation; *Int'l*, pg. 2822
IPLACEMENT, INC.; *U.S. Private*, pg. 2136
IPLANET INC.—See Mitsubishi Electric Corporation; *Int'l*, pg. 4944
IPLAYCO CORPORATION LTD.; *Int'l*, pg. 3797
I PLAY., INC.; *U.S. Private*, pg. 2020
IPLEX PIPELINES AUSTRALIA PTY LTD—See Fletcher Building Limited; *Int'l*, pg. 2699
IPLEX PIPELINES NZ LIMITED—See Fletcher Building Limited; *Int'l*, pg. 2699
IPL PLASTICS INC—See Madison Dearborn Partners, LLC; *U.S. Private*, pg. 2541
IPL RESEARCH LIMITED—See Computer & Technologies Holdings Limited; *Int'l*, pg. 1758
IPL SANTE ENVIRONNEMENT DURABLE ATLANTIQUE SAS—See Eurofins Scientific S.E.; *Int'l*, pg. 2542
IP MEDIA (XIAMEN) CO., LTD.—See International Press Softcom Limited; *Int'l*, pg. 3752

I & P MENARA SENDIRIAN BERHAD—See S P Setia Berhad; *Int'l*, pg. 6443
IPM ENERGY TRADING LIMITED—See ENGIE SA; *Int'l*, pg. 2432
IPM HOLDINGS, INC.; *Int'l*, pg. 3797
IPM HOLLAND B.V.—See Donegal Investment Group Plc; *Int'l*, pg. 2163
IPM INDIA WHOLESALE TRADING PRIVATE LIMITED—See Philip Morris International Inc.; *U.S. Public*, pg. 1685
IPM INFORMED PORTFOLIO MANAGEMENT AB—See Catella AB; *Int'l*, pg. 1359
IPM INTEGRATED PRESCRIPTION MANAGEMENT; *U.S. Private*, pg. 2136
IPM NISHIMOTO CO., LTD.—See Nishimoto Co., Ltd.; *Int'l*, pg. 5365
IP MORTGAGE BORROWER LLC—See Vornado Realty Trust; *U.S. Public*, pg. 2310
IPMOTION INC.—See Imagica Group Inc.; *Int'l*, pg. 3618
IPM PERTH LIMITED—See Donegal Investment Group Plc; *Int'l*, pg. 2163
IPM POTATO GROUP LIMITED—See Donegal Investment Group Plc; *Int'l*, pg. 2163
IPM SOFTWARE, INC.—See GI Manager L.P.; *U.S. Private*, pg. 1693
IPN CRM BV—See IPN Holding B.V.; *Int'l*, pg. 3797
IP NETWORKS, INC.; *U.S. Private*, pg. 2136
IPN EUROPE B.V.—See IPN Holding B.V.; *Int'l*, pg. 3797
IPN HEALTHCARE S.A.—See IPN Holding B.V.; *Int'l*, pg. 3797
IPN HOLDING B.V.; *Int'l*, pg. 3797
IPN LEARNING PTY LIMITED—See Sonic Healthcare Limited; *Int'l*, pg. 7097
IPN MEDICAL CENTRES (QLD) PTY LIMITED—See Sonic Healthcare Limited; *Int'l*, pg. 7097
IPN SERVICES PTY LIMITED—See Sonic Healthcare Limited; *Int'l*, pg. 7097
IPODEC CISTE MESTO A.S—See Veolia Environnement S.A.; *Int'l*, pg. 8159
IPO.GO AG; *Int'l*, pg. 3797
IPOH SPECIALIST HOSPITAL SDN BHD—See KPJ Healthcare Berhad; *Int'l*, pg. 4296
IPOINT-MEDIA LTD.; *Int'l*, pg. 3797
IPOINT-MEDIA LTD.—See iPoint-media Ltd.; *Int'l*, pg. 3797
IP-ONLY TELECOMMUNICATION AB—See EQT AB; *Int'l*, pg. 2475
IP OOO MINAVTO—See KAP Beteiligungs-AG; *Int'l*, pg. 4076
IPOPEMA BUSINESS CONSULTING SP. Z O.O.—See IPOPEMA Securities S.A.; *Int'l*, pg. 3797
IPOPEMA FINANCIAL ADVISORY SP. Z O.O.—See IPOPEMA Securities S.A.; *Int'l*, pg. 3797
IPOPEMA SECURITIES S.A.; *Int'l*, pg. 3797
IPOPEMA TOWARZYSTWO FUNDUSZY INWESTYCYJNYCH S.A.—See IPOPEMA Securities S.A.; *Int'l*, pg. 3797
I-POP NETWORKS PTE LTD—See InternetQ plc; *Int'l*, pg. 3754
I-PORK CORP. - HONJO PLANT—See Itoham Yonekyu Holdings Inc.; *Int'l*, pg. 3843
I-PORK CORP.—See Itoham Yonekyu Holdings Inc.; *Int'l*, pg. 3843
IPOSA PROPERTIES SOCIMI, S.A.; *Int'l*, pg. 3798
IPOWER INC.; *U.S. Public*, pg. 1167
I-POWER SOLUTIONS INDIA LTD.; *Int'l*, pg. 3564
IPOWERWEB INC.; *U.S. Private*, pg. 2137
IP PATHWAYS, LLC; *U.S. Private*, pg. 2136
IPPJ SDN BHD—See Johor Corporation; *Int'l*, pg. 3994
IP PLURIMEDIA SA—See Bertelsmann SE & Co. KGaA; *Int'l*, pg. 994
IPPLUS (UK) LIMITED—See The Yonder Digital Group Limited; *Int'l*, pg. 7705
IPPOKRATIS MAGNETIC TOMOGRAPHY S.A.—See AXON Holdings S.A.; *Int'l*, pg. 770
IPPOSHA OIL INDUSTRIES CO., LTD.—See Lion Corporation; *Int'l*, pg. 4517
IP-PRODUKTER OY—See K-Develop Oy; *Int'l*, pg. 4042
IPRAD SANTE; *Int'l*, pg. 3798
IPRAGAZ A.S.—See SHV Holdings N.V.; *Int'l*, pg. 6873
IPREL PROGETTI S.R.L.—See Sacmi Imola S.C.A.R.L.; *Int'l*, pg. 6463
IPR - GDF SUEZ AUSTRALIA PTY LTD - KWINANA COGENERATION PLANT—See ENGIE SA; *Int'l*, pg. 2432
IPR - GDF SUEZ AUSTRALIA PTY LTD—See ENGIE SA; *Int'l*, pg. 2432
IPR - GDF SUEZ LATIN AMERICA—See ENGIE SA; *Int'l*, pg. 2432
IPR - GDF SUEZ MIDDLE EAST, TURKEY & AFRICA—See ENGIE SA; *Int'l*, pg. 2433
IPR - GDF SUEZ NORTH AFRICA—See ENGIE SA; *Int'l*, pg. 2433
IPR - GDF SUEZ NORTH AMERICA—See ENGIE SA; *Int'l*, pg. 2433
I PRINT OY—See Ilkka Yhtymae Oyj; *Int'l*, pg. 3615
IPR LICENSING, INC.—See InterDigital, Inc.; *U.S. Public*, pg. 1144
IPRO DRESDEN; *Int'l*, pg. 3798
I-PROFESSIONAL SEARCH NETWORK, INC.—See Now Corporation; *Int'l*, pg. 5471

IPRO DRESDEN
CORPORATE AFFILIATIONS

IPROFILE, LLC.—See TA Associates, Inc.; *U.S. Private*, pg. 3915
I-PROJECTS B.V.—See Solutions 30 SE; *Int'l*, pg. 7077
IPROLAM SA BUCURESTI; *Int'l*, pg. 3798
I-PROMO PTE LTD—See Kingsmen Creatives Ltd; *Int'l*, pg. 4175
IPROMOTEU, INC.—See Champlain Capital Management LLC; *U.S. Private*, pg. 847
IPROPERTY.COM MALAYSIA SDN BHD—See News Corporation; *U.S. Public*, pg. 1521
IPROPERTY.COM PTY. LTD.—See News Corporation; *U.S. Public*, pg. 1520
IPROPERTY.COM SINGAPORE PTE. LTD.—See News Corporation; *U.S. Public*, pg. 1520
IPROPERTY GROUP LIMITED—See News Corporation; *U.S. Public*, pg. 1521
IPROSPECT—See Dentsu Group Inc.; *Int'l*, pg. 2037
IPRO TECH, LLC—See K1 Investment Management, LLC; *U.S. Private*, pg. 2252
IPRO TECHNOLOGY INC.—See EDOM Technology Co., Ltd.; *Int'l*, pg. 2313
IPR PHARMACEUTICAL INC.—See AstraZeneca PLC; *Int'l*, pg. 660
IPS ADHESIVES (JIASHAN) CO., LTD.—See IPS Corporation; *U.S. Private*, pg. 2137
IPSCO KOPPEL TUBULARS CORPORATION—See Techint S.p.A.; *Int'l*, pg. 7504
IPS CO., LTD; *Int'l*, pg. 3798
IPS CORPORATION; *U.S. Private*, pg. 2137
IPSCO TUBULARS INC.—See Techint S.p.A.; *Int'l*, pg. 7504
IPSCO TUBULARS (KENTUCKY) INC.—See Techint S.p.A.; *Int'l*, pg. 7504
IPSEN (BEIJING) PHARMACEUTICAL SCIENCE & TECHNOLOGY DEVELOPMENT CO., LTD.—See Ipsen S.A.; *Int'l*, pg. 3798
IPSEN BIOPHARMACEUTICALS CANADA INC.—See Ipsen S.A.; *Int'l*, pg. 3798
IPSEN BIOPHARMACEUTICALS, INC.—See Ipsen S.A.; *Int'l*, pg. 3798
IPSEN EPE—See Ipsen S.A.; *Int'l*, pg. 3798
IPSEN FARMACEUTICA B.V.—See Ipsen S.A.; *Int'l*, pg. 3798
IPSEN INDUSTRIES NORDISKA AB—See Quadriga Capital Beteiligungsberatung GmbH; *Int'l*, pg. 6150
IPSEN INTERNATIONAL GMBH—See Quadriga Capital Beteiligungsberatung GmbH; *Int'l*, pg. 6150
IPSEN INTERNATIONAL HOLDING GMBH—See Quadriga Capital Beteiligungsberatung GmbH; *Int'l*, pg. 6150
IPSEN INTERNATIONAL, INC.—See Quadriga Capital Beteiligungsberatung GmbH; *Int'l*, pg. 6150
IPSEN KOREA LTD.—See Ipsen S.A.; *Int'l*, pg. 3798
IPSEN N.V.—See Ipsen S.A.; *Int'l*, pg. 3798
IPSEN OOO—See Ipsen S.A.; *Int'l*, pg. 3798
IPSEN PHARMA GMBH—See Ipsen S.A.; *Int'l*, pg. 3798
IPSEN PHARMA S.A.—See Ipsen S.A.; *Int'l*, pg. 3798
IPSEN PHARMA S.A.S.—See Ipsen S.A.; *Int'l*, pg. 3798
IPSEN PHARMA S.R.O.—See Ipsen S.A.; *Int'l*, pg. 3798
IPSEN PTY LIMITED—See Ipsen S.A.; *Int'l*, pg. 3798
IPSEN S.A.; *Int'l*, pg. 3798
IPSEN (TIANJIN) PHARMACEUTICAL TRADE CO., LTD.—See Ipsen S.A.; *Int'l*, pg. 3798
IPSEN UKRAINE SERVICES LLC—See Ipsen S.A.; *Int'l*, pg. 3798
I & P SETIAWANGSA SDN.BHD.—See S P Setia Berhad; *Int'l*, pg. 6443
IPSH!—See Omnicom Group Inc.; *U.S. Public*, pg. 1600
IPSICOM SAS—See VINCI S.A.; *Int'l*, pg. 8223
IPSI L.L.C.—See Bechtel Group, Inc.; *U.S. Private*, pg. 510
IP SINGAPORE HOLDING PTE. LTD.—See International Paper Company; *U.S. Public*, pg. 1155
IPS - INNOVA PACKAGING SYSTEMS NV—See CABKA Group GmbH; *Int'l*, pg. 1245
IPS INTEGRATED PACKAGING SYSTEMS FZCO—See Krones AG; *Int'l*, pg. 4305
IPSIS, SAS—See IT Link S.A.; *Int'l*, pg. 3827
IPS METEOSTAR, INC.—See Danaher Corporation; *U.S. Public*, pg. 627
IPSOA EDITORE SRL—See Wolters Kluwer n.v.; *Int'l*, pg. 8445
IP SOFTCOM (AUSTRALIA) PTY LTD—See International Press Softcom Limited; *Int'l*, pg. 3752
IP SOFTCOM (MALAYSIA) SDN. BHD.—See International Press Softcom Limited; *Int'l*, pg. 3752
IP SOFTCOM (SHANGHAI) CO., LTD.—See International Press Softcom Limited; *Int'l*, pg. 3752
IP SOFTCOM (SHENZHEN) CO., LTD.—See International Press Softcom Limited; *Int'l*, pg. 3752
IP SOFTCOM (XIAMEN) CO., LTD.—See International Press Softcom Limited; *Int'l*, pg. 3752
IPSOGEN INC.—See QIAGEN N.V.; *Int'l*, pg. 6140
IPSOL ENERGY LIMITED—See Plutus PowerGen plc; *Int'l*, pg. 5899
IPSO MANAGEMENT LIMITED—See Plutus PowerGen plc; *Int'l*, pg. 5899
IPSOS AMERICA, INC.—See Ipsos S.A.; *Int'l*, pg. 3799
IPSOS AOM BOLIVIA—See Ipsos S.A.; *Int'l*, pg. 3799
IPSOS AOM—See Ipsos S.A.; *Int'l*, pg. 3799

IPSOS ARGENTINA S.A.—See Ipsos S.A.; *Int'l*, pg. 3799
IPSOS ASIA LTD.—See Ipsos S.A.; *Int'l*, pg. 3799
IPSOS ASI GMBH—See Ipsos S.A.; *Int'l*, pg. 3799
IPSOS-ASI, INC.—See Ipsos S.A.; *Int'l*, pg. 3801
IPSOS ASI ITALY—See Ipsos S.A.; *Int'l*, pg. 3800
IPSOS ASI—See Ipsos S.A.; *Int'l*, pg. 3799
IPSOS-ASI—See Ipsos S.A.; *Int'l*, pg. 3801
IPSOS-ASI—See Ipsos S.A.; *Int'l*, pg. 3801
IPSOS-ASI—See Ipsos S.A.; *Int'l*, pg. 3801
IPSOS ASI VENEZUELA CA—See Ipsos S.A.; *Int'l*, pg. 3799
IPSOS A/S—See Ipsos S.A.; *Int'l*, pg. 3799
IPSOS AS—See Ipsos S.A.; *Int'l*, pg. 3799
IPSOS AUSTRALIA PTY LTD—See Ipsos S.A.; *Int'l*, pg. 3799
IPSOS BAHNREISENFORSCHUNG GMBH—See Ipsos S.A.; *Int'l*, pg. 3799
IPSOS BELGIUM SA—See Ipsos S.A.; *Int'l*, pg. 3799
IPSOS BRASIL PESQUISAS DE MERCADO LTDA—See Ipsos S.A.; *Int'l*, pg. 3799
IPSOS BRAZIL LTDA.—See Ipsos S.A.; *Int'l*, pg. 3799
IPSOS BRUSSELS—See Ipsos S.A.; *Int'l*, pg. 3799
IPSOS B.V.—See Ipsos S.A.; *Int'l*, pg. 3799
IPSOS CANADA, INC.—See Ipsos S.A.; *Int'l*, pg. 3799
IPSOS CA—See Ipsos S.A.; *Int'l*, pg. 3799
IPSOS (CHILE) S.A.—See Ipsos S.A.; *Int'l*, pg. 3799
IPSOS (CHILE) S.A.S—See Ipsos S.A.; *Int'l*, pg. 3799
IPSOS CO., LTD.—See Ipsos S.A.; *Int'l*, pg. 3799
IPSOS COMCON LLC—See Ipsos S.A.; *Int'l*, pg. 3799
IPSOS COSTA RICA SA—See Ipsos S.A.; *Int'l*, pg. 3799
IPSOS D.O.O.—See Ipsos S.A.; *Int'l*, pg. 3801
IPSOS D.O.O.—See Ipsos S.A.; *Int'l*, pg. 3801
IPSOS D.O.O—See Ipsos S.A.; *Int'l*, pg. 3801
IPSOS ECUADOR SA—See Ipsos S.A.; *Int'l*, pg. 3799
IPSOS ESTUDIOS INTERNACIONALES SA—See Ipsos S.A.; *Int'l*, pg. 3800
IPSOS-FMC, INC.—See Ipsos S.A.; *Int'l*, pg. 3799
IPSOS FORWARD RESEARCH, INC.—See Ipsos S.A.; *Int'l*, pg. 3799
IPSOS FRANCE SAS—See Ipsos S.A.; *Int'l*, pg. 3799
IPSOS GMBH—See Ipsos S.A.; *Int'l*, pg. 3799
IPSOS GMBH—See Ipsos S.A.; *Int'l*, pg. 3799
IPSOS GROUP GIE—See Ipsos S.A.; *Int'l*, pg. 3799
IPSOS GROUP—See Ipsos S.A.; *Int'l*, pg. 3799
IPSOS HERRARTE, S.A. DE C.V.—See Ipsos S.A.; *Int'l*, pg. 3799
IPSOS HOLDING BELGIUM SA—See Ipsos S.A.; *Int'l*, pg. 3799
IPSOS HONG KONG LIMITED—See Ipsos S.A.; *Int'l*, pg. 3800
IPSOS HUNGARY ZRT—See Ipsos S.A.; *Int'l*, pg. 3800
IPSOS INC.—See Ipsos S.A.; *Int'l*, pg. 3800
IPSOS, INC.—See Ipsos S.A.; *Int'l*, pg. 3801
IPSOS INDONESIA PT—See Ipsos S.A.; *Int'l*, pg. 3800
IPSOS INSIGHT CORP.—See Ipsos S.A.; *Int'l*, pg. 3800
IPSOS INSIGHT INC—See Ipsos S.A.; *Int'l*, pg. 3800
IPSOS INTERACTIVE SERVICES CANADA LP—See Ipsos S.A.; *Int'l*, pg. 3800
IPSOS INTERACTIVE SERVICES SRL—See Ipsos S.A.; *Int'l*, pg. 3800
IPSOS-INVESTIGACION DE MERCADOS—See Ipsos S.A.; *Int'l*, pg. 3802
IPSOS JAPAN HOLDING KK—See Ipsos S.A.; *Int'l*, pg. 3800
IPSOS JSR KK—See Ipsos S.A.; *Int'l*, pg. 3800
IPSOS KK—See Ipsos S.A.; *Int'l*, pg. 3800
IPSOS KMG A.S.—See Ipsos S.A.; *Int'l*, pg. 3800
IPSOS LIMITED—See Ipsos S.A.; *Int'l*, pg. 3800
IPSOS LIMITED—See Ipsos S.A.; *Int'l*, pg. 3800
IPSOS LIMITED—See Ipsos S.A.; *Int'l*, pg. 3800
IPSOS LIMITED—See Ipsos S.A.; *Int'l*, pg. 3800
IPSOS LIMITED—See Ipsos S.A.; *Int'l*, pg. 3800
IPSOS LLC—See Ipsos S.A.; *Int'l*, pg. 3800
IPSOS LLP—See Ipsos S.A.; *Int'l*, pg. 3800
IPSOS LOYALTY GMBH—See Ipsos S.A.; *Int'l*, pg. 3799
IPSOS-LOYALTY, INC.—See Ipsos S.A.; *Int'l*, pg. 3802
IPSOS LOYALTY PTY LTD.—See Ipsos S.A.; *Int'l*, pg. 3800
IPSOS LTD.—See Ipsos S.A.; *Int'l*, pg. 3800
IPSOS LTD.—See Ipsos S.A.; *Int'l*, pg. 3800
IPSOS LTD.—See Ipsos S.A.; *Int'l*, pg. 3800
IPSOS (MALAYSIA) L.L.C.—See Ipsos S.A.; *Int'l*, pg. 3799
IPSOS MARKINOR PTY LTD—See Ipsos S.A.; *Int'l*, pg. 3800
IPSOS MORI—See Ipsos S.A.; *Int'l*, pg. 3802
IPSOS MORI UK LTD.—See Ipsos S.A.; *Int'l*, pg. 3800
IPSOS MOZAMBIQUE, LDA—See Ipsos S.A.; *Int'l*, pg. 3800
IPSOS MRBI LTD—See Ipsos S.A.; *Int'l*, pg. 3802
IPSOS NAPOLEON FRANCO & CO.—See Ipsos S.A.; *Int'l*, pg. 3800
IPSOS NAPOLEON FRANCO—See Ipsos S.A.; *Int'l*, pg. 3800
IPSOS NIGERIA LIMITED—See Ipsos S.A.; *Int'l*, pg. 3800
IPSOS NORM AB—See Ipsos S.A.; *Int'l*, pg. 3800
IPSOS NORTH AMERICA—See Ipsos S.A.; *Int'l*, pg. 3800
IPSOS NORTH AMERICA—See Ipsos S.A.; *Int'l*, pg. 3800
IPSOS NORWAY AS—See Ipsos S.A.; *Int'l*, pg. 3800
IPSOS NOVACTION KK—See Ipsos S.A.; *Int'l*, pg. 3800

IPSOS-NOVACTION LATIN AMERICA—See Ipsos S.A.; *Int'l*, pg. 3802
IPSOS-NOVACTION LATIN AMERICA—See Ipsos S.A.; *Int'l*, pg. 3802
IPSOS-NOVACTION LATIN AMERICA—See Ipsos S.A.; *Int'l*, pg. 3802
IPSOS-NPD CANADA INC.—See Ipsos S.A.; *Int'l*, pg. 3802
IPSOS NV (BELGIUM) SA—See Ipsos S.A.; *Int'l*, pg. 3800
IPSOS OBSERVER SA—See Ipsos S.A.; *Int'l*, pg. 3800
IPSOS OBSERVER SA—See Ipsos S.A.; *Int'l*, pg. 3800
IPSOS OOO LTD—See Ipsos S.A.; *Int'l*, pg. 3800
IPSOS OPERACIONES SA—See Ipsos S.A.; *Int'l*, pg. 3800
IPSOS OPERATIONS CANADA LP—See Ipsos S.A.; *Int'l*, pg. 3801
IPSOS OPERATIONS GMBH—See Ipsos S.A.; *Int'l*, pg. 3799
IPSOS OPERATIONS SRL—See Ipsos S.A.; *Int'l*, pg. 3801
IPSOS OPINION Y MERCADO S.A.—See Ipsos S.A.; *Int'l*, pg. 3801
IPSOS OPINION Y MERCADO SA—See Ipsos S.A.; *Int'l*, pg. 3801
IPSOS OTX CORP.—See Ipsos S.A.; *Int'l*, pg. 3800
IPSOS OTX INC.—See Ipsos S.A.; *Int'l*, pg. 3800
IPSOS PANAMA SA—See Ipsos S.A.; *Int'l*, pg. 3801
IPSOS POLSKA SP. Z.O.O.—See Ipsos S.A.; *Int'l*, pg. 3801
IPSOS PORTUGAL—See Ipsos S.A.; *Int'l*, pg. 3801
IPSOS (PTY) LTD.—See Ipsos S.A.; *Int'l*, pg. 3799
IPSOS PUBLIC AFFAIRS PTY LTD—See Ipsos S.A.; *Int'l*, pg. 3801
IPSOS PULS DOO SPLIT—See Ipsos S.A.; *Int'l*, pg. 3801
IPSOS REID CORP.—See Ipsos S.A.; *Int'l*, pg. 3801
IPSOS-REID PUBLIC AFFAIRS, INC.—See Ipsos S.A.; *Int'l*, pg. 3799
IPSOS RESEARCH PVT. LTD.—See Ipsos S.A.; *Int'l*, pg. 3801
IPSOS SARL—See Ipsos S.A.; *Int'l*, pg. 3801
IPSOS SARL—See Ipsos S.A.; *Int'l*, pg. 3801
IPSOS, S.A.—See Ipsos S.A.; *Int'l*, pg. 3801
IPSOS SA—See Ipsos S.A.; *Int'l*, pg. 3801
IPSOS S.A.; *Int'l*, pg. 3798
IPSOS SAUDI ARABIA LLC—See Ipsos S.A.; *Int'l*, pg. 3801
IPSOS SDN. BHD.—See Ipsos S.A.; *Int'l*, pg. 3801
IPSOS SENEGAL SASU—See Ipsos S.A.; *Int'l*, pg. 3801
IPSOS SINGAPORE PTE LTD—See Ipsos S.A.; *Int'l*, pg. 3801
IPSOS SP. Z. O. O.—See Ipsos S.A.; *Int'l*, pg. 3801
IPSOS SRL—See Ipsos S.A.; *Int'l*, pg. 3801
IPSOS SRL—See Ipsos S.A.; *Int'l*, pg. 3801
IPSOS STAT BAHRAIN W.L.L—See Ipsos S.A.; *Int'l*, pg. 3802
IPSOS STAT FZ. LLC—See Ipsos S.A.; *Int'l*, pg. 3802
IPSOS STAT JORDAN LTD.—See Ipsos S.A.; *Int'l*, pg. 3801
IPSOS-STAT—See Ipsos S.A.; *Int'l*, pg. 3802
IPSOS STRATEGIC MARKETING D.O.O.—See Ipsos S.A.; *Int'l*, pg. 3801
IPSOS STRATEGIC PULS D.O.O.E.L. SKOPJE—See Ipsos S.A.; *Int'l*, pg. 3801
IPSOS STRATEGIC PULS DOOEL—See Ipsos S.A.; *Int'l*, pg. 3798
IPSOS STRATEGIC PULS D.O.O.—See Ipsos S.A.; *Int'l*, pg. 3801
IPSOS STRATEGIC PULS SA'JEWO—See Ipsos S.A.; *Int'l*, pg. 3801
IPSOS STRATEGIC PULS SAS—See Ipsos S.A.; *Int'l*, pg. 3801
IPSOS (SUISSE) SA—See Ipsos S.A.; *Int'l*, pg. 3799
IPSOS SWEDEN AB—See Ipsos S.A.; *Int'l*, pg. 3801
IPSOS-SZONDA—See Ipsos S.A.; *Int'l*, pg. 3802
IPSOS TAIWAN LTD.—See Ipsos S.A.; *Int'l*, pg. 3801
IPSOS TAMBOR S.R.O.—See Ipsos S.A.; *Int'l*, pg. 3801
IPSOS TAMBOR SR S.R.O.—See Ipsos S.A.; *Int'l*, pg. 3801
IPSOS TANZANIA LIMITED—See Ipsos S.A.; *Int'l*, pg. 3801
IPSOS (THAILAND) LTD—See Ipsos S.A.; *Int'l*, pg. 3799
IPSOS UKRAINE LLC—See Ipsos S.A.; *Int'l*, pg. 3801
IPSOS USA, INC.—See Ipsos S.A.; *Int'l*, pg. 3799
IPSOS ZRT.—See Ipsos S.A.; *Int'l*, pg. 3801
IPSOTEK LTD.—See Atos SE; *Int'l*, pg. 692
THE IPS PARTNERSHIP PLC—See Epiris Managers LLP; *Int'l*, pg. 2461
IPS PENSIONS LIMITED—See Epiris Managers LLP; *Int'l*, pg. 2461
IPS SECUREX HOLDINGS LIMITED; *Int'l*, pg. 3798
IPS SECUREX PTE. LTD.—See IPS Securex Holdings Limited; *Int'l*, pg. 3798
IP STRATEGY LLC—See Eversource Energy; *U.S. Public*, pg. 801
IPSWICH BUILDING SOCIETY; *Int'l*, pg. 3802
IPSWICH CHRONICLE—See Gannett Co., Inc.; *U.S. Public*, pg. 902
IPSWICH SHELLFISH CO. INC.; *U.S. Private*, pg. 2137
IPSWITCH, INC.—See Progress Software Corporation; *U.S. Public*, pg. 1725

IPT ASSOCIATES LLC.; *U.S. Private*, pg. 2137
IPTE ANDELEC SARL—See IPTE Factory Automation n.v.; *Int'l*, pg. 3802
IPTE AUTOMATION OU—See IPTE Factory Automation n.v.; *Int'l*, pg. 3802
IPTE BEERNEM—See IPTE Factory Automation n.v.; *Int'l*, pg. 3802
IPTEC PTE. LTD.—See Zicom Group Limited; *Int'l*, pg. 8681
IPTE FACTORY AUTOMATION N.V.; *Int'l*, pg. 3802
IPTE GERMANY GMBH—See IPTE Factory Automation n.v.; *Int'l*, pg. 3802
IPTE IBERIA - AUTOMACAO INDUSTRIAL—See IPTE Factory Automation n.v.; *Int'l*, pg. 3802
IPTE INDUSTRIAL AUTOMATION (SHANGHAI) CO. LTD.—See IPTE Factory Automation n.v.; *Int'l*, pg. 3802
IPTE MEXICO S. DE R.L. DE C.V.—See IPTE Factory Automation n.v.; *Int'l*, pg. 3802
IPTE ORADEA—See IPTE Factory Automation n.v.; *Int'l*, pg. 3802
IPTE PLATZGUMMER GMBH—See IPTE Factory Automation n.v.; *Int'l*, pg. 3802
IPTE PRODEL FRANCE S.A.—See IPTE Factory Automation n.v.; *Int'l*, pg. 3803
IPTE SPAIN S.L.U.—See IPTE Factory Automation n.v.; *Int'l*, pg. 3803
IPTE USA—See IPTE Factory Automation n.v.; *Int'l*, pg. 3803
IPTIQ GROUP HOLDING LTD.—See Swiss Re Ltd.; *Int'l*, pg. 7372
IPURE LABS, INC.; *U.S. Public*, pg. 1167
IPVALUE MANAGEMENT, INC.—See Vector Capital Management, L.P.; *U.S. Private*, pg. 4351
IPVIDEO CORPORATION—See Motorola Solutions, Inc.; *U.S. Public*, pg. 1477
IPVISTA A/S—See Arrow Electronics, Inc.; *U.S. Public*, pg. 199
IPWA PLC; *Int'l*, pg. 3803
IQ3CORP LIMITED; *Int'l*, pg. 3803
IQA OPERATIOS GROUP, LTD.—See Elecnor, S.A.; *Int'l*, pg. 2347
IQAP CZECH, S.R.O.—See Avient Corporation; *U.S. Public*, pg. 247
IQAP MASTERBATCH GROUP, S.L.—See Avient Corporation; *U.S. Public*, pg. 247
IQ BACKOFFICE, INC.—See Ayala Corporation; *Int'l*, pg. 774
IQBLADE LIMITED—See TD Synnex Corp; *U.S. Public*, pg. 1986
I.Q.BRANDS AE—See Vikos S.A.; *Int'l*, pg. 8206
IQ CAPITAL (USA) LLC—See The IQ Group Global Ltd.; *Int'l*, pg. 7657
IQ CREDIT UNION; *U.S. Private*, pg. 2137
I.Q. DATA INTERNATIONAL, INC.—See Assurant, Inc.; *U.S. Public*, pg. 215
IQD FREQUENCY PRODUCTS INC.—See Wurth Verwaltungsgesellschaft mbH; *Int'l*, pg. 8511
IQD FREQUENCY PRODUCTS LIMITED—See Wurth Verwaltungsgesellschaft mbH; *Int'l*, pg. 8505
IQD GROUP LIMITED—See Wurth Verwaltungsgesellschaft mbH; *Int'l*, pg. 8505
IQD HOLDINGS LIMITED—See Wurth Verwaltungsgesellschaft mbH; *Int'l*, pg. 8505
IQE (EUROPE) LTD—See IQE plc; *Int'l*, pg. 3803
IQE INC.—See IQE plc; *Int'l*, pg. 3803
IQE KC LLC—See IQE plc; *Int'l*, pg. 3803
IQE PLC; *Int'l*, pg. 3803
IQE PROPERTIES INC.—See IQE plc; *Int'l*, pg. 3803
IQ EQ LUXEMBOURG SA; *Int'l*, pg. 3803
IQE RF LLC—See IQE plc; *Int'l*, pg. 3803
IQ ERP—See Interquest Group plc; *Int'l*, pg. 3757
IQE SILICON COMPOUNDS LTD—See IQE plc; *Int'l*, pg. 3803
IQE TAIWAN CORP.—See IQE plc; *Int'l*, pg. 3803
IQGEO AMERICA INC.—See KKR & Co. Inc.; *U.S. Public*, pg. 1253
IQGEO GERMANY GMBH—See KKR & Co. Inc.; *U.S. Public*, pg. 1253
IQGEO GROUP PLC—See KKR & Co. Inc.; *U.S. Public*, pg. 1253
IQGEO JAPAN KK—See KKR & Co. Inc.; *U.S. Public*, pg. 1253
IQGEO UK LIMITED—See KKR & Co. Inc.; *U.S. Public*, pg. 1253
IQ GMG INTENSIVE QUALITY GLOBAL MEDICAL GROUP PUBLIC LTD.; *Int'l*, pg. 3803
IQ GROUP (DONGGUAN) LTD.—See IQ Group Holdings Berhad; *Int'l*, pg. 3803
THE IQ GROUP GLOBAL LTD.; *Int'l*, pg. 7657
IQ GROUP HOLDINGS BERHAD; *Int'l*, pg. 3803
IQ GROUP SDN. BHD.—See IQ Group Holdings Berhad; *Int'l*, pg. 3803
IQ INTERNATIONAL AG; *Int'l*, pg. 3803
IQINVISION, INC.—See Vicon Industries, Inc.; *U.S. Private*, pg. 4377
IQIYI, INC.—See Baidu, Inc.; *Int'l*, pg. 801
IQ JAPAN CO., LTD.—See IQ Group Holdings Berhad; *Int'l*, pg. 3803

IQMS INC.—See Dassault Systemes S.A.; *Int'l*, pg. 1975
IQNAVIGATOR, INC.; *U.S. Private*, pg. 2137
IQNET SP. Z O.O.—See Unima 2000 Systemy Teleinformatyczne S.A.; *Int'l*, pg. 8048
IQ OFFICE PRODUCTS LLC; *U.S. Private*, pg. 2137
IQ-OPTIMIZE SOFTWARE AG—See United Internet AG; *Int'l*, pg. 8069
IQOR, INC.—See HGGC, LLC; *U.S. Private*, pg. 1930
IQ PARTNERS S.A.; *Int'l*, pg. 3803
IQ PHYSICAL DIAMOND TRUST; *U.S. Private*, pg. 2137
IQ PIPELINE; *U.S. Private*, pg. 2137
IQ RADIOLOGY PTY. LTD.—See Integral Diagnostics Limited; *Int'l*, pg. 3730
IQR CONSULTING, INC.—See ExlService Holdings, Inc.; *U.S. Public*, pg. 808
IQ RESEARCH LIMITED—See 1Spatial Plc; *Int'l*, pg. 3
IQS AVANTIQ LUXEMBOURG SARL—See Wolters Kluwer n.v.; *Int'l*, pg. 8445
IQS INSURANCE RETENTION GROUP, INC.—See Covenant Logistics Group, Inc.; *U.S. Public*, pg. 588
IQ SOLUTIONS GMBH—See Silver Investment Partners GmbH & Co. KG; *Int'l*, pg. 6923
IQ SOLUTIONS; *U.S. Private*, pg. 2137
IQSTEL INC.; *U.S. Public*, pg. 1167
IQ STUDENT ACCOMMODATION; *Int'l*, pg. 3803
IQ TECHNOLOGY—See Interquest Group plc; *Int'l*, pg. 3757
IQUEST GMBH & CO KG—See Allgeier SE; *Int'l*, pg. 338
IQUEST SCHWEIZ AG—See Allgeier SE; *Int'l*, pg. 338
IQUEST TECHNOLOGIES KFT—See Allgeier SE; *Int'l*, pg. 338
IQUEST TECHNOLOGIES SRL—See Allgeier SE; *Int'l*, pg. 338
IQUII S.R.L.—See TAMBURI INVESTMENT PARTNERS S.p.A; *Int'l*, pg. 7450
IQUINOSA FARMA S.A.—See FAES Farma, S.A.; *Int'l*, pg. 2601
IQUIQUE TERMINAL INTERNACIONAL S.A.—See Quinenco S.A.; *Int'l*, pg. 6164
IQVIA AG—See IQVIA Holdings Inc.; *U.S. Public*, pg. 1169
IQVIA AG—See IQVIA Holdings Inc.; *U.S. Public*, pg. 1168
IQVIA BIOTECH LLC—See IQVIA Holdings Inc.; *U.S. Public*, pg. 1169
IQVIA BIOTECH LTD.—See IQVIA Holdings Inc.; *U.S. Public*, pg. 1169
IQVIA COMMERCIAL GMBH & CO. OHG—See IQVIA Holdings Inc.; *U.S. Public*, pg. 1169
IQVIA COMMERCIAL SOFTWARE GMBH—See IQVIA Holdings Inc.; *U.S. Public*, pg. 1169
IQVIA COMMERCIAL SP. Z O.O.—See IQVIA Holdings Inc.; *U.S. Public*, pg. 1169
IQVIA COMMERICAL CONSULTING SP. Z O.O.—See IQVIA Holdings Inc.; *U.S. Public*, pg. 1169
IQVIA CONSULTING AND INFORMATION SERVICES INDIA PVT. LTD.—See IQVIA Holdings Inc.; *U.S. Public*, pg. 1168
IQVIA CONSULTING & INFORMATION SERVICES INDIA PRIVATE LIMITED—See IQVIA Holdings Inc.; *U.S. Public*, pg. 1169
IQVIA GOVERNMENT SOLUTIONS, INC.—See IQVIA Holdings Inc.; *U.S. Public*, pg. 1168
IQVIA HOLDINGS INC.; *U.S. Public*, pg. 1168
IQVIA INC.—See IQVIA Holdings Inc.; *U.S. Public*, pg. 1168
IQVIA LTD.—See IQVIA Holdings Inc.; *U.S. Public*, pg. 1169
IQVIA NEDERLAND—See IQVIA Holdings Inc.; *U.S. Public*, pg. 1170
IQVIA QUALITY METRIC INC.—See IQVIA Holdings Inc.; *U.S. Public*, pg. 1169
IQVIA RDS AG—See IQVIA Holdings Inc.; *U.S. Public*, pg. 1169
IQVIA RDS AG—See IQVIA Holdings Inc.; *U.S. Public*, pg. 1170
IQVIA RDS AND INTEGRATED SERVICES BELGIUM NV—See IQVIA Holdings Inc.; *U.S. Public*, pg. 1170
IQVIA RDS D.O.O. BEOGRAD—See IQVIA Holdings Inc.; *U.S. Public*, pg. 1169
IQVIA RDS EAST ASIA PTE LTD.—See IQVIA Holdings Inc.; *U.S. Public*, pg. 1169
IQVIA RDS EASTERN HOLDINGS GMBH—See IQVIA Holdings Inc.; *U.S. Public*, pg. 1170
IQVIA RDS ESTONIA OU—See IQVIA Holdings Inc.; *U.S. Public*, pg. 1169
IQVIA RDS ESTONIA OU—See IQVIA Holdings Inc.; *U.S. Public*, pg. 1170
IQVIA RDS FRANCE SAS—See IQVIA Holdings Inc.; *U.S. Public*, pg. 1170
IQVIA RDS GES.M.B.H—See IQVIA Holdings Inc.; *U.S. Public*, pg. 1170
IQVIA RDS (INDIA) PRIVATE LIMITED—See IQVIA Holdings Inc.; *U.S. Public*, pg. 1169
IQVIA RDS IRELAND LIMITED—See IQVIA Holdings Inc.; *U.S. Public*, pg. 1170
IQVIA RDS LATVIA SIA—See IQVIA Holdings Inc.; *U.S. Public*, pg. 1169
IQVIA RDS MAGYARORSZAG GYOGYSZERFEJLESZTESI ES TANACSADO KFT.—See IQVIA Holdings Inc.; *U.S. Public*, pg. 1170

IQVIA RDS PTY. LIMITED—See IQVIA Holdings Inc.; *U.S. Public*, pg. 1170
IQVIA RDS SLOVAKIA S.R.O.—See IQVIA Holdings Inc.; *U.S. Public*, pg. 1169
IQVIA RDS SWITZERLAND SARL—See IQVIA Holdings Inc.; *U.S. Public*, pg. 1169
IQVIA RDS UK HOLDINGS LIMITED—See IQVIA Holdings Inc.; *U.S. Public*, pg. 1170
IQVIA ROMANIA S.R.L.—See IQVIA Holdings Inc.; *U.S. Public*, pg. 1169
IQVIA SOLUTIONS ARGENTINA S.A.—See IQVIA Holdings Inc.; *U.S. Public*, pg. 1168
IQVIA SOLUTIONS ASIA PTE. LTD.—See IQVIA Holdings Inc.; *U.S. Public*, pg. 1168
IQVIA SOLUTIONS BANGLADESH LIMITED—See IQVIA Holdings Inc.; *U.S. Public*, pg. 1168
IQVIA SOLUTIONS DO BRASIL LTDA.—See IQVIA Holdings Inc.; *U.S. Public*, pg. 1169
IQVIA SOLUTIONS GMBH—See IQVIA Holdings Inc.; *U.S. Public*, pg. 1169
IQVIA SOLUTIONS (NZ) LIMITED—See IQVIA Holdings Inc.; *U.S. Public*, pg. 1168
IQVIA SOLUTIONS PAKISTAN (PRIVATE) LIMITED—See IQVIA Holdings Inc.; *U.S. Public*, pg. 1169
IQVIA SOLUTIONS PHILIPINES, INC.—See IQVIA Holdings Inc.; *U.S. Public*, pg. 1169
IQVIA SOLUTIONS PHILIPPINES, INC.—See IQVIA Holdings Inc.; *U.S. Public*, pg. 1169
IQVIA SOLUTIONS PHILIPPINES INC.—See IQVIA Holdings Inc.; *U.S. Public*, pg. 1168
IQVIA SOLUTIONS TAIWAN LTD.—See IQVIA Holdings Inc.; *U.S. Public*, pg. 1168
IQVIA SOLUTIONS UK LIMITED—See IQVIA Holdings Inc.; *U.S. Public*, pg. 1169
IQVIA TECHNOLOGY AND SERVICES AG—See IQVIA Holdings Inc.; *U.S. Public*, pg. 1169
IQVIA TECHNOLOGY & SERVICES AG—See IQVIA Holdings Inc.; *U.S. Public*, pg. 1169
IQVIA TECHNOLOGY SOLUTIONS UKRAINE LLC—See IQVIA Holdings Inc.; *U.S. Public*, pg. 1170
IQVIA (THAILAND) CO. LTD.—See IQVIA Holdings Inc.; *U.S. Public*, pg. 1169
IQVIA (THAILAND) CO. LTD.—See IQVIA Holdings Inc.; *U.S. Public*, pg. 1169
IQ WONING B.V.—See Ronesans Holding A.S.; *Int'l*, pg. 6396
IQX LIMITED; *Int'l*, pg. 3803
IQZAN HOLDING BERHAD; *Int'l*, pg. 3803
IRACORE INTERNATIONAL, INC.—See Lime Rock Partners, LLC; *U.S. Private*, pg. 2456
IRACORE INTERNATIONAL, INC.—See Thompson Street Capital Manager LLC; *U.S. Private*, pg. 4161
IRADIMED CORPORATION; *U.S. Public*, pg. 1171
IRADIO INC.—See ANSA McAL Limited; *Int'l*, pg. 477
IRA HIGDON GROCERY, INC.; *U.S. Private*, pg. 2137
IRAMA SEJATI SDN. BHD.—See Tropicana Corporation Berhad; *Int'l*, pg. 7939
IRANAIR; *Int'l*, pg. 3804
IRAN ARGHAM CO.; *Int'l*, pg. 3804
IRAN BEARING & BUSHING CO.; *Int'l*, pg. 3804
IRAN BEHNOUSH COMPANY; *Int'l*, pg. 3804
IRAN BOARD; *Int'l*, pg. 3804
IRAN CABLE COMPANY; *Int'l*, pg. 3804
IRAN CARBON COMPANY; *Int'l*, pg. 3804
IRAN CASTING INDUSTRIES; *Int'l*, pg. 3804
IRAN COMBINE MANUFACTURING COMPANY; *Int'l*, pg. 3804
IRAN COMPRESSOR MANUFACTURING COMPANY PLC; *Int'l*, pg. 3804
IRAN DAROU COMPANY—See Alborz Investment Company; *Int'l*, pg. 299
IRAN DARU PHARMACEUTICAL COMPANY—See Sobhan Pharmaceutical Company; *Int'l*, pg. 7030
IRAN ELECTRICITY METER MANUFACTURING COMPANY, PLC; *Int'l*, pg. 3804
IRAN FERROALLOY INDUSTRIES CO.; *Int'l*, pg. 3804
IRAN FERROSILICE CO.; *Int'l*, pg. 3804
IRANIAN CENTRAL OIL FIELDS COMPANY—See National Iranian Oil Company; *Int'l*, pg. 5160
IRANIAN FUEL CONSERVATION ORGANIZATION—See National Iranian Oil Company; *Int'l*, pg. 5160
IRANIAN OFF-SHORE OIL COMPANY—See National Iranian Oil Company; *Int'l*, pg. 5160
IRANIAN OIL TERMINALS COMPANY—See National Iranian Oil Company; *Int'l*, pg. 5160
IRAN INSULATOR COMPANY; *Int'l*, pg. 3804
IRANI PAPEL E EMBALAGEM S.A.; *Int'l*, pg. 3804
IRAN KHODRO COMPANY; *Int'l*, pg. 3804
IRAN KHODRO DIESEL COMPANY—See Iran Khodro Company; *Int'l*, pg. 3804
IRAN MANGANESE MINES COMPANY; *Int'l*, pg. 3804
IRAN MARITIME INDUSTRIAL COMPANY; *Int'l*, pg. 3804
IRAN MAYEH COMPANY—See Compagnie des Levures Lesaffre SA; *Int'l*, pg. 1739
IRAN MAYEH COMPANY - SOUTHEAST UNIT—See Compagnie des Levures Lesaffre SA; *Int'l*, pg. 1739
IRAN TRACTOR FOUNDRY COMPANY; *Int'l*, pg. 3804
IRAN TRACTOR MANUFACTURING COMPANY; *Int'l*, pg. 3804

IRAN TRANSFO CO.

CORPORATE AFFILIATIONS

IRAN TRANSFO CO.; *Int'l*, pg. 3804
IRAN YASA; *Int'l*, pg. 3804
IRAN ZINC PRODUCTION COMPANY LTD.—See National Iranian Lead & Zinc Company; *Int'l*, pg. 5160
IRAO LTD.—See Vienna Insurance Group AG Wiener Versicherung Gruppe; *Int'l*, pg. 8194
IRAQ CAPITAL AG; *Int'l*, pg. 3805
IRAQI AGRICULTURAL PRODUCTS; *Int'l*, pg. 3805
IRAQI CARPETS & UPHOLSTERY CO.; *Int'l*, pg. 3805
IRAQI CARTON MAUFACTURERS CO.; *Int'l*, pg. 3805
IRAQI COMPANY FOR ENGINEERING WORKS; *Int'l*, pg. 3805
IRAQI COMPANY FOR GENERAL TRANSPORTATION & OIL PRODUCTION; *Int'l*, pg. 3805
IRAQI DATE PROCESSING & MARKETING CO.; *Int'l*, pg. 3805
IRAQI FOR SEED PRODUCTION; *Int'l*, pg. 3805
THE IRAQI ISLAMIC BANK; *Int'l*, pg. 7657
IRAQI LAND TRANSPORT CO.—See Baghdad Soft Drinks Co.; *Int'l*, pg. 799
IRAQI MIDDLE EAST INVESTMENT BANK; *Int'l*, pg. 3805
IRATHANE SYSTEMS, INC.—See Lime Rock Partners, LLC; *U.S. Private*, pg. 2456
IRATHANE SYSTEMS, INC.—See Thompson Street Capital Manager LLC; *U.S. Private*, pg. 4161
IRA WYMAN, INC.—See Suburban Propane Partners, L.P.; *U.S. Public*, pg. 1958
IRAY EUROPE GMBH—See iRay Technology Company Limited; *Int'l*, pg. 3805
IRAY IMAGING LLC—See iRay Technology Company Limited; *Int'l*, pg. 3805
IRAY JAPAN LIMITED—See iRay Technology Company Limited; *Int'l*, pg. 3805
IRAY KOREA LIMITED—See iRay Technology Company Limited; *Int'l*, pg. 3805
IRAY TECHNOLOGY COMPANY LIMITED; *Int'l*, pg. 3805
IRBAL, S.A.—See Altrad Investment Authority SAS; *Int'l*, pg. 398
IRB ASSET MANAGEMENT SA—See IRB-Brasil Resseguros S.A.; *Int'l*, pg. 3806
IRB-BRASIL RESSEGUROS S.A.; *Int'l*, pg. 3805
IRB COMPANY INC.—See Genstar Capital, LLC; *U.S. Private*, pg. 1673
IRB INFRASTRUCTURE DEVELOPERS LTD.; *Int'l*, pg. 3805
IRB INFRASTRUCTURE PVT. LTD.—See IRB Infrastructure Developers Ltd.; *Int'l*, pg. 3805
IR BIOSCIENCES HOLDINGS, INC.; *U.S. Public*, pg. 1171
IRB KOLHAPUR INTEGRATED ROAD DEVELOPMENT COMPANY PVT. LTD.—See IRB Infrastructure Developers Ltd.; *Int'l*, pg. 3805
IRB MEDICAL EQUIPMENT, LLC; *U.S. Private*, pg. 2137
IRB SURAT DAHISAR TOLLWAY PVT. LTD.—See IRB Infrastructure Developers Ltd.; *Int'l*, pg. 3805
IRBY CONSTRUCTION COMPANY—See Quanta Services, Inc.; *U.S. Public*, pg. 1751
IRCAMERAS LLC—See HEICO Corporation; *U.S. Public*, pg. 1020
IRCE LTDA—See IRCE S.p.A.; *Int'l*, pg. 3806
IRCE S.L.—See IRCE S.p.A.; *Int'l*, pg. 3806
IRCE S.P.A.; *Int'l*, pg. 3806
IRC INC ADVANCED FILM DIVISION—See TT Electronics plc; *Int'l*, pg. 7959
IRC INC WIRE AND FILM TECHNOLOGY—See TT Electronics plc; *Int'l*, pg. 7959
IRC LIMITED—See Petropavlovsk PLC; *Int'l*, pg. 5832
IRC NIC A.D.; *Int'l*, pg. 3806
IRCON CHINA—See Fortive Corporation; *U.S. Public*, pg. 870
IRCON DRYING SYSTEMS AB—See Pomona-Gruppen AB; *Int'l*, pg. 5918
IRCON GMBH—See Schneider Electric SE; *Int'l*, pg. 6631
IRCON INC.—See Fortive Corporation; *U.S. Public*, pg. 870
IRCON INFRASTRUCTURE & SERVICES LIMITED—See Ircon International Limited; *Int'l*, pg. 3806
IRCON INTERNATIONAL LIMITED; *Int'l*, pg. 3806
IRC RETAIL CENTERS INC.—See DRA Advisors LLC; *U.S. Private*, pg. 1271
IRDETO ACCESS B.V.—See MultiChoice Group Limited; *Int'l*, pg. 5083
IRDETO - AUSTRALIA—See MultiChoice Group Limited; *Int'l*, pg. 5083
IRDETO - BRAZIL—See MultiChoice Group Limited; *Int'l*, pg. 5083
IRDETO B.V.—See MultiChoice Group Limited; *Int'l*, pg. 5083
IRDETO - CHINA—See MultiChoice Group Limited; *Int'l*, pg. 5083
IRDETO - SOUTH KOREA—See MultiChoice Group Limited; *Int'l*, pg. 5083
IR DEUTSCHE HOLDING GMBH—See Ingersoll Rand Inc.; *U.S. Public*, pg. 1121
IRDI SORIDEC GESTION SAS; *Int'l*, pg. 3806
IRD SOUTH ASIA PVT. LTD.—See Quarterhill Inc.; *Int'l*, pg. 6155
IRD U.S. CORP.—See Quarterhill Inc.; *Int'l*, pg. 6155
IREADER TECHNOLOGY CO., LTD.; *Int'l*, pg. 3806

IREDALE MINERAL COSMETICS LTD.—See San Francisco Equity Partners; *U.S. Private*, pg. 3540
IREIT GLOBAL GROUP PTE LTD—See Tikehau Capital Advisors SAS; *Int'l*, pg. 7747
IREKA CORPORATION BERHAD; *Int'l*, pg. 3806
IREKA DEVELOPMENT MANAGEMENT SDN. BHD.—See Ireka Corporation Berhad; *Int'l*, pg. 3806
IREKA ICAPITAL SDN. BHD.—See Ireka Corporation Berhad; *Int'l*, pg. 3806
IREKS FRANCE SARL—See IREKS GmbH; *Int'l*, pg. 3806
IREKS GMBH; *Int'l*, pg. 3806
IREKS (SHANGHAI) FOOD CO., LTD.—See IREKS GmbH; *Int'l*, pg. 3806
IRELAND BLYTH LIMITED; *Int'l*, pg. 3806
IRELAND GANNON ASSOCIATES INC.; *U.S. Private*, pg. 2137
IRELAND INC.; *U.S. Public*, pg. 1171
IRELL & MANELLA LLP; *U.S. Private*, pg. 2137
IREM CO., LTD.; *Int'l*, pg. 3807
IREMIT EUROPE REMITTANCE CONSULTING AG—See I-Remit, Inc.; *Int'l*, pg. 3564
IREMIT GLOBAL REMITTANCE LIMITED—See I-Remit, Inc.; *Int'l*, pg. 3564
I-REMIT, INC.; *Int'l*, pg. 3564
I-REMIT NEW ZEALAND LIMITED—See I-Remit, Inc.; *Int'l*, pg. 3564
IREM SOFTWARE ENGINEERING INC.—See EIZO Corporation; *Int'l*, pg. 2337
IRENE; *Int'l*, pg. 3807
IR ENGRAVING LLC—See Standex International; *U.S. Public*, pg. 1930
IREN S.P.A.; *Int'l*, pg. 3807
IRENT OTO KIRALAMA TIC. A.S.—See Loras Holding A.S.; *Int'l*, pg. 4557
IREP CO., LTD.—See Hakuhodo DY Holdings Incorporated; *Int'l*, pg. 3221
IRESEARCH SERVICES PVT. LTD.—See The Ugar Sugar Works Limited; *Int'l*, pg. 7697
I-RESOURCE CONSULTING INTERNATIONAL, INC.—See Now Corporation; *Int'l*, pg. 5471
IRESS FS LTD.—See IRESS Limited; *Int'l*, pg. 3808
IRESS LIMITED; *Int'l*, pg. 3808
IRESS PORTAL LIMITED—See IRESS Limited; *Int'l*, pg. 3808
IRESS WEALTH MANAGEMENT PTY LTD—See IRESS Limited; *Int'l*, pg. 3808
IRET - ASHLAND APARTMENTS, LLC—See Centerspace; *U.S. Public*, pg. 472
IRE-TEX ELECTRONICS SDN. BHD.—See IQZAN Holding Berhad; *Int'l*, pg. 3804
IRE-TEX (KL) SDN. BHD.—See IQZAN Holding Berhad; *Int'l*, pg. 3804
IRE-TEX (MALAYSIA) SDN. BHD.—See IQZAN Holding Berhad; *Int'l*, pg. 3804
IRE-TEX PRAHA S.R.O.—See IQZAN Holding Berhad; *Int'l*, pg. 3804
IRETI S.P.A.—See Iren S.p.A.; *Int'l*, pg. 3808
IRET - PARK MEADOWS, LLC—See Centerspace; *U.S. Public*, pg. 472
IRET PROPERTIES—See Centerspace; *U.S. Public*, pg. 472
IRET - VALLEY PARK MANOR, LLC—See Centerspace; *U.S. Public*, pg. 472
IRET - WHISPERING RIDGE APARTMENTS, LLC—See Centerspace; *U.S. Public*, pg. 472
IREVNA LIMITED—See S&P Global Inc.; *U.S. Public*, pg. 1830
IREWARD24 SA—See ComArch S.A.; *Int'l*, pg. 1707
IREX CORPORATION; *U.S. Private*, pg. 2137
IREX GROUP LTD.—See TyRex Group, Ltd.; *U.S. Private*, pg. 4269
IRFIS - FINANZIARIA PER LO SVILUPPO DELLA SICILIA S.P.A.—See UniCredit S.p.A.; *Int'l*, pg. 8034
IR (FOSHAN) BUILDING MATERIALS TRADING CO., LTD.—See Kuriyama Holdings Corporation; *Int'l*, pg. 4341
IRG BOP LTD.—See Investment Research Group Limited; *Int'l*, pg. 3785
IRHYTHM TECHNOLOGIES, INC.; *U.S. Public*, pg. 1171
IRHYTHM TECHNOLOGIES LIMITED—See iRhythm Technologies, Inc.; *U.S. Public*, pg. 1171
IRICO DISPLAY DEVICES CO., LTD.; *Int'l*, pg. 3808
IRICO GROUP NEW ENERGY COMPANY LIMITED; *Int'l*, pg. 3808
IRIDE S.A.—See Immofinanz AG; *Int'l*, pg. 3628
IRIDEX CORPORATION; *U.S. Public*, pg. 1171
IRIDEX S.A.—See IRIDEX Corporation; *U.S. Public*, pg. 1171
IRIDGE, INC.; *Int'l*, pg. 3808
IRIDIAN SPECTRAL TECHNOLOGIES, LTD.—See IDEX Corp; *U.S. Public*, pg. 1091
IRIDIO COLOR SERVICE INC.—See Chatham Asset Management, LLC; *U.S. Private*, pg. 863
IRIDIUM APARCAMIENTOS, S.L.—See ACS, Actividades de Construccion y Servicios, S.A.; *Int'l*, pg. 115
IRIDIUM COMMUNICATIONS INC.; *U.S. Public*, pg. 1171
IRIDIUM CONCESIONES DE INFRAESTRUCTURAS, S.A.—See ACS, Actividades de Construccion y Servicios, S.A.; *Int'l*, pg. 115

IRIDIUM GOVERNMENT SERVICES LLC—See Iridium Communications Inc.; *U.S. Public*, pg. 1171
IRIDIUM SATELLITE LLC—See Iridium Communications Inc.; *U.S. Public*, pg. 1171
IRIDIUM SERVICES DEUTSCHLAND GMBH—See E.ON SE; *Int'l*, pg. 2260
IRIDIUM TECHNOLOGY OPCO, LLC—See Levine Leichtman Capital Partners, LLC; *U.S. Private*, pg. 2435
IRIDIUM WORLD COMMUNICATIONS LTD.; *U.S. Public*, pg. 1171
IRIEL INDUSTRIA COMERCIO DE SISTEMAS ELECTRICOS LTDA.—See Siemens Aktiengesellschaft; *Int'l*, pg. 6887
IRIGNY EMPREENDIMENTOS IMOBILIARIOS S.A.—See Even Construtora e Incorporadora S.A.; *Int'l*, pg. 2562
IRIS ACQUISITION CORP.; *Int'l*, pg. 3808
IRIS AGROTECH SDN. BHD.—See IRIS Corporation Berhad; *Int'l*, pg. 3809
IRISA GROUP LIMITED—See Sun Capital Partners, Inc.; *U.S. Private*, pg. 3861
IRIS ASIA-PACIFIC PTY. LTD.—See init innovation in traffic systems SE; *Int'l*, pg. 3704
IRIS BUSINESS SERVICES LIMITED; *Int'l*, pg. 3808
IRISBUS IVECO - ANNONAY PLANT—See CNH Industrial N.V.; *Int'l*, pg. 1675
IRISBUS IVECO—See CNH Industrial N.V.; *Int'l*, pg. 1675
IRISBUS IVECO - VALLE UFITA PLANT—See CNH Industrial N.V.; *Int'l*, pg. 1675
IRIS CAPITAL FUND II GERMAN INVESTORS GMBH & CO. KG—See Munchener Ruckversicherungs AG; *Int'l*, pg. 5089
IRIS CERAMICA S.P.A.; *Int'l*, pg. 3808
IRIS CLOTHINGS LTD.; *Int'l*, pg. 3808
IRIS COMPUTERS D.D.; *Int'l*, pg. 3808
IRIS CORPORATION BERHAD; *Int'l*, pg. 3808
IRIS DIAGNOSTICS FRANCE S.A.—See Danaher Corporation; *U.S. Public*, pg. 625
IRIS DIAGNOSTICS (UK) LTD.—See Danaher Corporation; *U.S. Public*, pg. 625
IRIS DIGITAL LIMITED—See Samsung BioLogics Co., Ltd.; *Int'l*, pg. 6510
I.R.I.S. ECOMMUNICATION—See Canon Inc.; *Int'l*, pg. 1295
IRIS ECO POWER SDN. BHD.—See IRIS Corporation Berhad; *Int'l*, pg. 3809
IRIS ENERGY LIMITED; *Int'l*, pg. 3809
IRIS ENTERPRISE SOFTWARE (AUSTRALIA) PTY LTD—See HgCapital Trust plc; *Int'l*, pg. 3376
IRIS ENVIRONMENTAL—See RPS Group plc; *Int'l*, pg. 6415
IRISE; *U.S. Private*, pg. 2138
I.R.I.S. FRANCE SA—See Canon Inc.; *Int'l*, pg. 1295
IRIS GATEWAY SATELLITE SERVICES LIMITED—See Cyprus Telecommunications Authority; *Int'l*, pg. 1897
IRIS GERMANY GMBH—See iris Nation Worldwide Limited; *Int'l*, pg. 3809
IRIS GLOBAL CLINICAL TRIALS SOLUTIONS—See Omnicom Group Inc.; *U.S. Public*, pg. 1599
IRIS-GMBH INFRARED & INTELLIGENT SENSORS—See init innovation in traffic systems SE; *Int'l*, pg. 3704
I.R.I.S. GROUP S.A.—See Canon Inc.; *Int'l*, pg. 1295
IRISH BISCUITS (N.I.) LIMITED—See CapVest Limited; *Int'l*, pg. 1318
IRISH BULK LIQUID STORAGE LTD.—See Simon Group plc; *Int'l*, pg. 6932
IRISH BUSINESS SYSTEMS LIMITED—See Xerox Holdings Corporation; *U.S. Public*, pg. 2387
IRISH CEMENT LTD.—See CRH plc; *Int'l*, pg. 1844
IRISH CONTINENTAL GROUP PLC; *Int'l*, pg. 3809
IRISH DISTILLERS LTD.—See Pernod Ricard S.A.; *Int'l*, pg. 5810
IRISH DREDGING COMPANY LTD.—See HAL Trust N.V.; *Int'l*, pg. 3226
IRISH DRIVER-HARRIS CO., LTD.—See Driver-Harris Company; *U.S. Private*, pg. 1278
IRIS HELLAS REO S.A.—See Intrum AB; *Int'l*, pg. 3771
IRISH ESTATES (FACILITIES MANAGEMENT) LIMITED—See Aramark; *U.S. Public*, pg. 177
IRISH FERRIES—See Irish Continental Group plc; *Int'l*, pg. 3809
IRISH FERRIES (U.K.) SERVICES LIMITED—See Irish Continental Group plc; *Int'l*, pg. 3809
IRISH INDUSTRIAL EXPLOSIVES LIMITED—See Societe Anonyme d'Explosifs et de Produits Chimiques; *Int'l*, pg. 7035
IRIS HJALPMEDEL AB—See Indutrade AB; *Int'l*, pg. 3679
IRISH LIFE ASSURANCE PLC—See Power Corporation of Canada; *Int'l*, pg. 5943
IRISH LIFE GROUP LIMITED—See Power Corporation of Canada; *Int'l*, pg. 5943
IRISH MEDICAL SYSTEMS (COMPUTERS) LIMITED—See IMS MAXIMS plc; *Int'l*, pg. 3638
IRISH OXYGEN COMPANY LTD.—See SOL S.p.A.; *Int'l*, pg. 7067
IRISH PENSIONS TRUST LIMITED—See Marsh & McLennan Companies, Inc.; *U.S. Public*, pg. 1376
IRISH RECRUITMENT CONSULTANTS LIMITED—See HFBG Holding B.V.; *Int'l*, pg. 3375

COMPANY NAME INDEX

IRISH RESIDENTIAL PROPERTIES REIT PLC; *Int'l*, pg. 3809
IRISH SEAFOOD INVESTMENTS LIMITED—See Thai Union Group Public Company Limited; *Int'l*, pg. 7596
THE IRISH STOCK EXCHANGE PLC—See Euronext N.V.; *Int'l*, pg. 2554
IRISH STUDIO, LLC - IRELAND CORPORATE OFFICE—See Irish Studio, LLC; *U.S. Private*, pg. 2138
IRISH STUDIO, LLC; *U.S. Private*, pg. 2138
IRISH TIMES; *U.S. Private*, pg. 2138
IRIS ID SYSTEMS INC.; *U.S. Private*, pg. 2138
I.R.I.S. INC—See Canon Inc.; *Int'l*, pg. 1295
IRIS INFORMATION TECHNOLOGY SYSTEMS SDN. BHD.—See IRIS Corporation Berhad; *Int'l*, pg. 3809
IRIS INFRARED INNOVATION SYSTEMS GMBH; *Int'l*, pg. 3809
IRIS - INFRARED & INTELLIGENT SENSORES NA, INC.—See init innovation in traffic systems SE; *Int'l*, pg. 3704
IRIS INSTRUMENTS SA—See Bureau de Recherches Geologiques et Miniere; *Int'l*, pg. 1221
IRIS INTELLIGENT SENSING SASU—See init innovation in traffic systems SE; *Int'l*, pg. 3704
IRIS INTERNATIONAL, INC.—See Danaher Corporation; *U.S. Public*, pg. 625
IRIS KOREA LIMITED—See Samsung BioLogics Co., Ltd.; *Int'l*, pg. 6510
IRIS KOTO (M) SDN. BHD.—See IRIS Corporation Berhad; *Int'l*, pg. 3809
IRIS LOGIX SOLUTIONS PRIVATE LIMITED—See IRIS Business Services Limited; *Int'l*, pg. 3808
IRIS LONDON LIMITED—See Samsung BioLogics Co., Ltd.; *Int'l*, pg. 6510
I.R.I.S. LUXEMBOURG S.A.—See Canon Inc.; *Int'l*, pg. 1295
IRIS MEDICAL CENTRE LLC—See Kaya Limited; *Int'l*, pg. 4101
IRIS NATION WORLDWIDE LIMITED; *Int'l*, pg. 3809
IRIS NY—See iris Nation Worldwide Limited; *Int'l*, pg. 3809
IRISO COMPONENT CO., LTD.—See IRISO ELECTRONICS CO.,LTD; *Int'l*, pg. 3809
IRISO ELECTRONICS CO.,LTD - IBARAKI PLANT—See IRISO ELECTRONICS CO.,LTD; *Int'l*, pg. 3809
IRISO ELECTRONICS CO.,LTD; *Int'l*, pg. 0000
IRISO ELECTRONICS EUROPE GMBH—See IRISO ELECTRONICS CO.,LTD; *Int'l*, pg. 3809
IRISO ELECTRONICS (HONG KONG) LTD.—See IRISO ELECTRONICS CO.,LTD; *Int'l*, pg. 3809
IRISO ELECTRONICS PHILIPPINES, INC.—See IRISO ELECTRONICS CO.,LTD; *Int'l*, pg. 3809
IRISO ELECTRONICS (THAILAND) LTD.—See IRISO ELECTRONICS CO.,LTD; *Int'l*, pg. 3809
IRISO ELECTRONICS VIETNAM CO., LTD.—See IRISO ELECTRONICS CO.,LTD; *Int'l*, pg. 3809
IRISO (SHANGHAI) R&D CENTER CO., LTD.—See IRISO ELECTRONICS CO.,LTD; *Int'l*, pg. 3809
IRISO (SHANGHAI) TRADING CO., LTD.—See IRISO ELECTRONICS CO.,LTD; *Int'l*, pg. 3809
IRISO U.S.A., INC.—See IRISO ELECTRONICS CO.,LTD; *Int'l*, pg. 3809
IRIS POWER LP—See Koch Industries, Inc.; *U.S. Private*, pg. 2331
IRISS-ASIA PTY LTD—See IRISS, Inc.; *U.S. Private*, pg. 2139
IRIS SERVICE DELIVERY UK LTD.—See Nokia Corporation; *Int'l*, pg. 5404
IRISS, INC.; *U.S. Private*, pg. 2139
IRIS SINGAPORE—See iris Nation Worldwide Limited; *Int'l*, pg. 3809
IRISS, LLC—See IRISS, Inc.; *U.S. Private*, pg. 2139
IRIS SOFTWARE GROUP LTD.—See HgCapital Trust plc; *Int'l*, pg. 3376
IRIS SOFTWARE, INC.; *U.S. Private*, pg. 2138
IRIS SOLUTIONS, LLC—See Anatomy IT, LLC; *U.S. Private*, pg. 272
IRIS S.P.A.—See Onward Holdings Co., Ltd.; *Int'l*, pg. 5592
IRIS SYDNEY PTY LTD—See iris Nation Worldwide Limited; *Int'l*, pg. 3809
IRIS TECHNOLOGY CORPORATION; *U.S. Private*, pg. 2138
IRIS TELECOMMUNICATION AUSTRIA GMBH—See Nokia Corporation; *Int'l*, pg. 5404
IRIS TELECOMMUNICATION GMBH—See Nokia Corporation; *Int'l*, pg. 5404
IRIS TELECOMMUNICATION POLAND SP. Z O.O.—See Nokia Corporation; *Int'l*, pg. 5404
IRIS TELEKOMUNIKASYON MUHENDISLIK HIZMETLERI A.S.—See Nokia Corporation; *Int'l*, pg. 5404
IRIS THE VISUAL GROUP INC.—See Caisse de Depot et Placement du Quebec; *Int'l*, pg. 1254
IRIS THE VISUAL GROUP INC.—See FFL Partners, LLC; *U.S. Private*, pg. 1500
IRIS (USA) INC.—See Samsung BioLogics Co., Ltd.; *Int'l*, pg. 6510
IRIS WORLDWIDE INTEGRATED MARKETING PRIVATE LIMITED—See Samsung BioLogics Co., Ltd.; *Int'l*, pg. 6510

IRIS WORLDWIDE (THAILAND) LIMITED—See Samsung BioLogics Co., Ltd.; *Int'l*, pg. 6510
IRITEL AD BEOGRAD; *Int'l*, pg. 3810
IRIVER INC—See Dreamus Company; *Int'l*, pg. 2203
IRIX DESIGN GROUP INC.—See Global Education Communities Corp; *Int'l*, pg. 2995
IR JAPAN HOLDINGS, LTD.; *Int'l*, pg. 3804
IR JAPAN, INC.—See IR Japan Holdings, Ltd.; *Int'l*, pg. 3804
IRJB INSTITUT DE RADIOLOGIE DU JURA BERNOIS SA—See AEVIS VICTORIA SA; *Int'l*, pg. 183
IRLAB THERAPEUTICS AB; *Int'l*, pg. 3810
IR LOAN SERVICING, INC.—See Mitsubishi UFJ Financial Group, Inc.; *Int'l*, pg. 4968
IRL POLSKA SP. Z O.O.—See JSC INTER RAO UES; *Int'l*, pg. 4009
IRMA A/S—See FDB Group; *Int'l*, pg. 2628
IRMA S. MANN, STRATEGIC MARKETING INC.; *U.S. Private*, pg. 2139
IRM ENERGY LIMITED; *Int'l*, pg. 3810
IRMER + ELZE KOMPRESSOREN GMBH—See Atlas Copco AB; *Int'l*, pg. 679
IR (MIDDLE EAST) LLC—See CIMC-TianDa Holdings Company Limited; *Int'l*, pg. 1608
IRMOVO A.D.; *Int'l*, pg. 3810
IRMSCHER INC.; *U.S. Private*, pg. 2139
IRN PAYMENT SYSTEMS LLC—See Shift4 Payments, Inc.; *U.S. Public*, pg. 1874
IROBOT AUSTRIA GMBH—See iRobot Corp.; *U.S. Public*, pg. 1171
IROBOT CORP.; *U.S. Public*, pg. 1171
IROBOT (HK) LIMITED—See iRobot Corp.; *U.S. Public*, pg. 1171
IROBOT (INDIA) PRIVATE LIMITED—See iRobot Corp.; *U.S. Public*, pg. 1171
IROBOT ITALIA S.R.L.—See iRobot Corp.; *U.S. Public*, pg. 1171
IROBOT (SHANGHAI) LTD.—See iRobot Corp.; *U.S. Public*, pg. 1171
IROBOT - UK—See iRobot Corp.; *U.S. Public*, pg. 1171
IROC CO., LTD.; *Int'l*, pg. 3810
IROC TECHNOLOGIES—See BNP Paribas SA; *Int'l*, pg. 1089
IRODABUTOR MARTELA KFT—See Martela Oyj; *Int'l*, pg. 4703
IRO INC.—See Shenzhen Ellassay Fashion Co., Ltd.; *Int'l*, pg. 6808
IROKO PHARMACEUTICALS INC.; *U.S. Private*, pg. 2139
I'ROM CO., LTD.—See I'rom Group Co., Ltd.; *Int'l*, pg. 3562
I'ROM CS CO., LTD.—See I'rom Group Co., Ltd.; *Int'l*, pg. 3562
I'ROM EC CO., LTD.—See I'rom Group Co., Ltd.; *Int'l*, pg. 3562
IROMEZ S.R.O.—See Groupe BPCE; *Int'l*, pg. 3094
I'ROM GROUP CO., LTD.; *Int'l*, pg. 3562
I'ROM NA CO., LTD.—See I'rom Group Co., Ltd.; *Int'l*, pg. 3562
I'ROM PM CO., LTD.—See I'rom Group Co., Ltd.; *Int'l*, pg. 3562
IRONARCH TECHNOLOGY, LLC; *U.S. Private*, pg. 2140
IRONBARK ASSET MANAGEMENT FUND SERVICES LTD.—See Ironbark Asset Management Pty. Ltd.; *Int'l*, pg. 3810
IRONBARK ASSET MANAGEMENT PTY. LTD.; *Int'l*, pg. 3810
IRONBARK CAPITAL LIMITED; *Int'l*, pg. 3810
IRONBARK ZINC LIMITED; *Int'l*, pg. 3810
IRON BOW TECHNOLOGIES LLC; *U.S. Private*, pg. 2139
IRONBRIDGE CAPITAL; *Int'l*, pg. 3810
IRONBRIDGE EQUITY PARTNERS; *Int'l*, pg. 3810
IRON CITY INDUSTRIAL CLEANING CORP.; *U.S. Private*, pg. 2139
IRON DATA SOLUTIONS, INC.—See Tyler Technologies, Inc.; *U.S. Public*, pg. 2208
THE IRON DOOR COMPANY LLC; *U.S. Private*, pg. 4057
IRON DYNAMICS—See Steel Dynamics, Inc.; *U.S. Public*, pg. 1942
THE IRONEES COMPANY; *U.S. Private*, pg. 4057
IRON FORCE CORPORATION—See Iron Force Industrial Co., Ltd.; *Int'l*, pg. 3810
IRON FORCE INDUSTRIAL CO., LTD. - NANTOU DIVISION—See Iron Force Industrial Co., Ltd.; *Int'l*, pg. 3810
IRON FORCE INDUSTRIAL CO., LTD.; *Int'l*, pg. 3810
IRONGATE ENERGY SERVICES, LLC—See Clearlake Capital Group, L.P.; *U.S. Private*, pg. 935
IRONGATE REALTORS INC.; *U.S. Private*, pg. 2140
IRON HORSE ACQUISITION CORP.; *U.S. Private*, pg. 2139
IRON HORSE CORP.; *Int'l*, pg. 3810
IRON HORSE HOLDINGS INC.—See LendingTree, Inc.; *U.S. Public*, pg. 1305
IRONLINE COMPRESSION LIMITED PARTNERSHIP—See Staple Street Capital LLC; *U.S. Private*, pg. 3784
IRONMAN PARTS & SERVICES; *U.S. Private*, pg. 2140
IRONMAN SOUND INDUSTRIES, LLC—See Markeys Audio Visual Inc.; *U.S. Public*, pg. 2581

IRON MOUNTAIN INCORPORATED

IRON MINING GROUP, INC.; *U.S. Private*, pg. 2139
IRONMONGERYDIRECT LTD.—See Manutan International SA; *Int'l*, pg. 4679
IRON MOUNTAIN ANAMNIS GDM SAS—See Iron Mountain Incorporated; *U.S. Public*, pg. 1173
IRON MOUNTAIN ARSIVLEME HIZMETLERI AS—See Iron Mountain Incorporated; *U.S. Public*, pg. 1173
IRON MOUNTAIN A/S—See Iron Mountain Incorporated; *U.S. Public*, pg. 1173
IRON MOUNTAIN ASSURANCE CORPORATION—See Iron Mountain Incorporated; *U.S. Public*, pg. 1172
IRON MOUNTAIN AUSTRALIA GROUP PTY. LTD.—See Iron Mountain Incorporated; *U.S. Public*, pg. 1172
IRON MOUNTAIN AUSTRALIA PTY. LTD.—See Iron Mountain Incorporated; *U.S. Public*, pg. 1172
IRON MOUNTAIN AUSTRALIA SERVICES PTY LTD—See Iron Mountain Incorporated; *U.S. Public*, pg. 1172
IRON MOUNTAIN BAHRAIN CO., LTD.—See Iron Mountain Incorporated; *U.S. Public*, pg. 1172
IRON MOUNTAIN BULGARIA—See Iron Mountain Incorporated; *U.S. Public*, pg. 1172
IRON MOUNTAIN CANADA CORPORATION—See Iron Mountain Incorporated; *U.S. Public*, pg. 1172
IRON MOUNTAIN CANADA OPERATIONS ULC—See Iron Mountain Incorporated; *U.S. Public*, pg. 1172
IRON MOUNTAIN CESKA REPUBLIKA S.R.O.—See Iron Mountain Incorporated; *U.S. Public*, pg. 1173
IRON MOUNTAIN COLOMBIA, S.A.S.—See Iron Mountain Incorporated; *U.S. Public*, pg. 1172
IRON MOUNTAIN CYPRUS LIMITED—See Iron Mountain Incorporated; *U.S. Public*, pg. 1172
IRON MOUNTAIN DATA MANAGEMENT (BEIJING) CO., LTD.—See Iron Mountain Incorporated; *U.S. Public*, pg. 1172
IRON MOUNTAIN DATA MANAGEMENT CONSULTING (BEIJING) CO., LTD.—See Iron Mountain Incorporated; *U.S. Public*, pg. 1172
IRON MOUNTAIN DEUTSCHLAND GMBH—See Iron Mountain Incorporated; *U.S. Public*, pg. 1173
IRON MOUNTAIN DIMS LTD.—See Iron Mountain Incorporated; *U.S. Public*, pg. 1173
IRON MOUNTAIN DO BRASIL LTDA.—See Iron Mountain Incorporated; *U.S. Public*, pg. 1173
IRON MOUNTAIN D.O.O.—See Iron Mountain Incorporated; *U.S. Public*, pg. 1173
IRON MOUNTAIN ESPANA, S.A.—See Iron Mountain incorporated; *U.S. Public*, pg. 1173
IRON MOUNTAIN EUROPE LIMITED—See Iron Mountain Incorporated; *U.S. Public*, pg. 1172
IRON MOUNTAIN FINLAND OY—See Iron Mountain Incorporated; *U.S. Public*, pg. 1173
IRON MOUNTAIN FORGE CORPORATION—See MGA Entertainment, Inc.; *U.S. Private*, pg. 2694
IRON MOUNTAIN FOR INFORMATION DOCUMENTS STORING PSC—See Iron Mountain Incorporated; *U.S. Public*, pg. 1173
IRON MOUNTAIN FRANCE S.A.S.—See Iron Mountain Incorporated; *U.S. Public*, pg. 1173
IRON MOUNTAIN FZ-LLC—See Iron Mountain Incorporated; *U.S. Public*, pg. 1173
IRON MOUNTAIN HELLAS SA—See Iron Mountain Incorporated; *U.S. Public*, pg. 1173
IRON MOUNTAIN HOLDINGS GROUP, INC.—See Iron Mountain Incorporated; *U.S. Public*, pg. 1173
IRON MOUNTAIN HONG KONG LIMITED—See Iron Mountain Incorporated; *U.S. Public*, pg. 1173
IRON MOUNTAIN INCORPORATED; *U.S. Public*, pg. 1171
IRON MOUNTAIN (INDIA) PVT LTD.—See Iron Mountain Incorporated; *U.S. Public*, pg. 1172
IRON MOUNTAIN INFORMATION MANAGEMENT, LLC—See Iron Mountain Incorporated; *U.S. Public*, pg. 1173
IRON MOUNTAIN INTERNATIONAL HOLDINGS B.V.—See Iron Mountain Incorporated; *U.S. Public*, pg. 1173
IRON MOUNTAIN IRELAND LTD.—See Iron Mountain Incorporated; *U.S. Public*, pg. 1173
IRON MOUNTAIN (IRELAND) SERVICES LIMITED—See Iron Mountain Incorporated; *U.S. Public*, pg. 1172
IRON MOUNTAIN ITALIA S.P.A.—See Iron Mountain Incorporated; *U.S. Public*, pg. 1173
IRON MOUNTAIN KUWAIT FOR DOCUMENTS PRESERVATION AND DESTRUCTION SERVICES—See Iron Mountain Incorporated; *U.S. Public*, pg. 1173
IRON MOUNTAIN MAGYARORSZAG KERESKEDELMI ES SZOLGALTATO KFT.—See Iron Mountain Incorporated; *U.S. Public*, pg. 1173
IRON MOUNTAIN MAGYARORSZAQ KFT—See Iron Mountain Incorporated; *U.S. Public*, pg. 1173
IRON MOUNTAIN MUSCAT SPC—See Iron Mountain Incorporated; *U.S. Public*, pg. 1173
IRON MOUNTAIN NEDERLAND B.V.—See Iron Mountain Incorporated; *U.S. Public*, pg. 1173
IRON MOUNTAIN (NEDERLAND) SERVICES BV—See Iron Mountain Incorporated; *U.S. Public*, pg. 1173
IRON MOUNTAIN NORGE AS—See Iron Mountain Incorporated; *U.S. Public*, pg. 1173
IRON MOUNTAIN PERU S.A.—See Iron Mountain Incorporated; *U.S. Public*, pg. 1173

IRON MOUNTAIN INCORPORATED / CORPORATE AFFILIATIONS

IRON MOUNTAIN PHILIPPINES INC.—See Iron Mountain Incorporated; *U.S. Public*, pg. 1173
IRON MOUNTAIN POLSKA SP. Z O.O.—See Iron Mountain Incorporated; *U.S. Public*, pg. 1173
IRON MOUNTAIN RECORDS MANAGEMENT (SHANGHAI) CO LIMITED—See Iron Mountain Incorporated; *U.S. Public*, pg. 1173
IRON MOUNTAIN SHANGHAI CO. LTD—See Iron Mountain Incorporated; *U.S. Public*, pg. 1173
IRON MOUNTAIN SLOVAKIA S.R.O.—See Iron Mountain Incorporated; *U.S. Public*, pg. 1173
IRON MOUNTAIN SOUTH AFRICA (PTY) LTD—See Iron Mountain Incorporated; *U.S. Public*, pg. 1173
IRON MOUNTAIN SRL—See Iron Mountain Incorporated; *U.S. Public*, pg. 1173
IRON MOUNTAIN TAIWAN LTD.—See Iron Mountain Incorporated; *U.S. Public*, pg. 1173
IRON MOUNTAIN (THAILAND) LIMITED—See Iron Mountain Incorporated; *U.S. Public*, pg. 1172
IRON MOUNTAIN (UK) LTD.—See Iron Mountain Incorporated; *U.S. Public*, pg. 1172
IRON MOUNTAIN UKRAINE LLC—See Iron Mountain Incorporated; *U.S. Public*, pg. 1173
IRON MOUNTAIN (UK) SERVICES LIMITED—See Iron Mountain Incorporated; *U.S. Public*, pg. 1173
IRONNET, INC.; *U.S. Public*, pg. 1174
IRON ORE COMPANY OF CANADA—See Rio Tinto plc; *Int'l*, pg. 6347
IRON PATH CAPITAL, L.P.; *U.S. Private*, pg. 2139
IRON PEDDLERS, INC.; *U.S. Private*, pg. 2139
IRONPLANET, INC.—See RB Global, Inc.; *Int'l*, pg. 6226
IRONPLANET LIMITED—See RB Global, Inc.; *Int'l*, pg. 6226
IRON POINT PARTNERS, LLC; *U.S. Private*, pg. 2139
IRON PONY MOTORSPORTS GROUP, INC.; *U.S. Private*, pg. 2139
IRONRIDGE GLOBAL PARTNERS, LLC; *U.S. Private*, pg. 2140
IRONRIDGE INC.—See Esdec BV; *Int'l*, pg. 2502
IRON ROAD LIMITED—See The Sentient Group Limited; *Int'l*, pg. 7681
IRONSHORE AUSTRALIA HOLDINGS PTY LIMITED—See Liberty Mutual Holding Company Inc.; *U.S. Private*, pg. 2445
IRONSHORE CANADA LTD.—See Liberty Mutual Holding Company Inc.; *U.S. Private*, pg. 2445
IRONSHORE EUROPE DAC—See Hamilton Insurance Group, Ltd.; *Int'l*, pg. 3238
IRONSHORE HOLDINGS (U.S.) INC.—See Liberty Mutual Holding Company Inc.; *U.S. Private*, pg. 2445
IRONSHORE INC.—See Liberty Mutual Holding Company Inc.; *U.S. Private*, pg. 2445
IRONSHORE INSURANCE LTD. - SINGAPORE—See Liberty Mutual Holding Company Inc.; *U.S. Private*, pg. 2445
IRONSHORE INSURANCE LTD.—See Liberty Mutual Holding Company Inc.; *U.S. Private*, pg. 2445
THE IRONSIDE GROUP, INC.; *U.S. Private*, pg. 4057
IRON SOLUTIONS, INC—See Trimble, Inc.; *U.S. Public*, pg. 2190
IRON SOURCE, LLC—See Clairvest Group Inc.; *Int'l*, pg. 1641
IRONSOURCE LTD.—See Unity Software Inc.; *U.S. Public*, pg. 2254
IRON SPARK I INC.; *U.S. Private*, pg. 2139
IRONSTOB, LLC—See Forestar Group Inc.; *U.S. Public*, pg. 867
IRONSTONE AS—See Komplett ASA; *Int'l*, pg. 4244
IRON TRADE IMPORTS, INC.; *U.S. Private*, pg. 2140
IRONTRAFFIC.COM; *U.S. Private*, pg. 2140
IRONTREE INTERNET SERVICES (PTY.) LTD.—See Metrofile Holdings Limited; *Int'l*, pg. 4862
IRON TRUST DOO BEOGRAD—See Iron Mountain Incorporated; *U.S. Public*, pg. 1173
IRONVELD PLC; *Int'l*, pg. 3810
IRON VINE SECURITY, LLC—See ASGN Incorporated; *U.S. Public*, pg. 210
IRONWARE TECHNOLOGIES, LLC; *U.S. Private*, pg. 2140
IRONWAVE TECHNOLOGIES LLC; *U.S. Private*, pg. 2140
IRONWOOD CAPITAL MANAGEMENT LLC; *U.S. Private*, pg. 2140
IRONWOOD COURT, INC.—See Webster Financial Corporation; *U.S. Public*, pg. 2341
IRONWOOD EDUCATION LTD.; *Int'l*, pg. 3811
IRONWOOD ELECTRONICS INC.—See HEICO Corporation; *U.S. Public*, pg. 1020
IRONWOOD INSURANCE SERVICES LLC—See Marsh & McLennan Companies, Inc.; *U.S. Public*, pg. 1381
IRONWOOD LITHOGRAPHERS, INC.—See Chatham Asset Management, LLC; *U.S. Private*, pg. 862
IRONWOOD PARTNERS LLC; *U.S. Private*, pg. 2140
IRONWOOD PHARMACEUTICALS, INC.; *U.S. Public*, pg. 1174
IRONWOOD PLASTICS, INC.—See Berkshire Hathaway Inc.; *U.S. Public*, pg. 303
IRONWORKER MANAGEMENT PROGRESSIVE ACTION COOPERATIVE TRUST; *U.S. Private*, pg. 2140

IROOFING, LLC—See Porch Group, Inc.; *U.S. Public*, pg. 1702
IROQUOIS DIALYSIS, LLC—See DaVita Inc.; *U.S. Public*, pg. 640
IROQUOIS FALLS POWER CORP.—See Northland Power Inc.; *Int'l*, pg. 5445
IROQUOIS FEDERAL SAVINGS & LOAN ASSOCIATION—See IF Bancorp, Inc.; *U.S. Public*, pg. 1095
IROQUOIS GAS TRANSMISSION SYSTEM, LP—See Dominion Energy, Inc.; *U.S. Public*, pg. 674
IROQUOIS GAS TRANSMISSION SYSTEM, LP—See Iberdrola, S.A.; *Int'l*, pg. 3570
IROQUOIS GAS TRANSMISSION SYSTEM, LP—See TC Energy Corporation; *Int'l*, pg. 7482
IROQUOIS NURSING HOME, INC.; *U.S. Private*, pg. 2140
IROQUOIS PAVING CORPORATION; *U.S. Private*, pg. 2140
IRPC A&L CO., LTD.—See IRPC Public Company Limited; *Int'l*, pg. 3811
IRPC OIL CO., LTD.—See IRPC Public Company Limited; *Int'l*, pg. 3811
IRPC PUBLIC COMPANY LIMITED; *Int'l*, pg. 3811
IRP - INDUSTRIA DE REBOCOS DE PORTUGAL, S.A.—See SODIM, SGPS, SA; *Int'l*, pg. 7049
IRRADIANT PARTNERS, LP; *U.S. Private*, pg. 2140
IRRADIATION SOLUTIONS INC.—See A Brown Company, Inc.; *Int'l*, pg. 17
IRRAS AB; *Int'l*, pg. 3811
IRRAS GMBH—See IRRAS AB; *Int'l*, pg. 3811
IRRAS USA INC.—See IRRAS AB; *Int'l*, pg. 3811
IRRC CORPORATION; *Int'l*, pg. 3811
IRRI - AL TAL LTD.—See Water Ways Technologies Inc.; *Int'l*, pg. 8356
IRRIGATION DESIGN & CONSTRUCTION, LLC—See Jain Irrigation Systems Limited; *Int'l*, pg. 3872
IRRIGATION SPECIALISTS INC.; *U.S. Private*, pg. 2141
IRRIGATION STATION LLP; *U.S. Private*, pg. 2141
IRRITROL SYSTEMS—See The Toro Company; *U.S. Public*, pg. 2135
IR ROBOTICS INC.—See Vector Inc.; *Int'l*, pg. 8144
IRR SUPPLY CENTERS INC.; *U.S. Private*, pg. 2140
IRSA INVERSIONES Y REPRESENTACIONES SOCIEDAD ANONIMA; *Int'l*, pg. 3811
IRSA PROPIEDADES COMERCIALES S.A.—See IRSA Inversiones y Representaciones Sociedad Anonima; *Int'l*, pg. 3811
IR SECURITY TECHNOLOGIES—See Ingersoll Rand Inc.; *U.S. Public*, pg. 1121
IRS GIROD LTD—See Signaux Girod S.A.; *Int'l*, pg. 6911
IRSIK & DOLL FEED SERVICES INC.; *U.S. Private*, pg. 2141
IRS INTERNATIONAL PTY. LTD.—See Daikin Industries, Ltd.; *Int'l*, pg. 1935
IR SPECIALTY FOAM, LLC; *U.S. Private*, pg. 2137
IRS (S) PTE., LTD.—See IRISO ELECTRONICS CO.,LTD; *Int'l*, pg. 3809
IRS STAHLHANDEL GMBH—See L. Possehl & Co. mbH; *Int'l*, pg. 4383
IRTH SOLUTIONS, INC.; *U.S. Private*, pg. 2141
IRTH SOLUTIONS LLC—See Blackstone Inc.; *U.S. Public*, pg. 355
IRT LIVE OAK TRACE LOUISIANA, LLC—See Independence Realty Trust, Inc.; *U.S. Public*, pg. 1115
IRT NORTH AMERICA, INC.—See Storskogen Group AB; *Int'l*, pg. 7227
IRT OF TEXAS—See Interactive Response Technologies; *U.S. Private*, pg. 2108
IRT STONEBRIDGE CROSSING APARTMENTS OWNER, LLC—See Independence Realty Trust, Inc.; *U.S. Public*, pg. 1115
IRT WATERFORD LANDING APARTMENTS, LLC—See Independence Realty Trust, Inc.; *U.S. Public*, pg. 1115
IRTYSH-POLYMETAL JSC; *Int'l*, pg. 3811
IRU ELEKTRIJAAM OU—See Eesti Energia AS; *Int'l*, pg. 2317
IRUMA COUNTRY CLUB CO., LTD.—See Kuraray Co., Ltd.; *Int'l*, pg. 4336
IRUMOLD, S.L.U.—See Flex Ltd.; *Int'l*, pg. 2704
IRVIA MANTENIMIENTO FERROVIARIO, S.A.—See Alstom S.A.; *Int'l*, pg. 383
IRVIN AUTOMOTIVE PRODUCTS INC.—See Piston Group, LLC; *U.S. Private*, pg. 3190
IRVINE ACCESS FLOORS INC.; *U.S. Private*, pg. 2141
IRVINE APARTMENT COMMUNITIES INCORPORATED—See The Irvine Company Inc.; *U.S. Private*, pg. 4057
IRVINE COMMUNITY DEVELOPMENT COMPANY—See The Irvine Company Inc.; *U.S. Private*, pg. 4057
IRVINE COMMUNITY LAND TRUST; *U.S. Private*, pg. 2141
THE IRVINE COMPANY INC.; *U.S. Private*, pg. 4057
IRVINE IMPORTS, INC.—See AutoNation, Inc.; *U.S. Public*, pg. 235
IRVINE MARKETING COMMUNICATIONS; *U.S. Private*, pg. 2141
IRVINE MECHANICAL, INC.—See Halmos Capital Partners; *U.S. Private*, pg. 1845

IRVINE MECHANICAL, INC.—See Trivest Partners, LP; *U.S. Private*, pg. 4241
IRVINE RANCH WATER DISTRICT INC.; *U.S. Private*, pg. 2141
IRVINE REGIONAL HOSPITAL & MEDICAL CENTER—See Tenet Healthcare Corporation; *U.S. Public*, pg. 2008
IRVINE SCIENTIFIC SALES COMPANY, INC.—See FUJIFILM Holdings Corporation; *Int'l*, pg. 2823
IRVINE SPRING COMPANY LTD.—See Indutrade AB; *Int'l*, pg. 3679
IRVINE - WHITLOCK LIMITED—See Heidelberg Materials AG; *Int'l*, pg. 3316
IRVING BLENDING & PACKAGING LIMITED—See Irving Oil Limited; *Int'l*, pg. 3811
IRVING BURTON ASSOCIATES, LLC—See DLH Holdings Corp.; *U.S. Public*, pg. 670
IRVING MATERIALS INC.; *U.S. Private*, pg. 2141
IRVING OIL CORPORATION—See Irving Oil Limited; *Int'l*, pg. 3811
IRVING OIL LIMITED; *Int'l*, pg. 3811
IRVIN GOODON INDUSTRIES LTD.; *Int'l*, pg. 3811
IRVING PLACE CAPITAL MANAGEMENT, L.P.; *U.S. Private*, pg. 2141
IRVING PULP AND PAPER LTD.—See J.D. Irving, Limited; *Int'l*, pg. 3858
IRVINGQ FRANCE SAA—See TransDigm Group Incorporated; *U.S. Public*, pg. 2182
IRVIN-GQ LIMITED—See TransDigm Group Incorporated; *U.S. Public*, pg. 2182
IRVING RESOURCES INC.; *Int'l*, pg. 3811
IRVINGTON ELEVATOR COMPANY; *U.S. Private*, pg. 2142
IRVING WEBER ASSOCIATES, INC.—See Brown & Brown, Inc.; *U.S. Public*, pg. 401
IRVIN & JOHNSON HOLDING COMPANY (PTY) LIMITED—See AVI Limited; *Int'l*, pg. 740
IRWIN CONTRACTING INC.; *U.S. Private*, pg. 2142
IRWIN CORPORATION; *U.S. Private*, pg. 2142
IRWIN ENGINEERS INC.—See Pennoni Associates Inc.; *U.S. Private*, pg. 3136
IRWIN-HODSON COMPANY; *U.S. Private*, pg. 2142
IRWIN INDUSTRIAL LTD.; *Int'l*, pg. 3811
IRWIN INDUSTRIAL TOOL COMPANY—See Newell Brands Inc.; *U.S. Public*, pg. 1514
IRWIN INTERNATIONAL, INC.; *U.S. Private*, pg. 2142
IRWIN MITCHELL LLP; *Int'l*, pg. 3811
IRWIN NATURALS INC.; *Int'l*, pg. 3811
IRWIN NATURALS—See Irwin Naturals Inc.; *Int'l*, pg. 3811
IRWIN SEATING COMPANY INC.; *U.S. Private*, pg. 2142
IRWIN TELESCOPIC SEATING—See Irwin Seating Company Inc.; *U.S. Private*, pg. 2142
IRX THERAPEUTICS, INC.; *U.S. Private*, pg. 2142
IRYDION SP. Z O.O.—See PROCHEM S.A.; *Int'l*, pg. 5987
IRYD SP. Z O.O.—See PROCHEM S.A.; *Int'l*, pg. 5987
IRZ CONSULTING LLC—See Lindsay Corporation; *U.S. Public*, pg. 1319
ISAAC ENGINEERING CO., LTD.; *Int'l*, pg. 3812
ISAAC HEATING & AC; *U.S. Private*, pg. 2142
THE ISAACS COMPANY—See Fluid System Components Inc.; *U.S. Private*, pg. 1552
ISAACS ENTERPRISES INC.; *U.S. Private*, pg. 2142
ISAAC'S RESTAURANT & DELI INC.; *U.S. Private*, pg. 2142
ISAAC TIRE INC.; *U.S. Private*, pg. 2142
ISA ADVERTISING; *U.S. Private*, pg. 2142
ISAAS TECHNOLOGY LIMITED—See Watchstone Group plc; *Int'l*, pg. 8356
ISABEL BLOOM LLC; *U.S. Private*, pg. 2142
ISABELLA BANK CORPORATION; *U.S. Public*, pg. 1174
ISABELLA BANK—See Isabella Bank Corporation; *U.S. Public*, pg. 1174
ISABELLA OLIVER LTD.; *Int'l*, pg. 3812
ISABELLA STEWART GARDNER MUSEUM; *U.S. Private*, pg. 2142
ISABELLE RIDGWAY CARE CENTER; *U.S. Private*, pg. 2142
ISABERG RAPID AB—See ACCO Brands Corporation; *U.S. Public*, pg. 33
ISA BOLIVIA S.A.—See Ecopetrol S.A.; *Int'l*, pg. 2299
ISAB S.R.L.—See G.O.I. Energy Limited; *Int'l*, pg. 2866
ISA CAPITAL DO BRASIL S.A.—See Ecopetrol S.A.; *Int'l*, pg. 2299
ISACO INTERNATIONAL, INC.; *U.S. Private*, pg. 2142
ISACSSON FRUKT & GRONT AB—See Sysco Corporation; *U.S. Public*, pg. 1973
ISAF DRAHTWERK GMBH—See Lincoln Electric Holdings, Inc.; *U.S. Public*, pg. 1317
ISAGENIX INTERNATIONAL, LLC; *U.S. Private*, pg. 2142
ISAGEN S.A. E.S.P.—See Brookfield Corporation; *Int'l*, pg. 1186
ISAGRI S.A.; *Int'l*, pg. 3812
ISAGRO (ASIA) AGROCHEMICALS PVT, LTD.—See PI Industries Ltd.; *Int'l*, pg. 5859
ISAGRO HELLAS LTD—See Gowan Company LLC; *U.S. Private*, pg. 1747
ISAGRO ITALIA S.R.L.—See Gowan Company LLC; *U.S. Private*, pg. 1747

COMPANY NAME INDEX

ISAGRO S.P.A.—See Gowan Company LLC; *U.S. Private*, pg. 1747
ISAGRO USA, INC.—See Gowan Company LLC; *U.S. Private*, pg. 1747
ISA HOLDINGS LIMITED; *Int'l*, pg. 3812
ISA INDUSTRIAL LTD.; *Int'l*, pg. 3812
ISA INFORMATION SYSTEMS SERVICES—See Integrated Systems Analysts, Inc.; *U.S. Private*, pg. 2101
ISA INSTALLATION & DEPLOYMENT CENTER—See Integrated Systems Analysts, Inc.; *U.S. Private*, pg. 2101
ISA INSTALLATIONS-,STEUERUNGS UND AUTOMATISIERUNGS GMBH—See Icahn Enterprises L.P.; *U.S. Public*, pg. 1084
ISA INTELLIGENT SENSING ANYWHERE SA—See Anova Microsystems Inc.; *U.S. Private*, pg. 285
ISA INTERNATIONALE INC.; *Int'l*, pg. 3812
ISAK INTERNATIONAL HOLDING LTD—See Origo Partners Plc; *Int'l*, pg. 5631
ISAM AUTOMATION CANADA CORP.—See Hamburger Hafen und Logistik AG; *Int'l*, pg. 3237
ISAMAX SNACKS, INC.; *U.S. Private*, pg. 2143
ISAM MITCHELL & CO. INC.; *U.S. Private*, pg. 2143
ISAM NORTH AMERICA CORP.—See Hamburger Hafen und Logistik AG; *Int'l*, pg. 3237
ISAMU PAINT CO., LTD.; *Int'l*, pg. 3812
ISANGO! LTD.; *Int'l*, pg. 3812
ISANOR INVEST AS; *Int'l*, pg. 3812
ISAPRE BANMEDICA S.A.—See UnitedHealth Group Incorporated; *U.S. Public*, pg. 2242
ISAPRE NORTE GRANDE LTDA.—See Sociedad Quimica y Minera de Chile S.A.; *Int'l*, pg. 7032
ISAPRE SAN LORENZO LTDA—See Corporacion Nacional del Cobre de Chile; *Int'l*, pg. 1805
ISAPRE VIDA TRES S.A.—See UnitedHealth Group Incorporated; *U.S. Public*, pg. 2242
ISAR-DONAU-MORTEL GMBH & CO. KG—See BERGER Holding GmbH; *Int'l*, pg. 979
THE ISA RESORT CO., LTD.—See Veranda Resort Public Company Limited; *Int'l*, pg. 8164
ISATORI, INC.—See FitLife Brands, Inc.; *U.S. Public*, pg. 852
ISA-TRAESKO GMBH; *Int'l*, pg. 3812
ISBA MUTUAL INSURANCE COMPANY; *U.S. Private*, pg. 2143
ISBANK AG—See Turkiye Is Bankasi A.S.; *Int'l*, pg. 7976
ISBANK JSC; *Int'l*, pg. 3812
I&S BBDO INC.—See Omnicom Group Inc.; *U.S. Public*, pg. 1575
I&S/BBDO KANSAI REGIONAL HEAD OFFICE—See Omnicom Group Inc.; *U.S. Public*, pg. 1576
I&S/BBDO KYOTO REGIONAL HEAD OFFICE—See Omnicom Group Inc.; *U.S. Public*, pg. 1576
I&S/BBDO NAGOYA REGIONAL HEAD OFFICE—See Omnicom Group Inc.; *U.S. Public*, pg. 1576
I&S/BBDO SAPPORO BRANCH—See Omnicom Group Inc.; *U.S. Public*, pg. 1576
ISB CANARIAS SA—See Barclays PLC; *Int'l*, pg. 862
ISB CORPORATION; *Int'l*, pg. 3812
ISBELL CONSTRUCTION CO. LTD; *U.S. Private*, pg. 2143
ISBIR HOLDING A.S.; *Int'l*, pg. 3812
ISB UNIVERSALE BAU GMBH—See UniCredit S.p.A.; *Int'l*, pg. 8040
ISB VIETNAM COMPANY LIMITED—See ISB Corporation; *Int'l*, pg. 3812
ISC2 ASIA-PACIFIC—See International Information Systems Consortium Inc.; *U.S. Private*, pg. 2118
ISC2 EMEA—See International Information Systems Consortium Inc.; *U.S. Private*, pg. 2118
ISC2 JAPAN—See International Information Systems Consortium Inc.; *U.S. Private*, pg. 2118
ISCAL SUGAR B.V.—See Finasucre S.A.; *Int'l*, pg. 2670
ISCAL SUGAR S.A./N.V.—See Finasucre S.A.; *Int'l*, pg. 2670
ISCAN ONLINE, INC.; *U.S. Private*, pg. 2143
ISCA (PROPRIETARY) LIMITED—See DISTRIBUTION AND WAREHOUSING NETWORK LIMITED; *Int'l*, pg. 2136
ISCAR ALATI D.O.O—See Berkshire Hathaway Inc.; *U.S. Public*, pg. 307
ISCAR AUSTRIA GMBH—See Berkshire Hathaway Inc.; *U.S. Public*, pg. 307
ISCAR BENELUX S.A.—See Berkshire Hathaway Inc.; *U.S. Public*, pg. 307
ISCAR BLADES LTD.—See IDB Development Corporation Ltd.; *Int'l*, pg. 3588
ISCAR BULGARIA LTD—See Berkshire Hathaway Inc.; *U.S. Public*, pg. 307
ISCAR CR S.R.O.—See Berkshire Hathaway Inc.; *U.S. Public*, pg. 307
ISCAR FINLAND OY—See Berkshire Hathaway Inc.; *U.S. Public*, pg. 307
ISCAR FRANCE SAS—See Berkshire Hathaway Inc.; *U.S. Public*, pg. 307
ISCAR GERMANY GMBH—See Berkshire Hathaway Inc.; *U.S. Public*, pg. 307
ISCAR HARTMETALL AG—See Berkshire Hathaway Inc.; *U.S. Public*, pg. 307

ISCAR HUNGARY KFT.—See Berkshire Hathaway Inc.; *U.S. Public*, pg. 307
ISCAR IBERICA AS—See Berkshire Hathaway Inc.; *U.S. Public*, pg. 307
ISCAR ITALIA SRL—See Berkshire Hathaway Inc.; *U.S. Public*, pg. 307
ISCAR LTD.—See Berkshire Hathaway Inc.; *U.S. Public*, pg. 307
ISCAR NETHERLANDS BV—See Berkshire Hathaway Inc.; *U.S. Public*, pg. 307
ISCAR POLAND SP. Z O.O.—See Berkshire Hathaway Inc.; *U.S. Public*, pg. 307
ISCAR PORTUGAL SA—See Berkshire Hathaway Inc.; *U.S. Public*, pg. 307
ISCAR RUSSIA LLC—See Berkshire Hathaway Inc.; *U.S. Public*, pg. 307
ISCAR SLOVENIJA D.O.O.—See Berkshire Hathaway Inc.; *U.S. Public*, pg. 307
ISCAR SR, S.R.O.—See Berkshire Hathaway Inc.; *U.S. Public*, pg. 307
ISCAR SVERIGE AB—See Berkshire Hathaway Inc.; *U.S. Public*, pg. 307
ISCAR TOOLS LTD.—See Berkshire Hathaway Inc.; *U.S. Public*, pg. 307
ISCAR TOOLS SRL—See Berkshire Hathaway Inc.; *U.S. Public*, pg. 307
ISC BUSINESS TECHNOLOGY AG; *Int'l*, pg. 3812
ISC CO., LTD.; *Int'l*, pg. 3812
ISC.COM, LLC—See National Association for Stock Car Auto Racing, Inc.; *U.S. Private*, pg. 2845
ISC CONSTRUCTORS, LLC.; *U.S. Private*, pg. 2143
ISC CORP.; *U.S. Private*, pg. 2143
ISC GMBH—See Einhell Germany AG; *Int'l*, pg. 2334
I. SCHUMANN & COMPANY; *U.S. Private*, pg. 2026
ISC ITALIA S.R.L.—See Einhell Germany AG; *Int'l*, pg. 2334
ISC MICRO PRECISION SDN. BHD.—See NSK Ltd.; *Int'l*, pg. 5478
ISCM TECHNOLOGY (THAILAND) CO., LTD.—See D'nonce Technology Bhd.; *Int'l*, pg. 1900
ISCO HOLDING COMPANY INC.; *U.S. Private*, pg. 2143
ISCO INC.—See ASKO Holding A.S.; *Int'l*, pg. 625
ISCO INDUSTRIES LLC; *U.S. Private*, pg. 2143
ISCO INTERNATIONAL LLC; *U.S. Private*, pg. 2143
ISCO METALS & SUPPLY, LLC—See European Metal Recycling Limited; *Int'l*, pg. 2557
ISCOOL ENTERTAINMENT SA; *Int'l*, pg. 3813
IS COSTA RICA, S.A.—See Hewlett Packard Enterprise Company; *U.S. Public*, pg. 1032
ISC PUBLICATIONS, INC.—See National Association for Stock Car Auto Racing, Inc.; *U.S. Private*, pg. 2845
I-SCREAM MEDIA CO., LTD.—See Sigong Tech Co., Ltd.; *Int'l*, pg. 6912
ISC SOFTWARE PVT. LTD.—See CoreCard Corporation; *U.S. Public*, pg. 577
ISDALEN AS—See TINE SA; *Int'l*, pg. 7753
ISD CANTON, LLC—See DaVita Inc.; *U.S. Public*, pg. 639
ISD DUNAFERR ZRT.—See Industrial Union of Donbass Corporation; *Int'l*, pg. 3673
ISDEL ENERGY SAS—See VINCI S.A.; *Int'l*, pg. 8222
ISD HUTA CZESTOCHOWA SP. Z O.O.—See Industrial Union of Donbass Corporation; *Int'l*, pg. 3673
ISDIN, SA—See Laboratorios del Dr. Esteve, S.A.; *Int'l*, pg. 4390
ISD ITALIA S.R.L.—See HUB Cyber Security Ltd.; *Int'l*, pg. 3516
ISD KANSAS CITY, LLC—See DaVita Inc.; *U.S. Public*, pg. 639
ISD KENDALLVILLE, LLC—See DaVita Inc.; *U.S. Public*, pg. 639
ISDN HOLDINGS LIMITED; *Int'l*, pg. 3813
ISDN SOFTWARE BUSINESS PTE. LTD.—See ISDN Holdings Limited; *Int'l*, pg. 3813
IS DONGSEO CO., LTD.; *Int'l*, pg. 3811
ISEATZ INC.; *U.S. Private*, pg. 2143
ISEC HEALTHCARE LIMITED; *Int'l*, pg. 3813
ISE CHEMICALS CORPORATION; *Int'l*, pg. 3813
ISEC INCORPORATED; *U.S. Private*, pg. 2143
I-SEC INTERNATIONAL SECURITY B.V.—See ICTS International, N.V.; *Int'l*, pg. 3587
I-SEC INTERNATIONAL SECURITY B.V.—See ICTS International, N.V.; *Int'l*, pg. 3587
I-SEC ITALIA SERVICES S.R.L.—See ICTS International, N.V.; *Int'l*, pg. 3587
ISEC MYANMAR COMPANY LIMITED—See ISEC Healthcare Limited; *Int'l*, pg. 3813
ISE COMMERCE CO., LTD.; *Int'l*, pg. 3813
ISECO SA; *Int'l*, pg. 3814
ISEC PARTNERS, INC.—See NCC Group Plc; *Int'l*, pg. 5181
ISEC (PENANG) SDN. BHD.—See ISEC Healthcare Limited; *Int'l*, pg. 3813
ISEC SDN. BHD.—See ISEC Healthcare Limited; *Int'l*, pg. 3813
ISEC SECURITIZADORA S.A.S.; *Int'l*, pg. 3813
ISEC (SIBU) SDN. BHD.—See ISEC Healthcare Limited; *Int'l*, pg. 3813
I-SECURE COMPANY LIMITED—See Vintcom Technology Public Company Limited; *Int'l*, pg. 8242

ISETAN MITSUKOSHI HOLDINGS LTD.

ISECURETRAC CORP.—See Corrisoft LLC; *U.S. Private*, pg. 1059
ISE ETF VENTURES LLC—See Nasdaq, Inc.; *U.S. Public*, pg. 1491
ISE FLEET SERVICES, LLC—See Trimble, Inc.; *U.S. Public*, pg. 2190
ISEHAN CO., LTD.—See Tecnos Japan Inc.; *Int'l*, pg. 7517
ISEKI-CHANGZHOU MFG. CO., LTD.—See Iseki & Co., Ltd.; *Int'l*, pg. 3814
ISEKI & CO., LTD.; *Int'l*, pg. 3814
ISEKI FRANCE S.A.S—See Iseki & Co., Ltd.; *Int'l*, pg. 3814
ISEKI-KUMAMOTO MFG. CO., LTD.—See Iseki & Co., Ltd.; *Int'l*, pg. 3814
ISEKI KYUSHU CO., LTD.—See Iseki & Co., Ltd.; *Int'l*, pg. 3814
ISEKI MASCHINEN GMBH—See Iseki & Co., Ltd.; *Int'l*, pg. 3814
ISEKI-MATSUYAMA MFG. CO., LTD.—See Iseki & Co., Ltd.; *Int'l*, pg. 3814
ISEKI (THAILAND) CO., LTD.—See Iseki & Co., Ltd.; *Int'l*, pg. 3814
ISEKI TLS CO., LTD.—See Iseki & Co., Ltd.; *Int'l*, pg. 3814
ISEKI-TOHOKU CO., LTD.—See Iseki & Co., Ltd.; *Int'l*, pg. 3814
ISE LABS,CHINA, INC.—See ASE Technology Holding Co., Ltd.; *Int'l*, pg. 605
ISE LABS, INC.—See ASE Technology Holding Co., Ltd.; *Int'l*, pg. 604
ISELECTION HOLDING; *Int'l*, pg. 3814
ISELECTION SAS—See Nexity SA; *Int'l*, pg. 5244
ISELECT LTD.; *Int'l*, pg. 3814
ISE LIMITED; *U.S. Private*, pg. 2143
ISELI PRECISION LLC—See Precision Plus, Inc.; *U.S. Private*, pg. 3246
ISEMOTO CONTRACTING CO. LTD.; *U.S. Private*, pg. 2143
ISE MURATA MANUFACTURING CO., LTD.—See Murata Manufacturing Co., Ltd.; *Int'l*, pg. 5097
ISEND LLC—See ezetop Ltd.; *Int'l*, pg. 2594
ISENHOUR FURNITURE COMPANY; *U.S. Private*, pg. 2143
ISENSE & B.V.—See ManpowerGroup Inc.; *U.S. Public*, pg. 1362
ISENSE EINDHOVEN B.V.—See ManpowerGroup Inc.; *U.S. Public*, pg. 1362
I-SENS INC. - SONGDO FACTORY—See i-SENS Inc.; *Int'l*, pg. 3564
I-SENS INC.; *Int'l*, pg. 3564
I-SENS INC. - WONJU FACTORY—See i-SENS Inc.; *Int'l*, pg. 3564
I-SENS USA INC.—See i-SENS Inc.; *Int'l*, pg. 3564
ISENTIA GROUP LIMITED—See Pulsar Group; *Int'l*, pg. 6116
ISENTIA LIMITED—See Pulsar Group; *Int'l*, pg. 6116
ISENTIA (M) SDN. BHD.—See Pulsar Group; *Int'l*, pg. 6116
ISENTIA PTE LIMITED—See Pulsar Group; *Int'l*, pg. 6116
ISENTIA VIETNAM CO. INVESTMENT—See Pulsar Group; *Int'l*, pg. 6116
ISENTRIC SDN. BHD.—See IOUpay Limited; *Int'l*, pg. 3795
ISERO B.V.—See Grafton Group plc; *Int'l*, pg. 3051
ISERVEU TECHNOLOGY PRIVATE LIMITED—See Niyogin Fintech Limited; *Int'l*, pg. 5390
ISESAKI GAS CO., LTD.—See TOKAI Holdings Corporation; *Int'l*, pg. 7779
ISETAN (CHINA) CO., LTD.—See Isetan Mitsukoshi Holdings Ltd.; *Int'l*, pg. 3814
ISETAN CO., LTD.—See Isetan Mitsukoshi Holdings Ltd.; *Int'l*, pg. 3814
ISETAN (ITALIA) S.R.L.—See Isetan Mitsukoshi Holdings Ltd.; *Int'l*, pg. 3814
ISETAN KAIKAN CO., LTD.—See Isetan Mitsukoshi Holdings Ltd.; *Int'l*, pg. 3814
ISETAN MITSUKOSHI BUILDING MANAGEMENT SERVICE CO., LTD—See Isetan Mitsukoshi Holdings Ltd.; *Int'l*, pg. 3814
ISETAN MITSUKOSHI BUSINESS SUPPORT LTD.—See Isetan Mitsukoshi Holdings Ltd.; *Int'l*, pg. 3814
ISETAN MITSUKOSHI DIRECT SHOPPING LTD.—See Isetan Mitsukoshi Holdings Ltd.; *Int'l*, pg. 3814
ISETAN MITSUKOSHI FOOD SERVICE LTD.—See Isetan Mitsukoshi Holdings Ltd.; *Int'l*, pg. 3814
ISETAN MITSUKOSHI HOLDINGS LTD.; *Int'l*, pg. 3814
ISETAN MITSUKOSHI HUMAN SOLUTIONS LTD.—See Isetan Mitsukoshi Holdings Ltd.; *Int'l*, pg. 3814
ISETAN MITSUKOSHI INNOVATIONS LTD.—See Isetan Mitsukoshi Holdings Ltd.; *Int'l*, pg. 3814
ISETAN MITSUKOSHI LTD—See Isetan Mitsukoshi Holdings Ltd.; *Int'l*, pg. 3815
ISETAN MITSUKOSHI PROPERTY DESIGN LTD.—See Isetan Mitsukoshi Holdings Ltd.; *Int'l*, pg. 3815
ISETAN MITSUKOSHI SOLEIL, CO., LTD.—See Isetan Mitsukoshi Holdings Ltd.; *Int'l*, pg. 3815
ISETAN MITSUKOSHI SYSTEM SOLUTIONS LTD.—See Isetan Mitsukoshi Holdings Ltd.; *Int'l*, pg. 3815
ISETAN OF JAPAN SDN. BHD.—See Isetan Mitsukoshi Holdings Ltd.; *Int'l*, pg. 3815

ISETAN MITSUKOSHI HOLDINGS LTD.

CORPORATE AFFILIATIONS

ISETAN (SINGAPORE) LIMITED—See Isetan Mitsukoshi Holdings Ltd.; *Int'l*, pg. 3815
ISETAN SWING INC—See Isetan Mitsukoshi Holdings Ltd.; *Int'l*, pg. 3815
ISETAN (THAILAND) CO., LTD.—See Isetan Mitsukoshi Holdings Ltd.; *Int'l*, pg. 3814
ISETAN TIANJIN CO., LTD.—See Isetan Mitsukoshi Holdings Ltd.; *Int'l*, pg. 3814
ISEWAN DE MEXICO S.A. DE C.V.—See Isewan Terminal Service Co., Ltd.; *Int'l*, pg. 3816
ISEWAN EUROPE GMBH—See Isewan Terminal Service Co., Ltd.; *Int'l*, pg. 3816
ISEWAN (GUANGZHOU) INTERNATIONAL LOGISTICS CO., LTD.—See Isewan Terminal Service Co., Ltd.; *Int'l*, pg. 3816
ISEWAN (H.K.) LIMITED—See Isewan Terminal Service Co., Ltd.; *Int'l*, pg. 3816
ISEWAN (SHANGHAI) INTERNATIONAL LOGISTICS CO., LTD.—See Isewan Terminal Service Co., Ltd.; *Int'l*, pg. 3816
ISEWAN TAIWAN CO., LTD.—See Isewan Terminal Service Co., Ltd.; *Int'l*, pg. 3816
ISEWAN TERMINAL SERVICE CO., LTD.; *Int'l*, pg. 3815
ISEWAN (THAILAND) CO., LTD.—See Isewan Terminal Service Co., Ltd.; *Int'l*, pg. 3816
ISEWAN U.S.A. INC.—See Isewan Terminal Service Co., Ltd.; *Int'l*, pg. 3816
ISFAHAN PEGAH DAIRY COMPANY; *Int'l*, pg. 3816
ISFAHAN SAMAN GOSTAR COMPANY; *Int'l*, pg. 3816
IS FAKTORING A.S.; *Int'l*, pg. 3811
ISFEL COMPANY, INC.; *U.S. Private*, pg. 2143
ISFELD FORD SALES LTD; *Int'l*, pg. 3816
ISFI - INTERNATIONAL SPICE & FOOD IMPORT SA—See Gilde Equity Management (GEM) Benelux Partners B.V.; *Int'l*, pg. 2975
IS FINANSAL KIRALAMA A.S.—See Turkiye Is Bankasi A.S.; *Int'l*, pg. 7976
ISF INTERNATIONALE SCHULE FRANKFURT-RHEIN-MAIN GMBH & CO. KG—See General Motors Company; *U.S. Public*, pg. 927
ISF LIMITED; *Int'l*, pg. 3816
ISG ASIA CHINA LIMITED—See ISG PLC; *Int'l*, pg. 3816
ISG ASIA (HONG KONG) LIMITED—See ISG PLC; *Int'l*, pg. 3816
ISG ASIA INVESTMENT (HONG KONG) LIMITED—See ISG PLC; *Int'l*, pg. 3816
ISG ASIA (JAPAN) LIMITED—See ISG PLC; *Int'l*, pg. 3816
ISG ASIA (KOREA) LIMITED—See ISG PLC; *Int'l*, pg. 3816
ISG ASIA (MACAU) LIMITED—See ISG PLC; *Int'l*, pg. 3816
ISG ASIA MALAYSIA SDN BHD—See ISG PLC; *Int'l*, pg. 3816
ISG ASIA (SINGAPORE) PTE LIMITED—See ISG PLC; *Int'l*, pg. 3816
ISG ASIA—See ISG PLC; *Int'l*, pg. 3816
IS GAYRIMENKUL YATIRIM ORTAKLIGI A.S.; *Int'l*, pg. 3812
ISG CATHEDRAL LIMITED—See ISG PLC; *Int'l*, pg. 3816
ISG DEUTSCHLAND GMBH—See ISG PLC; *Int'l*, pg. 3816
ISG DEVELOPMENTS (SOUTHERN) LIMITED—See ISG PLC; *Int'l*, pg. 3816
ISGEC HEAVY ENGINEERING LTD.; *Int'l*, pg. 3816
ISGEC REDECAM ENVIRO SOLUTIONS PRIVATE LIMITED—See Isgec Heavy Engineering Ltd.; *Int'l*, pg. 3816
ISGETT DISTRIBUTORS INC.; *U.S. Private*, pg. 2143
ISG GROUP LLC—See Clearlake Capital Group, L.P.; *U.S. Private*, pg. 937
ISG GROUP LLC—See SkyKnight Capital LLC; *U.S. Private*, pg. 3685
ISG INFORMATION SERVICES GROUP AMERICAS, INC.—See Information Services Group, Inc.; *U.S. Public*, pg. 1118
ISG INGENIEURSERVICE GRUNDBAU GMBH—See PORR AG; *Int'l*, pg. 5923
IS GIRISIM SERMAYESI YATIRIM ORTAKLIGI A.S.; *Int'l*, pg. 3812
ISG JACKSON SPECIAL PROJECTS LIMITED—See ISG PLC; *Int'l*, pg. 3816
ISGN FULFILLMENT SERVICES, INC.—See CESC Limited; *Int'l*, pg. 1424
ISG NORDIC AB—See Lagercrantz Group AB; *Int'l*, pg. 4394
ISGN SOLUTIONS, INC.—See CESC Limited; *Int'l*, pg. 1424
ISGN TECHNOLOGIES LTD.—See K.K. Birla Group; *Int'l*, pg. 4044
ISGPAS GENERAL PURPOSE APPLICATIONS SYSTEMS GMBH—See Samsung Group; *Int'l*, pg. 6512
ISG PLC; *Int'l*, pg. 3816
I & S GROUP, INC.; *U.S. Private*, pg. 2020
ISG (SCHWEIZ) AG—See ISG PLC; *Int'l*, pg. 3816
ISG SERVICES, LLC—See Xerox Holdings Corporation; *U.S. Public*, pg. 2387
ISG SYSTEMS AB—See Lagercrantz Group AB; *Int'l*, pg. 4394
ISG TECHNOLOGY, INC.; *U.S. Private*, pg. 2143

ISGUS AMERICA LLC—See ISGUS GmbH; *Int'l*, pg. 3817
ISGUS GMBH—See ISGUS GmbH; *Int'l*, pg. 3817
ISGUS GMBH; *Int'l*, pg. 3817
ISGUS UK LIMITED—See ISGUS GmbH; *Int'l*, pg. 3817
ISHAAN INFRASTRUCTURES & SHELTERS LIMITED; *Int'l*, pg. 3817
ISHAN DYES & CHEMICALS LIMITED; *Int'l*, pg. 3817
ISHAP PERSONALDOKUMENTATIONS GMBH—See PORR AG; *Int'l*, pg. 5923
ISHARES GOLD BULLION FUND; *U.S. Public*, pg. 1174
ISHARES GOLD TRUST; *U.S. Public*, pg. 1174
ISHARP SDN BHD—See Khazanah Nasional Berhad; *Int'l*, pg. 4154
I-SHENG ELECTRIC WIRE & CABLE CO., LTD. - I-SHENG MANUFACTURING (SONG GANG) FACTORY—See I-Sheng Electric Wire & Cable Co., Ltd.; *Int'l*, pg. 3565
I-SHENG ELECTRIC WIRE & CABLE CO., LTD.; *Int'l*, pg. 3564
I-SHENG ELECTRONICS (KUNSHAN) CO., LTD.—See I-Sheng Electric Wire & Cable Co., Ltd.; *Int'l*, pg. 3565
I-SHENG JAPAN CO., LTD.—See I-Sheng Electric Wire & Cable Co., Ltd.; *Int'l*, pg. 3565
ISHIDA METAL CO., LTD.—See Sumitomo Corporation; *Int'l*, pg. 7269
ISHIGAKI FOODS CO., LTD.; *Int'l*, pg. 3817
ISHIHARA ARGENTINA S.A.—See Ishihara Sangyo Kaisha, Ltd.; *Int'l*, pg. 3817
ISHIHARA CHEMICAL CO., LTD.; *Int'l*, pg. 3817
ISHIHARA CHEMICAL (SHANGHAI) CO., LTD.—See Ishihara Chemical Co., Ltd.; *Int'l*, pg. 3817
ISHIHARA CORPORATION (U.S.A.)—See Ishihara Sangyo Kaisha, Ltd.; *Int'l*, pg. 3817
ISHIHARA-GIKEN CO., LTD.—See Yamazen Corporation; *Int'l*, pg. 8558
ISHIHARA KOHTETU CO., LTD.—See Sumitomo Corporation; *Int'l*, pg. 7269
ISHIHARA SANGYO KAISHA LIMITED, TOKYO—See Ishihara Sangyo Kaisha, Ltd.; *Int'l*, pg. 3817
ISHIHARA SANGYO KAISHA, LTD.; *Int'l*, pg. 3817
ISHII FOOD CO., LTD.; *Int'l*, pg. 3817
ISHII HYOKI (AMERICA), INC.—See Ishii Hyoki Co., Ltd.; *Int'l*, pg. 3817
ISHII HYOKI CO., LTD. - DISPLAY DIVISION—See Ishii Hyoki Co., Ltd.; *Int'l*, pg. 3817
ISHII HYOKI CO., LTD. - MACHINERY DIVISION—See Ishii Hyoki Co., Ltd.; *Int'l*, pg. 3817
ISHII HYOKI CO., LTD. - SOLAR SYSTEM DIVISION—See Ishii Hyoki Co., Ltd.; *Int'l*, pg. 3818
ISHII HYOKI CO., LTD.; *Int'l*, pg. 3817
ISHII IRON WORKS CO., LTD.; *Int'l*, pg. 3818
ISHIKARI ATSUTA GREEN ENERGY CO., LTD.—See Takasago Thermal Engineering Co., Ltd.; *Int'l*, pg. 7434
ISHIKARI DELICA CO., LTD.—See Kewpie Corporation; *Int'l*, pg. 4144
ISHIKARI TOYO KAISHA, LTD.—See Toyo Suisan Kaisha, Ltd.; *Int'l*, pg. 7858
ISHIKATSU EXTERIOR INC.—See Tokyu Fudosan Holdings Corporation; *Int'l*, pg. 7798
ISHIKAWA INK CO., LTD.—See Toyo Seikan Group Holdings, Ltd.; *Int'l*, pg. 7856
ISHIKAWAJIMA-HARIMA SUL-AMERICA LTDA.—See IHI Corporation; *Int'l*, pg. 3605
ISHIKAWAJIMA SCE (XIAMEN) CONSTRUCTION MACHINERY CO., LTD.—See IHI Corporation; *Int'l*, pg. 3605
ISHIKAWA SANKEN CO., LTD.—See Sanken Electric Co., Ltd.; *Int'l*, pg. 6540
ISHIKAWA SEISAKUSHO LTD.; *Int'l*, pg. 3818
ISHIKOTEC CO., LTD.—See NADEX CO., LTD.; *Int'l*, pg. 5123
ISHIMOKU EMORI CORPORATION—See JUTEC Holdings Corporation; *Int'l*, pg. 4032
ISHIMOTOBIO-CHEMICAL LABORATORY CO., LTD.—See MyunMoon Pharm Co., Ltd.; *Int'l*, pg. 5115
ISHIN HOTELS GROUP CO., LTD.—See Alpine Grove Partners LLP; *U.S. Private*, pg. 201
ISHIN HOTELS GROUP CO., LTD.—See Hoshino Resorts Inc.; *Int'l*, pg. 3483
ISHINO GASKET MFG. CO., LTD.—See NOK Corporation; *Int'l*, pg. 5401
ISHINOMAKI ATEX CO., LTD.—See NIPPON ANTENNA CO., LTD; *Int'l*, pg. 5310
ISHINOMAKI PLYWOOD MFG. CO., LTD.—See Noda Corporation; *Int'l*, pg. 5398
ISHI POWER SDN BHD—See IHI Corporation; *Int'l*, pg. 3605
ISHIR, INC.; *U.S. Private*, pg. 2143
ISHITA DRUGS & INDUSTRIES LIMITED; *Int'l*, pg. 3818
ISHIZAKI CO., LTD.—See Taiheiyo Cement Corporation; *Int'l*, pg. 7411
ISHIZUKA BUTSURYU SERVICE CO., LTD.—See Ishizuka Glass Co., Ltd.; *Int'l*, pg. 3818
ISHIZUKA GLASS CO., LTD. - FUKUSAKI PLANT—See Ishizuka Glass Co., Ltd.; *Int'l*, pg. 3818
ISHIZUKA GLASS CO., LTD. - HIMEJI PLANT—See Ishizuka Glass Co., Ltd.; *Int'l*, pg. 3818
ISHIZUKA GLASS CO., LTD.; *Int'l*, pg. 3818

ISHIZUKA MACHINE TECHNO CO., LTD.—See Ishizuka Glass Co., Ltd.; *Int'l*, pg. 3818
I & S HOLDINGS, LLC—See Stewart Information Services Corporation; *U.S. Public*, pg. 1947
ISHPI INFORMATION TECHNOLOGIES, INC.; *U.S. Private*, pg. 2143
ISHTIAQ TEXTILE MILLS LTD.; *Int'l*, pg. 3818
ISHWARSHAKTI HOLDINGS & TRADERS LIMITED; *Int'l*, pg. 3818
ISIA INTERNATIONAL UAE—See The Poul Due Jensen Foundation; *Int'l*, pg. 7676
ISIA S.P.A.—See The Poul Due Jensen Foundation; *Int'l*, pg. 7676
ISI AUTOMATION GMBH & CO. KG—See Jungheinrich AG; *Int'l*, pg. 4027
ISIC A/S—See Lagercrantz Group AB; *Int'l*, pg. 4394
ISI (CHINA) CO., LTD.—See DXC Technology Company; *U.S. Public*, pg. 695
ISID-AQ, LTD.—See Dentsu Group Inc.; *Int'l*, pg. 2038
ISID ASSIST, LTD.—See Dentsu Group Inc.; *Int'l*, pg. 2038
ISID BUSINESS CONSULTING, LTD.—See Dentsu Group Inc.; *Int'l*, pg. 2039
ISI-DENTSU OF EUROPE, LTD.—See Dentsu Group Inc.; *Int'l*, pg. 2038
ISI-DENTSU OF HONG KONG, LTD.—See Dentsu Group Inc.; *Int'l*, pg. 2038
ISI-DENTSU SHANGHAI CO., LTD.—See Dentsu Group Inc.; *Int'l*, pg. 2038
ISI-DENTSU SOUTH EAST ASIA PTE. LTD.—See Dentsu Group Inc.; *Int'l*, pg. 2038
ISI DESIGN AND INSTALLATION SOLUTIONS, INC.—See The Home Depot, Inc.; *U.S. Public*, pg. 2089
ISID FAIRNESS, LTD.—See Dentsu Group Inc.; *Int'l*, pg. 2038
ISID INTERTECHNOLOGIES, LTD.—See Dentsu Group Inc.; *Int'l*, pg. 2038
ISI ENVIRONMENTAL; *U.S. Private*, pg. 2144
ISIFLQ SAS—See Aalberts N.V.; *Int'l*, pg. 34
ISIGMA CAPITAL CORPORATION—See Marubeni Corporation; *Int'l*, pg. 4710
ISIGMA, LLC—See Energy Services Group, LLC; *U.S. Private*, pg. 1396
ISIGMA PARTNERS CORPORATION—See Marubeni Corporation; *Int'l*, pg. 4710
ISIGN MEDIA CORP.—See iSign Media Solutions Inc.; *Int'l*, pg. 3818
ISIGN MEDIA SOLUTIONS INC.; *Int'l*, pg. 3818
ISIGN SOLUTIONS INC.; *U.S. Public*, pg. 1174
ISIKARI CO., LTD.—See Mitsui Chemicals, Inc.; *Int'l*, pg. 4981
ISIKLAR AMBALAJ PAZ. A.S. - CUMRA FACTORY—See Isiklar Holding A.S.; *Int'l*, pg. 3819
ISIKLAR ENERJI VE YAPI HOLDING A.S.; *Int'l*, pg. 3818
ISIKLAR HOLDING A.S.; *Int'l*, pg. 3818
ISIKLAR PAPER SACK CO. LTD.—See Isiklar Holding A.S.; *Int'l*, pg. 3819
ISIK PLASTIK SANAYI VE DIS TICARET PAZARLAMA A.S.; *Int'l*, pg. 3818
ISILIS S.A.S.—See Majorel Group Luxembourg S.A.; *Int'l*, pg. 4655
ISI LOGISTICS SOUTH, LLC—See Roadrunner Transportation Systems, Inc.; *U.S. Public*, pg. 1802
ISILON SYSTEMS, LLC—See Dell Technologies Inc.; *U.S. Public*, pg. 651
ISIM S.P.A.—See Assicurazioni Generali S.p.A.; *Int'l*, pg. 643
ISI MUSTANG (ARGENTINA) S.A.—See John Wood Group PLC; *Int'l*, pg. 3983
IS INDUSTRIAL SERVICES AG; *Int'l*, pg. 3812
IS INFORMATICA SOFTWARE LTDA.—See Canada Pension Plan Investment Board; *Int'l*, pg. 1279
IS INFORMATICA SOFTWARE LTDA.—See Permira Advisers LLP; *Int'l*, pg. 5805
IS INFORMATIK SYSTEME GESELLSCHAFT FUR INFORMATIONSTECHNIK MBH—See CompuGroup Medical SE & Co. KGaA; *Int'l*, pg. 1757
IS INGENIERIE SAS—See VINCI S.A.; *Int'l*, pg. 8223
IS INKASSO SERVICE GMBH—See Permira Advisers LLP; *Int'l*, pg. 5807
ISIN LANKA PVT. LTD.—See Indorama Corporation Pte. Ltd.; *Int'l*, pg. 3658
ISI NORGREN, INC.—See IMI plc; *Int'l*, pg. 3626
ISIRONA, LLC; *U.S. Private*, pg. 2144
ISIS BELGIQUE SPRL—See Groupe Egis S.A.; *Int'l*, pg. 3102
ISIS CO., LTD.—See LTS, Inc.; *Int'l*, pg. 4571
ISIS CONCEPTS HOLDINGS LTD.; *Int'l*, pg. 3819
ISIS CONCEPTS LTD—See ISIS Concepts Holdings Ltd.; *Int'l*, pg. 3819
ISIS HEALTH CARE INDIA PRIVATE LIMITED—See Apollo Hospitals Enterprise Limited; *Int'l*, pg. 517
ISIS PARENTING, INC.; *U.S. Private*, pg. 2144
ISIS PROJECTS PTY LIMITED; *Int'l*, pg. 3819
ISIS S.A.S—See TXCOM S.A.; *Int'l*, pg. 7993
I&S IT-BERATUNG & SERVICE GMBH—See Capgemini SE; *Int'l*, pg. 1306
ISIT BV—See Proximus PLC; *Int'l*, pg. 6008
ISITE DESIGN INC.; *U.S. Private*, pg. 2144

COMPANY NAME INDEX

ISIT EDUCATION & SUPPORT BV—See Proximus PLC; *Int'l*, pg. 6008
I-SITE, INC.; *U.S. Private*, pg. 2026
ISI TELEMANAGEMENT SOLUTIONS, LLC—See Valent Capital Partners LLC; *U.S. Private*, pg. 4331
ISK AMERICAS, INC.—See Ishihara Sangyo Kaisha, Ltd.; *Int'l*, pg. 3817
ISKANDAR INVESTMENT BERHAD—See Khazanah Nasional Berhad; *Int'l*, pg. 4152
ISKANDAR WATERFRONT CITY BERHAD; *Int'l*, pg. 3819
ISKANDAR WATERFRONT HOLDINGS SDN. BHD.; *Int'l*, pg. 3819
ISK BIOSCIENCES CORPORATION—See Ishihara Sangyo Kaisha, Ltd.; *Int'l*, pg. 3817
ISK BIOSCIENCES EUROPE N.V.—See Ishihara Sangyo Kaisha, Ltd.; *Int'l*, pg. 3817
ISK BIOSCIENCES KOREA LTD.—See Ishihara Sangyo Kaisha, Ltd.; *Int'l*, pg. 3817
ISKENDERUN DEMIR VE CELIK A.S.—See Eregli Demir Ve Celik Fabrikalari T.A.S.; *Int'l*, pg. 2490
ISKENDERUN ENERJI URETIM VE TICARET A.S.—See OYAK Cement Group; *Int'l*, pg. 5677
ISKENDERUN ENERJI URETIM VE TICARET A.S. - SUGOZU POWER PLANT—See OYAK Cement Group; *Int'l*, pg. 5677
ISK KOREA CORPORATION—See Ishihara Sangyo Kaisha, Ltd.; *Int'l*, pg. 3817
ISKOOT TECHNOLOGIES, INC.—See QUALCOMM Incorporated; *U.S. Public*, pg. 1747
ISK OPTICS GMBH—See Jos. Schneider Optische Werke GmbH; *Int'l*, pg. 4000
ISKRA, D.D.; *Int'l*, pg. 3819
ISKRAEMECO BENELUX NV—See Iskraemeco, d.d.; *Int'l*, pg. 3819
ISKRAEMECO, D.D.; *Int'l*, pg. 3819
ISKRAEMECO FRANCE SAS—See Iskraemeco, d.d.; *Int'l*, pg. 3819
ISKRAEMECO GMBH—See Iskraemeco, d.d.; *Int'l*, pg. 3819
ISKRAEMECO (M) SDN. BHD.—See Iskraemeco, d.d.; *Int'l*, pg. 3819
ISKRAEMECO SARAJEVO, D.O.O.—See Iskraemeco, d.d.; *Int'l*, pg. 3819
ISKRAEMECO SVERIGE AB—See Iskraemeco, d.d.; *Int'l*, pg. 3819
ISKRAEMECO (UK) LTD.—See Iskraemeco, d.d.; *Int'l*, pg. 3819
ISKRA EMS, D.O.O.—See Iskra, d.d.; *Int'l*, pg. 3819
ISKRAFT HF—See TCS TurControlSysteme AG; *Int'l*, pg. 7485
ISKRA INDIA PVT LTD.—See Iskra, d.d.; *Int'l*, pg. 3819
ISKRA INVEST, D.D.—See Iskra, d.d.; *Int'l*, pg. 3819
ISKRA MIS, D.D.—See Iskra, d.d.; *Int'l*, pg. 3819
ISKRA SISTEMI, D.D.—See Iskra, d.d.; *Int'l*, pg. 3819
ISKRATELA L D. O. O.—See Iskra, d.d.; *Int'l*, pg. 3819
ISK SINGAPORE PTE. LTD.—See Ishihara Sangyo Kaisha, Ltd.; *Int'l*, pg. 3817
ISK TAIWAN CO., LTD.—See Ishihara Sangyo Kaisha, Ltd.; *Int'l*, pg. 3817
ISLA COMMUNICATIONS CO., INC.—See Deutsche Telekom AG; *Int'l*, pg. 2083
ISLA COOPERAGE CO. LTD.—See Tonnellerie Francois Freres; *Int'l*, pg. 7810
ISLAMI BANK BANGLADESH PLC; *Int'l*, pg. 3819
ISLAMI BANK SECURITIES LIMITED—See Islami Bank Bangladesh PLC; *Int'l*, pg. 3819
ISLAMIC ARAB INSURANCE CO. (P.S.C.)—See Dallah Al Baraka Holding Company E.C.; *Int'l*, pg. 1954
ISLAMIC BANK ZAMAN-BANK JSC; *Int'l*, pg. 3819
ISLAMIC CORPORATION FOR THE DEVELOPMENT OF THE PRIVATE SECTOR; *Int'l*, pg. 3819
ISLAMIC FINANCE AND INVESTMENT LIMITED; *Int'l*, pg. 3819
ISLAMIC FINANCIAL SECURITIES COMPNAY W.L.L.—See Islamic Holding Group (Q.S.C); *Int'l*, pg. 3820
ISLAMIC FOOD AND NUTRITION COUNCIL OF AMERICA; *U.S. Private*, pg. 2144
ISLAMIC HOLDING GROUP (Q.S.C); *Int'l*, pg. 3820
THE ISLAMIC INSURANCE CO. P.L.C.; *Int'l*, pg. 7657
ISLAMIC INTERNATIONAL ARAB BANK PLC—See Arab Bank plc; *Int'l*, pg. 529
ISLAMIC INVESTMENT COMPANY OF THE GULF (BAHAMAS) LIMITED—See Dar Al-Maal Al-Islami Trust; *Int'l*, pg. 1971
ISLAMI INSURANCE BANGLADESH LIMITED; *Int'l*, pg. 3819
ISLAMORADA FISH COMPANY LLC; *U.S. Private*, pg. 2144
ISLAND AGGREGATES LIMITED—See CEMEX, S.A.B. de C.V.; *Int'l*, pg. 1399
ISLAND AVIATION, INC.—See A. Soriano Corporation; *Int'l*, pg. 22
ISLAND CAPITAL GROUP LLC; *U.S. Private*, pg. 2144
ISLAND CO., LTD.—See Onward Holdings Co., Ltd.; *Int'l*, pg. 5592
ISLAND COMMUNICATIONS LTD.—See RHT Holding Ltd.; *Int'l*, pg. 6327
ISLAND COMPANY; *U.S. Private*, pg. 2145

ISLAND COMPUTER PRODUCTS, INC.; *U.S. Private*, pg. 2145
ISLAND DISPOSAL, INC.—See Waste Connections, Inc.; *Int'l*, pg. 8353
ISLAND EQUIPMENT INC; *U.S. Private*, pg. 2145
ISLANDER EAST PIPELINE COMPANY, L.L.C.—See Enbridge Inc.; *Int'l*, pg. 2397
ISLANDERS BANK—See Banner Corporation; *U.S. Public*, pg. 275
ISLAND FINANCE, INC.—See First BanCorp; *U.S. Public*, pg. 839
ISLAND FIRE SPRINKLER, INC.—See APi Group Corporation; *Int'l*, pg. 514
ISLAND GROVE AG PRODUCTS; *U.S. Private*, pg. 2145
ISLAND HOLDINGS, INC.; *U.S. Private*, pg. 2145
ISLAND HORTI-TECH HOLDINGS PTE. LIMITED—See The Bombay Burmah Trading Corporation Limited; *Int'l*, pg. 7627
ISLAND HOSPITALITY MANAGEMENT, LLC; *U.S. Private*, pg. 2145
ISLAND HOTEL (MADEIRA) LTD.—See LVMH Moet Hennessy Louis Vuitton SE; *Int'l*, pg. 4591
ISLANDIAN SARL—See ENL Limited; *Int'l*, pg. 2442
ISLAND INFORMATION & TECHNOLOGY, INC.; *Int'l*, pg. 3820
ISLAND INN CO. INC.; *U.S. Private*, pg. 2145
ISLAND INSURANCE COMPANY, LTD.—See Island Holdings, Inc.; *U.S. Private*, pg. 2145
ISLAND LANDSCAPE & NURSERY PTE LTD—See The Bombay Burmah Trading Corporation Limited; *Int'l*, pg. 7627
ISLAND LINCOLN-MERCURY, INC.; *U.S. Private*, pg. 2145
ISLAND LINE PTE LTD.—See MYP Ltd.; *Int'l*, pg. 5113
ISLAND LIVING LTD.—See ENL Limited; *Int'l*, pg. 2442
ISLANDMAGEE ENERGY LIMITED—See Harland & Wolff Group Holdings plc; *Int'l*, pg. 3277
ISLANDMAGEE STORAGE LIMITED—See Harland & Wolff Group Holdings plc; *Int'l*, pg. 3277
ISLAND MECHANICAL CORPORATION—See Quanta Services, Inc.; *U.S. Public*, pg. 1751
ISLAND MOVERS INC.; *U.S. Private*, pg. 2145
ISLAND NATURAL, INC.—See Nassau Candy Distributors Inc.; *U.S. Private*, pg. 2837
ISLAND OASIS FROZEN COCKTAIL CO.; *U.S. Private*, pg. 2145
ISLAND OPERATING COMPANY INC; *U.S. Private*, pg. 2145
ISLAND ORTHOPAEDIC CONSULTANTS PTE LTD—See OUE Limited; *Int'l*, pg. 5666
ISLAND PACIFIC HOMELOANS, LLC—See Central Pacific Financial Corporation; *U.S. Public*, pg. 473
ISLAND PACIFIC—See 3Q Holdings Limited; *Int'l*, pg. 9
THE ISLAND PACKET—See Chatham Asset Management, LLC; *U.S. Private*, pg. 867
ISLAND PEER REVIEW ORGANIZATION, INC.; *U.S. Private*, pg. 2145
ISLAND PERIODICALS INC.—See Periodical Management Group International Ltd.; *U.S. Private*, pg. 3150
ISLAND PEST CONTROL INC.—See Massey Services, Inc.; *U.S. Private*, pg. 2606
ISLAND PETROLEUM, INC.—See Par Pacific Holdings, Inc.; *U.S. Public*, pg. 1636
ISLAND PHARMACEUTICALS LIMITED; *Int'l*, pg. 3820
ISLAND PLANT COMPANY, LLC—See BrightView Holdings, Inc.; *U.S. Public*, pg. 384
ISLAND PREMIER INSURANCE COMPANY, LTD.—See Island Holdings, Inc.; *U.S. Private*, pg. 2145
ISLAND PRESS LIMITED—See MediaHouse Limited; *Int'l*, pg. 4772
ISLAND READY-MIX CONCRETE, INC.—See NOV, Inc.; *U.S. Public*, pg. 1544
ISLAND REALTY INC.; *U.S. Private*, pg. 2145
ISLAND RECREATIONAL; *U.S. Private*, pg. 2145
ISLAND REHABILITATION AND NURSING CENTER INC; *U.S. Private*, pg. 2145
ISLANDSBANKI HF; *Int'l*, pg. 3820
ISLAND SEAFOOD INC.—See Dulcich, Inc.; *U.S. Private*, pg. 1286
ISLANDS HOSPICE, INC.; *U.S. Private*, pg. 2145
ISLANDS MAGAZINE—See Bonnier AB; *Int'l*, pg. 1108
ISLAND SOFTWARE, INC.—See CP Software Group, Inc.; *U.S. Private*, pg. 1079
ISLANDS RESTAURANTS LP; *U.S. Private*, pg. 2146
ISLANDS WEST MANUFACTURERS LTD.; *Int'l*, pg. 3820
ISLAND TENNIS LP; *U.S. Private*, pg. 2145
ISLAND TEXTILE MILLS LTD.—See Tata Group of Companies Ltd.; *Int'l*, pg. 7466
ISLAND TUG & BARGE CO.; *U.S. Private*, pg. 2145
ISLAND WATER SPORTS, INC.; *U.S. Private*, pg. 2145
ISL CONSULTING LTD; *Int'l*, pg. 3819
ISLEBURN LTD.—See Global Energy (Holdings) Ltd.; *Int'l*, pg. 2995
ISLECHEM, LLC—See Aceto Corporation; *U.S. Private*, pg. 58
ISL ENGINEERING AND LAND SERVICES LTD; *Int'l*, pg. 3819
ISLE OF CAPRI BETTENDORF, L.C.—See Bally's Corporation; *U.S. Public*, pg. 268

ISOFTSTONE HOLDINGS LIMITED

ISLE OF CAPRI BLACK HAWK, LLC—See Bally's Corporation; *U.S. Public*, pg. 268
ISLE OF CAPRI CASINOS, INC.—See Bally's Corporation; *U.S. Public*, pg. 268
ISLE OF MAN BANK LIMITED—See NatWest Group plc; *Int'l*, pg. 5172
ISLE OF MAN ENTERPRISES PLC—See Sanlam Limited; *Int'l*, pg. 6545
ISLE OF MAN NEWSPAPERS LTD—See JPIMedia Holdings Limited; *Int'l*, pg. 4006
ISLE OF MAN POST OFFICE; *Int'l*, pg. 3820
THE ISLE OF MAN STEAM PACKET COMPANY LTD.—See Macquarie Group Limited; *Int'l*, pg. 4630
ISLET SCIENCES, INC.; *U.S. Private*, pg. 2146
ISLEWORTH HEALTHCARE ACQUISITION CORP.; *U.S. Public*, pg. 1174
ISL INTERNET SICHERHEITSLOSUNGEN GMBH—See MBB SE; *Int'l*, pg. 4751
ISMAIL ABUDAWOOD PROCTER & GAMBLE - DAMMAM—See The Procter & Gamble Company; *U.S. Public*, pg. 2120
ISMAIL INDUSTRIES LTD.; *Int'l*, pg. 3820
ISMAIL MOHAMMED ALDANAWI AL SADY GARDEN EQUIPMENT WLL—See Husqvarna AB; *Int'l*, pg. 3539
ISM COMMUNICATIONS CORPORATION; *Int'l*, pg. 3820
ISMECA EUROPE SEMICONDUCTOR SA—See Cohu, Inc.; *U.S. Public*, pg. 529
ISMECA MALAYSIA SDN. BHD.—See Cohu, Inc.; *U.S. Public*, pg. 529
ISMECA SEMICONDUCTOR HOLDING SA—See Cohu, Inc.; *U.S. Public*, pg. 529
ISMECA SEMICONDUCTOR (SUZHOU) CO. LTD.—See Cohu, Inc.; *U.S. Public*, pg. 529
ISMECA USA, INC.—See Cohu, Inc.; *U.S. Public*, pg. 529
ISMEDIA CO., LTD.; *Int'l*, pg. 3820
IS MERKEZLERI YONETIM VE ISLETIM A.S.—See Turkiye Is Bankasi A.S.; *Int'l*, pg. 7976
ISMET GMBH—See Phoenix Mecano AG; *Int'l*, pg. 5853
ISMET TRANSFORMATORY S.R.O.—See Phoenix Mecano AG; *Int'l*, pg. 5853
ISM INFORMATION SYSTEMS MANAGEMENT CORPORATION—See International Business Machines Corporation; *U.S. Public*, pg. 1146
ISMOBILE AB—See Telia Company AB; *Int'l*, pg. 7545
IS MOLAS S.P.A.—See Immsi S.p.a.; *Int'l*, pg. 3628
ISM RACEWAY—See National Association for Stock Car Auto Racing, Inc.; *U.S. Private*, pg. 2845
ISM RESOURCES CORP.; *Int'l*, pg. 3820
ISMT EUROPE—See ISMT Limited; *Int'l*, pg. 3820
ISMT LIMITED; *Int'l*, pg. 3820
ISMT LTD - JEJURI STEEL PLANT—See ISMT Limited; *Int'l*, pg. 3820
ISMT NORTH AMERICA—See ISMT Limited; *Int'l*, pg. 3820
IS NET ELEKTRONIK BILGI URET. DAG. TIC. VE ILET. HIZM. A.S.—See Turkiye Is Bankasi A.S.; *Int'l*, pg. 7976
ISN SOFTWARE CORP.; *U.S. Private*, pg. 2146
ISOBAR AUSTRALIA—See Dentsu Group Inc.; *Int'l*, pg. 2037
ISOBAR COMMERCE—See WPP plc; *Int'l*, pg. 8465
ISOBAR HONG KONG—See Dentsu Group Inc.; *Int'l*, pg. 2037
ISOBAR—See Dentsu Group Inc.; *Int'l*, pg. 2037
ISOBAR—See Dentsu Group Inc.; *Int'l*, pg. 2037
ISOBIONICS B.V.—See BASF SE; *Int'l*, pg. 884
ISOBOUW SYSTEMS BV—See BEWi ASA; *Int'l*, pg. 1004
ISOCAB FRANCE S.A.S.—See ThyssenKrupp AG; *Int'l*, pg. 7724
ISOCAB N.V.—See ThyssenKrupp AG; *Int'l*, pg. 7724
ISOCELE; *Int'l*, pg. 3820
ISOCHEM BETEILIGUNGS GMBH—See Aurelius Equity Opportunities SE & Co. KGaA; *Int'l*, pg. 708
ISOCHEM HOLDING GMBH—See Aurelius Equity Opportunities SE & Co. KGaA; *Int'l*, pg. 708
ISO CLAIMS SERVICES, INC.—See Verisk Analytics, Inc.; *U.S. Public*, pg. 2283
ISODIOL INTERNATIONAL, INC.; *Int'l*, pg. 3820
ISODRA GMBH—See IRCE S.p.A.; *Int'l*, pg. 3806
ISOENERGY LTD.; *Int'l*, pg. 3820
ISOFOL MEDICAL AB; *Int'l*, pg. 3820
ISOFOTON NORTH AMERICA INC—See Isofoton; *Int'l*, pg. 3821
ISOFOTON; *Int'l*, pg. 3821
ISOFT EHEALTH PTY LTD—See DXC Technology Company; *U.S. Public*, pg. 696
ISOFT INC.—See DXC Technology Company; *U.S. Public*, pg. 696
ISOFT SOLUTIONS (INTERNATIONAL) PTY LTD.—See DXC Technology Company; *U.S. Public*, pg. 696
ISOFTSTONE HOLDINGS LIMITED; *Int'l*, pg. 3821
ISOGARD SAS—See Johnson Controls International plc; *Int'l*, pg. 3987
ISOGRAPH LTD.—See Main Capital Partners B.V.; *Int'l*, pg. 4650
ISOHARA POLYURETHANE INDUSTRY CORPORATION—See NOK Corporation; *Int'l*, pg. 5402
ISOJOEN KONEHALLI OY—See Grafton Group plc; *Int'l*, pg. 3051

ISOKINETICS, INC. — CORPORATE AFFILIATIONS

ISOKINETICS, INC.; *U.S. Private*, pg. 2146
ISOLAFT AS—See Flakk Holding AS; *Int'l*, pg. 2698
ISOLAGEN EUROPE LTD.—See Castle Creek Pharmaceuticals Holdings, Inc.; *U.S. Public*, pg. 447
ISOLA GMBH—See TPG Capital, L.P.; *U.S. Public*, pg. 2174
ISOLA GROUP LTD.—See TPG Capital, L.P.; *U.S. Public*, pg. 2174
ISO-LANDSCAPE PTE. LTD.—See ISOTeam Ltd.; *Int'l*, pg. 3821
ISOLA S.P.A.—See SKion GmbH; *Int'l*, pg. 6987
ISOLATEC B.V.B.A.—See SIG plc; *Int'l*, pg. 6906
ISOLECTRA B.V.—See TKH Group N.V.; *Int'l*, pg. 7764
ISOLECTRA COMMUNICATIONS TECHNOLOGY SDN BHD—See TKH Group N.V.; *Int'l*, pg. 7764
ISOLECTRA FAR EAST PTE LTD—See TKH Group N.V.; *Int'l*, pg. 7764
ISOLENGE TERMO CONSTRUCOES LTDA.—See Illinois Tool Works Inc.; *U.S. Public*, pg. 1108
ISOLER LIMITED—See Northern Bear Plc; *Int'l*, pg. 5443
ISOLIERERZEUGNISSE GROSSROHRSDORF GMBH—See Dortmunder Gussasphalt GmbH & Co. KG; *Int'l*, pg. 2180
ISOLIERUNGEN LEIPZIG GMBH—See VINCI S.A.; *Int'l*, pg. 8238
ISOLINK, INC.—See Skyworks Solutions, Inc.; *U.S. Public*, pg. 1893
ISOLITE CORPORATION; *U.S. Private*, pg. 2146
ISOLITE GMBH—See Resonac Holdings Corporation; *Int'l*, pg. 6299
ISOLITE INSULATING PRODUCTS CO., LTD. - NANAO PLANT—See Isolite Insulating Products Co., Ltd.; *Int'l*, pg. 3821
ISOLITE INSULATING PRODUCTS CO., LTD. - OTOWA PLANT—See Isolite Insulating Products Co., Ltd.; *Int'l*, pg. 3821
ISOLITE INSULATING PRODUCTS CO., LTD.; *Int'l*, pg. 3821
ISOLITE (SHANGHAI) TRADE CO., LTD.—See Isolite Insulating Products Co., Ltd.; *Int'l*, pg. 3821
ISO LTD.—See Qube Holdings Limited; *Int'l*, pg. 6158
I-SOLUTIONS DIRECT, INC.—See Reliance Steel & Aluminum Co.; *U.S. Public*, pg. 1781
I SOLUTIONS INC.—See Emerson Electric Co.; *U.S. Public*, pg. 744
ISOLVED HCM LLC; *U.S. Private*, pg. 2146
ISOMEDIX INC.—See STERIS plc; *Int'l*, pg. 7209
ISOMEDIX OPERATIONS INC. - CHESTER—See STERIS plc; *Int'l*, pg. 7209
ISOMEDIX OPERATIONS INC. - EL PASO II—See STERIS plc; *Int'l*, pg. 7209
ISOMEDIX OPERATIONS INC. - EL PASO I—See STERIS plc; *Int'l*, pg. 7209
ISOMEDIX OPERATIONS INC. - GROVEPORT—See STERIS plc; *Int'l*, pg. 7210
ISOMEDIX OPERATIONS INC. - LIBERTYVILLE NORTH—See STERIS plc; *Int'l*, pg. 7210
ISOMEDIX OPERATIONS INC. - LIBERTYVILLE SOUTH—See STERIS plc; *Int'l*, pg. 7210
ISOMEDIX OPERATIONS INC. - MINNEAPOLIS—See STERIS plc; *Int'l*, pg. 7210
ISOMEDIX OPERATIONS INC. - SANDY—See STERIS plc; *Int'l*, pg. 7210
ISOMEDIX OPERATIONS INC.—See STERIS plc; *Int'l*, pg. 7209
ISOMEDIX OPERATIONS INC. - SPARTANBURG—See STERIS plc; *Int'l*, pg. 7210
ISOMEDIX OPERATIONS INC. - TEMECULA—See STERIS plc; *Int'l*, pg. 7210
ISOMEDIX OPERATIONS INC. - WHIPPANY—See STERIS plc; *Int'l*, pg. 7210
ISOMET AG—See IRCE S.p.A.; *Int'l*, pg. 3806
ISOMET CORPORATION; *U.S. Private*, pg. 2146
ISOMET (UK) LTD.—See Isomet Corporation; *U.S. Private*, pg. 2146
ISONAS, INC.—See Allegion Public Limited Company; *Int'l*, pg. 335
ISONEA (ISRAEL) LIMITED—See Respiri Limited; *Int'l*, pg. 6302
ISONEVAN TUULIPUISTO OY—See Taaleri Oyj; *Int'l*, pg. 7401
ISO NEW ENGLAND INC.; *U.S. Private*, pg. 2146
ISON GROUP; *Int'l*, pg. 3821
ISONOR IT AS—See TowerBrook Capital Partners, L.P.; *U.S. Private*, pg. 4195
ISON TECHNOLOGIES FZ LLC—See Ison Group; *Int'l*, pg. 3821
ISO PANELS, INC.—See Ergon, Inc.; *U.S. Private*, pg. 1418
ISOPLEXIS CORPORATION—See Bruker Corporation; *U.S. Public*, pg. 405
ISO POLY FILMS, INC.—See Alpha Industries, Inc.; *U.S. Private*, pg. 197
ISOPRA CO., LTD.; *Int'l*, pg. 3821
ISOPROFS BELGIE BVBA—See RWE AG; *Int'l*, pg. 6434
ISORAY MEDICAL, INC.—See Perspective Therapeutics, Inc.; *U.S. Public*, pg. 1678
ISOS ACQUISITION CORP.; *U.S. Public*, pg. 1174
ISOSBAR—See Dentsu Group Inc.; *Int'l*, pg. 2037

ISO SUPERMARKED A/S—See NorgesGruppen ASA; *Int'l*, pg. 5427
ISOSYSTEM DULLIKEN AG—See swisspor Management AG; *Int'l*, pg. 7374
ISO-SZER KFT.—See MOL Magyar Olaj- es Gazipari Nyrt.; *Int'l*, pg. 5020
ISOTEAM ACCESS PTE. LTD.—See ISOTeam Ltd.; *Int'l*, pg. 3821
ISOTEAM LTD.; *Int'l*, pg. 3821
ISOTECH LABORATORIES, INC.; *U.S. Private*, pg. 2146
ISO TECHNOLOGY SDN. BHD.—See Globetronics Technology Bhd.; *Int'l*, pg. 3007
ISOTECH PEST MANAGEMENT, INC.; *U.S. Private*, pg. 2146
ISOTECH PTE. LTD.—See PEC Ltd.; *Int'l*, pg. 5778
ISOTEK S.R.L.—See Endress+Hauser (International) Holding AG; *Int'l*, pg. 2408
ISOTEMP RESEARCH INC.—See Taitien Electronics Co., Ltd.; *Int'l*, pg. 7418
ISOTERM AS—See Wienerberger AG; *Int'l*, pg. 8405
ISOTRAK, INC.—See Horizon Capital LLP; *Int'l*, pg. 3479
ISOTRAK LIMITED—See Horizon Capital LLP; *Int'l*, pg. 3479
ISOTRON SYSTEMS B.V.—See Addtech AB; *Int'l*, pg. 134
ISOTTA FRASCHINI MOTORI S.P.A.—See Fincantieri S.p.A.; *Int'l*, pg. 2671
ISOVERA, LLC; *U.S. Private*, pg. 2146
ISPA BRATISLAVA SPOL SRO—See JCDecaux S.A.; *Int'l*, pg. 3921
ISPACE FURNITURE, INC.; *U.S. Private*, pg. 2146
ISPACE, INC.; *U.S. Private*, pg. 2146
ISPAC S.A.—See Tessenderlo Group NV; *Int'l*, pg. 7573
ISP ARGENTINA S.R.L.—See Ashland Inc.; *U.S. Public*, pg. 212
ISPARK LEARNING SOLUTIONS PVT LTD—See TCM Limited; *Int'l*, pg. 7484
ISP ASIA PACIFIC PTE. LTD.—See Ashland Inc.; *U.S. Public*, pg. 212
ISP BIOCHEMA SCHWABEN GMBH—See Ashland Inc.; *U.S. Public*, pg. 212
ISP CHEMICAL PRODUCTS LLC—See Ashland Inc.; *U.S. Public*, pg. 213
ISP CHEMICALS LLC—See Ashland Inc.; *U.S. Public*, pg. 212
ISP D INTERNATIONAL SOFTWARE PARTNERS GMBH—See SoftwareONE Holding AG; *Int'l*, pg. 7057
ISP DO BRASIL LTDA.—See Ashland Inc.; *U.S. Public*, pg. 213
ISPECIMEN INC.; *U.S. Public*, pg. 1174
ISP ELECTRO SOLUTIONS AG—See BKW AG; *Int'l*, pg. 1055
ISP FINANCE SERVICES LTD.; *Int'l*, pg. 3821
ISP FRANCE MARKETING SARL—See Ashland Inc.; *U.S. Public*, pg. 213
ISP GLOBAL LIMITED; *Int'l*, pg. 3821
ISP GLOBAL TECHNOLOGIES DEUTSCHLAND GMBH—See Ashland Inc.; *U.S. Public*, pg. 213
ISP GLOBAL TECHNOLOGIES INC.—See Ashland Inc.; *U.S. Public*, pg. 213
ISP HOLDINGS LIMITED; *Int'l*, pg. 3821
ISPICE LLC; *U.S. Private*, pg. 2146
I. SPIEWAK & SONS, INC.; *U.S. Private*, pg. 2026
ISP INDIA PVT. LTD—See Ashland Inc.; *U.S. Public*, pg. 213
ISP INTERIORS LIMITED—See ISP Holdings Limited; *Int'l*, pg. 3821
ISP INTERNATIONAL SOFTWARE PARTNERS, INC.—See Climb Global Solutions, Inc.; *U.S. Public*, pg. 515
ISPIRE TECHNOLOGY INC.; *U.S. Public*, pg. 1174
ISPIRI; *U.S. Private*, pg. 2146
ISP JAPAN LTD.—See Ashland Inc.; *U.S. Public*, pg. 213
ISP (KOREA) LIMITED—See Ashland Inc.; *U.S. Public*, pg. 212
ISPL PTE. LTD.—See ISP Global Limited; *Int'l*, pg. 3821
ISP MARL GMBH—See Ashland Inc.; *U.S. Public*, pg. 213
ISP MICROCAPS (U.K.) LIMITED—See Ashland Inc.; *U.S. Public*, pg. 213
ISP OPTICS CORP.—See LightPath Technologies, Inc.; *U.S. Public*, pg. 1315
ISP OPTICS LATVIA, SIA—See LightPath Technologies, Inc.; *U.S. Public*, pg. 1315
I-SPORT CO., LTD.—See Samart Corporation Public Company Limited; *Int'l*, pg. 6502
ISPOT.TV, INC.; *U.S. Private*, pg. 2146
ISP (POLSKA) SP.Z O.O.—See Ashland Inc.; *U.S. Public*, pg. 212
ISPR GMBH—See Vivendi SE; *Int'l*, pg. 8276
ISP SUPPLIES LLC; *U.S. Private*, pg. 2146
ISP SYNTHETIC ELASTOMERS LLC—See Ashland Inc.; *U.S. Public*, pg. 213
ISP TECHNOLOGIES INC.—See Ashland Inc.; *U.S. Public*, pg. 213
ISP (THAILAND) CO., LTD—See Ashland Inc.; *U.S. Public*, pg. 212
ISPT PTY. LTD.; *Int'l*, pg. 3821
ISP TURKEY—See Ashland Inc.; *U.S. Public*, pg. 213
ISP WEST S.R.O.—See CEZ, a.s.; *Int'l*, pg. 1428

ISQFT PARENT CORPORATION—See Roper Technologies, Inc.; *U.S. Public*, pg. 1814
I SQUARED CAPITAL ADVISORS (US) LLC; *U.S. Private*, pg. 2020
ISQUARE S.A.—See Quest Holdings S.A.; *Int'l*, pg. 6160
ISRACANN BIOSCIENCES INC.; *Int'l*, pg. 3821
ISRAEL ACQUISITIONS CORP.; *U.S. Public*, pg. 1175
ISRAEL A. ENGLANDER & CO., LLC; *U.S. Private*, pg. 2146
ISRAEL AEROSPACE INDUSTRIES LTD.; *Int'l*, pg. 3821
ISRAEL AIRCRAFT, ENGINES DIVISION/BEDEK AVIATION GROUP—See Israel Aerospace Industries Ltd.; *Int'l*, pg. 3822
ISRAEL AIRCRAFT INDUSTRIES MAMAN DIVISION—See Israel Aerospace Industries Ltd.; *Int'l*, pg. 3822
ISRAEL AIRCRAFT INDUSTRIES MBT DIVISION—See Israel Aerospace Industries Ltd.; *Int'l*, pg. 3822
ISRAEL AIRCRAFT INDUSTRIES MHT DIVISION—See Israel Aerospace Industries Ltd.; *Int'l*, pg. 3822
ISRAEL AIRCRAFT INDUSTRIES MISSILE & SPACE SYSTEMS GROUP—See Israel Aerospace Industries Ltd.; *Int'l*, pg. 3822
ISRAEL AIRCRAFT INDUSTRIES MLM DIVISION/MISSILE & SPACE SYSTEMS GROUP—See Israel Aerospace Industries Ltd.; *Int'l*, pg. 3822
ISRAEL AIRCRAFT INDUSTRIES TAMAM DIVISION/MISSILE & SPACE SYSTEMS GROUP—See Israel Aerospace Industries Ltd.; *Int'l*, pg. 3822
ISRAEL AIRCRAFT, MILITARY AIRCRAFT GROUP—See Israel Aerospace Industries Ltd.; *Int'l*, pg. 3822
ISRAEL AMPLIFY PROGRAM CORP.; *U.S. Public*, pg. 1175
ISRAEL ANDLER & SON INC.; *U.S. Private*, pg. 2147
ISRAEL CANADA TR LTD.; *Int'l*, pg. 3822
ISRAEL CAPITAL CANADA CORP.; *Int'l*, pg. 3822
ISRAEL CHINA BIOTECHNOLOGY ICB LTD.; *Int'l*, pg. 3822
ISRAEL CORPORATION LTD.; *Int'l*, pg. 3822
ISRAEL CREDIT CARDS LTD.—See IDB Development Corporation Ltd.; *Int'l*, pg. 3588
ISRAEL DISCOUNT BANK LTD.—See IDB Development Corporation Ltd.; *Int'l*, pg. 3588
ISRAEL DISCOUNT BANK OF NEW YORK—See IDB Development Corporation Ltd.; *Int'l*, pg. 3588
THE ISRAEL ELECTRIC CORPORATION LTD.; *Int'l*, pg. 7657
ISRAEL EXPORT INSTITUTE; *Int'l*, pg. 3823
ISRAEL INFRASTRUCTURE FUND—See Harel Insurance Investments & Financial Services Ltd.; *Int'l*, pg. 3274
THE ISRAEL LAND DEVELOPMENT CO., LTD.; *Int'l*, pg. 7657
ISRAEL LAND DEVELOPMENT URBAN RENEWAL LTD.; *Int'l*, pg. 3823
ISRAEL NATURAL GAS LINES LTD.; *Int'l*, pg. 3823
ISRAEL OPPORTUNITY ENERGY RESOURCES, LP; *Int'l*, pg. 3823
ISRAEL PETROCHEMICAL ENTERPRISES LTD.; *Int'l*, pg. 3824
ISRAEL PORTS DEVELOPMENT & ASSETS COMPANY LTD.; *Int'l*, pg. 3824
ISRAEL RAILWAYS LTD.; *Int'l*, pg. 3824
ISRAEL SHIPYARDS LTD.; *Int'l*, pg. 3824
ISRAEL TOBACCO CO. (M.T.) LTD.—See Dubek Ltd.; *Int'l*, pg. 2222
ISRAMCO, INC.—See Equital Ltd.; *Int'l*, pg. 2487
ISRAMCO NEGEV 2 LP; *Int'l*, pg. 3824
ISRAM WHOLESALE TOURS & TRAVEL LTD.; *U.S. Private*, pg. 2147
ISRA PARSYTEC GMBH—See Atlas Copco AB; *Int'l*, pg. 682
ISRAS INVESTMENT CO., LTD.; *Int'l*, pg. 3824
ISRA SURFACE VISION GMBH—See Atlas Copco AB; *Int'l*, pg. 682
ISRA SURFACE VISION INC.—See Atlas Copco AB; *Int'l*, pg. 682
ISRA VISION AG—See Atlas Copco AB; *Int'l*, pg. 682
ISRA VISION BRASIL—See Atlas Copco AB; *Int'l*, pg. 682
ISRA VISION FRANCE S.A.—See Atlas Copco AB; *Int'l*, pg. 682
ISRA VISION GMBH—See Atlas Copco AB; *Int'l*, pg. 682
ISRA VISION GRAPHIKON GMBH—See Atlas Copco AB; *Int'l*, pg. 682
ISRA VISION INDIA PRIVATE LIMITED—See Atlas Copco AB; *Int'l*, pg. 682
ISRA VISION IRAN—See Atlas Copco AB; *Int'l*, pg. 682
ISRA VISION ITALY—See Atlas Copco AB; *Int'l*, pg. 682
ISRA VISION JAPAN CORP LTD—See Atlas Copco AB; *Int'l*, pg. 683
ISRA VISION KOREA CO. LTD.—See Atlas Copco AB; *Int'l*, pg. 682
ISRA VISION LASOR GMBH—See Atlas Copco AB; *Int'l*, pg. 682
ISRA VISION LLC—See Atlas Copco AB; *Int'l*, pg. 683
ISRA VISION LTD.—See Atlas Copco AB; *Int'l*, pg. 682
ISRA VISION PARSYTEC AG—See Atlas Copco AB; *Int'l*, pg. 682

ISRA VISION PARSYTEC INC—See Atlas Copco AB; *Int'l*, pg. 683
ISRA VISION POLYMETRIC GMBH—See Atlas Copco AB; *Int'l*, pg. 683
ISRA VISION (SHANGHAI) CORP LTD—See Atlas Copco AB; *Int'l*, pg. 682
ISRA VISION SYSTEMS INC.—See Atlas Copco AB; *Int'l*, pg. 682
ISRA VISION TAIWAN—See Atlas Copco AB; *Int'l*, pg. 683
ISRA VISION TURKEY—See Atlas Copco AB; *Int'l*, pg. 682
ISRA VISION VISTEK A.S.—See Atlas Copco AB; *Int'l*, pg. 683
IS RAYFAST LIMITED—See Diploma PLC; *Int'l*, pg. 2128
ISRED PHARMA AND BIOTECH RESEARCH CO., LTD.—See YungShin Global Holding Corporation; *Int'l*, pg. 8614
ISR GROUP, INC.; *U.S. Private*, pg. 2146
ISRI GMBH—See AUNDE Achter & Ebels GmbH; *Int'l*, pg. 705
ISR IMMUNE SYSTEM REGULATION HOLDING AB; *Int'l*, pg. 3821
ISR INFORMATION PRODUCTS AG—See CENIT AG; *Int'l*, pg. 1401
ISRINGHAUSEN AB—See AUNDE Achter & Ebels GmbH; *Int'l*, pg. 705
ISRINGHAUSEN ASSENTOS, LDA.—See AUNDE Achter & Ebels GmbH; *Int'l*, pg. 705
ISRINGHAUSEN B.V.B.A.—See AUNDE Achter & Ebels GmbH; *Int'l*, pg. 705
ISRINGHAUSEN GMBH & CO. KG—See AUNDE Achter & Ebels GmbH; *Int'l*, pg. 705
ISRINGHAUSEN, INC.—See AUNDE Achter & Ebels GmbH; *Int'l*, pg. 706
ISRINGHAUSEN INDUSTRIAL LTDA.—See AUNDE Achter & Ebels GmbH; *Int'l*, pg. 705
ISRINGHAUSEN KOLTUK SISTEMLERI LTD.—See AUNDE Achter & Ebels GmbH; *Int'l*, pg. 705
ISRINGHAUSEN MEXICO S.A.DE C.V.—See AUNDE Achter & Ebels GmbH; *Int'l*, pg. 706
ISRINGHAUSEN OF SOUTH AFRICA (PTY) LTD.—See AUNDE Achter & Ebels GmbH; *Int'l*, pg. 706
ISRINGHAUSEN OTO YAN SANAYI, YEDEK PARCA VE KOLTUK SISTEMLERI SANAYI VE TICARET A.S.—See AUNDE Achter & Ebels GmbH; *Int'l*, pg. 706
ISRINGHAUSEN PTY. LTD.—See AUNDE Achter & Ebels GmbH; *Int'l*, pg. 706
ISRINGHAUSEN QUERETARO S.A. DE C.V.—See AUNDE Achter & Ebels GmbH; *Int'l*, pg. 706
ISRINGHAUSEN S.A.—See AUNDE Achter & Ebels GmbH; *Int'l*, pg. 706
ISRINGHAUSEN SPAIN S.L.U.—See AUNDE Achter & Ebels GmbH; *Int'l*, pg. 706
ISRINGHAUSEN S.P.A.—See AUNDE Achter & Ebels GmbH; *Int'l*, pg. 706
ISRINGHAUSEN UMEA AB—See AUNDE Achter & Ebels GmbH; *Int'l*, pg. 706
ISROTEL LTD.; *Int'l*, pg. 3824
ISR SHANGHAI INVESTMENT ADVISORY CO., LTD.—See Reenova Investment Holding Limited; *Int'l*, pg. 6249
ISS ABILIS FRANCE S.A.S.—See Onet SA; *Int'l*, pg. 5577
ISS AMERICA, INC.—See Daido Metal Corporation; *Int'l*, pg. 1922
ISSARA MINING LIMITED—See Kingsgate Consolidated Limited; *Int'l*, pg. 4174
ISS A/S—See EQT AB; *Int'l*, pg. 2476
ISS A/S—See The Goldman Sachs Group, Inc.; *U.S. Public*, pg. 2077
IS&S AVIATION, INC.—See Innovative Solutions & Support, Inc.; *U.S. Public*, pg. 1127
IS&S AVIATION, LLC—See Innovative Solutions & Support, Inc.; *U.S. Public*, pg. 1127
ISS CORPORATE SERVICES, INC.—See Deutsche Borse AG; *Int'l*, pg. 2064
ISS CORPORATION—See INES Corporation; *Int'l*, pg. 3683
IS&S DELAWARE, INC.—See Innovative Solutions & Support, Inc.; *U.S. Public*, pg. 1127
ISS EASTPOINT FACILITY SERVICES LIMITED—See EQT AB; *Int'l*, pg. 2476
ISS EASTPOINT FACILITY SERVICES LIMITED—See The Goldman Sachs Group, Inc.; *U.S. Public*, pg. 2077
ISSEL NORD S.R.L.—See Fincantieri S.p.A.; *Int'l*, pg. 2671
ISS FACILITY SERVICES AB—See EQT AB; *Int'l*, pg. 2476
ISS FACILITY SERVICES AB—See The Goldman Sachs Group, Inc.; *U.S. Public*, pg. 2077
ISS FACILITY SERVICES A.E.—See EQT AB; *Int'l*, pg. 2476
ISS FACILITY SERVICES A.E.—See The Goldman Sachs Group, Inc.; *U.S. Public*, pg. 2077
ISS FACILITY SERVICES AG—See EQT AB; *Int'l*, pg. 2477
ISS FACILITY SERVICES AG—See The Goldman Sachs Group, Inc.; *U.S. Public*, pg. 2078
ISS FACILITY SERVICES A/S—See EQT AB; *Int'l*, pg. 2476
ISS FACILITY SERVICES A/S—See EQT AB; *Int'l*, pg. 2476
ISS FACILITY SERVICES A/S—See The Goldman Sachs Group, Inc.; *U.S. Public*, pg. 2077
ISS FACILITY SERVICES A/S—See The Goldman Sachs Group, Inc.; *U.S. Public*, pg. 2077
ISS FACILITY SERVICES AUSTRALIA LIMITED—See EQT AB; *Int'l*, pg. 2476
ISS FACILITY SERVICES AUSTRALIA LIMITED—See The Goldman Sachs Group, Inc.; *U.S. Public*, pg. 2077
ISS FACILITY SERVICES GMBH—See EQT AB; *Int'l*, pg. 2476
ISS FACILITY SERVICES GMBH—See EQT AB; *Int'l*, pg. 2476
ISS FACILITY SERVICES GMBH—See The Goldman Sachs Group, Inc.; *U.S. Public*, pg. 2077
ISS FACILITY SERVICES GMBH—See The Goldman Sachs Group, Inc.; *U.S. Public*, pg. 2077
ISS FACILITY SERVICES, INC. - AUSTIN REGIONAL OFFICE—See EQT AB; *Int'l*, pg. 2476
ISS FACILITY SERVICES, INC. - AUSTIN REGIONAL OFFICE—See The Goldman Sachs Group, Inc.; *U.S. Public*, pg. 2077
ISS FACILITY SERVICES, INC. - DALLAS REGIONAL OFFICE—See EQT AB; *Int'l*, pg. 2476
ISS FACILITY SERVICES, INC. - DALLAS REGIONAL OFFICE—See The Goldman Sachs Group, Inc.; *U.S. Public*, pg. 2077
ISS FACILITY SERVICES, INC. - GREENSBORO REGIONAL OFFICE—See EQT AB; *Int'l*, pg. 2476
ISS FACILITY SERVICES, INC. - GREENSBORO REGIONAL OFFICE—See The Goldman Sachs Group, Inc.; *U.S. Public*, pg. 2077
ISS FACILITY SERVICES, INC. - HOUSTON REGIONAL OFFICE—See EQT AB; *Int'l*, pg. 2476
ISS FACILITY SERVICES, INC. - HOUSTON REGIONAL OFFICE—See The Goldman Sachs Group, Inc.; *U.S. Public*, pg. 2077
ISS FACILITY SERVICES, INC. - KANSAS CITY REGIONAL OFFICE—See EQT AB; *Int'l*, pg. 2476
ISS FACILITY SERVICES, INC. - KANSAS CITY REGIONAL OFFICE—See The Goldman Sachs Group, Inc.; *U.S. Public*, pg. 2078
ISS FACILITY SERVICES, INC. - LAS VEGAS REGIONAL OFFICE—See EQT AB; *Int'l*, pg. 2476
ISS FACILITY SERVICES, INC. - LAS VEGAS REGIONAL OFFICE—See The Goldman Sachs Group, Inc.; *U.S. Public*, pg. 2078
ISS FACILITY SERVICES, INC. - MEMPHIS REGIONAL OFFICE—See EQT AB; *Int'l*, pg. 2476
ISS FACILITY SERVICES, INC. - MEMPHIS REGIONAL OFFICE—See The Goldman Sachs Group, Inc.; *U.S. Public*, pg. 2078
ISS FACILITY SERVICES, INC. - PHOENIX REGIONAL OFFICE—See EQT AB; *Int'l*, pg. 2476
ISS FACILITY SERVICES, INC. - PHOENIX REGIONAL OFFICE—See The Goldman Sachs Group, Inc.; *U.S. Public*, pg. 2078
ISS FACILITY SERVICES, INC. - SAN ANTONIO REGIONAL OFFICE—See EQT AB; *Int'l*, pg. 2476
ISS FACILITY SERVICES, INC. - SAN ANTONIO REGIONAL OFFICE—See The Goldman Sachs Group, Inc.; *U.S. Public*, pg. 2078
ISS FACILITY SERVICES, INC.—See EQT AB; *Int'l*, pg. 2476
ISS FACILITY SERVICES, INC.—See The Goldman Sachs Group, Inc.; *U.S. Public*, pg. 2077
ISS FACILITY SERVICES LDA.—See EQT AB; *Int'l*, pg. 2476
ISS FACILITY SERVICES LDA.—See The Goldman Sachs Group, Inc.; *U.S. Public*, pg. 2077
ISS FACILITY SERVICES LIMITED—See EQT AB; *Int'l*, pg. 2476
ISS FACILITY SERVICES LIMITED—See EQT AB; *Int'l*, pg. 2477
ISS FACILITY SERVICES LIMITED—See The Goldman Sachs Group, Inc.; *U.S. Public*, pg. 2077
ISS FACILITY SERVICES LIMITED—See The Goldman Sachs Group, Inc.; *U.S. Public*, pg. 2078
ISS FACILITY SERVICES LTD. - LONDON—See EQT AB; *Int'l*, pg. 2477
ISS FACILITY SERVICES LTD. - LONDON—See The Goldman Sachs Group, Inc.; *U.S. Public*, pg. 2078
ISS FACILITY SERVICES S.A.—See EQT AB; *Int'l*, pg. 2476
ISS FACILITY SERVICES S.A.—See The Goldman Sachs Group, Inc.; *U.S. Public*, pg. 2077
ISS FACILITY SERVICES—See EQT AB; *Int'l*, pg. 2476
ISS FACILITY SERVICES—See The Goldman Sachs Group, Inc.; *U.S. Public*, pg. 2078
ISS FACILITY SERVICES SPOL. S R.O.—See EQT AB; *Int'l*, pg. 2476
ISS FACILITY SERVICES SPOL. S R.O.—See The Goldman Sachs Group, Inc.; *U.S. Public*, pg. 2077
ISS FACILITY SERVICES S.R.O.—See EQT AB; *Int'l*, pg. 2476
ISS FACILITY SERVICES S.R.O.—See The Goldman Sachs Group, Inc.; *U.S. Public*, pg. 2077
ISS GLOBAL A/S—See EQT AB; *Int'l*, pg. 2476
ISS GLOBAL A/S—See The Goldman Sachs Group, Inc.; *U.S. Public*, pg. 2077
ISSGR, INC.; *U.S. Private*, pg. 2147
ISS GROUP (ASIA) PTE. LTD.—See Advent International Corporation; *U.S. Private*, pg. 105
ISS GROUP EUROPE LIMITED—See Advent International Corporation; *U.S. Private*, pg. 105
ISS GROUP, INC.; *U.S. Private*, pg. 2147
ISSHIN INDUSTRIES CORPORATION—See NOK Corporation; *Int'l*, pg. 5402
ISS HOLDING A/S—See EQT AB; *Int'l*, pg. 2476
ISS HOLDING A/S—See The Goldman Sachs Group, Inc.; *U.S. Public*, pg. 2077
IS&S HOLDINGS, INC.—See Innovative Solutions & Support, Inc.; *U.S. Public*, pg. 1127
ISS HOSPITAL SERVICES B.V.—See EQT AB; *Int'l*, pg. 2477
ISS HOSPITAL SERVICES B.V.—See The Goldman Sachs Group, Inc.; *U.S. Public*, pg. 2078
ISSI JAPAN, INC.—See SummitView Capital Management Ltd.; *Int'l*, pg. 7302
ISS INC.—See Business Brain Showa-Ota Inc.; *Int'l*, pg. 1228
ISS INTEGRATED FACILITY SERVICES B.V.—See EQT AB; *Int'l*, pg. 2477
ISS INTEGRATED FACILITY SERVICES B.V.—See The Goldman Sachs Group, Inc.; *U.S. Public*, pg. 2078
ISS INTERNATIONAL SCIENTIFIC SERVICES CO.—See HORIBA Ltd; *Int'l*, pg. 3477
ISS IRELAND LTD.—See EQT AB; *Int'l*, pg. 2476
ISS IRELAND LTD.—See The Goldman Sachs Group, Inc.; *U.S. Public*, pg. 2078
ISS ISLAND EHF.—See EQT AB; *Int'l*, pg. 2476
ISS ISLAND EHF.—See The Goldman Sachs Group, Inc.; *U.S. Public*, pg. 2078
ISS MARKETING PTY LIMITED—See Enero Group Limited; *Int'l*, pg. 2424
ISS MEXICO MANUFACTURING, S.A. DE C.V.—See Daido Metal Corporation; *Int'l*, pg. 1922
ISS NEDERLAND B.V.—See EQT AB; *Int'l*, pg. 2476
ISS NEDERLAND B.V.—See The Goldman Sachs Group, Inc.; *U.S. Public*, pg. 2078
ISS N.V.—See EQT AB; *Int'l*, pg. 2476
ISS N.V.—See The Goldman Sachs Group, Inc.; *U.S. Public*, pg. 2078
ISS PALVELUT OY—See EQT AB; *Int'l*, pg. 2477
ISS PALVELUT OY—See The Goldman Sachs Group, Inc.; *U.S. Public*, pg. 2078
ISSPRO INC.; *U.S. Private*, pg. 2147
ISSQUARED INC.; *U.S. Private*, pg. 2147
ISS SCHWEIZ AG—See EQT AB; *Int'l*, pg. 2477
ISS SCHWEIZ AG—See The Goldman Sachs Group, Inc.; *U.S. Public*, pg. 2078
ISS SERVISYSTEM DO BRASIL LTDA.—See EQT AB; *Int'l*, pg. 2477
ISS SERVISYSTEM DO BRASIL LTDA.—See The Goldman Sachs Group, Inc.; *U.S. Public*, pg. 2078
ISS SERVISYSTEM D.O.O.—See EQT AB; *Int'l*, pg. 2477
ISS SERVISYSTEM D.O.O.—See The Goldman Sachs Group, Inc.; *U.S. Public*, pg. 2078
ISS SERVISYSTEM KFT.—See EQT AB; *Int'l*, pg. 2477
ISS SERVISYSTEM KFT.—See The Goldman Sachs Group, Inc.; *U.S. Public*, pg. 2078
ISS SHIPPING INDIA PVT. LTD.—See Albert Ballin KG; *Int'l*, pg. 295
ISS SOFTWARE GMBH—See Sopra Steria Group S.A.; *Int'l*, pg. 7110
ISSTA LINES LTD.; *Int'l*, pg. 3824
ISST HANDELS GMBH—See Stahlgruber Otto Gruber GmbH & Co. KG; *Int'l*, pg. 7164
ISS THORESEN AGENCIES LTD.—See Thoresen Thai Agencies Public Company Limited; *Int'l*, pg. 7718
ISS TMC SERVICES, INC.—See EQT AB; *Int'l*, pg. 2476
ISS TMC SERVICES, INC.—See The Goldman Sachs Group, Inc.; *U.S. Public*, pg. 2078
ISSUE MEDIA GROUP, LLC; *U.S. Private*, pg. 2147
ISSUER DIRECT CORPORATION; *U.S. Public*, pg. 1175
ISSUES & ANSWERS NETWORK, INC.—See Beyond Commerce, Inc.; *U.S. Public*, pg. 327
ISSUETRAK, INC.; *U.S. Private*, pg. 2147
ISS UK LIMITED—See EQT AB; *Int'l*, pg. 2477
ISS UK LIMITED—See The Goldman Sachs Group, Inc.; *U.S. Public*, pg. 2078
ISSUNBOU CO., LTD.; *Int'l*, pg. 3824
ISSUU, INC.—See Bending Spoons S.p.A.; *Int'l*, pg. 971
ISSYS ICT B.V.—See Dustin Group AB; *Int'l*, pg. 2235
ISTA BRASIL SERVICOS DE ENERGIA LTDA.—See CK Asset Holdings Limited; *Int'l*, pg. 1635
ISTA CESKA REPUBLICA S.R.O.—See CK Asset Holdings Limited; *Int'l*, pg. 1635
ISTA CIS—See CK Asset Holdings Limited; *Int'l*, pg. 1635
ISTA DANMARK A/S—See CK Asset Holdings Limited; *Int'l*, pg. 1635
ISTA DEUTSCHLAND GMBH—See CK Asset Holdings Limited; *Int'l*, pg. 1635
ISTA ENERGY SOLUTIONS LIMITED—See CK Asset Holdings Limited; *Int'l*, pg. 1635
ISTA ENERJI HIZMETLERI TIC. LTD. STI.—See CK Asset Holdings Limited; *Int'l*, pg. 1636

ISSUNBOU CO., LTD.

ISTA INTERNATIONAL GMBH—See CK Asset Holdings Limited; *Int'l*, pg. 1635
ISTA ITALIA S.R.L.—See CK Asset Holdings Limited; *Int'l*, pg. 1636
ISTA LUXEMBURG GMBH—See CK Asset Holdings Limited; *Int'l*, pg. 1636
ISTA MAGYARORSZAG MERESTECHNIKA SZERVIZ KFT.—See CK Asset Holdings Limited; *Int'l*, pg. 1636
ISTA MEASUREMENT TECHNOLOGY SERVICES (BEIJING) CO., LTD.—See CK Asset Holdings Limited; *Int'l*, pg. 1636
ISTA METERING SERVICES ESPANA, S.A.—See CK Asset Holdings Limited; *Int'l*, pg. 1636
ISTA MIDDLE EAST FZE—See CK Asset Holdings Limited; *Int'l*, pg. 1636
ISTANBUL GIDA DIS TICARET A.S.—See Yildiz Holding AS; *Int'l*, pg. 8583
ISTANBUL MAKINA A.S.—See Quaser Machine Tools, Inc.; *Int'l*, pg. 6157
ISTANBUL TICARET HIRDAVAT SANAYI A.S.—See Bunzl plc; *Int'l*, pg. 1218
ISTANBUL TICARET IS GUVENLIGI VE ENDUSTRIYEL SANAYI URUNLER A.S.—See Bunzl plc; *Int'l*, pg. 1218
ISTA NEDERLAND B.V.—See CK Asset Holdings Limited; *Int'l*, pg. 1636
ISTA NORGE AS—See CK Asset Holdings Limited; *Int'l*, pg. 1636
ISTA OSTERREICH GMBH—See CK Asset Holdings Limited; *Int'l*, pg. 1636
ISTA POLSKA SP.Z.O.O.—See CK Asset Holdings Limited; *Int'l*, pg. 1636
ISTAR APARTMENT HOLDINGS LLC—See Safehold Inc.; *U.S. Public*, pg. 1834
ISTAR ASSET SERVICES, INC.—See Safehold Inc.; *U.S. Public*, pg. 1834
ISTAR CORPORATION—See The Sumitomo Warehouse Co. Ltd.; *Int'l*, pg. 7689
ISTAR MARLIN LLC—See Safehold Inc.; *U.S. Public*, pg. 1834
ISTA ROMANIA SRL—See CK Asset Holdings Limited; *Int'l*, pg. 1636
ISTARSKA KREDITNA BANKA UMAG D.D.; *Int'l*, pg. 3824
ISTA RUS O.O.O.—See CK Asset Holdings Limited; *Int'l*, pg. 1636
ISTA SLOVAKIA S.R.O.—See CK Asset Holdings Limited; *Int'l*, pg. 1636
ISTA SWISS AG—See CK Asset Holdings Limited; *Int'l*, pg. 1636
I STATE TRUCK CENTER—See Interstate Companies, Inc.; *U.S. Private*, pg. 2124
I-STATE TRUCK CENTER—See Interstate Companies, Inc.; *U.S. Private*, pg. 2124
ISTAV MEDIA, S.R.O.—See Byggfakta Group Nordic HoldCo AB; *Int'l*, pg. 1234
I STAY MANAGEMENT SDN. BHD.—See AME Elite Consortium Berhad; *Int'l*, pg. 420
IST CO., LTD.—See ITbook Holdings Co., Ltd.; *Int'l*, pg. 3831
IST FARM MACHINERY CO., LTD.—See Iseki & Co., Ltd.; *Int'l*, pg. 3814
ISTIMEWA ELECTROTECHNIEK B.V.—See Fluor Corporation; *U.S. Public*, pg. 859
ISTITHMAR PJSC—See Dubai World Corporation; *Int'l*, pg. 2222
ISTITUTO DELLE VITAMINE SPA—See Koninklijke DSM N.V.; *Int'l*, pg. 4265
ISTITUTO DI RICHERCHE DI BIOLOGIA MOLECOLARE S.P.A.—See Merck & Co., Inc.; *U.S. Public*, pg. 1417
ISTITUTO GANASSINI SPA DI RICERCHE BIOCHIMICHE; *Int'l*, pg. 3824
ISTITUTO MARANGONI S.R.L.—See Providence Equity Partners L.L.C.; *U.S. Private*, pg. 3293
IST LIMITED; *Int'l*, pg. 3824
IST MANAGEMENT SERVICES, INC.; *U.S. Private*, pg. 2147
ISTMO COMPANIA DE REASEGUROS, INC.; *Int'l*, pg. 3824
ISTO BIOLOGICS, INC.—See Thompson Street Capital Manager LLC; *U.S. Private*, pg. 4161
ISTOCKPHOTO LP—See CC Capital Partners, LLC; *U.S. Private*, pg. 797
ISTONISH HOLDING COMPANY, INC.; *U.S. Private*, pg. 2147
ISTONISH INC.—See Istonish Holding Company, Inc.; *U.S. Private*, pg. 2147
ISTRA AVTO D.O.O.—See Avtotehna, d.d.; *Int'l*, pg. 751
ISTRABENZ, HOLDINSKA DRUZBA, D.D.; *Int'l*, pg. 3824
ISTRABENZ HOTELI PORTOROZ, D.O.O.—See Istrabenz, holdinska druzba, d.d.; *Int'l*, pg. 3824
ISTRABENZ PLINI, D.O.O.—See Linde plc; *Int'l*, pg. 4510
ISTRABENZ TURIZEM, D.D.—See Istrabenz, holdinska druzba, d.d.; *Int'l*, pg. 3824
ISTRAGRAFIKA D.D.—See CVC Capital Partners SICAV-FIS S.A.; *Int'l*, pg. 1881
ISTRATEGYLABS LLC—See WPP plc; *Int'l*, pg. 8483
ISTRATURIST UMAG D.D.—See Plava Laguna dd; *Int'l*, pg. 5894

ISTREAMPLANET CO., LLC—See Warner Bros. Discovery, Inc.; *U.S. Public*, pg. 2328
ISTREET NETWORK LIMITED; *Int'l*, pg. 3824
IST RESEARCH CORP.—See The Carlyle Group Inc.; *U.S. Public*, pg. 2056
ISTRINGS AVIATION CAPITAL CO., LTD.—See Marubeni Corporation; *Int'l*, pg. 4710
ISTROKAPITAL CZ, A.S.—See ISTROKAPITAL SE; *Int'l*, pg. 3824
ISTROKAPITAL SE; *Int'l*, pg. 3824
IST-SOFTWARE CO., LTD.—See I-Net Corporation; *Int'l*, pg. 3563
ISTYLE INC.; *Int'l*, pg. 3824
ISU ABXIS CO., LTD.—See ISU Chemical co., Ltd.; *Int'l*, pg. 3825
ISU CHEMICAL CO., LTD. - ONSAN FACTORY—See ISU Chemical co., Ltd.; *Int'l*, pg. 3825
ISU CHEMICAL CO., LTD.; *Int'l*, pg. 3825
ISU CHEMICAL CO., LTD. - ULSAN FACTORY—See ISU Chemical co., Ltd.; *Int'l*, pg. 3825
ISU CHEMICAL GERMANY GMBH—See ISU Chemical co., Ltd.; *Int'l*, pg. 3825
ISU ENGINEERING & CONSTRUCTION CO., LTD.—See ISU Chemical co., Ltd.; *Int'l*, pg. 3825
ISU EXABOARD CO., LTD.—See ISU Chemical co., Ltd.; *Int'l*, pg. 3825
ISU EXAFLEX CO., LTD.—See ISU Chemical co., Ltd.; *Int'l*, pg. 3825
ISUN, INC.; *U.S. Public*, pg. 1175
ISU PERSONALDIENSTLEISTUNGEN GMBH—See Randstad N.V.; *Int'l*, pg. 6203
ISUPETASYS CO., LTD.; *Int'l*, pg. 3825
ISU PETASYS CORPORATION—See ISU Chemical co., Ltd.; *Int'l*, pg. 3825
THE I SUPPLY COMPANY; *U.S. Private*, pg. 4055
ISURE INSURANCE BROKERS; *U.S. Private*, pg. 2147
ISU SYSTEMS CO., LTD—See ISU Chemical co., Ltd.; *Int'l*, pg. 3825
ISU VENTURE CAPITAL CO., LTD—See ISU Chemical co., Ltd.; *Int'l*, pg. 3825
ISUZU AUSTRALIA LIMITED—See Isuzu Motors Limited; *Int'l*, pg. 3825
ISUZU AUTOMOTIVE DEALERSHIP, INC.—See Ayala Corporation; *Int'l*, pg. 773
ISUZU AUTOMOTIVE EUROPE GMBH.—See Isuzu Motors Limited; *Int'l*, pg. 3825
ISUZU AUTOPARTS MANUFACTURING CORPORATION—See Isuzu Motors Limited; *Int'l*, pg. 3825
ISUZU AUTO-SERVICE CORPORATION—See Mitsubishi Corporation; *Int'l*, pg. 4939
ISUZU BANK GMBH—See Mitsubishi Corporation; *Int'l*, pg. 4939
ISUZU BENELUX N.V.—See Isuzu Motors Limited; *Int'l*, pg. 3825
ISUZU BUSINESS SUPPORT CORPORATION—See Mitsubishi Corporation; *Int'l*, pg. 4939
ISUZU (CHINA) HOLDING CO., LTD.—See Isuzu Motors Limited; *Int'l*, pg. 3825
ISUZU CHOU CORPORATION—See Mitsubishi Corporation; *Int'l*, pg. 4939
ISUZU COMMERCIAL TRUCK OF AMERICA, INC.—See Isuzu Motors Limited; *Int'l*, pg. 3825
ISUZU COMMERCIAL TRUCK OF CANADA, INC.—See Isuzu Motors Limited; *Int'l*, pg. 3825
ISUZU EAST AFRICA LTD.—See Isuzu Motors Limited; *Int'l*, pg. 3825
ISUZU ENGINE MANUFACTURING CO., (THAILAND) LTD.—See Isuzu Motors Limited; *Int'l*, pg. 3825
ISUZU HICOM MALAYSIA SDN. BHD.—See Isuzu Motors Limited; *Int'l*, pg. 3825
ISUZU LINEX CO., LTD.—See Isuzu Motors Limited; *Int'l*, pg. 3825
ISUZU MALAYSIA SDN. BHD.—See Mitsubishi Corporation; *Int'l*, pg. 4939
ISUZU MANAGEMENT SERVICE CORPORATION—See Mitsubishi Corporation; *Int'l*, pg. 4939
ISUZU MOTORS AMERICA INC.—See Isuzu Motors Limited; *Int'l*, pg. 3825
ISUZU MOTORS AMERICA INC.—See Isuzu Motors Limited; *Int'l*, pg. 3825
ISUZU MOTORS ASIA LTD.—See Isuzu Motors Limited; *Int'l*, pg. 3825
ISUZU MOTORS CHUBU CO., LTD.—See Isuzu Motors Limited; *Int'l*, pg. 3826
ISUZU MOTORS CO., (THAILAND) LTD.—See Isuzu Motors Limited; *Int'l*, pg. 3826
ISUZU MOTORS DE MEXICO S. DE R.L.—See Isuzu Motors Limited; *Int'l*, pg. 3826
ISUZU MOTORS DE MEXICO S. DE R.L.—See Mitsubishi Corporation; *Int'l*, pg. 4939
ISUZU MOTORS EUROPE LTD.—See Isuzu Motors Limited; *Int'l*, pg. 3826
ISUZU MOTORS EUROPE NV—See Isuzu Motors Limited; *Int'l*, pg. 3826
ISUZU MOTORS GERMANY GMBH—See Isuzu Motors Limited; *Int'l*, pg. 3826

CORPORATE AFFILIATIONS

ISUZU MOTORS INDIA PRIVATE LIMITED—See Mitsubishi Corporation; *Int'l*, pg. 4939
ISUZU MOTORS INTERNATIONAL FZE—See Isuzu Motors Limited; *Int'l*, pg. 3826
ISUZU MOTORS INTERNATIONAL OPERATIONS (THAILAND) CO., LTD.—See Mitsubishi Corporation; *Int'l*, pg. 4939
ISUZU MOTORS KINKI CO., LTD.—See Isuzu Motors Limited; *Int'l*, pg. 3826
ISUZU MOTORS LIMITED; *Int'l*, pg. 3825
ISUZU MOTORS OFF-HIGHWAY DIESEL ENGINE (SHANGHAI) CO., LTD.—See Isuzu Motors Limited; *Int'l*, pg. 3826
ISUZU MOTORS SYUTOKEN CO., LTD.—See Isuzu Motors Limited; *Int'l*, pg. 3826
ISUZU MOTORS TOKAI CO., LTD.—See Isuzu Motors Limited; *Int'l*, pg. 3826
ISUZU NETWORK CO., LTD—See Isuzu Motors Limited; *Int'l*, pg. 3826
ISUZU NORTH AMERICA CORPORATION—See Isuzu Motors Limited; *Int'l*, pg. 3826
ISUZU OPERATIONS (THAILAND) CO., LTD.—See Isuzu Motors Limited; *Int'l*, pg. 3826
ISUZU PHILIPPINES CORPORATION—See Isuzu Motors Limited; *Int'l*, pg. 3826
ISUZU SALES DEUTSCHLAND GMBH—See Isuzu Motors Limited; *Int'l*, pg. 3826
ISUZU SALES DEUTSCHLAND GMBH—See Mitsubishi Corporation; *Int'l*, pg. 4939
ISUZU SERVICE CENTER SDN. BHD.—See DRB-HICOM Berhad; *Int'l*, pg. 2201
ISUZU (SHANGHAI) TRADETECH CO., LTD.—See Isuzu Motors Limited; *Int'l*, pg. 3825
ISUZU TECHNICAL CENTER OF ASIA CO., LTD. (ITA)—See Isuzu Motors Limited; *Int'l*, pg. 3826
ISUZU TECHNICAL CENTER (THAILAND) CO., LTD.—See Isuzu Motors Limited; *Int'l*, pg. 3826
ISUZU TRUCK SOUTH AFRICA (PTY.) LIMITED—See General Motors Company; *U.S. Public*, pg. 926
ISUZU TRUCK (UK) LTD.—See Isuzu Motors Limited; *Int'l*, pg. 3826
ISUZU UTE AUSTRALIA PTY. LTD.—See Mitsubishi Corporation; *Int'l*, pg. 4939
ISUZU VIETNAM CO., LTD.—See Isuzu Motors Limited; *Int'l*, pg. 3826
ISUZU WAREHOUSE CORPORATION—See Mitsubishi Corporation; *Int'l*, pg. 4939
ISVA VERNICI SRL—See The Sherwin-Williams Company; *U.S. Public*, pg. 2128
ISVOR FIAT S.C.P.A.—See Stellantis N.V.; *Int'l*, pg. 7197
ISWILL ACQUISITION CORPORATION; *U.S. Private*, pg. 2147
ISXIS INVESTMENT PUBLIC LTD.; *Int'l*, pg. 3826
IS YATIRIM MENKUL DEGERLER A.S.—See Turkiye Is Bankasi A.S.; *Int'l*, pg. 7976
IS YATIRIM ORTAKLIGI AS; *Int'l*, pg. 3812
I.SYDEK ORIGINAL PACKAGE CO.,LTD.—See Iwatani Corporation; *Int'l*, pg. 3850
I SYNERGY GROUP LIMITED; *Int'l*, pg. 3562
I SYNERGY HOLDINGS BERHAD; *Int'l*, pg. 3562
I-SYS CORPORATION - EL DORADO HILLS—See System Development.Integration LLC; *U.S. Private*, pg. 3906
I-SYS CORPORATION—See System Development.Integration LLC; *U.S. Private*, pg. 3906
ISYS, INC.; *U.S. Private*, pg. 2147
ISYS LLC—See WidePoint Corporation; *U.S. Public*, pg. 2370
ISYS RTS GMBH—See Uno Minda Limited; *Int'l*, pg. 8084
ISZAO PPF INSURANCE—See Assicurazioni Generali S.p.A.; *Int'l*, pg. 646
IT21 INC.—See HSMC Orizon LLC; *U.S. Private*, pg. 1999
IT4LOGISTICS AG—See Deutsche Post AG; *Int'l*, pg. 2083
ITAAS, INC.—See Cognizant Technology Solutions Corporation; *U.S. Public*, pg. 524
ITAAS INDIA PRIVATE LIMITED—See Cognizant Technology Solutions Corporation; *U.S. Public*, pg. 524
ITABASHI KYOUDO SAGYO CO., LTD.—See Japan Pulp and Paper Company Limited; *Int'l*, pg. 3903
ITABASHI PAPER DISTRIBUTION CENTER CO., LTD.—See Japan Pulp and Paper Company Limited; *Int'l*, pg. 3903
ITABASHI TRADING CO., LTD.—See Menicon Co., Ltd.; *Int'l*, pg. 4816
ITAB BUTIKKINNREDNINGER AS OSLO—See ITAB Shop Concept AB; *Int'l*, pg. 3827
ITAB BUTIKKINNREDNINGER AS TRONDHEIM—See ITAB Shop Concept AB; *Int'l*, pg. 3827
ITAB EESTI QU—See ITAB Shop Concept AB; *Int'l*, pg. 3827
ITAB FINLAND OY—See ITAB Shop Concept AB; *Int'l*, pg. 3827
ITAB GERMANY GMBH—See ITAB Shop Concept AB; *Int'l*, pg. 3827
ITAB GUIDANCE AB—See ITAB Shop Concept AB; *Int'l*, pg. 3827
ITAB HARR GMBH—See ITAB Shop Concept AB; *Int'l*, pg. 3827

COMPANY NAME INDEX

ITAB INTERIORS LTD.—See ITAB Shop Concept AB; *Int'l*, pg. 3827
ITAB LINDCO AS—See ITAB Shop Concept AB; *Int'l*, pg. 3827
ITAB MERTENS N.V.—See ITAB Shop Concept AB; *Int'l*, pg. 3827
ITAB PAN OSTON OY—See ITAB Shop Concept AB; *Int'l*, pg. 3827
ITAB PHARMACY CONCEPT AB—See ITAB Shop Concept AB; *Int'l*, pg. 3827
ITAB PROLIGHT AB—See ITAB Shop Concept AB; *Int'l*, pg. 3827
ITAB PROLIGHT AS—See ITAB Shop Concept AB; *Int'l*, pg. 3827
ITAB PROLIGHT GERMANY GMBH—See ITAB Shop Concept AB; *Int'l*, pg. 3827
ITAB SCANFLOW AB—See ITAB Shop Concept AB; *Int'l*, pg. 3827
ITAB SHOP CONCEPT AB; *Int'l*, pg. 3827
ITAB SHOP CONCEPT A/S—See ITAB Shop Concept AB; *Int'l*, pg. 3827
ITAB SHOP CONCEPT BELGIUM N.V.—See ITAB Shop Concept AB; *Int'l*, pg. 3827
ITAB SHOP CONCEPT B.V.—See ITAB Shop Concept AB; *Int'l*, pg. 3827
ITAB SHOP CONCEPT CHINA CO. LTD.—See ITAB Shop Concept AB; *Int'l*, pg. 3827
ITAB SHOP CONCEPT CZ A.S—See ITAB Shop Concept AB; *Int'l*, pg. 3827
ITAB SHOP CONCEPT FINLAND OY—See ITAB Shop Concept AB; *Int'l*, pg. 3827
ITAB SHOP CONCEPT HUNGARY LLC—See ITAB Shop Concept AB; *Int'l*, pg. 3827
ITAB SHOP CONCEPT JONKOPING AB—See ITAB Shop Concept AB; *Int'l*, pg. 3827
ITAB SHOP CONCEPT LITHUANIA AB—See ITAB Shop Concept AB; *Int'l*, pg. 3827
ITAB SHOP CONCEPT NASSJO AB—See ITAB Shop Concept AB; *Int'l*, pg. 3827
ITAB SHOP CONCEPT POLSKA SP ZOO—See ITAB Shop Concept AB; *Int'l*, pg. 3827
ITAB SHOP PRODUCTS AB—See ITAB Shop Concept AB; *Int'l*, pg. 3828
ITAB SHOP PRODUCTS A/S—See ITAB Shop Concept AB; *Int'l*, pg. 3828
ITAB SISUSTUS AS—See ITAB Shop Concept AB; *Int'l*, pg. 3828
ITAB UK LTD.—See ITAB Shop Concept AB; *Int'l*, pg. 3828
ITACAMBA CEMENTO S.A.—See Cementos Molins S.A.; *Int'l*, pg. 1397
ITAC, LTD.—See ShinMaywa Industries, Ltd.; *Int'l*, pg. 6846
ITACONIX CORPORATION—See Itaconix PLC; *Int'l*, pg. 3828
ITACONIX PLC; *Int'l*, pg. 3828
ITAC SOFTWARE AG—See Durr AG; *Int'l*, pg. 2233
ITAC SOLUTIONS; *U.S. Private*, pg. 2148
ITAFOS; *U.S. Public*, pg. 1175
ITAG BUSINESS SOLUTIONS LTD.—See TCI Finance Ltd.; *Int'l*, pg. 7483
ITAGRA SA—See Mecanica Fina SA; *Int'l*, pg. 4765
ITAGROUP, INC.-ATLANTA—See ITAGroup, Inc.; *U.S. Private*, pg. 2148
ITAGROUP, INC.-CHICAGO—See ITAGroup, Inc.; *U.S. Private*, pg. 2148
ITAGROUP, INC.-DALLAS—See ITAGroup, Inc.; *U.S. Private*, pg. 2148
ITAGROUP, INC.-INDIANAPOLIS—See ITAGroup, Inc.; *U.S. Private*, pg. 2148
ITAGROUP, INC.-MINNEAPOLIS—See ITAGroup, Inc.; *U.S. Private*, pg. 2148
ITAGROUP, INC.; *U.S. Private*, pg. 2148
I-TAIL CORPORATION PCL—See Thai Union Group Public Company Limited; *Int'l*, pg. 7596
ITA, INC.—See The Kroger Co.; *U.S. Public*, pg. 2108
ITA INTERNATIONAL, LLC; *U.S. Private*, pg. 2148
ITA ISTITUTO TECNOLOGIE AVANZATE SRL—See RINA S.p.A.; *Int'l*, pg. 6342
ITAITO OY—See Dustin Group AB; *Int'l*, pg. 2235
ITAK (INTERNATIONAL) LIMITED—See Takashima & Co., Ltd.; *Int'l*, pg. 7435
ITAK INTERNATIONAL (SHANGHAI) LIMITED—See Takashima & Co., Ltd.; *Int'l*, pg. 7435
ITAK INTERNATIONAL (SHENZHEN) LIMITED—See Takashima & Co., Ltd.; *Int'l*, pg. 7435
ITAK INTERNATIONAL (THAILAND) LTD.—See Takashima & Co., Ltd.; *Int'l*, pg. 7435
ITALAISE, S.A. DE C.V.—See Grupo Lamosa S.A. de C.V.; *Int'l*, pg. 3132
ITAL-AMERICAS FOODS CORP.; *U.S. Private*, pg. 2148
ITALBRAS S.P.A.—See Umicore S.A./N.V.; *Int'l*, pg. 8024
ITALCEMENTI FINANCE—See Heidelberg Materials AG; *Int'l*, pg. 3317
ITALCEMENTI INGEGNERIA S.R.L.—See Heidelberg Materials AG; *Int'l*, pg. 3317
ITALCEMENTI S.P.A.—See Heidelberg Materials AG; *Int'l*, pg. 3316
ITALCERTIFER S.P.A.—See Ferrovie dello Stato Italiane S.p.A.; *Int'l*, pg. 2645

ITALCHIMICI S.P.A.—See Recordati S.p.A.; *Int'l*, pg. 6239
ITALCLEM S.P.A.—See Arab Electrical Industries; *Int'l*, pg. 530
ITALDESIGN-GIUGIARO S.P.A.—See Porsche Automobil Holding SE; *Int'l*, pg. 5926
ITALDRENI SRL—See Societa Esercizi Commerciali Industriali; *Int'l*, pg. 7034
ITALEAF S.P.A.; *Int'l*, pg. 3828
ITALEASE FINANCE S.P.A.—See Banco BPM S.p.A.; *Int'l*, pg. 818
ITALEASE GESTIONE BENI - OPERATIONAL HEADQUARTERS—See Banco BPM S.p.A.; *Int'l*, pg. 819
ITALEASE GESTIONE BENI S.P.A.—See Banco BPM S.p.A.; *Int'l*, pg. 818
ITALEASE NETWORK S.P.A.—See Banco BPM S.p.A.; *Int'l*, pg. 819
ITALEE OPTICS INC.; *U.S. Private*, pg. 2149
ITALENT INC.; *U.S. Private*, pg. 2149
ITALFERR S.P.A.—See Ferrovie dello Stato Italiane S.p.A.; *Int'l*, pg. 2645
ITALFONDIARIO S.P.A.—See doBank SpA; *Int'l*, pg. 2152
ITALGALVANO (TECHNIC GROUP) SLOVAKIA—See Technic Incorporated; *U.S. Private*, pg. 3953
ITALGAS RETI S.P.A.—See Italgas S.p.A.; *Int'l*, pg. 3828
ITALGAS S.P.A.; *Int'l*, pg. 3828
ITALGEN S.P.A.—See Italmobiliare S.p.A.; *Int'l*, pg. 3829
ITALGESTRA SRL—See Spirax-Sarco Engineering plc; *Int'l*, pg. 7137
ITALGRANI USA INC.—See James Richardson & Sons, Limited; *Int'l*, pg. 3878
ITALHOLDING S.R.L.—See Natuzzi S.p.A.; *Int'l*, pg. 5170
ITALIA ALIMENTARI S.P.A.—See Cremonini S.p.A.; *Int'l*, pg. 1838
ITALIA INDEPENDENT GROUP S.P.A.; *Int'l*, pg. 3828
ITALIA LOGISTICA SRL—See Poste Italiane S.p.A.; *Int'l*, pg. 5939
ITALIANA ASSICURAZIONI S.P.A.—See Societa Reale Mutua di Assicurazioni; *Int'l*, pg. 7034
ITALIANA AUDION S.R.L.—See Francotyp-Postalia Holding AG; *Int'l*, pg. 2761
ITALIANA EDIZIONI S.P.A.—See Stellantis N.V.; *Int'l*, pg. 7200
ITALIAN AMERICAN CORP.—See Central National Gottesman Inc.; *U.S. Private*, pg. 823
ITALIAN AUTOMOTIVE CENTER S.A.—See Stellantis N.V.; *Int'l*, pg. 7198
ITALIA NAVIGANDO S.P.A.—See Agenzia Nazionale per l'Attrazione degli Investimenti e lo Sviluppo d'Impresa SpA; *Int'l*, pg. 206
ITALIAN CAST STONE; *U.S. Private*, pg. 2149
ITALIAN EXHIBITION GROUP SPA; *Int'l*, pg. 3828
ITALIAN FRESH FOODS S.P.A.—See Emmi AG; *Int'l*, pg. 2384
ITALIAN GLASS MOULDS S.R.L.—See Zignago Vetro S.p.A.; *Int'l*, pg. 8682
ITALIAN MOTOR VILLAGE S.A.—See Stellantis N.V.; *Int'l*, pg. 7200
ITALIANO INSURANCE SERVICES, INC.—See GTCR LLC; *U.S. Private*, pg. 1803
ITALIAN ROSE GARLIC PRODUCTS, INC.—See Blue Point Capital Partners, LLC; *U.S. Private*, pg. 590
THE ITALIAN SEA GROUP S.P.A.; *Int'l*, pg. 7657
ITALIANSPED S.P.A.—See Sacmi Imola S.C.A.R.L.; *Int'l*, pg. 6463
ITALIAN TERRAZZO & TILE CO., OF BREVARD, INC.; *U.S. Private*, pg. 2149
ITALIAN-THAI DEVELOPMENT PCL - EQUIPMENT CENTER PRATOONAM PRA-IN FACTORY—See Italian-Thai Development pcl; *Int'l*, pg. 3829
ITALIAN-THAI DEVELOPMENT PCL - ITALIAN-THAI INDUSTRIAL FACTORY—See Italian-Thai Development pcl; *Int'l*, pg. 3829
ITALIAN-THAI DEVELOPMENT PCL - PATHUM THANI PRECAST CONCRETE FACTORY—See Italian-Thai Development pcl; *Int'l*, pg. 3829
ITALIAN-THAI DEVELOPMENT PCL - SAMUTPRAKARN FABRICATION FACTORY—See Italian-Thai Development pcl; *Int'l*, pg. 3829
ITALIAN-THAI DEVELOPMENT PCL; *Int'l*, pg. 3829
ITALIAN-THAI INTERNATIONAL CO., LTD.—See Italian-Thai Development pcl; *Int'l*, pg. 3829
ITALIAN-THAI POWER CO., LTD.—See Italian-Thai Development pcl; *Int'l*, pg. 3829
ITALIAN TOMATO LTD.—See BANDAI NAMCO Holdings Inc.; *Int'l*, pg. 829
ITALIAN WINE BRANDS S.P.A.; *Int'l*, pg. 3828
ITALIAONLINE S.P.A.—See VEON Ltd.; *Int'l*, pg. 8164
ITALIASSISTENZA S.P.A.—See Zambon Company S.p.A.; *Int'l*, pg. 8622
ITAL-ICE D.O.O—See Podravka d.d.; *Int'l*, pg. 5902
ITALMACERI S.R.L.—See DS Smith Plc; *Int'l*, pg. 2209
ITALMACERO S.R.L.—See ACEA S.p.A.; *Int'l*, pg. 95
ITALMATCH CHEMICALS S.P.A.—See Bain Capital, LP; *U.S. Private*, pg. 441
ITALMATCH USA CORPORATION—See Bain Capital, LP; *U.S. Private*, pg. 441
ITALMEX S.A.—See Sacmi Imola S.C.A.R.L.; *Int'l*, pg. 6464

ITALMEX S.P.A.—See Mex Holdings Co. Ltd.; *Int'l*, pg. 4869
ITALMOBILIARE INTERNATIONAL FINANCE LTD.—See Italmobiliare S.p.A.; *Int'l*, pg. 3829
ITALMOBILIARE S.P.A.; *Int'l*, pg. 3829
ITALO SVIZZERA DI ASSICURAZIONI SULLA VITA S.P.A.—See Helvetia Holding AG; *Int'l*, pg. 3340
ITALPARTS ITALIA S.R.L.—See Epiroc AB; *Int'l*, pg. 2463
ITALPASTA LIMITED; *Int'l*, pg. 3830
ITALPINAS DEVELOPMENT CORPORATION; *Int'l*, pg. 3830
ITALPIZZA S.R.L.—See Bakkavor Group plc; *Int'l*, pg. 806
ITALSOFA BAHIA LTDA.—See Natuzzi S.p.A.; *Int'l*, pg. 5170
ITALSOFA NORDESTE S/A—See Natuzzi S.p.A.; *Int'l*, pg. 5170
ITALSOFA ROMANIA S.R.L.—See Natuzzi S.p.A.; *Int'l*, pg. 5170
ITALSOFA SHANGHAI LTD.—See Natuzzi S.p.A.; *Int'l*, pg. 5170
ITALTEL S.P.A.—See Clayton, Dubilier & Rice, LLC; *U.S. Private*, pg. 925
ITALTHAI MARINE LTD.—See Italian-Thai Development pcl; *Int'l*, pg. 3829
ITALTHAI TREVI CO., LTD.—See Italian-Thai Development pcl; *Int'l*, pg. 3829
ITALTILE LIMITED; *Int'l*, pg. 3830
ITALTINTO EQUIPMENTS PVT. LIMITED—See I.C.T.C. Holdings Corporation; *Int'l*, pg. 3565
ITALTINTO S.R.L.—See I.C.T.C. Holdings Corporation; *Int'l*, pg. 3565
ITALTRACTOR ITM S.P.A.—See Titan International, Inc.; *U.S. Public*, pg. 2160
ITALTRACTOR ITM SPA—See Titan International, Inc.; *U.S. Public*, pg. 2160
ITALTRACTOR LANDRONI LTDA.—See Titan International, Inc.; *U.S. Public*, pg. 2160
ITALTRASFO SRL—See ABB Ltd.; *Int'l*, pg. 54
ITALTUBETTI, SPA—See Sonoco Products Company; *U.S. Public*, pg. 1904
ITALWARE S.R.L.—See Digital Value S.p.A.; *Int'l*, pg. 2123
ITALY1 INVESTMENT S.A.; *Int'l*, pg. 3830
ITALY INNOVAZIONI SPA; *Int'l*, pg. 3830
ITALY VADO TANK CLEANING S.R.L.—See Stolt-Nielsen Limited; *Int'l*, pg. 7221
ITAMAR MEDICAL, INC.—See Asahi Kasei Corporation; *Int'l*, pg. 597
ITAMAR MEDICAL LTD.—See Asahi Kasei Corporation; *Int'l*, pg. 597
IT AMERICA INC.; *U.S. Private*, pg. 2147
ITANDI, INC.—See GAtechnologies Co., Ltd.; *Int'l*, pg. 2888
ITAPEBI GERACAO DE ENERGIA S.A.; *Int'l*, pg. 3830
ITAPP INC.—See ServiceNow, Inc.; *U.S. Public*, pg. 1872
ITAR-TASS NEWS AGENCY; *Int'l*, pg. 3830
ITASCA BANCORP INC.; *U.S. Private*, pg. 2149
ITASCA BANK & TRUST CO.—See Itasca Bancorp Inc.; *U.S. Private*, pg. 2149
ITASCA RETAIL INFORMATION SYSTEMS, INC.—See Application Development Consultants, LLC; *U.S. Private*, pg. 298
ITASCA TECHNOLOGY INC.—See AcBel Polytech Inc.; *Int'l*, pg. 78
IT ASCENT, INC.; *U.S. Private*, pg. 2147
IT ASCENT, INC.-WALNUT CREEK—See IT Ascent, Inc.; *U.S. Private*, pg. 2148
ITA SERVICES PTY LTD.—See Microsoft Corporation; *U.S. Public*, pg. 1442
ITA SOFTWARE, INC.—See Alphabet Inc.; *U.S. Public*, pg. 83
ITAU BBA INTERNATIONAL PLC—See Itau Unibanco Holding S.A.; *Int'l*, pg. 3830
ITAU CORPBANCA COLOMBIA S. A.—See Itau Unibanco Holding S.A.; *Int'l*, pg. 3830
ITAUSA EMPREENDIMENTOS S.A.—See Itausa - Investimentos Itau S.A.; *Int'l*, pg. 3831
ITAUSA - INVESTIMENTOS ITAU S.A.; *Int'l*, pg. 3830
ITAU SEGUROS S.A.—See Itau Unibanco Holding S.A.; *Int'l*, pg. 3830
IT AUTHORITIES, INC.—See WidePoint Corporation; *U.S. Public*, pg. 2370
ITAU UNIBANCO HOLDING S.A.; *Int'l*, pg. 3830
ITAU UNIBANCO S.A—See Itau Unibanco Holding S.A.; *Int'l*, pg. 3830
ITAYAMAMEDICO CO., LTD.—See MatsukiyoCocokara & Co.; *Int'l*, pg. 4730
IT BANK JSC; *Int'l*, pg. 3826
ITBOOK CO., LTD.—See ITbook Holdings Co., Ltd.; *Int'l*, pg. 3831
ITBOOK HOLDINGS CO., LTD.; *Int'l*, pg. 3831
ITC-2, S.A.—See VINCI S.A.; *Int'l*, pg. 8222
ITCAMPUS SOFTWARE UND SYSTEMHAUS GMBH—See Silver Lake Group, LLC; *U.S. Private*, pg. 3660
ITCAMPUS (UK) LIMITED—See Silver Lake Group, LLC; *U.S. Private*, pg. 3660
ITC APT SP. Z.O.O.—See Empresaria Group Plc; *Int'l*, pg. 2389

1395

ITBOOK HOLDINGS CO., LTD.
CORPORATE AFFILIATIONS

ITC AUSTRALASIA PTY LTD—See ITC Learning Corp.; *U.S. Private*, pg. 2149
ITC BHADRACHALAM PAPERBOARDS LTD.—See ITC Limited; *Int'l*, pg. 3831
ITC CONCEPTS LTD; *Int'l*, pg. 3831
ITC CONSTRUCTION GROUP; *Int'l*, pg. 3831
ITC CORPORATION CO., LTD.—See Mitsubishi Corporation; *Int'l*, pg. 4938
ITC CS SP. Z.O.O.—See Empresaria Group Plc; *Int'l*, pg. 2389
ITC DISTRIBUTION, LLC—See ITV plc; *Int'l*, pg. 3845
IT-CE EIG—See Groupe BPCE; *Int'l*, pg. 3098
ITCEN CO., LTD.; *Int'l*, pg. 3832
ITC ENEX SOUTHEAST ASIA CO., LTD.—See Itochu Enex Co., Ltd.; *Int'l*, pg. 3841
ITC ENEX (THAILAND) CO., LTD.—See Itochu Enex Co., Ltd.; *Int'l*, pg. 3841
ITC GLOBAL AUSTRALIA—See Apax Partners LLP; *Int'l*, pg. 504
ITC GLOBAL GUINEA—See Apax Partners LLP; *Int'l*, pg. 504
ITC GLOBAL INC.—See Apax Partners LLP; *Int'l*, pg. 504
ITC GLOBAL UK—See Apax Partners LLP; *Int'l*, pg. 505
ITC GREEN & WATER CORP.—See ITOCHU Corporation; *Int'l*, pg. 3836
ITC GRID DEVELOPMENT, LLC—See Fortis Inc.; *U.S. Public*, pg. 2739
ITC HOLDING COMPANY, LLC; *U.S. Private*, pg. 2149
ITC HOLDINGS CORP.—See Fortis Inc.; *Int'l*, pg. 2739
ITC HOTELS LTD.—See ITC Limited; *Int'l*, pg. 3831
ITC INFOTECH DENMARK—See ITC Limited; *Int'l*, pg. 3831
ITC INFOTECH INDIA LTD.—See ITC Limited; *Int'l*, pg. 3831
ITC INFOTECH INDIA LTD.—See ITC Limited; *Int'l*, pg. 3831
ITC INFOTECH LTD.—See ITC Limited; *Int'l*, pg. 3831
ITC INFOTECH UK LTD.—See ITC Limited; *Int'l*, pg. 3831
ITC INFOTECH (USA) INC.—See ITC Limited; *Int'l*, pg. 3831
ITC INTERMEC TECHNOLOGIES CORPORATION AS—See Honeywell International Inc.; *U.S. Public*, pg. 1050
ITC INTERNATIONAL TIRE NV—See Compagnie Generale des Etablissements Michelin SCA; *Int'l*, pg. 1742
ITC INVESTMENT PARTNERS CORPORATION—See ASTMAX Trading, Inc.; *Int'l*, pg. 655
IT CITY PUBLIC COMPANY LIMITED; *Int'l*, pg. 3826
ITC LEARNING CORP.; *U.S. Private*, pg. 2149
ITC LIMITED; *Int'l*, pg. 3831
ITC MIDWEST LLC—See Fortis Inc.; *Int'l*, pg. 2740
ITCM NORTH AMERICA, INC.—See MPAC Group PLC; *Int'l*, pg. 5060
ITCONIC PORTUGAL, S.A.—See Equinix, Inc.; *U.S. Public*, pg. 788
ITCONS E-SOLUTIONS LIMITED; *Int'l*, pg. 3832
ITC PROPERTIES GROUP LIMITED; *Int'l*, pg. 3832
ITC RUBIS TERMINAL ANTWERP N.V.—See Mitsui & Co., Ltd.; *Int'l*, pg. 4973
ITC SERVICE GROUP, INC.—See Fujikura Ltd.; *Int'l*, pg. 2827
ITC TECHNOLOGY TAIWAN CORPORATION—See ITOCHU Corporation; *Int'l*, pg. 3836
ITD CEMENTATION INDIA LIMITED; *Int'l*, pg. 3832
IT DIRECT, LLC—See CompassMSP LLC; *U.S. Private*, pg. 999
ITDL IMAGETEC LIMITED—See Indian Toners & Developers Ltd.; *Int'l*, pg. 3654
ITD SOLUTIONS S.P.A.—See Digital Value S.p.A.; *Int'l*, pg. 2123
ITEAM CONSULTING, LLC—See Netsurit (Pty) Ltd; *Int'l*, pg. 5215
ITEB B.V.—See Allianz SE; *Int'l*, pg. 349
ITECA ALATOO—See Providence Equity Partners L.L.C.; *U.S. Private*, pg. 3293
ITECA ALATOO—See Searchlight Capital Partners, L.P.; *U.S. Private*, pg. 3588
ITECA KAZAKHSTAN—See Providence Equity Partners L.L.C.; *U.S. Private*, pg. 3293
ITECA KAZAKHSTAN—See Searchlight Capital Partners, L.P.; *U.S. Private*, pg. 3588
ITEC CONNECT LIMITED—See Xerox Holdings Corporation; *U.S. Public*, pg. 2386
ITEC CORPORATION—See KKR & Co. Inc.; *U.S. Public*, pg. 1260
ITEC HANKYU HANSHIN CO., LTD.—See Hankyu Hanshin Holdings Inc.; *Int'l*, pg. 3256
ITECHART GROUP, INC.; *U.S. Private*, pg. 2149
ITE CHINA—See Providence Equity Partners L.L.C.; *U.S. Private*, pg. 3292
ITE CHINA—See Searchlight Capital Partners, L.P.; *U.S. Private*, pg. 3587
ITECH MINERALS LTD.; *Int'l*, pg. 3832
I. TECHNICAL SERVICES LLC—See Prime Technological Services, LLC; *U.S. Private*, pg. 3262
ITECH SOLUTIONS, INC.—See Ampcus Inc.; *U.S. Private*, pg. 265
ITECH US, INC.—See SharedLABS, Inc.; *U.S. Private*, pg. 3626

ITECHX GMBH—See Profidata Group AG; *Int'l*, pg. 5989
ITEC INTELLIGENT SERVICES LTD.—See Permira Advisers LLP; *Int'l*, pg. 5804
ITEC LEASING CO., LTD.—See Tokyo Century Corporation; *Int'l*, pg. 7789
ITECMA S.A.S.—See Illinois Tool Works Inc.; *U.S. Public*, pg. 1104
ITECO NEPAL (PVT.) LTD.—See AFRY AB; *Int'l*, pg. 194
IT-ECONOMICS GMBH—See Sopra Steria Group S.A.; *Int'l*, pg. 7111
ITE ELECTRIC SYSTEMS CO PTE LTD; *Int'l*, pg. 3832
ITE EURASIAN EXHIBITIONS FZ LLC—See Providence Equity Partners L.L.C.; *U.S. Private*, pg. 3292
ITE EURASIAN EXHIBITIONS FZ LLC—See Searchlight Capital Partners, L.P.; *U.S. Private*, pg. 3588
ITEFIN PARTICIPATIONS SAS—See Apax Partners LLP; *Int'l*, pg. 504
ITEGRIA, LLC—See RIA in a Box LLC; *U.S. Private*, pg. 3424
ITE GULF FZ LLC—See Providence Equity Partners L.L.C.; *U.S. Private*, pg. 3292
ITE GULF FZ LLC—See Searchlight Capital Partners, L.P.; *U.S. Private*, pg. 3588
ITE (HOLDINGS) LIMITED; *Int'l*, pg. 3832
ITEK AS—See Addtech AB; *Int'l*, pg. 133
ITEK, INC.; *Int'l*, pg. 3832
ITEKNIK HOLDING CORPORATION; *U.S. Public*, pg. 1175
ITEK PL—See Addtech AB; *Int'l*, pg. 133
ITELAGEN INC; *U.S. Private*, pg. 2149
I-TELECOM LTD.—See Ireland Blyth Limited; *Int'l*, pg. 3807
I)TELE—See Vivendi SE; *Int'l*, pg. 8266
I TELEVISION—See Vivendi SE; *Int'l*, pg. 8266
ITELIOS S.A.S.—See Capgemini SE; *Int'l*, pg. 1307
ITE LLC MOSCOW—See Providence Equity Partners L.L.C.; *U.S. Private*, pg. 3292
ITE LLC MOSCOW—See Searchlight Capital Partners, L.P.; *U.S. Private*, pg. 3588
ITELLIGENCE AG—See Nippon Telegraph & Telephone Corporation; *Int'l*, pg. 5347
ITELLIGENCE AG—See Nippon Telegraph & Telephone Corporation; *Int'l*, pg. 5346
ITELLIGENCE A/S—See Nippon Telegraph & Telephone Corporation; *Int'l*, pg. 5347
ITELLIGENCE A.S.—See Nippon Telegraph & Telephone Corporation; *Int'l*, pg. 5347
ITELLIGENCE BUSINESS SOLUTIONS CANADA, INC.—See Nippon Telegraph & Telephone Corporation; *Int'l*, pg. 5347
ITELLIGENCE BUSINESS SOLUTIONS (UK) LTD.—See Nippon Telegraph & Telephone Corporation; *Int'l*, pg. 5347
ITELLIGENCE B.V.—See Nippon Telegraph & Telephone Corporation; *Int'l*, pg. 5347
ITELLIGENCE CONSULTING SHANGHAI LTD.—See Nippon Telegraph & Telephone Corporation; *Int'l*, pg. 5356
ITELLIGENCE, INC.—See Nippon Telegraph & Telephone Corporation; *Int'l*, pg. 5347
ITELLIGENCE SLOVAKIA, S.R.O.—See Silver Lake Group, LLC; *U.S. Private*, pg. 3658
ITELLIGENCE SOFTWARE SOLUTIONS WLL—See Nippon Telegraph & Telephone Corporation; *Int'l*, pg. 5343
ITELLIGENCE SP. Z O.O.—See Nippon Telegraph & Telephone Corporation; *Int'l*, pg. 5347
ITELLO AB; *Int'l*, pg. 3832
ITEL SP. Z O.O.—See PROCHEM S.A.; *Int'l*, pg. 5987
ITELYUM GROUP S.R.L.—See Stirling Square Capital Partners LLP; *Int'l*, pg. 7216
ITELYUM REGENERATION S.P.A.—See Stirling Square Capital Partners LLP; *Int'l*, pg. 7216
ITEM 9 LABS CORP.; *U.S. Public*, pg. 1175
ITEMA AMERICA, INC.—See Radici Partecipazioni S.p.A.; *Int'l*, pg. 6175
ITEMA HOLDING SPA—See Radici Partecipazioni S.p.A.; *Int'l*, pg. 6175
ITE MANAGEMENT L.P.; *U.S. Private*, pg. 2149
ITEMA S.P.A.—See Radici Partecipazioni S.p.A.; *Int'l*, pg. 6175
ITEMFIELD LIMITED—See Canada Pension Plan Investment Board; *Int'l*, pg. 1280
ITEMFIELD LIMITED—See Permira Advisers LLP; *Int'l*, pg. 5806
ITEMION GMBH & CO. KG—See Edenred S.A.; *Int'l*, pg. 2308
ITE MODA LTD.—See Providence Equity Partners L.L.C.; *U.S. Private*, pg. 3293
ITE MODA LTD.—See Searchlight Capital Partners, L.P.; *U.S. Private*, pg. 3588
ITEM PROFIILI OY—See Indutrade AB; *Int'l*, pg. 3679
ITEN INDUSTRIES INC.; *U.S. Private*, pg. 2149
ITE NORTH AMERICA INC.—See Providence Equity Partners L.L.C.; *U.S. Private*, pg. 3293
ITE NORTH AMERICA INC.—See Searchlight Capital Partners, L.P.; *U.S. Private*, pg. 3588
ITEOS THERAPEUTICS, INC; *U.S. Public*, pg. 1175
ITE POLAND SP. Z O.O.—See Providence Equity Partners L.L.C.; *U.S. Private*, pg. 3293

ITE POLAND SP. Z O.O.—See Searchlight Capital Partners, L.P.; *U.S. Private*, pg. 3588
ITEQ CORPORATION; *Int'l*, pg. 3832
ITEQ CORPORATION - TAIWAN FACTORY—See ITEQ Corporation; *Int'l*, pg. 3832
ITERA ASA; *Int'l*, pg. 3832
ITERA CONSULTING AS—See Itera ASA; *Int'l*, pg. 3832
ITERA CONSULTING GROUP DENMARK APS—See Itera ASA; *Int'l*, pg. 3832
ITERA CONSULTING GROUP SWEDEN AB—See Itera ASA; *Int'l*, pg. 3832
ITERA GAZETTE AS—See Itera ASA; *Int'l*, pg. 3833
ITERA NETWORKS AB—See Itera ASA; *Int'l*, pg. 3833
ITERA NETWORKS AS—See Itera ASA; *Int'l*, pg. 3833
ITERA OFFSHORING SERVICES AS—See Itera ASA; *Int'l*, pg. 3833
ITERA OIL AND GAS COMPANY LTD.—See OJSC Rosneftegaz; *Int'l*, pg. 5541
ITER CORPORATION—See Japan Investment Adviser Co., Ltd.; *Int'l*, pg. 3898
ITERGO INFORMATIONSTECHNOLOGIE GMBH—See Munchener Ruckversicherungs AG; *Int'l*, pg. 5089
I-TER/INFORMATICA & TERRITORIO S.P.A.—See Advanced Business Software & Solutions Ltd.; *Int'l*, pg. 157
ITERIO AB—See Multiconsult ASA; *Int'l*, pg. 5083
ITERIS, INC. - GRAND FORKS—See Almaviva S.p.A.; *Int'l*, pg. 363
ITERIS, INC.—See Almaviva S.p.A.; *Int'l*, pg. 363
IT-ERNITY INTERNET SERVICES BV—See Combell NV; *Int'l*, pg. 1708
ITERUM THERAPEUTICS PLC; *Int'l*, pg. 3833
ITES CO., LTD—See NHK Spring Co., Ltd.; *Int'l*, pg. 5257
ITESOFT DEUTSCHLAND GMBH—See ITESOFT S.A.; *Int'l*, pg. 3833
ITESOFT S.A.; *Int'l*, pg. 3833
ITESOFT UK LTD.—See ITESOFT S.A.; *Int'l*, pg. 3833
ITE TECH. INC; *Int'l*, pg. 3832
ITE TURKEY—See Providence Equity Partners L.L.C.; *U.S. Private*, pg. 3293
ITE TURKEY—See Searchlight Capital Partners, L.P.; *U.S. Private*, pg. 3588
ITEUVE CANARIAS, S.L.—See I Squared Capital Advisors (US) LLC; *U.S. Private*, pg. 2023
ITEUVE CANARIAS, S.L.—See TDR Capital LLP; *Int'l*, pg. 7492
ITE UZBEKISTAN—See Providence Equity Partners L.L.C.; *U.S. Private*, pg. 3293
ITE UZBEKISTAN—See Searchlight Capital Partners, L.P.; *U.S. Private*, pg. 3588
I-TEX CO., LTD.—See Unitika Ltd.; *Int'l*, pg. 8074
ITEX CORPORATION; *U.S. Public*, pg. 1175
ITEXICO LLC—See Trinity Hunt Management, L.P.; *U.S. Private*, pg. 4235
ITEXT SOFTWARE ASIA PTE. LTD.—See Hancom, Inc.; *Int'l*, pg. 3243
ITEXT SOFTWARE BVBA—See Hancom, Inc.; *Int'l*, pg. 3243
ITEXT SOFTWARE CORP.—See Hancom, Inc.; *Int'l*, pg. 3243
I.T EZHOP (HK) LIMITED—See IT Ltd; *Int'l*, pg. 3827
ITF CO., LTD.—See Inaba Denki Sangyo Co., Ltd.; *Int'l*, pg. 3643
ITF GERMANY GMBH—See Angelini ACRAF S.p.A.; *Int'l*, pg. 460
IT FIRST SOURCE; *U.S. Private*, pg. 2148
IT FORGING (THAILAND) CO., LTD. (ITF)—See Isuzu Motors Limited; *Int'l*, pg. 3825
ITFOR INC.; *Int'l*, pg. 3833
IT FREEDOM, LLC—See Court Square Capital Partners, L.P.; *U.S. Private*, pg. 1070
IT FRONTIER CORPORATION—See Mitsubishi Corporation; *Int'l*, pg. 4938
ITF S.P.A.—See Angelini ACRAF S.p.A.; *Int'l*, pg. 460
ITF SRL—See Sesa S.p.A.; *Int'l*, pg. 6728
ITF SUISSE AG—See DZ BANK AG Deutsche Zentral-Genossenschaftsbank; *Int'l*, pg. 2244
ITF TECHNOLOGIES INC.—See O-Net Technologies (Group) Limited; *Int'l*, pg. 5502
ITG AUSTRALIA LIMITED—See Virtu Financial, Inc.; *U.S. Public*, pg. 2300
ITG BRANDS, LLC—See Imperial Brands PLC; *Int'l*, pg. 3633
ITG CANADA CORP.—See Virtu Financial, Inc.; *U.S. Public*, pg. 2300
ITG FUTURES CO., LTD.—See Xiamen ITG Group Corp., Ltd.; *Int'l*, pg. 8524
ITG GLOBAL LOGISTICS B.V.—See Deutsche Post AG; *Int'l*, pg. 2081
ITG GMBH INTERNATIONALE SPEDITION UND LOGISTIK—See Carl Bennet AB; *Int'l*, pg. 1331
ITG HOLDINGS LLC; *U.S. Private*, pg. 2149
ITG HONG KONG LIMITED—See Virtu Financial, Inc.; *U.S. Public*, pg. 2300
ITG INTERNATIONALE SPEDITION GMBH—See Deutsche Post AG; *Int'l*, pg. 2081
ITG INTERNATIONAL TRANSPORTS, INC.—See Deutsche Post AG; *Int'l*, pg. 2081
IT GIRL PUBLIC RELATIONS; *U.S. Private*, pg. 2148

COMPANY NAME INDEX

ITG PLATFORMS INC.—See Virtu Financial, Inc.; *U.S. Public*, pg. 2300
ITG PLATFORMS INC.—See Virtu Financial, Inc.; *U.S. Public*, pg. 2300
ITG PLATFORMS SPAIN, S.L.—See Virtu Financial, Inc.; *U.S. Public*, pg. 2300
ITG REALTY LLC—See ITG Holdings LLC; *U.S. Private*, pg. 2149
ITG SOFTWARE INC.—See Insight Venture Management, LLC; *U.S. Private*, pg. 2091
ITG SOFTWARE SOLUTIONS, INC.—See Virtu Financial, Inc.; *U.S. Public*, pg. 2300
ITG SOLUTIONS NETWORK, INC.—See Virtu Financial, Inc.; *U.S. Public*, pg. 2300
THE IT GUYS, LLC—See BMI Systems Corporation; *U.S. Private*, pg. 601
IT GYMNASIET SVERIGE AB—See Bure Equity AB; *Int'l*, pg. 1221
ITHACA ENERGY INC.—See Delek Group Ltd.; *Int'l*, pg. 2012
ITHACA ENERGY (UK) LIMITED—See Delek Group Ltd.; *Int'l*, pg. 2012
THE ITHACA JOURNAL—See Gannett Co., Inc.; *U.S. Public*, pg. 900
ITHACA—See TKH Group N.V.; *Int'l*, pg. 7764
ITHAKA; *U.S. Private*, pg. 2149
IT-HANTVERKARNA SVERIGE AB—See Dustin Group AB; *Int'l*, pg. 2235
ITH ICOSERVE TECHNOLOGY FOR HEALTHCARE GMBH—See Siemens Aktiengesellschaft; *Int'l*, pg. 6887
ITHINK COMUNICACAO E PUBLICIDADE LTDA—See Publicis Groupe S.A.; *Int'l*, pg. 6111
ITHMAAR HOLDING B.S.C.—See Dar Al-Maal Al-Islami Trust; *Int'l*, pg. 1971
IT HOLDING S.P.A.; *Int'l*, pg. 3826
ITH PHARMA LTD.; *Int'l*, pg. 3833
ITHRAA CAPITAL LLC—See Atheeb Group; *Int'l*, pg. 669
ITIBITI SYSTEMS INC.—See Intertainment Media Inc.; *Int'l*, pg. 3762
ITI CAPITAL LIMITED—See Da Vinci Capital LLC; *Int'l*, pg. 1902
ITID CONSULTING, LTD.—See Dentsu Group Inc.; *Int'l*, pg. 2038
ITI GOLD LOANS LIMITED—See The Investment Trust of India Limited; *Int'l*, pg. 7656
ITI GROUP LTD.; *Int'l*, pg. 3833
ITI, INC.—See Intra-Cellular Therapies, Inc.; *U.S. Public*, pg. 1159
ITI INDUSTRIAL INVESTMENTS (UK) LTD.; *Int'l*, pg. 3833
ITI LIMITED - BANGALORE UNIT—See ITI Ltd; *Int'l*, pg. 3833
ITI LIMITED - MANKAPUR UNIT—See ITI Ltd; *Int'l*, pg. 3833
ITI LIMITED - NAINI UNIT—See ITI Ltd; *Int'l*, pg. 3833
ITI LIMITED - PALLAKAD UNIT—See ITI Ltd; *Int'l*, pg. 3833
ITI LTD; *Int'l*, pg. 3833
ITIM GROUP PLC; *Int'l*, pg. 3833
ITI PROFICIENCY LTD.—See Wipro Limited; *Int'l*, pg. 8432
ITIQUIRA ACQUISITION CORP.; *U.S. Public*, pg. 1175
ITI REFERENCE GROUP - FL—See Information Today Inc.; *U.S. Private*, pg. 2073
ITI REFERENCE GROUP - NJ—See Information Today Inc.; *U.S. Private*, pg. 2073
ITI SCOTLAND LIMITED—See Scottish Enterprise; *Int'l*, pg. 6652
ITI SECURITIES LIMITED—See Crest Ventures Limited; *Int'l*, pg. 1841
ITI TRAILERS & TRUCK BODIES, INC.; *U.S. Private*, pg. 2149
ITI TRANSCENDATA—See Wipro Limited; *Int'l*, pg. 8432
ITIVITI GROUP AB—See Broadridge Financial Solutions, Inc.; *U.S. Public*, pg. 391
ITIVITI LIMITED—See Broadridge Financial Solutions, Inc.; *U.S. Public*, pg. 391
IT-KAUPPA OY—See TT International Limited; *Int'l*, pg. 7960
ITK ENGINEERING GMBH—See Robert Bosch GmbH; *Int'l*, pg. 6361
ITK ENGINEERING JAPAN, INC.—See Robert Bosch GmbH; *Int'l*, pg. 6361
ITK ENGINEERING, LLC—See Robert Bosch GmbH; *Int'l*, pg. 6361
ITK HOLDING PLC.—See MOL Magyar Olaj- es Gazipari Nyrt.; *Int'l*, pg. 5020
I T K INTERNATIONALES TRANSPORT-KONTOR GMBH; *Int'l*, pg. 3562
ITL ASIA PACIFIC SDN. BHD.—See ITL Health Group Limited; *Int'l*, pg. 3833
ITLA S.P.A.—See Falck S.p.A.; *Int'l*, pg. 2610
ITL DESIGN AND MANUFACTURING PTY LIMITED—See ITL Health Group Limited; *Int'l*, pg. 3833
ITL HEALTHCARE PTY LIMITED—See Merit Medical Systems, Inc.; *U.S. Public*, pg. 1425
ITL HEALTH GROUP LIMITED; *Int'l*, pg. 3833
ITL INDUSTRIES LTD.; *Int'l*, pg. 3833

IT LINK S.A.; *Int'l*, pg. 3827
ITL NORTH AMERICA INC.—See ITL Health Group Limited; *Int'l*, pg. 3833
IT LTD; *Int'l*, pg. 3827
IT MANAGEMENT COMPANY LIMITED—See Bliss Intelligence Public Company Limited; *Int'l*, pg. 1064
ITMAX SYSTEM BERHAD; *Int'l*, pg. 3834
ITM CLOVER CO., LTD.—See Isetan Mitsukoshi Holdings Ltd.; *Int'l*, pg. 3815
ITM CO., LTD.—See Isolite Insulating Products Co.; *Int'l*, pg. 3821
ITM COMMUNICATIONS LTD.—See Aliter Capital LLP; *Int'l*, pg. 329
ITMEDIA INC.—See SoftBank Group Corp.; *Int'l*, pg. 7051
ITM ENTREPRISES S.A.; *Int'l*, pg. 3833
ITM INFORMATIONSTRANSPORT UND -MANAGEMENT GESELLSCHAFT M.B.H.—See Kapsch-Group Beteiligungs GmbH; *Int'l*, pg. 4077
ITM INSTRUMENTS, INC.; *Int'l*, pg. 3833
ITM MINING PTY. LTD.—See Titan International, Inc.; *U.S. Public*, pg. 2160
ITM POWER GMBH—See ITM Power Plc; *Int'l*, pg. 3834
ITM POWER PLC; *Int'l*, pg. 3833
ITM POWER (RESEARCH) LTD—See ITM Power Plc; *Int'l*, pg. 3834
ITM POWER (TRADING) LIMITED—See ITM Power Plc; *Int'l*, pg. 3834
ITM SEMICONDUCTOR CO., LTD.—See NICE Holdings Co., Ltd.; *Int'l*, pg. 5264
ITM TWENTYFIRST, LLC; *U.S. Private*, pg. 2150
ITMX GMBH—See Nippon Telegraph & Telephone Corporation; *Int'l*, pg. 5343
I.T.N. CONSOLIDATORS—See ZS Fund L.P.; *U.S. Private*, pg. 4609
IT/NET GROUP INC.; *Int'l*, pg. 3827
ITNETX (SWITZERLAND) LTD.—See Swisscom AG; *Int'l*, pg. 7374
ITN INTERNATIONAL INC.—See HGGC, LLC; *U.S. Private*, pg. 1929
ITN MARK (UK)—See Core Education and Technologies Ltd.; *Int'l*, pg. 1797
ITN NANOVATION AG—See SafBon Water Service (Holding) Inc., Shanghai; *Int'l*, pg. 6469
IT-NOVUM GMBH—See Allgeier SE; *Int'l*, pg. 338
IT NOVUM SCHWEIZ GMBH—See Allgeier SE; *Int'l*, pg. 337
ITOCHU AIRLEASE B.V.—See ITOCHU Corporation; *Int'l*, pg. 3837
ITOCHU ARGENTINA S.A.—See ITOCHU Corporation; *Int'l*, pg. 3837
ITOCHU AUSTRALIA LTD.—See ITOCHU Corporation; *Int'l*, pg. 3837
ITOCHU AUTOMOBILE AMERICA INC.—See ITOCHU Corporation; *Int'l*, pg. 3838
ITOCHU AUTOMOBILE CORPORATION—See ITOCHU Corporation; *Int'l*, pg. 3837
ITOCHU AVIATION CO., LTD.—See ITOCHU Corporation; *Int'l*, pg. 3837
ITOCHU AVIATION, INC.—See ITOCHU Corporation; *Int'l*, pg. 3838
ITOCHU BRASIL S.A.—See ITOCHU Corporation; *Int'l*, pg. 3837
ITOCHU CABLE SYSTEMS CORP.—See ITOCHU Corporation; *Int'l*, pg. 3837
ITOCHU CANADA LTD.—See ITOCHU Corporation; *Int'l*, pg. 3838
ITOCHU CAPITAL SECURITIES, LTD.—See ITOCHU Corporation; *Int'l*, pg. 3837
ITOCHU CERATECH CORP.—See ITOCHU Corporation; *Int'l*, pg. 3837
ITOCHU CHEMICAL FRONTIER CORPORATION—See ITOCHU Corporation; *Int'l*, pg. 3837
ITOCHU CHEMICALS AMERICA INC—See ITOCHU Corporation; *Int'l*, pg. 3838
ITOCHU CHILE S.A.—See ITOCHU Corporation; *Int'l*, pg. 3837
ITOCHU (CHINA) HOLDING CO., LTD.—See ITOCHU Corporation; *Int'l*, pg. 3837
ITOCHU (CHONGQING) TRADING CO., LTD.—See ITOCHU Corporation; *Int'l*, pg. 3837
ITOCHU CONSTRUCTION MACHINERY CO., LTD.—See ITOCHU Corporation; *Int'l*, pg. 3837
ITOCHU CORPORATION - OSAKA HEADQUARTERS—See ITOCHU Corporation; *Int'l*, pg. 3837
ITOCHU CORPORATION; *Int'l*, pg. 3834
ITOCHU (DALIAN) CO., LTD.—See ITOCHU Corporation; *Int'l*, pg. 3837
ITOCHU DEUTSCHLAND GMBH—See ITOCHU Corporation; *Int'l*, pg. 3837
ITOCHU ECUADOR S.A.—See ITOCHU Corporation; *Int'l*, pg. 3837
ITOCHU ENEX CO., LTD.; *Int'l*, pg. 3841
ITOCHU ENEX HOME-LIFE HOKKAIDO CO., LTD.—See Itochu Enex Co., Ltd.; *Int'l*, pg. 3842
ITOCHU ENEX HOME-LIFE KANSAI CO., LTD.—See Itochu Enex Co., Ltd.; *Int'l*, pg. 3842
ITOCHU ENEX HOME-LIFE NISHI-NIHON CO., LTD.—See Itochu Enex Co., Ltd.; *Int'l*, pg. 3842

ITOCHU ENEX CO., LTD.

ITOCHU ENEX HOME-LIFE TOHOKU CO., LTD.—See Itochu Enex Co., Ltd.; *Int'l*, pg. 3842
ITOCHU ENEX SUPPORT CO., LTD.—See Itochu Enex Co., Ltd.; *Int'l*, pg. 3842
ITOCHU ESPANA S.A.—See ITOCHU Corporation; *Int'l*, pg. 3837
ITOCHU EUROPE PLC—See ITOCHU Corporation; *Int'l*, pg. 3837
ITOCHU FASHION SYSTEM CO., LTD.—See ITOCHU Corporation; *Int'l*, pg. 3837
ITOCHU FEED MILLS CO., LTD.—See ITOCHU Corporation; *Int'l*, pg. 3837
ITOCHU FINANCE CORPORATION—See ITOCHU Corporation; *Int'l*, pg. 3837
ITOCHU FINANCE (EUROPE) PLC—See ITOCHU Corporation; *Int'l*, pg. 3837
ITOCHU FOOD SALES & MARKETING CO., LTD.—See ITOCHU Corporation; *Int'l*, pg. 3837
ITOCHU FRANCE S.A.S.—See ITOCHU Corporation; *Int'l*, pg. 3837
ITOCHU GENERAL SERVICES INC.—See ITOCHU Corporation; *Int'l*, pg. 3837
ITOCHU GUANGZHOU LTD.—See ITOCHU Corporation; *Int'l*, pg. 3837
ITOCHU HELLAS LTD.—See ITOCHU Corporation; *Int'l*, pg. 3838
ITOCHU HONG KONG LTD.—See ITOCHU Corporation; *Int'l*, pg. 3838
ITOCHU HOUSING CO., LTD.—See ITOCHU Corporation; *Int'l*, pg. 3837
ITOCHU HUMAN RESOURCE SERVICES INC.—See ITOCHU Corporation; *Int'l*, pg. 3838
ITOCHU HUNGARY KFT.—See ITOCHU Corporation; *Int'l*, pg. 3838
ITOCHU INDIA PVT. LTD.—See ITOCHU Corporation; *Int'l*, pg. 3838
ITOCHU INDUSTRIAL GAS CO., LTD.—See Itochu Enex Co., Ltd.; *Int'l*, pg. 3842
ITOCHU INTERACTIVE CORP.—See ITOCHU Corporation; *Int'l*, pg. 3838
ITOCHU INTERNATIONAL INC.—See ITOCHU Corporation; *Int'l*, pg. 3838
ITOCHU INTERNATIONAL—See ITOCHU Corporation; *Int'l*, pg. 3838
ITOCHU IRAN CO. LTD.—See ITOCHU Corporation; *Int'l*, pg. 3838
ITOCHU ITALIANA S.P.A.—See ITOCHU Corporation; *Int'l*, pg. 3839
ITOCHU KENZAI CORPORATION—See ITOCHU Corporation; *Int'l*, pg. 3839
ITOCHU KOREA LTD.—See ITOCHU Corporation; *Int'l*, pg. 3839
ITOCHU LATIN AMERICA, S.A.—See ITOCHU Corporation; *Int'l*, pg. 3839
ITOCHU LOGISTICS (CHINA) CO., LTD.—See ITOCHU Corporation; *Int'l*, pg. 3839
ITOCHU LOGISTICS CORP.—See ITOCHU Corporation; *Int'l*, pg. 3839
ITOCHU LOGISTICS (EUROPE) GMBH.—See ITOCHU Corporation; *Int'l*, pg. 3839
ITOCHU LOGISTICS (HK) LTD.—See ITOCHU Corporation; *Int'l*, pg. 3839
ITOCHU LOGISTICS (UK) LTD.—See ITOCHU Corporation; *Int'l*, pg. 3839
ITOCHU LOGISTICS (USA) CORP.—See ITOCHU Corporation; *Int'l*, pg. 3839
ITOCHU MACHINE-TECHNOS CORPORATION—See ITOCHU Corporation; *Int'l*, pg. 3839
ITOCHU METALS CORPORATION—See ITOCHU Corporation; *Int'l*, pg. 3839
ITOCHU MEXICO S.A. DE C.V.—See ITOCHU Corporation; *Int'l*, pg. 3839
ITOCHU MIDDLE EAST FZE—See ITOCHU Corporation; *Int'l*, pg. 3839
ITOCHU MINERAL RESOURCES DEVELOPMENT CORPORATION—See ITOCHU Corporation; *Int'l*, pg. 3839
ITOCHU MINERALS & ENERGY OF AUSTRALIA PTY LTD—See ITOCHU Corporation; *Int'l*, pg. 3839
ITOCHU MODEPAL CO., LTD.—See ITOCHU Corporation; *Int'l*, pg. 3839
ITOCHU NEW ZEALAND LTD.—See ITOCHU Corporation; *Int'l*, pg. 3837
ITOCHU NIGERIA LTD.—See ITOCHU Corporation; *Int'l*, pg. 3839
ITOCHU OIL EXPLORATION CO., LTD.—See ITOCHU Corporation; *Int'l*, pg. 3839
ITOCHU ORICO INSURANCE SERVICES CO., LTD.—See ITOCHU Corporation; *Int'l*, pg. 3839
ITOCHU PETROLEUM CO., (SINGAPORE) PTE. LTD.—See ITOCHU Corporation; *Int'l*, pg. 3839
ITOCHU PLANTECH INC.—See ITOCHU Corporation; *Int'l*, pg. 3839
ITOCHU PLASTICS INC.—See ITOCHU Corporation; *Int'l*, pg. 3839
ITOCHU PLASTICS PTE., LTD.—See ITOCHU Corporation; *Int'l*, pg. 3839
ITOCHU PROPERTY DEVELOPMENT, LTD.—See ITOCHU Corporation; *Int'l*, pg. 3839

ITOCHU ENEX CO., LTD.

CORPORATE AFFILIATIONS

ITOCHU PULP & PAPER CORP.—See ITOCHU Corporation; *Int'l*, pg. 3839
ITOCHU (QINGDAO) CO., LTD.—See ITOCHU Corporation; *Int'l*, pg. 3837
ITOCHU REIT MANAGEMENT CO., LTD.—See ITOCHU Corporation; *Int'l*, pg. 3839
ITOCHU RETAIL LINK CORPORATION—See ITOCHU Corporation; *Int'l*, pg. 3840
ITOCHU SHANGHAI LTD.—See ITOCHU Corporation; *Int'l*, pg. 3837
ITOCHU SHOKUHIN CO., LTD.—See ITOCHU Corporation; *Int'l*, pg. 3840
ITOCHU SINGAPORE PTE, LTD.—See ITOCHU Corporation; *Int'l*, pg. 3840
ITOCHU SUGAR CO., LTD.—See ITOCHU Corporation; *Int'l*, pg. 3840
ITOCHU SYSTECH CORPORATION—See ITOCHU Corporation; *Int'l*, pg. 3840
ITOCHU TAIWAN CORPORATION—See ITOCHU Corporation; *Int'l*, pg. 3840
ITOCHU TECHNOLOGY VENTURES. INC.—See ITOCHU Corporation; *Int'l*, pg. 3840
ITOCHU TECHNO-SOLUTIONS CORPORATION—See ITOCHU Corporation; *Int'l*, pg. 3840
ITOCHU TECHN-SOLUTIONS AMERICA, INC.—See ITOCHU Corporation; *Int'l*, pg. 3840
ITOCHU TEXTILE PROMINENT (ASIA) LTD.—See ITOCHU Corporation; *Int'l*, pg. 3840
ITOCHU (THAILAND) LTD—See ITOCHU Corporation; *Int'l*, pg. 3837
ITOCHU TUNISIA S.A.R.L.—See ITOCHU Corporation; *Int'l*, pg. 3840
ITOCHU URBAN COMMUNITY LTD.—See ITOCHU Corporation; *Int'l*, pg. 3840
ITOCHU VENEZUELA S.A.—See ITOCHU Corporation; *Int'l*, pg. 3840
ITOCHU WINDOWS CO., LTD.—See ITOCHU Corporation; *Int'l*, pg. 3840
ITOCO, INC.; *Int'l*, pg. 3842
ITO DENKI HANBAI CO., LTD.—See IWASAKI ELECTRIC Co., Ltd.; *Int'l*, pg. 3849
ITO EN AUSTRALIA PTY LIMITED—See ITO EN Ltd; *Int'l*, pg. 3834
ITO EN (HAWAII) LLC—See ITO EN Ltd; *Int'l*, pg. 3834
ITOEN-ITOCHU MINERAL WATERS CO., LTD.—See ITO EN Ltd; *Int'l*, pg. 3834
ITO EN KANSAI-CHAGYO, LTD.—See ITO EN Ltd; *Int'l*, pg. 3834
ITO EN LTD; *Int'l*, pg. 3834
ITO EN (NORTH AMERICA) INC.—See ITO EN Ltd; *Int'l*, pg. 3834
ITO EN SANGYO, LTD.—See ITO EN Ltd; *Int'l*, pg. 3834
ITO FRESH SALAD CO., LTD.—See Itoham Yonekyu Holdings Inc.; *Int'l*, pg. 3842
ITOHAM AMERICA, INC.—See Itoham Yonekyu Holdings Inc.; *Int'l*, pg. 3842
ITOHAM DAILY INC.—See Itoham Yonekyu Holdings Inc.; *Int'l*, pg. 3842
ITOHAM FOODS, INC. - FUNABASHI PLANT—See Itoham Yonekyu Holdings Inc.; *Int'l*, pg. 3842
ITOHAM FOODS, INC. - ITOHAM DAILY OTARU PLANT—See Itoham Yonekyu Holdings Inc.; *Int'l*, pg. 3842
ITOHAM FOODS, INC. - ITOHAM DAILY TOHOKU PLANT—See Itoham Yonekyu Holdings Inc.; *Int'l*, pg. 3843
ITOHAM FOODS, INC. - ITOHAM SHOKUHIN, OYABE PLANT—See Itoham Yonekyu Holdings Inc.; *Int'l*, pg. 3843
ITOHAM FOODS, INC. - KOBE PLANT—See Itoham Yonekyu Holdings Inc.; *Int'l*, pg. 3843
ITOHAM FOODS, INC. - NISHINOMIYA PLANT—See Itoham Yonekyu Holdings Inc.; *Int'l*, pg. 3843
ITOHAM FOODS, INC. - ROKKO PLANT—See Itoham Yonekyu Holdings Inc.; *Int'l*, pg. 3843
ITOHAM FOODS, INC.—See Itoham Yonekyu Holdings Inc.; *Int'l*, pg. 3842
ITOHAM FOODS, INC. - TOKYO PLANT—See Itoham Yonekyu Holdings Inc.; *Int'l*, pg. 3843
ITOHAM FOODS, INC. - TOYOHASHI PLANT—See Itoham Yonekyu Holdings Inc.; *Int'l*, pg. 3843
ITOHAM FOODS, INC. - WEST KYUSHU PLANT—See Itoham Yonekyu Holdings Inc.; *Int'l*, pg. 3843
ITOHAM YONEKYU HOLDINGS INC.; *Int'l*, pg. 3842
ITOH KOZAI CO., LTD.—See Nippon Steel Corporation; *Int'l*, pg. 5337
ITOHPIA HOME CO., LTD.—See ITOCHU Corporation; *Int'l*, pg. 3840
I TO I INTERNATIONAL PROJECTS LTD—See TUI AG; *Int'l*, pg. 7965
I-TO-I UK LIMITED—See TUI AG; *Int'l*, pg. 7969
ITOKI CORPORATION - INTERNATIONAL DIVISION—See Itoki Corporation; *Int'l*, pg. 3843
ITOKI CORPORATION - NY DESIGN BRANCH—See Itoki Corporation; *Int'l*, pg. 3843
ITOKI CORPORATION; *Int'l*, pg. 3843
ITOKI MALAYSIA SDN. BHD.—See Itoki Corporation; *Int'l*, pg. 3843

ITOKI MODERNFORM CO., LTD.—See Itoki Corporation; *Int'l*, pg. 3843
ITOKI (SHANGHAI) CORPORATION—See Itoki Corporation; *Int'l*, pg. 3843
ITOKI (SUZHOU) FURNITURE CO., LTD.—See Itoki Corporation; *Int'l*, pg. 3843
ITOKI SYSTEMS (SINGAPORE) PTE., LTD.—See Itoki Corporation; *Int'l*, pg. 3843
ITOKI (THAILAND) CO., LTD.—See Itoki Corporation; *Int'l*, pg. 3843
ITOKK, INC.; *U.S. Public*, pg. 1175
ITOKURO INC.; *Int'l*, pg. 3844
IT-ONE CO., LTD.—See Mitsubishi Research Institute, Inc.; *Int'l*, pg. 4968
ITONIS, INC.; *U.S. Public*, pg. 1175
ITOPIA ASSET MANAGEMENT CO., LTD.—See ITOCHU Corporation; *Int'l*, pg. 3840
ITOUCH LTD.—See Nippon Telegraph & Telephone Corporation; *Int'l*, pg. 5349
ITOUCH MOVILISTO PORTUGAL LDA.—See Nippon Telegraph & Telephone Corporation; *Int'l*, pg. 5349
ITOWNSTORE LLC; *U.S. Private*, pg. 2150
ITOXI CORP.; *Int'l*, pg. 3844
ITOX, LLC—See DFI Inc.; *Int'l*, pg. 2095
ITO YOGYO CO., LTD.; *Int'l*, pg. 3834
ITO-YOKADO CO., LTD.—See Seven & i Holdings Co., Ltd.; *Int'l*, pg. 6731
IT PEOPLE CORPORATION, INC.; *U.S. Private*, pg. 2148
ITP GMBH—See Renishaw plc; *Int'l*, pg. 6283
IT PROPHETS, LLC; *U.S. Private*, pg. 2148
THE IT PROS; *U.S. Private*, pg. 4057
IT PUBLICATIONS HELLAS LTD—See Liberis Publications SA; *Int'l*, pg. 4483
ITQAN CAPITAL—See Al Baraka Banking Group B.S.C.; *Int'l*, pg. 276
ITRAC LLC—See 424 Capital, LLC; *U.S. Private*, pg. 15
ITRAC LLC—See HealthEdge Investment Partners, LLC; *U.S. Private*, pg. 1896
ITRACS CORP.—See CommScope Holding Company, Inc.; *U.S. Public*, pg. 549
ITRADEFAIR.COM, INC.; *U.S. Private*, pg. 2150
ITRADENETWORK, INC.—See Roper Technologies, Inc.; *U.S. Public*, pg. 1814
ITRADENETWORK, LTD.—See Roper Technologies, Inc.; *U.S. Public*, pg. 1814
ITR CONCESSION COMPANY LLC—See Industry Super Holdings Pty. Ltd.; *Int'l*, pg. 3676
ITR CORP.—See ITOCHU Corporation; *Int'l*, pg. 3840
ITR D.O.O.—See INA-Industrija Nafte, d.d.; *Int'l*, pg. 3642
IT RE-ENGINEERING PTE. LTD.—See PEC Ltd.; *Int'l*, pg. 5778
ITRENEW, INC.—See Iron Mountain Incorporated; *U.S. Public*, pg. 1172
IT RESOURCES CORP.; *U.S. Private*, pg. 2148
IT RETAIL, INC.—See Dura Software Series A Qof LLC; *U.S. Private*, pg. 1292
ITR INDUSTRIES INC.; *U.S. Private*, pg. 2150
I&T RISK SOLUTIONS CO., LTD.—See ITOCHU Corporation; *Int'l*, pg. 3836
ITRON ARGENTINA S.A.—See Itron, Inc.; *U.S. Public*, pg. 1176
ITRON-AUSTRALASIA PTY LIMITED—See Itron, Inc.; *U.S. Public*, pg. 1176
ITRON AUSTRIA GMBH—See Itron, Inc.; *U.S. Public*, pg. 1176
ITRON BV—See Itron, Inc.; *U.S. Public*, pg. 1176
ITRON CANADA, INC.—See Itron, Inc.; *U.S. Public*, pg. 1176
ITRON CZECH REPUBLIC S.R.O.—See Itron, Inc.; *U.S. Public*, pg. 1176
ITRON DISTRIBUCION S.A. DE C.V.—See Itron, Inc.; *U.S. Public*, pg. 1176
ITRON FRANCE S.A.S.—See Itron, Inc.; *U.S. Public*, pg. 1176
ITRON GMBH—See Itron, Inc.; *U.S. Public*, pg. 1176
ITRON HOLDING GERMANY GMBH—See Itron, Inc.; *U.S. Public*, pg. 1176
ITRONICS INC.; *U.S. Public*, pg. 1176
ITRONICS METALLURGICAL, INC.—See Itronics Inc.; *U.S. Public*, pg. 1176
ITRON, INC. - OAKLAND—See Itron, Inc.; *U.S. Public*, pg. 1176
ITRON, INC.; *U.S. Public*, pg. 1175
ITRON INDIA PRIVATE LIMITED—See Itron, Inc.; *U.S. Public*, pg. 1176
ITRON ITALIA SPA—See Itron, Inc.; *U.S. Public*, pg. 1176
ITRONIX CORPORATION—See General Dynamics Corporation; *U.S. Public*, pg. 916
ITRONIX UK—See General Dynamics Corporation; *U.S. Public*, pg. 916
ITRON JAPAN CO., LTD.—See Itron, Inc.; *U.S. Public*, pg. 1176
ITRON LIQUID MEASUREMENT—See Itron, Inc.; *U.S. Public*, pg. 1176
ITRON LLC—See Itron, Inc.; *U.S. Public*, pg. 1176
ITRON MANAGEMENT SERVICES IRELAND, LIMITED—See Itron, Inc.; *U.S. Public*, pg. 1176
ITRON MEASUREMENTS & SYSTEMS (PROPRIETARY) LIMITED—See Itron, Inc.; *U.S. Public*, pg. 1176

ITRON METERING SOLUTIONS UK LTD—See Itron, Inc.; *U.S. Public*, pg. 1176
ITRON METERING SOLUTIONS UK LTD—See Itron, Inc.; *U.S. Public*, pg. 1176
ITRON METERING SYSTEMS (CHONGQING) CO., LTD.—See Itron, Inc.; *U.S. Public*, pg. 1176
ITRON METERING SYSTEMS SINGAPORE PTE LTD.—See Itron, Inc.; *U.S. Public*, pg. 1176
ITRON METERING SYSTEMS (SUZHOU) CO., LTD.—See Itron, Inc.; *U.S. Public*, pg. 1176
ITRON NEDERLAND B.V.—See Itron, Inc.; *U.S. Public*, pg. 1176
ITRON POLSKA SP. Z O.O.—See Itron, Inc.; *U.S. Public*, pg. 1176
ITRON PORTUGAL, UNIPESSOAL, LDA.—See Itron, Inc.; *U.S. Public*, pg. 1176
ITRON SISTEMAS DE MEDICAO LDA.—See Itron, Inc.; *U.S. Public*, pg. 1176
ITRON SOLUCIONES DE MEDIDA ESPANA SL—See Itron, Inc.; *U.S. Public*, pg. 1176
ITRON SOLUCOES PARA ENERGIA E AGUA LTDA.—See Itron, Inc.; *U.S. Public*, pg. 1176
ITRON SPAIN SLU—See Itron, Inc.; *U.S. Public*, pg. 1176
ITRON SWEDEN AB—See Itron, Inc.; *U.S. Public*, pg. 1176
ITRON (U.K.) LIMITED—See Noritake Co., Limited; *Int'l*, pg. 5428
ITRON UKRAINE—See Itron, Inc.; *U.S. Public*, pg. 1176
ITRON UNTERSTUTZUNGSKASSE GMBH—See Itron, Inc.; *U.S. Public*, pg. 1176
ITRON US GAS, LLC—See Itron, Inc.; *U.S. Public*, pg. 1176
ITRON ZAHLER & SYSTEMTECHNIK GMBH—See Itron, Inc.; *U.S. Public*, pg. 1176
ITRS GROUP LTD.—See TA Associates, Inc.; *U.S. Private*, pg. 3916
I-TRUE COMMUNICATIONS INC.—See istyle, Inc.; *Int'l*, pg. 3825
ITSAVVY LLC—See GenNx360 Capital Partners, L.P.; *U.S. Private*, pg. 1672
ITSBCHAIN, LLC—See IQSTEL Inc.; *U.S. Public*, pg. 1167
ITSCOPE GMBH—See 3U Holding AG; *Int'l*, pg. 10
ITS CORPORATION—See Kowa Co., Ltd.; *Int'l*, pg. 4294
ITSEMAP MEXICO, SERVICOS TECNOLOGICOS MAPFRE, S.A.—See MAPFRE S.A.; *Int'l*, pg. 4685
ITSEMAP S.A.—See MAPFRE S.A.; *Int'l*, pg. 4684
ITSEMAP VENEZUELA, SERVICOS TECNOLOGICOS MAPFRE, S.A.—See MAPFRE S.A.; *Int'l*, pg. 4685
ITS. FARM CO., LTD.—See ITOCHU Corporation; *Int'l*, pg. 3840
IT'S GREEK TO ME, INC.—See Hanesbrands Inc.; *U.S. Public*, pg. 983
ITS GROUP BENELUX SPRL—See ITS Group SA; *Int'l*, pg. 3844
ITS GROUP SA; *Int'l*, pg. 3844
IT'S HANBUL CO., LTD.—See Jumei International Holding Limited; *Int'l*, pg. 4026
ITSHOT.COM; *U.S. Private*, pg. 2150
ITS - INDUSTRIA TRANSFORMADORA DE SUBPRODUTOS ANIMAIS, S.A.—See SODIM, SGPS, SA; *Int'l*, pg. 7049
ITS INGENIEURGESELLSCHAFT MBH—See BKW AG; *Int'l*, pg. 1055
I.T.'S. INTERNATIONAL CO., LTD.—See Nippon Steel Corporation; *Int'l*, pg. 5337
IT'S JUST LUNCH INTERNATIONAL LLC—See The Riverside Company; *U.S. Private*, pg. 4109
I.T. SKILLFINDER LTD—See Skillfinder International Limited; *Int'l*, pg. 6986
ITS KONSORTIUM SDN. BHD.—See Muhibbah Engineering (M) Bhd.; *Int'l*, pg. 5078
ITSLEARNING AB—See Sanoma Oyj; *Int'l*, pg. 6553
ITSLEARNING A/S—See Sanoma Oyj; *Int'l*, pg. 6553
ITSLEARNING FRANCE S.A.—See Sanoma Oyj; *Int'l*, pg. 6553
ITSLEARNING GMBH—See Sanoma Oyj; *Int'l*, pg. 6553
ITSLEARNING NEDERLAND B.V.—See Sanoma Oyj; *Int'l*, pg. 6553
ITSLEARNING UK LTD.—See Sanoma Oyj; *Int'l*, pg. 6553
ITS LOGISTICS, INC.—See GHK Capital Partners LP; *U.S. Private*, pg. 1690
ITS MAGHIELSE LLC—See International Tooling Solutions LLC; *U.S. Private*, pg. 2121
ITS NETHERLANDS B.V.—See Parker Wellbore Company; *U.S. Public*, pg. 1650
IT SOLUTIONS CONSULTING LLC; *U.S. Private*, pg. 2148
IT SOLUTIONS, INC.; *U.S. Private*, pg. 2148
ITSOLUTIONS NET INC.—See MAXIMUS, Inc.; *U.S. Public*, pg. 1402
IT SONIX CUSTOM DEVELOPMENT GMBH—See Adecco Group AG; *Int'l*, pg. 140
I.T. SOURCE; *U.S. Private*, pg. 2027
ITSOURCE TECHNOLOGY INC.; *U.S. Private*, pg. 2150
ITS PARTNERS, LLC; *U.S. Private*, pg. 2150
ITS SCIENCE & MEDICAL PTE. LTD.—See HORIBA Ltd; *Int'l*, pg. 3477
ITS TECHNOLOGIES & LOGISTICS, LLC—See AMP Limited; *Int'l*, pg. 432

COMPANY NAME INDEX

ITS TESTING HOLDINGS CANADA LIMITED—See Intertek Group plc; *Int'l*, pg. 3762
IT'SUGAR LLC.—See Hilton Grand Vacations Inc.; *U.S. Public*, pg. 1039
ITSUMO, INC.; *Int'l*, pg. 3844
ITT AEROSPACE CONTROLS LLC—See ITT Inc.; *U.S. Public*, pg. 1177
ITTAR-IPP (PJ) SDN. BHD.—See KUB Malaysia Berhad; *Int'l*, pg. 4319
ITTAR SDN BHD—See KUB Malaysia Berhad; *Int'l*, pg. 4319
ITT BIW CONNECTOR SYSTEMS, LLC—See ITT Inc.; *U.S. Public*, pg. 1177
ITT BLAKERS PTY LTD—See ITT Inc.; *U.S. Public*, pg. 1177
ITT BOMBAS GOULDS DO BRASIL LTDA.—See ITT Inc.; *U.S. Public*, pg. 1177
ITT BORNEMANN GMBH—See ITT Inc.; *U.S. Public*, pg. 1177
ITT BRASIL EQUIPAMENTOSPARA BOMBEAMENTO E TRATAMENTO DE AGUA E EFLUENTES LTDA—See ITT Inc.; *U.S. Public*, pg. 1177
ITT CANNON DE MEXICO S.A. DE C.V.—See ITT Inc.; *U.S. Public*, pg. 1177
ITT CANNON GMBH—See ITT Inc.; *U.S. Public*, pg. 1177
ITT CANNON INTERNATIONAL, INC.—See ITT Inc.; *U.S. Public*, pg. 1177
ITT CANNON KOREA LTD.—See ITT Inc.; *U.S. Public*, pg. 1177
ITT CANNON VEAM ITALIA S.R.L.—See ITT Inc.; *U.S. Public*, pg. 1177
ITT COMMUNITY DEVELOPMENT CORP.—See ITT Inc.; *U.S. Public*, pg. 1178
ITT CONTROL TECHNOLOGIES EMEA GMBH—See ITT Inc.; *U.S. Public*, pg. 1178
ITT CONTROL TECHNOLOGIES GMBH—See ITT Inc.; *U.S. Public*, pg. 1178
ITT CORP. - NEWTON—See ITT Inc.; *U.S. Public*, pg. 1178
ITT CORPORATION INDIA PVT. LTD.—See ITT Inc.; *U.S. Public*, pg. 1178
ITT CORP. - SANTA ANA—See ITT Inc.; *U.S. Public*, pg. 1178
ITT CORP. - SUMTER—See ITT Inc.; *U.S. Public*, pg. 1178
ITT C'TREAT LLC—See ITT Inc.; *U.S. Public*, pg. 1177
ITT DELAWARE INVESTMENTS INC.—See ITT Inc.; *U.S. Public*, pg. 1178
IT TECH PACKAGING, INC.; *Int'l*, pg. 3827
ITT EDUCATIONAL SERVICES, INC.; *U.S. Private*, pg. 2150
ITTEFAQ IRON INDUSTRIES LTD.; *Int'l*, pg. 3844
ITTEHAD CHEMICALS LIMITED; *Int'l*, pg. 3844
I.T. TELECOM S.R.L.—See TIM S.p.A.; *Int'l*, pg. 7749
ITT ENGINEERED VALVES, LLC—See ITT Inc.; *U.S. Public*, pg. 1178
ITT ENIDINE INC.—See ITT Inc.; *U.S. Public*, pg. 1178
ITT FLUID TECHNOLOGY ASIA PTE LTD—See ITT Inc.; *U.S. Public*, pg. 1178
ITT FLUID TECHNOLOGY INTERNATIONAL, INC.—See ITT Inc.; *U.S. Public*, pg. 1178
ITT GOULDS PUMPS COLUMBIA S.A.S.—See ITT Inc.; *U.S. Public*, pg. 1178
ITT HIGH PRECISION MANUFACTURED PRODUCTS (WUXI) CO., LTD.—See ITT Inc.; *U.S. Public*, pg. 1178
ITTIERRE ACCESSORIES S.P.A.—See IT Holding S.p.A.; *Int'l*, pg. 3826
ITTIERRE S.P.A.—See IT Holding S.p.A.; *Int'l*, pg. 3826
ITTIHAD SCHOOLS CO P.L.C.; *Int'l*, pg. 3844
ITT INC.; *U.S. Public*, pg. 1177
ITT INDUSTRIES ENGINEERED PRODUCTS DIVISION—See ITT Inc.; *U.S. Public*, pg. 1178
ITT INDUSTRIES INC.—See ITT Inc.; *U.S. Public*, pg. 1178
ITT INDUSTRIES INC.—See ITT Inc.; *U.S. Public*, pg. 1178
ITT INDUSTRIES INC.—See ITT Inc.; *U.S. Public*, pg. 1178
ITT INDUSTRIES INC.—See ITT Inc.; *U.S. Public*, pg. 1178
ITT INDUSTRIES INC.—See ITT Inc.; *U.S. Public*, pg. 1178
ITT INDUSTRIES INC.—See ITT Inc.; *U.S. Public*, pg. 1178
ITT INDUSTRIES SPAIN SL—See ITT Inc.; *U.S. Public*, pg. 1178
ITT ITALIA S.R.L.—See ITT Inc.; *U.S. Public*, pg. 1178
ITT KOREA HOLDING B.V.—See ITT Inc.; *U.S. Public*, pg. 1178
ITT PURE-FLO (UK) LTD.—See ITT Inc.; *U.S. Public*, pg. 1178
ITT RHEINHUTTE BENELUX B.V.—See ITT Inc.; *U.S. Public*, pg. 1178
ITT RHEINHUTTE PUMPEN CO., LTD.—See ITT Inc.; *U.S. Public*, pg. 1178
ITT RHEINHUTTE PUMPEN GMBH—See ITT Inc.; *U.S. Public*, pg. 1178
ITT-USA, INC.—See Macquarie Group Limited; *Int'l*, pg. 4624

ITT VEAM LLC—See ITT Inc.; *U.S. Public*, pg. 1178
ITT-VIRGINIA, INC.—See Macquarie Group Limited; *Int'l*, pg. 4624
ITT WATER & WASTEWATER U.S.A., INC.—See ITT Inc.; *U.S. Public*, pg. 1178
ITTY, INC.—See TV Asahi Holdings Corporation; *Int'l*, pg. 7986
ITU ABSORBTECH, INC.; *U.S. Private*, pg. 2150
ITUB AS—See Berry Global Group, Inc; *U.S. Public*, pg. 326
ITUB DANMARK APS—See Berry Global Group, Inc; *U.S. Public*, pg. 326
ITUB EHF—See Berry Global Group, Inc; *U.S. Public*, pg. 322
ITUBOMBAS LOCACAO COMERCIO IMPORTACAO E EXPORTACAO LTDA.—See Atlas Copco AB; *Int'l*, pg. 683
ITUMA GMBH—See Datatec Limited; *Int'l*, pg. 1980
ITURAN ARGENTINA—See ITURAN Location & Control Ltd.; *Int'l*, pg. 3844
ITURAN BRAZIL—See ITURAN Location & Control Ltd.; *Int'l*, pg. 3844
ITURAN LOCATION & CONTROL LTD.; *Int'l*, pg. 3844
ITURAN USA LIFETRAK—See ITURAN Location & Control Ltd.; *Int'l*, pg. 3844
I'TUR GMBH—See TUI AG; *Int'l*, pg. 7965
IT USA INC.; *U.S. Private*, pg. 2148
ITUS—See A.A.G. STUCCHI s.r.l.; *Int'l*, pg. 23
ITUS VERWALTUNGS AG—See Munchener Ruckversicherungs AG; *Int'l*, pg. 5089
ITUX COMMUNICATION AB—See Tele2 AB; *Int'l*, pg. 7529
ITV-3, LLC—See Kuwait Investment Authority; *Int'l*, pg. 4345
ITV AMERICA INC.—See ITV plc; *Int'l*, pg. 3845
ITV ANGLIA—See ITV plc; *Int'l*, pg. 3845
ITVANTAGE, INC.—See Digerati Technologies, Inc.; *U.S. Public*, pg. 661
ITV BREAKFAST LIMITED—See ITV plc; *Int'l*, pg. 3845
ITV GLOBAL ENTERTAINMENT LIMITED—See ITV plc; *Int'l*, pg. 3845
ITV GMBH; *Int'l*, pg. 3844
ITV MERIDIAN—See ITV plc; *Int'l*, pg. 3845
ITV PLC; *Int'l*, pg. 3844
ITV PUBLIC COMPANY LIMITED; *Int'l*, pg. 3845
ITV SA—See SGS SA; *Int'l*, pg. 6743
ITV STUDIOS AUSTRALIA PTY LIMITED—See ITV plc; *Int'l*, pg. 3845
ITV STUDIOS GERMANY GMBH—See ITV plc; *Int'l*, pg. 3845
ITV STUDIOS HOLDING B.V.—See ITV plc; *Int'l*, pg. 3845
ITV STUDIOS, INC—See ITV plc; *Int'l*, pg. 3845
ITV STUDIOS LIMITED—See ITV plc; *Int'l*, pg. 3845
ITV STUDIOS NORWAY AS—See ITV plc; *Int'l*, pg. 3845
ITV STUDIOS SWEDEN AB—See ITV plc; *Int'l*, pg. 3845
ITV TYNE TEES TELEVISION—See ITV plc; *Int'l*, pg. 3845
ITV WALES—See ITV plc; *Int'l*, pg. 3845
ITW AIR MANAGEMENT—See Illinois Tool Works Inc.; *U.S. Public*, pg. 1104
ITW ANGLEBOARD AB—See Illinois Tool Works Inc.; *U.S. Public*, pg. 1104
ITW APPLIANCE COMPONENTS D.O.O.—See Illinois Tool Works Inc.; *U.S. Public*, pg. 1104
ITW ARK-LES CORPORATION—See Illinois Tool Works Inc.; *U.S. Public*, pg. 1104
ITW AUSTRALIA PROPERTY HOLDINGS PTY LTD.—See Illinois Tool Works Inc.; *U.S. Public*, pg. 1104
ITW AUSTRALIA PTY. LTD.—See Illinois Tool Works Inc.; *U.S. Public*, pg. 1104
ITW AUTOMOTIVE COMPONENTS (LANGFANG) CO., LTD.—See Illinois Tool Works Inc.; *U.S. Public*, pg. 1104
ITW AUTOMOTIVE FINISHING—See Illinois Tool Works Inc.; *U.S. Public*, pg. 1104
ITW AUTOMOTIVE KOREA, LLC—See Illinois Tool Works Inc.; *U.S. Public*, pg. 1104
ITW AUTOMOTIVE PRODUCTS GMBH—See Illinois Tool Works Inc.; *U.S. Public*, pg. 1104
ITW AUTOMOTIVE PRODUCTS MEXICO, S. DE R.L. DE C.V.—See Illinois Tool Works Inc.; *U.S. Public*, pg. 1104
ITW AUTO WAX COMPANY, INC.—See Illinois Tool Works Inc.; *U.S. Public*, pg. 1104
ITWAY FRANCE S.A.R.L.—See Itway S.p.A.; *Int'l*, pg. 3846
ITWAY HELLAS S.A.—See Itway S.p.A.; *Int'l*, pg. 3846
ITWAY IBERICA S.L.—See Itway S.p.A.; *Int'l*, pg. 3846
ITWAY S.P.A.; *Int'l*, pg. 3845
ITWAY VAD—See Esprinet S.p.A.; *Int'l*, pg. 2506
ITWAYVAD S.R.L.—See Itway S.p.A.; *Int'l*, pg. 3846
ITW BAILLY COMTE S.A.S.—See Illinois Tool Works Inc.; *U.S. Public*, pg. 1104
ITW BEFESTIGUNGSSYSTEME ALPEN GMBH—See Illinois Tool Works Inc.; *U.S. Public*, pg. 1104
ITW BEFESTIGUNGSSYSTEME GMBH—See Illinois Tool Works Inc.; *U.S. Public*, pg. 1104
ITW BELGIUM S.P.R.L.—See Illinois Tool Works Inc.; *U.S. Public*, pg. 1104
ITW BRANDS—See Illinois Tool Works Inc.; *U.S. Public*, pg. 1104

ITW BUILDEX—See Illinois Tool Works Inc.; *U.S. Public*, pg. 1104
ITW BUILDEX—See Illinois Tool Works Inc.; *U.S. Public*, pg. 1104
ITW BUILDING COMPONENTS GROUP INC.—See Illinois Tool Works Inc.; *U.S. Public*, pg. 1104
ITW CANADA INVESTMENTS LIMITED PARTNERSHIP—See Illinois Tool Works Inc.; *U.S. Public*, pg. 1105
ITW CANADA MANAGEMENT COMPANY—See Illinois Tool Works Inc.; *U.S. Public*, pg. 1105
ITW CER—See Illinois Tool Works Inc.; *U.S. Public*, pg. 1105
ITW CHEMICAL PRODUCTS LTDA—See Illinois Tool Works Inc.; *U.S. Public*, pg. 1105
ITW CHEMICAL PRODUCTS SCANDINAVIA APS—See Illinois Tool Works Inc.; *U.S. Public*, pg. 1105
ITW CHEMTRONICS—See Blackstone Inc.; *U.S. Public*, pg. 354
ITW CODING PRODUCTS—See Illinois Tool Works Inc.; *U.S. Public*, pg. 1105
ITW COLOMBIA S.A.S.—See Illinois Tool Works Inc.; *U.S. Public*, pg. 1105
ITW CONSTRUCTION PRODUCTS AB—See Illinois Tool Works Inc.; *U.S. Public*, pg. 1105
ITW CONSTRUCTION PRODUCTS APS—See Illinois Tool Works Inc.; *U.S. Public*, pg. 1105
ITW CONSTRUCTION PRODUCTS AS—See Illinois Tool Works Inc.; *U.S. Public*, pg. 1105
ITW CONSTRUCTION PRODUCTS CZ S.R.O.—See Illinois Tool Works Inc.; *U.S. Public*, pg. 1105
ITW CONSTRUCTION PRODUCTS ESPANA S.A.—See Illinois Tool Works Inc.; *U.S. Public*, pg. 1105
ITW CONSTRUCTION PRODUCTS ITALY SRL—See Illinois Tool Works Inc.; *U.S. Public*, pg. 1105
ITW CONSTRUCTION PRODUCTS OU—See Illinois Tool Works Inc.; *U.S. Public*, pg. 1105
ITW CONSTRUCTION PRODUCTS OY—See Illinois Tool Works Inc.; *U.S. Public*, pg. 1105
ITW CONSTRUCTION PRODUCTS (SINGAPORE) PTE. LTD.—See Illinois Tool Works Inc.; *U.S. Public*, pg. 1105
ITW CONSTRUCTION PRODUCTS—See Illinois Tool Works Inc.; *U.S. Public*, pg. 1105
ITW CONSTRUCTION PRODUCTS UK—See Illinois Tool Works Inc.; *U.S. Public*, pg. 1105
ITW CONSTRUCTION PRODUCTS UK—See Illinois Tool Works Inc.; *U.S. Public*, pg. 1105
ITW CONTAMINATION CONTROL B.V.—See Illinois Tool Works Inc.; *U.S. Public*, pg. 1105
ITW COVID SECURITY GROUP INC.—See Illinois Tool Works Inc.; *U.S. Public*, pg. 1105
ITW CP DISTRIBUTION CENTER HOLLAND BV—See Illinois Tool Works Inc.; *U.S. Public*, pg. 1105
ITW CPM S.A.S.—See Illinois Tool Works Inc.; *U.S. Public*, pg. 1105
ITW DE FRANCE S.A.S.—See Illinois Tool Works Inc.; *U.S. Public*, pg. 1108
ITW DELFAST DO BRASIL LTDA.—See Illinois Tool Works Inc.; *U.S. Public*, pg. 1105
ITW DENMARK APS—See Illinois Tool Works Inc.; *U.S. Public*, pg. 1105
ITW (DEUTSCHLAND) GMBH—See Illinois Tool Works Inc.; *U.S. Public*, pg. 1104
ITW DEVCON FUTURA COATINGS—See Illinois Tool Works Inc.; *U.S. Public*, pg. 1105
ITW DEVCON JAPAN—See Illinois Tool Works Inc.; *U.S. Public*, pg. 1105
ITW DEVCON—See Illinois Tool Works Inc.; *U.S. Public*, pg. 1105
ITW DO BRASIL INDUSTRIAL E COMERCIAL LTDA.—See Illinois Tool Works Inc.; *U.S. Public*, pg. 1108
ITW DRAWFORM—See Illinois Tool Works Inc.; *U.S. Public*, pg. 1106
ITW DYMON—See Illinois Tool Works Inc.; *U.S. Public*, pg. 1105
ITW DYNATEC ADHESIVE EQUIPMENT (SUZHOU) CO. LTD.—See Illinois Tool Works Inc.; *U.S. Public*, pg. 1105
ITW DYNATEC G.M.B.H.—See Illinois Tool Works Inc.; *U.S. Public*, pg. 1105
ITW DYNATEC KABUSHIKI KAISHA—See Illinois Tool Works Inc.; *U.S. Public*, pg. 1105
ITW DYNATEC—See Illinois Tool Works Inc.; *U.S. Public*, pg. 1105
ITW DYNATEC—See Illinois Tool Works Inc.; *U.S. Public*, pg. 1105
ITW EAE MEXICO, S DE RL DE CV—See Illinois Tool Works Inc.; *U.S. Public*, pg. 1105
ITW EF&C FRANCE SAS—See Illinois Tool Works Inc.; *U.S. Public*, pg. 1105
ITW EF&C SELB GMBH—See Illinois Tool Works Inc.; *U.S. Public*, pg. 1105
ITW ELECTRONIC BUSINESS ASIA CO., LIMITED—See Illinois Tool Works Inc.; *U.S. Public*, pg. 1105
ITW ELECTRONICS (SUZHOU) CO., LTD.—See Illinois Tool Works Inc.; *U.S. Public*, pg. 1105

ITWAY S.P.A.   CORPORATE AFFILIATIONS

ITW ESPANA, S.A.—See Illinois Tool Works Inc.; *U.S. Public*, pg. 1105
ITW - EVERCOAT—See Illinois Tool Works Inc.; *U.S. Public*, pg. 1104
ITW FASTEX—See Illinois Tool Works Inc.; *U.S. Public*, pg. 1105
ITW FEG HONG KONG LIMITED—See Illinois Tool Works Inc.; *U.S. Public*, pg. 1105
ITW FOILMARK—See Illinois Tool Works Inc.; *U.S. Public*, pg. 1105
ITW FOILS B.V.—See Illinois Tool Works Inc.; *U.S. Public*, pg. 1106
ITW FOILS—See Illinois Tool Works Inc.; *U.S. Public*, pg. 1105
ITW FOOD EQUIPMENT GROUP LLC—See Illinois Tool Works Inc.; *U.S. Public*, pg. 1106
ITW GERMAN REAL ESTATE MANAGEMENT GMBH & CO. KG—See Illinois Tool Works Inc.; *U.S. Public*, pg. 1106
ITW GLOBAL INVESTMENTS INC.—See Illinois Tool Works Inc.; *U.S. Public*, pg. 1106
ITW GLOBAL TIRE REPAIR EUROPE GMBH—See Illinois Tool Works Inc.; *U.S. Public*, pg. 1106
ITW GLOBAL TIRE REPAIR INC.—See Illinois Tool Works Inc.; *U.S. Public*, pg. 1106
ITW GRAPHICS ASIA LIMITED—See Illinois Tool Works Inc.; *U.S. Public*, pg. 1106
ITW GRAPHICS KOREA CO. LTD.—See Illinois Tool Works Inc.; *U.S. Public*, pg. 1106
ITW GRAPHICS—See Illinois Tool Works Inc.; *U.S. Public*, pg. 1106
ITW GRAPHICS (THAILAND) LTD.—See Illinois Tool Works Inc.; *U.S. Public*, pg. 1106
ITW GSE APS—See Illinois Tool Works Inc.; *U.S. Public*, pg. 1106
ITW GSE INC.—See Illinois Tool Works Inc.; *U.S. Public*, pg. 1103
ITW GUNTHER S.A.S.—See Illinois Tool Works Inc.; *U.S. Public*, pg. 1106
ITW HEARTLAND GEARS—See Illinois Tool Works Inc.; *U.S. Public*, pg. 1106
ITW HEARTLAND - STANDARD MACHINES—See Illinois Tool Works Inc.; *U.S. Public*, pg. 1106
ITW HI-CONE—See Illinois Tool Works Inc.; *U.S. Public*, pg. 1106
ITW HIGHLAND—See Illinois Tool Works Inc.; *U.S. Public*, pg. 1106
ITW IMAGEDATA—See Illinois Tool Works Inc.; *U.S. Public*, pg. 1106
ITW IMTRAN—See Illinois Tool Works Inc.; *U.S. Public*, pg. 1106
I.T.W. INC.—See Illinois Tool Works Inc.; *U.S. Public*, pg. 1104
ITW INDIA LIMITED—See Illinois Tool Works Inc.; *U.S. Public*, pg. 1106
ITW INDUSTRIAL FINISHING—See Illinois Tool Works Inc.; *U.S. Public*, pg. 1106
ITW INDUSTRY B.V.—See Illinois Tool Works Inc.; *U.S. Public*, pg. 1106
ITW INSULATION SYSTEMS MALAYSIA SDN BHD—See Illinois Tool Works Inc.; *U.S. Public*, pg. 1106
ITWIN TECHNOLOGY SDN, BHD.—See Cabnet Holding Berhad; *Int'l*, pg. 1246
ITW INTERNATIONAL HOLDINGS LLC—See Illinois Tool Works Inc.; *U.S. Public*, pg. 1106
ITW IRELAND—See Illinois Tool Works Inc.; *U.S. Public*, pg. 1106
ITW JAPAN LTD.—See Illinois Tool Works Inc.; *U.S. Public*, pg. 1106
ITW LIMITED—See Illinois Tool Works Inc.; *U.S. Public*, pg. 1106
ITW LLC & CO. KG—See Illinois Tool Works Inc.; *U.S. Public*, pg. 1106
ITW LYS FUSION S.R.L.—See Illinois Tool Works Inc.; *U.S. Public*, pg. 1106
ITW MAGNAFLUX—See Illinois Tool Works Inc.; *U.S. Public*, pg. 1106
ITW MARKING & CODING (SHANGHAI) CO., LTD.—See Illinois Tool Works Inc.; *U.S. Public*, pg. 1106
ITW MEDICAL PRODUCTS INC—See Illinois Tool Works Inc.; *U.S. Public*, pg. 1106
ITW MERITEX SDN. BHD.—See Illinois Tool Works Inc.; *U.S. Public*, pg. 1106
ITW METAL FASTENERS, S.L.—See Illinois Tool Works Inc.; *U.S. Public*, pg. 1106
ITW MIMA SYSTEMS S.A.S.—See Illinois Tool Works Inc.; *U.S. Public*, pg. 1106
ITW MORLOCK GMBH—See Illinois Tool Works Inc.; *U.S. Public*, pg. 1106
ITW MORTGAGE INVESTMENTS II, INC.—See Illinois Tool Works Inc.; *U.S. Public*, pg. 1106
ITW MOTION—See Illinois Tool Works Inc.; *U.S. Public*, pg. 1106
ITW MULLER—See Illinois Tool Works Inc.; *U.S. Public*, pg. 1106
ITW NEW ZEALAND LIMITED—See Illinois Tool Works Inc.; *U.S. Public*, pg. 1106
ITW NEXUS—See Illinois Tool Works Inc.; *U.S. Public*, pg. 1106

ITW NEXUS UK—See Illinois Tool Works Inc.; *U.S. Public*, pg. 1106
ITW (NINGBO) COMPONENTS & FASTENINGS SYSTEMS CO., LTD.—See Illinois Tool Works Inc.; *U.S. Public*, pg. 1106
IT WORKS! GLOBAL, INC.; *U.S. Private*, pg. 2148
IT WORKS INTERNET PTE. LTD.—See Dreamscape Networks Limited; *Int'l*, pg. 2203
I.T. WORKS RECRUITMENT INC.; *U.S. Private*, pg. 2027
IT WORKS S.A.—See Enterprise Investors Sp. z o.o.; *Int'l*, pg. 2452
ITW PACKAGING (SHANGHAI) CO., LTD.—See Crown Holdings, Inc.; *U.S. Public*, pg. 599
ITW PERFORMANCE PLASTIC (SHANGHAI) CO. LTD.—See Illinois Tool Works Inc.; *U.S. Public*, pg. 1106
ITW PERFORMANCE POLYMERS APS—See Illinois Tool Works Inc.; *U.S. Public*, pg. 1107
ITW PERFORMANCE POLYMERS & FLUIDS JAPAN CO. LTD.—See Illinois Tool Works Inc.; *U.S. Public*, pg. 1107
ITW PERFORMANCE POLYMERS & FLUIDS OOO—See Illinois Tool Works Inc.; *U.S. Public*, pg. 1107
ITW PERFORMANCE POLYMERS & FLUIDS PTE. LTD.—See Illinois Tool Works Inc.; *U.S. Public*, pg. 1107
ITW PERFORMANCE POLYMERS TRADING (SHANGHAI) CO. LTD.—See Illinois Tool Works Inc.; *U.S. Public*, pg. 1107
ITW PERMATEX CANADA—See Illinois Tool Works Inc.; *U.S. Public*, pg. 1107
ITW PERMATEX, INC.—See Illinois Tool Works Inc.; *U.S. Public*, pg. 1107
ITW PHILADELPHIA RESINS—See Illinois Tool Works Inc.; *U.S. Public*, pg. 1107
ITW PLASTIGLIDE—See Illinois Tool Works Inc.; *U.S. Public*, pg. 1107
ITW POLYMERS ADHESIVES NORTH AMERICA—See Illinois Tool Works Inc.; *U.S. Public*, pg. 1107
ITW POLYMERS & FLUIDS PTY, LTD.—See Illinois Tool Works Inc.; *U.S. Public*, pg. 1107
ITW POLYMERS SEALANTS NORTH AMERICA INC. - EASTERN DIVISION OFFICE—See Illinois Tool Works Inc.; *U.S. Public*, pg. 1107
ITW POLYMERS SEALANTS NORTH AMERICA INC.—See Illinois Tool Works Inc.; *U.S. Public*, pg. 1107
ITW POLY MEX, S. DE R.L. DE C.V.—See Illinois Tool Works Inc.; *U.S. Public*, pg. 1107
ITW POLYMEX, S. DE R.L. DE C.V.—See Illinois Tool Works Inc.; *U.S. Public*, pg. 1107
ITW POWERTRAIN FASTENING—See Illinois Tool Works Inc.; *U.S. Public*, pg. 1107
ITW PPF BRASIL ADESIVOS LTDA.—See Illinois Tool Works Inc.; *U.S. Public*, pg. 1107
ITW PRODUX—See Illinois Tool Works Inc.; *U.S. Public*, pg. 1107
ITW RAMSET/RED HEAD—See Illinois Tool Works Inc.; *U.S. Public*, pg. 1107
ITW REAL ESTATE MANAGEMENT GMBH—See Illinois Tool Works Inc.; *U.S. Public*, pg. 1107
ITW REYFLEX FRANCE S.A.S.—See Illinois Tool Works Inc.; *U.S. Public*, pg. 1107
ITW RICHMOND TECHNOLOGY—See Illinois Tool Works Inc.; *U.S. Public*, pg. 1107
ITW RIPPEY CORPORATION—See Illinois Tool Works Inc.; *U.S. Public*, pg. 1107
ITW RIVEX S.A.S.—See Illinois Tool Works Inc.; *U.S. Public*, pg. 1107
ITW ROCOL—See Illinois Tool Works Inc.; *U.S. Public*, pg. 1107
ITW SHAKEPROOF AUTOMOTIVE PRODUCTS—See Illinois Tool Works Inc.; *U.S. Public*, pg. 1107
ITW SHAKEPROOF GROUP—See Illinois Tool Works Inc.; *U.S. Public*, pg. 1107
ITW SHAKEPROOF—See Illinois Tool Works Inc.; *U.S. Public*, pg. 1107
ITW SHIPPERS S.P.R.L.—See Illinois Tool Works Inc.; *U.S. Public*, pg. 1107
ITW SMPI S.A.S.—See Illinois Tool Works Inc.; *U.S. Public*, pg. 1107
ITW SPAIN HOLDINGS, S.L.—See Illinois Tool Works Inc.; *U.S. Public*, pg. 1107
ITW SPECIALTY FILM LLC—See Illinois Tool Works Inc.; *U.S. Public*, pg. 1107
ITW SPECIALTY FILMS ITALY S.R.L.—See Illinois Tool Works Inc.; *U.S. Public*, pg. 1107
ITW SPECIALTY MATERIALS (SUZHOU) CO., LTD.—See Illinois Tool Works Inc.; *U.S. Public*, pg. 1107
ITW SPEEDLINE EQUIPMENT (SUZHOU) CO. LTD.—See Illinois Tool Works Inc.; *U.S. Public*, pg. 1107
ITW SPRAYTEC S.A.S.—See Illinois Tool Works Inc.; *U.S. Public*, pg. 1107
ITW STRETCH PACKAGING PARTS & TECHNICAL ASSISTANCE—See Illinois Tool Works Inc.; *U.S. Public*, pg. 1107
ITW SVERIGE AB—See Illinois Tool Works Inc.; *U.S. Public*, pg. 1107

ITW SWITCHES—See Illinois Tool Works Inc.; *U.S. Public*, pg. 1107
ITW SWITCHES—See Illinois Tool Works Inc.; *U.S. Public*, pg. 1107
ITW TEKFAST—See Illinois Tool Works Inc.; *U.S. Public*, pg. 1107
ITW TEMB (QUFU) AUTOMOTIVE COOLING SYSTEMS CO., LTD.—See Illinois Tool Works Inc.; *U.S. Public*, pg. 1108
ITW TEST & MEASUREMENT (CHINA) CO., LTD.—See Illinois Tool Works Inc.; *U.S. Public*, pg. 1108
ITW TEST & MEASUREMENT GMBH—See Illinois Tool Works Inc.; *U.S. Public*, pg. 1108
ITW TEST & MEASUREMENT ITALIA SRL—See Illinois Tool Works Inc.; *U.S. Public*, pg. 1108
ITW TEXWIPE—See Illinois Tool Works Inc.; *U.S. Public*, pg. 1108
ITW THERMAL FILMS (SHANGHAI) CO., LTD.—See Illinois Tool Works Inc.; *U.S. Public*, pg. 1108
ITW V.A.C. B.V.—See Illinois Tool Works Inc.; *U.S. Public*, pg. 1108
ITW WELDING PRODUCTS B.V.—See Illinois Tool Works Inc.; *U.S. Public*, pg. 1108
ITW WELDING PRODUCTS GROUP FZE—See Illinois Tool Works Inc.; *U.S. Public*, pg. 1108
ITW WELDING PRODUCTS ITALY SRL—See Illinois Tool Works Inc.; *U.S. Public*, pg. 1108
ITW WELDING PRODUCTS LIMITED LIABILITY COMPANY—See Illinois Tool Works Inc.; *U.S. Public*, pg. 1108
ITW ZIP-PAK PACKAGING (SHANGHAI) LTD.—See Illinois Tool Works Inc.; *U.S. Public*, pg. 1108
ITX-AI CO., LTD.; *Int'l*, pg. 3846
ITX COMMUNICATIONS INC.—See Nojima Corporation; *Int'l*, pg. 5401
ITX CORPORATION—See Nojima Corporation; *Int'l*, pg. 5401
ITX MERKEN, B.V.—See Industria de Diseno Textil, S.A.; *Int'l*, pg. 3666
ITX TRADING S.A.—See Industria de Diseno Textil, S.A.; *Int'l*, pg. 3666
ITZ CASH CARD LIMITED—See Ebix Inc.; *U.S. Public*, pg. 710
ITZ INFORMATIONSTECHNOLOGIE GMBH—See Bechtle AG; *Int'l*, pg. 938
IUK INC—See Intec Inc.; *Int'l*, pg. 3728
IUM OY—See Publicis Groupe S.A.; *Int'l*, pg. 6113
IUNIVERSE, LLC—See Najafi Companies, LLC; *U.S. Private*, pg. 2831
IUNLIMITED INC.; *U.S. Private*, pg. 2150
IUPAT DISTRICT COUNCIL 21; *U.S. Private*, pg. 2150
IUPAT DISTRICT COUNCIL 9; *U.S. Private*, pg. 2150
IUS SA; *Int'l*, pg. 3846
IUVO BIOSCIENCE, LLC; *U.S. Private*, pg. 2150
IUVO INDUSTRY CO., LTD.—See Dyaco International Inc.; *Int'l*, pg. 2238
IV3 SOLUTIONS INC.—See Real Matters, Inc.; *Int'l*, pg. 6233
IV4, INC.—See ProArch IT Solutions, Inc.; *U.S. Private*, pg. 3271
IVACON ENGINEERING B.V.; *Int'l*, pg. 3846
IVACO ROLLING MILLS, LP—See The Heico Companies, L.L.C.; *U.S. Private*, pg. 4050
IV-AGA TEXAS LLC—See Iv-Groep b.v.; *Int'l*, pg. 3846
I-VALO OY—See Fagerhult Group AB; *Int'l*, pg. 2602
IVALUA, INC.; *U.S. Private*, pg. 2150
IVAMOD D.O.O.—See Transition Evergreen; *Int'l*, pg. 7901
IVAN DOVERSPIKE CO.; *U.S. Private*, pg. 2150
IVAN GANDRUD CHEVROLET, INC.; *U.S. Private*, pg. 2150
IVANHOE CAMBRIDGE, INC.—See Caisse de Depot et Placement du Quebec; *Int'l*, pg. 1254
IVANHOE CAMBRIDGE—See Caisse de Depot et Placement du Quebec; *Int'l*, pg. 1254
IVANHOE COAL PTY LIMITED—See Banpu Public Company Limited; *Int'l*, pg. 852
IVANHOE ELECTRIC INC.; *Int'l*, pg. 3846
IVANHOE ENERGY, INC.; *Int'l*, pg. 3846
IVANHOE INDUSTRIES, INC.; *U.S. Private*, pg. 2150
IVANHOE MINES LTD.; *Int'l*, pg. 3846
IVANHOE PHILIPPINES INC.—See Rio Tinto plc; *Int'l*, pg. 6348
IVAN H. STEWART INC.; *U.S. Private*, pg. 2150
IVAN LEONARD CHEVROLET, INC.; *U.S. Private*, pg. 2150
IVANPLATS SYERSTON (PTY) LTD.—See Ivanhoe Mines Ltd.; *Int'l*, pg. 3846
IVAN SMITH FURNITURE, LLC; *U.S. Private*, pg. 2150
IVANTAGE HEALTH ANALYTICS, INC.—See Audax Group, Limited Partnership; *U.S. Private*, pg. 390
IVANTAGE INSURANCE BROKERS INC.—See The Allstate Corporation; *U.S. Public*, pg. 2033
IVANTI GERMANY GMBH—See Clearlake Capital Group, L.P.; *U.S. Private*, pg. 935
IVANTI SOFTWARE, INC.—See Clearlake Capital Group, L.P.; *U.S. Private*, pg. 935
IVARA CORPORATION—See Bentley Systems, Inc.; *U.S. Public*, pg. 297

COMPANY NAME INDEX

IVARI CANADA ULC—See Vestar Capital Partners, LLC; *U.S. Private*, pg. 4373
IVARS INC.; *U.S. Private*, pg. 2150
IVARSSON A/S—See Etex SA/NV; *Int'l*, pg. 2522
IVARSSON SVERIGE AB—See Etex SA/NV; *Int'l*, pg. 2522
IVAX ARGENTINA—See Teva Pharmaceutical Industries, Ltd.; *Int'l*, pg. 7579
IV-BOUW B.V.—See Iv-Groep b.v.; *Int'l*, pg. 3846
IVC GROUP LIMITED—See Mohawk Industries, Inc.; *U.S. Public*, pg. 1457
IVCI, LLC; *U.S. Private*, pg. 2151
IVC INDUSTRIAL COATINGS INC.—See PPG Industries, Inc.; *U.S. Public*, pg. 1707
IVC LUXEMBOURG S.A R.L.—See Mohawk Industries, Inc.; *U.S. Public*, pg. 1457
IV-CONSULT B.V.—See Iv-Groep b.v.; *Int'l*, pg. 3846
IV-CONSULT SDN BHD—See Iv-Groep b.v.; *Int'l*, pg. 3846
IVC-USA INC.; *U.S. Private*, pg. 2150
IVC US, INC.—See Mohawk Industries, Inc.; *U.S. Public*, pg. 1457
IVDESK HOLDINGS, INC.; *U.S. Private*, pg. 2151
IVD MEDICAL HOLDING LIMITED; *Int'l*, pg. 3846
IVECO ARAC SANAYI VE TICARET A.S.—See CNH Industrial N.V.; *Int'l*, pg. 1675
IVECO AUSTRIA GMBH—See CNH Industrial N.V.; *Int'l*, pg. 1675
IVECO BAYERN GMBH—See CNH Industrial N.V.; *Int'l*, pg. 1675
IVECO BELGIUM NV SA—See CNH Industrial N.V.; *Int'l*, pg. 1675
IVECO CAPITAL LIMITED—See Barclays PLC; *Int'l*, pg. 862
IVECO CAPITAL SERVICES S.R.L.—See CNH Industrial N.V.; *Int'l*, pg. 1675
IVECO CZECH REPUBLIC A.S.—See CNH Industrial N.V.; *Int'l*, pg. 1675
IVECO DANMARK A/S—See CNH Industrial N.V.; *Int'l*, pg. 1675
IVECO DEFENCE VEHICLES SPA—See CNH Industrial N.V.; *Int'l*, pg. 1675
IVECO ESPANA S.L.—See CNH Industrial N.V.; *Int'l*, pg. 1675
IVECO EST SAS—See CNH Industrial N.V.; *Int'l*, pg. 1675
IVECO FINANCE—See Barclays PLC; *Int'l*, pg. 862
IVECO FINANCE GMBH—See Barclays PLC; *Int'l*, pg. 862
IVECO FINANCE HOLDINGS LIMITED—See Barclays PLC; *Int'l*, pg. 862
IVECO FINANZIARIA S.P.A.—See Barclays PLC; *Int'l*, pg. 861
IVECO FINLAND OY—See CNH Industrial N.V.; *Int'l*, pg. 1675
IVECO FRANCE S.A.—See CNH Industrial N.V.; *Int'l*, pg. 1675
IVECO GROUP N.V.; *Int'l*, pg. 3847
IVECO INTERNATIONAL TRADE FINANCE S.A.—See CNH Industrial N.V.; *Int'l*, pg. 1675
IVECO LTD.—See CNH Industrial N.V.; *Int'l*, pg. 1675
IVECO L.V.I. S.A.S.—See CNH Industrial N.V.; *Int'l*, pg. 1675
IVECO MAGIRUS AG—See CNH Industrial N.V.; *Int'l*, pg. 1675
IVECO MAGIRUS FIREFIGHTING CAMIVA S.A.S.—See CNH Industrial N.V.; *Int'l*, pg. 1675
IVECO NORD NUTZFAHRZEUGE GMBH—See CNH Industrial N.V.; *Int'l*, pg. 1675
IVECO NORD-OST NUTZFAHRZEUGE GMBH—See CNH Industrial N.V.; *Int'l*, pg. 1675
IVECO NORD SAS—See CNH Industrial N.V.; *Int'l*, pg. 1675
IVECO NORGE A.S.—See CNH Industrial N.V.; *Int'l*, pg. 1675
IVECO OTOMOTIV TICARET A.S.—See CNH Industrial N.V.; *Int'l*, pg. 1675
IVECO PARTICIPATIONS S.A.S.—See CNH Industrial N.V.; *Int'l*, pg. 1675
IVECO POLAND SP. Z O.O.—See CNH Industrial N.V.; *Int'l*, pg. 1675
IVECO PROVENCE S.A.S.—See CNH Industrial N.V.; *Int'l*, pg. 1675
IVECO RETAIL LIMITED—See CNH Industrial N.V.; *Int'l*, pg. 1675
IVECO (SCHWEIZ) AG—See CNH Industrial N.V.; *Int'l*, pg. 1675
IVECO SLOVAKIA, S.R.O.—See CNH Industrial N.V.; *Int'l*, pg. 1676
IVECO S.P.A.—See CNH Industrial N.V.; *Int'l*, pg. 1675
IVECO SUD-WEST NUTZFAHRZEUGE GMBH—See CNH Industrial N.V.; *Int'l*, pg. 1676
IVECO SWEDEN A.B.—See CNH Industrial N.V.; *Int'l*, pg. 1676
IVECO TRUCK CENTRUM S.R.O.—See CNH Industrial N.V.; *Int'l*, pg. 1676
IVECO TRUCKS AUSTRALIA LTD—See CNH Industrial N.V.; *Int'l*, pg. 1676
IVECO TRUCK SERVICES S.R.L.—See CNH Industrial N.V.; *Int'l*, pg. 1676
IVECO UKRAINE LLC—See CNH Industrial N.V.; *Int'l*, pg. 1676
IVECO WEST NUTZFAHRZEUGE GMBH—See CNH Industrial N.V.; *Int'l*, pg. 1676
IVEDA SOLUTIONS, INC.; *U.S. Public*, pg. 1179
IVE GROUP LIMITED; *Int'l*, pg. 3846
IVENTA BRATISLAVA—See IVENTA Group Holding GmbH; *Int'l*, pg. 3847
IVENTA BUCHAREST—See IVENTA Group Holding GmbH; *Int'l*, pg. 3847
IVENTA CZECH MANAGEMENT CONSULTING S.R.O.—See IVENTA Group Holding GmbH; *Int'l*, pg. 3847
IVENTA GROUP HOLDING GMBH; *Int'l*, pg. 3847
IVENTA MANAGEMENT CONSULTING GMBH - GRAZ—See IVENTA Group Holding GmbH; *Int'l*, pg. 3847
IVENTA MANAGEMENT CONSULTING GMBH - LINZ—See IVENTA Group Holding GmbH; *Int'l*, pg. 3847
IVENTA MANAGEMENT CONSULTING GMBH - SALZBURG—See IVENTA Group Holding GmbH; *Int'l*, pg. 3847
IVENTURE SOLUTIONS, INC.; *U.S. Private*, pg. 2151
IVEO AB—See Storskogen Group AB; *Int'l*, pg. 7227
IVER AB—See EQT AB; *Int'l*, pg. 2478
IVERIC BIO, INC.—See Astellas Pharma Inc.; *Int'l*, pg. 653
IVERIFY US, INC.; *U.S. Private*, pg. 2151
IVERMEDI—See HORIBA Ltd; *Int'l*, pg. 3477
IVERSON'S LUMBER COMPANY INC.—See The Schockman Lumber Company, Inc.; *U.S. Private*, pg. 4114
IVES EQUIPMENT CORPORATION—See Frontenac Company LLC; *U.S. Private*, pg. 1614
IVEX PACKAGING CORPORATION—See Groupe IndusPac Emballage Inc.; *Int'l*, pg. 3104
IVEX PACKAGING LLC—See Groupe IndusPac Emballage Inc.; *Int'l*, pg. 3104
IVEY-COOPER SERVICES LLC—See Electricite de France S.A.; *Int'l*, pg. 2351
IVEY MECHANICAL COMPANY LLC; *U.S. Private*, pg. 2151
IVEYS CONSTRUCTION INC.; *U.S. Private*, pg. 2151
IVF AUSTRALIA PTY LTD—See Virtus Health Limited; *Int'l*, pg. 8248
IVF CENTRE (HONG KONG) LIMITED—See First Shanghai Investments Limited; *Int'l*, pg. 2687
IVF HARTMANN AG—See PAUL HARTMANN AG; *Int'l*, pg. 5760
IVF HARTMANN HOLDING AG—See PAUL HARTMANN AG; *Int'l*, pg. 5760
IV-GROEP B.V.; *Int'l*, pg. 3846
IVGSTORES LLC; *U.S. Private*, pg. 2151
I VIAGGI DES TURCHESE S.R.L.—See TUI AG; *Int'l*, pg. 7965
IVICT EUROPE GMBH—See Mitsubishi Corporation; *Int'l*, pg. 4938
IVIE & ASSOCIATES, INC.—See Quad/Graphics, Inc.; *U.S. Public*, pg. 1744
IVIEW DIGITAL VIDEO SOLUTIONS INC.—See Creative Vistas Inc.; *Int'l*, pg. 1834
I-VIEW PTY LTD.—See Ipsos S.A.; *Int'l*, pg. 3799
IVIGIL CORPORATION—See Ac&C International Co., Ltd.; *Int'l*, pg. 74
IVIGIL UK LIMITED—See Ac&C International Co., Ltd.; *Int'l*, pg. 74
IVILLAGE LLC—See Comcast Corporation; *U.S. Public*, pg. 540
IV-INDUSTRIE B.V.—See Iv-Groep b.v.; *Int'l*, pg. 3846
IVINEX; *U.S. Private*, pg. 2151
IV-INFRA B.V.—See Iv-Groep b.v.; *Int'l*, pg. 3846
IV-INFRA USA, LLC—See Iv-Groep b.v.; *Int'l*, pg. 3846
IVISION SCALE, LLC; *U.S. Private*, pg. 2151
IVISION TECH S.P.A.; *Int'l*, pg. 3847
IVISIT CORP.—See Relia, Inc.; *Int'l*, pg. 6260
IVISYS AB; *Int'l*, pg. 3847
IVIVVA ATHLETICA CANADA INC.—See lululemon athletica inc.; *Int'l*, pg. 4577
IVIZ GROUP, INC.; *U.S. Private*, pg. 2151
IVK-TUOTE OY—See Lindab International AB; *Int'l*, pg. 4503
IVOCLAR VIVADENT SAS; *Int'l*, pg. 3847
IVO ENERGI AB—See Fortum Oyj; *Int'l*, pg. 2741
IVOICEIDEAS, INC.; *U.S. Private*, pg. 2151
IV-OIL & GAS B.V.—See Iv-Groep b.v.; *Int'l*, pg. 3846
IVOIRE COTON S.A.—See Aga Khan Development Network; *Int'l*, pg. 199
IVOLUTION MEDICAL SYSTEMS, INC.; *U.S. Private*, pg. 2151
IVOLVE PTY. LTD.—See Topcon Corporation; *Int'l*, pg. 7814
IVONA SOFTWARE SP. Z O.O.—See Amazon.com, Inc.; *U.S. Public*, pg. 90
IVORY CAPITAL GROUP, LLC—See Affiliated Managers Group, Inc.; *U.S. Public*, pg. 55
IVORY HOMES; *U.S. Private*, pg. 2151
IVORY INTERNATIONAL, INC.; *U.S. Private*, pg. 2151
IVORY MEADOWS SDN. BHD.—See Ivory Properties Group Berhad; *Int'l*, pg. 3847
IVORY PROPERTIES GROUP BERHAD; *Int'l*, pg. 3847
IVOX SOLUTIONS, LLC; *U.S. Private*, pg. 2151
IVP LIMITED; *Int'l*, pg. 3847
IV PRODUKT AB; *Int'l*, pg. 3846
IVRCL LIMITED; *Int'l*, pg. 3847
IVRESSE CO., LTD.; *Int'l*, pg. 3847
IVRESSE CONSULTING LLC—See Ivresse Co., Ltd.; *Int'l*, pg. 3847
IVRESSE HOSPITALITY LLC—See Ivresse Co., Ltd.; *Int'l*, pg. 3847
IVS FRANCE S.A.S.—See IVS Group S.A.; *Int'l*, pg. 3848
IVS GROUP S.A.; *Int'l*, pg. 3848
IVS INDUSTRIEVERTRETUNG SCHWEIGER GMBH—See Doro AB; *Int'l*, pg. 2179
IVS ITALIA S.P.A.—See IVS Group S.A.; *Int'l*, pg. 3848
IV-TEC GMBH—See TKH Group N.V.; *Int'l*, pg. 7764
IVT INSTALLATIONS- UND VERBINDUNGSTECHNIK GMBH & CO. KG—See Wurth Verwaltungsgesellschaft mbH; *Int'l*, pg. 8505
IVU AUSTRIA GMBH—See IVU Traffic Technologies AG; *Int'l*, pg. 3848
IVU BENELUX B.V.—See IVU Traffic Technologies AG; *Int'l*, pg. 3848
IVU CHILE LTDA.—See IVU Traffic Technologies AG; *Int'l*, pg. 3848
IVU TRAFFIC TECHNOLOGIES AG; *Int'l*, pg. 3848
IVU TRAFFIC TECHNOLOGIES INC.—See IVU Traffic Technologies AG; *Int'l*, pg. 3848
IVU TRAFFIC TECHNOLOGIES ITALIA S.R.L.—See IVU Traffic Technologies AG; *Int'l*, pg. 3848
IVU TRAFFIC TECHNOLOGIES SCHWEIZ AG—See IVU Traffic Technologies AG; *Int'l*, pg. 3848
IVU TRAFFIC TECHNOLOGIES UK LTD.—See IVU Traffic Technologies AG; *Int'l*, pg. 3848
IV-WATER B.V.—See Iv-Groep b.v.; *Int'l*, pg. 3846
IVX HEALTH, INC.; *U.S. Private*, pg. 2151
IVY COMPTECH PRIVATE LIMITED—See Entain PLC; *Int'l*, pg. 2449
IVY COSMETICS CORPORATION - KYOTO PROMOTION DIVISION—See IVY Cosmetics Corporation; *Int'l*, pg. 3848
IVY COSMETICS CORPORATION - KYUSHU DIVISION—See IVY Cosmetics Corporation; *Int'l*, pg. 3848
IVY COSMETICS CORPORATION - MISATO PLANT—See IVY Cosmetics Corporation; *Int'l*, pg. 3848
IVY COSMETICS CORPORATION - OSAKA PROMOTION DIVISION—See IVY Cosmetics Corporation; *Int'l*, pg. 3848
IVY COSMETICS CORPORATION - SAN'IN DIVISION—See IVY Cosmetics Corporation; *Int'l*, pg. 3848
IVY COSMETICS CORPORATION; *Int'l*, pg. 3848
IVY CREDIT OPPORTUNITIES FUND; *U.S. Private*, pg. 2151
IVY EXEC, INC.; *U.S. Private*, pg. 2152
IVY GLOBAL SHARED SERVICES PRIVATE LIMITED—See Entain PLC; *Int'l*, pg. 2450
THE IVY GROUP, LTD.; *U.S. Private*, pg. 4057
THE IVY GROUP, LTD.—See The Ivy Group, Ltd.; *U.S. Private*, pg. 4058
IVY HIGH INCOME OPPORTUNITIES FUND; *U.S. Public*, pg. 1179
IVY H. SMITH COMPANY, LLC—See Dycom Industries, Inc.; *U.S. Public*, pg. 698
IVY INVESTMENT MANAGEMENT COMPANY—See Macquarie Group Limited; *Int'l*, pg. 4625
IVY PRODUCTIONS, INC.—See LOV Group Invest SAS; *Int'l*, pg. 4565
IVY SOFTWARE DEVELOPMENT SERVICES PRIVATE LIMITED—See Entain PLC; *Int'l*, pg. 2450
IVY SPORTS MEDICINE GMBH—See Stryker Corporation; *U.S. Public*, pg. 1955
IVY SPORTS MEDICINE, LLC—See Stryker Corporation; *U.S. Public*, pg. 1956
IVYSTONE GROUP, LLC - DALLAS—See Ivystone Group, LLC; *U.S. Private*, pg. 2152
IVYSTONE GROUP, LLC; *U.S. Private*, pg. 2152
IVY VENTURES, LLC—See ABRY Partners, LLC; *U.S. Private*, pg. 41
IVZ BAHAMAS PRIVATE LIMITED—See Invesco Ltd.; *U.S. Public*, pg. 1161
IWABUCHI CORPORATION; *Int'l*, pg. 3848
IWAFUJI INDUSTRIAL CO LTD—See ShinMaywa Industries, Ltd.; *Int'l*, pg. 6846
IWAGAWA JOZO CO., LTD.—See Kamigumi Co., Ltd.; *Int'l*, pg. 4062
IWAICOSMO HOLDINGS, INC.; *Int'l*, pg. 3848
IWAICOSMO SECURITIES CO., LTD.—See IwaiCosmo Holdings, Inc.; *Int'l*, pg. 3848
IWAI & OKAYA MACHINERY CO., LTD.—See Okaya & Co., Ltd.; *Int'l*, pg. 5546
IWAKI AMERICA INCORPORATED—See Iwaki Co., Ltd.; *Int'l*, pg. 3849
IWAKI BELGIUM BVBA—See Iwaki Co., Ltd.; *Int'l*, pg. 3848
IWAKI CO., LTD. - MIHARU PLANT—See Iwaki Co., Ltd.; *Int'l*, pg. 3849
IWAKI CO., LTD. - SAITAMA PLANT—See Iwaki Co., Ltd.; *Int'l*, pg. 3849
IWAKI CO., LTD.; *Int'l*, pg. 3848

IWAKI CO., LTD.

CORPORATE AFFILIATIONS

IWAKI DAIO PAPER CORPORATION—See Daio Paper Corporation; *Int'l*, pg. 1940
IWAKI EUROPE GMBH—See Iwaki Co., Ltd.; *Int'l*, pg. 3849
IWAKI FINE TECHNOLOGY CO., LTD.—See MISUMI Group Inc; *Int'l*, pg. 4922
IWAKI FRANCE S.A.—See Iwaki Co., Ltd.; *Int'l*, pg. 3849
IWAKI IBERICA PUMPS S.A.—See Iwaki Co., Ltd.; *Int'l*, pg. 3849
IWAKI ITALIA S.R.L.—See Iwaki Co., Ltd.; *Int'l*, pg. 3849
IWAKIM SDN. BHD.—See Iwaki Co., Ltd.; *Int'l*, pg. 3849
IWAKI NORDIC A/S—See Iwaki Co., Ltd.; *Int'l*, pg. 3848
IWAKI NORGE AS—See Iwaki Co., Ltd.; *Int'l*, pg. 3849
IWAKI PUMPS AUSTRALIA PTY. LTD.—See Iwaki Co., Ltd.; *Int'l*, pg. 3849
IWAKI PUMPS CO., LTD.—See Iwaki Co., Ltd.; *Int'l*, pg. 3849
IWAKI PUMPS (SHANGHAI) CO., LTD.—See Iwaki Co., Ltd.; *Int'l*, pg. 3849
IWAKI PUMPS TAIWAN CO., LTD.—See Iwaki Co., Ltd.; *Int'l*, pg. 3849
IWAKI PUMPS (UK) LIMITED—See Iwaki Co., Ltd.; *Int'l*, pg. 3849
IWAKI PUMPS VIETNAM CO., LTD.—See Iwaki Co., Ltd.; *Int'l*, pg. 3849
IWAKI SEIYAKU CO., LTD.—See Astena Holdings Co., Ltd.; *Int'l*, pg. 653
IWAKI SINGAPORE PTE LTD.—See Iwaki Co., Ltd.; *Int'l*, pg. 3849
IWAKI SUOMI OY—See Iwaki Co., Ltd.; *Int'l*, pg. 3849
IWAKI SVERIGE AB—See Iwaki Co., Ltd.; *Int'l*, pg. 3849
IWAKI (THAILAND) CO., LTD.—See Iwaki Co., Ltd.; *Int'l*, pg. 3849
IWAKUNI DAIICHI TRAFFIC LTD.—See Daiichi Koutsu Sangyo Co., Ltd.; *Int'l*, pg. 1928
IWAMA LOOM WORKS, LTD.—See Toyota Industries Corporation; *Int'l*, pg. 7866
IWAMI MURATA MANUFACTURING CO., LTD.—See Murata Manufacturing Co., Ltd.; *Int'l*, pg. 5097
IWANOHARA VINEYARD CO., LTD.—See Suntory Holdings Limited; *Int'l*, pg. 7326
IWAO & CO., LTD.—See Nisshinbo Holdings Inc.; *Int'l*, pg. 5373
IWASAKI ELECTRIC CO LTD - INTERNATIONAL BUSINESS DIVISION—See IWASAKI ELECTRIC Co., Ltd.; *Int'l*, pg. 3849
IWASAKI ELECTRIC CO., LTD.; *Int'l*, pg. 3849
IWASAKI ELECTRIC ENGINEERING SERVICE CO., LTD.—See IWASAKI ELECTRIC Co., Ltd.; *Int'l*, pg. 3849
IWASAKI SEISAKUSHO CO., LTD.—See Daifuku Co., Ltd.; *Int'l*, pg. 1926
IWATA BOLT USA INC.; *U.S. Private*, pg. 2152
IWATA CO., LTD.—See Takamiya Co., Ltd.; *Int'l*, pg. 7430
IWATA GRAND HOTEL INC.—See Hamamatsu Photonics K.K.; *Int'l*, pg. 3235
IWATANI CAMBOROUGH CO. LTD.—See Genus Plc; *Int'l*, pg. 2931
IWATANI CORPORATION EUROPE GMBH—See Iwatani Corporation; *Int'l*, pg. 3850
IWATANI CORPORATION HONG KONG LTD.—See Iwatani Corporation; *Int'l*, pg. 3850
IWATANI CORPORATION (KOREA) LTD.—See Iwatani Corporation; *Int'l*, pg. 3850
IWATANI CORPORATION OF AMERICA—See Iwatani Corporation; *Int'l*, pg. 3850
IWATANI CORPORATION SINGAPORE PTE. LTD.—See Iwatani Corporation; *Int'l*, pg. 3850
IWATANI CORPORATION; *Int'l*, pg. 3849
IWATANI CORPORATION TAIWAN LTD.—See Iwatani Corporation; *Int'l*, pg. 3850
IWATANI CORPORATION - TOKYO HEAD OFFICE—See Iwatani Corporation; *Int'l*, pg. 3850
IWATANI ELECTRONICS SHANGHAI CO., LTD.—See Iwatani Corporation; *Int'l*, pg. 3850
IWATANI INDUSTRIAL GAS PTE.LTD—See Iwatani Corporation; *Int'l*, pg. 3850
IWATANI NOX GAS PTE. LTD.—See Iwatani Corporation; *Int'l*, pg. 3850
IWATANI RIKA CO., LTD.—See New Japan Chemical Co., Ltd.; *Int'l*, pg. 5225
IWATA SANGYO CO., LTD.; *Int'l*, pg. 3849
IWATA SERVICE & SALES(M) SDN. BHD.—See ANEST IWATA Corporation; *Int'l*, pg. 458
IWATA SPECIALTY STEEL, INC.—See Nippon Steel Corporation; *Int'l*, pg. 5336
IWATAYA CO., LTD.—See Isetan Mitsukoshi Holdings Ltd.; *Int'l*, pg. 3815
IWATE-KENPOKU CLEAN CO., LTD.—See Takuma Co., Ltd.; *Int'l*, pg. 7442
IWATE MORI SHIGYO CO., LTD.—See Oji Holdings Corporation; *Int'l*, pg. 5537
IWATE MURATA MANUFACTURING CO., LTD.—See Murata Manufacturing Co., Ltd.; *Int'l*, pg. 5097
IWATE NOHMI CO., LTD.—See Nohmi Bosai Ltd.; *Int'l*, pg. 5400
IWATE OSAKI ELECTRIC CO., LTD.—See Osaki Electric Co., Ltd.; *Int'l*, pg. 5647
IWATE SHIBAURA ELECTRONICS CO., LTD.—See Shibaura Electronics Co., Ltd.; *Int'l*, pg. 6827
IWATSU ELECTRIC CO LTD—See AI Holdings Corp.; *Int'l*, pg. 227
IWATSU HONG KONG, LTD.—See AI Holdings Corp.; *Int'l*, pg. 227
IWATSUKA CONFECTIONERY CO., LTD.; *Int'l*, pg. 3850
IWATSU (MALAYSIA) SDN. BHD.—See AI Holdings Corp.; *Int'l*, pg. 227
IWATT, INC.—See Renesas Electronics Corporation; *Int'l*, pg. 6275
IWATT INTEGRATED CIRCUITS (SHENZHEN) LIMITED COMPANY—See Renesas Electronics Corporation; *Int'l*, pg. 6275
IWATT L.L.C.—See Renesas Electronics Corporation; *Int'l*, pg. 6275
IWAVE INFORMATION SYSTEMS INC.—See Incline MGMT Corp.; *U.S. Private*, pg. 2054
IW BANK S.P.A.—See Intesa Sanpaolo S.p.A.; *Int'l*, pg. 3766
IW CARGO HANDLERS, INC.—See International Container Terminal Services, Inc.; *Int'l*, pg. 3746
IWC MEDIA SERVICES—See Windjammer Capital Investors, LLC; *U.S. Private*, pg. 4538
IWC MEDIA—See De Agostini S.p.A.; *Int'l*, pg. 1994
IWCO DIRECT INC.—See Cerberus Capital Management, L.P.; *U.S. Private*, pg. 838
IWEB GROUP INC.—See Internap Holding LLC; *U.S. Private*, pg. 2114
IWEB TECHNOLOGIES INC.—See Internap Holding LLC; *U.S. Private*, pg. 2114
IWECO CHONOS LASITHIOU CRETE SA—See TERNA ENERGY SOCIETE ANONYME INDUSTRIAL COMMERCIAL TECHNICAL COMPANY S.A.; *Int'l*, pg. 7566
I-WELLNESS MARKETING GROUP, INC.; *U.S. Public*, pg. 1081
IWF SAN SIMEON PINES, L.P.—See Invest West Financial Corporation; *U.S. Private*, pg. 2131
IWG PLC; *Int'l*, pg. 3850
IW GROUP, INC. - NEW YORK OFFICE—See IW Group, Inc.; *U.S. Private*, pg. 2152
IW GROUP, INC. - SAN FRANCISCO OFFICE—See IW Group, Inc.; *U.S. Private*, pg. 2152
IW GROUP, INC.; *U.S. Private*, pg. 2152
IWI FUND MANAGEMENT LIMITED—See Investec Limited; *Int'l*, pg. 3777
IWI INC.; *U.S. Private*, pg. 2152
I-WILLING CORPORATION—See Mitsubishi Corporation; *Int'l*, pg. 4938
IWIN, INC.—See Flipside, Inc.; *U.S. Private*, pg. 1546
IWIN; *Int'l*, pg. 3850
IWIRED, INC.—See Vangeo Technology Group, LLC; *U.S. Private*, pg. 4343
I-WIRELESS INC.; *U.S. Private*, pg. 2026
I WIRELESS; *U.S. Private*, pg. 2026
IWIS-DAIDO LLC—See Daido Kogyo Co., Ltd.; *Int'l*, pg. 1921
IWISE AB—See Adecco Group AG; *Int'l*, pg. 140
IWK PACKAGING SYSTEMS, INC.—See ATS Corporation; *Int'l*, pg. 695
IWK VERPACKUNGSTECHNIK GMBH—See ATS Corporation; *Int'l*, pg. 695
IWL INTERNATIONALE WEIN LOGISTIK GMBH—See Hawesko Holding AG; *Int'l*, pg. 3288
IWM AG—See BKW AG; *Int'l*, pg. 1055
IWM AUTOMATION GMBH—See MAX Automation SE; *Int'l*, pg. 4733
IWOCA LTD.; *Int'l*, pg. 3850
IWORK SOFTWARE LLC—See Falk Integrated Technologies; *U.S. Private*, pg. 1467
IWOW TECHNOLOGY LIMITED; *Int'l*, pg. 3850
IWP INTERNATIONAL WEST PICTURES GMBH & CO. ERSTE PRODUKTIONS KG—See Commerzbank AG; *Int'l*, pg. 1718
IWS ACQUISITION CORPORATION—See Kingsway Financial Services Inc.; *U.S. Public*, pg. 1234
IWS ASSORTED PAPER COMPANY LIMITED—See Integrated Waste Solutions Group Holdings Limited; *Int'l*, pg. 3731
IWS ENVIRONMENTAL TECHNOLOGIES LIMITED—See Integrated Waste Solutions Group Holdings Limited; *Int'l*, pg. 3731
IWS REALTY CORPORATION—See Sumitomo Electric Industries, Ltd.; *Int'l*, pg. 7278
IWS WASTE MANAGEMENT COMPANY LIMITED—See Integrated Waste Solutions Group Holdings Limited; *Int'l*, pg. 3732
IX ACQUISITION CORP.; *Int'l*, pg. 3850
IXARIS SYSTEMS, LTD.; *Int'l*, pg. 3851
IX BIOPHARMA LTD.; *Int'l*, pg. 3851
IXCHANGE PTE LTD—See Khazanah Nasional Berhad; *Int'l*, pg. 4152
IXIA - AUSTIN—See Keysight Technologies, Inc.; *U.S. Public*, pg. 1227
IXIA PTE. LTD.—See Keysight Technologies, Inc.; *U.S. Public*, pg. 1227
IXIA—See Keysight Technologies, Inc.; *U.S. Public*, pg. 1227
IXIA TECHNOLOGIES EUROPE LIMITED—See Keysight Technologies, Inc.; *U.S. Public*, pg. 1227
IXICO PLC; *Int'l*, pg. 3851
IXI CORPORATION—See Equifax Inc.; *U.S. Public*, pg. 786
IXIR PRODUCTIONS, INC.; *Int'l*, pg. 3851
IXIT CORPORATION—See HS Holdings Co., Ltd.; *Int'l*, pg. 3503
IX KNOWLEDGE INC.; *Int'l*, pg. 3851
IXL LEARNING, INC.; *U.S. Private*, pg. 2152
IXMATION (ASIA) SDN. BHD.—See Durr AG; *Int'l*, pg. 2230
IXMATION INC.—See Durr AG; *Int'l*, pg. 2230
IXMATION (SUZHOU) CO., LTD.—See Durr AG; *Int'l*, pg. 2230
IXMATION (TIANJIN) CO., LTD.—See Durr AG; *Int'l*, pg. 2230
IXOM CHILE S.A.—See Keppel Corporation Limited; *Int'l*, pg. 4131
IXOM COLOMBIA S.A.S.—See Keppel Corporation Limited; *Int'l*, pg. 4131
IXOM HOLDCO. PTY. LTD.—See Keppel Corporation Limited; *Int'l*, pg. 4131
IXOM PERU S.A.C.—See Keppel Corporation Limited; *Int'l*, pg. 4131
IXONOS DENMARK APS—See Digitalist Group Oyj; *Int'l*, pg. 2123
IXONOS FINLAND MTSW LTD.—See Digitalist Group Oyj; *Int'l*, pg. 2123
IXONOS GERMANY GMBH—See Digitalist Group Oyj; *Int'l*, pg. 2123
IXONOS TECHNOLOGY CONSULTING LTD—See Digitalist Group Oyj; *Int'l*, pg. 2123
IXONOS TESTHOUSE LTD.—See Digitalist Group Oyj; *Int'l*, pg. 2123
IXONOS USA LTD.—See Digitalist Group Oyj; *Int'l*, pg. 2123
IXO PRIVATE EQUITY; *Int'l*, pg. 3851
IX PARTNERS LTD.—See Genpact Limited; *Int'l*, pg. 2927
IXREVEAL, INC.—See Springboard Capital, LLC; *U.S. Private*, pg. 3763
IXRF SYSTEMS, INC.; *U.S. Private*, pg. 2152
IX SYRINX PTY LTD.—See iX Biopharma Ltd.; *Int'l*, pg. 3851
IXTHUS INSTRUMENTATION LIMITED—See discoverIE Group plc; *Int'l*, pg. 2133
IXUP LIMITED; *Int'l*, pg. 3851
IXXI—See Regie Autonome des Transports Parisiens; *Int'l*, pg. 6253
IXYS CORPORATION—See Littelfuse, Inc.; *U.S. Public*, pg. 1327
IXYS GLOBAL SERVICES GMBH—See Littelfuse, Inc.; *U.S. Public*, pg. 1327
IXYS INTEGRATED CIRCUITS DIVISION INC.—See Littelfuse, Inc.; *U.S. Public*, pg. 1327
IXYS LONG BEACH INC.—See Littelfuse, Inc.; *U.S. Public*, pg. 1327
IXYS SEMICONDUCTOR GMBH—See Littelfuse, Inc.; *U.S. Public*, pg. 1327
IXYS SEMICONDUCTORS GMBH—See Littelfuse, Inc.; *U.S. Public*, pg. 1327
IXYS UK WESTCODE LIMITED—See Littelfuse, Inc.; *U.S. Public*, pg. 1327
IY FOODS K.K.—See Seven & i Holdings Co., Ltd.; *Int'l*, pg. 6730
IYKOT HITECH TOOLROOM LIMITED; *Int'l*, pg. 3851
IYO BANK LTD.—See Iyogin Holdings Co.,Ltd.; *Int'l*, pg. 3851
IYOGIN CAPITAL COMPANY LIMITED—See Iyogin Holdings Co.,Ltd.; *Int'l*, pg. 3851
IYOGIN COMPUTER SERVICE COMPANY LIMITED—See Iyogin Holdings Co.,Ltd.; *Int'l*, pg. 3851
IYOGIN HOLDINGS CO.,LTD.; *Int'l*, pg. 3851
IYOGIN LEASING COMPANY LIMITED—See Iyogin Holdings Co.,Ltd.; *Int'l*, pg. 3851
I YUAN PRECISION INDUSTRIAL CO., LTD.; *Int'l*, pg. 3562
IYUNO UK III LTD.—See The Carlyle Group Inc.; *U.S. Public*, pg. 2045
IYZI ODEME VE ELEKTRONIK PARA HIZMETLERI ANONIM SIRKETI—See Prosus N.V.; *Int'l*, pg. 6003
IZAFE GROUP AB; *Int'l*, pg. 3851
IZAMAX VENTURES, INC.—See Legal Graphicworks, Inc.; *U.S. Private*, pg. 2417
IZASA SCIENTIFIC, S.L.U.—See Werfen Life Group, S.A.U.; *Int'l*, pg. 8379
IZATCO TRADING COMPANY (PVT) LTD.—See Telefonaktiebolaget LM Ericsson; *Int'l*, pg. 7534
IZDEMIR ENERJI ELEKTRIK URETIM A.S.—See Izmir Demir Celik Sanayi AS; *Int'l*, pg. 3851
IZEA WORLDWIDE, INC.; *U.S. Public*, pg. 1179
IZENBERG APPRAISAL ASSOCIATES, INC.—See BBG Inc.; *U.S. Private*, pg. 498
IZENDA, INC.—See TA Associates, Inc.; *U.S. Private*, pg. 3915
IZEN INTERNATIONAL NV—See VINCI S.A.; *Int'l*, pg. 8223
IZENO PRIVATE LIMITED—See Datatec Limited; *Int'l*, pg. 1981

COMPANY NAME INDEX

IZEN RENEWABLE ENERGY BV—See VINCI S.A.; *Int'l*, pg. 8223
IZGRADNJA D.O.O.—See Bain Capital, LP; *U.S. Private*, pg. 443
IZGRADNJA D.O.O.—See Cinven Limited; *Int'l*, pg. 1613
IZ HAYVANCILIK TARIM VE GIDA SANAYI VE TICARET AS; *Int'l*, pg. 3851
IZHSTAL OAO—See Mechel PAO; *Int'l*, pg. 4766
IZHSTAL PAO—See Mechel PAO; *Int'l*, pg. 4766
IZICO HOLDING B.V.—See Egeria Capital Management B.V.; *Int'l*, pg. 2323
IZICO KATWIJK B.V.—See Egeria Capital Management B.V.; *Int'l*, pg. 2323
IZICO NEDERLAND B.V.—See Egeria Capital Management B.V.; *Int'l*, pg. 2323
IZI MEDICAL PRODUCTS, LLC—See Halma plc; *Int'l*, pg. 3232
IZMIR DEMIR CELIK SANAYI AS; *Int'l*, pg. 3851
IZMIR ELEKTRIK URETIM LIMITED SIRKETI—See Enka Insaat ve Sanayi A.S.; *Int'l*, pg. 2440
IZMIR ENTERNASYONAL OTELCILIK ANONIM SIRKETI—See Hilton Worldwide Holdings Inc.; *U.S. Public*, pg. 1041
IZMIR FIRCA SANAYI VE TICARET AS; *Int'l*, pg. 3851
IZMO LTD.; *Int'l*, pg. 3851
IZOBLOK GMBH—See BEWi ASA; *Int'l*, pg. 1004
IZOBLOK SA—See BEWi ASA; *Int'l*, pg. 1004
IZOCAM TIC. SAN. AS—See Koc Holding A.S.; *Int'l*, pg. 4223
IZOD—See PVH Corp.; *U.S. Public*, pg. 1739
IZOLA BANK P.L.C; *Int'l*, pg. 3851
IZOLACIJA HOLDING A.D.; *Int'l*, pg. 3851
IZOLACJA JAROCIN S.A.; *Int'l*, pg. 3851
IZOLIR A.D.; *Int'l*, pg. 3852
IZON NETWORK, INC.; *U.S. Public*, pg. 1179
IZOPOLI YAPI ELEMANLARI TAAHHUT SAN. VE TIC A.S - ADANA FACTORY—See Kingspan Group PLC; *Int'l*, pg. 4176
IZOPOLI YAPI ELEMANLARI TAAHHUT SAN. VE TIC A.S - BOLU FACTORY—See Kingspan Group PLC; *Int'l*, pg. 4176
IZOPOLI YAPI ELEMANLARI TAAHHUT SAN. VE TIC A.S—See Kingspan Group PLC; *Int'l*, pg. 4176
IZOPROGRES A.D.; *Int'l*, pg. 3852
IZOSTAL S.A.—See Stalprofil S.A., *Int'l*, pg. 7104
IZOTROPIC CORP.; *Int'l*, pg. 3852
I-ZOU HI-TECH (SZN) CO., LTD.—See I-CHIUN PRECISION INDUSTRY CO., LTD.; *Int'l*, pg. 3563
IZ TECHNOLOGIES, INC.; *U.S. Private*, pg. 2152
IZTOK PARKSIDE EOOD—See Arco Vara AS; *Int'l*, pg. 550
IZU DAIICHI TRAFFIC CO., LTD.—See Daiichi Koutsu Sangyo Co., Ltd.; *Int'l*, pg. 1928
IZUHAKONE RAILWAY CO., LTD.—See Seibu Holdings Inc.; *Int'l*, pg. 6684
IZUKYU CORP.—See Tokyu Corporation; *Int'l*, pg. 7797
IZUMI CO., LTD.—See RASA Corporation; *Int'l*, pg. 6212
IZUMI DENKI KOGYO CO., LTD.—See Daido Steel Co., Ltd.; *Int'l*, pg. 1923
THE IZUMI EXPRESS CO., LTD.—See The Sumitomo Warehouse Co. Ltd.; *Int'l*, pg. 7690
IZUMI FOOD MACHINERY CO., LTD. - AWAJI PLANT—See Sumitomo Heavy Industries, Ltd.; *Int'l*, pg. 7286
IZUMI FOOD MACHINERY CO., LTD.—See Sumitomo Heavy Industries, Ltd.; *Int'l*, pg. 7286
IZUMI INDUSTRY CO., LTD.—See Sumitomo Osaka Cement Co Ltd; *Int'l*, pg. 7296
IZUMI KOHAN CO., LTD.—See Nippon Steel Corporation; *Int'l*, pg. 5337
IZUMI KOHAN INDUSTRY INC.—See Nippon Steel Corporation; *Int'l*, pg. 5337
IZUMI MACHINE MFG. CO., LTD.—See Toyota Industries Corporation; *Int'l*, pg. 7866
IZUMI METAL CORPORATION—See UACJ Corporation; *Int'l*, pg. 7999
IZUMI PARK TOWN SERVICE CO., LTD.—See Mitsubishi Estate Co., Ltd.; *Int'l*, pg. 4946
IZUMI SANGYO CO., LTD.—See Tosoh Corporation; *Int'l*, pg. 7832
IZUMI SHOKO CO., LTD.—See Daido Kogyo Co., Ltd.; *Int'l*, pg. 1921
IZUMI SUPPORT CORPORATION—See Sumitomo Heavy Industries, Ltd.; *Int'l*, pg. 7286
IZUMI TRANSPORT CO., LTD.—See Sumitomo Osaka Cement Co Ltd; *Int'l*, pg. 7296
IZUMIYA CARD CO., LTD.—See H2O Retailing Corp.; *Int'l*, pg. 3200
IZUMIYA CO., LTD.—See H2O Retailing Corp.; *Int'l*, pg. 3200
IZUMO APPAREL LTD.—See Gunze Limited; *Int'l*, pg. 3186
IZUMO MURATA MANUFACTURING CO., LTD.—See Murata Manufacturing Co., Ltd.; *Int'l*, pg. 5097
IZUMO TEC CO., LTD.—See Hanwa Co., Ltd.; *Int'l*, pg. 3263
IZU SHABOTEN RESORT CO., LTD.; *Int'l*, pg. 3852
IZUSHI CABLE, INC.—See Hi-Lex Corporation; *Int'l*, pg. 3381

IZUTECH CORPORATION - SHINSHIRO PLANT—See Fair Friend Group; *Int'l*, pg. 2604
IZUTECH CORPORATION—See Fair Friend Group; *Int'l*, pg. 2604
IZUTSU MAISEN CO., LTD.—See Suntory Holdings Limited; *Int'l*, pg. 7326
IZUTSUYA CO., LTD.; *Int'l*, pg. 3852
IZUTSUYA WITH CARD CO., LTD.—See Yamaguchi Financial Group Inc.; *Int'l*, pg. 8548
IZVOR A.D.; *Int'l*, pg. 3852
IZZE BEVERAGE COMPANY—See PepsiCo, Inc.; *U.S. Public*, pg. 1669
IZZO INSURANCE SERVICES, INC.—See Brown & Brown, Inc.; *U.S. Public*, pg. 401
IZZY'S FRANCHISE SYSTEMS INC.; *U.S. Private*, pg. 2152

J

J2 ENGINEERING INC.; *U.S. Private*, pg. 2172
J2 GLOBAL CANADA, INC.—See Ziff Davis, Inc.; *U.S. Public*, pg. 2404
J2 GLOBAL IRELAND LIMITED—See Ziff Davis, Inc.; *U.S. Public*, pg. 2404
J2 INNOVATIONS, INC.—See Siemens Aktiengesellschaft; *Int'l*, pg. 6889
J2L HOLDING AB; *Int'l*, pg. 3859
J2 MANAGEMENT CORPORATION; *Int'l*, pg. 3859
J2 SOLUTIONS, INC.; *U.S. Private*, pg. 2172
J3 RESOURCES, INC.—See Eurofins Scientific S.E.; *Int'l*, pg. 2548
J4B SOFTWARE & PUBLISHING LIMITED—See IDOX PLC; *Int'l*, pg. 3596
J9 TECHNOLOGIES, INC.—See Axxiome AG; *Int'l*, pg. 773
JAAMDAROU CO.; *Int'l*, pg. 3859
JAANH, INC.; *Int'l*, pg. 3859
JAARBEURS HOLDING B.V.; *Int'l*, pg. 3859
JAARBEURS UTRECHT B.V.—See Jaarbeurs Holding B.V.; *Int'l*, pg. 3859
JAA - SERBIAN AUTHORS AGENCY; *Int'l*, pg. 3859
JABAFARMA PRODUTOS FARMACEUTICOS S.A.—See Recordati S.p.A.; *Int'l*, pg. 6239
JABA I INVERSIONES INMOBILIARIAS SOCIMI SA; *Int'l*, pg. 3864
JABAL OMAR DEVELOPMENT COMPANY; *Int'l*, pg. 3864
JABA RECORDATI S.A.—See Recordati S.p.A.; *Int'l*, pg. 6239
JA-BAR SILICONE CORPORATION—See Nolato AB; *Int'l*, pg. 5407
JABER EBNE HAYYAN PHARMACEUTICAL CO.; *Int'l*, pg. 3864
JAB HOLDING COMPANY S.A.R.L.; *Int'l*, pg. 3860
JAB HOLDINGS B.V.—See JAB Holding Company S.a.r.l.; *Int'l*, pg. 3861
JABIAN; *U.S. Private*, pg. 2173
JABIL ADVANCED MECHANICAL SOLUTIONS DE MEXICO, S DE RL DE C.V.—See Jabil Inc.; *U.S. Public*, pg. 1180
JABIL ADVANCED MECHANICAL SOLUTIONS, INC.—See Jabil Inc.; *U.S. Public*, pg. 1180
JABIL CHAD AUTOMATION—See Jabil Inc.; *U.S. Public*, pg. 1180
JABIL CIRCUIT AUSTRIA GMBH—See Jabil Inc.; *U.S. Public*, pg. 1181
JABIL CIRCUIT AUTOMOTIVE, SAS—See Jabil Inc.; *U.S. Public*, pg. 1181
JABIL CIRCUIT (BEIJING) LIMITED—See Jabil Inc.; *U.S. Public*, pg. 1180
JABIL CIRCUIT DE CHIHUAHUA S. DE R.L. DE C.V.—See Jabil Inc.; *U.S. Public*, pg. 1181
JABIL CIRCUIT DE MEXICO, S DE RL DE C.V.—See Jabil Inc.; *U.S. Public*, pg. 1181
JABIL CIRCUIT FINANCIAL, INC.—See Jabil Inc.; *U.S. Public*, pg. 1181
JABIL CIRCUIT GYARTO K.F.T.—See Jabil Inc.; *U.S. Public*, pg. 1181
JABIL CIRCUIT, INC. - SAN JOSE PLANT—See Jabil Inc.; *U.S. Public*, pg. 1181
JABIL CIRCUIT, INC. - TEMPE PLANT—See Jabil Inc.; *U.S. Public*, pg. 1181
JABIL CIRCUIT INDIA PVT. LTD.—See Jabil Inc.; *U.S. Public*, pg. 1181
JABIL CIRCUIT ITALIA, S.R.L—See Jabil Inc.; *U.S. Public*, pg. 1181
JABIL CIRCUIT ITALIA, S.R.L.—See Jabil Inc.; *U.S. Public*, pg. 1181
JABIL CIRCUIT JAPAN, INC.—See Jabil Inc.; *U.S. Public*, pg. 1181
JABIL CIRCUIT, LLC—See Jabil Inc.; *U.S. Public*, pg. 1181
JABIL CIRCUIT, LTD.—See Jabil Inc.; *U.S. Public*, pg. 1181
JABIL CIRCUIT OF MICHIGAN, INC.—See Jabil Inc.; *U.S. Public*, pg. 1181
JABIL CIRCUIT POLAND SP. Z O.O.—See Jabil Inc.; *U.S. Public*, pg. 1181
JABIL CIRCUIT, SAS—See Jabil Inc.; *U.S. Public*, pg. 1181

JABIL CIRCUIT (SHANGHAI) CO. LTD.—See Jabil Inc.; *U.S. Public*, pg. 1181
JABIL CIRCUIT (SHENZHEN) CO. LTD.—See Jabil Inc.; *U.S. Public*, pg. 1181
JABIL CIRCUIT (SINGAPORE) PTE. LTD.—See Jabil Inc.; *U.S. Public*, pg. 1181
JABIL CIRCUIT (SUZHOU) LTD.—See Jabil Inc.; *U.S. Public*, pg. 1181
JABIL CIRCUIT TECHNOLOGY INDIA PVT. LTD.—See Jabil Inc.; *U.S. Public*, pg. 1181
JABIL CIRCUIT U.K., LIMITED—See Jabil Inc.; *U.S. Public*, pg. 1181
JABIL DO BRASIL INDUSTRIA ELETROELETRONICA LTDA.—See Jabil Inc.; *U.S. Public*, pg. 1181
JABIL GLOBAL SERVICES DE MEXICO, S.A. DE C.V.—See Jabil Inc.; *U.S. Public*, pg. 1181
JABIL GLOBAL SERVICES INDIA PRIVATE LIMITED—See Jabil Inc.; *U.S. Public*, pg. 1181
JABIL GLOBAL SERVICES NETHERLANDS B.V.—See Jabil Inc.; *U.S. Public*, pg. 1181
JABIL GLOBAL SERVICES POLAND SP Z.O.O.—See Jabil Inc.; *U.S. Public*, pg. 1181
JABIL INC.; *U.S. Public*, pg. 1180
JABIL JAPAN, INC.—See Jabil Inc.; *U.S. Public*, pg. 1181
JABIL (MAURITIUS) HOLDINGS LTD.—See Jabil Inc.; *U.S. Public*, pg. 1180
JABIL SDN BHD LTD.—See Jabil Inc.; *U.S. Public*, pg. 1181
JABLONECKA TEPLARENSKA A REALITNI A.S.—See Groupe BPCE; *Int'l*, pg. 3094
JAB LUXURY GMBH—See JAB Holding Company S.a.r.l.; *Int'l*, pg. 3861
JABO SUPPLY CORPORATION; *U.S. Private*, pg. 2173
JABRA—See GN Store Nord A/S; *Int'l*, pg. 3016
JABREEN INTERNATIONAL DEVELOPMENT COMPANY SAOC—See Oman International Development & Investment Company SAOG; *Int'l*, pg. 5560
JABSCO MARINE ITALIA S.R.L.—See Xylem Inc.; *U.S. Public*, pg. 2396
JABUKA A.D; *Int'l*, pg. 3864
JAB WIRELESS, INC.; *U.S. Private*, pg. 2172
JACAM CHEMICAL COMPANY, INC.; *U.S. Private*, pg. 2173
JACARANDA FM PTY LTD.—See Kagiso Tiso Holdings Proprietary Limited; *Int'l*, pg. 4050
JA CARPENTRY, INC.; *U.S. Private*, pg. 2172
JACBO PFAHLGRUNDUNGEN GMBH—See L. Possehl & Co. mbH; *Int'l*, pg. 4383
JAC COMPUTER SERVICES LTD.—See Leonard Green & Partners, L.P.; *U.S. Private*, pg. 2430
JAC COMPUTER SERVICES LTD.—See TPG Capital, L.P.; *U.S. Private*, pg. 2177
JACCS CO., LTD.; *Int'l*, pg. 3864
JACCS FINANCE (CAMBODIA) PLC—See JACCS Co., Ltd.; *Int'l*, pg. 3864
JACCS FINANCE PHILIPPINES CORPORATION—See Sojitz Corporation; *Int'l*, pg. 7061
JACCS INTERNATIONAL VIETNAM FINANCE CO., LTD.—See JACCS Co., Ltd.; *Int'l*, pg. 3864
JACC STUDIOS INC.; *U.S. Private*, pg. 2173
JAC. DE VRIES GESTA B.V.—See NIBE Industrier AB; *Int'l*, pg. 5261
JACER CORPORATION; *U.S. Private*, pg. 2173
JAC HOLDINGS, LLC—See Argonaut Private Equity, LLC; *U.S. Private*, pg. 321
JAC HOLDINGS, LLC—See Hall Capital, LLC; *U.S. Private*, pg. 1843
JACINTOPORT INTERNATIONAL LLC—See Seaboard Corporation; *U.S. Public*, pg. 1850
JACK A. ALLEN INC.; *U.S. Private*, pg. 2173
JACKALOPE PUBLISHING, INC.—See Macari-Healey Publishing Company, LLC; *U.S. Private*, pg. 2534
JACKA RESOURCES LTD.; *Int'l*, pg. 3864
JACKASS CREEK LAND & LIVESTOCK COMPANY; *U.S. Private*, pg. 2175
JACK ASTOR'S (BOISBRIAND) REALTY INC.—See SIR Corp.; *Int'l*, pg. 6961
JACK ASTOR'S (DORVAL) REALTY INC.—See SIR Corp.; *Int'l*, pg. 6961
JACK ASTOR'S (GREENFIELD) REALTY INC.—See SIR Corp.; *Int'l*, pg. 6961
JACK ASTOR'S (LAVAL) REALTY INC.—See SIR Corp.; *Int'l*, pg. 6961
JACK BARCLAY LIMITED—See Berjaya Corporation Berhad; *Int'l*, pg. 983
JACK BECKER DISTRIBUTORS, INC.; *U.S. Private*, pg. 2173
JACK B. HENDERSON CONSTRUCTION CO. INC.; *U.S. Private*, pg. 2173
JACK B. KELLEY, INC.—See Ontario Municipal Employees Retirement System; *Int'l*, pg. 5585
JACK BLACK, L.L.C.—See Edgewell Personal Care Company; *U.S. Public*, pg. 718
JACK BOWKER FORD LEASING COMPANY; *U.S. Private*, pg. 2173
JACK BROWN PRODUCE, INC.; *U.S. Private*, pg. 2173
JACK BURFORD CHEVROLET-OLDSMOBILE-GEO, INC.; *U.S. Private*, pg. 2173

JACK BURFORD CHEVROLET-OLDSMOBILE-GEO, INC.   CORPORATE AFFILIATIONS

JACKBURN MANUFACTURING INC.—See Knox Enterprises Inc.; *U.S. Private*, pg. 2324
JACK BYRNE FORD & MERCURY, INC.; *U.S. Private*, pg. 2173
JACK CARTWRIGHT, INC.—See Boss Design Ltd.; *Int'l*, pg. 1117
JACK CARUSO REGENCY DODGE INC.; *U.S. Private*, pg. 2173
JACK CEWE LTD.; *Int'l*, pg. 3864
JACK CHIA INDUSTRIES (THAILAND) PUBLIC COMPANY LIMITED; *Int'l*, pg. 3864
JACK COOPER TRANSPORT CO., INC.; *U.S. Private*, pg. 2173
JACK COOPER TRANSPORT-TEAM AUTO PROCESSING INC.—See Jack Cooper Transport Co., Inc.; *U.S. Private*, pg. 2173
THE JACK COUNTY HERALD—See Alden Global Capital LLC; *U.S. Private*, pg. 156
JACK CREEK INVESTMENT CORP.—See Bridger Aerospace Group Holdings, Inc.; *U.S. Public*, pg. 382
JACK DANIEL DISTILLERY, LEM MOTLOW, PROP., INC.—See Brown-Forman Corporation; *U.S. Public*, pg. 403
JACK DANIEL'S PROPERTIES, INC.—See Brown-Forman Corporation; *U.S. Public*, pg. 403
JACK DEMMER FORD, INC.; *U.S. Private*, pg. 2173
JACK DOHENY SUPPLIES, INC.; *U.S. Private*, pg. 2173
JACKEL CHINA LTD.—See Ping An Insurance (Group) Company of China, Ltd.; *Int'l*, pg. 5869
JACKEL FRANCE SAS—See Li & Fung Limited; *Int'l*, pg. 4479
JACKEL INTERNATIONAL LIMITED—See Li & Fung Limited; *Int'l*, pg. 4479
JACKERY, INC.—See Shenzhen Hello Tech Energy Co., Ltd.; *Int'l*, pg. 6811
JACKERY JAPAN CO., LTD.—See Shenzhen Hello Tech Energy Co., Ltd.; *Int'l*, pg. 6811
JACK EVANS CHEVROLET CADILLAC; *U.S. Private*, pg. 2173
JACK FILTER HUNGARIA KFT.—See Mann+Hummel GmbH; *Int'l*, pg. 4673
JACK FILTER LUFTTECHNIK GMBH—See Mann+Hummel GmbH; *Int'l*, pg. 4673
JACK FROST ICE SERVICE, INC.—See H.I.G. Capital, LLC; *U.S. Private*, pg. 1829
JACK GARRETT FORD, INC.; *U.S. Private*, pg. 2173
JACK GIAMBALVO MOTOR CO., INC.; *U.S. Private*, pg. 2173
JACK GOSCH FORD, INC.; *U.S. Private*, pg. 2173
JACK GRAHAM INC.; *U.S. Private*, pg. 2174
JACK GRAY TRANSPORT, INC.; *U.S. Private*, pg. 2174
JACK GRIGGS INC.; *U.S. Private*, pg. 2174
JACK GUTTMAN, INC.—See Kohlberg & Company, LLC; *U.S. Private*, pg. 2338
JACK HENRY & ASSOCIATES, INC.; *U.S. Public*, pg. 1182
JACK HENRY BANKING—See Jack Henry & Associates, Inc.; *U.S. Public*, pg. 1182
JACK HENRY, LLC—See Jack Henry & Associates, Inc.; *U.S. Public*, pg. 1182
JACK HENRY SERVICES, LP—See Jack Henry & Associates, Inc.; *U.S. Public*, pg. 1182
JACK HENRY SYSTEMS, LP—See Jack Henry & Associates, Inc.; *U.S. Public*, pg. 1182
JACK HOOD TRANSPORTATION INC.; *U.S. Private*, pg. 2174
JACK HORNER COMMUNICATIONS; *U.S. Private*, pg. 2174
JACKIE COOPER BMW MINI; *U.S. Private*, pg. 2175
JACKIE COOPER PUBLIC RELATIONS—See Daniel J. Edelman, Inc.; *U.S. Private*, pg. 1155
JACKIE COOPER TIRE DISTRIBUTORS; *U.S. Private*, pg. 2175
JACKIN OPTICAL MARKETING COMPANY LIMITED—See AMCO United Holding Limited; *Int'l*, pg. 416
JACK IN THE BOX INC.; *U.S. Public*, pg. 1183
JACK JENNINGS & SONS, INC.; *U.S. Private*, pg. 2174
JACK & JILL OF AMERICA, INC.; *U.S. Private*, pg. 2173
JACK KAIN FORD, INC.; *U.S. Private*, pg. 2174
JACK KEY MOTOR COMPANY INC.; *U.S. Private*, pg. 2174
JACK KISSEE FORD AGENCY, INC.; *U.S. Private*, pg. 2174
JACK L. SLAGLE FIRE EQUIPMENT SUPPLY CO.; *U.S. Private*, pg. 2174
JACK MADDEN FORD SALES INC.; *U.S. Private*, pg. 2174
JACK MARSHALL FOODS INC.; *U.S. Private*, pg. 2174
JACK MAXTON CHEVROLET INCORPORATED; *U.S. Private*, pg. 2174
JACK MAY CHEVROLET BUICK GMC LIMITED; *Int'l*, pg. 3864
JACK M. BERRY INC.; *U.S. Private*, pg. 2174
JACK MORTON EXHIBITS—See The Interpublic Group of Companies, Inc.; *U.S. Public*, pg. 2096
JACK MORTON UK LIMITED—See The Interpublic Group of Companies, Inc.; *U.S. Public*, pg. 2096

JACK MORTON WORLDWIDE - SAN FRANCISCO—See The Interpublic Group of Companies, Inc.; *U.S. Public*, pg. 2097
JACK MORTON WORLDWIDE—See The Interpublic Group of Companies, Inc.; *U.S. Public*, pg. 2096
JACK MORTON WORLDWIDE—See The Interpublic Group of Companies, Inc.; *U.S. Public*, pg. 2096
JACK MORTON WORLDWIDE—See The Interpublic Group of Companies, Inc.; *U.S. Public*, pg. 2096
JACK MORTON WORLDWIDE—See The Interpublic Group of Companies, Inc.; *U.S. Public*, pg. 2096
JACK MORTON WORLDWIDE—See The Interpublic Group of Companies, Inc.; *U.S. Public*, pg. 2096
JACK MORTON WORLDWIDE—See The Interpublic Group of Companies, Inc.; *U.S. Public*, pg. 2096
JACK MORTON WORLDWIDE—See The Interpublic Group of Companies, Inc.; *U.S. Public*, pg. 2097
JACK MORTON WORLDWIDE—See The Interpublic Group of Companies, Inc.; *U.S. Public*, pg. 2097
JACK MORTON WORLDWIDE—See The Interpublic Group of Companies, Inc.; *U.S. Public*, pg. 2097
JACK MORTON WORLDWIDE—See The Interpublic Group of Companies, Inc.; *U.S. Public*, pg. 2097
JACK MORTON WORLDWIDE—See The Interpublic Group of Companies, Inc.; *U.S. Public*, pg. 2097
JACK MORTON WORLDWIDE—See The Interpublic Group of Companies, Inc.; *U.S. Public*, pg. 2096
JACK MYERS REPORT; *U.S. Private*, pg. 2174
JACK NADEL INC.; *U.S. Private*, pg. 2174
JACK NADEL INC. - SOUTHPORT OFFICE—See Jack Nadel Inc.; *U.S. Private*, pg. 2174
JACK NATHAN LIMITED—See Melewar Industrial Group Berhad; *Int'l*, pg. 4808
JACK NEAL & SON, INC.; *U.S. Private*, pg. 2174
JACK OF ALL GAMES, INC.—See TD Synnex Corp; *U.S. Public*, pg. 1984
THE JACK OLSTA COMPANY; *U.S. Private*, pg. 4058
JACKON AS; *Int'l*, pg. 3864
JACKOVICH INDUSTRIAL & CONSTRUCTION SUPPLY, INC.—See Colville Capital LLC; *U.S. Private*, pg. 979
THE JACK PARKER CORPORATION; *U.S. Private*, pg. 4058
JACK-POST CORPORATION; *U.S. Private*, pg. 2175
JACKPOT DIGITAL INC.; *Int'l*, pg. 3864
JACKPOT JUNCTION CASINO HOTEL; *U.S. Private*, pg. 2175
JACK POUST & COMPANY, INC.; *U.S. Private*, pg. 2174
JACKRABBIT TECHNOLOGIES, INC.; *U.S. Private*, pg. 2175
JACK RICE INSURANCE, INC.; *U.S. Private*, pg. 2174
JACK RICHESON & CO., INC.—See MPE Partners, LLC; *U.S. Private*, pg. 2803
JACK RICH INCORPORATED; *U.S. Private*, pg. 2174
JACK ROUSE ASSOCIATES, INC.—See RWS & Associates Entertainment, Inc.; *U.S. Private*, pg. 3509
JACK RUBIN & SONS INC.; *U.S. Private*, pg. 2174
JACKSAM CORPORATION; *U.S. Public*, pg. 1183
JACK'S AQUARIUM & PETS; *U.S. Private*, pg. 2175
JACK'S BEAN COMPANY, LLC; *U.S. Private*, pg. 2175
JACKSBORO GAZETTE-NEWS—See Alden Global Capital LLC; *U.S. Private*, pg. 156
JACK'S CAMERA INC.; *U.S. Private*, pg. 2175
JACK SCHMITT FORD INC.; *U.S. Private*, pg. 2174
JACK SCHWARTZ SHOES, INC.; *U.S. Private*, pg. 2174
JACK'S FAMILY RESTAURANTS INC.—See AEA Investors LP; *U.S. Private*, pg. 114
JACK'S FRUIT MARKET INC.; *U.S. Private*, pg. 2175
JACK'S HEAVY EQUIPMENT INCORPORATED; *U.S. Private*, pg. 2175
JACKSON ACQUISITION COMPANY; *U.S. Public*, pg. 1183
JACKSON ADEPT RESEARCH—See Jackson Associates, Inc.; *U.S. Private*, pg. 2175
JACKSON AND ASSOCIATES, INC.—See Forward Solutions; *U.S. Private*, pg. 1578
JACKSON & ASSOCIATES GENERAL CONTRACTORS, INC.; *U.S. Private*, pg. 2175
JACKSON ASSOCIATES, INC.; *U.S. Private*, pg. 2175
JACKSON AUTO GROUP; *U.S. Private*, pg. 2175
JACKSON & BLANC; *U.S. Private*, pg. 2175
JACKSON BUILDERS, INC.; *U.S. Private*, pg. 2175
JACKSON BUILDING CENTRES LTD. - CLASSIC HARDWARE—See Grafton Group plc; *Int'l*, pg. 3051
JACKSON & CHURCH HVAC GLOBAL—See AESYS Technologies, LLC; *U.S. Private*, pg. 120
JACKSON CLAYBORN, INC.; *U.S. Private*, pg. 2176
THE JACKSON CLINICS, LIMITED PARTNERSHIP—See U.S. Physical Therapy, Inc.; *U.S. Public*, pg. 2216
JACKSON COMFORT SYSTEMS, INC.—See Morgan Stanley; *U.S. Public*, pg. 1474
JACKSON & COOKSEY INC.—See BGC Group, Inc.; *U.S. Public*, pg. 329
JACKSON CORPORATION; *U.S. Private*, pg. 2176
JACKSON COUNTY BANK—See Bancorp of Southern Indiana; *U.S. Public*, pg. 269
JACKSON COUNTY FLORIDAN—See Lee Enterprises, Incorporated; *U.S. Public*, pg. 1299
JACKSON COUNTY HOME HEALTH, LLC—See UnitedHealth Group Incorporated; *U.S. Public*, pg. 2245

JACKSON COUNTY NEWSPAPERS INC.—See New West Newspapers Inc.; *U.S. Private*, pg. 2908
JACKSON COUNTY OIL CO., INC.; *U.S. Private*, pg. 2176
JACKSON COUNTY PULMONARY MEDICAL GROUP, LLC—See HCA Healthcare, Inc.; *U.S. Public*, pg. 999
JACKSON COUNTY RURAL ELECTRIC MEMBERSHIP CORPORATION; *U.S. Private*, pg. 2176
JACKSON DEAN CONSTRUCTION; *U.S. Private*, pg. 2176
JACKSON DESIGN & REMODELING, INC.; *U.S. Private*, pg. 2176
JACKSON ELECTRIC CO-OPERATIVE CORPORATION; *U.S. Private*, pg. 2176
JACKSON ELECTRIC MEMBERSHIP CORP.; *U.S. Private*, pg. 2176
JACKSON ENERGY AUTHORITY; *U.S. Private*, pg. 2176
JACKSON ENERGY COOPERATIVE; *U.S. Private*, pg. 2176
JACKSON FAMILY WINES, INC.; *U.S. Private*, pg. 2176
JACKSON FINANCIAL INC.; *U.S. Public*, pg. 1183
JACKSON FINANCIAL MANAGEMENT, INC.—See Genstar Capital, LLC; *U.S. Private*, pg. 1677
JACKSON FINANCIAL MANAGEMENT, INC.—See Keystone Group, L.P.; *U.S. Private*, pg. 2298
JACKSON FURNITURE INDUSTRIES; *U.S. Private*, pg. 2176
JACKSON GILMOUR & DOBBS, P.C.—See Kelley Drye & Warren LLP; *U.S. Private*, pg. 2275
THE JACKSON GROUP CORPORATION—See Chatham Asset Management, LLC; *U.S. Private*, pg. 863
THE JACKSON GROUP INC.—See Ares Management Corporation; *U.S. Public*, pg. 190
THE JACKSON GROUP INC.—See Leonard Green & Partners, L.P.; *U.S. Private*, pg. 2427
JACKSON HB MEDICAL SERVICES, LLC—See Community Health Systems, Inc.; *U.S. Public*, pg. 554
JACKSON HEALTHCARE, LLC; *U.S. Private*, pg. 2177
JACKSON HEALTH SYSTEM; *U.S. Private*, pg. 2176
JACKSON HEWITT TAX SERVICE INC.; *U.S. Private*, pg. 2177
JACKSON HMA, LLC—See Community Health Systems, Inc.; *U.S. Public*, pg. 554
JACKSON HOLE GOLF & TENNIS CLUB, INC.—See Vail Resorts, Inc.; *U.S. Public*, pg. 2271
JACKSON HOLE MOUNTAIN RESORT; *U.S. Private*, pg. 2177
JACKSON HOSPITAL CORPORATION—See Quorum Health Corporation; *U.S. Private*, pg. 3330
JACKSON HOSPITAL; *U.S. Private*, pg. 2177
JACKSON HOUSE; *U.S. Private*, pg. 2177
JACKSON HUNTER MORRIS & KNIGHT LLP; *U.S. Private*, pg. 2177
JACKSON INTEGRATED; *U.S. Private*, pg. 2177
JACKSON INVESTMENTS LIMITED; *Int'l*, pg. 3865
JACKSON KEARNEY GROUP; *U.S. Private*, pg. 2177
JACKSON KELLY PLLC - EVANSVILLE—See Jackson Kelly PLLC; *U.S. Private*, pg. 2177
JACKSON KELLY PLLC; *U.S. Private*, pg. 2177
THE JACKSON LABORATORY; *U.S. Private*, pg. 4058
JACKSONLEA POLISHING MATERIALS CO. LTD.—See Jason Industries, Inc.; *U.S. Private*, pg. 2190
JACKSON LEWIS LLP; *U.S. Private*, pg. 2177
JACKSON LUMBER AND MILLWORK CO.; *U.S. Private*, pg. 2177
JACKSON MARKETING GROUP, INC.; *U.S. Private*, pg. 2177
JACKSON MATTRESS COMPANY LLC; *U.S. Private*, pg. 2177
JACKSON MEDICAL CENTER, L.L.C.—See Tenet Healthcare Corporation; *U.S. Public*, pg. 2003
JACKSON MEDICAL MALL FOUNDATION; *U.S. Private*, pg. 2177
JACKSON METAL SERVICES INC.; *U.S. Private*, pg. 2178
JACKSON-MITCHELL, INC.—See Emmi AG; *Int'l*, pg. 2384
JACKSON NATIONAL ASSET MANAGEMENT LLC—See Jackson Financial Inc.; *U.S. Public*, pg. 1183
JACKSON NATIONAL LIFE DISTRIBUTORS LLC—See Jackson Financial Inc.; *U.S. Public*, pg. 1183
JACKSON NATIONAL LIFE INSURANCE COMPANY—See Jackson Financial Inc.; *U.S. Public*, pg. 1183
JACKSON OIL COMPANY, INC.; *U.S. Private*, pg. 2178
JACKSON OIL & SOLVENTS INC.; *U.S. Private*, pg. 2178
JACKSON PAPER COMPANY; *U.S. Private*, pg. 2178
JACKSON & PERKINS COMPANY—See Evergreen SC, LLC; *U.S. Private*, pg. 1440
JACKSON PHYSICIAN CORP.—See Quorum Health Corporation; *U.S. Private*, pg. 3330
JACKSON PLASTICS OPERATIONS INC—See Lancaster Colony Corporation; *U.S. Public*, pg. 1291
JACKSON PRODUCTS, INC.—See Kimberly-Clark Corporation; *U.S. Public*, pg. 1230
JACKSON PROPERTIES INC.; *U.S. Private*, pg. 2178
JACKSON RECOVERY CENTERS, INC.—See Rosecrance, Inc.; *U.S. Private*, pg. 3482
JACKSON SALES & STORAGE CO.—See National Presto Industries, Inc; *U.S. Public*, pg. 1497

COMPANY NAME INDEX

JACKSON SCHOOL VILLAGE, L.P.—See Essex Property Trust, Inc.; *U.S. Public*, pg. 796
JACKSON'S GARAGE INC.; *U.S. Private*, pg. 2179
JACKSON SQUARE AVIATION IRELAND LIMITED—See Mitsubishi HC Capital Inc.; *Int'l*, pg. 4951
JACKSON SQUARE AVIATION, LLC—See Mitsubishi HC Capital Inc.; *Int'l*, pg. 4951
JACKSON SQUARE PARTNERS, LLC—See Affiliated Managers Group, Inc.; *U.S. Public*, pg. 55
JACKSON SQUARE VENTURES, LLC; *U.S. Private*, pg. 2178
JACKSON SUMNER & ASSOCIATES, INC.; *U.S. Private*, pg. 2178
THE JACKSON SUN—See Gannett Co., Inc.; *U.S. Public*, pg. 900
JACKSON SUPPLY COMPANY; *U.S. Private*, pg. 2178
JACKSON SURGICAL CENTER, LLC—See Tenet Healthcare Corporation; *U.S. Public*, pg. 2010
JACKSON SYSTEMS, LLC; *U.S. Private*, pg. 2178
JACKSON, TENNESSEE HOSPITAL COMPANY, LLC—See Community Health Systems, Inc.; *U.S. Public*, pg. 554
JACKSON THORNTON & CO. PC; *U.S. Private*, pg. 2178
JACKSON-T, LLC—See Lithia Motors, Inc.; *U.S. Public*, pg. 1323
JACKSON TRANSPORT PROPRIETARY LIMITED—See OneLogix Group Limited; *Int'l*, pg. 5576
JACKSON TUBE SERVICE INC.; *U.S. Private*, pg. 2178
JACKSON & TULL; *U.S. Private*, pg. 2175
JACKSONVILLE BEACHES ANESTHESIA ASSOCIATES, INC.—See KKR & Co. Inc.; *U.S. Public*, pg. 1245
JACKSONVILLE BEACH SURGERY CENTER, LLC—See Bain Capital, LP; *U.S. Private*, pg. 446
JACKSONVILLE BUILDERS SUPPLY—See East Hardwood Co. Inc.; *U.S. Private*, pg. 1316
JACKSONVILLE BUSINESS JOURNAL—See Advance Publications, Inc.; *U.S. Private*, pg. 84
JACKSONVILLE CARENOW URGENT CARE, LLC—See HCA Healthcare, Inc.; *U.S. Public*, pg. 999
JACKSONVILLE ENDOSCOPY CENTERS, LLC—See Tenet Healthcare Corporation; *U.S. Public*, pg. 2004
JACKSONVILLE JAGUARS, LLC; *U.S. Private*, pg. 2179
JACKSONVILLE JETPORT LLC; *U.S. Private*, pg. 2179
JACKSONVILLE MULTISPECIALTY SERVICES, LLC—See HCA Healthcare, Inc.; *U.S. Public*, pg. 999
JACKSONVILLE ORTHOPEDIC INSTITUTE—See Baptist Health Medical Center; *U.S. Private*, pg. 470
THE JACKSONVILLE PORT AUTHORITY; *U.S. Private*, pg. 4058
JACKSONVILLE SPECIALISTS, LLC—See HCA Healthcare, Inc.; *U.S. Public*, pg. 999
JACKSONVILLE SURGERY CENTER, LTD.—See HCA Healthcare, Inc.; *U.S. Public*, pg. 999
JACKSONVILLE TBI REALTY, LLC—See Toll Brothers, Inc.; *U.S. Public*, pg. 2162
JACKSON WALKER LLP; *U.S. Private*, pg. 2178
JACKSON WELDING SUPPLY CO., INC.; *U.S. Private*, pg. 2178
JACKSON WHOLESALE HARDWARE; *U.S. Private*, pg. 2179
JACKSON WWS, INC.—See Hoshizaki Corporation; *Int'l*, pg. 3484
JACKSPEED CORPORATION LIMITED; *Int'l*, pg. 3865
JACKSPEED LEATHER SPECIAL MANUFACTURER (M) SDN. BHD.—See JACKSPEED CORPORATION LIMITED; *Int'l*, pg. 3865
JACKSPEED SINGAPORE PTE. LTD.—See JACKSPEED CORPORATION LIMITED; *Int'l*, pg. 3865
JACK'S SURF & SPORT; *U.S. Private*, pg. 2175
JACKS TIRE & OIL INC.—See Purcell Tire & Rubber Company Inc.; *U.S. Private*, pg. 3305
JACKS TIRE & OIL MANAGEMENT CO.—See Purcell Tire & Rubber Company Inc.; *U.S. Private*, pg. 3304
JACKSTONES, INC.; *Int'l*, pg. 3865
JACK'S WHOLESALE WINDOWS AND DESIGN; *U.S. Private*, pg. 2175
JACK TECHNOLOGY CO., LTD.; *Int'l*, pg. 3864
JACK VAN IMPE MINISTRIES INTERNATIONAL; *U.S. Private*, pg. 2175
JACK VICTOR LIMITED; *Int'l*, pg. 3864
JACK WALTERS & SONS CORP.; *U.S. Private*, pg. 2175
JACK WILLIAMS TIRE CO. INC.; *U.S. Private*, pg. 2175
JACK WILLS LTD.—See Frasers Group plc; *Int'l*, pg. 2765
JACK WINEGARDNER CHEVROLET, INC.; *U.S. Private*, pg. 2175
JACK WOLF CADILLAC GMC; *U.S. Private*, pg. 2175
JACK WOLFSKIN AUSTRIA GMBH—See Topgolf Callaway Brands Corp.; *U.S. Public*, pg. 2164
JACK WOLFSKIN BELGIUM BVBA—See Topgolf Callaway Brands Corp.; *U.S. Public*, pg. 2164
JACK WOLFSKIN GMBH & CO. KGAA—See Topgolf Callaway Brands Corp.; *U.S. Public*, pg. 2164
JACK WOLFSKIN ITALIA S.R.L.—See Topgolf Callaway Brands Corp.; *U.S. Public*, pg. 2164
JACK WOLFSKIN NETHERLANDS BV—See Topgolf Callaway Brands Corp.; *U.S. Public*, pg. 2164
JACK WOLFSKIN NORTH AMERICA, INC.—See Topgolf Callaway Brands Corp.; *U.S. Public*, pg. 2164

JACK WOLFSKIN UK LTD.—See Topgolf Callaway Brands Corp.; *U.S. Public*, pg. 2164
JACKY JONES FORD LINCOLN; *U.S. Private*, pg. 2179
JACKY'S ELECTRONICS LLC; *Int'l*, pg. 3865
JACKY'S ELECTRONICS (S) PTE. LTD.—See Jacky's Electronics LLC; *Int'l*, pg. 3865
JACKY'S INTERNATIONAL LTD.—See Jacky's Electronics LLC; *Int'l*, pg. 3865
JACLO INDUSTRIES—See Durst Corporation; *U.S. Private*, pg. 1294
JACLYN, INC.—See Golden Touch Imports, Inc.; *U.S. Private*, pg. 1734
JACMAR COMPANIES, INC.; *U.S. Private*, pg. 2179
JACMAR FOOD SERVICE—See Jacmar Companies, Inc.; *U.S. Private*, pg. 2179
JACMEL GROWTH PARTNERS MANAGEMENT LLC; *U.S. Private*, pg. 2179
JACOBACCI & PARTNERS S.P.A.—See Abril Abogados SLU; *Int'l*, pg. 69
JACOB BEK GMBH—See ThyssenKrupp AG; *Int'l*, pg. 7724
JACOB FORD VILLAGE, LLC—See Lone Star Global Acquisitions, LLC; *U.S. Private*, pg. 2488
JACOB HOLTZ COMPANY—See Dominus Capital, L.P.; *U.S. Private*, pg. 1256
JACOBI CARBONS AB—See Osaka Gas Co., Ltd.; *Int'l*, pg. 5645
JACOBIO PHARMACEUTICALS GROUP CO., LTD.; *Int'l*, pg. 3865
JACOBI SALES INC.; *U.S. Private*, pg. 2179
JACOBI, TOOMBS & LANZ, INC.—See NewHold Enterprises LLC; *U.S. Private*, pg. 2915
JACOB LEINENKUGEL BREWING COMPANY—See Molson Coors Beverage Company; *U.S. Public*, pg. 1459
JACOB LINDH AB—See Storskogen Group AB; *Int'l*, pg. 7227
JACOB NORTH LLC—See Midstates Group Company; *U.S. Private*, pg. 2718
JACO BRYANT PRINTING LLC—See Westshore Capital Partners LLC; *U.S. Private*, pg. 4500
JACOBS ADVANCED MANUFACTURING BV—See Jacobs Engineering Group, Inc.; *U.S. Public*, pg. 1185
JACOBS ADVISERS INC.—See Jacobs Engineering Group, Inc.; *U.S. Public*, pg. 1184
JACOBS AGENCY, INC.; *U.S. Private*, pg. 2179
JACOBS AUSTRALIA PTY. LIMITED—See Jacobs Engineering Group, Inc.; *U.S. Public*, pg. 1185
JACOBS AUTO ENTERPRISES INC.; *U.S. Private*, pg. 2179
JACOBS AUTO LAURENSBERG GMBH—See Penske Automotive Group, Inc.; *U.S. Public*, pg. 1665
JACOBS BELGIE NV—See Jacobs Engineering Group, Inc.; *U.S. Public*, pg. 1184
JACOBS BRASIL HOLDINGS S.A.—See Jacobs Engineering Group, Inc.; *U.S. Public*, pg. 1184
JACOBS CAPITAL, LLC; *U.S. Private*, pg. 2179
JACOBS CAPITAL (PTY) LTD.; *Int'l*, pg. 3865
JACOBS CHILE S.A.—See Jacobs Engineering Group, Inc.; *U.S. Public*, pg. 1185
JACOBS CHINA LIMITED—See Jacobs Engineering Group, Inc.; *U.S. Public*, pg. 1184
JACOBS CHINA LIMITED—See Jacobs Engineering Group, Inc.; *U.S. Public*, pg. 1185
JACOBS CLEAN ENERGY S.R.O.—See Jacobs Engineering Group, Inc.; *U.S. Public*, pg. 1184
JACOBS & CLEVENGER, INC.; *U.S. Private*, pg. 2179
JACOBS COLOMBIA S.A.S.—See Jacobs Engineering Group, Inc.; *U.S. Public*, pg. 1184
JACOBS CONSULTANCY SPOL S.R.O—See Jacobs Engineering Group, Inc.; *U.S. Public*, pg. 1184
JACOBS CONSULTANTS, INC.—See Jacobs Engineering Group, Inc.; *U.S. Public*, pg. 1184
JACOBS DOUWE EGBERTS AU PTY. LTD.—See JDE Peet's N.V.; *Int'l*, pg. 3925
JACOBS DOUWE EGBERTS BE B.V.B.A.—See JDE Peet's N.V.; *Int'l*, pg. 3925
JACOBS DOUWE EGBERTS DE GMBH—See JDE Peet's N.V.; *Int'l*, pg. 3925
JACOBS DOUWE EGBERTS DK APS—See JDE Peet's N.V.; *Int'l*, pg. 3925
JACOBS DOUWE EGBERTS ES S.L.U.—See JDE Peet's N.V.; *Int'l*, pg. 3925
JACOBS DOUWE EGBERTS FR S.A.S.—See JDE Peet's N.V.; *Int'l*, pg. 3925
JACOBS DOUWE EGBERTS GB LTD.—See JDE Peet's N.V.; *Int'l*, pg. 3925
JACOBS DOUWE EGBERTS KAZAKHSTAN LLP—See JDE Peet's N.V.; *Int'l*, pg. 3925
JACOBS DOUWE EGBERTS NL B.V.—See JAB Holding Company S.a.r.l.; *Int'l*, pg. 3862
JACOBS DOUWE EGBERTS NORGE AS—See JDE Peet's N.V.; *Int'l*, pg. 3925
JACOBS DOUWE EGBERTS PL SP. Z O.O.—See JDE Peet's N.V.; *Int'l*, pg. 3925
JACOBS DOUWE EGBERTS PRO NL B.V.—See JDE Peet's N.V.; *Int'l*, pg. 3925
JACOBS DOUWE EGBERTS RO S.R.L.—See JDE Peet's N.V.; *Int'l*, pg. 3925

JACOBS EAGLETON LLC—See Jacobs Engineering Group, Inc.; *U.S. Public*, pg. 1184
JACOBS E&C AUSTRALIA PTY. LTD.—See Jacobs Engineering Group, Inc.; *U.S. Public*, pg. 1185
JACOBS E&C LIMITED—See Jacobs Engineering Group, Inc.; *U.S. Public*, pg. 1186
JACOBSEN CONSTRUCTION COMPANY, INC.; *U.S. Private*, pg. 2180
JACOBS ENGINEERING AND CONSTRUCTION (THAILAND) LIMITED—See Jacobs Engineering Group, Inc.; *U.S. Public*, pg. 1184
JACOBS ENGINEERING DEUTSCHLAND GMBH—See Jacobs Engineering Group, Inc.; *U.S. Public*, pg. 1184
JACOBS ENGINEERING GROUP, INC. - ARLINGTON (NORTH GLEBE ROAD), VA—See Jacobs Engineering Group, Inc.; *U.S. Public*, pg. 1184
JACOBS ENGINEERING GROUP, INC. - BATON ROUGE, LA—See Jacobs Engineering Group, Inc.; *U.S. Public*, pg. 1184
JACOBS ENGINEERING GROUP, INC. - BOSTON, MA—See Jacobs Engineering Group, Inc.; *U.S. Public*, pg. 1184
JACOBS ENGINEERING GROUP, INC. - CINCINNATI, OH—See Jacobs Engineering Group, Inc.; *U.S. Public*, pg. 1184
JACOBS ENGINEERING GROUP, INC. - CONSHOHOCKEN, PA—See Jacobs Engineering Group, Inc.; *U.S. Public*, pg. 1184
JACOBS ENGINEERING GROUP, INC. - DENVER, CO—See Jacobs Engineering Group, Inc.; *U.S. Public*, pg. 1184
JACOBS ENGINEERING GROUP, INC. - GREENVILLE, SC—See Jacobs Engineering Group, Inc.; *U.S. Public*, pg. 1184
JACOBS ENGINEERING GROUP, INC. - MORRISTOWN, NJ—See Jacobs Engineering Group, Inc.; *U.S. Public*, pg. 1184
JACOBS ENGINEERING GROUP, INC. - NEW YORK, NY—See Jacobs Engineering Group, Inc.; *U.S. Public*, pg. 1184
JACOBS ENGINEERING GROUP, INC.; *U.S. Public*, pg. 1183
JACOBS ENGINEERING GROUP MALAYSIA SDN BHD—See Jacobs Engineering Group, Inc.; *U.S. Public*, pg. 1184
JACOBS ENGINEERING INDIA PRIVATE LIMITED—See Jacobs Engineering Group, Inc.; *U.S. Public*, pg. 1184
JACOBS ENGINEERING IRELAND LIMITED - BLACKROCK—See Jacobs Engineering Group, Inc.; *U.S. Public*, pg. 1184
JACOBS ENGINEERING IRELAND LIMITED—See Jacobs Engineering Group, Inc.; *U.S. Public*, pg. 1184
JACOBS ENGINEERING NEW YORK INC.—See Jacobs Engineering Group, Inc.; *U.S. Public*, pg. 1184
JACOBS ENGINEERING SA INTERNATIONAL—See Jacobs Engineering Group, Inc.; *U.S. Public*, pg. 1184
JACOBS ENGINEERING (SUZHOU) CO., LTD—See Jacobs Engineering Group, Inc.; *U.S. Public*, pg. 1185
JACOBS ENGINEERING UK LIMITED—See Jacobs Engineering Group, Inc.; *U.S. Public*, pg. 1185
JACOBSEN MANUFACTURING, INC.; *U.S. Private*, pg. 2180
JACOBSEN PROFESSIONAL LAWN CARE INC.—See Textron Inc.; *U.S. Public*, pg. 2028
JACOBS ENTERTAINMENT, INC.; *U.S. Private*, pg. 2179
JACOBSEN TEXTRON—See Textron Inc.; *U.S. Public*, pg. 2028
JACOBS EUROPEAN HOLDINGS LIMITED—See Jacobs Engineering Group, Inc.; *U.S. Public*, pg. 1185
JACOBS FIELD SERVICES AMERICAS INC.—See Jacobs Engineering Group, Inc.; *U.S. Public*, pg. 1185
JACOBS FIELD SERVICES NORTH AMERICA, INC.—See Jacobs Engineering Group, Inc.; *U.S. Public*, pg. 1185
JACOBS FINANCIAL GROUP, INC.; *U.S. Private*, pg. 2180
JACOBS GROUP (AUSTRALIA) PTY LTD—See Jacobs Engineering Group, Inc.; *U.S. Public*, pg. 1185
JACOBS HOLDING AG; *Int'l*, pg. 3865
JACOBS HOLDING GMBH—See Penske Automotive Group, Inc.; *U.S. Public*, pg. 1665
JACOBS INTERNATIONAL LIMITED—See Jacobs Engineering Group, Inc.; *U.S. Public*, pg. 1185
JACOBS ITALIA SPA—See Jacobs Engineering Group, Inc.; *U.S. Public*, pg. 1185
JACOBS MATASIS (PTY) LTD.—See Jacobs Engineering Group, Inc.; *U.S. Public*, pg. 1185
JACOBS MECHANICAL CO.; *U.S. Private*, pg. 2180
JACOBS MINERALS CANADA INC.—See Jacobs Engineering Group, Inc.; *U.S. Public*, pg. 1185
JACOBS MINERALS, INC.—See Jacobs Engineering Group, Inc.; *U.S. Public*, pg. 1185
JACOBS NEDERLAND BV—See Jacobs Engineering Group, Inc.; *U.S. Public*, pg. 1185
JACOBS NEW ZEALAND LIMITED—See Jacobs Engineering Group, Inc.; *U.S. Public*, pg. 1186
JACOBS NORWAY AS—See Jacobs Engineering Group, Inc.; *U.S. Public*, pg. 1185
JACOBSON CAPITAL SERVICES INC.; *U.S. Private*, pg. 2180

JACOBSON & COMPANY, INC.
CORPORATE AFFILIATIONS

JACOBSON & COMPANY, INC.; *U.S. Private*, pg. 2180
JACOBS ONE LIMITED—See Jacobs Engineering Group, Inc.; *U.S. Public*, pg. 1185
JACOBSON FLORAL SUPPLY INC.; *U.S. Private*, pg. 2180
JACOBSON HAT CO. INC.; *U.S. Private*, pg. 2180
JACOBSON MEDICAL (HONG KONG) LIMITED—See Jacobson Pharma Corporation Limited; *Int'l*, pg. 3865
JACOBSON PARTNERS; *U.S. Private*, pg. 2180
JACOBSON PHARMA CORPORATION LIMITED; *Int'l*, pg. 3865
JACOBSON ROST; *U.S. Private*, pg. 2180
JACOBSON (SHENZHEN) TRADING COMPANY LIMITED—See Chinney Alliance Group Limited; *Int'l*, pg. 1570
JACOBSON VAN DEN BERG (HONG KONG) LIMITED—See Chinney Alliance Group Limited; *Int'l*, pg. 1570
JACOBS PERU S.A.—See Jacobs Engineering Group, Inc.; *U.S. Public*, pg. 1185
JACOBS PROCESS B.V.—See Jacobs Engineering Group, Inc.; *U.S. Public*, pg. 1185
JACOBS PROCESS LIMITED—See Jacobs Engineering Group, Inc.; *U.S. Public*, pg. 1186
JACOBS PROFESSIONAL SERVICES INC.—See Jacobs Engineering Group, Inc.; *U.S. Public*, pg. 1185
JACOBS PROJECTS (PHILIPPINES) INC.—See Jacobs Engineering Group, Inc.; *U.S. Public*, pg. 1185
JACOBS PROJECTS (SHANGHAI) CO., LTD.—See Jacobs Engineering Group, Inc.; *U.S. Public*, pg. 1185
JACOBS REAL ESTATE SERVICES LLC—See The Richard E. Jacobs Group, LLC; *U.S. Private*, pg. 4106
JACOBSRIMELL—See Amdocs Limited; *Int'l*, pg. 419
JACOBS RUSSIA LLC—See Jacobs Engineering Group, Inc.; *U.S. Public*, pg. 1185
JACOBS SKM LTD—See Jacobs Engineering Group, Inc.; *U.S. Public*, pg. 1186
JACOBS STOBBARTS LTD—See Jacobs Engineering Group, Inc.; *U.S. Public*, pg. 1186
JACOBS STRATEGIC SOLUTIONS GROUP, INC.—See Jacobs Engineering Group, Inc.; *U.S. Public*, pg. 1185
JACOBS (SUZHOU) VEHICLE SYSTEMS CO., LTD—See Cummins Inc.; *U.S. Public*, pg. 608
JACOBS SVERIGE AB—See Jacobs Engineering Group, Inc.; *U.S. Public*, pg. 1185
JACOBS TECHNOLOGY, INC.—See Jacobs Engineering Group, Inc.; *U.S. Public*, pg. 1185
JACOBS TELECOMMUNICATIONS INC.—See Jacobs Engineering Group, Inc.; *U.S. Public*, pg. 1185
JACOB STERN & SONS, INC.; *U.S. Private*, pg. 2179
JACOB STERN & SONS, INC. - TEXAS DIVISION—See Jacob Stern & Sons, Inc.; *U.S. Private*, pg. 2179
JACOBS & THOMPSON INC.; *Int'l*, pg. 3865
JACOBS TRADING, LLC; *U.S. Private*, pg. 2180
JACOBS U.K. LIMITED—See Jacobs Engineering Group, Inc.; *U.S. Public*, pg. 1185
JACOBS VEHICLE SYSTEMS, INC.—See Cummins Inc.; *U.S. Public*, pg. 608
JACOBUS ENERGY, INC.; *U.S. Private*, pg. 2180
JACOBUS ENERGY - QUICKFLASH DIVISION—See Jacobus Energy, Inc.; *U.S. Private*, pg. 2180
JACOBUS PETROLEUM PRODUCTS, LLC—See Jacobus Energy, Inc.; *U.S. Private*, pg. 2180
JACOBY & MEYERS ATTORNEYS LLP—See Jacoby & Meyers, P.C.; *U.S. Private*, pg. 2180
JACOBY & MEYERS, LLC—See Jacoby & Meyers, P.C.; *U.S. Private*, pg. 2180
JACOBY & MEYERS, LLP—See Jacoby & Meyers, P.C.; *U.S. Private*, pg. 2180
JACOBY & MEYERS, P.C.; *U.S. Private*, pg. 2180
JACO ELECTRONICS, INC.; *U.S. Public*, pg. 1183
JACO ENVIRONMENTAL INC.; *U.S. Private*, pg. 2179
JACO MANUFACTURING CO. INC.; *U.S. Private*, pg. 2179
JACON AIRCRAFT SUPPLY CO. INC.; *U.S. Private*, pg. 2180
JACON EQUIPMENT PTY. LIMITED—See MAAS Group Holdings Limited; *Int'l*, pg. 4618
JACO OIL; *U.S. Private*, pg. 2179
JA COSMETICS CORP.—See TPG Capital, L.P.; *U.S. Public*, pg. 2174
JACOTTET INDUSTRIE SAS—See Carclo plc; *Int'l*, pg. 1321
J.A. COUNTER & ASSOCIATES, INC.—See Genstar Capital, LLC; *U.S. Private*, pg. 1674
JA-CO WELDING & CONSULTING LTD.; *Int'l*, pg. 3859
JAC PRODUCTS, INC. - JAC MOLDING PLANT—See Argonaut Private Equity, LLC; *U.S. Private*, pg. 321
JAC PRODUCTS, INC. - JAC MOLDING PLANT—See Hall Capital, LLC; *U.S. Private*, pg. 1843
JAC PRODUCTS, INC.—See Argonaut Private Equity, LLC; *U.S. Private*, pg. 321
JAC PRODUCTS, INC.—See Hall Capital, LLC; *U.S. Private*, pg. 1843
JACQUELINE EMPORIUM LIMITED—See King Fook Holdings Limited; *Int'l*, pg. 4168
JACQUELINE-EVE FASHIONS PTY. LIMITED—See Premier Investments Limited; *Int'l*, pg. 5960
JACQUELINE-EVE (LEASES) PTY. LIMITED—See Premier Investments Limited; *Int'l*, pg. 5960
JACQUELINE-EVE (RETAIL) PTY. LIMITED—See Premier Investments Limited; *Int'l*, pg. 5960
JACQUELINES WHOLESALE BAKERY, INC.—See Rich Holdings, Inc.; *U.S. Private*, pg. 3426
JACQUEMARD AVR SA—See Vossloh AG; *Int'l*, pg. 8308
JACQUES BOGART SA; *Int'l*, pg. 3866
JACQUES CHOCOLATERIE SA—See Sweet Products Logistics NV; *Int'l*, pg. 7366
JACQUES GEORGES DURAND INDUSTRIES, S.A.; *Int'l*, pg. 3866
JACQUES MORET, INC.; *U.S. Private*, pg. 2180
JACQUES TECHNOLOGIES PTY. LTD.—See TKH Group N.V.; *Int'l*, pg. 7764
JACQUES TORRES CHOCOLATE; *U.S. Private*, pg. 2180
JACQUES VERT GROUP LIMITED—See Sun Capital Partners, Inc.; *U.S. Private*, pg. 3861
JACQUES VERT GROUP LTD.—See Sun Capital Partners, Inc.; *U.S. Private*, pg. 3861
JACQUES WEIN-DEPOT WEIN-EINZELHANDEL GMBH—See Hawesko Holding AG; *Int'l*, pg. 3288
JACQUET BENELUX SA—See Jacquet Metal Service SA; *Int'l*, pg. 3866
JACQUET DEUTSCHLAND GMBH—See Jacquet Metal Service SA; *Int'l*, pg. 3866
JACQUET FINLAND OY—See Jacquet Metal Service SA; *Int'l*, pg. 3867
JACQUET HOUSTON INC.—See Jacquet Metal Service SA; *Int'l*, pg. 3867
JACQUET IBERICA S.A.—See Jacquet Metal Service SA; *Int'l*, pg. 3867
JACQUET INTERNATIONAL SAS—See Jacquet Metal Service SA; *Int'l*, pg. 3867
JACQUET ITALTAGLIO SRL—See Jacquet Metal Service SA; *Int'l*, pg. 3867
JACQUET LYON SASU—See Jacquet Metal Service SA; *Int'l*, pg. 3867
JACQUET METALLSERVICE GMBH—See Jacquet Metal Service SA; *Int'l*, pg. 3867
JACQUET METAL SERVICE SA; *Int'l*, pg. 3866
JACQUET MID ATLANTIC INC.—See Jacquet Metal Service SA; *Int'l*, pg. 3867
JACQUET MIDWEST INC.—See Jacquet Metal Service SA; *Int'l*, pg. 3867
JACQUET MILCAMPS BENELUX—See Groupe Limagrain Holding SA; *Int'l*, pg. 3107
JACQUET MONTREAL INC.—See Jacquet Metal Service SA; *Int'l*, pg. 3867
JACQUET NEDERLAND BV—See Jacquet Metal Service SA; *Int'l*, pg. 3867
JACQUET NORDPOL SP. Z O.O.—See Jacquet Metal Service SA; *Int'l*, pg. 3867
JACQUET NOVA SR—See Jacquet Metal Service SA; *Int'l*, pg. 3867
JACQUET OSIRO AG—See Jacquet Metal Service SA; *Int'l*, pg. 3867
JACQUET PARIS SAS—See Jacquet Metal Service SA; *Int'l*, pg. 3867
JACQUET POLSKA SP Z.O.O.—See Jacquet Metal Service SA; *Int'l*, pg. 3867
JACQUET PORTUGAL LDA—See Jacquet Metal Service SA; *Int'l*, pg. 3867
JACQUET SHANGHAI CO. LTD.—See Jacquet Metal Service SA; *Int'l*, pg. 3867
JACQUET SOUTHEAST INC.—See Jacquet Metal Service SA; *Int'l*, pg. 3867
JACQUET S.R.O.—See Jacquet Metal Service SA; *Int'l*, pg. 3867
JACQUET SVERIGE AB—See Jacquet Metal Service SA; *Int'l*, pg. 3867
JACQUET UK LTD—See Jacquet Metal Service SA; *Int'l*, pg. 3867
JACQUET WEST INC.—See Jacquet Metal Service SA; *Int'l*, pg. 3867
JACQUI SMALL LLP—See The Quarto Group, Inc.; *Int'l*, pg. 7677
JAC RECRUITMENT CO., LTD.; *Int'l*, pg. 3864
JAC RECRUITMENT (GERMANY) GMBH—See JAC Recruitment Co., Ltd.; *Int'l*, pg. 3864
JAC RECRUITMENT HONG KONG LTD.—See JAC Recruitment Co., Ltd.; *Int'l*, pg. 3864
JAC RECRUITMENT INDIA PVT. LTD.—See JAC Recruitment Co., Ltd.; *Int'l*, pg. 3864
JAC RECRUITMENT PTE. LTD.—See JAC Recruitment Co., Ltd.; *Int'l*, pg. 3864
JAC RECRUITMENT (UK) LIMITED—See JAC Recruitment Co., Ltd.; *Int'l*, pg. 3864
J.A. CROSON, L.L.C.; *U.S. Private*, pg. 2157
JACS CO., LTD.—See NIPPN Corporation; *Int'l*, pg. 5309
JACSTEN HOLDINGS, LLC; *U.S. Private*, pg. 2180
JACS UK LTD.; *Int'l*, pg. 3868
JAC TISSOT SOLUTIONS GMBH—See Li & Fung Limited; *Int'l*, pg. 4479
JACTRAVEL LIMITED—See Vitruvian Partners LLP; *Int'l*, pg. 8263
JACUZZI BRANDS CORPORATION—See Investindustrial Advisors Ltd.; *Int'l*, pg. 3779
JACUZZI CHILE S.A.—See Investindustrial Advisors Ltd.; *Int'l*, pg. 3779
JACUZZI DO BRASIL—See Investindustrial Advisors Ltd.; *Int'l*, pg. 3779
JACUZZI EUROPE S.P.A.—See Investindustrial Advisors Ltd.; *Int'l*, pg. 3779
JACUZZI HOT TUBS—See Investindustrial Advisors Ltd.; *Int'l*, pg. 3779
JACUZZI INC.—See Investindustrial Advisors Ltd.; *Int'l*, pg. 3779
JACUZZI LUXURY BATH—See Investindustrial Advisors Ltd.; *Int'l*, pg. 3779
JAC. VANDENBERG, INC.; *U.S. Private*, pg. 2173
JADACO BV—See Minerva Bunkering; *Int'l*, pg. 4907
JADAK EUROPE BV—See Novanta Inc.; *U.S. Public*, pg. 1548
JADAK, LLC—See Novanta Inc.; *U.S. Public*, pg. 1548
JADAR A.D.; *Int'l*, pg. 3868
JADARD TECHNOLOGY LIMITED—See Fitipower Integrated Technology, Inc.; *Int'l*, pg. 2695
JADASON ENTERPRISES (HK) LIMITED—See Jadason Enterprises Ltd; *Int'l*, pg. 3868
JADASON ENTERPRISES (JAPAN) LIMITED—See Jadason Enterprises Ltd; *Int'l*, pg. 3868
JADASON ENTERPRISES LTD; *Int'l*, pg. 3868
JADASON ENTERPRISES (THAILAND) LIMITED—See Jadason Enterprises Ltd; *Int'l*, pg. 3868
JADA TOYS CO., LTD—See SIMBA-DICKIE-GROUP GmbH; *Int'l*, pg. 6927
JADA TOYS, INC.—See SIMBA-DICKIE-GROUP GmbH; *Int'l*, pg. 6927
JADAWEL INTERNATIONAL COMPANY LIMITED; *Int'l*, pg. 3868
JADCORE LLC—See Arsenal Capital Management LP; *U.S. Private*, pg. 339
JAD CORPORATION—See Bain Capital, LP; *U.S. Private*, pg. 441
JADE ART GROUP INC.; *Int'l*, pg. 3868
JADE BIRD FIRE ALARM INTERNATIONAL (EUROPE) S.L.—See Jade Bird Fire Co., Ltd.; *Int'l*, pg. 3868
JADE BIRD FIRE CO., LTD.; *Int'l*, pg. 3868
JADE CITY INTERNATIONAL LIMITED—See Shui On Company Limited; *Int'l*, pg. 6869
JADE DESIGN, INC.; *U.S. Private*, pg. 2181
JADE EASTERN TRADING INC.; *U.S. Private*, pg. 2181
JADE EIGHT PROPERTIES LLC—See Safehold Inc.; *U.S. Public*, pg. 1834
JADE EQUIPMENT CORP.—See The Jordan Company, L.P.; *U.S. Private*, pg. 4060
JADE GLOBAL HOLDINGS, INC; *U.S. Public*, pg. 1186
JADE GLOBAL, INC.; *U.S. Private*, pg. 2181
JADE HOMES RESORT BERHAD—See Gamuda Berhad; *Int'l*, pg. 2879
JADE IMMOBILIEN MANAGEMENT GMBH—See ADLER Group SA; *Int'l*, pg. 150
JADE LEADER CORP.; *Int'l*, pg. 3868
JADE MARVEL GROUP BERHAD; *Int'l*, pg. 3868
JADE MOUNTAIN ACQUISITION CORP.; *Int'l*, pg. 3868
JADE POWER TRUST; *Int'l*, pg. 3868
JADE RESORTS PRIVATE LIMITED—See Country Club Hospitality & Holidays Limited; *Int'l*, pg. 1818
JADE ROAD INVESTMENTS LIMITED; *Int'l*, pg. 3868
JADE SOFTWARE CORPORATION LIMITED—See The Skipton Building Society; *Int'l*, pg. 7687
JADE SOFTWARE CORPORATION UK LIMITED—See The Skipton Building Society; *Int'l*, pg. 7687
JADES SUPER FOOD; *U.S. Private*, pg. 2181
JADE STEEL GROUP, LTD.; *U.S. Private*, pg. 2181
JADE-STERLING STEEL CO. INC.; *U.S. Private*, pg. 2181
JADESTONE ENERGY (AUSTRALIA) PTY. LTD.—See Jadestone Energy plc; *Int'l*, pg. 3868
JADESTONE ENERGY INC.—See Jadestone Energy plc; *Int'l*, pg. 3868
JADESTONE ENERGY PLC; *Int'l*, pg. 3868
JADESTONE ENERGY SDN. BHD.—See Jadestone Energy plc; *Int'l*, pg. 3868
JADESTONE ENERGY (SINGAPORE) PTE. LTD.—See Jadestone Energy plc; *Int'l*, pg. 3868
JADESTONE GROUP AB—See Light & Wonder, Inc.; *U.S. Public*, pg. 1315
JADE TRAVEL LTD.—See Success Universe Group Limited; *Int'l*, pg. 7250
JADE TRAVEL LTD.—See Success Universe Group Limited; *Int'l*, pg. 7250
J-AD GRAPHICS INC.; *U.S. Private*, pg. 2155
JADI IMAGING HOLDINGS BERHAD; *Int'l*, pg. 3868
JADI IMAGING TECHNOLOGIES SDN. BHD.—See Jadi Imaging Holdings Berhad; *Int'l*, pg. 3868
J. ADOLF BAEUERLE GMBH & CO. KG—See Georgsmarienhutte Holding GmbH; *Int'l*, pg. 2940
JADRAN AD; *Int'l*, pg. 3868
JADRAN A.D.; *Int'l*, pg. 3868
JADRAN D.D. CRIKVENIC; *Int'l*, pg. 3868
JADRAN GALENSKI LABORATORIJ D.D.; *Int'l*, pg. 3869
JADRANSKA BANKA D.D. SIBENIK; *Int'l*, pg. 3869
JADRANSKI NAFTOVOD, JOINT STOCK COMPANY; *Int'l*, pg. 3869
JADRANSKO OSIGURANJE D.D.; *Int'l*, pg. 3869
JADRAN TVORNICA CARAPA D.D.; *Int'l*, pg. 3869

COMPANY NAME INDEX

JADROAGENT D.D.; *Int'l*, pg. 3869
JADROPLOV LTD.; *Int'l*, pg. 3869
JAD SOLUTIONS PTE. LTD.—See Natural Cool Holdings Limited; *Int'l*, pg. 5167
JADUDA GMBH—See TX Group AG; *Int'l*, pg. 7992
JADWA INVESTMENT COMPANY; *Int'l*, pg. 3869
JADWA REIT SAUDI FUND; *Int'l*, pg. 3869
JAE BUSINESS SUPPORT, LTD.—See Japan Aviation Electronics Industry, Ltd.; *Int'l*, pg. 3886
JAECKLE MINNESOTA INC.—See Jaeckle Wholesale Inc.; *U.S. Private*, pg. 2181
JAECKLE WHOLESALE INC.; *U.S. Private*, pg. 2181
JAE DONGGUAN SERVICE CO., LTD.—See Japan Aviation Electronics Industry, Ltd.; *Int'l*, pg. 3886
JAE ELECTRONICS, INC.—See Japan Aviation Electronics Industry, Ltd.; *Int'l*, pg. 3886
JAE ENGINEERING, LTD.—See Japan Aviation Electronics Industry, Ltd.; *Int'l*, pg. 3886
JAE EUROPE, LTD.—See Japan Aviation Electronics Industry, Ltd.; *Int'l*, pg. 3886
JAE FOODS, LTD.—See Japan Aviation Electronics Industry, Ltd.; *Int'l*, pg. 3886
JAE FUJI, LTD.—See Japan Aviation Electronics Industry, Ltd.; *Int'l*, pg. 3886
THE JAEGER COMPANY'S SHOPS LIMITED—See Jaeger Limited; *Int'l*, pg. 3869
JAEGER ET BOSSHARD SA—See HIAG Immobilen Holding AG; *Int'l*, pg. 3382
JAEGER FRANCE SARL—See AdCapital AG; *Int'l*, pg. 126
JAEGER & HAINES, INC.—See Oklahoma General Agency, Inc.; *U.S. Private*, pg. 3007
JAEGER, INC.; *U.S. Private*, pg. 2181
JAEGER LIMITED; *Int'l*, pg. 3869
JAEGER LUMBER AND SUPPLY CO. INC.; *U.S. Private*, pg. 2181
JAEGER POWAY AUTOMOTIVE SYSTEMS (SHENZHEN) LTD.—See AdCapital AG; *Int'l*, pg. 126
JAEGER RESOURCES CORP.; *Int'l*, pg. 3869
JAE HAKKO, LTD.—See Japan Aviation Electronics Industry, Ltd.; *Int'l*, pg. 3886
JAE HIROSAKI, LTD.—See Japan Aviation Electronics Industry, Ltd.; *Int'l*, pg. 3886
JAE HONG KONG, LTD.—See Japan Aviation Electronics Industry, Ltd.; *Int'l*, pg. 3886
JAE HOUSTON, LLC—See Japan Aviation Electronics Industry, Ltd.; *Int'l*, pg. 3886
JAE KOREA, INC.—See Japan Aviation Electronics Industry, Ltd.; *Int'l*, pg. 3886
J A ELECTRONIC MANUFACTURING CO, INC.—See Brand Industrial Services, Inc.; *U.S. Private*, pg. 636
JA ELECTRONICS COMPANY—See Brance Krachy Company, Inc.; *U.S. Private*, pg. 635
JAENSCH IMMIGRATION LAW FIRM; *U.S. Private*, pg. 2181
JA ENVIROTANKS LTD.—See Original Steel Services Limited; *Int'l*, pg. 5630
JAE OREGON, INC.—See Japan Aviation Electronics Industry, Ltd.; *Int'l*, pg. 3886
JAE PHILIPPINES, INC.—See Japan Aviation Electronics Industry, Ltd.; *Int'l*, pg. 3886
JAEREN SPAREBANK; *Int'l*, pg. 3869
JAE SHANGHAI CO., LTD.—See Japan Aviation Electronics Industry, Ltd.; *Int'l*, pg. 3886
JAE SHINSHU, LTD.—See Japan Aviation Electronics Industry, Ltd.; *Int'l*, pg. 3886
JAE SINGAPORE PTE. LTD.—See Japan Aviation Electronics Industry, Ltd.; *Int'l*, pg. 3886
JAE TAIWAN, LTD.—See Japan Aviation Electronics Industry, Ltd.; *Int'l*, pg. 3886
JAE TIJUANA, S.A. DE C.V.—See Japan Aviation Electronics Industry, Ltd.; *Int'l*, pg. 3886
JAE WUJIANG CO., LTD.—See Japan Aviation Electronics Industry, Ltd.; *Int'l*, pg. 3886
JAE WUXI CO., LTD.—See Japan Aviation Electronics Industry, Ltd.; *Int'l*, pg. 3886
JAE YAMAGATA, LTD.—See Japan Aviation Electronics Industry, Ltd.; *Int'l*, pg. 3886
JAEYOUNG SOLUTEC CO., LTD. - CHIBA FACTORY—See Jaeyoung Solutec Co., Ltd.; *Int'l*, pg. 3869
JAEYOUNG SOLUTEC CO., LTD.; *Int'l*, pg. 3869
JAFARI CREDIT LIMITED—See Centum Investment Company Limited; *Int'l*, pg. 1416
JAFCO AMERICA VENTURES INC.—See JAFCO Group Co., Ltd.; *Int'l*, pg. 3869
JAFCO GROUP CO., LTD.; *Int'l*, pg. 3869
JAFCO INVESTMENT (ASIA PACIFIC) LTD; *Int'l*, pg. 3869
JAFCO INVESTMENT (KOREA) CO., LTD.—See JAFCO Group Co., Ltd.; *Int'l*, pg. 3869
JAFEC USA, INC.—See Japan Foundation Engineering Co., Ltd.; *Int'l*, pg. 3889
JAFFARIAN AUTOMOTIVE GROUP; *U.S. Private*, pg. 2181
JAFFE/BRAUNSTEIN FILMS, LTD.; *U.S. Private*, pg. 2181
JAFFER WELL DRILLING—See A.C. Schultes, Inc.; *U.S. Private*, pg. 24

JAFFE TILCHIN INVESTMENT PARTNERS, LLC; *U.S. Private*, pg. 2181
JA FLOWERS SERVICES INC.—See Armellini Industries, Inc.; *U.S. Private*, pg. 330
JAFRA COSMETICS AG—See Vorwerk & Co. KG; *Int'l*, pg. 8307
JAFRA COSMETICS GMBH & CO. KG—See Vorwerk & Co. KG; *Int'l*, pg. 8307
JAFRA COSMETICS INTERNATIONAL, INC.—See Betterware de Mexico S.A.P.I. de C.V.; *Int'l*, pg. 1004
JAFRA COSMETICS INTERNATIONAL LLC—See Vorwerk & Co. KG; *Int'l*, pg. 8307
JAFRA COSMETICS S.P.A.—See Vorwerk & Co. KG; *Int'l*, pg. 8307
JAFRA MANUFACTURING S.A. DE C.V.—See Vorwerk & Co. KG; *Int'l*, pg. 8307
JAFRA RUCHI COSMETICS INDIA PRIVATE LTD—See Vorwerk & Co. KG; *Int'l*, pg. 8307
J.A. FRATE TRANSPORT SERVICES, INC.; *U.S. Private*, pg. 2157
JAFRON BIOMEDICAL CO., LTD.; *Int'l*, pg. 3869
JAGAN LAMPS LIMITED; *Int'l*, pg. 3870
JAG APPAREL—See Apparel Group Pty. Ltd.; *Int'l*, pg. 519
JAGATJIT INDUSTRIES LIMITED - PLANT I—See Jagatjit Industries Limited; *Int'l*, pg. 3870
JAGATJIT INDUSTRIES LIMITED; *Int'l*, pg. 3870
JAG BERHAD; *Int'l*, pg. 3869
JAG CONSTRUCTION CO.; *U.S. Private*, pg. 2181
JAGEMANN STAMPING COMPANY; *U.S. Private*, pg. 2181
JAGENBERG AG; *Int'l*, pg. 3870
JAGENBERG, INC.—See Jagenberg AG; *Int'l*, pg. 3870
JAGENBERG PAPER SYSTEMS GMBH—See Jagenberg AG; *Int'l*, pg. 3870
JAGENBERG TEXTILE GMBH & CO. KG—See Jagenberg AG; *Int'l*, pg. 3870
JAGER & CO. GESELLSCHAFT MIT BESCHRANKTER HAFTUNG—See CEZ, a.s.; *Int'l*, pg. 1428
JAGER HEALTH KOLN GMBH—See IQVIA Holdings Inc.; *U.S. Public*, pg. 1169
JAGEX LTD.—See The Carlyle Group Inc.; *U.S. Public*, pg. 2047
JAG FIELD CO., LTD.—See Japan Asia Group Limited; *Int'l*, pg. 3885
JAG FOREST CO., LTD.—See Japan Asia Group Limited; *Int'l*, pg. 3885
JAGGED PEAK ENERGY INC.—See Pioneer Natural Resources Company; *U.S. Public*, pg. 1693
JAGGED PEAK, INC.—See ID Logistics SAS; *Int'l*, pg. 3587
JAGGER BROWN, INC.; *U.S. Private*, pg. 2182
JAG IDEAS COMPANY LIMITED—See Stream Ideas Group Ltd.; *Int'l*, pg. 7239
JAG IDEAS (MALAYSIA) SDN. BHD.—See Stream Ideas Group Ltd.; *Int'l*, pg. 7239
JAGJANANI TEXTILES LIMITED; *Int'l*, pg. 3870
J.A.G. MINES LTD.; *Int'l*, pg. 3857
JAGO AG—See HIAG Immobilen Holding AG; *Int'l*, pg. 3382
JAGRAN PRAKASHAN LIMITED; *Int'l*, pg. 3870
JAG SEABELL CO., LTD.—See Japan Asia Group Limited; *Int'l*, pg. 3885
JAGSON AIRLINES LIMITED; *Int'l*, pg. 3870
JAGSONPAL FINANCE & LEASING LTD; *Int'l*, pg. 3870
JAGSONPAL PHARMACEUTICALS LIMITED; *Int'l*, pg. 3870
JAG SPECIALTY FOODS, LLC.; *U.S. Private*, pg. 2181
JAGUAR CANADA INC.—See Tata Motors Limited; *Int'l*, pg. 7467
JAGUAR CARS LIMITED—See Tata Motors Limited; *Int'l*, pg. 7467
JAGUAR CARS OVERSEAS HOLDINGS LTD—See Tata Motors Limited; *Int'l*, pg. 7467
THE JAGUAR COLLECTION LTD—See Tata Motors Limited; *Int'l*, pg. 7468
JAGUAR CONSULTING, INC.—See FilmTrack Inc.; *U.S. Private*, pg. 1506
JAGUAR ELMHURST—See Elmhurst Auto Group; *U.S. Private*, pg. 1376
JAGUAR FINANCIAL CORPORATION; *Int'l*, pg. 3870
JAGUAR FUELING SERVICES, LLC; *U.S. Private*, pg. 2182
JAGUAR HEALTH, INC.; *U.S. Public*, pg. 1186
JAGUAR HISPANIA SL—See Tata Motors Limited; *Int'l*, pg. 7467
JAGUAR HONG KONG—See Tata Motors Limited; *Int'l*, pg. 7467
JAGUAR LAND ROVER AUSTRALIA PTY LTD—See Tata Motors Limited; *Int'l*, pg. 7467
JAGUAR LAND ROVER AUSTRIA GMBH—See Tata Motors Limited; *Int'l*, pg. 7467
JAGUAR LAND ROVER BELUX NV—See Tata Motors Limited; *Int'l*, pg. 7467
JAGUAR LAND ROVER CANADA ULC—See Tata Motors Limited; *Int'l*, pg. 7467
JAGUAR LAND ROVER DEUTSCHLAND GMBH—See Tata Motors Limited; *Int'l*, pg. 7467
JAGUAR LAND ROVER FRANCE, SAS—See Tata Motors Limited; *Int'l*, pg. 7467

JAGUAR LAND ROVER ITALIA SPA—See Tata Motors Limited; *Int'l*, pg. 7467
JAGUAR LAND ROVER JAPAN LTD—See Tata Motors Limited; *Int'l*, pg. 7467
JAGUAR LAND ROVER KOREA CO. LTD—See Tata Motors Limited; *Int'l*, pg. 7467
JAGUAR LAND ROVER MINNEAPOLIS—See Luther Holding Company; *U.S. Private*, pg. 2517
JAGUAR LAND ROVER NEDERLAND BV—See Tata Motors Limited; *Int'l*, pg. 7467
JAGUAR LAND ROVER NORTH AMERICA LLC—See Tata Motors Limited; *Int'l*, pg. 7467
JAGUAR LAND ROVER NORTH AMERICA, LLC—See Lithia Motors, Inc.; *U.S. Public*, pg. 1323
JAGUAR-LAND ROVER OF TACOMA—See Michael O'Brien Enterprises, Inc.; *U.S. Private*, pg. 2698
JAGUAR LAND ROVER PLC—See Tata Motors Limited; *Int'l*, pg. 7467
JAGUAR LAND ROVER (SOUTH AFRICA) (PTY) LTD—See Tata Motors Limited; *Int'l*, pg. 7467
JAGUAR MINING INC.; *Int'l*, pg. 3870
JAGUAR MOTORS (MACAU) LIMITED—See Tata Motors Limited; *Int'l*, pg. 7467
JAGUAR OF TAMPA—See Elder Automotive Group; *U.S. Private*, pg. 1350
JAGUAR RESOURCES INC.; *Int'l*, pg. 3870
JAHABOW INDUSTRIES INC.; *U.S. Private*, pg. 2182
JAHAN DENIZ KALA W.S.C—See Petrochemical Transportation Engineering Co.; *Int'l*, pg. 5826
JAHANGIR SIDDIQUI & CO. LTD.; *Int'l*, pg. 3871
JAHANGIR SIDDIQUI SECURITIES SERVICES LIMITED—See EFU Life Assurance Limited; *Int'l*, pg. 2321
JAHEN HOUSEHOLD PRODUCTS CO., LTD.; *Int'l*, pg. 3871
JAH ENTERPRISES, INC.; *U.S. Private*, pg. 2182
JAHNEL-KESTERMANN GETRIEBEWERKE GMBH & CO. KG—See Pyeong San Co., Ltd.; *Int'l*, pg. 6127
JAHN & SENGSTACK GMBH—See MLP SE; *Int'l*, pg. 5004
JAHNS & FRIENDS; *Int'l*, pg. 3871
JAHORINA AUTO D.O.O.—See Vienna Insurance Group AG Wiener Versicherung Gruppe; *Int'l*, pg. 8195
JAHORINA INSURANCE PLC—See Vienna Insurance Group AG Wiener Versicherung Gruppe; *Int'l*, pg. 8195
JAHORINA OC A.D; *Int'l*, pg. 3871
JAHR TOP SPECIAL VERLAG GMBH & CO. KG; *Int'l*, pg. 3871
JAHWA ELECTRONICS CO., LTD; *Int'l*, pg. 3871
JA HWA ELECTRONICS (M) SDN, BHD—See JAHWA ELECTRONICS CO., LTD; *Int'l*, pg. 3871
JAI BALAJI INDUSTRIES LTD; *Int'l*, pg. 3871
JAIC ASIA HOLDINGS PTE. LTD.—See Japan Asia Investment Co., Ltd.; *Int'l*, pg. 3886
JAIC BUSINESS SERVICE CO., LTD.—See JAIC Co., Ltd.; *Int'l*, pg. 3871
JAIC CO., LTD.; *Int'l*, pg. 3871
JAIC INTERNATIONAL (HONG KONG) CO., LTD.—See Japan Asia Investment Co., Ltd.; *Int'l*, pg. 3886
JAI CORP LTD; *Int'l*, pg. 3871
JAIC SECURITIES CO., LTD.—See Japan Asia Investment Co., Ltd.; *Int'l*, pg. 3886
JAIC (THAILAND) CO., LTD.—See Japan Asia Investment Co., Ltd.; *Int'l*, pg. 3886
JAI DINING SERVICES (EDINBURG), INC.—See RCI Hospitality Holdings, Inc.; *U.S. Public*, pg. 1767
JAI DINING SERVICES (HARLINGEN), INC.—See RCI Hospitality Holdings, Inc.; *U.S. Public*, pg. 1767
JAIHIND GREEN ENERGY LTD.—See Jaihind Projects Ltd.; *Int'l*, pg. 3871
JAIHIND PROJECTS LTD.; *Int'l*, pg. 3871
JAIHIND SYNTHETICS LIMITED; *Int'l*, pg. 3872
JAIKUMAR REAL ESTATES PRIVATE LIMITED—See Setubandhan Infrastructure Limited; *Int'l*, pg. 6730
JAI MATA GLASS LTD.; *Int'l*, pg. 3871
JAIMINI HEALTH, INC.—See Unum Group; *U.S. Public*, pg. 2263
JAIN (AMERICAS), INC.—See Jain Irrigation Systems Limited; *Int'l*, pg. 3872
JAINAM FERRO ALLOYS (I) LIMITED; *Int'l*, pg. 3872
JAINCO PROJECTS (INDIA) LIMITED; *Int'l*, pg. 3872
JAINDL FAMILY FARMS LLC; *U.S. Private*, pg. 2182
JAIN (EUROPE) LTD.—See Jain Irrigation Systems Limited; *Int'l*, pg. 3872
JAINEX AAMCOL LIMITED - AURANGABAD WORKS—See JAINEX AAMCOL LIMITED; *Int'l*, pg. 3872
JAINEX AAMCOL LIMITED; *Int'l*, pg. 3872
JAINGXI FIVE STAR PAPER CO., LTD.—See Wuzhou Special Paper Group Co., Ltd.; *Int'l*, pg. 8516
JAIN INTERNATIONAL TRADING BV—See Temasek Holdings (Private) Limited; *Int'l*, pg. 7550
JAIN IRRIGATION, INC.—See Jain Irrigation Systems Limited; *Int'l*, pg. 3872
JAIN IRRIGATION, INC.—See Jain Irrigation Systems Limited; *Int'l*, pg. 3872
JAIN IRRIGATION SYSTEMS LIMITED; *Int'l*, pg. 3872
JAIN MARMO INDUSTRIES LTD.; *Int'l*, pg. 3872
JA INTEGRATED THINKING; *U.S. Private*, pg. 2172

JA INTEGRATED THINKING

CORPORATE AFFILIATIONS

JA INTEGRATED THINKING—See JA Integrated Thinking; *U.S. Private*, pg. 2172
JAIPAN INDUSTRIES LIMITED; *Int'l*, pg. 3872
JAIPRAKASH ASSOCIATES LIMITED - JAYPEE BALAJI CEMENT PLANT—See Jaiprakash Associates Limited; *Int'l*, pg. 3872
JAIPRAKASH ASSOCIATES LIMITED - JAYPEE CEMENT BLENDING UNIT—See Jaiprakash Associates Limited; *Int'l*, pg. 3873
JAIPRAKASH ASSOCIATES LIMITED - JAYPEE CEMENT GRINDING UNIT—See Jaiprakash Associates Limited; *Int'l*, pg. 3873
JAIPRAKASH ASSOCIATES LIMITED - JAYPEE HIMACHAL CEMENT GRINDING & BLENDING UNIT—See Jaiprakash Associates Limited; *Int'l*, pg. 3873
JAIPRAKASH ASSOCIATES LIMITED - JAYPEE HIMACHAL CEMENT PLANT—See Jaiprakash Associates Limited; *Int'l*, pg. 3873
JAIPRAKASH ASSOCIATES LIMITED - JAYPEE REWA PLANT—See Jaiprakash Associates Limited; *Int'l*, pg. 3873
JAIPRAKASH ASSOCIATES LIMITED - JAYPEE ROORKEE CEMENT GRINDING UNIT—See Jaiprakash Associates Limited; *Int'l*, pg. 3873
JAIPRAKASH ASSOCIATES LIMITED - JAYPEE SIDHI CEMENT PLANT—See Jaiprakash Associates Limited; *Int'l*, pg. 3873
JAIPRAKASH ASSOCIATES LIMITED - JAYPEE SIKANDARABAD CEMENT GRINDING UNIT—See Jaiprakash Associates Limited; *Int'l*, pg. 3873
JAIPRAKASH ASSOCIATES LIMITED; *Int'l*, pg. 3872
JAIPRAKASH POWER VENTURES LTD.—See Jaiprakash Associates Limited; *Int'l*, pg. 3873
J-AIR CO., LTD.—See Japan Airlines Co., Ltd.; *Int'l*, pg. 3884
JAIR ELECTRONICS CORPORATION; *U.S. Private*, pg. 2182
JAIWAT CO., LTD.—See Penta-Ocean Construction Co., Ltd.; *Int'l*, pg. 5788
JAIX LEASING COMPANY—See FreightCar America, Inc.; *U.S. Public*, pg. 885
JAIZ BANK PLC; *Int'l*, pg. 3873
J.A.JACK & SONS, INC.—See Arcosa, Inc.; *U.S. Public*, pg. 186
JAJO, INC.; *U.S. Private*, pg. 2182
JAKAR ELECTRONICS, SPOL. S R.O.—See Arcline Investment Management LP; *U.S. Private*, pg. 314
JAKEL, INCORPORATED—See Regal Rexnord Corporation; *U.S. Public*, pg. 1773
JAKE SWEENEY AUTO LEASING, INC.—See Jake Sweeney Automotive Inc.; *U.S. Private*, pg. 2182
JAKE SWEENEY AUTOMOTIVE INC.; *U.S. Private*, pg. 2182
JAKE SWEENEY CHRYSLER JEEP DODGE, INC.—See Jake Sweeney Automotive Inc.; *U.S. Private*, pg. 2182
JAKHARIA FABRIC LTD.; *Int'l*, pg. 3873
JAKHARIA SYNTHETICS PVT. LTD.—See Jakharia Fabric Ltd.; *Int'l*, pg. 3873
JA KIRSCH CORPORATION—See Gellert Global Group; *U.S. Private*, pg. 1657
JAKKARAT UNIO FOOTWEAR CO., LTD.—See Saha-Union Public Company Limited; *Int'l*, pg. 6479
JAKKS PACIFIC GERMANY GMBH—See JAKKS Pacific, Inc.; *U.S. Public*, pg. 1186
JAKKS PACIFIC, INC.; *U.S. Public*, pg. 1186
JAKKS PACIFIC (UK) LTD.—See JAKKS Pacific, Inc.; *U.S. Public*, pg. 1186
JAKKS SALES CORPORATION—See JAKKS Pacific, Inc.; *U.S. Public*, pg. 1186
JAKOB ANTRIEBSTECHNIK GMBH—See Fukuda Corporation; *Int'l*, pg. 2839
JAKOB MARKETING PARTNERS, *U.S. Private*, pg. 2182
JAKOB MULLER AG; *Int'l*, pg. 3873
JAKOB WINTER GMBH; *Int'l*, pg. 3873
J.A. KOERNER & COMPANY; *U.S. Private*, pg. 2157
JAKPAISAN ESTATE PUBLIC COMPANY LIMITED; *Int'l*, pg. 3873
JAKROO INC.; *U.S. Private*, pg. 2182
JAKS RESOURCES BERHAD; *Int'l*, pg. 3873
JAKS SDN. BHD.—See JAKS Resources Berhad; *Int'l*, pg. 3873
JAKS STEEL INDUSTRIES SDN. BHD.—See JAKS Resources Berhad; *Int'l*, pg. 3873
JAL ABC, INC.—See Japan Airlines Co., Ltd.; *Int'l*, pg. 3882
JAL ACADEMY CO., LTD.—See Japan Airlines Co., Ltd.; *Int'l*, pg. 3882
JAL AEROPARTS CO., LTD.—See Japan Airlines Co., Ltd.; *Int'l*, pg. 3882
JAL AIRTECH CO., LTD.—See Japan Airlines Co., Ltd.; *Int'l*, pg. 3882
JALAN TRANSOLUTIONS (INDIA) LTD.; *Int'l*, pg. 3873
JALAPRATHAN CEMENT PUBLIC COMPANY LIMITED—See Heidelberg Materials AG; *Int'l*, pg. 3317
JAL AVIATION TECHNOLOGIES CO., LTD.—See Japan Airlines Co., Ltd.; *Int'l*, pg. 3882
JAL BRAND COMMUNICATIONS CO., LTD.—See Japan Airlines Co., Ltd.; *Int'l*, pg. 3882

JAL BUSINESS AVIATION CO., LTD.—See Marubeni Corporation; *Int'l*, pg. 4705
JAL CAPITAL CO., LTD.—See Japan Airlines Co., Ltd.; *Int'l*, pg. 3882
JALCARD, INC.—See Japan Airlines Co., Ltd.; *Int'l*, pg. 3883
JAL CARGO SALES CO., LTD.—See Japan Airlines Co., Ltd.; *Int'l*, pg. 3882
JALCO AUTOMOTIVE PTY. LTD.—See Pact Group Holdings Ltd.; *Int'l*, pg. 5693
JALCO ELECTRONICS HONG KONG LTD.—See Tohoku Tatsumi KK; *Int'l*, pg. 7777
JALCO HOLDINGS INC.; *Int'l*, pg. 3874
JAL CONSTRUCTION CO., LTD.—See Japan Airlines Co., Ltd.; *Int'l*, pg. 3882
JAL-DFS CO., LTD.—See Japan Airlines Co., Ltd.; *Int'l*, pg. 3883
JAL-DFS CO., LTD.—See Sojitz Corporation; *Int'l*, pg. 7061
J. ALEXANDER'S CORPORATION—See SoftBank Group Corp.; *Int'l*, pg. 7053
J. ALEXANDER'S HOLDINGS, INC.—See SoftBank Group Corp.; *Int'l*, pg. 7053
J. ALEXANDER'S OF TEXAS, INC.—See SoftBank Group Corp.; *Int'l*, pg. 7053
J. ALEXANDER'S RESTAURANTS, INC. - OHIO—See SoftBank Group Corp.; *Int'l*, pg. 7053
J. ALEXANDER'S RESTAURANTS, INC.—See SoftBank Group Corp.; *Int'l*, pg. 7054
J. ALEXANDER'S RESTAURANTS OF KANSAS, INC.—See SoftBank Group Corp.; *Int'l*, pg. 7053
JAL EXPRESS CO., LTD.—See Japan Airlines Co., Ltd.; *Int'l*, pg. 3884
JAL GROUP ITALIA S.R.L.; *Int'l*, pg. 3873
JAL HAWAII, INCORPORATED—See Japan Airlines Co., Ltd.; *Int'l*, pg. 3882
JAL HOTELS CO., LTD.—See Japan Airlines Co., Ltd.; *Int'l*, pg. 3882
JALINAN MASYHUR SDN BHD—See IJM Corporation Berhad; *Int'l*, pg. 3609
JAL INFORMATION TECHNOLOGY CO., LTD.—See Japan Airlines Co., Ltd.; *Int'l*, pg. 3882
JAL KANSAI AIRCARGO SYSTEM CO., LTD.—See Japan Airlines Co., Ltd.; *Int'l*, pg. 3882
JALLATTE S.A.S.—See JAL Group Italia S.r.l.; *Int'l*, pg. 3873
JAL LIVRE CO., LTD.—See Japan Airlines Co., Ltd.; *Int'l*, pg. 3882
JALLON SAS; *Int'l*, pg. 3874
JAL MAINTENANCE SERVICE CO., LTD.—See Japan Airlines Co., Ltd.; *Int'l*, pg. 3882
JALMAT ACTIVITES INTERNATIONALES, SA—See Altrad Investment Authority SAS; *Int'l*, pg. 398
JALMAT OUEST ATLANTIQUE, SA—See Altrad Investment Authority SAS; *Int'l*, pg. 398
JALMAT SUD OUEST, SA—See Altrad Investment Authority SAS; *Int'l*, pg. 398
JAL NARITA AIRCRAFT MAINTENANCE CO., LTD.—See Japan Airlines Co., Ltd.; *Int'l*, pg. 3882
JAL NAVIA FUKUOKA CO., LTD.—See Japan Airlines Co., Ltd.; *Int'l*, pg. 3882
JAL NAVIA OSAKA CO., LTD.—See Japan Airlines Co., Ltd.; *Int'l*, pg. 3882
JAL NAVIA SAPPORO CO., LTD.—See Japan Airlines Co., Ltd.; *Int'l*, pg. 3882
JAL NAVIA TOKYO CO., LTD.—See Japan Airlines Co., Ltd.; *Int'l*, pg. 3882
J.A. LOGISTICS, INC.—See J.A. Frate Transport Services, Inc.; *U.S. Private*, pg. 2157
JALPAC INDIA LTD.; *Int'l*, pg. 3874
JALPAK CO., LTD.—See Japan Airlines Co., Ltd.; *Int'l*, pg. 3883
JALPAK DE MEXICO SA DE CV—See Japan Airlines Co., Ltd.; *Int'l*, pg. 3883
JALPAK INTERNATIONAL ASIA PTE. LTD.—See Japan Airlines Co., Ltd.; *Int'l*, pg. 3883
JALPAK INTERNATIONAL (AUSTRIA) GES.M.B.H.—See Japan Airlines Co., Ltd.; *Int'l*, pg. 3883
JALPAK INTERNATIONAL (EUROPE) B.V.—See Japan Airlines Co., Ltd.; *Int'l*, pg. 3883
JALPAK INTERNATIONAL (FRANCE) S.A.S.—See Japan Airlines Co., Ltd.; *Int'l*, pg. 3883
JALPAK INTERNATIONAL (GERMANY) GMBH—See Japan Airlines Co., Ltd.; *Int'l*, pg. 3883
JALPAK INTERNATIONAL HONG KONG CO., LTD.—See Japan Airlines Co., Ltd.; *Int'l*, pg. 3883
JAL PASSENGER SERVICES AMERICA, INC.—See Japan Airlines Co., Ltd.; *Int'l*, pg. 3882
JAL PLAZA CO., LTD.—See Japan Airlines Co., Ltd.; *Int'l*, pg. 3882
JAL ROYAL CATERING CO., LTD.—See Japan Airlines Co., Ltd.; *Int'l*, pg. 3882
JAL SALES CO., LTD.—See Japan Airlines Co., Ltd.; *Int'l*, pg. 3882
JAL SATELLITE TRAVEL CO., LTD.—See Japan Airlines Co., Ltd.; *Int'l*, pg. 3883
JAL SHURI KANKO CO., LTD.—See Japan Airlines Co., Ltd.; *Int'l*, pg. 3882

JAL SIMULATOR ENGINEERING CO., LTD.—See Japan Airlines Co., Ltd.; *Int'l*, pg. 3883
JALSKY HAKODATE CO., LTD.—See Japan Airlines Co., Ltd.; *Int'l*, pg. 3884
JALSKY KANAZAWA CO., LTD.—See Japan Airlines Co., Ltd.; *Int'l*, pg. 3884
JALSKY KANSAI CO., LTD.—See Japan Airlines Co., Ltd.; *Int'l*, pg. 3884
JALSKY KYUSHU CO., LTD.—See Japan Airlines Co., Ltd.; *Int'l*, pg. 3884
JALSKY OSAKA CO., LTD.—See Japan Airlines Co., Ltd.; *Int'l*, pg. 3884
JALSKY SAPPORO CO., LTD.—See Japan Airlines Co., Ltd.; *Int'l*, pg. 3884
JALSKY SENDAI CO., LTD.—See Japan Airlines Co., Ltd.; *Int'l*, pg. 3884
JAL SKY SERVICE CO., LTD.—See Japan Airlines Co., Ltd.; *Int'l*, pg. 3883
JALSKY TOKYO CO., LTD.—See Japan Airlines Co., Ltd.; *Int'l*, pg. 3884
JALSOSA, S.L.—See Helvetia Holding AG; *Int'l*, pg. 3340
JAL SUNLIGHT CO., LTD.—See Japan Airlines Co., Ltd.; *Int'l*, pg. 3883
JAL TECHNO SERVICE CO., LTD.—See Japan Airlines Co., Ltd.; *Int'l*, pg. 3883
JAL TOKYO AIRCRAFT MAINTENANCE CO.,LTD.—See Japan Airlines Co., Ltd.; *Int'l*, pg. 3883
JALTOS CO., LTD.—See Japan Airlines Co., Ltd.; *Int'l*, pg. 3884
JAL TOURS CO., LTD.—See Japan Airlines Co., Ltd.; *Int'l*, pg. 3883
JAL TRAVEL HOKKAIDO CO., LTD.—See Japan Airlines Co., Ltd.; *Int'l*, pg. 3883
JALUX AIRPORT INC.—See Japan Airlines Co., Ltd.; *Int'l*, pg. 3883
JALUX AIRPORT. INC.—See Sojitz Corporation; *Int'l*, pg. 7061
JALUX AMERICAS, INC.—See Japan Airlines Co., Ltd.; *Int'l*, pg. 3883
JALUX AMERICAS, INC.—See Sojitz Corporation; *Int'l*, pg. 7061
JALUX ASIA LTD.—See Japan Airlines Co., Ltd.; *Int'l*, pg. 3883
JALUX ASIA LTD.—See Sojitz Corporation; *Int'l*, pg. 7061
JALUX EUROPE LTD.—See Japan Airlines Co., Ltd.; *Int'l*, pg. 3883
JALUX EUROPE LTD.—See Sojitz Corporation; *Int'l*, pg. 7061
JALUX FRESH FOODS, INC.—See Japan Airlines Co., Ltd.; *Int'l*, pg. 3883
JALUX FRESH FOODS, INC.—See Sojitz Corporation; *Int'l*, pg. 7062
JALUX HONG KONG CO., LTD.—See Japan Airlines Co., Ltd.; *Int'l*, pg. 3883
JALUX HONG KONG CO., LTD.—See Sojitz Corporation; *Int'l*, pg. 7062
JALUX INC.—See Japan Airlines Co., Ltd.; *Int'l*, pg. 3883
JALUX INC.—See Sojitz Corporation; *Int'l*, pg. 7062
JALUX INC.—See Japan Airlines Co., Ltd.; *Int'l*, pg. 3883
JALUX INC.—See Sojitz Corporation; *Int'l*, pg. 7061
JALUX INSURANCE & SERVICE INC.—See Japan Airlines Co., Ltd.; *Int'l*, pg. 3883
JALUX INSURANCE & SERVICE INC.—See Sojitz Corporation; *Int'l*, pg. 7062
JALUX SHANGHAI CO., LTD.—See Japan Airlines Co., Ltd.; *Int'l*, pg. 3883
JALUX SHANGHAI CO., LTD.—See Sojitz Corporation; *Int'l*, pg. 7062
JALUX SINGAPORE PTE. LTD.—See Japan Airlines Co., Ltd.; *Int'l*, pg. 3883
JALUX SINGAPORE PTE. LTD.—See Sojitz Corporation; *Int'l*, pg. 7062
JALUX STYLE INC.—See Japan Airlines Co., Ltd.; *Int'l*, pg. 3883
JALUX STYLE INC.—See Sojitz Corporation; *Int'l*, pg. 7062
JAL WAVE CO., LTD.—See Japan Airlines Co., Ltd.; *Int'l*, pg. 3883
JALWAYS CO., LTD.—See Japan Airlines Co., Ltd.; *Int'l*, pg. 3884
JAMAC INC.—See Janome Sewing Machine Co., Ltd.; *Int'l*, pg. 3880
JAMAICA AIRCRAFT REFUELLING SERVICES LTD.—See Petroleum Corporation of Jamaica Limited; *Int'l*, pg. 5829
JAMAICA BEARINGS CO. INC.; *U.S. Private*, pg. 2182
JAMAICA BEVERAGES LTD.—See S.M. Jaleel & Co. Ltd.; *Int'l*, pg. 6456
JAMAICA BROILERS GROUP LIMITED - JAMAICA EGG SERVICES DIVISION—See Jamaica Broilers Group Limited; *Int'l*, pg. 3874
JAMAICA BROILERS GROUP LIMITED; *Int'l*, pg. 3874
JAMAICA CONTAINER REPAIR SERVICES LTD—See Israel Corporation Ltd.; *Int'l*, pg. 3823
JAMAICA DISPATCH SERVICES LIMITED—See Goddard Enterprises Limited; *Int'l*, pg. 3019
JAMAICA FLOUR MILLS LIMITED—See Archer-Daniels-Midland Company; *U.S. Public*, pg. 185

COMPANY NAME INDEX

JAMAICA GYPSUM & QUARRIES LIMITED—See CEMEX, S.A.B. de C.V.; *Int'l*, pg. 1400
JAMAICA HOSPITAL MEDICAL CENTER; *U.S. Private*, pg. 2182
JAMAICA INTERNATIONAL INSURANCE COMPANY LIMITED—See GraceKennedy Limited; *Int'l*, pg. 3049
JAMAICA MONEY MARKET BROKERS LIMITED; *Int'l*, pg. 3874
JAMAICA NATIONAL BUILDING SOCIETY; *Int'l*, pg. 3874
JAMAICA NEWS NETWORK—See Radio Jamaica Limited; *Int'l*, pg. 6176
JAMAICAN TEAS LTD.; *Int'l*, pg. 3874
JAMAICA PEGASUS HOTEL; *Int'l*, pg. 3874
JAMAICA PRODUCERS GROUP LIMITED—See PanJam Investment Limited; *Int'l*, pg. 5728
JAMAICA PUBLIC SERVICES COMPANY LIMITED—See Marubeni Corporation; *Int'l*, pg. 4705
JAMAICA STOCK EXCHANGE; *Int'l*, pg. 3874
JAMAK FABRICATION-TEX LTD.—See JMK International, Inc.; *U.S. Private*, pg. 2216
JAMALCO—See Noble Group Holdings Limited; *Int'l*, pg. 5397
THE JAMAR COMPANY—See APi Group Corporation; *Int'l*, pg. 514
JA MARKETING CORP.; *U.S. Private*, pg. 2172
JAMA SOFTWARE INC.; *U.S. Private*, pg. 2182
JAM ASSOCIATES LLC; *U.S. Private*, pg. 2182
JAMBA, INC.—See Roark Capital Group Inc.; *U.S. Private*, pg. 3454
JAMBA JUICE COMPANY—See Roark Capital Group Inc.; *U.S. Private*, pg. 3454
JAMBOJET LIMITED—See Kenya Airways PLC; *Int'l*, pg. 4129
JAMBYL CEMENT LLP—See Vicat S.A.; *Int'l*, pg. 8185
JAM CITY, INC.—See Netmarble Corp.; *Int'l*, pg. 5214
JAMCO AERO DESIGN & ENGINEERING PTE LTD.—See Temasek Holdings (Private) Limited; *Int'l*, pg. 7551
JAMCO AEROMANUFACTURING CO. LTD.—See JAMCO Corporation; *Int'l*, pg. 3874
JAMCO AEROTECH CO., LTD.—See JAMCO Corporation; *Int'l*, pg. 3874
JAMCO AMERICA, INC.—See JAMCO Corporation; *Int'l*, pg. 3874
JAMCO CORPORATION; *Int'l*, pg. 3874
JAMCO INC.; *U.S. Private*, pg. 2182
JAMCO INTERNATIONAL INC.—See Littlejohn & Co., LLC; *U.S. Private*, pg. 2470
JAM COMMUNICATIONS, INC.—See Federated Media Inc.; *U.S. Private*, pg. 1492
JAMCO PHILIPPINES INC.—See JAMCO Corporation; *Int'l*, pg. 3874
JAMCO PRODUCTS, INC.—See Myers Industries, Inc.; *U.S. Public*, pg. 1488
JAMCO SINGAPORE PTE LTD.—See JAMCO Corporation; *Int'l*, pg. 3874
JAMCO TECHNICAL CENTER CO., LTD.—See JAMCO Corporation; *Int'l*, pg. 3874
JAMCRACKER, INC.—See Actua Corporation; *U.S. Private*, pg. 71
J.A.M. DISTRIBUTING COMPANY—See BRENNTAG SE; *Int'l*, pg. 1149
JAMEDA GMBH—See DocPlanner Group; *Int'l*, pg. 2153
J. AMERICA, INC.—See Blue Point Capital Partners, LLC; *U.S. Private*, pg. 590
JAMERSON & BAUWENS ELEC CONTRS; *U.S. Private*, pg. 2182
JAMERSON-LEWIS CONSTRUCTION INC.; *U.S. Private*, pg. 2182
JAMES A. ANDREW INC.; *U.S. Private*, pg. 2183
JAMES A. CUMMINGS, INC.—See Tutor Perini Corporation; *U.S. Public*, pg. 2206
JAMES A. HALEY VETERANS' HOSPITAL; *U.S. Private*, pg. 2183
JAMES A. JENNINGS CO. INC.; *U.S. Private*, pg. 2183
JAMES ALEXANDER CORPORATION; *U.S. Private*, pg. 2183
JAMES A. SCOTT & SON INC.; *U.S. Private*, pg. 2183
JAMES AUSTIN CO. - DELAND PLANT—See James Austin Co.; *U.S. Private*, pg. 2183
JAMES AUSTIN CO. - LUDLOW PLANT—See James Austin Co.; *U.S. Private*, pg. 2183
JAMES AUSTIN CO.; *U.S. Private*, pg. 2183
JAMES AUSTIN CO. - STATESVILLE PLANT—See James Austin Co.; *U.S. Private*, pg. 2183
JAMES AVERY CRAFTSMAN INC.; *U.S. Private*, pg. 2183
JAMES BATMASIAN; *U.S. Private*, pg. 2183
JAMES BAY ENERGY NIGERIA LIMITED—See James Bay Resources Limited; *Int'l*, pg. 3875
JAMES BAY RESOURCES LIMITED; *Int'l*, pg. 3875
JAMESBECK GLOBAL PARTNERS, LLC—See RFE Investment Partners; *U.S. Private*, pg. 3420
JAMES B. NUTTER & COMPANY; *U.S. Private*, pg. 2183
JAMES BRADEN FORD LTD.; *Int'l*, pg. 3875
JAMES BRIGGS LTD.—See Tetrosyl Ltd.; *Int'l*, pg. 7578
JAMES BROWN CONTRACTING INC.—See Navigation Capital Partners, Inc.; *U.S. Private*, pg. 2873
JAMES CAMPBELL CORPORATION; *U.S. Private*, pg. 2183

JAMES C. GREENE COMPANY—See Tenco Services, Inc.; *U.S. Private*, pg. 3965
JAMES CHAPPEL; *U.S. Private*, pg. 2183
JAMES C. JENKINS INSURANCE; *U.S. Private*, pg. 2183
JAMES CONEY ISLAND INC.; *U.S. Private*, pg. 2183
JAMES CONSTRUCTION GROUP LLC—See Primoris Services Corporation; *U.S. Public*, pg. 1718
JAMES CRAFT AND SON INC.; *U.S. Private*, pg. 2183
JAMES CROPPER CONVERTING LIMITED—See James Cropper Plc; *Int'l*, pg. 3875
JAMES CROPPER PLC; *Int'l*, pg. 3875
JAMES CROPPER SPECIALITY PAPERS LIMITED—See James Cropper Plc; *Int'l*, pg. 3875
JAMES DAWSON & SON LTD.—See Compagnie Generale des Etablissements Michelin SCA; *Int'l*, pg. 1745
JAMES DEWHURST LTD.—See Sioen Industries NV; *Int'l*, pg. 6960
JAMES D. MORRISSEY INC.; *U.S. Private*, pg. 2183
JAMES DOORCHECK, INC.—See Platinum Equity, LLC; *U.S. Private*, pg. 3208
JAMES DORAN COMPANY INC.; *U.S. Private*, pg. 2183
JAMES DRURY PARTNERS, LTD.; *U.S. Private*, pg. 2183
JAMES DURRANS GMBH—See James Durrans & Sons Limited; *Int'l*, pg. 3875
JAMES DURRANS & SONS LIMITED; *Int'l*, pg. 3875
JAMES DURRANS (TIANJIN) COATINGS LTD—See James Durrans & Sons Limited; *Int'l*, pg. 3875
JAMES E. BARNES ENTERPRISES INC.; *U.S. Private*, pg. 2183
JAMES ELECTRIC MOTOR SERVICES LTD.—See Ferguson plc; *Int'l*, pg. 2638
JAMES ELECTRONICS INC.—See Custom Magnetics, Inc.; *U.S. Private*, pg. 1129
JAMES E. ROBERTS-OBAYASHI CORPORATION—See Obayashi Corporation; *Int'l*, pg. 5509
JAMES E. WAGNER CULTIVATION CORP.; *Int'l*, pg. 3875
JAMES E. WATSON & CO.—See Atlas Copco AB; *Int'l*, pg. 683
JAMES FINLAY (BLANTYRE) LTD—See John Swire & Sons Limited; *Int'l*, pg. 3980
JAMES FINLAY MOMBASA LTD—See John Swire & Sons Limited; *Int'l*, pg. 3980
JAMES FISHER ASSET INFORMATION SERVICES LIMITED—See James Fisher & Sons Public Limited Company; *Int'l*, pg. 3876
JAMES FISHER AUSTRALIA PTY LTD—See James Fisher & Sons Public Limited Company; *Int'l*, pg. 3876
JAMES FISHER (CREWING SERVICES) LIMITED—See James Fisher & Sons Public Limited Company; *Int'l*, pg. 3876
JAMES FISHER DEFENCE LIMITED—See James Fisher & Sons Public Limited Company; *Int'l*, pg. 3876
JAMES FISHER DEFENCE NORTH AMERICA LIMITED—See James Fisher & Sons Public Limited Company; *Int'l*, pg. 3876
JAMES FISHER DEFENCE SWEDEN AKTIEBOLAG—See James Fisher & Sons Public Limited Company; *Int'l*, pg. 3876
JAMES FISHER EVERARD LIMITED—See James Fisher & Sons Public Limited Company; *Int'l*, pg. 3876
JAMES FISHER (LOGISTICS) LIMITED—See James Fisher & Sons Public Limited Company; *Int'l*, pg. 3876
JAMES FISHER MARINE SERVICES LIMITED—See James Fisher & Sons Public Limited Company; *Int'l*, pg. 3876
JAMES FISHER MFE LIMITED—See James Fisher & Sons Public Limited Company; *Int'l*, pg. 3876
JAMES FISHER MIMIC LIMITED—See James Fisher & Sons Public Limited Company; *Int'l*, pg. 3876
JAMES FISHER NUCLEAR GMBH—See James Fisher & Sons Public Limited Company; *Int'l*, pg. 3876
JAMES FISHER OFFSHORE LIMITED—See James Fisher & Sons Public Limited Company; *Int'l*, pg. 3876
JAMES FISHER OFFSHORE MALAYSIA SDN. BHD.—See James Fisher & Sons Public Limited Company; *Int'l*, pg. 3876
JAMES FISHER RUMIC LIMITED—See James Fisher & Sons Public Limited Company; *Int'l*, pg. 3876
JAMES FISHER (SHIPPING SERVICES) LIMITED—See James Fisher & Sons Public Limited Company; *Int'l*, pg. 3876
JAMES FISHER & SONS PUBLIC LIMITED COMPANY; *Int'l*, pg. 3875
JAMES FISHER SUBSEA EXCAVATION MEXICO S.A. DE C.V.—See James Fisher & Sons Public Limited Company; *Int'l*, pg. 3876
JAMES FISHER SUBSEA EXCAVATION PTE. LIMITED—See James Fisher & Sons Public Limited Company; *Int'l*, pg. 3876
JAMES FISHER TANKSHIPS HOLDINGS LIMITED—See James Fisher & Sons Public Limited Company; *Int'l*, pg. 3876
JAMES FISHER TECHNOLOGIES LLC—See James Fisher & Sons Public Limited Company; *Int'l*, pg. 3876
JAMES FISHER TESTING SERVICES (IRELAND) LIMITED—See James Fisher & Sons Public Limited Company; *Int'l*, pg. 3876
JAMES F. KNOTT REALITY GROUP; *U.S. Private*, pg. 2183

JAMES MARITIME HOLDINGS, INC.

JAMES GALL & ASSOCIATES PTY LIMITED—See Rubicor Group Limited; *Int'l*, pg. 6423
JAMES GALT & COMPANY LIMITED—See Koninklijke Jumbo BV; *Int'l*, pg. 4266
JAMES G. DAVIS CONSTRUCTION CORPORATION; *U.S. Private*, pg. 2184
JAMES GIBBONS FORMAT LTD.—See Newship Ltd; *Int'l*, pg. 5238
JAMES GLEN PTY. LTD.—See Wurth Verwaltungsgesellschaft mbH; *Int'l*, pg. 8509
JAMES G. MURPHY CO. INC.; *U.S. Private*, pg. 2184
JAMES G. PARKER INSURANCE ASSOCIATES; *U.S. Private*, pg. 2184
JAMES GRANT SPORTS MANAGEMENT—See Formation Group PLC; *Int'l*, pg. 2734
JAMES GROUP, INC.; *U.S. Private*, pg. 2184
JAMES HALSTEAD PLC; *Int'l*, pg. 3877
JAMES HAMILTON CONSTRUCTION CO.; *U.S. Private*, pg. 2184
JAMES HARDIE 117 PTY LTD—See James Hardie Industries plc; *Int'l*, pg. 3877
JAMES HARDIE AUSTRALIA PTY. LTD.—See James Hardie Industries plc; *Int'l*, pg. 3877
JAMES HARDIE BATIMENT S.A.S.—See James Hardie Industries plc; *Int'l*, pg. 3877
JAMES HARDIE BUILDING PRODUCTS INC.—See James Hardie Industries plc; *Int'l*, pg. 3877
JAMES HARDIE BUILDING PRODUCTS—See James Hardie Industries plc; *Int'l*, pg. 3877
JAMES HARDIE INDUSTRIES PLC; *Int'l*, pg. 3877
JAMES HARDIE PHILIPPINES, INC.—See James Hardie Industries plc; *Int'l*, pg. 3877
JAMES HARDIE RESEARCH (HOLDINGS) PTY LTD—See James Hardie Industries plc; *Int'l*, pg. 3877
JAMES HARDIE RESEARCH PTY LTD—See James Hardie Industries plc; *Int'l*, pg. 3877
JAMES HAY ADMINISTRATION COMPANY LIMITED—See Nucleus Financial Platforms Limited; *Int'l*, pg. 5485
JAMES HAY HOLDINGS LIMITED—See Nucleus Financial Platforms Limited; *Int'l*, pg. 5485
JAMES HAY PENSION TRUSTEES LIMITED—See Nucleus Financial Platforms Limited; *Int'l*, pg. 5485
JAMES HAY WRAP MANAGERS LIMITED—See Nucleus Financial Platforms Limited; *Int'l*, pg. 5485
JAMES H. CROSS CO.; *U.S. Private*, pg. 2184
JAMES H. DREW CORPORATION—See Paychex, Inc.; *U.S. Public*, pg. 1655
JAMES H. HEAL & COMPANY LIMITED—See Battery Ventures, L.P.; *U.S. Private*, pg. 489
JAMES H. MALOY INC.; *U.S. Private*, pg. 2184
JAMES HOTELS LIMITED; *Int'l*, pg. 3877
JAMES HOWDEN GROUP LIMITED—See Chart Industries, Inc.; *U.S. Public*, pg. 482
JAMES J. ANDERSON CONSTRUCTION CO. INC.; *U.S. Private*, pg. 2184
JAMES J. BOYLE & CO.; *U.S. Private*, pg. 2184
JAMES & JENKINS LTD; *Int'l*, pg. 3875
JAMES JONES COMPANY, LLC—See Mueller Water Products, Inc.; *U.S. Public*, pg. 1485
JAMES J. WELCH & CO., INC.; *U.S. Private*, pg. 2184
JAMES J. WILLIAMS BULK SERVICE TRANSPORT, INC.—See Trans-System Inc.; *U.S. Private*, pg. 4206
JAMES KEMBALL LIMITED—See Kawasaki Kisen Kaisha, Ltd.; *Int'l*, pg. 4100
JAMES LATHAM GATESHEAD LTD—See James Latham Plc; *Int'l*, pg. 3877
JAMES LATHAM LEEDS—See James Latham Plc; *Int'l*, pg. 3877
JAMES LATHAM PLC; *Int'l*, pg. 3877
JAMES LATHAM PURFLEET LTD—See James Latham Plc; *Int'l*, pg. 3877
JAMES LATHAMS DUDLEY LTD—See James Latham Plc; *Int'l*, pg. 3877
JAMES LATHAMS EASTLEIGH LTD—See James Latham Plc; *Int'l*, pg. 3877
JAMES LATHAMS HEMEL HEMPSTEAD LTD—See James Latham Plc; *Int'l*, pg. 3877
JAMES LATHAM THURROCK LTD—See James Latham Plc; *Int'l*, pg. 3877
JAMES LATHAM WIGSTON LTD—See James Latham Plc; *Int'l*, pg. 3877
JAMES LATHAM YATE LTD—See James Latham Plc; *Int'l*, pg. 3877
JAMES L. MAHER CENTER; *U.S. Private*, pg. 2184
JAMES L. MINITER INSURANCE AGENCY, INC.—See Hellman & Friedman LLC; *U.S. Private*, pg. 1909
JAMES L. TAYLOR MANUFACTURING CO.; *U.S. Private*, pg. 2184
JAMES LUMBER CO.; *U.S. Private*, pg. 2184
JAMES & LUTHER, INC.; *U.S. Private*, pg. 2183
JAMES L. WILLIAMS PTY. LTD.; *Int'l*, pg. 3877
JAMES MACHINE WORKS, LLC; *U.S. Private*, pg. 2184
THE JAMES MADISON INSTITUTE; *U.S. Private*, pg. 4058
JAMES MARINE INC.; *U.S. Private*, pg. 2184
JAMES MARITIME HOLDINGS, INC.; *U.S. Public*, pg. 1187

JAMESMARK BANCSHARES, INC.

CORPORATE AFFILIATIONS

JAMESMARK BANCSHARES, INC.; *U.S. Private*, pg. 2185
JAMES MARTIN SIGNATURE VANITIES, LLC—See Ferguson plc; *Int'l*, pg. 2638
JAMES MATTHEWS INC.; *U.S. Private*, pg. 2184
JAMES MCCULLAGH CO. INC.; *U.S. Private*, pg. 2184
JAMES MCHUGH CONSTRUCTION CO.—See McHugh Enterprises Inc.; *U.S. Private*, pg. 2636
JAMES M. JOHNSTON & ASSOCIATES INC.—See AlphaCore Capital LLC; *U.S. Private*, pg. 200
JAMES MONROE CAPITAL CORPORATION; *U.S. Public*, pg. 1187
JAMES MOORE & CO., P.L.; *U.S. Private*, pg. 2184
JAMES M. PLEASANTS COMPANY INC.; *U.S. Private*, pg. 2184
JAMESON, GILROY, AND B & L LIVESTOCK LTD.; *Int'l*, pg. 3878
JAMESON INNS, INC.—See J.E. Robert Company; *U.S. Private*, pg. 2162
JAMESON, LLC—See Platte River Ventures, LLC; *U.S. Private*, pg. 3211
JAMESON PUBLISHING INC.; *U.S. Private*, pg. 2185
JAMESON RESOURCES LIMITED; *Int'l*, pg. 3878
JAMES PASCOE LIMITED; *Int'l*, pg. 3878
JAMES P. HILL DISTRIBUTORS; *U.S. Private*, pg. 2184
JAMES PRECISION ENGINEERING PTE LTD—See Chien Wei Precise Technology Co., Ltd.; *Int'l*, pg. 1477
JAMES PURDEY & SONS LIMITED—See Compagnie Financiere Richemont S.A.; *Int'l*, pg. 1741
JAMES REAL ESTATE SERVICES, INC.—See Intelica Commercial Real Estate Company; *U.S. Private*, pg. 2104
JAMES REED & PARTNERS PLC; *Int'l*, pg. 3878
JAMES RICHARDSON & SONS, LIMITED; *Int'l*, pg. 3878
JAMES RITTER LUMBER COMPANY; *U.S. Private*, pg. 2185
JAMES RIVER COAL COMPANY; *U.S. Private*, pg. 2185
JAMES RIVER COAL SALES INC.—See James River Coal Company; *U.S. Private*, pg. 2185
JAMES RIVER COAL SERVICE CO.—See James River Coal Company; *U.S. Private*, pg. 2185
JAMES RIVER EQUIPMENT, CO.—See Brandt Holdings Company; *U.S. Private*, pg. 638
JAMES RIVER EQUIPMENT INC.; *U.S. Private*, pg. 2185
JAMES RIVER GROUP HOLDINGS, LTD.—See D. E. Shaw & Co., L.P.; *U.S. Private*, pg. 1139
JAMES RIVER GROUP, INC.—See D. E. Shaw & Co., L.P.; *U.S. Private*, pg. 1139
JAMES RIVER INSURANCE COMPANY—See D. E. Shaw & Co., L.P.; *U.S. Private*, pg. 1139
JAMES RIVER INTERNISTS, LLC—See HCA Healthcare, Inc.; *U.S. Public*, pg. 999
JAMES RIVER INTERNISTS, LLC—See HCA Healthcare, Inc.; *U.S. Public*, pg. 999
JAMES RIVER TRANSPORTATION; *U.S. Private*, pg. 2185
JAMES ROSS ADVERTISING; *U.S. Private*, pg. 2185
JAMES R. ROSENCRANTZ & SONS; *U.S. Private*, pg. 2185
JAMES R. THOMPSON INC.; *U.S. Private*, pg. 2185
JAMES R. VANNOY & SONS CONSTRUCTION COMPANY INC.; *U.S. Private*, pg. 2185
JAMES SKINNER BAKING COMPANY; *U.S. Private*, pg. 2185
JAMES & SONS LTD.; *U.S. Private*, pg. 2183
JAMES SOUTHALL & COMPANY LTD.; *Int'l*, pg. 3878
JAMES STEEL & TUBE COMPANY—See Avis Industrial Corporation; *U.S. Private*, pg. 407
JAMES & THOMAS, INC.; *U.S. Private*, pg. 2183
JAMES THOMPSON & CO. INC.; *U.S. Private*, pg. 2185
JAMESTOWN CONTAINER CORPORATION; *U.S. Private*, pg. 2185
JAMESTOWN CONTAINER CORP.—See Jamestown Container Corporation; *U.S. Private*, pg. 2185
JAMESTOWN CRA-B1, LLC—See Independence Realty Trust, Inc.; *U.S. Public*, pg. 1115
JAMESTOWN DISTRIBUTORS; *U.S. Private*, pg. 2185
JAMESTOWN ENTERTAINMENT; *U.S. Private*, pg. 2186
JAMESTOWN METAL MARINE SALES, INC.; *U.S. Private*, pg. 2186
JAMESTOWN PLASTICS INC.; *U.S. Private*, pg. 2186
THE JAMESTOWN SUN—See Forum Communications Company; *U.S. Private*, pg. 1577
JAMES TRUSS COMPANY; *U.S. Private*, pg. 2185
JAMES WALKER ASIA PACIFIC—See The James Walker Group Ltd; *Int'l*, pg. 7657
JAMES WALKER AUSTRALIA LTD—See The James Walker Group Ltd; *Int'l*, pg. 7657
JAMES WALKER BELGIUM—See The James Walker Group Ltd; *Int'l*, pg. 7657
JAMES WALKER BENELUX B.V.—See The James Walker Group Ltd; *Int'l*, pg. 7657
JAMES WALKER & COMPANY—See The James Walker Group Ltd; *Int'l*, pg. 7657
JAMES WALKER DEUTSCHLAND—See The James Walker Group Ltd; *Int'l*, pg. 7657
JAMES WALKER DO BRASIL TECNOLOGIA EM VEDACOES INDUSTRIALS LTDA—See The James Walker Group Ltd; *Int'l*, pg. 7658

JAMES WALKER FLEMINGS LTD—See The James Walker Group Ltd; *Int'l*, pg. 7657
JAMES WALKER FRANCE—See The James Walker Group Ltd; *Int'l*, pg. 7657
THE JAMES WALKER GROUP LTD; *Int'l*, pg. 7657
JAMES WALKER IBERICA—See The James Walker Group Ltd; *Int'l*, pg. 7657
JAMES WALKER INMARCO INDUSTRIES PVT LTD—See The James Walker Group Ltd; *Int'l*, pg. 7657
JAMES WALKER IRELAND—See The James Walker Group Ltd; *Int'l*, pg. 7657
JAMES WALKER ITALIANA—See The James Walker Group Ltd; *Int'l*, pg. 7658
JAMES WALKER KEAFLEX LTD—See The James Walker Group Ltd; *Int'l*, pg. 7658
JAMES WALKER MFG—See The James Walker Group Ltd; *Int'l*, pg. 7658
JAMES WALKER MOORFLEX LTD—See The James Walker Group Ltd; *Int'l*, pg. 7658
JAMES WALKER NEW ZEALAND—See The James Walker Group Ltd; *Int'l*, pg. 7658
JAMES WALKER NORGE AS—See The James Walker Group Ltd; *Int'l*, pg. 7658
JAMES WALKER OIL & GAS CO—See The James Walker Group Ltd; *Int'l*, pg. 7658
JAMES WALKER ROTABOLT LTD—See The James Walker Group Ltd; *Int'l*, pg. 7658
JAMES WALKER (SHANGHAI) SEALING TECHNOLOGY LTD—See The James Walker Group Ltd; *Int'l*, pg. 7657
JAMES WALKER SOUTH AFRICA—See The James Walker Group Ltd; *Int'l*, pg. 7658
JAMES WARREN TEA LIMITED—See Warren Tea Limited; *Int'l*, pg. 8346
JAMES WATTIE RETIREMENT VILLAGE LIMITED—See Ryman Healthcare Ltd.; *Int'l*, pg. 6439
JAMESWAY INCUBATOR COMPANY INC.—See FPS Food Processing Systems B.V.; *Int'l*, pg. 2757
JAMES W. BELL CO. INC.; *U.S. Private*, pg. 2185
JAMES W. HALTERMAN, INC.—See ARR Investments, LLC; *U.S. Private*, pg. 334
JAMF HOLDING CORP.; *U.S. Public*, pg. 1187
JAM FILLED ENTERTAINMENT, INC.—See Boat Rocker Media; *Int'l*, pg. 1095
JAMF JAPAN KK—See Jamf Holding Corp.; *U.S. Public*, pg. 1187
JAMF SOFTWARE PACIFIC LIMITED—See Jamf Holding Corp.; *U.S. Public*, pg. 1187
JAMF SOFTWARE UK LIMITED—See Jamf Holding Corp.; *U.S. Public*, pg. 1187
JAMF SWEDEN AB—See Jamf Holding Corp.; *U.S. Public*, pg. 1187
JAMIE GIBBS & ASSOCIATES; *U.S. Private*, pg. 2186
JAMIESON LABORATORIES LTD.—See Jamieson Wellness, Inc.; *Int'l*, pg. 3878
JAMIESON MANUFACTURING CO.—See ITOCHU Corporation; *Int'l*, pg. 3840
JAMIESON'S PET FOOD DISTRIBUTORS LTD.; *Int'l*, pg. 3878
JAMIESON WELLNESS, INC.; *Int'l*, pg. 3878
JAM INDUSTRIES LTD.—See DCC plc; *Int'l*, pg. 1990
JAMISON BEDDING, INC.—See Solstice Sleep Products, Inc.; *U.S. Private*, pg. 3710
JAMISON DOOR COMPANY; *U.S. Private*, pg. 2186
JAMISON/MCKAY LLC; *U.S. Private*, pg. 2186
JA MITSUI LEASING, LTD.; *Int'l*, pg. 3859
JA MITSUI LEASING USA HOLDINGS, INC.—See JA Mitsui Leasing, Ltd.; *Int'l*, pg. 3859
JAMMIN JAVA CORP.; *U.S. Public*, pg. 1187
JAMMU & KASHMIR BANK LTD.; *Int'l*, pg. 3878
JAMNA AUTO INDUSTRIES LTD - PLANT III—See Jamna Auto Industries Ltd.; *Int'l*, pg. 3878
JAMNA AUTO INDUSTRIES LTD - PLANT II—See Jamna Auto Industries Ltd.; *Int'l*, pg. 3878
JAMNA AUTO INDUSTRIES LTD - PLANT I—See Jamna Auto Industries Ltd.; *Int'l*, pg. 3878
JAMNA AUTO INDUSTRIES LTD.; *Int'l*, pg. 3878
JAMNAGAR PROPERTIES PRIVATE LIMITED—See Unilever PLC; *Int'l*, pg. 8044
JAMNICA D.O.O. BEOGRAD - RED BULL—See Red Bull GmbH; *Int'l*, pg. 6243
J.A. MOORE & SONS INC.; *U.S. Private*, pg. 2157
J. A. MOSS CONSTRUCTION CO. INC.; *U.S. Private*, pg. 2155
JAMPLAY LLC; *U.S. Private*, pg. 2186
JAMPT CORPORATION—See Sojitz Corporation; *Int'l*, pg. 7062
THE J.A.M.S. AGENCY CORPORATION—See Glockner Chevrolet Co. Inc.; *U.S. Private*, pg. 1720
JAMSAN TERVEYS OY—See Pihlajalinna Oy; *Int'l*, pg. 5865
JAMSHEDPUR UTILITIES & SERVICES COMPANY LIMITED—See Tata Sons Limited; *Int'l*, pg. 7471
J.A.M SHELL BUILDERS, INC.; *U.S. Private*, pg. 2158
JAMSHRI REALTY LIMITED; *Int'l*, pg. 3878
JAMS MEDIA LLC; *U.S. Private*, pg. 2186
JAMS, THE RESOLUTION EXPERTS; *U.S. Private*, pg. 2186
JAMUNA BANK PLC; *Int'l*, pg. 3878
JAMUNA OIL COMPANY LIMITED; *Int'l*, pg. 3878

JANAGAS S.R.L.—See Italgas S.p.A.; *Int'l*, pg. 3828
JANAKI FINANCE COMPANY LIMITED; *Int'l*, pg. 3879
JANAM TECHNOLOGIES LLC—See ASSA ABLOY AB; *Int'l*, pg. 637
JANANA DE MALUCHO TEXTILE MILLS LIMITED; *Int'l*, pg. 3879
JANA PARTNERS, LLC; *U.S. Private*, pg. 2186
JANASHAKTHI INSURANCE PLC; *Int'l*, pg. 3879
JANA SMALL FINANCE BANK; *Int'l*, pg. 3879
JANATA CAPITAL LTD.—See Global IME Bank Limited; *Int'l*, pg. 2997
JANATA INSURANCE COMPANY LTD.; *Int'l*, pg. 3879
JAN BECHER KARLOVARSKA BECHEROVKA, A/S—See Pernod Ricard S.A.; *Int'l*, pg. 5810
JANCO E-COMMERCE SOLUTIONS LIMITED—See Janco Holdings Limited; *Int'l*, pg. 3879
JANCO ELECTRONICS INC.; *U.S. Private*, pg. 2186
JANCO ENGINEERED PRODUCTS, LLC—See MacLean-Fogg Company; *U.S. Private*, pg. 2537
JANCO FOODS, INC.; *U.S. Private*, pg. 2186
JANCO HOLDINGS LIMITED; *Int'l*, pg. 3879
JANCO LTD.; *U.S. Private*, pg. 2186
THE JAN COMPANIES; *U.S. Private*, pg. 4058
JANDD MOUNTAINEERING, INC.; *U.S. Private*, pg. 2186
JANDIA PLAYA S.A.—See TUI AG; *Int'l*, pg. 7965
JANDL BAUGESELLSCHAFT M.B.H.—See PORR AG; *Int'l*, pg. 5923
JANE CHURCHILL LIMITED—See Colefax Group PLC; *Int'l*, pg. 1697
JANEL CORPORATION; *U.S. Public*, pg. 1187
JANEL GROUP, INC.—See Janel Corporation; *U.S. Public*, pg. 1187
THE JANEL GROUP OF GEORGIA, INC.—See Janel Corporation; *U.S. Public*, pg. 1187
JANELL INC.; *U.S. Private*, pg. 2186
JANE MANDER RETIREMENT VILLAGE LIMITED—See Ryman Healthcare Ltd.; *Int'l*, pg. 6439
JANES FAMILY FOODS LTD.—See Sofina Foods Inc.; *Int'l*, pg. 7050
JANESVILLE ACOUSTICS—See Jason Industries, Inc.; *U.S. Private*, pg. 2189
JANESVILLE DE MEXICO, S.A. DE C.V. - CELAYA PLANT—See Jason Industries, Inc.; *U.S. Private*, pg. 2189
JANESVILLE DE MEXICO, S.A. DE C.V.—See Jason Industries, Inc.; *U.S. Private*, pg. 2189
JANESVILLE GROUP LIMITED—See Societe BIC S.A.; *Int'l*, pg. 7036
JANESVILLE MALL LIMITED PARTNERSHIP—See CBL & Associates Properties, Inc.; *U.S. Public*, pg. 458
JANESVILLE SAND & GRAVEL CO; *U.S. Private*, pg. 2186
JANE TODD CRAWFORD MEMORIAL HOSP., INC.; *U.S. Private*, pg. 2186
JANETTO HOLDINGS PTY LTD—See Eagers Automotive Limited; *Int'l*, pg. 2263
JANEWAY PROPERTIES, INC.—See Edison Properties, LLC; *Int'l*, pg. 1337
JANE WINSTONE RETIREMENT VILLAGE LIMITED—See Ryman Healthcare Ltd.; *Int'l*, pg. 6439
JANFAIR PTY. LTD.—See China Rare Earth Resources And Technology Co., Ltd.; *Int'l*, pg. 1545
JANFUSUN FANCYWORLD CORP.; *Int'l*, pg. 3879
JANGADA MINES PLC; *Int'l*, pg. 3879
JANGHO CURTAIN WALL HONGKONG LTD—See Jangho Group Company Limited; *Int'l*, pg. 3879
JANGHO GROUP COMPANY LIMITED; *Int'l*, pg. 3879
JANGLE ADVERTISING; *U.S. Private*, pg. 2186
JANGWON TECH CO., LTD. - SECOND PLANT—See Jangwon Tech Co., Ltd.; *Int'l*, pg. 3879
JANGWON TECH CO., LTD.; *Int'l*, pg. 3879
JANGWON TECH CO., LTD. - THIRD PLANT—See Jangwon Tech Co., Ltd.; *Int'l*, pg. 3879
JANICKI ENVIRONMENTAL, INC.—See Environmental Science Associates; *U.S. Private*, pg. 1408
JANICO INVESTMENTS LTD.; *Int'l*, pg. 3879
JANIE & JACK LLC—See The Gap, Inc.; *U.S. Public*, pg. 2074
JANI KING FRANCHISING, INC.—See Jani-King International, Inc.; *U.S. Private*, pg. 2186
JANI KING, INC.—See Jani-King International, Inc.; *U.S. Private*, pg. 2187
JANI-KING INTERNATIONAL, INC.; *U.S. Private*, pg. 2186
JANI KING LEASING CORP.—See Jani-King International, Inc.; *U.S. Private*, pg. 2187
JANI KING OF CALIFORNIA, INC.—See Jani-King International, Inc.; *U.S. Private*, pg. 2187
JANI KING OF CALIFORNIA, INC.—See Jani-King International, Inc.; *U.S. Private*, pg. 2187
JANI KING OF CINCINNATI, INC.—See Jani-King International, Inc.; *U.S. Private*, pg. 2187
JANI KING OF CLEVELAND, INC.—See Jani-King International, Inc.; *U.S. Private*, pg. 2187
JANI KING OF COLORADO, INC.—See Jani-King International, Inc.; *U.S. Private*, pg. 2187
JANI KING OF DALLAS—See Jani-King International, Inc.; *U.S. Private*, pg. 2187

COMPANY NAME INDEX

JANI KING OF FLORIDA, INC.—See Jani-King International, Inc.; *U.S. Private*, pg. 2187
JANI KING OF HARTFORD, INC.—See Jani-King International, Inc.; *U.S. Private*, pg. 2187
JANI KING OF ILLINOIS, INC.—See Jani-King International, Inc.; *U.S. Private*, pg. 2187
JANI KING OF MIAMI, INC.—See Jani-King International, Inc.; *U.S. Private*, pg. 2187
JANI KING OF MICHIGAN, INC.—See Jani-King International, Inc.; *U.S. Private*, pg. 2187
JANI KING OF MINNESOTA, INC.—See Jani-King International, Inc.; *U.S. Private*, pg. 2187
JANI KING OF NASHVILLE, INC.—See Jani-King International, Inc.; *U.S. Private*, pg. 2187
JANI KING OF NEW JERSEY, INC.—See Jani-King International, Inc.; *U.S. Private*, pg. 2187
JANI-KING OF NEW YORK, INC.—See Jani-King International, Inc.; *U.S. Private*, pg. 2187
JANI KING OF OKLAHOMA, INC.—See Jani-King International, Inc.; *U.S. Private*, pg. 2187
JANI KING OF PHILADELPHIA, INC.—See Jani-King International, Inc.; *U.S. Private*, pg. 2187
JANI-KING OF PHOENIX—See Jani-King International, Inc.; *U.S. Private*, pg. 2187
JANI KING OF ST. LOUIS, INC.—See Jani-King International, Inc.; *U.S. Private*, pg. 2187
JANI KING OF WASHINGTON D.C., INC.—See Jani-King International, Inc.; *U.S. Private*, pg. 2187
JANIN ATLAS, INC.—See VINCI S.A.; *Int'l*, pg. 8235
JANISON EDUCATION GROUP LIMITED; *Int'l*, pg. 3879
JANITRONICS INC.; *U.S. Private*, pg. 2187
JANIVO HOLDING BV; *Int'l*, pg. 3879
JANJ A.D.; *Int'l*, pg. 3879
JAN KELLEY MARKETING; *Int'l*, pg. 3879
JANKLOW & NESBIT ASSOCIATES; *U.S. Private*, pg. 2187
JANKO STAJACIC A.D.; *Int'l*, pg. 3879
JANKOVICH COMPANY; *U.S. Private*, pg. 2187
JANKOWSKICO.; *U.S. Private*, pg. 2187
JANLYNN CORPORATION; *U.S. Private*, pg. 2187
JAN-MAR SALES LIMITED—See Bunzl plc; *Int'l*, pg. 1218
JANNAFARM SDN. BHD.—See Berjaya Corporation Berhad; *Int'l*, pg. 984
JANNAH HUNT OIL INC.—See Hunt Consolidated, Inc.; *U.S. Private*, pg. 2009
JANNELL MOTORS, INC.; *U.S. Private*, pg. 2187
JANNEY MONTGOMERY SCOTT LLC—See The Penn Mutual Life Insurance Company; *U.S. Private*, pg. 4092
JANOME AMERICA, INC.—See Janome Sewing Machine Co., Ltd.; *Int'l*, pg. 3880
JANOME AUSTRALIA PTY LTD.—See Janome Sewing Machine Co., Ltd.; *Int'l*, pg. 3880
JANOME CANADA LTD.—See Janome Sewing Machine Co., Ltd.; *Int'l*, pg. 3880
JANOME CREDIA CO., LTD.—See Janome Sewing Machine Co., Ltd.; *Int'l*, pg. 3880
JANOME DEUTSCHLAND GMBH—See Janome Sewing Machine Co., Ltd.; *Int'l*, pg. 3880
JANOME DIECASTING (THAILAND) CO., LTD.—See Janome Sewing Machine Co., Ltd.; *Int'l*, pg. 3880
JANOME DO BRASIL COMERCIO DE MAQUINAS LTDA.—See Janome Sewing Machine Co., Ltd.; *Int'l*, pg. 3880
JANOME EUROPE B.V.—See Janome Sewing Machine Co., Ltd.; *Int'l*, pg. 3880
JANOME INDUSTRIAL EQUIPMENT (SHANGHAI) CO., LTD.—See Janome Sewing Machine Co., Ltd.; *Int'l*, pg. 3880
JANOME INDUSTRIAL EQUIPMENT (TAIWAN) CO., LTD.—See Janome Sewing Machine Co., Ltd.; *Int'l*, pg. 3880
JANOME INDUSTRIAL EQUIPMENT USA, INC—See Janome Sewing Machine Co., Ltd.; *Int'l*, pg. 3880
JANOME MEXICO SERVICIOS LIMITADA S DE RL DE CV—See Janome Sewing Machine Co., Ltd.; *Int'l*, pg. 3880
JANOME NEW ZEALAND LTD.—See Janome Sewing Machine Co., Ltd.; *Int'l*, pg. 3880
JANOME SEWING MACHINE CO., LTD.; *Int'l*, pg. 3880
JANOME TAIWAN CO. LTD.—See Janome Sewing Machine Co., Ltd.; *Int'l*, pg. 3880
JANOME (THAILAND) CO. LTD.—See Janome Sewing Machine Co., Ltd.; *Int'l*, pg. 3880
JANOME UK LTD.—See Janome Sewing Machine Co., Ltd.; *Int'l*, pg. 3880
JANOSCHKA BARCELONA S.L.—See Janoschka GmbH; *Int'l*, pg. 3880
JANOSCHKA ESPANA S.L.—See Janoschka GmbH; *Int'l*, pg. 3880
JANOSCHKA GMBH; *Int'l*, pg. 3880
JANOSCHKA GRAPHIC SERVICES INDIA PRIVATE LTD.—See Janoschka GmbH; *Int'l*, pg. 3880
JANOSCHKA GRAPHICS FRANCE S.A.S.—See Janoschka GmbH; *Int'l*, pg. 3880
JANOSCHKA IZMIR AS—See Janoschka GmbH; *Int'l*, pg. 3880
JANOSCHKA KIPPENHEIM GMBH—See Janoschka GmbH; *Int'l*, pg. 3880

JANOSCHKA MEXICO SAPI DE C.V.—See Janoschka GmbH; *Int'l*, pg. 3880
JANOSCHKA PAVLOVSK LTD.—See Janoschka GmbH; *Int'l*, pg. 3880
JANOSCHKA POLSKA SP. Z.O.O.—See Janoschka GmbH; *Int'l*, pg. 3880
JANOSCHKA PORTUGAL LDA.—See Janoschka GmbH; *Int'l*, pg. 3880
JANOS TECHNOLOGY, LLC—See Fortive Corporation; *U.S. Public*, pg. 871
JANOTTA & HERNER, INC.; *U.S. Private*, pg. 2187
JANOVER INC.; *U.S. Public*, pg. 1187
JANOVIC-PLAZA INC.—See Berkshire Hathaway Inc.; *U.S. Public*, pg. 300
JANRAIN, INC.—See Akamai Technologies, Inc.; *U.S. Public*, pg. 69
JANRAIN UK LIMITED—See Akamai Technologies, Inc.; *U.S. Public*, pg. 69
JANSEN COASTAL PROPERTIES GROUP; *U.S. Private*, pg. 2187
THE JANSEN GROUP INC.; *U.S. Private*, pg. 4058
JANSEN RECYCLING GROUP—See The Jansen Group Inc.; *U.S. Private*, pg. 4058
JANSEN STRAWN CONSULTING ENGINEERS, INC.—See Ware Malcomb; *U.S. Private*, pg. 4441
JANSEN TEXTIL GMBH—See Wuensche Handelsgesellschaft International mbH & Co. KG; *Int'l*, pg. 8499
JANSEN VALK THOMPSON & REAHM PC; *U.S. Private*, pg. 2187
JANSER D.O.O.—See Janser GmbH; *Int'l*, pg. 3881
JANSER GMBH; *Int'l*, pg. 3880
JANSER GMBH—See Janser GmbH; *Int'l*, pg. 3880
JANSER POLSKA SP. Z O.O.—See Janser GmbH; *Int'l*, pg. 3880
JANSER S.A.—See Janser GmbH; *Int'l*, pg. 3880
JANSER SLOVENIJA—See Janser GmbH; *Int'l*, pg. 3881
JANSER, SPOL. S R.O.—See Janser GmbH; *Int'l*, pg. 3880
JANSER SPOL. S.R.O.—See Janser GmbH; *Int'l*, pg. 3881
JANSER UK LTD.—See Janser GmbH; *Int'l*, pg. 3881
JAN SNEL HD B.V.—See Daiwa House Industry Co., Ltd.; *Int'l*, pg. 1946
JANSON COMPUTERS PLC—See DCC plc; *Int'l*, pg. 1990
JANSONS ASSOCIATES, INC.; *U.S. Private*, pg. 2188
JANSPORT APPAREL CORP—See V. F. Corporation; *U.S. Public*, pg. 2269
JANSSEN ALZHEIMER IMMUNOTHERAPY RESEARCH & DEVELOPMENT, LLC—See Johnson & Johnson; *U.S. Public*, pg. 1196
JANSSEN BIOLOGICS B.V.—See Johnson & Johnson; *U.S. Public*, pg. 1196
JANSSEN BIOLOGICS (IRELAND)—See Johnson & Johnson; *U.S. Public*, pg. 1196
JANSSEN BIOTECH, INC.—See Johnson & Johnson; *U.S. Public*, pg. 1196
JANSSEN-CILAG AB—See Johnson & Johnson; *U.S. Public*, pg. 1197
JANSSEN-CILAG AG—See Johnson & Johnson; *U.S. Public*, pg. 1197
JANSSEN-CILAG A/S—See Johnson & Johnson; *U.S. Public*, pg. 1197
JANSSEN-CILAG A/S—See Johnson & Johnson; *U.S. Public*, pg. 1197
JANSSEN-CILAG B.V.—See Johnson & Johnson; *U.S. Public*, pg. 1197
JANSSEN-CILAG, C.A.—See Johnson & Johnson; *U.S. Public*, pg. 1197
JANSSEN-CILAG FARMACEUTICA, LDA.—See Johnson & Johnson; *U.S. Public*, pg. 1197
JANSSEN-CILAG FARMACEUTICA LTDA.—See Johnson & Johnson; *U.S. Public*, pg. 1197
JANSSEN CILAG FARMACEUTICA S.A.—See Johnson & Johnson; *U.S. Public*, pg. 1196
JANSSEN-CILAG GMBH—See Johnson & Johnson; *U.S. Public*, pg. 1197
JANSSEN-CILAG KFT.—See Johnson & Johnson; *U.S. Public*, pg. 1197
JANSSEN-CILAG LTD.—See Johnson & Johnson; *U.S. Public*, pg. 1197
JANSSEN-CILAG LTD.—See Johnson & Johnson; *U.S. Public*, pg. 1197
JANSSEN-CILAG (NEW ZEALAND) LIMITED—See Johnson & Johnson; *U.S. Public*, pg. 1197
JANSSEN-CILAG NV—See Johnson & Johnson; *U.S. Public*, pg. 1197
JANSSEN-CILAG OY—See Johnson & Johnson; *U.S. Public*, pg. 1197
JANSSEN-CILAG PHARMACEUTICA LIMITED—See Johnson & Johnson; *U.S. Public*, pg. 1197
JANSSEN-CILAG PHARMACEUTICAL S.A.C.I.—See Johnson & Johnson; *U.S. Public*, pg. 1197
JANSSEN-CILAG PHARMA GMBH—See Johnson & Johnson; *U.S. Public*, pg. 1197
JANSSEN-CILAG POLSKA, SP. Z O.O.—See Johnson & Johnson; *U.S. Public*, pg. 1197
JANSSEN-CILAG PTY. LIMITED—See Johnson & Johnson; *U.S. Public*, pg. 1197
JANSSEN-CILAG, S.A. DE C.V.—See Johnson & Johnson; *U.S. Public*, pg. 1197

JANSSEN-CILAG S.A.—See Johnson & Johnson; *U.S. Public*, pg. 1197
JANSSEN-CILAG S.A.—See Johnson & Johnson; *U.S. Public*, pg. 1197
JANSSEN-CILAG S.A.—See Johnson & Johnson; *U.S. Public*, pg. 1197
JANSSEN-CILAG S.P.A.—See Johnson & Johnson; *U.S. Public*, pg. 1197
JANSSEN-CILAG S.R.O—See Johnson & Johnson; *U.S. Public*, pg. 1197
JANSSEN INC.—See Johnson & Johnson; *U.S. Public*, pg. 1196
JANSSEN INTERNATIONAAL CVBA—See Johnson & Johnson; *U.S. Public*, pg. 1197
JANSSEN-ORTHO, INC.—See Johnson & Johnson; *U.S. Public*, pg. 1197
JANSSEN ORTHO, LLC—See Johnson & Johnson; *U.S. Public*, pg. 1196
JANSSEN ORTHO LLC—See Johnson & Johnson; *U.S. Public*, pg. 1196
JANSSEN PHARMACEUTICAL K.K.—See Johnson & Johnson; *U.S. Public*, pg. 1197
JANSSEN PHARMACEUTICAL LTD.—See Johnson & Johnson; *U.S. Public*, pg. 1197
JANSSEN PHARMACEUTICALS, INC.—See Johnson & Johnson; *U.S. Public*, pg. 1196
JANSSEN PHARMACEUTICA N.V.—See Johnson & Johnson; *U.S. Public*, pg. 1196
JANSSEN PHARMACEUTICA (PTY) LIMITED—See Johnson & Johnson; *U.S. Public*, pg. 1196
JANSSEN PHARMACEUTICA—See Johnson & Johnson; *U.S. Public*, pg. 1196
JANSSEN PRODUCTS, LP—See Johnson & Johnson; *U.S. Public*, pg. 1197
JANSSEN SCIENCES IRELAND UC—See Johnson & Johnson; *U.S. Public*, pg. 1197
JANSSEN SCIENCES IRELAND UC—See Johnson & Johnson; *U.S. Public*, pg. 1197
JANSSENS FIELD SERVICES BV—See Solutions 30 SE; *Int'l*, pg. 7077
JANSSEN VACCINE CORP.—See Johnson & Johnson; *U.S. Public*, pg. 1197
JANSSEN VACCINES AG—See Johnson & Johnson; *U.S. Public*, pg. 1195
JANSSEN VACCINES & PREVENTION B.V.—See Johnson & Johnson; *U.S. Public*, pg. 1197
JAN TABAK, N.V.—See Minor International PCL; *Int'l*, pg. 4911
JANTECH SERVICES, INC.—See Mitsubishi Heavy Industries, Ltd.; *Int'l*, pg. 4953
JANTEQ AUSTRALIA PTY. LIMITED—See General Dynamics Corporation; *U.S. Public*, pg. 916
JANTEQ CORP.—See General Dynamics Corporation; *U.S. Public*, pg. 916
JANTESA MEXICO, S.A. DE C.V.—See Jantsa Jant Sanayi ve Tic. A.S.; *Int'l*, pg. 3881
JANTSA JANT SANAYI VE TIC. A.S.; *Int'l*, pg. 3881
JANTSAN JANT PAZARLAMA VE TIC. A. S.—See Jantsa Jant Sanayi ve Tic. A.S.; *Int'l*, pg. 3881
JANTZEN APPAREL, LLC—See Perry Ellis International, Inc.; *U.S. Private*, pg. 3153
JANTZEN INC.—See Perry Ellis International, Inc.; *U.S. Private*, pg. 3154
JANTZEN INC.—See Perry Ellis International, Inc.; *U.S. Private*, pg. 3153
JANUS CORPORATION LIMITED; *Int'l*, pg. 3881
JANUS DISPLAYS; *U.S. Private*, pg. 2188
JANUS ET CIE—See Haworth, Inc.; *U.S. Private*, pg. 1883
JANUS HENDERSON ADMINISTRATION UK LIMITED—See Janus Henderson Group plc; *Int'l*, pg. 3881
JANUS HENDERSON FUND MANAGEMENT UK LIMITED—See Janus Henderson Group plc; *Int'l*, pg. 3881
JANUS HENDERSON GROUP PLC; *Int'l*, pg. 3881
JANUS HENDERSON INVESTORS (HONG KONG) LIMITED—See Janus Henderson Group plc; *Int'l*, pg. 3881
JANUS HENDERSON INVESTORS (SINGAPORE) LIMITED—See Janus Henderson Group plc; *Int'l*, pg. 3881
JANUS HENDERSON INVESTORS; *Int'l*, pg. 3881
JANUS HENDERSON INVESTORS UK LIMITED—See Janus Henderson Group plc; *Int'l*, pg. 3881
JANUS HENDERSON INVESTORS US LLC—See Janus Henderson Group plc; *Int'l*, pg. 3881
JANUS HENDERSON UK (HOLDINGS) LIMITED—See Janus Henderson Group plc; *Int'l*, pg. 3881
JANUS HENDERSON US (HOLDINGS) INC.—See Janus Henderson Group plc; *Int'l*, pg. 3881
JANUS HOTELS & RESORTS, INC.; *U.S. Private*, pg. 2188
JANUS INDEX & CALCULATION SERVICES LLC—See Janus Henderson Group plc; *Int'l*, pg. 3881
JANUS INTERNATIONAL GROUP, INC.—See Clearlake Capital Group, L.P.; *U.S. Private*, pg. 935
JANUX THERAPEUTICS, INC.; *U.S. Public*, pg. 1187
JANX INTEGRITY GROUP, INC.—See I Squared Capital Advisors (US) LLC; *U.S. Private*, pg. 2022

JANUX THERAPEUTICS, INC.   CORPORATE AFFILIATIONS

JANX INTEGRITY GROUP, INC.—See TDR Capital LLP; *Int'l*, pg. 7491
JAN X-RAY SERVICES INCORPORATED; *U.S. Private*, pg. 2186
JANZEN JOHNSTON & ROCKWELL EMERGENCY MEDICINE MANAGEMENT SERVICES, INC.; *U.S. Private*, pg. 2188
JAPAN 3D DEVICES CO., LTD.—See Minebea Mitsumi Inc.; *Int'l*, pg. 4902
JAPAN ABRASIVE GRAIN, LTD.—See Carlit Co., Ltd.; *Int'l*, pg. 1338
JAPANA CO., LTD.—See Alpen Co., Ltd.; *Int'l*, pg. 366
JAPAN ACRYLIC CHEMICAL CO., LTD.—See Dow Inc.; *U.S. Public*, pg. 685
JAPAN AEROFORGE, LTD.—See Kobe Steel, Ltd.; *Int'l*, pg. 4217
JAPAN AEROSPACE CORPORATION—See ITOCHU Corporation; *Int'l*, pg. 3840
JAPAN AGRIBIO CO., LTD.—See H2 Equity Partners B.V.; *Int'l*, pg. 3199
JAPAN AIRCARGO FORWARDERS ASSOCIATION—See Azuma Shipping Co., Ltd.; *Int'l*, pg. 782
JAPAN AIR COMMUTER CO., LTD.—See Japan Airlines Co., Ltd.; *Int'l*, pg. 3884
JAPAN AIR GASES, CO.—See L'Air Liquide S.A.; *Int'l*, pg. 4373
JAPAN AIRLINES CO., LTD. - LOS ANGELES REPRESENTATIVE OFFICE—See Japan Airlines Co., Ltd.; *Int'l*, pg. 3884
JAPAN AIRLINES CO., LTD. - NEW YORK REPRESENTATIVE OFFICE—See Japan Airlines Co., Ltd.; *Int'l*, pg. 3884
JAPAN AIRLINES CO., LTD.; *Int'l*, pg. 3881
JAPAN AIRLINES DOMESTIC CO., LTD.—See Japan Airlines Co., Ltd.; *Int'l*, pg. 3884
JAPAN AIRLINES MANAGEMENT CORP.—See Japan Airlines Co., Ltd.; *Int'l*, pg. 3884
JAPAN AIRPORT DELICA INC.—See Japan Airlines Co., Ltd.; *Int'l*, pg. 3883
JAPAN AIRPORT DELICA INC.—See Sojitz Corporation; *Int'l*, pg. 7062
JAPAN AIRPORT FUELING SERVICE CO., LTD.—See Japan Airlines Co., Ltd.; *Int'l*, pg. 3884
JAPAN AIRPORT SERVICE CO., LTD.—See Konoike Transport Co., Ltd.; *Int'l*, pg. 4274
JAPAN AIRPORT TECHNO CO., LTD.—See Japan Airport Terminal Co., Ltd.; *Int'l*, pg. 3885
JAPAN AIRPORT TERMINAL CO., LTD.; *Int'l*, pg. 3885
JAPAN AIRWAYS CO., LTD—See Konoike Transport Co., Ltd.; *Int'l*, pg. 4274
JAPAN AJAX MAGNETHERMIC CO., LTD.—See Park-Ohio Holdings Corp.; *U.S. Public*, pg. 1639
JAPAN ALTERNATIVE INVESTMENT CO., LTD.—See Mitsui & Co., Ltd.; *Int'l*, pg. 4973
JAPAN ALUMINA ASSOCIATES (AUSTRALIA) PTY. LTD.—See Press Metal Aluminium Holdings Bhd; *Int'l*, pg. 5965
JAPAN ALUMINA ASSOCIATES (AUSTRALIA) PTY. LTD.—See Sojitz Corporation; *Int'l*, pg. 7062
JAPAN ANALYST CORPORATION—See LECO Corporation; *U.S. Private*, pg. 2410
JAPAN ANIMAL REFERRAL MEDICAL CENTER CO., LTD.; *Int'l*, pg. 3885
JAPAN APPAREL SYSTEM SCIENCE INC.—See Toray Industries, Inc.; *Int'l*, pg. 7823
JAPAN ASIA ASSET MANAGEMENT CO., LTD.—See Japan Asia Group Limited; *Int'l*, pg. 3885
JAPAN ASIA FINANCIAL SERVICE CO., LTD.—See Japan Asia Group Limited; *Int'l*, pg. 3885
JAPAN ASIA GROUP LIMITED; *Int'l*, pg. 3885
JAPAN ASIA INVESTMENT (CHINA) CO., LTD.—See Japan Asia Investment Co., Ltd.; *Int'l*, pg. 3886
JAPAN ASIA INVESTMENT CO., LTD.; *Int'l*, pg. 3885
JAPAN ASIA LAND LIMITED—See Japan Land Limited; *Int'l*, pg. 3898
JAPAN ASIA (VIETNAM) COMPANY LTD.—See Japan Land Limited; *Int'l*, pg. 3898
JAPAN ASSET MARKETING CO., LTD.—See Pan Pacific International Holdings Corporation; *Int'l*, pg. 5715
JAPAN AUTO LEASING INC.; *Int'l*, pg. 3886
JAPAN AVIATION ELECTRONICS INDUSTRY, LTD. - AEROSPACE SALES DIVISION—See Japan Aviation Electronics Industry, Ltd.; *Int'l*, pg. 3886
JAPAN AVIATION ELECTRONICS INDUSTRY, LTD. - AKISHIMA PLANT—See Japan Aviation Electronics Industry, Ltd.; *Int'l*, pg. 3886
JAPAN AVIATION ELECTRONICS INDUSTRY, LTD. - INTERNATIONAL OPERATIONS PLANNING DIVISION—See Japan Aviation Electronics Industry, Ltd.; *Int'l*, pg. 3886
JAPAN AVIATION ELECTRONICS INDUSTRY, LTD.; *Int'l*, pg. 3886
JAPAN AVIATION ELECTRONICS INDUSTRY, LTD. - USER INTERFACE SOLUTIONS DIVISION—See Japan Aviation Electronics Industry, Ltd.; *Int'l*, pg. 3887
JAPAN BEST FOODS CO., LTD.—See Sojitz Corporation; *Int'l*, pg. 7062
JAPAN BEST RESCUE SYSTEM CO., LTD.; *Int'l*, pg. 3887

JAPAN BEVERAGE HOLDINGS INC.—See Suntory Holdings Limited; *Int'l*, pg. 7326
JAPAN BIKE AUCTION CO., LTD.—See USS Co., Ltd.; *Int'l*, pg. 8099
JAPAN BOTTLED WATER CO., LTD.—See Toyo Seikan Group Holdings, Ltd.; *Int'l*, pg. 7856
JAPAN BRAZIL PAPER AND PULP RESOURCES DEVELOPMENT CO., LTD.—See Oji Holdings Corporation; *Int'l*, pg. 5536
JAPAN BRIDGE CORPORATION—See OSJB Holdings Corporation; *Int'l*, pg. 5651
JAPAN BUSINESS LOGISTICS CO., LTD.—See Yasuda Logistics Corporation; *Int'l*, pg. 8570
JAPAN BUSINESS OPERATIONS CO., LTD.—See Oki Electric Industry Co., Ltd.; *Int'l*, pg. 5548
JAPAN BUTYL CO., LTD.—See JSR Corp.; *Int'l*, pg. 4014
JAPAN CABLECAST INC.; *Int'l*, pg. 3887
JAPAN CABLE TELEVISION, LTD.—See TV Asahi Holdings Corporation; *Int'l*, pg. 7986
JAPAN CARD PRODUCTS CO., LTD.—See Cartamundi N.V.; *Int'l*, pg. 1348
JAPAN CARGO CO., LTD.—See Bain Capital, LP; *U.S. Private*, pg. 444
JAPAN CARLIT CO., LTD.—See Carlit Co., Ltd.; *Int'l*, pg. 1338
JAPAN CARLIT (SHANGHAI) CO., LTD.—See Carlit Co., Ltd.; *Int'l*, pg. 1338
JAPAN CASH MACHINE CO., LTD. - NAGAHAMA PLANT—See Japan Cash Machine Co., Ltd.; *Int'l*, pg. 3887
JAPAN CASH MACHINE CO., LTD.; *Int'l*, pg. 3887
JAPAN CASTING & FORGING CORPORATION—See Mitsubishi Heavy Industries, Ltd.; *Int'l*, pg. 4953
JAPAN CATALYST, INC.—See Monex Group, Inc.; *Int'l*, pg. 5032
THE JAPAN CEE-BEE CHEMICAL CO., LTD.—See ITOCHU Corporation; *Int'l*, pg. 3841
JAPAN CERAMIC ENGINEERING CO., LTD.—See Mino Ceramic Co., Ltd.; *Int'l*, pg. 4910
JAPAN CERAMICS CO., LTD.—See Rinnai Corporation; *Int'l*, pg. 6344
JAPAN CHARGE NETWORK CO., LTD.—See Sumitomo Corporation; *Int'l*, pg. 7269
JAPAN CLINICAL LABORATORIES, INC.—See H.U. Group Holdings, Inc.; *Int'l*, pg. 3197
JAPAN CLINICAL SERVICE, INC.—See BML, Inc.; *Int'l*, pg. 1076
JAPAN COLLECTION SERVICE CO., LTD.—See Orient Corporation; *Int'l*, pg. 5621
JAPAN COLORING CO., LTD.—See JSR Corp.; *Int'l*, pg. 4014
JAPAN COMMERCIAL ESTABLISHMENT CO., LTD.—See Pan Pacific International Holdings Corporation; *Int'l*, pg. 5715
JAPAN COMMUNICATIONS, INC.; *Int'l*, pg. 3887
JAPAN COMPOSITE CO., LTD.—See Mitsui Chemicals, Inc.; *Int'l*, pg. 4981
JAPAN CONCENTRIX K.K—See TD Synnex Corp; *U.S. Public*, pg. 1984
JAPAN CORPORATE NEWS NETWORK (JCN) K.K.; *Int'l*, pg. 3887
JAPAN CREATIVE PLATFORM GROUP CO., LTD.; *Int'l*, pg. 3887
JAPAN CURRENT CO., LTD.; *Int'l*, pg. 3887
JAPAN DENTAL SUPPLY CO., LTD.—See GC Corporation; *Int'l*, pg. 2894
JAPAN DIGITAL LABORATORY CO., LTD.; *Int'l*, pg. 3887
JAPAN DISPLAY INC.; *Int'l*, pg. 3887
JAPAN DME CO.,LTD.—See Mitsubishi Gas Chemical Company, Inc.; *Int'l*, pg. 4948
JAPAN DRILLING CO., LTD.; *Int'l*, pg. 3888
JAPAN DROP FORGE CO., LTD.—See Daido Steel Co., Ltd.; *Int'l*, pg. 1923
JAPAN DUTY FREE FA-SO-LA ISETAN MITSUKOSHI CO., LTD.—See Japan Airport Terminal Co., Ltd.; *Int'l*, pg. 3885
JAPAN ECOLOGY CORPORATION—See Daito Chemix Corporation; *Int'l*, pg. 1943
JAPAN ECONOMIC RESEARCH INSTITUTE INC.—See Development Bank of Japan, Inc.; *Int'l*, pg. 2088
JAPAN ECOSYSTEM CO., LTD.; *Int'l*, pg. 3888
JAPAN ECVISION CO., LTD.—See Insight Venture Management, LLC; *U.S. Private*, pg. 2087
JAPAN EJECTOR ENGINEERING CO., LTD.—See Seika Corporation; *Int'l*, pg. 6685
JAPAN ELASTOMER CO., LTD.—See Asahi Kasei Corporation; *Int'l*, pg. 596
JAPAN ELECTRONIC MATERIALS CORPORATION - KUMAMOTO PLANT—See Japan Electronic Materials Corporation; *Int'l*, pg. 3888
JAPAN ELECTRONIC MATERIALS CORPORATION; *Int'l*, pg. 3888
JAPAN ELECTRONIC MONETARY CLAIM ORGANIZATION—See Mitsubishi UFJ Financial Group, Inc.; *Int'l*, pg. 4969
JAPAN ELEVATOR PARTS CO., LTD.—See Japan Elevator Service Holdings Co., Ltd.; *Int'l*, pg. 3888

JAPAN ELEVATOR SERVICE HOKKAIDO CO., LTD.—See Japan Elevator Service Holdings Co., Ltd.; *Int'l*, pg. 3888
JAPAN ELEVATOR SERVICE HOLDINGS CO., LTD.; *Int'l*, pg. 3888
JAPAN ELEVATOR SERVICE JYONAN CO., LTD.—See Japan Elevator Service Holdings Co., Ltd.; *Int'l*, pg. 3888
JAPAN ELEVATOR SERVICE JYOSAI CO., LTD.—See Japan Elevator Service Holdings Co., Ltd.; *Int'l*, pg. 3888
JAPAN ELEVATOR SERVICE KANAGAWA CO., LTD.—See Japan Elevator Service Holdings Co., Ltd.; *Int'l*, pg. 3888
JAPAN ELEVATOR SERVICE KANSAI CO., LTD.—See Japan Elevator Service Holdings Co., Ltd.; *Int'l*, pg. 3888
JAPAN ELEVATOR SERVICE TOKAI CO., LTD.—See Japan Elevator Service Holdings Co., Ltd.; *Int'l*, pg. 3888
JAPAN E-MARKET CO., LTD.—See Tokyo Electric Power Company Holdings, Incorporated; *Int'l*, pg. 7790
JAPAN EM CO., LTD.—See WAIDA MFG. CO., LTD.; *Int'l*, pg. 8331
JAPAN ENERGY E&P AUSTRALIA PTY. LTD.—See ENEOS Holdings, Inc.; *Int'l*, pg. 2417
JAPAN ENGINE CORPORATION; *Int'l*, pg. 3888
JAPAN ENGINEERING CO., LTD.—See Advantest Corporation; *Int'l*, pg. 166
JAPAN ENVIROCHEMICALS, LTD.—See Osaka Gas Co., Ltd.; *Int'l*, pg. 5645
JAPAN ENVIRONMENTAL SOLUTIONS, LTD.—See NIPPON KANZAI Holdings Co.,Ltd.; *Int'l*, pg. 5319
JAPAN ERI CO., LTD.—See ERI Holdings Co., Ltd.; *Int'l*, pg. 2491
JAPANESE ASSISTANCE NETWORK, INC.—See Relo Group, Inc.; *Int'l*, pg. 6265
JAPANESE HELP DESK INC.—See Prestige International Inc.; *Int'l*, pg. 5966
JAPANESE WEEKEND INC.; *U.S. Private*, pg. 2188
JAPANET BROADCASTING CO., LTD.—See Japanet Holdings Co., Ltd.; *Int'l*, pg. 3908
JAPANET HOLDINGS CO., LTD.; *Int'l*, pg. 3908
JAPAN EXCELLENT, INC.; *Int'l*, pg. 3888
JAPAN EXCHANGE GROUP, INC.; *Int'l*, pg. 3888
JAPAN EXLAN COMPANY, LIMITED—See Toyobo Co., Ltd.; *Int'l*, pg. 7860
JAPAN EXPRESS CO., LTD.—See Mitsui O.S.K. Lines, Ltd.; *Int'l*, pg. 4989
JAPAN EXPRESS CO., LTD.—See Mitsui O.S.K. Lines, Ltd.; *Int'l*, pg. 4989
JAPAN EXPRESS PACKING & TRANSPORT CO., LTD.—See Mitsui O.S.K. Lines, Ltd.; *Int'l*, pg. 4989
JAPAN EXPRESS TRANSPORTATION CO., LTD.—See Kawasaki Kisen Kaisha, Ltd.; *Int'l*, pg. 4099
JAPAN EXTERNAL TRADE ORGANIZATION; *Int'l*, pg. 3888
JAPAN EYELASH PRODUCTS INSTITUTE INC.—See Beauty Garage Inc.; *Int'l*, pg. 935
JAPAN FABWELD CO., LTD.—See Hagihara Industries Inc.; *Int'l*, pg. 3207
JAPAN FACILITY SOLUTIONS, INC.—See Azbil Corporation; *Int'l*, pg. 777
JAPAN FACILITY SOLUTIONS, INC.—See Kandenko Co., Ltd.; *Int'l*, pg. 4065
JAPAN FACILITY SOLUTIONS, INC.—See Mitsubishi Corporation; *Int'l*, pg. 4939
JAPAN FACILITY SOLUTIONS, INC.—See Sojitz Corporation; *Int'l*, pg. 7062
JAPAN FACILITY SOLUTIONS, INC.—See Tokyo Electric Power Company Holdings, Incorporated; *Int'l*, pg. 7790
JAPAN FAWICK CO., LTD.; *Int'l*, pg. 3888
JAPAN FILTER TECHNOLOGY, LTD.—See Japan Tobacco Inc.; *Int'l*, pg. 3907
JAPAN FINE CERAMICS CO., LTD.—See JGC Holdings Corporation; *Int'l*, pg. 3940
JAPAN FINECHEM COMPANY, INC.—See Mitsubishi Gas Chemical Company, Inc.; *Int'l*, pg. 4948
JAPAN FINE COATINGS CO., LTD.—See Bayer Aktiengesellschaft; *Int'l*, pg. 907
JAPAN FINE STEEL CO., LTD—See Kanai Juyo Kogyo Co.,Ltd; *Int'l*, pg. 4063
JAPAN FOOD CORP. (AUSTRALIA) PTY. LTD.—See Kikkoman Corporation; *Int'l*, pg. 4160
JAPAN FOOD CORPORATION—See NH Foods Ltd.; *Int'l*, pg. 5256
JAPAN FOOD (HAWAII), INC.—See Kikkoman Corporation; *Int'l*, pg. 4160
JAPAN FOOD & LIQUOR ALLIANCE INC.—See JFLA Holdings Inc.; *Int'l*, pg. 3939
JAPAN FOODS CO., LTD.—See Marubeni Corporation; *Int'l*, pg. 4710
JAPAN FOODS HOLDING LTD.; *Int'l*, pg. 3889
JAPAN FORMALIN COMPANY, INC.—See DIC Corporation; *Int'l*, pg. 2109
JAPAN FOUNDATION ENGINEERING CO., LTD.; *Int'l*, pg. 3889
JAPAN FRITO-LAY LTD.—See Calbee, Inc.; *Int'l*, pg. 1261
JAPAN FUND MANAGEMENT (LUXEMBOURG) S.A.—See Mizuho Financial Group, Inc.; *Int'l*, pg. 4997

COMPANY NAME INDEX

JAPAN GAS ENERGY CORPORATION—See ENEOS Holdings, Inc.; *Int'l*, pg. 2417
JAPAN GOLD CORP.; *Int'l*, pg. 3889
JAPAN GOLD KK—See Japan Gold Corp.; *Int'l*, pg. 3889
JAPAN H. L. LIMITED—See Jones Lang LaSalle Incorporated; *U.S. Public*, pg. 1202
JAPAN HOLIDAY TRAVEL CO., LTD.—See H.I.S. Co., Ltd.; *Int'l*, pg. 3195
JAPAN HOME (RETAIL) PTE. LTD.—See International Housewares Retail Company Limited; *Int'l*, pg. 3750
JAPAN HOME SHIELD CORPORATION—See LIXIL Group Corporation; *Int'l*, pg. 4534
JAPAN HOSPICE HOLDINGS, INC.; *Int'l*, pg. 3889
JAPAN HOTEL REIT INVESTMENT CORPORATION; *Int'l*, pg. 3889
JAPAN HOUSING MANAGEMENT CO.—See NIPPON KANZAI Holdings Co.,Ltd.; *Int'l*, pg. 5319
JAPAN HUMAN RESOURCES MEDICAL SCIENCE RESEARCH INSTITUTE CO., LTD.—See Nippon Kayaku Co., Ltd.; *Int'l*, pg. 5320
JAPAN HUNDSUN SOFTWARE INC.—See Hundsun Technologies Inc.; *Int'l*, pg. 3534
JAPAN HYDROGRAPHIC CHARTS & PUBLICATIONS CO.,LTD—See Mitsui O.S.K. Lines, Ltd.; *Int'l*, pg. 4989
JAPAN IDEX CO., LTD.—See Persol Holdings Co., Ltd.; *Int'l*, pg. 5819
JAPAN IMMUNORESEARCH LABORATORIES CO., LTD. (JIMRO)—See Otsuka Holdings Co., Ltd.; *Int'l*, pg. 5659
JAPAN INDUSTRIAL PARTNERS, INC.; *Int'l*, pg. 3889
JAPAN INDUSTRIAL TESTING CO., LTD.—See Sankyu, Inc.; *Int'l*, pg. 6544
JAPAN INFORMATION PROCESSING SERVICE CO.,LTD.—See Nippon Telegraph & Telephone Corporation; *Int'l*, pg. 5343
JAPAN INFRASTRUCTURE INITIATIVE COMPANY LIMITED—See Mitsubishi HC Capital Inc.; *Int'l*, pg. 4951
JAPAN INFRA WAYMARK CORPORATION—See Nippon Telegraph & Telephone Corporation; *Int'l*, pg. 5343
JAPAN INNOVATIONS CO., LTD.; *Int'l*, pg. 3898
THE JAPAN INSTITUTE FOR EDUCATIONAL MEASUREMENT, INC.—See EduLab, Inc.; *Int'l*, pg. 2316
JAPAN INSULATION CO., LTD.; *Int'l*, pg. 3898
JAPAN INTERNATIONAL BROADCASTING INC.—See Nippon Hoso Kyokai; *Int'l*, pg. 5318
JAPAN INTERNATIONAL FREIGHT FORWARDERS ASSOCIATION, INC.—See Azuma Shipping Co., Ltd.; *Int'l*, pg. 782
JAPAN INTERNET EXCHANGE CO. LTD.—See KDDI Corporation; *Int'l*, pg. 4111
JAPAN INTERNET NEWS CO., LTD.—See FUJISOFT INCORPORATED; *Int'l*, pg. 2830
JAPAN INVESTMENT ADVISER CO., LTD.; *Int'l*, pg. 3898
JAPAN INVESTMENT CORPORATION; *Int'l*, pg. 3898
JAPAN IRRADIATION SERVICE CO., LTD.—See Sumitomo Metal Mining Co., Ltd.; *Int'l*, pg. 7291
JAPAN JIFFY FOODS, INC.—See Kurabo Industries Ltd.; *Int'l*, pg. 4335
JAPAN JOINT SOLUTIONS CO., LTD.—See Minato Holdings Inc.; *Int'l*, pg. 4899
JAPAN JUICE PROCESSING COMPANY (JJPC)—See Marubeni Corporation; *Int'l*, pg. 4710
JAPAN JURONG ENGINEERING CO., LTD.—See IHI Corporation; *Int'l*, pg. 3605
JAPAN KANIGEN CO., LTD.—See Nihon Parkerizing Co., Ltd.; *Int'l*, pg. 5286
JAPAN KANTAR RESEARCH—See Bain Capital, LP; *U.S. Private*, pg. 448
JAPAN KENZAI CO., LTD.—See JK Holdings Co., Ltd.; *Int'l*, pg. 3972
JAPAN KOH YOUNG CO., LTD.—See Koh Young Technology Inc.; *Int'l*, pg. 4228
JAPAN KOTEI INFORMATICS CO., LTD.—See Wuhan Kotei Informatics Co., Ltd.; *Int'l*, pg. 8501
JAPAN LAIM CO., LTD.—See Ichishin Holdings Co., Ltd.; *Int'l*, pg. 3581
JAPAN LAND LIMITED; *Int'l*, pg. 3898
JAPAN LANTRONIX K.K.—See Lantronix, Inc.; *U.S. Public*, pg. 1293
JAPANLIFE CO., LTD.—See Hanwa Co., Ltd.; *Int'l*, pg. 3263
JAPAN LIFELINE CO., LTD.; *Int'l*, pg. 3898
THE JAPAN LIVING SERVICE CO., LTD.; *Int'l*, pg. 7658
JAPAN LOGISTICS CO., LTD.—See Kanematsu Corporation; *Int'l*, pg. 4068
JAPAN LOGISTICS DEVELOPMENT CO., LTD.—See AZ-COM MARUWA Holdings Inc.; *Int'l*, pg. 776
JAPAN LOGISTICS FUND, INC.; *Int'l*, pg. 3899
JAPAN LOGISTICS FUTURE INVESTMENT LIMITED—See SBS Holdings Inc.; *Int'l*, pg. 6607
JAPAN LOGISTIC SYSTEMS CORP.; *Int'l*, pg. 3898
JAPAN LUTRAVIL COMPANY LTD.—See Freudenberg SE; *Int'l*, pg. 2789
JAPAN MALAYSIA LNG CO.—See Petroliam Nasional Berhad; *Int'l*, pg. 5829
JAPAN MARINE SCIENCE INC.—See Nippon Yusen Kabushiki Kaisha; *Int'l*, pg. 5358

JAPAN MARINE UNITED CORPORATION—See IHI Corporation; *Int'l*, pg. 3605
JAPAN MARINE UNITED CORPORATION—See JFE Holdings, Inc.; *Int'l*, pg. 3938
JAPAN MARKETING OPERATIONS KK—See Ipsos S.A.; *Int'l*, pg. 3802
JAPAN M&A SOLUTION INCORPORATED; *Int'l*, pg. 3899
JAPAN MATERIAL CO., LTD.; *Int'l*, pg. 3899
JAPAN MATERIAL RECYCLE SYSTEM (JMR) CO., LTD.—See Osaka Soda Co., Ltd.; *Int'l*, pg. 5646
JAPAN MEAT CO., LTD.; *Int'l*, pg. 3899
JAPAN MEDICAL DYNAMIC MARKETING, INC.; *Int'l*, pg. 3899
JAPAN MEDICAL LEASE CORPORATION—See Mitsubishi HC Capital Inc.; *Int'l*, pg. 4951
JAPAN MEDICAL MATERIALS CORPORATION—See Kobe Steel, Ltd.; *Int'l*, pg. 4217
JAPAN MEDICAL MATERIALS CORPORATION—See KYOCERA Corporation; *Int'l*, pg. 4356
JAPAN MEDICAL MATERIALS CORP - SHIGA YOHKAICHI PLANT—See Kobe Steel, Ltd.; *Int'l*, pg. 4217
JAPAN MEDICAL MATERIALS CORP - SHIGA YOHKAICHI PLANT—See KYOCERA Corporation; *Int'l*, pg. 4356
JAPAN MEDICAL RESEARCH INSTITUTE CO., LTD.—See Nihon Chouzai Co., Ltd.; *Int'l*, pg. 5283
JAPAN MEDICAL TECHNOLOGY CO., LTD.—See Kaneka Corporation; *Int'l*, pg. 4067
JAPAN METHYL ETHER CO., LTD.—See Mitsubishi Gas Chemical Company, Inc.; *Int'l*, pg. 4948
JAPAN METROPOLITAN FUND INVESTMENT CORPORATION; *Int'l*, pg. 3899
JAPAN MORTGAGE CO., LTD.—See Fuyo General Lease Co., Ltd.; *Int'l*, pg. 2859
JAPAN MOTORS TRADING COMPANY LTD.—See Nissan Motor Co., Ltd.; *Int'l*, pg. 5367
JAPAN MULTIMEDIA SERVICES CORPORATION—See Sega Sammy Holdings Inc.; *Int'l*, pg. 6680
JAPAN NATURAL ENERGY COMPANY LIMITED—See Tokyo Electric Power Company Holdings, Incorporated; *Int'l*, pg. 7790
THE JAPAN NET BANK, LIMITED—See Sumitomo Mitsui Financial Group, Inc.; *Int'l*, pg. 7295
JAPAN NETWORK ENGINEERING CO., LTD.—See Electric Power Development Co., Ltd.; *Int'l*, pg. 2349
JAPAN NEW METALS CO., LTD.—See Mitsubishi Materials Corporation; *Int'l*, pg. 4963
JAPAN NUCLEAR FUEL LIMITED—See Tokyo Electric Power Company Holdings, Incorporated; *Int'l*, pg. 7790
JAPAN NUS CO., LTD.—See JGC Holdings Corporation; *Int'l*, pg. 3940
JAPAN NUTRITION CO., LTD. - KASHIMA PLANT—See ITOCHU Corporation; *Int'l*, pg. 3840
JAPAN NUTRITION CO., LTD.—See ITOCHU Corporation; *Int'l*, pg. 3840
JAPAN OFFICE ADVISORS, INC.—See Ichigo Asset Management, Ltd.; *Int'l*, pg. 3580
JAPAN OIL DEVELOPMENT CO., LTD.—See INPEX CORPORATION; *Int'l*, pg. 3717
JAPAN OIL TRANSPORTATION CO., LTD.; *Int'l*, pg. 3899
JAPAN PANA-USE CO., LTD.—See Ship Healthcare Holdings, Inc.; *Int'l*, pg. 6852
JAPAN PAPER TECHNOLOGY DONG NAI (VN) CO., LTD.—See Oji Holdings Corporation; *Int'l*, pg. 5536
JAPAN PAPER TECHNOLOGY (VN) CO., LTD.—See Oji Holdings Corporation; *Int'l*, pg. 5536
JAPAN PC SERVICE CO., LTD.; *Int'l*, pg. 3899
JAPAN PENSION NAVIGATOR CO., LTD.—See Sumitomo Mitsui Financial Group, Inc.; *Int'l*, pg. 7293
JAPAN PENSION SERVICE CO., LTD.—See Nippon Life Insurance Company; *Int'l*, pg. 5322
JAPAN PETROLEUM EXPLORATION CO. LTD.; *Int'l*, pg. 3900
JAPAN PHOTOCATALYST CENTER CO., LTD.—See Abalance Corporation Ltd.; *Int'l*, pg. 48
JAPAN PHOTO HOLDING NORGE AS—See CEWE Stiftung & Co. KGaA; *Int'l*, pg. 1425
JAPAN PILE CORPORATION—See ASIA PILE HOLDINGS CORPORATION; *Int'l*, pg. 614
JAPAN PIONICS CO., LTD.—See Mitsubishi Gas Chemical Company, Inc.; *Int'l*, pg. 4948
JAPAN PLACEMENT CENTER CO., LTD.—See Kyoritsu Maintenance Co., Ltd.; *Int'l*, pg. 4365
JAPAN POLYCHEM CORPORATION—See Mitsubishi Chemical Group Corporation; *Int'l*, pg. 4931
JAPAN POLYETHYLENE CORPORATION—See Mitsubishi Chemical Group Corporation; *Int'l*, pg. 4931
JAPAN POLYMARK CO.—See Illinois Tool Works Inc.; *U.S. Public*, pg. 1108
JAPAN POLYPROPYLENE CORPORATION—See Mitsubishi Chemical Group Corporation; *Int'l*, pg. 4931
JAPAN PORT INDUSTRY CO.—See Kamigumi Co., Ltd.; *Int'l*, pg. 4062
JAPAN POST BANK CO., LTD.—See Japan Post Holdings Co., Ltd.; *Int'l*, pg. 3900
JAPAN POST CO., LTD.—See Japan Post Holdings Co., Ltd.; *Int'l*, pg. 3900
JAPAN POST HOLDINGS CO., LTD.; *Int'l*, pg. 3900

JAPAN POST INFORMATION TECHNOLOGY CO., LTD.—See Japan Post Holdings Co., Ltd.; *Int'l*, pg. 3902
JAPAN POST INSURANCE CO., LTD.—See Japan Post Holdings Co., Ltd.; *Int'l*, pg. 3902
JAPAN POST SANKYU GLOBAL LOGISTICS CO., LTD.—See Sankyu, Inc.; *Int'l*, pg. 6544
JAPAN POTATO CORPORATION—See Hob Co., Ltd.; *Int'l*, pg. 3436
JAPAN POWDER COATINGS MANUFACTURING CO., LTD.—See Dai Nippon Toryo Co., Ltd.; *Int'l*, pg. 1916
JAPAN POWER BRAKES—See Carlisle Companies Incorporated; *U.S. Public*, pg. 437
JAPAN POWER FASTENING CO., LTD.—See NHK Spring Co., Ltd.; *Int'l*, pg. 5257
JAPAN POWER GENERATION LIMITED; *Int'l*, pg. 3902
JAPAN PREVENTIVE MEDICINE INC.—See Soiken Holdings Inc.; *Int'l*, pg. 7060
JAPAN PRIME REALTY INVESTMENT CORPORATION; *Int'l*, pg. 3903
JAPAN PRIVATE EQUITY CO., LTD—See Japan Asia Investment Co., Ltd.; *Int'l*, pg. 3886
JAPAN PRIVATE EQUITY CO., LTD.—See Nihon M&A Center Holdings Inc.; *Int'l*, pg. 5286
JAPAN PROCESS DEVELOPMENT CO., LTD.; *Int'l*, pg. 3903
JAPAN PROPERTY MANAGEMENT CENTER CO., LTD.; *Int'l*, pg. 3903
JAPAN PROPERTY SOLUTIONS CO., LTD.—See NIPPON KANZAI Holdings Co.,Ltd.; *Int'l*, pg. 5319
JAPAN PRO STAFF CO., LTD—See Bell-Park Co., Ltd.; *Int'l*, pg. 966
JAPAN PUBLICATIONS, INC.—See TOHAN CORPORATION; *Int'l*, pg. 7775
JAPAN PUBLICATIONS TRADING CO., LTD—See TOHAN CORPORATION; *Int'l*, pg. 7775
JAPAN PUBLIC FARE SERVICES CO., LTD.—See Transcosmos Inc.; *Int'l*, pg. 7898
JAPAN PULP AND PAPER COMPANY LIMITED; *Int'l*, pg. 3903
JAPAN PULP & PAPER (AUSTRALIA) PTY. LTD.—See Japan Pulp and Paper Company Limited; *Int'l*, pg. 3904
JAPAN PULP & PAPER CO., (H.K.) LTD.—See Japan Pulp and Paper Company Limited; *Int'l*, pg. 3904
JAPAN PULP & PAPER CO., LTD.—See Japan Pulp and Paper Company Limited; *Int'l*, pg. 3904
JAPAN PULP & PAPER GMBH—See Japan Pulp and Paper Company Limited; *Int'l*, pg. 3904
JAPAN PULP & PAPER (KOREA) CO., LTD.—See Japan Pulp and Paper Company Limited; *Int'l*, pg. 3904
JAPAN PULP & PAPER (M) SDN. BHD.—See Japan Pulp and Paper Company Limited; *Int'l*, pg. 3904
JAPAN PULP & PAPER (SHANGHAI) CO., LTD.—See Japan Pulp and Paper Company Limited; *Int'l*, pg. 3904
JAPAN PULP & PAPER (TAIWAN) CO., LTD.—See Japan Pulp and Paper Company Limited; *Int'l*, pg. 3904
JAPAN PULP & PAPER (THAILAND) CO., LTD.—See Japan Pulp and Paper Company Limited; *Int'l*, pg. 3904
JAPAN PULP & PAPER (U.S.A.) CORP.—See Japan Pulp and Paper Company Limited; *Int'l*, pg. 3904
JAPAN PURE CHEMICAL CO LTD; *Int'l*, pg. 3905
JAPAN RADIO CO., LTD. - MITAKA PLANT—See Nisshinbo Holdings Inc.; *Int'l*, pg. 5373
JAPAN RADIO CO., LTD. - SAITAMA PLANT—See Nisshinbo Holdings Inc.; *Int'l*, pg. 5373
JAPAN RADIO CO., LTD.—See Nisshinbo Holdings Inc.; *Int'l*, pg. 5373
JAPAN RADIO COMPANY (HK) LIMITED—See Nisshinbo Holdings Inc.; *Int'l*, pg. 5373
JAPAN RADIO GLASS CO., LTD.—See Nisshinbo Holdings Inc.; *Int'l*, pg. 5373
JAPAN RAILWAY SERVICE NET FUKUOKA COMPANY—See West Japan Railway Company; *Int'l*, pg. 8385
JAPAN RAILWAY SERVICE NET YONAGO COMPANY—See West Japan Railway Company; *Int'l*, pg. 8385
JAPAN REAL ESTATE ASSET MANAGEMENT CO., LTD.—See Mitsubishi Estate Co., Ltd.; *Int'l*, pg. 4946
JAPAN REAL ESTATE INVESTMENT CORPORATION; *Int'l*, pg. 3905
JAPAN RECYCLING CO.—See JFE Holdings, Inc.; *Int'l*, pg. 3934
JAPAN REGISTRY SERVICES CO., LTD.; *Int'l*, pg. 3905
JAPAN REIT ADVISORS CO., LTD.—See Marubeni Corporation; *Int'l*, pg. 4705
JAPAN RELIANCE SERVICE CORPORATION; *Int'l*, pg. 3905
JAPAN RENTAL GUARANTY CO.—See Tokyo Tatemono Co. Ltd.; *Int'l*, pg. 7796
THE JAPAN RESEARCH INSTITUTE, LIMITED—See Sumitomo Mitsui Financial Group, Inc.; *Int'l*, pg. 7295
THE JAPAN RESEARCH INSTITUTE (SHANGHAI) CONSULTING CO., LTD.—See Sumitomo Mitsui Financial Group, Inc.; *Int'l*, pg. 7295
THE JAPAN RESEARCH INSTITUTE (SHANGHAI) SOLUTION CO., LTD.—See Sumitomo Mitsui Financial Group, Inc.; *Int'l*, pg. 7296
JAPAN RESISTOR MFG CO., LTD.; *Int'l*, pg. 3905

JAPAN RESISTOR MFG CO., LTD.

JAPAN RESISTOR SALES CO., LTD.—See Japan Resistor Mfg Co., Ltd.; *Int'l*, pg. 3905
JAPAN SAFETY GUARD CO., LTD.—See SECOM Co., Ltd.; *Int'l*, pg. 6671
JAPAN SAUDI ARABIA METHANOL COMPANY, INC.—See Mitsubishi Gas Chemical Company, Inc.; *Int'l*, pg. 4948
JAPAN SEA WORKS CO., LTD.—See Kajima Corporation; *Int'l*, pg. 4055
JAPAN SECURITIES AGENTS, LTD.—See Japan Securities Finance Co., Ltd.; *Int'l*, pg. 3905
JAPAN SECURITIES CLEARING CORPORATION—See Japan Exchange Group, Inc.; *Int'l*, pg. 3888
JAPAN SECURITIES FINANCE CO., LTD.; *Int'l*, pg. 3905
JAPAN SECURITIES INCORPORATED—See Aizawa Securities Group Co., Ltd.; *Int'l*, pg. 255
JAPAN SEMICONDUCTOR CORPORATION—See Japan Industrial Partners, Inc.; *Int'l*, pg. 3889
JAPAN SEOUL SEMICONDUCTOR CO., LTD.—See Seoul Semiconductor Co., Ltd.; *Int'l*, pg. 6717
JAPAN SETTLEMENT INFORMATION CENTER LTD.—See GLORY Ltd.; *Int'l*, pg. 3010
JAPAN SHOTSHELL LTD.—See Daicel Corporation; *Int'l*, pg. 1919
JAPAN SHUTTLE CO., LTD.—See Shuttle Inc.; *Int'l*, pg. 6871
JAPAN SINBON ELECTRONICS CO.,LTD—See SINBON Electronics Co., Ltd.; *Int'l*, pg. 6936
JAPAN-SINGAPORE PETROCHEMICALS CO., LTD.—See Sumitomo Chemical Company, Limited; *Int'l*, pg. 7264
JAPAN SMALLER CAPITALIZATION FUND, INC.; *U.S. Public*, pg. 1187
JAPAN SOCIETY, INC.; *U.S. Private*, pg. 2188
JAPAN SOFTWARE DESIGN CO.,LTD.—See Cresco, Ltd.; *Int'l*, pg. 1840
JAPAN SPACE IMAGING CORPORATION—See Mitsubishi Corporation; *Int'l*, pg. 4939
JAPAN SPEED SHORE CO., LTD.—See Nishio Holdings Co., Ltd.; *Int'l*, pg. 5365
JAPAN SPORTS MARKETING INC.—See Tsuburaya Fields Holdings Inc.; *Int'l*, pg. 7955
JAPAN STEEL WORKS AMERICA, INC.—See The Japan Steel Works, Ltd.; *Int'l*, pg. 7658
JAPAN STEEL WORKS EUROPE GMBH—See The Japan Steel Works, Ltd.; *Int'l*, pg. 7658
JAPAN STEEL WORKS INDIA PRIVATE LIMITED—See The Japan Steel Works, Ltd.; *Int'l*, pg. 7658
THE JAPAN STEEL WORKS, LTD. - HIROSHIMA PLANT—See The Japan Steel Works, Ltd.; *Int'l*, pg. 7659
THE JAPAN STEEL WORKS, LTD. - MURORAN PLANT—See The Japan Steel Works, Ltd.; *Int'l*, pg. 7659
THE JAPAN STEEL WORKS, LTD. - ORDNANCE DIVISION—See The Japan Steel Works, Ltd.; *Int'l*, pg. 7659
THE JAPAN STEEL WORKS, LTD.; *Int'l*, pg. 7658
THE JAPAN STEEL WORKS, LTD. - YOKOHAMA PLANT—See The Japan Steel Works, Ltd.; *Int'l*, pg. 7659
JAPAN STEEL WORKS M&E, INC.—See The Japan Steel Works, Ltd.; *Int'l*, pg. 7658
THE JAPAN STEEL WORKS (SINGAPORE) PTE. LTD.—See The Japan Steel Works, Ltd.; *Int'l*, pg. 7659
THE JAPAN STEEL WORKS (THAILAND) CO., LTD.—See The Japan Steel Works, Ltd.; *Int'l*, pg. 7659
JAPAN SUN OIL COMPANY, LTD.—See Energy Transfer LP; *U.S. Public*, pg. 764
JAPAN SUPERCONDUCTOR TECHNOLOGY INC.—See Kobe Steel, Ltd.; *Int'l*, pg. 4217
JAPAN SUPER QUARTZ CORPORATION—See SUMCO Corporation; *Int'l*, pg. 7260
JAPAN SYNTHETIC ALCOHOL CO., LTD.—See Kirin Holdings Company, Limited; *Int'l*, pg. 4187
JAPAN SYSTEMS CO., LTD.—See DXC Technology Company; *U.S. Public*, pg. 696
JAPAN SYSTEMS ENGINEERING CORPORATION—See DTS Corporation; *Int'l*, pg. 2217
JAPAN SYSTEM TECHNIQUES CO., LTD.; *Int'l*, pg. 3905
JAPAN TELECOM AMERICA, INC.—See SoftBank Group Corp.; *Int'l*, pg. 7052
JAPAN TELECOM CHINA CO., LTD.—See SoftBank Group Corp.; *Int'l*, pg. 7052
JAPAN TELECOMMUNICATION ENGINEERING SERVICE CO., LTD.—See KDDI Corporation; *Int'l*, pg. 4111
JAPAN TEMPERED & LAMINATED GLASS CO., LTD.—See Central Glass Co., Ltd.; *Int'l*, pg. 1407
JAPAN THIRD PARTY OF AMERICA, INC.—See JTP Co., Ltd.; *Int'l*, pg. 4020
THE JAPAN TIMES LTD.—See News2u Holdings, Inc.; *Int'l*, pg. 5238
JAPAN TISSUE ENGINEERING CO., LTD.—See FUJIFILM Holdings Corporation; *Int'l*, pg. 2826
JAPAN TOBACCO INC.; *Int'l*, pg. 3905
JAPAN TRANSCITY CORPORATION - OVERSEAS BUSINESS MANAGEMENT DIVISION—See Japan Transcity Corporation; *Int'l*, pg. 3907

JAPAN TRANSCITY CORPORATION - SALES DEVELOPMENT DIVISION—See Japan Transcity Corporation; *Int'l*, pg. 3907
JAPAN TRANSCITY CORPORATION - SALES PROMOTION DIVISION—See Japan Transcity Corporation; *Int'l*, pg. 3907
JAPAN TRANSCITY CORPORATION - SCM DIVISION—See Japan Transcity Corporation; *Int'l*, pg. 3907
JAPAN TRANSCITY CORPORATION; *Int'l*, pg. 3907
JAPAN TRANSOCEAN AIR CO., LTD.—See Japan Airlines Co., Ltd.; *Int'l*, pg. 3884
JAPAN TRANSPORT ENGINEERING COMPANY—See East Japan Railway Company; *Int'l*, pg. 2270
JAPAN TRAVEL BUREAU (MALAYSIA) SDN. BHD.—See JTB Corp.; *Int'l*, pg. 4016
JAPAN TRINIDAD METHANOL COMPANY, INC.—See Mitsubishi Gas Chemical Company, Inc.; *Int'l*, pg. 4948
JAPAN TRUSTEE SERVICES BANK, LTD.; *Int'l*, pg. 3907
JAPAN TSS, INC.—See FTGroup Co Ltd.; *Int'l*, pg. 2800
JAPAN TUPPERWARE CO., LTD.—See Tupperware Brands Corporation; *U.S. Public*, pg. 2204
JAPAN TURBINE TECHNOLOGIES CO., LTD.—See RTX Corporation; *U.S. Public*, pg. 1823
JAPAN U-PICA COMPANY LTD. - MINE FACTORY—See Mitsubishi Gas Chemical Company, Inc.; *Int'l*, pg. 4948
JAPAN U-PICA COMPANY LTD. - SHONAN FACTORY—See Mitsubishi Gas Chemical Company, Inc.; *Int'l*, pg. 4949
JAPAN U-PICA COMPANY LTD.—See Mitsubishi Gas Chemical Company, Inc.; *Int'l*, pg. 4948
JAPAN VAM & POVAL CO., LTD—See Shin-Etsu Chemical Co. Ltd.; *Int'l*, pg. 6838
JAPAN VIETNAM FERTILIZER COMPANY - DONG NAI FACTORY—See Sojitz Corporation; *Int'l*, pg. 7062
JAPAN VIETNAM FERTILIZER COMPANY—See Sojitz Corporation; *Int'l*, pg. 7062
JAPAN VIETNAM PETROLEUM CO., LTD.—See ENEOS Holdings, Inc.; *Int'l*, pg. 2417
JAPAN VIEWORKS CO., LTD.—See Vieworks Co., Ltd.; *Int'l*, pg. 8204
JAPAN VILENE COMPANY, LTD.—See Freudenberg SE; *Int'l*, pg. 2789
JAPAN WASTE CORPORATION; *Int'l*, pg. 3908
JAPAN WHEELCHAIR-ACCESSIBLE VEHICLE DEALER CO., LTD.—See System Location Co., Ltd.; *Int'l*, pg. 7390
JAPAN WIND DEVELOPMENT CO., LTD.—See INFRONEER Holdings, Inc.; *Int'l*, pg. 3699
JAPAN WOOD CO., LTD.—See Tama Home Co., Ltd.; *Int'l*, pg. 7448
THE JAPAN WOOL TEXTILE CO., LTD.; *Int'l*, pg. 7659
JAPARA HEALTHCARE LIMITED—See Little Company of Mary Health Care Limited; *Int'l*, pg. 4528
JAPARA RETIREMENT LIVING 4 (COSGROVE COTTAGES) PTY. LTD.—See Little Company of Mary Health Care Limited; *Int'l*, pg. 4528
JAPARA RETIREMENT LIVING 6 (BARONGAROOK) PTY. LTD.—See Little Company of Mary Health Care Limited; *Int'l*, pg. 4528
JAPARA RETIREMENT LIVING 7 (THE HOMESTEAD) PTY. LTD.—See Little Company of Mary Health Care Limited; *Int'l*, pg. 4528
JAPAUL GOLD & VENTURES PLC; *Int'l*, pg. 3908
JAPAUTO MOTO; *Int'l*, pg. 3908
JAPCON INC.—See Sojitz Corporation; *Int'l*, pg. 7062
JAPCO., LTD.—See Carlit Co., Ltd.; *Int'l*, pg. 1338
JAPEX CORP.—See NOF Corporation; *Int'l*, pg. 5399
JAPEX ENERGY CO., LTD.—See Japan Petroleum Exploration Co. Ltd.; *Int'l*, pg. 3900
JAPEX GARRAF LTD.—See Japan Petroleum Exploration Co. Ltd.; *Int'l*, pg. 3900
JAPEX OFFSHORE LTD.—See Japan Petroleum Exploration Co. Ltd.; *Int'l*, pg. 3900
JAPEX PIPELINE LTD.—See Japan Petroleum Exploration Co. Ltd.; *Int'l*, pg. 3900
JAPEX SKS CORPORATION—See Japan Petroleum Exploration Co. Ltd.; *Int'l*, pg. 3900
JAPEX UK E&P LTD.—See Japan Petroleum Exploration Co. Ltd.; *Int'l*, pg. 3900
JAPEX (U.S.) CORP.—See Japan Petroleum Exploration Co. Ltd.; *Int'l*, pg. 3900
JAPFA LTD—See PT Japfa Comfeed Indonesia Tbk; *Int'l*, pg. 6049
JAPRA AD; *Int'l*, pg. 3908
JAPROTEK OY AB—See Lone Star Funds; *U.S. Private*, pg. 2486
JAPS-OLSON COMPANY—See Monomoy Capital Partners LLC; *U.S. Private*, pg. 2772
JAPY TECH S. A. S.—See Mutares SE & Co. KGaA; *Int'l*, pg. 5105

CORPORATE AFFILIATIONS

JAQUES INTERNATIONAL HOLDINGS PTY. LTD.—See Terex Corporation; *U.S. Public*, pg. 2020
JAQUES (THAILAND) LIMITED—See Terex Corporation; *U.S. Public*, pg. 2020
JARA CORPORATION; *Int'l*, pg. 3908
JARBOE'S PLUMBING, HEATING & COOLING, INC.; *U.S. Private*, pg. 2188
JARCHEM INDUSTRIES, INC.; *U.S. Private*, pg. 2188
JARDEN CORP.—See Newell Brands Inc.; *U.S. Public*, pg. 1515
JARDEN ZINC PRODUCTS, LLC—See Newell Brands Inc.; *U.S. Public*, pg. 1514
JARDILAND ENSEIGNES SAS—See Union InVivo - Union de Cooperatives Agricoles; *Int'l*, pg. 8053
JARDIM SISTEMAS AUTOMOTIVOS E INDUSTRIAIS, S.A.—See Cie Automotive S.A.; *Int'l*, pg. 1604
JARDINE CYCLE & CARRIAGE LIMITED—See Jardine Matheson Holdings Limited; *Int'l*, pg. 3910
JARDINE DISTRIBUTION, INC.—See Jardine Matheson Holdings Limited; *Int'l*, pg. 3908
THE JARDINE ENGINEERING CORPORATION LTD.—See Jardine Matheson Holdings Limited; *Int'l*, pg. 3909
JARDINE LLOYD THOMPSON ASIA PRIVATE LIMITED—See Marsh & McLennan Companies, Inc.; *U.S. Public*, pg. 1376
JARDINE LLOYD THOMPSON AUSTRALIA PTY LIMITED—See Marsh & McLennan Companies, Inc.; *U.S. Public*, pg. 1377
JARDINE LLOYD THOMPSON GROUP PLC—See Marsh & McLennan Companies, Inc.; *U.S. Public*, pg. 1376
JARDINE LLOYD THOMPSON KOREA LIMITED—See Marsh & McLennan Companies, Inc.; *U.S. Public*, pg. 1377
JARDINE LLOYD THOMPSON LIMITED—See Marsh & McLennan Companies, Inc.; *U.S. Public*, pg. 1377
JARDINE LLOYD THOMPSON LIMITED—See Marsh & McLennan Companies, Inc.; *U.S. Public*, pg. 1377
JARDINE LLOYD THOMPSON LIMITED—See Marsh & McLennan Companies, Inc.; *U.S. Public*, pg. 1377
JARDINE LLOYD THOMPSON LIMITED—See Marsh & McLennan Companies, Inc.; *U.S. Public*, pg. 1377
JARDINE LLOYD THOMPSON PTE LIMITED—See Marsh & McLennan Companies, Inc.; *U.S. Public*, pg. 1377
JARDINE LLOYD THOMPSON RISK & INSURANCE GROUP—See Marsh & McLennan Companies, Inc.; *U.S. Public*, pg. 1377
JARDINE LLOYD THOMPSON SDN BHD—See Marsh & McLennan Companies, Inc.; *U.S. Public*, pg. 1377
JARDINE LLOYD THOMPSON—See Marsh & McLennan Companies, Inc.; *U.S. Public*, pg. 1376
JARDINE LLOYD THOMPSON S.P.A.—See Marsh & McLennan Companies, Inc.; *U.S. Public*, pg. 1377
JARDINE MATHESON AUSTRALIA PTY. LTD.—See Jardine Matheson Holdings Limited; *Int'l*, pg. 3908
JARDINE MATHESON (CHINA) LTD.—See Jardine Matheson Holdings Limited; *Int'l*, pg. 3908
JARDINE, MATHESON & CO., LTD.—See Jardine Matheson Holdings Limited; *Int'l*, pg. 3909
JARDINE MATHESON EUROPE B.V.—See Jardine Matheson Holdings Limited; *Int'l*, pg. 3908
JARDINE MATHESON HOLDINGS LIMITED; *Int'l*, pg. 3908
JARDINE MATHESON INTERNATIONAL SERVICES LTD.—See Jardine Matheson Holdings Limited; *Int'l*, pg. 3908
JARDINE MATHESON LIMITED—See Jardine Matheson Holdings Limited; *Int'l*, pg. 3908
JARDINE MATHESON (MALAYSIA) SDN BHD—See Jardine Matheson Holdings Limited; *Int'l*, pg. 3908
JARDINE MATHESON (SINGAPORE) LTD.—See Jardine Matheson Holdings Limited; *Int'l*, pg. 3908
JARDINE MATHESON (THAILAND) LTD.—See Jardine Matheson Holdings Limited; *Int'l*, pg. 3908
JARDINE MATHESON (VIETNAM) LTD.—See Jardine Matheson Holdings Limited; *Int'l*, pg. 3908
JARDINE MOTORS GROUP LTD.—See Jardine Matheson Holdings Limited; *Int'l*, pg. 3908
JARDINE MOTORS GROUP UK LIMITED—See Lithia Motors, Inc.; *U.S. Public*, pg. 1323
JARDINE ONESOLUTION (2001) PTE. LTD.—See Jardine Matheson Holdings Limited; *Int'l*, pg. 3908
JARDINE ONESOLUTION (CHINA) LIMITED—See Jardine Matheson Holdings Limited; *Int'l*, pg. 3909
JARDINE ONESOLUTION (HK) LIMITED—See Jardine Matheson Holdings Limited; *Int'l*, pg. 3909
JARDINE PACIFIC HOLDINGS LTD—See Jardine Matheson Holdings Limited; *Int'l*, pg. 3908
JARDINE PACIFIC LTD.—See Jardine Matheson Holdings Limited; *Int'l*, pg. 3908
JARDINE PACIFIC (THAILAND) LTD.—See Jardine Matheson Holdings Limited; *Int'l*, pg. 3909
JARDINE RESTAURANT GROUP—See Jardine Matheson Holdings Limited; *Int'l*, pg. 3909
JARDINE SCHINDLER ELEVATOR CORPORATION—See Jardine Matheson Holdings Limited; *Int'l*, pg. 3909
JARDINE SCHINDLER ELEVATOR CORPORATION—See Schindler Holding AG; *Int'l*, pg. 6620

COMPANY NAME INDEX

JARDINE SCHINDLER GROUP—See Jardine Matheson Holdings Limited; *Int'l*, pg. 3909
JARDINE SCHINDLER GROUP—See Schindler Holding AG; *Int'l*, pg. 6620
JARDINE SCHINDLER LIFTS LTD.—See Otis Worldwide Corporation; *U.S. Public*, pg. 1623
JARDINE SCHINDLER LIFTS (MACAO) LTD.—See Schindler Holding AG; *Int'l*, pg. 6619
JARDINE SCHINDLER (THAI) LTD.—See Jardine Matheson Holdings Limited; *Int'l*, pg. 3909
JARDINE SCHINDLER (THAI) LTD.—See Schindler Holding AG; *Int'l*, pg. 6620
JARDINE SHIPPING HUB SERVICES PTE. LTD.—See Jardine Matheson Holdings Limited; *Int'l*, pg. 3909
JARDINE SHIPPING SERVICES (MALAYSIA) SDN BHD—See Jardine Matheson Holdings Limited; *Int'l*, pg. 3909
JARDINE SHIPPING SERVICES (VIETNAM) LTD—See Jardine Matheson Holdings Limited; *Int'l*, pg. 3909
JARDINE STRATEGIC HOLDINGS LTD.—See Jardine Matheson Holdings Limited; *Int'l*, pg. 3909
JARDINE TRANSPORT LTD.—See SeaFort Capital, Inc.; *Int'l*, pg. 6662
JARDINE TRAVEL LIMITED—See Jardine Matheson Holdings Limited; *Int'l*, pg. 3909
JARDINIER ALTERNATIVE IRRIGATION SYSTEMS, INC.; *U.S. Private*, pg. 2188
JARDINIER CORP.; *U.S. Private*, pg. 2188
JARDIS INDUSTRIES INC.; *U.S. Private*, pg. 2188
JARDON & HOWARD TECHNOLOGIES; *U.S. Private*, pg. 2188
J.A. REINHARDT & CO., INC.—See RTX Corporation; *U.S. Public*, pg. 1822
JARFALLA HARDVERKSTAD AB—See Georg Fischer AG; *Int'l*, pg. 2937
JARIET TECHNOLOGIES, INC.—See L3Harris Technologies, Inc.; *U.S. Public*, pg. 1280
J.A. RIGGS TRACTOR CO.; *U.S. Private*, pg. 2158
JARING METAL INDUSTRIES SDN. BHD.—See JAG Berhad; *Int'l*, pg. 3869
JARIR MARKETING COMPANY BAHRAIN—See JARIR MARKETING COMPANY; *Int'l*, pg. 3911
JARIR MARKETING COMPANY; *Int'l*, pg. 3911
JARISLOWSKY, FRASER LIMITED—See The Bank of Nova Scotia; *Int'l*, pg. 7617
JARIT GMBH—See Integra LifeSciences Holdings Corporation; *U.S. Public*, pg. 1136
JARLLYTEC CO., LTD.; *Int'l*, pg. 3911
JARLLY TECHNOLOGY (SHANGHAI) CO., LTD.—See Jarllytec Co., Ltd.; *Int'l*, pg. 3911
JARMEL KIZEL ARCHITECTS & ENGINEERS, INC.; *U.S. Private*, pg. 2188
JARNGRINDEN PROJEKTUTVECKLING AB—See Genova Property Group AB; *Int'l*, pg. 2926
J. ARON & COMPANY (SINGAPORE) PTE.—See The Goldman Sachs Group, Inc.; *U.S. Public*, pg. 2082
J. ARON & CO.—See The Goldman Sachs Group, Inc.; *U.S. Public*, pg. 2082
J. ARON HOLDINGS L.P.—See The Goldman Sachs Group, Inc.; *U.S. Public*, pg. 2081
JARPENO LIMITED—See Oil & Natural Gas Corporation Limited; *Int'l*, pg. 5534
JARRARD, NOWELL & RUSSELL, LLC; *U.S. Private*, pg. 2188
JARRELL CONTRACTING—See Charles E. Jarrell Contracting Company, Inc.; *U.S. Private*, pg. 852
JARRETT LOGISTICS SYSTEMS, INC.; *U.S. Private*, pg. 2188
JARROW FORMULAS, INC.—See New Mountain Capital, LLC; *U.S. Private*, pg. 2903
JARROW INDUSTRIES INCORPORATED; *U.S. Private*, pg. 2188
JARSON PRECISION TECHNOLOGY CO., LTD.—See Jarllytec Co., Ltd.; *Int'l*, pg. 3911
J. ARTHUR TRUDEAU MEMORIAL CENTER; *U.S. Private*, pg. 2155
JA-RU INC.; *U.S. Private*, pg. 2172
JA-RU INC.—See JA-RU INC.; *U.S. Private*, pg. 2172
JARVIS CONSTRUCTION (UK) LIMITED—See Jarvis Plc; *Int'l*, pg. 3911
JARVIS CUTTING TOOLS; *U.S. Private*, pg. 2188
JARVIS DOWNING & EMCH INC.; *U.S. Private*, pg. 2188
JARVIS ESTATES LIMITED—See Jarvis Plc; *Int'l*, pg. 3911
JARVIS FASTLINE LIMITED—See Jarvis Plc; *Int'l*, pg. 3911
JARVIS METALS RECYCLING INC.; *U.S. Private*, pg. 2188
JARVIS PAINTING, INC.—See BMS CAT, Inc.; *U.S. Private*, pg. 601
JARVIS PLC; *Int'l*, pg. 3911
THE JARVIS PRESS, INC.—See Chatham Asset Management, LLC; *U.S. Private*, pg. 863
JARVIS PROJECTS LIMITED—See Jarvis Plc; *Int'l*, pg. 3911
JARVIS SECURITIES PLC; *Int'l*, pg. 3911
JARVIS SUPPLY CO., INC.—See TruArc Partners, L.P.; *U.S. Private*, pg. 4245
JASACHEM SDN BHD—See Kuala Lumpur Kepong Berhad; *Int'l*, pg. 4318

JASA KITA BERHAD - FACTORY—See Jasa Kita Berhad; *Int'l*, pg. 3911
JASA KITA BERHAD; *Int'l*, pg. 3911
JASA KITA TRADING SDN. BHD.—See Jasa Kita Berhad; *Int'l*, pg. 3911
JASAN VIETNAM TEXTILE & DYEING CO., LTD.—See Zhejiang Jasan Holding Group Co., Ltd.; *Int'l*, pg. 8656
JAS ASSET PUBLIC COMPANY LIMITED; *Int'l*, pg. 3911
JASA TRANSIT, INC.; *U.S. Private*, pg. 2189
JASBA MOSAIK GMBH—See Deutsche Steinzeug Cremer & Breuer AG; *Int'l*, pg. 2083
JASCH INDUSTRIES LIMITED; *Int'l*, pg. 3911
JASCKSONLEA DE MEXICO S.A. DE C.V.—See Jason Industries, Inc.; *U.S. Private*, pg. 2190
JASCO ELECTRONICS HOLDINGS LIMITED - SCAFELL DIVISION—See Jasco Electronics Holdings Limited; *Int'l*, pg. 3911
JASCO ELECTRONICS HOLDINGS LIMITED; *Int'l*, pg. 3911
JASCO ELECTRONICS—See Jasco Electronics Holdings Limited; *Int'l*, pg. 3911
JASCO HEAT TREATING INC—See Jasco Tools Inc.; *U.S. Private*, pg. 2189
JASCO INDUSTRIES INC.; *U.S. Private*, pg. 2189
JAS CO., LTD.—See SBS Holdings Inc.; *Int'l*, pg. 6607
JASCO TOOLS INC.; *U.S. Private*, pg. 2189
JASCO TRADING (PTY) LIMITED—See Jasco Electronics Holdings Limited; *Int'l*, pg. 3911
JASCULCA/TERMAN AND ASSOCIATES; *U.S. Private*, pg. 2189
JAS DIAGNOSTICS, INC.—See Transasia Bio-Medicals Ltd.; *Int'l*, pg. 7896
JASENOVO A.D.; *Int'l*, pg. 3911
JAS FORWARDING INCORPORATED; *U.S. Private*, pg. 2188
JASH DEALMARK LIMITED; *Int'l*, pg. 3911
JASH ENGINEERING LIMITED; *Int'l*, pg. 3912
JAS HENNESSY & CO. LTD.—See LVMH Moet Hennessy Louis Vuitton SE; *Int'l*, pg. 4600
JAS HENNESSY & CO SCS—See LVMH Moet Hennessy Louis Vuitton SE; *Int'l*, pg. 4599
JASH USA INC.—See Jash Engineering Limited; *Int'l*, pg. 3912
JASLOW DENTAL LABORATORY INC.—See Cornerstone Dental Laboratories, LLC; *U.S. Private*, pg. 1052
JASMINAL S.A.R.L.—See Henkel AG & Co. KGaA; *Int'l*, pg. 3352
JASMINE INTERNATIONAL PUBLIC COMPANY LIMITED; *Int'l*, pg. 3912
JASMINE INTERNET CO., LTD.—See Jasmine International Public Company Limited; *Int'l*, pg. 3912
JASMINESOFT CO., LTD.—See Japan Pulp and Paper Company Limited; *Int'l*, pg. 3904
JASMINE SUBMARINE TELECOMMUNICATIONS CO., LTD.—See Jasmine International Public Company Limited; *Int'l*, pg. 3912
JASMINE TECHNOLOGY SOLUTION PUBLIC COMPANY LIMITED; *Int'l*, pg. 3912
JASMINE VINEYARDS, INC.; *U.S. Private*, pg. 2189
JASNIA SDN BHD—See Tambun Indah Land Berhad; *Int'l*, pg. 7450
JAS OCEANIA PTY LTD—See Bapcor Limited; *Int'l*, pg. 857
JAS OCEAN SERVICES INC.—See JAS Forwarding Incorporated; *U.S. Private*, pg. 2188
JA SOLAR AUSTRALIA PTY. LTD.—See JA Solar Technology Co., Ltd.; *Int'l*, pg. 3859
JA SOLAR BRAZIL CO., LTD.—See JA Solar Technology Co., Ltd.; *Int'l*, pg. 3859
JA SOLAR GMBH—See JA Solar Technology Co., Ltd.; *Int'l*, pg. 3859
JA SOLAR HOLDINGS CO., LTD.—See JA Solar Technology Co., Ltd.; *Int'l*, pg. 3859
JA SOLAR JAPAN LIMITED—See JA Solar Technology Co., Ltd.; *Int'l*, pg. 3859
JA SOLAR KOREA CO., LTD.—See JA Solar Technology Co., Ltd.; *Int'l*, pg. 3859
JA SOLAR MEXICO CO., LTD.—See JA Solar Technology Co., Ltd.; *Int'l*, pg. 3859
JA SOLAR TECHNOLOGY CO., LTD.; *Int'l*, pg. 3859
JA SOLAR TECHNOLOGY YANGZHOU CO., LTD.—See JA Solar Technology Co., Ltd.; *Int'l*, pg. 3859
JA SOLAR USA INC—See JA Solar Technology Co., Ltd.; *Int'l*, pg. 3859
JASON CO., LTD.; *Int'l*, pg. 3912
JASON ELECTRONICS (PTE) LTD—See Jason Marine Group Limited; *Int'l*, pg. 3912
JASON ELECTRONICS (THAILAND) CO., LTD.—See Jason Marine Group Limited; *Int'l*, pg. 3912
JASON ELEKTRONIK (M) SDN. BHD.—See Jason Marine Group Limited; *Int'l*, pg. 3912
JASON FURNITURE HANGZHOU CO LTD; *Int'l*, pg. 3912
JASON HOLDING GMBH—See Jason Industries, Inc.; *U.S. Private*, pg. 2189
JASON HOLDINGS UK LIMITED—See Jason Industries, Inc.; *U.S. Private*, pg. 2189
JASON INCORPORATED - BATTLE CREEK PLANT—See Jason Industries, Inc.; *U.S. Private*, pg. 2189

J.A. STREET & ASSOCIATES, INC.

JASON INCORPORATED - COLUMBUS PLANT—See Jason Industries, Inc.; *U.S. Private*, pg. 2189
JASON INCORPORATED - OLD FORT PLANT—See Jason Industries, Inc.; *U.S. Private*, pg. 2189
JASON INCORPORATED—See Jason Industries, Inc.; *U.S. Private*, pg. 2189
JASON INDUSTRIAL, INC.; *U.S. Private*, pg. 2189
JASON INDUSTRIES, INC.; *U.S. Private*, pg. 2189
JASON JONES TRUCKING, INC.—See OEP Capital Advisors, L.P.; *U.S. Private*, pg. 2999
JASON MARINE ELECTRONICS SPAIN, S.L.—See Jason Marine Group Limited; *Int'l*, pg. 3912
JASON MARINE GROUP LIMITED; *Int'l*, pg. 3912
JASON NATURAL PRODUCTS INC.—See The Hain Celestial Group, Inc.; *U.S. Public*, pg. 2087
JASON OHIO CORPORATION—See Jason Industries, Inc.; *U.S. Private*, pg. 2190
JASON PARQUET HOLDINGS LIMITED; *Int'l*, pg. 3912
JASON PARTNERS HOLDINGS INC.—See Jason Industries, Inc.; *U.S. Private*, pg. 2190
JASON (SHANGHAI) CO., LTD.—See Jason Marine Group Limited; *Int'l*, pg. 3912
JASON'S HAULING, LLC.; *U.S. Private*, pg. 2190
JASON SHIPPING ASA; *Int'l*, pg. 3912
JASPAR—See Toyota Tsusho Corporation; *Int'l*, pg. 7879
JASPER-ARA DIALYSIS L.L.P.—See Nautic Partners, LLC; *U.S. Private*, pg. 2870
JASPER CONTRACTORS INC; *U.S. Private*, pg. 2190
JASPER CORP.; *U.S. Private*, pg. 2190
JASPER DESIGN AUTOMATION, A.B.—See Cadence Design Systems, Inc.; *U.S. Public*, pg. 418
JASPER DESIGN AUTOMATION DO BRASIL INFORMATICA E MICROELECTRONICA LTDA.—See Cadence Design Systems, Inc.; *U.S. Public*, pg. 418
JASPER DESIGN AUTOMATION, INC.—See Cadence Design Systems, Inc.; *U.S. Public*, pg. 419
JASPER DESIGN AUTOMATION - ISRAEL, LTD.—See Cadence Design Systems, Inc.; *U.S. Public*, pg. 418
JASPER ELECTRIC MOTORS INC—See Jasper Engine & Transmission Exchange Inc.; *U.S. Private*, pg. 2190
JASPER ENGINEERING & EQUIPMENT CO.; *U.S. Private*, pg. 2190
JASPER ENGINE EXCHANGE INC.—See Jasper Engine & Transmission Exchange Inc.; *U.S. Private*, pg. 2190
JASPER ENGINES & TRANSMISSIONS, INC.—See Jasper Engine & Transmission Exchange Inc.; *U.S. Private*, pg. 2190
JASPER ENGINE & TRANSMISSION EXCHANGE INC. - JASPER ALTERNATE FUELS—See Jasper Engine & Transmission Exchange Inc.; *U.S. Private*, pg. 2190
JASPER ENGINE & TRANSMISSION EXCHANGE INC.; *U.S. Private*, pg. 2190
JASPER INVESTMENTS LIMITED; *Int'l*, pg. 3912
JASPER MINING CORPORATION; *Int'l*, pg. 3912
JASPER NEWS-BOY—See The Hearst Corporation; *U.S. Private*, pg. 4047
JASPER OIL COMPANY; *U.S. Private*, pg. 2190
JASPER OIL, INC.—See AIP, LLC; *U.S. Private*, pg. 136
JASPER RUBBER PRODUCTS INC.; *U.S. Private*, pg. 2190
JASPER SEATING CO., INC., JSI DIVISION—See Jasper Seating Co., Inc.; *U.S. Private*, pg. 2190
JASPER SEATING CO., INC.; *U.S. Private*, pg. 2190
JASPER SEATING COMPANY—See Jasper Seating Co., Inc.; *U.S. Private*, pg. 2190
JASPERSOFT CORPORATION—See Vista Equity Partners, LLC; *U.S. Private*, pg. 4402
JASPERSOFT GMBH—See Vista Equity Partners, LLC; *U.S. Private*, pg. 4402
JASPERSOFT LIMITED—See Vista Equity Partners, LLC; *U.S. Private*, pg. 4402
JASPERSOFT SARL—See Vista Equity Partners, LLC; *U.S. Private*, pg. 4402
JASPER STONE COMPANY—See L.G. Everist Inc.; *U.S. Private*, pg. 2366
JASPER TANK LTD—See Exchange Income Corporation; *Int'l*, pg. 2579
JASPER THERAPEUTICS, INC.; *U.S. Public*, pg. 1187
JASPER WYMAN & SON; *U.S. Private*, pg. 2190
JASSIM AL WAZZAN SONS GENERAL TRADING COMPANY W.L.L.—See Mezzan Holding Co KSC; *Int'l*, pg. 4870
JASSIM TRANSPORT & STEVEDORING COMPANY K.S.C.P.—See Kuwait Projects Company (Holding) K.S.C.P.; *Int'l*, pg. 4346
J. ASTAPHAN & CO (1970) LTD; *Int'l*, pg. 3854
JASTBOLAGET AB—See Orkla ASA; *Int'l*, pg. 5637
JASTEC CO., LTD.—See Nippon Telegraph & Telephone Corporation; *Int'l*, pg. 5346
JASTECH LTD.; *Int'l*, pg. 3913
JASTEC THAILAND CO., LTD.—See Japan System Techniques Co., Ltd.; *Int'l*, pg. 3905
JASTEL NETWORK CO., LTD.—See Jasmine International Public Company Limited; *Int'l*, pg. 3912
JASTICON INC.; *U.S. Private*, pg. 2191
J.A. STREET & ASSOCIATES, INC.; *U.S. Private*, pg. 2158
JASTRZEBSKA SPOLKA KOLEJOWA SP. Z O.O.—See Jastrzebska Spolka Weglowa S.A.; *Int'l*, pg. 3913

JASTRZEBSKA SPOLKA WEGLOWA S.A.

JASTRZEBSKA SPOLKA WEGLOWA S.A.; *Int'l*, pg. 3913
JASTRZEBSKIE ZAKLADY REMONTOWE SP. Z O.O.—See Jastrzebska Spolka Weglowa S.A.; *Int'l*, pg. 3913
JAST, S.A.—See ViaSat, Inc.; *U.S. Public*, pg. 2292
JAST TECHNIQUES PTE. LTD.—See Japan System Techniques Co., Ltd.; *Int'l*, pg. 3905
JASUINDO TIGA PERKASA TBK; *Int'l*, pg. 3913
JAS W. GLOVER LTD. INC; *U.S. Private*, pg. 2188
JAS WORLDWIDE, INC; *U.S. Private*, pg. 2188
JATAAYU SOFTWARE (P) LTD.—See Integra Micro Systems (P) Ltd.; *Int'l*, pg. 3730
JATA CARGO AB—See Storskogen Group AB; *Int'l*, pg. 7227
JATALIA GLOBAL VENTURES LIMITED; *Int'l*, pg. 3913
JATA LLC; *U.S. Private*, pg. 2191
JATASCO, INC.—See The Eads Company; *U.S. Private*, pg. 4024
JATAT FURNITURE INDUSTRIES SDN BHD—See Koda Ltd.; *Int'l*, pg. 4225
JATCO ENGINEERING LTD—See Nissan Motor Co., Ltd.; *Int'l*, pg. 5367
JATCO FRANCE SAS—See Nissan Motor Co., Ltd.; *Int'l*, pg. 5367
JATCO KOREA ENGINEERING CORP.—See Nissan Motor Co., Ltd.; *Int'l*, pg. 5367
JATCO KOREA SERVICE CORP.—See Nissan Motor Co., Ltd.; *Int'l*, pg. 5367
JATCO LTD—See Nissan Motor Co., Ltd.; *Int'l*, pg. 5367
JATCO PLANT TEC LTD—See Nissan Motor Co., Ltd.; *Int'l*, pg. 5367
JATCORP LIMITED; *Int'l*, pg. 3913
JATCO TOOL LTD—See Nissan Motor Co., Ltd.; *Int'l*, pg. 5367
JATCO USA INC.—See Nissan Motor Co., Ltd.; *Int'l*, pg. 5369
JATEC ELECTRIC LTD.; *Int'l*, pg. 3913
JATEC GMBH—See Quanex Building Products Corp.; *U.S. Public*, pg. 1749
JATET PETRO TECHNOLOGY PLC; *Int'l*, pg. 3913
J.A. TEXTILE MILLS LTD.—See National Group of Companies LLC; *Int'l*, pg. 5158
J.A. THOMAS & ASSOCIATES, INC.—See Microsoft Corporation; *U.S. Public*, pg. 1442
J. A. TIBERTI CONSTRUCTION CO., INC.—See Tiberti Organization; *U.S. Private*, pg. 4167
JATO DESIGN INTERNATIONAL LIMITED—See Shenzhen Jiang & Associates Creative Design Co., Ltd.; *Int'l*, pg. 6814
JAT OIL & SUPPLY INC.; *U.S. Private*, pg. 2191
JATOM SYSTEMS INC.; *Int'l*, pg. 3913
JATON CORP.; *U.S. Private*, pg. 2191
JATOS INC.—See Fuji Oozx Inc.; *Int'l*, pg. 2816
JAT PHARMACY, LLC—See Midwest Veterinary Supply, Inc.; *U.S. Private*, pg. 2723
JATRODIESEL, INC.; *U.S. Private*, pg. 2191
JATROSOLUTIONS GMBH—See EnBW Energie Baden-Wurttemberg AG; *Int'l*, pg. 2399
JAT SOFTWARE, INC.—See Greatland Corporation; *U.S. Private*, pg. 1770
JATTASHANKAR INDUSTRIES LIMITED; *Int'l*, pg. 3913
J.A .TUCKER COMPANY; *U.S. Private*, pg. 2157
JAUCH & HUEBENER SPOL. S.R.O.—See Aon plc; *Int'l*, pg. 491
JAUCH QUARTZ AMERICA, INC.—See Nantong Jianghai Capacitor Co., Ltd.; *Int'l*, pg. 5145
JAUCH QUARTZ FRANCE—See Nantong Jianghai Capacitor Co., Ltd.; *Int'l*, pg. 5145
JAUCH QUARTZ UK LTD.—See Nantong Jianghai Capacitor Co., Ltd.; *Int'l*, pg. 5145
JAUHARABAD SUGAR MILLS LIMITED; *Int'l*, pg. 3913
JAUNATO; *Int'l*, pg. 3913
JAUSS POLYMERS LIMITED; *Int'l*, pg. 3913
JAVA CITY; *U.S. Private*, pg. 2191
JAVA CONNECTIONS LLC; *U.S. Private*, pg. 2191
JAVAC PTY. LTD.—See Atlas Copco AB; *Int'l*, pg. 683
JAVA HOLDINGS CO., LTD.—See Phoenix Capital Co., Ltd.; *Int'l*, pg. 5849
JAVA MARINE LINES PTE. LTD.—See MMA Offshore Limited; *Int'l*, pg. 5005
JAVAN TECHNOLOGY INC; *U.S. Private*, pg. 2191
JAVED OMER VOHRA & COMPANY LIMITED; *Int'l*, pg. 3914
JAVELIN INNOVATIONS INC.—See Gilo Ventures, LLC; *U.S. Private*, pg. 1701
JAVELIN MORTGAGE INVESTMENT CORP.—See ARMOUR Residential REIT, Inc.; *U.S. Public*, pg. 193
JAVELIN—See Omnicom Group Inc.; *U.S. Public*, pg. 1586
JAVELIN SOUTHEAST CORPORATION; *U.S. Private*, pg. 2191
JAVIC PROPERTY LLC; *U.S. Private*, pg. 2191
JAVLYN INC.—See Krones AG; *Int'l*, pg. 4305
JAVLYN PROCESS SYSTEMS LLC—See Krones AG; *Int'l*, pg. 4305
JAVO BEVERAGE COMPANY, INC.; *U.S. Private*, pg. 2191
JAWALA INC.; *Int'l*, pg. 3914
JAWA POWER HOLDING GMBH—See Siemens Aktiengesellschaft; *Int'l*, pg. 6887

J.A. WOLL HANDELS GMBH—See B&M European Value Retail S.A.; *Int'l*, pg. 784
JAWONIO; *U.S. Private*, pg. 2191
JAWOOD BUSINESS PROCESS SOLUTIONS, LLC—See Genpact Limited; *Int'l*, pg. 2927
JAWOOD; *U.S. Private*, pg. 2191
J.A. WRIGHT & CO.—See TA Associates, Inc.; *U.S. Private*, pg. 3919
J.A. WRIGHT & CO.—See The Carlyle Group Inc.; *U.S. Public*, pg. 2057
JAWS HURRICANE ACQUISITION CORPORATION; *U.S. Public*, pg. 1187
JAWS JUGGERNAUT ACQUISITION CORPORATION; *U.S. Public*, pg. 1188
JAWS MUSTANG ACQUISITION CORPORATION; *U.S. Public*, pg. 1188
JAWS WILDCAT ACQUISITION CORPORATION; *U.S. Private*, pg. 2191
JAX ENTERPRISES INC.; *U.S. Private*, pg. 2191
JAX (J.ALEXANDER) REAL ESTATE—See SoftBank Group Corp.; *Int'l*, pg. 7054
JAX MARKETS—See Macber Inc.; *U.S. Private*, pg. 2535
JAXON ENTERPRISES; *U.S. Private*, pg. 2191
JAXON MINING INC.; *Int'l*, pg. 3914
JAXSON CORPORATION—See Mitani Sangyo Co., Ltd.; *Int'l*, pg. 4924
JAXSTA LIMITED; *Int'l*, pg. 3914
JAXX GMBH—See mybet Holding SE; *Int'l*, pg. 5111
JAXX UK LTD.—See mybet Holding SE; *Int'l*, pg. 5111
JAYA APPAREL; *U.S. Private*, pg. 2192
JAYABHARAT CREDIT LTD.; *Int'l*, pg. 3915
JAYA DIY MART SDN. BHD.—See Sunway Berhad; *Int'l*, pg. 7331
JAY ADVERTISING, INC.; *U.S. Private*, pg. 2191
JAYA HIND INDUSTRIES GROUP; *Int'l*, pg. 3914
JAYA HOLDINGS LIMITED; *Int'l*, pg. 3914
JAYA KONSTRUKSI MANGGALA PRATAMA TBK; *Int'l*, pg. 3914
JAYANT AGRO-ORGANICS LIMITED - UNIT 1—See Jayant Agro Organics Ltd; *Int'l*, pg. 3915
JAYANT AGRO-ORGANICS LIMITED - UNIT 2—See Jayant Agro Organics Ltd; *Int'l*, pg. 3915
JAYANT AGRO ORGANICS LTD; *Int'l*, pg. 3915
JAYANT INFRATECH LIMITED; *Int'l*, pg. 3915
JAYA REAL PROPERTY TBK; *Int'l*, pg. 3914
JAYASWAL NECO INDUSTRIES LIMITED; *Int'l*, pg. 3915
JAYA TIASA HOLDINGS BERHAD; *Int'l*, pg. 3915
JAYATMA ENTERPRISES LIMITED; *Int'l*, pg. 3915
JAYATMA INDUSTRIES LTD.; *Int'l*, pg. 3915
JAYA UNI'ANG (SABAH) SDN. BHD.—See Thong Guan Industries Berhad; *Int'l*, pg. 7717
JAY AUTOMOTIVE GROUP INC.—See Group 1 Automotive, Inc.; *U.S. Public*, pg. 971
JAYBEAM LIMITED—See Amphenol Corporation; *U.S. Public*, pg. 130
JAYBEAM WIRELESS SAS—See Amphenol Corporation; *U.S. Public*, pg. 130
JAYBEE ENG. (HOLDINGS) PTY. LTD.—See ANDRITZ AG; *Int'l*, pg. 456
JAY BHARAT MARUTI LTD; *Int'l*, pg. 3914
JAYBHARAT TEXTILES & REAL ESTATE LIMITED; *Int'l*, pg. 3915
JAYBIRD, LLC—See Logitech International S.A.; *U.S. Public*, pg. 1341
JAYBRAKE, LLC—See Dreison International, Inc.; *U.S. Private*, pg. 1276
JAYBRO GROUP PTY. LTD.—See CHAMP Private Equity Pty. Ltd.; *Int'l*, pg. 1439
JAY CASHMAN INC.; *U.S. Private*, pg. 2191
JAYCO CORPORATION PTY. LTD.; *Int'l*, pg. 3915
JAYCO INC.—See Thor Industries, Inc.; *U.S. Public*, pg. 2156
JAYCO INTERNATIONAL; *U.S. Private*, pg. 2192
JAYCORP BERHAD; *Int'l*, pg. 3915
JAYCORP HOME FURNISHINGS INC.—See Jaycorp Berhad; *Int'l*, pg. 3915
JAY COUNTY LANDFILL, L.L.C.—See Waste Management, Inc.; *U.S. Public*, pg. 2331
JAYCOX IMPLEMENT INC.; *U.S. Private*, pg. 2192
JAY DEE CONTRACTORS, INC.; *U.S. Private*, pg. 2191
JAYDEN RESOURCES INC.; *Int'l*, pg. 3915
JAY ENERGY & S. ENERGIES LIMITED; *Int'l*, pg. 3914
JAYEN INC.; *U.S. Private*, pg. 2192
JAYEX TECHNOLOGY LIMITED; *Int'l*, pg. 3915
JAYFER AUTOMOTIVE GROUP (MARKHAM) INC; *Int'l*, pg. 3915
JAY FRANCO & SONS INC.; *U.S. Private*, pg. 2191
JAY FULKROAD & SONS INC.; *U.S. Private*, pg. 2191
THE JAY GROUP; *U.S. Private*, pg. 4058
JAYHAWK PIPELINE, LLC—See CHS INC.; *U.S. Public*, pg. 491
JAY HENGES ENTERPRISES INC.; *U.S. Private*, pg. 2191
JAY INDUSTRIAL REPAIR, INC.; *U.S. Private*, pg. 2191
JAY INDUSTRIES INC.; *U.S. Private*, pg. 2192
JAY JAYS TRADEMARK PTY. LIMITED—See Premier Investments Limited; *Int'l*, pg. 5960
JAY JEMS INC.; *U.S. Private*, pg. 2192
JAYJUN COSMETIC INC.; *Int'l*, pg. 3915

CORPORATE AFFILIATIONS

JAY KADOWAKI INC.; *U.S. Private*, pg. 2192
JAYKAY ENTERPRISES LTD.; *Int'l*, pg. 3916
JAYKAY MARKETING SERVICES (PVT) LTD.—See John Keells Holdings PLC; *Int'l*, pg. 3978
JAYLYN SALES INC.; *U.S. Private*, pg. 2192
JAYMAN MASTERBUILT, INC.; *Int'l*, pg. 3916
JAY MAR INC.; *U.S. Private*, pg. 2192
JAY MART PUBLIC COMPANY LIMITED; *Int'l*, pg. 3914
JAYNE INDUSTRIES INC.; *Int'l*, pg. 3916
JAYNES CORPORATION; *U.S. Private*, pg. 2192
JAY N. NELSON INC.; *U.S. Private*, pg. 2192
JAY PACKAGING GROUP, INC.—See Wellspring Capital Management LLC; *U.S. Private*, pg. 4477
JAY PEAK, INC.—See Mont Saint-Sauveur International, Inc.; *Int'l*, pg. 5035
JAYPEE FERTILIZERS & INDUSTRIES LIMITED—See Jaiprakash Associates Limited; *Int'l*, pg. 3873
JAYPEE INFRATECH LIMITED—See Jaiprakash Associates Limited; *Int'l*, pg. 3873
JAYPEE SPORTS INTERNATIONAL LIMITED—See Jaiprakash Associates Limited; *Int'l*, pg. 3873
JAY PETROLEUM, INC.; *U.S. Private*, pg. 2192
JAY PETROLEUM LLC—See Equital Ltd.; *Int'l*, pg. 2487
JAY PLASTICS, INC.; *U.S. Private*, pg. 2192
JAY PONTIAC INC.; *U.S. Private*, pg. 2192
JAYRAY ADS & PR, INC.; *U.S. Private*, pg. 2192
JAYRIDE GROUP LIMITED; *Int'l*, pg. 3916
JAY R. SMITH MFG. CO.; *U.S. Private*, pg. 2192
JAYSET—See Nygard International Partnership; *Int'l*, pg. 5500
JAYSHREE CHEMICALS LTD.; *Int'l*, pg. 3916
JAY SHREE TEA & INDUSTRIES LTD; *Int'l*, pg. 3914
JAY & SILENT BOB'S SECRET STASH; *U.S. Private*, pg. 2191
JAY SOLUTIONS OY—See CapMan PLC; *Int'l*, pg. 1315
JAYSON OIL COMPANY INCORPORATED; *U.S. Private*, pg. 2192
JAY'S SPORTING GOODS, INC.; *U.S. Private*, pg. 2192
JAY'S TRANSPORTATION GROUP LTD.—See Mullen Group Ltd.; *Int'l*, pg. 5080
JAYSYNTH ANTHRAQUINONES LTD.—See JD Orgochem Limited; *Int'l*, pg. 3924
JAYSYNTH DYESTUFF (INDIA) LTD.; *Int'l*, pg. 3916
JAYUD GLOBAL LOGISTICS LIMITED; *Int'l*, pg. 3916
JAY USHIN LTD; *Int'l*, pg. 3914
JAYVEE PETROLEUM PTY LTD—See Ampol Limited; *Int'l*, pg. 436
JAYWAY APS—See Devoteam SA; *Int'l*, pg. 2090
JAYWAY HALMSTAD AB—See Devoteam SA; *Int'l*, pg. 2090
JAYWAY INC.—See Devoteam SA; *Int'l*, pg. 2090
JAYWAY MALMO AB—See Devoteam SA; *Int'l*, pg. 2090
JAYWAY STOCKHOLM AB—See Devoteam SA; *Int'l*, pg. 2090
JAYWING PLC; *Int'l*, pg. 3916
JAY WOLFE ACURA; *U.S. Private*, pg. 2192
JAY WOLFE TOYOTA OF WEST COUNTY; *U.S. Private*, pg. 2192
JAZAN DEVELOPMENT AND INVESTMENT COMPANY; *Int'l*, pg. 3916
JAZAN GAS PROJECTS COMPANY—See Air Products & Chemicals, Inc.; *U.S. Public*, pg. 66
JAZEERA AIRWAYS COMPANY KSC; *Int'l*, pg. 3916
JAZ HOTEL GMBH—See H World Group Limited; *Int'l*, pg. 3191
JAZ HOTEL GROUP S.A.E.—See TUI AG; *Int'l*, pg. 7965
JAZON SP. Z O.O.—See Chien Wei Precise Technology Co., Ltd.; *Int'l*, pg. 1477
JAZ TECHNOLOGY DEVELOPMENT (SHENZHEN) CO., LTD—See Asia Power Corporation Limited; *Int'l*, pg. 615
JAZWARES, INC.—See Berkshire Hathaway Inc.; *U.S. Public*, pg. 298
JAZZ AVIATION LP—See Chorus Aviation Inc.; *Int'l*, pg. 1584
JAZZ BASKETBALL INVESTORS, INC.; *U.S. Private*, pg. 2192
JAZZ CASINO COMPANY, LLC—See Caesars Entertainment, Inc.; *U.S. Public*, pg. 420
JAZZERCISE, INC.; *U.S. Private*, pg. 2193
JAZZ HIPSTER CORPORATION; *Int'l*, pg. 3916
JAZZ PHARMACEUTICALS COMMERCIAL CORP—See Jazz Pharmaceuticals plc; *Int'l*, pg. 3916
JAZZ PHARMACEUTICALS, INC. - PHILADELPHIA—See Jazz Pharmaceuticals plc; *Int'l*, pg. 3916
JAZZ PHARMACEUTICALS, INC.—See Jazz Pharmaceuticals plc; *Int'l*, pg. 3916
JAZZ PHARMACEUTICALS PLC; *Int'l*, pg. 3916
JAZZ PHARMACEUTICALS UK LIMITED—See Jazz Pharmaceuticals plc; *Int'l*, pg. 3916
JAZZ SEMICONDUCTOR, INC.—See Tower Semiconductor Ltd.; *Int'l*, pg. 7850
THE JAZZ STORE—See Musical Heritage Society Inc.; *U.S. Private*, pg. 2818
JAZZ TECHNOLOGIES, INC.—See Tower Semiconductor Ltd.; *Int'l*, pg. 7850
JAZZ TELECOM, S.A.U.—See Orange S.A.; *Int'l*, pg. 5609
JAZZ WIRELESS DATA INC.—See KORE Wireless Group, Inc.; *U.S. Private*, pg. 2343

COMPANY NAME INDEX

JB&A AVIATION INC.; *U.S. Private*, pg. 2193
JBA CONSULTING ENGINEERS (ASIA) LIMITED—See NV5 Global, Inc.; *U.S. Public*, pg. 1557
JBA CONSULTING ENGINEERS (ASIA) LIMITED—See NV5 Global, Inc.; *U.S. Public*, pg. 1557
JBA CONSULTING ENGINEERS SHANGHAI LIMITED—See NV5 Global, Inc.; *U.S. Public*, pg. 1557
JBA CONSULTING ENGINEERS—See NV5 Global, Inc.; *U.S. Public*, pg. 1557
JBA CONSULTING ENGINEERS VIETNAM LIMITED COMPANY—See NV5 Global, Inc.; *U.S. Public*, pg. 1557
JB ADVANCED TECHNOLOGY CORPORATION—See JBCC Holdings Inc.; *Int'l*, pg. 3917
JB ALLOY CORPORATION; *U.S. Private*, pg. 2193
J. BANICKI CONSTRUCTION, INC.—See Sterling Infrastructure, Inc.; *U.S. Public*, pg. 1946
J-BASE, INC.; *Int'l*, pg. 3854
JB ASSET MANAGEMENT CO., LTD.—See JB Financial Group Co., Ltd.; *Int'l*, pg. 3917
J. BAUER GMBH & CO. KG; *Int'l*, pg. 3854
JB AUTO CORE INC.—See John Boyd Enterprises Inc.; *U.S. Private*, pg. 2220
J&B AVIATION SERVICES INC.—See Illinois Tool Works Inc.; *U.S. Public*, pg. 1103
JBB BUILDERS INTERNATIONAL LIMITED; *Int'l*, pg. 3917
J.B. BOSTICK COMPANY; *U.S. Private*, pg. 2158
JBCC HOLDINGS INC.; *Int'l*, pg. 3917
JBCC (THAILAND) CO., LTD.—See JBCC Holdings Inc.; *Int'l*, pg. 3918
JB CHEMICALS & PHARMACEUTICALS LTD.; *Int'l*, pg. 3917
JBC HOLDING CO.; *U.S. Private*, pg. 2193
JBC INC.; *U.S. Private*, pg. 2193
J.B. CLARK OIL COMPANY INC.; *U.S. Private*, pg. 2158
JBCN (SHANGHAI) INFORMATION TECHNOLOGY CO., LTD.—See JBCC Holdings Inc.; *Int'l*, pg. 3918
JB COCOA FOODS (CHINA) CO., LTD.—See JB Foods Limited; *Int'l*, pg. 3917
JB COCOA, INC.—See JB Foods Limited; *Int'l*, pg. 3917
JB COCOA SDN BHD—See JB Foods Limited; *Int'l*, pg. 3917
JB CONTRACTING CORPORATION; *U.S. Private*, pg. 2193
J.B. COXWELL CONTRACTING, INC.; *U.S. Private*, pg. 2158
JBC TECHNOLOGIES, INC.; *U.S. Private*, pg. 2193
JB CUMBERLAND PR—See Didit.com, Inc.; *U.S. Private*, pg. 1227
J.B. DEWAR INC.; *U.S. Private*, pg. 2158
J.B. DOLLAR STRETCHER MAGAZINE; *U.S. Private*, pg. 2158
J.B. DUNN COMPANY INC.; *U.S. Private*, pg. 2158
J.BEE NP PUBLISHING, LTD.—See EOS Publishing, LLC; *U.S. Private*, pg. 1411
J BEESE VVS & BLIK A/S—See Bravida Holding AB; *Int'l*, pg. 1142
JB ELEKTRO AS—See Instalco AB; *Int'l*, pg. 3721
J. BERG & ASSOCIATES, INC.—See Integrity Marketing Group LLC; *U.S. Private*, pg. 2103
JBF BAHRAIN S.P.C—See JBF Industries Ltd; *Int'l*, pg. 3918
JB FINANCIAL GROUP CO., LTD.; *Int'l*, pg. 3917
JBF INDUSTRIES LTD; *Int'l*, pg. 3918
JBFM FLOUR MILL SDN BHD—See Kuok Brothers Sdn. Bhd.; *Int'l*, pg. 4334
JB FOODS LIMITED; *Int'l*, pg. 3917
JBF RAK LLC—See JBF Industries Ltd; *Int'l*, pg. 3918
JBG CORPORATION; *U.S. Private*, pg. 2193
JB GERMAN OIL GMBH & CO. KG—See Marquard & Bahls AG; *Int'l*, pg. 4699
JB GLOBAL LTD.; *Int'l*, pg. 3917
J.B. GOODWIN REAL ESTATE CO. INC.; *U.S. Private*, pg. 2158
JBG PROPERTIES; *U.S. Private*, pg. 2193
J&B GROUP, INC.; *U.S. Private*, pg. 2153
JBG SMITH PROPERTIES; *U.S. Public*, pg. 1188
J. B. HEALTHCARE PVT. LTD.—See JB Chemicals & Pharmaceuticals Ltd.; *Int'l*, pg. 3917
JB HI-FI (A) PTY LTD—See JB HI-FI Limited; *Int'l*, pg. 3917
JB HI-FI GROUP (NZ) LIMITED—See JB HI-FI Limited; *Int'l*, pg. 3917
JB HI-FI GROUP PTY LTD—See JB HI-FI Limited; *Int'l*, pg. 3917
JB HI-FI INSURANCE REPLACEMENTS—See JB HI-FI Limited; *Int'l*, pg. 3917
JB HI-FI LIMITED; *Int'l*, pg. 3917
JB HOWELL; *U.S. Private*, pg. 2193
J. B. HUDSON JEWELERS CO—See Pohlad Companies; *U.S. Private*, pg. 3220
J.B. HUNT LOGISTICS, INC.—See J.B. Hunt Transport Services, Inc.; *U.S. Public*, pg. 1180
J.B. HUNT TRANSPORT, INC.—See J.B. Hunt Transport Services, Inc.; *U.S. Public*, pg. 1180
J.B. HUNT TRANSPORT SERVICES, INC.; *U.S. Public*, pg. 1180

JBI ELECTRICAL SYSTEMS INCORPORATED; *U.S. Private*, pg. 2193
JBI, INC.; *U.S. Private*, pg. 2193
J&B IMPORTERS INC.; *U.S. Private*, pg. 2153
J&B IMPORTERS PACIFIC INC.—See J&B Importers Inc.; *U.S. Private*, pg. 2153
JB INDUSTRIES, INC.; *U.S. Private*, pg. 2193
JBI TECHNOLOGIES INC; *U.S. Private*, pg. 2193
J.B. JAMES CONSTRUCTION, LLC.; *U.S. Private*, pg. 2158
JBJ DISTRIBUTING INC.—See Veg-Land Sales Inc.; *U.S. Private*, pg. 4353
JBJ SALES & ASSOCIATES INC.; *U.S. Private*, pg. 2193
JBK ASSOCIATES INTERNATIONAL, INC.; *U.S. Private*, pg. 2193
J.B. KENEHAN, LLC; *U.S. Private*, pg. 2158
J BLACKWOOD & SON PTY LTD—See Wesfarmers Limited; *Int'l*, pg. 8381
JB LAVERDURE INC.; *Int'l*, pg. 3917
JBL HAWAII, LTD.; *U.S. Private*, pg. 2193
JBLH COMMUNICATIONS; *U.S. Private*, pg. 2194
JBL RESOURCES; *U.S. Private*, pg. 2194
JB MANAGEMENT INC.; *U.S. Private*, pg. 2193
J.B. MARTIN COMPANY; *U.S. Private*, pg. 2158
J&B MASKINTEKNIK AB—See Searchlight Capital Partners, L.P.; *U.S. Private*, pg. 3590
J&B MASKINTEKNIKK AS—See MEKO AB; *Int'l*, pg. 4805
J&B MATERIALS, INC.—See GMS Inc.; *U.S. Public*, pg. 948
J.B. MATHEWS COMPANY; *U.S. Private*, pg. 2158
JBM AUTO LTD.; *Int'l*, pg. 3918
J.B. METZLER'SCHE VERLAGSBUCHHANDLUNG UND C. E. POESCHEL VERLAG GMBH—See Verlagsgruppe Georg von Holtzbrinck GmbH; *Int'l*, pg. 8170
JBM INCORPORATED; *U.S. Private*, pg. 2194
JBM SAS—See Randstad N.V.; *Int'l*, pg. 6202
JBM TECHNOLOGIES, INC.; *U.S. Private*, pg. 2194
J.B.N. TELEPHONE CO.—See LICT Corporation; *U.S. Public*, pg. 1312
JBNV HOLDING CORP.; *U.S. Private*, pg. 2194
J. BOAG & SON PTY. LIMITED—See Kirin Holdings Company, Limited; *Int'l*, pg. 4189
JBO HOLDING COMPANY; *U.S. Private*, pg. 2194
J. BOUTARI & SON HOLDING S.A.; *Int'l*, pg. 3855
J. BOUTARI & SON WINERIES S.A.—See J. Boutari & Son Holding S.A.; *Int'l*, pg. 3855
J & B PARTNERSHIP LLP—See The Royal Health Group LLC; *U.S. Private*, pg. 4112
J.B. PEARL SALES & SERVICE INC.; *U.S. Private*, pg. 2158
J.B. POINDEXTER & CO., INC.; *U.S. Private*, pg. 2158
J&B PRODUCTS, INC.—See Federal Process Corporation; *U.S. Private*, pg. 1489
J BRAND, INC.—See Fast Retailing Co., Ltd.; *Int'l*, pg. 2621
J. BREED CLOTHING INC.; *U.S. Private*, pg. 2155
J. BRENLIN DESIGN, INC.; *U.S. Private*, pg. 2155
J&B RESTAURANT PARTNERS INC.; *U.S. Private*, pg. 2153
JBR INC.; *U.S. Private*, pg. 2194
JBR MEDIA VENTURES LLC; *U.S. Private*, pg. 2194
J BROWNE CONSTRUCTION LTD.—See Renew Holdings plc; *Int'l*, pg. 6278
JBS ARGENTINA S.A.—See Compagnie Financiere Richemont S.A.; *Int'l*, pg. 1741
J&B SAUSAGE COMPANY, INC.; *U.S. Private*, pg. 2153
JBS AUSTRALIA PTY LIMITED—See JBS S.A.; *Int'l*, pg. 3918
JBS AUTO-TECH SDN BHD - JOHOR BAHRU PLANT—See Solid Automotive Berhad; *Int'l*, pg. 7071
JBS FOODS INTERNATIONAL B.V.; *Int'l*, pg. 3918
JBS GLOBAL UK LIMITED—See JBS S.A.; *Int'l*, pg. 3918
JBS LIMITED; *U.S. Private*, pg. 2194
JBS LOGISTIC INC.; *U.S. Private*, pg. 2194
JBS MACHINERY CORPORATION—See Solitaire Machines Tools Limited; *Int'l*, pg. 7073
J.B. SMITH MFG CO., LLC—See Mueller Water Products, Inc.; *U.S. Public*, pg. 1485
JBSOLAR MALAGON, S.L.—See The AES Corporation; *U.S. Public*, pg. 2032
JBS PACKING COMPANY INC.; *U.S. Private*, pg. 2194
JBS PROJECT MANAGEMENT LLC—See H.I.G. Capital, LLC; *U.S. Private*, pg. 1827
JBS S.A.; *Int'l*, pg. 3918
JBS SHANGHAI, INC.—See Amiya Corporation; *Int'l*, pg. 428
J.B. SULLIVAN INC.; *U.S. Private*, pg. 2159
J&B SUPPLY, INC.; *U.S. Private*, pg. 2154
JBS USA FOOD COMPANY—See JBS S.A.; *Int'l*, pg. 3918
JBS USA HOLDINGS, INC.—See JBS S.A.; *Int'l*, pg. 3918
JBS USA, LLC - FOUR STAR BEEF, GREEN BAY—See JBS S.A.; *Int'l*, pg. 3918
JBS USA, LLC - FOUR STAR BEEF, PLAINWELL—See JBS S.A.; *Int'l*, pg. 3918
JBS USA, LLC - FOUR STAR BEEF, SOUDERTON—See JBS S.A.; *Int'l*, pg. 3918
JBS USA, LLC - FOUR STAR BEEF, TOLLESON—See JBS S.A.; *Int'l*, pg. 3918
JBS USA, LLC - HYRUM—See JBS S.A.; *Int'l*, pg. 3918

JBS USA, LLC—See JBS S.A.; *Int'l*, pg. 3918
JBS USA, LLC - WORTHINGTON—See JBS S.A.; *Int'l*, pg. 3919
JBT AEROTECH CORPORATION—See Oshkosh Corporation; *U.S. Public*, pg. 1620
JBT AEROTECH-GROUND SUPPORT EQUIPMENT—See Oshkosh Corporation; *U.S. Public*, pg. 1620
JBT AEROTECH SINGAPORE PTE. LTD.—See John Bean Technologies Corporation; *U.S. Public*, pg. 1191
JBT AEROTECH UK LIMITED—See John Bean Technologies Corporation; *U.S. Public*, pg. 1191
JBT ALCO-FOOD-MACHINES GMBH—See John Bean Technologies Corporation; *U.S. Public*, pg. 1191
JBT ELECTRIC, LLC—See Quanta Services, Inc.; *U.S. Public*, pg. 1751
JBT FOOD AND DAIRY SYSTEMS B.V.—See John Bean Technologies Corporation; *U.S. Public*, pg. 1191
JBT FOOD & DAIRY SYSTEMS INC.—See John Bean Technologies Corporation; *U.S. Public*, pg. 1191
JBT FOOD & DAIRY SYSTEMS SARL—See John Bean Technologies Corporation; *U.S. Public*, pg. 1192
JBT FOODTECH CITRUS SYSTEMS—See John Bean Technologies Corporation; *U.S. Public*, pg. 1191
JBT FOODTECH FORT PIERCE—See John Bean Technologies Corporation; *U.S. Public*, pg. 1191
JBT FOODTECH LINDSAY—See John Bean Technologies Corporation; *U.S. Public*, pg. 1191
JBT FOODTECH MADERA—See John Bean Technologies Corporation; *U.S. Public*, pg. 1191
JBT FOODTECH REDMOND—See John Bean Technologies Corporation; *U.S. Public*, pg. 1191
JBT FOODTECH SANDUSKY—See John Bean Technologies Corporation; *U.S. Public*, pg. 1191
J.B.T. INDUSTRIAL CO., LTD.—See Ji-Haw Industrial Co., Ltd.; *Int'l*, pg. 3941
JBT NETHERLANDS B.V.—See John Bean Technologies Corporation; *U.S. Public*, pg. 1191
JBT TRANSPORT; *Int'l*, pg. 3919
JBTV, INC.—See Aucnet Inc.; *Int'l*, pg. 700
JBT WOLF-TEC—See John Bean Technologies Corporation; *U.S. Public*, pg. 1191
JB UGLAND SHIPPING SINGAPORE PTE. LTD.—See Siva Ventures Limited; *Int'l*, pg. 6965
JB WATER & VACUUM SERVICE; *Int'l*, pg. 3917
JB WERE (NZ) PTY LIMITED—See National Australia Bank Limited; *Int'l*, pg. 5151
JBW GROUP LIMITED—See Bain Capital, LP; *U.S. Private*, pg. 434
J&B WHOLESALE DISTRIBUTING, INC.—See J&B Group, Inc.; *U.S. Private*, pg. 2153
JB WHOLESALE ROOFING & BUILDING SUPPLIES; *U.S. Private*, pg. 2193
JB&ZJMY HOLDING COMPANY; *Int'l*, pg. 3917
JC AB; *Int'l*, pg. 3919
JCAC TECHNOLOGIES INC—See Epiroc AB; *Int'l*, pg. 2463
J. CALNAN & ASSOCIATES, INC.; *U.S. Private*, pg. 2155
JCAM AGRI CO., LTD.—See Asahi Kasei Corporation; *Int'l*, pg. 596
J CAPITAL INVESTMENTS PTE LTD—See Johan Holdings Berhad; *Int'l*, pg. 3977
J. CARL H. BANCORPORATION; *U.S. Private*, pg. 2155
J. CARROLL & ASSOCIATES, INC.—See Louis F. Leeper Company; *U.S. Private*, pg. 2498
J-CASH MACHINE (THAILAND) CO., LTD.—See Japan Cash Machine Co., Ltd.; *Int'l*, pg. 3887
J CAST INC.—See JP Holdings, Inc.; *Int'l*, pg. 4005
JCAT GENERAL CONTRACTORS & MAINTENANCE; *U.S. Private*, pg. 2194
J C BAMFORD EXCAVATORS LIMITED; *Int'l*, pg. 3852
JCB CARD INTERNATIONAL (KOREA) CO., LTD.—See JCB Co., Ltd.; *Int'l*, pg. 3920
JCB CO., LTD.; *Int'l*, pg. 3919
JCB CONSTRUCTION EQUIPMENT AUSTRALIA—See CFC Group Pty. Ltd.; *Int'l*, pg. 1429
JCB FINANCE LTD—See J C Bamford Excavators Limited; *Int'l*, pg. 3852
JCB FINANCE SAS—See BNP Paribas SA; *Int'l*, pg. 1091
J.C. BILLION INC.; *U.S. Private*, pg. 2159
JCB INC.—See J C Bamford Excavators Limited; *Int'l*, pg. 3852
JCB INTERNATIONAL (ASIA) LTD.-TSIM SHA TSUI OFFICE—See JCB Co., Ltd.; *Int'l*, pg. 3920
JCB INTERNATIONAL ASIA PACIFIC PTE. LTD.—See JCB Co., Ltd.; *Int'l*, pg. 3920
JCB INTERNATIONAL BUSINESS CONSULTING (SHANGHAI) CO., LTD.—See JCB Co., Ltd.; *Int'l*, pg. 3920
JCB INTERNATIONAL CO., LTD.—See JCB Co., Ltd.; *Int'l*, pg. 3920
JCB INTERNATIONAL CREDIT CARD CO., LTD.—See JCB Co., Ltd.; *Int'l*, pg. 3920
JCB INTERNATIONAL (DEUTSCHLAND) GMBH—See JCB Co., Ltd.; *Int'l*, pg. 3920
JCB INTERNATIONAL DO BRASIL ADMINISTRADORA DE CARTOES DE PAGAMENTO LTDA.—See JCB Co., Ltd.; *Int'l*, pg. 3920
JCB INTERNATIONAL (EURASIA) LLC—See JCB Co., Ltd.; *Int'l*, pg. 3920

J.C. BILLION INC.

JCB INTERNATIONAL (EUROPE) LIMITED—See JCB Co., Ltd.; *Int'l*, pg. 3920
JCB INTERNATIONAL HOLDING (THAILAND) CO., LTD.—See JCB Co., Ltd.; *Int'l*, pg. 3920
JCB INTERNATIONAL (ITALY) S.P.A.—See JCB Co., Ltd.; *Int'l*, pg. 3920
JCB INTERNATIONAL (MICRONESIA) LTD.—See JCB Co., Ltd.; *Int'l*, pg. 3920
JCB INTERNATIONAL (OCEANIA) PTY LTD.-GOLD COAST—See JCB Co., Ltd.; *Int'l*, pg. 3920
JCB INTERNATIONAL (OCEANIA) PTY LTD.—See JCB Co., Ltd.; *Int'l*, pg. 3920
JCB INTERNATIONAL (SINGAPORE) PTE. LTD.—See JCB Co., Ltd.; *Int'l*, pg. 3920
JCB INTERNATIONAL (TAIWAN) CO., LTD.—See JCB Co., Ltd.; *Int'l*, pg. 3920
JC BIOTECH PRIVATE LIMITED—See Advanced Enzyme Technologies Limited; *Int'l*, pg. 159
JCBNEXT BERHAD; *Int'l*, pg. 3920
JC BOTTLING CO., LTD.—See Carlit Co., Ltd.; *Int'l*, pg. 1338
JCCA, INC.—See Bank of America Corporation; *U.S. Public*, pg. 272
J.C. CANNISTRARO, LLC; *U.S. Private*, pg. 2159
JCC ASSOCIATION; *U.S. Private*, pg. 2194
JCC COPPER STRIP COMPANY LIMITED—See Jiangxi Copper Company Limited; *Int'l*, pg. 3958
JCC FINANCIAL CO., LTD.—See Jiangxi Copper Company Limited; *Int'l*, pg. 3959
J.C. CHEEK CONTRACTORS, INC.; *U.S. Private*, pg. 2159
JC CHEMICAL CO., LTD.; *Int'l*, pg. 3919
JC CLARK LTD.; *Int'l*, pg. 3919
JC COMSA CORPORATION - FOODS MANUFACTURING DIVISION—See Delsole Corporation; *Int'l*, pg. 2015
JCC PAYMENT SYSTEMS LTD—See Bank of Cyprus Holdings Public Limited Company; *Int'l*, pg. 842
JCDECAUX ADVERTISING CO LTD. CHENGDU BRANCH—See JCDecaux S.A.; *Int'l*, pg. 3921
JCDECAUX ADVERTISING CO., LTD. - CHONGQING BRANCH—See JCDecaux S.A.; *Int'l*, pg. 3921
JCDECAUX ADVERTISING INDIA PVT LTD—See JCDecaux S.A.; *Int'l*, pg. 3921
JCDECAUX AIRPORT ESPANA—See JCDecaux S.A.; *Int'l*, pg. 3921
JCDECAUX AIRPORT FRANCE—See JCDecaux S.A.; *Int'l*, pg. 3921
JCDECAUX AIRPORT POLSKA SP Z O.O.—See JCDecaux S.A.; *Int'l*, pg. 3921
JCDECAUX AIRPORT PORTUGAL—See JCDecaux S.A.; *Int'l*, pg. 3921
JCDECAUX AIRPORT UK—See JCDecaux S.A.; *Int'l*, pg. 3921
JCDECAUX ANGOLA LIMITADA—See JCDecaux S.A.; *Int'l*, pg. 3921
JCDECAUX ARGENTINA/ URUGUAY—See JCDecaux S.A.; *Int'l*, pg. 3921
JCDECAUX ATA SAUDI LLC—See JCDecaux S.A.; *Int'l*, pg. 3922
JCDECAUX AUSTRALIA—See JCDecaux S.A.; *Int'l*, pg. 3921
JCDECAUX AUSTRALIA TRADING PTY LTD—See JCDecaux S.A.; *Int'l*, pg. 3920
JCDECAUX BELGIUM—See JCDecaux S.A.; *Int'l*, pg. 3921
JCDECAUX BILLBOARD—See JCDecaux S.A.; *Int'l*, pg. 3921
JCDECAUX BOTSWANA (PTY) LIMITED—See JCDecaux S.A.; *Int'l*, pg. 3921
JCDECAUX CHILE S.A.—See JCDecaux S.A.; *Int'l*, pg. 3921
JCDECAUX CHINA GROUP MARKETING—See JCDecaux S.A.; *Int'l*, pg. 3921
JCDECAUX DEUTSCHLAND/ABRIBUS CITYMEDIA—See JCDecaux S.A.; *Int'l*, pg. 3921
JCDECAUX DIGITAL VISION (HK) LTD.—See JCDecaux S.A.; *Int'l*, pg. 3921
JCDECAUX DO BRASIL, LTDA—See JCDecaux S.A.; pg. 3923
JCDECAUX DOMINICANA, SAS—See JCDecaux S.A.; *Int'l*, pg. 3921
JCDECAUX ECUADOR SA—See JCDecaux S.A.; *Int'l*, pg. 3921
JCDECAUX EESTI OU—See JCDecaux S.A.; *Int'l*, pg. 3921
JCDECAUX EL SALVADOR, S.A. DE C.V.—See JCDecaux S.A.; *Int'l*, pg. 3921
JCDECAUX ESPANA SLU—See JCDecaux S.A.; *Int'l*, pg. 3921
JCDECAUX ESWATINI (PROPRIETARY) LIMITED—See JCDecaux S.A.; *Int'l*, pg. 3921
JCDECAUX FINLAND OY—See JCDecaux S.A.; *Int'l*, pg. 3921
JCDECAUX FRANCE SAS—See JCDecaux S.A.; *Int'l*, pg. 3921
JCDECAUX GUATEMALA, S.A.—See JCDecaux S.A.; *Int'l*, pg. 3921
JCDECAUX HUNGARY ZRT—See JCDecaux S.A.; *Int'l*, pg. 3920

JCDECAUX IRELAND LTD.—See JCDecaux S.A.; *Int'l*, pg. 3921
JCDECAUX ISRAEL LTD.—See JCDecaux S.A.; *Int'l*, pg. 3922
JCDECAUX KOREA INC.—See JCDecaux S.A.; *Int'l*, pg. 3922
JCDECAUX LATVIJA SIA—See JCDecaux S.A.; *Int'l*, pg. 3922
JCDECAUX LESOTHO (PTY) LTD.—See JCDecaux S.A.; *Int'l*, pg. 3922
JCDECAUX LIETUVA UAB—See JCDecaux S.A.; *Int'l*, pg. 3922
JCDECAUX LTD.—See JCDecaux S.A.; *Int'l*, pg. 3922
JCDECAUX MACAU LTD.—See JCDecaux S.A.; *Int'l*, pg. 3922
JCDECAUX MADAGASCAR SA—See JCDecaux S.A.; *Int'l*, pg. 3922
JCDECAUX MESTSKY MOBILIAR SPOL S.R.O.—See JCDecaux S.A.; *Int'l*, pg. 3922
JCDECAUX MIDDLE EAST FZ-LLC—See JCDecaux S.A.; *Int'l*, pg. 3922
JCDECAUX MOBILIER URBAIN—See JCDecaux S.A.; *Int'l*, pg. 3922
JCDECAUX MOMENTUM SHANGHAI AIRPORT ADVERTISING CO., LTD.—See JCDecaux S.A.; *Int'l*, pg. 3921
JCDECAUX MONGOLIA LLC—See JCDecaux S.A.; *Int'l*, pg. 3922
JCDECAUX NEDERLAND B.V.—See JCDecaux S.A.; *Int'l*, pg. 3922
JCDECAUX NEONLIGHT POLAND—See JCDecaux S.A.; *Int'l*, pg. 3922
JCDECAUX NEONLIGHT—See JCDecaux S.A.; *Int'l*, pg. 3922
JCDECAUX NEONLIGHT—See JCDecaux S.A.; *Int'l*, pg. 3922
JCDECAUX NEONLIGHT SP ZOO—See JCDecaux S.A.; *Int'l*, pg. 3922
JCDECAUX NIGERIA OUTDOOR ADVERTISING LTD.—See JCDecaux S.A.; *Int'l*, pg. 3922
JCDECAUX NORGE—See JCDecaux S.A.; *Int'l*, pg. 3922
JCDECAUX NORTH AMERICA INC.—See JCDecaux S.A.; *Int'l*, pg. 3922
JCDECAUX ONE-STOP SHOP—See JCDecaux S.A.; *Int'l*, pg. 3922
JCDECAUX OUTDOOR ADVERTISING LTD.—See JCDecaux S.A.; *Int'l*, pg. 3922
JCDECAUX OUT OF HOME FZ-LLC—See JCDecaux S.A.; *Int'l*, pg. 3922
JCDECAUX PANAMA, S.A.—See JCDecaux S.A.; *Int'l*, pg. 3922
JCDECAUX PEARL & DEAN LTD—See JCDecaux S.A.; *Int'l*, pg. 3922
JCDECAUX PERU SAC—See JCDecaux S.A.; *Int'l*, pg. 3922
JCDECAUX PORTUGAL & JCDECAUX PUBLICIDADE LUMINOSA—See JCDecaux S.A.; *Int'l*, pg. 3922
JCDECAUX PORTUGAL—See JCDecaux S.A.; *Int'l*, pg. 3922
JCDECAUX PUBLICIDAD LUMINOSA—See JCDecaux S.A.; *Int'l*, pg. 3922
JCDECAUX S.A.; *Int'l*, pg. 3920
JCDECAUX SINGAPORE PTE. LTD.—See JCDecaux S.A.; *Int'l*, pg. 3922
JCDECAUX SLOVAKIA—See JCDecaux S.A.; *Int'l*, pg. 3922
JCDECAUX—See JCDecaux S.A.; *Int'l*, pg. 3921
JCDECAUX—See JCDecaux S.A.; *Int'l*, pg. 3921
JCDECAUX—See JCDecaux S.A.; *Int'l*, pg. 3921
JCDECAUX SOUTH AFRICA (PTY) LTD.—See JCDecaux S.A.; *Int'l*, pg. 3922
JCDECAUX SPAIN—See JCDecaux S.A.; *Int'l*, pg. 3922
JCDECAUX SVERIGE AB—See JCDecaux S.A.; *Int'l*, pg. 3922
JCDECAUX TANZANIA LTD.—See JCDecaux S.A.; *Int'l*, pg. 3922
JCDECAUX TOP MEDIA HONDURAS S.A.—See JCDecaux S.A.; *Int'l*, pg. 3922
JCDECAUX TOP MEDIA SERVICIOS DE PANAMA, S.A.—See JCDecaux S.A.; *Int'l*, pg. 3922
JCDECAUX UGANDA OUTDOOR ADVERTISING LTD.—See JCDecaux S.A.; *Int'l*, pg. 3922
JCDECAUX UK—See JCDecaux S.A.; *Int'l*, pg. 3922
JCDECAUX UNITED—See JCDecaux S.A.; *Int'l*, pg. 3922
JCDECAUX URUGUAY SA—See JCDecaux S.A.; *Int'l*, pg. 3922
JCDECAUX UZ. JV LTD.—See JCDecaux S.A.; *Int'l*, pg. 3922
JCDECAUX ZAMBIA LTD.—See JCDecaux S.A.; *Int'l*, pg. 3923
JCDECAUX ZIMBABWE (PVT) LTD.—See JCDecaux S.A.; *Int'l*, pg. 3922
JCE GROUP AB; *Int'l*, pg. 3923
JCEL CO., LTD.—See Central Glass Co., Ltd.; *Int'l*, pg. 1407
JCET GROUP CO., LTD.; *Int'l*, pg. 3923
JC FABRICA DE VALVULAS S.A.U.—See TTV, S.A.; *Int'l*, pg. 7961
JCF FLUID FLOW INDIA PRIVATE LIMITED—See Pentair plc; *Int'l*, pg. 5789

JC FINANCE & TAX INTERCONNECT HOLDING LTD.; *Int'l*, pg. 3919
JC FLOW CONTROLS PTE. LTD.—See TTV, S.A.; *Int'l*, pg. 7961
J.C. FLOWERS & CO. LLC; *U.S. Private*, pg. 2159
J.C. FLOWERS & CO. UK LTD.—See J.C. Flowers & Co. LLC; *U.S. Private*, pg. 2159
JC GARMENTS (M) SDN. BHD.—See Teo Guan Lee Corporation Berhad; *Int'l*, pg. 7562
JC GROUP (HK) LIMITED—See Tonking New Energy Group Holdings Limited; *Int'l*, pg. 7809
JCH CONSTRUCTION, LLC—See Brookfield Corporation; *Int'l*, pg. 1183
J-CHEMICAL, INC.—See Mitsubishi Gas Chemical Company, Inc.; *Int'l*, pg. 4948
J.C. HIGGINS CORP.—See EMCOR Group, Inc.; *U.S. Public*, pg. 738
J. CHRISTOF E & P SERVICES S.R.L.—See Christof Holding AG; *Int'l*, pg. 1587
J. CHRISTOF GESELLSCHAFT M.B.H.—See Christof Holding AG; *Int'l*, pg. 1587
J. CHRISTOF ROMANIA S.R.L.—See Christof Holding AG; *Int'l*, pg. 1587
J. CHRISTY CONSTRUCTION CO., INC.—See Delek Group Ltd.; *Int'l*, pg. 2012
JCH SYSTEMS INC.; *Int'l*, pg. 3923
JCHX MINING MANAGEMENT CO., LTD.; *Int'l*, pg. 3923
JCHYUN SYSTEMS, INC.—See Creative Technology Ltd.; *Int'l*, pg. 1833
JCI INDUSTRIES INC.; *U.S. Private*, pg. 2194
JCI JONES CHEMICALS, INC.-CORPORATE FINANCIAL CENTER—See JCI Jones Chemicals, Inc.; *U.S. Private*, pg. 2195
JCI JONES CHEMICALS, INC.-CSC—See JCI Jones Chemicals, Inc.; *U.S. Private*, pg. 2195
JCI JONES CHEMICALS, INC.; *U.S. Private*, pg. 2194
JCI METAL PRODUCTS, INC.—See J.F. Lehman & Company, Inc.; *U.S. Private*, pg. 2164
J. CINCO, INC.; *U.S. Private*, pg. 2155
JC INTERNATIONAL GROUP LTD; *Int'l*, pg. 3919
JCI USA INC.—See Nippon Chemical Industrial Co Ltd; *Int'l*, pg. 5313
JCJ ARCHITECTURE; *U.S. Private*, pg. 2195
JC JEANS & CLOTHES OY—See JC AB; *Int'l*, pg. 3919
JCK HOSPITALITY PUBLIC COMPANY LIMITED; *Int'l*, pg. 3923
JCK INTERNATIONAL PUBLIC LIMITED COMPANY; *Int'l*, pg. 3923
JCL AG; *Int'l*, pg. 3923
J CLARK AND SON LIMITED; *Int'l*, pg. 3852
JCL COMPANY LIMITED; *U.S. Private*, pg. 2195
J. C. LEWIS FORD, LLC; *U.S. Private*, pg. 2155
J.C. LEWIS PRIMARY HEALTH CARE CENTER INC.; *U.S. Private*, pg. 2160
J.C. MACELROY CO. INC.; *U.S. Private*, pg. 2160
J.C. MADIGAN INC.; *U.S. Private*, pg. 2160
J.C. MALONE ASSOCIATES—See Malone Workforce Solutions; *U.S. Private*, pg. 2558
JCM AMERICAN CORPORATION—See Japan Cash Machine Co., Ltd.; *Int'l*, pg. 3887
JC MARKETING ASSOCIATES INC.; *U.S. Private*, pg. 2194
JCMC, INC.; *U.S. Private*, pg. 2195
JCM EVENTS—See JC Marketing Associates Inc.; *U.S. Private*, pg. 2194
JCM GOLD (HK) LTD.—See Japan Cash Machine Co., Ltd.; *Int'l*, pg. 3887
JCM MEIHO CO., LTD.—See Japan Cash Machine Co., Ltd.; *Int'l*, pg. 3887
JCM PARTNERS, LLC; *U.S. Private*, pg. 2195
JCM TECHNO SUPPORT CO., LTD.—See Japan Cash Machine Co., Ltd.; *Int'l*, pg. 3887
JCM UNITED KINGDOM LTD.—See Japan Cash Machine Co., Ltd.; *Int'l*, pg. 3887
J.C. NEWMAN CIGAR CO.; *U.S. Private*, pg. 2160
JCN KANTO CO., LTD.—See Senko Group Holdings Co., Ltd.; *Int'l*, pg. 6709
J-CO AMERICA CORPORATION—See Taikisha Ltd.; *Int'l*, pg. 7413
JCO. CO., LTD.—See Sumitomo Metal Mining Co., Ltd.; *Int'l*, pg. 7291
JCOM CHINA CO., LTD.—See JTB Corp.; *Int'l*, pg. 4015
J-CO MEXICO, S. DE R.L. DE C.V.—See Taikisha Ltd.; *Int'l*, pg. 7413
J.CON SALON & SPA; *U.S. Private*, pg. 2160
J CORE CO., LTD.—See System Location Co., Ltd.; *Int'l*, pg. 7390
J.C. PALLET COMPANY, INC.; *U.S. Private*, pg. 2160
J.C. PAPER—See Central National Gottesman Inc.; *U.S. Private*, pg. 823
JCPE INVESTMENTS; *U.S. Private*, pg. 2195
J.C. PENNEY COMPANY, INC.; *U.S. Private*, pg. 2160
J.C. PENNEY CORPORATION, INC.—See J.C. Penney Company, Inc.; *U.S. Private*, pg. 2160
J.C. PENNEY PROPERTIES, INC.—See J.C. Penney Company, Inc.; *U.S. Private*, pg. 2160
JCP ENTREPRISE; *Int'l*, pg. 3923
JCP REALTY, INC.—See J.C. Penney Company, Inc.; *U.S. Private*, pg. 2160

COMPANY NAME INDEX

JC PRODUCTION SOLUTIONS, INC—See Smiths Group plc; *Int'l*, pg. 7010
JC PUBLIC RELATIONS, INC.; *U.S. Private*, pg. 2194
JCR-CHRISTOF CONSULTING S.R.L.—See Christof Holding AG; *Int'l*, pg. 1587
J.C.R. CONSTRUCTION CO., INC.—See Quanta Services, Inc.; *U.S. Public*, pg. 1751
JC RESTORATION INC.; *U.S. Private*, pg. 2194
J.CREW GROUP, INC.—See Leonard Green & Partners, L.P.; *U.S. Private*, pg. 2426
J.CREW GROUP, INC.—See TPG Capital, L.P.; *U.S. Public*, pg. 2174
J. CREW, INC.—See Leonard Green & Partners, L.P.; *U.S. Private*, pg. 2426
J. CREW, INC.—See TPG Capital, L.P.; *U.S. Public*, pg. 2174
J. CREW INTERNATIONAL, INC.—See Leonard Green & Partners, L.P.; *U.S. Private*, pg. 2426
J. CREW INTERNATIONAL, INC.—See TPG Capital, L.P.; *U.S. Public*, pg. 2174
J. CREW OPERATING CORP.—See Leonard Green & Partners, L.P.; *U.S. Private*, pg. 2426
J. CREW OPERATING CORP.—See TPG Capital, L.P.; *U.S. Public*, pg. 2174
J. CREW VIRGINIA, INC.—See Leonard Green & Partners, L.P.; *U.S. Private*, pg. 2426
J. CREW VIRGINIA, INC.—See TPG Capital, L.P.; *U.S. Public*, pg. 2174
THE J.C. ROBINSON SEED COMPANY; *U.S. Private*, pg. 4058
J. CROWDER CORPORATION—See Fluor Corporation; *U.S. Public*, pg. 859
JCR PHARMACEUTICALS CO., LTD. - KOBE NISHI PLANT—See JCR Pharmaceuticals Co., Ltd.; *Int'l*, pg. 3923
JCR PHARMACEUTICALS CO., LTD. - KOBE PLANT—See JCR Pharmaceuticals Co., Ltd.; *Int'l*, pg. 3923
JCR PHARMACEUTICALS CO., LTD. - MUROTANI PLANT—See JCR Pharmaceuticals Co., Ltd.; *Int'l*, pg. 3923
JCR PHARMACEUTICALS CO., LTD. - SEISHIN PLANT—See JCR Pharmaceuticals Co., Ltd.; *Int'l*, pg. 3923
JCR PHARMACEUTICALS CO., LTD.; *Int'l*, pg. 3923
JCS COMPUTER RESOURCE CORP.—See QXO, Inc.; *U.S. Public*, pg. 1758
JCSC SNA EUROPE INDUSTRIES BISOV—See Snap-on Incorporated; *U.S. Public*, pg. 1897
JCS DIGITAL SOLUTIONS PTE LTD—See Thai Beverage Public Company Limited; *Int'l*, pg. 7590
J.C. SMITH; *U.S. Private*, pg. 2160
JCS MONMOUTH MALL-NJ, LLC—See J.H. Whitney & Co., LLC; *U.S. Private*, pg. 2166
J.C. SNAVELY & SONS INC.; *U.S. Private*, pg. 2160
JCT600 LIMITED; *Int'l*, pg. 3924
JC TANLODEN VICTORIA PTY. LTD.—See Wingara Ag Limited; *Int'l*, pg. 8428
JC TECHNOLOGY, INC.; *U.S. Private*, pg. 2194
JCT ELECTRONICS LIMITED; *Int'l*, pg. 3924
JCT LIMITED; *Int'l*, pg. 3924
JCT LTD - FILAMENT PLANT—See JCT Limited; *Int'l*, pg. 3924
JCT LTD - TEXTILE PLANT—See JCT Limited; *Int'l*, pg. 3924
JC TRADING INC.; *U.S. Private*, pg. 2194
JCU CHEMICALS INDIA PVT. LTD.—See JCU Corporation; *Int'l*, pg. 3924
JCU CORPORATION - NIIGATA PLANT—See JCU Corporation; *Int'l*, pg. 3924
JCU CORPORATION; *Int'l*, pg. 3924
JCU INTERNATIONAL, INC.—See JCU Corporation; *Int'l*, pg. 3924
JCU KOREA CORPORATION - CHEONAN FACTORY—See JCU Corporation; *Int'l*, pg. 3924
JCU KOREA CORPORATION—See JCU Corporation; *Int'l*, pg. 3924
JCURVE SOLUTIONS LIMITED; *Int'l*, pg. 3924
JCURVE SOLUTIONS PHILIPPINES INC.—See JCurve Solutions Limited; *Int'l*, pg. 3924
JCU (SHANGHAI) TRADING CO., LTD.—See JCU Corporation; *Int'l*, pg. 3924
JCU SHENZHEN TECHNOLOGY CORPORATION—See JCU Corporation; *Int'l*, pg. 3924
J.C. VIRAMONTES INC.; *U.S. Private*, pg. 2160
J.C. WHITNEY & CO.; *U.S. Private*, pg. 2160
JCW SEARCH LTD.; *U.S. Private*, pg. 2195
JCY HDD TECHNOLOGY SDN BHD—See JCY International Berhad; *Int'l*, pg. 3924
JCY INTERNATIONAL BERHAD; *Int'l*, pg. 3924
JD2 INC. - LOS ANGELES—See JD2 Inc.; *U.S. Private*, pg. 2195
JD2 INC. - SAN DIEGO—See JD2 Inc.; *U.S. Private*, pg. 2195
JD2 INC.; *U.S. Private*, pg. 2195
J.D. ABRAMS LP—See Abrams International LLP; *U.S. Private*, pg. 40
JDA CHILE S.A.—See New Mountain Capital, LLC; *U.S. Private*, pg. 2902

JDA FRONTLINE, INC.—See Blue Engine Message & Media, LLC; *U.S. Private*, pg. 588
JDA GROUP LTD.; *Int'l*, pg. 3924
JDA INTERNATIONAL LTD.—See New Mountain Capital, LLC; *U.S. Private*, pg. 2902
JDAMC—See Deere & Company; *U.S. Public*, pg. 646
J. DANIEL & COMPANY, INC.—See The Danella Companies Inc.; *U.S. Private*, pg. 4018
JDA SOFTWARE ASIA PTE. LTD.—See New Mountain Capital, LLC; *U.S. Private*, pg. 2902
JDA SOFTWARE AUSTRALIA PTY. LTD.—See New Mountain Capital, LLC; *U.S. Private*, pg. 2902
JDA SOFTWARE BELGIUM—See New Mountain Capital, LLC; *U.S. Private*, pg. 2902
JDA SOFTWARE CANADA LTD.—See New Mountain Capital, LLC; *U.S. Private*, pg. 2902
JDA SOFTWARE FRANCE S.A.—See New Mountain Capital, LLC; *U.S. Private*, pg. 2902
JDA SOFTWARE GROUP, INC.—See New Mountain Capital, LLC; *U.S. Private*, pg. 2902
JDA SOFTWARE, INC. - AKRON—See New Mountain Capital, LLC; *U.S. Private*, pg. 2902
JDA SOFTWARE, INC. - ROCKVILLE—See New Mountain Capital, LLC; *U.S. Private*, pg. 2902
JDA SOFTWARE, INC.—See New Mountain Capital, LLC; *U.S. Private*, pg. 2902
JDA SOFTWARE, INC. - WEST DES MOINES—See New Mountain Capital, LLC; *U.S. Private*, pg. 2902
JDA SOFTWARE, INC. - WESTLAKE VILLAGE—See New Mountain Capital, LLC; *U.S. Private*, pg. 2902
JDA SOFTWARE INDIA PRIVATE LIMITED—See New Mountain Capital, LLC; *U.S. Private*, pg. 2902
JDA SOFTWARE ITALY S.R.L.—See New Mountain Capital, LLC; *U.S. Private*, pg. 2902
JDA SOFTWARE JAPAN CO., LTD.—See New Mountain Capital, LLC; *U.S. Private*, pg. 2902
JDA SOFTWARE KOREA, LTD.—See New Mountain Capital, LLC; *U.S. Private*, pg. 2902
JDA SOFTWARE NETHERLANDS B.V.—See New Mountain Capital, LLC; *U.S. Private*, pg. 2902
JDA SOFTWARE NORDIC AB—See New Mountain Capital, LLC; *U.S. Private*, pg. 2902
JDA SOFTWARE RUSSIA HOLDINGS, INC.—See New Mountain Capital, LLC; *U.S. Private*, pg. 2902
JDA SOFTWARE SHANGHAI CO. LTD.—See New Mountain Capital, LLC; *U.S. Private*, pg. 2902
JDA SOFTWARE (TAIWAN), INC.—See New Mountain Capital, LLC; *U.S. Private*, pg. 2902
JDA SOLUTIONS DO BRASIL LTDA.—See New Mountain Capital, LLC; *U.S. Private*, pg. 2903
JDA TECHNOLOGIES FINLAND OY LTD.—See New Mountain Capital, LLC; *U.S. Private*, pg. 2903
JDA TECHNOLOGIES, GMBH—See New Mountain Capital, LLC; *U.S. Private*, pg. 2903
JD BEAUTY CO., LLC—See ACON Investments, LLC; *U.S. Private*, pg. 62
J.D. & BILLY HINES TRUCKING, INC.; *U.S. Private*, pg. 2160
JDB INC.; *U.S. Private*, pg. 2195
JD BYRIDER AUTOMAX LLC; *U.S. Private*, pg. 2195
J.D. BYRIDER SYSTEMS, LLC—See Altamont Capital Partners; *U.S. Private*, pg. 205
JDC CORPORATION; *Int'l*, pg. 3925
JDC GROUP AG; *Int'l*, pg. 3925
JDC GROUP, LLC—See White Wolf Capital LLC; *U.S. Private*, pg. 4510
JD.COM, INC.; *Int'l*, pg. 3924
JD.COM INTERNATIONAL LIMITED—See JD.com, Inc.; *Int'l*, pg. 3924
JDC PLUS GMBH—See JDC Group AG; *Int'l*, pg. 3925
J.D. DADDARIO CO. INC.; *U.S. Private*, pg. 2160
J.D DEVELOPMENT CO., LTD.; *Int'l*, pg. 3857
J.D. DIFFENBAUGH, INC.; *U.S. Private*, pg. 2160
J. DEMPSEY INC.—See Principal Financial Group, Inc.; *U.S. Public*, pg. 1721
JDE PEET'S N.V.; *Int'l*, pg. 3925
JD EQUIPMENT INC.; *U.S. Private*, pg. 2195
J. DE SAEGHER STEENHANDEL N.V.—See CRH plc; *Int'l*, pg. 1844
J DEUTSCH ASSOCIATES INC.—See Aquiline Capital Partners LLC; *U.S. Private*, pg. 305
J-DEVICES CORPORATION—See Amkor Technology, Inc.; *U.S. Public*, pg. 124
J.D. FIELDS & COMPANY INC.; *U.S. Private*, pg. 2161
JD FIELD SERVICES, INC.—See National Energy Services, Inc.; *U.S. Private*, pg. 2853
J. & D. GEARS LIMITED—See Westinghouse Air Brake Technologies Corporation; *U.S. Public*, pg. 2358
JD GROUP LIMITED—See Steinhoff International Holdings N.V.; *Int'l*, pg. 7195
JDG TELEVISION INC.—See Griffin Holdings Inc.; *U.S. Private*, pg. 1788
JDH CAPITAL HOLDINGS, L.P.; *U.S. Private*, pg. 2195
JD HEALTH INTERNATIONAL INC.; *Int'l*, pg. 3924
J.D. HEISKELL & CO.; *U.S. Private*, pg. 2161
J.D. HONINGBERG INTERNATIONAL, INC.; *U.S. Private*, pg. 2161
JDH PACIFIC, INC.; *U.S. Private*, pg. 2195
JDI CHINA INC.—See Japan Display Inc.; *Int'l*, pg. 3887

JDI DISPLAY AMERICA, INC.—See Japan Display Inc.; *Int'l*, pg. 3887
JDI EUROPE GMBH—See Japan Display Inc.; *Int'l*, pg. 3887
JDI HONG KONG LIMITED—See Japan Display Inc.; *Int'l*, pg. 3887
JDI KOREA INC.—See Japan Display Inc.; *Int'l*, pg. 3887
J. DIRECTION CO., LTD.—See Onward Holdings Co., Ltd.; *Int'l*, pg. 5592
J.D. IRVING, LIMITED; *Int'l*, pg. 3857
JDI TAIWAN INC.—See Japan Display Inc.; *Int'l*, pg. 3887
JDK REAL ESTATE, LLC—See Kenco Group Inc.; *U.S. Private*, pg. 2283
JDL CASTLE CORPORATION; *U.S. Private*, pg. 2195
JDL DEVELOPMENT CORP.; *U.S. Private*, pg. 2195
JDL INTERNATIONAL ENVIRONMENTAL PROTECTION INC.—See Jiangxi JDL Environmental Protection Co., Ltd.; *Int'l*, pg. 3960
JDL MOTOR EXPRESS—See John Lenore & Company, Inc.; *U.S. Private*, pg. 2223
JD LOGISTICS, INC.; *Int'l*, pg. 3924
JDL TECHNOLOGIES, INC.—See TheIPGuys.Net LLC; *U.S. Private*, pg. 4141
J.D. MARTIN CO. INC.; *U.S. Private*, pg. 2161
J. D. MELLBERG FINANCIAL; *U.S. Private*, pg. 2155
JDM FOOD GROUP LIMITED—See Sunridge Partners (UK), LLP; *Int'l*, pg. 7321
JDM JINGDA MACHINE AMERICAS INC.—See JDM Jingda Machine(Ningbo) Co.,LTD; *Int'l*, pg. 3925
JDM JINGDA MACHINE(NINGBO) CO.,LTD; *Int'l*, pg. 3925
JDM MATERIALS COMPANY INCORPORATED; *U.S. Private*, pg. 2195
JDM TECHNOLOGY GROUP; *Int'l*, pg. 3925
J.D. MURCHISON INTERESTS INC.; *U.S. Private*, pg. 2161
JD NORMAN DE MEXICO, S. DE R.L. DE C.V.—See JD Norman Industries, Inc.; *U.S. Private*, pg. 2195
JD NORMAN INDUSTRIES, INC.; *U.S. Private*, pg. 2195
JD NORMAN INDUSTRIES-WINDSOR PLANT—See JD Norman Industries, Inc.; *U.S. Private*, pg. 2195
JD NORMAN LYDNEY LIMITED—See JD Norman Industries, Inc.; *U.S. Private*, pg. 2195
J-DOLPH PHARMACEUTICAL CO., LTD.—See TOWA PHARMACEUTICAL CO. LTD.; *Int'l*, pg. 7849
JD ORGOCHEM LIMITED; *Int'l*, pg. 3924
J.D. POWER—See Thoma Bravo, L.P.; *U.S. Private*, pg. 4148
J&D PRODUCE, INC.; *U.S. Private*, pg. 2154
JD RESEARCH INC.; *U.S. Private*, pg. 2195
JD RESTAURANTS INC.; *U.S. Private*, pg. 2195
J.D. RIVET & CO., INC.; *U.S. Private*, pg. 2161
JDRJ INC.—See Cintas Corporation; *U.S. Public*, pg. 496
JDR MICRODEVICES INC.; *U.S. Private*, pg. 2196
J.D. RUSH COMPANY INC.; *U.S. Private*, pg. 2161
J.D. RUSSELL COMPANY; *U.S. Private*, pg. 2161
JDS CAPITAL MANAGEMENT, INC.; *U.S. Private*, pg. 2196
J.D.S. FINANCE LIMITED—See Landon Capital Partners, LLC; *U.S. Private*, pg. 2386
J.D. SMITH CUSTOM HOMES, LLC; *U.S. Private*, pg. 2161
J&D SNACKS INC.—See Utz Brands, Inc.; *U.S. Public*, pg. 2267
JD SPORTS FASHION PLC—See Pentland Group Limited; *Int'l*, pg. 5792
JD STEEL CO. INC.; *U.S. Private*, pg. 2195
J. D. STEVENSON AND ASSOCIATES, INC.—See Gryphon Investors, LLC; *U.S. Private*, pg. 1798
J.D. STREETT & CO., INC.; *U.S. Private*, pg. 2161
J.D. STREETT & CO., INC. - ST. LOUIS PARK PLANT—See J.D. Streett & Co., Inc.; *U.S. Private*, pg. 2161
J.D. STREETT & CO., INC. - ST. LOUIS RIVER PLANT—See J.D. Streett & Co., Inc.; *U.S. Private*, pg. 2161
JDSU DO BRASIL LTDA. & CIA—See Viavi Solutions Inc.; *U.S. Public*, pg. 2295
JD SWEID FOODS LTD.—See Hallmark Poultry Processors Ltd.; *Int'l*, pg. 3230
JDVC RESOURCES CORPORATION—See Apollo Global Capital, Inc.; *Int'l*, pg. 517
JDV LIMITED—See Commonwealth Bank of Australia; *Int'l*, pg. 1720
JD WETHERSPOON PLC; *Int'l*, pg. 3924
J D W FINANCE LIMITED—See N Brown Group plc; *Int'l*, pg. 5115
J D WILLIAMS & CO. LIMITED—See N Brown Group plc; *Int'l*, pg. 5115
JD WILLIAMS & COMPANY LTD.—See N Brown Group plc; *Int'l*, pg. 5115
JDW MANAGEMENT CO.; *U.S. Private*, pg. 2196
JD SUGAR MILLS LTD.; *Int'l*, pg. 3925
JDW WRAP UP, INC.; *U.S. Private*, pg. 2196
JEAD AUTO SUPPLY INC.; *U.S. Private*, pg. 2196
JEANAVICE (TIANJIN) FOOD CO., LTD.—See Taiyo Kagaku Co., Ltd.; *Int'l*, pg. 7425
JEAN CACHAREL; *Int'l*, pg. 3925

JEAN CACHAREL

JEAN-CLAUDE BOISSET WINES U.S.A., INC.—See Boisset, La Famille des Grands Vins; *Int'l*, pg. 1101
JEAN CO., LTD.; *Int'l*, pg. 3925
THE JEAN COUTU GROUP (PJC) INC.—See Metro Inc.; *Int'l*, pg. 4860
JEAN DEVELOPMENT COMPANY, LLC—See MGM Resorts International; *U.S. Public*, pg. 1435
JEAN EGRETEAUD; *Int'l*, pg. 3926
JEAN LAIN ENTREPRISES; *Int'l*, pg. 3926
JEAN LEFEBVRE PACIFIQUE SA—See VINCI S.A.; *Int'l*, pg. 8223
JEAN LEFEVRE UK LTD.—See VINCI S.A.; *Int'l*, pg. 8223
JEAN-MARIE PHARMACAL COMPANY LIMITED—See Jacobson Pharma Corporation Limited; *Int'l*, pg. 3866
JEAN METZ S.A.S.—See Groupe Partouche S.A.; *Int'l*, pg. 3109
JEANNEAU AMERICA INC.—See Beneteau S.A; *Int'l*, pg. 972
JEANNE B. MCCOY COMMUNITY CENTER FOR THE ARTS; *U.S. Private*, pg. 2196
JEANNE LANVIN SAS—See Fosun International Limited; *Int'l*, pg. 2751
JEANNIE'S KIDS CLUB—See Kids Stuff, Inc.; *U.S. Private*, pg. 2303
JEAN PHILIPPE FRAGRANCES, LLC—See Inter Parfums, Inc.; *U.S. Public*, pg. 1140
JEAN SANDEL RETIREMENT VILLAGE LIMITED—See Ryman Healthcare Ltd.; *Int'l*, pg. 6439
JEANS.COM INC.; *U.S. Private*, pg. 2196
JEAN SIMPSON PERSONNEL SERVICES, INC.; *U.S. Private*, pg. 2196
JEANSKOMPANIET AS—See Coala-Life Group AB; *Int'l*, pg. 1680
JEANS MATE CORPORATION—See RIZAP GROUP, Inc.; *Int'l*, pg. 6354
JEANS WAREHOUSE, INC.; *U.S. Private*, pg. 2196
JEANSWEAR SERVICES FAR EAST LTD.—See Fingen S.p.A.; *Int'l*, pg. 2674
JEANSWEST CORPORATION PTY. LTD.—See Glorious Sun Enterprises Limited; *Int'l*, pg. 3009
JEANSWEST INTERNATIONAL (H.K.) LIMITED—See Glorious Sun Enterprises Limited; *Int'l*, pg. 3009
JE ARCHITECTS/ENGINEERS, P.C.—See Jacobs Engineering Group, Inc.; *U.S. Public*, pg. 1184
JEA; *U.S. Private*, pg. 2196
JEB AUTO. SDN. BHD.—See Kumpulan Jetson Berhad; *Int'l*, pg. 4332
JEB CO., LTD.—See Dentsu Group Inc.; *Int'l*, pg. 2039
JEBCOMMERCE LLC; *U.S. Private*, pg. 2196
JEBCO VENTURES, INC.; *U.S. Private*, pg. 2196
JEBENS GMBH—See AG der Dillinger Huttenwerke; *Int'l*, pg. 197
J.E. BERKOWITZ, LP; *U.S. Private*, pg. 2161
JEBILS FINANCE LIMITED; *Int'l*, pg. 3926
JEBRO INCORPORATED—See MDU Resources Group, Inc.; *U.S. Public*, pg. 1410
JEBSEN & JESSEN BUSINESS SERVICES (M) SDN. BHD.—See Jebsen & Jessen (SEA) Pte Ltd; *Int'l*, pg. 3926
JEBSEN & JESSEN BUSINESS SERVICES (S) PTE. LTD.—See Jebsen & Jessen (SEA) Pte Ltd; *Int'l*, pg. 3926
JEBSEN & JESSEN BUSINESS SERVICES (T) LTD.—See Jebsen & Jessen (SEA) Pte Ltd; *Int'l*, pg. 3926
JEBSEN & JESSEN CAMBODIA LTD—See Jebsen & Jessen (SEA) Pte Ltd; *Int'l*, pg. 3926
JEBSEN & JESSEN CHEMICALS (M) SDN BHD—See Jebsen & Jessen (SEA) Pte Ltd; *Int'l*, pg. 3926
JEBSEN & JESSEN CHEMICALS (P) INC—See Jebsen & Jessen (SEA) Pte Ltd; *Int'l*, pg. 3926
JEBSEN & JESSEN CHEMICALS (T) LTD—See Jebsen & Jessen (SEA) Pte Ltd; *Int'l*, pg. 3926
JEBSEN & JESSEN CHEMICALS VIETNAM CO LTD—See Jebsen & Jessen (SEA) Pte Ltd; *Int'l*, pg. 3926
JEBSEN & JESSEN COMMUNICATION SOLUTIONS (M) SDN BHD—See Jebsen & Jessen (SEA) Pte Ltd; *Int'l*, pg. 3926
JEBSEN & JESSEN COMMUNICATIONS (P) INC.—See Nippon Telegraph & Telephone Corporation; *Int'l*, pg. 5343
JEBSEN & JESSEN COMMUNICATIONS (T) LTD.—See Nippon Telegraph & Telephone Corporation; *Int'l*, pg. 5343
JEBSEN & JESSEN INGREDIENTS (P) INC.—See Jebsen & Jessen (SEA) Pte Ltd; *Int'l*, pg. 3926
JEBSEN & JESSEN OFFSHORE FZE—See Jebsen & Jessen (SEA) Pte Ltd; *Int'l*, pg. 3926
JEBSEN JESSEN OFFSHORE PTE LTD—See Jebsen & Jessen (SEA) Pte Ltd; *Int'l*, pg. 3926
JEBSEN & JESSEN PACKAGING (M) SDN BHD—See Jebsen & Jessen (SEA) Pte Ltd; *Int'l*, pg. 3926
JEBSEN & JESSEN PACKAGING VIETNAM CO LTD—See Jebsen & Jessen (SEA) Pte Ltd; *Int'l*, pg. 3926
JEBSEN & JESSEN (SEA) PTE LTD; *Int'l*, pg. 3926
JEBSEN & JESSEN TECHNOLOGY (S) PTE LTD—See Jebsen & Jessen (SEA) Pte Ltd; *Int'l*, pg. 3926
JEBSEN & JESSEN VIETNAM CO LTD—See Jebsen & Jessen (SEA) Pte Ltd; *Int'l*, pg. 3926
JEBSEN-MAZZUCCHELLI LTD—See Mazzucchelli 1849 S.p.a.; *Int'l*, pg. 4750
J.E. CARSTEN COMPANY; *U.S. Private*, pg. 2161
J.E. CHARLOTTE CONSTRUCTION CORP.; *U.S. Private*, pg. 2161
JECKERSON—See Stirling Square Capital Partners LLP; *Int'l*, pg. 7216
JECKING TOURS & TRAVEL LIMITED—See Corporate Travel Management Limited; *Int'l*, pg. 1805
JE CLEANTECH HOLDINGS LIMITED; *Int'l*, pg. 3925
JECO CO., LTD.—See Denso Corporation; *Int'l*, pg. 2032
JEDAT INC.—See Argo Graphics Inc.; *Int'l*, pg. 562
J&E DAVY HOLDINGS LIMITED; *Int'l*, pg. 3853
JEDBURG DIALYSIS, LLC—See DaVita Inc.; *U.S. Public*, pg. 640
JEDDAH BEVERAGE CAN MAKING CO. LTD.—See A.H. Algosaibi & Bros.; *Int'l*, pg. 24
JEDDAH BEVERAGE CAN MAKING CO. LTD.—See Crown Holdings, Inc.; *U.S. Public*, pg. 598
JEDDAH CABLE COMPANY—See El Sewedy Electric Company; *Int'l*, pg. 2341
JEDDO-HIGHLAND COAL CO. INC.—See Pagnotti Enterprises Inc.; *U.S. Private*, pg. 3075
THE JED FOUNDATION; *U.S. Private*, pg. 4058
JEDINSTVO A.D.; *Int'l*, pg. 3926
JEDINSTVO A.D.; *Int'l*, pg. 3926
JEDINSTVO GP A.D.; *Int'l*, pg. 3926
JEDINSTVO-METALOGRADNJA A.D.; *Int'l*, pg. 3926
J.E. DUNN CONSTRUCTION CO.—See J.E. Dunn Construction Group, Inc.; *U.S. Private*, pg. 2161
J.E. DUNN CONSTRUCTION CO.—See J.E. Dunn Construction Group, Inc.; *U.S. Private*, pg. 2161
J.E. DUNN CONSTRUCTION CO.—See J.E. Dunn Construction Group, Inc.; *U.S. Private*, pg. 2161
J.E. DUNN CONSTRUCTION CO.—See J.E. Dunn Construction Group, Inc.; *U.S. Private*, pg. 2161
J.E. DUNN CONSTRUCTION CO.—See J.E. Dunn Construction Group, Inc.; *U.S. Private*, pg. 2161
J.E. DUNN CONSTRUCTION GROUP, INC.; *U.S. Private*, pg. 2161
J.E. EKORNES APS—See QuMei Home Furnishings Group Co., Ltd.; *Int'l*, pg. 6166
J.E. EKORNES AS—See QuMei Home Furnishings Group Co., Ltd.; *Int'l*, pg. 6166
JEEN INTERNATIONAL CORP.—See H.I.G. Capital, LLC; *U.S. Private*, pg. 1832
JEEP CHRYSLER DODGE OF ONTARIO; *U.S. Private*, pg. 2196
JEEP CONSTRUCTION CO., LTD.—See Shimizu Corporation; *Int'l*, pg. 6835
JEERAN HOLDING COMPANY K.S.C.C.; *Int'l*, pg. 3927
JEEVAN SCIENTIFIC TECHNOLOGY LIMITED; *Int'l*, pg. 3927
JEEVES DEUTSCHLAND GMBH—See Battery Ventures, L.P.; *U.S. Private*, pg. 489
JEEVES FRANCE SAS—See Battery Ventures, L.P.; *U.S. Private*, pg. 489
JEEVES GMBH—See Battery Ventures, L.P.; *U.S. Private*, pg. 489
JEEVES INFORMATION SYSTEMS AB—See Battery Ventures, L.P.; *U.S. Private*, pg. 489
JEEVES INFORMATION SYSTEMS NORWAY—See Battery Ventures, L.P.; *U.S. Private*, pg. 489
JEEVES INFORMATION SYSTEMS UK LTD—See Battery Ventures, L.P.; *U.S. Private*, pg. 489
JEEVES OF BELGRAVIA LIMITED—See Timpson Group PLC; *Int'l*, pg. 7752
JEEVY COMPUTING, LLC; *U.S. Private*, pg. 2196
JEFF BANK—See Jeffersonville Bancorp; *U.S. Public*, pg. 1189
JEFF BELZER'S CHEVROLET DODGE KIA; *U.S. Private*, pg. 2196
JEFF BURGESS & ASSOCIATES, INC.—See DCC plc; *Int'l*, pg. 1990
JEFFCO FIBRES, INC.; *U.S. Private*, pg. 2197
JEFFCO LEASING COMPANY INC.; *U.S. Private*, pg. 2197
JEFF D'AMBROSIO AUTO GROUP; *U.S. Private*, pg. 2196
JEFF DAVIS BANCSHARES, INC.; *U.S. Private*, pg. 2196
JEFF DAVIS BANK & TRUST COMPANY—See Jeff Davis Bancshares, Inc.; *U.S. Private*, pg. 2196
JEFFERDS CORPORATION; *U.S. Private*, pg. 2197
JEFFERIES (AUSTRALIA) PTY. LTD.—See Jefferies Financial Group Inc.; *U.S. Public*, pg. 1188
JEFFERIES BACHE LIMITED—See Jefferies Financial Group Inc.; *U.S. Public*, pg. 1188
JEFFERIES BROADVIEW—See Jefferies Financial Group Inc.; *U.S. Public*, pg. 1189
JEFFERIES CAPITAL PARTNERS LLC—See Jefferies Financial Group Inc.; *U.S. Public*, pg. 1188
JEFFERIES ENERGY GROUP—See Jefferies Financial Group Inc.; *U.S. Public*, pg. 1188
JEFFERIES EXECUTION SERVICES, INC.—See Jefferies Financial Group Inc.; *U.S. Public*, pg. 1188
JEFFERIES FINANCE, LLC—See Jefferies Financial Group Inc.; *U.S. Public*, pg. 1188
JEFFERIES FINANCIAL GROUP INC.; *U.S. Public*, pg. 1188
JEFFERIES FINANCIAL SERVICES, INC.—See Jefferies Financial Group Inc.; *U.S. Public*, pg. 1188
JEFFERIES FUNDING LLC—See Jefferies Financial Group Inc.; *U.S. Public*, pg. 1188
JEFFERIES GROUP LLC—See Jefferies Financial Group Inc.; *U.S. Public*, pg. 1188
JEFFERIES HIGH YIELD HOLDINGS, LLC—See Jefferies Financial Group Inc.; *U.S. Public*, pg. 1188
JEFFERIES HONG KONG LIMITED—See Jefferies Financial Group Inc.; *U.S. Public*, pg. 1189
JEFFERIES INDIA PRIVATE LTD.—See Jefferies Financial Group Inc.; *U.S. Public*, pg. 1189
JEFFERIES INTERNATIONAL (HOLDINGS) LIMITED—See Jefferies Financial Group Inc.; *U.S. Public*, pg. 1188
JEFFERIES INTERNATIONAL LIMITED—See Jefferies Financial Group Inc.; *U.S. Public*, pg. 1188
JEFFERIES INVESTMENT ADVISERS, LLC—See Jefferies Financial Group Inc.; *U.S. Public*, pg. 1189
JEFFERIES (JAPAN) LIMITED—See Jefferies Financial Group Inc.; *U.S. Public*, pg. 1188
JEFFERIES LLC - LOS ANGELES—See Jefferies Financial Group Inc.; *U.S. Public*, pg. 1189
JEFFERIES LLC—See Jefferies Financial Group Inc.; *U.S. Public*, pg. 1189
JEFFERIES MORTGAGE FINANCE, LLC—See Jefferies Financial Group Inc.; *U.S. Public*, pg. 1189
JEFFERIES (SWITZERLAND) LTD.—See Jefferies Financial Group Inc.; *U.S. Public*, pg. 1188
JEFFER MANGELS BUTLER & MITCHELL LLP; *U.S. Private*, pg. 2197
JEFFER RESTAURANT CO., LTD.—See Wave Exponential Public Company Limited; *Int'l*, pg. 8359
JEFFERS, INC.; *U.S. Private*, pg. 2197
JEFFERSON ASPHALT PRODUCTS COMPANY; *U.S. Private*, pg. 2197
JEFFERSON AT MARINA DEL REY, L.P.—See UDR, Inc.; *U.S. Public*, pg. 2218
JEFFERSON AUTOMOTIVE GROUP; *Int'l*, pg. 3927
JEFFERSON BANK OF FLORIDA; *U.S. Private*, pg. 2197
JEFFERSON BANK OF MISSOURI—See Central Bancompany, Inc.; *U.S. Public*, pg. 472
JEFFERSON BANK & TRUST COMPANY—See First Mid Bancshares, Inc.; *U.S. Public*, pg. 846
JEFFERSON BLANKING INC.—See Shiloh Industries, Inc.; *U.S. Public*, pg. 3636
JEFFERSON CAPITAL SYSTEMS, LLC—See J.C. Flowers & Co. LLC; *U.S. Private*, pg. 2159
JEFFERSON CHEVROLET CO.; *U.S. Private*, pg. 2197
JEFFERSON CITY COCA-COLA BOTTLING CO.; *U.S. Private*, pg. 2197
JEFFERSON CITY OIL CO. INC.; *U.S. Private*, pg. 2197
JEFFERSON-COCKE COUNTY UTILITY DISTRICT; *U.S. Private*, pg. 2198
JEFFERSON COUNTY ADVERTISER—See Gannett Co., Inc.; *U.S. Public*, pg. 898
JEFFERSON COUNTY HMA, LLC—See Community Health Systems, Inc.; *U.S. Public*, pg. 554
JEFFERSON ELECTRIC INC.—See Guggenheim Partners, LLC; *U.S. Private*, pg. 1812
JEFFERSON ELORA CORPORATION—See G-TEKT Corporation; *Int'l*, pg. 2864
JEFFERSON ENERGY COOPERATIVE; *U.S. Private*, pg. 2197
JEFFERSON FINANCIAL CREDIT UNION; *U.S. Private*, pg. 2197
JEFFERSON HEALTH CARE, INC.—See The Ensign Group, Inc.; *U.S. Public*, pg. 2071
JEFFERSON HEALTH SYSTEM, INC.; *U.S. Private*, pg. 2197
JEFFERSON HOMEBUILDERS INC.; *U.S. Private*, pg. 2198
THE JEFFERSONIAN COMPANY, LLC—See Gannett Co., Inc.; *U.S. Public*, pg. 904
JEFFERSON INDUSTRIES CORPORATION; *U.S. Private*, pg. 2198
JEFFERSON INDUSTRIES CORPORATION—See G-TEKT Corporation; *Int'l*, pg. 2863
JEFFERSON MALL CMBS, LLC—See CBL & Associates Properties, Inc.; *U.S. Public*, pg. 458
JEFFERSON MANOR HEALTH CENTER; *U.S. Private*, pg. 2198
JEFFERSON PUBLIC RADIO; *U.S. Private*, pg. 2198
JEFFERSON QUARRY, LLC—See Summit Materials, Inc.; *U.S. Public*, pg. 1959
JEFFERSON REGIONAL HOMECARE, LLC—See UnitedHealth Group Incorporated; *U.S. Public*, pg. 2245
JEFFERSON REGIONAL MEDICAL CENTER; *U.S. Private*, pg. 2198
JEFFERSON SECURITY BANK; *U.S. Private*, pg. 2198
JEFFERSON SOLENOID VALVES USA, INC.—See Sophia Capital S.A.; *Int'l*, pg. 7108
JEFFERSON SOUTHERN CORPORATION—See G-TEKT Corporation; *Int'l*, pg. 2864
JEFFERSON SUDAMERICANA S.A.—See Sophia Capital S.A.; *Int'l*, pg. 7108
JEFFERSONVILLE BANCORP; *U.S. Public*, pg. 1189
JEFFERSON VINEYARDS; *U.S. Private*, pg. 2198

COMPANY NAME INDEX

JEFFERSON WELLS INTERNATIONAL, INC.—See ManpowerGroup Inc.; *U.S. Public*, pg. 1358
JEFFERSON YARNS; *U.S. Private*, pg. 2198
JEFFERSPET.COM—See Jeffers, Inc.; *U.S. Private*, pg. 2197
JEFFERY (WANDSWORTH) LIMITED—See General Motors Company; *U.S. Public*, pg. 928
JEFF HUNTER MOTORS, INC.; *U.S. Private*, pg. 2196
JEFF KERBER POOL PLASTERING, INC.; *U.S. Private*, pg. 2196
JEFF LUNGREN CHEVROLET, INC.; *U.S. Private*, pg. 2196
JEFFORDS STEEL & SPECIALTY CO.; *U.S. Private*, pg. 2198
JEFFREY AUTOMOTIVE GROUP; *U.S. Private*, pg. 2198
JEFFREY BUICK-NISSAN—See Jeffrey Automotive Group; *U.S. Private*, pg. 2198
JEFFREY CHAIN CORP—See Renold plc; *Int'l*, pg. 6284
JEFFREY FABRICS INC.; *U.S. Private*, pg. 2198
THE JEFFREY GROUP ARGENTINA—See WPP plc; *Int'l*, pg. 8466
THE JEFFREY GROUP BRAZIL—See WPP plc; *Int'l*, pg. 8467
THE JEFFREY GROUP, LLC—See WPP plc; *Int'l*, pg. 8466
THE JEFFREY GROUP MEXICO—See WPP plc; *Int'l*, pg. 8467
THE JEFFREY GROUP NEW YORK—See WPP plc; *Int'l*, pg. 8467
JEFFREY M. BROWN ASSOCIATES; *U.S. Private*, pg. 2198
JEFFREY M. CONSULTING LLC; *U.S. Private*, pg. 2198
JEFFREY RADER AB—See Hillenbrand, Inc.; *U.S. Public*, pg. 1037
JEFFREY RADER CANADA COMPANY—See Hillenbrand, Inc.; *U.S. Public*, pg. 1037
JEFFREY SCOTT AGENCY, INC.; *U.S. Private*, pg. 2198
JEFFRIES BROTHERS, INC.; *U.S. Private*, pg. 2198
JEFF'S BRANDS LTD.; *Int'l*, pg. 3927
JEFF SCHMITT AUTO GROUP; *U.S. Private*, pg. 2197
JEFF'S PEST CONTROL SERVICE, INC.—See Rollins, Inc.; *U.S. Public*, pg. 1809
JEFF WYLER ALEXANDRIA, INC.—See Jeff Wyler Automotive Family, Inc.; *U.S. Private*, pg. 2197
JEFF WYLER AUTOMOTIVE FAMILY, INC.; *U.S. Private*, pg. 2197
JEFF WYLER EASTGATE, INC.—See Jeff Wyler Automotive Family, Inc.; *U.S. Private*, pg. 2197
JEFF WYLER FAIRFIELD, INC.—See Jeff Wyler Automotive Family, Inc.; *U.S. Private*, pg. 2197
JEFF WYLER FLORENCE, INC.—See Jeff Wyler Automotive Family, Inc.; *U.S. Private*, pg. 2197
JEFF WYLER FRANKFORT, INC.—See Jeff Wyler Automotive Family, Inc.; *U.S. Private*, pg. 2197
JEFF WYLER FT. THOMAS, INC.—See Jeff Wyler Automotive Family, Inc.; *U.S. Private*, pg. 2197
JEFF WYLER LOUISVILLE II, INC.—See Jeff Wyler Automotive Family, Inc.; *U.S. Private*, pg. 2197
JEFF WYLER SPRINGFIELD, INC.—See Jeff Wyler Automotive Family, Inc.; *U.S. Private*, pg. 2197
JEFMAG; *Int'l*, pg. 3927
JEF UNITED CORP.—See The Furukawa Electric Co., Ltd.; *Int'l*, pg. 7646
JEG ARCHITECTURE NEVADA, INC.—See Jacobs Engineering Group, Inc.; *U.S. Public*, pg. 1184
JEGS AUTOMOTIVE INC.—See Greenbriar Equity Group, L.P.; *U.S. Private*, pg. 1776
J&E HALL INTERNATIONAL LTD.—See Daikin Industries, Ltd.; *Int'l*, pg. 1935
JEI AMERICA, INC.—See JEI Corporation; *Int'l*, pg. 3927
JEI CORPORATION JAPAN—See JEI Corporation; *Int'l*, pg. 3927
JEI CORPORATION; *Int'l*, pg. 3927
JEIL FEED CO., LTD.—See Harim Holdings Co., Ltd.; *Int'l*, pg. 3275
JEIL PHARMACEUTICAL CO., LTD.—See Jeil Pharma Holdings, Inc.; *Int'l*, pg. 3927
JEIL PHARMACEUTICAL CO., LTD. - YONGIN FACTORY—See Jeil Pharma Holdings, Inc.; *Int'l*, pg. 3927
JEIL PHARMA HOLDINGS, INC.; *Int'l*, pg. 3927
JEIL TECHNOS CO., LTD.; *Int'l*, pg. 3927
JEI SELF-LEARNING SYSTEMS, INC.—See JEI Corporation; *Int'l*, pg. 3927
JEI SELF LEARNING SYSTEMS NEW ZEALAND—See JEI Corporation; *Int'l*, pg. 3927
JEISYS MEDICAL INC.—See ArchiMed SAS; *Int'l*, pg. 548
J.E. JOHNSON INC.; *U.S. Private*, pg. 2162
JEJUAIR, CO., LTD.; *Int'l*, pg. 3927
JEJU BANK—See Shinhan Financial Group Co., Ltd.; *Int'l*, pg. 6843
JEJU BEER CO., LTD.; *Int'l*, pg. 3927
JEJU SEMICONDUCTOR CO.; *Int'l*, pg. 3927
JEK CARPET INC.; *U.S. Private*, pg. 2198
J.E. KINGHAM CONSTRUCTION CO., INC.; *U.S. Private*, pg. 2162
JEKYLL & HYDE BRAND BUILDERS INC.—See 1CM inc.; *Int'l*, pg. 3

JELAS PURI SDN. BHD.—See WCT Holdings Berhad; *Int'l*, pg. 8362
JEL-CAP VENDING INC.—See Legend Food Service LLC; *U.S. Private*, pg. 2418
JELD-WEN A/S—See ONEX Corporation; *Int'l*, pg. 5579
JELD-WEN AUSTRALIA PTY LTD—See Platinum Equity, LLC; *U.S. Private*, pg. 3205
JELD-WEN DEUTSCHLAND GMBH & CO. KG—See ONEX Corporation; *Int'l*, pg. 5579
JELD-WEN EESTI AS—See ONEX Corporation; *Int'l*, pg. 5579
JELD-WEN FRANCE S.A.S—See ONEX Corporation; *Int'l*, pg. 5579
JELD-WEN HOLDING, INC.—See ONEX Corporation; *Int'l*, pg. 5579
JELD-WEN, INC. - HAWKINS—See ONEX Corporation; *Int'l*, pg. 5579
JELD-WEN, INC. - PLYMOUTH—See ONEX Corporation; *Int'l*, pg. 5579
JELD-WEN, INC.—See ONEX Corporation; *Int'l*, pg. 5579
JELD-WEN LATVIJA SIA—See ONEX Corporation; *Int'l*, pg. 5579
JELD-WEN MAGYARORSZAG KFT.—See ONEX Corporation; *Int'l*, pg. 5579
JELD-WEN NORGE AS—See ONEX Corporation; *Int'l*, pg. 5579
JELD-WEN OF CANADA LTD. - SAINT APOLLINAIRE WINDOW PLANT—See ONEX Corporation; *Int'l*, pg. 5579
JELD-WEN OF CANADA LTD. - SAINT-HENRI DOOR PLANT—See ONEX Corporation; *Int'l*, pg. 5579
JELD-WEN OF CANADA LTD.—See ONEX Corporation; *Int'l*, pg. 5579
JELD-WEN OF CANADA LTD. - TORONTO WINDOW PLANT—See ONEX Corporation; *Int'l*, pg. 5579
JELD-WEN OF CANADA LTD. - WINNIPEG WINDOW PLANT—See ONEX Corporation; *Int'l*, pg. 5579
JELD-WEN POLSKA SP. Z.O.O.—See ONEX Corporation; *Int'l*, pg. 5579
JELD-WEN SUOMI OY—See ONEX Corporation; *Int'l*, pg. 5579
JELD-WEN TUREN GMBH—See ONEX Corporation; *Int'l*, pg. 5579
JELD-WEN UK LTD.—See ONEX Corporation; *Int'l*, pg. 5579
JELEC, INC.; *U.S. Private*, pg. 2198
JELEN D.D.; *Int'l*, pg. 3927
JELF CLARKE ROXBURGH—See Marsh & McLennan Companies, Inc.; *U.S. Public*, pg. 1378
JELF FINANCIAL PLANNING LIMITED—See Marsh & McLennan Companies, Inc.; *U.S. Public*, pg. 1378
JELF FINANCIAL PLANNING LIMITED—See Marsh & McLennan Companies, Inc.; *U.S. Public*, pg. 1378
JELF GROUP PLC—See Marsh & McLennan Companies, Inc.; *U.S. Public*, pg. 1377
JELF INSURANCE BROKERS LIMITED—See Marsh & McLennan Companies, Inc.; *U.S. Public*, pg. 1378
JELF LAMPIER—See Marsh & McLennan Companies, Inc.; *U.S. Public*, pg. 1378
JELF MANSON—See Marsh & McLennan Companies, Inc.; *U.S. Public*, pg. 1378
JELF WELLBEING LIMITED—See Marsh & McLennan Companies, Inc.; *U.S. Public*, pg. 1378
JELINEK HARDWARE INC.; *U.S. Private*, pg. 2198
JELLICO MEDICAL CENTER, INC.—See Rennova Health, Inc.; *U.S. Public*, pg. 1783
JELLIFF CORPORATION - FLORIDA FACILITY—See Jelliff Corporation; *U.S. Private*, pg. 2198
JELLIFF CORPORATION; *U.S. Private*, pg. 2198
JELLY BELLY CANDY COMPANY; *U.S. Private*, pg. 2198
JELLYFISH.COM, INC.—See Microsoft Corporation; *U.S. Public*, pg. 1441
THE JELLYVISION LAB, INC.; *U.S. Private*, pg. 4058
JELMAR COMPANY; *U.S. Private*, pg. 2199
JEL MARKETING (VIETNAM) JOINT VENTURE CO., LTD.—See GSH Corporation Limited; *Int'l*, pg. 3144
JELMOLI AG—See Swiss Prime Site AG; *Int'l*, pg. 7370
JELMOLI HOLDING AG—See Swiss Prime Site AG; *Int'l*, pg. 7370
JELMOLI LTD—See Swiss Prime Site AG; *Int'l*, pg. 7370
JELMOLI VERSAND AG—See Otto GmbH & Co. KG; *Int'l*, pg. 5662
JELRUS INTERNATIONAL—See Air Techniques, Inc.; *U.S. Private*, pg. 140
JELSCHEN GMBH—See KIRCHHOFF Gruppe; *Int'l*, pg. 4185
THE JEL SERT COMPANY; *U.S. Private*, pg. 4058
JELSINGRAD LIVAR LIVNICA CELIKA A. D.; *Int'l*, pg. 3927
JEL TRADING (BANGLADESH) LTD.—See Serial System Ltd.; *Int'l*, pg. 6723
JELUTONG DEVELOPMENT SDN BHD—See IJM Corporation Berhad; *Int'l*, pg. 3609
JEMA DISTRIBUTION; *Int'l*, pg. 3927
JEM AMERICA CORP.—See Japan Electronic Materials Corporation; *Int'l*, pg. 3888
JEMBAS ASSISTENCIA TECNICA, LDA; *Int'l*, pg. 3927
J.E.M. CAPITAL, INC.; *Int'l*, pg. 3858

JENNINGS ANDERSON FORD SALES

JEMENA LIMITED—See State Grid Corporation of China; *Int'l*, pg. 7183
JEMENA LIMITED—See Temasek Holdings (Private) Limited; *Int'l*, pg. 7551
JEM EUROPE S.A.R.L.—See Japan Electronic Materials Corporation; *Int'l*, pg. 3888
JEMEZ MOUNTAIN ELECTRIC CO-OP; *U.S. Private*, pg. 2199
JEM FINCO LIMITED—See American Securities LLC; *U.S. Private*, pg. 252
JEM (HONG KONG) CO., LTD.—See Japan Electronic Materials Corporation; *Int'l*, pg. 3888
JEMI INC.; *U.S. Private*, pg. 2199
JEMISON-DEMSEY METALS; *U.S. Private*, pg. 2199
JEMISON-DEMSEY METALS—See Jemison-Demsey Metals; *U.S. Private*, pg. 2199
JEM KOREA CO., LTD.—See Japan Electronic Materials Corporation; *Int'l*, pg. 3888
JEMS COATING LIMITED; *Int'l*, pg. 3927
JEM SHANGHAI CO., LTD.—See Japan Electronic Materials Corporation; *Int'l*, pg. 3888
JEMSTEP, INC.—See Invesco Ltd.; *U.S. Public*, pg. 1163
JEM TAIWAN PROBE CORP.—See Japan Electronic Materials Corporation; *Int'l*, pg. 3888
JEMTEC INC.; *Int'l*, pg. 3927
JENAER GEWINDETECHNIK GMBH—See Kuroda Precision Industries Ltd.; *Int'l*, pg. 4342
JENAER GLASWERK GMBH—See Carl-Zeiss-Stiftung; *Int'l*, pg. 1336
JENA-OPTRONIK GMBH—See Airbus SE; *Int'l*, pg. 245
JENAPHARM GMBH & CO. KG—See Bayer Aktiengesellschaft; *Int'l*, pg. 904
JENARK BUSINESS SYSTEMS, INC.—See Insight Venture Management, LLC; *U.S. Public*, pg. 2089
JENARK BUSINESS SYSTEMS, INC.—See Stone Point Capital LLC; *U.S. Private*, pg. 3822
JENAX INC.; *Int'l*, pg. 3927
JENBROOK PTY LTD—See EVE Health Group Limited; *Int'l*, pg. 2561
JENBURKT PHARMACEUTICALS LTD; *Int'l*, pg. 3928
JENCAP HOLDINGS LLC—See The Carlyle Group Inc.; *U.S. Public*, pg. 2047
JENCAP INSURANCE SERVICES INC.—See The Carlyle Group Inc.; *U.S. Public*, pg. 2047
JENCO PRODUCTIONS INC.; *U.S. Private*, pg. 2199
JENDEV—See Jersey Electricity plc; *Int'l*, pg. 3932
JENERATION ACQUISITION CORP.; *Int'l*, pg. 3928
JENERS DRUCKGUSSTECHNIK GMBH; *Int'l*, pg. 3928
JEN FLORIDA II, LLC—See Brookfield Corporation; *Int'l*, pg. 1183
JENG YUAN RECLAIMED RUBBER SDN. BHD.—See Polygreen Resources Co., Ltd.; *Int'l*, pg. 5915
JENKEM TECHNOLOGY CO., LTD.; *Int'l*, pg. 3928
JENKEM TECHNOLOGY USA, INC.—See Jenkem Technology Co., Ltd.; *Int'l*, pg. 3928
JENKINS BRICK COMPANY, INC. -ATTALLA—See Berkshire Hathaway Inc.; *U.S. Public*, pg. 298
JENKINS DIESEL POWER, INC.; *U.S. Private*, pg. 2199
JENKINS ELECTRIC CO.; *U.S. Private*, pg. 2199
JENKINS-ESSEX COMPANY; *U.S. Private*, pg. 2199
JENKINS FORD/MERCURY INC.; *U.S. Private*, pg. 2199
JENKINS GAS & OIL CO., INC.—See Suburban Propane Partners, L.P.; *U.S. Public*, pg. 1958
JENKINS GROUP, INC.; *U.S. Private*, pg. 2199
JENKINS HYUNDAI; *U.S. Private*, pg. 2199
JENKINS OIL COMPANY INC.; *U.S. Private*, pg. 2199
JENKINS SECURITY CONSULTANTS, INC.; *U.S. Private*, pg. 2199
JENKINS & WYNNE FORD INC.; *U.S. Private*, pg. 2199
JENKS & CATTELL ENGINEERING LTD.—See Newship Ltd; *Int'l*, pg. 5238
JENNA CONCRETE CORP.—See Vulcan Materials Company; *U.S. Public*, pg. 2314
JENNER & BLOCK LLP; *U.S. Private*, pg. 2199
JENNER CHEVROLET BUICK CORVETTE GMC; *Int'l*, pg. 3928
JENNER EQUIPMENT CO.; *U.S. Private*, pg. 2200
JENNER'S POND; *U.S. Private*, pg. 2200
JENNERSVILLE FAMILY MEDICINE, LLC—See Tower Health; *U.S. Private*, pg. 4193
JENN FENG INDUSTRIAL TOOLS CO., LTD.; *Int'l*, pg. 3928
JENNIE M. MELHAM MEMORIAL MEDICAL CENTER; *U.S. Private*, pg. 2200
JENNIE-O TURKEY STORE, INC.—See Hormel Foods Corporation; *U.S. Public*, pg. 1054
JENNIE-O TURKEY STORE INTERNATIONAL INC.—See Hormel Foods Corporation; *U.S. Public*, pg. 1054
JENNIE-O TURKEY STORE SALES, LLC—See Hormel Foods Corporation; *U.S. Public*, pg. 1054
JENNIFER CONVERTIBLES INC.—See Morris Home Holdings Limited; *Int'l*, pg. 5049
JENNINGS AERONAUTICS INC.—See AE Industrial Partners, LP; *U.S. Private*, pg. 112
JENNINGS AMERICAN LEGION HOSPITAL; *U.S. Private*, pg. 2200
JENNINGS ANDERSON FORD SALES; *U.S. Private*, pg. 2200

JENNINGS CENTER FOR OLDER ADULTS

JENNINGS CENTER FOR OLDER ADULTS; *U.S. Private,* pg. 2200
JENNINGS CHEVROLET, INC.; *U.S. Private,* pg. 2200
JENNINGS-DILL, INC.; *U.S. Private,* pg. 2200
JENNINGS-GOMER EQUITY INC.; *U.S. Private,* pg. 2200
JENNINGS TECHNOLOGY—See ABB Ltd.; *Int'l,* pg. 52
JENNINGS TIRE COMPANY INC.; *U.S. Private,* pg. 2200
JENNINGS VALUE CENTER; *U.S. Private,* pg. 2200
JENNINGS VOLKSWAGEN INC.; *U.S. Private,* pg. 2200
JENNISON ASSOCIATES LLC—See Prudential Financial, Inc.; *U.S. Public,* pg. 1731
JENNMAR CORPORATION OF WEST VIRGINIA INC.—See Frank Calandra, Inc.; *U.S. Private,* pg. 1594
JENNMAR CORPORATION—See Frank Calandra, Inc.; *U.S. Private,* pg. 1594
JENNMAR OF KENTUCKY INC.—See Frank Calandra, Inc.; *U.S. Private,* pg. 1594
JENNY CORPORATION OF OHIO; *U.S. Private,* pg. 2200
JENNY CRAIG DISTRIBUTION CENTER—See H.I.G. Capital, LLC; *U.S. Private,* pg. 1830
JENNY CRAIG, INC.—See H.I.G. Capital, LLC; *U.S. Private,* pg. 1829
JENNY CRAIG OPERATIONS, INC.—See H.I.G. Capital, LLC; *U.S. Private,* pg. 1830
JENNY CRAIG WEIGHT LOSS CENTRES (CANADA) COMPANY—See H.I.G. Capital, LLC; *U.S. Private,* pg. 1830
JENNY CRAIG WEIGHT LOSS CENTRES, INC.—See H.I.G. Capital, LLC; *U.S. Private,* pg. 1830
JENNY CRAIG WEIGHT LOSS CENTRES (NZ) LTD—See H.I.G. Capital, LLC; *U.S. Private,* pg. 1830
JENNY CRAIG WEIGHT LOSS CENTRES PTY. LTD.—See H.I.G. Capital, LLC; *U.S. Private,* pg. 1830
JENNY MARAGHY TEAM, INC.; *U.S. Private,* pg. 2200
JENNY PRODUCTS, INC.; *U.S. Private,* pg. 2200
JENOBA CO., LTD.; *Int'l,* pg. 3928
JENOPTIK ADVANCED SYSTEMS, LLC—See Jenoptik AG; *Int'l,* pg. 3928
JENOPTIK AG; *Int'l,* pg. 3928
JENOPTIK AUTOMATISIERUNGSTECHNIK GMBH—See Jenoptik AG; *Int'l,* pg. 3928
JENOPTIK AUTOMOTIVE NORTH AMERICA, LLC—See Jenoptik AG; *Int'l,* pg. 3928
JENOPTIK BENELUX B.V.—See Jenoptik AG; *Int'l,* pg. 3928
JENOPTIK COMPONENTS LLC—See Jenoptik AG; *Int'l,* pg. 3928
JENOPTIK DIODE LAB GMBH—See Jenoptik AG; *Int'l,* pg. 3928
JENOPTIK INDUSTRIAL METROLOGY GERMANY GMBH—See Jenoptik AG; *Int'l,* pg. 3928
JENOPTIK JAPAN CO LTD—See Jenoptik AG; *Int'l,* pg. 3928
JENOPTIK KATASORB GMBH—See Jenoptik AG; *Int'l,* pg. 3929
JENOPTIK KOREA CORPORATION LTD—See Jenoptik AG; *Int'l,* pg. 3929
JENOPTIK LASER TECHNOLOGIES USA CORP—See Jenoptik AG; *Int'l,* pg. 3928
JENOPTIK OPTICAL SYSTEMS GMBH—See Jenoptik AG; *Int'l,* pg. 3929
JENOPTIK OPTICAL SYSTEMS, INC.—See Jenoptik AG; *Int'l,* pg. 3928
JENOPTIK OPTICAL SYSTEMS, LLC—See Jenoptik AG; *Int'l,* pg. 3928
JENOPTIK POWER SYSTEMS GMBH—See Jenoptik AG; *Int'l,* pg. 3928
JENOPTIK ROBOT GMBH—See Jenoptik AG; *Int'l,* pg. 3929
JENOPTIK (SHANGHAI) PRECISION INSTRUMENTS AND EQUIPMENT CO., LTD.—See Jenoptik AG; *Int'l,* pg. 3928
JENOPTIK SSC GMBH—See Jenoptik AG; *Int'l,* pg. 3929
JENOPTIK TRAFFIC SOLUTIONS SWITZERLAND AG—See Jenoptik AG; *Int'l,* pg. 3928
JENOPTIK TRAFFIC SOLUTIONS UK LTD—See Jenoptik AG; *Int'l,* pg. 3928
JENOPTIK UK LIMITED—See Jenoptik AG; *Int'l,* pg. 3929
JENOVATION GMBH—See ManpowerGroup Inc.; *U.S. Public,* pg. 1362
JEN PARTNERS, LLC; *U.S. Private,* pg. 2199
JENSCARE SCIENTIFIC CO., LTD.; *Int'l,* pg. 3929
JENSEN AUDIO VISUAL; *U.S. Private,* pg. 2200
JENSEN BRIDGE & SUPPLY COMPANY; *U.S. Private,* pg. 2200
JENSEN BUILDERS LTD. (INC.)—See Moore Brothers Asphalt Inc.; *U.S. Private,* pg. 2779
JENSEN CONSTRUCTION COMPANY—See Rasmussen Group Inc.; *U.S. Private,* pg. 3357
JENSEN CONSTRUCTION MANAGEMENT, INC.—See Ventas, Inc.; *U.S. Public,* pg. 2278
JENSEN DISTRIBUTION SERVICES—See Ace Hardware Corporation; *U.S. Private,* pg. 56
JENSEN ENTERPRISES INC.; *U.S. Private,* pg. 2200
JENSEN FORD INC.; *U.S. Private,* pg. 2200
JENSEN GMBH—See Jensen-Group N.V.; *Int'l,* pg. 3929
JENSEN-GROUP N.V.; *Int'l,* pg. 3929
JENSEN HUGHES, INC. - MIDWEST—See Gryphon Investors, LLC; *U.S. Private,* pg. 1798

JENSEN HUGHES, INC.—See Gryphon Investors, LLC; *U.S. Private,* pg. 1798
JENSEN INDUSTRIAL GROUP A/S—See Jensen-Group N.V.; *Int'l,* pg. 3929
JENSEN INFORMATION TECHNOLOGIES INC; *U.S. Private,* pg. 2200
JENSEN INTERNATIONAL INC.; *U.S. Private,* pg. 2200
JENSEN ITALIA S.R.L.—See Jensen-Group N.V.; *Int'l,* pg. 3929
JENSEN JEWELERS OF IDAHO LLC; *U.S. Private,* pg. 2200
JENSEN LAUNDRY SYSTEMS AUSTRALIA PTY. LTD.—See Jensen-Group N.V.; *Int'l,* pg. 3929
JENSEN METAL PRODUCTS INC.; *U.S. Private,* pg. 2201
JENSEN & PILEGARD; *U.S. Private,* pg. 2200
JENSEN & SCHEELE BIL AS—See Bilia AB; *Int'l,* pg. 1029
JENSENS COMPLETE SHOPPING; *U.S. Private,* pg. 2201
JENSEN'S INC.—See Sun Communities, Inc.; *U.S. Public,* pg. 1961
JENSEN TIRE & AUTO CO.; *U.S. Private,* pg. 2201
JENSEN UK LTD.—See Jensen-Group N.V.; *Int'l,* pg. 3929
JENSEN UNDERGROUND UTILITIES, INC.; *U.S. Private,* pg. 2201
JENSEN USA, INC.—See Jensen-Group N.V.; *Int'l,* pg. 3929
JENSON & NICHOLSON (BANGLADESH) LIMITED—See Berger Paints Bangladesh Limited; *Int'l,* pg. 979
JENSON & NICHOLSON INDIA LTD; *Int'l,* pg. 3929
JENS S. TRANSMISJONER AS—See Axel Johnson Gruppen AB; *Int'l,* pg. 763
JENS S. TRANSMISSIONER AB—See Axel Johnson Gruppen AB; *Int'l,* pg. 763
JENS S. TRANSMISSIONER A/S—See Axel Johnson Gruppen AB; *Int'l,* pg. 763
JENTAYU SUSTAINABLES BERHAD; *Int'l,* pg. 3929
JENTECH PRECISION INDUSTRIAL CO., LTD.; *Int'l,* pg. 3929
JENTRAKEL SDN BHD—See Warisan TC Holdings Berhad; *Int'l,* pg. 8345
JENTSCHMANN AG—See Leggett & Platt, Incorporated; *U.S. Public,* pg. 1302
JENZABAR, INC.; *U.S. Private,* pg. 2201
JEOL ASIA PTE. LTD.—See JEOL Ltd.; *Int'l,* pg. 3930
JEOL ASIA(THAILAND)CO., LTD.—See JEOL Ltd.; *Int'l,* pg. 3930
JEOL (AUSTRALASIA) PTY. LTD.—See JEOL Ltd.; *Int'l,* pg. 3930
JEOL (BEIJING) CO., LTD.—See JEOL Ltd.; *Int'l,* pg. 3930
JEOL BRASIL INSTRUMENTOS CIENTIFICOS LTDA.—See JEOL Ltd.; *Int'l,* pg. 3930
JEOL CANADA, INC.—See JEOL Ltd.; *Int'l,* pg. 3930
JEOL DATUM SHANGHAI CO., LTD.—See JEOL Ltd.; *Int'l,* pg. 3930
JEOL DE MEXICO S.A. DE C.V.—See JEOL Ltd.; *Int'l,* pg. 3930
JEOL (EUROPE) B.V.—See JEOL Ltd.; *Int'l,* pg. 3930
JEOL (EUROPE) SAS—See JEOL Ltd.; *Int'l,* pg. 3930
JEOL (GERMANY) GMBH—See JEOL Ltd.; *Int'l,* pg. 3930
JEOL GULF FZCO—See JEOL Ltd.; *Int'l,* pg. 3930
JEOL INDIA PVT. LTD.—See JEOL Ltd.; *Int'l,* pg. 3930
JEOL (ITALIA) S.P.A.—See JEOL Ltd.; *Int'l,* pg. 3930
JEOL KOREA LTD.—See JEOL Ltd.; *Int'l,* pg. 3930
JEOL LTD.; *Int'l,* pg. 3929
JEOL (MALAYSIA) SDN BHD—See JEOL Ltd.; *Int'l,* pg. 3930
JEOL (NORDIC) AB—See JEOL Ltd.; *Int'l,* pg. 3930
JEOL RESONANCE INC.—See JEOL Ltd.; *Int'l,* pg. 3930
JEOL (RUS) LLC.—See JEOL Ltd.; *Int'l,* pg. 3930
JEOL SHANGHAI SEMICONDUCTORS LTD.—See JEOL Ltd.; *Int'l,* pg. 3930
JEOL (SKANDINAVISKA) A.B.—See JEOL Ltd.; *Int'l,* pg. 3930
JEOL TAIWAN SEMICONDUCTORS LTD.—See JEOL Ltd.; *Int'l,* pg. 3930
JEOL TECHNOSERVICE CO., LTD.—See JEOL Ltd.; *Int'l,* pg. 3930
JEOL (U.K.) LTD.—See JEOL Ltd.; *Int'l,* pg. 3930
JEOL USA, INC.—See JEOL Ltd.; *Int'l,* pg. 3930
JEONBUK BANK—See JB Financial Group Co., Ltd.; *Int'l,* pg. 3917
JEONBUK ENERGY SERVICE CO., LTD.—See SK Inc.; *Int'l,* pg. 6972
JEONBUK HYUNDAI MOTORS FC CO., LTD.—See Hyundai Motor Company; *Int'l,* pg. 3560
JEONGMOON INFORMATION CO., LTD.; *Int'l,* pg. 3930
JEONG POONG CO., LTD.—See Daesang Holdings Co., Ltd.; *Int'l,* pg. 1909
JEONJINBIO CO., LTD.; *Int'l,* pg. 3930
JEONSANTEX CO., LTD.—See Chonbang Co., Ltd.; *Int'l,* pg. 1578
JEONWOO PRECISION CO., LTD. - CHINA FACTORY—See Jeonwoo Precision Co., Ltd.; *Int'l,* pg. 3930
JEONWOO PRECISION CO., LTD.; *Int'l,* pg. 3930
JEOPARDY PRODUCTIONS, INC.—See Sony Group Corporation; *Int'l,* pg. 7105
JEOTEX, INC.; *Int'l,* pg. 3930

CORPORATE AFFILIATIONS

JEP HOLDINGS LTD.—See UMS Holdings Limited; *Int'l,* pg. 8026
JEP INDUSTRADES PTE.LTD.—See UMS Holdings Limited; *Int'l,* pg. 8027
JEP MANAGEMENT, INC.; *U.S. Private,* pg. 2201
JEPPESEN ASIA/PACIFIC PTE. LTD.—See The Boeing Company; *U.S. Public,* pg. 2039
JEPPESEN (CANADA) LTD.—See The Boeing Company; *U.S. Public,* pg. 2039
JEPPESEN DATAPLAN, INC.—See The Boeing Company; *U.S. Public,* pg. 2039
JEPPESEN GMBH—See The Boeing Company; *U.S. Public,* pg. 2039
JEPPESEN POLAND SPOLKA Z OGRANICZONA ODPOWIEDZIALNOSCIA—See The Boeing Company; *U.S. Public,* pg. 2039
JEPPESEN SANDERSON, INC.—See The Boeing Company; *U.S. Public,* pg. 2039
JEPPESEN SYSTEMS AB—See The Boeing Company; *U.S. Public,* pg. 2039
J & E PRECISION TOOL, LLC; *U.S. Private,* pg. 2152
JERA CO., LTD.—See Chubu Electric Power Co., Inc.; *Int'l,* pg. 1593
JERAISY CARDTEC—See Jeraisy Group; *Int'l,* pg. 3931
JERAISY COMPUTER & COMMUNICATION SERVICES—See Jeraisy Group; *Int'l,* pg. 3931
JERAISY COMPUTER PAPER PRODUCTS CO.—See Jeraisy Group; *Int'l,* pg. 3931
JERAISY GROUP; *Int'l,* pg. 3930
JERAL CONSTRUCTION SERVICES; *U.S. Private,* pg. 2201
THE JERALD DEVELOPMENT GROUP INC.; *U.S. Private,* pg. 4058
JERALD R. BREKKE, INC.—See McGrath RentCorp.; *U.S. Public,* pg. 1407
JERASH GARMENTS AND FASHIONS MANUFACTURING CO. LTD.—See Ford Glory International Limited; *Int'l,* pg. 2731
JERASH HOLDINGS (US), INC.; *U.S. Public,* pg. 1189
JERASIA APPAREL SDN. BHD.—See Jerasia Capital Berhad; *Int'l,* pg. 3931
JERASIA CAPITAL BERHAD; *Int'l,* pg. 3931
JERDON CONSTRUCTION SERVICES LLC; *U.S. Private,* pg. 2201
JERDON STYLE LLC; *U.S. Private,* pg. 2201
JERED, LLC—See Pohlad Companies; *U.S. Private,* pg. 3220
JEREH C-CREATE TECHNOLOGY CO., LTD.—See Yantai Jereh Oilfield Services Group Co., Ltd.; *Int'l,* pg. 8565
JEREH ENERGY EQUIPMENT & TECHNOLOGIES CORPORATION—See Yantai Jereh Oilfield Services Group Co., Ltd.; *Int'l,* pg. 8565
JEREH ENERGY SERVICES CORPORATION—See Yantai Jereh Oilfield Services Group Co., Ltd.; *Int'l,* pg. 8565
JEREH ENVIRONMENTAL PROTECTION TECHNOLOGY CO., LTD.—See Yantai Jereh Oilfield Services Group Co., Ltd.; *Int'l,* pg. 8565
JEREH GLOBAL DEVELOPMENT LLC—See Yantai Jereh Oilfield Services Group Co., Ltd.; *Int'l,* pg. 8565
JEREH OIL & GAS ENGINEERING CORPORATION—See Yantai Jereh Oilfield Services Group Co., Ltd.; *Int'l,* pg. 8565
JERGENS INC.; *U.S. Private,* pg. 2201
JERGENS INDIA PRIVATE, LTD.—See Jergens Inc.; *U.S. Private,* pg. 2201
JER HR GROUP LLC; *U.S. Private,* pg. 2201
JERICH AUSTRIA GMBH—See Jerich International GmbH; *Int'l,* pg. 3931
JERICH INTERNATIONAL GMBH; *Int'l,* pg. 3931
JERICHO ENERGY VENTURES INC.; *Int'l,* pg. 3931
JERICOL MINING INC.; *U.S. Private,* pg. 2201
JERITH MANUFACTURING LLC—See ASSA ABLOY AB; *Int'l,* pg. 639
JERMANN INGENIEURE UND GEOMETER AG—See BKW AG; *Int'l,* pg. 1055
JERNBANEVERKET; *Int'l,* pg. 3931
JERNBERG INDUSTRIES, LLC—See American Axle & Manufacturing Holdings, Inc.; *U.S. Public,* pg. 96
JERNBERG INDUSTRIES, LLC—See American Axle & Manufacturing Holdings, Inc.; *U.S. Public,* pg. 97
JERNBERG SALES, LLC—See American Axle & Manufacturing Holdings, Inc.; *U.S. Public,* pg. 96
JERNEH ASIA BERHAD—See Kuok Brothers Sdn. Bhd.; *Int'l,* pg. 4334
JERNIGAN CAPITAL, INC.; *U.S. Private,* pg. 2201
JERNIGAN OIL CO. INC.; *U.S. Private,* pg. 2201
J.E. ROBERT COMPANY; *U.S. Private,* pg. 2162
JEROME HAIMS REALTY, INC.—See BBG Inc.; *U.S. Private,* pg. 498
JEROME HOME; *U.S. Private,* pg. 2201
JEROME INDUSTRIES CORP.—See Tinicum Enterprises, Inc.; *U.S. Private,* pg. 4174
JEROME'S FURNITURE WAREHOUSE; *U.S. Private,* pg. 2201
JERONIMO MARTINS-DISTRIBUICAO DE PRODUTOS DE CONSUMO, LDA.—See Jeronimo Martins SGPS SA; *Int'l,* pg. 3931

COMPANY NAME INDEX

JERONIMO MARTINS DYSTRYBUCJA S.A.—See Jeronimo Martins SGPS SA; *Int'l*, pg. 3931
JERONIMO MARTINS-SERVICOS, S.A.—See Jeronimo Martins SGPS SA; *Int'l*, pg. 3931
JERONIMO MARTINS SGPS SA; *Int'l*, pg. 3931
JERR-DAN CORPORATION—See Oshkosh Corporation; *U.S. Public*, pg. 1620
JERRS PLUS INC.; *U.S. Private*, pg. 2202
JERRY BIGGERS CHEVROLET - ISUZU INC.; *U.S. Private*, pg. 2202
THE JERRY BROWN CO, INC.; *U.S. Private*, pg. 4059
JERRY BROWN, LTD.—See Stellex Capital Management LP; *U.S. Private*, pg. 3800
JERRY BRUCKHEIMER FILMS INC.; *U.S. Private*, pg. 2202
JERRY CHEN; *U.S. Private*, pg. 2202
JERRY ERWIN ASSOCIATES INC.; *U.S. Private*, pg. 2202
JERRY FERGUSON BUICK-GMC TRUCK LLC; *U.S. Private*, pg. 2202
JERRY FORD SALES LTD.; *Int'l*, pg. 3931
JERRY HAAG MOTORS INC.; *U.S. Private*, pg. 2202
JERRY HAMM CHEVROLET INC.; *U.S. Private*, pg. 2202
JERRY HEFLIN COURTESY CHEVROLET; *U.S. Private*, pg. 2202
JERRY LAWLEY INCORPORATED; *U.S. Private*, pg. 2202
JERRY LEE'S GROCERY, INC.; *U.S. Private*, pg. 2202
JERRY MEDICAL EQUIPMENT (SHANGHAI) CO., LTD.—See Cofoe Medical Technology Co., Ltd.; *Int'l*, pg. 1693
JERRY PATE TURF & IRRIGATION INC; *U.S. Private*, pg. 2202
JERRY SEINER CHEVROLET, INC.; *U.S. Private*, pg. 2202
JERRY SEINER SALT LAKE—See Jerry Seiner Chevrolet, Inc.; *U.S. Private*, pg. 2202
JERRY'S ENTERPRISES INC.; *U.S. Private*, pg. 2202
JERRY'S EXPRESS CARWASH—See Whitewater Express, Inc.; *U.S. Private*, pg. 4512
JERRY'S FAMOUS DELI, INC.; *U.S. Private*, pg. 2202
JERRY'S FORD SALES INC.; *U.S. Private*, pg. 2202
JERRY'S HOMES INC.; *U.S. Private*, pg. 2202
JERRY'S MARINE SERVICE FL, LLC—See Lewis Marine Supply Inc., *U.S. Private*, pg. 2430
JERRY SMITH CHEVROLET; *U.S. Private*, pg. 2202
JERRY'S SPORTS CENTER, INC.; *U.S. Private*, pg. 2202
JERRY'S SUPERMARKET INC.; *U.S. Private*, pg. 2202
JERRY ULM DODGE, INC.; *U.S. Private*, pg. 2202
JERRY W. BAILEY TRUCKING, INC.; *U.S. Private*, pg. 2202
JERSEY AIRTEL LIMITED—See Bharti Enterprises Limited; *Int'l*, pg. 1013
JERSEY CENTRAL POWER & LIGHT COMPANY—See FirstEnergy Corp.; *U.S. Public*, pg. 849
JERSEY CONSTRUCTION INCORPORATED; *U.S. Private*, pg. 2202
JERSEY DEEP FREEZE LIMITED—See Jersey Electricity plc; *Int'l*, pg. 3932
JERSEY ELECTRICITY PLC; *Int'l*, pg. 3932
JERSEY ELEVATOR CO. INC.—See Arcline Investment Management LP; *U.S. Private*, pg. 314
JERSEY HEALTH CONNECT; *U.S. Private*, pg. 2202
JERSEY HOME LOANS LIMITED—See J.C. Flowers & Co. LLC; *U.S. Private*, pg. 2160
JERSEY JOURNAL NEWSPAPER—See Advance Publications, Inc.; *U.S. Private*, pg. 86
JERSEY MIKE'S FRANCHISE SYSTEMS, INC.; *U.S. Private*, pg. 2203
JERSEY NATIONAL CAPTIAL—See Fedway Associates Inc.; *U.S. Private*, pg. 1492
JERSEY OIL & GAS PLC; *Int'l*, pg. 3932
THE JERSEY ROYAL COMPANY LIMITED—See Promethean Investments LLP; *Int'l*, pg. 5993
JERSEY SHORE BROADCASTING CORPORATION—See Beasley Broadcast Group, Inc.; *U.S. Public*, pg. 287
JERSEY SHORE HOSPITAL; *U.S. Private*, pg. 2203
JERSEY SHORE STATE BANK—See Penns Woods Bancorp, Inc.; *U.S. Public*, pg. 1663
JERSEY SHORE STEEL CO.; *U.S. Private*, pg. 2203
JERUSALEM CIGARETTE CO. LTD.—See Dubek Ltd.; *Int'l*, pg. 2222
THE JERUSALEM FOUNDATION, INC.; *U.S. Private*, pg. 4059
JERUSALEM INSURANCE COMPANY; *Int'l*, pg. 3932
JERUSALEM PHARMACEUTICALS CO.; *Int'l*, pg. 3932
JERUSALEM POST PUBLICATIONS LTD.; *Int'l*, pg. 3932
JERUSALEM REAL ESTATE INVESTMENT COMPANY P.L.C.; *Int'l*, pg. 3932
JERUSALEM TECHNOLOGY INVESTMENTS LTD.; *Int'l*, pg. 3932
JERVIS B. WEBB COMPANY LTD.—See Daifuku Co., Ltd.; *Int'l*, pg. 1925
JERVIS B. WEBB COMPANY OF CANADA LTD.—See Daifuku Co., Ltd.; *Int'l*, pg. 1925
JERVIS B. WEBB COMPANY—See Daifuku Co., Ltd.; *Int'l*, pg. 1925
JERVIS B. WEBB COMPANY—See Daifuku Co., Ltd.; *Int'l*, pg. 1925
JERVIS B. WEBB COMPANY—See Daifuku Co., Ltd.; *Int'l*, pg. 1925
JERVIS WEBB CHINA CO., LTD.—See Daifuku Co., Ltd.; *Int'l*, pg. 1925
JERVOIS GLOBAL LIMITED; *Int'l*, pg. 3932
JERYCO INDUSTRIES INC.; *U.S. Private*, pg. 2203
JERZEES—See Berkshire Hathaway Inc.; *U.S. Public*, pg. 305
JESCOBINA M SDN. BHD.—See JESCO Holdings, Inc.; *Int'l*, pg. 3932
JESCO CNS CO., LTD.—See JESCO Holdings, Inc.; *Int'l*, pg. 3932
JESCO CONSTRUCTION CORPORATION; *U.S. Private*, pg. 2203
JESCO HOA BINH ENGINEERING JSC—See JESCO Holdings, Inc.; *Int'l*, pg. 3932
JESCO HOLDINGS, INC.; *Int'l*, pg. 3932
JESCO, INC.—See W.G. Yates & Sons Construction Company; *U.S. Private*, pg. 4420
JESCO INC.; *U.S. Private*, pg. 2203
JESCO LIGHTING GROUP, LLC; *U.S. Private*, pg. 2203
J ESCOM HOLDINGS, INC.; *Int'l*, pg. 3852
JES CONSTRUCTION, LLC; *U.S. Private*, pg. 2203
JESCO WHOLESALE ELECTRICAL SUPPLIES INC.; *U.S. Private*, pg. 2203
JESDENE LIMITED—See African Rainbow Minerals Limited; *Int'l*, pg. 192
J.E. SHEKELL INC.; *U.S. Private*, pg. 2162
JES INTERNATIONAL HOLDINGS LIMITED; *Int'l*, pg. 3932
JESON ENTERPRISES INC.; *U.S. Private*, pg. 2203
JESPER OFFICE, LLC—See Unique Furniture A/S; *Int'l*, pg. 8059
J.E.S. RESTAURANT EQUIPMENT, INC.—See Trivest Partners, LP; *U.S. Private*, pg. 4240
JESS3; *U.S. Private*, pg. 2203
JESSE ENGINEERING COMPANY; *U.S. Private*, pg. 2203
JESSE KALISHER GALLERY, INC.—See Longwater Opportunities LLC; *U.S. Private*, pg. 2493
JESSHEIM STORSENTER AS—See Olav Thon Eiendomsselskap ASA; *Int'l*, pg. 5552
JESS HOWARD ELECTRIC COMPANY; *U.S. Private*, pg. 2203
JESSICA HOWARD, LTD.—See G-III Apparel Group, Ltd.; *U.S. Public*, pg. 894
JESSICA KINGSLEY (PUBLISHERS) LTD.—See Vivendi SE; *Int'l*, pg. 8271
JESSIE TRICE COMMUNITY HEALTH CENTER, INC.; *U.S. Private*, pg. 2203
JESS-LINK PRODUCTS CO., LTD.; *Int'l*, pg. 3932
JESSOP & COMPANY LTD.—See Ruia Group; *Int'l*, pg. 6426
THE JESSOP GROUP LIMITED—See Jessops plc; *Int'l*, pg. 3932
JESSOPS PLC; *Int'l*, pg. 3932
JESS SMITH & SONS COTTON; *U.S. Private*, pg. 2203
JESSUP AUTO PLAZA; *U.S. Private*, pg. 2203
JESSUP MANUFACTURING COMPANY, INC.; *U.S. Private*, pg. 2203
JESSY VENTURES CORP.; *Int'l*, pg. 3933
J. ESTINA CO., LTD.; *Int'l*, pg. 3855
J.E. STORK VENTILATOREN B.V.—See Zehnder Group AG; *Int'l*, pg. 8630
JESUP FURNITURE OUTLET INC.; *U.S. Private*, pg. 2203
JET2 PLC; *Int'l*, pg. 3933
JET ADVERTISING; *U.S. Private*, pg. 2203
JETA GARDENS (QLD) PTY. LTD.—See KPJ Healthcare Berhad; *Int'l*, pg. 4296
JET.AI INC.; *U.S. Public*, pg. 1189
JETAIRCENTER N.V.—See TUI AG; *Int'l*, pg. 7965
JETAIR N.V.—See TUI AG; *Int'l*, pg. 7965
JET AIR (SINGAPORE) PRIVATE LIMITED—See China Best Group Holding Limited; *Int'l*, pg. 1486
JETAIR TRAVEL DISTRIBUTION N.V.—See TUI AG; *Int'l*, pg. 7965
JET AIRWAYS (INDIA) LTD.; *Int'l*, pg. 3933
JET ALU MAROC SA; *Int'l*, pg. 3933
JET AVIATION AG—See General Dynamics Corporation; *U.S. Public*, pg. 916
JET AVIATION AUSTRALIA PTY LTD—See General Dynamics Corporation; *U.S. Public*, pg. 916
JET AVIATION BUSINESS JETS DEUTSCHLAND GMBH—See General Dynamics Corporation; *U.S. Public*, pg. 916
JET AVIATION GROUP—See General Dynamics Corporation; *U.S. Public*, pg. 913
JET AVIATION HOLDING GMBH—See General Dynamics Corporation; *U.S. Public*, pg. 916
JET AVIATION HOUSTON, INC.—See General Dynamics Corporation; *U.S. Public*, pg. 916
JET AVIATION MANAGEMENT—See General Dynamics Corporation; *U.S. Public*, pg. 913
JET AVIATION SERVICES GMBH—See General Dynamics Corporation; *U.S. Public*, pg. 916
JET AVIATION ST. LOUIS, INC.—See General Dynamics Corporation; *U.S. Public*, pg. 913
JET AVION CORPORATION—See HEICO Corporation; *U.S. Public*, pg. 1019
JETAVIVA; *U.S. Private*, pg. 2204

JETBEST CORP.; *Int'l*, pg. 3933
JETBLACK CORP.; *U.S. Public*, pg. 1189
JETBLUE AIRWAYS CORPORATION; *U.S. Public*, pg. 1189
JETBOIL, INC.—See Johnson Outdoors Inc.; *U.S. Public*, pg. 1200
JET BOX CO., INC.; *U.S. Private*, pg. 2203
JET BRAKEL AERO GMBH—See H2 Equity Partners B.V.; *Int'l*, pg. 3199
JETCAM INTERNATIONAL LTD.; *Int'l*, pg. 3933
JET CAPITAL TECHNOLOGY (SZ) LIMITED—See V-TAC Technology Co., Ltd.; *Int'l*, pg. 8105
JET CAPTIAL TECHNOLOGY (SZ) LIMITED—See V-TAC Technology Co., Ltd.; *Int'l*, pg. 8105
JETCENTERS, INC.—See Cordillera Corporation; *U.S. Private*, pg. 1047
JET CHEF—See Air France-KLM S.A.; *Int'l*, pg. 237
JET CITY ELECTRONICS INC.—See Renesas Electronics Corporation; *Int'l*, pg. 6276
JETCO DELIVERY, INC.—See GTI Transport Solutions, Inc.; *Int'l*, pg. 3151
J.E.T.CO., LTD.; *Int'l*, pg. 3858
JET.COM, INC.—See Walmart Inc.; *U.S. Public*, pg. 2325
JETCON CORPORATION LIMITED; *Int'l*, pg. 3933
JETCONNECT LIMITED—See Qantas Airways Limited; *Int'l*, pg. 6132
JETCORP TECHNICAL SERVICES INC.—See Directional Capital LLC; *U.S. Private*, pg. 1236
JETCROWN INDUSTRIAL (DONGGUAN) LIMITED—See Deswell Industries, Inc.; *Int'l*, pg. 2047
JETCROWN INDUSTRIAL (MACAO COMMERCIAL OFFSHORE) LIMITED—See Deswell Industries, Inc.; *Int'l*, pg. 2047
JET DISPATCH LIMITED—See China Best Group Holding Limited; *Int'l*, pg. 1486
JET EAST CORPORATE AVIATION, LLC—See The Sterling Group, L.P.; *U.S. Private*, pg. 4123
JETEC ELECTRONICS CO., LTD.; *Int'l*, pg. 3933
JETEC INGENIERIE SA—See VINCI S.A.; *Int'l*, pg. 8215
JET EDGE INTERNATIONAL LLC; *U.S. Private*, pg. 2203
J.E. TELFORD LIMITED—See Grafton Group plc; *Int'l*, pg. 3051
JETEMA CO., LTD.; *Int'l*, pg. 3933
JET ENERGY TRADING GMBH—See Phillips 66 Company; *U.S. Public*, pg. 1688
JET ENGINE LEASING PTY LTD—See Alliance Airlines; *Int'l*, pg. 338
JETER SYSTEMS—See H.S. Morgan Limited Partnership; *U.S. Private*, pg. 1835
JET EXPRESS INC.; *U.S. Private*, pg. 2203
JET FOOD STORES OF GEORGIA INC; *U.S. Private*, pg. 2204
JET FREIGHT LOGISTICS LIMITED; *Int'l*, pg. 3933
JET GAS CORPORATION; *U.S. Private*, pg. 2204
JET HOMELOANS, LLC—See Hilltop Holdings Inc.; *U.S. Public*, pg. 1039
JET INC.; *U.S. Private*, pg. 2204
JET INFRAVENTURE LTD; *Int'l*, pg. 3933
JET INTERNATIONAL CO., LLC; *U.S. Private*, pg. 2204
JET INTERNATIONAL TRAVEL CO., LTD.; *Int'l*, pg. 3933
JETION SOLAR HOLDINGS LIMITED - NANTONG FACTORY—See Jetion Solar Holdings Limited; *Int'l*, pg. 3933
JETION SOLAR HOLDINGS LIMITED; *Int'l*, pg. 3933
JETIT CORPORATION—See Azion Corp.; *Int'l*, pg. 780
JETIX EUROPE; *Int'l*, pg. 3933
JETKING INFOTRAIN LTD.; *Int'l*, pg. 3933
JET KNITWEARS LTD.; *Int'l*, pg. 3933
JETLINE ENGINEERING—See Illinois Tool Works Inc.; *U.S. Public*, pg. 1108
JET-LINE PRODUCTS INC.—See Pool Corporation; *U.S. Public*, pg. 1701
JET LINE PRODUCTS LONG ISLAND—See Pool Corporation; *U.S. Public*, pg. 1701
JET LINE PRODUCTS OF SOUTH JERSEY, LLC—See Pool Corporation; *U.S. Public*, pg. 1701
JET LINE PRODUCTS TEXAS, LLC—See Pool Corporation; *U.S. Public*, pg. 1701
JET-LINK AG—See ATON GmbH; *Int'l*, pg. 688
JET-LUBE OF CANADA LTD.—See CSW Industrials, Inc.; *U.S. Public*, pg. 601
JETLY S.A.—See Thermador Groupe; *Int'l*, pg. 7707
JET MACHINE & MANUFACTURING—See Wulco Inc.; *U.S. Private*, pg. 4575
JETMALL SPICES & MASALA LIMITED; *Int'l*, pg. 3933
JET MARKETING AGENCY LLC—See PopReach Corporation; *Int'l*, pg. 5921
JETMASTER (PTY) LTD—See ARGENT INDUSTRIAL LIMITED; *Int'l*, pg. 688
JET MULTIMEDIA TUNISIE SA—See Digital Virgo Group SAS; *Int'l*, pg. 2123
JET OPTOELECTRONICS CO., LTD.—See Jean Co., Ltd.; *Int'l*, pg. 3926
JETPAK BELGIUM B.V.—See Jetpak Top Holding AB; *Int'l*, pg. 3933
JETPAK GOTEBORG AB—See Jetpak Top Holding AB; *Int'l*, pg. 3933
JETPAK GROUP AB—See Jetpak Top Holding AB; *Int'l*, pg. 3933

JETPAK HANDLING A/S—See Jetpak Top Holding AB; *Int'l*, pg. 3933
JETPAK HELSINKI OY—See Jetpak Top Holding AB; *Int'l*, pg. 3933
JETPAK MALMO AB—See Jetpak Top Holding AB; *Int'l*, pg. 3933
JETPAK OSLO AS—See Jetpak Top Holding AB; *Int'l*, pg. 3934
JETPAK STOCKHOLM AB—See Jetpak Top Holding AB; *Int'l*, pg. 3934
JETPAK TOP HOLDING AB; *Int'l*, pg. 3934
JETPAY CORPORATION—See NCR Voyix Corporation.; *U.S. Public*, pg. 1502
JETPAY ISO SERVICES, LLC—See NCR Voyix Corporation.; *U.S. Public*, pg. 1502
JET PAY, LLC—See NCR Voyix Corporation.; *U.S. Public*, pg. 1502
JETPAY MERCHANT SERVICES, LLC—See NCR Voyix Corporation.; *U.S. Public*, pg. 1502
JET-PEP INC.; *U.S. Private*, pg. 2204
JET POLYMER RECYCLING, INC.—See Advanced Drainage Systems, Inc.; *U.S. Public*, pg. 46
JETPOOL, LLC; *U.S. Private*, pg. 2204
JET PREP. LTD.—See STERIS plc; *Int'l*, pg. 7209
JET PROPULSION LABORATORY—See California Institute of Technology; *U.S. Private*, pg. 719
JET RESOURCE, INC.—See Chemed Corporation; *U.S. Public*, pg. 484
JETRO CASH & CARRY ENTERPRISES, LLC; *U.S. Private*, pg. 2204
JETRO CASH & CARRY—See Jetro Cash & Carry Enterprises, LLC; *U.S. Private*, pg. 2204
JETRO CASH & CARRY—See Jetro Cash & Carry Enterprises, LLC; *U.S. Private*, pg. 2204
JETRO CASH & CARRY—See Jetro Cash & Carry Enterprises, LLC; *U.S. Private*, pg. 2204
JETRO CASH & CARRY—See Jetro Cash & Carry Enterprises, LLC; *U.S. Private*, pg. 2204
JETRO, NEW YORK—See Japan External Trade Organization; *Int'l*, pg. 3888
JETSEAL, INC.—See HEICO Corporation; *U.S. Public*, pg. 1021
JETSELECT, LLC—See Jet Edge International LLC; *U.S. Private*, pg. 2203
J.E.T. SEMI-CON. INTERNATIONAL TAIWAN INC.—See ZEUS CO., Ltd; *Int'l*, pg. 8640
JET SERVICES INC.—See Odyssey Investment Partners, LLC; *U.S. Private*, pg. 2995
JETS MRO, LLC; *U.S. Private*, pg. 2204
JETSON TV & APPLIANCE CENTERS; *U.S. Private*, pg. 2204
JET SPECIALTY, INC.; *U.S. Private*, pg. 2204
JETS SWIMWEAR PTY. LTD.—See Queens Lane Capital Pty Ltd; *Int'l*, pg. 6159
JETSTAR AIRWAYS PTY. LTD.—See Qantas Airways Limited; *Int'l*, pg. 6132
JETSTAR COMPANY LIMITED—See Jacobson Pharma Corporation Limited; *Int'l*, pg. 3866
JET STAR INC.; *U.S. Private*, pg. 2204
JET STREAM INTERNATIONAL; *U.S. Private*, pg. 2204
JETSTREAM OF HOUSTON, INC.—See Federal Signal Corporation; *U.S. Public*, pg. 826
JETSTREAM OF HOUSTON, LLP—See Federal Signal Corporation; *U.S. Public*, pg. 826
JETTA CORPORATION; *U.S. Private*, pg. 2204
JET TAGESLICHT & RWA GMBH—See H2 Equity Partners B.V.; *Int'l*, pg. 3199
JETTAINER GMBH—See Deutsche Lufthansa AG; *Int'l*, pg. 2068
JET TANK SERVICE, LLC—See Quanta Services, Inc.; *U.S. Public*, pg. 1751
JET TANKSTELLEN AUSTRIA GMBH—See Phillips 66 Company; *U.S. Public*, pg. 1688
JET TANKSTELLEN DEUTSCHLAND GMBH—See Phillips 66 Company; *U.S. Public*, pg. 1688
JETTA PRODUCTION COMPANY, INC.; *U.S. Private*, pg. 2204
JETTER AG—See Bucher Industries AG; *Int'l*, pg. 1207
JETTER AUTOMATION HUNGARY KFT.—See Bucher Industries AG; *Int'l*, pg. 1209
JETTER AUTOMATION TECHNOLOGY (SHANGHAI) CO., LTD.—See Bucher Industries AG; *Int'l*, pg. 1209
JETTER DISTRIBUTION LTD.—See Bucher Industries AG; *Int'l*, pg. 1207
JETTER OY—See Bucher Industries AG; *Int'l*, pg. 1207
JETTER TECHNOLOGIES PTE LTD.—See Bucher Industries AG; *Int'l*, pg. 1207
JETT FOR TOURISM & TRAVEL COMPANY—See Jordan Express Tourist Transportation Company; *Int'l*, pg. 3998
JETTICKET SOFTWARE GMBH—See CTS Eventim AG & Co. KGAA; *Int'l*, pg. 1873
JETT MECHANICAL INC.; *U.S. Private*, pg. 2204
JETTON ELECTRIC INC.; *U.S. Private*, pg. 2204
JET TRADING CO., LTD.—See Ashimori Industry Co., Ltd.; *Int'l*, pg. 607
JETWAY INFORMATION CO., LTD.; *Int'l*, pg. 3934
JETWELL COMPUTER CO., LTD.; *Int'l*, pg. 3934
JETWING SYMPHONY PLC; *Int'l*, pg. 3934
JET YARD, LLC—See Air T, Inc.; *U.S. Public*, pg. 67
JET YARD SOLUTIONS, LLC—See Air T, Inc.; *U.S. Public*, pg. 67

JEUDAN A/S; *Int'l*, pg. 3934
JEUGIA CORPORATION; *Int'l*, pg. 3934
JEUMONT DRIVES SYSTEMS SAS—See Altawest Group; *Int'l*, pg. 388
JEUMONT ELECTRIC INDIA PRIVATE LIMITED—See Altawest Group; *Int'l*, pg. 388
JEUMONT ELECTRIC MAINTENANCE—See Altawest Group; *Int'l*, pg. 388
JEUMONT ELECTRIC MIDDLE EAST—See Altawest Group; *Int'l*, pg. 388
JEUMONT ELECTRIC—See Altawest Group; *Int'l*, pg. 388
JEUNE BEAUTY CORPORATION—See NOF Corporation; *Int'l*, pg. 5399
JEUNESSE GLOBAL LLC; *U.S. Private*, pg. 2204
JEUNIQUE INTERNATIONAL INC.; *U.S. Private*, pg. 2204
JEUP INC.—See RH; *U.S. Public*, pg. 1796
JEVCO INSURANCE COMPANY—See Intact Financial Corporation; *Int'l*, pg. 3726
JEVEKA B.V.—See Bossard Holding AG; *Int'l*, pg. 1117
JEVI A/S—See NIBE Industrier AB; *Int'l*, pg. 5261
JEVIC NZ LIMITED—See OPTIMUS GROUP Co., Ltd.; *Int'l*, pg. 5605
JEVITH A/S—See SFS Group AG; *Int'l*, pg. 6739
JEVONS PROPERTIES, LLC—See MYND Property Management, Inc.; *U.S. Private*, pg. 2825
JEWELERS CREDIT CORP.—See Signet Jewelers Limited; *Int'l*, pg. 6911
JEWELER'S FINANCIAL SERVICE, INC.—See Signet Jewelers Limited; *Int'l*, pg. 6911
JEWELERS INC.; *U.S. Private*, pg. 2204
JEWELERS INTERNATIONAL SHOWCASE—See RELX plc; *Int'l*, pg. 6266
JEWELERS MUTUAL INSURANCE COMPANY; *U.S. Private*, pg. 2204
THE JEWELERS; *U.S. Private*, pg. 4059
JEWEL FOOD STORES, INC.—See Cerberus Capital Management, L.P.; *U.S. Private*, pg. 836
JEWELL ATTACHMENTS, LLC—See Stanley Black & Decker, Inc.; *U.S. Public*, pg. 1933
JEWELL COAL & COKE COMPANY, INC.—See SunCoke Energy, Inc.; *U.S. Public*, pg. 1964
THE JEWELLERY CHANNEL LIMITED—See Vaibhav Global Limited; *Int'l*, pg. 8108
JEWELLERY HOSPITAL COMPANY LIMITED—See King Fook Holdings Limited; *Int'l*, pg. 4168
JEWELL GRAIN COMPANY; *U.S. Private*, pg. 2205
JEWELL INSTRUMENTS, LLC; *U.S. Private*, pg. 2205
JEWELL INSURANCE ASSOCIATES, INC.—See TrueNorth Companies L.C.; *U.S. Private*, pg. 4249
JEWELL RESOURCES CORPORATION—See SunCoke Energy, Inc.; *U.S. Public*, pg. 1963
JEWELL SMOKELESS COAL CORPORATION—See SunCoke Energy, Inc.; *U.S. Public*, pg. 1964
JEWEL-OSCO—See Cerberus Capital Management, L.P.; *U.S. Private*, pg. 836
JEWEL RE-INSURANCE LTD.—See Signet Jewelers Limited; *Int'l*, pg. 6911
JEWELRY ASSET MANAGERS INC.—See Bookoff Group Holdings Ltd.; *Int'l*, pg. 1110
JEWELRY REPAIR ENTERPRISES, INC.; *U.S. Private*, pg. 2205
JEWELRY TO YOUR DOORSTEP; *U.S. Private*, pg. 2205
JEWETT-CAMERON LUMBER CORPORATION—See Jewett-Cameron Trading Company Ltd.; *U.S. Public*, pg. 1190
JEWETT-CAMERON SEED COMPANY—See Jewett-Cameron Trading Company Ltd.; *U.S. Public*, pg. 1190
JEWETT-CAMERON TRADING COMPANY LTD.; *U.S. Public*, pg. 1189
JEWETT CITY SAVINGS BANK; *U.S. Private*, pg. 2205
JEWETT ORTHOPAEDIC CLINIC, P.A.; *U.S. Private*, pg. 2205
JEWISH CHILD & FAMILY SERVICES; *U.S. Private*, pg. 2205
JEWISHCOLORADO; *U.S. Private*, pg. 2206
JEWISH COMMUNITY CENTER OF SAN FRANCISCO; *U.S. Private*, pg. 2205
JEWISH COMMUNITY CENTERS OF GREATER BOSTON, INC.; *U.S. Private*, pg. 2205
JEWISH COMMUNITY FOUNDATION OF GREATER KANSAS CITY; *U.S. Private*, pg. 2205
JEWISH COMMUNITY FOUNDATION OF SAN DIEGO; *U.S. Private*, pg. 2205
JEWISH COMMUNITY SERVICES; *U.S. Private*, pg. 2205
JEWISH COUNCIL FOR YOUTH SERVICES; *U.S. Private*, pg. 2205
JEWISH FAMILY AND CHILDREN'S SERVICES OF SAN FRANCISCO, THE PENINSULA, MARIN AND SONOMA COUNTIES; *U.S. Private*, pg. 2205
JEWISH FAMILY & CHILDREN'S SERVICE; *U.S. Private*, pg. 2205
JEWISH FAMILY SERVICE ASSOCIATION OF CLEVELAND; *U.S. Private*, pg. 2205
JEWISH FAMILY SERVICE OF LOS ANGELES; *U.S. Private*, pg. 2205
THE JEWISH FEDERATIONS OF NORTH AMERICA, INC.; *U.S. Private*, pg. 4059
JEWISH FOUNDATION FOR GROUP HOMES; *U.S. Private*, pg. 2206

JEWISH FUNDERS NETWORK; *U.S. Private*, pg. 2206
JEWISH HEALTHCARE CENTER; *U.S. Private*, pg. 2206
JEWISH HEALTHCARE FOUNDATION; *U.S. Private*, pg. 2206
JEWISH HOME LIFECARE; *U.S. Private*, pg. 2206
JEWISH HOME OF CINCINNATI; *U.S. Private*, pg. 2206
THE JEWISH HOME OF EASTERN PENNSYLVANIA; *U.S. Private*, pg. 4059
JEWISH MUSEUM; *U.S. Private*, pg. 2206
JEWISH RENAISSANCE MEDICAL CENTER INC.; *U.S. Private*, pg. 2206
JEWISH SENIOR SERVICES OF FAIRFIELD COUNTY INC.; *U.S. Private*, pg. 2206
JEWISH VOCATIONAL SERVICE AND EMPLOYMENT CENTER; *U.S. Private*, pg. 2206
JEWSON LTD.—See Compagnie de Saint-Gobain SA; *Int'l*, pg. 1733
JEXEL NUCLEAR COMPANY—See Exelon Corporation; *U.S. Public*, pg. 807
JEYCO (1992) PTY. LTD.—See Enerpac Tool Group Corp.; *U.S. Public*, pg. 766
THE JEYPORE SUGAR COMPANY LIMITED; *Int'l*, pg. 7659
JEZOWSKI & MARKEL CONTRACTORS INC.; *U.S. Private*, pg. 2206
JF AGRI LTD.—See Mitsubishi Corporation; *Int'l*, pg. 4939
J.F AHERN CO. - INDUSTRIAL & PROCESS PIPING DIVISION—See J.F. Ahern Co.; *U.S. Private*, pg. 2162
J.F. AHERN CO.; *U.S. Private*, pg. 2162
J.F. ALLEN COMPANY; *U.S. Private*, pg. 2162
JF APEX NOMINEES (ASING) SDN. BHD.—See Apex Equity Holdings Berhad; *Int'l*, pg. 509
JF APEX SECURITIES BERHAD—See Apex Equity Holdings Berhad; *Int'l*, pg. 509
J FARM CORPORATION—See JFE Holdings, Inc.; *Int'l*, pg. 3935
J-FAST CO., LTD.—See Taisei Corporation; *Int'l*, pg. 7415
J.F. BRENNAN CO., INC.; *U.S. Private*, pg. 2162
JFC AUSTRIA GMBH—See Kikkoman Corporation; *Int'l*, pg. 4160
JFC DE MEXICO S.A. DE C.V.—See Kikkoman Corporation; *Int'l*, pg. 4160
JFC DEUTSCHLAND GMBH—See Kikkoman Corporation; *Int'l*, pg. 4160
JFC FRANCE S.A.R.L.—See Kikkoman Corporation; *Int'l*, pg. 4160
JF CHICKEN CO., LTD.—See Mitsubishi Corporation; *Int'l*, pg. 4939
JFC HONG KONG LIMITED—See Kikkoman Corporation; *Int'l*, pg. 4160
JFC INTERNATIONAL (CANADA) INC.—See Kikkoman Corporation; *Int'l*, pg. 4160
JFC INTERNATIONAL (EUROPE) GMBH—See Kikkoman Corporation; *Int'l*, pg. 4160
JFC INTERNATIONAL INC.—See Kikkoman Corporation; *Int'l*, pg. 4160
JFC JAPAN INC.—See Kikkoman Corporation; *Int'l*, pg. 4160
JFC LLC—See Maschhoff Family Foods, LLC; *U.S. Private*, pg. 2601
JFC NEW ZEALAND LIMITED—See Kikkoman Corporation; *Int'l*, pg. 4160
JF CORP.—See MidOcean Partners, LLP; *U.S. Private*, pg. 2716
JFC RESTAURANT GMBH—See Kikkoman Corporation; *Int'l*, pg. 4160
JFC SINGAPORE PTE. LTD.—See Kikkoman Corporation; *Int'l*, pg. 4160
JFC (UK) LIMITED—See Kikkoman Corporation; *Int'l*, pg. 4160
JFD ADVERTISING & PUBLIC RELATIONS, INC.; *U.S. Private*, pg. 2206
JFD AUSTRALIA PTY. LTD.—See James Fisher & Sons Public Limited Company; *Int'l*, pg. 3876
JFD ORTEGA B.V.—See James Fisher & Sons Public Limited Company; *Int'l*, pg. 3876
JFD SINGAPORE PTE. LTD.—See James Fisher & Sons Public Limited Company; *Int'l*, pg. 3876
JFD SWEDEN AB—See James Fisher & Sons Public Limited Company; *Int'l*, pg. 3876
JFE ADVANCED LIGHT CORPORATION—See JFE Holdings, Inc.; *Int'l*, pg. 3934
JFE ADVANTECH CO., LTD.—See JFE Holdings, Inc.; *Int'l*, pg. 3934
JFE BARS & SHAPES CORP.—See JFE Holdings, Inc.; *Int'l*, pg. 3934
JFE BUSINESS SUPPORT YOKOHAMA CORPORATION—See JFE Holdings, Inc.; *Int'l*, pg. 3934
JFE CHEMICAL CORPORATION - CHIBA PLANT—See JFE Holdings, Inc.; *Int'l*, pg. 3934
JFE CHEMICAL CORPORATION - KASAOKA PLANT—See JFE Holdings, Inc.; *Int'l*, pg. 3934
JFE CHEMICAL CORPORATION - KEIHIN PLANT—See JFE Holdings, Inc.; *Int'l*, pg. 3934
JFE CHEMICAL CORPORATION - KURASHIKI PLANT—See JFE Holdings, Inc.; *Int'l*, pg. 3934
JFE CHEMICAL CORPORATION—See JFE Holdings, Inc.; *Int'l*, pg. 3934

JFE CIVIL ENGINEERING & CONSTRUCTION CORP.—See JFE Holdings, Inc.; *Int'l*, pg. 3934
JFE CONSULTING (SHANGHAI) CO., LTD.—See JFE Holdings, Inc.; *Int'l*, pg. 3938
JFE CONTAINER CO., LTD.—See JFE Holdings, Inc.; *Int'l*, pg. 3934
JFE ELECTRICAL & CONTROL SYSTEMS, INC.—See JFE Holdings, Inc.; *Int'l*, pg. 3934
JFE ELECTRICAL STEEL CO., LTD.—See JFE Holdings, Inc.; *Int'l*, pg. 3934
J-FEEL INC.—See Amuse Inc.; *Int'l*, pg. 442
JFE ENGINEERING CONSULTING (SHANGHAI) CO., LTD.—See JFE Holdings, Inc.; *Int'l*, pg. 3935
JFE ENGINEERING CORPORATION—See JFE Holdings, Inc.; *Int'l*, pg. 3934
JFE ENGINEERING CORPORATION-YANGON BRANCH—See JFE Holdings, Inc.; *Int'l*, pg. 3935
JFE ENGINEERING (M) SDN. BHD.—See JFE Holdings, Inc.; *Int'l*, pg. 3935
JFE ENVIRONMENTAL SERVICE CORPORATION—See JFE Holdings, Inc.; *Int'l*, pg. 3935
JFE GALVANIZING & COATING CO., LTD.—See JFE Holdings, Inc.; *Int'l*, pg. 3935
JFE HOLDINGS, INC.; *Int'l*, pg. 3934
JFE KANKYO CORPORATION—See JFE Holdings, Inc.; *Int'l*, pg. 3935
JFE KOZAI CORP.—See JFE Holdings, Inc.; *Int'l*, pg. 3935
JFE LEASE SYSTEM CORP.—See JFE Holdings, Inc.; *Int'l*, pg. 3935
JFE LIFE CORPORATION—See JFE Holdings, Inc.; *Int'l*, pg. 3935
JFE LOGISTICS CORP.—See JFE Holdings, Inc.; *Int'l*, pg. 3938
JFE MATERIAL CO., LTD.—See JFE Holdings, Inc.; *Int'l*, pg. 3935
JFE MECHANICAL CO., LTD.—See JFE Holdings, Inc.; *Int'l*, pg. 3935
JFE METAL PRODUCTS & ENGINEERING INC.—See JFE Holdings, Inc.; *Int'l*, pg. 3935
JFE MIE TECH. SERVICE CORPORATION—See JFE Holdings, Inc.; *Int'l*, pg. 3936
JFE MINERAL COMPANY, LTD. - ADVANCED MATERIALS WORKS—See JFE Holdings, Inc.; *Int'l*, pg. 3935
JFE MINERAL COMPANY, LTD. - CHIBA PLANT—See JFE Holdings, Inc.; *Int'l*, pg. 0005
JFE MINERAL COMPANY, LTD. - FUKUYAMA PLANT—See JFE Holdings, Inc.; *Int'l*, pg. 3935
JFE MINERAL COMPANY, LTD. - IIDE MINING WORKS—See JFE Holdings, Inc.; *Int'l*, pg. 3935
JFE MINERAL COMPANY, LTD. - KEIHIN PLANT—See JFE Holdings, Inc.; *Int'l*, pg. 3935
JFE MINERAL COMPANY, LTD. - KURASHIKI PLANT—See JFE Holdings, Inc.; *Int'l*, pg. 3935
JFE MINERAL COMPANY, LTD. - MUSASHINO MINING WORKS—See JFE Holdings, Inc.; *Int'l*, pg. 3936
JFE MINERAL COMPANY, LTD.—See JFE Holdings, Inc.; *Int'l*, pg. 3935
JFE MINERAL COMPANY, LTD. - TOCHIGI MINING WORKS—See JFE Holdings, Inc.; *Int'l*, pg. 3935
JFE MINERAL COMPANY, LTD. - TSUKUMI PLANT—See JFE Holdings, Inc.; *Int'l*, pg. 3936
JFE MINERAL COMPANY, LTD. - YOSII MINING WORKS—See JFE Holdings, Inc.; *Int'l*, pg. 3936
J&F ENTERPRISES INC.; *U.S. Private*, pg. 2154
JFE PIPE FITTING MFG. CO., LTD.—See JFE Holdings, Inc.; *Int'l*, pg. 3936
JFE PIPELINE ENGINEERING CORPORATION—See JFE Holdings, Inc.; *Int'l*, pg. 3935
JFE PLANT ENGINEERING CO., LTD.—See JFE Holdings, Inc.; *Int'l*, pg. 3938
JFE PLASTIC RESOURCE CORPORATION—See JFE Holdings, Inc.; *Int'l*, pg. 3936
JFE PRECISION CO., LTD.—See JFE Holdings, Inc.; *Int'l*, pg. 3936
JFE SEKKEI LTD.—See JFE Holdings, Inc.; *Int'l*, pg. 3936
JFE SHOJI AMERICA, LLC—See JFE Holdings, Inc.; *Int'l*, pg. 3936
JFE SHOJI COIL CENTER CORPORATION—See JFE Holdings, Inc.; *Int'l*, pg. 3936
JFE SHOJI CORMEC CO., LTD.—See JFE Holdings, Inc.; *Int'l*, pg. 3936
JFE SHOJI ELECTRICAL STEEL CO., LTD.—See JFE Holdings, Inc.; *Int'l*, pg. 3936
JFE SHOJI ELECTRONICS CORPORATION—See JFE Holdings, Inc.; *Int'l*, pg. 3936
JFE SHOJI JUTAKU SHIZAI CORPORATION—See JFE Holdings, Inc.; *Int'l*, pg. 3936
JFE SHOJI KOHNAN STEEL CENTER CO., LTD.—See JFE Holdings, Inc.; *Int'l*, pg. 3936
JFE SHOJI MACHINERY & MATERIALS CORPORATION—See JFE Holdings, Inc.; *Int'l*, pg. 3936
JFE SHOJI MATECH INC.—See JFE Holdings, Inc.; *Int'l*, pg. 3936
JFE SHOJI SERVICE CORPORATION—See JFE Holdings, Inc.; *Int'l*, pg. 3936
JFE SHOJI STEEL CONSTRUCTION MATERIALS CORPORATION—See JFE Holdings, Inc.; *Int'l*, pg. 3936

JFE SHOJI STEEL DE MEXICO S.A. DE C.V.—See JFE Holdings, Inc.; *Int'l*, pg. 3936
JFE SHOJI STEEL HAI PHONG CO., LTD.—See JFE Holdings, Inc.; *Int'l*, pg. 3936
JFE SHOJI STEEL INDIA PRIVATE LIMITED—See JFE Holdings, Inc.; *Int'l*, pg. 3936
JFE SHOJI STEEL MALAYSIA SDN. BHD.—See JFE Holdings, Inc.; *Int'l*, pg. 3936
JFE SHOJI STEEL PHILIPPINES, INC.—See JFE Holdings, Inc.; *Int'l*, pg. 3936
JFE SHOJI STEEL SERVICE CENTER BAJIO, S.A.P.I. DE C.V.—See JFE Holdings, Inc.; *Int'l*, pg. 3936
JFE SHOJI STEEL VIETNAM CO., LTD.—See JFE Holdings, Inc.; *Int'l*, pg. 3936
JFE SHOJI TERRE ONE CORPORATION—See JFE Holdings, Inc.; *Int'l*, pg. 3936
JFE SHOJI TINPLATE CENTER CORPORATION—See JFE Holdings, Inc.; *Int'l*, pg. 3936
JFE SHOJI TRADE AUSTRALIA PTY. LTD.—See JFE Holdings, Inc.; *Int'l*, pg. 3936
JFE SHOJI TRADE CORPORATION—See JFE Holdings, Inc.; *Int'l*, pg. 3936
JFE SHOJI TRADE CORP.—See JFE Holdings, Inc.; *Int'l*, pg. 3936
JFE SHOJI TRADE DO BRASIL LTDA.—See JFE Holdings, Inc.; *Int'l*, pg. 3936
JFE SHOJI TRADE KOREA LTD.—See JFE Holdings, Inc.; *Int'l*, pg. 3936
JFE SHOJI TRADE PHILIPPINES, INC.—See JFE Holdings, Inc.; *Int'l*, pg. 3936
JFE SHOJI TRADE THAILAND, LTD.—See JFE Holdings, Inc.; *Int'l*, pg. 3937
JFE SHOJI ZOSEN KAKO CORPORATION—See JFE Holdings, Inc.; *Int'l*, pg. 3937
JFE STEEL AMERICA, INC.—See JFE Holdings, Inc.; *Int'l*, pg. 3938
JFE STEEL AMERICA, INC.—See JFE Holdings, Inc.; *Int'l*, pg. 3938
JFE STEEL CORPORATION—See JFE Holdings, Inc.; *Int'l*, pg. 3937
JFE STEEL CORPORATION—See JFE Holdings, Inc.; *Int'l*, pg. 3938
JFE STEEL CORPORATION—See JFE Holdings, Inc.; *Int'l*, pg. 3938
JFE STEEL CORPORATION—See JFE Holdings, Inc.; *Int'l*, pg. 3938
JFE STEEL DO BRASIL LTDA—See JFE Holdings, Inc.; *Int'l*, pg. 3938
JFE STEEL GALVANIZING (THAILAND) LTD.—See JFE Holdings, Inc.; *Int'l*, pg. 3938
JFE STEEL PIPE CO., LTD.—See JFE Holdings, Inc.; *Int'l*, pg. 3938
JFE SYSTEMS, INC.—See JFE Holdings, Inc.; *Int'l*, pg. 3938
JFE TECHNO-DESIGN CORPORATION—See JFE Holdings, Inc.; *Int'l*, pg. 3938
JFE TECHNO MANILA, INC.—See JFE Holdings, Inc.; *Int'l*, pg. 3935
JFE TECHNOPHENIX CO., LTD.—See JFE Holdings, Inc.; *Int'l*, pg. 3938
JFE TECHNO-RESEARCH CORP—See JFE Holdings, Inc.; *Int'l*, pg. 3938
JFE TECHNOS CORPORATION—See JFE Holdings, Inc.; *Int'l*, pg. 3938
JFE TECHNO-WIRE CORP.—See JFE Holdings, Inc.; *Int'l*, pg. 3938
JFE TRADE HONG KONG LTD.—See JFE Holdings, Inc.; *Int'l*, pg. 3937
JFE TSU TECHNICAL WORKS CO., LTD.—See JFE Holdings, Inc.; *Int'l*, pg. 3938
JFE TUBIC CORP.—See JFE Holdings, Inc.; *Int'l*, pg. 3938
JFE URBAN RECYCLE CORP.—See JFE Holdings, Inc.; *Int'l*, pg. 3938
JFE WELDED PIPE MANUFACTURING CO., LTD.—See JFE Holdings, Inc.; *Int'l*, pg. 3938
JFE WEST JAPAN GS CO., LTD.—See JFE Holdings, Inc.; *Int'l*, pg. 3938
JFE WEST TECHNOLOGY CO., LTD.—See JFE Holdings, Inc.; *Int'l*, pg. 3938
JFE WING CORP.—See JFE Holdings, Inc.; *Int'l*, pg. 3938
JF FABER LIMITED—See Rcapital Partners LLP; *Int'l*, pg. 6227
JF FOODS CO., LTD.—See Mitsubishi Corporation; *Int'l*, pg. 4939
J F GOOD COMPANY INC—See Famous Enterprises Inc.; *U.S. Private*, pg. 1472
JFH CORP.—See Richelieu Hardware Ltd.; *Int'l*, pg. 6331
J.F. HILLEBRAND ARGENTINA SA—See Deutsche Post AG; *Int'l*, pg. 2081
J.F. HILLEBRAND BENELUX B.V.—See Deutsche Post AG; *Int'l*, pg. 2081
J.F. HILLEBRAND BRASIL LTDA—See Deutsche Post AG; *Int'l*, pg. 2081
JF HILLEBRAND CANADA INC.—See Deutsche Post AG; *Int'l*, pg. 2081

JF HILLEBRAND CENTRAL EUROPE GMBH—See Deutsche Post AG; *Int'l*, pg. 2081
JF HILLEBRAND CHILE LTDA—See Deutsche Post AG; *Int'l*, pg. 2081
JF HILLEBRAND CHINA CO. LTD—See Deutsche Post AG; *Int'l*, pg. 2081
JF HILLEBRAND DEUTSCHLAND GMBH—See Deutsche Post AG; *Int'l*, pg. 2081
JF HILLEBRAND FINLAND OY—See Deutsche Post AG; *Int'l*, pg. 2081
JF HILLEBRAND FRANCE SAS—See Deutsche Post AG; *Int'l*, pg. 2081
JF HILLEBRAND GROUP AG—See Deutsche Post AG; *Int'l*, pg. 2081
JF HILLEBRAND GROUP MANAGEMENT SERVICES—See Deutsche Post AG; *Int'l*, pg. 2081
JF HILLEBRAND IRELAND LTD—See Deutsche Post AG; *Int'l*, pg. 2081
JF HILLEBRAND ITALIA SPA—See Deutsche Post AG; *Int'l*, pg. 2081
JF HILLEBRAND JAPAN KK—See Deutsche Post AG; *Int'l*, pg. 2081
JF HILLEBRAND KOREA LTD.—See Deutsche Post AG; *Int'l*, pg. 2081
JF HILLEBRAND LIMITED—See Deutsche Post AG; *Int'l*, pg. 2081
JF HILLEBRAND MALAYSIA SDN BHD—See Deutsche Post AG; *Int'l*, pg. 2081
JF HILLEBRAND MEXICO SA DE CV—See Deutsche Post AG; *Int'l*, pg. 2081
JF HILLEBRAND MIDDLE EAST LLC—See Deutsche Post AG; *Int'l*, pg. 2081
JF HILLEBRAND NETHERLANDS—See Deutsche Post AG; *Int'l*, pg. 2081
JF HILLEBRAND PHILIPPINES INC—See Deutsche Post AG; *Int'l*, pg. 2081
JF HILLEBRAND PORTUGAL-TRANSITARIOS LDA—See Deutsche Post AG; *Int'l*, pg. 2081
JF HILLEBRAND RUSSIA (OOO)—See Deutsche Post AG; *Int'l*, pg. 2081
JF HILLEBRAND SCANDINAVIA A/S—See Deutsche Post AG; *Int'l*, pg. 2081
J.F. HILLEBRAND SCOTLAND LIMITED—See Deutsche Post AG; *Int'l*, pg. 2081
JF HILLEBRAND SINGAPORE PTE LTD—See Deutsche Post AG; *Int'l*, pg. 2081
JF HILLEBRAND SOUTH AFRICA (PTY) LTD—See Deutsche Post AG; *Int'l*, pg. 2081
JF HILLEBRAND SPAIN SA—See Deutsche Post AG; *Int'l*, pg. 2081
J.F. HILLEBRAND SVERIGE AB—See Deutsche Post AG; *Int'l*, pg. 2081
JF HILLEBRAND SWEDEN AB—See Deutsche Post AG; *Int'l*, pg. 2081
JF HILLEBRAND (THAILAND) LIMITED—See Deutsche Post AG; *Int'l*, pg. 2081
JF HILLEBRAND UK LIMITED—See Deutsche Post AG; *Int'l*, pg. 2081
JF HILLEBRAND URUGUAY—See Deutsche Post AG; *Int'l*, pg. 2081
JF HILLEBRAND USA INC—See Deutsche Post AG; *Int'l*, pg. 2081
JF HILLEBRAND VIETNAM CO., LTD—See Deutsche Post AG; *Int'l*, pg. 2081
J-FIBER GMBH—See LEONI AG; *Int'l*, pg. 4464
J-FILM CORPORATION - NARITA PLANT #1—See Mitsubishi Chemical Group Corporation; *Int'l*, pg. 4931
J-FILM CORPORATION - NARITA PLANT #2—See Mitsubishi Chemical Group Corporation; *Int'l*, pg. 4931
J-FILM CORPORATION—See Mitsubishi Chemical Group Corporation; *Int'l*, pg. 4931
J-FILM LOGISTICS, INC.—See Mitsubishi Chemical Group Corporation; *Int'l*, pg. 4931
J-FILM PHILIPPINES, INC.—See Mitsubishi Chemical Group Corporation; *Int'l*, pg. 4931
J&F INVESTIMENTOS S.A.; *Int'l*, pg. 3853
J FITZGIBBONS LLC; *U.S. Private*, pg. 2153
J. F. JOHNSON, INC.; *U.S. Private*, pg. 2156
J.F. JOHNSON LUMBER COMPANY; *U.S. Private*, pg. 2162
J.F. KIELY CONSTRUCTION CO.; *U.S. Private*, pg. 2162
JFK MEDICAL CENTER—See HCA Healthcare, Inc.; *U.S. Public*, pg. 999
JFK MEMORIAL HOSPITAL, INC.—See Tenet Healthcare Corporation; *U.S. Public*, pg. 2003
JFK NORTH SURGICENTER, LLC—See HCA Healthcare, Inc.; *U.S. Public*, pg. 999
JFK RINGS GMBH—See Apollo Global Management, Inc.; *U.S. Public*, pg. 162
JFLA HOLDINGS INC.; *Int'l*, pg. 3939
J.F. LEHMAN & COMPANY, INC.; *U.S. Private*, pg. 2162
J. FLETCHER CREAMER & SON, INC.—See J. Fletcher Creamer & Son Inc.; *U.S. Private*, pg. 2156
J. FLETCHER CREAMER & SON, INC.—See J. Fletcher Creamer & Son Inc.; *U.S. Private*, pg. 2156
J. FLETCHER CREAMER & SON INC.; *U.S. Private*, pg. 2156
J. FLETCHER CREAMER & SON, INC.—See J. Fletcher Creamer & Son Inc.; *U.S. Private*, pg. 2156

J.F. LOMMA INC.   CORPORATE AFFILIATIONS

J.F. LOMMA INC.; *U.S. Private*, pg. 2164
JF MICROTECHNOLOGY SDN. BHD.—See JF Technology Berhad; *Int'l*, pg. 3934
J.F. MILLS/WORLDWIDE; *U.S. Private*, pg. 2164
J.F. MONTALVO CASH & CARRY INC.; *U.S. Private*, pg. 2164
J.F. MOORE LITHOGRAPHERS INC.; *Int'l*, pg. 3858
JFN HOLDINGS LIMITED—See Rcapital Partners LLP; *Int'l*, pg. 6227
JFN LIMITED—See Rcapital Partners LLP; *Int'l*, pg. 6227
J. FONS CO INC—See Priority Waste LLC; *U.S. Private*, pg. 3267
J FOONG TECHNOLOGIES SDN. BHD.—See JF Technology Berhad; *Int'l*, pg. 3934
JFP FINANCIAL SERVICES LIMITED—See Kingswood Holdings Ltd.; *Int'l*, pg. 4180
JFR CARD CO., LTD.—See J. Front Retailing Co., Ltd.; *Int'l*, pg. 3855
JFR CONSULTING CO. LTD.—See J. Front Retailing Co., Ltd.; *Int'l*, pg. 3855
JFR CREATE CO., LTD.—See J. Front Retailing Co., Ltd.; *Int'l*, pg. 3855
J FRIENDLY, INC.—See Konoike Transport Co., Ltd.; *Int'l*, pg. 4274
JFR INFORMATION CENTER CO., LTD.—See J. Front Retailing Co., Ltd.; *Int'l*, pg. 3855
JFR KODOMO MIRAI CO., LTD.—See J. Front Retailing Co., Ltd.; *Int'l*, pg. 3855
JFR OFFICE SUPPORT CO., LTD.—See J. Front Retailing Co., Ltd.; *Int'l*, pg. 3855
JFROG LTD.; *U.S. Public*, pg. 1190
J. FRONT DESIGN & CONSTRUCTION CO., LTD.—See J. Front Retailing Co., Ltd.; *Int'l*, pg. 3855
J. FRONT FOODS CO., LTD.—See J. Front Retailing Co., Ltd.; *Int'l*, pg. 3855
J. FRONT RETAILING CO., LTD.; *Int'l*, pg. 3855
JFR SERVICE CO. LTD.—See J. Front Retailing Co., Ltd.; *Int'l*, pg. 3855
J.F. SHEA CO., INC.; *U.S. Private*, pg. 2164
J.F. SHEA CONSTRUCTION, INC.—See J.F. Shea Co., Inc.; *U.S. Private*, pg. 2164
J.F. SHELTON CO., INC.—See Kelso & Company, L.P.; *U.S. Private*, pg. 2278
JFSL PROJECTS LTD.—See Jacobs Engineering Group, Inc.; *U.S. Public*, pg. 1185
JF TECHNOLOGY BERHAD; *Int'l*, pg. 3934
JFT STRATEGIES FUND—See First Asset Investment Management Inc.; *Int'l*, pg. 2682
JF WEALTH HOLDINGS LTD.; *Int'l*, pg. 3934
J.F. WHITE CONTRACTING CO.—See ACS, Actividades de Construccion y Servicios, S.A.; *Int'l*, pg. 111
JGA BEACON—See Beacon Roofing Supply, Inc.; *U.S. Public*, pg. 286
JGB ENTERPRISES INC.—See HCI Equity Management, L.P.; *U.S. Private*, pg. 1889
JGB INDUSTRIES, INC.; *U.S. Private*, pg. 2207
JG BLACK BOOK OF TRAVEL; *U.S. Private*, pg. 2206
J.G. BOSWELL CO., INC.; *U.S. Private*, pg. 2165
J.G. BOSWELL CO., INC.—See J.G. Boswell Co., Inc.; *U.S. Private*, pg. 2165
JGB VENTURES INC.; *U.S. Private*, pg. 2207
JGC ALGERIA S.P.A.—See JGC Holdings Corporation; *Int'l*, pg. 3939
JGC AMERICA, INC.—See JGC Holdings Corporation; *Int'l*, pg. 3939
JGC ARABIA LIMITED—See JGC Holdings Corporation; *Int'l*, pg. 3939
JGC CATALYSTS & CHEMICALS LTD—See JGC Holdings Corporation; *Int'l*, pg. 3939
JGC CONSTRUCTION INTERNATIONAL PTE. LTD.—See JGC Holdings Corporation; *Int'l*, pg. 3940
JGC CORPORATION EUROPE B.V.—See JGC Holdings Corporation; *Int'l*, pg. 3940
JGC CORPORATION (UK) LTD.—See JGC Holdings Corporation; *Int'l*, pg. 3940
JGC ENERGY DEVELOPMENT (USA) INC.—See JGC Holdings Corporation; *Int'l*, pg. 3939
JGC ENGINEERING CONSULTANTS (SHANGHAI) CO., LTD.—See JGC Holdings Corporation; *Int'l*, pg. 3940
JGC EVERGREEN LTD.—See JGC Holdings Corporation; *Int'l*, pg. 3940
JGC FLUOR BC JOINT VENTURE—See Fluor Corporation; *U.S. Public*, pg. 858
JGC GULF INTERNATIONAL CO., LTD.—See JGC Holdings Corporation; *Int'l*, pg. 3940
JGC HOLDINGS CORPORATION; *Int'l*, pg. 3939
JGC INFORMATION SYSTEMS CO., LTD.—See JGC Holdings Corporation; *Int'l*, pg. 3940
JGC ITALY S. R. L.—See JGC Holdings Corporation; *Int'l*, pg. 3940
JGC-ITC RABIGH UTILITY CO., LTD.—See JGC Holdings Corporation; *Int'l*, pg. 3940
JGC JAPAN CORPORATION—See JGC Holdings Corporation; *Int'l*, pg. 3940
JGC KOREA CORPORATION—See JGC Holdings Corporation; *Int'l*, pg. 3940
JGC MIDDLE EAST FZE—See JGC Holdings Corporation; *Int'l*, pg. 3940

JGC NIGERIA LTD.—See JGC Holdings Corporation; *Int'l*, pg. 3940
JGC OCEANIA PTY. LTD.—See JGC Holdings Corporation; *Int'l*, pg. 3940
JG COMMUNICATION AB—See Nordic Morning Plc; *Int'l*, pg. 5422
JGC PHILIPPINES, INC.—See JGC Holdings Corporation; *Int'l*, pg. 3940
JGC PLANTECH AOMORI CO., LTD.—See JGC Holdings Corporation; *Int'l*, pg. 3940
JGC PLANTECH CO., LTD.—See JGC Holdings Corporation; *Int'l*, pg. 3940
JGC SINGAPORE PTE. LTD.—See JGC Holdings Corporation; *Int'l*, pg. 3940
JGC TECHNICAL ASSISTANCE SERVICES PHILIPPINES, INC.—See JGC Holdings Corporation; *Int'l*, pg. 3940
JGC TRADING & SERVICES CO., LTD.—See JGC Holdings Corporation; *Int'l*, pg. 3940
JGC (U.S.A.), INC.—See JGC Holdings Corporation; *Int'l*, pg. 3939
JGC VENTURES PTE. LTD.—See PT Modernland Realty Tbk; *Int'l*, pg. 6059
JGC VIETNAM CO., LTD.—See JGC Holdings Corporation; *Int'l*, pg. 3940
JGD ASSOCIATES INC.—See Fiedler Group; *U.S. Private*, pg. 1503
JGEAR; *U.S. Private*, pg. 2207
J.G. EDELEN CO. INC.; *U.S. Private*, pg. 2165
J.G. ELLIOTT INSURANCE CENTER—See Platte Valley Financial Service Companies Inc.; *U.S. Private*, pg. 3211
J.G. FINNERAN ASSOCIATES, INC.—See Porvair plc; *Int'l*, pg. 5935
J. GIBSON MCILVAIN COMPANY; *U.S. Private*, pg. 2156
JGI, INC.—See Japan Petroleum Exploration Co. Ltd.; *Int'l*, pg. 3900
JG MACLELLAN CONCRETE CO.; *U.S. Private*, pg. 2206
JG MANAGEMENT SYSTEMS, INC.; *U.S. Private*, pg. 2207
J.G. NIEDEREGGER GMBH & CO. KG; *Int'l*, pg. 3858
J.G. O'NEILL INC.; *U.S. Private*, pg. 2165
J. GOWDY CONSULTING, LLC—See Sustainserv, Inc.; *U.S. Private*, pg. 3886
J. GRADY RANDOLPH, INC.—See Daseke, Inc.; *U.S. Private*, pg. 1161
J GRAND CO., LTD.—See PT Bank JTrust Indonesia Tbk.; *Int'l*, pg. 6026
J.G. RIVE-SUD FRUITS & LEGUMES; *Int'l*, pg. 3858
J-GROUP HOLDINGS CORP.; *Int'l*, pg. 3854
JG SERVICE COMPANY; *U.S. Private*, pg. 2207
JGS SUPERMARKETS INC.; *U.S. Private*, pg. 2207
JG SUMMIT HOLDINGS, INC.; *Int'l*, pg. 3939
JG SUMMIT PETROCHEMICAL CORPORATION—See JG Summit Holdings, Inc.; *Int'l*, pg. 3939
JG TAX GROUP; *U.S. Private*, pg. 2207
J. G. TOWNSEND, JR. & COMPANY; *U.S. Private*, pg. 2156
THE J.G. WENTWORTH COMPANY—See JLL Partners, LLC; *U.S. Private*, pg. 2213
J.G. WENTWORTH HOME LENDING, LLC—See Freedom Mortgage Corporation; *U.S. Private*, pg. 1604
J.G. WENTWORTH SSC, L.P.—See JLL Partners, LLC; *U.S. Private*, pg. 2213
JH&A ADVERTISING INC.; *U.S. Private*, pg. 2207
JHABUA POWER LIMITED—See NTPC Limited; *Int'l*, pg. 5484
J.H. ALLEN INC.; *U.S. Private*, pg. 2165
JHANDEWALAS FOODS LIMITED; *Int'l*, pg. 3940
JHA PAYMENT PROCESSING SOLUTIONS, INC.—See Jack Henry & Associates, Inc.; *U.S. Public*, pg. 1182
J&H ASSET PROPERTY MANAGEMENT INC.; *U.S. Private*, pg. 2154
JHAVERI CREDITS & CAPITAL LIMITED; *Int'l*, pg. 3940
JHAVERI FLEXO INDIA LTD. - AURANGABAD FACTORY—See Jhaveri Flexo India Ltd.; *Int'l*, pg. 3940
JHAVERI FLEXO INDIA LTD. - DAPADA FACTORY—See Jhaveri Flexo India Ltd.; *Int'l*, pg. 3940
JHAVERI FLEXO INDIA LTD. - LUHARI FACTORY—See Jhaveri Flexo India Ltd.; *Int'l*, pg. 3940
JHAVERI FLEXO INDIA LTD.; *Int'l*, pg. 3940
JHAWAR INDUSTRIES, INC.—See Novacap Management Inc.; *Int'l*, pg. 5454
J.H. BARKAU & SONS INC.; *U.S. Private*, pg. 2165
J.H. BAXTER & COMPANY; *U.S. Private*, pg. 2165
JH BELGIUM, S.A.—See Minor International PCL; *Int'l*, pg. 4911
J.H. BENNETT & COMPANY INC.; *U.S. Private*, pg. 2165
J.H. BENNETT INC.; *U.S. Private*, pg. 2165
J.H. BERRA CONSTRUCTION CO., INC. - GRADING DIVISION—See J.H. Berra Holding Co., Inc.; *U.S. Private*, pg. 2165
J.H. BERRA CONSTRUCTION CO., INC. - LAND DEVELOPMENT DIVISION—See J.H. Berra Holding Co., Inc.; *U.S. Private*, pg. 2165
J.H. BERRA CONSTRUCTION CO., INC.—See J.H. Berra Holding Co., Inc.; *U.S. Private*, pg. 2165

J.H. BERRA CONSTRUCTION CO., INC. - UTILITY DIVISION—See J.H. Berra Holding Co., Inc.; *U.S. Private*, pg. 2165
J.H. BERRA ENGINEERING & SURVEYING CO., INC.—See J.H. Berra Holding Co., Inc.; *U.S. Private*, pg. 2165
J.H. BERRA HOLDING CO., INC.; *U.S. Private*, pg. 2165
J.H. BERRA PAVING CO., INC.—See J.H. Berra Holding Co., Inc.; *U.S. Private*, pg. 2165
JHB INC.; *U.S. Private*, pg. 2207
JH BIOTECH, INC.; *U.S. Private*, pg. 2207
J.H. BLADES & CO., INC.—See Lightyear Capital LLC; *U.S. Private*, pg. 2454
J. H. BLADES & CO., INC.—See Truist Financial Corporation; *U.S. Public*, pg. 2200
J.H. BUHRMASTER COMPANY INC.; *U.S. Private*, pg. 2165
JHC (INTERNATIONAL) LIMITED—See International Housewares Retail Company Limited; *Int'l*, pg. 3750
JHC STRUCTURES CORPORATION; *U.S. Private*, pg. 2207
JH DEUTSCHLAND GMBH—See Minor International PCL; *Int'l*, pg. 4911
JH EDUCATIONAL TECHNOLOGY INC.; *Int'l*, pg. 3940
J. HELLMAN FROZEN, INC.—See J. Hellman Produce, Inc.; *U.S. Private*, pg. 2156
J. HELLMAN PRODUCE, INC.; *U.S. Private*, pg. 2156
J.H. ELLWOOD & ASSOCIATES; *U.S. Private*, pg. 2165
J. HENRY HOLLAND CORPORATION—See Industrial Sales Company Inc.; *U.S. Private*, pg. 2068
JHEN VEI ELECTRONIC CO., LTD.; *Int'l*, pg. 3940
J.H. EVANS INC.; *U.S. Private*, pg. 2165
J.H. FAGAN COMPANY; *U.S. Private*, pg. 2165
J.H. FERGUSON & ASSOCIATES, LLC—See Paine Schwartz Partners, LLC; *U.S. Private*, pg. 3075
J.H. FINDORFF & SON, INC.; *U.S. Private*, pg. 2165
J.H. FLETCHER & CO.; *U.S. Private*, pg. 2165
J&H FOREST PRODUCTS; *U.S. Private*, pg. 2154
JH GLOBAL SERVICES, INC.; *U.S. Private*, pg. 2207
J.H. HARVEY CO., LLC—See Aldi Einkauf SE & Co. oHG; *Int'l*, pg. 304
J H HAYNES & CO LTD—See Apax Partners LLP; *Int'l*, pg. 502
J H HAYNES & CO LTD—See TowerBrook Capital Partners, L.P.; *U.S. Private*, pg. 4195
JH HOLLAND N.V.—See Minor International PCL; *Int'l*, pg. 4911
J. HILBURN; *U.S. Private*, pg. 2156
JHI OPTICAL GROUP—See The Wicks Group of Companies, LLC; *U.S. Private*, pg. 4135
JHI SOON MANUFACTURING INDUSTRIES SDN. BHD.—See New Hoong Fatt Holdings Berhad; *Int'l*, pg. 5224
JH. JANSER KFT.—See Janser GmbH; *Int'l*, pg. 3880
JHJ SOFTWARE, INC.—See Eli Global, LLC; *U.S. Private*, pg. 1360
J.H. KASPAR OIL CO.—See Stinker Stores, Inc.; *U.S. Private*, pg. 3813
JH KELLY LLC; *U.S. Private*, pg. 2207
J.H. LARSON ELECTRICAL COMPANY-HUDSON—See J.H. Larson Electrical Company; *U.S. Private*, pg. 2166
J.H. LARSON ELECTRICAL COMPANY; *U.S. Private*, pg. 2166
J.H. LARSON ELECTRICAL COMPANY—See J.H. Larson Electrical Company; *U.S. Private*, pg. 2166
J.H. LYNCH & SONS INC.; *U.S. Private*, pg. 2166
J.H. MCCORMICK, INC.; *U.S. Private*, pg. 2166
J.H. MCNAIRN LIMITED; *Int'l*, pg. 3858
JHM CONSOLIDATION BERHAD - KEDAH DARUL AMAN FACTORY—See JHM Consolidation Berhad; *Int'l*, pg. 3941
JHM CONSOLIDATION BERHAD; *Int'l*, pg. 3941
JHM CONSOLIDATION BERHAD - SUNGAI PETANI FACTORY—See JHM Consolidation Berhad; *Int'l*, pg. 3941
JHM DEVELOPMENT SA; *Int'l*, pg. 3941
JHM ENTERPRISES INC.; *U.S. Private*, pg. 2207
JHM FINANCIAL GROUP, LLC; *U.S. Private*, pg. 2207
JHM RESEARCH & DEVELOPMENT INC.; *U.S. Private*, pg. 2207
JHMS CO.,LTD.—See Nippon Kayaku Co., Ltd.; *Int'l*, pg. 5320
JHNA, INC.; *U.S. Private*, pg. 2208
JHOC INC.; *U.S. Private*, pg. 2208
J&H OIL COMPANY INC.; *U.S. Private*, pg. 2154
J-HOLDINGS CORP.; *Int'l*, pg. 3854
J-HORIZONS TRAVEL (M) SDN. BHD.; *Int'l*, pg. 3854
JH PARTNERS LLC; *U.S. Private*, pg. 2207
JHP SPOL. S.R.O.—See STRABAG SE; *Int'l*, pg. 7231
JHR CORPORATE RISK PTY LTD—See PSC Insurance Group Limited; *Int'l*, pg. 6016
JH RECYCLE CO., LTD.—See Japan Pulp and Paper Company Limited; *Int'l*, pg. 3903
JH RHODES COMPANY, INC. - CLINTON MANUFACTURING FACILITY—See Universal Photonics, Inc.; *U.S. Private*, pg. 4306
JH RHODES COMPANY, INC.—See Universal Photonics, Inc.; *U.S. Private*, pg. 4306
JH ROSE LOGISTICS INC.; *U.S. Private*, pg. 2207

COMPANY NAME INDEX

J.H. ROUTH PACKING CO.; *U.S. Private*, pg. 2166
J.H. RUDOLPH & CO. INC.; *U.S. Private*, pg. 2166
JHS CORPORATION—See Montgomery Chevrolet; *U.S. Private*, pg. 2776
JH SERVICES INC.; *U.S. Private*, pg. 2207
JHSF PARTICIPACOES S.A.; *Int'l*, pg. 3941
JHS INC.; *U.S. Private*, pg. 2208
JHS SVENDGAARD LABORATORIES LIMITED; *Int'l*, pg. 3941
JH TECHNOLOGIES INC.; *U.S. Private*, pg. 2207
JHT HOLDINGS, INC—See TFI International Inc.; *Int'l*, pg. 7586
JHT, INC.; *U.S. Private*, pg. 2208
J&H TRANSPORTATION INC.; *U.S. Private*, pg. 2154
J. HUNTER ADVERTISING INC.; *U.S. Private*, pg. 2156
J. HVIDTVED LARSEN A/S—See Bucher Industries AG; *Int'l*, pg. 1209
J. HVIDTVED LARSEN IRELAND LTD.—See Bucher Industries AG; *Int'l*, pg. 1209
J. HVIDTVED LARSEN UK LTD.—See Bucher Industries AG; *Int'l*, pg. 1209
J.H. WALKER INC.; *U.S. Private*, pg. 2166
J.H. WHITNEY CAPITAL PARTNERS, LLC—See J.H. Whitney & Co., LLC; *U.S. Private*, pg. 2166
J.H. WHITNEY & CO., LLC; *U.S. Private*, pg. 2166
J.H. WILLIAMS OIL COMPANY INC.; *U.S. Private*, pg. 2166
J.H. WILLIAMS TOOL GROUP—See Snap-on Incorporated; *U.S. Public*, pg. 1897
J.H. WRIGHT & ASSOCIATES INC.; *U.S. Private*, pg. 2166
JI2, INC.—See Soliton Systems, K.K.; *Int'l*, pg. 7073
JIACHEN HOLDING GROUP LIMITED; *Int'l*, pg. 3941
JIA CHI CO., LTD.—See Key Ware Electronics Co., Ltd.; *Int'l*, pg. 4145
JIADING INTERNATIONAL GROUP HOLDINGS LIMITED; *Int'l*, pg. 3941
JIAFENG WOOD (SUZHOU) CO., LTD.—See Emerald Plantation Holdings Limited; *Int'l*, pg. 2378
JIA GROUP HOLDINGS LIMITED; *Int'l*, pg. 3941
JIAHE FOODS INDUSTRY CO., LTD.; *Int'l*, pg. 3941
JIAHUA STORES HOLDINGS LIMITED; *Int'l*, pg. 3942
JIAJIA FOOD GROUP CO., LTD.; *Int'l*, pg. 0040
JIAJIAFU MODERN AGRICULTURE LIMITED; *Int'l*, pg. 3942
JIAJIAYUE GROUP CO LTD; *Int'l*, pg. 3942
JIALIJIA GROUP CORPORATION LIMITED; *Int'l*, pg. 3942
JIALONG LEADER (BEIJING) TRADING CO., LTD.—See Leader Electronics Corporation; *Int'l*, pg. 4432
JIAMEI FOOD PACKAGING (CHUZHOU) CO., LTD.; *Int'l*, pg. 3942
JIANA SCIENCE AND TECHNOLOGY CO., LTD.; *Int'l*, pg. 3942
JIAN EPAYMENT SYSTEMS LIMITED; *Int'l*, pg. 3942
JIANGBO PHARMACEUTICALS, INC.; *Int'l*, pg. 3942
JIANGHAI AMERICA INC.—See Nantong Jianghai Capacitor Co., Ltd.; *Int'l*, pg. 5145
JIANGHAI EUROPE ELECTRONIC COMPONENTS GMBH—See Nantong Jianghai Capacitor Co., Ltd.; *Int'l*, pg. 5145
JIANGHUAI (ANHUI) SONGZ AUTOMOBILE AIR CONDITIONING CO., LTD.—See Songzhi Kallang Automotive Air Conditioning Co., Ltd.; *Int'l*, pg. 7096
JIANGLING-ISUZU MOTORS CO., LTD.—See Isuzu Motors Limited; *Int'l*, pg. 3826
JIANGLING MOTORS CORPORATION, LTD; *Int'l*, pg. 3942
JIANGLONG BOAT POLYTRON TECHNOLOGIES INC—See Jianglong Shipbuilding Co., Ltd.; *Int'l*, pg. 3942
JIANGLONG SHIPBUILDING CO., LTD.; *Int'l*, pg. 3942
JIANGMEN ACE SURFACE TREATMENT CO., LTD.—See Ace Technologies Corp.; *Int'l*, pg. 95
JIANGMEN CHANGDA WOOD PRODUCTS COMPANY LIMITED—See Steed Oriental (Holdings) Company Limited; *Int'l*, pg. 7189
JIANGMEN COSCO SHIPPING ALUMINUM CO., LTD.—See China COSCO Shipping Corporation Limited; *Int'l*, pg. 1495
JIANGMEN GOLIK METAL MANUFACTURING CO., LTD.—See Golik Holdings Limited; *Int'l*, pg. 3036
JIANGMEN HANDSOME CHEMICAL DEVELOPMENT LIMITED—See Yips Chemical Holdings Limited; *Int'l*, pg. 8585
JIANGMEN HUAJIN METAL PRODUCT COMPANY LIMITED—See Huajin International Holdings Limited; *Int'l*, pg. 3512
JIANGMEN KANHOO INDUSTRY CO., LTD.; *Int'l*, pg. 3942
JIANGMEN KONG YUE JOLIMARK INFORMATION TECHNOLOGY LIMITED—See Jolimark Holdings Limited; *Int'l*, pg. 3996
JIANGMEN SENKEI CHEMICAL TANK STORAGE CO., LTD.—See Marubeni Corporation; *Int'l*, pg. 4705
JIANGMEN SUNTAK CIRCUIT TECHNOLOGY CO., LTD.—See Suntak Technology Co., Ltd.; *Int'l*, pg. 7324
JIANGMEN SYP ENGINEERING GLASS CO., LTD.—See Shanghai Yaohua Pilkington Glass Group Co., Ltd.; *Int'l*, pg. 6782
JIANGMEN TINGYI FOOD CO., LTD.—See Tingyi (Cayman Islands) Holding Corp.; *Int'l*, pg. 7754
JIANGMEN TOYO INK CO., LTD.—See Toyo Ink SC Holdings Co., Ltd.; *Int'l*, pg. 7853
JIANGMEN VA MANUFACTURING LTD.—See Ford Glory International Limited; *Int'l*, pg. 2731
JIANGMEN XINGHUI PAPER MILL CO., LTD.—See Hokuetsu Corporation; *Int'l*, pg. 3444
JIANGMEN YEEBO ELECTRONIC TECHNOLOGY CO., LTD.—See Yeebo (International Holdings) Limited; *Int'l*, pg. 8576
JIANGMEN YEEBO SEMICONDUCTOR CO., LTD.—See Yeebo (International Holdings) Limited; *Int'l*, pg. 8576
JIANG MEN YUAN HUI PROPERTY CO., LTD.—See China COSCO Shipping Corporation Limited; *Int'l*, pg. 1492
JIANGMEN ZHONGSHUN PAPER INDUSTRY CO., LTD.—See C&S Paper Co., Ltd.; *Int'l*, pg. 1239
JIANGNAN GROUP LIMITED; *Int'l*, pg. 3942
JIANGNAN MOULD & PLASTIC TECHNOLOGY CO., LTD.; *Int'l*, pg. 3942
JIANGNAN YIFAN MOTOR CO., LTD.; *Int'l*, pg. 3943
JIANGSHAN OUPAI DOOR INDUSTRY CO., LTD.; *Int'l*, pg. 3943
JIANGSHAN SHENDA ELECTRIC CO. LTD.—See Shenda International Engineering Co. Ltd.; *Int'l*, pg. 6800
JIANGSU AEROSPACE HYDRAULIC EQUIPMENTS CO., LTD.—See Shaanxi Aerospace Power High-tech Co., Ltd.; *Int'l*, pg. 6746
JIANGSU AEROSPACE POWER ELECTRIC CO., LTD.—See Shaanxi Aerospace Power High-tech Co., Ltd.; *Int'l*, pg. 6746
JIANGSU AIDEA PHARMACEUTICAL CO., LTD.; *Int'l*, pg. 3943
JIANGSU A-KERR BIO-IDENTIFICATION TECHNOLOGY CO., LTD.—See Huizhou Speed Wireless Technology Co., Ltd.; *Int'l*, pg. 3527
JIANGSU ALCHA ALUMINIUM GROUP CO., LTD.; *Int'l*, pg. 3943
JIANGSU ALLFAVOR INTELLIGENT CIRCUITS TECHNOLOGY CO., LTD.; *Int'l*, pg. 3943
JIANGSU ALLIST PHARMACEUTICAL CO., LTD.—See Shanghai Allist Pharmaceuticals Co., Ltd.; *Int'l*, pg. 6761
JIANGSU ALMADEN POWER INVESTMENT CO., LTD.—See Changzhou Almaden Stock Co., Ltd.; *Int'l*, pg. 1445
JIANGSU ALPHAMAB BIOPHARMACEUTICALS CO., LTD.; *Int'l*, pg. 3943
JIANGSU AMER NEW MATERIAL CO., LTD; *Int'l*, pg. 3943
JIANGSU ANIMALS BY-PRODUCTS IMPORT & EXPORT GROUP CORPORATION—See Jiangsu High Hope International Group Corporation; *Int'l*, pg. 3947
JIANGSU ANKURA INTELLIGENT POWER CO., LTD; *Int'l*, pg. 3943
JIANGSU AOBAO PRINTING TECHNOLOGY CO., LTD.—See ORG Technology Co., Ltd.; *Int'l*, pg. 5617
JIANGSU AOYANG HEALTH INDUSTRY CO., LTD.; *Int'l*, pg. 3943
JIANGSU APH METAL PRINTING TECHNOLOGY CO., LTD.—See Jiangsu Asia-Pacific Light Alloy Technology Co., Ltd.; *Int'l*, pg. 3943
JIANGSU APON MEDICAL TECHNOLOGY CO., LTD.; *Int'l*, pg. 3943
JIANGSU ASENTEC SENSOR PARTS CO., LTD.—See SJG Sejong Co., Ltd.; *Int'l*, pg. 6969
JIANGSU ASIA-PACIFIC ANSINDARALUMINIUM CO., LTD.—See Jiangsu Asia-Pacific Light Alloy Technology Co., Ltd.; *Int'l*, pg. 3943
JIANGSU ASIA-PACIFIC LIGHT ALLOY TECHNOLOGY CO., LTD.; *Int'l*, pg. 3943
JIANG SU ASICS CO., LTD.—See ASICS Corporation; *Int'l*, pg. 621
JIANGSU ATLANTIC WELDING CONSUMABLES LIMITED LIABILITY COMPANY—See Atlantic China Welding Consumables, Inc.; *Int'l*, pg. 674
JIANGSU AZURE CORPORATION; *Int'l*, pg. 3943
JIANGSU BAICHUAN HIGH-TECH NEW MATERIALS CO.,LTD.; *Int'l*, pg. 3944
JIANGSU BAOLI INTERNATIONAL INVESTMENT CO., LTD.; *Int'l*, pg. 3944
JIANGSU BEIREN ROBOT SYSTEM CO., LTD.; *Int'l*, pg. 3944
JIANGSU BIAOXIN KUBOTA INDUSTRIAL CO., LTD.—See Kubota Corporation; *Int'l*, pg. 4321
JIANGSU BIDE SCIENCE & TECHNOLOGY CO., LTD.; *Int'l*, pg. 3944
JIANGSU BIOPERFECTUS TECHNOLOGIES CO., LTD.; *Int'l*, pg. 3944
JIANGSU BOAMAX TECHNOLOGIES GROUP CO., LTD.; *Int'l*, pg. 3944
JIANGSU BOILN PLASTICS CO., LTD.; *Int'l*, pg. 3944
JIANGSU BOJUN INDUSTRIAL TECHNOLOGY CO., LTD.; *Int'l*, pg. 3944
JIANGSU BOMIN ELECTRONICS CO., LTD.—See Bomin Electronics Co., Ltd.; *Int'l*, pg. 1105
JIANGSU BOQIAN NEW MATERIALS CO., LTD.; *Int'l*, pg. 3944
JIANGSU BOSTIK ADHESIVE CO., LTD.—See Arkema S.A.; *Int'l*, pg. 571
JIANGSU BOXIN INVESTING & HOLDINGS CO., LTD.; *Int'l*, pg. 3944
JIANG SU BRIGHT STEEL FINE MACHINERY CO., LTD.—See Yeong Guan Energy Technology Group Co., Ltd.; *Int'l*, pg. 8577
JIANGSU BROADCASTING CABLE INFORMATION NETWORK CORPORATION LIMITED; *Int'l*, pg. 3944
JIANGSU BROTHER VITAMINS CO., LTD.—See Brother Enterprises Holding Co., Ltd.; *Int'l*, pg. 1196
JIANGSU BUDAOWENG FOODS CO., LTD.—See Ottogi Corporation; *Int'l*, pg. 5665
JIANGSU CANLON BUILDING MATERIALS CO., LTD.; *Int'l*, pg. 3944
JIANGSU CANOPUS WISDOM MEDICAL TECHNOLOGY CO., LTD.; *Int'l*, pg. 3944
JIANGSU CANYANG OPTOELECTRONICS LTD.—See Ennostar Inc.; *Int'l*, pg. 2444
JIANGSU CAS-IGBT TECHNOLOGY CO., LTD.; *Int'l*, pg. 3944
JIANG SU CASTFAST ELECTRONIC TECHNOLOGIES COMPANY LIMITED—See Karrie International Holdings Limited; *Int'l*, pg. 4085
JIANGSU CEREALS, OILS & FOODSTUFFS IMPORT & EXPORT GROUP CORP.—See Jiangsu High Hope International Group Corporation; *Int'l*, pg. 3947
JIANGSU CHANGBAO STEEL TUBE CO., LTD.; *Int'l*, pg. 3944
JIANGSU CHANGFENG CABLE CO., LTD.—See Jiangsu Zhongchao Holding Co., Ltd.; *Int'l*, pg. 3957
JIANGSU CHANGHAI COMPOSITE MATERIALS CO., LTD.; *Int'l*, pg. 3944
JIANGSU CHANGLING HYDRAULIC CO., LTD.; *Int'l*, pg. 3944
JIANGSU CHANGQING AGROCHEMICAL CO., LTD.; *Int'l*, pg. 3945
JIANGSU CHANGSHU AUTOMOTIVE TRIM GROUP CO., LTD.; *Int'l*, pg. 3945
JIANGSU CHANGSHU RURAL COMMERCIAL BANK CO., LTD.; *Int'l*, pg. 3945
JIANGSU CHANG TIAN ZHI YUAN TRANSPORTATION TECHNOLOGY CO., LTD.—See Jiangsu NandaSoft Technology Company Limited; *Int'l*, pg. 3951
JIANGSU CHEMICAL FERTILIZER CO., LTD.—See SOHO Holly Corporation; *Int'l*, pg. 7059
JIANGSU CHENGXING PHOSPH-CHEMICALS CO., LTD.; *Int'l*, pg. 3945
JIANGSU CHIATAI QINGJIANG PHARMACEUTICAL CO., LTD. - HUAIAN PLANT—See Sino Biopharmaceutical Limited; *Int'l*, pg. 6946
JIANGSU CHIATAI QINGJIANG PHARMACEUTICAL CO., LTD.—See Sino Biopharmaceutical Limited; *Int'l*, pg. 6946
JIANGSU CHINAGREEN BIOLOGICAL TECHNOLOGY CO., LTD.; *Int'l*, pg. 3945
JIANGSU CHUANZHIBOKE EDUCATION TECHNOLOGY CO., LTD.; *Int'l*, pg. 3945
JIANGSU CHUNG - HSIN PRECISION MACHINERY CO., LTD.—See Chung-Hsin Electric & Machinery Manufacturing Corp.; *Int'l*, pg. 1597
JIANGSU CHUNLAN REFRIGERATING EQUIPMENT CO., LTD.; *Int'l*, pg. 3945
JIANGSU C&M FILTRATION SOLUTIONS LIMITED—See Tex Year Industries Inc.; *Int'l*, pg. 7582
JIANGSU CNANO TECHNOLOGY CO., LTD.; *Int'l*, pg. 3945
JIANGSU CONTEMPORARY AMPEREX TECHNOLOGY LIMITED—See Contemporary Amperex Technology Co., Ltd.; *Int'l*, pg. 1779
JIANGSU CREVO SCIENCE & TECHNOLOGY CO., LTD.—See Sika AG; *Int'l*, pg. 6914
JIANGSU DAEDONG DOOR INC.—See Hi-Lex Corporation; *Int'l*, pg. 3381
JIANGSU DAE DONG HI-LEX INC.—See Hi-Lex Corporation; *Int'l*, pg. 3381
JIANGSU DAEWON ASIA AUTOMOBILE SPRING CO., LTD.—See Daewon Kang Up Co., Ltd.; *Int'l*, pg. 1910
JIANGSU DAGANG CO., LTD.; *Int'l*, pg. 3945
JIANGSU DAIFUKU RIXIN AUTOMATION CO., LTD.—See Daifuku Co., Ltd.; *Int'l*, pg. 1926
JIANGSU DALI FOODS CO., LTD.—See Dali Foods Group Co. Ltd.; *Int'l*, pg. 1951
JIANGSU DASHIJIUXIN MEDICAL TECHNOLOGY CO., LTD.—See Shenzhen DAS Intellitech Co., Ltd.; *Int'l*, pg. 6807
JIANGSU DAWEI PRECISION TECHNOLOGY CO., LTD.—See Nantong Guosheng Intelligence Technology Group Co., Ltd.; *Int'l*, pg. 5145
JIANGSU DAYBRIGHT INTELLIGENT ELECTRIC CO., LTD.; *Int'l*, pg. 3945
JIANGSU DEWEI ADVANCED MATERIALS CO., LTD.; *Int'l*, pg. 3945
JIANGSU DINGSHENG NEW MATERIAL JOINT-STOCK CO., LTD.; *Int'l*, pg. 3945

JIANGSU DONGGUANG MICRO-ELECTRONICS CO., LTD.

JIANGSU DONGGUANG MICRO-ELECTRONICS CO., LTD.; *Int'l*, pg. 3945
JIANGSU DONGHAI SAINT-GOBAIN CO. LTD.—See Compagnie de Saint-Gobain SA; *Int'l*, pg. 1723
JIANGSU DONGTAI TAISHENG POWER ENGINEERING MACHINERY CO., LTD.—See Shanghai Taisheng Wind Power Equipment Co., Ltd.; *Int'l*, pg. 6779
JIANGSU EASTERN SHENGHONG CO., LTD.; *Int'l*, pg. 3945
JIANGSU EAZYTEC CO., LTD.; *Int'l*, pg. 3945
JIANGSU ELECTRIC POWER COMPANY—See State Grid Corporation of China; *Int'l*, pg. 7183
JIANGSU ETERN COMPANY LIMITED; *Int'l*, pg. 3946
JIANGSU EXPRESSWAY COMPANY LIMITED; *Int'l*, pg. 3946
JIANGSU FAREVER PHARMA. CO., LTD.—See Jiangsu Nhwa Pharmaceutical Corporation Ltd.; *Int'l*, pg. 3951
JIANGSU FASTEN COMPANY LIMITED; *Int'l*, pg. 3946
JIANGSU FEILIKS INTERNATIONAL LOGISTICS INC.; *Int'l*, pg. 3946
JIANGSU FENGSHAN GROUP CO., LTD.; *Int'l*, pg. 3946
JIANGSU FEYMER TECHNOLOGY CO., LTD.; *Int'l*, pg. 3946
JIANGSU FINANCIAL LEASING CO., LTD.; *Int'l*, pg. 3946
JIANGSU FIVE STAR APPLIANCE CO., LTD.—See Jiayuan.com International Ltd.; *Int'l*, pg. 3962
JIANGSU FLAG CHEMICAL INDUSTRY CO., LTD.; *Int'l*, pg. 3946
JIANGSU FLAGCHEM INTERNATIONAL CO.—See Jiangsu Flag Chemical Industry Co., Ltd.; *Int'l*, pg. 3946
JIANGSU FLEXIBLE AUTO PARTS CO., LTD.—See Changzhou Tenglong Auto Parts Co., Ltd.; *Int'l*, pg. 1445
JIANGSU FUJITSU TELECOMMUNICATIONS TECHNOLOGY CO., LTD.—See Fujitsu Limited; *Int'l*, pg. 2835
JIANGSU FUSSON MOULD TECHNOLOGY CO., LTD.—See Jiangsu Tongda Power Technology Co., Ltd.; *Int'l*, pg. 3955
JIANGSU GANGRUI PRECISION MACHINERY CO., LTD.—See Yeong Guan Energy Technology Group Co., Ltd.; *Int'l*, pg. 8577
JIANGSU GENERAL SCIENCE TECHNOLOGY CO., LTD.; *Int'l*, pg. 3946
JIANGSU GIAN TECHNOLOGY CO., LTD.; *Int'l*, pg. 3946
JIANGSU GINAR PLASTIC TECHNOLOGY CO., LTD.—See Ginar Technology Co., Ltd.; *Int'l*, pg. 2976
JIANGSU GOLDEN MATERIAL TECHNOLOGY CO., LTD.—See Hongda Xingye Co., Ltd.; *Int'l*, pg. 3470
JIANGSU GOLDWIND SCIENCE & TECHNOLOGY CO., LTD.—See Xinjiang Goldwind Science & Technology Co., Ltd.; *Int'l*, pg. 8531
JIANGSU GOODWE POWER SUPPLY TECHNOLOGY CO., LTD.; *Int'l*, pg. 3946
JIANGSU GRAND XIANLE PHARMACEUTICAL CO., LTD.—See Grand Pharmaceutical Group Limited; *Int'l*, pg. 3056
JIANGSU GREENWISE ENVIRONMENTAL PROTECTION TECHNOLOGY CO., LTD.—See Jiangsu Rainbow Heavy Industries Co., Ltd.; *Int'l*, pg. 3952
JIANGSU GUOJING HOLDING GROUP CO., LTD.; *Int'l*, pg. 3946
JIANGSU GUOMAO REDUCER CO., LTD.; *Int'l*, pg. 3946
JIANGSU GUOQIANG TOOLS CO., LTD.—See Stanley Black & Decker, Inc.; *U.S. Public*, pg. 1933
JIANGSU GUOTAI INTERNATIONAL GROUP CO., LTD.; *Int'l*, pg. 3946
JIANGSU GUOXIN CORP., LTD.; *Int'l*, pg. 3946
JIANGSU HAGONG INTELLIGENT ROBOT CO., LTD.; *Int'l*, pg. 3947
JIANGSU HAILI WIND POWER EQUIPMENT TECHNOLOGY CO., LTD.; *Int'l*, pg. 3947
JIANGSU HANSOH PHARMACEUTICAL GROUP CO., LTD.; *Int'l*, pg. 3947
JIANGSU HANVO SAFETY PRODUCT CO., LTD.; *Int'l*, pg. 3947
JIANGSU HENGCHUANG PACKING MATERIAL CO., LTD.—See Shuangliang Eco-Energy Systems Company Limited; *Int'l*, pg. 6868
JIANGSU HENGLI HYDRAULIC CO., LTD.; *Int'l*, pg. 3947
JIANGSU HENGRUI MEDICINE CO., LTD.; *Int'l*, pg. 3947
JIANGSU HENGSHUN VINEGAR-INDUSTRY CO., LTD.; *Int'l*, pg. 3947
JIANGSU HENGXIN TECHNOLOGY CO., LTD.—See Hengxin Technology Ltd.; *Int'l*, pg. 3347
JIANGSU HIGH HOPE ARSER CO., LTD.—See Jiangsu High Hope International Group Corporation; *Int'l*, pg. 3947
JIANGSU HIGH HOPE BABY CO., LTD.—See Jiangsu High Hope International Group Corporation; *Int'l*, pg. 3947
JIANGSU HIGH HOPE COLD CHAIN LOGISTICS CO., LTD.—See Jiangsu High Hope International Group Corporation; *Int'l*, pg. 3947
JIANGSU HIGH HOPE CONVENTION & EXHIBITION CORP.—See Jiangsu High Hope International Group Corporation; *Int'l*, pg. 3947
JIANGSU HIGH HOPE INTERNATIONAL GROUP CORPORATION; *Int'l*, pg. 3947
JIANGSU HIGH HOPE INTERNATIONAL GROUP LAIY-INDA CO., LTD.—See Jiangsu High Hope International Group Corporation; *Int'l*, pg. 3947
JIANGSU HIGH HOPE INTERNATIONAL GROUP SUNSHINE IMPORT & EXPORT CORPORATION—See Jiangsu High Hope International Group Corporation; *Int'l*, pg. 3947
JIANGSU HIGH HOPE VENTURE CO., LTD.—See Jiangsu High Hope International Group Corporation; *Int'l*, pg. 3947
JIANGSU HOLLY CREATIONS CO., LTD.—See SOHO Holly Corporation; *Int'l*, pg. 7059
JIANGSU HOLLY ENVIRONMENTAL TECHNOLOGY INDUSTIRIAL CO., LTD.—See SOHO Holly Corporation; *Int'l*, pg. 7059
JIANGSU HOLLY EVERLASTING INC.—See SOHO Holly Corporation; *Int'l*, pg. 7059
JIANGSU HOLLY EVER-PRIME INTERNATIONAL CO., LTD.—See SOHO Holly Corporation; *Int'l*, pg. 7059
JIANGSU HOLLY INTERNATIONAL TECHNICAL ENGINEERING CO., LTD.—See SOHO Holly Corporation; *Int'l*, pg. 7059
JIANGSU HOLLY SHINE CO., LTD.—See SOHO Holly Corporation; *Int'l*, pg. 7059
JIANGSU HOLLY UWILL INT'L CO., LTD.—See SOHO Holly Corporation; *Int'l*, pg. 7060
JIANGSU HONGDE SPECIAL PARTS CO., LTD.; *Int'l*, pg. 3947
JIANGSU HONGDOU INDUSTRIAL CO., LTD.; *Int'l*, pg. 3947
JIANGSU HONGSHENG LEATHER CO., LTD.—See WW Holding Inc; *Int'l*, pg. 8516
JIANGSU HONGTIAN TECHNOLOGY CO., LTD.; *Int'l*, pg. 3948
JIANGSU HONGTU HIGH TECHNOLOGY CO., LTD.; *Int'l*, pg. 3948
JIANGSU HOPERUN SOFTWARE CO., LTD.; *Int'l*, pg. 3948
JIANGSU HORIEN CONTACT LENS CO., LTD.—See Ginko international Co., Ltd.; *Int'l*, pg. 2977
JIANGSU HUACHANG CHEMICAL CO., LTD.; *Int'l*, pg. 3948
JIANGSU HUADONG SYP GLASS CO., LTD.—See Shanghai Yaohua Pilkington Glass Group Co., Ltd.; *Int'l*, pg. 6782
JIANGSU HUAHONG TECHNOLOGY STOCK CO., LTD.; *Int'l*, pg. 3948
JIANGSU HUAI YIN CHIA TAI CO., LTD.—See Charoen Pokphand Foods Public Company Limited; *Int'l*, pg. 1453
JIANGSU HUALAN NEW PHARMACEUTICAL MATERIAL CO., LTD.; *Int'l*, pg. 3948
JIANGSU HUASHENG TIANLONG PHOTOELECTRIC CO., LTD.; *Int'l*, pg. 3948
JIANGSU HUAXICUN CO., LTD.; *Int'l*, pg. 3948
JIANGSU HUAXIN NEW MATERIAL CO., LTD.; *Int'l*, pg. 3948
JIANGSU HUIFENG BIO-AGRICULTURE CO., LTD.; *Int'l*, pg. 3948
JIANGSU IDEAL MEDICAL SCIENCE & TECHNOLOGY CO., LTD—See Shanghai Kinetic Medical Co., Ltd.; *Int'l*, pg. 6774
JIANGSU IHI FENGDONG VACUUM TECHNOLOGY CO., LTD.—See IHI Corporation; *Int'l*, pg. 3606
JIANGSU INNOVATIVE ECOLOGICAL NEW MATERIALS LTD.; *Int'l*, pg. 3948
JIANG SU INOAC JUTENG POLYMER CO., LTD—See INOAC Corporation; *Int'l*, pg. 3714
JIANGSU JFE SHOJI STEEL PRODUCTS CO., LTD.—See JFE Holdings, Inc.; *Int'l*, pg. 3937
JIANGSU JIANGNAN HIGH POLYMER FIBER CO., LTD.; *Int'l*, pg. 3948
JIANGSU JIANGNAN WATER CO., LTD.; *Int'l*, pg. 3948
JIANGSU JIANGYIN RURAL COMMERCIAL BANK.; *Int'l*, pg. 3949
JIANGSU JIBEIER PHARMACEUTICAL CO., LTD.; *Int'l*, pg. 3949
JIANGSU JIEJIE MICROELECTRONICS CO LTD; *Int'l*, pg. 3949
JIANGSU JINFANGYUAN CNC MACHINE CO., LTD.—See TRUMPF SE + Co. KG; *Int'l*, pg. 7942
JIANGSU JINGXUE INSULATION TECHNOLOGY CO., LTD.; *Int'l*, pg. 3949
JIANGSU JINGYUAN ENVIRONMENTAL PROTECTION CO., LTD.; *Int'l*, pg. 3949
JIANGSU JINJI INDUSTRIAL CO., LTD.; *Int'l*, pg. 3949
JIANGSU JINLING SPORTS EQUIPMENT CO., LTD.; *Int'l*, pg. 3949
JIANGSU JINSHENG INDUSTRY CO., LTD.; *Int'l*, pg. 3949
JIANGSU JIUWU HITECH CO., LTD.; *Int'l*, pg. 3949
JIANGSU JUJIE MICROFIBER TECHNOLOGY GROUP CO., LTD.; *Int'l*, pg. 3949
JIANGSU JURONG CHEMICAL CO., LTD.—See SunVic Chemical Holdings Limited; *Int'l*, pg. 7328
JIANGSU KAILONG BAODUN POWER TECHNOLOGY CO., LTD.—See Kailong High Technology Co., Ltd.; *Int'l*, pg. 4051
JIANGSU KANGBEI DE PHARMACEUTICAL CO.—See Zhejiang Jihua Group Co., Ltd.; *Int'l*, pg. 8657
JIANGSU KANION PHARMACEUTICAL CO., LTD.; *Int'l*, pg. 3949
JIANGSU KINFA SCI. & TECH. ADVANCED MATERIALS CO. LTD.—See Kingfa Sci &Tech Co., Ltd.; *Int'l*, pg. 4172
JIANGSU KINGFA SCI & TECH ADVANCED MATERIALS CO., LTD.—See Kingfa Sci &Tech Co., Ltd.; *Int'l*, pg. 4172
JIANGSU KING'S LUCK BREWERY JOINT-STOCK CO., LTD.; *Int'l*, pg. 3949
JIANGSU KUAIDA AGROCHEMICAL CO., LTD.—See Lier Chemical Co., Ltd.; *Int'l*, pg. 4492
JIANGSU KUANGDA AUTOMOBILE TEXTILE GROUP, INC - CHANGZHOU PLANT—See Kuangda Technology Group Co., Ltd.; *Int'l*, pg. 4319
JIANGSU KUANGDA ELECTRIC POWER INVESTMENT CO., LTD.—See Kuangda Technology Group Co., Ltd.; *Int'l*, pg. 4319
JIANGSU KUANGSHUN PHOTOSENSITIVITY NEW-MATERIAL STOCK CO., LTD. - GUANGZHOU DIVISION—See Jiangsu Kuangshun Photosensitivity New-Material Stock Co., Ltd.; *Int'l*, pg. 3949
JIANGSU KUANGSHUN PHOTOSENSITIVITY NEW-MATERIAL STOCK CO., LTD.; *Int'l*, pg. 3949
JIANGSU LANFENG BIO-CHEMICAL CO., LTD.; *Int'l*, pg. 3949
JIANGSU LEADER ELECTRONICS CO., LTD.—See Leader Electronics Inc.; *Int'l*, pg. 4433
JIANGSU LEADER ELECTRONICS INC.—See Leader Electronics Inc.; *Int'l*, pg. 4433
JIANGSU LEASTY CHEMICAL CO., LTD.—See Shuangliang Eco-Energy Systems Company Limited; *Int'l*, pg. 6868
JIANGSU LEE & MAN CHEMICAL LIMITED—See Lee & Man Chemical Company Limited; *Int'l*, pg. 4439
JIANGSU LEE & MAN PAPER MANUFACTURING COMPANY LIMITED—See Lee & Man Paper Manufacturing Limited; *Int'l*, pg. 4440
JIANGSU LEIKE DEFENSE TECHNOLOGY CO., LTD.; *Int'l*, pg. 3950
JIANGSU LEILI MOTOR CORPORATION LIMITED; *Int'l*, pg. 3950
JIANGSU LETTALL ELECTRONICS CO., LTD.; *Int'l*, pg. 3950
JIANGSU LIANCE ELECTROMECHANICAL TECHNOLOGY CO., LTD.; *Int'l*, pg. 3950
JIANGSU LIANFA TEXTILE CO., LTD.; *Int'l*, pg. 3950
JIANGSU LIANHUAN PHARMACEUTICAL CO., LTD.; *Int'l*, pg. 3950
JIANGSU LIANYUNGANG PORT CO., LTD.; *Int'l*, pg. 3950
JIANGSU LIBA ENTERPRISE JOINT-STOCK CO., LTD.; *Int'l*, pg. 3950
JIANGSU LIDAO NEW MATERIAL CO., LTD.; *Int'l*, pg. 3950
JIANGSU LIHUA ANIMAL HUSBANDRY STOCK CO., LTD.; *Int'l*, pg. 3950
JIANGSU LINYANG ENERGY CO., LTD.; *Int'l*, pg. 3950
JIANGSU LINYANG SOLARFUN CO., LTD.—See Hanwha Group; *Int'l*, pg. 3265
JIANGSU LIVON AUTOMOTIVE COMPONENTS TECHNOLOGY CO., LTD—See Ningbo Tianlong Electronics Co., Ltd.; *Int'l*, pg. 5306
JIANGSU LIXING GENERAL STEEL BALL CO., LTD.; *Int'l*, pg. 3950
JIANGSU LONGYUAN WIND POWER GENERATION CO., LTD.—See China Longyuan Power Group Corp Ltd.; *Int'l*, pg. 1515
JIANGSU LOPAL TECHNOLOGY CO., LTD.; *Int'l*, pg. 3950
JIANGSU LUCALA LIGHTING TECHNOLOGY CO., LTD.—See Jiangsu Linyang Energy Co., Ltd.; *Int'l*, pg. 3950
JIANGSU LUOKAI MECHANICAL & ELECTRICAL CO., LTD.; *Int'l*, pg. 3950
JIANGSU MAIXINLIN AVIATION SCIENCE & TECHNOLOGY CORP.; *Int'l*, pg. 3951
JIANGSU MAYSTA CHEMICAL CO., LTD.; *Int'l*, pg. 3951
JIANGSU MEMSTAR MEMBRANE MATERIAL TECHNOLOGY CO., LTD.—See Memstar Technology Ltd.; *Int'l*, pg. 4814
JIANGSU MINGFA INDUSTRIAL RAW MATERIAL CO., LTD.—See Mingfa Group (International) Company Limited; *Int'l*, pg. 4909
JIANGSU MOBIS AUTOMOTIVE PARTS CO., LTD.—See Hyundai MOBIS Co., Ltd.; *Int'l*, pg. 3558
JIANGSU NABTESCO KTK RAILROAD PRODUCTS CO., LTD.—See Nabtesco Corporation; *Int'l*, pg. 5119
JIANGSU NANDASOFT TECHNOLOGY COMPANY LIMITED; *Int'l*, pg. 3951
JIANGSU NANFANG BEARING CO., LTD.; *Int'l*, pg. 3951
JIANGSU NANFANG MEDICAL CO., LTD.; *Int'l*, pg. 3951
JIANGSU NATA OPTO-ELECTRONIC MATERIAL CO., LTD.; *Int'l*, pg. 3951
JIANGSU NEWAMSTAR PACKAGING MCHNRY CO LTD; *Int'l*, pg. 3951

COMPANY NAME INDEX

JIANGSU NEW ENERGY DEVELOPMENT CO., LTD.; *Int'l*, pg. 3951
JIANGSU NEW TRADE IMPORT & EXPORT CORP.—See Jiangsu Phoenix Publishing & Media Corporation Ltd.; *Int'l*, pg. 3952
JIANGSU NEW UNIVERSE ENVIRONMENTAL ENGINEERING MANAGEMENT LIMITED—See New Universe Environmental Group Limited; *Int'l*, pg. 5228
JIANGSU NEW YANGZI SHIPBUILDING CO., LTD—See Yangzijiang Shipbuilding (Holdings) Ltd; *Int'l*, pg. 8561
JIANGSU NHWA PHARMACEUTICAL CORPORATION LTD.; *Int'l*, pg. 3951
JIANGSU NISSIN-SINOTRANS INTERNATIONAL TRANSPORTATION CO., LTD.—See Nissin Corporation; *Int'l*, pg. 5375
JIANGSU NONGHUA INTELLIGENT AGRICULTURE TECHNOLOGY CO., LTD.; *Int'l*, pg. 3951
JIANGSU OFS HENGTONG OPTICAL TECHNOLOGY CO., LTD.—See The Furukawa Electric Co., Ltd.; *Int'l*, pg. 7646
JIANGSU OJI PAPER CO., LTD.—See Oji Holdings Corporation; *Int'l*, pg. 5536
JIANGSU OLIVE SENSORS HIGH-TECH CO LTD; *Int'l*, pg. 3951
JIANGSU O.R.G PACKING CO., LTD.—See ORG Technology Co., Ltd.; *Int'l*, pg. 5617
JIANGSU PACIFIC MILLENNIUM PACKAGING & PAPER INDUSTRIES CO., LTD.—See Pacific Millennium Packaging Group Corporation; *Int'l*, pg. 5691
JIANGSU PACIFIC PRECISION FORGING; *Int'l*, pg. 3951
JIANGSU PACIFIC QUARTZ CO., LTD.; *Int'l*, pg. 3951
JIANGSU PARKTEC PARKING EQUIPMENT CO., LTD.; *Int'l*, pg. 3951
JIANGSU PENGLING RUBBER HOSE CO., LTD.—See Tianjin Pengling Group Co., Ltd.; *Int'l*, pg. 7740
JIANGSU PEOPLE'S PUBLISHING HOUSE LTD.—See Jiangsu Phoenix Publishing & Media Corporation Ltd.; *Int'l*, pg. 3952
JIANGSU PEOPLE'S PUBLISHING LTD.—See Jiangsu Phoenix Publishing & Media Corporation Ltd.; *Int'l*, pg. 3952
JIANGSU PERMANENT EXPENSIVE NEW ENERGY TECHNOLOGY CO., LTD.—See Zhejiang Yonggui Electric Equipment Co., Ltd.; *Int'l*, pg. 0007
JIANGSU PHOENIX EDUCATION DEVELOPMENT LTD.—See Jiangsu Phoenix Publishing & Media Corporation Ltd.; *Int'l*, pg. 3952
JIANGSU PHOENIX PROPERTY INVESTMENT CO., LTD.; *Int'l*, pg. 3951
JIANGSU PHOENIX PUBLISHING & MEDIA CORPORATION LTD.; *Int'l*, pg. 3951
JIANGSU PHOENIX VOCATIONAL EDUCATION BOOKS LTD.—See Jiangsu Phoenix Publishing & Media Corporation Ltd.; *Int'l*, pg. 3952
JIANGSU PILKINGTON SYP GLASS CO. LTD.—See Shanghai Yaohua Pilkington Glass Group Co., Ltd.; *Int'l*, pg. 6782
JIANGSU PROTRULY TECHNOLOGY GROUP CO., LTD.; *Int'l*, pg. 3952
JIANGSU PROVINCIAL AGRICULTURAL RECLAMATION & DEVELOPMENT CO., LTD.; *Int'l*, pg. 3952
JIANGSU PULANNA COATING CO., LTD.—See The Sherwin-Williams Company; *U.S. Public*, pg. 2128
JIANGSU RAINBOW HEAVY INDUSTRIES CO., LTD.; *Int'l*, pg. 3952
JIANGSU RECBIO TECHNOLOGY CO., LTD.; *Int'l*, pg. 3952
JIANGSU RIJIU OPTOELECTRONICS JOINTSTOCK CO., LTD.; *Int'l*, pg. 3952
JIANGSU RIYING ELECTRONICS CO., LTD.; *Int'l*, pg. 3953
JIANGSU RONGTAI INDUSTRY CO., LTD.; *Int'l*, pg. 3953
JIANGSU ROTAM CHEMISTRY CO., LTD.—See Rotam Global AgroSciences Ltd.; *Int'l*, pg. 6402
JIANGSU ROYAL HOME USA, INC.; *U.S. Private*, pg. 2208
JIANGSU RUITAI NEW ENERGY MATERIALS CO., LTD.; *Int'l*, pg. 3953
JIANGSU RUTONG PETRO-MACHINERY CO,.LTD; *Int'l*, pg. 3953
JIANGSU SAFETY GROUP CO.,LTD; *Int'l*, pg. 3953
JIANGSU SAINTY APPAREL CO., LTD.—See Jiangsu Sainty Corp., Ltd.; *Int'l*, pg. 3953
JIANGSU SAINTY CHEMICAL STORAGE CO., LTD.—See Jiangsu Sainty Corp., Ltd.; *Int'l*, pg. 3953
JIANGSU SAINTY CORP., LTD.; *Int'l*, pg. 3953
JIANGSU SAINTY EAGLE & MFG CO., LTD.—See Jiangsu Sainty Corp., Ltd.; *Int'l*, pg. 3953
JIANGSU SAINTY FOOD TRADE CO., LTD.—See Jiangsu Sainty Corp., Ltd.; *Int'l*, pg. 3953
JIANGSU SAINTY FORTUNE CO., LTD.—See Jiangsu Sainty Corp., Ltd.; *Int'l*, pg. 3953
JIANGSU SAINTY HANDSOME CO., LTD.—See Jiangsu Sainty Corp., Ltd.; *Int'l*, pg. 3953
JIANGSU SAINTY JINTAN GARMENTS CO.—See Jiangsu Sainty Corp., Ltd.; *Int'l*, pg. 3953
JIANGSU SAINTY LAND-UP PRO-TRADING CO., LTD.—See Jiangsu Sainty Corp., Ltd.; *Int'l*, pg. 3953
JIANGSU SAINTY SAINTEK COMPANY LIMITED—See Jiangsu Sainty Corp., Ltd.; *Int'l*, pg. 3953
JIANGSU SAINTY SUITS CO., LTD.—See Jiangsu Sainty Corp., Ltd.; *Int'l*, pg. 3953
JIANGSU SANFANGXIANG CO., LTD.; *Int'l*, pg. 3953
JIANGSU SEAGULL COOLING TOWER CO., LTD.; *Int'l*, pg. 3953
JIANGSU SECOM SECURITY CO., LTD.—See SECOM Co., Ltd.; *Int'l*, pg. 6671
JIANGSU SENXUAN PHARMACEUTICAL & CHEMICAL CO., LTD.; *Int'l*, pg. 3953
JIANGSU SEUNG LIM ELECTRIC CO. LTD.—See Schunk GmbH; *Int'l*, pg. 6641
JIANGSU SHAGANG CO., LTD.; *Int'l*, pg. 3953
JIANGSU SHAGANG GROUP LTD.; *Int'l*, pg. 3954
JIANGSU SHEMAR ELECTRIC CO., LTD.; *Int'l*, pg. 3954
JIANGSU SHENHUA PHARMACEUTICAL CO., LTD.—See Fufeng Group Limited; *Int'l*, pg. 2804
JIANGSU SHENTONG VALVE CO., LTD.; *Int'l*, pg. 3954
JIANGSU SHUANGXING COLOR PLASTIC NEW MATERTALS CO., LTD.; *Int'l*, pg. 3954
JIANGSU SHUNFENG PHOTOVOLTAIC TECHNOLOGY CO., LTD.—See Shunfeng International Clean Energy Ltd.; *Int'l*, pg. 6870
JIANGSU SIDIKE NEW MATERIALS SCIENCE & TECHNOLOGY CO., LTD.; *Int'l*, pg. 3954
JIANGSU SIHUAN BIOENGINEERING CO., LTD.; *Int'l*, pg. 3954
JIANGSU SIMCERE PHARMACEUTICAL R&D CO., LTD.—See Simcere Pharmaceutical Group; *Int'l*, pg. 6928
JIANGSU SIMCERE VAXTEC BIO-PHARMACEUTICAL CO., LTD.—See Simcere Pharmaceutical Group; *Int'l*, pg. 6928
JIANGSU SINOJIT WIND ENERGY TECHNOLOGY CO., LTD.; *Int'l*, pg. 3954
JIANGSU SINOTEC CO., LTD.—See Shanghai Sinotec Co., Ltd.; *Int'l*, pg. 6778
JIANGSU SKYRAY INSTRUMENT CO., LTD.; *Int'l*, pg. 3954
JIANGSU SMARTWIN ELECTRONICS TECHNOLOGY CO., LTD.; *Int'l*, pg. 3954
JIANGSU SMITH NEW MATERIAL TECHNOLOGY CO., LTD.—See Shanghai Smith Adhesive New Material Co., Ltd.; *Int'l*, pg. 6779
JIANGSU SOPO CHEMICAL CO., LTD.; *Int'l*, pg. 3954
JIANGSU STANDARD-DIA BIOPHARMA CO., LTD.—See Standard Chem. & Pharm. Co., Ltd.; *Int'l*, pg. 7168
JIANGSU SUNEL TRANSFORMER CO., LTD.—See Guodian Nanjing Automation Co., Ltd.; *Int'l*, pg. 3186
JIANGSU SUNERA TECHNOLOGY CO., LTD.—See Valiant Co., Ltd.; *Int'l*, pg. 8115
JIANGSU SUNPOWER HEAT EXCHANGER & PRESSURE VESSEL CO., LTD.—See Sunpower Group Ltd.; *Int'l*, pg. 7320
JIANGSU SUNPOWER PIPING TECHNOLOGY CO., LTD.—See Sunpower Group Ltd.; *Int'l*, pg. 7320
JIANGSU SUNPOWER TECHNOLOGY CO., LTD.—See Sunpower Group Ltd.; *Int'l*, pg. 7320
JIANGSU SUNSHINE CO., LTD.; *Int'l*, pg. 3954
JIANGSU SUYAN JINGSHEN CO., LTD.; *Int'l*, pg. 3955
JIANGSU SUZHOU RURAL COMMERCIAL BANK CO., LTD; *Int'l*, pg. 3955
JIANGSU TAIJI INDUSTRY NEW MATERIALS CO., LTD.—See Wuxi Taiji Industry Co., Ltd.; *Int'l*, pg. 8516
JIANGSU TAISINTONG MACHINERY TECHNOLOGY CO., LTD.—See Sintokogio Ltd.; *Int'l*, pg. 6958
JIANGSU TAITONG FOOD LIMITED COMPANY—See Ottogi Corporation; *Int'l*, pg. 5665
JIANGSU TASLY DIYI PHARMACEUTICAL CO., LTD.—See Tasly Pharmaceutical Group Co., Ltd.; *Int'l*, pg. 7465
JIANGSU TELECOM COMPANY LIMITED—See China Telecommunications Corporation; *Int'l*, pg. 1558
JIANGSU TIANMU LAKE TOURISM CO., LTD.; *Int'l*, pg. 3955
JIANGSU TIMES TEXTILE TECHNOLOGY CO., LTD.; *Int'l*, pg. 3955
JIANGSU TOKYO ROPE CO., LTD.—See Tokyo Rope Manufacturing Co., Ltd.; *Int'l*, pg. 7794
JIANGSU TOLAND ALLOY CO., LTD.; *Int'l*, pg. 3955
JIANGSU TONGDA POWER TECHNOLOGY CO., LTD.; *Int'l*, pg. 3955
JIANGSU TONGGUANG ELECTRONIC WIRE & CABLE CORP., LTD.; *Int'l*, pg. 3955
JIANGSU TONGGUANG OPTICAL FIBER CABLE CO., LTD—See Jiangsu Tongguang Electronic Wire & Cable Corp., Ltd.; *Int'l*, pg. 3955
JIANGSU TONGGUANG TRANSMISSION LINES TECHNOLOGY CO.—See Jiangsu Tongguang Electronic Wire & Cable Corp., Ltd.; *Int'l*, pg. 3955
JIANGSU TONGLING ELECTRIC CO., LTD.; *Int'l*, pg. 3955
JIANGSU TONGLI RISHENG MACHINERY CO., LTD.; *Int'l*, pg. 3955
JIANGSU TONGRUN EQUIPMENT TECHNOLOGY CO., LTD.; *Int'l*, pg. 3955
JIANGSU TONGXINGBAO INTELLIGENT TRANSPORTATION TECHNOLOGY CO., LTD.; *Int'l*, pg. 3955
JIANGSU TONG YANG MACHINERY CO., LTD.—See Tym Corporation; *Int'l*, pg. 7995
JIANGSU TON YI TINPLATE CO., LTD.—See Uni-President Enterprises Corporation; *Int'l*, pg. 8028
JIANGSU TOYO RENXIN PIGMENT CO., LTD.—See Toyo Ink SC Holdings Co., Ltd.; *Int'l*, pg. 7853
JIANGSU TRANSIMAGE TECHNOLOGY CO., LTD.; *Int'l*, pg. 3955
JIANGSU TRIGIANT TECHNOLOGY CO., LTD.—See Trigiant Group Limited; *Int'l*, pg. 7921
JIANGSU TSC COATING CO., LTD.—See Hilong Holding Limited; *Int'l*, pg. 3393
JIANGSU TUV PRODUCT SERVICE LIMITED—See TUV SUD AG; *Int'l*, pg. 7984
JIANGSU TWB BEARINGS CO., LTD.—See The Timken Company; *U.S. Public*, pg. 2132
JIANGSU WANLIN MODERN LOGISTICS CO., LTD.; *Int'l*, pg. 3955
JIANGSU WANLIN WOOD INDUSTRIAL PARK CO., LTD.—See Jiangsu Wanlin Modern Logistics Co., Ltd.; *Int'l*, pg. 3955
JIANGSU WANLONG AUTOMATION EQUIPMENT CO., LTD.—See Endress+Hauser (International) Holding AG; *Int'l*, pg. 2408
JIANGSU WEIMING NEW MATERIAL CO., LTD.—See China Petrochemical Development Corp.; *Int'l*, pg. 1540
JIANGSU WENRUN OPTOELECTRONIC CO., LTD.—See Shin Hwa World Limited; *Int'l*, pg. 6836
JIANGSU WOTE ADVANCED MATERIALS TECHNOLOGY CO., LTD.—See Shenzhen Wote Advanced Materials Co., Ltd.; *Int'l*, pg. 6824
JIANGSU WUJIN STAINLESS STEEL PIPE GROUP CO., LTD; *Int'l*, pg. 3955
JIANGSU WUTONG INTERCONNECT TECHNOLOGY CO., LTD.—See Wutong Holding Group Co., Ltd.; *Int'l*, pg. 8514
JIANGSU WUZHONG PHARMACEUTICAL DEVELOPMENT CO., LTD.; *Int'l*, pg. 3955
JIANGSU XIANGYUAN ELECTRIC EQUIPMENT CO., LTD.—See Hubbell Incorporated; *U.S. Public*, pg. 1067
JIANGSU XIEHE ELECTRONIC CO., LTD.; *Int'l*, pg. 3956
JIANGSU XINGDA STEEL CORD CO., LTD.—See Xingda International Holdings Ltd; *Int'l*, pg. 8529
JIANGSU XINHUA DISTRIBUTION GROUP LTD.—See Jiangsu Phoenix Publishing & Media Corporation Ltd.; *Int'l*, pg. 3952
JIANGSU XINQUAN AUTOMOTIVE TRIM CO., LTD.; *Int'l*, pg. 3956
JIANGSU XINRI E-VEHICLE CO., LTD.; *Int'l*, pg. 3956
JIANGSU XIN YU ENVIRONMENTAL TECHNOLOGIES LIMITED—See New Universe Environmental Group Limited; *Int'l*, pg. 5228
JIANGSU XIUQIANG GLASS WORK CO., LTD.; *Int'l*, pg. 3956
JIANGSU YABANG DYESTUFF CO., LTD.; *Int'l*, pg. 3956
JIANGSU YANGDIAN SCIENCE & TECHNOLOGY CO., LTD.; *Int'l*, pg. 3956
JIANGSU YANGHE BREWERY JOINT-STOCK CO., LTD.; *Int'l*, pg. 3956
JIANGSU YANGJINXIN PRINTING & PACKAGING CO., LTD.—See MYS Group Co., Ltd.; *Int'l*, pg. 5114
JIANGSU YANGNONG CHEMICAL CO., LTD.; *Int'l*, pg. 3956
JIANGSU YANGZI-MITSUI SHIPBUILDING CO., LTD.—See Yangzijiang Shipbuilding (Holdings) Ltd; *Int'l*, pg. 8561
JIANGSU YAWEI MACHINE TOOL CO., LTD.; *Int'l*, pg. 3956
JIANGSU YAWEI STOCK CO.,LTD.—See Jiangsu Yawei Machine Tool Co., Ltd.; *Int'l*, pg. 3956
JIANGSU YIDA CHEMICAL CO., LTD.; *Int'l*, pg. 3956
JIANGSU YIKE FOOD GROUP CO., LTD.; *Int'l*, pg. 3956
JIANGSU YINGDA INFORMATION TECHNOLOGY CO., LTD.—See Global Infotech Co., Ltd.; *Int'l*, pg. 2997
JIANGSU YINHE ELECTRONICS CO., LTD.; *Int'l*, pg. 3956
JIANGSU YINHE TONGZHI NEW ENERGY TECHNOLOGY CO., LTD.—See Jiangsu Yinhe Electronics Co., Ltd.; *Int'l*, pg. 3956
JIANGSU YINREN GROUP CO., LTD.; *Int'l*, pg. 3956
JIANGSU YITONG HIGH-TECH CO., LTD.; *Int'l*, pg. 3956
JIANGSU YOKE TECHNOLOGY CO., LTD.; *Int'l*, pg. 3956
JIANGSU YUANFANG CABLE FACTORY CO., LTD.—See Jiangsu Zhongchao Holding Co., Ltd.; *Int'l*, pg. 3957
JIANGSU YUEDA GROUP CO., LTD.; *Int'l*, pg. 3957
JIANGSU YUEXIN PHARMACEUTICAL CO., LTD.—See Zhejiang Anglikang Pharmaceutical Co., Ltd.; *Int'l*, pg. 8648
JIANGSU YUNYI ELECTRIC CO., LTD.; *Int'l*, pg. 3957
JIANGSU YUNYONG ELECTRONICS & TECHNOLOGY CO., LTD.; *Int'l*, pg. 3957
JIANGSU YUXING FILM TECHNOLOGY CO., LTD.; *Int'l*, pg. 3957
JIANGSU YUYUE MEDICAL EQUIPMENT & SUPPLY CO., LTD.; *Int'l*, pg. 3957
JIANGSU ZEOCHEM TECHNOLOGY CO. LTD.—See CPH Chemie + Papier Holding AG; *Int'l*, pg. 1824
JIANGSU ZEYU INTELLIGENT ELECTRIC POWER CO., LTD.; *Int'l*, pg. 3957

JIANGSU ZEYU INTELLIGENT ELECTRIC POWER CO., LTD.

CORPORATE AFFILIATIONS

JIANGSU ZHANGJIAGANG CQRC VILLAGE & TOWNSHIP BANK CO., LTD.—See Chongqing Rural Commercial Bank Co., Ltd.; *Int'l*, pg. 1581
JIANGSU ZHANGJIAGANG RURAL COMMERCIAL BANK CO., LTD; *Int'l*, pg. 3957
JIANGSU ZHENGDAN CHEMICAL INDUSTRY CO., LTD.; *Int'l*, pg. 3957
JIANGSU ZHENJIANG NEW ENERGY EQUIPMENT CO., LTD.; *Int'l*, pg. 3957
JIANGSU ZHONGCHAO HOLDING CO., LTD.; *Int'l*, pg. 3957
JIANGSU ZHONGJI LAMINATION MATERIALS CO., LTD—See Shantou Wanshun New Material Group Co., Ltd.; *Int'l*, pg. 6785
JIANGSU ZHONGJIN MATAI MEDICINAL PACKAGING CO., LTD.—See Rengo Co., Ltd.; *Int'l*, pg. 6280
JIANGSU ZHONGKE INTELLIGENT SYSTEM CO., LTD.—See China Security Co., Ltd.; *Int'l*, pg. 1550
JIANGSU ZHONGLI GROUP CO., LTD.; *Int'l*, pg. 3957
JIANGSU ZHONGNAN CONSTRUCTION GROUP CO., LTD.; *Int'l*, pg. 3958
JIANGSU ZHONGSHE GROUP CO., LTD.; *Int'l*, pg. 3958
JIANGSU ZHONGSHENG GAOKE ENVIRONMENTAL CO., LTD; *Int'l*, pg. 3958
JIANGSU ZHONGTIAN TECHNOLOGY CO., LTD.; *Int'l*, pg. 3958
JIANGSU ZIJIN RURAL COMMERCIAL BANK CO., LTD.; *Int'l*, pg. 3958
JIANGSU ZITIAN MEDIA TECHNOLOGY CO., LTD.; *Int'l*, pg. 3958
JIANGSU ZIWEI FLAX CO., LTD.—See Kingdom Holdings Limited; *Int'l*, pg. 4172
JIANGSU ZONGYI CO., LTD.; *Int'l*, pg. 3958
JIANGXI ALBEMARLE LITHIUM CO., LTD.—See Albemarle Corporation; *U.S. Public*, pg. 73
JIANGXI ANDELI HIGH TECH CO., LTD.—See Foshan Golden Milky Way Intelligent Equipment Co., Ltd.; *Int'l*, pg. 2748
JIANGXI BAISHENG INTELLIGENT TECHNOLOGY CO., LTD.; *Int'l*, pg. 3958
JIANGXI BANK CO., LTD.; *Int'l*, pg. 3958
JIANGXI BLACK CAT CARBON BLACK CO., LTD.; *Int'l*, pg. 3958
JIANGXI BROTHER PHARMACEUTICAL CO., LTD.—Brother Enterprises Holding Co., Ltd.; *Int'l*, pg. 1196
JIANGXI BUILDING MATERIALS COMPANY—See Dalian Shide Group Co., Ltd.; *Int'l*, pg. 1952
JIANGXI CHANGELIGHT CO., LTD.—See Xiamen Changelight Co., Ltd.; *Int'l*, pg. 8523
JIANGXI CHANGHE SUZUKI AUTOMOBILE CO., LTD.—See Suzuki Motor Corporation; *Int'l*, pg. 7354
JIANGXI CHANGJIU BIOCHEMICAL INDUSTRY CO., LTD.; *Int'l*, pg. 3958
JIANGXI CHANGYUN CO., LTD.; *Int'l*, pg. 3958
JIANGXI CHENGUANG NEW MATERIALS CO., LTD.; *Int'l*, pg. 3958
JIANGXI COPPER COMPANY LIMITED; *Int'l*, pg. 3958
JIANGXI COPPER CORPJIANGXI COPPER CORPORATION MATERIAL & EQUIPMENT COMPANY—See Jiangxi Copper Company Limited; *Int'l*, pg. 3959
JIANGXI COPPER INTERNATIONAL TRADING CO., LTD.—See Jiangxi Copper Company Limited; *Int'l*, pg. 3959
JIANGXI CRYSTAL OPTECH CO., LTD.—See Zhejiang Crystal-optech Co., Ltd.; *Int'l*, pg. 8650
JIANGXI DATANG CHEMICALS CO., LTD.—See Daikin Industries, Ltd.; *Int'l*, pg. 1935
JIANGXI DOWA ENVIRONMENTAL MANAGEMENT CO., LTD.—See Dowa Holdings Co., Ltd.; *Int'l*, pg. 2183
JIANGXI EVERBRIGHT MEASUREMENT & CONTROL TECHNOLOGY CO., LTD.; *Int'l*, pg. 3959
JIANGXI FIRSTAR PANEL TECHNOLOGY CO LTD; *Int'l*, pg. 3959
JIANGXI FOCI FIBER OPTIC COMMUNICATION, INC.—See Foci Fiber Optic Communications, Inc.; *Int'l*, pg. 2718
JIANGXI FUXIANG PHARMACEUTICAL CO., LTD.; *Int'l*, pg. 3959
JIANGXI GANFENG LITHIUM CO., LTD.; *Int'l*, pg. 3959
JIANGXI GANNENG CO., LTD.; *Int'l*, pg. 3959
JIANGXI GANYUE EXPRESSWAY CO., LTD.; *Int'l*, pg. 3959
JIANGXI GEM RESOURCE RECYCLING CO., LTD.—See GEM Co., Ltd.; *Int'l*, pg. 2914
JIANGXI GEM SCRAPPED CAR RECYCLING CO., LTD.—See GEM Co., Ltd.; *Int'l*, pg. 2914
JIANGXI GETO NEW MATERIALS CORPORATION LIMITED; *Int'l*, pg. 3959
JIANGXI GLOBAL CHEMICAL INDUSTRIAL CO., LTD; *Int'l*, pg. 3959
JIANGXI GUOGUANG COMMERCIAL CHAINS CO., LTD.; *Int'l*, pg. 3959
JIANGXI GUOTAI GROUP CO., LTD.; *Int'l*, pg. 3959
JIANGXI HAIYUAN COMPOSITES TECHNOLOGY CO.,LTD.; *Int'l*, pg. 3959
JIANGXI HENGDA HI-TECH CO., LTD.; *Int'l*, pg. 3959
JIANGXI HONGCHENG ENVIRONMENT CO., LTD; *Int'l*, pg. 3959

JIANGXI HONGDU AVIATION INDUSTRY CO., LTD.; *Int'l*, pg. 3959
JIANGXI HUANGSHANGHUANG GROUP FOOD CO., LTD.; *Int'l*, pg. 3959
JIANGXI HUATE ELECTRONIC CHEMICAL CO., LTD.—See Guangdong Huate Gas Co., Ltd.; *Int'l*, pg. 3156
JIANGXI HUAWU BRAKE CO., LTD.; *Int'l*, pg. 3960
JIANGXI HUNGPAI NEW MATERIAL CO., LTD.; *Int'l*, pg. 3960
JIANGXI JDL ENVIRONMENTAL PROTECTION CO., LTD.; *Int'l*, pg. 3960
JIANGXI JIACHANG FORESTRY DEVELOPMENT CO., LTD.—See Emerald Plantation Holdings Limited; *Int'l*, pg. 2378
JIANGXI JOVO ENERGY CO., LTD.; *Int'l*, pg. 3960
JIANGXI KINWONG PRECISION CIRCUIT CO., LTD.—See Shenzhen Kinwong Electronic Co.,Ltd.; *Int'l*, pg. 6816
JIANGXI LANGHE MEDICAL INSTRUMENT CO., LTD.—See Well Lead Medical Co., Ltd.; *Int'l*, pg. 8373
JIANGXI LANTIAN WEI GUANG TECHNOLOGY COMPANY LIMITED—See Tech Pro Technology Development Limited; *Int'l*, pg. 7502
JIANGXI LDK SOLAR HI-TECH CO., LTD.—See LDK Solar Co., Ltd.; *Int'l*, pg. 4431
JIANGXI LEE & MAN CHEMICAL LIMITED—See Lee & Man Chemical Company Limited; *Int'l*, pg. 4439
JIANGXI LIANCHUANG OPTOELECTRONIC SCIENCE & TECHNOLOGY CO., LTD; *Int'l*, pg. 3960
JIANGXI LIDU WINE INDUSTRY CO., LTD.—See ZJLD Group Inc.; *Int'l*, pg. 8686
JIANGXI LINKTREND CABLE TECH CO., LTD.—See Jiangxi Lianchuang Optoelectronic Science & Technology Co., Ltd; *Int'l*, pg. 3960
JIANG XING ELECTRONICS LTD.—See Citizen Watch Co., Ltd.; *Int'l*, pg. 1625
JIANGXI PROVINCE PHARMACEUTICAL GROUP CORPORATION—See China Meheco Group Co., Ltd.; *Int'l*, pg. 1519
JIANGXI QIANGLIAN ELECTRIC PORCELAIN CO., LTD.—See Jinlihua Electric Co., Ltd.; *Int'l*, pg. 3969
JIANG XI SANXI MEDTEC CO., LTD.; *Int'l*, pg. 3942
JIANGXI SELON INDUSTRIAL CO., LTD.; *Int'l*, pg. 3960
JIANGXI SINOMA NEW SOLAR MATERIALS CO., LTD.—See China National Materials, Ltd.; *Int'l*, pg. 1532
JIANGXI SOUTH RARE-EARTH HIGH-TECH CO., LTD.—See Beijing Zhong Ke San Huan High-tech Co., Ltd.; *Int'l*, pg. 961
JIANGXI SPECIAL ELECTRIC MOTOR CO., LTD.; *Int'l*, pg. 3960
JIANGXI SUNREX TECHNOLOGY CORP.—See Sunrex Technology Corporation; *Int'l*, pg. 7321
JIANGXI SYNERGY PHARMACEUTICAL CO., LTD.; *Int'l*, pg. 3960
JIANGXI TAO-TAOGU E-COMMERCE CO., LIMITED—See FinTech Chain Limited; *Int'l*, pg. 2677
JIANGXI TECO ELECTRIC & MACHINERY CO., LTD.—See Teco Electric & Machinery Co., Ltd.; *Int'l*, pg. 7518
JIANGXI TIANLI TECHNOLOGY, INC.; *Int'l*, pg. 3960
JIANGXI TINCI CENTRAL ADVANCED MATERIALS CO., LTD.—See Central Glass Co., Ltd.; *Int'l*, pg. 1407
JIANGXI VANKE YIDA PROPERTY INVESTMENT COMPANY LIMITED—See China Vanke Co., Ltd.; *Int'l*, pg. 1562
JIANGXI WANNIANQING CEMENT CO., LTD.; *Int'l*, pg. 3960
JIANG XI WIRING SYSTEMS CO., LTD.—See Sumitomo Electric Industries, Ltd.; *Int'l*, pg. 7278
JIANGXI XIANGSHENG ENVIRONMENTAL PROTECTION TECHNOLOGY CO., LTD.—See Xiamen Zhongchuang Environmental Technology Co., Ltd.; *Int'l*, pg. 8526
JIANGXI XINYU GUOKE TECHNOLOGY CO., LTD.; *Int'l*, pg. 3960
JIANGXI YADONG CEMENT CO., LTD.—See Asia Cement Corporation; *Int'l*, pg. 611
JIANGXI YALI TRANSPORT CO., LTD.—See Asia Cement Corporation; *Int'l*, pg. 611
JIANGXI YONGDA RONGJIAN AUTOMOBILE SALES AND SERVICES CO., LTD.—See China Yongda Automobiles Services Holdings Limited; *Int'l*, pg. 1564
JIANGXI ZHENGBANG TECHNOLOGY CO., LTD.; *Int'l*, pg. 3960
JIANGXI ZHENGTONG ZETIAN AUTOMOBILE SALES SERVICES CO., LTD.—See China ZhengTong Auto Services Holdings Limited; *Int'l*, pg. 1566
JIANGXI ZHICHEN TECHNOLOGY CO. LTD.—See Shanghai Putailai New Energy Technology Co., Ltd.; *Int'l*, pg. 6777
JIANGYIN BAOZOU AUTOMOBILE SALES AND SERVICES CO., LTD.—See China Yongda Automobiles Services Holdings Limited; *Int'l*, pg. 1564
JIANGYIN CHANGDIAN ADVANCED PACKAGING CO., LTD.—See JCET Group Co., Ltd.; *Int'l*, pg. 3923
JIANGYIN DAODA AUTOMOBILE DECORATIVE PARTS CO., LTD.—See Jiangnan Mould & Plastic Technology Co., Ltd.; *Int'l*, pg. 3942

JIANGYIN DEGI TEC CASTING CO., LTD.—See Jiangnan Mould & Plastic Technology Co., Ltd.; *Int'l*, pg. 3942
JIANGYIN DUAL AUTOMOTIVE TEXTILE CO., LTD.—See DUAL Co. Ltd; *Int'l*, pg. 2217
JIANGYIN DUAL TECH CO., LTD—See DUAL Co. Ltd; *Int'l*, pg. 2217
JIANGYIN ELECTRICAL ALLOY CO., LTD.; *Int'l*, pg. 3960
JIANGYIN FUHUI TEXTILES LIMITED—See Fountain Set (Holdings) Limited; *Int'l*, pg. 2754
JIANGYIN HAIDA RUBBER AND PLASTIC CO., LTD.; *Int'l*, pg. 3960
JIANGYIN HANIL STEEL CO., LTD.—See HISTEEL Co., Ltd.; *Int'l*, pg. 3408
JIANGYIN HENGRUN HEAVY INDUSTRIES CO., LTD.; *Int'l*, pg. 3960
JIANGYIN HENGRUN RING FORGING CO., LTD.—See Jiangyin Hengrun Heavy Industries Co., Ltd.; *Int'l*, pg. 3960
JIANGYIN JIA HUA ADVANCED MATERIAL RESOURCES CO., LTD.—See Brookfield Corporation; *Int'l*, pg. 1181
JIANGYIN JIANGHUAMICRO ELCTRONIC MATERIALS CO., LTD.; *Int'l*, pg. 3960
JIANGYIN JINTIAN MACHINERY LIMITED—See Fountain Set (Holdings) Limited; *Int'l*, pg. 2754
JIANGYIN KAIYAN METAL MANUFACTURING CO., LTD.—See Changzhou Kaidi Electrical, Inc.; *Int'l*, pg. 1445
JIANGYIN LEICHI AUTOMOBILE SALES & SERVICES CO., LTD.—See China Yongda Automobiles Services Holdings Limited; *Int'l*, pg. 1564
JIANGYIN LITAI DECORATIVE MATERIALS CO., LTD.—See China Haida Ltd.; *Int'l*, pg. 1506
JIANGYIN LITAI ORNAMENTAL MATERIALS CO., LTD.—See China Haida Ltd.; *Int'l*, pg. 1506
JIANGYIN NANTAI HOME TEXTILES CORP. LTD.—See Nanjing Business and Tourism Corp., Ltd.; *Int'l*, pg. 5139
JIANGYIN PIVOT AUTOMOTIVE PRODUCTS CO., LTD.; *Int'l*, pg. 3961
JIANGYIN SINBON ELECTRONICS CO., LTD.—See SINBON Electronics Co., Ltd.; *Int'l*, pg. 6936
JIANGYIN SUGITA FASTEN SPRING WIRE CO., LTD.—See Kobe Steel, Ltd.; *Int'l*, pg. 4217
JIANGYIN SULI PHARMACEUTICAL TECHNOLOGY CO. LTD.—See Suli Co., Ltd.; *Int'l*, pg. 7255
JIANGYIN TUBOSCOPE TUBULAR DEVELOPMENT CO., LTD.—See NOV, Inc.; *U.S. Public*, pg. 1545
JIANGYIN WALSIN SPECIALTY ALLOY MATERIALS CO., LTD.—See Walsin Lihwa Corporation; *Int'l*, pg. 8335
JIANGYIN WALSIN STEEL CABLE CO., LTD.—See Walsin Lihwa Corporation; *Int'l*, pg. 8335
JIANGYIN XINGCHENG SPECIAL STEEL WORKS CO., LTD.—See CITIC Group Corporation; *Int'l*, pg. 1621
JIANGYIN XINREN TECHNOLOGY CO., LTD.—See Xin-Ren Aluminum Holdings Limited; *Int'l*, pg. 8533
JIANGYIN YANGTZE INTERNATIONAL COUNTRY CLUB CO LTD—See Keppel Corporation Limited; *Int'l*, pg. 4130
JIANGZHONG PHARMACEUTICAL CO., LTD.; *Int'l*, pg. 3961
JIANKUN INTERNATIONAL BERHAD; *Int'l*, pg. 3961
JI'AN MANKUN TECHNOLOGY CO., LTD.; *Int'l*, pg. 3941
JIANMIN PHARMACEUTICAL GROUP CO., LTD; *Int'l*, pg. 3961
JIANPU TECHNOLOGY INC.; *Int'l*, pg. 3961
JIAN SIN INDUSTRIAL CO., LTD.; *Int'l*, pg. 3942
JIANZHI EDUCATION TECHNOLOGY GROUP COMPANY LIMITED; *Int'l*, pg. 3961
JIANZHONG CONSTRUCTION DEVELOPMENT LIMITED; *Int'l*, pg. 3961
JIAOZUO JOINGARE BIOLOGICAL PRODUCT CO., LTD—See Joincare Pharmaceutical Industry Group Co., Ltd; *Int'l*, pg. 3994
JIAOZUO WANFANG ALUMINUM MANUFACTURING CO., LTD.; *Int'l*, pg. 3961
JIAOZUO ZHONGYU GAS CO., LTD.—See Zhongyu Energy Holdings Limited; *Int'l*, pg. 8676
JIAOZUO ZHONGYU GAS ENGINEERING INSTALLATION CO., LTD.—See Zhongyu Energy Holdings Limited; *Int'l*, pg. 8676
JIASHAN DOERRENBERG MOULD & DIE TRADING CO.—See Gesco AG; *Int'l*, pg. 2945
JIASHAN SUNKING POWER EQUIPMENT TECHNOLOGY CO., LTD.—See Sun.King Technology Group Limited; *Int'l*, pg. 7309
JIASHILI GROUP LIMITED; *Int'l*, pg. 3961
JIA SHI LUBRICANTS TRADING (SHANGHAI) CO., LTD.—See HF Sinclair Corporation; *U.S. Public*, pg. 1034
JIATE EXCELSIOR CO., LTD.—See Fresenius Medical Care AG; *Int'l*, pg. 2775
JIA TRUST CO., LTD.—See Japan Investment Adviser Co., Ltd.; *Int'l*, pg. 3898
JIA WEI LIFESTYLE, INC.; *Int'l*, pg. 3941
JIAWEI RENEWABLE ENERGY CO., LTD.; *Int'l*, pg. 3961
JIAWEI TECHNOLOGY (HK) LTD.—See Jiawei Renewable Energy Co., Ltd.; *Int'l*, pg. 3961

COMPANY NAME INDEX

JIM CRIVELLI CHEVROLET, INC.

Company Index

JIAWEI TECHNOLOGY (USA) LTD.—See Jiawei Renewable Energy Co., Ltd.; *Int'l*, pg. 3961
JIAXING AUCHAN HYPERMARKETS CO., LTD.—See Alibaba Group Holding Limited; *Int'l*, pg. 326
JIAXING BUILDING MATERIALS COMPANY—See Dalian Shide Group Co., Ltd.; *Int'l*, pg. 1952
JIAXING CIMC WOOD CO., LTD.—See China International Marine Containers (Group) Co., Ltd.; *Int'l*, pg. 1511
JIAXING CLINFLASH COMPUTER TECHNOLOGY CO., LTD.—See Hangzhou Tigermed Consulting Co., Ltd.; *Int'l*, pg. 3251
JIAXING EASTERN STEEL CORD CO., LTD.—See Shougang Century Holdings Limited; *Int'l*, pg. 6860
JIAXING GAS GROUP CO., LTD.; *Int'l*, pg. 3961
JIAXING GLEAD ELECTRONICS CO., LTD.—See Beijing BDstar Navigation Co., Ltd.; *Int'l*, pg. 946
JIAXING HAITAI CHEMICAL LOGISTICS COMPREHENSIVE SERVICE CO., LTD.—See Yongtaiyun Chemical Logistics Co., Ltd.; *Int'l*, pg. 8597
JIAXING KEM ELECTROMAGNETIC TECHNOLOGY CO., LTD.—See Keboda Technology Co., Ltd.; *Int'l*, pg. 4113
JIAXING KENLY PRECISION ELECTRONIC CO., LTD.—See Kenly Precision Industrial Co., Ltd.; *Int'l*, pg. 4127
JIAXING MINTH MACHINES CO., LTD.—See Minth Group Limited; *Int'l*, pg. 4914
JIAXING MURAKAMI CORPORATION—See Murakami Corporation; *Int'l*, pg. 5095
JIAXING NYC INDUSTRIAL CO., LTD.—See voestalpine AG; *Int'l*, pg. 8289
JIAXING SHUN ON ELECTRONIC TECHNOLOY CO.,LTD.—See Shun On Electronic Co, Ltd.; *Int'l*, pg. 6869
JIAXING YONGDA TONGCHENG AUTO SALES AND SERVICE CO., LTD.—See China Yongda Automobiles Services Holdings Limited; *Int'l*, pg. 1564
JIAXING ZANYU TECHNOLOGY DEVELOPMENT CO., LTD.—See Zanyu Technology Group Co., Ltd.; *Int'l*, pg. 8625
JIAXING ZHIBAO AUTOMOBILE SALES AND SERVICE CO., LTD.—See China Yongda Automobiles Services Holdings Limited; *Int'l*, pg. 1564
JIA XIN NEW MATERIALS (ANHUI) CO., LTD.—See Copartner Technology Corporation; *Int'l*, pg. 1793
JIA XIN PLASTIC (SHENZHEN) CO., LTD.—See Copartner Technology Corporation; *Int'l*, pg. 1793
JIAXIPERA COMPRESSOR LIMITED COMPANY—See Changhong Huayi Compressor Co., Ltd.; *Int'l*, pg. 1443
JIA YAO HOLDINGS LIMITED; *Int'l*, pg. 3941
JIA YI ENERGY CO., LTD.—See TOPCO Scientific Co., Ltd.; *Int'l*, pg. 7814
JIAYIN GROUP INC.; *Int'l*, pg. 3961
JIAYOU INTERNATIONAL LOGISTICS CO., LTD.; *Int'l*, pg. 3961
JIAYUAN.COM INTERNATIONAL LTD.; *Int'l*, pg. 3962
JIAYUAN INTERNATIONAL GROUP LIMITED; *Int'l*, pg. 3962
JIAYUAN SCIENCE & TECHNOLOGY CO., LTD.; *Int'l*, pg. 3962
JIAYUAN SERVICES HOLDINGS LIMITED; *Int'l*, pg. 3962
JIAYU HNA INDUSTRY DEVELOPMENT CO., LTD.—See Hainan Traffic Administration Holding Co., Ltd.; *Int'l*, pg. 3215
JIAYU HOLDING CO., LTD.; *Int'l*, pg. 3962
JIAZUO RAILWAY CABLE CO., LTD.—See China National Railway Signal & Communication Corp.; *Int'l*, pg. 1534
JIBANNET HOLDINGS CO. LTD.; *Int'l*, pg. 3962
JIBUHIN (THAILAND) CO., LTD.—See SPARX Group Co., Ltd.; *Int'l*, pg. 7128
JIC CAPITAL, LTD.—See Japan Investment Corporation; *Int'l*, pg. 3898
JICHODO CO., LTD.; *Int'l*, pg. 3962
JIC INSPECTION SERVICES PTE. LTD.—See ComfortDelGro Corporation Limited; *Int'l*, pg. 1713
J. I. CO., LTD.—See Senshu Ikeda Holdings, Inc.; *Int'l*, pg. 6713
JIDONG CEMENT LUANXIAN CO., LTD.—See Tangshan Jidong Cement Co., Ltd.; *Int'l*, pg. 7458
JIDOSHA BUHIN KOGYO CO., LTD. - MOKA FACTORY—See SPARX Group Co., Ltd.; *Int'l*, pg. 7128
JIDOSHA BUHIN KOGYO CO., LTD.—See SPARX Group Co., Ltd.; *Int'l*, pg. 7127
JIDOSHA YUSO KOGYO CO., LTD.—See Mercedes-Benz Group AG; *Int'l*, pg. 4825
JIECANG EUROPE GMBH—See Zhejiang Jiecang Linear Motion Technology Co., Ltd.; *Int'l*, pg. 8657
JIEC CO., LTD.—See Sumitomo Corporation; *Int'l*, pg. 7270
JIEN CANADA MINING LTD.—See Jilin Horoc Nonferrous Metal Group Co., Ltd.; *Int'l*, pg. 3963
JIEN NUNAVIK MINING EXPLORATION LTD.—See Jilin Horoc Nonferrous Metal Group Co., Ltd.; *Int'l*, pg. 3963
JIE SHENG COMMUNICATION SERVICES (SHANGHAI), INC.—See SECOM Co., Ltd.; *Int'l*, pg. 6671
JIETECH TRADING (SUZHOU) INC.—See Hitron Technologies Inc.; *Int'l*, pg. 3427
JIEYANG DINGJIE AUTOMOBILE SALES SERVICES CO., LTD.—See China ZhengTong Auto Services Holdings Limited; *Int'l*, pg. 1566
JIEYANG LUZE AUTOMOBILE SALES SERVICES CO., LTD.—See China ZhengTong Auto Services Holdings Limited; *Int'l*, pg. 1566
JIFFY AIR TOOL, INC.—See ShoreView Industries, LLC; *U.S. Private*, pg. 3642
JIFFY AS—See Jiffy International AS; *Int'l*, pg. 3962
JIFFY FRANCE S.A.R.L—See Jiffy International AS; *Int'l*, pg. 3962
JIFFY INTERNATIONAL AS; *Int'l*, pg. 3962
JIFFY LUBE INTERNATIONAL, INC.—See Shell plc; *Int'l*, pg. 6796
JIFFY LUBE INTERNATIONAL OF MARYLAND INC.—See Shell plc; *Int'l*, pg. 6796
JIFFY PREFORMA PRODUCTION K.K—See Jiffy International AS; *Int'l*, pg. 3962
JIFFY PRODUCTS ESPANA S.L.U.—See Jiffy International AS; *Int'l*, pg. 3962
JIFFY PRODUCTS GMBH—See Jiffy International AS; *Int'l*, pg. 3962
JIFFY PRODUCTS INTERNATIONAL AS—See Jiffy International AS; *Int'l*, pg. 3962
JIFFY PRODUCTS INTERNATIONAL B.V.—See Jiffy International AS; *Int'l*, pg. 3962
JIFFY PRODUCTS N.B LTD—See Jiffy International AS; *Int'l*, pg. 3962
JIFFY PRODUCTS OF AMERICA, INC.—See Jiffy International AS; *Int'l*, pg. 3962
JIFFY PRODUCTS S.L. (PRIVATE) LTD.—See Jiffy International AS; *Int'l*, pg. 3962
JIFFY PRODUCTS (UK) LTD.—See Jiffy International AS; *Int'l*, pg. 3962
JIF-PAK MANUFACTURING INC.—See Clayton, Dubilier & Rice, LLC; *U.S. Private*, pg. 926
JIGAR CABLES LIMITED; *Int'l*, pg. 3962
J.I. GARCIA CONSTRUCTION CO.; *U.S. Private*, pg. 2166
JIG.JP CO., LTD.; *Int'l*, pg. 3962
JIGRAF AB—See Volati AB; *Int'l*, pg. 8300
JIG-SAW INC.; *Int'l*, pg. 3962
JIGSAW SEARCH PTY. LTD.—See Bain Capital, LP; *U.S. Private*, pg. 434
JIGSY.COM; *Int'l*, pg. 3962
JIGYASA INFRASTRUCTURE LIMITED; *Int'l*, pg. 3962
JI-HAW AMERICA, INC.—See Ji-Haw Industrial Co., Ltd.; *Int'l*, pg. 3941
JI-HAW ELECTRONICS (KUNSHAN) CO., LTD.—See Ji-Haw Industrial Co., Ltd.; *Int'l*, pg. 3941
JI-HAW INDUSTRIAL CO., LTD.; *Int'l*, pg. 3941
JI-HAW OPTO-ELECTRICAL (AUHUI) CO., LTD.—See Ji-Haw Industrial Co., Ltd.; *Int'l*, pg. 3941
JI-HAW OPTO-ELECTRICAL (KUNSHAN) CO., LTD.—See Ji-Haw Industrial Co., Ltd.; *Int'l*, pg. 3941
JIH LIN TECHNOLOGY CO., LTD.; *Int'l*, pg. 3962
JIHOCESKA OBALOVNA, SPOL. S R.O.—See VINCI S.A.; *Int'l*, pg. 8219
JIHOMORAVSKA ARMATURKA SPOL. S.R.O.—See Zurn Elkay Water Solutions Corporation; *U.S. Public*, pg. 2413
JIH SUN FINANCIAL HOLDINGS CO., LTD.—See Fubon Financial Holding Co. Ltd.; *Int'l*, pg. 2802
JIHSUN FUTURES CO., LTD.—See Fubon Financial Holding Co. Ltd.; *Int'l*, pg. 2802
JIHSUN SECURITIES CO., LTD.—See Fubon Financial Holding Co. Ltd.; *Int'l*, pg. 2802
JIHUA GROUP CORPORATION LIMITED; *Int'l*, pg. 3963
JIIN YEEH DING ENTERPRISE CO., LTD.; *Int'l*, pg. 3963
JIKAI EQUIPMENT MANUFACTURING CO., LTD.; *Int'l*, pg. 3963
JIK INDUSTRIES LIMITED; *Int'l*, pg. 3963
J.I. KISLAK INC.; *U.S. Private*, pg. 2167
JILCO EQUIPMENT LEASING CO., INC.; *U.S. Private*, pg. 2208
J.I.L. COMMUNICATIONS, INC.—See Bluewave Technology Group, LLC; *U.S. Private*, pg. 599
JILGYUNGYI CO., LTD.; *Int'l*, pg. 3963
JILIN AODONG PHARMACEUTICAL GROUP CO., LTD.; *Int'l*, pg. 3963
JILIN BODA PHARMACEUTICAL CO., LTD.—See Simcere Pharmaceutical Group; *Int'l*, pg. 6928
JILIN CHEMICAL FIBRE CO., LTD.; *Int'l*, pg. 3963
JILIN CHENGCHENG GROUP CO., LTD.; *Int'l*, pg. 3963
JILIN CHUANGYUAN CHEMICAL CO., LTD.—See Planet Green Holdings Corp.; *U.S. Public*, pg. 1697
JILIN COMFORTDELGRO TAXI CO., LTD.—See ComfortDelGro Corporation Limited; *Int'l*, pg. 1713
JILIN DAHUA MACHINE MANUFACTURING CO., LTD.—See China North Industries Group Corporation; *Int'l*, pg. 1536
JILIN DALI FOODS CO., LTD.—See Dali Foods Group Co. Ltd.; *Int'l*, pg. 1951
JILIN DONGCHENG SUMIKA POLYMER COMPOUNDS CO., LTD.—See Sumitomo Chemical Company, Limited; *Int'l*, pg. 7264
JILIN ELECTRIC POWER COMPANY—See State Grid Corporation of China; *Int'l*, pg. 7183
JILIN EXPRESSWAY CO., LTD.; *Int'l*, pg. 3963
JILIN EXTRAWELL CHANGBAISHAN PHARMACEUTICAL CO., LTD.—See Extrawell Pharmaceutical Holdings Ltd.; *Int'l*, pg. 2592
JILIN HI-TECH RENEWABLE ENERGY CO., LTD.—See Shanghai Hi-Tech Control System Co., LTD.; *Int'l*, pg. 6770
JILIN HOROC NONFERROUS METAL GROUP CO., LTD.; *Int'l*, pg. 3963
JILIN JIAN YISHENG PHARMACEUTICAL CO., LTD.; *Int'l*, pg. 3963
JILIN JIEN NICKEL INDUSTRY CO., LTD.—See Jilin Horoc Nonferrous Metal Group Co., Ltd.; *Int'l*, pg. 3963
JILIN JINGUAN ELECTRIC CO LTD; *Int'l*, pg. 3963
JILIN JIUTAI RURAL COMMERCIAL BANK; *Int'l*, pg. 3963
JILIN JLU COMMUNICATION DESIGN INSTITUTE CO.,LTD; *Int'l*, pg. 3963
JILIN LIYUAN PRECISION MANUFACTURING CO., LTD.; *Int'l*, pg. 3963
JILIN OLED MATERIAL TECH CO., LTD.; *Int'l*, pg. 3964
JILIN POWER SHARE CO., LTD.; *Int'l*, pg. 3964
JILIN PROVINCE CHUNCHENG HEATING COMPANY LIMITED; *Int'l*, pg. 3964
JILIN PROVINCE HUINAN CHANGLONG BIO-PHARMACY COMPANY LIMITED; *Int'l*, pg. 3964
JILIN PROVINCE XIDIAN PHARMACEUTICAL SCI-TECH DEVELOPMENT CO., LTD.; *Int'l*, pg. 3964
JILIN QIFENG CHEMICAL FIBER CO., LTD.—See Jilin Chemical Fibre Co., Ltd.; *Int'l*, pg. 3963
JILIN QUANYANGQUAN CO., LTD.; *Int'l*, pg. 3964
JILIN SINO-MICROELECTRONICS CO., LTD.; *Int'l*, pg. 3964
JILIN YATAI CONSTRUCTION ENGINEERING CO., LTD.—See Jilin Yatai (Group) Co., Ltd.; *Int'l*, pg. 3964
JILIN YATAI (GROUP) BUILDING MATERIALS INVESTMENT CO., LTD.—See Jilin Yatai (Group) Co., Ltd.; *Int'l*, pg. 3964
JILIN YATAI (GROUP) CO., LTD.; *Int'l*, pg. 3964
JILIN YATAI (GROUP) PHARMACEUTICAL INVESTMENT CO., LTD.—See Jilin Yatai (Group) Co., Ltd.; *Int'l*, pg. 3964
JILIN YATAI REAL ESTATE DEVELOPMENT CO., LTD.—See Jilin Yatai (Group) Co., Ltd.; *Int'l*, pg. 3964
JILIN YIDA CHEMICAL CO., LTD.—See Jiangsu Yida Chemical Co., Ltd.; *Int'l*, pg. 3956
JILIN ZIXIN PHARMACEUTICAL INDUSTRIAL CO., LTD.; *Int'l*, pg. 3964
JILL S. SCHWARTZ & ASSOCIATES, P.A.; *U.S. Private*, pg. 2208
JILL STUART INTERNATIONAL LLC; *U.S. Private*, pg. 2208
JIL SANDER AG—See Onward Holdings Co., Ltd.; *Int'l*, pg. 5592
JIL SANDER AMERICA INC.—See Onward Holdings Co., Ltd.; *Int'l*, pg. 5592
JIL SANDER JAPAN K.K.—See Onward Holdings Co., Ltd.; *Int'l*, pg. 5592
JIMARI INTERNATIONAL, INC.; *U.S. Private*, pg. 2210
JIMARK S.R.O.—See Nayax Ltd.; *Int'l*, pg. 5178
JIM BAIER FORD LINCOLN MERCURY DODGE CHRYSLER JEEP; *U.S. Private*, pg. 2208
JIM BALL PONTIAC-BUICK-GMC, INC.; *U.S. Private*, pg. 2208
JIM BARNARD CHEVROLET, INC.; *U.S. Private*, pg. 2208
JIM BEAM BRANDS CO. - CLERMONT PLANT—See Suntory Holdings Limited; *Int'l*, pg. 7325
JIM BEAM BRANDS CO.—See Suntory Holdings Limited; *Int'l*, pg. 7325
JIMBO'S JUMBOS—See Conagra Brands, Inc.; *U.S. Public*, pg. 564
JIMBO SP. Z O.O.—See Marie Brizard Wine & Spirits S.A.; *Int'l*, pg. 4693
JIM BROWN CHEVROLET INC.; *U.S. Private*, pg. 2208
JIM BROWNE CHEVROLET, INC.—See General Motors Company; *U.S. Public*, pg. 926
JIM BURKE AUTOMOTIVE INC.; *U.S. Private*, pg. 2208
JIM BUTLER AUTO GROUP, LLC; *U.S. Private*, pg. 2208
JIM CAREY DISTRIBUTING COMPANY; *U.S. Private*, pg. 2208
JIM CARPENTER COMPANY—See The Lester Group Inc.; *U.S. Private*, pg. 4069
JIM CAUSLEY, INC.; *U.S. Private*, pg. 2208
JIM CLICK COLLISION CENTER EASTSIDE—See Jim Click, Inc.; *U.S. Private*, pg. 2208
JIM CLICK FORD, LINCOLN-MERCURY, INC.—See Jim Click, Inc.; *U.S. Private*, pg. 2208
JIM CLICK, INC.; *U.S. Private*, pg. 2208
JIM COGDILL COMPANY—See Lithia Motors, Inc.; *U.S. Public*, pg. 1323
JIMCO LAMP & MANUFACTURING, CO.—See Kohlberg & Company, LLC; *U.S. Private*, pg. 2338
JIM COLEMAN CADILLAC INC.—See Bethesda Investment Holding Co., Inc.; *U.S. Private*, pg. 546
JIM COLEMAN COMPANY; *U.S. Private*, pg. 2208
JIM COLEMAN TOYOTA, INC.—See Bethesda Investment Holding Co., Inc.; *U.S. Private*, pg. 546
JIMCO MAINTENANCE, INC.; *U.S. Private*, pg. 2210
JIMCOR AGENCY INC.; *U.S. Private*, pg. 2210
JIM CRIVELLI CHEVROLET, INC.; *U.S. Private*, pg. 2208

JIM CURLEY DEALERSHIP; U.S. Private, pg. 2208
JIMDO GMBH; Int'l, pg. 3964
JIMDO INC.—See Jimdo GmbH; Int'l, pg. 3964
JIM DOYLE FORD; U.S. Private, pg. 2208
JIM DUNWORTH INC.; U.S. Private, pg. 2208
JIM ELLIS ATLANTA INC.; U.S. Private, pg. 2208
JIMENEZ CUSTOM PAINTING, INC; U.S. Private, pg. 2210
JIM FLETCHER ARCHERY AIDS, INC.—See Escalade, Incorporated; U.S. Public, pg. 793
JIM FOREMAN PONTIAC INC.; U.S. Private, pg. 2208
JIM FUOCO MOTOR CO.; U.S. Private, pg. 2209
JIM F WEBB, INC.—See Cadent Energy Partners, LLC; U.S. Private, pg. 713
JIM GILMAN EXCAVATING INC.; U.S. Private, pg. 2209
JIM GLOVER CHEVROLET ISUZU; U.S. Private, pg. 2209
JIM HATHEWAY FORD SALES LIMITED; Int'l, pg. 3964
JIM HAWK GROUP INC.; U.S. Private, pg. 2209
THE JIM HENSON COMPANY; U.S. Private, pg. 4059
JIM HERRICK MOTORS INC.; U.S. Private, pg. 2209
JIM HICKS & COMPANY INC.; U.S. Private, pg. 2209
JIM HINTON OIL COMPANY INC.; U.S. Private, pg. 2209
JIM HUDSON AUTOMOTIVE GROUP; U.S. Private, pg. 2209
JIM KERAS CHEVROLET MEMPHIS; U.S. Private, pg. 2209
JIM KERAS SUBARU; U.S. Private, pg. 2209
JIM KOONS MANAGEMENT COMPANY—See Asbury Automotive Group, Inc.; U.S. Public, pg. 209
JIM KRANTZ ASSOCIATES INC; U.S. Private, pg. 2209
JIMLAR CORPORATION; U.S. Private, pg. 2210
JIM L. SHETAKIS DISTRIBUTING CO. INC.; U.S. Private, pg. 2209
JIM MACDONALD MOTORS LTD; Int'l, pg. 3964
JIM MARSH AMERICAN CORP.; U.S. Private, pg. 2209
JIM MCKAY CHEVROLET INC.; U.S. Private, pg. 2209
JIMMIE CROWDER EXCAVATING INC.; U.S. Private, pg. 2210
JIMMIE VICKERS; U.S. Private, pg. 2210
JIM MOFFATT CONSTRUCTION LTD.—See Petrowest Corp.; Int'l, pg. 5832
JIM MURPHY BUICK GMC, INC.; U.S. Private, pg. 2209
JIMMY BEANS WOOL; U.S. Private, pg. 2210
JIMMY CHOO PLC—See Capri Holdings Limited; Int'l, pg. 1316
JIMMY JOHN'S FRANCHISOR SPV, LLC—See Roark Capital Group Inc.; U.S. Private, pg. 3455
JIMMY JOHN'S LLC—See Roark Capital Group Inc.; U.S. Private, pg. 3455
JIMMY JONES TOYOTA OF ORANGEBURG; U.S. Private, pg. 2210
JIMMY SALES NECKWEAR CORP; U.S. Private, pg. 2210
JIMMY SANDERS, INC.—See Apollo Global Management, Inc.; U.S. Public, pg. 153
JIMMY WHITTINGTON LUMBER CO.; U.S. Private, pg. 2210
JIM OLIVER & ASSOCIATES—See Calvetti Ferguson, P.C.; U.S. Private, pg. 724
JIMOTO HOLDINGS, INC.; Int'l, pg. 3964
JIMOTY, INC.; Int'l, pg. 3965
JIM PALMER TRUCKING INC.; U.S. Private, pg. 2209
JIM PATTISON AUTO GROUP—See The Jim Pattison Group; Int'l, pg. 7660
JIM PATTISON AUTO GROUP—See The Jim Pattison Group; Int'l, pg. 7660
JIM PATTISON BROADCAST GROUP—See The Jim Pattison Group; Int'l, pg. 7660
JIM PATTISON ENTERTAINMENT LTD.—See The Jim Pattison Group; Int'l, pg. 7660
THE JIM PATTISON GROUP; Int'l, pg. 7659
JIM PATTISON LEASE—See The Jim Pattison Group; Int'l, pg. 7660
JIM PATTISON PACKAGING GROUP—See The Jim Pattison Group; Int'l, pg. 7660
JIM PENNEY LIMITED; Int'l, pg. 3964
JIM QUINLAN CHEVROLET CO.—See AutoNation, Inc.; U.S. Public, pg. 235
JIM RAYSIK INC.; U.S. Private, pg. 2209
JIM RIEHL'S FRIENDLY BUICK HONDA HUMMER; U.S. Private, pg. 2209
JIM ROBINSON INC.; U.S. Private, pg. 2209
JIMRO CO., LTD.—See Otsuka Holdings Co., Ltd.; Int'l, pg. 5659
JIM RYAN CHEVROLET INC.; U.S. Private, pg. 2209
JIM SCHMIDT CHEVROLET-OLDSMOBILE, INC.; U.S. Private, pg. 2209
JIM'S CONCRETE OF BREVARD INC.; U.S. Private, pg. 2210
JIM'S FORMAL WEAR INC.; U.S. Private, pg. 2210
JIM SKINNER FORD; U.S. Private, pg. 2209
JIM SKINNER HONDA; U.S. Private, pg. 2209
JIM SMITH BOATS, INC.; U.S. Private, pg. 2209
JIM SMITH CONTRACTING CO. LLC; U.S. Private, pg. 2210
JIM SMOLICH MOTORS, INC.—See Lithia Motors, Inc.; U.S. Public, pg. 1323
JIM'S SUPPLY CO. INC.; U.S. Private, pg. 2210

JIMSTONE CO OF LOUISIANA, INC.—See SiteOne Landscape Supply, Inc.; U.S. Public, pg. 1888
JIM TAYLOR CHEVROLET, LLC.; U.S. Private, pg. 2210
JIM TECHNOLOGY CORPORATION—See IHI Corporation; Int'l, pg. 3606
JIMTEN S.A.—See Aliaxis S.A./N.V.; Int'l, pg. 325
JIM THORPE NEIGHBORHOOD BANK—See JTNB Bancorp, Inc.; U.S. Public, pg. 1210
JIM THORP LUMBER PRODUCTS, INC.; U.S. Private, pg. 2210
JIM TIDWELL FORD, INC.—See Group 1 Automotive, Inc.; U.S. Public, pg. 971
JIM TRENARY CHEVROLET INC.; U.S. Private, pg. 2210
JIMU GROUP LIMITED; Int'l, pg. 3965
JIM VREELAND FORD; U.S. Private, pg. 2210
JIM WATERS CORPORATION—See Richards Building Supply Company; U.S. Private, pg. 3428
JIM WHITE LUMBER SALES INC.; U.S. Private, pg. 2210
JIM WILSON & ASSOCIATES, INC.; U.S. Private, pg. 2210
JIM WILSON CHEVROLET BUICK GMC; Int'l, pg. 3964
JIM WINTER BUICK-GMC TRUCK-NISSAN INC.; U.S. Private, pg. 2210
JIM WRIGHT ASSOCIATES; U.S. Private, pg. 2210
JIN AIR CO., LTD.; Int'l, pg. 3965
JINAN ACETATE CHEMICAL CO., LTD.; Int'l, pg. 3965
JINAN DALI FOODS CO., LTD.—See Dali Foods Group Co. Ltd.; Int'l, pg. 1951
JINAN GOLD PHOENIX BRAKE SYSTEMS CO., LTD.—See Shandong Gold Phoenix Co., Ltd.; Int'l, pg. 6753
JINAN GUOJI GROUP CO., LTD.; Int'l, pg. 3965
JINAN HIGH TECH DEVELOPMENT CO., LTD.; Int'l, pg. 3965
JINAN HI-TECH CONTROL SYSTEM CO., LTD.—See Shanghai Hi-Tech Control System CO., LTD.; Int'l, pg. 6770
JINAN HUAJIA SURFACE TECHNOLOGY CO., LTD.—See PPG Industries, Inc.; U.S. Public, pg. 1707
JINAN JIHLONG TECHNOLOGY CO., LTD.—See Jih Lin Technology Co., Ltd.; Int'l, pg. 3963
JINAN MECH PIPING TECHNOLOGY CO., LTD.—See Maike Tube Industry Holdings Limited; Int'l, pg. 4650
JINAN SYSMEX MEDICAL ELECTRONICS CO., LTD.—See Sysmex Corporation; Int'l, pg. 7388
JINAN UNITED CAN CO., LTD.—See Great China Metal Ind. Co., Ltd.; Int'l, pg. 3064
JINAN WANRUN MEAT PROCESSING CO., LTD.—See China Yurun Food Group Limited; Int'l, pg. 1566
JINAN ZHENGTE AUTOMATION TECHNOLOGY CO., LTD.—See Endress+Hauser (International) Holding AG; Int'l, pg. 2408
JINBANG STEEL CO., LTD.; Int'l, pg. 3965
JINCAI PRINTING & PACKAGING CO., LTD.—See MYS Group Co., Ltd.; Int'l, pg. 5114
JINCHI BIOTECH LIMITED; Int'l, pg. 3965
JINCHUAN GROUP INTERNATIONAL RESOURCES CO. LTD.; Int'l, pg. 3965
JINCHUAN GROUP LIMITED; Int'l, pg. 3965
JINCOSTECH CO., LTD.; Int'l, pg. 3966
JINDAL ARCHITECTURE LIMITED—See Jindal Holdings Limited; Int'l, pg. 3966
JINDAL CAPITAL LTD.; Int'l, pg. 3966
JINDAL COTEX LIMITED; Int'l, pg. 3966
JINDAL DRILLING & INDUSTRIES LTD; Int'l, pg. 3966
JINDALEE RESOURCES LIMITED; Int'l, pg. 3967
JINDAL FILMS EUROPE S.A.R.L—See Jindal Poly Films Ltd.; Int'l, pg. 3967
JINDAL HOLDINGS LIMITED; Int'l, pg. 3966
JINDAL HOTELS LTD; Int'l, pg. 3966
JINDAL INDIA THERMAL POWER LIMITED—See Jindal Poly Investment & Finance Company Limited; Int'l, pg. 3967
JINDAL IRON & STEEL COMPANY LIMITED—See Jindal Holdings Limited; Int'l, pg. 3966
JINDAL LEASEFIN LIMITED; Int'l, pg. 3966
JINDAL PHOTO INVESTMENTS LIMITED—See Consolidated Finvest & Holdings Limited; Int'l, pg. 1770
JINDAL PHOTO LTD.; Int'l, pg. 3966
JINDAL POLY FILMS LTD.; Int'l, pg. 3967
JINDAL POLY INVESTMENT & FINANCE COMPANY LIMITED; Int'l, pg. 3967
JINDAL POWER LIMITED—See Jindal Holdings Limited; Int'l, pg. 3966
JINDAL SAW LIMITED—See Jindal Holdings Limited; Int'l, pg. 3966
JINDAL STAINLESS LTD.—See Jindal Holdings Limited; Int'l, pg. 3966
JINDAL STAINLESS STEELWAY LIMITED—See Jindal Holdings Limited; Int'l, pg. 3966
JINDAL STEEL & POWER LTD.—See Jindal Holdings Limited; Int'l, pg. 3966
JINDAL TUBULAR USA LLC—See Jindal Holdings Limited; Int'l, pg. 3966
JINDAL WORLDWIDE LIMITED; Int'l, pg. 3967
JINDO CO., LTD.; Int'l, pg. 3967
JINDUICHENG MOLYBDENUM GROUP CO., LTD.; Int'l, pg. 3967

JINFA LABI MATERNITY & BABY ARTICLES CO., LTD.; Int'l, pg. 3967
JIN-FU XINNUO PRECISION PLASTIC COL,LTD—See Suzhou Jinfu Technology Co., Ltd.; Int'l, pg. 7351
JINGAO SOLAR CO., LTD.—See JA Solar Technology Co., Ltd.; Int'l, pg. 3859
JINGBO TECHNOLOGY, INC.; Int'l, pg. 3967
JINGCHUAN HENGXING FRUIT JUICE CO., LTD.—See QAF Limited; Int'l, pg. 6132
JINGDING ENGINEERING & CONSTRUCTION CO., LTD.—See CTCI Corporation; Int'l, pg. 1870
JINGGONG STEEL BUILDING GROUP; Int'l, pg. 3967
JINGHUA PHARMACEUTICAL GROUP CO., LTD—See Jiangsu Senxuan Pharmaceutical & Chemical Co., Ltd.; Int'l, pg. 3953
JING-JAN RETAIL BUSINESS CO., LTD.—See Radium Life Tech Co., Ltd.; Int'l, pg. 6176
JINGJIANG OHJI RUBBER CO., LTD.—See Kuriyama Holdings Corporation; Int'l, pg. 4341
JINGJIANG YINGLI PORT CO., LTD.—See Jiangsu Wanlin Modern Logistics Co., Ltd.; Int'l, pg. 3955
JINGJIN EQUIPMENT CO., LTD.; Int'l, pg. 3967
JING KING TECH HOLDINGS PTE LTD. - DONGGUAN PLANT—See Jing King Tech Holdings Pte Ltd.; Int'l, pg. 3967
JING KING TECH HOLDINGS PTE LTD. - SHENZHEN PLANT—See Jing King Tech Holdings Pte Ltd.; Int'l, pg. 3967
JING KING TECH HOLDINGS PTE LTD.; Int'l, pg. 3967
JINGLEBELL S.R.L.—See Canada Pension Plan Investment Board; Int'l, pg. 1280
JINGLEBELL S.R.L.—See EQT AB; Int'l, pg. 2482
JINGLEBELL S.R.L.—See Temasek Holdings (Private) Limited; Int'l, pg. 7548
JINGLE PUNKS MUSIC, LLC—See ole Media Management LP; Int'l, pg. 5553
JINGLV ENVIRONMENT SCIENCE & TECHNOLOGY CO., LTD.; Int'l, pg. 3967
JINGMEN BAOZE AUTOMOBILE SALES SERVICES CO., LTD.—See China ZhengTong Auto Services Holdings Limited; Int'l, pg. 1566
JINGMEN DEWEI GEM TUNGSTEN RESOURCE RECYCLING CO., LTD.—See GEM Co., Ltd.; Int'l, pg. 2914
JINGMEN GEM CO., LTD.—See GEM Co., Ltd.; Int'l, pg. 2914
JINGMEN GEM NEW MATERIAL CO., LTD—See GEM Co., Ltd.; Int'l, pg. 2914
JINGMEN HONGTU SPECIAL AIRCRAFT MANUFACTURING CO., LTD—See China International Marine Containers (Group) Co., Ltd.; Int'l, pg. 1511
JINGMEN LVYUAN ENVIRONMENTAL PROTECTION INDUSTRY DEVELOPMENT CO., LTD.—See GEM Co., Ltd.; Int'l, pg. 2914
JINGMEN PRATT VALVE CO, LTD.—See Mueller Water Products, Inc.; U.S. Public, pg. 1485
JING MU INTERNATIONAL EXHIBITION CO. LTD.—See Messe Munchen GmbH; Int'l, pg. 4841
JINGO INTERNATIONAL RECORDS CO., LTD.—See San Far Property Limited; Int'l, pg. 6520
JINGRUI HOLDINGS LIMITED; Int'l, pg. 3967
JINGTANG INTERNATIONAL CONTAINER TERMINAL CO. LTD.—See ACS, Actividades de Construccion y Servicios, S.A.; Int'l, pg. 115
JING TEA LIMITED—See Camellia Plc; Int'l, pg. 1271
JINGWEI INTERNATIONAL LIMITED; Int'l, pg. 3967
JINGWEI TEXTILE MACHINERY COMPANY, LTD.—See China Hi-Tech Group Corporation; Int'l, pg. 1508
JINGYE GROUP; Int'l, pg. 3968
JING YING INDUSTRIAL CO., LTD.—See voestalpine AG; Int'l, pg. 8289
JINGYOU INFORMATION TECHNOLOGY (SHANGHAI) CO., LTD—See IFCA MSC Berhad; Int'l, pg. 3599
JINGYOU TIMES INFORMATION TECHNOLOGY DEVELOPMENT CO., LTD.; Int'l, pg. 3968
JING YUEH ENERGY CO., LTD.—See TOPCO Scientific Co., Ltd.; Int'l, pg. 7814
JINGZHOU HENGLONG AUTOMOTIVE PARTS CO., LTD.—See China Automotive Systems, Inc.; Int'l, pg. 1484
JINGZHOU HENGSHENG AUTOMOTIVE SYSTEM CO., LTD.—See China Automotive Systems, Inc.; Int'l, pg. 1484
JINGZHOU XIANGDA CAMEL FEED CO., LTD—See Tangrenshen Group Co., Ltd.; Int'l, pg. 7458
JINHAI INTERNATIONAL GROUP HOLDINGS LIMITED; Int'l, pg. 3968
JINHE BIOTECHNOLOGY CO., LTD.; Int'l, pg. 3968
JIN HENG LI HARDWARE SDN BHD—See HG Metal Manufacturing Limited; Int'l, pg. 3375
JINHONG FASHION GROUP CO., LTD.; Int'l, pg. 3968
JINHUA CAPITAL CORPORATION; Int'l, pg. 3968
JINHUA CHUNGUANG TECHNOLOGY CO., LTD.; Int'l, pg. 3968
JINHUI HOLDINGS COMPANY LIMITED; Int'l, pg. 3968
JINHUI LIQUOR CO., LTD.; Int'l, pg. 3968
JINHUI SHIPPING & TRANSPORTATION LIMITED—See Jinhui Holdings Company Limited; Int'l, pg. 3968
JINJIAN CEREALS INDUSTRY CO., LTD.; Int'l, pg. 3968

COMPANY NAME INDEX

JINJIANG CHENGDA GEAR CO., LTD.—See S&C Engine Group Limited; *Int'l*, pg. 6444
JINJIANG HAINA MACHINERY COMPANY LIMITED—See Haina Intelligent Equipment International Holdings Limited; *Int'l*, pg. 3211
JINJIANG JINLONG INDUSTRIAL DEVELOPMENT CO., LTD.—See Powerlong Real Estate Holdings Limited; *Int'l*, pg. 5947
JINJIANG TAIYA SHOES DEVELOP CO.,LTD.—See Kingnet Network Co., Ltd.; *Int'l*, pg. 4174
JINJING TECHNOLOGY MALAYSIA SDN. BHD.—See Shandong Jinjing Science & Technology Co., Ltd.; *Int'l*, pg. 6755
JINKA MINERALS LTD—See REWARD MINERALS LTD; *Int'l*, pg. 6314
JINKE PROPERTY GROUP CO., LTD.; *Int'l*, pg. 3968
JINKE SMART SERVICES GROUP CO., LTD.; *Int'l*, pg. 3968
JINKO POWER TECHNOLOGY CO., LTD.; *Int'l*, pg. 3968
JINKOSOLAR HOLDING CO., LTD.; *Int'l*, pg. 3968
JINLEI TECHNOLOGY CO., LTD.; *Int'l*, pg. 3969
JINLI GROUP HOLDINGS LIMITED; *Int'l*, pg. 3969
JINLIHUA ELECTRIC CO., LTD.; *Int'l*, pg. 3969
JINLING HOTEL CORPORATION LTD.; *Int'l*, pg. 3969
JINLING HOTELS & RESORTS CORPORATION—See Jinling Hotel Corporation Ltd.; *Int'l*, pg. 3969
JINLING PHARMACEUTICAL COMPANY LIMITED; *Int'l*, pg. 3969
JINLONG MACHINERY & ELECTRONICS CO., LTD.; *Int'l*, pg. 3969
JINLONGYU GROUP CO., LTD.; *Int'l*, pg. 3969
JINMAO (CHINA) HOTEL INVESTMENTS AND MANAGEMENT LIMITED; *Int'l*, pg. 3969
JIN MAO INVESTMENT (CHANG SHA) CO., LTD.—See Sinochem Corporation; *Int'l*, pg. 6950
JIN MAO (SHANGHAI) REAL ESTATE CO., LTD.—See Sinochem Corporation; *Int'l*, pg. 6949
JIN MEDICAL INTERNATIONAL LIMITED; *Int'l*, pg. 3965
JINNENG GROUP CO., LTD.; *Int'l*, pg. 3969
JINNENG HOLDING SHANXI ELECTRIC POWER CO., LTD.; *Int'l*, pg. 3969
JINNENG SCIENCE & TECHNOLOGY CO., LTD.; *Int'l*, pg. 3969
JINNO CONSTRUCTION CO., LTD.—See Sala Corporation; *Int'l*, pg. 6490
JINNO OIL CENTER CO., LTD.—See Sala Corporation; *Int'l*, pg. 6490
JINNY BEAUTY SUPPLY CO. INC.; *U.S. Private*, pg. 2210
JINNY SOFTWARE LTD.—See Enghouse Systems Limited; *Int'l*, pg. 2427
JINPAN INTERNATIONAL (USA) LTD.—See Forebright Capital Management Ltd.; *Int'l*, pg. 2731
JINPAO PRECISION INDUSTRY CO., LTD—See JPP Holding Co., Ltd.; *Int'l*, pg. 4007
JINPAO PRECISION JAPAN CO., LTD.—See JPP Holding Co., Ltd.; *Int'l*, pg. 4007
JINPU LANDSCAPE ARCHITECTURE CO., LTD.; *Int'l*, pg. 3969
JINRI CONTAINER SERVICE CO., LTD.—See Maruzen Showa Unyu Co., Ltd.; *Int'l*, pg. 4716
JINRO DISTILLERS CO., LTD.; *Int'l*, pg. 3969
JINS EYEWEAR US, INC.—See Jins Holdings Inc.; *Int'l*, pg. 3969
JINSHANG BANK CO., LTD.; *Int'l*, pg. 3969
JINSHANG INTERNATIONAL FINANCIAL LEASING CO., LTD.—See Arta TechFin Corporation Limited; *Int'l*, pg. 581
JINS HOLDINGS INC.; *Int'l*, pg. 3969
JINSUNG GEORGIA, LLC—See JinSung T.E.C. Inc; *Int'l*, pg. 3970
JINSUNG JAPAN CORP.—See JinSung T.E.C. Inc; *Int'l*, pg. 3970
JINSUNG T.E.C. INC - NO. 2 PLANT—See JinSung T.E.C. Inc; *Int'l*, pg. 3970
JINSUNG T.E.C. INC; *Int'l*, pg. 3969
JINSUNG T.E.C. (YANTAI) CO., LTD.—See JinSung T.E.C. Inc; *Int'l*, pg. 3970
JINTAI ENERGY HOLDINGS LIMITED; *Int'l*, pg. 3970
JINTAI MINING GROUP, INC.; *Int'l*, pg. 3970
J. INTER CO., LTD.—See Japan Airlines Co., Ltd.; *Int'l*, pg. 3882
JINTIAN COPPER BAR COMPANY LTD.—See Ningbo Jintian Copper (Group) Co., Ltd.; *Int'l*, pg. 5303
JINTIAN COPPER (GERMANY) GMBH—See Ningbo Jintian Copper (Group) Co., Ltd.; *Int'l*, pg. 5302
JINTIAN COPPER JAPAN CO., LTD.—See Ningbo Jintian Copper (Group) Co., Ltd.; *Int'l*, pg. 5303
JINTIAN COPPER PLATE COMPANY LTD.—See Ningbo Jintian Copper (Group) Co., Ltd.; *Int'l*, pg. 5303
JINTIAN COPPER ROD COMPANY LTD.—See Ningbo Jintian Copper (Group) Co., Ltd.; *Int'l*, pg. 5303
JINTIAN COPPER (USA) CO., LTD.—See Ningbo Jintian Copper (Group) Co., Ltd.; *Int'l*, pg. 5303
JINTIAN COPPER (VIETNAM) CO., LTD.—See Ningbo Jintian Copper (Group) Co., Ltd.; *Int'l*, pg. 5303
JIN TONG LING TECHNOLOGY GROUP CO., LTD.; *Int'l*, pg. 3965
JINUSHI CO., LTD.; *Int'l*, pg. 3970

JIN WAN HONG INTERNATIONAL HOLDING LIMITED; *Int'l*, pg. 3970
JINXIANDAI INFORMATION INDUSTRY CO., LTD.; *Int'l*, pg. 3970
JINXI AXLE CO., LTD.—See China North Industries Group Corporation; *Int'l*, pg. 1535
JINXI INDUSTRIES GROUP CO., LTD.—See China North Industries Group Corporation; *Int'l*, pg. 1535
JINXIN COMPANY—See China National Railway Signal & Communication Corp.; *Int'l*, pg. 1534
JINX, INC.; *U.S. Private*, pg. 2211
JINXIN FERTILITY GROUP LIMITED; *Int'l*, pg. 3970
JINXI VODAR ENGINEERING CO., LTD.—See China Oriental Group Company Limited; *Int'l*, pg. 1538
JINXUAN COKING COAL LIMITED; *Int'l*, pg. 3970
JIN YANG PHARMACEUTICAL CO. LTD - ANSAN FACTORY—See Jin Yang Pharmaceutical Co. Ltd; *Int'l*, pg. 3965
JIN YANG PHARMACEUTICAL CO. LTD; *Int'l*, pg. 3965
JINYOUNG CO., LTD.; *Int'l*, pg. 3970
JINYUAN ENVIRONMENTAL PROTECTION CO., LTD.; *Int'l*, pg. 3970
JINYU BIO-TECHNOLOGY CO., LTD.; *Int'l*, pg. 3970
JINYU (HK) INTERNATIONAL MINING CO LTD—See Zijin Mining Group Company Limited; *Int'l*, pg. 8683
JINZAI CO., LTD.—See Zensho Holdings Co., Ltd.; *Int'l*, pg. 8634
JINZAI FOOD GROUP CO., LTD.; *Int'l*, pg. 3970
JINZHOU AOXIN YOUXIN DENTAL CLINIC CO., LTD.—See Aoxin Q & M Dental Group Limited; *Int'l*, pg. 498
JINZHOU CIHANG GROUP CO., LTD.; *Int'l*, pg. 3970
JINZHOU DONG WOO PRECISION CO., LTD.—See Wonder Auto Technology, Inc.; *Int'l*, pg. 8446
JINZHOU JINMAO PHOTOVOLTAIC TECHNOLOGY CO., LTD.—See Solargiga Energy Holdings Limited; *Int'l*, pg. 7070
JINZHOU PORT CO., LTD.; *Int'l*, pg. 3970
JINZHOU YANGGUANG ENERGY CO., LTD.—See Solargiga Energy Holdings Limited; *Int'l*, pg. 7070
JINZHOU YOUHUA SILICON MATERIALS CO., LTD.—See Solargiga Energy Holdings Limited; *Int'l*, pg. 7070
JINZHOU YUANCHENG BIO-CHEM TECHNOLOGY CO., LTD.—See Global Sweeteners Holdings Limited; *Int'l*, pg. 3001
JINZI HAM COMPANY LTD.; *Int'l*, pg. 3970
JIO CORPORATION—See LIXIL Group Corporation; *Int'l*, pg. 4534
JIO FINANCIAL SERVICES LTD.; *Int'l*, pg. 3970
JIONTO ENERGY INVESTMENT CO., LTD.; *Int'l*, pg. 3971
JIPAL CORPORATION—See TOWA Corporation; *Int'l*, pg. 7849
JIPAL (H.K.) COMPANY LTD.—See TOWA Corporation; *Int'l*, pg. 7849
JIPANGU INC.; *Int'l*, pg. 3971
JIP INFO BRIDGE CO., LTD.—See Nippon Telegraph & Telephone Corporation; *Int'l*, pg. 5343
JIP TECHNO SCIENCE CORPORATION—See Nippon Telegraph & Telephone Corporation; *Int'l*, pg. 5343
JIRDON AGRI CHEMICALS, INC.—See Western Cooperative Company; *U.S. Private*, pg. 4492
JIREH METAL PRODUCTS, INC.; *U.S. Private*, pg. 2211
JIREH SEMICONDUCTOR INCORPORATED—See Alpha and Omega Semiconductor Limited; *Int'l*, pg. 366
JIRONG REAL ESTATE CO., LTD.—See Chailease Holding Company Limited; *Int'l*, pg. 1437
JIS DISTRIBUTION LLC—See Jergens Inc.; *U.S. Private*, pg. 2201
JISHANYE, INC.; *Int'l*, pg. 3971
JISHI MEDIA CO., LTD.; *Int'l*, pg. 3971
JISL GLOBAL SA—See Jain Irrigation Systems Limited; *Int'l*, pg. 3872
JISL SYSTEMS SA—See Jain Irrigation Systems Limited; *Int'l*, pg. 3872
JITA OY—See Georg Fischer AG; *Int'l*, pg. 2937
JITCO GROUP LIMITED; *U.S. Private*, pg. 2211
JIT CORPORATION; *U.S. Private*, pg. 2211
JI TECH CO., LTD.; *Int'l*, pg. 3941
JITE TECHNOLOGIES INC.—See McVicar Industries Inc.; *Int'l*, pg. 4761
JITF INFRALOGISTICS LIMITED; *Int'l*, pg. 3971
JITNEYTRADE INC.—See Canaccord Genuity Group Inc.; *Int'l*, pg. 1277
JITPAY GMBH—See W.A.G Payment Solutions Plc; *Int'l*, pg. 8321
JITRAMAS CATERING CO., LTD.—See PTG Energy Public Company Limited; *Int'l*, pg. 6090
JITRAMAS CO., LTD.—See PTG Energy Public Company Limited; *Int'l*, pg. 6090
JITTERBIT, INC.—See KKR & Co. Inc.; *U.S. Public*, pg. 1254
JIT TRANS OY—See SSAB AB; *Int'l*, pg. 7153
JIUGUI LIQUOR CO., LTD.; *Int'l*, pg. 3971
JIUHE COMPANY LIMITED—See Sichuan Lutianhua Co., Ltd.; *Int'l*, pg. 6880
JIUJIANG DEYU CO., LTD.—See Honmyue Enterprise Co., Ltd.; *Int'l*, pg. 3472

JIUJIANG DONGBU TOYOTA AUTO SALES & SERVICES CO., LTD.—See China MeiDong Auto Holdings Limited; *Int'l*, pg. 1519
JIUJIANG GOLDEN EGRET HARDMATERIAL CO., LTD.—See Xiamen Tungsten Co., Ltd.; *Int'l*, pg. 8525
JIUJIANG SHANSHUI TECHNOLOGY CO., LTD.; *Int'l*, pg. 3971
JIUJIANG SUN.KING TECHNOLOGY CO., LTD.—See Sun.King Technology Group Limited; *Int'l*, pg. 7309
JIUJIANG XINLIANXIN FERTILISER CO., LTD.—See China XLX Fertiliser Ltd; *Int'l*, pg. 1563
JIUJIUWANG FOOD INTERNATIONAL LIMITED; *Int'l*, pg. 3971
JIULI USA, INC—See Zhejiang JIULI Hi-tech Metals Co., Ltd.; *Int'l*, pg. 8658
JIUMAOJIU INTERNATIONAL HOLDINGS LIMITED; *Int'l*, pg. 3971
JIU RONG HOLDINGS LTD; *Int'l*, pg. 3971
JIUSHENG ELECTRIC CO., LTD.; *Int'l*, pg. 3971
JIUTIAN CHEMICAL GROUP LIMITED; *Int'l*, pg. 3971
JIUXIN(CHANGZHOU)REAL ESTATE DEVELOPMENT CO., LTD.—See Daiwa House Industry Co., Ltd.; *Int'l*, pg. 1946
JIUZHITANG CO., LTD.; *Int'l*, pg. 3971
JIUZHITANG MAKER (BEIJING) CELL TECHNOLOGY CO., LTD.—See Jiuzhitang Co., Ltd.; *Int'l*, pg. 3971
JIUZI HOLDINGS, INC.; *Int'l*, pg. 3971
JIU ZUN DIGITAL INTERACTIVE ENTERTAINMENT GROUP HOLDINGS LIMITED; *Int'l*, pg. 3971
JIVAGRO LTD.—See PI Industries Ltd.; *Int'l*, pg. 5859
JIVE COMMUNICATIONS, INC.—See Elliott Management Corporation; *U.S. Private*, pg. 1368
JIVE COMMUNICATIONS, INC.—See Francisco Partners Management, LP; *U.S. Private*, pg. 1590
JIVE COMMUNICATIONS MEXICO, S. DE R.L. DE C.V.—See Elliott Management Corporation; *U.S. Private*, pg. 1368
JIVE COMMUNICATIONS MEXICO, S. DE R.L. DE C.V.—See Francisco Partners Management, LP; *U.S. Private*, pg. 1590
JIVE SOFTWARE AUSTRALIA PTY LTD.—See ESW Capital, LLC; *U.S. Private*, pg. 1430
JIVE SOFTWARE, INC.—See ESW Capital, LLC; *U.S. Private*, pg. 1430
JIVE TELECOMUNICACOES DO BRASIL, LTDA.—See Elliott Management Corporation; *U.S. Private*, pg. 1368
JIVE TELECOMUNICACOES DO BRASIL, LTDA.—See Francisco Partners Management, LP; *U.S. Private*, pg. 1590
JIWANRAM SHEODUTTRAI INDUSTRIES LIMITED; *Int'l*, pg. 3971
JIWA REALTY SDN. BHD.—See DutaLand Berhad; *Int'l*, pg. 2235
JIWOO ELECTRONICS CO., LTD.; *Int'l*, pg. 3972
JIYA ACQUISITION CORP.; *U.S. Public*, pg. 1190
JIYA ECO-PRODUCTS LIMITED; *Int'l*, pg. 3972
JI YAO HOLDING GROUP CO., LTD.; *Int'l*, pg. 3941
JIYI HOLDINGS LIMITED; *Int'l*, pg. 3972
JIYUAN PACKAGING HOLDINGS LIMITED; *Int'l*, pg. 3972
JIYUAN ZHONGYU GAS CO., LTD.—See Zhongyu Energy Holdings Limited; *Int'l*, pg. 8676
JIZE ZHONGYU GAS CO. LTD.—See Zhongyu Energy Holdings Limited; *Int'l*, pg. 8676
JIZHONG ENERGY RESOURCES CO., LTD.; *Int'l*, pg. 3972
J&J AG PRODUCTS, INC.; *U.S. Private*, pg. 2154
J.J.B. HILLIARD, W.L. LYONS, LLC—See Houchens Industries, Inc.; *U.S. Private*, pg. 1990
J & J CALIBRATION SERVICES, INC—See Aldinger Company; *U.S. Private*, pg. 160
J&J CARDS INC.; *U.S. Private*, pg. 2154
J.J. COLLINS SONS INC.; *U.S. Private*, pg. 2167
J.J. CROSS LIMITED—See Regent Gas Holdings Limited; *Int'l*, pg. 6252
J&J DENHOLM LTD.; *Int'l*, pg. 3853
JJ DETWEILER ENTERPRISES INC.; *U.S. Private*, pg. 2211
J&J DISTRIBUTING COMPANY; *U.S. Private*, pg. 2154
J&J DRIVE AWAY SYSTEMS, LLC—See Evanston Partners, LLC; *U.S. Private*, pg. 1435
THE J. J. ELEMER CORP.—See Action Bag Company; *U.S. Private*, pg. 67
JJ ENTERTAINMENT SE; *Int'l*, pg. 3972
J.J. EXPORTERS LTD.; *Int'l*, pg. 3858
J & J EXTERMINATING CO. INC.; *U.S. Private*, pg. 2152
JJ FERGUSON SAND & GRAVEL; *U.S. Private*, pg. 2211
J. J. FINANCE CORPORATION LIMITED; *Int'l*, pg. 3856
J & J FLEA MARKET—See United Flea Markets; *U.S. Private*, pg. 4292
J&J FLOORING GROUP, LLC—See Engineered Floors, LLC; *U.S. Private*, pg. 1398
JJF MANAGEMENT SERVICES, INC.; *U.S. Private*, pg. 2211
J&J FOODS INC.; *U.S. Private*, pg. 2154
J&J FURNITURE INCORPORATED; *U.S. Private*, pg. 2154
J.J. GOUGE & SON OIL CO. INC.; *U.S. Private*, pg. 2167
J.J. GUMBERG CO. INC.; *U.S. Private*, pg. 2167

J.J. HAINES & CO. INC.

J.J. HAINES & CO. INC.; *U.S. Private*, pg. 2167
JJ&H LTD.; *U.S. Private*, pg. 2211
J.JILL, INC.; *U.S. Public*, pg. 1180
J & J IMPORTS & FABRICATION, INC.; *U.S. Private*, pg. 2152
J & J INDUSTRIES INC.; *U.S. Private*, pg. 2152
JJJ FLOOR COVERING INC.; *U.S. Private*, pg. 2211
J.J. KELLER & ASSOCIATES, INC.; *U.S. Private*, pg. 2167
JJLA LLC; *U.S. Private*, pg. 2211
JJ-LAPP CABLE (S) PTE LTD—See Jebsen & Jessen (SEA) Pte Ltd; *Int'l*, pg. 3926
J&J MAINTENANCE INC.—See CBRE Group, Inc.; *U.S. Public*, pg. 460
J J MARSHALL & ASSOCIATES, INC.—See Arena Investors, LP; *U.S. Private*, pg. 318
J & J MARTS INC.; *U.S. Private*, pg. 2152
J & J MATERIALS CORP.—See SiteOne Landscape Supply, Inc.; *U.S. Public*, pg. 1888
JJM CONSTRUCTION LTD.; *Int'l*, pg. 3972
J & J MUNICIPAL SUPPLY, INC.—See Core & Main, Inc.; *U.S. Public*, pg. 576
JJ OPPORTUNITY CORP.; *U.S. Private*, pg. 2211
J. JOSEPHSON, INC.; *U.S. Private*, pg. 2156
J.J. PLANK CORPORATION—See ANDRITZ AG; *Int'l*, pg. 457
J.J. POWELL INC.; *U.S. Private*, pg. 2167
JJ PRINTING LIMITED—See SING TAO NEWS CORPORATION LIMITED; *Int'l*, pg. 6939
JJ-PUN (S) PTE LTD—See Jebsen & Jessen (SEA) Pte Ltd; *Int'l*, pg. 3926
JJ-PUN (S) PTE LTD—See Jebsen & Jessen (SEA) Pte Ltd; *Int'l*, pg. 3926
JJR ENTERPRISES INC.; *U.S. Private*, pg. 2211
JJR SOLUTIONS, LLC—See Logistics Management Institute; *U.S. Private*, pg. 2482
J.J. SKELTON OIL COMPANY INC.—See Star Group, L.P.; *U.S. Public*, pg. 1938
J&J SNACK FOODS CORP./MIA—See J&J Snack Foods Corporation; *U.S. Public*, pg. 1180
J&J SNACK FOODS CORP. OF CALIFORNIA—See J&J Snack Foods Corporation; *U.S. Public*, pg. 1180
J&J SNACK FOODS CORP. OF NEW JERSEY—See J&J Snack Foods Corporation; *U.S. Public*, pg. 1180
J&J SNACK FOODS CORPORATION; *U.S. Public*, pg. 1179
J&J SNACK FOODS CORP.—See J&J Snack Foods Corporation; *U.S. Public*, pg. 1180
J&J SNACK FOODS HANDHELDS CORP.—See J&J Snack Foods Corporation; *U.S. Public*, pg. 1180
J & J SNACK FOODS INVESTMENT CORP.—See J&J Snack Foods Corporation; *U.S. Public*, pg. 1179
J&J SNACK FOODS TRANSPORT CORP.—See J&J Snack Foods Corporation; *U.S. Public*, pg. 1180
JJS PROPERTIES, INC.—See Ventas, Inc.; *U.S. Public*, pg. 2278
J&J STAFFING RESOURCES INC.; *U.S. Private*, pg. 2154
J.J. TAYLOR COMPANIES INC.; *U.S. Private*, pg. 2167
J.J. TAYLOR DISTRIBUTING COMPANY OF MINNESOTA, INC.—See J.J. Taylor Companies Inc.; *U.S. Private*, pg. 2167
J.J. TAYLOR DISTRIBUTING OF FLORIDA, INC.—See J.J. Taylor Companies Inc.; *U.S. Private*, pg. 2167
J.J. TAYLOR DISTRIBUTING OF FLORIDA, INC.—See J.J. Taylor Companies Inc.; *U.S. Private*, pg. 2167
J & J TECHNICAL SERVICES, INC.—See Tonka Bay Equity Partners LLC; *U.S. Private*, pg. 4185
J.JUAN S.A.U.—See Brembo S.p.A.; *Int'l*, pg. 1145
JJ WADE & ASSOCIATES, INC.; *U.S. Private*, pg. 2211
J. J. WHITE, INC.—See Salini Costruttori S.p.A.; *Int'l*, pg. 6493
JK AGRI GENETICS LTD.—See JK Tyre & Industries Ltd.; *Int'l*, pg. 3972
JKAISER WORKSPACES, LLC; *U.S. Private*, pg. 2211
JK ASSOCIATES, INC.; *U.S. Private*, pg. 2211
JK CEMENT LTD; *Int'l*, pg. 3972
J.K. CEMENT WORKS (FUJAIRAH) FZC—See JK Cement Ltd; *Int'l*, pg. 3972
J-K CHEVROLET, INC.; *U.S. Private*, pg. 2155
JKC TRUCKING INC.; *U.S. Private*, pg. 2211
JKF AMERICAS INC.—See Bengal & Assam Company Ltd.; *Int'l*, pg. 973
J.K. FENNER (INDIA) LTD.—See Bengal & Assam Company Ltd.; *Int'l*, pg. 973
JK FILES & ENGINEERING LIMITED—See Raymond Limited; *Int'l*, pg. 6224
JK FINDINGS USA—See JK Jewelry Inc.; *U.S. Private*, pg. 2211
JK FOODS INC.; *U.S. Private*, pg. 2211
JKG LAND BERHAD; *Int'l*, pg. 3973
J.K. GROUP, INC.—See CyberGrants, LLC; *U.S. Private*, pg. 1133
JK GROUP SPA—See Dover Corporation; *U.S. Public*, pg. 681
JK GROUP USA, INC.—See Dover Corporation; *U.S. Public*, pg. 681
JK HOLDINGS CO., LTD.; *Int'l*, pg. 3972

J. KING'S FOOD SERVICE PROFESSIONALS INC.—See Sysco Corporation; *U.S. Public*, pg. 1974
J.K. INTERNATIONAL PTY. LTD.; *Int'l*, pg. 3858
JK JEWELRY INC.; *U.S. Private*, pg. 2211
JK LAKSHMI CEMENT LTD; *Int'l*, pg. 3972
JKL COPENHAGEN—See Publicis Groupe S.A.; *Int'l*, pg. 6103
JKL GOTEBORG—See Publicis Groupe S.A.; *Int'l*, pg. 6103
JKL HELSINKI—See Publicis Groupe S.A.; *Int'l*, pg. 6103
JKL OSLO—See Publicis Groupe S.A.; *Int'l*, pg. 6103
JKL PARTNERS, INC.; *Int'l*, pg. 3973
JKL STOCKHOLM—See Publicis Groupe S.A.; *Int'l*, pg. 6103
J.K. MARINE SERVICES LTD.—See Louisbourg Seafoods Ltd.; *Int'l*, pg. 4563
JK MAXX PAINT LIMITED—See JK Cement Ltd; *Int'l*, pg. 3972
JKM FERROTECH LIMITED—See Dynamatic Technologies Limited; *Int'l*, pg. 2239
JKMILNE ASSET MANAGEMENT; *U.S. Private*, pg. 2211
JK MINERAL DEVELOPMENT CORPORATION LIMITED—See NMDC Limited; *Int'l*, pg. 5393
JK MOVING & STORAGE INC.; *U.S. Private*, pg. 2211
JKN GLOBAL GROUP PUBLIC COMPANY LIMITED; *Int'l*, pg. 3973
J. KNIPPER & COMPANY, INC. - SOMERSET—See J. Knipper & Company, Inc.; *U.S. Private*, pg. 2156
J. KNIPPER & COMPANY, INC.; *U.S. Private*, pg. 2156
J&K NOVELTY, INC.; *U.S. Private*, pg. 2154
J. KOKOLAKIS CONTRACTING, INC.; *U.S. Private*, pg. 2156
J KOMFORT NERUHOMIST LLC—See Dragon Ukrainian Properties & Development Plc; *Int'l*, pg. 2199
J. KOSKI COMPANY—See APi Group Corporation; *Int'l*, pg. 514
JK PAPER LTD - JK PAPER MILLS—See JK Paper Ltd; *Int'l*, pg. 3972
JK PAPER LTD; *Int'l*, pg. 3972
JKP JABLANICA D.D.; *Int'l*, pg. 3973
J&K PLUMBING AND HEATING CO.; *U.S. Private*, pg. 2154
JKP VODOVOD I KANALIZACIJA D.D.; *Int'l*, pg. 3973
JK RECYCLE CO., LTD.—See Japan Pulp and Paper Company Limited; *Int'l*, pg. 3903
JKR EXCAVATING LTD.; *Int'l*, pg. 3973
J.K. SPINNING MILLS LTD.; *Int'l*, pg. 3858
JK SUCRALOSE EUROPE B.V.—See Liuzhou LMZ Co., Ltd.; *Int'l*, pg. 4529
JK SUCRALOSE INC.—See Liuzhou LMZ Co., Ltd.; *Int'l*, pg. 4529
JK SUCRALOSE INC.—See Liuzhou LMZ Co., Ltd.; *Int'l*, pg. 4529
JK TECHNOLOGY PTE. LTD.; *Int'l*, pg. 3972
JK TORNEL S.A. DE C.V.—See JK Tyre & Industries Ltd.; *Int'l*, pg. 3972
JK TRANS CO., LTD.—See Japan Oil Transportation Co., Ltd.; *Int'l*, pg. 3899
JK TYRE & INDUSTRIES LTD.; *Int'l*, pg. 3972
J. KUMAR INFRAPROJECTS LTD.; *Int'l*, pg. 3856
JKW CO., LTD.—See Kobe Steel, Ltd.; *Int'l*, pg. 4217
JKW HOLDINGS, LLC—See WillScot Mobile Mini Holdings Corp.; *U.S. Public*, pg. 2372
J.K. WIRE HARNESS SDN. BHD.—See Sumitomo Electric Industries, Ltd.; *Int'l*, pg. 7284
JK WOHNBAU AG; *Int'l*, pg. 3973
JKX HUNGARY B.V.—See JKX Oil & Gas Plc; *Int'l*, pg. 3973
JKX (NEDERLAND) B.V.—See JKX Oil & Gas Plc; *Int'l*, pg. 3973
JKX OIL & GAS PLC; *Int'l*, pg. 3973
JK YAMING INTERNATIONAL HOLDINGS PTE. LTD.—See Luma Investments, Ltd.; *Int'l*, pg. 4577
JLAB AUDIO, LLC—See Noritsu Koki Co., Ltd.; *Int'l*, pg. 5429
JLAB JAPAN CO., LTD.—See Noritsu Koki Co., Ltd.; *Int'l*, pg. 5429
JLA HOME, INC.—See E&E Co., Ltd.; *U.S. Private*, pg. 1301
JLA INFRAVILLE SHOPPERS LTD; *Int'l*, pg. 3973
JLA LIMITED—See Cinven Limited; *Int'l*, pg. 1612
J.L. ANDERSON COMPANY INC.; *U.S. Private*, pg. 2167
JL AUDIO, INC.—See Garmin Ltd.; *U.S. Public*, pg. 2885
J.L. BAINBRIDGE AND COMPANY, INC.; *U.S. Private*, pg. 2167
J.L. BECKER COMPANY—See Gasbarre Products Inc.; *U.S. Private*, pg. 1648
J.L. BRYAN EQUIPMENT & LEASE SERVICE, INC.—See Empeiria Capital Partners LLC; *U.S. Private*, pg. 1384
J.L. BUCHANAN INC.; *U.S. Private*, pg. 2167
J&L BUILDING MATERIALS INC.; *U.S. Private*, pg. 2154
J&L BUILDING MATERIALS OF DELAWARE INC.—See J&L Building Materials Inc.; *U.S. Private*, pg. 2154
J.L. BURKE CONTRACTING, INC.; *U.S. Private*, pg. 2167
JLC FOOD SYSTEMS INC.; *U.S. Private*, pg. 2212
J.L. CLARK, INC. - LANCASTER—See Henry Crown & Company; *U.S. Private*, pg. 1917
J.L. CLARK, INC.—See Henry Crown & Company; *U.S. Private*, pg. 1917

CORPORATE AFFILIATIONS

J.L. & COMPANY LIMITED—See Hermes International SCA; *Int'l*, pg. 3363
JLC RENOV; *Int'l*, pg. 3973
J.L. DAVIS COMPANIES; *U.S. Private*, pg. 2167
J.L. DE BALL CANADA INC.; *U.S. Private*, pg. 3858
J.L. DEGRAFFENREID & SONS, INC.—See DG Foods, LLC; *U.S. Private*, pg. 1221
J-LEASE CO., LTD.; *Int'l*, pg. 3854
JLE INDUSTRIES, LLC; *U.S. Private*, pg. 2212
JLE MANUFACTURING, INC.; *U.S. Private*, pg. 2212
JLEN ENVIRONMENTAL ASSETS GROUP LIMITED; *Int'l*, pg. 3973
J. LEUTENEGGER PTY LTD.—See E.C. Birch Proprietary Limited; *Int'l*, pg. 2251
J&L FIBER SERVICES, INC.—See Valmet Oyj; *Int'l*, pg. 8118
JL FILTRATION INC.—See Clean Harbors, Inc.; *U.S. Public*, pg. 510
JL FOODS CO., INC.; *U.S. Private*, pg. 2211
JL FURNISHINGS LLC; *U.S. Private*, pg. 2211
J.L. GADDY ENTERPRISES INC.; *U.S. Private*, pg. 2167
JLG DEUTSCHLAND GMBH—See Oshkosh Corporation; *U.S. Public*, pg. 1620
JLG EMEA B.V.—See Oshkosh Corporation; *U.S. Public*, pg. 1620
JLG EQUIPMENT SERVICES, INC.—See Oshkosh Corporation; *U.S. Public*, pg. 1620
JLG EQUIPMENT SERVICES LIMITED—See Oshkosh Corporation; *U.S. Public*, pg. 1620
JLG FINANCIAL SOLUTIONS—See Oshkosh Corporation; *U.S. Public*, pg. 1620
JLG FRANCE SARL—See Oshkosh Corporation; *U.S. Public*, pg. 1620
JLG GROUND SUPPORT EUROPE BVBA—See Oshkosh Corporation; *U.S. Public*, pg. 1620
JLG GROUP PLC; *Int'l*, pg. 3973
JLG INDUSTRIES GMBH—See Oshkosh Corporation; *U.S. Public*, pg. 1620
JLG INDUSTRIES, INC.—See Oshkosh Corporation; *U.S. Public*, pg. 1620
JLG INDUSTRIES, INC.—See Oshkosh Corporation; *U.S. Public*, pg. 1620
JLG INDUSTRIES, INC.—See Oshkosh Corporation; *U.S. Public*, pg. 1620
JLG INDUSTRIES INDIA PRIVATE LIMITED—See Oshkosh Corporation; *U.S. Public*, pg. 1620
JLG INDUSTRIES (ITALIA) S.R.L.—See Oshkosh Corporation; *U.S. Public*, pg. 1620
JLG INDUSTRIES (UNITED KINGDOM) LIMITED—See Oshkosh Corporation; *U.S. Public*, pg. 1620
JLG LATINO AMERICANA LTDA.—See Oshkosh Corporation; *U.S. Public*, pg. 1620
JLG NEW ZEALAND ACCESS EQUIPMENT & SERVICE—See Oshkosh Corporation; *U.S. Public*, pg. 1620
JLG PROPERTIES AUSTRALIA PTY LIMITED—See Oshkosh Corporation; *U.S. Public*, pg. 1620
JLG SVERIGE AB—See Oshkosh Corporation; *U.S. Public*, pg. 1620
J.L. HALEY ENTERPRISES, INC.—See Aterian Investment Management, L.P.; *U.S. Private*, pg. 367
J&L HOLDING COMPANY—See ITE Management L.P.; *U.S. Private*, pg. 2149
JLH PROPERTIES, INC.—See Tupperware Brands Corporation; *U.S. Public*, pg. 2204
JLH S A; *Int'l*, pg. 3973
J.LIEB FOODS, INC.; *U.S. Private*, pg. 2168
JL INDUSTRIES, INC.—See Activar, Inc.; *U.S. Private*, pg. 68
J&L JULI HOLDING (CANADA) LTD.—See Juli Sling Co., Ltd.; *Int'l*, pg. 4024
JLK, INC.; *Int'l*, pg. 3973
JLL CAPITAL MARKETS AB—See Jones Lang LaSalle Incorporated; *U.S. Public*, pg. 1202
JLL CORRETAGEM E TRASACOES IMOBILIARIAS LTDA.—See Jones Lang LaSalle Incorporated; *U.S. Public*, pg. 1202
JLL INCOME PROPERTY TRUST, INC.; *U.S. Private*, pg. 2212
JLL KNIGHTSBRIDGE—See Jones Lang LaSalle Incorporated; *U.S. Public*, pg. 1202
JLL LTD—See Jones Lang LaSalle Incorporated; *U.S. Public*, pg. 1202
JLL MACAU LIMITED—See Jones Lang LaSalle Incorporated; *U.S. Public*, pg. 1202
JLL MORTGAGE SERVICES PTY LTD—See Jones Lang LaSalle Incorporated; *U.S. Public*, pg. 1202
JLL PARTNERS, LLC; *U.S. Private*, pg. 2212
JLL PROPERTY SERVICES (MALAYSIA) SDN BHD—See Jones Lang LaSalle Incorporated; *U.S. Public*, pg. 1202
JLL TECHNOLOGY SOLUTIONS—See Jones Lang LaSalle Incorporated; *U.S. Public*, pg. 1202
JLL VALORACIONES SA—See Jones Lang LaSalle Incorporated; *U.S. Public*, pg. 1202
JL MAG RARE-EARTH CO., LTD.; *Int'l*, pg. 3973

COMPANY NAME INDEX J. MOORE & CO. INC.
Company Index

JL MARINE INSURANCE-BROKERS GMBH & CO. KG—See Marsh & McLennan Companies, Inc.; *U.S. Public*, pg. 1376
J.L. MAUPIN ENTERPRISES INC.; *U.S. Private*, pg. 2167
JLM COUTURE, INC.; *U.S. Public*, pg. 1190
JL MEDIA, INC.; *U.S. Private*, pg. 2212
J&L METROLOGY, INC.; *U.S. Private*, pg. 2154
JLM INDUSTRIES, INC.; *U.S. Private*, pg. 2213
JLMOORE, INC.; *U.S. Private*, pg. 2213
J.L. MORISON (INDIA) LTD.; *Int'l*, pg. 3858
JL MORISON (MALAYA) SDN BHD—See Berjaya Corporation Berhad; *Int'l*, pg. 984
JLM VERWALTUNGS GMBH—See Marsh & McLennan Companies, Inc.; *U.S. Public*, pg. 1376
JLM WHOLESALE INC.—See Dominus Capital, L.P.; *U.S. Private*, pg. 1257
J.LODGE, LLC; *U.S. Private*, pg. 2168
JLOGO HOLDINGS LTD.; *Int'l*, pg. 3973
J. LOHR WINERY CORPORATION; *U.S. Private*, pg. 2156
J. LORBER CO. INC.; *U.S. Private*, pg. 2156
J.L. RICHARDS & ASSOCIATES LIMITED; *Int'l*, pg. 3858
JLR, INC.—See Equifax Inc.; *U.S. Public*, pg. 786
J.L. ROTHROCK INC.; *U.S. Private*, pg. 2167
JLS CO., LTD.; *Int'l*, pg. 3973
JLS DIGITAL LTD.—See Swisscom AG; *Int'l*, pg. 7374
JLS GROUP INC.; *U.S. Private*, pg. 2213
JLS INVESTMENT GROUP LLC; *U.S. Private*, pg. 2213
JLS INVESTMENT REALTY; *U.S. Private*, pg. 2213
JLT ADVISORY LIMITED—See Marsh & McLennan Companies, Inc.; *U.S. Public*, pg. 1376
JLT BENEFIT SOLUTIONS LIMITED—See Marsh & McLennan Companies, Inc.; *U.S. Public*, pg. 1376
JLT BERMUDA LTD.—See Marsh & McLennan Companies, Inc.; *U.S. Public*, pg. 1376
JLT CLAMPS—See James L. Taylor Manufacturing Co.; *U.S. Private*, pg. 2184
JLT HOLDINGS JAPAN LIMITED—See Marsh & McLennan Companies, Inc.; *U.S. Public*, pg. 1376
JLT INDEPENDENT INSURANCE BROKERS PRIVATE LIMITED—See Marsh & McLennan Companies, Inc.; *U.S. Public*, pg. 1376
JLT INSURANCE BROKERS IRELAND LIMITED—See Marsh & McLennan Companies, Inc.; *U.S. Public*, pg. 1376
JLT INSURANCE MANAGEMENT (BERMUDA) LIMITED—See Marsh & McLennan Companies, Inc.; *U.S. Public*, pg. 1376
JLT INSURANCE MANAGEMENT (SINGAPORE) PTE LTD—See Marsh & McLennan Companies, Inc.; *U.S. Public*, pg. 1377
JLT INTERACTIVE PTE LTD—See Marsh & McLennan Companies, Inc.; *U.S. Public*, pg. 1377
JLT INVESTMENT MANAGEMENT LIMITED—See Marsh & McLennan Companies, Inc.; *U.S. Public*, pg. 1376
JLT JAPAN LIMITED—See Marsh & McLennan Companies, Inc.; *U.S. Public*, pg. 1376
JLT MOBILE COMPUTERS AB; *Int'l*, pg. 3973
JLT MOBILE COMPUTERS, INC.—See JLT Mobile Computers AB; *Int'l*, pg. 3974
JLT MOBILE COMPUTERS SWEDEN AB—See JLT Mobile Computers AB; *Int'l*, pg. 3974
J.L. TODD AUCTION CO.; *U.S. Private*, pg. 2168
JLT REINSURANCE BROKERS LIMITED—See Marsh & McLennan Companies, Inc.; *U.S. Public*, pg. 1376
JLT RE LIMITED—See Marsh & McLennan Companies, Inc.; *U.S. Public*, pg. 1376
JLT RISK SERVICES JAPAN LIMITED—See Marsh & McLennan Companies, Inc.; *U.S. Public*, pg. 1377
JLT RISK SOLUTIONS AB—See Marsh & McLennan Companies, Inc.; *U.S. Public*, pg. 1376
JLT RISK SOLUTIONS ASIA PTE LIMITED—See Marsh & McLennan Companies, Inc.; *U.S. Public*, pg. 1377
JLT SERVICES CORP.—See Aon plc; *Int'l*, pg. 489
JLT SPECIALTY LIMITED—See Marsh & McLennan Companies, Inc.; *U.S. Public*, pg. 1376
JLT WEALTH MANAGEMENT LIMITED—See Marsh & McLennan Companies, Inc.; *U.S. Public*, pg. 1376
J & L VENTURES LLC; *U.S. Private*, pg. 2152
J.L. WALLACE, INC.; *U.S. Private*, pg. 2168
JLY INVESTMENTS, INC.—See InCompass LLC; *U.S. Private*, pg. 2054
JM AB; *Int'l*, pg. 3974
J. MACEDO S.A.; *Int'l*, pg. 3856
JMAC INC.; *U.S. Private*, pg. 2214
JMACS JAPAN CO., LTD.; *Int'l*, pg. 3974
J&M ADVERTISING LLC; *U.S. Private*, pg. 2154
J&M ADVERTISING & PRODUCTIONS; *U.S. Private*, pg. 2154
JM&A GROUP—See JM Family Enterprises Inc.; *U.S. Private*, pg. 2214
JMA INFORMATION TECHNOLOGY; *U.S. Private*, pg. 2214
JMALUCELLI AGENCIAMENTO E SERVICOS LTDA.—See PARANA BCO S.A.; *Int'l*, pg. 5738
JMALUCELLI EQUIPAMENTOS LTDA—See J. Malucelli Holding SA; *Int'l*, pg. 3856
J. MALUCELLI HOLDING SA; *Int'l*, pg. 3856
JMALUCELLI INVESTIMENTOS LTDA.—See PARANA BCO S.A.; *Int'l*, pg. 5738
JMALUCELLI PREVIDENCIA—See J. Malucelli Holding SA; *Int'l*, pg. 3856
JMALUCELLI RESSEGURADORA S.A.—See PARANA BCO S.A.; *Int'l*, pg. 5739
JMALUCELLI SEGURADORA S.A—See J. Malucelli Holding SA; *Int'l*, pg. 3856
J. MANN INC.; *U.S. Private*, pg. 2156
JMA PROPERTIES LLC; *U.S. Private*, pg. 2214
JMARK BUSINESS SOLUTIONS, INC.; *U.S. Private*, pg. 2215
JMAR, LLC; *U.S. Private*, pg. 2214
JMAR RESEARCH, INC.—See JMAR, LLC; *U.S. Private*, pg. 2214
JMA SOLUTIONS; *U.S. Private*, pg. 2214
JMA VENTURES, LLC; *U.S. Private*, pg. 2214
J-MAX CO., LTD.; *Int'l*, pg. 3854
JMAX GLOBAL DISTRIBUTORS INC.; *Int'l*, pg. 3975
JMAX INTERNATIONAL LIMITED; *Int'l*, pg. 3975
JMB/245 PARK AVENUE ASSOCIATES, LTD.—See JMB Realty Corporation; *U.S. Private*, pg. 2215
J.M. BASTILLE ACIER INC.; *Int'l*, pg. 3858
JMB REALTY CORPORATION; *U.S. Private*, pg. 2215
JM BRUNEAU ESPANA SAU—See JM Bruneau SAS; *Int'l*, pg. 3974
JM BRUNEAU SAS; *Int'l*, pg. 3974
JM BULLION, INC.—See A-Mark Precious Metals, Inc.; *U.S. Public*, pg. 10
JMB WIND BRASIL LTDA.—See Schweiter Technologies AG; *Int'l*, pg. 6645
JMB WIND LTDA.—See Schweiter Technologies AG; *Int'l*, pg. 6645
JMC AMEA LTD.—See Vection Technologies Ltd.; *Int'l*, pg. 8143
JM CAPITAL II CORP.; *Int'l*, pg. 3974
J&M CATERING SERVICES NV—See Compass Group PLC; *Int'l*, pg. 1752
JMC CAPITAL PARTNERS LLC; *U.S. Private*, pg. 2215
JMC COMMUNITIES, INC.; *U.S. Private*, pg. 2215
JMC CORPORATION—See Kyung-In Synthetic Corporation; *Int'l*, pg. 4367
JMC CORPORATION; *Int'l*, pg. 3975
JMC EQUIPMENT LLC; *U.S. Private*, pg. 2215
J. MCGARVEY CONSTRUCTION COMPANY, INC.; *U.S. Private*, pg. 2156
JMC GROUP SRL—See Vection Technologies Ltd.; *Int'l*, pg. 8143
J & M CHEVROLET, INC.; *U.S. Private*, pg. 2152
JM CONSTRUCTION S.A.—See JM AB; *Int'l*, pg. 3974
J M CONSULTORES DE INFORMATICA E ARTES GRAFICAS, S.A.—See Reditus SGPS S.A.; *Int'l*, pg. 6248
JM CORPORATION—See Maeda Corporation; *Int'l*, pg. 4635
JM COX RESOURCES LP; *U.S. Private*, pg. 2213
JMC PROJECTS INDIA LTD; *Int'l*, pg. 3975
JMC VAN TRANS LIMITED—See An Post LLC; *Int'l*, pg. 443
JM DANMARK A/S—See JM AB; *Int'l*, pg. 3974
J.M. DAVIDSON INC.; *U.S. Private*, pg. 2168
JMDC, INC.—See OMRON Corporation; *Int'l*, pg. 5564
JMD COMMUNICATIONS; *U.S. Private*, pg. 2215
JM DIGITAL WORKS—See Jazzercise, Inc.; *U.S. Private*, pg. 2193
J&M DISTRIBUTING COMPANY, INC.; *U.S. Private*, pg. 2154
JMD MEDICO SERVICES LIMITED—See JMD Ventures Limited; *Int'l*, pg. 3975
JMD MHC LLC—See JMD Properties Inc.; *U.S. Public*, pg. 1190
JMD PROPERTIES INC.; *U.S. Public*, pg. 1190
JMD SECURITE SA—See Stanley Black & Decker, Inc.; *U.S. Public*, pg. 1933
JMD VENTURES LIMITED; *Int'l*, pg. 3975
JM EDUCATION GROUP; *Int'l*, pg. 3974
JME INCORPORATED; *U.S. Private*, pg. 2215
J. MENDEL, INC.—See Stallion, Inc.; *U.S. Private*, pg. 3776
JM ENERGY CORPORATION - CORPORATE PLANNING DIVISION—See JSR Corp.; *Int'l*, pg. 4013
JM ENERGY CORPORATION - MANUFACTURING DIVISION—See JSR Corp.; *Int'l*, pg. 4013
JM ENERGY CORPORATION—See JSR Corp.; *Int'l*, pg. 4013
JM ENTERPRISES 1, INC.—See Cardiff Lexington Corporation; *U.S. Public*, pg. 433
JM ENTREPRENAD AB—See JM AB; *Int'l*, pg. 3974
JM EQUIPMENT COMPANY INC.; *U.S. Private*, pg. 2213
J.M. FAHEY CONSTRUCTION COMPANY; *U.S. Private*, pg. 2168
JM FAMILY ENTERPRISES INC.; *U.S. Private*, pg. 2213
JMF COMPANY—See Zhejiang Hailiang Co., Ltd.; *Int'l*, pg. 8655
JM FINANCIAL ASSET MANAGEMENT PRIVATE LIMITED—See JM Financial Ltd.; *Int'l*, pg. 3974
JM FINANCIAL HOME LOANS LIMITED—See JM Financial Ltd.; *Int'l*, pg. 3974
JM FINANCIAL INSTITUTIONAL SECURITIES PRIVATE LIMITED—See JM Financial Ltd.; *Int'l*, pg. 3974
JM FINANCIAL LTD.; *Int'l*, pg. 3974
JM FINANCIAL MUTUAL FUND; *Int'l*, pg. 3974
JM FINANCIAL OVERSEAS HOLDINGS PRIVATE LIMITED—See JM Financial Ltd.; *Int'l*, pg. 3974
JM FINANCIAL SECURITIES INC.—See JM Financial Ltd.; *Int'l*, pg. 3974
JM FINANCIAL SERVICES PRIVATE LIMITED—See JM Financial Ltd.; *Int'l*, pg. 3974
JM FINANCIAL SINGAPORE PTE. LIMITED—See JM Financial Ltd.; *Int'l*, pg. 3974
J&M FOOD PRODUCTS COMPANY—See My Own Meals, Inc.; *U.S. Private*, pg. 2823
JMG CORPORATION LIMITED; *Int'l*, pg. 3975
JMG REALTY, INC.; *U.S. Private*, pg. 2215
J.M. GRIMSTAD INC.; *U.S. Private*, pg. 2168
THE JM GROUP (IT RECRUITMENT) LIMITED—See Staffing 360 Solutions, Inc.; *U.S. Public*, pg. 1925
JMGT STUDIOS SATELLITE TELEVISION NETWORK, LLC; *U.S. Private*, pg. 2215
J.M. HARTWELL L.P.—See Keystone Group, L.P.; *U.S. Private*, pg. 2297
JMH CAPITAL; *U.S. Private*, pg. 2215
JMH INTERNATIONAL, LLC—See EagleTree Capital, LP; *U.S. Private*, pg. 1312
JM HOLDINGS CO., LTD.; *Int'l*, pg. 3974
J.M. HUBER CORP.-NATURAL RESOURCES—See J.M. Huber Corporation; *U.S. Private*, pg. 2168
J.M. HUBER CORPORATION; *U.S. Private*, pg. 2168
J.M. HUBER FINLAND OY—See J.M. Huber Corporation; *U.S. Private*, pg. 2168
J.M. HUBER (INDIA) PVT. LTD.—See J.M. Huber Corporation; *U.S. Private*, pg. 2168
J.M. HUBER INVESTMENT (CHINA) LTD—See J.M. Huber Corporation; *U.S. Private*, pg. 2169
J.M. HUTTON & CO., INC.; *U.S. Private*, pg. 2169
JMIB HOLDINGS BV—See Marsh & McLennan Companies, Inc.; *U.S. Public*, pg. 1376
J. MICHAEL MALONEY, M.D., P.C.—See Epiphany Dermatology PA; *U.S. Private*, pg. 1413
J. MICHAELS, INC.; *Int'l*, pg. 3856
JMICRON TECHNOLOGY CORPORATION; *Int'l*, pg. 3975
JMI EQUITY—See JMI Services, Inc.; *U.S. Private*, pg. 2215
JMI EQUITY—See JMI Services, Inc.; *U.S. Private*, pg. 2216
J MILLIET BERCY BISTROT CASH BBC; *Int'l*, pg. 3852
JMIMX S.A. DE C.V.—See Jeongmoon Information Co., Ltd.; *Int'l*, pg. 3930
J&M INDUSTRIES INC.; *U.S. Private*, pg. 2154
JM INDUSTRIES INC.; *U.S. Private*, pg. 2214
J.MIRAI MEDICAL CO., LTD.—See Toho Holdings Co., Ltd.; *Int'l*, pg. 7776
JMI REALTY LLC—See JMI Services, Inc.; *U.S. Private*, pg. 2216
JMI SERVICES, INC.; *U.S. Private*, pg. 2215
JMI SPORTS LLC—See JMI Services, Inc.; *U.S. Private*, pg. 2216
JMI SYRINGES & MEDICAL DEVICES LIMITED; *Int'l*, pg. 3975
JMJ ASSOCIATES, LLC—See 3i Group plc; *Int'l*, pg. 9
J.M. JAYSON & CO., INC.; *U.S. Private*, pg. 2169
JMJ ENVIRONMENTAL INC.—See M.A. Bongiovanni Inc.; *U.S. Private*, pg. 2527
JMJ FINTECH LIMITED; *Int'l*, pg. 3975
JMJ ORGANICS, LTD.—See SiteOne Landscape Supply, Inc.; *U.S. Public*, pg. 1888
JMK AUTO SALES INC.; *U.S. Private*, pg. 2216
JMK INTERNATIONAL, INC.; *U.S. Private*, pg. 2216
JMK OPERATIONS INC.—See JMK International, Inc.; *U.S. Private*, pg. 2216
J.M. LAMBELET S.A.—See Romande Energie Holding S.A.; *Int'l*, pg. 6394
JM LEXUS—See JM Family Enterprises Inc.; *U.S. Private*, pg. 2214
JML OPTICAL INDUSTRIES, LLC—See Truist Financial Corporation; *U.S. Public*, pg. 2200
JML-SYSTEM AB—See Dustin Group AB; *Int'l*, pg. 2235
JML UNLIMITED; *U.S. Private*, pg. 2216
J. M. MARSCHUETZ CONSTRUCTION, CO.; *U.S. Private*, pg. 2156
JMMB BANK (JAMAICA) LIMITED; *Int'l*, pg. 3975
JMMB GROUP LTD.; *Int'l*, pg. 3975
JMMB INSURANCE BROKERS LTD—See Jamaica Money Market Brokers Limited; *Int'l*, pg. 3874
JMMB INTERNATIONAL LIMITED—See Jamaica Money Market Brokers Limited; *Int'l*, pg. 3874
JMMB SECURITIES LIMITED—See Jamaica Money Market Brokers Limited; *Int'l*, pg. 3874
J.M. MCCONKEY & CO. INC.; *U.S. Private*, pg. 2169
J.M. MCCORMICK COMPANY INC.; *U.S. Private*, pg. 2169
JMM MANAGEMENT GROUP, LLC—See Titan Cloud Software, LLC; *U.S. Private*, pg. 4177
J&M MOBILE HOMES INC.; *U.S. Private*, pg. 2154
J. M. MURRAY CENTER INC—See J.M. Murray Center Inc.; *U.S. Private*, pg. 2169
J.M. MURRAY CENTER INC.; *U.S. Private*, pg. 2169
JM NORGE AS—See JM AB; *Int'l*, pg. 3974
JM OIL COMPANY INC.; *U.S. Private*, pg. 2214
J. MOORE & CO. INC.; *U.S. Private*, pg. 2156

JMP ASSET MANAGEMENT LLC—See Citizens Financial Group, Inc.; *U.S. Public*, pg. 505
JMP COAL HOLDINGS, LLC; *U.S. Private*, pg. 2216
JMP CREDIT ADVISORS LLC—See Medalist Partners, LP; *U.S. Private*, pg. 2650
J.M. PERRONE CO., INC.; *U.S. Private*, pg. 2169
JMP GROUP INC.—See Citizens Financial Group, Inc.; *U.S. Public*, pg. 505
JMP GROUP LLC—See Citizens Financial Group, Inc.; *U.S. Public*, pg. 505
JMP REALTY TRUST INC.—See Citizens Financial Group, Inc.; *U.S. Public*, pg. 506
JMPR, INC.—See IMRE, LLC; *U.S. Private*, pg. 2051
JM PROCESS SYSTEMS INC.; *U.S. Private*, pg. 2214
JMP SECURITIES LLC - NEW YORK—See Citizens Financial Group, Inc.; *U.S. Public*, pg. 506
JMP SECURITIES LLC—See Citizens Financial Group, Inc.; *U.S. Public*, pg. 505
JMR ELECTRONICS INC.; *U.S. Private*, pg. 2216
JMR FINANCIAL GROUP, INC.; *U.S. Private*, pg. 2216
JMR-GESTAO DE EMPRESAS DE RETALHO, SGPS, S.A.—See Jeronimo Martins SGPS SA; *Int'l*, pg. 3931
J.M.R. MEDICAL, INC.—See AdaptHealth Corp.; *U.S. Public*, pg. 39
J.M. RODGERS CO., INC.; *U.S. Private*, pg. 2169
JMS ADRIATIC D.O.O.—See Jaquet Metal Service SA; *Int'l*, pg. 3867
JMS CO. LTD. - CHIYODA PLANT—See JMS Co., Ltd.; *Int'l*, pg. 3975
JMS CO. LTD. - IZUMO PLANT—See JMS Co., Ltd.; *Int'l*, pg. 3975
JMS CO. LTD. - MIYOSHI PLANT—See JMS Co., Ltd.; *Int'l*, pg. 3975
JMS CO. LTD. - ONO PLANT—See JMS Co., Ltd.; *Int'l*, pg. 3975
JMS CO., LTD.; *Int'l*, pg. 3975
JMS DALIAN MEDICAL SUPPLY CO., LTD.—See JMS Co., Ltd.; *Int'l*, pg. 3975
JMS DANMARK APS—See Jacquet Metal Service SA; *Int'l*, pg. 3867
JMS FOODSERVICE, LLC—See The J.M. Smucker Company; *U.S. Public*, pg. 2107
JMS HEALTHCARE PHL, INC.—See JMS Co., Ltd.; *Int'l*, pg. 3975
JMS HEALTHCARE (THAILAND) CO., LTD.—See JMS Co., Ltd.; *Int'l*, pg. 3975
J.M.S.(K) MEDICAL SUPPLY CO., LTD.—See JMS Co., Ltd.; *Int'l*, pg. 3975
JMS METALS ASIA PTE. LTD.—See Jacquet Metal Service SA; *Int'l*, pg. 3867
J.M. SMITH CORPORATION; *U.S. Private*, pg. 2169
THE J.M. SMUCKER COMPANY; *U.S. Public*, pg. 2106
J.M. SMUCKER LLC—See The J.M. Smucker Company; *U.S. Public*, pg. 2107
JMS NORTH AMERICA CORPORATION—See JMS Co., Ltd.; *Int'l*, pg. 3975
JM SORGE, INC.—See Sterling Investment Partners, L.P.; *U.S. Private*, pg. 3806
JMS REKLAMGARDEN AB; *Int'l*, pg. 3975
JMS RUSSEL METALS CORP.—See Russel Metals Inc.; *Int'l*, pg. 6430
JMS SERVICE CO., LTD.—See JMS Co., Ltd.; *Int'l*, pg. 3975
JMS SINGAPORE PTE. LTD.—See JMS Co., Ltd.; *Int'l*, pg. 3975
JM STEEL CO., LTD.—See SPARX Group Co., Ltd.; *Int'l*, pg. 7128
JM STEEL CORP.—See Frank Calandra, Inc.; *U.S. Private*, pg. 1594
J&M STEEL SOLUTIONS CO., LTD.—See JFE Holdings, Inc.; *Int'l*, pg. 3935
J.M. STEWART CORPORATION—See EBSCO Industries, Inc.; *U.S. Private*, pg. 1325
JM SUOMI OY—See JM AB; *Int'l*, pg. 3974
JM SWANK, LLC—See Platinum Equity, LLC; *U.S. Private*, pg. 3205
J&M TANK LINES INC.; *U.S. Private*, pg. 2154
JMT AUTO LIMITED—See Amtek Auto Limited; *Int'l*, pg. 441
JM TELECOM(CORP.); *Int'l*, pg. 3974
J.M. THOMPSON INSURANCE, INC.—See McGowan Insurance Group Inc.; *U.S. Private*, pg. 2635
JMT NETWORK SERVICES COMPANY LIMITED—See Jay Mart Public Company Limited; *Int'l*, pg. 3914
JMT PROPERTY CORP.—See Warburg Pincus LLC; *U.S. Private*, pg. 4438
JMT SK S.R.O—See JM Telecom(corp.); *Int'l*, pg. 3974
JMU DEFENSE SYSTEMS CO., LTD.—See JFE Holdings, Inc.; *Int'l*, pg. 3938
J. MURPHY & SONS LIMITED; *Int'l*, pg. 3856
JM WALKER LP; *U.S. Private*, pg. 2214
JMW HORECA UITZENDBUREAU BV—See Randstad N.V.; *Int'l*, pg. 6206
JMX INTERNATIONAL CORPORATION; *U.S. Private*, pg. 2216
JNANA THERAPEUTICS INC—See AbbVie Inc.; *U.S. Public*, pg. 24
JNANA THERAPEUTICS INC—See Bain Capital, LP; *U.S. Private*, pg. 441

JNBS FOUNDATION—See Jamaica National Building Society; *Int'l*, pg. 3874
JNBY DESIGN LIMITED; *Int'l*, pg. 3976
JNC CORPORATION; *Int'l*, pg. 3976
JN CHEVROLET; *U.S. Private*, pg. 2216
JN DATA A/S—See Jyske Bank A/S; *Int'l*, pg. 4037
JN ELINSTALLATORER AB—See Instalco AB; *Int'l*, pg. 3722
JNE LOGISTICS SINGAPORE PTE LTD—See Teckwah Industrial Corporation Ltd; *Int'l*, pg. 7515
J-NET RENTAL & LEASE CO., LTD.—See VT Holdings Co., Ltd.; *Int'l*, pg. 8315
JNE WELDING; *Int'l*, pg. 3976
JN FUND MANAGERS LIMITED—See Jamaica National Building Society; *Int'l*, pg. 3874
JNH AUSTRALIA PTY LTD—See Toys R Us ANZ Limited; *Int'l*, pg. 7881
JN-INTERNATIONAL MEDICAL CORPORATION; *U.S. Private*, pg. 2216
JNIT TECHNOLOGIES, INC.—See Magellanic Cloud Limited; *Int'l*, pg. 4637
JNJ EXPRESS INC.; *U.S. Private*, pg. 2216
JNJ MOBILE INC.; *U.S. Private*, pg. 2217
JNK GLOBAL CO., LTD.; *Int'l*, pg. 3976
THE J.N. PHILLIPS GLASS CO. INC.; *U.S. Private*, pg. 4058
JNPR SWEDEN AB—See Juniper Networks, Inc.; *U.S. Public*, pg. 1211
JNS HOLDINGS CORPORATION; *U.S. Public*, pg. 1190
JNS INSTRUMENTS LTD.—See Nippon Seiki Co., Ltd.; *Int'l*, pg. 5329
JNS MEDIA SPECIALISTS, INC.; *U.S. Private*, pg. 2217
JNS POWER & CONTROL SYSTEMS, INC.—See JNS Holdings Corporation; *U.S. Public*, pg. 1190
JNS-SMITHCHEM, LLC; *U.S. Private*, pg. 2217
JN SYSTEM PARTNERS CO., LTD.—See JSR Corp.; *Int'l*, pg. 4013
JNTC CO., LTD.; *Int'l*, pg. 3976
JNU GLOBAL INC.; *Int'l*, pg. 3976
J.N. WHITE ASSOCIATES, INC.; *U.S. Private*, pg. 2169
JOACHIM HERZ STIFTUNG; *Int'l*, pg. 3976
JOAN B. MARCUS COMMUNICATIONS LLC; *U.S. Private*, pg. 2217
JOANNE FABRICS INC.; *Int'l*, pg. 3976
JOANNE PLASTICS—See Burlington Basket Co.; *U.S. Private*, pg. 688
JOANN INC.; *U.S. Public*, pg. 1190
JO-ANN STORES, INC.—See Leonard Green & Partners, L.P.; *U.S. Private*, pg. 2426
JO-ANN STORES SUPPLY CHAIN MANAGEMENT, INC.—See Leonard Green & Partners, L.P.; *U.S. Private*, pg. 2426
JOAN PEARCE RESEARCH ASSOCIATES; *U.S. Private*, pg. 2217
JOAN SMITH ENTERPRISES INC.; *U.S. Private*, pg. 2217
JOAO DE DEUS & FILHOS S.A.—See Denso Corporation; *Int'l*, pg. 2031
JOAO FORTES ENGENHARIA S.A.; *Int'l*, pg. 3976
JOAO JACINTO TOME, S.A.—See Eiffage S.A.; *Int'l*, pg. 2331
J OASIS AIRBAG TECHNOLOGY PTE. LTD—See Tiong Woon Corporation Holding Ltd.; *Int'l*, pg. 7755
JOB ADDER OPERATIONS PTY. LTD.—See SEEK Limited; *Int'l*, pg. 6678
JOBAN JOINT POWER CO., LTD—See Tohoku Electric Power Co., Inc.; *Int'l*, pg. 7777
JOBAN KAIHATSU CO., LTD.; *Int'l*, pg. 3976
JOBAN KOSAN CO., LTD.; *Int'l*, pg. 3976
JOBAN KYODO PRINTING CO., LTD.—See Kyodo Printing Co. Ltd.; *Int'l*, pg. 4361
JOBARCO B.V.—See TKH Group N.V.; *Int'l*, pg. 7764
JOBAR INC.; *U.S. Private*, pg. 2217
JOBBERS AUTOMOTIVE WAREHOUSE; *U.S. Private*, pg. 2217
JOBBERS SERVICE OF SAN ANGELO—See Installer Sales & Service Incorporated; *U.S. Private*, pg. 2092
JOBBOARD ENTERPRISES GMBH—See SThree Plc.; *Int'l*, pg. 7214
JOBBOT, INC.; *U.S. Private*, pg. 2217
JOBBREISER AS—See Inin Group AS; *Int'l*, pg. 3703
JOBCASE, INC.; *U.S. Private*, pg. 2217
JOBE & COMPANY INC.; *U.S. Private*, pg. 2217
JOBELEPHANT.COM INC.; *U.S. Private*, pg. 2217
JOBE MATERIALS, L.P.; *U.S. Private*, pg. 2217
JOBEN BIO-MEDICAL CO., LTD.; *Int'l*, pg. 3976
JOBES, HENDERSON & ASSOCIATES, INC.—See Sterling Investment Partners, L.P.; *U.S. Private*, pg. 3806
JOBFAIR GMBH—See Bertrandt AG; *Int'l*, pg. 998
JOBFOX, INC.; *U.S. Private*, pg. 2217
JOBINDEX A/S; *Int'l*, pg. 3976
JOBING.COM, LLC; *U.S. Private*, pg. 2217
JOBMAN WORKWEAR AB—See New Wave Group AB; *Int'l*, pg. 5229
JOB & MEHR GMBH—See Veolia Environnement S.A.; *Int'l*, pg. 8153
JOBON CORPORATION—See Corporate Press Inc.; *U.S. Private*, pg. 1055
JOBREQ.COM, INC.; *U.S. Private*, pg. 2217
JOBS2WEB INC.—See SAP SE; *Int'l*, pg. 6568

JOBS AUTOMAZIONE S.P.A. - SACHMAN DIVISION—See Fair Friend Group; *Int'l*, pg. 2604
JOBS AUTOMAZIONE S.P.A.—See Fair Friend Group; *Int'l*, pg. 2604
JOBS BUILDING SERVICES LLC—See Valcourt Building Services LLC; *U.S. Private*, pg. 4330
JOBSCIENCE, INC.—See Insight Venture Management, LLC; *U.S. Private*, pg. 2087
THE JOBSCOPE CORPORATION—See Gower Corporation; *U.S. Private*, pg. 1747
JOBS DB RECRUITMENT (THAILAND) LIMITED—See SEEK Limited; *Int'l*, pg. 6678
JOBSERVE LTD.; *Int'l*, pg. 3976
JOBS GMBH—See Fair Friend Group; *Int'l*, pg. 2604
JOBS INC.—See Fair Friend Group; *Int'l*, pg. 2604
JOBSITE TRAILER CORP.—See Reliant Asset Management LLC; *U.S. Private*, pg. 3395
JOBSITE UK (WORLDWIDE) LIMITED—See Axel Springer SE; *Int'l*, pg. 767
JOBSOHIO BEVERAGE SYSTEM; *U.S. Private*, pg. 2217
JOB SOLUTION SWEDEN HOLDING AB; *Int'l*, pg. 3976
JOBSON HEALTHCARE INFORMATION LLC—See The Wicks Group of Companies, LLC; *U.S. Private*, pg. 4135
JOBSON MEDICAL INFORMATION LLC—See The Wicks Group of Companies, LLC; *U.S. Private*, pg. 4135
JOBSON PROFESSIONAL PUBLICATIONS GROUP—See The Wicks Group of Companies, LLC; *U.S. Private*, pg. 4135
JOBSON PUBLISHING CORPORATION—See The Wicks Group of Companies, LLC; *U.S. Private*, pg. 4135
JOBS PRC—See Fair Friend Group; *Int'l*, pg. 2604
JOBS SARL—See Fair Friend Group; *Int'l*, pg. 2604
JOB STORE INC.; *U.S. Private*, pg. 2217
JOBSTREET.COM PHILIPPINES INC.—See SEEK Limited; *Int'l*, pg. 6679
JOBSTREET.COM PTE. LTD.—See SEEK Limited; *Int'l*, pg. 6678
JOBSTUDIO PTE. LTD.—See BELLUNA CO. LTD.; *Int'l*, pg. 967
JOBTARGET LLC; *U.S. Private*, pg. 2217
JOBU CO., LTD. - MATERIAL RECYCLING PLANT—See Godo Steel, Ltd.; *Int'l*, pg. 3020
JOBU CO., LTD.—See Godo Steel, Ltd.; *Int'l*, pg. 3020
JOBURG INDUSTRIAL TRADING S.A. (PTY) LTD.—See Kirloskar Pneumatic Co. Ltd.; *Int'l*, pg. 4191
JOBVITE, INC.—See K1 Investment Management, LLC; *U.S. Private*, pg. 2252
JOBWINNER AG—See TX Group AG; *Int'l*, pg. 7992
JOBWORKS, INC.; *U.S. Private*, pg. 2217
JOBY AERO, INC.—See Joby Aviation, Inc.; *U.S. Public*, pg. 1190
JOBY AVIATION, INC.; *U.S. Public*, pg. 1190
JOCHEN SCHWEIZER GMBH—See ProSiebenSat.1 Media SE; *Int'l*, pg. 6000
JOCHEN SCHWEIZER MYDAYS HOLDING GMBH—See ProSiebenSat.1 Media SE; *Int'l*, pg. 6000
J. OCHSNER AG—See KIRCHHOFF Gruppe; *Int'l*, pg. 4185
JOCHU TECHNOLOGY CO., LTD.; *Int'l*, pg. 3977
JOCIL LIMITED—See The Andhra Sugars Limited; *Int'l*, pg. 7613
JOCKEY CLUB RACECOURSES LTD.; *Int'l*, pg. 3977
THE JOCKEY CLUB; *U.S. Private*, pg. 4059
JOCKEY INTERNATIONAL, INC.; *U.S. Private*, pg. 2217
JODAT LAW GROUP, P.A.; *U.S. Private*, pg. 2217
J.O. DELOTTO AND SONS, INC.; *U.S. Private*, pg. 2169
JODI KRISTOPHER INC.; *U.S. Private*, pg. 2218
JO-DI'S INC.; *U.S. Private*, pg. 2217
JODY MILLARD PEST CONTROL, LLC—See Rollins, Inc.; *U.S. Public*, pg. 1809
JOE-ANNE COMPANY INTERNATIONAL; *U.S. Private*, pg. 2219
JOE BANKS DRYWALL & ACOUSTICS INC.; *U.S. Private*, pg. 2218
JOE BASIL CHEVROLET, INC.; *U.S. Private*, pg. 2218
JOE BENBASSET INCORPORATED; *U.S. Private*, pg. 2218
JOE BLAND CONSTRUCTION, LP.; *U.S. Private*, pg. 2218
JOE BOXER COMPANY, LLC—See Iconix Acquisition LLC; *U.S. Private*, pg. 2033
JOE BRAND INC.; *U.S. Private*, pg. 2218
JOE BROWN COMPANY INC.; *U.S. Private*, pg. 2218
JOE COOPER FORD INC.; *U.S. Private*, pg. 2218
JOE CORBI'S WHOLESALE PIZZA INC.; *U.S. Private*, pg. 2218
JOE DANIELS CONSTRUCTION COMPANY; *U.S. Private*, pg. 2218
JOE DICKEY ELECTRIC INC.; *U.S. Private*, pg. 2218
JOE FISHER; *U.S. Private*, pg. 2218
JOE GARRELL & ASSOCIATES INC.; *U.S. Private*, pg. 2218
JOE GIBBS RACING INC.; *U.S. Private*, pg. 2218
JOE HALL FORD LINCOLN MERCURY NISSAN; *U.S. Private*, pg. 2218
JOE HOLDING BERHAD; *Int'l*, pg. 3977
JOE JOHNSON EQUIPMENT LLC—See Federal Signal Corporation; *U.S. Public*, pg. 826

COMPANY NAME INDEX

JOEKELS TEA PACKERS (PROPRIETARY) LTD—See Tata Sons Limited; *Int'l*, pg. 7470
JOE KIDD AUTOMOTIVE; *U.S. Private*, pg. 2218
JOE KOCH CONSTRUCTION, INC.; *U.S. Private*, pg. 2218
JOE KOZEK SAWMILLS LTD.; *Int'l*, pg. 3977
JO-EL ELECTRIC OY—See Schneider Electric SE; *Int'l*, pg. 6628
J.O.E.L. JERUSALEM OIL EXPLORATION LTD.—See Equital Ltd.; *Int'l*, pg. 2487
JOE LUNGHAMER CHEVROLET, INC.; *U.S. Private*, pg. 2218
JOE MACHENS CAPITAL CITY FORD LINCOLN; *U.S. Private*, pg. 2218
JOE MACHENS FORD INC.; *U.S. Private*, pg. 2218
JOE MACPHERSON FORD—See AutoNation, Inc.; *U.S. Public*, pg. 235
JOE MACPHERSON FORD—See AutoNation, Inc.; *U.S. Public*, pg. 236
JOE MACPHERSON INFINITI—See AutoNation, Inc.; *U.S. Public*, pg. 236
JOE McCLELLAND INC.; *U.S. Private*, pg. 2218
JOE MONEY MACHINERY CO. INC.; *U.S. Private*, pg. 2218
JOE MORGAN CHEVROLET CADILLAC, INC.—See General Motors Company; *U.S. Public*, pg. 926
JOE MYERS FORD; *U.S. Private*, pg. 2218
JOEONE CO., LTD.; *Int'l*, pg. 3977
JOE PIPER INC.; *U.S. Private*, pg. 2218
JOE RIZZA FORD, INC.; *U.S. Private*, pg. 2219
JOERNS HEALTHCARE, LLC; *U.S. Private*, pg. 2219
JOE & ROSS INC.—See Guggenheim Partners, LLC; *U.S. Private*, pg. 1812
JOE'S CRAB SHACK-ABINGDON MD, INC.—See J.H. Whitney & Co., LLC; *U.S. Private*, pg. 2166
JOE'S CRAB SHACK-ALABAMA PRIVATE CLUB INC.—See J.H. Whitney & Co., LLC; *U.S. Private*, pg. 2166
JOE'S CRAB SHACK-ANNE ARUNDEL MD, INC.—See J.H. Whitney & Co., LLC; *U.S. Private*, pg. 2166
JOE'S CRAB SHACK-HUNT VALLEY MD, INC.—See J.H. Whitney & Co., LLC; *U.S. Private*, pg. 2166
JOE'S CRAB SHACK-KANSAS, INC.—See J.H. Whitney & Co., LLC; *U.S. Private*, pg. 2166
JOE'S CRAB SHACK-MARYLAND, INC.—See J.H. Whitney & Co., LLC; *U.S. Private*, pg. 2166
JOE'S CRAB SHACK-REDONDO BEACH, INC.—See J.H. Whitney & Co., LLC; *U.S. Private*, pg. 2166
JOE'S CRAB SHACK-SAN DIEGO INC.—See J.H. Whitney & Co., LLC; *U.S. Private*, pg. 2166
JOE'S CRAB SHACK—See J.H. Whitney & Co., LLC; *U.S. Private*, pg. 2166
JOE'S CRAB SHACK-TEXAS, INC.—See J.H. Whitney & Co., LLC; *U.S. Private*, pg. 2166
JOE SELF CHEVROLET INC.; *U.S. Private*, pg. 2219
JOE'S JEANS SUBSIDIARY, INC.—See Centric Brands Inc.; *U.S. Private*, pg. 829
JOE'S REFRIGERATION, INC.; *U.S. Private*, pg. 2219
JOE SWARTZ ELECTRIC COMPANY; *U.S. Private*, pg. 2219
JOETSU NISSO CHEMICAL CO., LTD.—See Nippon Soda Co., Ltd.; *Int'l*, pg. 5334
JOETV/KZJO-TV—See Nexstar Media Group, Inc.; *U.S. Public*, pg. 1524
JOE VAN HORN CHEVROLET, INC.; *U.S. Private*, pg. 2219
JOE VELLA INSURANCE BROKERS PTY LTD—See Steadfast Group Limited; *Int'l*, pg. 7187
JOE WHEELER ELECTRIC MEMBERSHIP; *U.S. Private*, pg. 2219
JOE WHITE MALTINGS PTY. LTD.—See Cargill, Inc.; *U.S. Private*, pg. 755
THE JOEY CO.; *U.S. Private*, pg. 4059
JOEY NEW YORK, INC.; *U.S. Private*, pg. 1190
JOFCO INC.; *U.S. Private*, pg. 2219
JOFF FINTECH ACQUISITION CORP.; *U.S. Public*, pg. 1190
JOFFREY'S COFFEE & TEA CO.; *U.S. Private*, pg. 2219
J.O. GALLOUP COMPANY—See The Kendall Group, Inc.; *U.S. Private*, pg. 4064
JOGAN, INC.; *U.S. Private*, pg. 2219
JOHA GEBAEUDE- ERRICHTUNGS- UND VERMIETUNGS- GESELLSCHAFT M.B.H.—See UniCredit S.p.A.; *Int'l*, pg. 8034
J O HAMBRO CAPITAL MANAGEMENT LIMITED—See Westpac Banking Corporation; *Int'l*, pg. 8391
JOHAN HOLDINGS BERHAD; *Int'l*, pg. 3977
JOHAN INVESTMENT PRIVATE LIMITED—See Johan Holdings Berhad; *Int'l*, pg. 3977
JOHAN MANAGEMENT SERVICES SDN. BHD.—See Johan Holdings Berhad; *Int'l*, pg. 3977
JOHANNA FOODS, INC.; *U.S. Private*, pg. 2219
JOHANNES LEONARDO—See WPP plc; *Int'l*, pg. 8483
JOHANNESON'S INC.; *U.S. Private*, pg. 2219
JOHANN FROESCHEIS LYRA BLEISTIFT-FABRIK GMBH & CO. KG—See F.I.L.A. - Fabbrica Italiana Lapis ed Affini S.p.A.; *Int'l*, pg. 2597
JOHANN HALTERMANN LTD.—See Heritage Group; *U.S. Private*, pg. 1923
JOHANN HAY GMBH & CO. KG—See Musashi Seimitsu Industry Co., Ltd.; *Int'l*, pg. 5101
JOHAN RONNING HF—See Telefonaktiebolaget LM Ericsson; *Int'l*, pg. 7534
JOHANSEN & ANDERSON, INC.—See Partners Group Holding AG; *Int'l*, pg. 5750
JOHANSON DIELECTRICS, INC.; *U.S. Private*, pg. 2219
JOHANSON MANUFACTURING CORPORATION; *U.S. Private*, pg. 2219
JOHANSON TRANSPORTATION SERVICE; *U.S. Private*, pg. 2219
JOHBASE DEVELOPMENT SDN. BHD.—See BCB Berhad; *Int'l*, pg. 926
JOH. BERENBERG, GOSSLER & CO.; *Int'l*, pg. 3977
JOHCM (SINGAPORE) PTE LIMITED—See Perpetual Limited; *Int'l*, pg. 5812
JOHCM (USA) INC.—See Perpetual Limited; *Int'l*, pg. 5812
JOH. FRIEDRICH BEHRENS AG—See GreatStar Group Co., Ltd.; *Int'l*, pg. 3067
JOHLER NORDDRUCK GMBH; *Int'l*, pg. 3977
THE JOHN A. BECKER COMPANY; *U.S. Private*, pg. 4059
JOHN ABELL CORPORATION; *U.S. Private*, pg. 2220
JOHN A. BIEWER CO. INC.; *U.S. Private*, pg. 2219
JOHN ADAMS ASSOCIATES INC.—See Kellen Communications; *U.S. Private*, pg. 2274
JOHN ADAMS HEALTHCARE CENTER, LLC—See National HealthCare Corporation; *U.S. Public*, pg. 1495
JOHN ADAMS LIFE CORPORATION; *U.S. Public*, pg. 1190
JOHN ADCOCK INSURANCE AGENCY, INC.; *U.S. Private*, pg. 2220
JOHN A MARTIN AND ASSOCIATES OF NEVADA—See John A. Martin & Associates, Incorporated; *U.S. Private*, pg. 2220
JOHN A. MARTIN & ASSOCIATES, INCORPORATED; *U.S. Private*, pg. 2219
JOHN A. MARTIN & ASSOCIATES, LTD.—See John A. Martin & Associates, Incorporated; *U.S. Private*, pg. 2220
JOHAN ACADEMIC PREPARATORY INSTITUTE, INC.; *Int'l*, pg. 3984
JOHN A. PENNY CO. INC.; *U.S. Private*, pg. 2220
JOHN ASCUAGA'S NUGGET; *U.S. Private*, pg. 2220
JOHN ATENCIO GOLDSMITH, LTD.; *U.S. Private*, pg. 2220
JOHN A. VAN DEN BOSCH CO.; *U.S. Private*, pg. 2220
JOHN A. VASSILAROS & SON INC; *U.S. Private*, pg. 2220
JOHN AYLING & ASSOCIATES LIMITED; *Int'l*, pg. 3977
JOHN BEAN—See Snap-on Incorporated; *U.S. Public*, pg. 1897
JOHN BEAN TECHNOLOGIES AB—See John Bean Technologies Corporation; *U.S. Public*, pg. 1191
JOHN BEAN TECHNOLOGIES AUSTRALIA LTD.—See John Bean Technologies Corporation; *U.S. Public*, pg. 1191
JOHN BEAN TECHNOLOGIES AUTOMATED GUIDED VEHICLES, INC.—See Oshkosh Corporation; *U.S. Public*, pg. 1620
JOHN BEAN TECHNOLOGIES CORPORATION; *U.S. Public*, pg. 1191
JOHN BEAN TECHNOLOGIES GMBH—See John Bean Technologies Corporation; *U.S. Public*, pg. 1191
JOHN BEAN TECHNOLOGIES HONG KONG LIMITED—See John Bean Technologies Corporation; *U.S. Public*, pg. 1191
JOHN BEAN TECHNOLOGIES HONG KONG LTD. - PHILIPPINES OFFICE—See John Bean Technologies Corporation; *U.S. Public*, pg. 1191
JOHN BEAN TECHNOLOGIES IBERICA S.L.—See John Bean Technologies Corporation; *U.S. Public*, pg. 1191
JOHN BEAN TECHNOLOGIES INDIA PRIVATE LIMITED—See John Bean Technologies Corporation; *U.S. Public*, pg. 1191
JOHN BEAN TECHNOLOGIES INTERNATIONAL AB—See John Bean Technologies Corporation; *U.S. Public*, pg. 1191
JOHN BEAN TECHNOLOGIES K.K. - CITRUS DIVISION—See John Bean Technologies Corporation; *U.S. Public*, pg. 1191
JOHN BEAN TECHNOLOGIES K.K.—See John Bean Technologies Corporation; *U.S. Public*, pg. 1191
JOHN BEAN TECHNOLOGIES LTD.—See John Bean Technologies Corporation; *U.S. Public*, pg. 1191
JOHN BEAN TECHNOLOGIES MIDDLE EAST FZE—See John Bean Technologies Corporation; *U.S. Public*, pg. 1191
JOHN BEAN TECHNOLOGIES N.V.—See John Bean Technologies Corporation; *U.S. Public*, pg. 1191
JOHN BEAN TECHNOLOGIES (PROPRIETARY) LTD.—See John Bean Technologies Corporation; *U.S. Public*, pg. 1191
JOHN BEAN TECHNOLOGIES SA—See John Bean Technologies Corporation; *U.S. Public*, pg. 1192
JOHN BEAN TECHNOLOGIES (SHANGHAI) CO., LTD.—See John Bean Technologies Corporation; *U.S. Public*, pg. 1191
JOHN BEAN TECHNOLOGIES SPAIN S.L.—See John Bean Technologies Corporation; *U.S. Public*, pg. 1192
JOHN BEAN TECHNOLOGIES SPAIN S.L.U.—See John Bean Technologies Corporation; *U.S. Public*, pg. 1192
JOHN BEAN TECHNOLOGIES S.P.A.—See John Bean Technologies Corporation; *U.S. Public*, pg. 1192
JOHN BEAN TECHNOLOGIES SP. Z O.O.—See John Bean Technologies Corporation; *U.S. Public*, pg. 1192
JOHN BEAN TECHNOLOGIES (THAILAND) LTD.—See John Bean Technologies Corporation; *U.S. Public*, pg. 1191
JOHN BENJAMINS ANTIQUARIAT B.V.—See John Benjamins BV; *Int'l*, pg. 3977
JOHN BENJAMINS BV; *Int'l*, pg. 3977
JOHN BENJAMINS NORTH AMERICA INC.—See John Benjamins BV; *Int'l*, pg. 3977
JOHN BLEAKLEY RV CENTER INC.; *U.S. Private*, pg. 2220
JOHN BOOS & CO.—See JBC Holding Co.; *U.S. Private*, pg. 2193
JOHN BOUCHARD & SONS COMPANY - FOUNDRY DIVISION—See John Bouchard & Sons Company; *U.S. Private*, pg. 2220
JOHN BOUCHARD & SONS COMPANY; *U.S. Private*, pg. 2220
JOHN BOYD ENTERPRISES INC.; *U.S. Private*, pg. 2220
JOHN BRIDGEMAN LIMITED; *Int'l*, pg. 3977
JOHN BROWN MEDIA GROUP LTD.—See Dentsu Group Inc.; *Int'l*, pg. 2037
JOHN BROWN VOEST GMBH; *Int'l*, pg. 3977
JOHN B. RUDY COMPANY INC.; *U.S. Private*, pg. 2220
JOHN B. SANFILIPPO & SON, INC.; *U.S. Public*, pg. 1190
JOHN B. SANFILIPPO & SON, INC.—See John B. Sanfilippo & Son, Inc.; *U.S. Public*, pg. 1190
JOHN BUCK COMPANY; *U.S. Private*, pg. 2220
JOHN BULL COMPANY LIMITED; *Int'l*, pg. 3978
JOHN BULL STAMP AUCTIONS, LTD.—See Global Philatelic Network; *Int'l*, pg. 3000
JOHN BUNNING TRANSFER COMPANY; *U.S. Private*, pg. 2220
JOHN BURNS REAL ESTATE CONSULTING, INC.; *U.S. Private*, pg. 2220
JOHN BUTTINE INC.—See Kelso & Company, L.P.; *U.S. Private*, pg. 2280
JOHN CANNON HOMES INC.; *U.S. Private*, pg. 2220
JOHN CARETTI & CO.—See Paul J. Krez Company; *U.S. Private*, pg. 3113
JOHN CARLO, INC.—See Carlo Management Corporation; *U.S. Private*, pg. 764
JOHNCARLO WOODWORKING, INC.; *U.S. Private*, pg. 2225
JOHN C. BERRY & SONS INC.; *U.S. Private*, pg. 2220
JOHN C. DOLPH COMPANY—See SKion GmbH; *Int'l*, pg. 6988
JOHN CHANCE LAND SURVEYS, INC.—See Fugro N.V.; *Int'l*, pg. 2805
JOHN CHRISTNER TRUCKING INC.; *U.S. Private*, pg. 2220
JOHN CHUBB INSTRUMENTATION LTD.—See DEKRA e.V.; *Int'l*, pg. 2009
JOHN CHURCH CO.—See Theodore Presser Co.; *U.S. Private*, pg. 4141
THE JOHN CLARK MOTOR GROUP; *Int'l*, pg. 7660
JOHN C. NORDT CO., INC.—See Berkshire Hathaway Inc.; *U.S. Public*, pg. 316
JOHN COCKBURN BUILDING SUPPLIES LIMITED—See Fletcher Building Limited; *Int'l*, pg. 2700
JOHN COCKERILL INDIA LIMITED—See Euremis Holding SA; *Int'l*, pg. 2530
JOHN COLEMAN HAYES CONSTRUCTION CO.; *U.S. Private*, pg. 2221
JOHN CONTI COFFEE CO.; *U.S. Private*, pg. 2221
JOHN COPE'S FOOD PRODUCTS, INC.—See Farm Stand Foods; *U.S. Private*, pg. 1475
JOHN C. OTTO COMPANY, INC.—See Chatham Asset Management, LLC; *U.S. Private*, pg. 862
JOHN CRAIG (PTY) LTD.—See Steinhoff International Holdings N.V.; *Int'l*, pg. 7195
JOHN CRANE ARGENTINA SA—See Smiths Group plc; *Int'l*, pg. 7010
JOHN CRANE A.S.—See Smiths Group plc; *Int'l*, pg. 7010
JOHN CRANE AUSTRALIA PTY LTD.—See Smiths Group plc; *Int'l*, pg. 7010
JOHN CRANE BAKU LLC—See Smiths Group plc; *Int'l*, pg. 7010
JOHN CRANE BELGIUM N.V.—See Smiths Group plc; *Int'l*, pg. 7010
JOHN CRANE BENELUX—See Smiths Group plc; *Int'l*, pg. 7010
JOHN CRANE CANADA—See Smiths Group plc; *Int'l*, pg. 7010
JOHN CRANE CARIBE LTD.—See Smiths Group plc; *Int'l*, pg. 7010
JOHN CRANE CHINA LTD.—See Smiths Group plc; *Int'l*, pg. 7010
JOHN CRANE COLUMBIA—See Smiths Group plc; *Int'l*, pg. 7010

JOHN CRANE CZECH REPUBLIC—See Smiths Group plc; *Int'l*, pg. 7010
JOHN CRANE EGYPT SEALING SYSTEMS LLC—See Smiths Group plc; *Int'l*, pg. 7010
JOHN CRANE ENDUSTRIYEL SIZDIRMAZLIK SISTEMLERI LTD.—See Smiths Group plc; *Int'l*, pg. 7010
JOHN CRANE FRANCE S.A.S.—See Smiths Group plc; *Int'l*, pg. 7010
JOHN CRANE GES.M.B.H—See Smiths Group plc; *Int'l*, pg. 7010
JOHN CRANE GMBH—See Smiths Group plc; *Int'l*, pg. 7010
JOHN CRANE GROUP LIMITED—See Smiths Group plc; *Int'l*, pg. 7010
JOHN CRANE HELLAS - ENGINEERED SEALING SYSTEMS MONOPROSOPI EPE—See Smiths Group plc; *Int'l*, pg. 7011
JOHN CRANE HOLLAND, B.V.—See Smiths Group plc; *Int'l*, pg. 7010
JOHN CRANE HUNGARY KFT—See Smiths Group plc; *Int'l*, pg. 7011
JOHN CRANE IBERICA—See Smiths Group plc; *Int'l*, pg. 7010
JOHN CRANE, INC.—See Smiths Group plc; *Int'l*, pg. 7011
JOHN CRANE INTERNATIONAL INC.—See Smiths Group plc; *Int'l*, pg. 7011
JOHN CRANE (IRELAND) LIMITED—See Smiths Group plc; *Int'l*, pg. 7011
JOHN CRANE ITALIA SPA—See Smiths Group plc; *Int'l*, pg. 7011
JOHN CRANE (JAPAN) INC.—See Smiths Group plc; *Int'l*, pg. 7010
JOHN CRANE KAZAKHSTAN TOO—See Smiths Group plc; *Int'l*, pg. 7011
JOHN CRANE (KOREA) CO. LTD.—See Smiths Group plc; *Int'l*, pg. 7010
JOHN CRANE - KUWAIT—See Smiths Group plc; *Int'l*, pg. 7010
JOHN CRANE MALAYSIA SDN BHD—See Smiths Group plc; *Int'l*, pg. 7011
JOHN CRANE MEXICO SA DE CV—See Smiths Group plc; *Int'l*, pg. 7010
JOHN CRANE MIDDLE EAST-CENTRAL REGION—See Smiths Group plc; *Int'l*, pg. 7010
JOHN CRANE MIDDLE EAST FZE—See Smiths Group plc; *Int'l*, pg. 7011
JOHN CRANE NORGE—See Smiths Group plc; *Int'l*, pg. 7010
JOHN CRANE PACKING (PTY) LTD.—See Smiths Group plc; *Int'l*, pg. 7010
JOHN CRANE PERU SAC—See Smiths Group plc; *Int'l*, pg. 7011
JOHN CRANE POLAND SP. Z O.O.—See Smiths Group plc; *Int'l*, pg. 7011
JOHN CRANE PRODUCTION SOLUTIONS INC.—See Smiths Group plc; *Int'l*, pg. 7011
JOHN CRANE (PTY) LTD.—See Smiths Group plc; *Int'l*, pg. 7010
JOHN CRANE RUS LLC—See Smiths Group plc; *Int'l*, pg. 7010
JOHN CRANE SAFEMATIC OY—See Smiths Group plc; *Int'l*, pg. 7010
JOHN CRANE SAUDI ARABIA CO. LTD—See Smiths Group plc; *Int'l*, pg. 7010
JOHN CRANE SEALING SYSTEMS INDIA PVT. LTD.—See Smiths Group plc; *Int'l*, pg. 7010
JOHN CRANE SEALOL—See Smiths Group plc; *Int'l*, pg. 7011
JOHN CRANE SIGMA A.S.—See Smiths Group plc; *Int'l*, pg. 7010
JOHN CRANE SINGAPORE PTE. LTD.—See Smiths Group plc; *Int'l*, pg. 7010
JOHN CRANE SLOVAKIA SRO—See Smiths Group plc; *Int'l*, pg. 7011
JOHN CRANE SPA—See Smiths Group plc; *Int'l*, pg. 7010
JOHN CRANE SVERIGE AB—See Smiths Group plc; *Int'l*, pg. 7010
JOHN CRANE (SWITZERLAND) AG—See Smiths Group plc; *Int'l*, pg. 7010
JOHN CRANE TAIWAN—See Smiths Group plc; *Int'l*, pg. 7010
JOHN CRANE (THAILAND) LTD—See Smiths Group plc; *Int'l*, pg. 7010
JOHN CRANE TURKEY—See Smiths Group plc; *Int'l*, pg. 7010
JOHN CRANE UK LTD.—See Smiths Group plc; *Int'l*, pg. 7011
JOHN CRANE UK LTD.—See Smiths Group plc; *Int'l*, pg. 7011
JOHN CRANE VENEZUELA—See Smiths Group plc; *Int'l*, pg. 7011
JOHN CURTIS LETTINGS & MANAGEMENT LIMITED—See The Skipton Building Society; *Int'l*, pg. 7686
JOHN DAUGHERTY REALTORS INC.; *U.S. Private*, pg. 2221
JOHN DAVIDSON PIPES LTD.—See Tessenderlo Group NV; *Int'l*, pg. 7573

JOHN DAY COMPANY; *U.S. Private*, pg. 2221
JOHN D. DOVICH & ASSOCIATES, LLC—See Keystone Group, L.P.; *U.S. Private*, pg. 2297
JOHN DEERE AGRICULTURAL HOLDINGS, INC.—See Deere & Company; *U.S. Public*, pg. 647
JOHN DEERE BANK S.A.—See Deere & Company; *U.S. Public*, pg. 646
JOHN DEERE BRASIL LTDA.—See Deere & Company; *U.S. Public*, pg. 646
JOHN DEERE CANADA ULC—See Deere & Company; *U.S. Public*, pg. 646
JOHN DEERE CAPITAL CORPORATION—See Deere & Company; *U.S. Public*, pg. 646
JOHN DEERE COFFEYVILLE WORKS INC—See Deere & Company; *U.S. Public*, pg. 646
JOHN DEERE COMMERCIAL WORKSITE PRODUCTS, INC.—See Deere & Company; *U.S. Public*, pg. 646
JOHN DEERE CONSTRUCTION & FORESTRY COMPANY—See Deere & Company; *U.S. Public*, pg. 647
JOHN DEERE CONSUMER & COMMERCIAL EQUIPMENT, INC.—See Deere & Company; *U.S. Public*, pg. 646
JOHN DEERE CREDIT COMPANY—See Deere & Company; *U.S. Public*, pg. 646
JOHN DEERE CREDIT OY—See Deere & Company; *U.S. Public*, pg. 646
JOHN DEERE CREDIT SERVICES, INC.—See Deere & Company; *U.S. Public*, pg. 646
JOHN DEERE DAVENPORT WORKS—See Deere & Company; *U.S. Public*, pg. 647
JOHN DEERE DUBUQUE WORKS—See Deere & Company; *U.S. Public*, pg. 647
JOHN DEERE ELECTRONIC SOLUTIONS, INC.—See Deere & Company; *U.S. Public*, pg. 647
JOHN DEERE ENGINE WORKS—See Deere & Company; *U.S. Public*, pg. 646
JOHN DEERE FINANCIAL, F.S.B.—See Deere & Company; *U.S. Public*, pg. 646
JOHN DEERE FINANCIAL INC.—See Deere & Company; *U.S. Public*, pg. 646
JOHN DEERE FINANCIAL LIMITED—See Deere & Company; *U.S. Public*, pg. 646
JOHN DEERE FINANCIAL MEXICO, S.A. DE C.V. SOFOM, E.N.R.—See Deere & Company; *U.S. Public*, pg. 646
JOHN DEERE FOREIGN SALES CORPORATION LIMITED—See Deere & Company; *U.S. Public*, pg. 646
JOHN DEERE FORESTRY GROUP LLC—See Deere & Company; *U.S. Public*, pg. 647
JOHN DEERE GMBH & CO. KG—See Deere & Company; *U.S. Public*, pg. 646
JOHN DEERE GMBH & CO. KG—See Deere & Company; *U.S. Public*, pg. 646
JOHN DEERE HARVESTER WORKS—See Deere & Company; *U.S. Public*, pg. 647
JOHN DEERE HORICON WORKS—See Deere & Company; *U.S. Public*, pg. 647
JOHN DEERE IBERICA S.A.—See Deere & Company; *U.S. Public*, pg. 646
JOHN DEERE INDIA PRIVATE LIMITED—See Deere & Company; *U.S. Public*, pg. 646
JOHN DEERE INTERCONTINENTAL GMBH—See Deere & Company; *U.S. Public*, pg. 646
JOHN DEERE INTERNATIONAL GMBH—See Deere & Company; *U.S. Public*, pg. 646
JOHN DEERE-LANZ VERWALTUNGS-AKTIENGESELLSCHAFT—See Deere & Company; *U.S. Public*, pg. 647
JOHN DEERE LAWN AND GROUNDS CARE HOLDINGS, INC.—See Deere & Company; *U.S. Public*, pg. 646
JOHN DEERE LIMITED AUSTRALIA—See Deere & Company; *U.S. Public*, pg. 646
JOHN DEERE LTD.—See Deere & Company; *U.S. Public*, pg. 646
JOHN DEERE LTD.—See Deere & Company; *U.S. Public*, pg. 646
JOHN DEERE MEXICO S.A. DE C.V.—See Deere & Company; *U.S. Public*, pg. 647
JOHN DEERE OTTUMWA WORKS—See Deere & Company; *U.S. Public*, pg. 647
JOHN DEERE POLSKA SP. ZO.O—See Deere & Company; *U.S. Public*, pg. 647
JOHN DEERE POLSKA SP. Z O.O.—See Deere & Company; *U.S. Public*, pg. 647
JOHN DEERE POWER PRODUCTS, INC.—See Deere & Company; *U.S. Public*, pg. 647
JOHN DEERE (PTY.) LTD.—See Deere & Company; *U.S. Public*, pg. 647
JOHN DEERE RECEIVABLES, INC.—See Deere & Company; *U.S. Public*, pg. 647
JOHN DEERE S.A. DE C.V.—See Deere & Company; *U.S. Public*, pg. 647
JOHN DEERE S.A.S.—See Deere & Company; *U.S. Public*, pg. 647
JOHN DEERE TECHNOLOGIES CENTER—See Deere & Company; *U.S. Public*, pg. 647
JOHN DEERE THIBODAUX, INC.—See Deere & Company; *U.S. Public*, pg. 647

JOHN DEERE WALLDORF GMBH & CO. KG—See Deere & Company; *U.S. Public*, pg. 647
JOHN DEERE WATERLOO WORKS—See Deere & Company; *U.S. Public*, pg. 647
JOHN DEERE WORLDWIDE AGRICULTURAL EQUIPMENT—See Deere & Company; *U.S. Public*, pg. 647
JOHN DEERE WORLDWIDE CONSTRUCTION & FORESTRY—See Deere & Company; *U.S. Public*, pg. 647
JOHN DEERY MOTOR CO.; *U.S. Private*, pg. 2221
JOHN DI NASO & SONS INC.; *U.S. Private*, pg. 2221
JOHN DONOGHUE AUTOMOTIVE, INC.; *U.S. Private*, pg. 2221
JOHN DORY'S ADVERTISING (PTY) LTD.—See Spur Corporation; *Int'l*, pg. 7146
JOHN DORY'S FRANCHISE (PTY) LTD—See Spur Corporation; *Int'l*, pg. 7146
JOHN DRIGGS COMPANY, INC.; *U.S. Private*, pg. 2221
JOHN D STEPHENS INC.; *U.S. Private*, pg. 2221
JOHN EAGLE ACURA—See John Eagle A Management, LLC; *U.S. Private*, pg. 2221
JOHN EAGLE A MANAGEMENT, LLC; *U.S. Private*, pg. 2221
JOHN EAGLE HONDA OF HOUSTON—See John Eagle A Management, LLC; *U.S. Private*, pg. 2221
JOHN EAGLE SPORT CITY MOTORS, LLP—See John Eagle A Management, LLC; *U.S. Private*, pg. 2221
JOHN E. FELLS & SONS LTD.; *Int'l*, pg. 3978
JOHN E. GREEN CO.; *U.S. Private*, pg. 2221
JOHN E. KELLY & SONS ELECTRICAL CONSTRUCTION, INC.; *U.S. Private*, pg. 2221
JOHN E. PEAKES INSURANCE AGENCY, INC.—See PCF Insurance Services of The West, LLC; *U.S. Private*, pg. 3120
JOHN E. QUARLES CO.; *U.S. Private*, pg. 2221
JOHN EVANS' SONS, INC.; *U.S. Private*, pg. 2221
JOHN FAIRFAX LIMITED—See Nine Entertainment Co. Holdings Limited; *Int'l*, pg. 5298
JOHN FAYARD MOVING AND WAREHOUSING; *U.S. Private*, pg. 2221
JOHN F BUCHAN HOMES; *U.S. Private*, pg. 2221
JOHN F. KENNEDY CENTER FOR THE PERFORMING ARTS; *U.S. Private*, pg. 2221
JOHN FLYNN RETIREMENT VILLAGE PTY. LTD.—See Ryman Healthcare Ltd.; *Int'l*, pg. 6439
JOHN F MAHANEY, CO.—See Kinderhook Industries, LLC; *U.S. Private*, pg. 2306
JOHN FOGARTY CUSTOM BUILT HOMES; *U.S. Private*, pg. 2221
JOHN FRANCES LIMITED—See The Skipton Building Society; *Int'l*, pg. 7686
JOHN F. WATSON & COMPANY—See Peak Rock Capital LLC; *U.S. Private*, pg. 3124
JOHN GRAVES FOOD SERVICE INC.—See Menu Maker Foods Inc.; *U.S. Private*, pg. 2667
JOHN G. SHEDD AQUARIUM; *U.S. Private*, pg. 2221
JOHN GUEST CZECH S.R.O.—See Reliance Worldwide Corporation Limited; *Int'l*, pg. 6264
JOHN GUEST GMBH—See Reliance Worldwide Corporation Limited; *Int'l*, pg. 6264
JOHN GUEST KOREA LTD.—See Reliance Worldwide Corporation Limited; *Int'l*, pg. 6264
JOHN G. WEATHERFORD INC.; *U.S. Private*, pg. 2221
JOHN G. WILSON MACHINE LIMITED—See Tiercel Technology Corp.; *Int'l*, pg. 7744
JOHN HACKNEY AGENCY, INC.—See Genstar Capital, LLC; *U.S. Private*, pg. 1674
JOHN HANCOCK FINANCIAL CORPORATION—See Manulife Financial Corporation; *Int'l*, pg. 4678
JOHN HANCOCK FINANCIAL NETWORK, INC.—See Manulife Financial Corporation; *Int'l*, pg. 4678
JOHN HANCOCK FUNDS, LLC—See Manulife Financial Corporation; *Int'l*, pg. 4678
JOHN HANCOCK HEDGED EQUITY & INCOME FUND; *U.S. Public*, pg. 1192
JOHN HANCOCK INSURANCE AGENCY, INC.—See Manulife Financial Corporation; *Int'l*, pg. 4678
JOHN HANCOCK LIFE INSURANCE COMPANY OF NEW YORK—See Manulife Financial Corporation; *Int'l*, pg. 4678
JOHN HANCOCK LIFE INSURANCE COMPANY—See Manulife Financial Corporation; *Int'l*, pg. 4678
JOHN HANCOCK RETIREMENT PLAN SERVICES LLC—See Manulife Financial Corporation; *Int'l*, pg. 4678
JOHN HANCOCK SIGNATURE SERVICES, INC.—See Manulife Financial Corporation; *Int'l*, pg. 4678
JOHN HANCOCK STRATEGIC DIVERSIFIED INCOME FUND; *U.S. Public*, pg. 2222
JOHN HANCOCK VARIABLE LIFE INSURANCE COMPANY—See Manulife Financial Corporation; *Int'l*, pg. 4678
JOHN HARDY USA, INC.; *U.S. Private*, pg. 2222
JOHN HARVARD'S BREWHOUSE LLC; *U.S. Private*, pg. 2222
JOHN HASSALL, LLC—See KKR & Co. Inc.; *U.S. Public*, pg. 1262

COMPANY NAME INDEX

JOHN H. BONER COMMUNITY CENTER; *U.S. Private*, pg. 2222
JOHN H. BURROWS INC.; *U.S. Private*, pg. 2222
JOHN H. CARTER COMPANY INCORPORATED; *U.S. Private*, pg. 2222
JOHN H. DANIEL COMPANY INC.; *U.S. Private*, pg. 2222
JOHN HEATH & COMPANY INC—See R&Q Insurance Holdings Ltd.; *Int'l*, pg. 6168
JOHN HENRY FOSTER COMPANY OF SAINT LOUIS INC.; *U.S. Private*, pg. 2222
JOHN HENSHALL LIMITED—See Brown & Brown, Inc.; *U.S. Public*, pg. 401
JOHN H. FRISCHKORN, JR. INC.; *U.S. Private*, pg. 2222
JOHN H. HARLAND CO. OF PUERTO RICO—See MacAndrews & Forbes Incorporated; *U.S. Private*, pg. 2532
JOHN HINDERER HONDA; *U.S. Private*, pg. 2222
JOHN HINE AUTO & TRUCK CENTER; *U.S. Private*, pg. 2222
JOHN H. MYERS & SON INC.—See Bain Capital, LP; *U.S. Private*, pg. 451
JOHN HOGG & CO. LTD.; *Int'l*, pg. 3978
JOHN HOLLAND CONSTRUCTIONS PTY LTD.—See China Communications Construction Company Limited; *Int'l*, pg. 1491
JOHN HOLLAND GROUP PTY. LTD.—See China Communications Construction Company Limited; *Int'l*, pg. 1491
JOHN H. ROBINSON TESTING INC.—See Urban Engineers Inc.; *U.S. Private*, pg. 4314
JOHN HUBLER NISSAN-SUZUKI INC.; *U.S. Private*, pg. 2222
JOHN JACKSON MASONRY; *U.S. Private*, pg. 2222
JOHN J. CAMPBELL CO., INC.; *U.S. Private*, pg. 2222
JOHN J. DOODY & SON INC.; *U.S. Private*, pg. 2222
JOHN J HOLDEN INSURANCE COMPANY—See Reading Anthracite Company; *U.S. Private*, pg. 3366
JOHN J. KIRLIN INC. CAROLINAS DIV.—See John J. Kirlin Inc.; *U.S. Private*, pg. 2222
JOHN J. KIRLIN INC.; *U.S. Private*, pg. 2222
THE JOHN JOHNSON CO.; *U.S. Private*, pg. 4059
JOHN K. BURCH COMPANY INCORPORATED; *U.S. Private*, pg. 2222
JOHN KEELER & CO., INC.—See Blue Star Foods Corp.; *U.S. Public*, pg. 365
JOHN KEELLS COMPUTER SERVICES (PVT) LTD.—See John Keells Holdings PLC; *Int'l*, pg. 3978
JOHN KEELLS CONVENTIONS (PVT) LTD.—See John Keells Holdings PLC; *Int'l*, pg. 3978
JOHN KEELLS HOLDINGS PLC; *Int'l*, pg. 3978
JOHN KEELLS HOTELS PLC; *Int'l*, pg. 3979
JOHN KEELLS INTERNATIONAL (PVT) LTD.—See John Keells Holdings PLC; *Int'l*, pg. 3978
JOHN KEELLS MALDIVIAN RESORTS (PTE.) LTD.—See John Keells Holdings PLC; *Int'l*, pg. 3978
JOHN KEELLS OFFICE AUTOMATION PVT LTD.—See John Keells Holdings PLC; *Int'l*, pg. 3978
JOHN KEELLS PROPERTIES JA-ELA (PVT.) LTD.—See John Keells Holdings PLC; *Int'l*, pg. 3978
JOHN KEELLS RESIDENTIAL PROPERTIES (PVT) LTD.—See John Keells Holdings PLC; *Int'l*, pg. 3978
JOHN KEELLS STOCK BROKERS (PVT) LTD.—See John Keells Holdings PLC; *Int'l*, pg. 3978
JOHN KEELS LOGISTICS (PVT) LTD—See John Keells Holdings PLC; *Int'l*, pg. 3978
JOHN KENNEDY FORD LINCOLN MERCURY—See Kennedy Automotive Group Inc.; *U.S. Private*, pg. 2284
JOHN KENNEDY FORD OF PHOENIXVILLE—See Kennedy Automotive Group Inc.; *U.S. Private*, pg. 2284
JOHN KNOX VILLAGE OF FLORIDA, INC.; *U.S. Private*, pg. 2222
JOHN KOHL AUTO CENTER INC.; *U.S. Private*, pg. 2222
JOHN LAING GROUP PLC; *Int'l*, pg. 3979
JOHN LAING LIMITED—See John Laing Group plc; *Int'l*, pg. 3979
JOHN L. BOND INC.—See Calfee Company of Dalton, Inc.; *U.S. Private*, pg. 717
JOHN L. CONLEY INC.; *U.S. Private*, pg. 2222
JOHN L LENORE & COMPANY, INC.; *U.S. Private*, pg. 2222
JOHN LEWIS OF HUNGERFORD PLC; *Int'l*, pg. 3979
JOHN LEWIS PARTNERSHIP PLC; *Int'l*, pg. 3979
JOHN LEWIS PLC—See John Lewis Partnership plc; *Int'l*, pg. 3979
JOHN L. HINKLE HOLDINGS CO., INC.—See Riverside Partners, LLC; *U.S. Private*, pg. 3446
JOHN LISCOMBE LIMITED—See RS Group plc; *Int'l*, pg. 6417
JOHN LITTLE PRIVATE LTD.—See Robinson & Co. (S) Pte. Ltd.; *Int'l*, pg. 6370
JOHN L. JERSEY & SON INC.; *U.S. Private*, pg. 2222
JOHN LOBB SAS—See Hermes International SCA; *Int'l*, pg. 3363
JOHN L. SCOTT INC.; *U.S. Private*, pg. 2222
JOHN L. SULLIVAN INVESTMENTS INC.—See John Sullivan Automotive Group; *U.S. Private*, pg. 2225
JOHN L. WORTHAM & SON LLP—See Marsh & McLennan Companies, Inc.; *U.S. Public*, pg. 1383
JOHN MANEELY COMPANY—See Zekelman Industries Inc.; *U.S. Private*, pg. 4600

JOHN MARSHALL BANCORP, INC.; *U.S. Public*, pg. 1192
JOHN MATCHETT LIMITED—See Wilmington plc; *Int'l*, pg. 8422
JOHN MATTSON FASTIGHETS AB; *Int'l*, pg. 3979
JOHN MCASLAN PARTNERS LIMITED; *Int'l*, pg. 3979
JOHN M. DEAN CO., LLC—See SEI MetalTek; *U.S. Private*, pg. 3599
JOHN M. ELLSWORTH CO., INC.; *U.S. Private*, pg. 2223
JOHN MENZIES DISTRIBUTION—See Endless LLP; *Int'l*, pg. 2403
JOHN MENZIES PLC—See Agility; *Int'l*, pg. 210
JOHN MEUNIER INC.—See Veolia Environnement S.A.; *Int'l*, pg. 8163
JOHN M. FLOYD & ASSOCIATES, INC.—See Hammond, Kennedy, Whitney & Company, Inc.; *U.S. Private*, pg. 1850
JOHN M. HARTEL CO. INC.; *U.S. Private*, pg. 2223
JOHN M HENDERSON & CO LTD.; *Int'l*, pg. 3979
JOHN M. HESS AUCTION SERVICE, INC.; *U.S. Private*, pg. 2223
JOHN MIDDLETON INC.—See Altria Group, Inc.; *U.S. Public*, pg. 89
JOHN MILLS DISTRIBUTING CO. INC; *U.S. Private*, pg. 2223
JOHN MITCHELL HAULAGE & WAREHOUSING; *Int'l*, pg. 3979
JOHN M. LANCE FORD, LLC—See AutoNation, Inc.; *U.S. Public*, pg. 236
JOHN M. OLSON CORPORATION; *U.S. Private*, pg. 2223
JOHN MORIARTY & ASSOCIATES INC.; *U.S. Private*, pg. 2223
JOHN MORRELL & CO.—See WH Group Limited; *Int'l*, pg. 8395
JOHN MOURIER CONSTRUCTION, INC.; *U.S. Private*, pg. 2223
JOHN M. TAYLOR FUNERAL HOME, INC.—See Service Corporation International; *U.S. Public*, pg. 1871
JOHN MUIR HEALTH; *U.S. Private*, pg. 2223
JOHN MULLEN & CO, INC.; *U.S. Private*, pg. 2223
JOHN NEAL HOMES, INC.—See Estuary Investment Corp.; *U.S. Private*, pg. 1429
JOHN NEWCOMB ENTERPRISES INC.; *U.S. Private*, pg. 2223
JOHNNIC COMMUNICATION—See Vivendi SE; *Int'l*, pg. 8271
JOHNNIE-O; *U.S. Private*, pg. 2225
JOHN NOLAN ASSOCIATES LTD; *Int'l*, pg. 3979
JOHN NORTH FORD; *U.S. Private*, pg. 2223
JOHN N. SAUDER AUTO COMPANY; *U.S. Private*, pg. 2223
JOHNNY CUPCAKES; *U.S. Private*, pg. 2225
JOHNNY JANOSIK INC.; *U.S. Private*, pg. 2226
JOHNNY KETELSEN RECREATIONAL VEHICLES INC.; *U.S. Private*, pg. 2226
JOHNNY LONDOFF CHEVROLET, INC.; *U.S. Private*, pg. 2226
JOHNNY MACS' SPORTING GOODS STORES; *U.S. Private*, pg. 2226
JOHNNY RIBEIRO BUILDER INC.; *U.S. Private*, pg. 2226
THE JOHNNY ROCKETS GROUP, INC.—See Fog Cutter Capital Group Inc.; *U.S. Private*, pg. 1557
JOHNNY'S SEAFOOD COMPANY—See Dulcich, Inc.; *U.S. Private*, pg. 1286
JOHNNY WAS, LLC—See Oxford Industries, Inc.; *U.S. Public*, pg. 1629
JOHN OVENSTONE LTD—See African Equity Empowerment Investmts Limited; *Int'l*, pg. 191
JOHN PATON, INC.; *U.S. Private*, pg. 2223
JOHN PAUL MITCHELL SYSTEMS; *U.S. Private*, pg. 2223
JOHN PAUL PET, L.L.C.—See John Paul Mitchell Systems; *U.S. Private*, pg. 2223
JOHN PAUL RICHARD INC.; *U.S. Private*, pg. 2223
JOHN PAUL SAN FRANCISCO—See Accor S.A.; *Int'l*, pg. 92
THE JOHN P. BROOKS FAMILY CORPORATION; *U.S. Private*, pg. 4059
JOHN & PHIL'S TOYOTA-SUBARU INC.; *U.S. Private*, pg. 2219
JOHN PLAYER & SONS LTD—See Imperial Brands PLC; *Int'l*, pg. 3634
JOHN P. PICONE INC.—See ACS, Actividades de Construccion y Servicios, S.A.; *Int'l*, pg. 111
JOHN Q. HAMMONS HOTELS INC.; *U.S. Private*, pg. 2223
JOHN RANDOLPH MEDICAL CENTER—See HCA Healthcare, Inc.; *U.S. Public*, pg. 999
JOHN RANDOLPH OB/GYN, LLC—See HCA Healthcare, Inc.; *U.S. Public*, pg. 999
JOHN REYER COMPANY; *U.S. Private*, pg. 2224
JOHN RICHARD INCORPORATED; *U.S. Private*, pg. 2224
JOHN RICH & SONS—See Woolrich, Inc.; *U.S. Private*, pg. 4562
JOHN R. MCKENZIE JOBBER, INC.; *U.S. Private*, pg. 2223
JOHN R. MORREALE INCORPORATED; *U.S. Private*, pg. 2224

JOHN ROBERTS COMPANY; *U.S. Private*, pg. 2224
JOHN ROCK, INC.—See Freeman Spogli & Co. Incorporated; *U.S. Private*, pg. 1606
JOHN ROHRER CONTRACTING CO.; *U.S. Private*, pg. 2224
JOHN R. TURNER HOLDING COMPANY; *U.S. Private*, pg. 2224
JOHN R. WOOD, INC.; *U.S. Private*, pg. 2224
JOHN R. YOUNG & CO. INC.; *U.S. Private*, pg. 2224
JOHNS BROTHERS SECURITY INC.—See Schaubach Holdings Inc.; *U.S. Private*, pg. 3563
JOHNS-BYRNE CO.; *U.S. Private*, pg. 2226
JOHN S. CLARK COMPANY, LLC—See Obayashi Corporation; *Int'l*, pg. 5509
JOHNS EASTERN COMPANY INC.—See HGGC, LLC; *U.S. Private*, pg. 1929
JOHN S. FREY ENTERPRISES; *U.S. Private*, pg. 2224
JOHN SHEARER (HOLDINGS) LIMITED—See Arrowcrest Group Pty. Ltd.; *Int'l*, pg. 580
JOHN SHEARER LIMITED—See Arrowcrest Group Pty. Ltd.; *Int'l*, pg. 580
JOHNS HOPKINS ARAMCO HEALTHCARE COMPANY—See Saudi Arabian Oil Company; *Int'l*, pg. 6590
JOHNS HOPKINS HEALTH SYSTEM; *U.S. Private*, pg. 2226
JOHNS HOPKINS REAL ESTATE; *U.S. Private*, pg. 2226
THE JOHNS HOPKINS UNIVERSITY PRESS—See Johns Hopkins University; *U.S. Private*, pg. 2226
JOHNS HOPKINS UNIVERSITY; *U.S. Private*, pg. 2226
JOHN SISK AND SON (HOLDINGS) LIMITED—See Sicon Ltd.; *Int'l*, pg. 6881
JOHN SISK & SON LIMITED-IRELAND—See Sicon Ltd.; *Int'l*, pg. 6881
JOHN SISK & SON LIMITED-UK—See Sicon Ltd.; *Int'l*, pg. 6882
JOHN'S ISLAND CLUB, INC.; *U.S. Private*, pg. 2225
JOHN S. JAMES CO.; *U.S. Private*, pg. 2224
JOHN'S LUMBER & HARDWARE CO.—See Builders FirstSource, Inc.; *U.S. Public*, pg. 410
JOHNS LYNG GROUP LIMITED; *Int'l*, pg. 3984
JOHNS LYNG GROUP LIMITED; *Int'l*, pg. 3984
JOHNS MANVILLE CANADA INC. - INNISFAIL—See Berkshire Hathaway Inc.; *U.S. Public*, pg. 308
JOHNS MANVILLE CANADA INC.—See Berkshire Hathaway Inc.; *U.S. Public*, pg. 308
JOHNS MANVILLE CORP. - ENGINEERED PRODUCTS, WATERVILLE—See Berkshire Hathaway Inc.; *U.S. Public*, pg. 308
JOHNS MANVILLE CORPORATION—See Berkshire Hathaway Inc.; *U.S. Public*, pg. 308
JOHNS MANVILLE EUROPE GMBH—See Berkshire Hathaway Inc.; *U.S. Public*, pg. 308
JOHNS MANVILLE GMBH—See Berkshire Hathaway Inc.; *U.S. Public*, pg. 308
JOHNS MANVILLE SLOVAKIA, A.S.—See Berkshire Hathaway Inc.; *U.S. Public*, pg. 308
JOHNS MANVILLE—See Berkshire Hathaway Inc.; *U.S. Public*, pg. 308
JOHN SMEDLEY LTD.; *Int'l*, pg. 3979
JOHN SNOW, INC.; *U.S. Private*, pg. 2224
JOHNS OF NOTTINGHAM LTD; *Int'l*, pg. 3984
JOHNSON ACCESS (PROPRIETARY) LIMITED—See Hosken Consolidated Investments Limited; *Int'l*, pg. 3485
JOHNSON AND PHILLIPS (PAKISTAN) LIMITED; *Int'l*, pg. 3985
JOHNSON ARCHITECTURAL METAL COMPANY; *U.S. Private*, pg. 2226
JOHNSON AUTO PLAZA, INC.; *U.S. Private*, pg. 2226
JOHNSON BANK—See S.C. Johnson & Son, Inc.; *U.S. Private*, pg. 3516
JOHNSON & BLANTON; *U.S. Private*, pg. 2226
JOHNSON BROS. CORPORATION; *U.S. Private*, pg. 2226
JOHNSON BROS RUBBER CO.; *U.S. Private*, pg. 2226
JOHNSON BROTHERS BAKERY SUPPLY; *U.S. Private*, pg. 2227
JOHNSON BROTHERS CAROLINA DISTRIBUTING—See Johnson Brothers Liquor Company; *U.S. Private*, pg. 2227
JOHNSON BROTHERS LIQUOR COMPANY OF RHODE ISLAND—See Johnson Brothers Liquor Company; *U.S. Private*, pg. 2227
JOHNSON BROTHERS LIQUOR COMPANY; *U.S. Private*, pg. 2227
JOHNSON BRYCE INC—See Bryce Corporation; *U.S. Private*, pg. 674
JOHNSON CARLIER INC.; *U.S. Private*, pg. 2227
JOHNSON CARPET INC.; *U.S. Private*, pg. 2227
JOHNSON CHEMICAL PHARMACEUTICAL WORKS CO., LTD.; *Int'l*, pg. 3985
JOHNSON CITY BEDDING COMPANY—See Restonic Mattress Corporation; *U.S. Private*, pg. 3409
JOHNSON CITY CHEMICAL CO. INC.; *U.S. Private*, pg. 2227
JOHNSON CITY PRESS—See Sandusky Newspapers Inc.; *U.S. Private*, pg. 3545

JOHNSON CITY CHEMICAL CO. INC.
CORPORATE AFFILIATIONS

JOHNSON CLEANERS UK LTD.—See Timpson Group PLC; *Int'l*, pg. 7752

JOHNSON CLEANING SERVICES COMPANY LIMITED—See Hong Kong Johnson Holdings Company Limited; *Int'l*, pg. 3466

JOHNSON COMPANY, LTD.—See S.C. Johnson & Son, Inc.; *U.S. Private*, pg. 3516

JOHNSON CONCRETE CO.; *U.S. Private*, pg. 2227

JOHNSON CONTRACTING COMPANY; *U.S. Private*, pg. 2227

JOHNSON CONTRACTORS INC.; *U.S. Private*, pg. 2227

JOHNSON CONTROL & INTEGRATED SOLUTIONS FRANCE—See Johnson Controls International plc; *Int'l*, pg. 3988

JOHNSON CONTROLS, AO—See Johnson Controls International plc; *Int'l*, pg. 3986

JOHNSON CONTROLS AUTOBATTERIE GMBH—See Brookfield Corporation; *Int'l*, pg. 1175

JOHNSON CONTROLS AUTOBATTERIE GMBH—See Caisse de Depot et Placement du Quebec; *Int'l*, pg. 1254

JOHNSON CONTROLS AUTOMOTIVE SYSTEMS KK—See Adient plc; *Int'l*, pg. 148

JOHNSON CONTROLS BATTERIE AG—See Brookfield Corporation; *Int'l*, pg. 1175

JOHNSON CONTROLS BATTERIE AG—See Caisse de Depot et Placement du Quebec; *Int'l*, pg. 1254

JOHNSON CONTROLS BATTERIES LTD.—See Brookfield Corporation; *Int'l*, pg. 1175

JOHNSON CONTROLS BATTERIES LTD.—See Caisse de Depot et Placement du Quebec; *Int'l*, pg. 1254

JOHNSON CONTROLS BATTERY GROUP, LLC—See Brookfield Corporation; *Int'l*, pg. 1175

JOHNSON CONTROLS BATTERY GROUP, LLC—See Caisse de Depot et Placement du Quebec; *Int'l*, pg. 1254

JOHNSON CONTROLS BE ARGENTINA S.R.L.—See Johnson Controls International plc; *Int'l*, pg. 3985

JOHNSON CONTROLS BULGARIA EOOD—See Johnson Controls International plc; *Int'l*, pg. 3985

JOHNSON CONTROLS CHILE S.A.—See Johnson Controls International plc; *Int'l*, pg. 3985

JOHNSON CONTROLS COLOMBIA LIMITADA—See Johnson Controls International plc; *Int'l*, pg. 3985

JOHNSON CONTROLS CO., LTD.—See Johnson Controls International plc; *Int'l*, pg. 3985

JOHNSON CONTROLS CZECH SR.O.—See Johnson Controls International plc; *Int'l*, pg. 3985

JOHNSON CONTROLS DENMARK APS—See Johnson Controls International plc; *Int'l*, pg. 3985

JOHNSON CONTROLS - EGYPT—See Johnson Controls International plc; *Int'l*, pg. 3985

JOHNSON CONTROLS FINLAND OY—See Johnson Controls International plc; *Int'l*, pg. 3985

JOHNSON CONTROLS FIRE & SECURITY SOLUTIONS—See Johnson Controls International plc; *Int'l*, pg. 3985

JOHNSON CONTROLS FZE—See Johnson Controls International plc; *Int'l*, pg. 3985

JOHNSON CONTROLS, INC. - DALLAS OFFICE—See Johnson Controls International plc; *Int'l*, pg. 3986

JOHNSON CONTROLS, INC. - LITTLE ROCK OFFICE—See Johnson Controls International plc; *Int'l*, pg. 3986

JOHNSON CONTROLS, INC. - LOUISVILLE OFFICE—See Johnson Controls International plc; *Int'l*, pg. 3986

JOHNSON CONTROLS, INC. - MURFREESBORO PLANT—See Adient plc; *Int'l*, pg. 148

JOHNSON CONTROLS INC - NORMAL, OKLAHOMA—See Johnson Controls International plc; *Int'l*, pg. 3985

JOHNSON CONTROLS, INC. - SHREVEPORT OFFICE—See Johnson Controls International plc; *Int'l*, pg. 3986

JOHNSON CONTROLS, INC.—See Johnson Controls International plc; *Int'l*, pg. 3985

JOHNSON CONTROLS INDUSTRIES—See Johnson Controls International plc; *Int'l*, pg. 3985

JOHNSON CONTROLS INTEGRATED FIRE AND SECURITY CORPORATION SERVICIOS, S.A.—See Johnson Controls International plc; *Int'l*, pg. 3987

JOHNSON CONTROLS INTEGRATED FIRE & SECURITY N.V.—See Johnson Controls International plc; *Int'l*, pg. 3988

JOHNSON CONTROLS INTEGRATED FIRE & SECURITY (PORTUGAL), UNIPESSOAL LDA—See Johnson Controls International plc; *Int'l*, pg. 3989

JOHNSON CONTROLS INTERNATIONAL KFT—See Johnson Controls International plc; *Int'l*, pg. 3985

JOHNSON CONTROLS INTERNATIONAL KOREA CO., LTD.—See Johnson Controls International plc; *Int'l*, pg. 3987

JOHNSON CONTROLS INTERNATIONAL PLC; *Int'l*, pg. 3985

JOHNSON CONTROLS INTERNATIONAL ROMANIA S.R.L.—See Johnson Controls International plc; *Int'l*, pg. 3985

JOHNSON CONTROLS INTERNATIONAL SP.Z.O.O.—See Johnson Controls International plc; *Int'l*, pg. 3989

JOHNSON CONTROLS KOREA LTD.—See Johnson Controls International plc; *Int'l*, pg. 3985

JOHNSON CONTROLS LIMITED—See Johnson Controls International plc; *Int'l*, pg. 3985

JOHNSON CONTROLS LIMITED—See Johnson Controls International plc; *Int'l*, pg. 3985

JOHNSON CONTROLS L.P.—See Johnson Controls International plc; *Int'l*, pg. 3985

JOHNSON CONTROLS LTD.—See Johnson Controls International plc; *Int'l*, pg. 3985

JOHNSON CONTROLS MARINE SERVICES COMPANY LIMITED—See Johnson Controls International plc; *Int'l*, pg. 3987

JOHNSON CONTROLS MARINE SERVICES (SEAPLUS) CO., LTD.—See Johnson Controls International plc; *Int'l*, pg. 3987

JOHNSON CONTROLS PORTUGAL BE, LDA.—See Johnson Controls International plc; *Int'l*, pg. 3985

JOHNSON CONTROLS SYSTEMS & SERVICE AB—See Johnson Controls International plc; *Int'l*, pg. 3986

JOHNSON CONTROLS SYSTEMS & SERVICE GMBH—See Johnson Controls International plc; *Int'l*, pg. 3986

JOHNSON CONTROLS SYSTEMS & SERVICE GMBH—See Johnson Controls International plc; *Int'l*, pg. 3986

JOHNSON CONTROLS SYSTEMS & SERVICE ITALIA S.R.L.—See Johnson Controls International plc; *Int'l*, pg. 3986

JOHNSON CONTROLS TECHNISCHER SERVICE GMBH—See Johnson Controls International plc; *Int'l*, pg. 3986

JOHNSON CONTROLS VENEZUELA S.A.—See Johnson Controls International plc; *Int'l*, pg. 3986

JOHNSON CONTROLS YORK MARINE APS—See Johnson Controls International plc; *Int'l*, pg. 3986

THE JOHNSON CORPORATION—See Intact Financial Corporation; *Int'l*, pg. 3727

THE JOHNSON CORPORATION—See Tryg A/S; *Int'l*, pg. 7947

JOHNSON COUNTY BANK—See SKYLINE BANKSHARES, INC.; *U.S. Public*, pg. 1892

JOHNSON COUNTY NEUROLOGY, LLC—See HCA Healthcare, Inc.; *U.S. Public*, pg. 999

JOHNSON COUNTY NEUROLOGY, LLC—See HCA Healthcare, Inc.; *U.S. Public*, pg. 999

JOHNSON COUNTY WASTEWATER; *U.S. Private*, pg. 2227

JOHNSON CRUSHERS INTERNATIONAL, INC.—See Astec Industries, Inc.; *U.S. Public*, pg. 216

JOHNSON DESIGN GROUP; *U.S. Private*, pg. 2227

JOHNSON DIRECT; *U.S. Private*, pg. 2227

JOHNSON DODGE CHRYSLER JEEP, INC.; *U.S. Private*, pg. 2227

JOHNSON ELECTRIC AUTOMOTIVO BRASIL LTDA.—See Johnson Electric Holdings Limited; *Int'l*, pg. 3990

JOHNSON ELECTRIC (BEIHAI) CO., LTD.—See Johnson Electric Holdings Limited; *Int'l*, pg. 3990

JOHNSON ELECTRIC DOO—See Johnson Electric Holdings Limited; *Int'l*, pg. 3990

JOHNSON ELECTRIC ENGINEERING LIMITED—See Johnson Electric Holdings Limited; *Int'l*, pg. 3990

JOHNSON ELECTRIC GERMANY GMBH & CO. KG—See Johnson Electric Holdings Limited; *Int'l*, pg. 3990

JOHNSON ELECTRIC HATVAN KFT—See Johnson Electric Holdings Limited; *Int'l*, pg. 3990

JOHNSON ELECTRIC HOLDINGS LIMITED; *Int'l*, pg. 3990

JOHNSON ELECTRIC INDUSTRIAL MANUFACTORY, LIMITED—See Johnson Electric Holdings Limited; *Int'l*, pg. 3990

JOHNSON ELECTRIC INTERNATIONAL AG—See Johnson Electric Holdings Limited; *Int'l*, pg. 3990

JOHNSON ELECTRIC INTERNATIONAL (AT) GMBH—See Johnson Electric Holdings Limited; *Int'l*, pg. 3990

JOHNSON ELECTRIC INTERNATIONAL FRANCE S.A.R.L—See Johnson Electric Holdings Limited; *Int'l*, pg. 3990

JOHNSON ELECTRIC INTERNATIONAL (IT) S.R.L.—See Johnson Electric Holdings Limited; *Int'l*, pg. 3990

JOHNSON ELECTRIC INTERNATIONAL LIMITED—See Johnson Electric Holdings Limited; *Int'l*, pg. 3990

JOHNSON ELECTRIC INTERNATIONAL (UK) LIMITED—See Johnson Electric Holdings Limited; *Int'l*, pg. 3990

JOHNSON ELECTRIC (JIANGMEN) CO., LTD.—See Johnson Electric Holdings Limited; *Int'l*, pg. 3990

JOHNSON ELECTRIC KOREA (INDUSTRY)—See Johnson Electric Holdings Limited; *Int'l*, pg. 3990

JOHNSON ELECTRIC (NANJING) CO., LTD.—See Johnson Electric Holdings Limited; *Int'l*, pg. 3990

JOHNSON ELECTRIC NORTH AMERICA INC.—See Johnson Electric Holdings Limited; *Int'l*, pg. 3990

JOHNSON ELECTRIC OZD KFT—See Johnson Electric Holdings Limited; *Int'l*, pg. 3990

JOHNSON ELECTRIC POLAND SP.Z O.O.—See Johnson Electric Holdings Limited; *Int'l*, pg. 3990

JOHNSON ELECTRIC PRIVATE LIMITED—See Johnson Electric Holdings Limited; *Int'l*, pg. 3990

JOHNSON ELECTRIC SAINT REMY SAS—See Johnson Electric Holdings Limited; *Int'l*, pg. 3990

JOHNSON ELECTRIC SHANGHAI (INDUSTRY)—See Johnson Electric Holdings Limited; *Int'l*, pg. 3990

JOHNSON ELECTRIC (SHENZHEN) CO. LTD.—See Johnson Electric Holdings Limited; *Int'l*, pg. 3990

JOHNSON ELECTRIC SUPPLY CO.; *U.S. Private*, pg. 2227

JOHNSON ELECTRIC WORLD TRADE LTD.—See Johnson Electric Holdings Limited; *Int'l*, pg. 3990

JOHNSON ENGINEERING, INC.—See Apex Companies, LLC; *U.S. Private*, pg. 292

JOHNSON EQUIPMENT & CATTLE LLC—See Tym Corporation; *Int'l*, pg. 7995

JOHNSON EQUIPMENT COMPANY INC.; *U.S. Private*, pg. 2227

JOHNSON EQUIPMENT COMPANY S. DE R. L. DE C.V.—See Johnson Equipment Company Inc.; *U.S. Private*, pg. 2227

JOHNSON FEED INCORPORATED; *U.S. Private*, pg. 2227

JOHNSON FINANCIAL GROUP, INC.—See S.C. Johnson & Son, Inc.; *U.S. Private*, pg. 3516

JOHNSON FINCH & MCCLURE CONSTRUCTION, INC.; *U.S. Private*, pg. 2227

JOHNSON FITNESS (MALAYSIA) SDN. BHD.—See Johnson Health Tech. Co., Ltd.; *Int'l*, pg. 3991

JOHNSON FLOOR COMPANY, INC.; *U.S. Private*, pg. 2227

JOHNSON-FLUITEN S.R.L.—See Kadant Inc.; *U.S. Public*, pg. 1212

JOHNSON FOODS, INC.; *U.S. Private*, pg. 2228

JOHNSON GAS APPLIANCE CO.; *U.S. Private*, pg. 2228

THE JOHNSON GROUP, INC.; *U.S. Private*, pg. 4059

THE JOHNSON GROUP—See Deluxe Corporation; *U.S. Public*, pg. 653

THE JOHNSON GROUP; *U.S. Private*, pg. 4059

JOHNSON HARDWARE CO.; *U.S. Private*, pg. 2228

JOHNSON HEALTH CARE CO., LTD.—See Johnson Health Tech. Co., Ltd.; *Int'l*, pg. 3991

JOHNSON HEALTH TECH AUSTRALIA PTY. LTD.—See Johnson Health Tech. Co., Ltd.; *Int'l*, pg. 3991

JOHNSON HEALTH TECH. CO., LTD.; *Int'l*, pg. 3991

JOHNSON HEALTH TECH FRANCE S.A.S.—See Johnson Health Tech. Co., Ltd.; *Int'l*, pg. 3991

JOHNSON HEALTH TECH. GMBH—See Johnson Health Tech. Co., Ltd.; *Int'l*, pg. 3991

JOHNSON HEALTH TECH NORTH AMERICA INC—See Johnson Health Tech. Co., Ltd.; *Int'l*, pg. 3991

JOHNSON HEALTH TECH PHILIPPINES, INC.—See Johnson Health Tech. Co., Ltd.; *Int'l*, pg. 3991

JOHNSON HEALTH TECH. POLAND SP. Z.O.O.—See Johnson Health Tech. Co., Ltd.; *Int'l*, pg. 3991

JOHNSON HEALTH TECH RETAIL INC.—See Johnson Health Tech. Co., Ltd.; *Int'l*, pg. 3991

JOHNSON HEALTH TECH ROMANIA S.A—See Johnson Health Tech. Co., Ltd.; *Int'l*, pg. 3991

JOHNSON HICKEY MURCHISON, PC; *U.S. Private*, pg. 2228

JOHNSON & HOFFMAN, LLC; *U.S. Private*, pg. 2226

JOHNSON HOLDING CO.; *U.S. Private*, pg. 2228

JOHNSON HOMES OF MERIDIAN; *U.S. Private*, pg. 2228

JOHNSON HYUNDAI OF CARY INC.; *U.S. Private*, pg. 2228

JOHNSON INC.—See Intact Financial Corporation; *Int'l*, pg. 3727

JOHNSON INC.—See Tryg A/S; *Int'l*, pg. 7947

JOHNSON INDUSTRIES INTERNATIONAL, INC.—See Tetra Laval International S.A.; *Int'l*, pg. 7577

JOHNSON INSURANCE SERVICES, INC.—See S.C. Johnson & Son, Inc.; *U.S. Private*, pg. 3516

JOHNSON INTERNATIONAL CO.; *U.S. Private*, pg. 2228

JOHNSONITE CANADA INC.—See Tarkett S.A.; *Int'l*, pg. 7462

JOHNSONITE INC.—See Tarkett S.A.; *Int'l*, pg. 7463

JOHNSON & JOHNSON AB—See Johnson & Johnson; *U.S. Public*, pg. 1198

JOHNSON & JOHNSON AG—See Johnson & Johnson; *U.S. Public*, pg. 1198

JOHNSON & JOHNSON (CHINA) LTD.—See Johnson & Johnson; *U.S. Public*, pg. 1198

JOHNSON & JOHNSON COMERCIO E DISTRIBUICAO LTDA.—See Johnson & Johnson; *U.S. Public*, pg. 1198

JOHNSON & JOHNSON CONSUMER B.V.—See Kenvue Inc.; *U.S. Public*, pg. 1223

JOHNSON & JOHNSON CONSUMER FRANCE SAS—See Kenvue Inc.; *U.S. Public*, pg. 1223

JOHNSON & JOHNSON CONSUMER INC.—See Kenvue Inc.; *U.S. Public*, pg. 1223

JOHNSON & JOHNSON CONSUMER NV/SA—See Kenvue Inc.; *U.S. Public*, pg. 1223

JOHNSON & JOHNSON CONSUMER PRODUCTS—See Kenvue Inc.; *U.S. Public*, pg. 1223

JOHNSON & JOHNSON CONSUMER PRODUCTS—See Kenvue Inc.; *U.S. Public*, pg. 1223

COMPANY NAME INDEX

JOHNSON & JOHNSON DE ARGENTINA, S.A.C.E I.—See Kenvue Inc.; *U.S. Public*, pg. 1224
JOHNSON & JOHNSON DE COLOMBIA S.A.—See Kenvue Inc.; *U.S. Public*, pg. 1224
JOHNSON & JOHNSON DEL ECUADOR S.A.—See Kenvue Inc.; *U.S. Public*, pg. 1224
JOHNSON & JOHNSON DEL PERU S.A.—See Kenvue Inc.; *U.S. Public*, pg. 1224
JOHNSON & JOHNSON DE URUGUAY S.A.—See Johnson & Johnson; *U.S. Public*, pg. 1199
JOHNSON & JOHNSON DE VENEZUELA, S.A.—See Johnson & Johnson; *U.S. Public*, pg. 1199
JOHNSON & JOHNSON D.O.O.—See Johnson & Johnson; *U.S. Public*, pg. 1199
JOHNSON & JOHNSON FINANCE CORPORATION—See Johnson & Johnson; *U.S. Public*, pg. 1198
JOHNSON & JOHNSON FINANCE LIMITED—See Johnson & Johnson; *U.S. Public*, pg. 1198
JOHNSON & JOHNSON FINANCIAL SERVICES GMBH—See Johnson & Johnson; *U.S. Public*, pg. 1198
JOHNSON & JOHNSON GESELLSCHAFT M.B.H—See Kenvue Inc.; *U.S. Public*, pg. 1223
JOHNSON & JOHNSON GMBH—See Kenvue Inc.; *U.S. Public*, pg. 1224
JOHNSON & JOHNSON GROUP HOLDINGS GMBH—See Johnson & Johnson; *U.S. Public*, pg. 1198
JOHNSON & JOHNSON HEALTH AND WELLNESS SOLUTIONS, INC.—See Johnson & Johnson; *U.S. Public*, pg. 1198
JOHNSON & JOHNSON HEALTH CARE SYSTEMS INC.—See Johnson & Johnson; *U.S. Public*, pg. 1198
JOHNSON & JOHNSON HELLAS COMMERCIAL & INDUSTRIAL S.A.—See Kenvue Inc.; *U.S. Public*, pg. 1224
JOHNSON & JOHNSON HELLAS S.A.—See Johnson & Johnson; *U.S. Public*, pg. 1198
JOHNSON & JOHNSON HEMISFERICA S.A.—See Johnson & Johnson; *U.S. Public*, pg. 1198
JOHNSON & JOHNSON HOLDCO (NA) INC.—See Johnson & Johnson; *U.S. Public*, pg. 1197
JOHNSON & JOHNSON HOLDING AB—See Johnson & Johnson; *U.S. Public*, pg. 1198
JOHNSON & JOHNSON HOLDING GMBH—See Johnson & Johnson; *U.S. Public*, pg. 1198
JOHNSON & JOHNSON (HONG KONG) LIMITED—See Johnson & Johnson; *U.S. Public*, pg. 1198
JOHNSON & JOHNSON INC.—See Kenvue Inc.; *U.S. Public*, pg. 1224
JOHNSON & JOHNSON INDIA LTD.—See Johnson & Johnson; *U.S. Public*, pg. 1198
JOHNSON & JOHNSON INDUSTRIAL LTDA.—See Kenvue Inc.; *U.S. Public*, pg. 1224
JOHNSON & JOHNSON INNOVATION - JJDC, INC.—See Johnson & Johnson; *U.S. Public*, pg. 1198
JOHNSON & JOHNSON INNOVATION LIMITED—See Johnson & Johnson; *U.S. Public*, pg. 1198
JOHNSON & JOHNSON INNOVATION LLC—See Johnson & Johnson; *U.S. Public*, pg. 1198
JOHNSON & JOHNSON INTERNATIONAL S.A.—See Johnson & Johnson; *U.S. Public*, pg. 1198
JOHNSON & JOHNSON INTERNATIONAL—See Johnson & Johnson; *U.S. Public*, pg. 1198
JOHNSON & JOHNSON (IRELAND) LTD.—See Johnson & Johnson; *U.S. Public*, pg. 1198
JOHNSON & JOHNSON K.K.—See Johnson & Johnson; *U.S. Public*, pg. 1198
JOHNSON & JOHNSON KOREA, LTD.—See Kenvue Inc.; *U.S. Public*, pg. 1224
JOHNSON & JOHNSON LDA.—See Johnson & Johnson; *U.S. Public*, pg. 1198
JOHNSON & JOHNSON LTD.—See Johnson & Johnson; *U.S. Public*, pg. 1198
JOHNSON & JOHNSON MEDICAL B.V.—See Johnson & Johnson; *U.S. Public*, pg. 1198
JOHNSON & JOHNSON MEDICAL, INC; *Int'l*, pg. 3985
JOHNSON & JOHNSON MEDICAL KOREA LIMITED—See Johnson & Johnson; *U.S. Public*, pg. 1198
JOHNSON & JOHNSON MEDICAL LTD.—See Johnson & Johnson; *U.S. Public*, pg. 1198
JOHNSON & JOHNSON MEDICAL LTD.—See Johnson & Johnson; *U.S. Public*, pg. 1198
JOHNSON & JOHNSON MEDICAL N.V.—See Johnson & Johnson; *U.S. Public*, pg. 1199
JOHNSON & JOHNSON MEDICAL PRODUCTS GMBH—See Johnson & Johnson; *U.S. Public*, pg. 1199
JOHNSON & JOHNSON MEDICAL (PTY) LIMITED—See Johnson & Johnson; *U.S. Public*, pg. 1198
JOHNSON & JOHNSON MEDICAL PTY. LIMITED—See Johnson & Johnson; *U.S. Public*, pg. 1199
JOHNSON & JOHNSON MEDICAL S.A.—See Johnson & Johnson; *U.S. Public*, pg. 1199
JOHNSON & JOHNSON MEDICAL (SHANGHAI) LTD.—See Johnson & Johnson; *U.S. Public*, pg. 1198
JOHNSON & JOHNSON MEDICAL S.P.A.—See Johnson & Johnson; *U.S. Public*, pg. 1199

JOHNSON & JOHNSON MEDIKAL SANAYI VE TICARET LIMITED SIRKETI—See Johnson & Johnson; *U.S. Public*, pg. 1199
JOHNSON & JOHNSON MIDDLE EAST FZ-LLC—See Johnson & Johnson; *U.S. Public*, pg. 1199
JOHNSON & JOHNSON (MIDDLE EAST) INC.—See Johnson & Johnson; *U.S. Public*, pg. 1198
JOHNSON & JOHNSON (NEW ZEALAND) LIMITED—See Johnson & Johnson; *U.S. Public*, pg. 1198
JOHNSON & JOHNSON NORDIC AB—See Johnson & Johnson; *U.S. Public*, pg. 1199
JOHNSON & JOHNSON PACIFIC PTY. LTD.—See Kenvue Inc.; *U.S. Public*, pg. 1224
JOHNSON & JOHNSON PHARMACEUTICAL RESEARCH & DEVELOPMENT, LLC—See Johnson & Johnson; *U.S. Public*, pg. 1199
JOHNSON & JOHNSON (PHILIPPINES), INC.—See Johnson & Johnson; *U.S. Public*, pg. 1198
JOHNSON & JOHNSON PRIVATE LIMITED—See Johnson & Johnson; *U.S. Public*, pg. 1199
JOHNSON & JOHNSON, PRODAJA MEDICINSKIH IN FARMACEVTSKIH IZDELKOV, D.O.O—See Johnson & Johnson; *U.S. Public*, pg. 1199
JOHNSON & JOHNSON PRODUCTS INC.—See Johnson & Johnson; *U.S. Public*, pg. 1199
JOHNSON & JOHNSON PROFESSIONAL CO. (P.R.) INC.—See Johnson & Johnson; *U.S. Public*, pg. 1199
JOHNSON & JOHNSON (PROPRIETARY) LIMITED—See Johnson & Johnson; *U.S. Public*, pg. 1198
JOHNSON & JOHNSON PTE. LTD.—See Kenvue Inc.; *U.S. Public*, pg. 1224
JOHNSON & JOHNSON PTY. LIMITED—See Kenvue Inc.; *U.S. Public*, pg. 1224
JOHNSON & JOHNSON ROMANIA S.R.L.—See Johnson & Johnson; *U.S. Public*, pg. 1199
JOHNSON & JOHNSON, S.A. DE C.V.—See Kenvue Inc.; *U.S. Public*, pg. 1224
JOHNSON & JOHNSON SANTE BEAUTE FRANCE—See Kenvue Inc.; *U.S. Public*, pg. 1224
JOHNSON & JOHNSON S.A.—See Johnson & Johnson; *U.S. Public*, pg. 1199
JOHNSON & JOHNSON SDN. BHD.—See Johnson & Johnson; *U.S. Public*, pg. 1199
JOHNSON & JOHNSON S.E. D.O.O.—See Johnson & Johnson; *U.S. Public*, pg. 1199
JOHNSON & JOHNSON SERVICES INC.—See Johnson & Johnson; *U.S. Public*, pg. 1199
JOHNSON & JOHNSON SIHHI MALZEME SANAYI VE TICARET LIMITED SIRKETI—See Johnson & Johnson; *U.S. Public*, pg. 1199
JOHNSON & JOHNSON; *U.S. Public*, pg. 1193
JOHNSON & JOHNSON S.P.A.—See Johnson & Johnson; *U.S. Public*, pg. 1199
JOHNSON & JOHNSON, SPOL. S.R.O.—See Johnson & Johnson; *U.S. Public*, pg. 1199
JOHNSON & JOHNSON, S.R.O.—See Johnson & Johnson; *U.S. Public*, pg. 1199
JOHNSON & JOHNSON, S.R.O.—See Johnson & Johnson; *U.S. Public*, pg. 1199
JOHNSON & JOHNSON SURGICAL VISION, INC.—See Johnson & Johnson; *U.S. Public*, pg. 1199
JOHNSON & JOHNSON SURGICAL VISION, INC.—See Johnson & Johnson; *U.S. Public*, pg. 1199
JOHNSON & JOHNSON TAIWAN LTD.—See Johnson & Johnson; *U.S. Public*, pg. 1199
JOHNSON & JOHNSON VISION CARE, INC.—See Johnson & Johnson; *U.S. Public*, pg. 1199
JOHNSON & JOHNSON VISION CARE (IRELAND) LIMITED—See Johnson & Johnson; *U.S. Public*, pg. 1199
JOHNSON-LANCASTER & ASSOCIATES, INC.; *U.S. Private*, pg. 2229
JOHNSON LEVEL & TOOL MFG. CO., INC.—See Investment AB Latour; *Int'l*, pg. 3782
JOHNSON-LOCKLIN & ASSOCIATES INSURANCE CORPORATION—See GTCR LLC; *U.S. Private*, pg. 1803
JOHNSON LUMBER COMPANY; *U.S. Private*, pg. 2228
JOHNSON MACHINERY CO.; *U.S. Private*, pg. 2228
JOHNSON MACHINE WORKS INC.; *U.S. Private*, pg. 2228
JOHNSON-MANLEY LUMBER COMPANY; *U.S. Private*, pg. 2229
JOHNSON MATTHEY AB—See Johnson Matthey PLC; *Int'l*, pg. 3992
JOHNSON MATTHEY ARGENTINA S.A.—See Johnson Matthey PLC; *Int'l*, pg. 3992
JOHNSON MATTHEY ARGILLON (SHANGHAI) EMISSION CONTROL TECHNOLOGIES LTD.—See Johnson Matthey PLC; *Int'l*, pg. 3992
JOHNSON MATTHEY (AUST) LTD—See Johnson Matthey PLC; *Int'l*, pg. 3992
JOHNSON MATTHEY BATTERY MATERIALS GMBH—See Johnson Matthey PLC; *Int'l*, pg. 3992
JOHNSON MATTHEY BATTERY MATERIALS LTD.—See Johnson Matthey PLC; *Int'l*, pg. 3992
JOHNSON MATTHEY BELGIUM BVBA—See Johnson Matthey PLC; *Int'l*, pg. 3992

JOHNSON MATTHEY PLC

JOHNSON MATTHEY & BRANDENBERGER AG—See Johnson Matthey PLC; *Int'l*, pg. 3991
JOHNSON MATTHEY BRASIL LTDA.—See Johnson Matthey PLC; *Int'l*, pg. 3992
JOHNSON MATTHEY B.V.—See Johnson Matthey PLC; *Int'l*, pg. 3992
JOHNSON MATTHEY CATALOG CO.—See Johnson Matthey PLC; *Int'l*, pg. 3992
JOHNSON MATTHEY CATALYSTS (GERMANY) GMBH—See Johnson Matthey PLC; *Int'l*, pg. 3992
JOHNSON MATTHEY CATALYSTS KOREA LIMITED—See Johnson Matthey PLC; *Int'l*, pg. 3992
JOHNSON MATTHEY CATALYSTS LLC—See Johnson Matthey PLC; *Int'l*, pg. 3992
JOHNSON MATTHEY CATALYSTS—See Johnson Matthey PLC; *Int'l*, pg. 3992
JOHNSON MATTHEY CHEMICAL CATALYSTS—See Johnson Matthey PLC; *Int'l*, pg. 3992
JOHNSON MATTHEY CHEMICALS GMBH—See Johnson Matthey PLC; *Int'l*, pg. 3992
JOHNSON MATTHEY CHEMICALS INDIA PRIVATE LTD.—See Johnson Matthey PLC; *Int'l*, pg. 3992
JOHNSON MATTHEY & CO. GMBH.—See Johnson Matthey PLC; *Int'l*, pg. 3992
JOHNSON MATTHEY DE MEXICO, S.A. DE C.V.—See Johnson Matthey PLC; *Int'l*, pg. 3993
JOHNSON MATTHEY DOOEL SKOPJE—See Johnson Matthey PLC; *Int'l*, pg. 3992
JOHNSON MATTHEY FUEL CELLS LIMITED—See Johnson Matthey PLC; *Int'l*, pg. 3992
JOHNSON MATTHEY FUEL CELLS NA—See Johnson Matthey PLC; *Int'l*, pg. 3992
JOHNSON MATTHEY GMBH—See Johnson Matthey PLC; *Int'l*, pg. 3992
JOHNSON MATTHEY INC. - DOWNINGTOWN—See Johnson Matthey PLC; *Int'l*, pg. 3993
JOHNSON MATTHEY INC.—See Johnson Matthey PLC; *Int'l*, pg. 3993
JOHNSON MATTHEY ITALIA S.R.L.—See Johnson Matthey PLC; *Int'l*, pg. 3992
JOHNSON MATTHEY JAPAN G.K.—See Johnson Matthey PLC; *Int'l*, pg. 3992
JOHNSON MATTHEY KOREA LIMITED—See Johnson Matthey PLC; *Int'l*, pg. 3992
JOHNSON MATTHEY LIMITED—See Johnson Matthey PLC; *Int'l*, pg. 3992
JOHNSON MATTHEY LIMITED—See Johnson Matthey PLC; *Int'l*, pg. 3992
JOHNSON MATTHEY METAL PRODUCTS—See Johnson Matthey PLC; *Int'l*, pg. 3993
JOHNSON MATTHEY NOBLE METALS—See Johnson Matthey PLC; *Int'l*, pg. 3993
JOHNSON MATTHEY PCT—See Johnson Matthey PLC; *Int'l*, pg. 3992
JOHNSON MATTHEY PCT—See Johnson Matthey PLC; *Int'l*, pg. 3992
JOHNSON MATTHEY PCT—See Johnson Matthey PLC; *Int'l*, pg. 3992
JOHNSON MATTHEY PHARMACEUTICAL MATERIALS-USA—See Johnson Matthey PLC; *Int'l*, pg. 3992
JOHNSON MATTHEY PHARMACEUTICAL SERVICES (YANTAI) CO., LTD.—See Johnson Matthey PLC; *Int'l*, pg. 3992
JOHNSON MATTHEY PHARMA SERVICES—See Johnson Matthey PLC; *Int'l*, pg. 3992
JOHNSON MATTHEY PIEZO PRODUCTS GMBH—See Johnson Matthey PLC; *Int'l*, pg. 3992
JOHNSON MATTHEY PLC-COLOURS & COATINGS DIVISION—See Johnson Matthey PLC; *Int'l*, pg. 3993
JOHNSON MATTHEY PLC—See Johnson Matthey PLC; *Int'l*, pg. 3993
JOHNSON MATTHEY PLC; *Int'l*, pg. 3991
JOHNSON MATTHEY POLAND SPOLKA Z OGRANICZONA ODPOWIEDZIALNOCSCIA—See Johnson Matthey PLC; *Int'l*, pg. 3992
JOHNSON MATTHEY (PTY.) LIMITED—See Johnson Matthey PLC; *Int'l*, pg. 3992
JOHNSON MATTHEY REFINING, INC.—See Johnson Matthey PLC; *Int'l*, pg. 3993
JOHNSON MATTHEY SA—See Johnson Matthey PLC; *Int'l*, pg. 3992
JOHNSON MATTHEY SDN. BHD.—See Johnson Matthey PLC; *Int'l*, pg. 3992
JOHNSON MATTHEY (SHANGHAI) CHEMICALS LIMITED—See Johnson Matthey PLC; *Int'l*, pg. 3992
JOHNSON MATTHEY STATIONARY EMISSIONS CONTROL LLC—See Johnson Matthey PLC; *Int'l*, pg. 3992
JOHNSON MATTHEY TRADING (SHENZHEN) LTD—See Johnson Matthey PLC; *Int'l*, pg. 3993
JOHNSON MATTHEY VEHICLE TESTING & DEV. LLC—See Johnson Matthey PLC; *Int'l*, pg. 3993
JOHNSON MATTHEY (ZHANGJIAGANG) ENVIRONMENTAL PROTECTION TECHNOLOGY CO., LTD.—See Johnson Matthey PLC; *Int'l*, pg. 3992
JOHNSON MEDTECH (HK) LIMITED—See Johnson Electric Holdings Limited; *Int'l*, pg. 3990
JOHNSON MEDTECH LLC—See Johnson Electric Holdings Limited; *Int'l*, pg. 3990

JOHNSON MATTHEY PLC

JOHNSON METALL AB—See Norvestor Equity AS; *Int'l*, pg. 5447
JOHNSON, MIRMIRAN & THOMPSON, INC.; *U.S. Private*, pg. 2229
JOHNSON MORTGAGE COMPANY, LLC—See LINKBANCORP, Inc.; *U.S. Public*, pg. 1320
JOHNSON MOTOR SALES INC; *U.S. Private*, pg. 2228
JOHNSON MOTORS INC.; *U.S. Private*, pg. 2228
JOHNSON NEWSPAPER CORPORATION; *U.S. Private*, pg. 2228
JOHNSON O'CONNOR FERON & CARUCCI, LLP; *U.S. Private*, pg. 2228
JOHNSON O'HARE CO. INC; *U.S. Private*, pg. 2228
JOHNSON OIL COMPANY GAYLORD; *U.S. Private*, pg. 2228
JOHNSON OIL CO. OF HALLOCK; *U.S. Private*, pg. 2228
JOHNSON OUTDOORS CANADA, INC.—See Johnson Outdoors Inc.; *U.S. Public*, pg. 1200
JOHNSON OUTDOORS DIVING—See Johnson Outdoors Inc.; *U.S. Public*, pg. 1201
JOHNSON OUTDOORS FRANCE—See Johnson Outdoors Inc.; *U.S. Public*, pg. 1201
JOHNSON OUTDOORS GEAR LLC—See Johnson Outdoors Inc.; *U.S. Public*, pg. 1201
JOHNSON OUTDOORS INC.-MARINE ELECTRONICS GROUP—See Johnson Outdoors Inc.; *U.S. Public*, pg. 1201
JOHNSON OUTDOORS INC; *U.S. Public*, pg. 1200
JOHNSON OUTDOORS MARINE ELECTRONICS. INC.—See Johnson Outdoors Inc.; *U.S. Public*, pg. 1201
JOHNSON OUTDOORS VERTRIEBSGESELLSCHAFT GMBH—See Johnson Outdoors Inc.; *U.S. Public*, pg. 1201
JOHNSON OUTDOORS WATERCRAFT INC.—See Johnson Outdoors Inc.; *U.S. Public*, pg. 1201
JOHNSON OUTDOORS WATERCRAFT LTD.—See Johnson Outdoors Inc.; *U.S. Public*, pg. 1201
JOHNSON PACKINGS & INDUSTRIAL PRODUCTS, INC.—See Gallagher Fluid Seals Inc.; *U.S. Private*, pg. 1638
JOHNSON PARTNERS INC.; *U.S. Private*, pg. 2228
JOHNSON PHARMACARE LIMITED; *Int'l*, pg. 3993
JOHNSON POWER LTD.; *U.S. Private*, pg. 2228
JOHNSON PUBLISHING COMPANY, INC.; *U.S. Private*, pg. 2228
JOHNSON & QUIN, INC.; *U.S. Private*, pg. 2226
JOHNSONRAUHOFF MARKETING COMMUNICATIONS—See JohnsonRauhoff; *U.S. Private*, pg. 2229
JOHNSONRAUHOFF MARKETING COMMUNICATIONS—See JohnsonRauhoff; *U.S. Private*, pg. 2229
JOHNSONRAUHOFF; *U.S. Private*, pg. 2229
JOHNSON REGIONAL MEDICAL CENTER; *U.S. Private*, pg. 2228
JOHNSON SCANNELL & ASSOCIATES; *U.S. Private*, pg. 2229
JOHNSONS CONTROL SYSTEMS AND SERVICE GMBH—See Johnson Controls International plc; *Int'l*, pg. 3987
JOHNSON SCREENS, INC.—See Brookfield Corporation; *Int'l*, pg. 1182
JOHNSON SCREENS (INDIA) PRIVATE LIMITED—See Brookfield Corporation; *Int'l*, pg. 1182
JOHNSON SERVICE GROUP INC.; *U.S. Private*, pg. 2229
JOHNSON SERVICE GROUP PLC; *Int'l*, pg. 3993
JOHNSON SEWELL FORD LINCOLN MERCURY; *U.S. Private*, pg. 2229
JOHNSON'S GENERAL STORES INC.; *U.S. Private*, pg. 2229
JOHNSONS HOTEL LINEN LIMITED—See Johnson Service Group PLC; *Int'l*, pg. 3993
JOHNSONS HOTEL, RESTAURANT AND CATERING LINEN LIMITED—See Johnson Service Group PLC; *Int'l*, pg. 3993
JOHNSONS MEGA SAN BERNARDO S.A.—See Cencosud S.A.; *Int'l*, pg. 1400
JOHNSON SMITH COMPANY; *U.S. Private*, pg. 2229
JOHNSONS OF CHICKASHA INC.; *U.S. Private*, pg. 2229
JOHNSONS ROONEY WELCH, INC.—See Aon plc; *Int'l*, pg. 494
JOHNSONS STALBRIDGE LINEN SERVICES—See Johnson Service Group PLC; *Int'l*, pg. 3993
JOHNSON STEPHENS CONSULTING, INC.—See Dunes Point Capital, LLC; *U.S. Private*, pg. 1288
JOHNSONS TEXTILE SERVICES LIMITED—See Johnson Service Group PLC; *Int'l*, pg. 3993
JOHNSON'S TIRE SERVICE; *U.S. Private*, pg. 2229
JOHNSON STORAGE & MOVING COMPANY; *U.S. Private*, pg. 2229
JOHNSON SUPPLY & EQUIPMENT CORP.; *U.S. Private*, pg. 2229
JOHNSONS WAX DE PORTUGAL, LDA.—See S.C. Johnson & Son, Inc.; *U.S. Private*, pg. 3516
JOHNSONS WAX (EAST AFRICA) LTD.—See S.C. Johnson & Son, Inc.; *U.S. Private*, pg. 3516
JOHNSONS WAX ESPANOLA, S.A.—See S.C. Johnson & Son, Inc.; *U.S. Private*, pg. 3516
JOHNSON SYSTEM, INC.—See AGCO Corporation; *U.S. Public*, pg. 59
JOHNSON TECHNOLOGY—See General Electric Company; *U.S. Public*, pg. 919
JOHNSON THERMAL SYSTEMS INC.—See Mission Critical Group; *U.S. Private*, pg. 2747
JOHNSON TILES PTY LTD—See Norcros plc; *Int'l*, pg. 5415
JOHNSON & TOWERS, INC.; *U.S. Private*, pg. 2226
JOHNSON TRUCK BODIES, INC.—See Henry Crown & Company; *U.S. Private*, pg. 1917
JOHNSON TRUCK CENTER LLC—See Johnson & Towers, Inc.; *U.S. Private*, pg. 2226
JOHNSON UTILITIES, LLC—See EPCOR Utilities, Inc.; *Int'l*, pg. 2459
JOHNSON/V.B.C. INC.—See Van Blarcom Closures Inc.; *U.S. Private*, pg. 4339
JOHNSONVILLE, LLC; *U.S. Private*, pg. 2229
JOHNSONWAX DEL ECUADOR S.A.—See S.C. Johnson & Son, Inc.; *U.S. Private*, pg. 3516
JOHNSON WAX (EGYPT) CO.—See S.C. Johnson & Son, Inc.; *U.S. Private*, pg. 3516
JOHNSON WAX NEW ZEALAND LIMITED—See S.C. Johnson & Son, Inc.; *U.S. Private*, pg. 3516
JOHNSON WAX NIGERIA LIMITED—See S.C. Johnson & Son, Inc.; *U.S. Private*, pg. 3516
JOHNSON WAX S.P.A.—See S.C. Johnson & Son, Inc.; *U.S. Private*, pg. 3516
JOHNSON WESTERN GUNITE COMPANY; *U.S. Private*, pg. 2229
JOHN STAURULAKIS, LLC; *U.S. Private*, pg. 2224
JOHNSTECH INTERNATIONAL CORP.; *U.S. Private*, pg. 2229
JOHN STEWART CO. INC.; *U.S. Private*, pg. 2224
JOHN ST. INC.—See WPP plc; *Int'l*, pg. 8465
JOHNSTON BOILER COMPANY INC.—See Hines Corporation; *U.S. Private*, pg. 1949
JOHNSTON BROTHERS FARM; *U.S. Private*, pg. 2229
JOHNSTON BUILDERS LTD.; *Int'l*, pg. 3993
JOHNSTON COCA-COLA BOTTLING GROUP, INC.—See The Coca-Cola Company; *U.S. Public*, pg. 2065
JOHNSTONE FOODS INC.; *U.S. Private*, pg. 2230
JOHNSTON ENTERPRISES INC.; *U.S. Private*, pg. 2229
JOHNSTON ENTERPRISES INC.; *U.S. Private*, pg. 2230
JOHNSTONE SUPPLY INC.; *U.S. Private*, pg. 2230
JOHNSTONE SUPPLY, INC.—See Johnstone Supply Inc.; *U.S. Private*, pg. 2230
JOHNSTONE SUPPLY; *U.S. Private*, pg. 2230
JOHNSTON (FALKIRK) LTD—See JPIMedia Holdings Limited; *Int'l*, pg. 4006
JOHNSTON INDUSTRIAL SUPPLY, INC.; *U.S. Private*, pg. 2230
JOHNSTON INDUSTRIAL SUPPLY INC.; *U.S. Private*, pg. 2230
JOHNSTON INTEGRATION TECHNOLOGY LLC—See Johnston Industrial Supply Inc.; *U.S. Private*, pg. 2230
JOHNSTON, LEMON & CO. INC.; *U.S. Private*, pg. 2230
JOHNSTON LETTERBOX DIRECT LTD—See JPIMedia Holdings Limited; *Int'l*, pg. 4006
JOHNSTON LEWIS ASSOCIATES, INC.—See Hellman & Friedman LLC; *U.S. Private*, pg. 1909
JOHNSTON MOTOR SALES CO. LTD; *Int'l*, pg. 3993
JOHNSTON & MURPHY CO.—See Genesco Inc.; *U.S. Public*, pg. 930
JOHNSTON & MURPHY RETAIL/WHOLESALE STORES—See Genesco Inc.; *U.S. Public*, pg. 930
JOHNSTON NORTH AMERICA INC—See Bucher Industries AG; *Int'l*, pg. 1208
JOHNSTON PRESS PLC—See JPIMedia Holdings Limited; *Int'l*, pg. 4006
JOHNSTON PUBLISHING LTD—See JPIMedia Holdings Limited; *Int'l*, pg. 4006
JOHNSTON QUARRY GROUP LIMITED—See SigmaRoc Plc; *Int'l*, pg. 6909
JOHNSTON SUPPLY INC.; *U.S. Private*, pg. 2230
JOHNSTON SWEEPERS LTD—See Bucher Industries AG; *Int'l*, pg. 1208
JOHNSTON TEXTILES, INC.—See Meriturn Partners, LLC; *U.S. Private*, pg. 2675
JOHNSTON-TOMBIGBEE FURNITURE MFG. CO.—See Lounora Industries Inc.; *U.S. Private*, pg. 2500
JOHNSTONWELLS PUBLIC RELATIONS; *U.S. Private*, pg. 2230
JOHNSTOWN AMERICA, LLC—See FreightCar America, Inc.; *U.S. Public*, pg. 885
JOHNSTOWN REGIONAL ENERGY LLC—See Leaf Clean Energy Company; *Int'l*, pg. 4434
JOHNSTOWN WELDING & FABRICATION; *U.S. Private*, pg. 2230
JOHNSTOWN WIRE TECHNOLOGIES, INC.—See GFG Alliance Limited; *Int'l*, pg. 2956
JOHN SULLIVAN AUTOMOTIVE GROUP; *U.S. Private*, pg. 2224
JOHN SUTAK INSURANCE BROKERS, INC.—See Brookfield Reinsurance Ltd.; *Int'l*, pg. 1194
JOHN SWAN LIMITED—See H&H Group plc; *Int'l*, pg. 3191
JOHN SWIRE & SONS (CHINA) LIMITED—See John Swire & Sons Limited; *Int'l*, pg. 3980

CORPORATE AFFILIATIONS

JOHN SWIRE & SONS (GREEN INVESTMENTS) LTD—See John Swire & Sons Limited; *Int'l*, pg. 3980
JOHN SWIRE & SONS INC.—See John Swire & Sons Limited; *Int'l*, pg. 3980
JOHN SWIRE & SONS LIMITED; *Int'l*, pg. 3979
JOHN SWIRE & SONS (PNG) LIMITED—See John Swire & Sons Limited; *Int'l*, pg. 3980
JOHN SWIRE & SONS PTY LTD—See John Swire & Sons Limited; *Int'l*, pg. 3980
JOHN SWIRE & SONS (S.E. ASIA) PTE LIMITED—See John Swire & Sons Limited; *Int'l*, pg. 3980
JOHN T. DAVIS OIL CO. INC; *U.S. Private*, pg. 2225
JOHN T. HOWE INC.; *U.S. Private*, pg. 2225
JOHN T. MATHER MEMORIAL HOSPITAL; *U.S. Private*, pg. 2225
JOHN TRAYLOR INSURANCE—See Advanta Insurance Partners; *U.S. Private*, pg. 93
JOHN T. VUCUREVICH FOUNDATION; *U.S. Private*, pg. 2225
JOHN VANCE MOTORS INC.; *U.S. Private*, pg. 2225
JOHN VARVATOS APPAREL CORP.—See Lion Capital LLP; *Int'l*, pg. 4517
JOHN VARVATOS ENTERPRISES, INC.—See Lion Capital LLP; *Int'l*, pg. 4517
JOHN V. HEINEMAN COMPANY—See Paragon Food Service; *U.S. Private*, pg. 3091
JOHN VOLPI & CO., INC.; *U.S. Private*, pg. 2225
JOHN V. SCHULTZ CO.; *U.S. Private*, pg. 2225
JOHN WAGNER ASSOCIATES, INC. - PACIFIC DIVISION—See John Wagner Associates, Inc.; *U.S. Private*, pg. 2225
JOHN WAGNER ASSOCIATES, INC.; *U.S. Private*, pg. 2225
JOHN WALKDEN ET COMPAGNIE S.A.—See General Atlantic Service Company, L.P.; *U.S. Private*, pg. 1661
JOHN W. DANFORTH CO.; *U.S. Private*, pg. 2225
JOHN W. DANFORTH SERVICE CO.—See JWD Group Inc.; *U.S. Private*, pg. 2247
JOHN WEISS & SON LTD.—See Metall Zug AG; *Int'l*, pg. 4847
JOHN WEST FOODS LTD.—See Thai Union Group Public Company Limited; *Int'l*, pg. 7596
JOHN WEST HOLLAND BV—See Thai Union Group Public Company Limited; *Int'l*, pg. 7596
JOHN W. GLEIM, JR. INC.; *U.S. Private*, pg. 2225
JOHN W. HENRY & COMPANY, INC.; *U.S. Private*, pg. 2225
JOHN WHILE SPRINGS (SHANGHAI) CO., LTD.—See Beijer Alma AB; *Int'l*, pg. 943
JOHN WIELAND HOMES & NEIGHBORHOODS, INC.—See PulteGroup, Inc.; *U.S. Public*, pg. 1737
JOHN WIESNER INC.; *U.S. Private*, pg. 2225
JOHN WILEY & SONS (ASIA) PTE. LTD.—See John Wiley & Sons, Inc.; *U.S. Public*, pg. 1192
JOHN WILEY & SONS AUSTRALIA, LTD.—See John Wiley & Sons, Inc.; *U.S. Public*, pg. 1192
JOHN WILEY & SONS AUSTRALIA, LTD.—See John Wiley & Sons, Inc.; *U.S. Public*, pg. 1193
JOHN WILEY & SONS CANADA, LTD.—See John Wiley & Sons, Inc.; *U.S. Public*, pg. 1192
JOHN WILEY & SONS COMMERCIAL SERVICE (BEIJING) CO., LTD.—See John Wiley & Sons, Inc.; *U.S. Public*, pg. 1192
JOHN WILEY & SONS GMBH—See John Wiley & Sons, Inc.; *U.S. Public*, pg. 1192
JOHN WILEY & SONS (HK) LIMITED—See John Wiley & Sons, Inc.; *U.S. Public*, pg. 1192
JOHN WILEY & SONS, INC. - SOMERSET—See John Wiley & Sons, Inc.; *U.S. Public*, pg. 1193
JOHN WILEY & SONS, INC.; *U.S. Public*, pg. 1192
JOHN WILEY & SONS INTERNATIONAL RIGHTS, INC.—See John Wiley & Sons, Inc.; *U.S. Public*, pg. 1193
JOHN WILEY & SONS LTD A/S—See John Wiley & Sons, Inc.; *U.S. Public*, pg. 1193
JOHN-WILLIAM FINE FURNITURE & INTERIORS INC.; *U.S. Private*, pg. 2225
JOHN W. MCDOUGALL CO. INC.; *U.S. Private*, pg. 2225
JOHN & WONG SECURITIES COMPANY LIMITED—See Imagi International Holdings Ltd.; *Int'l*, pg. 3618
JOHN WOOD COMPANY, LLC—See Dunes Point Capital, LLC; *U.S. Private*, pg. 1288
JOHN WOOD GROUP PLC; *Int'l*, pg. 3981
JOHN W. ROOKER & ASSOCIATES INC.; *U.S. Private*, pg. 2225
JOHN W. STONE OIL DISTRIBUTORS LLC; *U.S. Private*, pg. 2225
JOHN WYETH & BROTHER LIMITED—See Pfizer Inc.; *U.S. Public*, pg. 1680
JOHN XXIII HOME; *U.S. Private*, pg. 2225
JOHN ZINK COMPANY LLC—See Koch Industries, Inc.; *U.S. Private*, pg. 2331
JOHN ZINK INTERNATIONAL LUXEMBOURG S.A.R.L.—See Koch Industries, Inc.; *U.S. Private*, pg. 2331
JOHN ZINK KEU GMBH—See Koch Industries, Inc.; *U.S. Private*, pg. 2331
JOHOR BAHRU FLOUR MILL SDN BHD—See Kuok Brothers Sdn. Bhd.; *Int'l*, pg. 4335

COMPANY NAME INDEX

JOHOR CORPORATION; *Int'l*, pg. 3994
JOHOR LAND BERHAD—See Johor Corporation; *Int'l*, pg. 3994
JOHOR PORT BERHAD—See MMC Corporation Berhad; *Int'l*, pg. 5005
JOHOR SHIPYARD & ENGINEERING SDN BHD—See E.A Technique (M) Bhd; *Int'l*, pg. 2250
JOHOR SKILLS DEVELOPMENT CENTRE SDN BHD—See Johor Corporation; *Int'l*, pg. 3994
JOHOR SPECIALIST HOSPITAL SDN BHD—See KPJ Healthcare Berhad; *Int'l*, pg. 4296
JOHOSPACE CO., LTD.—See sMedio Inc.; *Int'l*, pg. 7007
JOH. PENGG AG—See Berndorf AG; *Int'l*, pg. 987
JOHS. LASSEN FJELLEBROEN A/S—See The Middleby Corporation; *U.S. Public*, pg. 2114
JOHTOTEC OY—See Fortum Oyj; *Int'l*, pg. 2741
JOICO LABORATORIES INC.—See Henkel AG & Co. KGaA; *Int'l*, pg. 3354
JOIE DE VIVRE HOSPITALITY, LLC—See Commune Hotels & Resorts, LLC; *U.S. Private*, pg. 987
JOIGNET; *Int'l*, pg. 3994
J-OIL MILLS INC.; *Int'l*, pg. 3854
JOINCARE PHARMACEUTICAL INDUSTRY GROUP CO., LTD; *Int'l*, pg. 3994
JOINDRE CAPITAL SERVICES LTD.; *Int'l*, pg. 3995
JOIN ENTERTAINMENT HOLDINGS, INC.; *U.S. Private*, pg. 2230
JOINET SRL—See UniCredit S.p.A.; *Int'l*, pg. 8034
JOINN LABORATORIES CA INC.—See Joinn Laboratories (China) Co., Ltd.; *Int'l*, pg. 3995
JOINN LABORATORIES (CHINA) CO., LTD.; *Int'l*, pg. 3995
JOINN MEDSAFE CO., LTD.—See Joinn Laboratories (China) Co., Ltd.; *Int'l*, pg. 3995
JOINSOON ELECTRONICS MANUFACTURING CO., LTD.; *Int'l*, pg. 3995
JOINTA GALUSHA LLC—See The D.A. Collins Construction Co., Inc.; *U.S. Private*, pg. 4017
JOINT ANALYTICAL SYSTEMS GMBH; *Int'l*, pg. 3995
THE JOINT CORP.; *U.S. Public*, pg. 2107
JOINTECA EDUCATION SOLUTIONS LTD; *Int'l*, pg. 3996
JOINTEX COMPANY—See PLUS Corporation; *Int'l*, pg. 5898
JOINTEX GARMENT MANUFACTORY LIMITED—See Speedy Global Holdings Limited; *Int'l*, pg. 7133
JOINT HOLDINGS/BASIC METAL INDUSTRIES, INC.; *U.S. Private*, pg. 2230
JOINT INSURANCE BROKER CO., LTD.—See China United Insurance Service, Inc.; *Int'l*, pg. 1561
JOINTOWN PHARMACEUTICAL GROUP CO., LTD.; *Int'l*, pg. 3996
JOINT PROPERTY CO., LTD.—See Haseko Corporation; *Int'l*, pg. 3283
JOINT RESEARCH & DEVELOPMENT, INC.—See Broadtree Partners, LLC; *U.S. Private*, pg. 659
JOINT RESOURCES JSC; *Int'l*, pg. 3995
JOINT RETAIL LOGISTICS LIMITED—See Deutsche Post AG; *Int'l*, pg. 2081
JOINT STOCK COMMERCIAL BANK INVESTMENT AND DEVELOPMENT OF VIETNAM; *Int'l*, pg. 3995
JOINT STOCK COMMERCIAL BANK OF VIETNAM; *Int'l*, pg. 3995
JOINT-STOCK COMPANY AEROCOMPOSIT-ULYANOVSK—See PJSC United Aircraft Corporation; *Int'l*, pg. 5885
JOINT STOCK COMPANY CONCERN AVTOMATIKA—See Russian Technologies State Corporation; *Int'l*, pg. 6431
JOINT STOCK COMPANY HUNTSMAN-NMG B.V.—See Huntsman Corporation; *U.S. Public*, pg. 1075
JOINT-STOCK COMPANY INTER RAO - ELECTRICITY PLANTS—See JSC INTER RAO UES; *Int'l*, pg. 4009
JOINT-STOCK COMPANY KAPO-COMPOSIT—See PJSC United Aircraft Corporation; *Int'l*, pg. 5885
JOINT-STOCK COMPANY KAZAKHSTAN ELECTRICITY GRID OPERATING COMPANY; *Int'l*, pg. 3996
JOINT-STOCK COMPANY OLAINFARM KAZAKHSTAN—See AS Olainfarm; *Int'l*, pg. 590
JOINTSTOCK COMPANY RSHB-INSURANCE—See Russian Agricultural Bank JSC; *Int'l*, pg. 6430
JOINT-STOCK COMPANY TOMSK DISTRIBUTION COMPANY—See JSC ROSSETI; *Int'l*, pg. 4010
JOINT STOCK INSURANCE COMPANY WINNER-VIENNA INSURANCE GROUP—See Vienna Insurance Group AG Wiener Versicherung Gruppe; *Int'l*, pg. 8195
JOINT SUCCESS ENTERPRISES LIMITED—See Walsin Lihwa Corporation; *Int'l*, pg. 8335
JOINT VENTURE ITALKYR CLOSED JOINT STOCK COMPANY—See Hyatt Hotels Corporation; *U.S. Public*, pg. 1078
JOINT VENTURE MARKETING & COMMUNICATIONS; *U.S. Private*, pg. 2230
JOINT VENTURE PIPING INC.; *U.S. Private*, pg. 2230
JOINT VENTURE SUNRISE LOGISTICS CO., LTD.—See Mitsui-Soko Holdings Co., Ltd.; *Int'l*, pg. 4992
JOISER HOCH- UND TIEFBAU GMBH—See PORR AG; *Int'l*, pg. 5923
JOI'X CORPORATION—See ITOCHU Corporation; *Int'l*, pg. 3840

JOJO'S PIZZA KITCHEN INC.—See American Restaurant Holdings, Inc.; *U.S. Private*, pg. 246
JOKAKE CONSTRUCTION COMPANY; *U.S. Private*, pg. 2230
JO-KELL INCORPORATED; *U.S. Private*, pg. 2217
JOKILAAKSON PERHEKODIT OY—See Humana AB; *Int'l*, pg. 3530
JOKKI CO., LTD.—See Kyokuyo Co. Ltd.; *Int'l*, pg. 4363
JOKWANG I.L.I CO., LTD.; *Int'l*, pg. 3996
JOLIET AREA COMMUNITY HOSPICE; *U.S. Private*, pg. 2230
JOLIET SURGERY CENTER LIMITED PARTNERSHIP—See UnitedHealth Group Incorporated; *U.S. Public*, pg. 2242
JOLIFE AB—See Stryker Corporation; *U.S. Public*, pg. 1956
JOLIMARK HOLDINGS LIMITED; *Int'l*, pg. 3996
JOLIMARK (S) PTE. LTD.—See Jolimark Holdings Limited; *Int'l*, pg. 3996
JOLINA CAPITAL INC.; *Int'l*, pg. 3996
JOLLEY TROLLEY TRANSPORTATION OF CLEARWATER, INC.; *U.S. Private*, pg. 2230
JOLLIBEAN FOODS PTE LTD—See Berjaya Corporation Berhad; *Int'l*, pg. 984
JOLLIBEE FOODS CORPORATION; *Int'l*, pg. 3996
JOLLIBEE VIETNAM CO., LTD—See Jollibee Foods Corporation; *Int'l*, pg. 3996
JOLLIVILLE HOLDINGS CORPORATION; *Int'l*, pg. 3996
JOLLMAX COATING OY—See SP Group A/S; *Int'l*, pg. 7122
JOLLY BOARD LTD.; *Int'l*, pg. 3996
JOLLY BUYER ACQUISITION GMBH—See Artivion, Inc.; *U.S. Public*, pg. 208
JOLLY GARDENER PRODUCTS INC.—See CRH plc; *Int'l*, pg. 1846
JOLLY-PASTA CO., LTD.—See Zensho Holdings Co., Ltd.; *Int'l*, pg. 8634
JOLLY ROGER (AMUSEMENT RIDES) LIMITED—See ME Group International plc; *Int'l*, pg. 4762
JOLLY ROOFING & CONTRACTING CO., INC.; *U.S. Private*, pg. 2230
JOLODA HYDRAROLL LIMITED; *Int'l*, pg. 3996
JOLOHA ENTERPRISES, INC.—See Word Systems, Inc.; *U.S. Private*, pg. 4563
JOLOKIA CORPORATION—See Nextech3D.AI Corporation; *Int'l*, pg. 5249
JOLSEN MILJOPARK AS—See AF Gruppen ASA; *Int'l*, pg. 184
JOLT CAPITAL SAS; *Int'l*, pg. 3996
JOLT HEALTH INC.—See Uniserve Communications Corporation; *Int'l*, pg. 8061
JOLT ONLINE GAMING LIMITED (IRELAND)—See GameStop Corp.; *U.S. Public*, pg. 896
JOLYWOOD SUZHOU SUNWATT CO., LTD.; *Int'l*, pg. 3997
JOMAC CANADA—See Berkshire Hathaway Inc.; *U.S. Public*, pg. 311
JOMAR GROUP LTD.; *U.S. Private*, pg. 2230
JOMAR INVESTMENTS; *U.S. Private*, pg. 2231
JOMAR INVESTMENTS LC; *U.S. Private*, pg. 2230
JOMAR TEXTILES INC.; *U.S. Private*, pg. 2231
JOMATEL - EMPRESA DE MATERIAIS DE CONSTRUCAO S.A.—See Camargo Correa S.A.; *Int'l*, pg. 1268
JOMAX CONSTRUCTION COMPANY; *U.S. Private*, pg. 2231
JOMAX DRILLING (1988) LTD.; *Int'l*, pg. 3997
JOMIRA/ADVANCE; *U.S. Private*, pg. 2231
JOMIRA.COM—See Jomira/Advance; *U.S. Private*, pg. 2231
JOMO ELECTRIC RAILWAY CO., LTD.—See Tobu Railway Co., Ltd.; *Int'l*, pg. 7771
JOMO-NET CO., LTD.—See ENEOS Holdings, Inc.; *Int'l*, pg. 2417
JOMO RETAIL SERVICE CO., LTD.—See ENEOS Holdings, Inc.; *Int'l*, pg. 2417
J.O. MORY INC.; *U.S. Private*, pg. 2169
JOMOS BRANDSCHUTZ AG—See VINCI S.A.; *Int'l*, pg. 8223
JOMOS EUROSPRINKLER AG—See VINCI S.A.; *Int'l*, pg. 8223
JOM PHARMACEUTICAL SERVICES, INC.—See Johnson & Johnson; *U.S. Public*, pg. 1196
JONAN ENVIRONMENT TECHNOLOGY CO., LTD.—See Hitachi Zosen Corporation; *Int'l*, pg. 3411
JONAS BROWNE AND HUBBARD (GRENADA) LIMITED—See Goddard Enterprises Limited; *Int'l*, pg. 3019
JONAS & CO., LTD.—See Bain Capital, LP; *U.S. Private*, pg. 444
JONAS COMPUTING (UK) LTD.—See Constellation Software Inc.; *Int'l*, pg. 1773
JONAS MEDIZINTECHNIK HANDELS GMBH—See L'Air Liquide S.A.; *Int'l*, pg. 4374
JONAS PAUL EYEWEAR, LLC; *U.S. Private*, pg. 2231
JONAS SOFTWARE LTD.—See Constellation Software Inc.; *Int'l*, pg. 1773
JONATHAN ENGINEERED SOLUTIONS, CORP.—See JLL Partners, Inc.; *U.S. Private*, pg. 2212
JONATHAN GREEN & SONS; *U.S. Private*, pg. 2231

JONATHAN HIND FINANCIAL GROUP—See Principal Financial Group, Inc.; *U.S. Public*, pg. 1721
JONATHAN'S CO., LTD.—See Bain Capital, LP; *U.S. Private*, pg. 444
JONATHAN'S LANDING, INC.; *U.S. Private*, pg. 2231
JONATHAN'S PLACE; *U.S. Private*, pg. 2231
JON BYK ADVERTISING, INC.; *U.S. Private*, pg. 2231
JONDETECH SENSORS AB; *Int'l*, pg. 3997
JON-DON, LLC—See Incline MGMT Corp.; *U.S. Private*, pg. 2053
JONEN CORPORATION—See TAKAMISAWA CO., LTD.; *Int'l*, pg. 7430
JONES APPAREL GROUP CANADA, LP—See Premier Brands Group Holdings LLC; *U.S. Private*, pg. 3249
JONES BARCLAY BOSTON—See Clayton, Dubilier & Rice, LLC; *U.S. Private*, pg. 923
JONES BARCLAY BOSTON—See Stone Point Capital LLC; *U.S. Private*, pg. 3824
JONES & BARTLETT LEARNING, LLC—See Blackstone Inc.; *U.S. Public*, pg. 348
JONES & BARTLETT LEARNING, LLC—See Canada Pension Plan Investment Board; *Int'l*, pg. 1279
JONES-BLAIR COMPANY, LLC—See Hempel A/S; *Int'l*, pg. 3341
JONES BROS. DIRT & PAVING CONTRACTORS, INC.; *U.S. Private*, pg. 2231
JONES BROTHERS COMPANY INC.; *U.S. Private*, pg. 2231
JONES BROWN INC.—See Arthur J. Gallagher & Co.; *U.S. Public*, pg. 206
JONES CAPITAL, LLC; *U.S. Private*, pg. 2231
JONES CHEVROLET INCORPORATED; *U.S. Private*, pg. 2232
JONES COMMUNICATIONS, INC.—See Comcast Corporation; *U.S. Public*, pg. 538
JONES COMPANIES LTD.; *U.S. Private*, pg. 2232
JONES COMPANY, INC.; *U.S. Private*, pg. 2232
JONES COMPANY—See Nationwide Argosy Solutions, LLC; *U.S. Private*, pg. 2865
JONES & COOK STATIONERS, INC.—See Gateway Printing & Office Supply, Inc.; *U.S. Private*, pg. 1651
JONES CYBER SOLUTIONS, LTD.—See Jones International University; *U.S. Private*, pg. 2233
JONES DAIRY FARM; *U.S. Private*, pg. 2232
JONES DAY; *U.S. Private*, pg. 2232
JONES DEALERSHIPS; *U.S. Private*, pg. 2233
JONES EDMUNDS & ASSOCIATES, INC.; *U.S. Private*, pg. 2233
JONES E-GLOBAL LIBRARY, INC.—See Jones International University; *U.S. Private*, pg. 2233
JONES ENERGY FINANCE CORP.—See Jones Energy, Inc.; *U.S. Private*, pg. 2233
JONES ENERGY, INC.; *U.S. Private*, pg. 2233
JONES ENTERPRISES INC.; *U.S. Private*, pg. 2233
JONES FIBER PRODUCTS INC.—See Jones Companies Ltd.; *U.S. Private*, pg. 2232
JONES FISH HATCHERIES & DISTRIBUTORS, LLC—See Fort Point Capital, LLC; *U.S. Private*, pg. 1574
JONES FORD, INC.; *U.S. Private*, pg. 2233
JONES & FORREST, INC.—See Common Interest Management Services Inc.; *U.S. Private*, pg. 986
JONES-HAMILTON CO.; *U.S. Private*, pg. 2234
JONES HOMES (NORTHERN) LIMITED—See Emerson Developments (Holdings) Limited; *Int'l*, pg. 2379
JONES HOMES (SOUTHERN) LIMITED—See Emerson Developments (Holdings) Limited; *Int'l*, pg. 2380
JONES INTERACTIVE, INC.—See Jones International University; *U.S. Private*, pg. 2233
JONES INTERNATIONAL LIMITED—See Premier Brands Group Holdings LLC; *U.S. Private*, pg. 3249
JONES INTERNATIONAL UNIVERSITY; *U.S. Private*, pg. 2233
JONES & JONES INC.; *U.S. Private*, pg. 2231
JONES JUNCTION AUTO GROUP; *U.S. Private*, pg. 2233
JONES KING LAWYERS PTY LTD—See Collection House Limited; *Int'l*, pg. 1699
JONES KNOWLEDGE GROUP, INC.—See Jones International University; *U.S. Private*, pg. 2233
JONES KNOWLEDGE, INC.—See Jones International University; *U.S. Private*, pg. 2233
JONES LANG LASALLE AB—See Jones Lang LaSalle Incorporated; *U.S. Public*, pg. 1202
JONES LANG LASALLE (ACT INTEGRATED) PTY LIMITED—See Jones Lang LaSalle Incorporated; *U.S. Public*, pg. 1202
JONES LANG LASALLE (ACT) PTY LIMITED—See Jones Lang LaSalle Incorporated; *U.S. Public*, pg. 1202
JONES LANG LASALLE AG—See Jones Lang LaSalle Incorporated; *U.S. Public*, pg. 1202
JONES LANG LASALLE AMERICAS, INC; *U.S. Private*, pg. 2233
JONES LANG LASALLE AP LIMITED—See Jones Lang LaSalle Incorporated; *U.S. Public*, pg. 1203
JONES LANG LASALLE ARIZONA, LLC—See Jones Lang LaSalle Incorporated; *U.S. Public*, pg. 1202
JONES LANG LASALLE - ATLANTA—See Jones Lang LaSalle Incorporated; *U.S. Public*, pg. 1202

JONES LANG LASALLE AMERICAS, INC
CORPORATE AFFILIATIONS
Company Index

JONES LANG LASALLE AUSTRALIA PTY. LIMITED—See Jones Lang LaSalle Incorporated; *U.S. Public*, pg. 1202
JONES LANG LASALLE (BEIJING) CO., LTD.—See Jones Lang LaSalle Incorporated; *U.S. Public*, pg. 1202
JONES LANG LASALLE BV—See Jones Lang LaSalle Incorporated; *U.S. Public*, pg. 1205
JONES LANG LASALLE (CHINA) LIMITED—See Jones Lang LaSalle Incorporated; *U.S. Public*, pg. 1202
JONES LANG LASALLE CO., LTD.—See Jones Lang LaSalle Incorporated; *U.S. Public*, pg. 1203
JONES LANG LASALLE CONSTRUCTION COMPANY, INC.—See Jones Lang LaSalle Incorporated; *U.S. Public*, pg. 1203
JONES LANG LASALLE CORPORATE FINANCE LIMITED—See Jones Lang LaSalle Incorporated; *U.S. Public*, pg. 1203
JONES LANG LASALLE D.O.O.—See Jones Lang LaSalle Incorporated; *U.S. Public*, pg. 1205
JONES LANG LASALLE ESPANA, S.A.—See Jones Lang LaSalle Incorporated; *U.S. Public*, pg. 1203
JONES LANG LASALLE EUROPE LIMITED—See Jones Lang LaSalle Incorporated; *U.S. Public*, pg. 1203
JONES LANG LASALLE FACILITIES KABUSHIKI KAISHA—See Jones Lang LaSalle Incorporated; *U.S. Public*, pg. 1203
JONES LANG LASALLE FINLAND OY—See Jones Lang LaSalle Incorporated; *U.S. Public*, pg. 1203
JONES LANG LASALLE GAYRIMENKUL HIZMETLERI TICARET ANONIM SIRKETI—See Jones Lang LaSalle Incorporated; *U.S. Public*, pg. 1203
JONES LANG LASALLE (GENEVA) SA—See Jones Lang LaSalle Incorporated; *U.S. Public*, pg. 1202
JONES LANG LASALLE GLOBAL FINANCE LUXEMBOURG SARL—See Jones Lang LaSalle Incorporated; *U.S. Public*, pg. 1203
JONES LANG LASALLE GLOBAL SERVICES - RR, INC.—See Jones Lang LaSalle Incorporated; *U.S. Public*, pg. 1203
JONES LANG LASALLE HOLDINGS BV—See Jones Lang LaSalle Incorporated; *U.S. Public*, pg. 1203
JONES LANG LASALLE HOTELS & HOSPITALITY—See Jones Lang LaSalle Incorporated; *U.S. Public*, pg. 1203
JONES LANG LASALLE HOTELS (NSW) PTY LIMITED—See Jones Lang LaSalle Incorporated; *U.S. Public*, pg. 1203
JONES LANG LASALLE HOTELS (QLD) PTY LIMITED—See Jones Lang LaSalle Incorporated; *U.S. Public*, pg. 1203
JONES LANG LASALLE - HOUSTON—See Jones Lang LaSalle Incorporated; *U.S. Public*, pg. 1202
JONES LANG LASALLE INCORPORATED; *U.S. Public*, pg. 1201
JONES LANG LASALLE (INDIA) PRIVATE LIMITED—See Jones Lang LaSalle Incorporated; *U.S. Public*, pg. 1202
JONES LANG LASALLE INVESTMENT MANAGEMENT—See Jones Lang LaSalle Incorporated; *U.S. Public*, pg. 1203
JONES LANG LASALLE ISRAEL LIMITED—See Jones Lang LaSalle Incorporated; *U.S. Public*, pg. 1204
JONES LANG LASALLE KABUSHKI KAISHA—See Jones Lang LaSalle Incorporated; *U.S. Public*, pg. 1204
JONES LANG LASALLE KENYA LTD—See Jones Lang LaSalle Incorporated; *U.S. Public*, pg. 1204
JONES LANG LASALLE KFT—See Jones Lang LaSalle Incorporated; *U.S. Public*, pg. 1204
JONES LANG LASALLE LANKA (PRIVATE) LIMITED—See Jones Lang LaSalle Incorporated; *U.S. Public*, pg. 1204
JONES LANG LASALLE LIMITED LIABILITY COMPANY—See Jones Lang LaSalle Incorporated; *U.S. Public*, pg. 1204
JONES LANG LASALLE LIMITED—See Jones Lang LaSalle Incorporated; *U.S. Public*, pg. 1204
JONES LANG LASALLE LIMITED—See Jones Lang LaSalle Incorporated; *U.S. Public*, pg. 1204
JONES LANG LASALLE LLC—See Jones Lang LaSalle Incorporated; *U.S. Public*, pg. 1204
JONES LANG LASALLE LLP—See Jones Lang LaSalle Incorporated; *U.S. Public*, pg. 1204
JONES LANG LASALLE LTD.—See Jones Lang LaSalle Incorporated; *U.S. Public*, pg. 1204
JONES LANG LASALLE LTD—See Jones Lang LaSalle Incorporated; *U.S. Public*, pg. 1204
JONES LANG LASALLE (LUXEMBOURG) SECS—See Jones Lang LaSalle Incorporated; *U.S. Public*, pg. 1205
JONES LANG LASALLE MACHINERY & BUSINESS ASSETS LIMITED—See Jones Lang LaSalle Incorporated; *U.S. Public*, pg. 1203
JONES LANG LASALLE MICHIGAN, LLC—See Jones Lang LaSalle Incorporated; *U.S. Public*, pg. 1204
JONES LANG LASALLE (NSW) PTY LIMITED—See Jones Lang LaSalle Incorporated; *U.S. Public*, pg. 1203
JONES LANG LASALLE OF NEW YORK, LLC—See Jones Lang LaSalle Incorporated; *U.S. Public*, pg. 1205
JONES LANG LASALLE (PHILIPPINES), INC.—See Jones Lang LaSalle Incorporated; *U.S. Public*, pg. 1202
JONES LANG LASALLE PROPERTY CONSULTANTS PTE LTD—See Jones Lang LaSalle Incorporated; *U.S. Public*, pg. 1204
JONES LANG LASALLE (PUERTO RICO), INC.—See Jones Lang LaSalle Incorporated; *U.S. Public*, pg. 1202
JONES LANG LASALLE (QLD) PTY LIMITED—See Jones Lang LaSalle Incorporated; *U.S. Public*, pg. 1203
JONES LANG LASALLE REAL ESTATE SERVICES INCORPORATED—See Jones Lang LaSalle Incorporated; *U.S. Public*, pg. 1204
JONES LANG LASALLE REAL ESTATE SERVICES, INC.—See Jones Lang LaSalle Incorporated; *U.S. Public*, pg. 1204
JONES LANG LASALLE RESIDENTIAL DEVELOPMENT GMBH—See Jones Lang LaSalle Incorporated; *U.S. Public*, pg. 1204
JONES LANG LASALLE RESIDENTIAL PRIVATE LIMITED—See Jones Lang LaSalle Incorporated; *U.S. Public*, pg. 1204
JONES LANG LASALLE - SAN DIEGO—See Jones Lang LaSalle Incorporated; *U.S. Public*, pg. 1202
JONES LANG LASALLE (SA) PTY LIMITED—See Jones Lang LaSalle Incorporated; *U.S. Public*, pg. 1203
JONES LANG LASALLE SARL—See Jones Lang LaSalle Incorporated; *U.S. Public*, pg. 1204
JONES LANG LASALLE S.A.—See Jones Lang LaSalle Incorporated; *U.S. Public*, pg. 1204
JONES LANG LASALLE SAS—See Jones Lang LaSalle Incorporated; *U.S. Public*, pg. 1204
JONES LANG LASALLE SAUDI ARABIA LIMITED—See Jones Lang LaSalle Incorporated; *U.S. Public*, pg. 1204
JONES LANG LASALLE (SCOTLAND) LIMITED—See Jones Lang LaSalle Incorporated; *U.S. Public*, pg. 1203
JONES LANG LASALLE - SEATTLE—See Jones Lang LaSalle Incorporated; *U.S. Public*, pg. 1202
JONES LANG LASALLE SECS—See Jones Lang LaSalle Incorporated; *U.S. Public*, pg. 1204
JONES LANG LASALLE SERVICES AB—See Jones Lang LaSalle Incorporated; *U.S. Public*, pg. 1204
JONES LANG LASALLE SE—See Jones Lang LaSalle Incorporated; *U.S. Public*, pg. 1204
JONES LANG LASALLE - SILICON VALLEY—See Jones Lang LaSalle Incorporated; *U.S. Public*, pg. 1202
JONES LANG LASALLE, SOCIEDAD ANONIMA DE CAPITAL VARIABLE—See Jones Lang LaSalle Incorporated; *U.S. Public*, pg. 1205
JONES LANG LASALLE, SOCIEDADE DE MEDIACAO IMOBILIARIA, S.A.—See Jones Lang LaSalle Incorporated; *U.S. Public*, pg. 1205
JONES LANG LASALLE SOUTH AFRICA (PROPRIETARY) LTD—See Jones Lang LaSalle Incorporated; *U.S. Public*, pg. 1204
JONES LANG LASALLE S.P.A.—See Jones Lang LaSalle Incorporated; *U.S. Public*, pg. 1204
JONES LANG LASALLE SPOKA Z OGRANICZON ODPOWIEDZIALNOCECI—See Jones Lang LaSalle Incorporated; *U.S. Public*, pg. 1205
JONES LANG LASALLE SPRL—See Jones Lang LaSalle Incorporated; *U.S. Public*, pg. 1205
JONES LANG LASALLE SP. Z O.O.—See Jones Lang LaSalle Incorporated; *U.S. Public*, pg. 1204
JONES LANG LASALLE S.R.L.—See Jones Lang LaSalle Incorporated; *U.S. Public*, pg. 1204
JONES LANG LASALLE SRL—See Jones Lang LaSalle Incorporated; *U.S. Public*, pg. 1205
JONES LANG LASALLE S.R.O—See Jones Lang LaSalle Incorporated; *U.S. Public*, pg. 1205
JONES LANG LASALLE SSC (PHILIPPINES), INC.—See Jones Lang LaSalle Incorporated; *U.S. Public*, pg. 1204
JONES LANG LASALLE TAIWAN LIMITED—See Jones Lang LaSalle Incorporated; *U.S. Public*, pg. 1205
JONES LANG LASALLE - TEXAS, INC.—See Jones Lang LaSalle Incorporated; *U.S. Public*, pg. 1202
JONES LANG LASALLE (THAILAND) LIMITED—See Jones Lang LaSalle Incorporated; *U.S. Public*, pg. 1202
JONES LANG LASALLE UAE LIMITED—See Jones Lang LaSalle Incorporated; *U.S. Public*, pg. 1205
JONES LANG LASALLE (VIC) PTY LIMITED—See Jones Lang LaSalle Incorporated; *U.S. Public*, pg. 1203
JONES LANG LASALLE VIETNAM COMPANY LIMITED—See Jones Lang LaSalle Incorporated; *U.S. Public*, pg. 1205
JONES LANG LASALLE (WA) PTY LIMITED—See Jones Lang LaSalle Incorporated; *U.S. Public*, pg. 1203
JONES & LANIER ELECTRIC INC.; *U.S. Private*, pg. 2231
JONES LOGISTICS, LLC—See Jones Capital, LLC; *U.S. Private*, pg. 2232
JONES LUMBER COMPANY—See Bain Capital, LP; *U.S. Private*, pg. 451
JONES MANAGEMENT SERVICES, LLC—See Check Into Cash Inc.; *U.S. Private*, pg. 869
JONES, MARESCA & MCQUADE, P.A.; *U.S. Private*, pg. 2234
JONES MEDIA, INC.—See Adams Publishing Group, LLC; *U.S. Private*, pg. 75
JONES MEMORIAL HOSPITAL; *U.S. Private*, pg. 2233
JONES METAL PRODUCTS CO.; *U.S. Private*, pg. 2233
JONES & MITCHELL SPORTSWEAR—See Boxercraft Incorporated; *U.S. Private*, pg. 626
JONES MOTOR CO. INC.; *U.S. Private*, pg. 2233
JONES MOTOR CO., INC.—See Transport Investments, Inc.; *U.S. Private*, pg. 4210
JONES MOTOR GROUP, INC.—See Transport Investments, Inc.; *U.S. Private*, pg. 4210
JONES NEW YORK OUTERWEAR—See Amerex Group, Inc.; *U.S. Private*, pg. 219
JONES OIL CO. INC.; *U.S. Private*, pg. 2233
JONES-ONSLOW ELECTRIC MEMBERSHIP CORPORATION; *U.S. Private*, pg. 2234
JONES PACKAGING INC.; *Int'l*, pg. 3997
JONES PAINT & GLASS INC.; *U.S. Private*, pg. 2233
JONES PERINI JOINT VENTURE; *U.S. Private*, pg. 2233
JONES PETROLEUM COMPANY, INC.; *U.S. Private*, pg. 2233
JONES PLASTIC & ENGINEERING COMPANY, LLC - CAMDEN DIVISION—See Jones Plastic & Engineering Company, LLC; *U.S. Private*, pg. 2233
JONES PLASTIC & ENGINEERING COMPANY, LLC - JEFFERSONTOWN DIVISION—See Jones Plastic & Engineering Company, LLC; *U.S. Private*, pg. 2233
JONES PLASTIC & ENGINEERING COMPANY, LLC; *U.S. Private*, pg. 2233
JONES PLASTIC & ENGINEERING COMPANY, LLC - WILLIAMSBURG DIVISION—See Jones Plastic & Engineering Company, LLC; *U.S. Private*, pg. 2233
JONES PLASTIC & ENGINEERING DE MONTERREY, S.A. DE C.V.—See Jones Plastic & Engineering Company, LLC; *U.S. Private*, pg. 2234
JONES PRODUCE, INC.; *U.S. Private*, pg. 2234
JONES PROGRAMMING SERVICES, INC.—See Jones International University; *U.S. Private*, pg. 2233
JONES PROPERTIES, INC.—See Jones International University; *U.S. Private*, pg. 2233
JONES PROPERTIES, LLC—See Check Into Cash Inc.; *U.S. Private*, pg. 869
JONES PUBLIC AFFAIRS, INC.; *U.S. Private*, pg. 2234
JONES & SHIPMAN HARDINGE LIMITED—See Privet Fund Management, LLC; *U.S. Private*, pg. 3269
JONES & SHIPMAN S.A.R.L.—See Privet Fund Management, LLC; *U.S. Private*, pg. 3269
JONES SIGN CO., INC.; *U.S. Private*, pg. 2234
JONES SODA (CANADA) INC.—See Jones Soda Company; *U.S. Public*, pg. 1206
JONES SODA COMPANY; *U.S. Public*, pg. 1206
JONES SPACELINK, LTD.—See Jones International University; *U.S. Private*, pg. 2233
JONES STORES INC.; *U.S. Private*, pg. 2234
JONES-STUCKEY LTD., INC.—See Pennoni Associates Inc.; *U.S. Private*, pg. 3136
JONES TECH PLC; *Int'l*, pg. 3997
JONESTOWN BANK & TRUST COMPANY; *U.S. Private*, pg. 2234
JONES TRACTOR & EQUIPMENT CO., INC.; *U.S. Private*, pg. 2234
JONESTRADING INSTITUTIONAL SERVICES LLC; *U.S. Private*, pg. 2234
JONES VENDING & OCS DISTRIBUTING INC.; *U.S. Private*, pg. 2234
JONES & VINING INC. - CHINA FACTORY—See Jones & Vining Inc.; *U.S. Private*, pg. 2231
JONES & VINING INC. - LASTS FACTORY—See Jones & Vining Inc.; *U.S. Private*, pg. 2231
JONES & VINING INC. - MAINE FACTORY—See Jones & Vining Inc.; *U.S. Private*, pg. 2231
JONES & VINING INC.; *U.S. Private*, pg. 2231
JONES & VINING INC. - TAIWAN TBC FACTORY—See Jones & Vining Inc.; *U.S. Private*, pg. 2231
JONES & VINING INC. - VIETNAM FACTORY—See Jones & Vining Inc.; *U.S. Private*, pg. 2231
JONES-WILSON INSURANCE & INVESTMENTS, INC.—See Inszone Insurance Services, LLC; *U.S. Private*, pg. 2096
JON F. SWIFT INC.; *U.S. Private*, pg. 2231
JONGENEEL B.V.—See Blackstone Inc.; *U.S. Public*, pg. 356
JON HALL CHEVROLET, INC.; *U.S. Private*, pg. 2231
JON HALL HONDA; *U.S. Private*, pg. 2231
JON HART DESIGN CO.; *U.S. Private*, pg. 2231
JONI AND FRIENDS; *U.S. Private*, pg. 2234
JONIX SPA; *Int'l*, pg. 3997
JONJEE HI-TECH INDUSTRIAL & COMMERCIAL HOLDING CO., LTD.; *Int'l*, pg. 3997
JONJUA OVERSEAS LIMITED; *Int'l*, pg. 3997
JONKER BETON B.V.—See CRH plc; *Int'l*, pg. 1845
JONMANDY CORP.—See Ball Chain Mfg Co, Inc.; *U.S. Private*, pg. 459

COMPANY NAME INDEX

JON MURDOCK, INC.; *U.S. Private*, pg. 2231
JONQUIL STEEL & CONSTRUCTION CO.; *U.S. Private*, pg. 2234
JONRIE INTERTECH LLC—See Markey Machine LLC; *U.S. Private*, pg. 2581
JONVIEW CANADA INC.—See H.I.S. Co., Ltd.; *Int'l*, pg. 3195
JOOEUN INDUSTRIAL CO., LTD.—See KB Financial Group Inc.; *Int'l*, pg. 4104
JOOEUN LEASING CO., LTD.—See KB Financial Group Inc.; *Int'l*, pg. 4104
JOOLI.COM GMBH—See Elumeo SE; *Int'l*, pg. 2371
JOONDALUP HOSPITAL PTY LIMITED—See Ramsay Health Care Limited; *Int'l*, pg. 6199
JOONGANG ADVANCED MATERIALS CO., LTD; *Int'l*, pg. 3997
JOONGANG DAILY NEWS CALIFORNIA INC.—See JoongAng Media Network Co. Ltd.; *Int'l*, pg. 3997
JOONG ANG ENERVIS CO., LTD.; *Int'l*, pg. 3997
JOONGANG MEDIA NETWORK CO. LTD.; *Int'l*, pg. 3997
JOORNEY LLC; *U.S. Private*, pg. 2234
JOOYONTECH CO., LTD. - GOYANG FACTORY—See Jooyontech Co., Ltd.; *Int'l*, pg. 3997
JOOYONTECH CO., LTD.; *Int'l*, pg. 3997
J.O. PHARMA CO., LTD.—See Earth Corporation; *Int'l*, pg. 2268
JOPLIN PETRO—See Iowa 80 Group, Inc.; *U.S. Private*, pg. 2134
JOPLIN SUPPLY COMPANY—See Harry Cooper Supply Company; *U.S. Private*, pg. 1871
JOP, OVE & MYRTHU—See Omnicom Group Inc.; *U.S. Public*, pg. 1591
JOP, OVE & MYRTHU—See Omnicom Group Inc.; *U.S. Public*, pg. 1591
JORBAN-RISCOE ASSOCIATES INC.; *U.S. Private*, pg. 2234
JORDACHE ENTERPRISES; *U.S. Private*, pg. 2235
JORDAN ACADEMY FOR MARITIME STUDIES—See Jordan Nation Shipping Lines P.L.C; *Int'l*, pg. 3999
JORDAN AHLI BANK; *Int'l*, pg. 3997
JORDAN AIRCRAFT MAINTENANCE LIMITED—See Dubai Aerospace Enterprise Ltd; *Int'l*, pg. 2218
JORDAN AND PALESTINE FINANCIAL INVESTMENT CO.—See The Housing Bank for Trade & Finance; *Int'l*, pg. 7653
THE JORDAN AUTOMOTIVE GROUP; *U.S. Private*, pg. 4059
JORDAN-BLANCHARD CAPITAL, LLC—See The Jordan Company; *U.S. Private*, pg. 4059
JORDAN BROMINE COMPANY LIMITED—See Albemarle Corporation; *U.S. Public*, pg. 73
JORDAN BUSINESSMEN ASSOCIATIONS CO., LTD.—See Jordan Loan Guarantee Corporation; *Int'l*, pg. 3998
JORDAN CAPITAL AM, LLC—See The Jordan Company; *U.S. Private*, pg. 4059
JORDAN CARBONATE CO.—See Omya (Schweiz) AG; *Int'l*, pg. 5570
JORDAN CEMENT FACTORIES COMPANY PSC; *Int'l*, pg. 3997
JORDAN CHEMICAL INDUSTRIES CO. LTD; *Int'l*, pg. 3997
JORDAN CHEMICALS COMPANY LTD.—See Jordan Poultry Processing & Marketing Co Ltd.; *Int'l*, pg. 3999
JORDAN & CO INTERNATIONAL LIMITED—See An Post LLC; *U.S. Private*, pg. 443
JORDAN COMMERCIAL BANK; *Int'l*, pg. 3997
THE JORDAN COMPANY CHINA—See The Jordan Company, L.P.; *U.S. Private*, pg. 4062
THE JORDAN COMPANY, L.P.; *U.S. Private*, pg. 4059
THE JORDAN COMPANY; *U.S. Private*, pg. 4059
JORDAN CREEK FINANCIAL SOLUTIONS—See Cambridge Investment Group, Inc.; *U.S. Private*, pg. 727
JORDAN DAIRY; *Int'l*, pg. 3998
JORDAN DECAPOLIS PROPERTIES PLC; *Int'l*, pg. 3998
THE JORDAN, EDMISTON GROUP, INC.; *U.S. Private*, pg. 4063
JORDAN EMIRATES INSURANCE COMPANY—See Al-Sagr National Insurance Company; *Int'l*, pg. 288
JORDAN EMIRATES INSURANCE P.S.C.; *Int'l*, pg. 3998
JORDAN EXPORTERS ASSOCIATION LTD.—See Jordan Loan Guarantee Corporation; *Int'l*, pg. 3999
JORDAN EXPORT PORTAL LTD.—See Jordan Loan Guarantee Corporation; *Int'l*, pg. 3998
JORDAN EXPRESS TOURIST TRANSPORTATION COMPANY; *Int'l*, pg. 3998
JORDAN FAMILY HEALTH, L.L.C.—See HCA Healthcare, Inc.; *U.S. Public*, pg. 999
JORDAN FEED COMPANY—See Jordan Poultry Processing & Marketing Co Ltd.; *Int'l*, pg. 3999
JORDAN FORD INC.; *U.S. Private*, pg. 2235
JORDAN FRENCH INSURANCE CO. (P.L.C.); *Int'l*, pg. 3998
JORDAN GROUP FOR SHIPPING AGENCIES CO. LTD.—See Jordan Nation Shipping Lines P.L.C; *Int'l*, pg. 3999
JORDAN HEALTH COST MANAGEMENT SERVICES W.L.L.—See Munchener Ruckversicherungs AG; *Int'l*, pg. 5089

JORDAN HEALTH SERVICES, INC.—See Kelso & Company, L.P.; *U.S. Private*, pg. 2278
JORDAN HOTELS & TOURISM P.L.C.—See Zara Investment Holding Company Ltd.; *Int'l*, pg. 8625
JORDAN HOUSE CARE AS—See Orkla ASA; *Int'l*, pg. 5638
JORDANIAN CO. FOR DEVELOPING AND FINANCIAL INVESTMENT; *Int'l*, pg. 4000
JORDANIAN DUTY FREE SHOPS; *Int'l*, pg. 4000
JORDANIAN ELECTRIC POWER COMPANY LIMITED; *Int'l*, pg. 4000
JORDANIAN EXPATRIATES INVESTMENT HOLDING PLC; *Int'l*, pg. 4000
JORDANIAN MANAGEMENT & CONSULTANCY COMPANY; *Int'l*, pg. 4000
JORDANIAN MUTUAL FUNDS MANAGEMENT COMPANY; *Int'l*, pg. 4000
THE JORDANIAN PHARMACEUTICAL MANUFACTURING CO., P.L.C.; *Int'l*, pg. 7660
JORDANIAN REALESTATE COMPANY FOR DEVELOPMENT PLC; *Int'l*, pg. 4000
JORDANIAN SWISS COMPANY FOR MANUFACTURING & MARKETING CONSTRUCTION CHEMICALS COMPANY LTD.—See BASF SE; *Int'l*, pg. 884
JORDAN ICE AND AERATED WATER LTD.—See PepsiCo, Inc.; *U.S. Public*, pg. 1669
JORDAN IMPLEMENTS CO.; *U.S. Private*, pg. 2235
JORDAN INDUSTRIAL RESOURCES CO. LTD.; *Int'l*, pg. 3998
JORDAN INDUSTRIES, INC.; *U.S. Private*, pg. 2235
JORDAN INSURANCE COMPANY; *Int'l*, pg. 3998
JORDAN INTERNATIONAL CHARTERING COMPANY—See Jordan Nation Shipping Lines P.L.C; *Int'l*, pg. 3999
JORDAN INTERNATIONAL INSURANCE CO.; *Int'l*, pg. 3998
JORDAN INTERNATIONAL INVESTMENT CO.; *Int'l*, pg. 3998
JORDAN INTERNATIONAL TRADING CENTER CO., LTD.; *Int'l*, pg. 3998
JORDAN INVESTMENT & TOURISM TRANSPORT CO; *Int'l*, pg. 3998
JORDAN INVESTMENT TRUST P.L.C.; *Int'l*, pg. 3998
JORDAN ISLAMIC BANK—See Al Baraka Banking Group B.S.C.; *Int'l*, pg. 276
JORDAN, JONES AND GOULDING, INC.—See Jacobs Engineering Group, Inc.; *U.S. Public*, pg. 1186
JORDAN-KITT MUSIC INC.; *U.S. Private*, pg. 2235
JORDAN KUWAIT BANK PLC; *Int'l*, pg. 3998
JORDAN LAKE PRESERVE CORPORATION—See Hilton Grand Vacations Inc.; *U.S. Public*, pg. 1039
JORDAN LOAN GUARANTEE CORPORATION; *Int'l*, pg. 3998
JORDAN LUMBER & SUPPLY INC.; *U.S. Private*, pg. 2235
JORDAN MAGNESIA COMPANY—See Arab Potash Company PLC; *Int'l*, pg. 531
JORDAN MANUFACTURING LIMITED—See Redhall Group plc; *Int'l*, pg. 6247
JORDAN MARBLE COMPANY; *Int'l*, pg. 3999
JORDAN MASAKEN FOR LAND DEVELOPMENT & INDUSTRIAL PROJECTS; *Int'l*, pg. 3999
JORDAN MILLS INC—See Ceres Global Ag Corp.; *U.S. Public*, pg. 475
JORDAN MORTGAGE REFINANCING COMPANY LTD; *Int'l*, pg. 3999
JORDAN MOTORS, INC.; *U.S. Private*, pg. 2235
JORDAN NATION SHIPPING LINES P.L.C; *Int'l*, pg. 3999
JORDAN OIL SHALE COMPANY B.V.—See Shell plc; *Int'l*, pg. 6795
JORDANO'S FOOD SERVICE, INC.—See Jordano's, Inc.; *U.S. Private*, pg. 2236
JORDANO'S, INC.; *U.S. Private*, pg. 2235
JORDAN PAPER & CARDBOARD FACTORIES CO. PLC; *Int'l*, pg. 3999
JORDAN PEINTURE SA—See Akzo Nobel N.V.; *Int'l*, pg. 269
JORDAN PETROLEUM REFINERY COMPANY; *Int'l*, pg. 3999
JORDAN PHOSPHATE MINES COMPANY LTD.; *Int'l*, pg. 3999
JORDAN PIPES MANUFACTURING CO., LTD.; *Int'l*, pg. 3999
JORDAN PLASTICS LIMITED—See Berry Global Group, Inc; *U.S. Public*, pg. 322
JORDAN POULTRY PROCESSING & MARKETING CO LTD.; *Int'l*, pg. 3999
JORDAN PRESS FOUNDATION PLC; *Int'l*, pg. 3999
JORDAN PROJECTS FOR TOURISM DEVELOPMENT COMPANY; *Int'l*, pg. 3999
JORDAN PROPERTIES LTD.—See The Israel Electric Corporation Ltd.; *Int'l*, pg. 7657
JORDAN REFLECTORS LTD.—See Jordan Reflektoren GmbH & Co. KG; *Int'l*, pg. 3999
JORDAN REFLEKTOREN GMBH & CO. KG; *Int'l*, pg. 3999
JORDAN RESES SUPPLY COMPANY—See First Nation Group LLC; *U.S. Public*, pg. 1521

JORDAN'S FURNITURE, INC.—See Berkshire Hathaway Inc.; *U.S. Public*, pg. 308
THE JORDANS & RYVITA COMPANY LIMITED—See The Garfield Weston Foundation; *Int'l*, pg. 7649
JORDAN STEEL; *Int'l*, pg. 3999
JORDAN TECHNOLOGIES, LLC—See Turnbridge Capital, LLC; *U.S. Private*, pg. 4260
JORDAN TELECOM; *Int'l*, pg. 3999
JORDAN TRADE FACILITIES COMPANY PLC; *Int'l*, pg. 4000
JORDAN TRADING INC.—See The Siam Cement Public Company Limited; *Int'l*, pg. 7685
JORDAN VALLEY SEMICONDUCTOR CO LTD.—See Bruker Corporation; *U.S. Public*, pg. 406
JORDAN VALLEY SEMICONDUCTORS, INC.—See Bruker Corporation; *U.S. Public*, pg. 406
JORDAN VALLEY SEMICONDUCTORS KOREA LTD.—See Bruker Corporation; *U.S. Public*, pg. 406
JORDAN VALLEY SEMICONDUCTORS, LTD.—See Bruker Corporation; *U.S. Public*, pg. 406
JORDAN VALLEY SEMICONDUCTORS UK, LTD.—See Bruker Corporation; *U.S. Public*, pg. 406
JORDAN VEGETABLE OIL INDUSTRIES COMPANY—See Arab Supply & Trading Co.; *Int'l*, pg. 532
JORDAN-WILCOMB CONSTRUCTION, INC.; *U.S. Private*, pg. 2235
JORDAN WOOD INDUSTRIES CO.; *Int'l*, pg. 4000
JORDAN WORSTED MILLS COMPANY; *Int'l*, pg. 4000
JORDAN/ZALAZNICK ADVISERS, INC.; *U.S. Private*, pg. 2235
JORDY-CARTER INC.; *U.S. Private*, pg. 2236
JORF LASFAR ENERGY COMPANY 5&6 S.A.—See Taqa Morocco SA; *Int'l*, pg. 7461
JORGENSEN CONVEYORS, INC.—See Innovance, Inc.; *U.S. Private*, pg. 2081
JORGENSEN ENGINEERING A/S—See XANO Industri AB; *Int'l*, pg. 8519
JORGENSEN ENGINEERING USA INC.—See XANO Industri AB; *Int'l*, pg. 8519
JORGENSEN'S INC.; *U.S. Private*, pg. 2236
JORGENSON OPTICAL SUPPLY CY.—See EssilorLuxottica SA; *Int'l*, pg. 2513
JORJIN TECHNOLOGIES, INC.; *Int'l*, pg. 4000
JORLEASE INC.—See Jordano's, Inc.; *U.S. Private*, pg. 2236
JORMAC AEROSPACE, INC.; *U.S. Private*, pg. 2236
JORO FASHIONS INCORPORATED; *U.S. Private*, pg. 2236
JORUDAN CO., LTD.; *Int'l*, pg. 4000
JOS. A. BANK CLOTHIERS, INC.—See Tailored Brands, Inc.; *U.S. Public*, pg. 1979
JOSAM COMPANY—See Watts Water Technologies, Inc.; *U.S. Public*, pg. 2337
JOSAM RICHTTECKNIK GMBH—See Snap-on Incorporated; *U.S. Public*, pg. 1897
JOSANICA A.D.; *Int'l*, pg. 4000
JOSAPAR - JOAQUIM OLIVEIRA S/A PARTICIPACOES; *Int'l*, pg. 4000
JOS DISTRIBUTION—See Jardine Matheson Holdings Limited; *Int'l*, pg. 3908
JOSE DE MELLO IMOBILIARIA, SGPS, S.A.—See Jose de Mello, SGPS, S.A.; *Int'l*, pg. 4001
JOSE DE MELLO SAUDE, S.G.P.S., S.A.—See Jose de Mello, SGPS, S.A.; *Int'l*, pg. 4001
JOSE DE MELLO, SGPS, S.A.; *Int'l*, pg. 4001
JOSEF BLASSINGER GMBH + CO. KG—See THK CO., LTD.; *Int'l*, pg. 7711
JOSEF GARTNER & CO. UK LTD.—See Atlas Holdings, LLC; *U.S. Private*, pg. 377
JOSEF GARTNER & CO. UK LTD.—See Atlas Holdings, LLC; *U.S. Private*, pg. 377
JOSEF GARTNER CURTAIN WALL (SHANGHAI) CO. LTD.—See Atlas Holdings, LLC; *U.S. Private*, pg. 377
JOSEF GARTNER CURTAIN WALL (SUZHOU) CO. LTD—See Atlas Holdings, LLC; *U.S. Private*, pg. 377
JOSEF GARTNER GMBH—See Atlas Holdings, LLC; *U.S. Private*, pg. 377
JOSEF GARTNER SWITZERLAND AG—See Atlas Holdings, LLC; *U.S. Private*, pg. 377
JOSEF KIHLBERG AB—See Illinois Tool Works Inc.; *U.S. Public*, pg. 1108
JOSEF LAGEDER—See Michael Weinig AG; *Int'l*, pg. 4874
JOSEF MANNER & COMP AG; *Int'l*, pg. 4001
JOSEF MANNER S.R.O.—See Josef Manner & Comp AG; *Int'l*, pg. 4001
JOSEF MEISSNER GMBH & CO. KG; *Int'l*, pg. 4001
JOSEF MOBIUS BAU-AKTIENGESELLSCHAFT—See STRABAG SE; *Int'l*, pg. 7231
JOSEF RIEPL UNTERNEHMEN FUR HOCH- UND TIEFBAU GMBH—See STRABAG SE; *Int'l*, pg. 7231
JOSEF RIEPL UNTERNEHMEN FUR INGENIEUR- UND HOCHBAU GMBH—See STRABAG SE; *Int'l*, pg. 7231
JOSEF WITT GMBH—See Otto GmbH & Co. KG; *Int'l*, pg. 5663
JOSEMARIA RESOURCES INC.—See Lundin Mining Corporation; *Int'l*, pg. 4583

1445

JOSEPH A. BARANSKI LITERARY AGENCY—See Barancorp, Ltd.; *U.S. Private*, pg. 471
JOSEPH ABBOUD MANUFACTURING CORP.—See Tailored Brands, Inc.; *U.S. Public*, pg. 1979
JOSEPH A. NATOLI CONSTRUCTION CORP.; *U.S. Private*, pg. 2236
JOSEPH ASH LTD—See Hill & Smith PLC; *Int'l*, pg. 3391
JOSEPH AUTO GROUP; *U.S. Private*, pg. 2236
JOSEPH BEHR & SONS INC.; *U.S. Private*, pg. 2236
JOSEPH BETH BOOKSELLERS LLC; *U.S. Private*, pg. 2236
JOSEPH CONSTRUCTION CO. INC.; *U.S. Private*, pg. 2236
JOSEPH CORY HOLDINGS LLC—See J.B. Hunt Transport Services, Inc.; *U.S. Public*, pg. 1180
JOSEPH C. SANSONE COMPANY; *U.S. Private*, pg. 2236
JOSEPH DAIJI TAYLOR JR. ENTERPRISES, LLC—See J.F. Lehman & Company, Inc.; *U.S. Private*, pg. 2163
JOSEPH DAVIS, INC.; *U.S. Private*, pg. 2236
JOSEPH ELETTO TRANSFER INCORPORATED; *U.S. Private*, pg. 2236
JOSEPH F. BOENTE SONS INC.; *U.S. Private*, pg. 2236
JOSEPH G. PULITANO INSURANCE AGENCY INC.; *U.S. Private*, pg. 2236
JOSEPH HUGHES CONSTRUCTION; *U.S. Private*, pg. 2236
JOSEPH INDUSTRIES INC.—See Fastener Industries Inc.; *U.S. Private*, pg. 1482
JOSEPH J. BLAKE ASSOCIATES, INC.; *U.S. Private*, pg. 2236
JOSEPH J. HENDERSON & SON, INC.; *U.S. Private*, pg. 2236
JOSEPH JINGOLI & SON, INC.; *U.S. Private*, pg. 2236
JOSEPH L. ERTL, INC.; *U.S. Private*, pg. 2237
JOSEPH LTD.—See Onward Holdings Co., Ltd.; *Int'l*, pg. 5592
JOSEPH MCCORMICK CONSTRUCTION CO. INC.; *U.S. Private*, pg. 2237
JOSEPH MCDONNELL ENTERPRISES; *U.S. Private*, pg. 2237
JOSEPH MINTON INC.; *U.S. Private*, pg. 2237
JOSEPH M. SMITH COMMUNITY HEALTH CENTER, INC.; *U.S. Private*, pg. 2237
JOSEPH M. ZIMMER INC.; *U.S. Private*, pg. 2237
JOSEPH NETO & ASSOCIATES INC.—See Lerch Bates Inc.; *U.S. Private*, pg. 2431
JOSEPH OAT CORPORATION; *U.S. Private*, pg. 2237
JOSEPH P. ADDABBO FAMILY HEALTH CENTER, INC.; *U.S. Private*, pg. 2237
JOSEPH PARIS—See FAYAT SAS; *Int'l*, pg. 2625
JOSEPH P. CARRARA & SONS INC.; *U.S. Private*, pg. 2237
JOSEPH PEDOTT ADVERTISING & MARKETING, INC.; *U.S. Private*, pg. 2237
JOSEPH PHELPS VINEYARDS INC.—See LVMH Moet Hennessy Louis Vuitton SE; *Int'l*, pg. 4599
JOSEPH'S HOUSE OF CAMDEN; *U.S. Private*, pg. 2237
JOSEPH SMITH & SONS, INC.—See European Metal Recycling Limited; *Int'l*, pg. 2556
JOSEPH VICTORI WINES, INC.; *U.S. Private*, pg. 2237
JOSEPH VOGELE AG—See Deere & Company; *U.S. Public*, pg. 647
JOSEPH VOLKSWAGEN OF CINCINNATI—See Joseph Auto Group; *U.S. Private*, pg. 2236
JOSEPH WONES (HOLDINGS) LIMITED—See Heidelberg Materials AG; *Int'l*, pg. 3317
JOSERA GMBH & CO. KG; *Int'l*, pg. 4001
JOSER; *Int'l*, pg. 4001
JOS. ERTL GMBH—See Swietelsky Baugesellschaft m.b.H.; *Int'l*, pg. 7367
JOSE SILVA CARVALHO CATERING, S.A.—See Ibersol S.G.P.S., S.A.; *Int'l*, pg. 3574
JOSHEN PAPER & PACKAGING CO. INC.—See Bunzl plc; *Int'l*, pg. 1218
JOSHI KONOIKE TRANSPORT & INFRASTRUCTURE PVT. LTD.—See Konoike Transport Co., Ltd.; *Int'l*, pg. 4274
JOSHIN DENKI CO., LTD.; *Int'l*, pg. 4001
JOSH & JOHN'S HOME MADE ICE CREAM, INC.; *U.S. Private*, pg. 2237
JOSHUA & CO.; *U.S. Private*, pg. 2237
JOSHUA DIALYSIS, LLC—See DaVita Inc.; *U.S. Public*, pg. 640
JOSHUA GOLD RESOURCES INC.; *Int'l*, pg. 4001
JOSHUA GREEN CORPORATION; *U.S. Private*, pg. 2237
JOSHUA PARTNERS, LLC; *U.S. Private*, pg. 2237
JOSHUA STAR—See Alden Global Capital LLC; *U.S. Private*, pg. 156
JOSIE ACCESSORIES INC.; *U.S. Private*, pg. 2237
JOSINA LOTT RESIDENTIAL & COMMUNITY SERVICES; *U.S. Private*, pg. 2237
JOS INTERNATIONAL BREWERIES PLC; *Int'l*, pg. 4000
JOSLIN LESSER & ASSOCIATES, INC.—See NV5 Global, Inc.; *U.S. Public*, pg. 1557
JOSLYN CLARK CONTROLS, INC.—See Danaher Corporation; *U.S. Public*, pg. 627
JOSLYN HI-VOLTAGE COMPANY, LLC—See ABB Ltd.; *Int'l*, pg. 52

JOSLYN SUNBANK COMPANY LLC—See TransDigm Group Incorporated; *U.S. Public*, pg. 2181
JOSPER, S.A.—See The Middleby Corporation; *U.S. Public*, pg. 2114
JOS. SCHNEIDER OPTISCHE WERKE GMBH; *Int'l*, pg. 4000
JOSSEY-BASS, INC.—See John Wiley & Sons, Inc.; *U.S. Public*, pg. 1193
JOST BAUUNTERNEHMEN GMBH—See L. Possehl & Co. mbH; *Int'l*, pg. 4383
JOSTENS, INC.—See Platinum Equity, LLC; *U.S. Private*, pg. 3205
JOSTS ENGINEERING COMPANY LIMITED; *Int'l*, pg. 4001
JOST-WERKE GMBH—See Cinven Limited; *Int'l*, pg. 1612
JOTABEQU ADVERTISING—See WPP plc; *Int'l*, pg. 8472
JOTABEQU EL SALVADOR—See WPP plc; *Int'l*, pg. 8472
JOTABEQU INTEGRATO G2 SAN JOSE—See WPP plc; *Int'l*, pg. 8464
JOTA GMBH—See ATON GmbH; *Int'l*, pg. 689
JO TANKERS AS—See Stolt-Nielsen Limited; *Int'l*, pg. 7221
JOT AUTOMATION BEIJING LTD.—See Head Invest Oy; *Int'l*, pg. 3301
JOT AUTOMATION INC.—See Head Invest Oy; *Int'l*, pg. 3301
JOT AUTOMATION ITALY S.R.L—See Head Invest Oy; *Int'l*, pg. 3301
JOT AUTOMATION KFT.—See Head Invest Oy; *Int'l*, pg. 3301
JOT AUTOMATION LTD.—See Head Invest Oy; *Int'l*, pg. 3301
JOT AUTOMATION VIETNAM LTD.—See Head Invest Oy; *Int'l*, pg. 3301
JOTA-VERMOGENSVERWALTUNGSGESELLSCHAFT MBH—See Allianz SE; *Int'l*, pg. 353
JOTEC CARDIOVASCULAR S.L.—See Artivion, Inc.; *U.S. Public*, pg. 208
JOTEC GMBH—See Artivion, Inc.; *U.S. Public*, pg. 208
JOTECH METAL FABRICATION INDUSTRIES SDN. BHD.; *Int'l*, pg. 4001
JOTEC POLSKA SP. Z.O.O—See Artivion, Inc.; *U.S. Public*, pg. 208
JOTEC SALES GMBH—See Artivion, Inc.; *U.S. Public*, pg. 208
JOTEC S.R.L.—See Artivion, Inc.; *U.S. Public*, pg. 208
JOTEC UK LTD.—See Artivion, Inc.; *U.S. Public*, pg. 208
JOTETSU CORPORATION—See Tokyu Corporation; *Int'l*, pg. 7797
JOTEX AB—See Nordic Capital AB; *Int'l*, pg. 5420
JOTO PR AGENCY; *U.S. Private*, pg. 2238
JOTTAN INC.; *U.S. Private*, pg. 2238
JOTUL AS—See OpenGate Capital Management, LLC; *U.S. Private*, pg. 3030
JOTUL FRANCE S.A.—See OpenGate Capital Management, LLC; *U.S. Private*, pg. 3030
JOTUL HISPANIA, S.L.—See OpenGate Capital Management, LLC; *U.S. Private*, pg. 3030
JOTUL ITALIA SRL—See OpenGate Capital Management, LLC; *U.S. Private*, pg. 3030
JOTUL LITHUANIA—See OpenGate Capital Management, LLC; *U.S. Private*, pg. 3030
JOTUL NORTH AMERICA INC.—See OpenGate Capital Management, LLC; *U.S. Private*, pg. 3030
JOTUL POLSKA SP. Z.O.O.—See OpenGate Capital Management, LLC; *U.S. Private*, pg. 3030
JOTUN ABU DHABI (LLC)—See Jotun A/S; *Int'l*, pg. 4002
JOTUN ALGERIE SARL—See Jotun A/S; *Int'l*, pg. 4002
JOTUN A/S; *Int'l*, pg. 4001
JOTUN AUSTRALIA PTY. LTD.—See Jotun A/S; *Int'l*, pg. 4002
JOTUN BANGLADESH LTD.—See Jotun A/S; *Int'l*, pg. 4002
JOTUN BOYA SAN. VE TICARET A.S.—See Jotun A/S; *Int'l*, pg. 4002
JOTUN BRASIL IMP. EXP. & INDUSTRIA DE TINTAS LTDA.—See Jotun A/S; *Int'l*, pg. 4002
JOTUN BULGARIA EOOD—See Jotun A/S; *Int'l*, pg. 4002
JOTUN B.V.—See Jotun A/S; *Int'l*, pg. 4002
JOTUN COATINGS (ZHANGJIAGANG) CO. LTD—See Jotun A/S; *Int'l*, pg. 4002
JOTUN CYPRUS LTD—See Jotun A/S; *Int'l*, pg. 4002
JOTUN DANMARK A/S—See Jotun A/S; *Int'l*, pg. 4002
JOTUN (DEUTSCHLAND) GMBH—See Jotun A/S; *Int'l*, pg. 4002
JOTUN DO BRAZIL LTDA.—See Jotun A/S; *Int'l*, pg. 4003
JOTUN FRANCE S.A.—See Jotun A/S; *Int'l*, pg. 4002
JOTUN HELLAS LTD.—See Jotun A/S; *Int'l*, pg. 4002
JOTUN IBERICA S.A.—See Jotun A/S; *Int'l*, pg. 4002
JOTUN IBERICA S.A.—See Jotun A/S; *Int'l*, pg. 4002
JOTUN INDIA PVT. LTD.—See Jotun A/S; *Int'l*, pg. 4002
JOTUN (IRELAND) LTD.—See Jotun A/S; *Int'l*, pg. 4002
JOTUN ITALIA S.P.A.—See Jotun A/S; *Int'l*, pg. 4002
JOTUN (MALAYSIA) SDN. BHD.—See Jotun A/S; *Int'l*, pg. 4002
JOTUN OCEAN PAINT CO. LTD.—See Jotun A/S; *Int'l*, pg. 4002
JOTUN PAINTS CO. L.L.C.—See Jotun A/S; *Int'l*, pg. 4002

JOTUN PAINTS (H.K.) LTD.—See Jotun A/S; *Int'l*, pg. 4002
JOTUN PAINTS, INC. - HOUSTON—See Jotun A/S; *Int'l*, pg. 4002
JOTUN PAINTS, INC.—See Jotun A/S; *Int'l*, pg. 4002
JOTUN PAINTS OOO—See Jotun A/S; *Int'l*, pg. 4002
JOTUN PAINTS—See Jotun A/S; *Int'l*, pg. 4002
JOTUN PAINTS SOUTH AFRICA (PTY) LTD.—See Jotun A/S; *Int'l*, pg. 4002
JOTUN PAINTS (VIETNAM) CO. LTD.—See Jotun A/S; *Int'l*, pg. 4002
JOTUN (PHILIPPINES) INC.—See Jotun A/S; *Int'l*, pg. 4002
JOTUN POLSKA SP. Z.O.O.—See Jotun A/S; *Int'l*, pg. 4002
JOTUN POWDER COATINGS BULGARIA LTD.—See Jotun A/S; *Int'l*, pg. 4002
JOTUN POWDER COATINGS (CZ) A.S.—See Jotun A/S; *Int'l*, pg. 4002
JOTUN POWDER COATINGS (M) SDN. BHD.—See Jotun A/S; *Int'l*, pg. 4002
JOTUN POWDER COATINGS (N) AS—See Jotun A/S; *Int'l*, pg. 4002
JOTUN POWDER COATINGS PAKISTAN (PVT) LDA.—See Jotun A/S; *Int'l*, pg. 4003
JOTUN POWDER COATINGS SAUDI ARABIA LTD., CO.—See Jotun A/S; *Int'l*, pg. 4003
JOTUN POWDER COATINGS U.A.E. LLC—See Jotun A/S; *Int'l*, pg. 4003
JOTUN SAUDIA CO. LTD.—See Jotun A/S; *Int'l*, pg. 4003
JOTUN (SINGAPORE) PTE. LTD.—See Jotun A/S; *Int'l*, pg. 4002
JOTUN SVERIGE AB—See Jotun A/S; *Int'l*, pg. 4003
JOTUN THAILAND LTD.—See Jotun A/S; *Int'l*, pg. 4003
JOTUN TOZ BOYA SAN. VE TIC. A.S.—See Jotun A/S; *Int'l*, pg. 4003
JOTUN U.A.E. LTD. (LLC)—See Jotun A/S; *Int'l*, pg. 4003
JOUDER PRECISION INDUSTRY (KUNSHAN) CO., LTD; *Int'l*, pg. 4003
JOUFFRUIT; *Int'l*, pg. 4003
JOULE ASSETS, INC.; *U.S. Private*, pg. 2238
JOULE CAPITAL, LLC—See Joule Assets, Inc.; *U.S. Private*, pg. 2238
JOULE, INC.—See System One Holdings, LLC; *U.S. Private*, pg. 3906
JOULE MICROSYSTEMS INC.—See Banneker Partners, LLC; *U.S. Private*, pg. 469
JOULES LIMITED; *Int'l*, pg. 4003
JOULE—See WPP plc; *Int'l*, pg. 8474
JOULE—See WPP plc; *Int'l*, pg. 8465
JOULE STAFFING SERVICES, INC.—See System One Holdings, LLC; *U.S. Private*, pg. 3907
JOUNCE THERAPEUTICS, INC.—See Concentra Biosciences, LLC; *U.S. Private*, pg. 1008
JOURDAN PLC; *Int'l*, pg. 4003
JOURDAN RESOURCES INC.; *Int'l*, pg. 4003
JOURDANTON HOME CARE SERVICES, LLC—See Community Health Systems, Inc.; *U.S. Public*, pg. 554
JOURDENESS GROUP LIMITED; *Int'l*, pg. 4003
JOURNAL ADVOCATE—See Alden Global Capital LLC; *U.S. Private*, pg. 157
JOURNAL COMMUNITY PUBLISHING GROUP, INC.—See Gannett Co., Inc.; *U.S. Public*, pg. 898
JOURNAL & COURIER—See Gannett Co., Inc.; *U.S. Public*, pg. 898
THE JOURNAL-COURIER—See Independence Capital Partners, LLC; *U.S. Private*, pg. 2057
THE JOURNAL GAZETTE—See The Nutting Company, Inc.; *U.S. Private*, pg. 4086
JOURNALISTENSCHULE AXEL SPRINGER—See Axel Springer SE; *Int'l*, pg. 766
JOURNALISTGRUPPEN, JG AB—See Nordic Morning Plc; *Int'l*, pg. 5423
JOURNAL MEDIA GROUP, INC.—See Gannett Co., Inc.; *U.S. Public*, pg. 898
THE JOURNAL NEWS—See Gannett Co., Inc.; *U.S. Public*, pg. 900
JOURNAL PRODUCTIONS, INC.—See Lions Gate Entertainment Corp.; *Int'l*, pg. 4520
JOURNAL PUBLICATIONS, INC.; *U.S. Private*, pg. 2238
JOURNAL PUBLISHING CO. INC.—See CREATE Foundation; *U.S. Private*, pg. 1087
THE JOURNAL PUBLISHING CO. INC.—See The Nutting Company, Inc.; *U.S. Private*, pg. 4086
THE JOURNAL RECORD PUBLISHING CO., LLC—See The Dolan Company; *U.S. Private*, pg. 4022
THE JOURNAL-REGISTER—See The Retirement Systems of Alabama; *U.S. Private*, pg. 4106
JOURNAL SENTINEL, INC.—See Gannett Co., Inc.; *U.S. Public*, pg. 898
JOURNAL STAR, INC.—See Gannett Co., Inc.; *U.S. Public*, pg. 903
JOURNAL-STAR PRINTING CO.—See Lee Enterprises, Incorporated; *U.S. Public*, pg. 1299
JOURNAL TECHNOLOGIES, INC.—See Daily Journal Corporation; *U.S. Public*, pg. 620
THE JOURNAL TIMES—See Lee Enterprises, Incorporated; *U.S. Public*, pg. 1300
JOURNEO PLC; *Int'l*, pg. 4003

COMPANY NAME INDEX

JOURNEY BANK—See Muncy Columbia Financial Corporation; *U.S. Public*, pg. 1486
JOURNEYCARE, INC.—See Addus HomeCare Corporation; *U.S. Public*, pg. 40
JOURNEYED CANADA CORP.—See Snorrason Holdings ehf; *Int'l*, pg. 7028
JOURNEYED.COM, INC.—See Siris Capital Group, LLC; *U.S. Private*, pg. 3672
JOURNEY ENERGY INC.; *Int'l*, pg. 4003
JOURNEY FORWARD; *U.S. Private*, pg. 2238
JOURNEY GROUP PLC—See Harwood Capital LLP; *Int'l*, pg. 3282
JOURNEY HEALTH & LIFESTYLE—See Peloton Equity LLC; *U.S. Private*, pg. 3131
JOURNEY HOME HEALTHCARE OF SAN ANTONIO, LLC—See Tenet Healthcare Corporation; *U.S. Public*, pg. 2014
JOURNEY HOUSE, INC.; *U.S. Private*, pg. 2238
JOURNEYMAN CONSTRUCTION, INC.; *U.S. Private*, pg. 2238
JOURNEY MEDICAL CORPORATION; *U.S. Public*, pg. 1206
JOURNEY MENTAL HEALTH CENTER; *U.S. Private*, pg. 2238
JOURNEY MEXICO; *U.S. Private*, pg. 2238
JOURNEY PUBLISHING, INC—See Snorrason Holdings ehf; *Int'l*, pg. 7028
JOUVE, SA; *Int'l*, pg. 4003
JOVIAN ASSET MANAGEMENT INC.—See iA Financial Corporation Inc.; *Int'l*, pg. 3567
JOVIAN CAPITAL CORPORATION—See iA Financial Corporation Inc.; *Int'l*, pg. 3567
JOVIPAK CORPORATION—See Svenska Cellulosa Aktiebolaget SCA; *Int'l*, pg. 7356
JOVO ARCO ENERGY CO, LTD—See BP plc; *Int'l*, pg. 1131
JOWA AG—See The Federation of Migros Cooperatives; *Int'l*, pg. 7642
JOWAT ADHESIVES INDIA PVT. LTD.—See Jowat SE; *Int'l*, pg. 4003
JOWAT ATASOY YAPISTIRICI URUNLER TICARET A.S.—See Jowat SE; *Int'l*, pg. 4004
JOWAT (BEIJING) ADHESIVES CO. LTD.—See Jowat SE; *Int'l*, pg. 4003
JOWAT CANADA LTD.—See Jowat SE; *Int'l*, pg. 4004
JOWAT CHILE SPA—See Jowat SE; *Int'l*, pg. 4004
JOWAT CORPORATION—See Jowat SE; *Int'l*, pg. 4004
JOWAT DE MEXICO S. DE R.L. DE C.V.—See Jowat SE; *Int'l*, pg. 4004
JOWAT FRANCE SARL—See Jowat SE; *Int'l*, pg. 4004
JOWAT ITALIA S.R.L.—See Jowat SE; *Int'l*, pg. 4004
JOWAT (MALAYSIA) SDN. BHD.—See Jowat SE; *Int'l*, pg. 4003
JOWAT MANUFACTURING (SEA) SDN. BHD.—See Jowat SE; *Int'l*, pg. 4004
JOWAT MIDDLE EAST FZE—See Jowat SE; *Int'l*, pg. 4004
JOWAT NEDERLAND B.V.—See Jowat SE; *Int'l*, pg. 4004
JOWAT POLSKA SP. Z O.O. SP. K.—See Jowat SE; *Int'l*, pg. 4004
JOWAT SCANDINAVIA AB—See Jowat SE; *Int'l*, pg. 4004
JOWAT SE; *Int'l*, pg. 4003
JOWAT SWISS AG—See Jowat SE; *Int'l*, pg. 4004
JOWAT UK LTD.—See Jowat SE; *Int'l*, pg. 4004
JOWAT UNIVERSAL ADHESIVES AUSTRALIA PTY. LTD.—See Jowat SE; *Int'l*, pg. 4004
JOWELL GLOBAL LTD.; *Int'l*, pg. 4004
J.O. WILLIAMS MOTORS, INC.; *U.S. Private*, pg. 2169
JOWITT & RODGERS CO.—See SAK Industries Pvt Ltd; *Int'l*, pg. 6486
JOYAS INTERNATIONAL HOLDINGS LIMITED; *Int'l*, pg. 4004
JOYAS MANUFACTURING INTERNATIONAL LTD—See Joyas Manufacturing Limited; *Int'l*, pg. 4004
JOYAS MANUFACTURING LIMITED; *Int'l*, pg. 4004
JOYAU S.A.—See Deutsche Bahn AG; *Int'l*, pg. 2052
JOYCE & ASSOCIATES CONSTRUCTION, INC.; *U.S. Private*, pg. 2238
JOYCE BOUTIQUE HOLDINGS LIMITED; *Int'l*, pg. 4004
JOYCE BROS STORAGE & VAN CO.; *U.S. Private*, pg. 2238
JOYCE CHEN DIVISION—See Columbian Home Products; *U.S. Private*, pg. 978
JOYCE CORPORATION LTD; *Int'l*, pg. 4004
JOYCE/DAYTON CORP.—See Graham Holdings Company; *U.S. Public*, pg. 955
JOYCE FARMS, INC.; *U.S. Private*, pg. 2238
JOYCE FOAM PTY. LIMITED—See Sheela Foam Limited; *Int'l*, pg. 6792
JOYCE FOOD PRODUCTS INC.; *U.S. Private*, pg. 2239
JOYCE LESLIE INC.; *U.S. Private*, pg. 2239
JOYCE MANUFACTURING CO.; *U.S. Private*, pg. 2239
JOYCE MOTORS CORP.; *U.S. Private*, pg. 2239
JOYCE STEEL ERECTION, LLC—See Berkshire Hathaway Inc.; *U.S. Public*, pg. 309
JOYCITY CORPORATION; *Int'l*, pg. 4004
JOY CITY PROPERTY LTD.—See COFCO Limited; *Int'l*, pg. 1692

JOY! COMMUNICATIONS-FT. LAUDERDALE—See Joy! Communications; *U.S. Private*, pg. 2238
JOY! COMMUNICATIONS; *U.S. Private*, pg. 2238
JOY CONE COMPANY; *U.S. Private*, pg. 2238
JOY CONE COMPANY - WESTERN FACILITY—See Joy Cone Company; *U.S. Private*, pg. 2238
JOY DINING PRODUCTS K.K.—See Yoshimura Food Holdings K.K.; *Int'l*, pg. 8600
JO YEH COMPANY LIMITED—See BizLink Holding Inc.; *Int'l*, pg. 1053
JOYENT, INC.—See Samsung Group; *Int'l*, pg. 6512
JOY FOOD STORES INC.—See Supertest Oil Company Inc.; *U.S. Private*, pg. 3881
JOY FOR OUR YOUTH INC.; *U.S. Private*, pg. 2238
JOYFUL ATHLETIC CLUB CO., LTD.—See Joyful Honda Co., Ltd.; *Int'l*, pg. 4004
JOYFUL HONDA CO., LTD.; *Int'l*, pg. 4004
JOY GLOBAL AUSTRALIA PTY. LTD. -MURARRIE—See Komatsu Ltd.; *Int'l*, pg. 4236
JOY GLOBAL AUSTRALIA PTY. LTD.—See Komatsu Ltd.; *Int'l*, pg. 4236
JOY GLOBAL (BAOTOU) MINING MACHINERY CO. LT—See Komatsu Ltd.; *Int'l*, pg. 4235
JOY GLOBAL (CANADA) LTD.—See Komatsu Ltd.; *Int'l*, pg. 4235
JOY GLOBAL (CHILE) S.A.—See Komatsu Ltd.; *Int'l*, pg. 4235
JOY GLOBAL CONVEYORS INC.—See Stellex Capital Management LP; *U.S. Private*, pg. 3800
JOY GLOBAL .FRANCE S.A.R.L.—See Komatsu Ltd.; *Int'l*, pg. 4236
JOY GLOBAL INDUSTRIES LIMITED—See Komatsu Ltd.; *Int'l*, pg. 4235
JOY GLOBAL LONGVIEW OPERATIONS LLC—See Komatsu Ltd.; *Int'l*, pg. 4236
JOY GLOBAL MEXICO S.A. DE C.V.—See Komatsu Ltd.; *Int'l*, pg. 4236
JOY GLOBAL (PERU) S.A.C.—See Komatsu Ltd.; *Int'l*, pg. 4235
JOY GLOBAL (PERU) S.A.C.—See Mitsui & Co., Ltd.; *Int'l*, pg. 4973
JOY GLOBAL SOUTH AFRICA PTY LTD.—See Komatsu Ltd.; *Int'l*, pg. 4236
JOY GLOBAL SURFACE MINING INC.—See Komatsu Ltd.; *Int'l*, pg. 4236
JOY GLOBAL (TIANJIN) MINING MACHINERY CO. LTD.—See Komatsu Ltd.; *Int'l*, pg. 4235
JOY GLOBAL (UK) HOLDINGS CO. LIMITED—See Komatsu Ltd.; *Int'l*, pg. 4235
JOY GLOBAL (UK) LIMITED—See Komatsu Ltd.; *Int'l*, pg. 4236
JOY GLOBAL (UK) SURFACE LIMITED—See Komatsu Ltd.; *Int'l*, pg. 4236
JOY GLOBAL UNDERGROUND MINING LLC - ABINGDON SERVICE CENTER—See Komatsu Ltd.; *Int'l*, pg. 4236
JOY GLOBAL UNDERGROUND MINING LLC - FRANKLIN PLANT—See Komatsu Ltd.; *Int'l*, pg. 4236
JOY GLOBAL UNDERGROUND MINING LLC—See Komatsu Ltd.; *Int'l*, pg. 4236
JOYHANDS WELLNESS INC.—See MEDIROM Healthcare Technologies Inc.; *Int'l*, pg. 4780
JOYKEY INDUSTRIAL (PINGHU) LIMITED—See Quang Viet Enterprise Co., Ltd.; *Int'l*, pg. 6153
JOY KIE CORPORATION LIMITED; *Int'l*, pg. 4004
JOYLAB, INC.—See BEENOS Inc.; *Int'l*, pg. 939
JOY MANUFACTURING COMPANY (U.K.) LTD.—See Komatsu Ltd.; *Int'l*, pg. 4236
JOY MARK INC.; *U.S. Private*, pg. 2238
JOY MART CO., LTD.—See Zensho Holdings Co., Ltd.; *Int'l*, pg. 8634
JOY MIND LIMITED—See Lai Sun Garment (International) Limited; *Int'l*, pg. 4396
JOYNER SPORTSMEDICINE INSTITUTE, INC.—See Select Medical Holdings Corporation; *U.S. Public*, pg. 1858
JOYNET CO., LTD.—See TOKAI Holdings Corporation; *Int'l*, pg. 7779
JOYNEXT GMBH—See Ningbo Joyson Electronic Corp.; *Int'l*, pg. 5303
JOYN GMBH—See ProSiebenSat.1 Media SE; *Int'l*, pg. 6000
JOYN GMBH—See Warner Bros. Discovery, Inc.; *U.S. Public*, pg. 2327
THE JOYO BANK, LTD. - BUSINESS PLANNING DIVISION—See Mebuki Financial Group, Inc.; *Int'l*, pg. 4763
THE JOYO BANK, LTD.—See Mebuki Financial Group, Inc.; *Int'l*, pg. 4763
THE JOYO BUSINESS SERVICE CO., LTD.—See Mebuki Financial Group, Inc.; *Int'l*, pg. 4763
THE JOYO CASH SERVICE CO., LTD.—See Mebuki Financial Group, Inc.; *Int'l*, pg. 4763
THE JOYO COMPUTER SERVICE CO., LTD.—See Mebuki Financial Group, Inc.; *Int'l*, pg. 4763
THE JOYO CREDIT CO., LTD.—See Mebuki Financial Group, Inc.; *Int'l*, pg. 4764
THE JOYO CREDIT GUARANTEE CO., LTD.—See Mebuki Financial Group, Inc.; *Int'l*, pg. 4764

JOYY INC.

JOYO ELECTRIC CO., LTD.—See Beijing Sojo Electric Company Limited; *Int'l*, pg. 957
JOYO ENGINEERING CO., LTD.—See The Japan Steel Works, Ltd.; *Int'l*, pg. 7659
THE JOYO INDUSTRIAL RESEARCH INSTITUTE, LTD.—See Mebuki Financial Group, Inc.; *Int'l*, pg. 4764
JOYO REMICON CO., LTD.—See Taiheiyo Cement Corporation; *Int'l*, pg. 7411
JOYOUNG CO., LTD.—See JS Global Lifestyle Company Limited; *Int'l*, pg. 4008
JOYOUS FOODS CO., LTD.—See Nisshin Seifun Group, Inc.; *Int'l*, pg. 5372
JOY PIPE USA LLC; *U.S. Private*, pg. 2238
JOY REALTY LIMITED; *Int'l*, pg. 4004
JOYSON ANAND ABHISHEK SAFETY SYSTEMS PRIVATE LIMITED—See Ningbo Joyson Electronic Corp.; *Int'l*, pg. 5304
JOYSON PLASTEC GMBH—See Ningbo Joyson Electronic Corp.; *Int'l*, pg. 5303
JOYSON SAFETY SYSTEMS ACQUISITION LLC—See Ningbo Joyson Electronic Corp.; *Int'l*, pg. 5303
JOYSON SAFETY SYSTEMS ACQUISITION LLC—See Ningbo Joyson Electronic Corp.; *Int'l*, pg. 5303
JOYSON SAFETY SYSTEMS ARAD S.R.L.—See Ningbo Joyson Electronic Corp.; *Int'l*, pg. 5304
JOYSON SAFETY SYSTEMS ASCHAFFENBURG GMBH—See Ningbo Joyson Electronic Corp.; *Int'l*, pg. 5304
JOYSON SAFETY SYSTEMS ASCHAFFENBURG GMBH—See Ningbo Joyson Electronic Corp.; *Int'l*, pg. 5303
JOYSON SAFETY SYSTEMS BRASIL LTDA.—See Ningbo Joyson Electronic Corp.; *Int'l*, pg. 5304
JOYSON SAFETY SYSTEMS CZECH S.R.O.—See Ningbo Joyson Electronic Corp.; *Int'l*, pg. 5304
JOYSON SAFETY SYSTEMS CZECH S.R.O.—See Ningbo Joyson Electronic Corp.; *Int'l*, pg. 5303
JOYSON SAFETY SYSTEMS FRANCE EURL—See Ningbo Joyson Electronic Corp.; *Int'l*, pg. 5303
JOYSON SAFETY SYSTEMS HUNGARY KFT.—See Ningbo Joyson Electronic Corp.; *Int'l*, pg. 5303
JOYSON SAFETY SYSTEMS IGNITION GMBH—See Ningbo Joyson Electronic Corp.; *Int'l*, pg. 5303
JOYSON SAFETY SYSTEMS JAPAN G.K.—See Ningbo Joyson Electronic Corp.; *Int'l*, pg. 5304
JOYSON SAFETY SYSTEMS JAPAN KK—See Ningbo Joyson Electronic Corp.; *Int'l*, pg. 5303
JOYSON SAFETY SYSTEMS KOREA CO., LTD.—See Ningbo Joyson Electronic Corp.; *Int'l*, pg. 5304
JOYSON SAFETY SYSTEMS KOREA CO., LTD.—See Ningbo Joyson Electronic Corp.; *Int'l*, pg. 5303
JOYSON SAFETY SYSTEMS MAROC S.A R.L.—See Ningbo Joyson Electronic Corp.; *Int'l*, pg. 5303
JOYSON SAFETY SYSTEMS (M) SDN. BHD.—See Ningbo Joyson Electronic Corp.; *Int'l*, pg. 5303
JOYSON SAFETY SYSTEMS (PHILIPPINES) CORPORATION—See Ningbo Joyson Electronic Corp.; *Int'l*, pg. 5303
JOYSON SAFETY SYSTEMS PHILIPPINES CORPORATION—See Ningbo Joyson Electronic Corp.; *Int'l*, pg. 5303
JOYSON SAFETY SYSTEMS POLAND SP. Z O.O.—See Ningbo Joyson Electronic Corp.; *Int'l*, pg. 5304
JOYSON SAFETY SYSTEMS POLAND SP. Z O.O.—See Ningbo Joyson Electronic Corp.; *Int'l*, pg. 5303
JOYSON SAFETY SYSTEMS RUS LLC—See Ningbo Joyson Electronic Corp.; *Int'l*, pg. 5303
JOYSON SAFETY SYSTEMS SACHSEN GMBH—See Ningbo Joyson Electronic Corp.; *Int'l*, pg. 5303
JOYSON SAFETY SYSTEMS SHANGHAI CO., LTD.—See Ningbo Joyson Electronic Corp.; *Int'l*, pg. 5303
JOYSON SAFETY SYSTEMS SIBIU S.R.L.—See Ningbo Joyson Electronic Corp.; *Int'l*, pg. 5304
JOYSON SAFETY SYSTEMS SIBIU S.R.L.—See Ningbo Joyson Electronic Corp.; *Int'l*, pg. 5303
JOYSON SAFETY SYSTEMS TIANJIN CO., LTD.—See Ningbo Joyson Electronic Corp.; *Int'l*, pg. 5303
JOYSON SAFETY SYSTEMS TORINO S.R.L.—See Ningbo Joyson Electronic Corp.; *Int'l*, pg. 5303
JOYSON SAFETY SYSTEMS UK LIMITED—See Ningbo Joyson Electronic Corp.; *Int'l*, pg. 5303
JOYSON SAFETY SYSTEMS URUGUAY S.A.—See Ningbo Joyson Electronic Corp.; *Int'l*, pg. 5303
JOYSON-TOA SAFETY SYSTEMS CO., LTD.—See Ningbo Joyson Electronic Corp.; *Int'l*, pg. 5304
JOYSPEED GLOBAL CARGO CHINA LIMITED—See Hon Hai Precision Industry Co., Ltd.; *Int'l*, pg. 3457
JOY SPREADER GROUP INC.; *Int'l*, pg. 4004
JOYTECH EUROPE LIMITED—See Take-Two Interactive Software, Inc.; *U.S. Public*, pg. 1979
JOYUP CO., LTD.—See Ship Healthcare Holdings, Inc.; *Int'l*, pg. 6852
JOYVA CORPORATION; *U.S. Private*, pg. 2239
JOYVIO FOOD CO., LTD.; *Int'l*, pg. 4004
JOYWARE ELECTRONICS CO., LTD.; *Int'l*, pg. 4005
JOYWORKS INC.—See Business Brain Showa-Ota Inc.; *Int'l*, pg. 1228
JOYY INC.; *Int'l*, pg. 4005
J.O.Z. PEAB GROUP SIA—See Peab AB; *Int'l*, pg. 5772

J-PAC, LLC—See Public Pension Capital, LLC; *U.S. Private*, pg. 3300
JPAK GROUP INC.; *Int'l*, pg. 4005
J. PARPALA OY—See ANDRITZ AG; *Int'l*, pg. 456
J&PARTNERS L.P.; *Int'l*, pg. 3853
JP ASIAN ELECTRONICS MATERIALS (M) SDN. BHD.—See Japan Pulp and Paper Company Limited; *Int'l*, pg. 3903
THE J. PAUL GETTY TRUST; *U.S. Private*, pg. 4058
JP AUTOCESTE FBIH D.O.O.; *Int'l*, pg. 4005
J. PAWLEY MOTORS, INC.; *U.S. Private*, pg. 2156
J. P. BACHEM VERLAG GMBH; *Int'l*, pg. 3856
J.P.B. ENTERPRISES, INC.; *U.S. Private*, pg. 2170
JP BODEN & CO. LTD.; *Int'l*, pg. 4005
JPB PARTNERS, LLC—See J.P.B. Enterprises, Inc.; *U.S. Private*, pg. 2170
JP BUSINESS SERVICE CORPORATION—See Electric Power Development Co., Ltd.; *Int'l*, pg. 2349
JPC CABLE & WIRE INC.—See Jess-Link Products Co., Ltd.; *Int'l*, pg. 3932
JPC GROUP, INC.; *U.S. Private*, pg. 2239
JP CHEVROLET INC.; *U.S. Private*, pg. 2239
J & P COATS PAKISTAN (PVT) LIMITED—See Coats Group plc; *Int'l*, pg. 1682
JP CORELEX HOLDINGS CO., LTD.—See Japan Pulp and Paper Company Limited; *Int'l*, pg. 3903
JP CORELEX (VIETNAM) CO., LTD.—See Japan Pulp and Paper Company Limited; *Int'l*, pg. 3903
J.P. CULLEN & SONS INC.; *U.S. Private*, pg. 2169
JP DESIGN CO., LTD.—See Electric Power Development Co., Ltd.; *Int'l*, pg. 2349
J.P. DONMOYER, INC.—See Ono Transport Services, Inc.; *U.S. Private*, pg. 3027
JPEC CO., LTD.—See Electric Power Development Co., Ltd.; *Int'l*, pg. 2349
JP ELEKTROPRIVREDA BIH D.D.; *Int'l*, pg. 4005
JP ELEKTROPRIVREDA HZHB D.D. MOSTAR; *Int'l*, pg. 4005
JPEL PRIVATE EQUITY LIMITED; *Int'l*, pg. 4005
J. PEREZ ASSOCIATES INC.; *U.S. Private*, pg. 2157
J&P FLASH INC.; *U.S. Private*, pg. 2154
JPG PHARMA NV—See Fagron NV; *Int'l*, pg. 2603
JPG PLUMBING AND MECHANICAL SERVICES, INC.—See Huron Capital Partners LLC; *U.S. Private*, pg. 2012
JP GROUP LTD; *Int'l*, pg. 4005
J/P HAITIAN RELIEF ORGANIZATION; *U.S. Private*, pg. 2172
J.P. HART LUMBER COMPANY INC.; *U.S. Private*, pg. 2169
J-PHOENIX RESEARCH INC.—See SCALA Inc.; *Int'l*, pg. 6610
JP HOKKAI CO., LTD.—See Japan Pulp and Paper Company Limited; *Int'l*, pg. 3903
JP HOLDINGS, INC.; *Int'l*, pg. 4005
J&P HOLDINGS, LLC; *U.S. Private*, pg. 2155
JP HOUSEHOLD SUPPLY CO., LTD.—See Japan Pulp and Paper Company Limited; *Int'l*, pg. 3903
JP HT D.D. MOSTAR; *Int'l*, pg. 4005
J.P. HUNTER ENTERPRISES INC.; *U.S. Private*, pg. 2170
JPHYTEC CO., LTD.—See Electric Power Development Co., Ltd.; *Int'l*, pg. 2349
JPIMEDIA HOLDINGS LIMITED; *Int'l*, pg. 4006
JPIMEDIA LIMITED—See JPIMedia Holdings Limited; *Int'l*, pg. 4006
JPI NATIONAL CONSTRUCTION INC.; *U.S. Private*, pg. 2239
J.P. INGLIS COMPANY LIMITED—See Four Seas Mercantile Holdings Limited; *Int'l*, pg. 2755
J & P INVESTMENTS, INC.—See Revitalize Capital; *U.S. Private*, pg. 3416
J.P. JENKS, INC.—See R.W. Sidley, Incorporated; *U.S. Private*, pg. 3340
J P KENNY ENGINEERING LIMITED—See John Wood Group PLC; *Int'l*, pg. 3983
J P KENNY INC.—See John Wood Group PLC; *Int'l*, pg. 3983
J P KENNY PTY. LTD.—See John Wood Group PLC; *Int'l*, pg. 3983
JP KOMUS A.D.; *Int'l*, pg. 4005
J.P. KOTTS & CO.; *U.S. Private*, pg. 2170
J-PLASMA GMBH—See WEINERT Industries AG; *Int'l*, pg. 8370
JP LAWRENCE BIOMEDICAL, INC.; *U.S. Private*, pg. 2239
JPL CO., LTD.—See Kanda Holdings Co., Ltd.; *Int'l*, pg. 4065
JP LEASE PRODUCTS & SERVICES CO., LTD.—See Japan Investment Adviser Co., Ltd.; *Int'l*, pg. 3898
JPL INTEGRATED COMMUNICTIONS, INC.; *U.S. Private*, pg. 2239
JPL MANAGEMENT INC.; *U.S. Private*, pg. 2239
JP LOGINET CO., LTD.—See Japan Pulp and Paper Company Limited; *Int'l*, pg. 3903
JP LOGISTICS & MOTORSPORTS, INC.; *U.S. Private*, pg. 2239
JPL PRODUCTION II, INC.—See Quebecor Inc.; *Int'l*, pg. 6158

JPL PROJECT SP. Z O. O.—See Jacobs Engineering Group, Inc.; *U.S. Public*, pg. 1184
J. P. MASCARO & SONS; *U.S. Private*, pg. 2156
JP MATERIAL CHINA SHANGHAI PEAK INTERNATIONAL TRADE CO., LTD.—See WEDS CO., LTD.; *Int'l*, pg. 8367
J.P. MCDOUGALL & CO. LIMITED—See Akzo Nobel N.V.; *Int'l*, pg. 274
JP MCHALE PEST MANAGEMENT, LLC—See EQT AB; *Int'l*, pg. 2468
JP MEDIA DIRECT CO., LTD.—See Japan Post Holdings Co., Ltd.; *Int'l*, pg. 3900
JPMF JIANGYI CO., LTD.—See Lingyi iTech (Guangdong) Company; *Int'l*, pg. 4512
J.P. MORGAN ADMINISTRATIVE SERVICES AUSTRALIA LIMITED—See JPMorgan Chase & Co.; *U.S. Public*, pg. 1208
J.P. MORGAN AG—See JPMorgan Chase & Co.; *U.S. Public*, pg. 1208
JPMORGAN ASIA GROWTH & INCOME PLC; *Int'l*, pg. 4007
JPMORGAN ASSET MANAGEMENT (ASIA) INC.—See JPMorgan Chase & Co.; *U.S. Public*, pg. 1208
JPMORGAN ASSET MANAGEMENT (AUSTRALIA) LIMITED—See JPMorgan Chase & Co.; *U.S. Public*, pg. 1209
JPMORGAN ASSET MANAGEMENT (CANADA) INC.—See JPMorgan Chase & Co.; *U.S. Public*, pg. 1209
JPMORGAN ASSET MANAGEMENT (EUROPE) S.A.R.L.—See JPMorgan Chase & Co.; *U.S. Public*, pg. 1209
JPMORGAN ASSET MANAGEMENT HOLDINGS INC.—See JPMorgan Chase & Co.; *U.S. Public*, pg. 1208
JPMORGAN ASSET MANAGEMENT HOLDINGS (LUXEMBOURG) S.A.R.L.—See JPMorgan Chase & Co.; *U.S. Public*, pg. 1209
JPMORGAN ASSET MANAGEMENT INDIA PRIVATE LIMITED—See JPMorgan Chase & Co.; *U.S. Public*, pg. 1209
JPMORGAN ASSET MANAGEMENT (JAPAN) LIMITED—See JPMorgan Chase & Co.; *U.S. Public*, pg. 1209
JPMORGAN ASSET MANAGEMENT (KOREA) COMPANY LIMITED—See JPMorgan Chase & Co.; *U.S. Public*, pg. 1209
JPMORGAN ASSET MANAGEMENT LUXEMBOURG S.A.—See JPMorgan Chase & Co.; *U.S. Public*, pg. 1209
JPMORGAN ASSET MANAGEMENT (SINGAPORE) LIMITED—See JPMorgan Chase & Co.; *U.S. Public*, pg. 1209
J.P. MORGAN ASSET MANAGEMENT—See JPMorgan Chase & Co.; *U.S. Public*, pg. 1208
JPMORGAN ASSET MANAGEMENT (TAIWAN) LIMITED—See JPMorgan Chase & Co.; *U.S. Public*, pg. 1209
JPMORGAN ASSET MANAGEMENT (UK) LIMITED—See JPMorgan Chase & Co.; *U.S. Public*, pg. 1209
J.P. MORGAN AUSTRALIA GROUP PTY LIMITED—See JPMorgan Chase & Co.; *U.S. Public*, pg. 1208
J.P. MORGAN BANK CANADA—See JPMorgan Chase & Co.; *U.S. Public*, pg. 1208
J.P. MORGAN BANK INTERNATIONAL (LLC)—See JPMorgan Chase & Co.; *U.S. Public*, pg. 1209
J.P. MORGAN BANK (IRELAND) PLC—See JPMorgan Chase & Co.; *U.S. Public*, pg. 1208
J.P. MORGAN BANK LUXEMBOURG S.A.—See JPMorgan Chase & Co.; *U.S. Public*, pg. 1209
J.P. MORGAN BANK—See JPMorgan Chase & Co.; *U.S. Public*, pg. 1209
J.P. MORGAN BANK—See JPMorgan Chase & Co.; *U.S. Public*, pg. 1209
J.P. MORGAN BROKING (HONG KONG) LIMITED—See JPMorgan Chase & Co.; *U.S. Public*, pg. 1208
JPMORGAN CAZENOVE LTD.—See JPMorgan Chase & Co.; *U.S. Public*, pg. 1209
JPMORGAN CHASE BANK (CHINA) COMPANY LIMITED—See JPMorgan Chase & Co.; *U.S. Public*, pg. 1209
JPMORGAN CHASE BANK, DEARBORN—See JPMorgan Chase & Co.; *U.S. Public*, pg. 1209
JPMORGAN CHASE BANK, N.A. - LOUISVILLE—See JPMorgan Chase & Co.; *U.S. Public*, pg. 1209
JPMORGAN CHASE BANK, N.A.—See JPMorgan Chase & Co.; *U.S. Public*, pg. 1209
J.P. MORGAN CHASE COMMUNITY DEVELOPMENT GROUP—See JPMorgan Chase & Co.; *U.S. Public*, pg. 1208
JPMORGAN CHASE & CO.; *U.S. Public*, pg. 1206
JPMORGAN CHASE & CO.; *U.S. Public*, pg. 1206
JPMORGAN CHASE - MIDWEST REGIONAL OFFICE—See JPMorgan Chase & Co.; *U.S. Public*, pg. 1209
JPMORGAN CHASE - SOUTHERN REGIONAL OFFICE—See JPMorgan Chase & Co.; *U.S. Public*, pg. 1209

J.P. MORGAN CHASE (UK) HOLDINGS LTD.—See JPMorgan Chase & Co.; *U.S. Public*, pg. 1209
JPMORGAN CHASE - WESTERN REGIONAL OFFICE—See JPMorgan Chase & Co.; *U.S. Public*, pg. 1209
J.P. MORGAN CHILE LIMITADA—See JPMorgan Chase & Co.; *U.S. Public*, pg. 1208
J.P. MORGAN (CHINA) VENTURE CAPITAL INVESTMENT COMPANY LIMITED—See JPMorgan Chase & Co.; *U.S. Public*, pg. 1208
JPMORGAN CLAVERHOUSE INVESTMENT TRUST PLC; *Int'l*, pg. 4007
J.P. MORGAN CLEARING CORP.—See JPMorgan Chase & Co.; *U.S. Public*, pg. 1208
J.P. MORGAN CORRETORA DE CAMBIO E VALORES MOBILIARIOS S.A.—See JPMorgan Chase & Co.; *U.S. Public*, pg. 1208
JPMORGAN ELECT PLC; *Int'l*, pg. 4007
JPMORGAN EMERGING EUROPE, MIDDLE EAST & AFRICA SECURITIES PLC; *Int'l*, pg. 4007
J.P. MORGAN EQUITIES LIMITED—See JPMorgan Chase & Co.; *U.S. Public*, pg. 1208
JPMORGAN EUROPEAN INVESTMENT TRUST PLC; *Int'l*, pg. 4007
J.P. MORGAN EUROPE LIMITED—See JPMorgan Chase & Co.; *U.S. Public*, pg. 1208
J.P. MORGAN FONDS SERVICES GMBH—See JPMorgan Chase & Co.; *U.S. Public*, pg. 1208
JPMORGAN FUNDS (ASIA) LIMITED—See JPMorgan Chase & Co.; *U.S. Public*, pg. 1209
J.P. MORGAN FUTURES CO., LIMITED; *Int'l*, pg. 3858
J.P. MORGAN FUTURES INC.—See JPMorgan Chase & Co.; *U.S. Public*, pg. 1208
JPMORGAN GLOBAL CORE REAL ASSETS LIMITED; *Int'l*, pg. 4007
JPMORGAN GLOBAL EMERGING MARKETS INCOME TRUST PLC; *Int'l*, pg. 4007
JPMORGAN GLOBAL GROWTH & INCOME PLC; *Int'l*, pg. 4007
J.P. MORGAN GRUPO FINANCIERO S.A. DE C.V.—See JPMorgan Chase & Co.; *U.S. Public*, pg. 1208
J.P. MORGAN INTERNATIONAL INC.—See JPMorgan Chase & Co.; *U.S. Public*, pg. 1209
J.P. MORGAN INVESTMENT MANAGEMENT—See JPMorgan Chase & Co.; *U.S. Public*, pg. 1208
JPMORGAN JAPAN SMALL CAP GROWTH & INCOME PLC; *Int'l*, pg. 4007
J.P. MORGAN LIMITED—See JPMorgan Chase & Co.; *U.S. Public*, pg. 1209
J.P. MORGAN NOMINEES AUSTRALIA LIMITED—See JPMorgan Chase & Co.; *U.S. Public*, pg. 1208
J.P. MORGAN PARTNERS, LLC—See JPMorgan Chase & Co.; *U.S. Public*, pg. 1208
J.P. MORGAN PHYSICAL COPPER TRUST; *U.S. Private*, pg. 2170
J.P. MORGAN RESEARCH TOTAL RETURN FUND LLC—See JPMorgan Chase & Co.; *U.S. Public*, pg. 1208
J.P. MORGAN (S.E.A.) LIMITED—See JPMorgan Chase & Co.; *U.S. Public*, pg. 1208
J.P. MORGAN SECURITIES (ASIA PACIFIC) LIMITED—See JPMorgan Chase & Co.; *U.S. Public*, pg. 1208
J.P. MORGAN SECURITIES ASIA PTE. LTD.—See JPMorgan Chase & Co.; *U.S. Public*, pg. 1208
J.P. MORGAN SECURITIES INDIA PRIVATE LIMITED—See JPMorgan Chase & Co.; *U.S. Public*, pg. 1209
JPMORGAN SECURITIES JAPAN CO., LTD.—See JPMorgan Chase & Co.; *U.S. Public*, pg. 1209
JPMORGAN SECURITIES LLC—See JPMorgan Chase & Co.; *U.S. Public*, pg. 1208
J.P. MORGAN SECURITIES PLC—See JPMorgan Chase & Co.; *U.S. Public*, pg. 1208
J.P. MORGAN SECURITIES SINGAPORE PRIVATE LIMITED—See JPMorgan Chase & Co.; *U.S. Public*, pg. 1208
J.P. MORGAN SERVICES INC.—See JPMorgan Chase & Co.; *U.S. Public*, pg. 1208
J.P. MORGAN SERVICES INDIA PRIVATE LIMITED—See JPMorgan Chase & Co.; *U.S. Public*, pg. 1208
J.P. MORGAN SERVICES INDIA PRIVATE LIMITED—See JPMorgan Chase & Co.; *U.S. Public*, pg. 1208
J.P. MORGAN SERVICES (MALAYSIA) SDN. BHD.—See JPMorgan Chase & Co.; *U.S. Public*, pg. 1208
JPMORGAN SERVICIOS AUXILIARES, S.A.—See JPMorgan Chase & Co.; *U.S. Public*, pg. 1210
JPMORGAN SMALLER COMPANIES INVESTMENT TRUST PLC; *Int'l*, pg. 4007
J.P. MORGAN (SUISSE) S.A.—See JPMorgan Chase & Co.; *U.S. Public*, pg. 1209
J.P. MORGAN (SUISSE) SA—See JPMorgan Chase & Co.; *U.S. Public*, pg. 1208
JPMORGAN TRUST COMPANY (BAHAMAS) LIMITED—See JPMorgan Chase & Co.; *U.S. Public*, pg. 1210
JPMORGAN US SMALLER COMPANIES INVESTMENT TRUST PLC; *Int'l*, pg. 4007

COMPANY NAME INDEX

J.P. MORGAN VENTURES ENERGY CORPORATION—See JPMorgan Chase & Co.; *U.S. Public*, pg. 1208
JP MOTORS, INC.; *U.S. Private*, pg. 2239
JPMP CAPITAL CORP.—See JPMorgan Chase & Co.; *U.S. Public*, pg. 1208
JPM S.A.—See ASSA ABLOY AB; *Int'l*, pg. 639
J-PM SYSTEMS GMBH—See Taikisha Ltd.; *Int'l*, pg. 7413
JPN COLLECTION SERVICE CO., LTD.—See Credit Saison Co., Ltd.; *Int'l*, pg. 1836
JP NELSON ACCESS EQUIPMENT PTE LTD—See JP Nelson Equipment Pte Ltd; *Int'l*, pg. 4005
JP NELSON EQUIPMENT PTE LTD; *Int'l*, pg. 4005
JP NELSON (MALAYSIA) SDN BHD—See JP Nelson Equipment Pte Ltd; *Int'l*, pg. 4005
JP NELSON (TAIWAN) CORPORATION—See JP Nelson Equipment Pte Ltd; *Int'l*, pg. 4005
JP NELSON (THAILAND) LIMITED—See JP Nelson Equipment Pte Ltd; *Int'l*, pg. 4005
JPN HOLDINGS COMPANY, LIMITED—See Credit Saison Co., Ltd.; *Int'l*, pg. 1836
JPN INC.—See Ishii Hyoki Co., Ltd.; *Int'l*, pg. 3818
J.P. NOONAN TRANSPORTATION; *U.S. Private*, pg. 2170
JPO FAIRCONSULTING—See Messe Munchen GmbH; *Int'l*, pg. 4841
JP OIL COMPANY INC.; *U.S. Private*, pg. 2239
J.POND PRECISION METAL STAMPING (DONGGUAN) CO., LTD.—See J.Pond Precision Technology Co., Ltd.; *Int'l*, pg. 3858
J.POND PRECISION TECHNOLOGY CO., LTD.; *Int'l*, pg. 3858
JP ORIGINAL CORP.; *U.S. Private*, pg. 2239
J-POWER AUSTRALIA PTY. LTD.—See Electric Power Development Co., Ltd.; *Int'l*, pg. 2349
J-POWER ENTECH, INC.—See Electric Power Development Co., Ltd.; *Int'l*, pg. 2349
J-POWER HOLDINGS (THAILAND) CO., LTD.—See Electric Power Development Co., Ltd.; *Int'l*, pg. 2349
J-POWER RESOURCES CO., LTD.—See Electric Power Development Co., Ltd.; *Int'l*, pg. 2349
J-POWER SYSTEMS CORPORATION—See Proterial, Ltd.; *Int'l*, pg. 6006
J-POWER SYSTEMS CORPORATION—See Sumitomo Electric Industries, Ltd.; *Int'l*, pg. 7278
J-POWER USA DEVELOPMENT CO., LTD.—See Electric Power Development Co., Ltd.; *Int'l*, pg. 2349
J.P. PATTI TECTA AMERICA, LLC—See Altas Partners LP; *Int'l*, pg. 386
JPP FAR EAST (S) PTE. LTD.—See Japan Pulp and Paper Company Limited; *Int'l*, pg. 3903
JPP HOLDING CO., LTD.; *Int'l*, pg. 4007
JP PICCININI REAL ESTATE SERVICES LLC—See Aperion Management; *U.S. Private*, pg. 291
J P PLAST SLOVAKIA SPOL S R O—See Berry Global Group, Inc; *U.S. Public*, pg. 322
J P PLAST S R O—See Berry Global Group, Inc; *U.S. Public*, pg. 322
JP/POLITIKEN HUS A/S; *Int'l*, pg. 4005
JP RESOURCES CO., LTD.—See Japan Pulp and Paper Company Limited; *Int'l*, pg. 3903
J. PRESS, INC.—See Onward Holdings Co., Ltd.; *Int'l*, pg. 5592
JPR HOMES; *U.S. Private*, pg. 2239
J&P RICHARDSON INDUSTRIES PTY. LTD.—See VINCI S.A.; *Int'l*, pg. 8223
J. PRO CO., LTD.—See Japan Airlines Co., Ltd.; *Int'l*, pg. 3882
JP RYAN ENTERPRISES INC.; *U.S. Private*, pg. 2239
J.P. SAUER & SOHN GMBH—See SAN Swiss Arms AG; *Int'l*, pg. 6521
JPS COMPOSITE MATERIALS CORPORATION—See Steel Partners Holdings L.P.; *U.S. Public*, pg. 1943
JPS HEALTH NETWORK; *U.S. Private*, pg. 2239
JP SHIPPING SERVICES LTD—See PanJam Investment Limited; *Int'l*, pg. 5728
JP STEEL PLANTECH CO.—See JFE Holdings, Inc.; *Int'l*, pg. 3938
JP STEEL PLANTECH (SHANGHAI) CO., LTD.—See JFE Holdings, Inc.; *Int'l*, pg. 3938
JPT AMERICA, INC.—See TOHAN CORPORATION; *Int'l*, pg. 7775
J.P. TAYLOR COMPANY, L.L.C.—See Universal Corporation; *U.S. Public*, pg. 2254
JP TECH INSURANCE SERVICES INC.—See Arthur J. Gallagher & Co.; *U.S. Public*, pg. 206
JPT ELECTRONICS PTE. LTD.—See Shenzhen JPT Opto-Electronics Co., Ltd.; *Int'l*, pg. 6815
JPT EUROPE LTD.—See TOHAN CORPORATION; *Int'l*, pg. 7775
J.P. THIBODEAUX INC.; *U.S. Private*, pg. 2170
JPT PEPTIDE TECHNOLOGIES GMBH—See BioNTech SE; *Int'l*, pg. 1041
JP TRANSPORT SERVICE CO., LTD.—See Japan Pulp and Paper Company Limited; *Int'l*, pg. 3903
JPT SECURITIES LIMITED; *Int'l*, pg. 4007
JPTS ELECTRONICS MATERIALS (SHANGHAI) CO., LTD.—See Japan Pulp and Paper Company Limited; *Int'l*, pg. 3903

J.P. TURNER & COMPANY, LLC—See RCAP Holdings, LLC; *U.S. Private*, pg. 3361
J PUBLIC RELATIONS, INC.; *U.S. Private*, pg. 2153
JP VODOVOD I KANALIZACIJA D.O.O.; *Int'l*, pg. 4005
JPW CONSULTING; *U.S. Private*, pg. 2239
JPW INDUSTRIES INC.—See Tenex Capital Management, L.P.; *U.S. Private*, pg. 3966
JPW (TOOL) AG—See Tenex Capital Management, L.P.; *U.S. Private*, pg. 3966
JPX GLOBAL INC.; *U.S. Public*, pg. 1210
JQH ELECTRONICS INDIA LLP—See Shenzhen JingQuanHua Electronics Co., Ltd.; *Int'l*, pg. 6814
JQH INC.—See Shenzhen JingQuanHua Electronics Co., Ltd.; *Int'l*, pg. 6814
J-QUEST CO., LTD.—See ENEOS Holdings, Inc.; *Int'l*, pg. 2417
JQW PLC; *Int'l*, pg. 4007
J.R. ABBOTT CONSTRUCTION, INC.; *U.S. Private*, pg. 2170
JRAIFU SUPPORT CORPORATION—See JUTEC Holdings Corporation; *Int'l*, pg. 4032
J. RANCK ELECTRIC INC.; *U.S. Private*, pg. 2157
JR ANLEGG AS—See AF Gruppen ASA; *Int'l*, pg. 184
J.R. AUTOMATION - STEVENSVILLE—See Hitachi, Ltd.; *Int'l*, pg. 3423
J.R. AUTOMATION TECHNOLOGIES, LLC—See Hitachi, Ltd.; *Int'l*, pg. 3423
J. RAY MCDERMOTT (AUST.) HOLDING PTY LIMITED—See McDermott International, Inc.; *U.S. Public*, pg. 1405
J. RAY MCDERMOTT DE MEXICO, S.A. DE C.V.—See McDermott International, Inc.; *U.S. Public*, pg. 1405
J. RAYMOND CONSTRUCTION CORPORATION; *U.S. Private*, pg. 2157
JRB ATTACHMENTS, LLC—See Stanley Black & Decker, Inc.; *U.S. Public*, pg. 1933
J.R BIRKETT AND SONS LIMITED—See Greggs plc; *Int'l*, pg. 3078
JRC CZECH, A.S.—See Hamaga as; *Int'l*, pg. 3235
JRC DO BRASIL EMPREENDIMENTOS ELETRONICOS LTDA.—See Nisshinbo Holdings Inc.; *Int'l*, pg. 5373
JRC ENGINEERING CO., LTD.—See Nisshinbo Holdings Inc.; *Int'l*, pg. 5373
JR CENTRAL BUILDING CO., LTD.—See Central Japan Railway Company; *Int'l*, pg. 1408
JR CENTRAL CONSULTANTS COMPANY—See Central Japan Railway Company; *Int'l*, pg. 1408
JR CENTRAL PASSENGERS CO., LTD.—See Central Japan Railway Company; *Int'l*, pg. 1408
JR CIGARS.COM, INC.—See Imperial Brands PLC; *Int'l*, pg. 3634
JR CLANCY, INC.—See Wenger Corporation; *U.S. Private*, pg. 4481
JRC LOGISTICS; *U.S. Private*, pg. 2239
JRC MOBILITY INC.—See Nisshinbo Holdings Inc.; *Int'l*, pg. 5373
J.R. COLE INDUSTRIES INC.; *U.S. Private*, pg. 2170
J & R CONTRACTING CO. INC.—See Kohlberg & Company, LLC; *U.S. Private*, pg. 2337
J & R CONTRACTING CO. INC.—See Partners Group Holding AG; *Int'l*, pg. 5749
JRC CONTROLS INC.; *U.S. Private*, pg. 2239
JRC PIZZA LLC; *U.S. Private*, pg. 2240
JRC SHANGHAI CO., LTD.—See Nisshinbo Holdings Inc.; *Int'l*, pg. 5373
JRC TOKKI CO., LTD.—See Nisshinbo Holdings Inc.; *Int'l*, pg. 5373
JR DEVELOPMENT AND MANAGEMENT CORPORATION OF SHIZUOKA—See Central Japan Railway Company; *Int'l*, pg. 1408
JRD PACKAGING AND INDUSTRIAL SUPPLY; *U.S. Private*, pg. 2240
JR EAST JAPAN INFORMATION SYSTEMS COMPANY—See East Japan Railway Company; *Int'l*, pg. 2270
JR EAST NET STATION CO., LTD.—See East Japan Railway Company; *Int'l*, pg. 2270
JR EAST RETAIL NET CO., LTD.—See East Japan Railway Company; *Int'l*, pg. 2270
J. RECKNER ASSOCIATES INC.; *U.S. Private*, pg. 2157
JRE DEVELOPMENT CO., LTD.—See Japan Airlines Co., Ltd.; *Int'l*, pg. 3883
JRE DEVELOPMENT CO., LTD.—See Sojitz Corporation; *Int'l*, pg. 7062
J-RE-LIGHTS CO., LTD.—See Kyushu Electric Power Co., Inc.; *Int'l*, pg. 4367
J RENE HEBERT LTEE; *Int'l*, pg. 3852
J. RETTENMAIER BENELUX—See J. Rettenmaier & Sohne GmbH & Co. KG; *Int'l*, pg. 3856
J. RETTENMAIER LATINOAMERICANA LTDA.—See J. Rettenmaier & Sohne GmbH & Co. KG; *Int'l*, pg. 3856
J. RETTENMAIER & SOHNE GMBH & CO. KG - HEILBRONN PLANT—See J. Rettenmaier & Sohne GmbH & Co. KG; *Int'l*, pg. 3856
J. RETTENMAIER & SOHNE GMBH & CO. KG; *Int'l*, pg. 3856
J. RETTENMAIER USA, LP—See J. Rettenmaier & Sohne GmbH & Co. KG; *Int'l*, pg. 3856
J. REYNOLDS & CO.; *U.S. Private*, pg. 2157

J&R FILM & MOVIOLA DIGITAL CO.; *U.S. Private*, pg. 2155
J. R. FOODS LIMITED; *Int'l*, pg. 3856
JR. FOOD STORES, INC.—See Houchens Industries, Inc.; *U.S. Private*, pg. 1990
JRG ADVISORS, LLC—See Emerson Reid LLC; *U.S. Private*, pg. 1382
JRG FINCORP LIMITED—See Inditrade Capital Limited; *Int'l*, pg. 3656
JR GLOBAL LOGISTICS, INC.—See Jiayou International Logistics Co., Ltd.; *Int'l*, pg. 3962
JR GLOBAL REIT CO., LTD.; *Int'l*, pg. 4007
J&R HALL TRANSPORT INC.; *U.S. Private*, pg. 3853
JRH ELECTRONICS L.L.C.; *U.S. Private*, pg. 2240
JRH INDUSTRIES LLC; *U.S. Private*, pg. 2240
JR HOLDING ASI S.A.; *Int'l*, pg. 4007
JRI AMERICA, INC.—See Sumitomo Mitsui Financial Group, Inc.; *Int'l*, pg. 7295
JRI EUROPE, LIMITED—See Sumitomo Mitsui Financial Group, Inc.; *Int'l*, pg. 7295
JRI INDUSTRIES & INFRASTRUCTURE LIMITED; *Int'l*, pg. 4008
J&R INDUSTRIAL INC.—See ASE Technology Holding Co., Ltd.; *Int'l*, pg. 604
JR INSULATION SALES & SERVICE; *U.S. Private*, pg. 2239
JRI ORTHOPAEDICS LIMITED—See AK Medical Holdings Limited; *Int'l*, pg. 259
J. RIVEROS S.A.I.C.—See Mann+Hummel GmbH; *Int'l*, pg. 4673
JRJ INVESTMENTS, INC.—See AutoNation, Inc.; *U.S. Public*, pg. 235
J.R. JOHNSON, INC.—See Basset Creek Capital, Inc.; *U.S. Private*, pg. 486
J.R. JOHNSON, INC.—See Gladstone Management Corporation; *U.S. Private*, pg. 1705
JRJR33, INC.; *U.S. Private*, pg. 2240
JRJ VENTURES LLP; *Int'l*, pg. 4008
J.R. KELLY COMPANY INC.; *U.S. Private*, pg. 2170
JRL ENTERPRISES INC.; *U.S. Private*, pg. 2240
JRL ENTERPRISES, INC.; *U.S. Private*, pg. 2240
JR LICENSING, LLC—See XCel Brands, Inc.; *U.S. Public*, pg. 2385
JRL VENTURES, INC.; *U.S. Private*, pg. 2240
JR MANUFACTURING, INC.—See Nippon Steel Corporation; *Int'l*, pg. 5337
J.R. MCDADE COMPANY, INC.; *U.S. Private*, pg. 2170
JRM CONSTRUCTION MANAGEMENT, LLC; *U.S. Private*, pg. 2240
J & R MEDICAL, LLC—See ConvaTec Group PLC; *Int'l*, pg. 1786
JRM GROUP CO., LTD.—See Japan Resistor Mfg Co., Ltd.; *Int'l*, pg. 3905
J-R MOTORS COMPANY NORTH—See AutoNation, Inc.; *U.S. Public*, pg. 235
JRM (SHANGHAI) ELECTRONICS MANUFACTURING CO., LTD.—See Japan Resistor Mfg Co., Ltd.; *Int'l*, pg. 3905
JRM (THAILAND) CO., LTD.—See Japan Resistor Mfg Co., Ltd.; *Int'l*, pg. 3905
J&R MUSIC WORLD; *U.S. Private*, pg. 2155
J.R. NAVARRO & ASSOCIATES INC.; *U.S. Private*, pg. 2170
J. ROBERTS & COMPANY; *U.S. Private*, pg. 2157
J. ROBERT SCOTT INC.; *U.S. Private*, pg. 2157
J. ROMERO & ASSOCIATES; *Int'l*, pg. 3857
JR ORION SERVICES PTE. LTD.—See Sumner Group Health Limited; *Int'l*, pg. 7302
J. ROTHSCHILD CAPITAL MANAGEMENT LIMITED—See RIT Capital Partners plc; *Int'l*, pg. 6351
J ROYAL CO. INC.-BARRINGTON—See Diploma PLC; *Int'l*, pg. 2128
J. ROYAL CO. INC.—See Diploma PLC; *Int'l*, pg. 2128
JRP EDITIONS S.A.—See Ringier Holding AG; *Int'l*, pg. 6343
J.R. PIERCE PLUMBING CO., INC.; *U.S. Private*, pg. 2170
J&R PRODUCTS, INC.—See Pacific Avenue Capital Partners, LLC; *U.S. Private*, pg. 3065
JRS ADVERTISING; *U.S. Private*, pg. 2240
J&R SCHUGEL TRUCKING INC.; *U.S. Private*, pg. 2155
JRS COUNTRY STORE INC.; *U.S. Private*, pg. 2240
JRS HOLDING, INC.; *U.S. Private*, pg. 2240
J.R. SHORT MILLING COMPANY; *U.S. Private*, pg. 2170
J.R. SIMPLOT COMPANY, AGRI BUSINESS—See J.R. Simplot Company; *U.S. Private*, pg. 2170
J.R. SIMPLOT COMPANY FOOD GROUP—See J.R. Simplot Company; *U.S. Private*, pg. 2170
J.R. SIMPLOT COMPANY - LAND & LIVESTOCK—See J.R. Simplot Company; *U.S. Private*, pg. 2170
J.R. SIMPLOT COMPANY LATHROP PLANT—See J.R. Simplot Company; *U.S. Private*, pg. 2170
J.R. SIMPLOT COMPANY; *U.S. Private*, pg. 2170
J.R. SIMPLOT COMPANY—See J.R. Simplot Company; *U.S. Private*, pg. 2170
JRS INTERNATIONAL, LLC—See ICD Group International Inc.; *U.S. Private*, pg. 2030
JRSIS HEALTH CARE CORPORATION; *Int'l*, pg. 4008
J & R SLAW, INC.; *U.S. Private*, pg. 2152

J & R SLAW, INC.

CORPORATE AFFILIATIONS

J.R. SMITH MANUFACTURING COMPANY—See Jay R. Smith Mfg. Co.; *U.S. Private*, pg. 2192
JRS PHARMA LP - CEDAR RAPIDS PLANT—See J. Rettenmaier & Sohne GmbH & Co. KG; *Int'l*, pg. 3856
JRS PHARMA LP—See J. Rettenmaier & Sohne GmbH & Co. KG; *Int'l*, pg. 3856
JRS PHARMA OY—See J. Rettenmaier & Sohne GmbH & Co. KG; *Int'l*, pg. 3856
JRS PROZESSTECHNIK GMBH & CO KG—See J. Rettenmaier & Sohne GmbH & Co. KG; *Int'l*, pg. 3856
JRS RESOURCES, INC.—See Japan Pulp and Paper Company Limited; *Int'l*, pg. 3904
JRS SCHWEIZ AG—See J. Rettenmaier & Sohne GmbH & Co. KG; *Int'l*, pg. 3856
JRS TRUCKING SERVICE, INC.; *U.S. Private*, pg. 2240
JRT HEALTHCARE, INC.—See The Ensign Group, Inc.; *U.S. Public*, pg. 2071
J.R. THOMPSON COMPANY, LLC; *U.S. Private*, pg. 2171
JR TOKAI AGENCY CO., LTD.—See Central Japan Railway Company; *Int'l*, pg. 1408
JR TOKAI BUS COMPANY—See Central Japan Railway Company; *Int'l*, pg. 1408
JR TOKAI CONSTRUCTION CO., LTD.—See Central Japan Railway Company; *Int'l*, pg. 1408
JR TOKAI CORPORATION—See Central Japan Railway Company; *Int'l*, pg. 1408
JR TOKAI FOOD SERVICE CO., LTD.—See Central Japan Railway Company; *Int'l*, pg. 1408
JR TOKAI HOTELS CO., LTD.—See Central Japan Railway Company; *Int'l*, pg. 1408
JR TOKAI INFORMATION SYSTEMS COMPANY—See Central Japan Railway Company; *Int'l*, pg. 1408
JR TOKAI LOGISTICS CO., LTD.—See Central Japan Railway Company; *Int'l*, pg. 1408
JR TOKAI REAL ESTATE CO., LTD.—See Central Japan Railway Company; *Int'l*, pg. 1408
JR TOKAI TAKASHIMAYA CO., LTD.—See Central Japan Railway Company; *Int'l*, pg. 1408
JR TOKAI TOURS, INC.—See Central Japan Railway Company; *Int'l*, pg. 1408
J&R UNDERGROUND LLC—See Quanta Services, Inc.; *U.S. Public*, pg. 1751
J RUSSELL & ASSOCIATES LLC; *U.S. Private*, pg. 2153
J & R WELL SERVICE, LLC—See Rock Hill Capital Group, LLC; *U.S. Private*, pg. 3464
JR WEST FINANCIAL MANAGEMENT CO., LTD.—See West Japan Railway Company; *Int'l*, pg. 8385
JR WEST IT SOLUTIONS COMPANY—See West Japan Railway Company; *Int'l*, pg. 8385
JR WEST JAPAN COMMUNICATIONS COMPANY—See West Japan Railway Company; *Int'l*, pg. 8385
JR-WEST JAPAN CONSULTANTS COMPANY—See West Japan Railway Company; *Int'l*, pg. 8385
JR WEST JAPAN LINEN CO., LTD—See West Japan Railway Company; *Int'l*, pg. 8385
JR WEST JAPAN MARUNIX CO., LTD—See West Japan Railway Company; *Int'l*, pg. 8385
JR-WEST JAPAN REAL ESTATE & DEVELOPMENT COMPANY—See West Japan Railway Company; *Int'l*, pg. 8385
JR WEST MAINTEC CO., LTD.—See West Japan Railway Company; *Int'l*, pg. 8385
JR WEST MIYAJIMA FERRY CO., LTD.—See West Japan Railway Company; *Int'l*, pg. 8385
JR WEST PROPERTIES CO., LTD.—See Mitsubishi Heavy Industries, Ltd.; *Int'l*, pg. 4953
J. RYAN BONDING, INC.—See GTCR LLC; *U.S. Private*, pg. 1803
JS2 COMMUNICATIONS—See JS2 Communications; *U.S. Private*, pg. 2241
JS2 COMMUNICATIONS; *U.S. Private*, pg. 2241
JS ADWAYS MEDIA INC.—See Adways Inc.; *Int'l*, pg. 169
J. SAFRA SARASIN HOLDING AG—See Banco Safra S.A.; *Int'l*, pg. 824
JS AG PACKAGING, INC.—See Rainier Partners LP; *U.S. Private*, pg. 3348
JS&A GROUP, INC.; *U.S. Private*, pg. 2241
JSA HEALTHCARE CORPORATION; *U.S. Private*, pg. 2241
JSA HEALTHCARE NEVADA, LLC.—See DaVita Inc.; *U.S. Public*, pg. 640
J SAINSBURY PLC; *Int'l*, pg. 3852
JSA P5 NEVADA, LLC.—See DaVita Inc.; *U.S. Public*, pg. 640
JSA SERVICES LTD.; *Int'l*, pg. 4008
JSAT INTERNATIONAL INC.—See SKY Perfect JSAT Holdings Inc.; *Int'l*, pg. 6993
JSAT MOBILE COMMUNICATIONS INC.—See SKY Perfect JSAT Holdings Inc.; *Int'l*, pg. 6993
J&S AUDIO VISUAL COMMUNICATIONS, LLC—See Ashford Inc.; *U.S. Public*, pg. 211
JS BANK LIMITED—See Jahangir Siddiqui & Co. Ltd.; *Int'l*, pg. 3871
J.S.B. CO., LTD.; *Int'l*, pg. 3858
JSB GPB-MORTGAGE OJSC—See Gazprombank JSC; *Int'l*, pg. 2892
JSB GROUP A/S—See Gurit Holding AG; *Int'l*, pg. 3188
JSB INDUSTRIES INC.; *U.S. Private*, pg. 2241

J.S. BLADE ADVERTISING AGENCY, INC.; *U.S. Private*, pg. 2171
JSB LIGHTING—See Hancock & Gore Ltd.; *Int'l*, pg. 3242
JS BUILDERS, LLC—See Obayashi Corporation; *Int'l*, pg. 5508
JSC AEROKOMPOZIT—See PJSC United Aircraft Corporation; *Int'l*, pg. 5885
J&S CAFETERIA INC.; *U.S. Private*, pg. 2155
JSC AGRONOVA—See Public Joint Stock Company Acron; *Int'l*, pg. 6094
JSC AIST—See PJSC Rostelecom; *Int'l*, pg. 5884
JSC ALMAZY ANABARA—See PJSC Alrosa; *Int'l*, pg. 5878
JSC ALMETYEVSK HEATING NETWORKS—See PJSC Tatneft; *Int'l*, pg. 5885
JSC ALROSA AIR COMPANY—See PJSC Alrosa; *Int'l*, pg. 5878
JSC ALROSA-GAZ—See PJSC Alrosa; *Int'l*, pg. 5878
JSC ALROSA-LENA SHIPPING COMPANY—See PJSC Alrosa; *Int'l*, pg. 5878
JSC ALROSA-TORG—See PJSC Alrosa; *Int'l*, pg. 5878
JSC ALTYN BANK—See Halyk Bank of Kazakhstan JSC; *Int'l*, pg. 3234
JSCAPE LLC—See Redwood Software, Inc.; *U.S. Private*, pg. 3381
JSC ASTELLAS PHARMA—See Astellas Pharma Inc.; *Int'l*, pg. 653
JSC ATOMENERGOPROM—See State Atomic Energy Corporation ROSATOM; *Int'l*, pg. 7180
JSC ATOMREDMETZOLOTO—See State Atomic Energy Corporation ROSATOM; *Int'l*, pg. 7180
JSC AURORA AIRLINES—See PJSC Aeroflot Russian Airlines; *Int'l*, pg. 5878
JSC AVANGARD; *Int'l*, pg. 4008
JSC AVIAGARD-SP—See PJSC United Aircraft Corporation; *Int'l*, pg. 5885
JSC AVIATION GEARBOXES AND TRANSMISSIONS - PERM MOTORS—See Russian Technologies State Corporation; *Int'l*, pg. 6431
JSC AVIATION HOLDING COMPANY—See PJSC United Aircraft Corporation; *Int'l*, pg. 5885
J-S.C. AVTODIZEL—See Russian Technologies State Corporation; *Int'l*, pg. 6431
JSC AVTOVAZ—See Nissan Motor Co., Ltd.; *Int'l*, pg. 5367
JSC AVTOVAZ—See Renault S.A.; *Int'l*, pg. 6273
JSC AVTOVAZ—See Russian Technologies State Corporation; *Int'l*, pg. 6431
JSCB ALMAZERGIENBANK JSC; *Int'l*, pg. 4012
JSC BANK OF GEORGIA; *Int'l*, pg. 4008
JSC BASHINFORMSVYAZ—See PJSC Rostelecom; *Int'l*, pg. 5884
JSC BELON; *Int'l*, pg. 4008
JSC BENNET DISTRIBUTORS; *Int'l*, pg. 4008
JSC BETELTRANS—See JSC Russian Railways; *Int'l*, pg. 4011
JSCB FORSHTADT JSC; *Int'l*, pg. 4012
JSCB INTERNATIONAL FINANCIAL CLUB JSC—See Onexim Group Limited; *Int'l*, pg. 5581
JSC BOROVICHI REFRACTORIES PLANT; *Int'l*, pg. 4008
JSCB PERESVET PJSC; *Int'l*, pg. 4012
JSCB PRIMORYE; *Int'l*, pg. 4012
JSCB TENGE BANK—See Halyk Bank of Kazakhstan JSC; *Int'l*, pg. 3234
JSCB TRANSSTROIBANK JSC; *Int'l*, pg. 4012
JSC BUSINESS COMPUTER CENTER; *Int'l*, pg. 4008
JSC BVT EXIM—See Dohler GmbH; *Int'l*, pg. 2156
JSC CASPI NEFT TME—See Polytec Asset Holdings Limited; *Int'l*, pg. 5916
JSC CAUCASUS ENERGY & INFRASTRUCTURE; *Int'l*, pg. 4008
JSC CENTRAL TELEGRAPH—See OJSC Svyazinvest; *Int'l*, pg. 5612
JSC CHIRKEIGESSTROY—See PJSC RusHydro; *Int'l*, pg. 5884
JSC CITIBANK KAZAKHSTAN—See Citigroup Inc.; *U.S. Public*, pg. 504
JSC COMMERCIAL BANK - BANK OF MOSCOW—See PJSC VTB Bank; *Int'l*, pg. 5886
JSC COMMERCIAL PORT OF VLADIVOSTOK; *Int'l*, pg. 4008
JSC CONCERN OF AVIATION EQUIPMENT—See Russian Technologies State Corporation; *Int'l*, pg. 6432
JSC DNEPROPTROVSK TUBE WORKS—See Industrial Union of Donbass Corporation; *Int'l*, pg. 3673
JSC ECOSTIL—See R-Pharm CJSC; *Int'l*, pg. 6169
JSC EKATERINBURG NON-FERROUS METAL PROCESSING PLANT—See Renova Group; *Int'l*, pg. 6285
JSC ELECTRICAL EQUIPMENT MAINTENANCE FACTORY RETO—See JSC ROSSETI; *Int'l*, pg. 4010
JSC ENERGOTSENTR—See PJSC MOESK; *Int'l*, pg. 5883
JSC ESTRELLA BALTICS—See Intersnack Group GmbH & Co. KG; *Int'l*, pg. 3760
JSC EVAN—See NIBE Industrier AB; *Int'l*, pg. 5261
JSC FEDERAL FREIGHT—See JSC Russian Railways; *Int'l*, pg. 4012
JSC FEDERAL PASSENGER COMPANY—See JSC Russian Railways; *Int'l*, pg. 4012

JSC FE EFES KAZAKHSTAN BREWERY—See Anadolu Efes Biracilik ve Malt Sanayii A.S.; *Int'l*, pg. 445
JSC FLIGHT RESEARCH INSTITUTE N.A. M.M. GROMOV—See PJSC United Aircraft Corporation; *Int'l*, pg. 5885
JSC FRESENIUS SP—See Fresenius Medical Care AG; *Int'l*, pg. 2776
JSC GASO—See AS Infortar; *Int'l*, pg. 590
JSC GAZPROM NEFT—See PJSC Gazprom; *Int'l*, pg. 5879
JSC GEORGIAN CARD—See JSC Bank of Georgia; *Int'l*, pg. 4008
JSC GK KHIMIK; *Int'l*, pg. 4008
JSC GOLUBAYA VOLNA RESORT—See PJSC Alrosa; *Int'l*, pg. 5878
JSC GPI INSURANCE COMPANY HOLDING—See Vienna Insurance Group AG Wiener Versicherung Gruppe; *Int'l*, pg. 8195
JSC HALYK GLOBAL MARKETS—See Halyk Bank of Kazakhstan JSC; *Int'l*, pg. 3234
J. SCHNEIDER ELEKTROTECHNIK GMBH FACTORY II—See J. Schneider Elektrotechnik GmbH; *Int'l*, pg. 3857
J. SCHNEIDER ELEKTROTECHNIK GMBH; *Int'l*, pg. 3857
J. SCHNEIDER POWER SUPPLIES INC.—See J. Schneider Elektrotechnik GmbH; *Int'l*, pg. 3857
JSC HOLDING KAZEXPORTASTYK; *Int'l*, pg. 4008
JSC IC BOUREVESTNIK—See PJSC Alrosa; *Int'l*, pg. 5878
JSC INPROM; *Int'l*, pg. 4009
JSC INSURANCE COMPANY KAZKOMMERTS POLICY—See Halyk Bank of Kazakhstan JSC; *Int'l*, pg. 3234
JSC INTER RAO UES; *Int'l*, pg. 4009
JSC INTERREGIONAL DISTRIBUTION GRID COMPANY OF NORTH-WEST—See JSC ROSSETI; *Int'l*, pg. 4010
JSC ISBANK GEORGIA—See Turkiye Is Bankasi A.S.; *Int'l*, pg. 7976
JSC ISUZU RUS—See OJSC Sollers; *Int'l*, pg. 5542
JSC IZHEVSKY MEKHANICHESKY ZAVOD—See OJSC Concern Kalashnikov; *Int'l*, pg. 5539
JSC JV UZBAT A.O.—See British American Tobacco plc; *Int'l*, pg. 1167
JSC KALUGA PLANT REMPUTMASH—See JSC Russian Railways; *Int'l*, pg. 4012
JSC KAMENSK-URALSKY NON-FERROUS METAL WORKING PLANT—See Renova Group; *Int'l*, pg. 6285
JSC KARBOLIT—See Metafrax OJSC; *Int'l*, pg. 4844
JSC KAZMUNAIGAS EXPLORATION PRODUCTION—See JSC National Company KazMunayGas; *Int'l*, pg. 4010
JSC KAZTEMIRTRANS—See NC Kazakhstan Temir Zholy JSC; *Int'l*, pg. 5180
JSC KLAIPEDA SHIP REPAIR—See Koncernas Achemos Grupe; *Int'l*, pg. 4246
JSC KLIMOV—See Russian Technologies State Corporation; *Int'l*, pg. 6431
JSC KRASNOKAMSK METAL MESH WORKS; *Int'l*, pg. 4009
JSC KUZNETSOV—See Russian Technologies State Corporation; *Int'l*, pg. 6431
JSC LATVIJAS GAZE; *Int'l*, pg. 4009
JSC LC EUROPLAN—See Safmar Industrial & Financial Group; *Int'l*, pg. 6472
JSC LENENERGO—See JSC ROSSETI; *Int'l*, pg. 4010
JSC LENHYDROPROJECT—See PJSC RusHydro; *Int'l*, pg. 5884
JSC LIBERTY CONSUMER—See Bank of Georgia Group PLC; *Int'l*, pg. 843
JSC LIDSKOE PIVO—See Olvi Oyj; *Int'l*, pg. 5554
JSC LINDEKS; *Int'l*, pg. 4009
JSC LOGISTIKA-TERMINAL—See PJSC TransContainer; *Int'l*, pg. 5885
JSC LOMISI—See Anadolu Efes Biracilik ve Malt Sanayii A.S.; *Int'l*, pg. 445
JSC L-ZOS—See Russian Technologies State Corporation; *Int'l*, pg. 6431
JSC MARS FACTORY—See Russian Technologies State Corporation; *Int'l*, pg. 6432
JSC MASHINOSTROITELNY ZAVOD—See State Atomic Energy Corporation ROSATOM; *Int'l*, pg. 7181
JSC MINA—See Turkiye Sise ve Cam Fabrikalari A.S.; *Int'l*, pg. 7977
JSC MOBILE GTES—See OJSC Federal Grid Company of Unified Energy System; *Int'l*, pg. 5539
JSC MOESK-ENGINEERING—See PJSC MOESK; *Int'l*, pg. 5883
JSC MOTOVILIKHINSKIYE ZAVODY; *Int'l*, pg. 4009
JSC NATIONAL ATOMIC COMPANY KAZATOMPROM; *Int'l*, pg. 4009
JSC NATIONAL COMPANY KAZMUNAYGAS; *Int'l*, pg. 4009
JSC NATIONAL SETTLEMENT DEPOSITORY—See OJSC Moscow Exchange MICEX-RTS; *Int'l*, pg. 5540
JSC NEFAZ—See KAMAZ Publicly Traded Company; *Int'l*, pg. 4060
JSC NETRIS—See PJSC Rostelecom; *Int'l*, pg. 5884

COMPANY NAME INDEX

JSC NITI PROGRESS—See OJSC Concern Kalashnikov; *Int'l*, pg. 5539
JSC NIZHNIY NOVGOROD RETAIL COMPANY—See OAO AK Transneft; *Int'l*, pg. 5505
JSC NLMK-URAL—See Novolipetski Metallurgicheski Komb OAO; *Int'l*, pg. 5466
JSC NON-STATE PENSION FUND ALMAZNAYA OSEN—See PJSC Alrosa; *Int'l*, pg. 5878
JSC NORTH-WESTERN SHIPPING COMPANY—See Universal Cargo Logistics Holding B.V.; *Int'l*, pg. 8077
JSC NOVOROSLESEXPORT—See PJSC Novorossiysk Commercial Sea Port; *Int'l*, pg. 5883
JSC NPO NAUKA; *Int'l*, pg. 4010
JSC NPO SATURN—See Russian Technologies State Corporation; *Int'l*, pg. 6431
JSC NPP MOTOR—See Russian Technologies State Corporation; *Int'l*, pg. 6431
JSC OKA SHIPYARD—See Universal Cargo Logistics Holding B.V.; *Int'l*, pg. 8077
J'S COMMUNICATION CO., LTD.—See Segue Group Co., Ltd.; *Int'l*, pg. 6683
JS COMPUTEK LLC—See The 20 Msp Group LLC; *U.S. Private*, pg. 3980
J&S CONSTRUCTION COMPANY INC; *U.S. Private*, pg. 2155
JS CONSTRUCTION, S.E.; *U.S. Private*, pg. 2240
JSC OOIUPA NUR-TRUST—See Nurbank JSC; *Int'l*, pg. 5489
JSC OPIN—See Onexim Group Limited; *Int'l*, pg. 5581
JS CORPORATION; *Int'l*, pg. 4008
J.S. CORRUGATING MACHINERY CO., LTD.; *Int'l*, pg. 3858
JSCO SEVASTOPOL MARINE PLANT; *Int'l*, pg. 4012
JSC PCP RESPIRATOR—See Russian Technologies State Corporation; *Int'l*, pg. 6432
JSC PHARMSTANDARD; *Int'l*, pg. 4010
JSC POLIEF—See OAO SIBUR Holding; *Int'l*, pg. 5507
JSC POLYMETAL—See Solidcore Resources plc; *Int'l*, pg. 7072
JSC POLYUS KRASNOYARSK—See PJSC Polyus; *Int'l*, pg. 5883
JSC POLYUS RESEARCH INSTITUTE OF M.F.STELMAKH—See Russian Technologies State Corporation; *Int'l*, pg. 6401
JSC PRIME FITNESS—See Bank of Georgia Group PLC; *Int'l*, pg. 843
JSC PRIMORSK SHIPPING CORPORATION; *Int'l*, pg. 4010
JSC PROCREDIT BANK—See ProCredit Holding AG & Co. KGaA; *Int'l*, pg. 5987
JSC PROJEKTU CENTRAS—See Koncernas Achemos Grupe; *Int'l*, pg. 4246
JSC QUADRA-POWER GENERATION; *Int'l*, pg. 4010
JSC "KBP" INSTRUMENT DESIGN BUREAU—See Russian Technologies State Corporation; *Int'l*, pg. 6431
JSC RAILTRANSAUTO—See JSC Russian Railways; *Int'l*, pg. 4012
JSC RAILTRANSAUTO—See TransGroup AS, Ltd.; *Int'l*, pg. 7900
JSC RAKHAT—See Lotte Co., Ltd.; *Int'l*, pg. 4560
JSC REFSERVICE; *Int'l*, pg. 4010
JSC RG BRANDS—See RESMI Group Ltd.; *Int'l*, pg. 6297
JSC RIMERA—See PAO TMK; *Int'l*, pg. 5732
JSC ROSSETI; *Int'l*, pg. 4010
JSC ROSZHELDORPROJECT—See JSC Russian Railways; *Int'l*, pg. 4012
JSC RTI SYSTEMS CONCERN—See Sistema PJSFC; *Int'l*, pg. 6963
JSC RUSAL SAYANOGORSK—See United Company RUSAL Plc; *Int'l*, pg. 8066
JSC RUSATOM OVERSEAS COMPANY—See State Atomic Energy Corporation ROSATOM; *Int'l*, pg. 7181
JSC RUSSIAN AGENCY FOR EXPORT CREDIT AND INVESTMENT INSURANCE—See VEB.RF; *Int'l*, pg. 8143
JSC RUSSIAN AIRCRAFT CORPORATION—See PJSC United Aircraft Corporation; *Int'l*, pg. 5885
JSC RUSSIAN RAILWAYS; *Int'l*, pg. 4011
JSC RUSSIAN STANDARD BANK—See CJSC Russian Standard Corporation; *Int'l*, pg. 1634
JSC RUSSIAN STANDARD INSURANCE—See CJSC Russian Standard Corporation; *Int'l*, pg. 1634
JSC RZD LOGISTICS—See JSC Russian Railways; *Int'l*, pg. 4012
JSC RZDSTROY—See JSC Russian Railways; *Int'l*, pg. 4012
JSC RZD TRADING COMPANY—See JSC Russian Railways; *Int'l*, pg. 4012
JSC SANDOZ—See Novartis AG; *Int'l*, pg. 5457
JSC SB RBS (KAZAKHSTAN) LIMITED—See NatWest Group plc; *Int'l*, pg. 5171
JSC SDB TURBINA—See Russian Technologies State Corporation; *Int'l*, pg. 6431
JSC SEGEZHA PULP & PAPER MILL—See Sistema PJSFC; *Int'l*, pg. 6963
JSC SEVERSTAL-METIZ—See PAO Severstal; *Int'l*, pg. 5731
JSC SIAULIU PLENTAS; *Int'l*, pg. 4012
JSC SIBUR-PET—See OAO SIBUR Holding; *Int'l*, pg. 5507
JSC SISTEMA MASS MEDIA—See Sistema PJSFC; *Int'l*, pg. 6963
JSC SLAVNEFT-YANOS; *Int'l*, pg. 4012
JSC SOFRINSKY EXPERIMENTAL MECHANICAL PLANT; *Int'l*, pg. 4012
JSC STAR—See Russian Technologies State Corporation; *Int'l*, pg. 6431
JSC ST. PETERSBURG HEATING GRID—See PJSC Territorial Generating Company No 1; *Int'l*, pg. 5885
JSC SUEK; *Int'l*, pg. 4012
JSC SUMITOMO (SHI) DEMAG PLASTICS MACHINERY—See Sumitomo Heavy Industries, Ltd.; *Int'l*, pg. 7286
JSC TANECO—See PJSC Tatneft; *Int'l*, pg. 5885
JSC TBC BANK; *Int'l*, pg. 4012
JSC TBC INSURANCE—See TBC Bank Group PLC; *Int'l*, pg. 7479
JSC TELIANI VALLEY—See Bank of Georgia Group PLC; *Int'l*, pg. 843
JSC TEMIRBANK; *Int'l*, pg. 4012
JSC TENGRI BANK—See Punjab National Bank; *Int'l*, pg. 6120
JSC THIRD GENERATION COMPANY OF THE WHOLESALE ELECTRICITY MARKET—See PJSC MMC Norilsk Nickel; *Int'l*, pg. 5882
JSC TRANSCREDITBANK—See PJSC VTB Bank; *Int'l*, pg. 5886
JSC TRANSSERVICE—See PJSC MMC Norilsk Nickel; *Int'l*, pg. 5882
JSC TRANSTELECOM COMPANY—See JSC Russian Railways; *Int'l*, pg. 4012
JSC TULAMASHZAVOD—See Russian Technologies State Corporation; *Int'l*, pg. 6431
JSC TVEL—See State Atomic Energy Corporation ROSATOM; *Int'l*, pg. 7181
JSC TYUMENENERGO—See JSC ROSSETI; *Int'l*, pg. 4010
JSC UFA ENGINE INDUSTRIAL ASSOCIATION—See Russian Technologies State Corporation; *Int'l*, pg. 6431
JSC UKRSIB ASSET MANAGEMENT—See BNP Paribas SA; *Int'l*, pg. 1093
JSC UNITED TRANSPORT AND LOGISTICS COMPANY—See JSC Russian Railways; *Int'l*, pg. 4012
JSC URALSIBNEFTEPROVOD—See OAO AK Transneft; *Int'l*, pg. 5505
JSC VENTSPILS NAFTA—See Vitol Holding B.V.; *Int'l*, pg. 8260
JSC VETROPACK GOSTOMEL—See Vetropack Holding AG; *Int'l*, pg. 8181
JSC VNIIG—See PJSC RusHydro; *Int'l*, pg. 5884
JSC VO MASHPRIBORINTORG—See ESPEC Corp.; *Int'l*, pg. 2505
JSC YANTARENERGO—See JSC ROSSETI; *Int'l*, pg. 4010
JSC YARPOLIMERMASH-TATNEFT—See PJSC Tatneft; *Int'l*, pg. 5885
JSC ZALIV SHIPYARD; *Int'l*, pg. 4012
JSC ZAPSIBGAZPROM—See METROPOL Group of Companies; *Int'l*, pg. 4863
JSC ZHELDORIPOTEKA—See JSC Russian Railways; *Int'l*, pg. 4012
JSC ZOMZ—See Russian Technologies State Corporation; *Int'l*, pg. 6431
JSC ZVEZDA; *Int'l*, pg. 4012
JSE, INC.; *U.S. Private*, pg. 2241
JSE LIMITED; *Int'l*, pg. 4012
J&S ENGINEERING CORP.—See ESPEC Corp.; *Int'l*, pg. 2505
JSE PRIVATE PLACEMENTS PROPRIETARY LIMITED—See JSE Limited; *Int'l*, pg. 4012
JSE TRUSTEES (PTY) LIMITED—See JSE Limited; *Int'l*, pg. 4012
JS FINANCIAL SERVICES CO., INC.—See Stevens Group, Inc.; *U.S. Private*, pg. 3809
JSF INFORMATION TECHNOLOGY—See Japan Securities Finance Co., Ltd.; *Int'l*, pg. 3905
JS FOLSOM AUTOMOTIVE, INC.—See General Motors Company; *U.S. Public*, pg. 925
JSF TRUST AND BANKING CO., LTD.—See Japan Securities Finance Co., Ltd.; *Int'l*, pg. 3905
JS GENETICS, INC.—See Interpace Biosciences, Inc.; *U.S. Public*, pg. 1158
JS GLOBAL CAPITAL LIMITED—See Jahangir Siddiqui & Co. Ltd.; *Int'l*, pg. 3871
JS GLOBAL LIFESTYLE COMPANY LIMITED; *Int'l*, pg. 4008
J.S. HELD LLC—See Kelso & Company, L.P.; *U.S. Private*, pg. 2278
JS HUMIDIFIERS PLC—See Meier Capital AG; *Int'l*, pg. 4799
JSI MICROELECTRONICS—See JMAR, LLC; *U.S. Private*, pg. 2215
JS INDUSTRIAL S.A.C.—See HORIBA Ltd; *Int'l*, pg. 3477
JS INFOCOM LIMITED—See Jahangir Siddiqui & Co. Ltd.; *Int'l*, pg. 3871
JS INTERNATIONAL LIMITED—See Jahangir Siddiqui & Co. Ltd.; *Int'l*, pg. 3871
JS INVESTMENTS LIMITED—See Jahangir Siddiqui & Co. Ltd.; *Int'l*, pg. 3871
JSI SHIPPING; *U.S. Private*, pg. 2241
JSI STORE FIXTURES, INC.—See LSI Industries Inc.; *U.S. Public*, pg. 1344
JSJ CORPORATION; *U.S. Private*, pg. 2241
JSJ FURNITURE CORPORATION—See JSJ Corporation; *U.S. Private*, pg. 2241
J.S. JOHNSON & COMPANY LIMITED; *Int'l*, pg. 3858
JSJ PHARMACEUTICALS; *U.S. Private*, pg. 2241
JSJS DESIGNS (EUROPE) LIMITED—See LightWaveRF Plc; *Int'l*, pg. 4497
J.S. KARLTON COMPANY, INC.; *U.S. Private*, pg. 2171
JSKEM PRIVATE LIMITED—See PTT Public Company Limited; *Int'l*, pg. 6092
JSL CONSTRUCTION & DEVELOPMENT CO., LTD.; *Int'l*, pg. 4013
JS LEASING COMPANY INC.—See Slay Industries Inc.; *U.S. Private*, pg. 3687
JSL FOODS INC.; *U.S. Private*, pg. 2241
JSL INDUSTRIES LIMITED; *Int'l*, pg. 4013
JSL S.A.; *Int'l*, pg. 4013
JSL SOLUTIONS LLC—See Zebulon Solutions LLC; *U.S. Private*, pg. 4599
J. S. MACHINE INDIA PRIVATE LIMITED—See J.S. Corrugating Machinery Co., Ltd.; *Int'l*, pg. 3858
J & S MACHINE; *U.S. Private*, pg. 2152
J. SMART & CO. (CONTRACTORS) PLC; *Int'l*, pg. 3857
J&S MASONRY INC.; *U.S. Private*, pg. 2155
J.S. MCCARTHY INC.; *U.S. Private*, pg. 2171
J S MCCARTHY LIMITED—See SIG plc; *Int'l*, pg. 6906
J. SMITH LANIER & CO.—See Marsh & McLennan Companies, Inc.; *U.S. Public*, pg. 1381
JSML MEDIA, LLC; *U.S. Private*, pg. 2241
JSML MEDIA, LLC—See JSML Media, LLC; *U.S. Private*, pg. 2241
JSMN INTERNATIONAL INC.; *U.S. Private*, pg. 2241
JSOL CORPORATION—See Nippon Telegraph & Telephone Corporation; *Int'l*, pg. 5346
JSOL CORPORATION—See Sumitomo Mitsui Financial Group, Inc.; *Int'l*, pg. 7295
J. SOSNICK & SON INC.; *U.S. Private*, pg. 2157
J.S. O'WILL, INC.—See O'will Corporation; *Int'l*, pg. 5502
J.S. PALUCH CO. INC.; *U.S. Private*, pg. 2171
JSP CORPORATION—See Mitsubishi Gas Chemical Company, Inc.; *Int'l*, pg. 4948
JSP FOAM PRODUCTS PTE. LTD.—See Mitsubishi Gas Chemical Company, Inc.; *Int'l*, pg. 4948
JSP INTERNATIONAL GROUP LTD.—See Mitsubishi Gas Chemical Company, Inc.; *Int'l*, pg. 4948
JSP INTERNATIONAL S.A.R.L—See Mitsubishi Gas Chemical Company, Inc.; *Int'l*, pg. 4948
JSP INTERNATIONAL; *U.S. Private*, pg. 2241
JSP INTERNATIONAL S.R.O.—See Mitsubishi Gas Chemical Company, Inc.; *Int'l*, pg. 4948
J-SPIRAL STEEL PIPE CO., LTD.—See Maruichi Steel Tube Ltd; *Int'l*, pg. 4713
JSP MOLDING LTD.—See Mitsubishi Gas Chemical Company, Inc.; *Int'l*, pg. 4948
JSP MOLD LLC—See JSP International; *U.S. Private*, pg. 2241
J-SPORTS CORP.—See J-Holdings Corp.; *Int'l*, pg. 3854
JSP PLASTICS (SHANGHAI) CO., LTD.—See Mitsubishi Gas Chemical Company, Inc.; *Int'l*, pg. 4948
J.S.P. PROPERTY PUBLIC COMPANY LIMITED; *Int'l*, pg. 3858
JSPV CO LTD; *Int'l*, pg. 4013
J SQUARED INC.; *U.S. Private*, pg. 2153
JSR ACTIVE INNOVATION FUND, LLC—See JSR Corp.; *Int'l*, pg. 4013
JSR AMERICA, INC.—See JSR Corp.; *Int'l*, pg. 4013
JSR BST ELASTOMER CO., LTD.—See JSR Corp.; *Int'l*, pg. 4013
JSR BUSINESS SERVICE CO., LTD.—See JSR Corp.; *Int'l*, pg. 4013
JSR CORP. - CHIBA PLANT—See JSR Corp.; *Int'l*, pg. 4013
JSR CORP. - KASHIMA PLANT—See JSR Corp.; *Int'l*, pg. 4013
JSR CORP.; *Int'l*, pg. 4013
JSR CORP. - YOKKAICHI PLANT—See JSR Corp.; *Int'l*, pg. 4013
J.S. REDPATH CORPORATION—See ATON GmbH; *Int'l*, pg. 688
J. S. REDPATH LIMITED; *Int'l*, pg. 3857
JSR ELASTOMER AMERICA, INC.—See JSR Corp.; *Int'l*, pg. 4013
JSR ELASTOMER EUROPE GMBH—See JSR Corp.; *Int'l*, pg. 4013
JSR ELASTOMER INDIA PRIVATE LIMITED—See JSR Corp.; *Int'l*, pg. 4013
JSR ELASTOMER KOREA CO., LTD.—See JSR Corp.; *Int'l*, pg. 4013
JSR ELECTRONIC MATERIALS KOREA CO., LTD.—See JSR Corp.; *Int'l*, pg. 4013
JSR ENGINEERING CO., LTD.—See JSR Corp.; *Int'l*, pg. 4013
JSR LIFE SCIENCES CORPORATION—See JSR Corp.; *Int'l*, pg. 4013

JSR LOGISTICS & CUSTOMER CENTER CO., LTD.—See JSR Corp.; *Int'l*, pg. 4013
JSR MICRO (CHANGSHU) CO., LTD.—See JSR Corp.; *Int'l*, pg. 4013
JSR MICRO INC.—See ISC Co., Ltd.; *Int'l*, pg. 3813
JSR MICRO KOREA CO., LTD.—See ISC Co., Ltd.; *Int'l*, pg. 3813
JSR MICRO KYUSHU CO., LTD.—See JSR Corp.; *Int'l*, pg. 4013
JSR MICRO N.V.—See ISC Co., Ltd.; *Int'l*, pg. 3813
JSR MICRO TAIWAN CO., LTD.—See ISC Co., Ltd.; *Int'l*, pg. 3813
JSR MICROTECH INC.—See ISC Co., Ltd.; *Int'l*, pg. 3813
JSR OPTECH TSUKUBA CO., LTD.—See JSR Corp.; *Int'l*, pg. 4014
JSR (SHANGHAI) CO., LTD.—See JSR Corp.; *Int'l*, pg. 4013
JSRT MEXICO S.A. DE C.V.—See JSR Corp.; *Int'l*, pg. 4014
JSR TRADING BANGKOK CO., LTD.—See JSR Corp.; *Int'l*, pg. 4014
JSR TRADING CO., LTD.—See JSR Corp.; *Int'l*, pg. 4014
JSR TRADING (SHANGHAI) CO., LTD.—See JSR Corp.; *Int'l*, pg. 4014
JSR TRADING VIETNAM CO., LTD.—See JSR Corp.; *Int'l*, pg. 4014
JSS CORPORATION; *Int'l*, pg. 4014
JSSC UKRRICHFLOT—See Svarog Asset Management LLC; *Int'l*, pg. 7355
J.S.S ENTERPRISES (PVT) LTD.—See Daikin Industries, Ltd.; *Int'l*, pg. 1935
JSSF, INC.—See Frasco, Inc.; *U.S. Private*, pg. 1599
JSS MEDICAL RESEARCH, INC.—See Genesis Biotechnology Group, LLC; *U.S. Private*, pg. 1669
J-STAR CO. LTD.; *Int'l*, pg. 3854
J-STAR HOLDING CO., LTD.; *Int'l*, pg. 3854
J-STAR MOTION CORPORATION—See Zhejiang Jiecang Linear Motion Technology Co., Ltd.; *Int'l*, pg. 8657
J-STAR RESEARCH, INC.—See Porton Pharma Solutions Ltd.; *Int'l*, pg. 5935
JS TECHNOLOGY INC.—See Danaher Corporation; *U.S. Public*, pg. 627
J STEEL COMPANY HOLDINGS INC; *Int'l*, pg. 3852
J. STEPHEN SCHERER INC.; *U.S. Private*, pg. 2157
JSTI GROUP CO., LTD.; *Int'l*, pg. 4014
J. STOKES & ASSOCIATES, INC.; *U.S. Private*, pg. 2157
JST PERFORMANCE, INC.—See Genstar Capital, LLC; *U.S. Private*, pg. 1676
J-STREAM INC.; *Int'l*, pg. 3854
J. STRICKLAND & COMPANY; *U.S. Private*, pg. 2157
JST TRANSFORMATEURS SA; *Int'l*, pg. 4014
J. SUPOR & SON TRUCKING & RIGGING CO., INC.; *U.S. Private*, pg. 2157
J SUPPLY CO.; *U.S. Private*, pg. 2153
J-SUPPORT CO., LTD.—See TOKAI Holdings Corporation; *Int'l*, pg. 7779
JSU SP. Z O.O.—See Jastrzebska Spolka Weglowa S.A.; *Int'l*, pg. 3913
J. SUSSMAN, INC.; *U.S. Private*, pg. 2157
J.S. VENTURES, INC.; *U.S. Private*, pg. 2171
JS VINA LTD.—See JS Corporation; *Int'l*, pg. 4008
JSW AFTY CORPORATION—See The Japan Steel Works, Ltd.; *Int'l*, pg. 7659
JSW CLAD STEEL PLATE CO., LTD.—See The Japan Steel Works, Ltd.; *Int'l*, pg. 7658
JSW ELECTROMECHANICAL TRADING (SHANGHAI) CO., LTD.—See The Japan Steel Works, Ltd.; *Int'l*, pg. 7658
JSW ENERGY LIMITED—See Jindal Holdings Limited; *Int'l*, pg. 3966
JSW ENERGY (RATNAGIRI) LTD.—See Jindal Holdings Limited; *Int'l*, pg. 3966
J.S. WEST & COMPANY; *U.S. Private*, pg. 2171
JSW HIROSHIMA PLANT—See The Japan Steel Works, Ltd.; *Int'l*, pg. 7658
JSW HOLDINGS LTD.—See Jindal Holdings Limited; *Int'l*, pg. 3966
JSW INFRASTRUCTURE LTD.—See JSW Steel Ltd.; *Int'l*, pg. 4015
JSW ISPAT SPECIAL PRODUCTS LIMITED.—See Apollo Global Management, Inc.; *U.S. Public*, pg. 152
JSW ISPAT SPECIAL PRODUCTS LIMITED.—See JSW Steel Ltd.; *Int'l*, pg. 4015
JSW IT KOREA CO., LTD.—See The Japan Steel Works, Ltd.; *Int'l*, pg. 7658
JSW IT SERVICE CO.—See The Japan Steel Works, Ltd.; *Int'l*, pg. 7658
JSW IT SYSTEMS SP. Z O.O.—See Jastrzebska Spolka Weglowa S.A.; *Int'l*, pg. 3913
JSW KOKS S.A.—See Jastrzebska Spolka Weglowa S.A.; *Int'l*, pg. 3913
JSW LOGISTICS SP. Z O.O.—See Jastrzebska Spolka Weglowa S.A.; *Int'l*, pg. 3913
JSW MACHINE CENTER CO., LTD.—See The Japan Steel Works, Ltd.; *Int'l*, pg. 7658
JSW MACHINERY (NINGBO) CO., LTD.—See The Japan Steel Works, Ltd.; *Int'l*, pg. 7658
JSW MACHINERY TRADING (SHANGHAI) CO., LTD.—See The Japan Steel Works, Ltd.; *Int'l*, pg. 7658

JSW OCHRONA SP. Z O.O.—See Jastrzebska Spolka Weglowa S.A.; *Int'l*, pg. 3913
JSW PACIFIC CORP.; *Int'l*, pg. 4014
JSW PLASTIC MACHINERY (SHENZHEN) CO., LTD.—See The Japan Steel Works, Ltd.; *Int'l*, pg. 7658
JSW PLASTICS MACHINERY (H.K.) CO., LTD.—See The Japan Steel Works, Ltd.; *Int'l*, pg. 7658
JSW PLASTICS MACHINERY MEXICO S. DE R.L. DE C.V.—See The Japan Steel Works, Ltd.; *Int'l*, pg. 7658
JSW PLASTICS MACHINERY (M) SDN. BHD.—See The Japan Steel Works, Ltd.; *Int'l*, pg. 7658
JSW PLASTICS MACHINERY (PHILLIPPINES) INC.—See The Japan Steel Works, Ltd.; *Int'l*, pg. 7658
JSW PLASTICS MACHINERY (SHENZHEN) CO., LTD.—See The Japan Steel Works, Ltd.; *Int'l*, pg. 7658
JSW PLASTICS MACHINERY (TAIWAN) CORP.—See The Japan Steel Works, Ltd.; *Int'l*, pg. 7658
JSW PLASTICS MACHINERY VIETNAM LTD.—See The Japan Steel Works, Ltd.; *Int'l*, pg. 7658
JSW POWER TRADING COMPANY LTD—See Jindal Holdings Limited; *Int'l*, pg. 3966
JSW STEEL ITALY PIOMBINO S.P.A.—See JSW Steel Ltd.; *Int'l*, pg. 4015
JSW STEEL LTD.; *Int'l*, pg. 4014
JSW STEEL USA INC.—See JSW Steel Ltd.; *Int'l*, pg. 4015
JSW SZKOLENIE I GORNICTWO SP. Z O.O.—See Jastrzebska Spolka Weglowa S.A.; *Int'l*, pg. 3913
JSYL SOLUTION PTE LTD—See TCS TurControlSysteme AG; *Int'l*, pg. 7485
JSZ KAZAKHSTANCASPISHELF—See Marquard & Bahls AG; *Int'l*, pg. 4700
JTA INFORMATION & COMMUNICATION CO., LTD.—See Japan Airlines Co., Ltd.; *Int'l*, pg. 3883
J. TAPARIA PROJECTS LIMITED; *Int'l*, pg. 3857
J. TARRAN MARKETING INC.; *U.S. Private*, pg. 2157
JTA SOUTHERN SKY SERVICE CO., LTD.—See Japan Airlines Co., Ltd.; *Int'l*, pg. 3883
JTB AMERICAS, LTD.—See JTB Corp.; *Int'l*, pg. 4015
JTB AUSTRALIA PTY. LTD.—See JTB Corp.; *Int'l*, pg. 4015
JTB CORP.; *Int'l*, pg. 4015
JTB EUROPE LTD—See JTB Corp.; *Int'l*, pg. 4015
JTB FRANCE S.A.S.; *Int'l*, pg. 4016
JTB GERMANY GMBH—See JTB Corp.; *Int'l*, pg. 4015
JTB GREECE LTD.—See JTB Corp.; *Int'l*, pg. 4015
JTB (GUANGZHOU) INTERNATIONAL TOURS CO., LTD.—See JTB Corp.; *Int'l*, pg. 4015
JTB HAWAII, INC.—See JTB Corp.; *Int'l*, pg. 4015
JTB HAWAII TRAVEL, LLC—See JTB Corp.; *Int'l*, pg. 4015
JTB (HONG KONG) LTD—See JTB Corp.; *Int'l*, pg. 4015
JTB INDIA PRIVATE LIMITED—See JTB Corp.; *Int'l*, pg. 4015
JTB INTERNATIONAL (CANADA), LTD.—See JTB Corp.; *Int'l*, pg. 4015
JTB ITALY SRL—See JTB Corp.; *Int'l*, pg. 4015
JTB NEW ZEALAND LTD.—See JTB Corp.; *Int'l*, pg. 4015
JTB PTE. LTD.—See JTB Corp.; *Int'l*, pg. 4015
JTB SWITZERLAND S.A.—See JTB Corp.; *Int'l*, pg. 4015
JTB TAIWAN LTD.—See JTB Corp.; *Int'l*, pg. 4015
JTB (THAILAND) LIMITED—See JTB Corp.; *Int'l*, pg. 4015
JTB USA—See JTB Corp.; *Int'l*, pg. 4015
JTB VIAJES SPAIN, S.A.—See JTB Corp.; *Int'l*, pg. 4016
JTC ADMINISTRATION (UK) LIMITED—See JTC Group Holdings Ltd.; *Int'l*, pg. 4016
JTC (BVI) LIMITED—See JTC Group Holdings Ltd.; *Int'l*, pg. 4016
JTC (CAYMAN) LIMITED—See JTC Group Holdings Ltd.; *Int'l*, pg. 4016
JTC CORPORATE SERVICES (DIFC) LIMITED—See JTC PLC; *Int'l*, pg. 4016
JTC CORPORATE SERVICES (IRELAND) LIMITED—See JTC PLC; *Int'l*, pg. 4016
JTC FUND MANAGERS (GUERNSEY) LIMITED—See JTC Group Holdings Ltd.; *Int'l*, pg. 4016
JTC FUND SOLUTIONS (GUERNSEY) LIMITED—See JTC PLC; *Int'l*, pg. 4016
JTC FUND SOLUTIONS (IRELAND) LIMITED—See JTC PLC; *Int'l*, pg. 4016
JTC FUND SOLUTIONS RSA (PTY) LTD.—See JTC PLC; *Int'l*, pg. 4016
JTC GROUP HOLDINGS LTD.; *Int'l*, pg. 4016
JTC GROUP (NZ) LIMITED—See JTC Group Holdings Ltd.; *Int'l*, pg. 4016
JT CHINAE SAVING BANK, LTD.—See PT Bank JTrust Indonesia Tbk.; *Int'l*, pg. 6026
JTC (LUXEMBOURG) SA—See JTC Group Holdings Ltd.; *Int'l*, pg. 4016
JTC (MALTA) LIMITED—See JTC Group Holdings Ltd.; *Int'l*, pg. 4016
JTC (NETHERLANDS) B.V.—See JTC PLC; *Int'l*, pg. 4016
J&T COINS, LLC; *U.S. Private*, pg. 2155
JT CONSTRUCTION CO. INC.; *U.S. Private*, pg. 2241
JT CORPORATION; *Int'l*, pg. 4015
JTC PLC; *Int'l*, pg. 4016
JTC PRISON INDUSTRIES, LLC—See Liquidity Services, Inc.; *U.S. Public*, pg. 1321
JTC (SUISSE) SA—See JTC Group Holdings Ltd.; *Int'l*, pg. 4016

JTC TRUST COMPANY (SOUTH DAKOTA) LTD.—See JTC PLC; *Int'l*, pg. 4016
JTC TRUSTEES (SUISSE) SARL—See JTC PLC; *Int'l*, pg. 4016
JTC TRUSTEES (USA) LTD.—See JTC PLC; *Int'l*, pg. 4016
JTC (UK) LIMITED—See JTC Group Holdings Ltd.; *Int'l*, pg. 4016
JTD ENTERPRISES INC.; *U.S. Private*, pg. 2241
JTE CORPORATION; *Int'l*, pg. 4017
JTECH COMMUNICATIONS INC.—See HM Electronics Incorporated; *U.S. Private*, pg. 1954
JTECH MEDICAL INDUSTRIES, INC.—See ADDvise Group AB; *Int'l*, pg. 136
J. TECHNOLOGY CO., LTD.; *Int'l*, pg. 3857
J. TECH SALES, L.L.C.; *U.S. Private*, pg. 2157
JTEKT ASIA PACIFIC CO., LTD.—See JTEKT Corporation; *Int'l*, pg. 4017
JTEKT AUTOMOTIVA BRASIL LTDA.—See JTEKT Corporation; *Int'l*, pg. 4017
JTEKT AUTOMOTIVE ARGENTINA S.A.—See JTEKT Corporation; *Int'l*, pg. 4017
JTEKT AUTOMOTIVE CZECH PARDUBICE, S.R.O.—See JTEKT Corporation; *Int'l*, pg. 4017
JTEKT AUTOMOTIVE CZECH PLZEN, S.R.O.—See JTEKT Corporation; *Int'l*, pg. 4017
JTEKT AUTOMOTIVE DIJON SAINT-ETIENNE S.A.S.—See JTEKT Corporation; *Int'l*, pg. 4017
JTEKT AUTOMOTIVE ENGLAND LTD.—See JTEKT Corporation; *Int'l*, pg. 4017
JTEKT AUTOMOTIVE LYON S.A.S.—See JTEKT Corporation; *Int'l*, pg. 4017
JTEKT AUTOMOTIVE MALAYSIA—See Toyota Motor Corporation; *Int'l*, pg. 7872
JTEKT AUTOMOTIVE MEXICO, S.A. DE C.V.—See JTEKT Corporation; *Int'l*, pg. 4017
JTEKT AUTOMOTIVE NORTH AMERICA, INC.—See JTEKT Corporation; *Int'l*, pg. 4017
JTEKT AUTOMOTIVE SCIENCE & TECHNOLOGY CENTER (DALIAN) CO., LTD.—See JTEKT Corporation; *Int'l*, pg. 4017
JTEKT AUTOMOTIVE SOUTH CAROLINA INC.—See JTEKT Corporation; *Int'l*, pg. 4017
JTEKT AUTOMOTIVE TENNESSEE-MORRISTOWN, INC.—See JTEKT Corporation; *Int'l*, pg. 4017
JTEKT AUTOMOTIVE TENNESSEE-VONORE, CO.—See JTEKT Corporation; *Int'l*, pg. 4017
JTEKT AUTOMOTIVE TEXAS, L.P.—See JTEKT Corporation; *Int'l*, pg. 4017
JTEKT AUTOMOTIVE (THAILAND) CO., LTD.—See JTEKT Corporation; *Int'l*, pg. 4017
JTEKT AUTOMOTIVE (TIANJIN) CO., LTD.—See JTEKT Corporation; *Int'l*, pg. 4017
JTEKT AUTOMOTIVE UK LTD.—See JTEKT Corporation; *Int'l*, pg. 4017
JTEKT AUTOMOTIVE (WUXI) CO., LTD.—See JTEKT Corporation; *Int'l*, pg. 4017
JTEKT BEARINGS CANADA INC.—See JTEKT Corporation; *Int'l*, pg. 4018
JTEKT BEARINGS CZECH REPUBLIC S.R.O.—See JTEKT Corporation; *Int'l*, pg. 4018
JTEKT BEARINGS (DALIAN) CO., LTD.—See JTEKT Corporation; *Int'l*, pg. 4017
JTEKT BEARINGS DEUTSCHLAND GMBH—See JTEKT Corporation; *Int'l*, pg. 4018
JTEKT BEARINGS INDIA PRIVATE LIMITED—See JTEKT Corporation; *Int'l*, pg. 4018
JTEKT BEARINGS KOREA CO., LTD.—See JTEKT Corporation; *Int'l*, pg. 4018
JTEKT BEARINGS NORTH AMERICA LLC—See JTEKT Corporation; *Int'l*, pg. 4018
JTEKT BEARINGS(WUXI) CO., LTD.—See JTEKT Corporation; *Int'l*, pg. 4018
JTEKT BRASIL LTDA.—See JTEKT Corporation; *Int'l*, pg. 4018
JTEKT (CHINA) CO., LTD.—See JTEKT Corporation; *Int'l*, pg. 4017
JTEKT CORPORATION; *Int'l*, pg. 4017
JTEKT CORPORATION—See JTEKT Corporation; *Int'l*, pg. 4017
JTEKT CZECH REPUBLIC S.R.O.—See JTEKT Corporation; *Int'l*, pg. 4018
JTEKT DALIAN INNOVATION AUTOMOTIVE CO., LTD.—See JTEKT Corporation; *Int'l*, pg. 4018
JTEKT EUROPE BEARINGS B.V.—See JTEKT Corporation; *Int'l*, pg. 4018
JTEKT HPI S.A.S.—See JTEKT Corporation; *Int'l*, pg. 4018
JTEKT INDIA LIMITED; *Int'l*, pg. 4019
JTEKT IT CENTER AKITA CORPORATION—See JTEKT Corporation; *Int'l*, pg. 4018
JTEKT KOREA CO., LTD.—See JTEKT Corporation; *Int'l*, pg. 4018
JTEKT LATIN AMERICA, S.A.—See JTEKT Corporation; *Int'l*, pg. 4018
JTEKT LIOHO AUTOMOTIVE (FOSHAN) CO., LTD.—See JTEKT Corporation; *Int'l*, pg. 4018
JTEKT MACHINERY AMERICAS CORPORATION—See JTEKT Corporation; *Int'l*, pg. 4018

COMPANY NAME INDEX

JTEKT MACHINERY (DALIAN) CO., LTD.—See JTEKT Corporation; *Int'l*, pg. 4018
JTEKT MACHINERY EUROPE S.A.S.—See JTEKT Corporation; *Int'l*, pg. 4018
JTEKT MACHINERY (THAILAND) CO., LTD.—See JTEKT Corporation; *Int'l*, pg. 4018
JTEKT NORTH AMERICA, INC.—See JTEKT Corporation; *Int'l*, pg. 4017
JTEKT PHILIPPINES CORPORATION—See JTEKT Corporation; *Int'l*, pg. 4018
JTEKT RESEARCH & DEVELOPMENT CENTER (WUXI) CO., LTD.—See JTEKT Corporation; *Int'l*, pg. 4018
JTEKT SALES AUSTRALIA PTY. LTD.—See JTEKT Corporation; *Int'l*, pg. 4018
JTEKT SALES CANADA INC.—See JTEKT Corporation; *Int'l*, pg. 4018
JTEKT SALES DEUTSCHLAND GMBH—See JTEKT Corporation; *Int'l*, pg. 4018
JTEKT SALES FRANCE S.A.—See JTEKT Corporation; *Int'l*, pg. 4018
JTEKT SALES MIDDLE EAST FZCO—See JTEKT Corporation; *Int'l*, pg. 4018
JTEKT SALES UK LTD.—See JTEKT Corporation; *Int'l*, pg. 4018
JTEKT SONA AUTOMOTIVE INDIA LTD.—See JTEKT India Limited; *Int'l*, pg. 4019
JTEKT STEERING SYSTEMS (XIAMEN) CO., LTD.—See JTEKT Corporation; *Int'l*, pg. 4018
JTEKT (THAILAND) CO., LTD.—See JTEKT Corporation; *Int'l*, pg. 4017
JTEKT TORSEN EUROPE S.A.—See JTEKT Corporation; *Int'l*, pg. 4018
JTEKT TORSEN NORTH AMERICA, INC.—See JTEKT Corporation; *Int'l*, pg. 4018
JTEKT VENTAS MEXICO S.A. DE C.V.—See JTEKT Corporation; *Int'l*, pg. 4018
JTEKT WAZHOU AUTOMOTIVE (DALIAN) CO., LTD.—See JTEKT Corporation; *Int'l*, pg. 4018
JTE MACHINE SYSTEMS, INC.—See Druid Capital Partners, LLC; *U.S. Private*, pg. 1279
JTE MULTIMEDIA, LLC; *U.S. Private*, pg. 2241
JT ENGINEERING INC.—See Japan Tobacco Inc.; *Int'l*, pg. 3906
J&T ENTERPRISES INC., *U.S. Private*, pg. 2155
J-TEQ EMS SOLUTIONS LTD.—See Avnet, Inc.; *U.S. Public*, pg. 253
JTF BUSINESS SYSTEMS; *U.S. Private*, pg. 2242
JTF CONSTRUCTION, INC.; *U.S. Private*, pg. 2242
J.T. FENNELL CO. INC.; *U.S. Private*, pg. 2171
J&T FINANCE GROUP SE; *Int'l*, pg. 3854
JTF INTERNATIONAL HOLDINGS LIMITED; *Int'l*, pg. 4019
JTG TRADING BV—See B&S Group S.A.; *Int'l*, pg. 784
JTH FINANCIAL, LLC—See B. Riley Financial, Inc.; *U.S. Public*, pg. 261
JTH FINANCIAL, LLC—See Irradiant Partners, LP; *U.S. Private*, pg. 2140
J. THOMAS & CO. INC.; *U.S. Private*, pg. 2157
J. THOMSON COLOUR PRINTERS LTD.—See Bell & Bain Ltd.; *Int'l*, pg. 965
JTH TAX, INC.—See B. Riley Financial, Inc.; *U.S. Public*, pg. 261
JTH TAX, INC.—See Irradiant Partners, LP; *U.S. Private*, pg. 2140
JTI IRELAND LTD.—See Japan Tobacco Inc.; *Int'l*, pg. 3906
JTI-MACDONALD CORP.—See Japan Tobacco Inc.; *Int'l*, pg. 3906
JT INTERNATIONAL BUSINESS SERVICES LTD.—See Japan Tobacco Inc.; *Int'l*, pg. 3906
JT INTERNATIONAL CO. (CYPRUS) LTD.—See Japan Tobacco Inc.; *Int'l*, pg. 3906
JT INTERNATIONAL COMPANY NETHERLANDS BV—See Japan Tobacco Inc.; *Int'l*, pg. 3906
JT INTERNATIONAL COMPANY UKRAINE CJSC—See Japan Tobacco Inc.; *Int'l*, pg. 3906
JT INTERNATIONAL DO BRASIL LTDA—See Japan Tobacco Inc.; *Int'l*, pg. 3906
JT INTERNATIONAL D.O.O.—See Japan Tobacco Inc.; *Int'l*, pg. 3906
JT INTERNATIONAL FRANCE—See Japan Tobacco Inc.; *Int'l*, pg. 3906
JT INTERNATIONAL GERMANY GMBH—See Japan Tobacco Inc.; *Int'l*, pg. 3906
JT INTERNATIONAL HELLAS AEBE—See Japan Tobacco Inc.; *Int'l*, pg. 3906
JT INTERNATIONAL IBERIA SL—See Japan Tobacco Inc.; *Int'l*, pg. 3906
JT INTERNATIONAL INDIA PTE LIMITED—See Japan Tobacco Inc.; *Int'l*, pg. 3906
JT INTERNATIONAL ITALIA SRL—See Japan Tobacco Inc.; *Int'l*, pg. 3906
JT INTERNATIONAL KOREA, INC.—See Japan Tobacco Inc.; *Int'l*, pg. 3906
JT INTERNATIONAL MARKETING & SALES DOO—See Japan Tobacco Inc.; *Int'l*, pg. 3906
JT INTERNATIONAL (PHILIPPINES), INC.—See Japan Tobacco Inc.; *Int'l*, pg. 3906
JT INTERNATIONAL ROMANIA SRL—See Japan Tobacco Inc.; *Int'l*, pg. 3906
JT INTERNATIONAL S.A.—See Japan Tobacco Inc.; *Int'l*, pg. 3906
JT INTERNATIONAL (SINGAPORE) PTE. LTD.—See Japan Tobacco Inc.; *Int'l*, pg. 3906
JT INTERNATIONAL SPOL SRO—See Japan Tobacco Inc.; *Int'l*, pg. 3906
JT INTERNATIONAL TABANDOR SA—See Japan Tobacco Inc.; *Int'l*, pg. 3906
JT INTERNATIONAL (THAILAND) LIMITED—See Japan Tobacco Inc.; *Int'l*, pg. 3906
JT INTERNATIONAL TRADING SDN BHD—See Japan Tobacco Inc.; *Int'l*, pg. 3906
JTI SECURITIES LIMITED—See Heng Xin China Holdings Limited; *Int'l*, pg. 3345
JTI SWEDEN—See Japan Tobacco Inc.; *Int'l*, pg. 3906
JTI TUTUN URUNLERI PAZARLAMA AS—See Japan Tobacco Inc.; *Int'l*, pg. 3906
JTI TUTUN URUNLERI SANAYI A.S.—See Japan Tobacco Inc.; *Int'l*, pg. 3907
JTI (VIETNAM) PTE. LTD.—See Japan Tobacco Inc.; *Int'l*, pg. 3906
J.T. LANEHART ELECTRIC CO. INC.; *U.S. Private*, pg. 2171
JTL CAPITAL, LLC; *U.S. Private*, pg. 2242
JTL INDUSTRIES LIMITED; *Int'l*, pg. 4019
JTL INFRA LIMITED - MOHALI WORKS—See JTL Industries Limited; *Int'l*, pg. 4019
JTL INFRA LIMITED - RAIPUR WORKS—See JTL Industries Limited; *Int'l*, pg. 4020
JT LOGISTICS CO., LTD—See Japan Tobacco Inc.; *Int'l*, pg. 3906
JTMEC PTY LTD.—See Epiroc AB; *Int'l*, pg. 2463
J.T. MEGA MARKETING COMMUNICATIONS; *U.S. Private*, pg. 2171
JTM FOODS, LLC—See Tenex Capital Management, L.P.; *U.S. Private*, pg. 3966
JTNB BANCORP, INC.; *U.S. Public*, pg. 1210
JTO INC.; *U.S. Private*, pg. 2242
JTOP CO., LTD.—See EDION Corporation; *Int'l*, pg. 2310
JTOWER, INC.—See DigitalBridge Group, Inc.; *U.S. Public*, pg. 665
JT PACKARD & ASSOCIATES, INC.—See ABB Ltd.; *Int'l*, pg. 52
JTP CO., LTD.; *Int'l*, pg. 4020
JT PHARMA ALLIANCE CO., LTD—See Japan Tobacco Inc.; *Int'l*, pg. 3907
JTP HOMES PTY LIMITED—See Peet Limited; *Int'l*, pg. 5780
JTP SOUTH KOREA CO., LTD.—See JTP Co., Ltd.; *Int'l*, pg. 4020
JTP TRADING SDN BHD—See Johor Corporation; *Int'l*, pg. 3994
J TRANS KK—See Japan Transcity Corporation; *Int'l*, pg. 3907
JTR & CO. INC.; *U.S. Private*, pg. 2242
J&T RECYCLING CORPORATION—See JFE Holdings, Inc.; *Int'l*, pg. 3935
J TRUST ASIA PTE. LTD.—See J Trust Co., Ltd.; *Int'l*, pg. 3852
J TRUST CO., LTD.; *Int'l*, pg. 3852
J TRUST GLOBAL SECURITIES CO., LTD.—See PT Bank JTrust Indonesia Tbk.; *Int'l*, pg. 6026
J TRUST ROYAL BANK LTD.—See J Trust Co., Ltd.; *Int'l*, pg. 3852
J TRUST ROYAL BANK LTD.—See Royal Group of Companies Ltd.; *Int'l*, pg. 6412
JTS COMMUNITIES, INC.; *U.S. Private*, pg. 2242
JTS CONSTRUCTION; *U.S. Private*, pg. 2242
J.T. SHANNON LUMBER INC.; *U.S. Private*, pg. 2171
J.T. THORPE & SON, INC.—See Terra Millenium Corporation; *U.S. Private*, pg. 3970
JT TOBACCO INTERNATIONAL TAIWAN CORP.—See Japan Tobacco Inc.; *Int'l*, pg. 3906
J.T. TURNER CONSTRUCTION CO.; *U.S. Private*, pg. 2171
JT (UK) LTD.—See Japan Tobacco Inc.; *Int'l*, pg. 3906
JT UNITED (M) SDN BHD—See Shenzhen JT Automation Equipment Company Limited; *Int'l*, pg. 6815
JT UNIVERSAL (M) SDN BHD—See Shenzhen JT Automation Equipment Company Limited; *Int'l*, pg. 6815
JT UNIVERSAL PHILIPPINES INC.—See Shenzhen JT Automation Equipment Company Limited; *Int'l*, pg. 6815
JT UNIVERSAL PTE LTD—See Shenzhen JT Automation Equipment Company Limited; *Int'l*, pg. 6815
JT US, INC.—See Lang Inc; *Int'l*, pg. 4408
JTU (THAILAND) CO. LTD—See Shenzhen JT Automation Equipment Company Limited; *Int'l*, pg. 6815
JTU (VIETNAM) CO. LTD—See Shenzhen JT Automation Equipment Company Limited; *Int'l*, pg. 6815
J.T. VAUGHN CONSTRUCTION COMPANY INCORPORATED; *U.S. Private*, pg. 2171
J.T. WALKER INDUSTRIES, INC.; *U.S. Private*, pg. 2171
J.T. WIMSATT CONTRACTING CO., INC.; *U.S. Private*, pg. 2171
JUAN A. CALZADO S.A.R.L.—See DEKRA e.V.; *Int'l*, pg. 2010

JUAREZ BROTHERS TRUCKING INC.; *U.S. Private*, pg. 2242
JUAREZ MEXICO DIVISION—See Jones Plastic & Engineering Company, LLC; *U.S. Private*, pg. 2234
JUBAIL CHEMICAL INDUSTRIES LLC—See NAMA Chemicals Company; *Int'l*, pg. 5134
JUBAIL INTEGRATED PACKAGING COMPANY LIMITED LLC—See Boubyan Petrochemical Co. KSC; *Int'l*, pg. 1119
JUBAIL UNITED PETROCHEMICAL COMPANY—See Saudi Basic Industries Corporation; *Int'l*, pg. 6590
JUBA PERSONAL PROTECTIVE EQUIPMENT, S.L.U.—See Bunzl plc; *Int'l*, pg. 1218
JUBA'S INC.; *U.S. Private*, pg. 2242
JUBILANT BHARTIA GROUP; *Int'l*, pg. 4020
JUBILANT BIOSYS LIMITED—See Jubilant Bhartia Group; *Int'l*, pg. 4020
JUBILANT CADISTA PHARMACEUTICALS INC.—See Jubilant Bhartia Group; *Int'l*, pg. 4020
JUBILANT CHEMSYS LIMITED—See Jubilant Bhartia Group; *Int'l*, pg. 4020
JUBILANT CLINSYS INC.—See Jubilant Bhartia Group; *Int'l*, pg. 4020
JUBILANT CLINSYS LIMITED—See Jubilant Bhartia Group; *Int'l*, pg. 4020
JUBILANT DISCOVERY SERVICES INC.—See Jubilant Bhartia Group; *Int'l*, pg. 4020
JUBILANT FLAME INTERNATIONAL, LTD.; *Int'l*, pg. 4020
JUBILANT FOODWORKS LANKA (PVT.) LTD.—See Jubilant Bhartia Group; *Int'l*, pg. 4020
JUBILANT FOODWORKS LIMITED—See Jubilant Bhartia Group; *Int'l*, pg. 4020
JUBILANT HOLLISTERSTIER, LLC—See Jubilant Bhartia Group; *Int'l*, pg. 4020
JUBILANT INDUSTRIES INC.—See Jubilant Bhartia Group; *Int'l*, pg. 4020
JUBILANT INDUSTRIES LTD.—See Jubilant Bhartia Group; *Int'l*, pg. 4020
JUBILANT INGREVIA LIMITED; *Int'l*, pg. 4020
JUBILANT LIFE SCIENCES (USA) INC.—See Jubilant Bhartia Group; *Int'l*, pg. 4020
JUBILANT PHARMACEUTICALS NV—See Jubilant Bhartia Group; *Int'l*, pg. 4020
JUBILANT PHARMOVA LTD.—See Jubilant Bhartia Group; *Int'l*, pg. 4020
JUBILEE CORPORATION—See SMC Corporation; *Int'l*, pg. 7003
JUBILEE ENTERPRISE PUBLIC COMPANY LIMITED; *Int'l*, pg. 4020
JUBILEE GENERAL INSURANCE COMPANY LIMITED—See Aga Khan Development Network; *Int'l*, pg. 199
JUBILEE GOLD EXPLORATION LTD.; *Int'l*, pg. 4020
JUBILEE HOLDINGS LIMITED—See Aga Khan Development Network; *Int'l*, pg. 199
JUBILEE INDUSTRIES HOLDINGS LTD.—See Accrelist Ltd.; *Int'l*, pg. 93
JUBILEE INDUSTRIES (S) PTE LTD.—See Accrelist Ltd.; *Int'l*, pg. 93
THE JUBILEE INSURANCE COMPANY LTD—See Aga Khan Development Network; *Int'l*, pg. 199
THE JUBILEE INSURANCE COMPANY OF TANZANIA LTD—See Aga Khan Development Network; *Int'l*, pg. 199
THE JUBILEE INSURANCE COMPANY OF UGANDA LTD—See Aga Khan Development Network; *Int'l*, pg. 199
JUBILEE INSURANCE (MAURITIUS) LTD—See Aga Khan Development Network; *Int'l*, pg. 199
JUBILEE LIFE INSURANCE COMPANY LIMITED—See Aga Khan Development Network; *Int'l*, pg. 199
JUBILEE MANUFACTURING SDN BHD—See Accrelist Ltd.; *Int'l*, pg. 93
JUBILEE METALS GROUP PLC; *Int'l*, pg. 4020
JUBILEE METALS GROUP PLC; *Int'l*, pg. 4021
JUBILEE SPINNING & WEAVING MILLS LTD.; *Int'l*, pg. 4021
JUBITZ CORPORATION; *U.S. Private*, pg. 2242
J-U CARTER, INC.; *U.S. Private*, pg. 2155
THE JUDAICA PRESS, INC.; *U.S. Private*, pg. 4063
JUDCO MANUFACTURING INC.; *U.S. Private*, pg. 2242
JUDDS BROTHERS CONSTRUCTION COMPANY; *U.S. Private*, pg. 2242
JUDD WIRE, INC.—See Sumitomo Electric Industries, Ltd.; *Int'l*, pg. 7278
JUDEL PRODUCTS CORP.—See LVMH Moet Hennessy Louis Vuitton SE; *Int'l*, pg. 4603
JUDGE.COM, INC.—See The Judge Group, Inc.; *U.S. Private*, pg. 4063
THE JUDGE GROUP, INC.; *U.S. Private*, pg. 4063
JUDGE ROTENBERG EDUCATIONAL CENTER; *U.S. Private*, pg. 2242
JUDGES SCIENTIFIC PLC; *Int'l*, pg. 4021
JUDGE TECHNICAL SERVICES INC.—See The Judge Group, Inc.; *U.S. Private*, pg. 4063
JUDICIAL CORRECTION SERVICES, INC.; *U.S. Private*, pg. 2242
JUDICIAL WATCH, INC.; *U.S. Private*, pg. 2242

JUDITH HEFT ASSOCIATES, LLC—See Aon plc; *Int'l*, pg. 498
JUDITH RIPKA COMPANIES INC.; *U.S. Private*, pg. 2242
JUDLAU CONTRACTING, INC.—See Grupo Villar Mir, S.A.U.; *Int'l*, pg. 3139
JUDLIN FERMETURES S.A.R.L.—See dormakaba Holding AG; *Int'l*, pg. 2177
JUDO BANK PTY. LTD.—See Judo Capital Holdings Limited; *Int'l*, pg. 4021
JUDO CAPITAL HOLDINGS LIMITED; *Int'l*, pg. 4021
JUDSON A. SMITH COMPANY—See A.T. Wall Company; *U.S. Private*, pg. 28
JUDSON ENTERPRISES, LLC—See Great Day Improvements LLC; *U.S. Private*, pg. 1762
JUDSON SERVICES, INC.; *U.S. Private*, pg. 2242
JUDSON'S INC.; *U.S. Private*, pg. 2242
JUDY CONSTRUCTION COMPANY INC.; *U.S. Private*, pg. 2242
JUDY'S INSULATION CO., INC.—See Quad-C Management, Inc.; *U.S. Private*, pg. 3315
JUE-CHUNG ELECTRONICS CO., LTD—See Nidec Chaun-Choung Technology Corporation; *Int'l*, pg. 5274
JUEGOS KOMPAN S.A.—See KOMPAN A/S; *Int'l*, pg. 4243
JUEWEI FOOD CO., LTD.; *Int'l*, pg. 4021
JUFEEL INTERNATIONAL GROUP; *Int'l*, pg. 4021
JUFFALI AIR CONDITIONING, MECHANICAL & ELECTRICAL COMPANY - DUCTWORK FACILITY—See E.A. Juffali & Brothers Company; *Int'l*, pg. 2250
JUFFALI AIR CONDITIONING, MECHANICAL & ELECTRICAL COMPANY - LOW VOLTAGE PANEL BOARD FACILITY—See E.A. Juffali & Brothers Company; *Int'l*, pg. 2250
JUFFALI AIR CONDITIONING, MECHANICAL & ELECTRICAL COMPANY—See E.A. Juffali & Brothers Company; *Int'l*, pg. 2250
JUFFALI AUTOMOTIVE COMPANY—See E.A. Juffali & Brothers Company; *Int'l*, pg. 2250
JUFFALI CHEMICAL COMPANY—See E.A. Juffali & Brothers Company; *Int'l*, pg. 2250
JUFFALI-POLYONE MASTER BATCHES COMPANY—See Avient Corporation; *U.S. Public*, pg. 247
JUFFALI TECHNICAL EQUIPMENT COMPANY—See E.A. Juffali & Brothers Company; *Int'l*, pg. 2251
JUFFALI TYRES COMPANY—See E.A. Juffali & Brothers Company; *Int'l*, pg. 2251
JUGGERNAUT EXPLORATION LTD.; *Int'l*, pg. 4021
JUGGERNAUT MANAGEMENT, LLC; *U.S. Private*, pg. 2242
JUGOAGENT J.S.C.; *Int'l*, pg. 4021
JUGOBANKA A.D. BEOGRAD—See Societe Generale S.A.; *Int'l*, pg. 7040
JUGOCENTAR A.D.; *Int'l*, pg. 4021
JUGODRVO HOLDING A.D.; *Int'l*, pg. 4021
JUGOELEKTRO T.A.D.; *Int'l*, pg. 4021
JUGOINSPEKT A.D.; *Int'l*, pg. 4021
JUGOLEK A.D.; *Int'l*, pg. 4021
JUGOMETAL A.D.; *Int'l*, pg. 4022
JUGOPETROL AD—See HELLENIQ ENERGY Holdings S.A.; *Int'l*, pg. 3334
JUGOPREVOZ A.D.; *Int'l*, pg. 4022
JUGOPREVOZ-GACKO A.D.; *Int'l*, pg. 4022
JUGOPREVOZ KOVIN A.D.; *Int'l*, pg. 4022
JUGOPREVOZ KRUSEVAC A.D.; *Int'l*, pg. 4022
JUGOPREVOZ UGOPROMET A.D.; *Int'l*, pg. 4022
JUGOS DEL VALLE, S.A.B. DE C.V.—See Fomento Economico Mexicano, S.A.B. de C.V.; *Int'l*, pg. 2724
JUGOSLOVENSKI FOND ZA ZITA A.D.; *Int'l*, pg. 4022
JUGOSPED A.D.; *Int'l*, pg. 4022
JUGOTERM A.D.; *Int'l*, pg. 4022
JUGOZAN A.D.; *Int'l*, pg. 4022
JUHACHI CAPITAL CO., LTD.—See Fukuoka Financial Group, Inc.; *Int'l*, pg. 2840
THE JUHACHI-SHINWA BANK, LTD.—See Fukuoka Financial Group, Inc.; *Int'l*, pg. 2840
JUHAYNA FOOD INDUSTRIES CO.; *Int'l*, pg. 4022
JUHL ENERGY, INC.; *U.S. Private*, pg. 2243
JUHORTRANS A.D.; *Int'l*, pg. 4022
JUICEBLENDZ INTERNATIONAL INC.; *U.S. Private*, pg. 2243
JUICE COMMUNICATIONS; *U.S. Private*, pg. 2243
JUICE PRODUCTS NEW ZEALAND LTD.—See Sumitomo Corporation; *Int'l*, pg. 7269
JUICE RESOURCE SOLUTIONS LIMITED—See ManpowerGroup Inc.; *U.S. Public*, pg. 1359
JUICE TECHNOLOGIES, LLC; *U.S. Private*, pg. 2243
JUIC INTERNATIONAL CORP.; *Int'l*, pg. 4022
JUI LI EDSCHA BODY SYSTEMS, CO., LTD.—See Acek Desarrollo y Gestion Industrial SL; *Int'l*, pg. 96
JUI LI ENTERPRISE CO., LTD.; *Int'l*, pg. 4022
JUJAMCYN THEATRES CORP.; *U.S. Private*, pg. 2243
JUJIANG CONSTRUCTION GROUP CO., LTD.; *Int'l*, pg. 4022
JUJO THERMAL OY—See Nippon Paper Industries Co., Ltd.; *Int'l*, pg. 5327
JUJUBEE SA; *Int'l*, pg. 4022
JUJU COSMETICS CO., LTD.—See Kobayashi Pharmaceutical Co., Ltd.; *Int'l*, pg. 4216

JUKAN OPERATION CO., LTD.—See Mitsubishi Heavy Industries, Ltd.; *Int'l*, pg. 4953
JUKEIKAI CO., LTD.—See Daiwa House Industry Co., Ltd.; *Int'l*, pg. 1947
JUKEN ENGINEERING TECHNOLOGY SDN BHD - JOHOR BAHRU FACTORY—See Frencken Group Limited; *Int'l*, pg. 2772
JUKEN ENGINEERING TECHNOLOGY SDN BHD - KUALA LUMPUR FACTORY—See Frencken Group Limited; *Int'l*, pg. 2772
JUKEN (H.K.) CO., LIMITED—See Frencken Group Limited; *Int'l*, pg. 2772
JUKEN KOGYO CO. LTD.—See EMNI Co., Ltd; *Int'l*, pg. 2385
JUKEN MECPLAS TECHNOLOGY PTE LTD—See Frencken Group Limited; *Int'l*, pg. 2772
JUKEN MICRO-AIR (TIANJIN) TECHNOLOGY CO., LTD.—See Frencken Group Limited; *Int'l*, pg. 2773
JUKEN NISSHO LTD.—See WOOD ONE Co., Ltd.; *Int'l*, pg. 8449
JUKEN OPTICS (YANTAI) CO. LTD.—See EMNI Co., Ltd; *Int'l*, pg. 2385
JUKEN SWISS TECHNOLOGY AG—See Frencken Group Limited; *Int'l*, pg. 2773
JUKEN TECHNOLOGY (DONG-GUAN) CO. LTD.—See EMNI Co., Ltd; *Int'l*, pg. 2385
JUKEN TECHNOLOGY ENGINEERING SDN. BHD.—See EMNI Co., Ltd; *Int'l*, pg. 2385
JUKEN TECHNOLOGY (HUIZHOU) CO. LTD.—See EMNI Co., Ltd; *Int'l*, pg. 2385
JUKEN TECHNOLOGY LIMITED—See Frencken Group Limited; *Int'l*, pg. 2772
JUKEN (THAILAND) CO., LTD.—See Frencken Group Limited; *Int'l*, pg. 2772
JUKEN UNIPRODUCTS PVT LTD—See Frencken Group Limited; *Int'l*, pg. 2773
JUKEN (ZHUHAI) CO., LTD.—See Frencken Group Limited; *Int'l*, pg. 2772
JUKI AIZU CORPORATION—See Juki Corporation; *Int'l*, pg. 4022
JUKI AMERICA INC. - HOME SEWING DIVISION—See Juki Corporation; *Int'l*, pg. 4022
JUKI AMERICA, INC.—See Juki Corporation; *Int'l*, pg. 4022
JUKI AUTOMATION SYSTEMS AG—See Juki Corporation; *Int'l*, pg. 4023
JUKI AUTOMATION SYSTEMS CORPORATION—See Juki Corporation; *Int'l*, pg. 4023
JUKI AUTOMATION SYSTEMS GMBH—See Juki Corporation; *Int'l*, pg. 4023
JUKI AUTOMATION SYSTEMS INC.—See Juki Corporation; *Int'l*, pg. 4023
JUKI AUTOMATION SYSTEMS LTD—See Juki Corporation; *Int'l*, pg. 4023
JUKI BANGLADESH LTD.—See Juki Corporation; *Int'l*, pg. 4023
JUKI BANGLADESH LTD.—See Juki Corporation; *Int'l*, pg. 4023
JUKI CENTRAL EUROPE LTD.—See Juki Corporation; *Int'l*, pg. 4023
JUKI CENTRAL EUROPE SP.ZO.O. MOSCOW—See Juki Corporation; *Int'l*, pg. 4023
JUKI (CHINA) CO., LTD - DONGGUAN—See Juki Corporation; *Int'l*, pg. 4023
JUKI (CHINA) CO., LTD.-QINGDAO—See Juki Corporation; *Int'l*, pg. 4023
JUKI (CHINA) CO., LTD.—See Juki Corporation; *Int'l*, pg. 4023
JUKI CORPORATION - ELECTRONIC ASSEMBLY SYSTEMS BUSINESS UNIT - CYUBU NIHON CENTER—See Juki Corporation; *Int'l*, pg. 4022
JUKI CORPORATION - ELECTRONIC ASSEMBLY SYSTEMS BUSINESS UNIT - NISHI NIHON CENTER—See Juki Corporation; *Int'l*, pg. 4022
JUKI CORPORATION - ELECTRONIC ASSEMBLY SYSTEMS BUSINESS UNIT - SMT TRAINING CENTER—See Juki Corporation; *Int'l*, pg. 4022
JUKI CORPORATION - ELECTRONIC ASSEMBLY SYSTEMS BUSINESS UNIT—See Juki Corporation; *Int'l*, pg. 4022
JUKI CORPORATION - OHTAWARA PLANT—See Juki Corporation; *Int'l*, pg. 4023
JUKI CORPORATION; *Int'l*, pg. 4022
JUKI DO BRASIL COMERCIO E SERVICOS DE MAQUINAS LTDA.—See Juki Corporation; *Int'l*, pg. 4023
JUKI (EUROPE) GMBH TURKEY—See Juki Corporation; *Int'l*, pg. 4023
JUKI FRANCE SA—See Juki Corporation; *Int'l*, pg. 4023
JUKI GENERAL SERVICE CORPORATION—See Juki Corporation; *Int'l*, pg. 4023
JUKI HANOI SERVICE CENTER—See Juki Corporation; *Int'l*, pg. 4023
JUKI HIROSHIMA CORPORATION—See Juki Corporation; *Int'l*, pg. 4023
JUKI (HONG KONG) LTD.—See Juki Corporation; *Int'l*, pg. 4023
JUKI INDIA PRIVATE LIMITED—See Juki Corporation; *Int'l*, pg. 4023

JUKI INDIA PRIVATE LIMITED—See Juki Corporation; *Int'l*, pg. 4023
JUKI INDIA PRIVATE LIMITED—See Juki Corporation; *Int'l*, pg. 4023
JUKI INDIA PRIVATE LIMITED—See Juki Corporation; *Int'l*, pg. 4023
JUKI INDUSTRIAL EQUIPMENT TECHNOLOGY CORPORATION - DAISEN FACTORY—See Juki Corporation; *Int'l*, pg. 4023
JUKI INDUSTRIAL EQUIPMENT TECHNOLOGY CORPORATION—See Juki Corporation; *Int'l*, pg. 4023
JUKI INDUSTRIAL EQUIPMENT TECHNOLOGY CORPORATION - YOSHINO FACTORY—See Juki Corporation; *Int'l*, pg. 4023
JUKI ITALIA S.P.A.—See Juki Corporation; *Int'l*, pg. 4023
JUKI (LANGFANG) INDUSTRIAL CO., LTD.—See Juki Corporation; *Int'l*, pg. 4023
JUKI LANKA SERVICE CENTRE PVT. LTD.—See Juki Corporation; *Int'l*, pg. 4023
JUKI MACHINERY BANGLADESH LTD.—See Juki Corporation; *Int'l*, pg. 4023
JUKI MACHINERY VIETNAM CO., LTD.—See Juki Corporation; *Int'l*, pg. 4023
JUKI MATSUE CORPORATION—See Juki Corporation; *Int'l*, pg. 4023
JUKI METAL CORPORATION—See Juki Corporation; *Int'l*, pg. 4023
JUKI (MIDDLE EUROPE) GMBH MINSK—See Juki Corporation; *Int'l*, pg. 4023
JUKI (NINGBO) PRECISION CO., LTD.—See Juki Corporation; *Int'l*, pg. 4023
JUKI OHTAWARA CORPORATION—See Juki Corporation; *Int'l*, pg. 4023
JUKI PROSERVE CORPORATION—See Juki Corporation; *Int'l*, pg. 4023
JUKI (ROMANIA) S.R.L.—See Juki Corporation; *Int'l*, pg. 4023
JUKI SALES (JAPAN) CORPORATION—See Juki Corporation; *Int'l*, pg. 4023
JUKI (SHANGHAI) INDUSTRIAL CO., LTD .—See Juki Corporation; *Int'l*, pg. 4022
JUKI SINGAPORE PTE. LTD.—See Juki Corporation; *Int'l*, pg. 4024
JUKI SMT ASIA CO., LTD.—See Juki Corporation; *Int'l*, pg. 4023
JUKI TECHNOSOLUTIONS CORPORATION—See Juki Corporation; *Int'l*, pg. 4024
JUKI (THAILAND) COMPANY LIMITED—See Juki Corporation; *Int'l*, pg. 4023
JUKI UNION SPECIAL, MEXICO S.A. DE C.V.—See Juki Corporation; *Int'l*, pg. 4024
JUKI (VIETNAM) CO., LTD.—See Juki Corporation; *Int'l*, pg. 4023
JUKI XINXING INDUSTRY CO., LTD.—See Juki Corporation; *Int'l*, pg. 4023
JUKONSKI TRUCK SALES AND SERVICE; *U.S. Private*, pg. 2243
JULABO FRANCE SAS—See JULABO Labortechnik GmbH; *Int'l*, pg. 4024
JULABO ITALIA SRL—See JULABO Labortechnik GmbH; *Int'l*, pg. 4024
JULABO JAPAN CO., LTD.—See JULABO Labortechnik GmbH; *Int'l*, pg. 4024
JULABO KOREA CO., LTD.—See JULABO Labortechnik GmbH; *Int'l*, pg. 4024
JULABO LABORTECHNIK GMBH; *Int'l*, pg. 4024
JULABO LATIN AMERICA—See JULABO Labortechnik GmbH; *Int'l*, pg. 4024
JULABO NEDERLAND B.V.—See JULABO Labortechnik GmbH; *Int'l*, pg. 4024
JULABO SINGAPORE PTE., LTD.—See JULABO Labortechnik GmbH; *Int'l*, pg. 4024
JULABO TECHNOLOGY (BEIJING) CO. LTD.—See JULABO Labortechnik GmbH; *Int'l*, pg. 4024
JULABO UK LTD.—See JULABO Labortechnik GmbH; *Int'l*, pg. 4024
JULABO USA, INC.—See JULABO Labortechnik GmbH; *Int'l*, pg. 4024
JULESBURG ADVOCATE—See Alden Global Capital LLC; *U.S. Private*, pg. 157
JULES VERNE LTD—See REWE-Zentral-Aktiengesellschaft; *Int'l*, pg. 6314
JULIA B. FEE SOTHEBY'S INTERNATIONAL REALTY—See William Pitt Sotheby's International Realty; *U.S. Private*, pg. 4524
JULIA DYCKMAN ANDRUS MEMORIAL, INC.; *U.S. Private*, pg. 2243
JULIA JAPAN CO. ,LTD.—See GENDAI AGENCY INC.; *Int'l*, pg. 2917
JULIAN BOWEN LTD.—See Storskogen Group AB; *Int'l*, pg. 7227
JULIAN ELECTRIC INC.; *U.S. Private*, pg. 2243
JULIAN FREIRICH CO. INC.; *U.S. Private*, pg. 2243
JULIAN GOLD INC.; *U.S. Private*, pg. 2243
JULIANI KENNEY INVESTMENT CAPITAL, LLC; *U.S. Private*, pg. 2243
JULIAN LUMBER CO. INC.; *U.S. Private*, pg. 2243

COMPANY NAME INDEX

JULIAN ONG ENDOSCOPY & SURGERY PTE. LTD.—See HC Surgical Specialists Limited; *Int'l*, pg. 3297
JULIA VITRUM S.P.A.—See Zignago Vetro S.p.A.; *Int'l*, pg. 8682
JULIA WALLACE RETIREMENT VILLAGE LIMITED—See Ryman Healthcare Ltd.; *Int'l*, pg. 6439
JULIE A. LAITIN ENTERPRISES, INC.; *U.S. Private*, pg. 2243
JULIE EMOND PHYSICAL THERAPY, LIMITED PARTNERSHIP—See U.S. Physical Therapy, Inc.; *U.S. Public*, pg. 2214
JULIE LH BVBA—See KBC Group NV; *Int'l*, pg. 4105
JULIETTE FOWLER HOMES INC.; *U.S. Private*, pg. 2243
JULI PLC; *Int'l*, pg. 4024
JULISKA; *U.S. Private*, pg. 2243
JULI SLING CO., LTD.; *Int'l*, pg. 4024
JULIUS BAER ADVISORY S.A.E. LTD.—See Julius Baer Group Ltd.; *Int'l*, pg. 4024
JULIUS BAER CONSULTORES (PERU) S.A.C.—See Julius Baer Group Ltd.; *Int'l*, pg. 4024
JULIUS BAER CONSULTORES S.A.—See Julius Baer Group Ltd.; *Int'l*, pg. 4024
JULIUS BAER FIDUCIARIA S.R.L.—See Julius Baer Group Ltd.; *Int'l*, pg. 4024
JULIUS BAER FINANCIAL CONSULTANCY S.A.—See Julius Baer Group Ltd.; *Int'l*, pg. 4024
JULIUS BAER GROUP LTD.; *Int'l*, pg. 4024
JULIUS BAER (HONG KONG) LTD.—See Julius Baer Group Ltd.; *Int'l*, pg. 4024
JULIUS BAER INTERNATIONAL LTD.—See Julius Baer Group Ltd.; *Int'l*, pg. 4024
JULIUS BAER INVESTMENT ADVISORY GESMBH—See Julius Baer Group Ltd.; *Int'l*, pg. 4024
JULIUS BAER (MONACO) S.A.M.—See Julius Baer Group Ltd.; *Int'l*, pg. 4024
JULIUS BAER PATRIMOINE CONSEIL SARL—See Julius Baer Group Ltd.; *Int'l*, pg. 4024
JULIUS BAER PRIVATE BANKING—See Julius Baer Group Ltd.; *Int'l*, pg. 4024
JULIUS BAER (URUGUAY) S.A.—See Julius Baer Group Ltd.; *Int'l*, pg. 4024
JULIUS BERGER NIGERIA PLC—See Bilfinger SE; *Int'l*, pg. 1020
JULIUS BRANSCOME INC.; *U.S. Private*, pg. 2243
JULIUS HEYWINKEL GMBH—See NORD Holding Unternehmensbeteiligungsgesellschaft mbH; *Int'l*, pg. 5416
JULIUS MEINL BALIARNE, A.S.—See Julius Meinl Industrieholding GmbH; *Int'l*, pg. 4025
JULIUS MEINL COFFEE INTL., A.S.—See Julius Meinl Industrieholding GmbH; *Int'l*, pg. 4025
JULIUS MEINL GIDA SAN. VE TIC. LTD. STI.—See Julius Meinl Industrieholding GmbH; *Int'l*, pg. 4025
JULIUS MEINL GOURMET GMBH—See Julius Meinl Industrieholding GmbH; *Int'l*, pg. 4025
JULIUS MEINL HUNGARY KFT.—See Julius Meinl Industrieholding GmbH; *Int'l*, pg. 4025
JULIUS MEINL INDUSTRIEHOLDING GMBH; *Int'l*, pg. 4025
JULIUS MEINL ITALIA SPA—See Julius Meinl Industrieholding GmbH; *Int'l*, pg. 4025
JULIUS MEINL NAHRUNGSMITTEL PRODUKTIONS GES.M.B.H.—See Julius Meinl Industrieholding GmbH; *Int'l*, pg. 4025
JULIUS MEINL ROMANIA SRL.—See Julius Meinl Industrieholding GmbH; *Int'l*, pg. 4025
JULIUS MEINL UK LTD.—See Julius Meinl Industrieholding GmbH; *Int'l*, pg. 4025
JULIUS SCHEPPS COMPANY, INC.; *U.S. Private*, pg. 2243
JULIUS TALLBERG-KIINTEISTOET OYJ; *Int'l*, pg. 4025
JULIUS ZORN GMBH; *Int'l*, pg. 4025
JULIUS ZORN, INC.—See Julius Zorn GmbH; *Int'l*, pg. 4025
JULLUNDUR MOTOR AGENCY (DELHI) LTD.; *Int'l*, pg. 4025
JULONG CO., LTD.; *Int'l*, pg. 4025
JULY AUGUST COMMUNICATIONS AND PRODUCTIONS LTD.—See ProSiebenSat.1 Media SE; *Int'l*, pg. 6001
JULY STAR CO., LTD.—See Nippon Steel Corporation; *Int'l*, pg. 5337
JULY SYSTEMS, LLC—See Cisco Systems, Inc.; *U.S. Public*, pg. 499
JUMA AL MAJID CONCRETE PRODUCTS PLANTS L.L.C.—See Juma Al Majid Group; *Int'l*, pg. 4025
JUMA AL MAJID ELECTRO MECHANICAL WORKS L.L.C.—See Juma Al Majid Group; *Int'l*, pg. 4025
JUMA AL MAJID GROUP; *Int'l*, pg. 4025
JUMA TECHNOLOGY CORP.; *U.S. Public*, pg. 1210
JUMBA BAY—See Chow Tai Fook Enterprises Limited; *Int'l*, pg. 1585
JUMBO BAG LTD.; *Int'l*, pg. 4025
JUMBO CO., LTD.—See Encho Co., Ltd.; *Int'l*, pg. 2401
JUMBO ELECTRONICS COMPANY LTD.; *Int'l*, pg. 4026
JUMBO GAIN DEVELOPMENTS LIMITED—See Shenguan Holdings (Group) Limited; *Int'l*, pg. 6802
JUMBO GROUP LIMITED; *Int'l*, pg. 4026

JUMBO INTERACTIVE GMBH—See Jumbo Interactive Limited; *Int'l*, pg. 4026
JUMBO INTERACTIVE LIMITED; *Int'l*, pg. 4026
JUMBO INTERACTIVE NORTH AMERICA—See Jumbo Interactive Limited; *Int'l*, pg. 4026
JUMBO INTERACTIVE PTY. LTD.—See Jumbo Interactive Limited; *Int'l*, pg. 4026
JUMBO MARKT AG—See Maus Freres S.A.; *Int'l*, pg. 4732
JUMBO RETAIL ARGENTINA S.A.—See Cencosud S.A.; *Int'l*, pg. 1400
JUMBO S.A.; *Int'l*, pg. 4026
JUMBOSHRIMP ADVERTISING INC.; *U.S. Private*, pg. 2243
JUMBO SUPERMARKTEN B.V.; *Int'l*, pg. 4026
JUMBUCK AUSTRALIA PTY. LTD.—See Aumake Limited; *Int'l*, pg. 705
JUMEI INTERNATIONAL HOLDING LIMITED; *Int'l*, pg. 4026
JUMEIRAH GROUP LLC—See Dubai Holding LLC; *Int'l*, pg. 2218
JUMEIRAH INTERNATIONAL LLC—See Dubai Holding LLC; *Int'l*, pg. 2218
JUMIA TECHNOLOGIES AG; *Int'l*, pg. 4026
JUMP2 GROUP; *U.S. Private*, pg. 2243
JUMP DESIGN GROUP; *U.S. Private*, pg. 2243
JUMP DISTRIBUTORS (THAILAND) CO LTD—See Freudenberg SE; *Int'l*, pg. 2789
JUMPFORWARD LLC—See Global Payments Inc.; *U.S. Public*, pg. 943
JUMPGATE AB; *Int'l*, pg. 4026
JUMP INC.; *U.S. Private*, pg. 2243
JUMPING-JACKS SHOES DIV—See Munro & Company, Inc.; *U.S. Private*, pg. 2814
JUMP INTERNATIONAL TRADING (SHANGHAI) CO LTD—See Freudenberg SE; *Int'l*, pg. 2789
JUMPLUX TECHNOLOGY CO., LTD.—See Sunplus Technology Co., Ltd.; *Int'l*, pg. 7320
JUMP!; *U.S. Private*, pg. 2243
JUMP—See Omnicom Group Inc.; *U.S. Public*, pg. 1596
JUMPSTART AUTOMOTIVE MEDIA—See The Hearst Corporation; *U.S. Private*, pg. 4049
JUMPSTART GAMES, INC.—See NetDragon Websoft Holdings Limited; *Int'l*, pg. 5213
JUMPTIME, INC.—See Vivendi SE; *Int'l*, pg. 8270
JUMP WORLD HOLDING LIMITED; *Int'l*, pg. 4026
JUNCADELLA PROSEGUR INTERNACIONAL SA—See Prosegur Compania de Seguridad S.A.; *Int'l*, pg. 5999
JUN CERAMIC, INC.; *U.S. Private*, pg. 2244
JUNCKER BIKE PARTS B.V.—See Accell Group N.V.; *Int'l*, pg. 80
JUNCO FLORA SCHOOL CO., LTD.—See NIPPN Corporation; *Int'l*, pg. 5309
JUNCO STEEL CORPORATION; *U.S. Private*, pg. 2244
JUNCTION INTERNATIONAL, LLC; *U.S. Private*, pg. 2244
JUNCTION NETWORKS INC.—See Ooma, Inc.; *U.S. Public*, pg. 1605
JUNCTION SOLUTIONS, INC.; *U.S. Private*, pg. 2244
JUNDIAI SHOPPING CENTER LTDA.—See Multiplan Empreendimentos Imobiliarios S.A.; *Int'l*, pg. 5084
JUNEAU BIOSCIENCES, LLC; *U.S. Private*, pg. 2244
JUNEAU EMPIRE—See Gannett Co., Inc.; *U.S. Public*, pg. 903
JUNEAU PHYSICAL THERAPY, A PROFESSIONAL CORPORATION—See SouthEast Alaska Regional Health Consortium; *U.S. Private*, pg. 3724
JUNEE CORRECTIONAL CENTRE—See The GEO Group, Inc.; *U.S. Public*, pg. 2075
JUNEE LIMITED; *Int'l*, pg. 4026
JUNE EMBALLAGE AB—See Stora Enso Oyj; *Int'l*, pg. 7223
JUNE JACOBS SPA COLLECTION—See Peter Thomas Roth Labs LLC; *U.S. Private*, pg. 3159
JUNE LIFE, INC.—See BDT Capital Partners, LLC; *U.S. Private*, pg. 503
JUNE TAILOR, INC.—See WILsquare Capital LLC; *U.S. Private*, pg. 4532
JUNEYAO AIRLINES CO., LTD.; *Int'l*, pg. 4026
JUNGCLAUS-CAMPBELL CO. INC.; *U.S. Private*, pg. 2244
JUNGDAWN CO., LTD.; *Int'l*, pg. 4027
JUNG, DMS & CIE. AG—See JDC Group AG; *Int'l*, pg. 3925
JUNGE CONTROL, INC.—See Ag Growth International Inc.; *Int'l*, pg. 198
JUNGE & CO. VERSICHERUNGSMAKLER GMBH—See Lightyear Capital LLC; *U.S. Private*, pg. 2454
JUNGE FORD INC.; *U.S. Private*, pg. 2244
JUNGE LINCOLN MERCURY INC.; *U.S. Private*, pg. 2244
JUNGFRAUBAHN HOLDING AG; *Int'l*, pg. 4027
JUNG GUMMITECHNIK GMBH; *Int'l*, pg. 4026
JUNGHANS MICROTEC GMBH—See Diehl Stiftung & Co. KG; *Int'l*, pg. 2115
JUNGHANS T2M SAS—See Diehl Stiftung & Co. KG; *Int'l*, pg. 2115
JUNGHANS UHREN GMBH; *Int'l*, pg. 4027
JUNGHEINRICH AG; *Int'l*, pg. 4027

JUNGHEINRICH AG

JUNGHEINRICH AUSTRALIA PTY. LTD.—See Jungheinrich AG; *Int'l*, pg. 4027
JUNGHEINRICH AUSTRIA VERTRIEBS GES.M.B.H.—See Jungheinrich AG; *Int'l*, pg. 4027
JUNGHEINRICH BETEILIGUNGS-GMBH—See Jungheinrich AG; *Int'l*, pg. 4027
JUNGHEINRICH BUSINESS SERVICES ROMANIA S.R.L.—See Jungheinrich AG; *Int'l*, pg. 4027
JUNGHEINRICH COLOMBIA SAS—See Jungheinrich AG; *Int'l*, pg. 4027
JUNGHEINRICH (CR), S.R.O.—See Jungheinrich AG; *Int'l*, pg. 4027
JUNGHEINRICH DANMARK A/S—See Jungheinrich AG; *Int'l*, pg. 4027
JUNGHEINRICH DE ESPANA S.A.U.—See Jungheinrich AG; *Int'l*, pg. 4028
JUNGHEINRICH DEGEMPOINT AG & CO. KG—See Jungheinrich AG; *Int'l*, pg. 4027
JUNGHEINRICH DEGERNPOINT AG & CO. KG—See Jungheinrich AG; *Int'l*, pg. 4027
JUNGHEINRICH DESIGN CENTER HOUSTON CORPORATION—See Jungheinrich AG; *Int'l*, pg. 4027
JUNGHEINRICH D.O.O.—See Jungheinrich AG; *Int'l*, pg. 4028
JUNGHEINRICH ECUADOR S.A.—See Jungheinrich AG; *Int'l*, pg. 4027
JUNGHEINRICH EXPORT AG & CO. KG—See Jungheinrich AG; *Int'l*, pg. 4027
JUNGHEINRICH FINANCE AG & CO. KG—See Jungheinrich AG; *Int'l*, pg. 4027
JUNGHEINRICH FINANCE S.R.L.—See Jungheinrich AG; *Int'l*, pg. 4027
JUNGHEINRICH FINANCIAL SERVICES GMBH—See Jungheinrich AG; *Int'l*, pg. 4027
JUNGHEINRICH FINANCIAL SERVICES LTD.—See Jungheinrich AG; *Int'l*, pg. 4027
JUNGHEINRICH FINANCIAL SERVICES S.R.L.—See Jungheinrich AG; *Int'l*, pg. 4027
JUNGHEINRICH FLEET SERVICES S.L.—See Jungheinrich AG; *Int'l*, pg. 4027
JUNGHEINRICH FRANCE S.A.S.—See Jungheinrich AG; *Int'l*, pg. 4028
JUNGHEINRICH HELLAS EPE—See Jungheinrich AG; *Int'l*, pg. 4028
JUNGHEINRICH HUNGARIA KFT.—See Jungheinrich AG; *Int'l*, pg. 4028
JUNGHEINRICH ISTIF MAKINALARI SAN. VE TIC. LTD. STI.—See Jungheinrich AG; *Int'l*, pg. 4028
JUNGHEINRICH ITALIANA S.R.L.—See Jungheinrich AG; *Int'l*, pg. 4028
JUNGHEINRICH KATALOG GMBH & CO. KG—See Jungheinrich AG; *Int'l*, pg. 4028
JUNGHEINRICH LANDSBERG AG & CO. KG—See Jungheinrich AG; *Int'l*, pg. 4028
JUNGHEINRICH LIFT TRUCK COMERCIO DE EMPILHADEIRAS LTDA.—See Jungheinrich AG; *Int'l*, pg. 4028
JUNGHEINRICH LIFT TRUCK CORP.—See Jungheinrich AG; *Int'l*, pg. 4028
JUNGHEINRICH LIFT TRUCK FINANCE LTD.—See Jungheinrich AG; *Int'l*, pg. 4028
JUNGHEINRICH LIFT TRUCK INDIA PRIVATE LTD.—See Jungheinrich AG; *Int'l*, pg. 4028
JUNGHEINRICH LIFT TRUCK LIMITED—See Jungheinrich AG; *Int'l*, pg. 4028
JUNGHEINRICH LIFT TRUCK LTDA.—See Jungheinrich AG; *Int'l*, pg. 4028
JUNGHEINRICH LIFT TRUCK LTD.—See Jungheinrich AG; *Int'l*, pg. 4028
JUNGHEINRICH LIFT TRUCK MALAYSIA SDN. BHD.—See Jungheinrich AG; *Int'l*, pg. 4028
JUNGHEINRICH LIFT TRUCK MANUFACTURING (SHANGHAI) CO., LTD.—See Jungheinrich AG; *Int'l*, pg. 4028
JUNGHEINRICH LIFT TRUCK OOO—See Jungheinrich AG; *Int'l*, pg. 4028
JUNGHEINRICH LIFT TRUCK OY—See Jungheinrich AG; *Int'l*, pg. 4028
JUNGHEINRICH LIFT TRUCK (SHANGHAI) CO., LTD.—See Jungheinrich AG; *Int'l*, pg. 4028
JUNGHEINRICH LIFT TRUCK SIA—See Jungheinrich AG; *Int'l*, pg. 4028
JUNGHEINRICH LIFT TRUCK SINGAPORE PTE LTD.—See Jungheinrich AG; *Int'l*, pg. 4028
JUNGHEINRICH LIFT TRUCK TOV—See Jungheinrich AG; *Int'l*, pg. 4028
JUNGHEINRICH LIFT TRUCK UAB—See Jungheinrich AG; *Int'l*, pg. 4028
JUNGHEINRICH MOOSBURG AG & CO. KG—See Jungheinrich AG; *Int'l*, pg. 4028
JUNGHEINRICH MOOSBURG GMBH—See Jungheinrich AG; *Int'l*, pg. 4028
JUNGHEINRICH NEDERLAND B.V.—See Jungheinrich AG; *Int'l*, pg. 4028
JUNGHEINRICH NEW ZEALAND LTD.—See Jungheinrich AG; *Int'l*, pg. 4028
JUNGHEINRICH NORDERSTEDT AG & CO. KG—See Jungheinrich AG; *Int'l*, pg. 4028

JUNGHEINRICH AG

JUNGHEINRICH NORGE AS—See Jungheinrich AG; *Int'l*, pg. 4028
JUNGHEINRICH N.V./S.A.—See Jungheinrich AG; *Int'l*, pg. 4028
JUNGHEINRICH PERU S.A.C.—See Jungheinrich AG; *Int'l*, pg. 4028
JUNGHEINRICH POLSKA SP. Z.O.O.—See Jungheinrich AG; *Int'l*, pg. 4028
JUNGHEINRICH (PORTUGAL) EQUIPAMENTOS DE TRANSPORTE, LDA.—See Jungheinrich AG; *Int'l*, pg. 4027
JUNGHEINRICH PROFISHOP AG & CO. KG—See Jungheinrich AG; *Int'l*, pg. 4028
JUNGHEINRICH PROFISHOP GMBH—See Jungheinrich AG; *Int'l*, pg. 4028
JUNGHEINRICH RENTALIFT SPA—See Jungheinrich AG; *Int'l*, pg. 4028
JUNGHEINRICH ROMANIA S.R.L.—See Jungheinrich AG; *Int'l*, pg. 4028
JUNGHEINRICH SERVICE & PARTS AG & CO. KG—See Jungheinrich AG; *Int'l*, pg. 4028
JUNGHEINRICH SOUTH AFRICA (PTY) LTD.—See Jungheinrich AG; *Int'l*, pg. 4028
JUNGHEINRICH SPOL S.R.O.—See Jungheinrich AG; *Int'l*, pg. 4029
JUNGHEINRICH SVENSKA AB—See Jungheinrich AG; *Int'l*, pg. 4028
JUNGHEINRICH UK HOLDINGS LTD.—See Jungheinrich AG; *Int'l*, pg. 4028
JUNGHEINRICH UK LTD .—See Jungheinrich AG; *Int'l*, pg. 4028
JUNGHEINRICH VERTRIEB DEUTSCHLAND AG & CO. KG—See Jungheinrich AG; *Int'l*, pg. 4028
JUNGLE21 SA; *Int'l*, pg. 4029
JUNGLE DISK LLC—See Apollo Global Management, Inc.; *U.S. Public*, pg. 154
JUNG PUMPEN GMBH—See Pentair plc; *Int'l*, pg. 5790
JUNG PUMPEN HUNGARY KFT.—See Pentair plc; *Int'l*, pg. 5789
JUNG SEED GENETICS—See Bayer Aktiengesellschaft; *Int'l*, pg. 908
JUNGSEOK ENTERPRISE CO., LTD.—See Hanjin Kal Corp.; *Int'l*, pg. 3252
JUNG SHING WIRE CO., LTD.; *Int'l*, pg. 4026
JUNGS TRUCKING, INC.; *U.S. Private*, pg. 2244
JUNG TECHNOLOGIES HOLDING AG; *Int'l*, pg. 4027
JUNG VON MATT/DONAU—See Jung von Matt; *Int'l*, pg. 4027
JUNG VON MATT/ELBE—See Jung von Matt; *Int'l*, pg. 4027
JUNG VON MATT/LIMMAT—See Jung von Matt; *Int'l*, pg. 4027
JUNG VON MATT/NECKAR—See Jung von Matt; *Int'l*, pg. 4027
JUNG VON MATT; *Int'l*, pg. 4027
JUNG VON MATT/SPREE—See Jung von Matt; *Int'l*, pg. 4027
JUNG VON MATT/STROEMMEN—See Jung von Matt; *Int'l*, pg. 4027
JUNGWON MACHINERY IND. CO., LTD.—See DAE-IL Corporation; *Int'l*, pg. 1905
JUNHE PUMPS HOLDING CO., LTD.; *Int'l*, pg. 4029
JUNIATA MEMORIAL PARK LLC—See Axar Capital Management L.P.; *U.S. Private*, pg. 411
THE JUNIATA VALLEY BANK—See Juniata Valley Financial Corp.; *U.S. Public*, pg. 1210
JUNIATA VALLEY FINANCIAL CORP.; *U.S. Public*, pg. 1210
JUNIOR A.D.; *Int'l*, pg. 4029
JUNIOR FOOD STORES OF WEST FLORIDA, INC.—See TDR Capital LLP; *Int'l*, pg. 7494
JUNIOR GALLERY LTD.; *U.S. Private*, pg. 2244
JUNIOR'S BUILDING MATERIALS, INC.; *U.S. Private*, pg. 2244
JUNIOR SPORTS CORPORATION—See The Riverside Company; *U.S. Private*, pg. 4109
JUNIPER ASSISTED LIVING RESIDENCE I, LLC—See LTC Properties, Inc.; *U.S. Public*, pg. 1344
JUNIPER DEVELOPMENT GROUP; *Int'l*, pg. 4029
JUNIPER ELBOW CO. INC.; *U.S. Private*, pg. 2244
JUNIPER EXTENSIBLE SOLUTIONS S.R.L.—See TAMBURI INVESTMENT PARTNERS S.p.A.; *Int'l*, pg. 7450
JUNIPER GROUP, INC.; *U.S. Private*, pg. 2244
JUNIPER INDUSTRIAL HOLDINGS, INC.—See Clearlake Capital Group, L.P.; *U.S. Private*, pg. 935
JUNIPER INVESTMENT COMPANY, LLC; *U.S. Private*, pg. 2244
JUNIPER LANDSCAPING, INC.; *U.S. Private*, pg. 2244
JUNIPER NETWORKS AUSTRALIA LTD.—See Juniper Networks, Inc.; *U.S. Public*, pg. 1211
JUNIPER NETWORKS BRAZIL LTD.—See Juniper Networks, Inc.; *U.S. Public*, pg. 1211
JUNIPER NETWORKS B.V.—See Juniper Networks, Inc.; *U.S. Public*, pg. 1211
JUNIPER NETWORKS CHINA LTD.—See Juniper Networks, Inc.; *U.S. Public*, pg. 1211
JUNIPER NETWORKS FINLAND OY—See Juniper Networks, Inc.; *U.S. Public*, pg. 1211
JUNIPER NETWORKS FRANCE SARL—See Juniper Networks, Inc.; *U.S. Public*, pg. 1211
JUNIPER NETWORKS HOLDINGS INTERNATIONAL, INC.—See Juniper Networks, Inc.; *U.S. Public*, pg. 1211
JUNIPER NETWORKS (HONG KONG) LTD.—See Juniper Networks, Inc.; *U.S. Public*, pg. 1211
JUNIPER NETWORKS, INC.; *U.S. Public*, pg. 1210
JUNIPER NETWORKS INDIA PRIVATE LTD.—See Juniper Networks, Inc.; *U.S. Public*, pg. 1211
JUNIPER NETWORKS IRELAND LTD.—See Juniper Networks, Inc.; *U.S. Public*, pg. 1211
JUNIPER NETWORKS ITALY S.R.L.—See Juniper Networks, Inc.; *U.S. Public*, pg. 1211
JUNIPER NETWORKS KOREA, INC.—See Juniper Networks, Inc.; *U.S. Public*, pg. 1211
JUNIPER NETWORKS MALAYSIA SDN. BHD.—See Juniper Networks, Inc.; *U.S. Public*, pg. 1211
JUNIPER NETWORKS MEXICO S.A. DE C.V.—See Juniper Networks, Inc.; *U.S. Public*, pg. 1211
JUNIPER NETWORKS (SINGAPORE) PTE. LTD.—See Juniper Networks, Inc.; *U.S. Public*, pg. 1211
JUNIPER NETWORKS SPAIN SRL—See Juniper Networks, Inc.; *U.S. Public*, pg. 1211
JUNIPER NETWORKS SWITZERLAND GMBH—See Juniper Networks, Inc.; *U.S. Public*, pg. 1211
JUNIPER NETWORKS TAIWAN LIMITED CO.—See Juniper Networks, Inc.; *U.S. Public*, pg. 1211
JUNIPER NETWORKS U.K. LTD.—See Juniper Networks, Inc.; *U.S. Public*, pg. 1211
JUNIPER NETWORKS (US), INC.—See Juniper Networks, Inc.; *U.S. Public*, pg. 1211
JUNIPER PARK LP—See Omnicom Group Inc.; *U.S. Public*, pg. 1598
JUNIPER PAYMENTS, LLC—See Zucchetti Group S.p.A.; *Int'l*, pg. 8692
JUNIPER PHARMACEUTICALS (FRANCE) SA—See Catalent, Inc.; *U.S. Public*, pg. 448
JUNIPER PHARMACEUTICALS, INC.—See Catalent, Inc.; *U.S. Public*, pg. 448
JUNIPER PHARMA SERVICES LIMITED—See Catalent, Inc.; *U.S. Public*, pg. 448
JUNIPER ROCK CORPORATION—See Primoris Services Corporation; *U.S. Public*, pg. 1718
JUNIPER SYSTEMS—See Campbell Scientific, Inc.; *U.S. Private*, pg. 730
JUNKEN MEDICAL CO., LTD.—See Japan Lifeline Co., Ltd.; *Int'l*, pg. 3898
JUNKER INDUSTRIAL EQUIPMENT S.R.O.—See Otto Junker GmbH; *Int'l*, pg. 5664
JUNKFOOD CLOTHING COMPANY—See Delta Apparel, Inc.; *U.S. Public*, pg. 652
JUNKLUGGERS, LLC—See Apax Partners LLP; *Int'l*, pg. 502
JUNK MY CAR, LLC; *U.S. Private*, pg. 2244
JUNKUDO CO., LTD.—See Dai Nippon Printing Co., Ltd.; *Int'l*, pg. 1915
JUNMA TYRE CORD COMPANY LIMITED; *Int'l*, pg. 4029
JUNO CORP.—See Val-d'Or Mining Corporation; *Int'l*, pg. 8110
JUNO INVESTMENTS LLC; *U.S. Private*, pg. 2244
JUNOKAI GMBH—See Majorel Group Luxembourg S.A.; *Int'l*, pg. 4655
JUNO LIGHTING, LLC—See Acuity Brands, Inc.; *U.S. Public*, pg. 37
JUNOLL SERVICES—See Macquarie Group Limited; *Int'l*, pg. 4628
JUNO MINERALS LIMITED; *Int'l*, pg. 4029
JUNONIA LTD.; *U.S. Private*, pg. 2245
JUNOPACIFIC, INC.—See The Cretex Companies, Inc.; *U.S. Private*, pg. 4016
JUNO PHARMACEUTICALS, INC.; *Int'l*, pg. 4029
JUNO SEARCH PARTNERS, LLC—See Aon plc; *Int'l*, pg. 496
JUNO TECHNOLOGIES, INC.—See Sagewind Capital LLC; *U.S. Private*, pg. 3528
JUNO TECHNOLOGY CORPORATION; *U.S. Private*, pg. 2244
JUNO THERAPEUTICS, INC.—See Bristol-Myers Squibb Company; *U.S. Public*, pg. 386
JUNPUZI. CO., LTD.—See Chodai Co., Ltd.; *Int'l*, pg. 1577
JUNTENDO CO., LTD.; *Int'l*, pg. 4029
JUNTION DEVELOPMENT HONG KONG (HOLDING) LIMITED—See Longfor Group Holdings Limited; *Int'l*, pg. 4550
JUNTO DESIGN STUDIO, LLC; *U.S. Private*, pg. 2245
JUNWA FOOD CORPORATION—See Yoshimura Food Holdings K.K.; *Int'l*, pg. 8600
JUNXURE; *U.S. Private*, pg. 2245
JUOKU TECHNOLOGY CO., LTD.—See TYC Brother Industrial Co., Ltd.; *Int'l*, pg. 7994
JUPAI HOLDINGS LIMITED; *Int'l*, pg. 4029
JUPE FEEDS, INC.; *U.S. Private*, pg. 2245
JUPE MILLS, INC.; *U.S. Private*, pg. 2245
JUPITER ACQUISITION CORPORATION; *U.S. Public*, pg. 1211
JUPITER AIR (HONG KONG) LTD.—See Japan Airlines Co., Ltd.; *Int'l*, pg. 3884
JUPITER AIR OCEANIA LTD.—See Japan Airlines Co., Ltd.; *Int'l*, pg. 3884
JUPITER AIR SERVICES (MALAYSIA) SDN. BHD.—See Japan Airlines Co., Ltd.; *Int'l*, pg. 3884
JUPITER ALUMINUM CORPORATION - JUPITER COIL COATING DIVISION—See Jupiter Aluminum Corporation; *U.S. Private*, pg. 2245
JUPITER ALUMINUM CORPORATION; *U.S. Private*, pg. 2245
JUPITER ANESTHESIA ASSOCIATES, LLC—See KKR & Co. Inc.; *U.S. Public*, pg. 1245
JUPITER ASSET MANAGEMENT LIMITED—See Jupiter Fund Management plc; *Int'l*, pg. 4029
JUPITER BACH A/S; *Int'l*, pg. 4029
JUPITER BAND INSTRUMENTS, INC.—See K.H.S. Musical Instrument Co., Ltd.; *Int'l*, pg. 4043
JUPITER BEACH RESORT & SPA—See Ocean Properties, Ltd.; *U.S. Private*, pg. 2989
JUPITER CHEVROLET, LP; *U.S. Private*, pg. 2245
JUPITER COUNTRY CLUB, INC.—See Apollo Global Management, Inc.; *U.S. Public*, pg. 149
JUPITER COURIER NEWSWEEKLY—See Gannett Co., Inc.; *U.S. Public*, pg. 898
THE JUPITER DRAWING ROOM (PROPRIETARY) LIMITED; *Int'l*, pg. 7661
THE JUPITER DRAWING ROOM—See The Jupiter Drawing Room (Proprietary) Limited; *Int'l*, pg. 7661
JUPITER EFL IMAGING CENTER, LLC—See HCA Healthcare, Inc.; *U.S. Public*, pg. 999
JUPITER EMERGING & FRONTIER INCOME TRUST PLC; *Int'l*, pg. 4029
JUPITER ENERGY (KAZAKHSTAN) PTY LTD—See Jupiter Energy Limited; *Int'l*, pg. 4029
JUPITER ENERGY LIMITED; *Int'l*, pg. 4029
JUPITER EVENTS—See Mecklermedia Corporation; *U.S. Private*, pg. 2649
JUPITER EV—See Parkomat International Ltd.; *Int'l*, pg. 5744
JUPITER FUND MANAGEMENT PLC; *Int'l*, pg. 4029
JUPITER GLOBAL LIMITED—See Japan Airlines Co., Ltd.; *Int'l*, pg. 3884
JUPITER GOLD CORPORATION—See ATLAS LITHIUM CORPORATION; *Int'l*, pg. 686
JUPITER GOLF NETWORK CO., LTD.—See Sumitomo Corporation; *Int'l*, pg. 7269
JUPITER GREEN INVESTMENT TRUST PLC—See Jupiter Fund Management plc; *Int'l*, pg. 4029
JUPITER HOTELS LIMITED—See Singha Estate PCL; *Int'l*, pg. 6943
JUPITER IMAGING ASSOCIATES, INC.—See KKR & Co. Inc.; *U.S. Public*, pg. 1245
JUPITER INFOMEDIA LTD.; *Int'l*, pg. 4029
JUPITER INVESTMENT MANAGEMENT GROUP LIMITED—See Jupiter Fund Management plc; *Int'l*, pg. 4029
JUPITER JAPAN CO., LTD.—See Japan Airlines Co., Ltd.; *Int'l*, pg. 3884
JUPITER KIDNEY CENTER LLC—See Nautic Partners, LLC; *U.S. Private*, pg. 2870
JUPITER LIFE LINE HOSPITALS LIMITED; *Int'l*, pg. 4030
JUPITER MARINE INTERNATIONAL HOLDINGS, INC.; *U.S. Public*, pg. 1211
JUPITER MINES LIMITED; *Int'l*, pg. 4030
JUPITER MLC LOGISTICS (MYANMAR) LIMITED—See Mitsubishi Logistics Corporation; *Int'l*, pg. 4962
JUPITER MR SOLUTIONS CO., LTD.—See Cross Marketing Group Inc.; *Int'l*, pg. 1856
JUPITER NEUROSCIENCES, INC.; *U.S. Public*, pg. 1211
JUPITER PACIFIC FORWARDING JOINT VENTURE CO., LTD.—See Japan Airlines Co., Ltd.; *Int'l*, pg. 3884
JUPITER PORTFOLIO INVESTMENTS PUBLIC COMPANY LTD.—See Elma Holdings Public Company Ltd; *Int'l*, pg. 2367
JUPITER REALTY B.V—See SRV Group Plc; *Int'l*, pg. 7153
JUPITER REALTY CORPORATION; *U.S. Private*, pg. 2245
JUPITER RESEARCH, LLC—See TILT Holdings Inc.; *U.S. Public*, pg. 2159
JUPITER SHOP CHANNEL CO., LTD.—See KDDI Corporation; *Int'l*, pg. 4111
JUPITER SHOP CHANNEL CO., LTD.—See Sumitomo Corporation; *Int'l*, pg. 7269
JUPITER SINGAPORE PTE LTD.—See Japan Airlines Co., Ltd.; *Int'l*, pg. 3884
JUPITER TECHNOLOGY (WUXI) CO., LTD.—See Microelectronics Technology Company; *U.S. Private*, pg. 2703
JUPITER TELECOMMUNICATIONS CO., LTD.—See Sumitomo Corporation; *Int'l*, pg. 7269
JUPITER UK GROWTH INVESTMENT TRUST PLC; *Int'l*, pg. 4030
JUPITER WAGONS LIMITED; *Int'l*, pg. 4030
JUPITER WELLNESS ACQUISITION CORP.; *U.S. Public*, pg. 1211
JURA ENERGY CORPORATION—See Northern Financial Corporation; *Int'l*, pg. 5443
JURA-GUSS GMBH; *Int'l*, pg. 4030
JURA-HOLDING AG—See CRH plc; *Int'l*, pg. 1844

COMPANY NAME INDEX

JURA POLSKA SP. Z O.O.—See Pfleiderer GmbH; *Int'l*, pg. 5836
JURA SPEDITION GMBH—See Pfleiderer GmbH; *Int'l*, pg. 5836
JURA TRUST AG; *Int'l*, pg. 4030
JURCHEN TECHNOLOGY GMBH—See Lafayette Mittelstand Capital; *Int'l*, pg. 4392
JURCHEN TECHNOLOGY INDIA PRIVATE LIMITED—See Lafayette Mittelstand Capital; *Int'l*, pg. 4392
JURGENS CI (PTY) LIMITED—See Dubai World Corporation; *Int'l*, pg. 2221
JURGING GMBH & CO.; *Int'l*, pg. 4030
JURIDICA—See AXA S.A.; *Int'l*, pg. 759
JURIHAN SDN. BHD.—See Dominant Enterprise Berhad; *Int'l*, pg. 2161
JURINNOV LTD.—See Technology Concepts & Design, Inc.; *U.S. Private*, pg. 3955
JURLIQUE INTERNATIONAL PTY LTD—See Pola Orbis Holdings Inc.; *Int'l*, pg. 5905
THE JUROKU BANK, LTD.; *Int'l*, pg. 7661
JUROKU BUSINESS SERVICE CO., LTD.—See The Juroku Bank, Ltd.; *Int'l*, pg. 7661
JUROKU CAPITAL CO., LTD.—See The Juroku Bank, Ltd.; *Int'l*, pg. 7661
JUROKU COMPUTER SERVICE CO., LTD.—See The Juroku Bank, Ltd.; *Int'l*, pg. 7661
JUROKU DC CARD CO., LTD.—See The Juroku Bank, Ltd.; *Int'l*, pg. 7661
JUROKU FINANCIAL GROUP, INC.; *Int'l*, pg. 4030
JUROKU LEASE CO., LTD.—See The Juroku Bank, Ltd.; *Int'l*, pg. 7661
JURONG ENGINEERING LIMITED—See IHI Corporation; *Int'l*, pg. 3606
JURONG SHIPYARD PTE LTD.—See Sembcorp Industries Ltd.; *Int'l*, pg. 6703
JURPARTNER SERVICES GESELLSCHAFT FUR RECHTSSCHUTZ-SCHADENREGULIERUNG MBH—See AXA S.A.; *Int'l*, pg. 759
JURS MONTGOMERY BROKERAGE, LLC—See Simplicity Financial Marketing Holdings Inc.; *U.S. Private*, pg. 3667
JURUBINA SEMBAWANG (M) SDN BHD—See Punj Lloyd Ltd.; *Int'l*, pg. 6119
JURUENA MINERACAEO LTDA.—See Northwestern Enterprises Ltd.; *Int'l*, pg. 6447
JURU HEIGHTS SDN BHD—See Tambun Indah Land Berhad; *Int'l*, pg. 7450
JURUPA COMMUNITY SERVICES DISTRICT; *U.S. Private*, pg. 2245
JURUTERA PERUNDING AKAL SDN BHD—See Petra Energy Berhad; *Int'l*, pg. 5825
JUS BY JULIE LLC; *U.S. Private*, pg. 2245
JUS-COM INC.—See FTE Networks, Inc.; *U.S. Public*, pg. 889
JUSDA EUROPE S.R.O.—See Hon Hai Precision Industry Co., Ltd.; *Int'l*, pg. 3457
JU-SEE PUBLISHING CO., LTD.—See Daito Trust Construction Co., Ltd.; *Int'l*, pg. 1944
JUSEV CHARGING NETWORK SDN. BHD.—See Dancomech Holdings Berhad; *Int'l*, pg. 1959
JUSHI CANADA CO., LTD.—See China National Building Material Group Co., Ltd.; *Int'l*, pg. 1525
JUSHI CANADA FIBERGLASS CO. LTD.—See China Jushi Co., Ltd.; *Int'l*, pg. 1513
JUSHI FRANCE SAS—See China National Building Material Group Co., Ltd.; *Int'l*, pg. 1525
JUSHI GROUP (BZ) SINOSIA COMPOSITE MATERIALS CO., LTD.—See China Jushi Co., Ltd.; *Int'l*, pg. 1513
JUSHI GROUP CHENGDU CO., LTD.—See China Jushi Co., Ltd.; *Int'l*, pg. 1513
JUSHI GROUP CO., LTD.—See China National Building Material Group Co., Ltd.; *Int'l*, pg. 1525
JUSHI GROUP (HK) SINOSIA COMPOSITE MATERIALS CO., LTD.—See China Jushi Co., Ltd.; *Int'l*, pg. 1513
JUSHI GROUP HONG KONG CO., LIMITED—See China Jushi Co., Ltd.; *Int'l*, pg. 1513
JUSHI GROUP JIUJIANG CO., LTD.—See China Jushi Co., Ltd.; *Int'l*, pg. 1514
JUSHI GROUP (SA) SINOSIA COMPOSITE MATERIALS CO., LTD.—See China Jushi Co., Ltd.; *Int'l*, pg. 1513
JUSHI HOLDINGS INC.; *U.S. Public*, pg. 1211
JUSHI INDIA FIBERGLASS PVT LTD—See China Jushi Co., Ltd.; *Int'l*, pg. 1514
JUSHI ITALY SRL—See China Jushi Co., Ltd.; *Int'l*, pg. 1514
JUSHI JAPAN CO., LTD.—See China Jushi Co., Ltd.; *Int'l*, pg. 1514
JUSHI KOREA CO., LTD.—See China Jushi Co., Ltd.; *Int'l*, pg. 1514
JUSHI SINGAPORE PTE. LTD.—See China National Building Material Group Co., Ltd.; *Int'l*, pg. 1526
JUSHI SPAIN.S.A.—See China Jushi Co., Ltd.; *Int'l*, pg. 1514
JUSHI USA FIBERGLASS CO LTD—See China National Building Material Group Co., Ltd.; *Int'l*, pg. 1526
JUSHRI TECHNOLOGIES, INC.; *Int'l*, pg. 4030
JUST ADD PLASTICS INC.; *U.S. Private*, pg. 2245
JUST ANOTHER ACQUISITION CORP.; *U.S. Private*, pg. 2245

JUST ARRIVE, LLC—See Weldon, Williams & Lick, Inc.; *U.S. Private*, pg. 4474
JUST AUTOMOBILE LEASING CO., LTD—See Mitsubishi HC Capital Inc.; *Int'l*, pg. 4951
JUST BAKED SHOP LLC—See Tubby's Sub Shops, Inc.; *U.S. Private*, pg. 4255
JUSTBETTERCARS.COM INC.; *U.S. Private*, pg. 2246
JUST BORN, INC.; *U.S. Private*, pg. 2245
JUST BRIDGING LOANS PLC; *Int'l*, pg. 4030
JUST CAR CLINICS—See The Carlyle Group Inc.; *U.S. Public*, pg. 2050
JUST CASH FLOW PLC; *Int'l*, pg. 4030
JUST CO., LTD.—See The Japan Steel Works, Ltd.; *Int'l*, pg. 7659
JUST DESSERTS, INC.—See Trive Capital Inc.; *U.S. Private*, pg. 4240
JUST DIAL LTD; *Int'l*, pg. 4030
JUSTDICE GMBH—See Bertelsmann SE & Co. KGaA; *Int'l*, pg. 992
JUST DIGITAL GMBH—See Verve Group SE; *Int'l*, pg. 8176
JUST DYNAMICS SOFTWARE SOLUTIONS (PTY) LTD—See Capital Eye Investments Limited; *Int'l*, pg. 1311
JUST-EAT.CO.UK LTD.—See Just Eat Takeaway.com N.V.; *Int'l*, pg. 4030
JUST EAT PLC—See Just Eat Takeaway.com N.V.; *Int'l*, pg. 4030
JUST EAT TAKEAWAY.COM N.V.; *Int'l*, pg. 4030
JUSTEM CO., LTD.; *Int'l*, pg. 4031
JUST ENERGY GROUP INC.; *Int'l*, pg. 4030
JUST ENERGY, LLC—See Just Energy Group Inc.; *Int'l*, pg. 4031
JUST ENERGY TEXAS LP—See Just Energy Group Inc.; *Int'l*, pg. 4031
JUSTERINI & BROOKS LTD.—See Diageo plc; *Int'l*, pg. 2102
JUSTESA IMAGEN MEXICANA, S.A.—See Bracco S.p.A.; *Int'l*, pg. 1134
JUST FABULOUS, INC.; *U.S. Private*, pg. 2245
JUST FOR PETS LIMITED—See Pedigree Wholesale Ltd.; *Int'l*, pg. 5779
JUST FOR WRAPS; *U.S. Private*, pg. 2245
JUST GROUP LIMITED—See Premier Investments Limited; *Int'l*, pg. 5960
JUST GROUP PLC—See Permira Advisers LLP; *Int'l*, pg. 5806
JUSTICE FAMILY GROUP, LLC; *U.S. Private*, pg. 2246
JUSTICE RESOURCE INSTITUTE INC; *U.S. Private*, pg. 2246
JUSTICETRAX, INC.—See Banneker Partners, LLC; *U.S. Private*, pg. 469
JUSTICEWORKS YOUTHCARE INC.; *U.S. Private*, pg. 2246
JUSTIN ALLEN HOLDINGS LIMITED; *Int'l*, pg. 4031
JUSTIN BOOT COMPANY—See Berkshire Hathaway Inc.; *U.S. Public*, pg. 308
JUSTIN BRANDS, INC.—See Berkshire Hathaway Inc.; *U.S. Public*, pg. 308
JUSTIN CRAIG EDUCATION LIMITED—See Graham Holdings Company; *U.S. Public*, pg. 955
JUSTIN'S LLC—See Hormel Foods Corporation; *U.S. Public*, pg. 1054
JUSTIN VINEYARDS & WINERY LLC—See The Wonderful Company LLC; *U.S. Private*, pg. 4138
JUSTISS OIL COMPANY, INC.; *U.S. Private*, pg. 2246
JUSTIZZENTRUM IN HALLE WICHFORD & CO. KG—See Starwood Capital Group Global I, LLC; *U.S. Private*, pg. 3789
JUSTIZZENTRUM IN HALLE WICHFORD VERWALTUNGSGESELLSCHAFT MBH—See Starwood Capital Group Global I, LLC; *U.S. Private*, pg. 3789
JUST JAMIE AND PAULRICH LIMITED—See Li & Fung Limited; *Int'l*, pg. 4479
JUST JASMINE INVESTMENTS 201 (PTY) LIMITED—See Reunert Limited; *Int'l*, pg. 6312
JUST JEANS GROUP PTY LIMITED; *Int'l*, pg. 4031
JUST JEANS PTY. LTD.—See Premier Investments Limited; *Int'l*, pg. 5960
JUST KID, INC.; *U.S. Private*, pg. 2245
JUST KITCHEN HOLDINGS CORP.; *Int'l*, pg. 4031
JUST LANDLORDS INSURANCE SERVICES LTD.—See Arthur J. Gallagher & Co.; *U.S. Public*, pg. 206
JUST LIFE GROUP LIMITED; *Int'l*, pg. 4031
JUST LIKE FAMILY HOME CARE, LLC; *U.S. Private*, pg. 2245
JUST LOGISTICS, INC.—See Daiwa House Industry Co., Ltd.; *Int'l*, pg. 1946
JUST MANUFACTURING LLC—See Zurn Elkay Water Solutions Corporation; *U.S. Public*, pg. 2413
JUST MARKETING INTERNATIONAL LTD.—See Providence Equity Partners L.L.C.; *U.S. Private*, pg. 3291
JUST MEDIA, INC.; *U.S. Private*, pg. 2245
JUST MEDIA LTD.—See Just Media, Inc.; *U.S. Private*, pg. 2245
JUST MY SHOPPING INC.; *U.S. Private*, pg. 2245
JUSTNILE INTERNATIONAL CORP—See Y Ventures Group Ltd.; *Int'l*, pg. 8543

JUVA LIFE INC.

JUSTNILE PTE. LTD.—See Y Ventures Group Ltd.; *Int'l*, pg. 8543
JUSTNILE (SEA) PTE. LTD.—See Y Ventures Group Ltd.; *Int'l*, pg. 8543
JUST ON COSMETICS; *Int'l*, pg. 4031
JUST PLANNING INC.; *Int'l*, pg. 4031
JUST PLAY PRODUCTS, LLC; *U.S. Private*, pg. 2245
JUST RETIREMENT (HOLDINGS) LIMITED—See Permira Advisers LLP; *Int'l*, pg. 5806
JUST RETIREMENT LIMITED—See Permira Advisers LLP; *Int'l*, pg. 5806
JUST RETIREMENT SOLUTIONS LIMITED—See Permira Advisers LLP; *Int'l*, pg. 5806
JUST RIGHT PRODUCTS, INC.—See ADM Endeavors, Inc.; *U.S. Public*, pg. 42
JUST RITE ACOUSTICS INC.; *U.S. Private*, pg. 2245
JUSTRITE MANUFACTURING COMPANY, LLC—See The Riverside Company; *U.S. Private*, pg. 4109
JUSTRITE MANUFACTURING COMPANY—See The Riverside Company; *U.S. Private*, pg. 4109
JUSTSEARCH IRELAND LIMITED—See Oniva Online Group Europe AB; *Int'l*, pg. 5581
JUST SEARCH ITALIA S.R.L—See Oniva Online Group Europe AB; *Int'l*, pg. 5581
JUST-SHOP PTY. LIMITED—See Premier Investments Limited; *Int'l*, pg. 5960
JUST SLEEP HUALIEN ZHONGZHENG CO., LTD.—See Formosa International Hotels Corp.; *Int'l*, pg. 2734
JUST SLEEP KAOHSIUNG STATION CO., LTD.—See Formosa International Hotels Corp.; *Int'l*, pg. 2734
JUST SLEEP KAOHSIUNG ZHONGZHENG CO., LTD.—See Formosa International Hotels Corp.; *Int'l*, pg. 2734
JUST SLEEP OSAKA SHINSAIBASHI CO., LTD.—See Formosa International Hotels Corp.; *Int'l*, pg. 2734
JUST SLEEP TAINAN HUSHAN CO., LTD.—See Formosa International Hotels Corp.; *Int'l*, pg. 2734
JUST SLEEP TAIPEI NTU CO., LTD.—See Formosa International Hotels Corp.; *Int'l*, pg. 2734
JUST SLEEP TAIPEI SANCHONG CO., LTD.—See Formosa International Hotels Corp.; *Int'l*, pg. 2734
JUST SLEEP TAIPEI XIMENDING CO., LTD.—See Formosa International Hotels Corp.; *Int'l*, pg. 2734
JUST SLEEP YILAN JIAOXI CO., LTD.—See Formosa International Hotels Corp.; *Int'l*, pg. 2734
JUSTSYSTEMS CANADA, INC.—See JustSystems Corporation; *Int'l*, pg. 4031
JUSTSYSTEMS CORPORATION; *Int'l*, pg. 4031
JUST TECHNOLOGY(KUNSHAN)CO.,LTD.—See J.Pond Precision Technology Co., Ltd.; *Int'l*, pg. 3858
JUSTTRACK GMBH—See Bertelsmann SE & Co. KGaA; *Int'l*, pg. 993
JUST WATER NEW ZEALAND LIMITED—See Just Life Group Limited; *Int'l*, pg. 4031
JUST WHEELS & TIRES CO.—See Clearlake Capital Group, L.P.; *U.S. Private*, pg. 937
JUSTWORKS, INC.; *U.S. Public*, pg. 1211
JUSUNG ENGINEERING CO., LTD.; *Int'l*, pg. 4031
JUTAJATI SDN. BHD.—See Oriental Holdings Berhad; *Int'l*, pg. 5624
JUTAKUJOHOKAN CO., LTD.—See Iida Group Holdings Co., Ltd.; *Int'l*, pg. 3607
JUTAKUJOHOKAN FINANCIAL SERVICE CO., LTD.—See Iida Group Holdings Co., Ltd.; *Int'l*, pg. 3607
JUTAL OFFSHORE OIL SERVICES LIMITED; *Int'l*, pg. 4031
JUTAL OFFSHORE SHIPBUILDING SERVICES (DALIAN) COMPANY LIMITED—See Jutal Offshore Oil Services Limited; *Int'l*, pg. 4031
JUTAL OILFIELD SERVICES (TIANJIN) COMPANY LIMITED—See Jutal Offshore Oil Services Limited; *Int'l*, pg. 4031
JUTA PHARMA GMBH—See USV Pvt Ltd.; *Int'l*, pg. 8100
JUTASAMA SDN. BHD.—See Wah Seong Corporation Berhad; *Int'l*, pg. 8329
JUTEC AKITA CORPORATION—See JUTEC Holdings Corporation; *Int'l*, pg. 4032
JUTEC BUTSURYU CORPORATION—See JUTEC Holdings Corporation; *Int'l*, pg. 4032
JUTEC CORPORATION—See JUTEC Holdings Corporation; *Int'l*, pg. 4032
JUTEC HOLDINGS CORPORATION; *Int'l*, pg. 4031
JUTEC HOME CORPORATION—See JUTEC Holdings Corporation; *Int'l*, pg. 4032
JUTEKS D.D.—See Beaulieu International Group NV; *Int'l*, pg. 934
JU TENG INTERNATIONAL HOLDINGS LIMITED; *Int'l*, pg. 4020
JUTE SPINNERS LIMITED; *Int'l*, pg. 4031
JUTHAWAN MOLITEC (THAILAND) CO., LTD.—See Molitec Steel Co., Ltd.; *Int'l*, pg. 5022
JUTLANDER BANK A/S; *Int'l*, pg. 4032
JUTZE INTELLIGENCE TECHNOLOGY CO., LTD.; *Int'l*, pg. 4032
JUUAN DOLOMIITTIKALKKI OY—See SigmaRoc Plc; *Int'l*, pg. 6909
JUUT HOLDINGS INC.; *U.S. Private*, pg. 2246
JUVA LIFE INC.; *Int'l*, pg. 4032

JUVA LIFE INC.

CORPORATE AFFILIATIONS

JUVENIA (HONG KONG) COMPANY LIMITED—See Asia Commercial Holdings Limited; *Int'l*, pg. 611
JUVENIA MONTRES S.A.—See Asia Commercial Holdings Limited; *Int'l*, pg. 611
JUVENTEDC INC.—See COSCIENS Biopharma Inc.; *U.S. Public*, pg. 585
JUVENTUS FOOTBALL CLUB S.P.A—See Giovanni Agnelli B.V.; *Int'l*, pg. 2978
JUVER ALIMENTACION SA—See Hero AG; *Int'l*, pg. 3363
JUVO TECHNOLOGIES, LLC; *U.S. Private*, pg. 2246
JUWELO ITALIA S.R.L.—See Elumeo SE; *Int'l*, pg. 2371
JUWI AG—See MVV Energie AG; *Int'l*, pg. 5109
JUWI ENERGIA ODNAWIALNA SP. Z O.O.—See MVV Energie AG; *Int'l*, pg. 5109
JUWI ENERGIAS RENOVABLES - CENTRO AMERICA Y EL CARIBE, LTDA.—See MVV Energie AG; *Int'l*, pg. 5109
JUWI ENERGIAS RENOVABLES DE CHILE LTDA.—See MVV Energie AG; *Int'l*, pg. 5109
JUWI ENERGIAS RENOVABLES, S.L.U.—See MVV Energie AG; *Int'l*, pg. 5109
JUWI ENERGIE RINNOVABILI SRL—See MVV Energie AG; *Int'l*, pg. 5109
JUWI HELLAS A.E.—See MVV Energie AG; *Int'l*, pg. 5109
JUWI INDIA RENEWABLE ENERGIES PVT LTD—See MVV Energie AG; *Int'l*, pg. 5109
JUWI O&M GMBH—See MVV Energie AG; *Int'l*, pg. 5109
JUWI PHILIPPINES, INC.—See MVV Energie AG; *Int'l*, pg. 5109
JUWI RENEWABLE ENERGIES LIMITED—See MVV Energie AG; *Int'l*, pg. 5109
JUWI RENEWABLE ENERGIES PRIVATE LIMITED—See MVV Energie AG; *Int'l*, pg. 5109
JUWI RENEWABLE ENERGIES (PTY) LTD—See MVV Energie AG; *Int'l*, pg. 5109
JUWI RENEWABLE ENERGIES THAI CO., LTD—See MVV Energie AG; *Int'l*, pg. 5109
JUWI RENEWABLE ENERGY PTY—See MVV Energie AG; *Int'l*, pg. 5109
JUWI RENEWABLE IPP BETEILIGUNGS GMBH—See MVV Energie AG; *Int'l*, pg. 5109
JUWI SHIZEN ENERGY INC.—See MVV Energie AG; *Int'l*, pg. 5109
JUWI SOLAR INC.—See MVV Energie AG; *Int'l*, pg. 5109
JUWI S.R.O.—See MVV Energie AG; *Int'l*, pg. 5109
JUWI WIND, LLC—See MVV Energie AG; *Int'l*, pg. 5109
JUWI YENILENEBILIR ENERJI A.S—See MVV Energie AG; *Int'l*, pg. 5109
JUXT—See Project: Worldwide, Inc.; *U.S. Private*, pg. 3281
JUZEN CORPORATION—See Meiwa Corporation; *Int'l*, pg. 4805
JUZO SCANDINAVIA AB—See Julius Zorn GmbH; *Int'l*, pg. 4025
JUZO UK LTD.—See Julius Zorn GmbH; *Int'l*, pg. 4025
J VALUE CO., LTD.—See Japan Airlines Co., Ltd.; *Int'l*, pg. 3883
J VALUE CO., LTD.—See Sojitz Corporation; *Int'l*, pg. 7061
J. VAN VLIET B.V.—See HAL Trust N.V.; *Int'l*, pg. 3226
JVB FINANCIAL GROUP LLC—See Cohen & Company Inc.; *U.S. Public*, pg. 526
JVC AMERICA CORP.—See JVCKENWOOD Corporation; *Int'l*, pg. 4032
JVC BROADCASTING CORP.; *U.S. Private*, pg. 2246
JVC CANADA, INC.—See JVCKENWOOD Corporation; *Int'l*, pg. 4034
JVC CORPORATION; *U.S. Private*, pg. 2246
JVC DEUTSCHLAND GMBH—See JVCKENWOOD Corporation; *Int'l*, pg. 4034
JVC HOLDINGS, INC.—See LTC Properties, Inc.; *U.S. Public*, pg. 1344
JVC INDUSTRIAL AMERICA INC.—See JVCKENWOOD Corporation; *Int'l*, pg. 4032
JVC INTERNATIONAL (EUROPE) GMBH—See JVCKENWOOD Corporation; *Int'l*, pg. 4032
JVCKENWOOD AUSTRALIA PTY. LTD.—See JVCKENWOOD Corporation; *Int'l*, pg. 4032
JVCKENWOOD BELGIUM N.V.—See JVCKENWOOD Corporation; *Int'l*, pg. 4032
JVCKENWOOD (CHINA) INVESTMENT CO., LTD.—See JVCKENWOOD Corporation; *Int'l*, pg. 4032
JVCKENWOOD CORPORATION; *Int'l*, pg. 4032
JVCKENWOOD CREATIVE MEDIA CORPORATION—See JVCKENWOOD Corporation; *Int'l*, pg. 4032
JVCKENWOOD DESIGN CORPORATION—See JVCKENWOOD Corporation; *Int'l*, pg. 4033
JVCKENWOOD DEUTSCHLAND GMBH—See JVCKENWOOD Corporation; *Int'l*, pg. 4033
JVCKENWOOD ELECTRONICS MALAYSIA SDN. BHD.—See JVCKENWOOD Corporation; *Int'l*, pg. 4033
JVCKENWOOD ELECTRONICS (THAILAND) CO., LTD.—See JVCKENWOOD Corporation; *Int'l*, pg. 4033
JVCKENWOOD ENGINEERING CORPORATION—See JVCKENWOOD Corporation; *Int'l*, pg. 4033
JVCKENWOOD GULF FZE—See JVCKENWOOD Corporation; *Int'l*, pg. 4033
JVCKENWOOD HONG KONG HOLDINGS LIMITED—See JVCKENWOOD Corporation; *Int'l*, pg. 4033

JVCKENWOOD HONG KONG LTD.—See JVCKENWOOD Corporation; *Int'l*, pg. 4033
JVCKENWOOD IBERICA, S.A.—See JVCKENWOOD Corporation; *Int'l*, pg. 4033
JVCKENWOOD LATIN AMERICA, S.A.—See JVCKENWOOD Corporation; *Int'l*, pg. 4033
JVCKENWOOD MALAYSIA SDN. BHD.—See JVCKENWOOD Corporation; *Int'l*, pg. 4033
JVCKENWOOD NAGAOKA CORPORATION—See JVCKENWOOD Corporation; *Int'l*, pg. 4033
JVCKENWOOD NEDERLAND B.V.—See JVCKENWOOD Corporation; *Int'l*, pg. 4033
JVCKENWOOD SINGAPORE PTE. LTD.—See JVCKENWOOD Corporation; *Int'l*, pg. 4033
JVCKENWOOD TECHNOLOGIES SINGAPORE PTE. LTD.—See JVCKENWOOD Corporation; *Int'l*, pg. 4033
JVCKENWOOD (THAILAND) CO., LTD.—See JVCKENWOOD Corporation; *Int'l*, pg. 4032
JVCKENWOOD U.K. LIMITED—See JVCKENWOOD Corporation; *Int'l*, pg. 4033
JVCKENWOOD VIDEO TECH CORPORATION—See JVCKENWOOD Corporation; *Int'l*, pg. 4033
JVCKENWOOD YAMAGATA CORPORATION—See JVCKENWOOD Corporation; *Int'l*, pg. 4033
JVC MANUFACTURING MALAYSIA SDN. BHD.—See JVCKENWOOD Corporation; *Int'l*, pg. 4032
JVC MANUFACTURING (THAILAND) CO., LTD.—See JVCKENWOOD Corporation; *Int'l*, pg. 4032
JVC NETWORKS, INC.—See JVCKENWOOD Corporation; *Int'l*, pg. 4032
J.V. COCA-COLA ALMATY BOTTLERS LIMITED LIABILITY PARTNERSHIP—See Coca-Cola Icecek A.S.; *Int'l*, pg. 1686
JVC OPTICAL COMPONENTS (THAILAND) CO., LTD.—See JVCKENWOOD Corporation; *Int'l*, pg. 4032
JVC POLSKA SP. ZO. O.—See JVCKENWOOD Corporation; *Int'l*, pg. 4032
JVC PROFESSIONAL EUROPE LIMITED—See JVCKENWOOD Corporation; *Int'l*, pg. 4034
JVC TAIWAN CORP.—See JVCKENWOOD Corporation; *Int'l*, pg. 4032
JVC (U.K.) LTD.—See JVCKENWOOD Corporation; *Int'l*, pg. 4034
JVC U.S.A (PROFESSIONAL VIDEO DIV.)—See JVCKENWOOD Corporation; *Int'l*, pg. 4032
JVC U.S.A.—See JVCKENWOOD Corporation; *Int'l*, pg. 4032
J&V ENERGY TECHNOLOGY CO., LTD.; *Int'l*, pg. 3854
JV FUCHS MAST YLA UKRAINA—See FUCHS SE; *Int'l*, pg. 2804
JV GLOBAL LIMITED; *Int'l*, pg. 4032
JV GRANIFERT—See PJSC KuibyshevAzot; *Int'l*, pg. 5881
JVH EXPLOITATIE B.V.—See Novomatic AG; *Int'l*, pg. 5467
J VINEYARDS & WINERY—See E. & J. Gallo Winery; *U.S. Private*, pg. 1303
JV INKAI LLP—See JSC National Atomic Company Kazatomprom; *Int'l*, pg. 4009
JV INTERNATIONAL PTY LTD—See JV Global Limited; *Int'l*, pg. 4032
J. VINTON SCHAFER & SONS, INC.; *U.S. Private*, pg. 2157
JVIS MANUFACTURING—See JVIS USA LLC; *U.S. Private*, pg. 2246
JVIS USA LLC; *U.S. Private*, pg. 2246
JVK CONSTRUCTORS LLC; *U.S. Private*, pg. 2246
JVKELLYGROUP, INC.; *U.S. Private*, pg. 2246
JVK INTERNATIONAL MOVERS LTD.; *Int'l*, pg. 4034
JVL AGRO INDUSTRIES LIMITED; *Int'l*, pg. 4034
JVL OVERSEAS PTE. LTD.—See JVL Agro Industries Limited; *Int'l*, pg. 4034
JVM AG—See JVM Equipment Ltd.; *Int'l*, pg. 4034
JVM CO., LTD.; *Int'l*, pg. 4034
JVM EQUIPMENT INTERNATIONAL LTD.—See JVM Equipment Ltd.; *Int'l*, pg. 4034
JVM EQUIPMENT LTD.; *Int'l*, pg. 4034
JVM NEXT GMBH—See Jung von Matt; *Int'l*, pg. 4027
JV- NATH BIO-GENES CA LLC—See Nath Bio-Genes (India) Limited; *Int'l*, pg. 5149
J-VON REALTY—See Hyman Brickle & Son, Inc.; *U.S. Private*, pg. 2019
JVPK INC.; *U.S. Private*, pg. 2246
JV "BUSINESS CAR" CO. LTD.—See Toyota Tsusho Corporation; *Int'l*, pg. 7877
J.V. ROCKWELL PUBLISHING INC.; *U.S. Private*, pg. 2171
JV SARECO LLP—See JSC National Atomic Company Kazatomprom; *Int'l*, pg. 4009
JV SMITH COMPANIES; *U.S. Private*, pg. 2246
JVSPAC ACQUISITION CORP.; *Int'l*, pg. 4035
JVST, INC.—See CHR Group LLC; *U.S. Private*, pg. 889
J.V. (THAILAND) CO., LTD.—See JACKSPEED CORPORATION LIMITED; *Int'l*, pg. 3865
JV ZEISS-BELOMO OOO—See Carl-Zeiss-Stiftung; *Int'l*, pg. 1336
J. WAGNER AG; *Int'l*, pg. 3857
J. WAGNER GMBH—See J. Wagner AG; *Int'l*, pg. 3857
JWALCHER COMMUNICATIONS; *U.S. Private*, pg. 2246

J. WALTER THOMPSON ARGENTINA SRL—See WPP plc; *Int'l*, pg. 8479
J. WALTER THOMPSON AUSTRALIA PTY. LTD.—See WPP plc; *Int'l*, pg. 8480
J. WALTER THOMPSON AUSTRALIA PTY. LTD. - SYDNEY—See WPP plc; *Int'l*, pg. 8480
J. WALTER THOMPSON (BEIJING) CO., LTD.—See WPP plc; *Int'l*, pg. 8479
J. WALTER THOMPSON CANADA INC.—See WPP plc; *Int'l*, pg. 8479
J. WALTER THOMPSON CAPE TOWN (PTY) LTD.—See WPP plc; *Int'l*, pg. 8479
J. WALTER THOMPSON CARACAS—See WPP plc; *Int'l*, pg. 8479
J. WALTER THOMPSON CHILE LTDA.—See WPP plc; *Int'l*, pg. 8479
J. WALTER THOMPSON (CHINA) CO., LTD.—See WPP plc; *Int'l*, pg. 8479
J. WALTER THOMPSON COLOMBIA LTDA.—See WPP plc; *Int'l*, pg. 8479
J. WALTER THOMPSON CO., LTD.—See WPP plc; *Int'l*, pg. 8480
J. WALTER THOMPSON COMPANY—See WPP plc; *Int'l*, pg. 8478
J. WALTER THOMPSON DE MEXICO, S.A. DE C.V.—See WPP plc; *Int'l*, pg. 8479
J. WALTER THOMPSON DO BRASIL LTDA.—See WPP plc; *Int'l*, pg. 8479
J. WALTER THOMPSON EL SALVADOR—See WPP plc; *Int'l*, pg. 8479
J. WALTER THOMPSON ESPANA S.A. - BARCELONA—See WPP plc; *Int'l*, pg. 8479
J. WALTER THOMPSON ESPANA S.A.—See WPP plc; *Int'l*, pg. 8479
J. WALTER THOMPSON GMBH—See WPP plc; *Int'l*, pg. 8479
J. WALTER THOMPSON INDIA PVT. LTD.—See WPP plc; *Int'l*, pg. 8480
J. WALTER THOMPSON INTERNATIONAL (NZ) LTD.—See WPP plc; *Int'l*, pg. 8480
J. WALTER THOMPSON ITALIA - S.P.A.—See WPP plc; *Int'l*, pg. 8479
J. WALTER THOMPSON LDA.—See WPP plc; *Int'l*, pg. 8479
J. WALTER THOMPSON (M) SDN. BHD.—See WPP plc; *Int'l*, pg. 8479
J. WALTER THOMPSON POLAND SP. Z O.O.—See WPP plc; *Int'l*, pg. 8479
J. WALTER THOMPSON PORTUGAL—See WPP plc; *Int'l*, pg. 8479
J. WALTER THOMPSON PUERTO RICO, INC.—See WPP plc; *Int'l*, pg. 8479
J. WALTER THOMPSON ROMA S.R.L.—See WPP plc; *Int'l*, pg. 8479
J. WALTER THOMPSON S.A./N.V.—See WPP plc; *Int'l*, pg. 8479
J. WALTER THOMPSON SAS—See WPP plc; *Int'l*, pg. 8479
J. WALTER THOMPSON (SINGAPORE) PTE. LTD.—See WPP plc; *Int'l*, pg. 8480
J. WALTER THOMPSON SOUTH AFRICA (PTY) LTD.—See WPP plc; *Int'l*, pg. 8479
J. WALTER THOMPSON (TAIWAN) LIMITED—See WPP plc; *Int'l*, pg. 8480
J. WALTER THOMPSON (THAILAND) CO., LTD.—See WPP plc; *Int'l*, pg. 8480
J. WALTER THOMPSON UK LIMITED—See WPP plc; *Int'l*, pg. 8479
JW ALUMINUM CO.—See Wellspring Capital Management LLC; *U.S. Private*, pg. 4477
JW ALUMINUM CO.—See Wellspring Capital Management LLC; *U.S. Private*, pg. 4477
J. WASSON ENTERPRISES INC.; *U.S. Private*, pg. 2157
J WAY CO., LTD.; *Int'l*, pg. 3853
J.W. BAILEY CONSTRUCTION COMPANY; *U.S. Private*, pg. 2171
JW BOND CONSULTANTS, INC.—See Kelso & Company, L.P.; *U.S. Private*, pg. 2280
JWB REAL ESTATE CAPITAL LLC; *U.S. Private*, pg. 2246
J W BRETT, INC.—See RPM International Inc.; *U.S. Public*, pg. 1818
JW CAYMAN THERAPEUTICS COMPANY LIMITED; *Int'l*, pg. 4035
JWC CONSTRUCTION INC.; *U.S. Private*, pg. 2246
JWC ENVIRONMENTAL, LLC—See Sulzer Ltd.; *Int'l*, pg. 7257
JW CHEMITOWN—See JW Holdings Corporation; *Int'l*, pg. 4035
JWCH INSTITUTE, INC.; *U.S. Private*, pg. 2246
J.W. COLE FINANCIAL, INC.; *U.S. Private*, pg. 2172
J.W. CONSTRUCTION HOLDING S.A.; *Int'l*, pg. 3859
JW CREAGENE, INC.—See JW Holdings Corporation; *Int'l*, pg. 4035
J.W. D'ANGELO CO., INC.—See Core & Main, Inc.; *U.S. Public*, pg. 576
JWD ART SPACE CO., LTD.—See SCGJWD Logistics Public Company Limited; *Int'l*, pg. 6614

COMPANY NAME INDEX

JWD BOK SENG LOGISTICS (THAILAND) CO., LTD.—See SCGJWD Logistics Public Company Limited; *Int'l*, pg. 6614
JWD EXPRESS CO., LTD.—See SCGJWD Logistics Public Company Limited; *Int'l*, pg. 6614
JWD GROUP INC. - DANFORTH ALBANY FACILITY—See JWD Group Inc.; *U.S. Private*, pg. 2247
JWD GROUP INC. - DANFORTH ROCHESTER FACILITY—See JWD Group Inc.; *U.S. Private*, pg. 2247
JWD GROUP INC.; *U.S. Private*, pg. 2247
J. W. DIDADO ELECTRIC, LLC—See Quanta Services, Inc.; *U.S. Public*, pg. 1751
J.W.E. INC.; *U.S. Private*, pg. 2172
J-W ENERGY COMPANY; *U.S. Private*, pg. 2155
JW ENTERPRISES LTD.; *U.S. Private*, pg. 2246
J-WESCO LTD.—See The Sumitomo Warehouse Co. Ltd.; *Int'l*, pg. 7689
JW GLASS RECYCLING CO., LTD.—See ARE Holdings, Inc.; *Int'l*, pg. 557
J.W. GRAND INC.; *U.S. Private*, pg. 2172
J&W HARDIE LTD.—See Takara Holdings, Inc.; *Int'l*, pg. 7432
J.W. HARRIS CO., INC.—See Lincoln Electric Holdings, Inc.; *U.S. Public*, pg. 1317
JWH GROUP PTY LTD; *Int'l*, pg. 4035
JW HOLDINGS CORPORATION; *Int'l*, pg. 4035
JW HULME CO. LLC—See Olympus Holdings, LLC; *U.S. Private*, pg. 3013
JW ICU MEDICAL LIMITED—See Biosensors International Group, Ltd.; *Int'l*, pg. 1041
J&W INC.; *U.S. Private*, pg. 2155
JW INDUSTRIAL—See JW Holdings Corporation; *Int'l*, pg. 4035
JWIN ELECTRONICS CORP.; *U.S. Private*, pg. 2247
JWIPC TECHNOLOGY CO., LTD.; *Int'l*, pg. 4035
J-WITEX CORPORATION—See Nichia Steel Works Co., Ltd.; *Int'l*, pg. 5266
J.W. JONES COMPANY, LLC; *U.S. Private*, pg. 2172
J.W. JUNG SEED COMPANY; *U.S. Private*, pg. 2172
JWK INTERNATIONAL CORP.; *U.S. Private*, pg. 2247
J.W. KOEHLER ELECTRIC, INC.; *U.S. Private*, pg. 2172
JW LIFE SCIENCE—See JW Holdings Corporation; *Int'l*, pg. 4035
J.W. MAYS, INC.; *U.S. Public*, pg. 1180
JWM MANAGEMENT, INC.; *U.S. Private*, pg. 2247
JWM PRODUCTIONS, LLC; *U.S. Private*, pg. 2247
J WOOD REALTY, LLC; *U.S. Private*, pg. 2153
JW OPERATING COMPANY; *U.S. Private*, pg. 2246
JWORD, INC.—See GMO Internet Group, Inc.; *Int'l*, pg. 3013
J.W. PEPPER & SON INC.; *U.S. Private*, pg. 2172
J.W. PERRY INC.; *U.S. Private*, pg. 2172
JW PHARMACEUTICAL CORPORATION—See JW Holdings Corporation; *Int'l*, pg. 4035
J.W. PIERSON COMPANY INC.; *U.S. Private*, pg. 2172
JWP PUBLISHING LIMITED PARTNERSHIP—See GVIC Communications Corp.; *Int'l*, pg. 3189
J W R CONSTRUCTION SERVICES; *U.S. Private*, pg. 2153
J. WRIGHT BUILDING CENTER INC.; *U.S. Private*, pg. 2157
J.W.S. DELAVAU CO. INC.; *U.S. Private*, pg. 2172
JW SHINYAK CORPORATION—See JW Holdings Corporation; *Int'l*, pg. 4035
JWSIEG WINES; *U.S. Private*, pg. 2247
JW SOLUTION CO., LTD.—See World Holdings Co., Ltd.; *Int'l*, pg. 8457
J.W. SPEAKER CORPORATION; *U.S. Private*, pg. 2172
JWT AMSTERDAM—See WPP plc; *Int'l*, pg. 8479
JWT ASIA PACIFIC—See WPP plc; *Int'l*, pg. 8479
JWT ATLANTA—See WPP plc; *Int'l*, pg. 8480
JWT BAHRAIN—See WPP plc; *Int'l*, pg. 8480
JWT BANGALORE—See WPP plc; *Int'l*, pg. 8480
JWT BEIRUT—See WPP plc; *Int'l*, pg. 8480
JWT CAIRO—See WPP plc; *Int'l*, pg. 8480
JWT CASABLANCA—See WPP plc; *Int'l*, pg. 8480
JWT CHENNAI—See WPP plc; *Int'l*, pg. 8480
JWT COLOMBO—See WPP plc; *Int'l*, pg. 8480
JWT DAMASCUS—See WPP plc; *Int'l*, pg. 8480
JWT DIALOGUE—See WPP plc; *Int'l*, pg. 8479
JWT DUBAI—See WPP plc; *Int'l*, pg. 8480
JWT HELSINKI—See WPP plc; *Int'l*, pg. 8480
JW THERAPEUTICS (SUZHOU) CO., LTD.—See JW Cayman Therapeutics Company Limited; *Int'l*, pg. 4035
JW THERIAC PHARMACEUTICAL CORP.—See JW Holdings Corporation; *Int'l*, pg. 4035
JWT INSIDE—See WPP plc; *Int'l*, pg. 8480
JWT INSIDE—See WPP plc; *Int'l*, pg. 8480
JWT INSIDE—See WPP plc; *Int'l*, pg. 8481
JWT INSIDE—See WPP plc; *Int'l*, pg. 8481
JWT JAKARTA—See WPP plc; *Int'l*, pg. 8480
JWT JAPAN LIMITED—See WPP plc; *Int'l*, pg. 8480
JWT JEDDAH—See WPP plc; *Int'l*, pg. 8480
JWT KOLKATA—See WPP plc; *Int'l*, pg. 8480
JWT KOREA, LTD.—See WPP plc; *Int'l*, pg. 8480
JWT KUWAIT—See WPP plc; *Int'l*, pg. 8480
JWT LIMA—See WPP plc; *Int'l*, pg. 8480

JWT LITHUANIA SAN VILNIUS—See WPP plc; *Int'l*, pg. 8480
JWT MANILA—See WPP plc; *Int'l*, pg. 8480
JWT RIYADH—See WPP plc; *Int'l*, pg. 8480
JWT SPECIALIZED COMMUNICATIONS, INC.—See WPP plc; *Int'l*, pg. 8480
JWT SPECIALIZED COMMUNICATIONS—See WPP plc; *Int'l*, pg. 8481
JWT TUNIS—See WPP plc; *Int'l*, pg. 8481
JWT U.S.A., INC.—See WPP plc; *Int'l*, pg. 8481
JWT U.S.A., INC.—See WPP plc; *Int'l*, pg. 8481
JWT U.S.A., INC.—See WPP plc; *Int'l*, pg. 8481
JWT U.S.A., INC.—See WPP plc; *Int'l*, pg. 8481
JWT U.S.A., INC.—See WPP plc; *Int'l*, pg. 8481
JWT U.S.A., INC.—See WPP plc; *Int'l*, pg. 8481
JWT U.S.A., INC.—See WPP plc; *Int'l*, pg. 8481
JWT U.S.A., INC.—See WPP plc; *Int'l*, pg. 8481
JWT U.S.A., INC.—See WPP plc; *Int'l*, pg. 8481
JWT U.S.A., INC.—See WPP plc; *Int'l*, pg. 8481
JWT U.S.A., INC.—See WPP plc; *Int'l*, pg. 8481
JWT U.S.A., INC.—See WPP plc; *Int'l*, pg. 8481
JWT U.S.A., INC.—See WPP plc; *Int'l*, pg. 8481
JWT VIETNAM—See WPP plc; *Int'l*, pg. 8480
JWT WERBEAGENTUR GMBH—See WPP plc; *Int'l*, pg. 8481
J.W. WILLIAMS, INC.—See AECOM; *U.S. Public*, pg. 51
J.W. WINCO, INC.; *U.S. Private*, pg. 2172
JWW INVEST SA; *Int'l*, pg. 4035
JX ADVANCED METALS CORPORATION—See ENEOS Holdings, Inc.; *Int'l*, pg. 2415
JX ENERGY LTD.; *Int'l*, pg. 4035
JX ENTERPRISES INC.; *U.S. Private*, pg. 2247
JX GRAPHICS—See JX Enterprises Inc.; *U.S. Private*, pg. 2247
JX LUXVENTURE LIMITED; *Int'l*, pg. 4035
JX METALS PHILIPPINES, INC.—See ENEOS Holdings, Inc.; *Int'l*, pg. 2416
JX METALS PRECISION TECHNOLOGY CO., LTD.—See ENEOS Holdings, Inc.; *Int'l*, pg. 2416
JX METALS TRADING CO., LTD.—See ENEOS Holdings, Inc.; *Int'l*, pg. 2416
JX NIPPON ANCI CORP. - NARITA PLANT—See ENEOS Holdings, Inc.; *Int'l*, pg. 2417
JX NIPPON ANCI CORPORATION—See ENEOS Holdings, Inc.; *Int'l*, pg. 2417
JX NIPPON ANCI, INC.—See ENEOS Holdings, Inc.; *Int'l*, pg. 2417
JX NIPPON BUSINESS SERVICES CORPORATION—See ENEOS Holdings, Inc.; *Int'l*, pg. 2416
JX NIPPON COIL CENTER CO., LTD.—See ENEOS Holdings, Inc.; *Int'l*, pg. 2416
JX NIPPON DRILLING CO., LTD.—See ENEOS Holdings, Inc.; *Int'l*, pg. 2416
JX NIPPON ENVIRONMENTAL SERVICES CO., LTD.—See ENEOS Holdings, Inc.; *Int'l*, pg. 2416
JX NIPPON EXPLORATION & DEVELOPMENT CO., LTD.—See ENEOS Holdings, Inc.; *Int'l*, pg. 2416
JX NIPPON EXPLORATION & PRODUCTION (U.K.) LIMITED—See HitecVision AS; *Int'l*, pg. 3426
JX NIPPON FOUNDRY CO., LTD.—See ENEOS Holdings, Inc.; *Int'l*, pg. 2416
JX NIPPON INFORMATION TECHNOLOGY CO., LTD.—See ENEOS Holdings, Inc.; *Int'l*, pg. 2416
JX NIPPON MINING ECOMANAGEMENT, INC.—See ENEOS Holdings, Inc.; *Int'l*, pg. 2416
JX NIPPON MINING & METALS SINGAPORE PTE. LTD.—See ENEOS Holdings, Inc.; *Int'l*, pg. 2416
JX NIPPON MINING & METALS USA, INC.—See ENEOS Holdings, Inc.; *Int'l*, pg. 2416
JX NIPPON OIL & ENERGY ASIA PTE. LTD.—See ENEOS Holdings, Inc.; *Int'l*, pg. 2417
JX NIPPON OIL & ENERGY (AUSTRALIA) PTY. LTD.—See ENEOS Holdings, Inc.; *Int'l*, pg. 2417
JX NIPPON OIL & ENERGY TRADING CORPORATION—See ENEOS Holdings, Inc.; *Int'l*, pg. 2417
JX NIPPON OIL & ENERGY USA INC.—See ENEOS Holdings, Inc.; *Int'l*, pg. 2417
JX NIPPON OIL EXPLORATION (U.S.A.) LIMITED—See ENEOS Holdings, Inc.; *Int'l*, pg. 2417
JX NIPPON OIL & GAS EXPLORATION CORPORATION—See ENEOS Holdings, Inc.; *Int'l*, pg. 2416
JX NIPPON OIL & GAS EXPLORATION (MALAYSIA) LTD.—See ENEOS Holdings, Inc.; *Int'l*, pg. 2416
JX NIPPON PROCUREMENT CORPORATION—See ENEOS Holdings, Inc.; *Int'l*, pg. 2417
JX NIPPON RESEARCH INSTITUTE, LTD.—See ENEOS Holdings, Inc.; *Int'l*, pg. 2416
JX PACLEASE—See JX Enterprises Inc.; *U.S. Private*, pg. 2247
JXTG NIPPON OIL & ENERGY CORPORATION—See ENEOS Holdings, Inc.; *Int'l*, pg. 2417
J-YADO INC.—See Cybozu Inc.; *Int'l*, pg. 1894
JYE TAI PRECISION INDUSTRIAL CO., LTD. - DONG GUAN JT—See Lang Inc; *Int'l*, pg. 4408

JYE TAI PRECISION INDUSTRIAL CO., LTD. - SUZHOU JT FACTORY—See Lang Inc; *Int'l*, pg. 4408
JYE TAI PRECISION INDUSTRIAL (M) SDN. BHD.—See Lang Inc; *Int'l*, pg. 4408
JY GAS LIMITED; *Int'l*, pg. 4035
JY GRANDMARK HOLDINGS LIMITED; *Int'l*, pg. 4035
J & Y INTERNATIONAL COMPANY LIMITED—See Dream International Ltd; *Int'l*, pg. 2203
J.Y. LEGNER ASSOCIATES INC; *U.S. Private*, pg. 2172
JYNWEL CAPITAL LIMITED; *Int'l*, pg. 4035
JYOTHY CONSUMER PRODUCTS LTD.—See Jyothy Laboratories Ltd; *Int'l*, pg. 4036
JYOTHY FABRICARE SERVICES LTD—See Jyothy Laboratories Ltd; *Int'l*, pg. 4036
JYOTHY LABORATORIES LTD; *Int'l*, pg. 4036
JYOTI BIKASH BANK LTD.; *Int'l*, pg. 4036
JYOTI LTD. - ELECTRONICS & CONTROL SYSTEMS (RELAY DIVISION)—See Jyoti Ltd.; *Int'l*, pg. 4036
JYOTI LTD.; *Int'l*, pg. 4036
JYOTI LTD. - SWITCHGEAR DIVISION—See Jyoti Ltd.; *Int'l*, pg. 4036
JYOT INTERNATIONAL MARKETING LIMITED; *Int'l*, pg. 4036
JYOTI RESINS & ADHESIVES LTD. - GANDHINAGAR FACTORY—See Jyoti Resins & Adhesives Ltd.; *Int'l*, pg. 4036
JYOTI RESINS & ADHESIVES LTD.; *Int'l*, pg. 4036
JYOTIRGAMYA ENTERPRISES LIMITED; *Int'l*, pg. 4036
JYOTI STRUCTURES LTD; *Int'l*, pg. 4036
JYP ENTERTAINMENT CO., LTD.; *Int'l*, pg. 4036
JYSKE BANK A/S; *Int'l*, pg. 4036
JYSKE BANK (SCHWEIZ) AG—See Jyske Bank A/S; *Int'l*, pg. 4037
JYSKE FINANS A/S—See Jyske Bank A/S; *Int'l*, pg. 4037
JYSKE INVEST FUND MANAGEMENT A/S—See Jyske Bank A/S; *Int'l*, pg. 4037
JYSKE REALKREDIT, KGS.—See Jyske Bank A/S; *Int'l*, pg. 4037
JYSK-FYNSK KAPITAL A/S; *Int'l*, pg. 4036
JY STEEL PROCESSING CO., LTD.—See JFE Holdings, Inc.; *Int'l*, pg. 3937
JYUUKAN URBAN FACILITIES SERVICE CO., LTD.—See Mitsubishi Heavy Industries, Ltd.; *Int'l*, pg. 4953
JYVASKYLAN KAUPPAKATU 31 KOY—See Citycon Oyj; *Int'l*, pg. 1629
JZ ASSET MANAGEMENT UK LLP—See Jordan/Zalaznick Advisers, Inc.; *U.S. Private*, pg. 2235
JZ CAPITAL PARTNERS LIMITED; *Int'l*, pg. 4037
JZ INTERNATIONAL LTD.—See Jordan/Zalaznick Advisers, Inc.; *U.S. Private*, pg. 2235
JZ PARTNERS, LLC—See Jordan/Zalaznick Advisers, Inc.; *U.S. Private*, pg. 2235
JZR GOLD INC.; *Int'l*, pg. 4037
JZZ TECHNOLOGIES, INC.; *U.S. Private*, pg. 2247

K

K13 EXTENSIE BEHEER B.V.—See EBN B.V.; *Int'l*, pg. 2285
K1 INVESTMENT MANAGEMENT, LLC; *U.S. Private*, pg. 2252
K1 KASASTAJAT, OY—See I Squared Capital Advisors (US) LLC; *U.S. Private*, pg. 2023
K1 KASASTAJAT, OY—See TDR Capital LLP; *Int'l*, pg. 7492
K-1 PACKAGING GROUP—See Dunes Point Capital, LLC; *U.S. Private*, pg. 1288
K1 SOLUTION, INC.—See Federmann Enterprises, Ltd.; *Int'l*, pg. 2631
K1 SPEED, LLC; *U.S. Private*, pg. 2253
K-1 TECHNOLOGIES; *U.S. Private*, pg. 2250
K 2000, S.A.U.—See WPP plc; *Int'l*, pg. 8474
K2 ADVISORS LIMITED—See Franklin Resources, Inc.; *U.S. Public*, pg. 881
K2 ADVISORS L.L.C.—See Franklin Resources, Inc.; *U.S. Public*, pg. 881
K2A KNAUST & ANDERSSON FASTIGHETER AB; *Int'l*, pg. 4045
K2 ASSET MANAGEMENT HOLDINGS LTD.; *Int'l*, pg. 4044
K2 ASSET MANAGEMENT LTD.—See K2 Asset Management Holdings Ltd.; *Int'l*, pg. 4044
K2 CO., LTD.—See Capcom Co., Ltd.; *Int'l*, pg. 1302
K2 CONSULTANCY GROUP LIMITED—See HanmiGlobal Co., LTD.; *Int'l*, pg. 3257
K2 CORPORATE PARTNERS CO., LTD.—See SBS Holdings Inc.; *Int'l*, pg. 6607
K2 CORPORATION OF CANADA—See Kohlberg & Company, LLC; *U.S. Private*, pg. 2338
K2 DESIGN & STRATEGY, INC.; *U.S. Private*, pg. 2253
K2 DIAMOND COMPANY; *U.S. Private*, pg. 2253
K2 ENERGY LIMITED; *Int'l*, pg. 4044
K2 ENERGY SOLUTIONS, INC.; *U.S. Private*, pg. 2253
K2 F&B HOLDINGS LIMITED; *Int'l*, pg. 4044
K2FLY LIMITED; *Int'l*, pg. 4045
K2 GAMER (PVT) LTD.—See Gamer Pakistan Inc.; *U.S. Public*, pg. 895
K2 GOLD CORPORATION; *Int'l*, pg. 4045
K2 GROUP; *Int'l*, pg. 4045

K2 HOLDING S.A.

CORPORATE AFFILIATIONS

K2 HOLDING S.A.; *Int'l,* pg. 4045
K2 INDUSTRIAL INC.—See The Halifax Group LLC; *U.S. Private,* pg. 4042
K2 INDUSTRIAL SERVICES, INC.—See Arctic Slope Regional Corporation; *U.S. Private,* pg. 316
K2 INSURANCE SERVICES, LLC—See Warburg Pincus LLC; *U.S. Private,* pg. 4438
K2 KOREA CO. LTD.; *Int'l,* pg. 4045
K2L GMBH—See Microchip Technology Incorporated; *U.S. Public,* pg. 1436
K2 LT AB; *Int'l,* pg. 4045
K2-MDV HOLDINGS, LP—See Kohlberg & Company, LLC; *U.S. Private,* pg. 2338
K2M GERMANY GMBH—See Stryker Corporation; *U.S. Public,* pg. 1955
K2M GROUP HOLDINGS, INC.—See Stryker Corporation; *U.S. Public,* pg. 1955
K2M, INC.—See Stryker Corporation; *U.S. Public,* pg. 1955
K2M UK LIMITED—See Stryker Corporation; *U.S. Public,* pg. 1955
K2 PARTNERING SOLUTIONS, INC.; *U.S. Private,* pg. 2253
K2SHARE, LLC.; *U.S. Private,* pg. 2253
K2 SOLUTIONS, INC.; *U.S. Private,* pg. 2253
K2 SPORTS EUROPE GMBH—See Kohlberg & Company, LLC; *U.S. Private,* pg. 2338
K-2 SPORTS, LLC—See Kohlberg & Company, LLC; *U.S. Private,* pg. 2338
K3 BUSINESS SOLUTIONS—See K3 Business Technology Group plc; *Int'l,* pg. 4045
K3 BUSINESS TECHNOLOGY GROUP PLC; *Int'l,* pg. 4045
K3 CAPITAL GROUP LTD—See Sun Capital Partners, Inc.; *U.S. Private,* pg. 3861
K3 CONSTRUCTION GROUP, INC.; *U.S. Private,* pg. 2253
K3 ENTERPRISES INC.; *U.S. Private,* pg. 2253
K3 LANDSTEINAR NEDERLAND BV—See K3 Business Technology Group plc; *Int'l,* pg. 4045
K3 RETAIL AND BUSINESS SOLUTIONS LIMITED—See K3 Business Technology Group plc; *Int'l,* pg. 4045
K3 SUPPLY CHAIN SOLUTIONS LIMITED—See K3 Business Technology Group plc; *Int'l,* pg. 4045
K3 WORKS GMBH—See Gentherm Incorporated; *U.S. Public,* pg. 932
K4 SOLUTIONS, INC.; *U.S. Private,* pg. 2253
K7 LUMBER INC.; *Int'l,* pg. 4045
K92 MINING (AUSTRALIA) PTY LTD—See K92 Mining Inc.; *Int'l,* pg. 4045
K92 MINING INC.; *Int'l,* pg. 4045
K92 MINING LTD.—See K92 Mining Inc.; *Int'l,* pg. 4045
K9 GOLD CORP.; *Int'l,* pg. 4045
KAAL-TV LLC—See Hubbard Broadcasting, Inc.; *U.S. Private,* pg. 2000
KAANAPALI BEACH PROPERTIES, INC.—See KSL Capital Partners, LLC; *U.S. Private,* pg. 2355
KAANAPALI LAND, LLC; *U.S. Public,* pg. 1211
KAANAPALI LAND MANAGEMENT CORPORATION—See Kaanapali Land, LLC; *U.S. Public,* pg. 1211
KAANGO, LLC—See Kistefos AS; *Int'l,* pg. 4192
KAAR TECHNOLOGIES INDIA PVT LTD.; *Int'l,* pg. 4045
KAARYA FACILITIES & SERVICES LTD.; *Int'l,* pg. 4045
KAASHANDEL CULEMBORG B.V.—See Zuivelcooperatie FrieslandCampina U.A.; *Int'l,* pg. 8694
KAASUPORSSI OY—See Gasum Oy; *Int'l,* pg. 2888
KABA ACCESS CONTROL—See dormakaba Holding AG; *Int'l,* pg. 2177
KABA ACCESS SYSTEMS (SHANGHAI) CO., LTD.—See dormakaba Holding AG; *Int'l,* pg. 2178
KABADDI GAMES INC.—See Greenbank Capital Inc.; *Int'l,* pg. 3073
KABA DO BRASIL LTDA.—See dormakaba Holding AG; *Int'l,* pg. 2177
KABAFUSION HOLDINGS, LLC—See The Pritzker Group - Chicago, LLC; *U.S. Private,* pg. 4099
KABAFUSION - MICHIGAN—See The Pritzker Group - Chicago, LLC; *U.S. Private,* pg. 4099
KABA GALLENSCHUTZ GMBH—See dormakaba Holding AG; *Int'l,* pg. 2177
KABA GMBH—See dormakaba Holding AG; *Int'l,* pg. 2177
KABA ILCO CORP.—See dormakaba Holding AG; *Int'l,* pg. 2177
KABA ILCO INC.—See dormakaba Holding AG; *Int'l,* pg. 2177
KABA IMMOBILIEN GMBH—See dormakaba Holding AG; *Int'l,* pg. 2177
KABA JAYA SECURITY SDN. BHD.—See dormakaba Holding AG; *Int'l,* pg. 2179
KAB ALLGLASS GMBH—See AG Industries Limited; *Int'l,* pg. 198
KABA MAS LLC—See dormakaba Holding AG; *Int'l,* pg. 2177
KABAM, INC.; *U.S. Private,* pg. 2253
KABANA INC.; *U.S. Private,* pg. 2253
KABA NEW ZEALAND LIMITED—See dormakaba Holding AG; *Int'l,* pg. 2177
KA-BAR KNIVES, INC.—See CUTCO Corporation; *U.S. Private,* pg. 1131
KABA S.A.S.—See dormakaba Holding AG; *Int'l,* pg. 2177

KABA SRL—See dormakaba Holding AG; *Int'l,* pg. 2177
KABATEC GMBH & CO. KG—See Komax Holding AG; *Int'l,* pg. 4240
KABA WORKFORCE SOLUTIONS, LLC—See dormakaba Holding AG; *Int'l,* pg. 2177
KABCORP, INC.; *U.S. Private,* pg. 2253
KABC-TV INC.—See The Walt Disney Company; *U.S. Public,* pg. 2138
KABE GROUP AB; *Int'l,* pg. 4046
KABEL BW GMBH—See Permira Advisers LLP; *Int'l,* pg. 5808
KABELCOM RHEINHESSEN GMBH—See Morgan Stanley; *U.S. Public,* pg. 1473
KABEL DEUTSCHLAND HOLDING AG—See Vodafone Group Plc; *Int'l,* pg. 8284
KABELFERNSEHEN MUNCHEN SERVICENTER GMBH—See Morgan Stanley; *U.S. Public,* pg. 1473
KABELIN HARDWARE COMPANY INC.; *U.S. Private,* pg. 2253
KABELMAT WICKELTECHNIK GMBH.—See HELUKABEL GmbH; *Int'l,* pg. 3339
KABELPLUS GMBH—See EVN AG; *Int'l,* pg. 2571
KABELSCHLEPP CHINA CO., LTD.—See Tsubakimoto Chain Co.; *Int'l,* pg. 7953
KABELSCHLEPP FRANCE S.A.R.L.—See Tsubakimoto Chain Co.; *Int'l,* pg. 7954
KABELSCHLEPP GMBH—See Tsubakimoto Chain Co.; *Int'l,* pg. 7953
KABELSCHLEPP INDIA PVT. LTD.—See Tsubakimoto Chain Co.; *Int'l,* pg. 7954
KABELSCHLEPP ITALIA S.R.L.—See Tsubakimoto Chain Co.; *Int'l,* pg. 7954
KABELSCHLEPP SP. Z.O.O—See Tsubakimoto Chain Co.; *Int'l,* pg. 7954
KABELSCHLEPP SYSTEMTECHNIK SPOL. S.R.O.—See Tsubakimoto Chain Co.; *Int'l,* pg. 7954
KABELSIGNAL AG—See EVN AG; *Int'l,* pg. 2571
KABEL-TECHNIK-POLSKA SP. Z O.O.—See Samvardhana Motherson International Limited; *Int'l,* pg. 6516
KABELTROMMEL GESELLSCHAFT MBH & CO.KG—See Prysmian S.p.A.; *Int'l,* pg. 6012
KABELTROMMEL GMBH & CO. KG—See Nexans S.A.; *Int'l,* pg. 5241
KABELWERK EUPEN AG; *Int'l,* pg. 4046
KABELWERK MEISSEN WILHELM BALZER GMBH; *Int'l,* pg. 4046
KABE NO ANA PTE. LTD.—See RE&S Holdings Limited; *Int'l,* pg. 6230
KABETEX KULLAGER & TRANSMISSION AB—See Indutrade AB; *Int'l,* pg. 3679
KABILE-LB AD; *Int'l,* pg. 4046
KABIRDASS MOTOR COMPANY LTD—See BEST CAST IT LTD; *Int'l,* pg. 998
KABLAGEPRODUKTION I VASTERAS AB—See Lagercrantz Group AB; *Int'l,* pg. 4394
KABLE DISTRIBUTION SERVICES, INC.—See AMREP Corporation; *U.S. Public,* pg. 133
KABLE MEDIA SERVICES, INC.—See AMREP Corporation; *U.S. Public,* pg. 133
KABLE NEWS CO., INC.—See AMREP Corporation; *U.S. Public,* pg. 133
KABLE NEWS COMPANY—See AMREP Corporation; *U.S. Public,* pg. 133
KABLE STAFFING RESOURCES LLC; *U.S. Private,* pg. 2253
KABOKO MINING LIMITED; *Int'l,* pg. 4046
KABOODLE, INC.—See StyleSpot, Inc.; *U.S. Private,* pg. 3846
KABOOM!, INC.; *U.S. Private,* pg. 2253
KABRA COMMERCIAL LIMITED; *Int'l,* pg. 4046
KABRA DRUGS LIMITED; *Int'l,* pg. 4046
KABRA EXTRUSIONTECHNIK LTD; *Int'l,* pg. 4046
KAB SEATING AB—See Commercial Vehicle Group, Inc.; *U.S. Public,* pg. 547
KAB SEATING LIMITED—See Commercial Vehicle Group, Inc.; *U.S. Public,* pg. 547
KAB SEATING PTY. LTD.—See Commercial Vehicle Group, Inc.; *U.S. Public,* pg. 547
KAB SEATING SA—See Commercial Vehicle Group, Inc.; *U.S. Public,* pg. 547
KABSONS INDUSTRIES LIMITED; *Int'l,* pg. 4046
KAB STRABENSANIERUNG GMBH & CO KG—See STRABAG SE; *Int'l,* pg. 7231
KAB STRASSENSANIERUNG GMBH & CO KG—See STRABAG SE; *Int'l,* pg. 7231
KABU.COM SECURITIES CO., LTD.—See Mitsubishi UFJ Financial Group, Inc.; *Int'l,* pg. 4969
K.A. BUILDERS CONSTRUCTION PTE LTD—See INTRACO Limited; *Int'l,* pg. 3767
KABUKIZA CO., LTD.—See Shochiku Co., Ltd.; *Int'l,* pg. 6857
KABUKU INC.—See Futaba Corporation; *Int'l,* pg. 2850
KABUL INTERNATIONAL CO., LTD.—See KBI Group; *Int'l,* pg. 4107
KABUSHIKI KAISHA BRILLIANT SERVICE—See Cognizant Technology Solutions Corporation; *U.S. Public,* pg. 524

KABUSHIKI KAISHA HELENA KENKYUJYO—See Helena Laboratories Corporation; *U.S. Private,* pg. 1906
KABUSHIKI KAISHA SEIYOKEN; *Int'l,* pg. 4046
KABUSHIKI KAISHA VASCO DATA SECURITY JAPAN—See OneSpan Inc.; *U.S. Public,* pg. 1603
KABUTO DECOM, INC.; *Int'l,* pg. 4046
KABUTO INTERNATIONAL PHOENIX INC.—See Kabuto Decom, Inc.; *Int'l,* pg. 4046
KAC ALARM COMPANY LIMITED—See Honeywell International Inc.; *U.S. Public,* pg. 1051
KACAREVO A.D.; *Int'l,* pg. 4046
KACHCHH MINERALS LIMITED; *Int'l,* pg. 4046
KACO NEW ENERGY GMBH—See Siemens Aktiengesellschaft; *Int'l,* pg. 6887
KACO NEW ENERGY, INC.—See Siemens Aktiengesellschaft; *Int'l,* pg. 6887
KACO NEW ENERGY ITALIA S.R.L.—See Siemens Aktiengesellschaft; *Int'l,* pg. 6887
KACO NEW ENERGY SARL—See Siemens Aktiengesellschaft; *Int'l,* pg. 6887
KADANT AUSTRALIA PTY. LTD.—See Kadant Inc.; *U.S. Public,* pg. 1212
KADANT BC- LAMORT UK LIMITED—See Kadant Inc.; *U.S. Public,* pg. 1212
KADANT BLACK CLAWSON LLC—See Kadant Inc.; *U.S. Public,* pg. 1212
KADANT CANADA CORP.—See Kadant Inc.; *U.S. Public,* pg. 1212
KADANT FIBERLINE (CHINA) CO.—See Kadant Inc.; *U.S. Public,* pg. 1212
KADANT GRANTEK INC.—See Kadant Inc.; *U.S. Public,* pg. 1212
KADANT INC.; *U.S. Public,* pg. 1212
KADANT JOHNSON ARGENTINA S.R.L.—See Kadant Inc.; *U.S. Public,* pg. 1212
KADANT JOHNSON CORPORATION (WUXI) LTD.—See Kadant Inc.; *U.S. Public,* pg. 1212
KADANT JOHNSON DEUTSCHLAND GMBH—See Kadant Inc.; *U.S. Public,* pg. 1212
KADANT JOHNSON EUROPE BV—See Kadant Inc.; *U.S. Public,* pg. 1212
KADANT JOHNSON FRANCE B.V.—See Kadant Inc.; *U.S. Public,* pg. 1212
KADANT JOHNSON INC.—See Kadant Inc.; *U.S. Public,* pg. 1212
KADANT LAMORT AB—See Kadant Inc.; *U.S. Public,* pg. 1212
KADANT LAMORT S.A.S.—See Kadant Inc.; *U.S. Public,* pg. 1212
KADANT M-CLEAN AB—See Kadant Inc.; *U.S. Public,* pg. 1212
KADANT MEXICO S.A. DE C.V.—See Kadant Inc.; *U.S. Public,* pg. 1212
KADANT NORDIC AB—See Kadant Inc.; *U.S. Public,* pg. 1212
KADANT PAAL GMBH—See Kadant Inc.; *U.S. Public,* pg. 1212
KADANT PAAL S.A.U.—See Kadant Inc.; *U.S. Public,* pg. 1212
KADANT SOLUTIONS—See Kadant Inc.; *U.S. Public,* pg. 1212
KADANT SOUTH AMERICA LTDA.—See Kadant Inc.; *U.S. Public,* pg. 1212
KADANT UK LTD.—See Kadant Inc.; *U.S. Public,* pg. 1212
KADANT UNAFLEX LLC—See Kadant Inc.; *U.S. Public,* pg. 1212
KADDIS MANUFACTURING CORP.; *U.S. Private,* pg. 2253
KADDY LIMITED; *Int'l,* pg. 4046
KA.DE.GE KG—See Baader Bank AG; *Int'l,* pg. 791
KADEM SUSTAINABLE IMPACT CORPORATION; *U.S. Public,* pg. 1213
KADENCE INTERNATIONAL BUSINESS RESEARCH PTE. LTD.—See Cross Marketing Group Inc.; *Int'l,* pg. 1856
KADENCE INTERNATIONAL INC.—See Cross Marketing Group Inc.; *Int'l,* pg. 1856
KADENCE INTERNATIONAL LIMITED—See Cross Marketing Group Inc.; *Int'l,* pg. 1856
KADENCE INTERNATIONAL LTD.—See Cross Marketing Group Inc.; *Int'l,* pg. 1856
KADENCE INTERNATIONAL PVT., LTD.—See Cross Marketing Group Inc.; *Int'l,* pg. 1856
KADENCE INTERNATIONAL (THAILAND) CO., LTD.—See Cross Marketing Group Inc.; *Int'l,* pg. 1856
KADER HOLDINGS COMPANY LIMITED; *Int'l,* pg. 4046
KADER INDUSTRIAL COMPANY LIMITED—See Kader Holdings Company Limited; *Int'l,* pg. 4046
KADES CORP.; *U.S. Private,* pg. 2253
KADE TRADING GMBH—See Standard Motor Products, Inc.; *U.S. Public,* pg. 1929
KADIAC CO., LTD—See Coca-Cola Bottlers Japan Holdings Inc.; *Int'l,* pg. 1684
KADIKOY TANKERCILIK A.S.—See Koc Holding A.S.; *Int'l,* pg. 4223
KADIMASTEM LTD.; *Int'l,* pg. 4047
KADINJACA A.D.; *Int'l,* pg. 4047
KADINJACA A.D.; *Int'l,* pg. 4047

COMPANY NAME INDEX

KADISCO PAINT & ADHESIVE INDUSTRY S.C.—See Asian Paints Limited; *Int'l*, pg. 619
KADLEC REGIONAL MEDICAL CENTER; *U.S. Private*, pg. 2253
KADMON HOLDINGS, INC.—See Sanofi; *Int'l*, pg. 6548
KADMOS S.A.—See National Bank of Greece S.A.; *Int'l*, pg. 5153
KAD NEBUTU SALTA, UAB—See Tulikivi Corporation; *Int'l*, pg. 7969
KADOKAWA AMARIN COMPANY LIMITED—See Kadokawa Corporation; *Int'l*, pg. 4047
KADOKAWA CA (THAILAND) CO., LTD.—See Kadokawa Corporation; *Int'l*, pg. 4047
KADOKAWA CONTENTS ACADEMY CO., LTD.—See Kadokawa Corporation; *Int'l*, pg. 4047
KADOKAWA CORPORATION; *Int'l*, pg. 4047
KADOKAWA CORPORATION—See Kadokawa Corporation; *Int'l*, pg. 4047
KADOKAWA DAIEI STUDIO CO., LTD.—See Kadokawa Corporation; *Int'l*, pg. 4047
KADOKAWA GEMPAK STARZ SDN. BHD.—See Kadokawa Corporation; *Int'l*, pg. 4047
KADOKAWA HARUKI CORPORATION—See Tsuburaya Fields Holdings Inc.; *Int'l*, pg. 7955
KADOKAWA INTERCONTINENTAL PUBLISHING (ASIA) LTD.—See Lai Sun Group; *Int'l*, pg. 4396
KADOKAWA MEDIA HOUSE INC.—See Kadokawa Corporation; *Int'l*, pg. 4047
KADOKAWA MEDIA (TAIWAN) CO., LTD.—See Kadokawa Corporation; *Int'l*, pg. 4047
KADOKAWA TAIWAN CORPORATION—See Kadokawa Corporation; *Int'l*, pg. 4047
KADOMA SHIKI CO., LTD.—See Tomoku Co., Ltd.; *Int'l*, pg. 7801
KADOTA KOZAI CORPORATION—See JFE Holdings, Inc.; *Int'l*, pg. 3937
KADOWAKI STEEL MATERIAL'S CORPORATION—See JFE Holdings, Inc.; *Int'l*, pg. 3937
KADOYA SESAME MILLS INC.; *Int'l*, pg. 4047
KADUNA REFINING & PETROCHEMICAL COMPANY LIMITED—See Nigerian National Petroleum Corporation; *Int'l*, pg. 5282
KAEHLIG ANTRIEBSTECHNIK GMBH; *Int'l*, pg. 4047
KAE KRAFTWERKS- & ANLAGEN-ENGINEERING GMBH—See DKW AG; *Int'l*, pg. 1055
KAE: MARKETING INTELLIGENCE LTD.—See Optimisa PLC; *Int'l*, pg. 5604
KAEREK HOMES, INC.; *U.S. Private*, pg. 2253
KAESER & BLAIR INCORPORATED; *U.S. Private*, pg. 2254
KAESER COMPRESSORS INC.; *U.S. Private*, pg. 2254
KAESSBOHRER GELANDEFAHRZEUG AG; *Int'l*, pg. 4047
KAFAA FOR FINANCIAL & ECONOMICAL INVESTMENTS PLC; *Int'l*, pg. 4047
KAFEIN YAZILIM HIZMETLERI TICARET AS; *Int'l*, pg. 4047
KAFEVEND GROUP LIMITED—See Eden International SA; *Int'l*, pg. 2307
KAFFEBRYGGERIET AS—See Miko NV; *Int'l*, pg. 4892
KAFFEHUSET FRIELE A/S—See JAB Holding Company S.a.r.l.; *Int'l*, pg. 3862
KAFFEKNAPPEN AB—See Convini Sverige AB; *Int'l*, pg. 1787
KAFFEKNAPPEN NORGE AS—See Nestle S.A.; *Int'l*, pg. 5203
KAFFEKNAPPEN SVERIGE AB—See Nestle S.A.; *Int'l*, pg. 5203
KAFFEKOMPANIET DIN PAUSPARTNER AB—See Miko NV; *Int'l*, pg. 4892
KAFFENBARGER TRUCK EQUIPMENT CO.; *U.S. Private*, pg. 2254
KAFI BV—See ARCADIS N.V.; *Int'l*, pg. 541
KAF INVESTMENT BANK BERHAD—See KAF Securities Sdn. Bhd.; *Int'l*, pg. 4047
KAFR EL ZAYAT PESTICIDES & CHEMICALS CO.; *Int'l*, pg. 4047
KAFRIT INDUSTRIES LTD.; *Int'l*, pg. 4048
KAF-SEAGROATT & CAMPBELL BERHAD—See KAF Securities Sdn. Bhd.; *Int'l*, pg. 4047
KAF SECURITIES SDN. BHD.; *Int'l*, pg. 4047
KAF-TECH—See Clayton, Dubilier & Rice, LLC; *U.S. Private*, pg. 919
KAFUE HOUSE LIMITED—See Barclays PLC; *Int'l*, pg. 862
KA FUND ADVISORS LLC—See Kayne Anderson Capital Advisors, L.P.; *U.S. Private*, pg. 2267
KAGA AMUSEMENT CO., LTD.—See Kaga Electronics Co., Ltd.; *Int'l*, pg. 4048
KAGA AMUSEMENT MALAYSIA SDN. BHD.—See Kaga Electronics Co., Ltd.; *Int'l*, pg. 4049
KAGA COMPONENTS CO., LTD.—See Kaga Electronics Co., Ltd.; *Int'l*, pg. 4049
KAGA COMPONENTS (MALAYSIA) SDN. BHD.—See Kaga Electronics Co., Ltd.; *Int'l*, pg. 4049
KAGA CREATE CO., LTD.—See Kaga Electronics Co., Ltd.; *Int'l*, pg. 4049
KAGA (DALIAN) CO., LTD.—See Kaga Electronics Co., Ltd.; *Int'l*, pg. 4048

KAGA (DALIAN) ELECTRONICS CO., LTD.—See Kaga Electronics Co., Ltd.; *Int'l*, pg. 4048
KAGA DEVICES CO., LTD.—See Kaga Electronics Co., Ltd.; *Int'l*, pg. 4049
KAGA DEVICES (H.K.) LTD.—See Kaga Electronics Co., Ltd.; *Int'l*, pg. 4049
KAGA DEVICES INDIA PRIVATE LIMITED—See Kaga Electronics Co., Ltd.; *Int'l*, pg. 4049
KAGA EDUCATIONAL MARKETING CO., LTD.—See Kaga Electronics Co., Ltd.; *Int'l*, pg. 4048
KAGA ELECTRONICS CO., LTD.; *Int'l*, pg. 4048
KAGA ELECTRONICS INDIA PRIVATE LIMITED—See Kaga Electronics Co., Ltd.; *Int'l*, pg. 4049
KAGA ELECTRONICS INDONESIA, PT—See Kaga Electronics Co., Ltd.; *Int'l*, pg. 4049
KAGA ELECTRONICS (THAILAND) CO., LTD.—See Kaga Electronics Co., Ltd.; *Int'l*, pg. 4049
KAGA ELECTRONICS (USA) INC.—See Kaga Electronics Co., Ltd.; *Int'l*, pg. 4049
KAGA ELECTRONICS (VIETNAM) CO., LTD.—See Kaga Electronics Co., Ltd.; *Int'l*, pg. 4049
KAGA EMS TOWADA CO., LTD.—See Kaga Electronics Co., Ltd.; *Int'l*, pg. 4049
KAGA (EUROPE) ELECTRONICS B.V.—See Kaga Electronics Co., Ltd.; *Int'l*, pg. 4049
KAGA FIRST TRANSPORT SERVICE CO. LTD.—See Daiichi Koutsu Sangyo Co., Ltd.; *Int'l*, pg. 1928
KAGA HIGHTECH CO., LTD.—See Kaga Electronics Co., Ltd.; *Int'l*, pg. 4049
KAGA (H.K.) ELECTRONICS LTD.—See Kaga Electronics Co., Ltd.; *Int'l*, pg. 4048
KAGA (KOREA) ELECTRONICS CO., LTD.—See Kaga Electronics Co., Ltd.; *Int'l*, pg. 4049
KAGAKU UNYU CO., LTD.—See Mitsubishi Gas Chemical Company, Inc.; *Int'l*, pg. 4949
KAGAMAIISHI PLANT—See Nipro Corporation; *Int'l*, pg. 5361
KAGA MICRO SOLUTION CO., LTD.—See Kaga Electronics Co., Ltd.; *Int'l*, pg. 4049
KAGARA COPPER PTY LTD—See Kagara Ltd.; *Int'l*, pg. 4049
KAGARA LTD.; *Int'l*, pg. 4049
KAGA (SHANGHAI) ELECTRONICS CO., LTD.—See Kaga Electronics Co., Ltd.; *Int'l*, pg. 4049
KAGA (SHENZHEN) ELECTRONICS LTD.—See Kaga Electronics Co., Ltd.; *Int'l*, pg. 4049
KAGA (SHENZHEN) TRADING LTD.—See Kaga Electronics Co., Ltd.; *Int'l*, pg. 4049
KAGA (SINGAPORE) ELECTRONICS PTE. LTD.—See Kaga Electronics Co., Ltd.; *Int'l*, pg. 4049
KAGA SOLUTION NETWORK CO., LTD.—See Kaga Electronics Co., Ltd.; *Int'l*, pg. 4049
KAGA SPORTS CO., LTD.—See Kaga Electronics Co., Ltd.; *Int'l*, pg. 4048
KAGA (TAIWAN) ELECTRONICS CO., LTD.—See Kaga Electronics Co., Ltd.; *Int'l*, pg. 4049
KAGA TAXAN (SUZHOU) ELECTRONICS CO., LTD.—See Kaga Electronics Co., Ltd.; *Int'l*, pg. 4049
KAGA TECH CO., LTD.—See Kaga Electronics Co., Ltd.; *Int'l*, pg. 4049
KAGA TECHNOLOGY (SUZHOU) ELECTRONICS CO., LTD.—See Kaga Electronics Co., Ltd.; *Int'l*, pg. 4049
KAGA TECHNO SERVICE CO., LTD.—See Kaga Electronics Co., Ltd.; *Int'l*, pg. 4049
KAGA TOSHIBA ELECTRONICS COMPANY—See Japan Industrial Partners, Inc.; *Int'l*, pg. 3889
THE KAGAWA BANK, LTD.—See TOMONY Holdings, Inc.; *Int'l*, pg. 7802
KAGAWA PREFECTURE INFORMATION SERVICES CO., LTD.—See TOPPAN Holdings Inc.; *Int'l*, pg. 7816
KAGAWA TOKUYAMA CO., LTD.—See Tokuyama Corporation; *Int'l*, pg. 7787
KAGAYAKI CO., LTD.—See Zensho Holdings Co., Ltd.; *Int'l*, pg. 8634
KAGAZY RECYCLING LLP—See Kazakhstan Kagazy JSC; *Int'l*, pg. 4102
KAGEMA INDUSTRIEAUSRUSTUNGEN GMBH—See KSB SE & Co. KGaA; *Int'l*, pg. 4310
KAG ETHANOL LOGISTICS—See Ontario Municipal Employees Retirement System; *Int'l*, pg. 5585
KAGETSUENKANKO CO., LTD.; *Int'l*, pg. 4050
THE KAGIN ACCOUNTING SERVICE CO., LTD.—See Kyushu Financial Group, Inc; *Int'l*, pg. 4368
KAGISO ASSET MANAGEMENT (PTY.) LIMITED—See Kagiso Tiso Holdings Proprietary Limited; *Int'l*, pg. 4050
KAGISO MEDIA LIMITED—See Kagiso Tiso Holdings Proprietary Limited; *Int'l*, pg. 4050
KAGISO TISO HOLDINGS PROPRIETARY LIMITED; *Int'l*, pg. 4050
KAGISO VENTURES (PTY.) LIMITED—See Kagiso Tiso Holdings Proprietary Limited; *Int'l*, pg. 4050
KAG LOGISTICS, INC.—See Ontario Municipal Employees Retirement System; *Int'l*, pg. 5585
KAGOME AUSTRALIA PTY LTD.—See Kagome Co., Ltd.; *Int'l*, pg. 4050
KAGOME CO., LTD.; *Int'l*, pg. 4050
KAGOME DISTRIBUTION SERVICE CO LTD—See Kagome Co., Ltd.; *Int'l*, pg. 4050

KAGOME FOODS, INC.—See Kagome Co., Ltd.; *Int'l*, pg. 4050
KAGOME FUDOSAN CO., LTD.—See Kagome Co., Ltd.; *Int'l*, pg. 4050
KAGOME (HANGZHOU) FOOD CO., LTD.—See Kagome Co., Ltd.; *Int'l*, pg. 4050
KAGOME, INC.—See Kagome Co., Ltd.; *Int'l*, pg. 4050
KAGOME LABIO CO.—See Kagome Co., Ltd.; *Int'l*, pg. 4050
KAGOME NISSIN FOODS (H.K.) CO., LTD.—See Nissin Foods Holdings Co., Ltd.; *Int'l*, pg. 5376
KAGOME REAL ESTATE CO LTD—See Kagome Co., Ltd.; *Int'l*, pg. 4050
KAGOME (TIANJIN) FOOD INDUSTRY CO., LTD.—See Kagome Co., Ltd.; *Int'l*, pg. 4050
THE KAGOSHIMA BANK, LTD.—See Kyushu Financial Group, Inc; *Int'l*, pg. 4368
THE KAGOSHIMA CARD CO., LTD.—See Kyushu Financial Group, Inc; *Int'l*, pg. 4368
KAGOSHIMA DAIYA CO., LTD.—See Mitsubishi Heavy Industries, Ltd.; *Int'l*, pg. 4954
KAGOSHIMA HIKARI TELEVISION CO., INC.—See Kyushu Electric Power Co., Inc.; *Int'l*, pg. 4367
THE KAGOSHIMA LEASE CO., LTD.—See Kyushu Financial Group, Inc; *Int'l*, pg. 4368
KAGOSHIMA MORITA PUMP CORPORATION—See Morita Holdings Corporation; *Int'l*, pg. 5048
KAGOSHIMA SUNRISE FARM K.K.—See AEON Co., Ltd.; *Int'l*, pg. 177
KAGRA IX AS—See Umoe Gruppen AS; *Int'l*, pg. 8026
K. A. GROUP HOLDINGS PTE LTD—See INTRACO Limited; *Int'l*, pg. 3767
KAGUKURO CO., LTD.—See Nakabayashi Co., Ltd.; *Int'l*, pg. 5131
KAG WEST, LLC—See Ontario Municipal Employees Retirement System; *Int'l*, pg. 5585
KAHALA CORP.; *U.S. Private*, pg. 2254
KAHALA SENIOR LIVING COMMUNITY, INC.; *U.S. Private*, pg. 2254
KAH BINTANG AUTO SDN. BHD.—See Oriental Holdings Berhad; *Int'l*, pg. 5624
KAH CAPITAL MANAGEMENT, LLC—See Chimera Investment Corp.; *U.S. Public*, pg. 489
KAH CLASSIC AUTO SDN. BHD.—See Oriental Holdings Berhad; *Int'l*, pg. 5624
KAHEE CO., LTD. - GAJU MILL—See S Mark Co., Ltd.; *Int'l*, pg. 6443
KAHEE CO., LTD. - SINNI MILL—See S Mark Co., Ltd.; *Int'l*, pg. 6443
KAHIKI FOODS, INC.—See CJ Corporation; *Int'l*, pg. 1631
KAHIRA PHARMACEUTICALS & CHEMICAL INDUSTRIES COMPANY; *Int'l*, pg. 4050
KAHLE ENGINEERING CO.; *U.S. Private*, pg. 2254
KAHLER AUTOMATION CORPORATION; *U.S. Private*, pg. 2254
KAHLER-SENDERS GROUP INC.; *U.S. Private*, pg. 2254
KAHLIG ENTERPRISES INC.; *U.S. Private*, pg. 2254
KAHLO CHRYSLER JEEP DODGE RAM; *U.S. Private*, pg. 2254
KAHLO JEEP CHRYSLER DODGE; *U.S. Private*, pg. 2254
KAH MOTOR COMPANY SDN. BERHAD—See Oriental Holdings Berhad; *Int'l*, pg. 5624
KAHNAWAKE MANAGEMENT SERVICES INC.—See Entain PLC; *Int'l*, pg. 2450
KAHN-CARLIN + CO., INC.—See Kelso & Company, L.P.; *U.S. Private*, pg. 2280
KAHN DO BRASIL LTDA.—See Albert Kahn Associates, Inc.; *U.S. Private*, pg. 153
KAHN GLOBAL SERVICES, INC.—See Albert Kahn Associates, Inc.; *U.S. Private*, pg. 153
KAHN-LUCAS-LANCASTER INC.; *U.S. Private*, pg. 2254
KAHN SOUTH, INC.—See Albert Kahn Associates, Inc.; *U.S. Private*, pg. 153
KAHN VENTURES, INC.—See Berkshire Hathaway Inc.; *U.S. Public*, pg. 308
KAHO MANUFACTURING CO., LTD.—See Nittetsu Mining Co., Ltd.; *Int'l*, pg. 5383
KAHOOT! ASA—See The Goldman Sachs Group, Inc.; *U.S. Public*, pg. 2082
KAHO VALVE CO., LTD.—See Value Valves Co., Ltd.; *Int'l*, pg. 8124
KAH POWER PRODUCTS PTE. LTD.—See Oriental Holdings Berhad; *Int'l*, pg. 5624
KAHULUI TRUCKING & STORAGE, INC.—See Alexander & Baldwin, Inc.; *U.S. Public*, pg. 75
KAHU VETERINARY EQUIPMENT LIMITED—See Vimian Group AB; *Int'l*, pg. 8208
KAHYA CO., LTD.—See DCM Holdings Co., Ltd.; *Int'l*, pg. 1992
KAIBAB INDUSTRIES, INC.; *U.S. Private*, pg. 2254
KAIBO FOODS COMPANY LIMITED; *Int'l*, pg. 4051
KAI CORPORATION LTD.; *Int'l*, pg. 4050
KAI CORPORATION; *Int'l*, pg. 4050
KAI CUTLERY (H.K.) LTD.—See KAI Corporation; *Int'l*, pg. 4050
KAIDI ECOLOGICAL AND ENVIRONMENTAL TECHNOLOGY, CO., LTD.; *Int'l*, pg. 4051

KAIDI ECOLOGICAL AND ENVIRONMENTAL TECHNOLOGY CO., LTD.
CORPORATE AFFILIATIONS

KAIDI ELECTRICAL EUROPE GMBH—See Changzhou Kaidi Electrical, Inc.; *Int'l*, pg. 1445
KAIDI LLC—See Changzhou Kaidi Electrical, Inc.; *Int'l*, pg. 1445
KAIEMEI ELECTRONIC CORP.; *Int'l*, pg. 4051
KAI ENTERPRISES, INC.—See Kanematsu Corporation; *Int'l*, pg. 4069
KAI EUROPE GMBH—See KAI Corporation; *Int'l*, pg. 4050
KAIFENG HIROYOSHI AUTOMOTIVE TRIM CO., LTD.—See Hiroca Holdings Ltd.; *Int'l*, pg. 3404
KAIFENG KASAI AUTOMOTIVE TRIM PARTS CO., LTD.—See Kasai Kogyo Co., Ltd.; *Int'l*, pg. 4086
KAIFENG TAIYO KINMEI FOOD CO., LTD.—See Taiyo Kagaku Co., Ltd.; *Int'l*, pg. 7425
KAIFENG ZHUCHENG WIRING SYSTEMS, CO., LTD.—See Sumitomo Electric Industries, Ltd.; *Int'l*, pg. 7278
KAIGAI GIJYUTSU K.K.—See Shinwa Industrial Co., Ltd.; *Int'l*, pg. 6850
KAIGEN PHARMA CO., LTD.—See Sakai Chemical Industry Co., Ltd.; *Int'l*, pg. 6486
KAI GROUP—See Mohawk Industries, Inc.; *U.S. Public*, pg. 1457
KAIHAN CO., LTD.; *Int'l*, pg. 4051
KAIHATSUHIRYOU CO., LTD.—See Electric Power Development Co., Ltd.; *Int'l*, pg. 2349
KAI INDUSTRIES CO., LTD.—See KAI Corporation; *Int'l*, pg. 4050
KAI INVESTMENTS, LLC—See Howard Hughes Holdings Inc.; *U.S. Public*, pg. 1060
KAI JIA COMPUTER ACCESSORY CO., LTD.—See Casetek Holdings Limited; *Int'l*, pg. 1351
KAIJIRUSHI KOREA CORPORATION—See KAI Corporation; *Int'l*, pg. 4050
KAIJO CORPORATION—See Shibuya Corporation; *Int'l*, pg. 6827
KAIKAN KAIHATSU CO., LTD.—See Japan Airport Terminal Co., Ltd.; *Int'l*, pg. 3885
KAIKA SAS—See HORIBA Ltd; *Int'l*, pg. 3477
KAIKATSU FRONTIER INC.—See AOKI Holdings Inc.; *Int'l*, pg. 488
KAIKI SANGYO KABUSHIKI KAISHA—See NSK Ltd.; *Int'l*, pg. 5478
KAIKU KM0 S.L.—See Emmi AG; *Int'l*, pg. 2384
KAILASH AUTO FINANCE LIMITED; *Int'l*, pg. 4051
KAILASH BIKAS BANK LIMITED; *Int'l*, pg. 4051
KAILASH GROUP; *Int'l*, pg. 4051
KAILING HYDRAULIC TECHNOLOGY (SHANGHAI) CO., LTD.—See Daikin Industries, Ltd.; *Int'l*, pg. 1935
KAILI RESOURCES LIMITED; *Int'l*, pg. 4051
KAILO ENERGY—See Global Unicorn Holdings, Inc.; *U.S. Private*, pg. 1718
KAILONG HIGH TECHNOLOGY CO., LTD.; *Int'l*, pg. 4051
KAILONG LANFENG NEW MATERIAL TECHNOLOGY CO., LTD.—See Kailong High Technology Co., Ltd.; *Int'l*, pg. 4051
KAILOS GENETICS, INC.—See HealthOme Inc.; *U.S. Private*, pg. 1897
KAILUAN ENERGY CHEMICAL CO., LTD.; *Int'l*, pg. 4051
KAI MANAGEMENT SERVICES, LLC—See Marriott Vacations Worldwide Corporation; *U.S. Public*, pg. 1373
KAIMANN B.V.—See Compagnie de Saint-Gobain SA; *Int'l*, pg. 1723
KAIMANN FRANCE SAS—See Compagnie de Saint-Gobain SA; *Int'l*, pg. 1723
KAIMANN GMBH—See Compagnie de Saint-Gobain SA; *Int'l*, pg. 1723
KAIMANN IBERIA S.L.—See Compagnie de Saint-Gobain SA; *Int'l*, pg. 1723
KAIMANN ITALIA S.R.L—See Compagnie de Saint-Gobain SA; *Int'l*, pg. 1723
KAIMANN UK LTD—See Compagnie de Saint-Gobain SA; *Int'l*, pg. 1723
KAI MANUFACTURING INDIA PVT. LTD.—See KAI Corporation; *Int'l*, pg. 4050
KAI MEDICAL LABORATORY, LLC—See Empower Clinics Inc.; *Int'l*, pg. 2388
KAI MING INDUSTRIAL CO., LTD—See Tong Yang Industry Co., Ltd.; *Int'l*, pg. 7806
KAI MINING EOOD—See Mohawk Industries, Inc.; *U.S. Public*, pg. 1457
KAINANTU RESOURCES LTD.; *Int'l*, pg. 4051
KAIN AUTOMOTIVE, INC.—See NCM Associates, Inc.; *U.S. Private*, pg. 2876
KAIN CAPITAL, LLC; *U.S. Private*, pg. 2254
KA INDUSTRIAL SERVICES, LLC—See The Halifax Group LLC; *U.S. Private*, pg. 4042
KA INDUSTRIES INC.; *U.S. Private*, pg. 2253
THE KAIN LIMITED PARTNERSHIP; *Int'l*, pg. 7661
KAIN MANAGEMENT GROUP; *U.S. Private*, pg. 2254
KAINOS CAPITAL, LLC; *U.S. Private*, pg. 2254
KAINOS GROUP PLC; *Int'l*, pg. 4051
KAINOS LABORATORIES, INC; *Int'l*, pg. 4052
KAINOS MEDICINE, INC.; *Int'l*, pg. 4052
KAINOS PARTNERS INC.—See GTCR LLC; *U.S. Private*, pg. 1803
KAINOS SOFTWARE POLAND SPOLKA Z.O.O—See Kainos Group plc; *Int'l*, pg. 4052

KAINOS WORKSMART APS—See Kainos Group plc; *Int'l*, pg. 4052
KAINOS WORKSMART CANADA INC.—See Kainos Group plc; *Int'l*, pg. 4052
KAINOS WORKSMART LIMITED—See Kainos Group plc; *Int'l*, pg. 4052
KAIN & SHELTON (AGENCIES) PTY LTD—See K&S Corporation Limited; *Int'l*, pg. 4039
KAIN & SHELTON PTY LTD—See K&S Corporation Limited; *Int'l*, pg. 4039
KAINUUN SANOMAIN KIRJAPAINO OY—See Alma Media Corporation; *Int'l*, pg. 362
KAI PHARMACEUTICALS, INC.—See Amgen Inc.; *U.S. Public*, pg. 123
KAI PING ELEC & ELTEK COMPANY LIMITED—See Kingboard Holdings Limited; *Int'l*, pg. 4171
KAIPING ELEC & ELTEK NO. 3 COMPANY LIMITED—See Kingboard Holdings Limited; *Int'l*, pg. 4171
KAIPING ELEC & ELTEK NO. 5 COMPANY LIMITED—See Kingboard Holdings Limited; *Int'l*, pg. 4171
KAIPING HUI HUA TEXTILES LIMITED—See Fountain Set (Holdings) Limited; *Int'l*, pg. 2754
KAIPING KINGLY CAPSULES CO., LTD—See The United Laboratories International Holdings Ltd.; *Int'l*, pg. 7697
KAIPING PACIC INSULATING MATERIAL COMPANY LIMITED—See Kingboard Holdings Limited; *Int'l*, pg. 4170
KAI POLU SERVICES LLC; *U.S. Private*, pg. 2254
KAIRA CAN COMPANY LIMITED; *Int'l*, pg. 4052
KAIRAK INC.—See Illinois Tool Works Inc.; *U.S. Public*, pg. 1108
KAI R&D (GUANGZHOU) CO., LTD.—See KAI Corporation; *Int'l*, pg. 4050
KAIRIKIYA CO., LTD.; *Int'l*, pg. 4052
KAIRION GMBH—See ProSiebenSat.1 Media SE; *Int'l*, pg. 6000
KAIROS ACQUISITION CORP.; *U.S. Public*, pg. 1213
KAIROS AR, INC.; *U.S. Private*, pg. 2255
KAIROS ASSET MANAGEMENT SA—See Julius Baer Group Ltd.; *Int'l*, pg. 4024
KAIROS INDUSTRIAL HOLDINGS LTD.; *Int'l*, pg. 4052
KAIROS INDUSTRIES AG; *Int'l*, pg. 4052
KAIROS INVESTMENT MANAGEMENT LIMITED—See Julius Baer Group Ltd.; *Int'l*, pg. 4025
KAIROS INVESTMENT MANAGEMENT S.P.A.—See Julius Baer Group Ltd.; *Int'l*, pg. 4024
KAIROS MINERALS LIMITED; *Int'l*, pg. 4052
KAIROS NV—See Koninklijke BAM Groep N.V.; *Int'l*, pg. 4261
KAIROS PARTNERS SGR, S.P.A.—See ANIMA Holding S.p.A.; *Int'l*, pg. 471
KAIROUS ACQUISITION CORP. LIMITED; *Int'l*, pg. 4052
KAIRUIDE HOLDING CO., LTD.; *Int'l*, pg. 4052
KAISA CAPITAL INVESTMENT HOLDINGS LIMITED—See Kaisa Group Holdings Limited; *Int'l*, pg. 4052
KAISA GROUP HOLDINGS LIMITED; *Int'l*, pg. 4052
KAISA HEALTH GROUP HOLDINGS LIMITED; *Int'l*, pg. 4052
KAISA JIAYUN TECHNOLOGY INC.; *Int'l*, pg. 4052
KAISA PROSPERITY HOLDINGS LIMITED; *Int'l*, pg. 4052
KAISEN ENERGY CORP.; *Int'l*, pg. 4052
KAISER ALUMINUM ALEXCO LLC—See Kaiser Aluminum Corporation; *U.S. Public*, pg. 1213
KAISER ALUMINUM CANADA LIMITED—See Kaiser Aluminum Corporation; *U.S. Public*, pg. 1213
KAISER ALUMINUM CORPORATION; *U.S. Public*, pg. 1213
KAISER ALUMINUM FABRICATED PRODUCTS, LLC—See Kaiser Aluminum Corporation; *U.S. Public*, pg. 1213
KAISER ALUMINUM FABRICATED PRODUCTS—See Kaiser Aluminum Corporation; *U.S. Public*, pg. 1213
KAISER ALUMINUM FABRICATED PRODUCTS—See Kaiser Aluminum Corporation; *U.S. Public*, pg. 1213
KAISER ALUMINUM WARRICK, LLC—See Kaiser Aluminum Corporation; *U.S. Public*, pg. 1213
KAISER ALUMINUM WASHINGTON, LLC—See Kaiser Aluminum Corporation; *U.S. Public*, pg. 1213
KAISER ARTS & KRAFTS LIMITED; *Int'l*, pg. 4053
KAISER (CHINA) CULTURE CO., LTD.; *Int'l*, pg. 4052
KAISER CORPORATION LIMITED; *Int'l*, pg. 4053
KAISER FOUNDATION HEALTH PLAN, INC.—See Kaiser Permanente; *U.S. Private*, pg. 2255
KAISER FOUNDATION HEALTH PLAN OF GEORGIA, INC.—See Kaiser Permanente; *U.S. Private*, pg. 2255
KAISER FOUNDATION HEALTH PLAN OF THE MID-ATLANTIC STATES, INC.—See Kaiser Permanente; *U.S. Private*, pg. 2255
KAISER FOUNDATION HEALTH PLAN OF THE NORTHWEST—See Kaiser Permanente; *U.S. Private*, pg. 2255
KAISER FOUNDATION HEALTH PLAN OF WASHINGTON—See Kaiser Permanente; *U.S. Private*, pg. 2255
KAISER FOUNDATION HOSPITALS—See Kaiser Permanente; *U.S. Private*, pg. 2256
KAISER-FRANCIS OIL COMPANY; *U.S. Private*, pg. 2256

KAISER HEALTH PLAN ASSET MANAGEMENT, INC.—See Kaiser Permanente; *U.S. Private*, pg. 2256
KAISER HOSPITAL ASSET MANAGEMENT, INC.—See Kaiser Permanente; *U.S. Private*, pg. 2256
KAISER & KRAFT EUROPA—See Franz Haniel & Cie. GmbH; *Int'l*, pg. 2763
KAISER & KRAFT GMBH—See Franz Haniel & Cie. GmbH; *Int'l*, pg. 2763
KAISER MARKETING, INC.; *U.S. Private*, pg. 2255
KAISER OPTICAL SYSTEMS, INC.—See Endress+Hauser (International) Holding AG; *Int'l*, pg. 2407
KAISER OPTICAL SYSTEMS SARL—See RTX Corporation; *U.S. Public*, pg. 1823
KAISER PARTNER PRIVATBANK AG; *Int'l*, pg. 4053
KAISER PERMANENTE, COLORADO REGION—See Kaiser Permanente; *U.S. Private*, pg. 2256
KAISER PERMANENTE, GEORGIA REGION—See Kaiser Permanente; *U.S. Private*, pg. 2256
KAISER PERMANENTE, HAWAII REGION—See Kaiser Permanente; *U.S. Private*, pg. 2256
KAISER PERMANENTE INSURANCE COMPANY—See Kaiser Permanente; *U.S. Private*, pg. 2256
KAISER PERMANENTE, NORTHWEST REGION—See Kaiser Permanente; *U.S. Private*, pg. 2256
KAISER PERMANENTE; *U.S. Private*, pg. 2255
KAISER REEF LIMITED; *Int'l*, pg. 4053
KAISER SOHNE MINERALOLE GMBH & CO, KG—See Marquard & Bahls AG; *Int'l*, pg. 4699
KAISER TOBACCO STORE—See Kaiser Wholesale, Inc.; *U.S. Private*, pg. 2256
KAISER WHOLESALE, INC.; *U.S. Private*, pg. 2256
KAISHAN GROUP CO., LTD.; *Int'l*, pg. 4053
KAI SHING MANAGEMENT SERVICES LIMITED—See Sun Hung Kai Properties Limited; *Int'l*, pg. 7304
KAISHIN INDUSTRIA E COMERCIO LTDA.—See Miki Pulley Co., Ltd.; *Int'l*, pg. 4891
KAISUN HOLDINGS LIMITED; *Int'l*, pg. 4053
KAITA BIOMASS POWER CO., LTD.—See The Chugoku Electric Power Co., Inc.; *Int'l*, pg. 7632
THE KAITEKI INSTITUTE, INC.—See Mitsubishi Chemical Group Corporation; *Int'l*, pg. 4937
KAIT, LLC—See Gray Television, Inc.; *U.S. Public*, pg. 959
KAITORI OKOKU CO., LTD.; *Int'l*, pg. 4053
KAI U.S.A. LTD.—See KAI Corporation; *Int'l*, pg. 4050
KAIVAL BRANDS INNOVATIONS GROUP, INC.; *U.S. Public*, pg. 1213
KAI VIETNAM CO., LTD.—See KAI Corporation; *Int'l*, pg. 4050
KAIXIN AUTO HOLDINGS; *Int'l*, pg. 4053
KAIYO FOODS CO., LTD.—See Kyokuyo Co. Ltd.; *Int'l*, pg. 4363
KAIYUAN EDUCATION TECHNOLOGY GROUP CO., LTD.; *Int'l*, pg. 4053
KAI YUAN HOLDINGS LIMITED; *Int'l*, pg. 4050
KAI YURCONIC INSURANCE AGENCY, LLC—See Bain Capital, LP; *U.S. Private*, pg. 441
KAI YURCONIC INSURANCE AGENCY, LLC—See Keystone Insurers Group, Inc.; *U.S. Private*, pg. 2300
KAIZEN AUTOMOTIVE GROUP; *Int'l*, pg. 4053
THE KAIZEN COMPANY, LLC—See Tetra Tech, Inc.; *U.S. Public*, pg. 2024
KAIZEN DISCOVERY INC.—See Ivanhoe Electric Inc.; *Int'l*, pg. 3846
KAIZEN HOLDING LTD; *Int'l*, pg. 4053
KAIZEN PLATFORM, INC.; *Int'l*, pg. 4053
KAIZEN TECHNOLOGIES, INC.; *U.S. Private*, pg. 2256
KAIZHONG VOGT GMBH—See Shenzhen Kaizhong Precision Technology Co., Ltd; *Int'l*, pg. 6815
KAJAANI PROCESS MEASUREMENTS LTD.—See ABB Ltd.; *Int'l*, pg. 49
KAJANG RESOURCES CORPORATION SDN, BHD.—See MKH Berhad; *Int'l*, pg. 5002
KAJANG SPECIALIST HOSPITAL SDN BHD—See KPJ Healthcare Berhad; *Int'l*, pg. 4297
KAJARIA CERAMICS LTD; *Int'l*, pg. 4053
KAJARIA PLYWOOD PRIVATE LIMITED—See Kajaria Ceramics Ltd; *Int'l*, pg. 4053
KAJEET, INC.; *U.S. Private*, pg. 2256
KAJIHARA INDUSTRIAL CO., LTD.—See Denkyo Group Holdings Co.,Ltd.; *Int'l*, pg. 2028
KAJIMA AQUATECH CORPORATION—See Kajima Corporation; *Int'l*, pg. 4054
KAJIMA ASIA PACIFIC HOLDINGS PTE. LTD.—See Kajima Corporation; *Int'l*, pg. 4054
KAJIMA ASSOCIATE, INC.—See Kajima Corporation; *Int'l*, pg. 4054
KAJIMA AUSTRALIA PTY LTD—See Kajima Corporation; *Int'l*, pg. 4054
KAJIMA BUILDING & DESIGN GROUP, INC.—See Kajima Corporation; *Int'l*, pg. 4054
KAJIMA BUILDING & DESIGN, INC.—See Kajima Corporation; *Int'l*, pg. 4055
KAJIMA CORPORATION (CHINA) CO., LTD.—See Kajima Corporation; *Int'l*, pg. 4054
KAJIMA CORPORATION; *Int'l*, pg. 4054
KAJIMA CZECH DESIGN & CONSTRUCTION S.R.O.—See Kajima Corporation; *Int'l*, pg. 4054
KAJIMA DESIGN ASIA PTE. LTD.—See Kajima Corporation; *Int'l*, pg. 4055

COMPANY NAME INDEX

KAJIMA DEVELOPMENT CORPORATION—See Kajima Corporation; *Int'l*, pg. 4054
KAJIMA DEVELOPMENT PTE. LTD.—See Kajima Corporation; *Int'l*, pg. 4054
KAJIMA DEVELOPMENT PTE. LTD.—See Kajima Corporation; *Int'l*, pg. 4054
KAJIMA ESTATES (EUROPE) LTD.—See Kajima Corporation; *Int'l*, pg. 4054
KAJIMA EUROPE LOU ROUCAS S.A.R.L.—See Kajima Corporation; *Int'l*, pg. 4054
KAJIMA EUROPE S.A.S.—See Kajima Corporation; *Int'l*, pg. 4054
KAJIMA EUROPE U.K. HOLDING LTD.—See Kajima Corporation; *Int'l*, pg. 4054
KAJIMA FIT CO., LTD.—See Kajima Corporation; *Int'l*, pg. 4054
KAJIMA FRANCE DEVELOPMENT S.A.R.L.—See Kajima Corporation; *Int'l*, pg. 4054
KAJIMA INDIA PVT. LTD.—See Kajima Corporation; *Int'l*, pg. 4054
KAJIMA INFORMATION COMMUNICATION TECHNOLOGY CO., LTD.—See Kajima Corporation; *Int'l*, pg. 4054
KAJIMA INSTITUTE PUBLISHING CO., LTD.—See Kajima Corporation; *Int'l*, pg. 4054
KAJIMA INTERNATIONAL INC.—See Kajima Corporation; *Int'l*, pg. 4055
KAJIMA KRESS CO., LTD.—See Kajima Corporation; *Int'l*, pg. 4054
KAJIMA LEASING CORPORATION—See Kajima Corporation; *Int'l*, pg. 4054
KAJIMA (MALAYSIA) SDN. BHD.—See Kajima Corporation; *Int'l*, pg. 4055
KAJIMA MECHATRO ENGINEERING CO., LTD.—See Kajima Corporation; *Int'l*, pg. 4054
KAJIMA MYANMAR CO., LTD.—See Kajima Corporation; *Int'l*, pg. 4054
KAJIMA MYANMAR DEVELOPMENT & MANAGEMENT CO., LTD.—See Kajima Corporation; *Int'l*, pg. 4054
KAJIMA OVERSEAS ASIA PTE. LTD.—See Kajima Corporation; *Int'l*, pg. 4054
KAJIMA PARTNERSHIPS LTD.—See Kajima Corporation; *Int'l*, pg. 4054
KAJIMA PHILIPPINES INC.—See Kajima Corporation; *Int'l*, pg. 4055
KAJIMA POLAND SP. Z.O.O.—See Kajima Corporation; *Int'l*, pg. 4055
KAJIMA PROPERTY HOLDINGS LTD.—See Kajima Corporation; *Int'l*, pg. 4054
KAJIMA REAL ESTATE DEVELOPMENT INC.—See Kajima Corporation; *Int'l*, pg. 4055
KAJIMA REAL ESTATE INVESTMENT ADVISORS INC.—See Kajima Corporation; *Int'l*, pg. 4055
KAJIMA ROAD CO., LTD.—See Kajima Corporation; *Int'l*, pg. 4055
KAJIMA SHENYANG CONSTRUCTION MANAGEMENT & CONSULTING CO., LTD.—See Kajima Corporation; *Int'l*, pg. 4055
KAJIMA TATEMONO SOGO KANRI CO., LTD.—See Kajima Corporation; *Int'l*, pg. 4055
KAJIMA TECHNICAL RESEARCH INSTITUTE—See Kajima Corporation; *Int'l*, pg. 4055
KAJIMA TOHOKU KOUSAN CO., LTD.—See Kajima Corporation; *Int'l*, pg. 4055
KAJIMA U.S.A. INC.—See Kajima Corporation; *Int'l*, pg. 4055
KAJIMA VIETNAM CO., LTD.—See Kajima Corporation; *Int'l*, pg. 4055
KAJIMA YAESU KAIHATSU CO., LTD.—See Kajima Corporation; *Int'l*, pg. 4055
KAJITAKU INC.—See AEON Co., Ltd.; *Int'l*, pg. 177
KAJI TECHNOLOGY CORPORATION—See Mitsui E&S Holdings Co., Ltd.; *Int'l*, pg. 4984
KAJIYAMA WAREHOUSE CO., LTD.—See J Trust Co., Ltd.; *Int'l*, pg. 3853
KAJ LARSEN COMMUNICATION A/S—See Aiphone Co., Ltd.; *Int'l*, pg. 235
KAJOMI GMBH—See Stroer SE & Co. KGaA; *Int'l*, pg. 7242
KAJO NEUKIRCHEN MANAGEMENT UND BETEILIGUNGS GMBH; *Int'l*, pg. 4056
KAJUN KETTLE FOODS, INC.; *U.S. Private*, pg. 2256
KAKA AB—See Orkla ASA; *Int'l*, pg. 5637
KAKA INDUSTRIES LIMITED; *Int'l*, pg. 4056
KAKAKU.COM INC.; *Int'l*, pg. 4056
KAKAKU.COM INSURANCE, INC.—See Kakaku.Com Inc.; *Int'l*, pg. 4056
KAKAOBANK CORP.; *Int'l*, pg. 4056
KAKAO CORPORATION; *Int'l*, pg. 4056
KAKAO GAMES CORP.; *Int'l*, pg. 4056
KAKAO M.—See Kakao Corporation; *Int'l*, pg. 4056
KAKAOPAY CORPORATION; *Int'l*, pg. 4056
KAKATIYA CEMENT SUGAR & INDUSTRIES LIMITED - CEMENT WORKS—See Kakatiya Cement Sugar & Industries Limited; *Int'l*, pg. 4056
KAKATIYA CEMENT SUGAR & INDUSTRIES LIMITED; *Int'l*, pg. 4056

KAKATIYA CEMENT SUGAR & INDUSTRIES LIMITED - SUGAR WORKS—See Kakatiya Cement Sugar & Industries Limited; *Int'l*, pg. 4056
KAKATIYA TEXTILES LIMITED; *Int'l*, pg. 4056
KAKEL MAX AB; *Int'l*, pg. 4056
KAKEN PHARMACEUTICAL CO., LTD.; *Int'l*, pg. 4056
KAKEN SHOYAKU INC.—See Sawai Group Holdings Co., Ltd.; *Int'l*, pg. 6602
KAKE-TV—See Lockwood Broadcasting Inc.; *U.S. Private*, pg. 2478
KAKIVIK ASSET MANAGEMENT, LLC—See Bristol Bay Native Corporation; *U.S. Private*, pg. 656
KAKIYASU HONTEN CO., LTD.; *Int'l*, pg. 4056
KAKNES LANDSCAPE SUPPLY, INC.—See SiteOne Landscape Supply, Inc.; *U.S. Public*, pg. 1888
KA KOLN ASSEKURANZ.AGENTUR GMBH—See Munchener Ruckversicherungs AG; *Int'l*, pg. 5089
KAKTUS SPORTSWEAR INC.; *U.S. Private*, pg. 2256
KAKUNODATE SHIBAURA ELECTRONICS CO., LTD.—See Shibaura Electronics Co., Ltd.; *Int'l*, pg. 6827
KAKUTAMA SERVICE CO., LTD.—See Arakawa Chemical Industries, Ltd.; *Int'l*, pg. 534
KAKUYASU GROUP CO., LTD.; *Int'l*, pg. 4056
KAKUZI PLC—See Camellia Plc; *Int'l*, pg. 1271
KALABAKAN PLYWOOD SDN. BHD.—See Tekala Corporation Berhad; *Int'l*, pg. 7526
KALA BIO, INC.; *U.S. Public*, pg. 1213
KALAHARI DRY (THAILAND) CO., LTD.—See Taiheiyo Cement Corporation; *Int'l*, pg. 7411
KALAHARI GOLDRIDGE MINING CO LTD—See Harmony Gold Mining Company Limited; *Int'l*, pg. 3278
KALAHARI LIMITED—See BGC Group, Inc.; *U.S. Public*, pg. 329
KALAHARI MEDICAL DISTRIBUTORS (PROPRIETARY) LIMITED—See Clicks Group Limited; *Int'l*, pg. 1658
KALAHARI MINERALS PLC—See China Development Bank Corporation; *Int'l*, pg. 1497
KALAHARI MINERALS PLC—See China Guangdong Nuclear Power Holding Co., Ltd.; *Int'l*, pg. 1506
KALAHARI.NET—See Naspers Limited; *Int'l*, pg. 5148
KALALOU INC.; *U.S. Private*, pg. 2256
KALAMA EXPORTS LLC; *U.S. Private*, pg. 2256
KALAMARAKIS SAPOUNAS SA—See Max Weishaupt GmbH; *Int'l*, pg. 4735
KALAMAZOO DERMATOLOGY, P.C.—See Harvest Partners L.P.; *U.S. Private*, pg. 1876
KALAMAZOO FABRICATING—See Prab, Inc.; *U.S. Private*, pg. 3241
KALAMAZOO HOLDINGS, INC.; *U.S. Private*, pg. 2256
KALAMAZOO RESOURCES LIMITED; *Int'l*, pg. 4057
KALAMAZOO TRUCK SALES INC.; *U.S. Private*, pg. 2257
KALAMUNDA HOTEL (WA) PTY LTD—See Woolworths Group Limited; *Int'l*, pg. 8451
KALANEUVOS OY; *Int'l*, pg. 4057
KALARI HOLDINGS PTY LTD—See John Swire & Sons Limited; *Int'l*, pg. 3980
KALARI PTY LTD—See Qube Holdings Limited; *Int'l*, pg. 6158
KALAS MANUFACTURING, INC.; *U.S. Private*, pg. 2257
KALATUKKU E. ERIKSSON OY—See Kesko Corporation; *Int'l*, pg. 4142
KALAYAAN LAND CORPORATION—See Kimberly-Clark Corporation; *U.S. Public*, pg. 1229
KALBE INTERNATIONAL PTE. LTD.—See PT Kalbe Farma Tbk.; *Int'l*, pg. 6050
KALBE MALAYSIA SDN. BHD.—See PT Kalbe Farma Tbk.; *Int'l*, pg. 6050
KALBER DAIRY J.S. CO.; *Int'l*, pg. 4057
KALBE VISION PTE. LTD.—See PT Kalbe Farma Tbk.; *Int'l*, pg. 6050
KALB-TV NEWS CHANNEL 5—See Gray Television, Inc.; *U.S. Public*, pg. 960
KALCON (PTY) LTD.—See Wilson Bayly Holmes-Ovcon Limited; *Int'l*, pg. 8422
KALDERA COMPANY D.O.O.; *Int'l*, pg. 4057
KA' LE BAY SEAFOODS LTD—See Louisbourg Seafoods Ltd.; *Int'l*, pg. 4563
KALE ENVIRONMENTAL TECHNOLOGY (SHANGHAI) CO., LTD.; *Int'l*, pg. 4057
KALEGRAN LTD.—See MOL Magyar Olaj- es Gazipari Nyrt.; *Int'l*, pg. 5020
KALEIDA HEALTH; *U.S. Private*, pg. 2257
KALEIDESCAPE, INC.; *U.S. Private*, pg. 2257
KALEIDO BIOSCIENCES, INC.; *U.S. Public*, pg. 1213
KALEIDOSCOPE—See Omnicom Group Inc.; *U.S. Public*, pg. 1586
KALEKIM KIMYEVI MADDELER SANAYI VE TICARET A.S.; *Int'l*, pg. 4057
KAL ENERGY, INC.; *Int'l*, pg. 4057
KALERA PUBLIC LIMITED COMPANY; *U.S. Public*, pg. 1213
KALESERAMIK CANAKKALE KALEBODUR SERAMIK SANAYI A.S.; *Int'l*, pg. 4057
KALEX CIRCUIT BOARD (CHINA) LIMITED—See TTM Technologies, Inc.; *U.S. Public*, pg. 2203
KALEXSYN, INC.—See Dipharma Francis S.r.l.; *Int'l*, pg. 2128

KALEYRA, INC.; *U.S. Public*, pg. 1213
KALFANY SUSSE WERBUNG GMBH & CO. KG—See Zertus GmbH; *Int'l*, pg. 8639
KALF ENGINEERING PTE. LTD.—See UMS Holdings Limited; *Int'l*, pg. 8027
KALGOORLIE CONSOLIDATED GOLD MINES PTY LTD—See Northern Star Resources Ltd; *Int'l*, pg. 5444
KALGOORLIE GOLD MINING LIMITED; *Int'l*, pg. 4057
KALGOORLIE POWER SYSTEMS—See QIC Limited; *Int'l*, pg. 6141
KAL GROUP LIMITED; *Int'l*, pg. 4057
KALI AG—See K+S Aktiengesellschaft; *Int'l*, pg. 4041
KALIAKRA WIND POWER AD—See Mitsubishi Heavy Industries, Ltd.; *Int'l*, pg. 4954
KALIAN CORPORATION; *U.S. Private*, pg. 2257
KALIBRATE TECHNOLOGIES LTD.—See Hanover Investors Management LLP; *Int'l*, pg. 3258
KALIDA MANUFACTURING, INC.—See H-One Co., Ltd.; *Int'l*, pg. 3194
KALIDO INC.—See TA Associates, Inc.; *U.S. Private*, pg. 3915
KALIFF INSURANCE—See Scottish American Insurance General Agency, Inc.; *U.S. Private*, pg. 3578
KALIHI-PALAMA HEALTH CENTER; *U.S. Private*, pg. 2257
KALIKA LAGHUBITTA BITTIYA SANSTHA LTD.; *Int'l*, pg. 4057
KALILA MEDICAL, INC.—See Abbott Laboratories; *U.S. Public*, pg. 20
KALIL BOTTLING CO., INC.; *U.S. Private*, pg. 2257
KALINA POWER LIMITED; *Int'l*, pg. 4057
KALIN ENTERPRISES, INC.; *U.S. Private*, pg. 2257
KALIN FINANCIAL DIVISION—See Kalin Enterprises, Inc.; *U.S. Private*, pg. 2257
KALINGANAGAR SPECIAL STEEL PRIVATE LIMITED—See Balaji Amines Limited; *Int'l*, pg. 806
KALINGANAGAR SPECIAL STEEL PRIVATE LIMITED—See VISA Steel Limited; *Int'l*, pg. 8249
KALIO, INC.; *U.S. Private*, pg. 2257
KALISTRUT AEROSPACE S.A.S.—See Berkshire Hathaway Inc.; *U.S. Public*, pg. 314
KALITTA AIR, LLC; *U.S. Private*, pg. 2257
KALITTA CHARTERS, LLC.—See Kalitta Air, LLC; *U.S. Private*, pg. 2257
KALITTA TURBINE LEASING, LLC—See Kalitta Air, LLC; *U.S. Private*, pg. 2257
KALIUM LAKES LIMITED; *Int'l*, pg. 4057
KALI-UNION VERWALTUNGSGESELLSCHAFT MBH—See K+S Aktiengesellschaft; *Int'l*, pg. 4041
KALIX—See Coesia S.p.A.; *Int'l*, pg. 1690
KALIX; *U.S. Private*, pg. 2257
KALIZEA POLSKA SP.Z.O.O.—See Vivescia; *Int'l*, pg. 8279
KALIZEA S.A.S.—See Vivescia; *Int'l*, pg. 8279
KALKREUTH ROOFING & SHEETMETAL INC.; *U.S. Private*, pg. 2257
KALKSANDSTEINWERK AMBERG GMBH & CO. KG—See Heidelberg Materials AG; *Int'l*, pg. 3317
KAL KUSTOM ENTERPRISES; *U.S. Private*, pg. 2256
KALLAM TEXTILES LIMITED; *Int'l*, pg. 4057
KALLE AUSTRIA GMBH—See Clayton, Dubilier & Rice, LLC; *U.S. Private*, pg. 926
KALLEBACK PROPERTY INVEST AB; *Int'l*, pg. 4057
KALLE CHILE S.A.—See Clayton, Dubilier & Rice, LLC; *U.S. Private*, pg. 926
KALLE CZ, S.R.O.—See Clayton, Dubilier & Rice, LLC; *U.S. Private*, pg. 926
KALLE GMBH—See Clayton, Dubilier & Rice, LLC; *U.S. Private*, pg. 925
KALLE NALO POLSKA SP. Z O.O.—See Clayton, Dubilier & Rice, LLC; *U.S. Private*, pg. 926
KALLE NORDIC APS—See Clayton, Dubilier & Rice, LLC; *U.S. Private*, pg. 926
KALLESOE MACHINERY A/S—See Durr AG; *Int'l*, pg. 2233
KALLE USA INC.—See Clayton, Dubilier & Rice, LLC; *U.S. Private*, pg. 926
KALLFASS FRANCE SAS—See Kallfass Verpackungsmaschinen GmbH; *Int'l*, pg. 4057
KALLFASS VERPACKUNGSMASCHINEN GMBH; *Int'l*, pg. 4057
KALLIDUS INC.; *U.S. Private*, pg. 2257
KALLISTA, INC.—See Kohler Company; *U.S. Private*, pg. 2339
KALLO FOODS LTD—See PAI Partners S.A.S.; *Int'l*, pg. 5700
KALLO, INC.; *Int'l*, pg. 4057
KALLONI S.A.—See Hellenic Fishfarming S.A.; *Int'l*, pg. 3333
KALMAN FLOOR COMPANY; *U.S. Private*, pg. 2257
KALMAR AUSTRIA GMBH—See Cargotec Corporation; *Int'l*, pg. 1327
KALMAR BELGIUM NV/SA—See Cargotec Corporation; *Int'l*, pg. 1327
KALMAR B.V.—See Cargotec Corporation; *Int'l*, pg. 1327
KALMAR DANMARK A/S—See Cargotec Corporation; *Int'l*, pg. 1327
KALMAR EQUIPMENT (AUSTRALIA) PTY. LTD.—See Cargotec Corporation; *Int'l*, pg. 1327

KALMAR FRANCE S.A.—See Cargotec Corporation; *Int'l*, pg. 1327
KALMAR GERMANY GMBH—See Cargotec Corporation; *Int'l*, pg. 1328
KALMAR HEBEFAHRZEUGE HANDELSGESMBH—See Cargotec Corporation; *Int'l*, pg. 1327
KALMAR INDUSTRIES AB—See Cargotec Corporation; *Int'l*, pg. 1327
KALMAR INDUSTRIES CORPORATION—See Cargotec Corporation; *Int'l*, pg. 1327
KALMAR INDUSTRIES MAGNUM DIVISION—See Cargotec Corporation; *Int'l*, pg. 1327
KALMAR INDUSTRIES OY AB—See Cargotec Corporation; *Int'l*, pg. 1327
KALMAR INDUSTRIES SOUTH AFRICA (PTY) LTD—See Cargotec Corporation; *Int'l*, pg. 1327
KALMAR ITALIA S.R.L.—See Cargotec Corporation; *Int'l*, pg. 1328
KALMAR LTD.—See Cargotec Corporation; *Int'l*, pg. 1327
KALMAR MIDDLE EAST DMCC—See Cargotec Corporation; *Int'l*, pg. 1328
KALMAR NETHERLANDS B.V.—See Cargotec Corporation; *Int'l*, pg. 1328
KALMAR NORWAY AS—See Cargotec Corporation; *Int'l*, pg. 1327
KALMAR PORT MACHINERY (SHENZHEN) CO., LTD—See Cargotec Corporation; *Int'l*, pg. 1327
KALMAR PORTUGAL, S.A.—See Cargotec Corporation; *Int'l*, pg. 1328
KALMAR SOUTH EAST ASIA PTE. LTD.—See Cargotec Corporation; *Int'l*, pg. 1327
KALMAR SPAIN CARGO HANDLING SOLUTIONS S.A.—See Cargotec Corporation; *Int'l*, pg. 1328
KALMAR TURKEY YUK TASIMA SISTEMLERI ANONIM SIRKETI—See Cargotec Corporation; *Int'l*, pg. 1328
KALMAR USA INC.—See Cargotec Corporation; *Int'l*, pg. 1327
KALMBACH FEEDS, INC.; *U.S. Private*, pg. 2257
KALMBACH PUBLISHING CO.; *U.S. Private*, pg. 2257
KALNIN VENTURES LLC; *U.S. Private*, pg. 2258
KALNORTH GOLD MINES LIMITED; *Int'l*, pg. 4057
KALO GOLD CORP.; *Int'l*, pg. 4057
KALO, INC.; *U.S. Private*, pg. 2258
KALONA COOPERATIVE TELEPHONE COMPANY; *U.S. Private*, pg. 2258
KALON ACQUISITION CORP.; *Int'l*, pg. 4058
KALORIMETA GMBH; *Int'l*, pg. 4058
KALOS, INC.—See Fusion Health Technologies Corporation; *U.S. Private*, pg. 1625
KALOTI ENTERPRISES INC.; *U.S. Private*, pg. 2258
KALPA COMMERCIAL LIMITED; *Int'l*, pg. 4058
KALPATARU LTD.; *Int'l*, pg. 4058
KALPATARU POWER TRANSMISSION LIMITED—See Kalpataru Ltd.; *Int'l*, pg. 4058
KALPATARU POWER TRANSMISSION LTD. - BIOMASS ENERGY DIVISION—See Kalpataru Ltd.; *Int'l*, pg. 4058
KALPATARU POWER TRANSMISSION LTD. - GANDHINAGAR PLANT—See Kalpataru Ltd.; *Int'l*, pg. 4058
KALPATARU POWER TRANSMISSION USA INC.—See Kalpataru Ltd.; *Int'l*, pg. 4058
KALPATARU PROPERTIES (THANE) PVT. LTD.—See Kalpataru Ltd.; *Int'l*, pg. 4058
KALPATARU SATPURA TRANSCO PRIVATE LIMITED.—See Kalpataru Ltd.; *Int'l*, pg. 4058
KALRAY SA; *Int'l*, pg. 4058
KALREZ PETROLEUM (SERAM) LIMITED; *Int'l*, pg. 4058
KALSEC, INC.—See Kalamazoo Holdings, Inc.; *U.S. Private*, pg. 2257
KALSEP UK LTD.—See RLR, Inc.; *U.S. Private*, pg. 3451
KALSHOVEN AUTOMATION B.V.—See Advent International Corporation; *U.S. Private*, pg. 97
KALSHOVEN AUTOMATION B.V.—See Centerbridge Partners, L.P.; *U.S. Private*, pg. 813
KALSTAR ENTERPRISES LLC—See Kane Is Able, Inc.; *U.S. Private*, pg. 2260
KALTE 3000 AG—See Burkhalter Holding AG; *Int'l*, pg. 1225
KALTE ECKERT GMBH—See Triton Advisers Limited; *Int'l*, pg. 7931
KALTEHELDEN GMBH—See MEDIQON Group AG; *Int'l*, pg. 4780
KALTENBACH & VOIGT GMBH—See Danaher Corporation; *U.S. Public*, pg. 627
KALTHOFF LUFTFILTER UND FILTERMEDIEN GMBH; *Int'l*, pg. 4058
KALTURA, INC.; *U.S. Public*, pg. 1213
KALTURA LTD.—See Kaltura, Inc.; *U.S. Public*, pg. 1213
KALTY & SALIOS SALES INC.; *U.S. Private*, pg. 2258
KALUGA TURBINE WORKS OJSC—See OOO Severgrupp; *Int'l*, pg. 5594
KALUGSK SBYT COMPANY AO; *Int'l*, pg. 4058
K&A LUMBER COMPANY INC.—See Stock Building Supply; *U.S. Private*, pg. 3814
KALVISTA PHARMACEUTICALS, INC.; *U.S. Public*, pg. 1214
KALWALL CORPORATION; *U.S. Private*, pg. 2258
KALYAN CAPITALS LTD.; *Int'l*, pg. 4058

KALYANI CARPENTER SPECIAL STEELS LTD.—See Kalyani Group; *Int'l*, pg. 4059
KALYANI COMMERCIALS LIMITED; *Int'l*, pg. 4058
KALYANI FORGE LIMITED—See Kalyani Group; *Int'l*, pg. 4059
KALYANI GROUP; *Int'l*, pg. 4058
KALYANI INFOTECH SOLUTIONS LTD.—See Kalyani Group; *Int'l*, pg. 4059
KALYANI INVESTMENT COMPANY LIMITED; *Int'l*, pg. 4059
KALYANI STEELS LTD; *Int'l*, pg. 4059
KALYANI TECHNOFORGE LIMITED - BARAMATI PLANT—See Kalyani Group; *Int'l*, pg. 4059
KALYANI TECHNOFORGE LIMITED - MANESAR PLANT—See Kalyani Group; *Int'l*, pg. 4059
KALYANI TECHNOFORGE LIMITED - RANJANGAON PLANT—See Kalyani Group; *Int'l*, pg. 4059
KALYANI TECHNOFORGE LIMITED—See Kalyani Group; *Int'l*, pg. 4059
KALYANI TECHNOLOGIES LTD.—See Kalyani Group; *Int'l*, pg. 4059
KALYAN JEWELLERS FOR GOLDEN JEWELRY COMPANY, W.L.L—See Kalyan Jewellers India Limited; *Int'l*, pg. 4058
KALYAN JEWELLERS FZE—See Kalyan Jewellers India Limited; *Int'l*, pg. 4058
KALYAN JEWELLERS INDIA LIMITED; *Int'l*, pg. 4058
KALYAN JEWELLERS LLC—See Kalyan Jewellers India Limited; *Int'l*, pg. 4058
KALYANPUR CEMENTS LIMITED; *Int'l*, pg. 4059
KALYPSO, LP—See Rockwell Automation, Inc.; *U.S. Public*, pg. 3589
KALZIP ASIA PTE LIMITED—See Mutares SE & Co. KGaA; *Int'l*, pg. 5104
KALZIP FRANCE S.A.S.—See Mutares SE & Co. KGaA; *Int'l*, pg. 5105
KALZIP FZE—See Mutares SE & Co. KGaA; *Int'l*, pg. 5104
KALZIP GMBH—See Mutares SE & Co. KGaA; *Int'l*, pg. 5104
KALZIP GMBH—See Mutares SE & Co. KGaA; *Int'l*, pg. 5104
KALZIP GUANGZHOU LIMITED—See Mutares SE & Co. KGaA; *Int'l*, pg. 5104
KALZIP INC—See Mutares SE & Co. KGaA; *Int'l*, pg. 5104
KALZIP INDIA PRIVATE LIMITED—See Mutares SE & Co. KGaA; *Int'l*, pg. 5104
KALZIP ITALY SRL—See Mutares SE & Co. KGaA; *Int'l*, pg. 5104
KALZIP LIMITED—See Mutares SE & Co. KGaA; *Int'l*, pg. 5104
KALZIP LTD.—See Mutares SE & Co. KGaA; *Int'l*, pg. 5105
KALZIP SPAIN S.L.U.—See Mutares SE & Co. KGaA; *Int'l*, pg. 5104
KAMAAINA KIDS; *U.S. Private*, pg. 2258
KAMA CO., LTD.—See China Hi-Tech Group Corporation; *Int'l*, pg. 1508
KAMADA LTD.; *Int'l*, pg. 4059
KAMADGIRI FASHION LTD.; *Int'l*, pg. 4059
KAMA FRITID AB—See KABE Group AB; *Int'l*, pg. 4046
KAMA HOLDINGS LIMITED; *Int'l*, pg. 4059
KAMA INDUSTRIES LIMITED—See Aspen Pharmacare Holdings Limited; *Int'l*, pg. 629
KAMAISHI KOZAN CO., LTD.—See Nittetsu Mining Co., Ltd.; *Int'l*, pg. 5383
KAMAKEE DIALYSIS, LLC—See DaVita Inc.; *U.S. Public*, pg. 640
KAMAKURA CORPORATION—See SAS Institute Inc.; *U.S. Private*, pg. 3551
KAMAKURA INDUSTRY CO., LTD.—See UACJ Corporation; *Int'l*, pg. 7999
KAMAKURA JITAKU SOUGISHA INC.—See KAYAC Inc.; *Int'l*, pg. 4101
KAMAKURA SHINSHO, LTD.; *Int'l*, pg. 4059
KAMAKURA TECHNO-SCIENCE INC.—See Toray Industries, Inc.; *Int'l*, pg. 7823
KAMAL CORP.—See Trade Fair Corp.; *U.S. Private*, pg. 4201
KAMALI LEATHER LLC; *U.S. Private*, pg. 2258
KAMANA BIKASH BANK LIMITED—See Kamana Sewa Bikas Bank Ltd.; *Int'l*, pg. 4060
KAMAN AEROSPACE CORPORATION—See Arcline Investment Management LP; *U.S. Private*, pg. 314
KAMAN AEROSPACE GROUP, INC.—See Arcline Investment Management LP; *U.S. Private*, pg. 314
KAMANA SEWA BIKAS BANK LTD.; *Int'l*, pg. 4060
KAMAN AUTOMATION, INC.—See Littlejohn & Co., LLC; *U.S. Private*, pg. 2471
KAMAN COMPOSITES - UK HOLDINGS LIMITED—See Arcline Investment Management LP; *U.S. Private*, pg. 314
KAMAN COMPOSITES - VERMONT, INC.—See Arcline Investment Management LP; *U.S. Private*, pg. 314
KAMAN COMPOSITES - WICHITA, INC.—See Arcline Investment Management LP; *U.S. Private*, pg. 314
KAMAN CORPORATION—See Arcline Investment Management LP; *U.S. Private*, pg. 314
KAMAN ENGINEERING SERVICES, INC.—See Arcline Investment Management LP; *U.S. Private*, pg. 314

KAMAN FABRICATED PRODUCTS LIMITED—See Arcline Investment Management LP; *U.S. Private*, pg. 314
KAMAN FLUID POWER, LLC—See Littlejohn & Co., LLC; *U.S. Private*, pg. 2471
KAMAN INDUSTRIAL TECHNOLOGIES CORPORATION—See Littlejohn & Co., LLC; *U.S. Private*, pg. 2470
KAMAN MUSIC CORPORATION—See TPG Capital, L.P.; *U.S. Public*, pg. 2173
KAMAN PRECISION PRODUCTS, INC. - MIDDLETOWN—See Arcline Investment Management LP; *U.S. Private*, pg. 314
KAMAN PRECISION PRODUCTS, INC.—See Arcline Investment Management LP; *U.S. Private*, pg. 314
KAMAN'S ART SHOPPES INC.; *U.S. Private*, pg. 2258
KAMAN SPECIALTY BEARINGS & ENGINEERED PRODUCTS, GMBH—See Arcline Investment Management LP; *U.S. Private*, pg. 314
KAMANWALA HOUSING CONSTRUCTION LIMITED; *Int'l*, pg. 4060
KAMAPIM LTD.—See Floridienne SA; *Int'l*, pg. 2708
KAMA RESOURCES INC.; *Int'l*, pg. 4059
KAMAT HOTELS INDIA LTD; *Int'l*, pg. 4060
KAMATICS CORPORATION—See Arcline Investment Management LP; *U.S. Private*, pg. 314
KAMAX AUTOMOTIVE FASTENERS (CHINA) CO., LTD.—See KAMAX-Werke Rudolf Kellermann GmbH & Co. KG; *Int'l*, pg. 4060
KAMAX AUTOMOTIVE GMBH—See KAMAX-Werke Rudolf Kellermann GmbH & Co. KG; *Int'l*, pg. 4060
KAMAX GMBH & CO. KG—See KAMAX-Werke Rudolf Kellermann GmbH & Co. KG; *Int'l*, pg. 4060
KAMAX K.K.—See KAMAX-Werke Rudolf Kellermann GmbH & Co. KG; *Int'l*, pg. 4060
KAMAX K.S.—See KAMAX-Werke Rudolf Kellermann GmbH & Co. KG; *Int'l*, pg. 4060
KAMAX L.P.—See KAMAX-Werke Rudolf Kellermann GmbH & Co. KG; *Int'l*, pg. 4060
KAMAX S.A.U.—See KAMAX-Werke Rudolf Kellermann GmbH & Co. KG; *Int'l*, pg. 4060
KAMAX S.R.O.—See KAMAX-Werke Rudolf Kellermann GmbH & Co. KG; *Int'l*, pg. 4060
KAMAX-WERKE RUDOLF KELLERMANN GMBH & CO. KG; *Int'l*, pg. 4060
KAMAX (ZHENJIANG) AUTOMOTIVE FASTENERS TRADING CO., LTD.—See KAMAX-Werke Rudolf Kellermann GmbH & Co. KG; *Int'l*, pg. 4060
KAMAYA ELECTRIC CO., LTD.—See Walsin Technology Corporation; *Int'l*, pg. 8335
KAMAYA ELECTRIC (HK) LIMITED—See Walsin Technology Corporation; *Int'l*, pg. 8335
KAMAYA ELECTRIC(M) SDN. BHD.—See Walsin Technology Corporation; *Int'l*, pg. 8335
KAMAYA ELECTRONIC CO., LTD.—See Walsin Technology Corporation; *Int'l*, pg. 8335
KAMAYA, INC.—See Walsin Technology Corporation; *Int'l*, pg. 8335
KAMAYA KAGAKU KOGYO CO. LTD.; *Int'l*, pg. 4060
KAMAZ-ENERGO LLC—See KAMAZ Publicly Traded Company; *Int'l*, pg. 4060
KAMAZ-ENGINEERING JSC—See KAMAZ Publicly Traded Company; *Int'l*, pg. 4060
KAMAZ INTERNATIONAL TRADE COMPANY JSC—See KAMAZ Publicly Traded Company; *Int'l*, pg. 4060
KAMAZ PUBLICLY TRADED COMPANY; *Int'l*, pg. 4060
KAMAZZHILBYT LLC—See KAMAZ Publicly Traded Company; *Int'l*, pg. 4060
KAMBAL INTERNATIONAL CO.—See Dar Al Dawa Development & Investment Co.; *Int'l*, pg. 1971
KAMBI GROUP PLC; *Int'l*, pg. 4060
KAMBI MALTA LIMITED—See Kambi Group PLC; *Int'l*, pg. 4060
KAMBI PHILIPPINES INC.—See Kambi Group PLC; *Int'l*, pg. 4060
KAMBI SERVICES LIMITED—See Kambi Group PLC; *Int'l*, pg. 4060
KAMBI SWEDEN AB—See Kambi Group PLC; *Int'l*, pg. 4060
KAMBO LOCKSETS LIMITED—See Intelligent Living Application Group Inc.; *Int'l*, pg. 3734
KAM-BUS DD—See I Squared Capital Advisors (US) LLC; *U.S. Private*, pg. 2024
KAMCHATSKENERGO; *Int'l*, pg. 4061
KAMCO BUILDING SUPPLY CORPORATION OF PENNSYLVANIA—See Kamco Supply Corporation; *U.S. Private*, pg. 2258
KAMCO INVESTMENT COMPANY K.S.C.C.—See Kuwait Projects Company (Holding) K.S.C.P.; *Int'l*, pg. 4347
KAMCO INVESTMENT COMPANY SAUDI W.L.L.—See Kuwait Projects Company (Holding) K.S.C.P.; *Int'l*, pg. 4346
KAMCO SUPPLY CORPORATION OF BOSTON - KAMCO/O'CONNOR DOOR DIVISION—See Kamco Supply Corporation; *U.S. Private*, pg. 2258
KAMCO SUPPLY CORPORATION OF BOSTON - MAINE DOOR DIVISION—See Kamco Supply Corporation; *U.S. Private*, pg. 2258

COMPANY NAME INDEX

KAMCO SUPPLY CORPORATION OF BOSTON - MASSACHUSETTS DOOR DIVISION—See Kamco Supply Corporation; *U.S. Private*, pg. 2258
KAMCO SUPPLY CORPORATION OF BOSTON—See Kamco Supply Corporation; *U.S. Private*, pg. 2258
KAMCO SUPPLY CORPORATION OF NEW ENGLAND—See Kamco Supply Corporation; *U.S. Private*, pg. 2258
KAMCO SUPPLY CORPORATION; *U.S. Private*, pg. 2258
KAMCO SUPPLY CORPORATION—See GMS Inc.; *U.S. Public*, pg. 949
KAMCO SUPPLY OF NJ, LLC—See Kamco Supply Corporation; *U.S. Private*, pg. 2258
KAM-CRETE LTD.—See Bird Construction Inc.; *Int'l*, pg. 1047
KAMC-TV—See Mission Broadcasting, Inc.; *U.S. Private*, pg. 2747
KAMDAR (BRU) SDN. BHD.—See Kamdar Group (M) Berhad; *Int'l*, pg. 4061
KAMDAR GROUP (M) BERHAD; *Int'l*, pg. 4061
KAMDAR SDN. BERHAD—See Kamdar Group (M) Berhad; *Int'l*, pg. 4061
KAMDAR (SOUTH) SDN. BHD.—See Kamdar Group (M) Berhad; *Int'l*, pg. 4061
KAMDHENU LTD; *Int'l*, pg. 4061
KAMEDA SEIKA CO., LTD.; *Int'l*, pg. 4061
KAMEDA USA, INC.—See Kameda Seika Co., Ltd.; *Int'l*, pg. 4061
KAMEDDATA.COM, INC; *U.S. Private*, pg. 2258
KAMEI AUTO HOKKAIDO CORPORATION—See Kamei Corporation; *Int'l*, pg. 4061
KAMEI CORPORATION; *Int'l*, pg. 4061
KAMEI PROACT CORPORATION—See Kamei Corporation; *Int'l*, pg. 4061
KAME, LLC—See Sinclair, Inc.; *U.S. Public*, pg. 1885
KAMEN & CO.; *U.S. Private*, pg. 2258
KAMENI AGREGATI A.D.; *Int'l*, pg. 4062
KAMEN INDUSTRIAL SUPPLIES INC.—See Kamen Industrial Technologies; *U.S. Private*, pg. 2258
KAMEN INDUSTRIAL TECHNOLOGIES; *U.S. Private*, pg. 2258
KAMENITZA AD—See Anheuser-Busch InBev SA/NV; *Int'l*, pg. 466
KAMENIVO SLOVAKIA A.S.—See Heidelberg Materials AG; *Int'l*, pg. 3317
KAMENOLO MY CR S.R.O.—See STRABAG SE; *Int'l*, pg. 7231
KAMENOLOMY SR , S.R.O.—See STRABAG SE; *Int'l*, pg. 7231
KAMENSK-URALSKY METALLURGICAL WORKS J.S.CO; *Int'l*, pg. 4062
KAMES CAPITAL—See Aegon N.V.; *Int'l*, pg. 174
KAMEX LTD.—See Triumph Group, Inc.; *U.S. Public*, pg. 2196
KAMEYAMA CO., LTD.; *Int'l*, pg. 4062
KAM HING GLOBAL GARMENT COMPANY LIMITED—See Kam Hing International Holdings Limited; *Int'l*, pg. 4059
KAM HING INTERNATIONAL HOLDINGS LIMITED; *Int'l*, pg. 4059
KAM HING PIECE WORKS LIMITED—See Kam Hing International Holdings Limited; *Int'l*, pg. 4059
KAM HING PIECE WORKS (S) PTE LIMITED—See Kam Hing International Holdings Limited; *Int'l*, pg. 4059
KAM HING TEXTILE MACAO COMMERCIAL OFFSHORE COMPANY LIMITED—See Kam Hing International Holdings Limited; *Int'l*, pg. 4059
KAM HON PRINTING (SHENZHEN) CO., LTD.—See Neway Group Holdings Limited; *Int'l*, pg. 5232
KAMIAH DIALYSIS, LLC—See DaVita Inc.; *U.S. Public*, pg. 640
KAMI BUILDERS SDN BHD—See QI Ltd.; *Int'l*, pg. 6139
KAMIC AB—See Amplex AB; *Int'l*, pg. 4114
KAMIC COMPONENTS AB—See Amplex AB; *Int'l*, pg. 434
KAMIC INSTALLATION OY—See Amplex AB; *Int'l*, pg. 434
KAMIC LIGHT & SAFETY AB—See Amplex AB; *Int'l*, pg. 434
KAMI COLOURCERA PVT LTD.—See Keda Industrial Group Co., Ltd.; *Int'l*, pg. 4114
KAMIC SECURITY AB—See Amplex AB; *Int'l*, pg. 434
KAMIENINIU LASTELIU BANKAS UAB IMUNOLITA—See VITA 34 AG; *Int'l*, pg. 8257
KAMIGUMI AIR SERVICE CO., LTD.—See Kamigumi Co., Ltd.; *Int'l*, pg. 4062
KAMIGUMI CO., LTD. - HEAVY CARGO & ENERGY CARGO TRANSPORTATION DIVISION—See Kamigumi Co., Ltd.; *Int'l*, pg. 4062
KAMIGUMI CO., LTD. - INTERNATIONAL LOGISTICS DIVISION—See Kamigumi Co., Ltd.; *Int'l*, pg. 4062
KAMIGUMI CO., LTD. - PORT LOGISTICS DIVISION—See Kamigumi Co., Ltd.; *Int'l*, pg. 4062
KAMIGUMI CO., LTD.—See Kamigumi Co., Ltd.; *Int'l*, pg. 4062
KAMIGUMI CO., LTD.—See Kamigumi Co., Ltd.; *Int'l*, pg. 4062
KAMIGUMI CO., LTD.; *Int'l*, pg. 4062

KAMIGUMI-EFR LOGISTICS (MYANMAR) CO., LTD—See Kamigumi Co., Ltd.; *Int'l*, pg. 4062
KAMIGUMI GLOBAL SOLUTIONS MALAYSIA SDN. BHD.—See Kamigumi Co., Ltd.; *Int'l*, pg. 4062
KAMIGUMI (HONG KONG) CO., LTD.—See Kamigumi Co., Ltd.; *Int'l*, pg. 4062
KAMIGUMI INTERNATIONAL FORWADING (SHENZHEN) CO., LTD.—See Kamigumi Co., Ltd.; *Int'l*, pg. 4062
KAMIGUMI INTERNATIONAL FORWARDING (SHANGHAI) CO., LTD.—See Kamigumi Co., Ltd.; *Int'l*, pg. 4062
KAMIGUMI INTERNATIONAL FORWARDING (SHENZHEN) CO., LTD.—See Kamigumi Co., Ltd.; *Int'l*, pg. 4062
KAMIGUMI (MALAYSIA) SDN. BHD.—See Kamigumi Co., Ltd.; *Int'l*, pg. 4062
KAMIGUMI MARINE TRANSPORT CO., LTD.—See Kamigumi Co., Ltd.; *Int'l*, pg. 4062
KAMIGUMI MEIXCO, S.A. DE C.V.—See Kamigumi Co., Ltd.; *Int'l*, pg. 4062
KAMIGUMI MEXICO S.A. DE C.V.—See Kamigumi Co., Ltd.; *Int'l*, pg. 4062
KAMIGUMI MIDDLE EAST L.L.C.—See Kamigumi Co., Ltd.; *Int'l*, pg. 4062
KAMIGUMI SINGAPORE PTE. LTD.—See Kamigumi Co., Ltd.; *Int'l*, pg. 4062
KAMIGUMI (TAIWAN) CO., LTD.—See Kamigumi Co., Ltd.; *Int'l*, pg. 4062
KAMIGUMI USA INC.—See Kamigumi Co., Ltd.; *Int'l*, pg. 4062
KAMIGUMI (VIETNAM) CO., LTD.—See Kamigumi Co., Ltd.; *Int'l*, pg. 4062
KAMIJYO SEIKI CO., LTD.—See Unitika Ltd.; *Int'l*, pg. 8074
KAMIND IT INC.; *U.S. Private*, pg. 2258
KAMIN LLC—See IMin Partners, L.P.; *U.S. Private*, pg. 2047
KAMINOS S.A.—See Pasal Development S.A.; *Int'l*, pg. 5752
KAMINSKY SDN BHD—See Wilmar International Limited; *Int'l*, pg. 8421
KAMIOKA CERAMIC CO., LTD.—See Niterra Co., Ltd.; *Int'l*, pg. 5380
KAMITSU UNYU CO., LTD.—See Kamigumi Co., Ltd.; *Int'l*, pg. 4062
KAMIX CORP.—See Kamigumi Co., Ltd.; *Int'l*, pg. 4062
KAMIYA BIOMEDICAL CO.—See NITTO BOSEKI CO., LTD.; *Int'l*, pg. 5384
THE KAMLOOPS DAILY NEWS—See Glacier Media Inc.; *Int'l*, pg. 2987
KAMMERER GMBH; *Int'l*, pg. 4063
KAMMINGA & ROODVOETS INC.; *U.S. Private*, pg. 2258
KAMO ELECTRIC COOPERATIVE; *U.S. Private*, pg. 2258
THE KAMOGAWA GRAND HOTEL, LTD.; *Int'l*, pg. 7661
KAMOME CO., LTD.—See IBJ Inc.; *Int'l*, pg. 3576
KAMOTO COPPER COMPANY SA—See Glencore plc; *Int'l*, pg. 2991
KAMPAC INTERNATIONAL PLC; *Int'l*, pg. 4063
KAMPAC TRAVEL & TOURS LLC—See Kampac International PLC; *Int'l*, pg. 4063
KAMPANI CONSULTANTS LTD; *Int'l*, pg. 4063
KAMPFFMEYER FOOD INNOVATION GMBH—See Raiffeisen-Holding Niederosterreich-Wien reg. Gen.m.b.H.; *Int'l*, pg. 6185
KAMPFFMEYER MUHLEN GMBH—See Raiffeisen-Holding Niederosterreich-Wien reg. Gen.m.b.H.; *Int'l*, pg. 6185
KAMPF (HONG KONG) LTD—See Jagenberg AG; *Int'l*, pg. 3870
KAMPF MACHINERY CORPORATION—See Jagenberg AG; *Int'l*, pg. 3870
KAMPF MACHINERY INDIA PVT. LTD.—See Jagenberg AG; *Int'l*, pg. 3870
KAMPF MACHINERY (SHANGHAI) CO., LTD.—See Jagenberg AG; *Int'l*, pg. 3870
KAMPF SCHNEID- UND WICKELTECHNIK GMBH AND CO. KG—See Jagenberg AG; *Int'l*, pg. 3870
KAMPF WT LLC—See Jagenberg AG; *Int'l*, pg. 3870
KAMPGROUNDS OF AMERICA, INC.—See KOA Holdings Inc.; *U.S. Private*, pg. 2325
KAMPHENKEL GMBH & CO. VERTRIEBS KG—See Warsteiner Brauerei Haus Cramer KG; *Int'l*, pg. 8346
KAMPHUIS LASTECHNIEK BV—See ABIRD Holding BV; *Int'l*, pg. 62
KAM PLASTICS CORPORATION; *U.S. Private*, pg. 2258
KAMPS GMBH—See Holding Le Duff SA; *Int'l*, pg. 3450
KAMPS, INC.—See Freeman Spogli & Co. Incorporated; *U.S. Private*, pg. 1606
KAMPS INTERNATIONAL—See Holding Le Duff SA; *Int'l*, pg. 3450
KAMPS PROPANE, INC.—See Superior Plus Corp.; *Int'l*, pg. 7338
KAMPUCHEA FOOD CORPORATION CO., LTD.—See Royal Group of Companies Ltd.; *Int'l*, pg. 6413
KAMRAN & COMPANY, INC.; *U.S. Private*, pg. 2259
KAM & RONSON MEDIA GROUP INC.; *Int'l*, pg. 4059

KANA PIPELINE, INC.

KAMR-TV—See Nexstar Media Group, Inc.; *U.S. Public*, pg. 1522
KAMUX CORP.; *Int'l*, pg. 4063
KAM WING INTERNATIONAL TEXTILE COMPANY LIMITED—See Kam Hing International Holdings Limited; *Int'l*, pg. 4059
KAMYN INDUSTRIES LTD—See Aga Khan Development Network; *Int'l*, pg. 199
KANAAK CORPORATION—See Sealaska Corporation; *U.S. Private*, pg. 3585
KANAAN COMMUNICATIONS, LLC—See Dycom Industries, Inc.; *U.S. Public*, pg. 698
KANABO GROUP PLC; *Int'l*, pg. 4063
KANAC CORP.—See EXEO Group Inc.; *Int'l*, pg. 2583
KANADEN BRAIN CORPORATION—See Kanaden Corporation; *Int'l*, pg. 4063
KANADEN CORPORATION (H.K.) LTD.—See Kanaden Corporation; *Int'l*, pg. 4063
KANADEN CORPORATION (S.H.) LTD.—See Kanaden Corporation; *Int'l*, pg. 4063
KANADEN CORPORATION SINGAPORE PTE. LTD.—See Kanaden Corporation; *Int'l*, pg. 4063
KANADEN CORPORATION; *Int'l*, pg. 4063
KANADEN ENGINEERING CORPORATION—See Kanaden Corporation; *Int'l*, pg. 4063
KANADEN REINETSU CORPORATION—See Kanaden Corporation; *Int'l*, pg. 4063
KANADEN SUPPLY CORPORATION—See Kanaden Corporation; *Int'l*, pg. 4063
KANADEN TECHNO ENGINEERING CORPORATION—See Kanaden Corporation; *Int'l*, pg. 4063
KANADEN TELESYS CORPORATION—See Kanaden Corporation; *Int'l*, pg. 4063
KANADEN (THAILAND) CO., LTD.—See Kanaden Corporation; *Int'l*, pg. 4063
KANADEN TRADING (THAILAND) CO., LTD.—See Kanaden Corporation; *Int'l*, pg. 4063
KANADEN (VIETNAM) CO., LTD.—See Kanaden Corporation; *Int'l*, pg. 4063
KANAFLEX S.A. INDUSTRIA DE PLASTICOS—See Sansuy S.A.; *Int'l*, pg. 6557
KANAGATA CONSULTING CO., LTD.—See OSG Corporation; *Int'l*, pg. 5649
KANAGATA (THAILAND) CO., LTD.—See Toyo Seikan Group Holdings, Ltd.; *Int'l*, pg. 7856
KANAGAWA CHUO KOTSU CO., LTD.—See Odakyu Electric Railway Co., Ltd.; *Int'l*, pg. 5523
KANAGAWA FACTORY OF KANTOH DIETCOOK CO., LTD.—See Kenko Mayonnaise Co., Ltd.; *Int'l*, pg. 4127
KANAGAWA KAIHATSU KANKOU—See Dentsu Group Inc.; *Int'l*, pg. 2039
KANAGAWA K-TECHNO CO., LTD.—See Kandenko Co., Ltd.; *Int'l*, pg. 4065
KANAGAWA SEINO TRANSPORTATION CO., LTD.—See Seino Holdings Co., Ltd.; *Int'l*, pg. 6691
KANAGAWA SENKO TRANSPORT CO., LTD.—See Senko Group Holdings Co., Ltd.; *Int'l*, pg. 6710
KANAGAWA SUBARU INC.—See SUBARU CO., LTD.; *Int'l*, pg. 7246
KANAI JUYO KOGYO CO.,LTD - NON-WOVEN FACTORY—See Kanai Juyo Kogyo Co.,Ltd; *Int'l*, pg. 4063
KANAI JUYO KOGYO CO.,LTD; *Int'l*, pg. 4063
KANAI JUYO KOGYO CO.,LTD - TEXTILE MACHINERY FACTORY—See Kanai Juyo Kogyo Co.,Ltd; *Int'l*, pg. 4063
KANAI TOKUSEN SHANGHAI CO., LTD.—See Kanai Juyo Kogyo Co.,Ltd; *Int'l*, pg. 4064
KANAKIA GROUP; *Int'l*, pg. 4064
KANAK KRISHI IMPLEMENTS LIMITED; *Int'l*, pg. 4064
KANAL 24 NORGE AS—See Egmont Fonden; *Int'l*, pg. 2325
KANALBETRIEBE FRITZ WITHOFS GMBH—See Veolia Environnement S.A.; *Int'l*, pg. 8153
KANALY TRUST—See Genstar Capital, LLC; *U.S. Private*, pg. 1677
KANALY TRUST—See Keystone Group, L.P.; *U.S. Private*, pg. 2298
KANAME KOGYO CO., LTD.; *Int'l*, pg. 4064
KANAMIC NETWORK CO., LTD.; *Int'l*, pg. 4064
KANAMOTO CO., LTD.; *Int'l*, pg. 4064
KANAMOTO FECON HASSYU CONSTRUCTION EQUIPMENT RENTAL JSC—See Kanamoto Co., Ltd.; *Int'l*, pg. 4064
KANAMOTO (HK) CO., LTD.—See Kanamoto Co., Ltd.; *Int'l*, pg. 4064
KANAMOTO & JP NELSON EQUIPMENT (M) SDN. BHD.—See Kanamoto Co., Ltd.; *Int'l*, pg. 4064
KANAN, CORBIN, SCHUPAK & ARONOW, INC.; *U.S. Private*, pg. 2259
KANAN ENTERPRISES, INC.; *U.S. Private*, pg. 2259
KANANI INDUSTRIES LTD.; *Int'l*, pg. 4064
KANA PIPELINE, INC.; *U.S. Private*, pg. 2259
KANA SOFTWARE INC. - CHICAGO—See Verint Systems Inc.; *U.S. Public*, pg. 2281
KANA SOFTWARE, INC.—See Verint Systems Inc.; *U.S. Public*, pg. 2281

1465

KANA SOFTWARE KK—See Verint Systems Inc.; *U.S. Public*, pg. 2281
KANA SOFTWARE PTY LIMITED—See Verint Systems Inc.; *U.S. Public*, pg. 2281
KANA SOFTWARE—See Verint Systems Inc.; *U.S. Public*, pg. 2281
KANA SOFTWARE—See Verint Systems Inc.; *U.S. Public*, pg. 2281
KANA SOLUTIONS LTD—See Verint Systems Inc.; *U.S. Public*, pg. 2281
KANATA ELECTRONIC SERVICES LIMITED—See ShawCor Ltd.; *Int'l*, pg. 6791
KANATECH CO., LTD.—See Kanamoto Co., Ltd.; *Int'l*, pg. 4064
KANAWHA HOSPICE CARE, INC.; *U.S. Private*, pg. 2259
KANAWHA MANUFACTURING COMPANY; *U.S. Private*, pg. 2259
KANAWHA RIVER TERMINALS LLC—See SunCoke Energy, Inc.; *U.S. Public*, pg. 1964
KANAWHA SCALES & SYSTEMS INC.; *U.S. Private*, pg. 2259
KANAWHA STONE COMPANY INC.; *U.S. Private*, pg. 2259
KANAYA KNIT CO., LTD.—See Nippon Steel Corporation; *Int'l*, pg. 5337
KANAZAWA EIZO CENTER CORPORATION—See Nippon Television Holdings Inc.; *Int'l*, pg. 5356
KANAZAWA GERMAN BAKERY CO., LTD—See Yamazaki Baking Co., Ltd.; *Int'l*, pg. 8556
KANAZAWA MEIHAN CO., LTD.—See Meiji Holdings Co., Ltd.; *Int'l*, pg. 4800
KANAZAWA MURATA MANUFACTURING CO., LTD. - SENDAI PLANT—See Murata Manufacturing Co., Ltd.; *Int'l*, pg. 5097
KANAZAWA MURATA MANUFACTURING CO., LTD.—See Murata Manufacturing Co., Ltd.; *Int'l*, pg. 5097
KANAZAWA SOFTWARE CO., LTD.—See Computer Institute of Japan Ltd.; *Int'l*, pg. 1759
KANAZAWA TERMINAL DEVELOPMENT CO., LTD.—See West Japan Railway Company; *Int'l*, pg. 8385
KANAZU MFG. CO., LTD.—See Hitachi Astemo, Ltd.; *Int'l*, pg. 3408
KANAZU MURATA MANUFACTURING CO., LTD.—See Murata Manufacturing Co., Ltd.; *Int'l*, pg. 5097
KANBAKU CO., LTD.—See Suntory Holdings Limited; *Int'l*, pg. 7326
KANBARA DANBORU CO., LTD.—See Dynapac Co., Ltd.; *Int'l*, pg. 2241
KANBEN MINING CO., LTD.—See KUNIMINE INDUSTRIES CO., LTD.; *Int'l*, pg. 4333
KANBISHI CORPORATION—See Toyota Motor Corporation; *Int'l*, pg. 7870
KANBO BIOMEDICAL CO., LTD.—See TOPCO Scientific Co., Ltd.; *Int'l*, pg. 7814
KANBO PRAS CORPORATION—See Daiwabo Holdings Co., Ltd.; *Int'l*, pg. 1949
KANCELARIA PRAWNA - INKASO WEC SA; *Int'l*, pg. 4064
KANCELARIA PRAWNA RAVEN P.KRUPA SP. K.—See Kruk S.A.; *Int'l*, pg. 4308
KANCERA AB; *Int'l*, pg. 4064
KANCHANASINGKORN CO., LTD.—See Thai Beverage Public Company Limited; *Int'l*, pg. 7591
KANCHAN INTERNATIONAL LTD.; *Int'l*, pg. 4064
KANCHANMANIK SECURITIES PRIVATE LIMITED—See Ajcon Global Services Ltd.; *Int'l*, pg. 255
KANCHI KARPOORAM LIMITED; *Int'l*, pg. 4064
KANCO ENTERPRISES LTD; *Int'l*, pg. 4065
KANCO OVERSEAS—See Kanco Enterprises Ltd; *Int'l*, pg. 4065
KANCOR INGREDIENTS LTD.—See V. Mane Fils SA; *Int'l*, pg. 8105
KANCO TEA & INDUSTRIES LIMITED; *Int'l*, pg. 4065
KANDA CORE-TECHNO CO., LTD.—See Kanda Holdings Co., Ltd.; *Int'l*, pg. 4065
KANDAGIRI SPINNING MILLS LIMITED; *Int'l*, pg. 4065
KANDA HOLDINGS CO., LTD.; *Int'l*, pg. 4065
KANDARP DIGI SMART BPO LIMITED—See Reliable Data Services Ltd.; *Int'l*, pg. 6261
KANDA TSUSHINKI CO., LTD.; *Int'l*, pg. 4065
KANDELIUM BARIUM STRONTIUM GMBH & CO. KG—See Solvay S.A.; *Int'l*, pg. 7080
KANDEN AMENIX CORP.—See The Kansai Electric Power Co., Inc.; *Int'l*, pg. 7661
KANDEN E HOUSE CORP.—See The Kansai Electric Power Co., Inc.; *Int'l*, pg. 7661
KANDEN ENERGY SOLUTION CO., INC.—See The Kansai Electric Power Co., Inc.; *Int'l*, pg. 7661
KANDEN ENGINEERING CORP.—See The Kansai Electric Power Co., Inc.; *Int'l*, pg. 7661
KANDEN FACILITIES CO., LTD.—See The Kansai Electric Power Co., Inc.; *Int'l*, pg. 7661
KANDEN FUDOSAN CO., LTD.—See The Kansai Electric Power Co., Inc.; *Int'l*, pg. 7661
KANDEN GAS SUPPORT CO., INC.—See The Kansai Electric Power Co., Inc.; *Int'l*, pg. 7661
KANDEN JOY LIFE CO., LTD.—See The Kansai Electric Power Co., Inc.; *Int'l*, pg. 7661
KANDENKO CO., LTD.; *Int'l*, pg. 4065
KANDENKO ENGINEERING CONSULTING (SHANGHAI) CO., LTD.—See Kandenko Co., Ltd.; *Int'l*, pg. 4065
KANDENKO ENGINEERING (MALAYSIA) SDN. BHD.—See Kandenko Co., Ltd.; *Int'l*, pg. 4065
THE KANDEN L&A CO., LTD.—See The Kansai Electric Power Co., Inc.; *Int'l*, pg. 7662
KANDEN PLANT CORP.—See The Kansai Electric Power Co., Inc.; *Int'l*, pg. 7661
KANDEN POWER-TECH, CORP.—See The Kansai Electric Power Co., Inc.; *Int'l*, pg. 7662
KANDEN REALTY & DEVELOPMENT CO., LTD.—See The Kansai Electric Power Co., Inc.; *Int'l*, pg. 7662
KANDEN SECURITY OF SOCIETY, INC.—See The Kansai Electric Power Co., Inc.; *Int'l*, pg. 7661
KANDEN SYSTEM SOLUTIONS CO., INC.—See The Kansai Electric Power Co., Inc.; *Int'l*, pg. 7662
KANDERS & COMPANY, INC.; *U.S. Private*, pg. 2259
KANDI KOUNTRY EXPRESS, LTD.—See Monroe Truck Equipment, Inc.; *U.S. Private*, pg. 2774
KANDI TECHNOLOGIES GROUP, INC.; *Int'l*, pg. 4065
KANDMAD - SOCIEDADE GESTORA DE PARTICIPACOES SOCIAIS LDA—See Camargo Correa S.A.; *Int'l*, pg. 1268
K AND W LANDFILL INC.—See Waste Management, Inc.; *U.S. Public*, pg. 2331
KANDY HOTELS CO. (1938) PLC; *Int'l*, pg. 4066
KANDY PRIVATE HOSPITALS LTD—See Central Finance Company PLC; *Int'l*, pg. 1406
KANDY WALK INN LTD.—See John Keells Holdings PLC; *Int'l*, pg. 3978
KANE 3PL, LLC—See The Kane Company; *U.S. Private*, pg. 4064
KANE BIOTECH INC.; *Int'l*, pg. 4066
KANEBO COSMETICS (CHINA) CO.,LTD.—See Kao Corporation; *Int'l*, pg. 4074
KANEBO COSMETICS DEUTSCHLAND GMBH—See Kao Corporation; *Int'l*, pg. 4074
KANEBO COSMETICS (EUROPE) LTD.—See Kao Corporation; *Int'l*, pg. 4074
KANEBO COSMETICS INC.—See Kao Corporation; *Int'l*, pg. 4074
KANEBO COSMETICS ITALY SPA—See Kao Corporation; *Int'l*, pg. 4074
KANEBO COSMETICS KOREA CO., LTD.—See Kao Corporation; *Int'l*, pg. 4074
KANEBO COSMETICS MALAYSIA SDN. BHD.—See Kao Corporation; *Int'l*, pg. 4074
KANEBO COSMETICS RUS LLC—See Kao Corporation; *Int'l*, pg. 4074
KANEBO COSMETICS SALES CO., LTD.—See Kao Corporation; *Int'l*, pg. 4074
KANEBO COSMETICS THAILAND CO., LTD.—See Kao Corporation; *Int'l*, pg. 4074
KANEBO COSMETIQUES FRANCE S.A.R.L.—See Kao Corporation; *Int'l*, pg. 4074
KANEBO COSMILLION, LTD.—See Kao Corporation; *Int'l*, pg. 4074
KANEBRIDGE CORPORATION; *U.S. Private*, pg. 2260
KANE COMMUNICATIONS GROUP, LLC; *U.S. Private*, pg. 2259
THE KANE COMPANY; *U.S. Private*, pg. 4064
KANE CONSTRUCTIONS PTY LTD; *Int'l*, pg. 4066
KANE & FINKEL HEALTHCARE COMMUNICATIONS; *U.S. Private*, pg. 2259
KANE FREIGHT LINES INC.—See Kane Is Able, Inc.; *U.S. Private*, pg. 2260
KANE FURNITURE CORPORATION; *U.S. Private*, pg. 2259
KANEFUSA CHINA CORPORATION—See KANEFUSA CORPORATION; *Int'l*, pg. 4066
KANEFUSA CORPORATION; *Int'l*, pg. 4066
KANEFUSA EUROPE B.V.—See KANEFUSA CORPORATION; *Int'l*, pg. 4066
KANEFUSA INDIA PVT. LTD.—See KANEFUSA CORPORATION; *Int'l*, pg. 4066
KANEFUSA USA INC.—See KANEFUSA CORPORATION; *Int'l*, pg. 4066
KANE HOLDINGS LIMITED; *Int'l*, pg. 4066
KANE INFRASTRUCTURE SERVICES HOLDINGS, LLC—See Aterian Investment Management, L.P.; *U.S. Private*, pg. 366
KANE IS ABLE, INC.; *U.S. Private*, pg. 2260
KANEKA AEROSPACE LLC—See Kaneka Corporation; *Int'l*, pg. 4067
KANEKA AMERICAS HOLDING, INC.—See Kaneka Corporation; *Int'l*, pg. 4067
KANEKA ASIA CO., LTD.—See Kaneka Corporation; *Int'l*, pg. 4067
KANEKA BELGIUM N.V.—See Kaneka Corporation; *Int'l*, pg. 4067
KANEKA CORPORATION; *Int'l*, pg. 4066
KANEKA CREATIVE CONSULTING CO., LTD.—See Kaneka Corporation; *Int'l*, pg. 4067
KANEKA EUROGENTEC S.A.—See Kaneka Corporation; *Int'l*, pg. 4067
KANEKA FOAM PLASTICS CO., LTD.—See Kaneka Corporation; *Int'l*, pg. 4067
KANEKA FOODS CORPORATION—See Kaneka Corporation; *Int'l*, pg. 4067
KANEKA HOKEN CENTER CO., LTD.—See Kaneka Corporation; *Int'l*, pg. 4067
KANEKA HOKKAIDO CO., LTD.—See Kaneka Corporation; *Int'l*, pg. 4067
KANEKA KENTECH CO., LTD.—See Kaneka Corporation; *Int'l*, pg. 4067
KANEKA KOREA CORPORATION—See Kaneka Corporation; *Int'l*, pg. 4067
KANEKA (MALAYSIA) SDN. BHD.—See Kaneka Corporation; *Int'l*, pg. 4067
KANEKA MEDICAL TECH CORPORATION—See Kaneka Corporation; *Int'l*, pg. 4067
KANEKA NUTRIENTS L.P.—See Kaneka Corporation; *Int'l*, pg. 4067
KANEKA SOLAR MARKETING CO., LTD.—See Kaneka Corporation; *Int'l*, pg. 4067
KANEKA SOLARTECH CORPORATION—See Kaneka Corporation; *Int'l*, pg. 4067
KANEKA SUN SPICE CORPORATION—See Kaneka Corporation; *Int'l*, pg. 4067
KANEKA TAKASAGO SERVICE CENTER CO., LTD.—See Kaneka Corporation; *Int'l*, pg. 4067
KANEKA TECHNO RESEARCH CORPORATION—See Kaneka Corporation; *Int'l*, pg. 4067
KANEKA TEXAS CORP.—See Kaneka Corporation; *Int'l*, pg. 4067
KANEKA TRADING (SHANGHAI) CO., LTD.—See Kaneka Corporation; *Int'l*, pg. 4067
KANEKA YOUR HEALTH CARE CO., LTD.—See Kaneka Corporation; *Int'l*, pg. 4067
KANEKI CO., LTD.—See Hanwa Co., Ltd.; *Int'l*, pg. 3263
KANEKON CO., LTD.—See Riken Technos Corporation; *Int'l*, pg. 6341
KANEKO SANGYO CO., LTD.—See Nissui Corporation; *Int'l*, pg. 5378
KANEKO SEEDS CO., LTD.; *Int'l*, pg. 4067
KANEKO SEEDS (THAILAND) CO., LTD—See Kaneko Seeds Co., Ltd.; *Int'l*, pg. 4068
KANEKO SHOKUHIN CO., LTD.—See Nissui Corporation; *Int'l*, pg. 5378
KANEL INDUSTRIES LIMITED; *Int'l*, pg. 4068
KANE LPI SOLUTIONS (CAYMAN) LIMITED—See Kane Holdings Limited; *Int'l*, pg. 4066
KANE LPI SOLUTIONS LIMITED—See Kane Holdings Limited; *Int'l*, pg. 4066
KANE LPI SOLUTIONS (MALTA) LIMITED—See Kane Holdings Limited; *Int'l*, pg. 4066
KANE LPI SOLUTIONS (MENA) LIMITED—See Kane Holdings Limited; *Int'l*, pg. 4066
KANE LPI SOLUTIONS (USA), INC.—See Kane Holdings Limited; *Int'l*, pg. 4066
KANEMATSU ADVANCED MATERIALS CORP.—See Kanematsu Corporation; *Int'l*, pg. 4068
KANEMATSU AEROSPACE CORPORATION—See Kanematsu Corporation; *Int'l*, pg. 4068
KANEMATSU AGRITECH CO., LTD.—See Kanematsu Corporation; *Int'l*, pg. 4068
KANEMATSU AUSTRALIA LTD.—See Kanematsu Corporation; *Int'l*, pg. 4068
KANEMATSU CHEMICALS CORP.—See Kanematsu Corporation; *Int'l*, pg. 4068
KANEMATSU (CHINA) CO., LTD.—See Kanematsu Corporation; *Int'l*, pg. 4068
KANEMATSU COMMUNICATIONS LTD.—See Kanematsu Corporation; *Int'l*, pg. 4068
KANEMATSU CORPORATION; *Int'l*, pg. 4068
KANEMATSU DEVICES KOREA CORPORATION—See Kanematsu Corporation; *Int'l*, pg. 4068
KANEMATSU ELECTRONICS LTD.—See Kanematsu Corporation; *Int'l*, pg. 4068
KANEMATSU ENGINEERING CO., LTD.; *Int'l*, pg. 4069
KANEMATSU EUROPE PLC—See Kanematsu Corporation; *Int'l*, pg. 4068
KANEMATSU FOOD CORP.—See Kanematsu Corporation; *Int'l*, pg. 4068
KANEMATSU FUTURETECH SOLUTIONS CORPORATION—See Kanematsu Corporation; *Int'l*, pg. 4068
KANEMATSU G.M.B.H—See Kanematsu Corporation; *Int'l*, pg. 4068
KANEMATSU GRANKS, CORP.—See Kanematsu Corporation; *Int'l*, pg. 4068
KANEMATSU (HONG KONG) LTD.—See Kanematsu Corporation; *Int'l*, pg. 4068
KANEMATSU IRAN LTD.—See Kanematsu Corporation; *Int'l*, pg. 4068
KANEMATSU KGK CORP.—See Kanematsu Corporation; *Int'l*, pg. 4068
KANEMATSU KGK TRADE & SALES (SHANGHAI) CO., LTD.—See Kanematsu Corporation; *Int'l*, pg. 4068
KANEMATSU LOGISTICS & INSURANCE LTD.—See Kanematsu Corporation; *Int'l*, pg. 4069
KANEMATSU NEW ZEALAND LTD.—See Kanematsu Corporation; *Int'l*, pg. 4069
KANEMATSU-NNK CORPORATION - MATCH DEPARTMENT AWAJI FACTORY—See Kanematsu Sustech Corporation; *Int'l*, pg. 4069

COMPANY NAME INDEX

KANEMATSU-NNK CORPORATION - WOOD PRESERVATION DEPARTMENT KANSAI FACTORY—See Kanematsu Sustech Corporation; *Int'l*, pg. 4069
KANEMATSU-NNK CORPORATION - WOOD PRESERVATION DEPARTMENT KANTO FACTORY—See Kanematsu Sustech Corporation; *Int'l*, pg. 4069
KANEMATSU-NNK CORPORATION - WOOD PRESERVATION DEPARTMENT OKAYAMA FACTORY—See Kanematsu Sustech Corporation; *Int'l*, pg. 4069
KANEMATSU-NNK CORPORATION - WOOD PRESERVATION DEPARTMENT TOHOKU FACTORY—See Kanematsu Sustech Corporation; *Int'l*, pg. 4069
KANEMATSU PETROLEUM CORPORATION—See Kanematsu Corporation; *Int'l*, pg. 4069
KANEMATSU PWS LTD.—See Kanematsu Corporation; *Int'l*, pg. 4069
KANEMATSU SEMICONDUCTOR SINGAPORE PTE., LTD.—See Kanematsu Corporation; *Int'l*, pg. 4069
KANEMATSU SEMICONDUCTOR TAIWAN LTD.—See Kanematsu Corporation; *Int'l*, pg. 4069
KANEMATSU SOYTECH CORP.—See Kanematsu Corporation; *Int'l*, pg. 4069
KANEMATSU SUSTECH CORPORATION; *Int'l*, pg. 4069
KANEMATSU (THAILAND) LTD.—See Kanematsu Corporation; *Int'l*, pg. 4068
KANEMATSU TRADING CORP.—See Kanematsu Corporation; *Int'l*, pg. 4069
KANEMATSU USA INC.—See Kanematsu Corporation; *Int'l*, pg. 4069
KANEMATSU WELLNESS CORP.—See Kanematsu Corporation; *Int'l*, pg. 4069
KANEMATSU YUSO CO., LTD.—See Kanematsu Corporation; *Int'l*, pg. 4069
KANEMI CO., LTD.—See ITOCHU Corporation; *Int'l*, pg. 3836
KANE-MILLER CORP.; *U.S. Private*, pg. 2260
KANEMITSU CORPORATION - KASAI PLANT—See Kanemitsu Corporation; *Int'l*, pg. 4069
KANEMITSU CORPORATION - MIKI PLANT—See Kanemitsu Corporation; *Int'l*, pg. 4069
KANEMITSU CORPORATION; *Int'l*, pg. 4069
KANEPI GROUP PTY. LTD.—See mCloud Technologies Corp.; *Int'l*, pg. 4760
KANEPI PTE. LTD.—See mCloud Technologies Corp.; *Int'l*, pg. 4760
KANEQUIP, INC.; *U.S. Private*, pg. 2260
KAN EQUIPMENT INC.; *U.S. Private*, pg. 2259
KANESAWA SHIKI KOGYO CO., LTD.—See Tomoku Co., Ltd.; *Int'l*, pg. 7801
THE KANESHITA CONSTRUCTION CO., LTD.; *Int'l*, pg. 7661
KANESHO SOIL TREATMENT SPRL/BVBA—See Agro-Kanesho Co., Ltd.; *Int'l*, pg. 218
KANESO CO., LTD.; *Int'l*, pg. 4069
KANE STAFFING SERVICES, LLC—See The Kane Company; *U.S. Private*, pg. 4064
KANETA KOGYO CO., LTD.—See Honda Motor Co., Ltd.; *Int'l*, pg. 3463
KANE TRAFFIC SERVICES INC.—See Kane Is Able, Inc.; *U.S. Private*, pg. 2260
KANE TRANSPORT, INC.—See Transwood Carriers Inc.; *U.S. Private*, pg. 4211
KAN-ETSU SENKO LOGISTICS CO., LTD.—See Senko Group Holdings Co., Ltd.; *Int'l*, pg. 6710
KANE VETERINARY SUPPLIES, LTD.—See Patterson Companies, Inc.; *U.S. Public*, pg. 1654
KANE WAREHOUSING INC.—See Kane Is Able, Inc.; *U.S. Private*, pg. 2260
KANEX KROHNE ANLAGEN EXPORT GMBH—See Krohne International, Inc.; *Int'l*, pg. 4303
KANEX KROHNE GRODNO—See Krohne International, Inc.; *Int'l*, pg. 4303
KANEY AEROSPACE, INC.; *U.S. Private*, pg. 2260
KANEYO CO., LTD.—See Kanematsu Corporation; *Int'l*, pg. 4069
KANFA ARAGON AS—See Magnora ASA; *Int'l*, pg. 4641
KANFA AS—See TechnipFMC plc; *Int'l*, pg. 7507
KANGAROO BRANDS, INC.; *U.S. Private*, pg. 2260
KANGAROO ISLAND SEALINK PTY LTD—See Kelsian Group Limited; *Int'l*, pg. 4122
KANGAROO RESOURCES LIMITED—See PT. Bayan Resources Tbk.; *Int'l*, pg. 6084
KANGAS & ASSOCIATES, LLC; *U.S. Private*, pg. 2260
KANGDA NEW MATERIALS (GROUP) CO., LTD; *Int'l*, pg. 4070
KANGDE XIN COMPOSITE MATERIAL CO., LTD.; *Int'l*, pg. 4070
KANGEAN ENERGY INDONESIA LTD.—See Japan Petroleum Exploration Co. Ltd.; *Int'l*, pg. 3900
KANGER INTERNATIONAL BERHAD; *Int'l*, pg. 4070
KANGJI MEDICAL HOLDINGS LIMITED; *Int'l*, pg. 4070
KANGKAR RAYA BATU BATA SDN. BHD.—See Kia Lim Berhad; *Int'l*, pg. 4157
KANGLI (HK) LIMITED—See KangLi International Holdings Ltd.; *Int'l*, pg. 4070
KANGLI INTERNATIONAL HOLDINGS LTD.; *Int'l*, pg. 4070
KANGLIM CO., LTD.; *Int'l*, pg. 4070
KANGMEI PHARMACEUTICAL CO., LTD.; *Int'l*, pg. 4070

KANG NA HSIUNG ENTERPRISE CO., LTD. - SHANGHAI PLANT—See KNH Enterprise Co., Ltd.; *Int'l*, pg. 4206
KANGNAM CHEMICAL CO., LTD.—See DIC Corporation; *Int'l*, pg. 2109
KANGNAM JEVISCO CO., LTD.; *Int'l*, pg. 4070
KANGNI RAIL TRANSIT EQUIPMENT, CORP.—See Nanjing Kangni Mechanical & Electrical Co., Ltd.; *Int'l*, pg. 5140
KANGNI RAIL TRANSIT EQUIPMENT (THAILAND) CO., LTD.—See Nanjing Kangni Mechanical & Electrical Co., Ltd.; *Int'l*, pg. 5140
KANGNI TECHNOLOGY SERVICE S.A.R.L—See Nanjing Kangni Mechanical & Electrical Co., Ltd.; *Int'l*, pg. 5140
KANGPING TECHNOLOGY (SUZHOU) CO., LTD.; *Int'l*, pg. 4070
KANGSTEM BIOTECH CO., LTD; *Int'l*, pg. 4070
KANGWAL POLYESTER CO., LTD. - PHECTCHABURI FACTORY—See Kangwal Polyester Co., Ltd.; *Int'l*, pg. 4070
KANGWAL POLYESTER CO., LTD.; *Int'l*, pg. 4070
KANGWON LAND, INC.; *Int'l*, pg. 4070
KANGXIN NEW MATERIALS CO., LTD.; *Int'l*, pg. 4070
KANG YONG ELECTRIC PUBLIC COMPANY LIMITED—See Mitsubishi Electric Corporation; *Int'l*, pg. 4944
KANGYUE TECHNOLOGY COMPANY LIMITED; *Int'l*, pg. 4070
KANHAN TECHNOLOGIES LIMITED—See Aurum Pacific (China) Group Limited; *Int'l*, pg. 715
KAN HERB COMPANY, INC.—See PuraPharm Corporation Limited; *Int'l*, pg. 6121
KANHYM ESTATES PIC SOUTH AFRICA—See Genus Plc; *Int'l*, pg. 2931
KANIGEN (SHANGHAI) TRADE CO., LTD.—See Nihon Parkerizing Co., Ltd.; *Int'l*, pg. 5286
KANIGEN (THAILAND) CO., LTD.—See Nihon Parkerizing Co., Ltd.; *Int'l*, pg. 5286
KANIKA HOTELS PUBLIC COMPANY LTD; *Int'l*, pg. 4070
KANIKA INFRASTRUCTURE & POWER LIMITED; *Int'l*, pg. 4070
KANISHK STEEL INDUSTRIES LTD.; *Int'l*, pg. 4070
KANI WATER—See Ster Group; *Int'l*, pg. 7208
KANIZSA 2002 KFT.—See BNP Paribas SA; *Int'l*, pg. 1091
KANJANADIT PALM OIL CO., LTD.—See Energy Absolute Public Company Limited; *Int'l*, pg. 2422
KANKAI BIKAS BANK LIMITED; *Int'l*, pg. 4071
KANKAKEE DAILY JOURNAL COMPANY LLC—See Small Newspaper Group Inc.; *U.S. Private*, pg. 3690
KANKI CO., LTD.—See Kanamoto Co., Ltd.; *Int'l*, pg. 4064
KANKO DAIICHI TRAFFIC CO., LTD.—See Daiichi Koutsu Sangyo Co., Ltd.; *Int'l*, pg. 1928
KANKO FACILITIES CO LTD—See Kandenko Co., Ltd.; *Int'l*, pg. 4065
KANKO FUDOUSAN KANRI CO., LTD.—See Kandenko Co., Ltd.; *Int'l*, pg. 4065
KANKO POWER TECHNO CO LTD—See Kandenko Co., Ltd.; *Int'l*, pg. 4065
KANKO PRO CO., LTD.—See Mie Kotsu Group Holdings, Inc.; *Int'l*, pg. 4888
KANKO SYOJI CO LTD—See Kandenko Co., Ltd.; *Int'l*, pg. 4065
KANKYO ASSIST CO., LTD.—See Taiyo Yuden Company Ltd.; *Int'l*, pg. 7426
KANKYO RESEARCH INSTITUTE INC.—See TOYO KANETSU K.K.; *Int'l*, pg. 7855
KANKYORYOKKA CO.,LTD.—See Shimizu Corporation; *Int'l*, pg. 6835
KANKYO SOL-TECH CO., LTD.—See Takuma Co., Ltd.; *Int'l*, pg. 7442
KANKYOU BOUSAI CO., LTD.—See Founder's Consultants Holdings, Inc.; *Int'l*, pg. 2753
KANKYOUSEIBI CO., LTD.—See AEON Co., Ltd.; *Int'l*, pg. 177
KANMON DOCK SERVICE, LTD.—See Mitsubishi Heavy Industries, Ltd.; *Int'l*, pg. 4954
KANMONKAI CO., LTD.; *Int'l*, pg. 4071
KANMOR CONTROL SYSTEMS LTD.—See Watts Water Technologies, Inc.; *U.S. Public*, pg. 2337
KANNAKE OY—See Panostaja Oyj; *Int'l*, pg. 5729
KAN-NANMARU CORPORATION; *Int'l*, pg. 4063
KANNAPOLIS ENERGY PARTNERS LLC—See Peregrine Energy Corp.; *U.S. Private*, pg. 3147
KANNARU PRINTING CO., LTD.—See The Pack Corporation; *Int'l*, pg. 7672
KANNE CAFE GMBH—See Compass Group PLC; *Int'l*, pg. 1752
KANNEGIESSER AUE GMBH—See Hebert Kannegiesser GmbH; *Int'l*, pg. 3306
KANNEGIESSER AUGSBURG GMBH—See Hebert Kannegiesser GmbH; *Int'l*, pg. 3306
KANNEGIESSER AUSTRALIA PTY LTD—See Hebert Kannegiesser GmbH; *Int'l*, pg. 3306
KANNEGIESSER BENELUX B.V.—See Hebert Kannegiesser GmbH; *Int'l*, pg. 3306
KANNEGIESSER ESPANA, S.L—See Hebert Kannegiesser GmbH; *Int'l*, pg. 3306
KANNEGIESSER ETECH, INC.—See Hebert Kannegiesser GmbH; *Int'l*, pg. 3306

KANNEGIESSER FRANCE S.A.—See Hebert Kannegiesser GmbH; *Int'l*, pg. 3306
KANNEGIESSER GMBH—See Hebert Kannegiesser GmbH; *Int'l*, pg. 3306
KANNEGIESSER ITALIA S.R.L.—See Hebert Kannegiesser GmbH; *Int'l*, pg. 3306
KANNEGIESSER UK LTD.—See Hebert Kannegiesser GmbH; *Int'l*, pg. 3306
KANNET LIMITED—See Champion Technology Holdings Ltd; *Int'l*, pg. 1440
KANO LABORATORIES INC.—See Gryphon Investors, LLC; *U.S. Private*, pg. 1798
KANONADEN ENTREPRENAD AB—See AF Gruppen ASA; *Int'l*, pg. 184
THE KANOO GROUP, LLC; *Int'l*, pg. 7661
KANOO POWER SOLUTIONS—See Ebrahim K. Kanoo Company B.S.C.; *Int'l*, pg. 2286
KANOO SHIPPING—See The Kanoo Group, LLC; *Int'l*, pg. 7661
KANOO TRAVEL—See The Kanoo Group, LLC; *Int'l*, pg. 7661
KANORIA CHEMICALS & INDUSTRIES LTD; *Int'l*, pg. 4071
KANORIA ENERGY & INFRASTRUCTURE LIMITED; *Int'l*, pg. 4071
KANO UBE CONCRETE CO., LTD.—See UBE Corporation; *Int'l*, pg. 8001
KANPAI CO., LTD.—See Nippon Steel Corporation; *Int'l*, pg. 5337
KANPATSU SERVICE CO., LTD.—See K&O Energy Group Inc.; *Int'l*, pg. 4038
KANPUR FERTILIZERS & CHEMICALS LIMITED—See Jaiprakash Associates Limited; *Int'l*, pg. 3873
KANPUR ORGANICS PRIVATE LIMITED—See Raghuvansh Agrofams Ltd.; *Int'l*, pg. 6181
KANPUR PLASTIPACK LTD.; *Int'l*, pg. 4071
KAN RESEARCH INSTITUTE, INC.—See Eisai Co., Ltd.; *Int'l*, pg. 2335
KANRIKU CO., LTD.—See Konoike Transport Co., Ltd.; *Int'l*, pg. 4274
KANRO FOUR SEAS FOODS (SHANTOU) COMPANY LIMITED—See Four Seas Mercantile Holdings Limited; *Int'l*, pg. 2755
KANRO INC.; *Int'l*, pg. 4071
KANSAI AIRPORT GROUND SERVICE CO., LTD.—See Japan Airlines Co., Ltd.; *Int'l*, pg. 3885
KANSAI ALLIED COFFEE ROASTERS CO., LTD.—See S. ISHIMITSU & Co., LTD.; *Int'l*, pg. 6446
KANSAI-ALPHANAM PAINT CO., LTD.—See Kansai Paint Co., Ltd.; *Int'l*, pg. 4073
KANSAI ALTAN BOYA SANAYI VE TICARET ANONIM SIRKETI—See Kansai Paint Co., Ltd.; *Int'l*, pg. 4072
KANSAI BEVERAGE SERVICE COMPANY LIMITED—See Coca-Cola Bottlers Japan Holdings Inc.; *Int'l*, pg. 1684
KANSAI BUSINESS INFORMATION INC.—See Osaka Gas Co., Ltd.; *Int'l*, pg. 5645
KANSAI COKE AND CHEMICALS CO., LTD.—See Mitsubishi Chemical Group Corporation; *Int'l*, pg. 4931
KANSAI COSMO LOGISTICS CO., LTD.—See Cosmo Energy Holdings Co., Ltd.; *Int'l*, pg. 1812
KANSAI CSP K.K.—See Central Security Patrols Co., Ltd.; *Int'l*, pg. 1410
KANSAI DESIGN CO., LTD.—See Hitachi Zosen Corporation; *Int'l*, pg. 3411
KANSAI DIETCOOK CO., LTD.—See Kenko Mayonnaise Co., Ltd.; *Int'l*, pg. 4127
THE KANSAI ELECTRIC POWER CO., INC.; *Int'l*, pg. 7661
KANSAI ENERGYS CORPORATION—See NGK Insulators, Ltd.; *Int'l*, pg. 5254
KANSAI ENERGY SOLUTION (THAILAND) CO., LTD.—See The Kansai Electric Power Co., Inc.; *Int'l*, pg. 7662
KANSAI ENGINEERING CO., LTD.—See Kawasaki Heavy Industries, Ltd.; *Int'l*, pg. 4095
KANSAI FROZEN DISTRIBUTION CO., LTD.—See Ezaki Glico Co., Ltd.; *Int'l*, pg. 2593
KANSAI HELIOS COATINGS GMBH—See Kansai Paint Co., Ltd.; *Int'l*, pg. 4072
KANSAI HITACHI CO., LTD.—See Hitachi Co., Ltd.; *Int'l*, pg. 3423
KANSAI HOJU UNYU CO., LTD.—See Tomoku Co., Ltd.; *Int'l*, pg. 7801
KANSAIKAKO CO., LTD.—See Nitta Corporation; *Int'l*, pg. 5382
KANSAI KAKO CORPORATION—See SHO-BOND Holdings Co., Ltd.; *Int'l*, pg. 6857
KANSAI KIRIN BEVERAGE SERVICE CO., LTD.—See Kirin Holdings Company, Limited; *Int'l*, pg. 4187
KANSAI KOBUNSHI CO., LTD.—See Inabata & Co. Ltd.; *Int'l*, pg. 3644
KANSAI MARUWA LOGISTICS CO., LTD.—See AZ-COM MARUWA Holdings Inc.; *Int'l*, pg. 776
KANSAI MATECH CO., LTD.—See Taiheiyo Cement Corporation; *Int'l*, pg. 7411
KANSAI MAZDA CO., LTD.—See Mazda Motor Corporation; *Int'l*, pg. 4748
KANSAI MIRAI BANK, LIMITED—See Resona Holdings, Inc.; *Int'l*, pg. 6297

THE KANSAI ELECTRIC POWER CO., INC.   CORPORATE AFFILIATIONS

KANSAI MIRAI FINANCIAL GROUP, INC.—See Resona Holdings, Inc.; *Int'l*, pg. 6297
KANSAI NEROLAC PAINTS LTD.—See Kansai Paint Co., Ltd.; *Int'l*, pg. 4072
KANSAI NOK HANBAI CO., LTD.—See NOK Corporation; *Int'l*, pg. 5402
KANSAI OKAMURA MANUFACTURING CO., LTD—See Okamura Corporation; *Int'l*, pg. 5545
KANSAI OKURA CO., LTD.—See Okura Industrial Co., Ltd.; *Int'l*, pg. 5551
KANSAI PAINT (AMERICA), INC.—See Kansai Paint Co., Ltd.; *Int'l*, pg. 4072
KANSAI PAINT ASIA PACIFIC SDN. BHD.—See Kansai Paint Co., Ltd.; *Int'l*, pg. 4072
KANSAI PAINT (CHINA) INVESTMENT CO., LTD.—See Kansai Paint Co., Ltd.; *Int'l*, pg. 4072
KANSAI PAINT CO., LTD. - AMAGASAKI PLANT—See Kansai Paint Co., Ltd.; *Int'l*, pg. 4072
KANSAI PAINT CO., LTD. - HIRATSUKA PLANT—See Kansai Paint Co., Ltd.; *Int'l*, pg. 4072
KANSAI PAINT CO., LTD. - KANUMA PLANT—See Kansai Paint Co., Ltd.; *Int'l*, pg. 4072
KANSAI PAINT CO., LTD. - NAGOYA PLANT—See Kansai Paint Co., Ltd.; *Int'l*, pg. 4072
KANSAI PAINT CO., LTD. - ONO PLANT—See Kansai Paint Co., Ltd.; *Int'l*, pg. 4072
KANSAI PAINT CO., LTD.; *Int'l*, pg. 4071
KANSAI PAINT CO., LTD.-TECHNOLOGY & PRODUCTS DEVELOPMENT LABORATORY—See Kansai Paint Co., Ltd.; *Int'l*, pg. 4072
KANSAI PAINT EUROPE LIMITED—See Kansai Paint Co., Ltd.; *Int'l*, pg. 4072
KANSAI PAINT H.K., LTD.—See Kansai Paint Co., Ltd.; *Int'l*, pg. 4072
KANSAI PAINT MARINE (TAIWAN) CO., LTD.—See Kansai Paint Co., Ltd.; *Int'l*, pg. 4072
KANSAI PAINT MYANMAR CO., LTD.—See Kansai Paint Co., Ltd.; *Int'l*, pg. 4072
KANSAI PAINT PHILIPPINES, INC.—See Kansai Paint Co., Ltd.; *Int'l*, pg. 4072
KANSAI PAINT (SHENYANG) CO., LTD.—See Kansai Paint Co., Ltd.; *Int'l*, pg. 4072
KANSAI PAINT (SINGAPORE) PTE. LTD.—See Kansai Paint Co., Ltd.; *Int'l*, pg. 4072
KANSAI PAINTS LANKA (PRIVATE) LIMITED—See Kansai Paint Co., Ltd.; *Int'l*, pg. 4072
KANSAI PAINTS NEPAL PVT. LTD.—See Kansai Paint Co., Ltd.; *Int'l*, pg. 4072
KANSAI PIPE INDUSTRIES, LTD.—See Sumitomo Electric Industries, Ltd.; *Int'l*, pg. 7278
KANSAI PLASCON BOTSWANA (PROPRIETARY) LTD.—See Kansai Paint Co., Ltd.; *Int'l*, pg. 4072
KANSAI PLASCON KENYA LTD.—See Kansai Paint Co., Ltd.; *Int'l*, pg. 4072
KANSAI PLASCON MALAWI LTD.—See Kansai Paint Co., Ltd.; *Int'l*, pg. 4072
KANSAI PLASCON NAMIBIA (PROPRIETARY) LTD.—See Kansai Paint Co., Ltd.; *Int'l*, pg. 4072
KANSAI PLASCON (PTY) LTD—See Kansai Paint Co., Ltd.; *Int'l*, pg. 4072
KANSAI PLASCON SA—See Kansai Paint Co., Ltd.; *Int'l*, pg. 4072
KANSAI PLASCON SWAZILAND LTD.—See Kansai Paint Co., Ltd.; *Int'l*, pg. 4072
KANSAI PLASCON TANZANIA LTD.—See Kansai Paint Co., Ltd.; *Int'l*, pg. 4072
KANSAI PLASCON UGANDA LTD.—See Kansai Paint Co., Ltd.; *Int'l*, pg. 4072
KANSAI PLASCON ZAMBIA LTD.—See Kansai Paint Co., Ltd.; *Int'l*, pg. 4072
KANSAI PLASCON ZANZIBAR LTD.—See Kansai Paint Co., Ltd.; *Int'l*, pg. 4073
KANSAI RESIN (THAILAND) CO., LTD.—See Kansai Paint Co., Ltd.; *Int'l*, pg. 4073
KANSAI SHIPPING CO., LTD.—See Tosoh Corporation; *Int'l*, pg. 7832
KANSAI SUPERMARKET CO., LTD; *Int'l*, pg. 4073
KANSAI SUPER PREMIUM CO.,LTD.—See H2O Retailing Corp.; *Int'l*, pg. 3200
KANSAI TAIHEIYO MINERALS CORPORATION—See Taiheiyo Cement Corporation; *Int'l*, pg. 7411
KANSAI TELECASTING CORPORATION—See Fuji Media Holdings, Inc.; *Int'l*, pg. 2814
KANSAI TOKUYAMA TRADING CO., LTD.—See Tokuyama Corporation; *Int'l*, pg. 7787
KANSAI UBE CO., LTD.—See UBE Corporation; *Int'l*, pg. 8001
KANSAI U.S.A. CORPORATION—See Nippon Filcon Co., Ltd.; *Int'l*, pg. 5317
KANSAI WIRE NETTING CO., LTD. - AMAGASAKI FACTORY—See Nippon Filcon Co., Ltd.; *Int'l*, pg. 5317
KANSAI WIRE NETTING CO., LTD. - OSAKA FACTORY—See Nippon Filcon Co., Ltd.; *Int'l*, pg. 5318
KANSAI WIRE NETTING CO., LTD.—See Nippon Filcon Co., Ltd.; *Int'l*, pg. 5317
KANSAI WIRE NETTING CO., LTD. - TOKYO FACTORY—See Nippon Filcon Co., Ltd.; *Int'l*, pg. 5318
KANSAI WIRE NETTING TECHNOLOGY (KUNSHAN) CO., LTD.—See Nippon Filcon Co., Ltd.; *Int'l*, pg. 5318

KANSAS AVIATION OF INDEPENDENCE, L.L.C.—See VSE Corporation; *U.S. Public*, pg. 2313
THE KANSAS BANKERS SURETY COMPANY—See Berkshire Hathaway Inc.; *U.S. Public*, pg. 316
KANSAS CABLE HOLDINGS, INC.—See Gladstone Management Corporation; *U.S. Private*, pg. 1705
KANSAS CHILDREN'S SERVICE LEAGUE; *U.S. Private*, pg. 2260
KANSAS CITY AGGREGATE LLC—See Eagle Materials Inc.; *U.S. Public*, pg. 702
KANSAS CITY AUTO AUCTION INC.—See Cox Enterprises, Inc.; *U.S. Private*, pg. 1076
KANSAS CITY BUSINESS JOURNAL—See Advance Publications, Inc.; *U.S. Private*, pg. 84
KANSAS CITY CHIEFS FOOTBALL CLUB, INC.; *U.S. Private*, pg. 2260
KANSAS CITY ELECTRICAL SUPPLY CO.; *U.S. Private*, pg. 2260
KANSAS CITY FLY ASH LLC—See Eagle Materials Inc.; *U.S. Public*, pg. 702
KANSAS CITY FREIGHTLINER SALES INC.—See Penske Automotive Group, Inc.; *U.S. Public*, pg. 1664
KANSAS CITY GASTROENTEROLOGY & HEPATOLOGY PHYSICIANS GROUP, LLC—See HCA Healthcare, Inc.; *U.S. Public*, pg. 999
KANSAS CITY HOME CARE, INC.; *U.S. Private*, pg. 2260
KANSAS CITY HOSPICE & PALLIATIVE CARE; *U.S. Private*, pg. 2260
KANSAS CITY LIFE INSURANCE COMPANY; *U.S. Public*, pg. 1214
KANSAS CITY NEUROLOGY ASSOCIATES, LLC—See HCA Healthcare, Inc.; *U.S. Public*, pg. 999
KANSAS CITY OPTHALMICS LLC—See Carl-Zeiss-Stiftung; *Int'l*, pg. 1335
KANSAS CITY OPTHALMICS LLC—See EQT AB; *Int'l*, pg. 2473
KANSAS CITY PETERBILT INC.; *U.S. Private*, pg. 2260
KANSAS CITY PULMONOLOGY PRACTICE, LLC—See HCA Healthcare, Inc.; *U.S. Public*, pg. 1000
KANSAS CITY ROYALS BASEBALL CORPORATION; *U.S. Private*, pg. 2260
KANSAS CITY SAUSAGE COMPANY; *U.S. Private*, pg. 2260
KANSAS CITY SOUTHERN DE MEXICO S.A. DE C.V.—See Canadian Pacific Kansas City Limited; *Int'l*, pg. 1285
THE KANSAS CITY SOUTHERN RAILWAY COMPANY—See Canadian Pacific Kansas City Limited; *Int'l*, pg. 1285
KANSAS CITY SOUTHERN—See Canadian Pacific Kansas City Limited; *Int'l*, pg. 1285
THE KANSAS CITY STAR COMPANY—See Chatham Asset Management, LLC; *U.S. Private*, pg. 867
KANSAS CITY STEAK COMPANY, LLC—See Marfrig Global Foods S.A.; *Int'l*, pg. 4692
KANSAS CITY VASCULAR & GENERAL SURGERY GROUP, LLC—See HCA Healthcare, Inc.; *U.S. Public*, pg. 1000
KANSAS CITY WOMEN'S CLINIC GROUP, LLC—See HCA Healthcare, Inc.; *U.S. Public*, pg. 1000
KANSAS ELECTRIC POWER COOPERATIVE, INC.; *U.S. Private*, pg. 2260
KANSAS ELKS TRAINING CENTER FOR THE HANDICAPPED, INC.; *U.S. Private*, pg. 2261
KANSAS FEEDS, INC.; *U.S. Private*, pg. 2261
KANSAS GAS SERVICE COMPANY—See ONEOK, Inc.; *U.S. Public*, pg. 1603
KANSAS LIVESTOCK ASSOCIATION; *U.S. Private*, pg. 2261
KANSAS LOGOS, INC.—See Lamar Advertising Company; *U.S. Public*, pg. 1290
KANSAS LUMBER HOMESTORE INC.; *U.S. Private*, pg. 2261
KANSAS MASONIC HOME; *U.S. Private*, pg. 2261
KANSAS MEDICAL MUTUAL INSURANCE CO; *U.S. Private*, pg. 2261
KANSAS/OKLAHOMA MACHINE TOOLS, INC.; *U.S. Private*, pg. 2261
KANSAS PLASTICS COMPANY INC.—See MacLean-Fogg Company; *U.S. Private*, pg. 2537
KANSAS PULMONARY AND SLEEP SPECIALISTS, LLC—See HCA Healthcare, Inc.; *U.S. Public*, pg. 1000
KANSAS PULMONARY & SLEEP SPECIALISTS, LLC—See HCA Healthcare, Inc.; *U.S. Public*, pg. 1000
KANSAS RADIO NETWORKS—See Shivers Trading & Operating Company; *U.S. Private*, pg. 3638
KANSAS REHABILITATION HOSPITAL, INC.—See Encompass Health Corporation; *U.S. Public*, pg. 758
KANSAS SPEEDWAY CORPORATION—See National Association for Stock Car Auto Racing, Inc.; *U.S. Private*, pg. 2845
KANSAS SPEEDWAY DEVELOPMENT CORP.—See National Association for Stock Car Auto Racing, Inc.; *U.S. Private*, pg. 2845
KANSAS STAR CASINO, LLC—See Boyd Gaming Corporation; *U.S. Public*, pg. 377
KANSAS TRAUMA & CRITICAL CARE SPECIALISTS, LLC—See HCA Healthcare, Inc.; *U.S. Public*, pg. 1000
KANSAS TURNPIKE AUTHORITY; *U.S. Private*, pg. 2261

KANSEI CO., LTD.—See Punch Industry Co., Ltd.; *Int'l*, pg. 6118
KANSEKI CO., LTD.; *Int'l*, pg. 4073
KANSO TECHNOS CO., LTD.—See The Kansai Electric Power Co., Inc.; *Int'l*, pg. 7661
KAN S.P. Z O.O.—See Aalberts N.V.; *Int'l*, pg. 34
KANSSEN (YADONG) PIPE COATING SERVICE CO., LTD.—See Wah Seong Corporation Berhad; *Int'l*, pg. 8329
KANTAR DEUTSCHLAND GMBH—See Bain Capital, LP; *U.S. Private*, pg. 447
THE KANTAR GROUP LIMITED—See Bain Capital, LP; *U.S. Private*, pg. 447
THE KANTAR GROUP—See Bain Capital, LP; *U.S. Private*, pg. 448
KANTAR HEALTH—See Oracle Corporation; *U.S. Public*, pg. 1611
KANTAR IBOPE MEDIA—See Bain Capital, LP; *U.S. Private*, pg. 448
KANTAR MEDIA—See Bain Capital, LP; *U.S. Private*, pg. 448
KANTAR RETAIL—See Bain Capital, LP; *U.S. Private*, pg. 447
KANTAR WORLDPANEL—See Bain Capital, LP; *U.S. Private*, pg. 447
KANTATSU CO., LTD.—See Kanematsu Corporation; *Int'l*, pg. 4069
KAN-THERM GMBH—See Aalberts N.V.; *Int'l*, pg. 34
KANTI BIJLEE UTPADAN NIGAM LTD.—See NTPC Limited; *Int'l*, pg. 5484
KANTO AIR CARGO CO., LTD.—See Azuma Shipping Co., Ltd.; *Int'l*, pg. 782
KANTO BUSSAN CO., LTD.—See Makino Milling Machine Co., Ltd.; *Int'l*, pg. 4656
KANTO COIL CENTER CO., LTD.—See Toyota Tsusho Corporation; *Int'l*, pg. 7877
KANTO CONSTRUCTION CO., LTD.—See K&O Energy Group Inc.; *Int'l*, pg. 4038
KANTO CORPORATION; *U.S. Private*, pg. 2261
KANTO DAINICHISEIKA KOGYO CO., LTD.—See Dainichiseika Color & Chemicals Mfg. Co., Ltd.; *Int'l*, pg. 1939
KANTO D-BAR STEEL CORPORATION—See Godo Steel, Ltd.; *Int'l*, pg. 3020
KANTO DENKA KOGYO CO., LTD. - MIZUSHIMA PLANT—See Kanto Denka Kogyo Co., Ltd.; *Int'l*, pg. 4073
KANTO DENKA KOGYO CO., LTD. - SHIBUKAWA PLANT—See Kanto Denka Kogyo Co., Ltd.; *Int'l*, pg. 4073
KANTO DENKA KOGYO CO., LTD.; *Int'l*, pg. 4073
KANTO DENKA KOGYO (SHANGHAI) CO., LTD.—See Kanto Denka Kogyo Co., Ltd.; *Int'l*, pg. 4073
KANTO DENKA KOREA CO., LTD.—See Kanto Denka Kogyo Co., Ltd.; *Int'l*, pg. 4073
KANTOEISEN CO., LTD.—See Nippon Yusen Kabushiki Kaisha; *Int'l*, pg. 5358
KANTO GRAIN TERMINAL CO., LTD.—See Toyota Tsusho Corporation; *Int'l*, pg. 7877
KANTOH CO., LTD.—See Sala Corporation; *Int'l*, pg. 6490
KANTOH INOAC CO., LTD. - SAITAMA PLANT—See INOAC Corporation; *Int'l*, pg. 3714
KANTO HITACHI CO., LTD.—See Hitachi, Ltd.; *Int'l*, pg. 3423
KANTO MAZDA CO., LTD.—See Mazda Motor Corporation; *Int'l*, pg. 4748
KANTO MITSUBISHI MOTORS SALES CO., LTD.—See Mitsubishi Motors Corporation; *Int'l*, pg. 4966
KANTO NATURAL GAS DEVELOPMENT CO., LTD.—See K&O Energy Group Inc.; *Int'l*, pg. 4038
KANTONE HOLDINGS LTD—See Champion Technology Holdings Ltd; *Int'l*, pg. 1440
KANTONE PAGING COMPANY LIMITED—See Champion Technology Holdings Ltd; *Int'l*, pg. 1440
KANTO NIPPON FOOD, INC.—See NH Foods Ltd.; *Int'l*, pg. 5256
KANTO NOK HANBAI CO., LTD.—See NOK Corporation; *Int'l*, pg. 5402
KANTO OKURA CO., LTD.—See Okura Industrial Co., Ltd.; *Int'l*, pg. 5551
KANTO READY-MIXED CONCRETE TRANSPORTATION CO., LTD.—See UBE Corporation; *Int'l*, pg. 8001
KANTORWASSINK; *U.S. Private*, pg. 2261
KANTO SANGYO CO., LTD.—See Noritz Corporation; *Int'l*, pg. 5429
KANTO SANYO SEMICONDUCTOR CO., LTD.—See ON Semiconductor Corporation; *U.S. Public*, pg. 1601
KANTO SEIATSU KOGYO CO., LTD.—See Robert Bosch GmbH; *Int'l*, pg. 6361
KANTO-SEIATSU KOGYO CO., LTD.—See Robert Bosch GmbH; *Int'l*, pg. 6361
KANTO SEINO TRANSPORTATION CO., LTD.—See Seino Holdings Co., Ltd.; *Int'l*, pg. 6690
KANTO SENKO TRANSPORT CO., LTD.—See Senko Group Holdings Co., Ltd.; *Int'l*, pg. 6710
KANTO SODIUM SILICATE GLASS CO., LTD.—See Adeka Corporation; *Int'l*, pg. 142
KANTO SOGO SHIZAI CO., LTD.—See Fuji Sangyo Corporation; *Int'l*, pg. 2826

COMPANY NAME INDEX

KANTO STEEL LTD.—See Kyoei Steel Ltd.; *Int'l*, pg. 4362
KANTO STYRENE CO., LTD.—See Kaneka Corporation; *Int'l*, pg. 4067
KANTO TECHNICAL INSTITUTE—See Kawasaki Heavy Industries, Ltd.; *Int'l*, pg. 4095
KANTO TOHUN CO., LTD.—See Tomoku Co., Ltd.; *Int'l*, pg. 7801
KANTO UBE CONCRETE CO., LTD.—See UBE Corporation; *Int'l*, pg. 8001
KANTO UBE HOLDINGS CO., LTD.—See UBE Corporation; *Int'l*, pg. 8001
KANTOU SEIRAKU CO., LTD.—See Meiji Holdings Co., Ltd.; *Int'l*, pg. 4800
KANT-SLAM DOOR CHECK CO.—See The Bloomfield Manufacturing Co., Inc.; *U.S. Private*, pg. 3995
KANTSU CO., LTD.; *Int'l*, pg. 4073
KANU EQUIPMENT CONGO LIMITED—See Apex Partners Proprietary Limited; *Int'l*, pg. 512
KANU EQUIPMENT CONGO LIMITED—See TRG Management LP; *U.S. Private*, pg. 4219
KANU EQUIPMENT COTE'IVOIRE LIMITED—See Apex Partners Proprietary Limited; *Int'l*, pg. 512
KANU EQUIPMENT COTE'IVOIRE LIMITED—See TRG Management LP; *U.S. Private*, pg. 4219
KANU EQUIPMENT GHANA LIMITED—See Apex Partners Proprietary Limited; *Int'l*, pg. 512
KANU EQUIPMENT GHANA LIMITED—See TRG Management LP; *U.S. Private*, pg. 4219
KANU EQUIPMENT LIBERIA LTD.—See Apex Partners Proprietary Limited; *Int'l*, pg. 512
KANU EQUIPMENT LIBERIA LTD.—See TRG Management LP; *U.S. Private*, pg. 4219
KANU EQUIPMENT SIERRA LEONE—See Apex Partners Proprietary Limited; *Int'l*, pg. 512
KANU EQUIPMENT SIERRA LEONE—See TRG Management LP; *U.S. Private*, pg. 4220
KANUNGO FINANCIERS LIMITED; *Int'l*, pg. 4073
KANZACC CO., LTD.—See The Furukawa Electric Co., Ltd.; *Int'l*, pg. 7646
THE KANZA CO-OPERATIVE EXCHANGE, INC.; *U.S. Private*, pg. 4064
KANZAKI KOKYUKOKI MFG.CO., LTD.—See Yanmar Co., Ltd., *Int'l*, pg. 0500
KANZAKI SPECIALTY PAPERS INC.—See Oji Holdings Corporation; *Int'l*, pg. 5536
KANZAN SPEZIALPAPIERE GMBH—See Oji Holdings Corporation; *Int'l*, pg. 5536
KANZELSTEINBRUCH GRATKORN GMBH—See STRABAG SE; *Int'l*, pg. 7231
KANZEN MANAGEMENT SDN. BHD.—See FACB Industries Incorporated Berhad; *Int'l*, pg. 2600
KANZEN TETSU SDN. BHD.—See Kentzu Steel Sdn Bhd; *Int'l*, pg. 4129
KANZHUN LTD.; *Int'l*, pg. 4073
KANZLER GMBH—See Darling Ingredients Inc.; *U.S. Public*, pg. 634
KAO AUSTRALIA PTY. LIMITED—See Kao Corporation; *Int'l*, pg. 4074
KAO AUSTRIA HANDELSGESELLSCHAFT MBH—See Kao Corporation; *Int'l*, pg. 4074
KAO BRANDS EUROPE LTD.—See Kao Corporation; *Int'l*, pg. 4074
KAO CANADA LTD.—See Kao Corporation; *Int'l*, pg. 4074
KAO CHEMICAL CORPORATION SHANGHAI—See Kao Corporation; *Int'l*, pg. 4074
KAO CHEMICALS EUROPE, S.L.—See Kao Corporation; *Int'l*, pg. 4074
KAO CHEMICALS GMBH—See Kao Corporation; *Int'l*, pg. 4074
KAO CHIMIGRAF, S.L.—See Kao Corporation; *Int'l*, pg. 4074
KAO COLLINS INC.—See Kao Corporation; *Int'l*, pg. 4074
KAO COMMERCIAL (SHANGHAI) CO., LTD.—See Kao Corporation; *Int'l*, pg. 4074
KAO CONSUMER PRODUCTS (SOUTHEAST ASIA) CO., LTD—See Kao Corporation; *Int'l*, pg. 4074
KAO CORPORATION GMBH—See Kao Corporation; *Int'l*, pg. 4074
KAO CORPORATION S.A.—See Kao Corporation; *Int'l*, pg. 4074
KAO CORPORATION SHANGHAI—See Kao Corporation; *Int'l*, pg. 4074
KAO CORPORATION; *Int'l*, pg. 4073
KAO COSMETIC PRODUCTS ODAWARA CO., LTD.—See Kao Corporation; *Int'l*, pg. 4074
KAO CUSTOMER MARKETING CO., LTD.—See Kao Corporation; *Int'l*, pg. 4074
KAO DENMARK A/S—See Kao Corporation; *Int'l*, pg. 4074
KAO FONG MACHINERY CO., LTD.—See Hota Industrial Mfg. Co., Ltd.; *Int'l*, pg. 3487
KAO FRANCE SARL—See Kao Corporation; *Int'l*, pg. 4074
KAO GROUP CUSTOMER MARKETING CO., LTD.—See Kao Corporation; *Int'l*, pg. 4074
KAO HOLDINGS (THAILAND) CO., LTD.—See Kao Corporation; *Int'l*, pg. 4074
KAO (HONG KONG) LIMITED—See Kao Corporation; *Int'l*, pg. 4074

KAO HSIUNG CHANG IRON & STEEL CORP. - PEN FACTORY—See Kao Hsiung Chang Iron & Steel Corp.; *Int'l*, pg. 4075
KAO HSIUNG CHANG IRON & STEEL CORP.; *Int'l*, pg. 4075
KAO HSIUNG CHANG IRON & STEEL CORP. - YONG-AN FACTORY—See Kao Hsiung Chang Iron & Steel Corp.; *Int'l*, pg. 4075
KAOHSIUNG MONOMER COMPANY LIMITED—See Mitsubishi Chemical Group Corporation; *Int'l*, pg. 4930
KAOHSIUNG OPTO-ELECTRONICS INC.—See Wistron Corporation; *Int'l*, pg. 8438
KAOHSIUNG REFINERY—See CPC Corporation; *Int'l*, pg. 1824
KAO HULUDAO CASTING MATERIALS CO., LTD.—See Kao Corporation; *Int'l*, pg. 4075
KAO INDUSTRIAL (THAILAND) CO., LTD.—See Kao Corporation; *Int'l*, pg. 4075
KAO ITALY S.P.A.—See Kao Corporation; *Int'l*, pg. 4075
KAOLIN AD—See Quarzwerke GmbH; *Int'l*, pg. 6156
KAOLIN-UND TONWERKE SEILITZ-LOTHAIN GMBH—See SCR Sibelco SA; *Int'l*, pg. 6654
KA OLSSON & GEMS AB—See Indutrade AB; *Int'l*, pg. 3679
KAO (MALAYSIA) SDN., BHD.—See Kao Corporation; *Int'l*, pg. 4074
KAO (MALAYSIA) SDN. BHD.—See Kao Corporation; *Int'l*, pg. 4074
KAON AMERICA LATINA LTDA.—See KAONMEDIA CO, LTD.; *Int'l*, pg. 4075
KAONAVI, INC.; *Int'l*, pg. 4075
KAO NETHERLANDS B.V.—See Kao Corporation; *Int'l*, pg. 4075
KAO NEW ZEALAND LIMITED—See Kao Corporation; *Int'l*, pg. 4075
KAON GERMANY—See KAONMEDIA CO, LTD.; *Int'l*, pg. 4075
KAON INDIA PVT LTD.—See KAONMEDIA CO, LTD.; *Int'l*, pg. 4076
KAONMEDIA CO, LTD.; *Int'l*, pg. 4075
KAON MIDDLE EAST FZCO—See KAONMEDIA CO, LTD.; *Int'l*, pg. 4076
KAON NORWAY—See KAONMEDIA CO, LTD.; *Int'l*, pg. 4075
KAO NORWAY AS—See Kao Corporation; *Int'l*, pg. 4075
KAON RUSSIA—See KAONMEDIA CO, LTD.; *Int'l*, pg. 4075
KAO OLEOCHEMICAL (MALAYSIA) SDN. BHD.—See Kao Corporation; *Int'l*, pg. 4075
KAO PLASTICIZER (MALAYSIA) SDN. BHD.—See Kao Corporation; *Int'l*, pg. 4075
KAO PROFESSIONAL SALON SERVICES GMBH—See Kao Corporation; *Int'l*, pg. 4075
KAO PROFESSIONAL SERVICES CO., LTD.—See Kao Corporation; *Int'l*, pg. 4075
KAOPU GROUP, INC.; *Int'l*, pg. 4076
KAO-QUAKER CO., LTD.—See Kao Corporation; *Int'l*, pg. 4075
KAO-QUAKER CO., LTD. - TOYOHASHI PLANT—See Kao Corporation; *Int'l*, pg. 4075
KAORI HEAT TREATMENT CO., LTD. - BEN-CHOU PLANT—See Kaori Heat Treatment Co., Ltd.; *Int'l*, pg. 4076
KAORI HEAT TREATMENT CO., LTD.; *Int'l*, pg. 4076
KAORIME HONPO CO., LTD.—See Yoshimura Food Holdings K.K.; *Int'l*, pg. 8600
KAORI TECHNOLOGY (NINGBO) CO., LTD.—See Kaori Heat Treatment Co., Ltd.; *Int'l*, pg. 4076
KAO SALON JAPAN CO., LTD.—See Kao Corporation; *Int'l*, pg. 4075
KAO SANITARY PRODUCTS EHIME CO., LTD.—See Kao Corporation; *Int'l*, pg. 4075
KAO (SINGAPORE) PTE., LTD.—See Kao Corporation; *Int'l*, pg. 4075
KAO SOAP (MALAYSIA) SDN. BHD.—See Kao Corporation; *Int'l*, pg. 4075
KAO SOUTH AFRICA PTY. LTD.—See Kao Corporation; *Int'l*, pg. 4075
KAO SPECIALTIES AMERICAS—See Kao Corporation; *Int'l*, pg. 4075
KAO SWEDEN AB—See Kao Corporation; *Int'l*, pg. 4075
KAO SWITZERLAND AG—See Kao Corporation; *Int'l*, pg. 4075
KAO (TAIWAN) CORPORATION—See Kao Corporation; *Int'l*, pg. 4074
KAO TRADING CORPORATION SHANGHAI—See Kao Corporation; *Int'l*, pg. 4075
KAO (UK) LIMITED—See Kao Corporation; *Int'l*, pg. 4074
KAO USA INC.—See Kao Corporation; *Int'l*, pg. 4073
KAO USA, INC.—See Kao Corporation; *Int'l*, pg. 4075
KAO VIETNAM CO., LTD.—See Kao Corporation; *Int'l*, pg. 4075
KAPA CAPITAL, INC.; *Int'l*, pg. 4076
KAPALUA LAND COMPANY, LTD.—See Maui Land & Pineapple Company, Inc.; *U.S. Public*, pg. 1402
KAPALUA REALTY COMPANY, LTD.—See Maui Land & Pineapple Company, Inc.; *U.S. Public*, pg. 1402
KAPAR ENERGY VENTURES SDN. BHD.—See Tenaga Nasional Berhad; *Int'l*, pg. 7557

KAPOOR ENTERPRISES

KAP BETEILIGUNGS-AG; *Int'l*, pg. 4076
KAPCHORUA TEA KENYA PLC; *Int'l*, pg. 4076
KAPCO INCORPORATED; *U.S. Private*, pg. 2261
KAPDOM-INVEST GMBH—See Munchener Ruckversicherungs AG; *Int'l*, pg. 5089
KAPELE APPOINTMENTS (PTY) LIMITED - THE WORKING EARTH DIVISION—See ADvTECH Limited; *Int'l*, pg. 168
KAPELE APPOINTMENTS (PTY) LTD - VERTEX-KAPELE DIVISION—See ADvTECH Limited; *Int'l*, pg. 168
KAPELLEN SARL—See CLS Holdings plc; *Int'l*, pg. 1664
KAPELUSZ EDITORA, S.A.—See Promotora de Informaciones S.A.; *Int'l*, pg. 5995
KAPES, INC.—See Korea Electric Power Corporation; *Int'l*, pg. 4283
KAPE TECHNOLOGIES PLC; *Int'l*, pg. 4076
KAPIL COTEX LTD.; *Int'l*, pg. 4076
KAPIL RAJ FINANCE LTD.; *Int'l*, pg. 4076
KAPISH SERVICES PTY. LTD.—See Pacific Equity Partners Pty. Limited; *Int'l*, pg. 5689
KAPITAL YATIRIM HOLDING A.S.; *Int'l*, pg. 4076
KAPITOL, A.S.—See Vienna Insurance Group AG Wiener Versicherung Gruppe; *Int'l*, pg. 8195
KAPITOL POJISTOVACI A FINANCNI PORADENSTVI, A.S.—See Vienna Insurance Group AG Wiener Versicherung Gruppe; *Int'l*, pg. 8195
KAPLAMIN AMBALAJ SANAYI VE TICARET A.S.—See Cukurova Holding A.S.; *Int'l*, pg. 1876
KAPLAN AUTO GROUP; *U.S. Private*, pg. 2261
KAPLAN BUSINESS SCHOOL AUSTRALIA PTY LTD—See Graham Holdings Company; *U.S. Public*, pg. 955
KAPLAN BUSINESS SCHOOL PTY LTD.—See Graham Holdings Company; *U.S. Public*, pg. 955
KAPLAN CANADA INC.—See Graham Holdings Company; *U.S. Public*, pg. 955
KAPLAN COMPANIES INC.; *U.S. Private*, pg. 2261
KAPLAN CORPORATION; *U.S. Private*, pg. 2261
KAPLAN EARLY LEARNING COMPANY—See Kaplan Companies Inc.; *U.S. Private*, pg. 2261
KAPLAN EDUCATION PTY. LIMITED—See Graham Holdings Company; *U.S. Public*, pg. 955
KAPLAN FINANCIAL LIMITED—See Graham Holdings Company; *U.S. Public*, pg. 955
KAPLAN FINANCIAL—See Graham Holdings Company; *U.S. Public*, pg. 956
KAPLAN GLOBAL SOLUTIONS, LLC—See Graham Holdings Company; *U.S. Public*, pg. 955
KAPLAN HIGHER EDUCATION ACADEMY PTE. LTD.—See Graham Holdings Company; *U.S. Public*, pg. 955
KAPLAN HIGHER EDUCATION, LLC—See Graham Holdings Company; *U.S. Public*, pg. 955
KAPLAN, INC.—See Graham Holdings Company; *U.S. Public*, pg. 955
KAPLAN (INDIA) PRIVATE LIMITED—See Graham Holdings Company; *U.S. Public*, pg. 955
KAPLAN INSTITUTE LIMITED—See Graham Holdings Company; *U.S. Public*, pg. 956
KAPLAN INTERNATIONAL COLLEGE LONDON LIMITED—See Graham Holdings Company; *U.S. Public*, pg. 956
KAPLAN INTERNATIONAL COLLEGES, C.A.—See Graham Holdings Company; *U.S. Public*, pg. 955
KAPLAN INTERNATIONAL COLLEGES U.K. LIMITED—See Graham Holdings Company; *U.S. Public*, pg. 956
KAPLAN INTERNATIONAL ENGLISH (AUSTRALIA) PTY LIMITED—See Graham Holdings Company; *U.S. Public*, pg. 956
KAPLAN INTERNATIONAL (MANLY) PTY LIMITED—See Graham Holdings Company; *U.S. Public*, pg. 956
KAPLAN LAW SCHOOL LIMITED—See Graham Holdings Company; *U.S. Public*, pg. 956
KAPLAN OPEN LEARNING (ESSEX) LIMITED—See Graham Holdings Company; *U.S. Public*, pg. 956
KAPLAN PROFESSIONAL SCHOOLS, INC.—See Graham Holdings Company; *U.S. Public*, pg. 956
KAPLAN PROFESSIONAL—See Graham Holdings Company; *U.S. Public*, pg. 956
KAPLAN PUBLISHING LIMITED—See Graham Holdings Company; *U.S. Public*, pg. 956
KAPLANSKY INSURANCE AGENCY, INC.; *U.S. Private*, pg. 2261
THE KAPLAN THALER GROUP—See Publicis Groupe S.A.; *Int'l*, pg. 6112
KAPLAN TRUCKING COMPANY; *U.S. Private*, pg. 2261
KAPLAN TRUCKING—See Kaplan Trucking Company; *U.S. Private*, pg. 2261
KAP LIMITED—See Steinhoff International Holdings N.V.; *Int'l*, pg. 7194
KAPMAN ELEKTRIK VE ELEKTRONIK TIC. A.S.—See A.A.G. STUCCHI s.r.l.; *Int'l*, pg. 23
KAPOOR ENTERPRISES; *U.S. Private*, pg. 2261
KAPOSPLAST PLASTIC INDUSTRIAL CO. LTD.—See PannErgy Nyrt.; *Int'l*, pg. 5728
KAPPA BIOSCIENCE AS—See Balchem Corporation; *U.S. Public*, pg. 265

KAPPA BOOKS PUBLISHERS LLC—See Kappa Publishing Group, Inc.; *U.S. Private*, pg. 2262
KAPPA CREATE CO., LTD.; *Int'l*, pg. 4076
KAPP ADVERTISING SERVICE INCORPORATED; *U.S. Private*, pg. 2262
KAPPA FRANCE S.A.S.—See BasicNet S.p.A.; *Int'l*, pg. 886
KAPPA GRAPHICS, LP; *U.S. Private*, pg. 2262
KAPPAHL ALAND AB—See KappAhl Holding AB; *Int'l*, pg. 4077
KAPPAHL AS—See KappAhl Holding AB; *Int'l*, pg. 4077
KAPPAHL HOLDING AB; *Int'l*, pg. 4076
KAPPAHL OY—See KappAhl Holding AB; *Int'l*, pg. 4077
KAPPAHL POLSKA SP.Z.O.O.—See KappAhl Holding AB; *Int'l*, pg. 4077
KAPPA HOLDING (NEDERLAND) B.V.—See Smurfit Kappa Group plc; *Int'l*, pg. 7017
KAPPA KAPPA GAMMA; *U.S. Private*, pg. 2262
KAPPA MAP GROUP, LLC; *U.S. Private*, pg. 2262
KAPPA PUBLISHING GROUP, INC.; *U.S. Private*, pg. 2262
KAPPA QUAMA INTERNATIONAL B.V.—See Smurfit Kappa Group plc; *Int'l*, pg. 7017
KAPP-CHEMIE GMBH & CO. KG—See Stockmeier Holding GmbH; *Int'l*, pg. 7220
KAPP COMMUNICATIONS, INC.—See Interactive Services Network, Inc.; *U.S. Private*, pg. 2108
KAPP CONSTRUCTION COMPANY, INC.; *U.S. Private*, pg. 2262
KAPPE ASSOCIATES, INC.—See DXP Enterprises, Inc.; *U.S. Public*, pg. 697
KAPPELHOFF INDUSTRIETECHNIK GMBH—See VINCI S.A.; *Int'l*, pg. 8236
KAPPEL & KAPPEL INC.; *U.S. Private*, pg. 2262
KAPSCH (BEIJING) INFORMATION AND COMMUNICATION TECHNOLOGY CO., LTD.—See Kontron AG; *Int'l*, pg. 4276
KAPSCH BUSINESSCOM AG—See Kapsch-Group Beteiligungs GmbH; *Int'l*, pg. 4077
KAPSCH BUSINESSCOM KFT.—See Kapsch-Group Beteiligungs GmbH; *Int'l*, pg. 4077
KAPSCH BUSINESSCOM S.R.O.—See Kapsch-Group Beteiligungs GmbH; *Int'l*, pg. 4077
KAPSCH CARRIERCOM AG—See Kontron AG; *Int'l*, pg. 4276
KAPSCH CARRIERCOM DEUTSCHLAND GMBH—See Kontron AG; *Int'l*, pg. 4277
KAPSCH CARRIERCOM ESPANA, S.L.U.—See Kontron AG; *Int'l*, pg. 4277
KAPSCH CARRIERCOM FRANCE SAS—See Kontron AG; *Int'l*, pg. 4277
KAPSCH CARRIERCOM SP. Z O.O.—See Kontron AG; *Int'l*, pg. 4277
KAPSCH CARRIERCOM TAIWAN CO., LTD.—See Kontron AG; *Int'l*, pg. 4277
KAPSCH CARRIERCOM - UNIPESSOAL LDA—See Kontron AG; *Int'l*, pg. 4277
KAPSCH CARRIER SOLUTION GMBH—See Kontron AG; *Int'l*, pg. 4277
KAPSCH COMPONENTS GMBH & CO. KG—See Kapsch-Group Beteiligungs GmbH; *Int'l*, pg. 4077
KAPSCH COMPONENTS KG—See Kapsch-Group Beteiligungs GmbH; *Int'l*, pg. 4077
KAPSCH D.O.O.—See Kontron AG; *Int'l*, pg. 4277
KAPSCH EOOD—See Kontron AG; *Int'l*, pg. 4277
KAPSCH FE—See Kontron AG; *Int'l*, pg. 4277
KAPSCH-GROUP BETEILIGUNGS GMBH; *Int'l*, pg. 4077
KAPSCH PARTNER SOLUTIONS GMBH—See Kapsch-Group Beteiligungs GmbH; *Int'l*, pg. 4077
KAPSCH SMART ENERGY GMBH—See Kapsch-Group Beteiligungs GmbH; *Int'l*, pg. 4077
KAPSCH S.R.L.—See Kapsch-Group Beteiligungs GmbH; *Int'l*, pg. 4077
KAPSCH S.R.O.—See Kapsch-Group Beteiligungs GmbH; *Int'l*, pg. 4077
KAPSCH TELEMATIC SERVICES GMBH—See Kapsch-Group Beteiligungs GmbH; *Int'l*, pg. 4077
KAPSCH TELEMATIC SERVICES GMBH—See Kapsch-Group Beteiligungs GmbH; *Int'l*, pg. 4077
KAPSCH TELEMATIC SERVICES KFT.—See Kapsch-Group Beteiligungs GmbH; *Int'l*, pg. 4077
KAPSCH TELEMATIC SERVICES SOLUTIONS A/S—See Kapsch-Group Beteiligungs GmbH; *Int'l*, pg. 4077
KAPSCH TELEMATIC SERVICES SPOL. S.R.O.—See Kapsch-Group Beteiligungs GmbH; *Int'l*, pg. 4077
KAPSCH TELEMATIC SERVICES SP. Z O.O.—See Kapsch-Group Beteiligungs GmbH; *Int'l*, pg. 4077
KAPSCH TELEMATIC TECHNOLOGIES BULGARIA AD—See Kapsch-Group Beteiligungs GmbH; *Int'l*, pg. 4077
KAPSCH TELEMATIK TECHNOLOGIES BULGARIA EAD—See Kapsch-Group Beteiligungs GmbH; *Int'l*, pg. 4077
KAPSCH TRAFFICCOM AB—See Kapsch-Group Beteiligungs GmbH; *Int'l*, pg. 4077
KAPSCH TRAFFICCOM AG—See Kapsch-Group Beteiligungs GmbH; *Int'l*, pg. 4077
KAPSCH TRAFFICCOM ARCE SISTEMAS S.A.U.—See Kapsch-Group Beteiligungs GmbH; *Int'l*, pg. 4078
KAPSCH TRAFFICCOM ARGENTINA S.A.—See Kapsch-Group Beteiligungs GmbH; *Int'l*, pg. 4077
KAPSCH TRAFFICCOM AUSTRALIA PTY LTD.—See Kapsch-Group Beteiligungs GmbH; *Int'l*, pg. 4077
KAPSCH TRAFFICCOM CANADA INC.—See Kapsch-Group Beteiligungs GmbH; *Int'l*, pg. 4077
KAPSCH TRAFFICCOM CHILE S.A.—See Kapsch-Group Beteiligungs GmbH; *Int'l*, pg. 4077
KAPSCH TRAFFICCOM D.O.O.—See Kapsch-Group Beteiligungs GmbH; *Int'l*, pg. 4078
KAPSCH TRAFFICCOM FRANCE SAS—See Kapsch-Group Beteiligungs GmbH; *Int'l*, pg. 4077
KAPSCH TRAFFICCOM INC.—See Kapsch-Group Beteiligungs GmbH; *Int'l*, pg. 4077
KAPSCH TRAFFICCOM IVHS INC.—See Kapsch-Group Beteiligungs GmbH; *Int'l*, pg. 4077
KAPSCH TRAFFICCOM IVHS, S.A. DE C.V.—See Kapsch-Group Beteiligungs GmbH; *Int'l*, pg. 4077
KAPSCH TRAFFICCOM KAZAKHSTAN LLC—See Kapsch-Group Beteiligungs GmbH; *Int'l*, pg. 4077
KAPSCH TRAFFICCOM LTD.—See Kapsch-Group Beteiligungs GmbH; *Int'l*, pg. 4077
KAPSCH TRAFFICCOM LTD.—See Kapsch-Group Beteiligungs GmbH; *Int'l*, pg. 4077
KAPSCH TRAFFICCOM LTD.—See Kapsch-Group Beteiligungs GmbH; *Int'l*, pg. 4077
KAPSCH TRAFFICCOM PTE. LTD.—See Kapsch-Group Beteiligungs GmbH; *Int'l*, pg. 4077
KAPSCH TRAFFICCOM RUSSIA OOO—See Kapsch-Group Beteiligungs GmbH; *Int'l*, pg. 4078
KAPSCH TRAFFICCOM SA (PTY) LTD.—See Kapsch-Group Beteiligungs GmbH; *Int'l*, pg. 4078
KAPSCH TRAFFICCOM SAUDI ARABIA CO. LTD.—See Kapsch-Group Beteiligungs GmbH; *Int'l*, pg. 4078
KAPSCH TRAFFICCOM SOUTH AFRICA (PTY) LTD.—See Kapsch-Group Beteiligungs GmbH; *Int'l*, pg. 4078
KAPSCH TRAFFICCOM S.R.L.—See Kapsch-Group Beteiligungs GmbH; *Int'l*, pg. 4078
KAPSCH TRAFFICCOM S.R.L.—See Kapsch-Group Beteiligungs GmbH; *Int'l*, pg. 4078
KAPSCH TRAFFICCOM TRANSPORTATION BRASIL LTDA.—See Kapsch-Group Beteiligungs GmbH; *Int'l*, pg. 4078
KAPSCH TRAFFICCOM TRANSPORTATION S.A.U.—See Kapsch-Group Beteiligungs GmbH; *Int'l*, pg. 4078
KAPSTONE ASIA LIMITED—See WestRock Company; *U.S. Public*, pg. 2361
KAPSTONE CHARLESTON KRAFT, LLC—See WestRock Company; *U.S. Public*, pg. 2361
KAPSTONE CONTAINER CORPORATION - AMSTERDAM—See WestRock Company; *U.S. Public*, pg. 2361
KAPSTONE CONTAINER CORPORATION—See WestRock Company; *U.S. Public*, pg. 2361
KAPSTONE CONTAINER CORP. - TWIN FALLS—See WestRock Company; *U.S. Public*, pg. 2361
KAPSTONE KRAFT PAPER CORPORATION—See WestRock Company; *U.S. Public*, pg. 2361
KAPSTONE OAKLAND—See WestRock Company; *U.S. Public*, pg. 2361
KAPSTONE PACKAGING - LAWRENCEBURG SHEET PLANT—See WestRock Company; *U.S. Public*, pg. 2361
KAPSTONE PACKAGING - MINNEAPOLIS CORRUGATOR PLANT—See WestRock Company; *U.S. Public*, pg. 2361
KAPSTONE PACKAGING PLANT—See WestRock Company; *U.S. Public*, pg. 2361
KAPSTONE PACKAGING PLANT - SOUTH CAROLINA—See WestRock Company; *U.S. Public*, pg. 2361
KAPSTONE PACKAGING - WEST SPRINGFIELD SHEET PLANT—See WestRock Company; *U.S. Public*, pg. 2361
KAPSTONE PAPER & PACKAGING CORPORATION—See WestRock Company; *U.S. Public*, pg. 2361
KAPSTONE SEATTLE—See WestRock Company; *U.S. Public*, pg. 2361
KAPSTONE SPANISH FORK—See WestRock Company; *U.S. Public*, pg. 2361
KAPSTONE YAKIMA—See WestRock Company; *U.S. Public*, pg. 2361
KAPSTON SERVICES LIMITED; *Int'l*, pg. 4078
KAPSTREAM CAPITAL PTY LIMITED—See Janus Henderson Group plc; *Int'l*, pg. 3881
KAPTAN DEMIR CELIK ENDUSTRISI VE TICARET A.S. - KAPTAN DEMIR CELIK CORLU HADDEHANE TESISLERI PLANT—See Kaptan Demir Celik Endustrisi ve Ticaret A.S.; *Int'l*, pg. 4078
KAPTAN DEMIR CELIK ENDUSTRISI VE TICARET A.S. - KAPTAN DEMIR CELIK KARABUK HADDEHANE TESISLERI PLANT—See Kaptan Demir Celik Endustrisi ve Ticaret A.S.; *Int'l*, pg. 4078
KAPTAN DEMIR CELIK ENDUSTRISI VE TICARET A.S. - KAPTAN DEMIR CELIK M. EREGLISI IZABE TESISLERI PLANT—See Kaptan Demir Celik Endustrisi ve Ticaret A.S.; *Int'l*, pg. 4078
KAPTAN DEMIR CELIK ENDUSTRISI VE TICARET A.S.; *Int'l*, pg. 4078
KAPTAN METAL DIS TICARET VE NAKLIYAT A.S.—See Kaptan Demir Celik Endustrisi ve Ticaret A.S.; *Int'l*, pg. 4078
KAPTAS OY—See Addtech AB; *Int'l*, pg. 134
KAP-TECHNOLOGY JSC—See JSC National Atomic Company Kazatomprom; *Int'l*, pg. 4009
KAP TEXTILE HOLDINGS SA LTD.—See KAP Beteiligungs-AG; *Int'l*, pg. 4076
KAPTYN, INC.; *U.S. Private*, pg. 2262
KAPUTONE WOOL SCOUR LIMITED—See Lempriere Pty. Ltd.; *Int'l*, pg. 4450
KARACHI (PHARMA & DIA) ROCHE PAKISTAN LTD.—See Roche Holding AG; *Int'l*, pg. 6373
KARACHI STOCK EXCHANGE (GUARANTEE) LIMITED; *Int'l*, pg. 4078
KARADA LAB, INC.—See ARKRAY, Inc.; *Int'l*, pg. 572
KARADANOTE, INC.; *Int'l*, pg. 4078
KARADI TALES COMPANY PRIVATE LIMITED—See Future Corporate Resources Limited; *Int'l*, pg. 2853
KARAD PROJECTS & MOTORS LIMITED—See Kirloskar Brothers Limited; *Int'l*, pg. 4191
KARAFARIN BANK BROKERAGE CO.—See Karafarin Bank; *Int'l*, pg. 4078
KARAFARIN BANK INVESTMENT CO.—See Karafarin Bank; *Int'l*, pg. 4078
KARAFARIN BANK; *Int'l*, pg. 4078
KARAFARIN FOREIGN EXCHANGE CO.—See Karafarin Bank; *Int'l*, pg. 4078
KARAFARIN LEASING CO.—See Karafarin Bank; *Int'l*, pg. 4078
KARA FOODS—See Vision Capital, LLP; *Int'l*, pg. 8252
KARAGANDY ZHARYK LLP—See Kazakhstan Utility Systems LLP; *Int'l*, pg. 4102
KARAGANDYZHYLUSBYT LLP—See Kazakhstan Utility Systems LLP; *Int'l*, pg. 4102
KARA INDUSTRIAL MINERALS PTY LTD—See Tasmania Mines Limited; *Int'l*, pg. 7465
KARAKAS ATLANTIS KIYMETLI MADENLER KUYUMCULUK TELEKOMUNIKASYON SANAYI VE TICARET A.S.; *Int'l*, pg. 4078
KARAK LAND SDN. BHD.—See Bina Puri Holdings Bhd; *Int'l*, pg. 1032
KARAKSA HOTELS CORPORATION—See XYMAX Corporation; *Int'l*, pg. 8542
KARAKSA HOTELS KANSAI CORPORATION—See XYMAX Corporation; *Int'l*, pg. 8542
KARAKSA HOTELS SAPPORO CORPORATION—See XYMAX Corporation; *Int'l*, pg. 8542
KARAKSA HOTELS TOKYO CORPORATION—See XYMAX Corporation; *Int'l*, pg. 8542
KARAMBUNAI CORP BHD.—See Nagacorp Ltd.; *Int'l*, pg. 5124
KARAMBUNAI GOLF MANAGEMENT BHD.—See Nagacorp Ltd.; *Int'l*, pg. 5124
KARAMBUNAI RESORTS SDN. BHD.—See Nagacorp Ltd.; *Int'l*, pg. 5124
KARAM CERAMICS LIMITED - FACTORY—See Karam Ceramics Limited; *Int'l*, pg. 4078
KARAM CERAMICS LIMITED; *Int'l*, pg. 4078
KARAMOLEGOS BAKERY S.A.; *Int'l*, pg. 4078
KARAN ELECTRIC MANUFACTURING LIMITED—See Allan International Holdings Limited; *Int'l*, pg. 332
KARANJA TERMINAL & LOGISTICS PRIVATE LIMITED—See Mercantile Ports & Logistics Limited; *Int'l*, pg. 4819
KARAOLIS GROUP PUBLIC LTD; *Int'l*, pg. 4078
KARARA MINING LTD.—See Anshan Iron & Steel Group Corporation; *Int'l*, pg. 479
KARAS & KARAS GLASS CO. INC.; *U.S. Private*, pg. 2262
KARASUMA SHOJI CO., LTD.—See The Bank of Kyoto, Ltd.; *Int'l*, pg. 7615
KARAT PACKAGING INC.; *U.S. Public*, pg. 1214
KARATZIS S.A.; *Int'l*, pg. 4079
KARAVAN TRAILERS INC.; *U.S. Private*, pg. 2262
KARA VITA, INC.—See Dermazone Solutions, Inc.; *U.S. Private*, pg. 1210
KARAZHYRA JSC; *Int'l*, pg. 4079
KARBACH BREWING CO. LLC—See Anheuser-Busch InBev SA/NV; *Int'l*, pg. 465
KARBALA HOTELS; *Int'l*, pg. 4079
KARBOCHEM (PTY) LIMITED; *Int'l*, pg. 4079
KARBON BEAUTY LLC; *U.S. Private*, pg. 2262
KARBON-X CORP.; *Int'l*, pg. 4079
KARCHER AB—See Alfred Karcher GmbH & Co. KG; *Int'l*, pg. 316
KARCHER AG—See Alfred Karcher GmbH & Co. KG; *Int'l*, pg. 316
KARCHER ANLAGENVERMIETUNGS GMBH—See Alfred Karcher GmbH & Co. KG; *Int'l*, pg. 316
KARCHER AS—See Alfred Karcher GmbH & Co. KG; *Int'l*, pg. 316
KARCHER B.V.—See Alfred Karcher GmbH & Co. KG; *Int'l*, pg. 316
KARCHER CANADA, INC.—See Alfred Karcher GmbH & Co. KG; *Int'l*, pg. 316

COMPANY NAME INDEX

KARCHER CLEANING SYSTEMS A.E.—See Alfred Karcher GmbH & Co. KG; *Int'l*, pg. 316
KARCHER CLEANING SYSTEMS SDN. BHD.—See Alfred Karcher GmbH & Co. KG; *Int'l*, pg. 316
KARCHER CO., LTD. (SOUTH KOREA)—See Alfred Karcher GmbH & Co. KG; *Int'l*, pg. 316
KARCHER FLOOR CARE, INC.—See Alfred Karcher GmbH & Co. KG; *Int'l*, pg. 316
KARCHER FZE—See Alfred Karcher GmbH & Co. KG; *Int'l*, pg. 316
KARCHER HUNGARIA KFT.—See Alfred Karcher GmbH & Co. KG; *Int'l*, pg. 316
KARCHER INDUSTRIA E COMERCIO LTDA.—See Alfred Karcher GmbH & Co. KG; *Int'l*, pg. 316
KARCHER (JAPAN) CO., LTD.—See Alfred Karcher GmbH & Co. KG; *Int'l*, pg. 316
KARCHER LEASING GMBH—See Alfred Karcher GmbH & Co. KG; *Int'l*, pg. 316
KARCHER LIMITED—See Alfred Karcher GmbH & Co. KG; *Int'l*, pg. 316
KARCHER LTD—See Alfred Karcher GmbH & Co. KG; *Int'l*, pg. 316
KARCHER MEXICO, S.A. DE C.V.—See Alfred Karcher GmbH & Co. KG; *Int'l*, pg. 316
KARCHER NORTH AMERICA—See Alfred Karcher GmbH & Co. KG; *Int'l*, pg. 316
KARCHER N.V.—See Alfred Karcher GmbH & Co. KG; *Int'l*, pg. 316
KARCHER OY—See Alfred Karcher GmbH & Co. KG; *Int'l*, pg. 316
KARCHER POLAND LTD. SP. Z O.O.—See Alfred Karcher GmbH & Co. KG; *Int'l*, pg. 316
KARCHER PTY. LTD.—See Alfred Karcher GmbH & Co. KG; *Int'l*, pg. 317
KARCHER RENGORINGSSYSTEMER A/S—See Alfred Karcher GmbH & Co. KG; *Int'l*, pg. 317
KARCHER RESIDENTIAL SOLUTIONS, INC.—See Alfred Karcher GmbH & Co. KG; *Int'l*, pg. 317
KARCHER, S.A.—See Alfred Karcher GmbH & Co. KG; *Int'l*, pg. 317
KARCHER S.A.S.—See Alfred Karcher GmbH & Co. KG; *Int'l*, pg. 317
KARCHER SERVIS TICARET A.S.—See Alfred Karcher GmbH & Co. KG; *Int'l*, pg. 317
KARCHER (SHANGHAI) CLEANING SYSTEMS CO., LTD.—See Alfred Karcher GmbH & Co. KG; *Int'l*, pg. 316
KARCHER SOUTH EAST ASIA PTE LTD.—See Alfred Karcher GmbH & Co. KG; *Int'l*, pg. 317
KARCHER S.P.A.—See Alfred Karcher GmbH & Co. KG; *Int'l*, pg. 317
KARCHER SPOL. S R.O.—See Alfred Karcher GmbH & Co. KG; *Int'l*, pg. 317
KARCHER (UK) LTD.—See Alfred Karcher GmbH & Co. KG; *Int'l*, pg. 316
KARCHER UKRAINE—See Alfred Karcher GmbH & Co. KG; *Int'l*, pg. 317
KARDAN FINANCIAL SERVICES B.V.—See Kardan N.V.; *Int'l*, pg. 4079
KARDAN ISRAEL LTD.—See Kardan Yazamut (2011) Ltd.; *Int'l*, pg. 4079
KARDAN N.V.; *Int'l*, pg. 4079
KARDAN REAL ESTATE ENTERPRISE AND DEVELOPMENT LTD.—See Kardan N.V.; *Int'l*, pg. 4079
KARDAN YAZAMUT (2011) LTD.; *Int'l*, pg. 4079
KARDEMIR KARABUK DEMIR CELIK SANAYI VE TICARET A.S.; *Int'l*, pg. 4079
KARDEX AUSTRIA GMBH—See Kardex Holding AG; *Int'l*, pg. 4079
KARDEX DANMARK A/S—See Kardex Holding AG; *Int'l*, pg. 4079
KARDEX FAR EAST PRIVATE LTD—See Kardex Holding AG; *Int'l*, pg. 4079
KARDEX FINLAND OY—See Kardex Holding AG; *Int'l*, pg. 4079
KARDEX FRANCE SASU—See Kardex Holding AG; *Int'l*, pg. 4079
KARDEX HANDLING SOLUTIONS, LLC—See Kardex Holding AG; *Int'l*, pg. 4079
KARDEX HOLDING AG; *Int'l*, pg. 4079
KARDEX HUNGARIA KFT—See Kardex Holding AG; *Int'l*, pg. 4080
KARDEX INDIA STORAGE SOLUTIONS PRIVATE LTD.—See Kardex Holding AG; *Int'l*, pg. 4080
KARDEX ITALIA S.P.A.—See Kardex Holding AG; *Int'l*, pg. 4080
KARDEX LOGISTIC SYSTEM (BEIJING) CO. LTD.—See Kardex Holding AG; *Int'l*, pg. 4080
KARDEX MALAYSIA SDN BHD—See Kardex Holding AG; *Int'l*, pg. 4080
KARDEX MLOG—See Kardex Holding AG; *Int'l*, pg. 4080
KARDEX NORGE AS—See Kardex Holding AG; *Int'l*, pg. 4080
KARDEX POLSKA SP. Z O.O.—See Kardex Holding AG; *Int'l*, pg. 4080
KARDEX PORTUGAL, UNIPESSOAL LDA.—See Kardex Holding AG; *Int'l*, pg. 4080
KARDEX PRODUCTION USA INC—See Kardex Holding AG; *Int'l*, pg. 4080
KARDEX PRODUKTION DEUTSCHLAND GMBH—See Kardex Holding AG; *Int'l*, pg. 4080
KARDEX REMSTAR INC—See Kardex Holding AG; *Int'l*, pg. 4080
KARDEX REMSTAR SI D.O.O.—See Kardex Holding AG; *Int'l*, pg. 4080
KARDEX SASU ZA LA FONTAINE DU VAISSEAU—See Kardex Holding AG; *Int'l*, pg. 4080
KARDEX SCANDINAVIA AB—See Kardex Holding AG; *Int'l*, pg. 4080
KARDEX SISTEMAS S.A—See Kardex Holding AG; *Int'l*, pg. 4080
KARDEX SOUTH-AMERICA SAS—See Kardex Holding AG; *Int'l*, pg. 4080
KARDEX S.R.O.—See Kardex Holding AG; *Int'l*, pg. 4080
KARDEX STORAGE SYSTEMS, LLC—See Kardex Holding AG; *Int'l*, pg. 4080
KARDEX SVERIGE AB—See Kardex Holding AG; *Int'l*, pg. 4080
KARDEX SYSTEM AS—See Kardex Holding AG; *Int'l*, pg. 4080
KARDEX SYSTEMS AG—See Kardex Holding AG; *Int'l*, pg. 4080
KARDEX SYSTEMS AG—See Kardex Holding AG; *Int'l*, pg. 4080
KARDEX SYSTEMS BV—See Kardex Holding AG; *Int'l*, pg. 4080
KARDEX SYSTEMS IRELAND LTD.—See Kardex Holding AG; *Int'l*, pg. 4080
KARDEX SYSTEMS LTD—See Kardex Holding AG; *Int'l*, pg. 4080
KARDEX SYSTEMS ROMANIA SRL—See Kardex Holding AG; *Int'l*, pg. 4080
KARDEX SYSTEMS (UK) LTD.—See Kardex Holding AG; *Int'l*, pg. 4080
KARDEX TURKEY DEPOLAMA SISTEMLERI LTD. STI.—See Kardex Holding AG; *Int'l*, pg. 4080
KARDEX VCA PTY LTD—See Kardex Holding AG; *Int'l*, pg. 4080
KARDIA S.R.L.—See Asahi Intecc Co., Ltd.; *Int'l*, pg. 594
KAREEVLEI MINING PROPRIETORY LIMITED—See BlueeRock Diamonds plc; *Int'l*, pg. 1072
KARE FOR U SDN. BHD.—See Success Transformer Corporation Berhad; *Int'l*, pg. 7250
KARE INVESTMENT SECURITIES INC.—See Kiraca Holding A.S.; *Int'l*, pg. 4185
KAREL ELEKTRONIK SANAYI VE TICARET A.S.; *Int'l*, pg. 4080
KARELIA BULGARIA EOOD—See Karelia Tobacco Company Inc.; *Int'l*, pg. 4080
KARELIA INVESTMENT S.A—See Karelia Tobacco Company Inc.; *Int'l*, pg. 4080
KARELIAN DIAMOND RESOURCES PLC; *Int'l*, pg. 4081
KARELIA TOBACCO COMPANY INC.; *Int'l*, pg. 4080
KARELIA TOBACCO COMPANY (UK) LTD.—See Karelia Tobacco Company Inc.; *Int'l*, pg. 4080
KARELIA TUTUN VE TICARET A.S—See Karelia Tobacco Company Inc.; *Int'l*, pg. 4080
KAREN MILLER LTD.; *U.S. Private*, pg. 2262
KAREN MORSTAD & ASSOCIATES LLC.; *U.S. Private*, pg. 2262
KAREN PHARMACEUTICAL COMPANY LIMITED—See Jacobson Pharma Corporation Limited; *Int'l*, pg. 3866
KAREN RADLEY ACURA VOLKSWAGEN; *U.S. Private*, pg. 2262
KAREN SPRL—See Clariane SE; *Int'l*, pg. 1643
KAREO, INC.; *U.S. Private*, pg. 2262
KARESSA PHARMA HOLDING AB—See Klaria Pharma Holding AB; *Int'l*, pg. 4199
KARE-TV—See TEGNA Inc.; *U.S. Public*, pg. 1990
KAREX BERHAD; *Int'l*, pg. 4081
KARGA SEVEN PICTURES, LLC; *U.S. Private*, pg. 2262
KARGA SOLUTIONS LIMITED—See Karin Technology Holdings Limited; *Int'l*, pg. 4081
KARGER CHINA—See S. Karger AG; *Int'l*, pg. 6446
KARGER JAPAN, INC.—See S. Karger AG; *Int'l*, pg. 6446
THE KARGES FURNITURE COMPANY, INC.; *U.S. Private*, pg. 4064
KARGI KIZILIRMAK ENERJI A.S.—See Statkraft AS; *Int'l*, pg. 7185
KARHULAN LASI OY—See O-I Glass, Inc.; *U.S. Public*, pg. 1560
KARIBU HOLZTECHNIK GMBH—See Outside Living Industries France SARL; *Int'l*, pg. 5669
KARIMS INTERNATIONAL USA; *U.S. Private*, pg. 2262
KARIN ELECTRONIC SUPPLIES COMPANY LIMITED—See Karin Technology Holdings Limited; *Int'l*, pg. 4081
KARIN ELECTRONIC TRADING (SHENZHEN) CO., LTD.—See Karin Technology Holdings Limited; *Int'l*, pg. 4081
KARINE; *Int'l*, pg. 4081
KARINGAL ST LAURENCE LIMITED; *Int'l*, pg. 4081
KARIN INTERNATIONAL TRADING (SHANGHAI) CO., LTD.—See Karin Technology Holdings Limited; *Int'l*, pg. 4081
KARINPIA CO., LTD.—See Doshisha Co., Ltd.; *Int'l*, pg. 2180

KARL'S RENTAL CENTER INC.

KARINS ENGINEERING GROUP, INC.; *U.S. Private*, pg. 2262
KARINS ENGINEERING GROUP, INC. - ST. PETERSBURG OFFICE—See Karins Engineering Group, Inc.; *U.S. Private*, pg. 2262
KARIN TECHNOLOGY HOLDINGS LIMITED; *Int'l*, pg. 4081
KARIS CAPITAL PARTNERS, LLC—See Morgan Joseph TriArtisan Group Inc.; *U.S. Private*, pg. 2784
KARK AG; *Int'l*, pg. 4081
KARKKILAN LAAKARIKESKUS OY—See Componenta Corporation; *Int'l*, pg. 1753
KARKOTIS MANUFACTURING AND TRADING PUBLIC LTD.; *Int'l*, pg. 4081
KARLAND OTOMOTIV URUNLERI SANAYI VE TICARET A.S—See Kiraca Holding A.S.; *Int'l*, pg. 4185
KARL BAISCH GMBH; *Int'l*, pg. 4081
KARLCHEN'S BACKSTUBE GMBH; *Int'l*, pg. 4083
KARL DANZER GES.M.B.H.—See Danzer AG; *Int'l*, pg. 1970
KARL E. BRINKMANN GMBH; *Int'l*, pg. 4081
KARLEE CO.—See Littlejohn & Co., LLC; *U.S. Private*, pg. 2471
KARLEN WILLIAMS GRAYBILL ADVERTISING; *U.S. Private*, pg. 2263
KARL EUGEN FISCHER GMBH—See Deutsche Beteiligungs AG; *Int'l*, pg. 2063
KARLE UND JUNG GMBH—See Dieffenbacher Holding GmbH & Co. KG; *Int'l*, pg. 2114
KARL FLAMMER FORD, INC.; *U.S. Private*, pg. 2262
KARL GROSS EGYPT (LTD)—See Karl Gross Internationale Spedition GmbH; *Int'l*, pg. 4081
KARL GROSS INTERNATIONAL B.V.—See Karl Gross Internationale Spedition GmbH; *Int'l*, pg. 4081
KARL GROSS INTERNATIONALE SPEDITION GMBH; *Int'l*, pg. 4081
KARL GROSS LOGISTICS (SHANGHAI) CO., LTD.—See Karl Gross Internationale Spedition GmbH; *Int'l*, pg. 4081
KARL GROSS LOGISTICS VIET NAM CO., LTD.—See Karl Gross Internationale Spedition GmbH; *Int'l*, pg. 4082
KARLIN+PIMSLER; *U.S. Private*, pg. 2263
KARL JUNGBLUTH KETTENFABRIK GMBH & CO. KG; *Int'l*, pg. 4082
KARL KNAUZ MOTORS INC.; *U.S. Private*, pg. 2262
KARL MAYER (CHINA) LTD.—See KARL MAYER Textilmaschinenfabrik GmbH; *Int'l*, pg. 4082
KARL MAYER (H.K.) LTD.—See KARL MAYER Textilmaschinenfabrik GmbH; *Int'l*, pg. 4082
KARL MAYER INDIA PRIVATE LIMITED—See KARL MAYER Textilmaschinenfabrik GmbH; *Int'l*, pg. 4082
KARL MAYER LIBA TEXTILMASCHINENFABRIK GMBH—See KARL MAYER Textilmaschinenfabrik GmbH; *Int'l*, pg. 4082
KARL MAYER MALIMO TEXTILMASCHINENFABRIK GMBH—See KARL MAYER Textilmaschinenfabrik GmbH; *Int'l*, pg. 4082
KARL MAYER R&D GMBH—See KARL MAYER Textilmaschinenfabrik GmbH; *Int'l*, pg. 4082
KARL MAYER ROTAL S.R.L.—See KARL MAYER Textilmaschinenfabrik GmbH; *Int'l*, pg. 4082
KARL MAYER TEXTILE MACHINERY INDIA PRIVATE LIMITED—See KARL MAYER Textilmaschinenfabrik GmbH; *Int'l*, pg. 4082
KARL MAYER TEXTILE MACHINERY LTD.—See KARL MAYER Textilmaschinenfabrik GmbH; *Int'l*, pg. 4082
KARL MAYER TEXTILMASCHINEN AG—See KARL MAYER Textilmaschinenfabrik GmbH; *Int'l*, pg. 4082
KARL MAYER TEXTILMASCHINENFABRIK GMBH; *Int'l*, pg. 4082
KARL OTTO BRAUN KG—See PAUL HARTMANN AG; *Int'l*, pg. 5760
KARLOVACKA BANKA DD; *Int'l*, pg. 4083
KARL R. JOHNSON TRUCKING, INC.; *U.S. Private*, pg. 2262
KARLSBERG BRAUEREI GMBH; *Int'l*, pg. 4083
KARL SCHMIDT TRADING COMPANY S. DE R.L. DE C.V.—See Rheinmetall AG; *Int'l*, pg. 6322
KARL SCHMIDT UNISIA INC. - FORT WAYNE PLANT—See Rheinmetall AG; *Int'l*, pg. 6321
KARL SCHMIDT UNISIA - ZOLLNER DIVISION—See Rheinmetall AG; *Int'l*, pg. 6322
KARL SCHUMACHER DENTAL, LLC—See STERIS plc; *Int'l*, pg. 7209
KARLSHAMN EXPRESS AB—See DFDS A/S; *Int'l*, pg. 2095
KARLSHAMN KRAFT AB—See E.ON SE; *Int'l*, pg. 2255
KARL SIMON GMBH & CO. KG—See INDUS Holding AG; *Int'l*, pg. 3663
KARL'S RENTAL CENTER INC.; *U.S. Private*, pg. 2263
KARLSRUHER SANATORIUM AKTIENGESELLSCHAFT—See MK-Kliniken AG; *Int'l*, pg. 5001
KARL STORZ ADRIA EOS D.O.O.—See Karl Storz GmbH & Co.; *Int'l*, pg. 4082
KARL STORZ ENDOSCOPIA ARGENTINA S.A.—See Karl Storz GmbH & Co.; *Int'l*, pg. 4082

KARL STORZ ENDOSCOPIA IBERICA S.A.—See Karl Storz GmbH & Co.; *Int'l*, pg. 4082
KARL STORZ ENDOSCOPIA ITALIA S.R.L.—See Karl Storz GmbH & Co.; *Int'l*, pg. 4082
KARL STORZ ENDOSCOPIA LATINO AMERICA INC.—See Karl Storz GmbH & Co.; *Int'l*, pg. 4083
KARL STORZ ENDOSCOPIA MEXICO S.A. DE C.V.—See Karl Storz GmbH & Co.; *Int'l*, pg. 4082
KARL STORZ ENDOSCOPIA ROMANIA SRL—See Karl Storz GmbH & Co.; *Int'l*, pg. 4082
KARL STORZ ENDOSCOPIA—See Karl Storz GmbH & Co.; *Int'l*, pg. 4082
KARL STORZ ENDOSCOPIE FRANCE S.A.—See Karl Storz GmbH & Co.; *Int'l*, pg. 4082
KARL STORZ ENDOSCOPIJA D.O.O.—See Karl Storz GmbH & Co.; *Int'l*, pg. 4082
KARL STORZ ENDOSCOPY-AMERICA, INC.—See Karl Storz GmbH & Co.; *Int'l*, pg. 4083
KARL STORZ ENDOSCOPY ASIA MARKETING PTE. LTD.—See Karl Storz GmbH & Co.; *Int'l*, pg. 4082
KARL STORZ ENDOSCOPY AUSTRALIA PTY. LTD.—See Karl Storz GmbH & Co.; *Int'l*, pg. 4082
KARL STORZ ENDOSCOPY CANADA LTD.—See Karl Storz GmbH & Co.; *Int'l*, pg. 4082
KARL STORZ ENDOSCOPY CHINA LTD.—See Karl Storz GmbH & Co.; *Int'l*, pg. 4082
KARL STORZ ENDOSCOPY GULF & NEAR EAST—See Karl Storz GmbH & Co.; *Int'l*, pg. 4082
KARL STORZ ENDOSCOPY INDIA PRIVATE LTD.—See Karl Storz GmbH & Co.; *Int'l*, pg. 4082
KARL STORZ ENDOSCOPY JAPAN K. K.—See Karl Storz GmbH & Co.; *Int'l*, pg. 4082
KARL STORZ ENDOSCOPY KOREA CO. LTD.—See Karl Storz GmbH & Co.; *Int'l*, pg. 4082
KARL STORZ ENDOSCOPY (SHANGHAI) LTD.—See Karl Storz GmbH & Co.; *Int'l*, pg. 4082
KARL STORZ ENDOSCOPY SINGAPORE SALES PTE. LTD.—See Karl Storz GmbH & Co.; *Int'l*, pg. 4082
KARL STORZ ENDOSCOPY (SOUTH AFRICA) (PTY) LTD.—See Karl Storz GmbH & Co.; *Int'l*, pg. 4082
KARL STORZ ENDOSCOPY SUOMI OY—See Karl Storz GmbH & Co.; *Int'l*, pg. 4082
KARL STORZ ENDOSCOPY TAIWAN LTD.—See Karl Storz GmbH & Co.; *Int'l*, pg. 4082
KARL STORZ ENDOSCOPY (UK) LTD.—See Karl Storz GmbH & Co.; *Int'l*, pg. 4082
KARL STORZ ENDOSKOP AUSTRIA GMBH—See Karl Storz GmbH & Co.; *Int'l*, pg. 4082
KARL STORZ ENDOSKOPE BERLIN GMBH—See Karl Storz GmbH & Co.; *Int'l*, pg. 4082
KARL STORZ ENDOSKOPE GREECE LTD.—See Karl Storz GmbH & Co.; *Int'l*, pg. 4083
KARL STORZ ENDOSKOPE GREECE M.E.P.E.—See Karl Storz GmbH & Co.; *Int'l*, pg. 4083
KARL STORZ ENDOSKOPE, REGIONAL CENTER FOR ENDOSCOPY S.A.L.—See Karl Storz GmbH & Co.; *Int'l*, pg. 4083
KARL STORZ ENDOSKOPI DENMARK A/S—See Karl Storz GmbH & Co.; *Int'l*, pg. 4083
KARL STORZ ENDOSKOPI NORGE AS—See Karl Storz GmbH & Co.; *Int'l*, pg. 4083
KARL STORZ ENDOSKOP SVERIGE AB—See Karl Storz GmbH & Co.; *Int'l*, pg. 4082
KARL STORZ ENDOSZKOP MAGYARORSZAG KFT.—See Karl Storz GmbH & Co.; *Int'l*, pg. 4083
KARL STORZ ENDOVISION, INC.—See Karl Storz GmbH & Co.; *Int'l*, pg. 4083
KARL STORZ GMBH & CO. KG—See Karl Storz GmbH & Co.; *Int'l*, pg. 4083
KARL STORZ GMBH & CO.; *Int'l*, pg. 4082
KARL STORZ INDUSTRIAL—See Karl Storz GmbH & Co.; *Int'l*, pg. 4083
KARL STORZ MARKETING AMERICA DO SUL LTDA.—See Karl Storz GmbH & Co.; *Int'l*, pg. 4083
KARL STORZ VETERINARY ENDOSCOPY AMERICA, INC.—See Karl Storz GmbH & Co.; *Int'l*, pg. 4083
KARL STORZ VIDEO ENDOSCOPY ESTONIA OU—See Karl Storz GmbH & Co.; *Int'l*, pg. 4083
KARL THEIS GMBH—See BayWa AG; *Int'l*, pg. 918
KARL THOMSON FINANCE LIMITED—See Wisdom Wealth Resources Investment Holding Group Limited; *Int'l*, pg. 8435
KARL THOMSON INVESTMENT CONSULTANTS LIMITED—See Wisdom Wealth Resources Investment Holding Group Limited; *Int'l*, pg. 8435
KARL VOEGELE AG—See CCC S.A.; *Int'l*, pg. 1366
KARL WAECHTER AG—See BKW AG; *Int'l*, pg. 1055
KARL WOERWAG LACK-UND FARBENFABRIK GMBH & CO. KG—See PPG Industries, Inc.; *U.S. Public*, pg. 1707
KARMA ENERGY LIMITED—See Weizmann Limited; *Int'l*, pg. 8371
KARMAK INC.; *U.S. Private*, pg. 2263
KARMALOOP LLC—See Shiekh LLC; *U.S. Private*, pg. 3635
KARMAN MISSILE & SPACE SYSTEMS COMPANY—See Trive Capital Partners, LLC; *U.S. Private*, pg. 4240
KARMARAMA; *Int'l*, pg. 4083
KARMAR SA—See Bouygues S.A.; *Int'l*, pg. 1123

KARMART CHRYSLER DODGE VOLKSWAGEN MITSUBISHI; *U.S. Private*, pg. 2263
KARMARTS PUBLIC COMPANY LIMITED; *Int'l*, pg. 4083
KARMA SCIENCE, INC—See Meta Platforms, Inc.; *U.S. Public*, pg. 1427
KARMASPHERE, INC.; *U.S. Private*, pg. 2263
KARMAY INDUSTRIAL LIMITED—See Cosmos Machinery Enterprises Limited; *Int'l*, pg. 1813
KARMAY PLASTIC PRODUCTS (ZHUHAI) CO., LTD—See Cosmos Machinery Enterprises Limited; *Int'l*, pg. 1813
KARMIN EXPLORATION INC.—See Nexa Resources S.A.; *Int'l*, pg. 5239
KARNAK CORPORATION; *U.S. Private*, pg. 2263
KARNALI DEVELOPMENT BANK LTD.; *Int'l*, pg. 4083
KARNALYTE RESOURCES INC.; *Int'l*, pg. 4083
KARNAPHULI INSURANCE COMPANY LIMITED; *Int'l*, pg. 4083
KARNAVATI FINANCE LIMITED; *Int'l*, pg. 4083
KARNDEAN INTERNATIONAL GMBH—See James Halstead PLC; *Int'l*, pg. 3877
KARNERTA GMBH—See Raiffeisenlandesbank Oberosterreich Aktiengesellschaft; *Int'l*, pg. 6187
KARNIKA INDUSTRIES LIMITED; *Int'l*, pg. 4083
KARNIMATA COLD STORAGE LIMITED; *Int'l*, pg. 4083
KARNOV GROUP AB; *Int'l*, pg. 4084
KARNOV GROUP DENMARK A/S—See Karnov Group AB; *Int'l*, pg. 4084
KARNS PRIME AND FANCY FOOD; *U.S. Private*, pg. 2263
KAR NUT PRODUCTS COMPANY—See Palladium Equity Partners, LLC; *U.S. Private*, pg. 3077
KAROLINSKA DEVELOPMENT AB; *Int'l*, pg. 4084
KAROM DRINKS S.R.L.—See AMBRA S.A.; *Int'l*, pg. 415
KARONA, INC.—See ONEX Corporation; *Int'l*, pg. 5579
KARON PHUKET HOTEL CO., LTD.—See Central Plaza Hotel Public Company Limited; *Int'l*, pg. 1409
KAROO EXPLORATION CORP.; *Int'l*, pg. 4084
KAROON ENERGY INTERNATIONAL LTD.—See Karoon Energy Ltd.; *Int'l*, pg. 4084
KAROON ENERGY LTD.; *Int'l*, pg. 4084
KAROON GAS PTY. LTD.—See Karoon Energy Ltd.; *Int'l*, pg. 4084
KAROON OIL & GAS PRODUCTION COMPANY—See National Iranian Oil Company; *Int'l*, pg. 5160
KAROON PETROCHEMICAL CO.—See Persian Gulf Petrochemical Industry Commercial Company; *Int'l*, pg. 5815
KAROOOOO LTD.; *Int'l*, pg. 4084
KARO PHARMA AB—See EQT AB; *Int'l*, pg. 2478
KARORA RESOURCES INC.—See Westgold Resources Limited; *Int'l*, pg. 8390
KARO SP. Z O.O.—See Stalprodukt S.A.; *Int'l*, pg. 7164
KAROSSERIEWERK PORSCHE GMBH & CO. KG—See Porsche Automobil Holding SE; *Int'l*, pg. 5926
KAROUN DAIRIES, LLC—See Groupe Lactalis SA; *Int'l*, pg. 3106
KARPACKA SPOLKA GAZOWNICTWA SP. Z O.O.—See Polskie Gornictwo Naftowe i Gazownictwo S.A.; *Int'l*, pg. 5912
KARPELES FLIGHT SERVICES GMBH—See Deutsche Bahn AG; *Int'l*, pg. 2052
KARPREILLY, LLC; *U.S. Private*, pg. 2263
KARRAS S.A.—See Floridienne SA; *Int'l*, pg. 2708
KARR BARTH ASSOCIATES INC.; *U.S. Private*, pg. 2263
KARRIARKONSULTEN SVERIGE AB—See Storskogen Group AB; *Int'l*, pg. 7228
KARRIE INDUSTRIAL COMPANY LIMITED—See Karrie International Holdings Limited; *Int'l*, pg. 4085
KARRIE INTERNATIONAL HOLDINGS LIMITED; *Int'l*, pg. 4085
KARRIERS INC.; *U.S. Private*, pg. 2263
KARRIE TECHNOLOGIES COMPANY LIMITED—See Karrie International Holdings Limited; *Int'l*, pg. 4085
KARRO FOOD GROUP LIMITED—See CapVest Limited; *Int'l*, pg. 1318
KARSAN OTOMOTIV SANAYII VE TICARET A.S.—See Kiraca Holding A.S.; *Int'l*, pg. 4185
KARS CIMENTO AS—See Cementir Holding N.V.; *Int'l*, pg. 1397
KAR SIN BERHAD—See YNH Property Bhd; *Int'l*, pg. 8590
KARSON ASPHALT PAVING INC.—See Aecon Group Inc.; *Int'l*, pg. 172
KARSON KONSTRUCTION LIMITED—See Aecon Group Inc.; *Int'l*, pg. 172
KARSONS PHARMACY LIMITED—See Bestway (Holdings) Limited; *Int'l*, pg. 1001
KARSPACE MANAGEMENT LTD.—See Fundacion Bancaria Caixa d'Estalvis i Pensions de Barcelona, la Caixa; *Int'l*, pg. 2845
KARSTADT WARENHAUS GMBH—See SIGNA Holding GmbH; *Int'l*, pg. 6909
KARSTEN ENERGY CORP.; *Int'l*, pg. 4085
KARSTEN MANUFACTURING CORPORATION; *U.S. Private*, pg. 2263
KARSTEN S/A; *Int'l*, pg. 4085
KARSTENS INVESTMENT COUNSEL, INC.—See The CapFinancial Group, LLC; *U.S. Private*, pg. 4004

KARSTORP BILDEMONTERING AB—See LKQ Corporation; *U.S. Public*, pg. 1334
KARSUSAN KARADENIZ AQUACULTURE INDUSTRY, INC.; *Int'l*, pg. 4085
KARSU TEKSTIL AS; *Int'l*, pg. 4085
KARTAL KIMYA SANAYI VE TICARET A.S.—See BASF SE; *Int'l*, pg. 884
KARTENA AB—See Addnode Group AB; *Int'l*, pg. 130
KARTENHAUS TICKETSERVICE GMBH—See Live Nation Entertainment, Inc.; *U.S. Public*, pg. 1331
KARTEREDA HOLDING LTD—See ELLAKTOR S.A.; *Int'l*, pg. 2365
KARTESIA ADVISOR LLP; *Int'l*, pg. 4085
KARTIK AGRO CHEM. PVT LTD—See Shiva Global Agro Industries Ltd.; *Int'l*, pg. 6854
KARTIK INVESTMENTS TRUST LIMITED; *Int'l*, pg. 4085
KARTING; *Int'l*, pg. 4085
KARTONPACK DOBOZIPARI NYRT.; *Int'l*, pg. 4085
KARTONSAN KARTON SANAYI VE TICARET A.S.; *Int'l*, pg. 4085
KARTOON STUDIOS, INC.; *U.S. Public*, pg. 1214
KARTO OY; *Int'l*, pg. 4085
KARTPOL GROUP SP. Z O.O.—See Wentworth Technologies Co. Ltd.; *Int'l*, pg. 8377
KART, SPOL. S.R.O.—See CEZ, a.s.; *Int'l*, pg. 1428
KARTULI SHALI JSC; *Int'l*, pg. 4085
KARULA CO., LTD.; *Int'l*, pg. 4085
KARUNA THERAPEUTICS, INC.—See Bristol-Myers Squibb Company; *U.S. Public*, pg. 386
KARUR KCP PACKKAGINGS LTD. - MANUFACTURING UNIT—See Karur KCP Packkagings Ltd.; *Int'l*, pg. 4085
KARUR KCP PACKKAGINGS LTD. - PP & FIBC UNIT—See Karur KCP Packkagings Ltd.; *Int'l*, pg. 4085
KARUR KCP PACKKAGINGS LTD.; *Int'l*, pg. 4085
KARUR VYSYA BANK LTD; *Int'l*, pg. 4085
KARVY FINANCIAL SERVICES LIMITED; *Int'l*, pg. 4086
KARWIN ENGINEERING COMPANY LIMITED—See Karrie International Holdings Limited; *Int'l*, pg. 4085
KAR WO LIMITED—See Iseki & Co., Ltd.; *Int'l*, pg. 3814
KARWOSKI & COURAGE—See Omnicom Group Inc.; *U.S. Public*, pg. 1588
KARYA OUTDOOR SDN BHD—See Utusan Melayu (Malaysia) Berhad; *Int'l*, pg. 8102
KARYES INVESTMENT PUBLIC COMPANY LIMITED; *Int'l*, pg. 4086
KARYON INDUSTRIES BERHAD; *Int'l*, pg. 4086
KARYOPHARM EUROPE GMBH—See Karyopharm Therapeutics Inc.; *U.S. Public*, pg. 1214
KARYOPHARM THERAPEUTICS INC.; *U.S. Public*, pg. 1214
KASABA GAYRIMENKUL INSAAT TAAHHUT VE TICARET A.S.—See Turkiye Is Bankasi A.S.; *Int'l*, pg. 7976
KASA COMPANIES INC.; *U.S. Private*, pg. 2263
KASAGAMI MFG. CO., LTD.—See Nippon Thompson Co., Ltd.; *Int'l*, pg. 5357
KASAI (GERMANY) GMBH—See Kasai Kogyo Co., Ltd.; *Int'l*, pg. 4086
KASAI INDIA (CHENNAI) PRIVATE LIMITED—See Kasai Kogyo Co., Ltd.; *Int'l*, pg. 4086
KASAI KOGYO CO., LTD.; *Int'l*, pg. 4086
KASAI KOGYO CO., LTD. - YORII PLANT—See Kasai Kogyo Co., Ltd.; *Int'l*, pg. 4086
KASAIKOGYO MOROCCO S.A.R.L—See Kasai Kogyo Co., Ltd.; *Int'l*, pg. 4086
KASAI MEXICANA S.A DE C.V.—See Kasai Kogyo Co., Ltd.; *Int'l*, pg. 4086
KASA INDUSTRIAL CONTROLS INC.; *U.S. Private*, pg. 2263
KASAI NORTH AMERICA, INC. - MADISON PLANT—See Kasai Kogyo Co., Ltd.; *Int'l*, pg. 4086
KASAI NORTH AMERICA, INC. - PRATTVILLE PLANT—See Kasai Kogyo Co., Ltd.; *Int'l*, pg. 4086
KASAI NORTH AMERICA, INC.—See Kasai Kogyo Co., Ltd.; *Int'l*, pg. 4086
KASAI NORTH AMERICA, INC. - TALLADEGA PLANT—See Kasai Kogyo Co., Ltd.; *Int'l*, pg. 4086
KASAI NORTH AMERICA, INC. - UPPER SANDUSKY PLANT—See Kasai Kogyo Co., Ltd.; *Int'l*, pg. 4086
KASAI SAS—See HORIBA Ltd; *Int'l*, pg. 3477
KASAI SLOVAKIA S.R.O.—See Kasai Kogyo Co., Ltd.; *Int'l*, pg. 4086
KASAI SUPPORT SERVICE CO., LTD.—See Kasai Kogyo Co., Ltd.; *Int'l*, pg. 4086
KASAI TEC CO., LTD.—See Kasai Kogyo Co., Ltd.; *Int'l*, pg. 4086
KASAI TECK SEE CO., LTD.—See Kasai Kogyo Co., Ltd.; *Int'l*, pg. 4086
KASAI TECK SEE (MALAYSIA) SDN. BHD.—See Oriental Holdings Berhad; *Int'l*, pg. 5624
KASAI TECK SEE (THAILAND) CO., LTD. - PINTHONG PLANT—See Kasai Kogyo Co., Ltd.; *Int'l*, pg. 4086
KASAI TECK SEE (THAILAND) CO., LTD.—See Kasai Kogyo Co., Ltd.; *Int'l*, pg. 4086
KASAI UK LTD - MERTHYR PLANT—See Kasai Kogyo Co., Ltd.; *Int'l*, pg. 4086
KASAI UK LTD—See Kasai Kogyo Co., Ltd.; *Int'l*, pg. 4086
KASALIS INC.—See Jabil Inc.; *U.S. Public*, pg. 1181
KASAMBA, INC.—See LivePerson, Inc.; *U.S. Public*, pg. 1332

COMPANY NAME INDEX

KASAN CORP. (MALAYSIA) SDN. BHD.—See Kato Sansho Co., Ltd.; *Int'l*, pg. 4090
KASATI JOIN STOCK COMPANY; *Int'l*, pg. 4087
KASBAH RESOURCES LIMITED; *Int'l*, pg. 4087
KASBAR NATIONAL INDUSTRIES, INC.; *U.S. Private*, pg. 2263
KASB MODARABA; *Int'l*, pg. 4087
KASCO CO., LTD.—See Nippon Steel Corporation; *Int'l*, pg. 5337
KASCO CORPORATION; *U.S. Private*, pg. 2263
KASCO LLC—See Steel Partners Holdings L.P.; *U.S. Public*, pg. 1943
KASCO VENTURES INC.—See Kasco Corporation; *U.S. Private*, pg. 2263
KAS DIRECT, LLC—See S.C. Johnson & Son, Inc.; *U.S. Private*, pg. 3516
KASDORF S.A.—See Danone; *Int'l*, pg. 1966
KASEN INTERNATIONAL HOLDINGS LIMITED; *Int'l*, pg. 4087
KASEREI STUDER AG—See Emmi AG; *Int'l*, pg. 2385
KASET THAI BIO POWER CO., LTD.—See Kaset Thai International Sugar Corporation Public Company Limited; *Int'l*, pg. 4087
KASET THAI INTERNATIONAL SUGAR CORPORATION PUBLIC COMPANY LIMITED; *Int'l*, pg. 4087
KASEYA LLC—See Insight Venture Management, LLC; *U.S. Private*, pg. 2090
KASHFLOW SOFTWARE LTD—See HgCapital Trust plc; *Int'l*, pg. 3376
KASHI COMPANY—See WK Kellogg Co; *U.S. Public*, pg. 2376
KASHIDASU CO., LTD.—See FRANCE BED HOLDINGS CO. LTD.; *Int'l*, pg. 2759
KASHIHARA HIGH TRUST CO., LTD.—See Takuma Co., Ltd.; *Int'l*, pg. 7442
KASHII CO., LTD.—See Nippon Steel Corporation; *Int'l*, pg. 5337
KASHIMA ANTLERS F.C. CO., LTD.—See Mercari, Inc.; *Int'l*, pg. 4820
KASHIMA AROMATICS CO., LTD.—See ENEOS Holdings, Inc.; *Int'l*, pg. 2417
KASHIMA BERTH CO., LTD.—See AGC Inc.; *Int'l*, pg. 204
KASHIMA CHEMICAL CO., LTD.—See AGC Inc.; *Int'l*, pg. 204
KASHIMA OIL CO., LTD.—See ENEOS Holdings, Inc.; *Int'l*, pg. 2417
KASHIMA SANKEN CO., LTD.—See Sanken Electric Co., Ltd.; *Int'l*, pg. 6541
KASHIMA SOUTH JOINT POWER CORP.—See AGC Inc.; *Int'l*, pg. 204
KASHIMAYARI CO., LTD.—See Nippon Parking Development Co., Ltd.; *Int'l*, pg. 5328
KASHIN, INC.; *U.S. Public*, pg. 1214
KASHI RUICHENG NEW ENERGY TECHNOLOGY CO., LTD.—See Topray Solar Co., Ltd.; *Int'l*, pg. 7820
KASHIWA ENVIRONMENT TECHNOLOGY CO.,LTD—See Hitachi Zosen Corporation; *Int'l*, pg. 3411
KASHIWA SENKO TRANSPORT CO., LTD.—See Senko Group Holdings Co., Ltd.; *Int'l*, pg. 6710
KASHIWA UOICHIBA CO., LTD.—See Chuo Gyorui Co., Ltd.; *Int'l*, pg. 1598
KASHIYAMA DAIKANYAMA CO., LTD.—See Onward Holdings Co., Ltd.; *Int'l*, pg. 5592
KASHIYAMA (DALIAN) CO., LTD.—See Onward Holdings Co., Ltd.; *Int'l*, pg. 5592
KASHIYAMA SAGA CO., LTD.—See Onward Holdings Co., Ltd.; *Int'l*, pg. 5592
KASHTAN PETROLEUM LTD.—See Petrosibir AB; *Int'l*, pg. 5832
KASHTAN PETROLEUM LTD.—See Societe Generale S.A.; *Int'l*, pg. 7042
KA SHUI INTERNATIONAL HOLDINGS LIMITED; *Int'l*, pg. 4045
KA SHUI METAL MANUFACTURING (SHENZHEN) CO., LTD.—See Ka Shui International Holdings Limited; *Int'l*, pg. 4045
KA SHUI PLASTIC TECHNOLOGY COMPANY LIMITED—See Ka Shui International Holdings Limited; *Int'l*, pg. 4045
KA SHUI TECHNOLOGY (HUIZHOU) COMPANY LIMITED—See Ka Shui International Holdings Limited; *Int'l*, pg. 4045
KASHYAP TELE-MEDICINES LIMITED; *Int'l*, pg. 4087
KASIKORN ASSET MANAGEMENT CO., LTD.—See Kasikornbank Public Company Limited; *Int'l*, pg. 4087
KASIKORNBANK (CHINA) COMPANY LIMITED—See Kasikornbank Public Company Limited; *Int'l*, pg. 4087
KASIKORNBANK PUBLIC COMPANY LIMITED; *Int'l*, pg. 4087
KASIKORN FACTORING CO., LTD.—See Kasikornbank Public Company Limited; *Int'l*, pg. 4087
KASIKORN FACTORY & EQUIPMENT CO., LTD.—See Kasikornbank Public Company Limited; *Int'l*, pg. 4087
KASIKORN LABS CO., LTD.—See Kasikornbank Public Company Limited; *Int'l*, pg. 4087
KASIKORN LEASING CO., LTD.—See Kasikornbank Public Company Limited; *Int'l*, pg. 4087
KASIKORN PRO CO., LTD.—See Kasikornbank Public Company Limited; *Int'l*, pg. 4087

KASIKORN RESEARCH CENTER CO., LTD—See Kasikornbank Public Company Limited; *Int'l*, pg. 4087
KASIKORN SECURITIES PCL—See Kasikornbank Public Company Limited; *Int'l*, pg. 4087
KASIKORN SERVE CO., LTD.—See Kasikornbank Public Company Limited; *Int'l*, pg. 4087
KASIKORN SOFT CO., LTD.—See Kasikornbank Public Company Limited; *Int'l*, pg. 4087
KASIKORN TECHNOLOGY GROUP SECRETARIAT CO., LTD.—See Kasikornbank Public Company Limited; *Int'l*, pg. 4087
KASIKORNTHAI BANK LIMITED—See Kasikornbank Public Company Limited; *Int'l*, pg. 4087
KASIKORN X CO., LTD.—See Kasikornbank Public Company Limited; *Int'l*, pg. 4087
KAS INVESTMENT CO. INC.; *U.S. Private*, pg. 2263
KASKAD CORP.; *Int'l*, pg. 4088
KASKTAS KAYAR KALIP ALTYAPI SONDAJ KAZIK VE TECRIT ANONIM SIRKETI—See Enka Insaat ve Sanayi A.S.; *Int'l*, pg. 2440
KASON CORP.—See May River Capital, LLC; *U.S. Private*, pg. 2620
KASON INDUSTRIES INCORPORATED; *U.S. Private*, pg. 2264
KASOWITZ BENSON TORRES & FRIEDMAN LLP; *U.S. Private*, pg. 2264
THE KASPAR COMPANIES; *U.S. Private*, pg. 4064
KASPAR DIE & TOOL, INC.—See The Kaspar Companies; *U.S. Private*, pg. 4064
KASPAR ELECTROPLATING CORPORATION—See The Kaspar Companies; *U.S. Private*, pg. 4064
KASPAR WIRE WORKS, INC.—See The Kaspar Companies; *U.S. Private*, pg. 4064
KASPEN/JUNG VON MATT—See Jung von Matt; *Int'l*, pg. 4027
KASPER MACHINE CO.; *U.S. Private*, pg. 2264
KASPERSKY LAB AUSTRALIA PTY LTD—See Kaspersky Lab ZAO; *Int'l*, pg. 4088
KASPERSKY LAB, INC.—See Kaspersky Lab ZAO; *Int'l*, pg. 4088
KASPERSKY LAB INC.—See Kaspersky Lab ZAO; *Int'l*, pg. 4088
KASPERSKY LAB LDA—See Kaspersky Lab ZAO; *Int'l*, pg. 4088
KASPERSKY LAB POLSKA SP Z.O.O.—See Kaspersky Lab ZAO; *Int'l*, pg. 4088
KASPERSKY LABS ASIA PACIFIC LTD—See Kaspersky Lab ZAO; *Int'l*, pg. 4088
KASPERSKY LAB SEA SDN BHD—See Kaspersky Lab ZAO; *Int'l*, pg. 4088
KASPERSKY LABS GMBH—See Kaspersky Lab ZAO; *Int'l*, pg. 4088
KASPERSKY LABS INDIA PRIVATE LTD—See Kaspersky Lab ZAO; *Int'l*, pg. 4088
KASPERSKY LABS JAPAN K.K.—See Kaspersky Lab ZAO; *Int'l*, pg. 4088
KASPERSKY LAB SOUTH AFRICA (PTY) LTD—See Kaspersky Lab ZAO; *Int'l*, pg. 4088
KASPERSKY LAB UK LTD—See Kaspersky Lab ZAO; *Int'l*, pg. 4088
KASPERSKY LAB ZAO; *Int'l*, pg. 4088
KASPI BANK JSC—See Baring Vostok Capital Partners; *Int'l*, pg. 865
KASPIEN HOLDINGS INC.—See Kaspien Holdings Inc.; *U.S. Public*, pg. 1214
KASPIEN HOLDINGS INC.; *U.S. Public*, pg. 1214
KASPIEN, INC.—See Kaspien Holdings Inc.; *U.S. Public*, pg. 1214
KASPI.KZ JSC; *Int'l*, pg. 4088
KASSBOHRER ALL TERRAIN VEHICLES, INC.—See Kaessbohrer Gelandefahrzeug AG; *Int'l*, pg. 4047
KASSBOHRER E.S.E.—See Kaessbohrer Gelandefahrzeug AG; *Int'l*, pg. 4047
KASS BROS INC.; *U.S. Private*, pg. 2264
KASSEL EQUITY GROUP, LLC; *U.S. Private*, pg. 2264
KASSEM DARWISH FAKHRO & SONS; *Int'l*, pg. 4088
KAS SERVICES INDIA PRIVATE LIMITED—See Wesfarmers Limited; *Int'l*, pg. 8381
KASSIK MILLING CO.; *U.S. Private*, pg. 2264
KASS INDUSTRIAL SUPPLY CORP.; *U.S. Private*, pg. 2264
KASSON & KELLER—See Keymark Corporation; *U.S. Private*, pg. 2294
KASSOY, LLC; *U.S. Private*, pg. 2264
KAST CONSTRUCTION COMPANY, LLC; *U.S. Private*, pg. 2264
K.A. STEEL CHEMICALS INC.—See Olin Corporation; *U.S. Public*, pg. 1570
K. A. STEEL CHEMICALS INC.—See Olin Corporation; *U.S. Public*, pg. 1570
KASTEEL ENTERPRISES, INC.; *U.S. Private*, pg. 2264
KASTEEL VAN BRASSCHAAT NV—See Compass Group PLC; *Int'l*, pg. 1752
KASTEN MASONRY SALES INC.; *U.S. Private*, pg. 2264
KASTHAMANDAP DEVELOPMENT BANK LIMITED—See Kumari Bank Limited; *Int'l*, pg. 4329
KASTLE ELECTRIC COMPANY; *U.S. Private*, pg. 2264
KASTLE SYSTEMS INTERNATIONAL LLC; *U.S. Private*, pg. 2264

KASTLE SYSTEMS LLC—See Kastle Systems International LLC; *U.S. Private*, pg. 2264
KASTNER EXETER; *Int'l*, pg. 4088
KASTNER & PARTNERS - SAINT LOUIS—See Kastner & Partners; *U.S. Private*, pg. 2264
KASTNER & PARTNERS; *U.S. Private*, pg. 2264
KASTOR S.A.—See ELLAKTOR S.A.; *Int'l*, pg. 2364
KASTT, SPOL. S R.O.—See VINCI S.A.; *Int'l*, pg. 8223
KASUGA INDUSTRY LTD.—See Maruichi Steel Tube Ltd; *Int'l*, pg. 4713
KASUMI CO., LTD.—See AEON Co., Ltd.; *Int'l*, pg. 177
KASUMIGASEKI CAPITAL CO., LTD.; *Int'l*, pg. 4088
KASUMI KYODO JIGYO CO., LTD.—See Tosoh Corporation; *Int'l*, pg. 7832
KASUWA KHOLA HYDROPOWER LIMITED—See Radhi Bidhyut Co., Ltd.; *Int'l*, pg. 6173
KASW-TV—See The E.W. Scripps Company; *U.S. Public*, pg. 2068
KASY-TV—See Tamer Media, LLC; *U.S. Private*, pg. 3928
KATABAMI KOGYO CO., LTD.—See Kajima Corporation; *Int'l*, pg. 4055
KATADYN FRANCE—See Katadyn Holding AG; *Int'l*, pg. 4089
KATADYN GERMANY GMBH—See Katadyn Holding AG; *Int'l*, pg. 4089
KATADYN HOLDING AG; *Int'l*, pg. 4088
KATADYN NORTH AMERICA, INC.—See Katadyn Holding AG; *Int'l*, pg. 4089
KATADYN PRODUCTION SRL.—See Katadyn Holding AG; *Int'l*, pg. 4089
KATADYN SINGAPORE—See Katadyn Holding AG; *Int'l*, pg. 4089
KATAGIRI & CO., INC.—See Kamei Corporation; *Int'l*, pg. 4061
KATAHDIN BANKSHARES CORP.; *U.S. Public*, pg. 1214
KATAHDIN INDUSTRIES, INC.; *U.S. Private*, pg. 2264
KATAHDIN TRUST COMPANY—See Katahdin Bankshares Corp.; *U.S. Public*, pg. 1215
KATAKURA CAREER SUPPORT K.K.—See Katakura Industries Co., Ltd.; *Int'l*, pg. 4089
KATAKURA CARON SERVICE CORPORATION—See Katakura Industries Co., Ltd.; *Int'l*, pg. 4089
KATAKURA CONSTRUCTION CO., LTD.—See MIRAIT ONE Corporation; *Int'l*, pg. 4917
KATAKURA & CO-OP AGRI CORPORATION; *Int'l*, pg. 4089
KATAKURA INDUSTRIES CO., LTD.; *Int'l*, pg. 4089
KATAKURA INSURANCE SERVICE K.K.—See Katakura Industries Co., Ltd.; *Int'l*, pg. 4089
KATAKURA MACHINERY INDUSTRIES CO., LTD.—See Katakura Industries Co., Ltd.; *Int'l*, pg. 4089
KATALOGER I NORR AB—See Eniro Group AB; *Int'l*, pg. 2439
KATALYSATOR S.A.; *Int'l*, pg. 4089
KATALYST DATA MANAGEMENT LIMITED—See Katalyst Data Management LP; *Int'l*, pg. 4089
KATALYST DATA MANAGEMENT LLC—See Katalyst Data Management LP; *Int'l*, pg. 4089
KATALYST DATA MANAGEMENT LP - DENVER FACILITY—See Katalyst Data Management LP; *Int'l*, pg. 4089
KATALYST DATA MANAGEMENT LP - OKLAHOMA FACILITY—See Katalyst Data Management LP; *Int'l*, pg. 4089
KATALYST DATA MANAGEMENT LP; *Int'l*, pg. 4089
KATALYST PARTNERS, LLC; *U.S. Private*, pg. 2264
KATALYST SURGICAL, LLC—See Carl-Zeiss-Stiftung; *Int'l*, pg. 1334
KATANA ASSET MANAGEMENT LTD—See Katana Capital Limited; *Int'l*, pg. 4089
KATANA CAPITAL LIMITED; *Int'l*, pg. 4089
KATANGA MINING LIMITED—See Glencore plc; *Int'l*, pg. 2991
KATARE SPINNING MILLS LIMITED; *Int'l*, pg. 4089
KATARSIS CAPITAL ADVISORS SA—See Azimut Holding SpA; *Int'l*, pg. 779
KATAYAMA SEIYAKUSYO CO., LTD.—See Sakai Chemical Industry Co., Ltd.; *Int'l*, pg. 6486
KATAYAMA SEIYAKUSYO CO., LTD. - TOYAMA PLANT—See Sakai Chemical Industry Co., Ltd.; *Int'l*, pg. 6486
KATAYAMA STRATECH CORP.—See Shimizu Corporation; *Int'l*, pg. 6835
KATC COMMUNICATIONS, INC.—See Evening Post Publishing Co.; *U.S. Private*, pg. 1436
KATCHMARK CONSTRUCTION INC.—See Altas Partners LP; *Int'l*, pg. 386
KATEC CREATIVE RESOURCES CORPORATION—See Tung Ho Steel Enterprise Corporation; *Int'l*, pg. 7970
KATECH INGREDIENT SOLUTIONS GMBH—See Ingredion Incorporated; *U.S. Public*, pg. 1124
KATECH INGREDIENT SOLUTIONS LTD.—See Ingredion Incorporated; *U.S. Public*, pg. 1124
KATECH INGREDIENT SOLUTIONS SP. Z O.O.—See Ingredion Incorporated; *U.S. Public*, pg. 1124
KATE COWHIG INTERNATIONAL RECRUITMENT LIMITED—See Bain Capital, LP; *U.S. Private*, pg. 433
KATEK SE—See Kontron AG; *Int'l*, pg. 4277

KATEKS SISUSTUS—See Foga System International AB; *Int'l*, pg. 2721

KATENA PRODUCTS, INC.—See Audax Group, Limited Partnership; *U.S. Private*, pg. 388

KATERINSKA HOTELS S.R.O.—See Accor S.A.; *Int'l*, pg. 91

KATERINSKA OFFICE BUILDING S.R.O.—See PPF Group N.V.; *Int'l*, pg. 5950

KATER INTERNATIONAL LIMITED—See Cafe de Coral Holdings Limited; *Int'l*, pg. 1250

KATES-BOYLSTON PUBLICATIONS—See United Communications Group; *U.S. Private*, pg. 4289

KATE'S CAKES LTD—See Rhone Group, LLC; *U.S. Private*, pg. 3423

KATE SPADE & COMPANY LLC—See Tapestry, Inc.; *U.S. Public*, pg. 1981

KATE SPADE JAPAN CO., LTD.—See Tapestry, Inc.; *U.S. Public*, pg. 1981

KATE SPADE LLC—See Tapestry, Inc.; *U.S. Public*, pg. 1981

KATEX AD; *Int'l*, pg. 4089

KAT EXPLORATION, INC.; *Int'l*, pg. 4088

THE KATHARINE GIBBS CORPORATION-MELVILLE—See Perdoceo Education Corporation; *U.S. Public*, pg. 1673

KATHARINE GIBBS OF PHILADELPHIA, LLC—See Perdoceo Education Corporation; *U.S. Public*, pg. 1673

THE KATHARINE GIBBS SCHOOL OF NORWALK, INC.—See Perdoceo Education Corporation; *U.S. Public*, pg. 1673

THE KATHARINE GIBBS SCHOOL OF PISCATAWAY, INC.—See Perdoceo Education Corporation; *U.S. Public*, pg. 1673

KATHARINENHOF SENIOREHWOHN- UND PFLEGEANLAGE BETRIEBS-GMBH—See Deutsche Wohnen SE; *Int'l*, pg. 2085

KATHERINE'S COLLECTION INC.; *U.S. Private*, pg. 2264

K. ATHIENITIS CONTRACTORS-DEVELOPERS PUBLIC LTD; *Int'l*, pg. 4043

KATHIMERINI PUBLISHING SA; *Int'l*, pg. 4090

KATHMANDU PTY LIMITED—See KMD Brands Limited; *Int'l*, pg. 4204

KATHMANDU (U.K.) LIMITED—See KMD Brands Limited; *Int'l*, pg. 4204

KATHREIN PRIVATBANK AKTIENGESELLSCHAFT—See Raiffeisen Bank International AG; *Int'l*, pg. 6182

KATHRYN BEICH FUNDRAISING—See Lincolnshire Management, Inc.; *U.S. Private*, pg. 2459

KATHY CHOCOLATERIE N.V.—See Sweet Products Logistics NV; *Int'l*, pg. 7366

KATHY L. SUMMERS, M.D., PLLC—See HCA Healthcare, Inc.; *U.S. Public*, pg. 1000

KATILIM VARLIK KIRALAMA A.S.; *Int'l*, pg. 4090

KATIPULT TECHNOLOGY CORP.; *Int'l*, pg. 4090

KATITAS CO., LTD.; *Int'l*, pg. 4090

KATJES FASSIN GMBH & CO. KG—See Xaver Fassin GmbH; *Int'l*, pg. 8519

KATJESGREENFOOD GMBH & CO, KG—See Xaver Fassin GmbH; *Int'l*, pg. 8519

KATJES INTERNATIONAL GMBH & CO. KG—See Xaver Fassin GmbH; *Int'l*, pg. 8520

KAT LTD.—See KISWIRE LTD; *Int'l*, pg. 4193

KATMAILAND, INC.—See Bristol Bay Native Corporation; *U.S. Private*, pg. 656

KATMERCILER ARAC USTU EKIPMAN SANAYI VE TICARET A.S.; *Int'l*, pg. 4090

KATO DANBORU CO., LTD.—See Rengo Co., Ltd.; *Int'l*, pg. 6280

KATO ENGINEERING INC.—See Nidec Corporation; *Int'l*, pg. 5275

KATOEN NATIE AMSTERDAM B.V.—See Katoen Natie N.V.; *Int'l*, pg. 4091

KATOEN NATIE AUTOMOTIVE CONTRACTORS—See Katoen Natie N.V.; *Int'l*, pg. 4091

KATOEN NATIE BRASIL LTDA.—See Katoen Natie N.V.; *Int'l*, pg. 4091

KATOEN NATIE BULK TERMINALS LINKEROEVER—See Katoen Natie N.V.; *Int'l*, pg. 4091

KATOEN NATIE BULK TERMINALS NV—See Katoen Natie N.V.; *Int'l*, pg. 4091

KATOEN NATIE CANADA—See Katoen Natie N.V.; *Int'l*, pg. 4091

KATOEN NATIE CARGO AGENCY NV—See Katoen Natie N.V.; *Int'l*, pg. 4091

KATOEN NATIE CHEMICALS SOUTH AFRICA PTY LTD.—See Katoen Natie N.V.; *Int'l*, pg. 4091

KATOEN NATIE COMMODITIES ANTWERP—See Katoen Natie N.V.; *Int'l*, pg. 4091

KATOEN NATIE COTE D'IVOIRE SA—See Katoen Natie N.V.; *Int'l*, pg. 4091

KATOEN NATIE DE HENARES S.L.—See Katoen Natie N.V.; *Int'l*, pg. 4091

KATOEN NATIE DEUTSCHLAND GMBH—See Katoen Natie N.V.; *Int'l*, pg. 4091

KATOEN NATIE EESTI AS—See Katoen Natie N.V.; *Int'l*, pg. 4091

KATOEN NATIE FLANDERS CONTAINER TERMINALS NV—See Katoen Natie N.V.; *Int'l*, pg. 4091

KATOEN NATIE FRANCE—See Katoen Natie N.V.; *Int'l*, pg. 4091

KATOEN NATIE HAVENTRANSPORT NV—See Katoen Natie N.V.; *Int'l*, pg. 4091

KATOEN NATIE IBERICA S.L.—See Katoen Natie N.V.; *Int'l*, pg. 4091

KATOEN NATIE IOT LTD.—See Katoen Natie N.V.; *Int'l*, pg. 4091

KATOEN NATIE ITALIA SRL—See Katoen Natie N.V.; *Int'l*, pg. 4091

KATOEN NATIE LOJISTIK ANONIM SIRKETI—See Katoen Natie N.V.; *Int'l*, pg. 4091

KATOEN NATIE LOJISTIK A.S.—See Katoen Natie N.V.; *Int'l*, pg. 4091

KATOEN NATIE LOUISIANA—See Katoen Natie N.V.; *Int'l*, pg. 4091

KATOEN NATIE MEXICO—See Katoen Natie N.V.; *Int'l*, pg. 4091

KATOEN NATIE MIDWEST INC.—See Katoen Natie N.V.; *Int'l*, pg. 4091

KATOEN NATIE NORTHEAST INC.—See Katoen Natie N.V.; *Int'l*, pg. 4091

KATOEN NATIE NUTH B.V.—See Katoen Natie N.V.; *Int'l*, pg. 4091

KATOEN NATIE N.V.; *Int'l*, pg. 4090

KATOEN NATIE RUHR LOGISTIK GMBH.—See Katoen Natie N.V.; *Int'l*, pg. 4091

KATOEN NATIE SERVICES(THAILAND) LTD.—See Katoen Natie N.V.; *Int'l*, pg. 4091

KATOEN NATIE SINGAPORE (JURONG) PTE LTD—See Katoen Natie N.V.; *Int'l*, pg. 4091

KATOEN NATIE - TEESSIDE HANDLING & DISTRIBUTION LTD.—See Katoen Natie N.V.; *Int'l*, pg. 4091

KATOEN NATIE TERMINAL GENK NV—See Katoen Natie N.V.; *Int'l*, pg. 4091

KATOEN NATIE (THAILAND) LTD.—See Katoen Natie N.V.; *Int'l*, pg. 4091

KATOEN NATIE TRUCK & TRAILER SERVICE NV—See Katoen Natie N.V.; *Int'l*, pg. 4091

KATOEN NATIE USA—See Katoen Natie N.V.; *Int'l*, pg. 4091

KATOEN NATIE WESSELING LOGISTIK GMBH—See Katoen Natie N.V.; *Int'l*, pg. 4091

KATO HEAVY INDUSTRIES CONSTRUCTION MACHINERY CO., LTD.—See Kato Works Co., Ltd.; *Int'l*, pg. 4090

KATO (HONG KONG) HOLDINGS LIMITED; *Int'l*, pg. 4090

KATOH PRECISION MACHINERY CO., LTD.—See Sanoyas Holdings Corporation; *Int'l*, pg. 6554

KATOLEC AUTOMOTIVE SYSTEMS (GUANGZHOU) CO., LTD.—See Katolec Corporation; *Int'l*, pg. 4091

KATOLEC CORPORATION; *Int'l*, pg. 4091

KATOLEC DE BAJA CALIFORNIA, S.A. DE C.V.—See Katolec Corporation; *Int'l*, pg. 4091

KATOLEC DEVELOPMENT INC.—See Katolec Corporation; *Int'l*, pg. 4091

KATOLEC ENGINEERING (THAILAND) CO., LTD.—See Katolec Corporation; *Int'l*, pg. 4091

KATOLEC (HK) CO., LTD.—See Katolec Corporation; *Int'l*, pg. 4091

KATOLEC MALAYSIA SDN.BHD.—See Katolec Corporation; *Int'l*, pg. 4092

KATOLEC PHILIPPINES CORPORATION—See Katolec Corporation; *Int'l*, pg. 4091

KATOLEC SUZHOU CO., LTD.—See Katolec Corporation; *Int'l*, pg. 4091

KATOLEC (THAILAND) CO., LTD.—See Katolec Corporation; *Int'l*, pg. 4091

KATOLEC VIETNAM CORPORATION—See Katolec Corporation; *Int'l*, pg. 4092

KATOLEC WEST CO., LTD.—See Katolec Corporation; *Int'l*, pg. 4092

KATOM RESTAURANT SUPPLY INC; *U.S. Private*, pg. 2265

KATOMSK AS; *Int'l*, pg. 4092

KATONAH DEBT ADVISORS, L.L.C.—See LibreMax Capital, LLC; *U.S. Private*, pg. 2448

KATO SANGYO CO., LTD.; *Int'l*, pg. 4090

KATO SANSHO CO., LTD.; *Int'l*, pg. 4090

KATO SPRING (SHANGHAI) CO., LTD.—See Advanex Inc.; *Int'l*, pg. 163

KATO WORKS CO., LTD.; *Int'l*, pg. 4090

KATRINA GROUP LTD.; *Int'l*, pg. 4092

KATRIN FIELD INCORPORATED; *Int'l*, pg. 4092

KATRON SAVUNMA UZAY VE SIMULASYON TEKNOLOJILERI A.S.—See Koc Holding A.S.; *Int'l*, pg. 4223

KATSURAGAWA ELECTRIC CO., LTD.; *Int'l*, pg. 4092

KATSURAGI CO., LTD.—See Yamaha Corporation; *Int'l*, pg. 8549

KATSURA SANGYO CO., LTD.—See Hodogaya Chemical Co., Ltd.; *Int'l*, pg. 3439

KATSUTA CO., LTD.—See Takuma Co., Ltd.; *Int'l*, pg. 7442

KATSUYA (THAILAND) CO., LTD.—See AAPICO Hitech plc; *Int'l*, pg. 37

KATSUZAI CHEMICAL CORPORATION—See Mitsui Chemicals, Inc.; *Int'l*, pg. 4981

KATTEN MUCHIN ROSENMAN LLP; *U.S. Private*, pg. 2265

KATUN ARGENTINA S.R.L.—See General Plastic Industrial Co., Ltd.; *Int'l*, pg. 2919

KATUN BENELUX B.V.—See General Plastic Industrial Co., Ltd.; *Int'l*, pg. 2919

KATUN BRASIL COMERCIO DE SUPRIMENTOS PECAS E EQUIPAMENTOS LTDA.—See General Plastic Industrial Co., Ltd.; *Int'l*, pg. 2919

KATUN CORPORATION—See General Plastic Industrial Co., Ltd.; *Int'l*, pg. 2919

KATUN FRANCE S.A.R.L.—See General Plastic Industrial Co., Ltd.; *Int'l*, pg. 2919

KATUN GERMANY GMBH—See General Plastic Industrial Co., Ltd.; *Int'l*, pg. 2919

KATUN ITALY S.R.L.—See General Plastic Industrial Co., Ltd.; *Int'l*, pg. 2919

KATUN PORTUGAL S.A.—See General Plastic Industrial Co., Ltd.; *Int'l*, pg. 2919

KATUN SPAIN S.A.—See General Plastic Industrial Co., Ltd.; *Int'l*, pg. 2919

KATUN U.K. LTD.—See General Plastic Industrial Co., Ltd.; *Int'l*, pg. 2919

KATV, LLC—See Sinclair, Inc.; *U.S. Public*, pg. 1886

KATY ANUSA, LLC—See AutoNation, Inc.; *U.S. Public*, pg. 236

KATY ER CENTER LLC—See Adeptus Health Inc.; *U.S. Private*, pg. 78

KATY-H, INC.—See Lithia Motors, Inc.; *U.S. Public*, pg. 1323

KATY MILLS—See Simon Property Group, Inc.; *U.S. Public*, pg. 1882

KATZ 360 DIGITAL SALES—See iHeartMedia, Inc.; *U.S. Public*, pg. 1096

KATZ ADVANTAGE—See iHeartMedia, Inc.; *U.S. Public*, pg. 1096

KATZ COMMUNICATIONS, INC.—See iHeartMedia, Inc.; *U.S. Public*, pg. 1096

KATZ DIRECT—See iHeartMedia, Inc.; *U.S. Public*, pg. 1096

KATZ GROUP INC.; *Int'l*, pg. 4092

KATZ & KATZ TRANSFER, INC.; *U.S. Private*, pg. 2265

KATZKIN LEATHER INC.—See SECOM Co., Ltd.; *Int'l*, pg. 6670

KATZ & KLEIN—See EssilorLuxottica SA; *Int'l*, pg. 2513

KATZMAN FAMILY SUPPORT FOUNDATION; *U.S. Private*, pg. 2265

KATZ MARKETING SOLUTIONS—See iHeartMedia, Inc.; *U.S. Public*, pg. 1096

KATZ MEDIA GROUP, INC.—See iHeartMedia, Inc.; *U.S. Public*, pg. 1096

KATZ MILLENNIUM SALES & MARKETING INC.—See iHeartMedia, Inc.; *U.S. Public*, pg. 1096

KATZ NET RADIO SALES, INC.—See iHeartMedia, Inc.; *U.S. Public*, pg. 1096

KATZ RADIO GROUP—See iHeartMedia, Inc.; *U.S. Public*, pg. 1096

KATZ SAPPER & MILLER LLP; *U.S. Private*, pg. 2265

KATZSON BROS, INC.; *U.S. Private*, pg. 2265

KATZ TELEVISION GROUP—See iHeartMedia, Inc.; *U.S. Public*, pg. 1096

KAUAI COFFEE COMPANY, INC.—See Alexander & Baldwin, Inc.; *U.S. Public*, pg. 75

KAUAI COFFEE LLC.—See Segafredo Zanetti S.p.A.; *Int'l*, pg. 6682

KAUAI PETROLEUM CO., LTD.—See Par Pacific Holdings, Inc.; *U.S. Public*, pg. 1636

KAUBAMAJA AS—See Tallinna Kaubamaja AS; *Int'l*, pg. 7447

KAUCHUK J.S.CO.; *Int'l*, pg. 4092

K AUCTION INC.; *Int'l*, pg. 4037

KAUFEL GMBH & CO. KG—See ABB Ltd.; *Int'l*, pg. 52

KAUFFMAN ENGINEERING, INC.—See Monomoy Capital Partners LLC; *U.S. Private*, pg. 2772

KAUFFMAN POULTRY FARMS, INC.; *U.S. Private*, pg. 2265

KAUFFMAN TIRE INC.; *U.S. Private*, pg. 2265

KAUFFMAN TIRE SERVICE OF CINCINNATI INC.—See Kauffman Tire Inc.; *U.S. Private*, pg. 2265

KAUFHALLE GMBH—See Metro AG; *Int'l*, pg. 4857

KAUFHOF WARENHAUS ROSTOCK GMBH—See Metro AG; *Int'l*, pg. 4857

KAUFMAN ADVERTISING AGENCY; *U.S. Private*, pg. 2265

KAUFMAN & BROAD S.A.; *Int'l*, pg. 4092

KAUFMAN COMPANY INC.; *U.S. Private*, pg. 2265

KAUFMAN CONTAINER CO.; *U.S. Private*, pg. 2265

KAUFMAN, HALL & ASSOCIATES, LLC—See Vizient, Inc.; *U.S. Private*, pg. 4407

KAUFMAN LYNN CONSTRUCTION, INC.; *U.S. Private*, pg. 2265

KAUFMAN MFG. COMPANY; *U.S. Private*, pg. 2265

KAUFMANN & GOBLE ASSOCIATES, INC.—See Northwest Plan Services, Inc.; *U.S. Private*, pg. 2961

KAUFMANN & LINDGENS GMBH; *Int'l*, pg. 4092

KAUFMANN, ROSSIN & CO., PROFESSIONAL ASSOCIATION; *U.S. Private*, pg. 2265

KAUKAAN VOIMA OY—See Pohjolan Voima Oy; *Int'l*, pg. 5904

COMPANY NAME INDEX

KAUKO GMBH—See Aspo Oyj; *Int'l*, pg. 631
KAUKOMARKKINAT OY—See Aspo Oyj; *Int'l*, pg. 631
KAUKOMARKKINAT SHANGHAI LTD.—See Aspo Oyj; *Int'l*, pg. 631
KAUKORA OY—See NIBE Industrier AB; *Int'l*, pg. 5261
KAUKOTALO OY—See Valmet Oyj; *Int'l*, pg. 8118
KAUL GMBH—See Freudenberg SE; *Int'l*, pg. 2789
KAULIN MFG CO., LTD.; *Int'l*, pg. 4092
KAU MARKET EAF, S.L.—See Substrate Artificial Intelligence SA; *Int'l*, pg. 7249
KAUMY S.R.O.—See Fomento Economico Mexicano, S.A.B. de C.V.; *Int'l*, pg. 2724
KAUNET CO., LTD.—See Kokuyo Co., Ltd.; *Int'l*, pg. 4232
KAUNO ENERGIJA AB; *Int'l*, pg. 4092
KAUPPAHUONE HARJU OY—See Einhell Germany AG; *Int'l*, pg. 2333
KAUPPAKESKUS ISOKARHU OY—See Citycon Oyj; *Int'l*, pg. 1629
KAUPPALEHTI OY—See Alma Media Corporation; *Int'l*, pg. 362
KAUPULEHU DEVELOPMENTS—See Barnwell Industries, Inc.; *U.S. Public*, pg. 278
KAURI BUSINESS SYSTEMS LIMITED—See TA Associates, Inc.; *U.S. Private*, pg. 3914
KAUSHALYA INFRASTRUCTURE DEVELOPMENT CORPORATION LTD; *Int'l*, pg. 4092
KAUSHALYA LOGISTICS LIMITED; *Int'l*, pg. 4092
KAUSHALYA NIRMAN PVT. LTD.—See Kaushalya Infrastructure Development Corporation Ltd; *Int'l*, pg. 4092
KAUTEX ITALY—See PLASTECH Holding GmbH; *Int'l*, pg. 5892
KAUTEX MACHINES, INC.; *U.S. Private*, pg. 2265
KAUTEX MASCHINENBAU GMBH—See PLASTECH Holding GmbH; *Int'l*, pg. 5891
KAUTEX TEXTRON GMBH & CO. KG—See Textron Inc.; *U.S. Public*, pg. 2028
KAUTILYA INFOTECH LIMITED—See Alchemist Corporation Limited; *Int'l*, pg. 300
K AUTO OY—See Kesko Corporation; *Int'l*, pg. 4141
K AUTO PC OY—See Kesko Corporation; *Int'l*, pg. 4141
KAUT-TV—See Nexstar Media Group, Inc.; *U.S. Public*, pg. 1524
KAVALA, INC.; *U.S. Private*, pg. 2265
KAVANAGH COMMUNICATIONS; *Int'l*, pg. 4092
KAVANAUGH, INC.; *U.S. Private*, pg. 2265
KAVANGO RESOURCES PLC; *Int'l*, pg. 4092
KAV DANISMANLIK PAZ. TIC. AS—See Koc Holding A.S.; *Int'l*, pg. 4223
KAVED AG—See Pema Holding AG; *Int'l*, pg. 5784
KAVEH INDUSTRIAL CORPORATION - ISFAHAN FACTORY—See Kaveh Industrial Corporation; *Int'l*, pg. 4092
KAVEH INDUSTRIAL CORPORATION; *Int'l*, pg. 4092
KAVEH INDUSTRIAL CORPORATION - TEHRAN FACTORY—See Kaveh Industrial Corporation; *Int'l*, pg. 4092
KAVEH PAPER INDUSTRIES COMPANY; *Int'l*, pg. 4093
KAVERI GAS POWER LTD.; *Int'l*, pg. 4093
KAVERI SEED COMPANY LTD.; *Int'l*, pg. 4093
KAVERIT CRANES AND SERVICE ULC—See Konecranes Plc; *Int'l*, pg. 4251
KAVETT DIALYSIS, LLC—See DaVita Inc.; *U.S. Public*, pg. 640
KAVIENG PORT SERVICES LIMITED—See Steamships Trading Company Limited; *Int'l*, pg. 7188
KAVIM PUBLIC TRANSPORTATION LTD—See Mayer's Cars & Trucks Co. Ltd.; *Int'l*, pg. 4744
KAVIM RASKA A.D. RASKA; *Int'l*, pg. 4093
KAVITA FABRICS LIMITED; *Int'l*, pg. 4093
KAVO DENTAL GMBH—See Danaher Corporation; *U.S. Public*, pg. 627
KAVO DENTAL LTD.—See Danaher Corporation; *U.S. Public*, pg. 627
KAVO DENTAL TECHNOLOGIES, LLC—See Danaher Corporation; *U.S. Public*, pg. 627
KAVO DO BRASIL INDUSTRIA E COMERCIO LTDA.—See Danaher Corporation; *U.S. Public*, pg. 627
KAVTEK SOFTWARE CORP.; *U.S. Public*, pg. 1215
KAVVERI TELECOM PRODUCTS LTD; *Int'l*, pg. 4093
KAWABA RESORT CO., LTD.—See Nippon Parking Development Co., Ltd.; *Int'l*, pg. 5328
KAWABE BIOMASS POWER GENERATION CO., LTD.—See Japan Pulp and Paper Company Limited; *Int'l*, pg. 3904
KAWA CAPITAL MANAGEMENT, INC.; *U.S. Private*, pg. 2265
KAWACOM UGANDA LIMITED—See Ecom Agroindustrial Corporation Ltd; *Int'l*, pg. 2296
KAWADA CONSTRUCTION CO., LTD.—See Kawada Technologies Inc.; *Int'l*, pg. 4093
KAWADA INDUSTRIES, INC.—See Kawada Technologies Inc.; *Int'l*, pg. 4093
KAWADA ROBOTICS CORP.—See Kawada Technologies Inc.; *Int'l*, pg. 4093
KAWADA TECHNOLOGIES INC.; *Int'l*, pg. 4093
KAWADA TECHNOSYSTEM CO., LTD.—See Kawada Technologies Inc.; *Int'l*, pg. 4093
KAWADEN CORPORATION; *Int'l*, pg. 4093

KAWADER SERVICES—See Abu Dhabi Islamic Bank PJSC; *Int'l*, pg. 72
KAWAGISHI BRIDGE WORKS CO., LTD.; *Int'l*, pg. 4093
KAWAGOE SUISANSHIJO K.K.—See TOHTO SUISAN Co., Ltd.; *Int'l*, pg. 7778
KAWAGUCHI CHEMICAL INDUSTRY CO., LTD. - BUSINESS DEVELOPMENT DIVISION—See Kawaguchi Chemical Industry Co., Ltd.; *Int'l*, pg. 4093
KAWAGUCHI CHEMICAL INDUSTRY CO., LTD.; *Int'l*, pg. 4093
KAWAGUCHIKO COUNTRY CLUB CO., LTD.—See Tokyo Tatemono Co., Ltd.; *Int'l*, pg. 7796
KAWAGUCHI METAL INDUSTRIES CO., LTD.—See Kawakin Holdings Co., Ltd.; *Int'l*, pg. 4094
KAWAHIGASHI SHOJI CO., LTD.—See Takara Holdings, Inc.; *Int'l*, pg. 7432
KAWAI AMERICA CORPORATION—See Kawai Musical Instruments Mfg. Co., Ltd.; *Int'l*, pg. 4093
KAWAI AMERICA MANUFACTURING, INC.—See Kawai Musical Instruments Mfg. Co., Ltd.; *Int'l*, pg. 4093
KAWAI AUSTRALIA PTY. LTD.—See Kawai Musical Instruments Mfg. Co., Ltd.; *Int'l*, pg. 4093
KAWAICHI SANGYO CO., LTD.—See Daido Steel Co., Ltd.; *Int'l*, pg. 1923
KAWAI EUROPA GMBH—See Kawai Musical Instruments Mfg. Co., Ltd.; *Int'l*, pg. 4094
KAWAI FINISHING, INC.—See Kawai Musical Instruments Mfg. Co., Ltd.; *Int'l*, pg. 4094
KAWAI FRANCE SAS—See Kawai Musical Instruments Mfg. Co., Ltd.; *Int'l*, pg. 4094
KAWAI HIRYO CORPORATION—See Nagase & Co., Ltd.; *Int'l*, pg. 5126
KAWAI MUSICAL INSTRUMENTS MFG. CO., LTD.; *Int'l*, pg. 4093
KAWAI PIANO (RUSSIA) LLC—See Kawai Musical Instruments Mfg. Co., Ltd.; *Int'l*, pg. 4094
KAWAI TRADING (SHANGHAI) CO., LTD.—See Kawai Musical Instruments Mfg. Co., Ltd.; *Int'l*, pg. 4093
KAWAI UK LTD.—See Kawai Musical Instruments Mfg. Co., Ltd.; *Int'l*, pg. 4094
KAWAJU AKASHI ENGINEERING CO., LTD.—See Kawasaki Heavy Industries, Ltd.; *Int'l*, pg. 4095
KAWAJU FACILITECH CO., LTD.—See Kawasaki Heavy Industries, Ltd.; *Int'l*, pg. 4095
KAWAJU GIFU ENGINEERING CO., LTD.—See Kawasaki Heavy Industries, Ltd.; *Int'l*, pg. 4095
KAWAJU GIFU MANUFACTURING CO., LTD.—See Kawasaki Heavy Industries, Ltd.; *Int'l*, pg. 4095
KAWAJU GIFU SERVICE CO., LTD.—See Kawasaki Heavy Industries, Ltd.; *Int'l*, pg. 4095
KAWAJU KOBE SUPPORT CO., LTD.—See Kawasaki Heavy Industries, Ltd.; *Int'l*, pg. 4095
KAWAJU MARINE ENGINEERING CO., LTD.—See Kawasaki Heavy Industries, Ltd.; *Int'l*, pg. 4095
KAWAJU SERVICE CORP.—See Kawasaki Heavy Industries, Ltd.; *Int'l*, pg. 4095
KAWAJU STEEL WORK & ENGINEERING CO., LTD.—See Kawasaki Heavy Industries, Ltd.; *Int'l*, pg. 4096
KAWAJU SUPPORT CO., LTD.—See Kawasaki Heavy Industries, Ltd.; *Int'l*, pg. 4096
KAWAJYU SHOJI CO., LTD.—See Kawasaki Heavy Industries, Ltd.; *Int'l*, pg. 4096
KAWAKAMI PAINT MANUFACTURING CO., LTD.; *Int'l*, pg. 4094
KAWAKEN FINE CHEMICALS CO., LTD.—See Ajinomoto Company, Inc.; *Int'l*, pg. 257
KAWAKI KOSAN KAISHA, LTD.—See Kawasaki Kisen Kaisha, Ltd.; *Int'l*, pg. 4100
KAWAKI MEASURING INSTRUMENT CO., LTD.—See Yoshitake Inc.; *Int'l*, pg. 8601
KAWAKIN BUSINESS MANAGEMENT CO., LTD—See Kawakin Holdings Co., Ltd.; *Int'l*, pg. 4094
KAWAKIN CORE-TECH CO., LTD.—See Kawakin Holdings Co., Ltd.; *Int'l*, pg. 4094
KAWAKIN HOLDINGS CO., LTD.; *Int'l*, pg. 4094
KAWAKIN TECHNO SOLUTION CO., LTD. - HYOGO FACTORY—See Kawakin Holdings Co., Ltd.; *Int'l*, pg. 4094
KAWAKIN TECHNO SOLUTION CO., LTD.—See Kawakin Holdings Co., Ltd.; *Int'l*, pg. 4094
KAWAMATA SEIKI CO., LTD.—See Japan Industrial Partners, Inc.; *Int'l*, pg. 3890
KAWAMOTO CORPORATION; *Int'l*, pg. 4094
KAWAMURA QUANTITY SURVEYORS CO., LTD.—See Tokura Construction Co., Ltd.; *Int'l*, pg. 7786
KAWAN FOOD BERHAD; *Int'l*, pg. 4094
KAWAN FOOD MANUFACTURING SDN. BHD.—See Kawan Food Berhad; *Int'l*, pg. 4094
KAWANISHI LOGISTICS (S) PTE. LTD.—See Kawanishi Warehouse Co., Ltd.; *Int'l*, pg. 4094
KAWANISHI WAREHOUSE CO., LTD.; *Int'l*, pg. 4094
KAWARIN ENTERPRISE PTE LTD.—See JFE Holdings, Inc.; *Int'l*, pg. 3937
KAWARTHA DAIRY LIMITED; *Int'l*, pg. 4094
KAWASAKI BIOMASS POWER GENERATION CO., LTD.—See Fuluhashi EPO Corporation; *Int'l*, pg. 2844

KAWASAKI HEAVY INDUSTRIES, LTD.

KAWASAKI BIOMASS POWER GENERATION CO., LTD.—See Sumitomo Chemical Company, Limited; *Int'l*, pg. 7267
KAWASAKI BIOMASS POWER GENERATION CO., LTD.—See Sumitomo Forestry Co., Ltd.; *Int'l*, pg. 7285
KAWASAKI (CHONGQING) ROBOTICS ENGINEERING CO., LTD.—See Kawasaki Heavy Industries, Ltd.; *Int'l*, pg. 4096
KAWASAKI CHUNHUI PRECISION MACHINERY (ZHEJIANG) LTD.—See Kawasaki Heavy Industries, Ltd.; *Int'l*, pg. 4096
KAWASAKI & CO., LTD.; *Int'l*, pg. 4094
KAWASAKI CONSTRUCTION MACHINERY CORP. OF AMERICA—See Kawasaki Heavy Industries, Ltd.; *Int'l*, pg. 4096
KAWASAKI DO BRASIL INDUSTRIA E COMERCIO LTDA.—See Kawasaki Heavy Industries, Ltd.; *Int'l*, pg. 4098
KAWASAKI DO BRAZIL INDUSTRIA E COMERCIO LTDA.—See Kawasaki Heavy Industries, Ltd.; *Int'l*, pg. 4098
KAWASAKI ENGINEERING CO., LTD.—See Kawasaki Heavy Industries, Ltd.; *Int'l*, pg. 4096
KAWASAKI ENVIRONMENTAL PLANT ENGINEERING CO., LTD.—See Kawasaki Heavy Industries, Ltd.; *Int'l*, pg. 4096
KAWASAKI GAS TURBINE ASIA SDN. BHD.—See Kawasaki Heavy Industries, Ltd.; *Int'l*, pg. 4096
KAWASAKI GAS TURBINE EUROPE GMBH—See Kawasaki Heavy Industries, Ltd.; *Int'l*, pg. 4096
KAWASAKI GEOLOGICAL ENGINEERING CO., LTD.; *Int'l*, pg. 4095
KAWASAKI HEAVY INDUSTRIES-AKASHI TECHNICAL INSTITUTE—See Kawasaki Heavy Industries, Ltd.; *Int'l*, pg. 4096
KAWASAKI HEAVY INDUSTRIES-AKASHI WORKS—See Kawasaki Heavy Industries, Ltd.; *Int'l*, pg. 4096
KAWASAKI HEAVY INDUSTRIES-BANSHU WORKS—See Kawasaki Heavy Industries, Ltd.; *Int'l*, pg. 4096
KAWASAKI HEAVY INDUSTRIES (EUROPE) B.V.—See Kawasaki Heavy Industries, Ltd.; *Int'l*, pg. 4096
KAWASAKI HEAVY INDUSTRIES-GIFU WORKS—See Kawasaki Heavy Industries, Ltd.; *Int'l*, pg. 4096
KAWASAKI HEAVY INDUSTRIES-HARIMA WORKS—See Kawasaki Heavy Industries, Ltd.; *Int'l*, pg. 4096
KAWASAKI HEAVY INDUSTRIES (H.K.) LTD.—See Kawasaki Heavy Industries, Ltd.; *Int'l*, pg. 4096
KAWASAKI HEAVY INDUSTRIES-HYOGO WORKS—See Kawasaki Heavy Industries, Ltd.; *Int'l*, pg. 4096
KAWASAKI HEAVY INDUSTRIES (INDIA) PVT. LTD.—See Kawasaki Heavy Industries, Ltd.; *Int'l*, pg. 4096
KAWASAKI HEAVY INDUSTRIES-KOBE WORKS—See Kawasaki Heavy Industries, Ltd.; *Int'l*, pg. 4096
KAWASAKI HEAVY INDUSTRIES, LTD. - KAKOGAWA WORKS—See Kawasaki Heavy Industries, Ltd.; *Int'l*, pg. 4096
KAWASAKI HEAVY INDUSTRIES, LTD. - KCM CORPORATION MAIN PLANT—See Kawasaki Heavy Industries, Ltd.; *Int'l*, pg. 4096
KAWASAKI HEAVY INDUSTRIES, LTD. - NAGOYA WORKS 1—See Kawasaki Heavy Industries, Ltd.; *Int'l*, pg. 4096
KAWASAKI HEAVY INDUSTRIES, LTD. - NAGOYA WORKS 2—See Kawasaki Heavy Industries, Ltd.; *Int'l*, pg. 4096
KAWASAKI HEAVY INDUSTRIES, LTD. - NISHI-KOBE WORKS—See Kawasaki Heavy Industries, Ltd.; *Int'l*, pg. 4096
KAWASAKI HEAVY INDUSTRIES, LTD. - SAKAIDE WORKS—See Kawasaki Heavy Industries, Ltd.; *Int'l*, pg. 4096
KAWASAKI HEAVY INDUSTRIES, LTD. - SEISHIN WORKS—See Kawasaki Heavy Industries, Ltd.; *Int'l*, pg. 4096
KAWASAKI HEAVY INDUSTRIES, LTD.—See Kawasaki Heavy Industries, Ltd.; *Int'l*, pg. 4096
KAWASAKI HEAVY INDUSTRIES, LTD.; *Int'l*, pg. 4095
KAWASAKI HEAVY INDUSTRIES, LTD. (TOKYO)—See Kawasaki Heavy Industries, Ltd.; *Int'l*, pg. 4096
KAWASAKI HEAVY INDUSTRIES MACHINERY TRADING (SHANGHAI) CO., LTD.—See Kawasaki Heavy Industries, Ltd.; *Int'l*, pg. 4096
KAWASAKI HEAVY INDUSTRIES MANAGEMENT (SHANGHAI), LTD.—See Kawasaki Heavy Industries, Ltd.; *Int'l*, pg. 4096
KAWASAKI HEAVY INDUSTRIES MIDDLE EAST FZE—See Kawasaki Heavy Industries, Ltd.; *Int'l*, pg. 4096
KAWASAKI HEAVY INDUSTRIES-NAGOYA WORKS—See Kawasaki Heavy Industries, Ltd.; *Int'l*, pg. 4096
KAWASAKI HEAVY INDUSTRIES RUSSIA LLC—See Kawasaki Heavy Industries, Ltd.; *Int'l*, pg. 4096
KAWASAKI HEAVY INDUSTRIES (SINGAPORE) PTE. LTD.—See Kawasaki Heavy Industries, Ltd.; *Int'l*, pg. 4096
KAWASAKI HEAVY INDUSTRIES—See Kawasaki Heavy Industries, Ltd.; *Int'l*, pg. 4096

KAWASAKI HEAVY INDUSTRIES, LTD.

KAWASAKI HEAVY INDUSTRIES (THAILAND) CO., LTD.—See Kawasaki Heavy Industries, Ltd.; *Int'l*, pg. 4096
KAWASAKI HEAVY INDUSTRIES (UK) LTD.—See Kawasaki Heavy Industries, Ltd.; *Int'l*, pg. 4096
KAWASAKI HEAVY INDUSTRIES USA INC—See Kawasaki Heavy Industries, Ltd.; *Int'l*, pg. 4096
KAWASAKI HEAVY INDUSTRIES (U.S.A.), INC.—See Kawasaki Heavy Industries, Ltd.; *Int'l*, pg. 4096
KAWASAKI HYDROMECHANICS CORPORATION—See Kawasaki Heavy Industries, Ltd.; *Int'l*, pg. 4097
KAWASAKI KASEI CHEMICALS LTD. - KAWASAKI PLANT—See Air Water Inc.; *Int'l*, pg. 240
KAWASAKI KASEI CHEMICALS LTD.—See Air Water Inc.; *Int'l*, pg. 240
KAWASAKI KINKAI KISEN KAISHA, LTD.—See Kawasaki Kisen Kaisha, Ltd.; *Int'l*, pg. 4098
KAWASAKI KISEN KAISHA, LTD.; *Int'l*, pg. 4098
KAWASAKI KOKAN CO., LTD.—See JFE Holdings, Inc.; *Int'l*, pg. 3938
KAWASAKI LIFE CORPORATION—See Kawasaki Heavy Industries, Ltd.; *Int'l*, pg. 4097
KAWASAKI MACHINERY DO BRASIL MAQUINAS E EQUIPAMENTOS LTDA.—See Kawasaki Heavy Industries, Ltd.; *Int'l*, pg. 4097
KAWASAKI MACHINE SYSTEMS KOREA, LTD.—See Kawasaki Heavy Industries, Ltd.; *Int'l*, pg. 4097
KAWASAKI MACHINE SYSTEMS, LTD.—See Kawasaki Heavy Industries, Ltd.; *Int'l*, pg. 4097
KAWASAKI MARUUO CO., LTD.—See Yokohama Maruuo Co., Ltd.; *Int'l*, pg. 8595
KAWASAKI MOTOR ENTERPRISE THAILAND LTD.—See Kawasaki Heavy Industries, Ltd.; *Int'l*, pg. 4097
KAWASAKI MOTORES DO BRASIL LTDA.—See Kawasaki Heavy Industries, Ltd.; *Int'l*, pg. 4097
KAWASAKI MOTORS CORPORATION JAPAN—See Kawasaki Heavy Industries, Ltd.; *Int'l*, pg. 4097
KAWASAKI MOTORS CORP., U.S.A.—See Kawasaki Heavy Industries, Ltd.; *Int'l*, pg. 4097
KAWASAKI MOTORS ENTERPRISE (THAILAND) CO., LTD.—See Kawasaki Heavy Industries, Ltd.; *Int'l*, pg. 4097
KAWASAKI MOTORS EUROPE N.V.—See Kawasaki Heavy Industries, Ltd.; *Int'l*, pg. 4097
KAWASAKI MOTORS EUROPE N.V.—See Kawasaki Heavy Industries, Ltd.; *Int'l*, pg. 4097
KAWASAKI MOTORS EUROPE N.V.—See Kawasaki Heavy Industries, Ltd.; *Int'l*, pg. 4097
KAWASAKI MOTORS FINANCE CORPORATION—See Kawasaki Heavy Industries, Ltd.; *Int'l*, pg. 4097
KAWASAKI MOTORS HOLDING (MALAYSIA) SDN. BHD.—See Kawasaki Heavy Industries, Ltd.; *Int'l*, pg. 4097
KAWASAKI MOTORS MANUFACTURING CORP., U.S.A.—See Kawasaki Heavy Industries, Ltd.; *Int'l*, pg. 4097
KAWASAKI MOTORS (PHILS.) CORPORATION—See Kawasaki Heavy Industries, Ltd.; *Int'l*, pg. 4097
KAWASAKI MOTORS PTY. LTD.—See Kawasaki Heavy Industries, Ltd.; *Int'l*, pg. 4097
KAWASAKI MOTORS (SHANGHAI) , LTD.—See Kawasaki Heavy Industries, Ltd.; *Int'l*, pg. 4097
KAWASAKI MOTORS (UK) LTD.—See Kawasaki Heavy Industries, Ltd.; *Int'l*, pg. 4097
KAWASAKI MOTORS VIETNAM CO., LTD.—See Kawasaki Heavy Industries, Ltd.; *Int'l*, pg. 4097
KAWASAKI NATURAL GAS POWER GENERATION CO., LTD.—See ENEOS Holdings, Inc.; *Int'l*, pg. 2417
KAWASAKI NAVAL ENGINE SERVICE, LTD.—See Kawasaki Heavy Industries, Ltd.; *Int'l*, pg. 4097
KAWASAKI PLANT SYSTEMS, LTD.—See Kawasaki Heavy Industries, Ltd.; *Int'l*, pg. 4097
KAWASAKI PRECISION MACHINERY (SUZHOU) LTD.—See Kawasaki Heavy Industries, Ltd.; *Int'l*, pg. 4097
KAWASAKI PRECISION MACHINERY TRADING (SHANGHAI) CO., LTD.—See Kawasaki Heavy Industries, Ltd.; *Int'l*, pg. 4097
KAWASAKI PRECISION MACHINERY (UK) LTD.—See Kawasaki Heavy Industries, Ltd.; *Int'l*, pg. 4097
KAWASAKI PRECISION MACHINERY (U.S.A.), INC.—See Kawasaki Heavy Industries, Ltd.; *Int'l*, pg. 4097
KAWASAKI PRIME MOVER ENGINEERING CO., LTD.—See Kawasaki Heavy Industries, Ltd.; *Int'l*, pg. 4097
KAWASAKI RAIL CAR, INC.—See Kawasaki Heavy Industries, Ltd.; *Int'l*, pg. 4097
KAWASAKI ROBOTICS GMBH—See Kawasaki Heavy Industries, Ltd.; *Int'l*, pg. 4097
KAWASAKI ROBOTICS KOREA, LTD.—See Kawasaki Heavy Industries, Ltd.; *Int'l*, pg. 4097
KAWASAKI ROBOTICS (KUNSHAN) CO., LTD.—See Kawasaki Heavy Industries, Ltd.; *Int'l*, pg. 4097
KAWASAKI ROBOTICS (TIANJIN) CO., LTD.—See Kawasaki Heavy Industries, Ltd.; *Int'l*, pg. 4097
KAWASAKI ROBOTICS (UK) LTD.—See Kawasaki Heavy Industries, Ltd.; *Int'l*, pg. 4097
KAWASAKI ROBOTICS (U.S.A.), INC.—See Kawasaki Heavy Industries, Ltd.; *Int'l*, pg. 4097

KAWASAKI ROBOT SERVICE, LTD.—See Kawasaki Heavy Industries, Ltd.; *Int'l*, pg. 4097
KAWASAKI ROLLING STOCK COMPONENT CO., LTD.—See Kawasaki Heavy Industries, Ltd.; *Int'l*, pg. 4097
KAWASAKI ROLLING STOCK TECHNOLOGY CO., LTD.—See Kawasaki Heavy Industries, Ltd.; *Int'l*, pg. 4097
KAWASAKI SAFETY SERVICE INDUSTRIES, LTD.—See Kawasaki Heavy Industries, Ltd.; *Int'l*, pg. 4097
KAWASAKI SETSUBI KOGYO CO., LTD.—See Kandenko Co., Ltd.; *Int'l*, pg. 4065
KAWASAKI SHIPBUILDING CORPORATION—See Kawasaki Heavy Industries, Ltd.; *Int'l*, pg. 4098
KAWASAKI SHIPBUILDING CORPORATION—See Kawasaki Heavy Industries, Ltd.; *Int'l*, pg. 4098
KAWASAKI SUBSEA (UK) LTD.—See Kawasaki Heavy Industries, Ltd.; *Int'l*, pg. 4098
KAWASAKI TECHNOLOGY CO., LTD.—See Kawasaki Heavy Industries, Ltd.; *Int'l*, pg. 4098
KAWASAKI TECHNO WAVE CO., LTD.—See Kawasaki Heavy Industries, Ltd.; *Int'l*, pg. 4098
KAWASAKI THERMAL ENGINEERING CO., LTD.—See Kawasaki Heavy Industries, Ltd.; *Int'l*, pg. 4098
KAWASAKI TOKUYAMA READY MIXED CONCRETE CO., LTD.—See Tokuyama Corporation; *Int'l*, pg. 7787
KAWASAKI TRADING CO., LTD.—See Kawasaki Heavy Industries, Ltd.; *Int'l*, pg. 4098
KAWASAKI TRADING DO BRASIL LTDA.—See Kawasaki Heavy Industries, Ltd.; *Int'l*, pg. 4098
KAWASAKI TRADING (SHANGHAI) CO., LTD.—See Kawasaki Heavy Industries, Ltd.; *Int'l*, pg. 4098
KAWASAKI TSURUMI RINKO BUS CO., LTD.—See Keikyu Corporation; *Int'l*, pg. 4117
KAWASE COMPUTER SUPPLIES CO., LTD.; *Int'l*, pg. 4101
KAWASHIMA TEXTILE MANUFACTURERS (SHANGHAI) LTD.—See Toyota Boshoku Corporation; *Int'l*, pg. 7863
KAWASHO FOOD CORPORATION—See JFE Holdings, Inc.; *Int'l*, pg. 3937
KAWASUMI LABORATORIES AMERICA INC.—See Sumitomo Bakelite Co., Ltd.; *Int'l*, pg. 7263
KAWASUMI LABORATORIES INCORPORATED - MIE PLANT—See Sumitomo Bakelite Co., Ltd.; *Int'l*, pg. 7263
KAWASUMI LABORATORIES INCORPORATED - SAIKI PLANT—See Sumitomo Bakelite Co., Ltd.; *Int'l*, pg. 7263
KAWASUMI LABORATORIES INCORPORATED—See Sumitomo Bakelite Co., Ltd.; *Int'l*, pg. 7263
KAWASUMI LABORATORIES INCORPORATED - YAYOI PLANT—See Sumitomo Bakelite Co., Ltd.; *Int'l*, pg. 7263
KAWASUMI LABORATORIES (THAILAND) CO., LTD.—See Sumitomo Bakelite Co., Ltd.; *Int'l*, pg. 7263
KAWATA MACHINERY (HK) LIMITED—See KAWATA MFG CO., LTD.; *Int'l*, pg. 4101
KAWATA MARKETING SDN. BHD.—See KAWATA MFG CO., LTD.; *Int'l*, pg. 4101
KAWATA MFG CO., LTD. - OSAKA PLANT—See KAWATA MFG CO., LTD.; *Int'l*, pg. 4101
KAWATA MFG CO., LTD. - SANDA PLANT—See KAWATA MFG CO., LTD.; *Int'l*, pg. 4101
KAWATA MFG CO., LTD.; *Int'l*, pg. 4101
KAWATA MFG CO., LTD. - TOKYO PLANT—See KAWATA MFG CO., LTD.; *Int'l*, pg. 4101
KAWATA PACIFIC PTE. LTD.—See KAWATA MFG CO., LTD.; *Int'l*, pg. 4101
KAWATA (SHANGHAI) CO., LTD.—See KAWATA MFG CO., LTD.; *Int'l*, pg. 4101
KAWEAH CONSTRUCTION CO. INC.—See Lyles Diversified Inc.; *U.S. Private*, pg. 2520
KAWEFLEX WIRE AND CABLE INC.—See TKH Group N.V.; *Int'l*, pg. 7764
KAWNEER COMPANY CANADA LTD.—See Howmet Aerospace Inc.; *U.S. Public*, pg. 1062
KAWNEER COMPANY, INC.—See Howmet Aerospace Inc.; *U.S. Public*, pg. 1062
KAWNEER COMPANY, INC.—See Howmet Aerospace Inc.; *U.S. Public*, pg. 1062
KAWNEER COMPANY, INC.—See Howmet Aerospace Inc.; *U.S. Public*, pg. 1062
KAWNEER COMPANY, INC.—See Howmet Aerospace Inc.; *U.S. Public*, pg. 1062
KAWNEER COMPANY, INC. - SPRINGDALE—See Howmet Aerospace Inc.; *U.S. Public*, pg. 1062
KAWNEER FRANCE SA—See Howmet Aerospace Inc.; *U.S. Public*, pg. 1062
KAWNEER MAROC SA—See Howmet Aerospace Inc.; *U.S. Public*, pg. 1062
KAWNEER UK LIMITED—See Howmet Aerospace Inc.; *U.S. Public*, pg. 1062
KAW PIPE LINE COMPANY—See CHS INC.; *U.S. Public*, pg. 491
KAWTHER GRAIN (PRIVATE) LIMITED—See A.K. Al-Muhaidib & Sons Group of Companies; *Int'l*, pg. 25
KAW VALLEY COMPANIES, INC.; *U.S. Private*, pg. 2265
KAYA ASSOCIATES INC.; *U.S. Private*, pg. 2266

KAYABA EUROPE GMBH—See KYB Corporation; *Int'l*, pg. 4354
KAYABA HYDRAULICS SALES (SHANGHAI) LTD—See KYB Corporation; *Int'l*, pg. 4354
KAYABA INDUSTRY CO., LTD - GIFU NORTH PLANT—See KYB Corporation; *Int'l*, pg. 4354
KAYABA SPAIN S.A.—See KYB Corporation; *Int'l*, pg. 4354
KAYAC INC.; *Int'l*, pg. 4101
KAYA HOLDINGS, INC.; *U.S. Public*, pg. 1215
KAYAKO LIMITED—See ESW Capital, LLC; *U.S. Private*, pg. 1430
KAYAK SOFTWARE CORPORATION—See Booking Holdings, Inc.; *U.S. Public*, pg. 368
KAYAKU ADVANCED MATERIALS, INC.—See Nippon Kayaku Co., Ltd.; *Int'l*, pg. 5320
KAYAKU AKZO CORPORATION—See Akzo Nobel N.V.; *Int'l*, pg. 274
KAYAKU CHEMICAL (WUXI) CO., LTD—See Nippon Kayaku Co., Ltd.; *Int'l*, pg. 5320
KAYAKU CO., LTD.—See Pola Orbis Holdings Inc.; *Int'l*, pg. 5905
KAYAKU JAPAN CO., LTD.—See Nippon Kayaku Co., Ltd.; *Int'l*, pg. 5320
KAYAKU SAFETY SYSTEMS DE MEXICO, S.A. DE C.V.—See Nippon Kayaku Co., Ltd.; *Int'l*, pg. 5320
KAYAKU SAFETY SYSTEMS EUROPE A.S.—See Nippon Kayaku Co., Ltd.; *Int'l*, pg. 5320
KAYAKU SAFETY SYSTEMS (HUZHOU) CO., LTD.—See Nippon Kayaku Co., Ltd.; *Int'l*, pg. 5320
KAYAKU SAFETY SYSTEMS MALAYSIA SDN. BHD.—See Nippon Kayaku Co., Ltd.; *Int'l*, pg. 5320
KAYAKU (SHANGHAI) CO., LTD.—See Nippon Kayaku Co., Ltd.; *Int'l*, pg. 5320
KAYA LIMITED; *Int'l*, pg. 4101
KAYANGAN MANISAN (M) SDN. BHD.—See Kawan Food Berhad; *Int'l*, pg. 4094
KAY & ASSOCIATES INC.; *U.S. Private*, pg. 2266
KAY BVBA—See Ecolab Inc.; *U.S. Public*, pg. 714
KAYCAN LTD.—See Compagnie de Saint-Gobain SA; *Int'l*, pg. 1723
KAY CEE ENERGY & INFRA LIMITED; *Int'l*, pg. 4101
KAYCEE IND. LTD.—See CMS Computers Ltd.; *Int'l*, pg. 1672
KAYCEE INDUSTRIES LIMITED—See SALZER ELECTRONICS LIMITED; *Int'l*, pg. 6495
KAY CHEMICAL COMPANY—See Ecolab Inc.; *U.S. Public*, pg. 714
THE KAY COMPANY, INC.; *U.S. Private*, pg. 4064
KAY CONCRETE MATERIALS, CO.—See Monarch Cement Company; *U.S. Public*, pg. 1460
KAY COUNTY CLINIC COMPANY, LLC—See Community Health Systems, Inc.; *U.S. Public*, pg. 554
KAY COUNTY OKLAHOMA HOSPITAL COMPANY, LLC—See Community Health Systems, Inc.; *U.S. Public*, pg. 552
KAYDAV GROUP LIMITED; *Int'l*, pg. 4102
KAYDON CORPORATION—See SKF AB; *Int'l*, pg. 6985
KAYDON CUSTOM FILTRATION CORPORATION—See Madison Industries Holdings LLC; *U.S. Private*, pg. 2543
KAYDON RING & SEAL, INC.—See SKF AB; *Int'l*, pg. 6985
KAYE CORPORATION; *U.S. Private*, pg. 2266
KAYEMA ENERGY SOLUTIONS (PROPRIETARY) LIMITED—See Group Five Limited; *Int'l*, pg. 3089
KAYEM FOODS, INC.; *U.S. Private*, pg. 2266
KAYE PUBLISHING CORPORATION; *U.S. Private*, pg. 2266
KAYE-SMITH; *U.S. Private*, pg. 2266
KAY FLO INDUSTRIES, INC.—See The Andersons Incorporated; *U.S. Public*, pg. 2034
KAY FOODS INC.—See Kay Packing Company Inc.; *U.S. Private*, pg. 2266
KAY GRAFICAS AUTOMOTRICES S.A. DE C.V.—See Kay Screen Printing, Inc.; *U.S. Private*, pg. 2266
KAYHAN INTERNATIONAL LIMITED—See Business Office Systems Inc.; *U.S. Private*, pg. 695
KAY HOME PRODUCTS—See Akerue Industries, LLC; *U.S. Private*, pg. 145
KAYLA FOODS INT'L (BARBADOS) INC.—See Yogen Fruz; *Int'l*, pg. 8591
KAY-METZELER LIMITED—See TPG Capital, L.P.; *U.S. Public*, pg. 2175
KAYMUS RESOURCES INC.; *Int'l*, pg. 4102
KAYNAK TEKNIGI SANAYI VE TICARET A.S.—See Lincoln Electric Holdings, Inc.; *U.S. Public*, pg. 1317
KAYNE ANDERSON BDC, INC.; *U.S. Private*, pg. 2267
KAYNE ANDERSON CAPITAL ADVISORS, L.P.; *U.S. Private*, pg. 2267
KAYNE ANDERSON ENERGY INFRASTRUCTURE FUND, INC.—See Kayne Anderson Capital Advisors, L.P.; *U.S. Private*, pg. 2267
KAYNE ANDERSON NEXTGEN ENERGY & INFRASTRUCTURE, INC.—See Kayne Anderson Capital Advisors, L.P.; *U.S. Private*, pg. 2267
KAYNE ANDERSON RUDNICK INVESTMENT MANAGEMENT, LLC—See Virtus Investment Partners, Inc.; *U.S. Public*, pg. 2301
KAYNE DL 2021, INC.; *U.S. Private*, pg. 2267

COMPANY NAME INDEX

KAYNE & SON CUSTOM HARDWARE INC.; *U.S. Private*, pg. 2266
KAYNES TECHNOLOGY INDIA LIMITED; *Int'l*, pg. 4102
KAYO OF CALIFORNIA, INC.; *U.S. Private*, pg. 2267
KAY PACKING COMPANY INC.; *U.S. Private*, pg. 2266
KAYPENTAX—See Hoya Corporation; *Int'l*, pg. 3495
KAY POWER & PAPER LIMITED; *Int'l*, pg. 4101
KAY PREMIUM MARKING FILMS, LTD.—See Kay Screen Printing, Inc.; *U.S. Private*, pg. 2266
KAY PRIDE SDN BHD—See S P Setia Berhad; *Int'l*, pg. 6443
KAY & QUE (BANGLADESH) LTD.; *Int'l*, pg. 4101
KAY SCREEN PRINTING, INC.; *U.S. Private*, pg. 2266
KAYSER AUTOMOTIVE GROUP, LLC; *U.S. Private*, pg. 2267
KAYSER CHRYSLER CENTER, INC.—See Kayser Automotive Group, LLC; *U.S. Private*, pg. 2267
KAYSER CHRYSLER CENTER OF WATERTOWN, INC.—See Kayser Automotive Group, LLC; *U.S. Private*, pg. 2267
KAYSER CHRYSLER CENTER STOUGHTON—See Kayser Automotive Group, LLC; *U.S. Private*, pg. 2267
KAYSER FORD, INC.—See Kayser Automotive Group, LLC; *U.S. Private*, pg. 2267
KAYSERIGAZ KAYSERI DOGALGAZ DAGITIM PAZARLAMA VE TICARET A.S.—See EWE Aktiengesellschaft; *Int'l*, pg. 2575
KAYSER LIMITED—See Highway Holdings Limited; *Int'l*, pg. 3389
KAYSER-ROTH CORPORATION—See Golden Lady S.p.A.; *Int'l*, pg. 3030
KAYSER-ROTH CORPORATION—See Golden Lady S.p.A.; *Int'l*, pg. 3030
KAYSERSBERG PHARMACEUTICALS S.A.S.—See Recipharm AB; *Int'l*, pg. 6235
KAYS MEDICAL LTD; *Int'l*, pg. 4102
KAYSORN CONSTRUCTION COMPANY LIMITED—See Pruksa Holding Public Company Limited; *Int'l*, pg. 6010
KAY'S PROCESSING, INC.—See American Securities LLC; *U.S. Private*, pg. 250
KAYSUN CORPORATION; *U.S. Private*, pg. 2267
KAYSWAY CO., LTD.—See World Co., Ltd.; *Int'l*, pg. 8456
KAYTEE PRODUCTS, INC.—See Central Garden & Pet Company; *U.S. Public*, pg. 473
KAY TOLEDO TAG, INC.—See Ennis, Inc.; *U.S. Public*, pg. 769
KAYTON INTERNATIONAL, INC.; *U.S. Private*, pg. 2267
KAY UPHOSTERY; *U.S. Private*, pg. 2266
KAYWOODIE—See S.M. Frank & Co., Inc.; *U.S. Private*, pg. 3518
KAZAGROFINANCE JSC—See National Holding KazAgro JSC; *Int'l*, pg. 5158
KAZAGRO NATIONAL MANAGEMENT HOLDING JSC; *Int'l*, pg. 4102
KAZAKHALTYN MINING-METALLURGICAL CONCERN JSC; *Int'l*, pg. 4102
KAZAKHEXPORT EIC JSC—See National Managing Holding Baiterek JSC; *Int'l*, pg. 5161
KAZAKHEXPORT EXPORT INSURANCE COMPANY JSC—See National Managing Holding Baiterek JSC; *Int'l*, pg. 5161
KAZAKHINTRAKH JSC—See Halyk Bank of Kazakhstan JSC; *Int'l*, pg. 3234
KAZAKHMYS AKTOGAY LLP—See Nova Resources B.V.; *Int'l*, pg. 5452
KAZAKHMYS COPPER JSC; *Int'l*, pg. 4102
KAZAKHMYS INSURANCE JSC; *Int'l*, pg. 4102
KAZAKHMYS LLC—See Nova Resources B.V.; *Int'l*, pg. 5452
KAZAKH REPUBLICAN TRADING HOUSE ZANGAR JSC; *Int'l*, pg. 4102
KAZAKHSTAN CEMENT HOLDING B.V.—See Heidelberg Materials AG; *Int'l*, pg. 3317
KAZAKHSTAN HOUSING COMPANY JSC—See The National Bank of Kazakhstan; *Int'l*, pg. 7669
KAZAKHSTAN IJARA COMPANY JOINT STOCK COMPANY—See Aktif Yatirim Bankasi A.S.; *Int'l*, pg. 267
KAZAKHSTAN KAGAZY JSC; *Int'l*, pg. 4102
KAZAKHSTAN PIPE THREADERS LIMITED LIABILITY PARTNERSHIP—See Techint S.p.A.; *Int'l*, pg. 7503
KAZAKHSTAN POTASH CORPORATION LIMITED; *Int'l*, pg. 4102
KAZAKHSTAN PROJECT PREPARATION FUND LIMITED LIABILITY PARTNERSHIP—See National Managing Holding Baiterek JSC; *Int'l*, pg. 5161
KAZAKHSTAN SOLAR SILICON LLP—See Canadian Solar Inc.; *Int'l*, pg. 1286
KAZAKHSTAN SOLAR SILICON LLP—See ECM Technologies SAS; *Int'l*, pg. 2292
KAZAKHSTAN SOLAR SILICON LLP—See Kasen International Holdings Limited; *Int'l*, pg. 4087
KAZAKHSTAN SOLAR SILICON LLP—See Yadran-Oil Group; *Int'l*, pg. 8544
KAZAKHSTAN STOCK EXCHANGE JOINT-STOCK COMPANY; *Int'l*, pg. 4102
KAZAKHSTAN UTILITY SYSTEMS LLP; *Int'l*, pg. 4102
KAZAKHSTAN ZIRAAT INTERNATIONAL BANK—See Turkiye Cumhuriyeti Ziraat Bankasi A.S.; *Int'l*, pg. 7975

KAZAKHTELECOM JSC; *Int'l*, pg. 4102
KAZAN INTERNATIONAL, INC.; *U.S. Private*, pg. 2267
KAZAN INTERNATIONAL—See Kazan International, Inc.; *U.S. Private*, pg. 2267
KAZANKOMPESSORMASH OJSC—See HMS Hydraulic Machines & Systems Group plc; *Int'l*, pg. 3432
KAZATOMPROM-DAMU LLP—See JSC National Atomic Company Kazatomprom; *Int'l*, pg. 4009
KAZAX MINERALS INC.; *Int'l*, pg. 4102
KAZAZOTE JSC; *Int'l*, pg. 4103
KAZBEGI JSC—See Bank of Georgia Group PLC; *Int'l*, pg. 843
KAZ CANADA, INC.—See Helen of Troy Limited; *Int'l*, pg. 3329
KAZ CONSUMER PRODUCTS, S.L.U.—See Helen of Troy Limited; *Int'l*, pg. 3329
KAZERA GLOBAL PLC; *Int'l*, pg. 4103
KAZ EUROPE SARL—See Helen of Troy Limited; *Int'l*, pg. 3329
KAZ FRANCE SAS—See Helen of Troy Limited; *Int'l*, pg. 3329
KAZ HAUSGERATE GMBH—See Helen of Troy Limited; *Int'l*, pg. 3329
KAZ HOME APPLIANCE (SHENZHEN) COMPANY LIMITED—See Helen of Troy Limited; *Int'l*, pg. 3329
KAZIA THERAPEUTICS LIMITED; *Int'l*, pg. 4103
KAZI FOODS CORP. OF HAWAII—See Kazi Foods Inc.; *U.S. Private*, pg. 2267
KAZI FOODS INC.; *U.S. Private*, pg. 2267
KAZ, INC.—See Helen of Troy Limited; *Int'l*, pg. 3329
KAZINVESTBANK JSC; *Int'l*, pg. 4103
KAZKOMMERTSBANK JSC—See Halyk Bank of Kazakhstan JSC; *Int'l*, pg. 3234
KAZ MINERALS MANAGEMENT LLP—See Nova Resources B.V.; *Int'l*, pg. 5452
KAZ MINERALS PLC—See Nova Resources B.V.; *Int'l*, pg. 5452
KAZ MINERALS RUSSIA LLC—See Nova Resources B.V.; *Int'l*, pg. 5452
KAZMORTRANSFLOT LLP—See JSC National Company KazMunayGas; *Int'l*, pg. 4010
KAZMUNAYGAS ONIMDERY LLP—See JSC National Company KazMunayGas; *Int'l*, pg. 4010
KAZMUNAYTENIZ LLP—See JSC National Company KazMunayGas; *Int'l*, pg. 4010
KAZOKUTEI CO., LTD.—See SRS HOLDINGS CO.,LTD.; *Int'l*, pg. 7152
KAZOO & COMPANY; *U.S. Private*, pg. 2267
KAZOO, INC. - EDWARDS GARMENT DIVISION—See Kazoo, Inc.; *U.S. Private*, pg. 2268
KAZOO, INC.; *U.S. Private*, pg. 2267
KAZSTROYSERVICE GLOBAL B.V.—See OGCC KazStroyService JSC; *Int'l*, pg. 5531
KAZSTROYSERVICE INFRASTRUCTURE INDIA PVT. LTD.—See OGCC KazStroyService JSC; *Int'l*, pg. 5531
KAZSTROYSERVICE MIDDLE EAST—See OGCC KazStroyService JSC; *Int'l*, pg. 5531
KAZTRANSCOM JSC; *Int'l*, pg. 4103
KAZTRANSOIL JSC; *Int'l*, pg. 4103
KAZTRONIX, LLC; *U.S. Private*, pg. 2268
KAZUPACK LTD LLP—See Kazakhstan Kagazy JSC; *Int'l*, pg. 4102
KAZUSA ENVIRONMENTAL RESEARCH CENTER CO., LTD.—See Takasago Thermal Engineering Co., Ltd.; *Int'l*, pg. 7434
KAZ USA, INC.—See Helen of Troy Limited; *Int'l*, pg. 3329
KAZZINC LTD.—See Glencore plc; *Int'l*, pg. 2991
KBA ASIA-PACIFIC SDN. BHD.—See Koenig & Bauer AG; *Int'l*, pg. 4226
KBA AUSTRALASIA PTY. LTD.—See Koenig & Bauer AG; *Int'l*, pg. 4226
KBA-BERLIN GMBH—See Koenig & Bauer AG; *Int'l*, pg. 4226
KBA-BRASIL LTDA.—See Koenig & Bauer AG; *Int'l*, pg. 4226
KBACE TECHNOLOGIES, INC.—See Cognizant Technology Solutions Corporation; *U.S. Public*, pg. 524
KBA DOCUSYS, INC.; *U.S. Private*, pg. 2268
KBA-FRANCE SAS—See Koenig & Bauer AG; *Int'l*, pg. 4226
KBA-GRAFITEC S.R.O.—See Koenig & Bauer AG; *Int'l*, pg. 4226
KBA (HK) COMPANY LIMITED—See Koenig & Bauer AG; *Int'l*, pg. 4226
KBA-ITALIA S.P.A.—See Koenig & Bauer AG; *Int'l*, pg. 4226
KB ALLOYS, INC.—See AMG Critical Materials N.V.; *Int'l*, pg. 425
KBA-METRONIC AG—See Koenig & Bauer AG; *Int'l*, pg. 4226
KBA-METROPRINT AG—See Koenig & Bauer AG; *Int'l*, pg. 4226
KBA MORTGAGE, LLC—See Bank of America Corporation; *U.S. Public*, pg. 272
KBANE SAS—See Groupe Adeo S.A.; *Int'l*, pg. 3091
K BANK—See K Capital Corporation; *U.S. Private*, pg. 2249
KBA NORDIC A/S—See Koenig & Bauer AG; *Int'l*, pg. 4226

KBA NORTH AMERICA INC.—See Koenig & Bauer AG; *Int'l*, pg. 4226
KBA NOTASYS INDIA PVT. LTD.—See Koenig & Bauer AG; *Int'l*, pg. 4227
KBA-NOTASYS NORTH AMERICA, INC.—See Koenig & Bauer AG; *Int'l*, pg. 4227
KBA-NOTASYS SA—See Koenig & Bauer AG; *Int'l*, pg. 4226
KBA PRINTING MACHINERY (SHANGHAI) CO., LTD.—See Koenig & Bauer AG; *Int'l*, pg. 4226
KB ARBETSSTOLEN 3—See Atrium Ljungberg AB; *Int'l*, pg. 694
K. BARGER REALTY, LLC; *U.S. Private*, pg. 2251
KBA RUS OOO—See Koenig & Bauer AG; *Int'l*, pg. 4226
KB ASSET MANAGEMENT CO., LTD.—See KB Financial Group Inc.; *Int'l*, pg. 4103
KB ASSET MANAGEMENT SINGAPORE PTE. LTD.—See KB Financial Group Inc.; *Int'l*, pg. 4103
KBA-SWISS HOLDING SA—See Koenig & Bauer AG; *Int'l*, pg. 4227
KBA (UK) LTD.—See Koenig & Bauer AG; *Int'l*, pg. 4226
KB AUTOSYS CO., LTD; *Int'l*, pg. 4103
KB BANK MYANMAR CO., LTD.—See KB Financial Group Inc.; *Int'l*, pg. 4103
KBB JOINT OPERATING CO. SDN. BHD—See Petroliam Nasional Berhad; *Int'l*, pg. 5829
KBBM, INC.—See H.U. Group Holdings, Inc.; *Int'l*, pg. 3197
KB BUILDING SERVICES, INC.; *U.S. Private*, pg. 2268
KBC ADVANCED TECHNOLOGIES (BEIJING) CO., LTD—See Yokogawa Electric Corporation; *Int'l*, pg. 8592
KBC ADVANCED TECHNOLOGIES CANADA LIMITED—See Yokogawa Electric Corporation; *Int'l*, pg. 8592
KBC ADVANCED TECHNOLOGIES, INC.—See Yokogawa Electric Corporation; *Int'l*, pg. 8592
KBC ADVANCED TECHNOLOGIES LIMITED—See Yokogawa Electric Corporation; *Int'l*, pg. 8592
KBC ADVANCED TECHNOLOGY PTE. LTD.—See Yokogawa Electric Corporation; *Int'l*, pg. 8592
KBC ALPHA SFIO—See KBC Group NV; *Int'l*, pg. 4105
KBC ANCORA SCA—See Cera SCRL; *Int'l*, pg. 1421
KB CAPITAL CO., LTD.—See KB Financial Group Inc.; *Int'l*, pg. 4103
KBC ASSET MANAGEMENT SA—See KBC Group NV; *Int'l*, pg. 4105
KBC AUTOLEASE NV—See KBC Group NV; *Int'l*, pg. 4106
KBC BANKA A.D.—See KBC Group NV; *Int'l*, pg. 4105
KBC BANK FRANCE—See KBC Group NV; *Int'l*, pg. 4105
KBC BANK HONG KONG BRANCH—See KBC Group NV; *Int'l*, pg. 4105
KBC BANK IRELAND PLC—See KBC Group NV; *Int'l*, pg. 4105
KBC BANK NV LONDON BRANCH—See KBC Group NV; *Int'l*, pg. 4105
KBC BANK N.V. SINGAPORE BRANCH—See KBC Group NV; *Int'l*, pg. 4105
KBC BANK NV—See KBC Group NV; *Int'l*, pg. 4105
KBC BANK TAIPEI BRANCH—See KBC Group NV; *Int'l*, pg. 4105
KBC COMMERCIAL FINANCE—See KBC Group NV; *Int'l*, pg. 4105
KBC CORPORATION LTD.; *Int'l*, pg. 4104
KBC CREDIT INVESTMENTS NV—See KBC Group NV; *Int'l*, pg. 4105
KBC FINANCE IRELAND—See KBC Group NV; *Int'l*, pg. 4105
KBC FINANCIAL INDEMNITY INSURANCE SA—See KBC Group NV; *Int'l*, pg. 4106
KBC FINANCIAL PRODUCTS HONG KONG LIMITED—See KBC Group NV; *Int'l*, pg. 4105
KBC FINANCIAL PRODUCTS UK LIMITED—See KBC Group NV; *Int'l*, pg. 4105
KBC FINANCIAL SERVICES (IRELAND) LIMITED—See KBC Group NV; *Int'l*, pg. 4105
KBC FUND MANAGEMENT LIMITED—See KBC Group NV; *Int'l*, pg. 4105
KBC GLOBAL LIMITED; *Int'l*, pg. 4104
K.B.C. GROUP INC.; *U.S. Private*, pg. 2251
KBC GROUP NV; *Int'l*, pg. 4104
KBC GROUP RE SA—See KBC Group NV; *Int'l*, pg. 4106
KBC HEALTH & SAFETY PROPRIETARY LIMITED—See Workforce Holdings Ltd.; *Int'l*, pg. 8455
KBC HOMELOANS—See KBC Group NV; *Int'l*, pg. 4105
KBC IFIMA—See KBC Group NV; *Int'l*, pg. 4105
KBC, INC.; *U.S. Private*, pg. 2268
KBC INSURANCE NV—See KBC Group NV; *Int'l*, pg. 4106
KBC INTERNATIONALE FINANCIERINGSMAATSCHAPPIJ NV—See KBC Group NV; *Int'l*, pg. 4105
KBC INTERNATIONAL FINANCE NV—See KBC Group NV; *Int'l*, pg. 4105
KBC INVESTMENTS LIMITED—See KBC Group NV; *Int'l*, pg. 4105
KBC LEASE BELGIUM NV—See KBC Group NV; *Int'l*, pg. 4106

KBC, INC.

CORPORATE AFFILIATIONS

KBC LEASE (DEUTSCHLAND) VERWALTUNGS GMBH—See Merca Leasing GmbH & Co. KG; *Int'l*, pg. 4818
KBC LEASE FRANCE SA—See KBC Group NV; *Int'l*, pg. 4106
KBC LEASE HOLDING NV—See KBC Group NV; *Int'l*, pg. 4105
KBC LEASE (LUXEMBOURG) SA—See KBC Group NV; *Int'l*, pg. 4105
KBC LEASE (NEDERLAND) BV—See KBC Group NV; *Int'l*, pg. 4106
KBC LEASE (UK) LIMITED—See KBC Group NV; *Int'l*, pg. 4106
KB COMPONENTS AB; *Int'l*, pg. 4103
KB COMPONENTS CANADA, INC.—See KB Components AB; *Int'l*, pg. 4103
K-B CORPORATION; *U.S. Private*, pg. 2250
KBCO, THE POLARIZED LENS COMPANY—See EssilorLuxottica SA; *Int'l*, pg. 2513
KBC PROCESS TECHNOLOGY LTD. - JAPAN—See Yokogawa Electric Corporation; *Int'l*, pg. 8592
KBC PROCESS TECHNOLOGY LTD. - NETHERLANDS—See Yokogawa Electric Corporation; *Int'l*, pg. 8592
KBC PROCESS TECHNOLOGY LTD.—See Yokogawa Electric Corporation; *Int'l*, pg. 8592
KB CREDIT INFORMATION CO., LTD.—See KB Financial Group Inc.; *Int'l*, pg. 4104
KBC RUSTHUISVASTGOED NV—See KBC Group NV; *Int'l*, pg. 4106
KBC SECURITIES HUNGARY—See KBC Group NV; *Int'l*, pg. 4106
KBC SECURITIES NV—See KBC Group NV; *Int'l*, pg. 4106
KBC SECURITIES PATRIA—See KBC Group NV; *Int'l*, pg. 4106
KBC SECURITIES POLAND—See KBC Group NV; *Int'l*, pg. 4106
KBC TOOLS INCORPORATED - MACHINERY DIVISION—See KBC Tools Incorporated; *U.S. Private*, pg. 2268
KBC TOOLS INCORPORATED; *U.S. Private*, pg. 2268
KBC TOWARZYSTWO FUNDUSZY INWESTYCYJNYCH A.S.—See KBC Group NV; *Int'l*, pg. 4106
KBC VENDOR FINANCE (DEUTSCHLAND) GMBH—See Merca Leasing GmbH & Co. KG; *Int'l*, pg. 4818
KBC VENDOR LEASE (DEUTSCHLAND) SERVICE GMBH—See Merca Leasing GmbH & Co. KG; *Int'l*, pg. 4819
KB DAEHAN SPECIALIZED BANK PLC—See KB Financial Group Inc.; *Int'l*, pg. 4103
KB DATA SYSTEMS CO., LTD.—See KB Financial Group Inc.; *Int'l*, pg. 4103
KBD CONSTRUCTION SERVICES, INC.—See Kajima Corporation; *Int'l*, pg. 4055
KB DESIGN AS—See ITAB Shop Concept AB; *Int'l*, pg. 3828
KB DREAM TOGETHER 3RD SPECIAL PURPOSE ACQUISITION CO.; *Int'l*, pg. 4103
KBD TECHNIC—See CECO Environmental Corp.; *U.S. Public*, pg. 463
K&B DUCT—See CECO Environmental Corp.; *U.S. Public*, pg. 463
KBE BUILDING CORPORATION; *U.S. Private*, pg. 2268
KB EESTI OU—See Wulff-Group Plc; *Int'l*, pg. 8502
KB ELECTRONICS, INC.—See Nidec Corporation; *Int'l*, pg. 5277
KB ENGINEERING COATING SDN. BHD.—See Serba Dinamik Holdings Berhad; *Int'l*, pg. 6721
KB ENGINEERING, PC; *U.S. Private*, pg. 2268
KB ENTERPRISE CO., LTD.—See Keihan Holdings Co., Ltd.; *Int'l*, pg. 4116
KB EXPORTS PRIVATE LIMITED—See KRBL Limited; *Int'l*, pg. 4300
KBFG INSURANCE(CHINA) CO., LTD.—See KB Financial Group Inc.; *Int'l*, pg. 4104
KBFG SECURITIES AMERICA INC.—See KB Financial Group Inc.; *Int'l*, pg. 4104
KB FINA JOINT STOCK COMPANY—See KB Financial Group Inc.; *Int'l*, pg. 4103
KB FINANCIAL GROUP INC.; *Int'l*, pg. 4103
KB FUTURES CO., LTD.—See KB Financial Group Inc.; *Int'l*, pg. 4103
KBG CORP.; *Int'l*, pg. 4107
KB GOLDEN LIFE CARE CO., LTD.—See KB Financial Group Inc.; *Int'l*, pg. 4103
K.B. HALLEN MANAGEMENT A/S—See CTS Eventim AG & Co. KGAA; *Int'l*, pg. 1873
K BHINDI INTERNATIONAL; *U.S. Private*, pg. 2249
KBHL LLC; *U.S. Private*, pg. 2268
KB HOME CALIFORNIA LLC—See KB Home; *U.S. Public*, pg. 1215
KB HOME COLORADO, INC.—See KB Home; *U.S. Public*, pg. 1215
KB HOME GREATER LOS ANGELES, INC.—See KB Home; *U.S. Public*, pg. 1215
KB HOME GREATER LOS ANGELES INC.—See KB Home; *U.S. Public*, pg. 1215

KB HOME JACKSONVILLE LLC—See KB Home; *U.S. Public*, pg. 1215
KB HOME MORTGAGE COMPANY—See KB Home; *U.S. Public*, pg. 1215
KB HOME NEVADA INC.—See KB Home; *U.S. Public*, pg. 1215
KB HOME NEVADA INC.—See KB Home; *U.S. Public*, pg. 1215
KB HOME NORTHERN CALIFORNIA—See KB Home; *U.S. Public*, pg. 1215
KB HOME ORLANDO LLC—See KB Home; *U.S. Public*, pg. 1215
KB HOME PHOENIX INC.—See KB Home; *U.S. Public*, pg. 1215
KB HOME RALEIGH-DURHAM INC.—See KB Home; *U.S. Public*, pg. 1215
KB HOME SACRAMENTO INC.—See KB Home; *U.S. Public*, pg. 1215
KB HOME SACRAMENTO INC.—See KB Home; *U.S. Public*, pg. 1215
KB HOME/SHAW LOUISIANA LLC—See KB Home; *U.S. Public*, pg. 1215
KB HOME—See KB Home; *U.S. Public*, pg. 1215
KB HOME; *U.S. Public*, pg. 1215
KB HOME—See KB Home; *U.S. Public*, pg. 1215
KB HOME SOUTH BAY INC.—See KB Home; *U.S. Public*, pg. 1215
KB HOME TAMPA LLC—See KB Home; *U.S. Public*, pg. 1215
KBI BIOPHARMA, INC.—See JSR Corp.; *Int'l*, pg. 4013
KBI DONGKOOK IND. CO., LTD.—See KBI Group; *Int'l*, pg. 4107
KBI-E INC.—See Merck & Co., Inc.; *U.S. Public*, pg. 1417
KBI GROUP; *Int'l*, pg. 4107
KBI INSURANCE COMPANY, INC.—See Stock Yards Bancorp, Inc.; *U.S. Public*, pg. 1951
KBI JAPAN CO., LTD.—See KBI Group; *Int'l*, pg. 4107
KBI METAL CO., LTD.; *Int'l*, pg. 4107
KB INDUSTRIES, INC.—See Atlantic Wind & Solar, Inc.; *Int'l*, pg. 676
K-BIN INC.—See Shin-Etsu Chemical Co. Ltd.; *Int'l*, pg. 6838
KB INSURANCE COMPANY LTD.; *U.S. Private*, pg. 2268
KB INVESTMENT CO., LTD.—See KB Financial Group Inc.; *Int'l*, pg. 4103
KB INVESTMENT & SECURITIES CO., LTD.—See KB Financial Group Inc.; *Int'l*, pg. 4103
KBIO COMPANY INC.; *Int'l*, pg. 4107
KB J CAPITAL CO., LTD.—See KB Financial Group Inc.; *Int'l*, pg. 4103
KB JODDLAREN—See Atria Plc; *Int'l*, pg. 694
KBJR, INC.—See Silver Point Capital, L.P.; *U.S. Private*, pg. 3661
KB KABEL BETEILIGUNGS-GMBH—See LEONI AG; *Int'l*, pg. 4462
KBK CHEM-ENGINEERING PRIVATE LIMITED - PUNE UNIT—See Shree Renuka Sugars Limited; *Int'l*, pg. 6864
KBK CHEM-ENGINEERING PRIVATE LIMITED—See Shree Renuka Sugars Limited; *Int'l*, pg. 6864
KBK EUROPE GMBH—See Kyokuto Boeki Kaisha, Ltd.; *Int'l*, pg. 4362
KBK INC.—See Kyokuto Boeki Kaisha, Ltd.; *Int'l*, pg. 4362
KBK INSURANCE GROUP, INC.—See The Carlyle Group Inc.; *U.S. Public*, pg. 2050
KBK KONZERT- UND KUNSTLERAGENTUR GMBH—See DEAG Deutsche Entertainment AG; *Int'l*, pg. 1998
KB KOLAO LEASING CO., LTD.—See KB Financial Group Inc.; *Int'l*, pg. 4104
KB KOOKMIN CARD CO., LTD.—See KB Financial Group Inc.; *Int'l*, pg. 4104
KB KRANKENHAUSBETEILIGUNGSGESELLSCHAFT MBH & CO. KG—See Asklepios Kliniken GmbH & Co. KGaA; *Int'l*, pg. 623
KBK STEEL PRODUCTS CO., LTD.—See Kyokuto Boeki Kaisha, Ltd.; *Int'l*, pg. 4362
KBK TECHNOLOGIES, INC.; *U.S. Private*, pg. 2268
KBL EUROPEAN PRIVATE BANKERS S.A.—See KBL European Private Bankers S.A.; *Int'l*, pg. 4107
KBL EUROPEAN PRIVATE BANKERS S.A.; *Int'l*, pg. 4107
KB LIFE CO., LTD.—See KB Financial Group Inc.; *Int'l*, pg. 4104
KB LIFE PARTNERS CO., LTD.—See KB Financial Group Inc.; *Int'l*, pg. 4104
KBL MONACO CONSEIL ET COURTAGE EN ASSURANCE—See KBC Group NV; *Int'l*, pg. 4106
KBLUE S.R.L.—See Wurth Verwaltungsgesellschaft mbH; *Int'l*, pg. 8506
KBM ENTERPRISES INC.; *U.S. Private*, pg. 2268
KBM GROUP, INC.; *U.S. Private*, pg. 2268
KBM GROUP—See WPP plc; *Int'l*, pg. 8491
KBM-HOGUE; *U.S. Private*, pg. 2268
KBM MICROFINANCE MYANMAR CO., LTD.—See KB Financial Group Inc.; *Int'l*, pg. 4104
KBM INFOND, DRUZBA ZA UPRAVLJANJE, D.O.O.—See OTP Bank Plc; *Int'l*, pg. 5657
K&B MISSISSIPPI CORPORATION—See New Rite Aid, LLC; *U.S. Private*, pg. 2905

KBMT OPERATING COMPANY, LLC—See TEGNA Inc.; *U.S. Public*, pg. 1990
KB NO.5 SPECIAL PURPOSE ACQUISITION COMPANY; *Int'l*, pg. 4104
KB NO.8 SPECIAL PURPOSE ACQUSITION COMPANY; *Int'l*, pg. 4104
K-BOB'S USA INC.; *U.S. Private*, pg. 2250
KBO ENTERPRISES INC.; *U.S. Private*, pg. 2268
KB OF BALTIMORE INC.; *U.S. Private*, pg. 2268
KB PENSION SERVICES, INC.—See Kerkering, Barberio & Co.; *U.S. Private*, pg. 2290
KB PENZIJNI SPOLECNOST, A.S.—See Societe Generale S.A.; *Int'l*, pg. 7039
KB PIPELINE COMPANY—See Northwest Natural Holding Company; *U.S. Public*, pg. 1542
KB PRVO PENZISKO DRUSTVO AD—See Prva Group plc; *Int'l*, pg. 6010
KB PUBLIKUM INVEST AD—See Komercijalna Banka A.D. Skopje; *Int'l*, pg. 4242
KBR AL-YUSR LIMITED COMPANY—See KBR, Inc.; *U.S. Public*, pg. 1215
KBR CONSTRUCTION COMPANY, LLC—See KBR, Inc.; *U.S. Public*, pg. 1216
KB REAL ESTATE TRUST CO., LTD.—See KB Financial Group Inc.; *Int'l*, pg. 4104
KB REMICON LLC—See KBI Group; *Int'l*, pg. 4107
KBR ENGINEERING COMPANY, LLC—See KBR, Inc.; *U.S. Public*, pg. 1216
KBR HOLDINGS PTY LTD.—See KBR, Inc.; *U.S. Public*, pg. 1216
KBR, INC.; *U.S. Private*, pg. 2268
KBR, INC.; *U.S. Public*, pg. 1215
KBR INDUSTRIAL CANADA CO.—See KBR, Inc.; *U.S. Public*, pg. 1216
KBR NETHERLANDS INVESTMENTS B.V.—See KBR, Inc.; *U.S. Public*, pg. 1216
K-BRO LINEN INC.; *Int'l*, pg. 4042
K-BRO LINEN SYSTEMS INC - BUANDERIE HMR DIVISION—See K-Bro Linen Inc.; *Int'l*, pg. 4042
K-BRO LINEN SYSTEMS INC - LES BUANDERIES DEXTRAZE DIVISION—See K-Bro Linen Inc.; *Int'l*, pg. 4042
K-BRO LINEN SYSTEMS INC—See K-Bro Linen Inc.; *Int'l*, pg. 4042
KBR OVERSEAS, INC.—See KBR, Inc.; *U.S. Public*, pg. 1216
KBRWYLE AEROSPACE GROUP—See KBR, Inc.; *U.S. Public*, pg. 1216
KBRWYLE SCIENCE, TECHNOLOGY & ENGINEERING GROUP—See KBR, Inc.; *U.S. Public*, pg. 1216
KBR WYLE SERVICES LLC—See KBR, Inc.; *U.S. Public*, pg. 1216
KBRWYLE TECHNOLOGY SOLUTIONS, LLC—See KBR, Inc.; *U.S. Public*, pg. 1216
KBS AG—See Compagnie de Saint-Gobain SA; *Int'l*, pg. 1723
KBS BUILDERS, INC.—See Star Equity Holdings, Inc.; *U.S. Public*, pg. 1937
KBS CANE & SUGAR CO., LTD.—See Khonburi Sugar Public Company Limited; *Int'l*, pg. 4155
KBS CAPITAL ADVISORS, LLC—See KBS Realty Advisors, LLC; *U.S. Private*, pg. 2269
KBS CAPITAL MARKETS GROUP, LLC—See KBS Realty Advisors, LLC; *U.S. Private*, pg. 2269
KBS CONSTRUCTION, INC.; *U.S. Private*, pg. 2268
KBS CORPORATE SALES LIMITED—See Sun Capital Partners, Inc.; *U.S. Private*, pg. 3861
KBSD-TV—See Gray Television, Inc.; *U.S. Public*, pg. 960
KB SECURITIES CO., LTD.—See KB Financial Group Inc.; *Int'l*, pg. 4104
KB SEIREN CO., LTD. - HOKURIKU SYNTHETIC FIBERS PLANT—See Seiren Co., Ltd.; *Int'l*, pg. 6691
KB SEIREN CO., LTD. - NAGAHAMA PLANT—See Seiren Co., Ltd.; *Int'l*, pg. 6691
KB SEIREN DTY, LTD.—See Seiren Co., Ltd.; *Int'l*, pg. 6691
KB SEIREN LTD.—See Seiren Co., Ltd.; *Int'l*, pg. 6691
KBS FIRE PROTECTION SYSTEMS LTD.—See MITIE Group Plc; *Int'l*, pg. 4926
KBS GROWTH & INCOME REIT, INC.; *U.S. Public*, pg. 1216
KBSH-TV—See Gray Television, Inc.; *U.S. Public*, pg. 960
KBSIII ALMADEN FINANCIAL PLAZA, LLC—See KBS Real Estate Investment Trust III, Inc.; *U.S. Public*, pg. 1217
KBSIII ANCHOR CENTRE, LLC—See KBS Real Estate Investment Trust III, Inc.; *U.S. Public*, pg. 1217
KBSIII ONE WASHINGTONIAN, LLC—See KBS Real Estate Investment Trust III, Inc.; *U.S. Public*, pg. 1217
KBSIII TEN ALMADEN, LLC—See KBS Real Estate Investment Trust III, Inc.; *U.S. Public*, pg. 1217
KBSI LICENSEE L.P.—See Sinclair, Inc.; *U.S. Public*, pg. 1885
KBS INDIA LIMITED; *Int'l*, pg. 4107
KBS INTERNATIONAL HOLDINGS INC.; *Int'l*, pg. 4107
KBS INVESTMENT CO., LTD.—See Khonburi Sugar Public Company Limited; *Int'l*, pg. 4155
KBSI-TV—See Sinclair, Inc.; *U.S. Public*, pg. 1885

COMPANY NAME INDEX

KBS LEGACY PARTNERS APARTMENT REIT, INC.; *U.S. Private*, pg. 2268
KBSL-TV—See Gray Television, Inc.; *U.S. Public*, pg. 960
KBS MOTORSPORTS PTE. LTD.—See Zhongshi Minan Holdings Limited; *Int'l*, pg. 8675
K.B. SOCKS, INC.; *U.S. Private*, pg. 2251
KBS+P CANADA LP—See Stagwell, Inc.; *U.S. Public*, pg. 1927
KBS REAL ESTATE INVESTMENT TRUST III, INC.; *U.S. Public*, pg. 1217
KBS REALTY ADVISORS, LLC; *U.S. Private*, pg. 2268
KB STAFFING; *U.S. Private*, pg. 2268
KBS TRADING CO., LTD.—See Khonburi Sugar Public Company Limited; *Int'l*, pg. 4155
KB SYNTHETICS CO., LTD. - BUSAN FACTORY—See KB Synthetics Co., Ltd.; *Int'l*, pg. 4104
KB SYNTHETICS CO., LTD. - CHUK - JEON FACTORY—See KB Synthetics Co., Ltd.; *Int'l*, pg. 4104
KB SYNTHETICS CO., LTD.; *Int'l*, pg. 4104
K&B TIMBER AND HARDWARE PTY. LTD.—See Metcash Limited; *Int'l*, pg. 4852
K&B TRANSPORTATION; *U.S. Private*, pg. 2249
KB-TUOTE OY—See Wulff-Group Plc; *Int'l*, pg. 8502
KBTV-TV—See Sinclair, Inc.; *U.S. Public*, pg. 1885
KBW, INC.—See Stifel Financial Corp.; *U.S. Public*, pg. 1949
KB WINES, LLC—See TSG Consumer Partners LLC; *U.S. Private*, pg. 4253
KBXX-FM—See Urban One, Inc.; *U.S. Public*, pg. 2265
KBZ S.R.O.—See Zeleziarne Podbrezova a.s.; *Int'l*, pg. 8631
K CABLE TELEVISION CORPORATION, INC.—See The Kansai Electric Power Co., Inc.; *Int'l*, pg. 7661
KCA DEUTAG DRILLING GMBH—See Pamplona Capital Management LLP; *Int'l*, pg. 5711
KCA DEUTAG DRILLING LTD.—See Pamplona Capital Management LLP; *Int'l*, pg. 5711
KCA DEUTAG GMBH & CO. KG—See Pamplona Capital Management LLP; *Int'l*, pg. 5711
K-C ADVERTISING, INC.—See Kimberly-Clark Corporation; *U.S. Public*, pg. 1229
K-C AFC MANUFACTURING, S. DE R.L. DE C. V.—See Kimberly-Clark Corporation; *U.S. Public*, pg. 1229
KCA PARTNERS, LTD.; *U.S. Private*, pg. 2269
K CAPITAL CORPORATION; *U.S. Private*, pg. 2249
K CAR CO., LTD.; *Int'l*, pg. 4037
K CAREER PARTNERS CORP.—See Kawasaki Heavy Industries, Ltd.; *Int'l*, pg. 4095
KCAS, INC.—See Vitruvian Partners LLP; *Int'l*, pg. 8263
KCA SUPER PTY LIMITED—See Kimberly-Clark Corporation; *U.S. Public*, pg. 1229
KCAU-TV—See Nexstar Media Group, Inc.; *U.S. Public*, pg. 1522
KCB BANK KENYA LIMITED—See KCB Group PLC; *Int'l*, pg. 4108
KCB BANK UGANDA LTD.—See KCB Group PLC; *Int'l*, pg. 4108
KCB BELL, INC.; *U.S. Private*, pg. 2269
KCB GROUP PLC; *Int'l*, pg. 4108
KCB INTERLIGHT SP. Z O.O.—See Serafin Unternehmensgruppe GmbH; *Int'l*, pg. 6720
KCB MANAGEMENT LLC; *U.S. Private*, pg. 2269
KC BOBCAT INC.—See Berry Companies, Inc.; *U.S. Private*, pg. 538
KCBS-TV—See National Amusements, Inc.; *U.S. Private*, pg. 2840
KCB UMA GMBH—See Serafin Unternehmensgruppe GmbH; *Int'l*, pg. 6720
KCBX—See Koch Industries, Inc.; *U.S. Private*, pg. 2331
KCBY-TV—See Sinclair, Inc.; *U.S. Public*, pg. 1886
KCC BASILDON CHEMICAL CO., LTD.—See KCC Corporation; *Int'l*, pg. 4108
KCC (BEIJING) CO., LTD.—See KCC Corporation; *Int'l*, pg. 4108
KCC (CHONGQING) CO., LTD.—See KCC Corporation; *Int'l*, pg. 4108
KCC CONTRACTOR INC.; *U.S. Private*, pg. 2269
KCC CORPORATION - BEIJING PLANT—See KCC Corporation; *Int'l*, pg. 4108
KCC CORPORATION - CHENNAI PLANT—See KCC Corporation; *Int'l*, pg. 4108
KCC CORPORATION - GREECE PLANT—See KCC Corporation; *Int'l*, pg. 4108
KCC CORPORATION - HAMBURG PLANT—See KCC Corporation; *Int'l*, pg. 4108
KCC CORPORATION - HONG KONG PLANT—See KCC Corporation; *Int'l*, pg. 4108
KCC CORPORATION - KOCAELI PLANT—See KCC Corporation; *Int'l*, pg. 4108
KCC CORPORATION - MALAYSIA PLANT 2—See KCC Corporation; *Int'l*, pg. 4108
KCC CORPORATION; *Int'l*, pg. 4108
KCC CORPORATION - TOKYO PLANT—See KCC Corporation; *Int'l*, pg. 4108
KCC ENGINEERING & CONSTRUCTION CO., LTD; *Int'l*, pg. 4109
KC CENTRAL TRADING CO., LTD.—See Kamei Corporation; *Int'l*, pg. 4061

KCC EUROPE GMBH—See KCC Corporation; *Int'l*, pg. 4109
KCC GLASS CORPORATION; *Int'l*, pg. 4109
KCC (GUANGZHOU) CO., LTD.—See KCC Corporation; *Int'l*, pg. 4108
KCC (HANOI) CO., LTD.—See KCC Corporation; *Int'l*, pg. 4108
KCCI-TV—See The Hearst Corporation; *U.S. Private*, pg. 4048
KCC JAPAN CO., LTD.—See KCC Corporation; *Int'l*, pg. 4109
KCC (KUNSHAN) CO., LTD.—See KCC Corporation; *Int'l*, pg. 4108
KCCL PLASTIC LTD.; *Int'l*, pg. 4109
KC CO.,LTD.; *Int'l*, pg. 4108
KC CO., LTD.; *Int'l*, pg. 4107
KC COMPANY INC.; *U.S. Private*, pg. 2269
KC COTTRELL CO., LTD. - ANSEONG FACTORY—See KC Cottrell Co., Ltd.; *Int'l*, pg. 4108
KC COTTRELL CO., LTD.; *Int'l*, pg. 4108
KCC PAINT (INDIA) PVT. LTD.—See KCC Corporation; *Int'l*, pg. 4109
KCC PAINTS SDN. BHD.—See KCC Corporation; *Int'l*, pg. 4109
KCCS CAREER TECH INC.—See KYOCERA Corporation; *Int'l*, pg. 4356
KCC SINGAPORE PTE. LTD.—See KCC Corporation; *Int'l*, pg. 4109
KCCS MANAGEMENT CONSULTING, INC.—See KYOCERA Corporation; *Int'l*, pg. 4356
KCCS MOBILE ENGINEERING CO., LTD—See KYOCERA Corporation; *Int'l*, pg. 4356
KCC (VIETNAM NHON TRACH) CO., LTD.—See KCC Corporation; *Int'l*, pg. 4108
KCD, INC.; *U.S. Private*, pg. 2269
KCD INDUSTRIES INDIA LTD.; *Int'l*, pg. 4109
KC DISTRIBUTING, LLC—See Glazer's Family of Companies; *U.S. Private*, pg. 1707
KCE AMERICA INC.—See KCE Electronics Public Company Limited; *Int'l*, pg. 4109
KCE ELECTRONICS PUBLIC COMPANY LIMITED; *Int'l*, pg. 4109
K.C.E. INTERNATIONAL CO., LTD.—See KCE Electronics Public Company Limited; *Int'l*, pg. 4109
KC ELECTRIC ASSOCIATION; *U.S. Private*, pg. 2269
K CELLARS (HONG KONG) LIMITED—See Kader Holdings Company Limited; *Int'l*, pg. 4046
KCELL JSC—See Kazakhtelecom JSC; *Int'l*, pg. 4102
KCENC CO., LTD.—See KC CO., LTD.; *Int'l*, pg. 4107
KC ENERGIA CO., LTD.—See KC Green Holdings Co., Ltd.; *Int'l*, pg. 4108
KCENTRIC TECHNOLOGIES, INC.—See KKR & Co. Inc.; *U.S. Public*, pg. 1267
KC ENVIRO SERVICE CO., LTD.—See KC Green Holdings Co., Ltd.; *Int'l*, pg. 4108
KCEOC COMMUNITY ACTION PARTNERSHIP, INC.; *U.S. Private*, pg. 2269
K-C EQUIPMENT FINANCE L.P.—See Kimberly-Clark Corporation; *U.S. Public*, pg. 1229
KCE SINGAPORE PTE., LTD.—See KCE Electronics Public Company Limited; *Int'l*, pg. 4109
KCE TECHNOLOGY CO., LTD.—See KCE Electronics Public Company Limited; *Int'l*, pg. 4109
KCE (THAILAND) CO., LTD.—See KCE Electronics Public Company Limited; *Int'l*, pg. 4109
KC FEED CO., LTD.; *Int'l*, pg. 4108
KCG CORPORATION PUBLIC COMPANY LIMITED; *Int'l*, pg. 4109
KCGI CO., LTD.; *Int'l*, pg. 4109
KCG, INC.; *U.S. Private*, pg. 2269
K&C GLOBAL CO., LTD.; *Int'l*, pg. 4038
KC GREEN HOLDINGS CO., LTD.; *Int'l*, pg. 4108
K.C.G TEXTILE EGYPT S.A.; *Int'l*, pg. 4043
K C HARVEY ENVIRONMENTAL LLC—See Bernhard Capital Partners Management, LP; *U.S. Private*, pg. 537
KCI ASSOCIATES OF NORTH CAROLINA, P.A.—See KCI Holdings Inc.; *U.S. Private*, pg. 2269
KCI ASSOCIATES OF OHIO, P.A.—See KCI Holdings Inc.; *U.S. Private*, pg. 2269
KCI ASSOCIATES OF THE DISTRICT OF COLUMBIA, P.C.—See KCI Holdings Inc.; *U.S. Private*, pg. 2269
KCI AUSTRALIA PTY. LTD.—See 3M Company; *U.S. Public*, pg. 7
KCI AUSTRIA GMBH—See 3M Company; *U.S. Public*, pg. 7
KCI CLINIC SPAIN S.L.—See 3M Company; *U.S. Public*, pg. 7
KCI COMMUNICATIONS INFRASTRUCTURE—See KCI Holdings Inc.; *U.S. Private*, pg. 2270
KCI CONSTRUCTION CO.; *U.S. Private*, pg. 2269
KCI CRANES HOLDING (SINGAPORE) PTE LTD—See Konecranes Plc; *Int'l*, pg. 4251
KCID PT. KCC INDONESIA.—See KCC Corporation; *Int'l*, pg. 4108
KCI EUROPE HOLDING B.V.—See 3M Company; *U.S. Public*, pg. 8
KCI HOLDINGS INC.; *U.S. Private*, pg. 2269
KCI KK—See 3M Company; *U.S. Public*, pg. 7

KCI KONEPORTS AMERICAS—See Konecranes Plc; *Int'l*, pg. 4252
KCI LIMITED; *Int'l*, pg. 4109
KCI MEDICAL AB—See 3M Company; *U.S. Public*, pg. 7
KCI MEDICAL APS—See 3M Company; *U.S. Public*, pg. 7
KCI MEDICAL ASIA PTE. LTD.—See 3M Company; *U.S. Public*, pg. 7
KCI MEDICAL B.V.—See 3M Company; *U.S. Public*, pg. 7
KCI MEDICAL CANADA, INC.—See 3M Company; *U.S. Public*, pg. 7
KCI MEDICAL GMBH—See 3M Company; *U.S. Public*, pg. 7
KCI MEDICAL LTD.—See 3M Company; *U.S. Public*, pg. 8
KCI MEDICAL SOUTH AFRICA PTY. LTD.—See 3M Company; *U.S. Public*, pg. 8
KCI MEDICAL S.R.L.—See 3M Company; *U.S. Public*, pg. 8
KCI MEDIZINPRODUCKTE GMBH—See 3M Company; *U.S. Public*, pg. 8
KC INDUSTRIE SRL—See TKH Group N.V.; *Int'l*, pg. 7764
KC INDUSTRY CO., LTD.; *Int'l*, pg. 4108
KCI PROTECTION TECHNOLOGIES LLC—See KCI Holdings Inc.; *U.S. Private*, pg. 2270
KCI S.A.; *Int'l*, pg. 4109
KCI TECHNOLOGIES INC.—See KCI Holdings Inc.; *U.S. Private*, pg. 2269
K-CITYMARKET OY—See Kesko Corporation; *Int'l*, pg. 4141
KCI USA, INC.—See 3M Company; *U.S. Public*, pg. 8
KCKK-AM/FM—See Hunt Broadcasting, LLC; *U.S. Private*, pg. 2008
KC LANDFILL SERVICES CO., LTD.—See KC Green Holdings Co., Ltd.; *Int'l*, pg. 4108
KCL INFRA PROJECTS LIMITED; *Int'l*, pg. 4109
KC LTD.—See Macquarie Group Limited; *Int'l*, pg. 4626
KCMA CORPORATION—See Kawasaki Heavy Industries, Ltd.; *Int'l*, pg. 4095
KC MART INC.; *U.S. Private*, pg. 2269
KCM CAPITAL PARTNERS, LLC; *U.S. Private*, pg. 2270
KCM CORPORATION—See Noritake Co., Limited; *Int'l*, pg. 5428
K.C. METALSHEET PUBLIC COMPANY LIMITED; *Int'l*, pg. 4043
KCMJ CORPORATION—See Kawasaki Heavy Industries, Ltd.; *Int'l*, pg. 4095
KCNC-TV—See National Amusements, Inc.; *U.S. Private*, pg. 2840
K. COATINGS, LLC; *U.S. Private*, pg. 2251
KCO CAPITAL INC.; *Int'l*, pg. 4109
KCOE ISOM, LLP; *U.S. Private*, pg. 2270
KCOM CONTACT CENTRES LTD.—See Macquarie Group Limited; *Int'l*, pg. 4626
KCOM GROUP LIMITED—See Macquarie Group Limited; *Int'l*, pg. 4626
K&COMPANY, LLC—See GTCR LLC; *U.S. Private*, pg. 1806
K CONTROLS LIMITED—See Emerson Electric Co.; *U.S. Public*, pg. 747
KCOP TELEVISION, LLC—See Fox Corporation; *U.S. Public*, pg. 876
KCOY-TV—See Cowles Company; *U.S. Private*, pg. 1073
KCPAG FINANCIAL ADVISORS LLC—See Kemper CPA Group LLP; *U.S. Private*, pg. 2282
KCP BIOTECH UNIT—See KCP Ltd; *Int'l*, pg. 4110
KCP CEMENT DIVISION—See KCP Ltd; *Int'l*, pg. 4110
K.C. PETROLEUM, INC.; *U.S. Private*, pg. 2251
KCP HEAVY ENGINEERING DIVISION—See KCP Ltd; *Int'l*, pg. 4110
KCP HOLDCO, INC.; *U.S. Private*, pg. 2270
KCP HYDEL POWER DIVISION—See KCP Ltd; *Int'l*, pg. 4110
KCP&L GREATER MISSOURI OPERATIONS COMPANY—See Evergy, Inc.; *U.S. Public*, pg. 801
KCP LTD; *Int'l*, pg. 4110
KCPQ-TV—See Nexstar Media Group, Inc.; *U.S. Public*, pg. 1524
KC PROCESSING CO., LTD.—See Kuraray Co., Ltd.; *Int'l*, pg. 4336
K.C. PROPERTY PUBLIC COMPANY LIMITED; *Int'l*, pg. 4043
KCP SUGAR & INDUSTRIES CORPORATION LTD; *Int'l*, pg. 4110
KCP VIETNAM INDUSTRIES LIMITED—See KCP Ltd; *Int'l*, pg. 4110
KCRA-TV—See The Hearst Corporation; *U.S. Private*, pg. 4048
KCRG-TV—See Gray Television, Inc.; *U.S. Public*, pg. 960
KCR RESIDENTIAL REIT PLC; *Int'l*, pg. 4110
K.C.S.A. HOLDINGS (PTY.) LTD.—See Kimberly-Clark Corporation; *U.S. Public*, pg. 1229
KCS CO.,LTD.—See OYO Corporation; *Int'l*, pg. 5678
KCS CO., LTD.—See Nomura Research Institute, Ltd.; *Int'l*, pg. 5413
KCS HONG KONG LTD.—See CVC Capital Partners SICAV-FIS S.A.; *Int'l*, pg. 1886
KCS INTERNATIONAL, INC.—See MarineMax, Inc.; *U.S. Public*, pg. 1366
KCS KCC (SINGAPORE) PTE. LTD.—See KCC Corporation; *Int'l*, pg. 4109

KCS LIMITED—See CVC Capital Partners SICAV-FIS S.A.; *Int'l*, pg. 1886
KC SOLAR ENERGY CO., LTD.—See KC Green Holdings Co., Ltd.; *Int'l*, pg. 4108
KCSSA EAST AFRICA LIMITED—See Kimberly-Clark Corporation; *U.S. Public*, pg. 1229
KCS WEST, INC.—See Kajima Corporation; *Int'l*, pg. 4055
KCTC CO. LTD; *Int'l*, pg. 4110
KCTC INTERNATIONAL LTD.—See KCTC CO. Ltd; *Int'l*, pg. 4110
KCTECH TAIWAN CO., LTD.—See KC CO., LTD.; *Int'l*, pg. 4108
KCTNS CO., LTD.—See KC CO., LTD.; *Int'l*, pg. 4108
KC TRANSPORTATION INC.; *U.S. Private*, pg. 2269
KCTS TELEVISION; *U.S. Private*, pg. 2270
KCT TRADING PRIVATE LIMITED—See Japan Pulp and Paper Company Limited; *Int'l*, pg. 3904
KCTV-TV—See Meredith Corporation; *U.S. Public*, pg. 1423
KCV KCC (VIETNAM) CO., LTD.—See KCC Corporation; *Int'l*, pg. 4109
KCW CORPORATION; *Int'l*, pg. 4110
KD ACQUISITION I, LLC.; *U.S. Private*, pg. 2270
KDAF, LLC—See Nexstar Media Group, Inc.; *U.S. Public*, pg. 1524
KDAG BETEILIGUNGEN GMBH—See Siemens Aktiengesellschaft; *Int'l*, pg. 6887
KDA GROUP, INC.; *Int'l*, pg. 4111
KDB BANK (MAGYARORSZAG) RT.—See Korea Development Bank; *Int'l*, pg. 4282
KDB BANK UZBEKISTAN—See Korea Development Bank; *Int'l*, pg. 4282
KDBC-TV—See Ellis, McQuary, Stanley & Associates LLC; *U.S. Private*, pg. 1374
KDB IRELAND LTD.—See Korea Development Bank; *Int'l*, pg. 4282
KD CAPITAL MANAGEMENT S. A.—See KD Group dd; *Int'l*, pg. 4110
KDCHEM CO., LTD; *Int'l*, pg. 4111
KD CORPORATION; *Int'l*, pg. 4110
KDC REAL ESTATE DEVELOPMENT & INVESTMENTS; *U.S. Private*, pg. 2270
KDC REAL ESTATE DEVELOPMENT & INVESTMENTS - SOUTHEAST DIVISION—See KDC Real Estate Development & Investments; *U.S. Private*, pg. 2270
KDC SYSTEMS—See EMCOR Group, Inc.; *U.S. Public*, pg. 736
KD D.D.; *Int'l*, pg. 4110
KDD GROUP N.V.; *Int'l*, pg. 4111
KDDI AMERICA, INC.—See KDDI Corporation; *Int'l*, pg. 4111
KDDI CORPORATION; *Int'l*, pg. 4111
KDDI DEUTSCHLAND GMBH—See KDDI Corporation; *Int'l*, pg. 4111
KDDI DO BRASIL SOLUCOES EM TECNOLOGIA LTDA—See KDDI Corporation; *Int'l*, pg. 4111
KDDI ENGINEERING CORPORATION—See KDDI Corporation; *Int'l*, pg. 4111
KDDI EUROPE LTD.—See KDDI Corporation; *Int'l*, pg. 4111
KDDI EVOLVA INC—See KDDI Corporation; *Int'l*, pg. 4111
KDDI EVOLVA OKINAWA CORPORATION—See KDDI Corporation; *Int'l*, pg. 4111
KDDI FOUNDATION—See KDDI Corporation; *Int'l*, pg. 4111
KDDI FRANCE SAS—See KDDI Corporation; *Int'l*, pg. 4111
KDDI GLOBAL, LLC—See KDDI Corporation; *Int'l*, pg. 4111
KDDI GUANGZHOU CORPORATION—See KDDI Corporation; *Int'l*, pg. 4111
KDDI HONG KONG LTD.—See KDDI Corporation; *Int'l*, pg. 4111
KDDI INDIA PRIVATE, LTD.—See KDDI Corporation; *Int'l*, pg. 4111
KDDI KOREA CORPORATION—See KDDI Corporation; *Int'l*, pg. 4111
KDDI MALAYSIA SDN.BHD—See KDDI Corporation; *Int'l*, pg. 4111
KDDI OKINAWA CO., LTD.—See KDDI Corporation; *Int'l*, pg. 4111
KDDI PHILIPPINES CORPORATION—See KDDI Corporation; *Int'l*, pg. 4111
KDDI R & D LABORATORIES INC.—See KDDI Corporation; *Int'l*, pg. 4111
KDDI RESEARCH INSTITUTE, INC.—See KDDI Corporation; *Int'l*, pg. 4112
KDDI SINGAPORE PTE LTD.—See KDDI Corporation; *Int'l*, pg. 4112
KDDI TAIWAN CORPORATION—See KDDI Corporation; *Int'l*, pg. 4112
KDDI TECHNOLOGY CORPORATION—See KDDI Corporation; *Int'l*, pg. 4112
KDDI (THAILAND) LTD.—See KDDI Corporation; *Int'l*, pg. 4112
KDDI VIETNAM CORPORATION—See KDDI Corporation; *Int'l*, pg. 4112
KDDI WEB COMMUNICATIONS INC.—See KDDI Corporation; *Int'l*, pg. 4112

KDDL LIMITED; *Int'l*, pg. 4112
KDDL LTD - EIGEN ENGINEERING UNIT—See KDDL Limited; *Int'l*, pg. 4112
KDE INC.; *U.S. Private*, pg. 2270
KDE RECREATION BERHAD—See Berjaya Corporation Berhad; *Int'l*, pg. 983
KDES-FM—See Alpha Media LLC; *U.S. Private*, pg. 198
K-DEVELOP OY; *Int'l*, pg. 4042
K DEVELOPPEMENT SAS—See Rothschild & Co SCA; *Int'l*, pg. 6403
KDF FLUID TREATMENT INC.—See Palladium Equity Partners, LLC; *U.S. Private*, pg. 3078
KD FINANCNA TOCKA, PREMOZENJSKO SVETOVANJE, D. O. O.—See KD Group dd; *Int'l*, pg. 4110
KDF U.S., INC.—See Air Water Inc.; *Int'l*, pg. 240
KDFW-TV—See Fox Corporation; *U.S. Public*, pg. 876
KD GROUP DD; *Int'l*, pg. 4110
KDH DEFENSE SYSTEMS, INC.—See Spanos Barber Jesse & Co.; *U.S. Private*, pg. 3745
K-D HERMANN GMBH; *Int'l*, pg. 4042
KD HOLDING CORPORATION—See CTCI Corporation; *Int'l*, pg. 1870
K D HYDRAULICS, LTD.—See Daikin Industries, Ltd.; *Int'l*, pg. 1935
KDI AUTHENTIC S.A.S.—See Klockner & Co. SE; *Int'l*, pg. 4201
KDI CAPITAL PARTNERS, LLC—See Investors Management Corporation; *U.S. Private*, pg. 2132
KDI ELEMENTS; *U.S. Private*, pg. 2270
KDI EXPORT S.A.S.—See Klockner & Co. SE; *Int'l*, pg. 4202
KDI KLINIKSERVICE GMBH—See Fresenius SE & Co. KGaA; *Int'l*, pg. 2779
K & D INDUSTRIAL SERVICES INC.; *U.S. Private*, pg. 2249
KD INDUSTRIES INC.—See Kendale Industries, Inc.; *U.S. Private*, pg. 2283
KD INVESTMENTS A. D., BELGRADE—See KD Group dd; *Int'l*, pg. 4110
KD INVESTMENTS D. O. O.—See KD Group dd; *Int'l*, pg. 4110
KD INVESTMENTS EAD—See KD Group dd; *Int'l*, pg. 4110
KDI S.A.S.—See Klockner & Co. SE; *Int'l*, pg. 4201
KDJ HOLIDAYSCAPES & RESORTS LTD.; *Int'l*, pg. 4112
KD KAPITAL D. O. O.—See KD Group dd; *Int'l*, pg. 4110
KDK AUTOMOTIVE COATINGS CO., LTD.—See Kansai Paint Co., Ltd.; *Int'l*, pg. 4072
KDK CORP.—See Nippon Chemi-Con Corporation; *Int'l*, pg. 5312
KDK DONGKOOK AUTOMOTIVE SPAIN S.A.; *Int'l*, pg. 4112
KD KVART D. O. O.—See KD Group dd; *Int'l*, pg. 4110
KD LAMP CO—See ATC Group, Inc.; *U.S. Private*, pg. 365
KDL COMMUNICATIONS CORPORATION—See Windstream Holdings, Inc.; *U.S. Public*, pg. 2373
KD LEISURES LIMITED; *Int'l*, pg. 4110
KD LIFE ASIGURARI S. A.—See KD Group dd; *Int'l*, pg. 4110
KDM SHIPPING PUBLIC LIMITED; *Int'l*, pg. 4112
KDM SPECTRUMDATA PTY LTD—See Katalyst Data Management LP; *Int'l*, pg. 4089
KDM SPECTRUMDATA PTY LTD—See Katalyst Data Management LP; *Int'l*, pg. 4089
KDN FIRE PROTECTION LIMITED—See London Security PLC; *Int'l*, pg. 4547
KDNL-TV—See Sinclair, Inc.; *U.S. Public*, pg. 1885
KDNY ENTERPRISE; *U.S. Private*, pg. 2270
KDON 102 5 FM—See iHeartMedia, Inc.; *U.S. Public*, pg. 1097
KD PHARMA GROUP; *Int'l*, pg. 4110
K&D PRATT GROUP INC.; *Int'l*, pg. 4038
KDR BIOTECH CO LTD.—See Thermo Fisher Scientific Inc.; *U.S. Public*, pg. 2149
KDR INDUSTRIALS LTD.; *Int'l*, pg. 4112
KDR PRODUCTIONS/DOLLARWISE PUBLICATIONS; *U.S. Private*, pg. 2270
KDR SUPPLY, INC.; *U.S. Private*, pg. 2270
KDRV-TV—See Entertainment Studios, Inc.; *U.S. Private*, pg. 1405
KDS ACCESSORIES LTD.; *Int'l*, pg. 4112
KD SCIENTIFIC, INC.—See Harvard Bioscience, Inc.; *U.S. Public*, pg. 987
KD SERVIS A.S.—See Deutsche Bahn AG; *Int'l*, pg. 2052
KDS, INC.—See INES Corporation; *Int'l*, pg. 3683
KDS INTERIORS; *U.S. Private*, pg. 2270
KD SKLADI, D. O. O.—See KD Group dd; *Int'l*, pg. 4110
KDS KOMPRESSOREN- UND DRUCKLUFTSERVICE GMBH—See Atlas Copco AB; *Int'l*, pg. 683
KDS MANUFACTURING (M) SDN BHD—See Murata Machinery, Ltd.; *Int'l*, pg. 5096
KDSM, LLC—See Sinclair, Inc.; *U.S. Public*, pg. 1885
K.D. STEEL, INC.; *U.S. Private*, pg. 2251
K-D SUPPLY CORPORATION; *U.S. Private*, pg. 2250
KD TEC S.R.O.—See Kaga Electronics Co., Ltd.; *Int'l*, pg. 4049
KDT EUROPE SP Z O O—See Guangzhou KDT Machinery Co.,Ltd; *Int'l*, pg. 3166
K.D. TIMMONS INC.; *U.S. Private*, pg. 2251

KD TREND WEAR LIMITED; *Int'l*, pg. 4111
KDU COLLEGE (PG) SDN BHD—See Paramount Corporation Berhad; *Int'l*, pg. 5738
KDU COLLEGE SDN. BHD.—See Paramount Corporation Berhad; *Int'l*, pg. 5738
KDU MANAGEMENT DEVELOPMENT CENTRE SDN. BHD.—See Paramount Corporation Berhad; *Int'l*, pg. 5738
KD UPRAVLJANJE IMOVINOM D. O. O.—See KD Group dd; *Int'l*, pg. 4110
KDU SMART SCHOOL SDN. BHD.—See Paramount Corporation Berhad; *Int'l*, pg. 5738
KDU UNIVERSITY COLLEGE (PG) SDN. BHD.—See Paramount Corporation Berhad; *Int'l*, pg. 5738
KDV LABEL CO., INC.; *U.S. Private*, pg. 2270
KDVR-TV—See Nexstar Media Group, Inc.; *U.S. Public*, pg. 1524
KDW SALAS O'BRIEN, LLC—See Salas O'Brien Engineers, Inc.; *U.S. Private*, pg. 3530
KDX REALTY INVESTMENT CORPORATION; *Int'l*, pg. 4112
KD ZIVOTNO OSIGURANJE D. D.—See KD Group dd; *Int'l*, pg. 4110
KE2 THERM SOLUTIONS, INC.—See Acuity Brands, Inc.; *U.S. Public*, pg. 37
KEA ADVERTISING; *U.S. Private*, pg. 2271
KEADLE LUMBER ENTERPRISES, INC.—See Interfor Corporation; *Int'l*, pg. 3741
KEANDA (HONG KONG) INTERNATIONAL GROUP CO., LTD.—See Shenzhen Keanda Electronic Technology Corp., Ltd.; *Int'l*, pg. 6815
KEANE FRAC, LP—See Keane Group Holdings, LLC; *U.S. Private*, pg. 2271
KEANE GROUP HOLDINGS, LLC; *U.S. Private*, pg. 2271
KEANE HEALTHCARE SOLUTIONS—See Nippon Telegraph & Telephone Corporation; *Int'l*, pg. 5348
THE KEANE INSURANCE GROUP, INC.—See ABRY Partners, LLC; *U.S. Private*, pg. 43
KEANGNAM ENTERPRISES, LTD.; *Int'l*, pg. 4112
KEARFOTT CORPORATION—See Astronautics Corporation of America; *U.S. Private*, pg. 362
KEARFOTT GUIDANCE & NAVIGATION CORPORATION - KEARFOTT MOTION SYSTEM DIVISION—See Astronautics Corporation of America; *U.S. Private*, pg. 362
KEARFOTT GUIDANCE & NAVIGATION CORPORATION—See Astronautics Corporation of America; *U.S. Private*, pg. 362
KEARN DIALYSIS, LLC—See DaVita Inc.; *U.S. Public*, pg. 640
KEARNEY ELECTRIC, INC.; *U.S. Private*, pg. 2271
KEARNEY HUB PUBLISHING COMPANY INC.—See Lee Enterprises, Incorporated; *U.S. Public*, pg. 1298
KEARNEY O'DOHERTY PUBLIC AFFAIRS, LLC; *U.S. Private*, pg. 2271
KEARNS-TRIBUNE, LLC; *U.S. Private*, pg. 2271
KEARNY BANK—See Kearny Financial Corp.; *U.S. Public*, pg. 1217
KEARNY FINANCIAL CORP.; *U.S. Public*, pg. 1217
KEARNY MESA INFINITI; *U.S. Private*, pg. 2271
KEARSARGE TELEPHONE CO.—See Telephone & Data Systems, Inc.; *U.S. Public*, pg. 1998
KEATING BUILDING COMPANY—See Tutor Perini Corporation; *U.S. Public*, pg. 2206
KEATING & CO.; *U.S. Private*, pg. 2271
KEATING MAGEE MARKETING COMMUNICATIONS; *U.S. Private*, pg. 2271
KEATING, MUETHING & KLEKAMP PLL; *U.S. Private*, pg. 2271
KEATON ENERGY HOLDINGS LIMITED—See Salungano Group; *Int'l*, pg. 6495
KEAT RADIO CO. SDN. BHD.—See Pensonic Holdings Berhad; *Int'l*, pg. 5788
KEATS MANUFACTURING COMPANY; *U.S. Private*, pg. 2271
KEBA AG; *Int'l*, pg. 4113
KEBA GESELLSCHAFT FUR INTERNE SERVICES MBH—See Deutsche Bank Aktiengesellschaft; *Int'l*, pg. 2061
KEB ANTRIEBSTECHNIK AUSTRIA GMBH—See Karl E. Brinkmann GmbH; *Int'l*, pg. 4081
KEB ANTRIEBSTECHNIK GMBH—See Karl E. Brinkmann GmbH; *Int'l*, pg. 4081
KEB ASIA FINANCE LIMITED—See Hana Financial Group, Inc.; *Int'l*, pg. 3240
KEB AUSTRALIA LTD.—See Hana Financial Group, Inc.; *Int'l*, pg. 3240
KEB CAPITAL INC.—See Hana Financial Group, Inc.; *Int'l*, pg. 3240
KEBE ERSATZTEILE GMBH—See Enovis Corporation; *U.S. Public*, pg. 771
KEB ENTERPRISES LP; *U.S. Private*, pg. 2271
KEB FUTURES CO., LTD.—See Hana Financial Group, Inc.; *Int'l*, pg. 3240
KEB HANA BANK—See Hana Financial Group, Inc.; *Int'l*, pg. 3240
KEB HANA CARD CO., LTD.—See Hana Financial Group, Inc.; *Int'l*, pg. 3241
KEBI INDUSTRY CO., LTD.—See Daiwabo Holdings Co., Ltd.; *Int'l*, pg. 1949

COMPANY NAME INDEX

KEB INVESTORS SERVICES COMPANY—See Hana Financial Group, Inc.; *Int'l*, pg. 3240
KEB ITALIA S.R.L.—See Karl E. Brinkmann GmbH; *Int'l*, pg. 4081
KEB JAPAN LTD.—See Karl E. Brinkmann GmbH; *Int'l*, pg. 4081
KEB LA FINANCIAL CORP.—See Hana Financial Group, Inc.; *Int'l*, pg. 3240
KEB NY FINANCIAL CORP.—See Hana Financial Group, Inc.; *Int'l*, pg. 3240
KEBODA (CHONGQING) AUTOMOTIVE ELECTRONICS CO., LTD.—See Keboda Technology Co., Ltd.; *Int'l*, pg. 4113
KEBODA DEUTSCHLAND GMBH & CO. KG—See Keboda Technology Co., Ltd.; *Int'l*, pg. 4113
KEBODA (JIAXING) INDUSTRIAL CORP.—See Keboda Technology Co., Ltd.; *Int'l*, pg. 4113
KEBODA TECHNOLOGY CO., LTD.; *Int'l*, pg. 4113
KEBOL B.V.; *Int'l*, pg. 4113
KEB POWER TRANSMISSION TECHNOLOGY (SHANGHAI) CO., LTD.—See Karl E. Brinkmann GmbH; *Int'l*, pg. 4081
KEB RUS LTD.—See Karl E. Brinkmann GmbH; *Int'l*, pg. 4081
KEB TECHNOLOGY INDIA PRIVATE LIMITED—See KONA I Corporation; *Int'l*, pg. 4244
KEB (UK) LTD.—See Karl E. Brinkmann GmbH; *Int'l*, pg. 4081
KE-BURGMANN UK LTD.—See Freudenberg SE; *Int'l*, pg. 2789
KEB USA INTERNATIONAL CORP.—See Hana Financial Group, Inc.; *Int'l*, pg. 3240
KEC AMERICA CORP—See KEC Holdings Co., Ltd.; *Int'l*, pg. 4113
KEC CORPORATION; *Int'l*, pg. 4113
KEC CORPORATION—See Electric Power Development Co., Ltd.; *Int'l*, pg. 2349
KEC DEVICE CO.,LTD—See KEC Holdings Co., Ltd.; *Int'l*, pg. 4113
KEC HOLDINGS CO., LTD.; *Int'l*, pg. 4113
KEC INTERNATIONAL LIMITED; *Int'l*, pg. 4113
KEC INTERNATIONAL LIMITED - TRANSMISSION SOUTH ASIA UNIT—See KEC International Limited; *Int'l*, pg. 4113
KEC JAPAN CO.,LTD.—See KEC Holdings Co., Ltd.; *Int'l*, pg. 4113
KECK INC.; *U.S. Private*, pg. 2271
KECKLEY COMPANY; *U.S. Private*, pg. 2271
KECK SENG INVESTMENTS (HONG KONG) LIMITED; *Int'l*, pg. 4114
KECK SENG INVESTMENTS PTE. LTD.—See Keck Seng (Malaysia) Berhad; *Int'l*, pg. 4113
KECK SENG (MALAYSIA) BERHAD - PALM OIL FACTORY—See Keck Seng (Malaysia) Berhad; *Int'l*, pg. 4114
KECK SENG (MALAYSIA) BERHAD; *Int'l*, pg. 4113
K&E CO., LTD.—See Kumagai Gumi Co., Ltd.; *Int'l*, pg. 4329
K&E CO.,LTD.—See Kumagai Gumi Co., Ltd.; *Int'l*, pg. 4329
K-ECOMMERCE—See KKR & Co. Inc.; *U.S. Public*, pg. 1267
KEC SHANGHAI CO., LTD.—See KEC Holdings Co., Ltd.; *Int'l*, pg. 4113
KEC SINGAPORE PTE LTD—See KEC Holdings Co., Ltd.; *Int'l*, pg. 4113
KEC THAILAND COMPANY LIMITED—See KEC Corporation; *Int'l*, pg. 4113
KEDA (ANHUI) INDUSTRIAL CO., LTD.—See Keda Industrial Group Co., Ltd.; *Int'l*, pg. 4114
KEDA COMMUNICATIONS LTD; *Int'l*, pg. 4114
KEDA GROUP MATERIALS COMPANY—See Zhewen Interactive Group Co Ltd; *Int'l*, pg. 8671
KEDAH HOLDINGS SDN. BHD.—See Bina Darulaman Berhad; *Int'l*, pg. 1032
KEDAH SATO SDN. BHD.—See Toda Corporation; *Int'l*, pg. 7772
KEDA INDUSTRIAL GROUP CO., LTD.; *Int'l*, pg. 4114
KEDA INDUSTRIAL (INDIA) LTD.—See Keda Industrial Group Co., Ltd.; *Int'l*, pg. 4114
KEDA SEMICONDUCTOR CO., LTD.—See Zhewen Interactive Group Co Ltd; *Int'l*, pg. 8671
KEDA TRAFFIC APPLIANCES COMPANY—See Zhewen Interactive Group Co Ltd; *Int'l*, pg. 8671
KEDAUNG INDAH CAN TBK; *Int'l*, pg. 4114
KEDCO POWER LIMITED—See EQTEC plc; *Int'l*, pg. 2483
KEDDEM BIOSCIENCE LTD.—See Compugen Ltd.; *Int'l*, pg. 1755
KEDENTRANSSERVICE JSC; *Int'l*, pg. 4114
KEDGE CONSTRUCTION CO., LTD.; *Int'l*, pg. 4114
KEDIA CONSTRUCTION COMPANY LIMITED; *Int'l*, pg. 4114
KEDI HOLDINGS S.A.R.L.—See KKR & Co. Inc.; *U.S. Public*, pg. 1254
KEDING ENTERPRISES CO., LTD.; *Int'l*, pg. 4114
KEDINGTON (NI) LIMITED—See N.G. Bailey & Co. Ltd.; *Int'l*, pg. 5116

KEDI REFRIGERATION EQUIPMENT KUNSHAN CO., LTD.—See Mondragon Corporation; *Int'l*, pg. 5030
KEDPLASMA GMBH—See Kedrion S.p.A.; *Int'l*, pg. 4115
KEDPLASMA KFT.—See Kedrion S.p.A.; *Int'l*, pg. 4115
KEDPLASMA LLC—See Kedrion S.p.A.; *Int'l*, pg. 4115
KEDREN COMMUNITY HEALTH CENTER, INC.; *U.S. Private*, pg. 2271
KEDRION BIOPHARMA INC.—See Kedrion S.p.A.; *Int'l*, pg. 4115
KEDRION INTERNATIONAL GMBH—See Kedrion S.p.A.; *Int'l*, pg. 4115
KEDRION MEXICANA SA DE CV—See Kedrion S.p.A.; *Int'l*, pg. 4115
KEDRION PORTUGAL - DISTRIBUICAO DE PRODUTOS FARMACEUTICOS LDA—See Kedrion S.p.A.; *Int'l*, pg. 4115
KEDRION S.P.A.; *Int'l*, pg. 4115
KEDRION SWISS SARL—See Kedrion S.p.A.; *Int'l*, pg. 4115
KEDRIOS S.P.A.—See Cassa Depositi e Prestiti S.p.A.; *Int'l*, pg. 1354
KEE ACTION SPORTS CANADA—See KEE Action Sports LLC; *U.S. Private*, pg. 2271
KEE ACTION SPORTS EUROPE—See KEE Action Sports LLC; *U.S. Private*, pg. 2271
KEE ACTION SPORTS LLC; *U.S. Private*, pg. 2271
KEEBLER COMPANY—See Kellanova; *U.S. Public*, pg. 1217
KEECO, LLC; *U.S. Private*, pg. 2271
KEE ENVIRONMENTAL CONSTRUCTION CO., LTD.—See Kawasaki Heavy Industries, Ltd.; *Int'l*, pg. 4095
KEE ENVIRONMENTAL SERVICE, LTD.—See Kawasaki Heavy Industries, Ltd.; *Int'l*, pg. 4095
KEEEPER GMBH—See Mutares SE & Co. KGaA; *Int'l*, pg. 5106
KEEEPER S.A.—See Mutares SE & Co. KGaA; *Int'l*, pg. 5106
KEEEPER SP.Z O.O—See Mutares SE & Co. KGaA; *Int'l*, pg. 5106
KEE EUROPE GMBH—See Whole Easy Internet Technology Co., Ltd.; *Int'l*, pg. 8401
KEE FATT INDUSTRIES, SDN. BHD.—See Bando Chemical Industries, Ltd.; *Int'l*, pg. 830
KEEFE, BRUYETTE & WOODS INC. -SAN FRANCISCO—See Stifel Financial Corp.; *U.S. Public*, pg. 1950
KEEFE, BRUYETTE & WOODS INC.—See Stifel Financial Corp.; *U.S. Public*, pg. 1949
KEEFE, BRUYETTE & WOODS LIMITED—See Stifel Financial Corp.; *U.S. Public*, pg. 1950
KEEFE CONSTRUCTION SERVICES; *U.S. Private*, pg. 2272
KEEFE GROUP, INC.—See Centric Group LLC; *U.S. Private*, pg. 830
KEEFE SUPPLY COMPANY—See Centric Group LLC; *U.S. Private*, pg. 830
KEEGAN RESOURCES (GHANA) LIMITED—See Galiano Gold Inc.; *Int'l*, pg. 2873
KEE (GUANGDONG) GARMENT ACCESSORIES LIMITED—See China Apex Group Limited; *Int'l*, pg. 1483
KEE INTERFACE TECHNOLOGY, INC.—See Whole Easy Internet Technology Co., Ltd.; *Int'l*, pg. 8401
KEE (JINGMEN) GARMENT ACCESSORIES LIMITED—See China Apex Group Limited; *Int'l*, pg. 1483
K/E ELECTRIC SUPPLY CORP.; *U.S. Private*, pg. 2252
KE ELEKTRONIK GMBH—See Amphenol Corporation; *U.S. Public*, pg. 130
KE ELEKTRONIK GMBH—See Amphenol Corporation; *U.S. Public*, pg. 130
KEELER INSTRUMENTS INC.—See Halma plc; *Int'l*, pg. 3231
KEELER LIMITED—See Halma plc; *Int'l*, pg. 3232
KEELER MOTOR CAR COMPANY, INC.; *U.S. Private*, pg. 2272
THE KEELEY COMPANIES; *U.S. Private*, pg. 4064
KEELEY DEVELOPMENT GROUP, INC.—See The Keeley Companies; *U.S. Private*, pg. 4064
KEELEY-TETON ADVISORS, LLC—See Teton Advisors, Inc.; *U.S. Public*, pg. 2021
KEEL HOLDINGS, LLC—See Arlington Capital Partners LLC; *U.S. Private*, pg. 328
KEELING COMPANY; *U.S. Private*, pg. 2272
KEELING & WALKER LTD—See Amalgamated Metal Corporation PLC; *Int'l*, pg. 408
KEELLS FOOD PRODUCTS PLC—See John Keells Holdings PLC; *Int'l*, pg. 3978
KEELLS HOTEL MANAGEMENT SERVICES LTD.—See John Keells Holdings PLC; *Int'l*, pg. 3978
KEEL POINT ADVISORS, LLC—See Blue Creek Investment Partners; *U.S. Private*, pg. 586
KEEMO FASHION GROUP LIMITED; *Int'l*, pg. 4115
KEEN AIR SERVICES, INC.—See Dring Air Conditioning & Heating, LP; *U.S. Private*, pg. 1277
KEENAN & ASSOCIATES INC.—See New Mexico Mutual Casualty Company; *U.S. Private*, pg. 2898

KEENAN ENERGY COMPANY INCORPORATED; *U.S. Private*, pg. 2272
KEENAN, HOPKINS, SCHMIDT & STOWELL CONTRACTORS INC.; *U.S. Private*, pg. 2272
KEENAN-NAGLE ADVERTISING; *U.S. Private*, pg. 2272
KEEN BATTLE MEAD & CO.; *U.S. Private*, pg. 2272
KEEN BRANDING; *U.S. Private*, pg. 2272
KEEN BRANDING—See Keen Branding; *U.S. Private*, pg. 2272
KEEN BRANDING-WEST COAST—See Keen Branding; *U.S. Private*, pg. 2272
KEEN COMPRESSED GAS COMPANY; *U.S. Private*, pg. 2272
KEEN COMPRESSED GAS—See Keen Compressed Gas Company; *U.S. Private*, pg. 2272
KEENE BUILDING PRODUCTS COMPANY, INC.; *U.S. Private*, pg. 2272
KEENE CHRYSLER, INC.; *U.S. Private*, pg. 2272
KEENE DODGE CO. INC.; *U.S. Private*, pg. 2272
KEENELAND ASSOCIATION INC.; *U.S. Private*, pg. 2272
KEENELAND ASSOCIATION INC. - THE THOROUGHBRED CENTER DIVISION—See Keeneland Association Inc.; *U.S. Private*, pg. 2272
KEENE LUMBER CO.—See Bain Capital, LP; *U.S. Private*, pg. 451
KEENE PROMOTIONS, INC.; *U.S. Private*, pg. 2272
KEENE PROMOTIONS, INC.—See Keene Promotions, Inc.; *U.S. Private*, pg. 2272
KEENE PROMOTIONS, INC.—See Keene Promotions, Inc.; *U.S. Private*, pg. 2272
KEENER LUMBER COMPANY INC.; *U.S. Private*, pg. 2272
KEENE'S POINTE REALTY—See Murdock Holdings, LLC; *U.S. Private*, pg. 2814
KEENE STAR—See Alden Global Capital LLC; *U.S. Private*, pg. 156
KEENEY MANUFACTURING COMPANY—See United Plumbing Technologies; *U.S. Private*, pg. 4295
KEEN HEALTHCARE COMPANY; *U.S. Private*, pg. 2272
KEEN INFOTEK INC.; *U.S. Private*, pg. 2272
KEENNESS PRECISION ENGINEERING SDN. BHD.—See RGT Berhad; *Int'l*, pg. 6319
KEEN OCEAN INTERNATIONAL HOLDING LTD.; *Int'l*, pg. 4115
KEENPAC ITALIA S.R.L.—See Bunzl plc; *Int'l*, pg. 1218
KEENPAC (SWITZERLAND) SA—See Bunzl plc; *Int'l*, pg. 1218
KEEN POINT (EUROPE) GMBH.—See Xin Point Holdings Limited; *Int'l*, pg. 8529
KEENSIGHT CAPITAL SAS; *Int'l*, pg. 4115
KEENTECH COMPOSITE TECH. CO., LTD. - HOUXI PLANT—See Topkey Corporation; *Int'l*, pg. 7816
KEEN TECHNICAL SOLUTIONS LLC; *U.S. Private*, pg. 2272
KEEN TRANSPORT, INC.—See Wallenius Wilhelmsen ASA; *Int'l*, pg. 8334
KEEN VISION ACQUISITION CORPORATION; *U.S. Public*, pg. 1217
KEEPDATA CO., LTD.; *Int'l*, pg. 4115
KEEP ENTERPRISES, INC.; *U.S. Private*, pg. 2272
KEEPER-GRUPO SENSORMATIC S.A.—See Johnson Controls International plc; *Int'l*, pg. 3988
KEEPERS BRASIL LTDA—See Iron Mountain Incorporated; *U.S. Public*, pg. 1173
THE KEEPERS HOLDINGS, INC.; *Int'l*, pg. 7662
KEEPER TECHNICAL LABORATORY; *Int'l*, pg. 4115
KEEPER TECHNOLOGY CO., LTD.—See Tyntek Corporation; *Int'l*, pg. 7995
KEEPING CURRENT MATTERS, INC.; *U.S. Private*, pg. 2273
KEEPING KIDS SAFE INC.; *U.S. Private*, pg. 2273
KEEPING TRADITIONS INC.; *U.S. Private*, pg. 2273
KEEPITSAFE, INC.—See Ziff Davis, Inc.; *U.S. Public*, pg. 2403
KEEP-IT TECHNOLOGIES AS—See Scatec AS; *Int'l*, pg. 6613
KEEPMOAT LTD.—See Lloyds Banking Group plc; *Int'l*, pg. 4537
KEEPONPROSPECTING.COM—See Response Mail Express Inc.; *U.S. Private*, pg. 3408
KEEP ON TRUCKING COMPANY INCORPORATED; *U.S. Private*, pg. 2272
KEEPRS, INC.; *U.S. Private*, pg. 2273
KEEPSAKE PLANTS LTD—See Aris Horticulture, Inc.; *U.S. Private*, pg. 323
KEEPSAKE QUILTING, INC.—See The Riverside Company; *U.S. Private*, pg. 4109
KEEP SERVICES, INC.; *U.S. Private*, pg. 2273
KEE REAL ESTATE CO. OF DETROIT, INC; *U.S. Private*, pg. 2271
KEERTHI INDUSTRIES LIMITED; *Int'l*, pg. 4115
KEE SAFETY, INC.; *U.S. Private*, pg. 2271
KEESEE MOTOR CO.; *U.S. Private*, pg. 2273
KEE SHING HARDWARE SUPPLIES LIMITED—See Kee Shing Investment (BVI) Limited; *Int'l*, pg. 4115
KEE SHING INDUSTRIAL PRODUCTS LIMITED—See Kee Shing Investment (BVI) Limited; *Int'l*, pg. 4115
KEE SHING INVESTMENT (BVI) LIMITED; *Int'l*, pg. 4115

KEESING MEDIA GROUP B.V.—See Groupe Bruxelles Lambert SA; *Int'l*, pg. 3099
KEESING MEDIA GROUP B.V.—See Parcom Capital Management B.V.; *Int'l*, pg. 5739
KEE SONG BIO-TECHNOLOGY HOLDINGS LTD.; *Int'l*, pg. 4115
KEESON TECHNOLOGY CORPORATION LIMITED; *Int'l*, pg. 4115
KEE TAI PROPERTIES CO., LTD.; *Int'l*, pg. 4115
KEE TAIWAN CO., LTD.—See Whole Easy Internet Technology Co., Ltd.; *Int'l*, pg. 8401
KEETER MOTORS INC.; *U.S. Private*, pg. 2273
KEETON SERVICES, INC.—See Gibson Energy Inc.; *Int'l*, pg. 2963
KEETON'S OFFICE & ART SUPPLY CO.; *U.S. Private*, pg. 2273
KEEWATIN AIR LP—See Exchange Income Corporation; *Int'l*, pg. 2579
K & E EXCAVATING INC.; *U.S. Private*, pg. 2249
KEEYASK HYDROPOWER LIMITED PARTNERSHIP—See The Manitoba Hydro-Electric Board; *Int'l*, pg. 7665
KEEZ-FM—See Alpha Media LLC; *U.S. Private*, pg. 198
KEE (ZHEJIANG) GARMENT ACCESSORIES LIMITED—See China Apex Group Limited; *Int'l*, pg. 1483
KEE ZIPPERS CORPORATION LIMITED—See China Apex Group Limited; *Int'l*, pg. 1483
KEFFER HYUNDAI; *U.S. Private*, pg. 2273
KEFFER OF LITTLE RIVER, LLC—See Beach Automotive Group; *U.S. Private*, pg. 503
KE FIBERTEC AS—See Jysk-Fynsk Kapital A/S; *Int'l*, pg. 4036
KE FIBERTEC NORTH AMERICA INC.—See Jysk-Fynsk Kapital A/S; *Int'l*, pg. 4036
KEFI GOLD AND COPPER PLC; *Int'l*, pg. 4115
KEFI MINERALS (ETHIOPIA) LIMITED—See KEFI Gold and Copper plc; *Int'l*, pg. 4115
KEFI MINERALS PLC—See Starvest plc; *Int'l*, pg. 7180
K.E. FISCHER L.L.C.—See Deutsche Beteiligungs AG; *Int'l*, pg. 2063
KEF JAPAN, INC.—See Gold Peak Technology Group Limited; *Int'l*, pg. 3025
KE&G DEVELOPMENT LLC; *U.S. Private*, pg. 2270
KEGEL COMPANY INC.; *U.S. Private*, pg. 2273
KEGO AGRI S.A—See AMERRA Capital Management LLC; *Int'l*, pg. 424
KEGO AGRI S.A—See Mubadala Investment Company PJSC; *Int'l*, pg. 5076
KEGOYA DOCK CO., LTD.—See Penta-Ocean Construction Co., Ltd.; *Int'l*, pg. 5788
THE KEG ROYALTIES INCOME FUND; *Int'l*, pg. 7662
KE GUTRIDGE, LLC—See Kassel Equity Group, LLC; *U.S. Private*, pg. 2264
KEHE DISTRIBUTORS, LLC; *U.S. Private*, pg. 2273
THE KEHILLAH JEWISH EDUCATION FUND; *U.S. Private*, pg. 4064
KEHLIBAR EOOD—See Agria Group Holding JSC; *Int'l*, pg. 216
KEHM OIL COMPANY; *U.S. Private*, pg. 2273
KEHOE COMPONENT SALES INC.; *U.S. Private*, pg. 2273
KE HOLDINGS INC.; *Int'l*, pg. 4112
KEHUA DATA CO., LTD.; *Int'l*, pg. 4116
KEHUA HOLDINGS CO., LTD.; *Int'l*, pg. 4116
KEIDEL SUPPLY COMPANY INC.—See Winsupply, Inc.; *U.S. Private*, pg. 4545
KEIFUKU ELECTRIC RAILROAD CO., LTD.; *Int'l*, pg. 4116
KEIHAN AGENCY INC.—See Keihan Holdings Co., Ltd.; *Int'l*, pg. 4116
KEIHAN ASSET MANAGEMENT CO., LTD.—See Keihan Holdings Co., Ltd.; *Int'l*, pg. 4116
KEIHAN BUILDING TECHNO SERVICE CO., LTD.—See Keihan Holdings Co., Ltd.; *Int'l*, pg. 4116
KEIHAN BUS CO., LTD.—See Keihan Holdings Co., Ltd.; *Int'l*, pg. 4116
KEIHAN DEPARTMENT STORES CO., LTD.—See Keihan Holdings Co., Ltd.; *Int'l*, pg. 4116
KEIHAN ENGINEERING SERVICE CO., LTD.—See Keihan Holdings Co., Ltd.; *Int'l*, pg. 4116
KEIHAN GARDENING CO., LTD.—See Keihan Holdings Co., Ltd.; *Int'l*, pg. 4116
KEIHAN HOLDINGS CO., LTD.; *Int'l*, pg. 4116
KEIHAN HOTELS & RESORTS CO., LTD.—See Keihan Holdings Co., Ltd.; *Int'l*, pg. 4116
KEIHAN KIND CO., LTD.—See Keihan Holdings Co., Ltd.; *Int'l*, pg. 4116
KEIHANNA HELPER STATION CO., LTD.—See Senko Group Holdings Co., Ltd.; *Int'l*, pg. 6710
KEIHAN REAL ESTATE CO., LTD.—See Keihan Holdings Co., Ltd.; *Int'l*, pg. 4116
KEIHAN RYUTSU SYSTEMS CO., LTD.—See Keihan Holdings Co., Ltd.; *Int'l*, pg. 4116
KEIHANSHIN BUILDING CO., LTD.; *Int'l*, pg. 4116
KEIHAN TATEMONO CO., LTD.—See Keihan Holdings Co., Ltd.; *Int'l*, pg. 4116
KEIHAN THE STORE CO., LTD.—See Keihan Holdings Co., Ltd.; *Int'l*, pg. 4116

KEIHIN AIRCON NORTH AMERICA, INC.—See Hitachi Astemo, Ltd.; *Int'l*, pg. 3409
KEIHIN AIRFREIGHT CO., LTD.—See The Keihin Co., Ltd.; *Int'l*, pg. 7662
KEIHIN ASIA BANGKOK CO., LTD.—See Hitachi Astemo, Ltd.; *Int'l*, pg. 3408
KEIHIN AUTO PARTS (PHILIPPINES) CORP.—See Hitachi Astemo, Ltd.; *Int'l*, pg. 3408
KEIHIN AUTO PARTS (THAILAND) CO., LTD. - 2ND PLANT—See Hitachi Astemo, Ltd.; *Int'l*, pg. 3409
KEIHIN AUTO PARTS (THAILAND) CO., LTD.—See Hitachi Astemo, Ltd.; *Int'l*, pg. 3408
KEIHIN CAROLINA SYSTEM TECHNOLOGY, LLC—See Hitachi Astemo, Ltd.; *Int'l*, pg. 3409
THE KEIHIN CO., LTD.; *Int'l*, pg. 7662
KEIHIN CONTAINER TRANSPORT CO., LTD.—See The Keihin Co., Ltd.; *Int'l*, pg. 7662
KEIHIN CORPORATION - KAKUDA 1ST PLANT—See Hitachi Astemo, Ltd.; *Int'l*, pg. 3409
KEIHIN CORPORATION - KAKUDA 2ND PLANT—See Hitachi Astemo, Ltd.; *Int'l*, pg. 3409
KEIHIN CORPORATION - KAKUDA 3RD PLANT—See Hitachi Astemo, Ltd.; *Int'l*, pg. 3409
KEIHIN CORPORATION - MARUMORI PLANT—See Hitachi Astemo, Ltd.; *Int'l*, pg. 3409
KEIHIN CORPORATION - SAYAMA PLANT—See Hitachi Astemo, Ltd.; *Int'l*, pg. 3409
KEIHIN CORPORATION—See Hitachi Astemo, Ltd.; *Int'l*, pg. 3408
KEIHIN CORPORATION - SUZUKA PLANT—See Hitachi Astemo, Ltd.; *Int'l*, pg. 3409
KEIHIN DE MEXICO, S.A. DE C.V.—See Hitachi, Ltd.; *Int'l*, pg. 3423
KEIHIN DISTRIBUTION CO., LTD.—See The Keihin Co., Ltd.; *Int'l*, pg. 7662
KEIHIN DOCK CO., LTD.—See Nippon Yusen Kabushiki Kaisha; *Int'l*, pg. 5358
KEIHIN ELECTRONICS TECHNOLOGY INC—See Hitachi Astemo, Ltd.; *Int'l*, pg. 3409
KEIHIN-EVERETT FORWARDING CO., INC.—See The Keihin Co., Ltd.; *Int'l*, pg. 7662
KEIHIN FIE PVT LTD—See Hitachi Astemo, Ltd.; *Int'l*, pg. 3409
KEIHIN HARBOR TRANSPORT CO., LTD.—See The Keihin Co., Ltd.; *Int'l*, pg. 7662
KEIHIN IPT MFG., LLC—See Hitachi Astemo, Ltd.; *Int'l*, pg. 3409
KEIHIN KASEHIN CENTER CO., LTD.—See ENEOS Holdings, Inc.; *Int'l*, pg. 2416
KEIHIN KYUKO BUS CO., LTD.—See Keikyu Corporation; *Int'l*, pg. 4117
KEIHIN MARITIME CO., LTD.—See The Keihin Co., Ltd.; *Int'l*, pg. 7662
KEIHIN MICHIGAN MANUFACTURING, LLC—See Hitachi Astemo, Ltd.; *Int'l*, pg. 3409
KEIHIN MULTI-TRANS (HONG KONG) LIMITED—See The Keihin Co., Ltd.; *Int'l*, pg. 7662
KEIHIN MULTI-TRANS (SHANGHAI) CO., LTD.—See The Keihin Co., Ltd.; *Int'l*, pg. 7662
KEIHIN MULTI-TRANS (SINGAPORE) PTE LTD.—See The Keihin Co., Ltd.; *Int'l*, pg. 7662
KEIHIN MULTI-TRANS TAIWAN CO., LTD.—See The Keihin Co., Ltd.; *Int'l*, pg. 7662
KEIHIN MULTI-TRANS (VIETNAM) COMPANY LIMITED—See The Keihin Co., Ltd.; *Int'l*, pg. 7662
KEIHIN NAIGAI FORWARDING CO.,LTD.—See Mitsubishi Logistics Corporation; *Int'l*, pg. 4962
KEIHIN NORTH AMERICA, INC.—See Hitachi Astemo, Ltd.; *Int'l*, pg. 3409
KEIHIN PANALFA LTD.—See Hitachi Astemo, Ltd.; *Int'l*, pg. 3409
KEIHIN SALES AND DEVELOPMENT EUROPE GMBH—See Hitachi Astemo, Ltd.; *Int'l*, pg. 3409
KEIHIN SOGYO CO., LTD.—See Hitachi Astemo, Ltd.; *Int'l*, pg. 3409
KEIHIN (THAILAND) CO., LTD.—See Hitachi Astemo, Ltd.; *Int'l*, pg. 3408
KEIHIN TOKUSHU PRINTING CORPORATION—See The Pack Corporation; *Int'l*, pg. 7672
KEIHIN TRANSPORT CO., LTD.—See The Keihin Co., Ltd.; *Int'l*, pg. 7662
KEIHIN VALVE CORP—See Hitachi Astemo, Ltd.; *Int'l*, pg. 3409
KEIHIN WATARI CO., LTD.—See Hitachi Astemo, Ltd.; *Int'l*, pg. 3409
KEI INDUSTRIES LTD; *Int'l*, pg. 4116
KEI INDUSTRIES LTD - UNIT-1—See KEI Industries Ltd; *Int'l*, pg. 4116
KEI INDUSTRIES LTD - UNIT-2—See KEI Industries Ltd; *Int'l*, pg. 4116
KEIJIDOUSHAKAN CO., LTD.; *Int'l*, pg. 4116
KEIJI MAZDA CO., LTD.—See Mazda Motor Corporation; *Int'l*, pg. 4748
KEIKA VENTURES LLC; *U.S. Private*, pg. 2273
KEIKYU CONSTRUCTION CO., LTD.—See Gunze Limited; *Int'l*, pg. 3186
KEIKYU CORPORATION; *Int'l*, pg. 4117
KEIKYU DEPARTMENT STORE CO., LTD.—See Keikyu Corporation; *Int'l*, pg. 4117

KEIKYU ELECTRIC ENGINEERING CO., LTD.—See Keikyu Corporation; *Int'l*, pg. 4117
KEIKYU FINE-TEC CO., LTD.—See Keikyu Corporation; *Int'l*, pg. 4117
KEIKYU KAIHATSU CO., LTD.—See Keikyu Corporation; *Int'l*, pg. 4117
KEIKYU REAL ESTATE CO., LTD.—See Keikyu Corporation; *Int'l*, pg. 4117
KEIKYU STATION COMMERCE CO., LTD.—See Keikyu Corporation; *Int'l*, pg. 4117
KEIKYU STORE CO., LTD.—See Keikyu Corporation; *Int'l*, pg. 4117
KEI LEASE CO LTD—See Kandenko Co., Ltd.; *Int'l*, pg. 4065
KEILER & COMPANY; *U.S. Private*, pg. 2273
KEILHAUER INDUSTRIES LTD.; *Int'l*, pg. 4117
KEIM CHEVROLET INC.; *U.S. Private*, pg. 2273
KEIM CORP.; *U.S. Private*, pg. 2273
KEIM LUMBER COMPANY; *U.S. Private*, pg. 2274
KEIMOS 1988 U.S. INC.—See AMETEK, Inc.; *U.S. Public*, pg. 120
KEIM TS INC.; *U.S. Private*, pg. 2274
KEINARA CO., LTD.—See Nippon Light Metal Holdings Company, Ltd.; *Int'l*, pg. 5323
KEIN HING APPLIANCES SDN. BHD.—See Kein Hing International Berhad; *Int'l*, pg. 4117
KEIN HING INDUSTRY SDN. BHD.—See Kein Hing International Berhad; *Int'l*, pg. 4117
KEIN HING INTERNATIONAL BERHAD - FACTORY UK—See Kein Hing International Berhad; *Int'l*, pg. 4117
KEIN HING INTERNATIONAL BERHAD; *Int'l*, pg. 4117
KEIN HING MURAMOTO (VIETNAM) CO., LTD.—See Kein Hing International Berhad; *Int'l*, pg. 4117
KEIO AGENCY INC.; *Int'l*, pg. 4117
KEIO ATMAN CO., LTD.—See Keio Corporation; *Int'l*, pg. 4117
KEIO BUS CHUO CO., LTD.—See Keio Corporation; *Int'l*, pg. 4117
KEIO BUSINESS SUPPORT CO., LTD.—See Keio Corporation; *Int'l*, pg. 4117
KEIO BUS KOGANEI CO., LTD.—See Keio Corporation; *Int'l*, pg. 4117
KEIO CHIKA CHUSHAJOU CO., LTD.—See Keio Corporation; *Int'l*, pg. 4117
KEIO CORPORATION; *Int'l*, pg. 4117
KEIO JIDOUSHA CO., LTD.—See Keio Corporation; *Int'l*, pg. 4117
KEIO JUUKI SEIBI CO. LTD.—See Keio Corporation; *Int'l*, pg. 4117
KEIO PLAZA HOTEL CO., LTD.—See Keio Corporation; *Int'l*, pg. 4117
KEIO PLAZA HOTEL SAPPORO CO., LTD.—See Keio Corporation; *Int'l*, pg. 4117
KEIO PLAZA HOTEL TAMA—See Keio Corporation; *Int'l*, pg. 4117
KEIO PRESSO INN CO., LTD.—See Keio Corporation; *Int'l*, pg. 4117
KEIO RECREATION CO., LTD.—See Keio Corporation; *Int'l*, pg. 4117
KEIO RETAIL SERVICE CO., LTD.—See Keio Corporation; *Int'l*, pg. 4117
KEIO SETSUBI SERVICE CO., LTD.—See Keio Corporation; *Int'l*, pg. 4117
KEIO SHOKUHIN CO., LTD.—See Keio Corporation; *Int'l*, pg. 4117
KEIO SHOSEKI HANBAI CO., LTD.—See Keio Corporation; *Int'l*, pg. 4117
KEIO SINCERE STAFF CO., LTD.—See Keio Corporation; *Int'l*, pg. 4118
KEIO STORE CO., LTD.—See Keio Corporation; *Int'l*, pg. 4118
KEIOZU HOLDINGS COMPANY; *Int'l*, pg. 4118
KEI.PL SP. Z O.O.—See Cyber_Folks S.A.; *Int'l*, pg. 1892
KEISEI ELECTRIC RAILWAY CO., LTD.; *Int'l*, pg. 4118
KEISEIKING ENTERPRISES, LTD.—See IMV CORPORATION; *Int'l*, pg. 3638
KEIS GROUP—See HORIBA Ltd; *Int'l*, pg. 3477
KEITH BAGG STAFFING RESOURCES INC.; *Int'l*, pg. 4118
KEITH BAKER HOMES INC.; *U.S. Private*, pg. 2274
KEITH, BAYLEY, ROGERS & CO. LIMITED; *Int'l*, pg. 4118
KEITH DOYLE & ASSOCIATES INC.; *U.S. Private*, pg. 2274
KEITH HALL & SONS TRANSPORT LTD.—See TFI International Inc.; *Int'l*, pg. 7586
KEITH HAWTHORNE FORD; *U.S. Private*, pg. 2274
KEITHLEY INSTRUMENTS, LLC—See Fortive Corporation; *U.S. Public*, pg. 872
KEITHLY-WILLIAMS SEEDS INC.; *U.S. Private*, pg. 2274
KEITH MONUMENT COMPANY, INC.—See PKDM Holdings, Inc.; *U.S. Private*, pg. 3193
KEITH-PARK RETIREMENT VILLAGE LIMITED—See Ryman Healthcare Ltd.; *Int'l*, pg. 6439
KEITH PROWSE LIMITED—See Compass Group PLC; *Int'l*, pg. 1752
KEITH SMITH COMPANY, INC.; *U.S. Private*, pg. 2274
KEITH TITUS CORPORATION; *U.S. Private*, pg. 2274
KEITH ZARS POOLS; *U.S. Private*, pg. 2274
KEIWA INCORPORATED; *Int'l*, pg. 4118

COMPANY NAME INDEX

KEIWA INCORPORATED—See Keiwa Incorporated; *Int'l*, pg. 4118
KEIWA (NANJING) CO., LTD.—See Keiwa Incorporated; *Int'l*, pg. 4118
THE KEIYO BANK LIMITED; *Int'l*, pg. 7662
KEIYO CO., LTD.; *Int'l*, pg. 4118
KEIYO ETHYLENE CO., LTD.—See Sumitomo Chemical Company, Limited; *Int'l*, pg. 7264
KEIYO GAS CO., LTD.; *Int'l*, pg. 4118
KEIYO MONOMER CO., LTD.—See AGC Inc.; *Int'l*, pg. 204
KEIYO PIPELINE CO., LTD.—See INPEX CORPORATION; *Int'l*, pg. 3717
KEIYO UTILITY CO., LTD.—See Sapporo Holdings Limited; *Int'l*, pg. 6573
KEJA DONIA; *Int'l*, pg. 4118
KEJR, INC.; *U.S. Private*, pg. 2274
KEJURUTERAAN BINTAI KINDENKO SDN. BHD.—See Kinden Corporation; *Int'l*, pg. 4165
KEJURUTERAAN POWERWELL SDN. BHD.—See Powerwell Holdings Berhad; *Int'l*, pg. 5949
KEJURUTERAAN SAMUDRA TIMUR BERHAD; *Int'l*, pg. 4118
KEKE'S BREAKFAST CAFE INC.—See Denny's Corporation; *U.S. Public*, pg. 654
KEKKILA OY—See Vapo Oy; *Int'l*, pg. 8132
KEKROPS S.A.; *Int'l*, pg. 4118
KEKST & CO.—See Publicis Groupe S.A.; *Int'l*, pg. 6099
KELAB BANDAR LAGUNA MERBOK SDN. BHD.—See Paramount Corporation Berhad; *Int'l*, pg. 5738
KELA INVESTMENT FUND LTD; *Int'l*, pg. 4118
KELAIR PRODUCTS INC.—See Matot Inc.; *U.S. Private*, pg. 2611
KELANA JAYA MEDICAL CENTRE SDN. BHD.—See TDM Berhad; *Int'l*, pg. 7490
KELANI CABLES PLC; *Int'l*, pg. 4118
KELANI TYRES PLC; *Int'l*, pg. 4118
KELANI VALLEY PLANTATIONS LIMITED—See Hayleys PLC; *Int'l*, pg. 3291
KELATRON CORPORATION—See One Rock Capital Partners, LLC; *U.S. Private*, pg. 3022
KELBE BROS EQUIPMENT CO. INC.; *U.S. Private*, pg. 2274
KELBY MEDIA GROUP, INC.; *U.S. Private*, pg. 2274
KELBY TRAINING INC.—See Kelby Media Group, Inc.; *U.S. Private*, pg. 2274
KELCHNER, INC.—See John Wood Group PLC; *Int'l*, pg. 3984
KELCO INDUSTRIES INC.; *U.S. Private*, pg. 2274
KELCO LIMITED; *U.S. Private*, pg. 2274
KEL CONNECTORS, INC.—See KEL Corporation; *Int'l*, pg. 4118
KEL CORPORATION - MINAMI-ALPS FACTORY—See KEL Corporation; *Int'l*, pg. 4118
KEL CORPORATION - NAGANO FACTORY—See KEL Corporation; *Int'l*, pg. 4118
KEL CORPORATION; *Int'l*, pg. 4118
KEL CORPORATION - YAMANASHI FACTORY—See KEL Corporation; *Int'l*, pg. 4118
KELDA GROUP LIMITED—See Citigroup Inc.; *U.S. Public*, pg. 503
KELDA GROUP LIMITED—See GIC Pte. Ltd.; *Int'l*, pg. 2965
KELDA GROUP LIMITED—See HSBC Holdings plc; *Int'l*, pg. 3504
KELDA GROUP LIMITED—See M&G Group Limited; *Int'l*, pg. 4612
KELDON ELECTRIC & DATA LTD.; *Int'l*, pg. 4118
K-ELECTRIC LIMITED—See Abraaj Capital Limited; *Int'l*, pg. 67
KELE, INC.—See The Stephens Group, LLC; *U.S. Private*, pg. 4121
KELFRED HOLDINGS LIMITED; *Int'l*, pg. 4119
KELIAN PTY LIMITED—See Rio Tinto plc; *Int'l*, pg. 6346
KELI MOTOR GROUP CO., LTD.; *Int'l*, pg. 4119
KELIN ENVIRONMENTAL PROTECTION EQUIPMENT, INC.; *Int'l*, pg. 4119
KELINGTON ENGINEERING (SHANGHAI) CO., LTD.—See Kelington Group Berhad; *Int'l*, pg. 4119
KELINGTON ENGINEERING (S) PTE. LTD.—See Kelington Group Berhad; *Int'l*, pg. 4119
KELINGTON GROUP BERHAD; *Int'l*, pg. 4119
KELIN KRAFT AS—See Arendals Fossekompani ASA; *Int'l*, pg. 559
KELI SENSING TECHNOLOGY NINGBO CO., LTD.; *Int'l*, pg. 4119
KELKIN LIMITED—See DCC plc; *Int'l*, pg. 1991
KELK LTD.—See Komatsu Ltd.; *Int'l*, pg. 4235
KELKO QUAKER CHEMICAL, S.A.—See Quaker Chemical Corporation; *U.S. Public*, pg. 1746
KELLAL MAINTENANCE SA—See VINCI S.A.; *Int'l*, pg. 8223
KELLANDS AGRICULTURAL LTD.—See Alamo Group Inc.; *U.S. Public*, pg. 70
THE KELLAN GROUP PLC; *Int'l*, pg. 7662
KELLANOVA CANADA INC.—See Kellanova; *U.S. Public*, pg. 1217
KELLANOVA; *U.S. Public*, pg. 1217

KELLAWAY CRIDLAND PTY. LTD.—See Azimut Holding SpA; *Int'l*, pg. 779
KELLEHER ASSOCIATES, LLC—See AchieveNext, LLC; *U.S. Private*, pg. 59
THE KELLEHER CORPORATION; *U.S. Private*, pg. 4064
KELLEN COMMUNICATIONS; *U.S. Private*, pg. 2274
KELLEN COMMUNICATIONS—See Kellen Communications; *U.S. Private*, pg. 2274
KELLEN COMMUNICATIONS—See Kellen Communications; *U.S. Private*, pg. 2274
KELLEN COMMUNICATIONS—See Kellen Communications; *U.S. Private*, pg. 2274
KELLEN COMMUNICATIONS—See Kellen Communications; *U.S. Private*, pg. 2274
KELLEN EUROPE—See Kellen Communications; *U.S. Private*, pg. 2274
KELLER AUSTRALIA PTY LIMITED—See Keller Group plc; *Int'l*, pg. 4120
KELLER BROS MOTOR CO.; *U.S. Private*, pg. 2274
KELLER BUILDERS, INC.—See Swinerton Incorporated; *U.S. Private*, pg. 3894
KELLER CENTRAL ASIA LLP—See Keller Group plc; *Int'l*, pg. 4120
KELLER CIMENTACIONES CHILE SPA—See Keller Group plc; *Int'l*, pg. 4120
KELLER CIMENTACIONES DE LATINOAMERICA SA DE CV—See Keller Group plc; *Int'l*, pg. 4120
KELLER CIMENTACIONES SAC—See Keller Group plc; *Int'l*, pg. 4120
KELLER CIMENTACIONES S.L.U.—See Keller Group plc; *Int'l*, pg. 4120
KELLER CONSTRUCTION INC.; *U.S. Private*, pg. 2274
KELLER EGYPT LTD.—See Keller Group plc; *Int'l*, pg. 4120
KELLER ELECTRICAL INDUSTRIES, INC.; *U.S. Private*, pg. 2274
KELLER ENGENHARIA GEOTECNICA LTDA—See Keller Group plc; *Int'l*, pg. 4120
KELLER ENTERPRISES, INC.; *U.S. Private*, pg. 2274
KELLER FAY GROUP—See DGTL Holdings Inc.; *Int'l*, pg. 2097
KELLER FONDATIONS SPECIALES SAS—See Keller Group plc; *Int'l*, pg. 4120
KELLER FONDAZIONI S.R.L—See Keller Group plc; *Int'l*, pg. 4120
KELLER FOUNDATIONS LLC—See Keller Group plc; *Int'l*, pg. 4120
KELLER FOUNDATIONS LTD.—See Keller Group plc; *Int'l*, pg. 4120
KELLER FOUNDATIONS (SOUTH EAST ASIA) PTE LTD—See Keller Group plc; *Int'l*, pg. 4120
KELLER FOUNDATIONS VIETNAM CO., LIMITED—See Keller Group plc; *Int'l*, pg. 4120
KELLER FUNDERINGSTECHNIEKEN B.V.—See Keller Group plc; *Int'l*, pg. 4120
KELLER FUNDERINGSTEKNIK DANMARK APS—See Keller Group plc; *Int'l*, pg. 4120
KELLER GEOTEHNICA SRL—See Keller Group plc; *Int'l*, pg. 4120
KELLER GRADUATE SCHOOL OF MANAGEMENT—See Adtalem Global Education Inc.; *U.S. Public*, pg. 43
KELLER GRAIN & FEED INC.; *U.S. Private*, pg. 2275
KELLER GROUND ENGINEERING INDIA PRIVATE LTD—See Keller Group plc; *Int'l*, pg. 4120
KELLER GROUND ENGINEERING LLC—See Keller Group plc; *Int'l*, pg. 4120
KELLER GROUND ENGINEERING PTY LTD—See Keller Group plc; *Int'l*, pg. 4120
KELLER GROUND ENGINEERING—See Keller Group plc; *Int'l*, pg. 4120
KELLER GROUND ENGINEERING—See Keller Group plc; *Int'l*, pg. 4120
KELLER GROUP INC.; *U.S. Private*, pg. 2275
KELLER GROUP PLC; *Int'l*, pg. 4119
KELLER GRUNDBAU GES.MBH—See Keller Group plc; *Int'l*, pg. 4120
KELLER GRUNDBAU GMBH—See Keller Group plc; *Int'l*, pg. 4120
KELLER GRUNDBAU GMBH—See Keller Group plc; *Int'l*, pg. 4120
KELLER GRUNDBAU GMBH—See Keller Group plc; *Int'l*, pg. 4120
KELLER GRUNDLAGGNING AB—See Keller Group plc; *Int'l*, pg. 4120
KELLER HCW GMBH—See Groupe Legris Industries; *Int'l*, pg. 3106
KELLER HELLAS S.A.—See Keller Group plc; *Int'l*, pg. 4120
KELLER HOLDING GMBH—See Keller Group plc; *Int'l*, pg. 4120
KELLER HOMES, INC.—See Toll Brothers, Inc.; *U.S. Public*, pg. 2162
KELLER INC.; *U.S. Private*, pg. 2275
KELLER KITCHEN CABINETS, INC.; *U.S. Private*, pg. 2275
KELLER LABORATORIES INC.—See Cerberus Capital Management, L.P.; *U.S. Private*, pg. 839
KELLER LIMITED - COLCRETE EURODRILL DIVISION—See Keller Group plc; *Int'l*, pg. 4120
KELLER LIMITED - KELLER FOUNDATIONS DIVISION—See Keller Group plc; *Int'l*, pg. 4120

KELLIHER SAMETS VOLK

KELLER LIMITED - KELLER GEOTECHNIQUE DIVISION—See Keller Group plc; *Int'l*, pg. 4120
KELLER LIMITED—See Keller Group plc; *Int'l*, pg. 4120
KELLER (MALAYSIA) SDN. BHD.—See Keller Group plc; *Int'l*, pg. 4120
KELLER MANUFACTURING COMPANY, INC.; *U.S. Public*, pg. 1218
KELLER MEDICAL, INC.—See AbbVie Inc.; *U.S. Public*, pg. 23
KELLER MELYEPITO KFT—See Keller Group plc; *Int'l*, pg. 4120
KELLERMEYER BERGENSONS SERVICES, LLC—See Cerberus Capital Management, L.P.; *U.S. Private*, pg. 839
KELLER-MTS AG—See Keller Group plc; *Int'l*, pg. 4121
KELLER NEW ZEALAND LIMITED—See Keller Group plc; *Int'l*, pg. 4120
KELLER OIL COMPANY—See Reading Anthracite Company; *U.S. Private*, pg. 3366
KELLER POLSKA SP. Z O.O—See Keller Group plc; *Int'l*, pg. 4120
KELLER PTY. LTD.—See Keller Group plc; *Int'l*, pg. 4120
KELLER'S, INC.—See Capital Alignment Partners, Inc.; *U.S. Private*, pg. 738
KELLER'S, INC.—See Lynch Holdings, LLC; *U.S. Private*, pg. 2521
KELLER-SMITH SUPPLY, INC.; *U.S. Private*, pg. 2275
KELLER SPECIALNE ZAKLADANIE SPOL. S.R.O.—See Keller Group plc; *Int'l*, pg. 4120
KELLER SPECIALNE ZAKLADANI SPOL. S R.O.—See Keller Group plc; *Int'l*, pg. 4120
KELLERSTRASS ENTERPRISES LLC—See Parkland Corporation; *Int'l*, pg. 5743
KELLER SUPPLY COMPANY INC.; *U.S. Private*, pg. 2275
KELLER TECHNOLOGY CORPORATION; *U.S. Private*, pg. 2275
KELLER TURKI CO. LTD.—See Keller Group plc; *Int'l*, pg. 4121
KELLER UKRAINE LLC—See Keller Group plc; *Int'l*, pg. 4121
KELLER WILLIAMS CAPITAL PROPERTIES; *U.S. Private*, pg. 2275
KELLER WILLIAMS LEGACY BROKERAGE GROUP; *U.S. Private*, pg. 2275
KELLER WILLIAMS PLATINUM PARTNERS, INC.; *U.S. Private*, pg. 2275
KELLER WILLIAMS REALTY, INC.; *U.S. Private*, pg. 2275
KELLER ZEMIN MUHENDISLIGI LIMITED—See Keller Group plc; *Int'l*, pg. 4121
KELLEY AUTOMOTIVE GROUP; *U.S. Private*, pg. 2275
KELLEY BEAN CO., INC.; *U.S. Private*, pg. 2275
KELLEY BLUE BOOK CO., INC.—See Cox Enterprises, Inc.; *U.S. Private*, pg. 1076
KELLEY BROS; *U.S. Private*, pg. 2275
KELLEY CAWTHORNE, LLC; *U.S. Private*, pg. 2275
KELLEY CHEVROLET INC.; *U.S. Private*, pg. 2275
KELLEY & COMPANY; *U.S. Private*, pg. 2275
KELLEY CONNECT CO.; *U.S. Private*, pg. 2275
KELLEY DRYE & WARREN LLP; *U.S. Private*, pg. 2275
KELLEY ELECTRIC COMPANY—See The Townsend Corporation; *U.S. Private*, pg. 4127
KELLEY FOODS OF ALABAMA, INC.—See Ben E. Keith Company; *U.S. Private*, pg. 522
KELLEY HABIB JOHN; *U.S. Private*, pg. 2275
KELLEY HOLDINGS INC.; *U.S. Private*, pg. 2276
KELLEY STEEL ERECTORS INC.—See Kelley Holdings Inc.; *U.S. Private*, pg. 2276
KELLEY SWOFFORD ROY, INC.; *U.S. Private*, pg. 2276
KELLEY TRUCKING, INC.; *U.S. Private*, pg. 2276
KELLEY-WILLIAMSON COMPANY INC.; *U.S. Private*, pg. 2276
KELLFRI AB—See Volati AB; *Int'l*, pg. 8300
KELLFRI APS—See Volati AB; *Int'l*, pg. 8300
KELLIHER SAMETS VOLK NY—See Kelliher Samets Volk; *U.S. Private*, pg. 2276
KELLIHER SAMETS VOLK; *U.S. Private*, pg. 2276
KELLIHER SAMETS VOLK—See Kelliher Samets Volk; *U.S. Private*, pg. 2276
KELLMAN, S. DE R.L. DE C.V.—See Kellanova; *U.S. Public*, pg. 1218
KELLNER & KUNZ AG—See Wurth Verwaltungsgesellschaft mbH; *Int'l*, pg. 8507
KELLOGG ASIA PACIFIC PTE. LTD—See Kellanova; *U.S. Public*, pg. 1217
KELLOGG ASIA PRODUCTS SDN. BHD.—See Kellanova; *U.S. Public*, pg. 1217
KELLOGG ASIA SDN. BHD.—See Kellanova; *U.S. Public*, pg. 1217
KELLOGG (AUST.) PTY. LTD.—See Kellanova; *U.S. Public*, pg. 1217
KELLOGG AUSTRALIA HOLDINGS PTY LTD—See Kellanova; *U.S. Public*, pg. 1217
KELLOGG (AUSTRALIA) PROPRIETARY LTD.—See Kellanova; *U.S. Public*, pg. 1217
KELLOGG BROWN & ROOT ASIA PACIFIC PTE LTD—See KBR, Inc.; *U.S. Public*, pg. 1216
KELLOGG BROWN & ROOT (CANADA) COMPANY—See KBR, Inc.; *U.S. Public*, pg. 1216

KELLIHER SAMETS VOLK

KELLOGG BROWN & ROOT (GREENFORD) LIMITED—See KBR, Inc.; *U.S. Public*, pg. 1216
KELLOGG BROWN & ROOT HOLDINGS (U.K.) LIMITED—See KBR, Inc.; *U.S. Public*, pg. 1216
KELLOGG BROWN & ROOT INTERNATIONAL, INC.—See KBR, Inc.; *U.S. Public*, pg. 1216
KELLOGG BROWN & ROOT LLC—See KBR, Inc.; *U.S. Public*, pg. 1216
KELLOGG BROWN & ROOT SERVICES, INC.—See KBR, Inc.; *U.S. Public*, pg. 1216
KELLOGG CANADA, INC.—See Kellanova; *U.S. Public*, pg. 1217
KELLOGG CANADA INC.—See Kellanova; *U.S. Public*, pg. 1217
KELLOGG CARIBBEAN SERVICES COMPANY, INC.—See Kellanova; *U.S. Public*, pg. 1217
KELLOGG CO. - COOKIES & SNACKS BUSINESS—See Ferrero International S.A.; *Int'l*, pg. 2640
THE KELLOGG COLLECTION INC.; *U.S. Private*, pg. 4064
KELLOGG COMPANY MEXICO, S. DE R.L. DE C.V.—See Kellanova; *U.S. Public*, pg. 1218
KELLOGG COMPANY OF GREAT BRITAIN LIMITED—See Kellanova; *U.S. Public*, pg. 1218
KELLOGG COMPANY OF IRELAND LIMITED—See Kellanova; *U.S. Public*, pg. 1218
KELLOGG COMPANY OF SOUTH AFRICA (PTY.) LTD.—See Kellanova; *U.S. Public*, pg. 1218
KELLOGG CONVENIENCE FOOD PLANT—See WK Kellogg Co; *U.S. Public*, pg. 2376
KELLOGG DE MEXICO, S. DE R.L. DE C.V.—See Kellanova; *U.S. Public*, pg. 1218
KELLOGG (DEUTSCHLAND) GMBH—See Kellanova; *U.S. Public*, pg. 1218
KELLOGG ESPANA, S.L.—See Kellanova; *U.S. Public*, pg. 1218
KELLOGG EUROPE TRADING LIMITED—See Kellanova; *U.S. Public*, pg. 1218
KELLOGG FOODS (SHANGHAI) CO. LTD—See Kellanova; *U.S. Public*, pg. 1218
KELLOGG GROUP LIMITED—See Kellanova; *U.S. Public*, pg. 1218
KELLOGG INDIA PRIVATE LIMITED—See Kellanova; *U.S. Public*, pg. 1218
KELLOGG & KIMSEY, INC.; *U.S. Private*, pg. 2276
KELLOGG-LANCASTER PLANT—See WK Kellogg Co; *U.S. Public*, pg. 2376
KELLOGG MANUFACTURING ESPANA, S.L.—See Kellanova; *U.S. Public*, pg. 1218
KELLOGG MANUFACTURING GMBH & CO. KG—See Kellanova; *U.S. Public*, pg. 1217
KELLOGG MARKETING AND SALES COMPANY (UK) LIMITED—See Kellanova; *U.S. Public*, pg. 1218
KELLOGG-MEMPHIS PLANT—See WK Kellogg Co; *U.S. Public*, pg. 2376
KELLOGG (OSTERREICH) GMBH—See Kellanova; *U.S. Public*, pg. 1217
KELLOGG (QINGDAO) FOOD CO., LTD.—See Kellanova; *U.S. Public*, pg. 1217
KELLOGG SALES COMPANY—See Kellanova; *U.S. Public*, pg. 1218
KELLOGG SERVICIOS, S.C.—See Kellanova; *U.S. Public*, pg. 1218
KELLOGG'S PRODUITS ALIMENTAIRES, S.A.—See Kellanova; *U.S. Public*, pg. 1218
KELLOGG SUPPLY CO. INC.; *U.S. Private*, pg. 2276
KELLOGG SUPPLY INC.; *U.S. Private*, pg. 2276
KELLOGG (THAILAND) LIMITED—See Kellanova; *U.S. Public*, pg. 1217
KELLOGG USA INC.—See WK Kellogg Co; *U.S. Public*, pg. 2376
KELL SYSTEMS LTD—See Schneider Electric SE; *Int'l*, pg. 6628
KELLTON TECH SOLUTIONS LTD.; *Int'l*, pg. 4121
KELLTON TECH (UK) LIMITED—See Kellton Tech Solutions Ltd.; *Int'l*, pg. 4121
KELLVE GROUP AB; *Int'l*, pg. 4121
KELLVE SERVICE AB—See Kellve Group AB; *Int'l*, pg. 4121
KELLVE SWEDEN AB—See Kellve Group AB; *Int'l*, pg. 4121
KELLWOOD COMPANY - NEW YORK OFFICE—See Sun Capital Partners, Inc.; *U.S. Private*, pg. 3859
KELLWOOD COMPANY—See Sun Capital Partners, Inc.; *U.S. Private*, pg. 3859
KELLWOOD COMPANY - WESTERN REGION—See Sun Capital Partners, Inc.; *U.S. Private*, pg. 3859
KELLY AEROSPACE INC.—See Arcline Investment Management LP; *U.S. Private*, pg. 313
KELLY & ASSOCIATES INSURANCE GROUP, INC.; *U.S. Private*, pg. 2276
KELLY AUTOMOTIVE GROUP; *U.S. Private*, pg. 2276
KELLY AUTOMOTIVE SERVICES GROUP—See Kelly Services, Inc.; *U.S. Public*, pg. 1220
KELLY BMW; *U.S. Private*, pg. 2276
KELLY BOX & PACKAGING CORP.; *U.S. Private*, pg. 2276
KELLY CAPITAL, LLC; *U.S. Private*, pg. 2276

KELLYCO METAL DETECTOR SUPERSTORE; *U.S. Private*, pg. 2277
THE KELLY COMPANIES; *U.S. Private*, pg. 4064
KELLY COVE SALMON LTD.—See Cooke, Inc.; *Int'l*, pg. 1788
KELLY EDUCATIONAL STAFFING—See Kelly Services, Inc.; *U.S. Public*, pg. 1219
KELLY ENGINEERING RESOURCES—See Kelly Services, Inc.; *U.S. Public*, pg. 1220
KELLY FINANCIAL RESOURCES—See Kelly Services, Inc.; *U.S. Public*, pg. 1220
KELLY FOODS CORPORATION; *U.S. Private*, pg. 2276
KELLY GESELLSCHAFT M.B.H.—See Intersnack Group GmbH & Co. KG; *Int'l*, pg. 3760
KELLY GROUP LIMITED - RENWICK TALENT—See Adcorp Holdings Limited; *Int'l*, pg. 127
KELLY GROUP LIMITED—See Adcorp Holdings Limited; *Int'l*, pg. 127
KELLY IMPORTS INC.; *U.S. Private*, pg. 2276
KELLY INFORMATION TECHNOLOGY RESOURCES—See Kelly Services, Inc.; *U.S. Public*, pg. 1220
KELLY LAW REGISTRY—See TrustPoint International, LLC; *U.S. Private*, pg. 4251
KELLY LIMESTONE, LLC—See Arcosa, Inc.; *U.S. Public*, pg. 186
KELLY MANAGED SERVICES—See Kelly Services, Inc.; *U.S. Public*, pg. 1220
KELLY MANAGEMENT CORPORATION; *U.S. Private*, pg. 2276
KELLY MEDIA GROUP; *U.S. Private*, pg. 2276
KELLYMITCHELL GROUP, INC.; *U.S. Private*, pg. 2277
KELLY-MOORE PAINT COMPANY, INC.; *U.S. Private*, pg. 2277
KELLY, NANEY INSURANCE AGENCY, INC.—See Inszone Insurance Services, LLC; *U.S. Private*, pg. 2096
KELLY NISSAN INC.; *U.S. Private*, pg. 2276
KELLY PARTNERS GROUP HOLDINGS LIMITED; *Int'l*, pg. 4121
KELLY & PARTNERS, INC.—See Keystone Digital Imaging, Incorporated; *U.S. Private*, pg. 2296
KELLY PAYROLL SERVICES LIMITED—See Kelly Services, Inc.; *U.S. Public*, pg. 1219
KELLY & PICERNE INC.—See Picerne Real Estate Group; *U.S. Private*, pg. 3176
KELLY PIPE CO., LLC—See Shapco, Inc.; *U.S. Private*, pg. 3625
KELLY PIPE CO LLC—See Shapco, Inc.; *U.S. Private*, pg. 3625
KELLY PROPERTIES, INC.—See Kelly Services, Inc.; *U.S. Public*, pg. 1218
KELLY PROPERTY GROUP PTY. LTD.—See Kelly Partners Group Holdings Limited; *Int'l*, pg. 4121
KELLY RYAN EQUIPMENT COMPANY; *U.S. Private*, pg. 2276
KELLY'S CAJUN GRILL FRANCHISE; *U.S. Private*, pg. 2277
KELLY SCIENTIFIC RESOURCES—See Kelly Services, Inc.; *U.S. Public*, pg. 1220
KELLY, SCOTT & MADISON; *U.S. Private*, pg. 2277
KELLY, SCOTT & MADISON—See Kelly, Scott & Madison; *U.S. Private*, pg. 2277
KELLY SERVICES AB—See Kelly Services, Inc.; *U.S. Public*, pg. 1219
KELLY SERVICES (AUSTRALIA), LTD.—See Kelly Services, Inc.; *U.S. Public*, pg. 1218
KELLY SERVICES AUSTRALIA—See Kelly Services, Inc.; *U.S. Public*, pg. 1219
KELLY SERVICES CANADA, LTD.—See Kelly Services, Inc.; *U.S. Public*, pg. 1219
KELLY SERVICES - EMPRESSA DE TRABALHO TEMPORARIO, UNIPESSOAL, LDA.—See Kelly Services, Inc.; *U.S. Public*, pg. 1219
KELLY SERVICES FRANCE S.A.—See Kelly Services, Inc.; *U.S. Public*, pg. 1219
KELLY SERVICES GMBH NCO OHG—See Kelly Services, Inc.; *U.S. Public*, pg. 1219
KELLY SERVICES GMBH—See Kelly Services, Inc.; *U.S. Public*, pg. 1218
KELLY SERVICES HEALTHCARE UNIPESSOAL, LDA.—See Kelly Services, Inc.; *U.S. Public*, pg. 1219
KELLY SERVICES HUNGARY STAFFING, KFT.—See Kelly Services, Inc.; *U.S. Public*, pg. 1218
KELLY SERVICES, INC. - INTERNATIONAL DIVISION—See Kelly Services, Inc.; *U.S. Public*, pg. 1218
KELLY SERVICES, INC. - PROFESSIONAL TECHNICAL & STAFFING ALTERNATIVES DIVISION—See Kelly Services, Inc.; *U.S. Public*, pg. 1219
KELLY SERVICES, INC.; *U.S. Public*, pg. 1218
KELLY SERVICES (INDIA) PVT. LTD.—See Kelly Services, Inc.; *U.S. Public*, pg. 1219
KELLY SERVICES INTERIM (BELGIUM)—See Kelly Services, Inc.; *U.S. Public*, pg. 1219
KELLY SERVICES (IRELAND), LTD.—See Kelly Services, Inc.; *U.S. Public*, pg. 1219
KELLY SERVICES LUXEMBOURG, S.A.R.L.—See Kelly Services, Inc.; *U.S. Public*, pg. 1219

KELLY SERVICES (MALAYSIA) SDN. BHD.—See Kelly Services, Inc.; *U.S. Public*, pg. 1219
KELLY SERVICES MANAGEMENT S.A.R.L.—See Kelly Services, Inc.; *U.S. Public*, pg. 1219
KELLY SERVICES MEXICO S.A. DE C.V.—See Kelly Services, Inc.; *U.S. Public*, pg. 1219
KELLY SERVICES (NEDERLAND) B.V.—See Kelly Services, Inc.; *U.S. Public*, pg. 1219
KELLY SERVICES (NEW ZEALAND), LTD.—See Kelly Services, Inc.; *U.S. Public*, pg. 1219
KELLY SERVICES NORGE A/S—See Kelly Services, Inc.; *U.S. Public*, pg. 1219
KELLY SERVICES OF DENMARK, INC.—See Kelly Services, Inc.; *U.S. Public*, pg. 1219
KELLY SERVICES S.A.R.L.—See Kelly Services, Inc.; *U.S. Public*, pg. 1219
KELLY SERVICES SOCIETA DI FORNITURA DI LAVORO TEMPORANEO S.P.A.—See Kelly Services, Inc.; *U.S. Public*, pg. 1219
KELLY SERVICES—See Kelly Services, Inc.; *U.S. Public*, pg. 1219
KELLY SERVICES (S) PTE LTD—See Kelly Services, Inc.; *U.S. Public*, pg. 1218
KELLY SERVICES STAFFING & RECRUITMENT (THAILAND) CO., LTD.—See Kelly Services, Inc.; *U.S. Public*, pg. 1219
KELLY SERVICES (SUISSE) S.A.—See Kelly Services, Inc.; *U.S. Public*, pg. 1219
KELLY SERVICES (UK) LTD.—See Kelly Services, Inc.; *U.S. Public*, pg. 1219
KELLY'S INDUSTRIAL SERVICES, INC.—See Vantage Contractors, LLC; *U.S. Private*, pg. 4345
KELLY'S KIDS; *U.S. Private*, pg. 2277
KELLY SPICERS INC.—See Central National Gottesman Inc.; *U.S. Private*, pg. 823
KELLY'S PIPE & SUPPLY CO.—See Blackfriars Corp.; *U.S. Private*, pg. 575
KELLY SUBARU & MITSUBISHI; *U.S. Private*, pg. 2277
KELLY SUPPLY COMPANY; *U.S. Private*, pg. 2277
KELLY SYSTEMS INC.—See Novinger Group, Inc.; *U.S. Private*, pg. 2968
KELLY TOYS HOLDINGS, LLC—See Berkshire Hathaway Inc.; *U.S. Public*, pg. 298
KELLYTOY USA INC.; *U.S. Private*, pg. 2277
KELLY TRACTOR CO. INC.; *U.S. Private*, pg. 2277
KELLY VENTURES LTD.; *Int'l*, pg. 4121
KELMSCOTT COMMUNICATIONS, INC.; *U.S. Private*, pg. 2277
KELO-TV—See Nexstar Media Group, Inc.; *U.S. Public*, pg. 1522
KELOWNA FLIGHTCRAFT AIR CHARTER LTD.; *Int'l*, pg. 4121
KELOWNA FORD LINCOLN SALES LTD; *Int'l*, pg. 4121
KELOWNA MERCEDES-BENZ; *Int'l*, pg. 4121
KELPE CONTRACTING, INC.; *U.S. Private*, pg. 2277
KELPEN PLASTICS TECHNOLOGY SDN. BHD—See Ewein Berhad; *Int'l*, pg. 2576
KELPEN RESOURCES SDN BHD (KRSB)—See Ewein Berhad; *Int'l*, pg. 2576
KELP INDUSTRIES PTY. LTD.—See International Flavors & Fragrances Inc.; *U.S. Public*, pg. 1153
KELSEN GROUP A/S—See Ferrero International S.A.; *Int'l*, pg. 2641
KELSEN, INC.—See Ferrero International S.A.; *Int'l*, pg. 2641
KELSEN SOUTH AFRICA (PTY) LTD.—See Ferrero International S.A.; *Int'l*, pg. 2641
KELSER CORPORATION; *U.S. Private*, pg. 2277
KELSEY CONSTRUCTION, INC.; *U.S. Private*, pg. 2277
KELSEY-HAYES CANADA LIMITED—See ZF Friedrichshafen AG; *Int'l*, pg. 8645
KELSEY-HAYES COMPANY—See ZF Friedrichshafen AG; *Int'l*, pg. 8645
KELSEYS INTERNATIONAL, INC.—See Fairfax Financial Holdings Limited; *Int'l*, pg. 2608
KELSEY-TRAIL TRUCKING LTD.—See Daseke, Inc.; *U.S. Private*, pg. 1161
KEL SHANGHAI CO., LTD.—See KEL Corporation; *Int'l*, pg. 4118
KELSIAN GROUP LIMITED; *Int'l*, pg. 4121
KELSO-BURNETT COMPANY; *U.S. Private*, pg. 2281
KELSO & COMPANY, L.P.; *U.S. Private*, pg. 2277
KELSO GROUP HOLDINGS PLC; *Int'l*, pg. 4122
KELSO PLACE ASSET MANAGEMENT LLP; *Int'l*, pg. 4122
KELSO TECHNOLOGIES INC.; *Int'l*, pg. 4122
KELSO TECHNOLOGIES (USA) INC.—See Kelso Technologies Inc.; *Int'l*, pg. 4122
KELTA, INC.; *U.S. Private*, pg. 2281
KEL TAIWAN CO., LTD.—See KEL Corporation; *Int'l*, pg. 4118
KELTECH ENERGIES LTD.—See Chowgule & Company Pvt. Ltd.; *Int'l*, pg. 1585
KELTECH, INC.—See Bradford-White Corporation; *U.S. Private*, pg. 632
KELTEC PEOPLE; *Int'l*, pg. 4122
KELT EXPLORATION (LNG) LTD.—See Kelt Exploration Ltd.; *Int'l*, pg. 4122
KELT EXPLORATION LTD.; *Int'l*, pg. 4122

COMPANY NAME INDEX

KELTIC FINANCIAL SERVICES, LLC—See Ares Management Corporation; *U.S. Public*, pg. 189
KELTON RESEARCH, LLC—See Tailwind Capital Group, LLC; *U.S. Private*, pg. 3924
KELTRON CONNECTORS—See Keltron Electronics Corp.; *U.S. Private*, pg. 2281
KELTRON ELECTRONICS CORP.; *U.S. Private*, pg. 2281
KELTY, INC.—See Exxel Outdoors, Inc.; *U.S. Private*, pg. 1453
KELVIN ELECTRIC TRADING CO., LTD., *Int'l*, pg. 4122
KELVIN HUGHES LIMITED—See HENSOLDT AG; *Int'l*, pg. 3355
KELVIN HUGHES (NEDERLAND) B.V.—See HENSOLDT AG; *Int'l*, pg. 3355
KELVIN HUGHES (SINGAPORE) PTE. LTD.—See HENSOLDT AG; *Int'l*, pg. 3355
KELVIN MEDICAL, INC.; *U.S. Public*, pg. 1220
KELVION AB—See Triton Advisers Limited; *Int'l*, pg. 7931
KELVION BRAZED PHE GMBH—See Triton Advisers Limited; *Int'l*, pg. 7931
KELVION BVBA—See Triton Advisers Limited; *Int'l*, pg. 7931
KELVION B.V.—See Triton Advisers Limited; *Int'l*, pg. 7932
KELVION FZE—See Triton Advisers Limited; *Int'l*, pg. 7932
KELVION GMBH—See Triton Advisers Limited; *Int'l*, pg. 7932
KELVION HOLDING B.V.—See Triton Advisers Limited; *Int'l*, pg. 7932
KELVION HOLDING GMBH—See Triton Advisers Limited; *Int'l*, pg. 7931
KELVION, INC. - PHE SYSTEMS—See Triton Advisers Limited; *Int'l*, pg. 7932
KELVION, INC.—See Triton Advisers Limited; *Int'l*, pg. 7932
KELVION, INC. - THERMAL SOLUTIONS—See Triton Advisers Limited; *Int'l*, pg. 7932
KELVION INDIA PVT. LTD.—See Triton Advisers Limited; *Int'l*, pg. 7932
KELVION INTERCAMBIADORES LTDA.—See Triton Advisers Limited; *Int'l*, pg. 7932
KELVION LIMITED - PHE SYSTEMS—See Triton Advisers Limited; *Int'l*, pg. 7932
KELVION LIMITED - SEARLE SYSTEMS—See Triton Advisers Limited; *Int'l*, pg. 7932
KELVION LIMITED—See Triton Advisers Limited; *Int'l*, pg. 7932
KELVION MACHINE COOLING B.V.—See Triton Advisers Limited; *Int'l*, pg. 7932
KELVION MACHINE COOLING GMBH—See Triton Advisers Limited; *Int'l*, pg. 7932
KELVION MACHINE COOLING SP. Z O.O.—See Triton Advisers Limited; *Int'l*, pg. 7932
KELVION MASHIMPEKS LLC—See Triton Advisers Limited; *Int'l*, pg. 7932
KELVION OU—See Triton Advisers Limited; *Int'l*, pg. 7932
KELVION PHE B.V.—See Triton Advisers Limited; *Int'l*, pg. 7932
KELVION PHE GMBH—See Triton Advisers Limited; *Int'l*, pg. 7932
KELVION PTE. LTD.—See Triton Advisers Limited; *Int'l*, pg. 7932
KELVION RADIATOR GMBH—See Triton Advisers Limited; *Int'l*, pg. 7932
KELVION REFRIGERATION B.V.—See Triton Advisers Limited; *Int'l*, pg. 7932
KELVION REFRIGERATION GMBH—See Triton Advisers Limited; *Int'l*, pg. 7932
KELVION SAFETY HEAT EXCHANGERS GMBH—See Triton Advisers Limited; *Int'l*, pg. 7932
KELVION S.A.S.—See Triton Advisers Limited; *Int'l*, pg. 7932
KELVION SERVICES (PTY) LTD.—See Triton Advisers Limited; *Int'l*, pg. 7932
KELVION SP. Z O.O.—See Triton Advisers Limited; *Int'l*, pg. 7932
KELVION S.R.L. - PHE SYSTEMS—See Triton Advisers Limited; *Int'l*, pg. 7932
KELVION S.R.L.—See Triton Advisers Limited; *Int'l*, pg. 7932
KELVION S.R.O.—See Triton Advisers Limited; *Int'l*, pg. 7932
KELVION THERMAL SERVICES S.A.S.—See Triton Advisers Limited; *Int'l*, pg. 7932
KELVION THERMAL SOLUTIONS (PTY) LTD.—See Triton Advisers Limited; *Int'l*, pg. 7932
KELVION THERMAL SOLUTIONS S.A.S.—See Triton Advisers Limited; *Int'l*, pg. 7932
KELVION THERMAL SOLUTIONS S.A.U.—See Triton Advisers Limited; *Int'l*, pg. 7932
KELVION THERMAL SOLUTIONS W.L.L.—See Triton Advisers Limited; *Int'l*, pg. 7932
KELVYN PRESS INC.; *U.S. Private*, pg. 2281
KELWAY AFRICA—See Kelway Limited; *Int'l*, pg. 4122
KELWAY APAC—See Kelway Limited; *Int'l*, pg. 4122
KELWAY AUSTRALIA PTY LTD—See Kelway Limited; *Int'l*, pg. 4122
KELWAY FZ LLC—See Kelway Limited; *Int'l*, pg. 4122
KELWAY IRELAND—See Kelway Limited; *Int'l*, pg. 4122
KELWAY LIMITED; *Int'l*, pg. 4122

KELYNIAM GLOBAL, INC.; *U.S. Public*, pg. 1220
KEMACH EQUIPMENT (PTY) LTD.—See BH Botswana (Pty) Ltd.; *Int'l*, pg. 1009
KEMACH EQUIPMENT (PTY) LTD.—See Muscat Overseas Co., L.L.C.; *Int'l*, pg. 5102
KEMA INC.—See DNV GL Group AS; *Int'l*, pg. 2151
KEMAJUAN SEKIM BARU SDN. BHD.—See Mitrajaya Holdings Berhad; *Int'l*, pg. 4927
KEMA N.V.—See DNV GL Group AS; *Int'l*, pg. 2151
KEMA SERVICES INC. - ANAHEIM—See DNV GL Group AS; *Int'l*, pg. 2151
KEMA SERVICES INC. - MADISON—See DNV GL Group AS; *Int'l*, pg. 2151
KEMA SERVICES INC. - OAKLAND—See DNV GL Group AS; *Int'l*, pg. 2151
KEMA SERVICES INC.—See DNV GL Group AS; *Int'l*, pg. 2151
KEMA USA INC.—See DNV GL Group AS; *Int'l*, pg. 2151
KEMBA CREDIT UNION, INC.; *U.S. Private*, pg. 2281
KEMBA FINANCIAL CREDIT UNION; *U.S. Private*, pg. 2281
KEMBERTON HEALTHCARE SERVICES LLC—See GrowthCurve Capital LP; *U.S. Private*, pg. 1796
KEMBERTON HEALTHCARE SERVICES LLC—See Riverside Partners, LLC; *U.S. Private*, pg. 3446
K.E. MCKAY'S MARKET OF COOS BAY; *U.S. Private*, pg. 2252
KEMCO CO., LTD.—See Korea Zinc Company, Ltd.; *Int'l*, pg. 4287
KEMCO INDUSTRIES INC.; *U.S. Private*, pg. 2281
KEMCO KNOXVILLE—See GSK plc; *Int'l*, pg. 3149
KEMCO SYSTEMS, CO. LLC—See CECO Environmental Corp.; *U.S. Public*, pg. 463
KEMEERA INC.—See CORE Industrial Partners, LLC; *U.S. Private*, pg. 1049
KEMEK LLC—See Societe Anonyme d'Explosifs et de Produits Chimiques; *Int'l*, pg. 7035
KEMEK LTD.—See Societe Anonyme d'Explosifs et de Produits Chimiques; *Int'l*, pg. 7035
KEMEL ASIA PACIFIC PTE. LTD.—See Eagle Industry Co., Ltd.; *Int'l*, pg. 2265
KEMEL CO., LTD. - KURE FACTORY—See Eagle Industry Co., Ltd.; *Int'l*, pg. 2265
KEMEL CO., LTD.—See Eagle Industry Co., Ltd.; *Int'l*, pg. 2265
KEMEL CO., LTD. - TAKASAGO FACTORY—See Eagle Industry Co., Ltd.; *Int'l*, pg. 2265
KEMEL EUROPE LIMITED—See Eagle Industry Co., Ltd.; *Int'l*, pg. 2265
KEMEL SALES & SERVICE (SHANGHAI) CO., LTD.—See Eagle Industry Co., Ltd.; *Int'l*, pg. 2265
KEMENA INDUSTRIES SDN BHD—See IJM Corporation Berhad; *Int'l*, pg. 3609
KEMET BLUE POWDER CORPORATION—See Yageo Corporation; *Int'l*, pg. 8545
KEMET CORPORATION—See Yageo Corporation; *Int'l*, pg. 8545
KEMET DE MEXICO, S.A. DE C.V.—See Yageo Corporation; *Int'l*, pg. 8545
KEMET ELECTRONICS ASIA LIMITED—See Yageo Corporation; *Int'l*, pg. 8545
KEMET ELECTRONICS CORPORATION—See Yageo Corporation; *Int'l*, pg. 8545
KEMET ELECTRONICS ITALIA S.R.L.—See Yageo Corporation; *Int'l*, pg. 8545
KEMET ELECTRONICS LIMITED—See Yageo Corporation; *Int'l*, pg. 8545
KEMET ELECTRONICS OY—See Yageo Corporation; *Int'l*, pg. 8545
KEMET ELECTRONICS S.A.—See Yageo Corporation; *Int'l*, pg. 8545
KEMET JAPAN CO., LTD.—See Kitagawa Corporation; *Int'l*, pg. 4194
KEMETYL AB; *Int'l*, pg. 4122
KEMETYL BELGIUM NV—See Kemetyl AB; *Int'l*, pg. 4122
KEMETYL KIMYA SANAYI VE TICARET LIMITED SIRKETII—See Kemetyl AB; *Int'l*, pg. 4122
KEMETYL NEDERLAND B.V.—See Kemetyl AB; *Int'l*, pg. 4122
KEMETYL NORWAY AS—See Kemetyl AB; *Int'l*, pg. 4122
KEMETYL POLSKA SP.Z.O.O.—See Kemetyl AB; *Int'l*, pg. 4122
KEMETYL UK LIMITED—See Kemetyl AB; *Int'l*, pg. 4122
KEMFLO INTERNATIONAL CO. LTD; *Int'l*, pg. 4122
KEMIAO GARMENT HOLDING GROUP; *U.S. Public*, pg. 1220
KEMIFLOC A.S.—See Kemira Oyj; *Int'l*, pg. 4123
KEMIJA MOZIRJE—See Metalursko Kemicna Industrija Celje, d.d.; *Int'l*, pg. 4850
KEMIMEDI CO., LTD.; *Int'l*, pg. 4122
KEMINER REMMERS SPIEHS KARTONHANDELS GMBH—See Mayr-Melnhof Karton AG; *Int'l*, pg. 4745
KEMIN INDUSTRIES, INC.; *U.S. Private*, pg. 2281
KEMIN RESOURCES PLC; *Int'l*, pg. 4122
KEMIPOL SP. Z O.O.—See Kemira Oyj; *Int'l*, pg. 4123
KEMIRA ARGENTINA S.A.—See Kemira Oyj; *Int'l*, pg. 4122
KEMIRA (ASIA) CO., LTD.—See Kemira Oyj; *Int'l*, pg. 4122

KEMIRA AUSTRALIA PTY. LTD.—See Kemira Oyj; *Int'l*, pg. 4122
KEMIRA CELL SP. Z.O.O—See Kemira Oyj; *Int'l*, pg. 4123
KEMIRA CHEMICALS AS—See Kemira Oyj; *Int'l*, pg. 4123
KEMIRA CHEMICALS BRASIL—See Kemira Oyj; *Int'l*, pg. 4123
KEMIRA CHEMICALS B.V.—See Kemira Oyj; *Int'l*, pg. 4123
KEMIRA CHEMICALS CANADA INC.—See Kemira Oyj; *Int'l*, pg. 4123
KEMIRA CHEMICALS GERMANY GMBH—See Kemira Oyj; *Int'l*, pg. 4123
KEMIRA CHEMICALS, INC.—See Kemira Oyj; *Int'l*, pg. 4123
KEMIRA CHEMICALS, INC. - ST. CATHARINES PLANT—See Kemira Oyj; *Int'l*, pg. 4123
KEMIRA CHEMICALS, INC. - VANCOUVER PAPER CHEMICALS PLANT—See Kemira Oyj; *Int'l*, pg. 4123
KEMIRA CHEMICALS INDIA PRIVATE LIMITED—See Kemira Oyj; *Int'l*, pg. 4123
KEMIRA CHEMICALS KOREA CORPORATION—See Kemira Oyj; *Int'l*, pg. 4123
KEMIRA CHEMICALS OY—See Kemira Oyj; *Int'l*, pg. 4123
KEMIRA CHEMICALS OY - VAASA PAPER CHEMICALS PLANT—See Kemira Oyj; *Int'l*, pg. 4123
KEMIRA CHEMICALS S.A./N.V.—See Kemira Oyj; *Int'l*, pg. 4123
KEMIRA CHEMICALS (SHANGHAI) CO. LTD.—See Kemira Oyj; *Int'l*, pg. 4123
KEMIRA CHEMICALS (UK) LTD - BRADFORD DRY POLYACRYLAMIDE MANUFACTURING PLANT—See Kemira Oyj; *Int'l*, pg. 4123
KEMIRA CHEMICALS (UK) LTD - ELLESMERE PORT WATER TREATMENT PLANT—See Kemira Oyj; *Int'l*, pg. 4123
KEMIRA CHEMICALS (UK) LTD.—See Kemira Oyj; *Int'l*, pg. 4123
KEMIRA CHEMICALS (YANZHOU) CO., LTD—See Kemira Oyj; *Int'l*, pg. 4123
KEMIRA CHEMIE GMBH—See Kemira Oyj; *Int'l*, pg. 4123
KEMIRA CHEMIE GMBH—See Kemira Oyj; *Int'l*, pg. 4123
KEMIRA CHILE COMERCIAL LIMITADA—See Kemira Oyj; *Int'l*, pg. 4124
KEMIRA CHIMIE S.A.—See Kemira Oyj; *Int'l*, pg. 4123
KEMIRA CHIMIE S.A.S.U. - SAUSHEIM DEFOAMING & DEINKING CHEMICALS PLANT—See Kemira Oyj; *Int'l*, pg. 4123
KEMIRA CHIMIE S.A.S.U.—See Kemira Oyj; *Int'l*, pg. 4123
KEMIRA FINANCE SOLUTIONS B.V.—See Kemira Oyj; *Int'l*, pg. 4124
KEMIRA FRANCE SAS—See Kemira Oyj; *Int'l*, pg. 4124
KEMIRA GDANSK SP. Z O.O.—See Kemira Oyj; *Int'l*, pg. 4124
KEMIRA GERMANY GMBH - RHEINBERG WATER TREATMENT CHEMICALS PLANT—See Kemira Oyj; *Int'l*, pg. 4124
KEMIRA GERMANY GMBH—See Kemira Oyj; *Int'l*, pg. 4124
KEMIRA GERMANY SALES GMBH—See Kemira Oyj; *Int'l*, pg. 4124
KEMIRA IBERICA S.A. - DOS HERMANAS WATER TREATMENT CHEMICALS PLANT—See Kemira Oyj; *Int'l*, pg. 4124
KEMIRA IBERICA SALES AND MARKETING S.L.—See Kemira Oyj; *Int'l*, pg. 4124
KEMIRA IBERICA S.A.—See Kemira Oyj; *Int'l*, pg. 4124
KEMIRA IBERICA S.A. - ZARAMILLO WATER TREATMENT CHEMICALS PLANT—See Kemira Oyj; *Int'l*, pg. 4124
KEMIRA INTERNATIONAL FINANCE B.V.—See Kemira Oyj; *Int'l*, pg. 4124
KEMIRA ITALY SPA—See Kemira Oyj; *Int'l*, pg. 4123
KEMIRA JAPAN CO., LTD.—See Kemira Oyj; *Int'l*, pg. 4124
KEMIRA KEMI AB—See Kemira Oyj; *Int'l*, pg. 4124
KEMIRA KOREA CORPORATION—See Kemira Oyj; *Int'l*, pg. 4124
KEMIRA KTM D.O.O.—See Kemira Oyj; *Int'l*, pg. 4124
KEMIRA NEDERLAND HOLDING B.V.—See Kemira Oyj; *Int'l*, pg. 4124
KEMIRA OYJ - HARJAVALTA WATER TREATMENT CHEMICALS PLANT—See Kemira Oyj; *Int'l*, pg. 4124
KEMIRA OYJ; *Int'l*, pg. 4122
KEMIRA PIGMENTS OY—See Kemira Oyj; *Int'l*, pg. 4124
KEMIRA POLAR A/S—See Kemira Oyj; *Int'l*, pg. 4124
KEMIRA SOUTH AFRICA (PTY) LTD.—See Kemira Oyj; *Int'l*, pg. 4124
KEMIRA-SWIECIE SP. Z.O.O—See Kemira Oyj; *Int'l*, pg. 4124
KEMIRA TAIWAN CORPORATION—See Kemira Oyj; *Int'l*, pg. 4124
KEMIRA TEESPORT LIMITED—See Kemira Oyj; *Int'l*, pg. 4124
KEMIRA (THAILAND) CO., LTD.—See Kemira Oyj; *Int'l*, pg. 4122
KEMIRA URUGUAY S.A.—See Kemira Oyj; *Int'l*, pg. 4124
KEMIRA WATER DANMARK A/S—See Kemira Oyj; *Int'l*, pg. 4124

KEMIRA OYJ CORPORATE AFFILIATIONS

KEMIRA WATER SOLUTIONS CANADA INC. - OTTAWA WATER TREATMENT CHEMICALS PLANT—See Kemira Oyj; *Int'l*, pg. 4124
KEMIRA WATER SOLUTIONS CANADA INC—See Kemira Oyj; *Int'l*, pg. 4124
KEMIRA WATER SOLUTIONS, INC. - BALTIMORE WATER TREATMENT CHEMICALS PLANT—See Kemira Oyj; *Int'l*, pg. 4123
KEMIRA WATER SOLUTIONS, INC. - EAST CHICAGO WATER TREATMENT CHEMICALS PLANT—See Kemira Oyj; *Int'l*, pg. 4123
KEMIRA WATER SOLUTIONS, INC. - FONTANA WATER TREATMENT CHEMICALS PLANT—See Kemira Oyj; *Int'l*, pg. 4123
KEMIRA WATER SOLUTIONS, INC. - LONGVIEW POLYMER PLANT—See Kemira Oyj; *Int'l*, pg. 4123
KEMIRA WATER SOLUTIONS, INC. - MOJAVE WATER TREATMENT CHEMICALS PLANT—See Kemira Oyj; *Int'l*, pg. 4123
KEMIRA WATER SOLUTIONS, INC. - POLYMER PLANT—See Kemira Oyj; *Int'l*, pg. 4123
KEMIRA WATER SOLUTIONS, INC. - SAINT LOUIS WATER TREATMENT CHEMICALS PLANT—See Kemira Oyj; *Int'l*, pg. 4123
KEMIRA WATER SOLUTIONS, INC. - SAVANNAH WATER TREATMENT CHEMICALS PLANT—See Kemira Oyj; *Int'l*, pg. 4123
KEMIRA WATER SOLUTIONS, INC.—See Kemira Oyj; *Int'l*, pg. 4123
KEMIS BH D.O.O.—See Hisense Co., Ltd.; *Int'l*, pg. 3407
KEMIS-TERMOCLEAN D.O.O.—See Hisense Co., Ltd.; *Int'l*, pg. 3407
KEM KREST CORPORATION; *U.S. Private*, pg. 2281
KEMLON PRODUCTS & DEVELOPMENT CO.; *U.S. Private*, pg. 2281
KEMMONS WILSON, INC.; *U.S. Private*, pg. 2281
KEMMONS WILSON INSURANCE GROUP, LLC—See Virtus LLC; *U.S. Private*, pg. 4389
KEMNA MOTOR CO.; *U.S. Private*, pg. 2281
KEM ONE S.A.S.—See OpenGate Capital Management, LLC; *U.S. Private*, pg. 3030
KEMPAIR KLIMAATBEHEERSING B.V.—See CENTROTEC SE; *Int'l*, pg. 1414
KEMPARTNER AB—See Lifeclean International AB; *Int'l*, pg. 4494
KEMP & COMPANY LIMITED; *Int'l*, pg. 4124
KEMP & DENNING LIMITED; *Int'l*, pg. 4124
KEMPE ENGINEERING PTY. LTD.; *Int'l*, pg. 4125
KEMPEN CAPITAL MANAGEMENT BV—See Van Lanschot Kempen NV; *Int'l*, pg. 8126
KEMPEN FINANCE BV—See Van Lanschot Kempen NV; *Int'l*, pg. 8126
KEMPER AIP METALS LLC—See Gebr. Kemper GmbH & Co. KG; *Int'l*, pg. 2906
KEMPER ASIA PACIFIC TRADING LLP—See Gebr. Kemper GmbH & Co. KG; *Int'l*, pg. 2906
KEMPER B.V.—See KEMPER GmbH; *Int'l*, pg. 4125
KEMPER CAPITAL MANAGEMENT LLC—See Kemper CPA Group LLP; *U.S. Private*, pg. 2282
KEMPERCONNECT; *U.S. Private*, pg. 2282
KEMPER CORPORATION; *U.S. Public*, pg. 1220
KEMPER COST MANAGEMENT, INC.—See Commercial Warranty Solutions, LLC; *U.S. Private*, pg. 985
KEMPER CPA GROUP LLP; *U.S. Private*, pg. 2282
KEMPER EQUIPMENT INC.; *U.S. Private*, pg. 2282
KEMPER GMBH; *Int'l*, pg. 4125
KEMPER HOME SERVICE COMPANIES—See Kemper Corporation; *U.S. Public*, pg. 1220
KEMPER IBERICA, S.L.—See KEMPER GmbH; *Int'l*, pg. 4125
KEMPER INDEPENDENCE INSURANCE COMPANY—See Kemper Corporation; *U.S. Public*, pg. 1221
KEMPER INDIA PVT. LTD.—See KEMPER GmbH; *Int'l*, pg. 4125
KEMPER INVESTORS LIFE INSURANCE COMPANY—See Zurich Insurance Group Limited; *Int'l*, pg. 8699
KEMPERLESNIK; *U.S. Private*, pg. 2282
KEMPER SARL—See KEMPER GmbH; *Int'l*, pg. 4125
KEMPER SPECIALTY—See Kemper Corporation; *U.S. Public*, pg. 1221
KEMPER SPOL. S R.O.—See KEMPER GmbH; *Int'l*, pg. 4125
KEMPER SPORTS, INC.; *U.S. Private*, pg. 2282
KEMPER TECHNOLOGY CONSULTING—See Kemper CPA Group LLP; *U.S. Private*, pg. 2282
KEMPER TRADING SHANGHAI CO. LTD.—See Gebr. Kemper GmbH & Co. KG; *Int'l*, pg. 2906
KEMPER (U.K.) LTD.—See KEMPER GmbH; *Int'l*, pg. 4125
KEMPER VALVE & FITTINGS CORP.—See Caterpillar, Inc.; *U.S. Public*, pg. 452
KEMPES EL AB—See Instalco AB; *Int'l*, pg. 3722
KEMPKEY INSURANCE SERVICES, INC.—See Aon plc; *Int'l*, pg. 496
KEMP & LAURITZEN A/S; *Int'l*, pg. 4125
KEMP MANUFACTURING COMPANY; *U.S. Private*, pg. 2282

KEMPOWER OYJ; *Int'l*, pg. 4125
KEMP PROTEINS, LLC—See Six.02 Bioservices, LLC; *U.S. Private*, pg. 3677
KEMP & RUGE LAW GROUP; *U.S. Private*, pg. 2282
KEMPSEY CENTRAL PTY. LTD.—See Gowing Brothers Limited; *Int'l*, pg. 3044
KEMPS LLC—See Dairy Farmers of America, Inc.; *U.S. Private*, pg. 1146
KEMPSMITH MACHINE COMPANY; *U.S. Private*, pg. 2282
KEMP TECHNOLOGIES INC.—See Progress Software Corporation; *U.S. Public*, pg. 1725
KEMP TECHNOLOGIES INDIA PRIVATE LIMITED—See Progress Software Corporation; *U.S. Public*, pg. 1725
KEMP TECHNOLOGIES LIMITED—See Progress Software Corporation; *U.S. Public*, pg. 1725
KEMP TECHNOLOGIES PTE. LTD.—See Progress Software Corporation; *U.S. Public*, pg. 1725
KEMPTHORN MOTORS INC.; *U.S. Private*, pg. 2282
KEMPTON CHEVROLET BUICK LTD; *U.S. Private*, pg. 2282
KEMROCK INDUSTRIES & EXPORTS LTD.; *Int'l*, pg. 4125
KEMROCK INTERNATIONAL FZE—See Kemrock Industries & Exports Ltd.; *Int'l*, pg. 4125
KEMRON ENVIRONMENTAL SERVICES, INC.; *U.S. Private*, pg. 2282
THE KEMTAH GROUP INC.—See AE Industrial Partners, LP; *U.S. Private*, pg. 111
KEMWATER CRISTAL S.A.—See Kemira Oyj; *Int'l*, pg. 4124
KEMWATER PHIL. CORP.—See Kemira Oyj; *Int'l*, pg. 4124
KEMWATER PROCHEMIE S.R.O. - HULICE WATER TREATMENT CHEMICALS PLANT—See Kemira Oyj; *Int'l*, pg. 4124
KEMWATER PROCHEMIE S.R.O. - KOLIN WATER TREATMENT CHEMICALS PLANT—See Kemira Oyj; *Int'l*, pg. 4124
KEMWATER PROCHEMIE S.R.O.—See Kemira Oyj; *Int'l*, pg. 4124
KEMWELL BIOPHARMA PVT. LTD.; *Int'l*, pg. 4125
KENADYR METALS CORP.; *Int'l*, pg. 4125
KENAFRIC BISCUITS LIMITED—See The Bombay Burmah Trading Corporation Limited; *Int'l*, pg. 7627
KENAIDAN GROUP LTD.—See Obayashi Corporation; *Int'l*, pg. 5508
KENAI DRILLING LIMITED; *U.S. Private*, pg. 2283
KENALL MANUFACTURING CO.—See Legrand S.A.; *Int'l*, pg. 4445
KENALL MANUFACTURING CO.—See Legrand S.A.; *Int'l*, pg. 4444
THE KENAN ADVANTAGE GROUP, INC.—See Ontario Municipal Employees Retirement System; *Int'l*, pg. 5584
KENANGA CAPITAL ISLAMIC SDN BHD—See Bay Group Holdings Sdn Bhd; *Int'l*, pg. 901
KENANGA CAPITAL ISLAMIC SDN BHD—See Kenanga Investment Bank Berhad; *Int'l*, pg. 4125
KENANGA CAPITAL SDN BHD—See Kenanga Investment Bank Berhad; *Int'l*, pg. 4125
KENANGA FUNDS BERHAD—See Kenanga Investment Bank Berhad; *Int'l*, pg. 4125
KENANGA FUTURES SDN BHD—See Kenanga Investment Bank Berhad; *Int'l*, pg. 4125
KENANGA INVESTMENT BANK BERHAD; *Int'l*, pg. 4125
KENANGA INVESTORS BERHAD—See Kenanga Investment Bank Berhad; *Int'l*, pg. 4125
KENANGA ISLAMIC INVESTORS BERHAD—See Kenanga Investment Bank Berhad; *Int'l*, pg. 4125
KENAN TRANSPORT COMPANY—See Ontario Municipal Employees Retirement System; *Int'l*, pg. 5585
KEN-API SUPPLY INC.; *U.S. Private*, pg. 2283
KENBAR SERVICES INC.; *U.S. Private*, pg. 2283
KEN BETTRIDGE DISTRIBUTING INC.—See Parkland Corporation; *Int'l*, pg. 5743
THE KEN BLANCHARD COMPANIES; *U.S. Private*, pg. 4064
KEN BRATNEY COMPANY—See K.B.C. Group Inc.; *U.S. Private*, pg. 2251
KENCANA AGRI LIMITED; *Int'l*, pg. 4125
KENCANA HL SDN. BHD.—See Sapura Energy Berhad; *Int'l*, pg. 6574
KENCANA MARINE SDN. BHD.—See Sapura Energy Berhad; *Int'l*, pg. 6574
KENCANA PETROLEUM VENTURES SDN. BHD.—See Sapura Energy Berhad; *Int'l*, pg. 6574
KENCANA TORSCO SDN. BHD.—See Sapura Energy Berhad; *Int'l*, pg. 6574
KENCI S.L.—See Kennametal Inc.; *U.S. Public*, pg. 1222
KEN CLARK INTERNATIONAL; *U.S. Private*, pg. 2282
KENCOA AEROSPACE CORPORATION; *Int'l*, pg. 4125
KENCO GROUP INC.; *U.S. Private*, pg. 2283
KENCOIL INC.; *U.S. Private*, pg. 2283
KENCO INC.; *U.S. Private*, pg. 2283
KENCO LOGISTIC SERVICES INC.—See Kenco Group Inc.; *U.S. Private*, pg. 2283
KENCOM HOUSE LTD.—See KCB Group PLC; *Int'l*, pg. 4108

KEN COOK CO.; *U.S. Private*, pg. 2282
KENDALE INDUSTRIES, INC.; *U.S. Private*, pg. 2283
KENDAL KING GROUP; *U.S. Private*, pg. 2283
KENDALL AUTOMOTIVE GROUP INC.; *U.S. Private*, pg. 2283
KENDALL COUNTY RECORD, INC.—See The B. F. Shaw Printing Company; *U.S. Private*, pg. 3990
KENDALL CROSS HOLDINGS LIMITED—See Galliford Try Holdings plc; *Int'l*, pg. 2874
KENDALL ELECTRIC INC.—See The Kendall Group, Inc.; *U.S. Private*, pg. 4064
KENDALL ELECTRIC—See The Kendall Group, Inc.; *U.S. Private*, pg. 4064
THE KENDALL GROUP, INC.; *U.S. Private*, pg. 4064
KENDALL H LLC—See Kendall Automotive Group Inc.; *U.S. Private*, pg. 2283
KENDALL/HUNT PUBLISHING COMPANY INC.; *U.S. Private*, pg. 2283
KENDALL IMPORTS LLC; *U.S. Private*, pg. 2283
KENDALL-JACKSON—See Jackson Family Wines, Inc.; *U.S. Private*, pg. 2176
KENDALL-JACKSON WINE ESTATES, LTD.—See Jackson Family Wines, Inc.; *U.S. Private*, pg. 2176
KENDALL L LLC—See Kendall Automotive Group Inc.; *U.S. Private*, pg. 2283
KENDALL MOULDING & FRAMES, INC.; *U.S. Private*, pg. 2283
KENDALL PACKAGING CORPORATION - JEFFERSON—See Kendall Packaging Corporation; *U.S. Private*, pg. 2283
KENDALL PACKAGING CORPORATION - PITTSBURG FACILITY—See Kendall Packaging Corporation; *U.S. Private*, pg. 2283
KENDALL PACKAGING CORPORATION; *U.S. Private*, pg. 2283
KENDALL REGIONAL MEDICAL CENTER, LLC—See HCA Healthcare, Inc.; *U.S. Public*, pg. 1000
KENDALL REGIONAL URGENT CARE, LLC—See HCA Healthcare, Inc.; *U.S. Public*, pg. 1000
KENDALL, S.A.—See Medtronic plc; *U.S. Public*, pg. 4787
KENDALL'S BRASSERIE & BAR—See Delaware North Companies, Inc.; *U.S. Private*, pg. 1195
KENDALLVILLE FERTILIZER CO., INC.—See Sanimax Industries Inc.; *Int'l*, pg. 6539
KENDAL VETS4PETS LIMITED—See Pets at Home Group Plc; *Int'l*, pg. 5834
KENDA RUBBER CO., LTD.—See Kenda Rubber Industrial Co., Ltd.; *Int'l*, pg. 4126
KENDA RUBBER INDUSTRIAL CO. EUROPE GMBH—See Kenda Rubber Industrial Co., Ltd.; *Int'l*, pg. 4126
KENDA RUBBER INDUSTRIAL CO., LTD.; *Int'l*, pg. 4126
KENDA RUBBER (VIETNAM 2) CO., LTD.—See Kenda Rubber Industrial Co., Ltd.; *Int'l*, pg. 4126
KENDA RUBBER (VIETNAM) CO., LTD.—See Kenda Rubber Industrial Co., Ltd.; *Int'l*, pg. 4126
KENDA TIRE CO., LTD.—See Kenda Rubber Industrial Co., Ltd.; *Int'l*, pg. 4126
KENDA TYRE INC. CO., LTD.—See Kenda Rubber Industrial Co., Ltd.; *Int'l*, pg. 4126
KENDELL S.R.L.—See BASF SE; *Int'l*, pg. 884
KENDEN INDUSTRY CO., LTD.—See Tachibana Eletech Co., Ltd.; *Int'l*, pg. 7403
KEN DEPOT CORPORATION—See Kohnan Shoji Co., Ltd.; *Int'l*, pg. 4229
KEN DIXON AUTOMOTIVE GROUP; *U.S. Private*, pg. 2282
KENDON CORPORATION—See Cox Enterprises, Inc.; *U.S. Private*, pg. 1075
KENDO TRADING PTE. LTD.—See Emerging Glory Sdn Bhd; *Int'l*, pg. 2379
KENDRA SAINT PIERRE LIMITED—See ENL Limited; *Int'l*, pg. 2441
KENDRA SCOTT DESIGN, INC.; *U.S. Private*, pg. 2283
KENDRICK OIL CO. INC.; *U.S. Private*, pg. 2283
KENDRICK RESOURCES PLC; *Int'l*, pg. 4126
KENDRION AUTOMOTIVE (SIBIU) S.R.L.—See Kendrion N.V.; *Int'l*, pg. 4126
KENDRION BINDER MAGNETE S.R.L—See Kendrion N.V.; *Int'l*, pg. 4126
KENDRION BINDER MAGNETE VERTRIEBSGESELLSCHAFT MBH—See Kendrion N.V.; *Int'l*, pg. 4126
KENDRION BINDER MAGNETY S.R.O—See Kendrion N.V.; *Int'l*, pg. 4126
KENDRION (CHINA) CO., LTD.—See Kendrion N.V.; *Int'l*, pg. 4126
KENDRION (DONAUESCHINGEN/ENGELSWIES) GMBH—See Kendrion N.V.; *Int'l*, pg. 4126
KENDRION (EIBISWALD) GMBH—See Kendrion N.V.; *Int'l*, pg. 4126
KENDRION INDUSTRIAL (SIBIU) S.R.L—See Kendrion N.V.; *Int'l*, pg. 4126
KENDRION INTORQ GMBH—See Kendrion N.V.; *Int'l*, pg. 4126
KENDRION KUHNKE AUTOMATION GMBH—See Kendrion N.V.; *Int'l*, pg. 4126
KENDRION LINNIG GMBH—See Kendrion N.V.; *Int'l*, pg. 4126

COMPANY NAME INDEX

KENDRION (LINZ) GMBH—See Kendrion N.V.; *Int'l*, pg. 4126
KENDRION MAGNETA GMBH—See Kendrion N.V.; *Int'l*, pg. 4126
KENDRION MAGNETTECHNIK GMBH—See Kendrion N.V.; *Int'l*, pg. 4126
KENDRION (MARKDORF) GMBH—See Kendrion N.V.; *Int'l*, pg. 4126
KENDRION MISHAWAKA LLC—See Kendrion N.V.; *Int'l*, pg. 4126
KENDRION N.V.; *Int'l*, pg. 4126
KENDRION (PROSTEJOV) S.R.O.—See Kendrion N.V.; *Int'l*, pg. 4126
KENDRION (SHELBY) INC—See Kendrion N.V.; *Int'l*, pg. 4126
KENDRION (SHELBY) INC.—See Kendrion N.V.; *Int'l*, pg. 4126
KENDRION (SUZHOU) CO., LTD.—See Kendrion N.V.; *Int'l*, pg. 4126
KENDRION (SUZHOU) CO., LTD.—See Kendrion N.V.; *Int'l*, pg. 4126
KENDRION UK LTD.—See Kendrion N.V.; *Int'l*, pg. 4126
KENDRION (VILLINGEN) GMBH—See Kendrion N.V.; *Int'l*, pg. 4126
KENDRION (VILLINGEN) GMBH—See Kendrion N.V.; *Int'l*, pg. 4126
KENEDIX ADVISORS CO., LTD—See Sumitomo Corporation; *Int'l*, pg. 7275
KENEDIX ADVISORS CO., LTD—See Sumitomo Mitsui Financial Group, Inc.; *Int'l*, pg. 7295
KENEDIX, INC.—See Sumitomo Corporation; *Int'l*, pg. 7275
KENEDIX, INC.—See Sumitomo Mitsui Financial Group, Inc.; *Int'l*, pg. 7295
KENEDIX RESIDENTIAL NEXT INVESTMENT CORPORATION; *Int'l*, pg. 4127
KENEDIX RETAIL REIT CORPORATION; *Int'l*, pg. 4127
KENERGY CORP.; *U.S. Private*, pg. 2283
KENEXA CORPORATION—See International Business Machines Corporation; *U.S. Public*, pg. 1148
KENEXA LIMITED—See International Business Machines Corporation; *U.S. Public*, pg. 1148
KENEXA—See International Business Machines Corporation; *U.S. Public*, pg. 1148
KENEXA TECHNOLOGIES PRIVATE LIMITED—See International Business Machines Corporation; *U.S. Public*, pg. 1148
KENEX HOLDINGS LLC; *U.S. Private*, pg. 2284
KENFARMA, S.A.—See Pfizer Inc.; *U.S. Public*, pg. 1680
KENFOOD S.A.—See Loulis Food Ingredients S.A.; *Int'l*, pg. 4563
KEN FOWLER MOTORS INC; *U.S. Private*, pg. 2282
KEN GARFF NISSAN OF SALT LAKE—See Garff Enterprises, Inc.; *U.S. Private*, pg. 1644
KEN GARFF ST. GEORGE FORD LINCOLN—See Garff Enterprises, Inc.; *U.S. Private*, pg. 1644
KENGOO GROUP CO., LTD.; *Int'l*, pg. 4127
KEN GRODY FORD; *U.S. Private*, pg. 2282
KEN HOLDING CO., LTD.; *Int'l*, pg. 4125
KEN HOLDINGS BERHAD; *Int'l*, pg. 4125
KENILWORTH STEEL CO. INC.; *U.S. Private*, pg. 2284
KENILWORTH SYSTEMS CORP.; *U.S. Public*, pg. 1221
KENJO INC.; *U.S. Private*, pg. 2284
THE KENJYA GROUP, INC.; *U.S. Private*, pg. 4065
KEN KEN CO., LTD.—See Shinnihon Corporation; *Int'l*, pg. 6847
KENKI ENGINEERING CHIBA CO., LTD.—See Sumitomo Heavy Industries, Ltd.; *Int'l*, pg. 7286
KEN KOJAIAN HOMES, INC.; *U.S. Private*, pg. 2282
KENKO MAYONNAISE CO., LTD.; *Int'l*, pg. 4127
KENKOSYA CO., LTD.—See Kanematsu Corporation; *Int'l*, pg. 4069
KENKO UTILITY SUPPLY INC.; *U.S. Private*, pg. 2284
KENLAKE FOODS—See The Kroger Co.; *U.S. Public*, pg. 2108
KENLEE PRECISION CORPORATION; *U.S. Private*, pg. 2284
KENLOC, INC.; *U.S. Private*, pg. 2284
KEN LUNEACK CONSTRUCTION CO.; *U.S. Private*, pg. 2282
KENLY PRECISION INDUSTRIAL CO., LTD.; *Int'l*, pg. 4127
KEN-MAC METALS, INC.—See ThyssenKrupp AG; *Int'l*, pg. 7729
KENMAR CORPORATION; *U.S. Private*, pg. 2284
KENMARE RESOURCES PLC; *Int'l*, pg. 4127
KENMAR GLOBAL INVESTMENT MANAGEMENT LLC—See Ambroisie Capital Holding S.A.S.; *Int'l*, pg. 415
KENMAR GROUP INC.—See Ambroisie Capital Holding S.A.S.; *Int'l*, pg. 415
KENMAR SECURITIES INC—See Ambroisie Capital Holding S.A.S.; *Int'l*, pg. 415
KENMART VENDING SERVICES LIMITED—See Nayax Ltd.; *Int'l*, pg. 5178
KENMORE AIR HARBOR INC.; *U.S. Private*, pg. 2284
KENMORE CONSTRUCTION CO., INC.; *U.S. Private*, pg. 2284
KENMOR ELECTRIC CO. LP; *U.S. Private*, pg. 2284

KENMORE MERCY HOSPITAL—See Catholic Health System, Inc.; *U.S. Private*, pg. 791
KENNA BUILDING SUPPLIES LIMITED—See Fletcher Building Limited; *Int'l*, pg. 2700
KENNA COMMUNICATIONS LP—See Stagwell, Inc.; *U.S. Public*, pg. 1927
KENNAMETAL ADVANCED MATERIALS SOLUTIONS GROUP—See Kennametal Inc.; *U.S. Public*, pg. 1221
KENNAMETAL AMSG GMBH—See Kennametal Inc.; *U.S. Public*, pg. 1222
KENNAMETAL ARGENTINA S.A.—See Kennametal Inc.; *U.S. Public*, pg. 1221
KENNAMETAL AUSTRALIA PTY. LTD.—See Kennametal Inc.; *U.S. Public*, pg. 1221
KENNAMETAL BELGIUM S.P.R.L.—See Kennametal Inc.; *U.S. Public*, pg. 1222
KENNAMETAL CHILE LTDA.—See Kennametal Inc.; *U.S. Public*, pg. 1221
KENNAMETAL DE MEXICO, S.A. DE C.V.—See Kennametal Inc.; *U.S. Public*, pg. 1223
KENNAMETAL DEUTSCHLAND GMBH—See Kennametal Inc.; *U.S. Public*, pg. 1222
KENNAMETAL DO BRASIL LTDA.—See Kennametal Inc.; *U.S. Public*, pg. 1223
KENNAMETAL ENERGY, MINING & CONSTRUCTION SOLUTIONS—See Kennametal Inc.; *U.S. Public*, pg. 1221
KENNAMETAL EUROPE HOLDING GMBH—See Kennametal Inc.; *U.S. Public*, pg. 1222
KENNAMETAL EXTRUDE HONE LIMITED—See Kennametal Inc.; *U.S. Public*, pg. 1221
KENNAMETAL EXTRUDE HONE LTD.—See Kennametal Inc.; *U.S. Public*, pg. 1221
KENNAMETAL GMBH—See Kennametal Inc.; *U.S. Public*, pg. 1222
KENNAMETAL HARDPOINT (TAIWAN) INC.—See Kennametal Inc.; *U.S. Public*, pg. 1222
KENNAMETAL HOLDINGS EUROPE INC.—See Kennametal Inc.; *U.S. Public*, pg. 1222
KENNAMETAL HOLDINGS, LLC LUXEMBOURG S.C.S.—See Kennametal Inc.; *U.S. Public*, pg. 1222
KENNAMETAL HUNGARIA KFT.—See Kennametal Inc.; *U.S. Public*, pg. 1222
KENNAMETAL, INC. - INTERNATIONAL SPECIALTY ALLOYS—See AMG Critical Materials N.V.; *Int'l*, pg. 426
KENNAMETAL INC.; *U.S. Public*, pg. 1221
KENNAMETAL INDIA LTD.—See Kennametal Inc.; *U.S. Public*, pg. 1222
KENNAMETAL INFRASTRUCTURE GMBH—See Kennametal Inc.; *U.S. Public*, pg. 1222
KENNAMETAL IPG—See Kennametal Inc.; *U.S. Public*, pg. 1222
KENNAMETAL ITALIA PRODUZIONE S.R.L.—See Kennametal Inc.; *U.S. Public*, pg. 1222
KENNAMETAL ITALIA S.P.A.—See Kennametal Inc.; *U.S. Public*, pg. 1222
KENNAMETAL JAPAN LTD.—See Kennametal Inc.; *U.S. Public*, pg. 1222
KENNAMETAL KESICI TAKIMLAR SANAYI VE TICARET ANONIM SIRKETI—See Kennametal Inc.; *U.S. Public*, pg. 1222
KENNAMETAL KOREA LTD.—See Kennametal Inc.; *U.S. Public*, pg. 1222
KENNAMETAL LOGISTICS GMBH—See Kennametal Inc.; *U.S. Public*, pg. 1222
KENNAMETAL LOGISTICS UK LTD.—See Kennametal Inc.; *U.S. Public*, pg. 1222
KENNAMETAL METALWORKING SOLUTIONS & SERVICES GROUP—See Kennametal Inc.; *U.S. Public*, pg. 1222
KENNAMETAL NEDERLAND B.V.—See Kennametal Inc.; *U.S. Public*, pg. 1222
KENNAMETAL POLSKA SP. Z.O.O.—See Kennametal Inc.; *U.S. Public*, pg. 1222
KENNAMETAL PRODUKTIONS GMBH & CO. KG—See Kennametal Inc.; *U.S. Public*, pg. 1222
KENNAMETAL (SHANGHAI) CO., LTD.—See Kennametal Inc.; *U.S. Public*, pg. 1221
KENNAMETAL SHARED SERVICES PRIVATE LIMITED—See Kennametal Inc.; *U.S. Public*, pg. 1222
KENNAMETAL (SINGAPORE) PTE. LTD.—See Kennametal Inc.; *U.S. Public*, pg. 1221
KENNAMETAL SINTEC KERAMIK GMBH—See Kennametal Inc.; *U.S. Public*, pg. 1222
KENNAMETAL SOUTH AFRICA (PTY.) LTD.—See Kennametal Inc.; *U.S. Public*, pg. 1222
KENNAMETAL SP. Z O.O.—See Kennametal Inc.; *U.S. Public*, pg. 1222
KENNAMETAL STELLITE COATINGS S.R.L.—See Kennametal Inc.; *U.S. Public*, pg. 1222
KENNAMETAL STELLITE, L.P.—See Kennametal Inc.; *U.S. Public*, pg. 1223
KENNAMETAL STELLITE S.R.L.—See Kennametal Inc.; *U.S. Public*, pg. 1222
KENNAMETAL STELLRAM LIMITED—See Kennametal Inc.; *U.S. Public*, pg. 1223
KENNAMETAL (THAILAND) CO., LTD.—See Kennametal Inc.; *U.S. Public*, pg. 1221

KENNESAW MOTOR SALES, INC.

KENNAMETAL UK LIMITED—See Kennametal Inc.; *U.S. Public*, pg. 1222
KENNAMETAL WIDIA PRODUKTIONS GMBH & CO. KG—See Kennametal Inc.; *U.S. Public*, pg. 1222
KENNAMETAL WIDIA REAL ESTATE GMBH & CO. KG—See Kennametal Inc.; *U.S. Public*, pg. 1222
KENNAMETAL XUZHOU CO., LTD.—See Kennametal Inc.; *U.S. Public*, pg. 1223
THE KENNARDS HIRE GROUP; *Int'l*, pg. 7662
KENNA SECURITY, INC.—See Cisco Systems, Inc.; *U.S. Public*, pg. 499
KENN BOREK AIR LTD.—See Borek Construction, Ltd.; *Int'l*, pg. 1114
KENNEBEC JOURNAL—See MaineToday Media, Inc.; *U.S. Private*, pg. 2553
KENNEBEC SAVINGS BANK, MHC; *U.S. Private*, pg. 2284
KENNEBEC SAVINGS BANK—See Kennebec Savings Bank, MHC; *U.S. Private*, pg. 2284
KENNEBUNK SAVINGS BANK; *U.S. Private*, pg. 2284
KENNECOTT UTAH COPPER LLC—See Rio Tinto plc; *Int'l*, pg. 6346
KENNEDALE PRIMARY CARE PLLC—See HCA Healthcare, Inc.; *U.S. Public*, pg. 1000
KENNEDE ELECTRONICS MANUFACTURING CO., LTD.; *Int'l*, pg. 4127
KENNEDY ADVERTISING—See Kennedy Automotive Group Inc.; *U.S. Private*, pg. 2284
KENNEDY ASSOCIATES/ARCHITECTS, INC.; *U.S. Private*, pg. 2284
KENNEDY AUTOMOTIVE GROUP INC; *U.S. Private*, pg. 2284
KENNEDY CAPITAL MANAGEMENT, INC.; *U.S. Private*, pg. 2284
KENNEDY & COE WEALTH MANAGEMENT, LLC—See KCoe Isom, LLP; *U.S. Private*, pg. 2270
KENNEDY CONTRACTORS, INC.; *U.S. Private*, pg. 2284
KENNEDY CULVERT & SUPPLY COMPANY—See Ferguson plc; *Int'l*, pg. 2638
KENNEDY-DONOVAN CENTER, INC.; *U.S. Private*, pg. 2285
KENNEDY ENGINE CO., INC.; *U.S. Private*, pg. 2284
KENNEDY ENGINEERING & ASSOCIATES GROUP, LLC—See Volkert, Inc.; *U.S. Private*, pg. 4410
KENNEDY FORD SALES LIMITED; *Int'l*, pg. 4127
KENNEDY GROUP INC; *U.S. Private*, pg. 2285
THE KENNEDY GROUP LIMITED—See W.W. Grainger, Inc.; *U.S. Public*, pg. 2320
KENNEDY HEALTH SYSTEM; *U.S. Private*, pg. 2285
KENNEDY INK CO, INC; *U.S. Private*, pg. 2285
KENNEDY/JENKS CONSULTANTS INC.; *U.S. Private*, pg. 2285
KENNEDY LEWIS INVESTMENT MANAGEMENT LLC; *U.S. Private*, pg. 2285
KENNEDY MANUFACTURING COMPANY; *U.S. Private*, pg. 2285
KENNEDY MEMORIAL GARDENS, INC.—See Service Corporation International; *U.S. Public*, pg. 1869
KENNEDY RICE DRYERS LLC; *U.S. Private*, pg. 2285
KENNEDYS CMK LLP—See Kennedys Law LLP; *Int'l*, pg. 4127
KENNEDYS LAW LLP; *Int'l*, pg. 4127
KENNEDY TANK & MANUFACTURING COMPANY, INC.; *U.S. Private*, pg. 2285
KENNEDY TRANSPORTATION; *U.S. Private*, pg. 2285
KENNEDY TRANSPORTATION—See Kennedy Transportation; *U.S. Private*, pg. 2285
KENNEDY VALVE—See McWane, Inc.; *U.S. Private*, pg. 2645
KENNEDY WILSON AUCTION GROUP INC.—See Kennedy-Wilson Holdings, Inc.; *U.S. Public*, pg. 1223
KENNEDY-WILSON EUROPE LIMITED—See Kennedy-Wilson Holdings, Inc.; *U.S. Public*, pg. 1223
KENNEDY-WILSON HOLDINGS, INC.; *U.S. Public*, pg. 1223
KENNEDY-WILSON, INC.—See Kennedy-Wilson Holdings, Inc.; *U.S. Public*, pg. 1223
KENNEDY-WILSON INTERNATIONAL—See Kennedy-Wilson Holdings, Inc.; *U.S. Public*, pg. 1223
KENNEDY WILSON IRELAND LIMITED—See Kennedy-Wilson Holdings, Inc.; *U.S. Public*, pg. 1223
KENNEDY WILSON PENNSYLVANIA MANAGEMENT, INC.—See Kennedy-Wilson Holdings, Inc.; *U.S. Public*, pg. 1223
KENNEDY-WILSON PROPERTIES, LTD.; *U.S. Private*, pg. 2285
KENNEDY WILSON UK LIMITED—See Kennedy-Wilson Holdings, Inc.; *U.S. Public*, pg. 1223
KENNEDY WIRE ROPE & SLING CO.; *U.S. Private*, pg. 2285
KEN NELSON AUTO PLAZA INC.; *U.S. Private*, pg. 2282
KENNEL VACCINE VET SUPPLY CO.; *U.S. Private*, pg. 2285
KENNER & COMPANY, INC.; *U.S. Private*, pg. 2285
KENNERLEY-SPRATLING INC.; *U.S. Private*, pg. 2286
KENNESAW MOTOR SALES, INC.; *U.S. Private*, pg. 2286
KENNETH COLE PRODUCTIONS, INC.—See KCP Holdco, Inc.; *U.S. Private*, pg. 2270

KENNESAW MOTOR SALES, INC.   CORPORATE AFFILIATIONS

KENNETH CROSBY, LLC—See DXP Enterprises, Inc.; *U.S. Public*, pg. 697
KENNETH FOX SUPPLY CO.; *U.S. Private*, pg. 2286
KENNETH GORDON/IAG, INC.—See Individualized Apparel Group; *U.S. Private*, pg. 2064
KENNETH KO DESIGN CO., LTD.—See Shenzhen Bauing Construction Group Co., Ltd.; *Int'l*, pg. 6805
KENNETH MEYER CO INC.—See Dessin/Fournir, Inc.; *U.S. Private*, pg. 1215
KENNETH M. SEATON ENTERPRISES—See Family Inns of America, Inc.; *U.S. Private*, pg. 1470
KENNET PARTNERS LLC—See Kennet Partners Ltd; *Int'l*, pg. 4127
KENNET PARTNERS LTD; *Int'l*, pg. 4127
KENNETT HMA, INC.—See Community Health Systems, Inc.; *U.S. Public*, pg. 554
KENNEWICK INDUSTRIAL & ELECTRICAL SUPPLY INC.; *U.S. Private*, pg. 2286
KENNEY MACHINERY CORPORATION; *U.S. Private*, pg. 2286
KENNEY MANUFACTURING COMPANY; *U.S. Private*, pg. 2286
KENNICOTT BROS CO. INC.; *U.S. Private*, pg. 2286
KENNIE'S MARKETS INC.; *U.S. Private*, pg. 2286
KENNINGTON LTD., INC.; *U.S. Private*, pg. 2286
KENNY & COMPANY—See Kenny Pipe & Supply, Inc.; *U.S. Private*, pg. 2286
KENNY CONSTRUCTION COMPANY INC.—See Kenny Industries Inc.; *U.S. Private*, pg. 2286
KENNY ELECTRIC SERVICE INC.; *U.S. Private*, pg. 2286
KENNY INDUSTRIES INC.; *U.S. Private*, pg. 2286
KENNY KENT CHEVROLET CO. INC.; *U.S. Private*, pg. 2286
KENNY PIPE & SUPPLY, INC.; *U.S. Private*, pg. 2286
KENNY ROSS BUICK-GMC, INC.; *U.S. Private*, pg. 2286
KENNY'S CANDY COMPANY INC.—See KLN Enterprises Inc.; *U.S. Private*, pg. 2320
KENNY'S TILE & FLOORING, INC.; *U.S. Private*, pg. 2287
KENNY THOMAS ENTERPRISES INC.; *U.S. Private*, pg. 2286
KENNYWOOD ENTERTAINMENT, INC.—See Newgate Private Equity LLP; *Int'l*, pg. 5234
KENO AUCTIONS LLC; *U.S. Private*, pg. 2287
KENOGARD S.A.—See Sumitomo Chemical Company, Limited; *Int'l*, pg. 7266
KENOLKOBIL LIMITED—See Rubis SCA; *Int'l*, pg. 6423
KENONGWO GROUP US, INC.; *Int'l*, pg. 4127
KENON HOLDINGS LTD.; *Int'l*, pg. 4127
KENORLAND MINERALS LTD.; *Int'l*, pg. 4128
KENOSHA BEEF INTERNATIONAL LTD. INC.; *U.S. Private*, pg. 2287
KENOSHA COUNTY HUMANE SOCIETY—See Wisconsin Humane Society; *U.S. Private*, pg. 4548
KENOSHA SENIOR LIVING, INC.—See The Ensign Group, Inc.; *U.S. Public*, pg. 2070
KENOSIA CONSTRUCTION INC.; *U.S. Private*, pg. 2287
KENPAL FARM PRODUCTS INC.; *Int'l*, pg. 4128
KENRA PROFESSIONAL, LLC—See Henkel AG & Co. KGaA; *Int'l*, pg. 3353
KEN RIMBA SDN. BHD.—See Ken Holdings Berhad; *Int'l*, pg. 4125
KENROC BUILDING MATERIALS CO. LTD.; *Int'l*, pg. 4128
KENROC BUILDING MATERIALS CO. LTD.—See Kenroc Building Materials Co. Ltd.; *Int'l*, pg. 4128
KENROC BUILDING MATERIALS CO. LTD.—See Kenroc Building Materials Co. Ltd.; *Int'l*, pg. 4128
KENROC BUILDING MATERIALS CO. LTD.—See Kenroc Building Materials Co. Ltd.; *Int'l*, pg. 4128
KENROC BUILDING MATERIALS CO. LTD.—See Kenroc Building Materials Co. Ltd.; *Int'l*, pg. 4128
KENROC BUILDING MATERIALS CO. LTD.—See Kenroc Building Materials Co. Ltd.; *Int'l*, pg. 4128
KENROC BUILDING MATERIALS CO. LTD.—See Kenroc Building Materials Co. Ltd.; *Int'l*, pg. 4128
KENROC BUILDING MATERIALS CO. LTD.—See Kenroc Building Materials Co. Ltd.; *Int'l*, pg. 4128
KENROC BUILDING MATERIALS CO. LTD.—See Kenroc Building Materials Co. Ltd.; *Int'l*, pg. 4128
KENROC BUILDING MATERIALS CO. LTD.—See Kenroc Building Materials Co. Ltd.; *Int'l*, pg. 4128
KEN ROSS ARCHITECTS INC.—See Clark Nexsen, Inc.; *U.S. Private*, pg. 913
KENRY HOME IMPROVEMENT NETWORK, INC.; *U.S. Private*, pg. 2287
KEN'S BEVERAGE INC.—See Pentair plc; *Int'l*, pg. 5789
KENSEI INDUSTRY CO., LTD.—See A&D Co., Ltd.; *Int'l*, pg. 19
KENSEY FOODS LIMITED—See Samworth Brothers Ltd.; *Int'l*, pg. 6519
KENSEY NASH CORPORATION—See Koninklijke DSM N.V.; *Int'l*, pg. 4263
KENSEY NASH EUROPE GMBH—See Koninklijke DSM N.V.; *Int'l*, pg. 4263
KENSEY NASH HOLDING CORPORATION—See Koninklijke DSM N.V.; *Int'l*, pg. 4263

KEN'S FOODS, INC.; *U.S. Private*, pg. 2283
KENSHAW ELECTRICAL PTY LIMITED—See VivoPower International PLC; *Int'l*, pg. 8280
KENSHOO AMERICAS—See Kenshoo, Ltd.; *Int'l*, pg. 4128
KENSHOO AUSTRALIA—See Kenshoo, Ltd.; *Int'l*, pg. 4128
KENSHOO FRANCE—See Kenshoo, Ltd.; *Int'l*, pg. 4128
KENSHOO GERMANY—See Kenshoo, Ltd.; *Int'l*, pg. 4128
KENSHOO HONG KONG—See Kenshoo, Ltd.; *Int'l*, pg. 4128
KENSHOO JAPAN—See Kenshoo, Ltd.; *Int'l*, pg. 4128
KENSHOO, LTD.; *Int'l*, pg. 4128
KENSHOO SINGAPORE PTE. LTD.—See Kenshoo, Ltd.; *Int'l*, pg. 4128
KENSHOO UK—See Kenshoo, Ltd.; *Int'l*, pg. 4128
KENSINGTON AGRICULTURAL SERVICES LTD.; *Int'l*, pg. 4128
KENSINGTON CA, LLC—See Jones Lang LaSalle Incorporated; *U.S. Public*, pg. 1205
KENSINGTON CAPITAL ADVISORS, LLC—See Jones Lang LaSalle Incorporated; *U.S. Public*, pg. 1205
KENSINGTON CAPITAL PARTNERS LIMITED—See AGF Management Limited; *Int'l*, pg. 207
KENSINGTON CAPITAL PARTNERS, LLC; *U.S. Private*, pg. 2287
KENSINGTON COURT LIMITED; *Int'l*, pg. 4128
KENSINGTON MORTGAGES LIMITED—See Barclays PLC; *Int'l*, pg. 860
KENSINGTON PARK HOTEL—See Engage Hospitality LLC; *U.S. Private*, pg. 1397
KENSINGTON PUBLISHING CORP.; *U.S. Private*, pg. 2287
KENSINGTON STUDENT SERVICES LIMITED—See Graham Holdings Company; *U.S. Public*, pg. 956
KENSINGTON TECHNOLOGY GROUP—See ACCO Brands Corporation; *U.S. Public*, pg. 33
KENSINGTON VANGUARD NATIONAL LAND SERVICES, LLC—See Clayton, Dubilier & Rice, LLC; *U.S. Private*, pg. 927
KENSINGTON VANGUARD NATIONAL LAND SERVICES, LLC—See Mubadala Investment Company PJSC; *Int'l*, pg. 5076
KENSINGTON VANGUARD NATIONAL LAND SERVICES, LLC—See Stone Point Capital LLC; *U.S. Private*, pg. 3826
KENSIYUU CO., LTD.—See KYB Corporation; *Int'l*, pg. 4354
KENSOH CO., LTD.; *Int'l*, pg. 4128
K-ENSOL CO., LTD.; *Int'l*, pg. 4042
KENSON INVESTMENT LIMITED—See Oshidori International Holdings Limited; *Int'l*, pg. 5650
KEN'S SUPERFAIR FOODS; *U.S. Private*, pg. 2283
KENSTONE GMBH—See Commerzbank AG; *Int'l*, pg. 1718
KENS TREE CARE INC.—See Apax Partners LLP; *Int'l*, pg. 506
KENS-TV—See TEGNA Inc.; *U.S. Public*, pg. 1989
KEN TAME & ASSOCIATES PTY LTD—See Allianz SE; *Int'l*, pg. 353
KENT BEVERAGE COMPANY; *U.S. Private*, pg. 2287
KENT BUSINESS SYSTEMS CORP.; *U.S. Private*, pg. 2287
KENT CHAMOIS COMPANY LTD—See Spectrum Brands Holdings, Inc.; *U.S. Public*, pg. 1915
KENT CHEVROLET, CADILLAC, INC.; *U.S. Private*, pg. 2287
KENTCO INC.; *U.S. Private*, pg. 2288
KENT COMPANIES INC.; *U.S. Private*, pg. 2287
THE KENT COMPANIES; *U.S. Private*, pg. 4065
KENT CORPORATION; *U.S. Private*, pg. 2287
KENT COUNTY DAILY TIMES—See R.I.S.N. Operations Inc.; *U.S. Private*, pg. 3336
KENT DISTRIBUTORS INC.; *U.S. Private*, pg. 2287
KENTEC ELECTRONICS LTD.—See Hochiki Corporation; *Int'l*, pg. 3437
KEN TECHNOLOGY CO., LTD.—See Bain Capital, LP; *U.S. Private*, pg. 434
KENTEK OY—See Diploma PLC; *Int'l*, pg. 2128
KENT ELASTOMER PRODUCTS, INC.—See Meridian Industries, Inc.; *U.S. Private*, pg. 2673
KENT ENVIROPOWER LIMITED—See Fomento de Construcciones y Contratas, S.A.; *Int'l*, pg. 2723
KENT FAKTORING A.S.; *Int'l*, pg. 4128
KENT FRANCE SAS—See Berner SE; *Int'l*, pg. 988
KENT FROZEN FOODS—See Sysco Corporation; *U.S. Public*, pg. 1974
KENT GIDA MADDELERI SANAYII VE TICARET ANONIM SIRKETI—See Mondelez International, Inc.; *U.S. Public*, pg. 1461
KENT GROUP CO., LTD.—See Relo Group, Inc.; *Int'l*, pg. 6265
KENT GYPSUM SUPPLY INC.; *U.S. Private*, pg. 2287
KENTICO SOFTWARE BV—See Kentico Software s.r.o.; *Int'l*, pg. 4128
KENTICO SOFTWARE LLC—See Kentico Software s.r.o.; *Int'l*, pg. 4128
KENTICO SOFTWARE LTD.—See Kentico Software s.r.o.; *Int'l*, pg. 4128

KENTICO SOFTWARE PTY LTD.—See Kentico Software s.r.o.; *Int'l*, pg. 4129
KENTICO SOFTWARE S.R.O.; *Int'l*, pg. 4128
KENTIMA HOLDING AB; *Int'l*, pg. 4129
KENT IMMOBILEMANAGEMNT GMBH—See CR Capital Real Estate AG; *Int'l*, pg. 1827
KENT INDUSTRIAL CO., LTD.; *Int'l*, pg. 4128
KENT INDUSTRI DANMARK APS—See Berner SE; *Int'l*, pg. 988
KENT INTERNATIONAL INC.; *U.S. Private*, pg. 2287
KENT ISLAND MECHANICAL, LLC—See Crawford United Corporation; *U.S. Public*, pg. 592
KENT ITALIA S.R.L.—See Berner SE; *Int'l*, pg. 988
KENTMERE REHABILITATION AND HEALTHCARE CENTER; *U.S. Private*, pg. 2288
KENT-MICHAEL ENTERPRISES INC.; *U.S. Private*, pg. 2288
KENT M. LIM & COMPANY, INC.; *U.S. Private*, pg. 2288
KENT NEDERLAND B.V.—See Berner SE; *Int'l*, pg. 988
KENT NUTRITION GROUP, INC.—See Kent Corporation; *U.S. Private*, pg. 2287
KENTO DAIICHI TRAFFIC CO., LTD.—See Daiichi Koutsu Sangyo Co., Ltd.; *Int'l*, pg. 1928
KEN-TOOL—See Summit Tool Company; *U.S. Private*, pg. 3857
KENTOR AB—See Sopra Steria Group S.A.; *Int'l*, pg. 7109
KENT PET GROUP, INC.—See Kent Corporation; *U.S. Private*, pg. 2287
THE KENT POTATO COMPANY LIMITED—See Promethean Investments LLP; *Int'l*, pg. 5993
KENT PRECISION FOODS GROUP, INC.—See Kent Corporation; *U.S. Private*, pg. 2287
KENT RELIANCE BUILDING SOCIETY—See J.C. Flowers & Co. LLC; *U.S. Private*, pg. 2160
KENTROL/SEVCO, INC.—See F.W. Webb Company; *U.S. Private*, pg. 1457
KEN-TRON MANUFACTURING INC.; *U.S. Private*, pg. 2283
KENT RYLEE CHEVROLET-OLDSMOBILE, INC.; *U.S. Private*, pg. 2288
KENT SAND & GRAVEL, L.L.C.—See Haines & Kibblehouse Inc.; *U.S. Private*, pg. 1841
KENTS OIL SERVICE—See MDU Resources Group, Inc.; *U.S. Public*, pg. 1410
KENT'S OIL SERVICE—See MDU Resources Group, Inc.; *U.S. Public*, pg. 1410
KENT SPORTING GOODS COMPANY; *U.S. Private*, pg. 2288
KENTUCKIANA COMFORT CENTER, INC.; *U.S. Private*, pg. 2288
KENTUCKIANA MEDICAL CENTER, LLC—See Lennar Corporation; *U.S. Public*, pg. 1306
KENTUCKY ADVANCED FORGE, LLC—See JTEKT Corporation; *Int'l*, pg. 4018
KENTUCKY AMERICAN WATER—See American Water Works Company, Inc.; *U.S. Public*, pg. 112
KENTUCKY APPAREL LLP; *U.S. Private*, pg. 2288
KENTUCKY ASSOCIATION OF ELECTRIC COOPERATIVES, INC.; *U.S. Private*, pg. 2288
KENTUCKY AUTOMOTIVE CENTER OF GRAYSON; *U.S. Private*, pg. 2288
KENTUCKY BANCSHARES, INC.—See Stock Yards Bancorp, Inc.; *U.S. Public*, pg. 1951
KENTUCKY BANK—See Stock Yards Bancorp, Inc.; *U.S. Public*, pg. 1951
KENTUCKY BERWIND LAND COMPANY—See Berwind Corporation; *U.S. Private*, pg. 540
KENTUCKY BIOPROCESSING, INC.—See British American Tobacco plc; *Int'l*, pg. 1168
KENTUCKY EAGLE BEER INC.; *U.S. Private*, pg. 2288
KENTUCKY EDUCATION ASSOCIATION; *U.S. Private*, pg. 2288
KENTUCKY EMPLOYERS MUTUAL INSURANCE; *U.S. Private*, pg. 2288
KENTUCKY FARM BUREAU INSURANCE AGENCY INC.—See Kentucky Farm Bureau Mutual Insurance Company Inc.; *U.S. Private*, pg. 2288
KENTUCKY FARM BUREAU MUTUAL INSURANCE COMPANY INC.; *U.S. Private*, pg. 2288
KENTUCKY FARMERS BANK CORPORATION; *U.S. Private*, pg. 2288
KENTUCKY FIRST FEDERAL BANCORP—See First Federal MHC; *U.S. Private*, pg. 1518
KENTUCKY FRIED CHICKEN CANADA COMPANY—See Yum! Brands, Inc.; *U.S. Public*, pg. 2400
KENTUCKY FRIED CHICKEN (GREAT BRITAIN) LIMITED—See Yum! Brands, Inc.; *U.S. Public*, pg. 2400
KENTUCKY FRIED CHICKEN (GREAT BRITAIN) SERVICES LIMITED—See Yum! Brands, Inc.; *U.S. Public*, pg. 2400
KENTUCKY FRIED CHICKEN LIMITED—See Yum! Brands, Inc.; *U.S. Public*, pg. 2400
KENTUCKY FRIED CHICKEN (MALAYSIA) SDN. BHD.—See Johor Corporation; *Int'l*, pg. 3994
KENTUCKY FRIED CHICKEN PTY. LTD.—See Yum! Brands, Inc.; *U.S. Public*, pg. 2400
KENTUCKY HAULING, INC.—See Summit Materials, Inc.; *U.S. Public*, pg. 1960

COMPANY NAME INDEX

KENTUCKY HIGHLANDS INVESTMENT CORP.; *U.S. Private*, pg. 2288
KENTUCKY HOMECARE OF HENDERSON, LLC—See UnitedHealth Group Incorporated; *U.S. Public*, pg. 2245
KENTUCKY HOME LIFE INSURANCE COMPANY—See Forcht Group of Kentucky, Inc.; *U.S. Private*, pg. 1564
KENTUCKY INDIANA LUMBER - US LBM, LLC—See Bain Capital, LP; *U.S. Private*, pg. 451
KENTUCKY INTERACTIVE, LLC—See Tyler Technologies, Inc.; *U.S. Public*, pg. 2208
KENTUCKY LAKE OIL CO. INC.; *U.S. Private*, pg. 2288
KENTUCKY LOGOS, LLC—See Lamar Advertising Company; *U.S. Public*, pg. 1290
KENTUCKY LV, LLC—See UnitedHealth Group Incorporated; *U.S. Public*, pg. 2245
KENTUCKY MANUFACTURING CO.; *U.S. Private*, pg. 2288
KENTUCKY MEDICAL SERVICES FOUNDATION INC.; *U.S. Private*, pg. 2288
KENTUCKY MEDICAL SUPPLY, INC.—See AdaptHealth Corp.; *U.S. Public*, pg. 39
KENTUCKY NATIONAL INSURANCE COMPANY—See Forcht Group of Kentucky, Inc.; *U.S. Private*, pg. 1564
KENTUCKY NATIONAL INSURANCE GROUP, LLC—See Forcht Group of Kentucky, Inc.; *U.S. Private*, pg. 1564
KENTUCKY OIL GATHERING, LLC—See EnLink Midstream, LLC; *U.S. Public*, pg. 768
KENTUCKY OIL & REFINING COMPANY; *U.S. Private*, pg. 2288
KENTUCKYONE HEALTH, INC.—See University of Louisville; *U.S. Private*, pg. 4309
KENTUCKY ORGAN DONOR AFFILIATES; *U.S. Private*, pg. 2288
KENTUCKY ORTHOPEDIC REHABILITATION, LLC—See Select Medical Holdings Corporation; *U.S. Public*, pg. 1858
KENTUCKY PETROLEUM SUPPLY, INC.; *U.S. Private*, pg. 2288
KENTUCKY PHYSICIAN SERVICES, INC.—See Apollo Global Management, Inc.; *U.S. Public*, pg. 155
KENTUCKY POWER COMPANY—See American Electric Power Company, Inc.; *U.S. Public*, pg. 100
KENTUCKY RACEWAY, LLC—See Sonic Financial Corporation; *U.S. Private*, pg. 3713
KENTUCKY REHABILITATION SERVICES, INC.—See Select Medical Holdings Corporation; *U.S. Public*, pg. 1858
KENTUCKY RIVER HBP, LLC—See Quorum Health Corporation; *U.S. Private*, pg. 3330
KENTUCKY SPIRIT HEALTH PLAN, INC.—See Centene Corporation; *U.S. Public*, pg. 469
KENTUCKY STEEL CENTER, INC.—See Nippon Steel Corporation; *Int'l*, pg. 5338
KENTUCKY-TENNESSEE CLAY COMPANY; *U.S. Private*, pg. 2289
KENTUCKY TEXTILES INC.; *U.S. Private*, pg. 2289
KENTUCKY TRAILER TECHNOLOGIES—See Berkshire Hathaway Inc.; *U.S. Public*, pg. 299
KENTUCKY UTILITIES COMPANY—See PPL Corporation; *U.S. Public*, pg. 1711
KENT UK LTD.—See Berner SE; *Int'l*, pg. 988
KENTURN NANO TEC CO., LTD.; *Int'l*, pg. 4129
KENTVILLE CHRYSLER DODGE JEEP; *Int'l*, pg. 4129
KENTWOOD OFFICE FURNITURE INC.; *U.S. Private*, pg. 2289
KENTWOOD REAL ESTATE SERVICES LLC—See Berkshire Hathaway Inc.; *U.S. Public*, pg. 306
KENTWOOL COMPANY; *U.S. Private*, pg. 2289
KENTZ CORPORATION LIMITED—See AtkinsRealis Group Inc.; *Int'l*, pg. 671
KENTZU STEEL SDN BHD; *Int'l*, pg. 4129
KENUS LLP—See Alfa Laval AB; *Int'l*, pg. 312
KENVI JEWELS LTD.; *Int'l*, pg. 4129
KENVIN INCORPORATED; *U.S. Private*, pg. 2289
KENVUE INC.; *U.S. Public*, pg. 1223
KENWAL CANADA, INC.—See Kenwal Steel Corp.; *U.S. Private*, pg. 2289
KENWAL STEEL CORP.; *U.S. Private*, pg. 2289
KENWAL STEEL CORP—See Kenwal Steel Corp.; *U.S. Private*, pg. 2289
KENWAY CORPORATION—See Hill & Smith PLC; *Int'l*, pg. 3391
KENWAY DISTRIBUTORS INC.; *U.S. Private*, pg. 2289
KEN WEAVER MEATS INC.; *U.S. Private*, pg. 2282
KEN WILSON FORD INC.; *U.S. Private*, pg. 2282
KENWOOD ASC, LLC—See KKR & Co. Inc.; *U.S. Public*, pg. 1245
KENWOOD CORPORATION—See JVCKENWOOD Corporation; *Int'l*, pg. 4033
KENWOOD DEALER GROUP, INC.; *U.S. Private*, pg. 2289
KENWOOD DESIGN CORPORATION—See JVCKENWOOD Corporation; *Int'l*, pg. 4033
KENWOOD DEVICES CORPORATION—See JVCKENWOOD Corporation; *Int'l*, pg. 4033
KENWOOD ELECTRONICS AUSTRALIA PTY. LTD.—See JVCKENWOOD Corporation; *Int'l*, pg. 4033
KENWOOD ELECTRONICS BELGIUM N.V.—See JVCKENWOOD Corporation; *Int'l*, pg. 4033
KENWOOD ELECTRONICS BRAZIL LTDA.—See JVCKENWOOD Corporation; *Int'l*, pg. 4033
KENWOOD ELECTRONICS BRETAGNE S.A.—See JVCKENWOOD Corporation; *Int'l*, pg. 4033
KENWOOD ELECTRONICS CANADA, INC.—See JVCKENWOOD Corporation; *Int'l*, pg. 4033
KENWOOD ELECTRONICS DEUTSCHLAND GMBH—See JVCKENWOOD Corporation; *Int'l*, pg. 4033
KENWOOD ELECTRONICS FRANCE S.A.—See JVCKENWOOD Corporation; *Int'l*, pg. 4033
KENWOOD ELECTRONICS GULF FZE—See JVCKENWOOD Corporation; *Int'l*, pg. 4033
KENWOOD ELECTRONICS (HONG KONG) LTD.—See JVCKENWOOD Corporation; *Int'l*, pg. 4033
KENWOOD ELECTRONICS ITALIA S.P.A.—See JVCKENWOOD Corporation; *Int'l*, pg. 4033
KENWOOD ELECTRONICS LATIN AMERICA S.A.—See JVCKENWOOD Corporation; *Int'l*, pg. 4033
KENWOOD ELECTRONICS (MALAYSIA) SDN. BHD.—See JVCKENWOOD Corporation; *Int'l*, pg. 4033
KENWOOD ELECTRONICS SINGAPORE PTE. LTD.—See JVCKENWOOD Corporation; *Int'l*, pg. 4033
KENWOOD ELECTRONICS TECHNOLOGIES (S) PTE. LTD.—See JVCKENWOOD Corporation; *Int'l*, pg. 4033
KENWOOD ELECTRONICS TRADING (SHANGHAI) CO., LTD.—See JVCKENWOOD Corporation; *Int'l*, pg. 4034
KENWOOD ELECTRONICS U.K. LTD.—See JVCKENWOOD Corporation; *Int'l*, pg. 4033
KENWOOD ENGINEERING CORPORATION—See JVCKENWOOD Corporation; *Int'l*, pg. 4033
KENWOOD GEOBIT CORPORATION—See JVCKENWOOD Corporation; *Int'l*, pg. 4034
KENWOOD IBERICA S.A.—See JVCKENWOOD Corporation; *Int'l*, pg. 4034
KENWOOD KENEX CORPORATION—See JVCKENWOOD Corporation; *Int'l*, pg. 4034
KENWOOD LIMITED—See De'Longhi S.p.A.; *Int'l*, pg. 1997
KENWOOD LINCOLN MERCURY INC.; *U.S. Private*, pg. 2289
KENWOOD LIQUORS; *U.S. Private*, pg. 2289
KENWOOD MANUFACTURING GMBH—See De'Longhi S.p.A.; *Int'l*, pg. 1997
KENWOOD NAGANO CORPORATION—See JVCKENWOOD Corporation; *Int'l*, pg. 4034
KENWOOD PAINTED METALS, INC; *U.S. Private*, pg. 2289
KENWOOD PERSONNEL CORPORATION—See JVCKENWOOD Corporation; *Int'l*, pg. 4034
KENWOOD SERVICE (JAPAN) CORPORATION—See JVCKENWOOD Corporation; *Int'l*, pg. 4034
KENWOOD USA CORPORATION—See JVCKENWOOD Corporation; *Int'l*, pg. 4034
KENWOOD YAMAGATA CORPORATION—See JVCKENWOOD Corporation; *Int'l*, pg. 4034
KENWORTH MEXICANA, S.A. DE C.V.—See PACCAR Inc.; *U.S. Public*, pg. 1630
KENWORTH NORTHWEST, INC.; *U.S. Private*, pg. 2289
KENWORTH OF CENTRAL FLORIDA; *U.S. Private*, pg. 2289
KENWORTH OF CINCINNATI INC.; *U.S. Private*, pg. 2289
KENWORTH OF INDIANAPOLIS INC.; *U.S. Private*, pg. 2289
KENWORTH OF JACKSON INC.; *U.S. Private*, pg. 2289
KENWORTH OF JACKSONVILLE, INC.; *U.S. Private*, pg. 2289
KENWORTH OF ST. LOUIS INC.; *U.S. Private*, pg. 2289
KENWORTH SALES COMPANY, INC.; *U.S. Private*, pg. 2289
KENWORTH TRUCK CO.—See PACCAR Inc.; *U.S. Public*, pg. 1630
KENYA AIRWAYS PLC; *Int'l*, pg. 4129
KENYA ELECTRICITY GENERATING COMPANY LIMITED; *Int'l*, pg. 4129
KENYA LITHO LTD—See Aga Khan Development Network; *Int'l*, pg. 199
KENYAN ENTERPRISES INC.; *U.S. Private*, pg. 2289
KENYA POWER & LIGHTING COMPANY LIMITED; *Int'l*, pg. 4129
KENYA REINSURANCE CORPORATION LIMITED; *Int'l*, pg. 4129
KENYA REINSURANCE CORPORATION LTD.—See Kenya Reinsurance Corporation Limited; *Int'l*, pg. 4129
KENYA REINSURANCE CORPORATION UGANDA SMC LIMITED—See Kenya Reinsurance Corporation Limited; *Int'l*, pg. 4129
KENYA SHELL LTD.—See Shell plc; *Int'l*, pg. 6797
KENYA TEA DEVELOPMENT AGENCY LIMITED; *Int'l*, pg. 4129
KENYA TEA PACKERS LIMITED—See Kenya Tea Development Agency Limited; *Int'l*, pg. 4129
KENYA VEHICLE MANUFACTURERS LTD.—See Nissan Motor Co., Ltd.; *Int'l*, pg. 5367
KENYON COMPANIES; *U.S. Private*, pg. 2289
KENYON CONSTRUCTION, INC.; *U.S. Private*, pg. 2290
KENYON INDUSTRIES, INC.—See Hallwood Group, LLC; *U.S. Private*, pg. 1845

KEPI TECH CENTER INC.

KENYON INTERNATIONAL EMERGENCY SERVICES, INC.—See Wheels Up Experience Inc.; *U.S. Public*, pg. 2366
KENYON POWER BOATS INC.; *U.S. Private*, pg. 2290
KENZAN MEDIA, LLC—See Amdocs Limited; *Int'l*, pg. 420
KENZO BELGIQUE SA—See LVMH Moet Hennessy Louis Vuitton SE; *Int'l*, pg. 4594
KENZO DEUTSCHLAND GMBH—See LVMH Moet Hennessy Louis Vuitton SE; *Int'l*, pg. 4594
KENZO FASHION IBERICA—See LVMH Moet Hennessy Louis Vuitton SE; *Int'l*, pg. 4594
KENZO HOMME SA—See LVMH Moet Hennessy Louis Vuitton SE; *Int'l*, pg. 4594
KENZO PARFUMS ITALIA S.R.L—See LVMH Moet Hennessy Louis Vuitton SE; *Int'l*, pg. 4594
KENZO PARFUMS MEXICO—See LVMH Moet Hennessy Louis Vuitton SE; *Int'l*, pg. 4594
KENZO PARFUMS—See LVMH Moet Hennessy Louis Vuitton SE; *Int'l*, pg. 4594
KENZO PARFUMS—See LVMH Moet Hennessy Louis Vuitton SE; *Int'l*, pg. 4594
KENZO PARFUMS—See LVMH Moet Hennessy Louis Vuitton SE; *Int'l*, pg. 4594
KENZO PARFUMS—See LVMH Moet Hennessy Louis Vuitton SE; *Int'l*, pg. 4594
KENZO PARFUMS SPAIN—See LVMH Moet Hennessy Louis Vuitton SE; *Int'l*, pg. 4594
KENZO PARFUMS SWITZERLAND—See LVMH Moet Hennessy Louis Vuitton SE; *Int'l*, pg. 4594
KENZO PARIS K.K.—See LVMH Moet Hennessy Louis Vuitton SE; *Int'l*, pg. 4594
KENZO SA—See LVMH Moet Hennessy Louis Vuitton SE; *Int'l*, pg. 4594
KENZO UK LTD—See LVMH Moet Hennessy Louis Vuitton SE; *Int'l*, pg. 4592
KEOLIS S.A.—See SNCF; *Int'l*, pg. 7026
KEOLIS TRANSIT AMERICA, INC.—See SNCF; *Int'l*, pg. 7026
KEO MARKETING INC.; *U.S. Private*, pg. 2290
KEON CAPITAL INC.; *Int'l*, pg. 4129
KEONG HONG HOLDINGS LIMITED; *Int'l*, pg. 4129
KEONYS BELGIQUE SPRL—See CENIT AG; *Int'l*, pg. 1401
KEONYS NL BV—See CENIT AG; *Int'l*, pg. 1401
KEONYS SAS—See CENIT AG; *Int'l*, pg. 1401
KEO PLC; *Int'l*, pg. 4129
KEOPS—See L'Air Liquide S.A.; *Int'l*, pg. 4371
KEOPSYS SA—See Lumibird Group; *Int'l*, pg. 4578
KE OSTROV-ELEKTRIK S.R.O.—See Amphenol Corporation; *U.S. Public*, pg. 130
KE OSTROV ELEKTRIK S.R.O.—See Amphenol Corporation; *U.S. Public*, pg. 130
KE OSTROV ELEKTRIK S.R.O.—See Amphenol Corporation; *U.S. Public*, pg. 130
KEPCO AUSTRALIA PTY LTD.—See Korea Electric Power Corporation; *Int'l*, pg. 4283
KEPCO BYLONG AUSTRALIA PTY. LTD.—See Korea Electric Power Corporation; *Int'l*, pg. 4283
KEPCO CSC CO., LTD.—See Korea Electric Power Corporation; *Int'l*, pg. 4283
KEPCO E&C SERVICE CO., LTD.—See Korea Electric Power Corporation; *Int'l*, pg. 4283
KEPCO ENGINEERING & CONSTRUCTION COMPANY, INC.—See Korea Electric Power Corporation; *Int'l*, pg. 4283
KEPCO FMS CO., LTD.—See Korea Electric Power Corporation; *Int'l*, pg. 4283
KEPCO ILIJAN CORPORATION—See Korea Electric Power Corporation; *Int'l*, pg. 4283
KEPCO INC.; *U.S. Private*, pg. 2290
KEPCO KDN CO., LTD.—See Korea Electric Power Corporation; *Int'l*, pg. 4283
KEPCO KPS PHILIPPINES CORP.—See Korea Electric Power Corporation; *Int'l*, pg. 4283
KEPCO MCS CO., LTD.—See Korea Electric Power Corporation; *Int'l*, pg. 4283
KEPCO NUCLEAR FUEL CO., LTD.—See Korea Electric Power Corporation; *Int'l*, pg. 4283
KEPCO PHILIPPINES CORPORATION—See Korea Electric Power Corporation; *Int'l*, pg. 4283
KEPCO PHILIPPINES HOLDINGS INC.—See Korea Electric Power Corporation; *Int'l*, pg. 4283
KEPCO PLANT SERVICE & ENGINEERING CO., LTD; *Int'l*, pg. 4129
KEPCO SOLAR OF ALAMOSA, LLC—See Korea Electric Power Corporation; *Int'l*, pg. 4283
KEPCO SPC POWER CORPORATION—See Korea Electric Power Corporation; *Int'l*, pg. 4283
KEPCO-UHDE INC.—See Korea Electric Power Corporation; *Int'l*, pg. 4283
K.E.P. ELECTRIC, INC.—See IES Holdings, Inc.; *U.S. Public*, pg. 1094
KE PERSSON AB—See H&M Hennes & Mauritz AB; *Int'l*, pg. 3192
KEPHART TRUCKING COMPANY; *U.S. Private*, pg. 2290
KEPITAL MANAGEMENT LTD—See Keppel Corporation Limited; *Int'l*, pg. 4130
KEPI TECH CENTER INC.; *Int'l*, pg. 4130

KEPIT SYSTEMS OY—See Elisa Corporation; *Int'l*, pg. 2361
KEPLER ASSOCIATES LIMITED—See Marsh & McLennan Companies, Inc.; *U.S. Public*, pg. 1377
KEPLER CAPITAL MARKETS, INC.—See Kepler Capital Markets; *Int'l*, pg. 4130
KEPLER CAPITAL MARKETS; *Int'l*, pg. 4130
KEPLER-FONDS KAPITALANLAGEGESELLSCHAFT M.B.H.—See Raiffeisenlandesbank Oberosterreich Aktiengesellschaft; *Int'l*, pg. 6187
KEPLER GROUP LLC—See Kyu Investment, Inc.; *U.S. Private*, pg. 2361
KEPLER ROMINFO SA—See Alten S.A.; *Int'l*, pg. 390
KEPLER WEBER S.A.; *Int'l*, pg. 4130
KEPNER-TREGOE AUSTRALASIA PTY LTD—See Kepner-Tregoe, Inc.; *U.S. Private*, pg. 2290
KEPNER-TREGOE DEUTSCHLAND, LLC.—See Kepner-Tregoe, Inc.; *U.S. Private*, pg. 2290
KEPNER-TREGOE, INC.; *U.S. Private*, pg. 2290
KEPNER-TREGOE JAPAN, LLC—See Kepner-Tregoe, Inc.; *U.S. Private*, pg. 2290
KEPNER-TREGOE LTD.—See Kepner-Tregoe, Inc.; *U.S. Private*, pg. 2290
KEPNER-TREGOE (MALAYSIA) SDN. BHD.—See Kepner-Tregoe, Inc.; *U.S. Private*, pg. 2290
KEPNER-TREGOE SARL—See Kepner-Tregoe, Inc.; *U.S. Private*, pg. 2290
KEPNER-TREGOE, SA—See Kepner-Tregoe, Inc.; *U.S. Private*, pg. 2290
KEPNER-TREGOE SOUTHEAST ASIA LIMITED.—See Kepner-Tregoe, Inc.; *U.S. Private*, pg. 2290
KEPNER-TREGOE SOUTHEAST ASIA LTD—See Kepner-Tregoe, Inc.; *U.S. Private*, pg. 2290
KEPNER-TREGOE THAILAND, LLC—See Kepner-Tregoe, Inc.; *U.S. Private*, pg. 2290
KEPPEL AMFELS INC.—See Sembcorp Industries Ltd.; *Int'l*, pg. 6703
KEPPEL BATANGAS SHIPYARD INC—See Sembcorp Industries Ltd.; *Int'l*, pg. 6703
KEPPEL BAY PTE LTD—See Keppel Corporation Limited; *Int'l*, pg. 4130
KEPPEL CAPITAL HOLDINGS PTE LTD—See Keppel Corporation Limited; *Int'l*, pg. 4130
KEPPEL CORPORATION LIMITED; *Int'l*, pg. 4130
KEPPEL DC REIT MANAGEMENT PTE. LTD.; *Int'l*, pg. 4132
KEPPEL DC SINGAPORE 2 PTE. LTD—See Keppel Corporation Limited; *Int'l*, pg. 4130
KEPPEL DHCS PTE LTD—See Keppel Corporation Limited; *Int'l*, pg. 4130
KEPPEL ELECTRIC PTE LTD—See Keppel Corporation Limited; *Int'l*, pg. 4130
KEPPEL ENERGY PTE. LTD.—See Keppel Corporation Limited; *Int'l*, pg. 4130
KEPPEL ENVIRONMENTAL TECHNOLOGY CENTRE PTE LTD—See Keppel Corporation Limited; *Int'l*, pg. 4130
KEPPEL FELS BALTECH LTD.—See Sembcorp Industries Ltd.; *Int'l*, pg. 6703
KEPPEL FELS BRASIL SA—See Sembcorp Industries Ltd.; *Int'l*, pg. 6703
KEPPEL FELS ENGINEERING SHENZHEN CO. LTD—See Keppel Corporation Limited; *Int'l*, pg. 4130
KEPPEL FELS LTD.—See Sembcorp Industries Ltd.; *Int'l*, pg. 6703
KEPPEL FELS OFFSHORE & ENGINEERING SERVICES MUMBAI PTE LTD—See Sembcorp Industries Ltd.; *Int'l*, pg. 6703
KEPPEL FLOATEC LLC—See Keppel Corporation Limited; *Int'l*, pg. 4130
KEPPEL GAS PTE. LTD.—See Keppel Corporation Limited; *Int'l*, pg. 4131
KEPPEL HONG DA (TIANJIN ECO-CITY) PROPERTY DEVELOPMENT CO., LTD.—See Keppel Corporation Limited; *Int'l*, pg. 4130
KEPPEL INFRASTRUCTURE FUND MANAGEMENT PTE. LTD.—See Keppel Corporation Limited; *Int'l*, pg. 4131
KEPPEL INFRASTRUCTURE HOLDINGS PTE. LTD.—See Keppel Corporation Limited; *Int'l*, pg. 4131
KEPPEL INFRASTRUCTURE TRUST—See Keppel Corporation Limited; *Int'l*, pg. 4131
KEPPEL INTERNATIONAL FREIGHT FORWARDING (SHENZHEN) LTD—See Keppel Corporation Limited; *Int'l*, pg. 4131
KEPPEL LAKEFRONT (WUXI) PROPERTY DEVELOPMENT CO., LTD.—See Keppel Corporation Limited; *Int'l*, pg. 4131
KEPPEL LAND INTERNATIONAL LTD—See Keppel Corporation Limited; *Int'l*, pg. 4131
KEPPEL LAND LIMITED—See Keppel Corporation Limited; *Int'l*, pg. 4131
KEPPEL LAND (MAYFAIR) PTE LTD—See Keppel Corporation Limited; *Int'l*, pg. 4131
KEPPEL LAND (SHANGHAI) MANAGEMENT CO LTD—See Keppel Corporation Limited; *Int'l*, pg. 4131
KEPPEL LAND (TOWER D) PTE LTD—See Keppel Corporation Limited; *Int'l*, pg. 4131
KEPPEL LAND VIETNAM CO. LTD.—See Keppel Corporation Limited; *Int'l*, pg. 4131

KEPPEL LAND VIETNAM PROPERTIES PTE LTD—See Keppel Corporation Limited; *Int'l*, pg. 4131
KEPPEL LAND WATCO I CO., LTD.—See Keppel Corporation Limited; *Int'l*, pg. 4131
KEPPEL LETOURNEAU MIDDLE EAST FZE—See Sembcorp Industries Ltd.; *Int'l*, pg. 6703
KEPPEL LETOURNEAU USA, INC.—See Keppel Corporation Limited; *Int'l*, pg. 4131
KEPPEL LOGISTICS (HONG KONG) LTD—See China Merchants Group Limited; *Int'l*, pg. 1522
KEPPEL LOGISTICS (M) SDN BHD—See Keppel Corporation Limited; *Int'l*, pg. 4131
KEPPEL LOGISTICS PTE LTD—See Keppel Corporation Limited; *Int'l*, pg. 4131
KEPPEL MARINE AGENCIES INC.—See Sembcorp Industries Ltd.; *Int'l*, pg. 6703
KEPPEL MARINE AGENCIES INC.—See Sembcorp Industries Ltd.; *Int'l*, pg. 6703
KEPPEL MARINE AGENCIES INTERNATIONAL LLC—See Keppel Corporation Limited; *Int'l*, pg. 4131
KEPPEL MERLIMAU COGEN PTE. LTD.—See Keppel Corporation Limited; *Int'l*, pg. 4131
KEPPEL NANTONG SHIPYARD COMPANY LIMITED—See Sembcorp Industries Ltd.; *Int'l*, pg. 6703
KEPPEL OFFSHORE & MARINE LTD.—See Sembcorp Industries Ltd.; *Int'l*, pg. 6703
KEPPEL OFFSHORE & MARINE TECHNOLOGY CENTRE PTE LTD—See Sembcorp Industries Ltd.; *Int'l*, pg. 6703
KEPPEL OFFSHORE & MARINE USA, INC.—See Sembcorp Industries Ltd.; *Int'l*, pg. 6703
KEPPEL OIL & GAS SERVICES PTE. LTD.—See Keppel Corporation Limited; *Int'l*, pg. 4131
KEPPEL PACIFIC OAK US REIT; *Int'l*, pg. 4132
KEPPEL PHILIPPINES HOLDINGS, INC.—See Keppel Corporation Limited; *Int'l*, pg. 4131
KEPPEL PHILIPPINES MARINE INC—See Sembcorp Industries Ltd.; *Int'l*, pg. 6703
KEPPEL PHILIPPINES PROPERTIES INC.—See Keppel Corporation Limited; *Int'l*, pg. 4131
KEPPEL PRINCE ENGINEERING PTY LTD—See Sembcorp Industries Ltd.; *Int'l*, pg. 6703
KEPPEL REIT MANAGEMENT LTD.—See Keppel Corporation Limited; *Int'l*, pg. 4130
KEPPEL REIT; *Int'l*, pg. 4132
KEPPEL SEA SCAN PTE LTD—See Keppel Corporation Limited; *Int'l*, pg. 4130
KEPPEL SEGHERS BELGIUM NV—See Keppel Corporation Limited; *Int'l*, pg. 4131
KEPPEL SEGHERS DO BRASIL SISTEMAS AMBIENTAIS LTDA—See Keppel Corporation Limited; *Int'l*, pg. 4131
KEPPEL SEGHERS ENGINEERING SINGAPORE PTE LTD—See Keppel Corporation Limited; *Int'l*, pg. 4131
KEPPEL SEGHERS ENVIRONMENTAL ENGINEERING TECHNOLOGY (SHANGHAI) COMPANY LTD—See Keppel Corporation Limited; *Int'l*, pg. 4131
KEPPEL SEGHERS GMBH—See Keppel Corporation Limited; *Int'l*, pg. 4131
KEPPEL SEGHERS HONG KONG LTD—See Keppel Corporation Limited; *Int'l*, pg. 4132
KEPPEL SEGHERS INC—See Keppel Corporation Limited; *Int'l*, pg. 4132
KEPPEL SEGHERS NETHERLANDS BV—See Keppel Corporation Limited; *Int'l*, pg. 4132
KEPPEL SEGHERS PTE. LTD.—See Keppel Corporation Limited; *Int'l*, pg. 4132
KEPPEL SEGHERS UK LTD—See Keppel Corporation Limited; *Int'l*, pg. 4132
KEPPEL SHIPYARD LTD.—See Sembcorp Industries Ltd.; *Int'l*, pg. 6703
KEPPEL SINGMARINE BRASIL LTDA—See Keppel Corporation Limited; *Int'l*, pg. 4132
KEPPEL SINGMARINE PTE LTD—See Sembcorp Industries Ltd.; *Int'l*, pg. 6703
KEPPEL SUBIC SHIPYARD INC.—See Sembcorp Industries Ltd.; *Int'l*, pg. 6703
KEPPEL TELECOMMUNICATIONS & TRANSPORTATION, LTD.—See Keppel Corporation Limited; *Int'l*, pg. 4132
KE PRESOV ELEKTRIK, S.R.O.—See Amphenol Corporation; *U.S. Public*, pg. 130
KEPRO SOLUTIONS LIMITED—See Karin Technology Holdings Limited; *Int'l*, pg. 4081
KE PROTEZIONI SOLARI SRL—See BAT S.p.A.; *Int'l*, pg. 889
KEPR-TV—See Sinclair, Inc.; *U.S. Public*, pg. 1886
KEPU ELECTRONIC TECHNOLOGY (SHENZHEN) COMPANY LIMITED—See LED International Holdings Limited; *Int'l*, pg. 4438
KEPUNI HOLDINGS INC.; *Int'l*, pg. 4132
KERABITPRO OY—See Kingspan Group PLC; *Int'l*, pg. 4178
KERADOM S.R.L.—See Victoria Plc; *Int'l*, pg. 8189
KERAGLASS INDUSTRIES S.R.L.—See Cifin S.r.l.; *Int'l*, pg. 1606
KERAGLASS SNC—See Compagnie de Saint-Gobain SA; *Int'l*, pg. 1724
KERAGLASS SNC—See Corning Incorporated; *U.S. Public*, pg. 579

KERALA AYURVEDA LTD.; *Int'l*, pg. 4132
KERALTY BUSINESS GROUP; *Int'l*, pg. 4132
KERAMA MARAZZI—See Mohawk Industries, Inc.; *U.S. Public*, pg. 1457
KERAMA MARAZZI UKRAINE OOO—See Mohawk Industries, Inc.; *U.S. Public*, pg. 1457
KERAMIA-ALLATINI SA REAL ESTATE MANAGEMENT & HOLDING CO.; *Int'l*, pg. 4133
KERAMIKA - HOLDING A.D.; *Int'l*, pg. 4133
KERAMO WIENERBERGER IMMO NV—See Wienerberger AG; *Int'l*, pg. 8405
KERAS RESOURCES PLC; *Int'l*, pg. 4133
KERAVAN FOREVER OY—See Pihlajalinna Oy; *Int'l*, pg. 5865
KERBECK CADILLAC PONTIAC CHEVROLET, INC.; *U.S. Private*, pg. 2290
KERBER BROS. POOL PLASTERING, INC.; *U.S. Private*, pg. 2290
KERBS OIL COMPANY INC.; *U.S. Private*, pg. 2290
KER CADELAC SA—See Compagnie Financiere et de Participations Roullier SA; *Int'l*, pg. 1740
KERDOS GROUP S.A.; *Int'l*, pg. 4133
KERESKEDELMI ES HITELBANK RT.; *Int'l*, pg. 4133
KERETA KOMERSIL SELADANG (M) SDN BHD—See Warisan TC Holdings Berhad; *Int'l*, pg. 8345
KEREVITAS GIDA SANAYI VE TICARET A.S.—See Yildiz Holding AS; *Int'l*, pg. 8583
KERFORD LIMESTONE CO. INC.—See Constructors Inc.; *U.S. Private*, pg. 1025
KER, INC.; *U.S. Private*, pg. 2290
KERING EYEWEAR DACH GMBH—See Kering S.A.; *Int'l*, pg. 4134
KERING EYEWEAR FRANCE SAS—See Kering S.A.; *Int'l*, pg. 4134
KERING EYEWEAR JAPAN LTD—See Kering S.A.; *Int'l*, pg. 4134
KERING EYEWEAR SHANGHAI TRADING ENTERPRISES LTD.—See Kering S.A.; *Int'l*, pg. 4134
KERING EYEWEAR SPA—See Kering S.A.; *Int'l*, pg. 4134
KERING EYEWEAR TAIWAN LTD.—See Kering S.A.; *Int'l*, pg. 4134
KERING EYEWEAR UK LTD.—See Kering S.A.; *Int'l*, pg. 4134
KERING FINANCE—See Kering S.A.; *Int'l*, pg. 4135
KERING HOLLAND N.V.—See Kering S.A.; *Int'l*, pg. 4135
KERING S.A.; *Int'l*, pg. 4133
KERING VENTURE S.A.S.—See Kering S.A.; *Int'l*, pg. 4135
KERI SYSTEMS INC.; *U.S. Private*, pg. 2290
THE KERITE COMPANY—See Berkshire Hathaway Inc.; *U.S. Public*, pg. 310
KERJAYA PROSPEK GROUP BERHAD - IJOK FACTORY—See Kerjaya Prospek Group Berhad; *Int'l*, pg. 4136
KERJAYA PROSPEK GROUP BERHAD; *Int'l*, pg. 4136
KERJAYA PROSPEK PROPERTY BERHAD; *Int'l*, pg. 4136
KERKERING, BARBERIO & CO.; *U.S. Private*, pg. 2290
KERKERING BARBERIO FINANCIAL SERVICES, INC.—See Kerkering, Barberio & Co.; *U.S. Private*, pg. 2290
KERKSTRA PRECAST, INC.—See Solace Capital Partners, LLC; *U.S. Private*, pg. 3706
KERLIFE S.R.L.—See Ardian SAS; *Int'l*, pg. 555
KERLINK SA; *Int'l*, pg. 4137
KERMAN CEMENT INDUSTRIES GROUP INC.; *Int'l*, pg. 4137
KERMAN DIALYSIS CENTER, LLC—See Nautic Partners, LLC; *U.S. Private*, pg. 2870
KERMANS FINE FLOORING, INC.; *U.S. Private*, pg. 2290
KERMANSHAH PETROCHEMICAL INDUSTRIES CO.; *Int'l*, pg. 4137
KERMAS LTD; *Int'l*, pg. 4137
KERMIA HOTELS LTD—See Atlantica Hotels & Resorts Ltd; *Int'l*, pg. 676
KERMIA LTD—See Bank of Cyprus Holdings Public Limited Company; *Int'l*, pg. 842
KERMIA PROPERTIES & INVESTMENTS LTD—See Bank of Cyprus Holdings Public Limited Company; *Int'l*, pg. 842
KERMI GMBH—See Arbonia AG; *Int'l*, pg. 538
KERMI SP.Z.O.O.—See Arbonia AG; *Int'l*, pg. 538
KERMI S.R.O.—See Arbonia AG; *Int'l*, pg. 538
KERMODE RESOURCES LTD.; *Int'l*, pg. 4137
KERN & ASSOCIATES; *U.S. Private*, pg. 2290
KERN COUNTY TRACTOR PARTS, INC.—See Kinderhook Industries, LLC; *U.S. Private*, pg. 2306
KERN DEWENTER VIERE, LTD.—See Bergan Paulsen & Company PC; *U.S. Private*, pg. 530
KERN DOOR COMPANY—See Installed Building Products, Inc.; *U.S. Public*, pg. 1133
KERNEL GROUP HOLDINGS, INC.; *U.S. Public*, pg. 1224
KERNEL HOLDING S.A.; *Int'l*, pg. 4137
KERNEOS DO BRAZIL PRODUCAO E COMERCIO DE ALUMINOSOS LTDA—See Groupe Bruxelles Lambert SA; *Int'l*, pg. 3100
KERNEOS INC.—See Groupe Bruxelles Lambert SA; *Int'l*, pg. 3100

KERNEOS LTD.—See Groupe Bruxelles Lambert SA; *Int'l*, pg. 3100
KERNEOS SOUTHERN AFRICA (PTY) LTD.—See Groupe Bruxelles Lambert SA; *Int'l*, pg. 3100
KERNEX MICROSYSTEMS INDIA LTD; *Int'l*, pg. 4137
KERNEY SERVICE GROUP INC.; *U.S. Private*, pg. 2291
KERN FOOD DISTRIBUTING INC.; *U.S. Private*, pg. 2290
KERNKRAFTWERK BROKDORF GMBH—See E.ON SE; *Int'l*, pg. 2254
KERNKRAFTWERKE ISAR VERWALTUNGS GMBH—See E.ON SE; *Int'l*, pg. 2258
KERNKRAFTWERKE LIPPE-EMS GMBH—See RWE AG; *Int'l*, pg. 6434
KERNKRAFTWERKE GOSGEN-DANIKEN AG—See Axpo Holding AG; *Int'l*, pg. 771
KERNKRAFTWERK GUNDREMMINGEN GMBH—See RWE AG; *Int'l*, pg. 6434
KERNKRAFTWERK OBRIGHEIM GMBH—See EnBW Energie Baden-Wurttemberg AG; *Int'l*, pg. 2399
KERNKRAFTWERK STADE GMBH & CO. OHG—See E.ON SE; *Int'l*, pg. 2258
KERNKRAFTWERK UNTERWESER GMBH—See E.ON SE; *Int'l*, pg. 2254
KERN MACHINERY; *U.S. Private*, pg. 2291
KERN OIL & REFINING COMPANY—See Casey Co.; *U.S. Private*, pg. 782
THE KERN ORGANIZATION, INC.—See Omnicom Group Inc.; *U.S. Public*, pg. 1593
KERN PARTNERS LTD.; *Int'l*, pg. 4137
KERN REGIONAL CENTER; *U.S. Private*, pg. 2291
KERN RIVER GAS TRANSMISSION COMPANY—See Berkshire Hathaway Inc.; *U.S. Public*, pg. 300
KERNS MANUFACTURING CORP.; *U.S. Private*, pg. 2291
KERN & STELLY MEDIENTECHNIK GMBH—See Midwich Group Plc; *Int'l*, pg. 4887
KERNS TRUCKING INC.; *U.S. Private*, pg. 2291
KERN UND STELLY MEDIENTECHNIK GMBH—See Midwich Group Plc; *Int'l*, pg. 4887
KERONA GMBH—See Wurth Verwaltungsgesellschaft mbH; *Int'l*, pg. 8507
KEROS THERAPEUTICS, INC.; *U.S. Public*, pg. 1224
KERO-TV—See The E.W. Scripps Company; *U.S. Public*, pg. 2068
KERR BROTHERS (EXPORTS) PTY LIMITED—See Grove International Pty Limited; *Int'l*, pg. 3112
KERR CONCENTRATES, INC.—See Ingredion Incorporated; *U.S. Public*, pg. 1124
KERR CORPORATION—See Danaher Corporation; *U.S. Public*, pg. 628
KERR GMBH—See Danaher Corporation; *U.S. Public*, pg. 628
KERRICHER DIALYSIS, LLC—See DaVita Inc.; *U.S. Public*, pg. 640
KERRIDGE COMMERCIAL SYSTEMS (KSH) LIMITED—See KKR & Co. Inc.; *U.S. Public*, pg. 1256
KERRIDGE COMMERCIAL SYSTEMS LIMITED—See KKR & Co. Inc.; *U.S. Public*, pg. 1256
KERR ITALIA S.R.L.—See Danaher Corporation; *U.S. Public*, pg. 628
KERR LAKESIDE INC.; *U.S. Private*, pg. 2291
KERR-MCGEE OIL AND GAS CORPORATION—See Occidental Petroleum Corporation; *U.S. Public*, pg. 1561
KERR PACIFIC CORP.; *U.S. Private*, pg. 2291
KERR PUMP AND SUPPLY INC.; *U.S. Private*, pg. 2291
KERRVILLE CAMP-RESORT, LLC—See Sun Communities, Inc.; *U.S. Public*, pg. 1961
KERRY AGRIBUSINESS—See Kerry Group plc; *Int'l*, pg. 4138
KERRY BIO-SCIENCE B.V.—See Kerry Group plc; *Int'l*, pg. 4138
KERRY BIO-SCIENCE—See Kerry Group plc; *Int'l*, pg. 4138
KERRY BIO-SCIENCE—See Kerry Group plc; *Int'l*, pg. 4138
KERRY (CANADA) INC.—See Kerry Group plc; *Int'l*, pg. 4138
KERRY CARGO CENTRE LIMITED—See Kerry Group Limited; *Int'l*, pg. 4137
KERRY DISTRIBUTION (THAILAND) LIMITED—See Kerry Logistics Network Limited; *Int'l*, pg. 4140
KERRY DO BRASIL LTDA.—See Kerry Group plc; *Int'l*, pg. 4139
KERRY EAS LOGISTICS LIMITED—See Kerry Logistics Network Limited; *Int'l*, pg. 4140
KERRY EXPRESS (THAILAND) PUBLIC COMPANY LIMITED—See S.F. Holding Co., Ltd.; *Int'l*, pg. 6456
KERRY FACILITIES MANAGEMENT (HONG KONG) LIMITED—See Kerry Logistics Network Limited; *Int'l*, pg. 4140
KERRY FACILITIES MANAGEMENT SERVICES LIMITED—See Kerry Logistics Network Limited; *Int'l*, pg. 4140
KERRY FARM SUPPLIES LIMITED—See Kerry Group plc; *Int'l*, pg. 4138
KERRYFLEX SUPPLY CHAIN SOLUTIONS LIMITED—See Kerry Logistics Network Limited; *Int'l*, pg. 4140
KERRYFLEX SUPPLY CHAIN SOLUTIONS (MACAU) LIMITED—See Kerry Logistics Network Limited; *Int'l*, pg. 4140
KERRY FOOD INGREDIENTS (CEBU), INC.—See Kerry Group plc; *Int'l*, pg. 4138
KERRY FOOD INGREDIENTS (CORK) LIMITED—See Kerry Group plc; *Int'l*, pg. 4138
KERRY FOOD INGREDIENTS (HANGZHOU) COMPANY LIMITED—See Kerry Group plc; *Int'l*, pg. 4138
KERRY FOOD INGREDIENTS (PHILIPPINES)—See Kerry Group plc; *Int'l*, pg. 4138
KERRY FOODSERVICE—See Kerry Group plc; *Int'l*, pg. 4138
KERRY FOODS LIMITED—See Kerry Group plc; *Int'l*, pg. 4138
KERRY FOODS NOON GROUP—See Kerry Group plc; *Int'l*, pg. 4138
KERRY FORD INC.; *U.S. Private*, pg. 2291
KERRY FREIGHT (AUSTRALIA) PTY LTD.—See Kerry Logistics Network Limited; *Int'l*, pg. 4140
KERRY FREIGHT (HONG KONG) LIMITED—See Kerry Logistics Network Limited; *Int'l*, pg. 4140
KERRY FREIGHT INTERNATIONAL LIMITED—See Kerry Logistics Network Limited; *Int'l*, pg. 4140
KERRY FREIGHT (KOREA) INC.—See Kerry Logistics Network Limited; *Int'l*, pg. 4140
KERRY FREIGHT (TAIWAN) LIMITED—See Kerry Logistics Network Limited; *Int'l*, pg. 4140
KERRY FREIGHT (THAILAND) LIMITED—See Kerry Logistics Network Limited; *Int'l*, pg. 4140
THE KERRYGOLD COMPANY LTD—See Ornua Cooperative Limited; *Int'l*, pg. 5642
KERRY GROUP LIMITED; *Int'l*, pg. 4137
KERRY GROUP PLC; *Int'l*, pg. 4138
KERRY GUATEMALA, S.A.—See Kerry Group plc; *Int'l*, pg. 4138
KERRY HOLDING CO.—See Kerry Group plc; *Int'l*, pg. 4138
KERRY HOLDINGS (IRELAND) LIMITED—See Kerry Group plc; *Int'l*, pg. 4138
KERRY HUNGARIA KFT.—See Kerry Group plc; *Int'l*, pg. 4139
KERRY IBERIA TASTE & NUTRITION, S.L.U.—See Kerry Group plc; *Int'l*, pg. 4139
KERRY INC.—See Kerry Group plc; *Int'l*, pg. 4138
KERRY INGREDIENTS AUSTRALIA PTY. LIMITED—See Kerry Group plc; *Int'l*, pg. 4139
KERRY INGREDIENTS (DE MEXICO) S.A. DE C.V.—See Kerry Group plc; *Int'l*, pg. 4139
KERRY INGREDIENTS & FLAVORS CLARK MANUFACTURING FACILITY—See Kerry Group plc; *Int'l*, pg. 4138
KERRY INGREDIENTS & FLAVORS—See Kerry Group plc; *Int'l*, pg. 4138
KERRY INGREDIENTS & FLAVORS—See Kerry Group plc; *Int'l*, pg. 4138
KERRY INGREDIENTS & FLAVORS—See Kerry Group plc; *Int'l*, pg. 4138
KERRY INGREDIENTS & FLAVOURS ITALIA S.P.A.—See Kerry Group plc; *Int'l*, pg. 4139
KERRY INGREDIENTS & FLAVOURS LIMITED—See Kerry Group plc; *Int'l*, pg. 4139
KERRY INGREDIENTS GMBH—See Kerry Group plc; *Int'l*, pg. 4139
KERRY INGREDIENTS HOLDINGS (FRANCE) S.A.—See Kerry Group plc; *Int'l*, pg. 4139
KERRY INGREDIENTS INDIA PVT. LIMITED—See Kerry Group plc; *Int'l*, pg. 4139
KERRY INGREDIENTS (IRELAND) LIMITED—See Kerry Group plc; *Int'l*, pg. 4139
KERRY INGREDIENTS (M) SDN. BHD.—See Kerry Group plc; *Int'l*, pg. 4139
KERRY INGREDIENTS NIGERIA LIMITED—See Kerry Group plc; *Int'l*, pg. 4139
KERRY INGREDIENTS (NZ) LIMITED—See Kerry Group plc; *Int'l*, pg. 4139
KERRY INGREDIENTS—See Kerry Group plc; *Int'l*, pg. 4138
KERRY INGREDIENTS—See Kerry Group plc; *Int'l*, pg. 4138
KERRY INGREDIENTS SOUTH AFRICA (PTY) LIMITED—See Kerry Group plc; *Int'l*, pg. 4139
KERRY INGREDIENTS (THAILAND) LIMITED—See Kerry Group plc; *Int'l*, pg. 4139
KERRY INGREDIENTS TRADING (SHANGHAI) LIMITED—See Kerry Group plc; *Int'l*, pg. 4139
KERRY INGREDIENTS (UK) LIMITED—See Kerry Group plc; *Int'l*, pg. 4139
KERRY JAPAN KABUSHIKI KAISHA—See Kerry Group plc; *Int'l*, pg. 4139
KERRY KENYA LIMITED—See Kerry Group plc; *Int'l*, pg. 4139
KERRY LEISURE CONCEPTS SDN BHD—See Kuok Brothers Sdn. Bhd.; *Int'l*, pg. 4335
KERRY LOGISTICS (AUSTRALIA) PTY LTD—See Kerry Logistics Network Limited; *Int'l*, pg. 4140
KERRY LOGISTICS (BELGIUM) BVBA—See Kerry Logistics Network Limited; *Int'l*, pg. 4140
KERRY LOGISTICS (CENTRAL EUROPE) GMBH—See Kerry Logistics Network Limited; *Int'l*, pg. 4140
KERRY LOGISTICS (GERMANY) GMBH—See Kerry Logistics Network Limited; *Int'l*, pg. 4140
KERRY LOGISTICS GMBH—See Kerry Logistics Network Limited; *Int'l*, pg. 4140
KERRY LOGISTICS (MALAYSIA) SDN BHD—See Kerry Logistics Network Limited; *Int'l*, pg. 4140
KERRY LOGISTICS (NETHERLANDS) B.V.—See Kerry Logistics Network Limited; *Int'l*, pg. 4140
KERRY LOGISTICS NETWORK LIMITED; *Int'l*, pg. 4139
KERRY LOGISTICS (SHENZHEN YANTIAN) LTD.—See Kerry Logistics Network Limited; *Int'l*, pg. 4140
KERRY LOGISTICS (SINGAPORE) PTE. LTD.—See Kerry Logistics Network Limited; *Int'l*, pg. 4140
KERRY LOGISTICS (SWITZERLAND) GMBH—See Kerry Logistics Network Limited; *Int'l*, pg. 4140
KERRY LOGISTICS (THAILAND) LIMITED—See Kerry Logistics Network Limited; *Int'l*, pg. 4140
KERRY LOGISTICS (UK) LIMITED—See Kerry Logistics Network Limited; *Int'l*, pg. 4140
KERRY LOGISTICS (WESTERN EUROPE) SPRL—See Kerry Logistics Network Limited; *Int'l*, pg. 4140
THE KERRYMAN LIMITED—See Mediahuis Partners NV; *Int'l*, pg. 4772
THE KERRYMAN LIMITED—See VP Exploitatie N.V.; *Int'l*, pg. 8311
KERRY MENAT DMCC—See Kerry Group plc; *Int'l*, pg. 4139
KERRY (NEW ZEALAND) LIMITED—See Wilmar International Limited; *Int'l*, pg. 8421
KERRY (NL) B.V.—See Kerry Group plc; *Int'l*, pg. 4138
KERRY OILS & GRAINS (QINGDAO) LTD—See Wilmar International Limited; *Int'l*, pg. 8421
KERRY PANAMA, S.A.—See Kerry Group plc; *Int'l*, pg. 4139
KERRY POLSKA SP. Z.O.O.—See Kerry Group plc; *Int'l*, pg. 4139
KERRY PROJECT MANAGEMENT (H.K.) LIMITED—See Kerry Group Limited; *Int'l*, pg. 4137
KERRY PROPERTIES DEVELOPMENT MANAGEMENT (SHANGHAI) CO .LTD.—See Kerry Group Limited; *Int'l*, pg. 4137
KERRY PROPERTIES (H.K.) LIMITED—See Kerry Group Limited; *Int'l*, pg. 4137
KERRY PROPERTIES LTD.—See Kerry Group Limited; *Int'l*, pg. 4137
KERRY PROPERTIES (MACAU) LIMITED—See Kerry Group Limited; *Int'l*, pg. 4137
KERRY PROPERTIES (NORTH CHINA) DEVELOPMENT CO., LTD.—See Kerry Group Limited; *Int'l*, pg. 4137
KERRY PROPERTIES (SHENZHEN) CO. LTD.—See Kerry Group Limited; *Int'l*, pg. 4137
KERRY PROPERTY MANAGEMENT SERVICES LIMITED—See Kerry Group Limited; *Int'l*, pg. 4137
KERRY (QUEBEC) INC.—See Kerry Group plc; *Int'l*, pg. 4138
KERRY REAL ESTATE AGENCY LIMITED—See Kerry Group Limited; *Int'l*, pg. 4137
KERRY RECORDS MANAGEMENT SERVICES LIMITED—See Kerry Group Limited; *Int'l*, pg. 4137
KERRY ROCKFORD ENTERPRISES INC.—See A.P. Moller-Maersk A/S; *Int'l*, pg. 27
KERRY SAVORY, INC.—See Kerry Group plc; *Int'l*, pg. 4138
KERRY SAVOURY INGREDIENTS FRANCE S.A.S.—See Kerry Group plc; *Int'l*, pg. 4139
KERRY SIAM SEAPORT LIMITED—See Kerry Logistics Network Limited; *Int'l*, pg. 4140
KERRY TASTE & NUTRITION (VIETNAM) COMPANY LIMITED—See Kerry Group plc; *Int'l*, pg. 4139
KERRY TJ LOGISTICS COMPANY LIMITED—See Kerry Logistics Network Limited; *Int'l*, pg. 4140
KERRYTOWN SHOPS OF ANN ARBOR INC.—See O'Neal, Inc.; *U.S. Private*, pg. 2979
KERRY TOYOTA TOWNE; *U.S. Private*, pg. 2291
KERRY TREASURY SERVICES LIMITED—See Kerry Group plc; *Int'l*, pg. 4139
KERRY VOLKSWAGEN; *U.S. Private*, pg. 2291
KERRY WAREHOUSE (CHAI WAN) LIMITED—See Kerry Logistics Network Limited; *Int'l*, pg. 4140
KERRY WAREHOUSE (FANLING 1) LIMITED—See Kerry Logistics Network Limited; *Int'l*, pg. 4140
KERRY WAREHOUSE (HONG KONG) LIMITED—See Kerry Logistics Network Limited; *Int'l*, pg. 4140
KERRY WAREHOUSE (KWAI CHUNG) LIMITED—See Kerry Logistics Network Limited; *Int'l*, pg. 4140
KERRY WAREHOUSE (SHEUNG SHUI) LIMITED—See Kerry Logistics Network Limited; *Int'l*, pg. 4140
KERRY WAREHOUSE (TSUEN WAN) LIMITED—See Kerry Logistics Network Limited; *Int'l*, pg. 4140
KERSEN TECHNOLOGY CO., LTD; *Int'l*, pg. 4140
KERSHIP LORIENT SAS—See Naval Group SA; *Int'l*, pg. 5173
KERSHIP LORIENT SAS—See Piriou SAS; *Int'l*, pg. 5875
KERSHIP SAS—See Naval Group SA; *Int'l*, pg. 5173
KERSHIP SAS—See Piriou SAS; *Int'l*, pg. 5875
KERSHNER OFFICE FURNITURE; *U.S. Private*, pg. 2291

KERSHNER OFFICE FURNITURE

KERSTAR LTD.—See Absolent Air Care Group AB; *Int'l*, pg. 70
KERUR HOLDINGS LTD.; *Int'l*, pg. 4141
KERUSSO ACTIVEWEAR, INC.; *U.S. Private*, pg. 2291
KERVAN GIDA SANAYI VE TICARET A.S.; *Int'l*, pg. 4141
KERVANSARAY YATIRIM HOLDING A.S.; *Int'l*, pg. 4141
KERVERUS HOLDING IT (CYPRUS) PLC; *Int'l*, pg. 4141
KER-WESTERLUND FUNERAL HOME, INC.—See Service Corporation International; *U.S. Public*, pg. 1869
KERYX BIOPHARMACEUTICALS, INC.—See Akebia Therapeutics, Inc.; *U.S. Public*, pg. 69
KERZNER INTERNATIONAL LIMITED; *Int'l*, pg. 4141
KES ACQUISITION COMPANY—See Steel Dynamics, Inc.; *U.S. Public*, pg. 1942
KES AIRPORT EQUIPMENT FUELLING B.V.—See Air France-KLM S.A.; *Int'l*, pg. 237
KESAR ENTERPRISES LIMITED; *Int'l*, pg. 4141
KESAR INDIA LIMITED; *Int'l*, pg. 4141
KESAR MULTIMODAL LOGISTICS LIMITED—See Kesar Enterprises Limited; *Int'l*, pg. 4141
KESAR PETROPRODUCTS LIMITED; *Int'l*, pg. 4141
KESAR TERMINALS & INFRASTRUCTURE LIMITED—See Kesar Enterprises Limited; *Int'l*, pg. 4141
KESAS KENANGAN SDN BHD—See S P Setia Berhad; *Int'l*, pg. 6443
KESAS SDN. BHD.—See Gamuda Berhad; *Int'l*, pg. 2879
KESHAV MANGLAM IMPEX PVT LTD.—See Impex Tech Lab Inc.; *U.S. Private*, pg. 2050
KESHUN WATERPROOF TECHNOLOGIES CO., LTD.; *Int'l*, pg. 4141
KESKISUOMALAINEN OYJ; *Int'l*, pg. 4141
KESKO CORPORATION; *Int'l*, pg. 4141
KESKO-EASTERN FINLAND, KUOPIO—See Kesko Corporation; *Int'l*, pg. 4142
KESKO FINANCE AND ADMINISTRATION—See Kesko Corporation; *Int'l*, pg. 4142
KESKO FOOD LTD.—See Kesko Corporation; *Int'l*, pg. 4142
KESKO INFORMATION & LOGISTICS MANAGEMENT DIVISION—See Kesko Corporation; *Int'l*, pg. 4142
KESKO-NORTHERN FINLAND—See Kesko Corporation; *Int'l*, pg. 4142
KESKO ONNINEN INTERNATIONAL TRADING CO., LTD.—See Kesko Corporation; *Int'l*, pg. 4142
KESKO REAL ESTATE DIVISION—See Kesko Corporation; *Int'l*, pg. 4142
KESKO RESOURCE MANAGEMENT DIVISION—See Kesko Corporation; *Int'l*, pg. 4142
KESKO-SOUTHEASTERN FINLAND—See Kesko Corporation; *Int'l*, pg. 4142
KESKO-SOUTHWESTERN FINLAND—See Kesko Corporation; *Int'l*, pg. 4142
KESKO SVENSKA AB—See Kesko Corporation; *Int'l*, pg. 4142
KESKO-WESTERN FINLAND—See Kesko Corporation; *Int'l*, pg. 4142
KESLA GMBH—See Kesla Oyj; *Int'l*, pg. 4143
KESLA OYJ; *Int'l*, pg. 4143
KESLOG LTD—See Kesko Corporation; *Int'l*, pg. 4142
KESM INDUSTRIES BERHAD; *Int'l*, pg. 4143
KESM INDUSTRIES BERHAD—See KESM Industries Berhad; *Int'l*, pg. 4143
KESM INDUSTRIES (TIANJIN) CO. LTD.—See KESM Industries Berhad; *Int'l*, pg. 4143
KESM TEST (M) SDN. BHD.—See KESM Industries Berhad; *Int'l*, pg. 4143
KESO GMBH—See ASSA ABLOY AB; *Int'l*, pg. 640
KESORAM INDUSTRIES LIMITED - BIRLA SHAKTI CEMENT—See Kesoram Industries Limited; *Int'l*, pg. 4143
KESORAM INDUSTRIES LIMITED; *Int'l*, pg. 4143
KESPRO LTD—See Kesko Corporation; *Int'l*, pg. 4142
KESP SDN. BHD.—See KESM Industries Berhad; *Int'l*, pg. 4143
KES SCIENCE & TECHNOLOGY, INC.—See Applied UV, Inc.; *U.S. Public*, pg. 173
KESSEBOHMER OHG; *Int'l*, pg. 4143
KESSEL CONSTRUCTION INC.; *U.S. Private*, pg. 2291
KESSEL FESTIVAL GMBH—See DEAG Deutsche Entertainment AG; *Int'l*, pg. 1997
KESSELRUN RESOURCES LTD.; *Int'l*, pg. 4143
KESSEL (THAILAND) PTE., LTD.—See Siam Rajathanee Co., Ltd.; *Int'l*, pg. 6875
KESSINGER/HUNTER & CO. LC; *U.S. Private*, pg. 2291
KESSLER & CO AG—See Marsh & McLennan Companies, Inc.; *U.S. Public*, pg. 1377
KESSLER CONSULTING, INC.—See Marsh & McLennan Companies, Inc.; *U.S. Public*, pg. 1377
KESSLER-ELLIS PRODUCTS CO. INC.; *U.S. Private*, pg. 2291
THE KESSLER ENTERPRISE INC.; *U.S. Private*, pg. 4065
KESSLER GROUP INCORPORATED; *U.S. Private*, pg. 2291
KESSLER INDUSTRIES INC.; *U.S. Private*, pg. 2291
KESSLER INSTITUTE FOR REHABILITATION, INC.—See Select Medical Holdings Corporation; *U.S. Public*, pg. 1858

KESSLER ORTHOTIC & PROSTHETIC SERVICES, INC.—See Select Medical Holdings Corporation; *U.S. Public*, pg. 1858
KESSLER PREVOYANCE SA—See Marsh & McLennan Companies, Inc.; *U.S. Public*, pg. 1377
KESSLER REHAB CENTERS, INC.—See Select Medical Holdings Corporation; *U.S. Public*, pg. 1858
KESSLER SALES & DISTRIBUTION LLC—See Mueller Industries, Inc.; *U.S. Public*, pg. 1484
KESSLERS INCORPORATED; *U.S. Private*, pg. 2291
KESSLERS INTERNATIONAL LTD.—See Endless LLP; *Int'l*, pg. 2403
KESSLERS SPORT SHOP INC.—See ONEX Corporation; *Int'l*, pg. 5580
KES SYSTEMS, INC.—See Sunright Limited; *Int'l*, pg. 7321
KES SYSTEMS & SERVICE (1993) PTE. LTD. - PRODUCT DIVISION—See KESM Industries Berhad; *Int'l*, pg. 4143
KES SYSTEMS & SERVICE (1993) PTE. LTD.—See KESM Industries Berhad; *Int'l*, pg. 4143
KES SYSTEMS & SERVICE COSTA RICA SOCIEDAD ANONIMA—See KESM Industries Berhad; *Int'l*, pg. 4143
KES SYSTEMS & SERVICE (SHANGHAI) CO., LTD.—See KESM Industries Berhad; *Int'l*, pg. 4143
KESTE, LLC—See Trinity Hunt Management, L.P.; *U.S. Private*, pg. 4235
KESTEN-BROWN INSURANCE, LLC—See GTCR LLC; *U.S. Private*, pg. 1803
KESTER COMPONENTS (M) SDN. BHD.—See Illinois Tool Works Inc.; *U.S. Public*, pg. 1108
KESTER, INC.—See Element Solutions Inc.; *U.S. Public*, pg. 726
KESTONE CL ASIA HUB PTE. LTD.—See CL Educate Limited; *Int'l*, pg. 1640
KESTONE CL US LIMITED—See CL Educate Limited; *Int'l*, pg. 1640
KESTONE INTEGRATED MARKETING SERVICES PRIVATE LIMITED—See CL Educate Limited; *Int'l*, pg. 1640
KESTRA FINANCIAL, INC.—See Warburg Pincus LLC; *U.S. Private*, pg. 4439
KESTRA INVESTMENT SERVICES, LLC—See Warburg Pincus LLC; *U.S. Private*, pg. 4439
KESTRA KIINTEISTOPALVELUT OY—See Kesko Corporation; *Int'l*, pg. 4142
KESTREL-BCE LIMITED—See Epwin Group Plc; *Int'l*, pg. 2466
KESTREL COAL PTY. LTD.—See Rio Tinto plc; *Int'l*, pg. 6347
KESTREL COAL RESOURCES PTY. LTD.—See PT Adaro Energy Indonesia Tbk; *Int'l*, pg. 6019
KESTREL CORP.; *U.S. Private*, pg. 2291
KESTREL GOLD INC.; *Int'l*, pg. 4143
KESTREL PEST CONTROL LIMITED—See Rollins, Inc.; *U.S. Public*, pg. 1809
KESTRONICS ELECTRONICS (SHANGHAI PUDONG NEW AREA) CO. LTD.—See Sunright Limited; *Int'l*, pg. 7321
KESTRONICS PHILIPPINES, INC.—See Sunright Limited; *Int'l*, pg. 7321
KESTRONICS (S) PTE. LTD.—See Sunright Limited; *Int'l*, pg. 7321
KESTRONICS (THAILAND) CO., LTD.—See Sunright Limited; *Int'l*, pg. 7321
KEST SYSTEMS & SERVICE LTD.—See KESM Industries Berhad; *Int'l*, pg. 4143
KESWICK CORPORATION—See LVMH Moet Hennessy Louis Vuitton SE; *Int'l*, pg. 4591
KETA FOODS, LDA.—See Takara Holdings, Inc.; *Int'l*, pg. 7432
KETCHAM FOREST PRODUCTS, INC.; *U.S. Private*, pg. 2291
KETCHUM CANADA—See Omnicom Group Inc.; *U.S. Public*, pg. 1586
KETCHUM CHENGDU—See Omnicom Group Inc.; *U.S. Public*, pg. 1587
KETCHUM DIRECTORY ADVERTISING/KANSAS CITY—See Omnicom Group Inc.; *U.S. Public*, pg. 1587
KETCHUM DIRECTORY ADVERTISING/LOUISVILLE—See Omnicom Group Inc.; *U.S. Public*, pg. 1587
KETCHUM DIRECTORY ADVERTISING/PITTSBURGH—See Omnicom Group Inc.; *U.S. Public*, pg. 1587
KETCHUM, INC.—See Omnicom Group Inc.; *U.S. Public*, pg. 1586
KETCHUM PLEON GMBH—See Omnicom Group Inc.; *U.S. Public*, pg. 1587
KETCHUM PLEON MILANO—See Omnicom Group Inc.; *U.S. Public*, pg. 1587
KETCHUM PLEON ROMA—See Omnicom Group Inc.; *U.S. Public*, pg. 1587
KETCHUM PLEON—See Omnicom Group Inc.; *U.S. Public*, pg. 1587
KETCHUM PLEON—See Omnicom Group Inc.; *U.S. Public*, pg. 1587

CORPORATE AFFILIATIONS

KETCHUM PLEON—See Omnicom Group Inc.; *U.S. Public*, pg. 1587
KETCHUM PLEON STUTTGART—See Omnicom Group Inc.; *U.S. Public*, pg. 1587
KETCHUM PUBLICO—See Omnicom Group Inc.; *U.S. Public*, pg. 1587
KETCHUM-PUBLIC RELATIONS LTD.—See Omnicom Group Inc.; *U.S. Public*, pg. 1587
KETCHUM-PUBLIC RELATIONS—See Omnicom Group Inc.; *U.S. Public*, pg. 1587
KETCHUM-PUBLIC RELATIONS—See Omnicom Group Inc.; *U.S. Public*, pg. 1587
KETCHUM-PUBLIC RELATIONS—See Omnicom Group Inc.; *U.S. Public*, pg. 1587
KETCHUM SAMPARK PVT. LTD—See Omnicom Group Inc.; *U.S. Public*, pg. 1587
KETCHUM—See Omnicom Group Inc.; *U.S. Public*, pg. 1586
KETCHUM—See Omnicom Group Inc.; *U.S. Public*, pg. 1586
KETCHUM—See Omnicom Group Inc.; *U.S. Public*, pg. 1586
KETCHUM—See Omnicom Group Inc.; *U.S. Public*, pg. 1586
KETCHUM—See Omnicom Group Inc.; *U.S. Public*, pg. 1586
KETCHUM—See Omnicom Group Inc.; *U.S. Public*, pg. 1586
KETCHUM—See Omnicom Group Inc.; *U.S. Public*, pg. 1586
KETCHUM—See Omnicom Group Inc.; *U.S. Public*, pg. 1586
KETCHUM—See Omnicom Group Inc.; *U.S. Public*, pg. 1586
KETCHUM—See Omnicom Group Inc.; *U.S. Public*, pg. 1586
KETCHUM—See Omnicom Group Inc.; *U.S. Public*, pg. 1586
KETCHUM SPAIN—See Omnicom Group Inc.; *U.S. Public*, pg. 1587
KETCHUM TAIPEI—See Omnicom Group Inc.; *U.S. Public*, pg. 1587
KET ELECTRONICS (MALAYSIA) SDN. BHD.—See Kanematsu Corporation; *Int'l*, pg. 4068
KETER1 ACQUISITION CORP.; *U.S. Public*, pg. 1224
KETER ENVIRONMENTAL SERVICES, INC.—See TPG Capital, L.P.; *U.S. Public*, pg. 2174
KETER GROUP SA; *Int'l*, pg. 4143
KETER PLASTIC LTD.—See BC Partners LLP; *Int'l*, pg. 925
KETIC INC.—See Messe Munchen GmbH; *Int'l*, pg. 4841
KETJEN BLACK INTERNATIONAL COMPANY—See Lion Corporation; *Int'l*, pg. 4517
KETJEN CATALYSTS (SHANGHAI) COMPANY LIMITED—See Albemarle Corporation; *U.S. Public*, pg. 73
KETJEN CORPORATION—See Albemarle Corporation; *U.S. Public*, pg. 73
KETJEN HUNGARY LIMITED LIABILITY COMPANY—See Albemarle Corporation; *U.S. Public*, pg. 73
KETJEN INDIA PRIVATE LIMITED—See Albemarle Corporation; *U.S. Public*, pg. 73
KETJEN JAPAN GK—See Albemarle Corporation; *U.S. Public*, pg. 73
KETJEN KOREA LIMITED—See Albemarle Corporation; *U.S. Public*, pg. 73
KETJEN MALAYSIA SDN BHD.—See Albemarle Corporation; *U.S. Public*, pg. 73
KETJEN NETHERLANDS B.V.—See Albemarle Corporation; *U.S. Public*, pg. 73
KETJEN SINGAPORE PRIVATE LIMITED—See Albemarle Corporation; *U.S. Public*, pg. 73
KETJEN VIETNAM LIMITED LIABILITY CO., LTD.—See Albemarle Corporation; *U.S. Public*, pg. 73
KET MARINE ASIA PTE. LTD.—See GEA Group Aktiengesellschaft; *Int'l*, pg. 2903
KET MARINE INTERNATIONAL B.V.—See GEA Group Aktiengesellschaft; *Int'l*, pg. 2903
KET SOLUTION CO. LTD.—See Korea Electric Terminal Co., Ltd.; *Int'l*, pg. 4284
KETTELHUT CONSTRUCTION, INC.; *U.S. Private*, pg. 2292
KETTENBACH GMBH—See Steilmann Holding AG; *Int'l*, pg. 7193
KETT ENGINEERING CORPORATION; *U.S. Private*, pg. 2292
KETTERING ADVENTIST HEALTHCARE; *U.S. Private*, pg. 2292
KETTLEBY FOODS LIMITED—See Samworth Brothers Limited; *Int'l*, pg. 6519
KETTLE CUISINE, LLC—See Kainos Capital, LLC; *U.S. Private*, pg. 2255
KETTLE FALLS INTERNATIONAL RAILWAY, LLC—See The Broe Companies, Inc.; *U.S. Private*, pg. 4001
KETTLE FOODS, INC.—See Campbell Soup Company; *U.S. Public*, pg. 381
KETTLE-LAKES COOPERATIVE; *U.S. Private*, pg. 2292

COMPANY NAME INDEX

KETTLER AUSTRIA GMBH—See Lafayette Mittelstand Capital; *Int'l*, pg. 4392
KETTLER BENELUX B.V.—See Lafayette Mittelstand Capital; *Int'l*, pg. 4392
KETTLER (GB) LIMITED—See Lafayette Mittelstand Capital; *Int'l*, pg. 4392
KETTLER INTERNATIONAL, INC.—See Lafayette Mittelstand Capital; *Int'l*, pg. 4392
KETTLER INTERNATIONAL INC.—See Lafayette Mittelstand Capital; *Int'l*, pg. 4392
KETTLER ISRAEL LTD.—See Lafayette Mittelstand Capital; *Int'l*, pg. 4392
KETTLER POLSKA SP. Z O.O.—See Lafayette Mittelstand Capital; *Int'l*, pg. 4392
KETTLER S.A.R.L.—See Lafayette Mittelstand Capital; *Int'l*, pg. 4392
KETTLEY & COMPANY REALTORS-BATAVIA—See Kettley & Company Realtors Inc.; *U.S. Private*, pg. 2292
KETTLEY & COMPANY REALTORS-COMMERCIAL—See Kettley & Company Realtors Inc.; *U.S. Private*, pg. 2292
KETTLEY & COMPANY REALTORS INC.; *U.S. Private*, pg. 2292
KETTLEY & COMPANY REALTORS-OSWEGO—See Kettley & Company Realtors Inc.; *U.S. Private*, pg. 2292
KETTLEY & COMPANY REALTORS-SAINT CHARLES—See Kettley & Company Realtors Inc.; *U.S. Private*, pg. 2292
KETTLEY & COMPANY REALTORS-SANDWICH—See Kettley & Company Realtors Inc.; *U.S. Private*, pg. 2292
KETTLEY & COMPANY REALTORS-SUGAR GROVE—See Kettley & Company Realtors Inc.; *U.S. Private*, pg. 2292
KETTLEY & COMPANY REALTORS-YORKVILLE—See Kettley & Company Realtors Inc.; *U.S. Private*, pg. 2292
KETTLEY REALTORS—See Kettley & Company Realtors Inc.; *U.S. Private*, pg. 2292
KE TUBE INC.; *U.S. Private*, pg. 2270
KETV HEARST-ARGYLE TELEVISION, INC.—See The Hearst Corporation; *U.S. Private*, pg. 4048
KEUKA FOOTWEAR, INC.—See Genesco Inc.; *U.S. Public*, pg. 030
KEUM JUNG AKZO NOBEL PEROXIDES LTD—See Akzo Nobel N.V.; *Int'l*, pg. 274
KEUM KANG STEEL CO., LTD.; *Int'l*, pg. 4143
KEUM SUNG GRINDING WHEEL CO., LTD.—See Cheil Grinding Wheel Ind. Co., Ltd.; *Int'l*, pg. 1460
KEURIG CANADA INC.—See JAB Holding Company S.a.r.l.; *Int'l*, pg. 3862
KEURIG DR PEPPER INC.—See JAB Holding Company S.a.r.l.; *Int'l*, pg. 3861
KEURIG GREEN MOUNTAIN, INC.—See JAB Holding Company S.a.r.l.; *Int'l*, pg. 3862
KEURIG, INCORPORATED—See JAB Holding Company S.a.r.l.; *Int'l*, pg. 3862
KEVADIYA CONSTRUCTION PRIVATE LIMITED—See Udayshivakumar Infra Ltd.; *Int'l*, pg. 8014
KEVENOLL DO BRASIL PRODUTOS MEDICOS HOSPITALARES LTDA—See Top Glove Corporation Bhd.; *Int'l*, pg. 7812
KEV GROUP INC.; *Int'l*, pg. 4143
KEVINGTON BUILDING PRODUCTS LIMITED—See Ibstock plc; *Int'l*, pg. 3577
KEVIN JARVIS BUILDING SUPPLIES LIMITED—See Fletcher Building Limited; *Int'l*, pg. 2700
KEVIN'S WHOLESALE LLC; *U.S. Private*, pg. 2292
KEVIN WHITAKER CHEVROLET INC.; *U.S. Private*, pg. 2292
KEVITA, INC.—See PepsiCo, Inc.; *U.S. Public*, pg. 1669
KEVLIN CORPORATION—See Advent International Corporation; *U.S. Private*, pg. 100
KEVN-TV—See Gray Television, Inc.; *U.S. Public*, pg. 960
KEVON SDN. BHD.—See Ritamix Global Limited; *Int'l*, pg. 6351
KEVOTHERMAL LIMITED—See Sealed Air Corporation; *U.S. Public*, pg. 1853
KEVOTHERMAL LLC—See Sealed Air Corporation; *U.S. Public*, pg. 1853
KEWAL KIRAN CLOTHING LTD; *Int'l*, pg. 4144
KEWALO HARBOR, LLC—See Howard Hughes Holdings Inc.; *U.S. Public*, pg. 1060
KEWAUNEE FABRICATIONS, LLC—See Oshkosh Corporation; *U.S. Public*, pg. 1620
KEWAUNEE LABWAY ASIA PTE. LTD.—See Kewaunee Scientific Corporation; *U.S. Public*, pg. 1224
KEWAUNEE LABWAY INDIA PVT. LTD.—See Kewaunee Scientific Corporation; *U.S. Public*, pg. 1225
KEWAUNEE SCIENTIFIC CORPORATION INDIA PVT. LTD.—See Kewaunee Scientific Corporation; *U.S. Public*, pg. 1224
KEWAUNEE SCIENTIFIC CORPORATION; *U.S. Public*, pg. 1224
KEWEENAW BAY INDIAN COMMUNITY; *U.S. Private*, pg. 2292
KEWEENAW COPPER CO.—See Highland Copper Company Inc.; *Int'l*, pg. 3387

KEWEENAW LAND ASSOCIATION, LTD.; *U.S. Public*, pg. 1225
KEWEGO DEUTSCHLAND GMBH—See Piksel, Inc.; *U.S. Private*, pg. 3180
KEWELL TECHNOLOGY CO., LTD.; *Int'l*, pg. 4144
KEWILL BELGIUM NV—See Francisco Partners Management, LP; *U.S. Private*, pg. 1589
KEWILL BV—See Francisco Partners Management, LP; *U.S. Private*, pg. 1589
KEWILL CO., LTD.—See Francisco Partners Management, LP; *U.S. Private*, pg. 1589
KEWILL GMBH—See Francisco Partners Management, LP; *U.S. Private*, pg. 1589
KEWILL HOLDING B.V.—See Francisco Partners Management, LP; *U.S. Private*, pg. 1589
KEWILL INC.—See Francisco Partners Management, LP; *U.S. Private*, pg. 1589
KEWILL LIMITED—See Francisco Partners Management, LP; *U.S. Private*, pg. 1589
KEWILL PTE LTD—See Francisco Partners Management, LP; *U.S. Private*, pg. 1589
KEWILL SERVICE LOGISTICS B.V.—See Francisco Partners Management, LP; *U.S. Private*, pg. 1589
KEWILL—See Francisco Partners Management, LP; *U.S. Private*, pg. 1589
KEW MEDIA GROUP INC.; *Int'l*, pg. 4143
KEW MEDIA GROUP UK LIMITED—See Kew Media Group Inc.; *Int'l*, pg. 4143
KEW MEDIA INTERNATIONAL LIMITED—See Kew Media Group Inc.; *Int'l*, pg. 4144
KEWPIE CORPORATION; *Int'l*, pg. 4144
KEWPIE JYOZO CO., LTD.—See Kewpie Corporation; *Int'l*, pg. 4144
KEWPIE MALAYSIA SDN. BHD.—See Mitsubishi Corporation; *Int'l*, pg. 4939
KEWPIE VIETNAM CO., LTD.—See Mitsubishi Corporation; *Int'l*, pg. 4939
KEWSO SERVICES CORPORATION—See Kewpie Corporation; *Int'l*, pg. 4144
THE KEXIM ASIA LTD.—See The Export-Import Bank of Korea; *Int'l*, pg. 7641
KEXIM BANK (UK)—See The Export-Import Bank of Korea; *Int'l*, pg. 7641
KEXIM VIETNAM LEASING CO—See The Export-Import Bank of Korea; *Int'l*, pg. 7641
KEXING BIOPHARM CO., LTD.—See Shan Dong Kexing Bioproducts Co., Ltd.; *Int'l*, pg. 6751
KEY 103—See Heinrich Bauer Verlag KG; *Int'l*, pg. 3324
KEYAD, LLC; *U.S. Private*, pg. 2294
KEY ALLIANCE GROUP BERHAD; *Int'l*, pg. 4144
KEYANG ELECTRIC MACHINERY CO., LTD. - ANSAN PLANT—See Haesung Industrial Co., Ltd.; *Int'l*, pg. 3206
KEYANG ELECTRIC MACHINERY CO., LTD. - CHEONAN PLANT—See Haesung Industrial Co., Ltd.; *Int'l*, pg. 3206
KEYANG ELECTRIC MACHINERY CO., LTD.—See Haesung Industrial Co., Ltd.; *Int'l*, pg. 3205
KEYANG ELECTRIC MACHINERY (JIANGSU) CO., LTD.—See Haesung Industrial Co., Ltd.; *Int'l*, pg. 3205
KEYANG ELECTRIC MACHINERY (SUZHOU) CO., LTD.—See Haesung Industrial Co., Ltd.; *Int'l*, pg. 3206
KEYARCH ACQUISITION CORPORATION; *U.S. Public*, pg. 1225
KEY ASIC BERHAD; *Int'l*, pg. 4144
KEY ASIC LIMITED (SINGAPORE)—See Key ASIC Berhad; *Int'l*, pg. 4144
KEY ASSET MANAGEMENT (UK) LIMITED—See Skandinaviska Enskilda Banken AB; *Int'l*, pg. 6977
KEY ASSOCIATES CO., LTD.—See Key Coffee Inc.; *Int'l*, pg. 4145
KEY & ASSOCIATES PC; *U.S. Private*, pg. 2292
KEY AUTO CENTER—See Key Auto Group; *U.S. Private*, pg. 2292
KEY AUTO GROUP; *U.S. Private*, pg. 2292
KEYBANC CAPITAL MARKETS INC.—See KeyCorp; *U.S. Public*, pg. 1225
KEYBANK N.A. - KEY COMMUNITY BANK DIVISION—See KeyCorp; *U.S. Public*, pg. 1225
KEYBANK N.A. - KEY CORPORATE BANK DIVISION—See KeyCorp; *U.S. Public*, pg. 1225
KEYBANK NATIONAL ASSOCIATION—See KeyCorp; *U.S. Public*, pg. 1225
KEYBASE LLC—See Zoom Video Communications, Inc.; *U.S. Public*, pg. 2411
KEY BENEFIT ADMINISTRATORS, INC.—See Key Family of Companies; *U.S. Private*, pg. 2293
KEY BENEFIT ADMINISTRATORS—See Key Family of Companies; *U.S. Private*, pg. 2293
KEYBOARD CONCEPTS INC.; *U.S. Private*, pg. 2294
KEY BRAND ENTERTAINMENT, INC.; *U.S. Private*, pg. 2292
KEY BRAND FERTILIZER COMPANY LIMITED—See Buriram Sugar Public Company Limited; *Int'l*, pg. 1224
KEYBRIDGE CAPITAL LIMITED; *Int'l*, pg. 4145
KEY BS JLT W.L.L—See Arabi Holding Group Company K.S.C.C.; *Int'l*, pg. 532
KEY BUICK COMPANY; *U.S. Private*, pg. 2292
KEY CADILLAC, INC.; *U.S. Private*, pg. 2292

KEYENCE CORPORATION

KEYCAMP HOLIDAYS (IRELAND) LIMITED—See Cox & Kings Limited; *Int'l*, pg. 1822
KEYCAMP HOLIDAYS NETHERLANDS B.V.—See Cox & Kings Limited; *Int'l*, pg. 1822
KEY CAPTURE ENERGY, LLC—See SK Inc.; *Int'l*, pg. 6972
KEYCAST KOHLSWA AB—See The Riverside Company; *U.S. Private*, pg. 4109
KEYCAST LJUNGBY AB—See The Riverside Company; *U.S. Private*, pg. 4109
KEYCAST MEKO AB—See The Riverside Company; *U.S. Private*, pg. 4109
KEYCENTRIX—See CGF Industries, Inc.; *U.S. Private*, pg. 844
KEY CHEVROLET CADILLAC BUICK & GMC INC.; *Int'l*, pg. 4144
KEY CITY FURNITURE COMPANY; *U.S. Private*, pg. 2292
KEY CLUB MIAMI LLC—See Live Nation Entertainment, Inc.; *U.S. Public*, pg. 1329
KEYCO DISTRIBUTORS, INC.; *U.S. Private*, pg. 2294
KEY COFFEE INC.; *Int'l*, pg. 4145
KEY COMMUNICATIONS, INC.; *U.S. Private*, pg. 2292
KEY COMMUNITY DEVELOPMENT CORPORATION—See KeyCorp; *U.S. Public*, pg. 1225
KEY CONSTRUCTION INC.—See Wagman Companies, Inc.; *U.S. Private*, pg. 4426
KEY CONSTRUCTORS INC.; *U.S. Private*, pg. 2293
KEY CONTAINER CORPORATION; *U.S. Private*, pg. 2293
KEY COOPERATIVE; *U.S. Private*, pg. 2293
KEY CORP LIMITED; *Int'l*, pg. 4145
KEYCORP PTY. LIMITED—See Nordic Capital AB; *Int'l*, pg. 5420
KEYCORP REAL ESTATE CAPITAL MARKETS, INC.—See KeyCorp; *U.S. Public*, pg. 1226
KEYCORP; *U.S. Public*, pg. 1225
KEY CURRICULUM PRESS, INC.—See Platinum Equity, LLC; *U.S. Private*, pg. 3205
KEY DE PRECISE INDUSTRIS CO., LTD.—See Key Ware Electronics Co., Ltd.; *Int'l*, pg. 4145
KEYEAST CO., LTD; *Int'l*, pg. 4145
KEYEDIN SOLUTIONS HOLDINGS LIMITED—See KeyedIn Solutions, Inc.; *U.S. Private*, pg. 2294
KEYEDIN SOLUTIONS, INC.; *U.S. Private*, pg. 2294
KEYEDIN SOLUTIONS LIMITED—See KeyedIn Solutions, Inc.; *U.S. Private*, pg. 2294
KEYEDIN (UK) LIMITED—See KeyedIn Solutions, Inc.; *U.S. Private*, pg. 2294
KEY EDUCATION RESOURCES—See KeyCorp; *U.S. Public*, pg. 1225
KEYENCE AG—See Keyence Corporation; *Int'l*, pg. 4145
KEYENCE BRASIL COMERCIO DE PRODUTOS ELETRONICOS LTDA.—See Keyence Corporation; *Int'l*, pg. 4146
KEYENCE CANADA INC.—See Keyence Corporation; *Int'l*, pg. 4146
KEYENCE (CHINA) CO., LTD.—See Keyence Corporation; *Int'l*, pg. 4146
KEYENCE CORPORATION OF AMERICA—See Keyence Corporation; *Int'l*, pg. 4146
KEYENCE CORPORATION; *Int'l*, pg. 4145
KEYENCE DEUTSCHLAND GMBH—See Keyence Corporation; *Int'l*, pg. 4146
KEYENCE FRANCE S.A.—See Keyence Corporation; *Int'l*, pg. 4146
KEYENCE (HONG KONG) CO., LIMITED—See Keyence Corporation; *Int'l*, pg. 4145
KEYENCE HUNGARY KFT.—See Keyence Corporation; *Int'l*, pg. 4146
KEYENCE INTERNATIONAL (BELGIUM) NV/SA—See Keyence Corporation; *Int'l*, pg. 4146
KEYENCE ITALIA S.P.A.—See Keyence Corporation; *Int'l*, pg. 4146
KEYENCE (MALAYSIA) SDN. BHD.—See Keyence Corporation; *Int'l*, pg. 4145
KEYENCE MEXICO S.A. DE C.V.—See Keyence Corporation; *Int'l*, pg. 4146
KEYENCE PHILIPPINES INC.—See Keyence Corporation; *Int'l*, pg. 4146
KEYENCE POLAND SP. Z O.O.—See Keyence Corporation; *Int'l*, pg. 4146
KEYENCE SINGAPORE PTE. LTD.—See Keyence Corporation; *Int'l*, pg. 4146
KEYENCE SLOVENIA—See Keyence Corporation; *Int'l*, pg. 4146
KEYENCE TAIWAN CO., LTD.—See Keyence Corporation; *Int'l*, pg. 4146
KEYENCE (THAILAND) CO., LTD.—See Keyence Corporation; *Int'l*, pg. 4145
KEYENCE UK LTD.—See Keyence Corporation; *Int'l*, pg. 4146
KEYENCE VIETNAM CO., LTD.—See Keyence Corporation; *Int'l*, pg. 4146
KEY ENERGY QTS—See Key Energy Services, Inc.; *U.S. Public*, pg. 1225
KEY ENERGY SERVICES, INC.-APPALACHIAN DIVISION—See Key Energy Services, Inc.; *U.S. Public*, pg. 1225

KEYENCE CORPORATION

CORPORATE AFFILIATIONS

KEY ENERGY SERVICES, INC.-CALIFORNIA DIVISION—See Key Energy Services, Inc.; *U.S. Public*, pg. 1225
KEY ENERGY SERVICES, INC.-PERMIAN BASIN NORTH DIVISION—See Key Energy Services, Inc.; *U.S. Public*, pg. 1225
KEY ENERGY SERVICES, INC.-ROCKY MOUNTAIN DIVISION—See Key Energy Services, Inc.; *U.S. Public*, pg. 1225
KEY ENERGY SERVICES, INC.; *U.S. Public*, pg. 1225
KEY EQUIPMENT FINANCE INC.—See KeyCorp; *U.S. Public*, pg. 1225
KEY EQUIPMENT FINANCE INTERNATIONAL INC.—See KeyCorp; *U.S. Public*, pg. 1225
KEY EQUIPMENT & SUPPLY COMPANY; *U.S. Private*, pg. 2293
KEYERA CORPORATION; *Int'l*, pg. 4146
KEYERA ENERGY INC.—See Keyera Corporation; *Int'l*, pg. 4146
KEYERA ENERGY LTD.—See Keyera Corporation; *Int'l*, pg. 4146
KEYES ASSET MANAGEMENT—See The Keyes Company; *U.S. Private*, pg. 4065
THE KEYES COMPANY; *U.S. Private*, pg. 4065
KEYES LEXUS—See Keyes Motors, Inc.; *U.S. Private*, pg. 2294
KEYES MOTORS, INC.; *U.S. Private*, pg. 2294
KEYES NATIONAL REFERRAL—See The Keyes Company; *U.S. Private*, pg. 4065
KEYES TOYOTA—See Keyes Motors, Inc.; *U.S. Private*, pg. 2294
KEYE-TV—See Sinclair, Inc.; *U.S. Public*, pg. 1885
KEY FAMILY OF COMPANIES; *U.S. Private*, pg. 2293
KEY FINANCE LIMITED; *Int'l*, pg. 4145
KEY FINANCIAL ADMINISTRATORS, LTD.—See Key Family of Companies; *U.S. Private*, pg. 2293
KEY FOOD STORES CO-OPERATIVE, INC.; *U.S. Private*, pg. 2293
KEY FOUNDRY, INC.—See SK hynix Inc.; *Int'l*, pg. 6971
KEY FOUNDRY LTD.—See SK hynix Inc.; *Int'l*, pg. 6971
KEY FOUNDRY SHANGHAI CO., LTD.—See SK hynix Inc.; *Int'l*, pg. 6971
KEYGAMES NETWORK B.V.—See Azerion Group N.V.; *Int'l*, pg. 778
KEYG CONSULTING S.P.A.—See Stellantis N.V.; *Int'l*, pg. 7197
KEYGENT LLC; *U.S. Private*, pg. 2294
KEY GLASS LLC; *U.S. Private*, pg. 2293
KEY HANDLING SYSTEMS, INC.; *U.S. Private*, pg. 2293
KEYHAVEN CAPITAL PARTNERS LTD.; *Int'l*, pg. 4146
KEY HEALTH GROUP INC.—See Oasis Legal Finance LLC; *U.S. Private*, pg. 2986
KEYHOLDER, INC.; *Int'l*, pg. 4146
KEYHOLE TIG PTY. LIMITED—See K-TIG Limited; *Int'l*, pg. 4042
KEYHOLE TIG (USA) INC.—See K-TIG Limited; *Int'l*, pg. 4042
KEY HOLIDAYS—See United Rail, Inc.; *U.S. Public*, pg. 2234
KEY IMPACT & SALES SYSTEMS, INC.; *U.S. Private*, pg. 2293
KEYIMPACT SALES & SYSTEMS, INC.—See Prospect Hill Growth Partners, L.P.; *U.S. Private*, pg. 3288
KEY INDUSTRIES, INC.; *U.S. Private*, pg. 2293
KEY INFORMATION SYSTEMS, INC.; *U.S. Private*, pg. 2293
KEY INSURANCE COMPANY LIMITED—See GraceKennedy Limited; *Int'l*, pg. 3049
KEY INTERNATIONAL, INC.; *U.S. Private*, pg. 2293
KEYKERT USA, INC.—See China North Industries Group Corporation; *Int'l*, pg. 1535
KEY KNIFE INC.—See Kadant Inc.; *U.S. Public*, pg. 1212
KEYLIMETIE, LLC.; *U.S. Private*, pg. 2294
KEYLINE BUILDERS MERCHANT—See Travis Perkins plc; *Int'l*, pg. 7908
KEYLINE CONSULTING SDN. BHD.—See Chuan Huat Resources Berhad; *Int'l*, pg. 1589
KEYLOGIC ASSOCIATES, INC.—See System One Holdings, LLC; *U.S. Private*, pg. 3907
KEYLOGIC SYSTEMS, LLC—See System One Holdings, LLC; *U.S. Private*, pg. 3907
KEY LOGISTICS AB—See Mitsui-Soko Holdings Co., Ltd.; *Int'l*, pg. 4992
KEY LOGISTICS (PRIVATE) LIMITED—See TSL Limited; *Int'l*, pg. 7952
KEY MANUFACTURING INC—See Manar, Inc.; *U.S. Private*, pg. 2561
KEYMARK CORPORATION; *U.S. Private*, pg. 2294
KEYMARK, INC. - NORTHEAST—See Keymark, Inc.; *U.S. Private*, pg. 2294
KEYMARK, INC.; *U.S. Private*, pg. 2294
KEY MECHANICAL COMPANY; *U.S. Private*, pg. 2293
KEYMED BIOSCIENCES INC.; *Int'l*, pg. 4146
KEYMED IRELAND LTD.—See Olympus Corporation; *Int'l*, pg. 5557
KEYMED (MEDICAL & INDUSTRIAL EQUIPMENT) LTD.—See Olympus Corporation; *Int'l*, pg. 5557
KEYMILE AG—See DZS Inc.; *U.S. Public*, pg. 701
KEYMILE GMBH—See DZS Inc.; *U.S. Public*, pg. 701

KEYMILE KFT.—See DZS Inc.; *U.S. Public*, pg. 701
KEYMILE LLC—See DZS Inc.; *U.S. Public*, pg. 701
KEYMILE LTDA.—See DZS Inc.; *U.S. Public*, pg. 701
KEYMILE LTD.—See DZS Inc.; *U.S. Public*, pg. 701
KEYMILE NETWORKS GMBH—See DZS Inc.; *U.S. Public*, pg. 701
KEYMILE SP. Z O.O.—See DZS Inc.; *U.S. Public*, pg. 701
KEYMILE SYSTEMS JLT—See DZS Inc.; *U.S. Public*, pg. 701
KEYMILE SYSTEMS PTY. LTD—See DZS Inc.; *U.S. Public*, pg. 701
KEYMILE TEKNOLOJI SISTEMLERI LTD. STI.—See DZS Inc.; *U.S. Public*, pg. 701
KEYNE LTD.; *Int'l*, pg. 4146
KEYNETICS, INC.; *U.S. Private*, pg. 2294
KEYNOTE FINANCIAL SERVICES LIMITED; *Int'l*, pg. 4146
KEYNOTE LLC—See Dynatrace, Inc.; *U.S. Public*, pg. 700
KEYNOTER PUBLISHING COMPANY, INC.—See Chatham Asset Management, LLC; *U.S. Private*, pg. 866
KEYOR—See Perceva SAS; *Int'l*, pg. 5797
KEYOT, LLC—See 3 Bridge Solutions LLC; *U.S. Private*, pg. 7
KEY OUTDOOR INC.—See Boston Omaha Corporation; *U.S. Public*, pg. 372
KEY PARTNERS, INC.—See Key Family of Companies; *U.S. Private*, pg. 2293
KEYPATH EDUCATION INTERNATIONAL INC.—See Sterling Partners; *U.S. Private*, pg. 3806
KEYPATH EDUCATION LLC; *U.S. Private*, pg. 2294
KEY PERFORMANCE GROUP S.A.S.; *Int'l*, pg. 4145
KEY PERFORMANCE IDEAS INC.—See Century Park Capital Partners, LLC; *U.S. Private*, pg. 833
KEY PETROLEUM LIMITED; *Int'l*, pg. 4145
KEY PLASTICS PTY. LTD.—See Fletcher Building Limited; *Int'l*, pg. 2700
KEYPOINT CARRIERS LIMITED LAREDO FACILITY—See Keypoint Carriers Limited; *Int'l*, pg. 4146
KEYPOINT CARRIERS LIMITED; *Int'l*, pg. 4146
KEY POINT HEALTH SERVICES, INC.; *U.S. Private*, pg. 2293
KEY POLYMER CORPORATION—See Dalfort Capital Partners, LLC; *U.S. Private*, pg. 1149
KEYPORT SOLUTIONS, INC.—See SIOS Corp.; *Int'l*, pg. 6960
KEYPOWER CONSULTANTS IMPRIMIS LTD—See The Rethink Group Limited; *Int'l*, pg. 7678
KEYPROCESSOR B.V.—See TKH Group N.V.; *Int'l*, pg. 7764
KEY PRODUCTION COMPANY, INC.—See Coterra Energy Inc.; *U.S. Public*, pg. 587
KEY PROFESSIONAL MEDIA, INC.; *U.S. Private*, pg. 2293
KEY PROGRAM INCORPORATED; *U.S. Private*, pg. 2293
KEY PROPERTY SOLUTIONS, LLC; *U.S. Private*, pg. 2294
KEY PUNCH COMPUTER TEMPORARIES; *U.S. Private*, pg. 2294
KEY RESIN CO.—See RPM International Inc.; *U.S. Public*, pg. 1817
KEY RESOURCES, INC.—See Staffing 360 Solutions, Inc.; *U.S. Public*, pg. 1925
KEY RISK INSURANCE COMPANY—See W.R. Berkley Corporation; *U.S. Public*, pg. 2317
KEY RISK MANAGEMENT SERVICES, INC.—See W.R. Berkley Corporation; *U.S. Public*, pg. 2318
KEYRUS (CHINA) LTD.—See Keyrus SA; *Int'l*, pg. 4147
KEYRUS HONG KONG LIMITED—See Keyrus SA; *Int'l*, pg. 4147
KEYRUS INTERNATIONAL SA—See Keyrus SA; *Int'l*, pg. 4147
KEYRUS (ISRAEL) LTD.—See Keyrus SA; *Int'l*, pg. 4147
KEYRUS LUXEMBOURG SA—See Keyrus SA; *Int'l*, pg. 4147
KEYRUS MANAGEMENT S.A—See Keyrus SA; *Int'l*, pg. 4147
KEYRUS MAURITIUS LTD.—See Keyrus SA; *Int'l*, pg. 4147
KEYRUS N.V.—See Keyrus SA; *Int'l*, pg. 4147
KEYRUS SA; *Int'l*, pg. 4146
KEYRUS SPAIN SL—See Keyrus SA; *Int'l*, pg. 4147
KEYRUS TUNISIA SARL—See Keyrus SA; *Int'l*, pg. 4147
KEYRUS UK LIMITED—See Keyrus SA; *Int'l*, pg. 4147
KEYRUS US INC—See Keyrus SA; *Int'l*, pg. 4147
KEY SAFETY SYSTEMS, INC.—See Ningbo Joyson Electronic Corp.; *Int'l*, pg. 5303
KEY SAFETY SYSTEMS UK LIMITED—See Ningbo Joyson Electronic Corp.; *Int'l*, pg. 5303
KEYS AUTO CENTER—See Warren Henry Automobiles Inc.; *U.S. Private*, pg. 4444
KEYS COMMERCIAL REAL ESTATE LLC—See Lowe Enterprises, Inc.; *U.S. Private*, pg. 2504
KEYS EDUCATION & CARE LTD; *Int'l*, pg. 4147
KEYSEN ENGINEERING COMPANY LIMITED—See Great Eagle Holdings Limited; *Int'l*, pg. 3064
KEYS ENERGY SERVICES; *U.S. Private*, pg. 2295

KEYSEN PROPERTY MANAGEMENT SERVICES LIMITED—See Great Eagle Holdings Limited; *Int'l*, pg. 3064
KEYSER BROTHERS CADILLAC INC; *U.S. Private*, pg. 2295
KEYSER ENERGY—See Delos Capital, LLC; *U.S. Private*, pg. 1198
KEYSER, LLC; *U.S. Private*, pg. 2295
KEYSER & MILLER FORD INC.; *U.S. Private*, pg. 2295
KEYSHEEN (CAYMAN) HOLDINGS CO., LIMITED; *Int'l*, pg. 4147
KEYSIGHT TECHNOLOGIES, INC.; *U.S. Public*, pg. 1226
KEYSIGHT TECHNOLOGIES JAPAN G.K.—See Keysight Technologies, Inc.; *U.S. Public*, pg. 1227
KEYSIGHT TECHNOLOGIES UK LIMITED—See Keysight Technologies, Inc.; *U.S. Public*, pg. 1227
KEYSINO SEPARATION TECHNOLOGY, INC.; *Int'l*, pg. 4147
KEYSINO SEPARATION TECHNOLOGY (SINGAPORE) PTE. LTD.—See Keysino Separation Technology, Inc.; *Int'l*, pg. 4147
KEY-SOFT COMPUTER TECHNOLOGY PLC; *Int'l*, pg. 4145
KEY SOLUTIONS REAL ESTATE GROUP; *U.S. Private*, pg. 2294
KEYSOURCE MEDICAL, INC.; *U.S. Private*, pg. 2295
KEYS PRINTING COMPANY—See Chatham Asset Management, LLC; *U.S. Private*, pg. 862
KEYSTAR CORP.; *U.S. Public*, pg. 1227
KEYSTON BROS. INC.; *U.S. Private*, pg. 2295
KEYSTONE AERIAL SURVEYS, INC.—See Vexcel Holdings, Inc.; *U.S. Private*, pg. 4374
KEYSTONE AGENCY INVESTORS LLC; *U.S. Private*, pg. 2295
KEYSTONE AGENCY PARTNERS, LLC—See Bain Capital, LP; *U.S. Private*, pg. 441
KEYSTONE AGENCY PARTNERS, LLC—See Keystone Insurers Group, Inc.; *U.S. Private*, pg. 2300
KEYSTONE ANILINE CORP. - LIQUID MANUFACTURING TECHNICAL FACILITY—See Milliken & Company; *U.S. Private*, pg. 2737
KEYSTONE ANILINE CORP. - PACIFIC DIVISION—See Milliken & Company; *U.S. Private*, pg. 2737
KEYSTONE ANILINE CORP.—See Milliken & Company; *U.S. Private*, pg. 2737
KEYSTONE ASSET MANAGEMENT, INC.—See LRES Corp.; *U.S. Private*, pg. 2507
KEYSTONE AUTOMATIC TECHNOLOGY, INC.—See MetalKraft Industries, Inc.; *U.S. Private*, pg. 2681
KEYSTONE AUTOMOTIVE DISTRIBUTORS COMPANY, LLC—See LKQ Corporation; *U.S. Public*, pg. 1334
KEYSTONE AUTOMOTIVE INDUSTRIES - ATLANTA—See LKQ Corporation; *U.S. Public*, pg. 1334
KEYSTONE AUTOMOTIVE INDUSTRIES - BETHLEHEM—See LKQ Corporation; *U.S. Public*, pg. 1334
KEYSTONE AUTOMOTIVE INDUSTRIES - BUFFALO—See LKQ Corporation; *U.S. Public*, pg. 1334
KEYSTONE AUTOMOTIVE INDUSTRIES, INC.—See LKQ Corporation; *U.S. Public*, pg. 1334
KEYSTONE AUTOMOTIVE INDUSTRIES - NASHVILLE—See LKQ Corporation; *U.S. Public*, pg. 1334
KEYSTONE AUTOMOTIVE INDUSTRIES ON, INC.—See LKQ Corporation; *U.S. Public*, pg. 1334
KEYSTONE AUTOMOTIVE INDUSTRIES - STOCKTON—See LKQ Corporation; *U.S. Public*, pg. 1334
KEYSTONE AUTOMOTIVE OPERATIONS, INC.—See LKQ Corporation; *U.S. Public*, pg. 1334
KEYSTONE AVIATION, LLC—See Elevate Holdings, Inc.; *U.S. Private*, pg. 1358
KEYSTONE BANCSHARES, INC.; *U.S. Private*, pg. 2295
KEYSTONE BANK, NATIONAL ASSOCIATION—See Keystone Bancshares, Inc.; *U.S. Private*, pg. 2295
KEYSTONE BUILDERS RESOURCE GROUP, INC.; *U.S. Private*, pg. 2295
KEYSTONE CAPITAL, INC.; *U.S. Private*, pg. 2295
KEYSTONE CASE MANAGEMENT LIMITED—See Frenkel Topping Group plc; *Int'l*, pg. 2773
KEYSTONE CEMENT COMPANY—See Grupo Empresarial Kaluz S.A. de C.V.; *Int'l*, pg. 3127
KEYSTONE CENTER—See Universal Health Services, Inc.; *U.S. Public*, pg. 2260
KEYSTONE CHARLOTTE LLC—See Universal Health Services, Inc.; *U.S. Public*, pg. 2258
KEYSTONE CHEVROLET INC.; *U.S. Private*, pg. 2295
KEYSTONE CLEARWATER SOLUTIONS, LLC; *U.S. Private*, pg. 2295
KEYSTONE CLOSING SERVICES LLC—See Anywhere Real Estate Inc.; *U.S. Public*, pg. 141
KEYSTONE COFFEE COMPANY; *U.S. Private*, pg. 2295
KEYSTONE COMMUNITIES OF EAGAN, LLC—See Welltower Inc.; *U.S. Public*, pg. 2348
KEYSTONE COMMUNITIES OF PRIOR LAKE, LLC—See Welltower Inc.; *U.S. Public*, pg. 2348

COMPANY NAME INDEX

KEYSTONE COMMUNITY BANK—See Mercantile Bank Corporation; *U.S. Public*, pg. 1414
KEYSTONE CONSOLIDATED INDUSTRIES, INC.—See Contran Corporation; *U.S. Private*, pg. 1033
KEYSTONE CONSULTING ENGINEERS, INC.—See Keystone Consulting Engineers, Inc.; *U.S. Private*, pg. 2296
KEYSTONE CONSULTING ENGINEERS, INC.—See Keystone Consulting Engineers, Inc.; *U.S. Private*, pg. 2296
KEYSTONE CONSULTING ENGINEERS, INC.; *U.S. Private*, pg. 2295
KEYSTONE CORPORATION; *U.S. Private*, pg. 2296
KEYSTONE DEDICATED LOGISTICS; *U.S. Private*, pg. 2296
KEYSTONE DENTAL AB—See Keystone Dental, Inc.; *U.S. Private*, pg. 2296
KEYSTONE DENTAL GMBH—See Keystone Dental, Inc.; *U.S. Private*, pg. 2296
KEYSTONE DENTAL, INC.; *U.S. Private*, pg. 2296
KEYSTONE DENTAL S.A.S.—See Keystone Dental, Inc.; *U.S. Private*, pg. 2296
KEYSTONE DENTAL SPA—See Keystone Dental, Inc.; *U.S. Private*, pg. 2296
KEYSTONE DIGITAL IMAGING, INCORPORATED; *U.S. Private*, pg. 2296
KEYSTONE DODGE, INC.; *U.S. Private*, pg. 2296
KEYSTONE EDUCATION AND YOUTH SERVICES, LLC—See Universal Health Services, Inc.; *U.S. Public*, pg. 2258
KEYSTONE ELECTRICAL MANUFACTURING COMPANY; *U.S. Private*, pg. 2296
KEYSTONE ELECTRIC WIRE & CABLE CO. LTD.—See Prysmian S.p.A.; *Int'l*, pg. 6011
KEYSTONE EQUIPMENT FINANCE CORP.—See BDT Capital Partners, LLC; *U.S. Private*, pg. 502
KEYSTONE EXCAVATING LTD.; *Int'l*, pg. 4147
KEYSTONE FOODS LLC—See Tyson Foods, Inc.; *U.S. Public*, pg. 2209
KEYSTONE FORD; *U.S. Private*, pg. 2296
KEYSTONE FREIGHT CORP.—See National Retail Systems, Inc.; *U.S. Private*, pg. 2862
KEYSTONE FRICTION HINGE CO.; *U.S. Private*, pg. 2296
KEYSTONE FRUIT MARKETING INC.—See Arable Capital Partners LLC; *U.S. Private*, pg. 307
KEYSTONE FUELS, INC.; *U.S. Private*, pg. 2296
KEYSTONE FUNDING, INC.; *U.S. Private*, pg. 2296
KEYSTONE GROUP HOLDINGS INC.; *U.S. Private*, pg. 2296
KEYSTONE GROUP, L.P.; *U.S. Private*, pg. 2296
KEYSTONE HEALTH PLAN CENTRAL, INC.—See Capital BlueCross Inc.; *U.S. Private*, pg. 739
KEYSTONE HEALTH PLAN WEST, INC.—See Highmark Health; *U.S. Private*, pg. 1941
KEYSTONE INFORMATION SYSTEMS—See Valsef Group; *Int'l*, pg. 8123
KEYSTONE INFRA LTD.; *Int'l*, pg. 4147
KEYSTONE INSURERS GROUP, INC.; *U.S. Private*, pg. 2300
KEYSTONE LABORATORIES, INC.; *U.S. Private*, pg. 2300
KEYSTONE LAW GROUP PLC; *Int'l*, pg. 4147
KEYSTONE LIME COMPANY; *U.S. Private*, pg. 2300
KEYSTONE LINES, INC.—See US 1 Industries, Inc.; *U.S. Private*, pg. 4317
KEYSTONE LOGISTICS, LLC—See US 1 Industries, Inc.; *U.S. Private*, pg. 4317
KEYSTONE MCF CORPORATE FINANCE AB—See MCF Corporate Finance GmbH; *Int'l*, pg. 4758
KEYSTONE MICROTECH CORP.; *Int'l*, pg. 4147
KEYSTONE NATIONAL GROUP LLC; *U.S. Private*, pg. 2300
KEYSTONE NEWPORT NEWS, LLC—See Universal Health Services, Inc.; *U.S. Public*, pg. 2258
KEYSTONE NURSING HOME, INC.—See Welltower Inc.; *U.S. Public*, pg. 2348
KEYSTONE PAPER & BOX COMPANY, INC.—See Great Mill Rock LLC; *U.S. Private*, pg. 1766
KEYSTONE PARTNERS CO., LTD.; *Int'l*, pg. 4147
KEYSTONE PARTNERS—See Silver Oak Services Partners, LLC; *U.S. Private*, pg. 3661
KEYSTONE PEER REVIEW ORGANIZATION, INC.—See Apax Partners LLP; *Int'l*, pg. 504
KEYSTONE PHYSICS LIMITED—See Associates in Medical Physics, LLC; *U.S. Private*, pg. 358
KEYSTONE POWDERED METAL COMPANY - CHERRYVILLE—See Sumitomo Electric Industries, Ltd.; *Int'l*, pg. 7278
KEYSTONE POWDERED METAL COMPANY - LEWIS RUN—See Sumitomo Electric Industries, Ltd.; *Int'l*, pg. 7278
KEYSTONE POWDERED METAL COMPANY—See Sumitomo Electric Industries, Ltd.; *Int'l*, pg. 7278
KEYSTONE PRINTING INK CO.; *U.S. Private*, pg. 2300
KEYSTONE PROPERTY GROUP; *U.S. Private*, pg. 2300
KEYSTONE REALTORS LIMITED; *Int'l*, pg. 4147

KEYSTONE RESORT PROPERTY MANAGEMENT COMPANY—See Vail Resorts, Inc.; *U.S. Public*, pg. 2271
KEYSTONE RICHLAND CENTER LLC—See Universal Health Services, Inc.; *U.S. Public*, pg. 2258
KEYSTONE RISK PARTNERS, LLC—See Ryan Specialty Holdings, Inc.; *U.S. Public*, pg. 1827
KEYSTONE RV COMPANY—See Thor Industries, Inc.; *U.S. Public*, pg. 2156
KEYSTONE SHIPPING CO.; *U.S. Private*, pg. 2300
KEYSTONE SOLUTIONS INC.—See Rekor Systems, Inc.; *U.S. Public*, pg. 1778
KEYSTONE SPRING SERVICE, INC.—See American Securities LLC; *U.S. Private*, pg. 248
KEYSTONE STEEL & WIRE CO.—See Contran Corporation; *U.S. Private*, pg. 1033
KEYSTONE TOWER SYSTEMS, INC.—See NOV, Inc.; *U.S. Public*, pg. 1545
KEYSTONE TURBINE SERVICES LLC—See M International Inc.; *U.S. Private*, pg. 2523
KEYSTONE TURF CLUB, INC.—See International Turf Investment Co., Inc.; *U.S. Private*, pg. 2121
KEYSTONE VALVE (KOREA) LLC—See Emerson Electric Co.; *U.S. Public*, pg. 751
KEYSTONE WILDLIFE RESEARCH LTD.; *Int'l*, pg. 4147
KEYSTOPS LLC; *U.S. Private*, pg. 2300
KEYSTROKES TRANSCRIPTION SERVICE, INC.; *U.S. Private*, pg. 2300
KEYSTRUCT CONSTRUCTION, INC.; *U.S. Private*, pg. 2300
KEY SURGICAL GMBH—See STERIS plc; *Int'l*, pg. 7210
KEY SURGICAL, LLC—See STERIS plc; *Int'l*, pg. 7210
KEY-SYSTEMS GMBH—See Team Internet Group plc; *Int'l*, pg. 7500
KEYTEC CO., LTD.—See JK Holdings Co., Ltd.; *Int'l*, pg. 3972
KEY TECHNOLOGY AUSTRALIA PTY. LTD.—See Warburg Pincus LLC; *U.S. Private*, pg. 4438
KEY TECHNOLOGY B.V.—See Warburg Pincus LLC; *U.S. Private*, pg. 4438
KEY TECHNOLOGY, INC.—See Warburg Pincus LLC; *U.S. Private*, pg. 4437
KEY TOURS INTERNATIONAL INC.—See United Rail, Inc.; *U.S. Public*, pg. 2234
KEYTRADE BANK S.A.—See Confederation Nationale du Credit Mutuel; *Int'l*, pg. 1767
KEY TRAVEL LIMITED; *Int'l*, pg. 4145
KEYTREE LTD.; *Int'l*, pg. 4147
KEYTROLLER, LLC—See PowerFleet, Inc.; *U.S. Public*, pg. 1706
KEY TRONIC COMPUTER PERIPHERALS (SHANGHAI) CO. LTD—See Key Tronic Corporation; *U.S. Public*, pg. 1225
KEY TRONIC CORPORATION; *U.S. Public*, pg. 1225
KEYTRONICEMS COMPUTER PERIPHERAL CO.—See Key Tronic Corporation; *U.S. Public*, pg. 1225
KEY TRONIC JUAREZ S.A. DE CV—See Key Tronic Corporation; *U.S. Public*, pg. 1225
KEY TRONIC REYNOSA, S.A. DE CV—See Key Tronic Corporation; *U.S. Public*, pg. 1225
KEY VALVE TECHNOLOGIES LTD.—See Indutrade AB; *Int'l*, pg. 3679
KEYVENT AB—See Instalco AB; *Int'l*, pg. 3722
KEY WALLCOVERING INC.—See Mobile Paint Manufacturing Company of Delaware Inc.; *U.S. Private*, pg. 2757
KEY WARE ELECTRONICS CO., LTD.; *Int'l*, pg. 4145
KEYWARE SMART CARD DIVISION N.V.—See Keyware Technologies NV; *Int'l*, pg. 4147
KEYWARE SOLUTIONS INC.; *Int'l*, pg. 4147
KEYWARE TECHNOLOGIES NV; *Int'l*, pg. 4147
THE KEYW CORPORATION—See Jacobs Engineering Group, Inc.; *U.S. Public*, pg. 1186
KEYWELL LLC - FALCONER PROCESSING FACILITY—See Keywell LLC; *U.S. Private*, pg. 2300
KEYWELL LLC; *U.S. Private*, pg. 2300
KEYWELL LLC - WEST MIFFLIN PROCESSING FACILITY—See Keywell LLC; *U.S. Private*, pg. 2300
KEY WEST BOATS INC.; *U.S. Public*, pg. 2294
KEY WEST HMA, INC.—See Community Health Systems, Inc.; *U.S. Public*, pg. 554
KEY WEST LAMP COMPANY INC.; *U.S. Private*, pg. 2294
THE KEYW HOLDING CORPORATION—See Jacobs Engineering Group, Inc.; *U.S. Public*, pg. 1186
KEYWORD MARKETING INC.—See Vector Inc.; *Int'l*, pg. 8144
KEYWORDS INTERNATIONAL CO. LIMITED—See Canada Pension Plan Investment Board; *Int'l*, pg. 1280
KEYWORDS INTERNATIONAL CO. LIMITED—See EQT AB; *Int'l*, pg. 2482
KEYWORDS INTERNATIONAL CO. LIMITED—See Temasek Holdings (Private) Limited; *Int'l*, pg. 7548
KEYWORDS INTERNATIONAL CORPORATION INC.—See Canada Pension Plan Investment Board; *Int'l*, pg. 1280
KEYWORDS INTERNATIONAL CORPORATION INC.—See EQT AB; *Int'l*, pg. 2482

KEYWORDS INTERNATIONAL CORPORATION INC.—See Temasek Holdings (Private) Limited; *Int'l*, pg. 7548
KEYWORDS INTERNATIONAL INC.—See Canada Pension Plan Investment Board; *Int'l*, pg. 1280
KEYWORDS INTERNATIONAL INC.—See EQT AB; *Int'l*, pg. 2482
KEYWORDS INTERNATIONAL INC.—See Temasek Holdings (Private) Limited; *Int'l*, pg. 7548
KEYWORDS INTERNATIONAL PTE. LIMITED—See Canada Pension Plan Investment Board; *Int'l*, pg. 1280
KEYWORDS INTERNATIONAL PTE. LIMITED—See EQT AB; *Int'l*, pg. 2482
KEYWORDS INTERNATIONAL PTE. LIMITED—See Temasek Holdings (Private) Limited; *Int'l*, pg. 7548
KEYWORDS ITALIA SRL—See Canada Pension Plan Investment Board; *Int'l*, pg. 1280
KEYWORDS ITALIA SRL—See EQT AB; *Int'l*, pg. 2482
KEYWORDS ITALIA SRL—See Temasek Holdings (Private) Limited; *Int'l*, pg. 7548
KEYWORDS STUDIOS PLC—See Canada Pension Plan Investment Board; *Int'l*, pg. 1280
KEYWORDS STUDIOS PLC—See EQT AB; *Int'l*, pg. 2482
KEYWORDS STUDIOS PLC—See Temasek Holdings (Private) Limited; *Int'l*, pg. 7547
KEYYO; *Int'l*, pg. 4147
KE-ZAN HOLDINGS BERHAD—See OSK Holdings Berhad; *Int'l*, pg. 5651
KEZAR LIFE SCIENCES, INC.; *U.S. Public*, pg. 1227
KEZA SDN. BHD.—See PCCS Group Berhad; *Int'l*, pg. 5767
KEZI-TV—See Entertainment Studios, Inc.; *U.S. Private*, pg. 1405
KEZR-FM—See Alpha Media LLC; *U.S. Private*, pg. 198
KF (AUSTRALIA) PTY. LTD.—See Mondelez International, Inc.; *U.S. Public*, pg. 1461
KFAX SAN FRANCISCO—See Salem Media Group, Inc.; *U.S. Public*, pg. 1836
K & F BUSINESS BROKERS; *U.S. Private*, pg. 2249
KFC CHAMNORD SAS—See Yum! Brands, Inc.; *U.S. Public*, pg. 2400
KFC CORPORATION—See Yum! Brands, Inc.; *U.S. Public*, pg. 2400
KFC HOLDINGS JAPAN LTD.—See The Carlyle Group Inc.; *U.S. Public*, pg. 2048
KFC LTD.; *Int'l*, pg. 4147
KFC (PTY) LTD.—See Yum! Brands, Inc.; *U.S. Public*, pg. 2400
KFC RESTAURANTS ASIA PTE., LTD.—See Yum! Brands, Inc.; *U.S. Public*, pg. 2400
KFC RESTAURANTS SPAIN S.L.—See Yum! Brands, Inc.; *U.S. Public*, pg. 2400
K&F DISTRIBUTORS INC.; *U.S. Private*, pg. 2249
KFDM-TV—See Sinclair, Inc.; *U.S. Public*, pg. 1885
KFDX-TV—See Nexstar Media Group, Inc.; *U.S. Public*, pg. 1522
KFE HONG KONG CO., LIMITED—See Cosmos Machinery Enterprises Limited; *Int'l*, pg. 1813
KFE (SHENZHEN) CO., LTD.—See Cosmos Machinery Enterprises Limited; *Int'l*, pg. 1813
KFE (SUZHOU) CO., LTD.—See Cosmos Machinery Enterprises Limited; *Int'l*, pg. 1813
KFE (THAILAND) CO., LTD.—See Cosmos Machinery Enterprises Limited; *Int'l*, pg. 1813
KF FASTIGHETER AB—See Kooperativa Forbundet; *Int'l*, pg. 4279
KF FOODS CO., LTD.—See Maruha Nichiro Corporation; *Int'l*, pg. 4711
KFG RESOURCES LTD.; *U.S. Public*, pg. 1227
KFH CAPITAL INVESTMENTS COMPANY K.S.C.—See Kuwait Finance House K.S.C.; *Int'l*, pg. 4344
KFIC FINANCIAL BROKERAGE-K.S.C.C—See KFIC Invest K.S.C.P.; *Int'l*, pg. 4148
KFIC INVEST K.S.C.P.; *Int'l*, pg. 4148
K&F INDUSTRIES HOLDINGS, INC.—See Parker Hannifin Corporation; *U.S. Public*, pg. 1642
KF INDUSTRIES, INC.—See KKR & Co. Inc.; *U.S. Public*, pg. 1242
K&F INDUSTRIES, INC.—See Parker Hannifin Corporation; *U.S. Public*, pg. 1642
K-FIVE CONSTRUCTION CORPORATION - CHICAGO PLANT—See K-Five Construction Corporation; *U.S. Private*, pg. 2251
K-FIVE CONSTRUCTION CORPORATION - ELMHURST PLANT—See K-Five Construction Corporation; *U.S. Private*, pg. 2251
K-FIVE CONSTRUCTION CORPORATION - MARKHAM PLANT—See K-Five Construction Corporation; *U.S. Private*, pg. 2251
K-FIVE CONSTRUCTION CORPORATION - NAPERVILLE PLANT—See K-Five Construction Corporation; *U.S. Private*, pg. 2251
K-FIVE CONSTRUCTION CORPORATION; *U.S. Private*, pg. 2251
K.F. JACOBSON & CO. INC.—See R.B. Pamplin Corporation; *U.S. Private*, pg. 3334
K-F MANAGEMENT COMPANY, INC.; *U.S. Private*, pg. 2250
KFM ENTERPRISES, LLC; *U.S. Private*, pg. 2300

KFM ENTERPRISES, LLC

CORPORATE AFFILIATIONS

KFM HOLDINGS SDN. BHD.—See Khazanah Nasional Berhad; *Int'l*, pg. 4153
KFM KINGDOM HOLDINGS LIMITED - SHANGHAI PRODUCTION PLANT—See KFM Kingdom Holdings Limited; *Int'l*, pg. 4148
KFM KINGDOM HOLDINGS LIMITED - SHENZHEN PRODUCTION PLANT (GUANLAN)—See KFM Kingdom Holdings Limited; *Int'l*, pg. 4148
KFM KINGDOM HOLDINGS LIMITED - SHENZHEN PRODUCTION PLANT (XILI)—See KFM Kingdom Holdings Limited; *Int'l*, pg. 4148
KFM KINGDOM HOLDINGS LIMITED; *Int'l*, pg. 4148
KFM KINGDOM HOLDINGS LIMITED - SUZHOU PRODUCTION PLANT—See KFM Kingdom Holdings Limited; *Int'l*, pg. 4148
KFM-SCHAUMSTOFF GMBH—See Greiner Holding AG; *Int'l*, pg. 3078
KFN SENTINEL REIT LLC—See KKR & Co. Inc.; *U.S. Public*, pg. 1254
K-FOODS INC.; *U.S. Private*, pg. 2251
KFORCE GOVERNMENT HOLDINGS, INC.—See Kforce Inc.; *U.S. Public*, pg. 1227
KFORCE GOVERNMENT SOLUTIONS, INC.—See The Carlyle Group Inc.; *U.S. Public*, pg. 2048
KFORCE INC.; *U.S. Public*, pg. 1227
KFORCE—See Kforce Inc.; *U.S. Public*, pg. 1227
KFOR-TV—See Nexstar Media Group, Inc.; *U.S. Public*, pg. 1524
KFP INGENIEURE GMBH—See BKW AG; *Int'l*, pg. 1055
K FRIESE & ASSOCIATES, INC.—See H.W. Lochner, Inc.; *U.S. Private*, pg. 1836
KFS INC.; *U.S. Private*, pg. 2301
KFSM-TV—See Nexstar Media Group, Inc.; *U.S. Public*, pg. 1524
KF-SNF CO. LTD.—See SNF SAS; *Int'l*, pg. 7027
KFSN-TV INC.—See The Walt Disney Company; *U.S. Public*, pg. 2138
KFT INTERNATIONAL (MALAYSIA) SDN. BHD.—See KUB Malaysia Berhad; *Int'l*, pg. 4319
KFW CAPITAL GMBH & CO. KG—See KfW Group; *Int'l*, pg. 4148
KFW GROUP; *Int'l*, pg. 4148
KFW IPEX-BANK GMBH—See KfW Group; *Int'l*, pg. 4148
KFXO-TV—See News-Press & Gazette Company; *U.S. Private*, pg. 2917
KFYR-TV—See Gray Television, Inc.; *U.S. Public*, pg. 960
KG AGRI PRODUCTS, INC.—See Kanematsu Corporation; *Int'l*, pg. 4068
KG AIRCRAFT ROTABLES CO., LTD.—See Kanematsu Corporation; *Int'l*, pg. 4068
KGALAGADI SOAP INDUSTRIES (PTY) LTD.—See Sefalana Holdings Company Limited; *Int'l*, pg. 6679
KGAL ASSET MANAGEMENT OSTERREICH GMBH—See Commerzbank AG; *Int'l*, pg. 1718
KGAL GMBH & CO. KG—See Commerzbank AG; *Int'l*, pg. 1718
KG ALLAT CORP—See KGinicis Co. Ltd.; *Int'l*, pg. 4150
KGAN LICENSEE, LLC—See Sinclair, Inc.; *U.S. Public*, pg. 1885
KGAN-TV—See Sinclair, Inc.; *U.S. Public*, pg. 1885
KGBT-TV—See Sinclair, Inc.; *U.S. Public*, pg. 1885
KGB USA, INC.; *U.S. Private*, pg. 2301
KG CHEMICAL CORPORATION—See KG Eco Solution Co.,Ltd.; *Int'l*, pg. 4148
KGC LIFE & GIN CO., LTD.—See KT&G Corporation; *Int'l*, pg. 4316
KG COATING LIMITED—See Berkshire Hathaway Inc.; *U.S. Public*, pg. 314
K + G COMPLEX PUBLIC COMPANY LIMITED—See G.S. Galatariotis & Sons Ltd.; *Int'l*, pg. 2866
KG CREATIVE; *U.S. Private*, pg. 2301
KG DENIM LIMITED; *Int'l*, pg. 4148
KG ECO SOLUTION CO.,LTD.; *Int'l*, pg. 4148
KGEN POWER CORPORATION; *U.S. Private*, pg. 2301
K-GES CO., LTD.—See Kawasaki Heavy Industries, Ltd.; *Int'l*, pg. 4095
KGET-TV—See Nexstar Media Group, Inc.; *U.S. Public*, pg. 1522
KGF CO., LTD.—See Kaga Electronics Co., Ltd.; *Int'l*, pg. 4048
KG FLOWTECHNO CO., LTD.—See Kanamoto Co., Ltd.; *Int'l*, pg. 4064
KG HERMES VERSAND SERVICE GMBH & CO.—See Otto GmbH & Co. KG; *Int'l*, pg. 5663
KGHM CUPRUM SP. Z O.O.—See KGHM Polska Miedz S.A.; *Int'l*, pg. 4149
KGHM INTERNATIONAL LTD.—See KGHM Polska Miedz S.A.; *Int'l*, pg. 4149
KGHM INTERNATIONAL LTD. - TORONTO—See KGHM Polska Miedz S.A.; *Int'l*, pg. 4149
KGHM KUPFER AG—See KGHM Polska Miedz S.A.; *Int'l*, pg. 4149
KGHM KUPFERHANDELSGES.MBH—See KGHM Polska Miedz S.A.; *Int'l*, pg. 4149
KGHM LETIA - LEGNICKI PARK TECHNOLOGICZNY S.A.—See KGHM Polska Miedz S.A.; *Int'l*, pg. 4149
KGHM METRACO S.A.—See KGHM Polska Miedz S.A.; *Int'l*, pg. 4149

KGHM POLISH COPPER LTD—See KGHM Polska Miedz S.A.; *Int'l*, pg. 4149
KGHM POLSKA MIEDZ S.A.; *Int'l*, pg. 4148
KGHM (SHANGHAI) COPPER TRADING CO., LTD.—See KGHM Polska Miedz S.A.; *Int'l*, pg. 4149
KGHM TFI S.A.—See KGHM Polska Miedz S.A.; *Int'l*, pg. 4149
KGI ASIA (HOLDINGS) PTE. LTD.—See KGI Financial Holding Co., Ltd.; *Int'l*, pg. 4150
KGI ASIA LIMITED—See KGI Financial Holding Co., Ltd.; *Int'l*, pg. 4150
KGI BANK CO. LTD.—See KGI Financial Holding Co., Ltd.; *Int'l*, pg. 4150
KGI FINANCIAL HOLDING CO., LTD.; *Int'l*, pg. 4149
KGI FRASER SECURITIES PTE. LTD.—See KGI Financial Holding Co., Ltd.; *Int'l*, pg. 4150
KGI FUTURES CO. LTD.—See KGI Financial Holding Co., Ltd.; *Int'l*, pg. 4150
KGI HONG KONG LIMITED—See KGI Financial Holding Co., Ltd.; *Int'l*, pg. 4150
KGINICIS CO. LTD.; *Int'l*, pg. 4150
KG INTELLIGENCE CO., LTD.; *Int'l*, pg. 4148
KGI ONG CAPITAL PTE. LTD.—See KGI Financial Holding Co., Ltd.; *Int'l*, pg. 4150
KGI SECURITIES CO., LTD.—See KGI Financial Holding Co., Ltd.; *Int'l*, pg. 4150
KGI SECURITIES INVESTMENT TRUST CO., LTD.—See KGI Financial Holding Co., Ltd.; *Int'l*, pg. 4150
KGI SECURITIES (TAIWAN) CO., LTD.—See KGI Financial Holding Co., Ltd.; *Int'l*, pg. 4150
KGI SECURITIES (THAILAND) INTERNATIONAL HOLDINGS LIMITED—See KGI Securities (Thailand) Public Company Limited; *Int'l*, pg. 4150
KGI SECURITIES (THAILAND) PUBLIC COMPANY LIMITED; *Int'l*, pg. 4150
KGK CZECH S.R.O.—See Kanematsu Corporation; *Int'l*, pg. 4068
KGK ENGINEERING CORP.—See Kanematsu Corporation; *Int'l*, pg. 4068
KGK ENGINEERING (THAI) CO., LTD.—See Kanematsu Corporation; *Int'l*, pg. 4068
KGK INTERNATIONAL CORP.—See Kanematsu Corporation; *Int'l*, pg. 4068
KGL CAR RENTAL COMPANY W.L.L.—See Kuwait & Gulf Link Transport Co, KSCC; *Int'l*, pg. 4343
KGL LOGISTICS K.S.C.; *Int'l*, pg. 4150
KGL, LTD.—See Puncak Niaga Holdings Berhad; *Int'l*, pg. 6118
KGL RESOURCES LIMITED; *Int'l*, pg. 4150
KGL RESOURCES LTD.; *Int'l*, pg. 4150
K & G MED MARINAS MANAGEMENT S.A—See Kiriacoulis Mediterranean Cruises Shipping S.A.; *Int'l*, pg. 4186
K&G MEN'S CENTER, INC.—See Tailored Brands, Inc.; *U.S. Public*, pg. 1979
K&G MEN'S COMPANY INC.—See Tailored Brands, Inc.; *U.S. Public*, pg. 1979
KG MOBILIANS CO., LTD.; *Int'l*, pg. 4148
KG MOBILITY CORP.—See KG Eco Solution Co.,Ltd.; *Int'l*, pg. 4148
K.G. MOTORS, INC.—See The Zabel Companies, LLC; *U.S. Private*, pg. 4140
KGN INDUSTRIES LIMITED; *Int'l*, pg. 4150
KGO TELEVISION, INC.—See The Walt Disney Company; *U.S. Public*, pg. 2138
KG PASTRY MARKETING SDN. BHD.—See Kawan Food Berhad; *Int'l*, pg. 4094
KG PETROCHEM LIMITED; *Int'l*, pg. 4148
KGPE-TV—See Nexstar Media Group, Inc.; *U.S. Public*, pg. 1523
KGP GROUP, INC.; *U.S. Private*, pg. 2301
KG PROCESS INNOVATIONS, S.R.O.—See Koch Industries, Inc.; *U.S. Private*, pg. 2331
KGP TELECOMMUNICATIONS, INC.; *U.S. Private*, pg. 2301
K GROUND EXPERT CO., LTD.—See Konoike Transport Co., Ltd.; *Int'l*, pg. 4274
K GROUND SERVICE CO., LTD.—See Konoike Transport Co., Ltd.; *Int'l*, pg. 4274
KGS ELECTRONICS; *U.S. Private*, pg. 2301
KGS INSURANCE SERVICES, LLC—See Aon plc; *Int'l*, pg. 496
KGS KELLER GERATE & SERVICE GMBH—See Keller Group plc; *Int'l*, pg. 4120
KG SPECIALTIES LLC—See PEP Printing, Inc.; *U.S. Private*, pg. 3143
KGS SOURCING LIMITED—See Kering S.A.; *Int'l*, pg. 4134
KGS STEEL INC.; *U.S. Private*, pg. 2301
KG TECHNOLOGIES, INC.; *U.S. Private*, pg. 2301
KGTV—See The E.W. Scripps Company; *U.S. Public*, pg. 2068
KGUN-TV—See The E.W. Scripps Company; *U.S. Public*, pg. 2068
KGW-KRAFTWERK GRENZACH-WYHLEN GMBH—See E.ON SE; *Int'l*, pg. 2253
KHADIM INDIA LIMITED; *Int'l*, pg. 4150
KH ADVERTISING; *U.S. Private*, pg. 2301

KHAI QUOC TRADING & TECHNOLOGY DEVELOPMENT CO., LTD.—See Aiphone Co., Ltd.; *Int'l*, pg. 235
KHAIRPUR SUGAR MILLS LIMITED; *Int'l*, pg. 4150
KHAITAN CHEMICALS & FERTILIZERS LTD.; *Int'l*, pg. 4150
KHAITAN ELECTRICALS LIMITED; *Int'l*, pg. 4150
KHAITAN (INDIA) LIMITED; *Int'l*, pg. 4150
KHAI VAN TRADING COMPANY—See Shin Tai Industry Co., Ltd.; *Int'l*, pg. 6838
KHALEEJI BANK B.S.C.—See GFH Financial Group B.S.C.; *Int'l*, pg. 2956
KHALEEJ NATIONAL FLOUR MILLS—See Al Ghurair Investment LLC; *Int'l*, pg. 278
KHALID SIRAJ TEXTILE MILLS LIMITED; *Int'l*, pg. 4151
KHALISTA (LIUZHOU) CHEMICAL INDUSTRIES LTD—See PT AKR Corporindo Tbk; *Int'l*, pg. 6020
KHAN ACADEMY, INC.; *U.S. Private*, pg. 2301
KHAN ASPARUH AD—See Mohawk Industries, Inc.; *U.S. Public*, pg. 1457
KHAN BROTHERS PP WOVEN BAG INDUSTRIES LTD.; *Int'l*, pg. 4151
KHANDELWAL EXTRACTIONS LIMITED; *Int'l*, pg. 4151
KHANDELWAL EXTRACTIONS LIMITED - UNNAO FACTORY—See KHANDELWAL EXTRACTIONS LIMITED; *Int'l*, pg. 4151
KHANDWALA SECURITIES LIMITED; *Int'l*, pg. 4151
KHANG AN INVESTMENT REAL ESTATE JSC; *Int'l*, pg. 4151
KHANG DIEN HOUSE TRADING & INVESTMENT JOINT STOCK COMPANY; *Int'l*, pg. 4151
KHANG PHUC HOUSE TRADING INVESTMENT CO., LTD.—See Khang Dien House Trading & Investment Joint Stock Company; *Int'l*, pg. 4151
KHANH HOI IMPORT EXPORT JOINT STOCK COMPANY; *Int'l*, pg. 4151
KHANOM ELECTRICITY GENERATING CO. LTD.—See EGAT Public Company Limited; *Int'l*, pg. 2322
KHANOM ELECTRICITY GENERATING CO., LTD.—See Electricity Generating Public Co., Ltd.; *Int'l*, pg. 2352
KHANSAHEB SYKES LLC—See ANDREWS SYKES GROUP PLC; *Int'l*, pg. 452
KHAN'S SUPA IGA GROUP; *Int'l*, pg. 4151
KHAO KLA VENTURE CAPITAL MANAGEMENT CO., LTD.—See Kasikornbank Public Company Limited; *Int'l*, pg. 4087
KHARAFI NATIONAL CO. L.L.C.—See Kharafi National; *Int'l*, pg. 4151
KHARAFI NATIONAL FOR INFRASTRUCTURE PROJECTS DEVELOPMENTS CONSTRUCTION AND SERVICES S.A.E—See Kharafi National; *Int'l*, pg. 4151
KHARAFI NATIONAL KSC (CLOSED)—See Kharafi National; *Int'l*, pg. 4151
KHARAFI NATIONAL L.L.C.—See Kharafi National; *Int'l*, pg. 4151
KHARAFI NATIONAL; *Int'l*, pg. 4151
KHARAZMI INVESTMENT COMPANY; *Int'l*, pg. 4151
KHARG PETROCHEMICAL CO.; *Int'l*, pg. 4151
KHARIS CAPITAL ADVISORY BELGIUM SPRL—See KHARIS CAPITAL GP; *Int'l*, pg. 4151
KHARIS CAPITAL GP; *Int'l*, pg. 4151
KHARKH TOUR AMUZEMENT CITY; *Int'l*, pg. 4151
KHASH CEMENT COMPANY; *Int'l*, pg. 4151
KHATOR FIBRE & FABRICS LTD.; *Int'l*, pg. 4151
K&H AUTOPARK KFT.—See Kereskedelmi es Hitelbank Rt.; *Int'l*, pg. 4133
KHAVAR SPRING MFG COMPANY; *Int'l*, pg. 4151
KHAWAJA TANNERIES PVT. LTD.—See Mahmood Group of Companies LLC; *Int'l*, pg. 4649
KHAZANAH NASIONAL BERHAD; *Int'l*, pg. 4152
KHAZAR CEMENT CO.; *Int'l*, pg. 4154
KHAZAR EXPLORATION & PRODUCTION COMPANY—See National Iranian Oil Company; *Int'l*, pg. 5160
KHAZAR PLASTIC PRODUCTION & INDUSTRIAL COMPANY—See Pars Toushe Investment Company; *Int'l*, pg. 5746
KHAZAR SINTECH ELECTRO-MOTOR MANUFACTURING COMPANY—See Pars Toushe Investment Company; *Int'l*, pg. 5746
K&H BANK ZRT.—See KBC Group NV; *Int'l*, pg. 4105
KHC DUDEK & BOCK LLC—See Dudek & Bock Spring Manufacturing Company; *U.S. Private*, pg. 1284
K.H. CHAN TRADING SDN. BHD.—See HPI Resources Berhad; *Int'l*, pg. 3501
KHC LTD.—See Japan Asia Group Limited; *Int'l*, pg. 3885
KH CONSTRUCTION CO., LTD.; *Int'l*, pg. 4154
K&H CORRUGATED CASE CORP.—See Connecticut Container Corporation; *U.S. Private*, pg. 1015
K&H CSOPORTSZOLGALTATO KOZPONT KFT.—See Kereskedelmi es Hitelbank Rt.; *Int'l*, pg. 4133
K.H DELICA CO LTD—See Kagome Co., Ltd.; *Int'l*, pg. 4050
KHD HUMBOLDT WEDAG GMBH—See KHD Humboldt Wedag International AG; *Int'l*, pg. 4154
KHD HUMBOLDT WEDAG INDUSTRIAL SERVICES AG—See KHD Humboldt Wedag International AG; *Int'l*, pg. 4154
KHD HUMBOLDT WEDAG INTERNATIONAL AG; *Int'l*, pg. 4154

COMPANY NAME INDEX

KHOUZESTAN STEEL COMPANY

Company Index

K. HEEPS INC.; *U.S. Private*, pg. 2251
KHEE SAN BERHAD; *Int'l*, pg. 4154
KH ELECTRON CO., LTD.—See Corstone Corporation; *U.S. Private*, pg. 1060
KHEMANI DISTRIBUTORS & MARKETING LIMITED; *Int'l*, pg. 4154
KHEOBA CORP.; *Int'l*, pg. 4154
KHERA COMMUNICATIONS INC.; *U.S. Private*, pg. 2301
KHERSONGAZ, PJSC; *Int'l*, pg. 4154
K & H ESZKOZFINANSZIROZO PENZUGYI LIZING ZARTKORUEN MUKODO RESZVENYTARSASAG—See Kereskedelmi es Hitelbank Rt.; *Int'l*, pg. 4133
K&H FACTOR LTD.—See Kereskedelmi es Hitelbank Rt.; *Int'l*, pg. 4133
KHFM HOSPITALITY & FACILITY MANAGEMENT SERVICES LTD.; *Int'l*, pg. 4154
KH FOGES PTE LTD—See Kridhan Infra Limited; *Int'l*, pg. 4301
K. H. FOUNDATIONS LIMITED—See K. H. Group Holdings Ltd.; *Int'l*, pg. 4043
K&H FUND MANAGEMENT PLC—See Kereskedelmi es Hitelbank Rt.; *Int'l*, pg. 4133
K. H. GROUP HOLDINGS LTD.; *Int'l*, pg. 4043
KHI (DALIAN) COMPUTER TECHNOLOGY CO., LTD.—See Kawasaki Heavy Industries, Ltd.; *Int'l*, pg. 4095
KHI DESIGN & TECHNICAL SERVICE, INC.—See Kawasaki Heavy Industries, Ltd.; *Int'l*, pg. 4095
KHIDMAT MANTAP SDN. BHD.—See Naim Holdings Berhad; *Int'l*, pg. 5131
KHI JPS CO., LTD.—See Kawasaki Heavy Industries, Ltd.; *Int'l*, pg. 4095
KHI MANAGEMENT INTERNATIONAL LTD.—See Cobepa S.A.; *Int'l*, pg. 1683
KHI MECHANICAL SERVICES; *U.S. Private*, pg. 2301
KHIMJI RAMDAS SHIPPING LLC; *Int'l*, pg. 4154
KHIND ALLIANCES SDN. BHD.—See Khind Holdings Berhad; *Int'l*, pg. 4154
KHIND CUSTOMER SERVICE SDN. BHD.—See Khind Holdings Berhad; *Int'l*, pg. 4154
KHIND ELECTRICAL (HONG KONG) LIMITED—See Khind Holdings Berhad; *Int'l*, pg. 4155
KHIND ELECTRICAL (MALAYSIA) SDN. BHD.—See Khind Holdings Berhad; *Int'l*, pg. 4154
KHIND HOLDINGS BERHAD; *Int'l*, pg. 4154
KHIND MARKETING (M) SDN. BHD.—See Khind Holdings Berhad; *Int'l*, pg. 4154
KHIND MIDDLE EAST DMCC—See Khind Holdings Berhad; *Int'l*, pg. 4154
KHIND MIDDLE EAST FZE—See Khind Holdings Berhad; *Int'l*, pg. 4155
KHIND-MISTRAL (BORNEO) SDN. BHD.—See Khind Holdings Berhad; *Int'l*, pg. 4155
KHIND-MISTRAL INDUSTRIES SDN. BHD.—See Khind Holdings Berhad; *Int'l*, pg. 4155
KHIND-MISTRAL (M) SDN. BHD.—See Khind Holdings Berhad; *Int'l*, pg. 4155
KHIND-MISTRAL (SABAH) SDN. BHD.—See Khind Holdings Berhad; *Int'l*, pg. 4155
KHIND SYSTEMS (SINGAPORE) PTE. LTD.—See Khind Holdings Berhad; *Int'l*, pg. 4155
KH INTERNATIONAL, INC.—See Gellert Global Group; *U.S. Private*, pg. 1656
KHIRON LIFE SCIENCES CORP.; *Int'l*, pg. 4155
KHITKAN CO., LTD.—See Kawasaki Heavy Industries, Ltd.; *Int'l*, pg. 4095
KHK SALES CO., LTD.—See Piolax Inc.; *Int'l*, pg. 5871
K. H. LAND PTE LTD—See Keong Hong Holdings Limited; *Int'l*, pg. 4129
KH LAND SDN. BHD.—See DutaLand Berhad; *Int'l*, pg. 2235
K&H LEASE GROUP—See Kereskedelmi es Hitelbank Rt.; *Int'l*, pg. 4133
KHLITEC—See KHVatec Co., Ltd.; *Int'l*, pg. 4156
K & H LIZINGHAZ ZARTKORUEN MUKODO RESZVENYTARSASAG—See Kereskedelmi es Hitelbank Rt.; *Int'l*, pg. 4133
KHL MARKETING ASIA-PACIFIC PTE. LTD.—See SDAI Limited; *Int'l*, pg. 6657
K&H MANUFACTURING LLC—See Central Garden & Pet Company; *U.S. Public*, pg. 473
KHMELNITSKOBLENERGO, PJSC; *Int'l*, pg. 4155
KHMELNYTSKGAZ PJSC; *Int'l*, pg. 4155
KHMER CEMENT INDUSTRY COMPANY LIMITED—See Siam City Cement Public Company Limited; *Int'l*, pg. 6874
K&H MORTGAGE BANK LTD.—See Kereskedelmi es Hitelbank Rt.; *Int'l*, pg. 4133
KH NEOCHEM CO., LTD.—See Japan Industrial Partners, Inc.; *Int'l*, pg. 3889
KH NEOCHEM SINGAPORE—See Japan Industrial Partners, Inc.; *Int'l*, pg. 3889
KHNP USA LLC—See Korea Electric Power Corporation; *Int'l*, pg. 4283
KHN SOLUTIONS LLC; *U.S. Private*, pg. 2301
KHODAY INDIA LIMITED; *Int'l*, pg. 4155
KHOISAN TEA (PTY) LTD.—See Libstar Holdings Ltd.; *Int'l*, pg. 4487
KHONBURI BIO ENERGY CO., LTD.—See Khonburi Sugar Public Company Limited; *Int'l*, pg. 4155
KHONBURI POWER PLANT CO., LTD.—See Khonburi Sugar Public Company Limited; *Int'l*, pg. 4155
KHONBURI SUGAR PUBLIC COMPANY LIMITED; *Int'l*, pg. 4155
KHONG GUAN FOOD PRODUCTS (PTE.) LTD.—See Khong Guan Limited; *Int'l*, pg. 4155
KHONG GUAN LIMITED; *Int'l*, pg. 4155
KHON KAEN SUGAR INDUSTRY PUBLIC COMPANY LIMITED; *Int'l*, pg. 4155
KHON THAI SHOP LTD.—See Premier Marketing Public Company Limited; *Int'l*, pg. 5960
KHOOBSURAT LIMITED; *Int'l*, pg. 4155
KHOON GROUP LIMITED; *Int'l*, pg. 4155
KHOO SOON LEE REALTY SDN. BHD.—See KSL Holdings Berhad; *Int'l*, pg. 4314
KHORASAN PEGAH DAIRY COMPANY; *Int'l*, pg. 4155
KHOROS INTERNATIONAL, LLC—See Vista Equity Partners, LLC; *U.S. Private*, pg. 4398
KHOROS, LLC - AUSTRALIA OFFICE—See Vista Equity Partners, LLC; *U.S. Private*, pg. 4398
KHOROS, LLC - FRANCE OFFICE—See Vista Equity Partners, LLC; *U.S. Private*, pg. 4398
KHOROS, LLC—See Vista Equity Partners, LLC; *U.S. Private*, pg. 4398
KHOSLA VENTURES ACQUISITION CO.; *U.S. Public*, pg. 1227
KHOSLA VENTURES, LLC; *U.S. Private*, pg. 2301
KHOU HOLDINGS, INC.—See TEGNA Inc.; *U.S. Public*, pg. 1989
KHOURY INC.; *U.S. Private*, pg. 2301
KHOU-TV, INC.—See TEGNA Inc.; *U.S. Public*, pg. 1990
KHOUZESTAN PETROCHEMICAL CO.—See Persian Gulf Petrochemical Industry Commercial Company; *Int'l*, pg. 5815
KHOUZESTAN STEEL COMPANY; *Int'l*, pg. 4156
K. HOVNANIAN AMERICAN MORTGAGE LLC—See Hovnanian Enterprises, Inc.; *U.S. Public*, pg. 1056
K. HOVNANIAN ASPIRE AT APRICOT GROVE, LLC—See Hovnanian Enterprises, Inc.; *U.S. Public*, pg. 1056
K. HOVNANIAN ASPIRE AT AULD FARMS, LLC—See Hovnanian Enterprises, Inc.; *U.S. Public*, pg. 1056
K. HOVNANIAN ASPIRE AT CALITERRA RANCH, LLC—See Hovnanian Enterprises, Inc.; *U.S. Public*, pg. 1056
K. HOVNANIAN ASPIRE AT HAWKS RIDGE, LLC—See Hovnanian Enterprises, Inc.; *U.S. Public*, pg. 1056
K. HOVNANIAN ASPIRE AT PORT ST. LUCIE, LLC—See Hovnanian Enterprises, Inc.; *U.S. Public*, pg. 1056
K. HOVNANIAN ASPIRE AT RIVER TERRACE, LLC—See Hovnanian Enterprises, Inc.; *U.S. Public*, pg. 1056
K. HOVNANIAN ASPIRE AT SOLAIRE, LLC—See Hovnanian Enterprises, Inc.; *U.S. Public*, pg. 1056
K. HOVNANIAN ASPIRE AT STONES THROW, LLC—See Hovnanian Enterprises, Inc.; *U.S. Public*, pg. 1056
K. HOVNANIAN ASPIRE AT WATERSTONE, LLC—See Hovnanian Enterprises, Inc.; *U.S. Public*, pg. 1056
K. HOVNANIAN AT 240 MISSOURI, LLC—See Hovnanian Enterprises, Inc.; *U.S. Public*, pg. 1058
K. HOVNANIAN AT ALAMEDA POINT, LLC—See Hovnanian Enterprises, Inc.; *U.S. Public*, pg. 1058
K. HOVNANIAN AT ALEXANDER LAKES, LLC—See Hovnanian Enterprises, Inc.; *U.S. Public*, pg. 1058
K. HOVNANIAN AT AMBERLEY WOODS, LLC—See Hovnanian Enterprises, Inc.; *U.S. Public*, pg. 1058
K. HOVNANIAN AT ASHBY PLACE, LLC—See Hovnanian Enterprises, Inc.; *U.S. Public*, pg. 1058
K. HOVNANIAN AT ASHLEY POINTE LLC—See Hovnanian Enterprises, Inc.; *U.S. Public*, pg. 1058
K. HOVNANIAN AT ASPIRE AT APRICOT GROVE PH2, LLC—See Hovnanian Enterprises, Inc.; *U.S. Public*, pg. 1058
K. HOVNANIAN AT AUTUMN RIDGE, LLC—See Hovnanian Enterprises, Inc.; *U.S. Public*, pg. 1058
K. HOVNANIAN AT BEACON PARK AREA 129, LLC—See Hovnanian Enterprises, Inc.; *U.S. Public*, pg. 1058
K. HOVNANIAN AT BELLEWOOD, LLC—See Hovnanian Enterprises, Inc.; *U.S. Public*, pg. 1058
K. HOVNANIAN AT BENSEN'S MILL ESTATES, LLC—See Hovnanian Enterprises, Inc.; *U.S. Public*, pg. 1058
K. HOVNANIAN AT BLACKSTONE, LLC—See Hovnanian Enterprises, Inc.; *U.S. Public*, pg. 1058
K. HOVNANIAN AT BOCA DUNES, LLC—See Hovnanian Enterprises, Inc.; *U.S. Public*, pg. 1058
K. HOVNANIAN AT BOOTH FARM, LLC—See Hovnanian Enterprises, Inc.; *U.S. Public*, pg. 1058
K. HOVNANIAN AT BRADWELL ESTATES, LLC—See Hovnanian Enterprises, Inc.; *U.S. Public*, pg. 1058
K. HOVNANIAN AT BRITTANY MANOR, LLC—See Hovnanian Enterprises, Inc.; *U.S. Public*, pg. 1058
K. HOVNANIAN AT BURCH KOVE, LLC—See Hovnanian Enterprises, Inc.; *U.S. Public*, pg. 1058
K. HOVNANIAN AT CADENCE PARK, LLC—See Hovnanian Enterprises, Inc.; *U.S. Public*, pg. 1058
K. HOVNANIAN AT CASA DEL MAR, LLC—See Hovnanian Enterprises, Inc.; *U.S. Public*, pg. 1058
K. HOVNANIAN AT CEDAR LANE, LLC—See Hovnanian Enterprises, Inc.; *U.S. Public*, pg. 1058
K. HOVNANIAN AT CHRISTINA COURT, LLC—See Hovnanian Enterprises, Inc.; *U.S. Public*, pg. 1058
K. HOVNANIAN AT CHURCHILL FARMS LLC—See Hovnanian Enterprises, Inc.; *U.S. Public*, pg. 1058
K. HOVNANIAN AT COOPER'S LANDING, LLC—See Hovnanian Enterprises, Inc.; *U.S. Public*, pg. 1058
K. HOVNANIAN AT CORAL LAGO, LLC—See Hovnanian Enterprises, Inc.; *U.S. Public*, pg. 1058
K. HOVNANIAN AT COUNTRY VIEW ESTATES, LLC—See Hovnanian Enterprises, Inc.; *U.S. Public*, pg. 1058
K. HOVNANIAN AT DEER RIDGE, LLC—See Hovnanian Enterprises, Inc.; *U.S. Public*, pg. 1058
K. HOVNANIAN AT DORADO AT TWELVE BRIDGES, LLC—See Hovnanian Enterprises, Inc.; *U.S. Public*, pg. 1058
K. HOVNANIAN AT DOYLESTOWN, LLC—See Hovnanian Enterprises, Inc.; *U.S. Public*, pg. 1058
K. HOVNANIAN AT EDEN TERRACE, LLC—See Hovnanian Enterprises, Inc.; *U.S. Public*, pg. 1058
K. HOVNANIAN AT EMBREY MILL VILLAGE, LLC—See Hovnanian Enterprises, Inc.; *U.S. Public*, pg. 1058
K. HOVNANIAN AT ESTATES OF CHANCELLORSVILLE, LLC—See Hovnanian Enterprises, Inc.; *U.S. Public*, pg. 1058
K. HOVNANIAN AT ESTATES OF FOX CHASE, LLC—See Hovnanian Enterprises, Inc.; *U.S. Public*, pg. 1058
K. HOVNANIAN AT FAIRFIELD RIDGE, LLC—See Hovnanian Enterprises, Inc.; *U.S. Public*, pg. 1058
K. HOVNANIAN AT FIREFLY AT WINDING CREEK, LLC—See Hovnanian Enterprises, Inc.; *U.S. Public*, pg. 1058
K. HOVNANIAN AT FORK LANDING, LLC—See Hovnanian Enterprises, Inc.; *U.S. Public*, pg. 1058
K. HOVNANIAN AT GLEN OAKS, LLC—See Hovnanian Enterprises, Inc.; *U.S. Public*, pg. 1058
K. HOVNANIAN AT GRANDE PARK, LLC—See Hovnanian Enterprises, Inc.; *U.S. Public*, pg. 1058
K. HOVNANIAN AT HAMMOCK BREEZE, LLC—See Hovnanian Enterprises, Inc.; *U.S. Public*, pg. 1059
K. HOVNANIAN AT HAMPSHIRE FARMS, LLC—See Hovnanian Enterprises, Inc.; *U.S. Public*, pg. 1059
K. HOVNANIAN AT HAMPTON COVE, LLC—See Hovnanian Enterprises, Inc.; *U.S. Public*, pg. 1059
K. HOVNANIAN AT HARBOR'S EDGE AT BAYSIDE, LLC—See Hovnanian Enterprises, Inc.; *U.S. Public*, pg. 1059
K. HOVNANIAN AT HARVEST MEADOWS, LLC—See Hovnanian Enterprises, Inc.; *U.S. Public*, pg. 1059
K. HOVNANIAN AT HIDDEN BROOK, LLC—See Hovnanian Enterprises, Inc.; *U.S. Public*, pg. 1059
K. HOVNANIAN AT HILLTOP RESERVE, LLC—See Hovnanian Enterprises, Inc.; *U.S. Public*, pg. 1059
K. HOVNANIAN AT HUNTER'S POND, LLC—See Hovnanian Enterprises, Inc.; *U.S. Public*, pg. 1059
K. HOVNANIAN AT INDIAN WELLS, LLC—See Hovnanian Enterprises, Inc.; *U.S. Public*, pg. 1059
K. HOVNANIAN AT JACKS RUN, LLC—See Hovnanian Enterprises, Inc.; *U.S. Public*, pg. 1059
K. HOVNANIAN AT LAKE BURDEN, LLC—See Hovnanian Enterprises, Inc.; *U.S. Public*, pg. 1059
K. HOVNANIAN AT LAKE LECLARE, LLC—See Hovnanian Enterprises, Inc.; *U.S. Public*, pg. 1059
K. HOVNANIAN AT LAKE RANCHO VIEJO, LLC—See Hovnanian Enterprises, Inc.; *U.S. Public*, pg. 1059
K. HOVNANIAN AT LAUREL HILLS CROSSING, LLC—See Hovnanian Enterprises, Inc.; *U.S. Public*, pg. 1059
K. HOVNANIAN AT LILY ORCHARD, LLC—See Hovnanian Enterprises, Inc.; *U.S. Public*, pg. 1059
K. HOVNANIAN AT LINK CROSSING, LLC—See Hovnanian Enterprises, Inc.; *U.S. Public*, pg. 1059
K. HOVNANIAN AT LUKE LANDING, LLC—See Hovnanian Enterprises, Inc.; *U.S. Public*, pg. 1059
K. HOVNANIAN AT LUNA VISTA, LLC—See Hovnanian Enterprises, Inc.; *U.S. Public*, pg. 1059
K. HOVNANIAN AT MAIN STREET SQUARE, LLC—See Hovnanian Enterprises, Inc.; *U.S. Public*, pg. 1059
K. HOVNANIAN AT MAPLE HILL LLC—See Hovnanian Enterprises, Inc.; *U.S. Public*, pg. 1059
K. HOVNANIAN AT MARLBORO GROVE, LLC—See Hovnanian Enterprises, Inc.; *U.S. Public*, pg. 1059
K. HOVNANIAN AT MCCARTNEY RANCH, LLC—See Hovnanian Enterprises, Inc.; *U.S. Public*, pg. 1059
K. HOVNANIAN AT MEADOWRIDGE VILLAS, LLC—See Hovnanian Enterprises, Inc.; *U.S. Public*, pg. 1059
K. HOVNANIAN AT NEUSE RIVER, LLC—See Hovnanian Enterprises, Inc.; *U.S. Public*, pg. 1059
K. HOVNANIAN AT NEW POST, LLC—See Hovnanian Enterprises, Inc.; *U.S. Public*, pg. 1059
K. HOVNANIAN AT NORTH GROVE CROSSING, LLC—See Hovnanian Enterprises, Inc.; *U.S. Public*, pg. 1059
K. HOVNANIAN AT NORTH POINTE ESTATES LLC—See Hovnanian Enterprises, Inc.; *U.S. Public*, pg. 1059
K. HOVNANIAN AT NORTH RIDGE, LLC—See Hovnanian Enterprises, Inc.; *U.S. Public*, pg. 1059
K. HOVNANIAN AT OYSTER COVE, LLC—See Hovnanian Enterprises, Inc.; *U.S. Public*, pg. 1059

K. HOVNANIAN AT PALM VALLEY, L.L.C.—See Hovnanian Enterprises, Inc.; *U.S. Public*, pg. 1059
K. HOVNANIAN AT PARK PASEO, LLC—See Hovnanian Enterprises, Inc.; *U.S. Public*, pg. 1059
K. HOVNANIAN AT PINCKNEY FARM, LLC—See Hovnanian Enterprises, Inc.; *U.S. Public*, pg. 1059
K. HOVNANIAN AT PRAIRIE POINTE, LLC—See Hovnanian Enterprises, Inc.; *U.S. Public*, pg. 1059
K. HOVNANIAN AT QUAIL CREEK, L.L.C.—See Hovnanian Enterprises, Inc.; *U.S. Public*, pg. 1059
K. HOVNANIAN AT RANCHO CABRILLO, LLC—See Hovnanian Enterprises, Inc.; *U.S. Public*, pg. 1059
K. HOVNANIAN AT RANCHO EL DORADO, LLC—See Hovnanian Enterprises, Inc.; *U.S. Public*, pg. 1059
K. HOVNANIAN AT RANDALL HIGHLANDS, LLC—See Hovnanian Enterprises, Inc.; *U.S. Public*, pg. 1059
K. HOVNANIAN AT REDTAIL, LLC—See Hovnanian Enterprises, Inc.; *U.S. Public*, pg. 1059
K. HOVNANIAN AT RETREAT AT MILLSTONE, LLC—See Hovnanian Enterprises, Inc.; *U.S. Public*, pg. 1059
K. HOVNANIAN AT RIVER HILLS, LLC—See Hovnanian Enterprises, Inc.; *U.S. Public*, pg. 1059
K. HOVNANIAN AT ROCKLAND VILLAGE GREEN, LLC—See Hovnanian Enterprises, Inc.; *U.S. Public*, pg. 1059
K. HOVNANIAN AT SAGEBROOK, LLC—See Hovnanian Enterprises, Inc.; *U.S. Public*, pg. 1059
K. HOVNANIAN AT SAGE II HARVEST AT LIMONEIRA, LLC—See Hovnanian Enterprises, Inc.; *U.S. Public*, pg. 1059
K. HOVNANIAN AT SANDPIPER PLACE, LLC—See Hovnanian Enterprises, Inc.; *U.S. Public*, pg. 1059
K. HOVNANIAN AT SAUGANASH GLEN, LLC—See Hovnanian Enterprises, Inc.; *U.S. Public*, pg. 1059
K. HOVNANIAN AT SCOTTSDALE HEIGHTS, LLC—See Hovnanian Enterprises, Inc.; *U.S. Public*, pg. 1059
K. HOVNANIAN AT SEABROOK, LLC—See Hovnanian Enterprises, Inc.; *U.S. Public*, pg. 1059
K. HOVNANIAN AT SEASONS LANDING, LLC—See Hovnanian Enterprises, Inc.; *U.S. Public*, pg. 1059
K. HOVNANIAN AT SIERRA VISTA, LLC—See Hovnanian Enterprises, Inc.; *U.S. Public*, pg. 1059
K. HOVNANIAN AT SILVER LEAF, LLC—See Hovnanian Enterprises, Inc.; *U.S. Public*, pg. 1059
K. HOVNANIAN AT SOMERSET, LLC—See Hovnanian Enterprises, Inc.; *U.S. Public*, pg. 1059
K. HOVNANIAN AT SUMMERLAKE, LLC—See Hovnanian Enterprises, Inc.; *U.S. Public*, pg. 1059
K. HOVNANIAN AT SUMMIT CROSSING ESTATES, LLC—See Hovnanian Enterprises, Inc.; *U.S. Public*, pg. 1059
K. HOVNANIAN AT SUN CITY WEST, LLC—See Hovnanian Enterprises, Inc.; *U.S. Public*, pg. 1059
K. HOVNANIAN AT TAMARACK SOUTH LLC—See Hovnanian Enterprises, Inc.; *U.S. Public*, pg. 1056
K. HOVNANIAN AT TANGLEWOOD OAKS, LLC—See Hovnanian Enterprises, Inc.; *U.S. Public*, pg. 1059
K. HOVNANIAN AT THE HIGHLANDS AT SUMMERLAKE GROVE, LLC—See Hovnanian Enterprises, Inc.; *U.S. Public*, pg. 1059
K. HOVNANIAN AT THE PRESERVE, LLC—See Hovnanian Enterprises, Inc.; *U.S. Public*, pg. 1059
K. HOVNANIAN AT TORTOSA SOUTH, LLC—See Hovnanian Enterprises, Inc.; *U.S. Public*, pg. 1060
K. HOVNANIAN AT TOWNES AT COUNTY CENTER, LLC—See Hovnanian Enterprises, Inc.; *U.S. Public*, pg. 1060
K. HOVNANIAN AT TOWNSEND FIELDS, LLC—See Hovnanian Enterprises, Inc.; *U.S. Public*, pg. 1060
K. HOVNANIAN AT UNION PARK, LLC—See Hovnanian Enterprises, Inc.; *U.S. Public*, pg. 1060
K. HOVNANIAN AT UPPER PROVIDENCE, LLC—See Hovnanian Enterprises, Inc.; *U.S. Public*, pg. 1060
K. HOVNANIAN AT VALLETTA, LLC—See Hovnanian Enterprises, Inc.; *U.S. Public*, pg. 1060
K. HOVNANIAN AT VERRADO MARKETSIDE, LLC—See Hovnanian Enterprises, Inc.; *U.S. Public*, pg. 1060
K. HOVNANIAN AT VICTORY AT VERRADO, LLC—See Hovnanian Enterprises, Inc.; *U.S. Public*, pg. 1060
K. HOVNANIAN AT VILLAGE CENTER, LLC—See Hovnanian Enterprises, Inc.; *U.S. Public*, pg. 1060
K. HOVNANIAN AT VINEYARD HEIGHTS, LLC—See Hovnanian Enterprises, Inc.; *U.S. Public*, pg. 1060
K. HOVNANIAN AT WADE'S GRANT, LLC—See Hovnanian Enterprises, Inc.; *U.S. Public*, pg. 1060
K. HOVNANIAN AT WALKERS GROVE, LLC—See Hovnanian Enterprises, Inc.; *U.S. Public*, pg. 1060
K. HOVNANIAN AT WEST WINDSOR, L.L.C.—See Hovnanian Enterprises, Inc.; *U.S. Public*, pg. 1060
K. HOVNANIAN AT WILLOWSFORD GREENS III, LLC—See Hovnanian Enterprises, Inc.; *U.S. Public*, pg. 1060
K. HOVNANIAN BELDEN POINTE, LLC—See Hovnanian Enterprises, Inc.; *U.S. Public*, pg. 1056
K. HOVNANIAN BRITTANY MANOR BORROWER, LLC—See Hovnanian Enterprises, Inc.; *U.S. Public*, pg. 1056
K. HOVNANIAN BUILDING COMPANY, LLC—See Hovnanian Enterprises, Inc.; *U.S. Public*, pg. 1056

K. HOVNANIAN CAMBRIDGE HOMES, LLC—See Hovnanian Enterprises, Inc.; *U.S. Public*, pg. 1056
K. HOVNANIAN COMPANIES NORTHEAST, INC.—See Hovnanian Enterprises, Inc.; *U.S. Public*, pg. 1056
K. HOVNANIAN CORNERSTONE FARMS, LLC—See Hovnanian Enterprises, Inc.; *U.S. Public*, pg. 1056
K. HOVNANIAN DFW ASCEND AT JUSTIN CROSSING, LLC—See Hovnanian Enterprises, Inc.; *U.S. Public*, pg. 1056
K. HOVNANIAN DFW AUBURN FARMS, LLC—See Hovnanian Enterprises, Inc.; *U.S. Public*, pg. 1056
K. HOVNANIAN DFW BAYSIDE, LLC—See Hovnanian Enterprises, Inc.; *U.S. Public*, pg. 1056
K. HOVNANIAN DFW CANYON FALLS, LLC—See Hovnanian Enterprises, Inc.; *U.S. Public*, pg. 1056
K. HOVNANIAN DFW COMMODORE AT PRESTON, LLC—See Hovnanian Enterprises, Inc.; *U.S. Public*, pg. 1056
K. HOVNANIAN DFW DIAMOND CREEK ESTATES, LLC—See Hovnanian Enterprises, Inc.; *U.S. Public*, pg. 1056
K. HOVNANIAN DFW HARMON FARMS, LLC—See Hovnanian Enterprises, Inc.; *U.S. Public*, pg. 1056
K. HOVNANIAN DFW HERON POND, LLC—See Hovnanian Enterprises, Inc.; *U.S. Public*, pg. 1056
K. HOVNANIAN DFW HIGH POINTE, LLC—See Hovnanian Enterprises, Inc.; *U.S. Public*, pg. 1056
K. HOVNANIAN DFW HOMESTEAD, LLC—See Hovnanian Enterprises, Inc.; *U.S. Public*, pg. 1056
K. HOVNANIAN DFW LIBERTY CROSSING, LLC—See Hovnanian Enterprises, Inc.; *U.S. Public*, pg. 1057
K. HOVNANIAN DFW LIBERTY, LLC—See Hovnanian Enterprises, Inc.; *U.S. Public*, pg. 1057
K. HOVNANIAN DFW MIDTOWN PARK, LLC—See Hovnanian Enterprises, Inc.; *U.S. Public*, pg. 1057
K. HOVNANIAN DFW OAKMONT PARK, LLC—See Hovnanian Enterprises, Inc.; *U.S. Public*, pg. 1057
K. HOVNANIAN DFW SANFORD PARK, LLC—See Hovnanian Enterprises, Inc.; *U.S. Public*, pg. 1057
K. HOVNANIAN DFW SAPPHIRE BAY, LLC—See Hovnanian Enterprises, Inc.; *U.S. Public*, pg. 1057
K. HOVNANIAN DFW SEVENTEEN LAKES, LLC—See Hovnanian Enterprises, Inc.; *U.S. Public*, pg. 1057
K. HOVNANIAN DFW TRAILWOOD, LLC—See Hovnanian Enterprises, Inc.; *U.S. Public*, pg. 1057
K. HOVNANIAN DFW VILLAS AT MUSTANG PARK, LLC—See Hovnanian Enterprises, Inc.; *U.S. Public*, pg. 1057
K. HOVNANIAN DFW WATSON CREEK, LLC—See Hovnanian Enterprises, Inc.; *U.S. Public*, pg. 1057
K. HOVNANIAN DFW WELLINGTON VILLAS, LLC—See Hovnanian Enterprises, Inc.; *U.S. Public*, pg. 1057
K. HOVNANIAN DFW WILDRIDGE, LLC—See Hovnanian Enterprises, Inc.; *U.S. Public*, pg. 1057
K. HOVNANIAN ESTATES AT WEKIVA, LLC—See Hovnanian Enterprises, Inc.; *U.S. Public*, pg. 1057
K. HOVNANIAN FOUR SEASONS AT CHESTNUT RIDGE, LLC—See Hovnanian Enterprises, Inc.; *U.S. Public*, pg. 1057
K. HOVNANIAN FOUR SEASONS AT HOMESTEAD, LLC—See Hovnanian Enterprises, Inc.; *U.S. Public*, pg. 1057
K. HOVNANIAN GRAND CYPRESS, LLC—See Hovnanian Enterprises, Inc.; *U.S. Public*, pg. 1057
K. HOVNANIAN GREAT WESTERN BUILDING COMPANY, LLC—See Hovnanian Enterprises, Inc.; *U.S. Public*, pg. 1056
K. HOVNANIAN GREAT WESTERN HOMES, LLC—See Hovnanian Enterprises, Inc.; *U.S. Public*, pg. 1056
K. HOVNANIAN HOMES AT BROOK MANOR, LLC—See Hovnanian Enterprises, Inc.; *U.S. Public*, pg. 1057
K. HOVNANIAN HOMES AT CREEKSIDE, LLC—See Hovnanian Enterprises, Inc.; *U.S. Public*, pg. 1057
K. HOVNANIAN HOMES AT SHELL HALL, LLC—See Hovnanian Enterprises, Inc.; *U.S. Public*, pg. 1057
K. HOVNANIAN HOMES AT SHENANDOAH SPRINGS, LLC—See Hovnanian Enterprises, Inc.; *U.S. Public*, pg. 1057
K. HOVNANIAN HOMES AT SUMMIT POINTE, LLC—See Hovnanian Enterprises, Inc.; *U.S. Public*, pg. 1057
K. HOVNANIAN HOMES AT THE ABBY, LLC—See Hovnanian Enterprises, Inc.; *U.S. Public*, pg. 1057
K. HOVNANIAN HOMES - DFW, L.L.C.—See Hovnanian Enterprises, Inc.; *U.S. Public*, pg. 1057
K. HOVNANIAN HOMES OF MARYLAND I, LLC—See Hovnanian Enterprises, Inc.; *U.S. Public*, pg. 1057
K. HOVNANIAN HOMES OF MARYLAND, LLC—See Hovnanian Enterprises, Inc.; *U.S. Public*, pg. 1057
K. HOVNANIAN HOMES OF MINNESOTA AT ARBOR CREEK, LLC—See Hovnanian Enterprises, Inc.; *U.S. Public*, pg. 1057
K. HOVNANIAN HOMES OF MINNESOTA AT AUTUMN MEADOWS, LLC—See Hovnanian Enterprises, Inc.; *U.S. Public*, pg. 1057
K. HOVNANIAN HOMES OF MINNESOTA AT CEDAR HOLLOW, LLC—See Hovnanian Enterprises, Inc.; *U.S. Public*, pg. 1057

K. HOVNANIAN HOMES OF MINNESOTA AT FOUNDER'S RIDGE, LLC—See Hovnanian Enterprises, Inc.; *U.S. Public*, pg. 1057
K. HOVNANIAN HOMES OF MINNESOTA AT HARPERS STREET WOODS, LLC—See Hovnanian Enterprises, Inc.; *U.S. Public*, pg. 1057
K. HOVNANIAN HOMES OF MINNESOTA, L.L.C.—See Hovnanian Enterprises, Inc.; *U.S. Public*, pg. 1057
K. HOVNANIAN HOUSTON BALMORAL, LLC—See Hovnanian Enterprises, Inc.; *U.S. Public*, pg. 1057
K. HOVNANIAN HOUSTON BAYOU OAKS AT WEST OREM, LLC—See Hovnanian Enterprises, Inc.; *U.S. Public*, pg. 1057
K. HOVNANIAN HOUSTON CREEK BEND, LLC—See Hovnanian Enterprises, Inc.; *U.S. Public*, pg. 1057
K. HOVNANIAN HOUSTON DRY CREEK VILLAGE, LLC—See Hovnanian Enterprises, Inc.; *U.S. Public*, pg. 1057
K. HOVNANIAN HOUSTON ELDRIDGE PARK, LLC—See Hovnanian Enterprises, Inc.; *U.S. Public*, pg. 1057
K. HOVNANIAN HOUSTON GREATWOOD LAKE, LLC—See Hovnanian Enterprises, Inc.; *U.S. Public*, pg. 1057
K. HOVNANIAN HOUSTON KATY POINTE, LLC—See Hovnanian Enterprises, Inc.; *U.S. Public*, pg. 1057
K. HOVNANIAN HOUSTON LAKES OF BELLA TERRA WEST, LLC—See Hovnanian Enterprises, Inc.; *U.S. Public*, pg. 1057
K. HOVNANIAN HOUSTON LAUREL GLEN, LLC—See Hovnanian Enterprises, Inc.; *U.S. Public*, pg. 1057
K. HOVNANIAN HOUSTON MIDTOWN PARK I, LLC—See Hovnanian Enterprises, Inc.; *U.S. Public*, pg. 1057
K. HOVNANIAN HOUSTON PARK LAKES EAST, LLC—See Hovnanian Enterprises, Inc.; *U.S. Public*, pg. 1057
K. HOVNANIAN HOUSTON PARKWAY TRAILS, LLC—See Hovnanian Enterprises, Inc.; *U.S. Public*, pg. 1057
K. HOVNANIAN HOUSTON RIVER FARMS, LLC—See Hovnanian Enterprises, Inc.; *U.S. Public*, pg. 1057
K. HOVNANIAN HOUSTON SUNSET RANCH, LLC—See Hovnanian Enterprises, Inc.; *U.S. Public*, pg. 1057
K. HOVNANIAN HOUSTON TERRA DEL SOL, LLC—See Hovnanian Enterprises, Inc.; *U.S. Public*, pg. 1057
K. HOVNANIAN HOUSTON THUNDER BAY SUBDIVISION, LLC—See Hovnanian Enterprises, Inc.; *U.S. Public*, pg. 1057
K. HOVNANIAN HOUSTON TRANQUILITY LAKE ESTATES, LLC—See Hovnanian Enterprises, Inc.; *U.S. Public*, pg. 1057
K. HOVNANIAN HOUSTON WESTWOOD, LLC—See Hovnanian Enterprises, Inc.; *U.S. Public*, pg. 1057
K. HOVNANIAN LAKE PARKER, LLC—See Hovnanian Enterprises, Inc.; *U.S. Public*, pg. 1057
K. HOVNANIAN LANDINGS 40S, LLC—See Hovnanian Enterprises, Inc.; *U.S. Public*, pg. 1057
K. HOVNANIAN LEGACY AT VIA BELLA, LLC—See Hovnanian Enterprises, Inc.; *U.S. Public*, pg. 1057
K. HOVNANIAN LIBERTY ON BLUFF CREEK, LLC—See Hovnanian Enterprises, Inc.; *U.S. Public*, pg. 1057
K. HOVNANIAN MAGNOLIA AT WESTSIDE, LLC—See Hovnanian Enterprises, Inc.; *U.S. Public*, pg. 1057
K. HOVNANIAN MEADOW LAKES, LLC—See Hovnanian Enterprises, Inc.; *U.S. Public*, pg. 1057
K. HOVNANIAN MEADOW VIEW AT MOUNTAIN HOUSE, LLC—See Hovnanian Enterprises, Inc.; *U.S. Public*, pg. 1058
K. HOVNANIAN NORTON PLACE, LLC—See Hovnanian Enterprises, Inc.; *U.S. Public*, pg. 1058
K. HOVNANIAN OCOEE LANDINGS, LLC—See Hovnanian Enterprises, Inc.; *U.S. Public*, pg. 1058
K. HOVNANIAN OF HOUSTON II, L.L.C.—See Hovnanian Enterprises, Inc.; *U.S. Public*, pg. 1060
K. HOVNANIAN PRESERVE AT AVONLEA, LLC—See Hovnanian Enterprises, Inc.; *U.S. Public*, pg. 1058
K. HOVNANIAN REDFERN TRAILS, LLC—See Hovnanian Enterprises, Inc.; *U.S. Public*, pg. 1058
K. HOVNANIAN SAN SEBASTIAN, LLC—See Hovnanian Enterprises, Inc.; *U.S. Public*, pg. 1058
K. HOVNANIAN'S ASPIRE AT UNION VILLAGE, LLC—See Hovnanian Enterprises, Inc.; *U.S. Public*, pg. 1060
K. HOVNANIAN'S COVE AT ASBURY PARK URBAN RENEWAL, LLC—See Hovnanian Enterprises, Inc.; *U.S. Public*, pg. 1060
K. HOVNANIAN SERENO, LLC—See Hovnanian Enterprises, Inc.; *U.S. Public*, pg. 1058
K. HOVNANIAN'S FOUR SEASONS AT BAKERSFIELD, L.L.C.—See Hovnanian Enterprises, Inc.; *U.S. Public*, pg. 1056
K. HOVNANIAN'S FOUR SEASONS AT BAYMONT FARMS LLC—See Hovnanian Enterprises, Inc.; *U.S. Public*, pg. 1060
K. HOVNANIAN'S FOUR SEASONS AT BELLE TERRE, LLC—See Hovnanian Enterprises, Inc.; *U.S. Public*, pg. 1060
K. HOVNANIAN'S FOUR SEASONS AT CAROLINA OAKS, LLC—See Hovnanian Enterprises, Inc.; *U.S. Public*, pg. 1060

COMPANY NAME INDEX

K. HOVNANIAN'S FOUR SEASONS AT LAKES OF CANE BAY LLC—See Hovnanian Enterprises, Inc.; *U.S. Public*, pg. 1060
K. HOVNANIAN'S FOUR SEASONS AT NEW KENT VINEYARDS, L.L.C.—See Hovnanian Enterprises, Inc.; *U.S. Public*, pg. 1060
K. HOVNANIAN'S FOUR SEASONS AT RUSH CREEK, L.L.C.—See Hovnanian Enterprises, Inc.; *U.S. Public*, pg. 1060
K. HOVNANIAN'S FOUR SEASONS AT THE LAKES AT CANE BAY, LLC—See Hovnanian Enterprises, Inc.; *U.S. Public*, pg. 1060
K. HOVNANIAN'S FOUR SEASONS AT THE MANOR, LLC—See Hovnanian Enterprises, Inc.; *U.S. Public*, pg. 1060
K. HOVNANIAN'S FOUR SEASONS, LLC—See Hovnanian Enterprises, Inc.; *U.S. Public*, pg. 1060
K. HOVNANIAN SHERWOOD AT REGENCY, LLC—See Hovnanian Enterprises, Inc.; *U.S. Public*, pg. 1058
K. HOVNANIAN STERLING RANCH, LLC—See Hovnanian Enterprises, Inc.; *U.S. Public*, pg. 1058
K. HOVNANIAN SUMMIT HOMES, L.L.C.—See Hovnanian Enterprises, Inc.; *U.S. Public*, pg. 1058
K. HOVNANIAN T&C HOMES AT ILLINOIS, L.L.C.—See Hovnanian Enterprises, Inc.; *U.S. Public*, pg. 1058
K. HOVNANIAN UNION PARK, LLC—See Hovnanian Enterprises, Inc.; *U.S. Public*, pg. 1058
K. HOVNANIAN VILLAGE GLEN, LLC—See Hovnanian Enterprises, Inc.; *U.S. Public*, pg. 1058
K. HOVNANIAN VILLAS AT THE COMMONS, LLC—See Hovnanian Enterprises, Inc.; *U.S. Public*, pg. 1058
K. HOVNANIAN WINDING BAY PRESERVE, LLC—See Hovnanian Enterprises, Inc.; *U.S. Public*, pg. 1058
K. HOVNANIAN WINDWARD HOMES, LLC—See Hovnanian Enterprises, Inc.; *U.S. Public*, pg. 1058
K. HOVNANIAN WOODRIDGE PLACE, LLC—See Hovnanian Enterprises, Inc.; *U.S. Public*, pg. 1058
KHOY SUGAR CO.; *Int'l*, pg. 4156
KHOY TEXTILE CO.; *Int'l*, pg. 4156
KHQ, INCORPORATED—See Cowles Company; *U.S. Private*, pg. 1073
KHRG BORN LLC—See InterContinental Hotels Group PLC; *Int'l*, pg. 3738
KHRG LA PEER LLC—See InterContinental Hotels Group PLC; *Int'l*, pg. 3739
KHRG PALLADIAN LLC—See InterContinental Hotels Group PLC; *Int'l*, pg. 3739
KHRG PALOMAR PHOENIX LLC—See InterContinental Hotels Group PLC; *Int'l*, pg. 3739
KHRG PHILLY MONACO LLC—See InterContinental Hotels Group PLC; *Int'l*, pg. 3739
KHRONE SKARPENORD AS—See Krohne International, Inc.; *Int'l*, pg. 4303
KHRONOS ADVISORY LIMITED; *Int'l*, pg. 4156
THE KHRUNICHEV STATE RESEARCH & PRODUCTION SPACE CENTRE; *Int'l*, pg. 7662
KHRYSOS INDUSTRIES, INC.—See Youngevity International Corp.; *U.S. Public*, pg. 2399
KHS AG—See Salzgitter AG; *Int'l*, pg. 6497
KHS AG—See Salzgitter AG; *Int'l*, pg. 6497
KHS AG—See Salzgitter AG; *Int'l*, pg. 6497
KHS AG—See Salzgitter AG; *Int'l*, pg. 6497
KHS AG—See Salzgitter AG; *Int'l*, pg. 6497
KHS AG (THAILAND) LTD.—See Salzgitter AG; *Int'l*, pg. 6497
K & H SALES, INC.—See DoALL Company; *U.S. Private*, pg. 1250
KHS AMBULATORY SURGERY CENTER LLC—See Tenet Healthcare Corporation; *U.S. Public*, pg. 2010
KHS ANDES S.A.S.—See Salzgitter AG; *Int'l*, pg. 6496
KHS ARGENTINA S.A.—See Salzgitter AG; *Int'l*, pg. 6497
KHS ASIA PTE LTD—See Salzgitter AG; *Int'l*, pg. 6497
KHS AUSTRIA GMBH—See Salzgitter AG; *Int'l*, pg. 6497
KHS BENELUX B.V.—See Salzgitter AG; *Int'l*, pg. 6497
KHS BTC NIGERIA LTD.—See Salzgitter AG; *Int'l*, pg. 6497
KHS CORPOPLAST GMBH—See Salzgitter AG; *Int'l*, pg. 6496
KHS CORPOPLAST NORTH AMERICA INC.—See Salzgitter AG; *Int'l*, pg. 6496
KHS CORPOPLAST TRADING (SHANGHAI) CO., LTD.—See Salzgitter AG; *Int'l*, pg. 6496
KHS CORPOPLAST VERWALTUNGSGESELLSCHAFT MBH—See Salzgitter AG; *Int'l*, pg. 6496
KHS EAST AFRICA LTD.—See Salzgitter AG; *Int'l*, pg. 6496
KH SECURITY PTE. LTD.—See Advancer Global Limited; *Int'l*, pg. 163
KHS FRANCE S.A.R.L.—See Salzgitter AG; *Int'l*, pg. 6497
KHS GMBH—See Salzgitter AG; *Int'l*, pg. 6496
KHS HANDEL UND SERVICE GMBH—See Robert Bosch GmbH; *Int'l*, pg. 6361
KHS INDUSTRIA DE MAQUINAS LTDA.—See Salzgitter AG; *Int'l*, pg. 6497
KHS ITALIA S.R.L.—See Salzgitter AG; *Int'l*, pg. 6497
KHS JAPAN CORP.—See Salzgitter AG; *Int'l*, pg. 6497
KHS KOREA CO. LTD.—See Salzgitter AG; *Int'l*, pg. 6496
KHS MACHINE & EQUIPMENT (QINHUANGDAO) CO., LTD.—See Salzgitter AG; *Int'l*, pg. 6496

KHS MACHINERY PVT. LTD.—See Salzgitter AG; *Int'l*, pg. 6496
KHS MACHINES NIGERIA LIMITED—See Salzgitter AG; *Int'l*, pg. 6496
KHS MAKINE SANAYI VE TICARET LIMITED SIRKETI—See Salzgitter AG; *Int'l*, pg. 6496
KHS MANUFACTURING (SOUTH AFRICA) (PTY.) LTD.—See Salzgitter AG; *Int'l*, pg. 6496
KHS MEXICO S.A. DE C.V.—See Salzgitter AG; *Int'l*, pg. 6497
K.H. SMITH COMMUNICATIONS, INC—See Dycom Industries, Inc.; *U.S. Public*, pg. 698
K.H.S. MUSICAL INSTRUMENT CO., LTD.; *Int'l*, pg. 4043
KHS MYANMAR COMPANY LIMITED—See Salzgitter AG; *Int'l*, pg. 6496
KHS NORDIC APS—See Salzgitter AG; *Int'l*, pg. 6497
KHS PACIFIC PTY. LTD.—See Salzgitter AG; *Int'l*, pg. 6497
KHS PANAMERICANA SPA—See Salzgitter AG; *Int'l*, pg. 6496
KHS PLASMAX GMBH—See Salzgitter AG; *Int'l*, pg. 6496
KHS POLSKA SP. Z O.O.—See Salzgitter AG; *Int'l*, pg. 6496
KHS RUS OOO—See Salzgitter AG; *Int'l*, pg. 6496
KHS SCHWEIZ GMBH—See Salzgitter AG; *Int'l*, pg. 6496
KHS&S CONTRACTORS; *U.S. Private*, pg. 2301
KHS SKANDINAVIEN APS—See Salzgitter AG; *Int'l*, pg. 6497
KHS S.R.O.—See Salzgitter AG; *Int'l*, pg. 6497
KHS UK LTD.—See Salzgitter AG; *Int'l*, pg. 6497
KHS UKRAINE OOO—See Salzgitter AG; *Int'l*, pg. 6496
KHS USA, INC.—See Salzgitter AG; *Int'l*, pg. 6497
KHS USA, INC.—See Salzgitter AG; *Int'l*, pg. 6497
KHT FAHRZEUGTEILE GMBH—See Rupf Industries GmbH; *Int'l*, pg. 6429
K & H TRUCK PLAZA INC.—See Majors Management, LLC; *U.S. Private*, pg. 2555
KHTT—See Griffin Communications, LLC; *U.S. Private*, pg. 1787
KHUDUUGIIN TEEVER JOINT STOCK COMPANY; *Int'l*, pg. 4156
KHULNA POWER COMPANY LIMITED; *Int'l*, pg. 4156
KHULNA POWER COMPANY UNIT II LTD.—See Khulna Power Company Limited; *Int'l*, pg. 4156
KHURSHID SPINNING MILLS LIMITED; *Int'l*, pg. 4156
KHVATEC CO., LTD.; *Int'l*, pg. 4156
KHVATEC CO., LTD.—See KHVatec Co., Ltd.; *Int'l*, pg. 4156
KHV HUIZHOU PRECISION MANUFACTURING CO., LTD.—See KHVatec Co., Ltd.; *Int'l*, pg. 4156
KHV TIAJIN PRECISION MANUFACTURING CO., LTD.—See KHVatec Co., Ltd.; *Int'l*, pg. 4156
KHYATI MULTIMEDIA ENTERTAINMENT LIMITED; *Int'l*, pg. 4156
KHYBER TEXTILE MILLS LIMITED; *Int'l*, pg. 4156
KHYBER TOBACCO COMPANY LIMITED; *Int'l*, pg. 4156
KIA AMERICA, INC.—See Kia Corporation; *Int'l*, pg. 4156
KIA AUSTRALIA PTY LTD—See Kia Corporation; *Int'l*, pg. 4156
KIA AUTO AS—See Tallinna Kaubamaja AS; *Int'l*, pg. 7447
K.I. ABDULKADIR & PARTNERS CO. LTD.; *Int'l*, pg. 4043
KIA CANADA, INC.—See Kia Corporation; *Int'l*, pg. 4156
KIA CORPORATION; *Int'l*, pg. 4156
KIADIS PHARMA CANADA—See Sanofi; *Int'l*, pg. 6548
KIADIS PHARMA N.V.—See Sanofi; *Int'l*, pg. 6548
KIA GEORGIA, INC.—See Kia Corporation; *Int'l*, pg. 4156
KIA HELLAS S.A.—See AUTOHELLAS S.A.; *Int'l*, pg. 727
KIAH INC.—See Nexstar Media Group, Inc.; *U.S. Public*, pg. 1524
KIA JAPAN CO., LTD.—See Kia Corporation; *Int'l*, pg. 4156
KIA LIM BERHAD; *Int'l*, pg. 4157
KIAMICHI RAILROAD COMPANY L.L.C.—See Brookfield Infrastructure Partners L.P.; *Int'l*, pg. 1192
KIAMICHI RAILROAD COMPANY L.L.C.—See GIC Pte. Ltd.; *Int'l*, pg. 2966
KIA MOTORS AUSTRIA GMBH—See Kia Corporation; *Int'l*, pg. 4156
KIA MOTORS CZECH S.R.O.—See Kia Corporation; *Int'l*, pg. 4156
KIA MOTORS DEUTSCHLAND GMBH—See Kia Corporation; *Int'l*, pg. 4156
KIA MOTORS EUROPE GMBH—See Kia Corporation; *Int'l*, pg. 4156
KIA MOTORS HUNGARY KFT—See Kia Corporation; *Int'l*, pg. 4156
KIA MOTORS IBERIA SL—See Kia Corporation; *Int'l*, pg. 4157
KIA MOTORS NEDERLAND BV—See Kia Corporation; *Int'l*, pg. 4157
KIA MOTORS NEW ZEALAND LTD.—See Kia Corporation; *Int'l*, pg. 4157
KIA MOTORS POLSKA SP. Z.O.O.—See Kia Corporation; *Int'l*, pg. 4157
KIA MOTORS SALES SLOVENSKO S.R.O.—See Kia Corporation; *Int'l*, pg. 4157
KIA MOTORS SA (PTY) LIMITED—See Kia Corporation; *Int'l*, pg. 4157

KICE INDUSTRIES INC.

KIA MOTORS SLOVAKIA S.R.O.—See Kia Corporation; *Int'l*, pg. 4157
KIA MOTORS SWEDEN AB—See Kia Corporation; *Int'l*, pg. 4157
KIA MOTORS UK LIMITED—See Kia Corporation; *Int'l*, pg. 4157
KIAN ANN DISTRICENTRE PTE LTD—See Invicta Holdings Limited; *Int'l*, pg. 3788
KIAN ANN ENGINEERING LIMITED—See Invicta Holdings Limited; *Int'l*, pg. 3788
KIAN ANN ENGINEERING TRADING (SHANGHAI) CO., LTD.—See Invicta Holdings Limited; *Int'l*, pg. 3788
KIAN ANN INVESTMENT PTE. LTD.—See Invicta Holdings Limited; *Int'l*, pg. 3788
KIAN CAPITAL PARTNERS, LLC; *U.S. Private*, pg. 2302
KIAN CHUE HWA (INDUSTRIES) PTE LTD—See Invicta Holdings Limited; *Int'l*, pg. 3788
KIANG HUAT SEA GULL TRADING FROZEN FOOD PUBLIC COMPANY LIMITED; *Int'l*, pg. 4157
KIAN HO PTE LTD.; *Int'l*, pg. 4157
KIAN JOO CAN FACTORY BERHAD—See Can-One Berhad; *Int'l*, pg. 1276
KIAN JOO CANPACK SDN. BHD.—See Can-One Berhad; *Int'l*, pg. 1277
KIAN JOO CANPACK (SHAH ALAM) SDN. BHD.—See Can-One Berhad; *Int'l*, pg. 1276
KIAN JOO CAN (VIETNAM) CO., LTD.—See Can-One Berhad; *Int'l*, pg. 1276
KIAN JOO PACKAGING SDN BHD—See Can-One Berhad; *Int'l*, pg. 1277
KIAN JOO-VISYPAK SDN.BHD—See Can-One Berhad; *Int'l*, pg. 1277
KIAN SHEN CORPORATION; *Int'l*, pg. 4157
KIA OF SANTA FE; *U.S. Private*, pg. 2301
KIARA ADVISORS PTE. LTD.—See Korea Investment Holdings Co., Ltd.; *Int'l*, pg. 4285
KIARA CAPITAL PTE. LTD.—See Korea Investment Holdings Co., Ltd.; *Int'l*, pg. 4285
THE KIA STORE; *U.S. Private*, pg. 4065
KIATNAKIN BANK PUBLIC COMPANY LIMITED; *Int'l*, pg. 4157
KIATTANA TRANSPORT PUBLIC COMPANY LIMITED; *Int'l*, pg. 4157
KIAWAH ISLAND COMMUNITY ASSOCIATION, INC.; *U.S. Private*, pg. 2302
KIAWAH ISLAND GOLF RESORTS; *U.S. Private*, pg. 2302
KIAWAH PARTNERS; *U.S. Private*, pg. 2302
THE KIBAN CO., LTD.—See NOROO Paint & Coatings Co., Ltd.; *Int'l*, pg. 5431
KIBAN TECH CO., LTD.—See NOROO Paint & Coatings Co., Ltd.; *Int'l*, pg. 5431
KIBARU MANUFACTURING SDN BHD—See Ge-Shen Corporation Berhad; *Int'l*, pg. 2897
KIBBI, LLC—See AIP, LLC; *U.S. Private*, pg. 135
KIBBLE EQUIPMENT INC.—See Brandt Holdings Company; *U.S. Private*, pg. 639
KIBBLE EQUIPMENT—See Brandt Holdings Company; *U.S. Private*, pg. 639
KIBBLE & PRENTICE HOLDING COMPANY—See CPCM, LLC; *U.S. Private*, pg. 1080
KIBIKASEI CO., LTD.—See Mitsubishi Corporation; *Int'l*, pg. 4939
KIBING GROUP (M) SDN. BHD.—See Zhuzhou Kibing Group Co., Ltd.; *Int'l*, pg. 8680
KIBING GROUP (SINGAPORE) PTE. LTD.—See Zhuzhou Kibing Group Co., Ltd.; *Int'l*, pg. 8680
KIBING MINERALS (M) SDN. BHD.—See Zhuzhou Kibing Group Co., Ltd.; *Int'l*, pg. 8680
KIBION AB—See Orexo AB; *Int'l*, pg. 5617
KIBO CAPITAL PARTNERS LTD.; *Int'l*, pg. 4157
KIBO COMMERCE LTD.—See Vista Equity Partners, LLC; *U.S. Private*, pg. 4398
KIBO COMPRESSOR CORP.—See Burk Royalty Co.; *U.S. Private*, pg. 687
KIBO ENERGY PLC; *Int'l*, pg. 4157
KIBO - PETALUMA—See Vista Equity Partners, LLC; *U.S. Private*, pg. 4398
KIBO - SAN LUIS OBISPO—See Vista Equity Partners, LLC; *U.S. Private*, pg. 4398
KIBO SOFTWARE, INC.—See Vista Equity Partners, LLC; *U.S. Private*, pg. 4398
KIBUN FOODS INC.; *Int'l*, pg. 4157
KIBUN FOODS SINGAPORE PTE., LTD.—See Kibun Foods Inc.; *Int'l*, pg. 4157
KIBUN FOODS USA, INC.—See Kibun Foods Inc.; *Int'l*, pg. 4157
KIBUN FRESH SYSTEM INC.—See Kibun Foods Inc.; *Int'l*, pg. 4157
KIBUN TRADING INC.—See Kibun Foods Inc.; *Int'l*, pg. 4157
KICE INDUSTRIES INC.; *U.S. Private*, pg. 2302
K-I CHEMICAL DO BRASIL LTDA.—See Kumiai Chemical Industry Co., Ltd.; *Int'l*, pg. 4330
K-I CHEMICAL INDUSTRY CO., LTD.—See Kumiai Chemical Industry Co., Ltd.; *Int'l*, pg. 4330
K-I CHEMICAL U.S.A. INC.—See Kumiai Chemical Industry Co., Ltd.; *Int'l*, pg. 4330

KICE INDUSTRIES INC.
CORPORATE AFFILIATIONS

KI CHEMISTRY SARL—See Kulczyk Investments S.A.; *Int'l*, pg. 4327
KICHIRI HOLDINGS & CO., LTD.; *Int'l*, pg. 4158
KICHLER LIGHTING LLC—See Kingswood Capital Management LLC; *U.S. Private*, pg. 2312
KIC INNOENERGY S.E.—See EnBW Energie Baden-Wurttemberg AG; *Int'l*, pg. 2399
KICKAPOO TRIBE IN KANSAS; *U.S. Private*, pg. 2302
KICKAPOO VALLEY CHEESE CORP.; *U.S. Private*, pg. 2302
KICKERT SCHOOL BUS LINES, INC.—See Cook-Illinois Corp.; *U.S. Private*, pg. 1038
KICKHAEFER MANUFACTURING COMPANY INC.; *U.S. Private*, pg. 2302
KICK ICT GROUP LTD.—See BGF Group PLC; *Int'l*, pg. 1007
KICKING HORSE MOUNTAIN RESORT—See Resorts of the Canadian Rockies, Inc.; *Int'l*, pg. 6301
KICKSERV, INC.—See Gannett Co., Inc.; *U.S. Public*, pg. 898
KICKSTART VENTURES, INC.—See Globe Telecom, Inc.; *Int'l*, pg. 3006
KIC METALIKS LIMITED; *Int'l*, pg. 4158
KICO KUNSTSTOFFTECHNIK GMBH—See Mutares SE & Co. KGaA; *Int'l*, pg. 5105
KICO-POLSKA SP. Z.O.O.—See Mutares SE & Co. KGaA; *Int'l*, pg. 5105
KICTEAM, INC.—See Argosy Capital Group, LLC; *U.S. Private*, pg. 321
KICU-TV—See Apollo Global Management, Inc.; *U.S. Public*, pg. 164
KID CASTLE EDUCATIONAL CORPORATION; *Int'l*, pg. 4158
KIDCO CONSTRUCTION LTD.; *Int'l*, pg. 4158
KIDD & COMPANY LLC; *U.S. Private*, pg. 2302
KIDD CONSTRUCTION CO., INC.; *U.S. Private*, pg. 2302
KIDDE AEROSPACE—See RTX Corporation; *U.S. Public*, pg. 1822
KIDDE AUSTRALIA PTY LTD.—See Carrier Global Corporation; *U.S. Public*, pg. 441
KIDDE BRASIL LTDA.—See Carrier Global Corporation; *U.S. Public*, pg. 443
KIDDE-DEUGRA BRANDSCHUTZSYSTEME GMBH—See RTX Corporation; *U.S. Public*, pg. 1822
KIDDE-FENWAL, INC.—See Carrier Global Corporation; *U.S. Public*, pg. 441
KIDDE FIRE SAFETY—See Carrier Global Corporation; *U.S. Public*, pg. 440
KIDDE FIRE TRAINERS, INC.—See Carrier Global Corporation; *U.S. Public*, pg. 440
KIDDE GRAVINER LTD.—See RTX Corporation; *U.S. Public*, pg. 1822
KIDDE INTERNATIONAL LIMITED—See Carrier Global Corporation; *U.S. Public*, pg. 441
KIDDE PRODUCTS LIMITED—See Carrier Global Corporation; *U.S. Public*, pg. 441
KIDDER MATHEWS; *U.S. Private*, pg. 2302
KIDDER MATTHEW, LLC; *U.S. Private*, pg. 2303
KIDDESIGNS, INC.—See SDI Technologies, Inc.; *U.S. Private*, pg. 3581
KIDDE TECHNOLOGIES INC.—See RTX Corporation; *U.S. Public*, pg. 1822
KIDD GROUP; *U.S. Private*, pg. 2302
KIDDIELAND INTERNATIONAL LIMITED; *Int'l*, pg. 4158
KIDDIELAND TOYS LIMITED—See Kiddieland International Limited; *Int'l*, pg. 4158
KIDD JONES HENDERSON COUNTY; *U.S. Private*, pg. 2302
KIDD ROOFING; *U.S. Private*, pg. 2302
KIDDY'S CLASS ESPANA, S.A.—See Industria de Diseno Textil, S.A.; *Int'l*, pg. 3666
KIDE S.COOP—See Mondragon Corporation; *Int'l*, pg. 5030
KIDEX OY—See Martela Oyj; *Int'l*, pg. 4703
KID GALAXY INC.—See China Healthwise Holdings Limited; *Int'l*, pg. 1507
KID INTERIOR AS; *Int'l*, pg. 4158
KIDKRAFT INC.—See MidOcean Partners, LLP; *U.S. Private*, pg. 2717
KIDMAN RESOURCES LIMITED—See Wesfarmers Limited; *Int'l*, pg. 8381
KIDNEY CARE CENTERS OF CAMBRIDGE OHIO, LLC—See Nautic Partners, LLC; *U.S. Private*, pg. 2870
KIDNEY CARE CENTERS OF COSHOCTON OHIO, LLC—See Nautic Partners, LLC; *U.S. Private*, pg. 2870
KIDNEY CENTER OF ARVADA LLC—See Nautic Partners, LLC; *U.S. Private*, pg. 2870
KIDNEY CENTER OF BEAR CREEK, LLC—See Nautic Partners, LLC; *U.S. Private*, pg. 2870
KIDNEY CENTER OF BEXLEY, LLC—See Nautic Partners, LLC; *U.S. Private*, pg. 2870
KIDNEY CENTER OF LAFAYETTE LLC—See Nautic Partners, LLC; *U.S. Private*, pg. 2870
KIDNEY CENTER OF LAKEWOOD, LLC—See Nautic Partners, LLC; *U.S. Private*, pg. 2870
KIDNEY CENTER OF LONGMONT LLC—See Nautic Partners, LLC; *U.S. Private*, pg. 2870
KIDNEY CENTER OF NORTH DENVER, LLC—See Nautic Partners, LLC; *U.S. Private*, pg. 2870

THE KIDNEY CENTER OF SOUTH PHILADELPHIA, LLC—See Nautic Partners, LLC; *U.S. Private*, pg. 2871
KIDNEY CENTER OF WESTMINSTER LLC—See Nautic Partners, LLC; *U.S. Private*, pg. 2870
THE KIDNEY CENTER ON MAIN, LLC—See Nautic Partners, LLC; *U.S. Private*, pg. 2871
KIDNEY CENTERS OF MICHIGAN, LLC—See DaVita Inc.; *U.S. Public*, pg. 640
KIDNEY HOME CENTER, LLC—See DaVita Inc.; *U.S. Public*, pg. 640
KIDO GROUP CORP.; *Int'l*, pg. 4158
KIDOZ INC.; *Int'l*, pg. 4158
KIDPIK CORP.; *U.S. Public*, pg. 1227
KIDROBOT INC.—See National Entertainment Collectibles Association, Inc; *U.S. Private*, pg. 2853
KIDRON, INC.—See Temasek Holdings (Private) Limited; *Int'l*, pg. 7552
KIDS2, INC.; *U.S. Private*, pg. 2303
KIDS BEHAVIORAL HEALTH OF MONTANA, INC.—See Acadia Healthcare Company, Inc.; *U.S. Public*, pg. 29
KIDS BEHAVIORAL HEALTH OF UTAH, INC.—See Universal Health Services, Inc.; *U.S. Public*, pg. 2258
KIDS CLINIC @ BISHAN PTE. LTD.—See Singapore Medical Group Limited; *Int'l*, pg. 6940
KIDS FOOT LOCKER—See Foot Locker, Inc.; *U.S. Public*, pg. 863
KIDS IN NEED FOUNDATION; *U.S. Private*, pg. 2303
KIDS IN THE GAME LLC; *U.S. Private*, pg. 2303
KIDSLAND HK LIMITED—See Kidsland International Holdings Limited; *Int'l*, pg. 4158
KIDSLAND INTERNATIONAL HOLDINGS LIMITED; *Int'l*, pg. 4158
KIDS MEDICAL SYSTEMS LIMITED; *Int'l*, pg. 4158
KIDS ONLY, INC.—See JAKKS Pacific, Inc.; *U.S. Public*, pg. 1187
KIDSPEACE CORPORATION; *U.S. Private*, pg. 2303
KIDSPEACE; *U.S. Private*, pg. 2303
KIDSPOT.COM.AU PTY LIMITED—See News Corporation; *U.S. Public*, pg. 1519
KIDS PREFERRED INC.; *U.S. Private*, pg. 2303
KIDS SMILE HOLDINGS, INC.; *Int'l*, pg. 4158
KIDS STUFF, INC.; *U.S. Private*, pg. 2303
KIDSWELL BIO CORPORATION—See Noritsu Koki Co., Ltd.; *Int'l*, pg. 5429
KID-SYSTEME GMBH—See Airbus SE; *Int'l*, pg. 244
KIDUJA INDIA LIMITED; *Int'l*, pg. 4158
KIDVERTISERS, INC.; *U.S. Private*, pg. 2303
KIDVILLE, INC.; *U.S. Public*, pg. 1228
KIDWELL INC.; *U.S. Private*, pg. 2303
KIDY/KXVA OPERATING COMPANY, LLC—See TEGNA Inc.; *U.S. Public*, pg. 1990
KIDZMATTER INC.; *U.S. Private*, pg. 2303
KIDZTECH HOLDINGS LIMITED; *Int'l*, pg. 4158
KIDZ TEETH LIMITED—See BGH Capital Pty Ltd; *Int'l*, pg. 1008
KIDZ TEETH LIMITED—See Ontario Teachers' Pension Plan; *Int'l*, pg. 5586
KIEBACK GMBH & CO. KG—See INDUS Holding AG; *Int'l*, pg. 3663
KIEFER SPECIALTY FLOORING, INC.; *U.S. Private*, pg. 2303
KIEFFER & ASOCIADOS S.A.—See Willis Towers Watson Public Limited Company; *Int'l*, pg. 8416
KIEFFER & CO., INC.; *U.S. Private*, pg. 2303
KIEFFER LUMBER CO., INC.—See RP Lumber Co. Inc.; *U.S. Private*, pg. 3495
KIEFNER & ASSOCIATES INC.—See I Squared Capital Advisors (US) LLC; *U.S. Private*, pg. 2023
KIEFNER & ASSOCIATES INC.—See TDR Capital LLP; *Int'l*, pg. 7492
KIEFNER BROTHERS, INC.; *U.S. Private*, pg. 2303
KIEHL'S SINCE 1851 LLC—See L'Oreal S.A.; *Int'l*, pg. 4380
KIEKERT AG—See China North Industries Group Corporation; *Int'l*, pg. 1535
KIEKERT CS S.R.O.—See China North Industries Group Corporation; *Int'l*, pg. 1536
KIELER STADTENTWICKLUNGS- UND SANIERUNGSGESELLSCHAFT MBH—See Vonovia SE; *Int'l*, pg. 8305
KIEMLE-HANKINS COMPANY; *U.S. Private*, pg. 2303
KIEN GIANG BRICK TILE JOINT STOCK COMPANY; *Int'l*, pg. 4158
KIEN HUNG JOINT STOCK COMPANY; *Int'l*, pg. 4158
KIENLEN CONSTRUCTORS—See Alberici Corporation; *U.S. Private*, pg. 152
KIENLE + SPIESS GMBH—See Sumitomo Corporation; *Int'l*, pg. 7269
KIEN TAO ENGINEERING CO., LTD.—See M2I Corporation; *Int'l*, pg. 4617
KIEPE ELECTRIC CORPORATION—See Kiepe Electric GmbH; *Int'l*, pg. 4158
KIEPE ELECTRIC GES.M.B.H.—See Kiepe Electric GmbH; *Int'l*, pg. 4158
KIEPE ELECTRIC GMBH; *Int'l*, pg. 4158
KIEPE ELECTRIC LLC—See Kiepe Electric GmbH; *Int'l*, pg. 4158
KIEPE ELECTRIC SCHWEIZ AG—See Knorr-Bremse AG; *Int'l*, pg. 4210

KIEPE ELECTRIC S.R.L.—See Kiepe Electric GmbH; *Int'l*, pg. 4159
KIERAN LABEL CORP.—See I.D. Images LLC; *U.S. Private*, pg. 2027
KIER CONSTRUCTION CORPORATION; *U.S. Private*, pg. 2303
KIER CONSTRUCTION LIMITED—See Kier Group plc; *Int'l*, pg. 4159
KIER GROUP HOLDINGS, LLC; *U.S. Private*, pg. 2303
KIER GROUP PLC; *Int'l*, pg. 4159
KIER HARLOW LIMITED—See Kier Group plc; *Int'l*, pg. 4159
KIER HOMES LIMITED—See Kier Group plc; *Int'l*, pg. 4159
KIER LIMITED—See Kier Group plc; *Int'l*, pg. 4159
KIER MANAGED SERVICES LIMITED—See Kier Group plc; *Int'l*, pg. 4159
KIER PARTNERSHIP HOMES LIMITED—See Kier Group plc; *Int'l*, pg. 4159
KIER PLANT LIMITED—See Kier Group plc; *Int'l*, pg. 4159
KIER PROJECT INVESTMENT LIMITED—See Kier Group plc; *Int'l*, pg. 4159
KIER PROPERTY LIMITED—See Kier Group plc; *Int'l*, pg. 4159
KIERSTED SYSTEMS, L.P.—See Driven, Inc.; *U.S. Private*, pg. 1278
KIER STOKE LIMITED—See Kier Group plc; *Int'l*, pg. 4159
KIER TRADE CITY LLP—See Kier Group plc; *Int'l*, pg. 4159
KIESEL BAUCHEMIE GMBH & CO. KG; *Int'l*, pg. 4159
KIESEL BENELUX B. V.—See Kiesel Bauchemie GmbH & Co. KG; *Int'l*, pg. 4159
KIESEL POLSKA SP.Z.O.O.—See Kiesel Bauchemie GmbH & Co. KG; *Int'l*, pg. 4159
KIESEL SARL—See Kiesel Bauchemie GmbH & Co. KG; *Int'l*, pg. 4159
KIESEL S.R.O.—See Kiesel Bauchemie GmbH & Co. KG; *Int'l*, pg. 4159
KIESLER POLICE SUPPLY INC.; *U.S. Private*, pg. 2304
KIESLING MASCHINENTECHNIK GMBH—See Friedhelm Loh Stiftung & Co. KG; *Int'l*, pg. 2791
KIESS GMBH & CO. KG; *Int'l*, pg. 4159
KIESSLING TRANSIT, INC.—See Mobico Group PLC; *Int'l*, pg. 5008
KIESTAG STEINIGAND AG—See Vicat S.A.; *Int'l*, pg. 8186
KIESWERK AEBISHOLZ AG—See Vicat S.A.; *Int'l*, pg. 8185
KIESWERKE ANDRESEN GMBH—See Heidelberg Materials AG; *Int'l*, pg. 3317
KIESWERKE FLEMMINGEN GMBH—See Heidelberg Materials AG; *Int'l*, pg. 3317
KIESWERKE KIESER GMBH & CO. KG—See Heidelberg Materials AG; *Int'l*, pg. 3317
KIESWERK MAAS-ROELOFFS GMBH & CO. KG—See Heidelberg Materials AG; *Int'l*, pg. 3317
KIESWERK MAAS-ROELOFFS VERWALTUNGSGESELLSCHAFT MBH—See Heidelberg Materials AG; *Int'l*, pg. 3317
KIESWETTER MOTORS INC.; *Int'l*, pg. 4159
KIEWIT CONSTRUCTION GROUP, INC.—See Peter Kiewit Sons', Inc.; *U.S. Private*, pg. 3158
KIEWIT CORP.; *U.S. Private*, pg. 2304
KIEWIT INFRASTRUCTURE SOUTH CO.; *U.S. Private*, pg. 2304
KIEWIT INFRASTRUCTURE WEST CO. - VANCOUVER—See Peter Kiewit Sons', Inc.; *U.S. Private*, pg. 3158
KIEWIT MANAGEMENT LTD.—See Peter Kiewit Sons', Inc.; *U.S. Private*, pg. 3158
KIEWIT MINING GROUP, INC.—See Peter Kiewit Sons', Inc.; *U.S. Private*, pg. 3158
KIEWIT ROYALTY TRUST—See Peter Kiewit Sons', Inc.; *U.S. Private*, pg. 3158
KIFISSIA PASTRIES S.A.—See General Mills, Inc.; *U.S. Public*, pg. 922
KIFISSOS MALL SA—See Viohalco SA/NV; *Int'l*, pg. 8243
KI FRESH ACCESS, INC.—See Sumitomo Corporation; *Int'l*, pg. 7269
KIFS FINANCIAL SERVICES LTD.; *Int'l*, pg. 4159
KIFUKI U.S.A. CO., INC.—See Kewpie Corporation; *Int'l*, pg. 4144
KIGHT LUMBER CO. INC.; *U.S. Private*, pg. 2304
KIGO, INC.—See Thoma Bravo, L.P.; *U.S. Private*, pg. 4153
KIGO RENTAL SYSTEMS, S.L.—See Thoma Bravo, L.P.; *U.S. Private*, pg. 4153
KIGRE, INC.—See L3Harris Technologies, Inc.; *U.S. Public*, pg. 1281
KI GROUP S.P.A—See Bioera S.p.A.; *Int'l*, pg. 1037
KIHN SA—See Vossloh AG; *Int'l*, pg. 8309
KI HOLDINGS CO., LTD.—See Koito Manufacturing Co., Ltd.; *Int'l*, pg. 4230
KIIAN DIGITAL (SHANGHAI) CO., LTD.—See Dover Corporation; *U.S. Public*, pg. 681
KII CORPORATION - SAN MATEO—See Kii Corporation; *Int'l*, pg. 4159
KII CORPORATION; *Int'l*, pg. 4159

COMPANY NAME INDEX

KIINNIKEKESKUS SERVICES OY—See Panostaja Oyj; *Int'l*, pg. 5729
KIINNIKE-KOLMIO OY—See Indutrade AB; *Int'l*, pg. 3679
KIINTEISTOMAAILMA LTD.—See Sampo plc; *Int'l*, pg. 6508
KIINTEISTO MESTA OY—See Kesko Corporation; *Int'l*, pg. 4142
KIINTEISTO OY KAPSELI—See Orion Corporation; *Int'l*, pg. 5631
KIINTEISTO OY LAHDEN KARISMA—See Kesko Corporation; *Int'l*, pg. 4142
KIINTEISTO OY PIISPANPIHA 5—See EnviTec Biogas AG; *Int'l*, pg. 2456
KIINTEISTO OY RAISION LUOLASTO—See Elisa Corporation; *Int'l*, pg. 2361
KIINTEISTO OY—See Lassila & Tikanoja plc; *Int'l*, pg. 4421
KIINTEISTO OY TIR-TRANS—See Deutsche Bahn AG; *Int'l*, pg. 2052
KIINTEISTO OY VALIVAINION OSTOSKESKUS—See Kesko Corporation; *Int'l*, pg. 4142
KIINTEISTO OY VANTAAN TAHTAINKUJA 3—See Blackstone Inc.; *U.S. Public*, pg. 351
KIJCHAROEN ENGINEERING ELECTRIC PUBLIC COMPANY LIMITED; *Int'l*, pg. 4159
KIJKSHOP BV; *Int'l*, pg. 4159
KIK CUSTOM PRODUCTS INC.—See Centerbridge Partners, L.P.; *U.S. Private*, pg. 815
KIK (GEORGIA) LLC—See Centerbridge Partners, L.P.; *U.S. Private*, pg. 815
KIKINDSKI MLIN A.D; *Int'l*, pg. 4159
KIKKOMAN AUSTRALIA PTY. LIMITED—See Kikkoman Corporation; *Int'l*, pg. 4160
KIKKOMAN BUSINESS SERVICE COMPANY—See Kikkoman Corporation; *Int'l*, pg. 4160
KIKKOMAN CORPORATION; *Int'l*, pg. 4159
KIKKOMAN EUROPE R&D LABORATORY B.V.—See Kikkoman Corporation; *Int'l*, pg. 4160
KIKKOMAN FOOD PRODUCTS CO. - NODA PLANT—See Kikkoman Corporation; *Int'l*, pg. 4160
KIKKOMAN FOOD PRODUCTS CO. - TAKASAGO PLANT—See Kikkoman Corporation; *Int'l*, pg. 4160
KIKKOMAN FOODS EUROPE B.V.—See Kikkoman Corporation; *Int'l*, pg. 4160
KIKKOMAN FOODS, INC. - CALIFORNIA PLANT—See Kikkoman Corporation; *Int'l*, pg. 4160
KIKKOMAN FOODS, INC.—See Kikkoman Corporation; *Int'l*, pg. 4160
KIKKOMAN INTERNATIONAL INC.—See Kikkoman Corporation; *Int'l*, pg. 4160
KIKKOMAN L.O. CONSULTORIA. MARKETING E PROMOCOES LTDA.—See Kikkoman Corporation; *Int'l*, pg. 4160
KIKKOMAN MARKETING CENTER COMPANY LTD.—See Kikkoman Corporation; *Int'l*, pg. 4160
KIKKOMAN MARKETING & PLANNING, INC.—See Kikkoman Corporation; *Int'l*, pg. 4160
KIKKOMAN RESTAURANT, INC.—See Kikkoman Corporation; *Int'l*, pg. 4160
KIKKOMAN SALES USA, INC—See Kikkoman Corporation; *Int'l*, pg. 4160
KIKKOMAN SINGAPORE R&D LABORATORY PTE. LTD.—See Kikkoman Corporation; *Int'l*, pg. 4160
KIKKOMAN SOYFOODS CO., LTD.—See Kikkoman Corporation; *Int'l*, pg. 4160
KIKKOMAN (S) PTE. LTD.—See Kikkoman Corporation; *Int'l*, pg. 4160
KIKKOMAN TRADING ASIA PTE. LTD.—See Kikkoman Corporation; *Int'l*, pg. 4160
KIKKOMAN TRADING EUROPE GMBH—See Kikkoman Corporation; *Int'l*, pg. 4160
KIKKOMAN TRADING (S) PTE. LTD.—See Kikkoman Corporation; *Int'l*, pg. 4160
KIK POOL ADDITIVES INC.; *U.S. Private*, pg. 2304
KIK TEXTIL A NON-FOOD SPOL S.R.O.—See Tengelmann Warenhandelsgesellschaft KG; *Int'l*, pg. 7560
KIK TEXTIL ES NON-FOOD KFT.—See Tengelmann Warenhandelsgesellschaft KG; *Int'l*, pg. 7560
KIK TEXTILIEN UND NON-FOOD D.O.O.—See Tengelmann Warenhandelsgesellschaft KG; *Int'l*, pg. 7560
KIK TEXTILIEN UND NON-FOOD GMBH—See Tengelmann Warenhandelsgesellschaft KG; *Int'l*, pg. 7560
KIK TEXTIL SP. Z O. O.—See Tengelmann Warenhandelsgesellschaft KG; *Int'l*, pg. 7560
KIKUCHI (HONG KONG) LIMITED - CHINA FACTORY—See Kikuchi Seisakusho Co., Ltd.; *Int'l*, pg. 4161
KIKUCHI (HONG KONG) LIMITED—See Kikuchi Seisakusho Co., Ltd.; *Int'l*, pg. 4161
KIKUCHI INDUSTRY (THAILAND) CO., LTD.—See Takada Corporation; *Int'l*, pg. 7429
KIKUCHI SEISAKUSHO CO., LTD.; *Int'l*, pg. 4161
KIKUGAWA SEAL INDUSTRY CO., LTD.—See NOK Corporation; *Int'l*, pg. 5402
KIKUKAWA CO., LTD.—See Kobe Bussan Co., Ltd.; *Int'l*, pg. 4217
KIKUKAWA ENTERPRISE INC.; *Int'l*, pg. 4161
KIKUSUI AMERICA, INC.—See Kikusui Holdings Corporation; *Int'l*, pg. 4161

KIKUSUI CHEMICAL INDUSTRIES CO., LTD.; *Int'l*, pg. 4161
KIKUSUI HOLDINGS CORPORATION; *Int'l*, pg. 4161
KIK (VIRGINIA) LLC—See Centerbridge Partners, L.P.; *U.S. Private*, pg. 815
KIKXXL GMBH—See NORD Holding Unternehmensbeteiligungsgesellschaft mbH; *Int'l*, pg. 5416
KILAND LTD.; *Int'l*, pg. 4161
KILANG BIHUN BERSATU (EAST MALAYSIA) SDN BHD—See EKA Noodles Berhad; *Int'l*, pg. 2337
KILANG BIHUN BERSATU SDN BHD—See EKA Noodles Berhad; *Int'l*, pg. 2337
KILANG KOSFARM SDN BHD—See Far East Holdings Berhad; *Int'l*, pg. 2616
KILBURN CHEMICALS LTD.; *Int'l*, pg. 4161
KILBURN ENGINEERING LTD.; *Int'l*, pg. 4161
KILBURN OFFICE AUTOMATION LTD.; *Int'l*, pg. 4161
KILCOY PASTORAL COMPANY LTD.; *Int'l*, pg. 4161
KILDAIR SERVICE ULC—See Axel Johnson Gruppen AB; *Int'l*, pg. 765
KILDEMOES A/S—See Grimaldi Industri AB; *Int'l*, pg. 3086
KILER GAYRIMENKUL YATIRIM ORTAKLIGI A.S.—See Kiler Holding A.S.; *Int'l*, pg. 4161
KILER GYO A.S.—See Kiler Holding A.S.; *Int'l*, pg. 4161
KILER HOLDING A.S.; *Int'l*, pg. 4161
KILEY ADVISORS LLC—See FMI Corporation; *U.S. Private*, pg. 1554
KILEY GROUP, INC.; *U.S. Public*, pg. 1228
KILGORE COMPANIES, LLC—See Summit Materials, Inc.; *U.S. Public*, pg. 1960
KILGORE FLARES—See Chemring Group PLC; *Int'l*, pg. 1463
KILGORE INDUSTRIES; *U.S. Private*, pg. 2304
KILGUST MECHANICAL, INC.—See EMCOR Group, Inc.; *U.S. Public*, pg. 738
KILIA FLEISCHEREI-UND-SPEZIAL-MASCHINEN-FABRIK GMBH; *Int'l*, pg. 4161
KILIAN MANUFACTURING CORPORATION—See Regal Rexnord Corporation; *U.S. Public*, pg. 1772
KILIC DENIZ URUNLERI URETIMI IHRACAT ITHALAT VE TIC. A.S.; *Int'l*, pg. 4161
KIL INTERNATIONAL LIMITED—See Kanani Industries Ltd.; *Int'l*, pg. 4064
K I LIPTON INC.; *U.S. Private*, pg. 2249
KILITCH DRUGS (INDIA) LTD.; *Int'l*, pg. 4162
KILKENNY PEOPLE PUBLISHING LTD—See JPIMedia Holdings Limited; *Int'l*, pg. 4006
KILKEN PLATINUM PROPRIETARY LIMITED—See Andulela Investment Holdings Limited; *Int'l*, pg. 457
KILKIS PALEON TRIETHNES S.A.—See Metlen Energy & Metals S.A.; *Int'l*, pg. 4854
KILKIS SPINNING MILLS S.A.—See Hellenic Fabrics S.A.; *Int'l*, pg. 3333
KILLAM APARTMENT REAL ESTATE INVESTMENT TRUST; *Int'l*, pg. 4162
KILLAM OIL CO. LTD.; *U.S. Private*, pg. 2304
KILLARA FEEDLOT PTY. LTD.—See Elders Limited; *Int'l*, pg. 2346
KILLARK ELECTRIC—See Hubbell Incorporated; *U.S. Public*, pg. 1067
KILLARNEY HOTELS LTD.—See Liebherr-International AG; *Int'l*, pg. 4488
KILLBUCK BANCSHARES, INC.; *U.S. Public*, pg. 1228
THE KILLBUCK SAVINGS BANK COMPANY—See Killbuck Bancshares, Inc.; *U.S. Public*, pg. 1228
KILLEARN CONSTRUCTION, INC.—See Killearn Properties, Inc.; *U.S. Private*, pg. 2304
KILLEARN PROPERTIES, INC.; *U.S. Private*, pg. 2304
KILLEARN PROPERTIES OF GEORGIA—See Killearn Properties, Inc.; *U.S. Private*, pg. 2304
KILLEEN FURTNEY GROUP, INC.; *U.S. Private*, pg. 2304
KILLER BEE INC.—See Global Seafood Technologies; *U.S. Private*, pg. 1717
KILLER FILMS INC.; *U.S. Private*, pg. 2304
KILLER INTERACTIVE, LLC; *U.S. Private*, pg. 2304
KILLIAN BRANDING; *U.S. Private*, pg. 2304
KILLINEY DENTAL CENTRE PTE. LTD.—See Q&M Dental Group (Singapore) Limited; *Int'l*, pg. 6129
KILLINGTON LIMITED—See Powdr Corp.; *U.S. Private*, pg. 3236
KILLINGTON RESORT—See Powdr Corp.; *U.S. Private*, pg. 3236
KILLION INDUSTRIES INC.; *U.S. Private*, pg. 2304
KILLI RESOURCES LIMITED; *Int'l*, pg. 4162
KILMARNOCK VETS4PETS LIMITED—See Pets at Home Group Plc; *Int'l*, pg. 5834
KILMER WAGNER AND WISE PAPER CO. INC.—See Central National Gottesman Inc.; *U.S. Private*, pg. 823
KILN EUROPE SA—See Tokio Marine Holdings, Inc.; *Int'l*, pg. 7784
KILN GROUP LIMITED—See Tokio Marine Holdings, Inc.; *Int'l*, pg. 7784
KILN HONG KONG—See Tokio Marine Holdings, Inc.; *Int'l*, pg. 7782
KILN REGIONAL UNDERWRITING LIMITED—See Tokio Marine Holdings, Inc.; *Int'l*, pg. 7782
KILN SINGAPORE PTE LIMITED—See Tokio Marine Holdings, Inc.; *Int'l*, pg. 7784

KIMBERLITE CORP.

KILN SOUTH AFRICA (PROPRIETARY) LIMITED—See Tokio Marine Holdings, Inc.; *Int'l*, pg. 7784
KILN UNDERWRITING LIMITED—See Tokio Marine Holdings, Inc.; *Int'l*, pg. 7784
KILOMBERO SUGAR DISTRIBUTORS LIMITED—See ED&F Man Holdings Limited; *Int'l*, pg. 2303
KILOP USA, INC.; *U.S. Private*, pg. 2304
KILOVAL OY—See NIBE Industrier AB; *Int'l*, pg. 5261
KILPATRICK COMPANY INC.; *U.S. Private*, pg. 2304
KILPATRICK LIFE INSURANCE CO.; *U.S. Private*, pg. 2304
KILPATRICK SALES INC.; *U.S. Private*, pg. 2304
KILPATRICK & SCONYERS AGENCY—See Sherman & Hemstreet, Inc.; *U.S. Private*, pg. 3634
KILPATRICK TOWNSEND & STOCKTON LLP; *U.S. Private*, pg. 2304
KILPATRICK TURF & INDUSTRIAL EQUIPMENT—See Kilpatrick Company Inc.; *U.S. Private*, pg. 2304
KILPEST INDIA LIMITED; *Int'l*, pg. 4162
KILROY REALTY CORPORATION; *U.S. Public*, pg. 1228
KILROY REALTY FINANCE PARTNERSHIP, L.P.—See Kilroy Realty Corporation; *U.S. Public*, pg. 1228
KILROY REALTY, L.P.—See Kilroy Realty Corporation; *U.S. Public*, pg. 1228
KILROY SERVICES, LLC—See Kilroy Realty Corporation; *U.S. Public*, pg. 1228
KILWIN'S CHOCOLATES FRANCHISE, INC.—See Levine Leichtman Capital Partners, LLC; *U.S. Private*, pg. 2436
KIMAL LUMBER COMPANY—See Gulfeagle Supply, Inc.; *U.S. Private*, pg. 1817
KIMAL LUMBER COMPANY—See Gulfeagle Supply, Inc.; *U.S. Private*, pg. 1817
KIMBALL ELECTRONICS, INC.; *U.S. Public*, pg. 1228
KIMBALL ELECTRONICS INC.; *U.S. Private*, pg. 2305
KIMBALL ELECTRONICS INDIANAPOLIS, INC.—See Kimball Electronics, Inc.; *U.S. Public*, pg. 1228
KIMBALL ELECTRONICS MEXICO, INC.—See Kimball Electronics, Inc.; *U.S. Public*, pg. 1228
KIMBALL ELECTRONICS - MEXICO, S.A. DE C.V.—See Kimball Electronics, Inc.; *U.S. Public*, pg. 1228
KIMBALL ELECTRONICS (NANJING) CO., LTD.—See Kimball Electronics, Inc.; *U.S. Public*, pg. 1228
KIMBALL ELECTRONICS POLAND SP. Z O.O—See Kimball Electronics, Inc.; *U.S. Public*, pg. 1228
KIMBALL ELECTRONICS TAMPA, INC.—See Kimball Electronics, Inc.; *U.S. Public*, pg. 1228
KIMBALL ELECTRONICS (THAILAND), LTD.—See Kimball Electronics, Inc.; *U.S. Public*, pg. 1228
KIMBALL EQUIPMENT COMPANY; *U.S. Private*, pg. 2305
KIMBALL FURNITURE GROUP, LLC—See HNI Corporation; *U.S. Public*, pg. 1043
KIMBALL HOSPITALITY, INC.—See HNI Corporation; *U.S. Public*, pg. 1043
KIMBALL INTERNATIONAL, INC.—See HNI Corporation; *U.S. Public*, pg. 1043
KIMBALL INTERNATIONAL TRANSIT, INC.—See HNI Corporation; *U.S. Public*, pg. 1043
KIMBALL MEDICAL CENTER—See Barnabas Health, Inc.; *U.S. Private*, pg. 476
KIMBALL OFFICE, INC. - BORDEN—See HNI Corporation; *U.S. Public*, pg. 1043
KIMBALL OFFICE, INC. - JASPER, 15TH STREET—See HNI Corporation; *U.S. Public*, pg. 1043
KIMBALL OFFICE, INC. - JASPER, CHERRY STREET—See HNI Corporation; *U.S. Public*, pg. 1043
KIMBALL OFFICE, INC. - POST FALLS—See HNI Corporation; *U.S. Public*, pg. 1043
KIMBALL OFFICE, INC. - SALEM—See HNI Corporation; *U.S. Public*, pg. 1043
KIMBALL OFFICE, INC.—See HNI Corporation; *U.S. Public*, pg. 1043
KIMBELL ROYALTY PARTNERS, LP; *U.S. Public*, pg. 1228
KIMBELL TIGER ACQUISITION CORP.; *U.S. Public*, pg. 1228
KIMBERLEY CARPETS PTY LIMITED—See Bremworth Limited; *Int'l*, pg. 1145
KIMBERLEY DIAMONDS LTD.; *Int'l*, pg. 4162
KIMBERLEY FINE DIAMONDS; *Int'l*, pg. 4163
KIMBERLITE CORP.; *U.S. Private*, pg. 2305
KIMBERLY BOLIVIA S.A.—See Kimberly-Clark Corporation; *U.S. Public*, pg. 1229
KIMBERLY CARBONATES LLC—See Omya (Schweiz) AG; *Int'l*, pg. 5570
KIMBERLY-CLARK AMSTERDAM HOLDINGS B.V.—See Kimberly-Clark Corporation; *U.S. Public*, pg. 1229
KIMBERLY-CLARK ARGENTINA S.A.—See Kimberly-Clark Corporation; *U.S. Public*, pg. 1229
KIMBERLY-CLARK ASIA HOLDINGS PTE. LTD.—See Kimberly-Clark Corporation; *U.S. Public*, pg. 1229
KIMBERLY-CLARK ASIA PACIFIC PTE. LTD.—See Kimberly-Clark Corporation; *U.S. Public*, pg. 1229
KIMBERLY-CLARK AUSTRALIA HOLDINGS PTY. LIMITED—See Kimberly-Clark Corporation; *U.S. Public*, pg. 1229
KIMBERLY-CLARK AUSTRALIA PTY. LTD.—See Kimberly-Clark Corporation; *U.S. Public*, pg. 1229

KIMBERLY-CLARK BALLARD MEDICAL—See Kimberly-Clark Corporation; *U.S. Public*, pg. 1230
KIMBERLY-CLARK BOLIVIA S.A.—See Kimberly-Clark Corporation; *U.S. Public*, pg. 1229
KIMBERLY-CLARK BRASIL INDUSTRIA E COMERCIO DE PRODUTOS DE HIGIENE LTDA.—See Kimberly-Clark Corporation; *U.S. Public*, pg. 1229
KIMBERLY-CLARK CANADA INC.—See Kimberly-Clark Corporation; *U.S. Public*, pg. 1229
KIMBERLY-CLARK CENTRAL AMERICAN HOLDINGS, S.A.—See Kimberly-Clark Corporation; *U.S. Public*, pg. 1229
KIMBERLY-CLARK CHILE S.A.—See Kimberly-Clark Corporation; *U.S. Public*, pg. 1229
KIMBERLY-CLARK CHILE S.A.—See Kimberly-Clark Corporation; *U.S. Public*, pg. 1229
KIMBERLY-CLARK (CHINA) COMPANY LTD.—See Kimberly-Clark Corporation; *U.S. Public*, pg. 1229
KIMBERLY-CLARK COLOMBIA HOLDING LIMITADA—See Kimberly-Clark Corporation; *U.S. Public*, pg. 1229
KIMBERLY-CLARK CONWAY MILLS—See Kimberly-Clark Corporation; *U.S. Public*, pg. 1230
KIMBERLY-CLARK CORPORATION - CONSUMER TISSUE SECTOR—See Kimberly-Clark Corporation; *U.S. Public*, pg. 1229
KIMBERLY-CLARK CORPORATION - HOUSEHOLD PRODUCTS SECTOR—See Kimberly-Clark Corporation; *U.S. Public*, pg. 1229
KIMBERLY-CLARK CORPORATION - MOBILE—See Kimberly-Clark Corporation; *U.S. Public*, pg. 1229
KIMBERLY-CLARK CORPORATION - NEENAH PAPER—See Kimberly-Clark Corporation; *U.S. Public*, pg. 1229
KIMBERLY-CLARK CORPORATION - PERSONAL CARE SECTOR—See Kimberly-Clark Corporation; *U.S. Public*, pg. 1230
KIMBERLY-CLARK CORPORATION - PROFESSIONAL & OTHER AND HEALTH CARE SECTOR—See Kimberly-Clark Corporation; *U.S. Public*, pg. 1230
KIMBERLY-CLARK CORPORATION; *U.S. Public*, pg. 1228
KIMBERLY-CLARK CORPORATION—See Kimberly-Clark Corporation; *U.S. Public*, pg. 1229
KIMBERLY-CLARK CORPORATION—See Kimberly-Clark Corporation; *U.S. Public*, pg. 1229
KIMBERLY-CLARK CORPORATION—See Kimberly-Clark Corporation; *U.S. Public*, pg. 1229
KIMBERLY-CLARK CORPORATION—See Kimberly-Clark Corporation; *U.S. Public*, pg. 1229
KIMBERLY-CLARK CORPORATION—See Kimberly-Clark Corporation; *U.S. Public*, pg. 1229
KIMBERLY-CLARK CORPORATION—See Kimberly-Clark Corporation; *U.S. Public*, pg. 1229
KIMBERLY-CLARK CORPORATION—See Kimberly-Clark Corporation; *U.S. Public*, pg. 1230
KIMBERLY-CLARK CORPORATION—See Kimberly-Clark Corporation; *U.S. Public*, pg. 1230
KIMBERLY-CLARK CORPORATION—See Kimberly-Clark Corporation; *U.S. Public*, pg. 1230
KIMBERLY-CLARK CORPORATION—See Kimberly-Clark Corporation; *U.S. Public*, pg. 1230
KIMBERLY-CLARK CORPORATION—See Kimberly-Clark Corporation; *U.S. Public*, pg. 1230
KIMBERLY-CLARK CORPORATION—See Kimberly-Clark Corporation; *U.S. Public*, pg. 1230
KIMBERLY-CLARK CORPORATION—See Kimberly-Clark Corporation; *U.S. Public*, pg. 1230
KIMBERLY-CLARK CORPORATION—See Kimberly-Clark Corporation; *U.S. Public*, pg. 1230
KIMBERLY-CLARK DE CENTRO AMERICA S.A.—See Kimberly-Clark Corporation; *U.S. Public*, pg. 1231
KIMBERLY-CLARK DE MEXICO, S.A.B. DE C.V.—See Kimberly-Clark Corporation; *U.S. Public*, pg. 1231
KIMBERLY-CLARK ECUADOR S.A.—See Kimberly-Clark Corporation; *U.S. Public*, pg. 1230
KIMBERLY-CLARK EUROPE LIMITED—See Kimberly-Clark Corporation; *U.S. Public*, pg. 1230
KIMBERLY-CLARK FINANCE LIMITED—See Kimberly-Clark Corporation; *U.S. Public*, pg. 1230
KIMBERLY-CLARK GLOBAL SALES, LLC—See Kimberly-Clark Corporation; *U.S. Public*, pg. 1230
KIMBERLY-CLARK GMBH—See Kimberly-Clark Corporation; *U.S. Public*, pg. 1230
KIMBERLY-CLARK GMBH—See Kimberly-Clark Corporation; *U.S. Public*, pg. 1230
KIMBERLY-CLARK GMBH—See Kimberly-Clark Corporation; *U.S. Public*, pg. 1230
KIMBERLY-CLARK GUATEMALA, LIMITADA—See Kimberly-Clark Corporation; *U.S. Public*, pg. 1230
KIMBERLY-CLARK HEALTH CARE INC.—See Kimberly-Clark Corporation; *U.S. Public*, pg. 1230
KIMBERLY-CLARK HOLDING LTD—See Kimberly-Clark Corporation; *U.S. Public*, pg. 1230
KIMBERLY-CLARK HOLDING SRL—See Kimberly-Clark Corporation; *U.S. Public*, pg. 1230
KIMBERLY-CLARK (HONG KONG) LIMITED—See Kimberly-Clark Corporation; *U.S. Public*, pg. 1229

KIMBERLY-CLARK HYGIENE PRODUCTS PRIVATE LIMITED—See Kimberly-Clark Corporation; *U.S. Public*, pg. 1230
KIMBERLY-CLARK, INC.-HUNTSVILLE—See Kimberly-Clark Corporation; *U.S. Public*, pg. 1230
KIMBERLY-CLARK INC.—See Kimberly-Clark Corporation; *U.S. Public*, pg. 1230
KIMBERLY-CLARK INDIA PRIVATE LIMITED—See Kimberly-Clark Corporation; *U.S. Public*, pg. 1230
KIMBERLY-CLARK INTEGRATED SERVICES CORPORATION—See Kimberly-Clark Corporation; *U.S. Public*, pg. 1230
KIMBERLY-CLARK INTERNATIONAL SERVICES CORP.—See Kimberly-Clark Corporation; *U.S. Public*, pg. 1229
KIMBERLY-CLARK KAZAKHSTAN LIMITED LIABILITY PARTNERSHIP—See Kimberly-Clark Corporation; *U.S. Public*, pg. 1230
KIMBERLY-CLARK LDA.—See Kimberly-Clark Corporation; *U.S. Public*, pg. 1230
KIMBERLY-CLARK LIMITED—See Kimberly-Clark Corporation; *U.S. Public*, pg. 1230
KIMBERLY-CLARK MANUFACTURING (THAILAND) LIMITED—See Kimberly-Clark Corporation; *U.S. Public*, pg. 1230
KIMBERLY-CLARK OF SOUTH AFRICA (PTY) LTD.—See Kimberly-Clark Corporation; *U.S. Public*, pg. 1231
KIMBERLY-CLARK PAPER (SHANGHAI) CO. LTD.—See Kimberly-Clark Corporation; *U.S. Public*, pg. 1230
KIMBERLY-CLARK PARAGUAY, S.A.—See Kimberly-Clark Corporation; *U.S. Public*, pg. 1231
KIMBERLY-CLARK PENSION TRUSTS LTD.—See Kimberly-Clark Corporation; *U.S. Public*, pg. 1231
KIMBERLY-CLARK PERU S.R.L.—See Kimberly-Clark Corporation; *U.S. Public*, pg. 1231
KIMBERLY-CLARK PHILIPPINES INC.—See Kimberly-Clark Corporation; *U.S. Public*, pg. 1231
KIMBERLY-CLARK PUERTO RICO, INC.—See Kimberly-Clark Corporation; *U.S. Public*, pg. 1231
KIMBERLY-CLARK S.A.S.—See Kimberly-Clark Corporation; *U.S. Public*, pg. 1231
KIMBERLY-CLARK SAS—See Kimberly-Clark Corporation; *U.S. Public*, pg. 1231
KIMBERLY-CLARK (SINGAPORE) FINANCE PTE. LTD.—See Kimberly-Clark Corporation; *U.S. Public*, pg. 1229
KIMBERLY-CLARK SINGAPORE PTE. LTD.—See Kimberly-Clark Corporation; *U.S. Public*, pg. 1230
KIMBERLY-CLARK S.L.U.—See Kimberly-Clark Corporation; *U.S. Public*, pg. 1230
KIMBERLY-CLARK S.L.U.—See Kimberly-Clark Corporation; *U.S. Public*, pg. 1231
KIMBERLY-CLARK S.R.L.—See Kimberly-Clark Corporation; *U.S. Public*, pg. 1230
KIMBERLY-CLARK S.R.L.—See Kimberly-Clark Corporation; *U.S. Public*, pg. 1231
KIMBERLY-CLARK TAIWAN—See Kimberly-Clark Corporation; *U.S. Public*, pg. 1231
KIMBERLY-CLARK THAILAND LTD.—See Kimberly-Clark Corporation; *U.S. Public*, pg. 1230
KIMBERLY CLARK TRADING (MALAYSIA) SDN. BHD.—See Kimberly-Clark Corporation; *U.S. Public*, pg. 1230
KIMBERLY-CLARK TRADING (M) SDN. BHD.—See Kimberly-Clark Corporation; *U.S. Public*, pg. 1231
KIMBERLY-CLARK TUKETIM MALLARI SANAYI VE TICARET A.S.—See Kimberly-Clark Corporation; *U.S. Public*, pg. 1231
KIMBERLY-CLARK UK OPERATIONS LIMITED—See Kimberly-Clark Corporation; *U.S. Public*, pg. 1231
KIMBERLY-CLARK UKRAINE LLC—See Kimberly-Clark Corporation; *U.S. Public*, pg. 1231
KIMBERLY CLARK URUGUAY S.A.—See Kimberly-Clark Corporation; *U.S. Public*, pg. 1229
KIMBERLY-CLARK VIETNAM LTD.—See Kimberly-Clark Corporation; *U.S. Public*, pg. 1231
KIMBERLY-CLARK WORLDWIDE, INC.—See Kimberly-Clark Corporation; *U.S. Public*, pg. 1231
KIMBERLY PARRY ORGANICS, CORP.; *U.S. Public*, pg. 1228
KIMBER MFG. INC.; *U.S. Private*, pg. 2305
KIMBER PETROLEUM CORP.; *U.S. Private*, pg. 2305
KIMBLE BOMEX (BEIJING) GLASS CO. LTD.—See Gerresheimer AG; *Int'l*, pg. 2944
KIMBLE CHASE LIFE SCIENCE & RESEARCH PRODUCTS LLC - ROCHESTER PLANT—See OEP Capital Advisors, L.P.; *U.S. Public*, pg. 2999
KIMBLE CHASE LIFE SCIENCE & RESEARCH PRODUCTS LLC - ROCKWOOD PLANT—See OEP Capital Advisors, L.P.; *U.S. Public*, pg. 2999
KIMBLE CHASE LIFE SCIENCE & RESEARCH PRODUCTS LLC—See OEP Capital Advisors, L.P.; *U.S. Private*, pg. 2999
KIMBLE CHASSIS COMPANY—See Hines Corporation; *U.S. Private*, pg. 1949
KIMBLE COMPANIES INC.; *U.S. Private*, pg. 2305
KIMBLE MANUFACTURING COMPANY—See Hines Corporation; *U.S. Private*, pg. 1949

KIMBRELL INVESTMENTS INC.—See Furniture Distributors Inc.; *U.S. Private*, pg. 1624
KIMBRO OIL COMPANY INC.; *U.S. Private*, pg. 2305
KIMCO, INC.—See Kimco Realty Corporation; *U.S. Public*, pg. 1232
KIMCO OCALA 665, INC.—See Kimco Realty Corporation; *U.S. Public*, pg. 1231
KIMCO REALTY CORPORATION; *U.S. Public*, pg. 1231
KIMCO REALTY INC—See Kimco Realty Corporation; *U.S. Public*, pg. 1231
KIMCO REALTY INC—See Prometheus Real Estate Group, Inc.; *U.S. Private*, pg. 3283
KIMCO REALTY OP, LLC—See Kimco Realty Corporation; *U.S. Public*, pg. 1231
KIMCO STAFFING SERVICES INC.; *U.S. Private*, pg. 2305
KIMCO STEEL SALES LIMITED; *Int'l*, pg. 4163
KIMDEC CORPORATION SDN. BHD.; *Int'l*, pg. 4163
KIM ENG SECURITIES (HONG KONG) LIMITED—See Malayan Banking Berhad; *Int'l*, pg. 4660
KIM ENG SECURITIES INDIA PRIVATE LIMITED—See Malayan Banking Berhad; *Int'l*, pg. 4660
KIMFLOR AS—See Floridienne SA; *Int'l*, pg. 2708
KIMGRES AUSTRALIA PTY LTD.—See Kim Hin Industry Berhad; *Int'l*, pg. 4162
KIMGRES MARKETING SDN. BHD.—See Kim Hin Industry Berhad; *Int'l*, pg. 4162
KIM GUAN IMPEX SDN. BHD.—See Dominant Enterprise Berhad; *Int'l*, pg. 2161
KIM HANSEN CHEVROLET-OLDS; *U.S. Private*, pg. 2305
KIM HENG LIMITED; *Int'l*, pg. 4162
KIM HIAP LEE COMPANY PTE. LIMITED—See LHT Holdings Limited; *Int'l*, pg. 4479
KIM HIN CERAMIC (SEREMBAN) SDN. BHD.—See Kim Hin Industry Berhad; *Int'l*, pg. 4162
KIM HIN CERAMICS (SHANGHAI) CO., LTD.—See Kim Hin Industry Berhad; *Int'l*, pg. 4162
KIM HIN INDUSTRY BERHAD; *Int'l*, pg. 4162
KIM HIN JOO (MALAYSIA) BERHAD; *Int'l*, pg. 4162
KIM HIN PROPERTIES SDN. BHD.—See Kim Hin Industry Berhad; *Int'l*, pg. 4162
KIMIA BIOSCIENCES PVT LTD.; *Int'l*, pg. 4163
KIMIA SUCHI MARKETING SDN BHD—See Berjaya Corporation Berhad; *Int'l*, pg. 984
KIM INTERNATIONAL CORPORATION—See Greenlane Holdings, Inc.; *U.S. Public*, pg. 965
KIM KANG AQUACULTURE SDN BHD; *Int'l*, pg. 4162
KIM KING ASSOCIATES, LLC; *U.S. Private*, pg. 2305
KIMLEY-HORN AND ASSOCIATES, INC.; *U.S. Private*, pg. 2305
KIMLEY-HORN AND ASSOCIATES, INC.—See Kimley-Horn and Associates, Inc.; *U.S. Private*, pg. 2305
KIMLEY-HORN AND ASSOCIATES, INC.—See Kimley-Horn and Associates, Inc.; *U.S. Private*, pg. 2305
KIM LIGHTING—See Hubbell Incorporated; *U.S. Public*, pg. 1067
KIM LOONG RESOURCES BERHAD; *Int'l*, pg. 4162
KIMLUN CORPORATION BERHAD; *Int'l*, pg. 4163
KIMLY LIMITED; *Int'l*, pg. 4163
KIMLY SEAFOOD PTE. LTD.—See Kimly Limited; *Int'l*, pg. 4163
KIMLY SEAFOOD WEST PTE. LTD.—See Kimly Limited; *Int'l*, pg. 4163
KIMMEL & ASSOCIATES; *U.S. Private*, pg. 2305
KIMMERIDGE ENERGY MANAGEMENT COMPANY, LLC; *U.S. Private*, pg. 2305
KIMMERIDGE TEXAS GAS, LLC—See Kimmeridge Energy Management Company, LLC; *U.S. Private*, pg. 2305
KIMMINS CONTRACTING CORP.; *U.S. Private*, pg. 2305
KIMNICA SOCIEDAD ANONIMA—See Kimberly-Clark Corporation; *U.S. Public*, pg. 1231
KIMOCE; *Int'l*, pg. 4163
KIMO RHVAC CONTROLS GMBH—See BITZER SE; *Int'l*, pg. 1052
KIMOTO CO., LTD, - IBARAKI PLANT—See Kimoto Co., Ltd.; *Int'l*, pg. 4163
KIMOTO CO., LTD. - MIE PLANT—See Kimoto Co., Ltd.; *Int'l*, pg. 4163
KIMOTO CO., LTD.; *Int'l*, pg. 4163
KIMOTO INNOVATIVE TECHNOLOGIES (SHANGHAI) CO., LTD.—See Kimoto Co., Ltd.; *Int'l*, pg. 4163
KIMOTO LTD.—See Kimoto Co., Ltd.; *Int'l*, pg. 4163
KIMOTO TECH, INC.—See Kimoto Co., Ltd.; *Int'l*, pg. 4163
KIMOU ENVIRONMENTAL HOLDING LIMITED; *Int'l*, pg. 4163
KIM PARADISE PTE. LTD.—See Neo Group Limited; *Int'l*, pg. 5196
KIMPEX, INC—See Daeyang Electric Co., Ltd.; *Int'l*, pg. 1911
KIMPLAS LIMITED—See NORMA Group SE; *Int'l*, pg. 5430
KIMPLAS PIPING SYSTEMS LTD.—See NORMA Group SE; *Int'l*, pg. 5430
KIMPTON HOTEL MADERA—See InterContinental Hotels Group PLC; *Int'l*, pg. 3738
KIMPTON HOTEL & RESTAURANT GROUP, LLC—See InterContinental Hotels Group PLC; *Int'l*, pg. 3738

COMPANY NAME INDEX

KIMPTON MASON & ROOK HOTEL—See InterContinental Hotels Group PLC; *Int'l*, pg. 3738
KIMRAD TRANSPORT, LP.; *U.S. Private*, pg. 2306
KIMRAY, INC.; *U.S. Private*, pg. 2306
KIMREE, INC.; *Int'l*, pg. 4163
KIM & SCOTT'S, INC.; *U.S. Private*, pg. 2305
KIMS CUDDLES PRIVATE LIMITED—See Krishna Institute of Medical Sciences Limited; *Int'l*, pg. 4302
KIM SENG HENG ENGINEERING CONSTRUCTION (PTE) LTD—See KSH Holdings Limited; *Int'l*, pg. 4313
KIM SENG HENG REALTY PTE LTD—See KSH Holdings Limited; *Int'l*, pg. 4313
KIM SENG HUAT HARDWARE PTE LTD—See CosmoSteel Holdings Limited; *Int'l*, pg. 1814
KIM'S HOME CENTER INC.; *U.S. Private*, pg. 2305
KIM'S TOYOTA; *U.S. Private*, pg. 2305
KIM TECK CHEONG CONSOLIDATED BERHAD; *Int'l*, pg. 4162
KIM THAYER & ASSOCIATES—See Litigation Services, LLC; *U.S. Private*, pg. 2468
KIMUNYE TEA FACTORY COMPANY LIMITED—See Kenya Tea Development Agency Limited; *Int'l*, pg. 4129
KIMURA BREWERY INC.—See Tohokushinsha Film Corporation; *Int'l*, pg. 7777
KIMURA CHEMICAL PLANTS CO., LTD.; *Int'l*, pg. 4163
KIMURA CO., LTD.; *Int'l*, pg. 4163
KIMURA, INC.—See Kimura-Unity Co., Ltd.; *Int'l*, pg. 4163
KIMURA INFORMATION TECHNOLOGY CO., LTD.—See CMC Corporation; *Int'l*, pg. 1669
KIMURA KOHKI CO., LTD.; *Int'l*, pg. 4163
KIMURA SANGYO CO., LTD.—See Japan Asia Group Limited; *Int'l*, pg. 3885
KIMURATAN CORPORATION; *Int'l*, pg. 4164
KIMURA-UNITY CO., LTD. - INAZAWA PLANT—See Kimura-Unity Co., Ltd.; *Int'l*, pg. 4163
KIMURA-UNITY CO., LTD. - INUYAMA PLANT—See Kimura-Unity Co., Ltd.; *Int'l*, pg. 4163
KIMURA-UNITY CO., LTD. - KARIYA PLANT—See Kimura-Unity Co., Ltd.; *Int'l*, pg. 4163
KIMURA-UNITY CO., LTD. - MEIKO PLANT—See Kimura-Unity Co., Ltd.; *Int'l*, pg. 4164
KIMURA-UNITY CO., LTD.; *Int'l*, pg. 4163
KIMURA-UNITY CO., LTD. - TOYOTA PLANT—See Kimura-Unity Co., Ltd.; *Int'l*, pg. 4164
KIM VI INOX IMPORT EXPORT PRODUCTION JOINT STOCK COMPANY; *Int'l*, pg. 4162
KINA ASSET MANAGEMENT LIMITED—See Kina Securities Limited; *Int'l*, pg. 4164
KINA BANK LIMITED—See Kina Securities Limited; *Int'l*, pg. 4164
KINA-BIJAK SDN. BHD.—See Mitrajaya Holdings Berhad; *Int'l*, pg. 4927
KINALAJU SUPPLY SDN. BHD.—See B.I.G. Industries Berhad; *Int'l*, pg. 790
KIN AND CARTA COLOMBIA S.A.S.—See Kin and Carta plc; *Int'l*, pg. 4164
KIN AND CARTA PARTNERSHIPS LLC—See Kin and Carta plc; *Int'l*, pg. 4164
KIN AND CARTA PLC; *Int'l*, pg. 4164
KINA PETROLEUM LTD.; *Int'l*, pg. 4164
KINA SECURITIES LIMITED; *Int'l*, pg. 4164
KINATICO LTD; *Int'l*, pg. 4164
KINAXIS CHINA—See Kinaxis Inc.; *Int'l*, pg. 4165
KINAXIS HONG KONG—See Kinaxis Inc.; *Int'l*, pg. 4165
KINAXIS INC.; *Int'l*, pg. 4164
KINAXIS JAPAN K. K.—See Kinaxis Inc.; *Int'l*, pg. 4165
KINAXIS NETHERLANDS—See Kinaxis Inc.; *Int'l*, pg. 4165
KINAXO BIOTECHNOLOGIES GMBH—See Evotec SE; *Int'l*, pg. 2573
KINCAID FURNITURE COMPANY, INC.—See La-Z-Boy Incorporated; *U.S. Public*, pg. 1285
KINCAID GENERATION, L.L.C.—See Dominion Energy, Inc.; *U.S. Public*, pg. 674
KINCAID PRODUCTS, INC.; *U.S. Private*, pg. 2306
KINCAID UPHOLSTERY—See La-Z-Boy Incorporated; *U.S. Public*, pg. 1285
KIN + CARTA PLC—See BC Partners LLP; *Int'l*, pg. 925
KINCO AUTOMATION SHANGHAI CO., LTD.; *Int'l*, pg. 4165
KINCO CONSTRUCTORS LLC; *U.S. Private*, pg. 2306
KINCO ELECTRIC (SHENZHEN) LTD.—See Kinco Automation Shanghai Co., Ltd.; *Int'l*, pg. 4165
KINCO, LLC; *U.S. Private*, pg. 2306
KINCORA COPPER LIMITED; *Int'l*, pg. 4165
KINCROME AUSTRALIA PTY LTD; *Int'l*, pg. 4165
KINDAI CHEMICAL INDUSTRY CO., LTD.—See Toho Chemical Industry Co., Ltd.; *Int'l*, pg. 7775
KINDAI KAGAKU SHA CO., LTD.—See Impress Holdings Inc.; *Int'l*, pg. 3637
KINDASA WATER SERVICES COMPANY—See Sustained Infrastructure Holding Company SJSC; *Int'l*, pg. 7347
KIND CAMPAIGN; *U.S. Private*, pg. 2306
KINDCARD, INC.; *U.S. Private*, pg. 4165
KINDEE OIL & GAS LOUISIANA LLC—See OGI Group Ltd; *Int'l*, pg. 5531
KINDEE OIL & GAS TEXAS LLC—See OGI Group Ltd; *Int'l*, pg. 5531
KINDEL FURNITURE COMPANY; *U.S. Private*, pg. 2306

KINDEN CORPORATION; *Int'l*, pg. 4165
KINDEN DENRYOKU SERVICE COMPANY, INCORPORATED—See Kinden Corporation; *Int'l*, pg. 4165
KINDEN ELECTRICAL & MECHANICAL SERVICE COMPANY—See Kinden Corporation; *Int'l*, pg. 4165
KINDEN HIMEJI SERVICE COMPANY, INC.—See Kinden Corporation; *Int'l*, pg. 4165
KINDEN HYOGO SERVICE COMPANY, INC.—See Kinden Corporation; *Int'l*, pg. 4165
KINDEN INTERNATIONAL, LTD.—See Kinden Corporation; *Int'l*, pg. 4165
KINDEN KANSAI SERVICES COMPANY, INCORPORATED—See Kinden Corporation; *Int'l*, pg. 4165
KINDENKO (THAILAND) CO., LTD.—See Kinden Corporation; *Int'l*, pg. 4166
KINDEN KYOTO SERVICE COMPANY, INCORPORATED—See Kinden Corporation; *Int'l*, pg. 4165
KINDEN NAGOYA SERVICES COMPANY, INCORPORATED—See Kinden Corporation; *Int'l*, pg. 4165
KINDEN NARA SERVICE COMPANY INCORPORATED—See Kinden Corporation; *Int'l*, pg. 4165
KINDEN NISHINIHON SERVICE COMPANY, INC.—See Kinden Corporation; *Int'l*, pg. 4165
KINDEN PHILS CORPORATION—See Kinden Corporation; *Int'l*, pg. 4165
KINDEN SERVICE COMPANY, INCORPORATED—See Kinden Corporation; *Int'l*, pg. 4165
KINDEN SHIGA SERVICE COMPANY INCORPORATED—See Kinden Corporation; *Int'l*, pg. 4165
KINDEN SHOJI COMPANY, LTD—See Kinden Corporation; *Int'l*, pg. 4165
KINDENSPINET CORPORATION—See Kinden Corporation; *Int'l*, pg. 4166
KINDEN (THAILAND) CO., LTD.—See Kinden Corporation; *Int'l*, pg. 4165
KINDEN VIETNAM CO., LTD.—See Kinden Corporation; *Int'l*, pg. 4165
KINDERCARE EDUCATION LLC—See Partners Group Holding AG; *Int'l*, pg. 5750
KINDERCARE LEARNING CENTERS, INC.—See Partners Group Holding AG; *Int'l*, pg. 5750
KINDERCARE LEARNING COMPANIES, INC.; *U.S. Public*, pg. 1234
KINDER ELECTRIC COMPANY INC.; *U.S. Private*, pg. 2306
KINDERGARDEN NEDERLAND B.V.—See Bain Capital, LP; *U.S. Public*, pg. 437
KINDERGARDEN PLANTS LTD—See Ball Horticultural Company; *U.S. Public*, pg. 460
KINDERHOOK INDUSTRIES, LLC; *U.S. Private*, pg. 2306
KINDERHORT SALZBURGER LEITE GGMBH—See Asklepios Kliniken GmbH & Co. KGaA; *Int'l*, pg. 624
KINDER MORGAN ALTAMONT LLC—See Kinder Morgan, Inc.; *U.S. Public*, pg. 1233
KINDER MORGAN CANADA LIMITED—See Pembina Pipeline Corporation; *Int'l*, pg. 5785
KINDER MORGAN CO2 COMPANY, L.P.—See Kinder Morgan, Inc.; *U.S. Public*, pg. 1233
KINDER MORGAN (DELAWARE), INC.—See Kinder Morgan, Inc.; *U.S. Public*, pg. 1233
KINDER MORGAN ENERGY PARTNERS, L.P. - PACIFIC OPERATIONS—See Kinder Morgan, Inc.; *U.S. Public*, pg. 1233
KINDER MORGAN ENERGY PARTNERS, L.P.—See Kinder Morgan, Inc.; *U.S. Public*, pg. 1233
KINDER MORGAN G.P., INC.—See Kinder Morgan, Inc.; *U.S. Public*, pg. 1233
KINDER MORGAN, INC.; *U.S. Public*, pg. 1232
KINDER MORGAN PIPELINES (USA) INC.—See Kinder Morgan, Inc.; *U.S. Public*, pg. 1233
KINDER MORGAN SERVICES LLC—See Kinder Morgan, Inc.; *U.S. Public*, pg. 1233
KINDER MORGAN SOUTHEAST TERMINALS LLC - KNOXVILLE—See Kinder Morgan, Inc.; *U.S. Public*, pg. 1233
KINDER MORGAN SOUTHEAST TERMINALS LLC - ROANOKE—See Kinder Morgan, Inc.; *U.S. Public*, pg. 1233
KINDER MORGAN TEXAS PIPELINE, LP—See Kinder Morgan, Inc.; *U.S. Public*, pg. 1233
KINDER MORGAN TEXAS TERMINALS, L.P.—See Kinder Morgan, Inc.; *U.S. Public*, pg. 1233
KINDER MORGAN TREATING LP—See Kinder Morgan, Inc.; *U.S. Public*, pg. 1233
KINDER REESE; *U.S. Private*, pg. 2306
KINDHEART, LLC—See Intuitive Surgical, Inc.; *U.S. Public*, pg. 1160
KIND, INC.; *U.S. Private*, pg. 2306
KINDLE ENTERTAINMENT LIMITED—See Lions Gate Entertainment Corp.; *Int'l*, pg. 4521
KINDLIMANN AG—See Benteler International AG; *Int'l*, pg. 977

KINDLIMANN SA—See Benteler International AG; *Int'l*, pg. 977
KIND LLC; *U.S. Private*, pg. 2306
KINDLON ENTERPRISES, INC.; *U.S. Private*, pg. 2307
KINDLY MD, INC.; *U.S. Public*, pg. 1234
KINDOM CONSTRUCTION CORP.; *Int'l*, pg. 4166
KINDRED BIOSCIENCES, INC.—See Elanco Animal Health Incorporated; *U.S. Public*, pg. 723
KINDRED GROUP PLC; *Int'l*, pg. 4166
KINDRED HEALTHCARE, LLC—See Apollo Global Management, Inc.; *U.S. Public*, pg. 156
KINDRED HEALTHCARE OF ELIZABETH CITY—See Apollo Global Management, Inc.; *U.S. Public*, pg. 156
KINDRED HOSPICE MISSOURI, LLC—See Humana, Inc.; *U.S. Public*, pg. 1070
KINDRED HOSPITAL - ATLANTA—See Apollo Global Management, Inc.; *U.S. Public*, pg. 156
KINDRED HOSPITAL - BAY AREA - TAMPA—See Apollo Global Management, Inc.; *U.S. Public*, pg. 156
KINDRED HOSPITAL - CLEVELAND—See Apollo Global Management, Inc.; *U.S. Public*, pg. 156
KINDRED HOSPITAL - LOUISVILLE—See Apollo Global Management, Inc.; *U.S. Public*, pg. 156
KINDRED HOSPITAL PALM BEACH, L.L.C.—See Apollo Global Management, Inc.; *U.S. Public*, pg. 156
KINDRED HOSPITAL-PITTSBURGH-NORTH SHORE, L.L.C.—See Apollo Global Management, Inc.; *U.S. Public*, pg. 156
KINDRED HOSPITAL - SAN DIEGO—See Apollo Global Management, Inc.; *U.S. Public*, pg. 156
KINDRED HOSPITAL TUCSON—See Apollo Global Management, Inc.; *U.S. Public*, pg. 156
KINDRED NURSING AND REHABILITATION - BRAINTREE—See Apollo Global Management, Inc.; *U.S. Public*, pg. 157
KINDRED NURSING CENTERS LIMITED PARTNERSHIP—See Apollo Global Management, Inc.; *U.S. Public*, pg. 156
KINDRED NURSING CENTERS WEST, L.L.C.—See Apollo Global Management, Inc.; *U.S. Public*, pg. 156
KINDRED NURSING CENTERS WEST, LLC—See Apollo Global Management, Inc.; *U.S. Public*, pg. 156
KINDS RESOURCE SDN. BHD.—See Hai-O Enterprise Berhad; *Int'l*, pg. 3209
KINDSTAR GLOBALGENE TECHNOLOGY, INC.; *Int'l*, pg. 4166
KINDUCT TECHNOLOGIES, INC.; *Int'l*, pg. 4166
KINDY S.A.; *Int'l*, pg. 4166
KINECO EXEL COMPOSITES INDIA PRIVATE LIMITED—See Exel Composites Oyj; *Int'l*, pg. 2582
KINECO KAMAN COMPOSITES INDIA PRIVATE LIMITED—See Indo-National Limited; *Int'l*, pg. 3657
KINECT CONSULTING, LLC—See World Kinect Corporation; *U.S. Public*, pg. 2380
KINECT ENERGY DENMARK A/S—See World Kinect Corporation; *U.S. Public*, pg. 2380
KINECT ENERGY GERMANY GMBH—See World Kinect Corporation; *U.S. Public*, pg. 2380
KINECT ENERGY GREEN SERVICES AS—See World Kinect Corporation; *U.S. Public*, pg. 2380
KINECTIQ INC.; *U.S. Private*, pg. 2307
KINECTRICS INC—See Vision Capital, LLP; *Int'l*, pg. 8252
KINECT SOLAR, LLC; *U.S. Private*, pg. 2307
KINECT—See Omnicom Group Inc.; *U.S. Public*, pg. 1599
KINEDYNE CANADA LIMITED—See Kinedyne Corporation; *U.S. Private*, pg. 2307
KINEDYNE CORPORATION; *U.S. Private*, pg. 2307
KIN-EI CORP.—See Kintetsu Group Holdings Co.,Ltd.; *Int'l*, pg. 4183
KINEMASTER CORPORATION; *Int'l*, pg. 4166
KINEMED, INC.; *U.S. Private*, pg. 2307
KINEMETRICS, INC.—See OYO Corporation; *Int'l*, pg. 5678
KINEMETRICS SA—See OYO Corporation; *Int'l*, pg. 5678
KINEO S.A.—See AUTOHELLAS S.A.; *Int'l*, pg. 727
KINEPOLIS BRAINE SA—See Kinepolis Group N.V.; *Int'l*, pg. 4166
KINEPOLIS ESPANA SA—See Kinepolis Group N.V.; *Int'l*, pg. 4166
KINEPOLIS FILM DISTRIBUTION (KFD) NV—See Kinepolis Group N.V.; *Int'l*, pg. 4166
KINEPOLIS GROUP N.V.; *Int'l*, pg. 4166
KINEPOLIS HOLDING BV—See Kinepolis Group N.V.; *Int'l*, pg. 4166
KINEPOLIS MULHOUSE SA—See Kinepolis Group N.V.; *Int'l*, pg. 4166
KINEPOLIS POZNAN S.P.Z. O.O.—See Kinepolis Group N.V.; *Int'l*, pg. 4166
KINEPOLIS SCHWEIZ AG—See Kinepolis Group N.V.; *Int'l*, pg. 4166
KINEPOLIS THIONVILLE SA—See Kinepolis Group N.V.; *Int'l*, pg. 4166
KINERGY ADVANCEMENT BERHAD; *Int'l*, pg. 4166
KINERGY EMS (NANTONG) CO., LTD—See Kinergy Pte Ltd.; *Int'l*, pg. 4167
KINERGY MARKETING LLC—See Alto Ingredients, Inc.; *U.S. Public*, pg. 88
KINERGY PRECISION ENGINEERING (NANTONG) CO., LTD.—See Kinergy Pte Ltd.; *Int'l*, pg. 4167

KINERGY PTE LTD.
CORPORATE AFFILIATIONS

KINERGY PTE LTD.; *Int'l*, pg. 4167
KINERJAPAY CORP.; *Int'l*, pg. 4167
KINESIS INDUSTRY CO., LTD.; *Int'l*, pg. 4167
KINESYS INC.; *U.S. Private*, pg. 2307
KINETA, INC.; *U.S. Public*, pg. 1234
KINETEC S.A.—See Spronken Orthopedie NV; *Int'l*, pg. 7145
KINETEK CONSULTING, LLC; *U.S. Private*, pg. 2308
THE KINETIC CO., INC.—See Live Ventures Incorporated; *U.S. Public*, pg. 1332
KINETIC CONCEPTS, INC.—See 3M Company; *U.S. Public*, pg. 7
KINETIC CONSOLIDATED PTY LTD; *Int'l*, pg. 4167
KINETIC CONSTRUCTION LTD.; *Int'l*, pg. 4167
KINETIC CONTENT LLC—See ProSiebenSat.1 Media SE; *Int'l*, pg. 6000
KINETIC DESIGN & ADVERTISING PVT. LTD.—See WPP plc; *Int'l*, pg. 8475
KINETIC DEVELOPMENT GROUP LIMITED; *Int'l*, pg. 4167
KINETIC ELECTRONICS LTD.—See Komax Holding AG; *Int'l*, pg. 4240
KINETIC ENERGY, LLC—See EagleTree Capital, LP; *U.S. Private*, pg. 1311
KINETIC ENGINEERING, LTD.; *Int'l*, pg. 4167
KINETIC GROUP INC.; *U.S. Public*, pg. 1234
KINETIC GROUP SERVICES PTY LTD.; *Int'l*, pg. 4167
KINETIC ITALIA—See WPP plc; *Int'l*, pg. 8475
KINETICO BELGIUM HOLDINGS NV—See Axel Johnson Gruppen AB; *Int'l*, pg. 765
KINETICO DENMARK APS—See Axel Johnson Gruppen AB; *Int'l*, pg. 765
KINETICO FRANCE SARL—See Axel Johnson Gruppen AB; *Int'l*, pg. 765
KINETICO GERMANY GMBH—See Axel Johnson Gruppen AB; *Int'l*, pg. 765
KINETICO INCORPORATED—See Axel Johnson Gruppen AB; *Int'l*, pg. 765
KINETICO INCORPORATED—See Axel Johnson Gruppen AB; *Int'l*, pg. 765
KINETICOM, INC.; *U.S. Private*, pg. 2308
KINETICOM LTD.—See Kineticom, Inc.; *U.S. Private*, pg. 2308
KINETICO UK LIMITED—See Axel Johnson Gruppen AB; *Int'l*, pg. 765
KINETIC PROCESS SYSTEMS LTD—See Gemini Corporation; *Int'l*, pg. 2916
KINETIC PROJECTS INC—See Gemini Corporation; *Int'l*, pg. 2916
KINETIC PUBLISHING SERVICES, LLC—See Westchester Publishing Services, LLC; *U.S. Private*, pg. 4489
KINETICS DRIVE SOLUTIONS INC.—See Temasek Holdings (Private) Limited; *Int'l*, pg. 7552
KINETIC SEAS INCORPORATED; *U.S. Public*, pg. 1234
KINETICS GERMANY GMBH - DRESDEN OFFICE—See M+W Group GmbH; *Int'l*, pg. 4613
KINETICS GERMANY GMBH—See M+W Group GmbH; *Int'l*, pg. 4613
KINETICS HOLDING GMBH—See M+W Group GmbH; *Int'l*, pg. 4613
KINETICS LTD.—See Elbit Systems Limited; *Int'l*, pg. 2345
KINETICS MECHANICAL ENERGY; *U.S. Private*, pg. 2308
KINETICS NOISE CONTROL, INC.—See KPS Capital Partners, LP; *U.S. Private*, pg. 2347
KINETIC; *U.S. Private*, pg. 2308
KINETIC—See WPP plc; *Int'l*, pg. 8474
KINETIC—See WPP plc; *Int'l*, pg. 8474
KINETIC—See WPP plc; *Int'l*, pg. 8474
KINETIC—See WPP plc; *Int'l*, pg. 8474
KINETIC—See WPP plc; *Int'l*, pg. 8474
KINETIC—See WPP plc; *Int'l*, pg. 8474
KINETIC—See WPP plc; *Int'l*, pg. 8474
KINETIC—See WPP plc; *Int'l*, pg. 8474
KINETIC—See WPP plc; *Int'l*, pg. 8474
KINETIC—See WPP plc; *Int'l*, pg. 8474
KINETIC—See WPP plc; *Int'l*, pg. 8474
KINETIC—See WPP plc; *Int'l*, pg. 8474
KINETIC—See WPP plc; *Int'l*, pg. 8474
KINETIC—See WPP plc; *Int'l*, pg. 8474
KINETIC—See WPP plc; *Int'l*, pg. 8474
KINETICS PROCESS SYSTEMS PTE. LTD.—See M+W Group GmbH; *Int'l*, pg. 4613
KINETICS PROCESS SYSTEMS (SHANGHAI) LTD.—See M+W Group GmbH; *Int'l*, pg. 4613
KINETICS SYSTEMS MALAYSIA SDN. BHD. - KULIM OFFICE—See M+W Group GmbH; *Int'l*, pg. 4613
KINETICS SYSTEMS MALAYSIA SDN. BHD.—See M+W Group GmbH; *Int'l*, pg. 4613
KINETIC SYSTEMS, INC.—See M+W Group GmbH; *Int'l*, pg. 4613
KINETIC TECHNOLOGIES, INC.; *U.S. Private*, pg. 2308
KINETIC TRUST LTD.; *Int'l*, pg. 4168
KINETIC VENTURES, L.L.C.—See ITC Holding Company, LLC; *U.S. Private*, pg. 2149
KINETIC WORLDWIDE LTD—See Beekl Holding AG; *Int'l*, pg. 939

KINETIKA SARDEGNA SRL—See Clariane SE; *Int'l*, pg. 1643
KINETIK HOLDINGS INC.—See Kayne Anderson Capital Advisors, L.P.; *U.S. Private*, pg. 2267
KINETIKO ENERGY LTD; *Int'l*, pg. 4168
KINETIX SYSTEMS HOLDINGS LTD.; *Int'l*, pg. 4168
KINEX BEARINGS, A.S.—See CK Birla Group; *Int'l*, pg. 1636
KINEX-EXIM, SPOL. S R.O.—See HTC holding a.s.; *Int'l*, pg. 3508
KINEX INC.—See Planned Systems International, Inc.; *U.S. Private*, pg. 3196
KINEX-KLF, A.S.—See HTC holding a.s.; *Int'l*, pg. 3508
KING APPLIANCE CENTER INC.; *U.S. Private*, pg. 2308
KING ARCHITECTURAL METALS, INC.; *U.S. Private*, pg. 2308
THE KING ARTHUR FLOUR COMPANY, INC.; *U.S. Private*, pg. 4065
KING ASIA FOODS LTD.; *Int'l*, pg. 4168
KING ASPHALT, INC.—See Construction Partners, Inc.; *U.S. Public*, pg. 572
KING AUTO CENTER, INC.; *U.S. Private*, pg. 2308
KING BELGIUM NV—See Bunzl plc; *Int'l*, pg. 1218
KING BEVERAGE INC.; *U.S. Private*, pg. 2309
KINGBOARD COPPER FOIL HOLDINGS LIMITED—See Kingboard Holdings Limited; *Int'l*, pg. 4171
KINGBOARD ELECTRONIC RAW MATERIAL (JIANG YIN) CO., LTD.—See Kingboard Holdings Limited; *Int'l*, pg. 4171
KINGBOARD (FOGANG) LAMINATES CO. LIMITED—See Kingboard Holdings Limited; *Int'l*, pg. 4171
KINGBOARD (FOGANG) PAPER LAMINATES CO., LTD.—See Kingboard Holdings Limited; *Int'l*, pg. 4171
KINGBOARD (HEBEI) CHEMICAL CO. LIMITED—See Kingboard Holdings Limited; *Int'l*, pg. 4171
KINGBOARD (HEBEI) COKECHEM CO. LIMITED—See Kingboard Holdings Limited; *Int'l*, pg. 4171
KINGBOARD HOLDINGS LIMITED; *Int'l*, pg. 4170
KINGBOARD INVESTMENTS LIMITED—See Kingboard Holdings Limited; *Int'l*, pg. 4171
KINGBOARD (JIANGSU) CHEMICAL CO., LTD.—See Kingboard Holdings Limited; *Int'l*, pg. 4171
KINGBOARD LAMINATES HOLDINGS LIMITED—See Kingboard Holdings Limited; *Int'l*, pg. 4171
KINGBOARD LAMINATES (JIANGMEN) CO., LTD.—See Kingboard Holdings Limited; *Int'l*, pg. 4171
KINGBOARD LAMINATES (KUNSHAN) CO., LTD.—See Kingboard Holdings Limited; *Int'l*, pg. 4171
KINGBOARD LAMINATES (SHAOGUAN) LIMITED—See Kingboard Holdings Limited; *Int'l*, pg. 4171
KINGBOARD (LIANZHOU) FIBRE GLASS CO. LIMITED—See Kingboard Holdings Limited; *Int'l*, pg. 4171
KINGBOARD (PANYU NANSHA) PETROCHEMICAL COMPANY LIMITED—See Kingboard Holdings Limited; *Int'l*, pg. 4171
KINGBOARD (TAICANG) CHEMICAL CO., LTD.—See Kingboard Holdings Limited; *Int'l*, pg. 4171
KINGBO STRIKE LIMITED; *Int'l*, pg. 4170
KING BUICK GMC; *U.S. Private*, pg. 2309
KING BUSINESS FORMS CORP.; *U.S. Private*, pg. 2309
KINGCAN HOLDINGS LIMITED; *Int'l*, pg. 4171
KING CAN INDUSTRY CORPORATION—See Wei-Chuan Food Corporation; *Int'l*, pg. 8369
KING CANNON, INC; *U.S. Private*, pg. 2309
KING CAPITAL CORP.; *U.S. Private*, pg. 2309
KING CHOU MARINE TECHNOLOGY CO., LTD.; *Int'l*, pg. 4168
KING CHOU (VIETNAM) MARINE TECHNOLOGY CO., LTD.—See King Chou Marine Technology Co., Ltd.; *Int'l*, pg. 4168
KING CITY PHYSICIAN COMPANY, LLC—See Quorum Health Corporation; *U.S. Private*, pg. 3330
KINGCLEAN ELECTRIC CO., LTD.; *Int'l*, pg. 4171
KING CO., LTD.; *Int'l*, pg. 4168
KINGCOME SOFAS LIMITED—See Colefax Group PLC; *Int'l*, pg. 1697
KING.COM LIMITED—See Microsoft Corporation; *U.S. Public*, pg. 1439
KING & COMPANY INC,; *U.S. Private*, pg. 2308
KING + COMPANY; *U.S. Private*, pg. 2308
KING CONTENT PTY LTD—See Pulsar Group; *Int'l*, pg. 6116
KING CORE ELECTRONICS INC.; *Int'l*, pg. 4168
KING CORE ELECTRONICS (SUZHOU) CO., LTD.—See King Core Electronics Inc.; *Int'l*, pg. 4168
KING COTTON MOTOR COMPANY OF COVINGTON; *U.S. Private*, pg. 2309
KINGDEE INTERNATIONAL SOFTWARE GROUP COMPANY LTD.; *Int'l*, pg. 4171
KINGDEE INTERNATIONAL SOFTWARE GROUP (H.K.) CO., LTD.—See Kingdee International Software Group Company Ltd.; *Int'l*, pg. 4171
KINGDEE INTERNATIONAL SOFTWARE GROUP (SINGAPORE) PTE LTD.—See Kingdee International Software Group Company Ltd.; *Int'l*, pg. 4171
KINGDOM AGRICULTURE DEVELOPMENT COMPANY—See Kingdom Holding Company; *Int'l*, pg. 4172

KINGDOM EUROPE S.R.L.—See Kingdom Holdings Limited; *Int'l*, pg. 4172
KINGDOM FINE METAL LIMITED—See KFM Kingdom Holdings Limited; *Int'l*, pg. 4148
KINGDOM FOOD PRODUCTS APS—See Arla Foods amba; *Int'l*, pg. 573
KINGDOM HOLDING COMPANY; *Int'l*, pg. 4172
KINGDOM HOLDINGS LIMITED; *Int'l*, pg. 4172
KINGDOM HOTEL INVESTMENTS—See Kingdom Holding Company; *Int'l*, pg. 4172
KINGDOM INC.; *U.S. Private*, pg. 2310
KINGDOM OF MIND, LLC—See Live Nation Entertainment, Inc.; *U.S. Public*, pg. 1329
KINGDOM PROPERTIES CO. LIMITED—See Oriental Holdings Berhad; *Int'l*, pg. 5624
KINGDOMWAY NUTRITION, INC.; *U.S. Private*, pg. 2310
KINGDON-NICHOLS LLC; *U.S. Private*, pg. 2310
KING DRUG COMPANY OF FLORENCE INC.—See Lyndale Enterprises Inc.; *U.S. Private*, pg. 2521
KING DUAN INDUSTRIAL CO.,LTD.—See Universal Cement Corporation; *Int'l*, pg. 8078
KING ENGINEERING ASSOCIATES, INC.—See Littlejohn & Co., LLC; *U.S. Private*, pg. 2469
KINGENTA AUSTRALIA AG PTY. LTD.—See Kingenta Ecological Engineering Group Co., Ltd.; *Int'l*, pg. 4172
KINGENTA ECOLOGICAL ENGINEERING GROUP CO., LTD.; *Int'l*, pg. 4172
KINGENTA VIETNAM COMPANY LIMITED—See Kingenta Ecological Engineering Group Co., Ltd.; *Int'l*, pg. 4172
KINGERY PRINTING COMPANY; *U.S. Private*, pg. 2310
KING ESTATE OREGON WINES; *U.S. Private*, pg. 2309
KING ESTATE WINERY; *U.S. Private*, pg. 2309
KING FARM CENTER, LLC—See Regency Centers Corporation; *U.S. Public*, pg. 1774
KINGFA SCIENCE & TECHNOLOGY (INDIA) LTD.; *Int'l*, pg. 4172
KINGFA SCI &TECH CO., LTD.; *Int'l*, pg. 4172
KINGFA SCI. & TECH (MALAYSIA), LTD.—See Kingfa Sci &Tech Co., Ltd.; *Int'l*, pg. 4172
KINGFA SCI & TECH (USA), INC.—See Kingfa Sci &Tech Co., Ltd.; *Int'l*, pg. 4172
KING FEATURES SYNDICATE, INC.—See The Hearst Corporation; *U.S. Private*, pg. 4045
KINGFIELD HEATH LTD.; *Int'l*, pg. 4172
KING FINANCIAL PLANNING LLP—See Tavistock Investments PLC; *Int'l*, pg. 7477
THE KINGFISH COMPANY N.V.; *Int'l*, pg. 7662
KINGFISHER ASIA LTD—See Kingfisher plc; *Int'l*, pg. 4173
KINGFISHER BRIXHAM—See The Bidvest Group Limited; *Int'l*, pg. 7622
KINGFISHER B.V.—See Kingfisher plc; *Int'l*, pg. 4173
KINGFISHER CANADA HOLDINGS LLC—See Deutsche Bank Aktiengesellschaft; *Int'l*, pg. 2061
KINGFISHER CAPITAL, LLC—See Genstar Capital, LLC; *U.S. Private*, pg. 1677
KINGFISHER CAPITAL, LLC—See Keystone Group, L.P.; *U.S. Private*, pg. 2298
KINGFISHER ENVIRONMENTAL SERVICES LIMITED—See Marlowe Plc; *Int'l*, pg. 4698
KINGFISHER FRANCE S.A.S.—See Kingfisher plc; *Int'l*, pg. 4173
KINGFISHER METALS CORP.; *Int'l*, pg. 4173
KINGFISHER MINING LIMITED; *Int'l*, pg. 4173
KINGFISHER PLC; *Int'l*, pg. 4173
KINGFISHER REGIONAL HOSPITAL; *U.S. Private*, pg. 2311
KINGFISHER SYSTEMS, INC.; *U.S. Private*, pg. 2311
KINGFISH INC.; *U.S. Private*, pg. 2310
KINGFISH LIMITED; *Int'l*, pg. 4172
KING FOOK HOLDINGS LIMITED; *Int'l*, pg. 4168
KING FOOK INVESTMENT COMPANY LIMITED—See King Fook Holdings Limited; *Int'l*, pg. 4168
KING FOOK JEWELLERY GROUP LIMITED—See King Fook Holdings Limited; *Int'l*, pg. 4168
KING FOOK SECURITIES COMPANY LIMITED—See King Fook Holdings Limited; *Int'l*, pg. 4168
KING FORCE SECURITY LIMITED—See Greatwalle Inc.; *Int'l*, pg. 3068
KINGFORM HEALTH HOMETEXTILE GROUP LIMITED; *Int'l*, pg. 4173
KING FREIGHT LINES LIMITED.; *Int'l*, pg. 4168
KING GEN PUBLIC COMPANY LIMITED; *Int'l*, pg. 4168
KING GEORGE FINANCIAL CORPORATION; *Int'l*, pg. 4168
KING GEORGE LANDFILL, INC.—See Waste Management, Inc.; *U.S. Public*, pg. 2331
KING GLOBAL VENTURES INC.; *Int'l*, pg. 4168
THE KING GROUP; *U.S. Private*, pg. 4065
KING HAMM INDUSTRIAL CO., LTD.—See Quang Viet Enterprise Co., Ltd.; *Int'l*, pg. 6153
KING HENRY'S INC.; *U.S. Private*, pg. 2309
KING HICKORY FURNITURE COMPANY INC.; *U.S. Private*, pg. 2309
KINGHORN DRIVER HOUGH & CO.—See Pohlad Companies; *U.S. Private*, pg. 3220
KING HWA SIN INDUSTRIAL CO., LTD.; *Int'l*, pg. 4169
KING INDUSTRIES, INC.; *U.S. Private*, pg. 2309
KING INDUSTRIES; *U.S. Private*, pg. 2309

KING INSURANCE PARTNERS, LLC; U.S. Private, pg. 2309
KING INTERNATIONAL BULLION LIMITED—See Aceso Life Science Group Limited; Int'l, pg. 102
KING INTERNATIONAL FINANCIAL HOLDINGS LIMITED—See Aceso Life Science Group Limited; Int'l, pg. 102
KING JAMES GROUP COMPANY; Int'l, pg. 4169
KINGJARL CORPORATION—See Endress+Hauser (International) Holding AG; Int'l, pg. 2408
KING JIM CO., LTD.; Int'l, pg. 4169
KING JIM (HK) CO., LIMITED—See KING JIM CO., LTD.; Int'l, pg. 4169
KING JIM (MALAYSIA) SDN. BHD.—See KING JIM CO., LTD.; Int'l, pg. 4169
KING JIM (SHANGHAI) TRADING CO., LTD.—See KING JIM CO., LTD.; Int'l, pg. 4169
KING JIM (VIETNAM) CO., LTD.—See KING JIM CO., LTD.; Int'l, pg. 4169
KINGKEY FINANCIAL INTERNATIONAL (HOLDINGS) LIMITED; Int'l, pg. 4173
KINGKEY INTELLIGENCE CULTURE HOLDINGS LIMITED; Int'l, pg. 4173
KINGKOIL CORPORATION (M) SDN. BHD.—See OCB Berhad; Int'l, pg. 5515
KING KOIL LICENSING COMPANY INC.; U.S. Private, pg. 2309
KING KOLD FROZEN FOODS, INC.—See Saveur Food Group, LLC; U.S. Private, pg. 3556
KING KULLEN GROCERY COMPANY, INC.; U.S. Private, pg. 2309
KINGLAI HYGIENIC MATERIALS CO., LTD—See Kunshan Kinglai Hygienic Materials Co., Ltd.; Int'l, pg. 4333
KINGLAND GROUP HOLDINGS LIMITED; Int'l, pg. 4173
KINGLAND (SINO) COMPANY LIMITED—See Kingland Group Holdings Limited; Int'l, pg. 4173
KINGLAND SYSTEMS CORP.; U.S. Private, pg. 2311
KINGLAND TECHNOLOGY CO., LTD.; Int'l, pg. 4173
KING-LAR COMPANY; U.S. Private, pg. 2310
KING LOGISTICS, INC.; U.S. Private, pg. 2309
KING LONG TECHNOLOGY (SUZHOU) LTD.—See King Yuan Electronics Co., Ltd.; Int'l, pg. 4170
KING LUN HOLDINGS LIMITED; Int'l, pg. 4169
KINGLY SHIPPING LTD.—See Southern Cross Capital Management CA; Int'l, pg. 7118
KINGMAKER (CAMBODIA) FOOTWEAR CO., LTD.—See Kingmaker Footwear Holdings Limited; Int'l, pg. 4174
KINGMAKER FOOTWEAR HOLDINGS LIMITED; Int'l, pg. 4174
KINGMAKER (VIETNAM) FOOTWEAR CO., LTD.—See Kingmaker Footwear Holdings Limited; Int'l, pg. 4174
KINGMAN DAILY MINER—See Western Newspapers, Inc.; U.S. Private, pg. 4495
KINGMAN HOSPITAL, INC.; U.S. Private, pg. 2311
KINGMAN MINERALS LTD.; Int'l, pg. 4174
KINGMAN REGIONAL MEDICAL CENTER; U.S. Private, pg. 2311
KINGMAN RIVER RESOURCES INC.; Int'l, pg. 4174
KING MANUFACTURING CO. INC.; U.S. Private, pg. 2309
KING MARINE FOODS CO., LTD.—See Zen Corp Group PCL; Int'l, pg. 8632
KING & MAXWELL PRODUCTIONS INC.—See National Amusements, Inc.; U.S. Private, pg. 2841
KING MILLING COMPANY; U.S. Private, pg. 2309
KING MOTOR CO. INC.; U.S. Private, pg. 2309
KING MOTOR COMPANY; U.S. Private, pg. 2309
KINGNET NETWORK CO., LTD.; Int'l, pg. 4174
KING NUTRONICS CORPORATION—See L Squared Capital Management LP; U.S. Private, pg. 2362
KING NUTS HOLDING B.V.—See ACOMO N.V.; Int'l, pg. 108
KING NUTS & RAAPHORST B.V.—See ACOMO N.V.; Int'l, pg. 108
KING OCEAN SERVICES LIMITED; U.S. Private, pg. 2309
KING OF FANS, INC.; U.S. Private, pg. 2309
KING OF PINE CREEK MINING LTD.; U.S. Public, pg. 1234
KING OF STERLING HEIGHTS INC.—See Michigan Multi-King Inc.; U.S. Private, pg. 2701
KINGOLD JEWELRY, INC.; Int'l, pg. 4174
KING O'ROURKE CADILLAC; U.S. Private, pg. 2309
KING OSCAR AS—See Thai Union Group Public Company Limited; Int'l, pg. 7596
KING OSCAR INC.—See Thai Union Group Public Company Limited; Int'l, pg. 7596
KING PACIFIC LODGE—See Chow Tai Fook Enterprises Limited; Int'l, pg. 1585
KINGPAK TECHNOLOGY, INC.; Int'l, pg. 4174
KING PAR CORPORATION; U.S. Private, pg. 2309
KING PAWN II, INC.—See FirstCash Holdings, Inc.; U.S. Public, pg. 849
KING PAWN, INC.—See FirstCash Holdings, Inc.; U.S. Public, pg. 849
KING PIE HOLDINGS PROPRIETARY LIMITED—See The Bidvest Group Limited; Int'l, pg. 7624
KING PLASTIC CORPORATION; U.S. Private, pg. 2310
KING PLASTICS, INC.; U.S. Private, pg. 2310

KING POLYTECHNIC ENGINEERING CO., LTD.; Int'l, pg. 4169
KING POWER INTERNATIONAL CO., LTD.—See King Power International Group Co., Ltd.; Int'l, pg. 4169
KING POWER INTERNATIONAL GROUP CO., LTD.; Int'l, pg. 4169
KING PRICE FINANCIAL SERVICES (PROPRIETARY) LIMITED; Int'l, pg. 4169
KING & PRINCE SEAFOOD CORPORATION—See Nissui Corporation; Int'l, pg. 5379
KING PRIVILEGE WEALTH MANAGEMENT LIMITED—See KingKey Financial International (Holdings) Limited; Int'l, pg. 4173
KING RANCH, INC.; U.S. Private, pg. 2310
KING RECORDS CO., LTD.—See Kodansha Ltd.; Int'l, pg. 4225
KING RESOURCES, INC.; U.S. Public, pg. 1234
KING RIVER RESOURCES LIMITED; Int'l, pg. 4169
KINGRUN CO., LTD.—See Ship Healthcare Holdings, Inc.; Int'l, pg. 6852
KINGRUN HOKKAIDO CO., LTD.—See Ship Healthcare Holdings, Inc.; Int'l, pg. 6852
KINGRUN HOUNEST CO., LTD.—See Ship Healthcare Holdings, Inc.; Int'l, pg. 6852
KINGRUN KANSAI CO., LTD.—See Ship Healthcare Holdings, Inc.; Int'l, pg. 6852
KINGRUN KYUSHU CO., LTD.—See Ship Healthcare Holdings, Inc.; Int'l, pg. 6852
KINGRUN MEDICARE CO., LTD.—See Ship Healthcare Holdings, Inc.; Int'l, pg. 6852
KINGRUN RENEWAL CO., LTD.—See Ship Healthcare Holdings, Inc.; Int'l, pg. 6852
KINGS ARMS YARD VCT PLC; Int'l, pg. 4174
KINGS AUTO CO., LTD.—See PROTO CORPORATION; Int'l, pg. 6006
KINGSBRIDGE HOLDINGS LLC; U.S. Private, pg. 2311
KINGSBRIDGE PRIVATE PTY. LTD.—See Azimut Holding SpA; Int'l, pg. 779
KINGSBROOK JEWISH MEDICAL CENTER; U.S. Private, pg. 2311
KINGSBUD SP. Z O.O.—See Panevezio statybos trestas AB; Int'l, pg. 5727
KINGSBURY GMBH—See Kingsbury Inc.; U.S. Private, pg. 2311
KINGSBURY INC.; U.S. Private, pg. 2311
KINGSBURY MEADOWS (WAKEFIELD) MANAGEMENT COMPANY LIMITED—See Persimmon plc; Int'l, pg. 5816
KINGSBURY PACKAGING (LIMAVADY) LTD.—See Bunzl plc; Int'l, pg. 1218
THE KINGSBURY PLC—See Hayleys PLC; Int'l, pg. 3292
KINGS CHRYSLER JEEP DODGE; U.S. Private, pg. 2311
KINGSCLIFF TWEED COAST TAXIS PTY. LTD.—See ComfortDelGro Corporation Limited; Int'l, pg. 1712
KING'S COLONIAL FORD; U.S. Private, pg. 2310
KINGS COMMUNITY ACTION ORGANIZATION; U.S. Private, pg. 2311
KING'S CONSTRUCTION CO., INC.; U.S. Private, pg. 2310
KINGS & CONVICTS BREWING CO.; U.S. Private, pg. 2311
KINGS CREEK PLANTATION LLC; U.S. Private, pg. 2311
KINGSCROFT DEVELOPMENTS LIMITED—See Gallagher Holdings Ltd.; Int'l, pg. 2873
KINGSCROSS HYUNDAI; Int'l, pg. 4174
KING'S CROWN FORD, INC.—See AutoNation, Inc.; U.S. Public, pg. 236
KING'S CROWN FORD, INC.—See AutoNation, Inc.; U.S. Public, pg. 236
KINGSDALE PARTNERS LP—See Stagwell, Inc.; U.S. Public, pg. 1927
KINGS DELIGHT LTD., INC.; U.S. Private, pg. 2311
KINGS DOMINION LLC—See Six Flags Entertainment Corporation; U.S. Public, pg. 1890
KINGSDOWN, INC.—See Owen & Co. Ltd.; Int'l, pg. 5673
KINGSEMI CO., LTD.; Int'l, pg. 4174
KINGS ENTERTAINMENT GROUP INC.; Int'l, pg. 4174
KINGSETT CAPITAL; Int'l, pg. 4174
KINGSEY COGENERATION—See Boralex Inc.; Int'l, pg. 1112
KING'S FAMILY RESTAURANTS INC; U.S. Private, pg. 2310
THE KINGS FERRY LIMITED—See Mobico Group PLC; Int'l, pg. 5009
KING'S FLAIR INTERNATIONAL (HOLDINGS) LTD.; Int'l, pg. 4170
KINGS FORD INC.; U.S. Private, pg. 2311
KINGSFORD MANUFACTURING COMPANY—See The Clorox Company; U.S. Public, pg. 2063
THE KINGSFORD PRODUCTS COMPANY—See The Clorox Company; U.S. Public, pg. 2063
KINGSGATE CONSOLIDATED LIMITED; Int'l, pg. 4174
KINGSGATE TRANSPORTATION SERVICES, LLC; U.S. Private, pg. 2311
KINGS HAWAIIAN BAKERY WEST, INC.—See King's Hawaiian Holding Company, Inc.; U.S. Private, pg. 2310
KING'S HAWAIIAN HOLDING COMPANY, INC.; U.S. Private, pg. 2310

KING'S HAWAIIAN RETAIL, INC.—See King's Hawaiian Holding Company, Inc.; U.S. Private, pg. 2310
KING & SHAXSON ASSET MANAGEMENT—See Phillip Capital Pte. Ltd.; Int'l, pg. 5846
KING & SHAXSON CAPITAL LIMITED—See Phillip Capital Pte. Ltd.; Int'l, pg. 5846
KING & SHAXSON CAPITAL LIMITED—See Phillip Capital Pte. Ltd.; Int'l, pg. 5846
KING & SHAXSON LTD—See Phillip Capital Pte. Ltd.; Int'l, pg. 5846
KING'S HEAD DEVELOPMENT PLC; Int'l, pg. 4170
KINGS HILL ESTATE MANAGEMENT COMPANY LIMITED—See Prologis, Inc.; U.S. Public, pg. 1727
KINGS HILL PROPERTY MANAGEMENT LIMITED—See Prologis, Inc.; U.S. Public, pg. 1727
KINGS HILL RESIDENTIAL ESTATE MANAGEMENT COMPANY LIMITED—See Prologis, Inc.; U.S. Public, pg. 1727
KINGSIGNAL CABLE TECHNOLOGY (GANZHOU) CO.,LTD.—See Kingsignal Technology Co., Ltd.; Int'l, pg. 4175
KINGSIGNAL OPTICAL FIBER & CABLE (GANZHOU) CO.,LTD.—See Kingsignal Technology Co., Ltd.; Int'l, pg. 4175
KINGSIGNAL TECHNOLOGIES (INDIA) PVT. LTD.—See Kingsignal Technology Co., Ltd.; Int'l, pg. 4175
KINGSIGNAL TECHNOLOGY CO., LTD.; Int'l, pg. 4174
KINGSIGNAL TECHNOLOGY (THAILAND) CO., LTD.—See Kingsignal Technology Co., Ltd.; Int'l, pg. 4175
KINGS III OF AMERICA, LLC—See Arcline Investment Management LP; U.S. Private, pg. 314
KINGS INFRA VENTURES LIMITED; Int'l, pg. 4174
KINGS ISLAND COMPANY—See Six Flags Entertainment Corporation; U.S. Public, pg. 1890
KINGS ISLAND PARK LLC—See Six Flags Entertainment Corporation; U.S. Public, pg. 1890
KINGSISLE ENTERTAINMENT, INC.—See Verve Group SE; Int'l, pg. 8176
KINGSLAKE ENGINEERING SYSTEMS (PRIVATE) LIMITED—See Kingslake International Limited; Int'l, pg. 4175
KINGSLAKE ENGINEERING SYSTEMS (PVT) LTD.—See Kingslake International Limited; Int'l, pg. 4175
KINGSLAKE EUROPE BV—See Kingslake International Limited; Int'l, pg. 4175
KINGSLAKE INTERNATIONAL LIMITED; Int'l, pg. 4175
KINGSLAND ENERGY CORPORATION; Int'l, pg. 4175
THE KINGSLAND ENGINEERING CO. LTD—See Haco N.V.; Int'l, pg. 3205
KINGSLAND GLOBAL LTD.; Int'l, pg. 4175
KING'S LANDING LLC—See Independence Realty Trust, Inc.; U.S. Public, pg. 1115
KINGSLAND MINERALS LIMITED; Int'l, pg. 4175
KINGSLEY ASSOCIATES, INC.—See Stone Point Capital LLC; U.S. Private, pg. 3825
KINGSLEY CONSTRUCTORS INC.; U.S. Private, pg. 2311
KINGSLEY EDUGROUP LTD.—See China Maple Leaf Educational Systems Limited; Int'l, pg. 1517
KINGSLEY INTERNATIONAL SDN. BHD.—See China Maple Leaf Educational Systems Limited; Int'l, pg. 1517
KINGSLEY NAPLEY LLP; Int'l, pg. 4175
KING SLIDE TECHNOLOGY (CHINA) CO., LTD.—See King Slide Works Co., Ltd.; Int'l, pg. 4169
KING SLIDE TECHNOLOGY CO., LTD.—See King Slide Works Co., Ltd.; Int'l, pg. 4169
KING SLIDE USA, INC.—See King Slide Works Co., Ltd.; Int'l, pg. 4169
KING SLIDE WORKS CO., LTD.; Int'l, pg. 4169
KINGSMEN BEIJING CO., LTD.—See Kingsmen Creatives Ltd; Int'l, pg. 4175
KINGSMEN CMTI PCL; Int'l, pg. 4175
KINGSMEN CREATIVES LTD; Int'l, pg. 4175
KINGSMEN DESIGN PTE LTD—See Kingsmen Creatives Ltd; Int'l, pg. 4175
KINGSMEN ENVIRONMENTAL GRAPHICS PTE LTD—See Kingsmen Creatives Ltd; Int'l, pg. 4175
KINGSMEN EXHIBITS PTE LTD—See Kingsmen Creatives Ltd; Int'l, pg. 4175
KINGSMEN HONG KONG LTD.—See Kingsmen Creatives Ltd; Int'l, pg. 4175
KINGSMEN MACAU LIMITED—See Kingsmen Creatives Ltd; Int'l, pg. 4175
KINGSMEN MIDDLE EAST LLC—See Kingsmen Creatives Ltd; Int'l, pg. 4175
KINGSMEN OOH-MEDIA PTE. LTD.—See Kingsmen Creatives Ltd; Int'l, pg. 4175
KINGSMEN PROJECTS PTE LTD—See Kingsmen Creatives Ltd; Int'l, pg. 4175
KINGSMEN PROJECTS US—See Kingsmen Creatives Ltd; Int'l, pg. 4175
KINGSMEN RESOURCES LIMITED; Int'l, pg. 4176
KINGSMEN SDN BHD—See Kingsmen Creatives Ltd; Int'l, pg. 4175
KINGSMEN SHANGHAI CO., LTD.—See Kingsmen Creatives Ltd; Int'l, pg. 4175
KINGSMEN (SHENZHEN) CO LTD.—See Kingsmen Creatives Ltd; Int'l, pg. 4175

KINGSMEN SOFTWARE LLC; *U.S. Private*, pg. 2312
KINGSMEN TAIWAN INTERNATIONAL CO. LIMITED—See Kingsmen Creatives Ltd; *Int'l*, pg. 4175
KINGSMEN XPERIENCE, INC.—See Kingsmen Creatives Ltd; *Int'l*, pg. 4175
KING'S METAL FIBER TECHNOLOGIES CO., LTD.—See Tex-Ray Industrial Co., Ltd.; *Int'l*, pg. 7582
KINGSMILL REALTY INC.—See Anheuser-Busch InBev SA/NV; *Int'l*, pg. 465
KINGS NISSAN INC.; *U.S. Private*, pg. 2311
KINGSOAK HOMES LTD.—See Barratt Developments PLC; *Int'l*, pg. 868
KINGSOFT CORPORATION LIMITED; *Int'l*, pg. 4176
KING SOLUTIONS, INC.; *U.S. Private*, pg. 2310
KING SOOPERS INC.—See The Kroger Co.; *U.S. Public*, pg. 2107
KING & SPALDING LLP; *U.S. Private*, pg. 2308
KINGSPAN ACCESS FLOORS HOLDINGS LIMITED—See Kingspan Group PLC; *Int'l*, pg. 4176
KINGSPAN ACCESS FLOORS LIMITED—See Kingspan Group PLC; *Int'l*, pg. 4176
KINGSPAN A.S.—See Kingspan Group PLC; *Int'l*, pg. 4176
KINGSPAN B.V.—See Kingspan Group PLC; *Int'l*, pg. 4176
KINGSPAN CENTURY LIMITED—See Kingspan Group PLC; *Int'l*, pg. 4176
KINGSPAN DOOR COMPONENTS S.A.—See Kingspan Group PLC; *Int'l*, pg. 4176
KINGSPAN D.O.O.—See Kingspan Group PLC; *Int'l*, pg. 4178
KINGSPAN D.O.O.—See Kingspan Group PLC; *Int'l*, pg. 4178
KINGSPAN ENVIRONMENTAL -BELGIUIM—See Kingspan Group PLC; *Int'l*, pg. 4176
KINGSPAN ENVIRONMENTAL-FRANCE—See Kingspan Group PLC; *Int'l*, pg. 4176
KINGSPAN ENVIRONMENTAL LIMITED—See Kingspan Group PLC; *Int'l*, pg. 4176
KINGSPAN ENVIRONMENTAL—See Kingspan Group PLC; *Int'l*, pg. 4176
KINGSPAN ENVIRONMENT SP. Z O.O.—See Kingspan Group PLC; *Int'l*, pg. 4176
KINGSPAN FABRICATIONS—See Kingspan Group PLC; *Int'l*, pg. 4176
KINGSPAN FABRIK LIMITED—See Kingspan Group PLC; *Int'l*, pg. 4176
KINGSPAN FINANCE LTD.—See Kingspan Group PLC; *Int'l*, pg. 4176
KINGSPAN FUNDING EUROPE—See Kingspan Group PLC; *Int'l*, pg. 4176
KINGSPAN FUNDING UK—See Kingspan Group PLC; *Int'l*, pg. 4176
KINGSPAN GMBH—See Kingspan Group PLC; *Int'l*, pg. 4176
KINGSPAN GROUP LIMITED—See Kingspan Group PLC; *Int'l*, pg. 4176
KINGSPAN GROUP PLC; *Int'l*, pg. 4176
KINGSPAN HOLDING BELGIUM N.V.—See Kingspan Group PLC; *Int'l*, pg. 4176
KINGSPAN HOLDING GMBH—See Kingspan Group PLC; *Int'l*, pg. 4176
KINGSPAN HOLDINGS (INSULATION) LIMITED—See Kingspan Group PLC; *Int'l*, pg. 4177
KINGSPAN HOLDINGS (IRL) LIMITED—See Kingspan Group PLC; *Int'l*, pg. 4177
KINGSPAN HOLDINGS NETHERLANDS B.V.—See Kingspan Group PLC; *Int'l*, pg. 4177
KINGSPAN HOLDINGS (OVERSEAS) LIMITED—See Kingspan Group PLC; *Int'l*, pg. 4177
KINGSPAN HOLDINGS PANELS US INC.—See Kingspan Group PLC; *Int'l*, pg. 4177
KINGSPAN HOLDINGS (STRUCTURAL AND OFFSITE) LIMITED—See Kingspan Group PLC; *Int'l*, pg. 4177
KINGSPAN HOLDINGS US INC.—See Kingspan Group PLC; *Int'l*, pg. 4177
KINGSPAN HOT WATER SYSTEMS LIMITED—See Kingspan Group PLC; *Int'l*, pg. 4177
KINGSPAN INDIA PVT. LTD.—See Kingspan Group PLC; *Int'l*, pg. 4177
KINGSPAN INSULATED PANELS INC.—See Kingspan Group PLC; *Int'l*, pg. 4177
KINGSPAN INSULATED PANELS LIMITED—See Kingspan Group PLC; *Int'l*, pg. 4177
KINGSPAN INSULATED PANELS PTY LTD—See Kingspan Group PLC; *Int'l*, pg. 4177
KINGSPAN INSULATION B.V.—See Kingspan Group PLC; *Int'l*, pg. 4177
KINGSPAN INSULATION LIMITED—See Kingspan Group PLC; *Int'l*, pg. 4177
KINGSPAN INSULATION LIMITED—See Kingspan Group PLC; *Int'l*, pg. 4177
KINGSPAN INSULATION PTY LTD—See Kingspan Group PLC; *Int'l*, pg. 4177
KINGSPAN INSULATION SP. Z.O.O—See Kingspan Group PLC; *Int'l*, pg. 4177
KINGSPAN INTERNATIONAL FINANCE LTD.—See Kingspan Group PLC; *Int'l*, pg. 4177
KINGSPAN INVESTMENTS LIMITED—See Kingspan Group PLC; *Int'l*, pg. 4177

KINGSPAN KFT—See Kingspan Group PLC; *Int'l*, pg. 4177
KINGSPAN LIGHT & AIR LLC—See Kingspan Group PLC; *Int'l*, pg. 4177
KINGSPAN LIMITED—See Kingspan Group PLC; *Int'l*, pg. 4177
KINGSPAN LIMITED—See Kingspan Group PLC; *Int'l*, pg. 4177
KINGSPAN LIMITED—See Kingspan Group PLC; *Int'l*, pg. 4177
KINGSPAN LLC—See Kingspan Group PLC; *Int'l*, pg. 4177
KINGSPAN LVIV TOV—See Kingspan Group PLC; *Int'l*, pg. 4177
KINGSPAN MILJO AS—See Kingspan Group PLC; *Int'l*, pg. 4177
KINGSPAN N.V.—See Kingspan Group PLC; *Int'l*, pg. 4177
KINGSPAN OFF-SITE LTD.—See Kingspan Group PLC; *Int'l*, pg. 4177
KINGSPAN OU—See Kingspan Group PLC; *Int'l*, pg. 4177
KINGSPAN PANELS LIMITED—See Kingspan Group PLC; *Int'l*, pg. 4177
KINGSPAN PTE LIMITED—See Kingspan Group PLC; *Int'l*, pg. 4177
KINGSPAN RENEWABLES LIMITED—See Kingspan Group PLC; *Int'l*, pg. 4177
KINGSPAN RENEWABLES LTD. - GERMANY—See Kingspan Group PLC; *Int'l*, pg. 4177
KINGSPAN RENEWABLES LTD - POLAND—See Kingspan Group PLC; *Int'l*, pg. 4177
KINGSPAN RENEWABLES SRL—See Kingspan Group PLC; *Int'l*, pg. 4177
KINGSPAN SARL—See Kingspan Group PLC; *Int'l*, pg. 4177
KINGSPAN SIA—See Kingspan Group PLC; *Int'l*, pg. 4177
KINGSPAN SOLAR INC—See Kingspan Group PLC; *Int'l*, pg. 4177
KINGSPAN SP.Z O.O.—See Kingspan Group PLC; *Int'l*, pg. 4177
KINGSPAN S.R.L.—See Kingspan Group PLC; *Int'l*, pg. 4177
KINGSPAN S.R.O.—See Kingspan Group PLC; *Int'l*, pg. 4178
KINGSPAN SUELO TECHNICOS S.L.—See Kingspan Group PLC; *Int'l*, pg. 4177
KINGSPAN TAREC INDUSTRIAL INSULATION LTD.—See Kingspan Group PLC; *Int'l*, pg. 4177
KINGSPAN TEK GMBH—See Kingspan Group PLC; *Int'l*, pg. 4177
KINGSPORT BOOK, INC.—See Signet LLC; *U.S. Private*, pg. 3650
KINGSPORT POWER COMPANY—See American Electric Power Company, Inc.; *U.S. Public*, pg. 100
KINGS READY MIX, INC.—See Vulcan Materials Company; *U.S. Public*, pg. 2314
KING'S RESTAURANT & SUPERMARKET, INC.; *U.S. Private*, pg. 2310
KINGSROSE MINING LIMITED; *Int'l*, pg. 4179
KING'S SAFETYWEAR LIMITED—See Honeywell International Inc.; *U.S. Public*, pg. 1049
KINGS SEAFOOD COMPANY; *U.S. Private*, pg. 2311
KING'S SHOE MANUFACTURING PTE. LTD.—See Honeywell International Inc.; *U.S. Public*, pg. 1049
KINGS SUPER MARKETS, INC.—See MTN Capital Partners LLC; *U.S. Private*, pg. 2809
KINGS SUPER MARKETS, INC.—See TPG Capital, L.P.; *U.S. Public*, pg. 2168
KINGSTAR CONTRACTS—See Robore Holdings Ltd.; *Int'l*, pg. 6371
KINGSTATE ELECTRONICS CORPORATION; *Int'l*, pg. 4179
KING STEEL, INC.; *U.S. Private*, pg. 2310
KINGSTON BRIDGE ENGINEERING PTY LIMITED—See Fletcher Building Limited; *Int'l*, pg. 2700
KINGSTON COGEN LIMITED PARTNERSHIP—See Northland Power Inc.; *Int'l*, pg. 5446
KINGSTON COLLECTION—See Pyramid Management Group, Inc.; *U.S. Private*, pg. 3310
KINGSTON COMPANIES; *U.S. Private*, pg. 2312
KINGSTON DISTRIBUTION CENTER—See Corteva, Inc.; *U.S. Public*, pg. 584
KINGSTON DODGE CHRYSLER (1980) LTD.; *Int'l*, pg. 4179
KINGSTONE COMPANIES, INC.; *U.S. Public*, pg. 1234
KING STONE ENERGY GROUP LIMITED; *Int'l*, pg. 4169
KINGSTONE ENERGY TECHNOLOGY CORPORATION—See Wah Lee Industrial Corp.; *Int'l*, pg. 8329
KINGSTON ENVIRONMENTAL SERVICES, INC.; *U.S. Private*, pg. 2312
KINGSTON FINANCIAL GROUP LIMITED; *Int'l*, pg. 4179
KINGSTON FREEPORT TERMINAL LTD.—See CMA CGM S.A.; *Int'l*, pg. 1668
KINGSTON INFORMATION SERVICES LTD.—See Macquarie Group Limited; *Int'l*, pg. 4626
KINGSTON LOGISTICS CENTER LTD—See Israel Corporation Ltd.; *Int'l*, pg. 3823
KINGSTON MEDICAL SUPPLIES (PTE.) LTD.—See Fiamma Holdings Berhad; *Int'l*, pg. 2650

KINGSTON MINING, INC.—See Alpha Natural Resources, Inc.; *U.S. Private*, pg. 199
KINGSTON OIL SUPPLY CORP.—See PJSC Lukoil; *Int'l*, pg. 5882
KINGSTON PROCESSING, INC.—See Alpha Natural Resources, Inc.; *U.S. Private*, pg. 199
KINGSTON PROPANE—See UGI Corporation; *U.S. Public*, pg. 2221
KINGSTON PROPERTIES LIMITED; *Int'l*, pg. 4180
KINGSTON REPORTER—See Gannett Co., Inc.; *U.S. Public*, pg. 902
KINGSTON RESOURCES LIMITED; *Int'l*, pg. 4180
KINGSTON SALES CORPORATION—See Paychex, Inc.; *U.S. Public*, pg. 1655
KINGSTON TECHNOLOGY COMPANY, INC.; *U.S. Private*, pg. 2312
KINGSTON WHARVES LIMITED; *Int'l*, pg. 4180
KINGSTON WHIG-STANDARD—See Chatham Asset Management, LLC; *U.S. Private*, pg. 861
KING'S TOWN BANK; *Int'l*, pg. 4170
KING'S TOWN CONSTRUCTION CO., LTD.; *Int'l*, pg. 4170
KINGS TOYOTA—See Kenwood Dealer Group, Inc.; *U.S. Private*, pg. 2289
KING STREET CAPITAL MANAGEMENT, L.P.; *U.S. Private*, pg. 2310
KING STREET REAL ESTATE GP, L.L.C; *U.S. Private*, pg. 2310
KING STURGE MANAGEMENT SPRL—See Jones Lang LaSalle Incorporated; *U.S. Public*, pg. 1205
KINGSVIEW LLC; *U.S. Private*, pg. 2312
KINGSVIEW MINERALS LTD.; *Int'l*, pg. 4180
KINGSVILLE PUBLISHING COMPANY—See King Ranch, Inc.; *U.S. Private*, pg. 2310
KINGSVILLE STAMPING LTD.; *Int'l*, pg. 4180
KINGSWAY AMERICA INC.—See Kingsway Financial Services Inc.; *U.S. Public*, pg. 1234
KINGSWAY AMIGO INSURANCE COMPANY—See Kingsway Financial Services Inc.; *U.S. Public*, pg. 1234
KINGSWAY ARMS MANAGEMENT SERVICES INC.; *Int'l*, pg. 4180
KINGSWAY CHARITIES, INC.; *U.S. Private*, pg. 2312
KINGSWAY ENTERPRISES INC.; *U.S. Private*, pg. 2312
KINGSWAY FINANCIAL ASSESSMENTS PTY LTD—See Equifax Inc.; *U.S. Public*, pg. 786
KINGSWAY FINANCIAL SERVICES GROUP LIMITED—See Sunwah Internatiional Limited; *Int'l*, pg. 7328
KINGSWAY FINANCIAL SERVICES INC.; *U.S. Public*, pg. 1234
KINGS WAY HOMES INC.; *U.S. Private*, pg. 2311
KINGSWAY INSURANCE SERVICES LIMITED—See Brown & Brown, Inc.; *U.S. Public*, pg. 401
KINGSWAY REINSURANCE CORPORATION—See Kingsway Financial Services Inc.; *U.S. Public*, pg. 1234
KINGSWAY TRANSPORT—See TFI International Inc.; *Int'l*, pg. 7586
KINGSWOOD ACQUISITION CORP.; *U.S. Public*, pg. 1235
KINGSWOOD CAPITAL MANAGEMENT LLC; *U.S. Private*, pg. 2312
KINGSWOOD HOLDINGS LTD.; *Int'l*, pg. 4180
KING SYSTEMS CORPORATION—See Ambu A/S; *Int'l*, pg. 416
KING TACO RESTAURANT INC.; *U.S. Private*, pg. 2310
KING TAI TECHNOLOGY VIETNAM CO. LTD.—See King Chou Marine Technology Co., Ltd.; *Int'l*, pg. 4168
KING TELESERVICES LLC—See Skyview Capital, LLC; *U.S. Public*, pg. 3686
KING TESTER CORPORATION—See Salt Creek Capital Management, LLC; *U.S. Private*, pg. 3533
KING TOWER INC.—See Harsch Investment Corp.; *U.S. Private*, pg. 1872
KING VENTURE INC.; *U.S. Private*, pg. 2310
KING WAI CAPITAL LIMITED—See King Wai Group (Thailand) Public Company Limited; *Int'l*, pg. 4170
KING WAI GROUP (THAILAND) PUBLIC COMPANY LIMITED; *Int'l*, pg. 4169
KING WAI INSURANCE PUBLIC COMPANY LIMITED—See King Wai Group (Thailand) Public Company Limited; *Int'l*, pg. 4170
KING WAN CONSTRUCTION PTE LTD—See King Wan Corporation Limited; *Int'l*, pg. 4170
KING WAN CORPORATION LIMITED; *Int'l*, pg. 4170
KING WARE(CHONGQING) ELECTRONICS CO., LTD.—See Key Ware Electronics Co., Ltd.; *Int'l*, pg. 4145
KINGWAYTEK TECHNOLOGY CO., LTD.; *Int'l*, pg. 4180
KINGWELL GROUP LIMITED; *Int'l*, pg. 4180
KINGWEST RESOURCES LIMITED—See Brightstar Resources Limited; *Int'l*, pg. 1163
KING WIRE INC.; *U.S. Private*, pg. 2310
KINGWISOFT TECHNOLOGY GROUP COMPANY LIMITED; *Int'l*, pg. 4180
KINGWOOD ATHLETIC CLUB INC.—See Starmark Management Holdings LLC; *U.S. Private*, pg. 3787
KINGWOOD COVE GOLF CLUB—See OnCourse Strategies; *U.S. Private*, pg. 3019

COMPANY NAME INDEX

KINGWOOD MEDICAL CENTER—See HCA Healthcare, Inc.; *U.S. Public*, pg. 1000
KINGWOOD MEMORIAL PARK ASSOCIATION—See Axar Capital Management L.P.; *U.S. Private*, pg. 411
KINGWOOD MINING COMPANY, LLC—See Alpha Natural Resources, Inc.; *U.S. Private*, pg. 199
KINGWOOD PERSONNEL—See Murray Resources, Ltd.; *U.S. Private*, pg. 2816
KINGWOOD PHYSICAL THERAPY, LTD.—See U.S. Physical Therapy, Inc.; *U.S. Public*, pg. 2215
KINGWOOD SURGERY CENTER, LLC—See HCA Healthcare, Inc.; *U.S. Public*, pg. 1000
KINGWORLD MEDICINE HEALTHCARE LIMITED—See Kingworld Medicines Group Limited; *Int'l*, pg. 4180
KINGWORLD MEDICINES GROUP LIMITED; *Int'l*, pg. 4180
KING WORLD PRODUCTIONS, INC.—See National Amusements, Inc.; *U.S. Private*, pg. 2840
KINGWORLD RESOURCES LIMITED—See RH Petrogas Limited; *Int'l*, pg. 6319
KING WORLDWIDE INVESTOR RELATIONS—See Pacific Equity Partners Pty. Limited; *Int'l*, pg. 5689
KING YUAN ELECTRONICS CO., LTD. - CHU-NAN FACTORY—See King Yuan Electronics Co., Ltd.; *Int'l*, pg. 4170
KING YUAN ELECTRONICS CO., LTD.; *Int'l*, pg. 4170
KING YUAN ELECTRONICS CO., LTD. - SUZHOU FACTORY—See King Yuan Electronics Co., Ltd.; *Int'l*, pg. 4170
KING YUAN ELECTRONICS CO., LTD. - TONGLUO FACTORY—See King Yuan Electronics Co., Ltd.; *Int'l*, pg. 4170
KINH BAC CITY DEVELOPMENT HOLDING CORPORATION; *Int'l*, pg. 4180
KINIK COMPANY; *Int'l*, pg. 4180
KINIKSA PHARMACEUTICALS CORP.—See Kiniksa Pharmaceuticals, Ltd.; *Int'l*, pg. 4181
KINIKSA PHARMACEUTICALS, LTD.; *Int'l*, pg. 4180
KINISIS TRAVEL & TOURS INC.—See Top Kinisis Travel Public Ltd; *Int'l*, pg. 7813
KINJIRO CO., LTD.; *Int'l*, pg. 4181
KINKAI YUSEN LOGISTICS CO., LTD.—See Nippon Yusen Kabushiki Kaisha; *Int'l*, pg. 5358
KINK-FM—See Alpha Media LLC; *U.S. Private*, pg. 198
KINKI ABRADANT INDUSTRY CO., LTD.—See Nippon Light Metal Holdings Company, Ltd.; *Int'l*, pg. 5323
KINKI CONCRETE SALES COMPANY, LIMITED—See Kinden Corporation; *Int'l*, pg. 4166
KINKI FREIGHT SERVICE COMPANY, INCORPORATED—See Kinden Corporation; *Int'l*, pg. 4166
KINKI KENMAZAI KOGYO CO., LTD.—See Nippon Light Metal Holdings Company, Ltd.; *Int'l*, pg. 5323
KINKI MATSUSHITA TECHNICAL SERVICE—See Panasonic Holdings Corporation; *Int'l*, pg. 5717
KINKI MEIHAN CO., LTD.—See Meiji Holdings Co., Ltd.; *Int'l*, pg. 4800
KINKI NIPPON RAILWAY CO., LTD.—See Kintetsu Group Holdings Co.,Ltd.; *Int'l*, pg. 4183
KINKI OIL TRANSPORTATION CO., LTD.—See Japan Oil Transportation Co., Ltd.; *Int'l*, pg. 3899
KINKI OSAKA SHINYO HOSHO CO., LTD.—See Resona Holdings, Inc.; *Int'l*, pg. 6297
KINKI RYOJU ESTATE CO., LTD.—See Mitsubishi Heavy Industries, Ltd.; *Int'l*, pg. 4961
THE KINKI SHARYO CO., LTD.—See Kintetsu Group Holdings Co.,Ltd.; *Int'l*, pg. 4184
KINKI TRANSPORT & TERMINAL CO., LTD.—See Azuma Shipping Co., Ltd.; *Int'l*, pg. 782
KIN-KO ACE STORES INC.; *U.S. Private*, pg. 2306
KINKO OPTICAL CO., LTD.; *Int'l*, pg. 4181
KINKO SERVICE CO.,LTD.—See Mitsubishi Logistics Corporation; *Int'l*, pg. 4962
KINKO'S JAPAN CO., LTD.—See Konica Minolta, Inc.; *Int'l*, pg. 4257
KINLOCH ANDERSON LTD.—See Wonpung Mulsan Co., Ltd.; *Int'l*, pg. 8449
KIN LONG CONSTRUCTION MATERIALS TRADING L.L.C—See Guangdong Kinlong Hardware Prdcts Co., Ltd.; *Int'l*, pg. 3157
KIN LONG HARDWARE (INDIA) PRIVATE LIMITED—See Guangdong Kinlong Hardware Prdcts Co., Ltd.; *Int'l*, pg. 3157
KIN LONG HARDWARE (THAILAND) COMPANY LIMITED—See Guangdong Kinlong Hardware Prdcts Co., Ltd.; *Int'l*, pg. 3157
KIN LONG INDUSTRIAL (PHILIPPINES) INC.—See Guangdong Kinlong Hardware Prdcts Co., Ltd.; *Int'l*, pg. 3157
KIN LONG (MALAYSIA) SDN. BHD.—See Guangdong Kinlong Hardware Prdcts Co., Ltd.; *Int'l*, pg. 3157
KINLY HOLDING B.V.; *Int'l*, pg. 4181
KINNARPS AB; *Int'l*, pg. 4181
KINNARPS AS—See Kinnarps AB; *Int'l*, pg. 4181
KINNARPS, A. S.—See Kinnarps AB; *Int'l*, pg. 4181
KINNARPS A/S—See Kinnarps AB; *Int'l*, pg. 4181
KINNARPS DO BRASIL LTDA.—See Kinnarps AB; *Int'l*, pg. 4181
KINNARPS ITALIA SRL—See Kinnarps AB; *Int'l*, pg. 4181

KINNARPS LTDA—See Kinnarps AB; *Int'l*, pg. 4181
KINNARPS NEDERLAND BV—See Kinnarps AB; *Int'l*, pg. 4181
KINNARPS OF SWEDEN CO. LLC—See Kinnarps AB; *Int'l*, pg. 4181
KINNARPS OY—See Kinnarps AB; *Int'l*, pg. 4181
KINNARPS POLSKA SP. Z O. O.—See Kinnarps AB; *Int'l*, pg. 4181
KINNARPS PRODUCTION AB—See Kinnarps AB; *Int'l*, pg. 4181
KINNARPS PROJECT SOLUTIONS LLC—See Kinnarps AB; *Int'l*, pg. 4181
KINNARPS PROJECT SOLUTIONS—See Kinnarps AB; *Int'l*, pg. 4181
KINNARPS S.A. DE C.V—See Kinnarps AB; *Int'l*, pg. 4181
KINNARPS SAMAS GMBH—See Kinnarps AB; *Int'l*, pg. 4181
KINNARPS S.A.—See Kinnarps AB; *Int'l*, pg. 4181
KINNARPS, SPOL. S R.O.—See Kinnarps AB; *Int'l*, pg. 4181
KINNARPS SRL—See Kinnarps AB; *Int'l*, pg. 4181
KINNARPS (UK) LTD—See Kinnarps AB; *Int'l*, pg. 4181
KINNARPS UKRAINE LLC—See Kinnarps AB; *Int'l*, pg. 4181
KINNARPS USA INC.—See Kinnarps AB; *Int'l*, pg. 4181
KINNATE BIOPHARMA INC.—See XOMA Corporation; *U.S. Public*, pg. 2391
KINNEBROOK MOBILE HOME ASSOCIATES LP—See UMH Properties, Inc.; *U.S. Public*, pg. 2224
KINNERTON (CONFECTIONERY) AUSTRALIA PTY LIMITED—See Zertus GmbH; *Int'l*, pg. 8639
KINNERTON (CONFECTIONERY) COMPANY LIMITED—See Zertus GmbH; *Int'l*, pg. 8639
KINNEVIK AB; *Int'l*, pg. 4181
KINNEVIK CAPITAL LTD.—See Kinnevik AB; *Int'l*, pg. 4181
KINNEVIK ONLINE VENTURES AB—See Kinnevik AB; *Int'l*, pg. 4181
KINNEY BONDED WAREHOUSE INC.; *U.S. Private*, pg. 2313
KINNEY DRUGS INC.; *U.S. Private*, pg. 2313
KINNEY MOTORS; *U.S. Private*, pg. 2313
KINNEY WEST 83RD ST., INC.—See Eldridge Industries LLC; *U.S. Private*, pg. 1351
KINNICKINNIC REALTY CO.; *U.S. Private*, pg. 2313
KINNO HOSHI ENGINEERING CO., LTD.—See Inoue Rubber (Thailand) Public Company Limited; *Int'l*, pg. 3715
KINNSER SOFTWARE, INC.; *U.S. Private*, pg. 2313
KINO.DK A/S—See Egmont Fonden; *Int'l*, pg. 2325
KINOE TERMINAL CO., INC.—See Mitsubishi Gas Chemical Company, Inc.; *Int'l*, pg. 4949
KINOHELD GMBH—See CTS Eventim AG & Co. KGAA; *Int'l*, pg. 1873
KINO INTERNATIONAL CORP.; *U.S. Private*, pg. 2313
KINOPLEX SP. Z O.O—See Agora S.A.; *Int'l*, pg. 212
KINO POLSKA TV S.A.; *Int'l*, pg. 4182
KINOTON DIGITAL SOLUTIONS GMBH; *Int'l*, pg. 4182
KINOVATE LIFE SCIENCES, INC.—See Nitto Denko Corporation; *Int'l*, pg. 5384
KINOVO PLC; *Int'l*, pg. 4182
KINPAI CO., LTD.—See Osaka Gas Co., Ltd.; *Int'l*, pg. 5645
KINPAK, INC.—See OneWater Marine Inc.; *U.S. Public*, pg. 1604
KIN PANG HOLDINGS LIMITED; *Int'l*, pg. 4164
KINPLEX CORP.; *U.S. Private*, pg. 2313
KINPO ELECTRONICS, INC.; *Int'l*, pg. 4182
KIN POMPENTECHNIEK B.V.—See Indutrade AB; *Int'l*, pg. 3679
KINRARA GOLF CLUB SDN. BHD.—See S P Setia Berhad; *Int'l*, pg. 6443
KINRAY, INC.—See Cardinal Health, Inc.; *U.S. Public*, pg. 434
KINRO INVESTMENTS, INC.—See Rollins, Inc.; *U.S. Public*, pg. 1809
KINROSS BRASIL MINERACAO S.A.—See Kinross Gold Corporation; *Int'l*, pg. 4182
KINROSS GOLD CORPORATION; *Int'l*, pg. 4182
KINSALE BROKERS LIMITED—See Enstar Group Limited; *Int'l*, pg. 2449
KINSALE CAPITAL GROUP, INC.; *U.S. Public*, pg. 1235
KINSEI MATEC CO., LTD.—See INDUS Holding AG; *Int'l*, pg. 3664
KINSELLA MEDIA, LLC—See Exela Technologies, Inc.; *U.S. Public*, pg. 806
KINSEL MOTORS INC.; *U.S. Private*, pg. 2313
KINSETH HOSPITALITY COMPANY; *U.S. Private*, pg. 2313
KINSEY TECHNICAL SERVICES, INC.—See Science Applications International Corporation; *U.S. Public*, pg. 1848
KIN SHING HOLDINGS LIMITED; *Int'l*, pg. 4164
KINSHOFER APONOX OY—See Carl Bennet AB; *Int'l*, pg. 1332
KINSHOFER CZ S.R.O.—See Carl Bennet AB; *Int'l*, pg. 1332
KINSHOFER FRANCE S.A.R.L—See Carl Bennet AB; *Int'l*, pg. 1332

KINSHOFER GMBH—See Carl Bennet AB; *Int'l*, pg. 1332
KINSHOFER UK LTD.—See Carl Bennet AB; *Int'l*, pg. 1332
KINSLEY CONSTRUCTION INC.; *U.S. Private*, pg. 2313
KINSLEY GROUP, INC.; *U.S. Private*, pg. 2313
KINSLEY INDUSTRIAL—See Kinsley Construction Inc.; *U.S. Private*, pg. 2313
KINSLEY MANUFACTURING-STEEL FABRICATION & ERECTION—See Kinsley Construction Inc.; *U.S. Private*, pg. 2313
KINSMEDIC SDN. BHD.—See Fiamma Holdings Berhad; *Int'l*, pg. 2650
KINSOLE PTY LTD—See Hancock & Gore Ltd.; *Int'l*, pg. 3242
K-INSTITUUTTI OY—See Kesko Corporation; *Int'l*, pg. 4142
KINSUS INTERCONNECT TECHNOLOGY CORP.; *Int'l*, pg. 4182
KINSUS INTERCONNECT TECHNOLOGY CORP. - TAOYUAN FACTORY—See Kinsus Interconnect Technology Corp.; *Int'l*, pg. 4182
KINSUS INTERCONNECT TECHNOLOGY CORP. - XINGFENG FACTORY—See Kinsus Interconnect Technology Corp.; *Int'l*, pg. 4182
KINSUS SUZHOU CORP.—See Kinsus Interconnect Technology Corp.; *Int'l*, pg. 4182
KINTARA THERAPEUTICS, INC.; *U.S. Public*, pg. 1235
KINTA SUNWAY RESORT SDN. BHD.—See Sunway Berhad; *Int'l*, pg. 7328
KINTAVAR EXPLORATION INC.; *Int'l*, pg. 4182
KINTEC S.A.—See Siemens Aktiengesellschaft; *Int'l*, pg. 6887
KINTEC-SOLUTION GMBH—See Leggett & Platt, Incorporated; *U.S. Public*, pg. 1302
KINTETSU DEPARTMENT STORE CO., LTD.; *Int'l*, pg. 4182
KINTETSU ENTERPRISES COMPANY OF AMERICA—See Kintetsu Group Holdings Co.,Ltd.; *Int'l*, pg. 4183
KINTETSU GROUP HOLDINGS CO.,LTD.; *Int'l*, pg. 4182
KINTETSU INTERMODAL (TAIWAN), INC.—See Kintetsu Group Holdings Co.,Ltd.; *Int'l*, pg. 4183
KINTETSU INTERNATIONAL EXPRESS (U.S.A.), INC.—See Kintetsu Group Holdings Co.,Ltd.; *Int'l*, pg. 4183
KINTETSU MIYAKO HOTELS INTERNATIONAL, INC.—See Kintetsu Group Holdings Co.,Ltd.; *Int'l*, pg. 4183
KINTETSU RAILCAR ENGINEERING CO., LTD.—See Kintetsu Group Holdings Co.,Ltd.; *Int'l*, pg. 4183
KINTETSU TAXI COMPANY LIMITED—See Kintetsu Group Holdings Co.,Ltd.; *Int'l*, pg. 4183
KINTETSU WORLD EXPRESS (AUSTRALIA) PTY. LTD.—See Kintetsu Group Holdings Co.,Ltd.; *Int'l*, pg. 4183
KINTETSU WORLD EXPRESS (BENELUX) B.V.—See Kintetsu Group Holdings Co.,Ltd.; *Int'l*, pg. 4183
KINTETSU WORLD EXPRESS (DEUTSCHLAND) GMBH—See Kintetsu Group Holdings Co.,Ltd.; *Int'l*, pg. 4183
KINTETSU WORLD EXPRESS (FRANCE) S.A.—See Kintetsu Group Holdings Co.,Ltd.; *Int'l*, pg. 4183
KINTETSU WORLD EXPRESS (H.K.) LTD.—See Kintetsu Group Holdings Co.,Ltd.; *Int'l*, pg. 4183
KINTETSU WORLD EXPRESS, INC.—See Kintetsu Group Holdings Co.,Ltd.; *Int'l*, pg. 4183
KINTETSU WORLD EXPRESS (MALAYSIA) SDN. BHD.—See Kintetsu Group Holdings Co.,Ltd.; *Int'l*, pg. 4183
KINTETSU WORLD EXPRESS (TAIWAN), INC.—See Kintetsu Group Holdings Co.,Ltd.; *Int'l*, pg. 4183
KINTETSU WORLD EXPRESS (THAILAND) CO., LTD.—See Kintetsu Group Holdings Co.,Ltd.; *Int'l*, pg. 4183
KINTETSU WORLD EXPRESS (U.S.A.), INC.—See Kintetsu Group Holdings Co.,Ltd.; *Int'l*, pg. 4183
KINTIPS LIMITED—See Ahsay Backup Software Development Company Limited; *Int'l*, pg. 226
THE KINTOCK GROUP; *U.S. Private*, pg. 4065
KINTOR PHARMACEUTICAL (BEIJING) CO., LTD.—See Kintor Pharmaceutical Limited; *Int'l*, pg. 4184
KINTOR PHARMACEUTICAL LIMITED; *Int'l*, pg. 4184
KINTOR PHARMACEUTICALS HONG KONG LIMITED—See Kintor Pharmaceutical Limited; *Int'l*, pg. 4184
KINTOR PHARMACEUTICALS INC.—See Kintor Pharmaceutical Limited; *Int'l*, pg. 4184
KINUGAWA BRAKE PARTS CO., LTD.—See Development Bank of Japan, Inc.; *Int'l*, pg. 2088
KINUGAWA KORIYAMA CO., LTD.—See Development Bank of Japan, Inc.; *Int'l*, pg. 2088
KINUGAWA OITA CO., LTD.—See Development Bank of Japan, Inc.; *Int'l*, pg. 2088
KINUGAWA RUBBER INDUSTRIAL CO., LTD.—See Development Bank of Japan, Inc.; *Int'l*, pg. 2088
KINUTA FLOWER AUCTION CO., LTD.—See Aucnet Inc.; *Int'l*, pg. 700
KINVEY LLC—See Progress Software Corporation; *U.S. Public*, pg. 1725

KINTOR PHARMACEUTICAL LIMITED
CORPORATE AFFILIATIONS

KIN WAI TECHNOLOGY LTD.—See WE Components Pte. Ltd.; *Int'l*, pg. 8362
KIN WING FOUNDATIONS LIMITED—See Chinney Alliance Group Limited; *Int'l*, pg. 1570
KINWONG ELECTRONIC (HONGKONG) LTD.—See Shenzhen Kinwong Electronic Co.,Ltd.; *Int'l*, pg. 6816
KINWONG ELECTRONIC TECHNOLOGY (LONGCHUAN) CO., LTD.—See Shenzhen Kinwong Electronic Co.,Ltd.; *Int'l*, pg. 6816
KINX, INC.; *Int'l*, pg. 4184
KINYARA SUGAR WORKS LTD.; *Int'l*, pg. 4184
KIN YAT HOLDINGS LIMITED; *Int'l*, pg. 4164
KINYO EUROPE GMBH—See Kinyosha Co., Ltd.; *Int'l*, pg. 4184
KINYO GERMANY GMBH—See Kinyosha Co., Ltd.; *Int'l*, pg. 4184
KINYOSHA CO., LTD. - IWAMA PLANT—See Kinyosha Co., Ltd.; *Int'l*, pg. 4184
KINYOSHA CO., LTD. - MINORI PLANT—See Kinyosha Co., Ltd.; *Int'l*, pg. 4184
KINYOSHA CO., LTD. - SHIGA PLANT—See Kinyosha Co., Ltd.; *Int'l*, pg. 4184
KINYOSHA CO., LTD.; *Int'l*, pg. 4184
KINYOSHA CO., LTD. - TAKEHARA PLANT—See Kinyosha Co., Ltd.; *Int'l*, pg. 4184
KINYOSHA FRANCE SAS—See Kinyosha Co., Ltd.; *Int'l*, pg. 4184
KINYOSHA (HK) CO., LTD.—See Kinyosha Co., Ltd.; *Int'l*, pg. 4184
KINYOSHA IBERICA S.L.—See Kinyosha Co., Ltd.; *Int'l*, pg. 4184
KINYOSHA KANTO SALES CO., LTD.—See Kinyosha Co., Ltd.; *Int'l*, pg. 4184
KINYOSHA PRINTING CO., LTD.—See Kosaido Holdings Co., Ltd.; *Int'l*, pg. 4290
KINYOSHA (SHENZHEN) CO., LTD.—See Kinyosha Co., Ltd.; *Int'l*, pg. 4184
KINYOSHA (THAILAND) CO., LTD.—See Kinyosha Co., Ltd.; *Int'l*, pg. 4184
KINYOSHA VIETNAM CO., LTD.—See Kinyosha Co., Ltd.; *Int'l*, pg. 4184
KINYO SUPPLY CO.,LTD.—See Kinyosha Co., Ltd.; *Int'l*, pg. 4184
KINYO UK LTD.—See Kinyosha Co., Ltd.; *Int'l*, pg. 4184
KINYO VIRGINIA, INC.—See Kinyosha Co., Ltd.; *Int'l*, pg. 4184
KINZIE CAPITAL PARTNERS LP; *U.S. Private*, pg. 2313
KIOCL LIMITED; *Int'l*, pg. 4184
KIOLBASSA; *U.S. Private*, pg. 2313
KIONA SP. Z O.O.—See Carel Industries S.p.A.; *Int'l*, pg. 1324
KIONA VINEYARDS & WINERY; *U.S. Private*, pg. 2313
KION GROUP AG—See KKR & Co. Inc.; *U.S. Public*, pg. 1254
KION GROUP AG—See The Goldman Sachs Group, Inc.; *U.S. Public*, pg. 2078
KIONIX, INC.—See ROHM Co., Ltd.; *Int'l*, pg. 6385
KION NORTH AMERICA CORPORATION—See KKR & Co. Inc.; *U.S. Public*, pg. 1255
KION NORTH AMERICA CORPORATION—See The Goldman Sachs Group, Inc.; *U.S. Public*, pg. 2079
KIORA PHARMACEUTICALS, INC.; *U.S. Public*, pg. 1235
KIOR, INC.; *U.S. Private*, pg. 2313
KIORITZ CORPORATION—See Yamabiko Corporation; *Int'l*, pg. 8547
KIOSK EMBEDDED SYSTEMS GMBH—See Posiflex Technology Inc.; *Int'l*, pg. 5938
KIOSK INFORMATION SYSTEMS, INC.—See Posiflex Technology Inc.; *Int'l*, pg. 5938
KIOSK MEDICINE KENTUCKY, LLC—See The Kroger Co.; *U.S. Public*, pg. 2108
KIOS S.A.—See Quinenco S.A.; *Int'l*, pg. 6164
KIOTI GOLF CO., LTD.—See Daedong Corporation; *Int'l*, pg. 1906
KIP-CRAFT INCORPORATED; *U.S. Private*, pg. 2314
KIPER DEVELOPMENT, INC.; *U.S. Private*, pg. 2314
KIPLEPAY SDN. BHD.—See Green Packet Berhad; *Int'l*, pg. 3072
KIPLE SDN. BHD.—See Green Packet Berhad; *Int'l*, pg. 3072
KIPLINGERS PERSONAL FINANCE—See Future plc; *Int'l*, pg. 2857
THE KIPLINGER WASHINGTON EDITORS, INC.—See Future plc; *Int'l*, pg. 2857
KIPLIN METALS INC.; *Int'l*, pg. 4184
KIP MASTER JSC—See KAMAZ Publicly Traded Company; *Int'l*, pg. 4060
KIP MCGRATH EDUCATION CENTRES LTD; *Int'l*, pg. 4184
KIPOINT SPA—See Poste Italiane S.p.A.; *Int'l*, pg. 5939
KIPP & ZONEN B.V.—See Pic Investment Group Inc.; *Int'l*, pg. 5859
KIPP & ZONEN FRANCE S.A.R.L—See Pic Investment Group Inc.; *Int'l*, pg. 5859
KIP REAL ESTATE INVESTMENT TRUST; *Int'l*, pg. 4184
KIPS CO., LTD.; *Int'l*, pg. 4184
KIPSU, INC.; *U.S. Private*, pg. 2314
KIQ X INDUSTRIES INC.—See Kelso Technologies Inc.; *Int'l*, pg. 4122

KIRACA HOLDING A.S.; *Int'l*, pg. 4184
KIRA, INC.—See Tlingit Haida Tribal Business Corporation; *U.S. Private*, pg. 4179
KIRALYFI ES TARSA BT.—See PHOENIX Pharmahandel GmbH & Co. KG; *Int'l*, pg. 5854
KIRAMI OY—See Harvia Oyj; *Int'l*, pg. 3281
KIRAN PRINT PACK LTD.; *Int'l*, pg. 4185
KIRAN SYNTEX LIMITED; *Int'l*, pg. 4185
KIRAN VYAPAR LTD.—See Maharaja Shree Umaid Mills Ltd.; *Int'l*, pg. 4644
KIRAYAKA BANK, LTD.—See Jimoto Holdings, Inc.; *Int'l*, pg. 3964
KIRAZ 1 GAYRIMENKUL YATIRZM DANZSMANLIGI A.S.—See ESAS Holding A.S.; *Int'l*, pg. 2501
KIRBERG ROOFING INC.; *U.S. Private*, pg. 2314
KIRBY AGRI INC. - KIRBY AGRI INGREDIENTS FACILITY—See Kirby Agri Inc.; *U.S. Private*, pg. 2314
KIRBY AGRI INC.; *U.S. Private*, pg. 2314
KIRBY AGRI SERVICES—See Kirby Agri Inc.; *U.S. Private*, pg. 2314
KIRBY BATES ASSOCIATES, INC.—See Jackson Healthcare, LLC; *U.S. Private*, pg. 2177
KIRBY BUILDING SYSTEMS, INC.—See Nucor Corporation; *U.S. Public*, pg. 1553
KIRBY CORPORATION; *U.S. Public*, pg. 1235
KIRBY ENGINE SYSTEMS, INC.—See Kirby Corporation; *U.S. Public*, pg. 1235
KIRBY FOODS INC.; *U.S. Private*, pg. 2314
KIRBY INLAND MARINE, LP—See Kirby Corporation; *U.S. Public*, pg. 1235
KIRBY INLAND MARINE—See Kirby Corporation; *U.S. Public*, pg. 1235
KIRBY KANOY & ASSOCIATES, INC.; *U.S. Private*, pg. 2314
KIRBY LESTER, LLC—See Levine Leichtman Capital Partners, LLC; *U.S. Private*, pg. 2435
KIRBY MANUFACTURING INC.; *U.S. Private*, pg. 2314
KIRBY MARINE TRANSPORT CORPORATION—See Kirby Corporation; *U.S. Public*, pg. 1235
KIRBY MEDICAL CENTER; *U.S. Private*, pg. 2314
KIRBY NAGELHOUT CONSTRUCTION CO.; *U.S. Private*, pg. 2314
KIRBY NZ LIMITED—See Reece Limited; *Int'l*, pg. 6249
KIRBY OCEAN TRANSPORT CO. - HOUSTON OFFICE—See Kirby Corporation; *U.S. Public*, pg. 1236
KIRBY OCEAN TRANSPORT COMPANY—See Kirby Corporation; *U.S. Public*, pg. 1236
KIRBY OFFSHORE MARINE HAWAII, LLC—See Kirby Corporation; *U.S. Public*, pg. 1236
KIRBY RENTALS, LLC—See PRO EM Operations, LLC; *U.S. Private*, pg. 3269
KIRBY RISK CORPORATION; *U.S. Private*, pg. 2314
KIRBY-SMITH MACHINERY INC.; *U.S. Private*, pg. 2314
KIRBY WORLD HEADQUARTERS—See Berkshire Hathaway Inc.; *U.S. Public*, pg. 300
KIRCHHOFF ASPHALT-MISCHWERKE GMBH & CO. KG—See Strabag SE; *Int'l*, pg. 7231
KIRCHHOFF AUTOMOTIVE (CHONGQING) CO., LTD.—See KIRCHHOFF Gruppe; *Int'l*, pg. 4185
KIRCHHOFF AUTOMOTIVE DEUTSCHLAND GMBH—See KIRCHHOFF Gruppe; *Int'l*, pg. 4185
KIRCHHOFF AUTOMOTIVE GMBH—See KIRCHHOFF Gruppe; *Int'l*, pg. 4185
KIRCHHOFF AUTOMOTIVE PORTUGAL, S.A.—See KIRCHHOFF Gruppe; *Int'l*, pg. 4185
KIRCHHOFF AUTOMOTIVE ROMANIA SRL—See KIRCHHOFF Gruppe; *Int'l*, pg. 4185
KIRCHHOFF AUTOMOTIVE (SHENYANG) CO., LTD.—See KIRCHHOFF Gruppe; *Int'l*, pg. 4185
KIRCHHOFF AUTOMOTIVE (SUZHOU) CO., LTD.—See KIRCHHOFF Gruppe; *Int'l*, pg. 4185
KIRCHHOFF ESPANA, S.L.U.—See KIRCHHOFF Gruppe; *Int'l*, pg. 4185
KIRCHHOFF GMBH & CO. KG—See Mutares SE & Co. KGaA; *Int'l*, pg. 5105
KIRCHHOFF GRUPPE; *Int'l*, pg. 4185
KIRCHHOFF HUNGARIA KFT.—See KIRCHHOFF Gruppe; *Int'l*, pg. 4185
KIRCHHOFF IMMOBILIEN GMBH & CO. KG—See Mutares SE & Co. KGaA; *Int'l*, pg. 5105
KIRCHHOFF IRELAND LTD.—See KIRCHHOFF Gruppe; *Int'l*, pg. 4185
KIRCHHOFF POLSKA SP. ZO.O. - GLIWICE II PLANT—See KIRCHHOFF Gruppe; *Int'l*, pg. 4185
KIRCHHOFF POLSKA SP. ZO.O. - GLIWICE I PLANT—See KIRCHHOFF Gruppe; *Int'l*, pg. 4185
KIRCHHOFF POLSKA SP. Z O.O.—See KIRCHHOFF Gruppe; *Int'l*, pg. 4185
KIRCHHOFF PORTUGAL GAMETAL METALURGICA DA GANDARINHA S. A.—See KIRCHHOFF Gruppe; *Int'l*, pg. 4185
KIRCHHOFF WITTE GMBH—See KIRCHHOFF Gruppe; *Int'l*, pg. 4185
KIRCHMEYER & ASSOCIATES, INC.—See Real Matters, Inc.; *Int'l*, pg. 6233
KIRCHNER HOLDING GMBH—See STRABAG SE; *Int'l*, pg. 7231
KIRCHNER & VOLKER BAUUNTERNEHMUNG GMBH—See STRABAG SE; *Int'l*, pg. 7231

KIRCO; *U.S. Private*, pg. 2314
KIREI INC.—See Amuse Inc.; *Int'l*, pg. 442
KI REPLY GMBH—See Reply S.p.A.; *Int'l*, pg. 6291
KIRFIS S.A.—See GALAXIDI MARINE FARM S.A.; *Int'l*, pg. 2871
KIRIACOULIS MEDITERRANEAN CRUISES SHIPPING S.A.; *Int'l*, pg. 4186
KIRIBAI CHEMICAL CO., LTD.—See Kobayashi Pharmaceutical Co., Ltd.; *Int'l*, pg. 4216
KIRI DYES AND CHEMICALS LTD.—See Zhejiang Longsheng Group Co., Ltd.; *Int'l*, pg. 8659
KIRIHARA SHOTEN KK—See TOPPAN Holdings Inc.; *Int'l*, pg. 7817
KIRI INDUSTRIES LTD.; *Int'l*, pg. 4185
KIRILA CONTRACTORS INC.; *U.S. Private*, pg. 2314
KIRIN BEER MARKETING CO., LTD.—See Kirin Holdings Company, Limited; *Int'l*, pg. 4187
KIRIN BEVERAGE COMPANY, LIMITED—See Kirin Holdings Company, Limited; *Int'l*, pg. 4187
KIRIN BREWERY COMPANY, LIMITED—See Kirin Holdings Company, Limited; *Int'l*, pg. 4187
KIRIN BREWERY OF AMERICA, LLC—See Kirin Holdings Company, Limited; *Int'l*, pg. 4187
KIRIN BUSINESS SYSTEM CO., LTD.—See Kirin Holdings Company, Limited; *Int'l*, pg. 4187
KIRIN (CHINA) INVESTMENT CO., LTD.—See Kirin Holdings Company, Limited; *Int'l*, pg. 4187
KIRIN CITY CO., LTD.—See Kirin Holdings Company, Limited; *Int'l*, pg. 4187
KIRIN & COMMUNICATIONS CO., LTD—See Kirin Holdings Company, Limited; *Int'l*, pg. 4187
KIRIN DISTILLERY CO., LTD.—See Kirin Holdings Company, Limited; *Int'l*, pg. 4187
KIRINDO HOLDINGS CO., LTD.—See Bain Capital, LP; *U.S. Private*, pg. 441
KIRIN ECHO CO., LTD.—See Kirin Holdings Company, Limited; *Int'l*, pg. 4188
KIRIN ENGINEERING CO., LTD.—See Kirin Holdings Company, Limited; *Int'l*, pg. 4188
KIRIN EUROPE GMBH—See Kirin Holdings Company, Limited; *Int'l*, pg. 4188
KIRIN FOODS AUSTRALIA HOLDINGS PTY LTD—See Kirin Holdings Company, Limited; *Int'l*, pg. 4188
KIRIN GROUP HOLDINGS LIMITED; *Int'l*, pg. 4186
KIRIN GROUP OFFICE CO., LTD.—See Kirin Holdings Company, Limited; *Int'l*, pg. 4188
KIRIN HOLDINGS COMPANY, LIMITED; *Int'l*, pg. 4186
KIRIN HOLDINGS SINGAPORE PTE. LTD.—See Kirin Holdings Company, Limited; *Int'l*, pg. 4188
KIRIN KUNPENG (CHINA) BIO-PHARMACEUTICAL CO., LTD.—See Kirin Holdings Company, Limited; *Int'l*, pg. 4188
KIRIN LOGISTICS CO., LTD.—See Kirin Holdings Company, Limited; *Int'l*, pg. 4188
KIRIN MC DANONE WATERS CO., LTD.—See Kirin Holdings Company, Limited; *Int'l*, pg. 4188
KIRIN MERCHANDISING CO., LTD.—See Kirin Holdings Company, Limited; *Int'l*, pg. 4188
KIRIN TECHNO-SYSTEM CO., LTD.—See Kirin Holdings Company, Limited; *Int'l*, pg. 4188
KIRIN-TROPICANA INC.—See Kirin Holdings Company, Limited; *Int'l*, pg. 4188
KIRI RENEWABLE ENERGY PVT. LTD.—See Kiri Industries Ltd.; *Int'l*, pg. 4185
KIRISHIMA GEOTHERMAL CO., LTD.—See Nittetsu Mining Co., Ltd.; *Int'l*, pg. 5383
KIRISHINEFTEORGSINTEZ LTD—See Surgutneftegas OAO; *Int'l*, pg. 7344
KIRI TE KANAWA RETIREMENT VILLAGE LIMITED—See Ryman Healthcare Ltd.; *Int'l*, pg. 6439
KIRIU CORPORATION—See Sumitomo Corporation; *Int'l*, pg. 7269
KIRIU LIOHO CO.,LTD.—See Universal Cement Corporation; *Int'l*, pg. 8078
KIRIU TECHNO CORP.—See Sumitomo Corporation; *Int'l*, pg. 7269
KIRIU (THAILAND) CO., LTD.—See Sumitomo Corporation; *Int'l*, pg. 7269
KIRIU USA CORPORATION—See Sumitomo Corporation; *Int'l*, pg. 7269
KIRIWORKS, LLC—See i3 Verticals, Inc.; *U.S. Public*, pg. 1081
KIRK AG—See Kirkbi A/S; *Int'l*, pg. 4189
KIRK AG—See Kirkbi A/S; *Int'l*, pg. 4189
KIRK BEAUTY ONE GMBH—See CVC Capital Partners SICAV-FIS S.A.; *Int'l*, pg. 1883
KIRKBI A/S; *Int'l*, pg. 4189
KIRKBI PALAC KARLIN PROPERTY S.R.O—See Kirkbi A/S; *Int'l*, pg. 4189
KIRKBI REAL ESTATE INVESTMENT S.R.O—See Kirkbi A/S; *Int'l*, pg. 4189
KIRK & BLUM MANUFACTURING COMPANY INC.—See CECO Environmental Corp.; *U.S. Public*, pg. 463
KIRK BROTHERS FORD-LINCOLN, LLC; *U.S. Private*, pg. 2314
KIRKER ENTERPRISES, INC.—See RPM International Inc.; *U.S. Public*, pg. 1817
KIRKER TRAVEL LIMITED—See REWE-Zentral-Aktiengesellschaft; *Int'l*, pg. 6314

COMPANY NAME INDEX

KIRKESTUEN AS—See AF Gruppen ASA; *Int'l*, pg. 184
KIRKHAM HARDWOODS, INC.—See Maley & Wertz, Inc.; *U.S. Private*, pg. 2557
KIRKHILL AIRCRAFT PARTS CO.; *U.S. Private*, pg. 2314
KIRKHILL MANUFACTURING COMPANY INC.—See HEXPOL AB; *Int'l*, pg. 3372
KIRKHILL-TA COMPANY—See TransDigm Group Incorporated; *U.S. Public*, pg. 2181
KIRKHILL-TA—See TransDigm Group Incorporated; *U.S. Public*, pg. 2181
KIRK KAPITAL AG—See Kirk Kapital A/S; *Int'l*, pg. 4189
KIRK KAPITAL A/S; *Int'l*, pg. 4189
KIRK KEY INTERLOCK COMPANY LLC—See Halma plc; *Int'l*, pg. 3231
KIRKLAND & ELLIS INTERNATIONAL LLP—See Kirkland & Ellis LLP; *U.S. Private*, pg. 2315
KIRKLAND & ELLIS LLP; *U.S. Private*, pg. 2314
KIRKLAND LAKE DISCOVERIES CORP; *Int'l*, pg. 4191
KIRKLAND LAKE POWER CORP.—See Northland Power Inc.; *Int'l*, pg. 5446
KIRKLAND MOTORS—See AutoNation, Inc.; *U.S. Public*, pg. 236
KIRKLAND OF CHATTANOOGA INC.—See Kirkland's Inc.; *U.S. Public*, pg. 1236
KIRKLAND'S INC.; *U.S. Public*, pg. 1236
KIRKMAN GROUP, INC.—See Hemptown Organics Corp.; *Int'l*, pg. 3341
THE KIRKMAN OLIVER COMPANY—See Madison Dearborn Partners, LLC; *U.S. Private*, pg. 2541
KIRK & MATZ LTD.; *U.S. Private*, pg. 2314
KIRK NATIONALEASE CO. INC.—See KNL Holdings Inc.; *U.S. Private*, pg. 2322
KIRK & NICE, INC.—See Axar Capital Management L.P.; *U.S. Private*, pg. 411
KIRK & NICE SUBURBAN CHAPEL, INC.—See Axar Capital Management L.P.; *U.S. Private*, pg. 411
KIRKPATRICK BANK—See American BanCorp of Oklahoma; *U.S. Private*, pg. 223
KIRKPATRICK BROKERAGE CO.—See Acosta, Inc.; *U.S. Private*, pg. 64
KIRKPATRICK CONCRETE, INC—See Vicat S.A.; *Int'l*, pg. 8185
KIRKPATRICK SPRECKER & COMPANY, LLP—See Reyler Carr & Monroe LLP; *U.S. Private*, pg. 3399
KIRK PROPERTY A/S—See Kirk Kapital A/S; *Int'l*, pg. 4189
KIRKS AUTOMOTIVE INC.; *U.S. Private*, pg. 2315
THE KIRKSEY AGENCY, INC.—See Arthur J. Gallagher & Co.; *U.S. Public*, pg. 207
KIRKSTALL LIMITED—See Braveheart Investment Group Plc; *Int'l*, pg. 1141
KIRKSTALL LODGE LIMITED—See Sheikh Holdings Group (Investments) Limited; *Int'l*, pg. 6793
KIRKSTONE LTD.—See Mahwah Bergen Retail Group, Inc.; *U.S. Private*, pg. 2550
KIRKSVILLE ACADEMIC MEDICINE, LLC—See Community Health Systems, Inc.; *U.S. Public*, pg. 554
KIRKSVILLE CLINIC CORP.—See Community Health Systems, Inc.; *U.S. Public*, pg. 554
KIRKSVILLE MISSOURI HOSPITAL COMPANY, LLC—See Community Health Systems, Inc.; *U.S. Public*, pg. 554
KIRKSVILLE MOTOR COMPANY; *U.S. Private*, pg. 2315
KIRKSVILLE PHYSICAL THERAPY SERVICES, LLC—See Community Health Systems, Inc.; *U.S. Public*, pg. 554
KIRKWOOD BANCORPORATION CO.; *U.S. Private*, pg. 2315
KIRKWOOD BANK OF NEVADA—See JBNV Holding Corp.; *U.S. Private*, pg. 2194
KIRKWOOD BANK & TRUST CO.—See Kirkwood Bancorporation Co.; *U.S. Private*, pg. 2315
KIRKWOOD DIAMOND CANADA—See Diamond Estates Wines & Spirits, Inc.; *Int'l*, pg. 2105
KIRKWOOD DIGITAL LLC—See Kirkwood Holding, Inc.; *U.S. Private*, pg. 2315
KIRKWOOD HOLDING, INC.; *U.S. Private*, pg. 2315
KIRKWOOD MATERIAL SUPPLY, INC.—See SiteOne Landscape Supply, Inc.; *U.S. Public*, pg. 1889
KIRKWOOD MOUNTAIN RESORTS, LLC—See Vail Resorts, Inc.; *U.S. Public*, pg. 2271
KIRKWOOD PRINTING COMPANY, INC.; *U.S. Private*, pg. 2315
KIRKWOODS INC.; *U.S. Private*, pg. 2315
KIRLIN CUSTOM HOMES INC.; *U.S. Private*, pg. 2315
KIRLIN'S INC.; *U.S. Private*, pg. 2315
KIRLOSKAR BROTHERS INVESTMENTS LIMITED—See Kirloskar Brothers Limited; *Int'l*, pg. 4191
KIRLOSKAR BROTHERS LIMITED; *Int'l*, pg. 4191
KIRLOSKAR BROTHERS LTD - KONDHAPURI WORKS MANUFACTURING PLANT—See Kirloskar Brothers Limited; *Int'l*, pg. 4191
KIRLOSKAR BROTHERS LTD - SHIRWAL WORKS MANUFACTURING PLANT—See Kirloskar Brothers Limited; *Int'l*, pg. 4191
KIRLOSKAR BROTHERS (THAILAND) LIMITED—See Kirloskar Brothers Limited; *Int'l*, pg. 4191
KIRLOSKAR CONSTRUCTIONS & ENGINEERS LIMITED—See Kirloskar Brothers Limited; *Int'l*, pg. 4191

KIRLOSKAR CORROCOAT PRIVATE LIMITED—See Kirloskar Brothers Limited; *Int'l*, pg. 4191
KIRLOSKAR DMCC—See Kirloskar Pneumatic Co. Ltd.; *Int'l*, pg. 4191
KIRLOSKAR ELECTRIC COMPANY LTD; *Int'l*, pg. 4191
KIRLOSKAR FERROUS INDUSTRIES LTD.—See Kirloskar Industries Limited; *Int'l*, pg. 4191
KIRLOSKAR INDUSTRIES LIMITED; *Int'l*, pg. 4191
KIRLOSKAR OIL ENGINES LIMITED; *Int'l*, pg. 4191
KIRLOSKAR PNEUMATIC CO. LTD.; *Int'l*, pg. 4191
KIRLOSKAR POMPEN B.V.—See Kirloskar Brothers Limited; *Int'l*, pg. 4191
KIRLOSKAR SOUTH EAST ASIA CO. LTD—See Kirloskar Pneumatic Co. Ltd.; *Int'l*, pg. 4191
KIRLOSKAR TOYOTA TEXTILE MACHINERY PVT. LTD.—See Toyota Industries Corporation; *Int'l*, pg. 7866
KIRLOSKAR TOYOTA TEXTILE MACHINERY PVT. LTD.—See Toyota Industries Corporation; *Int'l*, pg. 7866
KIRMAC AUTOMOTIVE COLLISION SYSTEMS INC.; *Int'l*, pg. 4191
KIRO GRIFOLS S.L.—See Grifols, S.A.; *Int'l*, pg. 3085
KIROMIC BIOPHARMA, INC.; *U.S. Public*, pg. 1236
KIRONY CO., LTD.—See TOLI Corporation; *Int'l*, pg. 7798
KIRO RADIO—See Deseret Management Corporation; *U.S. Private*, pg. 1212
KIROWSKI ISOBAR ZRT—See Dentsu Group Inc.; *Int'l*, pg. 2037
KIRPART A.S.—See Kiraca Holding A.S.; *Int'l*, pg. 4185
KIRRIBILLY VINEYARDS PTY LIMITED—See Cheviot Bridge Limited; *Int'l*, pg. 1474
KIRRIBILLY VITICULTURE PTY LIMITED—See Cheviot Bridge Limited; *Int'l*, pg. 1474
KIRSCH KOHN & BRIDGE LLP—See Aprio, LLP; *U.S. Private*, pg. 301
KIRSCH PHARMA ASIA PACIFIC PTE. LTD.—See Kirsch Pharma GmbH; *Int'l*, pg. 4192
KIRSCH PHARMA AUSTRALIA PTY. LTD.—See Kirsch Pharma GmbH; *Int'l*, pg. 4192
KIRSCH PHARMA ESPANA SL—See Kirsch Pharma GmbH; *Int'l*, pg. 4192
KIRSCH PHARMA GMBH; *Int'l*, pg. 4192
KIRSCH PHARMA SHANGHAI CO., LTD.—See Kirsch Pharma GmbH; *Int'l*, pg. 4192
KIRSCH PHARMA SOUTH AFRICA (PTY.) LTD.—See Kirsch Pharma GmbH; *Int'l*, pg. 4192
KIRSHENBAUM BOND SENECAL + PARTNERS - MONTREAL—See Stagwell, Inc.; *U.S. Public*, pg. 1928
KIRSHENBAUM BOND SENECAL + PARTNERS—See Stagwell, Inc.; *U.S. Public*, pg. 1928
KIRSTEN MODEDESIGN GMBH & CO. KG—See Steilmann Holding AG; *Int'l*, pg. 7193
KIRTAS TECHNOLOGIES, INC.—See i2S SA; *Int'l*, pg. 3566
KIRTI INVESTMENTS LIMITED; *Int'l*, pg. 4192
KIRTIMAN AGRO GENETICS LTD—See Shiva Global Agro Industries Ltd.; *Int'l*, pg. 6854
KIRTLAND CAPITAL PARTNERS LLC; *U.S. Private*, pg. 2315
KIRTLEY-COLE ASSOCIATES, LLC.; *U.S. Private*, pg. 2315
KIRUS GMBH—See Schneider Electric SE; *Int'l*, pg. 6624
KIRYU INDUSTRY CO., LTD.—See Subaru Corporation; *Int'l*, pg. 7247
KISAN MOULDINGS LTD.; *Int'l*, pg. 4192
KISAN TELECOM CO., LTD.; *Int'l*, pg. 4192
KISAN TELECOM CO., LTD. - SUNGNAM PLANT—See Kisan Telecom Co., Ltd.; *Int'l*, pg. 4192
KISAQ, LLC—See Nana Regional Corporation, Inc.; *U.S. Private*, pg. 2832
KIS AS—See Kis Partners AS; *Int'l*, pg. 4192
KIS-BANK INC.—See Hyosung Corporation; *Int'l*, pg. 3552
KISCO CORP.—See KISCO Holdings Corp.; *Int'l*, pg. 4192
KISCO FOODS CO., LTD. - SHIMIZU FACTORY—See Kuze Co., Ltd.; *Int'l*, pg. 4348
KISCO FOODS CO., LTD.—See Kuze Co., Ltd.; *Int'l*, pg. 4348
KISCO FOODS INTERNATIONAL LIMITED—See Kuze Co., Ltd.; *Int'l*, pg. 4348
KISCO HOLDINGS CORP.; *Int'l*, pg. 4192
KISCO LTD.; *Int'l*, pg. 4192
KISH BANCORP, INC.; *U.S. Public*, pg. 1236
KISH BANK—See Kish Bancorp, Inc.; *U.S. Public*, pg. 1236
KISHIN CORPORATION—See Futaba Corporation; *Int'l*, pg. 2851
KISHIN MEGATEC CO., LTD.—See Futaba Corporation; *Int'l*, pg. 2851
KISHIN VIETNAM CO., LTD.—See Futaba Corporation; *Int'l*, pg. 2851
KISHIWADA CANCAN BAYSIDE MALL CORPORATION—See Sumitomo Corporation; *Int'l*, pg. 7269
KISH NAK OIL SEAL MFG. CO., LTD.—See NAK Sealing Technologies Corporation; *Int'l*, pg. 5131
KISHO KUROKAWA ARCHITECT & ASSOCIATES CO., LTD.—See Nippon Koei Co., Ltd.; *Int'l*, pg. 5321
KISIKANA D.O.O—See SOL S.p.A.; *Int'l*, pg. 7067

KISTOS HOLDINGS PLC

KIS INFORMATIK AG—See Cognizant Technology Solutions Corporation; *U.S. Public*, pg. 524
KIS INFORMATION & COMMUNICATION, INC.—See NICE Holdings Co., Ltd.; *Int'l*, pg. 5264
KIS INFORMATION SERVICES GMBH—See Cognizant Technology Solutions Corporation; *U.S. Public*, pg. 524
KISINGER CAMPO & ASSOCIATES CORP.; *U.S. Private*, pg. 2315
THE KISKUNGAZ CO., LTD.—See MOL Magyar Olaj- es Gazipari Nyrt.; *Int'l*, pg. 5021
KISLAK COMPANY—See J.I. Kislak Inc.; *U.S. Private*, pg. 2167
KISLAK NATIONAL BANK—See J.I. Kislak Inc.; *U.S. Private*, pg. 2167
KISLING AG—See Wurth Verwaltungsgesellschaft mbH; *Int'l*, pg. 8506
KISLING DEUTSCHLAND GMBH—See Wurth Verwaltungsgesellschaft mbH; *Int'l*, pg. 8506
KISMET ACQUISITION ONE CORP.; *Int'l*, pg. 4192
KISMET INTERNATIONAL LIMOUSINE SERVICE INC.; *U.S. Private*, pg. 2315
KISMET RESOURCES CORP.; *Int'l*, pg. 4192
KISMET RUBBER PRODUCTS INC.; *U.S. Private*, pg. 2315
KISO-JIBAN CONSULTANTS CO., LTD.—See Chodai Co., Ltd.; *Int'l*, pg. 1577
KISOJI CO., LTD.; *Int'l*, pg. 4192
KISOKOMAKOGEN KANKOKAIHATSU CO., LTD.—See Daido Steel Co., Ltd.; *Int'l*, pg. 1923
KIS PARTNERS AS; *Int'l*, pg. 4192
KIS PRICING—See Moody's Corporation; *U.S. Public*, pg. 1467
KISS 100—See Heinrich Bauer Verlag KG; *Int'l*, pg. 3324
KIS S.A.S.—See ME Group International plc; *Int'l*, pg. 4762
KISSEI COMTEC CO., LTD.—See KISSEI PHARMACEUTICAL CO. LTD.; *Int'l*, pg. 4192
KISSEI PHARMACEUTICAL CO. LTD.; *Int'l*, pg. 4192
KISSELBACK FORD; *U.S. Private*, pg. 2315
KISSES FROM ITALY, INC.; *U.S. Public*, pg. 1236
THE KISSIMMEE FL ENDOSCOPY ASC, LLC—See KKR & Co. Inc.; *U.S. Public*, pg. 1247
KISSIMMEE UTILITY AUTHORITY; *U.S. Private*, pg. 2315
KISSIN FRESH MEATS INC.; *U.S. Private*, pg. 2315
KISSINGER FINANCIAL—See Lee Equity Partners LLC; *U.S. Private*, pg. 2412
KISSMARK JAPAN CO., LTD.—See Alpen Co., Ltd.; *Int'l*, pg. 366
KISSNER GROUP HOLDINGS LP—See Stone Canyon Industries, LLC; *U.S. Private*, pg. 3817
KISSTIXX, LLC; *U.S. Private*, pg. 2315
KI-STAR REAL ESTATE CO., LTD.; *Int'l*, pg. 4156
KISTEFOS AS; *Int'l*, pg. 4192
KISTERS LIMITED—See Salzgitter AG; *Int'l*, pg. 6496
KISTLER AG—See PAUL HARTMANN AG; *Int'l*, pg. 5760
KISTLER TIFFANY BENEFITS CO.—See New Mountain Capital, LLC; *U.S. Private*, pg. 2901
KISTOS HOLDINGS PLC; *Int'l*, pg. 4193
KISTRON IN.—See KISWIRE LTD; *Int'l*, pg. 4193
KIS USA—See ME Group International plc; *Int'l*, pg. 4762
KISWIRE ARCELORMITTAL LTD.—See ArcelorMittal S.A.; *Int'l*, pg. 545
KISWIRE BALARAJA INDONESIA, PT—See KISWIRE LTD; *Int'l*, pg. 4193
KISWIRE CORD CZECH S.R.O.—See KISWIRE LTD; *Int'l*, pg. 4194
KISWIRE CORD LTD. - CHANGWON FACTORY—See KISWIRE LTD; *Int'l*, pg. 4193
KISWIRE CORD LTD. - POHANG FACTORY—See KISWIRE LTD; *Int'l*, pg. 4193
KISWIRE CORD LTD.—See KISWIRE LTD; *Int'l*, pg. 4193
KISWIRE CORD QINGDAO LTD.—See KISWIRE LTD; *Int'l*, pg. 4193
KISWIRE CORD RONGCHENG CO., LTD.—See KISWIRE LTD; *Int'l*, pg. 4193
KISWIRE CORD SDN. BHD.—See KISWIRE LTD; *Int'l*, pg. 4193
KISWIRE CORD VIETNAM LTD.—See KISWIRE LTD; *Int'l*, pg. 4193
KISWIRE CORD YANGTZE LTD.—See KISWIRE LTD; *Int'l*, pg. 4193
KISWIRE DIES SDN. BHD.—See KISWIRE LTD; *Int'l*, pg. 4193
KISWIRE FINE METAL (QINGDAO) LTD.—See KISWIRE LTD; *Int'l*, pg. 4194
KISWIRE INC. - BEAD WIRE DIVISION—See KISWIRE LTD; *Int'l*, pg. 4193
KISWIRE INC. - STEEL CORD DIVISION—See KISWIRE LTD; *Int'l*, pg. 4193
KISWIRE INDONESIA, PT—See KISWIRE LTD; *Int'l*, pg. 4193
KISWIRE INTERNATIONAL S. A.—See KISWIRE LTD; *Int'l*, pg. 4194
KISWIRE JAPAN CO.—See KISWIRE LTD; *Int'l*, pg. 4194
KISWIRE, LLC—See KISWIRE LTD; *Int'l*, pg. 4194
KISWIRE LOTUS CO., LTD.—See KISWIRE LTD; *Int'l*, pg. 4194
KISWIRE LTD. - BEAD WIRE FACTORY—See KISWIRE LTD; *Int'l*, pg. 4194

1509

KISTOS HOLDINGS PLC

KISWIRE LTD. - EONYANG FACTORY—See KISWIRE LTD; *Int'l*, pg. 4194
KISWIRE LTD. - GEONCHEON BEAD WIRE FACTORY—See KISWIRE LTD; *Int'l*, pg. 4194
KISWIRE LTD. - GEONCHEON SHAPED WIRE FACTORY—See KISWIRE LTD; *Int'l*, pg. 4194
KISWIRE LTD. - GUNBUK FACTORY—See KISWIRE LTD; *Int'l*, pg. 4194
KISWIRE LTD. - HYROPE FACTORY—See KISWIRE LTD; *Int'l*, pg. 4194
KISWIRE LTD; *Int'l*, pg. 4193
KISWIRE LTD. - SPRING WIRE FACTORY—See KISWIRE LTD; *Int'l*, pg. 4194
KISWIRE NEPTUNE SDN. BHD.—See KISWIRE LTD; *Int'l*, pg. 4194
KISWIRE PINE BLUFF, INC.—See KISWIRE LTD; *Int'l*, pg. 4194
KISWIRE QINGDAO LTD.—See KISWIRE LTD; *Int'l*, pg. 4194
KISWIRE R&D SDN. BHD.—See KISWIRE LTD; *Int'l*, pg. 4194
KISWIRE SDN.BHD. B.K.K—See KISWIRE LTD; *Int'l*, pg. 4194
KISWIRE SDN. BHD.—See KISWIRE LTD; *Int'l*, pg. 4194
KISWIRE (SHANGHAI) TRADING CO., LTD.—See KISWIRE LTD; *Int'l*, pg. 4193
KISWIRE SINGAPORE LTD.—See KISWIRE LTD; *Int'l*, pg. 4194
KISWIRE SZENTGOTTHARD LLC—See KISWIRE LTD; *Int'l*, pg. 4194
KISWIRE TRADING, INC.—See KISWIRE LTD; *Int'l*, pg. 4194
KITAC CORPORATION; *Int'l*, pg. 4194
KITAGAWA CORPORATION; *Int'l*, pg. 4194
KITAGAWA ENGINEERING CO., LTD.—See KITAGAWA SEIKI CO., LTD.; *Int'l*, pg. 4194
KITAGAWA EUROPE GMBH—See Kitagawa Corporation; *Int'l*, pg. 4194
KITAGAWA EUROPE LTD.—See Kitagawa Corporation; *Int'l*, pg. 4194
KITAGAWA INDIA PVT LTD.—See Kitagawa Corporation; *Int'l*, pg. 4194
KITAGAWA INDUSTRIES CO., LTD.—See NITTO KOGYO CORPORATION; *Int'l*, pg. 5387
KITAGAWA IRON WORKS (SHANGHAI) CO., LTD.—See Kitagawa Corporation; *Int'l*, pg. 4194
KITAGAWA KOREA AGENT CO., LTD.—See Kitagawa Corporation; *Int'l*, pg. 4194
KITAGAWA MEXICO, S.A. DE C.V.—See Nippon Steel Corporation; *Int'l*, pg. 5337
KITAGAWA-NORTHTECH INC.—See Nippon Steel Corporation; *Int'l*, pg. 5338
KITAGAWA SEIKI CO., LTD.; *Int'l*, pg. 4194
KITAGAWA (THAILAND) CO., LTD.—See Kitagawa Corporation; *Int'l*, pg. 4194
KITAHARA CAPITAL PARTNERS CO., LTD.; *Int'l*, pg. 4194
KITAHARA PONTIAC-BUICK-GMC, INC., *U.S. Private*, pg. 2316
KITAKAMI DELICA CO., LTD.—See Kewpie Corporation; *Int'l*, pg. 4144
KITAKAMI HITEC PAPER CORP.—See Mitsubishi Paper Mills Limited; *Int'l*, pg. 4967
KITAKAMI PAPER CO., LTD.—See Nippon Paper Industries Co., Ltd.; *Int'l*, pg. 5327
KITAKANTO MAZDA CO., LTD.—See Mazda Motor Corporation; *Int'l*, pg. 4748
KITA-KANTO SOHGO SECURITY SERVICES CO., LTD.—See Sohgo Security Services Co., Ltd.; *Int'l*, pg. 7059
KITA-KANTO STEEL CORPORATION—See JFE Holdings, Inc.; *Int'l*, pg. 3937
KITAKATA LIGHT METAL CO., LTD.—See Resonac Holdings Corporation; *Int'l*, pg. 6298
KITAKEI CO., LTD.; *Int'l*, pg. 4194
KITA KOUDENSHA CORPORATION; *Int'l*, pg. 4194
KITAKYUSHU FALTEC CO., LTD.—See TPR Co., Ltd.; *Int'l*, pg. 7884
KITAKYUSHU LIQUEFIED NATURAL GAS CO., INC.—See Kyushu Electric Power Co., Inc.; *Int'l*, pg. 4367
KITAKYUSHU NISSUI CO., LTD.—See Nissui Corporation; *Int'l*, pg. 5378
KITAKYUSHU UBE CONCRETE CO., LTD.—See UBE Corporation; *Int'l*, pg. 8001
KITALIVE INC.—See TerraSky Co., Ltd.; *Int'l*, pg. 7568
KITA MANUFACTURING CO., LTD.—See Cohu, Inc.; *U.S. Public*, pg. 529
KITAMI MOKUZAI CO., LTD.—See Yamaha Corporation; *Int'l*, pg. 8549
KITAMURA CO., LTD.—See Culture Convenience Club Co., Ltd.; *Int'l*, pg. 1877
KITANIHON ELECTRIC CABLE CO., LTD.—See Tohoku Electric Power Co., Inc.; *Int'l*, pg. 7777
KITANIHON GAS CO., LTD.—See Nippon Gas Co., Ltd.; *Int'l*, pg. 5318
KITANIHON SPINNING CO., LTD.; *Int'l*, pg. 4195
KITANIHONUNYU CORPORATION—See Senko Group Holdings Co., Ltd.; *Int'l*, pg. 6710

KITAN INDUSTRIES LTD.—See Access Industries, Inc.; *U.S. Private*, pg. 51
THE KITA-NIPPON BANK LTD.; *Int'l*, pg. 7663
KITANO ARMS CORPORATION; *U.S. Private*, pg. 2316
KITANO CONSTRUCTION CORP.; *Int'l*, pg. 4195
KITANOTATSUJIN CORPORATION; *Int'l*, pg. 4195
KITA-OSAKA KYUKO RAILWAY CO., LTD.—See Hankyu Hanshin Holdings Inc.; *Int'l*, pg. 3256
KITA-OSAKA SHIGYO CO., LTD.—See TOPPAN Holdings Inc.; *Int'l*, pg. 7817
KITASAN KOWA CO., LTD.—See Takashima & Co., Ltd.; *Int'l*, pg. 7435
KITASATO DAIICHI SANKYO VACCINE CO., LTD.—See Daiichi Sankyo Co., Ltd.; *Int'l*, pg. 1930
KITASATO OTSUKA BIOMEDICAL ASSAY LABORATORIES CO., LTD.—See Otsuka Holdings Co., Ltd.; *Int'l*, pg. 5658
KITASATO OTSUKA VIRUS ASSAY LABORATORIES CO., LTD.—See Otsuka Holdings Co., Ltd.; *Int'l*, pg. 5659
KITASHIBA ELECTRIC CO., LTD.—See Japan Industrial Partners, Inc.; *Int'l*, pg. 3890
KITASHIGA RYUOO, CO., LTD.—See Nippon Ski Resort Development Co., Ltd.; *Int'l*, pg. 5334
KITASHOKU CO., LTD.—See Tsukiji Uoichiba Co., Ltd.; *Int'l*, pg. 7956
KITAURA SOC CO., LTD.—See Sumitomo Osaka Cement Co Ltd; *Int'l*, pg. 7296
KITA USA, INC.—See Cohu, Inc.; *U.S. Public*, pg. 530
KITAZAWA SANGYO CO., LTD.; *Int'l*, pg. 4195
KITBAG LIMITED—See Kynetic LLC; *U.S. Private*, pg. 2360
KITCATT NOHR ALEXANDER SHAW, LTD.; *Int'l*, pg. 4195
KITCHELL CEM, INC.—See Kitchell Corporation; *U.S. Private*, pg. 2316
KITCHELL CONTRACTORS, INC. OF ARIZONA—See Kitchell Corporation; *U.S. Private*, pg. 2316
KITCHELL CORPORATION; *U.S. Private*, pg. 2316
KITCHELL DEVELOPMENT COMPANY—See Kitchell Corporation; *U.S. Private*, pg. 2316
KITCHEN ACADEMY—See Perdoceo Education Corporation; *U.S. Public*, pg. 1673
KITCHENAID—See Whirlpool Corporation; *U.S. Public*, pg. 2367
THE KITCHEN COLLECTION, LLC—See Hamilton Beach Brands Holding Company; *U.S. Public*, pg. 981
KITCHEN COOKED, INC.—See Utz Brands, Inc.; *U.S. Public*, pg. 2268
KITCHEN CRAFT OF CANADA—See MasterBrand, Inc.; *U.S. Public*, pg. 1394
KITCHEN CULTURE PTE. LTD.—See SDAI Limited; *Int'l*, pg. 6657
KITCHEN CULTURE SDN. BHD.—See SDAI Limited; *Int'l*, pg. 6657
KITCHENER AERO AVIONICS LTD.; *Int'l*, pg. 4195
KITCHEN FAIR—See Townecraft Homewares, LLC; *U.S. Private*, pg. 4198
KITCHEN FRESH FOODS INC.; *U.S. Private*, pg. 2316
THE KITCHEN GUILD; *U.S. Private*, pg. 4065
KITCHEN INC.—See TM Systems, LLC; *U.S. Private*, pg. 4179
KITCHEN INVESTMENT GROUP; *U.S. Private*, pg. 2316
KITCHEN KABOODLE II INC.; *U.S. Private*, pg. 2316
KITCHEN KOMPACT; *U.S. Private*, pg. 2316
KITCHEN LEO BURNETT—See Publicis Groupe S.A.; *Int'l*, pg. 6100
KITCHENMAN TERMINAL CO.—See George S. Coyne Chemical Co. Inc.; *U.S. Private*, pg. 1683
KITCHEN (PRO) LIMITED—See E, Bon Holdings Ltd; *Int'l*, pg. 2250
KITCHEN-QUIP, INC.; *U.S. Private*, pg. 2316
KITCHEN STUFF PLUS, INC.—See Fairfax Financial Holdings Limited; *Int'l*, pg. 2607
KITCHEN SUPPLIERS INCORPORATED; *U.S. Private*, pg. 2316
KITCHNER & PIERRO COMPANY, INC.; *U.S. Private*, pg. 2316
KIT DIGITAL LIMITED—See Piksel, Inc.; *U.S. Private*, pg. 3180
KIT DIGITAL PRAGUE A.S.—See Piksel, Inc.; *U.S. Private*, pg. 3180
KITE PHARMA EU B.V.—See Gilead Sciences, Inc.; *U.S. Public*, pg. 938
KITE PHARMA, INC.—See Gilead Sciences, Inc.; *U.S. Public*, pg. 938
KITE PHARMA UK, LTD—See Gilead Sciences, Inc.; *U.S. Public*, pg. 938
KITE REALTY GROUP, L.P.—See Kite Realty Group Trust; *U.S. Public*, pg. 1236
KITE REALTY GROUP TRUST; *U.S. Public*, pg. 1236
KITEX GARMENTS LIMITED; *Int'l*, pg. 4195
KITEX KIDSWEAR LIMITED—See Kitex Garments Limited; *Int'l*, pg. 4195
KIT FINANCE JSC; *Int'l*, pg. 4194
KITH KITCHENS, LLC—See Pfingsten Partners, LLC; *U.S. Private*, pg. 3164
KITH KITCHENS, LLC—See Promus Holdings, LLC; *U.S. Private*, pg. 3284

CORPORATE AFFILIATIONS

KITO AMERICAS, INC.—See The Carlyle Group Inc.; *U.S. Public*, pg. 2055
KITO CANADA INC.—See The Carlyle Group Inc.; *U.S. Public*, pg. 2055
KITO CORPORATION—See The Carlyle Group Inc.; *U.S. Public*, pg. 2054
KITO EUROPE GMBH—See The Carlyle Group Inc.; *U.S. Public*, pg. 2055
KITOKU AMERICA INC.—See Kitoku Shinryo Co., Ltd.; *Int'l*, pg. 4195
KITOKU SHINRYO CO., LTD.; *Int'l*, pg. 4195
KITRON AB—See Kitron ASA; *Int'l*, pg. 4195
KITRON ASA; *Int'l*, pg. 4195
KITRON AS—See Kitron ASA; *Int'l*, pg. 4195
KITRON ELECTROMECHANICAL (NINGBO) CO. LTD.—See Kitron ASA; *Int'l*, pg. 4195
KITRON ELECTRONICS MANUFACTURING (NINGBO) CO. LTD.—See Kitron ASA; *Int'l*, pg. 4195
KITRON GMBH—See Kitron ASA; *Int'l*, pg. 4195
KITRON INC.—See Kitron ASA; *Int'l*, pg. 4195
KITRON MICROELECTRONICS AB—See Kitron ASA; *Int'l*, pg. 4195
KITRON SOURCING AS—See Kitron ASA; *Int'l*, pg. 4195
KITRON SP. Z O.O—See Kitron ASA; *Int'l*, pg. 4195
KITRON TECHNOLOGIES INC.—See Kitron ASA; *Int'l*, pg. 4195
KITSAP BANK—See Olympic Bancorp; *U.S. Private*, pg. 3012
KITSAP PUBLIC SERVICES, INC.—See Kitsap Towing; *U.S. Private*, pg. 2316
KITSAP SUN, LLC—See Gannett Co., Inc.; *U.S. Public*, pg. 898
KITSAP TOWING; *U.S. Private*, pg. 2316
KITS EYECARE LTD.; *Int'l*, pg. 4195
KITSON & PARTNERS CLUBS—See Kitson & Partners, LLC; *U.S. Private*, pg. 2316
KITSON & PARTNERS COMMERCIAL—See Kitson & Partners, LLC; *U.S. Private*, pg. 2316
KITSON & PARTNERS COMMUNITIES—See Kitson & Partners, LLC; *U.S. Private*, pg. 2316
KITSON & PARTNERS, LLC; *U.S. Private*, pg. 2316
KITTIWAKE DEVELOPMENTS LIMITED—See Parker Hannifin Corporation; *U.S. Public*, pg. 1641
KITTLE'S HOME FURNISHINGS CENTER INC.; *U.S. Private*, pg. 2316
KITTLING RIDGE LTD.—See Magnotta Winery Corporation; *Int'l*, pg. 4641
KITTREDGE EQUIPMENT CO., INC.—See Singer Equipment Company; *U.S. Private*, pg. 3670
KITTRICH CORPORATION; *U.S. Private*, pg. 2316
KITTRICH LLC—See Kittrich Corporation; *U.S. Private*, pg. 2316
K&I TUBULAR CORPORATION—See JFE Holdings, Inc.; *Int'l*, pg. 3937
KITV-TV—See The Hearst Corporation; *U.S. Private*, pg. 4048
KITWARE, INC.; *U.S. Private*, pg. 2317
KITWAVE GROUP PLC; *Int'l*, pg. 4195
KITZ CORPORATION OF AMERICA—See KITZ CORPORATION; *Int'l*, pg. 4196
KITZ CORPORATION OF ASIA PACIFIC PTE. LTD.—See KITZ CORPORATION; *Int'l*, pg. 4196
KITZ CORPORATION OF EUROPE, S.A.—See KITZ CORPORATION; *Int'l*, pg. 4196
KITZ CORPORATION OF JIANGSU KUNSHAN—See KITZ CORPORATION; *Int'l*, pg. 4196
KITZ CORPORATION OF KUNSHAN—See KITZ CORPORATION; *Int'l*, pg. 4196
KITZ CORPORATION OF LIANYUNGANG—See KITZ CORPORATION; *Int'l*, pg. 4196
KITZ CORPORATION OF SHANGHAI—See KITZ CORPORATION; *Int'l*, pg. 4196
KITZ CORPORATION OF TAIWAN—See KITZ CORPORATION; *Int'l*, pg. 4196
KITZ CORPORATION; *Int'l*, pg. 4196
KITZ CORPORATION—See KITZ CORPORATION; *Int'l*, pg. 4196
KIT ZELLER, INC.—See Littlejohn & Co., LLC; *U.S. Private*, pg. 2471
KITZ ENGINEERING SERVICE CO., LTD.—See KITZ CORPORATION; *Int'l*, pg. 4196
KITZ EUROPE GMBH—See KITZ CORPORATION; *Int'l*, pg. 4196
KITZ HONG KONG COMPANY LIMITED—See KITZ CORPORATION; *Int'l*, pg. 4196
KITZMANS LTD.; *U.S. Private*, pg. 2317
KITZ METAL WORKS CORPORATION—See KITZ CORPORATION; *Int'l*, pg. 4196
KITZ MICRO FILTER CO., LTD.—See KITZ CORPORATION; *Int'l*, pg. 4196
KITZ & PFEIL INC.; *U.S. Private*, pg. 2317
KITZ SCT AMERICA CORPORATION—See KITZ CORPORATION; *Int'l*, pg. 4196
KITZ SCT CO., LTD.—See KITZ CORPORATION; *Int'l*, pg. 4196
KITZ SCT CORPORATION OF KUNSHAN—See KITZ CORPORATION; *Int'l*, pg. 4196
KITZ SCT OF KUNSHAN—See KITZ CORPORATION; *Int'l*, pg. 4196

COMPANY NAME INDEX

KITZ (THAILAND) LTD.—See KITZ CORPORATION; *Int'l*, pg. 4196
KITZ VALVE & ACTUATION (MALAYSIA) SDN. BHD.—See KITZ CORPORATION; *Int'l*, pg. 4196
KITZ VALVE & ACTUATION SINGAPORE PTE. LTD.—See KITZ CORPORATION; *Int'l*, pg. 4196
KITZ VALVE & ACTUATION (THAILAND) CO., LTD.—See KITZ CORPORATION; *Int'l*, pg. 4196
KITZ VALVE & ACTUATION VIETNAM CO., LTD.—See KITZ CORPORATION; *Int'l*, pg. 4196
KIU HUNG INDUSTRIES LIMITED—See Kiu Hung International Holdings Limited; *Int'l*, pg. 4197
KIU HUNG INTERNATIONAL HOLDINGS LIMITED; *Int'l*, pg. 4197
KIU HUNG TOYS COMPANY LIMITED—See Kiu Hung International Holdings Limited; *Int'l*, pg. 4197
KI (UK) LTD.—See Krueger International, Inc.; *U.S. Private*, pg. 2353
KIU KWONG INVESTMENT CO. LTD.—See Bank of China, Ltd.; *Int'l*, pg. 842
KIU LOK PROPERTIES (INTERNATIONAL) LIMITED—See FSE Services Group Limited; *Int'l*, pg. 2798
KIU LOK SERVICE MANAGEMENT COMPANY LIMITED—See FSE Services Group Limited; *Int'l*, pg. 2798
KIVATI SOFTWARE, LLC—See Resolute Solutions Corporation; *U.S. Private*, pg. 3406
KIVEL PROPERTIES LIMITED—See Heidelberg Materials AG; *Int'l*, pg. 3317
KIVETON PARK STEEL LIMITED; *Int'l*, pg. 4197
KIVI-TV—See The E.W. Scripps Company; *U.S. Public*, pg. 2068
KIV VERPACKUNGEN GMBH—See Groupe Guillin SA; *Int'l*, pg. 3104
KIWA BIO-TECH PRODUCTS GROUP CORP.; *U.S. Public*, pg. 1237
KIWETINOHK RESOURCES CORP.—See ARC Financial Corp.; *Int'l*, pg. 539
KIWIBOX.COM, INC.; *U.S. Private*, pg. 2317
KIWI CONSULTING EDV-BERATUNG GMBH—See adesso SE; *Int'l*, pg. 144
KIWI EXPRESS—See Freightways Group Limited; *Int'l*, pg. 2771
KIWI NORGE AS—See NorgesGruppen ASA; *Int'l*, pg. 5427
KIWIPLAN GMBH—See Illinois Tool Works Inc.; *U.S. Public*, pg. 1108
KIWIPLAN INC.—See Illinois Tool Works Inc.; *U.S. Public*, pg. 1109
KIWI PROPERTY GROUP LIMITED; *Int'l*, pg. 4197
KIWI STEEL N.Z. LIMITED—See SK Networks Co., Ltd.; *Int'l*, pg. 6974
KIWOOM ASSET MANAGEMENT CO., LTD.—See Saramin Co., Ltd.; *Int'l*, pg. 6576
KIWOOM ASSET PLANNER INC.—See Saramin Co., Ltd.; *Int'l*, pg. 6576
KIWOOM INVESTMENT CO., LTD.—See Daou Data Corp.; *Int'l*, pg. 1970
KIWOOM NO.3 SPECIAL PURPOSE ACQUISITION COMPANY; *Int'l*, pg. 4197
KIWOOM SECURITIES CO., LTD.; *Int'l*, pg. 4197
KIWS PROPERTY LLC—See dormakaba Holding AG; *Int'l*, pg. 2177
KIYA CORPORATION—See HOWA Corporation; *Int'l*, pg. 3492
THE KIYO BANK, LTD.; *Int'l*, pg. 7663
KIYOHARA SUMIDEN, LTD.—See Sumitomo Electric Industries, Ltd.; *Int'l*, pg. 7278
KIYO LEARNING CO., LTD.; *Int'l*, pg. 4197
KIYONNA CLOTHING, INC.; *U.S. Private*, pg. 2317
KIYOSUMI GOLF CLUB CO., LTD.—See Taiheiyo Cement Corporation; *Int'l*, pg. 7411
KIYOTA KOUGYO CO., LTD.—See Takasago Thermal Engineering Co., Ltd.; *Int'l*, pg. 7434
KIZAI CORPORATION—See Ishihara Chemical Co., Ltd.; *Int'l*, pg. 3817
KIZAN INTERNATIONAL INC.; *U.S. Private*, pg. 2317
KIZAN TECHNOLOGIES; *U.S. Private*, pg. 2317
KIZMEET, INC.—See Spark Networks SE; *Int'l*, pg. 7126
KIZUNA CORPORATION; *Int'l*, pg. 4197
KIZUNA HOLDINGS CORP.; *Int'l*, pg. 4197
KJAER GROUP A/S; *Int'l*, pg. 4197
KJAER GROUP US INC.—See KJAER GROUP A/S; *Int'l*, pg. 4197
KJARNAVORUR HF—See Orkla ASA; *Int'l*, pg. 5637
K. J. BEAMISH CONSTRUCTION CO., LIMITED; *Int'l*, pg. 4043
K.J. BEAMISH CONSTRUCTION CO., LIMITED; *Int'l*, pg. 4044
KJ CAN (JOHORE) SDN. BHD.—See Can-One Berhad; *Int'l*, pg. 1276
KJ CAN (SELANGOR) SDN. BHD.—See Can-One Berhad; *Int'l*, pg. 1276
KJC CORPORATION—See Career Technology (MFG.) Co., Ltd.; *Int'l*, pg. 1323
K&J CHEMICALS CO., LTD—See Kumyang Co., Ltd.; *Int'l*, pg. 4332

KJ CHEMICALS CORPORATION—See Seiko PMC Corporation; *Int'l*, pg. 6689
KJ CHEMICALS CORPORATION - YATSUSHIRO PLANT—See Seiko PMC Corporation; *Int'l*, pg. 6689
K & J CHEVROLET, INC.; *U.S. Private*, pg. 2249
KJDE CORP.; *U.S. Private*, pg. 2317
KJEDEHUSET AS—See Telenor ASA; *Int'l*, pg. 7539
KJELDSENS LIMITED—See Campbell Soup Company; *U.S. Public*, pg. 427
KJELL & COMPANY—See FSN Capital Partners AS; *Int'l*, pg. 2799
KJELL & CO NORWAY AS—See Kjell Group AB; *Int'l*, pg. 4197
KJELL GROUP AB; *Int'l*, pg. 4197
KJELLSTROM & LEE, INC.; *U.S. Private*, pg. 2317
KJ ENGINEERING SDN. BHD.—See Veolia Environnement S.A.; *Int'l*, pg. 8153
KJ INTERNATIONAL RESOURCES LTD.—See Leonard Green & Partners, L.P.; *U.S. Private*, pg. 2428
KJ INTERNATIONAL RESOURCES LTD.—See TTCP Management Services, LLC.; *U.S. Private*, pg. 4254
KJK CAPITAL OY; *Int'l*, pg. 4197
KJM ALUMINIUM CAN SDN. BHD.—See Can-One Berhad; *Int'l*, pg. 1276
KJMC CORPORATE ADVISORS (INDIA) LTD.; *Int'l*, pg. 4198
KJMC FINANCIAL SERVICES LTD.; *Int'l*, pg. 4198
KJO INTERNATIONAL SDN. BHD.—See Can-One Berhad; *Int'l*, pg. 1276
KJO SYSTEMS SDN. BHD.—See Can-One Berhad; *Int'l*, pg. 1276
K.J.P. LTD.—See Cinven Limited; *Int'l*, pg. 1612
KJ PRETECH ASIA HOLDING CO. LTD.—See EMNI Co., Ltd; *Int'l*, pg. 2385
K.J. QUINN S.A.S.—See Clariant AG; *Int'l*, pg. 1646
KJRH—See The E.W. Scripps Company; *U.S. Public*, pg. 2068
KJR MANAGEMENT—See KKR & Co. Inc.; *U.S. Public*, pg. 1255
KJS INDIA PRIVATE LIMITED—See Mondelez International, Inc.; *U.S. Public*, pg. 1461
KJ SPECIALTY PAPER CO., LTD.—See Mitsubishi Paper Mills Limited; *Int'l*, pg. 4967
KJ TECHNOLOGY CONSULTING, INC.; *U.S. Private*, pg. 2317
KJT GROUP, INC.; *U.S. Private*, pg. 2317
KJ WAJA ENGINEERING (M) SDN. BHD.; *Int'l*, pg. 4197
K & K ACTIVE OY—See Lagercrantz Group AB; *Int'l*, pg. 4394
KKALPANA INDUSTRIES (INDIA) LIMITED; *Int'l*, pg. 4198
KKALPANA PLASTICK LTD.—See Bbigplas Poly Pvt Ltd.; *Int'l*, pg. 920
K KAMPUS EDUCATION PRIVATE LIMITED—See KSS Limited; *Int'l*, pg. 4314
K.K. ARISTOCRAT TECHNOLOGIES—See Aristocrat Leisure Limited; *Int'l*, pg. 566
KKB DEUTSCHLAND GMBH—See Kleinkraftwerk Birseck AG (KKB); *Int'l*, pg. 4200
KKB ENGINEERING BERHAD; *Int'l*, pg. 4198
KKB INDUSTRIES (SABAH) SDN. BHD.—See KKB Engineering Berhad; *Int'l*, pg. 4198
K.K. BIRLA GROUP; *Int'l*, pg. 4044
KK BOLD; *U.S. Private*, pg. 2317
KKBOX HONG KONG LIMITED—See KDDI Corporation; *Int'l*, pg. 4112
KKBQ-FM—See Apollo Global Management, Inc.; *U.S. Public*, pg. 163
KKB VERWALTUNGS GMBH—See Kleinkraftwerk Birseck AG (KKB); *Int'l*, pg. 4200
KKC BEARING SERVICE CO., LTD.—See THK CO., LTD.; *Int'l*, pg. 7711
KKCG GROUP; *Int'l*, pg. 4198
K&K CORPORATION—See Krosaki Harima Corporation; *Int'l*, pg. 4307
K&K ELECTRIC, INC.—See Kian Capital Partners, LLC; *U.S. Private*, pg. 2302
K&K ELECTRIC, INC.—See RFE Investment Partners; *U.S. Private*, pg. 3419
KK ENTERPRISE (KUNSHAN) CO., LTD.—See Grand Pacific Petrochemical Corporation; *Int'l*, pg. 3055
KK ENTERPRISE (MALAYSIA) SDN. BHD.—See Grand Pacific Petrochemical Corporation; *Int'l*, pg. 3055
KKE SINGAPORE PTE. LTD.—See KOZO KEIKAKU ENGINEERING Inc; *Int'l*, pg. 4295
K&K EXPRESS LLC; *U.S. Private*, pg. 2249
K K FINCORP LIMITED—See Remi Group; *Int'l*, pg. 6271
KK FINE FOODS PLC—See What's Cooking Group NV; *Int'l*, pg. 8396
KKG KABELKOMMUNIKATION GUSTROW GMBH—See Morgan Stanley; *U.S. Public*, pg. 1473
K & K GLASS, INC.—See Driven Brands Holdings Inc.; *U.S. Public*, pg. 688
K&K GROUP AG; *Int'l*, pg. 4038
K&K INSURANCE BROKERS, INC. CANADA—See Aon plc; *Int'l*, pg. 495
K & K INSURANCE GROUP, INC.—See Aon plc; *Int'l*, pg. 494

K KIOSK AG—See Fomento Economico Mexicano, S.A.B. de C.V.; *Int'l*, pg. 2724
K&K IRON WORKS INC.; *U.S. Private*, pg. 2249
KKK GMBH & CO OHV—See E.ON SE; *Int'l*, pg. 2254
KKK GMBH & CO OHV—See Vattenfall AB; *Int'l*, pg. 8137
K.K. KINGSTON LTD.; *Int'l*, pg. 4044
K.K. KODAK INFORMATION SYSTEMS—See Eastman Kodak Company; *U.S. Public*, pg. 707
K.K. MARUSHIN—See Idemitsu Kosan Co., Ltd.; *Int'l*, pg. 3591
K.K. MEGURO GAJOEN—See Kowa Co., Ltd.; *Int'l*, pg. 4294
K.K. MELEXIS—See Melexis N.V.; *Int'l*, pg. 4808
KKO INTERNATIONAL SA; *Int'l*, pg. 4198
K-KONSULT ELTEKNIK I GAVLE AB—See Sweco AB; *Int'l*, pg. 7363
K. KOUIMTZIS S.A; *Int'l*, pg. 4043
KK PRECISION, INC.—See River Associates Investments, LLC; *U.S. Private*, pg. 3443
KKP TOWER COMPANY LIMITED—See Kiatnakin Bank Public Company Limited; *Int'l*, pg. 4157
K.K. PURAIDO—See ID Holdings Corporation; *Int'l*, pg. 3587
KKR 2006 FUND (GDG) L.P.—See KKR & Co. Inc.; *U.S. Public*, pg. 1255
KKR ALTERNATIVE INVESTMENT MANAGEMENT—See KKR & Co. Inc.; *U.S. Public*, pg. 1255
KKR ASIA LIMITED—See KKR & Co. Inc.; *U.S. Public*, pg. 1255
KKR AUSTRALIA INVESTMENT MANAGEMENT PTY. LIMITED—See KKR & Co. Inc.; *U.S. Public*, pg. 1256
KKR AUSTRALIA PTY LIMITED—See KKR & Co. Inc.; *U.S. Public*, pg. 1255
KKR CANADA ULC—See KKR & Co. Inc.; *U.S. Public*, pg. 1256
KKR CAPITAL MARKETS INDIA PRIVATE LIMITED—See KKR & Co. Inc.; *U.S. Public*, pg. 1256
KKR CAPITAL MARKETS JAPAN LIMITED—See KKR & Co. Inc.; *U.S. Public*, pg. 1256
KKR CAPITAL MARKETS LLC—See KKR & Co. Inc.; *U.S. Public*, pg. 1256
KKR & CO. INC.; *U.S. Public*, pg. 1237
KKR & CO. L.P. - MENLO PARK—See KKR & Co. Inc.; *U.S. Public*, pg. 1255
KKR CREDIT ADVISORS (EMEA) LLP—See KKR & Co. Inc.; *U.S. Public*, pg. 1256
KKR CREDIT ADVISORS (IRELAND)—See KKR & Co. Inc.; *U.S. Public*, pg. 1256
KKR CREDIT ADVISORS (US) LLC—See KKR & Co. Inc.; *U.S. Public*, pg. 1256
KKR CREDIT ADVISORY (UK) LLP—See KKR & Co. Inc.; *U.S. Public*, pg. 1256
KKR FINANCIAL HOLDINGS LLC—See KKR & Co. Inc.; *U.S. Public*, pg. 1256
KKR INDIA ADVISORS PRIVATE LIMITED—See KKR & Co. Inc.; *U.S. Public*, pg. 1256
KKR INDIA FINANCIAL SERVICES PRIVATE LIMITED—See KKR & Co. Inc.; *U.S. Public*, pg. 1256
K.K. RISING SUN—See Idemitsu Kosan Co., Ltd.; *Int'l*, pg. 3591
KKR JAPAN LIMITED—See KKR & Co. Inc.; *U.S. Public*, pg. 1256
KKR LUXEMBOURG S.A R.L.—See KKR & Co. Inc.; *U.S. Public*, pg. 1256
KKR MENA LIMITED—See KKR & Co. Inc.; *U.S. Public*, pg. 1256
KKR PRIVATE EQUITY CONGLOMERATE; *U.S. Private*, pg. 2317
KKRRAFTON DEVELOPERS LIMITED; *Int'l*, pg. 4198
KKR REAL ESTATE FINANCE TRUST INC.; *U.S. Public*, pg. 1267
KKR SAUDI LIMITED—See KKR & Co. Inc.; *U.S. Public*, pg. 1256
KK RWS GROUP—See RWS Holdings plc; *Int'l*, pg. 6437
K.K. SHINYO SEKIYU—See Idemitsu Kosan Co., Ltd.; *Int'l*, pg. 3591
KKS, LTD.—See TOKYO KIKAI SEISAKUSHO LTD.; *Int'l*, pg. 7793
KKSP PRECISION MACHINING, LLC—See Pine Grove Holdings, LLC; *U.S. Private*, pg. 3182
K&K SUPERSTORE SOUTHERN PUBLIC COMPANY LIMITED; *Int'l*, pg. 4038
K.K. SVC TOKYO—See Shell plc; *Int'l*, pg. 6795
KKT CHILLERS INC.—See NIBE Industrier AB; *Int'l*, pg. 5261
KKT CHILLERS—See NIBE Industrier AB; *Int'l*, pg. 5262
KKTC TELSIM; *Int'l*, pg. 4198
K.K. TERRE VERTE—See Seven & i Holdings Co., Ltd.; *Int'l*, pg. 6731
KKT INNOVATE CORPORATION—See Nippon Television Holdings Inc.; *Int'l*, pg. 5356
KKT KRAUS USA CORP—See NIBE Industrier AB; *Int'l*, pg. 5262
KKTV-TV—See Gray Television, Inc.; *U.S. Public*, pg. 960
KKV AGRO POWERS LTD.; *Int'l*, pg. 4198
KKW TRUCKING, INC.; *U.S. Private*, pg. 2317
K.K. YORK KEIBI—See Seven & i Holdings Co., Ltd.; *Int'l*, pg. 6731

K. KYTHREOTIS HOLDINGS PUBLIC LTD.

K. KYTHREOTIS HOLDINGS PUBLIC LTD.; *Int'l*, pg. 4043
K.LAB EDUCMEDIA GMBH—See Ernst Klett AG; *Int'l*, pg. 2495
KLABEN CHRYSLER JEEP DODGE RAM; *U.S. Private*, pg. 2317
KLABIN ARGENTINA S.A.—See Klabin S.A.; *Int'l*, pg. 4198
KLABIN AUSTRIA GMBH—See Klabin S.A.; *Int'l*, pg. 4198
KLAB INC.; *Int'l*, pg. 4198
KLABIN FOREST PRODUCTS COMPANY—See Klabin S.A.; *Int'l*, pg. 4198
KLABIN S.A.; *Int'l*, pg. 4198
KLAB VENTURES INC.—See KLab Inc.; *Int'l*, pg. 4198
KLABZUBA OIL & GAS; *U.S. Private*, pg. 2317
KLA CORPORATION; *U.S. Public*, pg. 1267
KL ACQUISITION CORP.; *U.S. Public*, pg. 1267
KLAD MANUFACTURING COMPANY, LTD.—See Berkshire Hathaway Inc.; *U.S. Public*, pg. 314
K&L ADVERTISING ASIA PTE LTD.—See K&L Inc.; *Int'l*, pg. 4038
K&L ADVERTISING HONG KONG LTD.—See K&L Inc.; *Int'l*, pg. 4038
KLAECKERIBOLAGET AB—See Lantmannen ek for; *Int'l*, pg. 4413
KLAFF REALTY, L.P.; *U.S. Private*, pg. 2317
KLAFF'S, INC.; *U.S. Private*, pg. 2317
KLAFS AG—See Kohler Company; *U.S. Private*, pg. 2339
KLAFS AMERICAS—See Kohler Company; *U.S. Private*, pg. 2339
KLAFS GMBH & CO. KG—See Kohler Company; *U.S. Private*, pg. 2339
KLAFS GMBH—See Kohler Company; *U.S. Private*, pg. 2339
KLAFS TECHNICAL LIMITED—See Kohler Company; *U.S. Private*, pg. 2339
KLAFTERS INC.; *U.S. Private*, pg. 2317
KLAGER PLASTIK GMBH; *Int'l*, pg. 4198
KLAIPEDA STEVEDORING COMPANY—See Koncernas Achemos Grupe; *Int'l*, pg. 4246
KLAIPEDOS NAFTA AB; *Int'l*, pg. 4199
KLAK EHF—See Origo hf.; *Int'l*, pg. 5630
KLAKKI EHF.; *Int'l*, pg. 4199
KLAMATH ENERGY, LLC—See Iberdrola, S.A.; *Int'l*, pg. 3570
KLAMATH PUBLISHING CO. INC.—See Pioneer Newspapers Inc.; *U.S. Private*, pg. 3187
KLAMATH PUBLISHING CO. LLC—See Pioneer Newspapers Inc.; *U.S. Private*, pg. 3187
KLAMFLEX PIPE COUPLINGS (PTY) LTD—See Zurn Elkay Water Solutions Corporation; *U.S. Public*, pg. 2413
K&L AMSTERDAM—See K&L Inc.; *Int'l*, pg. 4038
KLANG CO., LTD.—See Charoen Pokphand Foods Public Company Limited; *Int'l*, pg. 1453
KLANICA 8. OKTOBAR A.D.; *Int'l*, pg. 4199
KLANICA SO LADILNIK AD; *Int'l*, pg. 4199
KLANN PACKAGING GMBH—See Mutares SE & Co. KGaA; *Int'l*, pg. 5105
KLANT CONTACT SERVICES B.V—See Achmea B.V.; *Int'l*, pg. 103
KLARABO SVERIGE AB; *Int'l*, pg. 4199
KLARIA PHARMA HOLDING AB; *Int'l*, pg. 4199
KLARMOBIL GMBH—See freenet AG; *Int'l*, pg. 2770
KLARNA AB; *Int'l*, pg. 4199
KLARNA AUSTRIA GMBH—See Klarna AB; *Int'l*, pg. 4199
KLARNA BV—See Klarna AB; *Int'l*, pg. 4199
KLARNA GMBH—See Klarna AB; *Int'l*, pg. 4199
KLARNA NORGE AS—See Klarna AB; *Int'l*, pg. 4199
KLARNA UK LIMITED—See Klarna AB; *Int'l*, pg. 4199
KLARSEN SA; *Int'l*, pg. 4199
KLAS A.D.; *Int'l*, pg. 4199
KLAS D.D.; *Int'l*, pg. 4199
K LASER TECHNOLOGY (DONG GUAN) CO., LTD.—See K Laser Technology Inc.; *Int'l*, pg. 4037
K LASER TECHNOLOGY (HK) CO., LTD.—See K Laser Technology Inc.; *Int'l*, pg. 4037
K LASER TECHNOLOGY INC.; *Int'l*, pg. 4037
K LASER TECHNOLOGY JAPAN CO., LTD.—See K Laser Technology Inc.; *Int'l*, pg. 4037
K LASER TECHNOLOGY (KOREA) CO., LTD.—See K Laser Technology Inc.; *Int'l*, pg. 4037
K LASER TECHNOLOGY (THAILAND) CO., LTD.—See K Laser Technology Inc.; *Int'l*, pg. 4037
K LASER TECHNOLOGY (USA) CO., LTD.—See K Laser Technology Inc.; *Int'l*, pg. 4037
KLAS MANAGEMENT CO., LTD.—See Singha Estate PCL; *Int'l*, pg. 6944
KLASS CAPITAL CORP.; *Int'l*, pg. 4199
KLASSEN CORPORATION; *U.S. Private*, pg. 2318
KLASSIK RADIO AG; *Int'l*, pg. 4199
KLASSIK RADIO GMBH & CO. KG—See Bertelsmann SE & Co. KGaA; *Int'l*, pg. 995
KLASS INGREDIENTS INC.; *U.S. Private*, pg. 2317
KLASS PACK LIMITED—See Borosil Renewables Limited; *Int'l*, pg. 1114
KLAS - TV—See Nexstar Media Group, Inc.; *U.S. Public*, pg. 1522
KLA SYSTEMS, INC.—See Sciens Capital Management LLC; *U.S. Private*, pg. 3574
KLA-TENCOR ASIA-PAC DISTRIBUTION CORPORATION—See KLA Corporation; *U.S. Public*, pg. 1268
KLA-TENCOR CHINA CORPORATION—See KLA Corporation; *U.S. Public*, pg. 1268
KLA-TENCOR CORP. - TEXAS-FINLE DIVISION—See KLA Corporation; *U.S. Public*, pg. 1268
KLA-TENCOR GMBH—See KLA Corporation; *U.S. Public*, pg. 1268
KLA-TENCOR ITALY S.R.L.—See KLA Corporation; *U.S. Public*, pg. 1268
KLA-TENCOR MASSACHUSETTS—See KLA Corporation; *U.S. Public*, pg. 1268
KLA-TENCOR MIE GMBH—See KLA Corporation; *U.S. Public*, pg. 1268
KLA-TENCOR MIE INDIA PRIVATE LIMITED—See KLA Corporation; *U.S. Public*, pg. 1268
KLA-TENCOR (SINGAPORE) PTE. LTD.—See KLA Corporation; *U.S. Public*, pg. 1268
KLA-TENCOR SOFTWARE INDIA PRIVATE LIMITED—See KLA Corporation; *U.S. Public*, pg. 1268
KLATT FORDERTECHNIK GMBH—See Hormann Holding GmbH & Co. KG; *Int'l*, pg. 3480
KLAUBER BROTHERS INC.; *U.S. Private*, pg. 2318
KLAUER MANUFACTURING COMPANY; *U.S. Private*, pg. 2318
KLAUKE FRANCE SARL—See Emerson Electric Co.; *U.S. Public*, pg. 750
KLAUKE UK LIMITED—See Emerson Electric Co.; *U.S. Public*, pg. 750
KLAUS BERGER AUTOZUBEHOR GROSSHANDEL GMBH—See Stahlgruber Otto Gruber GmbH & Co. KG; *Int'l*, pg. 7164
KLAUSNER TRADING INTERNATIONAL GMBH; *Int'l*, pg. 4199
KLAUSNER TRADING USA, INC.—See Klausner Trading International GmbH; *Int'l*, pg. 4199
KLAUSSNER FURNITURE INDUSTRIES, INC.—See Monomoy Capital Partners LLC; *U.S. Private*, pg. 2772
KLAUS STEILMANN GMBH & CO. KG—See Steilmann Holding AG; *Int'l*, pg. 7193
KLAUS TECH, INC.; *U.S. Public*, pg. 1269
KLAUS UNION GMBH & CO. KG; *Int'l*, pg. 4199
KLAVENESS ASIA PTE. LTD.—See Rederiaksjeselskapet Torvald Klaveness; *Int'l*, pg. 6246
KLAVENESS COMBINATION CARRIERS ASA; *Int'l*, pg. 4199
KLAVENESS COMBINATION CARRIERS ASIA PTE. LTD.—See Klaveness Combination Carriers ASA; *Int'l*, pg. 4199
KLAVENESS MARINE HOLDING AS; *Int'l*, pg. 4200
KLAVIS INC.—See Money Forward, Inc.; *Int'l*, pg. 5032
KLAVIYO, INC.; *U.S. Public*, pg. 1269
KLAX LICENSING, INC.—See Spanish Broadcasting System Inc.; *U.S. Public*, pg. 1914
KLAY INSTRUMENTS B. V.—See TE Connectivity Ltd.; *Int'l*, pg. 7496
K&L BEVERAGE COMPANY, LLC—See Young's Holdings, Inc.; *U.S. Private*, pg. 4593
KLB INTRALOGISTIK GMBH—See Wuppermann AG; *Int'l*, pg. 8503
KLCC (HOLDINGS) SDN. BHD.—See Petroliam Nasional Berhad; *Int'l*, pg. 5829
KLCC PROPERTY HOLDINGS BERHAD—See Petroliam Nasional Berhad; *Int'l*, pg. 5829
KLC HOLDINGS, LTD.; *U.S. Private*, pg. 2318
KLC LAND COMPANY—See Walton Street Capital, LLC; *U.S. Private*, pg. 4435
K&L CREATIVE SEVICES—See K&L Inc.; *Int'l*, pg. 4038
KLDISCOVERY, INC.—See Pivotal Acquisition Corp.; *U.S. Private*, pg. 3192
KLDISCOVERY ONTRACK CANADA CO.—See Pivotal Acquisition Corp.; *U.S. Private*, pg. 3192
K & L DISTRIBUTORS, INC.; *U.S. Private*, pg. 2249
KLD LABS, INC.—See Ensco Inc.; *U.S. Public*, pg. 1402
KLEANGAS ENERGY TECHNOLOGIES, INC.; *U.S. Private*, pg. 2318
KLEANNARA CO., LTD - CHEONGJU FACTORY—See KleanNara Co., Ltd; *Int'l*, pg. 4200
KLEANNARA CO., LTD; *Int'l*, pg. 4200
KLEAR-VU CORPORATION; *U.S. Private*, pg. 2318
KLEBERG BANK, N.A.—See Kleberg & Company Bankers, Inc.; *U.S. Private*, pg. 2318
KLEBERG & COMPANY BANKERS, INC.; *U.S. Private*, pg. 2318
KLEBER LA PEROUSE SNC—See BNP Paribas SA; *Int'l*, pg. 1091
KLEBER PNEUMATIQUES SA—See Compagnie Generale des Etablissements Michelin SCA; *Int'l*, pg. 1743
KLEBER REIFEN GMBH—See Compagnie Generale des Etablissements Michelin SCA; *Int'l*, pg. 1743
KLECAR EUROPE SUD SCS—See BNP Paribas SA; *Int'l*, pg. 1091
KLECAR FONCIER ESPANA SA—See BNP Paribas SA; *Int'l*, pg. 1091
KLECAR FRANCE SNC—See BNP Paribas SA; *Int'l*, pg. 1091
KL ECO CITY SDN BHD—See S P Setia Berhad; *Int'l*, pg. 6443

CORPORATE AFFILIATIONS

KLEEMANN ASANSOR SAN. VE TIC. A.S.—See KLEEMANN HELLAS S.A.; *Int'l*, pg. 4200
KLEEMANN GMBH—See Deere & Company; *U.S. Public*, pg. 647
KLEEMANN HELLAS S.A.; *Int'l*, pg. 4200
KLEEMANN LIFTOVI D.O.O.—See KLEEMANN HELLAS S.A.; *Int'l*, pg. 4200
KLEEMANN LIFT RO S.R.L.—See KLEEMANN HELLAS S.A.; *Int'l*, pg. 4200
KLEEMANN LIFTS RUS—See KLEEMANN HELLAS S.A.; *Int'l*, pg. 4200
KLEEMANN LIFTS U.K. LTD—See KLEEMANN HELLAS S.A.; *Int'l*, pg. 4200
KLEENEZE UK LIMITED—See JRjr33, Inc.; *U.S. Private*, pg. 2240
KLEENHEAT PTY LTD—See Wesfarmers Limited; *Int'l*, pg. 8381
KLEENLINE, LLC—See Leonard Green & Partners, L.P.; *U.S. Private*, pg. 2428
KLEENMARK SERVICES CORP.; *U.S. Private*, pg. 2318
KLEEN-TECH BUILDING SERVICES; *U.S. Private*, pg. 2318
KLEEN-TECH SERVICES, LLC—See Concierge Building Services, LLC; *U.S. Private*, pg. 1009
KLEEN TEST PRODUCTS DIVISION MEQUON PLANT—See Meridian Industries, Inc.; *U.S. Private*, pg. 2673
KLEEN-TEX DO BRAZIL—See Kleen-Tex Industries, Inc.; *U.S. Private*, pg. 2318
KLEEN-TEX INDUSTRIES GMBH—See Kleen-Tex Industries, Inc.; *U.S. Private*, pg. 2318
KLEEN-TEX INDUSTRIES, INC.; *U.S. Private*, pg. 2318
KLEEN-TEX INDUSTRIES LTD.—See Kleen-Tex Industries, Inc.; *U.S. Private*, pg. 2318
KLEEN-TEX JAPAN, INC.—See Kleen-Tex Industries, Inc.; *U.S. Private*, pg. 2318
KLEEN-TEX POLSKA, SP. Z.O.O.—See Kleen-Tex Industries, Inc.; *U.S. Private*, pg. 2318
KLEEN-TEX SOUTH AFRICA (PTY) LTD.—See Kleen-Tex Industries, Inc.; *U.S. Private*, pg. 2318
KLEEN-TEX THAILAND CO. LTD.—See Kleen-Tex Industries, Inc.; *U.S. Private*, pg. 2318
KLEER VU DELUXE ALBUMS INC.; *Int'l*, pg. 4200
KLEET LUMBER COMPANY, INC.—See Builders First-Source, Inc.; *U.S. Public*, pg. 410
KLEFER A.E.—See Tecnolama S.A.; *Int'l*, pg. 7516
KLEGG ELECTRONICS, INC.; *U.S. Public*, pg. 1269
KLEIDER SOURCING LIMITED—See PDS Limited; *Int'l*, pg. 5770
KLEIDON & ASSOCIATES; *U.S. Private*, pg. 2318
KLEIN AGENCY, INC.—See Marsh & McLennan Companies, Inc.; *U.S. Public*, pg. 1381
KLEIN BROS. HOLDINGS, LTD.; *U.S. Private*, pg. 2318
KLEIN BROS. - SNACK & PACKAGED NUT DIVISON—See Klein Bros. Holdings, Ltd.; *U.S. Private*, pg. 2318
KLEIN & COSTA INSURANCE SERVICES—See Western Security Surplus Insurance Brokers, Inc.; *U.S. Private*, pg. 4496
KLEIN CUTLERY, LLC—See Klein Tools Inc.; *U.S. Private*, pg. 2319
KLEIN-DICKERT CO. INC.; *U.S. Private*, pg. 2319
KLEINE EQUIPMENT; *U.S. Private*, pg. 2319
KLEINER PERKINS CAUFIELD & BYERS; *U.S. Private*, pg. 2319
KLEINEWEFERS BETEILIGUNGS-GMBH—See Jagenberg AG; *Int'l*, pg. 3870
KLEINE WOLKE AG—See L. Possehl & Co. mbH; *Int'l*, pg. 4383
KLEINE WOLKE TEXTILGESELLSCHAFT MBH & CO. KG—See L. Possehl & Co. mbH; *Int'l*, pg. 4383
KLEINFELDER AUSTRALIA PTY LTD—See Goldberg Lindsay & Co., LLC; *U.S. Private*, pg. 1729
KLEINFELDER CENTRAL, INC.—See Goldberg Lindsay & Co., LLC; *U.S. Private*, pg. 1729
KLEINFELDER EAST, INC.—See Goldberg Lindsay & Co., LLC; *U.S. Private*, pg. 1729
THE KLEINFELDER GROUP, INC.—See Goldberg Lindsay & Co., LLC; *U.S. Private*, pg. 1729
KLEINFELDER GUAM, LLC—See Goldberg Lindsay & Co., LLC; *U.S. Private*, pg. 1729
KLEINFELDER INTERNATIONAL, INC.-CALGARY—See Goldberg Lindsay & Co., LLC; *U.S. Private*, pg. 1729
KLEINFELDER INTERNATIONAL, INC.—See Goldberg Lindsay & Co., LLC; *U.S. Private*, pg. 1729
KLEINFELDER NORTHEAST, INC.—See Goldberg Lindsay & Co., LLC; *U.S. Private*, pg. 1729
KLEINFELDER SOUTHEAST, INC.—See Goldberg Lindsay & Co., LLC; *U.S. Private*, pg. 1729
KLEINFELDER WEST, INC.—See Goldberg Lindsay & Co., LLC; *U.S. Private*, pg. 1730
KLEIN FINANCIAL ADVISORS INC.—See EP Wealth Advisors, LLC; *U.S. Public*, pg. 1411
KLEIN FOODS INC.; *U.S. Private*, pg. 2318
KLEIN & HEUCHAN, INC.; *U.S. Private*, pg. 2318
KLEIN-KAUFMAN CORP.; *U.S. Private*, pg. 2319
KLEINKNECHT ELECTRIC CO. INC.; *U.S. Private*, pg. 2319
KLEINKRAFTWERK BIRSECK AG (KKB); *Int'l*, pg. 4200

COMPANY NAME INDEX

KLEINMANN GMBH—See Illinois Tool Works Inc.; *U.S. Public*, pg. 1109
KLEIN MARINE SYSTEMS, INC.—See General Oceans AS; *Int'l*, pg. 2919
KLEINPARTNERS CAPITAL CORP.; *U.S. Private*, pg. 2319
KLEINPETER DAIRY FARM INC.; *U.S. Private*, pg. 2319
KLEINSCHMIDT AGENCY, INC.—See Arthur J. Gallagher & Co.; *U.S. Public*, pg. 206
KLEINSCHMIDT INC.; *U.S. Private*, pg. 2319
KLEIN'S INC.; *U.S. Private*, pg. 2319
KLEINS SUPERMARKETS INC.—See Klein's Inc.; *U.S. Private*, pg. 2319
KLEIN STEEL DIRECT ROCHESTER—See Klein Steel Service Inc.; *U.S. Private*, pg. 2319
KLEIN STEEL OF SYRACUSE—See Klein Steel Service Inc.; *U.S. Private*, pg. 2319
KLEIN STEEL OF WESTERN NEW YORK—See Klein Steel Service Inc.; *U.S. Private*, pg. 2319
KLEIN STEEL SERVICE INC.; *U.S. Private*, pg. 2319
KLEIN TOOLS DE MEXICO S DE R.L DE C.V.—See Klein Tools Inc.; *U.S. Private*, pg. 2319
KLEIN TOOLS INC.; *U.S. Private*, pg. 2319
KLEIN WANZLEBENER SAATZUCHT MAROC S.A.R.L.A.U.—See KWS SAAT SE & Co. KGaA; *Int'l*, pg. 4353
KLEINWORT BENSON BANK LIMITED—See Societe Generale S.A.; *Int'l*, pg. 7039
KLEINWORT BENSON (CHANNEL ISLANDS) LIMITED—See Societe Generale S.A.; *Int'l*, pg. 7039
KLEISS GEARS, INC.—See Victrex plc; *Int'l*, pg. 8190
KLEIWARENFABRIEK BUGGENUM B.V.—See CRH plc; *Int'l*, pg. 1845
KLEMENT SAUSAGE CO., INC.—See Altamont Capital Partners; *U.S. Private*, pg. 205
KLEM EURO RSCG—See Vivendi SE; *Int'l*, pg. 8269
KLEMKE MINING CORPORATION; *Int'l*, pg. 4200
KLEMM BOHRTECHNIK GMBH.—See BAUER Aktiengesellschaft; *Int'l*, pg. 893
KLEMM TANK LINES, INC.—See The Goldman Sachs Group, Inc.; *U.S. Public*, pg. 2080
KLEN INTERNATIONAL (74) PTY LTD.—See Avantor, Inc.; *U.S. Public*, pg. 242
KLEO HALBLEITERTECHNIK GMBH.—See Carl-Zeiss-Stiftung; *Int'l*, pg. 1336
KLEOPATRA HOLDINGS 2 S.C.A.—See Strategic Value Partners, LLC; *U.S. Private*, pg. 3836
KLEOS SPACE SA; *Int'l*, pg. 4200
KLEPIERRE ATHINON FONCIERE—See Klepierre SA; *Int'l*, pg. 4200
KLEPIERRE CONSEIL SNC—See Klepierre SA; *Int'l*, pg. 4200
KLEPIERRE CRETEIL SCI—See Klepierre SA; *Int'l*, pg. 4200
KLEPIERRE CZ SRO—See Klepierre SA; *Int'l*, pg. 4200
KLEPIERRE FINANCE SAS—See Klepierre SA; *Int'l*, pg. 4200
KLEPIERRE LARISSA LTD.—See Klepierre SA; *Int'l*, pg. 4200
KLEPIERRE MAKEDONIA FONCIERE—See Klepierre SA; *Int'l*, pg. 4200
KLEPIERRE MANAGEMENT ITALIA S.R.L.—See Klepierre SA; *Int'l*, pg. 4200
KLEPIERRE MANAGEMENT MAGYARORSZAG KFT.—See BNP Paribas SA; *Int'l*, pg. 1091
KLEPIERRE NEA EFKARPIA FONCIERE—See Klepierre SA; *Int'l*, pg. 4200
KLEPIERRE NEDERLAND B.V.—See Klepierre SA; *Int'l*, pg. 4200
KLEPIERRE NORDICA BV—See Klepierre SA; *Int'l*, pg. 4200
KLEPIERRE PLZEN A.S.—See Klepierre SA; *Int'l*, pg. 4200
KLEPIERRE POZNAN SP Z.O.O—See Klepierre SA; *Int'l*, pg. 4200
KLEPIERRE PRAHA SRO—See Klepierre SA; *Int'l*, pg. 4200
KLEPIERRE SA; *Int'l*, pg. 4200
KLEPIERRE VASTGOED ONTWIKKELING B.V.—See Klepierre SA; *Int'l*, pg. 4200
KLEPPER FALTBOOTWERFT AG; *Int'l*, pg. 4201
KLE PROJET 1 SAS—See BNP Paribas SA; *Int'l*, pg. 1091
KLERKX GROEP BV—See Macintosh Retail Group NV; *Int'l*, pg. 4622
KLESCH & COMPANY LIMITED—See Klesch & Company SA; *Int'l*, pg. 4201
KLESCH & COMPANY SA; *Int'l*, pg. 4201
KLETT BULGARIA EOOD—See Ernst Klett AG; *Int'l*, pg. 2495
KLETT CONSTRUCTION COMPANY; *U.S. Private*, pg. 2319
KLETT HELLAS E.M.E.—See Ernst Klett AG; *Int'l*, pg. 2495
KLETT IZDAVACKA KUCA D.O.O.—See Ernst Klett AG; *Int'l*, pg. 2495
KLETT NAKLADATELSTVI S.R.O.—See Ernst Klett AG; *Int'l*, pg. 2495
KLETT UND BALMER AG—See Ernst Klett AG; *Int'l*, pg. 2495

KLEVEN MARITIME A/S—See TDR Capital LLP; *Int'l*, pg. 7494
KLEVEN MARITIME TECHNOLOGY AS—See TDR Capital LLP; *Int'l*, pg. 7494
KLEVENS CAPITAL MANAGEMENT, INC.—See Mariner Wealth Advisors, LLC; *U.S. Private*, pg. 2575
KLEVEN VERFT AS—See TDR Capital LLP; *Int'l*, pg. 7494
KLEVERS GMBH & CO. KG; *Int'l*, pg. 4201
KLEWIN CONSTRUCTION INC.; *U.S. Private*, pg. 2319
KLEW-TV—See Sinclair, Inc.; *U.S. Public*, pg. 1886
KLEYSEN GROUP L.P.—See Mullen Group Ltd.; *Int'l*, pg. 5080
K&L FREIGHT MANAGEMENT, INC.; *U.S. Private*, pg. 2249
KLFY, LP—See Nexstar Media Group, Inc.; *U.S. Public*, pg. 1522
K&L GATES LLP; *U.S. Private*, pg. 2249
KLG CAPITAL SERVICES LIMITED; *Int'l*, pg. 4201
KLG, INC.—See Savills plc; *Int'l*, pg. 6599
KLH CAPITAL L.P.; *U.S. Private*, pg. 2319
KLH KALTETECHNIK GMBH—See Technotrans AG; *Int'l*, pg. 7511
KLICK COMMUNICATIONS INC.; *Int'l*, pg. 4201
KLICKENERGIE GMBH & CO. KG—See RWE AG; *Int'l*, pg. 6434
KLICK-LEWIS INC.; *U.S. Private*, pg. 2319
KLICKRENT GMBH—See Zeppelin GmbH; *Int'l*, pg. 8637
KLI CONSULTING GROUP, LLC—See SoftBank Group Corp.; *Int'l*, pg. 7053
KLIENTEC INTERNATIONAL SDN. BHD.—See Esthetics International Group Berhad; *Int'l*, pg. 2518
KLIGER-WEISS INFOSYSTEMS, INC.; *U.S. Private*, pg. 2320
KLIKKI AB—See Nordic Morning Plc; *Int'l*, pg. 5422
KLIKKI APS—See Nordic Morning Plc; *Int'l*, pg. 5422
KLIKKI AS—See Nordic Morning Plc; *Int'l*, pg. 5422
KLIKKICOM OY—See Nordic Morning Plc; *Int'l*, pg. 5422
KLIKLOK CORPORATION; *U.S. Private*, pg. 2320
KLIKLOK INTERNATIONAL—See Kliklok Corporation; *U.S. Private*, pg. 2320
KLIKON GROUP HOLDINGS PTY LIMITED; *Int'l*, pg. 4201
KLIK TECHNOLOGIES CORP.—See Checkalt, LLC; *U.S. Private*, pg. 869
KLIL INDUSTRIES LTD.; *Int'l*, pg. 4201
KLIL (UK) LTD.—See Klil Industries Ltd.; *Int'l*, pg. 4201
KLIMA BELGIUM NV—See VDL Groep B.V.; *Int'l*, pg. 8142
KLIMAMIETEN AS GMBH—See ANDREWS SYKES GROUP PLC; *Int'l*, pg. 452
KLIMAN SALES INC.; *U.S. Private*, pg. 2320
KLIMASAN KLIMA SANAYI VE TICARET AS; *Int'l*, pg. 4201
KLIMATEKNIKK OSLO AS—See Instalco AB; *Int'l*, pg. 3722
KLIMATEK VENTILATIONSMATERIEL A/S—See Lindab International AB; *Int'l*, pg. 4503
KLIMATROR I STOCKHOLM AB—See Instalco AB; *Int'l*, pg. 3722
KLIMAVENT D.D.; *Int'l*, pg. 4201
KLIM'TOP CONTROLS SAS—See VINCI S.A.; *Int'l*, pg. 8223
K&L INC.; *Int'l*, pg. 4038
KLINDWORTH-KRONOL ENERGIE GMBH & CO. KG—See Marquard & Bahls AG; *Int'l*, pg. 4699
K LINE ACCOUNTING AND FINANCE CO., LTD.—See Kawasaki Kisen Kaisha, Ltd.; *Int'l*, pg. 4099
K LINE AIR SERVICE (TAIWAN) LTD—See Kawasaki Kisen Kaisha, Ltd.; *Int'l*, pg. 4099
K LINE AIR TRAVEL LTD.—See Kawasaki Kisen Kaisha, Ltd.; *Int'l*, pg. 4100
K LINE AMERICA, INC.—See Kawasaki Kisen Kaisha, Ltd.; *Int'l*, pg. 4099
K LINE (AUSTRALIA) PTY. LTD.—See Kawasaki Kisen Kaisha, Ltd.; *Int'l*, pg. 4099
K LINE AUTO LOGISTICS PTY. LTD.—See Kawasaki Kisen Kaisha, Ltd.; *Int'l*, pg. 4099
K LINE AUTO LOGISTICS PTY. LTD.—See Qube Holdings Limited; *Int'l*, pg. 6158
K LINE (BELGIUM) NV—See Kawasaki Kisen Kaisha, Ltd.; *Int'l*, pg. 4099
K LINE BULK SHIPPING (UK) LIMITED—See Kawasaki Kisen Kaisha, Ltd.; *Int'l*, pg. 4099
K LINE BUSINESS SYSTEMS, LTD.—See Kawasaki Kisen Kaisha, Ltd.; *Int'l*, pg. 4099
K LINE CANADA LTD.—See Kawasaki Kisen Kaisha, Ltd.; *Int'l*, pg. 4099
K LINE (CHINA) LTD.—See Kawasaki Kisen Kaisha, Ltd.; *Int'l*, pg. 4099
K-LINE CONSTRUCTION LTD.; *Int'l*, pg. 4042
K LINE CONTAINER SERVICE (THAILAND) LTD.—See Kawasaki Kisen Kaisha, Ltd.; *Int'l*, pg. 4099
K LINE (DEUTSCHLAND) GMBH—See Kawasaki Kisen Kaisha, Ltd.; *Int'l*, pg. 4099
K LINE EUROPEAN SEA HIGHWAY SERVICES GMBH—See Kawasaki Kisen Kaisha, Ltd.; *Int'l*, pg. 4099
K LINE (EUROPE) LTD.—See Kawasaki Kisen Kaisha, Ltd.; *Int'l*, pg. 4099

KLINGELNBERG AG

K LINE (FINLAND) OY—See Kawasaki Kisen Kaisha, Ltd.; *Int'l*, pg. 4099
KLINE HILL PARTNERS LLC; *U.S. Private*, pg. 2320
K LINE HOLDING (EUROPE) LIMITED—See Kawasaki Kisen Kaisha, Ltd.; *Int'l*, pg. 4099
K LINE (HONG KONG) LTD.—See Kawasaki Kisen Kaisha, Ltd.; *Int'l*, pg. 4099
K LINE (KOREA) LTD.—See Kawasaki Kisen Kaisha, Ltd.; *Int'l*, pg. 4099
K LINE LNG SHIPPING (UK) LIMITED—See Kawasaki Kisen Kaisha, Ltd.; *Int'l*, pg. 4099
K LINE LOGISTICS (AUSTRALIA) PTY. LTD.—See Kawasaki Kisen Kaisha, Ltd.; *Int'l*, pg. 4100
K LINE LOGISTICS (CHINA) LTD.—See Kawasaki Kisen Kaisha, Ltd.; *Int'l*, pg. 4100
K LINE LOGISTICS FRANCE S.A.S—See Kawasaki Kisen Kaisha, Ltd.; *Int'l*, pg. 4100
K LINE LOGISTICS (HONG KONG) LTD.—See Kawasaki Kisen Kaisha, Ltd.; *Int'l*, pg. 4100
K LINE LOGISTICS, LTD.—See Kawasaki Kisen Kaisha, Ltd.; *Int'l*, pg. 4100
K LINE LOGISTICS (MALAYSIA) SDN BHD—See Kawasaki Kisen Kaisha, Ltd.; *Int'l*, pg. 4100
K LINE LOGISTICS (MEXICO), S.A. DE C.V—See Kawasaki Kisen Kaisha, Ltd.; *Int'l*, pg. 4100
K LINE LOGISTICS (SINGAPORE) PTE. LTD.—See Kawasaki Kisen Kaisha, Ltd.; *Int'l*, pg. 4100
K LINE LOGISTICS (THAILAND) LTD.—See Kawasaki Kisen Kaisha, Ltd.; *Int'l*, pg. 4100
K LINE LOGISTICS (U.K.) LTD.—See Kawasaki Kisen Kaisha, Ltd.; *Int'l*, pg. 4100
K LINE LOGISTICS (U.S.A.) INC.—See Kawasaki Kisen Kaisha, Ltd.; *Int'l*, pg. 4100
K LINE LOGISTICS (VIETNAM) CO., LTD.—See Kawasaki Kisen Kaisha, Ltd.; *Int'l*, pg. 4100
K LINE MARITIME (MALAYSIA) SDN BHD—See Kawasaki Kisen Kaisha, Ltd.; *Int'l*, pg. 4100
K LINE MEXICO SA DE CV—See Kawasaki Kisen Kaisha, Ltd.; *Int'l*, pg. 4100
K LINE (NEDERLAND) B.V.—See Kawasaki Kisen Kaisha, Ltd.; *Int'l*, pg. 4099
K LINE (NORWAY) AS—See Kawasaki Kisen Kaisha, Ltd.; *Int'l*, pg. 4099
K LINE OFFSHORE AS—See Kawasaki Kisen Kaisha, Ltd.; *Int'l*, pg. 4100
K LINE (PORTUGAL)-AGENTES DE NAVAGACAO, S.A.—See Kawasaki Kisen Kaisha, Ltd.; *Int'l*, pg. 4099
K-LINE PRAXISLOSUNGEN GMBH—See CompuGroup Medical SE & Co. KGaA; *Int'l*, pg. 1756
K LINE PTE LTD—See Kawasaki Kisen Kaisha, Ltd.; *Int'l*, pg. 4100
K LINE RORO & BULK AGENCIA MARITIMA LTDA.—See Kawasaki Kisen Kaisha, Ltd.; *Int'l*, pg. 4100
K LINE RORO BULK SHIP MANAGEMENT CO., LTD.—See Kawasaki Kisen Kaisha, Ltd.; *Int'l*, pg. 4100
K LINE RORO SERVICES LTD.—See Kawasaki Kisen Kaisha, Ltd.; *Int'l*, pg. 4100
K LINE (SCANDINAVIA) HOLDING A/S—See Kawasaki Kisen Kaisha, Ltd.; *Int'l*, pg. 4099
K LINE SHIP MANAGEMENT CO., LTD.—See Kawasaki Kisen Kaisha, Ltd.; *Int'l*, pg. 4100
K LINE SHIP MANAGEMENT (INDIA) PVT LTD—See Kawasaki Kisen Kaisha, Ltd.; *Int'l*, pg. 4100
K LINE SHIP MANAGEMENT (SINGAPORE) PTE LTD—See Kawasaki Kisen Kaisha, Ltd.; *Int'l*, pg. 4099
K LINE SHIPPING (SOUTH AFRICA) PTY. LTD.—See Kawasaki Kisen Kaisha, Ltd.; *Int'l*, pg. 4100
K LINE SHIPPING (SOUTH AFRICA) PTY. LTD.—See Kawasaki Kisen Kaisha, Ltd.; *Int'l*, pg. 4100
K LINE SHIPPING (SOUTH AFRICA) PTY. LTD.—See Kawasaki Kisen Kaisha, Ltd.; *Int'l*, pg. 4100
K LINE SHIPPING (SOUTH AFRICA) PTY. LTD.—See Kawasaki Kisen Kaisha, Ltd.; *Int'l*, pg. 4100
K LINE (SINGAPORE) PTE LTD—See Kawasaki Kisen Kaisha, Ltd.; *Int'l*, pg. 4099
K LINE (SWEDEN) AB—See Kawasaki Kisen Kaisha, Ltd.; *Int'l*, pg. 4099
K LINE SYSTEMS, LTD.—See Kawasaki Kisen Kaisha, Ltd.; *Int'l*, pg. 4100
K LINE (TAIWAN) LTD.—See Kawasaki Kisen Kaisha, Ltd.; *Int'l*, pg. 4099
K LINE (THAILAND) LTD.—See Kawasaki Kisen Kaisha, Ltd.; *Int'l*, pg. 4099
K LINE TRAVEL, LTD.—See Kawasaki Kisen Kaisha, Ltd.; *Int'l*, pg. 4100
KLINE VOLVO INC.; *U.S. Private*, pg. 2320
KLINGBEIL CAPITAL MANAGEMENT; *U.S. Private*, pg. 2320
KLINGE HOLDINGS PTY LTD—See Compagnie Generale des Etablissements Michelin SCA; *Int'l*, pg. 1743
KLINGEL-CARPENTER MORTUARY, INC.—See Service Corporation International; *U.S. Public*, pg. 1871
KLINGELNBERG AG; *Int'l*, pg. 4201
KLINGELNBERG AMERICA INC.—See Klingelnberg AG; *Int'l*, pg. 4201
KLINGELNBERG DO BRASIL—See Klingelnberg AG; *Int'l*, pg. 4201
KLINGELNBERG (FRANCE) SAS—See Klingelnberg AG; *Int'l*, pg. 4201

KLINGELNBERG AG

KLINGELNBERG IMEXMA SA—See Klingelnberg AG; *Int'l*, pg. 4201
KLINGELNBERG INDIA PRIVATE LTD.—See Klingelnberg AG; *Int'l*, pg. 4201
KLINGELNBERG ITALIANA SRL.—See Klingelnberg AG; *Int'l*, pg. 4201
KLINGELNBERG (JAPAN) LTD.—See Klingelnberg AG; *Int'l*, pg. 4201
KLINGELNBERG-KLAUSS ELECTRONICS B.V.; *Int'l*, pg. 4201
KLINGELNBERG MEXICO S.A. DE C.V.—See Klingelnberg AG; *Int'l*, pg. 4201
KLINGENBERG DEKORAMIK GMBH—See QuattroR SGR S.p.A.; *Int'l*, pg. 6157
KLINGENBURG GMBH—See Carel Industries S.p.A.; *Int'l*, pg. 1324
KLINGENBURG INTERNATIONAL SP. Z O.O.—See Carel Industries S.p.A.; *Int'l*, pg. 1324
KLINGENBURG UK LTD.—See Carel Industries S.p.A.; *Int'l*, pg. 1324
KLINGENBURG USA, LLC—See Carel Industries S.p.A.; *Int'l*, pg. 1324
KLINGENSTEIN, FIELDS & CO., L.P.; *U.S. Private*, pg. 2320
KLINGER COMPANIES INCORPORATED; *U.S. Private*, pg. 2320
KLINGLER & ASSOCIATES PC—See Smith Elliott Kearns & Company, LLC; *U.S. Private*, pg. 2320
KLINGLER TEXTIL AG—See Getzner Textil AG; *Int'l*, pg. 2954
KLINGSHIRN WINERY; *U.S. Private*, pg. 2320
KLINIK AM ROSENBERG HEIDEN—See Remgro Limited; *Int'l*, pg. 6270
KLINIK ANIS SDN. BHD.—See Qualitas Medical Group Limited; *Int'l*, pg. 6151
KLINIK BAD HERRENALB GMBH—See MK-Kliniken AG; *Int'l*, pg. 5001
KLINIK BIRSHOF AG—See Remgro Limited; *Int'l*, pg. 6270
KLINIK CATTERALL, KHOO AND RAJA MALEK SDN. BHD.—See Qualitas Medical Group Limited; *Int'l*, pg. 6151
KLINIK DAIMAN SDN. BHD.—See Qualitas Medical Group Limited; *Int'l*, pg. 6151
KLINIK DHAS SDN. BHD.—See Qualitas Medical Group Limited; *Int'l*, pg. 6151
KLINIK DR NUR AINITA SDN. BHD.—See Qualitas Medical Group Limited; *Int'l*, pg. 6151
KLINIKEN HERZBERG UND OSTERODE GMBH—See Fresenius SE & Co. KGaA; *Int'l*, pg. 2779
KLINIKEN MILTENBERG-ERLENBACH GMBH—See Fresenius SE & Co. KGaA; *Int'l*, pg. 2779
KLINIKEN MUNCHEN PASING UND PERLACH GMBH—See Fresenius SE & Co. KGaA; *Int'l*, pg. 2779
KLINIK FEUERBERG GMBH—See Asklepios Kliniken GmbH & Co. KGaA; *Int'l*, pg. 624
KLINIK FUR HERZCHIRURGIE DER HERZ- UND GEFASS-KLINIK GMBH—See Asklepios Kliniken GmbH & Co. KGaA; *Int'l*, pg. 624
KLINIK FUR HERZCHIRURGIE KARLSRUHE GMBH—See Fresenius SE & Co. KGaA; *Int'l*, pg. 2779
KLINIK HAUS FRANKEN GMBH—See Asklepios Kliniken GmbH & Co. KGaA; *Int'l*, pg. 624
KLINIK HILDESHEIMER LAND GMBH—See Fresenius SE & Co. KGaA; *Int'l*, pg. 2779
KLINIK HIRSLANDEN AG—See Remgro Limited; *Int'l*, pg. 6270
KLINIK JJ (JOHOR) SDN. BHD.—See Qualitas Medical Group Limited; *Int'l*, pg. 6151
KLINIK KIPFENBERG GMBH—See Fresenius SE & Co. KGaA; *Int'l*, pg. 2779
KLINIK LUDHER SDN. BHD.—See Qualitas Medical Group Limited; *Int'l*, pg. 6151
KLINIK PANTAI SDN. BHD.—See Qualitas Medical Group Limited; *Int'l*, pg. 6151
KLINIK PORT DICKSON SDN. BHD.—See Qualitas Medical Group Limited; *Int'l*, pg. 6151
KLINIK PYRAMIDE AM SEE AG; *Int'l*, pg. 4201
KLINIK SALAK SDN. BHD.—See Qualitas Medical Group Limited; *Int'l*, pg. 6151
KLINIK SALAK (SELANGOR) SDN. BHD.—See Qualitas Medical Group Limited; *Int'l*, pg. 6151
KLINIK SYED ALWI DAN CHANDRAN (PENANG) SDN. BHD.—See Qualitas Medical Group Limited; *Int'l*, pg. 6151
KLINIK THOMAS SDN. BHD.—See Qualitas Medical Group Limited; *Int'l*, pg. 6151
KLINIKUM ERFURT BEWACHUNGS GMBH—See Fresenius SE & Co. KGaA; *Int'l*, pg. 2780
KLINIKUM FRANKFURT (ODER) GMBH—See Asklepios Kliniken GmbH & Co. KGaA; *Int'l*, pg. 624
KLINIKUM GIFHORN GMBH—See Fresenius SE & Co. KGaA; *Int'l*, pg. 2779
KLINIKUM HILDESHEIM GMBH—See Fresenius SE & Co. KGaA; *Int'l*, pg. 2779
KLINIKUM MEININGEN GMBH—See Fresenius SE & Co. KGaA; *Int'l*, pg. 2779
KLINIKUM SALZGITTER GMBH—See Fresenius SE & Co. KGaA; *Int'l*, pg. 2779

KLINIKUM UELZEN GMBH—See Fresenius SE & Co. KGaA; *Int'l*, pg. 2779
THE KLINIQUE MEDICAL CLINIC PUBLIC COMPANY LIMITED; *Int'l*, pg. 7663
KLINISCH LABO RIGO BV B.V.B.A.—See Sonic Healthcare Limited; *Int'l*, pg. 7097
KLINKE BROTHERS ICE CREAM CO.; *U.S. Private*, pg. 2320
K&L INTERACTIVE INC.—See K&L Inc.; *Int'l*, pg. 4038
KLIPFEL HEFE AG—See Compagnie des Levures Lesaffre SA; *Int'l*, pg. 1738
KLIPPAN AB—See Celest Paper Klippan AB; *Int'l*, pg. 1392
KLIPSCH GROUP, INC.—See VOXX International Corporation; *U.S. Public*, pg. 2311
KLISCHEEWERKSTATT SCHOLLER GMBH—See Matthews International Corporation; *U.S. Public*, pg. 1399
KLJUC A.D.; *Int'l*, pg. 4201
KLK ASSURANCE (LABUAN) LTD—See Kuala Lumpur Kepong Berhad; *Int'l*, pg. 4318
KLK BIOENERGY SDN BHD—See Kuala Lumpur Kepong Berhad; *Int'l*, pg. 4318
KLK EMMERICH GMBH—See Kuala Lumpur Kepong Berhad; *Int'l*, pg. 4318
KL-KEPONG COMPLEX SDN BHD—See Kuala Lumpur Kepong Berhad; *Int'l*, pg. 4318
KL-KEPONG COUNTRY HOMES SDN BHD—See Kuala Lumpur Kepong Berhad; *Int'l*, pg. 4318
KL-KEPONG EDIBLE OIL SDN BHD—See Kuala Lumpur Kepong Berhad; *Int'l*, pg. 4318
KL-KEPONG INDUSTRIAL HOLDINGS SDN. BHD.—See Kuala Lumpur Kepong Berhad; *Int'l*, pg. 4318
KL-KEPONG INTERNATIONAL LTD—See Kuala Lumpur Kepong Berhad; *Int'l*, pg. 4318
KL-KEPONG PLANTATION HOLDINGS SDN BHD—See Kuala Lumpur Kepong Berhad; *Int'l*, pg. 4318
KL-KEPONG PROPERTY DEVELOPMENT SDN. BHD.—See Kuala Lumpur Kepong Berhad; *Int'l*, pg. 4318
KL-KEPONG PROPERTY MANAGEMENT SDN BHD—See Kuala Lumpur Kepong Berhad; *Int'l*, pg. 4318
KL-KEPONG RUBBER PRODUCTS SDN BHD—See Kuala Lumpur Kepong Berhad; *Int'l*, pg. 4318
KL-KEPONG (SABAH) SDN BHD—See Kuala Lumpur Kepong Berhad; *Int'l*, pg. 4318
KLK HARDWOOD FLOORING SDN. BHD.—See Batu Kawan Berhad; *Int'l*, pg. 891
KL-K HOLIDAY BUNGALOWS SDN BHD—See Kuala Lumpur Kepong Berhad; *Int'l*, pg. 4318
KLK KOLB SPECIALTIES BV—See Batu Kawan Berhad; *Int'l*, pg. 891
KLK LAND SDN BHD—See Batu Kawan Berhad; *Int'l*, pg. 891
KLK OLEO EMMERICH GMBH—See Kuala Lumpur Kepong Berhad; *Int'l*, pg. 4318
KLK OLEO (SHANGHAI) CO LTD—See Kuala Lumpur Kepong Berhad; *Int'l*, pg. 4318
KLK OLEO—See Kuala Lumpur Kepong Berhad; *Int'l*, pg. 4318
KLK OVERSEAS INVESTMENTS LTD—See Kuala Lumpur Kepong Berhad; *Int'l*, pg. 4318
KLK TENSACHEM SA—See Batu Kawan Berhad; *Int'l*, pg. 891
KLL EQUIPAMENTOS PARA TRANSPORTE LTDA.—See SAF-Holland S.A.; *Int'l*, pg. 6467
KLLM TRANSPORT SERVICES, INC.; *U.S. Private*, pg. 2320
KLM BUILDERS INC.; *U.S. Private*, pg. 2320
KLM CATERING SERVICES SCHIPHOL B.V.—See Air France-KLM S.A.; *Int'l*, pg. 237
K.L. MCCOY & ASSOCIATES; *U.S. Private*, pg. 2252
KLM CITYHOPPER—See Air France-KLM S.A.; *Int'l*, pg. 237
KLM EQUIPMENT SERVICES BV—See Air France-KLM S.A.; *Int'l*, pg. 238
KLM FINANCIAL SERVICES B.V.—See Air France-KLM S.A.; *Int'l*, pg. 237
KLM FLIGHT ACADEMY B.V.—See Koninklijke Luchtvaart Maatschappij N.V.; *Int'l*, pg. 4267
KLM HEALTH SERVICES B.V.—See Air France-KLM S.A.; *Int'l*, pg. 237
K&L MICROWAVE, INC.—See Dover Corporation; *U.S. Public*, pg. 679
KLM LABORATORIES, INC.; *U.S. Private*, pg. 2320
KLM LUCHTVAARTSCHOOL B.V.—See Air France-KLM S.A.; *Int'l*, pg. 237
KLM OLIEMAATSCHAPPIJ B.V.—See Air France-KLM S.A.; *Int'l*, pg. 237
KLM ROYAL DUTCH AIRLINES—See Air France-KLM S.A.; *Int'l*, pg. 237
KLM ROYAL DUTCH AIRLINES—See Air France-KLM S.A.; *Int'l*, pg. 237
KLM UK ENGINEERING LIMITED—See Air France-KLM S.A.; *Int'l*, pg. 237
KLM UK LTD.—See Air France-KLM S.A.; *Int'l*, pg. 237
KLNB, LLC; *U.S. Private*, pg. 2320
KLN ENTERPRISES INC.; *U.S. Private*, pg. 2320
KL-NET CORP.; *Int'l*, pg. 4198

CORPORATE AFFILIATIONS

KLN ULTRASCHALL AG—See Crest Group Inc.; *U.S. Private*, pg. 1096
KLN ULTRASONICS (SHANGHAI) CO., LTD.—See Crest Group Inc.; *U.S. Private*, pg. 1096
KLOCHER BAUGESELLSCHAFT M.B.H.—See ALPINE Bau GmbH; *Int'l*, pg. 371
KLOCKNER ALUMINIO IBERICA S.A.—See Klockner & Co. SE; *Int'l*, pg. 4202
KLOCKNER & CO DEUTSCHLAND GMBH—See Klockner & Co. SE; *Int'l*, pg. 4202
KLOCKNER & CO INTERNATIONAL GMBH—See Klockner & Co. SE; *Int'l*, pg. 4202
KLOCKNER & CO. SE; *Int'l*, pg. 4201
KLOCKNER DISTRIBUTION INDUSTRIELLE S.A.—See Klockner & Co. SE; *Int'l*, pg. 4202
KLOCKNER HOLSTEIN SEITZ S.A.—See Salzgitter AG; *Int'l*, pg. 6496
KLOCKNER INDUSTRIEBETEILIGUNGSGESELLSCHAFT MBH—See Deutsche Bank Aktiengesellschaft; *Int'l*, pg. 2061
KLOCKNER METALSNAB AD—See Klockner & Co. SE; *Int'l*, pg. 4202
KLOCKNER PARTICIPACIONES S.A.—See Klockner & Co. SE; *Int'l*, pg. 4202
KLOCKNER PENTAPLAST GMBH—See Strategic Value Partners, LLC; *U.S. Private*, pg. 3836
KLOCKNER PENTAPLAST LTD.—See Strategic Value Partners, LLC; *U.S. Private*, pg. 3836
KLOCKNER PENTAPLAST OF AMERICA, INC.—See Strategic Value Partners, LLC; *U.S. Private*, pg. 3836
KLOCKNER PET-TECHNOLOGIE GMBH—See Salzgitter AG; *Int'l*, pg. 6496
KLOCKNER STAHLHANDEL CZ, S.R.O.—See Klockner & Co. SE; *Int'l*, pg. 4202
KLOCKNER STAL I METAL POLSKA SP. Z O.O.—See Klockner & Co. SE; *Int'l*, pg. 4202
KLOECKNER DESMA ELASTOMERTECHNIK GMBH—See Salzgitter AG; *Int'l*, pg. 6497
KLOECKNER DESMA MACHINERY PVT. LTD.—See Salzgitter AG; *Int'l*, pg. 6497
KLOECKNER DESMA SCHUHMASCHINEN GMBH—See Salzgitter AG; *Int'l*, pg. 6497
KLOECKNER HANSEL PROCESSING GMBH—See Salzgitter AG; *Int'l*, pg. 6497
KLOECKNER METALS AUSTRIA GMBH & CO KG—See Klockner & Co. SE; *Int'l*, pg. 4202
KLOECKNER METALS BELGIUM N.V.—See Klockner & Co. SE; *Int'l*, pg. 4202
KLOECKNER METALS CORPORATION—See Klockner & Co. SE; *Int'l*, pg. 4202
KLOECKNER METALS FRANCE S.A.S.—See Klockner & Co. SE; *Int'l*, pg. 4203
KLOECKNER METALS GERMANY GMBH—See Klockner & Co. SE; *Int'l*, pg. 4203
KLOECKNER METALS ODS NEDERLANDS B.V.—See Klockner & Co. SE; *Int'l*, pg. 4203
KLOECKNER PENTAPLAST (SHANGHAI) CO., LTD.—See Strategic Value Partners, LLC; *U.S. Private*, pg. 3836
KLOEHN INC—See IMI plc; *Int'l*, pg. 3626
K LOGIX, LLC; *U.S. Private*, pg. 2249
KLOK CONTAINERS B.V.—See Renewi plc; *Int'l*, pg. 6279
KLOKKERHOLM KAROSSERIDELE A/S—See Indutrade AB; *Int'l*, pg. 3680
KLONDIKE CHEESE COMPANY; *U.S. Private*, pg. 2320
KLONDIKE GOLD CORP.; *Int'l*, pg. 4203
KLONDIKE MOTORS LTD; *Int'l*, pg. 4203
KLONDIKE SILVER CORP.—See Klondike Gold Corp.; *Int'l*, pg. 4203
KLONDYKE CONSTRUCTION LLC—See Goldberg Lindsay & Co., LLC; *U.S. Private*, pg. 1729
KLONE LAB, LLC—See Madison Parker Capital; *U.S. Private*, pg. 2544
KLONGLUANG UTILITIES CO., LTD.—See Electricity Generating Public Co., Ltd.; *Int'l*, pg. 2352
KLOPOTEK AG; *Int'l*, pg. 4203
KLOPOTEK BV—See Klopotek AG; *Int'l*, pg. 4203
KLOPOTEK NORTH AMERICA, INC.—See Klopotek AG; *Int'l*, pg. 4203
KLOPOTEK & PARTNER GMBH—See Klopotek AG; *Int'l*, pg. 4203
KLOPOTEK SAS—See Klopotek AG; *Int'l*, pg. 4203
KLOPOTEK SOFTWARE & TECHNOLOGY SERVICES ITALIA S.R.L.—See Klopotek AG; *Int'l*, pg. 4203
KLOPOTEK UK LTD.—See Klopotek AG; *Int'l*, pg. 4203
KLOS RADIO, LLC—See Meruelo Group LLC; *U.S. Private*, pg. 2677
KLOSTERMAN BAKING COMPANY, INC.—See New Water Capital, L.P.; *U.S. Private*, pg. 2908
KLOTE INTERNATIONAL CORP.; *U.S. Private*, pg. 2320
KLOTZ ASSOCIATES, INC.—See RPS Group plc; *Int'l*, pg. 6415
KL OUTDOOR LLC; *U.S. Private*, pg. 2317
KLOUT, INC.—See Vista Equity Partners, LLC; *U.S. Private*, pg. 4398
KLOVERN AB; *Int'l*, pg. 4203
KL-PARTS OY—See Oy Kaha AB; *Int'l*, pg. 5677
KLP KOMMUNEKREDITT—See Kommunal Landspensjonskasse gjensidig forsikringsselskap; *Int'l*, pg. 4242

COMPANY NAME INDEX

K.L. RESOURCES PTE. LTD.; *Int'l*, pg. 4044
KLRT-TV—See Mission Broadcasting, Inc.; *U.S. Private*, pg. 2747
KLS DOORS, LLC—See Patrick Industries, Inc.; *U.S. Public*, pg. 1652
KLSLV D.O.O—See I. KLOUKINAS - I. LAPPAS CONSTRUCTION & COMMERCE S.A.; *Int'l*, pg. 3565
KLS NETHERLANDS B.V—See TKH Group N.V.; *Int'l*, pg. 7764
KLS PROFESSIONAL ADVISORS GROUP, LLC—See Boston Private Financial Holdings, Inc.; *U.S. Public*, pg. 372
KLSS INC; *U.S. Private*, pg. 2320
KLS UGGLARPS—See Danish Crown AmbA; *Int'l*, pg. 1965
KL-TEHO OY—See Rapala VMC Oyj; *Int'l*, pg. 6209
KL TEXAS L.P.—See Freudenberg SE; *Int'l*, pg. 2786
KLUANG RUBBER COMPANY (MALAYA) BERHAD; *Int'l*, pg. 4203
KLUANG TIN AND CAN FACTORY SDN. BHD.—See Able Global Berhad; *Int'l*, pg. 63
KLUBER LUBRICACION MEXICANA S.A. DE C.V.—See Freudenberg SE; *Int'l*, pg. 2785
KLUBER LUBRICATION AG (SCHWEIZ)—See Freudenberg SE; *Int'l*, pg. 2785
KLUBER LUBRICATION ARGENTINA S.A.—See Freudenberg SE; *Int'l*, pg. 2785
KLUBER LUBRICATION A.S.—See Freudenberg SE; *Int'l*, pg. 2785
KLUBER LUBRICATION AUSTRALIA PTY. LTD.—See Freudenberg SE; *Int'l*, pg. 2785
KLUBER LUBRICATION AUSTRIA GMBH—See Freudenberg SE; *Int'l*, pg. 2785
KLUBER LUBRICATION BELGIUM NETHERLANDS S.A.—See Freudenberg SE; *Int'l*, pg. 2785
KLUBER LUBRICATION BENELUX S.A.—See Freudenberg SE; *Int'l*, pg. 2785
KLUBER LUBRICATION CHILE LTDA.—See Freudenberg SE; *Int'l*, pg. 2785
KLUBER LUBRICATION CHINA LTD.—See Freudenberg SE; *Int'l*, pg. 2785
KLUBER LUBRICATION CZ, S.R.O.—See Freudenberg SE; *Int'l*, pg. 2785
KLUBER LUBRICATION DEUTSCHLAND SE & CO. KG—See Freudenberg SE; *Int'l*, pg. 2785
KLUBER LUBRICATION FRANCE S.A.S.—See Freudenberg SE; *Int'l*, pg. 2785
KLUBER LUBRICATION GMBH IBERICA S.EN C.—See Freudenberg SE; *Int'l*, pg. 2785
KLUBER LUBRICATION GREAT BRITAIN LTD.—See Freudenberg SE; *Int'l*, pg. 2785
KLUBER LUBRICATION INDIA PVT. LTD. - MYSORE FACTORY—See Freudenberg SE; *Int'l*, pg. 2785
KLUBER LUBRICATION INDIA PVT. LTD.—See Freudenberg SE; *Int'l*, pg. 2785
KLUBER LUBRICATION ITALIA S.A.S.—See Freudenberg SE; *Int'l*, pg. 2785
KLUBER LUBRICATION (KOREA) LTD.—See Freudenberg SE; *Int'l*, pg. 2785
KLUBER LUBRICATION LUBRIFICANTES ESPECIAIS LTDA. & CIA.—See Freudenberg SE; *Int'l*, pg. 2786
KLUBER LUBRICATION (MALAYSIA) SDN. BHD.—See Freudenberg SE; *Int'l*, pg. 2785
KLUBER LUBRICATION MEXICANA S.A. DE C.V.—See Freudenberg SE; *Int'l*, pg. 2786
KLUBER LUBRICATION MUNCHEN SE & CO. KG—See Freudenberg SE; *Int'l*, pg. 2786
KLUBER LUBRICATION NORDIC A/S—See Freudenberg SE; *Int'l*, pg. 2786
KLUBER LUBRICATION NORTH AMERICA LP—See Freudenberg SE; *Int'l*, pg. 2786
KLUBER LUBRICATION OOO—See Freudenberg SE; *Int'l*, pg. 2786
KLUBER LUBRICATION POLSKA SP. Z O.O.—See Freudenberg SE; *Int'l*, pg. 2786
KLUBER LUBRICATION (PTY.) LTD.—See Freudenberg SE; *Int'l*, pg. 2785
KLUBER LUBRICATION (SHANGHAI) CO., LTD.—See Freudenberg SE; *Int'l*, pg. 2785
KLUBER LUBRICATION SOUTH EAST ASIA PTE. LTD.—See Freudenberg SE; *Int'l*, pg. 2786
KLUBER LUBRICATION YAGLAMA URUNLERI SANAYI VE TICARET A.S.—See Freudenberg SE; *Int'l*, pg. 2786
KLUB M5 (PTY) LTD—See Ascendis Health Limited; *Int'l*, pg. 601
KLUEBER LUBRICATION ROMANIA S.R.L.—See Freudenberg SE; *Int'l*, pg. 2789
KLUGE KLAVIATUREN GMBH—See Paulson & Co. Inc.; *U.S. Private*, pg. 3114
KLUH SERVICE MANAGEMENT GMBH; *Int'l*, pg. 4203
KLUIN WIJHE BV—See Aalberts N.V.; *Int'l*, pg. 34
KLUKWAN INC.; *U.S. Private*, pg. 2320
KLUMAN & BALTER LIMITED—See BRENNTAG SE; *Int'l*, pg. 1149
KLUMB LUMBER COMPANY INC. - INTERNATIONAL DIVISION—See Klumb Lumber Company Inc.; *U.S. Private*, pg. 2320
KLUMB LUMBER COMPANY INC.; *U.S. Private*, pg. 2320

KLUMPP COATINGS DO BRASIL LTD.—See The Sherwin-Williams Company; *U.S. Public*, pg. 2128
KLUNE INDUSTRIES, INC.—See Berkshire Hathaway Inc.; *U.S. Public*, pg. 315
KLUNGESS ELECTRONIC SUPPLY—See CCI Systems Inc.; *U.S. Private*, pg. 799
KLUNK & MILLAN ADVERTISING INC.; *U.S. Private*, pg. 2321
KLUS PHARMA INC.—See Sichuan Kelun Pharmaceutical Co., Ltd.; *Int'l*, pg. 6880
KLUTHE FRANCE; *Int'l*, pg. 4203
KLUTTS PROPERTY MANAGEMENT, INC.; *U.S. Private*, pg. 2321
KLUWER B.V.—See Wolters Kluwer n.v.; *Int'l*, pg. 8444
KLUWER LAW INTERNATIONAL B.V.—See Wolters Kluwer n.v.; *Int'l*, pg. 8444
KLUX A S.A.R.L.—See Kellanova; *U.S. Public*, pg. 1218
KLUZ PADOBRANI A.D.; *Int'l*, pg. 4203
KL-VARAOSAT OY—See Panostaja Oyj; *Int'l*, pg. 5729
KLVK AD—See Industrial Holding Bulgaria AD; *Int'l*, pg. 3672
KLW JOINERY PTE. LTD.—See HS Optimus Holdings Limited; *Int'l*, pg. 3503
KLW PLASTICS, INC.—See KODA Enterprises Group, LLC; *U.S. Private*, pg. 2335
KLW WOOD PRODUCTS SDN. BHD.—See HS Optimus Holdings Limited; *Int'l*, pg. 3503
KLX ENERGY SERVICES HOLDINGS, INC.; *U.S. Public*, pg. 1269
KLX ENERGY SERVICES—See The Boeing Company; *U.S. Public*, pg. 2040
K-MAATALOUS EXPERIMENTAL FARM—See Kesko Corporation; *Int'l*, pg. 4141
K-MAATALOUSKAUPAT OY—See Lantmannen ek for; *Int'l*, pg. 4413
K'MAC CO., LTD.—See Alconix Corporation; *Int'l*, pg. 302
K-MAC ENTERPRISES, INC.—See Brentwood Associates; *U.S. Private*, pg. 646
KMAC, INC.—See KKR & Co. Inc.; *U.S. Public*, pg. 1249
KM ACT CORP.—See KM Corp.; *Int'l*, pg. 4203
K-MAC TECHNOLOGY CORP.—See HB Solution Co., Ltd.; *Int'l*, pg. 3295
KM AGENCY SDN. BHD.—See Oriental Holdings Berhad; *Int'l*, pg. 5624
KMA GLOBAL SOLUTIONS INTERNATIONAL, INC.; *Int'l*, pg. 4203
KMA HOLDING, INC.; *U.S. Public*, pg. 1269
K - MAIL ORDER GMBH & CO. KG; *Int'l*, pg. 4037
KMA ONE, INC.—See Local Marketing Solutions Group, Inc.; *U.S. Private*, pg. 2477
KMART AUSTRALIA LIMITED—See Wesfarmers Limited; *Int'l*, pg. 8382
K&M ASSOCIATES—See American Biltrite Inc.; *U.S. Public*, pg. 98
K-MASTER SRL—See Edizione S.r.l.; *Int'l*, pg. 2312
KMA SUNBELT TRADING CORP.; *U.S. Private*, pg. 2321
K-MAX CORPORATION—See Arcline Investment Management LP; *U.S. Private*, pg. 314
KMBC HEARST-ARGYLE TELEVISION, INC.—See The Hearst Corporation; *U.S. Private*, pg. 4048
KMB CO., LTD. - PYUNGTAEK FACTORY—See KMB Co., Ltd.; *Int'l*, pg. 4203
KMB CO., LTD.; *Int'l*, pg. 4203
KMBH ADVERTISING; *U.S. Private*, pg. 2321
K.M.B. INTERNATIONAL COMPANY LIMITED—See Krung Thai Bank Public Company Limited; *Int'l*, pg. 4308
KM BIOLOGICS CO., LTD.—See Meiji Holdings Co., Ltd.; *Int'l*, pg. 4800
KMC AB—See Addtech AB; *Int'l*, pg. 131
KM CANADA RAIL HOLDINGS GP LIMITED—See Pembina Pipeline Corporation; *Int'l*, pg. 5785
K.M.C AUTOMOBILE TRANSMISSION CO., LTD.—See KMC (Kuei Meng) International Inc.; *Int'l*, pg. 4204
KMC CHAIN AMERICAN CORPORATION—See KMC (Kuei Meng) International Inc.; *Int'l*, pg. 4204
KMC CHAIN EUROPE N.V.—See KMC (Kuei Meng) International Inc.; *Int'l*, pg. 4204
KMC CONTROLS; *U.S. Private*, pg. 2321
KMC (KUEI MENG) INTERNATIONAL INC.; *Int'l*, pg. 4203
KMC MANAGEMENT CONSULTANTS GMBH & CO. KG; *Int'l*, pg. 4204
KMCO, LLC—See BRENNTAG SE; *Int'l*, pg. 1148
KM CORP.; *Int'l*, pg. 4203
KMC PROPERTIES ASA—See Logistea AB; *Int'l*, pg. 4542
KMC SPECIALTY HOSPITALS INDIA LTD.; *Int'l*, pg. 4204
KMC SYSTEMS INC.—See Elbit Systems Limited; *Int'l*, pg. 2344
KMC YTBEHANDLING AB—See Addtech AB; *Int'l*, pg. 134
KMD A/S—See NEC Corporation; *Int'l*, pg. 5183
KMD BRANDS LIMITED; *Int'l*, pg. 4204
KMD BRANDS MANAGED SERVICES (AU) PTY. LTD.—See KMD Brands Limited; *Int'l*, pg. 4204
KM DEVELOPMENT CORP.—See Zilber Ltd.; *U.S. Private*, pg. 4604
KM DISTRIBUCION DE MAQUINARIAS, S.A. DE C.V.—See Marubeni Corporation; *Int'l*, pg. 4705
KMDS CO., LTD.—See Kawasaki Kisen Kaisha, Ltd.; *Int'l*, pg. 4100

KME AMERICA INC.—See Intek Group S.p.A.; *Int'l*, pg. 3732
KME ARCHITECTURAL METALS GMBH & CO. KG—See Intek Group S.p.A.; *Int'l*, pg. 3732
KME BRASS FRANCE S.A.S.—See Intek Group S.p.A.; *Int'l*, pg. 3732
KME BRASS GERMANY GMBH—See Intek Group S.p.A.; *Int'l*, pg. 3732
KME BRASS ITALY SRL—See Intek Group S.p.A.; *Int'l*, pg. 3732
KME CO., LTD.—See Konami Group Corporation; *Int'l*, pg. 4245
KME EUROPA METAL AG—See Intek Group S.p.A.; *Int'l*, pg. 3732
KME EUROPA METAL AG—See Intek Group S.p.A.; *Int'l*, pg. 3732
KME FRANCE S.A.S.—See Intek Group S.p.A.; *Int'l*, pg. 3732
KME GERMANY AG—See Intek Group S.p.A.; *Int'l*, pg. 3732
KME GERMANY AG—See Intek Group S.p.A.; *Int'l*, pg. 3732
KME GERMANY GMBH & CO. K.G.—See Intek Group S.p.A.; *Int'l*, pg. 3732
KMEG-TV—See Ellis, McQuary, Stanley & Associates LLC; *U.S. Private*, pg. 1374
KME IBERTUBOS S.A.—See Intek Group S.p.A.; *Int'l*, pg. 3732
KME ITALY S.P.A.—See Intek Group S.p.A.; *Int'l*, pg. 3732
K&M ELECTRIC SUPPLY INC.; *U.S. Private*, pg. 2250
KME LOCSA S.A.—See Intek Group S.p.A.; *Int'l*, pg. 3732
KME METALS (SHANGHAI) TRADING LTD.—See Intek Group S.p.A.; *Int'l*, pg. 3733
KME MOULDS MEXICO S.A. DE C.V.—See Intek Group S.p.A.; *Int'l*, pg. 3732
KM ENTERPRISE SYSTEMS SDN BHD—See Kingslake International Limited; *Int'l*, pg. 4175
KME SERVICE RUSSLAND LTD.—See Intek Group S.p.A.; *Int'l*, pg. 3732
KME SPAIN S.A.U.—See Intek Group S.p.A.; *Int'l*, pg. 3733
KME SRL—See Intek Group S.p.A.; *Int'l*, pg. 3733
KME (SUISSE) S.A.—See Intek Group S.p.A.; *Int'l*, pg. 3732
K+M FAHRLEITUNGSTECHNIK GMBH—See Alpiq Holding AG; *Int'l*, pg. 372
KMF BUILDERS AND DEVELOPERS LTD.; *Int'l*, pg. 4204
KMG-BERNUTH, INC.—See Entegris, Inc.; *U.S. Public*, pg. 776
KMG CHEMICALS DO BRASIL LTDA—See Entegris, Inc.; *U.S. Public*, pg. 776
KMG CHEMICALS, INC.—See Entegris, Inc.; *U.S. Public*, pg. 776
KMG DE MEXICO, SA DE CV—See Entegris, Inc.; *U.S. Public*, pg. 776
KMG DRILLING&SERVICES LLP—See JSC National Company KazMunayGas; *Int'l*, pg. 4010
KMG ENTERPRISES INC.; *U.S. Private*, pg. 2321
KMG HAULING, INC.; *U.S. Private*, pg. 2321
KMGH-TV—See The E.W. Scripps Company; *U.S. Public*, pg. 2068
KMG MILK FOOD LIMITED; *Int'l*, pg. 4204
KM GOLD JSC; *Int'l*, pg. 4203
KMG SINGAPORE PTE. LTD.—See Entegris, Inc.; *U.S. Public*, pg. 776
KMG ULTRA PURE CHEMICALS LIMITED—See Entegris, Inc.; *U.S. Public*, pg. 776
KMG ULTRA PURE CHEMICALS SAS—See Entegris, Inc.; *U.S. Public*, pg. 776
K&M HAULIERS LTD.; *Int'l*, pg. 4038
KMH HI TECH CO., LTD.; *Int'l*, pg. 4204
KMH SHILLA LEISURE CO., LTD.; *Int'l*, pg. 4204
KMH SYSTEMS, INC.; *U.S. Private*, pg. 2321
KMI ACQUISITION, LLC—See Universal Health Services, Inc.; *U.S. Public*, pg. 2258
K MICRO INC.; *U.S. Private*, pg. 2249
K. MIKIMOTO & CO., LTD.; *Int'l*, pg. 4043
KM INDUSTRIAL, INC. - BENICIA DIVISION—See The Halifax Group LLC; *U.S. Private*, pg. 4042
KM INDUSTRIAL, INC. - LAS VEGAS DIVISION—See The Halifax Group LLC; *U.S. Private*, pg. 4042
KM INDUSTRIAL, INC.—See The Halifax Group LLC; *U.S. Private*, pg. 4042
KM INTERNATIONAL CORPORATION; *U.S. Private*, pg. 2321
KM INVESTMENT CORPORATION; *U.S. Private*, pg. 2321
KMI SERVICES PTE LTD—See Fair Friend Group; *Int'l*, pg. 2604
KMI SYSTEMS INC.; *U.S. Private*, pg. 2321
KMJ CONVENIENCE COMPANY; *U.S. Private*, pg. 2321
KMJQ-FM—See Urban One, Inc.; *U.S. Public*, pg. 2265
KMK CONSULTING COMPANY, LLC—See Keating, Muething & Klekamp PLL; *U.S. Private*, pg. 2271
KM KELLY, INC.; *U.S. Private*, pg. 2321
KMK INDUSTRIES, INC.—See Exhibit Systems, Inc.; *U.S. Private*, pg. 1448
KMK MUNAY AO; *Int'l*, pg. 4204

KMK MUNAY AO

KMLEE INVESTMENTS INC—See Just Eat Takeaway.com N.V.; *Int'l*, pg. 4030
KML SALES INC.; *U.S. Private*, pg. 2321
KML TECHNOLOGY GROUP LIMITED; *Int'l*, pg. 4204
K&M MACHINE-FABRICATING INC.—See McLoughlin Enterprises Inc.; *U.S. Private*, pg. 2641
KMM AD; *Int'l*, pg. 4204
KM MEXICO S.A. DE CV—See Kongsberg Gruppen ASA; *Int'l*, pg. 4255
KMM TELECOMMUNICATIONS; *U.S. Private*, pg. 2321
KMN CAPITAL LTD.; *Int'l*, pg. 4204
KMN CORPORATION—See KDDI Corporation; *Int'l*, pg. 4112
KM.ON GMBH—See KARL MAYER Textilmaschinenfabrik GmbH; *Int'l*, pg. 4082
KMOTR-MASNA KROMERIZ A.S.—See Agrofert Holding, a.s.; *Int'l*, pg. 219
KMOT-TV—See Gray Television, Inc.; *U.S. Public*, pg. 960
KMOV-TV, INC.—See Meredith Corporation; *U.S. Public*, pg. 1423
KMP BUROTECHNIK S.R.O.—See KMP PrintTechnik AG; *Int'l*, pg. 4204
KMP CRUSADER MANUFACTURING LTD.—See KMP PrintTechnik AG; *Int'l*, pg. 4205
KM PHARMACEUTICAL CO., LTD.; *Int'l*, pg. 4203
KMPH-TV—See Ellis, McQuary, Stanley & Associates LLC; *U.S. Private*, pg. 1374
KM PLANT SERVICES, INC. - PEKIN DIVISION—See The Halifax Group LLC; *U.S. Public*, pg. 4042
KM PLANT SERVICES, INC.—See The Halifax Group LLC; *U.S. Private*, pg. 4042
KMP PRINTTECHNIK AG; *Int'l*, pg. 4204
KMP PRINTTECHNIK POLSKA SP. Z O.O.—See KMP PrintTechnik AG; *Int'l*, pg. 4205
KMP PRINTTECHNIK S.R.L.—See KMP PrintTechnik AG; *Int'l*, pg. 4205
KM PROPPANTS, LLC—See Koch Industries, Inc.; *U.S. Private*, pg. 2333
KMRD PARTNERS, INC.; *U.S. Private*, pg. 2321
KMS ADVERTISING LTD.—See iHeartMedia, Inc.; *U.S. Public*, pg. 1095
KMSB-TV, INC.—See TEGNA Inc.; *U.S. Public*, pg. 1990
KMS ENTERPRISES, INC.; *U.S. Private*, pg. 2321
KMS FAB, LLC—See Reliance Steel & Aluminum Co.; *U.S. Public*, pg. 1780
KMS KATSUSHIRO MACHINERY (SHANDONG) CO., LTD.—See Komatsu Ltd.; *Int'l*, pg. 4235
KMS MEDISURGI LIMITED; *Int'l*, pg. 4205
KMSP-TV—See Fox Corporation; *U.S. Public*, pg. 876
KMS SERVICE INC.—See Kikkoman Corporation; *Int'l*, pg. 4160
KMS SOLUTIONS, LLC—See Subsystem Technologies, Inc.; *U.S. Private*, pg. 3847
KMS SOUTH, INC.—See Reliance Steel & Aluminum Co.; *U.S. Public*, pg. 1780
KMS TOOLS & EQUIPMENT LTD; *Int'l*, pg. 4205
K M SUGAR MILLS LIMITED; *Int'l*, pg. 4037
KMS VERTRIEB UND SERVICES AG—See PAO Severstal; *Int'l*, pg. 5731
KMS VERTRIEB UND SERVICES GMBH—See CompuGroup Medical SE & Co. KGaA; *Int'l*, pg. 1757
KMT BRRR!—See Americold Realty Trust, Inc.; *U.S. Public*, pg. 113
KM TECH LLC—See Kongsberg Gruppen ASA; *Int'l*, pg. 4255
KMTEX, LLC—See BRENNTAG SE; *Int'l*, pg. 1148
KMT GMBH—See AIP, LLC; *U.S. Private*, pg. 138
KMT GROUP AB—See AIP, LLC; *U.S. Private*, pg. 137
KMT-HANSA CORP.; *Int'l*, pg. 4205
KMT HEPATECH, INC.—See PhoenixBio Co., Ltd.; *Int'l*, pg. 5855
KMT HEPATECH INC.—See PhoenixBio Co., Ltd.; *Int'l*, pg. 5855
K&M TIRE, INC.; *U.S. Private*, pg. 2250
KMT KUNSTSTOFF- UND METALLTEILE AG—See Wurth Verwaltungsgesellschaft mbH; *Int'l*, pg. 8506
KMT PLANUNGSGESELLSCHAFT MBH—See BKW AG; *Int'l*, pg. 1055
KMT PRECISION GRINDING AB—See AIP, LLC; *U.S. Private*, pg. 137
KMT PRECISION GRINDING AB—See Nordstjernan AB; *Int'l*, pg. 5425
KMT PRECISION GRINDING GMBH—See AIP, LLC; *U.S. Private*, pg. 138
KMT PRECISION GRINDING, INC.—See AIP, LLC; *U.S. Private*, pg. 138
KMT PRECISION GRINDING TECHNOLOGY (BEIJING) CO., LTD—See Nordstjernan AB; *Int'l*, pg. 5425
KMT PRODUCTION MACHINERY INDIA PRIVATE LIMITED—See Nordstjernan AB; *Int'l*, pg. 5425
KMTR-TV—See Providence Equity Partners L.L.C.; *U.S. Private*, pg. 3293
KMTV-TV—See The E.W. Scripps Company; *U.S. Public*, pg. 2068
KMT WATERJET SYSTEMS, INC.—See AIP, LLC; *U.S. Private*, pg. 138
KMW ASIA PACIFIC PTE. LTD.—See Krauss-Maffei Wegmann GmbH & Co. KG; *Int'l*, pg. 4300

KMW DO BRASIL SISTEMAS DE DEFESA LTDA.—See Krauss-Maffei Wegmann GmbH & Co. KG; *Int'l*, pg. 4300
KMW DO BRASIL SISTEMAS MILITARES LTDA.—See Krauss-Maffei Wegmann GmbH & Co. KG; *Int'l*, pg. 4300
KM WEDDING EVENTS MANAGEMENT, INC.; *U.S. Public*, pg. 1269
THE KMW GROUP INC.; *U.S. Private*, pg. 4065
KMW INC.; *Int'l*, pg. 4205
KMW JAPAN INC—See KMW Inc.; *Int'l*, pg. 4205
KMWORLD—See Information Today, Inc.; *U.S. Private*, pg. 2073
KMW SAVUNMA TEKNOLOJILERI SAN VE TIC AS—See Krauss-Maffei Wegmann GmbH & Co. KG; *Int'l*, pg. 4300
KMW SCHWEISSTECHNIK GMBH—See Krauss-Maffei Wegmann GmbH & Co. KG; *Int'l*, pg. 4300
KMW U.S.A INC.—See KMW Inc.; *Int'l*, pg. 4205
KMYS-TV—See Sinclair, Inc.; *U.S. Public*, pg. 1885
KMYT-TV—See Providence Equity Partners L.L.C.; *U.S. Private*, pg. 3293
KNAACK-KRANE TRANSPORTTECHNIK GMBH; *Int'l*, pg. 4205
KNAACK LLC—See Triton Advisers Limited; *Int'l*, pg. 7935
KNACK SYSTEMS, LLC—See LKCM Headwater Investments; *U.S. Private*, pg. 2475
KNAFAIM HOLDINGS LIMITED; *Int'l*, pg. 4205
KNA FOODS LLC.—See Katadyn Holding AG; *Int'l*, pg. 4089
KN AGRI RESOURCES LIMITED; *Int'l*, pg. 4205
KN AIRLIFT GMBH—See Kuehne + Nagel International AG; *Int'l*, pg. 4324
KNAPE & VOGT MANUFACTURING COMPANY—See Wind Point Advisors LLC; *U.S. Private*, pg. 4534
THE KNAPHEIDE MANUFACTURING COMPANY; *U.S. Private*, pg. 4065
KNAPPCO CORPORATION—See Dover Corporation; *U.S. Public*, pg. 681
KNAPP FOODS INC.; *U.S. Private*, pg. 2321
KNAPP OIL CO. INC.; *U.S. Private*, pg. 2321
KNAPP SCHENCK & CO. INSURANCE AGENCY, INC.—See Cross Financial Corporation; *U.S. Private*, pg. 1105
KNAPSACK POWER GMBH & CO KG—See Statkraft AS; *Int'l*, pg. 7185
KNAUER'S WILBERT VAULT INC.—See Berkshire Hathaway Inc.; *U.S. Public*, pg. 298
KNAUF AFRICA TRADE—See Gebr. Knauf KG; *Int'l*, pg. 2906
KNAUF AG—See Gebr. Knauf KG; *Int'l*, pg. 2906
KNAUF ALCOPOR ITALIA S.P.A.—See Gebr. Knauf KG; *Int'l*, pg. 2906
KNAUF AMF CEILINGS LTD.—See Gebr. Knauf KG; *Int'l*, pg. 2906
KNAUF AMF D.O.O.—See Gebr. Knauf KG; *Int'l*, pg. 2906
KNAUF AMF EOOD—See Gebr. Knauf KG; *Int'l*, pg. 2906
KNAUF AMF FORROS DO BRASIL LTDA.—See Gebr. Knauf KG; *Int'l*, pg. 2906
KNAUF AMF FRANCE SARL—See Gebr. Knauf KG; *Int'l*, pg. 2906
KNAUF AMF GMBH & CO. KG—See Gebr. Knauf KG; *Int'l*, pg. 2906
KNAUF AMF HELLAS EPE—See Gebr. Knauf KG; *Int'l*, pg. 2906
KNAUF AMF INTERIORS HELLAS LTD.—See Gebr. Knauf KG; *Int'l*, pg. 2906
KNAUF AMF ITALIA CONTROSOFFITTI S.R.L.—See Gebr. Knauf KG; *Int'l*, pg. 2906
KNAUF AMF KFT.—See Gebr. Knauf KG; *Int'l*, pg. 2906
KNAUF AMF PLAFONDS BVBA—See Gebr. Knauf KG; *Int'l*, pg. 2906
KNAUF AMF PLAFONDSYSTEMEN B.V.—See Gebr. Knauf KG; *Int'l*, pg. 2906
KNAUF AMF SISTEMAS DE TECHOS S.L.—See Gebr. Knauf KG; *Int'l*, pg. 2906
KNAUF AMF S.R.O.—See Gebr. Knauf KG; *Int'l*, pg. 2906
KNAUF AQUAPANEL GMBH—See Gebr. Knauf KG; *Int'l*, pg. 2906
KNAUF A/S—See Gebr. Knauf KG; *Int'l*, pg. 2906
KNAUF A.S.—See Gebr. Knauf KG; *Int'l*, pg. 2906
KNAUF BATIMENT SAS—See Gebr. Knauf KG; *Int'l*, pg. 2906
KNAUF BAUPRODUKTE POLSKA SP. Z O. O.—See Gebr. Knauf KG; *Int'l*, pg. 2906
KNAUF BELCHATOW SP. Z O. O.—See Gebr. Knauf KG; *Int'l*, pg. 2906
KNAUF BRATISLAVA S.R.O.—See Gebr. Knauf KG; *Int'l*, pg. 2906
KNAUF BULGARIA EOOD—See Gebr. Knauf KG; *Int'l*, pg. 2906
KNAUF CO. LTD.—See Gebr. Knauf KG; *Int'l*, pg. 2906
KNAUF CYPRUS LIMITED—See Gebr. Knauf KG; *Int'l*, pg. 2906
KNAUF DANOGIPS A/S—See Gebr. Knauf KG; *Int'l*, pg. 2906
KNAUF DE CHILE LTDA.—See Gebr. Knauf KG; *Int'l*, pg. 2908

CORPORATE AFFILIATIONS

KNAUF DI LOTHAR KNAUF S.A.S.—See Gebr. Knauf KG; *Int'l*, pg. 2908
KNAUF DO BRASIL LTDA.—See Gebr. Knauf KG; *Int'l*, pg. 2908
KNAUF D.O.O.—See Gebr. Knauf KG; *Int'l*, pg. 2908
KNAUF EST SAS—See Gebr. Knauf KG; *Int'l*, pg. 2906
KNAUF FIBRE SAS—See Gebr. Knauf KG; *Int'l*, pg. 2906
KNAUF GES.M.B.H.—See Gebr. Knauf KG; *Int'l*, pg. 2906
KNAUF GIPS KG—See Gebr. Knauf KG; *Int'l*, pg. 2906
KNAUF GIPS S.R.L.—See Gebr. Knauf KG; *Int'l*, pg. 2906
KNAUF GYPSOPIIA ABEE—See Gebr. Knauf KG; *Int'l*, pg. 2907
KNAUF GYPSUM THAILAND LIMITED—See Gebr. Knauf KG; *Int'l*, pg. 2907
KNAUF ILE-DE-FRANCE SAS—See Gebr. Knauf KG; *Int'l*, pg. 2907
KNAUF INDUSTRIES EST—See Gebr. Knauf KG; *Int'l*, pg. 2907
KNAUF INDUSTRIES NORD—See Gebr. Knauf KG; *Int'l*, pg. 2907
KNAUF INDUSTRIES OUEST—See Gebr. Knauf KG; *Int'l*, pg. 2907
KNAUF INDUSTRIES SP. Z O. O.—See Gebr. Knauf KG; *Int'l*, pg. 2907
KNAUF INSULATION AB—See Gebr. Knauf KG; *Int'l*, pg. 2907
KNAUF INSULATION AE—See Gebr. Knauf KG; *Int'l*, pg. 2907
KNAUF INSULATION ARTIX SAS—See Gebr. Knauf KG; *Int'l*, pg. 2907
KNAUF INSULATION A/S—See Gebr. Knauf KG; *Int'l*, pg. 2907
KNAUF INSULATION B.V.—See Gebr. Knauf KG; *Int'l*, pg. 2907
KNAUF INSULATION CO. LTD—See Gebr. Knauf KG; *Int'l*, pg. 2907
KNAUF INSULATION D.O.O.—See Gebr. Knauf KG; *Int'l*, pg. 2907
KNAUF INSULATION, D.O.O.—See Gebr. Knauf KG; *Int'l*, pg. 2907
KNAUF INSULATION D.O.O.—See Gebr. Knauf KG; *Int'l*, pg. 2907
KNAUF INSULATION EOOD—See Gebr. Knauf KG; *Int'l*, pg. 2907
KNAUF INSULATION GMBH—See Gebr. Knauf KG; *Int'l*, pg. 2907
KNAUF INSULATION GMBH—See Gebr. Knauf KG; *Int'l*, pg. 2907
KNAUF INSULATION HOLDING AG—See Gebr. Knauf KG; *Int'l*, pg. 2907
KNAUF INSULATION HOLDING GMBH—See Gebr. Knauf KG; *Int'l*, pg. 2907
KNAUF INSULATION KFT.—See Gebr. Knauf KG; *Int'l*, pg. 2907
KNAUF INSULATION LANNEMEZAN SAS—See Gebr. Knauf KG; *Int'l*, pg. 2907
KNAUF INSULATION LLC—See Gebr. Knauf KG; *Int'l*, pg. 2907
KNAUF INSULATION LTD—See Gebr. Knauf KG; *Int'l*, pg. 2907
KNAUF INSULATION OOO—See Gebr. Knauf KG; *Int'l*, pg. 2907
KNAUF INSULATION OPERATION GMBH—See Gebr. Knauf KG; *Int'l*, pg. 2907
KNAUF INSULATION PTY LTD—See Gebr. Knauf KG; *Int'l*, pg. 2907
KNAUF INSULATION SAS—See Gebr. Knauf KG; *Int'l*, pg. 2907
KNAUF INSULATION - SHELBYVILLE—See Gebr. Knauf KG; *Int'l*, pg. 2907
KNAUF INSULATION S.L.—See Gebr. Knauf KG; *Int'l*, pg. 2907
KNAUF INSULATION SPA—See Gebr. Knauf KG; *Int'l*, pg. 2907
KNAUF INSULATION SPOL. S.R.O.—See Gebr. Knauf KG; *Int'l*, pg. 2907
KNAUF INSULATION SPRL—See Gebr. Knauf KG; *Int'l*, pg. 2907
KNAUF INSULATION SP. Z O. O.—See Gebr. Knauf KG; *Int'l*, pg. 2907
KNAUF INSULATION, S.R.O.—See Gebr. Knauf KG; *Int'l*, pg. 2907
KNAUF INTEGRAL KG—See Gebr. Knauf KG; *Int'l*, pg. 2907
KNAUF INTERFER POLSKA SP. Z O. O.—See Knauf Interfer SE; *Int'l*, pg. 4205
KNAUF INTERFER SE; *Int'l*, pg. 4205
KNAUF ISBA SAS—See Gebr. Knauf KG; *Int'l*, pg. 2907
KNAUF JAWORZNO III SP. Z O. O.—See Gebr. Knauf KG; *Int'l*, pg. 2907
KNAUF JORDAN—See Gebr. Knauf KG; *Int'l*, pg. 2907
KNAUF KFT.—See Gebr. Knauf KG; *Int'l*, pg. 2907
KNAUF LEBANON S.A.R.L.—See Gebr. Knauf KG; *Int'l*, pg. 2907
KNAUF LISBOA GMBH—See Gebr. Knauf KG; *Int'l*, pg. 2907
KNAUF LJUBLJANA D.O.O.—See Gebr. Knauf KG; *Int'l*, pg. 2907
KNAUF LLC—See Gebr. Knauf KG; *Int'l*, pg. 2907

COMPANY NAME INDEX

KNAUF LTD.—See Gebr. Knauf KG; *Int'l*, pg. 2907
KNAUF MAROKKO—See Gebr. Knauf KG; *Int'l*, pg. 2907
KNAUF NEW BUILDING MATERIAL PRODUCT CO., LTD.—See Gebr. Knauf KG; *Int'l*, pg. 2908
KNAUF NEW BUILDING MATERIAL (WUHU) CO. LTD—See Gebr. Knauf KG; *Int'l*, pg. 2908
KNAUF OUEST SAS—See Gebr. Knauf KG; *Int'l*, pg. 2908
KNAUF OY—See Gebr. Knauf KG; *Int'l*, pg. 2908
KNAUF PFT GMBH & CO. KG—See Gebr. Knauf KG; *Int'l*, pg. 2908
KNAUF PLASTERBOARD (JIANGSU) CO., LTD.—See Gebr. Knauf KG; *Int'l*, pg. 2908
KNAUF PLASTERBOARD PTY LTD—See Gebr. Knauf KG; *Int'l*, pg. 2908
KNAUF PLASTERBOARD TIANJIN CO. LTD.—See Gebr. Knauf KG; *Int'l*, pg. 2908
KNAUF PLATRES ET CIE. S.C.S.—See Gebr. Knauf KG; *Int'l*, pg. 2908
KNAUF PLATRES SARL—See Gebr. Knauf KG; *Int'l*, pg. 2908
KNAUF PORTO GMBH—See Gebr. Knauf KG; *Int'l*, pg. 2908
KNAUF RADIKA AD—See Gebr. Knauf KG; *Int'l*, pg. 2908
KNAUF RIESSLER GMBH & CO. KG—See Gebr. Knauf KG; *Int'l*, pg. 2906
KNAUF SH.P.K.—See Gebr. Knauf KG; *Int'l*, pg. 2908
KNAUF SIA—See Gebr. Knauf KG; *Int'l*, pg. 2908
KNAUF SINGAPORE PTE LTD.—See Gebr. Knauf KG; *Int'l*, pg. 2908
KNAUF SP. Z O. O.—See Gebr. Knauf KG; *Int'l*, pg. 2908
KNAUF SUD-EST SAS—See Gebr. Knauf KG; *Int'l*, pg. 2908
KNAUF SUD-OUEST SAS—See Gebr. Knauf KG; *Int'l*, pg. 2908
KNAUF SYRIA—See Gebr. Knauf KG; *Int'l*, pg. 2908
KNAUF TALLINN UU—See Gebr. Knauf KG; *Int'l*, pg. 2908
KNAUF TIRANA SHPK—See Gebr. Knauf KG; *Int'l*, pg. 2908
KNAUF TRADING (SHANGHAI) CO. LTD.—See Gebr. Knauf KG; *Int'l*, pg. 2908
KNAUF TRANS GMBH—See Gebr. Knauf KG; *Int'l*, pg. 2908
KNAUF UAB—See Gebr. Knauf KG; *Int'l*, pg. 2908
KNAUS TABBERT GMBH—See H.T.P. Investments BV; *Int'l*, pg. 0106
KNBC-TV—See Comcast Corporation; *U.S. Public*, pg. 539
KNCI-FM—See Deseret Management Corporation; *U.S. Private*, pg. 1212
KNC LABORATORIES CO., LTD.; *Int'l*, pg. 4205
KNDT UAE TECHNO INSPECTION LLC—See Orbitech Co., Ltd.; *Int'l*, pg. 5614
K. NEAL INTERNATIONAL TRUCKS, INC.; *U.S. Private*, pg. 2251
KNEAT.COM, INC.; *Int'l*, pg. 4205
KNEAT SOLUTIONS INC.—See kneat.com, Inc.; *Int'l*, pg. 4206
KNEAT SOLUTIONS LIMITED—See kneat.com, Inc.; *Int'l*, pg. 4206
KNECHT'S OF SPRINGFIELD INC.; *U.S. Private*, pg. 2321
KNEIP COMMUNICATION S.A.; *Int'l*, pg. 4206
KNEIPP GMBH—See PAUL HARTMANN AG; *Int'l*, pg. 5760
KNEIPP-HOF DUSSNANG AG—See Fresenius SE & Co. KGaA; *Int'l*, pg. 2780
KNEIPP JAPAN K.K.—See PAUL HARTMANN AG; *Int'l*, pg. 5761
KNEIPP NEDERLAND B.V.—See PAUL HARTMANN AG; *Int'l*, pg. 5761
KNEIPP VERWALTUNGSGESELLSCHAFT MBH—See PAUL HARTMANN AG; *Int'l*, pg. 5761
KNEIPP-WERKE KNEIPP-MITTEL-ZENTRALE—See PAUL HARTMANN AG; *Int'l*, pg. 5761
KNEISSL TIROL GMBH; *Int'l*, pg. 4206
K&N ELECTRIC INC.; *U.S. Private*, pg. 2250
K&N ELECTRIC MOTORS INC.; *U.S. Private*, pg. 2250
K&N ENGINEERING INC.; *U.S. Private*, pg. 2250
KNEOMEDIA LIMITED; *Int'l*, pg. 4206
KNEOWORLD UK LIMITED—See KNeoMedia Limited; *Int'l*, pg. 4206
KNESTRICK CONTRACTOR INC.; *U.S. Private*, pg. 2321
KNESTRICK PROPERTIES, LLC—See Knestrick Contractor Inc.; *U.S. Private*, pg. 2321
KNET CO. LTD.—See Hexatronic Group AB; *Int'l*, pg. 3371
KNETTSETRA AS—See SkiStar AB; *Int'l*, pg. 6990
KNEX PIPELINES & CABLES LTD.—See Renew Holdings plc; *Int'l*, pg. 6278
KNEXUS RESEARCH CORP.—See Lurie Investments, Inc; *U.S. Private*, pg. 2516
KNEZ BUILDING MATERIALS CO. INC.; *U.S. Private*, pg. 2321
K N FACILITIES CO., LTD.—See NIPPON KANZAI Holdings Co.,Ltd.; *Int'l*, pg. 5319
KNF FLODOS AG—See Verder International B.V.; *Int'l*, pg. 8166
KNF ITALIA S.R.L.—See Verder International B.V.; *Int'l*, pg. 8166
KNF JAPAN CO., LTD.—See Verder International B.V.; *Int'l*, pg. 8166

KNF KOREA LTD.—See Verder International B.V.; *Int'l*, pg. 8166
KNF MICRO AG—See Verder International B.V.; *Int'l*, pg. 8166
KNF NEUBERGER AB—See Verder International B.V.; *Int'l*, pg. 8166
KNF NEUBERGER AG—See Verder International B.V.; *Int'l*, pg. 8166
KNF NEUBERGER GMBH—See Verder International B.V.; *Int'l*, pg. 8166
KNF NEUBERGER, INC.—See Verder International B.V.; *Int'l*, pg. 8166
KNF NEUBERGER SAS—See Verder International B.V.; *Int'l*, pg. 8166
KNF NEUBERGER (UK) LTD—See Verder International B.V.; *Int'l*, pg. 8166
KNF PUMPS + SYSTEMS INDIA PVT. LTD.—See Verder International B.V.; *Int'l*, pg. 8166
KNF TAIWAN LTD.—See Verder International B.V.; *Int'l*, pg. 8166
KNF TECHNOLOGY (SHANGHAI) CO., LTD.—See Verder International B.V.; *Int'l*, pg. 8166
KNF-VERDER N.V.—See Verder International B.V.; *Int'l*, pg. 8166
K N GAS GATHERING, INC.—See Kinder Morgan, Inc.; *U.S. Public*, pg. 1233
KNG KRAFTWERKS- UND NETZGESELLSCHAFT MBH—See EnBW Energie Baden-Wurttemberg AG; *Int'l*, pg. 2399
KNG WELLTECHNO CO., LTD.—See K&O Energy Group Inc.; *Int'l*, pg. 4038
KNH ENTERPRISE CO., LTD.; *Int'l*, pg. 4206
KNH (SHANGHAI) CO., LTD.—See KNH Enterprise Co., Ltd.; *Int'l*, pg. 4206
KNICHEL LOGISTICS; *U.S. Private*, pg. 2322
KNICKERBOCKER DIALYSIS, INC.—See DaVita Inc.; *U.S. Public*, pg. 640
KNICKERBOCKER PARTITION CORPORATION; *U.S. Private*, pg. 2322
KNICK EXPLORATION INC.; *Int'l*, pg. 4206
KNICK KNACK, INC.; *U.S. Private*, pg. 2322
KNIFE RIVER CORPORATION - NORTH CENTRAL—See MDU Resources Group, Inc.; *U.S. Public*, pg. 1410
KNIFE RIVER CORPORATION - NORTHWEST—See MDU Resources Group, Inc.; *U.S. Public*, pg. 1410
KNIFE RIVER CORPORATION - SAULK RAPIDS—See MDU Resources Group, Inc.; *U.S. Public*, pg. 1410
KNIFE RIVER CORPORATION—See MDU Resources Group, Inc.; *U.S. Public*, pg. 1409
KNIFE RIVER CORPORATION - SOUTH—See MDU Resources Group, Inc.; *U.S. Public*, pg. 1411
KNIFE RIVER - EAST TEXAS DIVISION—See MDU Resources Group, Inc.; *U.S. Public*, pg. 1411
KNIFE RIVER HAWAII, INC.—See MDU Resources Group, Inc.; *U.S. Public*, pg. 1411
KNIFE RIVER MATERIALS - MEDFORD—See MDU Resources Group, Inc.; *U.S. Public*, pg. 1410
KNIFE RIVER MATERIALS—See MDU Resources Group, Inc.; *U.S. Public*, pg. 1410
KNIFE RIVER MATERIALS—See MDU Resources Group, Inc.; *U.S. Public*, pg. 1410
KNIFE RIVER-MEDFORD—See MDU Resources Group, Inc.; *U.S. Public*, pg. 1410
KNIFE RIVER-WACO READY MIX PLANT—See MDU Resources Group, Inc.; *U.S. Public*, pg. 1410
KNIGHT BENEDIKT AUSTRALIA PTY. LTD.—See Vimian Group AB; *Int'l*, pg. 8208
KNIGHT CANADA LIMITED—See IDEX Corp; *U.S. Public*, pg. 1091
KNIGHTEC AB; *Int'l*, pg. 4207
KNIGHT ENTERPRISES, INC.—See Guggenheim Partners, LLC; *U.S. Private*, pg. 1812
KNIGHT ENTERPRISES INC.; *U.S. Private*, pg. 2322
KNIGHT EQUIPMENT PTY., LTD.—See IDEX Corp; *U.S. Public*, pg. 1091
KNIGHT FRANK AUCKLAND LTD—See Knight Frank LLP; *Int'l*, pg. 4206
KNIGHT FRANK AUSTRALIA PTY. LTD.—See Knight Frank LLP; *Int'l*, pg. 4206
KNIGHT FRANK BOTSWANA LTD—See Knight Frank LLP; *Int'l*, pg. 4206
KNIGHT FRANK CAIRNS PTY LTD—See Knight Frank LLP; *Int'l*, pg. 4206
KNIGHT FRANK (CAMBODIA) PTE LTD—See Knight Frank LLP; *Int'l*, pg. 4206
KNIGHT FRANK ESPANA SA—See Knight Frank LLP; *Int'l*, pg. 4206
KNIGHT FRANK FRANKFURT GMBH—See Knight Frank LLP; *Int'l*, pg. 4206
KNIGHT FRANK (GAUTENG) (PTY) LTD—See Knight Frank LLP; *Int'l*, pg. 4206
KNIGHT FRANK GMBH CO KG—See Knight Frank LLP; *Int'l*, pg. 4206
KNIGHT FRANK HSC GMBH—See Knight Frank LLP; *Int'l*, pg. 4206
KNIGHT FRANK INDIA PVT LTD—See Knight Frank LLP; *Int'l*, pg. 4206
KNIGHT FRANK ITALIA S.R.L.—See Knight Frank LLP; *Int'l*, pg. 4206

KNIGHT SOLUTIONS

KNIGHT FRANK KENYA LTD—See Knight Frank LLP; *Int'l*, pg. 4206
KNIGHT FRANK KOREA—See Knight Frank LLP; *Int'l*, pg. 4206
KNIGHT FRANK LLP; *Int'l*, pg. 4206
KNIGHT FRANK (MALAWI) LTD—See Knight Frank LLP; *Int'l*, pg. 4206
KNIGHT FRANK MALAYSIA SDN BHD—See Knight Frank LLP; *Int'l*, pg. 4206
KNIGHT FRANK NIGERIA LIMITED—See Knight Frank LLP; *Int'l*, pg. 4206
KNIGHT FRANK (NORTHERN TERRITORY) PTY LTD—See Knight Frank LLP; *Int'l*, pg. 4206
KNIGHT FRANK PHUKET CO LTD—See Knight Frank LLP; *Int'l*, pg. 4206
KNIGHT FRANK PTE LTD—See Knight Frank LLP; *Int'l*, pg. 4207
KNIGHT FRANK SA—See Knight Frank LLP; *Int'l*, pg. 4207
KNIGHT FRANK (SHANGHAI) PROPERTY CONSULTANTS CO, LTD—See Knight Frank LLP; *Int'l*, pg. 4206
KNIGHT FRANK, SPOL. S R.O.—See Knight Frank LLP; *Int'l*, pg. 4206
KNIGHT FRANK SP. Z.O.O.—See Knight Frank LLP; *Int'l*, pg. 4207
KNIGHT FRANK TANZANIA LTD—See Knight Frank LLP; *Int'l*, pg. 4207
KNIGHT FRANK (THAILAND) LTD.—See Knight Frank LLP; *Int'l*, pg. 4206
KNIGHT FRANK UGANDA LTD—See Knight Frank LLP; *Int'l*, pg. 4207
KNIGHT FRANK (ZAMBIA) LTD—See Knight Frank LLP; *Int'l*, pg. 4207
KNIGHT FRANK ZAO—See Knight Frank LLP; *Int'l*, pg. 4207
KNIGHT FRANK ZIMBABWE—See Knight Frank LLP; *Int'l*, pg. 4207
KNIGHTHAWK INC.; *Int'l*, pg. 4207
KNIGHTHAWK PROTECTION, LLC—See Veteran Infrastructure Products LLC; *U.S. Private*, pg. 4373
KNIGHTHEAD CAPITAL MANAGEMENT LLC; *U.S. Private*, pg. 2322
KNIGHT INDUSTRIES & ASSOCIATES INC.; *U.S. Private*, pg. 2322
KNIGHT, LLC—See IDEX Corp; *U.S. Public*, pg. 1091
KNIGHT MARKETING ASSOCIATES, INC.; *U.S. Private*, pg. 2322
KNIGHTON ESTATES LIMITED—See Great Portland Estates Plc; *Int'l*, pg. 3065
KNIGHTON FOODS LIMITED—See Premier Foods plc; *Int'l*, pg. 5960
KNIGHT PAPER BOX COMPANY; *U.S. Private*, pg. 2322
KNIGHT PLANNING CORP.—See Winged Keel Group, LLC; *U.S. Private*, pg. 4541
KNIGHT PLASTICS, LLC—See Berry Global Group, Inc; *U.S. Public*, pg. 321
KNIGHT POINT SYSTEMS, LLC—See Veritas Capital Fund Management, LLC; *U.S. Private*, pg. 4364
KNIGHT PROTECTIVE SERVICE, INC.; *U.S. Private*, pg. 2322
KNIGHT RIFLES, INC.—See EBSCO Industries, Inc.; *U.S. Private*, pg. 1325
KNIGHTS APPAREL, INC.—See Hanesbrands Inc.; *U.S. Public*, pg. 983
KNIGHTS APPAREL LLC—See Hanesbrands Inc.; *U.S. Public*, pg. 983
KNIGHT'S ARMAMENT COMPANY; *U.S. Private*, pg. 2322
KNIGHTSBRIDGE BUSINESS SALES LIMITED—See Sun Capital Partners, Inc.; *U.S. Private*, pg. 3861
KNIGHTSBRIDGE CARPETS LIMITED—See Bremworth Limited; *Int'l*, pg. 1145
KNIGHTSBRIDGE CHEMICALS EGYPT SAE—See Knightsbridge Chemicals Ltd.; *Int'l*, pg. 4208
KNIGHTSBRIDGE CHEMICALS LTD.; *Int'l*, pg. 4208
KNIGHTSBRIDGE CHEMICALS LTD.—See Knightsbridge Chemicals Ltd.; *Int'l*, pg. 4208
KNIGHTSBRIDGE FURNITURE PRODUCTIONS LTD; *Int'l*, pg. 4208
KNIGHTSBRIDGE GUARDING LTD—See Rentokil Initial plc; *Int'l*, pg. 6287
KNIGHTSBRIDGE INVESTMENTS LIMITED—See Knightsbridge Chemicals Ltd.; *Int'l*, pg. 4208
KNIGHTSCOPE, INC.; *U.S. Public*, pg. 1269
KNIGHT SECURITY SYSTEMS, LLC—See Sentinel Capital Partners, L.L.C.; *U.S. Private*, pg. 3609
KNIGHT SEED COMPANY INC.; *U.S. Private*, pg. 2322
KNIGHTS GROUP HOLDINGS PLC; *Int'l*, pg. 4207
KNIGHT'S INC.; *U.S. Private*, pg. 2322
KNIGHTS & JOHNS MANAGEMENT LTD.—See Ireland Blyth Limited; *Int'l*, pg. 3807
KNIGHTS LIMITED—See Barbados Shipping & Trading Co. Ltd.; *Int'l*, pg. 858
KNIGHTS' MARINE & INDUSTRIAL SERVICES, INC.; *U.S. Private*, pg. 2322
KNIGHTS OF COLUMBUS; *U.S. Private*, pg. 2322
KNIGHT SOLUTIONS; *U.S. Private*, pg. 2322

KNIGHT SOLUTIONS

KNIGHTS PROFESSIONAL SERVICES LIMITED—See Knights Group Holdings PLC; *Int'l*, pg. 4208
KNIGHTSWAN ACQUISITION CORPORATION; *U.S. Public*, pg. 1270
KNIGHT-SWIFT TRANSPORTATION HOLDINGS INC.; *U.S. Public*, pg. 1269
KNIGHTSWOOD HOLDINGS LTD.—See Auxly Cannabis Group Inc.; *Int'l*, pg. 733
KNIGHTSWOOD PLACE (RAINHAM) RESIDENTS MANAGEMENT COMPANY LIMITED—See Persimmon plc; *Int'l*, pg. 5816
KNIGHT THERAPEUTICS INC.; *Int'l*, pg. 4207
KNIGHT TRANSPORTATION, INC.—See Knight-Swift Transportation Holdings Inc.; *U.S. Public*, pg. 1269
KNIGHT TRUCK & TRAILER SALES, LLC—See Knight-Swift Transportation Holdings Inc.; *U.S. Public*, pg. 1269
KNIGHT U.K. LTD.—See IDEX Corp; *U.S. Public*, pg. 1091
KNIGHT WENDLING GMBH—See GEMCO Engineers B.V.; *Int'l*, pg. 2915
KNIK CONSTRUCTION CO., INC.—See Lynden Incorporated; *U.S. Private*, pg. 2521
KNILAM PACKAGING (PTY) LTD—See Berry Global Group, Inc; *U.S. Public*, pg. 324
KNILL ENERGY HOLDING GMBH—See Knill Holding GmbH; *Int'l*, pg. 4208
KNILL HOLDING GMBH; *Int'l*, pg. 4208
KNILL TECHNOLOGY HOLDING GMBH—See Knill Holding GmbH; *Int'l*, pg. 4208
KN INFORMATION SYSTEMS CORPORATION—See Core Corporation; *Int'l*, pg. 1797
KNIPFING ASPHALT SOLUTIONS, INC.—See C & L Services LLC; *U.S. Private*, pg. 701
KNIPPING SYSTEM-TECHNIK GMBH—See RAG-Stiftung; *Int'l*, pg. 6179
KNIPPING VERBINDUNGSTECHNIK GMBH—See LISI S.A.; *Int'l*, pg. 4523
KNITCRAFT CORPORATION; *U.S. Private*, pg. 2322
KNIT-RITE INC.; *U.S. Private*, pg. 2322
KNIT TEXTILE INTEGRATED INDUSTRIES SDN. BHD.—See KTMG Limited; *Int'l*, pg. 4317
KNITWEAR FACTORY MAXIM C.M. PERTSINIDIS S.A.; *Int'l*, pg. 4208
KNITWORK PRODUCTIONS CORP.; *U.S. Private*, pg. 2322
KNITWORKS DESIGN ZONE, INC.; *U.S. Private*, pg. 2322
KNJAZ MILOS A.D.—See Mattoni 1873 a.s.; *Int'l*, pg. 4731
KNJAZ MILOS A.D.—See PepsiCo, Inc.; *U.S. Public*, pg. 1669
KNJ CO., LTD.; *Int'l*, pg. 4208
KNK COATINGS CO., LTD.—See Kansai Paint Co., Ltd.; *Int'l*, pg. 4072
K&N KENANGA HOLDINGS BERHAD—See Kenanga Investment Bank Berhad; *Int'l*, pg. 4125
KNL HOLDINGS INC.; *U.S. Private*, pg. 2322
KNL HOLDINGS, LLC; *U.S. Private*, pg. 2322
KNL INCORPORATED; *U.S. Private*, pg. 2322
KN (MAURITIUS) LIMITED—See Kuehne + Nagel International AG; *Int'l*, pg. 4324
KNM GROUP BERHAD; *Int'l*, pg. 4208
KNM PROCESS EQUIPMENT INC.—See KNM Group Berhad; *Int'l*, pg. 4209
KNM PROCESS SYSTEMS SDN. BHD.—See KNM Group Berhad; *Int'l*, pg. 4209
KNM SPECIAL PROCESS EQUIPMENT (CHANGSHU) CO., LTD.—See KNM Group Berhad; *Int'l*, pg. 4209
KNNEX HEALTH INC.—See Medacta Group SA; *Int'l*, pg. 4767
KNOAH SOLUTIONS, INC.—See Ontario Teachers' Pension Plan; *Int'l*, pg. 5585
KNOBBE MARTENS OLSON & BEAR LLP; *U.S. Private*, pg. 2323
KNOBIAS, INC.; *U.S. Private*, pg. 2323
KNOC CASPIAN LLP—See Korea National Oil Corporation; *Int'l*, pg. 4286
KNOC EAGLE FORD CORP.—See Korea National Oil Corporation; *Int'l*, pg. 4286
KNOCH, KERN & CO. KG; *Int'l*, pg. 4209
KNOCK, INC.; *U.S. Private*, pg. 2323
KNOCKINON, INC.—See Zenrin Co., Ltd.; *Int'l*, pg. 8634
KNOCK OUT PEST CONTROL PTY LIMITED—See Rentokil Initial plc; *Int'l*, pg. 6287
KNOCK TANKERS LTD.—See Fred. Olsen & Co.; *Int'l*, pg. 2769
KNOC TRADING SINGAPORE PTE. LTD.—See Korea National Oil Corporation; *Int'l*, pg. 4286
KNOEPFLER CHEVROLET CO.; *U.S. Private*, pg. 2323
KNOE-TV—See Gray Television, Inc.; *U.S. Public*, pg. 960
KNOLL AMERICA, INC.—See KNOLL Maschinenbau GmbH; *Int'l*, pg. 4209
KNOLL, INC.—See MillerKnoll, Inc.; *U.S. Public*, pg. 1447
KNOLL INTERNATIONAL S.A.—See MillerKnoll, Inc.; *U.S. Public*, pg. 1447
KNOLL INTERNATIONAL S.A.—See MillerKnoll, Inc.; *U.S. Public*, pg. 1447
KNOLL INTERNATIONAL U.K. LTD.—See MillerKnoll, Inc.; *U.S. Public*, pg. 1447
KNOLL MASCHINENBAU GMBH; *Int'l*, pg. 4209

KNOLL OVERSEAS, INC.—See MillerKnoll, Inc.; *U.S. Public*, pg. 1447
KNOLOGY, INC.—See WideOpenWest, Inc.; *U.S. Public*, pg. 2370
KNOLOGY OF FLORIDA, LLC—See WideOpenWest, Inc.; *U.S. Public*, pg. 2370
KNOLOGY OF HUNTSVILLE, INC.—See WideOpenWest, Inc.; *U.S. Public*, pg. 2370
KNOLOGY OF MONTGOMERY, INC.—See WideOpenWest, Inc.; *U.S. Public*, pg. 2370
KNOLOGY TOTAL COMMUNICATIONS, INC.—See WideOpenWest, Inc.; *U.S. Public*, pg. 2370
KNOPE ROOFING & FURNACE CO.—See Eponk Group Ltd.; *U.S. Private*, pg. 1414
KNOPF AUTOMOTIVE DO BRASIL LTDA—See Knopf Automotive Parts; *U.S. Private*, pg. 2323
KNOPF AUTOMOTIVE PARTS; *U.S. Private*, pg. 2323
KNOPF MOTORS INC.; *U.S. Private*, pg. 2323
KNOP-TV—See Gray Television, Inc.; *U.S. Public*, pg. 960
K.NORDANG AS—See Peab AB; *Int'l*, pg. 5772
KNORR ALIMENTARIA, S.A.—See Unilever PLC; *Int'l*, pg. 8044
KNORR BRAKE COMPANY—See Knorr-Bremse AG; *Int'l*, pg. 4210
KNORR BRAKE LTD.—See Knorr-Bremse AG; *Int'l*, pg. 4210
KNORR-BREMSE AG; *Int'l*, pg. 4209
KNORR-BREMSE ASIA PACIFIC (HOLDING) LTD.—See Knorr-Bremse AG; *Int'l*, pg. 4210
KNORR-BREMSE AUSTRALIA PTY. LTD.—See Knorr-Bremse AG; *Int'l*, pg. 4210
KNORR-BREMSE BENELUX B.V.B.A.—See Knorr-Bremse AG; *Int'l*, pg. 4211
KNORR-BREMSE BRAKE EQUIPMENT (SHANGHAI) CO., LTD.—See Knorr-Bremse AG; *Int'l*, pg. 4210
KNORR-BREMSE COMMERCIAL VEHICLE SYSTEMS JAPAN LTD.—See Knorr-Bremse AG; *Int'l*, pg. 4210
KNORR-BREMSE COMMERCIAL VEHICLE SYSTEMS (SHANGHAI) CO., LTD.—See Knorr-Bremse AG; *Int'l*, pg. 4210
KNORR-BREMSE DETC COMMERCIAL VEHICLE BRAKING TECHNOLOGY CO., LTD.—See Knorr-Bremse AG; *Int'l*, pg. 4210
KNORR-BREMSE FEKRENDSZEREK KFT.—See Knorr-Bremse AG; *Int'l*, pg. 4211
KNORR-BREMSE GES.M.B.H.—See Knorr-Bremse AG; *Int'l*, pg. 4211
KNORR-BREMSE IBERICA S.L.—See Knorr-Bremse AG; *Int'l*, pg. 4210
KNORR-BREMSE INDIA PRIVATE LTD.—See Knorr-Bremse AG; *Int'l*, pg. 4211
KNORR-BREMSE/NANKOU AIR SUPPLY UNIT (BEIJING) CO., LTD.—See Knorr-Bremse AG; *Int'l*, pg. 4211
KNORR-BREMSE NORDIC RAIL SERVICES AB—See Knorr-Bremse AG; *Int'l*, pg. 4210
KNORR-BREMSE PAMPLONA S.L.—See Knorr-Bremse AG; *Int'l*, pg. 4210
KNORR-BREMSE POLSKA SFN SP. Z O.O.—See Knorr-Bremse AG; *Int'l*, pg. 4210
KNORR-BREMSE RAILSERVICES (UK) LIMITED—See Mutares SE & Co. KGaA; *Int'l*, pg. 5105
KNORR-BREMSE RAIL SYSTEMS (BURTON) LTD.—See Knorr-Bremse AG; *Int'l*, pg. 4210
KNORR-BREMSE RAIL SYSTEMS CIS HOLDING OOO—See Knorr-Bremse AG; *Int'l*, pg. 4210
KNORR-BREMSE RAIL SYSTEMS ITALIA S.R.L.—See Knorr-Bremse AG; *Int'l*, pg. 4211
KNORR-BREMSE RAIL SYSTEMS JAPAN LTD.—See Knorr-Bremse AG; *Int'l*, pg. 4211
KNORR-BREMSE RAIL SYSTEMS KOREA LTD.—See Knorr-Bremse AG; *Int'l*, pg. 4211
KNORR-BREMSE RAIL SYSTEMS (MACHINING) LTD.—See Knorr-Bremse AG; *Int'l*, pg. 4210
KNORR-BREMSE RAIL SYSTEMS SCHWEIZ AG—See Knorr-Bremse AG; *Int'l*, pg. 4211
KNORR-BREMSE RAIL SYSTEMS (UK) LTD.—See Knorr-Bremse AG; *Int'l*, pg. 4211
KNORR-BREMSE RAIL TRANSPORTATION EQUIPMENT (CHENGDU) CO., LTD.—See Knorr-Bremse AG; *Int'l*, pg. 4211
KNORR-BREMSE RAILWAY TECHNOLOGIES (SHANGHAI) CO., LTD.—See Knorr-Bremse AG; *Int'l*, pg. 4211
KNORR-BREMSE RAYLI SISTEMLER SANAYI VE TICARET LIMITED SIRKETI—See Knorr-Bremse AG; *Int'l*, pg. 4211
KNORR-BREMSE S.A. (PTY.) LTD.—See Knorr-Bremse AG; *Int'l*, pg. 4211
KNORR-BREMSE SERVICES EUROPE S.R.O.—See Knorr-Bremse AG; *Int'l*, pg. 4211
KNORR-BREMSE SERVICES GMBH—See Knorr-Bremse AG; *Int'l*, pg. 4211
KNORR-BREMSE SISTEMAS PARA VEICULOS COMERCIAIS BRASIL LTDA.—See Knorr-Bremse AG; *Int'l*, pg. 4211
KNORR-BREMSE SISTEMAS PARA VEICULOS FERROVIARIOS LTDA.—See Knorr-Bremse AG; *Int'l*, pg. 4211

CORPORATE AFFILIATIONS

KNORR-BREMSE SISTEMI PER AUTOVEICOLI COMMERCIALI S.P.A.—See Knorr-Bremse AG; *Int'l*, pg. 4211
KNORR-BREMSE S.R.L.—See Knorr-Bremse AG; *Int'l*, pg. 4211
KNORR-BREMSE STEERING SYSTEMS JAPAN LTD.—See Knorr-Bremse AG; *Int'l*, pg. 4211
KNORR-BREMSE SYSTEME FUR NUTZFAHRZEUGE GMBH—See Knorr-Bremse AG; *Int'l*, pg. 4211
KNORR-BREMSE SYSTEME FUR SCHIENENFAHRZEUGE GMBH—See Knorr-Bremse AG; *Int'l*, pg. 4211
KNORR-BREMSE SYSTEMES FERROVIAIRES S.A.—See Knorr-Bremse AG; *Int'l*, pg. 4211
KNORR-BREMSE SYSTEMES POUR VEHICULES UTILITAIRES FRANCE S.A.—See Knorr-Bremse AG; *Int'l*, pg. 4211
KNORR-BREMSE SYSTEMES POUR VEHICULES UTILITAIRES FRANCE S.A.—See Knorr-Bremse AG; *Int'l*, pg. 4211
KNORR-BREMSE SYSTEMS FOR COMMERCIAL VEHICLES INDIA PVT. LTD.—See Knorr-Bremse AG; *Int'l*, pg. 4211
KNORR-BREMSE SYSTEMS FOR COMMERCIAL VEHICLES LTD.—See Knorr-Bremse AG; *Int'l*, pg. 4211
KNORR-BREMSE SYSTEMS FOR RAIL VEHICLES ENTERPRISE MANAGEMENT (BEIJING) CO., LTD.—See Knorr-Bremse AG; *Int'l*, pg. 4211
KNORR-BREMSE SYSTEMS FOR RAIL VEHICLES (SUZHOU) CO., LTD.—See Knorr-Bremse AG; *Int'l*, pg. 4211
KNORR-BREMSE SYSTEMY KOLEJOWE POLSKA SP. Z O.O.—See Knorr-Bremse AG; *Int'l*, pg. 4211
KNORR-BREMSE SYSTEMY PRO UITOVA VOZIDLA CR SPO—See Knorr-Bremse AG; *Int'l*, pg. 4211
KNORR-BREMSE SYSTEMY PRO UZITKOVA VOZILDA CR S.R.O.—See Knorr-Bremse AG; *Int'l*, pg. 4211
KNORR-BREMSE TECHNOLOGY CENTER INDIA PVT. LTD.—See Knorr-Bremse AG; *Int'l*, pg. 4211
KNORR-BREMSE VASUTI JARMU RENDSZEREK HUNGARIA KFT.—See Knorr-Bremse AG; *Int'l*, pg. 4211
KNORR SYSTEMS INC.—See Court Square Capital Partners, L.P.; *U.S. Private*, pg. 1069
KNOSYS LIMITED; *Int'l*, pg. 4212
KNOTEL AHOY! BERLIN GMBH—See Newmark Group, Inc.; *U.S. Public*, pg. 1515
KNOT OFFSHORE PARTNERS LP; *Int'l*, pg. 4212
KNOT STANDARD, LLC—See Billy Reid, Inc.; *U.S. Private*, pg. 559
KNOTT'S BERRY FARM LLC—See Six Flags Entertainment Corporation; *U.S. Public*, pg. 1890
KNOTTS CO. INC.; *U.S. Private*, pg. 2323
THE KNOT WORLDWIDE INC.—See Permira Advisers LLP; *Int'l*, pg. 5808
KNOUSE FOODS COOPERATIVE INC. - BIGLERVILLE, PA. PLANT—See Knouse Foods Cooperative Inc.; *U.S. Private*, pg. 2323
KNOUSE FOODS COOPERATIVE INC. - CHAMBERSBURG, PA. PLANT—See Knouse Foods Cooperative Inc.; *U.S. Private*, pg. 2323
KNOUSE FOODS COOPERATIVE INC. - GARDNERS, PA. PLANT—See Knouse Foods Cooperative Inc.; *U.S. Private*, pg. 2323
KNOUSE FOODS COOPERATIVE INC. - ORRTANNA, PA. PLANT—See Knouse Foods Cooperative Inc.; *U.S. Private*, pg. 2323
KNOUSE FOODS COOPERATIVE INC.; *U.S. Private*, pg. 2323
KNOVATION, INC.; *U.S. Private*, pg. 2323
KNOVEL CORPORATION; *U.S. Private*, pg. 2323
KNOWBE4, INC.—See Vista Equity Partners, LLC; *U.S. Private*, pg. 4398
KNOWBE4, LLC; *U.S. Private*, pg. 2323
KNOW IT AB; *Int'l*, pg. 4212
KNOW IT A-KRAFT AB—See Know IT AB; *Int'l*, pg. 4212
KNOWIT ARCHITECTURE AB—See Know IT AB; *Int'l*, pg. 4213
KNOWIT AS—See Know IT AB; *Int'l*, pg. 4213
KNOW-IT BUSINESS CONSULTING AB—See Know IT AB; *Int'l*, pg. 4212
KNOWIT BUSINESS CONSULTING AB—See Know IT AB; *Int'l*, pg. 4213
KNOW IT BUSINESS CONSULTING AS—See Know IT AB; *Int'l*, pg. 4212
KNOW IT CANDEO AB—See Know IT AB; *Int'l*, pg. 4212
KNOW IT CANDEO AB—See Know IT AB; *Int'l*, pg. 4212
KNOW IT CANDEO AB—See Know IT AB; *Int'l*, pg. 4212
KNOW IT CANDEO GAVLE AB—See Know IT AB; *Int'l*, pg. 4212
KNOWIT CLOUD AB—See Know IT AB; *Int'l*, pg. 4213
KNOWIT CLOUD & ARCHITECTURE AB—See Know IT AB; *Int'l*, pg. 4213
KNOWIT CONNECTIVITY AB—See Know IT AB; *Int'l*, pg. 4213
KNOW IT CONSULTING I GOTEBORG AB—See Know IT AB; *Int'l*, pg. 4212
KNOW IT CONSULTING I SODERTALJE AB—See Know IT AB; *Int'l*, pg. 4212
KNOWIT CORE AB—See Know IT AB; *Int'l*, pg. 4213

COMPANY NAME INDEX

KNOWIT CORE SYD AB—See Know IT AB; *Int'l*, pg. 4213
KNOW IT CREATE I LUND AB—See Know IT AB; *Int'l*, pg. 4212
KNOWIT CYBERSECURITY & LAW AB—See Know IT AB; *Int'l*, pg. 4213
KNOW IT DALARNA AB—See Know IT AB; *Int'l*, pg. 4212
KNOW IT DALSYS AB—See Know IT AB; *Int'l*, pg. 4213
KNOW IT DATAUNIT AB—See Know IT AB; *Int'l*, pg. 4213
KNOWIT DECISION HELIKOPTER AB—See Know IT AB; *Int'l*, pg. 4213
KNOWIT DECISION STOCKHOLM AB—See Know IT AB; *Int'l*, pg. 4213
KNOWIT DIGITAL MANAGEMENT AB—See Know IT AB; *Int'l*, pg. 4213
KNOW IT ESTONIA CONSULTING OU—See Know IT AB; *Int'l*, pg. 4213
KNOWIT EXPERIENCE OY—See Know IT AB; *Int'l*, pg. 4213
KNOWIT EXPERIENCE STOCKHOLM AB—See Know IT AB; *Int'l*, pg. 4213
KNOWIT FLX AB—See Know IT AB; *Int'l*, pg. 4213
KNOW IT GAVLEBORG AB—See Know IT AB; *Int'l*, pg. 4213
KNOW IT GOTEBORG AB—See Know IT AB; *Int'l*, pg. 4213
KNOW IT HRM AB—See Know IT AB; *Int'l*, pg. 4213
KNOW IT IM GOTEBORG AB—See Know IT AB; *Int'l*, pg. 4213
KNOW IT IM HELIKOPTER AB—See Know IT AB; *Int'l*, pg. 4213
KNOW IT IM INNOGRATE AB—See Know IT AB; *Int'l*, pg. 4213
KNOW IT IM LINKOPING AB—See Know IT AB; *Int'l*, pg. 4213
KNOW IT INFORMATION MANAGEMENT STOCKHOLM AB—See Know IT AB; *Int'l*, pg. 4213
KNOW IT INFORMATIONSSYNERIGI AB—See Know IT AB; *Int'l*, pg. 4213
KNOWIT INSIGHT ACCELERATE AB—See Know IT AB; *Int'l*, pg. 4213
KNOWIT INSIGHT SYD AB—See Know IT AB; *Int'l*, pg. 4213
KNOWIT INVATIVA AB—See Know IT AB; *Int'l*, pg. 4213
KNOWIT JONKOPING AB—See Know IT AB; *Int'l*, pg. 4213
KNOW IT KARLSTAD AB—See Know IT AB; *Int'l*, pg. 4213
KNOW IT MALARDALEN AB—See Know IT AB; *Int'l*, pg. 4213
KNOW IT MALARDALEN AB—See Know IT AB; *Int'l*, pg. 4213
KNOW IT MOBILE SYD AB—See Know IT AB; *Int'l*, pg. 4213
KNOW IT NET RESULT AB—See Know IT AB; *Int'l*, pg. 4213
KNOW IT NET RESULT INTERNATIONAL AB—See Know IT AB; *Int'l*, pg. 4213
KNOW IT NORRLAND AB—See Know IT AB; *Int'l*, pg. 4213
KNOWIT OREBRO AB—See Know IT AB; *Int'l*, pg. 4214
KNOWIT POLAND SP. Z O.O.—See Know IT AB; *Int'l*, pg. 4214
KNOW IT SECURE AB—See Know IT AB; *Int'l*, pg. 4213
KNOW IT SOFTWARE SOLUTIONS AB—See Know IT AB; *Int'l*, pg. 4213
KNOWIT SOFTWARE SOLUTIONS AS—See Know IT AB; *Int'l*, pg. 4213
KNOWIT SOLUTIONS COCREATE AB—See Know IT AB; *Int'l*, pg. 4214
KNOWIT SOLUTIONS DANMARK A/S—See Know IT AB; *Int'l*, pg. 4214
KNOWIT SOLUTIONS DATALYTICS AB—See Know IT AB; *Int'l*, pg. 4214
KNOW IT STAVANGER AS—See Know IT AB; *Int'l*, pg. 4213
KNOW IT STOCKHOLM AB—See Know IT AB; *Int'l*, pg. 4213
KNOW IT STOCKHOLM AMHS AB—See Know IT AB; *Int'l*, pg. 4213
KNOWIT SYDOST AB—See Know IT AB; *Int'l*, pg. 4214
KNOW IT SYSTEM DEVELOPMENT AB—See Know IT AB; *Int'l*, pg. 4213
KNOW IT TECHNOLOGY MANAGEMENT AB—See Know IT AB; *Int'l*, pg. 4213
KNOW IT TECHNOLOGY MANAGEMENT I STHLM AB—See Know IT AB; *Int'l*, pg. 4213
KNOW IT TECHNOWLEDGE I STOCKHOLM AB—See Know IT AB; *Int'l*, pg. 4213
KNOWIT UPPSALA AB—See Know IT AB; *Int'l*, pg. 4214
KNOWIT UPPSALA SOLUTIONS AB—See Know IT AB; *Int'l*, pg. 4214
KNOW IT YAHM SWEDEN AB—See Know IT AB; *Int'l*, pg. 4213
KNOW LABS, INC.; *U.S. Public*, pg. 1270
KNOWLAND GROUP INC.; *U.S. Private*, pg. 2323
KNOWLAN'S SUPER MARKETS INC.; *U.S. Private*, pg. 2323
KNOWLEDGE ADVANTAGE INC.; *U.S. Private*, pg. 2323
KNOWLEDGEADVISORS, INC.—See eXplorance, Inc.; *Int'l*, pg. 2588

KNOWLEDGE ANYWHERE, INC.; *U.S. Private*, pg. 2323
KNOWLEDGEBANK, INC.; *U.S. Private*, pg. 2323
KNOWLEDGE CAPITAL GROUP LLC—See Vizient, Inc.; *U.S. Private*, pg. 4407
KNOWLEDGECOM CORPORATION SDN. BHD.—See Censof Holdings Berhad; *Int'l*, pg. 1401
KNOWLEDGE CONTROL SYSTEMS LTD.—See Malam-Team Ltd.; *Int'l*, pg. 4659
KNOWLEDGE ECONOMIC CITY DEVELOPERS CO. LTD.; *Int'l*, pg. 4214
KNOWLEDGE FACTOR, INC.—See Polaris Growth Management, LLC; *U.S. Private*, pg. 3223
KNOWLEDGEFOX GMBH—See Fabasoft AG; *Int'l*, pg. 2598
KNOWLEDGE INFORMATION SOLUTIONS, INC.; *U.S. Private*, pg. 2323
KNOWLEDGE LABO, INC.—See Money Forward, Inc.; *Int'l*, pg. 5032
KNOWLEDGELAKE INC.; *U.S. Private*, pg. 2324
KNOWLEDGE LINK INC.—See Axiologic Solutions, LLC; *U.S. Private*, pg. 413
KNOWLEDGE MARINE & ENGINEERING WORKS LTD.; *Int'l*, pg. 4214
KNOWLEDGE MARKETING, LLC—See ESW Capital, LLC; *U.S. Private*, pg. 1430
KNOWLEDGE NETWORKS, INC.—See Advent International Corporation; *U.S. Private*, pg. 105
KNOWLEDGE PARTNERS INTERNATIONAL, LLC—See Sapiens International Corporation N.V.; *Int'l*, pg. 6571
KNOWLEDGEPOINT360 GROUP LLC—See Clayton, Dubilier & Rice, LLC; *U.S. Private*, pg. 928
KNOWLEDGE POWER CORPORATION; *Int'l*, pg. 4214
KNOWLEDGESUITE, INC.—See KDDI Corporation; *Int'l*, pg. 4112
KNOWLEDGE SUPPORT SYSTEMS INC.—See Hanover Investors Management LLP; *Int'l*, pg. 3258
KNOWLEDGE TOWER TRADING COMPANY; *Int'l*, pg. 4214
THE KNOWLEDGE TREE INC.; *U.S. Private*, pg. 4065
KNOWLEDGE WORKS, INC.—See Equifax Inc.; *U.S. Public*, pg. 786
KNOWLES ASSOCIATES, LLC; *U.S. Private*, pg. 2324
KNOWLES CAZENOVIA INC.—See Knowles Corporation; *U.S. Public*, pg. 1270
KNOWLES CAZENOVIA—See Knowles Corporation; *U.S. Public*, pg. 1270
KNOWLES CORPORATION; *U.S. Public*, pg. 1270
KNOWLES ELECTRONICS AUSTRIA GMBH—See Knowles Corporation; *U.S. Public*, pg. 1270
KNOWLES ELECTRONICS DENMARK APS—See Knowles Corporation; *U.S. Public*, pg. 1270
KNOWLES ELECTRONICS HOLDINGS, INC.—See Knowles Corporation; *U.S. Public*, pg. 1270
KNOWLES ELECTRONICS, LLC—See Knowles Corporation; *U.S. Public*, pg. 1270
KNOWLES ELECTRONICS (MALAYSIA) SDN. BHD.—See Knowles Corporation; *U.S. Public*, pg. 1270
KNOWLES ELECTRONICS TAIWAN, LTD.—See Knowles Corporation; *U.S. Public*, pg. 1270
KNOWLES ON SITE REPAIR, INC.—See American Securities LLC; *U.S. Private*, pg. 248
KNOWLES (UK) LTD—See Knowles Corporation; *U.S. Public*, pg. 1270
KNOWLOGY CORPORATION; *U.S. Private*, pg. 2324
THE KNOWLTON DEVELOPMENT CORPORATION—See Novacap Management Inc.; *Int'l*, pg. 5454
KNOWLTON TECHNOLOGIES LLC—See Eastman Chemical Company; *U.S. Public*, pg. 705
KNOWN GLOBAL LLC; *U.S. Private*, pg. 2324
KNOWNHOST LLC; *U.S. Private*, pg. 2324
KNOWSLEY SK LTD.—See Electricite de France S.A.; *Int'l*, pg. 2351
KNOX AREA RESCUE MINISTRIES; *U.S. Private*, pg. 2324
KNOX ASSOCIATES, INC.; *U.S. Private*, pg. 2324
KNOX ATTORNEY SERVICE INC.; *U.S. Private*, pg. 2324
KNOX CAPITAL HOLDINGS, LLC; *U.S. Private*, pg. 2324
KNOX CLINIC CORP.—See Quorum Health Corporation; *U.S. Private*, pg. 3330
KNOX COMMUNITY HOSPITAL; *U.S. Private*, pg. 2324
KNOX COUNTY STONE CO. INC.—See RiverStone Group, Inc.; *U.S. Private*, pg. 3446
KNOX CREEK COAL CORPORATION—See Alpha Natural Resources, Inc.; *U.S. Private*, pg. 198
KNOX DATA, CORP.—See ISB Corporation; *Int'l*, pg. 3812
KNOX ENERGY COOPERATIVE ASSOCIATION INC.; *U.S. Private*, pg. 2324
KNOX ENTERPRISES INC.; *U.S. Private*, pg. 2324
KNOX INVESTMENT PARTNERS LIMITED; *Int'l*, pg. 4214
KNOX LANE LP; *U.S. Private*, pg. 2324
KNOX OIL FIELD SUPPLY, INC.—See Applied Industrial Technologies, Inc.; *U.S. Public*, pg. 171
KNOX OIL OF TEXAS, INC.; *U.S. Private*, pg. 2324
KNOXVILLE CENTER, LLC—See Washington Prime Group Inc.; *U.S. Private*, pg. 4448
KNOXVILLE-CJD, LLC—See Lithia Motors, Inc.; *U.S. Public*, pg. 1323
KNOXVILLE EYE ANESTHESIA, LLC—See KKR & Co. Inc.; *U.S. Public*, pg. 1249

KNOXVILLE HB MEDICAL SERVICES, LLC—See Community Health Systems, Inc.; *U.S. Public*, pg. 554
KNOXVILLE HMA CARDIOLOGY PPM, LLC—See Community Health Systems, Inc.; *U.S. Public*, pg. 554
KNOXVILLE HMA PHYSICIAN MANAGEMENT, LLC—See Community Health Systems, Inc.; *U.S. Public*, pg. 554
KNOXVILLE HOME CARE SERVICES, LLC—See Community Health Systems, Inc.; *U.S. Public*, pg. 554
KNOXVILLE HOSPITAL & CLINICS; *U.S. Private*, pg. 2324
KNOXVILLE NEWS SENTINEL, LLC—See Gannett Co., Inc.; *U.S. Public*, pg. 898
KNOXVILLE'S COMMUNITY DEVELOPMENT CORP.; *U.S. Private*, pg. 2325
KNOXVILLE WHOLESALE FURNITURE CO. INC.; *U.S. Private*, pg. 2325
KN PLATECH AMERICA CORPORATION—See Nagase & Co., Ltd.; *Int'l*, pg. 5126
KN PROPERTIES; *U.S. Private*, pg. 2321
K.N.P. SUPPLY CO., LTD.—See Gunkul Engineering Co., Ltd.; *Int'l*, pg. 3183
KNR CONSTRUCTIONS LIMITED; *Int'l*, pg. 4214
KNR SHANKARAMPET PROJECT PRIVATE LIMITED—See KNR Constructions Limited; *Int'l*, pg. 4214
KNR SRIRANGAM INFRA PRIVATE LIMITED—See KNR Constructions Limited; *Int'l*, pg. 4214
KNR TIRUMALA INFRA PRIVATE LIMITED—See KNR Constructions Limited; *Int'l*, pg. 4214
KN RUBBER, LLC—See Kinderhook Industries, LLC; *U.S. Private*, pg. 2307
KNSD-TV—See Comcast Corporation; *U.S. Public*, pg. 539
KNSK WERBEAGENTUR GMBH—See Omnicom Group Inc.; *U.S. Public*, pg. 1576
KNT-CT HOLDINGS CO., LTD.—See Kintetsu Group Holdings Co.,Ltd.; *Int'l*, pg. 4183
KN-TECH CO., LTD.—See NITTAN Corporation; *Int'l*, pg. 5383
KNT HOLDINGS LIMITED; *Int'l*, pg. 4214
KNT MANUFACTURING INC.; *U.S. Private*, pg. 2325
KNTV-TV—See Comcast Corporation; *U.S. Public*, pg. 539
KNUD NIELSEN COMPANY INC.; *U.S. Private*, pg. 2325
KNUDSEN, GARDNER & HOWE, INC.; *U.S. Private*, pg. 2325
KNUDSEN & SONS, INC.—See The J.M. Smucker Company; *U.S. Public*, pg. 2107
KNUDSON MANUFACTURING, INC.; *U.S. Private*, pg. 2325
KNUDTSEN CHEVROLET COMPANY; *U.S. Private*, pg. 2325
KNUPP & WATSON & WALLMAN; *U.S. Private*, pg. 2325
KNUR MASCHINENBAU GMBH—See INDUS Holding AG; *Int'l*, pg. 3663
KNURR AG & CO. GRUNDBESITZ OHG—See Vertiv Holdings Co; *U.S. Public*, pg. 2289
KNURR AG—See Vertiv Holdings Co; *U.S. Public*, pg. 2289
KNURR ELECTRONICS GMBH & CO. GRUNDBESITZ OHG—See Vertiv Holdings Co; *U.S. Public*, pg. 2289
KNURR ELECTRONICS GMBH—See Vertiv Holdings Co; *U.S. Public*, pg. 2289
KNURR ELECTRONICS GMBH—See Vertiv Holdings Co; *U.S. Public*, pg. 2289
KNURR GMBH—See Vertiv Holdings Co; *U.S. Public*, pg. 2289
KNURR LTDA.—See Vertiv Holdings Co; *U.S. Public*, pg. 2289
KNURR-MECOR GMBH—See Vertiv Holdings Co; *U.S. Public*, pg. 2289
KNURR NORGE AS—See Vertiv Holdings Co; *U.S. Public*, pg. 2289
KNURR S.A.R.L.—See Vertiv Holdings Co; *U.S. Public*, pg. 2289
KNURR-SPECTRA (S.E.A.) PTE. LTD.—See Vertiv Holdings Co; *U.S. Public*, pg. 2289
KNURR TECHNICAL FURNITURE GMBH—See Vertiv Holdings Co; *U.S. Public*, pg. 2289
KNUSFORD BERHAD; *Int'l*, pg. 4214
KNUST-SBO FAR EAST PTE LTD.—See Schoeller-Bleckmann Oilfield Equipment AG; *Int'l*, pg. 6637
KNUST-SBO LTD.—See Schoeller-Bleckmann Oilfield Equipment AG; *Int'l*, pg. 6637
KNUT D.O.O.—See NIBE Industrier AB; *Int'l*, pg. 5261
KNUTSEN NYK OFFSHORE TANKERS AS—See Nippon Yusen Kabushiki Kaisha; *Int'l*, pg. 5358
KNUTSFORD DOMESTIC FUEL OIL COMPANY LIMITED—See NWF Group Plc; *Int'l*, pg. 5499
KNUTSFORD EXPRESS SERVICES LTD.; *Int'l*, pg. 4214
KNUTSON CONSTRUCTION SERVICES, INC.—See Knutson Construction Services; *U.S. Private*, pg. 2325
KNUTSON CONSTRUCTION SERVICES MIDWEST INC.—See Knutson Construction Services; *U.S. Private*, pg. 2325
KNUTSON CONSTRUCTION SERVICES; *U.S. Private*, pg. 2325
KNV ENERGIETECHNIK GMBH—See NIBE Industrier AB; *Int'l*, pg. 5261
KNW CO., LTD.; *Int'l*, pg. 4214
KNW HOLDINGS, INC.; *U.S. Private*, pg. 2325

KNW HOLDINGS, INC.

CORPORATE AFFILIATIONS

KNXV-TV—See The E.W. Scripps Company; *U.S. Public*, pg. 2068
KOA CAPITAL PARTNERS LLC; *U.S. Private*, pg. 2325
KOA CORPORATION; *Int'l*, pg. 4215
KOA CORPORATION—See H.W. Lochner, Inc.; *U.S. Private*, pg. 1836
KOA DAIICHI TRAFFIC CO., LTD.—See Daiichi Koutsu Sangyo Co., Ltd.; *Int'l*, pg. 1928
KOA DENKO (MALAYSIA) SDN.BHD.—See Koa Corporation; *Int'l*, pg. 4215
KOA ELECTRONICS (H.K.) LTD.—See Koa Corporation; *Int'l*, pg. 4215
KOA ELECTRONICS (TAICANG) CO., LTD.—See Koa Corporation; *Int'l*, pg. 4215
KOA EUROPE GMBH—See Koa Corporation; *Int'l*, pg. 4215
KOA HOLDINGS INC.; *U.S. Private*, pg. 2325
KOA ISEI CO., LTD.—See Koa Shoji Holdings Co., Ltd.; *Int'l*, pg. 4215
KOA KAOHSIUNG CORPORATION—See Koa Corporation; *Int'l*, pg. 4215
KOA KOGYO CO., LTD.—See Marubeni Corporation; *Int'l*, pg. 4705
KOAK POWER LIMITED—See Korea Electric Power Corporation; *Int'l*, pg. 4283
KOALA CAPITAL MANAGEMENT LIMITED—See KOALA Financial Group Ltd; *Int'l*, pg. 4215
KOALA FINANCIAL GROUP LTD; *Int'l*, pg. 4215
KOALA KARE PRODUCTS—See Bobrick Washroom Equipment, Inc.; *U.S. Private*, pg. 607
KOALA STUDIOS—See Tacony Corporation; *U.S. Private*, pg. 3921
KOALA TEE, INC.; *U.S. Private*, pg. 2325
KOAL SOFTWARE CO., LTD.; *Int'l*, pg. 4215
KOAM ENGINEERING SYSTEMS INC.; *U.S. Private*, pg. 2325
KO-AMEX GENERAL WHOLESALE INC.; *U.S. Private*, pg. 2325
KOAN HAO TECHNOLOGY CO., LTD.; *Int'l*, pg. 4215
KOANNA HEALTHCARE GMBH—See Shilpa Medicare Ltd; *Int'l*, pg. 6831
KOAS CO., LTD. - GIMPO FACTORY—See Koas Co., Ltd.; *Int'l*, pg. 4215
KOAS CO., LTD. - PAJU 1 FACTORY—See Koas Co., Ltd.; *Int'l*, pg. 4215
KOAS CO., LTD. - PAJU 2 FACTORY—See Koas Co., Ltd.; *Int'l*, pg. 4215
KOAS CO., LTD. - PAJU 4 FACTORY—See Koas Co., Ltd.; *Int'l*, pg. 4215
KOAS CO., LTD.; *Int'l*, pg. 4215
KOA SHOJI CO., LTD.—See Koa Shoji Holdings Co., Ltd.; *Int'l*, pg. 4215
KOA SHOJI HOLDINGS CO., LTD.; *Int'l*, pg. 4215
KOA SPEER ELECTRONICS INC.—See Koa Corporation; *Int'l*, pg. 4215
KOATECH TECHNOLOGY CORPORATION—See Taiflex Scientific Co., Ltd.; *Int'l*, pg. 7410
KOAT HEARST-ARGYLE TELEVISION, INC.—See The Hearst Corporation; *U.S. Private*, pg. 4048
KOATSU CHEMICAL INDUSTRIES, LTD.—See Arakawa Chemical Industries, Ltd.; *Int'l*, pg. 534
KOATSU GAS KOGYO CO., LTD.; *Int'l*, pg. 4215
KOATSU GAS KOGYO VIETNAM CO., LTD.—See Koatsu Gas Kogyo Co., Ltd.; *Int'l*, pg. 4215
KOATSU KOGYO CO., LTD.; *Int'l*, pg. 4215
KOAX CORP.—See NIBE Industrier AB; *Int'l*, pg. 5263
KOBALT BV; *Int'l*, pg. 4215
KOBA RESOURCES LIMITED; *Int'l*, pg. 4215
KOBAX CO., LTD.—See TORQ Inc.; *Int'l*, pg. 7829
KOBAYASHI HEALTHCARE EUROPE, LTD.—See Kobayashi Pharmaceutical Co., Ltd.; *Int'l*, pg. 4216
KOBAYASHI HEALTHCARE LLC—See Kobayashi Pharmaceutical Co., Ltd.; *Int'l*, pg. 4216
KOBAYASHI HEALTHCARE (MALAYSIA) SDN. BHD.—See Kobayashi Pharmaceutical Co., Ltd.; *Int'l*, pg. 4216
KOBAYASHI HEALTHCARE (THAILAND) CO., LTD.—See Kobayashi Pharmaceutical Co., Ltd.; *Int'l*, pg. 4216
KOBAYASHI PHARMACEUTICAL CO., LTD.; *Int'l*, pg. 4216
KOBAYASHI PHARMACEUTICAL (HONG KONG) CO., LTD.—See Kobayashi Pharmaceutical Co., Ltd.; *Int'l*, pg. 4216
KOBAYASHI PHARMACEUTICAL PLAX CO., LTD.—See Kobayashi Pharmaceutical Co., Ltd.; *Int'l*, pg. 4216
KOBAYASHI PHARMACEUTICAL (SINGAPORE) PTE. LTD.—See Kobayashi Pharmaceutical Co., Ltd.; *Int'l*, pg. 4216
KOBAYASHI PHARMACEUTICAL (TAIWAN) CO., LTD.—See Kobayashi Pharmaceutical Co., Ltd.; *Int'l*, pg. 4216
KOBAYASHI TRAVEL SERVICE LTD. INC.; *U.S. Private*, pg. 2326
KOBAYASHI YOKO CO., LTD.; *Int'l*, pg. 4216
KOBAY TECHNOLOGY BHD.; *Int'l*, pg. 4216
KOBE ALUMINUM AUTOMOTIVE PRODUCTS (CHINA) CO., LTD.—See Kobe Steel, Ltd.; *Int'l*, pg. 4218
KOBE ALUMINUM AUTOMOTIVE PRODUCTS, LLC—See Kobe Steel, Ltd.; *Int'l*, pg. 4217
KOBE BUSSAN (ANQIU) FOODS CO., LTD.—See Kobe Bussan Co., Ltd.; *Int'l*, pg. 4217
KOBE BUSSAN CO., LTD.; *Int'l*, pg. 4216
KOBE BUSSAN ECO GREEN HOKKAIDO CO., LTD.—See Kobe Bussan Co., Ltd.; *Int'l*, pg. 4217
KOBE CH WIRE (THAILAND) CO., LTD.—See Kobe Steel, Ltd.; *Int'l*, pg. 4218
KOBE COPPER (MALAYSIA) SDN. BHD.—See Kobe Steel, Ltd.; *Int'l*, pg. 4218
KOBE DAIICHI TRAFFIC CO., LTD.—See Daiichi Koutsu Sangyo Co., Ltd.; *Int'l*, pg. 1928
KOBE DIAMAINTENANCE CO.,LTD.—See Mitsubishi Logistics Corporation; *Int'l*, pg. 4962
KOBE ELECTRIC RAILWAY CO., LTD.; *Int'l*, pg. 4217
KOBE ELECTRONICS MATERIAL (THAILAND) CO., LTD.—See Kobe Steel, Ltd.; *Int'l*, pg. 4217
KOBE HEATING AND COOLING SUPPLY CO., LTD.—See Kobe Steel, Ltd.; *Int'l*, pg. 4217
KOBE HINO MOTOR LTD.—See Toyota Motor Corporation; *Int'l*, pg. 7871
KOBE JAPANESE STEAK HOUSE LLC—See Yamada Group USA Ltd.; *U.S. Private*, pg. 4585
KOBELCO ADVANCED COATING (AMERICA), INC.—See Kobe Steel, Ltd.; *Int'l*, pg. 4218
KOBELCO ADVANCED LUBE-SYSTEM ASIA CO., LTD.—See Kobe Steel, Ltd.; *Int'l*, pg. 4219
KOBELCO ALUMINUM PRODUCTS & EXTRUSIONS INC.—See Kobe Steel, Ltd.; *Int'l*, pg. 4219
KOBELCO ANGANG AUTO STEEL CO., LTD.—See Kobe Steel, Ltd.; *Int'l*, pg. 4219
KOBELCO AUTOMOTIVE ALUMINUM ROLLED PRODUCTS (CHINA) CO., LTD.—See Kobe Steel, Ltd.; *Int'l*, pg. 4219
KOBELCO BUSINESS PARTNERS CO., LTD.—See Kobe Steel, Ltd.; *Int'l*, pg. 4219
KOBELCO CAREER DEVELOPMENT CO., LTD.—See Kobe Steel, Ltd.; *Int'l*, pg. 4218
KOBELCO (CHINA) HOLDING CO., LTD.—See Kobe Steel, Ltd.; *Int'l*, pg. 4218
KOBELCO CH WIRE MEXICANA, S.A. DE C.V.—See Kobe Steel, Ltd.; *Int'l*, pg. 4219
KOBELCO COMPRESSORS AMERICA, INC.—See Kobe Steel, Ltd.; *Int'l*, pg. 4219
KOBELCO COMPRESSORS (CAMBODIA) CO., LTD.—See Kobe Steel, Ltd.; *Int'l*, pg. 4219
KOBELCO COMPRESSORS CORPORATION—See Kobe Steel, Ltd.; *Int'l*, pg. 4219
KOBELCO COMPRESSORS INDIA PVT. LTD.—See Kobe Steel, Ltd.; *Int'l*, pg. 4219
KOBELCO COMPRESSORS & MACHINERY PHILIPPINES CORPORATION—See Kobe Steel, Ltd.; *Int'l*, pg. 4219
KOBELCO COMPRESSORS MALAYSIA SDN. BHD.—See Kobe Steel, Ltd.; *Int'l*, pg. 4219
KOBELCO COMPRESSORS MANUFACTURING INDIANA, INC.—See Kobe Steel, Ltd.; *Int'l*, pg. 4218
KOBELCO COMPRESSORS MANUFACTURING (SHANGHAI) CORPORATION—See Kobe Steel, Ltd.; *Int'l*, pg. 4219
KOBELCO COMPRESSORS (SHANGHAI) CORPORATION—See Kobe Steel, Ltd.; *Int'l*, pg. 4219
KOBELCO COMPRESSORS (THAILAND) LTD.—See Kobe Steel, Ltd.; *Int'l*, pg. 4219
KOBELCO COMPRESSORS (VIETNAM) LTD.—See Kobe Steel, Ltd.; *Int'l*, pg. 4219
KOBELCO CONSTRUCTION EQUIPMENT INDIA PVT. LTD.—See Kobe Steel, Ltd.; *Int'l*, pg. 4219
KOBELCO CONSTRUCTION MACHINERY AUSTRALIA PTY. LTD.—See Kobe Steel, Ltd.; *Int'l*, pg. 4219
KOBELCO CONSTRUCTION MACHINERY (CHINA) CO., LTD.—See Kobe Steel, Ltd.; *Int'l*, pg. 4219
KOBELCO CONSTRUCTION MACHINERY CO., LTD.—See Kobe Steel, Ltd.; *Int'l*, pg. 4219
KOBELCO CONSTRUCTION MACHINERY ENGINEERING CO., LTD.—See Kobe Steel, Ltd.; *Int'l*, pg. 4219
KOBELCO CONSTRUCTION MACHINERY EUROPE B.V.—See Kobe Steel, Ltd.; *Int'l*, pg. 4219
KOBELCO CONSTRUCTION MACHINERY INTERNATIONAL TRADING CO., LTD.—See Kobe Steel, Ltd.; *Int'l*, pg. 4219
KOBELCO CONSTRUCTION MACHINERY JAPAN CO., LTD.—See Kobe Steel, Ltd.; *Int'l*, pg. 4219
KOBELCO CONSTRUCTION MACHINERY MALAYSIA SDN. BHD.—See Kobe Steel, Ltd.; *Int'l*, pg. 4219
KOBELCO CONSTRUCTION MACHINERY MIDDLE EAST & AFRICA FZCO.—See Kobe Steel, Ltd.; *Int'l*, pg. 4219
KOBELCO CONSTRUCTION MACHINERY SOUTHEAST ASIA CO., LTD.—See Kobe Steel, Ltd.; *Int'l*, pg. 4219
KOBELCO CONSTRUCTION MACHINERY U.S.A. INC.—See Kobe Steel, Ltd.; *Int'l*, pg. 4219
KOBELCO ECO-SOLUTIONS CO., LTD.—See Kobe Steel, Ltd.; *Int'l*, pg. 4219
KOBELCO ECO-SOLUTIONS VIETNAM CO., LTD.—See Kobe Steel, Ltd.; *Int'l*, pg. 4219
KOBELCO ENGINEERED CONSTRUCTION MATERIALS CO., LTD.—See Kobe Steel, Ltd.; *Int'l*, pg. 4219
KOBELCO EUROPE GMBH—See Kobe Steel, Ltd.; *Int'l*, pg. 4219
KOBELCO FINANCIAL CENTER, LTD.—See Kobe Steel, Ltd.; *Int'l*, pg. 4218
KOBELCO INDUSTRIAL MACHINERY INDIA PVT. LTD.—See Kobe Steel, Ltd.; *Int'l*, pg. 4219
KOBELCO INTERNATIONAL (S) CO., PTE. LTD.—See Kobe Steel, Ltd.; *Int'l*, pg. 4219
KOBELCO LOGISTICS INDIA PRIVATE LIMITED—See Kobe Steel, Ltd.; *Int'l*, pg. 4219
KOBELCO LOGISTICS, LTD.—See Kobe Steel, Ltd.; *Int'l*, pg. 4218
KOBELCO LOGISTICS (SHANGHAI) LTD.—See Kobe Steel, Ltd.; *Int'l*, pg. 4219
KOBELCO MACHINERY ASIA PTE. LTD.—See Kobe Steel, Ltd.; *Int'l*, pg. 4218
KOBELCO MACHINERY DO BRAZIL SERVICOS EMPRESARIAIS LTDA.—See Kobe Steel, Ltd.; *Int'l*, pg. 4220
KOBELCO MACHINERY INDIA PRIVATE LIMITED—See Kobe Steel, Ltd.; *Int'l*, pg. 4218
KOBELCO MACHINERY MIDDLE EAST FZE.—See Kobe Steel, Ltd.; *Int'l*, pg. 4219
KOBELCO MACHINERY PHILIPPINES INC.—See Kobe Steel, Ltd.; *Int'l*, pg. 4220
KOBELCO MACHINERY SYSTEM ENGINEERING QINGDAO CO., LTD.—See Kobe Steel, Ltd.; *Int'l*, pg. 4220
KOBELCO & MATERIALS COPPER TUBE, LTD.—See Kobe Steel, Ltd.; *Int'l*, pg. 4218
KOBELCO & MATERIALS COPPER TUBE (MALAYSIA) SDN. BHD.—See Kobe Steel, Ltd.; *Int'l*, pg. 4218
KOBELCO & MATERIALS COPPER TUBE (THAILAND) CO., LTD.—See Kobe Steel, Ltd.; *Int'l*, pg. 4218
KOBELCO MIG WIRE (THAILAND) CO., LTD.—See Kobe Steel, Ltd.; *Int'l*, pg. 4219
KOBELCO MILLCON STEEL CO., LTD.—See Kobe Steel, Ltd.; *Int'l*, pg. 4220
KOBELCO PERSONNEL CO., LTD.—See Kobe Steel, Ltd.; *Int'l*, pg. 4218
KOBELCO POWER KOBE INC.—See Kobe Steel, Ltd.; *Int'l*, pg. 4220
KOBELCO POWER MOKA INC.—See Kobe Steel, Ltd.; *Int'l*, pg. 4220
KOBELCO PRECISION PARTS (SUZHOU) CO., LTD.—See Kobe Steel, Ltd.; *Int'l*, pg. 4220
KOBELCO PROFESSIONAL SERVICE CO., LTD.—See Kobe Steel, Ltd.; *Int'l*, pg. 4220
KOBELCO RESEARCH INSTITUTE, INC.—See Kobe Steel, Ltd.; *Int'l*, pg. 4218
KOBELCO ROBOTICS SERVICE CO., LTD.—See Kobe Steel, Ltd.; *Int'l*, pg. 4218
KOBELCO SANKI SERVICE CO., LTD.—See Kobe Steel, Ltd.; *Int'l*, pg. 4218
KOBELCO SHINWA CO., LTD.—See Kobe Steel, Ltd.; *Int'l*, pg. 4220
KOBELCO SOUTH EAST ASIA LTD.—See Kobe Steel, Ltd.; *Int'l*, pg. 4220
KOBELCO SPRING WIRE (FOSHAN) CO., LTD.—See Kobelco Wire Co Ltd; *Int'l*, pg. 4221
KOBELCO STEWART BOLLING, INC.—See Kobe Steel, Ltd.; *Int'l*, pg. 4220
KOBELCO SYSTEMS CORPORATION—See Kobe Steel, Ltd.; *Int'l*, pg. 4218
KOBELCO TRADING (SHANGHAI) CO., LTD.—See Kobe Steel, Ltd.; *Int'l*, pg. 4220
KOBELCO TRAINING SERVICES CO., LTD.—See Kobe Steel, Ltd.; *Int'l*, pg. 4220
KOBELCO WELDING ASIA PACIFIC PTE. LTD.—See Kobe Steel, Ltd.; *Int'l*, pg. 4220
KOBELCO WELDING INDIA PVT. LTD.—See Kobe Steel, Ltd.; *Int'l*, pg. 4220
KOBELCO WELDING (MALAYSIA) SDN. BHD.—See Kobe Steel, Ltd.; *Int'l*, pg. 4220
KOBELCO WELDING OF AMERICA INC.—See Kobe Steel, Ltd.; *Int'l*, pg. 4220
KOBELCO WELDING OF EUROPE B.V.—See Kobe Steel, Ltd.; *Int'l*, pg. 4220
KOBELCO WELDING OF KOREA CO., LTD.—See Kobe Steel, Ltd.; *Int'l*, pg. 4220
KOBELCO WELDING OF QINGDAO CO., LTD.—See Kobe Steel, Ltd.; *Int'l*, pg. 4220
KOBELCO WELDING OF SHANGHAI CO., LTD.—See Kobe Steel, Ltd.; *Int'l*, pg. 4220
KOBELCO WELDING OF TANGSHAN CO., LTD.—See Kobe Steel, Ltd.; *Int'l*, pg. 4220
KOBELCO WELDING SOLUTION CO., LTD.—See Kobe Steel, Ltd.; *Int'l*, pg. 4220
KOBELCO WELDING TECHNOSOLUTIONS CO., LTD.—See Kobe Steel, Ltd.; *Int'l*, pg. 4220
KOBELCO WIRE CO LTD; *Int'l*, pg. 4221
KOBE LEATHER CLOTH CO., LTD.—See World Co., Ltd.; *Int'l*, pg. 8456
KOBE MEDICAL CARE PARTNERS CO., LTD.—See Kobe Steel, Ltd.; *Int'l*, pg. 4218
KOBE MIG WIRE (THAILAND) CO., LTD.—See Kobe Steel, Ltd.; *Int'l*, pg. 4218
KOBENHAVNS LUFTHAVNE A/S; *Int'l*, pg. 4222
KOBE PAINTS.—See Chugoku Marine Paints, Ltd.; *Int'l*, pg. 1595
KOBE PORT RECYCLE CO., LTD.—See Daiei Kankyo Co., Ltd.; *Int'l*, pg. 1924

COMPANY NAME INDEX

KOBE PRECISION, INC.—See Kobe Steel, Ltd.; *Int'l*, pg. 4218
KOBE PRECISION TECHNOLOGY SDN. BHD.—See Kobe Steel, Ltd.; *Int'l*, pg. 4218
KOBE REAL ESTATE CO LTD—See Kobe Steel, Ltd.; *Int'l*, pg. 4218
KOBE SC DEVELOPMENT COMPANY—See West Japan Railway Company; *Int'l*, pg. 8385
KOBE & SHINSHO TUBE SPECIALITIES SDN. BHD.—See Kobe Steel, Ltd.; *Int'l*, pg. 4217
KOBE SPECIAL STEEL WIRE PRODUCTS (PINGHU) CO., LTD.—See Kobe Steel, Ltd.; *Int'l*, pg. 4217
KOBE SPECIAL TUBE CO., LTD.—See Kobe Steel, Ltd.; *Int'l*, pg. 4217
KOBE STEEL ASIA PTE. LTD.—See Kobe Steel, Ltd.; *Int'l*, pg. 4218
KOBE STEEL ASIA PTE. LTD.—See Kobe Steel, Ltd.; *Int'l*, pg. 4218
KOBE STEEL CONSULTING CO., LTD.—See Kobe Steel, Ltd.; *Int'l*, pg. 4218
KOBE STEEL INTERNATIONAL (USA) INC.—See Kobe Steel, Ltd.; *Int'l*, pg. 4218
KOBE STEEL, LTD. - BEIJING—See Kobe Steel, Ltd.; *Int'l*, pg. 4218
KOBE STEEL, LTD. - CHOFU WORKS—See Kobe Steel, Ltd.; *Int'l*, pg. 4218
KOBE STEEL, LTD. - FUJISAWA WORKS—See Kobe Steel, Ltd.; *Int'l*, pg. 4218
KOBE STEEL, LTD. - FUKUCHIYAMA PLANT—See Kobe Steel, Ltd.; *Int'l*, pg. 4218
KOBE STEEL, LTD. - HARIMA PLANT—See Kobe Steel, Ltd.; *Int'l*, pg. 4218
KOBE STEEL, LTD. - IBARAKI PLANT—See Kobe Steel, Ltd.; *Int'l*, pg. 4218
KOBE STEEL, LTD. - INABE PLANT—See Kobe Steel, Ltd.; *Int'l*, pg. 4218
KOBE STEEL, LTD. - KAKOGAWA WORKS—See Kobe Steel, Ltd.; *Int'l*, pg. 4218
KOBE STEEL, LTD. - KOBE WORKS—See Kobe Steel, Ltd.; *Int'l*, pg. 4219
KOBE STEEL, LTD. - MOKA PLANT—See Kobe Steel, Ltd.; *Int'l*, pg. 4219
KOBE STEEL, LTD. - SAIJO PLANT—See Kobe Steel, Ltd.; *Int'l*, pg. 4219
KOBE STEEL, LTD.; *Int'l*, pg. 4217
KOBE STEEL, LTD. - TAKASAGO WORKS—See Kobe Steel, Ltd.; *Int'l*, pg. 4219
KOBE STEEL USA, INC. - NEW YORK OFFICE—See Kobe Steel, Ltd.; *Int'l*, pg. 4218
KOBE STEEL USA INC.—See Kobe Steel, Ltd.; *Int'l*, pg. 4218
KOBE SUNSO KOUN CO., LTD.—See Mitsui-Soko Holdings Co., Ltd.; *Int'l*, pg. 4992
KOBE WELDING OF KOREA CO., LTD.—See Kobe Steel, Ltd.; *Int'l*, pg. 4219
KOBE WELDING OF SHANGHAI CO.,LTD.—See Kobe Steel, Ltd.; *Int'l*, pg. 4219
KOBE WELDING OF TANGSHAN CO., LTD.—See Kobe Steel, Ltd.; *Int'l*, pg. 4217
KOBE WING STADIUM CO., LTD.—See Kobe Steel, Ltd.; *Int'l*, pg. 4217
KOBE WIRE PRODUCTS (FOSHAN) CO., LTD.—See Kobe Steel, Ltd.; *Int'l*, pg. 4219
KOBE YAMATO TRANSPORT CO., LTD.—See Yamato Holdings Co., Ltd.; *Int'l*, pg. 8554
KOB GMBH—See Deutsche Bahn AG; *Int'l*, pg. 2052
KOBIE MARKETING, INC.; *U.S. Private*, pg. 2326
KOBIL BURUNDI SA—See Rubis SCA; *Int'l*, pg. 6423
KOBIL ETHIOPIA LIMITED—See Rubis SCA; *Int'l*, pg. 6423
KOBILINE—See Koc Holding A.S.; *Int'l*, pg. 4223
KOBIL PETROLEUM RWANDA SARL—See Rubis SCA; *Int'l*, pg. 6423
KOBIL TANZANIA LIMITED—See Rubis SCA; *Int'l*, pg. 6423
KOBIOLABS, INC.; *Int'l*, pg. 4222
KOBMAND HERMAN SALLINGS FOND; *Int'l*, pg. 4222
KOB MEDICAL DEVICES (DEUTSCHLAND) GMBH—See PAUL HARTMANN AG; *Int'l*, pg. 5760
KOBO BIOTECH LTD.; *Int'l*, pg. 4222
KOBOLD GROUP LIMITED; *Int'l*, pg. 4222
KOBOT SYSTEMS PTY LTD—See Fuji Corporation; *Int'l*, pg. 2810
KOB (QINGDAO) MEDICAL DEVICES CO., LTD.—See PAUL HARTMANN AG; *Int'l*, pg. 5760
KOBRA INTERNATIONAL LTD.; *U.S. Private*, pg. 2326
KOBRAND CORPORATION; *U.S. Private*, pg. 2326
KOBRAND/WESTERN DIVISION—See Kobrand Corporation; *U.S. Private*, pg. 2326
KOBRASCO—See POSCO Holdings Inc.; *Int'l*, pg. 5936
KOBRASCO—See Vale S.A.; *Int'l*, pg. 8111
KOBRITE DONGGUAN CORPORATION—See Bright Led Electronics Corp.; *Int'l*, pg. 1161
KOBRITE TAIWAN CORPORATION—See Bright Led Electronics Corp.; *Int'l*, pg. 1161
KOB-TV, INC.—See Hubbard Broadcasting, Inc.; *U.S. Private*, pg. 2000
KOBUK DIALYSIS, LLC—See DaVita Inc.; *U.S. Public*, pg. 640
KOBUKURO TECHNO CO., LTD.—See Nittetsu Mining Co., Ltd.; *Int'l*, pg. 5383
KOBUNSHA CO., LTD.—See Kodansha Ltd.; *Int'l*, pg. 4225
KOBUSCH-SENGEWALD GMBH - HALLE—See Sun Capital Partners, Inc.; *U.S. Private*, pg. 3862
KOBUSCH SENGEWALD GMBH—See Sun Capital Partners, Inc.; *U.S. Private*, pg. 3862
KOBUSCH UK LIMITED—See Sun Capital Partners, Inc.; *U.S. Private*, pg. 3862
KOC BILGI GRUBU ILETISIM VE TEKNOLOJI SIRKETLERI AS—See Koc Holding A.S.; *Int'l*, pg. 4223
KOC BILGI VE SAVUNMA TEKNOLOJILERI A.S.—See Koc Holding A.S.; *Int'l*, pg. 4223
KOCB, INC.—See Sinclair, Inc.; *U.S. Public*, pg. 1885
KOCB LICENSEE, LLC—See Sinclair, Inc.; *U.S. Public*, pg. 1885
KOC BRYCE TEKNOLOJI EGITIM HIZMETLERI AS—See Koc Holding A.S.; *Int'l*, pg. 4223
KOC CO LTD—See Otsuka Holdings Co., Ltd.; *Int'l*, pg. 5659
KOC FIAT KREDI FINANSMAN A.S.; *Int'l*, pg. 4222
KOCHAB INCORPORADORA LTDA.—See PDG Realty S.A. Empreendimentos e Participacoes; *Int'l*, pg. 5770
KOCH AGRICULTURE COMPANY—See Koch Industries, Inc.; *U.S. Private*, pg. 2331
KOCH AGRONOMIC SERVICES, LLC—See Koch Industries, Inc.; *U.S. Private*, pg. 2333
KOCH AIR LLC—See Koch Enterprises, Inc.; *U.S. Private*, pg. 2326
KOCH AIR—See Koch Enterprises, Inc.; *U.S. Private*, pg. 2326
KOCH ALASKA PIPELINE COMPANY, LLC—See Koch Industries, Inc.; *U.S. Private*, pg. 2331
KOCH-ASIA PACIFIC, INC. - JOHN ZINK ASIA-PACIFIC DIVISION—See Koch Industries, Inc.; *U.S. Private*, pg. 2332
KOCH-ASIA PACIFIC, INC.—See Koch Industries, Inc.; *U.S. Private*, pg. 2332
KOCH ASPHALT SOLUTIONS—See Koch Industries, Inc.; *U.S. Private*, pg. 2331
KOCH & ASSOCIATES INC.—See Dover Corporation; *U.S. Public*, pg. 679
KOCH AUSTRALIA PTY. LTD.—See Koch Industries, Inc.; *U.S. Private*, pg. 2332
KOCHAVA, INC.; *U.S. Private*, pg. 2335
KOCH BUSINESS SOLUTIONS, LP—See Koch Industries, Inc.; *U.S. Private*, pg. 2331
KOCH CARBON, LLC—See Koch Industries, Inc.; *U.S. Private*, pg. 2331
KOCH CHEMICAL TECHNOLOGY GROUP INDIA PVT. LTD. - KOCH-GLITSCH BARODA DIVISION—See Koch Industries, Inc.; *U.S. Private*, pg. 2331
KOCH CHEMICAL TECHNOLOGY GROUP INDIA PVT. LTD. - KOCH-GLITSCH MUMBAI DIVISION—See Koch Industries, Inc.; *U.S. Private*, pg. 2331
KOCH CHEMICAL TECHNOLOGY GROUP LIMITED - KOCH-GLITSCH UK DIVISION—See Koch Industries, Inc.; *U.S. Private*, pg. 2332
KOCH CHEMICAL TECHNOLOGY GROUP LIMITED—See Koch Industries, Inc.; *U.S. Private*, pg. 2332
KOCH CHEMICAL TECHNOLOGY GROUP, LLC—See Koch Industries, Inc.; *U.S. Private*, pg. 2331
KOCH CHEMICAL TECHNOLOGY GROUP S.A. DE C.V.—See Koch Industries, Inc.; *U.S. Private*, pg. 2331
KOCH CHEMICAL TECHNOLOGY GROUP S.L. KOCH-GLITSCH DIVISION—See Koch Industries, Inc.; *U.S. Private*, pg. 2331
KOCH CONTAINER—See Buckeye Corrugated Inc.; *U.S. Private*, pg. 677
KOCH DEVELOPMENT CORPORATION; *U.S. Private*, pg. 2326
KOCH ENGINEERED SOLUTIONS, LLC—See Koch Industries, Inc.; *U.S. Private*, pg. 2332
KOCH ENTERPRISES, INC.; *U.S. Private*, pg. 2326
KOCH EQUITY DEVELOPMENT LLC—See Koch Industries, Inc.; *U.S. Private*, pg. 2332
KOCH EXPLORATION COMPANY LLC; *U.S. Private*, pg. 2326
KOCH FERTILISER AUSTRALIA PTY LTD—See Koch Industries, Inc.; *U.S. Private*, pg. 2333
KOCH FERTILISER, LTD.—See Koch Industries, Inc.; *U.S. Private*, pg. 2333
KOCH FERTILIZER CANADA, ULC—See Koch Industries, Inc.; *U.S. Private*, pg. 2333
KOCH FERTILIZER, LLC—See Koch Industries, Inc.; *U.S. Private*, pg. 2333
KOCH FILTER CORPORATION—See Canada Pension Plan Investment Board; *Int'l*, pg. 1281
KOCH FOODS, INC.; *U.S. Private*, pg. 2326
KOCH FOODS LLC—See Koch Foods, Inc.; *U.S. Private*, pg. 2326
KOCH FOODS LLC—See Koch Foods, Inc.; *U.S. Private*, pg. 2326
KOCH FORD LINCOLN SALES (2003) LTD.; *Int'l*, pg. 4224
KOCH-GLITSCH B.V.B.A.—See Koch Industries, Inc.; *U.S. Private*, pg. 2332
KOCH-GLITSCH CANADA, LP—See Koch Industries, Inc.; *U.S. Private*, pg. 2332
KOCH-GLITSCH CANADA, LP—See Koch Industries, Inc.; *U.S. Private*, pg. 2332
KOCH-GLITSCH FIELD SERVICE—See Koch Industries, Inc.; *U.S. Private*, pg. 2332
KOCH-GLITSCH ITALIA S.R.L.—See Koch Industries, Inc.; *U.S. Private*, pg. 2332
KOCH-GLITSCH, LP—See Koch Industries, Inc.; *U.S. Private*, pg. 2331
KOCH GRUPPE AUTOMOBILE AG; *Int'l*, pg. 4224
KOCH HC PARTNERSHIP BV—See Koch Industries, Inc.; *U.S. Private*, pg. 2333
KOCH HEAT TRANSFER CANADA, LP—See Koch Industries, Inc.; *U.S. Private*, pg. 2332
KOCH HEAT TRANSFER COMPANY, LP—See Koch Industries, Inc.; *U.S. Private*, pg. 2331
KOCH HEAT TRANSFER COMPANY, S.R.L.—See Koch Industries, Inc.; *U.S. Private*, pg. 2332
KOCH HEAT TRANSFER TECHNOLOGY CO.—See Koch Industries, Inc.; *U.S. Private*, pg. 2332
KOCHI DAIMARU CO., LTD.—See J. Front Retailing Co., Ltd.; *Int'l*, pg. 3855
KOCH INDUSTRIES, INC.—See Hillman Solutions Corp.; *U.S. Public*, pg. 1038
KOCH INDUSTRIES, INC.; *U.S. Private*, pg. 2326
KOCH INTERNATIONAL B.V—See Koch Industries, Inc.; *U.S. Private*, pg. 2332
KOCHI SOFTWARE CENTER LTD.—See Computer Institute of Japan Ltd.; *Int'l*, pg. 1759
KOCHI STYROL CO., LTD.—See Kaneka Corporation; *Int'l*, pg. 4067
KOCH KNIGHT LLC—See Koch Industries, Inc.; *U.S. Private*, pg. 2331
KOCH & LOWY, INC.; *U.S. Private*, pg. 2326
KOCHMAN CONSULTANTS LTD.—See TA Associates, Inc.; *U.S. Private*, pg. 3918
KOCH MEDIA AG—See Koch Media GmbH; *Int'l*, pg. 4225
KOCH MEDIA BENELUX—See Koch Media GmbH; *Int'l*, pg. 4225
KOCH MEDIA GMBH; *Int'l*, pg. 4224
KOCH MEDIA GMBH—See Koch Media GmbH; *Int'l*, pg. 4225
KOCH MEDIA LIMITED—See Koch Media GmbH; *Int'l*, pg. 4225
KOCH MEDIA LTD.—See Koch Media GmbH; *Int'l*, pg. 4225
KOCH MEDIA SAS—See Koch Media GmbH; *Int'l*, pg. 4225
KOCH MEDIA, S.L.U.—See Koch Media GmbH; *Int'l*, pg. 4225
KOCH MEDIA SRL—See Koch Media GmbH; *Int'l*, pg. 4225
KOCH MEMBRANE SYSTEMS, INC.—See Koch Industries, Inc.; *U.S. Private*, pg. 2332
KOCH METALS TRADING LIMITED—See Koch Industries, Inc.; *U.S. Private*, pg. 2333
KOCH MINERALS, LLC—See Koch Industries, Inc.; *U.S. Private*, pg. 2333
KOCH MINERALS S.A.—See Koch Industries, Inc.; *U.S. Private*, pg. 2333
KOCH MUSIKVERLAGE GMBH—See Universal Music Group N.V.; *Int'l*, pg. 8079
KOCH NITROGEN COMPANY, LLC—See Koch Industries, Inc.; *U.S. Private*, pg. 2333
KOCH OIL COMPANY—See Koch Industries, Inc.; *U.S. Private*, pg. 2333
KOC HOLDING A.S.; *Int'l*, pg. 4222
KOCH-OTTO YORK CO., INC.—See Koch Industries, Inc.; *U.S. Private*, pg. 2332
KOCH PIPELINE COMPANY, L.P—See Koch Industries, Inc.; *U.S. Private*, pg. 2333
KOCH POULTRY—See Koch Foods, Inc.; *U.S. Private*, pg. 2326
KOCH REFINING INTERNATIONAL PTE, LTD.—See Koch Industries, Inc.; *U.S. Private*, pg. 2333
KOCH'S CUT & SUPPLY STEEL CENTRE (PTY) LTD—See ARGENT INDUSTRIAL LIMITED; *Int'l*, pg. 560
KOCH SUPPLY & TRADING COMPANY LTD.—See Koch Industries, Inc.; *U.S. Private*, pg. 2333
KOCH SUPPLY & TRADING, LP—See Koch Industries, Inc.; *U.S. Private*, pg. 2333
KOCH TECNOLOGIA QUIMICA LTDA.—See Koch Industries, Inc.; *U.S. Private*, pg. 2332
KOCH TIEFKUHLKOST; *Int'l*, pg. 4225
KOCKUMS AB—See ThyssenKrupp AG; *Int'l*, pg. 7732
KOCKUMS INDUSTRIES (AUSTRALIA) PTY LTD—See Arrowcrest Group Pty. Ltd.; *Int'l*, pg. 580
KOCO CONNECTOR GMBH—See CompuGroup Medical SE & Co. KGaA; *Int'l*, pg. 1757
KOCOLENE MARKETING, LLC; *U.S. Private*, pg. 2335
KOCOM CO., LTD.; *Int'l*, pg. 4225
KOCO-TV—See The Hearst Corporation; *U.S. Private*, pg. 4048
KOCOUREK AUTOMOTIVE GROUP; *U.S. Private*, pg. 2335
KOCOUREK CHEVROLET, INC.; *U.S. Private*, pg. 2335

KOCOUREK WAUSAU IMPORTS—See Kocourek Automotive Group; *U.S. Private*, pg. 2335
KOCSISTEM BILGI VE ILETISIM HIZM. AS—See Koc Holding A.S.; *Int'l*, pg. 4223
KOC SISTEM BILGI VE ILETISIM HIZMETLERI A.S.—See Koc Holding A.S.; *Int'l*, pg. 4223
KOC SOLUTION CO., LTD.—See Mitsui Chemicals, Inc.; *Int'l*, pg. 4981
KOCTAS YAPI MARKETLERI TICARET S.A.—See Kingfisher plc; *Int'l*, pg. 4173
KOCTAS YAPI MARKETLERI TICARET S.A.—See Koc Holding A.S.; *Int'l*, pg. 4224
KODACO CO., LTD. - ANSEONG FACTORY—See KODACO Co., Ltd.; *Int'l*, pg. 4225
KODACO CO., LTD.; *Int'l*, pg. 4225
KODA ENTERPRISES GROUP, LLC; *U.S. Private*, pg. 2335
KODA FARMS, INC.; *U.S. Private*, pg. 2336
KODA INTERNATIONAL LTD.—See Koda Ltd.; *Int'l*, pg. 4225
KODAK ALARIS GERMANY GMBH—See Eastman Kodak Company; *U.S. Public*, pg. 707
KODAK AMERICAS LTDA.—See Eastman Kodak Company; *U.S. Public*, pg. 707
KODAK ARGENTINA S.A.I.C.—See Eastman Kodak Company; *U.S. Public*, pg. 707
KODAK A/S—See Eastman Kodak Company; *U.S. Public*, pg. 707
KODAK (AUSTRALASIA) PTY. LTD.—See Eastman Kodak Company; *U.S. Public*, pg. 707
KODAK CANADA INC.—See Eastman Kodak Company; *U.S. Public*, pg. 707
KODAK (CHINA) LTD.—See Eastman Kodak Company; *U.S. Public*, pg. 707
KODAK DA AMAZONIA INDUSTRIA E COMERCIO LTDA.—See Eastman Kodak Company; *U.S. Public*, pg. 708
KODAK DE COLOMBIA, SAS—See Eastman Kodak Company; *U.S. Public*, pg. 707
KODAK DE MEXICO S.A. DE C.V.—See Eastman Kodak Company; *U.S. Public*, pg. 708
KODAK DIGITAL PRODUCTS CENTER—See Eastman Kodak Company; *U.S. Public*, pg. 707
KODAK ELECTRONIC PRODUCTS (SHANGHAI) COMPANY LIMITED—See Eastman Kodak Company; *U.S. Public*, pg. 707
KODAK GESELLSCHAFT M.B.H.—See Eastman Kodak Company; *U.S. Public*, pg. 707
KODAK GMBH—See Eastman Kodak Company; *U.S. Public*, pg. 707
KODAK GRAPHIC COMMUNICATIONS CANADA COMPANY—See Eastman Kodak Company; *U.S. Public*, pg. 707
KODAK GRAPHIC COMMUNICATIONS GMBH—See Eastman Kodak Company; *U.S. Public*, pg. 707
KODAK GRAPHIC COMMUNICATIONS GROUP—See Eastman Kodak Company; *U.S. Public*, pg. 707
KODAK GRAPHIC COMMUNICATIONS—See Eastman Kodak Company; *U.S. Public*, pg. 707
KODAK GRAPHIC COMMUNICATIONS—See Eastman Kodak Company; *U.S. Public*, pg. 707
KODAK HOLDING GMBH—See Eastman Kodak Company; *U.S. Public*, pg. 707
KODAK (HONG KONG) LIMITED—See Eastman Kodak Company; *U.S. Public*, pg. 707
KODAK IL LTD—See Eastman Kodak Company; *U.S. Public*, pg. 707
KODAK IMAGING NETWORK, INC.—See Eastman Kodak Company; *U.S. Public*, pg. 707
KODAK INDIA LIMITED—See Eastman Kodak Company; *U.S. Public*, pg. 707
KODAK JAPAN INDUSTRIES LTD.—See Eastman Kodak Company; *U.S. Public*, pg. 707
KODAK (JAPAN) LTD.—See Eastman Kodak Company; *U.S. Public*, pg. 707
KODAK (KENYA) LIMITED—See Eastman Kodak Company; *U.S. Public*, pg. 707
KODAK KOREA LTD.—See Eastman Kodak Company; *U.S. Public*, pg. 707
KODAK LIMITED—See Eastman Kodak Company; *U.S. Public*, pg. 707
KODAK MEXICANA, S.A. DE C.V.—See Eastman Kodak Company; *U.S. Public*, pg. 707
KODAK NEDERLAND BV—See Eastman Kodak Company; *U.S. Public*, pg. 707
KODAK NEW ZEALAND LIMITED—See Eastman Kodak Company; *U.S. Public*, pg. 707
KODAK NORDIC AB—See Eastman Kodak Company; *U.S. Public*, pg. 707
KODAK NORGE A/S—See Eastman Kodak Company; *U.S. Public*, pg. 707
KODAK OOO—See Eastman Kodak Company; *U.S. Public*, pg. 708
KODAK OY—See Eastman Kodak Company; *U.S. Public*, pg. 708
KODAK-PATHE SAS—See Eastman Kodak Company; *U.S. Public*, pg. 708
KODAK PHILIPPINES, LTD.—See Eastman Kodak Company; *U.S. Public*, pg. 708

KODAK RAHOLA, INC.—See Eastman Kodak Company; *U.S. Public*, pg. 708
KODAK SA/NV—See Eastman Kodak Company; *U.S. Public*, pg. 708
KODAK, S.A.—See Eastman Kodak Company; *U.S. Public*, pg. 708
KODAK (SINGAPORE) PTE. LIMITED—See Eastman Kodak Company; *U.S. Public*, pg. 707
KODAK SOCIETE ANONYME—See Eastman Kodak Company; *U.S. Public*, pg. 708
KODAK S.P.A.—See Eastman Kodak Company; *U.S. Public*, pg. 708
KODAK (TAIWAN) LIMITED—See Eastman Kodak Company; *U.S. Public*, pg. 707
KODAK (THAILAND) LIMITED—See Eastman Kodak Company; *U.S. Public*, pg. 707
KODAL MINERALS PLC; *Int'l*, pg. 4225
KODA LTD.; *Int'l*, pg. 4225
KODAMA CHEMICAL INDUSTRY CO., LTD.—See Mitsubishi Chemical Group Corporation; *Int'l*, pg. 4931
KODAMA CO., LTD.—See Kamei Corporation; *Int'l*, pg. 4061
KODANSHA AMERICA LLC—See Kodansha Ltd.; *Int'l*, pg. 4225
KODANSHA BC CO., LTD.—See Kodansha Ltd.; *Int'l*, pg. 4225
KODANSHA EUROPE LTD.—See Kodansha Ltd.; *Int'l*, pg. 4225
KODANSHA LTD.; *Int'l*, pg. 4225
KODANSHA LTD—See Kodansha Ltd.; *Int'l*, pg. 4225
KODANSHA SCIENTIFIC LTD.—See Kodansha Ltd.; *Int'l*, pg. 4225
KODANSHA USA PUBLISHING, LLC—See Kodansha Ltd.; *Int'l*, pg. 4225
KODA SAIGON CO., LTD.—See Koda Ltd.; *Int'l*, pg. 4225
KODA SPECIALTY PRODUCTS GROUP—See KODA Enterprises Group, LLC; *U.S. Private*, pg. 2335
KODA WOODCRAFT SDN BHD—See Koda Ltd.; *Int'l*, pg. 4225
KODEN CO., LTD.—See Siemens Aktiengesellschaft; *Int'l*, pg. 6887
THE KODENSHA CO., LTD.; *Int'l*, pg. 7663
KODENSHI CORPORATION; *Int'l*, pg. 4225
KODENSHI DH CORP.—See Kodenshi Corporation; *Int'l*, pg. 4226
KODENSHI (HONG KONG) CO., LTD.—See Kodenshi Corporation; *Int'l*, pg. 4225
KODENSHI (SHANGHAI) CO., LTD.—See Kodenshi Corporation; *Int'l*, pg. 4226
KODENSHI SINGAPORE PTE., LTD.—See Kodenshi Corporation; *Int'l*, pg. 4226
KODENSHI (SY) CORP.—See Kodenshi Corporation; *Int'l*, pg. 4225
KODENSHI TK CORP.—See Kodenshi Corporation; *Int'l*, pg. 4226
KODE-TV—See Mission Broadcasting, Inc.; *U.S. Private*, pg. 2747
KODIAK BUILDING PARTNERS LLC; *U.S. Private*, pg. 2336
KODIAK CAKES, LLC—See Catterton Management Company, LLC; *U.S. Private*, pg. 793
KODIAK COPPER CORP.; *Int'l*, pg. 4226
KODIAK DAILY MIRROR—See Fairbanks Daily News-Miner Inc.; *U.S. Private*, pg. 1462
KODIAK ELECTRIC ASSOCIATION, INC.; *U.S. Private*, pg. 2336
KODIAK ENERGY, INC.; *Int'l*, pg. 4226
KODIAK FISHMEAL COMPANY; *U.S. Private*, pg. 2336
KODIAK GAS SERVICES, INC.—See EQT AB; *Int'l*, pg. 2478
KODIAK GAS SERVICES, LLC—See EQT AB; *Int'l*, pg. 2478
KODIAK GROUP HOLDINGS COMPANY—See V. F. Corporation; *U.S. Public*, pg. 2268
KODIAK MFG. INC.—See KPS Capital Partners, LP; *U.S. Private*, pg. 2347
KODIAK NETWORKS, INC.—See Motorola Solutions, Inc.; *U.S. Public*, pg. 1478
KODIAK PRODUCTS CO., INC.—See Brookfield Corporation; *Int'l*, pg. 1176
KODIAK SCIENCES INC.; *U.S. Public*, pg. 1270
KODIAK VENTURE PARTNERS, L.P.; *U.S. Private*, pg. 2336
KODI CO., LTD.; *Int'l*, pg. 4226
KODI KLIP CORPORATION—See Dayton Superior Corporation; *U.S. Private*, pg. 1178
KODY TECHNOLAB LIMITED; *Int'l*, pg. 4226
KOE AMERICAS INC.—See Japan Display Inc.; *Int'l*, pg. 3887
KOE ASIA PTE LTD.—See Wistron Corporation; *Int'l*, pg. 8438
KOECKRITZ RUGS, INC.; *U.S. Private*, pg. 2336
KOEDYKER & KENYON CONSTRUCTION, INC.; *U.S. Private*, pg. 2336
KOE EUROPE LTD.—See Wistron Corporation; *Int'l*, pg. 8438
KOEGEL MEATS INC.; *U.S. Private*, pg. 2336
KOEHLER-BRIGHT STAR, INC.—See Berkshire Hathaway Inc.; *U.S. Public*, pg. 310

KOEHLER LIGHTING PRODUCTS—See Berkshire Hathaway Inc.; *U.S. Public*, pg. 310
KOEI CHEMICAL CO., LTD.—See Sumitomo Chemical Company, Limited; *Int'l*, pg. 7264
KOEI CO., LTD.—See Marubeni Corporation; *Int'l*, pg. 4705
KOEI CONSULTANT CO., LTD.—See OYO Corporation; *Int'l*, pg. 5678
KOEI ENERGY CO., LTD.—See Nippon Koei Co., Ltd.; *Int'l*, pg. 5321
KOEI RESEARCH & CONSULTING INC.—See Nippon Koei Co., Ltd.; *Int'l*, pg. 5321
KOEI SHOJI CO., LTD.—See Kurabo Industries Ltd.; *Int'l*, pg. 4335
KOEI SYSTEM INC.—See Nippon Koei Co., Ltd.; *Int'l*, pg. 5321
KOEI TECMO BEIJING SOFTWARE CO., LTD.—See Koei Tecmo Holdings Co., Ltd.; *Int'l*, pg. 4226
KOEI TECMO HOLDINGS CO., LTD.; *Int'l*, pg. 4226
KOEI TECMO SINGAPORE PTE. LTD.—See Koei Tecmo Holdings Co., Ltd.; *Int'l*, pg. 4226
KOEI TECMO SOFTWARE VIETNAM CO., LTD.—See Koei Tecmo Holdings Co., Ltd.; *Int'l*, pg. 4226
KOEI TECMO TIANJIN SOFTWARE CO., LTD.—See Koei Tecmo Holdings Co., Ltd.; *Int'l*, pg. 4226
KOEI TECMO WAVE CO., LTD.—See Koei Tecmo Holdings Co., Ltd.; *Int'l*, pg. 4226
KOEMMERLING TIANJIN KUNSTSTOFF CO. LTD.—See Arcapita Group Holdings Limited; *Int'l*, pg. 542
K&O ENERGY GROUP INC.; *Int'l*, pg. 4038
KOENIG & BAUER AG; *Int'l*, pg. 4226
KOENIG & BAUER AG—See Koenig & Bauer AG; *Int'l*, pg. 4227
KOENIG & BAUER BANKNOTE SOLUTIONS (DE) GMBH—See Koenig & Bauer AG; *Int'l*, pg. 4227
KOENIG & BAUER BANKNOTE SOLUTIONS SA—See Koenig & Bauer AG; *Int'l*, pg. 4227
KOENIG & BAUER (DE) GMBH—See Koenig & Bauer AG; *Int'l*, pg. 4227
KOENIG & BAUER FLEXOTECNICA S.P.A.—See Koenig & Bauer AG; *Int'l*, pg. 4227
KOENIG & BAUER FT ENGINEERING GMBH—See Koenig & Bauer AG; *Int'l*, pg. 4227
KOENIG & BAUER GIESSEREI GMBH—See Koenig & Bauer AG; *Int'l*, pg. 4227
KOENIG & BAUER IBERICA, S.A.—See Koenig & Bauer AG; *Int'l*, pg. 4227
KOENIG & BAUER INDUSTRIAL GMBH—See Koenig & Bauer AG; *Int'l*, pg. 4227
KOENIG & BAUER IT S.R.L—See Koenig & Bauer AG; *Int'l*, pg. 4227
KOENIG & BAUER (JP) CO., LTD.—See Koenig & Bauer AG; *Int'l*, pg. 4227
KOENIG & BAUER KAMMANN GMBH—See Koenig & Bauer AG; *Int'l*, pg. 4227
KOENIG & BAUER METALPRINT GMBH—See Koenig & Bauer AG; *Int'l*, pg. 4227
KOENIG & BAUER SHEETFED AG & CO. KG—See Koenig & Bauer AG; *Int'l*, pg. 4227
KOENIG COMPANY INC.; *U.S. Private*, pg. 2336
KOENIG EQUIPMENT INC.; *U.S. Private*, pg. 2336
KOENIG FEINSTAHL AG—See Klockner & Co. SE; *Int'l*, pg. 4202
KOENIG FUEL & SUPPLY CO. INC.—See Koenig Company Inc.; *U.S. Private*, pg. 2336
KOENIG & MEYER GMBH & CO. KG; *Int'l*, pg. 4227
KOENIG SAND & GRAVEL LLC—See Koenig Company Inc.; *U.S. Private*, pg. 2336
KOENIGSEGG AUTOMOTIVE AB; *Int'l*, pg. 4227
KOENIGSTEINER AGENTUR GMBH—See WPP plc; *Int'l*, pg. 8481
KOENIG & STREY GMAC REAL ESTATE—See Berkshire Hathaway Inc.; *U.S. Public*, pg. 306
KOEPON HOLDINGS B.V.; *Int'l*, pg. 4227
KOEPPEL MAZDA; *U.S. Private*, pg. 2336
KOERNER DISTRIBUTOR INC.; *U.S. Private*, pg. 2336
KOERNER FORD OF SYRACUSE, INC.; *U.S. Private*, pg. 2336
KOESTLIN D.D.; *Int'l*, pg. 4227
KOETTER WOODWORKING INC.; *U.S. Private*, pg. 2336
KOETTING FORD, INC.; *U.S. Private*, pg. 2336
KOFAX AUSTRALIA PTY. LTD.—See Clearlake Capital Group, L.P.; *U.S. Private*, pg. 936
KOFAX AUSTRALIA PTY. LTD.—See TA Associates, Inc.; *U.S. Private*, pg. 3916
KOFAX AUSTRIA GMBH—See Clearlake Capital Group, L.P.; *U.S. Private*, pg. 936
KOFAX AUSTRIA GMBH—See TA Associates, Inc.; *U.S. Private*, pg. 3916
KOFAX BENELUX NV—See Clearlake Capital Group, L.P.; *U.S. Private*, pg. 936
KOFAX BENELUX NV—See TA Associates, Inc.; *U.S. Private*, pg. 3916
KOFAX DANMARK A/S—See Clearlake Capital Group, L.P.; *U.S. Private*, pg. 936
KOFAX DANMARK A/S—See TA Associates, Inc.; *U.S. Private*, pg. 3916
KOFAX DEUTSCHLAND AG—See Clearlake Capital Group, L.P.; *U.S. Private*, pg. 936

COMPANY NAME INDEX

KOFAX DEUTSCHLAND AG—See TA Associates, Inc.; *U.S. Private*, pg. 3916
KOFAX HOLDING AG—See Clearlake Capital Group, L.P.; *U.S. Private*, pg. 936
KOFAX HOLDING AG—See TA Associates, Inc.; *U.S. Private*, pg. 3916
KOFAX INC.—See Clearlake Capital Group, L.P.; *U.S. Private*, pg. 935
KOFAX INC.—See TA Associates, Inc.; *U.S. Private*, pg. 3916
KOFAX ITALIA S.R.L.—See Clearlake Capital Group, L.P.; *U.S. Private*, pg. 936
KOFAX ITALIA S.R.L.—See TA Associates, Inc.; *U.S. Private*, pg. 3916
KOFAX JAPAN CO. LTD.—See Clearlake Capital Group, L.P.; *U.S. Private*, pg. 936
KOFAX JAPAN CO. LTD.—See TA Associates, Inc.; *U.S. Private*, pg. 3916
KOFAX MALAYSIA SDN. BHD.—See Clearlake Capital Group, L.P.; *U.S. Private*, pg. 936
KOFAX MALAYSIA SDN. BHD.—See TA Associates, Inc.; *U.S. Private*, pg. 3916
KOFAX NETHERLANDS BV—See Clearlake Capital Group, L.P.; *U.S. Private*, pg. 936
KOFAX NETHERLANDS BV—See TA Associates, Inc.; *U.S. Private*, pg. 3916
KOFAX PORTUGAL, S.A.—See Clearlake Capital Group, L.P.; *U.S. Private*, pg. 936
KOFAX PORTUGAL, S.A.—See TA Associates, Inc.; *U.S. Private*, pg. 3916
KOFAX PRODUTOS DE IMAGEM DO BRASIL LTDA—See Clearlake Capital Group, L.P.; *U.S. Private*, pg. 936
KOFAX PRODUTOS DE IMAGEM DO BRASIL LTDA—See TA Associates, Inc.; *U.S. Private*, pg. 3916
KOFAX SCHWEIZ AG—See Clearlake Capital Group, L.P.; *U.S. Private*, pg. 936
KOFAX SCHWEIZ AG—See TA Associates, Inc.; *U.S. Private*, pg. 3916
KOFAX SINGAPORE PTE. LTD.—See Clearlake Capital Group, L.P.; *U.S. Private*, pg. 936
KOFAX SINGAPORE PTE. LTD.—See TA Associates, Inc.; *U.S. Private*, pg. 3916
KOFAX SOFTWARE IBERICA S.A.U.—See Clearlake Capital Group, L.P.; *U.S. Private*, pg. 936
KOFAX SOFTWARE IBERICA S.A.U.—See TA Associates, Inc.; *U.S. Private*, pg. 3916
KOFAX SVERIGE AB—See Clearlake Capital Group, L.P.; *U.S. Private*, pg. 936
KOFAX SVERIGE AB—See TA Associates, Inc.; *U.S. Private*, pg. 3916
KOFAX UK LTD.—See Clearlake Capital Group, L.P.; *U.S. Private*, pg. 936
KOFAX UK LTD.—See TA Associates, Inc.; *U.S. Private*, pg. 3916
KOFAX VIETNAM CO., LTD.—See Clearlake Capital Group, L.P.; *U.S. Private*, pg. 936
KOFAX VIETNAM CO., LTD.—See TA Associates, Inc.; *U.S. Private*, pg. 3916
KOFCO U.S.A, INC—See Korea Movenex Co., Ltd; *Int'l*, pg. 4286
KOFFEE BREAK PICTURES LTD.; *Int'l*, pg. 4227
KOFFLER SALES, LLC; *U.S. Private*, pg. 2337
KOFFOLK ANIMAL HEALTH & NUTRITION—See Phibro Animal Health Corporation; *U.S. Public*, pg. 1685
KOFFOLK LTD.—See Phibro Animal Health Corporation; *U.S. Public*, pg. 1685
KOFING, A.S.—See Promet Froup a.s.; *Int'l*, pg. 5993
KOFISA S.A.—See Koc Holding A.S.; *Int'l*, pg. 4223
KOFLER & KOMPANIE GMBH—See K&K Group AG; *Int'l*, pg. 4038
KOFOLA CESKOSLOVENSKO AS; *Int'l*, pg. 4227
KOFSTAD AGENCY INC.—See Principal Financial Group, Inc.; *U.S. Public*, pg. 1720
KOFU CASIO CO., LTD.—See Casio Computer Co., Ltd.; *Int'l*, pg. 1353
KOFU DAIICHI JITSUGYO CO., LTD.—See Rengo Co., Ltd.; *Int'l*, pg. 6280
KOFU DAIICHI-JITUGYO CO., LTD.—See Rengo Co., Ltd.; *Int'l*, pg. 6280
KOFU KYOWA DENGYO CO., LTD.—See Kyowa Electronic Instruments Co., Ltd.; *Int'l*, pg. 4366
KOFU MEDIENSHA ELECTRIC MFG CO., LTD.—See Meidensha Corporation; *Int'l*, pg. 4797
KOFU TOYO CO., LTD.—See Toyo Suisan Kaisha, Ltd.; *Int'l*, pg. 7858
KOFY, INC.—See Silver Point Capital, L.P.; *U.S. Private*, pg. 3661
KOGA B.V.—See Accell Group N.V.; *Int'l*, pg. 80
KOGA-CITY INFORMATION CENTER CO., LTD.—See Core Corporation; *Int'l*, pg. 1797
KOGA ENGINEERING & CONSTRUCTION, INC.; *U.S. Private*, pg. 2337
KOGAN.COM LTD; *Int'l*, pg. 4227
KOGA TOUCH CO., LTD.—See Sansheng Intellectual Education Technology Co., Ltd.; *Int'l*, pg. 6556
KOGA TRADING A.G.—See Accell Group N.V.; *Int'l*, pg. 81
KOGAZ RT.—See E.ON SE; *Int'l*, pg. 2253

KOGE EUROPE GMBH—See Koge Micro Tech Co., Ltd.; *Int'l*, pg. 4228
KOGE MICRO TECH CO., LTD.; *Int'l*, pg. 4228
KOGI CORPORATION - HIMEJI EAST FACTORY—See Kogi Corporation; *Int'l*, pg. 4228
KOGI CORPORATION; *Int'l*, pg. 4228
KOG-KTV FOOD PRODUCTS (INDIA) PRIVATE LIMITED—See Wilmar International Limited; *Int'l*, pg. 8421
KOGNITIV SINGAPORE PTE. LTD—See Aimia Inc.; *Int'l*, pg. 233
KOGNITIV UK LTD—See Aimia Inc.; *Int'l*, pg. 233
KOGOK CORPORATION; *U.S. Private*, pg. 2337
KO GOLD INC.; *Int'l*, pg. 4214
KOHA CO., LTD.—See Tamura Corporation; *Int'l*, pg. 7451
KOHANA COFFEE LLC—See Westrock Coffee Company; *U.S. Public*, pg. 2361
KOHAN KOGYO CO., LTD.—See Toyo Seikan Group Holdings, Ltd.; *Int'l*, pg. 7856
KOHAN SHOJI CO., LTD.—See Toyo Seikan Group Holdings, Ltd.; *Int'l*, pg. 7856
KO HARTOG VERKEERSTECHNIEK B.V.—See Addtech AB; *Int'l*, pg. 134
KOHAT CEMENT COMPANY LIMITED; *Int'l*, pg. 4228
KOHAT TEXTILE MILLS LIMITED—See Saif Holdings Limited; *Int'l*, pg. 6482
KOH BROTHERS BUILDING & CIVIL ENGINEERING CONTRACTOR (PTE.) LTD.—See Koh Brothers Group Limited; *Int'l*, pg. 4228
KOH BROTHERS DEVELOPMENT PTE LTD—See Koh Brothers Group Limited; *Int'l*, pg. 4228
KOH BROTHERS ECO ENGINEERING LTD.; *Int'l*, pg. 4228
KOH BROTHERS GROUP LIMITED; *Int'l*, pg. 4228
KOH BROTHERS INVESTMENT PTE LTD—See Koh Brothers Group Limited; *Int'l*, pg. 4228
KOHINOOR CHEMICAL COMPANY (BANGLADESH) LIMITED; *Int'l*, pg. 4228
KOHINOOR ENERGY LIMITED; *Int'l*, pg. 4229
KOHINOOR FOODS LIMITED; *Int'l*, pg. 4229
KOHINOOR FOODS USA INC—See Kohinoor Foods Limited; *Int'l*, pg. 4229
KOHINOOR INDUSTRIES LIMITED; *Int'l*, pg. 4229
KOHINOOR MAPLE LEAF GROUP; *Int'l*, pg. 4229
KOHINOOR MILLS LIMITED; *Int'l*, pg. 4229
KOHINOOR SPINNING MILLS LTD.—See Yousuf Weaving Mills Ltd.; *Int'l*, pg. 8604
KOHINOOR TECHNO ENGINEERS LIMITED; *Int'l*, pg. 4229
KOHINOOR TEXTILE MILLS LIMITED - RAIWIND DIVISION—See Kohinoor Maple Leaf Group; *Int'l*, pg. 4229
KOHINOOR TEXTILE MILLS LIMITED—See Kohinoor Maple Leaf Group; *Int'l*, pg. 4229
KOHJIN CO., LTD - SAIKI FACTORY—See Mitsubishi Corporation; *Int'l*, pg. 4939
KOHJIN CO., LTD.—See Mitsubishi Corporation; *Int'l*, pg. 4939
KOHJIN CO., LTD.- YATSUSHIRO FACTORY—See Mitsubishi Corporation; *Int'l*, pg. 4939
KOHLBERG & COMPANY, LLC; *U.S. Private*, pg. 2337
KOHLBERG KRAVIS ROBERTS & CO. LIMITED—See KKR & Co. Inc.; *U.S. Public*, pg. 1257
KOHLBERG KRAVIS ROBERTS & CO. PARTNERS LLP—See KKR & Co. Inc.; *U.S. Public*, pg. 1257
KOHLBERG KRAVIS ROBERTS & CO. SAS—See KKR & Co. Inc.; *U.S. Public*, pg. 1257
KOHLBERG KRAVIS ROBERTS (ESPANA) ASESORES SL—See KKR & Co. Inc.; *U.S. Public*, pg. 1257
KOHLBERG KRAVIS ROBERTS GMBH—See KKR & Co. Inc.; *U.S. Public*, pg. 1257
KOHLER AUSTRALIA—See Kohler Company; *U.S. Private*, pg. 2339
KOHLER CANADA CO. - HYTEC PLUMBING PRODUCTS DIVISION—See Kohler Company; *U.S. Private*, pg. 2339
KOHLER CANADA LTD.—See Kohler Company; *U.S. Private*, pg. 2339
KOHLER COMPANY; *U.S. Private*, pg. 2339
KOHLER CONSTRUCTION COMPANY INC.—See Dycom Industries, Inc.; *U.S. Public*, pg. 698
KOHLER DE MEXICO, S.A. DE C.V.—See Kohler Company; *U.S. Private*, pg. 2340
KOHLER FRANCE S.A.S.—See Kohler Company; *U.S. Private*, pg. 2340
KOHLER - GENERATOR DIVISION—See Kohler Company; *U.S. Private*, pg. 2339
KOHLER JAPAN K.K.—See Kohler Company; *U.S. Private*, pg. 2340
KOHLERS INC.; *U.S. Private*, pg. 2340
KOHLER (THAILAND) PUBLIC CO. LTD.—See Kohler Company; *U.S. Private*, pg. 2339
KOHLER WASTE SERVICES INC.—See Interstate Waste Services, Inc.; *U.S. Public*, pg. 2126
KOHL & FRISCH LIMITED; *Int'l*, pg. 4229
KOHL ROOFING & SIDING CO., INC.; *U.S. Private*, pg. 2337
KOHL'S CORPORATION; *U.S. Public*, pg. 1270

KOHL'S DEPARTMENT STORES—See Kohl's Corporation; *U.S. Public*, pg. 1270
KOHL'S INDIANA INC—See Kohl's Corporation; *U.S. Public*, pg. 1270
KOHL'S RANCH LODGE—See Apollo Global Management, Inc.; *U.S. Public*, pg. 150
KOHL'S RANCH LODGE—See Reverence Capital Partners LLC; *U.S. Private*, pg. 3415
KOHLS-WEELBORG FORD; *U.S. Private*, pg. 2340
KOHLTECH INTERNATIONAL LTD.; *Int'l*, pg. 4229
KOHMECA CO., LTD—See INZI Controls Co., Ltd; *Int'l*, pg. 3790
KOHNAN BLANKING SERVICE CORPORATION—See JFE Holdings, Inc.; *Int'l*, pg. 3937
KOHNAN SHOJI CO., LTD.; *Int'l*, pg. 4229
KOHNSTAMM COMMUNICATIONS—See Broadhead + Co., Inc.; *U.S. Private*, pg. 659
KOHO CO., LTD.—See Maeda Corporation; *Int'l*, pg. 4635
KOHOKU ELECTRONICS (M) SDN.BHD.—See Kohoku Kogyo Co., Ltd.; *Int'l*, pg. 4229
KOHOKU ELECTRONICS (S) PTE.LTD.—See Kohoku Kogyo Co., Ltd.; *Int'l*, pg. 4229
KOHOKU KOGYO CO., LTD.; *Int'l*, pg. 4229
KOHOKU LANKA (PVT.) LTD.—See Kohoku Kogyo Co., Ltd.; *Int'l*, pg. 4229
KOHO (TAIWAN) CO., LTD.—See Nichidenbo Corporation; *Int'l*, pg. 5268
KOHR BROTHERS, INC.; *U.S. Private*, pg. 2340
KOHSAI CO. LTD; *Int'l*, pg. 4229
KOHSEIYA CO., LTD.—See Valor Holdings Co., Ltd.; *Int'l*, pg. 8122
KOHSOKU CORPORATION; *Int'l*, pg. 4229
KOHT'AENE ENTERPRISES COMPANY, LLC—See Ahtna Incorporated; *U.S. Private*, pg. 131
KO HUTS, INC.; *U.S. Private*, pg. 2325
KOHWA PRECISION MOLDING (SHANGHAI) CO., LTD.—See Takagi Seiko Corporation; *Int'l*, pg. 7429
KOHWA SYSTEM CORPORATION—See NSW Inc.; *Int'l*, pg. 5481
KOHYO AMERICA, INC.—See AEON Co., Ltd.; *Int'l*, pg. 178
KOHYO CO., LTD.—See AEON Co., Ltd.; *Int'l*, pg. 178
KOHYO HOLLAND B.V.—See AEON Co., Ltd.; *Int'l*, pg. 178
KOH YOUNG AMERICA INC.—See Koh Young Technology Inc.; *Int'l*, pg. 4228
KOH YOUNG EUROPE GMBH—See Koh Young Technology Inc.; *Int'l*, pg. 4228
KOH YOUNG SE ASIA PTE. LTD.—See Koh Young Technology Inc.; *Int'l*, pg. 4228
KOH YOUNG TECHNOLOGY INC.; *Int'l*, pg. 4228
KOI AUTO PARTS-LOUISVILLE—See KOI Auto Parts; *U.S. Private*, pg. 2340
KOI AUTO PARTS; *U.S. Private*, pg. 2340
K-O-I ENTERPRISES INC.; *U.S. Private*, pg. 2251
KOIKE ARONSON, INC.—See Koike Sanso Kogyo Co., Ltd.; *Int'l*, pg. 4230
KOIKE ARONSON RANSOME—See Koike Sanso Kogyo Co., Ltd.; *Int'l*, pg. 4230
KOIKE ENGINEERING GERMANY GMBH—See Koike Sanso Kogyo Co., Ltd.; *Int'l*, pg. 4230
KOIKE ENGINEERING TANGSHAN CO., LTD.—See Koike Sanso Kogyo Co., Ltd.; *Int'l*, pg. 4230
KOIKE EUROPE B.V.—See ORIX Corporation; *Int'l*, pg. 5634
KOIKE MEDICAL CO., LTD.—See Koike Sanso Kogyo Co., Ltd.; *Int'l*, pg. 4230
KOIKE SANSO KOGYO CO., LTD.; *Int'l*, pg. 4229
KOIKE TECH CO., LTD.—See Koike Sanso Kogyo Co., Ltd.; *Int'l*, pg. 4230
KOIKE-YA INC.; *Int'l*, pg. 4230
KOIL ENERGY SOLUTIONS, INC.; *U.S. Public*, pg. 1270
KOIL METALS L.L.C.—See Cleveland-Cliffs, Inc.; *U.S. Public*, pg. 514
KOINE S.P.A.—See Nestle S.A.; *Int'l*, pg. 5203
KOINONIA FOSTER HOMES, INC.; *U.S. Private*, pg. 2340
KOIOS BEVERAGE CORP.; *Int'l*, pg. 4230
KOIS BROTHERS EQUIPMENT CO.; *U.S. Private*, pg. 2340
KOIT-FM—See Deseret Management Corporation; *U.S. Private*, pg. 1212
KOITO CZECH S.R.O.—See Koito Manufacturing Co., Ltd.; *Int'l*, pg. 4230
KOITO ELECTRIC INDUSTRIES, LTD.—See Koito Manufacturing Co., Ltd.; *Int'l*, pg. 4230
KOITO EUROPE LIMITED—See Koito Manufacturing Co., Ltd.; *Int'l*, pg. 4230
KOITO INSURANCE SERVICES CO., LTD.—See Koito Manufacturing Co., Ltd.; *Int'l*, pg. 4230
KOITO KYUSHU LIMITED—See Koito Manufacturing Co., Ltd.; *Int'l*, pg. 4230
KOITO MALAYSIA SDN. BHD.—See Koito Manufacturing Co., Ltd.; *Int'l*, pg. 4230
KOITO MANUFACTURING CO., LTD.; *Int'l*, pg. 4230
KOITO TRANSPORT CO., LTD.—See Koito Manufacturing Co., Ltd.; *Int'l*, pg. 4230
KOIWAI DAIRY PRODUCTS CO., LTD.—See Kirin Holdings Company, Limited; *Int'l*, pg. 4188

KOIZUMI LIGHTING TECHNOLOGY CORP.

KOIZUMI LIGHTING TECHNOLOGY CORP.; *Int'l,* pg. 4231
KOIZUMI LIGHTING TECHNOLOGY (SHANGHAI) CO., LTD.—See KOIZUMI Lighting Technology Corp.; *Int'l,* pg. 4231
KOIZUMI LIGHTING TECHNOLOGY (SINGAPORE) CORP PTE. LTD.—See KOIZUMI Lighting Technology Corp.; *Int'l,* pg. 4231
KO JA (CAYMAN) CO., LTD.; *Int'l,* pg. 4214
KOJAK BUS CO., LTD.—See Keihan Holdings Co., Ltd.; *Int'l,* pg. 4116
KOJAMO OYJ; *Int'l,* pg. 4231
KOJIMA CO., LTD.; *Int'l,* pg. 4231
KOJIMA IRON WORKS CO., LTD.; *Int'l,* pg. 4231
KOJIMA IRON WORKS CO., LTD. - YAHATA PLANT—See Kojima Iron Works Co., Ltd.; *Int'l,* pg. 4231
KOKAI SAS; *Int'l,* pg. 4231
KOKA KFT.—See STRABAG SE; *Int'l,* pg. 7231
KOKANDO & KYOSO MIRAI ASIA PTE. LTD.—See Toho Holdings Co., Ltd.; *Int'l,* pg. 7776
KOKANKYO ENGINEERING CORPORATION (EAE)—See Daiwa House Industry Co., Ltd.; *Int'l,* pg. 1946
KOKEN BORING MACHINE CO., LTD. - ATSUGI FACTORY—See KOKEN BORING MACHINE CO.,LTD.; *Int'l,* pg. 4231
KOKEN BORING MACHINE CO.,LTD.; *Int'l,* pg. 4231
KOKEN BORING MACHINE CO., LTD. - SUWA FACTORY—See KOKEN BORING MACHINE CO.,LTD.; *Int'l,* pg. 4231
KOKEN LTD.; *Int'l,* pg. 4231
KOKEN MANUFACTURING COMPANY, INC.—See Takara Belmont Corporation; *Int'l,* pg. 7431
KOKH-TV—See Sinclair, Inc.; *U.S. Public,* pg. 1886
KOKI HOLDINGS AMERICA LTD. - CANADA—See KKR & Co. Inc.; *U.S. Public,* pg. 1257
KOKI HOLDINGS AMERICA LTD.—See KKR & Co. Inc.; *U.S. Public,* pg. 1257
KOKI HOLDINGS CO., LTD.—See KKR & Co. Inc.; *U.S. Public,* pg. 1257
KOKI SALES CO., LTD.—See KKR & Co. Inc.; *U.S. Public,* pg. 1257
KOKI-TV—See Providence Equity Partners L.L.C.; *U.S. Private,* pg. 3293
KOKKO CO., LTD.—See Yuasa Trading Co., Ltd.; *Int'l,* pg. 8609
KOKKO (HONG KONG) CO., LTD.—See Yuasa Trading Co., Ltd.; *Int'l,* pg. 8609
KOKKOLAN VOIMA OY—See Pohjolan Voima Oy; *Int'l,* pg. 5904
KOKKO (SHENZHEN) TRADING CO., LTD.—See Yuasa Trading Co., Ltd.; *Int'l,* pg. 8609
KOKKO SYSTEMS CO., LTD.—See MIRAIT ONE Corporation; *Int'l,* pg. 4917
KOKOBUY INC.—See Onward Holdings Co., Ltd.; *Int'l,* pg. 5592
KOKO HOTELS CO., LTD.—See Polaris Holdings Co., Ltd.; *Int'l,* pg. 5907
KOKOLO SAS—See Leonard Green & Partners, L.P.; *U.S. Private,* pg. 2424
KOKOMO GRAIN CO., INC.; *U.S. Private,* pg. 2340
KOKOMO GRAIN CO., INC. - WINAMAC—See Kokomo Grain Co., Inc.; *U.S. Private,* pg. 2340
KOKOPELLI, INC.; *Int'l,* pg. 4231
KOKORO COMPANY LTD—See Sanrio Company, Ltd.; *Int'l,* pg. 6554
KOKOSING CONSTRUCTION COMPANY, INC. - HEAVY INDUSTRIAL DIVISION—See Kokosing Construction Company, Inc.; *U.S. Private,* pg. 2340
KOKOSING CONSTRUCTION COMPANY, INC. - HIGHWAY DIVISION—See Kokosing Construction Company, Inc.; *U.S. Private,* pg. 2340
KOKOSING CONSTRUCTION COMPANY, INC.; *U.S. Private,* pg. 2340
KOKOSING CONSTRUCTION COMPANY INC—See Kokosing Construction Company, Inc.; *U.S. Private,* pg. 2340
KOKOSING MATERIALS, INC. - CLEVELAND PLANT—See Kokosing Construction Company, Inc.; *U.S. Private,* pg. 2340
KOKOSING MATERIALS, INC. - COLUMBIA STATION PLANT—See Kokosing Construction Company, Inc.; *U.S. Private,* pg. 2340
KOKOSING MATERIALS, INC. - COLUMBUS PLANT—See Kokosing Construction Company, Inc.; *U.S. Private,* pg. 2340
KOKOSING MATERIALS, INC. - EAST CLARIDON PLANT—See Kokosing Construction Company, Inc.; *U.S. Private,* pg. 2340
KOKOSING MATERIALS, INC. - GARFIELD PLANT—See Kokosing Construction Company, Inc.; *U.S. Private,* pg. 2341
KOKOSING MATERIALS, INC. - SHEFFIELD PLANT—See Kokosing Construction Company, Inc.; *U.S. Private,* pg. 2341
KOKOSING MATERIALS, INC.—See Kokosing Construction Company, Inc.; *U.S. Private,* pg. 2340
KOKSOWNIA PRZYJAZN SP. Z O.O.—See Jastrzebska Spolka Weglowa S.A.; *Int'l,* pg. 3913

KOKUBU FOOD LOGISTICS MALAYSIA SDN. BHD.—See Texchem Resources Bhd.; *Int'l,* pg. 7583
KOKUBU INDUSTRIAL CO., LTD.—See Nichias Corporation; *Int'l,* pg. 5267
KOKUDO BUILAC CORPORATION—See JDC Corporation; *Int'l,* pg. 3925
KOKUDO KAIHATSU INDUSTRY CO., LTD.—See JDC Corporation; *Int'l,* pg. 3925
KOKUEI PAPER CO., LTD.—See Nippon Paper Industries Co., Ltd.; *Int'l,* pg. 5327
KOKUKA SANGYO CO., LTD.—See Mitsubishi Gas Chemical Company, Inc.; *Int'l,* pg. 4949
KOKURA ENTERPRISE CO., LTD.—See Biken Techno Corporation Ltd.; *Int'l,* pg. 1023
KOKURA KOSAN ENERGY CO., LTD.—See Itochu Enex Co., Ltd.; *Int'l,* pg. 3842
KOKUSAI ASSET MANAGEMENT CO., LTD.—See Mitsubishi UFJ Financial Group, Inc.; *Int'l,* pg. 4969
KOKUSAI BEIJING LIMITED—See Japan Asia Group Limited; *Int'l,* pg. 3885
KOKUSAI BULK TERMINAL CO., LTD.—See Maruzen Showa Unyu Co., Ltd.; *Int'l,* pg. 4716
KOKUSAI BUNKAZAI CO., LTD.—See Japan Asia Group Limited; *Int'l,* pg. 3885
KOKUSAI BUTSURYU CO., LTD.—See Isewan Terminal Service Co., Ltd.; *Int'l,* pg. 3816
KOKUSAI CABLE SHIP CO., LTD.—See KDDI Corporation; *Int'l,* pg. 4112
KOKUSAI CHART CORPORATION—See Nakabayashi Co., Ltd.; *Int'l,* pg. 5131
KOKUSAI CO., LTD.; *Int'l,* pg. 4231
KOKUSAI ELECTRIC ASIA PACIFIC CO., LTD.—See KKR & Co. Inc.; *U.S. Public,* pg. 1258
KOKUSAI ELECTRIC CORPORATION—See KKR & Co. Inc.; *U.S. Public,* pg. 1257
KOKUSAI ELECTRIC EUROPE GMBH—See KKR & Co. Inc.; *U.S. Public,* pg. 1258
KOKUSAI ELECTRIC SEMICONDUCTOR SERVICE INC.—See KKR & Co. Inc.; *U.S. Public,* pg. 1258
KOKUSAI EUROPE GMBH—See KOKUSAI CO., LTD; *Int'l,* pg. 4231
KOKUSAI INCORPORATED—See KOKUSAI CO., LTD; *Int'l,* pg. 4231
KOKUSAI KIGYO CO., LTD.—See Taiheiyo Cement Corporation; *Int'l,* pg. 7411
KOKUSAI KOGYO CO., LTD.—See The Carlyle Group Inc.; *U.S. Public,* pg. 2055
KOKUSAI LAND (VIETNAM) LIMITED—See Japan Asia Group Limited; *Int'l,* pg. 3885
KOKUSAI SEMICONDUCTOR EQUIPMENT CORPORATION—See KKR & Co. Inc.; *U.S. Public,* pg. 1257
KOKUSAI (SHANGHAI) CO., LTD.—See KOKUSAI CO., LTD; *Int'l,* pg. 4231
KOKUSAKU KIKO CO., LTD.—See Nippon Paper Industries Co., Ltd.; *Int'l,* pg. 5327
KOKUYO CAMLIN LTD.—See Kokuyo Co., Ltd.; *Int'l,* pg. 4232
KOKUYO CHUBU SALES CO., LTD.—See Kokuyo Co., Ltd.; *Int'l,* pg. 4232
KOKUYO CO., LTD.; *Int'l,* pg. 4231
KOKUYO CO., LTD.—See Kokuyo Co., Ltd.; *Int'l,* pg. 4232
KOKUYO CO., LTD.—See Kokuyo Co., Ltd.; *Int'l,* pg. 4232
KOKUYO COMMERCE (SHANGHAI) CO., LTD.—See Kokuyo Co., Ltd.; *Int'l,* pg. 4232
KOKUYO DESIGN CONSULTANTS (SHANGHAI) CO., LTD.—See Kokuyo Co., Ltd.; *Int'l,* pg. 4232
KOKUYO ENGINEERING & TECHNOLOGY CO., LTD.—See Kokuyo Co., Ltd.; *Int'l,* pg. 4232
KOKUYO FINANCE CO., LTD.—See Kokuyo Co., Ltd.; *Int'l,* pg. 4232
KOKUYO FURNITURE (CHINA) CO., LTD.—See Kokuyo Co., Ltd.; *Int'l,* pg. 4232
KOKUYO FURNITURE COMMERCE AND TRADING (SHANGHAI) CO., LTD.—See Kokuyo Co., Ltd.; *Int'l,* pg. 4232
KOKUYO HOKKAIDO SALES CO., LTD.—See Kokuyo Co., Ltd.; *Int'l,* pg. 4231
KOKUYO HOKURIKU NIIGATA SALES CO., LTD.—See Kokuyo Co., Ltd.; *Int'l,* pg. 4231
KOKUYO-IK (THAILAND) CO., LTD.—See Kokuyo Co., Ltd.; *Int'l,* pg. 4232
KOKUYO INTERNATIONAL ASIA CO., LTD.—See Kokuyo Co., Ltd.; *Int'l,* pg. 4232
KOKUYO INTERNATIONAL CO., LTD.—See Kokuyo Co., Ltd.; *Int'l,* pg. 4232
KOKUYO INTERNATIONAL (MALAYSIA) SDN. BHD.—See Kokuyo Co., Ltd.; *Int'l,* pg. 4232
KOKUYO INTERNATIONAL (THAILAND) CO., LTD.—See Kokuyo Co., Ltd.; *Int'l,* pg. 4232
KOKUYO K HEART CO., LTD.—See Kokuyo Co., Ltd.; *Int'l,* pg. 4232
KOKUYO KINKI SALES CO., LTD.—See Kokuyo Co., Ltd.; *Int'l,* pg. 4232
KOKUYO KITAKANTO SALES CO., LTD.—See Kokuyo Co., Ltd.; *Int'l,* pg. 4231
KOKUYO KYUSHU SALES CO., LTD.—See Kokuyo Co., Ltd.; *Int'l,* pg. 4232

CORPORATE AFFILIATIONS

KOKUYO LOGITEM CO., LTD.—See Kokuyo Co., Ltd.; *Int'l,* pg. 4232
KOKUYO (MALAYSIA) SDN. BHD.—See Kokuyo Co., Ltd.; *Int'l,* pg. 4232
KOKUYO MARKETING CO., LTD.—See Kokuyo Co., Ltd.; *Int'l,* pg. 4232
KOKUYO MVP CO., LTD.—See Kokuyo Co., Ltd.; *Int'l,* pg. 4232
KOKUYO NISHIKANTO SALES CO., LTD.—See Kokuyo Co., Ltd.; *Int'l,* pg. 4232
KOKUYO & PARTNERS CO., LTD.—See Kokuyo Co., Ltd.; *Int'l,* pg. 4232
KOKUYO PRODUCT SHIGA CO., LTD.—See Kokuyo Co., Ltd.; *Int'l,* pg. 4232
KOKUYO RIDDHI PAPER PRODUCTS PVT., LTD.—See Kokuyo Co., Ltd.; *Int'l,* pg. 4232
KOKUYO SANYO SHIKOKU SALES CO., LTD.—See Kokuyo Co., Ltd.; *Int'l,* pg. 4232
KOKUYO (SHANGHAI) MANAGEMENT CO., LTD.—See Kokuyo Co., Ltd.; *Int'l,* pg. 4232
KOKUYO STORE CREATION CO., LTD.—See Kokuyo Co., Ltd.; *Int'l,* pg. 4232
KOKUYO STORE CREATION (SHANGHAI) CO., LTD.—See Kokuyo Co., Ltd.; *Int'l,* pg. 4232
KOKUYO TOHOKU SALES CO., LTD.—See Kokuyo Co., Ltd.; *Int'l,* pg. 4232
KOKUYO TOKAI SALES CO., LTD.—See Kokuyo Co., Ltd.; *Int'l,* pg. 4232
KOKUYO TRADING (SHANGHAI) CO., LTD.—See Kokuyo Co., Ltd.; *Int'l,* pg. 4232
KOKUYO VIETNAM CO., LTD.—See Kokuyo Co., Ltd.; *Int'l,* pg. 4232
KOKUYO VIETNAM TRADING CO., LTD.—See Kokuyo Co., Ltd.; *Int'l,* pg. 4232
KOLA MINING AND METALLURGICAL COMPANY—See PJSC MMC Norilsk Nickel; *Int'l,* pg. 5882
KOLAR GOLD PTY LTD.—See Tally Ltd.; *Int'l,* pg. 7448
KOLB DISTRIBUTION AG—See Kuala Lumpur Kepong Berhad; *Int'l,* pg. 4318
KOLB DISTRIBUTION BV—See Kuala Lumpur Kepong Berhad; *Int'l,* pg. 4318
KOLBE & KOLBE MILLWORK CO., INC.; *U.S. Private,* pg. 2341
KOLB ELEKTRO AG—See Burkhalter Holding AG; *Int'l,* pg. 1225
KOLBEN HYDRAULICS LIMITED—See Yuken India Ltd.; *Int'l,* pg. 8612
KOLBENSCHMIDT DE MEXICO S. DE R.L. DE C.V. - CELAYA PLANT—See Rheinmetall AG; *Int'l,* pg. 6322
KOLBENSCHMIDT DE MEXICO S. DE R.L. DE C.V.—See Rheinmetall AG; *Int'l,* pg. 6322
KOLBENSCHMIDT K.K.—See Rheinmetall AG; *Int'l,* pg. 6322
KOLBENSCHMIDT PIERBURG AG—See Rheinmetall AG; *Int'l,* pg. 6322
KOLBENSCHMIDT PIERBURG INNOVATIONS GMBH—See Rheinmetall AG; *Int'l,* pg. 6322
KOLBENSCHMIDT USA INC.—See Rheinmetall AG; *Int'l,* pg. 6322
KOLBERG-PIONEER, INC.—See Astec Industries, Inc.; *U.S. Public,* pg. 216
KOL BIOMEDICAL INSTRUMENTS INC.; *U.S. Private,* pg. 2341
KOLB SP. Z O.O.—See Stalprofil S.A.; *Int'l,* pg. 7164
KOLCRAFT ENTERPRISES, INC.; *U.S. Private,* pg. 2341
KOLDING SALATFABRIK A/S—See Orkla ASA; *Int'l,* pg. 5637
KOLD, LLC—See Gray Television, Inc.; *U.S. Public,* pg. 959
KOLD TRANS, LLC—See Knight-Swift Transportation Holdings Inc.; *U.S. Public,* pg. 1269
KOLDT & RYO EL A/S—See AddLife AB; *Int'l,* pg. 129
KOLDWATER TECHNOLOGIES LLC—See Business Industrial Network; *U.S. Private,* pg. 695
KOLE CONSTRUCTION COMPANY, INC.; *U.S. Private,* pg. 2341
KOLEKTOR ATP D.O.O.—See Kolektor Group d.o.o.; *Int'l,* pg. 4232
KOLEKTOR AUTOMOTIVE NANJING CO. LTD.—See Kolektor Group d.o.o.; *Int'l,* pg. 4232
KOLEKTOR BOSNA D.O.O.—See Kolektor Group d.o.o.; *Int'l,* pg. 4232
KOLEKTOR COMMUTATOR WUXI CO., LTD.—See Kolektor Group d.o.o.; *Int'l,* pg. 4232
KOLEKTOR COMTRADE GMBH—See Kolektor Group d.o.o.; *Int'l,* pg. 4232
KOLEKTOR FEBO D.O.O.—See Kolektor Group d.o.o.; *Int'l,* pg. 4233
KOLEKTOR GROUP D.O.O.; *Int'l,* pg. 4232
KOLEKTOR KAUTT & BUX GMBH—See Kolektor Group d.o.o.; *Int'l,* pg. 4233
KOLEKTOR KOLING INZENIRING, INSTALACIJE, PROIZVODNJA D.O.O.—See Kolektor Group d.o.o.; *Int'l,* pg. 4233
KOLEKTOR LIV D.O.O.—See Fluidmaster, Inc.; *U.S. Private,* pg. 1552
KOLEKTOR LIV POSTOJNA, D.D.—See Kolektor Group d.o.o.; *Int'l,* pg. 4233

COMPANY NAME INDEX

KOLEKTOR MAGMA D.O.O—See Kolektor Group d.o.o.; *Int'l*, pg. 4233
KOLEKTOR MAGNET TECHNOLOGY GMBH—See Kolektor Group d.o.o.; *Int'l*, pg. 4233
KOLEKTOR MISSEL SCHWAB GMBH—See Kolektor Group d.o.o.; *Int'l*, pg. 4233
KOLEKTOR PROKOS D.O.O.—See Kolektor Group d.o.o.; *Int'l*, pg. 4233
KOLEKTOR SIKOM D.O.O.—See Kolektor Group d.o.o.; *Int'l*, pg. 4233
KOLEKTOR SINABIT D.O.O.—See Kolektor Group d.o.o.; *Int'l*, pg. 4233
KOLEKTOR SINYUNG INDUSTRIAL CO., LTD.—See Kolektor Group d.o.o.; *Int'l*, pg. 4233
KOLEKTOR SYNATEC D.O.O.—See Kolektor Group d.o.o.; *Int'l*, pg. 4233
KOLEKTOR TKI INC.—See Kolektor Group d.o.o.; *Int'l*, pg. 4233
KOLETZKY IMPLEMENT, INC.; *U.S. Private*, pg. 2341
KOLHAPUR OXYGEN AND ACETYLENE PRIVATE LIMITED—See Chowgule & Company Pvt. Ltd.; *Int'l*, pg. 1585
THE KOLHAPUR STEEL LIMITED—See Kirloskar Brothers Limited; *Int'l*, pg. 4191
KOLIBRI KAPITAL AS; *Int'l*, pg. 4233
KOLICEVO KARTON PROIZVODNJA KARTONA, D.O.O.—See Mayr-Melnhof Karton AG; *Int'l*, pg. 4745
KOLIGO THERAPEUTICS, INC.—See Orgenesis Inc.; *U.S. Public*, pg. 1617
KOLING AD; *Int'l*, pg. 4233
KOLIN INSAAT TURIZM SANAYI VE TICARET A.S.; *Int'l*, pg. 4233
KOLINPHARMA S.P.A.; *Int'l*, pg. 4233
KOLKHORST PETROLEUM COMPANY; *U.S. Private*, pg. 2341
KOLLAKORN CORPORATION LIMITED; *Int'l*, pg. 4233
KOLLER ASSET & MANAGEMENT GMBH & CO. KG—See MB Holding Company LLC; *Int'l*, pg. 4750
KOLLE REBBE GMBH—See Accenture plc; *Int'l*, pg. 87
KOLLER ENTERPRISES, INC. - KOLLER-CRAFT SOUTH DIVISION—See Koller Enterprises, Inc.; *U.S. Private*, pg. 2341
KOLLER ENTERPRISES, INC.; *U.S. Private*, pg. 2341
KOLLER MASCHINEN UND ANLAGENBAU GMBH—See MB Holding Company LLC; *Int'l*, pg. 4750
KOLLER + SCHWEMMER GMBH—See Robert Bosch GmbH; *Int'l*, pg. 6361
KOLLER TRANSPORTE - KIES - ERDBAU GMBH—See PORR AG; *Int'l*, pg. 5923
KOLLER WORKOVER & DRILLING GMBH—See MB Holding Company LLC; *Int'l*, pg. 4750
KOLLEX GMBH—See COCA-COLA EUROPACIFIC PARTNERS PLC; *Int'l*, pg. 1685
KOLLMAN LABEL GROUP, LLC; *U.S. Private*, pg. 2341
KOLLMORGEN AUTOMATION AB—See Regal Rexnord Corporation; *U.S. Public*, pg. 1772
KOLLMORGEN CORPORATION—See Regal Rexnord Corporation; *U.S. Public*, pg. 1772
KOLLMORGEN ELECTRO-OPTICAL—See L3Harris Technologies, Inc.; *U.S. Public*, pg. 1281
KOLLMORGEN EUROPE GMBH—See Regal Rexnord Corporation; *U.S. Public*, pg. 1772
KOLLMORGEN SRL—See Regal Rexnord Corporation; *U.S. Public*, pg. 1772
KOLLMORGEN STEUERUNGSTECHNIK GMBH; *Int'l*, pg. 4233
KOLLSMAN, INC.—See Elbit Systems Limited; *Int'l*, pg. 2344
KOLMARBNH CO., LTD.; *Int'l*, pg. 4233
KOLMAR COSMETICS (WUXI) CO., LTD.—See Korea Kolmar Holdings Co., Ltd; *Int'l*, pg. 4286
KOLMAR DE MEXICO, S.A. DE C.V.; *Int'l*, pg. 4233
KOLMAR KOREA CO., LTD. - MAKEUP FACTORY 1—See Korea Kolmar Holdings Co., Ltd; *Int'l*, pg. 4286
KOLMAR KOREA CO., LTD. - MAKEUP FACTORY 2—See Korea Kolmar Holdings Co., Ltd; *Int'l*, pg. 4286
KOLMAR KOREA CO., LTD. - SKIN CARE FACTORY 1—See Korea Kolmar Holdings Co., Ltd; *Int'l*, pg. 4286
KOLMAR KOREA CO., LTD. - SKIN CARE FACTORY 2—See Korea Kolmar Holdings Co., Ltd; *Int'l*, pg. 4286
KOLMAR LABORATORIES, INC.—See Novacap Management Inc.; *Int'l*, pg. 5454
KOLME S.R.L.—See Sesa S.p.A.; *Int'l*, pg. 6728
KOLMI-HOPEN SAS—See A.R. Medicom Inc.; *Int'l*, pg. 28
KOLNER AUSSENWERBUNG GESELLSCHAFT MIT BESCHRANKTER HAFTUNG—See Stroer SE & Co. KGaA; *Int'l*, pg. 7242
KOLOGIK CAPITAL, LLC—See Kologik LLC; *U.S. Private*, pg. 2341
KOLOGIK LLC; *U.S. Private*, pg. 2341
KOLOK AFRICA (PTY) LIMITED—See The Bidvest Group Limited; *Int'l*, pg. 7624
KOLOK (NAMIBIA) (PTY) LIMITED—See The Bidvest Group Limited; *Int'l*, pg. 7624
KOLOK (PTY) LIMITED—See The Bidvest Group Limited; *Int'l*, pg. 7624
KOLONA PAINTING & GENERAL CONSTRUCTION, INC.—See Equal Earth Corp.; *U.S. Private*, pg. 1415
KOLON CORP.; *Int'l*, pg. 4233

KOLON ENVIRONMENTAL SERVICE CO. LTD.; *Int'l*, pg. 4233
KOLON EU GMBH—See Kolon Industries, Inc.; *Int'l*, pg. 4234
KOLON FASHION MATERIAL, INC.—See Kolon Corp.; *Int'l*, pg. 4233
KOLON GLOBAL CORPORATION—See Kolon Corp.; *Int'l*, pg. 4233
KOLON GP CHEMICAL CO., LTD—See Kolon Industries, Inc.; *Int'l*, pg. 4233
KOLON HUIZHOU CO., LTD.—See Kolon Industries, Inc.; *Int'l*, pg. 4234
KOLON INDUSTRIES BINH DUONG COMPANY LIMITED—See Kolon Industries, Inc.; *Int'l*, pg. 4234
KOLON INDUSTRIES INC.-CHEMICAL ORGANIZATION—See Kolon Industries, Inc.; *Int'l*, pg. 4234
KOLON INDUSTRIES, INC. - GIMCHEON PLANT 1—See Kolon Industries, Inc.; *Int'l*, pg. 4234
KOLON INDUSTRIES, INC. - GIMCHEON PLANT 2—See Kolon Industries, Inc.; *Int'l*, pg. 4234
KOLON INDUSTRIES, INC. - GUMI PLANT—See Kolon Industries, Inc.; *Int'l*, pg. 4234
KOLON INDUSTRIES INC. - GYEONGSAN PLANT—See Kolon Industries, Inc.; *Int'l*, pg. 4234
KOLON INDUSTRIES, INC. - INCHEON PLANT—See Kolon Industries, Inc.; *Int'l*, pg. 4234
KOLON INDUSTRIES, INC.; *Int'l*, pg. 4233
KOLON INDUSTRIES, INC. - ULSAN PLANT—See Kolon Industries, Inc.; *Int'l*, pg. 4234
KOLON INDUSTRIES, INC. - YEOSU PLANT—See Kolon Industries, Inc.; *Int'l*, pg. 4234
KOLON LIFE SCIENCE INC.; *Int'l*, pg. 4234
KOLON NANJING CO., LTD.—See Kolon Industries, Inc.; *Int'l*, pg. 4234
KOLON PLASTICS INC.—See Kolon Corp.; *Int'l*, pg. 4233
KOLON TISSUEGENE, INC.; *U.S. Public*, pg. 1270
KOLON USA INC.—See Kolon Industries, Inc.; *Int'l*, pg. 4234
KOLORFUSION INTERNATIONAL, INC.; *U.S. Public*, pg. 1270
KOLOS CEMENT LTD.; *Int'l*, pg. 4234
KOLOS MADAGASCAR LTD.—See Kolos Cement Ltd.; *Int'l*, pg. 4234
KOLOSSO AUTO SALES INC.; *U.S. Private*, pg. 2341
KOLOS S.R.O.—See Osterreichische Post AG; *Int'l*, pg. 5653
KOLO VEIDEKKE AS—See Veidekke ASA; *Int'l*, pg. 8148
KOLPAK—See Ali Holding S.r.l; *Int'l*, pg. 322
KOLPIN OUTDOORS, INC.—See Polaris, Inc.; *U.S. Public*, pg. 1700
KOLSCHE BLISTER GMBH—See Medios AG; *Int'l*, pg. 4778
KOLS CONTAINERS—See O. Berk Company L.L.C.; *U.S. Private*, pg. 2981
KOLTE PATIL DEVELOPERS LTD; *Int'l*, pg. 4234
KOLTER COMMERCIAL LLC—See The Kolter Group LLC; *U.S. Private*, pg. 4065
THE KOLTER GROUP LLC; *U.S. Private*, pg. 4065
KOLTER HOMES, LLC—See The Kolter Group LLC; *U.S. Private*, pg. 4065
KOLTER LAND PARTNERS LLC—See The Kolter Group LLC; *U.S. Private*, pg. 4065
KOLTOV INC.; *U.S. Private*, pg. 2341
KOLTSO URALA CB LLC; *Int'l*, pg. 4234
KOLUBARA UNIVERZAL D.O.O.—See Continental Aktiengesellschaft; *Int'l*, pg. 1781
KOLUSZKY FOUNDRY SP. Z.O.O.—See Haco N.V.; *Int'l*, pg. 3205
KOLUT A.D.; *Int'l*, pg. 4234
KOMAIHALTEC INC. - FRAMEWORK TEST FACILITY—See Komaihaltec Inc.; *Int'l*, pg. 4234
KOMAIHALTEC INC. - FUTTSU PLANT—See Komaihaltec Inc.; *Int'l*, pg. 4234
KOMAIHALTEC INC. - OSAKA PLANT—See Komaihaltec Inc.; *Int'l*, pg. 4234
KOMAIHALTEC INC.; *Int'l*, pg. 4234
KOMAIHALTEC INC. - WAKAYAMA WORKS—See Komaihaltec Inc.; *Int'l*, pg. 4234
KOMAIHALTEC Inc. - WIND TUNNEL FACILITY—See Komaihaltec Inc.; *Int'l*, pg. 4234
KOMALI FERTILITY CENTRE LLP—See Aster DM Healthcare Ltd.; *Int'l*, pg. 654
THE KOMAN GROUP, LLC—See The Keeley Companies; *U.S. Private*, pg. 4064
KOMAN INC.; *U.S. Private*, pg. 2341
KOMAN SPORTSWEAR MANUFACTURING CORP.; *U.S. Private*, pg. 2341
KOMA PRECISION INC.; *U.S. Private*, pg. 2341
KOMAR COMPANY; *U.S. Private*, pg. 2341
KOMAR INDUSTRIES, LLC; *U.S. Private*, pg. 2342
KOMARKCORP BERHAD; *Int'l*, pg. 4234
KOMARKETING ASSOCIATES LLC—See Walker Sands, Inc.; *U.S. Private*, pg. 4429
KOMARK INTERNATIONAL (M) SDN. BHD.—See Komarkcorp Berhad; *Int'l*, pg. 4234
KOMARK (THAILAND) CO,. LTD.—See Komarkcorp Berhad; *Int'l*, pg. 4234
KOMAR SCREW CORP.; *U.S. Private*, pg. 2342

KOMATSU AMERICA CORP. - LSP DIVISION—See Komatsu Ltd.; *Int'l*, pg. 4235
KOMATSU AMERICA CORPORATION—See Komatsu Ltd.; *Int'l*, pg. 4235
KOMATSU AMERICA CORP.—See Komatsu Ltd.; *Int'l*, pg. 4235
KOMATSU AMERICA INDUSTRIES, LLC—See Komatsu Ltd.; *Int'l*, pg. 4235
KOMATSU ASIA & PACIFIC PTE. LTD.—See Komatsu Ltd.; *Int'l*, pg. 4236
KOMATSU ASIA & PACIFIC PTE. LTD.—See Komatsu Ltd.; *Int'l*, pg. 4236
KOMATSU AUSTRALIA CORPORATE FINANCE PTY. LTD.—See Komatsu Ltd.; *Int'l*, pg. 4236
KOMATSU AUSTRALIA PTY. LTD.—See Komatsu Ltd.; *Int'l*, pg. 4236
KOMATSU AUSTRALIA PTY LTD—See Komatsu Ltd.; *Int'l*, pg. 4236
KOMATSU BANGKOK LEASING CO., LTD.—See Komatsu Ltd.; *Int'l*, pg. 4236
KOMATSU BOTL FINANCE CIS, LLC.—See Komatsu Ltd.; *Int'l*, pg. 4236
KOMATSU BRASIL INTERNATIONAL LTDA.—See Komatsu Ltd.; *Int'l*, pg. 4236
KOMATSU BUSINESS SUPPORT LTD.—See Komatsu Ltd.; *Int'l*, pg. 4236
KOMATSU CABTEC CO., LTD.—See Komatsu Ltd.; *Int'l*, pg. 4236
KOMATSU CASTEX JAPAN LTD. (KCX)—See Komatsu Ltd.; *Int'l*, pg. 4236
KOMATSU CASTEX LTD.—See Komatsu Ltd.; *Int'l*, pg. 4236
KOMATSU (CHANGZHOU) CONSTRUCTION MACHINERY CORP.—See Komatsu Ltd.; *Int'l*, pg. 4235
KOMATSU (CHANGZHOU) FOUNDRY CORPORATION—See Komatsu Ltd.; *Int'l*, pg. 4235
KOMATSU (CHANGZHOU) REBUILD CO., LTD—See Komatsu Ltd.; *Int'l*, pg. 4235
KOMATSU CHINA LTD.—See Komatsu Ltd.; *Int'l*, pg. 4236
KOMATSU CHINA MINING LIMITED—See Komatsu Ltd.; *Int'l*, pg. 4236
KOMATSU CIS LLC—See Komatsu Ltd.; *Int'l*, pg. 4236
KOMATSU CONSTRUCTION ATTACHMENT CHANGZHOU CO., LTD.—See Komatsu Ltd.; *Int'l*, pg. 4236
KOMATSU CONSTRUCTION EQUIPMENT SALES & SERVICE JAPAN LTD.—See Komatsu Ltd.; *Int'l*, pg. 4236
KOMATSU CORPORATE SERVICES LTD.—See Komatsu Ltd.; *Int'l*, pg. 4236
KOMATSU CUMMINS CHILE ARRIENDA S.A.—See Komatsu Ltd.; *Int'l*, pg. 4236
KOMATSU CUMMINS CHILE LTDA.—See Cummins Inc.; *U.S. Public*, pg. 608
KOMATSU CUMMINS CHILE LTDA.—See Komatsu Ltd.; *Int'l*, pg. 4236
KOMATSU CUMMINS ENGINE CO., LTD.—See Cummins Inc.; *U.S. Public*, pg. 608
KOMATSU CUMMINS ENGINE CO., LTD.—See Komatsu Ltd.; *Int'l*, pg. 4237
KOMATSU CUSTOMER SUPPORT JAPAN LTD.—See Komatsu Ltd.; *Int'l*, pg. 4237
KOMATSU DIESEL CO., LTD.—See Komatsu Ltd.; *Int'l*, pg. 4237
KOMATSU DO BRASIL LTDA.—See Komatsu Ltd.; *Int'l*, pg. 4238
KOMATSU ELECTRONICS, INC.—See Komatsu Ltd.; *Int'l*, pg. 4237
KOMATSU EQUIPMENT COMPANY—See Komatsu Ltd.; *Int'l*, pg. 4235
KOMATSU ESPANA S.A.—See Komatsu Ltd.; *Int'l*, pg. 4237
KOMATSU EUROPE COORDINATION CENTER N.V.—See Komatsu Ltd.; *Int'l*, pg. 4237
KOMATSU EUROPE INTERNATIONAL N.V.—See Komatsu Ltd.; *Int'l*, pg. 4237
KOMATSU FAR EAST LTD.—See Komatsu Ltd.; *Int'l*, pg. 4237
KOMATSU FINANCE AMERICA INC.—See Komatsu Ltd.; *Int'l*, pg. 4237
KOMATSU FINANCE CHILE S.A.—See Komatsu Ltd.; *Int'l*, pg. 4237
KOMATSU FINANCE MEXICO, S.A. DE C.V—See Komatsu Ltd.; *Int'l*, pg. 4237
KOMATSU FINANCIAL EUROPE N.V.—See Komatsu Ltd.; *Int'l*, pg. 4237
KOMATSU FINANCIAL LEASING CHINA LTD.—See Komatsu Ltd.; *Int'l*, pg. 4237
KOMATSU FINANCIAL LIMITED PARTNERSHIP—See Komatsu Ltd.; *Int'l*, pg. 4235
KOMATSU FOREST AB—See Komatsu Ltd.; *Int'l*, pg. 4237
KOMATSU FOREST A/S—See Komatsu Ltd.; *Int'l*, pg. 4237
KOMATSU FOREST GMBH—See Komatsu Ltd.; *Int'l*, pg. 4237
KOMATSU FOREST LIMITED—See Komatsu Ltd.; *Int'l*, pg. 4237
KOMATSU FOREST LTDA.—See Komatsu Ltd.; *Int'l*, pg. 4237

KOMATSU FOREST OY—See Komatsu Ltd.; *Int'l*, pg. 4237
KOMATSU FOREST PTY. LTD.—See Komatsu Ltd.; *Int'l*, pg. 4237
KOMATSU FORKLIFT AUSTRALIA PTY LTD.—See Komatsu Ltd.; *Int'l*, pg. 4237
KOMATSU FORKLIFT CO., LTD.—See Komatsu Ltd.; *Int'l*, pg. 4237
KOMATSU FORKLIFT JAPAN LTD.—See Komatsu Ltd.; *Int'l*, pg. 4237
KOMATSU FORKLIFT U.S.A., LLC—See Komatsu Ltd.; *Int'l*, pg. 4237
KOMATSU FRANCE S.A.—See Komatsu Ltd.; *Int'l*, pg. 4237
KOMATSU GENERAL SERVICES LTD.—See Komatsu Ltd.; *Int'l*, pg. 4237
KOMATSU HANOMAG GMBH—See Komatsu Ltd.; *Int'l*, pg. 4237
KOMATSU HOLDING SOUTH AMERICA LTDA.—See Komatsu Ltd.; *Int'l*, pg. 4237
KOMATSU HUANAN LTD.—See Komatsu Ltd.; *Int'l*, pg. 4237
KOMATSU INDIA PRIVATE LIMITED—See Komatsu Ltd.; *Int'l*, pg. 4236
KOMATSU INDUSTRIES CORPORATION—See Komatsu Ltd.; *Int'l*, pg. 4237
KOMATSU INDUSTRIES EUROPE GMBH—See Komatsu Ltd.; *Int'l*, pg. 4237
KOMATSU INDUSTRIES MEXICO S.A. DE C.V.—See Komatsu Ltd.; *Int'l*, pg. 4237
KOMATSU INDUSTRIES (SHANGHAI) LTD.—See Komatsu Ltd.; *Int'l*, pg. 4237
KOMATSU INDUSTRIES (THAILAND) CO., LTD.—See Komatsu Ltd.; *Int'l*, pg. 4237
KOMATSU INTERLINK CO., LTD.—See KOMATSU MATERE Co.,Ltd.; *Int'l*, pg. 4239
KOMATSU ITALIA MANUFACTURING S.P.A.—See Komatsu Ltd.; *Int'l*, pg. 4237
KOMATSU ITALIA S.P.A.—See Komatsu Ltd.; *Int'l*, pg. 4237
KOMATSU JAKARTA OFFICE—See Komatsu Ltd.; *Int'l*, pg. 4237
KOMATSU KVX LLC—See Komatsu Ltd.; *Int'l*, pg. 4235
KOMATSU LATIN AMERICA CORP.—See Komatsu Ltd.; *Int'l*, pg. 4237
KOMATSU LEASING (CAMBODIA) PLC—See Komatsu Ltd.; *Int'l*, pg. 4238
KOMATSU LOGISTICS CORP.—See Komatsu Ltd.; *Int'l*, pg. 4238
KOMATSU LTD. - KANAZAWA PLANT—See Komatsu Ltd.; *Int'l*, pg. 4238
KOMATSU LTD. - KORIYAMA PLANT—See Komatsu Ltd.; *Int'l*, pg. 4238
KOMATSU LTD. - OSAKA PLANT—See Komatsu Ltd.; *Int'l*, pg. 4238
KOMATSU LTD. - OYAMA PLANT—See Komatsu Ltd.; *Int'l*, pg. 4238
KOMATSU LTD. - ROKKO PLANT—See Komatsu Ltd.; *Int'l*, pg. 4238
KOMATSU LTD.; *Int'l*, pg. 4234
KOMATSU LTD. - TOCHIGI PLANT—See Komatsu Ltd.; *Int'l*, pg. 4238
KOMATSU MACHINERY CORPORATION—See Komatsu Ltd.; *Int'l*, pg. 4238
KOMATSU MANUFACTURING RUS, LLC—See Komatsu Ltd.; *Int'l*, pg. 4236
KOMATSU MARKETING SUPPORT AUSTRALIA PTY LTD—See Komatsu Ltd.; *Int'l*, pg. 4238
KOMATSU MATERE CO.,LTD.; *Int'l*, pg. 4239
KOMATSU MEXICANA S.A. DE C.V.—See Komatsu Ltd.; *Int'l*, pg. 4238
KOMATSU MIDDLE EAST FZE—See Komatsu Ltd.; *Int'l*, pg. 4238
KOMATSU MINING CORP.—See Komatsu Ltd.; *Int'l*, pg. 4235
KOMATSU-MITSUI MAQUINARIAS PERU S.A.—See Mitsui & Co., Ltd.; *Int'l*, pg. 4973
KOMATSU MURATA MANUFACTURING CO., LTD.—See Murata Manufacturing Co., Ltd.; *Int'l*, pg. 5097
KOMATSU NTC LTD. - AWAZU PLANT—See Komatsu Ltd.; *Int'l*, pg. 4238
KOMATSU NTC LTD. - FUKUNO PLANT—See Komatsu Ltd.; *Int'l*, pg. 4238
KOMATSU NTC LTD.—See Komatsu Ltd.; *Int'l*, pg. 4238
KOMATSU PAKISTAN SOFT (PVT) LTD.—See Komatsu Ltd.; *Int'l*, pg. 4238
KOMATSU PARKERIZING CO., LTD.—See Nihon Parkerizing Co., Ltd.; *Int'l*, pg. 5286
KOMATSU PARTS ASIA CO., LTD.—See Komatsu Ltd.; *Int'l*, pg. 4238
KOMATSU POWER GENERATION SYSTEMS (SHANGHAI) LTD.—See Komatsu Ltd.; *Int'l*, pg. 4238
KOMATSU RENTAL LTD.—See Komatsu Ltd.; *Int'l*, pg. 4238
KOMATSU SAFETY TRAINING CENTER LTD.—See Komatsu Ltd.; *Int'l*, pg. 4238
KOMATSU SEIREN CO., LTD. - MIKAWA FACTORY—See KOMATSU MATERE Co.,Ltd.; *Int'l*, pg. 4239

KOMATSU SEIREN (SUZHOU) TEXTILE DYEING CO., LTD.—See KOMATSU MATERE Co.,Ltd.; *Int'l*, pg. 4239
KOMATSU (SHANDONG) CONSTRUCTION MACHINERY CORP.—See Komatsu Ltd.; *Int'l*, pg. 4235
KOMATSU (SHANGHAI) LTD.—See Komatsu Ltd.; *Int'l*, pg. 4235
KOMATSU SHANTUI CONSTRUCTION MACHINERY CO., LTD.—See Komatsu Ltd.; *Int'l*, pg. 4238
KOMATSU SHEARING CO., LTD.—See Komatsu Ltd.; *Int'l*, pg. 4238
KOMATSU SILICON AMERICA, INC.—See Komatsu Ltd.; *Int'l*, pg. 4238
KOMATSU SOUTHERN AFRICA (PTY) LTD.—See Komatsu Ltd.; *Int'l*, pg. 4238
KOMATSU SWELOG SKOGSMASKINER HB—See Komatsu Ltd.; *Int'l*, pg. 4237
KOMATSU TOCHIGI INC.—See Fujii Sangyo Corporation; *Int'l*, pg. 2826
KOMATSU TOKKI CORPORATION—See Komatsu Ltd.; *Int'l*, pg. 4238
KOMATSU UK LTD.—See Komatsu Ltd.; *Int'l*, pg. 4238
KOMATSU UNDERCARRIAGE CHINA CORPORATION—See Neturen Co., Ltd.; *Int'l*, pg. 5216
KOMATSU USED EQUIPMENT CORP.—See Komatsu Ltd.; *Int'l*, pg. 4238
KOMATSU UTILITY EUROPE S.P.A.—See Komatsu Ltd.; *Int'l*, pg. 4238
KOMATSU WALL INDUSTRY CO., LTD.; *Int'l*, pg. 4239
KOMATSU ZENOAH CO.—See Komatsu Ltd.; *Int'l*, pg. 4238
KOM AUTOMATION, INC.—See Graybar Electric Company, Inc.; *U.S. Private*, pg. 1760
KOMAX AG—See Komax Holding AG; *Int'l*, pg. 4240
KOMAX AUSTRIA GMBH—See Komax Holding AG; *Int'l*, pg. 4240
KOMAX AUTOMATION INDIA PVT. LTD.—See Komax Holding AG; *Int'l*, pg. 4240
KOMAX BELGIUM N.V.—See Komax Holding AG; *Int'l*, pg. 4240
KOMAX BULGARIA EOOD—See Komax Holding AG; *Int'l*, pg. 4240
KOMAX COMERCIAL DO BRASIL LTDA—See Komax Holding AG; *Int'l*, pg. 4240
KOMAX CORPORATION; *U.S. Private*, pg. 2342
KOMAX CORP—See Komax Holding AG; *Int'l*, pg. 4240
KOMAX CZECH REPUBLIC TRADING S.R.O.—See Komax Holding AG; *Int'l*, pg. 4240
KOMAX DE MEXICO S. DE R.L. DE C.V.—See Komax Holding AG; *Int'l*, pg. 4241
KOMAX DEUTSCHLAND GMBH—See Komax Holding AG; *Int'l*, pg. 4240
KOMAX DISTRIBUTION (THAILAND) CO., LTD.—See Komax Holding AG; *Int'l*, pg. 4240
KOMAX FRANCE SARL—See Komax Holding AG; *Int'l*, pg. 4240
KOMAX HOLDING AG; *Int'l*, pg. 4240
KOMAX HUNGARY KFT.—See Komax Holding AG; *Int'l*, pg. 4240
KOMAX JAPAN K.K.—See Komax Holding AG; *Int'l*, pg. 4240
KOMAX KL—See Komax Holding AG; *Int'l*, pg. 4240
KOMAX MANAGEMENT AG—See Komax Holding AG; *Int'l*, pg. 4240
KOMAX MAROC SARL—See Komax Holding AG; *Int'l*, pg. 4240
KOMAXON CO., LTD. - HAKUSAN FACTORY—See KOMATSU MATERE Co.,Ltd.; *Int'l*, pg. 4239
KOMAXON CO., LTD.—See KOMATSU MATERE Co.,Ltd.; *Int'l*, pg. 4239
KOMAX PORTUGUESA S.A.—See Komax Holding AG; *Int'l*, pg. 4240
KOMAX ROMANIA TRADING S.R.L.—See Komax Holding AG; *Int'l*, pg. 4240
KOMAX SA (PTY) LTD—See Komax Holding AG; *Int'l*, pg. 4240
KOMAX SHANGHAI CO. LTD.—See Komax Holding AG; *Int'l*, pg. 4240
KOMAX SINGAPORE PTE LTD—See Komax Holding AG; *Int'l*, pg. 4240
KOMAX SLE GMBH & CO. KG—See Komax Holding AG; *Int'l*, pg. 4241
KOMAX SLOVAKIA S.R.O.—See Komax Holding AG; *Int'l*, pg. 4240
KOMAX TAPING GMBH & CO. KG—See Komax Holding AG; *Int'l*, pg. 4240
KOMAX TESTING BULGARIA EOOD—See Komax Holding AG; *Int'l*, pg. 4240
KOMAX TESTING GERMANY GMBH—See Komax Holding AG; *Int'l*, pg. 4240
KOMAX TESTING INDIA PVT. LTD.—See Komax Holding AG; *Int'l*, pg. 4240
KOMAX TESTING MAROC FT S.A.R.L.—See Komax Holding AG; *Int'l*, pg. 4240
KOMAX TESTING MEXICO, S DE R.L. DE C.V.—See Komax Holding AG; *Int'l*, pg. 4240
KOMAX TESTING ROMANIA S.R.L.—See Komax Holding AG; *Int'l*, pg. 4240

KOMAX TESTING TUNISIA S.A.R.L.—See Komax Holding AG; *Int'l*, pg. 4240
KOMAX TESTING TURKIYE TEST SISTEMLERI SAN. LTD. STI.—See Komax Holding AG; *Int'l*, pg. 4240
KOMAX THONAUER KFT.—See Komax Holding AG; *Int'l*, pg. 4241
KOMAX TSK MAROC SARL.—See Komax Holding AG; *Int'l*, pg. 4240
KOMBASSAN HOLDING A.S.; *Int'l*, pg. 4241
KOMBET DZIALDOWO SP. Z O.O—See Dekpol S.A.; *Int'l*, pg. 2006
KOMBI, LTD.; *U.S. Private*, pg. 2342
KOMBINAT KOKSOCHEMICZNY ZABRZE S.A.; *Int'l*, pg. 4241
KOMBITERMINAL BURGHAUSEN GMBH—See Deutsche Bahn AG; *Int'l*, pg. 2051
KOM-DIA GMBH—See Veolia Environnement S.A.; *Int'l*, pg. 8153
KOMEC HELSEN N.V.—See Lonza Group AG; *Int'l*, pg. 4553
KOMEDA HOLDINGS CO., LTD.; *Int'l*, pg. 4241
KOMEHYO HOLDINGS CO., LTD.; *Int'l*, pg. 4241
KOMELON CORPORATION - KOMELON FRANCE DIVISION—See Komelon Corporation; *Int'l*, pg. 4241
KOMELON CORPORATION - KOMELON STEEL DIVISION—See Komelon Corporation; *Int'l*, pg. 4241
KOMELON CORPORATION; *Int'l*, pg. 4241
KOMELON USA CORPORATION—See Komelon Corporation; *Int'l*, pg. 4241
KOME ON COMMUNICATION LTD.; *Int'l*, pg. 4241
KOMERCIJALNA BANKA A.D. BANJA LUKA; *Int'l*, pg. 4242
KOMERCIJALNA BANKA A.D. SKOPJE; *Int'l*, pg. 4242
KOMERCIJALNO-INVESTICIONA BANKA D.D.; *Int'l*, pg. 4242
KOMERCNI BANKA, A.S.—See Societe Generale S.A.; *Int'l*, pg. 7039
KOMERCNI BANKA BRATISLAVA, A.S.—See Societe Generale S.A.; *Int'l*, pg. 7040
KOMERCNI POJHTOVNA—See Societe Generale S.A.; *Int'l*, pg. 7040
KOMERI CO., LTD.; *Int'l*, pg. 4242
KOMET MALI SARL—See Roscan Gold Corp.; *Int'l*, pg. 6399
KOMGRAD A.D.; *Int'l*, pg. 4242
KOMICO EQUIPMENT PARTS SHENZHEN CO., LTD.—See MiCo Ltd.; *Int'l*, pg. 4876
KOMICO HILLSBORO LLC—See KoMiCo Ltd; *Int'l*, pg. 4242
KOMICO LTD.—See MiCo Ltd.; *Int'l*, pg. 4876
KOMICO LTD; *Int'l*, pg. 4242
KOMICO TECHNOLOGY INC.—See MiCo Ltd.; *Int'l*, pg. 4876
KOMICO TECHNOLOGY SINGAPORE PTE. LTD.—See MiCo Ltd.; *Int'l*, pg. 4876
KOMICO TECHNOLOGY TAIWAN LTD.—See MiCo Ltd.; *Int'l*, pg. 4876
KOMI ELECTRONICS CO., LTD.—See Samjin LND Co., Ltd.; *Int'l*, pg. 6506
KOMIEXPERT S R.O.—See Tulikivi Corporation; *Int'l*, pg. 7969
KOMIPHARM INTERNATIONAL CO., LTD. - OSONG PLANT—See Komipharm International Co., Ltd.; *Int'l*, pg. 4242
KOMIPHARM INTERNATIONAL CO., LTD.; *Int'l*, pg. 4242
KOMIPHARM INTERNATIONAL CO., LTD. - YESAN PLANT—See Komipharm International Co., Ltd.; *Int'l*, pg. 4242
KOMIPO SERVICE CO., LTD.—See Korea Electric Power Corporation; *Int'l*, pg. 4283
KOMLINE-SANDERSON CORPORATION; *U.S. Private*, pg. 2342
KOMMANDITBOLAGET CEMENTEN—See Heidelberg Materials AG; *Int'l*, pg. 3318
KOMMANDITGESELLSCHAFT ZARA DEUTSCHLAND B.V. & CO.—See Industria de Diseno Textil, S.A.; *Int'l*, pg. 3666
KOMMENERGIE GMBH—See E.ON SE; *Int'l*, pg. 2258
KOMMERLING CHEMISCHE FABRIK GMBH—See H.B. Fuller Company; *U.S. Public*, pg. 978
KOMMERLING USA, INC.—See Arcapita Group Holdings Limited; *Int'l*, pg. 542
KOMMUNALKREDIT AUSTRIA AG; *Int'l*, pg. 4242
KOMMUNAL LANDSPENSJONSKASSE GJENSIDIG FORSIKRINGSSELSKAP; *Int'l*, pg. 4242
KOMO A.D.; *Int'l*, pg. 4242
KOMODIDAD DISTRIBUTORS INC.; *U.S. Private*, pg. 2342
KOMODO HEALTH, INC.; *U.S. Private*, pg. 2342
KOMOLINE AEROSPACE LIMITED; *Int'l*, pg. 4242
KOMO MACHINE INC.; *U.S. Private*, pg. 2342
KOMORI AMERICA CORPORATION—See Komori Corporation; *Int'l*, pg. 4242
KOMORI-CHAMBON S.A.—See Komori Corporation; *Int'l*, pg. 4243
KOMORI CORPORATION; *Int'l*, pg. 4242
KOMORI CORPORATION - TSUKUBA PLANT—See Komori Corporation; *Int'l*, pg. 4242

KOMORI CURRENCY TECHNOLOGY UK LTD—See Komori Corporation; *Int'l*, pg. 4242
KOMORI ELECTRONICS CO., LTD.—See Komori Corporation; *Int'l*, pg. 4242
KOMORI ENGINEERING CO., LTD.—See Komori Corporation; *Int'l*, pg. 4242
KOMORI FRANCE S.A.—See Komori Corporation; *Int'l*, pg. 4242
KOMORI HONG KONG LIMITED—See Komori Corporation; *Int'l*, pg. 4242
KOMORI INDIA PRIVATE LIMITED—See Komori Corporation; *Int'l*, pg. 4243
KOMORI INTERNATIONAL (EUROPE) B.V.—See Komori Corporation; *Int'l*, pg. 4243
KOMORI INTERNATIONAL NETHERLANDS B.V.—See Komori Corporation; *Int'l*, pg. 4243
KOMORI ITALIA S.R.L.—See Komori Corporation; *Int'l*, pg. 4243
KOMORI KOSAN CO LTD—See Komori Corporation; *Int'l*, pg. 4243
KOMORI LEASING INCORPORATED—See Komori Corporation; *Int'l*, pg. 4242
KOMORI MACHINERY CO., LTD.—See Komori Corporation; *Int'l*, pg. 4243
KOMORI MALAYSIA SDN. BHD.—See Komori Corporation; *Int'l*, pg. 4243
KOMORI PRECISION CO., LTD.—See Komori Corporation; *Int'l*, pg. 4243
KOMORI PRINTING MACHINE (SHENZHEN) CO., LTD.—See Komori Corporation; *Int'l*, pg. 4243
KOMORI REALTY CO., LTD.—See Komori Corporation; *Int'l*, pg. 4243
KOMORI (SHENZHEN) PRINT ENGINEERING CO., LTD.—See Komori Corporation; *Int'l*, pg. 4242
KOMORI SOUTHEAST ASIA PTE. LTD.—See Komori Corporation; *Int'l*, pg. 4243
KOMORI TAIWAN LIMITED—See Komori Corporation; *Int'l*, pg. 4243
KOMORI U.K. LIMITED—See Komori Corporation; *Int'l*, pg. 4243
KOMORO MURATA MANUFACTURING CO., LTD.—See Murata Manufacturing Co., Ltd.; *Int'l*, pg. 5097
KOMOS CO.,LTD.—See Ecoplastic Corporation; *Int'l*, pg. 2299
KOMO-TV—See Sinclair, Inc.; *U.S. Public*, pg. 1800
KOMPAKAR INC BHD.—See Temasek Holdings (Private) Limited; *Int'l*, pg. 7553
KOMPAN A/S; *Int'l*, pg. 4243
KOMPAN BARNLAND AB—See KOMPAN A/S; *Int'l*, pg. 4243
KOMPAN B.V.—See KOMPAN A/S; *Int'l*, pg. 4243
KOMPAN COMMERCIAL SYSTEMS SA—See KOMPAN A/S; *Int'l*, pg. 4243
KOMPAN DICA A/S—See KOMPAN A/S; *Int'l*, pg. 4243
KOMPAN GMBH—See KOMPAN A/S; *Int'l*, pg. 4243
KOMPANIA PIWOWARSKA S.A.—See Asahi Group Holdings Ltd.; *Int'l*, pg. 593
KOMPANI GROUP; *U.S. Private*, pg. 2342
KOMPANIJA BOBAR D.O.O.; *Int'l*, pg. 4243
KOMPANIJA GRADITELJ AD; *Int'l*, pg. 4244
KOMPANIJA MISIC A.D.; *Int'l*, pg. 4244
KOMPAN, INC.—See KOMPAN A/S; *Int'l*, pg. 4243
KOMPAN ITALIA S.R.L.—See KOMPAN A/S; *Int'l*, pg. 4243
KOMPAN LTD.—See KOMPAN A/S; *Int'l*, pg. 4243
KOMPAN MIDDLE EAST AND AFRICA—See KOMPAN A/S; *Int'l*, pg. 4243
KOMPAN NORGE AS—See KOMPAN A/S; *Int'l*, pg. 4243
KOMPAN NV/SA—See KOMPAN A/S; *Int'l*, pg. 4243
KOMPAN PLAYSCAPE PTY. LTD.—See KOMPAN A/S; *Int'l*, pg. 4243
KOMPAN S.A.S.—See KOMPAN A/S; *Int'l*, pg. 4243
KOMPAN SUOMI OY—See KOMPAN A/S; *Int'l*, pg. 4243
KOMPAS A.D.; *Int'l*, pg. 4244
KOMPAS MEDUGORJE D.D.; *Int'l*, pg. 4244
KOMPAS MTS D.D.; *Int'l*, pg. 4244
KOMPASS ALGERIE INTERNATIONAL, EURL—See Ratos AB; *Int'l*, pg. 6216
KOMPASS AZERBAIJAN CO.—See Ratos AB; *Int'l*, pg. 6217
KOMPASS BELGIUM SA-NV—See Ratos AB; *Int'l*, pg. 6217
KOMPASS BILGI DAGITIM HIZMETLERI A.S.—See Ratos AB; *Int'l*, pg. 6217
KOMPASS B.V.—See Ratos AB; *Int'l*, pg. 6217
KOMPASS CZECH REPUBLIC S.R.O.—See Ratos AB; *Int'l*, pg. 6217
KOMPASS DANMARK A/S—See Ratos AB; *Int'l*, pg. 6217
KOMPASS FINLAND OY—See Ratos AB; *Int'l*, pg. 6217
KOMPASS GEORGIA—See Ratos AB; *Int'l*, pg. 6216
KOMPASS GMBH—See Ratos AB; *Int'l*, pg. 6217
KOMPASS INDIA INFORMATION PVT. LTD.—See Ratos AB; *Int'l*, pg. 6217
KOMPASS INFO DOO—See Ratos AB; *Int'l*, pg. 6217
KOMPASS INTERNATIONAL NEUENSCHWANDER SA—See Axon Active AG; *Int'l*, pg. 770
KOMPASS INTERNATIONAL S.A.—See Ratos AB; *Int'l*, pg. 6217
KOMPASS IRAN CO.—See Ratos AB; *Int'l*, pg. 6217
KOMPASS JAPAN K.K.—See Ratos AB; *Int'l*, pg. 6217

KOMPASS KAZAKHSTAN—See Ratos AB; *Int'l*, pg. 6217
KOMPASS KOREA INC.—See Ratos AB; *Int'l*, pg. 6217
KOMPASS LANKA (PVT) LTD.—See Ratos AB; *Int'l*, pg. 6217
KOMPASS NORGE AS—See Ratos AB; *Int'l*, pg. 6217
KOMPASS ROMANIA SRL—See Ratos AB; *Int'l*, pg. 6217
KOMPASS SLOVAKIA A.S.—See Ratos AB; *Int'l*, pg. 6217
KOMPASS SVERIGE AB—See Ratos AB; *Int'l*, pg. 6217
KOMPASS UK LTD—See Ratos AB; *Int'l*, pg. 6217
KOMPASS UKRAINE JSC—See Ratos AB; *Int'l*, pg. 6217
KOMPETENSUTVECKLINGSINSTITUTET SVERIGE AB—See AcadeMedia AB; *Int'l*, pg. 77
KOMPETENZNETZ RAIL BERLIN BRANDENBURG GMBH—See Havellandische Eisenbahn AG; *Int'l*, pg. 3286
KOMPETENZZENTRUM AUTOMOBIL- UND INDUSTRIEELEKTRONIK GMBH—See Infineon Technologies AG; *Int'l*, pg. 3687
KOMPETENZZENTRUM FUR SICHERE ENTSORGUNG GMBH—See Eckert & Ziegler Strahlen- und Medizintechnik AG; *Int'l*, pg. 2290
KOMPLETT ASA; *Int'l*, pg. 4244
KOMPLETT SERVICES SWEDEN AB—See Komplett ASA; *Int'l*, pg. 4244
KOMPLIGENS FASTIGHETER AB—See Peab AB; *Int'l*, pg. 5772
KOMPLI HOLDINGS PLC; *Int'l*, pg. 4244
KOMPOGAS SLO LLC—See Hitachi Zosen Corporation; *Int'l*, pg. 3411
KOMPONENTA A.—See P-Duke Technology Co., Ltd.; *Int'l*, pg. 5681
KOMPONENT KFT.—See WAMGROUP S.p.A.; *Int'l*, pg. 8338
KOMPRESOR A.D.; *Int'l*, pg. 4244
KOMPRESSORTEKNIK AB—See Instalco AB; *Int'l*, pg. 3722
KOMPUTRONIK S.A.; *Int'l*, pg. 4244
KOMTECH (PTY) LTD.—See Komax Holding AG; *Int'l*, pg. 4240
KOMTES CHRUDIM S.R.O.—See W.A.G Payment Solutions Plc; *Int'l*, pg. 8321
KOMTES SK S.R.O.—See W.A.G Payment Solutions Plc; *Int'l*, pg. 8321
KOMUNALAC MODRICA A.D.; *Int'l*, pg. 4244
KOMUNALAC TESLIC A.D.; *Int'l*, pg. 4244
KOMUNALNA POISFOVNA, A.S.—See Vienna Insurance Group AG Wiener Versicherung Gruppe; *Int'l*, pg. 8195
KOMUNALNA POIST'OVNA, A.S.—See Vienna Insurance Group AG Wiener Versicherung Gruppe; *Int'l*, pg. 8195
KOMUNALNE USLUGE AD; *Int'l*, pg. 4244
KOMUNALNO A.D.; *Int'l*, pg. 4244
KOMUNO GMBH—See Helaba Landesbank Hessen-Thuringen; *Int'l*, pg. 3328
KOMYAPI INSAAT A.S.—See Bera Holding A.S.; *Int'l*, pg. 978
KONA BREWERY LLC—See Anheuser-Busch InBev SA/NV; *Int'l*, pg. 465
KONA C CO., LTD.—See KONA I Corporation; *Int'l*, pg. 4244
KONAFISH COMPANY INC.—See Tropic Fish & Vegetable Center Inc.; *U.S. Private*, pg. 4242
KONA GRILL INC.—See The ONE Group Hospitality, Inc.; *U.S. Public*, pg. 2118
KONA HR CONSULTING GROUP LLC; *U.S. Private*, pg. 2342
KONA I CORPORATION; *Int'l*, pg. 4244
KONAKA CO., LTD.; *Int'l*, pg. 4244
KONA M CO., LTD.—See KONA I Corporation; *Int'l*, pg. 4244
KONAMI AMUSEMENT CO., LTD.—See Konami Group Corporation; *Int'l*, pg. 4245
KONAMI AMUSEMENT OF EUROPE LTD.—See Konami Group Corporation; *Int'l*, pg. 4245
KONAMI AUSTRALIA PTY LTD.—See Konami Group Corporation; *Int'l*, pg. 4245
KONAMI COMPUTER ENTERTAINMENT STUDIO, INC.—See Konami Group Corporation; *Int'l*, pg. 4245
KONAMI COMPUTER ENTERTAINMENT TOKYO, INC.—See Konami Group Corporation; *Int'l*, pg. 4245
KONAMI CORPORATION OF AMERICA INC.—See Konami Group Corporation; *Int'l*, pg. 4245
KONAMI CORPORATION—See Konami Group Corporation; *Int'l*, pg. 4245
KONAMI CROSS MEDIA NY, INC.—See Konami Group Corporation; *Int'l*, pg. 4245
KONAMI DIGITAL ENTERTAINMENT B.V.—See Konami Group Corporation; *Int'l*, pg. 4245
KONAMI DIGITAL ENTERTAINMENT B.V.—See Konami Group Corporation; *Int'l*, pg. 4245
KONAMI DIGITAL ENTERTAINMENT CO., LTD.—See Konami Group Corporation; *Int'l*, pg. 4245
KONAMI DIGITAL ENTERTAINMENT, INC.—See Konami Group Corporation; *Int'l*, pg. 4245
KONAMI DIGITAL ENTERTAINMENT LTD.—See Konami Group Corporation; *Int'l*, pg. 4245
KONAMI GAMING, INC.—See Konami Group Corporation; *Int'l*, pg. 4245
KONAMI GROUP CORPORATION; *Int'l*, pg. 4245

KONAMI MANUFACTURING AND SERVICE, INC.—See Konami Group Corporation; *Int'l*, pg. 4245
KONAMI MUSIC ENTERTAINMENT, INC.—See Konami Group Corporation; *Int'l*, pg. 4245
KONAMI REAL ESTATE, INC.—See Konami Group Corporation; *Int'l*, pg. 4245
KONAMI SPORTS & LIFE CO., LTD.—See Konami Group Corporation; *Int'l*, pg. 4245
KONAN INDUSTRY CO., LTD.—See Yamato Holdings Co., Ltd.; *Int'l*, pg. 8554
KONAN KOGYO CO., LTD.—See AISIN Corporation; *Int'l*, pg. 253
KONAN KUCYOU CO., LTD.—See Mitsubishi Heavy Industries, Ltd.; *Int'l*, pg. 4954
KONARED CORPORATION; *U.S. Public*, pg. 1271
KONARK INFRATECH PRIVATE LIMITED—See Konark Synthetic Ltd.; *Int'l*, pg. 4245
KONARK SYNTHETIC LTD. - BENGALURU UNIT—See Konark Synthetic Ltd.; *Int'l*, pg. 4245
KONARK SYNTHETIC LTD.; *Int'l*, pg. 4245
KONAR LEBENSMITTELHANDELS GMBH—See Podravka d.d.; *Int'l*, pg. 5903
KONA SUSHI, INC.—See The ONE Group Hospitality, Inc.; *U.S. Public*, pg. 2118
KONATEL INC.—See KonaTel, Inc.; *U.S. Public*, pg. 1271
KONATEL, INC.; *U.S. Public*, pg. 1271
KONA TEXAS RESTAURANTS, INC.—See The ONE Group Hospitality, Inc.; *U.S. Public*, pg. 2118
KONBINISUTESHON CO., LTD—See TKP Corporation; *Int'l*, pg. 7766
KONCAR - DIGITAL LTD.—See KONCAR - Electrical Industry Inc; *Int'l*, pg. 4246
KONCAR - DISTRIBUTION AND SPECIAL TRANSFORMERS INC—See KONCAR - Electrical Industry Inc; *Int'l*, pg. 4246
KONCAR - DISTRIBUTIVNI I SPECIJALNI TRANSFORMATORI D.D.; *Int'l*, pg. 4245
KONCAR DISTRIBUTIVNI & SPECIJALNI TRANSFORMATORI DD; *Int'l*, pg. 4246
KONCAR - ELECTRICAL ENGINEERING INSTITUTE INC.—See KONCAR - Electrical Industry Inc; *Int'l*, pg. 4246
KONCAR - ELECTRICAL INDUSTRY INC; *Int'l*, pg. 4245
KONCAR - ELECTRIC VEHICLES INC.—See KONCAR - Electrical Industry Inc; *Int'l*, pg. 4246
KONCAR - ELECTRONICS & INFORMATICS INC.—See KONCAR - Electrical Industry Inc; *Int'l*, pg. 4246
KONCAR-ELEKTROINDUSTRIJA D.D.; *Int'l*, pg. 4246
KONCAR-ENERGETSKI TRANSFORMATORI, D.O.O.—See Siemens Aktiengesellschaft; *Int'l*, pg. 6887
KONCAR - ENGINEERING CO. LTD.—See KONCAR - Electrical Industry Inc; *Int'l*, pg. 4246
KONCAR - ENGINEERING FOR PLANT INSTALLATION & COMMISSIONING INC.—See Koncar-Elektroindustrija d.d.; *Int'l*, pg. 4246
KONCAR - GENERATORS & MOTORS INC.—See KONCAR - Electrical Industry Inc; *Int'l*, pg. 4246
KONCAR - HOUSEHOLD APPLIANCES LTD—See KONCAR - Electrical Industry Inc; *Int'l*, pg. 4246
KONCAR - INFRASTRUCTURE & SERVICES LTD.—See KONCAR - Electrical Industry Inc; *Int'l*, pg. 4246
KONCAR - INSTRUMENT TRANSFORMERS INC.—See KONCAR - Electrical Industry Inc; *Int'l*, pg. 4246
KONCAR - LOW VOLTAGE SWITCHES & CIRCUIT BRAKERS INC.—See KONCAR - Electrical Industry Inc; *Int'l*, pg. 4246
KONCAR - METALNE KONSTRUKCIJE D.D.—See KONCAR - Electrical Industry Inc; *Int'l*, pg. 4246
KONCAR - MOTORS AND ELECTRICAL SYSTEMS LTD.—See Koncar-Elektroindustrija d.d.; *Int'l*, pg. 4246
KONCAR - POWER PLANT & ELECTRIC TRACTION ENGINEERING INC.—See KONCAR - Electrical Industry Inc; *Int'l*, pg. 4246
KONCAR - RENEWABLE ENERGY SOURCES LTD.—See KONCAR - Electrical Industry Inc; *Int'l*, pg. 4246
KONCAR - SMALL ELECTRICAL MACHINES INC.—See KONCAR - Electrical Industry Inc; *Int'l*, pg. 4246
KONCAR - SWITCHGEAR INC.—See KONCAR - Electrical Industry Inc; *Int'l*, pg. 4246
KONCEPO SCIENTECH INTERNATIONAL PVT. LTD.—See Kewaunee Scientific Corporation; *U.S. Public*, pg. 1225
KONCEPT SP. Z O.O.—See Zaklady Chemiczne POLICE S.A.; *Int'l*, pg. 8621
KONCEPT TECHNOLOGIES INC; *U.S. Private*, pg. 2342
KONCERNAS ACHEMOS GRUPE; *Int'l*, pg. 4246
KONCERN ENERGETYCZNA ENERGA SA; *Int'l*, pg. 4246
KONDATOR AB—See Lagercrantz Group AB; *Int'l*, pg. 4394
KONDO CHEMICAL INDUSTRY CO., LTD.; *Int'l*, pg. 4246
KONDO CHEMICAL INDUSTRY CO., LTD. - TOKUSHIMA PLANT—See KONDO Chemical Industry Co., Ltd.; *Int'l*, pg. 4247
KONDOH SHOKAI CO., LTD.—See Uchida Yoko Co., Ltd.; *Int'l*, pg. 8012
KONDOSERVIS MANAGEMENT SDN. BHD.—See IGB Berhad; *Int'l*, pg. 3601

KONDOSERVIS SDN. BHD.—See IGB Berhad; *Int'l*, pg. 3601
KONDOTEC INC.; *Int'l*, pg. 4247
KONE AB—See KONE Oyj; *Int'l*, pg. 4247
KONE AG—See KONE Oyj; *Int'l*, pg. 4247
KONE AKSJESELSKAP—See KONE Oyj; *Int'l*, pg. 4248
KONE ASANSOR SANAYI VE TICARET A.S.—See KONE Oyj; *Int'l*, pg. 4248
KONE ASCENSORI S.P.A.—See KONE Oyj; *Int'l*, pg. 4248
KONE ASCENSORUL S.A.—See KONE Oyj; *Int'l*, pg. 4248
KONE ASSARAIN LLC—See KONE Oyj; *Int'l*, pg. 4248
KONE A/S—See KONE Oyj; *Int'l*, pg. 4247
KONE A/S—See KONE Oyj; *Int'l*, pg. 4247
KONE BAHRAIN W.L.L.—See KONE Oyj; *Int'l*, pg. 4248
KONE BELGIUM S.A.—See KONE Oyj; *Int'l*, pg. 4248
KONE BUSINESS SERVICES, S.R.O.—See KONE Oyj; *Int'l*, pg. 4248
KONE B.V.—See KONE Oyj; *Int'l*, pg. 4248
KONECRANES AB—See Konecranes Plc; *Int'l*, pg. 4251
KONECRANES AG—See Konecranes Plc; *Int'l*, pg. 4251
KONECRANES AND DEMAG AG—See Konecranes Plc; *Int'l*, pg. 4253
KONECRANES AND DEMAG, LDA.—See Konecranes Plc; *Int'l*, pg. 4253
KONECRANES AND DEMAG PRIVATE LIMITED—See Konecranes Plc; *Int'l*, pg. 4253
KONECRANES AND DEMAG (PTY) LTD.—See Konecranes Plc; *Int'l*, pg. 4253
KONECRANES AND DEMAG S.R.O.—See Konecranes Plc; *Int'l*, pg. 4253
KONECRANES A/S—See Konecranes Plc; *Int'l*, pg. 4251
KONECRANES AS—See Konecranes Plc; *Int'l*, pg. 4251
KONECRANES BV—See Konecranes Plc; *Int'l*, pg. 4251
KONECRANES CANADA, INC.—See Konecranes Plc; *Int'l*, pg. 4251
KONECRANES CHILE.—See Konecranes Plc; *Int'l*, pg. 4251
KONECRANES COMPANY LTD.—See Konecranes Plc; *Int'l*, pg. 4251
KONECRANES DEMAG BRASIL LTDA.—See Konecranes Plc; *Int'l*, pg. 4253
KONECRANES FINANCE OY—See Konecranes Plc; *Int'l*, pg. 4251
KONECRANES FINLAND OY—See Konecranes Plc; *Int'l*, pg. 4251
KONECRANES (FRANCE) S.A.—See Konecranes Plc; *Int'l*, pg. 4251
KONECRANES (FRANCE)—See Konecranes Plc; *Int'l*, pg. 4251
KONECRANES GMBH - ANSBACH—See Konecranes Plc; *Int'l*, pg. 4251
KONECRANES GMBH - BERLIN—See Konecranes Plc; *Int'l*, pg. 4251
KONECRANES GMBH—See Konecranes Plc; *Int'l*, pg. 4251
KONECRANES HELLAS LIFTING EQUIPMENT AND SERVICES S.A.—See Konecranes Plc; *Int'l*, pg. 4251
KONECRANES HOLDING BV—See Konecranes Plc; *Int'l*, pg. 4251
KONECRANES HOLDING GMBH—See Konecranes Plc; *Int'l*, pg. 4251
KONECRANES, INC. - HOUSTON PLANT—See Konecranes Plc; *Int'l*, pg. 4252
KONECRANES, INC.—See Konecranes Plc; *Int'l*, pg. 4252
KONECRANES INDIA PRIVATE LTD.—See Konecranes Plc; *Int'l*, pg. 4251
KONECRANES KFT.—See Konecranes Plc; *Int'l*, pg. 4251
KONECRANES LATVIA—See Konecranes Plc; *Int'l*, pg. 4251
KONECRANES LIFTING SYSTEMS GMBH—See Konecranes Plc; *Int'l*, pg. 4251
KONECRANES LIFTING SYSTEMS GMBH—See Konecranes Plc; *Int'l*, pg. 4251
KONECRANES LIFTTRUCKS AB—See Konecranes Plc; *Int'l*, pg. 4251
KONECRANES MACHINE TOOL SERVICE LTD.—See Konecranes Plc; *Int'l*, pg. 4252
KONECRANES MACHINE TOOL SERVICES LTD.—See Konecranes Plc; *Int'l*, pg. 4252
KONECRANES MEXICO S.A. DE C.V.—See Konecranes Plc; *Int'l*, pg. 4252
KONECRANES NORWAY HOLDING A/S—See Konecranes Plc; *Int'l*, pg. 4252
KONECRANES NUCLEAR EQUIPMENT & SERVICES, LLC—See Konecranes Plc; *Int'l*, pg. 4252
KONECRANES ORLEY MEYER—See Konecranes Plc; *Int'l*, pg. 4252
KONECRANES OU—See Konecranes Plc; *Int'l*, pg. 4252
KONECRANES OYJ; *Int'l*, pg. 4251
KONECRANES PERU S.R.L—See Konecranes Plc; *Int'l*, pg. 4252
KONECRANES PLC; *Int'l*, pg. 4251
KONECRANES PORT SERVICES (BENELUX)—See Konecranes Plc; *Int'l*, pg. 4253
KONECRANES PTE LTD.—See Konecranes Plc; *Int'l*, pg. 4252
KONECRANES PTY LTD.—See Konecranes Plc; *Int'l*, pg. 4252
KONECRANES PTY LTD.—See Konecranes Plc; *Int'l*, pg. 4252
KONECRANES PTY LTD—See Konecranes Plc; *Int'l*, pg. 4252
KONECRANES SA/NV—See Konecranes Plc; *Int'l*, pg. 4252
KONECRANES S.A.—See Konecranes Plc; *Int'l*, pg. 4252
KONECRANES SDN. BHD.—See Konecranes Plc; *Int'l*, pg. 4252
KONECRANES SERVICE OY—See Konecranes Plc; *Int'l*, pg. 4252
KONECRANES (SHANGHAI) CO. LTD.—See Konecranes Plc; *Int'l*, pg. 4251
KONECRANES SLOVAKIA S.R.O.—See Konecranes Plc; *Int'l*, pg. 4252
KONECRANES SP. Z.O.O.—See Konecranes Plc; *Int'l*, pg. 4252
KONECRANES SUPPLY HUNGARY KFT.—See Konecranes Plc; *Int'l*, pg. 4252
KONECRANES SWEDEN HOLDING AB—See Konecranes Plc; *Int'l*, pg. 4252
KONECRANES TALHAS, PONTES ROLANTES E SERVICOS LTDA.—See Konecranes Plc; *Int'l*, pg. 4252
KONECRANES (THAILAND) LTD.—See Konecranes Plc; *Int'l*, pg. 4251
KONECRANES TICARET VE SERVIS LIMITED SIRKETI—See Konecranes Plc; *Int'l*, pg. 4252
KONECRANES UK LIMITED—See Konecranes Plc; *Int'l*, pg. 4252
KONECRANES UK LTD. - INDUSTRIAL CRANE DIVISION—See Konecranes Plc; *Int'l*, pg. 4252
KONECRANES VIETNAM CO.,LTD—See Konecranes Plc; *Int'l*, pg. 4252
KONECRANES YARDIT OY—See Konecranes Plc; *Int'l*, pg. 4252
KONECTA ARGENTINA—See Grupo Konectanet S.L.; *Int'l*, pg. 3130
KONECTA BTO, S.L.—See Grupo Konectanet S.L.; *Int'l*, pg. 3130
KONECTA CHILE SA—See Grupo Konectanet S.L.; *Int'l*, pg. 3130
KONECTA PORTUGAL, LDA—See Grupo Konectanet S.L.; *Int'l*, pg. 3130
KONECTA UK LTD—See Grupo Konectanet S.L.; *Int'l*, pg. 3130
KONECTBUS LIMITED—See GLOBALVIA Inversiones, S.A.U.; *Int'l*, pg. 3005
KONECTBUS LIMITED—See Kinetic Group Services Pty Ltd.; *Int'l*, pg. 4167
KONE DEURSYSTEMEN B.V.—See KONE Oyj; *Int'l*, pg. 4248
KONE D O O LJUBLJANA—See KONE Oyj; *Int'l*, pg. 4248
KONE DOOR AB—See KONE Oyj; *Int'l*, pg. 4248
KONE D.O.O.—See KONE Oyj; *Int'l*, pg. 4250
KONE D.O.O.—See KONE Oyj; *Int'l*, pg. 4250
KONE D.O.O.—See KONE Oyj; *Int'l*, pg. 4250
KONE EHF—See KONE Oyj; *Int'l*, pg. 4250
KONE ELEVADORES, S.A.—See KONE Oyj; *Int'l*, pg. 4248
KONE ELEVATOR A/S—See KONE Oyj; *Int'l*, pg. 4248
KONE ELEVATOR & ESCALATOR—See KONE Oyj; *Int'l*, pg. 4248
KONE ELEVATOR (H.K.) LTD.—See KONE Oyj; *Int'l*, pg. 4248
KONE ELEVATOR INDIA LTD.—See KONE Oyj; *Int'l*, pg. 4248
KONE ELEVATOR (M) SDN. BHD.—See KONE Oyj; *Int'l*, pg. 4248
KONE ELEVATOR PTE. LTD.—See KONE Oyj; *Int'l*, pg. 4248
KONE ELEVATORS AND ESCALATORS SARL AU—See KONE Oyj; *Int'l*, pg. 4248
KONE ELEVATORS CO., LTD.—See KONE Oyj; *Int'l*, pg. 4248
KONE ELEVATORS CO., LTD.—See KONE Oyj; *Int'l*, pg. 4248
KONE ELEVATORS CYPRUS LIMITED—See KONE Oyj; *Int'l*, pg. 4248
KONE ELEVATORS EMPLOYEE BENEFITS PTY LIMITED—See KONE Oyj; *Int'l*, pg. 4248
KONE ELEVATORS FINLAND—See KONE Oyj; *Int'l*, pg. 4248
KONE ELEVATOR (SHANGHAI) CO., LTD.—See KONE Oyj; *Int'l*, pg. 4248
KONE ELEVATORS PTY. LTD.—See KONE Oyj; *Int'l*, pg. 4248
KONE ELEVATORS PTY LTD—See KONE Oyj; *Int'l*, pg. 4248
KONE ELEVATORS SOUTH AFRICA (PTY) LTD.—See KONE Oyj; *Int'l*, pg. 4248
KONE ELEVATORS TAIWAN CO. LTD.—See KONE Oyj; *Int'l*, pg. 4248
KONE ELEVATORS W.L.L.—See KONE Oyj; *Int'l*, pg. 4248
KONE EOOD—See KONE Oyj; *Int'l*, pg. 4248
KONE FELVONO KFT.—See KONE Oyj; *Int'l*, pg. 4248
KONE GARANT AUFZUG GMBH—See KONE Oyj; *Int'l*, pg. 4248
KONE GMBH—See KONE Oyj; *Int'l*, pg. 4248
KONE HISSIT OY—See KONE Oyj; *Int'l*, pg. 4248
KONE HOLDING FRANCE S.A.S.—See KONE Oyj; *Int'l*, pg. 4248
KONE HOLDING GMBH—See KONE Oyj; *Int'l*, pg. 4248
KONE HOLLAND B.V.—See KONE Oyj; *Int'l*, pg. 4248
KONE INC. - ELEVATORS NORTH AMERICA—See KONE Oyj; *Int'l*, pg. 4249
KONE INC. - ESCALATOR DIVISION—See KONE Oyj; *Int'l*, pg. 4249
KONE INC. - SERVICE CENTER—See KONE Oyj; *Int'l*, pg. 4249
KONE INC.—See KONE Oyj; *Int'l*, pg. 4248
KONE INC.—See KONE Oyj; *Int'l*, pg. 4249
KONE, INC.—See KONE Oyj; *Int'l*, pg. 4250
KONE LTD.—See KONE Oyj; *Int'l*, pg. 4249
KONE INC. - SPARES—See KONE Oyj; *Int'l*, pg. 4249
KONE INDUSTRIAL OY—See KONE Oyj; *Int'l*, pg. 4249
KONE INDUSTRIAL S.A. DE C.V.—See KONE Oyj; *Int'l*, pg. 4249
KONE INDUSTRIAL SERVICIOS S.A. DE C.V.—See KONE Oyj; *Int'l*, pg. 4249
KONE INDUSTRIAL S.P.A.—See KONE Oyj; *Int'l*, pg. 4249
KONE INTERNATIONAL S.A.—See KONE Oyj; *Int'l*, pg. 4249
KONE INVESTITION GMBH—See KONE Oyj; *Int'l*, pg. 4249
KONE (IRELAND) LIMITED—See KONE Oyj; *Int'l*, pg. 4247
KONE JAPAN CO. LTD.—See KONE Oyj; *Int'l*, pg. 4249
KONE KENYA LIMITED—See KONE Oyj; *Int'l*, pg. 4249
KONEKESKO EESTI AS—See Kesko Corporation; *Int'l*, pg. 4142
KONEKESKO LATVIJA SIA—See Kesko Corporation; *Int'l*, pg. 4142
KONEKESKO LIETUVA UAB—See Kesko Corporation; *Int'l*, pg. 4142
KONEKESKO LTD.—See Kesko Corporation; *Int'l*, pg. 4142
KONEKESKO OOO—See Kesko Corporation; *Int'l*, pg. 4142
KONEKSA HEALTH LLC—See Merck & Co., Inc.; *U.S. Public*, pg. 1417
KONEKT AUSTRALIA PTY LTD.—See Konekt Limited; *Int'l*, pg. 4253
KONEKT EMPLOYMENT PTY LTD—See Konekt Limited; *Int'l*, pg. 4253
KONEKT LIMITED; *Int'l*, pg. 4253
KONEKT WORKPLACE HEALTH SOLUTIONS PTY LTD.—See Konekt Limited; *Int'l*, pg. 4253
KONE LIFTS LLC—See KONE Oyj; *Int'l*, pg. 4249
KONE LIFTS S.R.O.—See KONE Oyj; *Int'l*, pg. 4249
KONE LLC—See KONE Oyj; *Int'l*, pg. 4249
KONE LTD.—See KONE Oyj; *Int'l*, pg. 4249
KONE LUXEMBOURG S.A.R.L.—See KONE Oyj; *Int'l*, pg. 4249
KONE MAKEDONIJA DOOEL SKOPJE—See KONE Oyj; *Int'l*, pg. 4249
KONE MAKEDONIJA DOOEL—See KONE Oyj; *Int'l*, pg. 4249
K-ONE MANUFACTURING SDN. BHD.—See K-One Technology Berhad; *Int'l*, pg. 4042
KONEMATIC GMBH—See KONE Oyj; *Int'l*, pg. 4250
KONE METRO AB—See KONE Oyj; *Int'l*, pg. 4249
KONE MEXICO, S.A. DE C.V.—See KONE Oyj; *Int'l*, pg. 4250
KONE MONTAGE GMBH—See KONE Oyj; *Int'l*, pg. 4249
KONE NEDERLAND HOLDING B.V.—See KONE Oyj; *Int'l*, pg. 4249
KONE (NI) LIMITED—See KONE Oyj; *Int'l*, pg. 4247
KONE OYJ; *Int'l*, pg. 4247
KONE PLC-GLASGOW—See KONE Oyj; *Int'l*, pg. 4249
KONE PLC—See KONE Oyj; *Int'l*, pg. 4249
KONE PORTUGAL- ELEVADORES LDA.—See KONE Oyj; *Int'l*, pg. 4249
KONE PTE. LTD.—See KONE Oyj; *Int'l*, pg. 4249
KONE PUBLIC COMPANY LIMITED—See KONE Oyj; *Int'l*, pg. 4249
KONE QUEBEC, INC.—See KONE Oyj; *Int'l*, pg. 4249
KONE RULLETRAPPER AS—See KONE Oyj; *Int'l*, pg. 4249
KONE RULLTRAPPOR A.B.—See KONE Oyj; *Int'l*, pg. 4249
KONE S.A.—See KONE Oyj; *Int'l*, pg. 4249
KONE S.A.—See KONE Oyj; *Int'l*, pg. 4249
KONE SCANDINAVIA AB—See KONE Oyj; *Int'l*, pg. 4250
KONE (SCHWEIZ) AG—See KONE Oyj; *Int'l*, pg. 4247
KONE SERVICEZENTRALE GMBH—See KONE Oyj; *Int'l*, pg. 4250
KONE S.P.A.—See KONE Oyj; *Int'l*, pg. 4249
KONE SP. Z O.O.—See KONE Oyj; *Int'l*, pg. 4250
KONE S.R.O.—See KONE Oyj; *Int'l*, pg. 4250
KONE SSC S.R.O.—See KONE Oyj; *Int'l*, pg. 4250
KONETA, INC.—See Kinderhook Industries, LLC; *U.S. Private*, pg. 2307
K-ONE TECHNOLOGY BERHAD; *Int'l*, pg. 4042
KONE UGANDA LIMITED—See KONE Oyj; *Int'l*, pg. 4250
KONE (UK)-KEIGHLEY—See KONE Oyj; *Int'l*, pg. 4249
KONE VIETNAM LIMITED LIABILITY COMPANY—See KONE Oyj; *Int'l*, pg. 4250

COMPANY NAME INDEX

KONEXUS CONSULTING GROUP GMBH—See Capgemini SE; *Int'l*, pg. 1307
KONFECTION E ELECTRONIK GMBH—See Amphenol Corporation; *U.S. Public*, pg. 130
KONFOONG MATERIALS INTERNATIONAL CO., LTD.; *Int'l*, pg. 4253
KONFRUT GIDA SANAYI VE TICARET AS; *Int'l*, pg. 4253
KONGAZ A.S.—See Bera Holding A.S.; *Int'l*, pg. 978
KONG DENTAL SURGERY SINGAPORE PVT LTD.—See OUE Limited; *Int'l*, pg. 5666
KONG NUON GROUP CO., LTD.—See Bridgestone Corporation; *Int'l*, pg. 1160
KONGREGATE INC.—See Modern Times Group MTG AB; *Int'l*, pg. 5014
KONGSBERG ACTUATION SYSTEMS BV—See Kongsberg Automotive ASA; *Int'l*, pg. 4254
KONGSBERG ACTUATION SYSTEMS GMBH—See Kongsberg Automotive ASA; *Int'l*, pg. 4254
KONGSBERG ACTUATION SYSTEMS II INC—See Kongsberg Automotive ASA; *Int'l*, pg. 4254
KONGSBERG ACTUATION SYSTEMS LTD—See Kongsberg Automotive ASA; *Int'l*, pg. 4254
KONGSBERG ACTUATION SYSTEMS SL—See Kongsberg Automotive ASA; *Int'l*, pg. 4254
KONGSBERG AUTOMOTIVE AB—See Kongsberg Automotive ASA; *Int'l*, pg. 4254
KONGSBERG AUTOMOTIVE ASA; *Int'l*, pg. 4253
KONGSBERG AUTOMOTIVE AS—See Kongsberg Automotive ASA; *Int'l*, pg. 4254
KONGSBERG AUTOMOTIVE DRIVELINE SYSTEM INDIA LTD.—See Kongsberg Automotive ASA; *Int'l*, pg. 4254
KONGSBERG AUTOMOTIVE GMBH—See Kongsberg Automotive ASA; *Int'l*, pg. 4254
KONGSBERG AUTOMOTIVE INC. - MILAN—See Kongsberg Automotive ASA; *Int'l*, pg. 4254
KONGSBERG AUTOMOTIVE INC.—See Kongsberg Automotive ASA; *Int'l*, pg. 4254
KONGSBERG AUTOMOTIVE INC. - SUFFIELD—See Kongsberg Automotive ASA; *Int'l*, pg. 4254
KONGSBERG AUTOMOTIVE INC. - VAN WERT—See Kongsberg Automotive ASA; *Int'l*, pg. 4254
KONGSBERG AUTOMOTIVE INC. - WILLIS—See Kongsberg Automotive ASA; *Int'l*, pg. 4254
KONGSBERG AUTOMOTIVE (INDIA) PRIVATE LTD.—See Kongsberg Automotive ASA; *Int'l*, pg. 4254
KONGSBERG AUTOMOTIVE JAPAN KK—See Kongsberg Automotive ASA; *Int'l*, pg. 4254
KONGSBERG AUTOMOTIVE, KFT—See Kongsberg Automotive ASA; *Int'l*, pg. 4254
KONGSBERG AUTOMOTIVE LIMITED—See Kongsberg Automotive ASA; *Int'l*, pg. 4254
KONGSBERG AUTOMOTIVE LTDA.—See Kongsberg Automotive ASA; *Int'l*, pg. 4254
KONGSBERG AUTOMOTIVE LTD. - NORMANTON—See Kongsberg Automotive ASA; *Int'l*, pg. 4254
KONGSBERG AUTOMOTIVE LTD.—See Kongsberg Automotive ASA; *Int'l*, pg. 4254
KONGSBERG AUTOMOTIVE SARL—See Kongsberg Automotive ASA; *Int'l*, pg. 4254
KONGSBERG AUTOMOTIVE (SHANGHAI) CO., LTD.—See Kongsberg Automotive ASA; *Int'l*, pg. 4254
KONGSBERG AUTOMOTIVE—See Kongsberg Automotive ASA; *Int'l*, pg. 4254
KONGSBERG AUTOMOTIVE SP. Z O.O.—See Kongsberg Automotive ASA; *Int'l*, pg. 4254
KONGSBERG AUTOMOTIVE SRL DE CV—See Kongsberg Automotive ASA; *Int'l*, pg. 4254
KONGSBERG AUTOMOTIVE S.R.O—See Kongsberg Automotive ASA; *Int'l*, pg. 4254
KONGSBERG AUTOMOTIVE (WUXI) LTD.—See Kongsberg Automotive ASA; *Int'l*, pg. 4254
KONGSBERG AVIATION MAINTENANCE SERVICES AS—See Kongsberg Gruppen ASA; *Int'l*, pg. 4255
KONGSBERG DEFENCE & AEROSPACE AS—See Kongsberg Gruppen ASA; *Int'l*, pg. 4255
KONGSBERG DEFENCE OY—See Kongsberg Gruppen ASA; *Int'l*, pg. 4255
KONGSBERG DEVOTEK AS; *Int'l*, pg. 4254
KONGSBERG DISCOVERY US, LLC—See Kongsberg Gruppen ASA; *Int'l*, pg. 4255
KONGSBERG DRILLING MANAGMENT SOLUTIONS AS—See Kongsberg Gruppen ASA; *Int'l*, pg. 4255
KONGSBERG DRIVELINE SYSTEMS GMBH—See Kongsberg Automotive ASA; *Int'l*, pg. 4254
KONGSBERG DRIVELINE SYSTEMS SAS—See Kongsberg Automotive ASA; *Int'l*, pg. 4254
KONGSBERG ESCO AB—See Kongsberg Esco AS; *Int'l*, pg. 4255
KONGSBERG ESCO AS; *Int'l*, pg. 4254
KONGSBERG ESCO MPV AS—See Kongsberg Esco AS; *Int'l*, pg. 4255
KONGSBERG EVOTEC AS—See Kongsberg Gruppen ASA; *Int'l*, pg. 4255
KONGSBERG GEOACOUSTICS PTE. LTD.—See Kongsberg Gruppen ASA; *Int'l*, pg. 4255
KONGSBERG GRUPPEN ASA BUSINESS DEVELOPMENT—See Kongsberg Gruppen ASA; *Int'l*, pg. 4255
KONGSBERG GRUPPEN ASA; *Int'l*, pg. 4255

KONGSBERG INC—See Kongsberg Automotive ASA; *Int'l*, pg. 4254
KONGSBERG INTEGRATED TACTICAL SYSTEMS INC.—See Kongsberg Gruppen ASA; *Int'l*, pg. 4255
KONGSBERG INTERIOR SYSTEMS KFT—See Kongsberg Automotive ASA; *Int'l*, pg. 4254
KONGSBERG INTERIOR SYSTEMS S. DE RL DE CV—See Kongsberg Automotive ASA; *Int'l*, pg. 4254
KONGSBERG MARITIME AS—See Kongsberg Gruppen ASA; *Int'l*, pg. 4255
KONGSBERG MARITIME CANADA LTD.—See Kongsberg Gruppen ASA; *Int'l*, pg. 4255
KONGSBERG MARITIME CHINA (JIANGSU) LTD.—See Kongsberg Gruppen ASA; *Int'l*, pg. 4255
KONGSBERG MARITIME CHINA LTD.—See Kongsberg Gruppen ASA; *Int'l*, pg. 4255
KONGSBERG MARITIME CM KOREA LTD.—See Kongsberg Gruppen ASA; *Int'l*, pg. 4256
KONGSBERG MARITIME DENMARK A/S—See Kongsberg Gruppen ASA; *Int'l*, pg. 4256
KONGSBERG MARITIME DO BRASIL S.A.—See Kongsberg Gruppen ASA; *Int'l*, pg. 4256
KONGSBERG MARITIME ENGINEERING AS—See Kongsberg Gruppen ASA; *Int'l*, pg. 4255
KONGSBERG MARITIME FRANCE S.A.R.L.—See Kongsberg Gruppen ASA; *Int'l*, pg. 4255
KONGSBERG MARITIME GMBH—See Kongsberg Gruppen ASA; *Int'l*, pg. 4255
KONGSBERG MARITIME HELLAS SA—See Kongsberg Gruppen ASA; *Int'l*, pg. 4255
KONGSBERG MARITIME HOI TUNG HOLDING LTD.—See Kongsberg Gruppen ASA; *Int'l*, pg. 4255
KONGSBERG MARITIME HOLLAND BV—See Kongsberg Gruppen ASA; *Int'l*, pg. 4255
KONGSBERG MARITIME INC.—See Kongsberg Gruppen ASA; *Int'l*, pg. 4255
KONGSBERG MARITIME INDIA PVT. LTD.—See Kongsberg Gruppen ASA; *Int'l*, pg. 4256
KONGSBERG MARITIME JAPAN CO. LTD.—See Kongsberg Gruppen ASA; *Int'l*, pg. 4256
KONGSBERG MARITIME KOREA LTD.—See Kongsberg Gruppen ASA; *Int'l*, pg. 4256
KONGSBERG MARITIME LTD.—See Kongsberg Gruppen ASA; *Int'l*, pg. 4256
KONGSBERG MARITIME MEXICO S.A.DE C.V.—See Kongsberg Gruppen ASA; *Int'l*, pg. 4256
KONGSBERG MARITIME MIDDLE EAST DMCCO—See Kongsberg Gruppen ASA; *Int'l*, pg. 4256
KONGSBERG MARITIME NAMIBIA PTY. LTD.—See Kongsberg Gruppen ASA; *Int'l*, pg. 4256
KONGSBERG MARITIME NETHERLANDS B.V.—See Kongsberg Gruppen ASA; *Int'l*, pg. 4256
KONGSBERG MARITIME POLAND SP. Z.O.O—See Kongsberg Gruppen ASA; *Int'l*, pg. 4256
KONGSBERG MARITIME PTE. LTD.—See Kongsberg Gruppen ASA; *Int'l*, pg. 4256
KONGSBERG MARITIME SIMULATION INC.—See Kongsberg Gruppen ASA; *Int'l*, pg. 4256
KONGSBERG MARITIME SIMULATION LTD.—See Kongsberg Gruppen ASA; *Int'l*, pg. 4256
KONGSBERG MARITIME SRL.—See Kongsberg Gruppen ASA; *Int'l*, pg. 4256
KONGSBERG MARITIME SWEDEN AB—See Kongsberg Gruppen ASA; *Int'l*, pg. 4256
KONGSBERG MARITIME TURKEY DENIZCILIK SANAYI VE TICARET LIMITED—See Kongsberg Gruppen ASA; *Int'l*, pg. 4256
KONGSBERG MESOTECH LTD.—See Kongsberg Gruppen ASA; *Int'l*, pg. 4256
KONGSBERG NAERINGSEIENDOM AS—See Kongsberg Gruppen ASA; *Int'l*, pg. 4256
KONGSBERG NORCONTROL IT AS—See Kongsberg Gruppen ASA; *Int'l*, pg. 4255
KONGSBERG NORCONTROL IT PTY. LTD.—See Kongsberg Gruppen ASA; *Int'l*, pg. 4255
KONGSBERG NORCONTROL LIMITED—See Kongsberg Gruppen ASA; *Int'l*, pg. 4255
KONGSBERG NORCONTROL PTE. LTD—See Kongsberg Gruppen ASA; *Int'l*, pg. 4255
KONGSBERG NORCONTROL SURVEILLANCE PVT. LTD.—See Kongsberg Gruppen ASA; *Int'l*, pg. 4255
KONGSBERG OIL & GAS TECHNOLOGIES AS—See Kongsberg Gruppen ASA; *Int'l*, pg. 4256
KONGSBERG OIL & GAS TECHNOLOGIES INC.—See Kongsberg Gruppen ASA; *Int'l*, pg. 4256
KONGSBERG OIL & GAS TECHNOLOGIES LTD.—See Kongsberg Gruppen ASA; *Int'l*, pg. 4256
KONGSBERG OIL & GAS TECHNOLOGIES PVT LTD.—See Kongsberg Gruppen ASA; *Int'l*, pg. 4256
KONGSBERG POWER PRODUCTS SYSTEMS AB—See Kongsberg Automotive ASA; *Int'l*, pg. 4254
KONGSBERG POWER PRODUCTS SYSTEMS SRL—See Kongsberg Automotive ASA; *Int'l*, pg. 4254
KONGSBERG PROCESS SIMULATION PVT LTD.—See Kongsberg Gruppen ASA; *Int'l*, pg. 4256
KONGSBERG PROTECH SYSTEMS AUSTRALIA PTY LTD.—See Kongsberg Gruppen ASA; *Int'l*, pg. 4256

KONGSBERG PROTECH SYSTEMS USA CORPORATION INC.—See Kongsberg Gruppen ASA; *Int'l*, pg. 4256
KONGSBERG PROTECH SYSTEMS USA CORPORATION—See Kongsberg Gruppen ASA; *Int'l*, pg. 4255
KONGSBERG RAUFOSS DISTRIBUTION SAS—See Kongsberg Automotive ASA; *Int'l*, pg. 4254
KONGSBERG SEATEX AS—See Kongsberg Gruppen ASA; *Int'l*, pg. 4256
KONGSBERG SPACETEC AS—See Kongsberg Gruppen ASA; *Int'l*, pg. 4255
KONGSBERG SRL—See Kongsberg Automotive ASA; *Int'l*, pg. 4254
KONGSBERG TEKNOLOGIPARK AS—See Kongsberg Gruppen ASA; *Int'l*, pg. 4256
KONGSKILDE HOWARD FRANCE S.A.—See Kongskilde Industries A/S; *Int'l*, pg. 4257
KONGSKILDE IBERICA, S.A.—See Kongskilde Industries A/S; *Int'l*, pg. 4257
KONGSKILDE INDUSTRIES A/S; *Int'l*, pg. 4257
KONGSKILDE INDUSTRIES INC.—See Kongskilde Industries A/S; *Int'l*, pg. 4257
KONGSKILDE INDUSTRIETECHNIK GMBH—See Kongskilde Industries A/S; *Int'l*, pg. 4257
KONGSKILDE POLSKA SPOLKA Z O.O.—See Kongskilde Industries A/S; *Int'l*, pg. 4257
KONGSKILDE RUS LLC—See Kongskilde Industries A/S; *Int'l*, pg. 4257
KONG SUN HOLDINGS LIMITED; *Int'l*, pg. 4253
KONG-TV, INC.—See TEGNA Inc.; *U.S. Public*, pg. 1990
KONG YOUNG INDUSTRIAL CO., LTD.—See Korea Electric Terminal Co., Ltd.; *Int'l*, pg. 4284
KONGZHONG CORPORATION; *Int'l*, pg. 4257
KONIAG INC.; *U.S. Private*, pg. 2342
KONI BV—See ITT Inc.; *U.S. Public*, pg. 1178
KONICA MINOLTA BALTIA UAB—See Konica Minolta, Inc.; *Int'l*, pg. 4257
KONICA MINOLTA BIZCOM CO., LTD.—See Konica Minolta, Inc.; *Int'l*, pg. 4257
KONICA MINOLTA BUSINESS ASSOCIATES CO., LTD.—See Konica Minolta, Inc.; *Int'l*, pg. 4257
KONICA MINOLTA BUSINESS EXPERT, INC.—See Konica Minolta, Inc.; *Int'l*, pg. 4257
KONICA MINOLTA BUSINESS SOLUTIONS AUSTRALIA PTY. LTD.—See Konica Minolta, Inc.; *Int'l*, pg. 4257
KONICA MINOLTA BUSINESS SOLUTIONS AUSTRIA GMBH—See Konica Minolta, Inc.; *Int'l*, pg. 4257
KONICA MINOLTA BUSINESS SOLUTIONS (BELGIUM) N.V.—See Konica Minolta, Inc.; *Int'l*, pg. 4257
KONICA MINOLTA BUSINESS SOLUTIONS (CANADA) LTD.—See Konica Minolta, Inc.; *Int'l*, pg. 4257
KONICA MINOLTA BUSINESS SOLUTIONS (CHINA) CO., LTD.—See Konica Minolta, Inc.; *Int'l*, pg. 4257
KONICA MINOLTA BUSINESS SOLUTIONS CZECH SPOL. S.R.O.—See Konica Minolta, Inc.; *Int'l*, pg. 4258
KONICA MINOLTA BUSINESS SOLUTIONS DE MEXICO SA DE C.V.—See Konica Minolta, Inc.; *Int'l*, pg. 4259
KONICA MINOLTA BUSINESS SOLUTIONS DENMARK A/S—See Konica Minolta, Inc.; *Int'l*, pg. 4258
KONICA MINOLTA BUSINESS SOLUTIONS DEUTSCHLAND GMBH—See Konica Minolta, Inc.; *Int'l*, pg. 4257
KONICA MINOLTA BUSINESS SOLUTIONS DO BRASIL LTDA.—See Konica Minolta, Inc.; *Int'l*, pg. 4259
KONICA MINOLTA BUSINESS SOLUTIONS EAST LTD.—See Konica Minolta, Inc.; *Int'l*, pg. 4258
KONICA MINOLTA BUSINESS SOLUTIONS EUROPE GMBH—See Konica Minolta, Inc.; *Int'l*, pg. 4257
KONICA MINOLTA BUSINESS SOLUTIONS FINLAND OY—See Konica Minolta, Inc.; *Int'l*, pg. 4258
KONICA MINOLTA BUSINESS SOLUTIONS FRANCE S.A.S.—See Konica Minolta, Inc.; *Int'l*, pg. 4258
KONICA MINOLTA BUSINESS SOLUTIONS (HK) LTD.—See Konica Minolta, Inc.; *Int'l*, pg. 4257
KONICA MINOLTA BUSINESS SOLUTIONS ITALIA S.P.A.—See Konica Minolta, Inc.; *Int'l*, pg. 4258
KONICA MINOLTA BUSINESS SOLUTIONS JAPAN CO., LTD.—See Konica Minolta, Inc.; *Int'l*, pg. 4258
KONICA MINOLTA BUSINESS SOLUTIONS (M) SDN. BHD.—See Konica Minolta, Inc.; *Int'l*, pg. 4257
KONICA MINOLTA BUSINESS SOLUTIONS NETHERLANDS B.V.—See Konica Minolta, Inc.; *Int'l*, pg. 4258
KONICA MINOLTA BUSINESS SOLUTIONS NEW ZEALAND LTD.—See FUJIFILM Holdings Corporation; *Int'l*, pg. 2825
KONICA MINOLTA BUSINESS SOLUTIONS NORWAY AS—See Konica Minolta, Inc.; *Int'l*, pg. 4258
KONICA MINOLTA BUSINESS SOLUTIONS POLSKA S.P.Z.O.O.—See Konica Minolta, Inc.; *Int'l*, pg. 4258
KONICA MINOLTA BUSINESS SOLUTIONS PORTUGAL LDA.—See Konica Minolta, Inc.; *Int'l*, pg. 4258
KONICA MINOLTA BUSINESS SOLUTIONS ROMANIA S.R.L.—See Konica Minolta, Inc.; *Int'l*, pg. 4258
KONICA MINOLTA BUSINESS SOLUTIONS RUSSIA LLC—See Konica Minolta, Inc.; *Int'l*, pg. 4258
KONICA MINOLTA BUSINESS SOLUTIONS SLOVENIA D.O.O.—See Konica Minolta, Inc.; *Int'l*, pg. 4258

KONIAG INC.

KONICA MINOLTA BUSINESS SOLUTIONS—See Konica Minolta, Inc.; *Int'l*, pg. 4258
KONICA MINOLTA BUSINESS SOLUTIONS SPAIN S.A.—See Konica Minolta, Inc.; *Int'l*, pg. 4258
KONICA MINOLTA BUSINESS SOLUTIONS (S) PTE. LTD.—See Konica Minolta, Inc.; *Int'l*, pg. 4257
KONICA MINOLTA BUSINESS SOLUTIONS SWEDEN AB—See Konica Minolta, Inc.; *Int'l*, pg. 4257
KONICA MINOLTA BUSINESS SOLUTIONS (UK) LTD.—See Konica Minolta, Inc.; *Int'l*, pg. 4257
KONICA MINOLTA BUSINESS SOLUTIONS USA, INC.—See Konica Minolta, Inc.; *Int'l*, pg. 4258
KONICA MINOLTA BUSINESS TECHNOLOGIES (DONGGUAN) CO., LTD.—See Konica Minolta, Inc.; *Int'l*, pg. 4259
KONICA MINOLTA BUSINESS TECHNOLOGIES, INC.—See Konica Minolta, Inc.; *Int'l*, pg. 4259
KONICA MINOLTA BUSINESS TECHNOLOGIES MANUFACTURING (HK) LTD.—See Konica Minolta, Inc.; *Int'l*, pg. 4259
KONICA MINOLTA BUSINESS TECHNOLOGIES (WUXI) CO., LTD.—See Konica Minolta, Inc.; *Int'l*, pg. 4259
KONICA MINOLTA CHEMICAL CO., LTD.—See Konica Minolta, Inc.; *Int'l*, pg. 4259
KONICA MINOLTA (CHINA) INVESTMENT LTD.—See Konica Minolta, Inc.; *Int'l*, pg. 4257
KONICA MINOLTA CONSULTING (SHENZHEN) CO., LTD.—See Konica Minolta, Inc.; *Int'l*, pg. 4259
KONICA MINOLTA ELECTRONICS CO., LTD.—See Konica Minolta, Inc.; *Int'l*, pg. 4259
KONICA MINOLTA ENGINEERING CO., LTD.—See Konica Minolta, Inc.; *Int'l*, pg. 4259
KONICA MINOLTA EUROPE B.V.—See Konica Minolta, Inc.; *Int'l*, pg. 4258
KONICA MINOLTA GLASS TECH. CO., LTD.—See Konica Minolta, Inc.; *Int'l*, pg. 4259
KONICA MINOLTA GRAPHIC IMAGING USA, INC.—See Konica Minolta, Inc.; *Int'l*, pg. 4258
KONICA MINOLTA HEALTH CARE CO., LTD.—See Konica Minolta, Inc.; *Int'l*, pg. 4259
KONICA MINOLTA HEALTHCARE INDIA, PRIVATE LTD.—See Konica Minolta, Inc.; *Int'l*, pg. 4259
KONICA MINOLTA HEALTH CARE SYSTEM SUPPORT CO., LTD.—See Konica Minolta, Inc.; *Int'l*, pg. 4259
KONICA MINOLTA HUNGARY BUSINESS SOLUTIONS LTD.—See Konica Minolta, Inc.; *Int'l*, pg. 4258
KONICA MINOLTA IJ TECHNOLOGIES, INC.—See Konica Minolta, Inc.; *Int'l*, pg. 4259
KONICA MINOLTA IJ TEXTILE EUROPE S.R.L.—See Konica Minolta, Inc.; *Int'l*, pg. 4259
KONICA MINOLTA, INC.; *Int'l*, pg. 4257
KONICA MINOLTA INFORMATION SYSTEM CO., LTD.—See Konica Minolta, Inc.; *Int'l*, pg. 4259
KONICA MINOLTA INTERNATIONAL TRADING (SHANGHAI) CO., LTD.—See Konica Minolta, Inc.; *Int'l*, pg. 4259
KONICA MINOLTA JAPAN, INC.—See Konica Minolta, Inc.; *Int'l*, pg. 4259
KONICA MINOLTA LOGISTICS CO., LTD.—See Konica Minolta, Inc.; *Int'l*, pg. 4259
KONICA MINOLTA MECHATRONICS CO., LTD.—See Konica Minolta, Inc.; *Int'l*, pg. 4259
KONICA MINOLTA MEDICAL & GRAPHIC IMAGING EUROPE B.V.—See Konica Minolta, Inc.; *Int'l*, pg. 4259
KONICA MINOLTA MEDICAL & GRAPHIC IMAGING EUROPE GMBH—See Konica Minolta, Inc.; *Int'l*, pg. 4259
KONICA MINOLTA MEDICAL & GRAPHIC, INC.—See Konica Minolta, Inc.; *Int'l*, pg. 4259
KONICA MINOLTA MEDICAL & GRAPHIC (SHANGHAI) CO., LTD.—See Konica Minolta, Inc.; *Int'l*, pg. 4259
KONICA MINOLTA MEDICAL IMAGING USA, INC.—See Konica Minolta, Inc.; *Int'l*, pg. 4258
KONICA MINOLTA OFFICE PRODUCTS, INC.—See Konica Minolta, Inc.; *Int'l*, pg. 4258
KONICA MINOLTA OPTICAL PRODUCTS (SHANGHAI) CO., LTD.—See Konica Minolta, Inc.; *Int'l*, pg. 4259
KONICA MINOLTA OPTO (DALIAN) CO., LTD.—See Konica Minolta, Inc.; *Int'l*, pg. 4259
KONICA MINOLTA OPTO DEVICES CO., LTD.—See Konica Minolta, Inc.; *Int'l*, pg. 4259
KONICA MINOLTA OPTO PRODUCTS CO., LTD.—See Konica Minolta, Inc.; *Int'l*, pg. 4259
KONICA MINOLTA PHOTO IMAGING AUSTRIA GMBH—See Konica Minolta, Inc.; *Int'l*, pg. 4258
KONICA MINOLTA PHOTO IMAGING CANADA, INC.—See Konica Minolta, Inc.; *Int'l*, pg. 4259
KONICA MINOLTA PHOTO IMAGING, INC.—See Konica Minolta, Inc.; *Int'l*, pg. 4259
KONICA MINOLTA PHOTO IMAGING, INC.—See Konica Minolta, Inc.; *Int'l*, pg. 4259
KONICA MINOLTA PHOTO IMAGING (THAILAND) CO., LTD.—See Konica Minolta, Inc.; *Int'l*, pg. 4259
KONICA MINOLTA PHOTO IMAGING (UK) LTD.—See Konica Minolta, Inc.; *Int'l*, pg. 4259
KONICA MINOLTA PLANETARIUM CO., LTD.—See Konica Minolta, Inc.; *Int'l*, pg. 4259
KONICA MINOLTA PRINTING SOLUTIONS JAPAN CO., LTD.—See Konica Minolta, Inc.; *Int'l*, pg. 4259

KONICA MINOLTA PRINTING SOLUTIONS USA, INC.—See Konica Minolta, Inc.; *Int'l*, pg. 4258
KONICA MINOLTA SENSING EUROPE B.V.—See Konica Minolta, Inc.; *Int'l*, pg. 4259
KONICA MINOLTA SENSING, INC.—See Konica Minolta, Inc.; *Int'l*, pg. 4260
KONICA MINOLTA SLOVAKIA SPOL. S.R.O.—See Konica Minolta, Inc.; *Int'l*, pg. 4258
KONICA MINOLTA SOFTWARE DEVELOPMENT (DALIAN) CO., LTD.—See Konica Minolta, Inc.; *Int'l*, pg. 4260
KONICA MINOLTA SOFTWARE LABORATORY CO., LTD.—See Konica Minolta, Inc.; *Int'l*, pg. 4260
KONICA MINOLTA SOGO SERVICE CO., LTD.—See Konica Minolta, Inc.; *Int'l*, pg. 4260
KONICA MINOLTA SUPPLIES MANUFACTURING FRANCE S.A.S.—See Konica Minolta, Inc.; *Int'l*, pg. 4260
KONICA MINOLTA SUPPLIES MANUFACTURING KANSAI CO., LTD.—See Konica Minolta, Inc.; *Int'l*, pg. 4260
KONICA MINOLTA SUPPLIES MANUFACTURING U.S.A., INC.—See Konica Minolta, Inc.; *Int'l*, pg. 4260
KONICA MINOLTA TECHNOLOGY CENTER, INC.—See Konica Minolta, Inc.; *Int'l*, pg. 4260
KONICA MINOLTA TECHNOPRODUCTS CO., LTD.—See Konica Minolta, Inc.; *Int'l*, pg. 4260
KONICA MINOLTA TECHNOSEARCH CORPORATION—See Konica Minolta, Inc.; *Int'l*, pg. 4260
KONICA MINOLTA UKRAINE—See Konica Minolta, Inc.; *Int'l*, pg. 4260
KONIC GLORY CO., LTD.; *Int'l*, pg. 4257
KONIG LUDWIG GMBH & CO. KG SCHLOSSBRAUEREI KALTENBERG—See Warsteiner Brauerei Haus Cramer KG; *Int'l*, pg. 8346
KONIGSFURT URANIA VERLAG GMBH—See Cartamundi N.V.; *Int'l*, pg. 1348
KONIGSWARTER & EBELL CHEMISCHE FABRIK GMBH—See TIB Chemicals AG; *Int'l*, pg. 7742
KONI NA LLC—See ITT Inc.; *U.S. Public*, pg. 1178
KONING & HARTMAN BV—See VINCI S.A.; *Int'l*, pg. 8223
KONING RESTAURANTS INTERNATIONAL, LTD.; *U.S. Private*, pg. 2342
KONINGSHOF, B.V.—See Minor International PCL; *Int'l*, pg. 4911
KONINKLIJKE AHOLD DELHAIZE N.V.; *Int'l*, pg. 4260
KONINKLIJKE AHREND N.V.—See HAL Trust N.V.; *Int'l*, pg. 3223
KONINKLIJKE BAM GROEP N.V.; *Int'l*, pg. 4261
KONINKLIJKE BRILL N.V.; *Int'l*, pg. 4261
KONINKLIJKE DELFTSCH AARDEWERKFABRIEK N.V.; *Int'l*, pg. 4261
KONINKLIJKE DE RUIJTER BV—See 3G Capital Inc.; *U.S. Private*, pg. 9
KONINKLIJKE DE RUIJTER BV—See Berkshire Hathaway Inc.; *U.S. Public*, pg. 317
KONINKLIJKE DIRKZWAGER B.V.—See Electricite de France S.A.; *Int'l*, pg. 2351
KONINKLIJKE DOUWE EGBERTS B.V.—See JAB Holding Company S.a.r.l.; *Int'l*, pg. 3862
KONINKLIJKE DSM N.V.; *Int'l*, pg. 4262
KONINKLIJKE FRIESLANDCAMPINA N.V.—See Zuivelcooperatie FrieslandCampina U.A.; *Int'l*, pg. 8694
KONINKLIJKE GAZELLE N.V.—See Pon Holdings B.V.; *Int'l*, pg. 5918
KONINKLIJKE GROLSCH N.V.—See Asahi Group Holdings Ltd.; *Int'l*, pg. 593
KONINKLIJKE HASKONINGDHV GROEP B.V.; *Int'l*, pg. 4266
KONINKLIJKE JUMBO BV; *Int'l*, pg. 4266
KONINKLIJKE KPN N.V.; *Int'l*, pg. 4266
KONINKLIJKE LUCHTVAART MAATSCHAPPIJ N.V.; *Int'l*, pg. 4267
KONINKLIJKE MOSA BV.—See Egeria Capital Management B.V.; *Int'l*, pg. 2323
KONINKLIJKE NEDSCHROEF HOLDING B.V.—See Shanghai Electric Group Company Limited; *Int'l*, pg. 6766
KONINKLIJKE PEIJNENBURG B.V.—See Lotus Bakeries N.V.; *Int'l*, pg. 4561
KONINKLIJKE PEITSMAN B.V.—See Mohawk Industries, Inc.; *U.S. Public*, pg. 1457
KONINKLIJKE PHILIPS N.V.; *Int'l*, pg. 4267
KONINKLIJKE POSTNL BV—See PostNL N.V.; *Int'l*, pg. 5940
KONINKLIJKE SANDERS BV—See 3i Group plc; *Int'l*, pg. 9
KONINKLIJKE TEN CATE, B.V.—See ABN AMRO Group N.V.; *Int'l*, pg. 64
KONINKLIJKE TEN CATE, B.V.—See Gilde Buy Out Partners B.V.; *Int'l*, pg. 2974
KONINKLIJKE TEN CATE, B.V.—See Parcom Capital Management B.V.; *Int'l*, pg. 5740
KONINKLIJKE VOLKERWESSELS N.V.; *Int'l*, pg. 4271
KONINKLIJKE VOPAK N.V.; *Int'l*, pg. 4272
KONINKLIJKE WEGENER B.V.—See DPG Media Group NV; *Int'l*, pg. 2188
KONINKLIJKE WEGENER N.V.—See DPG Media Group NV; *Int'l*, pg. 2188

CORPORATE AFFILIATIONS

KONINKLIJKE WOHRMANN B.V.—See Chevrillon Philippe Industrie; *Int'l*, pg. 1474
KONI NORTH AMERICA, INC.—See ITT Inc.; *U.S. Public*, pg. 1178
KONISHI CO., LTD.; *Int'l*, pg. 4273
KONISHI MEDICAL INSTRUMENTS CO., LTD.—See Ship Healthcare Holdings, Inc.; *Int'l*, pg. 6852
KONKA GROUP CO., LTD.; *Int'l*, pg. 4274
KONKAN LNG LIMITED—See GAIL (India) Limited; *Int'l*, pg. 2869
KONKOLA COPPER MINES PLC—See Vedanta Resources Ltd.; *Int'l*, pg. 8145
KONKRIT UTARA SDN. BHD.—See Oriental Holdings Berhad; *Int'l*, pg. 5624
KONNDOR INDUSTRIES LIMITED; *Int'l*, pg. 4274
KONOHANA TRANSPORT CO., LTD.—See Konoike Transport Co., Ltd.; *Int'l*, pg. 4275
KONOIKE AIR PORT SERVICE CO., LTD.—See Konoike Transport Co., Ltd.; *Int'l*, pg. 4275
KONOIKE ASIA (CAMBODIA) CO., LTD.—See Konoike Transport Co., Ltd.; *Int'l*, pg. 4275
KONOIKE ASIA (INDIA) PVT. LTD.—See Konoike Transport Co., Ltd.; *Int'l*, pg. 4274
KONOIKE ASIA(JIANGSU) CO., LTD.—See Konoike Transport Co., Ltd.; *Int'l*, pg. 4274
KONOIKE ASIA (MYANMAR) CO., LTD—See Konoike Transport Co., Ltd.; *Int'l*, pg. 4274
KONOIKE ASIA (THAILAND) CO., LTD.—See Konoike Transport Co., Ltd.; *Int'l*, pg. 4274
KONOIKE CONSTRUCTION CO., LTD.—See Sekisui House, Ltd.; *Int'l*, pg. 6697
KONOIKE COOL LOGISTICS (THAILAND) CO., LTD.—See Konoike Transport Co., Ltd.; *Int'l*, pg. 4275
KONOIKE COOL LOGISTICS TOHOKU CO., LTD.—See Konoike Transport Co., Ltd.; *Int'l*, pg. 4275
KONOIKE CORPORATE SERVICE CO., LTD.—See Konoike Transport Co., Ltd.; *Int'l*, pg. 4275
KONOIKE ENGINEERING CO., LTD—See Konoike Transport Co., Ltd.; *Int'l*, pg. 4275
KONOIKE-E STREET, INC.—See Konoike Transport Co., Ltd.; *Int'l*, pg. 4274
KONOIKE-EURO LOGISTICS (BANGLADESH) LTD.—See Konoike Transport Co., Ltd.; *Int'l*, pg. 4275
KONOIKE EXPRESS CO., LTD.—See Konoike Transport Co., Ltd.; *Int'l*, pg. 4274
KONOIKE EXPRESS (THAILAND) CO., LTD.—See Konoike Transport Co., Ltd.; *Int'l*, pg. 4274
KONOIKE-GENERAL, INC.—See Konoike Transport Co., Ltd.; *Int'l*, pg. 4274
KONOIKE IT SOLUTIONS CO., LTD.—See Konoike Transport Co., Ltd.; *Int'l*, pg. 4275
KONOIKE J.TRANSPORT (THAILAND) CO., LTD.—See Konoike Transport Co., Ltd.; *Int'l*, pg. 4275
KONOIKE LOGISTICS (SHANGHAI) CO., LTD.—See Konoike Transport Co., Ltd.; *Int'l*, pg. 4274
KONOIKE LOGISTICS (SHENZHEN) CO., LTD.—See Konoike Transport Co., Ltd.; *Int'l*, pg. 4275
KONOIKE MEDICAL CO., LTD.—See Konoike Transport Co., Ltd.; *Int'l*, pg. 4274
KONOIKE MEXICO S.A, DE C.V—See Konoike Transport Co., Ltd.; *Int'l*, pg. 4274
KONOIKE MYANMAR CO., LTD.—See Konoike Transport Co., Ltd.; *Int'l*, pg. 4275
KONOIKE-PACIFIC CALIFORNIA, INC.—See Konoike Transport Co., Ltd.; *Int'l*, pg. 4275
KONOIKE SHIPPING CO., LTD.—See Konoike Transport Co., Ltd.; *Int'l*, pg. 4274
KONOIKE SKY SUPPORT CO., LTD.—See Konoike Transport Co., Ltd.; *Int'l*, pg. 4275
KONOIKE-SOTUS VENTURE CO., LTD—See Konoike Transport Co., Ltd.; *Int'l*, pg. 4274
KONOIKE TRANSPORT CO., LTD.; *Int'l*, pg. 4274
KONOIKE TRANSPORT & ENGINEERING (H.K.) LTD.—See Konoike Transport Co., Ltd.; *Int'l*, pg. 4274
KONOIKE TRANSPORT & ENGINEERING (S) PTE LTD.—See Konoike Transport Co., Ltd.; *Int'l*, pg. 4274
KONOIKE TRANSPORT & ENGINEERING (USA), INC.—See Konoike Transport Co., Ltd.; *Int'l*, pg. 4274
KONOIKE VINATRANS LOGISTICS CO., LTD—See Konoike Transport Co., Ltd.; *Int'l*, pg. 4274
KONOSHIMA CHEMICAL CO., LTD.; *Int'l*, pg. 4275
KONOSHIMA CHEMICAL CO., LTD. - TAKUMA FACTORY—See Konoshima Chemical Co., Ltd.; *Int'l*, pg. 4275
KONOVER COMMERCIAL CORPORATION—See The Simon Konover Company; *U.S. Private*, pg. 4118
KONOVER HOTEL CORPORATION—See The Simon Konover Company; *U.S. Private*, pg. 4118
KONOVER RESIDENTIAL CORPORATION—See The Simon Konover Company; *U.S. Private*, pg. 4118
KONOVER SOUTH, LLC—See The Simon Konover Company; *U.S. Private*, pg. 4118
KONPLAN S.R.O.—See Krones AG; *Int'l*, pg. 4305
KONRAD BEYER & CO SPEZIALBAU GMBH—See ALPINE Bau GmbH; *Int'l*, pg. 371
KONRAD HORNSCHUCH AG—See Continental Aktiengesellschaft; *Int'l*, pg. 1780
KONRAD MERKT GMBH; *Int'l*, pg. 4275

KONRAD REITZ VENTILATOREN GMBH & CO. KG; *Int'l*, pg. 4275
KONRAD SCHAFER GMBH—See INDUS Holding AG; *Int'l*, pg. 3663
KONRAD WITTWER GMBH; *Int'l*, pg. 4275
KONSBERG NORSPACE AS—See Kongsberg Gruppen ASA; *Int'l*, pg. 4256
KONSEPTI OY; *Int'l*, pg. 4275
KONSORCJUM STALI S.A.; *Int'l*, pg. 4275
KONSORTIUM BAS EKSPRES SEMENANJUNG (M) SDN. BHD.—See One Glove Group Berhad; *Int'l*, pg. 5575
KONSORTIUM LEBUHRAYA BUTTERWORTH-KULIM SDN BHD—See Khazanah Nasional Berhad; *Int'l*, pg. 4153
KONSORTIUM LOGISTIK BERHAD—See DRB-HICOM Berhad; *Int'l*, pg. 2201
KONSORTIUM PELABUHAN KEMAMAN SDN. BHD.—See Terengganu Incorporated Sdn. Bhd.; *Int'l*, pg. 7564
KONSORTIUM TRANSNASIONAL BERHAD; *Int'l*, pg. 4275
KONSTANCE PNEUMATICS—See Penn-Air & Hydraulics Corp.; *U.S. Private*, pg. 3135
KONSUL INKASSO GMBH—See Deutsche Bank Aktiengesellschaft; *Int'l*, pg. 2061
KONSULTBOLAG1 SYD AB—See AFRY AB; *Int'l*, pg. 194
KONSYL PHARMACEUTICALS INC.—See ICC Industries, Inc.; *U.S. Private*, pg. 2030
K-ON SYSTEMS, INC.—See Ship Healthcare Holdings, Inc.; *Int'l*, pg. 6852
KONTAFARMA CHINA HOLDINGS LIMITED; *Int'l*, pg. 4276
KONTAGENT INC.; *U.S. Private*, pg. 2342
KONTAK MANUFACTURING CO. LTD.—See General Electric Company; *U.S. Public*, pg. 918
KONTALI ANALYSE AS—See Arendals Fossekompani ASA; *Int'l*, pg. 559
KONTASET KFT.; *Int'l*, pg. 4276
KONTEIN, UNA DIVISION DE SIGMA, S. A. DE C.V.—See Sigma S.A. de C.V.; *Int'l*, pg. 6908
KONTENA NASIONAL BERHAD—See MMC Corporation Berhad; *Int'l*, pg. 5005
KONTEXT DRUCKEREI GMBH—See voestalpine AG; *Int'l*, pg. 8295
KONTIGO CARE AB; *Int'l*, pg. 4276
KONTIKAB AB—See Investment AB Latour; *Int'l*, pg. 3782
KONTINENTALE BAUGESELLSCHAFT M.B.H.—See Swietelsky Baugesellschaft m.b.H.; *Int'l*, pg. 7367
KONTINENT-EMO-TRANS GMBH—See Kontinent Spedition GmbH; *Int'l*, pg. 4276
KONTINENT SPEDITION GMBH; *Int'l*, pg. 4276
KONTO D.O.O.; *Int'l*, pg. 4276
KONTOOR BRANDS, INC.; *U.S. Public*, pg. 1271
KONTORA FAMILY OFFICE GMBH—See Cerberus Capital Management, L.P.; *U.S. Private*, pg. 838
KONTORA FAMILY OFFICE GMBH—See GoldenTree Asset Management LP; *U.S. Private*, pg. 1734
KONTORA FAMILY OFFICE GMBH—See J.C. Flowers & Co. LLC; *U.S. Private*, pg. 2159
KONTOR NEW MEDIA GMBH—See Edel SE & Co. KGaA; *Int'l*, pg. 2305
KONTOR RECORDS GMBH—See Edel SE & Co. KGaA; *Int'l*, pg. 2305
KONTOR SPACE LIMITED; *Int'l*, pg. 4276
KONTOUR XIAN MEDICAL TECHNOLOGY CO., LTD.; *Int'l*, pg. 4276
KONTRAM OY—See Indutrade AB; *Int'l*, pg. 3680
KONTRA—See Mohammed Jalal & Sons WLL; *Int'l*, pg. 5018
KONTROL BUILDINGS INC.—See Kontrol Technologies Corp.; *Int'l*, pg. 4276
KONTROLFREEK, LLC—See SteelSeries ApS; *Int'l*, pg. 7190
KONTROLLAUTOMATIK SVENSKA AB—See Indutrade AB; *Int'l*, pg. 3680
KONTROLMATIK TEKNOLOJI ENERJI VE MUHENDISLIK A.S.; *Int'l*, pg. 4276
KONTROL TECHNOLOGIES CORP.; *Int'l*, pg. 4276
KONTRON AG; *Int'l*, pg. 4276
KONTRON AIS GMBH—See Kontron AG; *Int'l*, pg. 4277
KONTRON AMERICA INC.—See Kontron AG; *Int'l*, pg. 4277
KONTRON ASIA INC.—See Kontron AG; *Int'l*, pg. 4277
KONTRON AUSTRIA GMBH—See Kontron AG; *Int'l*, pg. 4277
KONTRON CANADA—See Kontron AG; *Int'l*, pg. 4277
KONTRON ELECTRONICS AG—See Kontron AG; *Int'l*, pg. 4277
KONTRON ELECTRONICS GMBH—See Kontron AG; *Int'l*, pg. 4277
KONTRON EMBEDDED COMPUTERS GMBH—See Kontron AG; *Int'l*, pg. 4277
KONTRON EUROPE GMBH—See Kontron AG; *Int'l*, pg. 4277
KONTRON MODULAR COMPUTERS S.A.—See Kontron AG; *Int'l*, pg. 4277
KONTRON S&T AG—See Kontron AG; *Int'l*, pg. 4277
KONTRON TECHNOLOGIES GMBH—See Kontron AG; *Int'l*, pg. 4277
KONTRON TRANSPORTATION GMBH—See Kontron AG; *Int'l*, pg. 4277
KON TUM SUGAR JOINT STOCK COMPANY; *Int'l*, pg. 4244
KONTUUR-LEO BURNETT—See Publicis Groupe S.A.; *Int'l*, pg. 6100
KONVEI KOMPETANSESENTER AS—See Inin Group AS; *Int'l*, pg. 3703
KONXIN TRADE CO., LTD.—See Korea Electric Terminal Co., *Int'l*, pg. 4284
KONYA CIMENTO SANAYII AS; *Int'l*, pg. 4278
KONYA CIMENTO—See Vicat S.A.; *Int'l*, pg. 8186
KONYA HAZIR BETON SANAYI VE TICARET A.S.—See Vicat S.A.; *Int'l*, pg. 8186
KONYA KAGIT SAN. VE TIC. A.S.—See Bera Holding A.S.; *Int'l*, pg. 978
KONYA PETROL A.S.—See Bera Holding A.S.; *Int'l*, pg. 978
KONY, INC.—See Temenos AG; *Int'l*, pg. 7554
KONY INDIA PRIVATE LIMITED—See Temenos AG; *Int'l*, pg. 7554
KONY SOLUTIONS, INC.; *U.S. Private*, pg. 2343
KONZA VALLEY CAPITAL INC.; *U.S. Private*, pg. 2343
KONZERN US HOLDING CORPORATION—See CHINA MEDICINE CORPORATION; *Int'l*, pg. 1518
KONZUL D.O.O.—See Ameropa AG; *Int'l*, pg. 424
KOOEE COMMUNICATIONS PTY LTD—See CK Hutchison Holdings Limited; *Int'l*, pg. 1638
KOOEE COMMUNICATIONS PTY LTD—See Vodafone Group Plc; *Int'l*, pg. 8285
KOOEE PTY LTD—See CK Hutchison Holdings Limited; *Int'l*, pg. 1638
KOOEE PTY LTD—See Vodafone Group Plc; *Int'l*, pg. 8285
KOOKABURRA CONTAINERS PTY LIMITED—See United Rentals, Inc.; *U.S. Public*, pg. 2235
KOOKJE ELECTRIC KOREA CO., LTD.—See KKR & Co. Inc.; *U.S. Public*, pg. 1257
KOOKMIN BANK CAMBODIA PLC.—See KB Financial Group Inc.; *Int'l*, pg. 4104
KOOKMIN BANK HONG KONG LIMITED—See KB Financial Group Inc.; *Int'l*, pg. 4104
KOOKMIN BANK—See KB Financial Group Inc.; *Int'l*, pg. 4104
KOOK SOON DANG CO LTD; *Int'l*, pg. 4278
KOOL2PLAY SA; *Int'l*, pg. 4278
KOOLAN IRON ORE PTY LTD—See Mount Gibson Iron Limited; *Int'l*, pg. 5056
KOOLANT KOOLERS INC.—See The Glen Dimplex Group; *Int'l*, pg. 7650
KOOL AUTOMOTIVE; *U.S. Private*, pg. 2343
KOOL CHEVROLET, OLDSMOBILE, CADILLAC, INC.; *U.S. Private*, pg. 2343
KOOLE TANKTRANSPORT B.V.—See JPMorgan Chase & Co.; *U.S. Public*, pg. 1209
KOOLSEE NEW MEDIA GROUP LTD.; *Int'l*, pg. 4278
KOOMBER TEA COMPANY LIMITED—See Camellia Plc; *Int'l*, pg. 1271
KOON CONSTRUCTION & TRANSPORT CO., PTE. LTD.—See Koon Holdings Limited; *Int'l*, pg. 4278
KOONENBERRY GOLD LIMITED; *Int'l*, pg. 4278
KOON HOLDINGS LIMITED; *Int'l*, pg. 4278
KOONS FORD INC.; *U.S. Private*, pg. 2343
KOONS LINCOLN MERCURY, INC.; *U.S. Private*, pg. 2343
KOONS OF MANASSAS INC.; *U.S. Private*, pg. 2343
KOONS OF TYSONS CORNER CHEVY CHRYSLER—See Asbury Automotive Group, Inc.; *U.S. Public*, pg. 209
KOONS SILVER SPRING FORD LINCOLN; *U.S. Private*, pg. 2343
KOONS WESTMINSTER TOYOTA; *U.S. Private*, pg. 2343
KOONTZ-WAGNER CUSTOM CONTROLS HOLDINGS, LLC—See The Toronto-Dominion Bank; *Int'l*, pg. 7696
KOONTZ-WAGNER ELECTRIC COMPANY; *U.S. Private*, pg. 2343
KOOPERATIVA FORBUNDET; *Int'l*, pg. 4279
KOOPERATIVA POISFOVNA, A.S.—See Vienna Insurance Group AG Wiener Versicherung Gruppe; *Int'l*, pg. 8195
KOOPERATIVA POJISTOVNA, A.S.—See Vienna Insurance Group AG Wiener Versicherung Gruppe; *Int'l*, pg. 8195
KOOPMAN LUMBER CO. INC.; *U.S. Private*, pg. 2343
KOOPMAN OSTBO; *U.S. Private*, pg. 2343
KOOPS FURNESS N.V.; *Int'l*, pg. 4279
KOOR INDUSTRIES LTD.—See IDB Development Corporation Ltd.; *Int'l*, pg. 3588
KOORSEN PROTECTION SERVICES; *U.S. Private*, pg. 2343
KOOSHAREM, LLC—See Affiliated Managers Group, Inc.; *U.S. Public*, pg. 54
KOOSHAREM, LLC—See Anchorage Capital Group, L.L.C.; *U.S. Private*, pg. 274
KOOTENAY SILVER INC.; *Int'l*, pg. 4279
KOOTENAY ZINC CORP.; *Int'l*, pg. 4279
KOOTH PLC; *Int'l*, pg. 4279
KOOVS PLC; *Int'l*, pg. 4279
KOOY BAKSTEENCENTRUM B.V.—See CRH plc; *Int'l*, pg. 1845
KOOYMAN B.V.; *Int'l*, pg. 4279
KOOZIE GROUP—See Societe BIC S.A.; *Int'l*, pg. 7036
KOPALNIA WAPIENIA CZATOWICE SP. Z O.O.—See Poludniowy Koncern Energetyczny S.A.; *Int'l*, pg. 5913
KOPANO COPIER COMPANY (PTY) LIMITED—See Reunert Limited; *Int'l*, pg. 6312
KOPAONIK A.D.; *Int'l*, pg. 4279
KOPAONIK A.D.; *Int'l*, pg. 4279
KOP-COAT, INC.—See RPM International Inc.; *U.S. Public*, pg. 1819
KOP-COAT NEW ZEALAND LTD.—See RPM International Inc.; *U.S. Public*, pg. 1819
KOPCO INC.; *U.S. Private*, pg. 2343
KOPERASI ANGKATAN TENTERA MALAYSIA BERHAD; *Int'l*, pg. 4279
KOPERNIK DEVELOPMENT SP.Z.O.O.—See Warimpex Finanz- und Beteiligungs AG; *Int'l*, pg. 8345
KOPEX S.A.—See TDJ S.A.; *Int'l*, pg. 7487
KOPFWERK DATENSYSTEME GMBH—See Henry Schein, Inc.; *U.S. Public*, pg. 1027
KOPIER NET—See Perpetual Capital, LLC; *U.S. Private*, pg. 3153
KOPIJYVA OY—See Panostaja Oyj; *Int'l*, pg. 5729
KOPIN CORPORATION; *U.S. Public*, pg. 1271
KOPLA AMERICA INC.—See BGFecomaterials CO., LTD.; *Int'l*, pg. 1007
KOPLAR COMMUNICATIONS INTERNATIONAL, INC.; *U.S. Private*, pg. 2343
KOPLAR PROPERTIES INC—See Koplar Communications International, Inc.; *U.S. Private*, pg. 2343
KOP LIMITED; *Int'l*, pg. 4279
KOPPARBERG BRYGGERI AB; *Int'l*, pg. 4279
KOPPARBERG MINING EXPLORATION AB—See Copperstone Resources AB; *Int'l*, pg. 1794
KOPPER GLO FUEL, INC.—See Quintana Capital Group, L.P.; *U.S. Private*, pg. 3328
KOPPER GLO MINING, LLC; *U.S. Private*, pg. 2343
KOPPERMANN & CO. GMBH; *Int'l*, pg. 4279
KOPPERMANN ITALIA—See Koppermann & Co. GmbH; *Int'l*, pg. 4279
KOPPERS ASHCROFT INC.—See Koppers Holdings Inc.; *U.S. Public*, pg. 1271
KOPPERS DEUTSCHLAND GMBH—See Koppers Holdings Inc.; *U.S. Public*, pg. 1271
KOPPERS HOLDINGS INC.; *U.S. Public*, pg. 1271
KOPPERS INC.—See Koppers Holdings Inc.; *U.S. Public*, pg. 1271
KOPPERS LATVIA SIA—See Koppers Holdings Inc.; *U.S. Public*, pg. 1272
KOPPERS NORWAY AS—See Koppers Holdings Inc.; *U.S. Public*, pg. 1272
KOPPERS PERFORMANCE CHEMICALS AUSTRALIA PTY LTD—See Koppers Holdings Inc.; *U.S. Public*, pg. 1272
KOPPERS PERFORMANCE CHEMICALS INC.—See Koppers Holdings Inc.; *U.S. Public*, pg. 1272
KOPPERS PERFORMANCE CHEMICALS NEW ZEALAND—See Koppers Holdings Inc.; *U.S. Public*, pg. 1272
KOPPERS RAILROAD STRUCTURES INC.—See Koppers Holdings Inc.; *U.S. Public*, pg. 1272
KOPPERS SPECIALTY CHEMICALS LIMITED—See Koppers Holdings Inc.; *U.S. Public*, pg. 1272
KOPPERS SWEDEN AB—See Koppers Holdings Inc.; *U.S. Public*, pg. 1272
KOPPERS (TIANJIN) TRADING CO., LTD.—See Koppers Holdings Inc.; *U.S. Public*, pg. 1271
KOPPERS UK LIMITED—See Koppers Holdings Inc.; *U.S. Public*, pg. 1272
KOPPERS UTILITY & INDUSTRIAL PRODUCTS INC.—See Koppers Holdings Inc.; *U.S. Public*, pg. 1272
KOPPERS WORLDWIDE VENTURES CORPORATION—See Koppers Holdings Inc.; *U.S. Public*, pg. 1272
KOPP GLASS, INC.; *U.S. Public*, pg. 1271
KOPRAN LTD.; *Int'l*, pg. 4279
KOPRAN RESEARCH LABORATORIES LTD.—See Kopran Ltd.; *Int'l*, pg. 4279
KOPRIVNICA OPSKRBA D.O.O.—See RWE AG; *Int'l*, pg. 6434
KOPRIVNICA PLIN D.O.O.—See RWE AG; *Int'l*, pg. 6434
KOPRODUKT A.D.; *Int'l*, pg. 4279
KOPTER GROUP AG—See Leonardo S.p.A.; *Int'l*, pg. 4459
K-OPTICOM CORP.—See The Kansai Electric Power Co., Inc.; *Int'l*, pg. 7661
KOPY GOLDFIELDS AB; *Int'l*, pg. 4279
KOPY KWEEN INCORPORATED; *U.S. Private*, pg. 2343
KORAB RESOURCES LTD.; *Int'l*, pg. 4279
KORADO BULGARIA; *Int'l*, pg. 4280
KORALLE SANITARPRODUKTE GMBH—See Arbonia AG; *Int'l*, pg. 538
KOR ALTA CONSTRUCTION LTD.; *Int'l*, pg. 4279
KORAMCO ENERGY PLUS REIT CO., LTD.; *Int'l*, pg. 4280
KORAMCO THE ONE REIT; *Int'l*, pg. 4280

KORAMCO THE ONE REIT / CORPORATE AFFILIATIONS

KORAMIC2ENGAGE NV—See Koramic Real Estate NV; *Int'l*, pg. 4280
KORAMIC REAL ESTATE NV; *Int'l*, pg. 4280
KORAMIS GMBH—See Zech Group SE; *Int'l*, pg. 8628
KORATRADE MTMC LTD.—See Koc Holding A.S.; *Int'l*, pg. 4223
KORAT THAI TECH COMPANY LIMITED—See Srithai Superware Public Company Limited; *Int'l*, pg. 7151
KORBA WEST POWER COMPANY LIMITED—See Avantha Group; *Int'l*, pg. 735
KORBER AG; *Int'l*, pg. 4280
KORBER MEDIPAK SYSTEMS AG—See Korber AG; *Int'l*, pg. 4281
KORBER MEDIPAK SYSTEMS GMBH—See Korber AG; *Int'l*, pg. 4280
KORBER MEDIPAK SYSTEMS NORTH AMERCIA INC.—See Korber AG; *Int'l*, pg. 4280
KORBER PROCESS SOLUTIONS GMBH—See Korber AG; *Int'l*, pg. 4281
KORBER SCHLEIFRING MACHINERY (SHANGHAI) CO. LTD.—See United Grinding Group AG; *Int'l*, pg. 8067
KORCOM PORTER NOVELLI—See Omnicom Group Inc.; *U.S. Public*, pg. 1591
KORDA KAGIT PAZARLAMA VE TICARET ANONIM IRKETI—See Inapa - Investimentos, Participacoes e Gestao, SA; *Int'l*, pg. 3645
KORDELLOS CH. BROS S.A.; *Int'l*, pg. 4281
KORD HOLDINGS, INC.; *Int'l*, pg. 4281
KORD PARTY FAVOUR MANUFACTORY LTD.—See Kord Holdings, Inc.; *Int'l*, pg. 4281
KORDSA, INC.—See Haci Omer Sabanci Holding A.S.; *Int'l*, pg. 3204
KORDSA TEKNIK TEKSTIL A.S.—See Haci Omer Sabanci Holding A.S.; *Int'l*, pg. 3204
KORD TECHNOLOGIES, INC.—See KBR, Inc.; *U.S. Public*, pg. 1216
KOREA AEROSPACE INDUSTRIES LTD. - SANCHEONG FACTORY—See Korea Aerospace Industries Ltd.; *Int'l*, pg. 4281
KOREA AEROSPACE INDUSTRIES LTD.; *Int'l*, pg. 4281
KOREA AIRPORT SERVICE CO., LTD.; *Int'l*, pg. 4281
KOREA ALCOHOL INDUSTRIAL CO., LTD.; *Int'l*, pg. 4281
KOREA ARLICO PHARM CO., LTD.; *Int'l*, pg. 4282
KOREA ASSET IN TRUST CO LTD; *Int'l*, pg. 4282
KOREA ASSET INVESTMENT SECURITIES CO., LTD.; *Int'l*, pg. 4282
KOREA ATOMIC ENERGY RESEARCH INSTITUTE—See Korea Electric Power Corporation; *Int'l*, pg. 4283
KOREA AUTOGLASS CORPORATION—See KCC GLASS Corporation; *Int'l*, pg. 4109
KOREA CABLE T.V CHUNG-BUK SYSTEM CO., LTD.; *Int'l*, pg. 4282
KOREA CAPTAIN COMPANY LIMITED—See Korea National Oil Corporation; *Int'l*, pg. 4286
KOREA CAST IRON PIPE IND. CO., LTD. - POHANG PLANT—See Korea Cast Iron Pipe Ind. Co., Ltd.; *Int'l*, pg. 4282
KOREA CAST IRON PIPE IND. CO., LTD.; *Int'l*, pg. 4282
KOREA CEMENT CO., LTD.—See Gangdong Industry Co., Ltd.; *Int'l*, pg. 2880
KOREACENTER CO., LTD.; *Int'l*, pg. 4288
KOREA CHINO CORPORATION—See CHINO Corporation; *Int'l*, pg. 1571
KOREA CIRCUIT CO LTD; *Int'l*, pg. 4282
KOREA COMPOSITES INC.—See HANKUK CARBON Co., Ltd.; *Int'l*, pg. 3254
KOREA COMPUTER INC; *Int'l*, pg. 4282
KOREA COMPUTER & SYSTEMS INC; *Int'l*, pg. 4282
KOREA COMPUTER TERMINAL INC.; *Int'l*, pg. 4282
KOREA CONVEYOR IND. CO., LTD.—See Tsubakimoto Chain Co.; *Int'l*, pg. 7953
KOREA CRAWLER TRACK LTD.—See Hoe Leong Corporation Ltd.; *Int'l*, pg. 3439
KOREA CREDIT GUARANTEE FUND; *Int'l*, pg. 4282
KOREA DELPHI AUTOMOTIVE SYSTEMS CORPORATION—See Aptiv PLC; *Int'l*, pg. 525
KOREA DEPOSIT INSURANCE CORPORATION; *Int'l*, pg. 4282
KOREA DEVELOPMENT BANK; *Int'l*, pg. 4282
KOREA DEVELOPMENT CORPORATION—See Daelim Industrial Co., Ltd.; *Int'l*, pg. 1908
KOREA DEVELOPMENT FINANCING CORPORATION; *Int'l*, pg. 4283
KOREA DISTRICT HEATING CORPORATION; *Int'l*, pg. 4283
KOREA DISTRICT HEATING ENGINEERING CO., LTD.—See Korea District Heating Corporation; *Int'l*, pg. 4283
KOREA DRY BEARING CO., LTD.—See Daido Metal Corporation; *Int'l*, pg. 1922
KOREA EAST-WEST POWER CO., LTD.—See Korea Electric Power Corporation; *Int'l*, pg. 4283
THE KOREA ECONOMIC BROADCASTING CO., LTD; *Int'l*, pg. 7663
KOREA ELECTRIC POWER CORPORATION; *Int'l*, pg. 4283
KOREA ELECTRIC POWER CORPORATION—See Korea Electric Power Corporation; *Int'l*, pg. 4283

KOREA ELECTRIC POWER INDUSTRIAL DEVELOPMENT CO., LTD.; *Int'l*, pg. 4284
KOREA ELECTRIC TERMINAL CO., LTD.; *Int'l*, pg. 4284
KOREA ELECTRONIC CERTIFICATION AUTHORITY, INC.; *Int'l*, pg. 4284
KOREA ELECTRONIC MATERIAL CO., LTD.—See Japan Industrial Partners, Inc.; *Int'l*, pg. 3890
KOREA ELECTRO-OPTICS CO., LTD.—See SSNewTech Co., Ltd.; *Int'l*, pg. 7157
KOREA ELECTRO TECHNOLOGY RESEARCH INSTITUTE—See Korea Electric Power Corporation; *Int'l*, pg. 4283
KOREA ENERGY ECONOMICS INSTITUTE; *Int'l*, pg. 4284
KOREA ENGINEERING CO., LTD—See KCTC CO. Ltd; *Int'l*, pg. 4110
KOREA ENGINEERING CONSULTANTS CORP.; *Int'l*, pg. 4284
KOREA ENGINEERING PLASTICS CO., LTD.—See Mitsubishi Gas Chemical Company, Inc.; *Int'l*, pg. 4949
KOREA EXCHANGE BANK (DEUTSCHLAND) AG—See Hana Financial Group, Inc.; *Int'l*, pg. 3241
KOREA EXCHANGE BANK OF CANADA—See Hana Financial Group, Inc.; *Int'l*, pg. 3241
KOREA EXCHANGE; *Int'l*, pg. 4284
KOREA EXCHANGE - STOCK MARKET DIVISION—See Korea Exchange; *Int'l*, pg. 4284
KOREA EXPORT PACKAGING INDUSTRIAL CO., LTD.; *Int'l*, pg. 4284
KOREA EXPRESS EUROPE GMBH—See CJ Corporation; *Int'l*, pg. 1633
KOREA EXPRESS HONG KONG CO., LTD.—See CJ Corporation; *Int'l*, pg. 1633
KOREA EXPRESS JAPAN CO., LTD.—See CJ Corporation; *Int'l*, pg. 1633
KOREA EXPRESS SHANGHAI CO., LTD.—See CJ Corporation; *Int'l*, pg. 1633
KOREA EXPRESS TIANJIN CO., LTD.—See CJ Corporation; *Int'l*, pg. 1633
KOREA EXPRESS U.S.A. INC.—See CJ Corporation; *Int'l*, pg. 1633
KOREA FANUC CORPORATION—See FANUC Corporation; *Int'l*, pg. 2615
KOREA FA SYSTEMS CO., LTD.—See Fuji Electric Co., Ltd.; *Int'l*, pg. 2812
KOREA FLANGE CO., LTD. - NO. 2 FACTORY—See Korea Movenex Co., Ltd; *Int'l*, pg. 4286
KOREA FLANGE CO., LTD. - NO. 3 FACTORY—See Korea Movenex Co., Ltd; *Int'l*, pg. 4286
KOREA FOODIPHARM, CO., LTD—See Korea Kolmar Holdings Co., Ltd; *Int'l*, pg. 4286
KOREA FUEL-TECH CORPORATION - GONGDO FACTORY—See KOREA FUEL-TECH CORPORATION; *Int'l*, pg. 4285
KOREA FUEL-TECH CORPORATION - GYEONGJU FACTORY—See KOREA FUEL-TECH CORPORATION; *Int'l*, pg. 4285
KOREA FUEL-TECH CORPORATION; *Int'l*, pg. 4285
KOREA FURNITURE CO., LTD.; *Int'l*, pg. 4285
KOREA GAS CORPORATION—See Korea Electric Power Corporation; *Int'l*, pg. 4283
KOREA GINSENG (CHINA) CORP.—See KT&G Corporation; *Int'l*, pg. 4316
KOREA GINSENG CORPORATION—See KT&G Corporation; *Int'l*, pg. 4316
KOREA HD BROADCASTING CORP.—See KT Corporation; *Int'l*, pg. 4315
KOREA HEAT TREATMENT CO., LTD.—See Neturen Co., Ltd.; *Int'l*, pg. 5216
THE KOREA HEAVY MACHINERY CO., LTD.—See HNK Machine Tool Co., Ltd.; *Int'l*, pg. 3434
KOREA HOSIDEN ELECTRONICS CO., LTD.—See Hosiden Corporation; *Int'l*, pg. 3484
KOREA HOUGHTON CORPORATION—See Quaker Chemical Corporation; *U.S. Public*, pg. 1746
KOREA HYDRO AND NUCLEAR POWER CO., LTD.—See Korea Electric Power Corporation; *Int'l*, pg. 4283
KOREA INDUSTRIAL CO., LTD.; *Int'l*, pg. 4285
KOREA INDUSTRY—See Sajodongaone Co., Ltd.; *Int'l*, pg. 6486
KOREA INFORMATION CERTIFICATE AUTHORITY, INC.; *Int'l*, pg. 4285
KOREA INFORMATION & COMMUNICATION; *Int'l*, pg. 4285
KOREA INFORMATION ENGINEERING SERVICES CO., LTD.; *Int'l*, pg. 4285
KOREA INOUE KASEI CO., LTD.—See INOAC Corporation; *Int'l*, pg. 3714
KOREA INVESTMENT CAPITAL CO., LTD.—See Korea Investment Holdings Co., Ltd.; *Int'l*, pg. 4285
KOREA INVESTMENT HOLDINGS CO., LTD.; *Int'l*, pg. 4285
KOREA INVESTMENT MANAGEMENT ASIA LIMITED—See Korea Investment Holdings Co., Ltd.; *Int'l*, pg. 4285
KOREA INVESTMENT MUTUAL SAVING BANK CO., LTD.—See Korea Investment Holdings Co., Ltd.; *Int'l*, pg. 4285

KOREA INVESTMENT MUTUAL SAVINGS BANK—See Korea Investment Holdings Co., Ltd.; *Int'l*, pg. 4285
KOREA INVESTMENT PARTNERS CO., LTD.—See Korea Investment Holdings Co., Ltd.; *Int'l*, pg. 4285
KOREA INVESTMENT PRIVATE EQUITY CO. LTD.—See Korea Investment Holdings Co., Ltd.; *Int'l*, pg. 4285
KOREA INVESTMENT & SECURITIES ASIA LIMITED—See Korea Investment Holdings Co., Ltd.; *Int'l*, pg. 4285
KOREA INVESTMENT & SECURITIES CO., LTD.—See Korea Investment Holdings Co., Ltd.; *Int'l*, pg. 4285
KOREA INVESTMENT & SECURITIES EUROPE LIMITED—See Korea Investment Holdings Co., Ltd.; *Int'l*, pg. 4285
KOREA INVESTMENT & SECURITIES SINGAPORE PTE. LTD.—See Korea Investment Holdings Co., Ltd.; *Int'l*, pg. 4285
KOREA INVESTMENT TRUST MANAGEMENT CO., LTD.—See Korea Investment Holdings Co., Ltd.; *Int'l*, pg. 4285
KOREA INVESTMENT VALUE ASSET MANAGEMENT—See Korea Investment Holdings Co., Ltd.; *Int'l*, pg. 4285
KOREA INVESTORS SERVICE, INC.—See Moody's Corporation; *U.S. Public*, pg. 1467
KOREA JOHNSON CO., LTD.—See S.C. Johnson & Son, Inc.; *U.S. Private*, pg. 3516
KOREA KEYENCE CO., LTD.—See Keyence Corporation; *Int'l*, pg. 4145
KOREA KOKUSAI CO., LTD.—See KOKUSAI CO., LTD; *Int'l*, pg. 4231
KOREA KOLMAR CO., LTD.; *Int'l*, pg. 4285
KOREA KOLMAR HOLDINGS CO., LTD; *Int'l*, pg. 4286
KOREA KYONG NAM TAIYO YUDEN CO., LTD—See Taiyo Yuden Company Ltd.; *Int'l*, pg. 7426
KOREA LEASE FINANCING CO., LTD.—See DGB Financial Group Co., Ltd.; *Int'l*, pg. 2096
KOREA LINE CORPORATION; *Int'l*, pg. 4286
KOREA LINE (SINGAPORE) PTE LTD—See Korea Line Corporation; *Int'l*, pg. 4286
KOREA LUXSHARE-ICT CO., LTD.—See Luxshare Precision Industry Co., Ltd.; *Int'l*, pg. 4589
KOREA MIDLAND POWER CO., LTD.—See Korea Electric Power Corporation; *Int'l*, pg. 4284
KOREA MIRACLE PEOPLE CO., LTD.; *Int'l*, pg. 4286
KOREA MITSUMI CO., LTD.—See Minebea Mitsumi Inc.; *Int'l*, pg. 4902
KOREA MIURA CO., LTD.—See Miura Co., Ltd.; *Int'l*, pg. 4994
KOREA MOVENEX CO., LTD.; *Int'l*, pg. 4286
KOREA MURATA ELECTRONICS COMPANY, LIMITED—See Murata Manufacturing Co., Ltd.; *Int'l*, pg. 5097
KOREAN AIR LINES CO., LTD. - CHINA DIVISION—See Korean Air Lines Co., Ltd.; *Int'l*, pg. 4288
KOREAN AIR LINES CO., LTD. - FRANCE DIVISION—See Korean Air Lines Co., Ltd.; *Int'l*, pg. 4288
KOREAN AIR LINES CO., LTD.; *Int'l*, pg. 4288
KOREAN AIR LINES CO., LTD. - US DIVISION—See Korean Air Lines Co., Ltd.; *Int'l*, pg. 4288
KOREA NATIONAL OIL CORPORATION; *Int'l*, pg. 4286
KOREAN DRUG CO., LTD.; *Int'l*, pg. 4288
KOREAN ENVIRONMENT TECHNOLOGY CO., LTD.; *Int'l*, pg. 4288
KOREA NETUREN CO., LTD.—See Neturen Co., Ltd.; *Int'l*, pg. 5216
KOREA NEW NETWORK CO., LTD.; *Int'l*, pg. 4286
KOREAN HELICOPTER DEVELOPMENT SUPPORT LTD.—See Airbus SE; *Int'l*, pg. 247
KOREA NITTA MOORE CORP—See Nitta Corporation; *Int'l*, pg. 5382
KOREA NITTO DENKO CO., LTD.—See Nitto Denko Corporation; *Int'l*, pg. 5384
KOREA NITTO OPTICAL CO., LTD.—See Nitto Denko Corporation; *Int'l*, pg. 5384
KOREA NON-BANK LEASE FINANCING CO. LTD—See DGB Financial Group Co., Ltd.; *Int'l*, pg. 2096
KOREAN RED GINSENG CORP., INC—See KT&G Corporation; *Int'l*, pg. 4316
KOREAN REINSURANCE COMPANY; *Int'l*, pg. 4288
KOREAN REINSURANCE SWITZERLAND AG—See Korean Reinsurance Company; *Int'l*, pg. 4288
KOREAN RE UNDERWRITING LTD.—See Korean Reinsurance Company; *Int'l*, pg. 4288
KOREA NUCLEAR FUEL CO., LTD.—See Korea Electric Power Corporation; *Int'l*, pg. 4284
KOREAN WOMEN'S ASSOCIATION; *U.S. Private*, pg. 2343
KOREA OCEAN BUSINESS CORPORATION; *Int'l*, pg. 4287
KOREA OPTICAL HIGHTECH CO., LTD.—See Nitto Denko Corporation; *Int'l*, pg. 5384
KOREA OTSUKA PHARMACEUTICAL CO., LTD.—See Otsuka Pharmaceutical Co., Ltd.; *Int'l*, pg. 5659
KOREA PETRO CHEMICAL IND CO - ONSAN PLANT—See Korea Petro Chemical Ind Co; *Int'l*, pg. 4287
KOREA PETRO CHEMICAL IND CO; *Int'l*, pg. 4287

COMPANY NAME INDEX

KOREA PETRO CHEMICAL IND CO - ULSAN PLANT—See Korea Petro Chemical Ind Co; *Int'l*, pg. 4287
KOREA PETROLEUM INDUSTRIAL CO., LTD.; *Int'l*, pg. 4287
KOREA PHARMA CO., LTD.; *Int'l*, pg. 4287
KOREA PILLAR PACKING CO., LTD.—See Nippon Pillar Packing Co., Ltd.; *Int'l*, pg. 5328
KOREA PLANT SERVICE & ENGINEERING—See Korea Electric Power Corporation; *Int'l*, pg. 4284
KOREA PLASMA TECHNOLOGY U CO., LTD.—See Alutec Co., Ltd.; *Int'l*, pg. 401
KOREA POLYACETAL CO., LTD.—See Mitsubishi Gas Chemical Company, Inc.; *Int'l*, pg. 4949
KOREA PORT LOGISTICS CO., LTD.—See KCTC CO. Ltd; *Int'l*, pg. 4110
KOREA POWER EXCHANGE—See Korea Electric Power Corporation; *Int'l*, pg. 4284
KOREA RATINGS CORP.; *Int'l*, pg. 4287
KOREA REAL ESTATE INVESTMENT & TRUST CO., LTD.; *Int'l*, pg. 4287
KOREA RED GINSENG CORPORATION—See KT&G Corporation; *Int'l*, pg. 4316
KOREA REFRACTORIES CO., LTD.; *Int'l*, pg. 4287
KOREA RENTAL CORPORATION—See IS Dongseo Co., Ltd.; *Int'l*, pg. 3811
KOREA ROBOT MANUFACTURING CO., LTD.; *Int'l*, pg. 4287
KOREA SANKEN CO., LTD.—See Sanken Electric Co., Ltd.; *Int'l*, pg. 6541
KOREA SANYOU CO., LTD.—See Sanyou Corporation Limited; *Int'l*, pg. 6565
KOREA SATORI CO., LTD.—See SATORI ELECTRIC CO., LTD.; *Int'l*, pg. 6586
KOREA SCHRODER FUND MANAGEMENT LIMITED—See Schroders plc; *Int'l*, pg. 6639
KOREA SECURITIES DEPOSITORY—See Korea Exchange; *Int'l*, pg. 4284
KOREA SEMICONDUCTOR SYSTEM CO., LTD.; *Int'l*, pg. 4287
KOREA SEVEN CO., LTD—See Lotte Co., Ltd.; *Int'l*, pg. 4560
KOREA SHINKO MICROELECTRONICS CO., LTD.—See Fujitsu Limited; *Int'l*, pg. 2837
KOREA SHINKO TRADING CO., LTD.—See Fujitsu Limited; *Int'l*, pg. 2838
KOREA SHINTO CO., LTD.—See Dong-A Socio Holdings Co., Ltd.; *Int'l*, pg. 2165
KOREA SHIPBUILDING & OFFSHORE ENGINEERING CO., LTD.—See Hyundai Heavy Industries Co., Ltd.; *Int'l*, pg. 3557
KOREA SHOWA CHEMICALS CO.—See Resonac Holdings Corporation; *Int'l*, pg. 6298
KOREA SILO CO., LTD.—See Daehan Flour Mills co., Ltd; *Int'l*, pg. 1907
KOREA SINBON ELECTRONICS CO., LTD.—See SINBON Electronics Co., Ltd.; *Int'l*, pg. 6936
KOREA SINTERED METAL CO., LTD.—See Sumitomo Electric Industries, Ltd.; *Int'l*, pg. 7278
KOREA SINTO CO., LTD.—See Sintokogio Ltd.; *Int'l*, pg. 6958
KOREA SOUTH-EAST POWER CO., LTD.—See Korea Electric Power Corporation; *Int'l*, pg. 4284
KOREA SOUTHERN POWER CO., LTD.—See Korea Electric Power Corporation; *Int'l*, pg. 4284
KOREA STEEL CO., LTD; *Int'l*, pg. 4287
KOREA STEEL SHAPE CO., LTD. - CHILSEO-STEEL MILL—See Korea Steel Co., Ltd; *Int'l*, pg. 4287
KOREA STEEL SHAPE CO., LTD. - NOK-SAN PLANT—See Korea Steel Co., Ltd; *Int'l*, pg. 4287
KOREA SUNERGY CO., LTD—See China Sunergy Co., Ltd.; *Int'l*, pg. 1556
KOREA TAIYO YUDEN CO., LTD.—See Taiyo Yuden Company Ltd.; *Int'l*, pg. 7426
KOREA TAJIMA CO., LTD.—See Tajima Industries Ltd.; *Int'l*, pg. 7428
KOREA TDK CO. LTD.—See TDK Corporation; *Int'l*, pg. 7487
KOREA TECHNIC CO. LTD.—See Technic Incorporated; *U.S. Private*, pg. 3953
KOREA TELECOM AMERICA, INC.—See KT Corporation; *Int'l*, pg. 4315
KOREA TELECOM JAPAN CO., LTD.—See KT Corporation; *Int'l*, pg. 4315
KOREA THUMB VET CO., LTD.—See Harim Holdings Co., Ltd.; *Int'l*, pg. 3276
KOREA TIMES CO., LTD.; *Int'l*, pg. 4287
KOREA TIMES LOS ANGELES INC.—See Korea Times Co., Ltd.; *Int'l*, pg. 4287
KOREA TONG YANG YUJUN CO. LTD—See Taiyo Yuden Company Ltd.; *Int'l*, pg. 7427
KOREA TRANSFORMER CO. LTD.—See Diamond Electric Mfg. Co., Ltd.; *Int'l*, pg. 2105
KOREA UCB CO LTD.—See UCB S.A.; *Int'l*, pg. 8011
KOREA UNITED PHARM INC; *Int'l*, pg. 4287
KOREA VACUUM LIMITED—See ShinMaywa Industries, Ltd.; *Int'l*, pg. 6846
KOREA VALUE ASSET MANAGEMENT CO., LTD.—See Korea Investment Holdings Co., Ltd.; *Int'l*, pg. 4285
KOREA WESTERN POWER CO., LTD.—See Korea Electric Power Corporation; *Int'l*, pg. 4284
KOREA ZERUST CO., LTD.—See Northern Technologies International Corporation; *U.S. Public*, pg. 1538
KOREA ZINC COMPANY, LTD.; *Int'l*, pg. 4287
KORECTYPE CORPORATION—See Ko-Rec-Type Corp.; *U.S. Private*, pg. 2325
KO-REC-TYPE CORP.; *U.S. Private*, pg. 2325
KORE FOODS LIMITED; *Int'l*, pg. 4281
KORE MINING LTD.; *Int'l*, pg. 4281
KOREMURA ASAHI DIAMOND INDUSTRIAL CO., LTD.—See Asahi Diamond Industrial Co. Ltd.; *Int'l*, pg. 592
KORE POTASH LIMITED—See Kore Potash PLC; *Int'l*, pg. 4281
KORE POTASH PLC; *Int'l*, pg. 4281
KORE POWER, INC.; *U.S. Private*, pg. 2343
KORE TELEMATICS—See KORE Wireless Group, Inc.; *U.S. Private*, pg. 2343
KORE WIRELESS GROUP, INC.; *U.S. Private*, pg. 2343
KOREX CORPORATION—See Pensler Capital Corporation; *U.S. Private*, pg. 3139
KOREX LIMITED—See Aminex PLC; *Int'l*, pg. 428
KOREY KAY & PARTNERS; *U.S. Private*, pg. 2343
KORFEZ GAYRIMENKUL YATIRIM ORTAKLIGI AS; *Int'l*, pg. 4288
KORFEZ ULASTIRMA A.S.—See Koc Holding A.S.; *Int'l*, pg. 4224
KORGAN-KAZATOMPROM LLP—See JSC National Atomic Company Kazatomprom; *Int'l*, pg. 4009
KORGES ENTERPRISES, INC.—See Lazydays Holdings, Inc.; *U.S. Public*, pg. 1295
KORG EUROPE LIMITED—See Korg Inc.; *Int'l*, pg. 4288
KORG HK LTD.—See Korg Inc.; *Int'l*, pg. 4288
KORG INC.; *Int'l*, pg. 4288
KORG ITALY S.P.A.—See Korg Inc.; *Int'l*, pg. 4288
KORG MIDDLE EAST—See Korg Inc.; *Int'l*, pg. 4288
KORGTECH INC.—See Korg Inc.; *Int'l*, pg. 4288
KORG (UK) LIMITED—See Korg Inc.; *Int'l*, pg. 4288
KORG USA, INC.—See Korg Inc.; *Int'l*, pg. 4288
KORIAN DEUTSCHLAND AG—See Clariane SE; *Int'l*, pg. 1643
KORIAN LES OLIVIERS JSC—See Clariane SE; *Int'l*, pg. 1643
KORIAN LES TROIS TOURS JSC—See Clariane SE; *Int'l*, pg. 1643
KORI CONSTRUCTION (M) SDN. BHD.—See Kori Holdings Limited; *Int'l*, pg. 4288
KORI HOLDINGS LIMITED; *Int'l*, pg. 4288
KORINDO GROUP - BALIKPAPAN DIVISION—See Korindo Group; *Int'l*, pg. 4288
KORINDO GROUP - PANGKALAN BUN DIVISION—See Korindo Group; *Int'l*, pg. 4289
KORINDO GROUP; *Int'l*, pg. 4288
KORINDO WIND TOWER DIVISION—See Korindo Group; *Int'l*, pg. 4289
KORIN TECHNOLOGY CO., LIMITED—See Toyota Tsusho Corporation; *Int'l*, pg. 7877
KORINTHOS POWER S.A.—See Iberdrola, S.A.; *Int'l*, pg. 3573
KORIYAMA HIROSE ELECTRIC CO., LTD—See Hirose Electric Co., Ltd.; *Int'l*, pg. 3405
KORKEN SCHIESSER GES.M.B.H.—See CORTICEIRA AMORIM, S.G.P.S., S.A.; *Int'l*, pg. 1808
KORKKITRIO OY—See CORTICEIRA AMORIM, S.G.P.S., S.A.; *Int'l*, pg. 1808
KORLAM NV—See VINCI S.A.; *Int'l*, pg. 8223
KORLOFF PARIS—See Korloff SA; *Int'l*, pg. 4289
KORLOFF SA; *Int'l*, pg. 4289
KORLOY, INC.—See Sumitomo Electric Industries, Ltd.; *Int'l*, pg. 7278
KORMAK PRAHA A.S.—See EnBW Energie Baden-Wurttemberg AG; *Int'l*, pg. 2399
KORMAN RESIDENTIAL PROPERTIES, INC.—See Korman Services, L.P.; *U.S. Private*, pg. 2344
KORMAN SERVICES, L.P.; *U.S. Private*, pg. 2344
KORNBRENNEREI BERENTZEN GMBH—See Berentzen-Gruppe AG; *Int'l*, pg. 978
KORN FERRY A/S—See Korn Ferry; *U.S. Public*, pg. 1273
KORN FERRY (AT) GMBH—See Korn Ferry; *U.S. Public*, pg. 1272
KORN FERRY (AU) PTY. LTD. - MELBOURNE—See Korn Ferry; *U.S. Public*, pg. 1272
KORN FERRY (AU) PTY. LTD.—See Korn Ferry; *U.S. Public*, pg. 1272
KORN FERRY (BE) BVBA—See Korn Ferry; *U.S. Public*, pg. 1272
KORN FERRY (BR) CONSULTORES LTDA. - RIO DE JANEIRO—See Korn Ferry; *U.S. Public*, pg. 1272
KORN FERRY (BR) CONSULTORES LTDA.—See Korn Ferry; *U.S. Public*, pg. 1272
KORN FERRY (CA) LTD. - CALGARY—See Korn Ferry; *U.S. Public*, pg. 1273
KORN FERRY (CA) LTD.—See Korn Ferry; *U.S. Public*, pg. 1273
KORN FERRY (CA) LTD. - VANCOUVER—See Korn Ferry; *U.S. Public*, pg. 1273
KORN FERRY CR S.R.L.—See Korn Ferry; *U.S. Public*, pg. 1273

KORN FERRY

KORN FERRY (DE) GMBH—See Korn Ferry; *U.S. Public*, pg. 1273
KORN FERRY (DK) A/S—See Korn Ferry; *U.S. Public*, pg. 1273
KORN FERRY (FR) SARL—See Korn Ferry; *U.S. Public*, pg. 1273
KORN FERRY FUTURESTEP (THE PHILIPPINES) INC.—See Korn Ferry; *U.S. Public*, pg. 1273
KORN FERRY (HK) LIMITED—See Korn Ferry; *U.S. Public*, pg. 1273
KORN/FERRY INTERNATIONAL AB - GOTHENBURG—See Korn Ferry; *U.S. Public*, pg. 1274
KORN/FERRY INTERNATIONAL AB—See Korn Ferry; *U.S. Public*, pg. 1274
KORN/FERRY INTERNATIONAL BELNORDE S.A. DE C.V.—See Korn Ferry; *U.S. Public*, pg. 1274
KORN/FERRY INTERNATIONAL BUDAPEST INDIVIDUAL CONSULTING & SERVICE LTD.—See Korn Ferry; *U.S. Public*, pg. 1274
KORN/FERRY INTERNATIONAL - COLOMBIA—See Korn Ferry; *U.S. Public*, pg. 1274
KORN/FERRY INTERNATIONAL CONSULTORES ASOCIADOS, C.A.—See Korn Ferry; *U.S. Public*, pg. 1274
KORN/FERRY INTERNATIONAL (KOREA) LIMITED—See Korn Ferry; *U.S. Public*, pg. 1274
KORN/FERRY INTERNATIONAL LIMITED—See Korn Ferry; *U.S. Public*, pg. 1274
KORN/FERRY INTERNATIONAL MUSAVIRILIK LIMITED SIRKETI—See Korn Ferry; *U.S. Public*, pg. 1274
KORN/FERRY INTERNATIONAL OY—See Korn Ferry; *U.S. Public*, pg. 1274
KORN/FERRY INTERNATIONAL-PERU SOCIEDAD ANONIMA—See Korn Ferry; *U.S. Public*, pg. 1274
KORN/FERRY INTERNATIONAL PRIVATE LIMITED—See Korn Ferry; *U.S. Public*, pg. 1274
KORN/FERRY INTERNATIONAL S.A. DE C.V.—See Korn Ferry; *U.S. Public*, pg. 1274
KORN FERRY INTERNATIONAL S.A.—See Korn Ferry; *U.S. Public*, pg. 1273
KORN FERRY INTERNATIONAL S.A.—See Korn Ferry; *U.S. Public*, pg. 1273
KORN FERRY INTERNATIONAL S.A.—See Korn Ferry; *U.S. Public*, pg. 1273
KORN FERRY INTERNATIONAL S.A.—See Korn Ferry; *U.S. Public*, pg. 1273
KORN FERRY INTERNATIONAL S.A.—See Korn Ferry; *U.S. Public*, pg. 1273
KORN/FERRY INTERNATIONAL (TAIWAN) CO. LIMITED—See Korn Ferry; *U.S. Public*, pg. 1274
KORN FERRY (IT) S.R.L. - ROME—See Korn Ferry; *U.S. Public*, pg. 1273
KORN FERRY (IT) S.R.L.—See Korn Ferry; *U.S. Public*, pg. 1273
KORN FERRY (JAPAN) LTD.—See Korn Ferry; *U.S. Public*, pg. 1273
KORN FERRY LEADERSHIP CONSULTING CORPORATION—See Korn Ferry; *U.S. Public*, pg. 1273
KORN FERRY LIMITED—See Korn Ferry; *U.S. Public*, pg. 1274
KORN FERRY LLC—See Korn Ferry; *U.S. Public*, pg. 1274
KORN FERRY (LUXEMBOURG) S.A.R.L.—See Korn Ferry; *U.S. Public*, pg. 1273
KORN FERRY (NL) B.V.—See Korn Ferry; *U.S. Public*, pg. 1273
KORN FERRY (NZ)—See Korn Ferry; *U.S. Public*, pg. 1273
KORN FERRY (PL) SP. Z O.O.—See Korn Ferry; *U.S. Public*, pg. 1273
KORN FERRY RECRUITMENT (THAILAND) LTD.—See Korn Ferry; *U.S. Public*, pg. 1274
KORN FERRY RPOPS (HONG KONG) LTD.—See Korn Ferry; *U.S. Public*, pg. 1273
KORN FERRY RPOPS (SG) PTE. LTD.—See Korn Ferry; *U.S. Public*, pg. 1273
KORN FERRY RPO (SWEDEN) AB—See Korn Ferry; *U.S. Public*, pg. 1274
KORN FERRY S.A.—See Korn Ferry; *U.S. Public*, pg. 1274
KORN FERRY (SCHWEIZ) GMBH—See Korn Ferry; *U.S. Public*, pg. 1273
KORN FERRY (SG) PTE. LTD.—See Korn Ferry; *U.S. Public*, pg. 1273
KORN FERRY (SHANGHAI) HUMAN CAPITAL CONSULTING CO., LTD.—See Korn Ferry; *U.S. Public*, pg. 1274
KORN FERRY (SK) S.R.O.—See Korn Ferry; *U.S. Public*, pg. 1274
KORN FERRY; *U.S. Public*, pg. 1272
KORN FERRY SP LLC—See Korn Ferry; *U.S. Public*, pg. 1274
KORN FERRY S.R.O.—See Korn Ferry; *U.S. Public*, pg. 1274
KORN FERRY (SWEDEN) AB—See Korn Ferry; *U.S. Public*, pg. 1273
KORN/FERRY (THAILAND) LIMITED—See Korn Ferry; *U.S. Public*, pg. 1274

KORN FERRY — CORPORATE AFFILIATIONS

KORN FERRY (US)—See Korn Ferry; *U.S. Public*, pg. 1273
KORNIC AUTOMATION CO., LTD.; *Int'l*, pg. 4289
KORNIT DIGITAL LTD.; *Int'l*, pg. 4289
KORN-OG FODERSTOF KOMPAGNIET (KFK) A/S—See Norsk Hydro ASA; *Int'l*, pg. 5435
KORNS GALVANIZING CO., INC.—See Hill & Smith PLC; *Int'l*, pg. 3392
KOROBERI INC.; *U.S. Private*, pg. 2344
KORONA DEVELOPMENT LLC—See Dragon Ukrainian Properties & Development Plc; *Int'l*, pg. 2199
KORONA INVEST OY; *Int'l*, pg. 4289
KORONA JV SP ZOO—See SNF SAS; *Int'l*, pg. 7027
KOROSEAL INTERIOR PRODUCTS LLC—See Sangetsu Co., Ltd.; *Int'l*, pg. 6537
KOROSEAL WALL COVERINGS WEST—See RJF International Corporation; *U.S. Private*, pg. 3449
KOROSKA BANKA D.D.—See Nova Ljubljanska banka d.d.; *Int'l*, pg. 5451
KOROTKIN-SCHLESINGER & ASSOCIATES, INC.; *U.S. Private*, pg. 2344
KORPORACJA BUDOWLANA DOM S.A.; *Int'l*, pg. 4289
KORPORACJA GOSPODARCZA EFEKT S.A.; *Int'l*, pg. 4289
KORPORACJA KGL SA; *Int'l*, pg. 4289
KORPORATA ELEKTROENERGJITIKE SHQIPTARE; *Int'l*, pg. 4289
KORPORATSIYA TRANSAGRO OJSC—See OJSC Pava; *Int'l*, pg. 5541
KORRES S.A. NATURAL PRODUCTS; *Int'l*, pg. 4289
KORRIO, INC.—See Waud Capital Partners LLC; *U.S. Private*, pg. 4457
KORR MEDICAL TECHNOLOGIES INC; *U.S. Private*, pg. 2344
KORRY ELECTRONICS CO.—See TransDigm Group Incorporated; *U.S. Public*, pg. 2181
KORS ENGINEERING COMPANY, INC.—See Francisco Partners Management, LP; *U.S. Private*, pg. 1591
KORSHUNOV MINING PLANT OAO—See Mechel PAO; *Int'l*, pg. 4766
KORSNAS AB - FROVI—See Billerud AB; *Int'l*, pg. 1030
KORSNAS AB—See Billerud AB; *Int'l*, pg. 1030
KORSNAS GMBH—See Billerud AB; *Int'l*, pg. 1030
KORSNAS ROCKHAMMAR AB—See Billerud AB; *Int'l*, pg. 1030
KORSNAS SHANGHAI TRADING LTD.—See Billerud AB; *Int'l*, pg. 1030
KORTEC, INC.; *U.S. Private*, pg. 2344
KORTE CONSTRUCTION COMPANY INC.; *U.S. Private*, pg. 2344
KORTE CONSTRUCTION; *U.S. Private*, pg. 2344
KORTE DESIGNS, INC.—See Korte Construction Company Inc.; *U.S. Private*, pg. 2344
KORTE DOES IT ALL; *U.S. Private*, pg. 2344
KORTEK AUSTRALIA PTY LTD—See Kortek Corporation; *Int'l*, pg. 4289
KORTEK CORPORATION; *Int'l*, pg. 4289
KORTEKS MENSUCAT SANAYI VE TICARET AS; *Int'l*, pg. 4289
KORTEK USA INC—See Kortek Corporation; *Int'l*, pg. 4289
KORTEK VINA CO., LTD.—See Kortek Corporation; *Int'l*, pg. 4289
KORTH DIRECT MORTGAGE INC.; *U.S. Private*, pg. 2344
KORT REHABILITATION AT HOME, LLC—See Select Medical Holdings Corporation; *U.S. Public*, pg. 1858
KORTROS GROUP—See Renova Group; *Int'l*, pg. 6285
KORTX, LLC; *U.S. Private*, pg. 2344
KORU MEDICAL SYSTEMS, INC.; *U.S. Public*, pg. 1275
KORUM MOTORS INC.; *U.S. Private*, pg. 2344
KORUS CONSULTING CIS LLC—See OJSC Sberbank of Russia; *Int'l*, pg. 5542
KORUTRANS INTERNATIONAL INC.; *U.S. Private*, pg. 2344
KORVER CORP.; *U.S. Public*, pg. 1275
KORVEST GALVANISERS—See Korvest Ltd.; *Int'l*, pg. 4289
KORVEST LTD.; *Int'l*, pg. 4289
KORV-GORANS KEBAB OY—See Atria Plc; *Int'l*, pg. 694
KORVIS AUTOMATION INC; *U.S. Private*, pg. 2344
KORYO CREDIT INFORMATION CO., LTD.; *Int'l*, pg. 4289
KORYO ENGINEERING CO., LTD.—See Mitsubishi Heavy Industries, Ltd.; *Int'l*, pg. 4954
KORYOJYUHAN CO., LTD.; *Int'l*, pg. 4289
KOSAIDO HOLDINGS CO., LTD.; *Int'l*, pg. 4290
KOSAKA SMELTING & REFINING CO., LTD—See Dowa Holdings Co., Ltd.; *Int'l*, pg. 2183
KOSAKI TMI D.D.; *Int'l*, pg. 4290
KOSAN GAS A/S—See UGI Corporation; *U.S. Public*, pg. 2222
KOSAN GAS FINLAND OY—See UGI Corporation; *U.S. Public*, pg. 2222
KOSAN GAS NORGE A/S—See UGI Corporation; *U.S. Public*, pg. 2222
KOSAN GAS SVERIGE AB—See UGI Corporation; *U.S. Public*, pg. 2222
KOSAN KANRI SERVICE CO.,LTD.—See Mitsui O.S.K. Lines, Ltd.; *Int'l*, pg. 4989

KOSAN KANRI SERVICE WEST CO., LTD.—See Mitsui O.S.K. Lines, Ltd.; *Int'l*, pg. 4989
KOSA-TV CBS 7—See Gray Television, Inc.; *U.S. Public*, pg. 960
KOSAYA GORA IRON WORKS PJSC; *Int'l*, pg. 4290
KOSCIUSZKO THREDBO PTY LIMITED—See Event Hospitality & Entertainment Limited; *Int'l*, pg. 2562
KOSCOM CORPORATION—See Korea Exchange; *Int'l*, pg. 4284
KOSE AMERICA, INC.—See KOSE Corporation; *Int'l*, pg. 4290
KOSE BRASIL COMERCIO DE COSMETICOS LTDA.—See KOSE Corporation; *Int'l*, pg. 4290
KOSE CORPORATION INDIA PVT. LTD.—See KOSE Corporation; *Int'l*, pg. 4290
KOSE CORPORATION; *Int'l*, pg. 4290
KOSE COSMENIENCE CO., LTD.—See KOSE Corporation; *Int'l*, pg. 4290
KOSE COSMEPIA CO., LTD.—See KOSE Corporation; *Int'l*, pg. 4290
KOSE COSMEPORT CORP.—See KOSE Corporation; *Int'l*, pg. 4290
KOSE COSMETICS CO., LTD. (CHINA)—See Nihon Kolmar Co., Ltd.; *Int'l*, pg. 5286
KOSEC TIM D.O.O.—See Inles d.d.; *Int'l*, pg. 3705
KOSEC TIM D.O.O.—See Inles d.d.; *Int'l*, pg. 3705
KOSE (HONG KONG) CO., LTD.—See KOSE Corporation; *Int'l*, pg. 4290
KOSEI ALUMINUM CO., LTD.; *Int'l*, pg. 4290
KOSE INDUSTRIES CO., LTD.—See KOSE Corporation; *Int'l*, pg. 4290
KOSE INSURANCE SERVICE CO., LTD.—See KOSE Corporation; *Int'l*, pg. 4290
THE KOSEI SECURITIES CO., LTD.; *Int'l*, pg. 7663
KOSEI ST. MARYS CORPORATION—See Kosei Aluminum Co., Ltd.; *Int'l*, pg. 4290
KOSE KOREA CO., LTD.—See KOSE Corporation; *Int'l*, pg. 4290
KOSE (MALAYSIA) SDN. BHD.—See KOSE Corporation; *Int'l*, pg. 4290
KOSE MARUHO CO., LTD.—See KOSE Corporation; *Int'l*, pg. 4290
KO-SENKO LOGISTICS CO., LTD.—See Senko Group Holdings Co., Ltd.; *Int'l*, pg. 6710
KOSEN SERVICE CO., LTD.—See Kobelco Wire Co Ltd; *Int'l*, pg. 4221
KOSE PROVISION CO., LTD.—See KOSE Corporation; *Int'l*, pg. 4290
KOSE R.E. CO., LTD.; *Int'l*, pg. 4290
KOSE SALES CO., LTD.—See KOSE Corporation; *Int'l*, pg. 4290
KOSE SINGAPORE PTE., LTD.—See KOSE Corporation; *Int'l*, pg. 4290
KOSE (THAILAND) CO., LTD.—See KOSE Corporation; *Int'l*, pg. 4290
KOSHIDAKA HOLDINGS CO., LTD.; *Int'l*, pg. 4290
KOSHIDAKA INTERNATIONAL PTE. LTD.—See Koshidaka Holdings Co., Ltd.; *Int'l*, pg. 4291
KOSHIDAKA KOREA CO., LTD.—See Koshidaka Holdings Co., Ltd.; *Int'l*, pg. 4291
KOSHIN KOGAKU CO., LTD.—See YAMAICHI ELECTRONICS Co Ltd; *Int'l*, pg. 8552
KOSHIN KOGAKU CO., LTD.- TOGAWA PLANT—See YAMAICHI ELECTRONICS Co Ltd; *Int'l*, pg. 8552
KOSHIN KOGYO CO., LTD.—See Marubeni Construction Material Lease Co., Ltd.; *Int'l*, pg. 4704
KOSHU DAIICHI TRAFFIC CO., LTD.—See Daiichi Koutsu Sangyo Co., Ltd.; *Int'l*, pg. 1928
KOSHUHA CO., LTD.—See DKK Co., Ltd.; *Int'l*, pg. 2139
KOSINSKI ARCHITECTURE, INC.; *U.S. Private*, pg. 2344
KOS INTERNATIONAL HOLDINGS LTD.; *Int'l*, pg. 4289
KOS INTERNATIONAL LIMITED—See KOS International Holdings Ltd.; *Int'l*, pg. 4290
KOSITZKA & WICKS CO.; *U.S. Private*, pg. 2344
KOSKIKESKUKSEN HUOLTO OY—See Citycon Oyj; *Int'l*, pg. 1629
KOSKISEN CORP.; *Int'l*, pg. 4291
KOSLAND PTE. LTD.—See Koh Brothers Group Limited; *Int'l*, pg. 4228
KOSMAJ A.D.; *Int'l*, pg. 4291
KOSMAJ MERMER A.D.; *Int'l*, pg. 4291
KOSMAS GROUP INTERNATIONAL INC.; *U.S. Private*, pg. 2344
KOSME GESELLSCHAFT MBH—See Krones AG; *Int'l*, pg. 4305
KOSME S.R.L.—See Krones AG; *Int'l*, pg. 4305
KOSMOS ENERGY GHANA HC—See Kosmos Energy Ltd.; *U.S. Public*, pg. 1275
KOSMOS ENERGY, LLC—See Kosmos Energy Ltd.; *U.S. Public*, pg. 1275
KOSMOS ENERGY LTD.; *U.S. Public*, pg. 1275
KOSMOS ENERGY OFFSHORE MOROCCO HC—See Kosmos Energy Ltd.; *U.S. Public*, pg. 1275
KOSO CORPORATION—See Hamamatsu Photonics K.K.; *Int'l*, pg. 3235
KOSOKU PAPER LTD.—See Japan Pulp and Paper Company Limited; *Int'l*, pg. 3904
KOSOVOPROJEKT INZENJERING A.D.; *Int'l*, pg. 4291

KOSPA CORPORATION—See Mitsubishi Gas Chemical Company, Inc.; *Int'l*, pg. 4948
KOSPO POWER SERVICES LTDA.—See Korea Electric Power Corporation; *Int'l*, pg. 4283
KOSSAN RUBBER INDUSTRIES BHD; *Int'l*, pg. 4291
KOSS CORPORATION; *U.S. Public*, pg. 1275
KOSSEN CO., LTD. - BUAN FACTORY—See IREM Co., Ltd.; *Int'l*, pg. 3807
KOSSE PARTNERS I, LLC—See Vspeed Capital, LLC; *U.S. Private*, pg. 4415
KOSS EUROPE S.A.—See Koss Corporation; *U.S. Public*, pg. 1275
KOSSMAN DEVELOPMENT COMPANY; *U.S. Private*, pg. 2344
KOSSMAN'S, INC.; *U.S. Private*, pg. 2345
KOSSODO S.A.C.—See HORIBA Ltd; *Int'l*, pg. 3477
KOS SPA—See Compagnia Finanziaria de Benedetti S.p.A.; *Int'l*, pg. 1722
KOS SPEZIALTUREN GMBH—See ASSA ABLOY AB; *Int'l*, pg. 638
KOSS-WINN BANCSHARES, INC.; *U.S. Private*, pg. 2344
KOSTA ABRAS AD; *Int'l*, pg. 4291
KOSTA FORLAG AB—See New Wave Group AB; *Int'l*, pg. 5229
KOSTAL BULGARIA AUTOMOTIVE EOOD—See Leopold Kostal GmbH & Co. KG; *Int'l*, pg. 4465
KOSTAL BULGARIA LTD.—See Leopold Kostal GmbH & Co. KG; *Int'l*, pg. 4465
KOSTAL (CHANGCHUN) AUTOMOTIVE ELECTRIC CO., LTD.—See Leopold Kostal GmbH & Co. KG; *Int'l*, pg. 4465
KOSTAL CR, SPOL. S R.O.—See Leopold Kostal GmbH & Co. KG; *Int'l*, pg. 4465
KOSTAL DA AMAZONIA INDUSTRIA E COMERCIO DE AUTO PECAS LTDA.—See Leopold Kostal GmbH & Co. KG; *Int'l*, pg. 4466
KOSTAL DA AMAZONIA INDUSTRIA E COMURCIO DE AUTO PECAS LTDA.—See Leopold Kostal GmbH & Co. KG; *Int'l*, pg. 4466
KOSTAL ELECTRICA S. A.—See Leopold Kostal GmbH & Co. KG; *Int'l*, pg. 4465
KOSTAL ELETROMECANICA LTDA.—See Leopold Kostal GmbH & Co. KG; *Int'l*, pg. 4465
KOSTAL FRANCE—See Leopold Kostal GmbH & Co. KG; *Int'l*, pg. 4465
KOSTAL INDIA PRIVATE LIMITED—See Leopold Kostal GmbH & Co. KG; *Int'l*, pg. 4465
KOSTAL INDUSTRIE ELEKTRIK GMBH—See Leopold Kostal GmbH & Co. KG; *Int'l*, pg. 4465
KOSTAL IRELAND GMBH—See Leopold Kostal GmbH & Co. KG; *Int'l*, pg. 4465
KOSTAL ITALIA S. R. L.—See Leopold Kostal GmbH & Co. KG; *Int'l*, pg. 4465
KOSTAL JAPAN CO., LTD.—See Leopold Kostal GmbH & Co. KG; *Int'l*, pg. 4465
KOSTAL KONTAKT SYSTEME GMBH—See Leopold Kostal GmbH & Co. KG; *Int'l*, pg. 4465
KOSTAL KONTAKT SYSTEME GMBH—See Leopold Kostal GmbH & Co. KG; *Int'l*, pg. 4465
KOSTAL KONTAKT SYSTEME, INC.—See Leopold Kostal GmbH & Co. KG; *Int'l*, pg. 4465
KOSTAL KOREA LTD.—See Leopold Kostal GmbH & Co. KG; *Int'l*, pg. 4465
KOSTAL MAROC, SARL—See Leopold Kostal GmbH & Co. KG; *Int'l*, pg. 4465
KOSTAL MEXICANA, S.A. DE C.V.—See Leopold Kostal GmbH & Co. KG; *Int'l*, pg. 4465
KOSTAL NTTF AUTOMOTIVE INDIA PVT. LTD.—See Leopold Kostal GmbH & Co. KG; *Int'l*, pg. 4465
KOSTAL OF AMERICA, INC.—See Leopold Kostal GmbH & Co. KG; *Int'l*, pg. 4466
KOSTAL S.A.—See Leopold Kostal GmbH & Co. KG; *Int'l*, pg. 4465
KOSTAL (SHANGHAI) KONTAKT SYSTEME MANUFACTURING CO., LTD.—See Leopold Kostal GmbH & Co. KG; *Int'l*, pg. 4465
KOSTAL SOFIASOFT BULGARIA OOD—See Leopold Kostal GmbH & Co. KG; *Int'l*, pg. 4465
KOSTAL SOLAR ELECTRIC FRANCE SARL—See Leopold Kostal GmbH & Co. KG; *Int'l*, pg. 4465
KOSTAL SOLAR ELECTRIC GMBH—See Leopold Kostal GmbH & Co. KG; *Int'l*, pg. 4465
KOSTAL SOLAR ELECTRIC HELLAS E.P.E.—See Leopold Kostal GmbH & Co. KG; *Int'l*, pg. 4465
KOSTAL SOLAR ELECTRIC IBERICA S.L.—See Leopold Kostal GmbH & Co. KG; *Int'l*, pg. 4465
KOSTAL SOLAR ELECTRIC ITALIA SRL—See Leopold Kostal GmbH & Co. KG; *Int'l*, pg. 4465
KOSTAL SWEDEN AB—See Leopold Kostal GmbH & Co. KG; *Int'l*, pg. 4465
KOSTAL UK LTD.—See Leopold Kostal GmbH & Co. KG; *Int'l*, pg. 4466
KOSTAL UKRAINA TOV—See Leopold Kostal GmbH & Co. KG; *Int'l*, pg. 4466
KOSTEK SYSTEMS, INC.; *Int'l*, pg. 4291
KOSTELECKE UZENINY A.S.—See Agrofert Holding, a.s.; *Int'l*, pg. 219
KOSTENETS-HHI JSC; *Int'l*, pg. 4291

COMPANY NAME INDEX

KOSTER AFDICHTINGSSYSTEMEN BV—See Koster Bauchemie AG; *Int'l*, pg. 4291
KOSTER AMERICAN CORP.—See Koster Bauchemie AG; *Int'l*, pg. 4291
KOSTER AQUATECNIC LTD.—See Koster Bauchemie AG; *Int'l*, pg. 4291
KOSTER BAUCHEMIE AG; *Int'l*, pg. 4291
KOSTER BELGIE VLAANDEREN—See Koster Bauchemie AG; *Int'l*, pg. 4291
KOSTER BULGARIA LTD.—See Koster Bauchemie AG; *Int'l*, pg. 4291
KOSTER & CO. GMBH—See INDUS Holding AG; *Int'l*, pg. 3663
KOSTER CZ S.R.O.—See INDUS Holding AG; *Int'l*, pg. 3663
KOSTER HRVATSKA D.O.O.—See Koster Bauchemie AG; *Int'l*, pg. 4291
KOSTER IMP, UNIPESSOAL, LDA.—See Koster Bauchemie AG; *Int'l*, pg. 4291
KOSTER JAPAN CORP.—See Koster Bauchemie AG; *Int'l*, pg. 4291
KOSTER POLSKA SP. Z O.O.—See Koster Bauchemie AG; *Int'l*, pg. 4291
KOSTER YAPIKIMYASALLARI INSAAT VE TICARET A.S.—See Koster Bauchemie AG; *Int'l*, pg. 4291
KOSTIAL COMPANY, LLC; *U.S. Private*, pg. 2345
KOSTKA ENTERPRISES INC.; *U.S. Private*, pg. 2345
KOSTMAYER CONSTRUCTION INC.; *U.S. Private*, pg. 2345
KOSTO FOOD PRODUCTS CO.; *U.S. Private*, pg. 2345
KOSTRITZER SCHWARZBIERBRAUEREI GMBH & CO.—See Bitburger Braugruppe GmbH; *Int'l*, pg. 1049
KOSTROMA LTD.—See G-III Apparel Group, Ltd.; *U.S. Public*, pg. 894
KOSTROMSKAYA SBYTOVAYA COMPANIA PJSC; *Int'l*, pg. 4291
KOSUGI SANGYO CO., LTD.—See Asia Development Capital Co., Ltd.; *Int'l*, pg. 611
KOSUN BIO CO., LTD.; *Int'l*, pg. 4291
KOSYU SAISEKI CO., LTD—See Taiheiyo Cement Corporation; *Int'l*, pg. 7411
KOT ADDU POWER COMPANY LIMITED; *Int'l*, pg. 4291
KOTA ELECTRICITY DISTRIBUTION LIMITED—See CESC Limited; *Int'l*, pg. 1424
KOTAGALA PLANTATIONS PLC; *Int'l*, pg. 4291
KOTAK INVESTMENT ADVISORS LIMITED—See Kotak Mahindra Bank Limited; *Int'l*, pg. 4292
KOTAK MAHINDRA ASSET MANAGEMENT COMPANY LIMITED—See Kotak Mahindra Bank Limited; *Int'l*, pg. 4292
KOTAK MAHINDRA BANK LIMITED; *Int'l*, pg. 4292
KOTAK MAHINDRA CAPITAL COMPANY LIMITED—See Kotak Mahindra Bank Limited; *Int'l*, pg. 4292
KOTAK MAHINDRA, INC.—See Kotak Mahindra Bank Limited; *Int'l*, pg. 4292
KOTAK MAHINDRA (INTERNATIONAL) LIMITED—See Kotak Mahindra Bank Limited; *Int'l*, pg. 4292
KOTAK MAHINDRA PRIME LIMITED—See Kotak Mahindra Bank Limited; *Int'l*, pg. 4292
KOTAK MAHINDRA (UK) LIMITED—See Kotak Mahindra Bank Limited; *Int'l*, pg. 4292
KOTAK SECURITIES LIMITED—See Kotak Mahindra Bank Limited; *Int'l*, pg. 4292
KOTA RAYA DEVELOPMENT SDN BHD—See Berjaya Corporation Berhad; *Int'l*, pg. 983
KOTA TINGGI OIL PALM PLANTATIONS SDN. BHD.—See Keck Seng (Malaysia) Berhad; *Int'l*, pg. 4114
KOTECS CO., LTD.—See Topy Industries, Ltd.; *Int'l*, pg. 7821
KOTECS KOGYO CO., LTD.—See Topy Industries, Ltd.; *Int'l*, pg. 7821
KOTEKS VISCOFAN D.O.O.—See Viscofan SA; *Int'l*, pg. 8250
KOTEM HUNGARY LTD.—See Quality Vision International Inc.; *U.S. Private*, pg. 3321
KOTEM TECHNOLOGIES INC.—See Quality Vision International Inc.; *U.S. Private*, pg. 3321
THE KOTERET GROUP—See Omnicom Group Inc.; *U.S. Public*, pg. 1578
KOTHARI FERMENTATION & BIOCHEM LIMITED; *Int'l*, pg. 4292
KOTHARI INDUSTRIAL CORPORATION LIMITED; *Int'l*, pg. 4292
KOTHARI PETROCHEMICALS, LTD.; *Int'l*, pg. 4292
KOTHARI PRODUCTS LIMITED; *Int'l*, pg. 4292
KOTHARI PRODUCTS SINGAPORE PTE. LIMITED—See Kothari Products Limited; *Int'l*, pg. 4292
KOTHARI SUGARS & CHEMICALS LIMITED; *Int'l*, pg. 4292
KOTHARI WORLD FINANCE LIMITED; *Int'l*, pg. 4292
KOTHEN ENERGIE GMBH.—See MVV Energie AG; *Int'l*, pg. 5108
KOTHEN ENERGIE NETZ GMBH.—See MVV Energie AG; *Int'l*, pg. 5108
KOTIA ENTERPRISES LIMITED; *Int'l*, pg. 4292
KOTIKOKKI.NET OY—See Alma Media Corporation; *Int'l*, pg. 362
KOTIMAAN ENERGIA OY—See Fortum Oyj; *Int'l*, pg. 2742

KOT INSURANCE COMPANY, AG.—See Petroleos Mexicanos; *Int'l*, pg. 5828
KOTIPIZZA GROUP OYJ—See Orkla ASA; *Int'l*, pg. 5637
KOTIPIZZA OYJ—See Orkla ASA; *Int'l*, pg. 5637
KOTIS DESIGN LLC; *U.S. Private*, pg. 2345
KOTIVIEP 'B KFT.—See Betonut Szolgaltato es Epito Rt.; *Int'l*, pg. 1003
KOTLOSTROENE JSCO—See Favorit Hold AD; *Int'l*, pg. 2623
KOTOBUKI CORPORATION; *Int'l*, pg. 4292
KOTOBUKI INDUSTRY CO., LTD.—See AISIN Corporation; *Int'l*, pg. 253
KOTOBUKI KASEI CORP.—See Nagase & Co., Ltd.; *Int'l*, pg. 5126
KOTOBUKI KOGYO CO., LTD.—See Aichi Electric Co., Ltd.; *Int'l*, pg. 229
KOTOBUKI SPIRITS CO., LTD.; *Int'l*, pg. 4292
KOTOBUKIYA CO., LTD.; *Int'l*, pg. 4292
KOTOBUYIKA CO.; *Int'l*, pg. 4292
KOTO, INC.—See Kotobuyika Co.; *Int'l*, pg. 4293
KOTON MAGAZACILIK TEKSTIL SANAYI VE TICARET AS; *Int'l*, pg. 4293
KOTOUC STRAMBERK SPOL, S.R.O.—See CEZ, a.s.; *Int'l*, pg. 1428
KOTRA INDUSTRIES BERHAD; *Int'l*, pg. 4293
KOTRA PHARMA (M) SDN. BHD.—See Kotra Industries Berhad; *Int'l*, pg. 4293
KOTTER GMBH & CO. KG; *Int'l*, pg. 4293
KOTTKE TRUCKING, INC.; *U.S. Private*, pg. 2345
KOTV INC.—See Griffin Communications, LLC; *U.S. Private*, pg. 1787
KOTYARK INDUSTRIES LIMITED; *Int'l*, pg. 4293
KOUEI INDUSTRY CO., LTD.—See Freesia Macross Corporation; *Int'l*, pg. 2771
KOUFU GROUP LIMITED—See Dominus Capital, L.P.; *U.S. Private*, pg. 1256
KOUKANDEKIRUKUN, INC.; *Int'l*, pg. 4293
KOUKI CORP.—See Daiei Kankyo Co., Ltd.; *Int'l*, pg. 1924
KOUKOU SANGYO CORPORATION—See Daiken Corporation; *Int'l*, pg. 1931
KOUNAN TSUSHO CO., LTD.—See RAIZNEXT Corporation; *Int'l*, pg. 6192
KOUNRAD COPPER COMPANY LLP—See Central Asia Metals plc; *Int'l*, pg. 1404
KOUNT INC—See Equifax Inc.; *U.S. Public*, pg. 786
KOURAKUEN HOLDINGS CORPORATION; *Int'l*, pg. 4293
KOURT SECURITY PARTNERS LLC; *U.S. Private*, pg. 2345
KOURY CORPORATION; *U.S. Private*, pg. 2345
KOUSA INTERNATIONAL, LLC—See Korindo Group; *Int'l*, pg. 4289
KOUSHI INTEC INC.—See TIS Inc.; *Int'l*, pg. 7757
KOUSHIN MAZDA CO., LTD.—See Mazda Motor Corporation; *Int'l*, pg. 4748
KOUTADLY - CONSULTADORIA ECONOMICA E PARTICIPACOES, S.A.—See L. Possehl & Co. mbH; *Int'l*, pg. 4383
KOUT FOOD GROUP K.S.C.C.; *Int'l*, pg. 4293
KOUVO AUTOMATION OY—See Addtech AB; *Int'l*, pg. 134
KOU YOU KAI, LTD.; *U.S. Private*, pg. 2345
KOUZA ECO-CREATION CO., LTD.—See Mitsubishi Heavy Industries, Ltd.; *Int'l*, pg. 4954
KOUZIRO CO LTD—See Yamada Holdings Co., Ltd.; *Int'l*, pg. 8548
KOVACK REALTORS—See Berkshire Hathaway Inc.; *U.S. Public*, pg. 308
KOVA FERTILIZER INC. - OHIO DIVISION—See Kova Fertilizer Inc.; *U.S. Private*, pg. 2345
KOVA FERTILIZER INC.; *U.S. Private*, pg. 2345
KOVAI MEDICAL CENTER & HOSPITAL LIMITED; *Int'l*, pg. 4293
KOVAIR SOFTWARE, INC.—See Surge Ventures, LLC; *U.S. Private*, pg. 3884
KOVALAM INVESTMENT & TRADING CO.LTD; *Int'l*, pg. 4293
KOVALAM RESORT PRIVATE LIMITED—See HLV Ltd.; *Int'l*, pg. 3431
KOVALCHICK SALVAGE CO.; *U.S. Private*, pg. 2345
KOVALSKY-CARR ELECTRIC SUPPLY CO, INC.—See United Electric Supply Company, Inc.; *U.S. Private*, pg. 4291
KOVARUS, INC.; *U.S. Private*, pg. 2345
KOVA SOLUTIONS, INC.—See Berkshire Hathaway Inc.; *U.S. Public*, pg. 312
KOVATCH MOBILE EQUIPMENT CORP.—See AIP, LLC; *U.S. Private*, pg. 135
KOVDORSKIY GOK JSC; *Int'l*, pg. 4293
KOVEL/FULLER; *U.S. Private*, pg. 2345
KOVILPATTI LAKSHMI ROLLER FLOUR MILLS LIMITED; *Int'l*, pg. 4293
KOVINOPLASTIKA LOZ, D.D.—See KJK Capital Oy; *Int'l*, pg. 4197
KOVINOPLASTIKA ZAGREB D.O.O.—See KJK Capital Oy; *Int'l*, pg. 4198
KOVITZ INVESTMENT GROUP, LLC—See Clayton, Dubilier & Rice, LLC; *U.S. Private*, pg. 923
KOVITZ INVESTMENT GROUP, LLC—See Stone Point Capital LLC; *U.S. Private*, pg. 3824

KOVROVSKIY MEKHANICHESKIY ZAVOD OAO—See State Atomic Energy Corporation ROSATOM; *Int'l*, pg. 7181
KOVR-TV—See National Amusements, Inc.; *U.S. Private*, pg. 2840
KOVUHUTY, A.S.—See Umcor AG; *Int'l*, pg. 8022
KOWA AMERICAN CORPORATION—See Kowa Co., Ltd.; *Int'l*, pg. 4294
KOWA ASIA LIMITED—See Kowa Co., Ltd.; *Int'l*, pg. 4294
KOWA ASIA PACIFIC PTE., LTD.—See Kowa Co., Ltd.; *Int'l*, pg. 4294
KOWA CO., LTD.; *Int'l*, pg. 4293
KOWA ESTATE CO., LTD.—See Kowa Co., Ltd.; *Int'l*, pg. 4294
KOWA EUROPE GMBH—See Kowa Co., Ltd.; *Int'l*, pg. 4294
KOWA EYECON CO., LTD.—See Kowa Co., Ltd.; *Int'l*, pg. 4294
KOWA HEALTH CARE AMERICA, INC.—See Kowa Co., Ltd.; *Int'l*, pg. 4294
KOWA INDIA PVT. LTD.—See Kowa Co., Ltd.; *Int'l*, pg. 4294
KOWA KASEI CO., LTD.—See Totetsu Kogyo Co., Ltd.; *Int'l*, pg. 7845
KOWA KOGYO CO., LTD.—See Mitsubishi Heavy Industries, Ltd.; *Int'l*, pg. 4954
KOWA KOREA CO., LTD.—See Kowa Co., Ltd.; *Int'l*, pg. 4294
KOWAL CONSTRUCTION LTD.; *Int'l*, pg. 4294
KOWALSKI CO., INC.; *U.S. Private*, pg. 2345
KOWALSKI COMPANIES INC.; *U.S. Private*, pg. 2345
KOWALSKI COMPANIES INC.; *U.S. Private*, pg. 2345
KOWALSKI'S WHITE BEAR LAKE MARKET—See Kowalski Companies Inc.; *U.S. Private*, pg. 2345
KOWA LUMBER CO., LTD.—See Sumitomo Forestry Co., Ltd.; *Int'l*, pg. 7285
KOWA OPTICAL PRODUCTS CO., LTD.—See Kowa Co., Ltd.; *Int'l*, pg. 4294
KOWA OPTIMED EUROPE LTD.—See Kowa Co., Ltd.; *Int'l*, pg. 4294
KOWA PHARMACEUTICAL EUROPE CO. LTD.—See Kowa Co., Ltd.; *Int'l*, pg. 4294
KOWA PHARMACEUTICALS CO., LTD.—See Alfresa Holdings Corporation; *Int'l*, pg. 317
KOWA RESEARCH INSTITUTE, INC.—See Kowa Co., Ltd.; *Int'l*, pg. 4294
KOWA SANGYO CO., LTD.—See Rengo Co., Ltd.; *Int'l*, pg. 6280
KOWA SEIKO CO., LTD.—See Dowa Holdings Co., Ltd.; *Int'l*, pg. 2183
KOWA (SHANGHAI) CO., LTD.—See Kowa Co., Ltd.; *Int'l*, pg. 4294
KOWA (SHANGHAI) OPTICAL INSTRUMENTS INTERNATIONAL CO., LTD.—See Kowa Co., Ltd.; *Int'l*, pg. 4294
KOWA (SHANGHAI) PHARMA CONSULTING CO., LTD.—See Kowa Co., Ltd.; *Int'l*, pg. 4294
KOWA TAIWAN TSUSHO CO., LTD.—See Kowa Co., Ltd.; *Int'l*, pg. 4294
KOWA (THAILAND) CO., LTD.—See Kowa Co., Ltd.; *Int'l*, pg. 4294
KOWEPO LAO INTERNATIONAL CO., LTD.—See Korea Electric Power Corporation; *Int'l*, pg. 4283
KOWLOONBAY INTERNATIONAL TRADE & EXHIBITION CENTRE—See Hopewell Holdings Limited; *Int'l*, pg. 3473
KOWLOON DEVELOPMENT COMPANY LIMITED; *Int'l*, pg. 4294
KOWLOON DEVELOPMENT FINANCE LIMITED—See Kowloon Development Company Limited; *Int'l*, pg. 4295
KOWLOON FUNERAL PARLOUR COMPANY LIMITED—See Grand Peace Group Holdings Limited; *Int'l*, pg. 3056
THE KOWLOON HOTEL LIMITED—See CK Asset Holdings Limited; *Int'l*, pg. 1635
THE KOWLOON MOTOR BUS COMPANY (1933) LIMITED—See Transport International Holdings Limited; *Int'l*, pg. 7905
KOWLOON PANDA HOTEL LIMITED—See Hopewell Holdings Limited; *Int'l*, pg. 3473
KOYA CORP.—See Hirata Corporation; *Int'l*, pg. 3404
KOYA LEADERSHIP PARTNERS LLC; *U.S. Private*, pg. 2345
KOY HELSINGIN ITAKATU 11—See Blackstone Inc.; *U.S. Public*, pg. 351
KOYJ CO., LTD.; *Int'l*, pg. 4295
KOYKER MFG. CO.—See Sioux Steel Company; *U.S. Private*, pg. 3671
KOY KUNINKAANKAARI—See Blackstone Inc.; *U.S. Public*, pg. 351
KOY NIMISMIEHENNIITTY—See Blackstone Inc.; *U.S. Public*, pg. 351
KOYO AUSTRALIA PTY. LTD.—See JTEKT Corporation; *Int'l*, pg. 4018
KOYO AUTO CO., LTD.—See VT Holdings Co., Ltd.; *Int'l*, pg. 8315
KOYO AUTOMOTIVE PARTS (WUXI) CO., LTD.—See JTEKT Corporation; *Int'l*, pg. 4018
KOYO BEARING DALIAN CO., LTD.—See JTEKT Corporation; *Int'l*, pg. 4018

KOYJ CO., LTD.

CORPORATE AFFILIATIONS

KOYO BEARINGS CANADA INC.—See JTEKT Corporation; *Int'l*, pg. 4018
KOYO BEARINGS CESKA REPUBLIKA S.R.O.—See JTEKT Corporation; *Int'l*, pg. 4018
KOYO BEARINGS DEUTSCHLAND GMBH—See JTEKT Corporation; *Int'l*, pg. 4018
KOYO BEARINGS (EUROPE) LTD.—See JTEKT Corporation; *Int'l*, pg. 4018
KOYO BEARINGS INDIA PRIVATE LTD.—See JTEKT Corporation; *Int'l*, pg. 4018
KOYO BEARINGS VIERZON MAROMME SAS—See JTEKT Corporation; *Int'l*, pg. 4018
KOYO CANADA INC.—See JTEKT Corporation; *Int'l*, pg. 4018
KO YO CHEMICAL (GROUP) LTD.; *Int'l*, pg. 4215
KOYO CO., LTD.—See Toho Holdings Co., Ltd.; *Int'l*, pg. 7776
KOYO CORPORATION OF U.S.A.—See JTEKT Corporation; *Int'l*, pg. 4018
KOYO CORPORATION OF U.S.A.—See JTEKT Corporation; *Int'l*, pg. 4018
KOYO DEUTSCHLAND GMBH—See JTEKT Corporation; *Int'l*, pg. 4018
KOYO ELECTRONICS INDUSTRIES CO., LTD.; *Int'l*, pg. 4295
KOYO ENGINEERING (S.E. ASIA) PTE. LTD—See Koyo International Limited; *Int'l*, pg. 4295
KOYO FRANCE S.A.—See JTEKT Corporation; *Int'l*, pg. 4018
KOYO IBERICA, S.L.—See JTEKT Corporation; *Int'l*, pg. 4018
KOYO INTERNATIONAL LIMITED; *Int'l*, pg. 4295
KOYO ITALIA S.R.L.—See JTEKT Corporation; *Int'l*, pg. 4019
KOYO JICO KOREA CO., LTD.—See JTEKT Corporation; *Int'l*, pg. 4019
KOYO JOINT (THAILAND) CO., LTD.—See JTEKT Corporation; *Int'l*, pg. 4019
KOYO KENKI LEASE CO., LTD.—See Aktio Holdings Corporation; *Int'l*, pg. 267
KOYO-KOWA CO., LTD.—See JTEKT Corporation; *Int'l*, pg. 4019
KOYO KULLAGER SCANDINAVIA A.B.—See JTEKT Corporation; *Int'l*, pg. 4019
KOYO KYUEI CO., LTD.—See JTEKT Corporation; *Int'l*, pg. 4019
KOYO LATIN AMERICA, S.A.—See JTEKT Corporation; *Int'l*, pg. 4019
KOYO LINE, LTD—See Marubeni Corporation; *Int'l*, pg. 4705
KOYO LIOHO (FOSHAN) AUTOMOTIVE PARTS CO., LTD.—See JTEKT Corporation; *Int'l*, pg. 4019
KOYO MACHINE INDUSTRIES CO., LTD.—See JTEKT Corporation; *Int'l*, pg. 4019
KOYO M&E PTE. LTD—See Koyo International Limited; *Int'l*, pg. 4295
KOYOMETALTEC CO., LTD.—See JTEKT Corporation; *Int'l*, pg. 4019
KOYO MEXICANA, S.A. DE C.V.—See JTEKT Corporation; *Int'l*, pg. 4019
KOYO MIDDLE EAST FZCO—See JTEKT Corporation; *Int'l*, pg. 4019
KOYO NEEDLE BEARINGS (WUXI) CO., LTD.—See JTEKT Corporation; *Int'l*, pg. 4019
KOYO NICHIJIKU CO., LTD.—See JTEKT Corporation; *Int'l*, pg. 4019
KOYO PAPER MFG. CO., LTD.—See Nippon Paper Industries Co., Ltd.; *Int'l*, pg. 5327
KOYO ROLAMENTOS DO BRASIL LTDA.—See JTEKT Corporation; *Int'l*, pg. 4019
KOYO ROMANIA S.A.—See JTEKT Corporation; *Int'l*, pg. 4019
KOYO SANGYO CO., LTD.—See Bando Chemical Industries, Ltd.; *Int'l*, pg. 830
KOYO SEALING TECHNO CO., LTD.—See Koyo Electronics Industries Co., Ltd.; *Int'l*, pg. 4295
KOYO SEIKI CO., LTD.—See Kawakin Holdings Co., Ltd.; *Int'l*, pg. 4094
KOYOSHA CO., LTD.—See Japan Pulp and Paper Company Limited; *Int'l*, pg. 3904
KOYOSHA INC.; *Int'l*, pg. 4295
KOYO SINGAPORE BEARINGS (PTE) LTD.—See JTEKT Corporation; *Int'l*, pg. 4019
KOYOSUNTECH CO., LTD.—See Yoshitake Inc.; *Int'l*, pg. 8601
KOYO SYSTEM KIKI CO., LTD.—See Yamau Holdings Co., Ltd.; *Int'l*, pg. 8555
KOYO THERMO SYSTEMS CO., LTD.—See Koyo Electronics Industries Co., Ltd.; *Int'l*, pg. 4295
KOYOU INNOTEX CO., LTD.—See Koyou Rentia Co., Ltd.; *Int'l*, pg. 4295
KOYO (U.K.) LIMITED—See JTEKT Corporation; *Int'l*, pg. 4019
KOYOU LOGI-X CO., LTD.—See Koyou Rentia Co., Ltd.; *Int'l*, pg. 4295
KOYOU RENTIA CO., LTD.; *Int'l*, pg. 4295
KOYOU SERVICE CO., LTD.—See Koyou Rentia Co., Ltd.; *Int'l*, pg. 4295

KOYO YAKUHIN CO., LTD.—See MatsukiyoCocokara & Co.; *Int'l*, pg. 4730
KOY ZEPPELININ CITY KESKUS—See Blackstone Inc.; *U.S. Public*, pg. 351
KOZA ALTIN ISLETMELERI AS; *Int'l*, pg. 4295
KOZA ANADOLU METAL MADENCILIK ISLETMELERI AS; *Int'l*, pg. 4295
KOZAKURA SHOKAI CO., LTD.—See Chori Co., Ltd.; *Int'l*, pg. 1583
KOZARA A.D.; *Int'l*, pg. 4295
KOZARAPREVOZ A.D.; *Int'l*, pg. 4295
KOZARAPUTEVI D.O.O. BANJA LUKA—See Grupa Fortis d.o.o. Banja Luka; *Int'l*, pg. 3116
KOZHAN JSC—See Geo-Jade Petroleum Corporation; *Int'l*, pg. 2932
KOZIENICE II SP. Z O.O.—See ENEA S.A.; *Int'l*, pg. 2410
KOZO KEIKAKU ENGINEERING INC; *Int'l*, pg. 4295
KOZOSUSHI CO., LTD.; *Int'l*, pg. 4295
KOZUKI DENSO CO., LTD.—See Teikoku Electric Mfg. Co., Ltd.; *Int'l*, pg. 7524
KOZY SHACK ENTERPRISES INC.—See Land O'Lakes, Inc.; *U.S. Private*, pg. 2383
KPA-BM HOLDINGS LIMITED; *Int'l*, pg. 4296
K.P.A. COMPANY LIMITED—See China Financial Services Holdings Limited; *Int'l*, pg. 1503
KPA LLC; *U.S. Private*, pg. 2345
KPA PENSIONSFORSAKRING AB—See Folksam omsesidig sakforsakring; *Int'l*, pg. 2721
K PAR K—See Compagnie de Saint-Gobain SA; *Int'l*, pg. 1723
KPA SERVICES, LLC—See Providence Equity Partners L.L.C.; *U.S. Private*, pg. 3293
KP BUILDING PRODUCTS LTD.—See Compagnie de Saint-Gobain SA; *Int'l*, pg. 1723
KPC HEALTHCARE HOLDINGS, INC.; *U.S. Private*, pg. 2346
KPC HEALTHCARE, INC.—See KPC Healthcare Holdings, Inc.; *U.S. Private*, pg. 2346
KP CO. LTD.—See Mitsubishi Gas Chemical Company, Inc.; *Int'l*, pg. 4948
KP COMPONENTS INC.—See Segulah Advisor AB; *Int'l*, pg. 6684
K/P CORPORATION; *U.S. Private*, pg. 2252
KPC PHARMACEUTICALS INC.; *Int'l*, pg. 4296
KPC PROMISE HEALTHCARE, LLC—See KPC Healthcare Holdings, Inc.; *U.S. Private*, pg. 2346
KPC PROMISE HOSPITAL OF BATON ROUGE, LLC—See KPC Healthcare Holdings, Inc.; *U.S. Private*, pg. 2346
KPC PROMISE HOSPITAL OF DALLAS, LLC—See KPC Healthcare Holdings, Inc.; *U.S. Private*, pg. 2346
KPC PROMISE HOSPITAL OF OVERLAND PARK, LLC—See KPC Healthcare Holdings, Inc.; *U.S. Private*, pg. 2346
KPC PROMISE HOSPITAL OF PHOENIX, LLC—See KPC Healthcare Holdings, Inc.; *U.S. Private*, pg. 2346
KPC PROMISE HOSPITAL OF SALT LAKE, LLC—See KPC Healthcare Holdings, Inc.; *U.S. Private*, pg. 2346
KPC PROMISE HOSPITAL OF VICKSBURG, LLC—See KPC Healthcare Holdings, Inc.; *U.S. Private*, pg. 2346
KPC PROMISE HOSPITAL OF WICHITA FALLS, LLC—See KPC Healthcare Holdings, Inc.; *U.S. Private*, pg. 2346
KPC PROMISE SKILLED NURSING FACILITY OF OVERLAND PARK, LLC—See KPC Healthcare Holdings, Inc.; *U.S. Private*, pg. 2346
KPC PROMISE SKILLED NURSING FACILITY OF WICHITA FALLS, LLC—See KPC Healthcare Holdings, Inc.; *U.S. Private*, pg. 2346
KP CREDIT GAIN FINANCE COMPANY LIMITED—See China Financial Services Holdings Limited; *Int'l*, pg. 1503
KPD INSURANCE, INC.—See IMA Financial Group, Inc.; *U.S. Private*, pg. 2043
KPDX-TV—See Meredith Corporation; *U.S. Public*, pg. 1423
KP ENERGY LIMITED; *Int'l*, pg. 4295
KPF - CHUNGJU FACTORY—See KPF; *Int'l*, pg. 4296
KPFF INC.; *U.S. Private*, pg. 2346
KPF, LLC—See The Kroger Co.; *U.S. Public*, pg. 2108
KPF; *Int'l*, pg. 4296
KPF USA—See KPF; *Int'l*, pg. 4296
KPH-CONSOLIDATION, INC.—See HCA Healthcare, Inc.; *U.S. Public*, pg. 999
KPH HOLDINGS, LLC—See Dreison International, Inc.; *U.S. Private*, pg. 1276
KPHO BROADCASTING CORPORATION—See Meredith Corporation; *U.S. Public*, pg. 1423
KP HOLDINGS LLC; *U.S. Private*, pg. 2345
KPHO-TV—See Meredith Corporation; *U.S. Public*, pg. 1423
KPI 2 INCORPORATED; *U.S. Private*, pg. 2346
KPIC DAWN POLYMER (SHANGHAI) CO., LTD.—See Shandong Dawn Polymer Co., Ltd.; *Int'l*, pg. 6752
KPIC-TV—See Sinclair, Inc.; *U.S. Public*, pg. 1886
KPI DIRECT LLC; *U.S. Private*, pg. 2346
KPI ELEVATORS, INC.—See KONE Oyj; *Int'l*, pg. 4250
KPI GREEN ENERGY LIMITED; *Int'l*, pg. 4296

KPI LOGISTICS, INC.—See P&S Transportation, Inc.; *U.S. Private*, pg. 3059
K & P INTERNATIONAL HOLDINGS LIMITED; *Int'l*, pg. 4037
KPI PARTNERS, INC.; *U.S. Private*, pg. 2346
KPIT CUMMINS GLOBAL BUSINESS SOLUTIONS LTD.—See KPIT Technologies Ltd; *Int'l*, pg. 4296
KPIT INFORSYSTEMS INCORPORATED—See KPIT Technologies Ltd; *Int'l*, pg. 4296
KPIT INFOSYSTEMS CENTRAL EUROPE SP.Z O.O.—See KPIT Technologies Ltd; *Int'l*, pg. 4296
KPIT INFOSYSTEMS INCORPORATED—See KPIT Technologies Ltd; *Int'l*, pg. 4296
KPIT (SHANGHAI) SOFTWARE TECHNOLOGY CO., LIMITED—See KPIT Technologies Ltd; *Int'l*, pg. 4296
KPIT TECHNOLOGIES GK—See KPIT Technologies Ltd; *Int'l*, pg. 4296
KPIT TECHNOLOGIES GMBH—See KPIT Technologies Ltd; *Int'l*, pg. 4296
KPIT TECHNOLOGIES INC.—See KPIT Technologies Ltd; *Int'l*, pg. 4296
KPIT TECHNOLOGIES LTD; *Int'l*, pg. 4296
KPIT TECHNOLOGIES NETHERLANDS B.V.—See KPIT Technologies Ltd; *Int'l*, pg. 4296
KPIT TECHNOLOGIES (UK) LIMITED—See KPIT Technologies Ltd; *Int'l*, pg. 4296
KPIX-TV—See National Amusements, Inc.; *U.S. Private*, pg. 2840
KPJ HEALTHCARE BERHAD; *Int'l*, pg. 4296
KPJ HEALTHCARE UNIVERSITY COLLEGE SDN BHD—See KPJ Healthcare Berhad; *Int'l*, pg. 4297
KPJ HEALTHSHOPPE SDN BHD—See KPJ Healthcare Berhad; *Int'l*, pg. 4296
KPK DORE OG VINDUER A/S—See Ratos AB; *Int'l*, pg. 6220
KP KOMPONENTER A/S—See Segulah Advisor AB; *Int'l*, pg. 6684
KP KOMUNALAC A.D.; *Int'l*, pg. 4295
KPLC, LLC—See Gray Television, Inc.; *U.S. Public*, pg. 959
KPLR, INC.—See Nexstar Media Group, Inc.; *U.S. Public*, pg. 1524
K-PLUS OY—See Kesko Corporation; *Int'l*, pg. 4142
K PLUS S AFRICA (PTY) LTD.—See K+S Aktiengesellschaft; *Int'l*, pg. 4040
K PLUS S IBERIA S.L.—See K+S Aktiengesellschaft; *Int'l*, pg. 4040
K PLUS S MIDDLE EAST FZE—See K+S Aktiengesellschaft; *Int'l*, pg. 4040
KPM ANALYTICS, INC.—See Union Park Capital; *U.S. Private*, pg. 4285
K.P. MCNAMARA COMPANY, INC.—See HCI Equity Management, L.P.; *U.S. Private*, pg. 1889
K.P. MCNAMARA OF GEORGIA, INC—See HCI Equity Management, L.P.; *U.S. Private*, pg. 1889
KPMF USA INC—See Kay Screen Printing, Inc.; *U.S. Private*, pg. 2266
KPMG ADVISORY BCVBA—See KPMG Europe LLP; *Int'l*, pg. 4297
KPMG AFRICA LIMITED; *Int'l*, pg. 4297
KPMG AG/SA—See KPMG Europe LLP; *Int'l*, pg. 4297
KPMG AG WIRTSCHAFTSPRUFUNGSGESELLSCHAFT—See KPMG Europe LLP; *Int'l*, pg. 4297
KPMG BAGIMSIZ DENETIM VE SERBEST MUHASEBECI MALI MUSAVIRILIK A.S.; *Int'l*, pg. 4297
KPMG CORPORATE FINANCE, LLC—See KPMG LLP; *U.S. Private*, pg. 2346
KPMG EUROPE LLP NIEDERLASSUNG DEUTSCHLAND—See KPMG Europe LLP; *Int'l*, pg. 4297
KPMG EUROPE LLP; *Int'l*, pg. 4297
KPMG INTERNATIONAL COOPERATIVE; *Int'l*, pg. 4297
KPMG LLP; *U.S. Private*, pg. 2346
KPMG LLP—See KPMG Europe LLP; *Int'l*, pg. 4297
KPMG N.V.—See KPMG Europe LLP; *Int'l*, pg. 4297
KPMG, S.A.—See KPMG Europe LLP; *Int'l*, pg. 4297
KPMG SERVICES (PROPRIETARY) LIMITED—See KPMG Africa Limited; *Int'l*, pg. 4297
KPMG S.P.A.; *Int'l*, pg. 4297
KPM HOLDING LIMITED; *Int'l*, pg. 4297
KPM INDUSTRIES LTD.—See Sika AG; *Int'l*, pg. 6914
KP MOTORS LLC—See Asbury Automotive Group, Inc.; *U.S. Public*, pg. 209
KPM TECH CO., LTD; *Int'l*, pg. 4297
KPM-UK TAXIS PLC—See Bowmark Capital LLP; *Int'l*, pg. 1124
KPN B.V.—See Koninklijke KPN N.V.; *Int'l*, pg. 4266
KPN EURORINGS B.V.—See GTT Communications, Inc.; *U.S. Private*, pg. 1808
KPN EURORINGS GBMH—See Koninklijke KPN N.V.; *Int'l*, pg. 4267
KPN INTERNATIONAL—See GTT Communications, Inc.; *U.S. Private*, pg. 1808
KPN INTERNATIONAL—See GTT Communications, Inc.; *U.S. Private*, pg. 1808
KPN INTERNATIONAL—See GTT Communications, Inc.; *U.S. Private*, pg. 1808

COMPANY NAME INDEX

KPN MOBILE INTERNATIONAL B.V.—See Koninklijke KPN N.V.; *Int'l*, pg. 4267
KPNX-TV—See TEGNA Inc.; *U.S. Public*, pg. 1990
KPPD-SZCZECINEK S.A.; *Int'l*, pg. 4298
KPP GROUP HOLDINGS CO., LTD.; *Int'l*, pg. 4297
K'(PRIME) TECHNOLOGIES INC.—See Nanalysis Scientific Corp.; *Int'l*, pg. 5138
K.P.R., INC.—See Northlane Capital Partners, LLC; *U.S. Private*, pg. 2956
KPR MILL LIMITED; *Int'l*, pg. 4298
K-PROVISION CO., LTD.—See Kajima Corporation; *Int'l*, pg. 4054
KPRS CONSTRUCTION SERVICES, INC.; *U.S. Private*, pg. 2346
KPRZ 1210AM RADIO INC—See Salem Media Group, Inc.; *U.S. Public*, pg. 1836
KPS AG—See Bridgepoint Group Plc; *Int'l*, pg. 1154
KPS (BEIJING) PETROLEUM EQUIPMENT TRADING CO, LTD.—See Dover Corporation; *U.S. Public*, pg. 681
KPS CAPITAL PARTNERS, LP; *U.S. Private*, pg. 2346
KPS CEE S.R.O.—See Dover Corporation; *U.S. Public*, pg. 681
KPS CO., LTD.—See Konoike Transport Co., Ltd.; *Int'l*, pg. 4274
KPS CONSORTIUM BERHAD; *Int'l*, pg. 4299
KPS CONSULTING—See Bridgepoint Group Plc; *Int'l*, pg. 1154
KPS CORP; *Int'l*, pg. 4299
KPS FRANCE SARL—See Dover Corporation; *U.S. Public*, pg. 681
KPS FUELING SOLUTIONS SDN. BHD.—See Dover Corporation; *U.S. Public*, pg. 681
KP SHAW, LLC—See The Shaw Group Inc.; *U.S. Private*, pg. 4117
KPSI PROPERTY INC—See Keppel Corporation Limited; *Int'l*, pg. 4130
KP SNACKS LTD.—See Intersnack Group GmbH & Co. KG; *Int'l*, pg. 3760
KPS N.A., INC.—See Koito Manufacturing Co., Ltd.; *Int'l*, pg. 4230
KPS PLYWOOD SDN. BHD.—See KPS Consortium Berhad; *Int'l*, pg. 4299
KPSS GOVERNMENT SOLUTIONS, INC.—See Kratos Defense & Security Solutions, Inc.; *U.S. Public*, pg. 1276
KPSS HONG KONG LTD.—See Kao Corporation; *Int'l*, pg. 4075
KPSS - KAO PROFESSIONAL SALON SERVICES GMBH—See Kao Corporation; *Int'l*, pg. 4073
KPSS NEDERLAND B.V.—See Kao Corporation; *Int'l*, pg. 4074
KPSS (UK) LIMITED—See Kao Corporation; *Int'l*, pg. 4075
KPS UK LIMITED—See Dover Corporation; *U.S. Public*, pg. 681
KPTCC CO., LTD.; *Int'l*, pg. 4299
KPT. GRZEGORZ GORSKI POLSTEAM (MOROCCO) S.A.R.L—See Polska Zegluga Morska; *Int'l*, pg. 5911
KPTI LIMITED—See Brown & Brown, Inc.; *U.S. Public*, pg. 401
KPT INDUSTRIES LTD.; *Int'l*, pg. 4299
KP TISSUE INC.; *Int'l*, pg. 4296
KP TOPLANA A.D.; *Int'l*, pg. 4296
KPWR-FM—See Meruelo Group LLC; *U.S. Private*, pg. 2677
KPX CHEMICAL CO., LTD.; *Int'l*, pg. 4299
KPX CHEMICAL CO., LTD. - ULSAN PLANT—See KPX Chemical Co., Ltd.; *Int'l*, pg. 4299
KPX DEVELOPMENT CO., LTD.—See KPX Holdings Co., Ltd.; *Int'l*, pg. 4299
KPX FINE CHEMICAL CO., LTD.—See Hanwha Group; *Int'l*, pg. 3266
KPX HOLDINGS CO., LTD.; *Int'l*, pg. 4299
KPX VINA CO., LTD.—See KPX Holdings Co., Ltd.; *Int'l*, pg. 4299
KQED INC.; *U.S. Private*, pg. 2348
KQKS-FM—See AUDACY, INC.; *U.S. Public*, pg. 226
KRACHT GMBH—See Atlas Copco AB; *Int'l*, pg. 683
KRACIE FOODS, LTD.—See Hoyu Co., Ltd.; *Int'l*, pg. 3499
KRACIE FOODS SALES, LTD.—See Hoyu Co., Ltd.; *Int'l*, pg. 3499
KRACIE HOLDINGS, LTD.—See Hoyu Co., Ltd.; *Int'l*, pg. 3499
KRACIE HOME PRODUCTS, LTD.—See Hoyu Co., Ltd.; *Int'l*, pg. 3499
KRACIE HOME PRODUCTS SALES LTD.—See Hoyu Co., Ltd.; *Int'l*, pg. 3499
KRACIE PHARMACEUTICAL, LTD.—See Hoyu Co., Ltd.; *Int'l*, pg. 3499
KRACIE PHARMA, LTD.—See Hoyu Co., Ltd.; *Int'l*, pg. 3499
KRACK CORPORATION—See Panasonic Holdings Corporation; *Int'l*, pg. 5720
KRACKELER SCIENTIFIC INC.; *U.S. Private*, pg. 2348
KRACO ENTERPRISES, LLC—See Sun Capital Partners, Inc.; *U.S. Private*, pg. 3860
KRACOR, INC.—See Yamaha Corporation; *Int'l*, pg. 8550
KRA CORPORATION; *U.S. Private*, pg. 2348
KRAEFT LOGISTIK GMBH—See HELM AG; *Int'l*, pg. 3338
KRAEMER BROTHERS, LLC; *U.S. Private*, pg. 2348

KRAEMER NORTH AMERICA, LLC—See Obayashi Corporation; *Int'l*, pg. 5508
KRAEMER PHARMACEUTICAL (SHANGHAI) EQUIPMENT CO., LTD.—See Indutrade AB; *Int'l*, pg. 3680
KRAEMER'S NURSERY INC.; *U.S. Private*, pg. 2348
KRAEMER US, LLC—See Indutrade AB; *Int'l*, pg. 3680
KRAFCOR UNLIMITED—See Specialty Industries, Inc.; *U.S. Private*, pg. 3750
KRAFFT HAESTFODER AB—See Lantmannen ek for; *Int'l*, pg. 4413
KRAFT AND WARME ROHR- UND ANLAGENTECHNIK GMBH—See PORR AG; *Int'l*, pg. 5923
KRAFTANLAGEN HAMBURG GMBH—See Alpiq Holding AG; *Int'l*, pg. 372
KRAFTANLAGEN HEIDELBERG GMBH—See Alpiq Holding AG; *Int'l*, pg. 372
KRAFTANLAGEN MUNCHEN GMBH—See Bouygues S.A.; *Int'l*, pg. 1123
KRAFTANLAGEN POWER PLANTS GMBH—See Alpiq Holding AG; *Int'l*, pg. 372
KRAFTANLAGEN ROMANIA S.R.L.—See Alpiq Holding AG; *Int'l*, pg. 372
KRAFT BANK ASA; *Int'l*, pg. 4299
KRAFT CANADA, INC.-INGLESIDE—See 3G Capital Inc.; *U.S. Private*, pg. 10
KRAFT CANADA, INC.-INGLESIDE—See Berkshire Hathaway Inc.; *U.S. Public*, pg. 318
KRAFT CANADA, INC.-MOUNT-ROYAL—See 3G Capital Inc.; *U.S. Private*, pg. 10
KRAFT CANADA, INC.-MOUNT-ROYAL—See Berkshire Hathaway Inc.; *U.S. Public*, pg. 318
KRAFT CANADA INC.—See 3G Capital Inc.; *U.S. Private*, pg. 10
KRAFT CANADA INC.—See Berkshire Hathaway Inc.; *U.S. Public*, pg. 318
KRAFT CHEMICAL COMPANY; *U.S. Private*, pg. 2348
KRAFT FOOD INGREDIENTS CORP.—See 3G Capital Inc.; *U.S. Private*, pg. 10
KRAFT FOOD INGREDIENTS CORP.—See Berkshire Hathaway Inc.; *U.S. Public*, pg. 318
KRAFT FOODS CEEMA GMBH—See Mondelez International, Inc.; *U.S. Public*, pg. 1462
KRAFT FOODS COLOMBIA LTDA.—See Mondelez International, Inc.; *U.S. Public*, pg. 1461
KRAFT FOODS COSTA RICA, S.A.—See Mondelez International, Inc.; *U.S. Public*, pg. 1461
KRAFT FOODS DE NICARAGUA S.A.—See Mondelez International, Inc.; *U.S. Public*, pg. 1461
KRAFT FOODS DEVELOPING MARKETS—See Mondelez International, Inc.; *U.S. Public*, pg. 1461
KRAFT FOODS EESTI OSAUHING—See Mondelez International, Inc.; *U.S. Public*, pg. 1462
KRAFT FOODS EGYPT L.L.C.—See Mondelez International, Inc.; *U.S. Public*, pg. 1461
KRAFT FOODS ENTITY HOLDINGS B.V.—See Mondelez International, Inc.; *U.S. Public*, pg. 1462
KRAFT FOODS FINLAND PRODUCTION OY—See Mondelez International, Inc.; *U.S. Public*, pg. 1462
KRAFT FOODS FRANCE INTELLECTUAL PROPERTY S.A.S.—See Mondelez International, Inc.; *U.S. Public*, pg. 1463
KRAFT FOODS GROUP PUERTO RICO, LLC—See 3G Capital Inc.; *U.S. Private*, pg. 10
KRAFT FOODS GROUP PUERTO RICO, LLC—See Berkshire Hathaway Inc.; *U.S. Public*, pg. 318
KRAFT FOODS (MIDDLE EAST & AFRICA) LTD.—See Mondelez International, Inc.; *U.S. Public*, pg. 1462
KRAFT FOODS PANAMA, S.A.—See Mondelez International, Inc.; *U.S. Public*, pg. 1462
KRAFT FOODS (PUERTO RICO), LLC—See Mondelez International, Inc.; *U.S. Public*, pg. 1461
KRAFT FOODS SVERIGE HOLDING AB—See Mondelez International, Inc.; *U.S. Public*, pg. 1462
KRAFT GIDA SANAYI VE TICARET A. S.—See Mondelez International, Inc.; *U.S. Public*, pg. 1461
THE KRAFT GROUP LLC; *U.S. Private*, pg. 4065
KRAFT HEINZ COMPANY - ADDISON—See 3G Capital Inc.; *U.S. Private*, pg. 10
KRAFT HEINZ COMPANY - ADDISON—See Berkshire Hathaway Inc.; *U.S. Public*, pg. 318
KRAFT HEINZ COMPANY - CHARLOTTE—See 3G Capital Inc.; *U.S. Private*, pg. 10
KRAFT HEINZ COMPANY - CHARLOTTE—See Berkshire Hathaway Inc.; *U.S. Public*, pg. 318
KRAFT HEINZ COMPANY - COLUMBIA—See 3G Capital Inc.; *U.S. Private*, pg. 10
KRAFT HEINZ COMPANY - COLUMBIA—See Berkshire Hathaway Inc.; *U.S. Public*, pg. 318
KRAFT HEINZ COMPANY - COSHOCTON—See 3G Capital Inc.; *U.S. Private*, pg. 10
KRAFT HEINZ COMPANY - COSHOCTON—See Berkshire Hathaway Inc.; *U.S. Public*, pg. 318
KRAFT HEINZ COMPANY - DOVER—See 3G Capital Inc.; *U.S. Private*, pg. 10
KRAFT HEINZ COMPANY - DOVER—See Berkshire Hathaway Inc.; *U.S. Public*, pg. 318
KRAFT HEINZ COMPANY - FULLERTON—See 3G Capital Inc.; *U.S. Private*, pg. 10

KRAFT POWER CORP.

KRAFT HEINZ COMPANY - FULLERTON—See Berkshire Hathaway Inc.; *U.S. Public*, pg. 318
KRAFT HEINZ COMPANY - GARLAND—See 3G Capital Inc.; *U.S. Private*, pg. 10
KRAFT HEINZ COMPANY - GARLAND—See Berkshire Hathaway Inc.; *U.S. Public*, pg. 318
KRAFT HEINZ COMPANY - GRANITE CITY—See 3G Capital Inc.; *U.S. Private*, pg. 10
KRAFT HEINZ COMPANY - GRANITE CITY—See Berkshire Hathaway Inc.; *U.S. Public*, pg. 318
KRAFT HEINZ COMPANY - IRVINE—See 3G Capital Inc.; *U.S. Private*, pg. 10
KRAFT HEINZ COMPANY - IRVINE—See Berkshire Hathaway Inc.; *U.S. Public*, pg. 318
KRAFT HEINZ COMPANY - LEHIGH VALLEY—See 3G Capital Inc.; *U.S. Private*, pg. 10
KRAFT HEINZ COMPANY - LEHIGH VALLEY—See Berkshire Hathaway Inc.; *U.S. Public*, pg. 318
KRAFT HEINZ COMPANY - LIVERMORE—See 3G Capital Inc.; *U.S. Private*, pg. 10
KRAFT HEINZ COMPANY - LIVERMORE—See Berkshire Hathaway Inc.; *U.S. Public*, pg. 318
KRAFT HEINZ COMPANY - LOUIS RICH—See 3G Capital Inc.; *U.S. Private*, pg. 10
KRAFT HEINZ COMPANY - LOUIS RICH—See Berkshire Hathaway Inc.; *U.S. Public*, pg. 318
KRAFT HEINZ COMPANY - LOWVILLE—See 3G Capital Inc.; *U.S. Private*, pg. 11
KRAFT HEINZ COMPANY - LOWVILLE—See Berkshire Hathaway Inc.; *U.S. Public*, pg. 318
KRAFT HEINZ COMPANY - MASON CITY—See 3G Capital Inc.; *U.S. Private*, pg. 11
KRAFT HEINZ COMPANY - MASON CITY—See Berkshire Hathaway Inc.; *U.S. Public*, pg. 318
KRAFT HEINZ COMPANY - MAXWELL HOUSE COFFEE—See 3G Capital Inc.; *U.S. Private*, pg. 11
KRAFT HEINZ COMPANY - MAXWELL HOUSE COFFEE—See Berkshire Hathaway Inc.; *U.S. Public*, pg. 318
KRAFT HEINZ COMPANY - NEW ULM—See 3G Capital Inc.; *U.S. Private*, pg. 11
KRAFT HEINZ COMPANY - NEW ULM—See Berkshire Hathaway Inc.; *U.S. Public*, pg. 318
KRAFT HEINZ COMPANY - OSCAR MAYER—See 3G Capital Inc.; *U.S. Private*, pg. 11
KRAFT HEINZ COMPANY - OSCAR MAYER—See Berkshire Hathaway Inc.; *U.S. Public*, pg. 318
KRAFT HEINZ COMPANY - PLANTERS—See 3G Capital Inc.; *U.S. Private*, pg. 11
KRAFT HEINZ COMPANY - PLANTERS—See Berkshire Hathaway Inc.; *U.S. Public*, pg. 318
KRAFT HEINZ COMPANY - RICHMOND—See 3G Capital Inc.; *U.S. Private*, pg. 11
KRAFT HEINZ COMPANY - RICHMOND—See Berkshire Hathaway Inc.; *U.S. Public*, pg. 318
KRAFT HEINZ COMPANY - SAN LEANDRO—See 3G Capital Inc.; *U.S. Private*, pg. 11
KRAFT HEINZ COMPANY - SAN LEANDRO—See Berkshire Hathaway Inc.; *U.S. Public*, pg. 318
THE KRAFT HEINZ COMPANY—See 3G Capital Inc.; *U.S. Private*, pg. 9
THE KRAFT HEINZ COMPANY—See Berkshire Hathaway Inc.; *U.S. Public*, pg. 317
KRAFT HEINZ COMPANY - SPRINGFIELD—See 3G Capital Inc.; *U.S. Private*, pg. 11
KRAFT HEINZ COMPANY - SPRINGFIELD—See Berkshire Hathaway Inc.; *U.S. Public*, pg. 318
KRAFT HEINZ COMPANY - TULARE—See 3G Capital Inc.; *U.S. Private*, pg. 11
KRAFT HEINZ COMPANY - TULARE—See Berkshire Hathaway Inc.; *U.S. Public*, pg. 318
KRAFT HEINZ COMPANY - WAUSAU—See 3G Capital Inc.; *U.S. Private*, pg. 11
KRAFT HEINZ COMPANY - WAUSAU—See Berkshire Hathaway Inc.; *U.S. Public*, pg. 318
KRAFT HEINZ COMPANY - WILKES BARRE—See 3G Capital Inc.; *U.S. Private*, pg. 11
KRAFT HEINZ COMPANY - WILKES BARRE—See Berkshire Hathaway Inc.; *U.S. Public*, pg. 318
KRAFT HEINZ FOODS COMPANY—See 3G Capital Inc.; *U.S. Private*, pg. 9
KRAFT HEINZ FOODS COMPANY—See Berkshire Hathaway Inc.; *U.S. Public*, pg. 317
KRAFT & KENNEDY, INC.; *U.S. Private*, pg. 2348
KRAFTMAID CABINETRY, INC.—See AIP, LLC; *U.S. Private*, pg. 133
KRAFTMAID CABINETRY—See AIP, LLC; *U.S. Private*, pg. 133
KRAFT MART—See AGCO Inc.; *U.S. Private*, pg. 126
KRAFTMEK OY—See Kuroda Precision Industries Ltd.; *Int'l*, pg. 4342
KRAFT MOTORCAR COMPANY OF TALLAHASSEE, INC.; *U.S. Private*, pg. 2348
KRAFT OF ASIA PAPERBOARD & PACKAGING CO., LTD.—See Marubeni Corporation; *Int'l*, pg. 4705
KRAFTON, INC.; *Int'l*, pg. 4299
KRAFT POWER CORP.; *U.S. Private*, pg. 2349
KRAFTSZER KFT.—See Alpiq Holding AG; *Int'l*, pg. 373

KRAFT POWER CORP.
CORPORATE AFFILIATIONS

KRAFTSZER VALLALKOZASI KFT.—See Alpiq Holding AG; *Int'l*, pg. 373
KRAFT TOOL COMPANY INC.; *U.S. Private*, pg. 2349
KRAFTVERKEHRSGESELLSCHAFT PADERBORN MBH—See E.ON SE; *Int'l*, pg. 2253
KRAFTWAY CORPORATION PLC; *Int'l*, pg. 4299
KRAFTWERK CO., LTD.—See Transaction Co., Ltd.; *Int'l*, pg. 7895
KRAFTWERK MEHRUM GMBH—See Energeticky a Prumyslovy Holding, a.s.; *Int'l*, pg. 2420
KRAFTWERK SCHKOPAU GMBH—See E.ON SE; *Int'l*, pg. 2253
KRAFTWERK SCHWEDT GMBH & CO. KG—See Beijing Enterprises Holdings Limited; *Int'l*, pg. 950
KRAGNES FARMERS ELEVATOR CO.; *U.S. Private*, pg. 2349
KRAHULIK - MASOZAVOD KRAHULCI, A.S.—See Agrofert Holding, a.s.; *Int'l*, pg. 219
KRAICHGAU-KLINIK AKTIENGESELLSCHAFT—See Asklepios Kliniken GmbH & Co. KGaA; *Int'l*, pg. 623
KRAICHGAU-KLINIK BAD RAPPENAU GMBH & CO. KG—See Asklepios Kliniken GmbH & Co. KGaA; *Int'l*, pg. 623
KRAIG BIOCRAFT LABORATORIES, INC.; *U.S. Public*, pg. 1275
KRA INTERNATIONAL, LLC—See Patrick Industries, Inc.; *U.S. Public*, pg. 1652
KRAJINAPETROL A.D.; *Int'l*, pg. 4299
KRAKCHEMIA S.A.; *Int'l*, pg. 4299
KRAKEN ENERGY CORP.; *Int'l*, pg. 4299
KRAKEN POWER GMBH—See Kraken Robotics Inc.; *Int'l*, pg. 4299
KRAKEN ROBOTICS INC.; *Int'l*, pg. 4299
KRAKOWSKI KREDENS SP. Z O.O.—See Alma Market S.A.; *Int'l*, pg. 361
KRAKPOL SP. Z O.O.—See Impel S.A.; *Int'l*, pg. 3632
KRAMER AG—See Indutrade AB; *Int'l*, pg. 3680
KRAMER AUCTIONS LTD.—See RB Global, Inc.; *Int'l*, pg. 6226
KRAMER BEVERAGE CO. INC.; *U.S. Private*, pg. 2349
KRAMER BROS LUMBER CO. INC.; *U.S. Private*, pg. 2349
KRAMER DIRECT; *U.S. Private*, pg. 2349
KRAMER LABORATORIES, INC.—See Avista Capital Partners, L.P.; *U.S. Private*, pg. 408
KRAMER & LEONARD INC.; *U.S. Private*, pg. 2349
KRAMER LEVIN NAFTALIS & FRANKEL LLP; *U.S. Private*, pg. 2349
KRAMER-SMILKO—See Valsef Group; *Int'l*, pg. 8123
KRAMER TIRE CO. INC.; *U.S. Private*, pg. 2349
KRAMER-WERKE GMBH—See Wacker Neuson SE; *Int'l*, pg. 8324
KRAMER-WILSON CO. INC.; *U.S. Private*, pg. 2349
KRAMME CONSOLIDATED INC.; *U.S. Private*, pg. 2349
KRAMP GROEP BV—See SHV Holdings N.V.; *Int'l*, pg. 6872
KRAMSKI GMBH; *Int'l*, pg. 4299
KRAMSKI NORTH AMERICA, INC.—See KRAMSKI GmbH; *Int'l*, pg. 4299
KRAMZ—See En+ Group Ltd.; *Int'l*, pg. 2395
KRANBAU KOETHEN GMBH—See Georgsmarienhutte Holding GmbH; *Int'l*, pg. 2940
K.R. ANDERSON CO. INC.; *U.S. Private*, pg. 2252
KRANEKS INTERNATIONAL CO., LTD.—See Komatsu Ltd.; *Int'l*, pg. 4235
KRANICH'S JEWELERS, INC.; *U.S. Private*, pg. 2349
KRANKENHAUS CUXHAVEN GMBH—See Asklepios Kliniken GmbH & Co. KGaA; *Int'l*, pg. 624
KRANKENHAUS KOTHEN GMBH—See Fresenius SE & Co. KGaA; *Int'l*, pg. 2779
KRANKENHAUS ST. BARBARA ATTENDORN GMBH—See Fresenius SE & Co. KGaA; *Int'l*, pg. 2779
KRANKENHEIM RUHESITZ AM WANNSEE-SENIORENHEIMSTATT GMBH—See Clariane SE; *Int'l*, pg. 1643
KRANKEN-TRANSPORT HERZIG GMBH—See Lundbeckfonden; *Int'l*, pg. 4583
KRANOR AS—See Peab AB; *Int'l*, pg. 5772
KRANSERVICE RHEINBERG GMBH—See Konecranes Plc; *Int'l*, pg. 4253
KRANTECHNIK OST GMBH—See Ralf Teichmann GmbH; *Int'l*, pg. 6196
KRANTI INDUSTRIES LTD.; *Int'l*, pg. 4299
KRANZ, INC.—See Bain Capital, LP; *U.S. Private*, pg. 440
KRAPF'S COACHES INC.; *U.S. Private*, pg. 2349
KRAS B.V.—See TUI AG; *Int'l*, pg. 7965
KRASCOMMERCE D.O.O.—See MESNA INDUSTRIJA BRACA PIVAC d.o.o.; *Int'l*, pg. 4840
KRAS CZ SPOL.S R.O.—See MESNA INDUSTRIJA BRACA PIVAC d.o.o.; *Int'l*, pg. 4840
KRASDALE FOODS INC.; *U.S. Private*, pg. 2349
KRAS D.D.—See MESNA INDUSTRIJA BRACA PIVAC d.o.o.; *Int'l*, pg. 4840
KRAS KOMERC D.O.O.—See MESNA INDUSTRIJA BRACA PIVAC d.o.o.; *Int'l*, pg. 4840
KRASNAPOLSKY BELGIAN SHARES, B.V.—See Minor International PCL; *Int'l*, pg. 4911
KRASNAPOLSKY HOTELS LTD.—See Minor International PCL; *Int'l*, pg. 4911

KRASNAPOLSKY HOTELS & RESTAURANTS, N.V.—See Minor International PCL; *Int'l*, pg. 4911
KRASNOYARSKENERGOSBYT PJSC; *Int'l*, pg. 4300
KRAS SLOVAKIA S.R.O.—See MESNA INDUSTRIJA BRACA PIVAC d.o.o.; *Int'l*, pg. 4840
KRAS-TRGOVINA D.O.O.—See MESNA INDUSTRIJA BRACA PIVAC d.o.o.; *Int'l*, pg. 4840
KRASTSVETMET JSC; *Int'l*, pg. 4300
KRATON CHEMICAL A.B.—See Daelim Industrial Co., Ltd.; *Int'l*, pg. 1908
KRATON CHEMICAL B.V.—See Daelim Industrial Co., Ltd.; *Int'l*, pg. 1908
KRATON CHEMICAL, LLC—See Daelim Industrial Co., Ltd.; *Int'l*, pg. 1908
KRATON CORPORATION—See Daelim Industrial Co., Ltd.; *Int'l*, pg. 1908
KRATON FORMOSA POLYMERS CORPORATION—See Daelim Industrial Co., Ltd.; *Int'l*, pg. 1908
KRATON POLYMERS DO BRASIL INDUSTRIA E COMERCIO DE PRODUTOS PETROQUIMICOS LTDA.—See Daelim Industrial Co., Ltd.; *Int'l*, pg. 1908
KRATON POLYMERS JAPAN LTD.—See Daelim Industrial Co., Ltd.; *Int'l*, pg. 1908
KRATON POLYMERS U.S. LLC—See Daelim Industrial Co., Ltd.; *Int'l*, pg. 1908
KRATOS ANALYTICAL INC.—See Shimadzu Corporation; *Int'l*, pg. 6831
KRATOS ANALYTICAL LTD.—See Shimadzu Corporation; *Int'l*, pg. 6831
KRATOS ARABIA, LTD.—See Kratos Defense & Security Solutions, Inc.; *U.S. Public*, pg. 1276
KRATOS COMMUNICATIONS LTD.—See Kratos Defense & Security Solutions, Inc.; *U.S. Public*, pg. 1276
KRATOS DEFENSE ENGINEERING SOLUTIONS, INC.—See Kratos Defense & Security Solutions, Inc.; *U.S. Public*, pg. 1276
KRATOS DEFENSE & ROCKET SUPPORT SERVICES, INC.—See Kratos Defense & Security Solutions, Inc.; *U.S. Public*, pg. 1276
KRATOS DEFENSE & SECURITY SOLUTIONS, INC.; *U.S. Public*, pg. 1275
KRATOS ENERGY & INFRASTRUCTURE LIMITED; *Int'l*, pg. 4300
KRATOS-GENERAL MICROWAVE ISRAEL—See Kratos Defense & Security Solutions, Inc.; *U.S. Public*, pg. 1276
KRATOS INTEGRAL SYSTEMS EUROPE S.A.S.—See Kratos Defense & Security Solutions, Inc.; *U.S. Public*, pg. 1276
KRATOS-INTEGRAL SYSTEMS, INC.—See Kratos Defense & Security Solutions, Inc.; *U.S. Public*, pg. 1276
KRATOS INTEGRAL SYSTEMS INTERNATIONAL, INC.—See Kratos Defense & Security Solutions, Inc.; *U.S. Public*, pg. 1276
KRATOS MID-ATLANTIC, INC.—See Kratos Defense & Security Solutions, Inc.; *U.S. Public*, pg. 1276
KRATOS NETWORKS, INC.—See Kratos Defense & Security Solutions, Inc.; *U.S. Public*, pg. 1276
KRATOS NORWAY AS—See Kratos Defense & Security Solutions, Inc.; *U.S. Public*, pg. 1276
KRATOS PUBLIC SAFETY & SECURITY SOLUTIONS, INC.—See Securitas AB; *Int'l*, pg. 6675
KRATOS SOUTHWEST, L.P.—See Kratos Defense & Security Solutions, Inc.; *U.S. Public*, pg. 1276
KRATOS SPACE & MISSILE DEFENSE SYSTEMS, INC.—See Kratos Defense & Security Solutions, Inc.; *U.S. Public*, pg. 1276
KRATOS TECHNOLOGY & TRAINING SOLUTIONS, INC.—See Kratos Defense & Security Solutions, Inc.; *U.S. Public*, pg. 1276
KRATOS UNMANNED SYSTEMS SOLUTIONS, INC.—See Kratos Defense & Security Solutions, Inc.; *U.S. Public*, pg. 1276
KRAUS-ANDERSON CAPITAL INC—See Kraus-Anderson Incorporated; *U.S. Private*, pg. 2349
KRAUS-ANDERSON COMMUNICATIONS GROUP—See Kraus-Anderson Incorporated; *U.S. Private*, pg. 2349
KRAUS-ANDERSON CONSTRUCTION COMPANY, INC.—See Kraus-Anderson Incorporated; *U.S. Private*, pg. 2349
KRAUS-ANDERSON INCORPORATED; *U.S. Private*, pg. 2349
KRAUS-ANDERSON INSURANCE—See Kraus-Anderson Incorporated; *U.S. Private*, pg. 2349
KRAUS-ANDERSON MORTGAGE COMPANY—See Kraus-Anderson Incorporated; *U.S. Private*, pg. 2350
KRAUS-ANDERSON REALTY COMPANY—See Kraus-Anderson Incorporated; *U.S. Private*, pg. 2350
KRAUS CARPET MILLS LIMITED—See Hilco Trading, LLC; *U.S. Private*, pg. 1944
KRAUS CONSTRUCTION INC.; *U.S. Private*, pg. 2349
KRAUSE ADVERTISING; *U.S. Private*, pg. 2350
KRAUSE GENTLE CORPORATION; *U.S. Private*, pg. 2350
KRAUSE PUBLICATIONS, INC.—See Tinicum Enterprises, Inc.; *U.S. Private*, pg. 4174
KRAUS-REISEN OMNIBUSBETRIEBS GMBH—See Metropolitan European Transport Limited; *Int'l*, pg. 4864

KRAUSSMAFFEI AUSTRIA GES.MBH—See Luger Gesellschaft m.b.H.; *Int'l*, pg. 4575
KRAUSSMAFFEI BERSTORFF GMBH—See China National Chemical Corporation; *Int'l*, pg. 1528
KRAUSSMAFFEI COMPANY LIMITED—See China National Chemical Corporation; *Int'l*, pg. 1528
KRAUSSMAFFEI GROUP FRANCE SAS—See China National Chemical Corporation; *Int'l*, pg. 1528
KRAUSSMAFFEI GROUP GMBH—See China National Chemical Corporation; *Int'l*, pg. 1528
KRAUSSMAFFEI GROUP UK LTD.—See China National Chemical Corporation; *Int'l*, pg. 1528
KRAUSSMAFFEI TECHNOLOGIES GMBH—See China National Chemical Corporation; *Int'l*, pg. 1528
KRAUSS-MAFFEI WEGMANN GMBH & CO. KG; *Int'l*, pg. 4300
KRAUS USA - DISTRIBUTION CENTER—See Hilco Trading, LLC; *U.S. Private*, pg. 1944
KRAUS USA PLUMBING LLC—See Masco Corporation; *U.S. Public*, pg. 1390
KRAUSZ INDUSTRIES LTD.—See Mueller Water Products, Inc.; *U.S. Public*, pg. 1485
KRAUSZ USA INC.—See Mueller Water Products, Inc.; *U.S. Public*, pg. 1485
K-RAUTA AB—See Kesko Corporation; *Int'l*, pg. 4141
K RAUTA SIA—See Kesko Corporation; *Int'l*, pg. 4141
KRAUTER & COMPANY, LLC—See Kelso & Company, L.P.; *U.S. Private*, pg. 2280
KRAUTERHAUS WILD GMBH & CO. KG—See Laurens Spethmann Holding Aktiengesellschaft & Co. KG; *Int'l*, pg. 4424
KRAVAG UMWELTSCHUTZ UND SICHERHEITSTECHNIK GMBH—See DZ BANK AG Deutsche Zentral-Genossenschaftsbank; *Int'l*, pg. 2244
KRAVCO SIMON COMPANY; *U.S. Private*, pg. 2350
KRAVE PURE FOODS, INC.—See Sonoma Brands LLC; *U.S. Private*, pg. 3714
KRAVET CANADA—See Kravet, Inc.; *U.S. Private*, pg. 2350
KRAVET FABRICS INC.; *U.S. Private*, pg. 2350
KRAVET, INC.; *U.S. Private*, pg. 2350
KRAVET MEXICO—See Kravet Fabrics Inc.; *U.S. Private*, pg. 2350
KRAYDEN, INC.—See Audax Group, Limited Partnership; *U.S. Private*, pg. 388
KRAZ , PJSC—See PJSC AutoKrAZ; *Int'l*, pg. 5878
KRBL DMCC GROUP—See KRBL Limited; *Int'l*, pg. 4300
KRBL LIMITED; *Int'l*, pg. 4300
KRB MACHINERY CO. INC.; *U.S. Private*, pg. 2350
KRB MANAGEMENT, INC.—See Caisse de Depot et Placement du Quebec; *Int'l*, pg. 1256
KRB MANAGEMENT, INC.—See KKR & Co. Inc.; *U.S. Public*, pg. 1265
KR CAPITAL ADVISORS INC.; *U.S. Private*, pg. 2348
KRC CAPITAL B.V.; *Int'l*, pg. 4300
KRC CO., LTD.—See Kajima Corporation; *Int'l*, pg. 4054
KRC RESEARCH—See The Interpublic Group of Companies, Inc.; *U.S. Public*, pg. 2105
KRC RESEARCH—See The Interpublic Group of Companies, Inc.; *U.S. Public*, pg. 2105
K.R.C. TRANSPORT & SERVICE CO., LTD.—See Nippon Yusen Kabushiki Kaisha; *Int'l*, pg. 5358
KRCW-TV—See Nexstar Media Group, Inc.; *U.S. Public*, pg. 1524
KREAB AB—See Omnicom Group Inc.; *U.S. Public*, pg. 1587
KREAB BRUSSELS—See Omnicom Group Inc.; *U.S. Public*, pg. 1587
KREAB ESPANA S.L. - BARCELONA—See Omnicom Group Inc.; *U.S. Public*, pg. 1587
KREAB ESPANA S.L.—See Omnicom Group Inc.; *U.S. Public*, pg. 1587
KREAB (HONG KONG) LIMITED—See Omnicom Group Inc.; *U.S. Public*, pg. 1587
KREAB K.K.—See Omnicom Group Inc.; *U.S. Public*, pg. 1587
KREAB LIMITED—See Omnicom Group Inc.; *U.S. Public*, pg. 1587
KREAB LISBON—See Omnicom Group Inc.; *U.S. Public*, pg. 1587
KREAB OY—See Omnicom Group Inc.; *U.S. Public*, pg. 1588
KREAB PTE. LTD.—See Omnicom Group Inc.; *U.S. Public*, pg. 1588
KREAB WORLDWIDE AB—See Omnicom Group Inc.; *U.S. Public*, pg. 1587
KREAGER BROTHERS EXCAVATING; *U.S. Private*, pg. 2350
KREATECH BIOTECHNOLOGY BV—See Danaher Corporation; *U.S. Public*, pg. 628
KREATE GROUP PLC; *Int'l*, pg. 4300
KREATE OY—See Kreate Group Plc; *Int'l*, pg. 4300
KREATE PTY. LIMITED—See Academies Australasia Group Limited; *Int'l*, pg. 77
KREATIONS INC.; *U.S. Private*, pg. 2350
KREATIVA NEW FORMULA D.O.O.—See Alkemy SpA; *Int'l*, pg. 331
KREATOPARAGOGIKI KAVALAS S.A.; *Int'l*, pg. 4300
KREBER GRAPHICS INC.; *U.S. Private*, pg. 2350

COMPANY NAME INDEX

KREBER L.L.C.—See Kreber Graphics Inc.; *U.S. Private*, pg. 2350
KREBS BIOCHEMICALS & INDUSTRIES LTD.; *Int'l*, pg. 4300
KREBS FRANCE SARL—See KREBS & RIEDEL Schleifscheibenfabrik GmbH & Co KG.; *Int'l*, pg. 4300
KREBS & RIEDEL SCHLEIFSCHEIBENFABRIK GMBH & CO KG.; *Int'l*, pg. 4300
KREBS & RIEDEL SHANGHAI CO., LTD.—See KREBS & RIEDEL Schleifscheibenfabrik GmbH & Co KG; *Int'l*, pg. 4300
KREDIETBANK INFORMATIQUE GIE—See KBC Group NV; *Int'l*, pg. 4106
KREDIETFINANCE CORPORATION (SEPTEMBER) LIMITED—See KBC Group NV; *Int'l*, pg. 4106
KREDIETRUST LUXEMBOURG S.A.—See KBL European Private Bankers S.A.; *Int'l*, pg. 4107
KREDITBANKEN A/S; *Int'l*, pg. 4301
KREDIT-INKASSO AB—See Svenska Handelsbanken AB; *Int'l*, pg. 7358
KREDITKORT HF—See Islandsbanki hf.; *Int'l*, pg. 3820
KREDITSERVICES NORD GMBH—See Norddeutsche Landesbank Girozentrale; *Int'l*, pg. 5416
KREDITT INKASSO AS—See Svenska Handelsbanken AB; *Int'l*, pg. 7358
KREDOBANK SA—See PKO Bank Polski SA; *Int'l*, pg. 5887
KREDO R—See Publicis Groupe S.A.; *Int'l*, pg. 6099
KREDYT INKASO S.A.; *Int'l*, pg. 4301
KREFFT GROBKUCHENTECHNIK GMBH—See Ali Holding S.r.l; *Int'l*, pg. 321
KREG CORPORATION - CONNECTICUT OFFICE—See Vizient, Inc.; *U.S. Private*, pg. 4407
KREG CORPORATION—See Vizient, Inc.; *U.S. Private*, pg. 4407
KREHALON AUSTRALIA PTY. LTD.—See Kureha Corporation; *Int'l*, pg. 4338
KREHALON B.V.—See Kureha Corporation; *Int'l*, pg. 4338
KREHALON B.V.—See Kureha Corporation; *Int'l*, pg. 4338
KREHALON B.V.—See Kureha Corporation; *Int'l*, pg. 4338
KREHALON B.V.—See Kureha Corporation; *Int'l*, pg. 4338
KREHALON FRANCE S.A.S.—See Kureha Corporation; *Int'l*, pg. 4338
KREHALON INDUSTRIE B.V.—See Kureha Corporation; *Int'l*, pg. 4338
KREHALON UK LTD.—See Kureha Corporation; *Int'l*, pg. 4338
KREHER STEEL CO. - DETROIT—See Duferco S.A.; *Int'l*, pg. 2223
KREHER STEEL COMPANY, LLC—See Duferco S.A.; *Int'l*, pg. 2223
KREHER WIRE PROCESSING, INC.—See Duferco S.A.; *Int'l*, pg. 2223
KREI ARCHITECTURE INC—See Parametrix, Inc.; *U.S. Private*, pg. 3092
KREIDER SERVICES, INC.; *U.S. Private*, pg. 2350
KREILKAMP TRUCKING INC.; *U.S. Private*, pg. 2350
KREISEL GMBH UND CO. KG; *Int'l*, pg. 4301
KREISER FUEL SERVICE INC.; *U.S. Private*, pg. 2350
KREISKRANKENHAUS GIFHORN GMBH—See Asklepios Kliniken GmbH & Co. KGaA; *Int'l*, pg. 624
KREISLER BORG FLORMAN GENERAL CONSTRUCTION COMPANY INC.; *U.S. Private*, pg. 2350
KREISLER INDUSTRIAL CORPORATION—See Smiths Group plc; *Int'l*, pg. 7012
KREISLER MANUFACTURING CORPORATION—See Smiths Group plc; *Int'l*, pg. 7012
KREISS COLLECTION ARIZONA INC.—See Kreiss Enterprises Inc.; *U.S. Private*, pg. 2350
KREISS COLLECTION ATLANTA INC.—See Kreiss Enterprises Inc.; *U.S. Private*, pg. 2351
KREISS COLLECTION COLORADO INC.—See Kreiss Enterprises Inc.; *U.S. Private*, pg. 2351
KREISS COLLECTION FLORIDA INC.—See Kreiss Enterprises Inc.; *U.S. Private*, pg. 2351
KREISS COLLECTION ILLINOIS INC.—See Kreiss Enterprises Inc.; *U.S. Private*, pg. 2351
KREISS COLLECTION NEVADA INC.—See Kreiss Enterprises Inc.; *U.S. Private*, pg. 2351
KREISS ENTERPRISES INC.; *U.S. Private*, pg. 2350
KREIS WASSER AG—See Burkhalter Holding AG; *Int'l*, pg. 1225
K-REIT ASIA INVESTMENT PTE LTD—See Keppel Corporation Limited; *Int'l*, pg. 4130
KRELE, LLC—See TONIX PHARMACEUTICALS HOLDING CORP.; *U.S. Public*, pg. 2162
KRELL ADVERTISING; *U.S. Private*, pg. 2351
KRELLER GROUP INC.; *U.S. Private*, pg. 2351
KRELL INDUSTRIES, INC.; *U.S. Private*, pg. 2351
KREMENCHUKGAZ, PJSC; *Int'l*, pg. 4301
KREMENTZ & COMPANY; *U.S. Private*, pg. 2351
KREMLIN REXSON POLSKA SP. Z O.O.—See Exel Industries SA; *Int'l*, pg. 2583
KREMLIN REXSON PTE LTD—See Exel Industries SA; *Int'l*, pg. 2583
KREMLIN-REXSON SA—See Exel Industries SA; *Int'l*, pg. 2582
KREMLIN REXSON S.P.A—See Exel Industries SA; *Int'l*, pg. 2583

KREMOINT PHARMA PRIVATE LIMITED—See Bliss Gvs Pharma Ltd.; *Int'l*, pg. 1063
KREMPP LUMBER CO.; *U.S. Private*, pg. 2351
KRENZEN CADILLAC-PONTIAC INC.; *U.S. Private*, pg. 2351
KREON FINNANCIAL SERVICES LIMITED; *Int'l*, pg. 4301
KREPE-KRAFT, INC.—See MOD-PAC CORP.; *U.S. Private*, pg. 2759
KREPEZHNI IZDELIA AD; *Int'l*, pg. 4301
KRESS CORPORATION; *U.S. Private*, pg. 2351
KRESSON VIEW CENTER—See Formation Capital, LLC; *U.S. Private*, pg. 1571
KRESS STORES OF PUERTO RICO; *U.S. Private*, pg. 2351
KRESTA HOLDINGS LIMITED—See Ningbo Xianfeng New Material Co. Ltd; *Int'l*, pg. 5307
KRESTMARK INDUSTRIES, LP—See Seven Group Holdings Limited; *Int'l*, pg. 6732
KRETAM HOLDINGS BERHAD; *Int'l*, pg. 4301
THE KRETSINGER GROUP, INC.; *U.S. Private*, pg. 4066
KRETTO SYSCON LIMITED; *Int'l*, pg. 4301
KRETZ LUMBER CO., INC.; *U.S. Private*, pg. 2351
KREUZ ENGINEERING LTD.—See Headland Capital Partners Limited; *Int'l*, pg. 3301
KREUZ HOLDINGS LIMITED—See Headland Capital Partners Limited; *Int'l*, pg. 3301
KREUZ INTERNATIONAL PTE LTD—See Headland Capital Partners Limited; *Int'l*, pg. 3301
KREUZ OFFSHORE CONTRACTORS LTD.—See Headland Capital Partners Limited; *Int'l*, pg. 3301
KREUZ OFFSHORE MARINE PTE LTD—See Headland Capital Partners Limited; *Int'l*, pg. 3301
KREUZ SHIPBUILDING & ENGINEERING PTE LTD—See Headland Capital Partners Limited; *Int'l*, pg. 3301
KREUZ SUBSEA PTE. LTD.—See Headland Capital Partners Limited; *Int'l*, pg. 3301
KREX-TV—See Nexstar Media Group, Inc.; *U.S. Public*, pg. 1522
KREZUS SPOLKA AKCYJNA; *Int'l*, pg. 4301
KR FASTIGHETER I ESKILSTUNA AB—See Kesko Corporation; *Int'l*, pg. 4142
KR FASTIGHETER I UPPLAND AB—See Kesko Corporation; *Int'l*, pg. 4142
KRF UK LTD.; *Int'l*, pg. 4301
KRG CAPITAL MANAGEMENT, L.P.; *U.S. Private*, pg. 2351
KRGP INC.—See The Kroger Co.; *U.S. Public*, pg. 2108
KRG RIVERS EDGE, LLC—See Kite Realty Group Trust; *U.S. Public*, pg. 1236
KR HOLDINGS CORPORATION—See create restaurants holdings inc.; *Int'l*, pg. 1832
KRIDHAN INFRA LIMITED; *Int'l*, pg. 4301
KRIEGER AUTO GROUP; *U.S. Private*, pg. 2351
KRIEGER FORD INC.; *U.S. Private*, pg. 2351
KRIEGER MOTOR COMPANY INC.; *U.S. Private*, pg. 2351
KRIEG, SCHLUPP, BURGE WERBEAGENTUR AG; *Int'l*, pg. 4301
KRIENIK ADVERTISING, INC.; *U.S. Private*, pg. 2351
KRIER FOODS, INC.; *U.S. Private*, pg. 2351
THE KRIETE GROUP; *U.S. Private*, pg. 4066
KRI INTERNATIONAL CORPORATION—See Nippon Koei Co., Ltd.; *Int'l*, pg. 5321
KRI KRI MILK INDUSTRY S.A.; *Int'l*, pg. 4301
KRILLION, INC.—See Local Corporation; *U.S. Public*, pg. 1337
K&R INDUSTRIES INC.; *U.S. Private*, pg. 2250
KRINGLE PHARMA, INC.; *Int'l*, pg. 4301
KRINOS FOODS INC.; *U.S. Private*, pg. 2351
KR INVESTMENT LTD.; *Int'l*, pg. 4299
KRIO INTEZET ZRT.—See VITA 34 AG; *Int'l*, pg. 8257
KRIPALU CENTER FOR YOGA & HEALTH; *U.S. Private*, pg. 2351
KRIS AUTOMATED PACKAGING SYSTEMS PRIVATE LIMITED—See Sealed Air Corporation; *U.S. Public*, pg. 1853
KRIS COMMUNICATIONS INC.—See Evening Post Publishing Co.; *U.S. Private*, pg. 1436
KRISENERGY BANGLADESH LIMITED—See KrisEnergy Ltd.; *Int'l*, pg. 4301
KRISENERGY (CAMBODIA) LTD.—See KrisEnergy Ltd.; *Int'l*, pg. 4301
KRISENERGY (GULF OF THAILAND) LTD.—See KrisEnergy Ltd.; *Int'l*, pg. 4301
KRISENERGY LTD.; *Int'l*, pg. 4301
KRISER'S; *U.S. Private*, pg. 2352
KRISHCA STRAPPING SOLUTIONS LIMITED; *Int'l*, pg. 4301
KRISHNA BUILDTECH PVT. LTD.—See TARC Limited; *Int'l*, pg. 7462
KRISHNA CAPITAL & SECURITIES LTD.; *Int'l*, pg. 4301
KRISHNA FERRO PRODUCTS LIMITED; *Int'l*, pg. 4301
KRISHNA FILAMENT INDUSTRIES LIMITED; *Int'l*, pg. 4302
KRISHNA HOLDINGS PTE. LTD.—See The Braj Binani Group; *Int'l*, pg. 7627
KRISHNA INSTITUTE OF MEDICAL SCIENCES LIMITED; *Int'l*, pg. 4302

KRKA, D.D., NOVO MESTO

KRISHNA LANDI RENZO INDIA PRIVATE LTD.—See Landi Renzo S.p.a.; *Int'l*, pg. 4406
KRISHNA PHOSCHEM LIMITED; *Int'l*, pg. 4302
KRISHNA VENTURES LIMITED; *Int'l*, pg. 4302
KRISPI OIL RUSSIA LLC—See Mewah International Inc.; *Int'l*, pg. 4868
KRISPI OILS POLAND SP. Z.O.O.—See Mewah International Inc.; *Int'l*, pg. 4868
KRISPI OIL (TURKEY) LTD STI—See Mewah International Inc.; *Int'l*, pg. 4868
KRISPY KREME DOUGHNUT CORPORATION—See Krispy Kreme, Inc.; *U.S. Public*, pg. 1277
KRISPY KREME DOUGHNUTS, INC.—See Krispy Kreme, Inc.; *U.S. Public*, pg. 1277
KRISPY KREME, INC.; *U.S. Public*, pg. 1277
KRISPY KREME UK LTD.—See Alcuin Capital Partners LLP; *Int'l*, pg. 303
KRISTAL 1923 AD VELES; *Int'l*, pg. 4302
KRISTAL A.D.; *Int'l*, pg. 4302
KRISTAL CADILLAC, CHEVROLET, & GEO IMPORTS; *U.S. Private*, pg. 2352
KRISTAL KOLA VE MESRUBAT SANAYI TICARET A.S.; *Int'l*, pg. 4302
KRISTEN DISTRIBUTING CO.; *U.S. Private*, pg. 2352
KRISTERA AD—See Agria Group Holding JSC; *Int'l*, pg. 216
KRISTERA-AGRO EOOD—See Agria Group Holding JSC; *Int'l*, pg. 216
KRISTIINE KESKUS OU—See Citycon Oyj; *Int'l*, pg. 1629
KRIST SEVEN LTD.—See Windmoeller & Hoelscher KG; *Int'l*, pg. 8426
KRISUMI CORPORATION PRIVATE LIMITED—See Sumitomo Corporation; *Int'l*, pg. 7269
KRIS-WAY TRUCK LEASING INC.—See Mitsui & Co., Ltd.; *Int'l*, pg. 4980
KRIS-WAY TRUCK LEASING INC.—See Penske Automotive Group, Inc.; *U.S. Public*, pg. 1665
KRIS-WAY TRUCK LEASING INC.—See Penske Corporation; *U.S. Private*, pg. 3139
K-RITE CONSTRUCTION LTD.; *Int'l*, pg. 4042
KRITI INDUSTRIES INDIA LTD; *Int'l*, pg. 4302
KRITIKA WIRES LTD.; *Int'l*, pg. 4302
KRITI NUTRIENTS LIMITED; *Int'l*, pg. 4302
KRITON ARTOS SA; *Int'l*, pg. 4302
KRIV-TV—See Fox Corporation; *U.S. Public*, pg. 876
KRIYA CAPITAL, LLC; *U.S. Private*, pg. 2352
KRIZ-DAVIS CO., INC.; *U.S. Private*, pg. 2352
KRKA AUSSENHANDELS GMBH—See Krka, d.d., Novo Mesto; *Int'l*, pg. 4302
KRKA BELGIUM, SA—See Krka, d.d., Novo Mesto; *Int'l*, pg. 4303
KRKA BULGARIA EOOD—See Krka, d.d., Novo Mesto; *Int'l*, pg. 4303
KRKA CR, S. R. O.—See Krka, d.d., Novo Mesto; *Int'l*, pg. 4302
KRKA, D.D., NOVO MESTO - LJUBLJANA FACILITY—See Krka, d.d., Novo Mesto; *Int'l*, pg. 4303
KRKA, D.D., NOVO MESTO - LJUTOMER FACILITY—See Krka, d.d., Novo Mesto; *Int'l*, pg. 4303
KRKA, D.D., NOVO MESTO - NOVO MESTO FACILITY—See Krka, d.d., Novo Mesto; *Int'l*, pg. 4303
KRKA, D.D., NOVO MESTO; *Int'l*, pg. 4302
KRKA FARMACEUTICA, S.L.—See Krka, d.d., Novo Mesto; *Int'l*, pg. 4303
KRKA FARMACEUTICA UNIPESSOAL LDA—See Krka, d.d., Novo Mesto; *Int'l*, pg. 4302
KRKA FARMACEUTICI MILANO, S.R.L.—See Krka, d.d., Novo Mesto; *Int'l*, pg. 4302
KRKA-FARMA D.O.O. NOVI SAD—See Krka, d.d., Novo Mesto; *Int'l*, pg. 4303
KRKA FARMA, D. O. O.—See Krka, d.d., Novo Mesto; *Int'l*, pg. 4302
KRKA-FARMA DOO—See Krka, d.d., Novo Mesto; *Int'l*, pg. 4303
KRKA FARMA, D. O. O., ZAGREB—See Krka, d.d., Novo Mesto; *Int'l*, pg. 4302
KRKA FINLAND OY—See Krka, d.d., Novo Mesto; *Int'l*, pg. 4303
KRKA FRANCE EURL—See Krka, d.d., Novo Mesto; *Int'l*, pg. 4303
KRKA HELLAS E.P.E.—See Krka, d.d., Novo Mesto; *Int'l*, pg. 4303
KRKA MAGYARORSZAG KERESKEDELMI KEPVISELET—See Krka, d.d., Novo Mesto; *Int'l*, pg. 4302
KRKA PHARMA DUBLIN LIMITED—See Krka, d.d., Novo Mesto; *Int'l*, pg. 4302
KRKA PHARMA GMBH—See Krka, d.d., Novo Mesto; *Int'l*, pg. 4302
KRKA POLSKA SP. Z O.O.—See Krka, d.d., Novo Mesto; *Int'l*, pg. 4302
KRKA ROMANIA S.R.L.—See Krka, d.d., Novo Mesto; *Int'l*, pg. 4303
KRKA SLOVENSKO, S.R.O.—See Krka, d.d., Novo Mesto; *Int'l*, pg. 4303
KRKA SVERIGE AB—See Krka, d.d., Novo Mesto; *Int'l*, pg. 4303
KRKA UK LTD.—See Krka, d.d., Novo Mesto; *Int'l*, pg. 4303

KRKA, D.D., NOVO MESTO

CORPORATE AFFILIATIONS

KRKA UKRAINE LLC—See Krka, d.d., Novo Mesto; *Int'l*, pg. 4303
KRKA USA, LLC—See Krka, d.d., Novo Mesto; *Int'l*, pg. 4303
KR LEASE CORPORATION—See Kajima Corporation; *Int'l*, pg. 4054
KRM22 PLC; *Int'l*, pg. 4303
KR MOTORS CO., LTD.; *Int'l*, pg. 4299
KRM SERVICE AG—See Kardex Holding AG; *Int'l*, pg. 4079
K ROAD POWER, INC.; *U.S. Private*, pg. 2249
KROBEL PROMET D.O.O.—See TCS TurControlSysteme AG; *Int'l*, pg. 7485
KROCHET KIDS INTL.; *U.S. Private*, pg. 2352
KROEHLER FURNITURE MANUFACTURING COMPANY, INC.—See Schottenstein Stores Corporation; *U.S. Private*, pg. 3569
KROEKER FARMS LTD.; *Int'l*, pg. 4303
KROENKE ARENA COMPANY, LLC—See Kroenke Sports & Entertainment, LLC; *U.S. Private*, pg. 2352
KROENKE SPORTS & ENTERTAINMENT, LLC; *U.S. Private*, pg. 2352
KROESCHELL ENGINEERING CO. INC.—See Kroeschell, Inc.; *U.S. Private*, pg. 2352
KROESCHELL ENGINEERING NORTH, INC.—See Kroeschell, Inc.; *U.S. Private*, pg. 2352
KROESCHELL ENGINEERING SERVICE, INC.—See Kroeschell, Inc.; *U.S. Private*, pg. 2352
KROESCHELL, INC.; *U.S. Private*, pg. 2352
KROESCHELL OPERATIONS INC.—See Kroeschell, Inc.; *U.S. Private*, pg. 2352
KROFAM INC.; *U.S. Private*, pg. 2352
KROFTA TECHNOLOGIES, LLC—See Ecolab Inc.; *U.S. Public*, pg. 714
KROGAB SVERIGE AB—See Arla Foods amba; *Int'l*, pg. 573
THE KROGER CO. OF MICHIGAN—See The Kroger Co.; *U.S. Public*, pg. 2109
THE KROGER CO.; *U.S. Public*, pg. 2107
KROGER DELTA MARKETING AREA—See The Kroger Co.; *U.S. Public*, pg. 2108
KROGER GREIFERTECHNIK GMBH CO. & KG—See RAG-Stiftung; *Int'l*, pg. 6179
KROGER LIMITED PARTNERSHIP I—See The Kroger Co.; *U.S. Public*, pg. 2108
KROGER PRESCRIPTION PLANS, INC.—See The Kroger Co.; *U.S. Public*, pg. 2108
KROGER SPECIALTY INFUSION AL, LLC—See The Kroger Co.; *U.S. Public*, pg. 2108
KROGER SPECIALTY INFUSION CA, LLC—See The Kroger Co.; *U.S. Public*, pg. 2108
KROGER SPECIALTY INFUSION TX, LLC—See The Kroger Co.; *U.S. Public*, pg. 2108
KROGER SPECIALTY PHARMACY FL 2 LLC—See The Kroger Co.; *U.S. Public*, pg. 2108
KROGER SPECIALTY PHARMACY, INC.—See The Kroger Co.; *U.S. Public*, pg. 2108
KROGER SPECIALTY PHARMACY LA, LLC—See The Kroger Co.; *U.S. Public*, pg. 2108
KROGSVEEN AS—See Pareto Group; *Int'l*, pg. 5741
KROHARI CHIKURO CORPORATION—See Krosaki Harima Corporation; *Int'l*, pg. 4307
KROHNE AG—See Krohne International, Inc.; *Int'l*, pg. 4304
KROHNE AUSTRALIA PTY. LTD.—See Krohne International, Inc.; *Int'l*, pg. 4304
KROHNE BELGIUM NV—See Krohne International, Inc.; *Int'l*, pg. 4304
KROHNE CANADA INC.—See Krohne International, Inc.; *Int'l*, pg. 4304
KROHNE CONAUT INSTRUMENTACAO LTDA.—See Krohne International, Inc.; *Int'l*, pg. 4304
KROHNE CZ, SPOL S.R.O.—See Krohne International, Inc.; *Int'l*, pg. 4304
KROHNE DE MEXICO, SA DE CV—See Krohne International, Inc.; *Int'l*, pg. 4303
KROHNE ENGINEERING GMBH—See Krohne International, Inc.; *Int'l*, pg. 4304
KROHNE GESELLSCHAFT M.B.H.—See Krohne International, Inc.; *Int'l*, pg. 4304
KROHNE IBERIA, S.R.L.—See Krohne International, Inc.; *Int'l*, pg. 4303
KROHNE, INC.—See Krohne International, Inc.; *Int'l*, pg. 4304
KROHNE INSTRUMENTATION AS—See Krohne International, Inc.; *Int'l*, pg. 4304
KROHNE INTERNATIONAL, INC.; *Int'l*, pg. 4303
KROHNE ITALIA SRL—See Krohne International, Inc.; *Int'l*, pg. 4304
KROHNE JAPAN KK—See Krohne International, Inc.; *Int'l*, pg. 4303
KROHNE KAZAKHSTAN LLP—See Krohne International, Inc.; *Int'l*, pg. 4303
KROHNE LTD.—See Krohne International, Inc.; *Int'l*, pg. 4304
KROHNE (MALAYSIA) SDN. BHD.—See Krohne International, Inc.; *Int'l*, pg. 4304
KROHNE MARSHALL LTD.—See Krohne International, Inc.; *Int'l*, pg. 4304

KROHNE MEASUREMENT INSTRUMENTS (SHANGHAI) CO. LTD.—See Krohne International, Inc.; *Int'l*, pg. 4304
KROHNE MEASUREMENT TECHNOLOGY (SHANGHAI) CO., LTD.—See Krohne International, Inc.; *Int'l*, pg. 4303
KROHNE MESSTECHNIK GMBH & CO. KG—See Krohne International, Inc.; *Int'l*, pg. 4304
KROHNE NEDERLAND B.V.—See Krohne International, Inc.; *Int'l*, pg. 4304
KROHNE NEW ZEALAND LTD—See Krohne International, Inc.; *Int'l*, pg. 4303
KROHNE OIL & GAS B.V.—See Krohne International, Inc.; *Int'l*, pg. 4304
KROHNE OIL & GAS LLC—See Krohne International, Inc.; *Int'l*, pg. 4304
KROHNE OIL & GAS MALAYSIA SDN BHD—See Krohne International, Inc.; *Int'l*, pg. 4304
KROHNE OIL & GAS (UK) LIMITED—See Krohne International, Inc.; *Int'l*, pg. 4304
KROHNE OTOMASYON SANAYI VE TICARET LIMITED SIRKETI—See Krohne International, Inc.; *Int'l*, pg. 4304
KROHNE POLSKA SP. Z O.O.—See Krohne International, Inc.; *Int'l*, pg. 4304
KROHNE PRESSURE SOLUTIONS GMBH—See Krohne International, Inc.; *Int'l*, pg. 4303
KROHNE PTY. LTD.—See Krohne International, Inc.; *Int'l*, pg. 4304
KROHNE S.A.S.—See Krohne International, Inc.; *Int'l*, pg. 4304
KROHNE SKARPENORD A/S—See Krohne International, Inc.; *Int'l*, pg. 4303
KROHNE (SOUTH EAST ASIA) PTE., LTD.—See Krohne International, Inc.; *Int'l*, pg. 4303
KROHNE (THAILAND) CO. LTD.—See Krohne International, Inc.; *Int'l*, pg. 4304
KROK BROTHERS HOLDINGS (PTY) LTD—See Aspen Pharmacare Holdings Limited; *Int'l*, pg. 629
KROKUS PRIVATE EQUITY SP. Z O.O.—See Groupe BPCE; *Int'l*, pg. 3095
KROKUS PRIVATE EQUITY SP. Z O.O.—See Polian Financial Services Sp. z o.o.; *Int'l*, pg. 5909
KROLL ASSOCIATES (ASIA) LTD.—See Permira Advisers LLP; *Int'l*, pg. 5807
KROLL ASSOCIATES BRASIL LTDA.—See Permira Advisers LLP; *Int'l*, pg. 5807
KROLL ASSOCIATES IBERIA, S.L.—See Permira Advisers LLP; *Int'l*, pg. 5807
KROLL ASSOCIATES SA—See Permira Advisers LLP; *Int'l*, pg. 5807
KROLL ASSOCIATES SRL—See Permira Advisers LLP; *Int'l*, pg. 5807
KROLL, BECKER & WING, LLC; *U.S. Private*, pg. 2353
KROLL CANADA—See Permira Advisers LLP; *Int'l*, pg. 5807
KROLL CRANES A/S—See Muhibbah Engineering (M) Bhd.; *Int'l*, pg. 5078
KROLL DIRECT MARKETING INC.; *U.S. Private*, pg. 2353
KROLL FACTUAL DATA, LLC—See Permira Advisers LLP; *Int'l*, pg. 5807
KROLL FRANCE SAS—See Permira Advisers LLP; *Int'l*, pg. 5807
KROLL HOLDCO, LLC—See Permira Advisers LLP; *Int'l*, pg. 5807
KROLL HOLDINGS LIMITED—See Permira Advisers LLP; *Int'l*, pg. 5807
KROLL, LLC—See Permira Advisers LLP; *Int'l*, pg. 5807
KROLL MEXICO—See Permira Advisers LLP; *Int'l*, pg. 5807
KROLL ONTRACK BELGIUM—See Pivotal Acquisition Corp.; *U.S. Private*, pg. 3192
KROLL ONTRACK GMBH—See Pivotal Acquisition Corp.; *U.S. Private*, pg. 3192
KROLL ONTRACK (HK) LTD.—See Pivotal Acquisition Corp.; *U.S. Private*, pg. 3192
KROLL ONTRACK LIMITED—See Pivotal Acquisition Corp.; *U.S. Private*, pg. 3192
KROLL ONTRACK, LLC—See Pivotal Acquisition Corp.; *U.S. Private*, pg. 3192
KROLL ONTRACK PTY LTD.—See Pivotal Acquisition Corp.; *U.S. Private*, pg. 3192
KROLL ONTRACK SARL—See Pivotal Acquisition Corp.; *U.S. Private*, pg. 3192
KROLL ONTRACK SP. Z O.O.—See Pivotal Acquisition Corp.; *U.S. Private*, pg. 3192
KROLL ONTRACK (SWITZERLAND) GMBH—See Pivotal Acquisition Corp.; *U.S. Private*, pg. 3192
KROLL SECURITIES, LLC—See Permira Advisers LLP; *Int'l*, pg. 5807
KROMBACHER BRAUEREI BERNHARD SCHADEBERG GMBH & CO. KG; *Int'l*, pg. 4304
KROMEK GROUP PLC; *Int'l*, pg. 4304
KROMET ASIA LTD.—See Kromet International Inc.; *Int'l*, pg. 4304
KROMET INTERNATIONAL INC. - ALUMABRITE DIVISION—See Kromet International Inc.; *Int'l*, pg. 4304

KROMET INTERNATIONAL INC.; *Int'l*, pg. 4304
KROMI CZ S.R.O.—See KROMI Logistik AG; *Int'l*, pg. 4305
KROMI LOGISTICA DO BRASIL LTDA.—See KROMI Logistik AG; *Int'l*, pg. 4305
KROMI LOGISTIK AG—See KROMI Logistik AG; *Int'l*, pg. 4305
KROMI LOGISTIK AG—See KROMI Logistik AG; *Int'l*, pg. 4305
KROMI LOGISTIK AG; *Int'l*, pg. 4304
KROMI LOGISTIK SPAIN S.L.—See KROMI Logistik AG; *Int'l*, pg. 4305
KROMI SLOVAKIA S.R.O.—See KROMI Logistik AG; *Int'l*, pg. 4305
KROMO ALI SPA—See Ali Holding S.r.l.; *Int'l*, pg. 321
KROMSCHRODER & PFANNENSCHMIDT GMBH—See ITV plc; *Int'l*, pg. 3845
KRONAN FASTIGHETER I KARLSKRONA AB—See Eurocommercial Properties N.V.; *Int'l*, pg. 2534
KRONANS DROGHANDEL APOTEK AB—See Oriola Corporation; *Int'l*, pg. 5631
KRON & ASSOCIATES ADVERTISING INC.; *U.S. Private*, pg. 2353
KRONE KALTE+KLIMA VERTRIEBS-GMBH—See INDUS Holding AG; *Int'l*, pg. 3664
KRONES AG—See Krones AG; *Int'l*, pg. 4305
KRONES AG; *Int'l*, pg. 4305
KRONES ANDINA LTDA.—See Krones AG; *Int'l*, pg. 4305
KRONES ANGOLA - REPRESENTACOES, COMERCIO E INDUSTRIA, LDA.—See Krones AG; *Int'l*, pg. 4305
KRONES ASIA LTD.—See Krones AG; *Int'l*, pg. 4305
KRONES BANGLADESH LIMITED—See Krones AG; *Int'l*, pg. 4305
KRONES CHILE SPA—See Krones AG; *Int'l*, pg. 4305
KRONES DO BRAZIL LTDA.—See Krones AG; *Int'l*, pg. 4306
KRONES FILIPINAS INC.—See Krones AG; *Int'l*, pg. 4305
KRONES IBERICA, S.A.U.—See Krones AG; *Int'l*, pg. 4305
KRONES INC.—See Krones AG; *Int'l*, pg. 4305
KRONES INDIA PVT. LTD.—See Krones AG; *Int'l*, pg. 4305
KRONES-IZUMI PROCESSING PTE. LTD.—See Krones AG; *Int'l*, pg. 4306
KRONES JAPAN CO. LTD.—See Krones AG; *Int'l*, pg. 4305
KRONES KAZAKHSTAN TOO—See Krones AG; *Int'l*, pg. 4305
KRONES KOREA LTD.—See Krones AG; *Int'l*, pg. 4305
KRONES LCS CENTER EAST AFRICA LIMITED—See Krones AG; *Int'l*, pg. 4305
KRONES LCS CENTER WEST AFRICA LIMITED—See Krones AG; *Int'l*, pg. 4305
KRONES MACHINERY CO. LTD.—See Krones AG; *Int'l*, pg. 4305
KRONES MACHINERY MALAYSIA SDN. BHD.—See Krones AG; *Int'l*, pg. 4305
KRONES MACHINERY (TAICANG) CO. LTD.—See Krones AG; *Int'l*, pg. 4305
KRONES MAKINA SANAYI VE TIKARET LTD.—See Krones AG; *Int'l*, pg. 4305
KRONES MEX S.A. DE C.V.—See Krones AG; *Int'l*, pg. 4306
KRONES NEDERLAND B.V.—See Krones AG; *Int'l*, pg. 4306
KRONES NEW ZEALAND LIMITED—See Krones AG; *Int'l*, pg. 4306
KRONES NORDIC APS—See Krones AG; *Int'l*, pg. 4306
KRONES O.O.O—See Krones AG; *Int'l*, pg. 4306
KRONES PACIFIC PTY LIMITED—See Krones AG; *Int'l*, pg. 4306
KRONES PORTUGAL EQUIPAMENTOS INDUSTRIAIS LDA.—See Krones AG; *Int'l*, pg. 4306
KRONES ROMANIA PROD. S.R.L.—See Krones AG; *Int'l*, pg. 4306
KRONES SALES (BEIJING) CO. LTD.—See Krones AG; *Int'l*, pg. 4306
KRONES S.A.R.L—See Krones AG; *Int'l*, pg. 4306
KRONES SERVICE EUROPE EOOD—See Krones AG; *Int'l*, pg. 4306
KRONES SERVICE EUROPE KFT.—See Krones AG; *Int'l*, pg. 4306
KRONES SOUTHERN AFRICA (PROP) LTD.—See Krones AG; *Int'l*, pg. 4306
KRONES SPOLKA Z.O.O.—See Krones AG; *Int'l*, pg. 4306
KRONES S.R.O.—See Krones AG; *Int'l*, pg. 4306
KRONES SURLATINA S.A.—See Krones AG; *Int'l*, pg. 4306
KRONES (THAILAND) CO. LTD.—See Krones AG; *Int'l*, pg. 4305
KRONES UK LTD.—See Krones AG; *Int'l*, pg. 4306
KRONES UKRAINE LLC—See Krones AG; *Int'l*, pg. 4306
KRONFAGEL AB—See Scandi Standard AB; *Int'l*, pg. 6612
KRONHOLM INSURANCE SERVICES—See Brown & Brown, Inc.; *U.S. Public*, pg. 401
KRONICLES (SINGAPORE) PTE. LTD.—See Kronologi Asia Berhad; *Int'l*, pg. 4306
KRONOLOGI ASIA BERHAD; *Int'l*, pg. 4306

COMPANY NAME INDEX

KRONOS ADVANCED TECHNOLOGIES, INC.; *U.S. Private*, pg. 2353
KRONOS AUSTRALIA PTY LTD—See Hellman & Friedman LLC; *U.S. Private*, pg. 1910
KRONOS AUTOMOBILES S.A.—See s.a. D'Ieteren n.v.; *Int'l*, pg. 6448
KRONOS BIO, INC.; *U.S. Public*, pg. 1277
KRONOS B.V.—See Contran Corporation; *U.S. Private*, pg. 1033
KRONOS CANADA, INC.—See Contran Corporation; *U.S. Private*, pg. 1033
KRONOS CHEMIE GMBH—See Contran Corporation; *U.S. Private*, pg. 1033
KRONOS DE MEXICO SA DE CV—See Hellman & Friedman LLC; *U.S. Private*, pg. 1911
KRONOS EUROPE S.A./N.V.—See Contran Corporation; *U.S. Private*, pg. 1033
KRONOS EXPRESS LTD—See Kronos Press Distribution Agency Plc Ltd; *Int'l*, pg. 4306
KRONOS FOODS CORP.—See Entrepreneurial Equity Partners, LLC; *U.S. Private*, pg. 1406
KRONOS, INCORPORATED - HIRING SOLUTIONS GROUP—See Hellman & Friedman LLC; *U.S. Private*, pg. 1911
KRONOS, INCORPORATED - ISERIES SOLUTIONS GROUP—See Hellman & Friedman LLC; *U.S. Private*, pg. 1911
KRONOS, INCORPORATED—See Hellman & Friedman LLC; *U.S. Private*, pg. 1910
KRONOS, INCORPORATED - TELESTAFF SOLUTIONS GROUP—See Hellman & Friedman LLC; *U.S. Private*, pg. 1911
KRONOS INTERNATIONAL, INC.—See Contran Corporation; *U.S. Private*, pg. 1033
KRONOS LIMITED—See Contran Corporation; *U.S. Private*, pg. 1033
KRONOS LOUISIANA, INC.—See Contran Corporation; *U.S. Private*, pg. 1033
KRONOS NORGE A/S—See Contran Corporation; *U.S. Private*, pg. 1033
KRONOS PRESS DISTRIBUTION AGENCY PLC LTD; *Int'l*, pg. 4306
KRONOS SINGAPORE PTE. LTD—See Hellman & Friedman LLC; *U.S. Private*, pg. 1910
KRONOS SYSTEMS BVBA—See Hellman & Friedman LLC; *U.S. Private*, pg. 1910
KRONOS SYSTEMS B.V.—See Hellman & Friedman LLC; *U.S. Private*, pg. 1910
KRONOS SYSTEMS INDIA PRIVATE LIMITED—See Hellman & Friedman LLC; *U.S. Private*, pg. 1910
KRONOS SYSTEMS LTD—See Hellman & Friedman LLC; *U.S. Private*, pg. 1910
KRONOS TITAN A/S—See Contran Corporation; *U.S. Private*, pg. 1033
KRONOS TITAN GMBH—See Contran Corporation; *U.S. Private*, pg. 1033
KRONOS (US) INC—See Hellman & Friedman LLC; *U.S. Private*, pg. 1910
KRONOS WORLDWIDE, INC.—See Contran Corporation; *U.S. Private*, pg. 1033
KRONPRINZ GMBH—See Crestview Partners, L.P.; *U.S. Private*, pg. 1097
KRON TELECOMMUNICATION TECHNOLOGIES PRIVATE LIMITED—See Kron Telekomunikasyon Hizmetleri A.S.; *Int'l*, pg. 4305
KRON TELEKOMUNIKASYON HIZMETLERI A.S.; *Int'l*, pg. 4305
KRON-TV—See Nexstar Media Group, Inc.; *U.S. Public*, pg. 1523
KROPP HOLDINGS, INC.—See World Kinect Corporation; *U.S. Public*, pg. 2380
KROPYVNYTSKYI OEP PJSC—See Kernel Holding S.A.; *Int'l*, pg. 4137
KROPZ PLC; *Int'l*, pg. 4307
KROSAKI AMR REFRACTARIOS S.A.U.—See Krosaki Harima Corporation; *Int'l*, pg. 4307
KROSAKI HARIMA CORPORATION - AKO PLANT—See Krosaki Harima Corporation; *Int'l*, pg. 4307
KROSAKI HARIMA CORPORATION - CHIBA PLANT—See Krosaki Harima Corporation; *Int'l*, pg. 4307
KROSAKI HARIMA CORPORATION - FINE CERAMICS PLANT—See Krosaki Harima Corporation; *Int'l*, pg. 4307
KROSAKI HARIMA CORPORATION - FURNACE DIVISION—See Krosaki Harima Corporation; *Int'l*, pg. 4307
KROSAKI HARIMA CORPORATION - KISARAZU MONOLITHIC PLANT—See Krosaki Harima Corporation; *Int'l*, pg. 4307
KROSAKI HARIMA CORPORATION - NAGOYA TAPHOLE CLAY PLANT—See Krosaki Harima Corporation; *Int'l*, pg. 4307
KROSAKI HARIMA CORPORATION - OITA TAPHOLE CLAY PLANT—See Krosaki Harima Corporation; *Int'l*, pg. 4307
KROSAKI HARIMA CORPORATION; *Int'l*, pg. 4307
KROSAKI HARIMA CORPORATION - TAKASAGO MONOLITHIC PLANT—See Krosaki Harima Corporation; *Int'l*, pg. 4307

KROSAKI HARIMA CORPORATION - TAKASAGO PLANT—See Krosaki Harima Corporation; *Int'l*, pg. 4307
KROSAKI HARIMA CORPORATION - YAHATA MONOLITHIC PLANT—See Krosaki Harima Corporation; *Int'l*, pg. 4307
KROSAKI HARIMA CORPORATION - YAHATA PLANT—See Krosaki Harima Corporation; *Int'l*, pg. 4307
KROSAKI HARIMA EUROPE B.V.—See Krosaki Harima Corporation; *Int'l*, pg. 4307
KROSAKI HARIMA (SHANGHAI) ENTERPRISE MANAGEMENT CO., LTD.—See Krosaki Harima Corporation; *Int'l*, pg. 4307
KROSAKI HARIMA (SHANGHAI) INTERNATIONAL TRADING CO., LTD.—See Krosaki Harima Corporation; *Int'l*, pg. 4307
KROSAKI USA INC.—See Krosaki Harima Corporation; *Int'l*, pg. 4307
KROSSOVER INTELLIGENCE INC.—See Agile Sports Technologies, Inc.; *U.S. Private*, pg. 128
KROSWANG GMBH; *Int'l*, pg. 4307
KROW COMMUNICATIONS LIMITED—See The Mission Group Public Limited Company; *Int'l*, pg. 7667
KROY INDUSTRIES, INC.; *U.S. Private*, pg. 2353
KROY LLC—See Pubco Corporation; *U.S. Private*, pg. 3298
KROY SIGN SYSTEMS, LLC—See Pubco Corporation; *U.S. Private*, pg. 3298
KR PLUS—See Korea Ratings Corp.; *Int'l*, pg. 4287
K.R.S. CORPORATION; *Int'l*, pg. 4044
KRSNAA DIAGNOSTICS LTD.; *Int'l*, pg. 4307
KRT MARKETING, INC.—See Recruitics, LLC; *U.S. Private*, pg. 3372
K&R TRANSPORTATION, LLC—See California Cartage Company LLC; *U.S. Private*, pg. 718
KRUD KUTTER, INC.—See RPM International Inc.; *U.S. Public*, pg. 1817
KRUEGER ASSOCIATES INC.; *U.S. Private*, pg. 2353
KRUEGER FLORAL-N-GIFTS; *U.S. Private*, pg. 2353
KRUEGER-GILBERT HEALTH PHYSICS, INC.—See Blue Sea Capital Management LLC; *U.S. Private*, pg. 592
KRUEGER INTERNATIONAL, INC.; *U.S. Private*, pg. 2353
KRUEGER SHEET METAL; *U.S. Private*, pg. 2353
KRUGE-AIR, INC.—See H.I.G. Capital, LLC; *U.S. Private*, pg. 1831
KRUGER AKVAPUR AB—See Veolia Environnement S.A.; *Int'l*, pg. 8161
KRUGER AQUACARE—See Veolia Environnement S.A.; *Int'l*, pg. 8161
KRUGER A/S—See Veolia Environnement S.A.; *Int'l*, pg. 8161
KRUGER - BRAMPTON MILL—See Kruger Inc.; *Int'l*, pg. 4307
KRUGER - BROMPTONVILLE MILL—See Kruger Inc.; *Int'l*, pg. 4307
KRUGER BROWN HOLDINGS, LLC; *U.S. Private*, pg. 2353
KRUGER FOODS INC.; *U.S. Private*, pg. 2353
KRUGER INC.; *Int'l*, pg. 4307
KRUGER KALDNES AS—See Veolia Environnement S.A.; *Int'l*, pg. 8161
KRUGER - LA SALLE MILL—See Kruger Inc.; *Int'l*, pg. 4307
KRUGER - MONTREAL MILL—See Kruger Inc.; *Int'l*, pg. 4307
KRUGER OY—See Veolia Environnement S.A.; *Int'l*, pg. 8161
KRUGER PLASTIC PRODUCTS, LLC—See HC Private Investments LLC; *U.S. Private*, pg. 1888
KRUGER PRODUCTS L.P. - CRABTREE MILL—See Kruger Inc.; *Int'l*, pg. 4308
KRUGER PRODUCTS L.P. - GATINEAU MILL—See Kruger Inc.; *Int'l*, pg. 4308
KRUGER PRODUCTS L.P. - MEMPHIS MILL—See Kruger Inc.; *Int'l*, pg. 4308
KRUGER PRODUCTS L.P. - NEW WESTMINSTER MILL—See Kruger Inc.; *Int'l*, pg. 4308
KRUGER PRODUCTS L.P. - SHERBROOKE MILL—See Kruger Inc.; *Int'l*, pg. 4308
KRUGER PRODUCTS L.P.—See Kruger Inc.; *Int'l*, pg. 4308
KRUGER - TROIS RIVIERES MILL—See Kruger Inc.; *Int'l*, pg. 4307
KRUGER URBAN FOREST PRODUCTS, INC.—See Kruger Inc.; *Int'l*, pg. 4308
KRUGER WAYAGAMACK INC.—See Kruger Inc.; *Int'l*, pg. 4308
KRUGER WINES AND SPIRITS - MONTREAL PRODUCTION PLANT—See Kruger Inc.; *Int'l*, pg. 4308
KRUGER WINES AND SPIRITS—See Kruger Inc.; *Int'l*, pg. 4308
KRUG INC; *Int'l*, pg. 4307
KRUG, VINS FINS DE CHAMPAGNE S.A.—See LVMH Moet Hennessy Louis Vuitton SE; *Int'l*, pg. 4599
KRUIDVAT RETAIL BV—See CK Hutchison Holdings Limited; *Int'l*, pg. 1636
KRUIZINGA BV—See Manutan International SA; *Int'l*, pg. 4679

KRUK CESKA A SLOVENSKA REPUBLIKA S.R.O.—See Kruk S.A.; *Int'l*, pg. 4308
KRUK DEUTSCHLAND GMBH—See Kruk S.A.; *Int'l*, pg. 4308
KRUK ESPANA S.L. UNIPERSONAL—See Kruk S.A.; *Int'l*, pg. 4308
KRUK S.A.; *Int'l*, pg. 4308
KRUMLAND CO. LLC; *U.S. Private*, pg. 2353
KRUNGDHEP DOCUMENT CO., LTD.—See Krungdhep Sophon Public Company Limited; *Int'l*, pg. 4309
KRUNGDHEP SOPHON PUBLIC COMPANY LIMITED; *Int'l*, pg. 4309
KRUNGSRI ASSET MANAGEMENT CO., LTD.—See Mitsubishi UFJ Financial Group, Inc.; *Int'l*, pg. 4969
KRUNGSRI AYUDHYA AMC LTD.—See Mitsubishi UFJ Financial Group, Inc.; *Int'l*, pg. 4969
KRUNGSRIAYUDHYA CARD CO., LTD.—See Mitsubishi UFJ Financial Group, Inc.; *Int'l*, pg. 4969
KRUNGSRI FACTORING CO., LTD.—See Mitsubishi UFJ Financial Group, Inc.; *Int'l*, pg. 4969
KRUNGSRI GENERAL INSURANCE BROKER LIMITED—See Mitsubishi UFJ Financial Group, Inc.; *Int'l*, pg. 4969
KRUNGSRI LIFE ASSURANCE BROKER LIMITED—See Mitsubishi UFJ Financial Group, Inc.; *Int'l*, pg. 4969
KRUNGSRI SECURITIES PUBLIC COMPANY LIMITED—See Mitsubishi UFJ Financial Group, Inc.; *Int'l*, pg. 4969
KRUNG THAI ASSET MANAGEMENT—See Krung Thai Bank Public Company Limited; *Int'l*, pg. 4308
KRUNGTHAI-AXA LIFE INSURANCE CO., LTD.—See AXA S.A.; *Int'l*, pg. 759
KRUNGTHAI-AXA LIFE INSURANCE CO., LTD.—See Krung Thai Bank Public Company Limited; *Int'l*, pg. 4308
KRUNG THAI BANK PUBLIC COMPANY LIMITED; *Int'l*, pg. 4308
KRUNGTHAI CARD PUBLIC COMPANY LIMITED; *Int'l*, pg. 4309
KRUNGTHAI CAR RENT & LEASE PUBLIC COMPANY LIMITED; *Int'l*, pg. 4309
KRUNGTHAI CHAROENSRI COMPANY LIMITED—See Krung Thai Bank Public Company Limited; *Int'l*, pg. 4308
KRUNG THAI COMPUTER SERVICES COMPANY LIMITED—See Krung Thai Bank Public Company Limited; *Int'l*, pg. 4308
KRUNGTHAI HOLDING COMPANY LIMITED—See Krung Thai Bank Public Company Limited; *Int'l*, pg. 4308
KRUNG THAI IBJ LEASING COMPANY LIMITED—See Krung Thai Bank Public Company Limited; *Int'l*, pg. 4308
KRUNGTHAI MIZUHO LEASING COMPANY LIMITED—See Mizuho Leasing Company, Limited; *Int'l*, pg. 4999
KRUNGTHAI PANICH INSURANCE COMPANY LIMITED—See Krung Thai Bank Public Company Limited; *Int'l*, pg. 4308
KRUNGTHAI THANAKIT PUBLIC COMPANY LIMITED—See Krung Thai Bank Public Company Limited; *Int'l*, pg. 4308
KRUPKE HOLDING GMBH; *Int'l*, pg. 4309
KRUPP BILSTEIN OF AMERICA INC.—See ThyssenKrupp AG; *Int'l*, pg. 7732
KRUPP CANADA INC.—See ThyssenKrupp AG; *Int'l*, pg. 7724
KRUPP HOESCH SUSPENSIONS INC.—See ThyssenKrupp AG; *Int'l*, pg. 7732
KRUPP INFORMATIK GESELLSCHAFT MIT BESCHRANKTER HAFTUNG—See ThyssenKrupp AG; *Int'l*, pg. 7724
KRUPP KOMMUNICATIONS; *U.S. Private*, pg. 2353
KRUPP L CONSTRUCTION INC.; *U.S. Private*, pg. 2353
KRUPP MODULOS AUTOMOTIVOS DO BRASIL LTDA.—See Porsche Automobil Holding SE; *Int'l*, pg. 5929
KRUPP MODULOS AUTOMOTIVOS DO BRASIL LTDA.—See ThyssenKrupp AG; *Int'l*, pg. 7732
KRUPP NIROSTA GMBH-WERK DILLENBURG—See ThyssenKrupp AG; *Int'l*, pg. 7730
KRUPS GMBH—See SEB S.A.; *Int'l*, pg. 6668
KRUPS NORTH AMERICA, INC.—See SEB S.A.; *Int'l*, pg. 6668
KRUSELL INTERNATIONAL AB—See Northbaze Group AB; *Int'l*, pg. 5442
KRUSE-WARTHAN DUBUQUE AUTO PLAZA; *U.S. Private*, pg. 2353
KRUSE WORLDWIDE COURIER, LTD.; *U.S. Private*, pg. 2353
KRUSIK-PLASTIKA A.D.; *Int'l*, pg. 4309
KRUSKOPF COONTZ; *U.S. Private*, pg. 2353
KRV AS—See Addtech AB; *Int'l*, pg. 134
KR WAVEMAKER—See WPP plc; *Int'l*, pg. 8473
KRX ENERGY PTE LTD—See Lion Energy Limited; *Int'l*, pg. 4518
KRXI, LLC—See Sinclair, Inc.; *U.S. Public*, pg. 1885
KRYNICA VITAMIN SA; *Int'l*, pg. 4309
KRYNICKI RECYKLING S.A.—See SCR Sibelco SA; *Int'l*, pg. 6654

KRYNICA VITAMIN SA

CORPORATE AFFILIATIONS

KRYPT INC.—See ArchLynk, LLC; *U.S. Private*, pg. 311
KRYPTON INDUSTRIES LIMITED; *Int'l*, pg. 4309
KRYPTON INDUSTRIES LTD.; *Int'l*, pg. 4309
KRYPTOS NETWORKS PVT LTD—See Crayon Group AS; *Int'l*, pg. 1829
KRYSO RESOURCES LIMITED—See China Nonferrous Gold Limited; *Int'l*, pg. 1535
KRYSTAL AVIATION SERVICES PVT LTD—See Krystal Integrated Services Pvt. Ltd.; *Int'l*, pg. 4309
KRYSTAL BIOTECH, INC.; *U.S. Public*, pg. 1277
KRYSTAL GOURMET SERVICES PVT LTD—See Krystal Integrated Services Pvt. Ltd.; *Int'l*, pg. 4309
KRYSTAL INFINITY LLC; *U.S. Private*, pg. 2354
KRYSTAL INTEGRATED SERVICES PVT. LTD.; *Int'l*, pg. 4309
KRYSTAL KLEAN INC.—See ACON Investments, LLC; *U.S. Private*, pg. 62
KRYSTAL KLEAN USA INC.—See ACON Investments, LLC; *U.S. Private*, pg. 62
KRYSTAL RESTAURANTS LLC—See SoftBank Group Corp.; *Int'l*, pg. 7054
KRZ PORT - BOURGAS AD—See Industrial Holding Bulgaria AD; *Int'l*, pg. 3672
K+S AGRICOLTURA S.P.A.—See K+S Aktiengesellschaft; *Int'l*, pg. 4040
K S AGRI RESOURCES PTE. LTD.—See K.S. Oils Ltd; *Int'l*, pg. 4044
K+S AGRO MEXICO S.A. DE C.V.—See K+S Aktiengesellschaft; *Int'l*, pg. 4040
KSA INDUSTRIES INC.; *U.S. Private*, pg. 2354
K+S AKTIENGESELLSCHAFT - PLANT SALZDETFURTH—See K+S Aktiengesellschaft; *Int'l*, pg. 4040
K+S AKTIENGESELLSCHAFT; *Int'l*, pg. 4039
KS ALUMINIUM-TECHNOLOGIE GMBH—See Rheinmetall AG; *Int'l*, pg. 6321
K+S AN-INSTITUTS VERWALTUNGSGESELLSCHAFT MBH—See K+S Aktiengesellschaft; *Int'l*, pg. 4040
KSA REALTY CORPORATION—See A. Soriano Corporation; *Int'l*, pg. 22
KSARIA CORPORATION—See ITT Inc.; *U.S. Public*, pg. 1179
KSASHMTSSI GMBH—See Atlassian Corporation; *Int'l*, pg. 686
K+S ASIA PACIFIC PTE. LTD.—See K+S Aktiengesellschaft; *Int'l*, pg. 4040
KS ATAG GMBH—See Rheinmetall AG; *Int'l*, pg. 6321
KS AUTOMOTIVE INC—See Kennerley-Spratling Inc.; *U.S. Private*, pg. 2286
KSAX-TV, INC.—See Hubbard Broadcasting, Inc.; *U.S. Private*, pg. 2000
KSB ALGERIE EURL—See KSB SE & Co. KGaA; *Int'l*, pg. 4311
KSB-AMVI, S.A.—See KSB SE & Co. KGaA; *Int'l*, pg. 4312
KSB-AMVI S.A.—See KSB SE & Co. KGaA; *Int'l*, pg. 4312
KS BANCORP INC.; *U.S. Public*, pg. 1277
KS BANK, INC.—See KS Bancorp Inc.; *U.S. Public*, pg. 1277
KSB ARMATUREN GMBH—See KSB SE & Co. KGaA; *Int'l*, pg. 4311
KSB ARTRU SERVICES RHONE ALPES S.A.S.—See KSB SE & Co. KGaA; *Int'l*, pg. 4311
KSB A/S—See KSB SE & Co. KGaA; *Int'l*, pg. 4311
K+S BAUSTOFFRECYCLING GMBH—See K+S Aktiengesellschaft; *Int'l*, pg. 4040
KSB AUSTRALIA PTY LTD.—See KSB SE & Co. KGaA; *Int'l*, pg. 4311
KSB AUSTRALIA PTY. LTD.—See KSB SE & Co. KGaA; *Int'l*, pg. 4311
KSB BELGIUM S.A.—See KSB Limited; *Int'l*, pg. 4310
KSB BOMBAS E VALVULAS S.A.—See KSB SE & Co. KGaA; *Int'l*, pg. 4311
KSB BOMBAS HIDRAULICAS S.A.—See KSB SE & Co. KGaA; *Int'l*, pg. 4311
KSB BRASIL LTDA.—See KSB SE & Co. KGaA; *Int'l*, pg. 4311
KSB CERPADLA A ARMATURY—See KSB SE & Co. KGaA; *Int'l*, pg. 4311
KSB CHILE S.A.—See KSB SE & Co. KGaA; *Int'l*, pg. 4311
KSB COLOMBIA SAS—See KSB SE & Co. KGaA; *Int'l*, pg. 4311
KSB COMPANIA SUDAMERICANA DE BOMBAS S.A.—See KSB SE & Co. KGaA; *Int'l*, pg. 4311
KSB CONTROLADORA S.A. DE C.V.—See KSB SE & Co. KGaA; *Int'l*, pg. 4311
KSB DE MEXICO, S.A. DE C.V.—See KSB SE & Co. KGaA; *Int'l*, pg. 4312
KSB DUBRIC, INC.—See KSB SE & Co. KGaA; *Int'l*, pg. 4311
KS BEARINGS—See KS International Investment Corp.; *U.S. Private*, pg. 2354
K+S BENELUX B.V.—See K+S Aktiengesellschaft; *Int'l*, pg. 4040
K+S BETEILIGUNGS GMBH—See K+S Aktiengesellschaft; *Int'l*, pg. 4040
KSB FINANCE NEDERLAND B.V.—See KSB SE & Co. KGaA; *Int'l*, pg. 4311

KSB FINLAND OY—See KSB SE & Co. KGaA; *Int'l*, pg. 4311
KSB FLUID SYSTEMS GMBH—See KSB SE & Co. KGaA; *Int'l*, pg. 4311
KSB GIW, INC.—See KSB SE & Co. KGaA; *Int'l*, pg. 4311
KSBG KOMMUNALE BETEILIGUNGSGESELLSCHAFT GMBH & CO. KG; *Int'l*, pg. 4313
KSB HUNGARY KFT.—See KSB SE & Co. KGaA; *Int'l*, pg. 4311
KSB-HYDRAULOR SERVICES—See KSB SE & Co. KGaA; *Int'l*, pg. 4312
KSB INC.—See KSB SE & Co. KGaA; *Int'l*, pg. 4311
KSB ITALIA S.P.A.—See KSB SE & Co. KGaA; *Int'l*, pg. 4311
KSB ITUR SPAIN S.A.—See KSB SE & Co. KGaA; *Int'l*, pg. 4311
KSB KOREA LTD.—See KSB SE & Co. KGaA; *Int'l*, pg. 4311
KSB LIMITED—See KSB SE & Co. KGaA; *Int'l*, pg. 4311
KSB LIMITED; *Int'l*, pg. 4310
KSB LIMITED—See KSB SE & Co. KGaA; *Int'l*, pg. 4311
KSB LTD.—See KSB SE & Co. KGaA; *Int'l*, pg. 4311
KSB MALAYSIA PUMPS & VALVES SDN. BHD.—See KSB SE & Co. KGaA; *Int'l*, pg. 4311
KSB MEXICANA S.A. DE C.V.—See KSB SE & Co. KGaA; *Int'l*, pg. 4311
KSB MIDDLE EAST FZE—See KSB SE & Co. KGaA; *Int'l*, pg. 4311
KSB MIL CONTROLS LIMITED—See KSB SE & Co. KGaA; *Int'l*, pg. 4311
KSB NEDERLAND B.V.—See KSB SE & Co. KGaA; *Int'l*, pg. 4311
KSB NEW ZEALAND LIMITED—See KSB SE & Co. KGaA; *Int'l*, pg. 4311
KSB NORGE AS—See KSB SE & Co. KGaA; *Int'l*, pg. 4311
KSB ON SITE MACHINING BVBA—See KSB SE & Co. KGaA; *Int'l*, pg. 4313
KSB OOO—See KSB SE & Co. KGaA; *Int'l*, pg. 4311
KSB OSTERREICH GES.MBH—See KSB SE & Co. KGaA; *Int'l*, pg. 4312
KSB PERU S.A.—See KSB SE & Co. KGaA; *Int'l*, pg. 4312
KSB PHILIPPINES, INC.—See KSB SE & Co. KGaA; *Int'l*, pg. 4312
KSB POLSKA SP. Z O.O.—See KSB SE & Co. KGaA; *Int'l*, pg. 4312
KSB-POMPA, ARMATUR SANAYI VE TICARET A.S.—See KSB SE & Co. KGaA; *Int'l*, pg. 4312
KSB POMPE—See KSB SE & Co. KGaA; *Int'l*, pg. 4312
KSB POMPES ET ROBINETTERIES S.A.R.L. D'ASSOCIE UNIQUE—See KSB SE & Co. KGaA; *Int'l*, pg. 4312
KSB POMPY I ARMATURA SP. ZO.O—See KSB SE & Co. KGaA; *Int'l*, pg. 4312
KSB PUMPE I ARMATURE D.O.Q. BEOGRAD—See KSB SE & Co. KGaA; *Int'l*, pg. 4312
KSB PUMPE I ARMATURE D.Q.O.—See KSB Limited; *Int'l*, pg. 4310
KSB PUMPS AND VALVES (PTY) LTD.—See KSB SE & Co. KGaA; *Int'l*, pg. 4312
KSB PUMPS ARABIA LTD.—See KSB SE & Co. KGaA; *Int'l*, pg. 4312
KSB PUMPS CO. LTD., LAHORE—See KSB SE & Co. KGaA; *Int'l*, pg. 4312
KSB PUMPS CO. LTD.—See KSB SE & Co. KGaA; *Int'l*, pg. 4312
KSB PUMPS, INC.—See KSB SE & Co. KGaA; *Int'l*, pg. 4312
KSB PUMPS LIMITED, PUNE—See KSB SE & Co. KGaA; *Int'l*, pg. 4312
KSB PUMPS (S.A.) (PTY.) LTD.—See KSB SE & Co. KGaA; *Int'l*, pg. 4312
KSB PUMPS & VALVES LIMITED—See KSB SE & Co. KGaA; *Int'l*, pg. 4312
KSB PUMPS & VALVES LTD.—See KSB SE & Co. KGaA; *Int'l*, pg. 4312
KSB PUMPY & ARMATURY S.R.O.—See KSB SE & Co. KGaA; *Int'l*, pg. 4312
K+S BRASILEIRA FERTILIZANTES E PRODUTOS INDUSTRIAIS LTDA.—See K+S Aktiengesellschaft; *Int'l*, pg. 4040
KSB S.A.S—See KSB SE & Co. KGaA; *Int'l*, pg. 4312
KSB (SCHWEIZ) AG—See KSB SE & Co. KGaA; *Int'l*, pg. 4310
KSB SE & CO. KGAA; *Int'l*, pg. 4310
KSB SEIL CO., LTD.—See KSB SE & Co. KGaA; *Int'l*, pg. 4312
KSB SERVICE EITB-SITELEC—See KSB SE & Co. KGaA; *Int'l*, pg. 4312
KSB SERVICE GMBH—See KSB SE & Co. KGaA; *Int'l*, pg. 4312
KSB SERVICE ITALIA S.R.L.—See KSB SE & Co. KGaA; *Int'l*, pg. 4311
KSB SERVICE ROBINETTERIE—See KSB SE & Co. KGaA; *Int'l*, pg. 4312
KSB SERVICE SUCIBA S.L.U.—See KSB SE & Co. KGaA; *Int'l*, pg. 4312
KSB SHANGHAI PUMP CO., LTD.—See KSB SE & Co. KGaA; *Int'l*, pg. 4312

KSB SINGAPORE (ASIA PACIFIC) PTE. LTD.—See KSB SE & Co. KGaA; *Int'l*, pg. 4312
KSB SVERIGE AB—See KSB SE & Co. KGaA; *Int'l*, pg. 4312
KSB (SWITZERLAND) LTD—See KSB SE & Co. KGaA; *Int'l*, pg. 4310
KSB SZIVATTYU ES ARMATURA KFT.—See KSB SE & Co. KGaA; *Int'l*, pg. 4312
KSB TAIWAN CO. LTD.—See KSB SE & Co. KGaA; *Int'l*, pg. 4312
KSB TECH PVT. LTD.—See KSB SE & Co. KGaA; *Int'l*, pg. 4312
KSB TESMA AG—See KSB SE & Co. KGaA; *Int'l*, pg. 4312
KSB VALVES (CHANGZHOU) CO., LTD.—See KSB SE & Co. KGaA; *Int'l*, pg. 4312
KSB VENEZOLANA C.A.—See KSB SE & Co. KGaA; *Int'l*, pg. 4312
KSB VIETNAM CO., LTD.—See KSB SE & Co. KGaA; *Int'l*, pg. 4312
KSBW-TV—See The Hearst Corporation; *U.S. Private*, pg. 4048
KSBY COMMUNICATIONS, INC.—See Evening Post Publishing Co.; *U.S. Private*, pg. 1436
KSB ZAMBIA LIMITED—See KSB SE & Co. KGaA; *Int'l*, pg. 4312
KSCA-FM—See ForgeLight, LLC; *U.S. Private*, pg. 1568
KSCA-FM—See Searchlight Capital Partners, L.P.; *U.S. Private*, pg. 3590
K+S CHILE S.A.—See K+S Aktiengesellschaft; *Int'l*, pg. 4040
K. SCHWEIZER AG—See Burkhalter Holding AG; *Int'l*, pg. 1225
KSCMF LTD.—See Rallis India Limited; *Int'l*, pg. 6196
K+S CONSULTING GMBH—See K+S Aktiengesellschaft; *Int'l*, pg. 4040
K&S CORPORATION LIMITED; *Int'l*, pg. 4038
KSC STUDIO, LLC—See Bertram Capital Management, LLC; *U.S. Private*, pg. 540
K+S CZ A.S.—See K+S Aktiengesellschaft; *Int'l*, pg. 4040
KS CZ MOTORSERVICE S.R.O.—See Rheinmetall AG; *Int'l*, pg. 6321
KSD ENTERPRISES LTD.—See Keck Seng (Malaysia) Berhad; *Int'l*, pg. 4114
KSD HAULAGE CONTRACTORS LTD; *Int'l*, pg. 4313
KS DISTRIBUTION (MALAYSIA) SDN. BHD.—See KS Energy Limited; *Int'l*, pg. 4309
KS DISTRIBUTION PTE LTD—See KS Energy Limited; *Int'l*, pg. 4309
KS DISTRIBUTION (SHANGHAI) LTD.—See KS Energy Limited; *Int'l*, pg. 4309
KSDK-TV—See TEGNA Inc.; *U.S. Public*, pg. 1990
KS DRILLING PTE LTD—See KS Energy Limited; *Int'l*, pg. 4310
KSEC INTELLIGENT TECHNOLOGY CO., LTD.; *Int'l*, pg. 4313
KSEE TELEVISION, INC.—See Nexstar Media Group, Inc.; *U.S. Public*, pg. 1523
KSE LIMITED; *Int'l*, pg. 4313
KS ENERGY LIMITED; *Int'l*, pg. 4309
KS ENERGY SERVICES, LLC—See Clayton, Dubilier & Rice, LLC; *U.S. Private*, pg. 919
K. SENG SENG CORPORATION BHD; *Int'l*, pg. 4043
K. SENG SENG MANUFACTURING SDN BHD—See K. Seng Seng Corporation Bhd; *Int'l*, pg. 4043
K+S ENTSORGUNG GMBH—See K+S Aktiengesellschaft; *Int'l*, pg. 4040
K+S ENTSORGUNG (SCHWEIZ) AG—See Thommen-Furler AG; *Int'l*, pg. 7714
KS EQUIPMENT (SHANGHAI) LTD.—See KS Energy Limited; *Int'l*, pg. 4309
K SERA SERA MINIPLEX PRIVATE LIMITED—See KSS Limited; *Int'l*, pg. 4314
K SERA SERA PRODUCTIONS FZE—See KSS Limited; *Int'l*, pg. 4314
K+S FERTILIZERS (INDIA) PRIVATE LIMITED—See K+S Aktiengesellschaft; *Int'l*, pg. 4040
K+S FINANCE BELGIUM BVBA—See K+S Aktiengesellschaft; *Int'l*, pg. 4040
KS FLOW CONTROL PTE. LTD.—See KS Energy Limited; *Int'l*, pg. 4309
K&S FREIGHTERS LIMITED—See K&S Corporation Limited; *Int'l*, pg. 4039
K&S FREIGHTERS PTY. LTD.—See K&S Corporation Limited; *Int'l*, pg. 4039
K&S FUELS—See K&S Corporation Limited; *Int'l*, pg. 4039
KSFY-TV—See Gray Television, Inc.; *U.S. Public*, pg. 960
KSG AGRO S.A.; *Int'l*, pg. 4313
KSG DISTRIBUTING, INC.; *U.S. Private*, pg. 2354
KSG ENTERPRISES LTD.—See Keck Seng (Malaysia) Berhad; *Int'l*, pg. 4114
KSG KARTEN-VERRECHNUNGS- UND SERVICEGESELLSCHAFT M.B.H.—See UniCredit S.p.A.; *Int'l*, pg. 8034
KS GLEITLAGER DE MEXICO, S. DE R.L. DE C.V.—See Rheinmetall AG; *Int'l*, pg. 6321
KS GLEITLAGER GMBH—See Rheinmetall AG; *Int'l*, pg. 6321

COMPANY NAME INDEX

KS GLEITLAGER NORTH AMERICA LLC—See Rheinmetall AG; *Int'l*, pg. 6321
KS GLEITLAGER USA INC.—See Rheinmetall AG; *Int'l*, pg. 6321
K&S GROUP PTY LTD—See K&S Corporation Limited; *Int'l*, pg. 4039
K+S GUBRE VE ENDUSTRI URUNLERI SAN. VE TIC. LTD. STI.—See K+S Aktiengesellschaft; *Int'l*, pg. 4040
K + S HAUSTECHNIK PLANUNGSGESELLSCHAFT MBH—See TUV SUD AG; *Int'l*, pg. 7984
KSHB-TV—See The E.W. Scripps Company; *U.S. Public*, pg. 2068
KSHE-FM—See Hubbard Broadcasting, Inc.; *U.S. Private*, pg. 2000
KSH HOLDINGS LIMITED; *Int'l*, pg. 4313
KSHITIJ POLYLINE LTD.; *Int'l*, pg. 4313
KSHITIZ INVESTMENTS LIMITED; *Int'l*, pg. 4313
K'S HOLDINGS CORPORATION; *Int'l*, pg. 4039
KSH PROPERTY DEVELOPMENT PTE LTD—See KSH Holdings Limited; *Int'l*, pg. 4313
KSH SOLUTIONS INC.—See AFRY AB; *Int'l*, pg. 194
KSIGN CO., LTD.; *Int'l*, pg. 4313
KSI.INC—See Qurate Retail, Inc.; *U.S. Public*, pg. 1758
KS INDUSTRIES, L.P.; *U.S. Private*, pg. 2354
K&S INTEGRATED DISTRIBUTION PTY LTD—See K&S Corporation Limited; *Int'l*, pg. 4039
KS INTERNATIONAL HOLDINGS CORP.; *U.S. Public*, pg. 1277
KS INTERNATIONAL INVESTMENT CORP.; *U.S. Private*, pg. 2354
KS INTERNATIONAL LLC—See D.C. Capital Partners, LLC; *U.S. Private*, pg. 1141
KSIP (SINGAPORE) PTE. LTD.—See Kee Shing Investment (BVI) Limited; *Int'l*, pg. 4115
K+S ITALIA S.R.L.—See K+S Aktiengesellschaft; *Int'l*, pg. 4040
KSI TRADING COMPANY; *U.S. Private*, pg. 2354
KSI TRADING CORP.—See Investcorp Holdings B.S.C.; *Int'l*, pg. 3776
K+S IT-SERVICES GMBH—See K+S Aktiengesellschaft; *Int'l*, pg. 4040
KSJ & ASSOCIATES; *U.S. Private*, pg. 2354
K+S KALI ATLANTIQUE S.A.S.—See K+S Aktiengesellschaft; *Int'l*, pg. 4040
K+S KALI DU ROURE S.A.S.—See K+S Aktiengesellschaft; *Int'l*, pg. 4040
K+S KALI FRANCE S.A.S.—See K+S Aktiengesellschaft; *Int'l*, pg. 4040
K+S KALI GMBH - NEUHOF-ELLERS PLANT—See K+S Aktiengesellschaft; *Int'l*, pg. 4040
K+S KALI GMBH - SIGMUNDSHALL PLANT—See K+S Aktiengesellschaft; *Int'l*, pg. 4040
K+S KALI GMBH—See K+S Aktiengesellschaft; *Int'l*, pg. 4040
K+S KALI GMBH - WERK BERGMANNSSEGEN-HUGO PLANT—See K+S Aktiengesellschaft; *Int'l*, pg. 4040
K+S KALI GMBH - WERRA PLANT—See K+S Aktiengesellschaft; *Int'l*, pg. 4040
K+S KALI GMBH - ZIELITZ PLANT—See K+S Aktiengesellschaft; *Int'l*, pg. 4040
K+S KALI WITTENHEIM S.A.S.—See K+S Aktiengesellschaft; *Int'l*, pg. 4040
KSK AUTOMOTIVE COMPONENTS (PINGHU) CO., LTD.—See Keboda Technology Co., Ltd.; *Int'l*, pg. 4113
KSK CO., LTD.—See VITAL KSK HOLDINGS, INC.; *Int'l*, pg. 8258
KSK CO., LTD.; *Int'l*, pg. 4314
KSK ENERGY LIMITED—See KSK Power Ventur plc; *Int'l*, pg. 4314
KSK ENERGY VENTURES LIMITED; *Int'l*, pg. 4314
KSK KYUSHU CORPORATION—See KSK CO., LTD.; *Int'l*, pg. 4314
KSKN TELEVISION, INC.—See TEGNA Inc.; *U.S. Public*, pg. 1990
KS KOLBENSCHMIDT CZECH REBUBLIC A.S.—See Rheinmetall AG; *Int'l*, pg. 6321
KS KOLBENSCHMIDT FRANCE S.A.S.—See Rheinmetall AG; *Int'l*, pg. 6321
KS KOLBENSCHMIDT GMBH—See Rheinmetall AG; *Int'l*, pg. 6321
KS KOLBENSCHMIDT US, INC.—See Rheinmetall AG; *Int'l*, pg. 6321
KSK POWER VENTUR PLC; *Int'l*, pg. 4314
K SKY CO., LTD.—See Konoike Transport Co.; *Int'l*, pg. 4274
KSLA, LLC—See Gray Television, Inc.; *U.S. Public*, pg. 959
KS LARGE BORE PISTONS INC.—See Rheinmetall AG; *Int'l*, pg. 6321
KSL CAPITAL PARTNERS, LLC; *U.S. Private*, pg. 2354
KSL CHEMICAL CO., LTD.—See Khon Kaen Sugar Industry Public Company Limited; *Int'l*, pg. 4155
KSL DEVELOPMENT SDN. BHD.—See KSL Holdings Berhad; *Int'l*, pg. 4314
KSL EXPORT TRADING CO.—See Khon Kaen Sugar Industry Public Company Limited; *Int'l*, pg. 4155
KSL HOLDINGS BERHAD; *Int'l*, pg. 4314
KSL HOLDINGS LIMITED; *Int'l*, pg. 4314

KSL KUTTLER AUTOMATION SYSTEMS GMBH—See Suntech Power Holdings Co., Ltd.; *Int'l*, pg. 7325
KSL MEDIA, INC.; *U.S. Private*, pg. 2355
KSL MEDIA, INC.—See KSL Media, Inc.; *U.S. Private*, pg. 2355
KSLP (CHINA) CO. LTD.—See Rheinmetall AG; *Int'l*, pg. 6321
KSL PROPERTIES SDN. BHD.—See KSL Holdings Berhad; *Int'l*, pg. 4314
KSL REAL ESTATE CO., LTD.—See Khon Kaen Sugar Industry Public Company Limited; *Int'l*, pg. 4155
KSL RESORTS—See KSL Capital Partners, LLC; *U.S. Private*, pg. 2355
KSL-TV—See Deseret Management Corporation; *U.S. Private*, pg. 1212
KS MARKEDET—See BNP Paribas SA; *Int'l*, pg. 1091
K&S MARKET INC.; *U.S. Private*, pg. 2250
K. S. M. CO., LTD.—See Kurogane Kosakusho Ltd.; *Int'l*, pg. 4342
KSM ELECTRONICS INC.; *U.S. Private*, pg. 2355
K+S MINERALS & AGRICULTURE GMBH—See K+S Aktiengesellschaft; *Int'l*, pg. 4040
K+S MINING ARGENTINA S.A.—See K+S Aktiengesellschaft; *Int'l*, pg. 4040
KSM METALS CO., LTD.—See Australian Strategic Materials Limited; *Int'l*, pg. 722
KSM MINING ULC—See Seabridge Gold Inc.; *Int'l*, pg. 6661
K+S MONTANA HOLDINGS LLC—See K+S Aktiengesellschaft; *Int'l*, pg. 4040
KSMO-TV—See Meredith Corporation; *U.S. Public*, pg. 1423
KSM PARTNERS; *Int'l*, pg. 4314
KS NALOZBE D.D.; *Int'l*, pg. 4310
KS NATURAL RESOURCES PTE. LTD.—See K.S. Oils Ltd; *Int'l*, pg. 4044
K+S NETHERLANDS HOLDING B.V.—See K+S Aktiengesellschaft; *Int'l*, pg. 4040
KSNET, INC.—See Lesaka Technologies, Inc.; *Int'l*, pg. 4468
KSNF-TV—See Nexstar Media Group, Inc.; *U.S. Public*, pg. 1523
K+S NORTH AMERICA CORPORATION—See K+S Aktiengesellschaft; *Int'l*, pg. 4040
K+S NORTH AMERICA SALT HOLDINGS LLC—See K+S Aktiengesellschaft; *Int'l*, pg. 4040
K&S (NZ) LIMITED—See K&S Corporation Limited; *Int'l*, pg. 4038
KSOFT SYSTEMS INC.—See Virinchi Ltd.; *Int'l*, pg. 8248
K. S. OILS LIMITED; *Int'l*, pg. 4043
K.S. OILS LTD; *Int'l*, pg. 4044
KSOLUTIONS SPA—See Giovanni Agnelli B.V.; *Int'l*, pg. 2978
KSOLVES INDIA LIMITED; *Int'l*, pg. 4314
KSOLVES LLC—See Ksolves India Limited; *Int'l*, pg. 4314
K-SOLV GROUP, LLC; *U.S. Private*, pg. 2251
KSP CO., LTD.; *Int'l*, pg. 4314
KS PERSONALDIENSTLEISTUNGSGESELLSCHAFT MBH I.L.—See Rheinmetall AG; *Int'l*, pg. 6321
K+S PERU S.A.C.—See K+S Aktiengesellschaft; *Int'l*, pg. 4041
KSPG AG—See Rheinmetall AG; *Int'l*, pg. 6321
KSPG AUTOMOTIVE BRAZIL LTDA. - MS MOTOR SERVICE BRAZIL DIVISION—See Rheinmetall AG; *Int'l*, pg. 6321
KSPG AUTOMOTIVE BRAZIL LTDA. - PIERBURG PUMP TECHNOLOGY DIVISION—See Rheinmetall AG; *Int'l*, pg. 6321
KSPG AUTOMOTIVE BRAZIL LTDA.—See Rheinmetall AG; *Int'l*, pg. 6321
KSPG AUTOMOTIVE INDIA PRIVATE LTD.—See Rheinmetall AG; *Int'l*, pg. 6322
KSPG (CHINA) INVESTMENT CO. LTD.—See Rheinmetall AG; *Int'l*, pg. 6321
KSPG MALTA HOLDING LTD—See Rheinmetall AG; *Int'l*, pg. 6322
KSPG NETHERLANDS HOLDING B.V.—See Rheinmetall AG; *Int'l*, pg. 6322
KSP-KABELSERVICE PRENZLAU GMBH—See Morgan Stanley; *U.S. Public*, pg. 1473
KSP MANUFACTURING SDN BHD—See Kuala Lumpur Kepong Berhad; *Int'l*, pg. 4318
K+S POLSKA SP. Z O.O—See K+S Aktiengesellschaft; *Int'l*, pg. 4041
K+S POTASH CANADA—See K+S Aktiengesellschaft; *Int'l*, pg. 4041
KS-QUADRO BAUSYSTEME GMBH—See H+H International A/S; *Int'l*, pg. 3194
K+S SALT LLC—See K+S Aktiengesellschaft; *Int'l*, pg. 4040
K+S SALT OF THE AMERICAS HOLDING B.V.—See K+S Aktiengesellschaft; *Int'l*, pg. 4041
K+S SALZ GMBH—See K+S Aktiengesellschaft; *Int'l*, pg. 4041
K.S. SANOYAS CO., LTD.—See Sanoyas Holdings Corporation; *Int'l*, pg. 6554
K&S SERVICES INC.; *U.S. Private*, pg. 2250
KSS ISKER—See OGCC KazStroyService JSC; *Int'l*, pg. 5531

KSS LIMITED; *Int'l*, pg. 4314
KSS LINE LTD.; *Int'l*, pg. 4314
KSS RETAIL LIMITED—See Tesco PLC; *Int'l*, pg. 7572
KS SUMMIT STEEL CO., LTD.—See Sumitomo Corporation; *Int'l*, pg. 7269
K-STAR SPORTS LIMITED; *Int'l*, pg. 4042
KSTC-TV, LLC—See Hubbard Broadcasting, Inc.; *U.S. Private*, pg. 2000
KST DATA INC.; *U.S. Private*, pg. 2355
KS-TECH CO., LTD.—See Kurimoto Ltd; *Int'l*, pg. 4339
KST ELECTRIC, LTD.—See Rosendin Electric, Inc.; *U.S. Private*, pg. 3483
KST ELECTRIC POWER COMPANY, S.A.P.I. DE C.V.—See Korea Electric Power Corporation; *Int'l*, pg. 4283
K.S. TERMINALS INC.; *Int'l*, pg. 4044
KST MARITIME—See Keppel Corporation Limited; *Int'l*, pg. 4130
K & S TOOL, DIE & MANUFACTURING, INC.; *U.S. Private*, pg. 2249
KSTP-FM, LLC—See Hubbard Broadcasting, Inc.; *U.S. Private*, pg. 2000
KSTP-TV, LLC—See Hubbard Broadcasting, Inc.; *U.S. Private*, pg. 2000
K.S TRADING (PVT) LTD.—See Daikin Industries, Ltd.; *Int'l*, pg. 1935
K S TRAINING LTD.—See MBH Corporation Plc; *Int'l*, pg. 4752
K+S TRANSPORT GMBH—See K+S Aktiengesellschaft; *Int'l*, pg. 4041
K&S TRANSPORT MANAGEMENT PTY LTD—See K&S Corporation Limited; *Int'l*, pg. 4039
KSTU LICENSE, LLC—See Nexstar Media Group, Inc.; *U.S. Public*, pg. 1524
KSTU-TV—See Nexstar Media Group, Inc.; *U.S. Public*, pg. 1524
K+S UK & EIRE LTD.—See K+S Aktiengesellschaft; *Int'l*, pg. 4041
K S UK LIMITED—See E-Land World Ltd.; *Int'l*, pg. 2248
K-SUN CORPORATION—See Seiko Epson Corporation; *Int'l*, pg. 6686
KSUS INTERNATIONAL LLC.—See Rheinmetall AG; *Int'l*, pg. 6322
K+S VERSICHERUNGSVERMITTLUNGS GMBH—See K+S Aktiengesellschaft; *Int'l*, pg. 4041
KSVI-TV—See Nexstar Media Group, Inc.; *U.S. Public*, pg. 1523
KSWB INC.—See Nexstar Media Group, Inc.; *U.S. Public*, pg. 1524
KSW, INC.—See The Related Companies, L.P.; *U.S. Private*, pg. 4103
K+S WINDSOR SALT LTD.—See K+S Aktiengesellschaft; *Int'l*, pg. 4041
K.S.WIRE CO., LTD.—See KISWIRE LTD; *Int'l*, pg. 4193
K-SWISS AUSTRALIA—See E-Land World Ltd.; *Int'l*, pg. 2248
K-SWISS CANADA—See E-Land World Ltd.; *Int'l*, pg. 2248
K-SWISS DIRECT, INC—See E-Land World Ltd.; *Int'l*, pg. 2248
K-SWISS EUROPE B.V.—See E-Land World Ltd.; *Int'l*, pg. 2248
K-SWISS (HONG KONG) LTD.—See E-Land World Ltd.; *Int'l*, pg. 2248
K-SWISS INC.—See E-Land World Ltd.; *Int'l*, pg. 2248
K-SWISS PACIFIC INC.—See E-Land World Ltd.; *Int'l*, pg. 2248
K-SWISS RETAIL LTD.—See E-Land World Ltd.; *Int'l*, pg. 2248
K-SWISS SALES CORP.—See E-Land World Ltd.; *Int'l*, pg. 2248
KSW MECHANICAL SERVICES, INC.—See The Related Companies, L.P.; *U.S. Private*, pg. 4103
KTAB-TV—See Nexstar Media Group, Inc.; *U.S. Public*, pg. 1523
KT ACQUISITION LLC—See Crawford United Corporation; *U.S. Public*, pg. 592
KTA GROUP INC.—See Bowman Consulting Group Ltd.; *U.S. Public*, pg. 376
K-TALOUSPALVELUKESKUS OY—See Kesko Corporation; *Int'l*, pg. 4141
KT ALPHA CO., LTD.—See KT Corporation; *Int'l*, pg. 4315
KT ALPHA CO., LTD.—See KT Corporation; *Int'l*, pg. 4315
KTAL-TV—See Nexstar Media Group, Inc.; *U.S. Public*, pg. 1523
KT AMC CO., LTD.—See KT Corporation; *Int'l*, pg. 4315
KT ANDINA S.A.C.—See Kepner-Tregoe, Inc.; *U.S. Private*, pg. 2290
KTB ADVISORY CO., LTD.—See Krung Thai Bank Public Company Limited; *Int'l*, pg. 4308
KTB ASIA ADVISORS PTE. LTD.—See KTB Investment & Securities Co., Ltd.; *Int'l*, pg. 4316
KTB ASSET MANAGEMENT CO., LTD.—See KTB Investment & Securities Co., Ltd.; *Int'l*, pg. 4316
KTB COMPUTER SERVICES CO., LTD.—See Krung Thai Bank Public Company Limited; *Int'l*, pg. 4308
KTBC-TV—See Fox Corporation; *U.S. Public*, pg. 876

1543

K & S TOOL, DIE & MANUFACTURING, INC.

CORPORATE AFFILIATIONS

KTB GENERAL SERVICES AND SECURITY COMPANY LIMITED—See Krung Thai Bank Public Company Limited; *Int'l*, pg. 4308
KTB GENERAL SERVICES CO., LTD.—See Krung Thai Bank Public Company Limited; *Int'l*, pg. 4308
KTB INVESTMENT MANAGEMENT CO., LTD.—See KTB Investment & Securities Co., Ltd.; *Int'l*, pg. 4316
KTB INVESTMENT & SECURITIES CO., LTD.; *Int'l*, pg. 4316
KTB LEASING CO., LTD.—See Krungthai Card Public Company Limited; *Int'l*, pg. 4309
KTB PRIVATE EQUITY CO., LTD.—See KTB Investment & Securities Co., Ltd.; *Int'l*, pg. 4316
KTB SECURITIES (THAILAND) COMPANY LIMITED—See KTB Investment & Securities Co., Ltd.; *Int'l*, pg. 4316
KTB SPECIAL PURPOSE ACQUISITION COMPANY 1 CO., LTD; *Int'l*, pg. 4316
KTC (EDIBLES) LIMITED—See Endless LLP; *Int'l*, pg. 2403
KTC KOMMUNIKATIONS- UND TRAININGS-CENTER KONIGSTEIN GMBH—See Commerzbank AG; *Int'l*, pg. 1718
KT CLOUD CO., LTD.—See KT Corporation; *Int'l*, pg. 4315
KT CLOUD LAB LLP—See Kazakhtelecom JSC; *Int'l*, pg. 4102
KTC MANAGEMENT CORPORATION—See The Goldman Sachs Group, Inc.; *U.S. Public*, pg. 2080
KT CORPORATION; *Int'l*, pg. 4314
KT CS CORP.; *Int'l*, pg. 4315
KTDS CO., LTD.—See KT Corporation; *Int'l*, pg. 4315
K-TEC CORP.—See Kawasaki Heavy Industries, Ltd.; *Int'l*, pg. 4095
K-TECH CONSTRUCTION PUBLIC COMPANY LIMITED; *Int'l*, pg. 4042
K-TECH CORP.; *U.S. Private*, pg. 2251
K-TECHNOLOGIES, INC.; *U.S. Private*, pg. 2251
K-TEC INCORPORATED; *U.S. Private*, pg. 2251
K-TEC VERWALTUNGSGESELLSCHAFT MBH—See Schunk GmbH; *Int'l*, pg. 6641
KT EDUI CO., LTD.—See KT Corporation; *Int'l*, pg. 4315
K-TEION FOODS CO., LTD.—See Kato Sangyo Co., Ltd.; *Int'l*, pg. 4090
K-TEK CORPORATION, INC.—See Griffiths Corporation; *U.S. Private*, pg. 1789
K-TEK INSTRUMENTS (PTY) LTD.—See ABB Ltd.; *Int'l*, pg. 55
K.TEK SYSTEMS, INC.; *U.S. Private*, pg. 2252
K-TEL DIRECT, INC.—See K-Tel International Inc.; *Int'l*, pg. 4042
K-TEL INTERNATIONAL INC.; *Int'l*, pg. 4042
K-TEL MULTIMEDIA (UK) LIMITED—See K-Tel International Inc.; *Int'l*, pg. 4042
KTESIOS REAL ESTATE SOCIMI, S.A.; *Int'l*, pg. 4316
KTG AGRAR SE; *Int'l*, pg. 4316
KT&G CORPORATION; *Int'l*, pg. 4315
KTG KABELTROMMEL GMBH & CO. KG—See Prysmian S.p.A.; *Int'l*, pg. 6011
KTGL-FM—See Digity Companies, LLC; *U.S. Private*, pg. 1231
KT GRANT, INC.—See The Pritzker Organization, LLC; *U.S. Private*, pg. 4100
KT&G TUTUN MAMULLERI SANAYI VE TICARET A.S.—See KT&G Corporation; *Int'l*, pg. 4316
K & T HEATING SERVICES LIMITED—See Cap10 Partners LLP; *Int'l*, pg. 1301
KTH LEESBURG PRODUCTS, LLC—See H-One Co., Ltd.; *Int'l*, pg. 3194
KTH PARTS INDUSTRIES INC.; *U.S. Private*, pg. 2355
KTH SHELBURNE MFG., INC.—See Honda Motor Co., Ltd.; *Int'l*, pg. 3463
KTHV-TV—See TEGNA Inc.; *U.S. Public*, pg. 1990
KTI BELGIUM N.V.—See VDL Groep B.V.; *Int'l*, pg. 8140
KTI BIO-FUELS, INC.—See Casella Waste Systems, Inc.; *U.S. Public*, pg. 446
K-TIG LIMITED; *Int'l*, pg. 4042
KTI, INC.; *U.S. Private*, pg. 2355
KTIMA KOSTAS LAZARIDIS S.A.; *Int'l*, pg. 4316
KT INVEST A.S.; *Int'l*, pg. 4315
KTIS BIO FERTILISER CO., LTD.—See Kaset Thai International Sugar Corporation Public Company Limited; *Int'l*, pg. 4087
K..TIS CORPORATION—See Kewpie Corporation; *Int'l*, pg. 4144
KTIS CORPORATION; *Int'l*, pg. 4316
KTIV-TV—See Gray Television, Inc.; *U.S. Public*, pg. 961
KTK GROUP CO., LTD.; *Int'l*, pg. 4316
KTK INC.; *Int'l*, pg. 4316
KT KIRA SERTIFIKALARI VARLIK KIRALAMA A.S.; *Int'l*, pg. 4315
KTLA INC.—See Nexstar Media Group, Inc.; *U.S. Public*, pg. 1524
KTL GLOBAL LIMITED; *Int'l*, pg. 4316
KT LINKUS—See KT Corporation; *Int'l*, pg. 4315
KTL LOGAN PTE. LTD.—See KTL Global Limited; *Int'l*, pg. 4317
KTLN-TV—See OTA Broadcasting, LLC; *U.S. Private*, pg. 3048
KTL OFFSHORE PTE. LTD.—See KTL Global Limited; *Int'l*, pg. 4317

KTL SOLUTIONS, INC.; *U.S. Private*, pg. 2355
KTM AG—See Pierer Konzerngesellschaft mbH; *Int'l*, pg. 5862
KTM CANADA INC.—See Pierer Konzerngesellschaft mbH; *Int'l*, pg. 5862
KTM CENTRAL EAST EUROPE S.R.O.—See Pierer Konzerngesellschaft mbH; *Int'l*, pg. 5863
KTMG LIMITED; *Int'l*, pg. 4317
KTMHOWS CO., LTD.—See KT Corporation; *Int'l*, pg. 4315
K T M, INC.—See World Kinect Corporation; *U.S. Public*, pg. 2380
KTM INDUSTRIES INC.—See TemperPack Technologies, Inc.; *U.S. Private*, pg. 3963
KT M MOBILE CO., LTD.—See KT Corporation; *Int'l*, pg. 4315
KTM NORDIC OY—See Pierer Konzerngesellschaft mbH; *Int'l*, pg. 5863
KTM NORTH AMERICA, INC.—See Pierer Konzerngesellschaft mbH; *Int'l*, pg. 5863
KT MOS NAMBU CO., LTD.—See KT Corporation; *Int'l*, pg. 4315
KT MOTORS CO., LTD.—See TPR Co., Ltd.; *Int'l*, pg. 7884
KTM-RACING AG—See Pierer Konzerngesellschaft mbH; *Int'l*, pg. 5863
KTM-SPORTMOTORCYCLE AG—See Pierer Konzerngesellschaft mbH; *Int'l*, pg. 5863
KTM-SPORTMOTORCYCLE BELGIUM S.A.—See Pierer Konzerngesellschaft mbH; *Int'l*, pg. 5863
KTM-SPORTMOTORCYCLE ESPANA S.L.—See Pierer Konzerngesellschaft mbH; *Int'l*, pg. 5863
KTM-SPORTMOTORCYCLE ITALIA S.R.L.—See Pierer Konzerngesellschaft mbH; *Int'l*, pg. 5863
KTM-SPORTMOTORCYCLE SCANDINAVIA AB—See Pierer Konzerngesellschaft mbH; *Int'l*, pg. 5863
KTM-SPORTMOTORCYCLE UK LTD.—See Pierer Konzerngesellschaft mbH; *Int'l*, pg. 5863
KTM TECHNOLOGIES GMBH—See Pierer Konzerngesellschaft mbH; *Int'l*, pg. 5863
KT NETWORKS CORP.—See KT Corporation; *Int'l*, pg. 4315
KTNQ-AM—See ForgeLight, LLC; *U.S. Private*, pg. 1568
KTNQ-AM—See Searchlight Capital Partners, L.P.; *U.S. Private*, pg. 3590
KTNV-TV—See The E.W. Scripps Company; *U.S. Public*, pg. 2068
K-TOOL CORPORATION MICHIGAN; *U.S. Private*, pg. 2251
K-TOP REITS CO., LTD.; *Int'l*, pg. 4042
K TORK INTERNATIONAL INC.—See Rotork Plc; *Int'l*, pg. 6406
KTP INDUSTRIES, INC.—See Toray Industries, Inc.; *Int'l*, pg. 7823
KTP KUNSTSTOFF PALETTENTECHNIK GMBH; *Int'l*, pg. 4317
KT POWERTEL CO. LTD.; *Int'l*, pg. 4315
KTR BENELUX B.V. - BELGIUM OFFICE—See KTR Kupplungstechnik GmbH; *Int'l*, pg. 4317
KTR BENELUX B.V.—See KTR Kupplungstechnik GmbH; *Int'l*, pg. 4317
KTR BRAKE SYSTEMS GMBH—See KTR Kupplungstechnik GmbH; *Int'l*, pg. 4317
KTR CAPITAL PARTNERS, LLC—See Norges Bank; *Int'l*, pg. 5427
KTR CAPITAL PARTNERS, LLC—See Prologis, Inc.; *U.S. Public*, pg. 1727
KTR CORPORATION—See KTR Kupplungstechnik GmbH; *Int'l*, pg. 4317
KTR COUPLINGS (INDIA) PVT. LTD.—See KTR Kupplungstechnik GmbH; *Int'l*, pg. 4317
KTR COUPLINGS LTD.—See KTR Kupplungstechnik GmbH; *Int'l*, pg. 4317
KTR COUPLINGS SOUTH AFRICA (PTY) LTD.—See KTR Kupplungstechnik GmbH; *Int'l*, pg. 4317
KTR CR, SPOL. S. R. O.—See KTR Kupplungstechnik GmbH; *Int'l*, pg. 4317
KTR DO BRASIL LTDA.—See KTR Kupplungstechnik GmbH; *Int'l*, pg. 4317
KTR FINLAND OY—See KTR Kupplungstechnik GmbH; *Int'l*, pg. 4317
KTR FRANCE—See KTR Kupplungstechnik GmbH; *Int'l*, pg. 4317
KTR JAPAN CO., LTD.—See KTR Kupplungstechnik GmbH; *Int'l*, pg. 4317
KTR KOREA LTD.—See KTR Kupplungstechnik GmbH; *Int'l*, pg. 4317
KTRK TELEVISION, INC.—See The Walt Disney Company; *U.S. Public*, pg. 2138
KTR KUPPLUNGSTECHNIK AG—See KTR Kupplungstechnik GmbH; *Int'l*, pg. 4317
KTR KUPPLUNGSTECHNIK GMBH; *Int'l*, pg. 4317
KTR KUPPLUNGSTECHNIK NORGE AS—See KTR Kupplungstechnik GmbH; *Int'l*, pg. 4317
K-TRON CHINA LTD.—See Hillenbrand, Inc.; *U.S. Public*, pg. 1036
K-TRON ELECTRONICS—See Hillenbrand, Inc.; *U.S. Public*, pg. 1037

K-TRONICS (SUZHOU) TECHNOLOGY CO., LTD.—See BOE Technology Group Co., Ltd.; *Int'l*, pg. 1099
K-TRON INTERNATIONAL, INC.—See Hillenbrand, Inc.; *U.S. Public*, pg. 1036
K-TRON INVESTMENT CO.—See Hillenbrand, Inc.; *U.S. Public*, pg. 1037
K-TRON PROCESS GROUP—See Hillenbrand, Inc.; *U.S. Public*, pg. 1037
K-TRON (SHANGHAI) CO. LTD.—See Hillenbrand, Inc.; *U.S. Public*, pg. 1036
KTR POLSKA SP. Z. O. O.—See KTR Kupplungstechnik GmbH; *Int'l*, pg. 4317
KTR POWER TRANSMISSION TECHNOLOGY (SHANGHAI) CO. LTD.—See KTR Kupplungstechnik GmbH; *Int'l*, pg. 4317
KTR PRIVODNAYA TECHNIKA, LLC—See KTR Kupplungstechnik GmbH; *Int'l*, pg. 4317
KTR SVERIGE AB—See KTR Kupplungstechnik GmbH; *Int'l*, pg. 4317
KTR TAIWAN LTD.—See KTR Kupplungstechnik GmbH; *Int'l*, pg. 4317
KTR TURKEY GUC AKTARMA SISTEMLERI SAN. TIC. LTD. STI.—See KTR Kupplungstechnik GmbH; *Int'l*, pg. 4317
KTSA-FM/AM—See Alpha Media LLC; *U.S. Private*, pg. 198
KT SAT CO., LTD.—See KT Corporation; *Int'l*, pg. 4315
KTSC JANITORIAL INC.—See Concierge Building Services, LLC; *U.S. Private*, pg. 1009
KT'S KITCHENS, INC.; *U.S. Private*, pg. 2355
KTS KUNSTSTOFF TECHNIK SCHMOLLN GMBH—See AdCapital AG; *Int'l*, pg. 126
KT SKYLIFE CO., LTD.; *Int'l*, pg. 4315
KT SPORTS CO., LTD.—See KT Corporation; *Int'l*, pg. 4315
KT SUBMARINE CORP.; *Int'l*, pg. 4315
KTS VERWALTUNGS GMBH—See AcadeMedia AB; *Int'l*, pg. 77
KTTC-TV—See Gray Television, Inc.; *U.S. Public*, pg. 961
KT TELECOP CO., LTD.—See KT Corporation; *Int'l*, pg. 4315
KTTU-TV, INC.—See TEGNA Inc.; *U.S. Public*, pg. 1990
KTTV—See Fox Corporation; *U.S. Public*, pg. 876
K-TUBE CORPORATION—See Cook Group Incorporated; *U.S. Private*, pg. 1037
KTUL, LLC—See Sinclair, Inc.; *U.S. Public*, pg. 1886
KTVA-TV—See Liberty Broadband Corporation; *U.S. Public*, pg. 1310
KTVE-TV—See Mission Broadcasting, Inc.; *U.S. Private*, pg. 2747
KTVI-TV—See Nexstar Media Group, Inc.; *U.S. Public*, pg. 1524
KTVK-3TV—See Meredith Corporation; *U.S. Public*, pg. 1423
KTVK, INC.—See Meredith Corporation; *U.S. Public*, pg. 1423
KTVL-TV—See Sinclair, Inc.; *U.S. Public*, pg. 1885
KTVT BROADCASTING COMPANY LP—See National Amusements, Inc.; *U.S. Private*, pg. 2840
KTVU, INC.—See Apollo Global Management, Inc.; *U.S. Public*, pg. 164
KTVU, LLC—See Apollo Global Management, Inc.; *U.S. Public*, pg. 164
KTVX-TV—See Nexstar Media Group, Inc.; *U.S. Public*, pg. 1523
KTW GMBH & CO. KG—See Nifco Inc.; *Int'l*, pg. 5281
KTXD OPERATING COMPANY, LLC—See SunTx Capital Partners, L.P.; *U.S. Private*, pg. 3874
KTZ-FREIGHT TRANSPORTATION LLP—See NC Kazakhstan Temir Zholy JSC; *Int'l*, pg. 5180
KUAJISHAN SHAOXING WINE CO., LTD.; *Int'l*, pg. 4317
KUAISHOU TECHNOLOGY CO., LTD.; *Int'l*, pg. 4317
KUALA LUMPUR GOLF & COUNTRY CLUB BERHAD—See Sime Darby Berhad; *Int'l*, pg. 6930
KUALA LUMPUR KEPONG BERHAD; *Int'l*, pg. 4317
KUALA TERENGGANU SPECIALIST HOSPITAL SDN. BHD.—See TDM Berhad; *Int'l*, pg. 7490
KUALITI ALAM SDN BHD—See Khazanah Nasional Berhad; *Int'l*, pg. 4152
KUALITI KINTA SDN. BHD.—See Y&G Corporation Berhad; *Int'l*, pg. 8543
KUAL TECHNOLOGIES SDN. BHD.—See Kobay Technology Bhd.; *Int'l*, pg. 4216
KUANGCHI SCIENCE LIMITED; *Int'l*, pg. 4319
KUANG-CHI TECHNOLOGIES CO., LTD.; *Int'l*, pg. 4319
KUANGDA AUTOMOBILE TRIM PARTS CO., LTD.—See Kuangda Technology Group Co., Ltd.; *Int'l*, pg. 4319
KUANGDA TECHNOLOGY GROUP CO., LTD.; *Int'l*, pg. 4319
KUANG HONG ARTS MANAGEMENT, INC.; *Int'l*, pg. 4319
KUANGLI BIO-TECH HOLDINGS CO., LTD.; *Int'l*, pg. 4319
KUANG MING SHIPPING CORP—See Yang Ming Marine Transport Corporation; *Int'l*, pg. 8560
KUANG PEI SAN FOOD PRODUCTS PUBLIC CO., LTD.; *Int'l*, pg. 4319
KUANG ROCK PRODUCTS SDN BHD—See IJM Corporation Berhad; *Int'l*, pg. 3609

COMPANY NAME INDEX

KUANTAN MEDICAL CENTRE SDN. BHD.—See TDM Berhad; *Int'l*, pg. 7490
KUANTAN PORT CONSORTIUM SDN BHD—See IJM Corporation Berhad; *Int'l*, pg. 3609
KUANTAN TEMBELING RESORT SDN. BHD.—See Pasdec Holdings Berhad; *Int'l*, pg. 5752
KUANTUM PAPERS LTD.; *Int'l*, pg. 4319
KUAN YUEH TECHNOLOGY ENGINEERING CO., LTD.—See TOPCO Scientific Co., Ltd.; *Int'l*, pg. 7814
KUAYUE-EXPRESS GROUP CO., LTD.—See JD Logistics, Inc.; *Int'l*, pg. 3924
KUB AGRO HOLDINGS SDN. BHD.—See KUB Malaysia Berhad; *Int'l*, pg. 4319
KUB AGROTECH SDN. BHD.—See KUB Malaysia Berhad; *Int'l*, pg. 886
KUBALD GMBH; *Int'l*, pg. 4320
KUBAN AGROHOLDING—See Basic Element Company; *Int'l*, pg. 886
KUBANENERGO PJSC—See JSC ROSSETI; *Int'l*, pg. 4010
KUBATRONIK-LEITERPLATTEN GMBH; *Int'l*, pg. 4320
KUBB LAND SDN BHD; *Int'l*, pg. 4320
KUB EKUITI SDN. BHD.—See KUB Malaysia Berhad; *Int'l*, pg. 4319
KUBELL CO LTD; *Int'l*, pg. 4320
KUBE PAK CORP.; *U.S. Private*, pg. 2355
KUBERAN GLOBAL EDU SOLUTIONS LIMITED; *Int'l*, pg. 4320
KUBER RESOURCES CORPORATION; *Int'l*, pg. 4320
KUBER UDYOG LTD.; *Int'l*, pg. 4320
KUBE-STAHL GMBH & CO. KG; *Int'l*, pg. 4320
KUBETECH CUSTOM MOLDING INC.—See Sun Capital Partners, Inc.; *U.S. Private*, pg. 3859
KUBE-TV—See Ellis, McQuary, Stanley & Associates LLC; *U.S. Private*, pg. 1374
KUB-FUJITSU TELECOMMUNICATIONS (MALAYSIA) SDN BHD—See KUB Malaysia Berhad; *Int'l*, pg. 4320
KUB GAZ SDN. BHD.—See KUB Malaysia Berhad; *Int'l*, pg. 4320
KUBIENT, INC.; *U.S. Public*, pg. 1277
KUBIK B.V.—See Kubik Inc.; *Int'l*, pg. 4320
KUBIKENBORG ALUMINIUM AB—See United Company RUSAL Plc; *Int'l*, pg. 8066
KUBIK INC. - NEW JERSEY FACILITY—See Kubik Inc.; *Int'l*, pg. 4320
KUBIK INC. - SAVAGE FACILITY—See Kubik Inc.; *Int'l*, pg. 4320
KUBIK INC.; *Int'l*, pg. 4320
KUBIN-NICHOLSON CORP., CHICAGO—See Kubin-Nicholson Corporation; *U.S. Private*, pg. 2356
KUBIN-NICHOLSON CORP., NEW YORK—See Kubin-Nicholson Corporation; *U.S. Private*, pg. 2356
KUBIN-NICHOLSON CORPORATION; *U.S. Private*, pg. 2355
KUBIN-NICHOLSON CORP.—See Kubin-Nicholson Corporation; *U.S. Private*, pg. 2356
KUBIQ SDN BHD—See Signature International Berhad; *Int'l*, pg. 6910
KUB MAJU MILL SDN. BHD.—See KUB Malaysia Berhad; *Int'l*, pg. 4319
KUB MALAYSIA BERHAD; *Int'l*, pg. 4319
KUBODERA CO., LTD.; *Int'l*, pg. 4320
KUBOO, INC.; *U.S. Public*, pg. 1277
KUBOTA AGRICULTURAL MACHINERY INDIA PVT., LTD.—See Kubota Corporation; *Int'l*, pg. 4321
KUBOTA AGRICULTURAL MACHINERY (SUZHOU) CO., LTD.—See Kubota Corporation; *Int'l*, pg. 4321
KUBOTA AGRO-INDUSTRIAL MACHINERY PHILIPPINES, INC.—See Kubota Corporation; *Int'l*, pg. 4321
KUBOTA AIR CONDITIONER, LTD.—See Kubota Corporation; *Int'l*, pg. 4321
KUBOTA BAUMASCHINEN GMBH—See Kubota Corporation; *Int'l*, pg. 4321
KUBOTA CANADA LTD.—See Kubota Corporation; *Int'l*, pg. 4321
KUBOTA CHINA FINANCIAL LEASING LTD.—See Kubota Corporation; *Int'l*, pg. 4321
KUBOTA CHINA HOLDINGS CO., LTD.—See Kubota Corporation; *Int'l*, pg. 4321
KUBOTA-C.I. CO., LTD.—See Kubota Corporation; *Int'l*, pg. 4322
KUBOTA CONSTRUCTION CO., LTD.—See Kubota Corporation; *Int'l*, pg. 4321
KUBOTA CONSTRUCTION MACHINERY JAPAN CORPORATION—See Kubota Corporation; *Int'l*, pg. 4321
KUBOTA CONSTRUCTION MACHINERY (SHANGHAI) CO., LTD.—See Kubota Corporation; *Int'l*, pg. 4321
KUBOTA CONSTRUCTION MACHINERY (WUXI) CO., LTD.—See Kubota Corporation; *Int'l*, pg. 4321
KUBOTA CORPORATION; *Int'l*, pg. 4320
KUBOTA CREDIT CO., LTD.—See Kubota Corporation; *Int'l*, pg. 4321
KUBOTA CREDIT CORPORATION U.S.A.—See Kubota Corporation; *Int'l*, pg. 4321
KUBOTA (DEUTSCHLAND) GMBH—See Kubota Corporation; *Int'l*, pg. 4321
KUBOTA ENGINE AMERICA CORPORATION—See Kubota Corporation; *Int'l*, pg. 4321

KUBOTA ENGINE JAPAN CORPORATION—See Kubota Corporation; *Int'l*, pg. 4321
KUBOTA ENGINE (SHANGHAI) CO., LTD.—See Kubota Corporation; *Int'l*, pg. 4321
KUBOTA ENGINE (THAILAND) CO., LTD.—See Kubota Corporation; *Int'l*, pg. 4321
KUBOTA ENVIRONMENTAL SERVICE CO., LTD.—See Kubota Corporation; *Int'l*, pg. 4321
KUBOTA ESPANA S.A.—See Kubota Corporation; *Int'l*, pg. 4321
KUBOTA EUROPE S.A.—See Kubota Corporation; *Int'l*, pg. 4321
KUBOTA FARM & INDUSTRIAL MACHINERY SERVICE LTD—See Kubota Corporation; *Int'l*, pg. 4321
KUBOTA FARM MACHINERY EUROPE S.A.S.—See Kubota Corporation; *Int'l*, pg. 4321
KUBOTA INDUSTRIAL EQUIPMENT CORPORATION—See Kubota Corporation; *Int'l*, pg. 4321
KUBOTA INSURANCE CORPORATION—See Kubota Corporation; *Int'l*, pg. 4321
KUBOTA KOREA CO., LTD.—See Kubota Corporation; *Int'l*, pg. 4321
KUBOTA LOGISTICS CORPORATION—See Kubota Corporation; *Int'l*, pg. 4321
KUBOTA MACHINERY TRADING CO., LTD.—See Kubota Corporation; *Int'l*, pg. 4321
KUBOTA MANUFACTURING OF AMERICA CORPORATION—See Kubota Corporation; *Int'l*, pg. 4322
KUBOTA MATERIALS CANADA CORPORATION—See Kubota Corporation; *Int'l*, pg. 4322
KUBOTA MEMBRANE EUROPE LTD.—See Kubota Corporation; *Int'l*, pg. 4322
KUBOTA MEMBRANE U.S.A. CORPORATION—See Kubota Corporation; *Int'l*, pg. 4322
KUBOTA METAL CORPORATION—See Kubota Corporation; *Int'l*, pg. 4322
KUBOTA MYANMAR CO., LTD.—See Kubota Corporation; *Int'l*, pg. 4322
KUBOTA PHARMACEUTICAL HOLDINGS CO., LTD.; *Int'l*, pg. 4322
KUBOTA SAUDI ARABIA COMPANY, LLC—See Kubota Corporation; *Int'l*, pg. 4322
KUBOTA SEIKI CO., LTD.—See Kubota Corporation; *Int'l*, pg. 4321
KUBOTA SYSTEMS INC.—See Kubota Corporation; *Int'l*, pg. 4322
KUBOTA TRACTOR (AUSTRALIA) PTY. LTD.—See Kubota Corporation; *Int'l*, pg. 4322
KUBOTA TRACTOR CORPORATION - ATLANTA—See Kubota Corporation; *Int'l*, pg. 4322
KUBOTA TRACTOR CORPORATION—See Kubota Corporation; *Int'l*, pg. 4322
KUBOTA (UK) LTD.—See Kubota Corporation; *Int'l*, pg. 4322
KUBOTA VIETNAM CO., LTD.—See Kubota Corporation; *Int'l*, pg. 4322
KUBO TECH AG—See Diploma PLC; *Int'l*, pg. 2128
KUBO TECH GMBH—See Diploma PLC; *Int'l*, pg. 2128
KUBOTEK CORPORATION - KYOTO 1ST FACTORY—See KUBOTEK Corporation; *Int'l*, pg. 4322
KUBOTEK CORPORATION - KYOTO 2ND FACTORY—See KUBOTEK Corporation; *Int'l*, pg. 4322
KUBOTEK CORPORATION; *Int'l*, pg. 4322
KUBOTEK EUROPE SRL—See KUBOTEK Corporation; *Int'l*, pg. 4322
KUBOTEK KOREA CO., LTD.—See KUBOTEK Corporation; *Int'l*, pg. 4322
KUBOTEK USA, INC.—See KUBOTEK Corporation; *Int'l*, pg. 4322
KUB POWER SDN. BHD.—See KUB Malaysia Berhad; *Int'l*, pg. 4319
KUBRICKY CONSTRUCTION CORP.—See The D.A. Collins Construction Co., Inc.; *U.S. Private*, pg. 4017
KUB SEPADU SDN BHD—See KUB Malaysia Berhad; *Int'l*, pg. 4320
KUB TELEKOMUNIKASI SDN BHD—See KUB Malaysia Berhad; *Int'l*, pg. 4320
KUCERA PROPERTIES; *U.S. Private*, pg. 2356
KUCHAI DEVELOPMENT BERHAD—See Sungei Bagan Rubber Company (MALAYA) Berhad; *Int'l*, pg. 7314
KUCHE & CO GMBH—See Otto GmbH & Co. KG; *Int'l*, pg. 5663
KU CHI ENTERPRISE LIMITED; *Int'l*, pg. 4317
KUCHING PLYWOOD BHD.—See W T K Holdings Berhad; *Int'l*, pg. 8320
KUCHING RIVERINE RESORT MANAGEMENT SDN BHD—See IJM Corporation Berhad; *Int'l*, pg. 3609
KUCUKER TEKSTIL SANAYI VE TICARET A.S.; *Int'l*, pg. 4322
KUDAN, INC.; *Int'l*, pg. 4322
KUDELSKI S.A.; *Int'l*, pg. 4323
KUDELSKI SECURITY - ATLANTA—See Kudelski S.A.; *Int'l*, pg. 4323
KUDELSKI SECURITY INC.—See Kudelski S.A.; *Int'l*, pg. 4323
KUDELSKI SECURITY—See Kudelski S.A.; *Int'l*, pg. 4323

KUDGI TRANSMISSION LIMITED—See Larsen & Toubro Limited; *Int'l*, pg. 4418
KUDICK CHEVROLET-BUICK, INC.; *U.S. Private*, pg. 2356
KUDO CORPORATION; *Int'l*, pg. 4323
KUDONG ELECTRIC WIRE CO., LTD—See Nexans S.A.; *Int'l*, pg. 5241
KUDOS FILM & TELEVISION LIMITED—See LOV Group Invest SAS; *Int'l*, pg. 4565
KUDOS INDUSTRIAL COMPANY; *Int'l*, pg. 4323
KUDOS (LAW) LIMITED—See LOV Group Invest SAS; *Int'l*, pg. 4565
KUDSK & DAHL A/S—See Cementir Holding N.V.; *Int'l*, pg. 1397
KUDU INDUSTRIES INC.; *Int'l*, pg. 4324
KUDU INVESTMENT MANAGEMENT LLC; *U.S. Private*, pg. 2356
KUDZU FABRICS INCORPORATED; *U.S. Private*, pg. 2356
KUEHNE CHEMICAL COMPANY, INC.; *U.S. Private*, pg. 2356
KUEHNE & NAGEL AB—See Kuehne + Nagel International AG; *Int'l*, pg. 4324
KUEHNE + NAGEL AE—See Kuehne + Nagel International AG; *Int'l*, pg. 4324
KUEHNE + NAGEL (AG & CO.) KG—See Kuehne + Nagel International AG; *Int'l*, pg. 4324
KUEHNE & NAGEL (ANGOLA) TRANSITARIOS LDA.—See Kuehne + Nagel International AG; *Int'l*, pg. 4324
KUEHNE + NAGEL AS—See Kuehne + Nagel International AG; *Int'l*, pg. 4324
KUEHNE + NAGEL AS—See Kuehne + Nagel International AG; *Int'l*, pg. 4324
KUEHNE + NAGEL A/S—See Kuehne + Nagel International AG; *Int'l*, pg. 4324
KUEHNE + NAGEL COMPANY LIMITED—See Kuehne + Nagel International AG; *Int'l*, pg. 4324
KUEHNE + NAGEL COMPANY W.L.L.—See Kuehne + Nagel International AG; *Int'l*, pg. 4324
KUEHNE + NAGEL D.O.O.E.L.—See Kuehne + Nagel International AG; *Int'l*, pg. 4325
KUEHNE + NAGEL D.O.O.—See Kuehne + Nagel International AG; *Int'l*, pg. 4325
KUEHNE + NAGEL DOO—See Kuehne + Nagel International AG; *Int'l*, pg. 4325
KUEHNE + NAGEL D.O.O.—See Kuehne + Nagel International AG; *Int'l*, pg. 4325
KUEHNE + NAGEL EASTERN EUROPE AG—See Kuehne + Nagel International AG; *Int'l*, pg. 4324
KUEHNE + NAGEL EUROSHIPPING GMBH—See Kuehne + Nagel International AG; *Int'l*, pg. 4324
KUEHNE + NAGEL FPE—See Kuehne + Nagel International AG; *Int'l*, pg. 4324
KUEHNE + NAGEL GESELLSCHAFT M.B.H.—See Kuehne + Nagel International AG; *Int'l*, pg. 4324
KUEHNE + NAGEL INC.—See Kuehne + Nagel International AG; *Int'l*, pg. 4324
KUEHNE + NAGEL INC.—See Kuehne + Nagel International AG; *Int'l*, pg. 4324
KUEHNE + NAGEL INTERMODAL GMBH—See Kuehne + Nagel International AG; *Int'l*, pg. 4324
KUEHNE + NAGEL INTERNATIONAL AG; *Int'l*, pg. 4324
KUEHNE + NAGEL INTERNATIONALE TRANSPORT-GESELLSCHAFT M.B.H.—See Kuehne + Nagel International AG; *Int'l*, pg. 4324
KUEHNE & NAGEL (IRELAND) LIMITED—See Kuehne + Nagel International AG; *Int'l*, pg. 4324
KUEHNE & NAGEL JORDAN LTD.—See Kuehne + Nagel International AG; *Int'l*, pg. 4324
KUEHNE + NAGEL KFT—See Kuehne + Nagel International AG; *Int'l*, pg. 4324
KUEHNE + NAGEL LDA.—See Kuehne + Nagel International AG; *Int'l*, pg. 4324
KUEHNE + NAGEL LIMITED—See Kuehne + Nagel International AG; *Int'l*, pg. 4324
KUEHNE + NAGEL LIMITED—See Kuehne + Nagel International AG; *Int'l*, pg. 4324
KUEHNE + NAGEL LIMITED—See Kuehne + Nagel International AG; *Int'l*, pg. 4324
KUEHNE + NAGEL LIMITED—See Kuehne + Nagel International AG; *Int'l*, pg. 4324
KUEHNE + NAGEL LIMITED—See Kuehne + Nagel International AG; *Int'l*, pg. 4324
KUEHNE + NAGEL LIMITED—See Kuehne + Nagel International AG; *Int'l*, pg. 4324
KUEHNE + NAGEL LIMITED—See Kuehne + Nagel International AG; *Int'l*, pg. 4324
KUEHNE + NAGEL LIMITED—See Kuehne + Nagel International AG; *Int'l*, pg. 4324
KUEHNE + NAGEL L.L.C.—See Kuehne + Nagel International AG; *Int'l*, pg. 4324
KUEHNE + NAGEL LOGISTICS B.V.—See Kuehne + Nagel International AG; *Int'l*, pg. 4324
KUEHNE + NAGEL LOGISTICS LANGENAU GMBH—See Kuehne + Nagel International AG; *Int'l*, pg. 4324

KUEHNE + NAGEL LTDA.—See Kuehne + Nagel International AG; *Int'l*, pg. 4325
KUEHNE + NAGEL LTD.—See Kuehne + Nagel International AG; *Int'l*, pg. 4324
KUEHNE & NAGEL LTD.—See Kuehne + Nagel International AG; *Int'l*, pg. 4324
KUEHNE + NAGEL LTD.—See Kuehne + Nagel International AG; *Int'l*, pg. 4325
KUEHNE + NAGEL LTD.—See Kuehne + Nagel International AG; *Int'l*, pg. 4325
KUEHNE + NAGEL LTD.—See Kuehne + Nagel International AG; *Int'l*, pg. 4325
KUEHNE + NAGEL LTD.—See Kuehne + Nagel International AG; *Int'l*, pg. 4325
KUEHNE + NAGEL LTD.—See Kuehne + Nagel International AG; *Int'l*, pg. 4325
KUEHNE + NAGEL LTD.—See Kuehne + Nagel International AG; *Int'l*, pg. 4324
KUEHNE + NAGEL MANAGEMENT SASU—See Kuehne + Nagel International AG; *Int'l*, pg. 4325
KUEHNE + NAGEL NV—See Kuehne + Nagel International AG; *Int'l*, pg. 4325
KUEHNE + NAGEL N.V.—See Kuehne + Nagel International AG; *Int'l*, pg. 4325
KUEHNE + NAGEL (PRIVATE) LIMITED—See Kuehne + Nagel International AG; *Int'l*, pg. 4324
KUEHNE + NAGEL PRIVATE LIMITED—See Kuehne + Nagel International AG; *Int'l*, pg. 4325
KUEHNE & NAGEL PTY. LTD.—See Kuehne + Nagel International AG; *Int'l*, pg. 4324
KUEHNE & NAGEL (PTY.) LTD.—See Kuehne + Nagel International AG; *Int'l*, pg. 4324
KUEHNE & NAGEL (PVT.) LTD.—See Kuehne + Nagel International AG; *Int'l*, pg. 4324
KUEHNE + NAGEL PVT. LTD.—See Kuehne + Nagel International AG; *Int'l*, pg. 4325
KUEHNE + NAGEL S.A. DE C.V.—See Kuehne + Nagel International AG; *Int'l*, pg. 4325
KUEHNE + NAGEL S.A.—See Kuehne + Nagel International AG; *Int'l*, pg. 4325
KUEHNE + NAGEL S.A.—See Kuehne + Nagel International AG; *Int'l*, pg. 4325
KUEHNE + NAGEL S. A.—See Kuehne + Nagel International AG; *Int'l*, pg. 4325
KUEHNE + NAGEL S.A.—See Kuehne + Nagel International AG; *Int'l*, pg. 4325
KUEHNE + NAGEL S.A.—See Kuehne + Nagel International AG; *Int'l*, pg. 4325
KUEHNE + NAGEL S.A.—See Kuehne + Nagel International AG; *Int'l*, pg. 4325
KUEHNE + NAGEL S.A.—See Kuehne + Nagel International AG; *Int'l*, pg. 4325
KUEHNE + NAGEL S.A.—See Kuehne + Nagel International AG; *Int'l*, pg. 4325
KUEHNE + NAGEL S.A.—See Kuehne + Nagel International AG; *Int'l*, pg. 4325
KUEHNE + NAGEL S.A.—See Kuehne + Nagel International AG; *Int'l*, pg. 4325
KUEHNE + NAGEL S.A.S.—See Kuehne + Nagel International AG; *Int'l*, pg. 4325
KUEHNE + NAGEL SDN. BHD.—See Kuehne + Nagel International AG; *Int'l*, pg. 4325
KUEHNE + NAGEL SERVICOS LOGISTICOS LTDA.—See Kuehne + Nagel International AG; *Int'l*, pg. 4325
KUEHNE + NAGEL SE—See Kuehne + Nagel International AG; *Int'l*, pg. 4325
KUEHNE + NAGEL SPA—See Kuehne + Nagel International AG; *Int'l*, pg. 4325
KUEHNE + NAGEL SRL—See Kuehne + Nagel International AG; *Int'l*, pg. 4325
KUEHNE & NAGEL UAB—See Kuehne + Nagel International AG; *Int'l*, pg. 4324
KUEHNE + NAGEL WLL—See Kuehne + Nagel International AG; *Int'l*, pg. 4325
KUEHN MOTOR COMPANY; *U.S. Private*, pg. 2356
KUEN LING MACHINERY REFRIGERATING (SHANGHAI) CO., LTD.—See Kuen Ling Refrigerating Machinery Co., Ltd.; *Int'l*, pg. 4326
KUEN LING MACHINERY REFRIGERATING (SUZHOU) CO., LTD.—See Kuen Ling Refrigerating Machinery Co., Ltd.; *Int'l*, pg. 4326
KUEN LING REFRIGERATING MACHINERY CO., LTD.; *Int'l*, pg. 4325
K&U ENTERPRISE CO., LTD.—See Kyokuyo Co. Ltd.; *Int'l*, pg. 4363
KUERT CONCRETE INCORPORATED; *U.S. Private*, pg. 2356
KUFU COMPANY INC.; *Int'l*, pg. 4326
KUGA CO., LTD.—See Oji Holdings Corporation; *Int'l*, pg. 5537
KUGELFINK GMBH—See THK CO., LTD.; *Int'l*, pg. 7711
KUGLER COMPANY - CULBERTSON PRODUCTION PLANT—See Kugler Company; *U.S. Private*, pg. 2356
KUGLER COMPANY - RAPID CITY PRODUCTION PLANT—See Kugler Company; *U.S. Private*, pg. 2356
KUGLER COMPANY; *U.S. Private*, pg. 2356
KUGLER COMPANY - STERLING PRODUCTION PLANT—See Kugler Company; *U.S. Private*, pg. 2356

KUGLER COMPANY - ULYSSES PRODUCTION PLANT—See Kugler Company; *U.S. Private*, pg. 2356
KUGLER OIL CO.; *U.S. Private*, pg. 2356
KUHIO MOTORS INC.; *U.S. Private*, pg. 2356
KUHLKE CONSTRUCTION & ASSOCIATES, INC.; *U.S. Private*, pg. 2356
KUHLMAN CONCRETE LLC—See Kuhlman Corporation; *U.S. Private*, pg. 2356
KUHLMAN CONSTRUCTION PRODUCTS, INC.—See Kuhlman Corporation; *U.S. Private*, pg. 2356
KUHLMAN CORPORATION; *U.S. Private*, pg. 2356
KUHLMAN ELECTRIC CORPORATION—See ABB Ltd.; *Int'l*, pg. 52
KUHLMAN, INC.; *U.S. Private*, pg. 2356
KUHLMAN LLC—See BorgWarner Inc.; *U.S. Public*, pg. 371
KUHLMANN FRANCE S.A.S.—See Tessenderlo Group NV; *Int'l*, pg. 7573
KUHN-AUDUREAU SA—See Bucher Industries AG; *Int'l*, pg. 1209
KUHN BAUMASCHINEN DEUTSCHLAND GMBH—See KUHN Holding GmbH; *Int'l*, pg. 4326
KUHN BAUMASCHINEN GMBH—See KUHN Holding GmbH; *Int'l*, pg. 4326
KUHN-BLANCHARD SAS—See Bucher Industries AG; *Int'l*, pg. 1209
KUHN DO BRASIL S/A—See Bucher Industries AG; *Int'l*, pg. 1209
KUHN D.O.O.—See KUHN Holding GmbH; *Int'l*, pg. 4326
KUHNE ELECTRONIC GMBH—See Alaris Holdings Limited; *Int'l*, pg. 291
KUHNE GMBH; *Int'l*, pg. 4326
KUHNE & VOGEL GMBH—See VINCI S.A.; *Int'l*, pg. 8223
KUHN FARM MACHINERY LTD—See Bucher Industries AG; *Int'l*, pg. 1209
KUHN FARM MACHINERY PTY LTD—See Bucher Industries AG; *Int'l*, pg. 1209
KUHN FARM MACHINERY SARL—See Bucher Industries AG; *Int'l*, pg. 1209
KUHN FEUERSCHUTZ G.M.B.H.—See London Security PLC; *Int'l*, pg. 4547
KUHN FOLDMUNKAGEP KFT.—See KUHN Holding GmbH; *Int'l*, pg. 4326
KUHN-GELDROP B.V.—See Bucher Industries AG; *Int'l*, pg. 1209
KUHN GROUP SAS—See Bucher Industries AG; *Int'l*, pg. 1209
KUHN HOLDING GMBH; *Int'l*, pg. 4326
KUHN HONDA; *U.S. Private*, pg. 2356
KUHN HRVATSKA D.O.O.—See KUHN Holding GmbH; *Int'l*, pg. 4326
KUHN-HUARD S.A.—See Bucher Industries AG; *Int'l*, pg. 1209
KUHN IBERICA SA—See Bucher Industries AG; *Int'l*, pg. 1209
KUHN ITALIA SRL.—See Bucher Industries AG; *Int'l*, pg. 1209
KUHN KRAUSE, INC.—See Bucher Industries AG; *Int'l*, pg. 1209
KUHN LADETECHNIK GMBH—See KUHN Holding GmbH; *Int'l*, pg. 4326
KUHN MASCHINEN-VERTRIEB GMBH—See Bucher Industries AG; *Int'l*, pg. 1209
KUHN MASZYNY ROLNICZE SP. Z.O.O—See Bucher Industries AG; *Int'l*, pg. 1209
KUHN MGM SAS—See Bucher Industries AG; *Int'l*, pg. 1209
KUHN-MONTANA INDUSTRIA DE MAQUINAS S/A—See Bucher Industries AG; *Int'l*, pg. 1209
KUHN-MT S.R.O.—See KUHN Holding GmbH; *Int'l*, pg. 4326
KUHN NORTH AMERICA, INC.—See Bucher Industries AG; *Int'l*, pg. 1209
KUHN POLSKA SP.Z.O.O—See KUHN Holding GmbH; *Int'l*, pg. 4326
KUHN S.A.—See Bucher Industries AG; *Int'l*, pg. 1209
KUHN SCHWEIZ AG—See KUHN Holding GmbH; *Int'l*, pg. 4326
KUHNS EQUIPMENT COMPANY; *U.S. Private*, pg. 2356
KUHNS & HELLER CUSTOM WINDOW TREATMENTS; *U.S. Private*, pg. 2356
KUHN SLOVAKIA S.R.O.—See KUHN Holding GmbH; *Int'l*, pg. 4326
KUHN VOSTOK LLC—See Bucher Industries AG; *Int'l*, pg. 1209
KUHN & WITTENBORN, INC.; *U.S. Private*, pg. 2356
KU HOLDINGS CO., LTD.; *Int'l*, pg. 4317
THE KUIKEN BROTHERS COMPANY, INC.; *U.S. Private*, pg. 4066
KUIK & PARTNERS GERECHTSDEURWAARDERS & INCASSOBUREAU B.V.—See Munchener Ruckversicherungs AG; *Int'l*, pg. 5089
KUI SHENG TECHNOLOGY (SHENZHEN) CO., LTD.—See Zhen Ding Technology Holding Limited; *Int'l*, pg. 8669
KUJU LIMITED—See NorthEdge Capital LLP; *Int'l*, pg. 5442
KUKA AKTIENGESELLSCHAFT—See Midea Group Co., Ltd.; *Int'l*, pg. 4884

KUKA ASSEMBLY AND TEST CORP.—See Midea Group Co., Ltd.; *Int'l*, pg. 4885
KUKA AUTOMATION EQUIPMENT (SHANGHAI) CO., LTD.—See Midea Group Co., Ltd.; *Int'l*, pg. 4885
KUKA AUTOMATION TAIWAN LTD.—See Midea Group Co., Ltd.; *Int'l*, pg. 4885
KUKA AUTOMATISERING + ROBOTS N.V.—See Midea Group Co., Ltd.; *Int'l*, pg. 4885
KUKA AUTOMATISME + ROBOTIQUE S.A.S.—See Midea Group Co., Ltd.; *Int'l*, pg. 4885
KUKA DE MEXICO S. DE R. L. DE C. V.—See Midea Group Co., Ltd.; *Int'l*, pg. 4885
KUKA FLEXIBLE MANUFACTURING SYSTEMS (SHANGHAI) CO., LTD.—See Midea Group Co., Ltd.; *Int'l*, pg. 4885
KUKA HUNGARIA KFT.—See Midea Group Co., Ltd.; *Int'l*, pg. 4885
KUKA NORDIC AB—See Midea Group Co., Ltd.; *Int'l*, pg. 4885
KUKA ROBOT AUTOMATION MALAYSIA SDN. BHD.—See Midea Group Co., Ltd.; *Int'l*, pg. 4885
KUKA ROBOTER ITALIA S. P. A.—See Midea Group Co., Ltd.; *Int'l*, pg. 4885
KUKA ROBOTICS CANADA LTD.—See Midea Group Co., Ltd.; *Int'l*, pg. 4885
KUKA ROBOTICS CORP.—See Midea Group Co., Ltd.; *Int'l*, pg. 4885
KUKA ROBOTICS (INDIA) PVT. LTD.—See Midea Group Co., Ltd.; *Int'l*, pg. 4885
KUKA ROBOTICS JAPAN KK—See Midea Group Co., Ltd.; *Int'l*, pg. 4885
KUKA ROBOTICS RUSSIA OOO—See Midea Group Co., Ltd.; *Int'l*, pg. 4885
KUKA ROBOTS IBERICA, S.A.—See Midea Group Co., Ltd.; *Int'l*, pg. 4885
KUKA SLOVAKIA S R.O.—See Midea Group Co., Ltd.; *Int'l*, pg. 4884
KUKA SYSTEMS DE MEXICO, S. DE R. L. DE C. V.—See Midea Group Co., Ltd.; *Int'l*, pg. 4885
KUKA SYSTEMS DO BRASIL LTDA.—See Midea Group Co., Ltd.; *Int'l*, pg. 4885
KUKA SYSTEMS DO BRASZIL LTDA.—See Midea Group Co., Ltd.; *Int'l*, pg. 4885
KUKA SYSTEMS GMBH - BOP FRANCE—See Midea Group Co., Ltd.; *Int'l*, pg. 4885
KUKA SYSTEMS GMBH—See Midea Group Co., Ltd.; *Int'l*, pg. 4885
KUKA SYSTEMS NORTH AMERICA LLC—See Midea Group Co., Ltd.; *Int'l*, pg. 4885
KUKA SYSTEMS UK LIMITED—See Midea Group Co., Ltd.; *Int'l*, pg. 4885
KUKA TOLEDO PRODUCTION OPERATIONS LLC—See Midea Group Co., Ltd.; *Int'l*, pg. 4885
KUKBO DESIGN CO., LTD; *Int'l*, pg. 4326
KUKBO LOGISTICS CO., LTD.; *Int'l*, pg. 4327
KUKBO VINA CO., LTD.—See KUKBO DESIGN Co., Ltd; *Int'l*, pg. 4326
KUKDO CHEMICAL CO., LTD. - SIWHA FACTORY—See Kukdo Chemical Co Ltd; *Int'l*, pg. 4327
KUKDO CHEMICAL CO LTD; *Int'l*, pg. 4327
KUKDONG APPAREL INC.—See Kukdong Corporation; *Int'l*, pg. 4327
KUKDONG CORPORATION; *Int'l*, pg. 4327
KUKDONG ELECTRIC WIRE CO. LTD—See Nexans S.A.; *Int'l*, pg. 5241
KUKDONG OIL & CHEMICAL CO., LTD. - LPG DIVISION—See Kukdong Oil & Chemical Co., Ltd.; *Int'l*, pg. 4327
KUKDONG OIL & CHEMICAL CO., LTD.; *Int'l*, pg. 4327
KUKDONG OIL & CHEMICAL CO., LTD. - WATERPROOFING MEMBRANE DIVISION—See Kukdong Oil & Chemical Co., Ltd.; *Int'l*, pg. 4327
KUKDONG OIL & CHEMICALS CO. LTD.—See Kukdong Oil & Chemical Co., Ltd.; *Int'l*, pg. 4327
KUKDONG TEXTILE S.A. DE C.V.—See Kukdong Corporation; *Int'l*, pg. 4327
KUKE MUSIC HOLDING LIMITED; *Int'l*, pg. 4327
K.U.K. HOFZUCKERBACKER CH. DEMEL—See DO & CO Aktiengesellschaft; *Int'l*, pg. 2152
KUKIL METAL CO., LTD.; *Int'l*, pg. 4327
KUK-IL PAPER MFG. CO., LTD.; *Int'l*, pg. 4326
KUK-IL PAPER MFG. CO., LTD. - YONG-IN PLANT—See Kuk-Il Paper Mfg. Co., Ltd.; *Int'l*, pg. 4326
KUKJEON PHARMACEUTICAL CO., LTD.; *Int'l*, pg. 4327
KUKJE PHARMACEUTICAL INDUSTRIAL COMPANY LIMITED - ANSAN PLANT—See Kukje Pharma Co., Ltd.; *Int'l*, pg. 4327
KUKJE PHARMA CO., LTD.; *Int'l*, pg. 4327
KUKUI'ULA DEVELOPMENT COMPANY, INC.—See Alexander & Baldwin, Inc.; *U.S. Public*, pg. 75
KUKUI'ULA VILLAGE LLC—See Alexander & Baldwin, Inc.; *U.S. Public*, pg. 75
KUK YOUNG G&M CO., LTD.; *Int'l*, pg. 4326
KULA GOLD LIMITED—See Geopacific Resources Limited; *Int'l*, pg. 2934
KULA MAKINA IMALAT SAN. TIC. LTD. STI.—See Chien Wei Precise Technology Co., Ltd.; *Int'l*, pg. 1477
KULA PRODUCE CO, LTD.—See Sysco Corporation; *U.S. Public*, pg. 1974

COMPANY NAME INDEX

KULA SUSHI USA, INC.—See Kura Sushi, Inc.; *Int'l*, pg. 4335
KULBACK'S CONSTRUCTION, INC.; *U.S. Private*, pg. 2356
KULCZYK INVESTMENTS S.A.; *Int'l*, pg. 4327
KULESA FAUL INC. *U.S. Private*, pg. 2356
KULE YON. VE ORG. VE DANISMANLIK A.S.—See Loras Holding A.S.; *Int'l*, pg. 4557
KULICKE AND SOFFA DIE BONDING GMBH—See Kulicke & Soffa Industries, Inc.; *Int'l*, pg. 4329
KULICKE AND SOFFA PTE. LTD.—See Kulicke & Soffa Industries, Inc.; *Int'l*, pg. 4329
KULICKE & SOFFA (ASIA) LIMITED—See Kulicke & Soffa Industries, Inc.; *Int'l*, pg. 4328
KULICKE & SOFFA ASIAPAC INC.—See Kulicke & Soffa Industries, Inc.; *Int'l*, pg. 4328
KULICKE & SOFFA GMBH—See Kulicke & Soffa Industries, Inc.; *Int'l*, pg. 4328
KULICKE & SOFFA HOLDING COMPANY PTE. LTD.—See Kulicke & Soffa Industries, Inc.; *Int'l*, pg. 4328
KULICKE & SOFFA INDUSTRIES, INC.; *Int'l*, pg. 4328
KULICKE & SOFFA INDUSTRIES INC.—See Kulicke & Soffa Industries, Inc.; *Int'l*, pg. 4329
KULICKE & SOFFA INDUSTRIES—See Kulicke & Soffa Industries, Inc.; *Int'l*, pg. 4329
KULICKE & SOFFA (ISRAEL) LTD.—See Kulicke & Soffa Industries, Inc.; *Int'l*, pg. 4328
KULICKE & SOFFA (JAPAN) LTD.—See Kulicke & Soffa Industries, Inc.; *Int'l*, pg. 4328
KULICKE & SOFFA KOREA INC.—See Kulicke & Soffa Industries, Inc.; *Int'l*, pg. 4329
KULICKE & SOFFA LITEQ B.V.—See Kulicke & Soffa Industries, Inc.; *Int'l*, pg. 4329
KULICKE & SOFFA (MALAYSIA) SDN. BHD.—See Kulicke & Soffa Industries, Inc.; *Int'l*, pg. 4328
KULICKE & SOFFA ORTHODYNE GMBH—See Kulicke & Soffa Industries, Inc.; *Int'l*, pg. 4329
KULICKE & SOFFA (PHILS.) INC.—See Kulicke & Soffa Industries, Inc.; *Int'l*, pg. 4328
KULICKE & SOFFA (SHANGHAI) INTERNATIONAL TRADING CO., LTD.—See Kulicke & Soffa Industries, Inc.; *Int'l*, pg. 4328
KULICKE & SOFFA—See Kulicke & Soffa Industries, Inc.; *Int'l*, pg. 4328
KULICKE & SOFFA—See Kulicke & Soffa Industries, Inc.; *Int'l*, pg. 4328
KULICKE & SOFFA (SUZHOU) LIMITED—See Kulicke & Soffa Industries, Inc.; *Int'l*, pg. 4328
KULICKE & SOFFA (SWITZERLAND) MANAGEMENT GMBH—See Kulicke & Soffa Industries, Inc.; *Int'l*, pg. 4328
KULICKE & SOFFA TECHNOLOGY (M) SDN. BHD.—See Kulicke & Soffa Industries, Inc.; *Int'l*, pg. 4329
KULICKE & SOFFA (THAILAND) LTD.—See Kulicke & Soffa Industries, Inc.; *Int'l*, pg. 4329
KULIM INDUSTRIAL GASES SDN. BHD.—See Air Products & Chemicals, Inc.; *U.S. Public*, pg. 66
KULIM LIVESTOCK SDN BHD—See Johor Corporation; *Int'l*, pg. 3994
KULIM (MALAYSIA) BERHAD—See Johor Corporation; *Int'l*, pg. 3994
KULIM MEWAH SDN BHD—See IJM Corporation Berhad; *Int'l*, pg. 3609
KULINAARIA OU—See Tallinna Kaubamaja AS; *Int'l*, pg. 7447
KULINARIS AS—See TINE SA; *Int'l*, pg. 7753
KULITE ITALIA, SRL—See Kulite Semiconductor Products, Inc.; *U.S. Private*, pg. 2357
KULITE SEMI-CONDUCTOR, GMBH—See Kulite Semiconductor Products, Inc.; *U.S. Private*, pg. 2357
KULITE SEMICONDUCTOR PRODUCTS, INC.; *U.S. Private*, pg. 2357
KULITE SENSORS CHINA, INC.—See Kulite Semiconductor Products, Inc.; *U.S. Private*, pg. 2357
KULITE SENSORS, LTD.—See Kulite Semiconductor Products, Inc.; *U.S. Private*, pg. 2357
THE KULJIAN CORPORATION; *U.S. Private*, pg. 4066
KULKER S.A.S.—See Groupe ELYDAN; *Int'l*, pg. 3102
KULLANATMARKET ELEKTRONIK PAZARLAMA TICARET ANONIM SIRKETI—See Bunzl plc; *Int'l*, pg. 1218
KULLMAN BUILDINGS CORP.; *U.S. Private*, pg. 2357
KULMAKOMPONENTIDE OU—See Beijer Ref AB; *Int'l*, pg. 944
KULMBACHER BRAUEREI AG—See L'Arche Green N.V.; *Int'l*, pg. 4376
KULMBACHER BRAUEREI AG—See Schorghuber Stiftung & Co. Holding KG; *Int'l*, pg. 6639
KULR TECHNOLOGY GROUP, INC.; *U.S. Public*, pg. 1277
KULTHORN KIRBY FOUNDRY COMPANY LIMITED—See Kulthorn Kirby Public Co., Ltd.; *Int'l*, pg. 4329
KULTHORN KIRBY PUBLIC CO., LTD.; *Int'l*, pg. 4329
KULTHORN PREMIER COMPANY LIMITED—See Kulthorn Kirby Public Co., Ltd.; *Int'l*, pg. 4329
KULTHORN RESEARCH & DEVELOPMENT COMPANY LIMITED—See Kulthorn Kirby Public Co., Ltd.; *Int'l*, pg. 4329

KULTHORN STEEL COMPANY LIMITED—See Kulthorn Kirby Public Co., Ltd.; *Int'l*, pg. 4329
KULT TEKSTIL TURIZM YAYINCILIK A.S.; *Int'l*, pg. 4329
KULTURFORMAT GMBH—See JCDecaux S.A.; *Int'l*, pg. 3923
KULTUR IM PARK GMBH—See DEAG Deutsche Entertainment AG; *Int'l*, pg. 1998
KULTUR-MEDIEN HAMBURG GMBH GESELLSCHAFT FUR KULTURINFORMATIONSANLAGEN—See Stroer SE & Co. KGaA; *Int'l*, pg. 7242
KULTUR- UND KONGRESSZENTRUM JAHRHUNDERTHALLE GMBH—See DEAG Deutsche Entertainment AG; *Int'l*, pg. 1998
KULZER DENTAL LTD.—See Mitsui Chemicals, Inc.; *Int'l*, pg. 4981
KULZER GMBH—See Mitsui Chemicals, Inc.; *Int'l*, pg. 4981
KULZER JAPAN CO., LTD.—See Mitsui Chemicals, Inc.; *Int'l*, pg. 4981
KUMAGAI AUSTRALIA FINANCE PTY. LTD.—See JINUSHI Co., Ltd.; *Int'l*, pg. 3970
KUMAGAI AUSTRALIA PTY. LTD.—See JINUSHI Co., Ltd.; *Int'l*, pg. 3970
KUMAGAI GUMI CO., LTD.; *Int'l*, pg. 4329
KUMAGAI GUMI CO., LTD.—See Kumagai Gumi Co., Ltd.; *Int'l*, pg. 4329
KUMAGAYA OHKA CO., LTD.—See Tokyo Ohka Kogyo Co., Ltd.; *Int'l*, pg. 7794
KUMALIFT CO., LTD.—See SECOM Co., Ltd.; *Int'l*, pg. 6671
KUMAMOTO AUTOBACS INC.—See Autobacs Seven Co., Ltd.; *Int'l*, pg. 726
THE KUMAMOTO BANK, LTD.—See Fukuoka Financial Group, Inc.; *Int'l*, pg. 2840
KUMAMOTO DAIICHI TRAFFIC LTD—See Daiichi Koutsu Sangyo Co., Ltd.; *Int'l*, pg. 1928
KUMAMOTO FISHING TACKLE CO., LTD.—See Shimano, Inc.; *Int'l*, pg. 6833
KUMAMOTO HINO MOTOR LTD.—See Toyota Motor Corporation; *Int'l*, pg. 7871
KUMAMOTO MANUFACTURING FACILITY—See Honda Motor Co., Ltd.; *Int'l*, pg. 3463
KUMAMOTO MORIROKU KASEI CO., LTD.—See Moriroku Holdings Company, Ltd.; *Int'l*, pg. 5047
KUMAMOTO NICHIAS CORPORATION—See Nichias Corporation; *Int'l*, pg. 5267
KUMAMOTO NOK CORPORATION—See NOK Corporation; *Int'l*, pg. 5402
KUMANO DAIICHI TRAFFIC CO., LTD.—See Daiichi Koutsu Sangyo Co., Ltd.; *Int'l*, pg. 1928
KUMARI BANK LIMITED; *Int'l*, pg. 4329
KUMARINA RESOURCES LIMITED—See ICM Limited; *Int'l*, pg. 3582
KUMAR WIRE CLOTH MANUFACTURING COMPANY LIMITED; *Int'l*, pg. 4329
KUMAS MANYEZIT SANAYI A.S.—See Eregli Demir Ve Celik Fabrikalari T.A.S.; *Int'l*, pg. 2490
KUMA STAINLESS TUBES LIMITED—See Maruichi Steel Tube Ltd; *Int'l*, pg. 4713
KUMBA IRON ORE LTD.—See Anglo American PLC; *Int'l*, pg. 462
KUMBA SINGAPORE PTE. LTD.—See Anglo American PLC; *Int'l*, pg. 462
KUMBI CO., LTD.; *Int'l*, pg. 4329
KUMEYAAY WIND LLC—See Infigen Energy Limited; *Int'l*, pg. 3685
KUM GMBH & CO KG; *Int'l*, pg. 4329
KUM & GO—See Krause Gentle Corporation; *U.S. Private*, pg. 2350
KUMHO ASIANA CULTURAL FOUNDATION CO, LTD.—See Kumho Asiana Group; *Int'l*, pg. 4330
KUMHO ASIANA GROUP; *Int'l*, pg. 4330
KUMHO BUSLINES CO., LTD.; *Int'l*, pg. 4330
KUMHO ELECTRIC, INC.; *Int'l*, pg. 4330
KUMHO ENGINEERING & CONSTRUCTION CO., LTD.; *Int'l*, pg. 4330
KUMHO HT, INC.; *Int'l*, pg. 4330
KUMHO MITSUI CHEMICALS, INC.—See Kumho Asiana Group; *Int'l*, pg. 4330
KUMHO MITSUI CHEMICALS, INC.—See Mitsui Chemicals, Inc.; *Int'l*, pg. 4983
KUMHO MITSUI CHEMICALS, INC.—See Takeda Pharmaceutical Company Limited; *Int'l*, pg. 7437
KUMHO P&B CHEMICALS, INC.—See Kumho Asiana Group; *Int'l*, pg. 4330
KUMHO PETRO CHEMICAL CO., LTD.—See Kumho Asiana Group; *Int'l*, pg. 4330
KUMHO POLYCHEM CO., LTD.—See JSR Corp.; *Int'l*, pg. 4014
KUMHO POLYCHEM CO., LTD.—See Kumho Asiana Group; *Int'l*, pg. 4330
KUMHO RESORT INC.—See Kumho Asiana Group; *Int'l*, pg. 4330
KUMHO TIRE CANADA INC.—See Kumho Asiana Group; *Int'l*, pg. 4330
KUMHO TIRE CO., INC.—See Kumho Asiana Group; *Int'l*, pg. 4330
KUMHO TIRE U.S.A., INC.—See Kumho Asiana Group; *Int'l*, pg. 4330

KUMIAI CHEMICAL INDUSTRY CO., LTD.; *Int'l*, pg. 4330
KUMIKA LOGISTICS CO., LTD.—See Kumiai Chemical Industry Co., Ltd.; *Int'l*, pg. 4330
KUMKANG AMERICA, INC.—See Kumkang Kind; *Int'l*, pg. 4331
KUMKANG KIND - CHANGNYEONG FACTORY—See Kumkang Kind; *Int'l*, pg. 4331
KUMKANG KIND EAST AFRICA LIMITED—See Kumkang Kind; *Int'l*, pg. 4331
KUMKANG KIND - EONYANG FACTORY—See Kumkang Kind; *Int'l*, pg. 4331
KUMKANG KIND - EUMSEONG 1 FACTORY—See Kumkang Kind; *Int'l*, pg. 4331
KUMKANG KIND - EUMSEONG 2 FACTORY—See Kumkang Kind; *Int'l*, pg. 4331
KUMKANG KIND INDIA PRIVATE LIMITED—See Kumkang Kind; *Int'l*, pg. 4331
KUMKANG KIND - JINCHEON 1 FACTORY—See Kumkang Kind; *Int'l*, pg. 4331
KUMKANG KIND - JINCHEON 2 FACTORY—See Kumkang Kind; *Int'l*, pg. 4331
KUMKANG KIND - MODULAR FACTORY—See Kumkang Kind; *Int'l*, pg. 4331
KUMKANG KIND (M) SDN. BHD.—See Kumkang Kind; *Int'l*, pg. 4331
KUMKANG KIND; *Int'l*, pg. 4331
KUMKANG KIND VIETNAM CO., LTD.—See Kumkang Kind; *Int'l*, pg. 4331
KUMMEL FAHRZEUGTEILE GMBH & CO. KG; *Int'l*, pg. 4331
KUMMLER+MATTER AG—See Bouygues S.A.; *Int'l*, pg. 1123
KUMNAMU ENTERTAINMENT, INC.—See Sunny Side Up Group Inc.; *Int'l*, pg. 7319
KUMO HI-TECH CO., LTD.; *Int'l*, pg. 4331
KUMPU GMBH—See Metso Oyj; *Int'l*, pg. 4865
KUMPULAN BERTAM PLANTATIONS BERHAD—See Johor Corporation; *Int'l*, pg. 3994
KUMPULAN DARUL EHSAN BERHAD; *Int'l*, pg. 4331
KUMPULAN FIMA BERHAD; *Int'l*, pg. 4331
KUMPULAN GAPADU SDN BHD—See MALTON BERHAD; *Int'l*, pg. 4664
KUMPULAN HARTANAH SELANGOR BERHAD—See Kumpulan Darul Ehsan Berhad; *Int'l*, pg. 4331
KUMPULAN H & L HIGH-TECH BERHAD; *Int'l*, pg. 4331
KUMPULAN IKRAM (SABAH) SDN BHD—See Protasco Berhad; *Int'l*, pg. 6003
KUMPULAN IKRAM (SARAWAK) SDN BHD—See Protasco Berhad; *Int'l*, pg. 6003
KUMPULAN IKRAM SDN BHD—See Protasco Berhad; *Int'l*, pg. 6003
KUMPULAN JETSON BERHAD; *Int'l*, pg. 4332
KUMPULAN KESUMA SDN BHD—See Nylex (Malaysia) Berhad; *Int'l*, pg. 5500
KUMPULAN KITACON BERHAD; *Int'l*, pg. 4332
KUMPULAN MEDIC IMAN SDN. BHD.—See TDM Berhad; *Int'l*, pg. 7490
KUMPULAN MEDIC (K.L.) SDN. BHD.—See Qualitas Medical Group Limited; *Int'l*, pg. 6151
KUMPULAN MEDIC (SELANGOR) SDN. BHD.—See Qualitas Medical Group Limited; *Int'l*, pg. 6151
KUMPULAN PENGURUSAN KAYU KAYAN TERENGGANU SDN BHD—See Golden Pharos Berhad; *Int'l*, pg. 3031
KUMPULAN PERANGSANG SELANGOR BERHAD—See Kumpulan Darul Ehsan Berhad; *Int'l*, pg. 4331
KUMPUNIEMEN VOIMA OY—See Metsaliitto Osuuskunta; *Int'l*, pg. 4864
KUMSUNG INDUSTRIAL CO., LTD.—See Daewon Cable Co., Ltd.; *Int'l*, pg. 1909
KUMTOR GOLD COMPANY—See Centerra Gold Inc.; *Int'l*, pg. 1403
KUMULUS VAPE SA; *Int'l*, pg. 4332
KUMV-TV—See Gray Television, Inc.; *U.S. Public*, pg. 960
KUMWELL CORPORATION PUBLIC COMPANY LIMITED; *Int'l*, pg. 4332
KUMYANG CHEMICAL (SHANGHAI) CO., LTD.—See Kumyang Co., Ltd.; *Int'l*, pg. 4332
KUMYANG CO., LTD.; *Int'l*, pg. 4332
KUMYANG CORPORATION—See Kumyang Co., Ltd.; *Int'l*, pg. 4332
KUMYANG GREEN POWER CO., LTD.; *Int'l*, pg. 4332
KUMYANG (LIANYUNGANG) CHEMICAL CO., LTD.—See Kumyang Co., Ltd.; *Int'l*, pg. 4332
KUMYANG NEIMENGGU CHEMICAL CO., LTD.—See Kumyang Co., Ltd.; *Int'l*, pg. 4332
KUMYANG USA INC.—See Kumyang Co., Ltd.; *Int'l*, pg. 4332
KUNA MEAT CO, INC.; *U.S. Private*, pg. 2357
KUNAU IMPLEMENT CO. INC.; *U.S. Private*, pg. 2357
KUNCAI AMERICAS LLC—See Fujian Kuncai Material Technology Co., Ltd.; *Int'l*, pg. 2818
KUNCAI EUROPE B.V.—See Fujian Kuncai Material Technology Co., Ltd.; *Int'l*, pg. 2818
KUNCAI INTERNATIONAL INDIA PVT. LTD.—See Fujian Kuncai Material Technology Co., Ltd.; *Int'l*, pg. 2818
KUNDAN EDIFICE LTD.; *Int'l*, pg. 4332
KUNDA NORDIC CEMENT CORP.—See Heidelberg Materials AG; *Int'l*, pg. 3318

KUNDELL COMMUNICATIONS, INC.

KUNDELL COMMUNICATIONS, INC.; *U.S. Private*, pg. 2357
KUNDEN CLUB GMBH DES VOLKSWAGEN-KONZERNS—See Porsche Automobil Holding SE; *Int'l*, pg. 5929
KUNDERT MOTORS INC.; *U.S. Private*, pg. 2357
KUNDINGER FLUID POWER, INC.; *U.S. Private*, pg. 2357
KUNDISCH BETEILIGUNGS-GMBH—See Phoenix Mecano AG; *Int'l*, pg. 5852
KUNDISCH GMBH + CO. KG—See Phoenix Mecano AG; *Int'l*, pg. 5852
KUNDKRAFT AB—See Schibsted ASA; *Int'l*, pg. 6616
KUNDKRAFT I SVERIGE AB—See Schibsted ASA; *Int'l*, pg. 6617
KUNENE MOTOR HOLDINGS LIMITED—See The Bidvest Group Limited; *Int'l*, pg. 7625
KUNES CHEVROLET; *U.S. Private*, pg. 2357
KUNES' COUNTRY FORD-LINCOLN-MERCURY, INC.; *U.S. Private*, pg. 2357
KUNFU PAPER (KUNSAN) CO., LTD.—See Cheng Loong Corp.; *Int'l*, pg. 1466
KUNG LONG BATTERIES INDUSTRIAL CO., LTD. - BEN LUC FACTORY—See Kung Long Batteries Industrial Co., Ltd.; *Int'l*, pg. 4332
KUNG LONG BATTERIES INDUSTRIAL CO., LTD. - DUC HOA FACTORY—See Kung Long Batteries Industrial Co., Ltd.; *Int'l*, pg. 4332
KUNG LONG BATTERIES INDUSTRIAL CO., LTD.; *Int'l*, pg. 4332
KUNGSFISKAREN BYGG & FASTIGHET AB—See Peab AB; *Int'l*, pg. 5772
KUNG SING ENGINEERING CORPORATION; *Int'l*, pg. 4332
KUNGSLEDEN AB; *Int'l*, pg. 4332
KUNGSLEDEN FASTIGHETS AB—See Kungsleden AB; *Int'l*, pg. 4332
KUNGSLEDEN FRIAB AB—See Kungsleden AB; *Int'l*, pg. 4332
KUNGSLEDEN MATTAN AB—See Kungsleden AB; *Int'l*, pg. 4332
KUNGSLEDEN OST B AB—See Kungsleden AB; *Int'l*, pg. 4332
KUNGSLEDEN OST G AB—See Kungsleden AB; *Int'l*, pg. 4332
KUNGSLEDEN REAL ESTATE BV—See Kungsleden AB; *Int'l*, pg. 4332
KUNGSLEDEN SERVICE AB—See Kungsleden AB; *Int'l*, pg. 4332
KUNGSLEDEN SYD AB—See Kungsleden AB; *Int'l*, pg. 4332
KUNGSORS MEKANISKA VERKSTAD AB—See XANO Industri AB; *Int'l*, pg. 8519
KUNI AUTO CENTER—See Holman Automotive Group, Inc.; *U.S. Private*, pg. 1967
KUNI DENVER MOTORS, LLC—See Holman Automotive Group, Inc.; *U.S. Private*, pg. 1967
KUNI ENTERPRISES, INC.—See Holman Automotive Group, Inc.; *U.S. Private*, pg. 1967
KUNI GERMAN MOTORS, LLC—See Holman Automotive Group, Inc.; *U.S. Private*, pg. 1967
KUNIHIRO INC.—See Nissui Corporation; *Int'l*, pg. 5378
KUNI HONDA; *U.S. Private*, pg. 2357
KUNI HUBACHER MOTORS, LLC—See Holman Automotive Group, Inc.; *U.S. Private*, pg. 1967
KUNIKO LIMITED; *Int'l*, pg. 4333
KUNIMAIN CO., LTD.—See KUNIMINE INDUSTRIES CO., LTD.; *Int'l*, pg. 4333
KUNIMINE INDUSTRIES CO., LTD.; *Int'l*, pg. 4333
KUNIMINE MARKETING CO., LTD.—See KUNIMINE INDUSTRIES CO., LTD.; *Int'l*, pg. 4333
KUNIMINE (THAILAND) CO., LTD.—See KUNIMINE INDUSTRIES CO., LTD.; *Int'l*, pg. 4333
KUNIMOKU HOUSE CO., LTD.—See NAC Co., Ltd.; *Int'l*, pg. 5121
KUNITAKARA ELECTRIC CO., LTD.—See Ya Horng Electronic Co., Ltd.; *Int'l*, pg. 8544
KUNKEL MILLER & HAMENT; *U.S. Private*, pg. 2357
THE KUNKEL SERVICE COMPANY INC.; *U.S. Private*, pg. 4066
KUNKLE REALTY, LLC; *U.S. Private*, pg. 2357
KUNLUN ENERGY CO. LTD.—See China National Petroleum Corporation; *Int'l*, pg. 1533
KUNLUN TECH CO., LTD.; *Int'l*, pg. 4333
KUNMING APPLE KAIXIN FOODS INGREDIENTS CO., LTD.—See Apple Flavor & Fragrance Group Co., Ltd.; *Int'l*, pg. 520
KUNMING BAKER NORTON PHARMACEUTICAL CO. LTD.—See KPC Pharmaceuticals Inc.; *Int'l*, pg. 4296
KUNMING CHINA INTERNATIONAL TRAVEL SERVICE CO., LTD.—See China Tourism Group Duty Free Corporation Limited; *Int'l*, pg. 1560
KUNMING CHUAN JIN NUO CHEMICAL CO., LTD.; *Int'l*, pg. 4333
KUNMING COLOR PRINTING CO., LTD.—See Shenzhen Jinjia Group Co., Ltd.; *Int'l*, pg. 6814
KUNMING CONDELL ELECTRONICS CO., LTD.—See Endress+Hauser (International) Holding AG; *Int'l*, pg. 2408
KUNMING DIANCHI WATER TREATMENT CO., LTD.; *Int'l*, pg. 4333
KUNMING FIRMENICH AROMATICS CO. LTD.—See Firmenich International SA; *Int'l*, pg. 2681
KUNMING FUTIAN FOOD CO., LTD.—See Zhuhai Zhongfu Enterprise Co., Ltd.; *Int'l*, pg. 8679
KUNMING IRON & STEEL GROUP CO., LTD.; *Int'l*, pg. 4333
KUNMING JINGRUN FOOD CO., LTD.—See ORG Technology Co., Ltd.; *Int'l*, pg. 5617
KUNMING JIN JIANG HOTEL COMPANY LIMITED—See Shanghai Jin Jiang Capital Company Limited; *Int'l*, pg. 6772
KUNMING KUMYANG CHEMICAL CO., LTD—See Kumyang Co., Ltd.; *Int'l*, pg. 4332
KUNMING LONGJIN PHARMACEUTICAL CO., LTD.; *Int'l*, pg. 4333
KUNMING NANTIAN COMPUTER SYSTEM CO., LTD.—See Yunnan Nantian Electronics Information Co., Ltd.; *Int'l*, pg. 8616
KUNMING SHENGHUO PHARMACEUTICAL (GROUP) CO., LTD.—See China Resources Sanjiu Medical & Pharmaceutical Co., Ltd.; *Int'l*, pg. 1549
KUNMING TONGREN HOSPITAL CO., LTD.—See China Medical & HealthCare Group Limited; *Int'l*, pg. 1518
KUNMING YUNNEI POWER CO., LTD.; *Int'l*, pg. 4333
KUNMING YUNZHE HIGH TECHNOLOGY CO., LTD.—See Yunnan Lincang Xinyuan Germanium Industrial Co., Ltd.; *Int'l*, pg. 8615
KUNNEPPU SEKKAI KOGYO INC.—See Taiheiyo Kouhatsu Incorporated; *Int'l*, pg. 7412
KUNO OIL COMPANY INC.; *U.S. Private*, pg. 2357
KUN PENG INTERNATIONAL LTD.; *Int'l*, pg. 4332
KUN-SAN TAIFLEX ELECTRONIC MATERIAL CO., LTD.—See Taiflex Scientific Co., Ltd.; *Int'l*, pg. 7410
KUNSHAN ACHILLES ARTIFICIAL LEATHER CO., LTD.—See Achilles Corporation; *Int'l*, pg. 103
KUNSHAN ACHILLES NEW MATERIAL TECHNOLOGY CO., LTD.—See Achilles Corporation; *Int'l*, pg. 103
KUNSHAN AICA KOGYO CO., LTD.—See AICA Kogyo Company, Limited; *Int'l*, pg. 229
KUNSHAN ASIA AROMA CORP., LTD.; *Int'l*, pg. 4333
KUNSHAN AT&MIK CO., LTD.—See Advanced Technology & Materials Co., Ltd.; *Int'l*, pg. 162
KUNSHAN BAOZEN AUTOMOBILE SALES AND SERVICES CO., LTD.—See China Yongda Automobiles Services Holdings Limited; *Int'l*, pg. 1564
KUNSHAN CHAITAI-XINCHENG PRECISION FORGING CO., LTD.—See AAPICO Hitech plc; *Int'l*, pg. 37
KUNSHAN CHUHO SPRING CO., LTD.—See Chuo Spring Co., Ltd.; *Int'l*, pg. 1599
KUNSHAN DONGWEI TECHNOLOGY CO., LTD.; *Int'l*, pg. 4333
KUNSHAN DOWA THERMO FURNACE CO., LTD.—See Dowa Holdings Co., Ltd.; *Int'l*, pg. 2184
KUNSHAN DRAGONSTATE ELECTRONIC TECHNOLOGY CO., LTD.—See Concraft Holding Co., Ltd.; *Int'l*, pg. 1765
KUNSHAN ECO WATER SYSTEMS CO., LTD—See Hyflux Ltd; *Int'l*, pg. 3548
KUNSHAN ENDO LIGHTING CO., LTD.—See ENDO Lighting Corporation; *Int'l*, pg. 2405
KUNSHAN ESON PRECISION ENGINEERING CO., LTD.—See Eson Precision Ind. Co., Ltd.; *Int'l*, pg. 2504
KUNSHAN EVERWIN PRECISION TECHNOLOGY CO., LTD.—See Shenzhen Everwin Precision Technology Co., Ltd.; *Int'l*, pg. 6809
KUNSHAN EWPT PRECISION TECHNOLOGY CO., LTD.—See Shenzhen Everwin Precision Technology Co., Ltd.; *Int'l*, pg. 6809
KUNSHAN FRD ELECTRONIC MATERIALS CO., LTD.—See Shenzhen FRD Science & Technology Co., Ltd.; *Int'l*, pg. 6810
KUNSHAN FUJI MACHINE MFG. CO., LTD.—See Fuji Corporation; *Int'l*, pg. 2810
KUNSHAN FULFIL TECH CO., LTD.—See Syncmold Enterprise Corp.; *Int'l*, pg. 7382
KUNSHAN GIANTPLUS OPTOELECTRONICS TECHNOLOGY CO., LTD.—See TOPPAN Holdings Inc.; *Int'l*, pg. 7817
KUNSHAN HK ELEVATOR SYSTEMS CO., LTD—See KLEEMANN HELLAS S.A.; *Int'l*, pg. 4200
KUNSHAN HUADE METAL PACKAGING CONTAINER CO., LTD.—See Crown Holdings, Inc.; *U.S. Public*, pg. 599
KUNSHAN HUBBLE RADIO ELECTRONIC TECHNOLOGY CO., LTD.—See Shenzhen Everwin Precision Technology Co., Ltd.; *Int'l*, pg. 6809
KUNSHAN HUGUANG AUTO HARNESS CO., LTD.; *Int'l*, pg. 4333
KUNSHAN HUTEK CORPORATION—See RITEK CORPORATION; *Int'l*, pg. 6351
KUNSHAN JENG JEA COMPUTER FITTINGS CO., LTD.—See Shin Zu Shing Co., Ltd.; *Int'l*, pg. 6838
KUNSHAN JINNJI PRECISION MOLD CO., LTD.—See CHIALIN Precision Industrial Co., Ltd.; *Int'l*, pg. 1475
KUNSHAN JUST CONN. PRECISION COMPONENTS CO., LTD.—See Shenzhen Everwin Precision Technology Co., Ltd.; *Int'l*, pg. 6809

CORPORATE AFFILIATIONS

KUNSHAN KANEFUSA CORPORATION—See KANEFUSA CORPORATION; *Int'l*, pg. 4066
KUNSHAN KEY WARE ELECTRONICS CO., LTD.—See Key Ware Electronics Co., Ltd.; *Int'l*, pg. 4145
KUNSHAN KING CHOU FISH NET MFG. CO., LTD.—See King Chou Marine Technology Co., Ltd.; *Int'l*, pg. 4168
KUNSHAN KING CHOU NET MFG. CO., LTD.—See King Chou Marine Technology Co., Ltd.; *Int'l*, pg. 4168
KUNSHAN KINGLAI HYGIENIC MATERIALS CO., LTD.; *Int'l*, pg. 4333
KUNSHAN KOATECH TECHNOLOGY CORPORATION—See Taiflex Scientific Co., Ltd.; *Int'l*, pg. 7410
KUNSHAN KUANGRUI PACKAGE MATERIAL CO., LTD.—See Eson Precision Ind. Co., Ltd.; *Int'l*, pg. 2504
KUNSHAN LASERWARE LASER TECHNOLOGY CO., LTD.—See Key Ware Electronics Co., Ltd.; *Int'l*, pg. 4145
KUNSHAN LEMTECH ELECTRONICS TECHNOLOGY CO., LTD.—See LemTech Holdings Co., Ltd.; *Int'l*, pg. 4450
KUNSHAN LEMTECH SLIDE TECHNOLOGY CO., LTD.—See LemTech Holdings Co., Ltd.; *Int'l*, pg. 4450
KUNSHAN LGMSK COMPUTER CO., LTD.—See LG Corp.; *Int'l*, pg. 4474
KUNSHAN LUN TENG SYSTEM CO., LTD.—See Twinhead International Corp.; *Int'l*, pg. 7990
KUNSHAN MACAUTO AUTOMOBILE PARTS INDUSTRY CO., LTD.—See Macauto Industrial Co., Ltd.; *Int'l*, pg. 4620
KUNSHAN MAOSHUN SEALING PRODUCTS INDUSTRIAL CO., LTD.—See NAK Sealing Technologies Corporation; *Int'l*, pg. 5131
KUNSHAN NEW KIKUKAWA EQUIPMENT CO., LTD.—See Kikukawa Enterprise Inc.; *Int'l*, pg. 4161
KUNSHAN NISHOKU PLASTIC ELECTRONIC CO., LTD.—See Nishoku Technology Inc.; *Int'l*, pg. 5366
KUNSHAN NSK CO., LTD.—See NSK Ltd.; *Int'l*, pg. 5478
KUNSHAN OJI FILTER CO., LTD.—See Oji Holdings Corporation; *Int'l*, pg. 5537
KUNSHAN POLYSTAR ELECTRONICS CO., LTD.—See Polytronics Technology Corp.; *Int'l*, pg. 5917
KUNSHAN PROTEK CO. LTD.—See RITEK CORPORATION; *Int'l*, pg. 6351
KUNSHAN Q TECHNOLOGY LIMITED—See Q Technology (Group) Company Limited; *Int'l*, pg. 6129
KUNSHAN QUASER MACHINE TOOLS, INC.—See Quaser Machine Tools, Inc.; *Int'l*, pg. 6157
KUNSHAN RADIANT INNOVATION CO., LTD.—See Radiant Innovation, Inc.; *Int'l*, pg. 6174
KUNSHAN RINGFEDER POWER TRANSMISSION CO., LTD.—See VBG Group AB; *Int'l*, pg. 8138
KUNSHAN RITEK TRADING COMPANY, LTD.—See RITEK CORPORATION; *Int'l*, pg. 6351
KUNSHAN SINO SILICON TECHNOLOGY CO., LTD.—See Sino-American Silicon Products Inc.; *Int'l*, pg. 6948
KUNSHAN SMITH XINGYE ELECTRONIC MATERIALS CO., LTD.—See Shanghai Smith Adhesive New Material Co., Ltd.; *Int'l*, pg. 6779
KUNSHAN STAFLEX TEXTILE CO., LTD. - JIANGSU FACTORY—See Dynic Corporation; *Int'l*, pg. 2243
KUNSHAN STAFLEX TEXTILE CO., LTD.—See Dynic Corporation; *Int'l*, pg. 2243
KUNSHAN SUNWILL ELECTRIC APPLIANCES CO., LTD.—See Guangdong Sunwill Precising Plastic Co., Ltd.; *Int'l*, pg. 3160
KUNSHAN TAIBO PRECISION TECHNOLOGY CO., LTD.—See Shenzhen Everwin Precision Technology Co., Ltd.; *Int'l*, pg. 6809
KUNSHAN TAIFLEX ELECTRONIC CO., LTD.—See Taiflex Scientific Co., Ltd.; *Int'l*, pg. 7410
KUNSHAN TAIMIDE TECH, INC.—See Taimide Tech. Inc.; *Int'l*, pg. 7415
KUNSHAN TIANYANG HOT MELT ADHESIVES CO., LTD.—See Tianyang New Materials (Shanghai) Technology Co., Ltd.; *Int'l*, pg. 7742
KUNSHAN TONGHE TOYOTA SERVICE CO.,LTD.—See Universal Cement Corporation; *Int'l*, pg. 8078
KUNSHAN TON YI INDUSTRIAL CO., LTD.—See Uni-President Enterprises Corporation; *Int'l*, pg. 8028
KUNSHAN TOPA INTELLIGENT EQUIPMENT CO., LTD.; *Int'l*, pg. 4333
KUNSHAN TOYOTA BOSHOKU AUTOMOTIVE PARTS CO., LTD.—See Toyota Boshoku Corporation; *Int'l*, pg. 7864
KUN SHAN TYC HIGH PERFORMANCE LIGHTING TECH CO., LTD.—See TYC Brother Industrial Co., Ltd.; *Int'l*, pg. 7994
KUNSHAN WANHE PRECISION ELECTRON CO., LTD.—See Sinher Technology Inc.; *Int'l*, pg. 6945
KUNSHAN WCON ELECTRONICS CO., LTD.—See Wcon Electronics (Guangdong) Co., Ltd.; *Int'l*, pg. 8361
KUNSHAN YATTAO CHEMICAL CO., LTD.—See Kingboard Holdings Limited; *Int'l*, pg. 4171
KUNSHAN YUAN MAO ELECTRONICS TECHNOLOGY CO., LTD.—See Global Brands Manufacture Ltd.; *Int'l*, pg. 2993

KUNSTHAUS LEASING GMBH—See UniCredit S.p.A.; *Int'l*, pg. 8037
KUNSTSCHULE WANDSBEK GMBH—See MEDIQON Group AG; *Int'l*, pg. 4780
KUNSTSTOFFE INDUSTRIES LTD.; *Int'l*, pg. 4333
KUNSTSTOFFVERARBEITUNG UEBIGAU GMBH—See uesa GmbH; *Int'l*, pg. 8014
KUNSUL CHEMICAL INDUSTRIAL CO., LTD. - ANYANG FACTORY—See Kangnam Jevisco Co., Ltd.; *Int'l*, pg. 4070
KUNSUL CHEMICAL INDUSTRIAL CO., LTD. - HAMAN FACTORY—See Kangnam Jevisco Co., Ltd.; *Int'l*, pg. 4070
KUNSUL CHEMICAL INDUSTRIAL CO., LTD. - PYEONGTAEK FACTORY—See Kangnam Jevisco Co., Ltd.; *Int'l*, pg. 4070
KUNTHIRO.HOMETECH CORPORATION—See JUTEC Holdings Corporation; *Int'l*, pg. 4032
KUNTNER & CO., KG—See REHAU Verwaltungszentrale AG; *Int'l*, pg. 6255
KUNTSCHAR U. SCHLUTER GMBH—See CENTROTEC SE; *Int'l*, pg. 1414
KUNTZ ELECTROPLATING INC.; *Int'l*, pg. 4333
KUNTZMAN TRUCKING INC.; *U.S. Private*, pg. 2357
KUNWHA PHARMACEUTICAL CO., LTD. - KOREA PLANT—See Lotus Pharmaceutical Co., Ltd.; *Int'l*, pg. 4561
KUNWU JIUDING INVESTMENT HOLDINGS CO., LTD.; *Int'l*, pg. 4333
KUNYUE DEVELOPMENT CO., LTD.; *Int'l*, pg. 4334
KUNZ FASERPLATTENWERK BARUTH GMBH—See Pfleiderer GmbH; *Int'l*, pg. 5836
KUNZLI PAPIER AG—See MAY+SPIES GMBH; *Int'l*, pg. 4743
KUO AEROSPACE, S.A. DE C.V.—See Grupo Kuo, S.A.B. de C.V.; *Int'l*, pg. 3131
KUOBROTHERS CORP.; *Int'l*, pg. 4334
KUO CONCENTRADORA, S.A. DE C.V.—See Grupo Kuo, S.A.B. de C.V.; *Int'l*, pg. 3131
KUO HORNG CO., LTD.—See Idemitsu Kosan Co., Ltd.; *Int'l*, pg. 3591
KUOK BROTHERS SDN. BHD.; *Int'l*, pg. 4334
KUOK (SINGAPORE) LIMITED; *Int'l*, pg. 4334
KUONI DESTINATION MANAGEMENT A/S—See JTB Corp.; *Int'l*, pg. 4016
KUONI DESTINATION MANAGEMENT B.V.—See JTB Corp.; *Int'l*, pg. 4016
KUONI DESTINATION MANAGEMENT GES.M.B.H—See JTB Corp.; *Int'l*, pg. 4016
KUONI DESTINATION MANAGEMENT S.L.—See JTB Corp.; *Int'l*, pg. 4016
KUONI DESTINATION MANAGEMENT S.P.A.—See JTB Corp.; *Int'l*, pg. 4016
KUONI GLOBAL TRAVEL SERVICES AG—See JTB Corp.; *Int'l*, pg. 4016
KUONI HOLDING DELAWARE, INC.—See JTB Corp.; *Int'l*, pg. 4016
KUONI REISEN HOLDING AG—See EQT AB; *Int'l*, pg. 2478
KUONI TRAVEL (CHINA) LTD.—See Fairfax Financial Holdings Limited; *Int'l*, pg. 2608
KUO TOONG INTERNATIONAL; *Int'l*, pg. 4334
KUO YANG CONSTRUCTION; *Int'l*, pg. 4334
KUOZUI MOTORS, LTD.—See Toyota Motor Corporation; *Int'l*, pg. 7872
KUPALA BELARUSIAN-AUSTRIAN CLOSED JOINT STOCK INSURANCE COMPANY—See Vienna Insurance Group AG Wiener Versicherung Gruppe; *Int'l*, pg. 8195
KUPELE DUDINCE AS; *Int'l*, pg. 4335
KUPER REALTY CORP.; *U.S. Private*, pg. 2357
KUPFERBERGBAU STADTBERGE ZU NIEDERMARSBERG GMBH—See GEA Group Aktiengesellschaft; *Int'l*, pg. 2903
KUPFER COPPER GERMANY GMBH—See Anglo American PLC; *Int'l*, pg. 462
KUPFEREXPLORATIONSGESELLSCHAFT MBH—See GEA Group Aktiengesellschaft; *Int'l*, pg. 2903
KUPFERRHEYDT GMBH—See Umcor AG; *Int'l*, pg. 8022
KUPINA GRUNDSTUCKS-VERWALTUNGSGESELLSCHAFT MBH & CO. KG—See Metro AG; *Int'l*, pg. 4857
KUPKE + WOLF GMBH; *Int'l*, pg. 4335
KUPPER CHEVROLET, INC.; *U.S. Private*, pg. 2357
KUQI LICENSEE, LLC—See Sinclair, Inc.; *U.S. Public*, pg. 1885
KURABO CHEMICAL WORKS CO., LTD.—See Kurabo Industries Ltd.; *Int'l*, pg. 4335
KURABO DENIM INTERNATIONAL LTD.—See Kurabo Industries Ltd.; *Int'l*, pg. 4335
KURABO DRIVING SCHOOL CO., LTD.—See Kurabo Industries Ltd.; *Int'l*, pg. 4335
KURABO ENGINEERING WORK SERVICE CO., LTD.—See Kurabo Industries Ltd.; *Int'l*, pg. 4335
KURABO INDUSTRIES LTD. - ANJO MILL—See Kurabo Industries Ltd.; *Int'l*, pg. 4335
KURABO INDUSTRIES LTD. - GUNMA PLANT—See Kurabo Industries Ltd.; *Int'l*, pg. 4335

KURABO INDUSTRIES LTD. - HOJO MILL—See Kurabo Industries Ltd.; *Int'l*, pg. 4335
KURABO INDUSTRIES LTD. - KAMOGATA PLANT—See Kurabo Industries Ltd.; *Int'l*, pg. 4335
KURABO INDUSTRIES LTD. - MARUGAME MILL—See Kurabo Industries Ltd.; *Int'l*, pg. 4335
KURABO INDUSTRIES LTD. - MIE PLANT—See Kurabo Industries Ltd.; *Int'l*, pg. 4335
KURABO INDUSTRIES LTD. - NEYAGAWA PLANT—See Kurabo Industries Ltd.; *Int'l*, pg. 4335
KURABO INDUSTRIES LTD.; *Int'l*, pg. 4335
KURABO INDUSTRIES LTD. - SUSONO PLANT—See Kurabo Industries Ltd.; *Int'l*, pg. 4335
KURABO INDUSTRIES LTD. - TOKUSHIMA PLANT—See Kurabo Industries Ltd.; *Int'l*, pg. 4335
KURABO INTERNATIONAL CO., LTD.—See Kurabo Industries Ltd.; *Int'l*, pg. 4335
KURABO PLANT SYSTEM CO., LTD.—See Kurabo Industries Ltd.; *Int'l*, pg. 4335
KURABO SHANGHAI CO., LTD.—See Kurabo Industries Ltd.; *Int'l*, pg. 4335
KURABO TECHNO SYSTEM LTD.—See Kurabo Industries Ltd.; *Int'l*, pg. 4335
KURABO VIETNAM CO., LTD.—See Kurabo Industries Ltd.; *Int'l*, pg. 4336
KURAFLEX CO., LTD.—See Kuraray Co., Ltd.; *Int'l*, pg. 4336
KURAKI AMERICA CORPORATION—See Kurabo Industries Ltd.; *Int'l*, pg. 4336
KURAKI COMPANY LTD.—See Kurabo Industries Ltd.; *Int'l*, pg. 4336
KURAKI SHANGHAI CO., LTD.—See Kurabo Industries Ltd.; *Int'l*, pg. 4336
KURAKI TAIWAN CO., LTD.—See Kurabo Industries Ltd.; *Int'l*, pg. 4336
KURAMOTO CO., LTD. - HANAIZUMI FACTORY—See KURAMOTO Co., Ltd.; *Int'l*, pg. 4336
KURAMOTO CO., LTD. - MIE FACTORY—See KURAMOTO Co., Ltd.; *Int'l*, pg. 4336
KURAMOTO CO., LTD.; *Int'l*, pg. 4336
KURANI INCORPORATED; *U.S. Private*, pg. 2357
KURA ONCOLOGY, INC.; *U.S. Public*, pg. 1277
KURARAY ADVANCED CHEMICALS (THAILAND) CO., LTD.—See Kuraray Co., Ltd.; *Int'l*, pg. 4336
KURARAY AMERICA, INC.—See Kuraray Co., Ltd.; *Int'l*, pg. 4336
KURARAY AQUA CO., LTD.—See Kuraray Co., Ltd.; *Int'l*, pg. 4336
KURARAY ASIA PACIFIC PTE. LTD.—See Kuraray Co., Ltd.; *Int'l*, pg. 4336
KURARAY BUSINESS SERVICES CO., LTD.—See Kuraray Co., Ltd.; *Int'l*, pg. 4336
KURARAY CHEMICAL CO., LTD.—See Kuraray Co., Ltd.; *Int'l*, pg. 4336
KURARAY CHEMICAL CO., LTD. - TSURUMI PLANT—See Kuraray Co., Ltd.; *Int'l*, pg. 4336
KURARAY CHINA CO., LTD.—See Kuraray Co., Ltd.; *Int'l*, pg. 4337
KURARAY CO., LTD. - KASHIMA PLANT—See Kuraray Co., Ltd.; *Int'l*, pg. 4337
KURARAY CO., LTD. - KURASHIKI PLANT (SAKAZU)—See Kuraray Co., Ltd.; *Int'l*, pg. 4337
KURARAY CO., LTD. - KURASHIKI PLANT (TAMASHIMA)—See Kuraray Co., Ltd.; *Int'l*, pg. 4337
KURARAY CO., LTD. - NIIGATA PLANT—See Kuraray Co., Ltd.; *Int'l*, pg. 4337
KURARAY CO., LTD. - OKAYAMA PLANT—See Kuraray Co., Ltd.; *Int'l*, pg. 4337
KURARAY CO., LTD. - SAIJO PLANT—See Kuraray Co., Ltd.; *Int'l*, pg. 4337
KURARAY CO., LTD.; *Int'l*, pg. 4336
KURARAY DENTAL BENELUX B.V.—See Kuraray Co., Ltd.; *Int'l*, pg. 4337
KURARAY DENTAL ITALIA S.R.L.—See Kuraray Co., Ltd.; *Int'l*, pg. 4337
KURARAY ENGINEERING CO., LTD.—See Kuraray Co., Ltd.; *Int'l*, pg. 4337
KURARAY EUROPE GMBH—See Kuraray Co., Ltd.; *Int'l*, pg. 4337
KURARAY EUROPE NORDIC AB OY—See Kuraray Co., Ltd.; *Int'l*, pg. 4337
KURARAY FASTENING CO., LTD. - MARUOKA PLANT—See Kuraray Co., Ltd.; *Int'l*, pg. 4337
KURARAY FASTENING CO, LTD.—See Kuraray Co., Ltd.; *Int'l*, pg. 4337
KURARAY FUDOSAN CO., LTD.—See Kuraray Co., Ltd.; *Int'l*, pg. 4337
KURARAY HOLDINGS U.S.A., INC.—See Kuraray Co., Ltd.; *Int'l*, pg. 4336
KURARAY HONG KONG CO., LTD.—See Kuraray Co., Ltd.; *Int'l*, pg. 4337
KURARAY INDIA PRIVATE LIMITED—See Kuraray Co., Ltd.; *Int'l*, pg. 4337
KURARAY INTERIOR CO., LTD.—See Kuraray Co., Ltd.; *Int'l*, pg. 4337
KURARAY KOREA LTD.—See Kuraray Co., Ltd.; *Int'l*, pg. 4337
KURARAY KURAFLEX CO., LTD.—See Kuraray Co., Ltd.; *Int'l*, pg. 4337

KURARAY LIVING CO., LTD.—See Kuraray Co., Ltd.; *Int'l*, pg. 4337
KURARAY MAGICTAPE (SHANGHAI) CO., LTD.—See Kuraray Co., Ltd.; *Int'l*, pg. 4337
KURARAY MEDICAL INC.—See Kuraray Co., Ltd.; *Int'l*, pg. 4337
KURARAY METHACRYLATE (ZHANG JIA GANG) CO., LTD.—See Kuraray Co., Ltd.; *Int'l*, pg. 4337
KURARAY NORDIC AB OY—See Kuraray Co., Ltd.; *Int'l*, pg. 4337
KURARAY NORITAKE DENTAL INC.—See Kuraray Co., Ltd.; *Int'l*, pg. 4337
KURARAY OKAYAMA SPINNING CO., LTD.—See Kuraray Co., Ltd.; *Int'l*, pg. 4337
KURARAY PLASTICS CO., LTD. - IBUKI PLANT—See Kuraray Co., Ltd.; *Int'l*, pg. 4337
KURARAY PLASTICS CO., LTD.—See Kuraray Co., Ltd.; *Int'l*, pg. 4337
KURARAY SAIJO CO., LTD.—See Kuraray Co., Ltd.; *Int'l*, pg. 4337
KURARAY SOUTH AMERICA LTDA.—See Kuraray Co., Ltd.; *Int'l*, pg. 4337
KURARAY SOUTH AMERICA REPRESENTACOES LTDA.—See Kuraray Co., Ltd.; *Int'l*, pg. 4337
KURARAY TAMASHIMA CO., LTD.—See Kuraray Co., Ltd.; *Int'l*, pg. 4337
KURARAY TECHNO CO., LTD.—See Kuraray Co., Ltd.; *Int'l*, pg. 4337
KURARAY (THAILAND) CO., LTD.—See Kuraray Co., Ltd.; *Int'l*, pg. 4337
KURARAY TRADING CO., LTD.—See Kuraray Co., Ltd.; *Int'l*, pg. 4337
KURARAY TRADING (SHANGHAI) CO., LTD.—See Kuraray Co., Ltd.; *Int'l*, pg. 4337
KURARAY TRADING VIETNAM CO., LTD.—See Kuraray Co., Ltd.; *Int'l*, pg. 4337
KURARAY TRAVEL SERVICE CORP.—See Kuraray Co., Ltd.; *Int'l*, pg. 4337
KURASHIKI CABLE TELEVISION INC.—See TOKAI Holdings Corporation; *Int'l*, pg. 7779
KURASHIKI CHEMICAL PRODUCTS DO BRASIL LTDA.—See Kurabo Industries Ltd.; *Int'l*, pg. 4336
KURASHIKI DO BRASIL TEXTIL LTDA.—See Kurabo Industries Ltd.; *Int'l*, pg. 4335
KURASHIKI ENVIRONMENT TECHNOLOGY CO., LTD.—See Hitachi Zosen Corporation; *Int'l*, pg. 3411
KURASHIKI IVY SQUARE, LTD.—See Kurabo Industries Ltd.; *Int'l*, pg. 4335
KURASHIKI KAKO CO., LTD.—See Mazda Motor Corporation; *Int'l*, pg. 4748
KURASHIKI KOKUSAI HOTEL, LTD.—See Kuraray Co., Ltd.; *Int'l*, pg. 4337
KURASHIKI ROYAL ART HOTEL CO., LTD.—See Striders Corporation; *Int'l*, pg. 7240
KURASHIKI STYLE CO., LTD.—See PAL GROUP Holdings Co., Ltd.; *Int'l*, pg. 5705
KURASHIKI TEXTILE MANUFACTURING CO., LTD.—See Kurabo Industries Ltd.; *Int'l*, pg. 4336
KURASHI NET JP CO., LTD.—See Japan Pulp and Paper Company Limited; *Int'l*, pg. 3904
KURASHINO SAISON CO., LTD.—See Credit Saison Co., Ltd.; *Int'l*, pg. 1836
KURA SUSHI, INC.; *Int'l*, pg. 4335
KURA SUSHI TAIWAN CO, LTD—See Kura Sushi, Inc.; *Int'l*, pg. 4335
KURA SUSHI USA, INC.—See Kura Sushi, Inc.; *Int'l*, pg. 4335
KURATLE & JAECKER AG—See Holzwerkstoff Holding AG; *Int'l*, pg. 3454
KURAUDIA HOLDINGS CO., LTD.; *Int'l*, pg. 4338
KURAYA KASEI, INC.—See Medipal Holdings Corporation; *Int'l*, pg. 4779
KURAYA (USA) CORPORATION—See Medipal Holdings Corporation; *Int'l*, pg. 4779
KURAYOSHI GUNZE CO., LTD.—See Gunze Limited; *Int'l*, pg. 3186
KURBO, INC.—See WW International, Inc.; *U.S. Public*, pg. 2384
KURDISTAN INTERNATIONAL BANK FOR INVESTMENT & DEVELOPMENT; *Int'l*, pg. 4338
KURE ASSOCIATES LLC—See M&B Corporation; *U.S. Private*, pg. 2524
KURE GRINDING WHEEL CO., LTD. - CHIBA PLANT—See Kure Grinding Wheel Co., Ltd.; *Int'l*, pg. 4338
KURE GRINDING WHEEL CO., LTD. - ENIWA PLANT—See Kure Grinding Wheel Co., Ltd.; *Int'l*, pg. 4338
KURE GRINDING WHEEL CO., LTD. - KOKUFU PLANT—See Kure Grinding Wheel Co., Ltd.; *Int'l*, pg. 4338
KURE GRINDING WHEEL CO., LTD. - KURE PLANT—See Kure Grinding Wheel Co., Ltd.; *Int'l*, pg. 4338
KURE GRINDING WHEEL CO., LTD.; *Int'l*, pg. 4338
KURE GRINDING WHEEL (THAILAND) CO.,LTD.—See Kure Grinding Wheel Co., Ltd.; *Int'l*, pg. 4338
KUREHA ADVANCED MATERIALS, INC.—See Kureha Corporation; *Int'l*, pg. 4338

KURE GRINDING WHEEL CO., LTD.

CORPORATE AFFILIATIONS

KUREHA AMERICA INC.—See Kureha Corporation; *Int'l*, pg. 4338
KUREHA CERAMIC CO., LTD.—See Hokuriku Electric Industry Co., Ltd.; *Int'l*, pg. 3445
KUREHA (CHANGSHU) FLUOROPOLYMERS CO., LTD.—See Kureha Corporation; *Int'l*, pg. 4338
KUREHA CHEMICALS SHANGHAI CO., LTD.—See Kureha Corporation; *Int'l*, pg. 4338
KUREHA (CHINA) INVESTMENT CO., LTD.—See Kureha Corporation; *Int'l*, pg. 4338
KUREHA CORPORATION - IWAKI FACTORY—See Kureha Corporation; *Int'l*, pg. 4338
KUREHA CORPORATION - PLASTICS PROCESSING FACTORY—See Kureha Corporation; *Int'l*, pg. 4338
KUREHA CORPORATION; *Int'l*, pg. 4338
KUREHA ECOLOGY MANAGEMENT CO., LTD.—See Kureha Corporation; *Int'l*, pg. 4338
KUREHA ENERGY SOLUTIONS LLC—See Kureha Corporation; *Int'l*, pg. 4338
KUREHA ENGINEERING CO., LTD.—See Kureha Corporation; *Int'l*, pg. 4338
KUREHA EUROPE B.V.—See Kureha Corporation; *Int'l*, pg. 4338
KUREHA EXTECH CO., LTD.—See Kureha Corporation; *Int'l*, pg. 4338
KUREHA EXTRON CO., LTD.—See Kureha Corporation; *Int'l*, pg. 4338
KUREHA GMBH—See Kureha Corporation; *Int'l*, pg. 4338
KUREHA GOHSEN CO., LTD.—See Kureha Corporation; *Int'l*, pg. 4338
KUREHA GOSEN CO., LTD.—See Kureha Corporation; *Int'l*, pg. 4338
KUREHA-KAI MEDICAL CORPORATION—See Kureha Corporation; *Int'l*, pg. 4339
KUREHA LTD.—See Toyobo Co., Ltd.; *Int'l*, pg. 7860
KUREHANISHIKI CONSTRUCTION CO., LTD.—See Kureha Corporation; *Int'l*, pg. 4339
KUREHA PGA LLC—See Kureha Corporation; *Int'l*, pg. 4339
KUREHA PLASTICS CO., LTD.—See Kureha Corporation; *Int'l*, pg. 4339
KUREHA SERVICE CO., LTD.—See Kureha Corporation; *Int'l*, pg. 4339
KUREHA (SHANGHAI) CARBON FIBER MATERIALS CO., LTD.—See Kureha Corporation; *Int'l*, pg. 4338
KUREHA SHANGHAI TRADING CO., LTD.—See Kureha Corporation; *Int'l*, pg. 4339
KUREHA SPECIAL LABORATORY CO., LTD.—See Kureha Corporation; *Int'l*, pg. 4339
KUREHA STAFF SERVICE CO., LTD.—See Kureha Corporation; *Int'l*, pg. 4339
KUREHA TRADING CO., LTD.—See Kureha Corporation; *Int'l*, pg. 4339
KUREHA UNYU CO., LTD.—See Kureha Corporation; *Int'l*, pg. 4339
KUREHA VIETNAM CO., LTD.—See Kureha Corporation; *Int'l*, pg. 4339
KUREIJI, INC.; *U.S. Private*, pg. 2357
KURGAN GRUNDSTUCKS-VERWALTUNGSGESELLSCHAFT MBH & CO. OHG—See E.ON SE; *Int'l*, pg. 2258
KURGANSKAYA GENERIRUYUSHCHAYA KOMPANIYA OAO; *Int'l*, pg. 4339
KURHESSISCHE SPIELBANK KASSEL/BADWILDUNGEN GMBH & CO. KG—See Novomatic AG; *Int'l*, pg. 5467
KURIBAYASHI SEISAKUSHO CO., LTD.—See NSK Ltd.; *Int'l*, pg. 5478
KURIBAYASHI STEAMSHIP CO., LTD.; *Int'l*, pg. 4339
KURIER DIREKTSERVICE DRESDEN GMBH—See Bertelsmann SE & Co. KGaA; *Int'l*, pg. 993
KURIERVERLAGS GMBH & CO. KG; *Int'l*, pg. 4339
KURIMOTO BUSINESS ASSOCIATES CO., LTD.—See Kurimoto Ltd; *Int'l*, pg. 4339
KURIMOTO CONCRETE INDUSTRIES, LTD.—See Kurimoto Ltd; *Int'l*, pg. 4339
KURIMOTO CONCRETE INDUSTRY CO., LTD.—See Sumitomo Osaka Cement Co Ltd; *Int'l*, pg. 7296
KURIMOTO LOGISTICS CORPORATION—See Kurimoto Ltd; *Int'l*, pg. 4339
KURIMOTO LTD - CHITA FACTORY—See Kurimoto Ltd; *Int'l*, pg. 4339
KURIMOTO LTD - FUKUOKA FACTORY—See Kurimoto Ltd; *Int'l*, pg. 4339
KURIMOTO LTD - KAGAYA FACTORY—See Kurimoto Ltd; *Int'l*, pg. 4339
KURIMOTO LTD - KATANO FACTORY—See Kurimoto Ltd; *Int'l*, pg. 4339
KURIMOTO LTD - KOGA FACTORY—See Kurimoto Ltd; *Int'l*, pg. 4339
KURIMOTO LTD - MATSUDO FACTORY—See Kurimoto Ltd; *Int'l*, pg. 4339
KURIMOTO LTD - OKAYAMA FACTORY—See Kurimoto Ltd; *Int'l*, pg. 4339
KURIMOTO LTD - SAKAI FACTORY—See Kurimoto Ltd; *Int'l*, pg. 4339
KURIMOTO LTD - SAPPORO FACTORY—See Kurimoto Ltd; *Int'l*, pg. 4339
KURIMOTO LTD - SENDAI FACTORY—See Kurimoto Ltd; *Int'l*, pg. 4339

KURIMOTO LTD; *Int'l*, pg. 4339
KURIMOTO LTD - SUMIYOSHI FACTORY—See Kurimoto Ltd; *Int'l*, pg. 4339
KURIMOTO PIPE ENGINEERING CO., LTD.—See Kurimoto Ltd; *Int'l*, pg. 4339
KURIMOTO PLASTICS CO., LTD.—See Kurimoto Ltd; *Int'l*, pg. 4339
KURIMOTO POLYMERS CO., LTD.—See Kurimoto Ltd; *Int'l*, pg. 4339
KURIMOTO TRADING CO., LTD.—See Kurimoto Ltd; *Int'l*, pg. 4339
KURIMOTO USA, INC.—See Kurimoto Ltd; *Int'l*, pg. 4339
KURION, INC.—See Veolia Environnement S.A.; *Int'l*, pg. 8158
KURITA AMERICA HOLDINGS INC.—See Kurita Water Industries Ltd.; *Int'l*, pg. 4340
KURITA AMERICA INC.—See Kurita Water Industries Ltd.; *Int'l*, pg. 4340
KURITA ANALYSIS SERVICE CO., LTD.—See Kurita Water Industries Ltd.; *Int'l*, pg. 4340
KURITA BMS CO., LTD.—See Kurita Water Industries Ltd.; *Int'l*, pg. 4340
KURITA BUIL-TECH CO., LTD.—See Kurita Water Industries Ltd.; *Int'l*, pg. 4340
KURITA CHEMICAL KANTO LTD.—See Kurita Water Industries Ltd.; *Int'l*, pg. 4340
KURITA CHEMICAL MANUFACTURING LTD.—See Kurita Water Industries Ltd.; *Int'l*, pg. 4340
KURITA CHEMICALS HOKKAIDO LTD.—See Kurita Water Industries Ltd.; *Int'l*, pg. 4340
KURITA CHEMICALS KANSAI LTD.—See Kurita Water Industries Ltd.; *Int'l*, pg. 4340
KURITA CHEMICALS KUMAMOTO LTD.—See Kurita Water Industries Ltd.; *Int'l*, pg. 4340
KURITA CHEMICALS OITA LTD.—See Kurita Water Industries Ltd.; *Int'l*, pg. 4340
KURITA CHEMICALS SANYO CO. LTD.—See Kurita Water Industries Ltd.; *Int'l*, pg. 4340
KURITA CHEMICALS TOKAI CO., LTD.—See Kurita Water Industries Ltd.; *Int'l*, pg. 4340
KURITA CHEMICALS WEST JAPAN LTD.—See Kurita Water Industries Ltd.; *Int'l*, pg. 4340
KURITA CREATION CO., LTD.—See Kurita Water Industries Ltd.; *Int'l*, pg. 4340
KURITA DO BRASIL LTDA.—See Kurita Water Industries Ltd.; *Int'l*, pg. 4341
KURITA ENGINEERING CO., LTD.—See Kurita Water Industries Ltd.; *Int'l*, pg. 4340
KURITA EUROPE GMBH—See Kurita Water Industries Ltd.; *Int'l*, pg. 4340
KURITA FRANCE S.A.S.—See Kurita Water Industries Ltd.; *Int'l*, pg. 4340
KURITA-GK CHEMICAL CO., LTD.—See Kurita Water Industries Ltd.; *Int'l*, pg. 4341
KURITA-GK VIETNAM CO., LTD.—See Kurita Water Industries Ltd.; *Int'l*, pg. 4341
KURITA HOKKAIDO LTD.—See Kurita Water Industries Ltd.; *Int'l*, pg. 4340
KURITA HOKURIKU LTD.—See Kurita Water Industries Ltd.; *Int'l*, pg. 4340
KURITA IBERICA SL—See Kurita Water Industries Ltd.; *Int'l*, pg. 4340
KURITA KANSAI LTD.—See Kurita Water Industries Ltd.; *Int'l*, pg. 4340
KURITA KANTO LTD.—See Kurita Water Industries Ltd.; *Int'l*, pg. 4340
KURITA KITAKANTOU CO., LTD.—See Kurita Water Industries Ltd.; *Int'l*, pg. 4340
KURITA KYUSYU LTD.—See Kurita Water Industries Ltd.; *Int'l*, pg. 4340
KURITA MEIKI LTD.—See Kurita Water Industries Ltd.; *Int'l*, pg. 4340
KURITA MIDDLE EAST FZE—See Kurita Water Industries Ltd.; *Int'l*, pg. 4341
KURITA POLSKA SP.Z.O.O.—See Kurita Water Industries Ltd.; *Int'l*, pg. 4341
KURITA R&D ASIA PTE. LTD.—See Kurita Water Industries Ltd.; *Int'l*, pg. 4341
KURITA SANYO LTD.—See Kurita Water Industries Ltd.; *Int'l*, pg. 4340
KURITA (SINGAPORE) PTE. LTD.—See Kurita Water Industries Ltd.; *Int'l*, pg. 4340
KURITA SOGO SERVICE CO., LTD.—See Kurita Water Industries Ltd.; *Int'l*, pg. 4341
KURITA SVERIGE AB—See Kurita Water Industries Ltd.; *Int'l*, pg. 4341
KURITA (TAIWAN) CO., LTD.—See Kurita Water Industries Ltd.; *Int'l*, pg. 4340
KURITA TOKAI LTD.—See Kurita Water Industries Ltd.; *Int'l*, pg. 4341
KURITA TURKEY KIMYA A.S.—See Kurita Water Industries Ltd.; *Int'l*, pg. 4341
KURITA WATER INDUSTRIES (DALIAN) CO., LTD.—See Kurita Water Industries Ltd.; *Int'l*, pg. 4341
KURITA WATER INDUSTRIES (JIANGYIN) CO., LTD.—See Kurita Water Industries Ltd.; *Int'l*, pg. 4341
KURITA WATER INDUSTRIES LTD. - SHIZUOKA PLANT—See Kurita Water Industries Ltd.; *Int'l*, pg. 4341

KURITA WATER INDUSTRIES LTD.; *Int'l*, pg. 4340
KURITA WATER INDUSTRIES LTD. - TOYOURA PLANT—See Kurita Water Industries Ltd.; *Int'l*, pg. 4341
KURITA WATER INDUSTRIES LTD. - TSURUGA PLANT—See Kurita Water Industries Ltd.; *Int'l*, pg. 4341
KURITA WATER INDUSTRIES LTD. - YAMAGUCHI PLANT—See Kurita Water Industries Ltd.; *Int'l*, pg. 4341
KURITA WATER INDUSTRIES (SUZHOU) LTD.—See Kurita Water Industries Ltd.; *Int'l*, pg. 4341
KURITA WATER (MALAYSIA) SDN. BHD.—See Kurita Water Industries Ltd.; *Int'l*, pg. 4341
KURITA WATER TECHNOLOGY (TAIWAN) CO., LTD.—See Kurita Water Industries Ltd.; *Int'l*, pg. 4341
KURITAZ CO., LTD.—See Kurita Water Industries Ltd.; *Int'l*, pg. 4341
KURI TEC CORPORATION—See Kuriyama Holdings Corporation; *Int'l*, pg. 4341
KURI TEC MANUFACTURING, INC.—See Kuriyama Holdings Corporation; *Int'l*, pg. 4341
KURITEC SERVICE CO. LTD.—See Kurita Water Industries Ltd.; *Int'l*, pg. 4341
KURITEC (SHANGHAI) CO., LTD.—See Kurita Water Industries Ltd.; *Int'l*, pg. 4341
KURITETSU (SHANGHAI) TRADING CO., LTD.—See Kurimoto Ltd; *Int'l*, pg. 4339
KURIYAMA CANADA, INC.—See Kuriyama Holdings Corporation; *Int'l*, pg. 4342
KURIYAMA DE MEXICO, S.D.E.R.L.DE.C.V.—See Kuriyama Holdings Corporation; *Int'l*, pg. 4342
KURIYAMA EUROPE COOPERATIEF U.A.—See Kuriyama Holdings Corporation; *Int'l*, pg. 4342
KURIYAMA HOLDINGS CORPORATION; *Int'l*, pg. 4341
KURIYAMA JAPAN CORPORATION—See Kuriyama Holdings Corporation; *Int'l*, pg. 4342
KURIYAMA OF AMERICA, INC.—See Kuriyama Holdings Corporation; *Int'l*, pg. 4342
KURIYAMA-OHJI (THAILAND) LTD. - RAYONG FACTORY—See Kuriyama Holdings Corporation; *Int'l*, pg. 4342
KURIYAMA-OHJI (THAILAND) LTD.—See Kuriyama Holdings Corporation; *Int'l*, pg. 4342
KURIYAMA (SHANGHAI) CORPORATION—See Kuriyama Holdings Corporation; *Int'l*, pg. 4341
KURIYAMA (THAILAND) CO., LTD.—See Kuriyama Holdings Corporation; *Int'l*, pg. 4341
KURMAN COMMUNICATIONS, INC.; *U.S. Private*, pg. 2357
KURNIA OUTDOOR SDN. BHD.—See Media Prima Berhad; *Int'l*, pg. 4771
KUROBANE NIKON CO., LTD.—See Nikon Corporation; *Int'l*, pg. 5292
KURODA ELECTRIC CO., LTD.—See MBK Partners Ltd.; *Int'l*, pg. 4753
KURODA JENA TEC, INC.—See Kuroda Precision Industries Ltd.; *Int'l*, pg. 4342
KURODA PNEUMATICS LTD.—See Parker Hannifin Corporation; *U.S. Public*, pg. 1641
KURODA PRECISION INDUSTRIES KOREA LTD.—See Kuroda Precision Industries Ltd.; *Int'l*, pg. 4342
KURODA PRECISION INDUSTRIES LTD.; *Int'l*, pg. 4342
KURODA PRECISION INDUSTRIES (M) SDN BHD—See JFE Holdings, Inc.; *Int'l*, pg. 3937
KURODA PRECISION INDUSTRIES—See Kuroda Precision Industries Ltd.; *Int'l*, pg. 4342
KURODA RECYCLE CO., LTD.—See Envipro Holdings Inc.; *Int'l*, pg. 2454
KUROGANE KOSAKUSHO LTD.; *Int'l*, pg. 4342
KUROGANE KOSAN CO., LTD.—See Kurogane Kosakusho Ltd.; *Int'l*, pg. 4342
KURON CORPORATION LIMITED—See Do Day Dream PCL; *Int'l*, pg. 2152
KUROS BIOSCIENCES AG; *Int'l*, pg. 4342
KUROS BIOSCIENCES AG; *Int'l*, pg. 4342
KUROS BIOSCIENCES B.V.—See Kuros Biosciences AG; *Int'l*, pg. 4342
KUROS BIOSCIENCES USA, INC.—See Kuros Biosciences AG; *Int'l*, pg. 4342
KUROSE SUISAN CO., LTD.—See Nissui Corporation; *Int'l*, pg. 5378
KUROSHIO SUISAN CO., LTD.—See Kyokuyo Co. Ltd.; *Int'l*, pg. 4363
KUROTANI CORPORATION; *Int'l*, pg. 4342
KURSANA AG—See Dussmann Stiftung & Co. KGaA; *Int'l*, pg. 2234
KURTEC INSPECTION SERVICES SDN BHD—See I Squared Capital Advisors (US) LLC; *U.S. Private*, pg. 2023
KURTEC INSPECTION SERVICES SDN BHD—See TDR Capital LLP; *Int'l*, pg. 7493
KURT GEIGER LIMITED—See Cinven Limited; *Int'l*, pg. 1612
KURTIS CHEVROLET, INC.; *U.S. Private*, pg. 2358
KURT J. LESKER COMPANY; *U.S. Private*, pg. 2357
KURT MANUFACTURING CO. INC. - KURT ENGINEERED SYSTEMS DIVISION—See Kurt Manufacturing Co. Inc.; *U.S. Private*, pg. 2357

COMPANY NAME INDEX

KURT MANUFACTURING CO. INC. - KURT HYDRAULICS DIVISION—See Kurt Manufacturing Co. Inc.; *U.S. Private*, pg. 2358
KURT MANUFACTURING CO. INC. - KURT INDUSTRIAL PRODUCTS DIVISION—See Kurt Manufacturing Co. Inc.; *U.S. Private*, pg. 2358
KURT MANUFACTURING CO. INC. - KURT KINETIC DIVISION—See Kurt Manufacturing Co. Inc.; *U.S. Private*, pg. 2358
KURT MANUFACTURING CO. INC. - KURT MACHINING DIVISION—See Kurt Manufacturing Co. Inc.; *U.S. Private*, pg. 2358
KURT MANUFACTURING CO. INC. - KURT MANUFACTURING CORPORATE, GEAR, AND MACHINING DIVISION—See Kurt Manufacturing Co. Inc.; *U.S. Private*, pg. 2358
KURT MANUFACTURING CO. INC. - KURT SCREW MACHINING AND HYDRAULICS DIVISIONS—See Kurt Manufacturing Co. Inc.; *U.S. Private*, pg. 2358
KURT MANUFACTURING CO. INC.; *U.S. Private*, pg. 2357
KURT OBERMEIER GMBH & CO. KG, *Int'l*, pg. 4342
KURT ORBAN PARTNERS, LLC; *U.S. Private*, pg. 2358
KURT S. ADLER, INC.; *U.S. Private*, pg. 2358
KURT SAFARI (PTY) LTD.—See TUI AG; *Int'l*, pg. 7965
KURT SALMON ASSOCIATES, INC.—See Accenture plc; *Int'l*, pg. 86
KURT VERSEN, INC.—See Hubbell Incorporated; *U.S. Public*, pg. 1067
KURT WEISS GREENHOUSES INC.; *U.S. Private*, pg. 2358
KURT WEISS GREENHOUSES OF CONNECTICUT INC.—See Kurt Weiss Greenhouses Inc.; *U.S. Private*, pg. 2358
KURT WEISS OF NJ, INC.—See Kurt Weiss Greenhouses Inc.; *U.S. Private*, pg. 2358
KURT WEISS OF PENNSYLVANIA, INC.—See Kurt Weiss Greenhouses Inc.; *U.S. Private*, pg. 2358
KURTZ AMBULANCE SERVICE, INC.—See KKR & Co. Inc.; *U.S. Public*, pg. 1251
KURTZ BROS., INC.; *U.S. Private*, pg. 2358
KURTZ BROS. INC.; *U.S. Private*, pg. 2358
KURTZ ERSA S.A.DE C.V.—See Kurtz Holding GmbH & Co. Beteiligungs KG; *Int'l*, pg. 4342
KURTZ FAR EAST LTD.—See Kurtz Holding GmbH & Co. Beteiligungs KG; *Int'l*, pg. 4342
KURTZ FRANCE S.A.R.L.—See Kurtz Holding GmbH & Co. Beteiligungs KG; *Int'l*, pg. 4342
KURTZ GMBH—See Kurtz Holding GmbH & Co. Beteiligungs KG; *Int'l*, pg. 4342
KURTZ GRAVEL COMPANY. INC.—See Vulcan Materials Company; *U.S. Public*, pg. 2314
KURTZ HOLDING GMBH & CO. BETEILIGUNGS KG; *Int'l*, pg. 4342
KURTZ ITALIA SRL—See Kurtz Holding GmbH & Co. Beteiligungs KG; *Int'l*, pg. 4343
KURTZMAN CARSON CONSULTANTS LLC—See GCP Capital Partners Holdings LLC; *U.S. Private*, pg. 1654
KURTZ NORTH AMERICA INC.—See Kurtz Holding GmbH & Co. Beteiligungs KG; *Int'l*, pg. 4343
KURTZ SHANGHAI LTD.—See Kurtz Holding GmbH & Co. Beteiligungs KG; *Int'l*, pg. 4343
KURTZ SOUTH EAST ASIA PRIVATE LTD.—See Kurtz Holding GmbH & Co. Beteiligungs KG; *Int'l*, pg. 4343
KURTZ SYSTEMS AFRICA (PTY) LTD.—See Kurtz Holding GmbH & Co. Beteiligungs KG; *Int'l*, pg. 4343
KURTZ ZHUHAI MANUFACTURING LTD.—See Kurtz Holding GmbH & Co. Beteiligungs KG; *Int'l*, pg. 4343
KURUME HIGH TRUST CO., LTD.—See Takuma Co., Ltd.; *Int'l*, pg. 7442
KURUME-NISHITETSU TAXI CO., LTD.—See Nishi-Nippon Railroad Co., Ltd.; *Int'l*, pg. 5364
KURZ CHEERS INC.—See Leonhard Kurz GmbH & Co. KG; *Int'l*, pg. 4462
KURZ CS SPOL.SR.O.—See Leonhard Kurz GmbH & Co. KG; *Int'l*, pg. 4462
KURZ DIGITAL SOLUTIONS GMBH & CO. KG—See Leonhard Kurz GmbH & Co. KG; *Int'l*, pg. 4462
KURZ DO BRASIL—See Leonhard Kurz GmbH & Co. KG; *Int'l*, pg. 4462
KURZ ELECTRIC SOLUTIONS INC.; *U.S. Private*, pg. 2358
KURZEMES ATSLEGA 1 A/S; *Int'l*, pg. 4343
KURZ - FORWARD COMPANY LTD.—See Leonhard Kurz GmbH & Co. KG; *Int'l*, pg. 4462
KURZ FRANCE S.A.R.L.—See Leonhard Kurz GmbH & Co. KG; *Int'l*, pg. 4462
KURZ GROUP, INC.—See Ryan, LLC; *U.S. Private*, pg. 3511
KURZ (INDIA) PVT. LTD.—See Leonhard Kurz GmbH & Co. KG; *Int'l*, pg. 4462
KURZ JAPAN LTD.—See Leonhard Kurz GmbH & Co. KG; *Int'l*, pg. 4462
KURZ-KASCH, INC.—See Monomoy Capital Partners LLC; *U.S. Private*, pg. 2772
KURZ-KASCH WABASH—See Monomoy Capital Partners LLC; *U.S. Private*, pg. 2772
KURZ MEXICO S.DE R.L.DE C.V.—See Leonhard Kurz GmbH & Co. KG; *Int'l*, pg. 4462

KURZ NEW ZEALAND LTD.—See Leonhard Kurz GmbH & Co. KG; *Int'l*, pg. 4462
KURZ NORTH AFRICA SARL—See Leonhard Kurz GmbH & Co. KG; *Int'l*, pg. 4462
KURZ PRAGEFOLIEN AG—See Leonhard Kurz GmbH & Co. KG; *Int'l*, pg. 4462
KURZ STAMPING TECHNOLOGY (HEFEI) CO., LTD.—See Leonhard Kurz GmbH & Co. KG; *Int'l*, pg. 4462
KURZ (THAILAND) LTD.—See Leonhard Kurz GmbH & Co. KG; *Int'l*, pg. 4462
KURZ TRANSFER PRODUCTS, INC.—See Leonhard Kurz GmbH & Co. KG; *Int'l*, pg. 4462
KURZ TRANSFER PRODUCTS, L.P.—See Leonhard Kurz GmbH & Co. KG; *Int'l*, pg. 4462
KURZ TRANSFER PRODUCTS L.P.—See Leonhard Kurz GmbH & Co. KG; *Int'l*, pg. 4462
KURZ TYPOFOL GMBH—See Leonhard Kurz GmbH & Co. KG; *Int'l*, pg. 4462
KURZWEIL/INTELLITOOLS, INC.—See Veritas Capital Fund Management, LLC; *U.S. Private*, pg. 4361
KUSAKABE MARITIME ENGINEERING CO., LTD.—See Mitsui O.S.K. Lines, Ltd.; *Int'l*, pg. 4989
KUSAM ELECTRICAL INDUSTRIES LIMITED; *Int'l*, pg. 4343
KUSATEK GMBH—See Harvia Oyj; *Int'l*, pg. 3281
KUSA-TV—See TEGNA Inc.; *U.S. Public*, pg. 1990
KUSCHALL AG—See Invacare Corporation; *U.S. Private*, pg. 2131
KUSHAL LTD.; *Int'l*, pg. 4343
KUSHCO HOLDINGS, INC.—See Greenlane Holdings, Inc.; *U.S. Private*, pg. 964
KUSHIKATSU TANAKA CO., LTD.; *Int'l*, pg. 4343
(KUSHIKINO) DAIICHI TRAFFIC CO., LTD.—See Daiichi Koutsu Sangyo Co., Ltd.; *Int'l*, pg. 1928
KUSHIM INC.—See V-cube, Inc.; *Int'l*, pg. 8104
KUSH INDUSTRIES LIMITED; *Int'l*, pg. 4343
KUSHIRO TOHSUI REITO K.K.—See TOHTO SUISAN Co., Ltd.; *Int'l*, pg. 7778
KUSHIRO UBE CO., LTD.—See UBE Corporation; *Int'l*, pg. 8001
KUSHNER COMPANIES; *U.S. Private*, pg. 2358
KUSH SUPPLY CO. LLC—See Greenlane Holdings, Inc.; *U.S. Private*, pg. 965
KLISSKE FINANCIAL ASSET MANAGEMENT, INC.—See Arthur J. Gallagher & Co.; *U.S. Public*, pg. 206
KUSTANNUSOSAKEYHTIO ILTALEHTI—See Alma Media Corporation; *Int'l*, pg. 362
KUSTANNUS OY AAMULEHTI—See Alma Media Corporation; *Int'l*, pg. 362
KUSTERS ZIMA CORPORATION—See Jagenberg AG; *Int'l*, pg. 3870
THE KUSTO GROUP INC.; *Int'l*, pg. 7663
KUSTOMER, INC.—See Meta Platforms, Inc.; *U.S. Public*, pg. 1427
KUSTOM GROUP; *U.S. Private*, pg. 2358
KUSTOM SIGNALS, INC.—See Ecco Safety Group; *U.S. Private*, pg. 1326
KUSTOM US, INC.; *U.S. Private*, pg. 2358
KUSTUR KUSADASI TURIZM ENDUSTRISI A.S.; *Int'l*, pg. 4343
KUSUM SPICES PRIVATE LIMITED—See Foods & Inns Ltd.; *Int'l*, pg. 2727
KUSURINOAOKI CO., LTD.; *Int'l*, pg. 4343
KUSURI NO AOKI HOLDINGS CO., LTD.; *Int'l*, pg. 4343
KUSURINOFUKUTARO CO., LTD.—See Tsuruha Holdings Inc.; *Int'l*, pg. 7958
KUTAHYA PORSELEN SANAYI A.S.; *Int'l*, pg. 4343
KUTAK ROCK LLP; *U.S. Private*, pg. 2358
KUTAMA SINTHUMULE CORRECTIONAL CENTRE—See The GEO Group, Inc.; *U.S. Public*, pg. 2075
KUTCHINS, ROBBINS & DIAMOND, LTD.; *U.S. Private*, pg. 2358
KUTCHO COPPER CORP.; *Int'l*, pg. 4343
KUTIR, CORP.; *U.S. Private*, pg. 2358
KUTLICK REALTY, LLC—See Steve Platz Realty Inc.; *U.S. Private*, pg. 3808
KUTP-TV—See Fox Corporation; *U.S. Public*, pg. 876
KUTTLER AUTOMATION SYSTEMS (SUZHOU) CO., LTD.—See Suntech Power Holdings Co., Ltd.; *Int'l*, pg. 7325
KUTTNER PRINTS INC.—See Safer Prints Inc.; *U.S. Private*, pg. 3524
KUTV-TV—See Sinclair, Inc.; *U.S. Public*, pg. 1885
KUUHUBB INC.; *Int'l*, pg. 4343
KUULOPIIRI OY—See Demant A/S; *Int'l*, pg. 2023
KUUSIOLINNA TERVEYS OY—See Pihlajalinna Oy; *Int'l*, pg. 5865
KUVARE US HOLDINGS, INC.; *U.S. Private*, pg. 2358
KUWAIT AIRWAYS CORPORATION - CANADA OFFICE—See Kuwait Airways Corporation; *Int'l*, pg. 4344
KUWAIT AIRWAYS CORPORATION; *Int'l*, pg. 4343
KUWAIT AIRWAYS CORPORATION - US OFFICE—See Kuwait Airways Corporation; *Int'l*, pg. 4344
KUWAIT AVIATION FUELING COMPANY K.S.C.—See Kuwait Petroleum Corporation; *Int'l*, pg. 4345
KUWAIT AVIATION SERVICES CO.—See Kuwait Airways Corporation; *Int'l*, pg. 4344

KUWAIT BOXES CARTON MANUFACTURING COMPANY K.S.C.C.—See The Securities House K.S.C.C.; *Int'l*, pg. 7681
KUWAIT BUSINESS TOWN REAL ESTATE COMPANY KSCC; *Int'l*, pg. 4344
KUWAIT CABLE VISION COMPANY SAK; *Int'l*, pg. 4344
KUWAIT CEMENT COMPANY K.S.C.; *Int'l*, pg. 4344
KUWAIT CEMENT READY-MIX COMPANY—See Kuwait Cement Company K.S.C.; *Int'l*, pg. 4344
KUWAIT COMMERCIAL MARKETS COMPLEX CO. (S.A.K.); *Int'l*, pg. 4344
THE KUWAIT COMPANY FOR PROCESS PLANT CONSTRUCTION & CONTRACTING K.S.C.; *Int'l*, pg. 7663
KUWAIT CONTINENTAL HOTEL CO.—See Fouad Alghanim & Sons Group of Companies; *Int'l*, pg. 2753
KUWAIT DRILLING CO.—See Kuwait Petroleum Corporation; *Int'l*, pg. 4345
KUWAIT FINANCE HOUSE B.S.C.—See Kuwait Finance House K.S.C.; *Int'l*, pg. 4345
KUWAIT FINANCE HOUSE K.S.C.; *Int'l*, pg. 4344
KUWAIT FINANCIAL CENTRE S.A.K.—See National Industries Group Holding S.A.K.; *Int'l*, pg. 5159
KUWAIT FLOUR MILLS & BAKERIES CO. S.A.K.; *Int'l*, pg. 4345
KUWAIT FOOD COMPANY (AMERICANA) S.A.K.—See Adeptio LLC; *Int'l*, pg. 143
KUWAIT FOOD COMPANY (UAE)—See Adeptio LLC; *Int'l*, pg. 143
KUWAIT FOREIGN PETROLEUM EXPLORATION COMPANY K.S.C.—See Kuwait Petroleum Corporation; *Int'l*, pg. 4345
KUWAIT FOUNDRY CO. (S.A.K.P); *Int'l*, pg. 4345
KUWAIT & GULF LINK TRANSPORT CO. KSCC; *Int'l*, pg. 4345
KUWAIT GULF OIL COMPANY K.S.C.—See Kuwait Petroleum Corporation; *Int'l*, pg. 4345
KUWAIT GYPSUM MANUFACTURING & TRADING CO. S.A.K.C.; *Int'l*, pg. 4345
KUWAIT HOTELS COMPANY K.S.C.P.—See Kuwait Projects Company (Holding) K.S.C.P.; *Int'l*, pg. 4346
KUWAIT INDO TRADING COMPANY W.L.L.—See Mezzan Holding Co KSC; *Int'l*, pg. 4870
KUWAIT INSURANCE COMPANY S.A.K.; *Int'l*, pg. 4345
KUWAIT INTERNATIONAL BANK K.S.C.; *Int'l*, pg. 4345
KUWAIT INTERNATIONAL FAIR COMPANY K.S.C.—See Kuwait Investment Company (S.A.K.); *Int'l*, pg. 4345
KUWAIT INVEST HOLDING COMPANY K.S.C.C.; *Int'l*, pg. 4345
KUWAIT INVESTMENT AUTHORITY; *Int'l*, pg. 4345
KUWAIT INVESTMENT COMPANY (S.A.K.); *Int'l*, pg. 4345
KUWAIT & MIDDLE EAST FINANCIAL INVESTMENT COMPANY K.S.C.C.—See Kuwait Finance House K.S.C.; *Int'l*, pg. 4344
KUWAIT NATIONAL CINEMA COMPANY K.S.C.; *Int'l*, pg. 4345
KUWAIT NATIONAL PETROLEUM COMPANY—See Kuwait Petroleum Corporation; *Int'l*, pg. 4345
KUWAIT NETWORK ELECTRONIC TECHNOLOGY COMPANY W.L.L—See Fouad Alghanim & Sons Group of Companies; *Int'l*, pg. 2753
KUWAIT OIL COMPANY K.S.C.—See Kuwait Petroleum Corporation; *Int'l*, pg. 4346
KUWAIT OIL TANKER COMPANY S.A.K.—See Kuwait Petroleum Corporation; *Int'l*, pg. 4346
KUWAIT PACKING MATERIALS MANUFACTURING COMPANY K.S.C.C.; *Int'l*, pg. 4346
KUWAIT PAINT CO.—See Al-Babtain Group; *Int'l*, pg. 284
KUWAIT PEARLS CATERING CO.—See Ali Abdullah Al Tamimi Company; *Int'l*, pg. 319
KUWAIT PETROLEUM CORPORATION; *Int'l*, pg. 4345
KUWAIT PETROLEUM INTERNATIONAL—See Kuwait Petroleum Corporation; *Int'l*, pg. 4346
KUWAIT PIPE INDUSTRIES & OIL SERVICES COMPANY K.S.C.- JOHN PICKLE MIDDLE EAST—See Kuwait Pipe Industries & Oil Services Company K.S.C.; *Int'l*, pg. 4346
KUWAIT PIPE INDUSTRIES & OIL SERVICES COMPANY K.S.C.; *Int'l*, pg. 4346
KUWAIT PORTLAND CEMENT CO. K.S.C.C.; *Int'l*, pg. 4346
KUWAIT PROJECTS COMPANY (HOLDING) K.S.C.P.; *Int'l*, pg. 4346
KUWAIT QATAR INSURANCE COMPANY K.S.C.C—See Qatar Insurance Company S.A.Q.; *Int'l*, pg. 6134
KUWAIT REAL ESTATE CO. (K.S.C.); *Int'l*, pg. 4347
KUWAIT REAL ESTATE HOLDING COMPANY K.P.S.C.; *Int'l*, pg. 4347
KUWAIT REINSURANCE CO. K.S.C.C.; *Int'l*, pg. 4348
KUWAIT REMAL REAL ESTATE COMPANY K.P.S.C.; *Int'l*, pg. 4348
KUWAIT RESORTS COMPANY (K.S.C.); *Int'l*, pg. 4348
KUWAIT STOCK EXCHANGE; *Int'l*, pg. 4348
KUWAIT SWEDISH CLEANING SERVICES CO. S.A.K.; *Int'l*, pg. 4348
KUWAIT SYRIAN HOLDING CO. K.S.C.; *Int'l*, pg. 4348
KUWAIT TURKISH PARTICIPATION BANK INC.—See Kuwait Finance House K.S.C.; *Int'l*, pg. 4345

KUWAIT SYRIAN HOLDING CO. K.S.C. CORPORATE AFFILIATIONS

KUWAIT UNITED CONSTRUCTION MANAGEMENT COMPANY W.L.L.—See Kuwait Projects Company (Holding) K.S.C.P.; *Int'l*, pg. 4347
KUWAIT UNITED FACILITIES MANAGEMENT COMPANY S.A.K. (CLOSED)—See Kuwait Projects Company (Holding) K.S.C.P.; *Int'l*, pg. 4347
KUWANA SERVICE CO.,LTD—See Toyo Tire Corporation; *Int'l*, pg. 7859
KUWAYAMA CORPORATION; *Int'l*, pg. 4348
KUWAYAMA CORPORATION - TOYAMA FACTORY—See Kuwayama Corporation; *Int'l*, pg. 4348
KUWAYAMA EUROPE N.V.—See Kuwayama Corporation; *Int'l*, pg. 4348
KUWAZAWA HOLDINGS CORP.; *Int'l*, pg. 4348
KUWER INDUSTRIES LIMITED; *Int'l*, pg. 4348
KUYA SILVER CORPORATION; *Int'l*, pg. 4348
KUYAS YATIRIM A.S.; *Int'l*, pg. 4348
KUYKENDAHL MEDICAL CENTER LLC—See Adeptus Health Inc.; *U.S. Private*, pg. 78
KUYKENDALL GARDNER; *U.S. Private*, pg. 2359
KUYKENDALL & POWELL OIL CO.; *U.S. Private*, pg. 2359
KUZBASS POWER SALES COMPANY—See Mechel PAO; *Int'l*, pg. 4766
KUZCO LIGHTING, INC.; *Int'l*, pg. 4348
KUZE (CHENGDU) TRADING CO., LTD.—See Kuze Co., Ltd.; *Int'l*, pg. 4348
KUZE CO., LTD.; *Int'l*, pg. 4348
KUZEY KIBRIS SANTRAL MADENCILIK LTD.—See Parsan Makina Parcalari Sanayii AS; *Int'l*, pg. 5747
KUZNIA POLSKA S.A.—See Mangata Holding S.A.; *Int'l*, pg. 4670
KUZULUK KAPLICA INSAAT TURIZM SAGLIK VE PETROL URUNLERI TIC. A.S.—See Ihlas Holding A.S.; *Int'l*, pg. 3606
KUZUU LIMESTONE AGGREGATE CO., LTD.—See Nittetsu Mining Co., Ltd.; *Int'l*, pg. 5383
KUZZEN'S, INC.—See Lipman & Lipman, Inc.; *U.S. Private*, pg. 2465
KVAERNER CANADA LTD.—See Aker Solutions ASA; *Int'l*, pg. 263
KVAERNER LLC—See Aker Solutions ASA; *Int'l*, pg. 263
KVALITEETTEHNIKA OU—See Max Weishaupt GmbH; *Int'l*, pg. 4735
KVALITETSKONTROLL AS—See SmartCraft ASA; *Int'l*, pg. 7002
KVAL-TV—See Sinclair, Inc.; *U.S. Public*, pg. 1886
KVANTUM GROUP DD; *Int'l*, pg. 4348
KVASAC D.O.O.—See Compagnie des Levures Lesaffre SA; *Int'l*, pg. 1738
K-VA-T FOOD STORES, INC.; *U.S. Private*, pg. 2251
KVAZAR-MICRO HUNGARY KFT.; *Int'l*, pg. 4348
KVB KUNLUN NEW ZEALAND LIMITED—See CITIC Securities Co., Ltd.; *Int'l*, pg. 1622
KVB KUNLUN PTY LIMITED—See CITIC Securities Co., Ltd.; *Int'l*, pg. 1622
KVB KUNSTSTOFFVERWERTUNG BRANDENBURG GMBH—See Alba SE; *Int'l*, pg. 293
KVC CONNECTORS SDN BHD—See KVC Industrial Supplies Sdn. Bhd.; *Int'l*, pg. 4349
KVC DEVELOPMENT; *U.S. Private*, pg. 2359
KVC INDUSTRIAL SUPPLIES (JOHOR) SDN. BHD.—See KVC Industrial Supplies Sdn. Bhd.; *Int'l*, pg. 4349
KVC INDUSTRIAL SUPPLIES (KUANTAN) SDN. BHD.—See KVC Industrial Supplies Sdn. Bhd.; *Int'l*, pg. 4349
KVC INDUSTRIAL SUPPLIES (MELAKA) SDN. BHD.—See KVC Industrial Supplies Sdn. Bhd.; *Int'l*, pg. 4349
KVC INDUSTRIAL SUPPLIES (N.S.) SDN. BHD.—See KVC Industrial Supplies Sdn. Bhd.; *Int'l*, pg. 4349
KVC INDUSTRIAL SUPPLIES (PENANG) SDN. BHD.—See KVC Industrial Supplies Sdn. Bhd.; *Int'l*, pg. 4349
KVC INDUSTRIAL SUPPLIES (PERAK) SDN. BHD.—See KVC Industrial Supplies Sdn. Bhd.; *Int'l*, pg. 4349
KVC INDUSTRIAL SUPPLIES SDN. BHD.; *Int'l*, pg. 4349
KVC INDUSTRIAL SUPPLIES (THAILAND) CO. LTD.—See Sonepar S.A.; *Int'l*, pg. 7091
KVC INDUSTRIES SDN. BHD.—See KVC Industrial Supplies Sdn. Bhd.; *Int'l*, pg. 4349
KVC INSTALLATION MATERIAL STORE SDN. BHD.—See KVC Industrial Supplies Sdn. Bhd.; *Int'l*, pg. 4349
KVC (UK) LTD—See Federal International (2000) Ltd; *Int'l*, pg. 2630
KVCW, LLC—See Sinclair, Inc.; *U.S. Public*, pg. 1885
KVD KVARNDAMMEN AB—See Ratos AB; *Int'l*, pg. 6220
KV ENTERPRISES BV—See Sembcorp Industries Ltd.; *Int'l*, pg. 6703
KVERNELAND ASA—See Kubota Corporation; *Int'l*, pg. 4322
KVERNELAND GROUP DEUTSCHLAND GMBH—See Kubota Corporation; *Int'l*, pg. 4322
KVERNELAND GROUP FRANCE S.A.S.—See Kubota Corporation; *Int'l*, pg. 4322
KVERNELAND GROUP LES LANDES GENUSSON S.A.S.—See Kubota Corporation; *Int'l*, pg. 4322
KVERNELAND GROUP OPERATIONS NORWAY AS—See Kubota Corporation; *Int'l*, pg. 4322

KVERVA AS; *Int'l*, pg. 4349
KVH EUROPE A/S—See KVH Industries Inc; *U.S. Public*, pg. 1278
KVH INDUSTRIES A/S—See KVH Industries Inc; *U.S. Public*, pg. 1278
KVH INDUSTRIES INC; *U.S. Public*, pg. 1277
KVH INDUSTRIES JAPAN CO. LTD.—See KVH Industries Inc; *U.S. Public*, pg. 1278
KVH INDUSTRIES NORWAY A/S—See KVH Industries Inc; *U.S. Public*, pg. 1278
KVH MEDIA GROUP LTD.—See KVH Industries Inc; *U.S. Public*, pg. 1278
KVH MEDIA GROUP LTD.—See KVH Industries Inc; *U.S. Public*, pg. 1278
KV HOLDING CO., INC.—See Hubbell Incorporated; *U.S. Public*, pg. 1067
KVIE, INC.; *U.S. Private*, pg. 2359
KVIKA BANKI HF; *Int'l*, pg. 4349
KVIKMYNDAHOLLIN EHF.—See Heimar hf.; *Int'l*, pg. 3323
KVJ MUVEK ZRT.—See Videoton Holding Zrt.; *Int'l*, pg. 8191
KVK CORPORATION; *Int'l*, pg. 4349
KVK PARABIT, A.S.—See Sika AG; *Int'l*, pg. 6915
KVK PHILIPPINES INC.—See KVK CORPORATION; *Int'l*, pg. 4349
KVK USA INC.—See DIC Corporation; *Int'l*, pg. 2109
KVL AUDIO VISUAL SERVICES; *U.S. Private*, pg. 2359
KVLY-TV—See Gray Television, Inc.; *U.S. Public*, pg. 960
KV MART CO.; *U.S. Private*, pg. 2359
KVM-CONHEAT A/S—See NIBE Industrier AB; *Int'l*, pg. 5261
KVM-GENVEX A/S—See NIBE Industrier AB; *Int'l*, pg. 5261
KVOA COMMUNICATIONS, INC.—See Gray Television, Inc.; *U.S. Public*, pg. 961
KVOS-TV—See OTA Broadcasting, LLC; *U.S. Private*, pg. 3048
KVP PHARMA+VETERINAR PRODUKTE GMBH—See Bayer Aktiengesellschaft; *Int'l*, pg. 905
KVT-FASTENING AG—See Bossard Holding AG; *Int'l*, pg. 1117
KVT FASTENING GMBH—See Bossard Holding AG; *Int'l*, pg. 1117
KVT-FASTENING SPOL. S.R.O.—See Bossard Holding AG; *Int'l*, pg. 1117
KVT FASTENING SP Z O.O.—See Bossard Holding AG; *Int'l*, pg. 1117
KVT-FASTENING S.R.L.—See Bossard Holding AG; *Int'l*, pg. 1117
KVT-FASTENING, ZWEIGNIEDERLASSUNG DER BOSSARD AG—See Bossard Holding AG; *Int'l*, pg. 1117
KVT-TEHNIKA PRITRJEVANJA, D.O.O.—See Bossard Holding AG; *Int'l*, pg. 1117
KVUE TELEVISION, INC.—See TEGNA Inc.; *U.S. Public*, pg. 1990
KVUE-TV—See TEGNA Inc.; *U.S. Public*, pg. 1990
KVVU-TV—See Meredith Corporation; *U.S. Public*, pg. 1423
KW 1 ACQUISITION CO. LLC; *U.S. Private*, pg. 2359
K. WAH ASPHALT LIMITED—See Galaxy Entertainment Group Limited; *Int'l*, pg. 2871
K. WAH CONSTRUCTION MATERIALS LIMITED—See Galaxy Entertainment Group Limited; *Int'l*, pg. 2871
K. WAH INTERNATIONAL HOLDINGS LIMITED; *Int'l*, pg. 4043
K. WAH MANAGEMENT SERVICES LIMITED—See K. Wah International Holdings Limited; *Int'l*, pg. 4043
KWALITY CREDIT & LEASING LIMITED; *Int'l*, pg. 4349
KWALITY DAIRY PRODUCTS, FZE—See Kwality Limited; *Int'l*, pg. 4349
KWALITY LIMITED; *Int'l*, pg. 4349
KWALITY PHARMACEUTICALS LIMITED; *Int'l*, pg. 4349
KWALU—See DuraGroup LLC; *U.S. Private*, pg. 1292
KWANGDONG HEALTHBIO CO., LTD.—See Kwang Dong Pharmaceutical Co., Ltd.; *Int'l*, pg. 4350
KWANG DONG HOUSEHOLD AND HEALTHCARE INC.,—See Kwang Dong Pharmaceutical Co., Ltd.; *Int'l*, pg. 4350
KWANG DONG ORIENTAL HOSPITAL—See Kwang Dong Pharmaceutical Co., Ltd.; *Int'l*, pg. 4350
KWANG DONG PHARMACEUTICAL CO., LTD. - GMP PLANT—See Kwang Dong Pharmaceutical Co., Ltd.; *Int'l*, pg. 4350
KWANGDONG PHARMACEUTICAL CO., LTD.-SONGTAN PLANT—See Kwang Dong Pharmaceutical Co., Ltd.; *Int'l*, pg. 4350
KWANG DONG PHARMACEUTICAL CO., LTD.; *Int'l*, pg. 4350
KWANG JIN IND. CO., LTD.; *Int'l*, pg. 4350
KWANGJU BANK CO., LTD.—See JB Financial Group Inc.; *Int'l*, pg. 3917
KWANG MING SILK MILL CO., LTD.; *Int'l*, pg. 4350
KWANGMU CO., LTD.; *Int'l*, pg. 4350
KWANG MYUNG ELECTRIC CO., LTD.; *Int'l*, pg. 4350
KWANG YANG MOTOR CO., LTD.; *Int'l*, pg. 4350
KWAN HENMI ARCHITECTURE & PLANNING, INC.—See DLR Group, LLC; *U.S. Private*, pg. 1247
KWAN ON HOLDINGS LIMITED; *Int'l*, pg. 4350

KWANTAS CORPORATION BERHAD; *Int'l*, pg. 4350
KWANTAS OIL SDN BHD—See Kwantas Corporation Berhad; *Int'l*, pg. 4350
KWANTAS PLANTATIONS SDN. BHD.—See Kwantas Corporation Berhad; *Int'l*, pg. 4350
KWANTUM BELGIUM BV—See Macintosh Retail Group NV; *Int'l*, pg. 4622
KWANTUM NEDERLAND BV—See Macintosh Retail Group NV; *Int'l*, pg. 4622
KWAN YONG HOLDINGS LIMITED; *Int'l*, pg. 4350
KWA-ROR I YSTAD AB—See Instalco AB; *Int'l*, pg. 3722
KW ASSOCIATES LLC; *U.S. Private*, pg. 2359
KWATANI GLOBAL (PTY.) LTD.—See Sandvik AB; *Int'l*, pg. 6529
KWATANI (PTY.) LTD.—See Sandvik AB; *Int'l*, pg. 6529
KWB GERMANY GMBH—See Einhell Germany AG; *Int'l*, pg. 2334
KWBQ-TV—See Tamer Media, LLC; *U.S. Public*, pg. 3928
K&W CAFETERIAS INC.; *U.S. Private*, pg. 2250
KW CANTATA TRAIL, LLC—See Kennedy-Wilson Holdings, Inc.; *U.S. Public*, pg. 1223
KWC CAPITAL PARTNERS PTY. LTD.; *Int'l*, pg. 4350
KWC FUNDS PTY. LTD.—See KWC Capital Partners Pty. Ltd.; *Int'l*, pg. 4350
KWCH-TV—See Gray Television, Inc.; *U.S. Public*, pg. 960
KWC LOGISTICS CO., LTD.—See Krungdhep Sophon Public Company Limited; *Int'l*, pg. 4309
K.W.C. WAREHOUSE CO., LTD.—See Krungdhep Sophon Public Company Limited; *Int'l*, pg. 4309
KWEICHOW MOUTAI CO., LTD.; *Int'l*, pg. 4350
KWE-KINTETSU WORLD EXPRESS(S)PTE LTD.—See Kintetsu Group Holdings Co., Ltd.; *Int'l*, pg. 4183
KWENA CONCRETE PRODUCTS (PTY) LTD—See Botswana Development Corporation Limited; *Int'l*, pg. 1118
KWE PARTNERS, INC.; *U.S. Private*, pg. 2359
KWESST INC.—See KWESST Micro Systems Inc.; *Int'l*, pg. 4350
KWESST MICRO SYSTEMS INC.; *Int'l*, pg. 4350
KWESTO—See Franz Haniel & Cie. GmbH; *Int'l*, pg. 2763
KW FIRE PROTECTION LIMITED—See London Security PLC; *Int'l*, pg. 4547
KW FOUR POINTS, LLC—See Kennedy-Wilson Holdings, Inc.; *U.S. Public*, pg. 1223
KW FUELS INC.; *U.S. Private*, pg. 2359
KWGC, INC. ADVERTISING & DESIGN; *U.S. Private*, pg. 2359
KWG GROUP HOLDINGS LIMITED; *Int'l*, pg. 4350
KWG IMMOBILIEN GMBH—See Vonovia SE; *Int'l*, pg. 8305
KWG KOMMUNALE WOHNEN GMBH—See Vonovia SE; *Int'l*, pg. 8305
KWG LIVING GROUP HOLDINGS LIMITED; *Int'l*, pg. 4350
KWGN INC.—See Nexstar Media Group, Inc.; *U.S. Public*, pg. 1524
KWG RESOURCES INC.; *Int'l*, pg. 4351
KWG S.A.—See PBG S.A.; *Int'l*, pg. 5765
KWH CONSTRUCTORS, INC.—See KWH Constructors Ltd.; *Int'l*, pg. 4351
KWH CONSTRUCTORS LTD.; *Int'l*, pg. 4351
KWH GROUP LTD; *Int'l*, pg. 4351
KWI ASSET MANAGEMENT CO., LTD.—See King Wai Group (Thailand) Public Company Limited; *Int'l*, pg. 4169
KWIAT INC.; *U.S. Private*, pg. 2359
KWICKIE/FLASH FOODS, INC.—See Jones Company, Inc.; *U.S. Private*, pg. 2232
KWI INSURANCE PCL—See King Wai Group (Thailand) Public Company Limited; *Int'l*, pg. 4169
KWIK AUTO BODY SUPPLIES, INC.—See LKQ Corporation; *U.S. Public*, pg. 1334
KWIKBUILD CORPORATION—See Lonrho Limited; *Int'l*, pg. 4552
KWIKCLICK, INC.; *U.S. Public*, pg. 1278
KWIK-FIT FLEET—See ITOCHU Corporation; *Int'l*, pg. 3837
KWIK-FIT (GB) LIMITED—See ITOCHU Corporation; *Int'l*, pg. 3837
KWIK-FIT GROUP LIMITED—See ITOCHU Corporation; *Int'l*, pg. 3837
KWIK JOBS, INC.—See Labor Smart Inc.; *U.S. Public*, pg. 1285
KWIK LOK AUSTRALIA PTY LTD—See KLC Holdings, Ltd.; *U.S. Private*, pg. 2318
KWIK LOK CORP. - NEW HAVEN—See KLC Holdings, Ltd.; *U.S. Private*, pg. 2318
KWIK LOK CORPORATION—See KLC Holdings, Ltd.; *U.S. Private*, pg. 2318
KWIK LOK (IRELAND) LTD—See KLC Holdings, Ltd.; *U.S. Private*, pg. 2318
KWIK LOK JAPAN LTD.—See KLC Holdings, Ltd.; *U.S. Private*, pg. 2318
KWIK LOK LTD.—See KLC Holdings, Ltd.; *U.S. Private*, pg. 2318
KWIKOT (PTY) LTD.—See AB Electrolux; *Int'l*, pg. 41
KWIKPART SDN BHD—See Hup Soon Global Corporation Limited; *Int'l*, pg. 3538

COMPANY NAME INDEX

KWIKSET CORPORATION—See Spectrum Brands Holdings, Inc.; *U.S. Public*, pg. 1917
KWIK-SET FASTENERS, INC.; *U.S. Private*, pg. 2359
KWIK SHOP INC.—See TDR Capital LLP; *Int'l*, pg. 7494
KWIK TEK INC.—See Falconhead Capital, LLC; *U.S. Private*, pg. 1467
KWIK TRIP INC.; *U.S. Private*, pg. 2359
KWI LIFE INSURANCE PCL.—See King Wai Group (Thailand) Public Company Limited; *Int'l*, pg. 4169
KW INVESTMENT MANAGEMENT LTD.—See Kennedy-Wilson Holdings, Inc.; *U.S. Public*, pg. 1223
KWITTKEN & COMPANY LIMITED—See Stagwell, Inc.; *U.S. Public*, pg. 1927
KWITTKEN & COMPANY; *U.S. Private*, pg. 2359
KWITTKEN LP—See Stagwell, Inc.; *U.S. Public*, pg. 1927
KWIZDA AGRO GMBH—See Kwizda Holding GmbH; *Int'l*, pg. 4351
KWIZDA HOLDING GMBH; *Int'l*, pg. 4351
KWIZDA PHARMA GMBH—See Kwizda Holding GmbH; *Int'l*, pg. 4351
KWJ ENGINEERING INC.—See Interlink Electronics, Inc.; *U.S. Public*, pg. 1144
KW LEASING INC.; *U.S. Private*, pg. 2359
K W LEE CLINIC & SURGERY FOR WOMEN PTE. LTD.—See Singapore O&G Ltd.; *Int'l*, pg. 6941
KW/LF MALIBU SANDS, LLC—See Kennedy-Wilson Holdings, Inc.; *U.S. Public*, pg. 1223
KW MARINA VIEW, LLC—See Kennedy-Wilson Holdings, Inc.; *U.S. Public*, pg. 1223
KWM BEACH MANUFACTURING CO INC.; *U.S. Private*, pg. 2359
K.W. METAL WORK PCL; *Int'l*, pg. 4044
K&W MOBILE LOO SERVICES PTE LTD—See King Wan Corporation Limited; *Int'l*, pg. 4170
K W NELSON INTERIOR DESIGN AND CONTRACTING GROUP LIMITED; *Int'l*, pg. 4038
KWONG FONG INDUSTRIES CORPORATION; *Int'l*, pg. 4351
KWONG LEE SHUN TRADING CO., LTD.—See Global-Tech Advanced Innovations Inc.; *Int'l*, pg. 3003
KWONG LUEN ENGINEERING HOLDINGS LTD.; *Int'l*, pg. 4351
KWONG LUNG ENTERPRIS CO., LTD.—See Kwong Lung Enterprise Co., Ltd.; *Int'l*, pg. 4351
KWONG LUNG ENTERPRISE CO., LTD.; *Int'l*, pg. 4351
KWONG LUNG EUROPE SP. Z O.O.—See Kwong Lung Enterprise Co., Ltd.; *Int'l*, pg. 4351
KWONG LUNG JAPAN CO., LTD.—See Kwong Lung Enterprise Co., Ltd.; *Int'l*, pg. 4351
KWONG LUNG-MEKO CO., LTD.—See Kwong Lung Enterprise Co., Ltd.; *Int'l*, pg. 4351
KWONG LUNG MEKO II CO., LTD.—See Kwong Lung Enterprise Co., Ltd.; *Int'l*, pg. 4351
KWONG LUNG-O MON COMPANY LIMITED—See Kwong Lung Enterprise Co., Ltd.; *Int'l*, pg. 4351
KWONG LUNG (SUZHOU) CO.,LTD.—See Kwong Lung Enterprise Co., Ltd.; *Int'l*, pg. 4351
KWONG MAN KEE GROUP LTD.; *Int'l*, pg. 4351
KWONG WAN REALTY LIMITED—See Hysan Development Company Limited; *Int'l*, pg. 3554
KWOON CHUNG BUS HOLDINGS LIMITED; *Int'l*, pg. 4351
KWOON CHUNG MOTORS COMPANY, LIMITED—See KWOON CHUNG BUS HOLDINGS LIMITED; *Int'l*, pg. 4351
K & W OPTICAL LTD.—See EssilorLuxottica SA; *Int'l*, pg. 2515
K W PETROLEUM SERVICES LTD.; *Int'l*, pg. 4038
KW PLASTICS; *U.S. Private*, pg. 2359
K & W POPCORN INC.—See Preferred Popcorn LLC; *U.S. Private*, pg. 3248
KW PROPERTY MANAGEMENT, LLC; *U.S. Private*, pg. 2359
K.W. REESE INC.; *U.S. Private*, pg. 2252
KW SACRAMENTO, LLC—See Kennedy-Wilson Holdings, Inc.; *U.S. Public*, pg. 1223
KWS ARGENTINA S.A.—See Grupo Don Mario; *Int'l*, pg. 3126
KWS AUSTRIA SAAT GMBH—See KWS SAAT SE & Co. KGaA; *Int'l*, pg. 4352
KWS BENELUX B.V.—See KWS SAAT SE & Co. KGaA; *Int'l*, pg. 4352
KWS BENELUX B.V.—See KWS SAAT SE & Co. KGaA; *Int'l*, pg. 4352
KWS BENELUX B.V.—See KWS SAAT SE & Co. KGaA; *Int'l*, pg. 4352
KWS BENELUX B.V.—See KWS SAAT SE & Co. KGaA; *Int'l*, pg. 4352
KWS BERLIN GMBH—See KWS SAAT SE & Co. KGaA; *Int'l*, pg. 4352
KWS BULGARIA E.O.O.D.—See KWS SAAT SE & Co. KGaA; *Int'l*, pg. 4352
KWS BULGARIA EOOD.—See KWS SAAT SE & Co. KGaA; *Int'l*, pg. 4352
KWS CEREALS USA LLC—See KWS SAAT SE & Co. KGaA; *Int'l*, pg. 4352
KWS CHILE LTDA.—See KWS SAAT SE & Co. KGaA; *Int'l*, pg. 4352
KWS FRANCE S.A.R.L—See KWS SAAT SE & Co. KGaA; *Int'l*, pg. 4352
KWS GATEWAY RESEARCH CENTER LLC—See KWS SAAT SE & Co. KGaA; *Int'l*, pg. 4352
KWS INFRA BV—See Koninklijke VolkerWessels N.V.; *Int'l*, pg. 4271
KWS INTERSAAT GMBH—See KWS SAAT SE & Co. KGaA; *Int'l*, pg. 4352
KWS ITALIA S.P.A.—See KWS SAAT SE & Co. KGaA; *Int'l*, pg. 4352
KWS KLOSTERGUT WIEBRECHTSHAUSEN GMBH—See KWS SAAT SE & Co. KGaA; *Int'l*, pg. 4352
KWS KOMMUNAL-WASSERVERSORGUNG SAAR GMBH—See RWE AG; *Int'l*, pg. 6434
KWS LANDWIRTSCHAFT GMBH—See KWS SAAT SE & Co. KGaA; *Int'l*, pg. 4352
KWS LOCHOW GMBH—See KWS SAAT SE & Co. KGaA; *Int'l*, pg. 4352
KWS LOCHOW POLSKA SP. Z O.O.—See KWS SAAT SE & Co. KGaA; *Int'l*, pg. 4352
KWS MAGYARORSZAG KFT—See KWS SAAT SE & Co. KGaA; *Int'l*, pg. 4352
KWS MAIS FRANCE S.A.R.L.—See KWS SAAT SE & Co. KGaA; *Int'l*, pg. 4352
KWS MAIS GMBH—See KWS SAAT SE & Co. KGaA; *Int'l*, pg. 4352
KWS MANUFACTURING COMPANY, LTD.—See Kadant Inc.; *U.S. Public*, pg. 1212
KWS MOMONT S.A.S.—See KWS SAAT SE & Co. KGaA; *Int'l*, pg. 4352
KWS OSIVA S.R.O.—See KWS SAAT SE & Co. KGaA; *Int'l*, pg. 4352
KWS POLSKA SP. Z O.O.—See KWS SAAT SE & Co. KGaA; *Int'l*, pg. 4352
KWS POTATO B.V.—See KWS SAAT SE & Co. KGaA; *Int'l*, pg. 4352
KWS R&D CHINA LTD.—See KWS SAAT SE & Co. KGaA; *Int'l*, pg. 4352
KWS R&D RUS LLC—See KWS SAAT SE & Co. KGaA; *Int'l*, pg. 4352
KWS SAAT SE & CO. KGAA; *Int'l*, pg. 4351
KWS SCANDINAVIA A/S—See KWS SAAT SE & Co. KGaA; *Int'l*, pg. 4353
KWS SEEDS INC.—See KWS SAAT SE & Co. KGaA; *Int'l*, pg. 4353
KWS SEMENA S.R.O.—See KWS SAAT SE & Co. KGaA; *Int'l*, pg. 4352
KWS SEMENTES LTDA.—See KWS SAAT SE & Co. KGaA; *Int'l*, pg. 4353
KWS SEMILLAS CANARIAS S.L.U.—See KWS SAAT SE & Co. KGaA; *Int'l*, pg. 4353
KWS SEMILLAS IBERICA S.L.—See KWS SAAT SE & Co. KGaA; *Int'l*, pg. 4353
KWS SEMINTE S.R.L.—See KWS SAAT SE & Co. KGaA; *Int'l*, pg. 4352
KWS SERVICES DEUTSCHLAND GMBH—See KWS SAAT SE & Co. KGaA; *Int'l*, pg. 4352
KWS SERVICES EAST GMBH—See KWS SAAT SE & Co. KGaA; *Int'l*, pg. 4352
KWS SERVICES MEDITERRANEAN S.A.S.—See KWS SAAT SE & Co. KGaA; *Int'l*, pg. 4352
KWS SERVICES NORTH AMERICA LLC—See KWS SAAT SE & Co. KGaA; *Int'l*, pg. 4353
KWS SERVICES NORTH B.V.—See KWS SAAT SE & Co. KGaA; *Int'l*, pg. 4352
KWS SERVICOS E PARTICIPACOES SOUTH AMERICA LTDA.—See KWS SAAT SE & Co. KGaA; *Int'l*, pg. 4353
KWS SJEME D.O.O.—See KWS SAAT SE & Co. KGaA; *Int'l*, pg. 4352
KWS SRBIJA D.O.O.—See KWS SAAT SE & Co. KGaA; *Int'l*, pg. 4352
KWS SUISSE SA—See KWS SAAT SE & Co. KGaA; *Int'l*, pg. 4353
KWS TURK TARYM TICARET A.S.—See KWS SAAT SE & Co. KGaA; *Int'l*, pg. 4353
KWS UK LTD.—See KWS SAAT SE & Co. KGaA; *Int'l*, pg. 4353
KWS UKRAINE T.O.W.—See KWS SAAT SE & Co. KGaA; *Int'l*, pg. 4352
KWT GLOBAL, LLC—See Stagwell, Inc.; *U.S. Public*, pg. 1927
KWT GLOBAL LP—See Stagwell, Inc.; *U.S. Public*, pg. 1927
KWT GLOBAL LTD.—See Stagwell, Inc.; *U.S. Public*, pg. 1927
K&W TIRE COMPANY INC.; *U.S. Private*, pg. 2250
KWT RAILWAY, INC.—See Brookfield Infrastructure Partners L.P.; *Int'l*, pg. 1192
KWT RAILWAY, INC.—See GIC Pte. Ltd.; *Int'l*, pg. 2966
KW TRANSPORTATION SERVICES, LLC—See Kennedy-Wilson Holdings, Inc.; *U.S. Public*, pg. 1223
KW TRICENTER, LLC—See Kennedy-Wilson Holdings, Inc.; *U.S. Public*, pg. 1223
KWUNG'S HOLDINGS LIMITED; *Int'l*, pg. 4353
KWV GMBH—See L. Possehl & Co. mbH; *Int'l*, pg. 4383
KWWL-TV—See Gray Television, Inc.; *U.S. Public*, pg. 961
KWYK SAS—See Vivendi SE; *Int'l*, pg. 8271
KXAN LLC—See Nexstar Media Group, Inc.; *U.S. Public*, pg. 1523
KXAS-TV—See Comcast Corporation; *U.S. Public*, pg. 539
KX INNOVATION CO LTD; *Int'l*, pg. 4353
KXOJ INC.—See Stephens Media Group Management, LLC; *U.S. Private*, pg. 3803
KXRM-TV—See Nexstar Media Group, Inc.; *U.S. Public*, pg. 1523
KX SYSTEMS, INC.—See FD Technologies PLC; *Int'l*, pg. 2628
KXTV INC.—See TEGNA Inc.; *U.S. Public*, pg. 1990
KYAGALANYI COFFEE LIMITED—See ED&F Man Holdings Limited; *Int'l*, pg. 2303
KYALAMI & MITRAJAYA BUILDERS (PTY) LTD.—See Mitrajaya Holdings Berhad; *Int'l*, pg. 4927
KYANA PACKAGING & INDUSTRIAL SUPPLY, INC.; *U.S. Private*, pg. 2359
KYANITE MINING CORPORATION; *U.S. Private*, pg. 2360
KYB ADVANCED MANUFACTURING SPAIN, S.A.U.—See KYB Corporation; *Int'l*, pg. 4353
KYB AMERICA LLC—See KYB Corporation; *Int'l*, pg. 4353
KYB AMERICA LLC—See KYB Corporation; *Int'l*, pg. 4353
KYB ASIAN PACIFIC CORP. LTD.—See KYB Corporation; *Int'l*, pg. 4353
KYB (CHINA) INVESTMENT CO., LTD.—See KYB Corporation; *Int'l*, pg. 4353
KYB CHITA MANUFACTURING EUROPE S.R.O.—See KYB Corporation; *Int'l*, pg. 4353
KYB-CONMAT PVT. LTD.—See KYB Corporation; *Int'l*, pg. 4354
KYB CORPORATION; *Int'l*, pg. 4353
KYB ENGINEERING & SERVICE CO., LTD.—See KYB Corporation; *Int'l*, pg. 4353
KYB EUROPE GMBH—See KYB Corporation; *Int'l*, pg. 4354
KYB EUROPE GMBH—See KYB Corporation; *Int'l*, pg. 4353
KYB HYDRAULICS INDUSTRY (ZHENJIANG) LTD—See KYB Corporation; *Int'l*, pg. 4354
KYB IBERIA—See KYB Corporation; *Int'l*, pg. 4354
KYB INDUSTRIAL MACHINERY (ZHENJIANG) LTD—See KYB Corporation; *Int'l*, pg. 4354
KYB ITALY GMBH—See KYB Corporation; *Int'l*, pg. 4353
KYB KANAYAMA CO., LTD.—See KYB Corporation; *Int'l*, pg. 4353
KYB LATINOMERICA S.A DE C.V—See KYB Corporation; *Int'l*, pg. 4354
KYB LOGISTICS CO., LTD.—See KYB Corporation; *Int'l*, pg. 4353
KYB MANUFACTURING CZECH S.R.O—See KYB Corporation; *Int'l*, pg. 4354
KYB MANUFACTURING DO BRASIL FABRICANTE DE AUTOPECAS S.A.—See KYB Corporation; *Int'l*, pg. 4354
KYB MANUFACTURING NORTH AMERICA INC.—See KYB Corporation; *Int'l*, pg. 4353
KYB MANUFACTURING TAIWAN CO LTD—See KYB Corporation; *Int'l*, pg. 4354
KYB MANUFACTURING VIETNAM CO., LTD.—See KYB Corporation; *Int'l*, pg. 4354
KYB MEXICO S.A. DE C.V.—See KYB Corporation; *Int'l*, pg. 4354
KYB MIDDLE EAST FZE—See KYB Corporation; *Int'l*, pg. 4354
KYB MOTORCYCLE SUSPENSION CO., LTD.—See KYB Corporation; *Int'l*, pg. 4354
KYB MOTORCYCLE SUSPENSION INDIA PVT. LTD.—See KYB Corporation; *Int'l*, pg. 4354
KYB STAGE ENGINEERING CO., LTD.—See KYB Corporation; *Int'l*, pg. 4354
KYB STEERING (THAILAND) CO LTD—See KYB Corporation; *Int'l*, pg. 4354
KYB SUSPENSIONS EUROPE, S.A.—See KYB Corporation; *Int'l*, pg. 4354
KYB (THAILAND) CO LTD—See KYB Corporation; *Int'l*, pg. 4354
KYB TRONDULE CO., LTD.—See KYB Corporation; *Int'l*, pg. 4354
KYB TURKEY CORPORATION—See KYB Corporation; *Int'l*, pg. 4354
KYB UK LTD.—See KYB Corporation; *Int'l*, pg. 4354
KYB-UMW MALAYSIA SDN BHD—See KYB Corporation; *Int'l*, pg. 4354
KYB-UMW MALAYSIA SDN BHD—See Sime Darby Berhad; *Int'l*, pg. 6930
KYB-UMW STEERING MALAYSIA SDN BHD—See Sime Darby Berhad; *Int'l*, pg. 6930
KYBURZ-CARLSON CONSTRUCTION; *U.S. Private*, pg. 2360
KYB-YS CO., LTD.—See KYB Corporation; *Int'l*, pg. 4354
KYCKR IRELAND LIMITED—See Kyckr Limited; *Int'l*, pg. 4354
KYCKR LIMITED; *Int'l*, pg. 4354
KYC MACHINE CO., LTD.—See Fair Friend Group; *Int'l*, pg. 2604
KYC MACHINE INDUSTRY CO. LTD. - NISHIWAKI PLANT—See Fair Friend Group; *Int'l*, pg. 2604

KYC MACHINE INDUSTRY CO. LTD.—See Fair Friend Group; *Int'l*, pg. 2604
KYCOM HOLDINGS CO., LTD.; *Int'l*, pg. 4354
KYC SORIMACHI CO., LTD.—See Fair Friend Group; *Int'l*, pg. 2604
KYDEX, LLC—See Sekisui Chemical Co., Ltd.; *Int'l*, pg. 6694
KYEC JAPAN - ALDETE CORPORATION—See King Yuan Electronics Co., Ltd.; *Int'l*, pg. 4170
KYEC JAPAN K.K.—See King Yuan Electronics Co., Ltd.; *Int'l*, pg. 4170
KYEC USA INC.—See King Yuan Electronics Co., Ltd.; *Int'l*, pg. 4170
KYEONG NAM STEEL CO., LTD.; *Int'l*, pg. 4355
KYERYONG CONSTRUCTION INDUSTRIAL CO., LTD; *Int'l*, pg. 4355
KYERYONG-KHABAROVSK CO., LTD.—See Kyeryong Construction Industrial Co., Ltd; *Int'l*, pg. 4355
KYE SYSTEMS AMERICA CORPORATION—See KYE Systems Corp.; *Int'l*, pg. 4355
KYE SYSTEMS CORP.; *Int'l*, pg. 4355
KYE SYSTEMS EUROPE GMBH—See KYE Systems Corp.; *Int'l*, pg. 4355
KYE SYSTEMS H.K. CORP. LTD.—See KYE Systems Corp.; *Int'l*, pg. 4355
KYE SYSTEMS UK LTD.—See KYE Systems Corp.; *Int'l*, pg. 4355
KYGO-FM—See AUDACY, INC.; *U.S. Public*, pg. 226
KYH AB—See AcadeMedia AB; *Int'l*, pg. 77
KYIVSTAR GSM JSC—See VEON Ltd.; *Int'l*, pg. 8164
THE KYJEN COMPANY, LLC—See Prospect Hill Growth Partners, L.P.; *U.S. Private*, pg. 3288
KYK ADVERTISING MARKETING PROMOTIONS; *U.S. Private*, pg. 2360
KYLAND TECHNOLOGY CO., LTD.; *Int'l*, pg. 4355
KYLAND TECHNOLOGY EMEA GMBH—See Kyland Technology Co., Ltd.; *Int'l*, pg. 4355
KYLE CONTI CONSTRUCTION, L.L.C.; *U.S. Private*, pg. 2360
KYLE ENTERPRISES LLC; *U.S. Private*, pg. 2360
KYLE RAILROAD COMPANY—See Brookfield Infrastructure Partners L.P.; *Int'l*, pg. 1192
KYLE RAILROAD COMPANY—See GIC Pte. Ltd.; *Int'l*, pg. 2966
KYLE'S CUSTOM WOOD SHOP, INC.—See 1847 Holdings LLC; *U.S. Public*, pg. 2
KYLMA AB—See Beijer Ref AB; *Int'l*, pg. 944
KYMERA INTERNATIONAL—See Palladium Equity Partners, LLC; *U.S. Private*, pg. 3077
KYMERA THERAPEUTICS, INC.; *U.S. Public*, pg. 1278
KYMETA CORPORATION; *U.S. Private*, pg. 2360
KYM HOLDINGS BHD.; *Int'l*, pg. 4355
KYM INDUSTRIES (M) SDN. BHD. —See KYM Holdings Bhd.; *Int'l*, pg. 4355
KYMI PAPER OY—See UPM-Kymmene Corporation; *Int'l*, pg. 8090
KYN CAPITAL GROUP, INC.; *U.S. Public*, pg. 1278
KYNDALYN PARK PTY LTD—See Select Harvests Limited; *Int'l*, pg. 6699
KYNDRYL HOLDINGS INC.; *U.S. Public*, pg. 1278
KYNECTIS SA—See Atos SE; *Int'l*, pg. 692
KYNER'S AUTO SALES, INC.; *U.S. Private*, pg. 2360
KYNETIC LLC; *U.S. Private*, pg. 2360
KYNEX INC—See Genstar Capital, LLC; *U.S. Private*, pg. 1678
KYNOCH FERTILIZERS (PTY) LTD.—See Farmsecure Holdings (Pty) Ltd.; *Int'l*, pg. 2620
KYNOL EUROPA GMBH—See Gun Ei Chemical Industry Co., Ltd.; *Int'l*, pg. 3183
KYNOL EUROPA IMPORT-EXPORT GMBH—See Gun Ei Chemical Industry Co., Ltd.; *Int'l*, pg. 3183
KYOBO 5 SPECIAL PURPOSE ACQUISITION COMPANY; *Int'l*, pg. 4355
KYOBO AXA GENERAL INSURANCE CO. LTD.—See AXA S.A.; *Int'l*, pg. 759
KYOBO INFORMATION & COMMUNICATION CO., LTD.—See Kyobo Life Insurance Co., Ltd.; *Int'l*, pg. 4355
KYOBO LIFE INSURANCE CO., LTD.; *Int'l*, pg. 4355
KYOBO SECURITIES CO., LTD.; *Int'l*, pg. 4355
KYOBUNDO CO., LTD.—See KYORIN Holdings, Inc.; *Int'l*, pg. 4364
KYOCERA AMERICA, INC.—See KYOCERA Corporation; *Int'l*, pg. 4359
KYOCERA AMOEBA MANAGEMENT CONSULTING (SHANGHAI) CO. LTD.—See KYOCERA Corporation; *Int'l*, pg. 4356
KYOCERA ASIA PACIFIC (INDIA) PVT. LTD.—See KYOCERA Corporation; *Int'l*, pg. 4356
KYOCERA ASIA PACIFIC PTE. LTD.—See KYOCERA Corporation; *Int'l*, pg. 4356
KYOCERA ASIA PACIFIC (THAILAND) CO., LTD.—See KYOCERA Corporation; *Int'l*, pg. 4356
KYOCERA AUTOMOTIVE & INDUSTRIAL SOLUTIONS GMBH—See KYOCERA Corporation; *Int'l*, pg. 4356
KYOCERA AVX COMPONENTS CORPORATION—See KYOCERA Corporation; *Int'l*, pg. 4356
KYOCERA BILGITAS DOCUMENT SOLUTIONS TURKEY A.S.—See KYOCERA Corporation; *Int'l*, pg. 4356
KYOCERA CHEMICAL CORP. - KAWAGUCHI WORKS—See KYOCERA Corporation; *Int'l*, pg. 4356
KYOCERA CHEMICAL CORP. - KAWASAKI WORKS—See KYOCERA Corporation; *Int'l*, pg. 4356
KYOCERA CHEMICAL CORP. - KORIYAMA WORKS—See KYOCERA Corporation; *Int'l*, pg. 4356
KYOCERA CHEMICAL CORP. - MOKA WORKS—See KYOCERA Corporation; *Int'l*, pg. 4356
KYOCERA CHEMICAL CORPORATION—See KYOCERA Corporation; *Int'l*, pg. 4356
KYOCERA CHEMICAL (HONG KONG) LTD.—See KYOCERA Corporation; *Int'l*, pg. 4356
KYOCERA CHEMICAL SINGAPORE PTE. LTD.—See KYOCERA Corporation; *Int'l*, pg. 4356
KYOCERA CHEMICAL (WUXI) CO., LTD.—See KYOCERA Corporation; *Int'l*, pg. 4356
KYOCERA (CHINA) SALES & TRADING CORPORATION—See KYOCERA Corporation; *Int'l*, pg. 4356
KYOCERA CIRCUIT DESIGN PHILIPPINES, INC.—See KYOCERA Corporation; *Int'l*, pg. 4356
KYOCERA CIRCUIT SOLUTIONS INC.—See KYOCERA Corporation; *Int'l*, pg. 4356
KYOCERA COMMUNICATIONS, INC.—See KYOCERA Corporation; *Int'l*, pg. 4359
KYOCERA COMMUNICATION SYSTEMS CO., LTD.—See KYOCERA Corporation; *Int'l*, pg. 4356
KYOCERA COMMUNICATION SYSTEMS (SHANGHAI) CO., LTD.—See KYOCERA Corporation; *Int'l*, pg. 4356
KYOCERA COMMUNICATION SYSTEMS SINGAPORE PTE. LTD.—See KYOCERA Corporation; *Int'l*, pg. 4356
KYOCERA COMMUNICATION SYSTEMS VIETNAM CO. LTD.—See KYOCERA Corporation; *Int'l*, pg. 4356
KYOCERA CONNECTOR PRODUCTS CORPORATION—See KYOCERA Corporation; *Int'l*, pg. 4357
KYOCERA CONNECTOR PRODUCTS (DONGGUAN) CO. LTD.—See KYOCERA Corporation; *Int'l*, pg. 4357
KYOCERA CONNECTOR PRODUCTS HONG KONG LTD.—See KYOCERA Corporation; *Int'l*, pg. 4357
KYOCERA CONNECTOR PRODUCTS KOREA CO., LTD.—See KYOCERA Corporation; *Int'l*, pg. 4357
KYOCERA CORP. - FINE CERAMICS GROUP—See KYOCERA Corporation; *Int'l*, pg. 4357
KYOCERA CORPORATION - FUKUSHIMA TANAGURA PLANT—See KYOCERA Corporation; *Int'l*, pg. 4360
KYOCERA CORPORATION - HOKKAIDO KITAMI PLANT—See KYOCERA Corporation; *Int'l*, pg. 4360
KYOCERA CORPORATION - KAGOSHIMA HAYATO PLANT—See KYOCERA Corporation; *Int'l*, pg. 4360
KYOCERA CORPORATION - KAGOSHIMA KOKUBU PLANT—See KYOCERA Corporation; *Int'l*, pg. 4360
KYOCERA CORPORATION - KAGOSHIMA SENDAI PLANT—See KYOCERA Corporation; *Int'l*, pg. 4360
KYOCERA CORPORATION - MIE ISE PLANT—See KYOCERA Corporation; *Int'l*, pg. 4360
KYOCERA CORPORATION - NAGANO OKAYA PLANT—See KYOCERA Corporation; *Int'l*, pg. 4360
KYOCERA CORPORATION - SHIGA GAMO PLANT—See KYOCERA Corporation; *Int'l*, pg. 4360
KYOCERA CORPORATION - SHIGA YASU PLANT—See KYOCERA Corporation; *Int'l*, pg. 4360
KYOCERA CORPORATION - SHIGA YOHKAICHI PLANT—See KYOCERA Corporation; *Int'l*, pg. 4360
KYOCERA CORPORATION; *Int'l*, pg. 4355
KYOCERA CRYSTAL DEVICE PHILIPPINES, INC.—See KYOCERA Corporation; *Int'l*, pg. 4356
KYOCERA CTC PRECISION TOOLS PRIVATE LIMITED—See KYOCERA Corporation; *Int'l*, pg. 4356
KYOCERA DISPLAY CORPORATION—See KYOCERA Corporation; *Int'l*, pg. 4357
KYOCERA DISPLAY EUROPE GMBH—See KYOCERA Corporation; *Int'l*, pg. 4357
KYOCERA DISPLAY (ZHANGJIAGANG) CO. LTD.—See KYOCERA Corporation; *Int'l*, pg. 4357
KYOCERA DO BRASIL COMPONENTES INDUSTRIAIS LTDA.—See KYOCERA Corporation; *Int'l*, pg. 4360
KYOCERA DOCUMENT SOLUTIONS AMERICA, INC.—See KYOCERA Corporation; *Int'l*, pg. 4357
KYOCERA DOCUMENT SOLUTIONS ASIA LIMITED—See KYOCERA Corporation; *Int'l*, pg. 4357
KYOCERA DOCUMENT SOLUTIONS AUSTRALIA PTY. LTD.—See KYOCERA Corporation; *Int'l*, pg. 4357
KYOCERA DOCUMENT SOLUTIONS AUSTRIA GMBH—See KYOCERA Corporation; *Int'l*, pg. 4357
KYOCERA DOCUMENT SOLUTIONS BELGIUM N.V./S.A.—See KYOCERA Corporation; *Int'l*, pg. 4358
KYOCERA DOCUMENT SOLUTIONS BRAZIL LTDA.—See KYOCERA Corporation; *Int'l*, pg. 4357
KYOCERA DOCUMENT SOLUTIONS CANADA, LTD.—See KYOCERA Corporation; *Int'l*, pg. 4357
KYOCERA DOCUMENT SOLUTIONS CHILE SPA—See KYOCERA Corporation; *Int'l*, pg. 4357
KYOCERA DOCUMENT SOLUTIONS (CHINA) CORPORATION—See KYOCERA Corporation; *Int'l*, pg. 4357
KYOCERA DOCUMENT SOLUTIONS CZECH, S.R.O.—See KYOCERA Corporation; *Int'l*, pg. 4357
KYOCERA DOCUMENT SOLUTIONS DANMARK A/S—See KYOCERA Corporation; *Int'l*, pg. 4358
KYOCERA DOCUMENT SOLUTIONS DEUTSCHLAND GMBH—See KYOCERA Corporation; *Int'l*, pg. 4358
KYOCERA DOCUMENT SOLUTIONS ESPANA, S.A.—See KYOCERA Corporation; *Int'l*, pg. 4358
KYOCERA DOCUMENT SOLUTIONS EUROPE B.V.—See KYOCERA Corporation; *Int'l*, pg. 4357
KYOCERA DOCUMENT SOLUTIONS FINLAND OY—See KYOCERA Corporation; *Int'l*, pg. 4358
KYOCERA DOCUMENT SOLUTIONS FRANCE S.A.S.—See KYOCERA Corporation; *Int'l*, pg. 4358
KYOCERA DOCUMENT SOLUTIONS HONG KONG LIMITED—See KYOCERA Corporation; *Int'l*, pg. 4357
KYOCERA DOCUMENT SOLUTIONS INC.—See KYOCERA Corporation; *Int'l*, pg. 4357
KYOCERA DOCUMENT SOLUTIONS INDIA PRIVATE LIMITED—See KYOCERA Corporation; *Int'l*, pg. 4357
KYOCERA DOCUMENT SOLUTIONS ITALIA S.P.A.—See KYOCERA Corporation; *Int'l*, pg. 4358
KYOCERA DOCUMENT SOLUTIONS JAPAN INC.—See KYOCERA Corporation; *Int'l*, pg. 4358
KYOCERA DOCUMENT SOLUTIONS MEXICO, S.A. DE C.V.—See KYOCERA Corporation; *Int'l*, pg. 4358
KYOCERA DOCUMENT SOLUTIONS NEDERLAND B.V.—See KYOCERA Corporation; *Int'l*, pg. 4358
KYOCERA DOCUMENT SOLUTIONS NEW ZEALAND LTD.—See KYOCERA Corporation; *Int'l*, pg. 4358
KYOCERA DOCUMENT SOLUTIONS NORDIC AB—See KYOCERA Corporation; *Int'l*, pg. 4358
KYOCERA DOCUMENT SOLUTIONS PORTUGAL LDA.—See KYOCERA Corporation; *Int'l*, pg. 4358
KYOCERA DOCUMENT SOLUTIONS RUSSIA LLC—See KYOCERA Corporation; *Int'l*, pg. 4358
KYOCERA DOCUMENT SOLUTIONS SINGAPORE PTE. LTD.—See KYOCERA Corporation; *Int'l*, pg. 4357
KYOCERA DOCUMENT SOLUTIONS SOUTH AFRICA (PTY) LTD.—See KYOCERA Corporation; *Int'l*, pg. 4358
KYOCERA DOCUMENT SOLUTIONS TAIWAN CORPORATION—See KYOCERA Corporation; *Int'l*, pg. 4357
KYOCERA DOCUMENT SOLUTIONS (THAILAND) CORP., LTD.—See KYOCERA Corporation; *Int'l*, pg. 4357
KYOCERA DOCUMENT SOLUTIONS (U.K.) LTD.—See KYOCERA Corporation; *Int'l*, pg. 4357
KYOCERA DOCUMENT TECHNOLOGY (DONGGUAN) CO., LTD.—See KYOCERA Corporation; *Int'l*, pg. 4357
KYOCERA ELECTRONIC DEVICES, LLC—See KYOCERA Corporation; *Int'l*, pg. 4359
KYOCERA EUROPE GMBH—See KYOCERA Corporation; *Int'l*, pg. 4358
KYOCERA FINECERAMICS GMBH—See KYOCERA Corporation; *Int'l*, pg. 4357
KYOCERA FINECERAMICS ITALY S.R.L.—See KYOCERA Corporation; *Int'l*, pg. 4358
KYOCERA FINECERAMICS LIMITED—See KYOCERA Corporation; *Int'l*, pg. 4357
KYOCERA FINECERAMICS PRECISION GMBH—See KYOCERA Corporation; *Int'l*, pg. 4358
KYOCERA FINECERAMICS S.A.S.—See KYOCERA Corporation; *Int'l*, pg. 4357
KYOCERA FINECERAMICS SOLUTIONS GMBH—See KYOCERA Corporation; *Int'l*, pg. 4358
KYOCERA HONG KONG LOGISTICS CO., LTD.—See KYOCERA Corporation; *Int'l*, pg. 4356
KYOCERA (HONG KONG) SALES & TRADING LIMITED—See KYOCERA Corporation; *Int'l*, pg. 4356
KYOCERA INDUSTRIAL TOOLS CORPORATION—See KYOCERA Corporation; *Int'l*, pg. 4358
KYOCERA INDUSTRIAL TOOLS SALES CORPORATION—See KYOCERA Corporation; *Int'l*, pg. 4358
KYOCERA INTERNATIONAL ELECTRONICS CO., LTD.—See KYOCERA Corporation; *Int'l*, pg. 4358
KYOCERA INTERNATIONAL, INC.—See KYOCERA Corporation; *Int'l*, pg. 4358
KYOCERA KINSEKI CORPORATION—See KYOCERA Corporation; *Int'l*, pg. 4359
KYOCERA KINSEKI HERTZ CORPORATION—See KYOCERA Corporation; *Int'l*, pg. 4359
KYOCERA KINSEKI HOKKAIDO CORP. - MIKASA PLANT—See KYOCERA Corporation; *Int'l*, pg. 4359
KYOCERA KINSEKI HOKKAIDO CORP.—See KYOCERA Corporation; *Int'l*, pg. 4359
KYOCERA KINSEKI YAMAGATA CORP.—See KYOCERA Corporation; *Int'l*, pg. 4359
KYOCERA KOREA CO., LTD.—See KYOCERA Corporation; *Int'l*, pg. 4359
KYOCERA (MALAYSIA) SDN. BHD.—See KYOCERA Corporation; *Int'l*, pg. 4356
KYOCERA MEXICANA, S.A. DE C.V.—See KYOCERA Corporation; *Int'l*, pg. 4359
KYOCERA MEXICO SERVICES, S.A. DE C.V.—See KYOCERA Corporation; *Int'l*, pg. 4359
KYOCERA OPTEC CO., LTD.—See KYOCERA Corporation; *Int'l*, pg. 4359
KYOCERA OPTEC (DONGGUAN) CO., LTD.—See KYOCERA Corporation; *Int'l*, pg. 4359

KYOCERA PRECISION TOOLS (GANZHOU) CO., LTD.—See KYOCERA Corporation; *Int'l*, pg. 4359
KYOCERA PRECISION TOOLS KOREA CO., LTD.—See KYOCERA Corporation; *Int'l*, pg. 4359
KYOCERA PRECISION TOOLS (ZHUHAI) CO., LTD.—See KYOCERA Corporation; *Int'l*, pg. 4359
KYOCERA REALTY DEVELOPMENT CO., LTD.—See KYOCERA Corporation; *Int'l*, pg. 4359
KYOCERA RYOBI (DALIAN) MACHINERY CO., LTD.—See KYOCERA Corporation; *Int'l*, pg. 4358
KYOCERA SENCO EMEA B.V.—See KYOCERA Corporation; *Int'l*, pg. 4360
KYOCERA SENCO INDUSTRIAL TOOLS, INC.—See KYOCERA Corporation; *Int'l*, pg. 4360
KYOCERA SENCO JAPAN CORPORATION—See KYOCERA Corporation; *Int'l*, pg. 4360
KYOCERA SENCO (NZ) LTD.—See KYOCERA Corporation; *Int'l*, pg. 4359
KYOCERA SGS PRECISION TOOLS EUROPE LTD.—See KYOCERA Corporation; *Int'l*, pg. 4359
KYOCERA SGS PRECISION TOOLS, INC.—See KYOCERA Corporation; *Int'l*, pg. 4359
KYOCERA SOC CORPORATION—See KYOCERA Corporation; *Int'l*, pg. 4360
KYOCERA SOLAR CORPORATION—See KYOCERA Corporation; *Int'l*, pg. 4360
KYOCERA SOLAR DO BRASIL LTDA.—See KYOCERA Corporation; *Int'l*, pg. 4360
KYOCERA SOLAR EUROPE S.R.O.—See KYOCERA Corporation; *Int'l*, pg. 4360
KYOCERA SOLAR INC.—See KYOCERA Corporation; *Int'l*, pg. 4360
KYOCERA TELECOM EQUIPMENT (MALAYSIA) SDN. BHD—See KYOCERA Corporation; *Int'l*, pg. 4360
KYOCERA (THAILAND) CO., LTD.—See KYOCERA Corporation; *Int'l*, pg. 4356
KYOCERA (TIANJIN) SALES & TRADING CORPORATION—See KYOCERA Corporation; *Int'l*, pg. 4356
KYOCERA (TIANJIN) SOLAR ENERGY CO., LTD.—See KYOCERA Corporation; *Int'l*, pg. 4356
KYOCERA TIKITIN LTD.—See KYOCERA Corporation; *Int'l*, pg. 4360
KYOCERA TYCOM CANADA, LTD.—See KYOCERA Corporation; *Int'l*, pg. 4359
KYOCERA TYCOM CORPORATION—See KYOCERA Corporation; *Int'l*, pg. 4359
KYOCERA-UBE RF TEC CORPORATION—See KYOCERA Corporation; *Int'l*, pg. 4360
KYOCERA UNIMERCO TOOLING A/S—See KYOCERA Corporation; *Int'l*, pg. 4360
KYOCERA UNIMERCO TOOLING INC.—See KYOCERA Corporation; *Int'l*, pg. 4360
KYOCERA VIETNAM COMPANY LIMITED—See KYOCERA Corporation; *Int'l*, pg. 4360
KYOCERA (WUXI) ELECTRONIC MATERIALS CO., LTD.—See KYOCERA Corporation; *Int'l*, pg. 4356
KYOCHON F&B CO., LTD.; *Int'l*, pg. 4360
KYODEN CO., LTD.—See The Carlyle Group Inc.; *U.S. Public*, pg. 2048
KYODO ADVERTISING CO., LTD.; *Int'l*, pg. 4360
KYODO ADVERTISING CO., LTD.—See Kyodo Advertising Co., Ltd.; *Int'l*, pg. 4360
KYODO ADVERTISING CO., LTD.—See Kyodo Advertising Co., Ltd.; *Int'l*, pg. 4360
KYODO ADVERTISING CO., LTD.—See Kyodo Advertising Co., Ltd.; *Int'l*, pg. 4360
KYODO ADVERTISING CO., LTD.—See Kyodo Advertising Co., Ltd.; *Int'l*, pg. 4360
KYODO ADVERTISING CO., LTD.—See Kyodo Advertising Co., Ltd.; *Int'l*, pg. 4360
KYODO ADVERTISING CO., LTD.—See Kyodo Advertising Co., Ltd.; *Int'l*, pg. 4360
KYODO ADVERTISING CO., LTD.—See Kyodo Advertising Co., Ltd.; *Int'l*, pg. 4360
KYODO-ALLIED INDUSTRIES LTD.; *Int'l*, pg. 4361
KYODO-ALLIED TECHNOLOGY PTE LTD—See Kyodo-Allied Industries Ltd.; *Int'l*, pg. 4361
KYODO-ALLIED TRADING (SHANGHAI) CO., LTD.—See Kyodo-Allied Industries Ltd.; *Int'l*, pg. 4361
KYODO CARBON CO., LTD.—See Mitsui Chemicals, Inc.; *Int'l*, pg. 4981
KYODO CHEMICAL CO., LTD.—See Sakai Chemical Industry Co., Ltd.; *Int'l*, pg. 6486
KYODO COMPUTER CO., LTD.—See KYCOM Holdings Co., Ltd.; *Int'l*, pg. 4355
KYODO DIE-WORKS (THAILAND) CO., LTD.—See Hoden Seimitsu Kako Kenkyusho Co., Ltd.; *Int'l*, pg. 3438
KYODO DIE-WORKS (THAILAND) CO., LTD.—See LIXIL Group Corporation; *Int'l*, pg. 4534
KYODO EDIT, INC.—See Fuji Media Holdings, Inc.; *Int'l*, pg. 2814
KYODO ENGINEERING CORPORATION—See Bain Capital, LP; *U.S. Private*, pg. 434
KYODO FOOD PRODUCTS CO., LTD.—See NH Foods Ltd.; *Int'l*, pg. 5256
KYODOH DOBOKU CO., LTD.—See Daiei Kankyo Co., Ltd.; *Int'l*, pg. 1924
KYODO HOUSING LOAN CO., LTD.—See The Norinchukin Bank; *Int'l*, pg. 7671
KYODO IGAKU LABORATORIES, INC.—See BML, Inc.; *Int'l*, pg. 1076
KYODO KAIUN CO., LTD.—See Toyo Seikan Group Holdings, Ltd.; *Int'l*, pg. 7856
KYODO LOGISTICS CO., LTD—See Kyodo Printing Co. Ltd.; *Int'l*, pg. 4361
KYODO NEWS PR WIRE—See Dentsu Group Inc.; *Int'l*, pg. 2039
KYODO PAPER HOLDINGS; *Int'l*, pg. 4360
KYODO PRINTING CO., LTD - COMMERCIAL PRINTING DIVISION—See Kyodo Printing Co. Ltd.; *Int'l*, pg. 4361
KYODO PRINTING CO., LTD - FINE ART REPRODUCTIONS DIVISION—See Kyodo Printing Co. Ltd.; *Int'l*, pg. 4361
KYODO PRINTING CO., LTD - GOKA PLANT—See Kyodo Printing Co. Ltd.; *Int'l*, pg. 4361
KYODO PRINTING CO., LTD - KAWAJIMA PLANT—See Kyodo Printing Co. Ltd.; *Int'l*, pg. 4361
KYODO PRINTING CO., LTD - KOISHIKAWA PLANT—See Kyodo Printing Co. Ltd.; *Int'l*, pg. 4361
KYODO PRINTING CO., LTD - MORIYA PLANT—See Kyodo Printing Co. Ltd.; *Int'l*, pg. 4361
KYODO PRINTING CO., LTD - PACKAGING PRINTING DIVISION—See Kyodo Printing Co. Ltd.; *Int'l*, pg. 4361
KYODO PRINTING CO., LTD - SALES PROMOTION CENTER—See Kyodo Printing Co. Ltd.; *Int'l*, pg. 4361
KYODO PRINTING CO., LTD - SMART CARD DIVISION—See Kyodo Printing Co. Ltd.; *Int'l*, pg. 4361
KYODO PRINTING CO. LTD.; *Int'l*, pg. 4361
KYODO PRINTING CO., LTD - TECHNICAL SUPERVISORY DIVISION—See Kyodo Printing Co. Ltd.; *Int'l*, pg. 4361
KYODO PRINTING CO., LTD - TSURUGASHIMA PLANT—See Kyodo Printing Co. Ltd.; *Int'l*, pg. 4361
KYODO PRINTING CO., LTD - WAKAYAMA PLANT—See Kyodo Printing Co. Ltd.; *Int'l*, pg. 4361
KYODO PRINTING MARKETING SOLUTIONS CO., LTD.—See Kyodo Printing Co. Ltd.; *Int'l*, pg. 4361
KYODO PRINTING MEDIA PRODUCT CO., LTD.—See Kyodo Printing Co. Ltd.; *Int'l*, pg. 4361
KYODO PRINTING NISHINIHON CO., LTD.—See Kyodo Printing Co. Ltd.; *Int'l*, pg. 4361
KYODO PRINTING (VIETNAM) CO. LTD.—See Kyodo Printing Co. Ltd.; *Int'l*, pg. 4361
KYODO PUBLIC RELATIONS CO., LTD.; *Int'l*, pg. 4361
KYODO SAKUSAN CO. LTD.—See Daicel Corporation; *Int'l*, pg. 1919
KYODO SEMINAR CO., LTD.—See The Norinchukin Bank; *Int'l*, pg. 7671
KYODO SOJITZ FEED COMPANY LIMITED—See Sojitz Corporation; *Int'l*, pg. 7062
KYODOSUISAN CO., LTD.—See Tsukiji Uoichiba Co., Ltd.; *Int'l*, pg. 7956
KYODO TELEVISION,LTD.—See Fuji Media Holdings, Inc.; *Int'l*, pg. 2814
KYOE DAIICHI TRAFFIC INDUSTRIAL LTD—See Daiichi Koutsu Sangyo Co., Ltd.; *Int'l*, pg. 1928
THE KYOEI ANNUITY HOME CO., LTD.—See Prudential Financial, Inc.; *U.S. Public*, pg. 1733
THE KYOEI BUILDING MANAGEMENT CO., LTD.—See Prudential Financial, Inc.; *U.S. Public*, pg. 1733
KYOEI COMMUNICATION INDUSTRY CO., LTD.—See NANYO Corporation; *Int'l*, pg. 5146
KYOEI CORPORATION—See Key Coffee Inc.; *Int'l*, pg. 4145
KYOEI DANBORU CO., LTD.—See Rengo Co., Ltd.; *Int'l*, pg. 6280
KYOEI DATA CENTER CO., LTD.—See KYCOM Holdings Co., Ltd.; *Int'l*, pg. 4355
KYOEI DO BRASIL COMPANHIA DE SEGUROS—See Prudential Financial, Inc.; *U.S. Public*, pg. 1733
KYOEI ELECTRONICS HONG KONG LIMITED—See Kyoei Sangyo Co., Ltd.; *Int'l*, pg. 4361
KYOEI ELECTRONICS SHANGHAI CO., LTD.—See Kyoei Sangyo Co., Ltd.; *Int'l*, pg. 4361
KYOEI ELECTRONICS SINGAPORE PTE LTD.—See Kyoei Sangyo Co., Ltd.; *Int'l*, pg. 4361
KYOEI ELECTRONICS (THAILAND) CO., LTD.—See Kyoei Sangyo Co., Ltd.; *Int'l*, pg. 4361
KYOEI ENGINEERING CO., LTD.—See Nippon Seiki Co., Ltd.; *Int'l*, pg. 5329
THE KYOEI FIRE & MARINE INSURANCE CO., LTD.; *Int'l*, pg. 7663
KYOEI FIRE & MARINE INSURANCE CO., (U.K.) LTD.—See The Kyoei Fire & Marine Insurance Co., Ltd.; *Int'l*, pg. 7663
KYOEI FUTABA ENGINEERING CO., LTD.—See Cosmos Machinery Enterprises Limited; *Int'l*, pg. 1813
KYOEI INDUSTRIAL CO., LTD.—See Kyoei Steel Ltd.; *Int'l*, pg. 4362
KYOEI KASAI BUSINESS SERVICE CO., LTD.—See The Kyoei Fire & Marine Insurance Co., Ltd.; *Int'l*, pg. 7663
KYOEI KASAI CLAIMS RESEARCH CO., LTD.—See The Kyoei Fire & Marine Insurance Co., Ltd.; *Int'l*, pg. 7663
KYOEI KASAI FINANCE CO., LTD.—See The Kyoei Fire & Marine Insurance Co., Ltd.; *Int'l*, pg. 7663
KYOEI KASAI MARINE SERVICE CO., LTD.—See The Kyoei Fire & Marine Insurance Co., Ltd.; *Int'l*, pg. 7663
KYOEI KASAI SHINRAI LIFE INSURANCE CO. LTD—See Fukoku Mutual Life Insurance Company; *Int'l*, pg. 2839
KYOEI KASAI TRAINING SERVICE CO., LTD.—See The Kyoei Fire & Marine Insurance Co., Ltd.; *Int'l*, pg. 7663
KYOEI LOAN MANAGEMENT SERVICE CO., LTD.—See The Kyoei Fire & Marine Insurance Co., Ltd.; *Int'l*, pg. 7663
KYOEI MARINE TECHNOLOGY CO., LTD.—See Kyoei Sangyo Co., Ltd.; *Int'l*, pg. 4361
KYOEI MESONA INC.—See Kyoei Steel Ltd.; *Int'l*, pg. 4362
KYOEI PLASTIC MFG. CO., LTD.—See Riken Technos Corporation; *Int'l*, pg. 6341
KYOEI RECYCLING CO., LTD.—See Kyoei Steel Ltd.; *Int'l*, pg. 4362
KYOEI SANGYO CO., LTD.; *Int'l*, pg. 4361
KYOEI SECURITY SERVICE CO., LTD.; *Int'l*, pg. 4361
KYOEI SHOJI CO., LTD.—See AGC Inc.; *Int'l*, pg. 204
KYOEI SHOKUSAN CO. LTD.—See Daicel Corporation; *Int'l*, pg. 1919
KYOEI STEEL LTD - HIRAKATA DIVISION—See Kyoei Steel Ltd.; *Int'l*, pg. 4362
KYOEI STEEL LTD - NAGOYA DIVISION—See Kyoei Steel Ltd.; *Int'l*, pg. 4362
KYOEI STEEL LTD.; *Int'l*, pg. 4362
KYOEI STEEL LTD YAMAGUCHI DIVISION—See Kyoei Steel Ltd.; *Int'l*, pg. 4362
KYOEI STEEL VIETNAM COMPANY LIMITED—See Kyoei Steel Ltd.; *Int'l*, pg. 4362
KYOEI SYSTEM CO., LTD.—See Kyoei Sangyo Co., Ltd.; *Int'l*, pg. 4361
KYOEI TANKER CO., LTD.; *Int'l*, pg. 4362
KYOE MARUZEN (THAILAND) CO., LTD.—See Maruzen Showa Unyu Co., Ltd.; *Int'l*, pg. 4716
KYOGIN BUSINESS SERVICE CO., LTD.—See The Bank of Kyoto, Ltd.; *Int'l*, pg. 7615
KYOGIN CARD SERVICE CO., LTD.—See The Bank of Kyoto, Ltd.; *Int'l*, pg. 7615
KYOGIN LEASE & CAPITAL CO., LTD.—See The Bank of Kyoto, Ltd.; *Int'l*, pg. 7615
KYOGOKU UNYU SHOJI CO., LTD.; *Int'l*, pg. 4362
KYOKUREI INC.—See Nichirei Corporation; *Int'l*, pg. 5270
KYOKUREI OPERATION INC.—See Nichirei Corporation; *Int'l*, pg. 5269
KYOKURYO WAREHOUSE CO.,LTD.—See Mitsubishi Logistics Corporation; *Int'l*, pg. 4962
KYOKUSHIN TRANSPORT CO., LTD.—See Nippon Paper Industries Co., Ltd.; *Int'l*, pg. 5327
KYOKUTO BOEKI KAISHA, LTD.; *Int'l*, pg. 4362
KYOKUTO CO., LTD.; *Int'l*, pg. 4362
KYOKUTO KAIHATSU KOGYO CO. LTD. - FUKUOKA PLANT—See Kyokuto Kaihatsu Kogyo Co. Ltd.; *Int'l*, pg. 4363
KYOKUTO KAIHATSU KOGYO CO. LTD. - MIKI PLANT—See Kyokuto Kaihatsu Kogyo Co. Ltd.; *Int'l*, pg. 4363
KYOKUTO KAIHATSU KOGYO CO. LTD. - NAGOYA PLANT—See Kyokuto Kaihatsu Kogyo Co. Ltd.; *Int'l*, pg. 4363
KYOKUTO KAIHATSU KOGYO CO. LTD.; *Int'l*, pg. 4362
KYOKUTO KAIHATSU KOGYO CO. LTD. - YOKOHAMA PLANT—See Kyokuto Kaihatsu Kogyo Co. Ltd.; *Int'l*, pg. 4363
KYOKUTO KAIHATSU (KUNSHAN) MACHINERY CO., LTD.—See Kyokuto Kaihatsu Kogyo Co. Ltd.; *Int'l*, pg. 4363
KYOKUTO KAIHATSU PARKING CO., LTD.—See Kyokuto Kaihatsu Kogyo Co. Ltd.; *Int'l*, pg. 4363
KYOKUTO PROPERTY CO., LTD.—See Kyokuto Securities Co., Ltd.; *Int'l*, pg. 4363
KYOKUTO SANKI CO., LTD.; *Int'l*, pg. 4363
KYOKUTO SECURITIES CO., LTD.; *Int'l*, pg. 4363
KYOKUTO SERVICE ENGINEERING CO., LTD.—See Kyokuto Kaihatsu Kogyo Co. Ltd.; *Int'l*, pg. 4363
KYOKUTO SERVICE ENGINEERING HOKKAIDO CO., LTD.—See Kyokuto Kaihatsu Kogyo Co. Ltd.; *Int'l*, pg. 4363
KYOKUTO SPECIAL AUTOMOBILE TRADING (SHANGHAI) CO., LTD.—See Kyokuto Kaihatsu Kogyo Co. Ltd.; *Int'l*, pg. 4363
KYOKUTO TRADING (INDIA) PRIVATE LIMITED—See Kyokuto Boeki Kaisha, Ltd.; *Int'l*, pg. 4362
KYOKUTO TRADING (SHANGHAI) CO., LTD.—See Kyokuto Boeki Kaisha, Ltd.; *Int'l*, pg. 4362
KYOKUYO AKITSU REIZO CO., LTD.—See Kyokuyo Co. Ltd.; *Int'l*, pg. 4363
KYOKUYO AMERICA CORP.—See Kyokuyo Co. Ltd.; *Int'l*, pg. 4363
KYOKUYO CO. LTD.; *Int'l*, pg. 4363
KYOKUYO ELECTRIC CO., LTD.—See Daeyang Electric Co., Ltd.; *Int'l*, pg. 1911
KYOKUYO EUROPE B.V.—See Kyokuyo Co. Ltd.; *Int'l*, pg. 4364
KYOKUYO FEED ONE MARINE CO., LTD.—See Kyokuyo Co. Ltd.; *Int'l*, pg. 4364
KYOKUYO FOODS CO., LTD.—See Kyokuyo Co. Ltd.; *Int'l*, pg. 4364

KYOKUYO CO. LTD.

CORPORATE AFFILIATIONS

KYOKUYO FRESH CO., LTD.—See Kyokuyo Co. Ltd.; *Int'l*, pg. 4364
KYOKUYO MARINE EHIME CO., LTD.—See Kyokuyo Co. Ltd.; *Int'l*, pg. 4364
KYOKUYO MARINE FARM CO., LTD.—See Kyokuyo Co. Ltd.; *Int'l*, pg. 4364
KYOKUYO SHOJI CO., LTD.—See Kyokuyo Co. Ltd.; *Int'l*, pg. 4364
KYOKUYO SHOKUHIN CO., LTD.—See Kyokuyo Co. Ltd.; *Int'l*, pg. 4364
KYOKUYO SOUGOU SERVICE CO., LTD.—See Kyokuyo Co. Ltd.; *Int'l*, pg. 4364
KYOKUYO SUISAN CO., LTD.—See Kyokuyo Co. Ltd.; *Int'l*, pg. 4364
KYOKUYO (THAILAND) CO., LTD.—See Kyokuyo Co. Ltd.; *Int'l*, pg. 4363
KYON AG—See Vimian Group AB; *Int'l*, pg. 8208
KYONGBO PHARMACEUTICAL CO., LTD.; *Int'l*, pg. 4364
KYONGNAM BANK CO., LTD.—See BNK Financial Group Inc.; *Int'l*, pg. 1079
KYORIN HOLDINGS, INC.; *Int'l*, pg. 4364
KYORIN PHARMACEUTICAL CO., LTD., - NOSHIRO PLANT—See KYORIN Holdings, Inc.; *Int'l*, pg. 4364
KYORIN PHARMACEUTICAL CO., LTD.—See KYORIN Holdings, Inc.; *Int'l*, pg. 4364
KYORIN PHARMACEUTICAL GROUP FACILITIES CO., LTD.—See KYORIN Holdings, Inc.; *Int'l*, pg. 4364
KYORIN PHARMACEUTICAL - OKAYA PLANT—See KYORIN Holdings, Inc.; *Int'l*, pg. 4364
KYORIN RIMEDIO CO., LTD.—See KYORIN Holdings, Inc.; *Int'l*, pg. 4364
KYORITSU AIR TECH INC.; *Int'l*, pg. 4364
THE KYORITSU CO., LTD.; *Int'l*, pg. 7663
KYORITSU COMPUTER & COMMUNICATION CO., LTD.; *Int'l*, pg. 4364
KYORITSU ELECTRIC CORPORATION; *Int'l*, pg. 4364
KYORITSU ELECTRIC INDIA PVT LTD.—See Kyoritsu Electric Corporation; *Int'l*, pg. 4364
KYORITSU ELECTRIC (MALAYSIA) SDN., BHD.—See Kyoritsu Electric Corporation; *Int'l*, pg. 4364
KYORITSU ELECTRIC (SHANGHAI) CO., LTD.—See Kyoritsu Electric Corporation; *Int'l*, pg. 4364
KYORITSU ELECTRIC (SHENZHEN) CO., LTD.—See Kyoritsu Electric Corporation; *Int'l*, pg. 4364
KYORITSU ELECTRIC TECH (PHILIPPINES), INC.—See Kyoritsu Electric Corporation; *Int'l*, pg. 4364
KYORITSU ELECTRIC (THAILAND) CO., LTD.—See Kyoritsu Electric Corporation; *Int'l*, pg. 4364
KYORITSU ELECTRIC (VIETNAM) CO., LTD.—See Kyoritsu Electric Corporation; *Int'l*, pg. 4364
KYORITSU ENGINEERING (THAILAND) CO. LTD.—See Kyoritsu Electric Corporation; *Int'l*, pg. 4364
KYORITSU FOODS SERVICE CO., LTD.—See Kyoritsu Maintenance Co., Ltd.; *Int'l*, pg. 4365
KYORITSU IRRIGATE CO., LTD.—See Yanmar Co., Ltd.; *Int'l*, pg. 8563
KYORITSU MACHINERY CORPORATION—See Kyoritsu Electric Corporation; *Int'l*, pg. 4365
KYORITSU MAINTENANCE CO., LTD.; *Int'l*, pg. 4365
KYORITSU PRINTING CO., LTD.; *Int'l*, pg. 4365
KYORITSU RADIO SERVICE CO., LTD.—See Furuno Electric Co., Ltd.; *Int'l*, pg. 2848
KYORITSU SAISEKISHO CO., LTD.—See NANYO Corporation; *Int'l*, pg. 5146
KYORITSU SETSUBI CO., LTD.—See Takuma Co., Ltd.; *Int'l*, pg. 7442
KYORITSU TEST SYSTEM CO., LTD.—See Kyoritsu Electric Corporation; *Int'l*, pg. 4365
KYORITSU TRUST CO., LTD.—See Kyoritsu Maintenance Co., Ltd.; *Int'l*, pg. 4365
KYOSAN DENKI AMERICA, INC.—See Denso Corporation; *Int'l*, pg. 2032
KYOSAN DENKI CO., LTD. - PLANT 2—See Denso Corporation; *Int'l*, pg. 2032
KYOSAN DENKI CO., LTD.—See Denso Corporation; *Int'l*, pg. 2032
KYOSAN DENKI CO., LTD - YUKI PLANT—See Denso Corporation; *Int'l*, pg. 2032
KYOSAN DENSO MANUFACTURING KENTUCKY, LLC.—See Denso Corporation; *Int'l*, pg. 2032
KYOSAN ELECTRICAL CONSTRUCTION CO.,—See Kyosan Electric Manufacturing Co., Ltd.; *Int'l*, pg. 4365
KYOSAN ELECTRIC MANUFACTURING CO., LTD.; *Int'l*, pg. 4365
KYOSAN ENGINEERING SERVICE CO., LTD.—See Kyosan Electric Manufacturing Co., Ltd.; *Int'l*, pg. 4365
KYOSAN INDIA PVT. LTD.—See Kyosan Electric Manufacturing Co., Ltd.; *Int'l*, pg. 4365
KYOSAN KOGYO CO., LTD.—See Kyosan Electric Manufacturing Co., Ltd.; *Int'l*, pg. 4365
KYOSAN LIGHT METAL CO., LTD.—See Shoko Co., Ltd.; *Int'l*, pg. 6858
KYOSAN METAL INDUSTRY CO., LTD.—See Kyosan Electric Manufacturing Co., Ltd.; *Int'l*, pg. 4365
KYOSAN SEIKI CO., LTD.—See Kyosan Electric Manufacturing Co., Ltd.; *Int'l*, pg. 4365
KYOSAN SERVICE CORPORATION—See Denso Corporation; *Int'l*, pg. 2032

KYOSAN SYSTEM CO., LTD.—See Kyosan Electric Manufacturing Co., Ltd.; *Int'l*, pg. 4365
KYOSAN USA INC.—See Kyosan Electric Manufacturing Co., Ltd.; *Int'l*, pg. 4365
KYOSEI CHEMICAL CO., LTD. - NAKAJO PLANT—See Kuraray Co., Ltd.; *Int'l*, pg. 4337
KYOSEI CHEMICAL CO., LTD.—See Kuraray Co., Ltd.; *Int'l*, pg. 4337
KYOSEI RENTEMU CO., LTD.—See Aktio Holdings Corporation; *Int'l*, pg. 267
KYOSHA CO., LTD. - KYUSHU PLANT—See KYOSHA CO., LTD.; *Int'l*, pg. 4365
KYOSHA CO., LTD. - NIIGATA PLANT—See KYOSHA CO., LTD.; *Int'l*, pg. 4365
KYOSHA CO., LTD.; *Int'l*, pg. 4365
KYOSHA HONG KONG CO., LTD.—See KYOSHA CO., LTD.; *Int'l*, pg. 4365
KYOSHA MALAYSIA CIRCUIT TECHNOLOGY SDN. BHD.—See KYOSHA CO., LTD.; *Int'l*, pg. 4365
KYOSHA NORTH AMERICA, INC.—See KYOSHA CO., LTD.; *Int'l*, pg. 4365
KYOSHA (THAILAND) CO., LTD.—See KYOSHA CO., LTD.; *Int'l*, pg. 4365
KYOSHIN COMMUNICATIONS CO LTD.—See Restar Holdings Corporation; *Int'l*, pg. 6303
KYOSHIN EUROPE LTD.—See Nitto Denko Corporation; *Int'l*, pg. 5384
KYOSHIN INDUSTRY ASIA PTE LTD.—See Rhythm Co., Ltd.; *Int'l*, pg. 6328
KYOSHIN KENKO CO., LTD.; *Int'l*, pg. 4365
KYOSHINSHA CO., LTD.—See Tomoku Co., Ltd.; *Int'l*, pg. 7801
KYOSHIN TECHNOSONIC (ASIA) LTD.—See Restar Holdings Corporation; *Int'l*, pg. 6303
KYOSHIN TECHNOSONIC CO., LTD.—See Restar Holdings Corporation; *Int'l*, pg. 6303
KYOSHIN TECHNOSONIC (K) CO., LTD.—See Restar Holdings Corporation; *Int'l*, pg. 6303
KYOSHIN TECHNOSONIC (SHENZHEN) LTD.—See Restar Holdings Corporation; *Int'l*, pg. 6303
KYOSHIN VIETNAM CO., LTD.—See Rhythm Co., Ltd.; *Int'l*, pg. 6328
KYOTARU CO., LTD.—See Yoshinoya Holdings Co., Ltd.; *Int'l*, pg. 8600
KYOTO BUS CO., LTD.—See Keihan Holdings Co., Ltd.; *Int'l*, pg. 4116
KYOTO CENTURY HOTEL CO., LTD.—See Keihan Holdings Co., Ltd.; *Int'l*, pg. 4116
KYOTO CREDIT SERVICE CO., LTD.—See The Bank of Kyoto, Ltd.; *Int'l*, pg. 7616
KYOTO EKI-KANKO DEPARTMENT STORE COMPANY—See West Japan Railway Company; *Int'l*, pg. 8385
KYOTO ELEX CO., LTD.—See DKS Co. Ltd.; *Int'l*, pg. 2140
KYOTO FINANCIAL GROUP, INC.; *Int'l*, pg. 4365
KYOTO GROUP AS; *Int'l*, pg. 4365
KYOTO GUARANTY SERVICE CO., LTD.—See The Bank of Kyoto, Ltd.; *Int'l*, pg. 7616
KYOTO HINO MOTOR LTD.—See Toyota Motor Corporation; *Int'l*, pg. 7871
THE KYOTO HOTEL, LTD.; *Int'l*, pg. 7663
KYOTO KAMI SHOJI CO., LTD.—See Japan Pulp and Paper Company Limited; *Int'l*, pg. 3904
KYOTO KANKYO CO., LTD.—See Daiei Kankyo Co., Ltd.; *Int'l*, pg. 1924
KYOTO KIMONO YUZEN HOLDINGS CO., LTD.; *Int'l*, pg. 4366
KYOTO MARUBENI CO., LTD—See Marubeni Corporation; *Int'l*, pg. 4705
KYOTO PURPLE SANGA COMPANY LIMITED—See KYOCERA Corporation; *Int'l*, pg. 4360
KYOTO RESEARCH INSTITUTE, INC.—See The Bank of Kyoto, Ltd.; *Int'l*, pg. 7616
KYOTO RESEARCH PARK CORP—See Osaka Gas Co., Ltd.; *Int'l*, pg. 5646
KYOTO SENKO TRANSPORT CO., LTD.—See Senko Group Holdings Co., Ltd.; *Int'l*, pg. 6710
KYOTO STATION BUILDING DEVELOPMENT CO., LTD—See West Japan Railway Company; *Int'l*, pg. 8385
KYOTO STATION CENTER CO., LTD.—See West Japan Railway Company; *Int'l*, pg. 8385
KYOTO TOOL CO., LTD.; *Int'l*, pg. 4366
KYOTO TOWER CO., LTD.—See Keihan Holdings Co., Ltd.; *Int'l*, pg. 4116
KYOUDOU KASANKASUISO CORPORATION—See Mitsubishi Gas Chemical Company, Inc.; *Int'l*, pg. 4949
KYOUDOU POLYMER CO., LTD.—See Daicel Corporation; *Int'l*, pg. 1919
KYOUEI CO., LTD.—See Ichinen Holdings Co., Ltd.; *Int'l*, pg. 3580
KYOUEI SEITAI K.K.—See Nippon Paper Industries Co., Ltd.; *Int'l*, pg. 5327
KYOUEI SHOKUSAN CO., LTD.—See Daicel Corporation; *Int'l*, pg. 1919
KYOURYOU MAINTENANCE, INC.—See Kawada Technologies Inc.; *Int'l*, pg. 4093

KYOWA AMERICAS INC.—See Kyowa Electronic Instruments Co., Ltd.; *Int'l*, pg. 4366
KYOWA CARTON CO., LTD.—See Asahi Printing Co., Ltd.; *Int'l*, pg. 598
KYOWA CO., LTD.—See Sankyo Kasei Corporation; *Int'l*, pg. 6543
KYOWA CRITICARE CO., LTD.—See NMC Health PLC; *Int'l*, pg. 5392
KYOWA DENGYO MALAYSIA SDN. BHD.—See Kyowa Electronic Instruments Co., Ltd.; *Int'l*, pg. 4366
KYOWA DENGYO (THAILAND) CO., LTD.—See Kyowa Electronic Instruments Co., Ltd.; *Int'l*, pg. 4366
KYOWA DENKO CO., LTD.—See Kyoritsu Electric Corporation; *Int'l*, pg. 4365
KYOWA ELECTRIC MFG. CO., LTD.—See Teikoku Electric Mfg. Co., Ltd.; *Int'l*, pg. 7524
KYOWA ELECTRONIC INSTRUMENTS CO., LTD.; *Int'l*, pg. 4366
KYOWA ELECTRONIC (SHANGHAI) TRADING CO., LTD.—See Kyowa Electronic Instruments Co., Ltd.; *Int'l*, pg. 4366
KYOWA ENGINEERING CONSULTANTS CO., LTD.; *Int'l*, pg. 4366
KYOWA HAKKO BIO CO., LTD.—See Kirin Holdings Company, Limited; *Int'l*, pg. 4188
KYOWA HAKKO CHEMICAL AMERICAS, INC.—See Japan Industrial Partners, Inc.; *Int'l*, pg. 3889
KYOWA HAKKO EUROPE GMBH—See Kirin Holdings Company, Limited; *Int'l*, pg. 4188
KYOWA HAKKO (H.K.) CO., LTD.—See Kirin Holdings Company, Limited; *Int'l*, pg. 4188
KYOWA HAKKO KIRIN AMERICA, INC.—See Kirin Holdings Company, Limited; *Int'l*, pg. 4188
KYOWA HAKKO KIRIN CHINA PHARMACEUTICAL CO., LTD.—See Kirin Holdings Company, Limited; *Int'l*, pg. 4189
KYOWA HAKKO KIRIN CO., LTD. - FUJI PLANT—See Kirin Holdings Company, Limited; *Int'l*, pg. 4188
KYOWA HAKKO KIRIN CO., LTD. - SAKAI PLANT—See Kirin Holdings Company, Limited; *Int'l*, pg. 4188
KYOWA HAKKO KIRIN CO., LTD. - TAKASAKI PLANT—See Kirin Holdings Company, Limited; *Int'l*, pg. 4188
KYOWA HAKKO KIRIN CO., LTD. - UBE PLANT—See Kirin Holdings Company, Limited; *Int'l*, pg. 4188
KYOWA HAKKO KIRIN (HONG KONG) CO., LTD.—See Kirin Holdings Company, Limited; *Int'l*, pg. 4188
KYOWA HAKKO KIRIN KOREA CO., LTD.—See Kirin Holdings Company, Limited; *Int'l*, pg. 4188
KYOWA HAKKO KIRIN KOREA CO., LTD.—See Kirin Holdings Company, Limited; *Int'l*, pg. 4188
KYOWA HAKKO KIRIN PHARMA, INC.—See Kirin Holdings Company, Limited; *Int'l*, pg. 4188
KYOWA HAKKO KIRIN (SINGAPORE) PTE. LTD.—See Kirin Holdings Company, Limited; *Int'l*, pg. 4188
KYOWA HAKKO KIRIN (TAIWAN) CO., LTD.—See Kirin Holdings Company, Limited; *Int'l*, pg. 4188
KYOWA HAKKO KIRIN (THAILAND) CO., LTD.—See Kirin Holdings Company, Limited; *Int'l*, pg. 4188
KYOWA HAKKO KIRIN U.K. LTD.—See Kirin Holdings Company, Limited; *Int'l*, pg. 4188
KYOWA HAKKO (MALAYSIA) SDN BHD—See Kirin Holdings Company, Limited; *Int'l*, pg. 4188
KYOWA HAKKO U.S.A., INC.—See Kirin Holdings Company, Limited; *Int'l*, pg. 4188
KYOWA HIGH TECH CO., LTD.—See Kyowa Electronic Instruments Co., Ltd.; *Int'l*, pg. 4366
KYOWA INDUSTRIAL CO., LTD.—See Mitsui Chemicals, Inc.; *Int'l*, pg. 4981
KYOWA INDUSTRIAL CO., LTD.—See Mitsui Chemicals, Inc.; *Int'l*, pg. 4981
KYOWA ITALIANA FARMACEUTICI S.R.L.—See Kirin Holdings Company, Limited; *Int'l*, pg. 4189
KYOWA KANKO KAIHATSU (M) BERHAD—See Zavarco PLC; *Int'l*, pg. 8626
KYOWA KIKAKU LTD.—See Nippon Telegraph & Telephone Corporation; *Int'l*, pg. 5350
KYOWA KIRIN CO, LTD.—See Kirin Holdings Company, Limited; *Int'l*, pg. 4188
KYOWA KIRIN PHARMACEUTICAL RESEARCH, INC.—See Kirin Holdings Company, Limited; *Int'l*, pg. 4188
KYOWAKOGYOSYO CO., LTD.; *Int'l*, pg. 4366
KYOWAKOUGYOU CO., LTD.—See Iwabuchi Corporation; *Int'l*, pg. 3848
KYOWA LEATHER CLOTH CO., LTD.; *Int'l*, pg. 4366
KYOWA MACHINERY (SHANDONG) CO., LTD.—See Kyowakogyosyo Co., Ltd.; *Int'l*, pg. 4366
KYOWA MANUFACTURING CO., LTD—See Press Kogyo Co., Ltd.; *Int'l*, pg. 5964
KYOWA MEASUREMENT ENGINEERING CO., LTD.—See Kyowa Electronic Instruments Co., Ltd.; *Int'l*, pg. 4366
KYOWA MEDICAL CORPORATION; *Int'l*, pg. 4366
KYOWA MEDICAL PROMOTION CO., LTD.—See Kirin Holdings Company, Limited; *Int'l*, pg. 4189
KYOWANISSEI CO., LTD.; *Int'l*, pg. 4366
KYOWA PHARMACEUTICAL INDUSTRY CO., LTD.—See Unison Capital, Inc.; *Int'l*, pg. 8061

COMPANY NAME INDEX

KYOWA SANGYO CORP.—See Toyota Boshoku Corporation; *Int'l*, pg. 7864
KYOWA SERVICE CENTER CO., LTD.—See Kyowa Electronic Instruments Co., Ltd.; *Int'l*, pg. 4366
KYOWA SHIGYO CO., LTD.—See Rengo Co., Ltd.; *Int'l*, pg. 6280
KYOWA SHIPPING CO.—See Sankyu, Inc.; *Int'l*, pg. 6544
KYOWA STEEL CO., LTD.—See Kanematsu Corporation; *Int'l*, pg. 4069
KYOWA SUISAN CO., LTD—See Nissui Corporation; *Int'l*, pg. 5378
KYOWA SYNCHRO TECHNOLOGY EUROPE S.A.S.—See Sojitz Corporation; *Int'l*, pg. 7062
KYOYU LEASE CO., LTD.—See Marubeni Construction Material Lease Co., Ltd.; *Int'l*, pg. 4704
KYPROU FINANCE (NL) B.V.—See Bank of Cyprus Holdings Public Limited Company; *Int'l*, pg. 842
KYPROU INSURANCE SERVICES LTD—See Bank of Cyprus Holdings Public Limited Company; *Int'l*, pg. 842
KYPROU MUTUAL FUND MANAGEMENT COMPANY S.A.—See Bank of Cyprus Holdings Public Limited Company; *Int'l*, pg. 842
KYPROU SECURITIES SA—See Bank of Cyprus Holdings Public Limited Company; *Int'l*, pg. 842
KYRA SOLUTIONS INC.; *U.S. Private*, pg. 2360
KYRGYZ INVESTMENT AND CREDIT BANK LTD—See Aga Khan Development Network; *Int'l*, pg. 199
KYRGYZKOMMERTSBANK OJSC—See Halyk Bank of Kazakhstan JSC; *Int'l*, pg. 3234
KYRIBA CORPORATION—See Bridgepoint Group Plc; *Int'l*, pg. 1155
KYRON LABORATORIES (PTY) LTD—See Ascendis Health Limited; *Int'l*, pg. 601
KYRON SAHKO OY—See Instalco AB; *Int'l*, pg. 3722
KYROS KEBAB SDN BHD—See Cab Cakaran Corporation Berhad; *Int'l*, pg. 1245
KYRUUS, INC.; *U.S. Private*, pg. 2360
KYSOR WARREN CORP.—See EPTA S.p.a.; *Int'l*, pg. 2466
KYSOR/WARREN DE MEXICO, S. DE R.L. DE C.V.—See Lennox International Inc.; *U.S. Public*, pg. 1307
KYSOR WARREN EPTA US CORP.—See EPTA S.p.a.; *Int'l*, pg. 2466
KYTE BROKING LIMITED—See R.J. O'Brien & Associates, LLC; *U.S. Private*, pg. 3337
KYTO TECHNOLOGY & LIFE SCIENCE, INC.; *U.S. Public*, pg. 1278
KYTX OPERATING COMPANY, LLC—See TEGNA Inc.; *U.S. Public*, pg. 1990
KYUBEIYA CO., LTD.—See Zensho Holdings Co., Ltd.; *Int'l*, pg. 8634
KYUDEN BUSINESS FRONT INC.—See Kyushu Electric Power Co., Inc.; *Int'l*, pg. 4367
KYUDEN BUSINESS SOLUTIONS CO., INC.—See Kyushu Electric Power Co., Inc.; *Int'l*, pg. 4368
KYUDEN ECOSOL CO., LTD.—See Kyushu Electric Power Co., Inc.; *Int'l*, pg. 4368
KYUDEN GOOD LIFE FUKUOKA JOSUI COMPANY, INC.—See Kyushu Electric Power Co., Inc.; *Int'l*, pg. 4368
KYUDEN GOOD LIFE HIGASHIFUKUOKA COMPANY, INC.—See Kyushu Electric Power Co., Inc.; *Int'l*, pg. 4368
KYUDEN GOOD LIFE KAGOSHIMA COMPANY, INC.—See Kyushu Electric Power Co., Inc.; *Int'l*, pg. 4368
KYUDEN GOOD LIFE KUMAMOTO COMPANY, INC.—See Kyushu Electric Power Co., Inc.; *Int'l*, pg. 4368
KYUDEN HOME SECURITY CO., INC.—See Kyushu Electric Power Co., Inc.; *Int'l*, pg. 4368
KYUDEN INFOCOM COMPANY, INC.—See Kyushu Electric Power Co., Inc.; *Int'l*, pg. 4368
KYUDEN INTERNATIONAL CORPORATION—See Kyushu Electric Power Co., Inc.; *Int'l*, pg. 4368
KYUDENKO CORPORATION; *Int'l*, pg. 4366
KYUDENKO MALAYSIA SDN. BHD.—See Kyudenko Corporation; *Int'l*, pg. 4366
KYUDENKO-OHSIS (THAILAND) CO., LTD.—See Kyudenko Corporation; *Int'l*, pg. 4366
KYUDENKO SOUTH EAST ASIA PTE. LTD.—See Kyudenko Corporation; *Int'l*, pg. 4366
KYUDENKO (THAILAND) CO., LTD.—See Kyudenko Corporation; *Int'l*, pg. 4366
KYUDENKO VIETNAM CO., LTD.—See Kyudenko Corporation; *Int'l*, pg. 4366
KYUDEN MIRAI ENERGY COMPANY, INCORPORATED—See Kyushu Electric Power Co., Inc.; *Int'l*, pg. 4368
KYUDEN SANGYO CO., INC.—See Kyushu Electric Power Co., Inc.; *Int'l*, pg. 4368
KYUDEN SHARED BUSINESS CO., LTD.—See Kyushu Electric Power Co., Inc.; *Int'l*, pg. 4368
KYUDEN TECHNOSYSTEMS CORPORATION—See Kyushu Electric Power Co., Inc.; *Int'l*, pg. 4368
KYUDO CO., LTD.—See Central Institute for Experimental Animals; *Int'l*, pg. 1408

KYUHEN CO., INC.—See Daihen Corporation; *Int'l*, pg. 1926
KYU INVESTMENT, INC.; *U.S. Private*, pg. 2360
KYUKI CORPORATION—See Kyushu Electric Power Co., Inc.; *Int'l*, pg. 4368
KYUKO-LEASE INC.—See ORIX Corporation; *Int'l*, pg. 5634
KYULIEN ENVIRONMENT IMPROVING CO., LTD.—See Kyudenko Corporation; *Int'l*, pg. 4366
KYUNG CHANG INDUSTRIAL CO., LTD.; *Int'l*, pg. 4366
KYUNG CHANG PRECISION CO., LTD.—See Kyung Chang Industrial Co., Ltd.; *Int'l*, pg. 4366
KYUNG CHANG PRECISION INDUSTRIAL CO., LTD.—See Kyung Chang Industrial Co., Ltd.; *Int'l*, pg. 4367
KYUNGDONG CITY GAS CO., LTD.; *Int'l*, pg. 4367
KYUNGDONG INVEST CO., LTD.; *Int'l*, pg. 4367
KYUNGDONG NAVIEN CO., LTD.; *Int'l*, pg. 4367
KYUNG DONG ONE RUS LLC—See KyungDong Navien Co., Ltd.; *Int'l*, pg. 4367
KYUNGDONG PHARMACEUTICAL CO., LTD. - HWASEONG PLANT—See Kyungdong Pharmaceutical Co., Ltd.; *Int'l*, pg. 4367
KYUNGDONG PHARMACEUTICAL CO., LTD.; *Int'l*, pg. 4367
KYUNGDONG PHARMACEUTICAL CO., LTD. - YANGGAM PLANT—See Kyungdong Pharmaceutical Co., Ltd.; *Int'l*, pg. 4367
KYUNGIN AMERICA INC.—See Kyung In Electronics Co., Ltd; *Int'l*, pg. 4367
KYUNG IN ELECTRONICS CO., LTD.; *Int'l*, pg. 4367
KYUNGIN ELECTRONICS (SHEN ZHEN) CO., LTD.—See Kyung In Electronics Co., Ltd; *Int'l*, pg. 4367
KYUNGIN ELECTRONICS(TIAN JIN) CO., LTD.—See Kyung In Electronics Co., Ltd; *Int'l*, pg. 4367
KYUNGIN MEXICO, SA DE C.V.—See Kyung In Electronics Co., Ltd; *Int'l*, pg. 4367
KYUNGIN PRECISION CO., LTD.—See Kyung In Electronics Co., Ltd; *Int'l*, pg. 4367
KYUNG-IN SYNTHETIC CORPORATION; *Int'l*, pg. 4367
KYUNG NAM PHARM CO., LTD.; *Int'l*, pg. 4367
KYUNGNONG CORPORATION; *Int'l*, pg. 4367
KYUNGSHIN CORPORATION—See Sumitomo Electric Industries, Ltd.; *Int'l*, pg. 7278
KYUQUOT POWER LTD.—See Synex Renewable Energy Corporation; *Int'l*, pg. 7385
KYUSHU ALPHA CO., LTD.—See ALPHA Corporation; *Int'l*, pg. 367
KYUSHU CALCIUM CO., LTD.—See Maruo Calcium Co., Ltd.; *Int'l*, pg. 4714
KYUSHU CARD CO., LTD.—See The Nishi-Nippon City Bank, Ltd.; *Int'l*, pg. 7670
KYUSHU CREATE MEDIC CO., LTD.—See CREATE MEDIC CO. LTD.; *Int'l*, pg. 1832
KYUSHU DAIKI ALUMINIUM CO., LTD.—See Daiki Aluminium Industry Co., Ltd.; *Int'l*, pg. 1931
KYUSHU DAINICHISEIKA KOGYO CO., LTD—See Dainichiseika Color & Chemicals Mfg. Co., Ltd.; *Int'l*, pg. 1939
KYUSHU DAISHINKU CORP—See Daishinku Corp.; *Int'l*, pg. 1942
KYUSHU DIETCOOK CO., LTD.—See Kenko Mayonnaise Co., Ltd.; *Int'l*, pg. 4127
KYUSHU DTS CORPORATION—See DTS Corporation; *Int'l*, pg. 2217
KYUSHU ECONOMIC RESEARCH INSTITUTE CO., LTD.—See Kyushu Financial Group, Inc.; *Int'l*, pg. 4368
KYUSHU ELECTRIC POWER CO., INC.; *Int'l*, pg. 4367
KYUSHU ENERGY CO., LTD.—See Itochu Enex Co., Ltd.; *Int'l*, pg. 3842
KYUSHU ENVIRONMENTAL MANAGEMENT CORPORATION—See Kyushu Electric Power Co., Inc.; *Int'l*, pg. 4368
KYUSHU F.C.C. CO., LTD.—See F.C.C. Co., Ltd.; *Int'l*, pg. 2596
KYUSHU FINANCIAL GROUP, INC; *Int'l*, pg. 4368
KYUSHU F-TECH INC.—See F-Tech Inc.; *Int'l*, pg. 2595
KYUSHU GOMU KAKO CO., LTD.—See JSR Corp.; *Int'l*, pg. 4014
KYUSHU GUNZE CO., LTD.—See Gunze Limited; *Int'l*, pg. 3186
KYUSHU HITACHI SYSTEMS, LTD.—See Hitachi, Ltd.; *Int'l*, pg. 3423
KYUSHU INAX CORPORATION—See LIXIL Group Corporation; *Int'l*, pg. 4534
KYUSHU INDUSTRIAL GAS, INC.—See Mitsui Chemicals, Inc.; *Int'l*, pg. 4981
KYUSHU JUKAN OPERATION CO., LTD.—See Mitsubishi Heavy Industries, Ltd.; *Int'l*, pg. 4954
KYUSHU KASAI CO., LTD.—See Kasai Kogyo Co., Ltd.; *Int'l*, pg. 4086
KYUSHU KENSAN CO., LTD.—See Kanamoto Co., Ltd.; *Int'l*, pg. 4064
KYUSHU KOUSHUHA NETUREN CO.LTD.—See Neturen Co., Ltd.; *Int'l*, pg. 5216
KYUSHU KYOEI SYSTEMS CO., LTD.—See KYCOM Holdings Co., Ltd.; *Int'l*, pg. 4355
KYUSHU LEASING SERVICE CO., LTD.; *Int'l*, pg. 4368

KYUSHU MARUICHI STEEL TUBE LTD.—See Maruichi Steel Tube Ltd; *Int'l*, pg. 4713
KYUSHU MARUWA LOGISTICS CO., LTD.—See AZ-COM MARUWA Holdings Inc.; *Int'l*, pg. 776
KYUSHU MAZDA CO., LTD.—See Mazda Motor Corporation; *Int'l*, pg. 4749
KYUSHU MEINYU HANBAI CO., LTD—See Meiji Holdings Co., Ltd.; *Int'l*, pg. 4800
KYUSHU MORI SHIGYO CO., LTD.—See Oji Holdings Corporation; *Int'l*, pg. 5536
KYUSHU MUSASHI SEIMITSU CO., LTD.—See Musashi Seimitsu Industry Co., Ltd.; *Int'l*, pg. 5101
KYUSHU OKI TELECOMMUNICATION SYSTEMS—See Oki Electric Industry Co., Ltd.; *Int'l*, pg. 5548
KYUSHU OKURA CO., LTD.—See Okura Industrial Co., Ltd.; *Int'l*, pg. 5551
KYUSHU PADO CORP.—See RIZAP GROUP, Inc.; *Int'l*, pg. 6354
KYUSHU RAILWAY COMPANY; *Int'l*, pg. 4368
KYUSHU RINSAN KK—See Kyushu Electric Power Co., Inc.; *Int'l*, pg. 4368
KYUSHU RION CO., LTD.—See RION Co. Ltd.; *Int'l*, pg. 6348
KYUSHU RYOSO TRANSPORTATION CO.,LTD.—See Mitsubishi Logistics Corporation; *Int'l*, pg. 4962
KYUSHU SANGYO KOTSU HOLDINGS CO., LTD.—See H.I.S. Co., Ltd.; *Int'l*, pg. 3195
KYUSHU SANKO UNYU CO., LTD.—See Konoike Transport Co., Ltd.; *Int'l*, pg. 4275
KYUSHU SEINO TRANSPORTATION CO., LTD.—See Seino Holdings Co., Ltd.; *Int'l*, pg. 6690
KYUSHU SEKISUI KENZAI CO., LTD.—See Sekisui Chemical Co., Ltd.; *Int'l*, pg. 6693
KYUSHU SHIROKI CO., LTD.—See AISIN CORPORATION; *Int'l*, pg. 253
KYUSHU SHIZUKI CO., INC.—See Shizuki Electric Company, Inc.; *Int'l*, pg. 6855
KYUSHU SMELTING TECHNOLOGY CORPORATION—See Toyota Tsusho Corporation; *Int'l*, pg. 7877
KYUSHU SUMIDEN SEIMITSU LTD.—See Sumitomo Electric Industries, Ltd.; *Int'l*, pg. 7278
KYUSHU SUMITOMO BAKELITE CO., LTD.—See Sumitomo Bakelite Co., Ltd.; *Int'l*, pg. 7263
KYUSHU SUNTORY TECHNO PRODUCTS LTD.—See Suntory Holdings Limited; *Int'l*, pg. 7326
KYUSHU-TECH CORPORATION—See JFE Holdings, Inc.; *Int'l*, pg. 3937
KYUSHU TELECOMMUNICATION NETWORK CO., INC.—See Kyushu Electric Power Co., Inc.; *Int'l*, pg. 4368
KYUSHU TOHO CO., LTD.—See Toho Holdings Co., Ltd.; *Int'l*, pg. 7776
KYUSHU TOKUYAMA READY MIXED CONCRETE CO., LTD.—See Tokuyama Corporation; *Int'l*, pg. 7787
KYUSHU TORISHIMA CO.,LTD.—See Torishima Pump Mfg. Co., Ltd.; *Int'l*, pg. 7828
KYUSHU TRAINING CENTER—See Rinnai Corporation; *Int'l*, pg. 6344
KYUSHU TS CO., LTD.—See TS Tech Co Ltd; *Int'l*, pg. 7948
KYUSHU UOICHI CO., LTD.—See Maruha Nichiro Corporation; *Int'l*, pg. 4711
KYUSHU WACOAL MANUFACTURING CORP. - FUKUOKA FACTORY—See Wacoal Holdings Corp.; *Int'l*, pg. 8325
KYUSHU WACOAL MANUFACTURING CORP. - KUMAMOTO FACTORY—See Wacoal Holdings Corp.; *Int'l*, pg. 8325
KYUSHU WACOAL MANUFACTURING CORP.—See Wacoal Holdings Corp.; *Int'l*, pg. 8325
KYUSHU WHEEL KOGYO, LTD.—See Topy Industries, Ltd.; *Int'l*, pg. 7822
KYUSIN KAIHATSU INC.—See Mitsui Fudosan Co., Ltd.; *Int'l*, pg. 4986
KYUSO COMPANY, LTD.—See Zero Co., Ltd.; *Int'l*, pg. 8638
KYUSYU DTS CORPORATION—See DTS Corporation; *Int'l*, pg. 2217
KYUSYU NETWORK CABLE CO., LTD.—See The Furukawa Electric Co., Ltd.; *Int'l*, pg. 7646
KYUSYU REPURO CO., LTD.—See Marubeni Construction Material Lease Co., Ltd.; *Int'l*, pg. 4704
KYUSYU TS CO., LTD.—See TS Tech Co Ltd; *Int'l*, pg. 7948
KYUZITUHACK CO., LTD.—See Lion Corporation; *Int'l*, pg. 4517
KYVERNA THERAPEUTICS, INC.; *U.S. Public*, pg. 1278
KY VY CORPORATION—See Nippon Paper Industries Co., Ltd.; *Int'l*, pg. 5327
KYW-TV—See National Amusements, Inc.; *U.S. Private*, pg. 2840
KYYBA, INC.; *U.S. Private*, pg. 2361
KYZEN BVBA—See Kyzen Corporation; *U.S. Private*, pg. 2361
KYZEN CORPORATION - NORTH AMERICAN OPERATIONS FACILITY—See Kyzen Corporation; *U.S. Private*, pg. 2361
KYZEN CORPORATION; *U.S. Private*, pg. 2361

KYZEN CORPORATION

KYZEN SDN. BHD.—See Kyzen Corporation; *U.S. Private*, pg. 2361
KZ CO.—See IDEX Corp; *U.S. Public*, pg. 1091
KZ GREEN TECH CO., LTD.—See Korea Zinc Company, Ltd.; *Int'l*, pg. 4287
KZ HANDELS AB—See Addtech AB; *Int'l*, pg. 134
K.Z. KALSIUM SDN. BHD.—See Omya (Schweiz) AG; *Int'l*, pg. 5570
K. Z. LEASING & FINANCE LTD.; *Int'l*, pg. 4043
KZ-PRANDA CO., LTD.—See Korea Zinc Company, Ltd.; *Int'l*, pg. 4287
KZRV, L.P.—See Thor Industries, Inc.; *U.S. Public*, pg. 2156
KZS ADVERTISING; *U.S. Private*, pg. 2361
K. ZUGHAIBI & B. KABBANI GENERAL PARTNERSHIP; *Int'l*, pg. 4043
KZ X CO., LTD.—See Korea Zinc Company, Ltd.; *Int'l*, pg. 4287

L

L1 BAL HARBOUR LLC—See Fosun International Limited; *Int'l*, pg. 2751
L1 ENERGY LIMITED—See LetterOne Holdings S.A.; *Int'l*, pg. 4470
L1 LONG SHORT FUND LTD.; *Int'l*, pg. 4386
L2 CAPITAL PARTNERS; *U.S. Private*, pg. 2367
L2C, INC.—See TransUnion; *U.S. Public*, pg. 2184
L2F INC.—See The Middleby Corporation; *U.S. Public*, pg. 2114
L2I - FINANCIAL SOLUTIONS INC.—See Mobius Eco-Capital plc; *Int'l*, pg. 5012
L2T MEDIA; *U.S. Private*, pg. 2367
L37 LLC—See BCD Holdings N.V.; *Int'l*, pg. 926
L3 ADAPTIVE METHODS—See L3Harris Technologies, Inc.; *U.S. Public*, pg. 1284
L-3 ADVANCED LASER SYSTEMS TECHNOLOGY—See L3Harris Technologies, Inc.; *U.S. Public*, pg. 1281
L-3 APPLIED SIGNAL & IMAGE TECHNOLOGY—See L3Harris Technologies, Inc.; *U.S. Public*, pg. 1281
L-3 APPLIED TECHNOLOGIES, INC.—See L3Harris Technologies, Inc.; *U.S. Public*, pg. 1281
L3 AVIATION PRODUCTS, INC.—See L3Harris Technologies, Inc.; *U.S. Public*, pg. 1284
L-3 AVIATION RECORDERS—See L3Harris Technologies, Inc.; *U.S. Public*, pg. 1281
L-3 AVIONICS SYSTEMS, INC.—See L3Harris Technologies, Inc.; *U.S. Public*, pg. 1281
L-3 AVISYS—See L3Harris Technologies, Inc.; *U.S. Public*, pg. 1281
L-3 CHESAPEAKE SCIENCES CORPORATION—See L3Harris Technologies, Inc.; *U.S. Public*, pg. 1281
L-3 CINCINNATI ELECTRONICS—See L3Harris Technologies, Inc.; *U.S. Public*, pg. 1281
L-3 COMMAND & CONTROL SYSTEMS AND SOFTWARE—See L3Harris Technologies, Inc.; *U.S. Public*, pg. 1281
L3 COMMERCIAL TRAINING SOLUTIONS LIMITED—See L3Harris Technologies, Inc.; *U.S. Public*, pg. 1284
L-3 COMMUNICATION APPLIED TECHNOLOGIES/JAYCOR—See L3Harris Technologies, Inc.; *U.S. Public*, pg. 1281
L-3 COMMUNICATIONS ADVANCED LASER SYSTEMS TECHNOLOGY INC—See L3Harris Technologies, Inc.; *U.S. Public*, pg. 1281
L-3 COMMUNICATIONS AEROMET, INC.—See L3Harris Technologies, Inc.; *U.S. Public*, pg. 1281
L-3 COMMUNICATIONS ASA LIMITED—See L3Harris Technologies, Inc.; *U.S. Public*, pg. 1281
L-3 COMMUNICATIONS AUSTRALIA GROUP PTY LTD—See L3Harris Technologies, Inc.; *U.S. Public*, pg. 1281
L-3 COMMUNICATIONS BRASHEAR—See L3Harris Technologies, Inc.; *U.S. Public*, pg. 1282
L-3 COMMUNICATIONS CINCINNATI ELECTRONICS CORPORATION—See L3Harris Technologies, Inc.; *U.S. Public*, pg. 1282
L-3 COMMUNICATIONS COMBAT PROPULSION SYSTEMS—See L3Harris Technologies, Inc.; *U.S. Public*, pg. 1282
L-3 COMMUNICATIONS COMCEPT—See L3Harris Technologies, Inc.; *U.S. Public*, pg. 1282
L-3 COMMUNICATIONS COMMUNICATION SYSTEMS-EAST—See L3Harris Technologies, Inc.; *U.S. Public*, pg. 1282
L-3 COMMUNICATIONS COMMUNICATION SYSTEMS-WEST—See L3Harris Technologies, Inc.; *U.S. Public*, pg. 1282
L3 COMMUNICATIONS CORP. - PULSE SCIENCES—See L3Harris Technologies, Inc.; *U.S. Public*, pg. 1284
L-3 COMMUNICATIONS CYTERRA CORPORATION—See L3Harris Technologies, Inc.; *U.S. Public*, pg. 1282
L-3 COMMUNICATIONS DATRON—See L3Harris Technologies, Inc.; *U.S. Public*, pg. 1282
L-3 COMMUNICATIONS-DISPLAY SYSTEMS—See L3Harris Technologies, Inc.; *U.S. Public*, pg. 1283
L-3 COMMUNICATIONS ELAC NAUTIK GMBH—See L3Harris Technologies, Inc.; *U.S. Public*, pg. 1282

L-3 COMMUNICATIONS ELECTRON DEVICES—See L3Harris Technologies, Inc.; *U.S. Public*, pg. 1282
L-3 COMMUNICATIONS ELECTRON DEVICES—See L3Harris Technologies, Inc.; *U.S. Public*, pg. 1282
L-3 COMMUNICATIONS ELECTRONIC SYSTEMS—See L3Harris Technologies, Inc.; *U.S. Public*, pg. 1282
L-3 COMMUNICATIONS ELECTRON TECHNOLOGIES INC—See L3Harris Technologies, Inc.; *U.S. Public*, pg. 1282
L-3 COMMUNICATIONS EO/IR INC—See L3Harris Technologies, Inc.; *U.S. Public*, pg. 1282
L-3 COMMUNICATIONS ESSCO COLLINS LTD.—See Odyssey Investment Partners, LLC; *U.S. Private*, pg. 2994
L-3 COMMUNICATIONS FLIGHT INTERNATIONAL AVIATION LLC—See L3Harris Technologies, Inc.; *U.S. Public*, pg. 1282
L-3 COMMUNICATIONS GLOBAL NETWORK SOLUTIONS—See L3Harris Technologies, Inc.; *U.S. Public*, pg. 1282
L-3 COMMUNICATIONS INFRARED PRODUCTS—See L3Harris Technologies, Inc.; *U.S. Public*, pg. 1282
L-3 COMMUNICATIONS INTEGRATED SYSTEMS GROUP—See L3Harris Technologies, Inc.; *U.S. Public*, pg. 1282
L-3 COMMUNICATIONS INTEGRATED SYSTEMS L.P.—See L3Harris Technologies, Inc.; *U.S. Public*, pg. 1282
L-3 COMMUNICATIONS INTEGRATED SYSTEMS—See L3Harris Technologies, Inc.; *U.S. Public*, pg. 1282
L-3 COMMUNICATIONS KLEIN ASSOCIATES, INC.—See L3Harris Technologies, Inc.; *U.S. Public*, pg. 1282
L-3 COMMUNICATIONS KOREA CO., LTD.—See L3Harris Technologies, Inc.; *U.S. Public*, pg. 1280
L-3 COMMUNICATIONS MAGNET-MOTOR GMBH—See L3Harris Technologies, Inc.; *U.S. Public*, pg. 1282
L-3 COMMUNICATIONS MAPPS INC.—See L3Harris Technologies, Inc.; *U.S. Public*, pg. 1282
L-3 COMMUNICATIONS MARINE HOLDINGS AS—See L3Harris Technologies, Inc.; *U.S. Public*, pg. 1282
L-3 COMMUNICATIONS MARINE SYSTEMS UK LTD—See L3Harris Technologies, Inc.; *U.S. Public*, pg. 1282
L-3 COMMUNICATIONS MARIPRO INC—See L3Harris Technologies, Inc.; *U.S. Public*, pg. 1282
L-3 COMMUNICATIONS MAS (CANADA) INC.—See L3Harris Technologies, Inc.; *U.S. Public*, pg. 1282
L-3 COMMUNICATIONS MOBILE-VISION, INC.—See L3Harris Technologies, Inc.; *U.S. Public*, pg. 1282
L-3 COMMUNICATIONS NARDA MICROWAVE-EAST—See L3Harris Technologies, Inc.; *U.S. Public*, pg. 1282
L-3 COMMUNICATIONS NARDA MICROWAVE-WEST—See L3Harris Technologies, Inc.; *U.S. Public*, pg. 1282
L-3 COMMUNICATIONS NARDA SATELLITE NETWORKS—See L3Harris Technologies, Inc.; *U.S. Public*, pg. 1282
L-3 COMMUNICATIONS NOVA ENGINEERING, INC.—See L3Harris Technologies, Inc.; *U.S. Public*, pg. 1282
L-3 COMMUNICATIONS OCEANIA PTY LIMITED—See L3Harris Technologies, Inc.; *U.S. Public*, pg. 1283
L-3 COMMUNICATIONS OCEAN SYSTEMS—See L3Harris Technologies, Inc.; *U.S. Public*, pg. 1283
L-3 COMMUNICATIONS RANDTRON ANTENNA SYSTEMS—See L3Harris Technologies, Inc.; *U.S. Public*, pg. 1283
L-3 COMMUNICATIONS SECURITY AND DETECTION SYSTEMS, INC.—See L3Harris Technologies, Inc.; *U.S. Public*, pg. 1283
L-3 COMMUNICATIONS SINGAPORE PTE LTD—See L3Harris Technologies, Inc.; *U.S. Public*, pg. 1283
L-3 COMMUNICATIONS SONOMA EO INC—See L3Harris Technologies, Inc.; *U.S. Public*, pg. 1283
L-3 COMMUNICATIONS—See L3Harris Technologies, Inc.; *U.S. Public*, pg. 1281
L-3 COMMUNICATIONS SPACE & NAVIGATION—See EMCORE Corporation; *U.S. Public*, pg. 739
L-3 COMMUNICATIONS SSG-TINSLEY—See L3Harris Technologies, Inc.; *U.S. Public*, pg. 1283
L-3 COMMUNICATIONS TARGA SYSTEMS—See L3Harris Technologies, Inc.; *U.S. Public*, pg. 1283
L-3 COMMUNICATIONS TELEMETRY-WEST—See L3Harris Technologies, Inc.; *U.S. Public*, pg. 1283
L-3 COMMUNICATIONS UK LTD—See L3Harris Technologies, Inc.; *U.S. Public*, pg. 1283
L-3 COMMUNICATIONS VALMARINE AS—See L3Harris Technologies, Inc.; *U.S. Public*, pg. 1283
L-3 COMMUNICATIONS WESTWOOD CORPORATION-NMP DIVISION—See L3Harris Technologies, Inc.; *U.S. Public*, pg. 1283
L-3 COMMUNICATIONS WESTWOOD CORPORATION—See L3Harris Technologies, Inc.; *U.S. Public*, pg. 1283
L-3 COMMUNICATIONS WESTWOOD CORPORATION-TANO DIVISION—See L3Harris Technologies, Inc.; *U.S. Public*, pg. 1283

CORPORATE AFFILIATIONS

L-3 CRESTVIEW AEROSPACE—See AIP, LLC; *U.S. Private*, pg. 133
L3 CTS AIRLINE ACADEMY (NZ) LIMITED—See L3Harris Technologies, Inc.; *U.S. Public*, pg. 1284
L-3 D.P. ASSOCIATES INC.—See L3Harris Technologies, Inc.; *U.S. Public*, pg. 1283
L3 ELECTRON DEVICES, INC.—See L3Harris Technologies, Inc.; *U.S. Public*, pg. 1284
L-3 ELECTRON TECHNOLOGIES, INC.—See L3Harris Technologies, Inc.; *U.S. Public*, pg. 1283
L-3 EOTECH, INC.—See L3Harris Technologies, Inc.; *U.S. Public*, pg. 1284
L3 FUZING & ORDNANCE SYSTEMS, INC.—See L3Harris Technologies, Inc.; *U.S. Public*, pg. 1284
L-3 FUZING & ORDNANCE SYSTEMS—See L3Harris Technologies, Inc.; *U.S. Public*, pg. 1283
L-3 G.A. INTERNATIONAL, INC.—See L3Harris Technologies, Inc.; *U.S. Public*, pg. 1283
L3HARRIS MAS INC.—See L3Harris Technologies, Inc.; *U.S. Public*, pg. 1284
L3HARRIS TECHNOLOGIES, INC.; *U.S. Public*, pg. 1279
L-3 INTERSTATE ELECTRONICS CORPORATION—See L3Harris Technologies, Inc.; *U.S. Public*, pg. 1283
L3 LATITUDE, LLC—See L3Harris Technologies, Inc.; *U.S. Public*, pg. 1284
L-3 MARINE SYSTEMS—See L3Harris Technologies, Inc.; *U.S. Public*, pg. 1283
L3 MARIPRO, INC.—See L3Harris Technologies, Inc.; *U.S. Public*, pg. 1284
L-3 MARITIME SYSTEMS—See L3Harris Technologies, Inc.; *U.S. Public*, pg. 1283
L-3 MAS CANADA—See L3Harris Technologies, Inc.; *U.S. Public*, pg. 1283
L3 MICREO PTY LIMITED—See L3Harris Technologies, Inc.; *U.S. Public*, pg. 1284
L-3 MICRODYNE OUTSOURCING, INC.—See L3Harris Technologies, Inc.; *U.S. Public*, pg. 1283
L3 MOBILE-VISION, INC.—See Keystone Group, L.P.; *U.S. Private*, pg. 2296
L-3 MUSTANG TECHNOLOGY—See L3Harris Technologies, Inc.; *U.S. Public*, pg. 1283
L-3 NARDA-MITEQ—See L3Harris Technologies, Inc.; *U.S. Public*, pg. 1283
L3 OCEANIA PTY LIMITED—See L3Harris Technologies, Inc.; *U.S. Public*, pg. 1284
L3 OCEANSERVER, INC.—See L3Harris Technologies, Inc.; *U.S. Public*, pg. 1284
L-3 PHOTONICS—See L3Harris Technologies, Inc.; *U.S. Public*, pg. 1283
L-3 POWER & CONTROL SYSTEMS GROUP—See L3Harris Technologies, Inc.; *U.S. Public*, pg. 1283
L3 SECURITY & DETECTION SYSTEMS, INC.—See L3Harris Technologies, Inc.; *U.S. Public*, pg. 1284
L-3 SONOMA EO—See L3Harris Technologies, Inc.; *U.S. Public*, pg. 1283
L-3 SPD ELECTRICAL SYSTEMS, INC.—See L3Harris Technologies, Inc.; *U.S. Public*, pg. 1283
L-3 SYSTEMS & IMAGERY—See L3Harris Technologies, Inc.; *U.S. Public*, pg. 1283
L3 TECHNOLOGIES CANADA INC.—See L3Harris Technologies, Inc.; *U.S. Public*, pg. 1284
L3 TECHNOLOGIES, INC.—See L3Harris Technologies, Inc.; *U.S. Public*, pg. 1280
L3 TECHNOLOGIES MAS INC.—See L3Harris Technologies, Inc.; *U.S. Public*, pg. 1284
L3 UNIDYNE, INC.—See L3Harris Technologies, Inc.; *U.S. Public*, pg. 1284
L-3 UNIDYNE—See L3Harris Technologies, Inc.; *U.S. Public*, pg. 1283
L-3 UNMANNED SYSTEMS—See L3Harris Technologies, Inc.; *U.S. Public*, pg. 1283
L-3 WESCAM INC.—See L3Harris Technologies, Inc.; *U.S. Public*, pg. 1283
L3 WESTWOOD CORPORATION—See L3Harris Technologies, Inc.; *U.S. Public*, pg. 1284
L-3 WOLF COACH—See L3Harris Technologies, Inc.; *U.S. Public*, pg. 1284
L5E LLC; *U.S. Private*, pg. 2367
L8 SOUTH COAST PLAZA LLC—See Fosun International Limited; *Int'l*, pg. 2751
LAACO, LTD.—See CubeSmart; *U.S. Public*, pg. 604
LA ADA DE ACUNA, S. DE R.L. DE C.V.—See Kimberly-Clark Corporation; *U.S. Public*, pg. 1231
LA AGENCIA DE ORCI & ASOCIADOS; *U.S. Private*, pg. 2367
LAAGLAND B.V.—See Rotrada Holding B.V.; *Int'l*, pg. 6406
LAAKIRCHEN PAPIER AG—See Heinzel Holding GmbH; *Int'l*, pg. 3325
LA AMAPOLA, INC.; *U.S. Private*, pg. 2367
LA AMISTAD BEHAVIORAL HEALTH SERVICES—See Universal Health Services, Inc.; *U.S. Public*, pg. 2260
LA AMISTAD RESIDENTIAL TREATMENT CENTER, LLC—See Universal Health Services, Inc.; *U.S. Public*, pg. 2258
LAAN HEILOO B.V.—See Orkla ASA; *Int'l*, pg. 5638
LA ANONIMA; *Int'l*, pg. 4386
LAAN & SPAR BANK A/S; *Int'l*, pg. 4389

COMPANY NAME INDEX

LAARS HEATING SYSTEMS CO.—See Bradford-White Corporation; *U.S. Private*, pg. 632
LA ASH, INC.—See Seven Group Holdings Limited; *Int'l*, pg. 6732
LA ASSOCIATES, INC.; *U.S. Private*, pg. 2367
LAB21 HEALTHCARE LTD.—See Novacyt SA; *Int'l*, pg. 5454
LAB21 LTD.—See Novacyt SA; *Int'l*, pg. 5454
LAB 21 SA—See RINA S.p.A.; *Int'l*, pg. 6342
LAB 231 S.R.L.—See Iren S.p.A.; *Int'l*, pg. 3808
LABADIE AUTO INC.; *U.S. Private*, pg. 2370
LA BAGUETTE FRENCH BREAD & PASTRY SHOP; *U.S. Private*, pg. 2368
LABAIRE SYSTEMS CO—See Activar, Inc.; *U.S. Private*, pg. 68
LA BANQUE CENTRALE DE MADAGASCAR; *Int'l*, pg. 4386
LA BANQUE DE FRANCE; *Int'l*, pg. 4386
LA BANQUE POSTALE—See La Poste S.A.; *Int'l*, pg. 4388
LABARGE COATING, LLC—See Womble Company Inc.; *U.S. Private*, pg. 4556
LABA ROYALTY SUB LLC—See Innoviva, Inc.; *U.S. Public*, pg. 1127
LA BASQUAISE DE CD—See Compagnie de Saint-Gobain SA; *Int'l*, pg. 1724
LABAT AFRICA LTD.; *Int'l*, pg. 4389
LABAT-ANDERSON INC.—See Corporate Risk Holdings LLC; *U.S. Private*, pg. 1056
LABATT BREWERIES ATLANTIC REGION—See Anheuser-Busch InBev SA/NV; *Int'l*, pg. 466
LABATT BREWERIES OF LONDON—See Anheuser-Busch InBev SA/NV; *Int'l*, pg. 466
LABATT BREWERIES OF NEWFOUNDLAND—See Anheuser-Busch InBev SA/NV; *Int'l*, pg. 466
LABATT BREWERIES ONTARIO LTD.—See Anheuser-Busch InBev SA/NV; *Int'l*, pg. 466
LABATT BREWERIES PRAIRIE REGION—See Anheuser-Busch InBev SA/NV; *Int'l*, pg. 466
LABATT BREWING COMPANY LIMITED—See Anheuser-Busch InBev SA/NV; *Int'l*, pg. 466
LABATT FOOD SERVICE; *U.S. Private*, pg. 2370
LABATT USA LLC—See Florida Ice and Farm Co. S.A.; *Int'l*, pg. 2708
LABAY-SUMMERS INTERNATIONAL INC.; *U.S. Private*, pg. 2370
LABBIOTECH LTD.—See HORIBA Ltd; *Int'l*, pg. 3477
LABCONCO CORPORATION; *U.S. Private*, pg. 2370
LABCONNECT LLC; *U.S. Private*, pg. 2370
LABCONSULT GMBH.—See Sonic Healthcare Limited; *Int'l*, pg. 7097
LABCOR, INC.—See Morgan Stanley; *U.S. Public*, pg. 1474
LABCORP - BATON ROUGE—See Laboratory Corporation of America Holdings; *U.S. Public*, pg. 1287
LABCORP BVBA—See Laboratory Corporation of America Holdings; *U.S. Public*, pg. 1287
LABCORP - CHEYENNE—See Laboratory Corporation of America Holdings; *U.S. Public*, pg. 1287
LABCORP CLINICAL TRIALS—See Laboratory Corporation of America Holdings; *U.S. Public*, pg. 1287
LABCORP EMPLOYER SERVICES, INC.—See Laboratory Corporation of America Holdings; *U.S. Public*, pg. 1287
LABCORP JAPAN, G.K.—See Laboratory Corporation of America Holdings; *U.S. Public*, pg. 1287
LAB CRAFTERS INC.—See Huron Capital Partners LLC; *U.S. Private*, pg. 2012
LABCYTE, INC.—See Danaher Corporation; *U.S. Public*, pg. 624
LAB DEPOT S.A.—See HORIBA Ltd; *Int'l*, pg. 3477
LA/BEACH STRATEGIC ALLIANCE, LLC—See Marsh & McLennan Companies, Inc.; *U.S. Public*, pg. 1381
LABEGE AUTO SPORT S.A.S.; *Int'l*, pg. 4389
LABEL-AIRE A/S—See Impaxx, Inc.; *U.S. Private*, pg. 2049
LABEL-AIRE, INC.—See Impaxx, Inc.; *U.S. Private*, pg. 2049
LABEL ART—See Platinum Equity, LLC; *U.S. Private*, pg. 3206
LABEL CRAFTS JAMAICA LTD.—See Goddard Enterprises Limited; *Int'l*, pg. 3019
LABEL IMPRESSION, INC.—See Genstar Capital, LLC; *U.S. Private*, pg. 1676
LABEL INDUSTRIES, INC.—See Sycamore Partners Management, LP; *U.S. Private*, pg. 3896
LABELING SYSTEMS LLC—See Leonard Green & Partners, L.P.; *U.S. Private*, pg. 2428
LABELKRAFT TECHNOLOGIES LIMITED; *Int'l*, pg. 4389
LABELLA ASSOCIATES, D.P.C.; *U.S. Private*, pg. 2370
LABELLA SAUSAGE, LLC—See The Anderson Group, LLC; *U.S. Private*, pg. 3986
LA BELLE FASHIONS INC.; *U.S. Private*, pg. 2368
LABELLE STRATEGIC RESOURCES, INC.—See Knowledge Anywhere, Inc.; *U.S. Private*, pg. 2323
LABEL SAS—See Advent International Corporation; *U.S. Private*, pg. 100
LABELS BY ANDRES NV—See Damartex SA; *Int'l*, pg. 1956
THE LABEL SMITH LLC—See Heartwood Partners, LLC; *U.S. Private*, pg. 1901

LABELS WEST, INC.—See Ares Management Corporation; *U.S. Public*, pg. 190
LABEL TECH, INC.—See Harvest Partners L.P.; *U.S. Private*, pg. 1876
LABELTEC—See J.R. Cole Industries Inc.; *U.S. Private*, pg. 2170
LABELTEX MILLS INCORPORATED; *U.S. Private*, pg. 2370
LABEL WORKS—See Taylor Corporation; *U.S. Private*, pg. 3938
LABELWORX INC.—See Resilience Capital Partners, LLC; *U.S. Private*, pg. 3405
LAB ENTREPRENOR AS—See AF Gruppen ASA; *Int'l*, pg. 184
LAB ESCAPE, INC.—See Teikametrics LLC; *U.S. Private*, pg. 3958
LABESFAL LABORATORIOS ALMIRO S.A—See Fresenius SE & Co. KGaA; *Int'l*, pg. 2778
LABETTE HEALTH; *U.S. Private*, pg. 2370
LABEYRIE FINE FOODS SAS—See Lur Berri; *Int'l*, pg. 4586
LABEYRIE SA—See Lur Berri; *Int'l*, pg. 4586
LABFORWARD GMBH; *Int'l*, pg. 4389
LABGEAR AUSTRALIA PTY. LTD.—See Paragon Care Limited; *Int'l*, pg. 5736
LABGENOMICS CO., LTD.; *Int'l*, pg. 4389
LAB GMBH—See CNIM Constructions Industrielles de la Mediterranee SA; *Int'l*, pg. 1677
LABIANA HEALTH SA; *Int'l*, pg. 4389
LABIANA LIFE SCIENCES, S.A.; *Int'l*, pg. 4389
LA BI.CO DUE S.R.L.—See A2A S.p.A.; *Int'l*, pg. 29
LABIMEX SRO—See HORIBA Ltd; *Int'l*, pg. 3477
LABINAL DE CHIHUAHUA, SA DE CV—See Safran SA; *Int'l*, pg. 6474
LABINAL DE MEXICO, SA DE CV—See Safran SA; *Int'l*, pg. 6474
LABINAL SALISBURY, INC.—See Safran SA; *Int'l*, pg. 6474
LABINAL SERVICES—See Safran SA; *Int'l*, pg. 6474
LABINAL VICHY—See Safran SA; *Int'l*, pg. 6474
LABINAL VILLEMUR—See Safran SA; *Int'l*, pg. 6474
LABITE.COM, INC.—See Just Eat Takeaway.com N.V.; *Int'l*, pg. 4030
LABIXIAOXIN (FUJIAN) FOOD STUFF INDUSTRY CO., LTD—See Labixiaoxin Snacks Group Limited; *Int'l*, pg. 4389
LABIXIAOXIN SNACKS GROUP LIMITED; *Int'l*, pg. 4389
LA BIZNAGA S.A.—See Ledesma S.A.A.I.; *Int'l*, pg. 4439
LABKOTEC OY—See Indutrade Ab; *Int'l*, pg. 3680
LAB. LIERAC SA—See Impala SAS; *Int'l*, pg. 3631
LAB LOGISTICS LLC—See Atlantic Street Capital Management LLC; *U.S. Private*, pg. 374
LABMAG SERVICES INC.—See Abaxx Technologies Inc.; *Int'l*, pg. 48
LAB MANAGER—See LabX Media Group; *Int'l*, pg. 4391
LAB MASTER SDN. BHD.—See Hiap Huat Holdings Bhd; *Int'l*, pg. 3382
LAB M HOLDINGS—See Neogen Corporation; *U.S. Public*, pg. 1505
LAB M LIMITED—See Neogen Corporation; *U.S. Public*, pg. 1505
LABNAC INC.—See Liston Brick Company of Corona Inc.; *U.S. Private*, pg. 2467
LA BODEGA INC.; *U.S. Private*, pg. 2368
LABO-LOKEREN B.V.B.A.—See Sonic Healthcare Limited; *Int'l*, pg. 7097
LA BONITA OLE, INC.; *U.S. Private*, pg. 2368
LABOPHARM EUROPE LIMITED—See Endo International plc; *Int'l*, pg. 2404
LABO PRINT S.A.; *Int'l*, pg. 4389
LABOR 28 AG—See Sonic Healthcare Limited; *Int'l*, pg. 7097
LABOR 28 MANAGEMENT GMBH—See Sonic Healthcare Limited; *Int'l*, pg. 7097
LABORATOIRE D AUDITION DE ARCEAUX SARL—See Amplifon S.p.A.; *Int'l*, pg. 435
LABORATOIRE DE DERMO-COSMETIQUE ANIMALE S.A.S.—See Vimian Group AB; *Int'l*, pg. 8208
LABORATOIRE DE LA MER SAS—See Perrigo Company plc; *Int'l*, pg. 5813
LABORATOIRE ELAIAPHARM SA—See Lundbeckfonden; *Int'l*, pg. 4583
LABORATOIRE GARANCIA SAS—See Unilever PLC; *Int'l*, pg. 8044
LABORATOIRE GLAXOSMITHKLINE—See GSK plc; *Int'l*, pg. 3149
LABORATOIRE KALISTERRA SAS—See PAI Partners S.A.S.; *Int'l*, pg. 5700
LABORATOIRE KCI MEDICAL—See 3M Company; *U.S. Public*, pg. 8
LABORATOIRE MONIQUE REMY—See International Flavors & Fragrances Inc.; *U.S. Public*, pg. 1153

LABORATOIRE NEGMA S.A.S.—See Wockhardt Limited; *Int'l*, pg. 8441
LABORATOIRE OENOBIOL S.A.S.—See Sanofi; *Int'l*, pg. 6548
LABORATOIRE OPHTALMIC B&T; *Int'l*, pg. 4390
LABORATOIRES ALCON S.A.—See Novartis AG; *Int'l*, pg. 5457
LABORATOIRES ANIOS S.A.—See Ecolab Inc.; *U.S. Public*, pg. 714
LABORATOIRE SANOFLORE SA—See L'Oreal S.A.; *Int'l*, pg. 4380
LABORATOIRES BOIRON SRL—See Boiron Group; *Int'l*, pg. 1101
LABORATOIRES BOUCHARA RECORDATI S.A.S.—See Recordati S.p.A.; *Int'l*, pg. 6239
LABORATOIRES CLARINS S.A.; *Int'l*, pg. 1649
LABORATOIRES COLOPLAST—See Coloplast A/S; *Int'l*, pg. 1704
LABORATOIRES CONVATEC SAS—See ConvaTec Group PLC; *Int'l*, pg. 1786
LABORATOIRES DECLEOR S.A.S.—See L'Oreal S.A.; *Int'l*, pg. 4380
LABORATOIRES DIETETIQUE ET SANTE SAS—See Otsuka Holdings Co., Ltd.; *Int'l*, pg. 5658
LABORATOIRES DR. N.G. PAYOT—See LBO France S.a.r.l.; *Int'l*, pg. 4429
LABORATOIRE SERVICES INTERNATIONAL (LSI) SAS—See Thermo Fisher Scientific Inc.; *U.S. Public*, pg. 2149
LABORATOIRES EXPANSCIENCE; *Int'l*, pg. 4390
LABORATOIRES FILORGA COSMETIQUES ESPANA S.L.U.—See Colgate-Palmolive Company; *U.S. Public*, pg. 533
LABORATOIRES FILORGA COSMETIQUES S.A.—See Colgate-Palmolive Company; *U.S. Public*, pg. 533
LABORATOIRES FUJIFILM SA—See FUJIFILM Holdings Corporation; *Int'l*, pg. 2822
LABORATOIRES GALDERMA SAS—See Abu Dhabi Investment Authority; *Int'l*, pg. 71
LABORATOIRES GALDERMA SAS—See EQT Corporation; *U.S. Public*, pg. 785
LABORATOIRES GALDERMA SAS—See Public Sector Pension Investment Board; *Int'l*, pg. 6096
LABORATOIRES GARNIER PARIS—See L'Oreal S.A.; *Int'l*, pg. 4380
LABORATOIRES GRUNENTHAL S.A.S.—See Grunenthal GmbH; *Int'l*, pg. 3115
LABORATOIRES LEO S.A—See LEO Pharma A/S; *Int'l*, pg. 4457
LABORATOIRES LOHMANN & RAUSCHER S.A.—See Lohmann & Rauscher International GmbH & Co. KG; *Int'l*, pg. 4544
LABORATOIRES MERCK SHARP & DOHME-CHIBRET SNC—See Merck & Co., Inc.; *U.S. Public*, pg. 1417
LABORATOIRES OMEGA PHARMA FRANCE SAS—See Perrigo Company plc; *Int'l*, pg. 5813
LABORATOIRES PAUL HARTMANN S.A.R.L.—See PAUL HARTMANN AG; *Int'l*, pg. 5761
LABORATOIRES PHYTOSOLBA—See Impala SAS; *Int'l*, pg. 3631
LABORATOIRES RADIATEX S.A.—See Sagami Rubber Industries Co., Ltd.; *Int'l*, pg. 6478
LABORATOIRES TAKEDA—See Takeda Pharmaceutical Company Limited; *Int'l*, pg. 7439
LABORATOIRES TERUMO FRANCE S.A.—See Terumo Corporation; *Int'l*, pg. 7569
LABORATORI CAT-GAIRIN, S.L.U.—See Eurofins Scientific S.E.; *Int'l*, pg. 2550
LABORATORIE DR RENAUD INC.—See Bausch Health Companies Inc.; *Int'l*, pg. 898
LABORATORIES 3M SANTE SAS—See 3M Company; *U.S. Public*, pg. 6
LABORATORIES TORRENT, S.A. DE C.V.—See Torrent Pharmaceuticals Limited; *Int'l*, pg. 7831
LABORATORIO ALAC LTDA.—See Eurofins Scientific S.E.; *Int'l*, pg. 2550
LABORATORIO ANALISI CLINICHE MEDICHE IANNACCONE S.R.L.—See Bios S.p.A.; *Int'l*, pg. 1041
LABORATORIO CHILE S.A.—See Teva Pharmaceutical Industries, Ltd.; *Int'l*, pg. 7579
LABORATORIO DE ANALISES CLINICAS J. PINTO DE BARROS, S.A.—See Eurofins Scientific S.E.; *Int'l*, pg. 2551
LABORATORIO DE ANALISES CLINICAS SAO LUCAS LTDA.—See Centro de Imagem Diagnosticos S.A.; *Int'l*, pg. 1413
LABORATORIO DE CONTROL ARJ, S. A. DE C. V.—See ALS Limited; *Int'l*, pg. 378
LABORATORIO DE ENSAYOS METROLOGICOS, S.L.—See I Squared Capital Advisors (US) LLC; *U.S. Private*, pg. 2023
LABORATORIO DE ENSAYOS METROLOGICOS, S.L.—See TDR Capital LLP; *Int'l*, pg. 7492
LABORATORIO FARMACEUTICO ERFO S.P.A.; *Int'l*, pg. 4390
LABORATORIO FRANCO COLOMBIANO LAFRANCOL S.A.S.—See Abbott Laboratories; *U.S. Public*, pg. 20

LABORATORIO FARMACEUTICO ERFO S.P.A.

CORPORATE AFFILIATIONS

LABORATORIO GESSYMA GALEA, S.L.—See Eurofins Scientific S.E.; *Int'l*, pg. 2550
LABORATORIO LKM SA—See Advent International Corporation; *U.S. Private*, pg. 103
LABORATORIO PASTEUR DE ANALISES CLINICAS LTDA.—See Eurofins Scientific S.E.; *Int'l*, pg. 2550
LABORATORIO REIG JOFRE, S.A.; *Int'l*, pg. 4390
LABORATORIO ROE S.A.—See UnitedHealth Group Incorporated; *U.S. Public*, pg. 2242
LABORATORIO SAO LUCAS LTDA.—See Eurofins Scientific S.E.; *Int'l*, pg. 2550
LABORATORIOS ARSAL SA DE CV—See HORIBA Ltd; *Int'l*, pg. 3477
LABORATORIOS BAGO COLOMBIA—See Bago Group; *Int'l*, pg. 799
LABORATORIOS BAGO DE BOLIVIA S.A.—See Bago Group; *Int'l*, pg. 799
LABORATORIOS BAGO DE GUATEMALA S.A.—See Bago Group; *Int'l*, pg. 799
LABORATORIOS BAGO DEL ECUADOR S.A.—See Bago Group; *Int'l*, pg. 799
LABORATORIOS BAGO DEL PERU S.A.—See Bago Group; *Int'l*, pg. 799
LABORATORIOS BAGO DO BRASIL S.A.—See Bago Group; *Int'l*, pg. 799
LABORATORIOS BAGO S.A.—See Bago Group; *Int'l*, pg. 799
LABORATORIOS B.BRAUN S.A.—See B. Braun Melsungen AG; *Int'l*, pg. 787
LABORATORIOS BETA S.A.; *Int'l*, pg. 4390
LABORATORIOS BUCKMAN S.A.—See Bulab Holdings, Inc.; *U.S. Private*, pg. 684
LABORATORIOS COMBIX S.L.—See Zydus Lifesciences Limited; *Int'l*, pg. 8700
LABORATORIOS DEL DR. ESTEVE, S.A.; *Int'l*, pg. 4390
LABORATORIOS DELTA SA—See Viatris Inc.; *U.S. Public*, pg. 2293
LABORATORIOS FARMACEUTICOS DE NICARAGUA, S.A.—See GSK plc; *Int'l*, pg. 3149
LABORATORIOS FARMACEUTICOS GUERBET S.A.—See Guerbet SA; *Int'l*, pg. 3172
LABORATORIOS FARMACEUTICOS ROVI S.A.; *Int'l*, pg. 4390
LABORATORIOS FERRING LTDA—See Ferring Holding SA; *Int'l*, pg. 2642
LABORATORIOS FERRING SA—See Ferring Holding SA; *Int'l*, pg. 2642
LABORATORIOS FROSST, S.A.—See Merck & Co., Inc.; *U.S. Public*, pg. 1417
LABORATORIOS GALDERMA, S.A.—See Nestle S.A.; *Int'l*, pg. 5203
LABORATORIOS GRIFFITH DE CENTRO AMERICA S.A.—See Griffith Laboratories, Inc.; *U.S. Private*, pg. 1789
LABORATORIOS GRIFFITH DE MEXICO S.A. DE C.V.—See Griffith Laboratories, Inc.; *U.S. Private*, pg. 1789
LABORATORIOS GRIFOLS, S.A.—See Grifols, S.A.; *Int'l*, pg. 3085
LABORATORIOS GRIN, S.A. DE C.V.—See Lupin Limited; *Int'l*, pg. 4586
LABORATORIOS GROSSMAN, S.A.—See Bausch Health Companies Inc.; *Int'l*, pg. 897
LABORATORIOS HARTMANN S.A.—See PAUL HARTMANN AG; *Int'l*, pg. 5761
LABORATORIOS HEEL ESPANA, S.A.U.—See Delton AG; *Int'l*, pg. 2021
LABORATORIOS INDAS, S.A.U.—See PT Sinar Mas Group; *Int'l*, pg. 6073
LABORATORIOS INTERVET S.A.—See Merck & Co., Inc.; *U.S. Public*, pg. 1417
LABORATORIOS KARIZOO, S.A. DE C.V.—See SeQuent Scientific Limited; *Int'l*, pg. 6719
LABORATORIOS KARIZOO, S.A.—See SeQuent Scientific Limited; *Int'l*, pg. 6719
LABORATORIOS MONTORO BOTELLA SL—See Eurofins Scientific S.E.; *Int'l*, pg. 2551
LABORATORIOS PARKE DAVIS, S.L.—See Pfizer Inc.; *U.S. Public*, pg. 1680
LABORATORIOS PFIZER, LDA.—See Pfizer Inc.; *U.S. Public*, pg. 1680
LABORATORIOS PFIZER LTDA.—See Pfizer Inc.; *U.S. Public*, pg. 1680
LABORATORIOS PHOENIX SOCIEDAD ANONIMA INDUSTRIAL COMERCIAL Y FINANCIERA—See GSK plc; *Int'l*, pg. 3149
LABORATORIOS RECALCINE S.A.—See Abbott Laboratories; *U.S. Public*, pg. 20
LABORATORIOS SANFER S.A. DE C.V.—See Invekra S.A.P.I. de C.V.; *Int'l*, pg. 3772
LABORATORIOS SILESIA S.A.—See Grunenthal GmbH; *Int'l*, pg. 3115
LABORATORIOS STADA, S.L.—See Bain Capital, LP; *U.S. Private*, pg. 443
LABORATORIO STADA, S.L.—See Cinven Limited; *Int'l*, pg. 1613
LABORATORIOS TORRENT MALAYSIA SDN. BHD.—See Torrent Pharmaceuticals Limited; *Int'l*, pg. 7831

LABORATORIOS TORRENT, S.A. DE CV—See Torrent Pharmaceuticals Limited; *Int'l*, pg. 7831
LABORATORIOS VERIS S.A.—See FAES Farma, S.A.; *Int'l*, pg. 2601
LABORATORIOS VICKS, S.L.—See The Procter & Gamble Company; *U.S. Public*, pg. 2120
LABORATORIOS VIRBAC COSTA RICA SA—See Virbac S.A.; *Int'l*, pg. 8246
LABORATORIOS VIRBAC MEXICO S.A. DE C.V.—See Virbac S.A.; *Int'l*, pg. 8246
LABORATORIOS VITAL, S.L.U.—See Eurofins Scientific S.E.; *Int'l*, pg. 2551
LABORATORIOS VITORIA S.A.—See FAES Farma, S.A.; *Int'l*, pg. 2601
LABORATORIO SYNTHESIS S.A.S.—See Abbott Laboratories; *U.S. Public*, pg. 20
LABORATORY CORPORATION OF AMERICA HOLDINGS; *U.S. Public*, pg. 1285
LABORATORY SERVICES MSO LLC; *U.S. Private*, pg. 2370
LABORATORY SPECIALITIES PROPRIETARY LTD.—See Thermo Fisher Scientific Inc.; *U.S. Public*, pg. 2147
LABORATORY STAFFING INC.—See Xenspire, Inc.; *U.S. Private*, pg. 4581
LABORCHEMIE APOLDA GMBH—See HEYL Chemisch-pharmazeutische Fabrik GmbH und Co. KG; *Int'l*, pg. 3374
LABORDIAGNOSZTIKA KFT.—See HORIBA Ltd; *Int'l*, pg. 3477
LABORD-MED-APARELHAGEM DE PRECISAO LTDA.—See Mauna Kea Technologies SA; *Int'l*, pg. 4732
LABORELEC C.V.—See ENGIE SA; *Int'l*, pg. 2431
THE LABORERS PACIFIC SOUTHWEST REGIONAL ORGANIZING COALITION; *U.S. Private*, pg. 4067
LABOREX BURKINA S.A.—See Toyota Tsusho Corporation; *Int'l*, pg. 7876
LABOREX CAMEROUN SA—See Toyota Tsusho Corporation; *Int'l*, pg. 7876
LABOREX KENYA LIMITED—See Toyota Tsusho Corporation; *Int'l*, pg. 7876
LABOREX MALI S.A—See Toyota Tsusho Corporation; *Int'l*, pg. 7876
LABOREX SENEGAL—See Toyota Tsusho Corporation; *Int'l*, pg. 7876
LABOREX TANZANIE—See Toyota Tsusho Corporation; *Int'l*, pg. 7876
LABOREX UGANDA LIMITED—See Toyota Tsusho Corporation; *Int'l*, pg. 7876
LABOR HAKO S.A.S.—See L. Possehl & Co. mbH; *Int'l*, pg. 4383
LABOR HAMBURG - LUEBECK MVZ GMBH—See Sonic Healthcare Limited; *Int'l*, pg. 7097
LABOR HANNOVER MVZ GMBH—See Sonic Healthcare Limited; *Int'l*, pg. 7097
LABORIE BELGIUM—See Investor AB; *Int'l*, pg. 3786
LABORIE CANADA—See Investor AB; *Int'l*, pg. 3786
LABORIE CHINA—See Investor AB; *Int'l*, pg. 3786
LABORIE EUROPE LTD—See Investor AB; *Int'l*, pg. 3786
LABORIE FRANCE—See Investor AB; *Int'l*, pg. 3786
LABORIE GERMANY—See Investor AB; *Int'l*, pg. 3786
LABORIE MEDICAL TECHNOLOGIES, CORP.—See Investor AB; *Int'l*, pg. 3786
LABORIE MEDICAL TECHNOLOGIES, ULC—See Investor AB; *Int'l*, pg. 3786
LABOR LADEMANNBOGEN MVZ GMBH—See Sonic Healthcare Limited; *Int'l*, pg. 7097
LABOR MANAGEMENT CONCEPTS, INC.; *U.S. Private*, pg. 2370
LABOR-MANAGEMENT HEALTHCARE FUND; *U.S. Private*, pg. 2370
LABORMED PHARMA S.A.—See Advent International Corporation; *U.S. Private*, pg. 103
LABOR READY MID-ATLANTIC, INC.—See TrueBlue, Inc.; *U.S. Public*, pg. 2198
LABOR READY MIDWEST, INC.—See TrueBlue, Inc.; *U.S. Public*, pg. 2198
LABOR READY SOUTHEAST, INC.—See TrueBlue, Inc.; *U.S. Public*, pg. 2198
LABOR READY SOUTHWEST, INC.—See TrueBlue, Inc.; *U.S. Public*, pg. 2198
LABOR RELATIONS INSTITUTE, INC.; *U.S. Private*, pg. 2370
LABOR SAVING DEVICES, INC.—See George Risk Industries, Inc.; *U.S. Public*, pg. 934
LABOR SCHOTTDORF ADMINISTRATION GMBH—See Sonic Healthcare Limited; *Int'l*, pg. 7097
LABOR SMART INC.; *U.S. Public*, pg. 1285
LABOR STAFFING, INC.; *U.S. Private*, pg. 2370
LABOR TRES LABORATORIOS E CONSULTORIA TECNICA LTDA.—See Eurofins Scientific S.E.; *Int'l*, pg. 2550
LABOR-ZENTRAL.CH AG—See IDEXX Laboratories, Inc.; *U.S. Public*, pg. 1093
LABOSPORT SAS; *Int'l*, pg. 4390
LABOTECH INTERNATIONAL CO., LTD.—See Furuno Electric Co., Ltd.; *Int'l*, pg. 2848
LABOTEC INC.; *U.S. Private*, pg. 2370
LABOTEC, INC.—See BML, Inc.; *Int'l*, pg. 1076

LABOUESSE; *Int'l*, pg. 4390
LABOUR SOLUTIONS AUSTRALIA PROPRIETARY LIMITED—See Adcorp Holdings Limited; *Int'l*, pg. 127
LABOV MECHANICAL, INC.—See EMCOR Group, Inc.; *U.S. Public*, pg. 738
LABPLAS SDN BHD—See Jebsen & Jessen (SEA) Pte Ltd; *Int'l*, pg. 3926
LAB PRODUCTS, INC.—See Bio Medic Corporation; *U.S. Private*, pg. 561
LABRADA BODYBUILDING NUTRITION INC.; *U.S. Private*, pg. 2370
LABRADOR GOLD CORP.; *Int'l*, pg. 4390
LABRADOR IRON MINES HOLDINGS LIMITED; *Int'l*, pg. 4390
LABRADOR IRON ORE ROYALTY CORPORATION; *Int'l*, pg. 4390
LABRADOR MINERAL RESOURCES INC.—See Mega-Watt Lithium and Battery Metals Corp.; *Int'l*, pg. 4794
LABRADOR RESOURCES INC.; *Int'l*, pg. 4390
LABRADOR URANIUM INC.—See ATHA Energy Corp.; *Int'l*, pg. 669
LABRADOR VENTURES, L.P.; *U.S. Private*, pg. 2370
LA BRASSERIE LABATT—See Anheuser-Busch InBev SA/NV; *Int'l*, pg. 466
LA BRAYER INDUSTRIES LTD.; *Int'l*, pg. 4387
LA BREA BAKERY, INC.—See ARYZTA AG; *Int'l*, pg. 588
LABRECHE; *U.S. Private*, pg. 2371
LABRIOLA BAKING COMPANY; *U.S. Private*, pg. 2371
LABROBOT PRODUCTS AB—See Addtech AB; *Int'l*, pg. 134
LABROUSSE S.A.—See Tessenderlo Group NV; *Int'l*, pg. 7573
LABRUM AB—See ADDvise Group AB; *Int'l*, pg. 136
LAB SCIENCE SOLUTION SDN BHD—See HORIBA Ltd; *Int'l*, pg. 3477
LABSKE STERKOPISKY A BETON S.R.O.—See Heidelberg Materials AG; *Int'l*, pg. 3318
LABSO CHIMIE FINE S.A.R.L—See C.H. Boehringer Sohn AG & Co. KG; *Int'l*, pg. 1242
LABSPHERE, INC.—See Halma plc; *Int'l*, pg. 3231
LABSTYLE INNOVATION LTD.—See DarioHealth Corp.; *U.S. Public*, pg. 633
LAB SUPPORT, LLC—See ASGN Incorporated; *U.S. Public*, pg. 211
LABTECH INTERIORS LLC—See Dubai Investments PJSC; *Int'l*, pg. 2219
LABTECH SERVICES LTD.—See Global Energy (Holdings) Ltd.; *Int'l*, pg. 2995
LABTECH SOFTWARE, LLC; *U.S. Private*, pg. 2371
LABTECH SOFTWARE—See LabTech Software, LLC; *U.S. Private*, pg. 2371
LABTESTS LIMITED—See Brookfield Corporation; *Int'l*, pg. 1176
LABTEST—See Intertek Group plc; *Int'l*, pg. 3763
LAB TOP PERU S.R.L—See HORIBA Ltd; *Int'l*, pg. 3477
LABUAN INTERNATIONAL FINANCIAL EXCHANGE INC.—See Bursa Malaysia Berhad; *Int'l*, pg. 1227
LABUDDE GROUP, INC.; *U.S. Private*, pg. 2371
LABUR BINA SDN. BHD.—See WCT Holdings Berhad; *Int'l*, pg. 8362
L.A. BURDICK CHOCOLATE; *U.S. Private*, pg. 2364
LABU SAYONG CAFE SDN. BHD.—See Perak Corporation Berhad; *Int'l*, pg. 5796
LA BUVETTE S.A.S.; *Int'l*, pg. 4387
LABVANTAGE SOLUTIONS INC.; *U.S. Private*, pg. 2371
LAB-VENT CONTROLS A/S—See AddLife AB; *Int'l*, pg. 129
LAB VISION CORPORATION—See Thermo Fisher Scientific Inc.; *U.S. Public*, pg. 2152
LABWIRE, INC.; *U.S. Public*, pg. 1287
LABWORLD (PTY) LTD.—See AFGRI Limited; *Int'l*, pg. 188
LABX MEDIA GROUP; *Int'l*, pg. 4390
LABX—See LabX Media Group; *Int'l*, pg. 4391
LABYRINTH INC.—See Harbor Business Compliance Corporation; *U.S. Private*, pg. 1858
LABYRINTH RESOURCES LIMITED; *Int'l*, pg. 4391
LABYRINTH SOLUTIONS INC.—See BGF Group PLC
LA CADENA INVESTMENTS; *U.S. Private*, pg. 2368
LA CAFETIERE (UK) LIMITED—See Lifetime Brands, Inc.; *U.S. Public*, pg. 1313
LA CALA GOLF CLUB S.L.—See Farmer Business Developments plc; *Int'l*, pg. 2619
LA CAMPAGNOLA S.A.C.I.—See Arcor Sociedad Anonima, Industrial y Comercial; *Int'l*, pg. 550
LA CANADA TOCHOSA, S.A.—See Nefinsa S.A.; *Int'l*, pg. 5192
LA CANASTA FURNISHINGS; *U.S. Private*, pg. 2368
LA CAPITAL CABLE S.A.—See Grupo Clarin S.A.; *Int'l*, pg. 3125
LA CAPITALE CIVIL SERVICE INSURER INC.—See La Capitale Civil Service Mutual; *Int'l*, pg. 4387
LA CAPITALE CIVIL SERVICE MUTUAL; *Int'l*, pg. 4387
LA CAPITALE FINANCIAL GROUP INC.—See La Capitale Civil Service Mutual; *Int'l*, pg. 4387
LA CAPITALE FINANCIAL SECURITY INSURANCE COMPANY—See La Capitale Civil Service Mutual; *Int'l*, pg. 4387

COMPANY NAME INDEX

LA CAPITALE GENERAL INSURANCE INC.—See La Capitale Civil Service Mutual; *Int'l*, pg. 4387
LA. CARRIERS,L.L.C.; *U.S. Private*, pg. 2370
LA CARTERIE HALLMARK—See Hallmark Cards, Inc.; *U.S. Private*, pg. 1845
LA CASA DE DON PEDRO, INC.; *U.S. Private*, pg. 2368
LACAVA & SOWERSBY INC.; *U.S. Private*, pg. 2371
LA CAVE WAREHOUSE—See Vino Vault, Inc.; *U.S. Private*, pg. 4386
LAC CO., LTD.; *Int'l*, pg. 4391
LAC DES ILES MINES LTD.—See Impala Platinum Holdings Limited; *Int'l*, pg. 3630
LACE FOODSERVICE CORPORATION; *U.S. Private*, pg. 2371
THE LACEK GROUP—See WPP plc; *Int'l*, pg. 8488
LACE LASTIC COMPANY; *U.S. Private*, pg. 2371
LA CENA FINE FOODS LTD.—See Diaz Wholesale & Manufacturing Co., Inc.; *U.S. Private*, pg. 1225
LACERTA GROUP, INC.—See SK Capital Partners, LP; *U.S. Private*, pg. 3679
LACERTE SOFTWARE CORPORATION—See Intuit Inc.; *U.S. Public*, pg. 1160
LACES GROUP, INC.—See ONEX Corporation; *Int'l*, pg. 5578
LACEY MANUFACTURING COMPANY LLC—See NN, Inc.; *U.S. Public*, pg. 1531
LAC GROUP; *U.S. Private*, pg. 2371
LA CHAINE INFO—See Television Francaise 1 S.A.; *Int'l*, pg. 7542
LA CHARTREUSE—See Carrefour SA; *Int'l*, pg. 1345
LA CHATEAU BONNE ENTENTE—See Pomerleau Inc.; *Int'l*, pg. 5917
LACHAT INSTRUMENTS—See Danaher Corporation; *U.S. Public*, pg. 628
LA CHAUSSERIA SA; *Int'l*, pg. 4387
LACHAUX PAYSAGES—See FAYAT SAS; *Int'l*, pg. 2625
LACHENMEIER APS—See Illinois Tool Works Inc.; *U.S. Public*, pg. 1109
LACHER & ASSOCIATES INSURANCE AGENCY, INC.; *U.S. Private*, pg. 2371
LACHLAN STAR LIMITED; *Int'l*, pg. 4391
LACIE AB—See Seagate Technology Holdings PLC; *Int'l*, pg. 6663
LACIE ASIA LIMITED—See Seagate Technology Holdings PLC; *Int'l*, pg. 6663
LACIE ELECTRONIQUE D2, S.A.—See Seagate Technology Holdings PLC; *Int'l*, pg. 6663
LACIE LIMITED—See Seagate Technology Holdings PLC; *Int'l*, pg. 6663
LACIE LTD—See Seagate Technology Holdings PLC; *Int'l*, pg. 6663
LA CIE MCCORMICK CANADA CO.—See McCormick & Company, Incorporated; *U.S. Public*, pg. 1404
LACIE PERIPHERALS INC.—See Seagate Technology Holdings PLC; *Int'l*, pg. 6663
LACIE PTY LTD.—See Seagate Technology Holdings PLC; *Int'l*, pg. 6663
LACIE S.A.S.—See Seagate Technology Holdings PLC; *Int'l*, pg. 6663
LACIE S.A.S.—See Seagate Technology Holdings PLC; *Int'l*, pg. 6663
LACIE SPRL—See Seagate Technology Holdings PLC; *Int'l*, pg. 6663
LACIE SRL.—See Seagate Technology Holdings PLC; *Int'l*, pg. 6663
LACIMA INC.; *U.S. Private*, pg. 2371
LA CIMENTERIE DE LUKALA S.A.R.L.—See Heidelberg Materials AG; *Int'l*, pg. 3318
LACKAWANNA CASUALTY COMPANY—See Group One Thousand One, LLC; *U.S. Private*, pg. 1794
LACKAWANNA PRODUCTS CORP.; *U.S. Private*, pg. 2371
THE LACKEY GROUP; *U.S. Private*, pg. 4067
LACKEY MEMORIAL HOSPITAL; *U.S. Private*, pg. 2371
LACKIER CENTER GLAUCHAU GMBH—See Porsche Automobil Holding SE; *Int'l*, pg. 5933
LACKIER CENTRUM OBERLAND GMBH—See Porsche Automobil Holding SE; *Int'l*, pg. 5933
LACKPROM PLC.—See Synergon Holding PLC; *Int'l*, pg. 7384
LACK'S AARONSON, INC.; *U.S. Private*, pg. 2371
LACKS ENTERPRISES, INC.; *U.S. Private*, pg. 2371
LACKS TRIM SYSTEMS, INC.—See Lacks Enterprises, Inc.; *U.S. Private*, pg. 2371
LACK'S VALLEY STORES LTD.—See Lack's Aaronson, Inc.; *U.S. Private*, pg. 2371
LACKS WHEEL TRIM SYSTEMS, INC.—See Lacks Enterprises, Inc.; *U.S. Private*, pg. 2371
LAC LA BICHE TRANSPORT LTD.; *Int'l*, pg. 4391
LACLEDE CHAIN MANUFACTURING CO., LLC - MARYVILLE—See C3 Capital Partners, LP; *U.S. Private*, pg. 710
LACLEDE CHAIN MANUFACTURING COMPANY, LLC—See C3 Capital Partners, LP; *U.S. Private*, pg. 710
LACLEDE DEVELOPMENT COMPANY—See Spire, Inc; *U.S. Public*, pg. 1918
LACLEDE ELECTRIC COOPERATIVE INC.; *U.S. Private*, pg. 2371

LACLEDE ENERGY RESOURCES, INC.—See Spire, Inc; *U.S. Public*, pg. 1918
LACLEDE GAS FAMILY SERVICES, INC.—See Spire, Inc; *U.S. Public*, pg. 1918
LACLEDE INSURANCE RISK SERVICES, INC.—See Spire, Inc; *U.S. Public*, pg. 1918
LACLEDE INVESTMENT LLC—See Spire, Inc; *U.S. Public*, pg. 1918
LACLEDE MILL—See Idaho Forest Group, LLC; *U.S. Private*, pg. 2035
LACLEDE PIPELINE COMPANY—See Spire, Inc; *U.S. Public*, pg. 1918
LACLEDE VENTURE CORP.—See Spire, Inc; *U.S. Public*, pg. 1918
LA CLINICA DE LA RAZA INC.; *U.S. Private*, pg. 2368
LA CLINIQUE DE PARIS (HK) LIMITED—See Meilleure Health International Industry Group Limited; *Int'l*, pg. 4803
LA CLINIQUE DU MOUSSEAU SAS—See Ramsay Health Care Limited; *Int'l*, pg. 6200
LA CLIPPERS LLC; *U.S. Private*, pg. 2368
LACO ASSOCIATES, INC.; *U.S. Private*, pg. 2372
LA COCINERA—See Nestle S.A.; *Int'l*, pg. 5205
LA-CO INDUSTRIES EUROPE S.A.S.—See LA-CO Industries Markal Co., Inc.; *U.S. Private*, pg. 2370
LA-CO INDUSTRIES MARKAL CO., INC.; *U.S. Private*, pg. 2370
LACOMBE FORD SALES LTD; *Int'l*, pg. 4391
LACOMED, SPOL. S R.O.—See CEZ, a.s.; *Int'l*, pg. 1429
LA COMPAGNIE BENJAMIN DE ROTHSCHILD S.A.—See Edmond de Rothschild Holding S.A.; *Int'l*, pg. 2313
LA COMPAGNIE DU VENT SAS—See ENGIE SA; *Int'l*, pg. 2434
LA COMPAGNIE FINANCIERE EDMOND DE ROTHSCHILD BANQUE—See Edmond de Rothschild Holding S.A.; *Int'l*, pg. 2313
LA COMPAGNIE FINANCIERE EDMOND DE ROTHSCHILD—See Edmond de Rothschild Holding S.A.; *Int'l*, pg. 2313
LA.COM—See Alden Global Capital LLC; *U.S. Private*, pg. 156
LA COMUNIDAD—See Publicis Groupe S.A.; *Int'l*, pg. 6110
LA COMUNIDAD—See Publicis Groupe S.A.; *Int'l*, pg. 6110
LA CONCORDE HOLDINGS LIMITED—See Niveus Investments Limited; *Int'l*, pg. 5389
L&A CONTRACTING COMPANY INC.; *U.S. Private*, pg. 2362
LA COOPERATIVE ARTERRIS SCA; *Int'l*, pg. 4387
LA COOPERATIVE WELCOOP SA; *Int'l*, pg. 4387
LACOPRODUCTORA, S.L.—See Promotora de Informaciones S.A.; *Int'l*, pg. 5995
LA CORNUE SAS—See The Middleby Corporation; *U.S. Public*, pg. 2114
LA CORNUE SAS—See The Middleby Corporation; *U.S. Public*, pg. 2114
LA CORNUE SAS—See The Middleby Corporation; *U.S. Public*, pg. 2114
LA CORNUE SAS—See The Middleby Corporation; *U.S. Public*, pg. 2114
LA CORTEZ ENERGY COLOMBIA E.U.—See LA CORTEZ ENERGY, INC.; *Int'l*, pg. 4387
LA CORTEZ ENERGY COLOMBIA, INC.—See LA CORTEZ ENERGY, INC.; *Int'l*, pg. 4387
LA CORTEZ ENERGY, INC.; *Int'l*, pg. 4387
LA COSTA DENTAL GROUP—See Espire Dental Practice, LLC; *U.S. Private*, pg. 1427
LACOSTE S.A.—See Maus Freres S.A.; *Int'l*, pg. 4732
LA COTE BLEUE S.A.S.—See KNEIP Communication S.A.; *Int'l*, pg. 4206
L-ACOUSTICS, INC.—See L-Acoustics SAS; *Int'l*, pg. 4381
L-ACOUSTICS SAS; *Int'l*, pg. 4381
LACOX INC.—See Ergon, Inc.; *U.S. Private*, pg. 1418
LACOX PROPANE GAS COMPANY INC.—See Ergon, Inc.; *U.S. Private*, pg. 1418
LA CREMA, INC.—See Jackson Family Wines, Inc.; *U.S. Private*, pg. 2176
LA CREME COFFEE & TEA—See DeCoty Coffee Company; *U.S. Private*, pg. 1188
LA CRETE TRANSPORT 79 LTD.—See TFI International Inc.; *Int'l*, pg. 7586
LACROIX ELECTRONICS FRANCE—See LACROIX S.A.; *Int'l*, pg. 4391
LACROIX ELECTRONICS—See LACROIX S.A.; *Int'l*, pg. 4391
LACROIX ELECTRONICS ZOO—See LACROIX S.A.; *Int'l*, pg. 4391
LACROIX + KRESS GMBH—See LS Corp.; *Int'l*, pg. 4569
LACROIX + KRESS GMBH—See LS Corp.; *Int'l*, pg. 4569
LACROIX S.A.; *Int'l*, pg. 4391
LACROIX S.A.; *Int'l*, pg. 4391
LACROIX SIGNALISATION—See LACROIX S.A.; *Int'l*, pg. 4391
LACROIX SINGAPORE PTE. LTD.—See LACROIX S.A.; *Int'l*, pg. 4391
LACROIX SOFREL ESPANA S.L.U.—See LACROIX S.A.; *Int'l*, pg. 4391
LACROIX SOFREL—See LACROIX S.A.; *Int'l*, pg. 4391

LACROIX SOFREL SRL—See LACROIX S.A.; *Int'l*, pg. 4391
LACROIX SPARKLING WATER, INC.—See National Beverage Corp.; *U.S. Public*, pg. 1494
LACROIX TRAFIC—See LACROIX S.A.; *Int'l*, pg. 4391
LA CROMOGRAFICA SRL—See Platinum Equity, LLC; *U.S. Private*, pg. 3206
LACROSSE FOOTWEAR, INC.—See ABC-Mart, Inc.; *Int'l*, pg. 57
LA CROSSE LUMBER COMPANY; *U.S. Private*, pg. 2368
LA CROSSE PLUMBING SUPPLY CO. INC.—See First Supply LLC; *U.S. Private*, pg. 1529
LA CROSSE PUBLIC LIBRARY; *U.S. Private*, pg. 2368
LA CROSSE TECHNOLOGY; *Int'l*, pg. 4387
LA CROSSE TRIBUNE—See Lee Enterprises, Incorporated; *U.S. Public*, pg. 1299
LA CROSSE TRUCK CENTER INC.; *U.S. Private*, pg. 2368
LACTALIS-ALBA S.R.L.—See Groupe Lactalis SA; *Int'l*, pg. 3106
LACTALIS AMERICAN GROUP, INC.—See Groupe Lactalis SA; *Int'l*, pg. 3106
LACTALIS CANADA INC.—See Groupe Lactalis SA; *Int'l*, pg. 3106
LACTALIS DELI, INC.—See Groupe Lactalis SA; *Int'l*, pg. 3106
LACTALIS DEUTSCHLAND GMBH—See Groupe Lactalis SA; *Int'l*, pg. 3106
LACTALIS EUROPE DU NORD S.A.—See Groupe Lactalis SA; *Int'l*, pg. 3106
LACTALIS HONGRIE, S.R.O.—See Groupe Lactalis SA; *Int'l*, pg. 3106
LACTALIS INTERNATIONAL SNC—See Groupe Lactalis SA; *Int'l*, pg. 3106
LACTALIS LUXEMBOURG SENC—See Groupe Lactalis SA; *Int'l*, pg. 3106
LACTALIS MCLELLAND—See Groupe Lactalis SA; *Int'l*, pg. 3106
LACTALIS POLSKA. SP. Z O.O.—See Groupe Lactalis SA; *Int'l*, pg. 3106
LACTALIS PORTUGAL, LDA—See Groupe Lactalis SA; *Int'l*, pg. 3106
LACTALIS SINGAPORE PTE. LTD.—See Bega Cheese Ltd.; *Int'l*, pg. 940
LACTALIS-UKRAINE, CJSC—See Groupe Lactalis SA; *Int'l*, pg. 3106
LACTALIS UNITED KINGDOM LTD—See Groupe Lactalis SA; *Int'l*, pg. 3106
LACTATE NATURA S.A.—See Societatea de Investitii Financiare Oltenia S.A.; *Int'l*, pg. 7034
LACTEAS GARCIA BAQUERO, SA; *Int'l*, pg. 4391
LACTEC AUTOMATIC PAINTING SYSTEMS (CHANGCHUN) LTD.—See LacTec GmbH; *Int'l*, pg. 4391
LACTEC GMBH; *Int'l*, pg. 4391
LACTEC SERVICZ S.R.O.—See LacTec GmbH; *Int'l*, pg. 4391
LACTEC USA LLC—See LacTec GmbH; *Int'l*, pg. 4391
LACTEOS CAPRINOS S.A.—See Lacteas Garcia Baquero, SA; *Int'l*, pg. 4391
LACTINA; *Int'l*, pg. 4391
L'ACTION MUNICIPALE—See Vivendi SE; *Int'l*, pg. 8271
LACTO ASIA (M) SDN. BHD.—See Lacto Japan Co., Ltd.; *Int'l*, pg. 4391
LACTO ASIA PTE. LTD.—See Lacto Japan Co., Ltd.; *Int'l*, pg. 4392
LACTO JAPAN CO., LTD.; *Int'l*, pg. 4391
LACTOSAN A/S—See Thornico A/S; *Int'l*, pg. 7719
LACTOSAN CHINA LTD.—See Thornico A/S; *Int'l*, pg. 7719
LACTOSAN JAPAN LTD.—See Thornico A/S; *Int'l*, pg. 7719
LACTOSAN LTD.—See Thornico A/S; *Int'l*, pg. 7719
LACTOSAN-SANOVO INGREDIENTS GROUP—See Thornico A/S; *Int'l*, pg. 7719
LACTOSAN (UK) LTD.—See Thornico A/S; *Int'l*, pg. 7719
LACTOSAN URUGUAY S.A.—See Thornico A/S; *Int'l*, pg. 7720
LACTOSE (INDIA) LIMITED—See Kerry Group plc; *Int'l*, pg. 4139
LACY & MIDDLEMISS SHIPBROKERS LTD.—See J&J Denholm Ltd.; *Int'l*, pg. 3853
LADAM AFFORDABLE HOUSING LIMITED; *Int'l*, pg. 4392
L.A. DARLING COMPANY—See Berkshire Hathaway Inc.; *U.S. Public*, pg. 311
LADAS DOMAINS LLC—See Ladas & Parry; *U.S. Private*, pg. 2372
LADAS & PARRY, CALIFORNIA—See Ladas & Parry; *U.S. Private*, pg. 2372
LADAS & PARRY, ENGLAND—See Ladas & Parry; *U.S. Private*, pg. 2372
LADAS & PARRY, ILLINOIS—See Ladas & Parry; *U.S. Private*, pg. 2372
LADAS & PARRY, LLP, GERMANY—See Ladas & Parry; *U.S. Private*, pg. 2372
LADAS & PARRY; *U.S. Private*, pg. 2372
LADBIBLE GROUP LIMITED—See LBG Media Plc; *Int'l*, pg. 4429

LADBIBLE IRELAND LIMITED—See LBG Media Plc; *Int'l*, pg. 4429
LADBROKES BETTING & GAMING LIMITED—See Entain PLC; *Int'l*, pg. 2450
LADBROKES CORAL GROUP LIMITED—See Entain PLC; *Int'l*, pg. 2450
LADBROKES GROUP FINANCE PLC—See Entain PLC; *Int'l*, pg. 2450
LADCE BETON S.R.O.—See BERGER Holding GmbH; *Int'l*, pg. 979
LADCO COMPANY LIMITED; *Int'l*, pg. 4392
LADDAWN INC.—See Berry Global Group, Inc; *U.S. Public*, pg. 322
LADD DISTRIBUTION LLC—See TE Connectivity Ltd.; *Int'l*, pg. 7497
LADDER CAPITAL ADVISER LLC—See Ladder Capital Corp.; *U.S. Public*, pg. 1288
LADDER CAPITAL ASSET MANAGEMENT LLC—See Ladder Capital Corp.; *U.S. Public*, pg. 1288
LADDER CAPITAL CORP.; *U.S. Public*, pg. 1287
LADDER CAPITAL FINANCE HOLDINGS LLLP—See Ladder Capital Corp.; *U.S. Public*, pg. 1288
LADDER CAPITAL SECURITIES LLC—See Ladder Capital Corp.; *U.S. Public*, pg. 1288
LADDER INDUSTRIES, INC.—See Holden Industries, Inc.; *U.S. Private*, pg. 1962
LADDERUP CORPORATE ADVISORY PRIVATE LIMITED—See Ladderup Finance Ltd; *Int'l*, pg. 4392
LADDERUP FINANCE LTD; *Int'l*, pg. 4392
LADDERUP WEALTH MANAGEMENT PRIVATE LIMITED—See Ladderup Finance Ltd; *Int'l*, pg. 4392
LADD HANFORD AUTO GROUP; *U.S. Private*, pg. 2372
LADD INDUSTRIES, LLC—See TE Connectivity Ltd.; *Int'l*, pg. 7497
LADENBURG THALMANN ANNUITY INSURANCE SERVICES, LLC—See Reverence Capital Partners LLC; *U.S. Private*, pg. 3414
LADENBURG, THALMANN & CO. INC.—See Reverence Capital Partners LLC; *U.S. Private*, pg. 3414
LADENBURG THALMANN FINANCIAL SERVICES INC.—See Reverence Capital Partners LLC; *U.S. Private*, pg. 3414
LADENSO OY—See Stora Enso Oyj; *Int'l*, pg. 7223
LADE PROFESIONAL S.A.—See Fortive Corporation; *U.S. Public*, pg. 872
LADERA RANCH MAINTENANCE CORP.; *U.S. Private*, pg. 2372
LA DIFF SARL—See Vivendi SE; *Int'l*, pg. 8272
LAD IMAGING, LLC—See HCA Healthcare, Inc.; *U.S. Public*, pg. 1000
LADONNA CO., LTD.—See KING JIM CO., LTD.; *Int'l*, pg. 4169
LA DORIA S.P.A.—See Investindustrial Advisors Ltd.; *Int'l*, pg. 3779
LADPRAO GENERAL HOSPITAL PUBLIC COMPANY LIMITED; *Int'l*, pg. 4392
LADRX CORPORATION; *U.S. Public*, pg. 1288
LAD'S PET SUPPLIES—See Summit Partners, L.P.; *U.S. Private*, pg. 3855
LADUN INVESTMENT COMPANY; *Int'l*, pg. 4392
LADY ALICE MINES PTY LTD—See Cobra Resources plc; *Int'l*, pg. 1683
LADY ANN CRUISES INC.; *U.S. Private*, pg. 2372
LADYBIRD BOOKS LTD—See Bertelsmann SE & Co. KGaA; *Int'l*, pg. 991
LADYBUG RESOURCE GROUP, INC.; *U.S. Public*, pg. 1288
LADY BURD EXCLUSIVE PRIVATE LABEL COSMETICS; *U.S. Private*, pg. 2372
LADY CAKE-FEINE KUCHEN GMBH—See Suddeutsche Zuckerruben-Verwertungs-Genossenschaft eG; *Int'l*, pg. 7252
LADY DRUG STORE CO., LTD.; *Int'l*, pg. 4392
LADY ESTER LINGERIE CORP.; *U.S. Private*, pg. 2372
LADY FITNESS INC.—See AEA Investors LP; *U.S. Private*, pg. 113
LADY FITNESS INC.—See Ontario Teachers' Pension Plan; *Int'l*, pg. 5587
LADY FOOT LOCKER—See Foot Locker, Inc.; *U.S. Public*, pg. 863
LADY GRACE STORES INC.; *U.S. Private*, pg. 2372
LADY MANHATTAN COSMETICS GMBH—See JAB Holding Company S.a.r.l.; *Int'l*, pg. 3860
LADY PRIMROSE'S, INC.; *U.S. Private*, pg. 2372
LADY PRISON PRODUCTIONS, INC.—See Lions Gate Entertainment Corp.; *Int'l*, pg. 4520
LAEBON DEVELOPMENTS LTD.; *Int'l*, pg. 4392
LAEIS (DALIAN) TRADING CO. LTD.—See Sacmi Imola S.C.A.R.L.; *Int'l*, pg. 6464
LAEIS GMBH—See Sacmi Imola S.C.A.R.L.; *Int'l*, pg. 6464
LAEMCHABANG INTERNATIONAL RO-RO TERMINAL LTD.—See Nippon Yusen Kabushiki Kaisha; *Int'l*, pg. 5358
LAEM CHAROEN SEAFOOD COMPANY LIMITED—See MK Restaurant Group Public Company Limited; *Int'l*, pg. 5000
LAEMPE MOSSNER SINTO GMBH—See Sintokogio Ltd.; *Int'l*, pg. 6958
LAEP INVESTMENTS, LTD.; *Int'l*, pg. 4392

LAERDAL MEDICAL CORPORATION; *U.S. Private*, pg. 2372
LA ESFERA DE LOS LIBROS S.L.—See RCS MediaGroup S.p.A.; *Int'l*, pg. 6229
LA ESPIGA DE ORO TORTILLA FACTORY; *U.S. Private*, pg. 2368
LAESTI AS—See Norvik hf; *Int'l*, pg. 5448
LAETITIA VINEYARD & WINERY—See Vintage Wine Estates, Inc.; *U.S. Public*, pg. 2298
LAETUS FRANCE SARL—See Coesia S.p.A.; *Int'l*, pg. 1690
LAETUS GMBH—See Coesia S.p.A.; *Int'l*, pg. 1690
LAETUS IBERICA—See Coesia S.p.A.; *Int'l*, pg. 1690
LAETUS MEXICO S. DE R.L. DE C.V.—See Coesia S.p.A.; *Int'l*, pg. 1690
LA FABRICA JOTABEQU—See WPP plc; *Int'l*, pg. 8472
LAFAIVE OIL CO.; *U.S. Private*, pg. 2372
LA FAMILIA PAWN & JEWELRY—See Simple Management Group, Inc.; *U.S. Private*, pg. 3666
LAFANG CHINA CO LTD; *Int'l*, pg. 4392
LA FANTANA SRL—See Axel Johnson Gruppen AB; *Int'l*, pg. 765
LAFARGE AFRICA PLC.—See Holcim Ltd.; *Int'l*, pg. 3448
LAFARGE ALGERIE—See Holcim Ltd.; *Int'l*, pg. 3448
LAFARGE BEOCINSKA FABRIKA CEMENTA D.O.O.—See Holcim Ltd.; *Int'l*, pg. 3448
LAFARGE BETONS - AGENCE—See Holcim Ltd.; *Int'l*, pg. 3449
LAFARGE BETONS CENTRALE BPE QUIMPER—See Holcim Ltd.; *Int'l*, pg. 3449
LAFARGE CANADA INC.—See Holcim Ltd.; *Int'l*, pg. 3449
LAFARGE CANADA INC.—See Holcim Ltd.; *Int'l*, pg. 3449
LAFARGE CEMENT AS—See Holcim Ltd.; *Int'l*, pg. 3448
LAFARGE CEMENT D.O.O.—See Holcim Ltd.; *Int'l*, pg. 3448
LAFARGE CEMENT HUNGARY LTD.—See Holcim Ltd.; *Int'l*, pg. 3448
LAFARGE CEMENT MALAWI LTD.—See Holcim Ltd.; *Int'l*, pg. 3448
LAFARGE CEMENT S.A.—See Holcim Ltd.; *Int'l*, pg. 3448
LAFARGE CEMENT SINGAPORE PTE. LTD.—See YTL Corporation Berhad; *Int'l*, pg. 8606
LAFARGE CEMENT SYRIA—See Holcim Ltd.; *Int'l*, pg. 3448
LAFARGE CEMENT ZIMBABWE LIMITED—See Holcim Ltd.; *Int'l*, pg. 3448
LAFARGE CIMENTS ANTILLES—See Holcim Ltd.; *Int'l*, pg. 3448
LAFARGE DUJIANGYAN CEMENT CO. LTD.—See Shui On Company Limited; *Int'l*, pg. 6869
LAFARGE DUNDAS QUARRY—See Holcim Ltd.; *Int'l*, pg. 3449
LAFARGE GIPS BV—See Holcim Ltd.; *Int'l*, pg. 3448
LAFARGE GYPSUM (PTY) LTD.—See Holcim Ltd.; *Int'l*, pg. 3448
LAFARGEHOLCIM BANGLADESH LIMITED—See Cementos Molins S.A.; *Int'l*, pg. 1398
LAFARGEHOLCIM BANGLADESH LIMITED—See Holcim Ltd.; *Int'l*, pg. 3449
LAFARGEHOLCIM (BRASIL) S.A. - BARROSO PLANT—See Companhia Siderurgica Nacional; *Int'l*, pg. 1748
LAFARGEHOLCIM (BRASIL) S.A. - CANTAGALO PLANT—See Companhia Siderurgica Nacional; *Int'l*, pg. 1748
LAFARGEHOLCIM (BRASIL) S.A.—See Companhia Siderurgica Nacional; *Int'l*, pg. 1748
LAFARGEHOLCIM ESPANA S.A.—See Holcim Ltd.; *Int'l*, pg. 3449
LAFARGEHOLCIM FRANCE SAS—See Holcim Ltd.; *Int'l*, pg. 3449
LAFARGEHOLCIM GUINEE—See Holcim Ltd.; *Int'l*, pg. 3449
LAFARGEHOLCIM MAROC—See Holcim Ltd.; *Int'l*, pg. 3448
LAFARGEHOLCIM RUSSIA—See Holcim Ltd.; *Int'l*, pg. 3449
LAFARGE INDUSTRIES SOUTH AFRICA (PTY) LTD.—See Holcim Ltd.; *Int'l*, pg. 3448
LAFARGE KRUSZYWA I BETON SP. Z O.O.—See Holcim Ltd.; *Int'l*, pg. 3448
LAFARGE LOGISTIQUE ALGERIE LLA—See Holcim Ltd.; *Int'l*, pg. 3448
LAFARGE MAROC HOLDING—See Holcim Ltd.; *Int'l*, pg. 3448
LAFARGE (MAURITIUS) CEMENT LTD—See Holcim Ltd.; *Int'l*, pg. 3448
LAFARGE NORTH AMERICA INC.—See Holcim Ltd.; *Int'l*, pg. 3449
LAFARGE NORTH AMERICA INC. - WHITEHALL CEMENT PLANT—See Holcim Ltd.; *Int'l*, pg. 3449
LAFARGE READYMIX NIGERIA LIMITED—See Holcim Ltd.; *Int'l*, pg. 3448
LAFARGE ROAD MARKING—See Holcim Ltd.; *Int'l*, pg. 3449
LAFARGE ROOFING CO. LTD.—See PAI Partners S.A.S.; *Int'l*, pg. 5701
LAFARGE SERVICE GROUP - R&D CENTER LYON—See Holcim Ltd.; *Int'l*, pg. 3449

LAFARGE SOUTH AFRICA HOLDINGS (PTY) LTD.—See Holcim Ltd.; *Int'l*, pg. 3448
LAFARGE ZEMENTWERKE GMBH—See Holcim Ltd.; *Int'l*, pg. 3449
LA FAVORITA INC.—See Novus Inc.; *U.S. Private*, pg. 2968
LAFAYETTE AMBASSADOR BANK—See Fulton Financial Corporation; *U.S. Public*, pg. 892
LAFAYETTE COCA-COLA BOTTLING COMPANY—See Coca-Cola Bottling Co. United, Inc.; *U.S. Private*, pg. 958
LAFAYETTE COMPANY; *U.S. Private*, pg. 2372
THE LAFAYETTE DENVER, LLC—See Highlands REIT, Inc.; *U.S. Private*, pg. 1940
LAFAYETTE ENGLISH APARTMENTS, LP—See RAIT Financial Trust; *U.S. Private*, pg. 3349
LAFAYETTE GENERAL HEALTH SYSTEM; *U.S. Private*, pg. 2372
LAFAYETTE HEALTH CARE CENTER, INC.—See Apollo Global Management, Inc.; *U.S. Public*, pg. 157
LAFAYETTE INSTRUMENT COMPANY, INC.—See Branford Castle, Inc.; *U.S. Private*, pg. 639
LAFAYETTE INSURANCE COMPANY—See United Fire Group, Inc.; *U.S. Public*, pg. 2230
THE LAFAYETTE LIFE INSURANCE COMPANY—See Western & Southern Financial Group, Inc.; *U.S. Private*, pg. 4490
LAFAYETTE MITTELSTAND CAPITAL; *Int'l*, pg. 4392
LAFAYETTE MOTOR SALES INC.; *U.S. Private*, pg. 2372
LAFAYETTE OB HOSPITALISTS, LLC—See HCA Healthcare, Inc.; *U.S. Public*, pg. 1000
LAFAYETTE PARK HOTEL CORP.—See Woodside Hotels & Resorts; *U.S. Private*, pg. 4560
LAFAYETTE PHARMACEUTICALS LLC—See Mallinckrodt Public Limited Company; *Int'l*, pg. 4663
LAFAYETTE REAL ESTATE LLC—See Prologis, Inc.; *U.S. Public*, pg. 1727
LAFAYETTE REGIONAL HEALTH CENTER—See HCA Healthcare, Inc.; *U.S. Public*, pg. 1000
LAFAYETTE SERVICES LASER—See BNP Paribas SA; *Int'l*, pg. 1091
LAFAYETTE SERVICES LASER—See Galeries Lafayette SA; *Int'l*, pg. 2872
LAFAYETTE SPECIALTY HOSPITAL, LLC—See Apollo Global Management, Inc.; *U.S. Public*, pg. 157
LAFAYETTE SQUARE USA, INC.; *U.S. Private*, pg. 2372
LAFAYETTE SURGERY CENTER LIMITED PARTNERSHIP—See HCA Healthcare, Inc.; *U.S. Public*, pg. 1000
LAFAYETTE SURGICARE, INC.—See HCA Healthcare, Inc.; *U.S. Public*, pg. 1000
LAFAYETTE TV, LLC—See Entertainment Studios, Inc.; *U.S. Private*, pg. 1405
LAFAYETTE VENETIAN BLIND INC.; *U.S. Private*, pg. 2372
LAFE CORPORATION LIMITED; *Int'l*, pg. 4392
LA FEDERATION CONTINENTALE COMPAGNIE D'ASSURANCES SUR LA VIE S.A.—See Assicurazioni Generali S.p.A.; *Int'l*, pg. 645
LA FEMME PERFUMERY INC.; *U.S. Private*, pg. 2368
LA FERRETERA VIZCAINA S.A—See Whittan Storage Systems Ltd.; *Int'l*, pg. 8400
LA FERRETERA VIZCAINA S.A—See Whittan Storage Systems Ltd.; *Int'l*, pg. 8400
LAFERT ELEKTROMOTORJI D.O.O.—See Sumitomo Heavy Industries, Ltd.; *Int'l*, pg. 7287
LAFERT GMBH—See Sumitomo Heavy Industries, Ltd.; *Int'l*, pg. 7287
LAFERT SERVO DRIVES S.R.L.—See Sumitomo Heavy Industries, Ltd.; *Int'l*, pg. 7287
LAFERT SERVO MOTORS S.P.A.—See Sumitomo Heavy Industries, Ltd.; *Int'l*, pg. 7287
LAFERT S.P.A.—See Sumitomo Heavy Industries, Ltd.; *Int'l*, pg. 7287
LAFERT (SUZHOU) CO., LTD.—See Sumitomo Heavy Industries, Ltd.; *Int'l*, pg. 7287
LAFFANS PETROCHEMICALS LIMITED—See Huntsman Corporation; *U.S. Public*, pg. 1074
LAFFERTY CHEVROLET, INC.; *U.S. Private*, pg. 2373
LAFFEY INTERNATIONAL REALTY, LLC—See Berkshire Hathaway Inc.; *U.S. Public*, pg. 306
LAFFITTE MANAGEMENT GROUP LLC—See Live Nation Entertainment, Inc.; *U.S. Public*, pg. 1329
LAFI LOGICIELS APPLICATION FORMATION INFORMATION S.A.S.—See Droege Group AG; *Int'l*, pg. 2205
LA FINANCIERE ATALIAN SAS; *Int'l*, pg. 4387
LA FINANCIERE PATRIMONIALE D'INVESTISSEMENT S.A.S.; *Int'l*, pg. 4387
LAFITTE; *Int'l*, pg. 4393
LAFITTE TP SAS—See VINCI S.A.; *Int'l*, pg. 8223
LAFLECHE ENVIRONMENTAL INC.—See TFI International, Inc.; *Int'l*, pg. 7586
LAFLEUR MINERALS INC.; *Int'l*, pg. 4393
LA FONCIERE VERTE SA; *Int'l*, pg. 4393
LAFONTAINE AUTOMOTIVE GROUP, LLC; *U.S. Private*, pg. 2373
LAFONTAINE IMPORT MOTORS INC.; *U.S. Private*, pg. 2373

COMPANY NAME INDEX

LA FONTE DELLA VITA SRL—See Bioera S.p.A.; *Int'l*, pg. 1037
LA FOODS; *U.S. Private*, pg. 2368
LA FORCE LLC—See DNS Capital, LLC; *U.S. Private*, pg. 1249
LA FORET ENGINEERING CO., LTD.—See AGC Inc.; *Int'l*, pg. 204
LAFORO IRON FOUNDRY; *Int'l*, pg. 4393
LA FORTEZZA ASIA SDN BHD—See ITAB Shop Concept AB; *Int'l*, pg. 3828
LA FORTEZZA MIDDLE EAST DMCC—See ITAB Shop Concept AB; *Int'l*, pg. 3828
LA FORTEZZA SUDAMERICANA S.A.—See ITAB Shop Concept AB; *Int'l*, pg. 3828
LA FOURCHETTE NETHERLANDS B.V.—See TripAdvisor, Inc.; *U.S. Public*, pg. 2195
LA FOURCHETTE SAS—See TripAdvisor, Inc.; *U.S. Public*, pg. 2195
LAFOURCHETTE SWEDEN AB—See TripAdvisor, Inc.; *U.S. Public*, pg. 2195
LA FRANCAISE DE L ENERGIE SA; *Int'l*, pg. 4388
LA FRANCAISE DES JEUX SA; *Int'l*, pg. 4388
LAFRANCE ASSOCIATES, LLC; *U.S. Private*, pg. 2373
LAFRANCE CORPORATION - BENMATT INDUSTRIES DIVISION—See LaFrance Corporation; *U.S. Private*, pg. 2373
LAFRANCE CORPORATION - J.A.T. CREATIVE PRODUCTS DIVISION—See LaFrance Corporation; *U.S. Private*, pg. 2373
LAFRANCE CORPORATION - PACTEC CUSTOM DIVISION—See LaFrance Corporation; *U.S. Private*, pg. 2373
LAFRANCE CORPORATION - PACTEC STANDARD DIVISION—See LaFrance Corporation; *U.S. Private*, pg. 2373
LAFRANCE CORPORATION; *U.S. Private*, pg. 2373
LAFRANCOL INTERNACIONAL S.A.S.—See Abbott Laboratories; *U.S. Public*, pg. 20
LAFRONTERIZA LLC—See Grupo Bimbo, S.A.B. de C.V.; *Int'l*, pg. 3122
LA FUGUE—See LVMH Moet Hennessy Louis Vuitton SE; *Int'l*, pg. 4592
LAFUMA AMERICA, INC.—See Calida Holding AG; *Int'l*, pg. 1264
LAFUMA BV—See Calida Holding AG; *Int'l*, pg. 1264
LAFUMA GROUP GMBH—See Calida Holding AG; *Int'l*, pg. 1264
LAFUMA HK LTD.—See Calida Holding AG; *Int'l*, pg. 1264
LAFUMA HUNGARIA—See Calida Holding AG; *Int'l*, pg. 1264
LAFUMA MOBILIER SAS—See Calida Holding AG; *Int'l*, pg. 1264
LAFUMA SA—See Calida Holding AG; *Int'l*, pg. 1264
LAGAAY MEDICAL GROUP B.V.—See B&S Group S.A.; *Int'l*, pg. 784
LA GAIANA S.P.A.—See Marcegaglia S.p.A.; *Int'l*, pg. 4689
LAGA INDUSTRIES LTD—See Steamships Trading Company Limited; *Int'l*, pg. 7188
LA-GAJJAR MACHINERIES PRIVATE LIMITED—See Kirloskar Oil Engines Limited; *Int'l*, pg. 4191
LAGAN ASPHALT LTD—See Lagan Holdings Ltd.; *Int'l*, pg. 4393
LAGAN BITUMEN LTD—See Lagan Holdings Ltd.; *Int'l*, pg. 4393
LAGAN BRICK LTD.—See Lagan Holdings Ltd.; *Int'l*, pg. 4393
LAGAN CEMENT B.V.—See Lagan Holdings Ltd.; *Int'l*, pg. 4393
LAGAN CEMENT LTD—See Lagan Holdings Ltd.; *Int'l*, pg. 4393
LAGAN CONCRETE LIMITED—See Lagan Holdings Ltd.; *Int'l*, pg. 4393
LAGAN HOLDINGS LTD.; *Int'l*, pg. 4393
LAGAN HOMES—See Lagan Holdings Ltd.; *Int'l*, pg. 4393
LAGARDERE ACTIVE DIGITAL SAS—See Vivendi SE; *Int'l*, pg. 8274
LAGARDERE ACTIVE ENTREPRISES JAPAN—See Vivendi SE; *Int'l*, pg. 8274
LAGARDERE ACTIVE FINANCES (SAS)—See Vivendi SE; *Int'l*, pg. 8274
LAGARDERE ACTIVE RADIO INTERNATIONAL S.A.—See Vivendi SE; *Int'l*, pg. 8274
LAGARDERE ACTIVE SAS—See Vivendi SE; *Int'l*, pg. 8274
LAGARDERE ACTIVE TV—See Vivendi SE; *Int'l*, pg. 8274
LAGARDERE ENTERTAINMENT SAS—See Vivendi SE; *Int'l*, pg. 8275
LAGARDERE FINANCE—See Vivendi SE; *Int'l*, pg. 8276
LAGARDERE GLOBAL ADVERTISING SA—See Vivendi SE; *Int'l*, pg. 8272
LAGARDERE MEDIA CONSULTING—See Vivendi SE; *Int'l*, pg. 8274
LAGARDERE MEDIA SAS—See Vivendi SE; *Int'l*, pg. 8272
LAGARDERE NEWS—See Vivendi SE; *Int'l*, pg. 8274
LAGARDERE NORTH AMERICA—See Vivendi SE; *Int'l*, pg. 8277
LAGARDERE PARIS RACING RESSOURCES SASP—See Vivendi SE; *Int'l*, pg. 8277
LAGARDERE PARTICIPATIONS—See Vivendi SE; *Int'l*, pg. 8277
LAGARDERE PUBLICITE SAS—See Czech Media Invest as; *Int'l*, pg. 1898
LAGARDERE RESSOURCES S.A.S.—See Vivendi SE; *Int'l*, pg. 8277
LAGARDERE SA—See Vivendi SE; *Int'l*, pg. 8271
LAGARDERE SERVICES BULGARIA LTD—See Vivendi SE; *Int'l*, pg. 8276
LAGARDERE SERVICES CHINA CO LIMITED—See Vivendi SE; *Int'l*, pg. 8276
LAGARDERE SERVICES DISTRIBUTION SAS—See Adriatic Media Investors LLC; *U.S. Private*, pg. 82
LAGARDERE SERVICES HONG KONG LIMITED—See Vivendi SE; *Int'l*, pg. 8276
LAGARDERE SERVICES SINGAPORE PTE LTD—See Vivendi SE; *Int'l*, pg. 8276
LAGARDERE SPORTS & ENTERTAINMENT S.A.S—See Vivendi SE; *Int'l*, pg. 8277
LAGARDERE STUDIOS DISTRIBUTION, SA—See Vivendi SE; *Int'l*, pg. 8277
LAGARDERE STUDIOS SAS—See Vivendi SE; *Int'l*, pg. 8277
LAGARDERE THEMATIQUES—See Vivendi SE; *Int'l*, pg. 8274
LAGARDERE TRAVEL RETAIL AS—See Vivendi SE; *Int'l*, pg. 8277
LAGARDERE TRAVEL RETAIL AUSTRIA GMBH—See Vivendi SE; *Int'l*, pg. 8277
LAGARDERE TRAVEL RETAIL EHF—See Vivendi SE; *Int'l*, pg. 8277
LAGARDERE TRAVEL RETAIL FRANCE SNC—See Vivendi SE; *Int'l*, pg. 8277
LAGARDERE TRAVEL RETAIL HONG KONG LTD.—See Vivendi SE; *Int'l*, pg. 8277
LAGARDERE TRAVEL RETAIL ITALIA SRL—See Vivendi SE; *Int'l*, pg. 8277
LAGARDERE TRAVEL RETAIL LUXEMBOURG SARL—See Vivendi SE; *Int'l*, pg. 8277
LAGARDERE TRAVEL RETAIL NETHERLANDS HOLDING BV—See Vivendi SE; *Int'l*, pg. 8277
LAGARDERE TRAVEL RETAIL SAS—See Vivendi SE; *Int'l*, pg. 8275
LAGARDERE TRAVEL RETAIL SINGAPORE PTE. LTD—See Vivendi SE; *Int'l*, pg. 8277
LAGARDERE TRAVEL RETAIL—See Vivendi SE; *Int'l*, pg. 8273
LAGARDERE TRAVEL RETAIL SP ZOO—See Vivendi SE; *Int'l*, pg. 8278
LAGARDERE TRAVEL RETAIL UK LTD.—See Vivendi SE; *Int'l*, pg. 8278
LAGARDERE UK LTD.—See Vivendi SE; *Int'l*, pg. 8278
LAGARDERE UNLIMITED LIVE ENTERTAINMENT—See Vivendi SE; *Int'l*, pg. 8276
LAGARDERE UNLIMITED SAS—See Vivendi SE; *Int'l*, pg. 8276
LAGARDERE UNLIMITED STADIUM SOLUTIONS SAS—See Vivendi SE; *Int'l*, pg. 8276
LAGARDERE UNLIMITED TALENTS UK LIMITED—See Vivendi SE; *Int'l*, pg. 8277
LAGARRIGUE; *Int'l*, pg. 4393
LAGASSE, INC.—See Sycamore Partners Management, LP; *U.S. Private*, pg. 3897
L.A. GAUGE CO.; *U.S. Private*, pg. 2364
L.A. GEAR CALIFORNIA, INC.—See ACI International; *U.S. Private*, pg. 59
L.A. GEAR, INC.—See ACI International; *U.S. Private*, pg. 59
L'AGEFI—See Financiere Pinault SCA; *Int'l*, pg. 2668
L'AGENCE AUTOMOBILIERE S.A.; *Int'l*, pg. 4369
LAGENDA PROPERTIES BERHAD; *Int'l*, pg. 4393
LAGERCRANTZ ASIA LTD—See Lagercrantz Group AB; *Int'l*, pg. 4394
LAGERCRANTZ A/S—See Lagercrantz Group AB; *Int'l*, pg. 4394
LAGERCRANTZ COMMUNICATION AB—See Lagercrantz Group AB; *Int'l*, pg. 4394
LAGERCRANTZ GROUP AB; *Int'l*, pg. 4393
LAGERHAUS E-SERVICE GMBH—See BayWa AG; *Int'l*, pg. 918
LAGERHAUS FRANCHISE GMBH—See BayWa AG; *Int'l*, pg. 918
LAGERHAUS LANDQUART AG—See Wurth Verwaltungsgesellschaft mbH; *Int'l*, pg. 8506
LAGERHAUS TECHNIK-CENTER GMBH & CO. KG—See BayWa AG; *Int'l*, pg. 918
LAGERHAUS TECHNIK-CENTER GMBH—See BayWa AG; *Int'l*, pg. 918
LAGERMAX LEASING GMBH—See UniCredit S.p.A.; *Int'l*, pg. 8037
LAGERMEX S.A. DE C.V.—See ThyssenKrupp AG; *Int'l*, pg. 7730
LAGERMIX RULLPORTAR AB—See Troax Group AB; *Int'l*, pg. 7937
LAGER'S, INC.; *U.S. Private*, pg. 2373
LAGEV IMMOBILIEN LEASING GESELLSCHAFT M.B.H.—See UniCredit S.p.A.; *Int'l*, pg. 8037
LA GIULIA IND. S.P.A.—See Perfetti Van Melle Holding B.V.; *Int'l*, pg. 5800
LAGKAGEHUSET A/S—See FSN Capital Partners AS; *Int'l*, pg. 2799
LAGLASSE & OMHOVERE—See FAYAT SAS; *Int'l*, pg. 2625
LAGLER AUSTRALIA—See Eugen Lagler GmbH; *Int'l*, pg. 2526
L.A. GLO INTERNATIONAL, INC.; *U.S. Private*, pg. 2364
LAGNAM SPINTEX LIMITED; *Int'l*, pg. 4395
LAGO BUILDERS INC.; *U.S. Private*, pg. 2373
LAGO MAR PROPERTIES, INC.; *U.S. Private*, pg. 2373
LAGOON CREEK RESOURCES PTY. LTD.—See Laramide Resources Ltd.; *Int'l*, pg. 4418
LAGOS INC.; *U.S. Private*, pg. 2373
LAGOSTINA SPA—See SEB S.A.; *Int'l*, pg. 6667
LA GRANDE EPICERIE—See LVMH Moet Hennessy Louis Vuitton SE; *Int'l*, pg. 4598
LA GRANDE OBSERVER—See Western Communications Inc.; *U.S. Public*, pg. 4491
LAGRANGE ASSOCIATES, LLC—See Wheeler Real Estate Investment Trust, Inc.; *U.S. Public*, pg. 2366
LAGRANGE ENERGIE - UND GEBAUDETECHNIK GMBH—See VINCI S.A.; *Int'l*, pg. 8237
LA GRANGE GROCERY CO.; *U.S. Private*, pg. 2368
LAGRANGE PRODUCTION—See Compagnie de Saint-Gobain SA; *Int'l*, pg. 1724
LAGRANGE TWM GMBH—See VINCI S.A.; *Int'l*, pg. 8223
LAGRAPHICO; *U.S. Private*, pg. 2373
LAGREZE—See Tonnellerie Francois Freres; *Int'l*, pg. 7810
LA GROU MOTOR SERVICE INCORPORATED; *U.S. Private*, pg. 2368
LAG SERVICE POLSKA SP. Z O.O.—See CIMC Vehicle (Group) Co., Ltd.; *Int'l*, pg. 1608
LAGTA GROUP TRAINING LIMITED—See SPX Technologies, Inc.; *U.S. Public*, pg. 1921
LAG TRAILERS N.V.—See China International Marine Containers (Group) Co., Ltd.; *Int'l*, pg. 1512
LAGUARDIA ASSOCIATES; *U.S. Private*, pg. 2373
LAGUELLE SA; *Int'l*, pg. 4395
LAGUNA BAY GROUP PTY LTD; *Int'l*, pg. 4395
LAGUNA COOKIE COMPANY, INC.—See Meiji Holdings Co., Ltd.; *Int'l*, pg. 4800
LAGUNA DAI-ICHI, INC.—See I-PEX Inc.; *Int'l*, pg. 3564
LAGUNA GATEWAY INLAND CONTAINER TERMINAL INC.—See International Container Terminal Services, Inc.; *Int'l*, pg. 3746
LAGUNA HOLIDAY CLUB LIMITED—See Banyan Tree Holdings; *Int'l*, pg. 855
LAGUNA LIFE D.A.C.—See Enstar Group Limited; *Int'l*, pg. 2449
LAGUNA PRODUKTER AS—See TINE SA; *Int'l*, pg. 7753
LAGUNA RESORTS & HOTELS PUBLIC COMPANY LIMITED—See Banyan Tree Holdings Ltd.; *Int'l*, pg. 855
LAGUNA TEN BOSCH CO., LTD.—See H.I.S. Co., Ltd.; *Int'l*, pg. 3195
LAGUNA TOOLS INC.; *U.S. Private*, pg. 2373
LAGUNA TREATMENT HOSPITAL, LLC—See AAC Holdings, Inc.; *U.S. Public*, pg. 30
THE LAGUNITAS BREWING COMPANY—See L'Arche Green N.V.; *Int'l*, pg. 4377
LA HABRA RELOCATIONS, INC.—See Wheaton Van Lines, Inc.; *U.S. Private*, pg. 4505
LA HACIENDA LIMITED—See Griffon Corporation; *U.S. Public*, pg. 969
LAHAD DATU EDIBLE OILS SDN BHD—See Kuok Brothers Sdn. Bhd.; *Int'l*, pg. 4335
LAHAV L R REAL ESTATE LTD.; *Int'l*, pg. 4395
LAHAYE ATLANTIQUE; *Int'l*, pg. 4395
L.A. HAZARD & SONS INC.—See IRR Supply Centers Inc.; *U.S. Private*, pg. 2140
LAHDEN PROJEKTIIMI OY—See Sweco AB; *Int'l*, pg. 7363
LAHDEN TERATEOS OY—See Investment AB Latour; *Int'l*, pg. 3781
LAHDEN TRIO KOY—See Citycon Oyj; *Int'l*, pg. 1629
L.A. HEARNE COMPANY; *U.S. Private*, pg. 2364
LAHERA PRODUCTION—See LBO France S.a.r.l.; *Int'l*, pg. 4430
LAHEY CLINIC; *U.S. Private*, pg. 2373
LA HIPOTECARIA (HOLDING), INC.; *Int'l*, pg. 4388
LAHMEYER AGUA Y ENERGIA S.A.—See Lahmeyer Holding GmbH; *Int'l*, pg. 4395
LAHMEYER BERLIN GMBH—See Lahmeyer Holding GmbH; *Int'l*, pg. 4395
LAHMEYER CONSULTING ENGINEERS (T) LIMITED—See Lahmeyer Holding GmbH; *Int'l*, pg. 4395
LAHMEYER GKW CONSULT GMBH—See Lahmeyer Holding GmbH; *Int'l*, pg. 4395
LAHMEYER HOLDING GMBH; *Int'l*, pg. 4395
LAHMEYER HYDROPROJEKT GMBH—See Lahmeyer Holding GmbH; *Int'l*, pg. 4395
LAHMEYER IDP CONSULT INC.—See Lahmeyer Holding GmbH; *Int'l*, pg. 4396
LAHMEYER INTERNATIONAL (INDIA) PVT. LTD.—See Lahmeyer Holding GmbH; *Int'l*, pg. 4396
LAHMEYER INTERNATIONAL QATAR LLC—See Lahmeyer Holding GmbH; *Int'l*, pg. 4396

LAHMEYER HOLDING GMBH

LAHMEYER MUNCHEN INGENIEURGESELLSCHAFT MBH—See Lahmeyer Holding GmbH; *Int'l*, pg. 4396
LAHNPAPER GMBH—See KAJO NEUKIRCHEN Management und Beteiligungs GmbH; *Int'l*, pg. 4056
LAHORE COMPOST (PVT) LTD.—See Saif Holdings Limited; *Int'l*, pg. 6482
LAHORE STOCK EXCHANGE (GUARANTEE) LTD.; *Int'l*, pg. 4396
LAHOTI OVERSEAS LIMITED; *Int'l*, pg. 4396
LA HUNE S.A.S.—See Madrigall SA; *Int'l*, pg. 4635
LAHVARNA BROD D.O.O.—See Vitkovice Holding, A.S.; *Int'l*, pg. 8260
LAIBE CORPORATION; *U.S. Private*, pg. 2373
LAI BEC PTE. LTD.—See HC Surgical Specialists Limited; *Int'l*, pg. 3297
LAIDE AUDITIVE SA—See Amplifon S.p.A.; *Int'l*, pg. 435
LAIDLAW ASIA LIMITED—See Rutland Partners LLP; *Int'l*, pg. 6432
LAIDLAW CARRIERS BULK LP—See TFI International Inc.; *Int'l*, pg. 7585
LAIDLAW CARRIERS TANK—See TFI International Inc.; *Int'l*, pg. 7585
LAIDLAW CARRIERS VAN LP—See TFI International Inc.; *Int'l*, pg. 7585
LAIDLAW ENERGY GROUP, INC.; *U.S. Private*, pg. 2373
LAIDLAW GLOBAL CORPORATION; *U.S. Private*, pg. 2373
LAIDLAW INTERIORS GROUP LTD—See Rutland Partners LLP; *Int'l*, pg. 6432
LAIDLAW INTERIORS GULF LLC—See Rutland Partners LLP; *Int'l*, pg. 6432
LAI FUNG HOLDINGS LIMITED—See Lai Sun Group; *Int'l*, pg. 4396
LAI GA TOYS CO. LIMITED—See Amuse Group Holding Ltd.; *Int'l*, pg. 442
LAI GONGCHANG CO., LTD.—See RITEK CORPORATION; *Int'l*, pg. 6351
LAI GROUP HOLDING COMPANY LIMITED; *Int'l*, pg. 4396
LAI INTERNATIONAL, INC.-MINNEAPOLIS—See Monroe Capital LLC; *U.S. Private*, pg. 2773
LAI INTERNATIONAL, INC.-MINNEAPOLIS—See The RLJ Companies, LLC; *U.S. Private*, pg. 4111
LAI INTERNATIONAL, INC.—See Monroe Capital LLC; *U.S. Private*, pg. 2773
LAI INTERNATIONAL, INC.—See The RLJ Companies, LLC; *U.S. Private*, pg. 4111
LAI INTERNATIONAL, INC.-WESTMINSTER—See Monroe Capital LLC; *U.S. Private*, pg. 2773
LAI INTERNATIONAL, INC.-WESTMINSTER—See The RLJ Companies, LLC; *U.S. Private*, pg. 4111
LAIKA CARAVANS S.P.A.—See Thor Industries, Inc.; *U.S. Public*, pg. 2156
LAIKA, INC.; *U.S. Private*, pg. 2373
LAIKI FINANCIAL SERVICES LTD—See Bank of Cyprus Holdings Public Limited Company; *Int'l*, pg. 842
LAIMING INSURANCE GROUP—See Lander Van Gundy Agency, Inc.; *U.S. Private*, pg. 2385
LA IMPERIAL RESOURCES INC.; *Int'l*, pg. 4388
LAINAAMO OY—See Taaleri Oyj; *Int'l*, pg. 7401
L.A. INC.—See J.B. Hunt Transport Services, Inc.; *U.S. Public*, pg. 1180
LA INDIAN OAKS QRS INC.—See Apartment Investment and Management Company; *U.S. Public*, pg. 144
LAING O'ROURKE AUSTRALIA PTY LIMITED—See Laing O'Rourke Plc; *Int'l*, pg. 4396
LAING O'ROURKE PLC; *Int'l*, pg. 4396
LAING O'ROURKE TECHNICAL SERVICES (INDIA) PRIVATE LIMITED—See Laing O'Rourke Plc; *Int'l*, pg. 4396
LAING THERMOTECH, INC.—See Xylem Inc.; *U.S. Public*, pg. 2396
LAINIERE DE PICARDIE ARGENTINA S.A.—See Chargeurs SA; *Int'l*, pg. 1449
LAINIERE DE PICARDIE BC—See Chargeurs SA; *Int'l*, pg. 1449
LAINIERE DE PICARDIE DEUTSCHLAND GMBH—See Chargeurs SA; *Int'l*, pg. 1449
LAINIERE DE PICARDIE GOLAPLAST BRAZIL TEXTIL LTDA—See Chargeurs SA; *Int'l*, pg. 1449
LAINIERE DE PICARDIE, INC.—See Chargeurs SA; *Int'l*, pg. 1449
LAINIERE DE PICARDIE KOREA CO. LTD—See Chargeurs SA; *Int'l*, pg. 1449
LAINIERE DE PICARDIE UK LTD—See Chargeurs SA; *Int'l*, pg. 1449
LAINIERE DE PICARDIE URUGUAY S.A.—See Chargeurs SA; *Int'l*, pg. 1449
LA INSTITUT LANCOME—See L'Oreal S.A.; *Int'l*, pg. 4380
LA INTERNATIONAL COMPUTER CONSULTANTS LTD.; *Int'l*, pg. 4388
L & A INTERNATIONAL HOLDINGS LIMITED; *Int'l*, pg. 4368
LAIPPLE OIL INC.; *U.S. Private*, pg. 2373
LAIQON AG; *Int'l*, pg. 4397
LAIRD CHRISTIANSON ADVERTISING, INC.; *U.S. Private*, pg. 2374
LAIRD & COMPANY, INC.; *U.S. Private*, pg. 2373

LAIRD CONNECTIVITY, INC.—See Audax Group, Limited Partnership; *U.S. Private*, pg. 388
LAIRD CONTROLS UK LIMITED—See DuPont de Nemours, Inc.; *U.S. Public*, pg. 693
LAIRD ELECTRIC LNC.—See Bird Construction Inc.; *Int'l*, pg. 1047
LAIRD LIMITED—See DuPont de Nemours, Inc.; *U.S. Public*, pg. 693
LAIRD NOLLER AUTOMOTIVE INC.; *U.S. Private*, pg. 2374
LAIRD NOLLER FORD INCORPORATED; *U.S. Private*, pg. 2374
LAIRD NORTON COMPANY, LLC; *U.S. Private*, pg. 2374
LAIRD NORTON PROPERTIES—See Laird Norton Company, LLC; *U.S. Private*, pg. 2374
LAIRD NORTON TYEE—See Laird Norton Company, LLC; *U.S. Private*, pg. 2374
LAIRD + PARTNERS NEW YORK LLC—See Stagwell, Inc.; *U.S. Public*, pg. 1927
LAIRD PLASTICS, INC.—See Blackfriars Corp.; *U.S. Private*, pg. 575
LAIRD SUPERFOOD, INC.; *U.S. Public*, pg. 1288
LAIRD TECHNOLOGIES GMBH; *Int'l*, pg. 4397
LAIRD TECHNOLOGIES GOTHENBURG AB; *Int'l*, pg. 4397
LAIRD TECHNOLOGIES, INC.—See DuPont de Nemours, Inc.; *U.S. Public*, pg. 693
LAIRD TECHNOLOGIES, INDIA PRIVATE LIMITED; *Int'l*, pg. 4397
LAIRD TECHNOLOGIES JAPAN, INC.—See DuPont de Nemours, Inc.; *U.S. Public*, pg. 693
LAIRD TECHNOLOGIES KOREA Y.H.—See DuPont de Nemours, Inc.; *U.S. Public*, pg. 693
LAIRD TECHNOLOGIES LTD—See DuPont de Nemours, Inc.; *U.S. Public*, pg. 693
LAIRD TECHNOLOGIES (M) SDN BHD—See DuPont de Nemours, Inc.; *U.S. Public*, pg. 693
LAIRD TECHNOLOGIES S. DE R. L. DE C. V.—See DuPont de Nemours, Inc.; *U.S. Public*, pg. 693
LAIRD TECHNOLOGIES (SEA) PTE LIMITED—See DuPont de Nemours, Inc.; *U.S. Public*, pg. 693
LAIRD TECHNOLOGIES (SHANGHAI) LIMITED—See DuPont de Nemours, Inc.; *U.S. Public*, pg. 693
LAIRD TECHNOLOGIES (SHENZHEN) LIMITED—See DuPont de Nemours, Inc.; *U.S. Public*, pg. 693
LAIRD TECHNOLOGIES S.R.O.—See DuPont de Nemours, Inc.; *U.S. Public*, pg. 693
LAIRD TECHNOLOGIES TAIWAN, INC.—See DuPont de Nemours, Inc.; *U.S. Public*, pg. 693
LAIRD TECHONOLGIES (SEA) PTE., LTD.—See DuPont de Nemours, Inc.; *U.S. Public*, pg. 693
LAIRD WINE & SPIRITS OF PA CO.—See Laird & Company, Inc.; *U.S. Private*, pg. 2373
L'AIR LIQUIDE S.A.; *Int'l*, pg. 4369
LAISHUI JIDONG CEMENT CO., LTD.—See Tangshan Jidong Cement Co., Ltd.; *Int'l*, pg. 7458
LAI SI ENTERPRISE HOLDING LIMITED; *Int'l*, pg. 4396
LAISSE PASSE CO., LTD.—See LOOK INCORPORATED; *Int'l*, pg. 4555
LAI SUN DEVELOPMENT COMPANY LIMITED—See Lai Sun Group; *Int'l*, pg. 4396
LAI SUN GARMENT (INTERNATIONAL) LIMITED; *Int'l*, pg. 4396
LAI SUN GROUP; *Int'l*, pg. 4396
THE LAITRAM LLC; *U.S. Private*, pg. 4067
LAITRAM MACHINERY APS—See The Laitram LLC; *U.S. Private*, pg. 4067
LAITRAM MACHINERY INC.—See The Laitram LLC; *U.S. Private*, pg. 4067
LAI WAH FOOTWEAR TRADING LIMITED—See Hillhouse Investment Management Limited; *Int'l*, pg. 3393
LAIWU STEEL GROUP, LTD.; *Int'l*, pg. 4397
LAIX INC.; *Int'l*, pg. 4397
LAJAVI INVERSIONES SL; *Int'l*, pg. 4397
LAJIN ENTERTAINMENT NETWORK GROUP LIMITED; *Int'l*, pg. 4397
LA JOHNSON FRANCAISE S.A.—See S.C. Johnson & Son, Inc.; *U.S. Private*, pg. 3516
LA JOLLA BEACH & TENNIS CLUB INC.; *U.S. Private*, pg. 2368
THE LA JOLLA ENDOSCOPY CENTER, L.P.—See KKR & Co. Inc.; *U.S. Public*, pg. 1247
LA JOLLA LOGIC—See Enlightenment Capital LLC; *U.S. Private*, pg. 1400
LA JOLLA PHARMACEUTICAL COMPANY—See Innoviva, Inc.; *U.S. Public*, pg. 1127
LA JOLLA PHARMACEUTICAL II B.V.—See Innoviva, Inc.; *U.S. Public*, pg. 1127
LA JOLLA SKILLED, INC.—See The Ensign Group, Inc.; *U.S. Public*, pg. 2071
LAKALA PAYMENT CO., LTD.; *Int'l*, pg. 4397
LA KATTOHUOLTO OY—See Kingspan Group PLC; *Int'l*, pg. 4178
LAKE AIR METAL PRODUCTS LLC; *U.S. Private*, pg. 2374
LAKE AREA CORN PROCESSORS, LLC; *U.S. Private*, pg. 2374
LAKE AREA PHYSICIAN SERVICES, LLC—See Community Health Systems, Inc.; *U.S. Public*, pg. 554

CORPORATE AFFILIATIONS

LAKE ARROWHEAD DIV.—See Purcell Co., Inc.; *U.S. Private*, pg. 3304
LAKE AUSTIN SPA RESORT; *U.S. Private*, pg. 2374
LAKE BUSINESS PRODUCTS, INC.; *U.S. Private*, pg. 2374
LAKE CABLE LLC; *U.S. Private*, pg. 2374
LAKE CAMERON, LLC—See DRA Advisors LLC; *U.S. Private*, pg. 1271
LAKE CAMERON, LLC—See Fogelman Properties, LLC; *U.S. Private*, pg. 1557
LAKE CAPITAL MANAGEMENT LLC; *U.S. Private*, pg. 2374
LAKE CATHERINE—See Munro & Company, Inc.; *U.S. Private*, pg. 2814
LAKE CHARLES COCA-COLA BOTTLING COMPANY—See Coca-Cola Bottling Co. United, Inc.; *U.S. Private*, pg. 958
LAKE CITY BANK INVESTMENTS LIMITED—See Lakeland Financial Corporation; *U.S. Public*, pg. 1288
LAKE CITY BANK—See Lakeland Financial Corporation; *U.S. Public*, pg. 1288
LAKE CITY FORD SALES LTD.; *Int'l*, pg. 4397
LAKE CITY HEAT TREATING CORP.—See Bodycote plc; *Int'l*, pg. 1098
LAKE CITY IMAGING, LLC—See HCA Healthcare, Inc.; *U.S. Public*, pg. 1000
LAKE CITY MEDICAL CENTER—See HCA Healthcare, Inc.; *U.S. Public*, pg. 1000
LAKE CITY PARTNERSHIP COUNCIL; *U.S. Private*, pg. 2374
LAKE CITY REGIONAL MEDICAL GROUP, LLC—See HCA Healthcare, Inc.; *U.S. Public*, pg. 1000
LAKE CITY REPORTER—See Community Newspapers Inc.; *U.S. Private*, pg. 996
LAKE COEUR D'ALENE CRUISES INC.—See The Hagadone Corporation; *U.S. Private*, pg. 4041
LAKE COMMUNICATIONS LIMITED—See Searchlight Capital Partners, L.P.; *U.S. Private*, pg. 3589
LAKE CONSUMER PRODUCTS, INC.—See Wisconsin Pharmacal Company, LLC; *U.S. Private*, pg. 4548
LAKE COUNTRY CAPITAL LLC; *U.S. Private*, pg. 2374
LAKE COUNTRY FOODS; *U.S. Private*, pg. 2374
LAKE COUNTRY POWER; *U.S. Private*, pg. 2374
LAKE COUNTRY RADIO—See Alden Global Capital LLC; *U.S. Private*, pg. 156
THE LAKE COUNTRY SUN—See Alden Global Capital LLC; *U.S. Private*, pg. 156
LAKE COUNTY DODGE INC.; *U.S. Private*, pg. 2375
LAKE COUNTY GAS—See UGI Corporation; *U.S. Public*, pg. 2221
LAKE COUNTY PRESS; *U.S. Private*, pg. 2375
LAKE COUNTY RECORD-BEE—See Alden Global Capital LLC; *U.S. Private*, pg. 156
LAKE CUMBERLAND CARDIOLOGY ASSOCIATES, LLC—See Apollo Global Management, Inc.; *U.S. Public*, pg. 158
LAKE CUMBERLAND REGIONAL HOSPITAL, LLC—See Apollo Global Management, Inc.; *U.S. Public*, pg. 158
LAKE CUMBERLAND SURGERY CENTER, LP—See Apollo Global Management, Inc.; *U.S. Public*, pg. 158
LAKEDALE COMMUNICATIONS LLC—See Windstream Holdings, Inc.; *U.S. Public*, pg. 2373
LAKEDALE WHITELEY MEADOWS (NORTH WHITELEY) MANAGEMENT COMPANY LIMITED—See Persimmon plc; *Int'l*, pg. 5816
LAKEEL, INC.; *Int'l*, pg. 4397
LAKE ELMO BANK; *U.S. Private*, pg. 2375
LAKE ENDOSCOPY CENTER, LLC—See Tenet Healthcare Corporation; *U.S. Public*, pg. 2004
LAKE ERIE ELECTRIC INC-HIRSCH DIVISION—See Lake Erie Electric, Inc.; *U.S. Private*, pg. 2375
LAKE ERIE ELECTRIC, INC.; *U.S. Private*, pg. 2375
LAKE FOREST AM, LTD—See American Realty Investors, Inc.; *U.S. Public*, pg. 108
LAKE FOREST BANK & TRUST COMPANY, N.A.—See Wintrust Financial Corporation; *U.S. Public*, pg. 2375
LAKE FOREST SPORTSCARS LTD.; *U.S. Private*, pg. 2375
LAKEFRONT LINES, INC.—See Stagecoach Group plc; *Int'l*, pg. 7163
LAKEFRONT MEDICAL ASSOCIATES, LLC—See Tenet Healthcare Corporation; *U.S. Public*, pg. 2014
LAKEFRONT RESIDENCE SDN. BHD.—See Avaland Berhad; *Int'l*, pg. 734
LAKE GENEVA REGIONAL NEWS—See Lee Enterprises, Incorporated; *U.S. Public*, pg. 1299
LAKE GEORGE VENTURES INC.—See Galesi Group; *U.S. Private*, pg. 1637
LAKE GRANBURY HOSPITAL-BASED PROFESSIONAL SERVICES—See Community Health Systems, Inc.; *U.S. Public*, pg. 554
LAKE GRAY DIALYSIS CENTER LLC—See Nautic Partners, LLC; *U.S. Private*, pg. 2870
LAKE GROUP MEDIA, INC.; *U.S. Private*, pg. 2375
LAKEHEAD CONSTRUCTORS, INC.—See Lakehead Holding Corp.; *U.S. Private*, pg. 2376
LAKEHEAD HOLDING CORP.; *U.S. Private*, pg. 2376
LAKEHEAD MARINE & INDUSTRIAL INC.—See Upper Lakes Group Inc.; *Int'l*, pg. 8093

COMPANY NAME INDEX LAKES REGION VISITING NURSE ASSOCIATION
Company Index

LAKEHEAD SHIPPING COMPANY LIMITED—See Blue Wolf Capital Partners LLC; *U.S. Private*, pg. 594
LAKE HOSPITAL SYSTEM, INC.; *U.S. Private*, pg. 2375
LAKE HOUSTON PHYSICAL THERAPY, LIMITED PARTNERSHIP—See U.S. Physical Therapy, Inc.; *U.S. Public*, pg. 2215
LAKE INTERNATIONAL TECHNOLOGIES (PTY) LIMITED—See AECI Limited; *Int'l*, pg. 171
LAKE JAMES LODGE; *U.S. Private*, pg. 2375
LAKE JEANETTE DEVELOPMENT CO—See Hudson Advisors LLC; *U.S. Private*, pg. 2001
LAKE KEOWEE CHRYSLER DODGE JEEP RAM; *U.S. Private*, pg. 2375
LAKELAND ANIMAL NUTRITION, INC.—See Alltech, Inc.; *U.S. Private*, pg. 194
LAKELAND ARGENTINA, SRL—See Lakeland Industries, Inc.; *U.S. Public*, pg. 1289
LAKELAND AUTO AUCTION—See Cox Enterprises, Inc.; *U.S. Private*, pg. 1076
LAKELAND BANCORP, INC.—See Provident Financial Services, Inc.; *U.S. Public*, pg. 1730
LAKELAND BANK—See Provident Financial Services, Inc.; *U.S. Public*, pg. 1730
LAKELAND BEHAVIORAL HEALTH SYSTEM—See Acadia Healthcare Company, Inc.; *U.S. Public*, pg. 29
LAKELAND (BEIJING) SAFETY PRODUCTS, CO., LTD.—See Lakeland Industries, Inc.; *U.S. Public*, pg. 1288
LAKELAND COMMUNITY HOSPITAL, INC.—See Curae Health, Inc.; *U.S. Private*, pg. 1124
LAKELAND COOPERATIVE; *U.S. Private*, pg. 2376
LAKELAND DAIRIES AGRIBUSINESS—See Lakeland Dairies Co-Operative Society Ltd.; *Int'l*, pg. 4397
LAKELAND DAIRIES CO-OPERATIVE SOCIETY LTD.; *Int'l*, pg. 4397
LAKELAND DAIRIES FOOD INGREDIENTS—See Lakeland Dairies Co-Operative Society Ltd.; *Int'l*, pg. 4397
LAKELAND ELECTRIC; *U.S. Private*, pg. 2376
LAKELAND FINANCIAL CORPORATION; *U.S. Public*, pg. 1288
THE LAKELAND FL ENDOSCOPY ASC, LLC—See KKR & Co. Inc.; *U.S. Public*, pg. 1247
LAKELAND GLOVES AND SAFETY APPAREL PRIVATE LTD.—See Lakeland Industries, Inc.; *U.S. Public*, pg. 1289
LAKELAND HOME CARE SERVICES, LLC—See Community Health Systems, Inc.; *U.S. Public*, pg. 554
LAKELAND INDIA PRIVATE LIMITED—See Lakeland Industries, Inc.; *U.S. Public*, pg. 1289
LAKELAND INDUSTRIES EUROPE LTD.—See Lakeland Industries, Inc.; *U.S. Public*, pg. 1289
LAKELAND INDUSTRIES, INC. AGENCIA EN CHILE—See Lakeland Industries, Inc.; *U.S. Public*, pg. 1289
LAKELAND INDUSTRIES, INC.; *U.S. Public*, pg. 1288
LAKELAND LEDGER PUBLISHING CORPORATION—See Gannett Co., Inc.; *U.S. Public*, pg. 905
LAKELAND LIMITED; *Int'l*, pg. 4397
LAKELAND PAPER CORPORATION; *U.S. Private*, pg. 2376
LAKELAND PRINTING CO INC; *U.S. Private*, pg. 2376
LAKELAND PROTECTIVE WEAR, INC.—See Lakeland Industries, Inc.; *U.S. Public*, pg. 1289
LAKELAND SQUARE MALL, LLC—See Brookfield Corporation; *Int'l*, pg. 1185
LAKELAND TOURS, LLC—See Eurazeo SE; *Int'l*, pg. 2529
LAKELAND & WATERWAYS RAILWAY—See Canadian National Railway Company; *Int'l*, pg. 1284
LAKE LANSING ASC PARTNERS, LLC—See Tenet Healthcare Corporation; *U.S. Public*, pg. 2011
LAKE LAS VEGAS MARINA LLC—See Centerbridge Partners, L.P.; *U.S. Private*, pg. 815
LAKELINE PLAZA, LLC—See Washington Prime Group Inc.; *U.S. Private*, pg. 4448
LAKE LIVINGSTON TELEPHONE COMPANY; *U.S. Private*, pg. 2375
LAKE LOUIE BREWING LLC—See Wisconsin Brewing Company LLC; *U.S. Private*, pg. 4548
LAKE LYNDON B. JOHNSON IMPROVEMENT CORPORATION; *U.S. Private*, pg. 2375
LAKE MAITLAND PTY LTD—See Mega Uranium Ltd.; *Int'l*, pg. 4793
LAKE MANAWA NISSAN INC.; *U.S. Private*, pg. 2375
LAKEMARY CENTER INC.; *U.S. Private*, pg. 2376
LAKE MARY SURGERY CENTER, L.L.C.—See Bain Capital, LP; *U.S. Private*, pg. 445
LAKE MATERIALS CO., LTD.; *Int'l*, pg. 4397
LAKE MECHANICAL CONTRACTORS; *U.S. Private*, pg. 2375
LAKE METROPARKS; *U.S. Private*, pg. 2375
LAKE MICHIGAN CREDIT UNION; *U.S. Private*, pg. 2375
LAKE MILLS FEED & GRAIN INC.—See Vita Plus Corporation; *U.S. Private*, pg. 4405
LAKE MINDEN RESORT—See Equity LifeStyle Properties, Inc.; *U.S. Public*, pg. 790
LAKE NONA EMERGENCY PHYSICIANS, LLC—See HCA Healthcare, Inc.; *U.S. Public*, pg. 1000
LAKE NONA GOLF & COUNTRY CLUB, LLC—See Tavistock Group, Inc.; *U.S. Private*, pg. 3937
LAKE NONA INPATIENT SERVICES, LLC—See HCA Healthcare, Inc.; *U.S. Public*, pg. 1000
LAKE NORMAN BENEFITS, INC.—See ABRY Partners, LLC; *U.S. Private*, pg. 43
LAKE NORMAN LANDFILL, INC.—See Republic Services, Inc.; *U.S. Public*, pg. 1786
LAKE NORMAN TRACTOR COMPANY—See BobCo Inc.; *U.S. Private*, pg. 607
LAKEN SHIPPING CORPORATION SMT (USA) INC.—See Algoma Central Corporation; *Int'l*, pg. 318
LAKE OKEECHOBEE REAL ESTATE MAGAZINE—See Independent Newspapers, Inc.; *U.S. Private*, pg. 2060
LAKE OSWEGO HOLDINGS INC.—See St. John Holdings Inc.; *U.S. Private*, pg. 3772
LAKE PACIFIC PARTNERS, LLC; *U.S. Private*, pg. 2375
LAKEPARK INDUSTRIES, INC.—See Midway Products Group, Inc.; *U.S. Private*, pg. 2719
LAKEPARK INDUSTRIES OF INDIANA, INC.—See Midway Products Group, Inc.; *U.S. Private*, pg. 2719
LAKE PARK MUNICIPAL UTILITIES; *U.S. Private*, pg. 2375
LAKE PARK OF MADISON LLC—See Healthtique Group LLC; *U.S. Private*, pg. 1898
LAKEPHARMA, INC.; *U.S. Private*, pg. 2376
LAKE POINTE OPERATING COMPANY, L.L.C.—See Tenet Healthcare Corporation; *U.S. Public*, pg. 2006
LAKE POINTE PARTNERS, LTD.—See Tenet Healthcare Corporation; *U.S. Public*, pg. 2006
LAKE PRESTON COOPERATIVE ASSOCIATION; *U.S. Private*, pg. 2375
LAKE REGION CO-OP OIL ASSOCIATION; *U.S. Private*, pg. 2375
LAKE REGION ELECTRIC COOP; *U.S. Private*, pg. 2375
LAKE REGION HEALTHCARE; *U.S. Private*, pg. 2376
LAKE REGION MANUFACTURING, INC.—See Integer Holdings Corporation; *U.S. Public*, pg. 1135
LAKE REGION MEDICAL GMBH—See Integer Holdings Corporation; *U.S. Public*, pg. 1135
LAKE REGION MEDICAL HOLDINGS, INC—See Integer Holdings Corporation; *U.S. Public*, pg. 1135
LAKE REGION MEDICAL, INC.—See Integer Holdings Corporation; *U.S. Public*, pg. 1135
LAKE REGION MEDICAL LIMITED—See Integer Holdings Corporation; *U.S. Public*, pg. 1135
LAKE REGION MEDICAL LTD—See Integer Holdings Corporation; *U.S. Public*, pg. 1135
LAKE REGION MEDICAL - SALEM—See Integer Holdings Corporation; *U.S. Public*, pg. 1135
LAKE REGION MEDICAL SDN. BHD.—See Integer Holdings Corporation; *U.S. Public*, pg. 1135
LAKE REGION MEDICAL - TRENTON—See Integer Holdings Corporation; *U.S. Public*, pg. 1135
LAKE RESOURCES N.L.; *Int'l*, pg. 4397
LAKERS TAVERN (WA) PTY LTD—See Woolworths Group Limited; *Int'l*, pg. 8451
LAKES AREA COOPERATIVE; *U.S. Private*, pg. 2376
LAKES AREA NONPROFIT SUPPORT FOUNDATION; *U.S. Private*, pg. 2376
LAKES BLUE ENERGY NL; *Int'l*, pg. 4397
LAKE SEMINOLE SQUARE, LLC—See Brookdale Senior Living Inc.; *U.S. Public*, pg. 395
LAKES GAMING & RESORTS, LLC—See Golden Entertainment, Inc.; *U.S. Public*, pg. 950
LAKES GAS COMPANY; *U.S. Private*, pg. 2376
LAKESHORE ACQUISITION I CORP.; *Int'l*, pg. 4397
LAKE SHORE BANCORP, INC.; *U.S. Public*, pg. 1288
LAKE SHORE BEHAVIORAL HEALTH, INC.; *U.S. Private*, pg. 2376
LAKESHORE BIOPHARMA CO., LTD.; *Int'l*, pg. 4397
LAKESHORE CAPITAL PARTNERS LLC; *U.S. Private*, pg. 2377
LAKESHORE DISPOSAL, INC.—See Waste Connections, Inc.; *Int'l*, pg. 8353
LAKESHORE ENTERTAINMENT CORP.; *U.S. Private*, pg. 2377
LAKESHORE ESTATES INC; *U.S. Private*, pg. 2377
LAKESHORE FITTINGS, INC.—See MiddleGround Management, LP; *U.S. Private*, pg. 2711
LAKESHORE FOODS CORP.; *U.S. Private*, pg. 2377
LAKESHORE LANDINGS, LLC—See Sun Communities, Inc.; *U.S. Public*, pg. 1961
LAKESHORE LEARNING MATERIALS; *U.S. Private*, pg. 2377
LAKESHORE MACHINE TOOLS—See The 600 Group PLC; *Int'l*, pg. 7609
LAKESHORE MANAGEMENT GROUP; *U.S. Private*, pg. 2377
LAKE SHORE NEWSPAPERS INC.; *U.S. Private*, pg. 2376
LAKE SHORE PRESS, INC.—See PLBY Group, Inc.; *U.S. Public*, pg. 1698
LAKE SHORE RADIATOR INC.; *U.S. Private*, pg. 2376
LAKESHORE RECYCLING SYSTEMS, LLC—See Macquarie Group Limited; *Int'l*, pg. 4628
LAKE SHORE SAVINGS BANK—See Lake Shore Bancorp, Inc.; *U.S. Public*, pg. 1288
LAKESHORE STAFFING INC.—See Jordan Industries, Inc.; *U.S. Private*, pg. 2235
LAKESHORE SYSTEM SERVICES OF FLORIDA, INC.—See Encompass Health Corporation; *U.S. Public*, pg. 758
LAKESHORE UTILITY TRAILER INC.; *U.S. Private*, pg. 2377
LAKESIDE BANCSHARES, INC.; *U.S. Public*, pg. 1289
LAKESIDE BANK; *U.S. Private*, pg. 2377
LAKESIDE BANK—See Lakeside Bancshares, Inc.; *U.S. Public*, pg. 1289
LAKESIDE BANK—See PFBS Holdings, Inc.; *U.S. Private*, pg. 3164
LAKESIDE BOOK COMPANY—See Atlas Holdings, LLC; *U.S. Private*, pg. 376
LAKESIDE CHEVROLET BUICK GMC LTD.—See General Motors Company; *U.S. Public*, pg. 926
LAKESIDE COUNTRY CLUB; *U.S. Private*, pg. 2377
LAKESIDE FOODS, INC. - BELGIUM PLANT—See Lakeside Foods, Inc.; *U.S. Private*, pg. 2377
LAKESIDE FOODS, INC. - BROOTEN PLANT—See Lakeside Foods, Inc.; *U.S. Private*, pg. 2377
LAKESIDE FOODS, INC. - MANITOWOC PLANT—See Lakeside Foods, Inc.; *U.S. Private*, pg. 2377
LAKESIDE FOODS, INC. - NEW RICHMOND PLANT—See Lakeside Foods, Inc.; *U.S. Private*, pg. 2377
LAKESIDE FOODS, INC. - OWATONNA PLANT—See Lakeside Foods, Inc.; *U.S. Private*, pg. 2377
LAKESIDE FOODS, INC. - PLAINVIEW PLANT—See Lakeside Foods, Inc.; *U.S. Private*, pg. 2377
LAKESIDE FOODS, INC. - RANDOM LAKE PLANT—See Lakeside Foods, Inc.; *U.S. Private*, pg. 2377
LAKESIDE FOODS, INC. - REEDSBURG PLANT—See Lakeside Foods, Inc.; *U.S. Private*, pg. 2377
LAKESIDE FOODS, INC. - SEYMOUR PLANT—See Lakeside Foods, Inc.; *U.S. Private*, pg. 2377
LAKESIDE FOODS, INC.; *U.S. Private*, pg. 2377
LAKESIDE FOODS—See Lakeside Foods, Inc.; *U.S. Private*, pg. 2377
LAKESIDE IMPORTS INC.; *U.S. Private*, pg. 2378
LAKESIDE INDUSTRIES - ABERDEEN PLANT—See Lakeside Industries; *U.S. Private*, pg. 2378
LAKESIDE INDUSTRIES - CENTRALIA PLANT—See Lakeside Industries; *U.S. Private*, pg. 2378
LAKESIDE INDUSTRIES - FOSTER ROAD PLANT—See Lakeside Industries; *U.S. Private*, pg. 2378
LAKESIDE INDUSTRIES - FREMONT PLANT—See Lakeside Industries; *U.S. Private*, pg. 2378
LAKESIDE INDUSTRIES - HILLSBORO PLANT—See Lakeside Industries; *U.S. Private*, pg. 2378
LAKESIDE INDUSTRIES - ISSAQUAH PLANT—See Lakeside Industries; *U.S. Private*, pg. 2378
LAKESIDE INDUSTRIES - KENT PLANT—See Lakeside Industries; *U.S. Private*, pg. 2378
LAKESIDE INDUSTRIES - LONGVIEW PLANT—See Lakeside Industries; *U.S. Private*, pg. 2378
LAKESIDE INDUSTRIES - MONROE PLANT—See Lakeside Industries; *U.S. Private*, pg. 2378
LAKESIDE INDUSTRIES - PORT ANGELES PLANT—See Lakeside Industries; *U.S. Private*, pg. 2378
LAKESIDE INDUSTRIES - PORTLAND PLANT—See Lakeside Industries; *U.S. Private*, pg. 2378
LAKESIDE INDUSTRIES; *U.S. Private*, pg. 2378
LAKESIDE INDUSTRIES - VALLEY PAVING PLANT—See Lakeside Industries; *U.S. Private*, pg. 2378
LAKESIDE INSULATION, LLC—See Installed Building Products, Inc.; *U.S. Public*, pg. 1133
LAKESIDE INTERNATIONAL LLC—See Lakeside International Trucks Inc.; *U.S. Private*, pg. 2378
LAKESIDE INTERNATIONAL TRUCKS INC.; *U.S. Private*, pg. 2378
LAKESIDE MEDICAL GROUP, INC.; *U.S. Private*, pg. 2378
LAKESIDE METALS INC.; *U.S. Private*, pg. 2378
LAKESIDE MILL LLC—See UDR, Inc.; *U.S. Public*, pg. 2218
LAKESIDE PAINTING, INC.—See Painters USA, Inc.; *U.S. Private*, pg. 3076
LAKESIDE PLASTICS, INC.; *U.S. Private*, pg. 2378
LAKE SIDE PRINTING FACTORY LIMITED—See Fountain Set (Holdings) Limited; *Int'l*, pg. 2754
LAKESIDE PROCESS CONTROLS LTD.; *Int'l*, pg. 4397
LAKESIDE PRODUCTIONS INC.; *U.S. Private*, pg. 2378
LAKESIDE PROPERTY DEVELOPMENT CO., LTD.—See Pearson plc; *Int'l*, pg. 5775
LAKESIDE SUPPLY CO. INC.; *U.S. Private*, pg. 2378
LAKESIDE TRANSPORTATION INC.—See Cook-Illinois Corp.; *U.S. Private*, pg. 1038
LAKESIDE WOMEN'S HOSPITAL—See INTEGRIS Health, Inc.; *U.S. Private*, pg. 2102
LAKES OF NORTHDALE APARTMENTS LLC—See Independence Realty Trust, Inc.; *U.S. Public*, pg. 1115
LAKES PIPE & SUPPLY CORP.; *U.S. Private*, pg. 2376
LAKES REGION TUBULAR PRODUCTS, INC.—See Smiths Group plc; *Int'l*, pg. 7012
LAKES REGION VISITING NURSE ASSOCIATION; *U.S. Private*, pg. 2376

LAKES & RIVERS TRANSFER DIV.—See Jack Gray Transport, Inc.; *U.S. Private*, pg. 2174
LAKE SUPERIOR BREWING COMPANY; *U.S. Private*, pg. 2376
LAKE SUPERIOR CONSULTING—See ShawCor Ltd.; *Int'l*, pg. 6791
LAKE TAHOE CRUISES, INC.—See Aramark; *U.S. Public*, pg. 176
LAKE TANSI VILLAGE INC.—See Equity LifeStyle Properties, Inc.; *U.S. Public*, pg. 790
THE LAKE TERMINAL RAILROAD COMPANY—See United States Steel Corporation; *U.S. Public*, pg. 2236
THE LAKE TODAY—See Wehco Media, Inc.; *U.S. Private*, pg. 4470
LAKETON INVESTMENTS—See Power Corporation of Canada; *Int'l*, pg. 5944
LAKE VICTORIA MINING COMPANY, INC., *Int'l*, pg. 4397
LAKEVIEW ACQUISITION CORPORATION; *U.S. Public*, pg. 1289
LAKEVIEW CAPITAL, INC.; *U.S. Private*, pg. 2378
LAKE VIEW CHEESE CO.; *U.S. Private*, pg. 2376
LAKEVIEW CONSTRUCTION INC.; *U.S. Private*, pg. 2378
LAKEVIEW ENDOSCOPY CENTER—See HCA Healthcare, Inc.; *U.S. Public*, pg. 1000
LAKEVIEW EQUITY PARTNERS, LLC; *U.S. Private*, pg. 2378
LAKEVIEW FARMS, INC.; *U.S. Private*, pg. 2378
LAKEVIEW FARMS, INC.—See Lakeview Farms, Inc.; *U.S. Private*, pg. 2378
LAKEVIEW FARMS LLC; *U.S. Private*, pg. 2378
LAKEVIEW HEALTH SYSTEMS, L.L.C.—See Lee Equity Partners LLC; *U.S. Private*, pg. 2412
LAKEVIEW HOSPITAL PHYSICIAN SERVICES, LLC—See HCA Healthcare, Inc.; *U.S. Public*, pg. 1000
LAKEVIEW HOSPITAL—See HCA Healthcare, Inc.; *U.S. Public*, pg. 1000
LAKEVIEW HOTEL INVESTMENT CORP.—First Canadian Management Corporation; *Int'l*, pg. 2682
LAKEVIEW INTERNAL MEDICINE, LLC—See HCA Healthcare, Inc.; *U.S. Public*, pg. 1000
LAKEVIEW MEDICAL CENTER, LLC—See HCA Healthcare, Inc.; *U.S. Public*, pg. 1000
LAKE VIEW MEMORIAL GARDENS, INC.—See Service Corporation International; *U.S. Public*, pg. 1869
LAKEVIEW NEUROSURGERY CLINIC, LLC—See HCA Healthcare, Inc.; *U.S. Public*, pg. 1000
LAKEVIEW REGIONAL PHYSICIAN GROUP, LLC—See HCA Healthcare, Inc.; *U.S. Public*, pg. 1000
LAKEVIEW SURGERY CENTER, LLC—See Ventas, Inc.; *U.S. Public*, pg. 2278
LAKE VILLAGE SEED & TIRE CO.; *U.S. Private*, pg. 2376
LAKEVILLE MOTOR EXPRESS INC.—See Wren Corporation; *U.S. Private*, pg. 4572
LAKE WALES CLINIC CORP.—See Community Health Systems, Inc.; *U.S. Public*, pg. 554
LAKE WALES HOSPITAL CORPORATION—See Adventist Health System Sunbelt Healthcare Corporation; *U.S. Private*, pg. 109
LAKEWAY MECHANICAL CONTRACTORS; *U.S. Private*, pg. 2378
LAKEWAY PUBLISHERS INCORPORATED; *U.S. Private*, pg. 2378
LAKEWAY REGIONAL HOSPITAL—See Community Health Systems, Inc.; *U.S. Public*, pg. 554
LAKEWAY TRUCKING INCORPORATED; *U.S. Private*, pg. 2378
LAKE WELDING SUPPLY COMPANY, INC.—See Linde plc; *Int'l*, pg. 4508
LAKE WINN RESOURCES CORP.; *Int'l*, pg. 4397
LAKEWOOD-AMEDEX INC.; *U.S. Private*, pg. 2379
LAKEWOOD CAPITAL, LLC; *U.S. Private*, pg. 2378
LAKEWOOD CHEVROLET—See AutoCanada Inc.; *Int'l*, pg. 726
LAKEWOOD FORD; *U.S. Private*, pg. 2379
LAKEWOOD MERIDIAN LLC—See Brookdale Senior Living Inc.; *U.S. Public*, pg. 395
LAKEWOOD RANCH GOLF & COUNTRY CLUB; *U.S. Private*, pg. 2379
LAKEWOOD REGIONAL MEDICAL CENTER, INC.—See UCI Health; *U.S. Private*, pg. 4274
LAKEWOOD RESOURCE & REFERRAL CENTER; *U.S. Private*, pg. 2379
LAKEWOOD SURGERY CENTER, LLC—See Tenet Healthcare Corporation; *U.S. Public*, pg. 2011
LAKHANI INDIA LIMITED; *Int'l*, pg. 4398
LAKHOTIA POLYESTER (INDIA) LIMITED; *Int'l*, pg. 4398
LAKIN GENERAL CORPORATION; *U.S. Private*, pg. 2379
LAKIN TIRE WEST INC.—See The Carlyle Group Inc.; *U.S. Private*, pg. 2048
LAKIPERINTA OY—See Otava Ltd.; *Int'l*, pg. 5656
LAKNORD—See Richelieu Hardware Ltd.; *Int'l*, pg. 6331
LAKOINGATLAN-FORGALMAZO KFT—See Intrum AB; *Int'l*, pg. 3771
LAKSANA WIBAWA SDN.BHD.—See YLI Holdings Berhad; *Int'l*, pg. 8590
LAKSHMI AUTOMATIC LOOM WORKS LIMITED; *Int'l*, pg. 4398
LAKSHMI AUTOMATIC LOOM WORKS LTD. - UNIT 1—See Lakshmi Automatic Loom Works Limited; *Int'l*, pg. 4398
LAKSHMI AUTOMATIC LOOM WORKS LTD. - UNIT 2—See Lakshmi Automatic Loom Works Limited; *Int'l*, pg. 4398
LAKSHMI ELECTRICAL CONTROL SYSTEMS LIMITED; *Int'l*, pg. 4398
LAKSHMI FINANCE & INDUSTRIAL CORPORATION LIMITED; *Int'l*, pg. 4398
LAKSHMI MACHINE WORKS LIMITED MACHINE TOOL DIVISION & FOUNDRY DIVISION—See Lakshmi Machine Works Ltd.; *Int'l*, pg. 4398
LAKSHMI MACHINE WORKS LIMITED MACHINE TOOL DIVISION—See Lakshmi Machine Works Ltd.; *Int'l*, pg. 4398
LAKSHMI MACHINE WORKS LIMITED UNIT 2—See Lakshmi Machine Works Ltd.; *Int'l*, pg. 4398
LAKSHMI MACHINE WORKS LTD.; *Int'l*, pg. 4398
THE LAKSHMI MILLS COMPANY LIMITED; *Int'l*, pg. 7663
THE LAKSHMI MILLS COMPANY LIMITED - UNIT 2—See The Lakshmi Mills Company Limited; *Int'l*, pg. 7664
LAKSHMI PRECISION SCREWS LTD.; *Int'l*, pg. 4398
LAKSHMI VENKATESH TG COLLEGE OF NURSING—See TGV Sraac Limited; *Int'l*, pg. 7588
LAKSHMI VENKATESH TG COLLEGE OF PHYSIOTHERAPY—See TGV Sraac Limited; *Int'l*, pg. 7588
LAKSHYA FORUM FOR COMPETITIONS PVT. LTD.—See MT EDUCARE LIMITED; *Int'l*, pg. 5069
LAKSON BUSINESS SOLUTIONS LIMITED—See Lakson Group of Companies; *Int'l*, pg. 4398
LAKSON GROUP OF COMPANIES; *Int'l*, pg. 4398
LAKSON INVESTMENTS LIMITED—See COLGATE-PALMOLIVE (PAKISTAN) LTD; *Int'l*, pg. 1698
LAKS- & VILDTCENTRALEN AS—See Austevoll Seafood ASA; *Int'l*, pg. 717
L.A. LACY, INC.—See The Branch Group, Inc.; *U.S. Private*, pg. 3999
LA-LA IMPORTS INC.; *U.S. Private*, pg. 2370
LALANCE FINANCIAL GROUP, INC.—See State Farm Mutual Automobile Insurance Company; *U.S. Private*, pg. 3792
LALAPORT MANAGEMENT CO., LTD. - LALAPORT KASHIWANOHA FACILITY—See Mitsui Fudosan Co., Ltd.; *Int'l*, pg. 4986
LALAPORT MANAGEMENT CO., LTD. - LALAPORT SHIN MISATO FACILITY—See Mitsui Fudosan Co., Ltd.; *Int'l*, pg. 4986
LALAPORT MANAGEMENT CO., LTD. - LALAPORT TOKYO-BAY FACILITY—See Mitsui Fudosan Co., Ltd.; *Int'l*, pg. 4986
LALAPORT MANAGEMENT CO., LTD. - LALAPORT YOKOHAMA FACILITY—See Mitsui Fudosan Co., Ltd.; *Int'l*, pg. 4986
LALAPORT MANAGEMENT CO., LTD. - MITSUI OUTLET PARK IRUMA FACILITY—See Mitsui Fudosan Co., Ltd.; *Int'l*, pg. 4986
LALAPORT MANAGEMENT CO., LTD. - MITSUI OUTLET PARK JAZZ DREAM NAGASHIMA FACILITY—See Mitsui Fudosan Co., Ltd.; *Int'l*, pg. 4986
LALAPORT MANAGEMENT CO., LTD. - MITSUI OUTLET PARK MARINE PIER KOBE FACILITY—See Mitsui Fudosan Co., Ltd.; *Int'l*, pg. 4986
LALAPORT MANAGEMENT CO., LTD. - MITSUI OUTLET PARK SENDAI MINATO FACILITY—See Mitsui Fudosan Co., Ltd.; *Int'l*, pg. 4986
LALAPORT MANAGEMENT CO.,LTD. - MITSUI OUTLET PARK TAMA MINAMI OSAWA FACILITY—See Mitsui Fudosan Co., Ltd.; *Int'l*, pg. 4986
LALAPORT MANAGEMENT CO., LTD. - MITSUI OUTLET PARK YOKOHAMA BAYSIDE FACILITY—See Mitsui Fudosan Co., Ltd.; *Int'l*, pg. 4986
LALAPORT MANAGEMENT CO., LTD. - URBAN DOCK LALAPORT TOYOSU FACILITY—See Mitsui Fudosan Co., Ltd.; *Int'l*, pg. 4986
LA LATINOAMERICANA, SEGUROS, S.A.; *Int'l*, pg. 4388
LALBHAI GROUP; *Int'l*, pg. 4398
LALEHAM HEALTHCARE LIMITED—See DCC plc; *Int'l*, pg. 1991
LA LEY—See Wolters Kluwer n.v.; *Int'l*, pg. 8444
LALIN PROPERTY PUBLIC COMPANY LIMITED; *Int'l*, pg. 4399
LALIQUE ASIA LIMITED—See Lalique Group S.A.; *Int'l*, pg. 4399
LALIQUE ASIA LTD.—See Lalique Group S.A.; *Int'l*, pg. 4399
LALIQUE BEAUTY DISTRIBUTION SASU—See Lalique Group S.A.; *Int'l*, pg. 4399
LALIQUE CRYSTAL SINGAPORE LTD.—See Lalique Group S.A.; *Int'l*, pg. 4399
LALIQUE GMBH—See Lalique Group S.A.; *Int'l*, pg. 4399
LALIQUE GROUP S.A.; *Int'l*, pg. 4399
LALIQUE LTD.—See Lalique Group S.A.; *Int'l*, pg. 4399
LALIQUE NORTH AMERICA INC.—See Lalique Group S.A.; *Int'l*, pg. 4399
LALIQUE S.A.—See Lalique Group S.A.; *Int'l*, pg. 4399
LALIQUE (SHANGHAI) LIMITED—See Lalique Group S.A.; *Int'l*, pg. 4399
LALIT POLYMERS & ELECTRONICS LTD.; *Int'l*, pg. 4399
LALLEMAND / AMERICAN YEAST CORPORATION—See Lallemand, Inc.; *Int'l*, pg. 4399
LALLEMAND AUSTRALIA PTY LTD—See Lallemand, Inc.; *Int'l*, pg. 4399
LALLEMAND BAKING SOLUTIONS LTD.—See Lallemand, Inc.; *Int'l*, pg. 4399
LALLEMAND BIO-INGREDIENTS INC—See Lallemand, Inc.; *Int'l*, pg. 4399
LALLEMAND CHILE Y CIA. LTDA.—See Lallemand, Inc.; *Int'l*, pg. 4399
LALLEMAND HUMAN NUTRITION A/S—See Lallemand, Inc.; *Int'l*, pg. 4399
LALLEMAND, INC.; *Int'l*, pg. 4399
LALLEMAND MEXICO S.A. DE C.V.—See Lallemand, Inc.; *Int'l*, pg. 4400
LALLEMAND SA—See Lallemand, Inc.; *Int'l*, pg. 4399
LALLEMAND SPECIALTIES INC.—See Lallemand, Inc.; *Int'l*, pg. 4400
LALLEMAND SP. Z.O.O—See Lallemand, Inc.; *Int'l*, pg. 4400
LALLY PIPE & TUBE—See L B Industries, Inc.; *U.S. Private*, pg. 2361
LALPIR POWER LTD.; *Int'l*, pg. 4400
LA LUZ, S.A.—See Grupo Boluda; *Int'l*, pg. 3123
LA MADELEINE DE CORPS, INC.—See Holding Le Duff SA; *Int'l*, pg. 3450
LA MADELEINE INC.; *U.S. Private*, pg. 2368
LA MADELEINE OF MARYLAND, INC.—See La Madeleine Inc.; *U.S. Private*, pg. 2369
LA MAISON BLEUE SA—See Activa Capital S.A.S.; *Int'l*, pg. 119
LA MAISON MOREAU S.A.S.—See Onward Holdings Co., Ltd.; *Int'l*, pg. 5592
LAMAJAK INC.; *U.S. Private*, pg. 2379
LAMAN BV—See Descours & Cabaud SA; *Int'l*, pg. 2044
LA MANCHA RESOURCES INC.; *Int'l*, pg. 4388
LA MANSION DEL RIO INC.; *U.S. Private*, pg. 2369
LAMAR ADVERTISING COMPANY - SEATTLE—See Clear Channel Outdoor Holdings, Inc.; *U.S. Public*, pg. 512
LAMAR ADVERTISING COMPANY; *U.S. Public*, pg. 1290
LAMAR ADVERTISING CO. - RICHMOND BRANCH—See Lamar Advertising Company; *U.S. Public*, pg. 1290
LAMAR ADVERTISING OF COLORADO SPRINGS, INC.—See Lamar Advertising Company; *U.S. Public*, pg. 1290
LAMAR ADVERTISING OF MICHIGAN, INC.—See Lamar Advertising Company; *U.S. Public*, pg. 1290
LAMAR ADVERTISING OF OKLAHOMA, INC.—See Lamar Advertising Company; *U.S. Public*, pg. 1290
LAMAR ADVERTISING OF PENN, LLC—See Lamar Advertising Company; *U.S. Public*, pg. 1290
LAMAR ADVERTISING OF SOUTH DAKOTA, INC.—See Lamar Advertising Company; *U.S. Public*, pg. 1290
LAMAR ADVERTISING OF YOUNGSTOWN, INC.—See Lamar Advertising Company; *U.S. Public*, pg. 1290
LAMAR ALLIANCE AIRPORT ADVERTISING CO.—See Lamar Advertising Company; *U.S. Public*, pg. 1290
LAMAR CENTRAL OUTDOOR, LLC—See Lamar Advertising Company; *U.S. Public*, pg. 1291
LA MARCHE MANUFACTURING COMPANY; *U.S. Private*, pg. 2369
LAMAR CONSTRUCTION COMPANY; *U.S. Private*, pg. 2379
LAMAR CORPORATION—See Lamar Advertising Company; *U.S. Public*, pg. 1290
LAMAR HOLDING CORP.; *Int'l*, pg. 4400
LAMAR INVESTMENTS, LLC—See Lamar Advertising Company; *U.S. Public*, pg. 1291
THE LAMARJEAN GROUP, INC.; *U.S. Private*, pg. 4067
L&A MARKETING & ADVERTISING, INC.; *U.S. Private*, pg. 2362
LAMAR LEDGER—See Alden Global Capital LLC; *U.S. Private*, pg. 157
LAMAR MEDIA CORP.—See Lamar Advertising Company; *U.S. Public*, pg. 1291
LAMAR OBIE CORPORATION—See Lamar Advertising Company; *U.S. Public*, pg. 1291
LA MAROCAINE VIE S.A.—See Societe Generale S.A.; *Int'l*, pg. 7040
LAMAR PARTNERING CORPORATION; *U.S. Private*, pg. 2379
LAMAR PENSACOLA TRANSIT, INC.—See Lamar Advertising Company; *U.S. Public*, pg. 1291
LAMAR TECHNOLOGIES CORPORATION—See Aeries Enterprises, LLC; *U.S. Private*, pg. 117
LAMAR TENNESSEE, L.L.C.—See Lamar Advertising Company; *U.S. Public*, pg. 1291
LAMAR TEXAS LIMITED PARTNERSHIP—See Lamar Advertising Company; *U.S. Public*, pg. 1291
LAMARTHE S.A.—See Veropam S.A.; *Int'l*, pg. 8173
LAMAR TRANSIT ADVERTISING CANADA LTD.—See Lamar Advertising Company; *U.S. Public*, pg. 1291
LA MARZOCCO INTERNATIONAL, LLC—See De'Longhi S.p.A.; *Int'l*, pg. 1997
L.A. MAZDA; *U.S. Public*, pg. 4385
LAMAZE INTERNATIONAL; *U.S. Private*, pg. 2379

COMPANY NAME INDEX

LAMB & ASSOCIATES INC.; *U.S. Private*, pg. 2379
LAMB COUNTY ELECTRIC COOPERATIVE, INC.; *U.S. Private*, pg. 2379
LAMBDA GENERAL CONTRACTORS INC.; *Int'l*, pg. 4400
LAMBDA PHYSIK JAPAN CO., LTD.—See Coherent Corp.; *U.S. Public*, pg. 527
LAMBDA RESEARCH OPTICS, INC.; *U.S. Private*, pg. 2379
LAMBDA SYSTEM INC.—See Core Corporation; *Int'l*, pg. 1797
LAMBDA TD SOFTWARE, INC.; *U.S. Private*, pg. 2379
LAMBDA THERAPEUTIC RESEARCH, INC.—See Lambda Therapeutic Research Ltd.; *Int'l*, pg. 4400
LAMBDA THERAPEUTIC RESEARCH LTD.; *Int'l*, pg. 4400
LAMBDA THERAPEUTIC RESEARCH SP.Z O.O.—See Lambda Therapeutic Research Ltd.; *Int'l*, pg. 4400
LAMBENT TECHNOLOGIES—See H.I.G. Capital, LLC; *U.S. Private*, pg. 1832
LAMBERT & CO.; *U.S. Private*, pg. 2379
LAMBERT OIL COMPANY INC.; *U.S. Private*, pg. 2380
LAMBERT, RIDDLE, SCHIMMEL & COMPANY, LLLP—See Brown & Brown, Inc.; *U.S. Public*, pg. 397
LAMBERTS BAY FOODS (PTY) LTD.—See Famous Brands Limited; *Int'l*, pg. 2612
LAMBERT'S CABLE SPLICING COMPANY, LLC—See Dycom Industries, Inc.; *U.S. Public*, pg. 698
LAMBERTS HEALTHCARE LTD.—See Merck KGaA; *Int'l*, pg. 4831
LAMBERT SMITH HAMPTON GROUP LTD.—See The Skipton Building Society; *Int'l*, pg. 7686
LAMBERT SMITH HAMPTON LTD.—See The Skipton Building Society; *Int'l*, pg. 7686
LAMBERT'S POINT BARGE COMPANY, INC.—See Norfolk Southern Corporation; *U.S. Public*, pg. 1536
LAMBERT'S POINT DOCKS, INC.—See Norfolk Southern Corporation; *U.S. Public*, pg. 1535
LAMBERTSSON OY—See Peab AB; *Int'l*, pg. 5772
LAMBERTSSONS KRAN AB—See Peab AB; *Int'l*, pg. 5772
LAMBERTSSON SVERIGE AB—See Peab AB; *Int'l*, pg. 5772
LAMBERT VET SUPPLY; *U.S. Private*, pg. 2380
LAMBESIS, INC.; *U.S. Private*, pg. 2380
LAMBETH HOUSE, INC.; *U.S. Private*, pg. 2380
L'AMBIANCE BEACHES LTD.; *U.S. Private*, pg. 2363
LAMBIE-NAIRN & COMPANY LIMITED—See WPP plc; *Int'l*, pg. 8465
LAMBODHARA TEXTILES LIMITED; *Int'l*, pg. 4401
LAMBO GROUP BERHAD; *Int'l*, pg. 4400
LAMBORGHINI ARTIMARCA S.P.A.—See Porsche Automobil Holding SE; *Int'l*, pg. 5926
LAMB PRODUCTIONS, INC.—See Lions Gate Entertainment Corp.; *Int'l*, pg. 4520
LAMBRAKIS PRESS S.A.; *Int'l*, pg. 4401
LAMBRETTA SOUTH INCORPORATED; *U.S. Private*, pg. 2380
LAMBRO INDUSTRIES INC.; *U.S. Private*, pg. 2380
LAMBS FARM, INC.; *U.S. Private*, pg. 2380
LAMB SIGN; *U.S. Private*, pg. 2379
LAMBSON LIMITED—See Arkema S.A.; *Int'l*, pg. 571
LAMB'S TIRE & AUTOMOTIVE CENTERS; *U.S. Private*, pg. 2379
THE LAMBTON MOTORS LIMITED; *Int'l*, pg. 7664
LAMB & WEBSTER INC.; *U.S. Private*, pg. 2379
LAMB WESTON BSW, LLC—See Lamb Weston Holdings, Inc.; *U.S. Public*, pg. 1291
LAMB WESTON CANADA ULC—See Lamb Weston Holdings, Inc.; *U.S. Public*, pg. 1291
LAMB WESTON HOLDINGS, INC.; *U.S. Public*, pg. 1291
LAMB WESTON, INC.—See Lamb Weston Holdings, Inc.; *U.S. Public*, pg. 1291
LAMB WESTON SALES, INC.—See Lamb Weston Holdings, Inc.; *U.S. Public*, pg. 1291
LAMCOL NV—See VINCI S.A.; *Int'l*, pg. 8223
LAMDA DEVELOPMENT SA; *Int'l*, pg. 4401
LAMDA ESTATE DEVELOPMENT S.A.—See Lamda Development SA; *Int'l*, pg. 4401
LAMDA FLISVOS MARINA A.E.—See Lamda Development SA; *Int'l*, pg. 4401
LAMDA HELLIX S.A—See Digital Realty Trust, Inc.; *U.S. Public*, pg. 663
LAMDA OLYMPIA VILLAGE S.A.—See Lamda Development SA; *Int'l*, pg. 4401
LAMDA PRIMA PROPERTIES S.A.—See Lamda Development SA; *Int'l*, pg. 4401
LAMDONG FOODSTUFFS JOINT STOCK COMPANY; *Int'l*, pg. 4401
LAM DONG INVESTMENT HYDRAULIC CONSTRUCTION JOINT STOCK COMPANY; *Int'l*, pg. 4400
LAM DONG MINERALS & BUILDING MATERIALS JOIN STOCK COMPANY; *Int'l*, pg. 4400
LAMDONG PHARMACEUTICAL JSC; *Int'l*, pg. 4401
LAMELEE IRON ORE LTD.; *Int'l*, pg. 4401
LA MERIDIONAL COMPANIA ARGENTINA DE SEGUROS S.A.—See Fairfax Financial Holdings Limited; *Int'l*, pg. 2607

LAMERS HIGH TECH SYSTEMS B.V.—See Aalberts N.V.; *Int'l*, pg. 4401
LA MESA RV CENTER, INC.; *U.S. Private*, pg. 2369
LAMEX B.V.—See Lamex Foods UK Limited; *Int'l*, pg. 4401
LAMEX FOODS A.B.—See Lamex Foods UK Limited; *Int'l*, pg. 4401
LAMEX FOODS B.V.—See Lamex Foods UK Limited; *Int'l*, pg. 4401
LAMEX FOODS EUROPE AG—See Lamex Foods UK Limited; *Int'l*, pg. 4401
LAMEX FOODS INC.—See Lamex Foods UK Limited; *Int'l*, pg. 4401
LAMEX FOODS UK LIMITED; *Int'l*, pg. 4401
LAMF GLOBAL VENTURES CORP. I—See Holdco Nuvo Group D.G Ltd.; *U.S. Public*, pg. 1044
LAM HO INVESTMENTS PTE. LIMITED—See Keck Seng Investments (Hong Kong) Limited; *Int'l*, pg. 4114
LAMILUX HEINRICH STRUNZ HOLDING GMBH & CO. KG; *Int'l*, pg. 4401
LAMINAR CAPITAL PTY. LTD.—See Perpetual Limited; *Int'l*, pg. 5812
LAMIN-ART, INC.—See Arborite; *Int'l*, pg. 539
LAMINATE TECHNOLOGIES INC.; *U.S. Private*, pg. 2380
LAMINATE TECHNOLOGIES OF TENNESSEE—See Laminate Technologies Inc.; *U.S. Private*, pg. 2380
LAMINATE WORKS INC.; *U.S. Private*, pg. 2380
LAMINATING PAPERS LTD.—See Stora Enso Oyj; *Int'l*, pg. 7225
LAMINATING SERVICES INC.; *U.S. Private*, pg. 2380
LAMINATION DEPOT INC.; *U.S. Private*, pg. 2380
LAMINATIONS, INC.—See Simona AG; *Int'l*, pg. 6932
LAMINATION SPECIALTIES CORP.—See UPG Enterprises LLC; *U.S. Private*, pg. 4311
LAMINATORS INC.; *U.S. Private*, pg. 2380
LAMINCER S.A.—See ThyssenKrupp AG; *Int'l*, pg. 7724
LAMINEX (AUSTRALIA) PTY. LTD.—See Fletcher Building Limited; *Int'l*, pg. 2700
LAMINEX GROUP PTY LIMITED—See Fletcher Building Limited; *Int'l*, pg. 2700
LAMINEX, INC.; *U.S. Private*, pg. 2380
LAMINEX US HOLDINGS PTY LIMITED—See Fletcher Building Limited; *Int'l*, pg. 2700
LA MINUTE & SES COMPLICATIONS SA—See LVMH Moet Hennessy Louis Vuitton SE; *Int'l*, pg. 4598
LAMI WOOD PRODUCTS CORPORATION; *U.S. Private*, pg. 2380
LAMKIN CORPORATION; *U.S. Private*, pg. 2380
LAMKONE RESTAURANTS INC.; *U.S. Private*, pg. 2380
LAMKO TOOL & MOLD INC.; *U.S. Private*, pg. 4401
L.A.M. LOMBARDA ASCENSORI MONTACARICHI S.R.L.—See KONE Oyj; *Int'l*, pg. 4250
LAMM FOOD SERVICE, LLC—See Alvarez & Marsal, Inc.; *U.S. Private*, pg. 213
LAMM FOOD SERVICE, LLC—See Highview Capital, LLC; *U.S. Private*, pg. 1942
LAMMHULTS DESIGN GROUP AB; *Int'l*, pg. 4401
LAMMICO INSURANCE AGENCY INC.—See Louisiana Medical Mutual Insurance Company; *U.S. Private*, pg. 2500
LA MODE CO., LTD.—See World Co., Ltd.; *Int'l*, pg. 8457
LA MODE EN IMAGES—See Omnicom Group Inc.; *U.S. Public*, pg. 1596
LA MODERNA DE TOLUCA, S.A. DE C.V.—See Grupo La Moderna, S.A.B. de C.V.; *Int'l*, pg. 3131
LAMONICA FINE FOODS; *U.S. Private*, pg. 2380
LAMONS GASKET COMPANY—See TriMas Corporation; *U.S. Public*, pg. 2189
LAMONT BIT SERVICES LTD.—See Vertex Resource Group Ltd.; *Int'l*, pg. 8174
LAMONT DIGITAL SYSTEMS INC.; *U.S. Private*, pg. 2380
LAMONT HANLEY & ASSOCIATES; *U.S. Private*, pg. 2380
LAMOR BEIJING CO., LTD.—See Lamor Corporation PLC; *Int'l*, pg. 4401
LAMOR COLOMBIA S.A.S.—See Lamor Corporation PLC; *Int'l*, pg. 4401
LAMOR CORPORATION PLC; *Int'l*, pg. 4401
LAMOR CORPORATION UK LTD.—See Lamor Corporation PLC; *Int'l*, pg. 4401
LAMOR ENVIRONMENTAL SOLUTIONS SPAIN S.L.—See Lamor Corporation PLC; *Int'l*, pg. 4401
LAMOR INDIA PRIVATE LTD.—See Lamor Corporation PLC; *Int'l*, pg. 4401
LAMOR MIDDLE EAST LLC—See Lamor Corporation PLC; *Int'l*, pg. 4401
LAMOR PERU S.A.C.—See Lamor Corporation PLC; *Int'l*, pg. 4401
LAMORTE BURNS & CO INC.; *U.S. Private*, pg. 2380
LAMOR USA CORPORATION—See Lamor Corporation PLC; *Int'l*, pg. 4401
LAMOR VOSTOK LLC—See Lamor Corporation PLC; *Int'l*, pg. 4401
LAMOSA DESARROLLOS INMOBILIARIOS, S.A. DE C.V.—See Grupo Lamosa S.A. de C.V.; *Int'l*, pg. 3132
LAMOSA REVESTIMIENTOS (GUADALAJARA), S.A. DE C.V.—See Grupo Lamosa S.A. de C.V.; *Int'l*, pg. 3132
LAMOSA REVESTIMIENTOS (MONTERREY), S.A. DE C.V.—See Grupo Lamosa S.A. de C.V.; *Int'l*, pg. 3132

LAM RESEARCH CORPORATION

LAMOSA REVESTIMIENTOS (TLAXCALA), S.A DE C.V.—See Grupo Lamosa S.A. de C.V.; *Int'l*, pg. 3132
L.A. MOVERS; *U.S. Private*, pg. 2364
LAMPE EQUITY MANAGEMENT GMBH—See Dr. August Oetker KG; *Int'l*, pg. 2190
LAMPE PRIVATINVEST MANAGEMENT GMBH—See Dr. August Oetker KG; *Int'l*, pg. 2190
LAMPERD LESS LETHAL, INC.; *Int'l*, pg. 4401
LAMPERT YARDS, INC.; *U.S. Private*, pg. 2381
LAMPGALLERIAN I VAXJO AB—See BHG Group AB; *Int'l*, pg. 1015
LAMPIRIS S.A.—See TotalEnergies SE; *Int'l*, pg. 7837
LAMPLIGHT FARMS INCORPORATED—See W.C. Bradley Co.; *U.S. Private*, pg. 4419
LAMPO-TUKKU OY—See Panostaja Oyj; *Int'l*, pg. 5729
LAMP POST FRANCHISE CORPORATION; *U.S. Private*, pg. 2380
LAMPRECHT PHARMA LOGISTICS LTD.—See Lamprecht Transport AG; *Int'l*, pg. 4402
LAMPRECHT TRANSPORT AG; *Int'l*, pg. 4401
LAMPRECHT TRANSPORT LTD.—See Lamprecht Transport AG; *Int'l*, pg. 4402
LAMPRELL DUBAI LLC—See Lamprell plc; *Int'l*, pg. 4402
LAMPRELL ENERGY FZCO.—See Lamprell plc; *Int'l*, pg. 4402
LAMPRELL ENERGY LIMITED—See Lamprell plc; *Int'l*, pg. 4402
LAMPRELL PLC; *Int'l*, pg. 4402
LAMPRELL SHARJAH WLL—See Lamprell plc; *Int'l*, pg. 4402
LAMPRELL - SUNBELT H2S SAFETY SERVICES, BAUTINO HYDROTEST FACILITY—See Lamprell plc; *Int'l*, pg. 4402
LAMPRELL - SUNBELT H2S SAFETY SERVICES—See Lamprell plc; *Int'l*, pg. 4402
LAMPREY HEALTH CARE; *U.S. Private*, pg. 2381
LAMPROS STEEL, INC.—See Reliance Steel & Aluminum Co.; *U.S. Public*, pg. 1780
LAMPSA HELLENIC HOTELS S.A.; *Int'l*, pg. 4402
LAMPSON AUSTRALIA PTY LTD—See Lampson International, LLC; *U.S. Private*, pg. 2381
LAMPSON CANADA, LTD—See Lampson International, LLC; *U.S. Private*, pg. 2381
LAMPSON INTERNATIONAL, LLC; *U.S. Private*, pg. 2381
LAMPS PLUS INC.; *U.S. Private*, pg. 2381
LAMPTON-LOVE, INC.—See Ergon, Inc.; *U.S. Private*, pg. 1418
LAMPTON-LOVE, INC.—See Ergon, Inc.; *U.S. Private*, pg. 1418
LAMPTON-LOVE, INC.—See Ergon, Inc.; *U.S. Private*, pg. 1418
LAMPTON-LOVE, INC.—See Ergon, Inc.; *U.S. Private*, pg. 1418
LAMPTON-LOVE, INC.—See Ergon, Inc.; *U.S. Private*, pg. 1418
LAMP WORKS—See ELK Group International, Inc.; *U.S. Private*, pg. 1362
LAM RESEARCH AG—See Lam Research Corporation; *U.S. Public*, pg. 1289
LAM RESEARCH B.V.—See Lam Research Corporation; *U.S. Public*, pg. 1289
LAM RESEARCH CO., LTD. - HIROSHIMA SERVICE CENTER—See Lam Research Corporation; *U.S. Public*, pg. 1289
LAM RESEARCH CO., LTD.—See Lam Research Corporation; *U.S. Public*, pg. 1289
LAM RESEARCH CO., LTD.—See Lam Research Corporation; *U.S. Public*, pg. 1289
LAM RESEARCH CO., LTD.—See Lam Research Corporation; *U.S. Public*, pg. 1289
LAM RESEARCH CO., LTD.—See Lam Research Corporation; *U.S. Public*, pg. 1289
LAM RESEARCH CO., LTD.—See Lam Research Corporation; *U.S. Public*, pg. 1289
LAM RESEARCH CORPORATION—See Lam Research Corporation; *U.S. Public*, pg. 1289
LAM RESEARCH CORPORATION; *U.S. Public*, pg. 1289
LAM RESEARCH CORPORATION—See Lam Research Corporation; *U.S. Public*, pg. 1289
LAM RESEARCH CORPORATION—See Lam Research Corporation; *U.S. Public*, pg. 1289
LAM RESEARCH CORPORATION—See Lam Research Corporation; *U.S. Public*, pg. 1289
LAM RESEARCH GMBH—See Lam Research Corporation; *U.S. Public*, pg. 1289
LAM RESEARCH HOLDING GMBH—See Lam Research Corporation; *U.S. Public*, pg. 1289
LAM RESEARCH ILLINOIS IAG, INC.—See Lam Research Corporation; *U.S. Public*, pg. 1290
LAM RESEARCH (INDIA) PRIVATE LTD.—See Lam Research Corporation; *U.S. Public*, pg. 1289
LAM RESEARCH INTERNATIONAL HOLDING COMPANY—See Lam Research Corporation; *U.S. Public*, pg. 1290
LAM RESEARCH INTERNATIONAL SARL—See Lam Research Corporation; *U.S. Public*, pg. 1290
LAM RESEARCH (IRELAND) LIMITED—See Lam Research Corporation; *U.S. Public*, pg. 1289
LAM RESEARCH (ISRAEL) LTD.—See Lam Research Corporation; *U.S. Public*, pg. 1289

LAM RESEARCH KOREA LTD.—See Lam Research Corporation; *U.S. Public*, pg. 1290
LAM RESEARCH MALAYSIA SDN. BHD.—See Lam Research Corporation; *U.S. Public*, pg. 1290
LAM RESEARCH MANAGEMENT GMBH—See Lam Research Corporation; *U.S. Public*, pg. 1289
LAM RESEARCH MANUFACTURING KOREA, LLC—See Lam Research Corporation; *U.S. Public*, pg. 1290
LAM RESEARCH SAS—See Lam Research Corporation; *U.S. Public*, pg. 1290
LAM RESEARCH SAS—See Lam Research Corporation; *U.S. Public*, pg. 1290
LAM RESEARCH SERVICE CO., LTD.—See Lam Research Corporation; *U.S. Public*, pg. 1290
LAM RESEARCH SERVICES U.S. INC.—See Lam Research Corporation; *U.S. Public*, pg. 1290
LAM RESEARCH (SHANGHAI) CO., LTD.—See Lam Research Corporation; *U.S. Public*, pg. 1289
LAM RESEARCH SINGAPORE PTE. LTD.—See Lam Research Corporation; *U.S. Public*, pg. 1290
LAM RESEARCH SRL—See Lam Research Corporation; *U.S. Public*, pg. 1290
LAMSCO WEST, INC.—See Inflexion Private Equity Partners LLP; *Int'l*, pg. 3688
LAMSON & GOODNOW MANUFACTURING CO.; *U.S. Private*, pg. 2381
LAM SON SUGAR JOINT STOCK CORPORATION; *Int'l*, pg. 4400
LAM SOON BALL YAMAMURA INC.—See Nihon Yamamura Glass Co., Ltd.; *Int'l*, pg. 5288
LAM SOON EDIBLE OILS SDN. BHD.—See Lam Soon (Thailand) Public Company Limited; *Int'l*, pg. 4400
LAM SOON (HONG KONG) LIMITED; *Int'l*, pg. 4400
LAM SOON PRODUCTS SUPPLY (HONG KONG) COMPANY LIMITED—See LAM SOON (HONG KONG) LIMITED; *Int'l*, pg. 4400
LAM SOON SINGAPORE PTE LTD—See Lam Soon (Thailand) Public Company Limited; *Int'l*, pg. 4400
LAM SOON (THAILAND) PUBLIC COMPANY LIMITED; *Int'l*, pg. 4400
LAMTEX HOLDINGS LIMITED; *Int'l*, pg. 4402
LAM THAO FERTILIZERS & CHEMICALS JOINT STOCK COMPANY; *Int'l*, pg. 4400
LAM VALVES INC.—See Eggelhof Incorporated; *U.S. Private*, pg. 1344
LAMVIN, INC.—See Sound Seal, Inc.; *U.S. Private*, pg. 3717
LAMY LIAISONS S.A.S.—See Karnov Group AB; *Int'l*, pg. 4084
LAMY LUTTI S.A.S.—See Xaver Fassin GmbH; *Int'l*, pg. 8520
LAMY; *U.S. Private*, pg. 2381
LANA DUKE CONSULTING; *U.S. Private*, pg. 2381
LANAKAM S.A.; *Int'l*, pg. 4402
LANA, S. COOP.—See Mondragon Corporation; *Int'l*, pg. 5030
LAN ASSISTANS SVERIGE AB—See Storskogen Group AB; *Int'l*, pg. 7228
LANAS TRINIDAD SA—See Chargeurs SA; *Int'l*, pg. 1450
LANA UNLIMITED COMPANY; *U.S. Private*, pg. 2381
LAN CARGO S.A.—See LATAM Airlines Group S.A.; *Int'l*, pg. 4422
LANCASHIRE EVENING POST LTD—See JPIMedia Holdings Limited; *Int'l*, pg. 4006
LANCASHIRE HOLDINGS LIMITED; *Int'l*, pg. 4402
LANCASHIRE INSURANCE COMPANY (UK) LIMITED—See Lancashire Holdings Limited; *Int'l*, pg. 4402
LANCASHIRE INSURANCE MARKETING SERVICES LIMITED—See Lancashire Holdings Limited; *Int'l*, pg. 4402
LANCASHIRE PUBLICATIONS LTD—See JPIMedia Holdings Limited; *Int'l*, pg. 4006
LANCASHIRE SYNDICATES LIMITED—See Lancashire Holdings Limited; *Int'l*, pg. 4402
LANCASTER AUTO GROUP; *U.S. Private*, pg. 2381
LANCASTER BEHAVIORAL HEALTH HOSPITAL, LLC—See Universal Health Services, Inc.; *U.S. Public*, pg. 2258
LANCASTER BINGO CO. INC.; *U.S. Private*, pg. 2381
LANCASTER CARS LIMITED—See Lithia Motors, Inc.; *U.S. Public*, pg. 1323
LANCASTER CLINIC CORP.—See Community Health Systems, Inc.; *U.S. Public*, pg. 554
LANCASTER COLONY COMMERCIAL PRODUCTS, INC.—See Lancaster Colony Corporation; *U.S. Public*, pg. 1291
LANCASTER COLONY CORPORATION; *U.S. Public*, pg. 1291
LANCASTER COUNTY TIMBER FRAMES, INC.; *U.S. Private*, pg. 2381
LANCASTER COUNTY WEEKLIES INC.—See Lancaster Newspapers Inc.; *U.S. Private*, pg. 2381
LANCASTER EMERGENCY MEDICAL SERVICES ASSOCIATION—See Community Health Systems, Inc.; *U.S. Public*, pg. 554
LANCASTER EQUIPMENT CORPORATION—See Leuner Inc.; *U.S. Private*, pg. 2433

LANCASTER FASTENER CO LTD—See Trifast plc; *Int'l*, pg. 7921
LANCASTER FINE FOODS, INC.—See Wind Point Advisors LLC; *U.S. Private*, pg. 4536
LANCASTER FOODS, INC.—See Continental Grain Company; *U.S. Private*, pg. 1029
LANCASTER GENERAL HEALTH; *U.S. Private*, pg. 2381
LANCASTER HOME CARE SERVICES, LLC—See Community Health Systems, Inc.; *U.S. Public*, pg. 554
LANCASTER HOSPITAL CORPORATION—See Universal Health Services, Inc.; *U.S. Public*, pg. 2258
LANCASTER HOST RESORT & CONFERENCE CENTER; *U.S. Private*, pg. 2381
LANCASTER IMAGING CENTER, LLC—See Community Health Systems, Inc.; *U.S. Public*, pg. 554
LANCASTER LEAF TOBACCO COMPANY OF PENNSYLVANIA, INC.—See Universal Corporation; *U.S. Public*, pg. 2254
LANCASTER LEAF TOBACCO CO. OF PENNSYLVANIA—See Universal Corporation; *U.S. Public*, pg. 2254
LANCASTER MEDICAL GROUP, LLC—See Community Health Systems, Inc.; *U.S. Public*, pg. 554
LANCASTER & MORECAMBE NEWSPAPERS LTD—See JPIMedia Holdings Limited; *Int'l*, pg. 4006
LANCASTER MOTOR COMPANY LIMITED—See Lithia Motors, Inc.; *U.S. Public*, pg. 1323
LANCASTER NEWSPAPERS INC.; *U.S. Private*, pg. 2381
LANCASTER OIL COMPANY—See Aurora Capital Group, LLC; *U.S. Private*, pg. 394
LANCASTER OUTPATIENT IMAGING, LLC—See Community Health Systems, Inc.; *U.S. Public*, pg. 554
THE LANCASTER PA ENDOSCOPY ASC, L.P.—See KKR & Co. Inc.; *U.S. Public*, pg. 1247
LANCASTER PLC—See Lithia Motors, Inc.; *U.S. Public*, pg. 1323
LANCASTER POLLARD HOLDINGS, INC.; *U.S. Private*, pg. 2381
LANCASTER PRE-CAST (PTY) LIMITED—See Afrimat Limited; *Int'l*, pg. 193
LANCASTER RAIL PRODUCTS—See Metalurgica Gerdau S.A.; *Int'l*, pg. 4850
LANCASTER REDEVELOPMENT CORP; *U.S. Private*, pg. 2381
LANCASTER SPECIALIST CARS LIMITED—See Lithia Motors, Inc.; *U.S. Public*, pg. 1323
LANCASTER SPECIALTY SURGERY CENTER, LLC—See Tenet Healthcare Corporation; *U.S. Public*, pg. 2004
LANCASTER SPORTS CARS LIMITED—See Lithia Motors, Inc.; *U.S. Public*, pg. 1323
LANCASTER TELEPHONE COMPANY—See Comporium Group; *U.S. Private*, pg. 1002
LANCASTER TOYOTA INC.; *U.S. Private*, pg. 2381
LANCASTER VETS4PETS LIMITED—See Pets at Home Group Plc; *Int'l*, pg. 5834
LANCE BISSETT LTD; *Int'l*, pg. 4402
LANCE CAMPER MANUFACTURING CORPORATION—See AIP, LLC; *U.S. Private*, pg. 135
LANCE FUNK FARMS; *U.S. Private*, pg. 2382
LANCE INDUSTRIES INC.; *U.S. Private*, pg. 2382
LANCE INVESTIGATION SERVICE; *U.S. Private*, pg. 2382
LANCEL SOGEDI S.A.—See Piquadro SpA; *Int'l*, pg. 5873
LANCER CLAIMS SERVICES, INC.—See Brown & Brown, Inc.; *U.S. Public*, pg. 401
LANCER CONTAINER LINES LIMITED; *Int'l*, pg. 4402
LANCER CORPORATION—See Hoshizaki Corporation; *Int'l*, pg. 3484
LANCER DISPERSIONS INC.; *U.S. Private*, pg. 2382
LANCER EUROPE, S.A.—See Hoshizaki Corporation; *Int'l*, pg. 3484
LANCER HOLLAND B.V.—See Getinge AB; *Int'l*, pg. 2949
LANCER INC.—See Getinge AB; *Int'l*, pg. 2951
LANCER INTERNATIONAL SALES, INC.—See Hoshizaki Corporation; *Int'l*, pg. 3484
LANCER ORTHODONTICS INC.; *U.S. Public*, pg. 1292
LANCER SALES USA INC—See Getinge AB; *Int'l*, pg. 2951
LANCERS, INC.; *Int'l*, pg. 4402
LANCER S.N.C.—See Getinge AB; *Int'l*, pg. 2949
LANCER UK LTD.—See Getinge AB; *Int'l*, pg. 2951
LANCER USA INC.—See Getinge AB; *Int'l*, pg. 2949
LANCE SHIPPING S.A.—See Dynagas LNG Partners LP; *Int'l*, pg. 2239
LANCESOFT INC.; *U.S. Private*, pg. 2382
LANCET DATA SCIENCES; *U.S. Private*, pg. 2382
LANCET INDEMNITY RISK RETENTION GROUP, INC.; *U.S. Private*, pg. 2382
THE LANCET—See RELX plc; *Int'l*, pg. 6268
LANCET TECHNOLOGY INC—See ESO Solutions, Inc.; *U.S. Private*, pg. 1426
LANCEWOOD HOLDINGS PTY. LTD.—See Libstar Holdings Ltd.; *Int'l*, pg. 4487
LANCIA AUTOMOBILES S.P.A.—See Stellantis N.V.; *Int'l*, pg. 7200
LANCO ASSEMBLY SYSTEMS; *U.S. Private*, pg. 2382
LANCO CONSTRUCTION & ENGINEERING PTE LTD; *Int'l*, pg. 4402
LANCO CORP.; *U.S. Private*, pg. 2382

LAN-CO DEVELOPMENT INC.; *U.S. Private*, pg. 2381
LANCO INTERNATIONAL INC.; *U.S. Private*, pg. 2382
LANCO MANUFACTURING CORP.; *U.S. Private*, pg. 2382
LANCOME PARFUMS ET BEAUTE—See L'Oreal S.A.; *Int'l*, pg. 4380
LAN CONTROL SYSTEMS LIMITED—See Halma plc; *Int'l*, pg. 3232
LANCOPE, LLC—See Cisco Systems, Inc.; *U.S. Public*, pg. 499
LANCOR GUDUVANCHERY DEVELOPMENTS LIMITED—See Lancor Holdings Ltd.; *Int'l*, pg. 4403
LANCOR HOLDINGS LTD.; *Int'l*, pg. 4403
LANCOR MAINTENANCE & SERVICES LTD.—See Lancor Holdings Ltd.; *Int'l*, pg. 4403
LANCOR PROJECTS LIMITED—See Compuage Infocom Ltd.; *Int'l*, pg. 1754
LANCY CO., LTD.; *Int'l*, pg. 4403
LANCY MIXJET—See Sany Group Co., Ltd.; *Int'l*, pg. 6563
LANDAAL PACKAGING SYSTEMS; *U.S. Private*, pg. 2384
LANDACORP, INC.—See ExlService Holdings, Inc.; *U.S. Public*, pg. 808
LAND AIR EXPRESS INC.; *U.S. Private*, pg. 2382
LAND AIR EXPRESS OF NEW ENGLAND; *U.S. Private*, pg. 2382
LANDAIR SURVEYING COMPANY OF GEORGIA—See KCI Holdings Inc.; *U.S. Private*, pg. 2270
LANDAIR TRANSPORT, INC.; *U.S. Private*, pg. 2384
LANDAI TECHNOLOGY GROUP CORP., LTD.; *Int'l*, pg. 4404
LANDALE LIMITED; *Int'l*, pg. 4404
LAND AND HOUSES FREEHOLD & LEASEHOLD PROPERTY FUND; *Int'l*, pg. 4404
LAND AND HOUSES FUND MANAGEMENT CO., LTD.—See Land & Houses Public Company Limited; *Int'l*, pg. 4403
LAND AND HOUSES NORTH CO., LTD.—See Land & Houses Public Company Limited; *Int'l*, pg. 4403
LAND AND HOUSES NORTH-EAST CO., LTD.—See Land & Houses Public Company Limited; *Int'l*, pg. 4403
LAND AND HOUSES PROPERTY FUND 1—See Land & Houses Public Company Limited; *Int'l*, pg. 4403
LAND AND HOUSES PROPERTY FUND 2—See Land & Houses Public Company Limited; *Int'l*, pg. 4403
LAND AND HOUSES RETAIL BANK PLC—See Land & Houses Public Company Limited; *Int'l*, pg. 4403
LANDAU BUILDING COMPANY; *U.S. Private*, pg. 2384
LANDAU DIRECT; *U.S. Private*, pg. 2384
LANDAU ELECTRONIC GMBH—See Robert Bosch GmbH; *Int'l*, pg. 6361
LANDAUER AUSTRALASIA PTY. LTD.—See Fortive Corporation; *U.S. Public*, pg. 871
LANDAUER EUROPE, LTD.—See Fortive Corporation; *U.S. Public*, pg. 871
LANDAUER EUROPE SAS—See Fortive Corporation; *U.S. Public*, pg. 871
LANDAUER, INC.—See Fortive Corporation; *U.S. Public*, pg. 871
LANDAUER LTD.—See Westindia AB; *Int'l*, pg. 8390
LANDAUER-MEDSTAR—See Quadrant Management, Inc.; *U.S. Private*, pg. 3316
LANDAU, NASELLA & KLATSKY, LLC; *U.S. Private*, pg. 2384
LANDAU UNIFORMS INCORPORATED; *U.S. Private*, pg. 2384
LANDAVAZO BROS. INC.; *U.S. Private*, pg. 2384
LANDA WATER CLEANING SYSTEMS—See Alfred Karcher GmbH & Co. KG; *Int'l*, pg. 316
LANDBASE INDIA LIMITED—See ITC Limited; *Int'l*, pg. 3831
LANDBAY INC; *Int'l*, pg. 4404
LANDBEES CORPORATION—See Manila Electric Company; *Int'l*, pg. 4671
LAND BRIDGE TERMINALS, INC.—See Pyramid Industries, Inc.; *U.S. Private*, pg. 3310
LAND & BUILDINGS INVESTMENT MANAGEMENT, LLC; *U.S. Private*, pg. 2382
LAND BUSINESS CO., LTD.; *Int'l*, pg. 4404
LANDCARE LANDSCAPING, INC.; *U.S. Private*, pg. 2384
LANDCATCH NATURAL SELECTION LIMITED—See Hendrix Genetics B.V.; *Int'l*, pg. 3345
LANDCOAST INSULATION INC.; *U.S. Private*, pg. 2385
LAND & COATES, INC.; *U.S. Private*, pg. 2382
LANDCO CONSTRUCTION; *U.S. Private*, pg. 2384
LAND CO., LTD.; *Int'l*, pg. 4404
LANDCOM INC.; *U.S. Private*, pg. 2385
LAND CONCIERGE, INC.—See EnBio Holdings Inc.; *Int'l*, pg. 2396
L AND C WINDSOR CABLES LTD.—See Leggett & Platt, Incorporated; *U.S. Public*, pg. 1302
LANDEC AG—See Lifecore Biomedical, Inc.; *U.S. Public*, pg. 1312
LANDED HOME LOANS LLC—See Rithm Capital Corp.; *U.S. Public*, pg. 1800
LANDE GMBH—See E.ON SE; *Int'l*, pg. 2258
LANDELIJKE ASSOCIATIE VAN GERECHTSDEURWAARDERS B.V.—See Munchener Ruckversicherungs AG; *Int'l*, pg. 5089

COMPANY NAME INDEX

LANDERS AUTO GROUP INC.; U.S. Private, pg. 2385
LANDERS AUTO SALES, LLC—See Penske Automotive Group, Inc.; U.S. Public, pg. 1665
LANDER SIMULATION & TRAINING SOLUTIONS, S.A.—See Construcciones y Auxiliar de Ferrocarriles S.A.; Int'l, pg. 1777
LANDERS-MCLARTY BENTONVILLE LLC; U.S. Private, pg. 2385
LANDERS & PARTNERS, INC.; U.S. Private, pg. 2385
LANDERS & PARTNERS, INC.—See Landers & Partners, Inc.; U.S. Private, pg. 2385
LANDER SPORTS DEVELOPMENT CO., LTD.; Int'l, pg. 4404
LANDERS UNDERWRITING INC.—See Jackson Sumner & Associates, Inc.; U.S. Private, pg. 2178
LANDER VALLEY PHYSICIAN PRACTICES, LLC—See Apollo Global Management, Inc.; U.S. Public, pg. 158
LANDER VAN GUNDY AGENCY, INC.; U.S. Private, pg. 2385
LANDESBANK BADEN-WURTTEMBERG CAPITAL MARKETS PLC—See Landesbank Baden-Wurttemberg; Int'l, pg. 4405
LANDESBANK BADEN-WURTTEMBERG; Int'l, pg. 4404
LANDESBANK BADEN-WURTTEMBERG—See Landesbank Baden-Wurttemberg; Int'l, pg. 4405
LANDESBANK BERLIN AG—See Deutscher Sparkassen- und Giroverband e.V.; Int'l, pg. 2085
LANDESBANK BERLIN HOLDING AG—See Deutscher Sparkassen- und Giroverband e.V.; Int'l, pg. 2085
LANDESBANK RHEINLAND-PFALZ INTERNATIONAL S.A.—See Landesbank Baden-Wurttemberg; Int'l, pg. 4405
LANDESBANK SAAR; Int'l, pg. 4406
LANDES CANADA INC.—See Medike, Inc.; U.S. Private, pg. 2656
LANDES HONG KONG LIMITED—See Medike, Inc.; U.S. Private, pg. 2657
LANDES-HYPOTHEKENBANK STEIERMARK AKTIENGESELLSCHAFT—See Raiffeisen-Landesbank Steiermark AG; Int'l, pg. 6186
LANDESKRANKENANSTALTEN-BETRIEBSGESELLSCHAFT; Int'l, pg. 4406
LANDES LEDERWARENFABRIK GMBH—See Medike, Inc.; U.S. Private, pg. 2656
LANDES OIL INC.; U.S. Private, pg. 2385
LAND & GENERAL BERHAD; Int'l, pg. 4403
LANDHANDEL KNAUP GMBH—See BayWa AG; Int'l, pg. 918
LANDHOF GESMBH & CO. KG—See Raiffeisenlandesbank Oberosterreich Aktiengesellschaft; Int'l, pg. 6187
LAND & HOMES GROUP LIMITED; Int'l, pg. 4403
LANDHOPE CORPORATION; U.S. Private, pg. 2385
LAND & HOUSES PUBLIC COMPANY LIMITED; Int'l, pg. 4403
LAND & HOUSES SECURITIES PUBLIC COMPANY LIMITED—See LH Financial Group Public Company Limited; Int'l, pg. 4477
LANDING ENTERTAINMENT KOREA CO., LTD—See Shin Hwa World Limited; Int'l, pg. 6836
LANDING JEJU DEVELOPMENT CO., LTD—See Shin Hwa World Limited; Int'l, pg. 6836
LANDINGS CLUB INC.; U.S. Private, pg. 2385
LAND INSTRUMENTS INTERNATIONAL—See AMETEK, Inc.; U.S. Public, pg. 118
LANDI RENZO PARS PRIVATE JOINT STOCK COMPANY—See Landi Renzo S.p.a.; Int'l, pg. 4406
LANDI RENZO POLSKA SP. Z O.O.—See Landi Renzo S.p.a.; Int'l, pg. 4406
LANDI RENZO RO S.R.L.—See Landi Renzo S.p.a.; Int'l, pg. 4406
LANDI RENZO S.P.A.; Int'l, pg. 4406
LANDI RENZO USA CORPORATION—See Landi Renzo S.p.a.; Int'l, pg. 4406
LANDI RENZO VE C.A.—See Landi Renzo S.p.a.; Int'l, pg. 4406
LANDIS C. DECK & SONS SITE CONTRACTORS—See Haines & Kibblehouse Inc.; U.S. Private, pg. 1841
LANDIS COMMUNICATIONS INC.; U.S. Private, pg. 2385
LANDIS CONSTRUCTION CO., LLC.; U.S. Private, pg. 2385
LANDIS EXPRESS, INC.—See S&H Express, Inc.; U.S. Private, pg. 3513
LANDIS+GYR AB—See Japan Industrial Partners, Inc.; Int'l, pg. 3890
LANDIS+GYR A.E.—See Japan Industrial Partners, Inc.; Int'l, pg. 3890
LANDIS+GYR AG—See Japan Industrial Partners, Inc.; Int'l, pg. 3890
LANDIS+GYR-ALEXANDRIA—See Japan Industrial Partners, Inc.; Int'l, pg. 3890
LANDIS+GYR A/S—See Japan Industrial Partners, Inc.; Int'l, pg. 3890
LANDIS+GYR AS—See Japan Industrial Partners, Inc.; Int'l, pg. 3890
LANDIS+GYR B.V.—See Japan Industrial Partners, Inc.; Int'l, pg. 3890
LANDIS+GYR D.O.O.—See Japan Industrial Partners, Inc.; Int'l, pg. 3890

LANDIS+GYR GMBH—See Japan Industrial Partners, Inc.; Int'l, pg. 3890
LANDIS+GYR GMBH—See Japan Industrial Partners, Inc.; Int'l, pg. 3890
LANDIS+GYR INC.—See Japan Industrial Partners, Inc.; Int'l, pg. 3890
LANDIS+GYR N.V.—See Japan Industrial Partners, Inc.; Int'l, pg. 3890
LANDIS+GYR OY—See Japan Industrial Partners, Inc.; Int'l, pg. 3890
LANDIS+GYR (PTY.) LTD.—See Japan Industrial Partners, Inc.; Int'l, pg. 3890
LANDIS+GYR S.A.S.—See Japan Industrial Partners, Inc.; Int'l, pg. 3890
LANDIS+GYR S.A.U.—See Japan Industrial Partners, Inc.; Int'l, pg. 3890
LANDIS+GYR—See Japan Industrial Partners, Inc.; Int'l, pg. 3890
LANDIS+GYR S.P.A—See Japan Industrial Partners, Inc.; Int'l, pg. 3890
LANDIS+GYR SP.Z O.O—See Japan Industrial Partners, Inc.; Int'l, pg. 3890
LANDIS+GYR S.R.O—See Japan Industrial Partners, Inc.; Int'l, pg. 3890
LANDIS HOLDINGS LLC—See The Manitowoc Company, Inc.; U.S. Public, pg. 2111
LANDIS MACHINE—See NESCO, Inc.; U.S. Private, pg. 2886
LANDIS SUPER MARKET, INC.; U.S. Private, pg. 2385
LANDIS SUPPLY OF NEW JERSEY, INC.—See Hendricks Holding Company, Inc.; U.S. Private, pg. 1915
LANDIS TAIPEI HOTEL CO., LTD.; Int'l, pg. 4406
LANDIX, INC.; Int'l, pg. 4406
LAND & LEGAL SOLUTIONS; U.S. Private, pg. 2382
LANDLORDCENTRE.CO.UK LIMITED—See Paragon Banking Group PLC; Int'l, pg. 5735
LANDLUST GMBH; Int'l, pg. 4406
LAND MANAGEMENT GROUP, INC.—See The Davey Tree Expert Company; U.S. Private, pg. 4018
LAND MANAGEMENT INC.—See Kurita Water Industries Ltd.; Int'l, pg. 4341
LANDMANN GERMANY GMBH—See The Social Chain AG; Int'l, pg. 7687
LANDMANN HUNGARIA KFT.—See The Social Chain AG; Int'l, pg. 7687
LANDMANN LIMITED—See The Social Chain AG; Int'l, pg. 7687
LANDMANN POLSKA SP. Z O.O.—See The Social Chain AG; Int'l, pg. 7687
LANDMARC LEISURE CORPORATION LIMITED; Int'l, pg. 4406
LANDMARC SUPPORT SERVICES LTD.—See Interserve Plc; Int'l, pg. 3759
LANDMAR GROUP L.L.C.—See Crescent Resources, LLC; U.S. Private, pg. 1094
LAND-MARINE CARGO, INC.—See ArcBest Corporation; U.S. Public, pg. 180
LAND & MARINE ENGINEERING LTD.—See J. Murphy & Sons Limited; Int'l, pg. 3856
LANDMARK BANCORP, INC.; U.S. Public, pg. 1292
LANDMARK BANK, N.A.—See Landrum Company; U.S. Private, pg. 2386
LANDMARK BANK—See Clinton Bancshares, Inc.; U.S. Private, pg. 944
LANDMARK CARS LIMITED; Int'l, pg. 4406
LANDMARK CENTRAL MARKET CO. LLC—See Landmark Retail Holdings 1 Limited; Int'l, pg. 4407
LANDMARK COMMUNITY NEWSPAPERS, LLC—See Irish Times; U.S. Private, pg. 2138
LANDMARK CONSTRUCTION COMPANY, INC.; U.S. Private, pg. 2385
LANDMARK DIVIDEND LLC—See DigitalBridge Group, Inc.; U.S. Public, pg. 664
LANDMARK EARTH SOLUTIONS, INC.—See Leggett & Platt, Incorporated; U.S. Public, pg. 1302
LANDMARK EDUCATION SERVICES—See Irish Times; U.S. Private, pg. 2139
LAND MARK ELECTRIC, INC.; U.S. Private, pg. 2382
LANDMARK ELEVATOR, INC.—See L Squared Capital Management LP; U.S. Private, pg. 2362
LANDMARK ENGINEERING AND SURVEYING CORP.; U.S. Private, pg. 2385
LANDMARK EQUIPMENT; U.S. Private, pg. 2385
LANDMARK EVENT STAFFING SERVICES, INC.—See Allied Universal Manager LLC; U.S. Private, pg. 190
LANDMARK FAS LTD.—See Daily Mail & General Trust plc; Int'l, pg. 1938
LANDMARK FINANCIAL ADVISORS, LLC—See TA Associates, Inc.; U.S. Private, pg. 3919
LANDMARK GRAPHICS CORPORATION—See Halliburton Company; U.S. Public, pg. 980
LANDMARK GROUP OF BRIGHTON, INC.—See Aon plc; Int'l, pg. 497
LANDMARK GROWTH CAPITAL PARTNERS, LP; U.S. Private, pg. 2385
LANDMARK HEALTHCARE, INC.; U.S. Private, pg. 2385
LANDMARK HEALTH, LLC—See UnitedHealth Group Incorporated; U.S. Public, pg. 2242

LANDMARK HEALTH OF CALIFORNIA, LLC—See UnitedHealth Group Incorporated; U.S. Public, pg. 2242
LANDMARK HEALTH OF NORTH CAROLINA, LLC—See UnitedHealth Group Incorporated; U.S. Public, pg. 2242
LANDMARK HEALTH OF OREGON, LLC—See UnitedHealth Group Incorporated; U.S. Public, pg. 2242
LANDMARK HEALTH OF PENNSYLVANIA, LLC—See UnitedHealth Group Incorporated; U.S. Public, pg. 2242
LANDMARK HEALTH OF WASHINGTON, LLC—See UnitedHealth Group Incorporated; U.S. Public, pg. 2242
LANDMARK HEALTH TECHNOLOGIES PRIVATE LIMITED—See UnitedHealth Group Incorporated; U.S. Public, pg. 2242
LANDMARK HOMES OF TENNESSEE, INC.—See Century Communities, Inc.; U.S. Public, pg. 475
LANDMARK HOME WARRANTY, LLC—See frontdoor, inc.; U.S. Public, pg. 887
LANDMARK INFORMATION GROUP—See Daily Mail & General Trust plc; Int'l, pg. 1938
LANDMARK INFRASTRUCTURE PARTNERS LP—See DigitalBridge Group, Inc.; U.S. Public, pg. 665
LANDMARK JORDAN PSC LIMITED—See Landmark Retail Holdings 1 Limited; Int'l, pg. 4407
LANDMARK MALL L.L.C.—See Howard Hughes Holdings Inc.; U.S. Public, pg. 1060
LANDMARK MEDIA ENTERPRISES, LLC—See Irish Times; U.S. Private, pg. 2138
LANDMARK MEDICAL CENTER—See Prime Healthcare Services, Inc.; U.S. Private, pg. 3261
LANDMARK MEDICAL OF MASSACHUSETTS, PLLC—See UnitedHealth Group Incorporated; U.S. Public, pg. 2242
LANDMARK NATIONAL BANK—See Landmark Bancorp, Inc.; U.S. Public, pg. 1292
LANDMARK NETWORK INC.—See Gridiron Capital, LLC; U.S. Private, pg. 1786
LANDMARK NURSERIES INC.; U.S. Private, pg. 2385
LANDMARK OPTOELECTRONICS CORPORATION; Int'l, pg. 4407
LANDMARK PARTNERS, LLC—See Ares Management Corporation; U.S. Public, pg. 189
LANDMARK PLASTIC CORPORATION; U.S. Private, pg. 2385
LAND MARK PRODUCTS, INC.—See One Rock Capital Partners, LLC; U.S. Private, pg. 3022
LANDMARK PROPERTY DEVELOPMENT COMPANY LIMITED—See Dalmia Bharat Limited; Int'l, pg. 1954
LANDMARK PROPERTY MANAGEMENT JSC—See Alfa Finance Holding AD; Int'l, pg. 307
LANDMARK PUBLISHING—See Irish Times; U.S. Private, pg. 2139
LANDMARK RETAIL CORP.; U.S. Private, pg. 2385
LANDMARK RETAIL HOLDINGS 1 LIMITED—See Landmark Retail Holdings 1 Limited; Int'l, pg. 4407
LANDMARK RETAIL HOLDINGS 1 LIMITED; Int'l, pg. 4407
LANDMARK RETAIL LEBANON SARL—See Landmark Retail Holdings 1 Limited; Int'l, pg. 4407
LANDMARKS BERHAD; Int'l, pg. 4407
LANDMARK SCHOOL, INC.; U.S. Private, pg. 2385
LANDMARK SERVICE CO. LLC—See Worth & Co., Inc.; U.S. Private, pg. 4570
LANDMARK SERVICES COOPERATIVE; U.S. Private, pg. 2386
LANDMARK SPINNING INDUSTRIES LIMITED—See Hashwani Group; Int'l, pg. 3283
LANDMARKS SA—See Hasgrove plc; Int'l, pg. 3283
LANDMARK SURGICAL SUITES, LLC—See Tenet Healthcare Corporation; U.S. Public, pg. 2004
LANDMARK UNDERWRITING AGENCY (PTY.) LTD.—See Talanx AG; Int'l, pg. 7445
LANDMARK WHITE (BRISBANE) PTY LTD—See Acumentis Group Limited; Int'l, pg. 121
LANDMARK WHITE (GOLD COAST) PTY LTD—See Acumentis Group Limited; Int'l, pg. 121
LANDMARK WHITE (SYDNEY) PTY LTD—See Acumentis Group Limited; Int'l, pg. 121
LANDMARK WHITE (VIC) PTY LTD—See Acumentis Group Limited; Int'l, pg. 121
LANDMART HOMES; Int'l, pg. 4407
LAND MEAT NEW ZEALAND LIMITED—See AFFCO Holdings Limited; Int'l, pg. 186
LAND 'N' SEA DISTRIBUTING, INC.—See Brunswick Corporation; U.S. Public, pg. 407
LAND 'N SEA, INC.; U.S. Private, pg. 2382
LANDO CO., LTD.—See Shih Wei Navigation Co., Ltd.; Int'l, pg. 6828
LAND OF LINCOLN CREDIT UNION; U.S. Private, pg. 2383
LAND O'FROST, INC.; U.S. Private, pg. 2383
LANDOIN EMBALLAGES; Int'l, pg. 4407
LAND O'LAKES ANIMAL MILK PRODUCTS COMPANY - BLACK RIVER FALLS PLANT—See Land O'Lakes, Inc.; U.S. Private, pg. 2383
LAND O'LAKES ANIMAL MILK PRODUCTS COMPANY—See Land O'Lakes, Inc.; U.S. Private, pg. 2383

LAND O'LAKES FINANCE CO.—See Land O'Lakes, Inc.; *U.S. Private*, pg. 2383
LAND O'LAKES, INC. - CARLISLE—See Land O'Lakes, Inc.; *U.S. Private*, pg. 2383
LAND O'LAKES, INC. - FOOD INGREDIENTS DIVISION—See Land O'Lakes, Inc.; *U.S. Private*, pg. 2383
LAND O'LAKES, INC. - INTERNATIONAL DIVISION—See Land O'Lakes, Inc.; *U.S. Private*, pg. 2383
LAND O'LAKES, INC. - KENT—See Land O'Lakes, Inc.; *U.S. Private*, pg. 2383
LAND O'LAKES, INC. - KIEL—See Land O'Lakes, Inc.; *U.S. Private*, pg. 2383
LAND O'LAKES, INC. - NASHVILLE—See Land O'Lakes, Inc.; *U.S. Private*, pg. 2383
LAND O'LAKES, INC.; *U.S. Private*, pg. 2383
LAND O'LAKES PURINA FEED LLC—See Land O'Lakes, Inc.; *U.S. Private*, pg. 2383
LAND O'LAKES PURINA FEED—See Land O'Lakes, Inc.; *U.S. Private*, pg. 2383
LANDOLL CORPORATION - DREXEL—See Landoll Corporation; *U.S. Private*, pg. 2386
LANDOLL CORPORATION; *U.S. Private*, pg. 2386
LANDOLT & CIE SA—See ODDO BHF SCA; *Int'l*, pg. 5524
LANDON CAPITAL PARTNERS, LLC; *U.S. Private*, pg. 2386
LANDON TITLE COMPANY, LLC—See Stewart Information Services Corporation; *U.S. Public*, pg. 1947
LANDOR ASSOCIATES—See WPP plc; *Int'l*, pg. 8483
LANDOR ASSOCIATES—See WPP plc; *Int'l*, pg. 8483
LANDOR ASSOCIATES—See WPP plc; *Int'l*, pg. 8483
LANDOR ASSOCIATES—See WPP plc; *Int'l*, pg. 8483
LANDOR ASSOCIATES—See WPP plc; *Int'l*, pg. 8483
LANDOR ASSOCIATES—See WPP plc; *Int'l*, pg. 8483
LANDOR ASSOCIATES—See WPP plc; *Int'l*, pg. 8483
LANDOR ASSOCIATES—See WPP plc; *Int'l*, pg. 8483
LANDOR ASSOCIATES—See WPP plc; *Int'l*, pg. 8483
LANDOR ASSOCIATES—See WPP plc; *Int'l*, pg. 8483
LANDOR CARTONS HOLDINGS LTD.; *Int'l*, pg. 4407
LANDOR CARTONS LTD.—See Landor Cartons Holdings Ltd.; *Int'l*, pg. 4407
LANDORE RESOURCES CANADA INC.—See Landore Resources Ltd; *Int'l*, pg. 4407
LANDORE RESOURCES LTD; *Int'l*, pg. 4407
LANDOS BIOPHARMA, INC.—See AbbVie Inc.; *U.S. Public*, pg. 24
LAND-O-SUN DAIRIES LLC—See Dean Foods Company; *U.S. Private*, pg. 1183
LAND O'SUN MANAGEMENT CORPORATION; *U.S. Private*, pg. 2383
LANDPARK ADVISORS, LLC; *U.S. Private*, pg. 2386
LANDPOINT INC.; *U.S. Private*, pg. 2386
LAND POWER SRL—See Public Power Corporation S.A.; *Int'l*, pg. 6095
LAND PROPERTIES INC.; *U.S. Private*, pg. 2383
LANDQART AG—See Schweizerische Nationalbank; *Int'l*, pg. 6646
LANDQWEST COMMERCIAL, LLC; *U.S. Private*, pg. 2386
LANDRETH LUMBER COMPANY; *U.S. Private*, pg. 2386
LANDRICH HOLDING LIMITED; *Int'l*, pg. 4407
LAND-RON, INC.; *U.S. Private*, pg. 2384
LAND ROVER BELUX SA/NV—See Tata Motors Limited; *Int'l*, pg. 7467
LAND ROVER ESPANA SL—See Tata Motors Limited; *Int'l*, pg. 7467
LAND ROVER HUNTINGTON—See Marubeni Corporation; *Int'l*, pg. 4706
LAND ROVER IRELAND LTD—See Tata Motors Limited; *Int'l*, pg. 7467
LANDROVER ORLANDO; *U.S. Private*, pg. 2386
LAND ROVER SAN JOSE; *U.S. Private*, pg. 2384
LAND ROVER—See Tata Motors Limited; *Int'l*, pg. 7467
LANDROW LIMITED—See Salini Costruttori S.p.A.; *Int'l*, pg. 6493
LANDRUM & BROWN, INCORPORATED; *U.S. Private*, pg. 2386
LANDRUM COMPANY; *U.S. Private*, pg. 2386
LANDRUM CONSULTING, INC.—See Landrum Human Resource Companies, Inc.; *U.S. Private*, pg. 2386
LANDRUM HUMAN RESOURCE COMPANIES, INC.; *U.S. Private*, pg. 2386
LANDRUM PROFESSIONAL EMPLOYER SERVICES, INC.—See Landrum Human Resource Companies, Inc.; *U.S. Private*, pg. 2386
LANDRUM STAFFING SERVICES, INC.—See Landrum Human Resource Companies, Inc.; *U.S. Private*, pg. 2386
LANDRY HARRIS & CO. INC.; *U.S. Private*, pg. 2386
LANDRY'S, INC.—See Fertitta Entertainment, Inc.; *U.S. Private*, pg. 1499
LANDSAFE FLOOD DETERMINATION, INC.—See Bank of America Corporation; *U.S. Public*, pg. 272
LANDSAFE, INC.—See Bank of America Corporation; *U.S. Public*, pg. 272

LANDSAFE TITLE AGENCY, INC.—See Bank of America Corporation; *U.S. Public*, pg. 272
LAND SAPPORT INC.—See GENDAI AGENCY INC.; *Int'l*, pg. 2917
LANDSBANKINN HF.; *Int'l*, pg. 4407
LANDSBERG BENNETT PRIVATE WEALTH MANAGEMENT; *U.S. Private*, pg. 2387
LANDSBERRY & JAMES MARKETING PTY LTD—See Brookfield Corporation; *Int'l*, pg. 1178
LANDSBERRY & JAMES MARKETING PTY LTD—See Elliott Management Corporation; *U.S. Private*, pg. 1371
LANDSCAPE CARE CO.—See Bruce Company of Wisconsin, Inc.; *U.S. Private*, pg. 671
LANDSCAPE CONCEPTS MANAGEMENT, INC.; *U.S. Private*, pg. 2387
LANDSCAPE DEVELOPMENTAL INC.; *U.S. Private*, pg. 2387
LANDSCAPE FORMS, INC.; *U.S. Private*, pg. 2387
LANDSCAPE MAINTENANCE PROFESSIONALS, INC.; *U.S. Private*, pg. 2387
LANDSCAPE PARCSUD SL—See Banco de Sabadell, S.A.; *Int'l*, pg. 821
THE LANDSCAPE PARTNERS, LTD.—See Aspen Grove Landscape Companies, LLC; *U.S. Private*, pg. 352
LANDSCAPE SERVICE PROFESSIONALS, INC.—See Centre Partners Management LLC; *U.S. Private*, pg. 829
LANDSCAPE SERVICE PROFESSIONALS, INC.—See LP First Capital; *U.S. Private*, pg. 2507
LANDSCAPE STRUCTURES INC.; *U.S. Private*, pg. 2387
LANDSCAPES UNLIMITED LLC; *U.S. Private*, pg. 2387
LANDSCAPES WORKSHOP, INC.—See Carousel Capital Partners; *U.S. Private*, pg. 769
LANDSEA CAMP AND CATERING SERVICES LTD.—See Aramark; *U.S. Public*, pg. 178
LANDSEA GREEN LIFE SERVICE COMPANY LIMITED; *Int'l*, pg. 4407
LANDSEA GREEN MANAGEMENT LIMITED; *Int'l*, pg. 4407
LANDSEA HOMES CORP.; *U.S. Public*, pg. 1292
LANDSEA HOMES OF ARIZONA, LLC—See Landsea Green Management Limited; *Int'l*, pg. 4407
LAND & SEA, INC.—See Power Test, Inc.; *U.S. Private*, pg. 3239
LAND & SEA INSTRUMENTATION LTD—See Black & McDonald Limited; *Int'l*, pg. 1056
LAND & SEA PETROLEUM, INC.—See RKA Petroleum Companies, LLC; *U.S. Private*, pg. 3450
LAND SECURITIES GROUP PLC; *Int'l*, pg. 4404
LAND SECURITIES PLC—See Land Securities Group Plc; *Int'l*, pg. 4404
LAND SECURITIES PROPERTIES LIMITED—See Land Securities Group Plc; *Int'l*, pg. 4404
LANDS' END DIRECT MERCHANTS, INC.—See Lands' End, Inc.; *U.S. Public*, pg. 1292
LANDS' END EUROPE LIMITED—See Lands' End, Inc.; *U.S. Public*, pg. 1292
LANDS' END GMBH—See Lands' End, Inc.; *U.S. Public*, pg. 1292
LANDS' END, INC.; *U.S. Public*, pg. 1292
LANDS' END JAPAN, K.K.—See Lands' End, Inc.; *U.S. Public*, pg. 1292
LANDS END MARINA HOLDING COMPANY, INC.; *U.S. Private*, pg. 2387
LANDS END MARINA—See Lands End Marina Holding Company, Inc.; *U.S. Private*, pg. 2387
LANDS END RESOURCES LTD; *Int'l*, pg. 4407
LANDSHIRE, INC.; *U.S. Private*, pg. 2387
LANDSNET HF.—See Landsvirkjun - The Na; *Int'l*, pg. 4408
LAND SOLUTION INC.—See Kurita Water Industries Ltd.; *Int'l*, pg. 4341
LAND SOLUTIONS, INC.; *U.S. Private*, pg. 2384
LANDSON EMISSION TECHNOLOGIES A/S; *Int'l*, pg. 4407
LAND SOUTH CONSTRUCTION LLC; *U.S. Private*, pg. 2384
LAND SOUTH HOLDINGS, LLC; *U.S. Private*, pg. 2384
LAND SOUTH REALTY, LLC—See Land South Holdings, LLC; *U.S. Private*, pg. 2384
LAND SPAN INC.—See Watkins Associated Industries Inc.; *U.S. Private*, pg. 4454
LANDSTAR BLUE LLC—See Landstar System, Inc.; *U.S. Public*, pg. 1292
LANDSTAR DEVELOPMENT CORPORATION; *U.S. Private*, pg. 2387
LANDSTAR EXPRESS AMERICA, INC.—See Landstar System, Inc.; *U.S. Public*, pg. 1292
LANDSTAR GEMINI, INC.—See Landstar System, Inc.; *U.S. Public*, pg. 1292
LANDSTAR GLOBAL LOGISTICS, INC.—See Landstar System, Inc.; *U.S. Public*, pg. 1292
LANDSTAR INWAY, INC.—See Landstar System, Inc.; *U.S. Public*, pg. 1292
LANDSTAR LIGON, INC.—See Landstar System, Inc.; *U.S. Public*, pg. 1292
LANDSTAR RANGER, INC.—See Landstar System, Inc.; *U.S. Public*, pg. 1292

LANDSTAR SYSTEM HOLDINGS, INC.—See Landstar System, Inc.; *U.S. Public*, pg. 1292
LANDSTAR SYSTEM, INC. - ROCKFORD SERVICE CENTER—See Landstar System, Inc.; *U.S. Public*, pg. 1292
LANDSTAR SYSTEM, INC.; *U.S. Public*, pg. 1292
LANDSTAR TITLE AGENCY INC.; *U.S. Private*, pg. 2387
LANDSTAR TRANSPORTATION LOGISTICS, INC.—See Landstar System, Inc.; *U.S. Public*, pg. 1292
LANDSTED, LLC; *U.S. Private*, pg. 2387
LANDSVAKI HF.—See Landsbankinn hf.; *Int'l*, pg. 4407
LANDSVIRKJUN POWER EHF.—See Landsvirkjun - The Na; *Int'l*, pg. 4408
LANDSVIRKJUN - THE NATIONAL POWER CO.; *Int'l*, pg. 4407
LANDTECH DATA CORP.—See AccuTitle LLC; *U.S. Private*, pg. 55
LANDTECHNIK STEIGRA GMBH—See AGRAVIS Raiffeisen AG; *Int'l*, pg. 215
LANDTEC SEKIWA CHUBU, LTD—See Sekisui House, Ltd.; *Int'l*, pg. 6697
LANDTEC SEKIWA, LTD—See Sekisui House, Ltd.; *Int'l*, pg. 6697
LANDTEC NORTH AMERICA, INC.—See Graco, Inc.; *U.S. Public*, pg. 954
LAND TITLE AND ESCROW, INC.—See Anywhere Real Estate Inc.; *U.S. Public*, pg. 142
LAND TITLE GUARANTEE COMPANY INC.; *U.S. Private*, pg. 2384
LANDTRAN EXPRESS INC.—See Landtran Systems Inc.; *Int'l*, pg. 4408
LANDTRAN LOGISTICS INC.—See Landtran Systems Inc.; *Int'l*, pg. 4408
LAND TRANSPORT AUTHORITY OF SINGAPORE; *Int'l*, pg. 4404
LANDTRAN SYSTEMS INC.; *Int'l*, pg. 4408
LAND TRUCKING CO. INC.—See Laney & Duke Terminal Warehouse Co. Inc.; *U.S. Private*, pg. 2388
LAND TRUST ALLIANCE; *U.S. Private*, pg. 2384
LAND TRUST OF SANTA CRUZ COUNTY; *U.S. Private*, pg. 2384
LANDURA, LLC—See UFP Industries, Inc.; *U.S. Public*, pg. 2219
LANDUS COOPERATIVE; *U.S. Private*, pg. 2387
LANDVELAR HF; *Int'l*, pg. 4408
LANDVEST INC.; *U.S. Private*, pg. 2387
LAND VIEW FERTILIZER INC.; *U.S. Private*, pg. 2384
LANDWEHR WASSERTECHNIK GMBH—See E.ON SE; *Int'l*, pg. 2258
THE LANDWELL COMPANY LP—See Contran Corporation; *U.S. Private*, pg. 1034
LANDWELL PRICEWATERHOUSECOOPERS TAX & LEGAL SERVICES S.L.—See PricewaterhouseCoopers, S.L.; *Int'l*, pg. 5973
LAND WIN ELECTRONIC CORP.—See Koch Industries, Inc.; *U.S. Private*, pg. 2335
LANDWIRTH'S GMBH—See Berentzen-Gruppe AG; *Int'l*, pg. 978
LANDWIRTSCHAFTLICHE PRODUKTIONSGESELLSCHAFT MBH—See KTG Agrar SE; *Int'l*, pg. 4316
LANDWOOD TITLE CO. INC.—See Tarbell Financial Corporation; *U.S. Private*, pg. 3933
LANDY COURTAGE S.A.S.—See Assicurazioni Generali S.p.A.; *Int'l*, pg. 647
LANE AVIATION CORPORATION; *U.S. Private*, pg. 2387
LANEBRIDGE INVESTMENT MANAGEMENT LTD—See Rothschild & Co SCA; *Int'l*, pg. 6403
LANE BRYANT CHARITIES, INC.—See Sycamore Partners Management, LP; *U.S. Private*, pg. 3896
LANE BRYANT, INC.—See Sycamore Partners Management, LP; *U.S. Private*, pg. 3896
LANEBURY GROWTH CAPITAL LTD.; *Int'l*, pg. 4408
LANECO CONSTRUCTION SYSTEMS INC.; *U.S. Private*, pg. 2388
LANE COMPANY; *U.S. Private*, pg. 2387
THE LANE CONSTRUCTION CORPORATION—See Salini Costruttori S.p.A.; *Int'l*, pg. 6493
LANE CONVEYORS & DRIVES, INC.; *U.S. Private*, pg. 2387
LANE ENERGY POLAND SP. Z.O.O—See SalvaRx Group Plc; *Int'l*, pg. 6495
LANE ENTERPRISES INC.; *U.S. Private*, pg. 2388
LANE EQUIPMENT CO. INC.; *U.S. Private*, pg. 2388
LANE FURNITURE INDUSTRIES—See Heritage Home Group, LLC; *U.S. Private*, pg. 1924
LANE HOME FURNISHINGS RETAIL, INC.—See Heritage Home Group, LLC; *U.S. Private*, pg. 1924
LANE INDUSTRIES INCORPORATED—See Salini Costruttori S.p.A.; *Int'l*, pg. 6493
LANELABS USA INC.; *U.S. Private*, pg. 2388
LANE LIMITED—See Skandinavisk Holding A/S; *Int'l*, pg. 6976
LANE MARKETING—See Lane PR; *U.S. Private*, pg. 2388
LANE POWELL PC; *U.S. Private*, pg. 2388
LANE PRESS, INC.; *U.S. Private*, pg. 2388
LANE PR; *U.S. Private*, pg. 2388
LANE QUINN BENEFIT CONSULTANTS LTD.—See People Corporation; *Int'l*, pg. 5793

COMPANY NAME INDEX

LANESBOROUGH REAL ESTATE INVESTMENT TRUST; *Int'l*, pg. 4408
LANE SOUTHERN ORCHARDS; *U.S. Private*, pg. 2388
LANE SUPPLY INC.; *U.S. Private*, pg. 2388
LANETERRALEVER; *U.S. Private*, pg. 2388
LANETRO ZED S.A.; *Int'l*, pg. 4408
LANEVENTURE—See Heritage Home Group, LLC; *U.S. Private*, pg. 1924
LANEY & DUKE TERMINAL WAREHOUSE CO. INC.; *U.S. Private*, pg. 2388
LANEY'S INC.; *U.S. Private*, pg. 2388
LAN FA TEXTILE CO., LTD.; *Int'l*, pg. 4402
LAN FA TEXTILE CO., LTD. - TAO YUAN FACTORY—See LAN FA TEXTILE CO., LTD.; *Int'l*, pg. 4402
LAN FA TEXTILE CO., LTD. - ZU BAY FACTORY—See LAN FA TEXTILE CO., LTD.; *Int'l*, pg. 4402
LANFRANCHI NICKEL MINES PTY LTD—See Panoramic Resources Limited; *Int'l*, pg. 5729
LANFRANCHI NORTH AMERICA, INC.—See Lanfranchi S.r.l.; *Int'l*, pg. 4408
LANFRANCHI NORTH EUROPE S.A.S—See Lanfranchi S.r.l.; *Int'l*, pg. 4408
LANFRANCHI S.R.L.; *Int'l*, pg. 4408
LANGAN AUTOMOTIVE GROUP; *U.S. Private*, pg. 2388
LANGAN ENGINEERING & ENVIRONMENTAL SERVICES INC.; *U.S. Private*, pg. 2388
LANGAN ENGINEERING & ENVIRONMENTAL SERVICES, INC.—See Langan Engineering & Environmental Services, Inc.; *U.S. Private*, pg. 2389
LANGAN ENGINEERING & ENVIRONMENTAL SERVICES, INC.—See Langan Engineering & Environmental Services, Inc.; *U.S. Private*, pg. 2389
LANGAN ENGINEERING & ENVIRONMENTAL SERVICES, INC.—See Langan Engineering & Environmental Services, Inc.; *U.S. Private*, pg. 2389
LANGAN ENGINEERING & ENVIRONMENTAL SERVICES, INC.; *U.S. Private*, pg. 2388
LANGAN ENGINEERING & ENVIRONMENTAL SERVICES, INC.—See Langan Engineering & Environmental Services, Inc.; *U.S. Private*, pg. 2388
LANGAN ENGINEERING & ENVIRONMENTAL SERVICES, INC.—See Langan Engineering & Environmental Services, Inc.; *U.S. Private*, pg. 2389
LANGAN ENGINEERING & ENVIRONMENTAL SERVICES, INC.—See Langan Engineering & Environmental Services, Inc.; *U.S. Private*, pg. 2389
LANGAN ENGINEERING & ENVIRONMENTAL SERVICES, INC.—See Langan Engineering & Environmental Services, Inc.; *U.S. Private*, pg. 2389
LANGAN ENGINEERING & ENVIRONMENTAL SERVICES, INC.—See Langan Engineering & Environmental Services, Inc.; *U.S. Private*, pg. 2389
LANGAN ENGINEERING & ENVIRONMENTAL SERVICES, INC.—See Langan Engineering & Environmental Services, Inc.; *U.S. Private*, pg. 2389
LANGAN ENGINEERING & ENVIRONMENTAL SERVICES, INC.—See Langan Engineering & Environmental Services, Inc.; *U.S. Private*, pg. 2389
LANGAN ENGINEERING & ENVIRONMENTAL SERVICES, INC.—See Langan Engineering & Environmental Services, Inc.; *U.S. Private*, pg. 2389
LANGAN ENGINEERING & ENVIRONMENTAL SERVICES, INC.—See Langan Engineering & Environmental Services, Inc.; *U.S. Private*, pg. 2389
LANGAN ENGINEERING & ENVIRONMENTAL SERVICES, INC.—See Langan Engineering & Environmental Services, Inc.; *U.S. Private*, pg. 2389
LANGAN ENGINEERING & ENVIRONMENTAL SERVICES, INC.—See Langan Engineering & Environmental Services, Inc.; *U.S. Private*, pg. 2389
LANGAN INTERNATIONAL, LLC - ABU DHABI—See Langan Engineering & Environmental Services, Inc.; *U.S. Private*, pg. 2389
LANGAN INTERNATIONAL, LLC - GREECE—See Langan Engineering & Environmental Services, Inc.; *U.S. Private*, pg. 2389
LANGAN INTERNATIONAL, LLC - QATAR—See Langan Engineering & Environmental Services, Inc.; *U.S. Private*, pg. 2389
LANGAN INTERNATIONAL, LLC - TURKEY—See Langan Engineering & Environmental Services, Inc.; *U.S. Private*, pg. 2389
LANGAN INTERNATIONAL, LLC - UNITED ARAB EMIRATES—See Langan Engineering & Environmental Services, Inc.; *U.S. Private*, pg. 2389
LANGAN TREADWELL ROLLO - OAKLAND—See Langan Engineering & Environmental Services, Inc.; *U.S. Private*, pg. 2389
LANGAN TREADWELL ROLLO - SACRAMENTO—See Langan Engineering & Environmental Services, Inc.; *U.S. Private*, pg. 2389
LANGAN TREADWELL ROLLO - SAN JOSE—See Langan Engineering & Environmental Services, Inc.; *U.S. Private*, pg. 2389
LANGAN TREADWELL ROLLO—See Langan Engineering & Environmental Services, Inc.; *U.S. Private*, pg. 2389
THE LANG COMPANY, INC.; *U.S. Private*, pg. 4067
THE LANGDALE COMPANY; *U.S. Private*, pg. 4067

LANGDALE E3 PTE. LTD.—See Insas Berhad; *Int'l*, pg. 3718
LANGEBERG & ASHTON FOODS PROPRIETARY LIMITED—See Tiger Brands Ltd.; *Int'l*, pg. 7746
LANGENPAC NV—See MPAC Group PLC; *Int'l*, pg. 5060
LANGENSCHEIDT KOMMANDITGESELLSCHAFT; *Int'l*, pg. 4408
LANGE PLUMBING SUPPLY, INC.; *U.S. Private*, pg. 2389
LANGER ELECTRIC COMPANY; *U.S. Private*, pg. 2389
THE LANGER GROUP—See PC GROUP, INC.; *U.S. Private*, pg. 3119
LANGER HEINRICH URANIUM (PTY) LTD.—See China National Nuclear Corporation; *Int'l*, pg. 1532
LANGER HEINRICH URANIUM (PTY) LTD.—See Paladin Energy Ltd.; *Int'l*, pg. 5705
LANGER INSTRUMENTS CORPORATION—See Halma plc; *Int'l*, pg. 3232
LANGER JUICE COMPANY, INC.; *U.S. Private*, pg. 2389
LANGER TRANSPORT; *U.S. Private*, pg. 2389
LANGE-STEGMANN CO., INC.; *U.S. Private*, pg. 2389
LANGE UHREN GMBH—See Reinet Investments S.C.A.; *Int'l*, pg. 6257
LANGEVELD/SLEEGERS BV—See What's Cooking Group NV; *Int'l*, pg. 8397
LANG EXTERIOR, INC.; *U.S. Private*, pg. 2388
LANGFANG DEVELOPMENT CO., LTD.; *Int'l*, pg. 4409
LANGFANG D&G MACHINERY TECHNOLOGY COMPANY LIMITED—See D&G TECHNOLOGY HOLDING CO., LTD.; *Int'l*, pg. 1899
LANGFANG HUADE METAL PACKAGING CONTAINER CO., LTD.—See Crown Holdings, Inc.; *U.S. Public*, pg. 599
LANGFANG NIPPON PAINT CO., LTD.—See Nippon Paint Holdings Co., Ltd.; *Int'l*, pg. 5325
LANGFANG ZHONGBEN PACKAGE CO., LTD.—See Inabata & Co. Ltd.; *Int'l*, pg. 3644
LANG GMBH & CO. KG; *Int'l*, pg. 4408
LANGHAM HOSPITALITY GROUP LIMITED—See Great Eagle Holdings Limited; *Int'l*, pg. 3064
LANGHAM HOSPITALITY INVESTMENTS LIMITED; *Int'l*, pg. 4409
LANGHAM HOTELS INTERNATIONAL LIMITED—See Great Eagle Holdings Limited; *Int'l*, pg. 3064
LANGHAM LOGISTICS INC.; *U.S. Private*, pg. 2389
THE LANGHAM MELBOURNE—See Great Eagle Holdings Limited; *Int'l*, pg. 3064
LANGHAMMER GMBH—See Korber AG; *Int'l*, pg. 4281
LANGHAM PLACE HOTEL (HK) LIMITED—See Langham Hospitality Investments Limited; *Int'l*, pg. 4409
LANGHOLM CAPITAL LLP; *Int'l*, pg. 4409
LANGHORNE DIALYSIS LLC—See Nautic Partners, LLC; *U.S. Private*, pg. 2870
LANG INC; *Int'l*, pg. 4408
LANGKAWI HOLIDAY VILLA SDN. BHD.—See Advance Synergy Berhad; *Int'l*, pg. 156
LANG KFT.—See LKQ Corporation; *U.S. Public*, pg. 1335
LANGLE & STAUB SANITARPLANUNG GMBH—See Burkhalter Holding AG; *Int'l*, pg. 1225
LANGLEY AGENCY, INC.—See GTCR LLC; *U.S. Private*, pg. 1803
LANGLEY HOLDINGS PLC; *Int'l*, pg. 4409
LANGLEY MOTOR CO., INC.; *U.S. Private*, pg. 2389
LANGLEYS SOLICITORS LLP—See Knights Group Holdings PLC; *Int'l*, pg. 4208
LANGLEY TOYOTATOWN; *Int'l*, pg. 4411
LANGLEY WHOLESALE LTD.—See Nayax Ltd.; *Int'l*, pg. 5178
LANGLEY WIRE CLOTH PRODUCTS—See Graycliff Partners LP; *U.S. Private*, pg. 1760
LANGLOIS SOBRETI; *Int'l*, pg. 4411
LANGOLD REAL ESTATE CO., LTD.; *Int'l*, pg. 4411
LANG REALTY, INC.; *U.S. Private*, pg. 2388
LANG & SCHWARZ AKTIENGESELLSCHAFT; *Int'l*, pg. 4408
LANGSHYTTAN SLIPSERVICE AB—See Investment AB Latour; *Int'l*, pg. 3782
LANGSON ENERGY, INC.; *U.S. Private*, pg. 2389
LANGSTON COMPANIES, INC.; *U.S. Private*, pg. 2389
LANGSTON COMPANY; *U.S. Private*, pg. 2390
LANGSTONE SUPPLIES LIMITED—See Park-Ohio Holdings Corp.; *U.S. Public*, pg. 1639
LANGUAGE LINE SERVICES UK LTD.—See Teleperformance SE; *Int'l*, pg. 7540
LANGUAGELINE SOLUTIONS, INC.—See ABRY Partners, LLC; *U.S. Private*, pg. 42
LANGUAGELINE SOLUTIONS—See Teleperformance SE; *Int'l*, pg. 7540
LANGUAGE LINKS INTERNATIONAL PTY. LIMITED—See Academies Australasia Group Limited; *Int'l*, pg. 77
LANGUAGE SCIENTIFIC, INC.; *U.S. Private*, pg. 2390
LANGUAGE SERVICES ASSOCIATES, INC.; *U.S. Private*, pg. 2390
LANGUAGE TRAINING CENTER; *U.S. Private*, pg. 2390
LANGUAGE TRANSLATION INC.—See Lingualinx Inc.; *U.S. Private*, pg. 2461
LANGUAGE WEAVER INC.—See RWS Holdings plc; *Int'l*, pg. 6437
LANGUAGE WEAVER SRL—See RWS Holdings plc; *Int'l*, pg. 6437

THE LANGUAGE WORKS, INC.—See Euromezzanine Conseil SAS; *Int'l*, pg. 2554
THE LANGUAGE WORKS, INC.—See Indigo Capital LLP; *Int'l*, pg. 3655
LANHAI MEDICAL INVESTMENT CO., LTD.; *Int'l*, pg. 4411
LANHAM BROTHERS GENERAL CONTRACTORS; *U.S. Private*, pg. 2390
LAN HANDLING TECHNOLOGIES BV - HALFWEG FACTORY—See Hydratec Industries NV; *Int'l*, pg. 3546
LAN HANDLING TECHNOLOGIES BV—See Hydratec Industries NV; *Int'l*, pg. 3546
LANIER AUSTRALIA PTY LTD—See Ricoh Company, Ltd.; *Int'l*, pg. 6333
LANIER CONSTRUCTION COMPANY; *U.S. Private*, pg. 2390
LANIER PARKING INC.; *U.S. Private*, pg. 2390
LANIER UPSHAW, INC.; *U.S. Private*, pg. 2390
LANIFICIO ANGELICO SRL; *Int'l*, pg. 4411
LANITIS BROS LTD.—See Coca-Cola HBC AG; *Int'l*, pg. 1686
LANITIS BROS PUBLIC LTD.—See Coca-Cola HBC AG; *Int'l*, pg. 1686
LANITIS GOLF PUBLIC CO., LTD.; *Int'l*, pg. 4411
LANKA ALUMINIUM INDUSTRIES PLC; *Int'l*, pg. 4411
LANKA ASHOK LEYLAND PLC; *Int'l*, pg. 4411
LANKABANGLA ASSET MANAGEMENT COMPANY LIMITED—See LankaBangla Finance Ltd.; *Int'l*, pg. 4412
LANKABANGLA FINANCE LTD.; *Int'l*, pg. 4412
LANKABANGLA INFORMATION SYSTEM LIMITED—See LankaBangla Finance Ltd.; *Int'l*, pg. 4412
LANKABANGLA INVESTMENTS LIMITED—See LankaBangla Finance Ltd.; *Int'l*, pg. 4412
LANKABANGLA SECURITIES LIMITED—See LankaBangla Finance Ltd.; *Int'l*, pg. 4412
LANKA CANNERIES LIMITED—See Hunter & Company PLC; *Int'l*, pg. 3536
LANKA CEMENT PLC; *Int'l*, pg. 4411
LANKA CERAMIC PLC—See Royal Ceramics Lanka PLC; *Int'l*, pg. 6411
LANKA COMMUNICATION SERVICES (PVT) LIMITED—See Temasek Holdings (Private) Limited; *Int'l*, pg. 7553
LANKA GRAPHITE LIMITED; *Int'l*, pg. 4411
THE LANKA HOSPITALS CORPORATION PLC; *Int'l*, pg. 7664
LANKA INDUSTRIAL ESTATES LIMITED—See DFCC Bank PLC; *Int'l*, pg. 2094
LANKA IOC PLC—See Indian Oil Corporation Limited; *Int'l*, pg. 3654
LANKA MARINE SERVICES (PVT.) LTD.—See John Keells Holdings PLC; *Int'l*, pg. 3978
LANKA MILK FOODS (CWE) PLC; *Int'l*, pg. 4412
LANKAN ALLIANCE FINANCE LIMITED—See Peoples Leasing & Finance PLC; *Int'l*, pg. 5794
LANKA SECURITIES PVT. LTD.—See Bank of Ceylon; *Int'l*, pg. 841
LANKA SECURITIES PVT. LTD.—See First Capital Securities Corporation Limited; *Int'l*, pg. 2682
LANKA SPECIAL STEELS LTD—See E.B. Creasy & Company PLC; *Int'l*, pg. 2251
LANKA SUGAR COMPANY (PVT.) LIMITED; *Int'l*, pg. 4412
LANKA TILES PLC; *Int'l*, pg. 4412
LANKA VENTURES PLC; *Int'l*, pg. 4412
LANKA WALLTILE PLC; *Int'l*, pg. 4412
LANKELMA LTD—See HAL Trust N.V.; *Int'l*, pg. 3226
LANKEM CEYLON PLC; *Int'l*, pg. 4412
LANKEM TEA & RUBBER PLANTATIONS (PVT) LTD.—See E.B. Creasy & Company PLC; *Int'l*, pg. 2251
LANKHORST TASELAAR B.V.—See Brunswick Corporation; *U.S. Public*, pg. 408
LANK OIL CO. INC.; *U.S. Private*, pg. 2390
LANKOM ELECTRONICS CO LTD—See Lankom Electronics Limited; *Int'l*, pg. 4412
LANKOM ELECTRONICS LIMITED; *Int'l*, pg. 4412
LANKOM SALES LTD—See Lankom Electronics Limited; *Int'l*, pg. 4412
LANKWITZER COATING LTD.—See Lankwitzer Lackfabrik GmbH; *Int'l*, pg. 4412
LANKWITZER DO BRASIL LTDA—See Lankwitzer Lackfabrik GmbH; *Int'l*, pg. 4412
LANKWITZER GEORGIA LTD.—See Lankwitzer Lackfabrik GmbH; *Int'l*, pg. 4412
LANKWITZER LACKFABRIK BEL—See Lankwitzer Lackfabrik GmbH; *Int'l*, pg. 4412
LANKWITZER LACKFABRIK CR, SPOL S.R.O.—See Lankwitzer Lackfabrik GmbH; *Int'l*, pg. 4412
LANKWITZER LACKFABRIK GMBH - LEIPZIG PLANT—See Lankwitzer Lackfabrik GmbH; *Int'l*, pg. 4412
LANKWITZER LACKFABRIK GMBH - OSTERWIECK PLANT—See Lankwitzer Lackfabrik GmbH; *Int'l*, pg. 4412
LANKWITZER LACKFABRIK GMBH; *Int'l*, pg. 4412
LANKWITZER POLSKA SP. Z.O.O.—See Lankwitzer Lackfabrik GmbH; *Int'l*, pg. 4412

LANKWITZER LACKFABRIK GMBH

CORPORATE AFFILIATIONS

LANKWITZER SLOVENSKO, S.R.O.—See Lankwitzer Lackfabrik GmbH; *Int'l*, pg. 4412
LANLOGIC, INC.—See Brown Brothers Harriman & Co.; *U.S. Private*, pg. 667
LANMAN & KEMP-BARCLAY CO., INC.; *U.S. Private*, pg. 2390
LANMAN OIL COMPANY, INC.; *U.S. Private*, pg. 2390
THE LANMARK GROUP INC.; *U.S. Private*, pg. 4067
LANMARK TECHNOLOGY INC.; *U.S. Private*, pg. 2390
LAN MED NAUTILUS LTD—See TIM S.p.A.; *Int'l*, pg. 7750
LANNAN CHEVROLET INC.; *U.S. Private*, pg. 2390
LANNA RESOURCES PCL; *Int'l*, pg. 4412
LANNA (SINGAPORE) PTE LTD—See Lanna Resources pcl; *Int'l*, pg. 4412
LANNEBO FONDER AB—See Lannebo & Partners AB; *Int'l*, pg. 4413
LANNEBO & PARTNERS AB; *Int'l*, pg. 4413
LANNETT COMPANY, INC.; *U.S. Public*, pg. 1292
LANNETT HOLDINGS, INC.—See Lannett Company, Inc.; *U.S. Public*, pg. 1293
LANO EQUIPMENT INC.; *U.S. Private*, pg. 2390
LA NOUBA SARL—See U10 Corp SA; *Int'l*, pg. 7998
LANPEC TECHNOLOGIES LIMITED; *Int'l*, pg. 4413
LAN PERU S.A.—See LATAM Airlines Group S.A.; *Int'l*, pg. 4422
LANPHERE ENTERPRISES INC.; *U.S. Private*, pg. 2390
LANSA JAPAN LTD.—See TIS Inc.; *Int'l*, pg. 7757
LANSDOWNE OIL & GAS PLC; *Int'l*, pg. 4413
LANSDOWNE PARK VILLAGE LIMITED—See Arvida Group Limited; *Int'l*, pg. 587
LANSDOWNE PARTNERS LIMITED; *Int'l*, pg. 4413
LANSDOWNE PARTNERS (UK) LLP—See Lansdowne Partners Limited; *Int'l*, pg. 4413
LANSDOWNE SECURITY, INC.; *Int'l*, pg. 4413
LANSDOWNE TECHNOLOGIES INC.—See Upper Lakes Group Inc.; *Int'l*, pg. 8093
LANSEN PHARMACEUTICAL HOLDINGS CO., LTD.; *Int'l*, pg. 4413
LANS HOLDINGS, INC.; *U.S. Public*, pg. 1293
LANSING BUILDING PRODUCTS, INC. - NORFOLK—See Lansing Building Products, Inc.; *U.S. Private*, pg. 2390
LANSING BUILDING PRODUCTS, INC.; *U.S. Private*, pg. 2390
LANSING ETHANOL SERVICES, LLC—See The Andersons Incorporated; *U.S. Public*, pg. 2034
LANSING ICE AND FUEL COMPANY; *U.S. Private*, pg. 2390
LANSING LOUISIANA, LLC—See The Andersons Incorporated; *U.S. Public*, pg. 2034
LANSING MALL, LLC—See Brookfield Corporation; *Int'l*, pg. 1185
LANSING STATE JOURNAL—See Gannett Co., Inc.; *U.S. Public*, pg. 897
LANSING TRADE GROUP LLC—See The Andersons Incorporated; *U.S. Public*, pg. 2034
LANSINOH LABORATORIES INC.; *U.S. Private*, pg. 2390
LANSMONT CORP.—See Battery Ventures, L.P.; *U.S. Private*, pg. 488
LANSON-BCC; *Int'l*, pg. 4413
LANSPEED; *U.S. Private*, pg. 2391
LANTA-BANK JSC; *Int'l*, pg. 4413
LANTANA COMMUNICATIONS CORP.; *U.S. Private*, pg. 2391
LANTAU TOURS LIMITED—See KWOON CHUNG BUS HOLDINGS LIMITED; *Int'l*, pg. 4351
LANTA VEJKIJ CO., LTD.—See Thonburi Healthcare Group PCL; *Int'l*, pg. 7716
LANTBUTIKEN SVERIGE AB—See Volati AB; *Int'l*, pg. 8300
LANTECH DRILLING SERVICES INC.—See Orbit Garant Drilling Inc.; *Int'l*, pg. 5614
LANTECH INC.; *U.S. Private*, pg. 2391
LANTEC OF LOUISIANA, LLC; *U.S. Private*, pg. 2391
LANTERN HOTEL GROUP LIMITED; *Int'l*, pg. 4413
LANTERN PHARMA INC.; *U.S. Public*, pg. 1293
LANTHANEIN RESOURCES LIMITED; *Int'l*, pg. 4413
LANTHEUS HOLDINGS, INC.—See Avista Capital Partners, L.P.; *U.S. Private*, pg. 408
LANTHEUS MEDICAL IMAGING, INC.—See Avista Capital Partners, L.P.; *U.S. Private*, pg. 408
LANTIC, INC.—See Rogers Sugar Inc.; *Int'l*, pg. 6384
LANTIS CO., LTD.—See BANDAI NAMCO Holdings Inc.; *Int'l*, pg. 829
THE LANTIS EYEWEAR CORPORATION; *U.S. Private*, pg. 4067
LANTMANNEN AGROENERGI AB—See Lantmannen ek for; *Int'l*, pg. 4413
LANTMANNEN AS-FAKTOR AB—See Lantmannen ek for; *Int'l*, pg. 4413
LANTMANNEN ASPEN AB—See Lantmannen ek for; *Int'l*, pg. 4413
LANTMANNEN BIOAGRI AB—See Lantmannen ek for; *Int'l*, pg. 4414
LANTMANNEN BYGGLANT AB—See Lantmannen ek for; *Int'l*, pg. 4414
LANTMANNEN CEREALIA AB—See Lantmannen ek for; *Int'l*, pg. 4414
LANTMANNEN CEREALIA A/S—See Lantmannen ek for; *Int'l*, pg. 4414

LANTMANNEN EK FOR; *Int'l*, pg. 4413
LANTMANNEN ENERGI AB—See Lantmannen ek for; *Int'l*, pg. 4414
LANTMANNEN INVEST AB—See Lantmannen ek for; *Int'l*, pg. 4414
LANTMANNEN LANTBRUK—See Lantmannen ek for; *Int'l*, pg. 4414
LANTMANNEN MASKIN AB—See Lantmannen ek for; *Int'l*, pg. 4414
LANTMANNEN MASKINIMPORT AB—See Lantmannen ek for; *Int'l*, pg. 4414
LANTMANNEN SCHULSTAD A/S—See Lantmannen ek for; *Int'l*, pg. 4414
LANTMANNEN SOLANUM AB—See Lantmannen ek for; *Int'l*, pg. 4414
LANTMANNEN UNIBAKE GMBH & CO KG—See Lantmannen ek for; *Int'l*, pg. 4414
LANTMANNEN UNIBAKE INTERNATIONAL—See Lantmannen ek for; *Int'l*, pg. 4414
LANTMANNEN UNIBAKE RUSSIA LLC—See Lantmannen ek for; *Int'l*, pg. 4414
LANTMANNEN UNIBAKE SWEDEN AB—See Lantmannen ek for; *Int'l*, pg. 4414
LANTMANNEN UNIBAKE UK LTD—See Lantmannen ek for; *Int'l*, pg. 4414
LANTMANNEN UNIBAKE USA, INC—See Lantmannen ek for; *Int'l*, pg. 4414
LANTRO (CAMBODIA) CO., LTD.—See MIRAIT ONE Corporation; *Int'l*, pg. 4917
LANTRO (HK) LIMITED—See MIRAIT ONE Corporation; *Int'l*, pg. 4917
LANTRO (MALAYSIA) SDN BHD—See MIRAIT ONE Corporation; *Int'l*, pg. 4917
LANTRO MYANMAR CO., LTD.—See MIRAIT ONE Corporation; *Int'l*, pg. 4917
LANTRONIX HONG KONG LTD.—See Lantronix, Inc.; *U.S. Public*, pg. 1293
LANTRONIX, INC.; *U.S. Public*, pg. 1293
LANTRONIX JAPAN K.K.—See Lantronix, Inc.; *U.S. Public*, pg. 1293
LANTRONIX NETHERLANDS B.V.—See Lantronix, Inc.; *U.S. Public*, pg. 1293
LANTRO (PENANG) SDN BHD—See MIRAIT ONE Corporation; *Int'l*, pg. 4917
LANTRO (SHANGHAI) CO., LTD.—See MIRAIT ONE Corporation; *Int'l*, pg. 4917
LANTRO (S) PTE LTD—See MIRAIT ONE Corporation; *Int'l*, pg. 4917
LANTRO (TAIWAN) LTD.—See MIRAIT ONE Corporation; *Int'l*, pg. 4917
LANTRO TECHNOLOGIES INDIA PRIVATE LIMITED—See MIRAIT ONE Corporation; *Int'l*, pg. 4917
LANTROVISION KOREA CO. LTD.—See MIRAIT ONE Corporation; *Int'l*, pg. 4917
LANTROVISION (S) LTD—See MIRAIT ONE Corporation; *Int'l*, pg. 4917
LANTZ CONSTRUCTION COMPANY; *U.S. Private*, pg. 2391
LANVIN ASIA PACIFIC LTD.—See Fosun International Limited; *Int'l*, pg. 2751
LANVIN GROUP HOLDINGS LIMITED—See Fosun International Limited; *Int'l*, pg. 2751
LANVIN INC.—See Fosun International Limited; *Int'l*, pg. 2751
LANVIN JAPAN K.K.—See Fosun International Limited; *Int'l*, pg. 2751
LANWEHR ASPHALT GMBH—See Eiffage S.A.; *Int'l*, pg. 2331
LANWEHR BAU GMBH—See Eiffage S.A.; *Int'l*, pg. 2331
LANWORKS PTE LTD—See HgCapital Trust plc; *Int'l*, pg. 3377
LANXESS ACCOUNTING GMBH—See LANXESS AG; *Int'l*, pg. 4415
LANXESS ADDITIVES TAIWAN LTD.—See LANXESS AG; *Int'l*, pg. 4415
LANXESS AG; *Int'l*, pg. 4414
LANXESS BUNA GMBH—See LANXESS AG; *Int'l*, pg. 4415
LANXESS BUTYL PTE. LTD.—See LANXESS AG; *Int'l*, pg. 4415
LANXESS CANADA COMPANY—See LANXESS AG; *Int'l*, pg. 4415
LANXESS CENTRAL EASTERN EUROPE S.R.O.—See LANXESS AG; *Int'l*, pg. 4415
LANXESS (CHANGZHOU) CO., LTD.—See LANXESS AG; *Int'l*, pg. 4415
LANXESS CHEMICAL (CHINA) CO., LTD.—See LANXESS AG; *Int'l*, pg. 4415
LANXESS CHEMICAL (SHANGHAI) CO., LTD.—See LANXESS AG; *Int'l*, pg. 4415
LANXESS CHEMICALS, S.L.—See LANXESS AG; *Int'l*, pg. 4415
LANXESS CHROME MINING (PTY) LTD.—See LANXESS AG; *Int'l*, pg. 4415
LANXESS CISA (PTY) LIMITED—See Brother Enterprises Holding Co., Ltd.; *Int'l*, pg. 1196
LANXESS CISA (PTY) LTD.—See LANXESS AG; *Int'l*, pg. 4415

LANXESS CORPORATION—See LANXESS AG; *Int'l*, pg. 4415
LANXESS DEUTSCHLAND GMBH—See LANXESS AG; *Int'l*, pg. 4415
LANXESS DISTRIBUTION GMBH—See LANXESS AG; *Int'l*, pg. 4415
LANXESS FINANCE B.V.—See LANXESS AG; *Int'l*, pg. 4415
LANXESS HOLDING HISPANIA, SL—See LANXESS AG; *Int'l*, pg. 4415
LANXESS HONG KONG LIMITED—See LANXESS AG; *Int'l*, pg. 4415
LANXESS INDIA PRIVATE LIMITED—See LANXESS AG; *Int'l*, pg. 4415
LANXESS INDUSTRIA DE CHEMICALS E PLASTICOS LTDA—See LANXESS AG; *Int'l*, pg. 4415
LANXESS INDUSTRIA DE PRODUTOS QUIMICOS E PLASTICOS LTDA.—See LANXESS AG; *Int'l*, pg. 4416
LANXESS INTERNATIONAL HOLDING GMBH—See LANXESS AG; *Int'l*, pg. 4416
LANXESS INTERNATIONAL SA—See LANXESS AG; *Int'l*, pg. 4416
LANXESS K.K.—See LANXESS AG; *Int'l*, pg. 4416
LANXESS KOREA LIMITED—See LANXESS AG; *Int'l*, pg. 4416
LANXESS LIMITED—See LANXESS AG; *Int'l*, pg. 4416
LANXESS (LIYANG) POLYOLS CO., LTD.—See LANXESS AG; *Int'l*, pg. 4415
LANXESS MIDDLE EAST GMBH—See LANXESS AG; *Int'l*, pg. 4416
LANXESS MINING (PTY) LTD.—See LANXESS AG; *Int'l*, pg. 4415
LANXESS (NINGBO) PIGMENTS CO., LTD.—See LANXESS AG; *Int'l*, pg. 4415
LANXESS NV—See LANXESS AG; *Int'l*, pg. 4416
LANXESS PTE. LTD.—See LANXESS AG; *Int'l*, pg. 4416
LANXESS (PTY) LTD.—See LANXESS AG; *Int'l*, pg. 4415
LANXESS (PTY) LTD.—See LANXESS AG; *Int'l*, pg. 4415
LANXESS (PTY) LTD.—See LANXESS AG; *Int'l*, pg. 4415
LANXESS PTY. LTD.—See LANXESS AG; *Int'l*, pg. 4416
LANXESS S.A. DE C.V.—See LANXESS AG; *Int'l*, pg. 4416
LANXESS S.A.—See LANXESS AG; *Int'l*, pg. 4416
LANXESS S.A.S.—See LANXESS AG; *Int'l*, pg. 4416
LANXESS SOLUTIONS K.K.—See LANXESS AG; *Int'l*, pg. 4415
LANXESS SOLUTIONS UK LTD.—See LANXESS AG; *Int'l*, pg. 4415
LANXESS SOLUTIONS US INC.—See LANXESS AG; *Int'l*, pg. 4415
LANXESS S.R.L.—See LANXESS AG; *Int'l*, pg. 4416
LANXESS SWITZERLAND GMBH—See LANXESS AG; *Int'l*, pg. 4415
LANXESS SYBRON CHEMICALS, INC.—See LANXESS AG; *Int'l*, pg. 4415
LANXESS TAIWAN LTD.—See LANXESS AG; *Int'l*, pg. 4415
LANXESS (WUXI) HIGH PERFORMANCE COMPOSITE MATERIALS COMPANY LIMITED—See LANXESS AG; *Int'l*, pg. 4415
LANYON, INC.—See Blackstone Inc.; *U.S. Public*, pg. 353
LANYON INVESTMENT COMPANY LIMITED; *Int'l*, pg. 4416
LANYON SOLUTIONS, INC.—See Blackstone Inc.; *U.S. Public*, pg. 353
L'ANZA EP SWEDEN AB—See Storskogen Group AB; *Int'l*, pg. 7228
LANZA, S.A. DE C.V.—See Promotora de Informaciones S.A.; *Int'l*, pg. 5995
LANZATECH GLOBAL, INC.; *U.S. Public*, pg. 1293
LANZHOU CENTER STEEL STRUCTURE CO., LTD—See Center International Group Co Ltd; *Int'l*, pg. 1403
LANZHOU FOCI PHARMACEUTICAL CO., LTD.; *Int'l*, pg. 4416
LANZHOU GREATWALL ELECTRICAL CO., LTD.; *Int'l*, pg. 4416
LANZHOU GREAT WALL ELECTRICAL POWER EQUIPMENT CO., LTD.—See Lanzhou Greatwall Electrical Co., Ltd.; *Int'l*, pg. 4416
LANZHOU HAIMO ENERGY TECHNOLOGY CO., LTD.—See Haimo Technologies Group Corp.; *Int'l*, pg. 3211
LANZHOU HUANGHE ENTERPRISE CO., LTD.; *Int'l*, pg. 4416
LANZHOU LISHANG GUOCHAO INDUSTRIAL GROUP CO., LTD.; *Int'l*, pg. 4416
LANZHOU LS HEAVY EQUIPMENT CO., LTD.; *Int'l*, pg. 4416
LANZHOU MEIDONG LEXUS AUTO SALES & SERVICES CO., LTD.—See China MeiDong Auto Holdings Limited; *Int'l*, pg. 1519
LANZHOU ZHONGFU CONTAINER CO., LTD.—See Zhuhai Zhongfu Enterprise Co., Ltd.; *Int'l*, pg. 8679
LANZHOU ZHUANGYUAN PASTURE CO LTD; *Int'l*, pg. 4416
LANZO CONSTRUCTION COMPANY FLORIDA INC.—See Lanzo Construction Company, Inc.; *U.S. Private*, pg. 2391

COMPANY NAME INDEX

LANZO CONSTRUCTION COMPANY INC.; *U.S. Private*, pg. 2391
LAO AIRLINES; *Int'l*, pg. 4417
LAOBAIXING PHARMACY CHAIN JOINT STOCK COMPANY; *Int'l*, pg. 4417
LAO CAI MINERAL EXPLOITATION & PROCESSING JOINT STOCK COMPANY; *Int'l*, pg. 4417
LAO FENG XIANG CO., LTD.; *Int'l*, pg. 4417
LAO HOLDING STATE ENTERPRISE; *Int'l*, pg. 4417
LAO-JAGRO DEVELOPMENT XIENGKHOUANG CO., LTD.—See Vietnam Dairy Products Joint Stock Company; *Int'l*, pg. 8198
LAO NISHIMATSU CONSTRUCTION CO., LTD.—See Nishimatsu Construction Co., Ltd.; *Int'l*, pg. 5365
LAO NISSIN SMT CO., LTD.—See Nissin Corporation; *Int'l*, pg. 5375
LAON MEDI INC.—See Laon People Inc.; *Int'l*, pg. 4417
LAON PEOPLE INC.; *Int'l*, pg. 4417
LA OPALA RG LIMITED; *Int'l*, pg. 4388
LAO-VIET J.V. BANK—See Joint Stock Commercial Bank Investment and Development of Vietnam; *Int'l*, pg. 3995
LAOX CO., LTD.; *Int'l*, pg. 4417
LA OXIGENA PARAGUAYA S.A.—See L'Air Liquide S.A.; *Int'l*, pg. 4375
LAOX MEDIA SOLUTIONS CO., LTD.—See Laox Co., Ltd.; *Int'l*, pg. 4417
LAOX REAL ESTATE CO., LTD.—See Laox Co., Ltd.; *Int'l*, pg. 4417
LAPAK ISRAEL LTD—See ILAPAK S.A.; *Int'l*, pg. 3613
LA PALETTE ROUGE DEUTSCHLAND GMBH—See LPR Logistic Packaging Return S.A.S.; *Int'l*, pg. 4568
LA PALETTE ROUGE IBERICA SA—See LPR Logistic Packaging Return S.A.S.; *Int'l*, pg. 4568
LA PALETTE ROUGE POLAND SP. Z O.O.—See LPR Logistic Packaging Return S.A.S.; *Int'l*, pg. 4568
LA PALMA INTERCOMMUNITY HOSPITAL—See Prime Healthcare Services, Inc.; *U.S. Private*, pg. 3261
LA PALOMA TREATMENT CENTER, LLC—See Universal Health Services, Inc.; *U.S. Public*, pg. 2258
LAPARANZA, S.A.—See Banco Santander, S.A.; *Int'l*, pg. 826
LA PAZ MINING CORP.; *U.S. Private*, pg. 2369
LA PAZ REGIONAL HOSPITAL; *U.S. Private*, pg. 2369
LAPCO HOLDINGS LIMITED; *Int'l*, pg. 4417
LAPEER COUNTY PRESS—See JAMO Media LLC; *U.S. Private*, pg. 2186
LAPENSEE PLUMBING INC.; *U.S. Private*, pg. 2391
LA PERLA FASHION HOLDING N.V.—See Tennor Holding BV; *Int'l*, pg. 7561
LA PERLA GROUP FRANCE S.A.R.L.—See Tennor Holding BV; *Int'l*, pg. 7561
LA PERLA NORTH AMERICA INC.—See Tennor Holding BV; *Int'l*, pg. 7561
LAPEYRA & TALTAVULL COMERCIAL S.L.—See Windmoeller & Hoelscher KG; *Int'l*, pg. 8426
LAPEYRE SAS—See Mutares SE & Co. KGaA; *Int'l*, pg. 5105
LAPEYRE SERVICES (LGS)—See Compagnie de Saint-Gobain SA; *Int'l*, pg. 1724
LAPEYRE STAIR, INC.—See The Laitram LLC; *U.S. Private*, pg. 4067
LAPHAM DIALYSIS, LLC—See DaVita Inc.; *U.S. Public*, pg. 640
LAPHAM-HICKEY STEEL CORP. - FAIRFIELD DIVISION—See Lapham-Hickey Steel Corp.; *U.S. Private*, pg. 2391
LAPHAM-HICKEY STEEL CORP. - LITTLE CANADA DIVISION—See Lapham-Hickey Steel Corp.; *U.S. Private*, pg. 2391
LAPHAM-HICKEY STEEL CORP.—See Lapham-Hickey Steel Corp.; *U.S. Private*, pg. 2391
LAPHAM-HICKEY STEEL CORP.; *U.S. Private*, pg. 2391
LAPHAM-HICKEY STEEL CORP—See Lapham-Hickey Steel Corp.; *U.S. Private*, pg. 2391
LAPHAM HICKEY STEEL (WI)—See Lapham-Hickey Steel Corp.; *U.S. Private*, pg. 2391
LAPIDOTH CAPITAL LTD.; *Int'l*, pg. 4417
LAPIDOTH HELETZ LP—See Lapidoth Capital Ltd.; *Int'l*, pg. 4417
LA PIE QUI CHANTE SA—See Mondelez International, Inc.; *U.S. Public*, pg. 1461
LAPINE CO., LTD.; *Int'l*, pg. 4417
LAPINE TRUCK SALES & EQUIPMENT CO. INC.; *U.S. Private*, pg. 2391
LAPIN KANSA OY—See Alma Media Corporation; *Int'l*, pg. 362
LAPINUS FIBRES B.V.—See ROCKWOOL A/S; *Int'l*, pg. 6381
LAPISNET CO., LTD.—See MIRAIT ONE Corporation; *Int'l*, pg. 4917
LAPIS SOFTWARE ASSOCIATES LLC—See Light & Wonder, Inc.; *U.S. Public*, pg. 1314
LAPIZ—See Publicis Groupe S.A.; *Int'l*, pg. 6100
LA PIZZA LOCA, INC.—See Meruelo Group LLC; *U.S. Private*, pg. 2677
LAP KEI ENGINEERING (HOLDINGS) LIMITED; *Int'l*, pg. 4417
LAPKER ZRT.—See Vivendi SE; *Int'l*, pg. 8276
LAPLACA COHEN; *U.S. Private*, pg. 2391

LA PLACE B.V.—See Jumbo Supermarkten B.V.; *Int'l*, pg. 4026
LAPLAND CAR TEST AKTIEBOLAG—See Mercedes-Benz Group AG; *Int'l*, pg. 4825
LAPLANTE CADILLAC CHEVROLET BUICK GMC LTD.—See General Motors Company; *U.S. Public*, pg. 926
LAPLANTE CHEVROLET PONTIAC BUICK GMC LTD; *Int'l*, pg. 4417
LA PLATA ELECTRIC ASSOCIATION; *U.S. Private*, pg. 2369
LA PLATEFORME DU BATIMENT—See Compagnie de Saint-Gobain SA; *Int'l*, pg. 1724
LAPLING ELECTRONICS CO., LTD.—See Ligitek Electronics Co., Ltd.; *Int'l*, pg. 4497
LAPLINK SOFTWARE, INC.; *U.S. Private*, pg. 2391
LAPMASTER GROUP HOLDINGS LLC—See Angeles Equity Partners, LLC; *U.S. Private*, pg. 282
LAPMASTER GROUP HOLDINGS LLC—See Bison Capital Asset Management, LLC; *U.S. Private*, pg. 566
LAPMASTER INDIA PRIVATE LIMITED—See Angeles Equity Partners, LLC; *U.S. Private*, pg. 282
LAPMASTER INDIA PRIVATE LIMITED—See Bison Capital Asset Management, LLC; *U.S. Private*, pg. 566
LAPMASTER WOLTERS GMBH—See Angeles Equity Partners, LLC; *U.S. Private*, pg. 282
LAPMASTER WOLTERS GMBH—See Bison Capital Asset Management, LLC; *U.S. Private*, pg. 566
LAPMASTER WOLTERS LIMITED—See Angeles Equity Partners, LLC; *U.S. Private*, pg. 282
LAPMASTER WOLTERS LIMITED—See Bison Capital Asset Management, LLC; *U.S. Private*, pg. 566
LAPMASTER WOLTERS LLC—See Angeles Equity Partners, LLC; *U.S. Private*, pg. 282
LAPMASTER WOLTERS LLC—See Bison Capital Asset Management, LLC; *U.S. Private*, pg. 566
LAP OF LOVE, INC.; *U.S. Private*, pg. 2391
LAPOLLA INDUSTRIES, INC.—See Huntsman Corporation; *U.S. Public*, pg. 1075
LAPORTE CUSTOM METAL PROCESSING, LLC—See Acerinox, S.A.; *Int'l*, pg. 101
LAPORTE HERALD ARGUS—See Paxton Media Group LLC; *U.S. Private*, pg. 3116
LA PORTE MEDICAL CENTER LLC—See Adeptus Health Inc.; *U.S. Private*, pg. 78
LAPORTE MEDICAL GROUP SURGICAL CENTER, LLC—See Community Health Systems, Inc.; *U.S. Public*, pg. 554
LA POSITIVA SEGUROS; *Int'l*, pg. 4388
LA POSTE S.A.; *Int'l*, pg. 4388
LA POSTE TELECOM—See Tofane Global SAS; *Int'l*, pg. 7774
LAPOUYADE—See Blackstone Inc.; *U.S. Public*, pg. 348
LAPPEENRANNAN VILLIMIEHEN VITONEN OY—See Citycon Oyj; *Int'l*, pg. 1629
L'APPEL MEDICAL—See Randstad N.V.; *Int'l*, pg. 6202
LAPPEN AUTO SUPPLY CO. INC.; *U.S. Private*, pg. 2391
LAPPERRE BHAC N.V.—See Sonova Holding AG; *Int'l*, pg. 7100
LAPPIN ELECTRIC COMPANY—See Blackfriars Corp.; *U.S. Private*, pg. 574
LAPP INSULATOR COMPANY, LLC; *U.S. Private*, pg. 2391
LAPPLAND GOLDMINERS AB; *Int'l*, pg. 4417
LAPPLAND GOLDMINERS OY—See Lappland Goldminers AB; *Int'l*, pg. 4417
LA PRAIRIE GROUP DEUTSCHLAND GMBH—See maxingvest ag; *Int'l*, pg. 4741
LA PRAIRIE GROUP FRANCE S.A.S.—See maxingvest ag; *Int'l*, pg. 4741
LA PRAIRIE GROUP IBERIA S.A.U.—See maxingvest ag; *Int'l*, pg. 4741
LA PRAIRIE GROUP (RUS) LLC—See maxingvest ag; *Int'l*, pg. 4741
LA PRAIRIE HONG KONG LIMITED—See maxingvest ag; *Int'l*, pg. 4741
LA PRAIRIE, INC.—See maxingvest ag; *Int'l*, pg. 4739
LA PRAIRIE JAPAN K.K.—See maxingvest ag; *Int'l*, pg. 4741
LA PRAIRIE KOREA LTD—See maxingvest ag; *Int'l*, pg. 4741
LA PRAIRIE MIDDLE EAST—See maxingvest ag; *Int'l*, pg. 4741
LA PRAIRIE (SHANGHAI) CO. LTD.—See maxingvest ag; *Int'l*, pg. 4741
LA PRAIRIE (UK) LIMITED—See maxingvest ag; *Int'l*, pg. 4741
LA PREFERIDA, INC.; *U.S. Private*, pg. 2369
LA PRENSA LIBRE—See Wehco Media, Inc.; *U.S. Private*, pg. 4470
LA PRIMA CATERING; *U.S. Private*, pg. 2369
LAPTV LLC—See The Walt Disney Company; *U.S. Public*, pg. 2140
LA PUENTE HIGHLANDER—See Alden Global Capital LLC; *U.S. Private*, pg. 158
LA RABIDA CHILDREN'S HOSPITAL; *U.S. Private*, pg. 2369
LA RADIO, LLC—See Cumulus Media Inc.; *U.S. Public*, pg. 610

LARA EXPLORATION LTD.; *Int'l*, pg. 4417
LARAGEN INCORPORATED—See Thompson Street Capital Manager LLC; *U.S. Private*, pg. 4161
LARAIB ENERGY LIMITED—See The Hub Power Company Limited; *Int'l*, pg. 7653
THE LARAMAR GROUP, LLC; *U.S. Private*, pg. 4067
LARAMIDE RESOURCES LTD.; *Int'l*, pg. 4417
LARAMIE ENERGY, LLC—See Par Pacific Holdings, Inc.; *U.S. Public*, pg. 1636
LARAMIE ENTERPRISES, INC.; *U.S. Private*, pg. 2391
LA RANCHERA INC.; *U.S. Private*, pg. 2369
LARA STEFANEL SAS—See Stefanel S.p.A.; *Int'l*, pg. 7192
LA RATIONNELLE NETTOYAGE INDUSTRIEL; *Int'l*, pg. 4388
L'ARCHE GREEN N.V.; *Int'l*, pg. 4376
L'ARCHEVEQUE & RIVEST LIMITED; *Int'l*, pg. 4377
LARCO ENTERPRISES INC.; *U.S. Private*, pg. 2391
LARCOM INSURANCE, LTD.—See Valaris Limited; *Int'l*, pg. 8110
LARD OIL CO. INC.; *U.S. Private*, pg. 2391
LARD OIL COMPANY OF ACADIANA—See Lard Oil Co. Inc.; *U.S. Private*, pg. 2391
LARD OIL COMPANY—See Lard Oil Co. Inc.; *U.S. Private*, pg. 2391
LARDOSA INVESTMENTS BV—See Israel Aerospace Industries Ltd.; *Int'l*, pg. 3822
LAREAU INSURANCE BROKERS; *Int'l*, pg. 4418
LA RECETTA SOLUCIONES GASTRONOMICAS INTEGRADAS S.A.S.—See Grupo Nutresa S.A.; *Int'l*, pg. 3133
LAREDO ALARM SYSTEMS INC.; *U.S. Private*, pg. 2392
THE LAREDO COCA-COLA BOTTLING COMPANY, INC.—See The Coca-Cola Company; *U.S. Public*, pg. 2065
LAREDO FED JV1, LLC—See Universal Health Services, Inc.; *U.S. Public*, pg. 2258
LAREDO GONZALEZ AUTO PARTS; *U.S. Private*, pg. 2392
LAREDO MIDSTREAM SERVICES, LLC—See Vital Energy, Inc.; *U.S. Public*, pg. 2306
LAREDO MORNING TIMES—See The Hearst Corporation; *U.S. Private*, pg. 4047
LAREDO OIL, INC.; *U.S. Public*, pg. 1293
LAREDO OUTLET SHOPPES, LLC—See CBL & Associates Properties, Inc.; *U.S. Public*, pg. 458
LAREDO PAVING INC.; *U.S. Private*, pg. 2392
LAREDO REGIONAL MEDICAL CENTER, L.P.—See Universal Health Services, Inc.; *U.S. Public*, pg. 2258
LAREDO RIDGE WIND, LLC—See BlackRock, Inc.; *U.S. Public*, pg. 345
LA REDOUTE CATALOG BENELUX—See Galeries Lafayette SA; *Int'l*, pg. 2872
LA REDOUTE PORTUGAL—See Galeries Lafayette SA; *Int'l*, pg. 2872
LA REDOUTE SA—See Galeries Lafayette SA; *Int'l*, pg. 2872
LA REDOUTE SUISSE SA—See Galeries Lafayette SA; *Int'l*, pg. 2872
LA REFINERIA DOMINICANA DE PETROLEO, S.A.—See Shell plc; *Int'l*, pg. 6797
LA REGALE LLC; *U.S. Private*, pg. 2369
LA REGINA DI SAN MARZANO USA; *U.S. Private*, pg. 2369
LA REINA COMPANY; *U.S. Private*, pg. 2369
LA REINE BLANCHE SAS—See VINCI S.A.; *Int'l*, pg. 8223
L'ARENA DES CANADIENS, INC.—See Club de hockey Canadien, Inc.; *Int'l*, pg. 1664
LAR ESPANA REAL ESTATE SOCIMI, S.A.; *Int'l*, pg. 4417
LARGA KITIKMEOT LTD.—See Nunasi Corporation; *Int'l*, pg. 5489
LARGAN (DONGGUAN) OPTRONIC LTD.—See Largan Precision Co., Ltd.; *Int'l*, pg. 4418
LARGAN HEALTH AI-TECH CO., LTD.—See Largan Precision Co., Ltd.; *Int'l*, pg. 4418
LARGAN INDUSTRIAL OPTICS CO., LTD.—See Largan Precision Co., Ltd.; *Int'l*, pg. 4418
LARGAN MEDICAL CO., LTD.—See Largan Precision Co., Ltd.; *Int'l*, pg. 4418
LARGAN PRECISION CO., LTD.; *Int'l*, pg. 4418
LARGO CONCRETE INC.; *U.S. Private*, pg. 2392
LARGO ENDOSCOPY CENTER, L.P.—See Bain Capital, LP; *U.S. Public*, pg. 445
LARGO INC.; *Int'l*, pg. 4418
LARGO LEASING GESELLSCHAFT M.B.H.—See Uni-Credit S.p.A.; *Int'l*, pg. 8035
LARGO MEDICAL CENTER-INDIAN ROCKS RD. CAMPUS—See Largo Medical Center; *U.S. Private*, pg. 2392
LARGO MEDICAL CENTER; *U.S. Private*, pg. 2392
LARGO PHYSICIAN GROUP, LLC—See HCA Healthcare, Inc.; *U.S. Public*, pg. 1000
LARGO SA; *Int'l*, pg. 4418
LARGO SURGERY, LLC—See Bain Capital, LP; *U.S. Private*, pg. 445
LARIAT PARTNERS LP; *U.S. Private*, pg. 2392
LARIAT SERVICES, INC.—See SandRidge Energy, Inc.; *U.S. Public*, pg. 1839

LARIMAR THERAPEUTICS, INC.　　　　　　　　　　　　　　　　　　　　　　　　　　　　　　　　CORPORATE AFFILIATIONS

LARIMAR THERAPEUTICS, INC.; *U.S. Public*, pg. 1293
LARIMART SPA—See Leonardo S.p.A.; *Int'l*, pg. 4460
LA RINASCENTE S.R.L.—See Investitori Associati Societa di Gestione del Risparmio (SGR) S.p.A.; *Int'l*, pg. 3780
LARIO OIL & GAS COMPANY - DENVER DIVISION—See O's Companies Inc.; *U.S. Private*, pg. 2980
LARIO OIL & GAS COMPANY—See O's Companies Inc.; *U.S. Private*, pg. 2980
LARIS MEDIA ACQUISITION CORP.; *U.S. Public*, pg. 1293
LARITECH INC.; *U.S. Private*, pg. 2392
LARIVIERE SAS—See SIG plc; *Int'l*, pg. 6906
LARIX AS—See Alten S.A.; *Int'l*, pg. 390
LARIX SWEDEN AB—See Alten S.A.; *Int'l*, pg. 390
LARK AVE CAR WASH CORPORATION; *U.S. Private*, pg. 2392
LARK DISTILLING CO., LTD.; *Int'l*, pg. 4418
LARKEN INC.; *U.S. Private*, pg. 2392
LARKIN CHASE CENTER—See Formation Capital, LLC; *U.S. Private*, pg. 1571
L.A.R.K. INDUSTRIES, INC.—See Littlejohn & Co., LLC; *U.S. Private*, pg. 2470
L.A.R.K. INDUSTRIES, INC.—See Platinum Equity, LLC; *U.S. Private*, pg. 3205
LARKIN ENTERPRISES, INC.; *U.S. Private*, pg. 2392
LARKIN ERVIN & SHIRLEY, LLP—See Calvetti Ferguson, P.C.; *U.S. Private*, pg. 724
LARKIN INGRASSIA, PLLC; *U.S. Private*, pg. 2392
LARK.PL S.A.; *Int'l*, pg. 4418
LARKSPUR RESTAURANT & BAR, LLC—See Vail Resorts, Inc.; *U.S. Public*, pg. 2271
LARM & TELETEKNIK I MOTALA AB—See Instalco AB; *Int'l*, pg. 3722
LARNACA ZENON FLOURMILLS LTD—See Mitsides Public Company Ltd; *Int'l*, pg. 4928
LAROCCO ENTERPRISES INC.; *U.S. Private*, pg. 2392
LA ROCHE CHEVROLET-OLDSMOBILE-CADILLAC, INC.; *U.S. Private*, pg. 2369
LA ROCHE-POSAY LABORATOIRE PHARMACEUTIQUE—See L'Oreal S.A.; *Int'l*, pg. 4380
LAROHN INC.; *U.S. Private*, pg. 2392
LARON, INC.—See Genstar Capital, LLC; *U.S. Private*, pg. 1678
LAROSA BUILDING GROUP LLC; *U.S. Private*, pg. 2392
LA ROSA DEL MONTE EXPRESS INC.; *U.S. Private*, pg. 2369
LA ROSA HOLDINGS CORP.; *U.S. Private*, pg. 2369
LA ROSA'S, INC.; *U.S. Private*, pg. 2369
LAROSA TORTILLA FACTORY; *U.S. Private*, pg. 2392
LAROUSSE EDITORIAL S.L.—See Vivendi SE; *Int'l*, pg. 8273
LAROUSSE—See Vivendi SE; *Int'l*, pg. 8273
LAROX INDIA PRIVATE LTD.—See Metso Oyj; *Int'l*, pg. 4865
LARQ SA; *Int'l*, pg. 4418
LARRAIN VIAL S.A. CORREDORA DE BOLSA—See Larrain Vial SpA; *Int'l*, pg. 4418
LARRAIN VIAL SPA; *Int'l*, pg. 4418
LARROC LTD.; *U.S. Private*, pg. 2392
LARRY BLUMBERG & ASSOCIATES; *U.S. Private*, pg. 2392
LARRY C. MCCRAE INC.; *U.S. Private*, pg. 2392
LARRY FANNIN CHEVROLET-PONTIAC-BUICK; *U.S. Private*, pg. 2392
LARRY FU INSURANCE AGENCY INC—See Inszone Insurance Services, LLC; *U.S. Private*, pg. 2096
LARRY H. MILLER FORD MESA—See Larry H. Miller Group of Companies; *U.S. Private*, pg. 2392
LARRY H. MILLER GROUP DEALERSHIPS—See Larry H. Miller Group of Companies; *U.S. Private*, pg. 2392
LARRY H. MILLER GROUP OF COMPANIES; *U.S. Private*, pg. 2392
LARRY H. MILLER HONDA—See Larry H. Miller Group of Companies; *U.S. Private*, pg. 2393
LARRY H. MILLER SPORTS & ENTERTAINMENT GROUP OF COMPANIES—See Larry H. Miller Group of Companies; *U.S. Private*, pg. 2393
LARRY H. MILLER VOLKSWAGEN LAKEWOOD—See Larry H. Miller Group of Companies; *U.S. Private*, pg. 2393
LARRY HUDSON CHEVROLET BUICK GMC INC.; *Int'l*, pg. 4418
LARRY JEWELRY INTERNATIONAL COMPANY LIMITED; *Int'l*, pg. 4418
LARRY J. OVERTON & ASSOCIATES INC.; *U.S. Private*, pg. 2393
LARRY KLINE WHOLESALE MEATS, INC.; *U.S. Private*, pg. 2393
LARRY L. ROTHCHILD'S—See S. Rothschild & Co., Inc.; *U.S. Private*, pg. 3515
LARRY MACDONALD CHEVROLET BUICK GMC LTD.; *Int'l*, pg. 4418
LARRY MATHIS FINANCIAL PLANNING, LLC; *U.S. Private*, pg. 2393
LARRY METHVIN INSTALLATION; *U.S. Private*, pg. 2393
LARRY MILLER SUNDANCE DODGE; *U.S. Private*, pg. 2393
LARRY PEEL & CO., INC.; *U.S. Private*, pg. 2393

LARRY REID'S BLOOMINGTON CHRYSLER JEEP DODGE RAM; *U.S. Private*, pg. 2393
LARRY RENAUD FORD & R.V. SALES; *Int'l*, pg. 4418
LARRY'S MARKET, INC.; *U.S. Private*, pg. 2393
LARRY'S MARKETS, INC.; *U.S. Private*, pg. 2393
LARRY'S MINING, INC.; *U.S. Private*, pg. 2393
LARRY SNYDER & CO.; *U.S. Private*, pg. 2393
LARS & ASSOCIATES; *U.S. Private*, pg. 2393
LARSEN COOPERATIVE CO.—See CHS INC.; *U.S. Public*, pg. 492
LARSEN MARINE SERVICE INC.; *U.S. Private*, pg. 2393
LARSENS CREAMERY INC.; *U.S. Private*, pg. 2393
LARSEN & SHAW LIMITED; *Int'l*, pg. 4418
LARSEN; *U.S. Private*, pg. 2393
LARSEN—See Larsen; *U.S. Private*, pg. 2393
LARSEN SUPPLY COMPANY INC.; *U.S. Private*, pg. 2393
LARSEN & TOUBRO (EAST ASIA) SDN BHD—See Larsen & Toubro Limited; *Int'l*, pg. 4419
LARSEN & TOUBRO ELECTROMECH LLC—See Larsen & Toubro Limited; *Int'l*, pg. 4419
LARSEN & TOUBRO INFOTECH CANADA LIMITED—See Larsen & Toubro Limited; *Int'l*, pg. 4419
LARSEN & TOUBRO INTERNATIONAL FZE—See Larsen & Toubro Limited; *Int'l*, pg. 4419
LARSEN & TOUBRO KUWAIT CONSTRUCTION GENERAL CONTRACTING COMPANY WLL—See Larsen & Toubro Limited; *Int'l*, pg. 4419
LARSEN & TOUBRO LIMITED; *Int'l*, pg. 4418
LARSEN & TOUBRO (QINGDAO) RUBBER MACHINERY COMPANY LIMITED—See Larsen & Toubro Limited; *Int'l*, pg. 4419
LARSEN & TOUBRO (WUXI) ELECTRIC COMPANY LIMITED—See Larsen & Toubro Limited; *Int'l*, pg. 4419
LARS LARSEN GROUP; *Int'l*, pg. 4418
LARSON BOATS LLC—See Polaris, Inc.; *U.S. Public*, pg. 1700
LARSON CABLE TRAILERS, INC.—See Felling Trailers, Inc.; *U.S. Private*, pg. 1494
LARSON CONTRACTING CENTRAL, LLC; *U.S. Private*, pg. 2393
LARSON DAIRY INC.; *U.S. Private*, pg. 2393
LARSON-DANIELSON CONSTRUCTION COMPANY, INC.; *U.S. Private*, pg. 2394
LARSON DESIGN GROUP - APALACHIN—See Larson Design Group; *U.S. Private*, pg. 2394
LARSON DESIGN GROUP—See Larson Design Group; *U.S. Private*, pg. 2394
LARSON DESIGN GROUP—See Larson Design Group; *U.S. Private*, pg. 2394
LARSON DESIGN GROUP—See Larson Design Group; *U.S. Private*, pg. 2394
LARSON DESIGN GROUP; *U.S. Private*, pg. 2393
LARSON DESIGN GROUP—See Larson Design Group; *U.S. Private*, pg. 2394
LARSON DESIGN GROUP—See Larson Design Group; *U.S. Private*, pg. 2394
LARSON DESIGN GROUP—See Larson Design Group; *U.S. Private*, pg. 2394
LARSON DESIGN GROUP—See Larson Design Group; *U.S. Private*, pg. 2394
LARSON FINANCIAL GROUP, LLC—See Larson Financial Holdings, LLC; *U.S. Private*, pg. 2394
LARSON FINANCIAL HOLDINGS, LLC; *U.S. Private*, pg. 2394
LARSON FINANCIAL SECURITIES, LLC—See Larson Financial Holdings, LLC; *U.S. Private*, pg. 2394
LARSON FINANCIAL SERVICES, INC.; *U.S. Private*, pg. 2394
THE LARSON GROUP, INC.; *U.S. Private*, pg. 4067
THE LARSON GROUP; *U.S. Private*, pg. 4067
LARSON IMPLEMENT INC.—See Minnesota Ag Group Inc.; *U.S. Private*, pg. 2743
LARSON, INCORPORATED—See Paschal Home Services, LLC; *U.S. Private*, pg. 3104
LARSON-JUHL US LLC—See Berkshire Hathaway Inc.; *U.S. Public*, pg. 298
LARSON MANAGEMENT, INC.; *U.S. Private*, pg. 2394
LARSON MANUFACTURING COMPANY, INC—See Fortune Brands Innovations, Inc.; *U.S. Public*, pg. 873
LARSON PACKAGING COMPANY, LLC; *U.S. Private*, pg. 2394
LARSONS APPLIANCE COMPANY; *U.S. Private*, pg. 2394
LARSON WEALTH PARTNERS, LLC—See Larson Financial Holdings, LLC; *U.S. Private*, pg. 2394
LARSTAN INDUSTRIES, INC.—See Banks Bros. Corporation; *U.S. Private*, pg. 468
L'ARTISAN PARFUMEUR S.A.—See Paine Schwartz Partners, LLC; *U.S. Private*, pg. 3076
L'ARTISAN PARFUMEUR USA—See Paine Schwartz Partners, LLC; *U.S. Private*, pg. 3076
LARTOM INC.; *U.S. Private*, pg. 2394
LARUE DISTRIBUTING COMPANY; *U.S. Private*, pg. 2394
LARU GMBH—See Darling Ingredients Inc.; *U.S. Public*, pg. 634
LA RURAL S.A. DE SEGUROS—See Tokio Marine Holdings, Inc.; *Int'l*, pg. 7782
LARUS ENERGY LIMITED; *Int'l*, pg. 4420
LARUSSO CONCRETE COMPANY INC.; *U.S. Private*, pg. 2394

LARVOTTO RESOURCES LIMITED; *Int'l*, pg. 4420
LARZEP, S.A.—See Enerpac Tool Group Corp.; *U.S. Public*, pg. 766
LARZUL SA—See Floridienne SA; *Int'l*, pg. 2708
LASACO ASSURANCE PLC; *Int'l*, pg. 4420
LASACO PROPERTIES LTD.—See LASACO Assurance Plc; *Int'l*, pg. 4420
LASACO TRADING AND INVESTMENT LTD.—See LASACO Assurance Plc; *Int'l*, pg. 4420
LASALLE AMBULANCE, INC.—See KKR & Co. Inc.; *U.S. Public*, pg. 1249
LASALLE BANCORP, INC.; *U.S. Private*, pg. 2394
LASALLE BRISTOL CORP.—See ASSA ABLOY AB; *Int'l*, pg. 639
LASALLE CAPITAL GROUP PARTNERS, LLC—See LSCG Management, Inc.; *U.S. Private*, pg. 2508
LASALLE EXPLORATION CORP.—See Harfang Exploration Inc.; *Int'l*, pg. 3274
LASALLE FUNDS MANAGEMENT LIMITED—See Jones Lang LaSalle Incorporated; *U.S. Public*, pg. 1203
LASALLE GMBH—See Jones Lang LaSalle Incorporated; *U.S. Public*, pg. 1205
LASALLE HOTEL PROPERTIES—See Pebblebrook Hotel Trust; *U.S. Public*, pg. 1660
LASALLE INTERNATIONAL PARTNER; *U.S. Private*, pg. 2394
LASALLE INVESTMENT (LUXEMBOURG) SARL—See Jones Lang LaSalle Incorporated; *U.S. Public*, pg. 1204
LASALLE INVESTMENT MANAGEMENT ASIA PTE LTD—See Jones Lang LaSalle Incorporated; *U.S. Public*, pg. 1203
LASALLE INVESTMENT MANAGEMENT AUSTRALIA PTY LTD—See Jones Lang LaSalle Incorporated; *U.S. Public*, pg. 1205
LASALLE INVESTMENT MANAGEMENT BV—See Jones Lang LaSalle Incorporated; *U.S. Public*, pg. 1203
LASALLE INVESTMENT MANAGEMENT BV—See Jones Lang LaSalle Incorporated; *U.S. Public*, pg. 1203
LASALLE INVESTMENT MANAGEMENT (CANADA)—See Jones Lang LaSalle Incorporated; *U.S. Public*, pg. 1203
LASALLE INVESTMENT MANAGEMENT CO., LTD.—See Jones Lang LaSalle Incorporated; *U.S. Public*, pg. 1205
LASALLE INVESTMENT MANAGEMENT ESPANA, S.L.U.—See Jones Lang LaSalle Incorporated; *U.S. Public*, pg. 1203
LASALLE INVESTMENT MANAGEMENT HONG KONG LIMITED—See Jones Lang LaSalle Incorporated; *U.S. Public*, pg. 1205
LASALLE INVESTMENT MANAGEMENT, INC.—See Jones Lang LaSalle Incorporated; *U.S. Public*, pg. 1204
LASALLE INVESTMENT MANAGEMENT LUXEMBOURG SARL—See Jones Lang LaSalle Incorporated; *U.S. Public*, pg. 1204
LASALLE INVESTMENT MANAGEMENT S.A.S.—See Jones Lang LaSalle Incorporated; *U.S. Public*, pg. 1203
LASALLE INVESTMENT MANAGEMENT SECURITIES, LLC—See Jones Lang LaSalle Incorporated; *U.S. Public*, pg. 1204
LASALLE INVESTMENT MANAGEMENT (SHANGHAI) CO., LTD.—See Jones Lang LaSalle Incorporated; *U.S. Public*, pg. 1205
LASALLE INVESTMENT MANAGEMENT—See Jones Lang LaSalle Incorporated; *U.S. Public*, pg. 1203
LASALLE LOGIPORT REIT; *Int'l*, pg. 4420
THE LASALLE NETWORK; *U.S. Private*, pg. 4067
LASALLE PARTNERS, S. DE R.L. DE C.V.—See Jones Lang LaSalle Incorporated; *U.S. Public*, pg. 1205
LASALLE REIT ADVISORS K.K.—See Jones Lang LaSalle Incorporated; *U.S. Public*, pg. 1205
LA SALLE STREET SECURITIES; *U.S. Private*, pg. 2369
LASALLE SYSTEMS LEASING, INC.—See American Securities LLC; *U.S. Private*, pg. 250
LASALLE VENTURES ONE LTD.—See Lasalle International Partner; *U.S. Private*, pg. 2395
LASALLE WASHINGTON ONE LESSEE, INC.—See Pebblebrook Hotel Trust; *U.S. Public*, pg. 1660
LA SALSA, INC.—See Fresh Enterprises, LLC; *U.S. Private*, pg. 1609
LA SALTENA S.A.—See Molinos Rio de la Plata S.A.; *Int'l*, pg. 5022
LA SAMANNA S.A.S.—See LVMH Moet Hennessy Louis Vuitton SE; *Int'l*, pg. 4591
LA SAN MARCO S.P.A.—See Segafredo Zanetti S.p.A.; *Int'l*, pg. 6682
LASANTE CO., LTD.—See EM Systems Co., Ltd.; *Int'l*, pg. 2372
LASA PROSPECCOES SA—See CGG; *Int'l*, pg. 1432
LASA SCHIENENTECHNIK GMBH—See voestalpine AG; *Int'l*, pg. 8290
LASA SUPERGENERICS LIMITED; *Int'l*, pg. 4420
LA SAVOISIENNE DE CD—See Compagnie de Saint-Gobain SA; *Int'l*, pg. 1724
LA SAVONNERIE DE NYONS S.A.; *Int'l*, pg. 4389
LASCAD S.N.C.—See L'Oreal S.A.; *Int'l*, pg. 4380

COMPANY NAME INDEX

LAS-CAL CORPORATION; *U.S. Private*, pg. 2394
LASCARIS & SONS INC.; *U.S. Private*, pg. 2395
LASCHINGER SEAFOOD GMBH—See Mowi ASA; *Int'l*, pg. 5058
LASCO COMPOSITES, LP—See Crane NXT, Co.; *U.S. Public*, pg. 590
LASCO CONSTRUCTION, INC.; *U.S. Private*, pg. 2395
LASCO ENTERPRISES; *U.S. Private*, pg. 2395
LASCO FITTINGS INC.—See Aalberts N.V.; *Int'l*, pg. 35
LAS COLINAS SURGERY CENTER, LTD.—See HCA Healthcare, Inc.; *U.S. Public*, pg. 1000
LASCO MANUFACTURING LIMITED; *Int'l*, pg. 4420
LASCOM SA; *Int'l*, pg. 4420
LASCOM SOLUTIONS, INC.—See Lascom SA; *Int'l*, pg. 4420
LASCOR S.P.A.—See The Swatch Group Ltd.; *Int'l*, pg. 7691
LAS CRUCES AUTOMOTIVE GROUP, INC.—See General Motors Company; *U.S. Public*, pg. 926
LAS CRUCES MEDICAL CENTER, LLC—See Community Health Systems, Inc.; *U.S. Public*, pg. 554
LAS CRUCES PHYSICIAN SERVICES, LLC—See Community Health Systems, Inc.; *U.S. Public*, pg. 554
LAS CRUCES SUN-NEWS—See Gannett Co., Inc.; *U.S. Public*, pg. 899
LAS CRUCES SURGERY CENTER - TELSHOR, LLC—See Community Health Systems, Inc.; *U.S. Public*, pg. 554
LA SEDA DE BARCELONA, S.A.; *Int'l*, pg. 4389
LA SEGUNDA S.A.—See Asociacion de Cooperativas Argentinas C.L.; *Int'l*, pg. 628
LASELEC SA—See Komax Holding AG; *Int'l*, pg. 4240
LAS ENCINAS HOSPITAL—See HCA Healthcare, Inc.; *U.S. Public*, pg. 1000
LAS ENCINAS HOSPITAL—See HCA Healthcare, Inc.; *U.S. Public*, pg. 1000
LA SENZA CORPORATION—See Regent, L.P.; *U.S. Private*, pg. 3388
LASEPARTNER A/S—See ASSA ABLOY AB; *Int'l*, pg. 640
LASER 2000 GMBH—See Gimv NV; *Int'l*, pg. 2976
LASERAGE TECHNOLOGY CORP.—See AMETEK, Inc.; *U.S. Public*, pg. 120
LASER AND OUTPATIENT SURGERY CENTER, LLC—See Bain Capital, LP; *U.S. Private*, pg. 445
LASER APP SOFTWARE, INC.—See Roper Technologies, Inc.; *U.S. Public*, pg. 1812
LASERBOND LIMITED; *Int'l*, pg. 4420
LASERCARD CORPORATION—See ASSA ABLOY AB; *Int'l*, pg. 637
LASER CARGO S.R.L.—See LATAM Airlines Group S.A.; *Int'l*, pg. 4422
LASER CONTROL SYSTEMS LIMITED.—See FARO Technologies, Inc.; *U.S. Public*, pg. 823
LASERCUT INC.—See El.En. S.p.A.; *Int'l*, pg. 2342
LASERCYCLE USA, INC.; *U.S. Private*, pg. 2395
LASER DESIGN, INC.—See Nordson Corporation; *U.S. Public*, pg. 1532
LASER DIAGNOSTIC TECHNOLOGIES—See Carl-Zeiss-Stiftung; *Int'l*, pg. 1334
LASERDONTICS LIMITED—See Human Health Holdings Limited; *Int'l*, pg. 3529
LASER DYNAMICS AUSTRALIA PTY LTD.—See BlueScope Steel Limited; *Int'l*, pg. 1073
LASER ENERGETICS, INC.; *U.S. Public*, pg. 1293
LA-SER EUROPE LIMITED; *Int'l*, pg. 4389
LASER EXCEL, INC.; *U.S. Private*, pg. 2395
LASERFLASH S.A.—See ArcelorMittal S.A.; *Int'l*, pg. 546
LASERFLEX CORPORATION—See Ryerson Holding Corporation; *U.S. Public*, pg. 1829
LASERGEN, INC.—See Agilent Technologies, Inc.; *U.S. Public*, pg. 62
LASER IMAGE CORPORATION—See Didit.com, Inc.; *U.S. Private*, pg. 1228
LASER IMAGE PLUS IMAGING PRODUCTS, INC.—See Magnum Print Solutions, Inc.; *U.S. Private*, pg. 2549
LASER IMAGING SYSTEMS GMBH & CO. KG—See KLA Corporation; *U.S. Public*, pg. 1268
LASER INFOMEDIA LTD.—See CDI International Limited; *Int'l*, pg. 1371
LASER LIGHT TECHNOLOGIES, LLC—See DuPont de Nemours, Inc.; *U.S. Public*, pg. 694
LASERLINE GMBH—See CEWE Stiftung & Co. KGaA; *Int'l*, pg. 1425
LASERLINE SAFETY AND SECURITY SYSTEMS S.R.L.; *Int'l*, pg. 4420
LASERMASTER INTERNATIONAL; *U.S. Public*, pg. 1294
LASERMICRONICS GMBH—See LPKF Laser & Electronics AG; *Int'l*, pg. 4568
LASEROP LTD.—See AEM Holdings Ltd.; *Int'l*, pg. 175
LASER-PACIFIC MEDIA CORPORATION—See Eastman Kodak Company; *U.S. Public*, pg. 708
LASERPERFORMANCE (EUROPE) LIMITED—See Full Moon Holdings Limited; *Int'l*, pg. 2842
LASER PHOTONICS CORPORATION; *U.S. Public*, pg. 1294
LASER POLSKA—See BNP Paribas SA; *Int'l*, pg. 1091
LASER POLSKA—See Galeries Lafayette SA; *Int'l*, pg. 2872
LASER PRINT PLUS, INC.—See GI Manager L.P.; *U.S. Private*, pg. 1692
LASER PROJECTION TECHNOLOGIES, INC.—See FARO Technologies, Inc.; *U.S. Public*, pg. 823
LASER PROS INTERNATIONAL CORP.; *U.S. Private*, pg. 2395
LASER QUANTUM GMBH—See Novanta Inc.; *U.S. Public*, pg. 1548
LASER QUANTUM LIMITED—See Novanta Inc.; *U.S. Public*, pg. 1548
LA SERRANA S.A.—See Arcor Sociedad Anonima, Industrial y Comercial; *Int'l*, pg. 550
LASER REPRODUCTIONS INC.—See Trilantic Capital Management L.P.; *U.S. Private*, pg. 4231
LASER SALES INC.; *Int'l*, pg. 4420
LASER SPECIALTIES, INC.—See Lorraine Capital LLC; *U.S. Private*, pg. 2496
LASER SPECTRA SERVICES INDIA PVT. LTD.—See HORIBA Ltd; *Int'l*, pg. 3477
LASER SPINE INSTITUTE, LLC; *U.S. Private*, pg. 2395
LASERSSEL CO., LTD.; *Int'l*, pg. 4420
LASER SYSTEMS, INC.—See Loffler Companies, Inc.; *U.S. Private*, pg. 2480
LASER SYSTEMS & SOLUTIONS OF EUROPE SASU—See Screen Holdings Co., Ltd.; *Int'l*, pg. 6656
LASERTEC CORPORATION; *Int'l*, pg. 4420
LASER TECHNOLOGY, INC.; *U.S. Private*, pg. 2395
LASERTEC, INC.; *U.S. Private*, pg. 2395
LASERTEC KOREA CORPORATION—See Lasertec Corporation; *Int'l*, pg. 4420
LASERTEC TAIWAN INC.—See Lasertec Corporation; *Int'l*, pg. 4420
LASERTEC U.S.A., INC.—See Lasertec Corporation; *Int'l*, pg. 4420
LASER TEK (KUNSHAN) CO., LTD.—See Laser Tek Taiwan Co., Ltd.; *Int'l*, pg. 4420
LASERTEK SINGAPORE PTE. LTD.—See Laser Tek Taiwan Co., Ltd.; *Int'l*, pg. 4420
LASER TEK TAIWAN CO., LTD.; *Int'l*, pg. 4420
LASER VENTURES, INC.—See Altaris Capital Partners, LLC; *U.S. Private*, pg. 206
L & A SERVICES PTY LIMITED—See Sonic Healthcare Limited; *Int'l*, pg. 7097
LASGO CHRYSALIS—See Bertelsmann SE & Co. KGaA; *Int'l*, pg. 990
LASHBACK, LLC—See PerformLine Inc.; *U.S. Private*, pg. 3150
LASH EXCAVATING & PAVING; *U.S. Private*, pg. 2395
THE LASH GROUP, INC.—See Cencora, Inc.; *U.S. Public*, pg. 467
LA SIA S.P.A.; *Int'l*, pg. 4389
LASIK GERMANY GMBH—See EuroEyes International Eye Clinic Limited; *Int'l*, pg. 2535
THE LASIK SURGERY CLINIC PTE. LTD.—See Singapore Medical Group Limited; *Int'l*, pg. 6941
THE LASIK VISION INSTITUTE, LLC; *U.S. Private*, pg. 4067
LASINGOO NORGE AS—See MEKO AB; *Int'l*, pg. 4805
LASITER CONSTRUCTION INC.; *U.S. Private*, pg. 2395
LASIT LASER DEUTSCHLAND GMBH—See El.En. S.p.A.; *Int'l*, pg. 2342
LASIT LASER IBERICA, S.L.—See El.En. S.p.A.; *Int'l*, pg. 2342
LASIT LASER POLSKA SP. Z O.O.—See El.En. S.p.A.; *Int'l*, pg. 2342
LASIT LASER UK LTD.—See El.En. S.p.A.; *Int'l*, pg. 2342
LASIT SPA—See El.En. S.p.A.; *Int'l*, pg. 2342
LASIT USA INC.—See El.En. S.p.A.; *Int'l*, pg. 2342
LASKO PRODUCTS, LLC; *U.S. Private*, pg. 2395
LA SOCIETE DE PROMOTION DE LA POINTE SIMON ET SES ENVIRONS—See Guardian Holdings Limited; *Int'l*, pg. 3171
LA SOCIETE DES BINGOS DU QUEBEC, INC.—See Loto-Quebec; *Int'l*, pg. 4559
LA SOCIETE DES CASINOS DU QUEBEC, INC.—See Loto-Quebec; *Int'l*, pg. 4559
LA SOCIETE DES LOTERIES VIDEO DU QUEBEC, INC.—See Loto-Quebec; *Int'l*, pg. 4559
LA SOCIETE NOUVELLE D'HLM DE MARSEILLE; *Int'l*, pg. 4389
LA SOCIETE STEPHANOISE DES EAUX—See Veolia Environnement S.A.; *Int'l*, pg. 8155
LAS OLAS DE SEQUOIA, LLC—See DaVita Inc.; *U.S. Public*, pg. 640
LASONIC ELECTRONICS CORPORATION; *U.S. Private*, pg. 2395
LAS PALMAS DEL SOL HEALTHCARE—See HCA Healthcare, Inc.; *U.S. Public*, pg. 1000
LAS PALMAS DEL SOL URGENT CARE, PLLC—See HCA Healthcare, Inc.; *U.S. Public*, pg. 1000
LA SPEZIA CONTAINER TERMINAL S.P.A.—See EUROKAI GmbH & Co. KGaA; *Int'l*, pg. 2553
LAS PIEDRAS CONSTRUCTION CORP.; *U.S. Private*, pg. 2394
LASSE HOLST AS—See AF Gruppen ASA; *Int'l*, pg. 184
LASSELSBERGER A.S.—See Lasselsberger GmbH; *Int'l*, pg. 4420
LASSELSBERGER GMBH; *Int'l*, pg. 4420

LAS VEGAS BOAT HARBOR INC.

LASSELSBERGER HUNGARIA KFT.—See Lasselsberger GmbH; *Int'l*, pg. 4420
LASSELSBERGER ITALY S.R.L.—See Lasselsberger GmbH; *Int'l*, pg. 4420
LASSELSBERGER-KNAUF D.O.O.—See Lasselsberger GmbH; *Int'l*, pg. 4421
LASSELSBERGER-KNAUF KFT.—See Gebr. Knauf KG; *Int'l*, pg. 2908
LASSELSBERGER-KNAUF S.R.L.—See Lasselsberger GmbH; *Int'l*, pg. 4421
LASSELSBERGER, S.R.O.—See Lasselsberger GmbH; *Int'l*, pg. 4421
LASSEN DIALYSIS, LLC—See DaVita Inc.; *U.S. Public*, pg. 640
LASSEN TOUR & TRAVEL, INC.—See JTB Corp.; *Int'l*, pg. 4015
LAS SERENAS SENIOR APARTMENTS LP—See Berkshire Hathaway Inc.; *U.S. Public*, pg. 298
LASSERVICE AS; *Int'l*, pg. 4421
LASSETER IMPLEMENT COMPANY, LLC—See Lasseter Tractor Co.; *U.S. Private*, pg. 2395
LASSETERS HEALTH CLUB PTY. LTD.—See Lasseters International Holdings Limited; *Int'l*, pg. 4421
LASSETERS INTERNATIONAL HOLDINGS LIMITED; *Int'l*, pg. 4421
LASSETER TRACTOR CO., INC.; *U.S. Private*, pg. 2395
LASSIE B.V.—See Ebro Foods S.A.; *Int'l*, pg. 2286
LASSILA & TIKANOJA PLC; *Int'l*, pg. 4421
LASSILA & TIKANOJA SERVICE AB—See Lassila & Tikanoja plc; *Int'l*, pg. 4421
LASSITER-WARE INC.; *U.S. Private*, pg. 2395
LASSO MARKETING, INC.—See IQVIA Holdings Inc.; *U.S. Public*, pg. 1169
LASSONDE BEVERAGES CANADA—See Lassonde Industries, Inc.; *Int'l*, pg. 4421
LASSONDE INDUSTRIES, INC.; *Int'l*, pg. 4421
LASSONDE PAPPAS & CO., INC.—See Lassonde Industries, Inc.; *Int'l*, pg. 4421
LASSONDE SPECIALITIES INC.—See Lassonde Industries, Inc.; *Int'l*, pg. 4421
LASSONDE WESTERN CANADA—See Lassonde Industries, Inc.; *Int'l*, pg. 4421
LASSUS BROS. OIL INC.; *U.S. Private*, pg. 2395
LASSUS WHERLEY & ASSOCIATES, P.C.—See Peapack-Gladstone Financial Corporation; *U.S. Public*, pg. 1659
LASTA A.D.; *Int'l*, pg. 4422
L.A. STEELCRAFT PRODUCTS CO.—See Hindman Manufacturing Co.; *U.S. Private*, pg. 1948
LASTENSUOJELUYKSIKKO LEPPALINTU OY—See Humana AB; *Int'l*, pg. 3530
LASTENSUOJELUYKSIKKO PIHAKOIVU OY—See Humana AB; *Int'l*, pg. 3530
THE LASTER GROUP; *U.S. Private*, pg. 4068
LASTER TECH AUTOMOTIVE (SHANGHAI) CO., LTD.—See Laster Tech Co., Ltd.; *Int'l*, pg. 4422
LASTER TECH CO., LTD.; *Int'l*, pg. 4422
LASTER TECH ELECTRONICS (DONGGUAN) CO., LTD.—See Laster Tech Co., Ltd.; *Int'l*, pg. 4422
LASTER TECH OPTO (JIAYUGUAN) CO., LTD.—See Laster Tech Co., Ltd.; *Int'l*, pg. 4422
LASTER TECH OPTO (SHENZHEN) CO., LTD.—See Laster Tech Co., Ltd.; *Int'l*, pg. 4422
LASTER TECH (THAILAND) CO., LTD.—See Laster Tech Co., Ltd.; *Int'l*, pg. 4422
LASTING IMPRESSIONS FOOD CO., LTD.—See DO & CO Aktiengesellschaft; *Int'l*, pg. 2152
LASTING IMPRESSIONS INC.; *U.S. Private*, pg. 2395
LAST LAP S.L.—See RCS MediaGroup S.p.A.; *Int'l*, pg. 6230
LASTLINE G.K.—See Dell Technologies Inc.; *U.S. Public*, pg. 651
LASTLINE INC.; *U.S. Private*, pg. 2395
LAST MILE ENTERPRISES LTD.; *Int'l*, pg. 4422
LASTMINUTE.COM.AU PTY. LIMITED—See Expedia Group, Inc.; *U.S. Public*, pg. 810
LAST ONE MILE CO., LTD.—See Vector Inc.; *Int'l*, pg. 8144
LASTRA ATTREZZATURE S.R.L.—See Agfa-Gevaert N.V.; *Int'l*, pg. 209
LA SUISSE ASSURANCES (FRANCE)—See Swiss Life Holding; *Int'l*, pg. 7368
LA SUISSE ASSURANCES IARD (FRANCE)—See Swiss Life Holding; *Int'l*, pg. 7368
LA SUISSE ASSURANCES-VIE (FRANCE)—See Swiss Life Holding; *Int'l*, pg. 7368
LA SUISSE WATCH COMPANY LIMITED—See Oriental Watch Holdings Limited; *Int'l*, pg. 5627
LA SUPPLY CO.; *U.S. Private*, pg. 2369
LAS VEGAS AIR CONDITIONING, INC.—See Baum Capital Partners Management LLC; *U.S. Private*, pg. 490
LAS VEGAS AMERICA CORP.—See Ark Restaurants Corp.; *U.S. Public*, pg. 193
LAS VEGAS ARENA MANAGEMENT, LLC—See MGM Resorts International; *U.S. Public*, pg. 1435
LAS VEGAS BOAT HARBOR INC.; *U.S. Private*, pg. 2394
THE LAS VEGAS EAST OPHTHALMOLOGY ASC, LLC—See KKR & Co. Inc.; *U.S. Public*, pg. 1247
LAS VEGAS FESTIVAL FOOD CORP.—See Ark Restaurants Corp.; *U.S. Public*, pg. 193

LAS VEGAS BOAT HARBOR INC.   CORPORATE AFFILIATIONS

THE LAS VEGAS GOLDEN KNIGHTS—See Black Knight Sports & Entertainment LLC; *U.S. Private*, pg. 572
LAS VEGAS HEALTHCARE AND REHABILITATION CENTER—See Apollo Global Management, Inc.; *U.S. Public*, pg. 157
LAS VEGAS MAGAZINE—See The Greenspun Corporation; *U.S. Private*, pg. 4039
LAS VEGAS MEDICAL GROUP, LLC—See Universal Health Services, Inc.; *U.S. Public*, pg. 2258
LAS VEGAS MOTOR SPEEDWAY—See Sonic Financial Corporation; *U.S. Private*, pg. 3713
LAS VEGAS MUTUAL TRADING CO., INC.—See Takara Holdings, Inc.; *Int'l*, pg. 7433
THE LAS VEGAS PALM—See Palm Restaurant Group; *U.S. Private*, pg. 3080
LAS VEGAS PEDIATRIC DIALYSIS, LLC—See DaVita Inc.; *U.S. Public*, pg. 640
LAS VEGAS POLICE PROTECTIVE ASSOCIATION CIVILIAN EMPLOYEES, INC.; *U.S. Private*, pg. 2394
LAS VEGAS ROOFING SUPPLY, LLC—See Beacon Roofing Supply, Inc.; *U.S. Public*, pg. 286
LAS VEGAS SANDS CORP.; *U.S. Public*, pg. 1293
LAS VEGAS SANDS, LLC—See Las Vegas Sands Corp.; *U.S. Public*, pg. 1293
LAS VEGAS SOLARI HOSPICE CARE, LLC—See DaVita Inc.; *U.S. Public*, pg. 640
LAS VEGAS SUN, INC.—See The Greenspun Corporation; *U.S. Private*, pg. 4039
LAS VEGAS SUNSET PROPERTIES—See Western Alliance Bancorporation; *U.S. Public*, pg. 2354
LAS VEGAS SURGERY CENTER—See HCA Healthcare, Inc.; *U.S. Public*, pg. 1000
LAS VEGAS VALLEY WATER DISTRICT; *U.S. Private*, pg. 2394
LAS VEGAS VENICE DELI CORP.—See Ark Restaurants Corp.; *U.S. Public*, pg. 193
LAS VEGAS WEEKLY—See The Greenspun Corporation; *U.S. Private*, pg. 4039
LAS VENTANAS AL PARAISO—See JTL Capital, LLC; *U.S. Private*, pg. 2242
LAS YARETAS S.A.—See McEwen Mining Inc.; *Int'l*, pg. 4758
LATA ENVIRONMENTAL SERVICES OF KENTUCKY, LLC—See Los Alamos Technical Associates, Inc.; *U.S. Private*, pg. 2496
LATA-KEMRON REMEDIATION, LLC—See Los Alamos Technical Associates, Inc.; *U.S. Private*, pg. 2496
LATAM AIRLINES GROUP S.A.; *Int'l*, pg. 4422
LATAM AUTOS LIMITED; *Int'l*, pg. 4422
LATA-MERRICK ENGINEERING & ENVIRONMENT, LLC—See Los Alamos Technical Associates, Inc.; *U.S. Private*, pg. 2496
LATAM EXCHANGES DATA INC.—See SIX Group AG; *Int'l*, pg. 6966
LA TAPATIA - NORCAL, INC.; *U.S. Private*, pg. 2369
L.A.T APPAREL, LLC; *U.S. Private*, pg. 2364
LATA-SHARP REMEDIATION SERVICES, LLC—See Los Alamos Technical Associates, Inc.; *U.S. Private*, pg. 2496
LATAS INDUSTRIA DE EMBALAGENS DE ALUMINIO DE BRASIL LTDA.—See Ball Corporation; *U.S. Public*, pg. 267
LATCHA+ASSOCIATES; *U.S. Private*, pg. 2396
LATCH, INC.; *U.S. Public*, pg. 1294
LATCHWAYS PLC—See MSA Safety Incorporated; *U.S. Public*, pg. 1481
LAT CO., LTD.; *Int'l*, pg. 4422
LATECIS CANADA INC.—See Searchlight Capital Partners, L.P.; *U.S. Private*, pg. 3588
LATECIS UK LIMITED—See Searchlight Capital Partners, L.P.; *U.S. Private*, pg. 3588
LATECOERE INC.—See Searchlight Capital Partners, L.P.; *U.S. Private*, pg. 3588
LATECOERE SA—See Searchlight Capital Partners, L.P.; *U.S. Private*, pg. 3588
LATECOERE SERVICES GMBH—See Searchlight Capital Partners, L.P.; *U.S. Private*, pg. 3588
LATE JULY SNACKS LLC; *U.S. Private*, pg. 2396
LATELEC—See Searchlight Capital Partners, L.P.; *U.S. Private*, pg. 3588
LATENT LIGHT FINANCE LIMITED; *Int'l*, pg. 4422
LATENT VIEW ANALYTICS B.V.—See Latent View Analytics Limited; *Int'l*, pg. 4422
LATENT VIEW ANALYTICS CORPORATION—See Latent View Analytics Limited; *Int'l*, pg. 4422
LATENT VIEW ANALYTICS GMBH—See Latent View Analytics Limited; *Int'l*, pg. 4422
LATENT VIEW ANALYTICS LIMITED; *Int'l*, pg. 4422
LATENT VIEW ANALYTICS PTE. LTD.—See Latent View Analytics Limited; *Int'l*, pg. 4422
LATENT VIEW ANALYTICS UK LIMITED—See Latent View Analytics Limited; *Int'l*, pg. 4422
LATE ROOMS LIMITED—See Rest Easy Group Ltd.; *Int'l*, pg. 6303
LA TERRA FINA, INC.; *U.S. Private*, pg. 2369
LATEX CONSTRUCTION COMPANY; *U.S. Private*, pg. 2396
LATEXX MANUFACTURING SDN. BHD.—See Semperit AG Holding; *Int'l*, pg. 6706

LATEXX PARTNERS BERHAD—See Semperit AG Holding; *Int'l*, pg. 6706
LATFOOD A/S—See Orkla ASA; *Int'l*, pg. 5638
LATHAM FORD-F, LLC—See Lithia Motors, Inc.; *U.S. Public*, pg. 1323
LATHAM GROUP, INC.; *U.S. Public*, pg. 1294
LATHAM HI-TECH HYBRIDS, INC.; *U.S. Private*, pg. 2396
LATHAM MOTORS INC.; *U.S. Private*, pg. 2396
LATHAM POOL PRODUCTS, INC.—See Pamplona Capital Management LLP; *Int'l*, pg. 5711
LATHAMS LIMITED—See James Latham Plc; *Int'l*, pg. 3878
LATHAMS LTD—See James Latham Plc; *Int'l*, pg. 3878
LATHAM & WATKINS LLP; *U.S. Public*, pg. 2396
LATHIAN SYSTEMS, INC.—See D&R Lathian LLC; *U.S. Private*, pg. 1138
THE LATHROP COMPANY, INC.—See ACS, Actividades de Construccion y Servicios, S.A.; *Int'l*, pg. 113
LATHROP DIALYSIS, LLC—See DaVita Inc.; *U.S. Public*, pg. 640
LATHROP ENGINEERING, INC.—See Tecan Group AG; *Int'l*, pg. 7501
LATHROP & GAGE LLP; *U.S. Private*, pg. 2396
LATHROP-TROTTER CO, INC.—See Koch Enterprises, Inc.; *U.S. Private*, pg. 2326
LATICINIOS CAROLINA LTDA—See General Mills, Inc.; *U.S. Public*, pg. 922
LATICRETE INTERNATIONAL, INC.; *U.S. Private*, pg. 2396
LA TIENDA FOODS INC.; *U.S. Private*, pg. 2370
LATI FRANCE S.A.S.—See Lati Industria Termoplastici S.p.A.; *Int'l*, pg. 4422
LATI IBERICA, S.L. UNIPERSONAL—See Lati Industria Termoplastici S.p.A.; *Int'l*, pg. 4423
LATI INDUSTRIA TERMOPLASTICI DEUTSCHLAND GMBH—See Lati Industria Termoplastici S.p.A.; *Int'l*, pg. 4423
LATI INDUSTRIA TERMOPLASTICI S.p.A.; *Int'l*, pg. 4422
LATIMER GROUP LIMITED—See Post Holdings, Inc.; *U.S. Public*, pg. 1703
LA TIM METAL & INDUSTRIES LIMITED; *Int'l*, pg. 4389
LATINA MEDIA VENTURES, LLC; *U.S. Private*, pg. 2397
LATIN AMERICAN AGRIBUSINESS DEVELOPMENT CORPORATION; *U.S. Private*, pg. 2397
LATIN-AMERICAN HOLDINGS CORPORATION—See Koninklijke Philips N.V.; *Int'l*, pg. 4268
LATIN AMERICAN INVESTMENT BANK BAHAMAS LIMITED—See Citigroup Inc.; *U.S. Public*, pg. 504
LATIN AMERICAN NAUTILUS PERU S.A.—See TIM S.p.A.; *Int'l*, pg. 7750
LATIN AMERICAN NAUTILUS USA INC.—See TIM S.p.A.; *Int'l*, pg. 7750
LATIN AMERICAN YOUTH CENTER INC.; *U.S. Private*, pg. 2397
LATINA NIAGARA IMPORTING CO.; *U.S. Private*, pg. 2397
LATIN CONNECTION—See Hanson Watson Associates; *U.S. Private*, pg. 1857
LATIN ENERGY ARGENTINA—See BP plc; *Int'l*, pg. 1131
LATINEX HOLDINGS, INC.; *Int'l*, pg. 4423
LATIN METALS INC.; *Int'l*, pg. 4423
LATINOAMERICANA DE GESTION HOTELERA, S.L.—See Minor International PCL; *Int'l*, pg. 4911
LATIN PERCUSSION INC.; *U.S. Private*, pg. 2397
LATIN RESOURCES LIMITED; *Int'l*, pg. 4423
LATIN UNUM AMERICA HOLDINGS—See Unum Group; *U.S. Public*, pg. 2263
LATINWAM TRADING, S DE RL DE CV—See WAM-GROUP S.p.A.; *Int'l*, pg. 8339
LATINWORKS MARKETING, INC.—See Omnicom Group Inc.; *U.S. Public*, pg. 1588
LATIN WORLD ENTERTAINMENT AGENCY; *U.S. Private*, pg. 2397
LATISYS-ASHBURN, LLC—See DigitalBridge Group, Inc.; *U.S. Public*, pg. 665
LATISYS-ASHBURN, LLC—See EQT AB; *Int'l*, pg. 2481
LATISYS-CHICAGO, LLC—See DigitalBridge Group, Inc.; *U.S. Public*, pg. 665
LATISYS-CHICAGO, LLC—See EQT AB; *Int'l*, pg. 2481
LATI THERMOPLASTICS DO BRASIL LTDA—See Lati Industria Termoplastici S.p.A.; *Int'l*, pg. 4423
LATITUDE 25 OY—See NoHo Partners Plc; *Int'l*, pg. 5400
LATITUDE 34 TECHNOLOGIES, LLC—See Team Solutions Group, Inc.; *U.S. Private*, pg. 3950
LATITUDE 360, INC.; *U.S. Private*, pg. 2397
LATITUDE 36, INC.—See DBAY Advisors Limited; *Int'l*, pg. 1987
LATITUDE BEVERAGE COMPANY; *U.S. Private*, pg. 2397
LATITUDE GROUP HOLDINGS LIMITED; *Int'l*, pg. 4423
LATITUDE MANAGEMENT REAL ESTATE INVESTORS, INC.—See Jones Lang LaSalle Incorporated; *U.S. Public*, pg. 1204
LATITUDEPAY AUSTRALIA PTY. LTD.—See Latitude Group Holdings Limited; *Int'l*, pg. 4423
LATITUDEPAY MALAYSIA SDN. BHD.—See Latitude Group Holdings Limited; *Int'l*, pg. 4423
LATITUDEPAY SINGAPORE PTE. LTD.—See Latitude Group Holdings Limited; *Int'l*, pg. 4423

LATITUDE—See The Richards Group, Inc.; *U.S. Private*, pg. 4107
LATITUDE TREE FURNITURE SDN BHD—See Rhong Khen International Berhad; *Int'l*, pg. 6327
LATITUDE TREE VIETNAM JSC—See Rhong Khen International Berhad; *Int'l*, pg. 6327
LATI UK LIMITED—See Lati Industria Termoplastici S.p.A.; *Int'l*, pg. 4423
LATI U.S.A., INC.—See Lati Industria Termoplastici S.p.A.; *Int'l*, pg. 4423
LATOFF WAINER & COMPANY; *U.S. Private*, pg. 2397
LA TOQUE ANGEVINE S.A.S.—See LDC SA; *Int'l*, pg. 4431
LATORRA, PAUL & McCANN; *U.S. Private*, pg. 2397
LATO SUPPLY CORPORATION; *U.S. Private*, pg. 2397
LA TOUCHE BOND SOLON TRAINING LIMITED—See Wilmington plc; *Int'l*, pg. 8422
LATOUR CAPITAL MANAGEMENT SAS; *Int'l*, pg. 4423
LATOUR FUTURE SOLUTIONS AB—See Investment AB Latour; *Int'l*, pg. 3781
LATOUR-GRUPPEN AB—See Investment AB Latour; *Int'l*, pg. 3781
LATOUR INDUSTRIES AB—See Investment AB Latour; *Int'l*, pg. 3782
LA TOURISM & CONVENTION BOARD; *U.S. Private*, pg. 2370
LA TOURS, INC.—See Mitsui Fudosan Co., Ltd.; *Int'l*, pg. 4986
LAT PURSER & ASSOCIATES, INC.; *U.S. Private*, pg. 2395
LATROBE DIALYSIS, LLC—See DaVita Inc.; *U.S. Public*, pg. 640
LATROBE MAGNESIUM LIMITED; *Int'l*, pg. 4423
LATROBE PALLET, INC.; *U.S. Private*, pg. 2397
LATROBE POWER PARTNERSHIP—See ENGIE SA; *Int'l*, pg. 2432
LATROBE SPECIALTY METALS COMPANY, LLC—See Carpenter Technology Corporation; *U.S. Public*, pg. 439
LATROBE SPECIALTY STEEL COMPANY DISTRIBUTION—See Carpenter Technology Corporation; *U.S. Public*, pg. 439
LATROBE VALLEY BV—See Snowy Hydro Limited; *Int'l*, pg. 7028
LATROBE VALLEY FUNERAL SERVICES PTY LTD—See Propel Funeral Partners Limited; *Int'l*, pg. 5997
LATSHAW DRILLING AND EXPLORATION COMPANY; *U.S. Private*, pg. 2397
LATSIN SIA—See Kinnevik AB; *Int'l*, pg. 4181
LATTEC I/S—See Foss A/S; *Int'l*, pg. 2749
LATTER & BLUM, INC.—See Compass, Inc.; *U.S. Public*, pg. 561
LATTER & BLUM OF TEXAS, LLC—See Compass, Inc.; *U.S. Public*, pg. 561
LATTEYS INDUSTRIES LTD.; *Int'l*, pg. 4423
LATTICE BIOLOGICS LTD.; *U.S. Public*, pg. 1294
LATTICE ENGINES, INC.—See Cannae Holdings, Inc.; *U.S. Public*, pg. 430
LATTICE ENGINES, INC.—See CC Capital Partners, LLC; *U.S. Private*, pg. 798
LATTICE ENGINES, INC.—See Intercontinental Exchange, Inc.; *U.S. Public*, pg. 1142
LATTICE INC.; *U.S. Public*, pg. 1294
LATTICE SEMICONDUCTEURS SARL—See Lattice Semiconductor Corporation; *U.S. Public*, pg. 1294
LATTICE SEMICONDUCTOR CORPORATION; *U.S. Public*, pg. 1294
LATTICE SEMICONDUCTOR GMBH—See Lattice Semiconductor Corporation; *U.S. Public*, pg. 1294
LATTICE SEMICONDUCTOR JAPAN KK—See Lattice Semiconductor Corporation; *U.S. Public*, pg. 1294
LATTICE SEMICONDUCTOR K.K.—See Lattice Semiconductor Corporation; *U.S. Public*, pg. 1294
LATTICE SEMICONDUCTOR (PH) CORPORATION—See Lattice Semiconductor Corporation; *U.S. Public*, pg. 1294
LATTICE SEMICONDUCTOR (SHANGHAI) CO., LTD.—See Lattice Semiconductor Corporation; *U.S. Public*, pg. 1294
LATTICE SEMICONDUCTOR S.R.L.—See Lattice Semiconductor Corporation; *U.S. Public*, pg. 1294
LATTICE SEMICONDUCTOR UK LIMITED—See Lattice Semiconductor Corporation; *U.S. Public*, pg. 1294
LATTICE SG PTE. LTD.—See Lattice Semiconductor Corporation; *U.S. Public*, pg. 1294
LATTICE STRATEGIES LLC—See The Hartford Financial Services Group, Inc.; *U.S. Public*, pg. 2088
LATTIMORE MATERIALS COMPANY, L.P.—See Holcim Ltd.; *Int'l*, pg. 3446
LATTKLINKERBETONG AB—See Peab AB; *Int'l*, pg. 5772
LATT MAXCY CORPORATION; *U.S. Private*, pg. 2397
LATTNER ENTERTAINMENT GROUP ILLINOIS, LLC—See Boyd Gaming Corporation; *U.S. Public*, pg. 377
L'ATTRAIT ASIA (THAILAND) CO., LTD.—See L'attrait Co., Ltd.; *Int'l*, pg. 4378
L'ATTRAIT CO., LTD.; *Int'l*, pg. 4378
LATTY 2RS GMBH—See Latty International S. A.; *Int'l*, pg. 4423

COMPANY NAME INDEX

LATTY ARGENTINA S.A.—See Latty International S. A.; *Int'l*, pg. 4423
LATTY DICHTUNGSTECHNIK AG—See Latty International S. A.; *Int'l*, pg. 4423
LATTY IBERICA S.L.—See Latty International S. A.; *Int'l*, pg. 4423
LATTY INTERNATIONAL S. A.; *Int'l*, pg. 4423
LATTY MAROC TECHNISEALS SARL—See Latty International S. A.; *Int'l*, pg. 4423
LATTY SOUTH AFRICA LTD—See Latty International S. A.; *Int'l*, pg. 4423
L.A. TURBINE—See Chart Industries, Inc.; *U.S. Public*, pg. 482
LATUR RENEWABLE PRIVATE LIMITED—See Torrent Power Limited; *Int'l*, pg. 7831
LATVIAN FOREST CO AB; *Int'l*, pg. 4423
LATVIAN NEWS SERVICE SIA; *Int'l*, pg. 4423
LATVIAN SNACKS SIA—See PepsiCo, Inc.; *U.S. Public*, pg. 1669
LATVIJAS ENERGOCELTNIEKS SIA; *Int'l*, pg. 4423
LATVIJAS JURAS MEDICINAS CENTRS; *Int'l*, pg. 4423
LATVIJAS VALSTS RADIO UN TELEVIZIJAS CENTRS; *Int'l*, pg. 4423
LAU ASSOCIATES LLC—See Bryn Mawr Bank Corporation; *U.S. Public*, pg. 408
LAUBERGE NEWCO, LLC—See IMH Financial Corporation; *U.S. Private*, pg. 2047
LAUBER IWISA AG—See Poenina Holding AG; *Int'l*, pg. 5903
LAUBEUF SAS—See CRH plc; *Int'l*, pg. 1844
LAUCEL; *Int'l*, pg. 4424
LAUDA AMERICA LATINA C.A.—See Lauda Dr. R. Wobser GmbH & Co. KG; *Int'l*, pg. 4424
LAUDA-BRINKMANN, LP—See Lauda Dr. R. Wobser GmbH & Co. KG; *Int'l*, pg. 4424
LAUDA CHINA CO., LTD.—See Lauda Dr. R. Wobser GmbH & Co. KG; *Int'l*, pg. 4424
LAUDA DR. R. WOBSER GMBH & CO. KG; *Int'l*, pg. 4424
LAUDA FRANCE S.A.R.L.—See Lauda Dr. R. Wobser GmbH & Co. KG; *Int'l*, pg. 4424
LAUDA ITALIA S.R.L.—See Lauda Dr. R. Wobser GmbH & Co. KG; *Int'l*, pg. 4424
LAUDA-NOAH, LP—See Lauda Dr. R. Wobser GmbH & Co. KG; *Int'l*, pg. 4424
LAUDA PRODUCTION CHINA CO., LTD.—See Lauda Dr. R. Wobser GmbH & Co. KG; *Int'l*, pg. 4424
LAUDA SINGAPORE PTE. LTD.—See Lauda Dr. R. Wobser GmbH & Co. KG; *Int'l*, pg. 4424
LAUDA TECHNOLOGY LTD.—See Lauda Dr. R. Wobser GmbH & Co. KG; *Int'l*, pg. 4424
LAUDA ULTRACOOL S.L.—See Lauda Dr. R. Wobser GmbH & Co. KG; *Int'l*, pg. 4424
LAUD COLLIER & COMPANY, LLC; *U.S. Private*, pg. 2397
LAUDERDALE-MIAMI AUTO AUCTION INC.—See Cox Enterprises, Inc.; *U.S. Private*, pg. 1076
LAUDY BOUW & ONTWIKKELING B.V.—See Ronesans Holding A.S.; *Int'l*, pg. 6396
THE LAUERER MARKIN GROUP, INC.; *U.S. Private*, pg. 4068
LAUER-FISCHER GMBH—See CompuGroup Medical SE & Co. KGaA; *Int'l*, pg. 1757
LAUFER GROUP INTERNATIONAL LTD.; *U.S. Private*, pg. 2397
LAUGHERY VALLEY AG CO-OP, INC.; *U.S. Private*, pg. 2397
LAUGHING SAMURAI; *U.S. Private*, pg. 2397
LAUGHLIN/CONSTABLE, INC.; *U.S. Private*, pg. 2398
LAUGHLIN/CONSTABLE, INC.—See Laughlin/Constable, Inc.; *U.S. Private*, pg. 2398
LAUGHLIN/CONSTABLE NEW YORK—See Laughlin/Constable, Inc.; *U.S. Private*, pg. 2398
LAUGHLIN MEMORIAL HOSPITAL—See Mountain States Health Alliance; *U.S. Private*, pg. 2800
LAUGHLIN OIL COMPANY; *U.S. Private*, pg. 2397
LAU INDUSTRIES—See Canada Pension Plan Investment Board; *Int'l*, pg. 1281
LAUING HEATEC CO., LTD.—See Bilfinger SE; *Int'l*, pg. 1028
LAUMA LINGERIE AS—See Silvano Fashion Group AS; *Int'l*, pg. 6922
LAUNCH AGENCY; *U.S. Private*, pg. 2398
LAUNCH CREATIVE MARKETING; *U.S. Private*, pg. 2398
LAUNCH DIAGNOSTICS LIMITED—See Avacta Group plc; *Int'l*, pg. 733
LAUNCH DIGITAL MARKETING LLC—See Cars.com Inc.; *U.S. Public*, pg. 444
LAUNCHEQUITY PARTNERS, LLC; *U.S. Private*, pg. 2398
LAUNCH EUROPE GMBH—See Launch Tech Company Limited; *Int'l*, pg. 4424
LAUNCHFAX.COM INC.; *U.S. Private*, pg. 2398
THE LAUNCH GROUP; *Int'l*, pg. 7664
LAUNCH IBERICA S.L.—See Launch Tech Company Limited; *Int'l*, pg. 4424
LAUNCH ITALY GMBH—See Launch Tech Company Limited; *Int'l*, pg. 4424
LAUNCHPAD ADVERTISING LLC; *U.S. Private*, pg. 2398

LAUNCHPAD HOME GROUP—See RFE Investment Partners; *U.S. Private*, pg. 3419
LAUNCH PAD MARKETING CORPORATION; *Int'l*, pg. 4424
LAUNCHPAD; *U.S. Private*, pg. 2398
LAUNCHROCK, INC.—See Fundable LLC; *U.S. Private*, pg. 1622
LAUNCH; *U.S. Private*, pg. 2398
LAUNCH TECH COMPANY LIMITED - SHANGHAI FACTORY—See Launch Tech Company Limited; *Int'l*, pg. 4424
LAUNCH TECH COMPANY LIMITED; *Int'l*, pg. 4424
LAUNCH TECH INTERNATIONAL CO., LTD.—See Launch Tech Company Limited; *Int'l*, pg. 4424
LAUNCH TECH JAPAN INC—See Launch Tech Company Limited; *Int'l*, pg. 4424
LAUNCH TECH (M) SDN. BHD.—See Launch Tech Company Limited; *Int'l*, pg. 4424
LAUNCH TECHNICAL WORKFORCE SOLUTIONS, LLC—See The Argentum Group; *U.S. Private*, pg. 3988
LAUNCH TECHNOLOGIES CO., LTD.—See Advanced International Multitech Co., Ltd.; *Int'l*, pg. 160
LAUNCH TECHNOLOGIES SA (PTY) LTD—See Launch Tech Company Limited; *Int'l*, pg. 4424
LAUNCH TECH PTY. LTD—See Launch Tech Company Limited; *Int'l*, pg. 4424
LAUNCH TECH UK LIMITED—See Launch Tech Company Limited; *Int'l*, pg. 4424
LAUNCH TECH USA (CANADA) INC.—See Launch Tech Company Limited; *Int'l*, pg. 4424
LAUNCH TECH (USA) INC—See Launch Tech Company Limited; *Int'l*, pg. 4424
LAUNDRIMATE SERVICE LIMITED—See ISP Holdings Limited; *Int'l*, pg. 3821
LAUNDRY LOCKER INC.—See Mulberrys, LLC; *U.S. Private*, pg. 2811
LAUNDRYLUX INC.; *U.S. Private*, pg. 2398
LAUNDRY PRO OF FLORIDA, INC.—See EVI Industries, Inc.; *U.S. Public*, pg. 803
LAUN-DRY SUPPLY COMPANY INC.; *U.S. Private*, pg. 2398
LAUNDRY SYSTEMS OF TENNESSEE, LLC—See EVI Industries, Inc.; *U.S. Public*, pg. 803
LAURA ASHLEY CEE COUNTRIES BV—See Gordon Brothers Group, LLC; *U.S. Private*, pg. 1742
LAURA ASHLEY ESPANA SA—See Gordon Brothers Group, LLC; *U.S. Private*, pg. 1742
LAURA ASHLEY HOLDINGS PLC—See Gordon Brothers Group, LLC; *U.S. Private*, pg. 1742
LAURA ASHLEY, INC.—See Gordon Brothers Group, LLC; *U.S. Private*, pg. 1742
LAURA ASHLEY (IRELAND) LTD.—See Gordon Brothers Group, LLC; *U.S. Private*, pg. 1742
LAURA ASHLEY JAPAN CO., LTD.—See Gordon Brothers Group, LLC; *U.S. Private*, pg. 1742
LAURA ASHLEY LTD.—See Gordon Brothers Group, LLC; *U.S. Private*, pg. 1742
LAURA ASHLEY NV—See Gordon Brothers Group, LLC; *U.S. Private*, pg. 1742
LAURA ASHLEY SA—See Gordon Brothers Group, LLC; *U.S. Private*, pg. 1742
LAURA ASHLEY SA—See Gordon Brothers Group, LLC; *U.S. Private*, pg. 1742
LAURA ASHLEY S.P.A.—See Gordon Brothers Group, LLC; *U.S. Private*, pg. 1742
LAURABADA SHIPPING SERVICES LIMITED—See Steamships Trading Company Limited; *Int'l*, pg. 7188
LAURA DAVIDSON PUBLIC RELATIONS, INC.; *U.S. Private*, pg. 2398
LAURA PEARCE, LTD.; *U.S. Private*, pg. 2398
LAURA SECORD—See Nutriart Inc.; *Int'l*, pg. 5492
LAURA'S LEAN BEEF COMPANY—See Meyer Natural Angus, LLC; *U.S. Private*, pg. 2692
LAUREATE BIOPHARMACEUTICAL SERVICES, INC.—See Saints Capital, LLC; *U.S. Private*, pg. 3530
LAUREATE EDUCATION, INC.—See KKR & Co. Inc.; *U.S. Public*, pg. 1259
LAUREATE INSURANCE PARTNERS, LLC—See The Baldwin Insurance Group, Inc.; *U.S. Private*, pg. 2036
LAUREL AGGREGATES LLC—See Sun Capital Partners, Inc.; *U.S. Private*, pg. 3861
LAUREL AGGREGATES OF DELAWARE, LLC—See Natural Resource Partners L.P.; *U.S. Public*, pg. 1499
LAUREL FOODSYSTEMS INC.; *U.S. Private*, pg. 2398
LAUREL FORD LINCOLN-MERCURY; *U.S. Private*, pg. 2398
LAUREL GROCERY COMPANY LLC; *U.S. Private*, pg. 2398
LAUREL HEALTH RESOURCES, INC.—See Welltower Inc.; *U.S. Public*, pg. 2348
LAUREL HEALTH SYSTEMS; *U.S. Private*, pg. 2398
LAUREL HIGHLANDS LANDFILL, INC.—See Waste Management, Inc.; *U.S. Public*, pg. 2331
LAUREL HIGHLANDS, LLC—See Hovnanian Enterprises, Inc.; *U.S. Public*, pg. 1060
LAUREL HILL CAPITAL PARTNERS LLC; *U.S. Private*, pg. 2398
LAUREL HOLDINGS INC.; *U.S. Private*, pg. 2398

LAURUS TECHNOLOGIES, INC.

LAUREL IMPORTS INC.—See Laurel Motors Holding Company; *U.S. Private*, pg. 2399
LAUREL MANAGEMENT COMPANY—See Laurel Holdings Inc.; *U.S. Private*, pg. 2399
THE LAUREL MD ENDOSCOPY ASC, LLC—See KKR & Co. Inc.; *U.S. Public*, pg. 1248
LAUREL MOTORS HOLDING COMPANY; *U.S. Private*, pg. 2399
LAUREL OAKS BEHAVIORAL HEALTH CENTER, INC.—See Universal Health Services, Inc.; *U.S. Public*, pg. 2258
LAUREL ORGANICS LTD.—See KIMIA Biosciences Pvt Ltd.; *Int'l*, pg. 4163
THE LAUREL OUTLOOK—See Yellowstone Communications; *U.S. Private*, pg. 4588
LAUREL RACING ASSOCIATION, INC.—See The Stronach Group Inc.; *Int'l*, pg. 7689
LAUREL RIDGE HEALTH CARE CENTER—See Athena Health Care Systems; *U.S. Private*, pg. 367
LAUREL RIDGE—See Reading Anthracite Company; *U.S. Private*, pg. 3366
LAUREL STEEL LIMITED—See Nucor Corporation; *U.S. Public*, pg. 1553
LAUREL TECHNOLOGIES CO. LTD.—See Beijing Highlander Digital Technology Co., Ltd.; *Int'l*, pg. 951
LAUREL TECHNOLOGIES PARTNERSHIP—See Leonardo S.p.A.; *Int'l*, pg. 4459
LAURELTON DIAMONDS BELGIUM BVBA—See LVMH Moet Hennessy Louis Vuitton SE; *Int'l*, pg. 4603
LAURELTON DIAMONDS (BOTSWANA) (PROPRIETARY) LIMITED—See LVMH Moet Hennessy Louis Vuitton SE; *Int'l*, pg. 4603
LAURELTON DIAMONDS, INC.—See LVMH Moet Hennessy Louis Vuitton SE; *Int'l*, pg. 4603
LAUREL TRUCKING COMPANY INC.—See Laurel Grocery Company LLC; *U.S. Private*, pg. 2398
LAUREL VALLEY MOTORS INC.—See Laurel Motors Holding Company; *U.S. Private*, pg. 2399
LAUREL WEALTH ADVISORS, INC.—See Integrated Wealth Concepts, LLC; *U.S. Private*, pg. 2101
LAURELWOOD PROPERTIES INC—See The Goodyear Tire & Rubber Company; *U.S. Public*, pg. 2084
LAUREN BHARAT ENGINEERING PRIVATE LIMITED—See Lauren Holdings Inc.; *U.S. Private*, pg. 2399
LAUREN ENGINEERS & CONSTRUCTORS INC.—See Lauren Holdings Inc.; *U.S. Private*, pg. 2399
LAUREN ENGINEERS & CONSTRUCTORS, ULC—See Lauren Holdings Inc.; *U.S. Private*, pg. 2399
LAUREN HOLDINGS INC.; *U.S. Private*, pg. 2399
LAUREN INTERNATIONAL INC.; *U.S. Private*, pg. 2399
LAUREN LAND COMPANY—See Alpha Natural Resources, Inc.; *U.S. Private*, pg. 198
LAUREN PLASTICS LLC—See Cooper-Standard Holdings Inc.; *U.S. Public*, pg. 574
LAURENS COMMISSION OF PUBLIC WORKS; *U.S. Private*, pg. 2399
LAURENS ELECTRIC COOPERATIVE; *U.S. Private*, pg. 2399
LAURENS RESTORATION, INC.; *U.S. Private*, pg. 2399
LAURENS SPETHMANN HOLDING AKTIENGESELLSCHAFT & CO. KG; *Int'l*, pg. 4424
LAURENTIAN BANK OF CANADA; *Int'l*, pg. 4425
LAURENTIAN BANK SECURITIES INC.—See Laurentian Bank of Canada; *Int'l*, pg. 4425
LAURENTIAN MOTORS SUDBURY LTD.; *Int'l*, pg. 4425
LAURENTIDE CONTROLS LTD.; *Int'l*, pg. 4425
LAURENT LAUGIER SA; *Int'l*, pg. 4424
LAURENT LEBLANC LTD.; *Int'l*, pg. 4424
LAURENT-PELLIET SA; *Int'l*, pg. 4424
LAURENT-PERRIER UK LTD.—See Champagne Laurent-Perrier; *Int'l*, pg. 1440
LAURENT REIFEN GMBH—See Compagnie Generale des Etablissements Michelin SCA; *Int'l*, pg. 1743
LAUREY PEAT & ASSOCIATES INC.; *U.S. Private*, pg. 2399
LAURIDSEN GROUP INC.; *U.S. Private*, pg. 2399
LAURIER ENTERPRISES INC.; *U.S. Private*, pg. 2400
LAURINBURG KFC TAKE HOME INC.—See ZV Pate Inc.; *U.S. Public*, pg. 4610
LAURIN PUBLISHING CO., INC.; *U.S. Private*, pg. 2400
LAURION MINERAL EXPLORATION INC.; *Int'l*, pg. 4425
LAURIS MODA LTD.—See Tekstilpromet d.d; *Int'l*, pg. 7528
LAURISTON PARK RETIREMENT VILLAGE LIMITED—See Arvida Group Limited; *Int'l*, pg. 587
LAURITZEN CORPORATION; *U.S. Private*, pg. 2400
LAURITZEN KOSAN A/S—See BW Epic Kosan Ltd.; *Int'l*, pg. 1231
LAURUS CAPITAL MANAGEMENT, LLC; *U.S. Private*, pg. 2400
LAURUS CORP.—See Ethika Investments LLC; *U.S. Private*, pg. 1431
LAURUS INTERNATIONAL B.V.—See Jumbo Supermarkten B.V.; *Int'l*, pg. 4026
LAURUS LABS LIMITED—See Evotec SE; *Int'l*, pg. 2573
LAURUS NEDERLAND B.V.—See Jumbo Supermarkten B.V.; *Int'l*, pg. 4026
LAURUS TECHNOLOGIES, INC.; *U.S. Private*, pg. 2400

1577

LAURUS TECHNOLOGIES, INC.

CORPORATE AFFILIATIONS

LAURUS TRANSACTION ADVISORS L.L.C.—See CBIZ, Inc.; *U.S. Public*, pg. 457
LAUSELL INC.; *U.S. Private*, pg. 2400
LAUSITZER VERLAGSSERVICE GMBH—See Neue Pressegesellschaft mbH & Co. KG; *Int'l*, pg. 5218
LAUTAN LUAS SINGAPORE PTE LTD—See PT. Lautan Luas Tbk; *Int'l*, pg. 6087
LAUTH GROUP, INC; *U.S. Private*, pg. 2400
LAUTNER ENEGIESPARTECHNIK GMBH—See Systemair AB; *Int'l*, pg. 7391
LAUTUS TRADING BVBA—See Elsan Ltd.; *Int'l*, pg. 2370
LAUX CONSTRUCTION, LLC—See Rival Holdings, LLC.; *U.S. Private*, pg. 3442
LAVABAU LLC—See Einhell Germany AG; *Int'l*, pg. 2333
LAVACA PIPE LINE COMPANY—See Formosa Plastics Corporation; *U.S. Private*, pg. 2736
LAVALIER INSURANCE SERVICES, LLC—See W.R. Berkley Corporation; *U.S. Public*, pg. 2318
LAVALLEY BUILDING SUPPLY INC.; *U.S. Private*, pg. 2400
LAVA MEDTECH ACQUISITION CORP.; *U.S. Public*, pg. 1294
LAVANTE INC.—See PRGX Global, Inc.; *U.S. Private*, pg. 3257
LAVANTURE PRODUCTS COMPANY INC.; *U.S. Private*, pg. 2400
LAVARETUS UNDERWRITING AB—See Marsh & McLennan Companies, Inc.; *U.S. Public*, pg. 1377
LAVASA CORPORATION LIMITED—See Hindustan Construction Co. Ltd; *Int'l*, pg. 3399
LAVATEC ASIA PACIFIC CO LTD—See Lavatec Laundry Technology GmbH; *Int'l*, pg. 4425
LAVATEC LAUNDRY TECHNOLOGY GMBH; *Int'l*, pg. 4425
LAVATEC LAUNDRY TECHNOLOGY INC.—See Lavatec Laundry Technology GmbH; *Int'l*, pg. 4425
LAVATEC NEDERLAND BV—See Lavatec Laundry Technology GmbH; *Int'l*, pg. 4425
LAVA THERAPEUTICS NV; *Int'l*, pg. 4425
LAVAZZA COFFEE (UK) LTD.—See Luigi Lavazza S.p.A.; *Int'l*, pg. 4575
LAVAZZA DEUTSCHLAND GMBH—See Luigi Lavazza S.p.A.; *Int'l*, pg. 4575
LAVAZZA DO BRASIL IND. E COM. LTDA—See Luigi Lavazza S.p.A.; *Int'l*, pg. 4575
LAVAZZA KAFFEE GMBH—See Luigi Lavazza S.p.A.; *Int'l*, pg. 4575
LAVAZZA PREMIUM COFFEES CORP.—See Luigi Lavazza S.p.A.; *Int'l*, pg. 4575
LAVELLE INDUSTRIES INC.; *U.S. Private*, pg. 2400
LAVENA AD; *Int'l*, pg. 4425
LAVENDER FIELDS (SOUTH WOOTTON) RESIDENTS MANAGEMENT COMPANY LTD.—See Persimmon plc; *Int'l*, pg. 5816
LAVENDON ACCESS SERVICES (FRANCE) SA—See Loxam SAS; *Int'l*, pg. 4566
LAVENDON ACCESS SERVICES (UK) LIMITED—See Loxam SAS; *Int'l*, pg. 4566
LAVENDON GROUP LIMITED—See Loxam SAS; *Int'l*, pg. 4566
LA VENECIA IBERIAGLASS S.L.—See Compagnie de Saint-Gobain SA; *Int'l*, pg. 1724
LA VENECIANA CENTRO S.A.—See Compagnie de Saint-Gobain SA; *Int'l*, pg. 1724
LA VENEZIA ASSICURAZIONI S.P.A.—See Assicurazioni Generali S.p.A.; *Int'l*, pg. 643
LAVENIA SMITH & SUMMERS HOME FOR FUNERALS—See Flanner & Buchanan, Inc.; *U.S. Private*, pg. 1540
L'AVENIR—See AdVini S.A.; *Int'l*, pg. 168
LAVERANA GMBH & CO. KG; *Int'l*, pg. 4425
LAVERDA AGCO SPA—See AGCO Corporation; *U.S. Public*, pg. 59
LA VERDAD MULTIMEDIA, SA—See Vocento, S.A.; *Int'l*, pg. 8284
LAVERDA S.P.A—See AGCO Corporation; *U.S. Public*, pg. 59
LAVERDIERE CONSTRUCTION INC.; *U.S. Private*, pg. 2400
LAVERNE HIGHLANDER—See Alden Global Capital LLC; *U.S. Private*, pg. 158
LA VETA SURGICAL CENTER—See Encompass Health Corporation; *U.S. Public*, pg. 758
LAVET S.R.L.—See LCI Industries; *U.S. Public*, pg. 1295
LAVG ZUID B.V.—See Munchener Ruckversicherungs AG; *Int'l*, pg. 5087
LAVIDGE & ASSOCIATES INC.; *U.S. Private*, pg. 2400
THE LAVIDGE COMPANY; *U.S. Private*, pg. 4068
LAVIE BIO LTD.—See Corteva, Inc.; *U.S. Public*, pg. 584
LA VIE—See Nestle S.A.; *Int'l*, pg. 5210
LAVI INDUSTRIES INC. - NEW YORK FACILITY—See Lavi Industries Inc.; *U.S. Private*, pg. 2400
LAVI INDUSTRIES INC.; *U.S. Private*, pg. 2400
LAVIPHARM HELLAS S.A.—See LAVIPHARM S.A.; *Int'l*, pg. 4425
LAVIPHARM S.A.; *Int'l*, pg. 4425
LAVISH DINE CATERING PTE LTD—See Neo Group Limited; *Int'l*, pg. 5196

LAVISH LABORATORY COMPANY LIMITED—See Gift Infinite Public Company Limited; *Int'l*, pg. 2970
LAVISTA LICENSEE SOLUTIONS PTY LIMITED—See ClearView Wealth Limited; *Int'l*, pg. 1657
LAVO GALLERY SDN. BHD.—See Focus Dynamics Group Berhad; *Int'l*, pg. 2719
LAVOIE STRATEGIC COMMUNICATIONS GROUP, INC.; *U.S. Private*, pg. 2400
LAVORO BANK AG—See BNP Paribas SA; *Int'l*, pg. 1089
LAVORO LIMITED; *Int'l*, pg. 4425
LAVORWASH BRASIL IND. E COM. LTDA—See Emak S.p.A.; *Int'l*, pg. 2373
LAVORWASH BRASIL IND. LTDA.—See Emak S.p.A.; *Int'l*, pg. 2373
LAVORWASH FRANCE S.A.S.—See Emak S.p.A.; *Int'l*, pg. 2373
LAVORWASH GB LTD—See Lavorwash S.p.A.; *Int'l*, pg. 4425
LAVORWASH IBERICA S.L.—See Emak S.p.A.; *Int'l*, pg. 2373
LAVORWASH POLSKA S.P. Z O.O.—See Emak S.p.A.; *Int'l*, pg. 2373
LAVORWASH S.P.A.; *Int'l*, pg. 4425
LAVO.TV AS; *Int'l*, pg. 4425
LA VOZ DEL INTERIOR S.A.—See Grupo Clarin S.A.; *Int'l*, pg. 3124
LAVSIM HIGIENIZACAO TEXTIL S.A.—See Servizi Italia SpA; *Int'l*, pg. 6726
LAW BULLETIN PUBLISHING COMPANY; *U.S. Private*, pg. 2400
LAW CENTRAL CO. PTY. LTD.—See Count Limited; *Int'l*, pg. 1818
THE LAW COMPANY, INC.; *U.S. Private*, pg. 4068
LAW.COM—See Apax Partners LLP; *Int'l*, pg. 504
LAWCROSSING, INC.; *U.S. Private*, pg. 2400
THE LAW DEBENTURE CORPORATION P.L.C.; *Int'l*, pg. 7664
LAW DEBENTURE TRUST (ASIA) LIMITED—See The Law Debenture Corporation p.l.c.; *Int'l*, pg. 7664
LAW DEBENTURE TRUST COMPANY OF NEW YORK—See The Law Debenture Corporation p.l.c.; *Int'l*, pg. 7664
THE LAW DEBENTURE TRUST CORPORATION (CHANNEL ISLANDS) LIMITED—See The Law Debenture Corporation p.l.c.; *Int'l*, pg. 7664
L.A WEB OFFSET PRINTING INC.; *U.S. Private*, pg. 2364
LAWECO MASCHINEN- UND APPARATEBAU GMBH; *Int'l*, pg. 4425
LA WEEKLY, LP—See Semanal Media, LLC; *U.S. Private*, pg. 3603
LA-WELL SYSTEMS GMBH—See CompuGroup Medical SE & Co. KGaA; *Int'l*, pg. 1756
LAW ENFORCEMENT ASSOCIATES CORPORATION; *U.S. Private*, pg. 2400
LAW ENFORCEMENT HEALTH BENEFITS, INC.; *U.S. Private*, pg. 2400
LAW ENFORCEMENT OFFICERS & FIREFIGHTERS HEALTH AND WELFARE TRUST; *U.S. Private*, pg. 2400
LAW ENFORCEMENT TECHNOLOGY GROUP—See Vista Equity Partners, LLC; *U.S. Private*, pg. 4395
LAWFINANCE LTD.; *Int'l*, pg. 4425
THE LAW FIRM OF ANIDJAR & LEVINE, P.A.; *U.S. Private*, pg. 4068
LAWFRONT GROUP LIMITED—See Blixt Group Limited; *Int'l*, pg. 1064
LAW & KENNETH SAATCHI & SAATCHI PRIVATE LIMITED—See Publicis Groupe S.A.; *Int'l*, pg. 6107
LAWLER BALLARD VAN DURAND; *U.S. Private*, pg. 2400
LAWLER BALLARD VAN DURAND—See Lawler Ballard Van Durand; *U.S. Private*, pg. 2401
LAWLER FOODS LTD.—See Gryphon Investors, LLC; *U.S. Private*, pg. 1798
LAWLEY AUTOMOTIVE GROUP; *U.S. Private*, pg. 2401
LAWLEY AUTOMOTIVE—See Lawley Service Inc.; *U.S. Private*, pg. 2401
LAWLEY BENEFITS GROUP, LLC—See Lawley Service Inc.; *U.S. Private*, pg. 2401
LAWLEY MOTORS LLC; *U.S. Private*, pg. 2401
LAWLEY SERVICE INC.; *U.S. Private*, pg. 2401
LAWLINK (UK) LTD.—See Daily Mail & General Trust plc; *Int'l*, pg. 1938
LAWLOGIX GROUP, INC.—See Equifax Inc.; *U.S. Public*, pg. 786
LAWMAN HEATING & COOLING, INC.; *U.S. Private*, pg. 2401
LAWMEN'S SAFETY SUPPLY INC.—See Kanders & Company, Inc.; *U.S. Private*, pg. 2259
LAWMEN SUPPLY COMPANY OF NEW JERSEY, INC.; *U.S. Private*, pg. 2401
LAWNAMERICA, INC.—See TruGreen Limited Partnership; *U.S. Private*, pg. 4249
LAWN AND GOLF SUPPLY CO., INC.; *U.S. Private*, pg. 2401
LAWN BUTLER INC.; *U.S. Private*, pg. 2401
LAWN DOCTOR INC; *U.S. Private*, pg. 2401
LAWN PRIDE INC.—See Harvest Partners L.P.; *U.S. Private*, pg. 1876

LAWN STAR PTY. LTD.—See Einhell Germany AG; *Int'l*, pg. 2333
LAWN TECH INC.—See Green Group Holdings LLC; *U.S. Private*, pg. 1773
LAWN TENNIS ASSOCIATION OF AUSTRALIA LIMITED; *Int'l*, pg. 4425
LAWNWOOD CARDIOVASCULAR SURGERY, LLC—See HCA Healthcare, Inc.; *U.S. Public*, pg. 1000
LAWNWOOD PAVILION PHYSICIAN SERVICES, LLC—See HCA Healthcare, Inc.; *U.S. Public*, pg. 1000
LAWNWOOD REGIONAL MEDICAL CENTER—See HCA Healthcare, Inc.; *U.S. Public*, pg. 1000
LAWO AG; *Int'l*, pg. 4426
LAWO GROUP USA INC.—See Lawo AG; *Int'l*, pg. 4426
LAWO INTERNATIONAL GMBH—See Lawo AG; *Int'l*, pg. 4426
LAWO NORTH AMERICA CORP.—See Lawo AG; *Int'l*, pg. 4426
LAWRENCE A. BROOKS INC.; *U.S. Private*, pg. 2401
LAWRENCEBURG DIALYSIS, LLC—See DaVita Inc.; *U.S. Public*, pg. 640
LAWRENCE COUNTY ECONOMIC DEVELOPMENT CORPORATION; *U.S. Private*, pg. 2401
LAWRENCE COUNTY MEMORIAL HOSPITAL; *U.S. Private*, pg. 2401
LAWRENCE COUNTY NEWSPAPERS, INC.; *U.S. Private*, pg. 2401
LAWRENCE FINANCIAL CORPORATION; *U.S. Private*, pg. 2401
LAWRENCE FRASER BROKERS LIMITED—See Brown & Brown, Inc.; *U.S. Public*, pg. 401
LAWRENCE HALL CHEVROLET INC.; *U.S. Private*, pg. 2401
LAWRENCE HALL CHEVROLET OLDSMOBILE BUICK INC.; *U.S. Private*, pg. 2401
LAWRENCE HARVEY SEARCH & SELECTION LTD.; *Int'l*, pg. 4426
LAWRENCE-LYNCH CORPORATION; *U.S. Private*, pg. 2402
LAWRENCE OIL CO. INC.; *U.S. Private*, pg. 2401
LAWRENCE PAPER COMPANY; *U.S. Private*, pg. 2401
LAWRENCE PARK HEALTH & WELLNESS CLINIC INC.—See Empower Clinics Inc.; *Int'l*, pg. 2388
LAWRENCE PLUMBING SUPPLY CO.—See Ferguson plc; *Int'l*, pg. 2638
LAWRENCE PUMPS, INC.—See Flowserve Corporation; *U.S. Public*, pg. 856
LAWRENCE PUMPS (SHANGHAI) COMPANY LIMITED—See Flowserve Corporation; *U.S. Public*, pg. 856
LAWRENCE RAGAN COMMUNICATIONS, INC.; *U.S. Private*, pg. 2402
LAWRENCE READY MIXED CONCRETE CO.—See Boston Sand & Gravel Company; *U.S. Public*, pg. 373
LAWRENCE RUBEN CO.; *U.S. Private*, pg. 2402
LAWRENCE SCHIFF SILK MILLS, INC.—See Revolution Capital Group, LLC; *U.S. Private*, pg. 3416
LAWRENCE & SCHILLER, INC.; *U.S. Private*, pg. 2401
LAWRENCE TRACTOR COMPANY INC.; *U.S. Private*, pg. 2402
LAWRENCE TRANSPORTATION COMPANY—See Rihm Motor Company; *U.S. Private*, pg. 3436
LAWRENCE TRANSPORTATION SERVICES, INC.; *U.S. Private*, pg. 2402
LAWRENCE TRANSPORTATION SYSTEMS, INC.; *U.S. Private*, pg. 2402
LAWRENCEVILLE FORD LINCOLN MERCURY; *U.S. Private*, pg. 2402
LAWRENCEVILLE SURGERY CENTER, L.L.C.—See Tenet Healthcare Corporation; *U.S. Public*, pg. 2011
LAWRESHWAR FOOTCARE PRIVATE LIMITED—See Lehar Footwears Limited; *Int'l*, pg. 4446
LAWROOM—See EverFi, Inc.; *U.S. Private*, pg. 1438
LAWRY FREIGHT SYSTEM, INC.; *U.S. Private*, pg. 2402
LAWRY'S RESTAURANTS, INC.; *U.S. Private*, pg. 2402
LAWSON ATM NETWORKS INC.—See Lawson, Inc.; *Int'l*, pg. 4426
LAWSON CHEVROLET INC.; *U.S. Private*, pg. 2402
THE LAWSON COMPANIES, INC.; *U.S. Private*, pg. 4068
LAWSON ELECTRIC COMPANY; *U.S. Private*, pg. 2402
LAWSON, INC.; *Int'l*, pg. 4426
LAWSON INDUSTRIES INC.—See Pella Corporation; *U.S. Private*, pg. 3131
LAWSON MECHANICAL CONTRACTORS; *U.S. Private*, pg. 2402
LAWSON PHILIPPINES, INC.—See Lawson, Inc.; *Int'l*, pg. 4426
LAWSON PRODUCTS INC. (ONTARIO)—See Distribution Solutions Group, Inc.; *U.S. Public*, pg. 668
LAWSON PRODUCTS, INC.—See Distribution Solutions Group, Inc.; *U.S. Public*, pg. 669
LAWSON PRODUCTS, INC.—See Distribution Solutions Group, Inc.; *U.S. Public*, pg. 668
LAWSON PRODUCTS, INC.—See Distribution Solutions Group, Inc.; *U.S. Public*, pg. 668
LAWSON PRODUCTS, INC.—See Distribution Solutions Group, Inc.; *U.S. Public*, pg. 668
LAWSON PRODUCTS, INC.—See Distribution Solutions Group, Inc.; *U.S. Public*, pg. 669

COMPANY NAME INDEX

LAWSON STORE100, INC.—See Lawson, Inc.; *Int'l*, pg. 4426
LAWSON TRAVELS & TOURS (INDIA) PRIVATE LIMITED—See Ebix Inc.; *U.S. Public*, pg. 710
LAWTER ARGENTINA S.A.—See Harima Chemicals Group, Inc.; *Int'l*, pg. 3276
LAWTER BVBA—See Harima Chemicals Group, Inc.; *Int'l*, pg. 3276
LAWTER CHEMICALS (SHANGHAI) CO., LTD.—See Harima Chemicals Group, Inc.; *Int'l*, pg. 3276
LAWTER INC. - R&D—See Harima Chemicals Group, Inc.; *Int'l*, pg. 3276
LAWTER, INC.—See Harima Chemicals Group, Inc.; *Int'l*, pg. 3276
LAWTER MAASTRICHT B.V.—See Harima Chemicals Group, Inc.; *Int'l*, pg. 3276
LAWTER (N.Z.) LTD.—See Harima Chemicals Group, Inc.; *Int'l*, pg. 3276
LAWTON DEVELOPMENT CO., LTD.; *Int'l*, pg. 4426
LAWTON DIALYSIS CENTER, LLC—See Nautic Partners, LLC; *U.S. Private*, pg. 2870
LAWTON HEALTHCARE CENTER—See Apollo Global Management, Inc.; *U.S. Public*, pg. 157
LAWTONS DRUG STORES LIMITED—See Empire Company Limited; *Int'l*, pg. 2387
THE LAWTON TUBE CO., LTD.; *Int'l*, pg. 7664
LAW TRUSTED THIRD PARTY SERVICES (PTY) LTD—See Etion Limited; *Int'l*, pg. 2523
LAW UNION & ROCK INS. PLC; *Int'l*, pg. 4425
LAWVALE PTY LTD—See Wesfarmers Limited; *Int'l*, pg. 8382
LAWYERS AND MERCHANTS TRANSLATION BUREAU INC.—See RWS Holdings plc; *Int'l*, pg. 6437
LAWYERS TITLE INSURANCE CORPORATION—See Fidelity National Financial, Inc.; *U.S. Public*, pg. 831
LAWYERS TITLE OF ARIZONA—See Fidelity National Financial, Inc.; *U.S. Public*, pg. 831
LAWYERS TITLE OF EL PASO, INC.—See Fidelity National Financial, Inc.; *U.S. Public*, pg. 831
LAXAI PHARMA, LTD.; *U.S. Private*, pg. 2402
LAXAPANA BATTERIES PLC.—See E.B. Creasy & Company PLC; *Int'l*, pg. 2251
LAXEY PARTNERS LTD.; *Int'l*, pg. 4426
LAXEY PARTNERS (UK) LIMITED—See Laxey Partners Ltd.; *Int'l*, pg. 4426
LAXMI BANK LIMITED; *Int'l*, pg. 4426
LAXMI CAPITAL MARKET LIMITED—See Laxmi Bank Limited; *Int'l*, pg. 4426
LAXMI COTSPIN LIMITED.; *Int'l*, pg. 4426
LAXMI DEVELOPERS PRIVATE LIMITED—See Laxmi Goldorna House Limited; *Int'l*, pg. 4426
LAXMI GOLDORNA HOUSE LIMITED; *Int'l*, pg. 4426
LAXMI ITALY S.R.L.—See Laxmi Organic Industries Limited; *Int'l*, pg. 4426
LAXMI LAGHUBITTA BITTIYA SANSTHA LTD.; *Int'l*, pg. 4426
LAXMI LIFESCIENCES PRIVATE LTD.—See Laxmi Organic Industries Limited; *Int'l*, pg. 4426
LAXMI ORGANIC INDUSTRIES (EUROPE) BV—See Laxmi Organic Industries Limited; *Int'l*, pg. 4426
LAXMI ORGANIC INDUSTRIES LIMITED; *Int'l*, pg. 4426
LAXMIPATI ENGINEERING WORKS LIMITED; *Int'l*, pg. 4426
LAXMI PETROCHEM MIDDLE EAST FZE—See Laxmi Organic Industries Limited; *Int'l*, pg. 4426
LAXMI SUNRISE BANK LIMITED—See Laxmi Bank Limited; *Int'l*, pg. 4426
LAXUS TECHNOLOGIES INC.—See World Co., Ltd.; *Int'l*, pg. 8457
LAYA HEALTHCARE LIMITED—See AXA S.A.; *Int'l*, pg. 759
LAYA MAX TRADING CO., LTD.—See Fulgent Sun International (Holding) Co., Ltd.; *Int'l*, pg. 2842
LAYA OUTDOOR PRODUCTS LIMITED—See Fulgent Sun International (Holding) Co., Ltd.; *Int'l*, pg. 2842
LAYAR REAL RESERVA, S.A.—See Tecnicas Reunidas, S.A.; *Int'l*, pg. 7515
LAY BROTHERS INC.; *U.S. Private*, pg. 2402
LAYDE STEEL S.L.—See Tata Sons Limited; *Int'l*, pg. 7472
LAYDON COMPOSITES LTD.—See ZF Friedrichshafen AG; *Int'l*, pg. 8641
LAYERTEX S.L.—See Helvetia Holding AG; *Int'l*, pg. 3340
LAYERWISE NV—See 3D Systems Corporation; *U.S. Public*, pg. 4
LAY HONG BERHAD; *Int'l*, pg. 4427
LAYLA TEXTILE & TRADERS LIMITED; *Int'l*, pg. 4427
LAYMAN BROTHERS INSULATION, LLC—See Installed Building Products, Inc.; *U.S. Public*, pg. 1133
LAYMAN CANDY COMPANY, INC.; *U.S. Private*, pg. 2402
LAYNE CHRISTENSEN COMPANY—See Granite Construction Incorporated; *U.S. Public*, pg. 957
LAYNE DRILLING ZAMBIA—See Granite Construction Incorporated; *U.S. Public*, pg. 958
LAYNE ENERGY, INC.—See Granite Construction Incorporated; *U.S. Public*, pg. 958
LAYNE GEOCONSTRUCTION—See Granite Construction Incorporated; *U.S. Public*, pg. 958
LAYNE HEAVY CIVIL, INC.—See Reynolds Construction, LLC; *U.S. Private*, pg. 3418

LAYNE SOUTHWEST, INC.—See Reynolds Construction, LLC; *U.S. Private*, pg. 3418
LAYNE TEXAS, INCORPORATED—See Granite Construction Incorporated; *U.S. Public*, pg. 958
LAYN EUROPE SRL—See Guilin Layn Natural Ingredients Corp.; *Int'l*, pg. 3173
LAYNE-WESTERN CO., INC.—See Granite Construction Incorporated; *U.S. Public*, pg. 958
LAYN USA, INC.—See Guilin Layn Natural Ingredients Corp.; *Int'l*, pg. 3173
LAY-OUT PLANNING CONSULTANTS CO., LTD.; *Int'l*, pg. 4427
LAYSTER INVESTMENTS PLC; *Int'l*, pg. 4427
LAYTEC AG—See Nynomic AG; *Int'l*, pg. 5501
LAYTON CONSTRUCTION COMPANY, LLC—See STO Building Group Inc.; *U.S. Private*, pg. 3813
LAYTON FAMILY PRACTICE, LLC—See HCA Healthcare, Inc.; *U.S. Public*, pg. 1000
LAYTON HILLS DODGE INC.; *U.S. Private*, pg. 2402
LAZADA GROUP; *Int'l*, pg. 4427
LAZARD AB—See Lazard Ltd.; *Int'l*, pg. 4427
LAZARD ALTERNATIVE INVESTMENTS LLC—See Lazard Ltd.; *Int'l*, pg. 4427
LAZARD ALTERNATIVE MANAGEMENT LLC—See Lazard Ltd.; *Int'l*, pg. 4427
LAZARD ARGENTINA S.A.—See Lazard Ltd.; *Int'l*, pg. 4427
LAZARD ASIA (HK) LIMITED—See Lazard Ltd.; *Int'l*, pg. 4427
LAZARD ASIA (HONG KONG) LIMITED—See Lazard Ltd.; *Int'l*, pg. 4427
LAZARD ASIA LIMITED—See Lazard Ltd.; *Int'l*, pg. 4427
LAZARD ASSET MANAGEMENT (CANADA), INC.—See Lazard Ltd.; *Int'l*, pg. 4427
LAZARD ASSET MANAGEMENT (DEUTSCHLAND) GMBH—See Lazard Ltd.; *Int'l*, pg. 4427
LAZARD ASSET MANAGEMENT (HK) LIMITED—See Lazard Ltd.; *Int'l*, pg. 4427
LAZARD ASSET MANAGEMENT LIMITED—See Lazard Ltd.; *Int'l*, pg. 4427
LAZARD ASSET MANAGEMENT LLC—See Lazard Ltd.; *Int'l*, pg. 4427
LAZARD ASSET MANAGEMENT PACIFIC CO.—See Lazard Ltd.; *Int'l*, pg. 4427
LAZARD ASSET MANAGEMENT SCHWEIZ AG—See Lazard Ltd.; *Int'l*, pg. 4427
LAZARD ASSET MANAGEMENT (SINGAPORE) PTE. LTD.—See Lazard Ltd.; *Int'l*, pg. 4427
LAZARD AUSTRALIA PRIVATE EQUITY PTY LTD—See Lazard Ltd.; *Int'l*, pg. 4427
LAZARD AUSTRALIA PTY LTD—See Lazard Ltd.; *Int'l*, pg. 4427
LAZARD BUSINESS CONSULTING (BEIJING) CO., LTD.—See Lazard Ltd.; *Int'l*, pg. 4428
LAZARD BV—See Lazard Ltd.; *Int'l*, pg. 4427
LAZARD BV/SRL—See Lazard Ltd.; *Int'l*, pg. 4427
LAZARD CANADA INC.—See Lazard Ltd.; *Int'l*, pg. 4428
LAZARD CARNEGIE WYLIE INVESTMENT MANAGEMENT PTY. LTD.—See Lazard Ltd.; *Int'l*, pg. 4428
LAZARD CARNEGIE WYLIE PTY. LTD.—See Lazard Ltd.; *Int'l*, pg. 4428
LAZARD CHILE S.P.A.—See Lazard Ltd.; *Int'l*, pg. 4428
LAZARD CHINA LIMITED—See Lazard Ltd.; *Int'l*, pg. 4428
LAZARD & CO., HOLDINGS LIMITED—See Lazard Ltd.; *Int'l*, pg. 4427
LAZARD COLOMBIA S.A.S.—See Lazard Ltd.; *Int'l*, pg. 4428
LAZARD & CO., LTD.—See Lazard Ltd.; *Int'l*, pg. 4427
LAZARD FRERES BANQUE SA—See Lazard Ltd.; *Int'l*, pg. 4428
LAZARD FRERES & CO., LLC—See Lazard Ltd.; *Int'l*, pg. 4428
LAZARD FRERES GESTION—See Lazard Ltd.; *Int'l*, pg. 4427
LAZARD FRERES K.K.—See Lazard Ltd.; *Int'l*, pg. 4428
LAZARD FRERES SAS—See Lazard Ltd.; *Int'l*, pg. 4428
LAZARD FUND MANAGERS (IRELAND) LIMITED—See Lazard Ltd.; *Int'l*, pg. 4428
LAZARD GLOBAL TOTAL RETURN & INCOME FUND, INC.; *U.S. Private*, pg. 2402
LAZARD GROUP LLC—See Lazard Ltd.; *Int'l*, pg. 4427
LAZARD GULF LIMITED—See Lazard Ltd.; *Int'l*, pg. 4428
LAZARD INDIA PRIVATE LIMITED—See Lazard Ltd.; *Int'l*, pg. 4428
LAZARD JAPAN ASSET MANAGEMENT K.K.—See Lazard Ltd.; *Int'l*, pg. 4428
LAZARD KOREA ASSET MANAGEMENT CO., LTD.—See Lazard Ltd.; *Int'l*, pg. 4428
LAZARD KOREA LIMITED—See Lazard Ltd.; *Int'l*, pg. 4428
LAZARD LTD.; *Int'l*, pg. 4427
LAZARD MIDDLE MARKET LLC—See Lazard Ltd.; *Int'l*, pg. 4428
LAZARD PANAMA S.A.—See Lazard Ltd.; *Int'l*, pg. 4428
LAZARD PTY LTD—See Lazard Ltd.; *Int'l*, pg. 4428
LAZARD REAL ESTATE PARTNERS LLC—See Lazard Ltd.; *Int'l*, pg. 4427
LAZARD SAUDI ARABIA LIMITED—See Lazard Ltd.; *Int'l*, pg. 4428

LBC EXPRESS HOLDINGS, INC.

LAZARD SPRL—See Lazard Ltd.; *Int'l*, pg. 4428
LAZARD WORLD DIVIDEND & INCOME FUND, INC.; *U.S. Private*, pg. 2402
LAZARE KAPLAN BELGIUM N.V.—See Lazare Kaplan International, Inc.; *U.S. Private*, pg. 2402
LAZARE KAPLAN INTERNATIONAL, INC.; *U.S. Private*, pg. 2402
LAZAR INDUSTRIES LLC; *U.S. Private*, pg. 2402
LAZAR NESIC A.D.; *Int'l*, pg. 4427
LAZAR PARTNERS LTD.—See Finn Partners, Inc.; *U.S. Private*, pg. 1510
LAZARUS REFINING & MARKETING, LLC—See Blue Dolphin Energy Company; *U.S. Public*, pg. 364
LA-Z-BOY INCORPORATED; *U.S. Public*, pg. 1284
LA-Z-BOY LOGISTICS, INC.—See La-Z-Boy Incorporated; *U.S. Public*, pg. 1285
LA-Z-BOY RESIDENTIAL—See La-Z-Boy Incorporated; *U.S. Public*, pg. 1285
LA-Z-BOY SOUTH—See La-Z-Boy Incorporated; *U.S. Public*, pg. 1285
LA-Z-BOY TENNESSEE—See La-Z-Boy Incorporated; *U.S. Public*, pg. 1285
LA-Z-BOY (THAILAND) LTD.—See La-Z-Boy Incorporated; *U.S. Public*, pg. 1285
LA-Z-BOY WEST—See La-Z-Boy Incorporated; *U.S. Public*, pg. 1285
LAZER SPORT N.V.—See Shimano, Inc.; *Int'l*, pg. 6833
LAZER SPOT, INC.—See Harvest Partners L.P.; *U.S. Private*, pg. 1876
LAZLO INTERNATIONAL SA—See FAES Farma, S.A.; *Int'l*, pg. 2601
LAZORD—See HAK Algahtani Group of Companies; *Int'l*, pg. 3219
LAZORPOINT, LLC; *U.S. Private*, pg. 2403
LAZ PARKING LTD, LLC; *U.S. Private*, pg. 2402
LA-Z-RECLINER SHOP INC.; *U.S. Private*, pg. 2370
LAZURDE COMPANY FOR JEWELRY; *Int'l*, pg. 4428
LAZURITON NANO BIOTECHNOLOGY (U.S.A.) INC.; *Int'l*, pg. 4428
LAZY-BOY FURNITURE GALLERIES; *U.S. Private*, pg. 2403
LAZYDAYS HOLDINGS, INC.; *U.S. Public*, pg. 1294
LAZY DAYS' R.V. CENTER, INC.—See Lazydays Holdings, Inc.; *U.S. Public*, pg. 1295
LAZZARA YACHT CORP.; *U.S. Private*, pg. 2403
LBA GROUP, INC.; *U.S. Private*, pg. 2403
LBA HAYNES STRAND, PLLC—See Aprio, LLP; *U.S. Private*, pg. 301
LB ALUMINIUM BERHAD; *Int'l*, pg. 4428
LB ALUMINIUM (SARAWAK) SDN. BHD.—See LB Aluminium Berhad; *Int'l*, pg. 4428
LB ALUMINIUM (SINGAPORE) PTE LTD.—See LB Aluminium Berhad; *Int'l*, pg. 4428
LBA REALTY LLC; *U.S. Private*, pg. 2403
LB BOHLE LLC—See L.B. BOHLE Maschinen + Verfahren GmbH; *Int'l*, pg. 4385
L.B. BOHLE MASCHINEN + VERFAHREN GMBH; *Int'l*, pg. 4385
LBBW ASSET MANAGEMENT GMBH—See Landesbank Baden-Wurttemberg; *Int'l*, pg. 4405
LBBW CORPORATE REAL ESTATE MANAGEMENT GMBH—See Landesbank Baden-Wurttemberg; *Int'l*, pg. 4405
LBBW DUBLIN MANAGEMENT GMBH—See Landesbank Baden-Wurttemberg; *Int'l*, pg. 4405
LBBW GVZ ENTWICKLUNGSGESELLSCHAFT LEIPZIG MBH—See Landesbank Baden-Wurttemberg; *Int'l*, pg. 4405
LBBW IMMOBILIEN ASSET MANAGEMENT GMBH—See Landesbank Baden-Wurttemberg; *Int'l*, pg. 4405
LBBW IMMOBILIEN CAPITAL GMBH—See Landesbank Baden-Wurttemberg; *Int'l*, pg. 4405
LBBW IMMOBILIEN KOMMUNALENTWICKLUNG GMBH—See Landesbank Baden-Wurttemberg; *Int'l*, pg. 4405
LBBW IMMOBILIEN ROMANIA S.R.L.—See Landesbank Baden-Wurttemberg; *Int'l*, pg. 4405
LBBW LEASING GMBH—See Landesbank Baden-Wurttemberg; *Int'l*, pg. 4405
LBBW LUXEMBURG S.A.—See Landesbank Baden-Wurttemberg; *Int'l*, pg. 4405
LBBW MEXICO S.A. DE C.V.—See Landesbank Baden-Wurttemberg; *Int'l*, pg. 4405
LBBW (SCHWEIZ) AG—See Landesbank Baden-Wurttemberg; *Int'l*, pg. 4405
LBBW TRUST GMBH—See Landesbank Baden-Wurttemberg; *Int'l*, pg. 4405
LBBW US REAL ESTATE INVESTMENT LLC—See Landesbank Baden-Wurttemberg; *Int'l*, pg. 4405
LBBW VENTURE CAPITAL GMBH—See Landesbank Baden-Wurttemberg; *Int'l*, pg. 4405
LBC CAPITAL LTD.—See Laurentian Bank of Canada; *Int'l*, pg. 4425
LBC CREDIT PARTNERS, INC.—See Independence Capital Partners, LLC; *U.S. Private*, pg. 2055
LBC EXPRESS HOLDINGS, INC.; *Int'l*, pg. 4429
LBC EXPRESS, INC.—See LBC Express Holdings, Inc.; *Int'l*, pg. 4429

LBC FINANCIAL SERVICES INC.—See Laurentian Bank of Canada; *Int'l*, pg. 4425
LBC MABUHAY USA CORP.—See LBC Express Holdings, Inc.; *Int'l*, pg. 4429
LB CO., LTD.—See Polaris Capital Group Co., Ltd.; *Int'l*, pg. 5907
LB CO., LTD.—See Asahi Group Holdings Ltd.; *Int'l*, pg. 594
LBC TRUST INC.—See Laurentian Bank of Canada; *Int'l*, pg. 4425
LB ELECTRIC SUPPLY CO. INC.; *U.S. Private*, pg. 2403
LBEST INC.—See HS Ad Inc.; *Int'l*, pg. 3502
LBF ENTERPRISES; *U.S. Private*, pg. 2403
L. B. FINANCE PLC; *Int'l*, pg. 4381
L.B. FOSTER BALL WINCH, INC.—See L.B. Foster Company; *U.S. Public*, pg. 1278
L.B. FOSTER CO. - BEDFORD—See L.B. Foster Company; *U.S. Public*, pg. 1278
L.B. FOSTER COMPANY; *U.S. Public*, pg. 1278
L.B. FOSTER RAIL TECHNOLOGIES CANADA LTD—See L.B. Foster Company; *U.S. Public*, pg. 1278
L. B. FOSTER RAIL TECHNOLOGIES, INC.—See L.B. Foster Company; *U.S. Public*, pg. 1278
L.B. FOSTER RAIL TECHNOLOGIES, INC.—See L.B. Foster Company; *U.S. Public*, pg. 1279
L.B. FOSTER RAIL TECHNOLOGIES (UK) LTD.—See L.B. Foster Company; *U.S. Public*, pg. 1278
L.B. FOSTER UK LTD.—See L.B. Foster Company; *U.S. Public*, pg. 1279
LBG LIMITED—See B. Grimm Group; *Int'l*, pg. 788
LBG MEDIA PLC; *Int'l*, pg. 4429
LB HUNET—See LB Semicon Co., Ltd.; *Int'l*, pg. 4429
LBI BELGIUM; *Int'l*, pg. 4429
LBI CAPITAL BERHAD; *Int'l*, pg. 4429
LBI HF.; *Int'l*, pg. 4429
LBI INTERNATIONAL N.V.—See Publicis Groupe S.A.; *Int'l*, pg. 6098
L. BILODEAU & FILS LTD; *Int'l*, pg. 4381
LB IMMOBILIENBEWERTUNGSGESELLSCHAFT MBH—See BayernLB Holding AG; *Int'l*, pg. 914
L.B. INDUSTRIES, INC.; *U.S. Private*, pg. 2364
L B INDUSTRIES, INC.; *U.S. Private*, pg. 2361
LBI NORDIC HOLDING A/S—See Publicis Groupe S.A.; *Int'l*, pg. 6098
LB INTERNATIONAL, INC.; *U.S. Private*, pg. 2403
LB INVESTMENT INC.—See LB Semicon Co., Ltd.; *Int'l*, pg. 4429
LBIQ GMBH—See Publicis Groupe S.A.; *Int'l*, pg. 6111
LB&L CABLE INC.; *U.S. Private*, pg. 2403
LBL COMMUNICATION GROUP; *Int'l*, pg. 4429
LBL LIGHTING LLC—See AEA Investors LP; *U.S. Private*, pg. 114
LBLUSEM CO. LTD.; *Int'l*, pg. 4429
LBM CONSTRUCTION COMPANY, INC.; *U.S. Private*, pg. 2403
LBM CORP.; *U.S. Private*, pg. 2403
LB MEDIA GROUP, LLC—See Leafbuyer Technologies, Inc.; *U.S. Public*, pg. 1296
LBMP, LLC—See Lithia Motors, Inc.; *U.S. Public*, pg. 1323
LBM S.R.L.—See Compass Diversified Holdings; *U.S. Public*, pg. 560
LBN PARTNERS LLC - LOS ANGELES OFFICE—See Ansira Partners, Inc.; *U.S. Private*, pg. 286
LBN PARTNERS LLC—See Ansira Partners, Inc.; *U.S. Private*, pg. 286
LBO FRANCE S.A.R.L.; *Int'l*, pg. 4429
L.B.O. HOLDING, INC.—See Vail Resorts, Inc.; *U.S. Public*, pg. 2271
L. BOSENDORFER KLAVIERFABRIK GMBH—See Yamaha Corporation; *Int'l*, pg. 8549
L&B PAPER INC.; *U.S. Private*, pg. 2362
LBP COMMUNICATIONS; *Int'l*, pg. 4430
L B PIPE & COUPLING PRODUCTS, LLC—See L.B. Foster Company; *U.S. Public*, pg. 1278
L B PIPE & COUPLING PRODUCTS, LLC—See L B Industries, Inc.; *U.S. Private*, pg. 2361
LBP MANUFACTURING LLC—See Sabert Corporation; *U.S. Private*, pg. 3520
LB PRIVATE EQUITY INC.—See LB Semicon Co., Ltd.; *Int'l*, pg. 4429
LBQ FOUNDRY S.A. DE C.V.—See Le Belier SA; *Int'l*, pg. 4431
L&B REALTY ADVISORS, INC.; *U.S. Private*, pg. 2362
LBS BAYERISCHE LANDESBAUSPARKASSE—See BayernLB Holding AG; *Int'l*, pg. 913
LBS BINA GROUP BERHAD; *Int'l*, pg. 4430
LBS COMMUNICATIONS INC—See Bertelsmann SE & Co. KGaA; *Int'l*, pg. 995
LB SEMICON CO., LTD.; *Int'l*, pg. 4428
LBS FINANCIAL CREDIT UNION; *U.S. Private*, pg. 2403
LB-SHELL PLC; *Int'l*, pg. 4429
LBS IMMOBILIEN GMBH—See Helaba Landesbank Hessen-Thuringen; *Int'l*, pg. 3328
LBS LIMITED PARTNERSHIP—See Ventas, Inc.; *U.S. Public*, pg. 2278
LBS SAAR GMBH—See Landesbank Saar; *Int'l*, pg. 4406
LB STEEL, LLC—See L B Industries, Inc.; *U.S. Private*, pg. 2361
LBT INNOVATIONS LTD.; *Int'l*, pg. 4430

L&B TRANSPORT INC.—See L&B Transport Inc.; *U.S. Private*, pg. 2362
L&B TRANSPORT INC.; *U.S. Private*, pg. 2362
LBU, INC.; *U.S. Private*, pg. 2403
LBU PERSONAL COMPLETE GMBH—See Zalaris ASA; *Int'l*, pg. 8621
L/B WATER SERVICE INC.; *U.S. Private*, pg. 2367
L.B. WHITE COMPANY INC.; *U.S. Private*, pg. 2364
LBX COMPANY LLC—See Sumitomo Heavy Industries, Ltd.; *Int'l*, pg. 7289
LBX DO BRASIL COMERICO DE EQUIPMENTOS INDUSTRIAIS LTDA—See Sumitomo Heavy Industries, Ltd.; *Int'l*, pg. 7287
LC3S INC.; *U.S. Private*, pg. 2403
LCA CONSULTING OY—See Etteplan Oyj; *Int'l*, pg. 2525
LCAM SAS—See Eurofins Scientific S.E.; *Int'l*, pg. 2542
L CAPITAL ASIA ADVISORS PLC—See LVMH Moet Hennessy Louis Vuitton SE; *Int'l*, pg. 4592
L CAPITAL MANAGEMENT SAS—See LVMH Moet Hennessy Louis Vuitton SE; *Int'l*, pg. 4592
L-CARE CO., LTD.—See LONGLIFE HOLDING Co., Ltd.; *Int'l*, pg. 4551
L CATTERTON ASIA ACQUISITION CORP.; *Int'l*, pg. 4369
L CATTERTON LATIN AMERICA ACQUISITION CORP.; *U.S. Public*, pg. 1278
LC AUTOMATION LTD.; *Int'l*, pg. 4430
LCA-VISION INC.; *U.S. Private*, pg. 2403
L&C BIO CO., LTD.; *Int'l*, pg. 4369
LCC BELGIUM N.V.—See Mahindra & Mahindra Limited; *Int'l*, pg. 4647
LCC FOCKE SERVICE ST.-PB—See Focke & Co. (GmbH & Co.) Verpackungsmaschinen; *Int'l*, pg. 2718
LCCG UK LIMITED—See Utmost International Group Holdings Limited; *Int'l*, pg. 8101
L&C CHANGSHA CABLE INDUSTRIES LTD.—See Leggett & Platt, Incorporated; *U.S. Public*, pg. 1302
LCC, UNITED KINGDOM, LIMITED—See Mahindra & Mahindra Limited; *Int'l*, pg. 4647
LCD COMMUNICATIONS LLC—See PulteGroup, Inc.; *U.S. Public*, pg. 1737
LCD (INDOCHINA) PTE LTD—See Aspial Corporation Limited; *Int'l*, pg. 630
LCD (INDOCHINA) PTE LTD—See Fragrance Group Limited; *Int'l*, pg. 2758
THE L.C. DOANE COMPANY; *U.S. Private*, pg. 4067
LCD PROPERTY MANAGEMENT PTE LTD—See Aspial Corporation Limited; *Int'l*, pg. 630
LCD PROPERTY MANAGEMENT PTE LTD—See Fragrance Group Limited; *Int'l*, pg. 2758
LCD (VIETNAM) PTE LTD—See Aspial Corporation Limited; *Int'l*, pg. 630
LCD (VIETNAM) PTE LTD—See Fragrance Group Limited; *Int'l*, pg. 2758
LCEL COLLECTIBLES INC.; *U.S. Private*, pg. 2403
LC ENTERPRISES LLC; *U.S. Private*, pg. 2403
LCG, LLC—See Entravision Communications Corporation; *U.S. Public*, pg. 779
L.C.G. MALMBERG B.V.—See Sanoma Oyj; *Int'l*, pg. 6553
LC GROUP LLC; *U.S. Private*, pg. 2403
LCG TECHNOLOGIES CORPORATION; *U.S. Private*, pg. 2403
LCH GROUP HOLDINGS LIMITED—See London Stock Exchange Group plc; *Int'l*, pg. 4548
LCH LIMITED—See London Stock Exchange Group plc; *Int'l*, pg. 4548
L.C. HOTELS PTE LTD—See A-Smart Holdings Ltd.; *Int'l*, pg. 20
LCI CLASQUIN SA—See Clasquin S.A.; *Int'l*, pg. 1652
LCI CORPORATION INTERNATIONAL—See Nederman Holding AB; *Int'l*, pg. 5188
LCI EDUCATION NETWORK; *Int'l*, pg. 4430
LCI, INC.—See Verisk Analytics, Inc.; *U.S. Public*, pg. 2283
LCI INDUSTRIES; *U.S. Public*, pg. 1295
L.C. INDUSTRIES FOR THE BLIND INC.; *U.S. Private*, pg. 2365
L.C. INDUSTRIES INC.; *U.S. Private*, pg. 2365
LCL ACQUISITIONS LIMITED—See Lovell Minnick Partners LLC; *U.S. Private*, pg. 2502
LC LAUSANNE CITES S.A.—See TX Group AG; *Int'l*, pg. 7992
LCL BULK TRANSPORT INC.—See P&S Investment Company Inc.; *U.S. Private*, pg. 3059
LCL GROUP LIMITED—See Lovell Minnick Partners LLC; *U.S. Private*, pg. 2502
LCL LOGISTIX (INDIA) PVT. LTD.—See CMA CGM S.A.; *Int'l*, pg. 1668
LCL LOGISTIX TANZANIA LTD.—See CMA CGM S.A.; *Int'l*, pg. 1668
L.C. LOGISTICS PTE LTD—See Aspial Corporation Limited; *Int'l*, pg. 630
L.C. LOGISTICS PTE LTD—See Fragrance Group Limited; *Int'l*, pg. 2758
L.C. (LONDON) LTD—See Aspial Corporation Limited; *Int'l*, pg. 630
L.C. (LONDON) LTD—See Fragrance Group Limited; *Int'l*, pg. 2758
LCL RESOURCES LIMITED; *Int'l*, pg. 4430
LCL SERVICES (IOM) LIMITED—See Lovell Minnick Partners LLC; *U.S. Private*, pg. 2502

LCL SERVICES (IRELAND) LIMITED—See Lovell Minnick Partners LLC; *U.S. Private*, pg. 2502
LCL TRANSIT COMPANY—See P&S Investment Company Inc.; *U.S. Private*, pg. 3059
LC LUXCONTROL ASBL—See TUV Rheinland Berlin-Brandenburg Pfalz e.V.; *Int'l*, pg. 7982
LC MANUFACTURING LLC—See MW Universal Inc.; *U.S. Private*, pg. 2822
LCMC HEALTH HOLDINGS, INC.; *U.S. Private*, pg. 2403
LC MORTGAGE CORPORATION; *U.S. Private*, pg. 2403
LCM PRECISION TECHNOLOGY S.R.L.—See Hurco Companies, Inc.; *U.S. Public*, pg. 1076
LCNB CORP.; *U.S. Public*, pg. 1296
LCNB NATIONAL BANK—See LCNB Corp.; *U.S. Public*, pg. 1296
LCN CLOSERS—See Allegion Public Limited Company; *Int'l*, pg. 335
LCN SAS—See Eurofins Scientific S.E.; *Int'l*, pg. 2543
L-COM GLOBAL CONNECTIVITY CORP. - FLORIDA—See Genstar Capital, LLC; *U.S. Private*, pg. 1677
L-COM, INC.—See Genstar Capital, LLC; *U.S. Private*, pg. 1677
L-CON CONSTRUCTORS COMPANY—See Lexicon, Inc.; *U.S. Private*, pg. 2440
LC PACKAGING INTERNATIONAL BV; *Int'l*, pg. 4430
LC PACKAGING UK LTD - SCOTLAND—See LC Packaging International BV; *Int'l*, pg. 4430
LC PACKAGING UK LTD—See LC Packaging International BV; *Int'l*, pg. 4430
LCP ACQUISITION CORP.; *U.S. Private*, pg. 2403
LCP HOLDINGS AND INVESTMENTS PUBLIC LTD.—See Bank of Cyprus Holdings Public Limited Company; *Int'l*, pg. 842
LCP LEUNA CARBOXYLATION PLANT GMBH—See Daicel Corporation; *Int'l*, pg. 1919
LCP LIBERA AG—See Alexander Forbes Group Holdings Limited; *Int'l*, pg. 307
LCP S.R.L.—See Investment AB Latour; *Int'l*, pg. 3781
LCR CONTRACTORS, INC.—See TopBuild Corp.; *U.S. Public*, pg. 2163
LCR ELECTRONICS, INC.—See Tinicum Enterprises, Inc.; *U.S. Private*, pg. 4174
LCR GROUP PTY LTD—See Qube Holdings Limited; *Int'l*, pg. 6158
LCR HALLCREST LLC—See Harbour Group Industries, Inc.; *U.S. Private*, pg. 1861
LCR HALLCREST LTD—See Harbour Group Industries, Inc.; *U.S. Private*, pg. 1861
LCR HIGHWAYS LTD—See VINCI S.A.; *Int'l*, pg. 8220
LCS CONSTRUCTORS, INC.; *U.S. Private*, pg. 2403
LCS HOLDINGS INC.; *U.S. Private*, pg. 2403
LCS IMOBILIAR SA; *Int'l*, pg. 4430
LCS INC.—See Dunes Point Capital, LLC; *U.S. Private*, pg. 1288
LCS SERVICES LANDFILL, INC.—See Waste Management, Inc.; *U.S. Public*, pg. 2331
LCS TECHNOLOGIES, INC.; *U.S. Private*, pg. 2404
LC SUREFOOT; *U.S. Private*, pg. 2403
LC-TEC HOLDING AB; *Int'l*, pg. 4430
LCT GLOBAL RESOURCES, INC.; *U.S. Private*, pg. 2404
LCTH CORPORATION BHD—See Fu Yu Corporation Limited; *Int'l*, pg. 2801
LCTI LOW CARBON TECHNOLOGIES INTERNATIONAL INC.; *U.S. Public*, pg. 1296
LCV CAPITAL MANAGEMENT, LLC; *U.S. Private*, pg. 2404
LCV CORPORATION—See TOKAI Holdings Corporation; *Int'l*, pg. 7779
L.C. WHITFORD CO. INC.; *U.S. Private*, pg. 2365
L.C. WILLIAMS & ASSOCIATES, LLC; *U.S. Private*, pg. 2365
LCY CHEMICAL CORP.—See KKR & Co. Inc.; *U.S. Public*, pg. 1258
LCY ELASTOMERS LP—See KKR & Co. Inc.; *U.S. Public*, pg. 1258
LD ACQUISITION COMPANY 8 LLC—See DigitalBridge Group, Inc.; *U.S. Public*, pg. 665
L. D'AGOSTINI & SONS INC.; *U.S. Private*, pg. 2364
L&D APPLIANCES CORPORATION; *U.S. Private*, pg. 2362
LD BULK ASIA PTE LTD.—See Louis Dreyfus Armateurs; *Int'l*, pg. 4561
LDC ARGENTINA S.A.—See Louis Dreyfus Company B.V.; *Int'l*, pg. 4562
LDC (CHINA) TRADING COMPANY LTD.—See Louis Dreyfus Company B.V.; *Int'l*, pg. 4562
LDC DENTAL PUBLIC COMPANY LIMITED; *Int'l*, pg. 4430
LD CELULOSE S.A.—See Lenzing Aktiengesellschaft; *Int'l*, pg. 4415
LDC ENTERPRISES AUSTRALIA PTY. LTD.—See Louis Dreyfus Company B.V.; *Int'l*, pg. 4562
LDC (HOLDINGS) PLC—See The Unite Group plc; *Int'l*, pg. 7697
LDC (MANAGERS) LIMITED—See Lloyds Banking Group plc; *Int'l*, pg. 4537
LDC PRECISION ENGINEERING CO., LTD.—See LemTech Holdings Co., Ltd.; *Int'l*, pg. 4450

COMPANY NAME INDEX

LDC SA; *Int'l*, pg. 4430
LDC (TIANJIN) FOOD TECHNOLOGY LIMITED LIABILITY COMPANY—See Louis Dreyfus Company B.V.; *Int'l*, pg. 4562
LDC TRADING & SERVICES CO. S.A.—See Raizen S.A.; *Int'l*, pg. 6192
LD&D AUSTRALIA PTY. LTD.—See Bega Cheese Ltd.; *Int'l*, pg. 940
L.D. DAVIS INDUSTRIES INC.; *U.S. Private*, pg. 2365
LDD FIRE PROTECTION—See Robore Holdings Ltd.; *Int'l*, pg. 6371
LD DIDACTIC GMBH—See Aurelius Equity Opportunities SE & Co. KGaA; *Int'l*, pg. 708
LDD SPECIAL WORKS—See Robore Holdings Ltd.; *Int'l*, pg. 6371
LDF FOOD GROUP; *U.S. Private*, pg. 2404
LDG REINSURANCE CORPORATION—See Tokio Marine Holdings, Inc.; *Int'l*, pg. 7784
LDG SAN ANTONIO—See Larson Design Group; *U.S. Private*, pg. 2394
LDG - TRANSPORTATION ENGINEERING—See Larson Design Group; *U.S. Private*, pg. 2393
LDH (LA DORIA) LTD—See Investindustrial Advisors Ltd.; *Int'l*, pg. 3779
LDI INDUSTRIES, INC.; *U.S. Private*, pg. 2404
LDI LTD., LLC; *U.S. Private*, pg. 2404
LDISCOVERY, LLC - FORT LAUDERDALE—See Pivotal Acquisition Corp.; *U.S. Private*, pg. 3192
LDISCOVERY, LLC - PHILADELPHIA—See Pivotal Acquisition Corp.; *U.S. Private*, pg. 3192
LDIS, LLC—See Tetra Tech, Inc.; *U.S. Public*, pg. 2023
LDJ PRODUCTIONS; *U.S. Private*, pg. 2404
LDK SOLAR CANADA INC—See LDK Solar Co., Ltd.; *Int'l*, pg. 4431
LDK SOLAR CO., LTD.; *Int'l*, pg. 4431
LDK SOLAR HI-TECH (NANCHANG) CO., LTD.—See LDK Solar Co., Ltd.; *Int'l*, pg. 4431
LDK SOLAR INTERNATIONAL COMPANY LIMITED—See LDK Solar Co., Ltd.; *Int'l*, pg. 4431
LDK SOLAR ITALIA S.R.L.—See LDK Solar Co., Ltd.; *Int'l*, pg. 4431
LDK SOLAR POWER TECHNOLOGY (XINYU) ENGINEERING CO., LTD.—See LDK Solar Co., Ltd.; *Int'l*, pg. 4431
LDK SOLAR SPAIN, S.L.—See LDK Solar Co., Ltd.; *Int'l*, pg. 4431
LDK SOLAR TECH USA, INC.—See LDK Solar Co., Ltd.; *Int'l*, pg. 4431
LDK SOLAR USA INC.—See LDK Solar Co., Ltd.; *Int'l*, pg. 4431
LDK TRADING SERVICE GERMANY GMBH—See LDK Solar Co., Ltd.; *Int'l*, pg. 4431
LDLC.COM SA; *Int'l*, pg. 4431
LDLC, LLC—See Lithia Motors, Inc.; *U.S. Public*, pg. 1323
LDM B.V.—See Outokumpu Oyj; *Int'l*, pg. 5667
LDMI; *U.S. Private*, pg. 2404
LD PORTS & LOGISTICS—See Louis Dreyfus Armateurs; *Int'l*, pg. 4561
LDR BRASIL COMERCIO, IMPORTACAO E EXPORTACAO LTDA.—See Zimmer Biomet Holdings, Inc.; *U.S. Public*, pg. 2406
LD RECYCLING GMBH—See PORR AG; *Int'l*, pg. 5923
LD RETI S.R.L.—See A2A S.p.A.; *Int'l*, pg. 29
LDR GROWTH PARTNERS; *U.S. Private*, pg. 2404
LDR HOLDING CORPORATION—See Zimmer Biomet Holdings, Inc.; *U.S. Public*, pg. 2406
LDR INDUSTRIES, INC.; *U.S. Private*, pg. 2404
LDR MEDICAL S.A.S.—See Zimmer Biomet Holdings, Inc.; *U.S. Public*, pg. 2406
LDR SPINE USA, INC.—See Zimmer Biomet Holdings, Inc.; *U.S. Public*, pg. 2406
L.D.S. METAL WORKS COMPANY LIMITED—See Tirathai Public Company Limited; *Int'l*, pg. 7756
LDT INC.; *Int'l*, pg. 4431
LDT LASER DISPLAY TECHNOLOGY GMBH—See Rheinmetall AG; *Int'l*, pg. 6323
LDT—See James Latham Plc; *Int'l*, pg. 3878
LDV INC.; *U.S. Private*, pg. 2404
LDV UNITED—See WPP plc; *Int'l*, pg. 8467
LEACH COLOUR LIMITED—See Chargeurs SA; *Int'l*, pg. 1450
LEACHGARNER—See Berkshire Hathaway Inc.; *U.S. Public*, pg. 316
LEACH INTERNATIONAL CORPORATION—See TransDigm Group Incorporated; *U.S. Public*, pg. 2181
LEACH INTERNATIONAL EUROPE S.A.—See TransDigm Group Incorporated; *U.S. Public*, pg. 2181
LEACH RHODES WALKER LTD.; *Int'l*, pg. 4432
LEACKCO BANK HOLDING COMPANY, INC.; *U.S. Private*, pg. 2405
LEACO RURAL TELEPHONE COOP INC.; *U.S. Private*, pg. 2405
LEA COUNTY ELECTRIC COOP; *U.S. Private*, pg. 2405
LEACY MG LTD.; *Int'l*, pg. 4432
LEAD5 MEDIA, LLC.; *U.S. Private*, pg. 2405
LEADAGE ALLOYS INDIA LIMITED—See EXIDE INDUSTRIES LIMITED; *Int'l*, pg. 2585
LEADBETTER FOODS INC.—See Premium Brands Holdings Corporation; *Int'l*, pg. 5963

LEAD BY SALES, LLC; *U.S. Private*, pg. 2405
LEADCLOUD, LLC—See The Allstate Corporation; *U.S. Public*, pg. 2033
THE LEAD CO., INC.; *Int'l*, pg. 7664
LEADCOM COSTA RICA S.A—See Mahindra & Mahindra Limited; *Int'l*, pg. 4647
LEADCOM DE COLOMBIA S.A—See Mahindra & Mahindra Limited; *Int'l*, pg. 4647
LEADCOM DEL ECUADOR S.A—See Mahindra & Mahindra Limited; *Int'l*, pg. 4647
LEADCOM INTEGRATED SOLUTIONS LIMITED—See Mahindra & Mahindra Limited; *Int'l*, pg. 4647
LEADCOM PERU S.A.C—See Mahindra & Mahindra Limited; *Int'l*, pg. 4647
LEADCOM TANZANIA LTD.—See Mahindra & Mahindra Limited; *Int'l*, pg. 4647
LEADCOM TELECOMUNICATIONES DE CHILE S.A—See Mahindra & Mahindra Limited; *Int'l*, pg. 4647
LEADCORP INC.; *Int'l*, pg. 4432
LEADCREATIONS.COM LLC; *U.S. Private*, pg. 2405
LEAD DATA INC.; *Int'l*, pg. 4432
LEADDESK OYJ; *Int'l*, pg. 4432
LEADDOG MARKETING GROUP; *U.S. Private*, pg. 2405
LEAD EASTERN INVESTMENT CO., LTD.; *Int'l*, pg. 4432
LEADEC BV & CO. KG—See Triton Advisers Limited; *Int'l*, pg. 7933
LEADEC CORP.—See Triton Advisers Limited; *Int'l*, pg. 7933
LEADEC DO BRASIL LTDA.—See Triton Advisers Limited; *Int'l*, pg. 7933
LEADEC FM BV & CO. KG—See Triton Advisers Limited; *Int'l*, pg. 7933
LEADEC HOLDING BV & CO. KG—See Triton Advisers Limited; *Int'l*, pg. 7933
LEADEC INDIA PVT. LTD.—See Triton Advisers Limited; *Int'l*, pg. 7933
LEADEC KFT.—See Triton Advisers Limited; *Int'l*, pg. 7933
LEADEC LIMITED—See Triton Advisers Limited; *Int'l*, pg. 7933
LEADEC MEXICO S. DE R.L. DE C.V.—See Triton Advisers Limited; *Int'l*, pg. 7933
LEADEC OSTERREICH GMBH—See Triton Advisers Limited; *Int'l*, pg. 7933
LEADEC SP. Z O.O.—See Triton Advisers Limited; *Int'l*, pg. 7933
LEADEC S.R.O.—See Triton Advisers Limited; *Int'l*, pg. 7933
LEADEC S.R.O.—See Triton Advisers Limited; *Int'l*, pg. 7933
LEAD EDGE CAPITAL MANAGEMENT, LLC; *U.S. Private*, pg. 2405
LEAD EDGE GROWTH OPPORTUNITIES, LTD.; *U.S. Public*, pg. 1296
LEADER ASSOCIATED NEWSPAPERS PTY. LIMITED—See News Corporation; *U.S. Public*, pg. 1520
LEADER AUTO RESOURCES LAR INC.; *Int'l*, pg. 4432
LEADER BANK, N.A.; *U.S. Private*, pg. 2405
LEADER CABLE INDUSTRY BERHAD—See Sarawak Cable Berhad; *Int'l*, pg. 6576
LEADER CAPITAL HOLDINGS CORP.; *Int'l*, pg. 4432
LEADER & CRESCENDO ELECTRONICS INTERNATIONAL PTE LTD.—See Leader Electronics Inc.; *Int'l*, pg. 4433
LEADER DISTRIBUTION SYSTEMS, INC.; *U.S. Private*, pg. 2406
LEADER ELECTRONICS CORPORATION; *Int'l*, pg. 4432
LEADER ELECTRONICS INC.; *Int'l*, pg. 4432
LEADER ELECTRONICS N.A. INC.—See Leader Electronics Inc.; *Int'l*, pg. 4433
LEADER ELECTRONICS PHILIPPINE BRANCH INCORPORATED—See Leader Electronics Inc.; *Int'l*, pg. 4433
LEADER EMERGENCY VEHICLES—See AIP, LLC; *U.S. Private*, pg. 135
LEADER ENERGY SERVICES LTD.—See Key Energy Services, Inc.; *U.S. Public*, pg. 1225
LEADER ENVIRONMENTAL TECHNOLOGIES LIMITED; *Int'l*, pg. 4432
LEADER FAITH INTERNATIONAL—See Sinolink Worldwide Holdings Limited; *Int'l*, pg. 6952
LEADERFLUSH & SHAPLAND HOLDINGS LIMITED—See SIG plc; *Int'l*, pg. 6906
LEADER HARMONIOUS DRIVE SYSTEMS CO., LTD.; *Int'l*, pg. 4433
LEADER HILL CORPORATION; *Int'l*, pg. 4433
LEADER HOME CENTERS INC.; *U.S. Private*, pg. 2406
LEADER INSTRUMENTS CORPORATION—See Leader Electronics Corporation; *Int'l*, pg. 4432
LEADER & KALKASKIAN—See Alden Global Capital LLC; *U.S. Private*, pg. 156
LEADERLEASE S.A.; *Int'l*, pg. 4433
LEADER MARINE CONT. L.L.C.—See Build King Holdings Limited; *Int'l*, pg. 1212
LEADER METAL INDUSTRY CO., LTD.—See Berkshire Hathaway Inc.; *U.S. Public*, pg. 311
LEADER ONE FINANCIAL CORP.; *U.S. Private*, pg. 2406
LEADERONE FINANCIAL; *U.S. Private*, pg. 2406

LEADLIFE SOLUTIONS INC.

LEADER PAPER PRODUCTS INC.; *U.S. Private*, pg. 2406
LEADER PHYSICAL THERAPY, LIMITED PARTNERSHIP—See U.S. Physical Therapy, Inc.; *U.S. Public*, pg. 2215
LEADER POST—See Chatham Asset Management, LLC; *U.S. Private*, pg. 861
THE LEADERS BANK—See Providence Financial Corporation; *U.S. Private*, pg. 3294
LEADERS COSMETICS CO., LTD.; *Int'l*, pg. 4433
LEADERS CREDIT UNION; *U.S. Private*, pg. 2406
THE LEADERS GROUP, INC.; *U.S. Private*, pg. 4068
LEADERSHIP DEVELOPMENT SOLUTIONS SRL; *Int'l*, pg. 4433
THE LEADERSHIP INSTITUTE; *U.S. Private*, pg. 4068
LEADER'S HOLDING COMPANY; *U.S. Private*, pg. 2406
LEADERS IN ONCOLOGY CARE LIMITED—See HCA Healthcare, Inc.; *U.S. Public*, pg. 1000
LEADERS INTERNATIONAL UK LTD—See Daeyang Electric Co., Ltd.; *Int'l*, pg. 1911
LEADERS MERCHANT SERVICES, LLC—See Paysafe Limited; *Int'l*, pg. 5764
LEADER SPORTS EUROPE S.A.—See Opti-Coating Laboratories, Inc.; *Int'l*, pg. 5602
LEADERS TECHNOLOGY INVESTMENT CO., LTD.; *Int'l*, pg. 4433
LEADER STEEL HOLDINGS BERHAD; *Int'l*, pg. 4433
LEADER STEEL SDN. BHD.—See Leader Steel Holdings Berhad; *Int'l*, pg. 4433
LEADER STEEL SERVICE CENTRE SDN. BHD.—See Leader Steel Holdings Berhad; *Int'l*, pg. 4433
LEADER TECH, INC.—See HEICO Corporation; *U.S. Public*, pg. 1020
LEADER TRAILER, INC.—See International Industries, Inc.; *U.S. Private*, pg. 2117
LEAD FINANCIAL SERVICES LIMITED; *Int'l*, pg. 4432
LEADFORMANCE S.A.S—See Solocal Group; *Int'l*, pg. 7074
LEADFORMIX INC.—See SAP SE; *Int'l*, pg. 6567
LEAD GENERATION SOLUTIONS; *U.S. Private*, pg. 2405
LEADGENESYS; *U.S. Private*, pg. 2406
LEADID LLC; *U.S. Private*, pg. 2406
LEADING BRANDS OF AMERICA, INC.—See Liquid Media Group Ltd.; *Int'l*, pg. 4523
LEADING BRANDS OF CANADA, INC.—See Liquid Media Group Ltd.; *Int'l*, pg. 4523
LEADING EDGE AUTO REFINISHES, INC.—See Wesco Group, Inc.; *U.S. Private*, pg. 4482
LEADING EDGE AVIATION, INC.; *U.S. Private*, pg. 2406
LEADING EDGE AVIATION SERVICES INC.—See Vance Street Capital LLC; *U.S. Private*, pg. 4342
LEADING EDGE AVIATION SOLUTIONS, LLC; *U.S. Private*, pg. 2406
LEADING EDGE CO., LTD.—See CREEK & RIVER Co., Ltd.; *Int'l*, pg. 1837
LEADING EDGE ENGINEERING, PC—See Adaptive Corp.; *U.S. Private*, pg. 76
LEADING EDGE JET CENTER LLC—See Leading Edge Aviation, Inc.; *U.S. Private*, pg. 2406
THE LEADING EDGE MARKET RESEARCH CONSULTANTS PTY LIMITED—See Enero Group Limited; *Int'l*, pg. 2424
LEADING EDGE MATERIALS CORP.; *Int'l*, pg. 4433
LEADING EDGE MISSISSIPPI INC.; *U.S. Private*, pg. 2406
LEADING EDGE RECOVERY SOLUTIONS, LLC; *U.S. Private*, pg. 2406
LEADING EDJE; *U.S. Private*, pg. 2406
LEADING ENERGY CORPORATION—See CTCI Corporation; *Int'l*, pg. 1870
LEADING HOLDINGS GROUP LIMITED; *Int'l*, pg. 4433
THE LEADING HOTELS OF THE WORLD, LTD.; *U.S. Private*, pg. 4068
LEADING INTERCONNECT SEMICONDUCTOR TECHNOLOGY QINHUANGDAO CO., LTD.—See Zhen Ding Technology Holding Limited; *Int'l*, pg. 8669
LEADING INVESTMENT & SECURITIES CO., LTD.; *Int'l*, pg. 4433
LEADING LADY COMPANIES; *U.S. Private*, pg. 2406
LEADING LEASING FINANCE & INVESTMENT COMPANY LTD.; *Int'l*, pg. 4433
LEADING MARK, INC.—See Vector Inc.; *Int'l*, pg. 8144
LEADING RIDGE MANAGEMENT, LLC; *U.S. Private*, pg. 2406
LEADING SOLUTIONS CO., LTD.—See Tanabe Consulting Group Co., Ltd.; *Int'l*, pg. 7454
LEADING TECHNOLOGY GROUP PTY LTD.; *Int'l*, pg. 4433
LEADING THE WAY WITH DR. MICHAEL YOUSSEF; *U.S. Private*, pg. 2406
LEADING WAY APPAREL SHANGHAI LIMITED—See Dickson Concepts (International) Limited; *Int'l*, pg. 2112
LEAD INNOVATION CORP.; *Int'l*, pg. 4432
LEAD INTELLIGENCE, INC.—See Verisk Analytics, Inc.; *U.S. Public*, pg. 2283
LEAD IT CORPORATION; *U.S. Private*, pg. 2405
LEADJEN, INC.; *U.S. Private*, pg. 2406
LEADLIFE SOLUTIONS INC.; *U.S. Private*, pg. 2406

1581

LEADLIFE SOLUTIONS INC.

LEADMAKER SERVICES LTD.—See Komax Holding AG; *Int'l*, pg. 4241
LEAD MANAGEMENT ENGINEERING & CONSTRUCTION PTE. LTD.—See M+W Group GmbH; *Int'l*, pg. 4613
LEAD MANAGEMENT ENGINEERING (MALAYSIA) SDN. BHD.—See M+W Group GmbH; *Int'l*, pg. 4613
LEAD MANAGEMENT ENGINEERING (SHANGHAI) CO., LTD.—See M+W Group GmbH; *Int'l*, pg. 4613
LEADMAN ELECTRONICS USA, INC.; *U.S. Private*, pg. 2406
LEADMD, INC.; *U.S. Private*, pg. 2407
LEADNOMICS; *U.S. Private*, pg. 2407
LEAD REAL ESTATE CO., LTD.; *Int'l*, pg. 4432
LEAD RESEARCH GROUP, LLC; *U.S. Private*, pg. 2405
LEADS360 INC.; *U.S. Private*, pg. 2407
LEADS BIO CO., LTD.—See Jinli Group Holdings Limited; *Int'l*, pg. 3969
LEADS.COM—See Siris Capital Group, LLC; *U.S. Private*, pg. 3675
LEADSCOPE, INC.—See ArchiMed SAS; *Int'l*, pg. 548
LEADSHINE AMERICA INC.—See China Leadshine Technology Co., Ltd.; *Int'l*, pg. 1514
LEAD SHOJI CO., LTD.—See Shimojima Co., Ltd.; *Int'l*, pg. 6836
THE LEADS NETWORK, LLC; *U.S. Private*, pg. 4068
LEADSONLINE LLC; *U.S. Private*, pg. 2407
LEADSPACE, INC.; *U.S. Private*, pg. 2407
LEADTECH CO., LTD.—See Helios Techno Holding Co., Ltd.; *Int'l*, pg. 3330
LEAD TECHNOLOGIES, INC.—See Thoma Bravo, L.P.; *U.S. Private*, pg. 4146
LEADTEK RESEARCH INC.; *Int'l*, pg. 4433
LEADTREND TECHNOLOGY CORP.; *Int'l*, pg. 4433
LEAD VIEW SDN BHD—See YNH Property Bhd; *Int'l*, pg. 8590
LEADVILLE INSURANCE COMPANY—See Macy's, Inc.; *U.S. Public*, pg. 1353
LEADVISE REPLY GMBH—See Reply S.p.A.; *Int'l*, pg. 6291
LEADVISION MEDIA, LLC; *U.S. Private*, pg. 2407
LEADWAY ASSURANCE COMPANY LIMITED; *Int'l*, pg. 4434
LEADWAY TECHNOLOGY INVESTMENT GROUP LIMITED; *Int'l*, pg. 4434
LEAF AREENA OY—See Pihlajalinna Oy; *Int'l*, pg. 5865
LEAFBUYER TECHNOLOGIES, INC.; *U.S. Public*, pg. 1296
THE LEAF-CHRONICLE—See Gannett Co., Inc.; *U.S. Public*, pg. 900
LEAF CLEAN ENERGY COMPANY; *Int'l*, pg. 4434
LEAF COMMERCIAL CAPITAL, INC.—See M&T Bank Corporation; *U.S. Public*, pg. 1351
LEAFFILTER NORTH INC.; *U.S. Private*, pg. 2407
LEAF FINANCIAL CORP.—See Island Capital Group LLC; *U.S. Private*, pg. 2144
LEAF GROUP LTD.—See Graham Holdings Company; *U.S. Public*, pg. 956
LEAF HOME, LLC; *U.S. Private*, pg. 2407
LEAFIELD FEEDS LTD.—See ForFarmers Group B.V.; *Int'l*, pg. 2732
LEAF MOBILE, INC.; *Int'l*, pg. 4434
LEAFNXT CO., LTD.—See Nisso Corporation; *Int'l*, pg. 5377
LEAF OF FAITH BEVERAGE INC.; *U.S. Public*, pg. 1296
LEAF RESOURCES LIMITED; *Int'l*, pg. 4434
LEAF RIVER ENERGY CENTER LLC—See New Jersey Resources Corporation; *U.S. Public*, pg. 1511
LEAF RIVER HOME HEALTH CARE, LLC—See UnitedHealth Group Incorporated; *U.S. Public*, pg. 2245
LEAF TRADING COMPANY LTD.—See Pyxus International, Inc.; *U.S. Public*, pg. 1740
LEAGAS DELANEY HAMBURG GMBH—See Leagas Delaney Limited; *Int'l*, pg. 4434
LEAGAS DELANEY ITALIA S.R.L.—See Leagas Delaney Limited; *Int'l*, pg. 4434
LEAGAS DELANEY LIMITED; *Int'l*, pg. 4434
LEAGAS DELANEY LONDON LIMITED—See Leagas Delaney Limited; *Int'l*, pg. 4434
LEAGAS DELANEY SHANGHAI CO., LTD.—See Leagas Delaney Limited; *Int'l*, pg. 4434
LEAGAS DELANEY TOKYO—See Leagas Delaney Limited; *Int'l*, pg. 4434
LEAGAS DELANEY USA INC.—See Leagas Delaney Limited; *Int'l*, pg. 4434
LEAGEL S.R.L.—See International Flavors & Fragrances Inc.; *U.S. Public*, pg. 1153
LEAGUE CITY-H, INC.—See Lithia Motors, Inc.; *U.S. Public*, pg. 1323
LEAGUE OF CONSERVATION VOTERS, INC.; *U.S. Private*, pg. 2407
LEAGUE PIPELINE SERVICES LTD.; *Int'l*, pg. 4434
LEAGUER SHENZHEN MICROELECTRONICS CORP.; *Int'l*, pg. 4434
LEAGUESAFE, LLC—See SharpLink Gaming, Inc.; *U.S. Public*, pg. 1874
LEAHY ORCHARDS INC.; *Int'l*, pg. 4434
LEAKE AUCTION CO.—See RB Global, Inc.; *Int'l*, pg. 6226

LEAKE OIL CO. INC.; *U.S. Private*, pg. 2407
LEAKE & WATTS SERVICES INC.; *U.S. Private*, pg. 2407
LEAKTITE CORPORATION; *U.S. Private*, pg. 2407
LEALEA ENTERPRISE CO., LTD.; *Int'l*, pg. 4434
LEALEA HOTELS & RESORTS CO., LTD.; *Int'l*, pg. 4434
LEAMAAT OMIKRON B.V.—See Heidelberg Materials AG; *Int'l*, pg. 3318
LEAMAN CO., LTD.—See Nakabayashi Co., Ltd.; *Int'l*, pg. 5131
LEAMAN CONTAINER INC.; *U.S. Private*, pg. 2407
LEAMINGTON SPA MYTON ROAD VETS4PETS LIMITED—See Pets at Home Group Plc; *Int'l*, pg. 5834
LEAMINGTON SPA VETS4PETS LIMITED—See Pets at Home Group Plc; *Int'l*, pg. 5834
LEANCOR LLC—See TPG Capital, L.P.; *U.S. Public*, pg. 2177
LEANDOG; *U.S. Private*, pg. 2407
LEA NETWORKS, LLC—See HF Company; *Int'l*, pg. 3374
LEANIN' TREE, INC.; *U.S. Private*, pg. 2407
LEANIN' TREE, INC.; *U.S. Private*, pg. 2407
LEANLIFE HEALTH INC.; *Int'l*, pg. 4434
LEAN MEAN FIGHTING MACHINE LTD.—See M&C Saatchi plc; *Int'l*, pg. 4611
LEANNETWORKING KFT.—See adesso SE; *Int'l*, pg. 144
LEA NORTH AMERICA INC.—See Panariagroup Industrie Ceramiche S.p.A.; *Int'l*, pg. 5717
LEAN STAFFING SOLUTIONS, INC.; *U.S. Private*, pg. 2407
LEANSWIFT AB—See Wipro Limited; *Int'l*, pg. 8432
LEANSWIFT SOLUTIONS, INC.—See Wipro Limited; *Int'l*, pg. 8432
LEAN TEIK SOON SDN. BHD.—See ATA IMS Berhad; *Int'l*, pg. 665
LEANTEQ CO., LTD.—See Enpro Inc.; *U.S. Public*, pg. 775
LEANTEQ LLC—See Enpro Inc.; *U.S. Public*, pg. 775
LEAPED SERVICES SDN BHD—See Khazanah Nasional Berhad; *Int'l*, pg. 4152
LEAPFORCE, INC.—See Appen Limited; *Int'l*, pg. 519
LEAPFROG ENTERPRISES, INC.—See VTech Holdings Ltd.; *Int'l*, pg. 8317
LEAPFROG INTERACTIVE; *U.S. Private*, pg. 2407
LEAPFROG RESEARCH & PLANNING LIMITED—See Arsenal Capital Management LP; *U.S. Private*, pg. 338
LEAPFROG SOLUTIONS, INC.; *U.S. Private*, pg. 2407
LEAP HOLDINGS GROUP LTD.; *Int'l*, pg. 4434
LEAPING GROUP CO., LTD.; *Int'l*, pg. 4434
LEAP MOTION, INC.—See Ultrahaptics Ltd.; *Int'l*, pg. 8018
LEAP PARTNERS; *U.S. Private*, pg. 2407
LEAP TECHNOLOGIES, INC.—See Trajan Group Holdings Limited; *Int'l*, pg. 7891
LEAP THERAPEUTICS, INC.; *U.S. Public*, pg. 1296
LEAP THERAPEUTICS LTD.—See Leap Therapeutics, Inc.; *U.S. Public*, pg. 1296
LEAPTRON ENGINEERING PTE LTD—See ISDN Holdings Limited; *Int'l*, pg. 3813
LEAR AUTOMOTIVE INDIA PRIVATE LIMITED—See Lear Corporation; *U.S. Public*, pg. 1297
LEAR AUTOMOTIVE MOROCCO SAS—See Lear Corporation; *U.S. Public*, pg. 1297
LEAR CANADA INVESTMENTS LTD.—See Lear Corporation; *U.S. Public*, pg. 1297
LE ARC CORPORATION—See Parigi International Inc.; *U.S. Private*, pg. 3094
LEAR CORPORATION ASIENTOS S.L.—See Lear Corporation; *U.S. Public*, pg. 1297
LEAR CORPORATION BELGIUM CVA—See Lear Corporation; *U.S. Public*, pg. 1297
LEAR CORPORATION BETEILIGUNGS GMBH—See Lear Corporation; *U.S. Public*, pg. 1297
LEAR CORPORATION CHANGCHUN AUTOMOTIVE INTERIOR SYSTEMS CO., LTD.—See Lear Corporation; *U.S. Public*, pg. 1297
LEAR CORPORATION CZECH REPUBLIC S.R.O.—See Lear Corporation; *U.S. Public*, pg. 1297
LEAR CORPORATION GMBH & CO. KG—See Lear Corporation; *U.S. Public*, pg. 1297
LEAR CORPORATION HUNGARY AUTOMOTIVE MANUFACTURING KFT.—See Lear Corporation; *U.S. Public*, pg. 1297
LEAR CORPORATION ITALIA S.R.L.—See Lear Corporation; *U.S. Public*, pg. 1297
LEAR CORPORATION JARNY, S.A.S.—See Lear Corporation; *U.S. Public*, pg. 1297
LEAR CORPORATION POLAND II SP. Z O.O.—See Lear Corporation; *U.S. Public*, pg. 1297
LEAR CORPORATION PONTEVEDRA, S.A.U.—See Lear Corporation; *U.S. Public*, pg. 1297
LEAR CORPORATION PORTUGAL - COMPONENTES PARA AUTOMOVEIS S.A.—See Lear Corporation; *U.S. Public*, pg. 1297
LEAR CORPORATION ROMANIA S.R.L.—See Lear Corporation; *U.S. Public*, pg. 1297
LEAR CORPORATION SEATING FRANCE FEIGNIES SAS—See Lear Corporation; *U.S. Public*, pg. 1297
LEAR CORPORATION SEATING FRANCE SAS—See Lear Corporation; *U.S. Public*, pg. 1297
LEAR CORPORATION (SHANGHAI) LIMITED—See Lear Corporation; *U.S. Public*, pg. 1297

CORPORATE AFFILIATIONS

LEAR CORPORATION; *U.S. Public*, pg. 1296
LEAR CORPORATION SWEDEN AB—See Lear Corporation; *U.S. Public*, pg. 1297
LEAR CORPORATION (UK) LIMITED—See Lear Corporation; *U.S. Public*, pg. 1297
LEAR CORPORATION VIGO, S.A.U.—See Lear Corporation; *U.S. Public*, pg. 1297
LEAR EUROPEAN HOLDING S.L.—See Lear Corporation; *U.S. Public*, pg. 1297
LEARFIELD COMMUNICATIONS, LLC—See Atairos Group, Inc.; *U.S. Private*, pg. 363
LEARFIELD COMMUNICATIONS, LLC—See Atairos Group, Inc.; *U.S. Private*, pg. 363
LEARFIELD LICENSING PARTNERS, LLC—See Atairos Group, Inc.; *U.S. Private*, pg. 363
LEARFIELD NEWS—See Atairos Group, Inc.; *U.S. Private*, pg. 364
LEAR HOLDINGS (HUNGARY) KFT.—See Lear Corporation; *U.S. Public*, pg. 1297
LEAR MEXICAN SEATING CORPORATION—See Lear Corporation; *U.S. Public*, pg. 1297
LEAR MEXICAN TRIM OPERATIONS, S. DE R.L. DE C.V.—See Lear Corporation; *U.S. Public*, pg. 1297
LEARN AFRICA PLC; *Int'l*, pg. 4434
LEARN CW INVESTMENT CORP.; *U.S. Public*, pg. 1298
LEARNDIRECT LIMITED—See Dimensions Training Solutions Ltd.; *Int'l*, pg. 2126
LEARNED LUMBER; *U.S. Private*, pg. 2408
LEARNERS EDGE, INC.—See Quad-C Management, Inc.; *U.S. Private*, pg. 3315
LEARNIFY AB—See Grimaldi Industri AB; *Int'l*, pg. 3085
LEARNING ALLY, INC.; *U.S. Private*, pg. 2408
LEARNING ANNEX HOLDINGS, LLC; *U.S. Private*, pg. 2408
THE LEARNING ANNEX LLC—See Learning Annex Holdings, LLC; *U.S. Private*, pg. 2408
LEARNING CARE GROUP, INC.—See American Securities LLC; *U.S. Private*, pg. 249
LEARNING EDGE ACADEMY OF PROFESSIONALS LTD.; *Int'l*, pg. 4434
THE LEARNING EDGE INTERNATIONAL PTY LTD—See Pearson plc; *Int'l*, pg. 5778
LEARNING EVOLUTION, LLC; *U.S. Private*, pg. 2408
THE LEARNING EXPERIENCE—See Golden Gate Capital Management II, LLC; *U.S. Private*, pg. 1731
LEARNING INTERNET INC.—See Educomp Solutions, Ltd.; *Int'l*, pg. 2315
THE LEARNING NETWORK INC.—See Pluribus Technologies Inc.; *Int'l*, pg. 5898
LEARNING OBJECTS, INC.—See Apax Partners LLP; *Int'l*, pg. 503
LEARNING OBJECTS, INC.—See Apollo Global Management, Inc.; *U.S. Public*, pg. 168
LEARNING OBJECTS, INC.—See KKR & Co. Inc.; *U.S. Public*, pg. 1256
LEARNING OBJECTS, INC.—See Searchlight Capital Partners, L.P.; *U.S. Private*, pg. 3587
LEARNING POOL LIMITED—See Marlin Equity Partners, LLC; *U.S. Private*, pg. 2584
LEARNING RESOURCES, INC.; *U.S. Private*, pg. 2408
LEARNING TECHNOLOGIES GROUP GMBH—See Learning Technologies Group plc; *Int'l*, pg. 4435
LEARNING TECHNOLOGIES GROUP (HONG KONG) LIMITED—See Learning Technologies Group plc; *Int'l*, pg. 4435
LEARNING TECHNOLOGIES GROUP PLC; *Int'l*, pg. 4434
LEARNING TECHNOLOGIES GROUP PTY LIMITED—See Learning Technologies Group plc; *Int'l*, pg. 4435
LEARNING TREE INTERNATIONAL AB—See Learning Tree International, Inc.; *U.S. Public*, pg. 1298
LEARNING TREE INTERNATIONAL, INC.; *U.S. Public*, pg. 1298
LEARNING TREE INTERNATIONAL INC.—See Learning Tree International, Inc.; *U.S. Public*, pg. 1298
LEARNING TREE INTERNATIONAL, K.K.—See Learning Tree International, Inc.; *U.S. Public*, pg. 1298
LEARNING TREE INTERNATIONAL LTD.—See Learning Tree International, Inc.; *U.S. Public*, pg. 1298
LEARNING TREE INTERNATIONAL USA, INC.—See Learning Tree International, Inc.; *U.S. Public*, pg. 1298
LEARNING TRENDS, LLC; *U.S. Private*, pg. 2408
LEARNING WINGS PTE LTD—See MBH Corporation Plc; *Int'l*, pg. 4752
LEARN IT SYSTEMS LLC—See Gryphon Investors, LLC; *U.S. Private*, pg. 1799
LEARNKEY INCORPORATED; *U.S. Private*, pg. 2408
LEARNLIVE TECHNOLOGIES; *U.S. Private*, pg. 2408
LEAR NORTH EUROPEAN OPERATIONS GMBH—See Lear Corporation; *U.S. Public*, pg. 1297
LEARNOSITY LTD.; *U.S. Private*, pg. 2408
LEARN-S CO., LTD.—See EQT AB; *Int'l*, pg. 2467
LEARNSHIP NETWORKS GMBH—See THI Investments GmbH; *Int'l*, pg. 7708
LEARNVEST INC.—See The Northwestern Mutual Life Insurance Company; *U.S. Private*, pg. 4085
LEAR SEWING (PTY.) LTD.—See Lear Corporation; *U.S. Public*, pg. 1297
LEAR SHANGHAI AUTOMOTIVE METALS CO., LTD.—See Lear Corporation; *U.S. Public*, pg. 1297

COMPANY NAME INDEX

LEAR TEKNIK OTO YAN SANAYI LTD. SIRKET—See Lear Corporation; *U.S. Public*, pg. 1297
LEARTIKER ELIKAGAIEN TEKNOLOGIA—See Mondragon Corporation; *Int'l*, pg. 5031
LEASAFRIC GHANA LIMITED—See C & I Leasing Plc.; *Int'l*, pg. 1237
LEASCO INC—See Transwood Carriers Inc.; *U.S. Private*, pg. 4211
LEASEACCELERATOR INC.; *U.S. Private*, pg. 2408
LEASE A SALES REP; *U.S. Private*, pg. 2408
LEASE CRUTCHER LEWIS; *U.S. Private*, pg. 2408
LEASEDIMENSIONS, INC.—See Genpact Limited; *Int'l*, pg. 2927
LEASEDIMENSIONS, INC.—See Genpact Limited; *Int'l*, pg. 2927
LEASEDIRECT FINANCE LIMITED—See Investec Limited; *Int'l*, pg. 3778
LEASE IT PUBLIC COMPANY LIMITED—See SVOA Public Company Limited; *Int'l*, pg. 7359
LEASE LINE INC.; *U.S. Private*, pg. 2408
LEASELINK SP. Z O.O.—See Pragma Inkaso S.A.; *Int'l*, pg. 5953
LEASE ONE CORP.; *U.S. Private*, pg. 2408
LEASE OPERATORS LIMITED; *Int'l*, pg. 4435
LEASEPLAN CORPORATION N.V.—See Societe Generale S.A.; *Int'l*, pg. 7040
LEASEPLAN ITALIA S.P.A.—See Societe Generale S.A.; *Int'l*, pg. 7040
LEASEPLAN NEDERLAND N.V.—See Societe Generale S.A.; *Int'l*, pg. 7040
LEASEPLAN POTUGAL—See Societe Generale S.A.; *Int'l*, pg. 7040
LEASE PORTFOLIO MANAGEMENT LTD—See Rothschild & Co SCA; *Int'l*, pg. 6403
LEASEQ, INC.—See SoftBank Group Corp.; *Int'l*, pg. 7053
LEASESERVICE PARTNER B.V.—See LKQ Corporation; *U.S. Public*, pg. 1335
LEASEWAY OF PUERTO RICO INC.; *U.S. Private*, pg. 2408
LEASFINANZ GMBH—See UniCredit S.p.A.; *Int'l*, pg. 8035
LEASING ASSOCIATES INC.; *U.S. Private*, pg. 2408
THE LEASING EXPERTS INC.; *U.S. Private*, pg. 4068
LEASING GROUP JSC; *Int'l*, pg. 4435
LEASING INNOVATIONS INC.; *U.S. Private*, pg. 2408
LEASING KHODRO GHADIR CO.; *Int'l*, pg. 4435
LEASING TECHNOLOGIES INTERNATIONAL INC.; *U.S. Private*, pg. 2408
LEASING TOTAL S.A.; *Int'l*, pg. 4436
LEASINT S.P.A.—See Intesa Sanpaolo S.p.A.; *Int'l*, pg. 3766
LEASINVEST IMMO LUX SA—See Ackermans & van Haaren NV; *Int'l*, pg. 106
LEASINVEST SERVICES NV—See Ackermans & van Haaren NV; *Int'l*, pg. 106
LEATEC FINE CERAMICS CO., LTD.; *Int'l*, pg. 4436
LEATEC FINE CERAMICS (KUNSHAN) CO., LTD.—See Leatec Fine Ceramics Co., Ltd.; *Int'l*, pg. 4436
LEATHER CREATIONS INC.; *U.S. Private*, pg. 2409
THE LEATHER FACTORY OF CANADA LTD.—See Tandy Leather Factory, Inc.; *U.S. Public*, pg. 1980
LEATHER INDUSTRIES OF KENYA LTD—See Aga Khan Development Network; *Int'l*, pg. 199
LEATHERMAN TOOL GROUP, INC.; *U.S. Private*, pg. 2409
LEATHERS ENTERPRISES INC.—See S&S Petroleum Inc.; *U.S. Private*, pg. 3514
LEATHERSTOCKING CORP.; *U.S. Private*, pg. 2409
LEATHER UP LIMITED; *Int'l*, pg. 4436
LEATT CORPORATION; *Int'l*, pg. 4436
LEAVELOGIC, INC.—See Unum Group; *U.S. Public*, pg. 2263
LEAVENS VOLKSWAGEN INC.; *Int'l*, pg. 4436
THE LEAVITT CORPORATION; *U.S. Private*, pg. 4068
LEAVITT GROUP ENTERPRISES, INC.; *U.S. Private*, pg. 2409
LEAVITT GROUP FOUR CORNERS INSURANCE INC.—See Leavitt Group Enterprises, Inc.; *U.S. Private*, pg. 2409
LEAVITT INTERNATIONAL (FSC CORP.)—See The Leavitt Corporation; *U.S. Private*, pg. 4068
LEAVITT MACHINERY LTD.; *Int'l*, pg. 4436
LEAVITT MEDICAL ASSOCIATES OF FLORIDA, INC.—See Harvest Partners L.P.; *U.S. Private*, pg. 1876
LEAVITTS FREIGHT SERVICE, INC.—See Daseke, Inc.; *U.S. Private*, pg. 1161
LEAVITT TUBE COMPANY LLC - JACKSON PLANT—See Maruichi Steel Tube Ltd; *Int'l*, pg. 4713
LEAWOOD TCP, LLC—See Washington Prime Group Inc.; *U.S. Private*, pg. 4449
LEAX ARKIVATOR SWEDEN AB—See Leax Group AB; *Int'l*, pg. 4436
LEAX ARKIVATOR TELECOM AB—See Leax Group AB; *Int'l*, pg. 4436
LEAX BALTIC SIA—See Leax Group AB; *Int'l*, pg. 4436
LEAX BRINKMANN GMBH—See Leax Group AB; *Int'l*, pg. 4436
LEAX COMPONENTS AB—See Leax Group AB; *Int'l*, pg. 4436

LEAX DO BRASIL LTDA.—See Leax Group AB; *Int'l*, pg. 4436
LEAX FALUN AB—See Leax Group AB; *Int'l*, pg. 4436
LEAX GROUP AB; *Int'l*, pg. 4436
LEAX HUNGARY ZRT.—See Leax Group AB; *Int'l*, pg. 4436
LEAX INDUSTRY (KUNSHAN) CO., LTD.—See Leax Group AB; *Int'l*, pg. 4436
LEAX MEKANISKA AB—See Leax Group AB; *Int'l*, pg. 4436
LEAX QUALITY AB—See Leax Group AB; *Int'l*, pg. 4436
LEAX REZEKNE SIA—See Leax Group AB; *Int'l*, pg. 4436
LEBAKKENS, INC. OF WISCONSIN; *U.S. Private*, pg. 2409
LEBAMOFF ENTERPRISES INC.; *U.S. Private*, pg. 2409
THE LEBANESE CERAMICS INDUSTRIES (S.A.L.)—See Lecico Egypt S.A.E.; *Int'l*, pg. 4437
THE LEBANESE COMPANY FOR THE DEVELOPMENT AND RECONSTRUCTION OF BEIRUT CENTRAL DISTRICT S.A.L; *Int'l*, pg. 7664
LEBANESE LEASING COMPANY SAL—See Fransabank SAL; *Int'l*, pg. 2762
LEBANESE REAL ESTATE COMMERCIAL COMPANY S.A.R.L.—See Mohammed Abdulmohsin Al-Kharafi & Sons WLL; *Int'l*, pg. 5018
LEBANON DAILY NEWS—See Gannett Co., Inc.; *U.S. Public*, pg. 900
LEBANON DISTRIBUTION CENTER—See The Maple-Vail Book Manufacturing Group; *U.S. Private*, pg. 4074
LEBANON ENDOSCOPY CENTER, LLC—See Tenet Healthcare Corporation; *U.S. Public*, pg. 2011
LEBANON EXPRESS—See Lee Enterprises, Incorporated; *U.S. Public*, pg. 1299
LEBANON HMA, INC.—See Community Health Systems, Inc.; *U.S. Public*, pg. 554
LEBANON HMA SURGERY CENTER, LLC—See Community Health Systems, Inc.; *U.S. Public*, pg. 554
LEBANON POWER & APPARATUS COMPANY, INC.—See Air Hydro Power Inc.; *U.S. Private*, pg. 139
LEBANON PUBLISHING COMPANY INC.—See Sandusky Newspapers Inc.; *U.S. Private*, pg. 3545
LEBANON SEABOARD CORPORATION; *U.S. Private*, pg. 2409
LEBANON SURGERY CENTER, LLC—See Community Health Systems, Inc.; *U.S. Public*, pg. 554
LEBANON VALLEY COLD STORAGE, LP—See Bonduelle SAS; *Int'l*, pg. 1106
LEBARONBROWN INDUSTRIES LLC; *U.S. Private*, pg. 2409
LEBARONBROWN SPECIALITIES LLC—See LeBaronBrown Industries LLC; *U.S. Private*, pg. 2409
LEBBING ENGINEERING & CONSULTING GMBH—See Jagenberg AG; *Int'l*, pg. 3870
LE BELIER LUSHUN (DALIAN) FOUNDRY CO., LTD.—See Le Belier SA; *Int'l*, pg. 4431
LE BELIER SA; *Int'l*, pg. 4431
LEBEN CLEAN ENERGY CO., LTD.—See Mirarth Holdings, Inc.; *Int'l*, pg. 4918
LEBEN COMMUNITY CO., LTD.—See Mirarth Holdings, Inc.; *Int'l*, pg. 4918
LEBEN HOME BUILD CO., LTD.—See Mirarth Holdings, Inc.; *Int'l*, pg. 4918
L'EBENOID S.A.—See ABB Ltd.; *Int'l*, pg. 54
LEBENTHAL & CO. LLC; *U.S. Private*, pg. 2409
LEBEN ZESTOCK CO., LTD.—See Mirarth Holdings, Inc.; *Int'l*, pg. 4918
LEBERGE & CURTIS, INC.—See Cazenovia Equipment Co., Inc.; *U.S. Private*, pg. 796
LEBERMUTH COMPANY; *U.S. Private*, pg. 2409
LEBHAR-FRIEDMAN INC.; *U.S. Private*, pg. 2409
LE BISON GOURMAND SARL—See Derichebourg S.A.; *Int'l*, pg. 2042
LE BLEU CORPORATION; *U.S. Private*, pg. 2404
LEBLON HOLDINGS LLC.—See Bacardi Limited; *Int'l*, pg. 794
LEBOA IT SOLUTIONS (PTY) LTD—See Stellar Capital Partners Limited; *Int'l*, pg. 7204
LE BON MARCHE SA—See LVMH Moet Hennessy Louis Vuitton SE; *Int'l*, pg. 4598
LEBOS SHOE STORE INC.; *U.S. Private*, pg. 2409
LE BOULANGER INC.; *U.S. Private*, pg. 2405
LE BOURGET S.A.—See CSP International Fashion Group S.p.A.; *Int'l*, pg. 1867
LE BOZEC FILTRATION ET SYSTEMES, S.A.S.—See Donaldson Company, Inc.; *U.S. Public*, pg. 676
LE BRUN TOYOTA—See West Herr Automotive Group, Inc.; *U.S. Private*, pg. 4485
LEBTECH BERHAD; *Int'l*, pg. 4436
LEBUS MANUFACTURING CO.—See KKR & Co. Inc.; *U.S. Public*, pg. 1264
LECA (GREAT BRITAIN) LIMITED—See Heidelberg Materials AG; *Int'l*, pg. 3318
LECCO TRASPORTI S.C.A.R.L.—See Deutsche Bahn AG; *Int'l*, pg. 2052
LE CENTRE D'INSEMINATION PORCINE DU QUEBEC (C.I.P.Q.) INC.—See Investissement Quebec; *Int'l*, pg. 3780
LECESSE DEVELOPMENT CORPORATION; *U.S. Private*, pg. 2409

LECO CORPORATION

LE CHAMEAU SAS—See Marwyn Investment Management LLP; *Int'l*, pg. 4718
LE CHAMP (SOUTH EAST ASIA) PTE LTD.—See Takebishi Corporation; *Int'l*, pg. 7436
LE CHAPERON ROUGE; *U.S. Private*, pg. 2405
LECHASE CONSTRUCTION SERVICES, LLC; *U.S. Private*, pg. 2409
LECHE GLORIA S.A.; *Int'l*, pg. 4436
LEC HELLAS SA—See Lectra SA; *Int'l*, pg. 4437
LECHLER AB—See Lechler GmbH; *Int'l*, pg. 4436
LECHLER FRANCE S.A—See Lechler GmbH; *Int'l*, pg. 4436
LECHLER GMBH; *Int'l*, pg. 4436
LECHLER, INC.—See Lechler GmbH; *Int'l*, pg. 4436
LECHLER INDIA PVT. LTD.—See Lechler GmbH; *Int'l*, pg. 4436
LECHLER LTD.—See Lechler GmbH; *Int'l*, pg. 4436
LECHLER OY—See Lechler GmbH; *Int'l*, pg. 4436
LECHLER S.A./N.V.—See Lechler GmbH; *Int'l*, pg. 4436
LECHLER, S.A.—See Lechler GmbH; *Int'l*, pg. 4436
LECHLER (TIANJIN) INTERNATIONAL TRADING COMPANY LTD.—See Lechler GmbH; *Int'l*, pg. 4436
LECHWERKE AG—See RWE AG; *Int'l*, pg. 6434
LECICO EGYPT S.A.E.; *Int'l*, pg. 4437
LECICO FRANCE SARL—See Lecico Egypt S.A.E.; *Int'l*, pg. 4437
LECICO POLAND—See Lecico Egypt S.A.E.; *Int'l*, pg. 4437
LECICO (UK) LTD.—See Lecico Egypt S.A.E.; *Int'l*, pg. 4437
LECIEN (CAMBODIA) CO., LTD.—See Wacoal Holdings Corp.; *Int'l*, pg. 8325
LECIEN CORPORATION—See Wacoal Holdings Corp.; *Int'l*, pg. 8326
LECIEN NAGASAKI CORPORATION—See Wacoal Holdings Corp.; *Int'l*, pg. 8326
LECIEN (VIETNAM) CO., LTD.—See Wacoal Holdings Corp.; *Int'l*, pg. 8325
LEC, INC.; *Int'l*, pg. 4436
LEC INDUSTRIES CO., LTD.—See Daiki Axis Co., Ltd.; *Int'l*, pg. 1932
LECIP ARCONTIA AB—See LECIP Holdings Corporation; *Int'l*, pg. 4437
LECIP CORPORATION—See LECIP Holdings Corporation; *Int'l*, pg. 4437
LECIP DIGITAL SIGNAGE CORPORATION—See LECIP Holdings Corporation; *Int'l*, pg. 4437
LECIP ELECTRONICS CORPORATION—See LECIP Holdings Corporation; *Int'l*, pg. 4437
LECIP ENGINEERING CORPORATION—See LECIP Holdings Corporation; *Int'l*, pg. 4437
LECIP HOLDINGS CORPORATION; *Int'l*, pg. 4437
LECIP INC.—See LECIP Holdings Corporation; *Int'l*, pg. 4437
LECIP SANGYO LTD.—See LECIP Holdings Corporation; *Int'l*, pg. 4437
LECIP (SINGAPORE) PTE LTD—See LECIP Holdings Corporation; *Int'l*, pg. 4437
LECIP SLP CORPORATION—See LECIP Holdings Corporation; *Int'l*, pg. 4437
LECIP THAI CO., LTD.—See LECIP Holdings Corporation; *Int'l*, pg. 4437
LECKIE & LECKIE LIMITED—See News Corporation; *U.S. Public*, pg. 1519
LECKPATRICK DAIRIES LIMITED—See Kerry Group plc; *Int'l*, pg. 4139
L'ECLAIRAGE TECHNIQUE S.A.; *Int'l*, pg. 4378
LE CLAIRE INVESTMENT INC.—See RiverStone Group, Inc.; *U.S. Private*, pg. 3447
LE CLAIR INDUSTRIES INC.; *U.S. Private*, pg. 2405
LECLANCHE GMBH—See Oakridge Global Energy Solutions, Inc.; *U.S. Public*, pg. 1560
LECLANCHE SA—See Oakridge Global Energy Solutions, Inc.; *U.S. Public*, pg. 1560
LECO AFRICA (PTY.) LTD.—See LECO Corporation; *U.S. Private*, pg. 2410
LECO ARGENTINA S.A.—See LECO Corporation; *U.S. Private*, pg. 2410
LECO AUSTRALIA PTY. LTD.—See LECO Corporation; *U.S. Private*, pg. 2410
LECO CORPORATION; *U.S. Private*, pg. 2410
LECO CORPORATION SVENSKA AB—See LECO Corporation; *U.S. Private*, pg. 2410
LECO EUROPE B.V.—See LECO Corporation; *U.S. Private*, pg. 2410
LECO FRANCE—See LECO Corporation; *U.S. Private*, pg. 2410
LECO INSTRUMENTE GMBH—See LECO Corporation; *U.S. Private*, pg. 2410
LECO INSTRUMENTE PLZEN S.R.O.—See LECO Corporation; *U.S. Private*, pg. 2410
LECO INSTRUMENTOS LTDA.—See LECO Corporation; *U.S. Private*, pg. 2410
LECO INSTRUMENTOS S.L.—See LECO Corporation; *U.S. Private*, pg. 2410
LECO INSTRUMENTS HONG KONG LTD.—See LECO Corporation; *U.S. Private*, pg. 2410
LECO INSTRUMENTS LTD.—See LECO Corporation; *U.S. Private*, pg. 2410

LECO INSTRUMENTS (M) SDN. BHD.—See LECO Corporation; *U.S. Private*, pg. 2410
LECO INSTRUMENTS S.A.—See LECO Corporation; *U.S. Private*, pg. 2410
LECO INSTRUMENTS TAIWAN LTD.—See LECO Corporation; *U.S. Private*, pg. 2410
LECO INSTRUMENTS (THAILAND) LTD.—See LECO Corporation; *U.S. Private*, pg. 2410
LECO INSTRUMENTS UK LTD.—See LECO Corporation; *U.S. Private*, pg. 2410
LECO ITALY, S.R.L.—See LECO Corporation; *U.S. Private*, pg. 2410
LECO JAPAN CORPORATION—See LECO Corporation; *U.S. Private*, pg. 2410
LECO KOREA CO. LTD.—See LECO Corporation; *U.S. Private*, pg. 2410
LE COLVERT SPRL—See Clariane SE; *Int'l*, pg. 1643
LECO MEXICO S.A. DE C.V.—See LECO Corporation; *U.S. Private*, pg. 2410
LECON, INC.—See KKR & Co. Inc.; *U.S. Public*, pg. 1263
LECO POLSKA SP. Z O.O.—See LECO Corporation; *U.S. Private*, pg. 2410
L.E. COPPERSMITH INC.; *U.S. Private*, pg. 2365
LECO PRODUCTS B.V.—See Aalberts N.V.; *Int'l*, pg. 35
LECORA AB—See Orkla ASA; *Int'l*, pg. 5638
LE CORDON BLEU COLLEGE OF CULINARY ARTS IN CHICAGO—See Perdoceo Education Corporation; *U.S. Public*, pg. 1673
LE CORDON BLEU COLLEGE OF CULINARY ARTS—See Perdoceo Education Corporation; *U.S. Public*, pg. 1673
LE CORDON BLEU COLLEGE OF CULINARY ARTS—See Perdoceo Education Corporation; *U.S. Public*, pg. 1673
LE CORDON BLEU COLLEGE OF CULINARY ARTS—See Perdoceo Education Corporation; *U.S. Public*, pg. 1673
LE CORDON BLEU NORTH AMERICA, LLC—See Perdoceo Education Corporation; *U.S. Public*, pg. 1673
LECORP, INC.; *U.S. Private*, pg. 2410
LECORPIO, LLC—See Insight Venture Management, LLC; *U.S. Private*, pg. 2087
LECO TECHNOLOGIES-PHILIPPINE MARKETING CORPORATION—See LECO Corporation; *U.S. Private*, pg. 2410
LECOT SAS—See PSB Industries SA; *Int'l*, pg. 6014
LECO (VIETNAM) CO., LTD.—See LECO Corporation; *U.S. Private*, pg. 2410
LEC REFRIGERATION—See The Glen Dimplex Group; *Int'l*, pg. 7650
LECRON INDUSTRIAL DEVELOPMENT GROUP CO., LTD.; *Int'l*, pg. 4437
LECROY LIGHTSPEED CORPORATION—See Teledyne Technologies Incorporated; *U.S. Public*, pg. 1994
LEC; *U.S. Private*, pg. 2409
LECSTAR TELECOM, INC.—See Integracore, Inc.; *U.S. Private*, pg. 2098
LECTA BENELUX SA—See CVC Capital Partners SICAV-FIS S.A.; *Int'l*, pg. 1888
LECTA DEUTSCHLAND GMBH—See CVC Capital Partners SICAV-FIS S.A.; *Int'l*, pg. 1887
LECTA HQ SA—See CVC Capital Partners SICAV-FIS S.A.; *Int'l*, pg. 1887
LECTA MAROC SARL—See CVC Capital Partners SICAV-FIS S.A.; *Int'l*, pg. 1888
LECTA MEXICO S. DE R.L. DE C.V.—See CVC Capital Partners SICAV-FIS S.A.; *Int'l*, pg. 1888
LECTA NORTH AMERICA INC—See CVC Capital Partners SICAV-FIS S.A.; *Int'l*, pg. 1888
LECTA PAPER UK LTD—See CVC Capital Partners SICAV-FIS S.A.; *Int'l*, pg. 1888
LECTA S.A.—See CVC Capital Partners SICAV-FIS S.A.; *Int'l*, pg. 1887
LECTORUM PUBLICATIONS, INC.; *U.S. Private*, pg. 2410
LECTRA AUSTRALIA PTY LTD—See Lectra SA; *Int'l*, pg. 4437
LECTRA BALTIC OU—See Lectra SA; *Int'l*, pg. 4437
LECTRA BRASIL LTDA—See Lectra SA; *Int'l*, pg. 4437
LECTRA CANADA INC—See Lectra SA; *Int'l*, pg. 4437
LECTRA CHILE SA—See Lectra SA; *Int'l*, pg. 4437
LECTRA DANMARK A/S—See Lectra SA; *Int'l*, pg. 4437
LECTRA DEUTSCHLAND GMBH—See Lectra SA; *Int'l*, pg. 4437
LECTRA HONG KONG LTD.—See Lectra SA; *Int'l*, pg. 4437
LECTRA ISRAEL LTD—See Lectra SA; *Int'l*, pg. 4437
LECTRA ITALIA SPA—See Lectra SA; *Int'l*, pg. 4437
LECTRA JAPAN LTD—See Lectra SA; *Int'l*, pg. 4437
LECTRA KOREA LTD.—See Lectra SA; *Int'l*, pg. 4437
LECTRA MAROC SARL—See Lectra SA; *Int'l*, pg. 4438
LECTRA PHILIPPINES INC—See Lectra SA; *Int'l*, pg. 4438
LECTRA PORTUGAL LDA—See Lectra SA; *Int'l*, pg. 4438
LECTRA RUSSIA OOO—See Lectra SA; *Int'l*, pg. 4438
LECTRA SA; *Int'l*, pg. 4437
LECTRA SINGAPORE PTE LTD—See Lectra SA; *Int'l*, pg. 4438
LECTRA SISTEMAS ESPANOLA SA—See Lectra SA; *Int'l*, pg. 4438

LECTRA—See Lectra SA; *Int'l*, pg. 4437
LECTRA—See Lectra SA; *Int'l*, pg. 4437
LECTRA SUOMI OY—See Lectra SA; *Int'l*, pg. 4438
LECTRA SVERIGE AB—See Lectra SA; *Int'l*, pg. 4438
LECTRA SYSTEMES CAD CAM AS—See Lectra SA; *Int'l*, pg. 4438
LECTRA SYSTEMES SA DE CV—See Lectra SA; *Int'l*, pg. 4438
LECTRA SYSTEMES TUNISIE SA—See Lectra SA; *Int'l*, pg. 4438
LECTRA SYSTEMS (CANADA) INC.—See Lectra SA; *Int'l*, pg. 4438
LECTRA SYSTEMS INC.—See Lectra SA; *Int'l*, pg. 4438
LECTRA SYSTEMS INC.—See Lectra SA; *Int'l*, pg. 4438
LECTRA SYSTEMS SA (PTY) LTD.—See Lectra SA; *Int'l*, pg. 4438
LECTRA SYSTEMS (SHANGHAI) CO. LTD—See Lectra SA; *Int'l*, pg. 4438
LECTRA TAIWAN CO. LTD—See Lectra SA; *Int'l*, pg. 4438
LECTRA TECHNOLOGIES INDIA PRIVATE LTD—See Lectra SA; *Int'l*, pg. 4438
LECTRA UK LTD—See Lectra SA; *Int'l*, pg. 4438
LECTRA USA INC.—See Lectra SA; *Int'l*, pg. 4438
LECTRODRYER LLC; *U.S. Private*, pg. 2410
LECTRUS, INC.—See RFE Investment Partners; *U.S. Private*, pg. 3419
LECZYNSKA ENERGETYKA SP. Z O.O.—See Lubelski Wegiel BOGDANKA Spolka Akcyjna; *Int'l*, pg. 4572
LEDA BVBA—See Nederman Holding AB; *Int'l*, pg. 5189
LEDA FURNITURE LTD; *Int'l*, pg. 4438
LEDAX CO., LTD.; *Int'l*, pg. 4438
LEDCOR CONSTRUCTION—See Ledcor Group of Companies; *Int'l*, pg. 4438
LEDCOR GROUP OF COMPANIES; *Int'l*, pg. 4438
LEDCOR INDUSTRIAL—See Ledcor Group of Companies; *Int'l*, pg. 4438
LEDDARTECH HOLDINGS INC.; *Int'l*, pg. 4438
LEDDARTECH INC.—See LeddarTech Holdings Inc.; *Int'l*, pg. 4438
LED DENTAL INC—See Level Equity Management, LLC; *U.S. Private*, pg. 2434
LEDD TECHNOLOGIES W.L.L.—See Gulf Warehousing Company QSC; *Int'l*, pg. 3182
LED ENGIN, INC.—See ams AG; *Int'l*, pg. 438
LEDERER GMBH—See Freudenberg SE; *Int'l*, pg. 2789
LEDERMANN IMMOBILIEN AG; *Int'l*, pg. 4439
LEDER REINHARDT GMBH; *Int'l*, pg. 4439
LEDERWERKE WIEMAN GMBH—See M.M. Warburg & Co. KGaA; *Int'l*, pg. 4616
LEDESMA S.A.A.I.; *Int'l*, pg. 4439
LEDESMA S.A.—See Ledesma S.A.A.I.; *Int'l*, pg. 4439
LEDGER DISPATCH—See Alden Global Capital LLC; *U.S. Private*, pg. 155
LEDGERPAY, INC.—See Quisitive Technology Solutions, Inc.; *Int'l*, pg. 6165
LEDGE WEALTH MANAGEMENT, INC.—See Dakota Wealth Management LLC; *U.S. Private*, pg. 1148
LEDGEWOOD HEALTH CARE CORPORATION—See Apollo Global Management, Inc.; *U.S. Public*, pg. 157
LEDGEWOOD REHABILITATION AND SKILLED NURSING CENTER—See Apollo Global Management, Inc.; *U.S. Public*, pg. 157
LEDIC MANAGEMENT GROUP; *U.S. Private*, pg. 2410
LED INTERNATIONAL HOLDINGS LIMITED - SHENZHEN FACTORY—See LED International Holdings Limited; *Int'l*, pg. 4438
LED INTERNATIONAL HOLDINGS LIMITED; *Int'l*, pg. 4438
LEDISO ITALIA S.R.L.—See Demant A/S; *Int'l*, pg. 2024
THE LEDLIE GROUP; *U.S. Private*, pg. 4068
LED LINEAR GMBH—See Fagerhult Group AB; *Int'l*, pg. 2602
LED LINEAR UK LTD.—See Fagerhult Group AB; *Int'l*, pg. 2602
LED LINEAR USA INC.—See Fagerhult Group AB; *Int'l*, pg. 2602
LEDLINK OPTICS, INC.; *Int'l*, pg. 4439
LEDMAN OPTOELECTRONIC CO., LTD.; *Int'l*, pg. 4439
LED-MARK ITS A/S—See Solix Group AB; *Int'l*, pg. 7073
LEDNOVATION, INC.; *U.S. Private*, pg. 2411
LE DOMAINE DU PLESSIS SAS—See VINCI S.A.; *Int'l*, pg. 8223
LEDO TEA COMPANY LIMITED; *Int'l*, pg. 4439
LEDRA ESTATE LTD.—See Bank of Cyprus Holdings Public Limited Company; *Int'l*, pg. 842
LEDS-C4, S.A.; *Int'l*, pg. 4439
LED SOURCE, LLC; *U.S. Private*, pg. 2410
LEDSTIERNAN AB; *Int'l*, pg. 4439
LEDSTIERNAN VENTURE AB—See Ledstiernan AB; *Int'l*, pg. 4439
LED SUPPLY CO.—See Applied UV, Inc.; *U.S. Public*, pg. 173
LEDTECH ELECTRONICS CORPORATION; *Int'l*, pg. 4439
LEDUC CHRYSLER JEEP; *Int'l*, pg. 4439
LEDUC & DEXTER INC.; *U.S. Private*, pg. 2411
LE DUFF AMERICA, INC.—See Holding Le Duff SA; *Int'l*, pg. 3450

LEDUS LIGHTING TECHNOLOGY LIMITED—See Tech Pro Technology Development Limited; *Int'l*, pg. 7502
LEDYARD COMPANY; *U.S. Private*, pg. 2411
LEDYARD FINANCIAL GROUP, INC.; *U.S. Public*, pg. 1298
LEE ADVERTISING; *U.S. Private*, pg. 2411
LEE A. FOLGER INC.; *U.S. Private*, pg. 2411
LEEANN CHIN, INC.; *U.S. Private*, pg. 2414
LEE & ASSOCIATES COMMERCIAL REAL ESTATE; *U.S. Private*, pg. 2411
LEE & ASSOCIATES, INC.; *U.S. Private*, pg. 2411
LEE & ASSOCIATES LICENSING AND ADMINISTRATION CO., LP; *U.S. Private*, pg. 2411
LEE AUTOMOTIVE GROUP INC.; *U.S. Private*, pg. 2411
LEE BANK—See Berkshire Financial Services, Inc.; *U.S. Private*, pg. 533
LEE BANK; *U.S. Private*, pg. 2411
LEE BEVERAGE CO. INC.; *U.S. Private*, pg. 2411
LEE BIOSOLUTIONS, INC.—See DevCo Partners Oy; *Int'l*, pg. 2086
LEEBO B.V.; *Int'l*, pg. 4441
LEE BRASS COMPANY; *U.S. Private*, pg. 2411
LEE BROS FOODSERVICE INC.; *U.S. Private*, pg. 2411
LEE BROTHERS BILSTON LIMITED—See Bunzl plc; *Int'l*, pg. 1218
LEE BUILDER MART INC.; *U.S. Private*, pg. 2411
LEE CHANG YUNG TECHNOLOGY CORPORATION—See KKR & Co. Inc.; *U.S. Public*, pg. 1258
LEECHES U.S.A. LTD.—See Accurate Chemical & Scientific Corporation; *U.S. Private*, pg. 55
LEECHI ENTERPRISES CO., LTD.; *Int'l*, pg. 4441
LEE+CHO TRADING CO.—See Einhell Germany AG; *Int'l*, pg. 2334
LEE COMPANY S.A.—See The Lee Company; *U.S. Private*, pg. 4068
THE LEE COMPANY SCANDINAVIA AB—See The Lee Company; *U.S. Private*, pg. 4069
LEE COMPANY; *U.S. Private*, pg. 2411
THE LEE COMPANY; *U.S. Private*, pg. 4068
LEE CONSTRUCTION CO.—See W.C. English Incorporated; *U.S. Private*, pg. 4419
LEE CONSUMER PRODUCTS DIVISION—See Lee Pharmaceuticals; *U.S. Public*, pg. 1300
LEE CONTAINER CORPORATION, INC.—See Greif Inc.; *U.S. Public*, pg. 968
LEE CORP HOMES INC.; *U.S. Private*, pg. 2411
LEECO STEEL, LLC—See O'Neal Industries, Inc.; *U.S. Private*, pg. 2979
LEE COUNTY ELECTRIC COOPERATIVE, INC.; *U.S. Private*, pg. 2411
LEE COUNTY LANDFILL, INC.—See Republic Services, Inc.; *U.S. Public*, pg. 1786
LEE COUNTY LANDFILL SC, LLC—See Republic Services, Inc.; *U.S. Public*, pg. 1786
LEEDEN DISTRIBUTION PTE LTD—See Mitsubishi Chemical Group Corporation; *Int'l*, pg. 4936
LEEDEN HERCULES SDN BHD—See Mitsubishi Chemical Group Corporation; *Int'l*, pg. 4936
LEEDEN INTERNATIONAL PTE. LTD.—See Mitsubishi Chemical Group Corporation; *Int'l*, pg. 4936
LEEDEN INVESTMENT PTE LTD—See Mitsubishi Chemical Group Corporation; *Int'l*, pg. 4936
LEEDEN NATIONAL OXYGEN LTD.—See Mitsubishi Chemical Group Corporation; *Int'l*, pg. 4936
LEEDEN PHILIPPINES INC.—See Mitsubishi Chemical Group Corporation; *Int'l*, pg. 4936
LEEDEN POWERWELD SDN BHD—See Mitsubishi Chemical Group Corporation; *Int'l*, pg. 4936
LEEDEN SDN BHD—See Mitsubishi Chemical Group Corporation; *Int'l*, pg. 4936
LEE DENTAL & ORTHODONTICS DIVISION—See Lee Pharmaceuticals; *U.S. Public*, pg. 1300
LEEDEN WELDING SDN BHD—See Mitsubishi Chemical Group Corporation; *Int'l*, pg. 4936
LEED FABRICATION SERVICES, LLC—See First Reserve Management, L.P.; *U.S. Private*, pg. 1526
LEEDO MANUFACTURING CO.; *U.S. Private*, pg. 2414
LEEDOM & ASSOCIATES, LLC—See Leedom Management Group, Inc.; *U.S. Private*, pg. 2414
LEEDOM MANAGEMENT GROUP, INC.; *U.S. Private*, pg. 2414
LEE DRYWALL, INC.; *U.S. Private*, pg. 2411
LEEDS BUILDING SOCIETY; *Int'l*, pg. 4441
LEED SELLING TOOLS CORPORATION; *U.S. Private*, pg. 2414
LEEDS EQUITY PARTNERS, LLC; *U.S. Private*, pg. 2414
LEEDS FINANCIAL SERVICES LTD.—See Leeds Building Society; *Int'l*, pg. 4441
LEEDS KIRKSTALL VETS4PETS LIMITED—See Pets at Home Group Plc; *Int'l*, pg. 5834
LEEDS MORTGAGE FUNDING LTD.—See Leeds Building Society; *Int'l*, pg. 4441
LEEDS NOVAMARK CAPITAL; *U.S. Private*, pg. 2415
LEEDS PRECISION INSTRUMENTS; *U.S. Private*, pg. 2415
LEEDS WELD & CO.; *U.S. Private*, pg. 2415
LEED TOOL CORPORATION—See Superior Energy Services, Inc.; *U.S. Private*, pg. 3877

COMPANY NAME INDEX

LEEDY MANUFACTURING CO. INC.; *U.S. Private,* pg. 2415
LEE EDWARDS INC.; *U.S. Private,* pg. 2411
LEE ELECTRICAL CONSTRUCTION, LLC—See Quanta Services, Inc.; *U.S. Public,* pg. 1751
LEE ENTERPRISES, INCORPORATED; *U.S. Public,* pg. 1298
LEE EQUITY PARTNERS LLC; *U.S. Private,* pg. 2411
LEEF BRANDS INC; *Int'l,* pg. 4441
LEE F. COWPER, INC., *U.S. Private,* pg. 2413
LEE FEED MILL PUBLIC COMPANY LIMITED; *Int'l,* pg. 4440
LEE FOUNDATION—See Lee Enterprises, Incorporated; *U.S. Public,* pg. 1299
LEEHAR DISTRIBUTORS, LLC—See UnitedHealth Group Incorporated; *U.S. Public,* pg. 2247
LEE HARTMAN & SONS INC.; *U.S. Private,* pg. 2413
LEE HECHT HARRISON AG—See Adecco Group AG; *Int'l,* pg. 139
LEE HECHT HARRISON HK LIMITED—See Adecco Group AG; *Int'l,* pg. 141
LEE HECHT HARRISON, INC.—See Adecco Group AG; *Int'l,* pg. 138
LEE HECHT HARRISON LIMITED—See Adecco Group AG; *Int'l,* pg. 139
LEE HECHT HARRISON, LLC—See Adecco Group AG; *Int'l,* pg. 139
LEE HECHT HARRISON POLSKA SP. Z O.O.—See Adecco Group AG; *Int'l,* pg. 141
LEE HECHT HARRISON—See Adecco Group AG; *Int'l,* pg. 138
LEE HECHT HARRISON—See Adecco Group AG; *Int'l,* pg. 138
LEE HECHT HARRISON—See Adecco Group AG; *Int'l,* pg. 138
LEE HECHT HARRISON—See Adecco Group AG; *Int'l,* pg. 138
LEE HECHT HARRISON—See Adecco Group AG; *Int'l,* pg. 138
LEE HEDGES PLC; *Int'l,* pg. 4440
LEE HING DEVELOPMENT LIMITED; *Int'l,* pg. 4440
LEE HWA JEWELLERY PTE. LTD.—See Aspial Corporation Limited; *Int'l,* pg. 630
LEE HYDRAULISCHE MINIATURKOMPONENTEN—See The Lee Company; *U.S. Private,* pg. 4068
LEE HY PAVING CORPORATION; *U.S. Private,* pg. 2413
LEE HYUNDAI INC.; *U.S. Private,* pg. 2413
LEE INDUSTRIES INC.; *U.S. Private,* pg. 2413
LEEJAM SPORTS CO; *Int'l,* pg. 4441
LEE JEANS—See Kontoor Brands, Inc.; *U.S. Public,* pg. 1271
LEE JOFA, INC.—See Kravet Fabrics Inc.; *U.S. Private,* pg. 2350
LEE KEE GROUP LIMITED—See Lee Kee Holdings Limited; *Int'l,* pg. 4440
LEE KEE HOLDINGS LIMITED; *Int'l,* pg. 4440
LEE KENNEDY CO. INC.; *U.S. Private,* pg. 2413
LEE KIM TAH HOLDINGS LTD.; *Int'l,* pg. 4440
LEE KIM TAH (PTE) LTD—See Lee Kim Tah Holdings Ltd.; *Int'l,* pg. 4440
LEE KINSTLE CHEVROLET-OLDSMOBILE INC.; *U.S. Private,* pg. 2413
LEE KU INDUSTRIAL CO., LTD.; *Int'l,* pg. 4440
LEE KUM KEE (EUROPE) LIMITED—See SYSU International, Inc.; *Int'l,* pg. 7393
LEE KUM KEE LIMITED - CANADA OFFICE—See SYSU International, Inc.; *Int'l,* pg. 7393
LEE KUM KEE LIMITED—See SYSU International, Inc.; *Int'l,* pg. 7393
LEE KUM KEE (MALAYSIA) SDN. BHD.—See SYSU International, Inc.; *Int'l,* pg. 7393
LEE KUM KEE (USA) FOODS INC.—See SYSU International, Inc.; *Int'l,* pg. 7393
LEE KUM KEE (U.S.A.) INC.—See SYSU International, Inc.; *Int'l,* pg. 7393
LEEK UNITED BUILDING SOCIETY; *Int'l,* pg. 4441
LEELAND BAKING CO., LLC—See Flowers Foods, Inc.; *U.S. Public,* pg. 855
LEEL ELECTRICALS LTD.; *Int'l,* pg. 4441
LEE LEWIS CONSTRUCTION, INC.; *U.S. Private,* pg. 2413
LEE LONGLAND & CO. LTD.; *Int'l,* pg. 4440
LEELOWE INC.; *U.S. Private,* pg. 2415
LEE LUMBER & BUILDING MATERIAL CORP.; *U.S. Private,* pg. 2413
LEEMAH CORPORATION; *U.S. Private,* pg. 2415
LEEMAH ELECTRONICS INC—See Leemah Corporation; *U.S. Private,* pg. 2415
LEEMAH PROPERTY INC—See Leemah Corporation; *U.S. Private,* pg. 2415
LEE & MAN CHEMICAL COMPANY LIMITED; *Int'l,* pg. 4439
LEE & MAN COMPANY LIMITED—See Best Food Holding Company Limited; *Int'l,* pg. 999
LEE & MAN DEVELOPMENT LIMITED—See Lee & Man Chemical Company Limited; *Int'l,* pg. 4439
LEE & MAN HANDBAG MANUFACTURING CO. LTD.—See Best Food Holding Company Limited; *Int'l,* pg. 999

LEE & MAN MANAGEMENT CO. LTD.—See Best Food Holding Company Limited; *Int'l,* pg. 999
LEE & MAN PAPER MANUFACTURING LIMITED; *Int'l,* pg. 4439
LEE MASONRY PRODUCTS, LLC; *U.S. Private,* pg. 2413
LEE MATHEWS EQUIPMENT INC.; *U.S. Private,* pg. 2413
LEE MEMORIAL HEALTH SYSTEM; *U.S. Private,* pg. 2413
LEE MENTAL HEALTH CENTER, INC.; *U.S. Private,* pg. 2413
LEE METAL GROUP LTD.—See BRC Asia Limited; *Int'l,* pg. 1143
LEE MICHAELS JEWELERS INC.; *U.S. Private,* pg. 2413
LEE-MOORE CAPITAL COMPANY; *U.S. Private,* pg. 2414
LEE MUNDER CAPITAL GROUP, LLC—See Royal Bank of Canada; *Int'l,* pg. 6409
LEEN ALKHAIR TRADING COMPANY; *Int'l,* pg. 4441
LEENA THEME PAINTING LIMITED—See Yau Lee Holdings Limited; *Int'l,* pg. 8571
LEE NATIONAL CORPORATION; *U.S. Private,* pg. 2413
LEE & NEE SOFTWARE EXPORTS LTD.; *Int'l,* pg. 4440
LEENGATE INDUSTRIAL & WELDING SUPPLIES LIMITED—See Linde plc; *Int'l,* pg. 4507
LEENGATE INDUSTRIAL & WELDING SUPPLIES (NORTH EAST) LIMITED—See Linde plc; *Int'l,* pg. 4507
LEENGATE INDUSTRIAL & WELDING SUPPLIES (NOTTINGHAM) LIMITED—See Linde plc; *Int'l,* pg. 4507
LEENGATE INDUSTRIAL & WELDING SUPPLIES (SCOTLAND) LIMITED—See Linde plc; *Int'l,* pg. 4507
LEENGATE VALVES LIMITED; *Int'l,* pg. 4441
LEE & NIGHTINGALE ADVERTISING LTD.; *Int'l,* pg. 4440
LEEN MENKEN FOODSERVICE LOGISTICS BV—See bpost NV/SA; *Int'l,* pg. 1133
LEENO INDUSTRIAL, INC.; *Int'l,* pg. 4441
LEE PATTANA AGRO SILO CO., LTD.—See Lee Feed Mill Public Company Limited; *Int'l,* pg. 4440
LEE PATTANA FEED MILL CO., LTD.—See Lee Feed Mill Public Company Limited; *Int'l,* pg. 4440
LEE PHARMACEUTICALS; *U.S. Public,* pg. 1300
LEEP INC; *U.S. Public,* pg. 1301
LEE PONTIAC-GMC, INC.—See Lee Automotive Group Inc.; *U.S. Private,* pg. 2411
LEEPORT (HOLDINGS) LIMITED; *Int'l,* pg. 4441
LEEPORT MACHINERY (SHANGHAI) COMPANY LIMITED—See Leeport (Holdings) Limited; *Int'l,* pg. 4441
LEEPORT MACHINERY (TAIWAN) CO., LIMITED—See Leeport (Holdings) Limited; *Int'l,* pg. 4441
LEEPORT MACHINE TOOL (SHENZHEN) COMPANY LIMITED—See Leeport (Holdings) Limited; *Int'l,* pg. 4441
LEEPORT MACHINE TOOL TRADING (CHINA) LIMITED—See Leeport (Holdings) Limited; *Int'l,* pg. 4441
LEEPORT METALFORMING MACHINERY LIMITED—See Leeport (Holdings) Limited; *Int'l,* pg. 4441
LEEPORT METROLOGY (DONGGUAN) LIMITED—See Leeport (Holdings) Limited; *Int'l,* pg. 4441
LEEPORT METROLOGY MACAO COMMERCIAL OFFSHORE LIMITED—See Leeport (Holdings) Limited; *Int'l,* pg. 4442
LEEPORT PRECISION MACHINE TOOL COMPANY LIMITED—See Leeport (Holdings) Limited; *Int'l,* pg. 4442
LEEPORT (SINGAPORE) PTE LTD—See Leeport (Holdings) Limited; *Int'l,* pg. 4441
LEEPORT TOOLS LIMITED—See Leeport (Holdings) Limited; *Int'l,* pg. 4442
LEEPORT TOOLS MACAO COMMERCIAL OFFSHORE LIMITED—See Leeport (Holdings) Limited; *Int'l,* pg. 4442
LEE PROCUREMENT SOLUTIONS CO.—See Lee Enterprises, Incorporated; *U.S. Public,* pg. 1299
LEE PRODUCTS LTD.—See The Lee Company; *U.S. Private,* pg. 4068
LEEPS SUPPLY CO. INC.; *U.S. Private,* pg. 2415
LEE PUBLICATIONS, INC.—See Lee Enterprises, Incorporated; *U.S. Public,* pg. 1299
LEE RANCH COAL COMPANY—See Peabody Energy Corporation; *U.S. Public,* pg. 1659
LEE REEDY INC.; *U.S. Private,* pg. 2413
LEER INC.—See Dexter Apache Holdings, Inc.; *U.S. Private,* pg. 1220
LEERINK PARTNERS LLC—See Bain Capital, LP; *U.S. Private,* pg. 432
LEESAR, INC.; *U.S. Private,* pg. 2415
LEESBURG MOTORS, LLC—See AutoNation, Inc.; *U.S. Public,* pg. 236
LEESBURG SOUTHERN ELECTRIC INC; *U.S. Private,* pg. 2415
LEE'S CURTAIN CO., INC.; *U.S. Private,* pg. 2414
LEES DIALYSIS, LLC—See DaVita Inc.; *U.S. Public,* pg. 640
LEE'S FAMOUS RECIPES INC.; *U.S. Private,* pg. 2414
LEES FOODS LIMITED—See DBAY Advisors Limited; *Int'l,* pg. 1986
LEE-SILSBY COMPOUNDING PHARMACY—See Osceola Capital Management, LLC; *U.S. Private,* pg. 3047

LEE-SIMPSON ASSOCIATES, INC.—See Comvest Group Holdings LLC; *U.S. Private,* pg. 1007
LEES OF SCOTLAND LIMITED—See DBAY Advisors Limited; *Int'l,* pg. 1986
LEESON ELECTRIC - GROVE GEAR—See Regal Rexnord Corporation; *U.S. Public,* pg. 1773
LEE'S PET CLUB INC.; *U.S. Private,* pg. 2414
LEE'S PHARMACEUTICAL (HK) LIMITED—See Lee's Pharmaceutical Holdings Limited; *Int'l,* pg. 4441
LEE'S PHARMACEUTICAL HOLDINGS LIMITED; *Int'l,* pg. 4441
LEE SPRING COMPANY LLC; *U.S. Private,* pg. 2413
LEES READY MIX & TRUCKING, INC.; *U.S. Private,* pg. 2415
LEE SRL—See The Lee Company; *U.S. Private,* pg. 4068
LEE'S SUMMIT HONDA INC.; *U.S. Private,* pg. 2414
LEE'S SUMMIT JOURNAL—See Chatham Asset Management, LLC; *U.S. Private,* pg. 866
LEE'S SUMMIT MEDICAL CENTER—See HCA Healthcare, Inc.; *U.S. Public,* pg. 1001
LEE STEEL CORPORATION; *U.S. Private,* pg. 2413
LEE'S TRASH SERVICES, INC.—See Macquarie Group Limited; *Int'l,* pg. 4628
LEE SUPPLY COMPANY INC.—See Core & Main, Inc.; *U.S. Public,* pg. 576
LEE SUPPLY CORP.; *U.S. Private,* pg. 2414
LEESVILLE AUTO WRECKERS, INC.—See Stellex Capital Management LP; *U.S. Private,* pg. 3800
LEE SWEE KIAT GROUP BERHAD; *Int'l,* pg. 4440
LEE THEATRE REALTY LIMITED—See Hysan Development Company Limited; *Int'l,* pg. 3554
LEE THONG HUNG TRADING & TRANSPORT SDN. BHD.—See Vibrant Group Limited; *Int'l,* pg. 8184
LEE TRANSPORT INC.; *U.S. Private,* pg. 2414
LEEUWENHORST CONGRES CENTER, B.V.—See Minor International PCL; *Int'l,* pg. 4911
LEEUWIN METALS LTD.; *Int'l,* pg. 4442
LEEVERS FOODS INC.; *U.S. Private,* pg. 2415
LEEVERS SUPERMARKETS INC.; *U.S. Private,* pg. 2415
LEE WAI HANDBAG MANUFACTURING CO., LTD.—See Lee & Man Chemical Company Limited; *Int'l,* pg. 4439
LEEWARD ASPHALT, L.L.C.—See Haines & Kibblehouse Inc.; *U.S. Private,* pg. 1841
LEEWARD CONSTRUCTION, INC.; *U.S. Private,* pg. 2415
LEE WETHERINGTON HOMES INC.; *U.S. Private,* pg. 2414
LEEWRANGLER INTERNATIONAL SAGL—See V. F. Corporation; *U.S. Public,* pg. 2268
LEE & WYRSCH; *U.S. Private,* pg. 2411
LEEYO SOFTWARE INC.—See Zuora, Inc.; *U.S. Public,* pg. 2412
LEFAUBAS—See Carrefour SA; *Int'l,* pg. 1345
LEFEBVRE COMPANIES, INC.; *U.S. Private,* pg. 2415
LEFEBVRE & SONS INC.—See LeFebvre Companies, Inc.; *U.S. Private,* pg. 2415
LEFF ELECTRIC - BEDFORD HEIGHTS—See The H. Leff Electric Company; *U.S. Private,* pg. 4040
LEFF ELECTRIC - ELYRIA—See The H. Leff Electric Company; *U.S. Private,* pg. 4040
LEFF ELECTRIC - MENTOR—See The H. Leff Electric Company; *U.S. Private,* pg. 4040
LEFF ELECTRIC - STRONGSVILLE—See The H. Leff Electric Company; *U.S. Private,* pg. 4040
LEFF ELECTRIC - WARREN—See The H. Leff Electric Company; *U.S. Private,* pg. 4041
LEFF ELECTRIC - YOUNGSTOWN—See The H. Leff Electric Company; *U.S. Private,* pg. 4041
LEFFERTS OIL TERMINAL INC.; *U.S. Private,* pg. 2415
LEFFINGWELL AG SALES CO. INC.; *U.S. Private,* pg. 2415
LEFFLER AGENCY, INC.; *U.S. Private,* pg. 2415
LEFKA ORI S.A.—See Attica Group; *Int'l,* pg. 696
LEFORM BERHAD; *Int'l,* pg. 4442
LEFORT FRANCHETEAU S.A.S.—See VINCI S.A.; *Int'l,* pg. 8237
LE FOYER STEPHANAIS; *Int'l,* pg. 4431
LEFRAK ORGANIZATION INC.; *U.S. Private,* pg. 2415
LEFROY EXPLORATION LIMITED; *Int'l,* pg. 4442
LEFT BEHIND GAMES, INC.; *U.S. Private,* pg. 2415
LEFTERIS ACQUISITION CORP.; *U.S. Public,* pg. 1301
LEFT FIELD LABS, LLC—See Stagwell, Inc.; *U.S. Public,* pg. 1927
LEFTFIELD PICTURES; *U.S. Private,* pg. 2415
LEFT FIELD PRINTING GROUP LTD.—See Lion Rock Group Ltd; *Int'l,* pg. 4519
LEFTIES ESPANA, S.A.—See Industria de Diseno Textil, S.A.; *Int'l,* pg. 3666
THE LEGACY AGENCY, INC. - NEWPORT BEACH—See Gatemore Capital Management LLP; *Int'l,* pg. 2889
THE LEGACY AGENCY, INC. - NEW YORK—See Gatemore Capital Management LLP; *Int'l,* pg. 2889
LEGACY AUDIO, INC.; *U.S. Private,* pg. 2416
LEGACY AUTOMOTIVE GROUP; *U.S. Private,* pg. 2416
LEGACY AVIATION SERVICES INC.; *U.S. Private,* pg. 2416
LEGACY BAKEHOUSE, LLC—See Benford Capital Partners, LLC; *U.S. Private,* pg. 526
LEGACY BANK OF FLORIDA—See Seacoast Banking Corporation of Florida; *U.S. Public,* pg. 1851

LEGACY AVIATION SERVICES INC. CORPORATE AFFILIATIONS

LEGACY BANK OF TEXAS—See Legacy Texas Group, Inc.; *U.S. Private*, pg. 2417
LEGACY BANK—See InBankshares Corp.; *U.S. Public*, pg. 1114
LEGACY BANK—See Midstate Bancorp, Inc.; *U.S. Private*, pg. 2717
LEGACY BANK & TRUST COMPANY—See Century Bancshares, Inc.; *U.S. Private*, pg. 832
LEGACY BROADCASTING, LLC; *U.S. Private*, pg. 2416
LEGACY BUILDING SERVICES, INC.—See Dempsey Construction, Inc.; *U.S. Private*, pg. 1204
LEGACY.COM, INC.—See Pamplona Capital Management LLP; *Int'l*, pg. 5711
LEGACY COMMERCIAL PROPERTY—See Highland Ventures, Ltd.; *U.S. Private*, pg. 1939
LEGACY COMMUNITY FEDERAL CREDIT UNION; *U.S. Private*, pg. 2416
LEGACY COMMUNITY HEALTH; *U.S. Private*, pg. 2416
THE LEGACY COMPANIES; *U.S. Private*, pg. 4069
LEGACY CONTRACTING SOLUTIONS, INC; *U.S. Private*, pg. 2416
LEGACY CONVERTING, INC.—See Essity Aktiebolag; *Int'l*, pg. 2517
LEGACY CUSTOM BUILDING & REMODELING, INC.—See Dreamstyle Remodeling, Inc.; *U.S. Private*, pg. 1275
LEGACY EDUCATION ALLIANCE, INC.; *U.S. Public*, pg. 1301
LEGACY EDUCATION INC.; *U.S. Public*, pg. 1301
LEGACY EMANUEL CHILDREN'S HOSPITAL—See Legacy Health System; *U.S. Private*, pg. 2416
LEGACY EMANUEL HOSPITAL & HEALTH CENTER—See Legacy Health System; *U.S. Private*, pg. 2416
LEGACY FINANCIAL PLANNING LLC—See TA Associates, Inc.; *U.S. Private*, pg. 3919
LEGACY FIRE PROTECTION, INC.—See TruArc Partners, L.P.; *U.S. Private*, pg. 4244
LEGACY FOOTWEAR LIMITED; *Int'l*, pg. 4442
LEGACY FORD-MERCURY INC.—See Legacy Automotive Group; *U.S. Private*, pg. 2416
LEGACY FOUNDATION, INC.; *U.S. Private*, pg. 2416
LEGACY GOLF MANAGEMENT LLC; *U.S. Private*, pg. 2416
LEGACY GOOD SAMARITAN HOSPITAL & MEDICAL CENTER—See Legacy Health System; *U.S. Private*, pg. 2416
LEGACY HEALTHCARE ADVISORS LLC; *U.S. Private*, pg. 2416
LEGACY HEALTH SYSTEM; *U.S. Private*, pg. 2416
LEGACY HOUSING CORPORATION; *U.S. Public*, pg. 1301
LEGACY INFINITI; *U.S. Private*, pg. 2416
LEGACY IRON ORE LIMITED; *Int'l*, pg. 4442
LEGACY LANDS, LLC—See Five Point Holdings, LLC; *U.S. Public*, pg. 852
LEGACY LONG DISTANCE INTERNATIONAL, INC.; *U.S. Private*, pg. 2416
LEGACY MARKETING GROUP—See Regan Holding Corporation; *U.S. Private*, pg. 3386
LEGACY MEASUREMENT SOLUTIONS, INC.—See White Deer Management LLC; *U.S. Private*, pg. 4508
LEGACY MEDICAL EQUIPMENT—See Catholic Health Initiatives; *U.S. Private*, pg. 789
LEGACY MEDICAL, LLC—See AdaptHealth Corp.; *U.S. Public*, pg. 39
LEGACY MERCANTILE LTD.; *Int'l*, pg. 4442
LEGACY MERIDIAN PARK HOSPITAL—See Legacy Health System; *U.S. Private*, pg. 2416
LEGACY MINERALS HOLDINGS LIMITED; *Int'l*, pg. 4442
LEGACY MOUNT HOOD MEDICAL CENTER—See Legacy Health System; *U.S. Private*, pg. 2416
LEGACY NISSAN; *U.S. Private*, pg. 2416
LEGACY OXYGEN & HOME CARE EQUIPMENT, LLC—See Quipt Home Medical Corp.; *U.S. Public*, pg. 1757
LEGACY PARTNERS INC.; *U.S. Private*, pg. 2416
LEGACY PHARMACEUTICALS SWITZERLAND GMBH; *Int'l*, pg. 4442
LEGACY PROFESSIONALS LLP; *U.S. Private*, pg. 2416
LEGACY PUBLICATIONS INC.—See Pace Communications Inc.; *U.S. Private*, pg. 3063
LEGACY PUBLISHING COMPANY; *U.S. Private*, pg. 2416
LEGACY RESERVES, INC.; *U.S. Private*, pg. 2417
LEGACY RESERVES SERVICES INC.—See Legacy Reserves, Inc.; *U.S. Private*, pg. 2417
LEGACY RESOURCE CORPORATION; *U.S. Private*, pg. 2417
LEGACY SALMON CREEK HOSPITAL—See Legacy Health System; *U.S. Private*, pg. 2416
LEGACY SENIOR SERVICES; *U.S. Private*, pg. 2417
LEGACY STRUCTURES, LLC—See Maugel Architects Inc; *U.S. Private*, pg. 2614
LEGACY SUPPLY CHAIN SERVICES - BRAMPTON—See LEGACY Supply Chain Services; *U.S. Private*, pg. 2417
LEGACY SUPPLY CHAIN SERVICES - FONTANA—See LEGACY Supply Chain Services; *U.S. Private*, pg. 2417

LEGACY SUPPLY CHAIN SERVICES - GARDEN GROVE—See LEGACY Supply Chain Services; *U.S. Private*, pg. 2417
LEGACY SUPPLY CHAIN SERVICES - ONTARIO—See LEGACY Supply Chain Services; *U.S. Private*, pg. 2417
LEGACY SUPPLY CHAIN SERVICES - RENO—See LEGACY Supply Chain Services; *U.S. Private*, pg. 2417
LEGACY SUPPLY CHAIN SERVICES; *U.S. Private*, pg. 2417
LEGACY TECHNOLOGIES INC.; *U.S. Private*, pg. 2417
LEGACYTEXAS FINANCIAL GROUP, INC.—See Prosperity Bancshares, Inc.; *U.S. Public*, pg. 1728
LEGACY TEXAS GROUP, INC.; *U.S. Private*, pg. 2417
LEGACYTEXAS INSURANCE SERVICES, INC.—See Prosperity Bancshares, Inc.; *U.S. Public*, pg. 1728
LEGACYTEXAS TITLE CO.—See Prosperity Bancshares, Inc.; *U.S. Public*, pg. 1728
LEGACY TRANSPORTATION SERVICES; *U.S. Private*, pg. 2417
LEGACY VENTURES INTERNATIONAL, INC.; *Int'l*, pg. 4442
LEGACY VIVINT SMART HOME, INC.—See NRG Energy, Inc.; *U.S. Public*, pg. 1551
LEGACYXCHANGE, INC.; *U.S. Private*, pg. 2417
LE GAGA HOLDINGS LIMITED; *Int'l*, pg. 4431
LEGAL ACCESS PLANS LLC; *U.S. Private*, pg. 2417
LEGAL AID BUREAU, INC.; *U.S. Private*, pg. 2417
LEGAL AID CENTER OF SOUTHERN NEVADA; *U.S. Private*, pg. 2417
LEGAL AID FOUNDATION OF LOS ANGELES; *U.S. Private*, pg. 2417
LEGAL AID OF NORTHWEST TEXAS; *U.S. Private*, pg. 2417
LEGAL AID SERVICES OF OKLAHOMA, INC.; *U.S. Private*, pg. 2417
LEGAL AID SOCIETY OF SUFFOLK COUNTY INC.; *U.S. Private*, pg. 2417
LEGAL APPOINTMENTS LTD—See Randstad N.V.; *Int'l*, pg. 6204
LEGAL BRAND MARKETING, L.L.C.; *U.S. Private*, pg. 2417
LEGAL CHILE S.A.—See MetLife, Inc.; *U.S. Public*, pg. 1430
LEGAL-EYE LIMITED—See ULS Technology plc; *Int'l*, pg. 8017
LEGAL & GENERAL AMERICA INC.—See Legal & General Group Plc; *Int'l*, pg. 4443
LEGAL & GENERAL ASSURANCE (PENSIONS MANAGEMENT) LIMITED—See Legal & General Group Plc; *Int'l*, pg. 4443
LEGAL & GENERAL ASSURANCE SOCIETY LIMITED—See Legal & General Group Plc; *Int'l*, pg. 4443
LEGAL & GENERAL BANK (FRANCE) SA—See Legal & General Group Plc; *Int'l*, pg. 4443
LEGAL & GENERAL (FRANCE) SA—See Groupe Apicil; *Int'l*, pg. 3091
LEGAL & GENERAL GROUP PLC; *Int'l*, pg. 4442
LEGAL & GENERAL HOMES MODULAR LIMITED—See Legal & General Group Plc; *Int'l*, pg. 4443
LEGAL & GENERAL INSURANCE LTD.—See Allianz SE; *Int'l*, pg. 353
LEGAL & GENERAL INVESTMENT MANAGEMENT AMERICA INC.—See Legal & General Group Plc; *Int'l*, pg. 4443
LEGAL & GENERAL INVESTMENT MANAGEMENT LIMITED—See Legal & General Group Plc; *Int'l*, pg. 4443
LEGAL & GENERAL PENSIONS LIMITED—See Legal & General Group Plc; *Int'l*, pg. 4443
LEGAL & GENERAL PROPERTY LIMITED—See Legal & General Group Plc; *Int'l*, pg. 4443
LEGAL & GENERAL RESOURCES LIMITED—See Legal & General Group Plc; *Int'l*, pg. 4443
LEGAL & GENERAL SURVEYING SERVICES LIMITED—See Legal & General Group Plc; *Int'l*, pg. 4443
LEGAL & GENERAL (UNIT TRUST MANAGERS) LIMITED—See Legal & General Group Plc; *Int'l*, pg. 4443
LEGAL GRAPHICWORKS, INC.; *U.S. Private*, pg. 2417
THE LEGAL GROUP INC.—See Noor, Inc.; *U.S. Private*, pg. 2935
LEGALL HOLDINGS, INC.; *U.S. Private*, pg. 2418
LEGAL RESEARCH CENTER, INC.; *U.S. Private*, pg. 2418
LEGAL SEA FOODS INC.—See PPX Hospitality Brands Inc.; *U.S. Private*, pg. 3241
LEGAL SERVICES NYC; *U.S. Private*, pg. 2418
LEGAL SERVICES OF NEW JERSEY; *U.S. Private*, pg. 2418
LEGAL SHRED INC.; *U.S. Private*, pg. 2418
LEGALZOOM.COM, INC.; *U.S. Public*, pg. 1301
LEGAMASTER BVBA—See Edding AG; *Int'l*, pg. 2304
LEGAMASTER GMBH—See Edding AG; *Int'l*, pg. 2304
LEGAMASTER INTERNATIONAL BV—See Edding AG; *Int'l*, pg. 2304

LEGATIO TECHNOLOGIES LTD.—See GTCR LLC; *U.S. Private*, pg. 1804
LEGATO LEASING GMBH—See UniCredit S.p.A.; *Int'l*, pg. 8036
LEGATO MERGER CORP.; *U.S. Public*, pg. 1301
LEGATO PUBLISHERS GROUP—See Perseus Books, LLC; *U.S. Private*, pg. 3155
LEG BADEN-WURTTEMBERG VERWALTUNGS-GMBH—See Landesbank Baden-Wurttemberg; *Int'l*, pg. 4405
LEGENCE HOLDINGS LLC—See Blackstone Inc.; *U.S. Public*, pg. 355
LEGEND ADVISORY LLC—See Lincoln Investment Planning Inc.; *U.S. Private*, pg. 2458
LEGENDARY ENTERTAINMENT, LLC—See Dalian Wanda Group Corporation Ltd.; *Int'l*, pg. 1953
LEGENDARY HOLDING, INC.; *U.S. Private*, pg. 2418
LEGENDARY MOTORCAR COMPANY LTD.; *Int'l*, pg. 4444
LEGENDARY PICTURES PRODUCTIONS, LLC—See Dalian Wanda Group Corporation Ltd.; *Int'l*, pg. 1953
LEGENDARY TELEVISION, LLC—See Dalian Wanda Group Corporation Ltd.; *Int'l*, pg. 1953
LEGENDARY VENTURES, INC.; *Int'l*, pg. 4444
LEGEND BIOTECH CORPORATION; *U.S. Public*, pg. 1301
LEGEND BIOTECH USA INCORPORATED—See Legend Biotech Corporation; *U.S. Public*, pg. 1301
LEGEND BRANDS, INC.—See RPM International Inc.; *U.S. Public*, pg. 1817
LEGEND CAPITAL CO., LTD—See Legend Holdings Corporation; *Int'l*, pg. 4443
LEGEND CLASSIC HOMES LTD.; *U.S. Private*, pg. 2418
LEGEND CORPORATE SERVICES PTY LTD—See Adamantem Capital Management Pty Limited; *Int'l*, pg. 123
LEGEND CORPORATION LIMITED—See Adamantem Capital Management Pty Limited; *Int'l*, pg. 123
LEGEND CREATIVE GROUP; *U.S. Private*, pg. 2418
LEGEND CREDIT, INC.—See Bitcoin Brands Inc.; *U.S. Private*, pg. 567
LEGEND FINANCIAL ADVISORS, INC; *U.S. Private*, pg. 2418
LEGEND FOOD SERVICE LLC; *U.S. Private*, pg. 2418
THE LEGEND GROUP—See Lincoln Investment Planning Inc.; *U.S. Private*, pg. 2458
LEGEND HOLDINGS CORPORATION; *Int'l*, pg. 4443
LEGEND HOME CORP.; *U.S. Private*, pg. 2418
LEGEND HOMES CORPORATION; *U.S. Private*, pg. 2418
LEGEND INVESTMENTS LTD.—See Mercedes-Benz Group AG; *Int'l*, pg. 4825
LEGEND MEDIA, INC.; *Int'l*, pg. 4443
LEGEND MINING LIMITED; *Int'l*, pg. 4443
LEGEND OIL AND GAS, LTD.; *U.S. Public*, pg. 1301
LEGEND POWER SYSTEMS INC.; *Int'l*, pg. 4443
LEGENDS HOSPITALITY, LLC—See Sixth Street Partners LLC; *U.S. Private*, pg. 3677
LEGEND SPICES, INC.; *Int'l*, pg. 4443
LEGEND STRATEGY INTERNATIONAL HOLDINGS GROUP; *Int'l*, pg. 4444
LEGEND STUDIOS, INC.—See Bitcoin Brands Inc.; *U.S. Private*, pg. 567
LEGEND UPSTAR HOLDINGS LIMITED; *Int'l*, pg. 4444
LEGGAT MCCALL PROPERTIES LLC; *U.S. Private*, pg. 2418
LEGGAT MCCALL PROPERTIES, LLC.; *U.S. Private*, pg. 2418
LEGGETTE, BRASHEARS & GRAHAM, INC.—See WSP Global, Inc.; *Int'l*, pg. 8497
LEGGETT & PLATT ADMINISTRADORA, S.A. DE C.V.—See Leggett & Platt, Incorporated; *U.S. Public*, pg. 1303
LEGGETT & PLATT AEROSPACE MIDDLETOWN, LLC—See Leggett & Platt, Incorporated; *U.S. Public*, pg. 1303
LEGGETT & PLATT - AMCO DIVISION—See Leggett & Platt, Incorporated; *U.S. Public*, pg. 1303
LEGGETT & PLATT ASIA LIMITED—See Leggett & Platt, Incorporated; *U.S. Public*, pg. 1303
LEGGETT & PLATT CANADA CO.—See Leggett & Platt, Incorporated; *U.S. Public*, pg. 1303
LEGGETT & PLATT COMMERCIAL VEHICLE PRODUCTS, INC.—See Leggett & Platt, Incorporated; *U.S. Public*, pg. 1303
LEGGETT & PLATT COMPONENTS COMPANY, INC.—See Leggett & Platt, Incorporated; *U.S. Public*, pg. 1303
LEGGETT & PLATT COMPONENTS EUROPE LIMITED—See Leggett & Platt, Incorporated; *U.S. Public*, pg. 1303
LEGGETT & PLATT DE MEXICO, S. DE R.L. DE C.V.—See Leggett & Platt, Incorporated; *U.S. Public*, pg. 1303
LEGGETT & PLATT DO BRASIL LTDA.—See Leggett & Platt, Incorporated; *U.S. Public*, pg. 1303
LEGGETT & PLATT FRANCE S.A.S.—See Leggett & Platt, Incorporated; *U.S. Public*, pg. 1303
LEGGETT & PLATT (GUANGZHOU) CO. LTD.—See Leggett & Platt, Incorporated; *U.S. Public*, pg. 1302

COMPANY NAME INDEX

LEGGETT & PLATT, INC. - CHICAGO—See Leggett & Platt, Incorporated; *U.S. Public*, pg. 1303
LEGGETT & PLATT, INCORPORATED; *U.S. Public*, pg. 1301
LEGGETT & PLATT, INC. - OXFORD—See Leggett & Platt, Incorporated; *U.S. Public*, pg. 1303
LEGGETT & PLATT INDUSTRY (HUIZHOU) CO LTD—See Leggett & Platt, Incorporated; *U.S. Public*, pg. 1303
LEGGETT & PLATT INTERNATIONAL DEVELOPMENT CO.—See Leggett & Platt, Incorporated; *U.S. Public*, pg. 1303
LEGGETT & PLATT INTERNATIONAL SERVICE CORPORATION—See Leggett & Platt, Incorporated; *U.S. Public*, pg. 1303
LEGGETT & PLATT (JIAXING) CO. LTD.—See Leggett & Platt, Incorporated; *U.S. Public*, pg. 1302
LEGGETT & PLATT OFFICE COMPONENTS INTERNATIONAL S.R.L.—See Leggett & Platt, Incorporated; *U.S. Public*, pg. 1303
LEGGETT & PLATT OFFICE COMPONENTS, LLC—See Leggett & Platt, Incorporated; *U.S. Public*, pg. 1303
LEGGETT & PLATT RESIDENCIAL, S. DE R.L. DE C.V.—See Leggett & Platt, Incorporated; *U.S. Public*, pg. 1303
LEGGETT & PLATT (SHANGHAI) CO. LTD.—See Leggett & Platt, Incorporated; *U.S. Public*, pg. 1302
LEGGETT & PLATT (SHANGHAI) MACHINERY TECHNOLOGY CO. LTD—See Leggett & Platt, Incorporated; *U.S. Public*, pg. 1302
LEGGETT & PLATT (TAIZHOU) CO. LTD.—See Leggett & Platt, Incorporated; *U.S. Public*, pg. 1302
LEGG INC.; *U.S. Private*, pg. 2418
LEGGIUNO S.P.A.—See S. Kumars Nationwide Limited; *Int'l*, pg. 6447
LEGG MASON ASSET MANAGEMENT (SINGAPORE) PTE LTD.—See Franklin Resources, Inc.; *U.S. Public*, pg. 882
LEGG MASON CAPITAL MANAGEMENT INC.—See Franklin Resources, Inc.; *U.S. Public*, pg. 882
LEGG MASON, INC.—See Franklin Resources, Inc.; *U.S. Public*, pg. 881
LEGG MASON INVESTMENTS (EUROPE) LIMITED—See Franklin Resources, Inc.; *U.S. Public*, pg. 882
LEGG MASON INVESTMENTS (LUXEMBOURG) S.A.—See Franklin Resources, Inc.; *U.S. Public*, pg. 882
LEGG MASON INVESTMENTS (SWITZERLAND) GMBH—See Franklin Resources, Inc.; *U.S. Public*, pg. 881
LEGG MASON INVESTOR SERVICES, LLC—See Franklin Resources, Inc.; *U.S. Public*, pg. 882
LEGGO SRL—See Caltagirone Editore S.p.A.; *Int'l*, pg. 1266
LEGIAL AG—See Munchener Ruckversicherungs AG; *Int'l*, pg. 5089
LEGIC IDENTSYSTEMS AG—See dormakaba Holding AG; *Int'l*, pg. 2179
LEGIER & COMPANY—See Cherry Bekaert LLP; *U.S. Private*, pg. 874
LEGILITY, LLC; *U.S. Private*, pg. 2418
LEG IMMOBILIEN SE; *Int'l*, pg. 4442
LEGION ADVERTISING; *U.S. Private*, pg. 2418
LEGION CONSORTIUM LIMITED; *Int'l*, pg. 4444
LEGION GROUP PLC—See OCS Group Limited; *Int'l*, pg. 5521
LEGION (H.K.) LIMITED; *Int'l*, pg. 4444
LEGION INDUSTRIES, INC.—See The Legacy Companies; *U.S. Private*, pg. 4069
LEGION PAPER CORPORATION—See Gould Paper Corporation; *U.S. Private*, pg. 1745
LEGION UK LTD.—See Vivendi SE; *Int'l*, pg. 8274
LEGISLATIVE INFORMATION SERVICES OF AMERICA, LLC—See The Dolan Company; *U.S. Private*, pg. 4022
LEG MANAGEMENT GMBH—See LEG Immobilien SE; *Int'l*, pg. 4442
LEGMAS S.A.; *Int'l*, pg. 4444
LEGO ASSET MANAGEMENT LIMITED—See LFG Investment Holdings Limited; *Int'l*, pg. 4473
LEGO A/S—See Kirkbi A/S; *Int'l*, pg. 4190
LEGO AUSTRALIA PTY. LTD.—See Kirkbi A/S; *Int'l*, pg. 4190
LEGO BELGIUM N.V.—See Kirkbi A/S; *Int'l*, pg. 4190
LEGO BRAND RETAIL INC.—See Kirkbi A/S; *Int'l*, pg. 4190
LEGO BRAND RETAIL S.A.S—See Kirkbi A/S; *Int'l*, pg. 4190
LEGO CANADA INC.—See Kirkbi A/S; *Int'l*, pg. 4190
LEGOCHEM BIOSCIENCES INC. - ANSEONG PLANT—See LegoChem Biosciences Inc.; *Int'l*, pg. 4444
LEGOCHEM BIOSCIENCES INC.; *Int'l*, pg. 4444
LEGO COMPANY LIMITED—See Kirkbi A/S; *Int'l*, pg. 4190
LEGO COMPANY LIMITED—See Kirkbi A/S; *Int'l*, pg. 4190
LEGO COMPANY LTD.—See Kirkbi A/S; *Int'l*, pg. 4190
LEGO CORPORATE FINANCE LIMITED—See LFG Investment Holdings Limited; *Int'l*, pg. 4473
LEGO EDUCATION EUROPE LTD.—See Kirkbi A/S; *Int'l*, pg. 4190

LEGO GMBH—See Kirkbi A/S; *Int'l*, pg. 4190
LEGO HANDELSGESELLS. GMBH—See Kirkbi A/S; *Int'l*, pg. 4190
LEGO HONG KONG LIMITED—See Kirkbi A/S; *Int'l*, pg. 4190
LEGO HUNGARIA KFT.—See Kirkbi A/S; *Int'l*, pg. 4190
LEGO JAPAN LTD.—See Kirkbi A/S; *Int'l*, pg. 4190
LEGO KOREA CO. LTD.—See Kirkbi A/S; *Int'l*, pg. 4190
LEGOLAND APS—See Merlin Entertainments plc; *Int'l*, pg. 4837
LEGOLAND CALIFORNIA LLC—See Merlin Entertainments plc; *Int'l*, pg. 4837
LEGOLAND DEUTSCHLAND FREIZEITPARK GMBH—See Merlin Entertainments plc; *Int'l*, pg. 4837
LEGOLAND DISCOVERY CENTER ARIZONA LLC—See Merlin Entertainments plc; *Int'l*, pg. 4837
LEGOLAND DISCOVERY CENTER COLUMBUS LLC—See Merlin Entertainments plc; *Int'l*, pg. 4837
LEGOLAND DISCOVERY CENTER MICHIGAN LLC—See Merlin Entertainments plc; *Int'l*, pg. 4837
LEGOLAND DISCOVERY CENTER PHILADELPHIA LLC—See Merlin Entertainments plc; *Int'l*, pg. 4837
LEGOLAND DISCOVERY CENTER SAN ANTONIO LLC—See Merlin Entertainments plc; *Int'l*, pg. 4837
LEGOLAND DISCOVERY CENTRE DEUTSCHLAND GMBH—See Merlin Entertainments plc; *Int'l*, pg. 4837
LEGOLAND HOLIDAYS DEUTSCHLAND GMBH—See Merlin Entertainments plc; *Int'l*, pg. 4837
LEGO LIFESTYLE INTERNATIONAL LTD.—See Kirkbi A/S; *Int'l*, pg. 4190
LEGO MANUFACTURING KFT.—See Kirkbi A/S; *Int'l*, pg. 4190
LEGO MEXICO S.A. DE C.V—See Kirkbi A/S; *Int'l*, pg. 4190
LEGO NEW ZEALAND LTD.—See Kirkbi A/S; *Int'l*, pg. 4190
LEGO NORGE A/S—See Kirkbi A/S; *Int'l*, pg. 4190
LEGO OPERACIONES DE MEXICO S.A. DE C.V.—See Kirkbi A/S; *Int'l*, pg. 4190
LEGO PARK HOLDING UK LTD.—See Kirkbi A/S; *Int'l*, pg. 4190
LEGO POLSKA SP. Z.O.O.—See Kirkbi A/S; *Int'l*, pg. 4190
LEGO PRODUCTION S.R.O.—See Kirkbi A/S; *Int'l*, pg. 4190
LEGO S.A.—See Kirkbi A/S; *Int'l*, pg. 4190
LEGO S.A.S.—See Kirkbi A/S; *Int'l*, pg. 4190
LEGO SECURITIES LIMITED—See LFG Investment Holdings Limited; *Int'l*, pg. 4473
LEGO SINGAPORE PTE. LTD.—See Kirkbi A/S; *Int'l*, pg. 4190
LEGO SOUTH AFRICA (PTY.) LTD.—See Kirkbi A/S; *Int'l*, pg. 4190
LEGO S.P.A.—See Kirkbi A/S; *Int'l*, pg. 4190
LEGOSYS SOLUTIONS, LLC—See Central Iowa Power Cooperative; *U.S. Private*, pg. 822
LEGO SYSTEMS A/S—See Kirkbi A/S; *Int'l*, pg. 4190
LEGO SYSTEMS, INC.—See Kirkbi A/S; *Int'l*, pg. 4190
LEGO SYSTEMS—See Kirkbi A/S; *Int'l*, pg. 4190
LEGO TOY CO., LTD.—See Kirkbi A/S; *Int'l*, pg. 4190
LEGO TOY MANUFACTURING CO., LTD.—See Kirkbi A/S; *Int'l*, pg. 4190
LEGO TRADING CO LTD—See Kirkbi A/S; *Int'l*, pg. 4190
LEGO TRADING S.R.O.—See Kirkbi A/S; *Int'l*, pg. 4190
LEGOUEIX SAS—See Rubix Group International Limtied; *Int'l*, pg. 6423
LEGRAND AV, INC.—See Legrand S.A.; *Int'l*, pg. 4445
LEGRAND AV NETHERLANDS B.V.—See Legrand S.A.; *Int'l*, pg. 4445
LEGRAND CANADA, INC.—See Legrand S.A.; *Int'l*, pg. 4445
LEGRAND CHINA—See Legrand S.A.; *Int'l*, pg. 4445
LEGRAND COLOMBIA SA—See Legrand S.A.; *Int'l*, pg. 4445
LEGRAND ELECTRICAL—See Legrand S.A.; *Int'l*, pg. 4445
LEGRAND ELECTRICA S.A—See Legrand S.A.; *Int'l*, pg. 4445
LEGRAND ELECTRIC LTD—See Legrand S.A.; *Int'l*, pg. 4445
LEGRAND ELECTRIQUE SA—See Legrand S.A.; *Int'l*, pg. 4445
LEGRAND ELEKTRIK SAN. A.S.—See Legrand S.A.; *Int'l*, pg. 4445
LEGRAND ESPANA SL—See Legrand S.A.; *Int'l*, pg. 4445
LEGRAND FRANCE SA—See Legrand S.A.; *Int'l*, pg. 4444
LEGRAND GMBH—See Legrand S.A.; *Int'l*, pg. 4445
LEGRAND GROUP PTY LTD—See Legrand S.A.; *Int'l*, pg. 4445
LEGRAND HOLDING INC.—See Legrand S.A.; *Int'l*, pg. 4445
LEGRAND INDIA PVT LTD - JALGAON MANUFACTURING UNIT—See Legrand S.A.; *Int'l*, pg. 4445
LEGRAND INDIA PVT LTD - NASHIK MANUFACTURING UNIT—See Legrand S.A.; *Int'l*, pg. 4445
LEGRAND INDIA PVT LTD—See Legrand S.A.; *Int'l*, pg. 4445
LEGRAND JOHNSON CONSTRUCTION CO.—See Summit Materials, Inc.; *U.S. Private*, pg. 1960

LEHMAN BROTHERS HOLDINGS INC. PLAN TRUST

LEGRAND NEDERLAND B.V.—See Legrand S.A.; *Int'l*, pg. 4445
LEGRAND NORTH AMERICA, LLC—See Legrand S.A.; *Int'l*, pg. 4445
LEGRAND ROMANIA SRL—See Legrand S.A.; *Int'l*, pg. 4446
LEGRAND S.A.; *Int'l*, pg. 4444
LEGRAND SCANDINAVIA APS—See Legrand S.A.; *Int'l*, pg. 4444
LEGRAND SLV D.O.O—See Legrand S.A.; *Int'l*, pg. 4444
LEGRAND S.R.O.—See Legrand S.A.; *Int'l*, pg. 4446
LEGRAND (SUISSE) S.A.—See Legrand S.A.; *Int'l*, pg. 4445
LEGRAND UKRAINE LTD—See Legrand S.A.; *Int'l*, pg. 4444
LEG RESOURCE INC.; *U.S. Private*, pg. 2415
LEGRIS DANMARK APS—See Parker Hannifin Corporation; *U.S. Public*, pg. 1645
LEGRIS DO BRASIL LTDA.—See Parker Hannifin Corporation; *U.S. Public*, pg. 1645
LEGRIS HUNGARIA KFT—See Parker Hannifin Corporation; *U.S. Public*, pg. 1645
LEGRIS INDIA PVT. LTD.—See Parker Hannifin Corporation; *U.S. Public*, pg. 1645
LEGRIS POLAND SP. Z.O.O.—See Parker Hannifin Corporation; *U.S. Public*, pg. 1645
LEGRIS S.A.S.—See Parker Hannifin Corporation; *U.S. Public*, pg. 1645
LEGRIS, S.R.O.—See Parker Hannifin Corporation; *U.S. Public*, pg. 1645
LE GROUPE MASTER S.E.C; *Int'l*, pg. 4431
LEGS (SHANGHAI) CULTURAL & CREATIVE COMPANY, LTD.—See CL Holdings Inc.; *Int'l*, pg. 1640
LEGS (SHANGHAI) TRADING COMPANY, LTD.—See CL Holdings Inc.; *Int'l*, pg. 1640
LEGUIDE.COM S.A.—See Vivendi SE; *Int'l*, pg. 8278
LEGUME FRUCTE S.A.—See SIF Banat-Crisana S.A.; *Int'l*, pg. 6905
LEGUM & NORMAN INC.; *U.S. Private*, pg. 2418
LEHAR FOOTWEARS LIMITED; *Int'l*, pg. 4446
LEHIGH ACRES DIALYSIS CENTER, LLC—See Nautic Partners, LLC; *U.S. Private*, pg. 2870
LEHIGH ASPHALT, PAVING & CONSTRUCTION—See Barletta Materials & Construction; *U.S. Private*, pg. 476
LEHIGH CEMENT COMPANY LLC—See Heidelberg Materials AG; *Int'l*, pg. 3313
LEHIGH CEMENT CO.—See Heidelberg Materials AG; *Int'l*, pg. 3313
LEHIGH CEMENT - INDIANA PLANT—See Heidelberg Materials AG; *Int'l*, pg. 3317
LEHIGH CEMENT—See Heidelberg Materials AG; *Int'l*, pg. 3313
LEHIGH ENGINEERING ASSOCIATES, INC.; *U.S. Private*, pg. 2418
LEHIGH ENGINEERING LLC—See Reading Anthracite Company; *U.S. Private*, pg. 3366
LEHIGH FUELS—See Reading Anthracite Company; *U.S. Private*, pg. 3366
LEHIGH HANSON CANADA—See Heidelberg Materials AG; *Int'l*, pg. 3313
LEHIGH HANSON ECC, INC.—See Heidelberg Materials AG; *Int'l*, pg. 3317
LEHIGH HANSON MATERIALS LIMITED—See Heidelberg Materials AG; *Int'l*, pg. 3318
LEHIGH HEAVY FORGE CORP—See Park Corp.; *U.S. Private*, pg. 3096
LEHIGH HMA, LLC—See Prime Healthcare Services, Inc.; *U.S. Private*, pg. 3261
LEHIGH NORTHEAST CEMENT CO.—See Heidelberg Materials AG; *Int'l*, pg. 3313
LEHIGH NORTHWEST CEMENT COMPANY—See Heidelberg Materials AG; *Int'l*, pg. 3314
LEHIGH NORTHWEST MARINE, LLC—See Heidelberg Materials AG; *Int'l*, pg. 3318
LEHIGH OUTFITTERS, LLC—See Rocky Brands, Inc.; *U.S. Public*, pg. 1807
LEHIGH REALTY COMPANY—See Heidelberg Materials AG; *Int'l*, pg. 3318
LEHIGH SOUTHWEST CEMENT COMPANY—See Heidelberg Materials AG; *Int'l*, pg. 3313
LEHIGH TECHNOLOGIES INC.—See Compagnie Generale des Etablissements Michelin SCA; *Int'l*, pg. 1743
LEHIGH VALLEY HEALTH NETWORK EMS—See Lehigh Valley Health Network, Inc.; *U.S. Private*, pg. 2419
LEHIGH VALLEY HEALTH NETWORK, INC.; *U.S. Private*, pg. 2418
LEHIGH VALLEY PLASTICS INC.; *U.S. Private*, pg. 2419
LEHIGH VALLEY RESPIRATORY CARE - LANCASTER, INC.—See AdaptHealth Corp.; *U.S. Public*, pg. 39
LEHIGH WHITE CEMENT COMPANY—See Cementir Holding N.V.; *Int'l*, pg. 1397
LEHIGH WHITE CEMENT COMPANY - WACO PLANT—See Cementir Holding N.V.; *Int'l*, pg. 1397
LEH INSURANCE GROUP, LLC—See Sharing Services Global Corporation; *U.S. Public*, pg. 1873
LEHMAN BROTHERS HOLDINGS INC. PLAN TRUST; *U.S. Private*, pg. 2419

1587

LEHMAN BROTHERS HOLDINGS INC. PLAN TRUST

LEHMAN BROTHERS HOLDINGS PLC—See Lehman Brothers Holdings Inc. Plan Trust; *U.S. Private*, pg. 2419
LEHMAN BROTHERS INC.—See Lehman Brothers Holdings Inc. Plan Trust; *U.S. Private*, pg. 2419
LEHMAN COMMERCIAL PAPER INC.—See Lehman Brothers Holdings Inc. Plan Trust; *U.S. Private*, pg. 2419
LEHMAN DEALERSHIP ENTERPRISES, INC.—See Lithia Motors, Inc.; *U.S. Public*, pg. 1323
LEHMANMILLET EUROPE—See LehmanMillet; *U.S. Private*, pg. 2419
LEHMANMILLET; *U.S. Private*, pg. 2419
LEHMANMILLET—See LehmanMillet; *U.S. Private*, pg. 2419
LEHMAN PRINTING CENTER—See Alden Global Capital LLC; *U.S. Private*, pg. 157
LEHMAN-ROBERTS COMPANY; *U.S. Private*, pg. 2419
LEHMAN TRIKES USA, INC.; *U.S. Private*, pg. 2419
LEHNER INVESTMENTS AG; *Int'l*, pg. 4446
LEHNHOFF HARTSTAHL GMBH—See Komatsu Ltd.; *Int'l*, pg. 4238
LEHOUX ET JACQUE—See L'Oreal S.A.; *Int'l*, pg. 4380
LEHR CONSTRUCTION COMPANY; *U.S. Private*, pg. 2419
LEHRER MCGOVERN INTERNATIONAL LTD—See Lendlease Corporation Limited; *Int'l*, pg. 4451
LEHRER'S FLOWERS INC.; *U.S. Private*, pg. 2419
LEHRKINDS INC.; *U.S. Private*, pg. 2419
LEHTIKANTA OY—See Sanoma Oyj; *Int'l*, pg. 6553
LEHTO GROUP OYJ; *Int'l*, pg. 4446
LEIBER GMBH; *Int'l*, pg. 4446
LEIBLER-BRONFMAN LUBALIN; *U.S. Private*, pg. 2419
LEIB SOLUTIONS, INC.; *U.S. Private*, pg. 2419
LEIBUR AS—See Lantmannen ek for; *Int'l*, pg. 4414
LEICA BIOSYSTEMS IMAGING INC.—See Danaher Corporation; *U.S. Public*, pg. 628
LEICA BIOSYSTEMS NEWCASTLE LIMITED—See Danaher Corporation; *U.S. Public*, pg. 628
LEICA BIOSYSTEMS NUSSLOCH GMBH—See Danaher Corporation; *U.S. Public*, pg. 628
LEICA BIOSYSTEMS RICHMOND, INC.—See Danaher Corporation; *U.S. Public*, pg. 628
LEICA CAMERA AG—See Blackstone Inc.; *U.S. Public*, pg. 360
LEICA CAMERA AG—See SOCRATES Privatstiftung; *Int'l*, pg. 7044
LEICA CAMERA, INC.—See Blackstone Inc.; *U.S. Public*, pg. 360
LEICA CAMERA, INC.—See SOCRATES Privatstiftung; *Int'l*, pg. 7044
LEICA GEOSYSTEMS AG METROLOGY DIVISION—See Hexagon AB; *Int'l*, pg. 3367
LEICA GEOSYSTEMS AG—See Hexagon AB; *Int'l*, pg. 3367
LEICA GEOSYSTEMS GR, LLC—See Hexagon AB; *Int'l*, pg. 3368
LEICA GEOSYSTEMS, INC. - COSTA MESA—See Hexagon AB; *Int'l*, pg. 3368
LEICA GEOSYSTEMS, INC.—See Hexagon AB; *Int'l*, pg. 3368
LEICA GEOSYSTEMS LTD.—See Hexagon AB; *Int'l*, pg. 3367
LEICA MICROSYSTEMS B.V.—See Danaher Corporation; *U.S. Public*, pg. 628
LEICA MICROSYSTEMS CAMBRIDGE LIMITED—See Danaher Corporation; *U.S. Public*, pg. 628
LEICA MICROSYSTEMS CANADA—See Danaher Corporation; *U.S. Public*, pg. 628
LEICA MICROSYSTEMS GMBH—See Danaher Corporation; *U.S. Public*, pg. 628
LEICA MICROSYSTEMS, INC.—See Danaher Corporation; *U.S. Public*, pg. 628
LEICA MICROSYSTEMS IR GMBH—See Danaher Corporation; *U.S. Public*, pg. 628
LEICA MICROSYSTEMS KK—See Danaher Corporation; *U.S. Public*, pg. 628
LEICA MICROSYSTEMS LIMITED—See Danaher Corporation; *U.S. Public*, pg. 628
LEICA MICROSYSTEMS (SEA) PTE LTD—See Danaher Corporation; *U.S. Public*, pg. 628
LEICA MICROSYSTEMS TRADING (SHANGHAI) LTD.—See Danaher Corporation; *U.S. Public*, pg. 628
LEICA MIKROSYSTEME (AUSTRIA) GMBH—See Danaher Corporation; *U.S. Public*, pg. 628
LEICA MIKROSYSTEME VERTRIEB GMBH—See Danaher Corporation; *U.S. Public*, pg. 628
LEICESTER HOLDINGS CO., LTD.—See Restar Holdings Corporation; *Int'l*, pg. 6303
THE LEICESTER NUFFIELD HOSPITAL—See Nuffield Health; *Int'l*, pg. 5487
LEICHTMETALL ALUMINIUM GIESSEREI HANNOVER GMBH—See Quantum Capital Partners AG; *Int'l*, pg. 6154
LEICHT TRANSFER & STORAGE COMPANY; *U.S. Private*, pg. 2419
LEIDEN CABINET CO.; *U.S. Private*, pg. 2419
LEIDERDORP INSTRUMENTS BV—See Indutrade AB; *Int'l*, pg. 3680

LEIDOS BIOMEDICAL RESEARCH, INC.—See Leidos Holdings, Inc.; *U.S. Public*, pg. 1304
LEIDOS CANADA—See Leidos Holdings, Inc.; *U.S. Public*, pg. 1304
LEIDOS CYBER, INC.—See Capgemini SE; *Int'l*, pg. 1307
LEIDOS ENGINEERING OF NORTH CAROLINA, INC.—See Leidos Holdings, Inc.; *U.S. Public*, pg. 1304
LEIDOS ENGINEERING—See Leidos Holdings, Inc.; *U.S. Public*, pg. 1304
LEIDOS ENGINEERING—See Leidos Holdings, Inc.; *U.S. Public*, pg. 1304
LEIDOS ENGINEERING—See Leidos Holdings, Inc.; *U.S. Public*, pg. 1304
LEIDOS ENGINEERING—See Leidos Holdings, Inc.; *U.S. Public*, pg. 1304
LEIDOS HEALTH, LLC—See ManpowerGroup Inc.; *U.S. Public*, pg. 1362
LEIDOS HOLDINGS, INC.; *U.S. Public*, pg. 1304
LEIDOS, INC.—See Leidos Holdings, Inc.; *U.S. Public*, pg. 1304
LEIDSCHE VERZEKERING MAATSCHAPIJ N.V.—See Reinsurance Group of America, Inc.; *U.S. Public*, pg. 1777
LEIFELD METAL SPINNING GMBH—See Sumitomo Heavy Industries, Ltd.; *Int'l*, pg. 7287
LEIF GRIMSRUD AS—See Veidekke ASA; *Int'l*, pg. 8148
LEIFHEIT AG; *Int'l*, pg. 4446
LEIFHEIT AG—See Leifheit AG; *Int'l*, pg. 4447
LEIFHEIT-BIRAMBEAU S.A.S.—See Leifheit AG; *Int'l*, pg. 4447
LEIFHEIT CZ A.S.—See Leifheit AG; *Int'l*, pg. 4447
LEIFHEIT DISTRIBUTION S.R.L.—See Leifheit AG; *Int'l*, pg. 4447
LEIFHEIT ESPANA S.A.—See Leifheit AG; *Int'l*, pg. 4447
LEIFHEIT INTERNATIONAL U.S.A. INC—See Leifheit AG; *Int'l*, pg. 4447
LEIFHEIT OSTERREICH GMBH—See Leifheit AG; *Int'l*, pg. 4447
LEIFHEIT POLSKA SP. Z O.O.—See Leifheit AG; *Int'l*, pg. 4447
LEIF HOEGH (U.K.) LIMITED—See Hoegh LNG Holding Ltd.; *Int'l*, pg. 3439
LEIF JOHNSON FORD INC.; *U.S. Private*, pg. 2419
LEIGH FIBERS, INC.; *U.S. Private*, pg. 2419
LEIGH FIBERS, INC., WAREHOUSE & DISTRIBUTION—See Leigh Fibers, Inc.; *U.S. Private*, pg. 2419
LEIGHFISHER INC.—See Jacobs Engineering Group, Inc.; *U.S. Public*, pg. 1186
LEIGHFISHER LTD.—See Jacobs Engineering Group, Inc.; *U.S. Public*, pg. 1186
LEIGH MARCUS, INC.; *U.S. Private*, pg. 2419
LEIGH-MARDON PACIFIC PACKAGING PTE LTD.—See AMVIG Holdings Limited; *Int'l*, pg. 442
LEIGHOW OIL COMPANY INCORPORATED; *U.S. Private*, pg. 2420
LEIGHTON ASSOCIATES, INC.—See Kelso & Company, L.P.; *U.S. Private*, pg. 2278
LEIGHTON BROADCASTING - FERGUS FALLS—See Leighton Enterprises, Inc.; *U.S. Private*, pg. 2420
LEIGHTON BROADCASTING - WINONA—See Leighton Enterprises, Inc.; *U.S. Private*, pg. 2420
LEIGHTON CONTRACTORS PTY. LIMITED—See ACS, Actividades de Construccion y Servicios, S.A.; *Int'l*, pg. 113
LEIGHTON CONTRACTORS PTY. LIMITED—See Apollo Global Management, Inc.; *U.S. Public*, pg. 153
LEIGHTON ENTERPRISES, INC.; *U.S. Private*, pg. 2420
LEIGHTON PROPERTIES PTY LIMITED—See ACS, Actividades de Construccion y Servicios, S.A.; *Int'l*, pg. 115
LEIGHTON ROAD HOTEL MANAGEMENT SERVICES LIMITED—See SEA Holdings Limited; *Int'l*, pg. 6660
LEI INDUSTRIES (H.K.) LIMITED—See Leader Electronics Inc.; *Int'l*, pg. 4433
LEI JAPAN CO., LTD.—See Leader Electronics Inc.; *Int'l*, pg. 4433
LEILIAN CO., LTD.—See ITOCHU Corporation; *Int'l*, pg. 3840
LEI MALAYSIA SDN. BHD.—See Leader Electronics Inc.; *Int'l*, pg. 4433
LEIMEN ENTERPRISE LTD.—See Korea Electric Terminal Co., Ltd.; *Int'l*, pg. 4284
LEINBACH MACHINERY CO.; *U.S. Private*, pg. 2420
LEINER PAK GELATINE LIMITED; *Int'l*, pg. 4447
LEINGANG HOME CENTER—See True Home Value, Inc.; *U.S. Private*, pg. 4247
LEIN HING HOLDINGS SDN. BHD.—See Kato Sangyo Co., Ltd.; *Int'l*, pg. 4090
LEINSTER EXPRESS NEWSPAPERS LTD—See JPIMedia Holdings Limited; *Int'l*, pg. 4006
LEINSTER LEADER LTD—See JPIMedia Holdings Limited; *Int'l*, pg. 4006
LEIPNIK-LUNDENBURGER INVEST BETEILIGUNGS AG—See Raiffeisen-Holding Niederosterreich-Wien reg. Gen.m.b.H.; *Int'l*, pg. 6185
LEIPURIN ESTONIA AS—See Aspo Oyj; *Int'l*, pg. 631
LEIPURIN OY—See Aspo Oyj; *Int'l*, pg. 631
LEIPURIN PLC—See Aspo Oyj; *Int'l*, pg. 631

CORPORATE AFFILIATIONS

LEISURE ACQUISITION CORP.; *U.S. Public*, pg. 1304
LEISURE ARTS, INC.—See Lions Gate Entertainment Corp.; *Int'l*, pg. 4521
LEISURE BAY DISTRIBUTING CO. INC.—See Leisure Bay Industries, Inc.; *U.S. Private*, pg. 2420
LEISURE BAY INDUSTRIES, INC.; *U.S. Private*, pg. 2420
LEISURE CAPITAL CORPORATION—See Hilton Grand Vacations Inc.; *U.S. Public*, pg. 1040
LEISURE CARE, INC.; *U.S. Private*, pg. 2420
LEISURE CONSTRUCTION LLC—See Leisure Hotel Corporation; *U.S. Private*, pg. 2420
LEISURE CORP PRIVATE LIMITED—See Ebix Inc.; *U.S. Public*, pg. 710
LEISURE FARM CORPORATION SDN BHD—See Mulpha International Bhd.; *Int'l*, pg. 5081
LEISURE HOTEL CORPORATION; *U.S. Private*, pg. 2420
LEISURE HOTEL LLC—See Leisure Hotel Corporation; *U.S. Private*, pg. 2420
LEISURE INN PENNY ROYAL PTY. LTD.—See Seibu Holdings Inc.; *Int'l*, pg. 6684
LEISURE INN POKOLBIN RESORT PTY. LIMITED—See Seibu Holdings Inc.; *Int'l*, pg. 6685
LEISURE INN SPIRES RESORT PTY. LIMITED—See Seibu Holdings Inc.; *Int'l*, pg. 6685
LEISURELINK INC.—See VacationRoost Group Inc.; *U.S. Private*, pg. 4329
LEISURE LIVING LIMITED—See Blackstone Inc.; *U.S. Public*, pg. 358
LEISURE PASS GROUP LIMITED—See Exponent Private Equity LLP; *Int'l*, pg. 2589
LEISURE RE ADVISORS LLC—See Leisure Hotel Corporation; *U.S. Private*, pg. 2420
LEISURE & RESORTS WORLD CORPORATION; *Int'l*, pg. 4447
LEISURE SPORTS INC.; *U.S. Private*, pg. 2420
LEISURE TIME MARKETING INC.; *U.S. Private*, pg. 2420
LEISURE TRENDS GROUP, LLC—See The NPD Group, Inc.; *U.S. Private*, pg. 4085
LEISURE, WERDEN & TERRY AGENCY, INC.; *U.S. Private*, pg. 2420
LEISURE WORLD OF MARYLAND; *U.S. Private*, pg. 2420
LEISUREWORLD SENIOR CARE LP—See Sienna Senior Living Inc.; *Int'l*, pg. 6904
LEISZLER OIL CO., INC.; *U.S. Private*, pg. 2420
THE LEITH AGENCY—See Arsenal Capital Management LP; *U.S. Public*, pg. 338
LEITH HONDA ABERDEEN; *U.S. Private*, pg. 2420
LEITH INC.—See Holman Automotive Group, Inc.; *U.S. Private*, pg. 1967
LEITMOTIF CREATORS GMBH—See Highlight Communications AG; *Int'l*, pg. 3388
LEITNER GESELLSCHAFT M.B.H—See STRABAG SE; *Int'l*, pg. 7231
LEITNER SHRIRAM MANUFACTURING LIMITED—See SEPC Limited; *Int'l*, pg. 6718
LEITNER TOURISTIK GMBH—See ECM Equity Capital Management GmbH; *Int'l*, pg. 2291
LEITRIM OBSERVER LTD—See JPIMedia Holdings Limited; *Int'l*, pg. 4006
LEITUNGSPARTNER GMBH—See RWE AG; *Int'l*, pg. 6434
LEITZ ACCO BRANDS GMBH & CO. KG—See ACCO Brands Corporation; *U.S. Public*, pg. 33
LEIVERS BROTHERS LTD.—See Danish Crown AmbA; *Int'l*, pg. 1965
LE JARDIN D'ACCLIMATATION—See LVMH Moet Hennessy Louis Vuitton SE; *Int'l*, pg. 4598
LEJAY LAGOUTE; *Int'l*, pg. 4447
LE JEAN BLEU INC.; *Int'l*, pg. 4431
LE JEUNE INVESTMENT INC.; *U.S. Private*, pg. 2405
LEJEUNE MOTOR COMPANY INC.; *U.S. Private*, pg. 2420
LEJEUNE STEEL COMPANY—See APi Group Corporation; *Int'l*, pg. 514
LEJI INTERMEDIACAO S.A.—See Companhia Brasileira de Distribuicao; *Int'l*, pg. 1746
L.E. JOHNSON PRODUCTS INC.; *U.S. Private*, pg. 2365
LEJU HOLDINGS LIMITED; *Int'l*, pg. 4447
LEKANG FILTER AS—See Indutrade AB; *Int'l*, pg. 3680
LEKANG MASKIN AS—See Indutrade AB; *Int'l*, pg. 3680
L.E.K. CONSULTING AUSTRALIA PTY. LTD.—See L.E.K. Consulting Group Limited; *Int'l*, pg. 4386
L.E.K. CONSULTING GMBH—See L.E.K. Consulting Group Limited; *Int'l*, pg. 4386
L.E.K. CONSULTING GROUP LIMITED; *Int'l*, pg. 4385
L.E.K. CONSULTING (INTERNATIONAL) LIMITED—See L.E.K. Consulting Group Limited; *Int'l*, pg. 4386
L.E.K. CONSULTING LLC—See L.E.K. Consulting Group Limited; *Int'l*, pg. 4386
L.E.K. CONSULTING S.A.R.L.—See L.E.K. Consulting Group Limited; *Int'l*, pg. 4386
L.E.K. CONSULTING (SHANGHAI) CO., LTD.—See L.E.K. Consulting Group Limited; *Int'l*, pg. 4386
L.E.K. CONSULTING (SINGAPORE) PTE. LTD.—See L.E.K. Consulting Group Limited; *Int'l*, pg. 4386
L.E.K. CONSULTING UK LIMITED—See L.E.K. Consulting Group Limited; *Int'l*, pg. 4386

COMPANY NAME INDEX

LEKIR BULK TERMINAL SDN. BHD.—See Tenaga Nasional Berhad; *Int'l*, pg. 7557
LEKKA TRADING CO., LTD.—See RiverRock European Capital Partners LLP; *Int'l*, pg. 6353
LEKKERLAND AG & CO. KG—See REWE-Zentral-Aktiengesellschaft; *Int'l*, pg. 6315
LEKKERLAND A/S—See NorgesGruppen ASA; *Int'l*, pg. 5427
LEKKERLAND CZESKA REPUBLIKA S.R.O—See REWE-Zentral-Aktiengesellschaft; *Int'l*, pg. 6315
LEKKERLAND DEUTSCHLAND GMBH & CO. KG—See REWE-Zentral-Aktiengesellschaft; *Int'l*, pg. 6315
LEKKERLAND HANDELS- UND DIENSTLEISTUNGS AG—See REWE-Zentral-Aktiengesellschaft; *Int'l*, pg. 6315
LEKKERLAND NEDERLAND B.V.—See REWE-Zentral-Aktiengesellschaft; *Int'l*, pg. 6315
LEKKERLAND POLSKA S.A.—See REWE-Zentral-Aktiengesellschaft; *Int'l*, pg. 6315
LEKKERLAND (SCHWEIZ) AG—See REWE-Zentral-Aktiengesellschaft; *Int'l*, pg. 6315
LEKKERLAND VENDING SERVICES B.V.—See REWE-Zentral-Aktiengesellschaft; *Int'l*, pg. 6315
LEKOIL LIMITED; *Int'l*, pg. 4447
LEK PHARMACEUTICALS D.D.—See Sandoz Group AG; *Int'l*, pg. 6526
LEK PHARMACEUTICALS D.D.—See Sandoz Group AG; *Int'l*, pg. 6526
LEK & SAKERHET AB—See KOMPAN A/S; *Int'l*, pg. 4243
LEK S.A.—See Novartis AG; *Int'l*, pg. 5457
LEK & SIKKERHET AS—See KOMPAN A/S; *Int'l*, pg. 4243
LEK SKOPJE D.O.O.—See Sandoz Group AG; *Int'l*, pg. 6526
LEKTRO INC.—See John Bean Technologies Corporation; *U.S. Public*, pg. 1192
LEKUE, S.L.—See Espiga Capital Gestion S.G.E.C.R, S.A.; *Int'l*, pg. 2506
LEKUE USA, INC.—See Espiga Capital Gestion S.G.E.C.R, S.A.; *Int'l*, pg. 2506
LE&LA LHOIST ENGINEERING & LIME APPLICATION—See Lhoist S.A.; *Int'l*, pg. 4478
LELAND PROPERTIES—See ITT Inc.; *U.S. Public*, pg. 1178
LE LAVOIR LTD.; *Int'l*, pg. 4431
LE LIVRE PARIS SNC—See Vivendi SE; *Int'l*, pg. 8273
LELON ELECTRONICS CORP.; *Int'l*, pg. 4447
LELON ELECTRONICS (HUIZHOU) CO., LTD.—See Lelon Electronics Corp.; *Int'l*, pg. 4447
LELON ELECTRONICS (SUZHOU) CO., LTD.—See Lelon Electronics Corp.; *Int'l*, pg. 4447
LELOUP ENTREPRISE GENERALE SPRL—See Ackermans & van Haaren NV; *Int'l*, pg. 104
LE LUNDBERG FASTIGHETS AB—See L. E. Lundbergforetagen AB; *Int'l*, pg. 4381
L. E. LUNDBERGFORETAGEN AB; *Int'l*, pg. 4381
LELY AUSTRALIA PTY LTD—See AGCO Corporation; *U.S. Public*, pg. 59
LELYNX S.A.S.—See Gruppo MutuiOnline S.p.A; *Int'l*, pg. 3141
LEMAITRE MEDICAL TECHNOLOGY (SHANGHAI) CO., LTD.—See LeMaitre Vascular, Inc.; *U.S. Public*, pg. 1304
LEMAITRE VASCULAR AS—See LeMaitre Vascular, Inc.; *U.S. Public*, pg. 1304
LEMAITRE VASCULAR GK—See LeMaitre Vascular, Inc.; *U.S. Public*, pg. 1304
LEMAITRE VASCULAR GMBH—See LeMaitre Vascular, Inc.; *U.S. Public*, pg. 1304
LEMAITRE VASCULAR, INC.; *U.S. Public*, pg. 1304
LEMAITRE VASCULAR, LTD—See LeMaitre Vascular, Inc.; *U.S. Public*, pg. 1305
LEMAITRE VASCULAR PTY LTD—See LeMaitre Vascular, Inc.; *U.S. Public*, pg. 1305
LEMAITRE VASCULAR SWITZERLAND GMBH—See LeMaitre Vascular, Inc.; *U.S. Public*, pg. 1305
LEMAITRE VASCULAR ULC—See LeMaitre Vascular, Inc.; *U.S. Public*, pg. 1305
LEMAN CONSULTING SA—See Kudelski S.A.; *Int'l*, pg. 4323
LE MANOIR AG—See Swiss Prime Site AG; *Int'l*, pg. 7370
LEMANS CORPORATION; *U.S. Private*, pg. 2420
LE MANS STADIUM S.A.S.—See VINCI S.A.; *Int'l*, pg. 8223
LEMAPACK B.V.—See S.A Industrias Celulosa Aragonesa CIF; *Int'l*, pg. 6447
LEMARCO S.A.—See Gellert Global Group; *U.S. Private*, pg. 1657
LEMARNE CORPORATION LIMITED; *Int'l*, pg. 4448
LE MARS INSURANCE COMPANY—See Donegal Group Inc.; *U.S. Public*, pg. 676
LEMARTEC ENGINEERING & CONSTRUCTION CORPORATION; *U.S. Private*, pg. 2420
LEMASTER STEEL ERECTORS INC.; *U.S. Private*, pg. 2420
LE MAT' ELECTRIQUE—See Sonepar S.A.; *Int'l*, pg. 7091
LEMAUVIEL AUTOMOBILES VIRE; *Int'l*, pg. 4448
LEMAY AUTO GROUP; *U.S. Private*, pg. 2421
LEMAY ONLINE; *Int'l*, pg. 4448

LEMBAGA KEMAJUAN TANAH PERSEKUTUAN; *Int'l*, pg. 4448
LEMBAGA TABUNG ANGKATAN TENTERA; *Int'l*, pg. 4448
LEMBAGA TABUNG HAJI; *Int'l*, pg. 4449
LEMBAH LANGAT DEVELOPMENT SDN. BHD.—See Petaling Tin Berhad; *Int'l*, pg. 5823
LEM BELGIUM SPRL-BVBA—See LEM Holding SA; *Int'l*, pg. 4447
LEM CAPITAL, L.P.—See Independence Capital Partners, LLC; *U.S. Private*, pg. 2056
LEMCON NETWORKS MEXICO S. DE R.L. DE C.V.—See Lemcon USA Corporation; *U.S. Private*, pg. 2421
LEM CONSTRUCTION; *U.S. Private*, pg. 2420
LEMCON USA CORPORATION; *U.S. Private*, pg. 2421
LEME, INC.—See Saugatuck Capital Company; *U.S. Private*, pg. 3554
LEM ELECTRONICS CO. LTD—See LEM Holding SA; *Int'l*, pg. 4447
LE MERIDIEN ATLANTA PERIMETER—See Marriott International, Inc.; *U.S. Public*, pg. 1371
LE MERIDIEN NEW ORLEANS—See Marriott International, Inc.; *U.S. Public*, pg. 1372
LEM EUROPE GMBH—See LEM Holding SA; *Int'l*, pg. 4447
LEMFORDER ELECTRONIC GMBH—See ZF Friedrichshafen AG; *Int'l*, pg. 8641
LEM FRANCE S.A.R.L.—See LEM Holding SA; *Int'l*, pg. 4447
LEM HOLDING SA; *Int'l*, pg. 4447
LEMIEUX GROUP L.P.; *U.S. Private*, pg. 2421
LE MIN INDUSTRIAL CO., LTD.—See Allis Electric Co., Ltd.; *Int'l*, pg. 359
LEM INTERNATIONAL S.A.—See LEM Holding SA; *Int'l*, pg. 4447
LEM ITALIA S.R.L.—See LEM Holding SA; *Int'l*, pg. 4447
LEM JAPAN K.K.—See LEM Holding SA; *Int'l*, pg. 4448
LEMKE LAND SURVEYING, LLC—See Parkhill, Smith & Cooper, Inc.; *U.S. Private*, pg. 3098
LEMKEN AGRICULTURAL MACHINERY (QINGDAO) CO. LTD.—See Lemken GmbH & Co. KG; *Int'l*, pg. 4449
LEMKEN AUSTRIA GMBH—See Lemken GmbH & Co. KG; *Int'l*, pg. 4449
LEMKEN BELGIUM BVBA—See Lemken GmbH & Co. KG; *Int'l*, pg. 4449
LEMKEN CANADA INC.—See Lemken GmbH & Co. KG; *Int'l*, pg. 4449
LEMKEN CZECH, S.R.O.—See Lemken GmbH & Co. KG; *Int'l*, pg. 4449
LEMKEN FRANCE SARL—See Lemken GmbH & Co. KG; *Int'l*, pg. 4449
LEMKEN GMBH & CO. KG; *Int'l*, pg. 4449
LEMKEN HUNGARIA KFT.—See Lemken GmbH & Co. KG; *Int'l*, pg. 4449
LEMKEN IBERIA S.L—See Lemken GmbH & Co. KG; pg. 4449
LEMKEN INDIA AGRO EQUIPMENT PVT LTD.—See Lemken GmbH & Co. KG; *Int'l*, pg. 4449
LEMKEN ITALIA S.R.L.—See Lemken GmbH & Co. KG; *Int'l*, pg. 4449
LEMKEN NEDERLAND B.V.—See Lemken GmbH & Co. KG; *Int'l*, pg. 4449
LEMKEN-NIEDERLASSUNG SCHWEIZ—See Lemken GmbH & Co. KG; *Int'l*, pg. 4449
LEMKEN POLSKA SP.Z.O.O.—See Lemken GmbH & Co. KG; *Int'l*, pg. 4449
LEMKEN ROMANIA SRL—See Lemken GmbH & Co. KG; *Int'l*, pg. 4449
LEMKEN SKANDINAVIEN APS—See Lemken GmbH & Co. KG; *Int'l*, pg. 4449
LEMKEN SLOVAKIA S.R.O.—See Lemken GmbH & Co. KG; *Int'l*, pg. 4449
LEMKEN SOUTH AFRICA PTY. LTD.—See Lemken GmbH & Co. KG; *Int'l*, pg. 4449
LEMKEN UK—See Lemken GmbH & Co. KG; *Int'l*, pg. 4449
LEMKEN USA INC—See Lemken GmbH & Co. KG; *Int'l*, pg. 4449
LEMKEN WERK HETZERATH AG—See Lemken GmbH & Co. KG; *Int'l*, pg. 4449
LEMKEN WERK MEPPEN AG—See Lemken GmbH & Co. KG; *Int'l*, pg. 4449
LEM MARKETS INC.; *U.S. Private*, pg. 2420
LEMMEN OIL COMPANY—See Sun Capital Partners, Inc.; *U.S. Private*, pg. 3860
LEMMINKAINEN ANLEGG AS—See YIT Corporation; *Int'l*, pg. 8586
LEMMINKAINEN A/S—See YIT Corporation; *Int'l*, pg. 8586
LEMMINKAINEN BETONITUOTE OY—See YIT Corporation; *Int'l*, pg. 8586
LEMMINKAINEN (CHINA) CO., LTD.—See YIT Corporation; *Int'l*, pg. 8586
LEMMINKAINEN EESTI AS—See YIT Corporation; *Int'l*, pg. 8586
LEMMINKAINEN INDUSTRI AS—See YIT Corporation; *Int'l*, pg. 8586
LEMMINKAINEN INFRA OY—See YIT Corporation; *Int'l*, pg. 8586

LEMTECH HOLDINGS CO., LTD.

LEMMINKAINEN KATTO OY—See YIT Corporation; *Int'l*, pg. 8586
LEMMINKAINEN NORGE AS—See YIT Corporation; *Int'l*, pg. 8586
LEMMINKAINEN OYJ—See YIT Corporation; *Int'l*, pg. 8586
LEMMINKAINEN POLSKA SP. Z O.O.—See YIT Corporation; *Int'l*, pg. 8586
LEMMINKAINEN PP OY—See YIT Corporation; *Int'l*, pg. 8586
LEMMINKAINEN RAKENNUSTUOTTEET OY—See CRH plc; *Int'l*, pg. 1848
LEMMINKAINEN SVERIGE AB—See YIT Corporation; *Int'l*, pg. 8586
LEMMINKAINEN TALO OY INTERNATIONAL—See YIT Corporation; *Int'l*, pg. 8586
LEMMINKAINEN TALO OY RUSSIA—See YIT Corporation; *Int'l*, pg. 8586
LEMMINKAINEN TALO OY—See YIT Corporation; *Int'l*, pg. 8586
LEMMINKAINEN TALOTEKNIIKKA OY—See Onvest Oy; *Int'l*, pg. 5592
LEMMON FUNERAL HOME OF DULANEY VALLEY, INC.—See Service Corporation International; *U.S. Public*, pg. 1869
THE LEMNA CORPORATION; *U.S. Private*, pg. 4069
LEMNA INTERNATIONAL INC.—See The Lemna Corporation; *U.S. Private*, pg. 4069
LEMNATEC GMBH—See Nynomic AG; *Int'l*, pg. 5501
LEMNA TECHNOLOGIES, INC.—See The Lemna Corporation; *U.S. Private*, pg. 4069
LEMNA USA INC.—See The Lemna Corporation; *U.S. Private*, pg. 4069
LEMO ASIA PTE LTD—See Lemo S.A.; *Int'l*, pg. 4449
LEMO CANADA, INC—See Lemo S.A.; *Int'l*, pg. 4449
LEMO CONNECTORS NEDERLAND BV—See Lemo S.A.; *Int'l*, pg. 4449
LEMO DENMARK A/S—See Lemo S.A.; *Int'l*, pg. 4450
LEMO ELECTRONICS (SHANGHAI) CO., LTD.—See Lemo S.A.; *Int'l*, pg. 4450
LEMO ELEKTRONIK GESMBH—See Lemo S.A.; *Int'l*, pg. 4450
LEMO FRANCE SARL—See Lemo S.A.; *Int'l*, pg. 4450
LEMO GMBH—See Lemo S.A.; *Int'l*, pg. 4450
LEMO HONG KONG LTD—See Lemo S.A.; *Int'l*, pg. 4450
THE LEMOINE COMPANY INCORPORATED; *U.S. Private*, pg. 4069
LEMO ITALIA SRL—See Lemo S.A.; *Int'l*, pg. 4450
LEMO JAPAN—See Lemo S.A.; *Int'l*, pg. 4450
LEMONADE, INC.; *U.S. Public*, pg. 1305
LEMONADE SOFTWARE DEVELOPMENT S.L.—See Sword Group SE; *Int'l*, pg. 7376
LEMONBEAT GMBH—See RWE AG; *Int'l*, pg. 6434
LEMON CO., LTD.; *Int'l*, pg. 4450
LE MONDE DES GRANDS BORDEAUX CHATEAU CLASSIC S.A.R.L.—See Hawesko Holding AG; *Int'l*, pg. 3288
LEMONLIGHT MEDIA, INC.; *U.S. Private*, pg. 2421
LEMO NORDIC AB—See Lemo S.A.; *Int'l*, pg. 4450
LEMO NORWAY A/S—See Lemo S.A.; *Int'l*, pg. 4450
LEMON SISTEMI S.P.A.; *Int'l*, pg. 4450
LEMONS LANDFILL, LLC—See Republic Services, Inc.; *U.S. Public*, pg. 1786
LEMONSOFT OYJ; *Int'l*, pg. 4450
LEMON TREE HOTELS LTD.; *Int'l*, pg. 4450
LEMON-X CORPORATION—See Highlander Partners, LP.; *U.S. Private*, pg. 1939
LEMO S.A.; *Int'l*, pg. 4449
LEMOS LABS, LLC; *U.S. Private*, pg. 2421
LEMO U.K.—See Lemo S.A.; *Int'l*, pg. 4450
LEMO U.S.A. INC.—See Lemo S.A.; *Int'l*, pg. 4450
LEMO VERKAUF AG—See Lemo S.A.; *Int'l*, pg. 4450
LEMPRIERE (AUSTRALIA) PTY. LTD.—See Lempriere Pty. Ltd.; *Int'l*, pg. 4450
LEMPRIERE GRAIN PTY. LTD.—See Lempriere Pty. Ltd.; *Int'l*, pg. 4450
LEMPRIERE PTY. LTD.; *Int'l*, pg. 4450
LEM RUSSIA LTD.—See LEM Holding SA; *Int'l*, pg. 4448
LEMSYS SA—See Teradyne, Inc.; *U.S. Public*, pg. 2018
LEMTAPES OY—See H.B. Fuller Company; *U.S. Public*, pg. 978
LEMTECH-EAHWA PRECISION TECHNONLOGY CO., LTD.—See LemTech Holdings Co., Ltd.; *Int'l*, pg. 4451
LEMTECH ELECTRONICS TECHNOLOGY (CHANGSHU) CO., LTD.—See LemTech Holdings Co., Ltd.; *Int'l*, pg. 4450
LEMTECH ENERGY SOLUTIONS CORPORATION—See LemTech Holdings Co., Ltd.; *Int'l*, pg. 4450
LEMTECH GLOBAL INDUSTRIES LTD.—See LemTech Holdings Co., Ltd.; *Int'l*, pg. 4450
LEMTECH GLOBAL SOLUTION CO. LTD.—See LemTech Holdings Co., Ltd.; *Int'l*, pg. 4450
LEMTECH HOLDINGS CO., LTD.; *Int'l*, pg. 4450
LEMTECH INDUSTRIAL SERVICES LTD.—See LemTech Holdings Co., Ltd.; *Int'l*, pg. 4450
LEMTECH INTERNATIONAL LIMITED—See LemTech Holdings Co., Ltd.; *Int'l*, pg. 4450
LEMTECH PRECISION ENGINEERING (TIANJIN) CO., LTD.—See LemTech Holdings Co., Ltd.; *Int'l*, pg. 4450

LEMTECH HOLDINGS CO., LTD.

LEMTECH PRECISION MATERIAL (CHINA) CO., LTD.—See LemTech Holdings Co., Ltd.; *Int'l*, pg. 4451
LEMTECH PRECISION MATERIAL (CZECH) S.R.O.—See LemTech Holdings Co., Ltd.; *Int'l*, pg. 4450
LEMTECH TECHNOLOGY LIMITED—See LemTech Holdings Co., Ltd.; *Int'l*, pg. 4451
LEMTECH USA INC.—See LemTech Holdings Co., Ltd.; *Int'l*, pg. 4451
LEM UK LTD.—See LEM Holding SA; *Int'l*, pg. 4448
LEM USA INC.—See LEM Holding SA; *Int'l*, pg. 4448
LEMUSIMUN/Y&R—See WPP plc; *Int'l*, pg. 8491
THE L.E. MYERS CO.—See MYR Group Inc.; *U.S. Public*, pg. 1489
LENAJA SA DISTRIBUTION; *Int'l*, pg. 4451
LENA LIGHTING S.A.; *Int'l*, pg. 4451
LENAPE FORGE, INC.; *U.S. Private*, pg. 2421
LENATI LLC—See Concentrix Corporation; *U.S. Public*, pg. 565
LENA TOURS AND TRAVEL—See Seera Group Holding Co.; *Int'l*, pg. 6679
LENAWEE FUELS INC.; *U.S. Private*, pg. 2421
LEN CHEONG HOLDING BERHAD; *Int'l*, pg. 4451
LENCI CALZATURE SPA—See Li & Fung Limited; *Int'l*, pg. 4480
LENCO, INC. - PMC—See PMC Group, Inc.; *U.S. Private*, pg. 3218
LENCO MARINE SOLUTIONS, LLC—See Brunswick Corporation; *U.S. Public*, pg. 408
LENCO MOBILE INC.; *U.S. Private*, pg. 2421
LENDA, INC.—See Reali, Inc.; *U.S. Private*, pg. 3368
LENDBUZZ, INC.; *U.S. Private*, pg. 2421
LENDDIRECT CORP.—See CURO Group Holdings Corp.; *U.S. Public*, pg. 611
LENDERLIVE NETWORK, LLC—See Computershare Limited; *Int'l*, pg. 1760
LENDER'S CHOICE INC.—See LRES Corp.; *U.S. Private*, pg. 2507
LENDER'S CONSULTING GROUP, INC.; *U.S. Private*, pg. 2421
LENDERS INSPECTION COMPANY—See Old Republic International Corporation; *U.S. Public*, pg. 1569
LENDERS TITLE COMPANY—See Knox Capital Holdings, LLC; *U.S. Private*, pg. 2324
LENDINGCLUB CORPORATION; *U.S. Public*, pg. 1305
LENDINGONE, LLC; *U.S. Private*, pg. 2421
LENDINGPOINT LLC; *U.S. Private*, pg. 2421
LENDINGPOT PRIVATE LIMITED—See IFS Capital Limited; *Int'l*, pg. 3600
LENDING SCIENCE DM, INC.; *U.S. Private*, pg. 2421
LENDING SPACE INC.; *U.S. Private*, pg. 2421
LENDINGTREE, INC.; *U.S. Public*, pg. 1305
LENDINGTREE, LLC—See LendingTree, Inc.; *U.S. Public*, pg. 1305
LENDINVEST PLC; *Int'l*, pg. 4451
LENDIO INC.; *U.S. Private*, pg. 2421
LENDI PTY. LTD.—See Bailador Technology Investments Limited; *Int'l*, pg. 802
LEND LEASE (AUSTRALIA) COMMUNITIES LIMITED—See Lendlease Corporation Limited; *Int'l*, pg. 4451
LEND LEASE BUILDING JAPAN INC.—See Lendlease Corporation Limited; *Int'l*, pg. 4452
LEND LEASE BUILDING PTY, LTD. - NEW ZEALAND—See Lendlease Corporation Limited; *Int'l*, pg. 4452
LEND LEASE BUILDING PTY. LTD.—See Lendlease Corporation Limited; *Int'l*, pg. 4452
LEND LEASE BUILDING PTY. LTD.—See Lendlease Corporation Limited; *Int'l*, pg. 4452
LEND LEASE BUILDING PTY. LTD.—See Lendlease Corporation Limited; *Int'l*, pg. 4452
LEND LEASE COMMUNITIES (AUSTRALIA) LIMITED—See Lendlease Corporation Limited; *Int'l*, pg. 4452
LEND LEASE COMMUNITIES INC.—See Lendlease Corporation Limited; *Int'l*, pg. 4452
LEND LEASE CONSTRUCTION (EMEA) LIMITED—See Lendlease Corporation Limited; *Int'l*, pg. 4452
LEND LEASE CONSTRUCTION HOLDINGS (EMEA) LIMITED—See Lendlease Corporation Limited; *Int'l*, pg. 4452
LEND LEASE CONSULTING (EMEA) LIMITED—See Lendlease Corporation Limited; *Int'l*, pg. 4452
LENDLEASE CORPORATION LIMITED; *Int'l*, pg. 4451
LEND LEASE DELFIN DEVELOPMENT—See Lendlease Corporation Limited; *Int'l*, pg. 4452
LEND LEASE DEVELOPMENT INC.—See Lendlease Corporation Limited; *Int'l*, pg. 4452
LEND LEASE DEVELOPMENT INC.—See Lendlease Corporation Limited; *Int'l*, pg. 4452
LEND LEASE DEVELOPMENT INC.—See Lendlease Corporation Limited; *Int'l*, pg. 4452
LEND LEASE DEVELOPMENT LIMITED—See Lendlease Corporation Limited; *Int'l*, pg. 4452
LEND LEASE ENGINEERING PTY LIMITED—See Lendlease Corporation Limited; *Int'l*, pg. 4452
LEND LEASE ESPANA S.A.—See Lendlease Corporation Limited; *Int'l*, pg. 4452

LEND LEASE EUROPE GP LIMITED—See Lendlease Corporation Limited; *Int'l*, pg. 4452
LEND LEASE EUROPE LIMITED—See Lendlease Corporation Limited; *Int'l*, pg. 4452
LEND LEASE FACILITIES MANAGEMENT (EMEA) LIMITED—See Lendlease Corporation Limited; *Int'l*, pg. 4452
LEND LEASE FINANCE LIMITED—See Lendlease Corporation Limited; *Int'l*, pg. 4452
LENDLEASE GLOBAL COMMERCIAL REIT; *Int'l*, pg. 4453
LEND LEASE GLOBAL INVESTMENT PLC—See Lendlease Corporation Limited; *Int'l*, pg. 4452
LEND LEASE INFRASTRUCTURE PTY LIMITED—See Lendlease Corporation Limited; *Int'l*, pg. 4452
LEND LEASE INFRASTRUCTURE PTY LIMITED—See Lendlease Corporation Limited; *Int'l*, pg. 4452
LEND LEASE INTERNATIONAL PTY LIMITED—See Lendlease Corporation Limited; *Int'l*, pg. 4452
LEND LEASE INVESTMENT MANAGEMENT PTE. LTD.—See Lendlease Corporation Limited; *Int'l*, pg. 4452
LEND LEASE JAPAN PTY LTD—See Lendlease Corporation Limited; *Int'l*, pg. 4452
LEND LEASE PRIMELIFE LIMITED—See Lendlease Corporation Limited; *Int'l*, pg. 4452
LEND LEASE PROJECT MANAGEMENT & CONSTRUCTION (AUSTRALIA) PTY LIMITED—See Lendlease Corporation Limited; *Int'l*, pg. 4452
LEND LEASE PROJECT MANAGEMENT & CONSTRUCTION (SHANGHAI) CO., LTD—See Lendlease Corporation Limited; *Int'l*, pg. 4452
LEND LEASE PROPERTY MANAGEMENT PTY LIMITED—See Lendlease Corporation Limited; *Int'l*, pg. 4452
LEND LEASE REAL ESTATE INVESTMENT SERVICES LTD—See Lendlease Corporation Limited; *Int'l*, pg. 4453
LEND LEASE REAL ESTATE INVESTMENTS LTD—See Lendlease Corporation Limited; *Int'l*, pg. 4453
LEND LEASE RESIDENTIAL GROUP (EMEA) LIMITED—See Lendlease Corporation Limited; *Int'l*, pg. 4453
LEND LEASE RESPONSIBLE ENTITY LIMITED—See Lendlease Corporation Limited; *Int'l*, pg. 4453
LEND LEASE (SCOTLAND) LTD—See Lendlease Corporation Limited; *Int'l*, pg. 4452
LEND LEASE SINGAPORE PTE LIMITED—See Lendlease Corporation Limited; *Int'l*, pg. 4453
LEND LEASE (TAIWAN) PTY. LTD.—See Lendlease Corporation Limited; *Int'l*, pg. 4452
LEND LEASE (US) CAPITAL, INC.—See Lendlease Corporation Limited; *Int'l*, pg. 4452
LEND LEASE (US) CONSTRUCTION HOLDINGS, INC.—See Lendlease Corporation Limited; *Int'l*, pg. 4452
LEND LEASE (US) CONSTRUCTION INC—See Lendlease Corporation Limited; *Int'l*, pg. 4452
LEND LEASE (US) CONSTRUCTION, LMB, INC.—See Lendlease Corporation Limited; *Int'l*, pg. 4452
LEND LEASE (US) HEALTHCARE DEVELOPMENT LLC—See Lendlease Corporation Limited; *Int'l*, pg. 4452
LEND LEASE (US) HOLDINGS, INC.—See Lendlease Corporation Limited; *Int'l*, pg. 4452
LEND LEASE (US) PUBLIC PARTNERSHIPS LLC—See Lendlease Corporation Limited; *Int'l*, pg. 4452
LEND LEASE VENTURES PTY LTD—See Lendlease Corporation Limited; *Int'l*, pg. 4453
LENDLOCK GROUP LIMITED; *Int'l*, pg. 4453
LENDMARK FINANCIAL SERVICES, INC.—See Lightyear Capital LLC; *U.S. Private*, pg. 2454
LENDMARK FINANCIAL SERVICES, INC.—See Ontario Teachers' Pension Plan; *Int'l*, pg. 5586
LENDO AB—See Schibsted ASA; *Int'l*, pg. 6617
LENDO APS—See Schibsted ASA; *Int'l*, pg. 6617
LENDO AS—See Schibsted ASA; *Int'l*, pg. 6617
LENDO OY—See Schibsted ASA; *Int'l*, pg. 6617
LENDO SP. Z.O.O—See Schibsted ASA; *Int'l*, pg. 6617
LENDO TOPCO AS—See Schibsted ASA; *Int'l*, pg. 6617
LENDR, LLC; *U.S. Private*, pg. 2421
LENDWAY, INC.; *U.S. Public*, pg. 1305
LENEL SYSTEMS INTERNATIONAL INC.—See Carrier Global Corporation; *U.S. Public*, pg. 441
L'ENFANT DC HOTEL LLC—See Stanford Hotels Corporation; *U.S. Private*, pg. 3782
LENFEST GROUP LLC; *U.S. Private*, pg. 2422
LENG AIK ENGINEERING PTE. LTD.—See EXEO Group Inc.; *Int'l*, pg. 2583
LENG UNIVERSAL, INC.; *U.S. Private*, pg. 2422
LENNAR ARIZONA CONSTRUCTION, INC—See Lennar Corporation; *U.S. Public*, pg. 1306
LENNAR CHICAGO, INC.—See Lennar Corporation; *U.S. Public*, pg. 1306
LENNAR COLORADO, LLC—See Lennar Corporation; *U.S. Public*, pg. 1306
LENNAR COMMUNITIES, INC.—See Lennar Corporation; *U.S. Public*, pg. 1306
LENNAR CORPORATION; *U.S. Public*, pg. 1305

CORPORATE AFFILIATIONS

LENNAR DESIGN STUDIO HOME—See Lennar Corporation; *U.S. Public*, pg. 1306
LENNARD MANUFACTURING (PVT) LTD—See Innscor Africa Ltd.; *Int'l*, pg. 3713
LENNARDS NIGERIA PLC; *Int'l*, pg. 4453
LENNAR FINANCIAL SERVICES, INC.—See Lennar Corporation; *U.S. Public*, pg. 1306
LENNAR HOMES, COLORADO DIV—See Lennar Corporation; *U.S. Public*, pg. 1306
LENNAR HOMES, INC. - ORLANDO—See Lennar Corporation; *U.S. Public*, pg. 1306
LENNAR HOMES, INC.—See Lennar Corporation; *U.S. Public*, pg. 1306
LENNAR HOMES, INC.—See Lennar Corporation; *U.S. Public*, pg. 1306
LENNAR HOMES, INC.—See Lennar Corporation; *U.S. Public*, pg. 1306
LENNAR HOMES, INC.—See Lennar Corporation; *U.S. Public*, pg. 1306
LENNAR HOMES, INC.—See Lennar Corporation; *U.S. Public*, pg. 1306
LENNAR HOMES, INC.—See Lennar Corporation; *U.S. Public*, pg. 1306
LENNAR HOMES OF TENNESSEE, LLC—See Lennar Corporation; *U.S. Public*, pg. 1306
LENNAR HOMES OF TEXAS LAND AND CONSTRUCTION, LTD.—See Lennar Corporation; *U.S. Public*, pg. 1306
LENNAR HOMES OF UTAH, INC.—See Lennar Corporation; *U.S. Public*, pg. 1305
LENNAR MARE ISLAND, LLC—See Lennar Corporation; *U.S. Public*, pg. 1306
LENNAR MORTGAGE, LLC—See Lennar Corporation; *U.S. Public*, pg. 1306
LENNAR MULTIFAMILY COMMUNITIES, LLC—See Lennar Corporation; *U.S. Public*, pg. 1306
LENNAR SACRAMENTO, INC.—See Lennar Corporation; *U.S. Public*, pg. 1306
LENNAR—See Lennar Corporation; *U.S. Public*, pg. 1306
LENNAR TITLE, INC.—See Lennar Corporation; *U.S. Public*, pg. 1306
LENNAR TITLE, LLC—See Lennar Corporation; *U.S. Public*, pg. 1306
LENNAR US HOMES—See Lennar Corporation; *U.S. Public*, pg. 1306
LENNAR WINNCREST, LLC—See Lennar Corporation; *U.S. Public*, pg. 1306
LENNEPER GMBH & CO.KG; *Int'l*, pg. 4453
LENNOX FRANCE S.A.S.—See Lennox International Inc.; *U.S. Public*, pg. 1307
LENNOX INDUSTRIES INC.—See Lennox International Inc.; *U.S. Public*, pg. 1307
LENNOX INTERNATIONAL INC.; *U.S. Public*, pg. 1307
LENNOX NATIONAL ACCOUNT SERVICES INC.—See Lennox International Inc.; *U.S. Public*, pg. 1307
LENNOX POLSKA SP. Z.O.O.—See Lennox International Inc.; *U.S. Public*, pg. 1308
LENNTECH BV; *Int'l*, pg. 4453
LENNY & LARRY'S; *U.S. Private*, pg. 2422
LE NOBLE AGE SANTE SA; *Int'l*, pg. 4431
LE NOBLE LUMBER CO. INC.; *U.S. Private*, pg. 2405
LE NOIR CAFE - SOLE PROPRIETORSHIP LLC—See Alpha Dhabi Holding PJSC; *Int'l*, pg. 367
LENOIR CITY UTILITIES BOARD INC.; *U.S. Private*, pg. 2422
LENORD, BAUER & CO. GMBH—See Fukuda Corporation; *Int'l*, pg. 2839
LENORD S.R.L.—See FNM S.p.A.; *Int'l*, pg. 2718
LENOTRE SA—See Sodexo S.A.; *Int'l*, pg. 7045
LENOVO-ASIAINFO TECHNOLOGIES, INC—See CITIC Group Corporation; *Int'l*, pg. 1619
LENOVO (BEIJING) LIMITED—See Lenovo Group Limited; *Int'l*, pg. 4453
LENOVO (DANMARK) APS—See Lenovo Group Limited; *Int'l*, pg. 4453
LENOVO (DEUTSCHLAND) GMBH—See Lenovo Group Limited; *Int'l*, pg. 4453
LENOVO ENTERPRISE SOLUTIONS (SINGAPORE) PTE. LTD.—See Lenovo Group Limited; *Int'l*, pg. 4453
LENOVO (FRANCE) SAS—See Lenovo Group Limited; *Int'l*, pg. 4453
LENOVO GROUP LIMITED; *Int'l*, pg. 4453
LENOVO (ITALY) S.R.L.—See Lenovo Group Limited; *Int'l*, pg. 4453
LENOVO (JAPAN) LTD.—See Lenovo Group Limited; *Int'l*, pg. 4453
LENOVO MEXICO, S. DE R.L. DE C.V.—See Lenovo Group Limited; *Int'l*, pg. 4454
LENOVO (SCHWEIZ) GMBH—See Lenovo Group Limited; *Int'l*, pg. 4453
LENOVO (SHENZHEN) ADVANCED SYSTEM DESIGN CENTRE—See Lenovo Group Limited; *Int'l*, pg. 4453
LENOVO (SINGAPORE) PTE. LTD.—See Lenovo Group Limited; *Int'l*, pg. 4453
LENOVO (SOUTH AFRICA) (PTY) LIMITED—See Lenovo Group Limited; *Int'l*, pg. 4453
LENOVO (SWEDEN) A.B.—See Lenovo Group Limited; *Int'l*, pg. 4453

COMPANY NAME INDEX

LENOVO TECHNOLOGY B.V. SP. Z O.O.—See Lenovo Group Limited; *Int'l*, pg. 4454
LENOVO TECHNOLOGY (UNITED KINGDOM) LIMITED—See Lenovo Group Limited; *Int'l*, pg. 4454
LENOVO TECNOLOGIA (BRASIL) LTDA.—See Lenovo Group Limited; *Int'l*, pg. 4454
LENOVO (UNITED STATES) INC.—See Lenovo Group Limited; *Int'l*, pg. 4453
LENOVO (UNITED STATES) INC. - US SALES HEADQUARTERS—See Lenovo Group Limited; *Int'l*, pg. 4453
LENOX CORPORATION—See Centre Lane Partners, LLC; *U.S. Private*, pg. 827
LENOX FARMS LIMITED PARTNERSHIP—See UDR, Inc.; *U.S. Private*, pg. 2218
LENOX - KINSTON PLANT—See Centre Lane Partners, LLC; *U.S. Private*, pg. 827
LENOX—See Stanley Black & Decker, Inc.; *U.S. Public*, pg. 1933
LENOX WEALTH MANAGEMENT, INC.—See Creative Planning, LLC; *U.S. Private*, pg. 1090
LENSAR, INC.; *U.S. Public*, pg. 1308
LENSCLEAN, INC.—See Radians, Inc.; *U.S. Private*, pg. 3343
LENSER ASIA SDN. BHD.—See ANDRITZ AG; *Int'l*, pg. 456
LENSER FILTRATION GMBH—See ANDRITZ AG; *Int'l*, pg. 456
LENSING WHOLESALE INC.; *U.S. Private*, pg. 2422
LENS TECHNOLOGY CO., LTD.; *Int'l*, pg. 4454
LEN STOLER INC.; *U.S. Private*, pg. 2421
LENSWISTA AG; *Int'l*, pg. 4454
LENTA LTD.—See SeverGroup OOO; *Int'l*, pg. 6735
LEN-TEX CORP.; *U.S. Private*, pg. 2421
LENTEX S.A.; *Int'l*, pg. 4454
LEN THE PLUMBER, LLC—See Catterton Management Company, LLC; *U.S. Private*, pg. 793
LENTHOR ENGINEERING, LLC—See Arsenal Capital Management LP; *U.S. Private*, pg. 338
LENTINE MANAGEMENT INC.; *U.S. Private*, pg. 2422
LENTI S.R.L.—See Safilo Group S.p.A.; *Int'l*, pg. 6472
LENTOR INVESTMENTS PTE. LTD.—See Temasek Holdings (Private) Limited; *Int'l*, pg. 7548
LEN-TRAN, INC.; *U.S. Private*, pg. 2422
L'ENTREPRISE ELECTRIQUE—See VINCI S.A., *Int'l*, pg. 8237
LENT TORMOZ IRAN COMPANY; *Int'l*, pg. 4454
LENTUO INTERNATIONAL INC.; *Int'l*, pg. 4454
LENTZ MILLING COMPANY—See Platinum Equity, LLC; *U.S. Private*, pg. 3205
LENZE AB—See Lenze SE; *Int'l*, pg. 4454
LENZE AC TECHNOLOGY CORP.—See Lenze SE; *Int'l*, pg. 4454
LENZE AMERICAS CORPORATION—See Lenze SE; *Int'l*, pg. 4454
LENZE ANTRIEBSTECHNIK GMBH—See Lenze SE; *Int'l*, pg. 4454
LENZE ANTRIEBSTECHNIK HANDELSGESELLSCHAFT MBH—See Lenze SE; *Int'l*, pg. 4454
LENZE ARGENTINA AUTOMATIZACION S.A.—See Lenze SE; *Int'l*, pg. 4454
LENZE A/S—See Lenze SE; *Int'l*, pg. 4454
LENZE AS—See Lenze SE; *Int'l*, pg. 4454
LENZE AUSTRIA HOLDING GMBH—See Lenze SE; *Int'l*, pg. 4454
LENZE AUTOMATION GMBH—See Lenze SE; *Int'l*, pg. 4454
LENZE BACHOFEN AG—See Lenze SE; *Int'l*, pg. 4454
LENZE BRASIL AUTOMACAO LTDA.—See Lenze SE; *Int'l*, pg. 4454
LENZE B.V.B.A.—See Lenze SE; *Int'l*, pg. 4454
LENZE B.V.—See Lenze SE; *Int'l*, pg. 4454
LENZE DELEGACION BILBAO SRL—See Lenze SE; *Int'l*, pg. 4454
LENZE DRIVES OY—See Lenze SE; *Int'l*, pg. 4455
LENZE DRIVE SYSTEMS FRANCE SARL—See Lenze SE; *Int'l*, pg. 4455
LENZE DRIVE SYSTEMS GMBH—See Lenze SE; *Int'l*, pg. 4455
LENZE DRIVE SYSTEMS (SHANGHAI) CO. LTD.—See Lenze SE; *Int'l*, pg. 4454
LENZE GERIT S.R.L.—See Lenze SE; *Int'l*, pg. 4455
LENZE GMBH & CO KG—See Lenze SE; *Int'l*, pg. 4455
LENZE HAJTASTECHNIKA KFT.—See Lenze SE; *Int'l*, pg. 4455
LENZE ITALIA S.R.L.—See Lenze SE; *Int'l*, pg. 4455
LENZE LTD.—See Lenze SE; *Int'l*, pg. 4455
LENZE MECHATRONICS PVT. LTD.—See Lenze SE; *Int'l*, pg. 4455
LENZE MEHATRONIKA-POGONSKA TEHNIKA D.O.O.—See Lenze SE; *Int'l*, pg. 4455
LENZE MUHENDISLIK SAN. VE. TIC. A.S.—See Lenze SE; *Int'l*, pg. 4455
LENZE POGONSKA TEKNIKA, D.O.O.—See Lenze SE; *Int'l*, pg. 4455
LENZE POLSKA SP. Z O.O.—See Lenze SE; *Int'l*, pg. 4455
LENZE SAS—See Lenze SE; *Int'l*, pg. 4455
LENZE S.E.A. SDN. BHD.—See Lenze SE; *Int'l*, pg. 4455
LENZE SERVICE GMBH—See Lenze SE; *Int'l*, pg. 4455
LENZE SE; *Int'l*, pg. 4454
LENZE SLOVAKIA, S.R.O.—See Lenze SE; *Int'l*, pg. 4455
LENZE SOUTH EAST ASIA PTE. LTD—See Lenze SE; *Int'l*, pg. 4455
LENZE, S.R.O.—See Lenze SE; *Int'l*, pg. 4455
LENZE TRANSMISIONES S.A.—See Lenze SE; *Int'l*, pg. 4455
LENZE UAB—See Lenze SE; *Int'l*, pg. 4455
LENZE VERBINDUNGSTECHNIK GMBH—See Lenze SE; *Int'l*, pg. 4455
LENZE ZADVIZHVASTA TEHNIKA EOOD—See Lenze SE; *Int'l*, pg. 4455
LENZ INC.; *U.S. Private*, pg. 2422
LENZING AKTIENGESELLSCHAFT; *Int'l*, pg. 4455
LENZING BETEILIGUNGS GMBH—See Lenzing Aktiengesellschaft; *Int'l*, pg. 4455
LENZING BIOCEL PASKOV A.S—See Lenzing Aktiengesellschaft; *Int'l*, pg. 4455
LENZING FIBERS GMBH—See Lenzing Aktiengesellschaft; *Int'l*, pg. 4455
LENZING FIBERS GRIMSBY LIMITED—See Lenzing Aktiengesellschaft; *Int'l*, pg. 4455
LENZING FIBERS HOLDING GMBH—See Lenzing Aktiengesellschaft; *Int'l*, pg. 4455
LENZING FIBERS (HONG KONG) LTD—See Lenzing Aktiengesellschaft; *Int'l*, pg. 4455
LENZING FIBERS INC.—See Lenzing Aktiengesellschaft; *Int'l*, pg. 4455
LENZING FIBERS INDIA PRIVATE LIMITED—See Lenzing Aktiengesellschaft; *Int'l*, pg. 4455
LENZING FIBERS (SHANGHAI) CO., LTD.—See Lenzing Aktiengesellschaft; *Int'l*, pg. 4455
LENZING HOLDING GMBH—See Lenzing Aktiengesellschaft; *Int'l*, pg. 4455
LENZING KOREA YUHAN HOESA—See Lenzing Aktiengesellschaft; *Int'l*, pg. 4455
LENZING (NANJING) FIBERS CO., LTD.—See Lenzing Aktiengesellschaft; *Int'l*, pg. 4455
LENZING PLASTICS GMBH & CO. KG—See Raiffeisenlandesbank Oberosterreich Aktiengesellschaft; *Int'l*, pg. 6187
LENZING SINGAPORE PTE. LTD.—See Lenzing Aktiengesellschaft; *Int'l*, pg. 4455
LENZING TAIWAN FIBERS LTD.—See Lenzing Aktiengesellschaft; *Int'l*, pg. 4456
LENZING TECHNIK GMBH—See Lenzing Aktiengesellschaft; *Int'l*, pg. 4456
LENZING (THAILAND) CO., LTD.—See Lenzing Aktiengesellschaft; *Int'l*, pg. 4455
LENZLINGER SOHNE AG; *Int'l*, pg. 4456
LENZLINGER SOHNE AG - USTER—See Lenzlinger Sohne AG; *Int'l*, pg. 4456
LENZOLOTO OAO—See PJSC Polyus; *Int'l*, pg. 5883
LENZ + PARTNER AG—See Infront ASA; *Int'l*, pg. 3699
LENZ THERAPEUTICS, INC.; *U.S. Public*, pg. 1308
LENZ THERAPEUTICS OPERATIONS, INC.—See Lenz Therapeutics, Inc.; *U.S. Public*, pg. 1308
LEO ACQUISITIONS CORP.; *Int'l*, pg. 4456
LEO A. DALY COMPANY; *U.S. Private*, pg. 2422
LEO BURING PTY. LTD.—See Treasury Wine Estates Limited; *Int'l*, pg. 7909
LEO BURNETT ADVERTISING S.R.O.—See Publicis Groupe S.A.; *Int'l*, pg. 6101
LEO BURNETT ANNONSBYRA—See Publicis Groupe S.A.; *Int'l*, pg. 6101
LEO BURNETT ASSOCIATES—See Publicis Groupe S.A.; *Int'l*, pg. 6101
LEO BURNETT-BEIJING—See Publicis Groupe S.A.; *Int'l*, pg. 6102
LEO BURNETT BELGIUM—See Publicis Groupe S.A.; *Int'l*, pg. 6101
LEO BURNETT BUDAPEST—See Publicis Groupe S.A.; *Int'l*, pg. 6101
LEO BURNETT BUSINESS—See Publicis Groupe S.A.; *Int'l*, pg. 6101
LEO BURNETT CASABLANCA—See Publicis Groupe S.A.; *Int'l*, pg. 6101
LEO BURNETT CHILE—See Publicis Groupe S.A.; *Int'l*, pg. 6101
LEO BURNETT COLOMBIA, S.A.—See Publicis Groupe S.A.; *Int'l*, pg. 6101
LEO BURNETT COMPANY LTD.—See Publicis Groupe S.A.; *Int'l*, pg. 6101
LEO BURNETT COMUNICA, S.A.—See Publicis Groupe S.A.; *Int'l*, pg. 6101
LEO BURNETT CO., S.R.L.—See Publicis Groupe S.A.; *Int'l*, pg. 6101
LEO BURNETT CO. S.R.L.—See Publicis Groupe S.A.; *Int'l*, pg. 6101
LEO BURNETT DEL PERU S.A.—See Publicis Groupe S.A.; *Int'l*, pg. 6101
LEO BURNETT DETROIT, INC.—See Publicis Groupe S.A.; *Int'l*, pg. 6101
LEO BURNETT GMBH—See Publicis Groupe S.A.; *Int'l*, pg. 6101
LEO BURNETT-GUANGZHOU—See Publicis Groupe S.A.; *Int'l*, pg. 6102
LEO BURNETT-HONG KONG—See Publicis Groupe S.A.; *Int'l*, pg. 6102
LEO BURNETT INC.—See Publicis Groupe S.A.; *Int'l*, pg. 6101
LEO BURNETT INC.—See Publicis Groupe S.A.; *Int'l*, pg. 6101
LEO BURNETT INC., SUCURSAL ARGENTINA—See Publicis Groupe S.A.; *Int'l*, pg. 6101
LEO BURNETT INDIA—See Publicis Groupe S.A.; *Int'l*, pg. 6101
LEO BURNETT INDIA—See Publicis Groupe S.A.; *Int'l*, pg. 6101
LEO BURNETT JORDAN—See Publicis Groupe S.A.; *Int'l*, pg. 6101
LEO BURNETT KIEV—See Publicis Groupe S.A.; *Int'l*, pg. 6101
LEO BURNETT KOREA—See Publicis Groupe S.A.; *Int'l*, pg. 6101
LEO BURNETT KREASINDO INDONESIA—See Publicis Groupe S.A.; *Int'l*, pg. 6101
LEO BURNETT - LOS ANGELES—See Publicis Groupe S.A.; *Int'l*, pg. 6101
LEO BURNETT, LTD.—See Publicis Groupe S.A.; *Int'l*, pg. 6102
LEO BURNETT MANILA—See Publicis Groupe S.A.; *Int'l*, pg. 6101
LEO BURNETT MELBOURNE—See Publicis Groupe S.A.; *Int'l*, pg. 6101
LEO BURNETT MEXICO S.A. DE C.V.—See Publicis Groupe S.A.; *Int'l*, pg. 6101
LEO BURNETT MOSCOW—See Publicis Groupe S.A.; *Int'l*, pg. 6101
LEO BURNETT PANAMA, S.A.—See Publicis Groupe S.A.; *Int'l*, pg. 6101
LEO BURNETT PUBLICIDADE, LTDA.—See Publicis Groupe S.A.; *Int'l*, pg. 6101
LEO BURNETT PUBLICIDADE, LTDA.—See Publicis Groupe S.A.; *Int'l*, pg. 6101
LEO BURNETT ROME—See Publicis Groupe S.A.; *Int'l*, pg. 6101
LEO BURNETT SHANGHAI ADVERTISING CO., LTD.—See Publicis Groupe S.A.; *Int'l*, pg. 6101
LEO BURNETT SOLUTIONS INC.—See Publicis Groupe S.A.; *Int'l*, pg. 6101
LEO BURNETT SYDNEY—See Publicis Groupe S.A.; *Int'l*, pg. 6102
LEO BURNETT & TARGET SA—See Publicis Groupe S.A.; *Int'l*, pg. 6101
LEO BURNETT USA—See Publicis Groupe S.A.; *Int'l*, pg. 6102
LEO BURNETT VILNIUS—See Publicis Groupe S.A.; *Int'l*, pg. 6102
LEO BURNETT WARSAW SP.Z.O.O.—See Publicis Groupe S.A.; *Int'l*, pg. 6102
LEO BURNETT WERBEAGENTUR GMBH & CO. KG—See Publicis Groupe S.A.; *Int'l*, pg. 6102
LEO BURNETT WORLDWIDE, INC.—See Publicis Groupe S.A.; *Int'l*, pg. 6100
LEO BURNETT WORLDWIDE - LATIN AMERICA—See Publicis Groupe S.A.; *Int'l*, pg. 6102
LEOCH ACCUPOWER (M) SDN BHD—See Leoch International Technology Limited; *Int'l*, pg. 4457
LEOCH BATTERIES INDIA PRIVATE LIMITED—See Leoch International Technology Limited; *Int'l*, pg. 4457
LEOCH BATTERY COMPANY LIMITED—See Leoch International Technology Limited; *Int'l*, pg. 4457
LEOCH BATTERY CORPORATION—See Leoch International Technology Limited; *Int'l*, pg. 4457
LEOCH BATTERY (JIANGSU) CORP.—See Leoch International Technology Limited; *Int'l*, pg. 4457
LEOCH BATTERY PTE. LTD.—See Leoch International Technology Limited; *Int'l*, pg. 4457
LEOCH BATTERY UK LTD.—See Leoch International Technology Limited; *Int'l*, pg. 4457
LEOCH EMEA S.A.—See Leoch International Technology Limited; *Int'l*, pg. 4457
LEOCH INTERNATIONAL TECHNOLOGY LIMITED; *Int'l*, pg. 4457
LEOCH ITALIA S.R.L.—See Leoch International Technology Limited; *Int'l*, pg. 4457
LEOCH LANKA (PRIVATE) LTD.—See Leoch International Technology Limited; *Int'l*, pg. 4457
LEOCLAN CO., LTD.; *Int'l*, pg. 4457
LEOCONNECT INC.—See SCALA Inc.; *Int'l*, pg. 6610
LEO CONSTRUCTION COMPANY; *U.S. Private*, pg. 2422
LEOCOR GOLD, INC.; *Int'l*, pg. 4457
LEOCZECH SPOL S.R.O—See Huhtamaki Oyj; *Int'l*, pg. 3525
LEO FARMACEUTICOS LDA.—See LEO Pharma A/S; *Int'l*, pg. 4456
LE OFFICINE RIUNITE - UDINE S.P.A.—See IMER International S.p.A.; *Int'l*, pg. 3623
LEOFOO DEVELOPMENT CO., LTD.; *Int'l*, pg. 4457
LEO GLOBAL LOGISTICS PUBLIC COMPANY LIMITED; *Int'l*, pg. 4456
LEO GROUP CO., LTD.; *Int'l*, pg. 4456
LEO J. BRENNAN, INC.; *U.S. Private*, pg. 2422
LEO JOURNAGAN CONSTRUCTION CO.; *U.S. Private*, pg. 2422

LEO J. ROTH CORP.
CORPORATE AFFILIATIONS

LEO J. ROTH CORP.; *U.S. Private,* pg. 2422
LEO J. SHAPIRO & ASSOCIATES, LLC; *U.S. Private,* pg. 2422
LEO LABORATORIES, LTD.—See LEO Pharma A/S; *Int'l,* pg. 4457
LEO LABORATORIES LTD.—See LEO Pharma A/S; *Int'l,* pg. 4456
LEO LEARNING BRASIL—See Learning Technologies Group plc; *Int'l,* pg. 4435
LEO LEARNING LIMITED—See Learning Technologies Group plc; *Int'l,* pg. 4435
LEO MART CO., LTD.—See Isetan Mitsukoshi Holdings Ltd.; *Int'l,* pg. 3815
LEOMINSTER CREDIT UNION; *U.S. Private,* pg. 2422
LEOMINSTER NEWS INC.; *U.S. Private,* pg. 2422
LEO MOTORS, INC.; *Int'l,* pg. 4456
LEO MYANMAR LOGISTICS COMPANY LIMITED—See LEO Global Logistics Public Company Limited; *Int'l,* pg. 4456
LEONARD A. FEINBERG INCORPORATED; *U.S. Private,* pg. 2423
LEONARD BUS SALES INC.; *U.S. Private,* pg. 2423
THE LEONARD COMPANY; *U.S. Private,* pg. 4069
LEONARD CONSULTING LLC; *U.S. Private,* pg. 2423
LEONARD DRAKE (HK) LTD.—See Esthetics International Group Berhad; *Int'l,* pg. 2518
LEONARD DRAKE (M) SDN. BHD.—See Esthetics International Group Berhad; *Int'l,* pg. 2518
LEONARD E. BELCHER, INC.—See Petroleum Marketing Group Inc.; *U.S. Private,* pg. 3162
LEONARD FASHION S.A.S.—See Sankyo Seiko Co., Ltd.; *Int'l,* pg. 6543
LEONARD & FINCO PUBLIC RELATIONS INC.—See Kane Communications Group, LLC; *U.S. Private,* pg. 2259
LEONARD GREEN & PARTNERS, L.P.; *U.S. Private,* pg. 2423
LEONARDI & CO. USA INC.—See Savino Del Bene S.p.A.; *Int'l,* pg. 6600
LEONARDI & C SPA—See Savino Del Bene S.p.A.; *Int'l,* pg. 6600
LEONARDI GMBH & CO. KG—See Compass Group PLC; *Int'l,* pg. 1752
LEONARDI HPM GMBH—See Compass Group PLC; *Int'l,* pg. 1752
LEONARDI IBERIA S.A.—See Savino Del Bene S.p.A.; *Int'l,* pg. 6600
LEONARD INSURANCE SERVICES AGENCY INC.—See GTCR LLC; *U.S. Private,* pg. 1803
LEONARD SVM GMBH—See Compass Group PLC; *Int'l,* pg. 1752
LEONARD KREUSCH GMBH & CO.—See Leonard Kreusch, Inc.; *U.S. Private,* pg. 2430
LEONARD KREUSCH, INC.; *U.S. Private,* pg. 2430
LEONARDO AUSTRALIA PTY. LTD.—See Leonardo S.p.A.; *Int'l,* pg. 4459
LEONARDO CANADA CO.—See Leonardo S.p.A.; *Int'l,* pg. 4459
LEONARDO (CHINA) CO., LTD.—See Leonardo S.p.A.; *Int'l,* pg. 4459
LEONARDO & CO. S.P.A.—See Houlihan Lokey, Inc.; *U.S. Public,* pg. 1055
LEONARDO DO BRASIL LTDA.—See Leonardo S.p.A.; *Int'l,* pg. 4459
LEONARDO DRS, INC.—See Leonardo S.p.A.; *Int'l,* pg. 4458
LEONARDO FOR TRADING OF MACHINERY EQUIPMENT & DEVICES WLL—See Leonardo S.p.A.; *Int'l,* pg. 4459
LEONARDO GERMANY GMBH—See Leonardo S.p.A.; *Int'l,* pg. 4459
LEONARDO GLOBAL SOLUTIONS SPA—See Leonardo S.p.A.; *Int'l,* pg. 4459
LEONARDO HELICOPTERS USA, INC.—See Leonardo S.p.A.; *Int'l,* pg. 4459
LEONARDO HISPANIA SAU—See Leonardo S.p.A.; *Int'l,* pg. 4459
LEONARDO INTERNATIONAL SPA—See Leonardo S.p.A.; *Int'l,* pg. 4459
LEONARDO MALAYSIA SDN BHD—See Leonardo S.p.A.; *Int'l,* pg. 4459
LEONARDO MW LIMITED—See Leonardo S.p.A.; *Int'l,* pg. 4460
LEONARDO POLAND SP. Z O.O.—See Leonardo S.p.A.; *Int'l,* pg. 4459
LEONARDO PORTUGAL S.A.—See Leonardo S.p.A.; *Int'l,* pg. 4460
LEONARDO ROMANIA AEROSPACE, DEFENCE & SECURITY S.A.—See Leonardo S.p.A.; *Int'l,* pg. 4460
LEONARDO SINGAPORE PTE. LTD.—See Leonardo S.p.A.; *Int'l,* pg. 4460
LEONARDO S.P.A.; *Int'l,* pg. 4457
LEONARDO TECHNOLOGIES & SERVICES LTD.—See
LEONARDO TURKEI HAVACILIK SAVUNMA VE GUVENLIK SISTEMLERI A.S.—See Leonardo S.p.A.; *Int'l,* pg. 4460
LEONARDO US AIRCRAFT INC.—See Leonardo S.p.A.; *Int'l,* pg. 4460

LEONARD PETERSON & CO., INC.; *U.S. Private,* pg. 2430
LEONARD'S CARPET SERVICE INC.; *U.S. Private,* pg. 2430
LEONARD'S EXPRESS INC.; *U.S. Private,* pg. 2430
LEONARD S. FIORE, INC.; *U.S. Private,* pg. 2430
LEONARDTOWN SURGERY CENTER, LLC—See Tenet Healthcare Corporation; *U.S. Public,* pg. 2004
LEONARD VALVE COMPANY—See Bessemer Investment Partners LLC; *U.S. Private,* pg. 541
LEONA'S PIZZERIA INC.; *U.S. Private,* pg. 2423
LEON BEKAERT S.P.A.—See NV Bekaert SA; *Int'l,* pg. 5496
LEON CO.—See Central Security Patrols Co., Ltd.; *Int'l,* pg. 1410
LEON D. DEMATTEIS CONSTRUCTION; *U.S. Private,* pg. 2422
LEON DE BRUXELLES SA—See Eurazeo SE; *Int'l,* pg. 2529
LEONE ASSET MANAGEMENT, INC.; *U.S. Public,* pg. 1308
LEONE FILM GROUP S.P.A.; *Int'l,* pg. 4461
LEONE & KEEBLE INC.; *U.S. Private,* pg. 2430
LEONETTI & ASSOCIATES, LLC—See Lee Equity Partners LLC; *U.S. Private,* pg. 2412
LEONETTI CELLAR; *U.S. Private,* pg. 2430
LEON E. WINTERMYER INC.—See L.E.W. Holding Co. Inc.; *U.S. Private,* pg. 2365
LEON FARMER AND COMPANY INC.; *U.S. Private,* pg. 2422
LEON FRAZER & ASSOCIATES INC.—See iA Financial Corporation Inc.; *Int'l,* pg. 3567
LEON FUAT BERHAD; *Int'l,* pg. 4457
LEON FUAT HARDWARE SDN. BHD.—See Leon Fuat Berhad; *Int'l,* pg. 4457
LEONG HIN PILING (PTE) LTD—See Enviro-Hub Holdings Ltd.; *Int'l,* pg. 2454
LEONG HIN SAN SDN. BHD.—See United Malacca Berhad; *Int'l,* pg. 8070
LEONG HUP FOOD PTE. LTD.—See Leong Hup International Berhad; *Int'l,* pg. 4461
LEONG HUP HOLDINGS BERHAD—See Emerging Glory Sdn Bhd; *Int'l,* pg. 2379
LEONG HUP INTERNATIONAL BERHAD; *Int'l,* pg. 4461
LEONG HUP (PHILIPPINES), INC.—See Leong Hup International Berhad; *Int'l,* pg. 4461
LEON GROSSE AQUITAINE—See Leon Grosse; *Int'l,* pg. 4457
LEON GROSSE ELECTRICITE (LGE)—See Leon Grosse; *Int'l,* pg. 4457
LEON GROSSE; *Int'l,* pg. 4457
LEONHARD KURZ (AUST.) PTY. LTD.—See Leonhard Kurz GmbH & Co. KG; *Int'l,* pg. 4462
LEONHARD KURZ BENELUX B.V.—See Leonhard Kurz GmbH & Co. KG; *Int'l,* pg. 4462
LEONHARD KURZ (FAR EAST) LTD.—See Leonhard Kurz GmbH & Co. KG; *Int'l,* pg. 4462
LEONHARD KURZ GMBH & CO. KG; *Int'l,* pg. 4461
LEONHARD KURZ HUNGARIA KFT.—See Leonhard Kurz GmbH & Co. KG; *Int'l,* pg. 4462
LEONHARD KURZ IRELAND LTD.—See Leonhard Kurz GmbH & Co. KG; *Int'l,* pg. 4462
LEONHARD KURZ SOUTH-EAST EUROPE KFT.—See Leonhard Kurz GmbH & Co. KG; *Int'l,* pg. 4462
LEONHARD KURZ (U.K.) LTD.—See Leonhard Kurz GmbH & Co. KG; *Int'l,* pg. 4462
LEONHARD MOLL BETONWERKE GMBH & CO KG; *Int'l,* pg. 4462
LEONHARD MOLL HOCH- UND TIEFBAU GMBH—See STRABAG SE; *Int'l,* pg. 7231
LEON HATOT SA—See The Swatch Group Ltd.; *Int'l,* pg. 7691
LEON HENRY, INC.; *U.S. Private,* pg. 2422
LEONI AG; *Int'l,* pg. 4462
LEONI AUTOKABEL POLSKA SP.Z.O.O—See LEONI AG; *Int'l,* pg. 4463
LEONI AUTOKABEL SLOWAKIA SPOL S.R.O.—See LEONI AG; *Int'l,* pg. 4463
LEONI AUTOMOTIVE DO BRASIL LTDA—See LEONI AG; *Int'l,* pg. 4463
LEONI AUTOMOTIVE LEADS GMBH—See LEONI AG; *Int'l,* pg. 4463
LEONI BORDNETZ-SYSTEME GMBH & CO., KG—See LEONI AG; *Int'l,* pg. 4462
LEONI CABLE ASSEMBLIES GMBH—See LEONI AG; *Int'l,* pg. 4463
LEONI CABLE BELGIUM N.V—See LEONI AG; *Int'l,* pg. 4463
LEONI CABLE (CHANGZHOU) CO LTD—See LEONI AG; *Int'l,* pg. 4463
LEONI CABLE DE CHIHUAHUA S.A. DE C.V.—See LEONI AG; *Int'l,* pg. 4463
LEONI CABLE INC—See EnBW Energie Baden-Wurttemberg AG; *Int'l,* pg. 2399
LEONI CABLE MAROC SARL—See LEONI AG; *Int'l,* pg. 4463
LEONI CABLE S.A DE C.V.—See LEONI AG; *Int'l,* pg. 4463

LEONI CABLE SLOVAKIA SPOL S.R.O—See LEONI AG; *Int'l,* pg. 4463
LEONI CABLE SOLUTIONS (INDIA) PRIVATE LIMITED—See LEONI AG; *Int'l,* pg. 4463
LEONI CABLE (XIAMEN) CO LTD—See LEONI AG; *Int'l,* pg. 4463
LEONI DRAHT GMBH—See LEONI AG; *Int'l,* pg. 4463
LEONI ELECTRICAL SYSTEMS (JINING) CO., LTD.—See LEONI AG; *Int'l,* pg. 4463
LEONI ELECTRICAL SYSTEMS (PENGLAI) CO., LTD.—See LEONI AG; *Int'l,* pg. 4463
LEONI ELECTRICAL SYSTEMS (SHANGHAI) CO. LTD.—See LEONI AG; *Int'l,* pg. 4463
LEONI ELOCAB GMBH—See LEONI AG; *Int'l,* pg. 4464
LEONI ELOCAB LTD—See LEONI AG; *Int'l,* pg. 4463
LEONI ENGINEERING PRODUCTS & SERVICES INC.—See LEONI AG; *Int'l,* pg. 4463
LEONI FIBER OPTICS GMBH—See LEONI AG; *Int'l,* pg. 4463
LEONI FIBER OPTICS GMBH—See LEONI AG; *Int'l,* pg. 4463
LEONI FIBER OPTICS INC.—See LEONI AG; *Int'l,* pg. 4463
LEONI FURAS S.L—See LEONI AG; *Int'l,* pg. 4463
LEONI FURUKAWA WIRING SYSTEMS SAS—See The Furukawa Electric Co., Ltd.; *Int'l,* pg. 7646
LEONI HIGHTEMP SOLUTIONS GMBH—See LEONI AG; *Int'l,* pg. 4463
LEONI ITALY S.R.L.—See LEONI AG; *Int'l,* pg. 4463
LEONI KABEL GMBH—See LEONI AG; *Int'l,* pg. 4463
LEONI KABELGYAR HUNGARIA KFT—See LEONI AG; *Int'l,* pg. 4464
LEONI KABEL HOLDING GMBH—See LEONI AG; *Int'l,* pg. 4463
LEONI KABEL POLSKA SP.Z.O.O—See LEONI AG; *Int'l,* pg. 4463
LEONI KABELSYSTEME GMBH—See LEONI AG; *Int'l,* pg. 4464
LEONI KABLO VE TEKNOLOJILERI SANAYI VE TICARET LIMITED SIRKETI—See LEONI AG; *Int'l,* pg. 4464
LEONI KERPEN GMBH—See LEONI AG; *Int'l,* pg. 4464
LEONI MIDDLE EAST FZE—See LEONI AG; *Int'l,* pg. 4463
LEON INSPECTION & TESTING INDIA PRIVATE LIMITED—See China Leon Inspection Holding Limited; *Int'l,* pg. 1514
LEON INSPECTION TESTING SERVICES SDN. BHD—See China Leon Inspection Holding Limited; *Int'l,* pg. 1514
LEONI PROTEC CABLE SYSTEMS GMBH—See LEONI AG; *Int'l,* pg. 4464
LEONISA USA; *U.S. Private,* pg. 2431
LEONISA HOLDING INC.—See LEONI AG; *Int'l,* pg. 4464
LEONISCHE PORTUGAL LDA—See LEONI AG; *Int'l,* pg. 4464
LEONI SCHWEIZ AG—See LEONI AG; *Int'l,* pg. 4464
LEONI (S.E.A) PTE LTD—See LEONI AG; *Int'l,* pg. 4463
LEONI SILITHERMS S.R.L—See LEONI AG; *Int'l,* pg. 4464
LEONI SLOVAKIA SPOL. S.R.O.—See LEONI AG; *Int'l,* pg. 4463
LEONI SLOWAKIA SPOL S.R.O—See LEONI AG; *Int'l,* pg. 4464
LEONI SPECIAL CABLES (CHANGZHOU) CO LTD—See LEONI AG; *Int'l,* pg. 4464
LEONI SPECIAL CABLES GMBH—See LEONI AG; *Int'l,* pg. 4463
LEONI SPECIAL CABLES IBERICA S.A—See LEONI AG; *Int'l,* pg. 4464
LEONI STUDER GMBH—See LEONI AG; *Int'l,* pg. 4464
LEONI TEMCO LTD—See LEONI AG; *Int'l,* pg. 4464
LEONI TUNISIE SARL—See LEONI AG; *Int'l,* pg. 4464
LEONI WIRE & CABLE SOLUTIONS JAPAN K.K—See LEONI AG; *Int'l,* pg. 4464
LEONI WIRE (CHANGZHOU) CO LTD—See LEONI AG; *Int'l,* pg. 4464
LEONI WIRE INC—See LEONI AG; *Int'l,* pg. 4464
LEONI WIRING SYSTEMS AIN SEBAA SA—See LEONI AG; *Int'l,* pg. 4463
LEONI WIRING SYSTEMS ARAD SRL—See LEONI AG; *Int'l,* pg. 4464
LEONI WIRING SYSTEMS BOUSKOURA SA—See LEONI AG; *Int'l,* pg. 4463
LEONI WIRING SYSTEMS (CHANGCHUN) CO. LTD.—See LEONI AG; *Int'l,* pg. 4464
LEONI WIRING SYSTEMS CZECH, S.R.O.—See LEONI AG; *Int'l,* pg. 4463
LEONI WIRING SYSTEMS DE DURANGO S.A. DE CV—See LEONI AG; *Int'l,* pg. 4463
LEONI WIRING SYSTEMS DE TORREON S.A. DE CV—See LEONI AG; *Int'l,* pg. 4463
LEONI WIRING SYSTEMS EGYPT S.A.E.—See LEONI AG; *Int'l,* pg. 4463
LEONI WIRING SYSTEMS FRANCE S.A—See LEONI AG; *Int'l,* pg. 4464
LEONI WIRING SYSTEMS HERMOSILLO S.A DE C.V—See LEONI AG; *Int'l,* pg. 4464

COMPANY NAME INDEX

LEONI WIRING SYSTEMS, INC.—See LEONI AG; *Int'l*, pg. 4464
LEONI WIRING SYSTEMS ITALY S.R.L.—See LEONI AG; *Int'l*, pg. 4463
LEONI WIRING SYSTEMS KOREA INC—See LEONI AG; *Int'l*, pg. 4464
LEONI WIRING SYSTEMS MATEUR NORD SA—See LEONI AG; *Int'l*, pg. 4464
LEONI WIRING SYSTEMS MEXICANA S.A DE C.V—See LEONI AG; *Int'l*, pg. 4464
LEONI WIRING SYSTEMS PITESTI SRL—See LEONI AG; *Int'l*, pg. 4464
LEONI WIRING SYSTEMS (PUNE) PVT LTD—See LEONI AG; *Int'l*, pg. 4464
LEONI WIRING SYSTEMS RO S.R.L.—See LEONI AG; *Int'l*, pg. 4463
LEONI WIRING SYSTEMS SOUTHEAST D.O.O.—See LEONI AG; *Int'l*, pg. 4463
LEONI WIRING SYSTEMS SPAIN S.L.—See LEONI AG; *Int'l*, pg. 4463
LEONI WIRING SYSTEMS (TIELING) CO., LTD.—See LEONI AG; *Int'l*, pg. 4463
LEONI WIRING SYSTEMS TUNISIA SARL—See LEONI AG; *Int'l*, pg. 4463
LEONI WIRING SYSTEM UA GMBH—See LEONI AG; *Int'l*, pg. 4464
LEONI WIRING SYSTEM U.K LTD—See LEONI AG; *Int'l*, pg. 4464
LEON JONES FEED AND GRAIN INC.; *U.S. Private*, pg. 2423
LEON KOROL COMPANY; *U.S. Private*, pg. 2423
LEON MAX INC.; *U.S. Private*, pg. 2423
LEON MEDICAL CENTERS, INC.; *U.S. Private*, pg. 2423
LEON N. WEINER & ASSOCIATES; *U.S. Private*, pg. 2423
LEON OVERSEAS PTE. LTD—See China Leon Inspection Holding Limited; *Int'l*, pg. 1514
LEONOVUS INC.; *Int'l*, pg. 4464
LEON'S FINE FOODS, INC.; *U.S. Private*, pg. 2423
LEON'S FURNITURE LIMITED; *Int'l*, pg. 4457
LEON SPEAKERS, INC.; *U.S. Private*, pg. 2423
LEON SULLIVAN HEALTH CARE CENTER; *U.S. Private*, pg. 2423
LEON TECHNOLOGY CO LTD; *Int'l*, pg. 4457
LEONTEQ AG; *Int'l*, pg. 4464
LEONTEQ SECURITIES AG—See Leonteq AG; *Int'l*, pg. 4465
LEONTEQ SECURITIES (EUROPE) GMBH—See Leonteq AG; *Int'l*, pg. 4464
LEONTEQ SECURITIES (HONG KONG) LTD.—See Leonteq AG; *Int'l*, pg. 4464
LEONTEQ SECURITIES (JAPAN) LTD.—See Leonteq AG; *Int'l*, pg. 4464
LEONTEQ SECURITIES (MONACO) SAM—See Leonteq AG; *Int'l*, pg. 4464
LEONTEQ SECURITIES (SINGAPORE) PTE. LTD.—See Leonteq AG; *Int'l*, pg. 4465
LEOO SAS—See ADLPartner SA; *Int'l*, pg. 151
LEOPALACE21 BUSINESS CONSULTING (SHANGHAI) CO., LTD.—See Leopalace21 Corporation; *Int'l*, pg. 4465
LEOPALACE21 CORPORATION; *Int'l*, pg. 4465
LEOPALACE21 PHILIPPINES INC.—See Leopalace21 Corporation; *Int'l*, pg. 4465
LEOPALACE21 SINGAPORE PTE. LTD.—See Leopalace21 Corporation; *Int'l*, pg. 4465
LEOPALACE21 (THAILAND) CO., LTD.—See Leopalace21 Corporation; *Int'l*, pg. 4465
LEOPALACE GUAM CORPORATION—See Leopalace21 Corporation; *Int'l*, pg. 4465
LEOPALACE INSURANCE CO., LTD.—See Leopalace21 Corporation; *Int'l*, pg. 4465
LEOPALACE LEASING CORPORATION—See Leopalace21 Corporation; *Int'l*, pg. 4465
LEOPALACE POWER CORPORATION—See Leopalace21 Corporation; *Int'l*, pg. 4465
LEOPALACE SMILE CO., LTD.—See Leopalace21 Corporation; *Int'l*, pg. 4465
LEOPARDO COMPANIES INC.; *U.S. Private*, pg. 2431
LEO PHARMA AB—See LEO Pharma A/S; *Int'l*, pg. 4456
LEO PHARMA ASIA PTE LTD.—See LEO Pharma A/S; *Int'l*, pg. 4456
LEO PHARMA A/S; *Int'l*, pg. 4456
LEO PHARMA AS—See LEO Pharma A/S; *Int'l*, pg. 4456
LEO PHARMA BV—See LEO Pharma A/S; *Int'l*, pg. 4456
LEO PHARMACEUTICAL PRODUCTS LLC—See LEO Pharma A/S; *Int'l*, pg. 4456
LEO PHARMACEUTICAL PRODUCTS SARATH LTD.—See LEO Pharma A/S; *Int'l*, pg. 4456
LEO PHARMACEUTICALS, S. DE R.L. DE C.V.—See LEO Pharma A/S; *Int'l*, pg. 4456
LEO PHARMA GMBH—See LEO Pharma A/S; *Int'l*, pg. 4456
LEO PHARMA GMBH—See LEO Pharma A/S; *Int'l*, pg. 4456
LEO PHARMA INC.—See LEO Pharma A/S; *Int'l*, pg. 4456
LEO PHARMA INC.—See LEO Pharma A/S; *Int'l*, pg. 4456
LEO PHARMA K.K.—See LEO Pharma A/S; *Int'l*, pg. 4456
LEO PHARMA LTD.—See LEO Pharma A/S; *Int'l*, pg. 4456

LEO PHARMA NV—See LEO Pharma A/S; *Int'l*, pg. 4456
LEO PHARMA OY—See LEO Pharma A/S; *Int'l*, pg. 4456
LEO PHARMA PTY LTD—See LEO Pharma A/S; *Int'l*, pg. 4456
LEO PHARMA SARL—See LEO Pharma A/S; *Int'l*, pg. 4456
LEO PHARMA S.P.A.—See LEO Pharma A/S; *Int'l*, pg. 4456
LEO PHARMA SP. Z O.O.—See LEO Pharma A/S; *Int'l*, pg. 4456
LEO PHARMA S.R.O.—See LEO Pharma A/S; *Int'l*, pg. 4456
LEOPOLD KETEL & PARTNERS; *U.S. Private*, pg. 2431
LEOPOLD KOSTAL GMBH & CO. KG; *Int'l*, pg. 4465
LEO PROPERTY MANAGEMENT PRIVATE LIMITED—See Allgreen Properties Ltd.; *Int'l*, pg. 338
LEO S.A.—See Enovos International S.A.; *Int'l*, pg. 2444
LEO'S FOODS, INC.—See Flowers Foods, Inc.; *U.S. Public*, pg. 855
LEOTEK ELECTRONICS CORP.—See Lite-On Technology Corporation; *Int'l*, pg. 4525
LEOTEK ELECTRONICS USA LLC—See Lite-On Technology Corporation; *Int'l*, pg. 4525
LEOTEX CO., LTD.—See Isetan Mitsukoshi Holdings Ltd.; *Int'l*, pg. 3815
LEO TIDWELL EXCAVATING CORP; *U.S. Private*, pg. 2422
LEO US HOLDING, INC.—See LEO Pharma A/S; *Int'l*, pg. 4456
LEOVEGAS AB; *Int'l*, pg. 4466
LEO VISION S.A.S.—See Vivendi SE; *Int'l*, pg. 8275
LEO VISTA SDN. BHD.—See Mitrajaya Holdings Berhad; *Int'l*, pg. 4928
LE PAFE, INC.; *U.S. Private*, pg. 2405
LEPAGE BAKERIES, INC.—See Flowers Foods, Inc.; *U.S. Public*, pg. 854
LEPAGE'S CORPORATION; *U.S. Private*, pg. 2431
LE PALAIS PRAHA S.R.O.—See Warimpex Finanz- und Beteiligungs AG; *Int'l*, pg. 8345
LEPANTO CONSOLIDATED MINING COMPANY; *Int'l*, pg. 4466
LEPANTO INVESTMENT & DEVELOPMENT CORPORATION—See Lepanto Consolidated Mining Company; *Int'l*, pg. 4466
LE PASSAGE TO INDIA TOURS & TRAVELS PVT LTD—See TUI AG; *Int'l*, pg. 7965
LEPEL CORPORATION—See Indel, Inc.; *U.S. Private*, pg. 2055
LEPENSKI VIR A.D.; *Int'l*, pg. 4466
LEPERCQ, DE NEUFLIZE & CO. INC; *U.S. Private*, pg. 2431
LEPERMISLIBRE SA; *Int'l*, pg. 4466
LE PETIT BASQUE; *Int'l*, pg. 4431
LE PETIT-FILS DE L.U. CHOPARD FRANCE SAS—See Chopard & Cie S.A.; *Int'l*, pg. 1582
LEPIDICO LTD.; *Int'l*, pg. 4466
LEPIERS' INC.; *U.S. Private*, pg. 2431
LE POINT—See Financiere Pinault SCA; *Int'l*, pg. 2668
LEPOUTRE TERNYNCK—See Chargeurs SA; *Int'l*, pg. 1449
LEPPINKS INC.; *U.S. Private*, pg. 2431
LEPPO INC.; *U.S. Private*, pg. 2431
LEPRINO FOODS COMPANY; *U.S. Private*, pg. 2431
LEPTON GLOBAL SOLUTIONS LLC—See Kymeta Corporation; *U.S. Private*, pg. 2360
LEPU BIOPHARMA CO., LTD.; *Int'l*, pg. 4466
LE PUBLIC SYSTEME; *Int'l*, pg. 4431
LEPU MEDICAL TECHNOLOGY (BEIJING) CO., LTD.; *Int'l*, pg. 4466
LEPU SCIENTECH MEDICAL TECHNOLOGY (SHANGHAI) CO., LTD.; *Int'l*, pg. 4466
LE PUY ENROBES SAS—See VINCI S.A.; *Int'l*, pg. 8223
L'EQUITE COMPAGNIE D'ASSURANCES ET DE REASSURANCES CONTRE LES RISQUES DE TOUTE NATURE S.A.—See Assicurazioni Generali S.p.A.; *Int'l*, pg. 645
L'EQUITE IARD S.A.—See Assicurazioni Generali S.p.A.; *Int'l*, pg. 645
L'EQUITE S.A.—See Assicurazioni Generali S.p.A.; *Int'l*, pg. 645
LERADO CHINA LIMITED—See Lerado Financial Group Company Limited; *Int'l*, pg. 4466
LERADO FINANCIAL GROUP COMPANY LIMITED; *Int'l*, pg. 4466
LERADO GLOBAL (MACAO COMMERCIAL OFFSHORE) LIMITED—See Lerado Financial Group Company Limited; *Int'l*, pg. 4466
LERADO GROUP (HOLDING) COMPANY LIMITED - ZHONGSHAN FACTORY—See Lerado Financial Group Company Limited; *Int'l*, pg. 4466
LERBS AG—See Rubix Group International Limtied; *Int'l*, pg. 6423
LERCARI INTERNATIONAL LTD.—See Gruppo MutuiOnline S.p.A.; *Int'l*, pg. 3141
LERCARI MOTOR S.R.L.—See Gruppo MutuiOnline S.p.A.; *Int'l*, pg. 3141
LERCARI S.R.L.—See Gruppo MutuiOnline S.p.A.; *Int'l*, pg. 3141
LERCH BATES INC.; *U.S. Private*, pg. 2431

L'EREMO DI MIAZZINA S.R.L.—See Garofalo Health Care SpA; *Int'l*, pg. 2886
LERER HIPPEAU ACQUISITION CORP.; *U.S. Public*, pg. 1308
LE RESEAU SANTE SOCIALE SAS—See CompuGroup Medical SE & Co. KGaA; *Int'l*, pg. 1757
LE RESERVOIR MASSAL—See FAYAT SAS; *Int'l*, pg. 2625
LE RESERVOIR—See FAYAT SAS; *Int'l*, pg. 2625
LERETA LLC—See Edwards Capital, LLC; *U.S. Private*, pg. 1342
LERETA LLC—See Vestar Capital Partners, LLC; *U.S. Private*, pg. 4372
LERK THAI RESTAURANT PTE LTD—See Select Group Limited; *Int'l*, pg. 6699
LERNER CORPORATION; *U.S. Private*, pg. 2431
LERNER ENTERPRISES, INC.; *U.S. Private*, pg. 2431
LERNER ENTERPRISES; *U.S. Private*, pg. 2431
LERNER NEW YORK, INC.—See Irving Place Capital Management, L.P.; *U.S. Private*, pg. 2142
LERNER REAL ESTATE ADVISORS, INC.; *U.S. Private*, pg. 2431
LE ROUGE AB—See Frontier Digital Ventures Limited; *Int'l*, pg. 2795
LEROUX & LOTZ MAINTYS SAS—See Altawest Group; *Int'l*, pg. 388
LEROUX & LOTZ TECHNOLOGIES SA—See Altawest Group; *Int'l*, pg. 388
LEROY ALFHEIM AS—See Austevoll Seafood ASA; *Int'l*, pg. 717
LEROY AURORA AS—See Austevoll Seafood ASA; *Int'l*, pg. 717
LEROY BULANDET AS—See Austevoll Seafood ASA; *Int'l*, pg. 717
LEROY COOPERATIVE ASSOCIATION INC.; *U.S. Private*, pg. 2431
LEROY DELICO AS—See Austevoll Seafood ASA; *Int'l*, pg. 717
LEROY FINLAND OY—See Austevoll Seafood ASA; *Int'l*, pg. 717
LEROY FOSSEN AS—See Austevoll Seafood ASA; *Int'l*, pg. 717
LEROY HILL COFFEE COMPANY INC.; *U.S. Private*, pg. 2431
LEROY HOLDING CO., INC.; *U.S. Private*, pg. 2431
LEROY MERLIN BRESIL LTDA—See Groupe Adeo S.A.; *Int'l*, pg. 3091
LEROY MERLIN BRICOLAJ ROMANIA SRL—See Groupe Adeo S.A.; *Int'l*, pg. 3091
LEROY MERLIN ESPANA S.L.U.—See Groupe Adeo S.A.; *Int'l*, pg. 3091
LEROY MERLIN ITALY S.R.L—See Groupe Adeo S.A.; *Int'l*, pg. 3091
LEROY MERLIN POLOGNE SP. Z.O.O.—See Groupe Adeo S.A.; *Int'l*, pg. 3091
LEROY MIDT AS—See Austevoll Seafood ASA; *Int'l*, pg. 717
LEROY NORGE AS—See Austevoll Seafood ASA; *Int'l*, pg. 717
LEROY NORWAY SEAFOODS AS—See Austevoll Seafood ASA; *Int'l*, pg. 717
LEROY PORTUGAL LDA.—See Austevoll Seafood ASA; *Int'l*, pg. 717
LEROY PROCESSING SPAIN SL—See Austevoll Seafood ASA; *Int'l*, pg. 717
LEROY SEAFOOD AB—See Austevoll Seafood ASA; *Int'l*, pg. 717
LEROY SEAFOOD AS—See Austevoll Seafood ASA; *Int'l*, pg. 717
LEROY SEAFOOD AS—See Austevoll Seafood ASA; *Int'l*, pg. 717
LEROY SEAFOOD DANMARK A/S—See Austevoll Seafood ASA; *Int'l*, pg. 717
LEROY SEAFOOD GROUP ASA—See Austevoll Seafood ASA; *Int'l*, pg. 717
LEROY SEAFOOD HOLDING B.V.—See Austevoll Seafood ASA; *Int'l*, pg. 717
LEROY SEAFOOD ITALY S.R.L.—See Austevoll Seafood ASA; *Int'l*, pg. 718
LEROY SEAFOOD NETHERLANDS B.V.—See Austevoll Seafood ASA; *Int'l*, pg. 718
LEROY SEAFOOD UK LTD.—See Austevoll Seafood ASA; *Int'l*, pg. 718
LEROY SEAFOOD USA INC.—See Austevoll Seafood ASA; *Int'l*, pg. 718
LEROY SJOMATGRUPPEN AS—See Austevoll Seafood ASA; *Int'l*, pg. 718
LEROY SMOGEN SEAFOOD AB—See Austevoll Seafood ASA; *Int'l*, pg. 717
LEROY-SOMER B.V.—See Nidec Corporation; *Int'l*, pg. 5276
LEROY-SOMER CANADA LTD.—See Nidec Corporation; *Int'l*, pg. 5276
LEROY-SOMER DENMARK A/S—See Nidec Corporation; *Int'l*, pg. 5277
LEROY SOMER ELEKTOMEKANIK SISTEMLER TICARET LTD. STI—See Nidec Corporation; *Int'l*, pg. 5276

LEROY HOLDING CO., INC.

CORPORATE AFFILIATIONS

LEROY-SOMER ELEKTROANTRIEBE GMBH—See Nidec Corporation; *Int'l*, pg. 5277
LEROY-SOMER MARBAISE GMBH—See Nidec Corporation; *Int'l*, pg. 5277
LEROY-SOMER NORDEN AB—See Nidec Corporation; *Int'l*, pg. 5277
LEROY-SOMER NORGE A/S—See Nidec Corporation; *Int'l*, pg. 5277
LEROY-SOMER OY—See Nidec Corporation; *Int'l*, pg. 5277
LEROY-SOMER (PTY) LTD.—See Nidec Corporation; *Int'l*, pg. 5276
LEROY SPRINGS & COMPANY INC.; *U.S. Private*, pg. 2431
LEROY SVERIGE AB—See Austevoll Seafood ASA; *Int'l*, pg. 717
LEROY TRONDHEIM AS—See Austevoll Seafood ASA; *Int'l*, pg. 717
LEROY TURKEY SU URUNLERI SAN. VE TIC A.S.—See Austevoll Seafood ASA; *Int'l*, pg. 717
LEROY VEST AS—See Austevoll Seafood ASA; *Int'l*, pg. 717
LERRI SOLAR TECHNOLOGY CO., LTD.—See LONGi Green Energy Technology Co., Ltd.; *Int'l*, pg. 4550
LERRO CORPORATION; *U.S. Private*, pg. 2431
LERTHAI GROUP LIMITED; *Int'l*, pg. 4466
LES ACIERS FINS DE LA SARRE S.A.—See Saarstahl AG; *Int'l*, pg. 6461
LES ACIERS SOFATEC INC.; *Int'l*, pg. 4467
LESAFFRE ARGENTINA S.A.—See Compagnie des Levures Lesaffre SA; *Int'l*, pg. 1738
LESAFFRE AUSTRALIA PACIFIC PTY LTD—See Compagnie des Levures Lesaffre SA; *Int'l*, pg. 1738
LESAFFRE AUSTRIA AG—See Compagnie des Levures Lesaffre SA; *Int'l*, pg. 1739
LESAFFRE BULGARIA EOOD—See Compagnie des Levures Lesaffre SA; *Int'l*, pg. 1739
LESAFFRE CESKO, A.S.—See Compagnie des Levures Lesaffre SA; *Int'l*, pg. 1739
LESAFFRE CHILE S.A.—See Compagnie des Levures Lesaffre SA; *Int'l*, pg. 1739
LESAFFRE COLOMBIA LTDA—See Compagnie des Levures Lesaffre SA; *Int'l*, pg. 1739
LESAFFRE (FAR EAST) LTD.—See Compagnie des Levures Lesaffre SA; *Int'l*, pg. 1738
LESAFFRE IBERICA S.A.—See Compagnie des Levures Lesaffre SA; *Int'l*, pg. 1739
LESAFFRE INGREDIENTS SERVICES POLSKA SP. Z O.O.—See Compagnie des Levures Lesaffre SA; *Int'l*, pg. 1738
LESAFFRE INGREDIENTS SERVICES SA—See Compagnie des Levures Lesaffre SA; *Int'l*, pg. 1738
LESAFFRE INTERNATIONAL CORP.—See Compagnie des Levures Lesaffre SA; *Int'l*, pg. 1739
LESAFFRE ITALIA S.P.A.—See Compagnie des Levures Lesaffre SA; *Int'l*, pg. 1739
LESAFFRE MAGYARORSZAG ELESZTOGYARTO ES KERESKEDELMI KFT.—See Compagnie des Levures Lesaffre SA; *Int'l*, pg. 1739
LESAFFRE MANAGEMENT (SHANGHAI) CO., LTD.—See Compagnie des Levures Lesaffre SA; *Int'l*, pg. 1739
LESAFFRE MAROC—See Compagnie des Levures Lesaffre SA; *Int'l*, pg. 1739
LESAFFRE (MINGGUANG) CO., LTD.—See Compagnie des Levures Lesaffre SA; *Int'l*, pg. 1738
LESAFFRE NORDIC AB—See Compagnie des Levures Lesaffre SA; *Int'l*, pg. 1739
LESAFFRE PERU S.A.C.—See Compagnie des Levures Lesaffre SA; *Int'l*, pg. 1739
LESAFFRE POLSKA S.A.—See Compagnie des Levures Lesaffre SA; *Int'l*, pg. 1739
LESAFFRE ROMANIA S.R.L.—See Compagnie des Levures Lesaffre SA; *Int'l*, pg. 1739
LESAFFRE RS D.O.O.—See Compagnie des Levures Lesaffre SA; *Int'l*, pg. 1739
LESAFFRE SLOVENSKO, A.S.—See Compagnie des Levures Lesaffre SA; *Int'l*, pg. 1739
LESAFFRE UKRAINE LLC—See Compagnie des Levures Lesaffre SA; *Int'l*, pg. 1739
LESAFFRE URUGUAY S.A.—See Compagnie des Levures Lesaffre SA; *Int'l*, pg. 1739
LESAFFRE YEAST CORP.—See Compagnie des Levures Lesaffre SA; *Int'l*, pg. 1739
LES AGENCES DE PAPA S.A; *Int'l*, pg. 4467
LESAGE SAS—See Brookfield Corporation; *Int'l*, pg. 1188
LESAINT CHEMICAL LOGISTICS—See LeSaint Logistics LLC; *U.S. Private*, pg. 2432
LESAINT LOGISTICS LLC; *U.S. Private*, pg. 2432
LESAINT LOGISTICS—See LeSaint Logistics LLC; *U.S. Private*, pg. 2432
LESAINT LOGISTICS TRANSPORTATION, INC.—See LeSaint Logistics LLC; *U.S. Private*, pg. 2432
LESAKA TECHNOLOGIES, INC.; *Int'l*, pg. 4468
LESA LATARIA ENGIADINAISA SA—See Emmi AG; *Int'l*, pg. 2385
LES ALIMENTS DA VINCI LTD.; *Int'l*, pg. 4467
LES ALIMENTS DOMINION CITRUS—See Dominion Holding Corporation; *Int'l*, pg. 2161

LES ALLEES D'HELVETIA COMMERCIAL CENTRE LIMITED—See ENL Limited; *Int'l*, pg. 2441
LES AMBASSADEURS CLUB LIMITED—See Shin Hwa World Limited; *Int'l*, pg. 6836
LES ATELIERS DU GOUT—See Sysco Corporation; *U.S. Public*, pg. 1974
LES ATELIERS HORLOGERS LOUIS VUITTON SA—See LVMH Moet Hennessy Louis Vuitton SE; *Int'l*, pg. 4595
LES ATELIERS HORLOGERS LVMH SA—See LVMH Moet Hennessy Louis Vuitton SE; *Int'l*, pg. 4603
LES ATELIERS JOAILLERS LOUIS VUITTON SAS—See LVMH Moet Hennessy Louis Vuitton SE; *Int'l*, pg. 4598
LE SAUNDA HOLDINGS LIMITED; *Int'l*, pg. 4432
LES BOISERIES ROUSSEAU INC.; *Int'l*, pg. 4467
LES BOISES LA FLEUR INC.; *Int'l*, pg. 4467
LES BOUTIQUES BOUCHERON SAS—See Kering S.A.; *Int'l*, pg. 4135
LES BRASSERIES DU CAMEROUN SA; *Int'l*, pg. 4467
LES CABLES BEN-MOR INC.; *Int'l*, pg. 4467
LES CALCAIRES REGIONAUX SAS—See VINCI S.A.; *Int'l*, pg. 8223
LESCARDEN, INC.; *U.S. Public*, pg. 1308
LESCARE KITCHENS INC.; *U.S. Private*, pg. 2432
LES CARS JACQUEMARD—See Regie Autonome des Transports Parisiens; *Int'l*, pg. 6253
LES CASTORS ANGEVINS; *Int'l*, pg. 4467
LES CELLIERS DE CALAIS S.A.S.—See SoftBank Group Corp.; *Int'l*, pg. 7053
LES CHANTIERS DE CHIBOUGAMAU LTEE; *Int'l*, pg. 4467
LES CHARMILLES SA—See Clariane SE; *Int'l*, pg. 1643
LES CHARMILLES—See LDC SA; *Int'l*, pg. 4431
LES CHAUSSURES STC INC.; *Int'l*, pg. 4467
LESCHUPLAT GMBH—See Buzzi SpA; *Int'l*, pg. 1230
L.E. SCHWARTZ & SON INC.; *U.S. Private*, pg. 2365
LES CIMENTS DE BIZERTE; *Int'l*, pg. 4467
LESCO DISTRIBUTING; *U.S. Private*, pg. 2432
LESCO GMBH & COMPANY KG—See Inles d.d.; *Int'l*, pg. 3705
LES COLLECTIONS SHAN INC.; *Int'l*, pg. 4467
LES COMPAGNONS—See Groupe Crit, S.A.; *Int'l*, pg. 3101
LES CONSTRUCTEURS DU BOIS SA; *Int'l*, pg. 4467
LES DERIVES RESINIQUES ET TERPENIQUES SA—See Firmenich International SA; *Int'l*, pg. 2681
LES DESSOUS BOUTIQUE DIFFUSION S.A.—See V. F. Corporation; *U.S. Public*, pg. 2268
LES DISTRIBUTIONS MARC BOIVIN INC.; *Int'l*, pg. 4467
LES DOCKS DES PETROLES D'AMBES SA; *Int'l*, pg. 4467
LESEA BROADCASTING CORPORATION; *U.S. Private*, pg. 2432
LES EAUX MINERALES D'OULMES SA; *Int'l*, pg. 4467
LES ECHOS FORMATION SAS—See LVMH Moet Hennessy Louis Vuitton SE; *Int'l*, pg. 4598
LES ECHOS MEDIAS SNC—See LVMH Moet Hennessy Louis Vuitton SE; *Int'l*, pg. 4598
LES ECHOS SA—See LVMH Moet Hennessy Louis Vuitton SE; *Int'l*, pg. 4592
LES ECHOS SERVICES SAS—See LVMH Moet Hennessy Louis Vuitton SE; *Int'l*, pg. 4598
LES EDITIONS ALBERT RENE S.A.R.L.—See Vivendi SE; *Int'l*, pg. 8273
LES EDITIONS CEC, INC.—See Quebecor Inc.; *Int'l*, pg. 6158
LES EDITIONS DIDIER S.N.C.—See Vivendi SE; *Int'l*, pg. 8273
LES EDITIONS DU TRECARRE, INC.—See Quebecor Inc.; *Int'l*, pg. 6158
LES EDITIONS FOUCHER S N C—See Vivendi SE; *Int'l*, pg. 8273
LES EDITIONS HATIER S.A.—See Vivendi SE; *Int'l*, pg. 8274
LES EDITIONS MUSICALES FRANCOIS 1ER SNC—See Vivendi SE; *Int'l*, pg. 8278
LES EDITIONS QUEBEC-LIVRES—See Quebecor Inc.; *Int'l*, pg. 6158
LES ENPHANTS GROUP; *Int'l*, pg. 4467
LESENS ACTEA SAS—See VINCI S.A.; *Int'l*, pg. 8223
LESENS CENTRE VAL DE LOIRE SAS—See VINCI S.A.; *Int'l*, pg. 8223
LESENS ELECTRICITE SAS—See VINCI S.A.; *Int'l*, pg. 8223
LES ENTRETIENS DU CARLA—See Pierre Fabre S.A.; *Int'l*, pg. 5864
LES FABRICATIONS HAMMOND QUEBEC INC—See Hammond Manufacturing Co. Ltd.; *Int'l*, pg. 3238
LES FILE DRYWALL INCORPORATED; *U.S. Private*, pg. 2431
LES FLOTS LLC—See Clariane SE; *Int'l*, pg. 1643
LES GARAGES SARCELLOIS SA; *Int'l*, pg. 4467
LES GRANDS GARAGES DE LANNION; *Int'l*, pg. 4467
LES GRANDS MOULINS DE DAKAR—See Seaboard Corporation; *U.S. Public*, pg. 1850
LESHA INDUSTRIES LTD; *Int'l*, pg. 4469
LESHAN ELECTRIC POWER CO., LTD.; *Int'l*, pg. 4469
LESHAN GAOCE NEW ENERGY TECHNOLOGY CO., LTD.—See Qingdao GaoCe Technology Co., Ltd.; *Int'l*, pg. 6143

LESHAN GIANTSTAR FARMING & HUSBANDRY CORPORATION; *Int'l*, pg. 4469
LESHAN-PHOENIX SEMICONDUCTOR CO., LTD.—See ON Semiconductor Corporation; *U.S. Public*, pg. 1600
LESHAN SCANA MACHINERY CO.—See Scana ASA; *Int'l*, pg. 6611
LESHAN TOPRAY CELL CO., LTD.—See Topray Solar Co., Ltd.; *Int'l*, pg. 7820
LES HAUTS DE GENOLIER SA—See AEVIS VICTORIA SA; *Int'l*, pg. 183
LES HUILES DIESEL A. ROY INC.; *Int'l*, pg. 4467
LESIC & CAMPER COMMUNICATIONS; *U.S. Private*, pg. 2432
LESIC & CAMPER COMMUNICATIONS—See Lesic & Camper Communications; *U.S. Private*, pg. 2432
LESICO LTD; *Int'l*, pg. 4469
L.E. SIMMONS & ASSOCIATES, INC.; *U.S. Private*, pg. 2365
LES INDUSTRIES CEDAN INC.—See Richelieu Hardware Ltd.; *Int'l*, pg. 6331
LES INDUSTRIES MAIBEC INC; *Int'l*, pg. 4467
LES INDUSTRIES RAILWEL INC.—See CVC Capital Partners SICAV-FIS S.A.; *Int'l*, pg. 1887
LES INDUSTRIES SODEVAMERICA INC—See Sodeva; *Int'l*, pg. 7045
LES INDUSTRIES TOUCH INC.; *Int'l*, pg. 4467
LES INGREDIENTS ALIMENTAIRES BSA INC.—See International Flavors & Fragrances Inc.; *U.S. Public*, pg. 1153
LESJOFORS AB—See Beijer Alma AB; *Int'l*, pg. 943
LESJOFORS A/S—See Beijer Alma AB; *Int'l*, pg. 943
LESJOFORS A/S—See Beijer Alma AB; *Int'l*, pg. 943
LESJOFORS AUTOMOTIVE AB—See Beijer Alma AB; *Int'l*, pg. 943
LESJOFORS AUTOMOTIVE LTD—See Beijer Alma AB; *Int'l*, pg. 943
LESJOFORS BANDDETALJER AB—See Beijer Alma AB; *Int'l*, pg. 943
LESJOFORS CHINA LTD—See Beijer Alma AB; *Int'l*, pg. 943
LESJOFORS FJADRAR AB—See Beijer Alma AB; *Int'l*, pg. 943
LESJOFORS GAS SPRINGS LV—See Beijer Alma AB; *Int'l*, pg. 943
LESJOFORS HEAVY SPRINGS UK LTD.—See Beijer Alma AB; *Int'l*, pg. 943
LESJOFORS INDUSTRIAL SPRINGS & PRESSINGS GMBH—See Beijer Alma AB; *Int'l*, pg. 943
LESJOFORS INDUSTRIFJADRAR AB—See Beijer Alma AB; *Int'l*, pg. 943
LESJOFORS SPRINGS GMBH—See Beijer Alma AB; *Int'l*, pg. 943
LESJOFORS SPRINGS LV—See Beijer Alma AB; *Int'l*, pg. 943
LESJOFORS SPRINGS OY—See Beijer Alma AB; *Int'l*, pg. 943
LESJOFORS SPRINGS & PRESSINGS AB—See Beijer Alma AB; *Int'l*, pg. 943
LESJOFORS SPRINGS SLOVAKIA S.R.O.—See Beijer Alma AB; *Int'l*, pg. 943
LESJOFORS STOCKHOLMS FJADER AB—See Beijer Alma AB; *Int'l*, pg. 943
LESJOFORS STOCK SPRING AB—See Beijer Alma AB; *Int'l*, pg. 943
LESK AO; *Int'l*, pg. 4469
LESKOM DSP—See Safwood S.p.A.; *Int'l*, pg. 6477
LESKOVACKI SAJAM AD; *Int'l*, pg. 4469
LES LABORATOIRES SERVIER SAS; *Int'l*, pg. 4467
LESLIE CONTROLS, INC.—See KKR & Co. Inc.; *U.S. Public*, pg. 1242
THE LESLIE CORPORATION; *U.S. Private*, pg. 4069
LESLIE DAVIS LIMITED—See Signet Jewelers Limited; *Int'l*, pg. 6911
LESLIE EQUIPMENT COMPANY - MARIETTA—See Leslie Equipment Company; *U.S. Private*, pg. 2432
LESLIE EQUIPMENT COMPANY; *U.S. Private*, pg. 2432
LESLIE EQUIPMENT COMPANY—See Leslie Equipment Company; *U.S. Private*, pg. 2432
LESLIE EQUIPMENT COMPANY—See Leslie Equipment Company; *U.S. Private*, pg. 2432
LESLIE EQUIPMENT COMPANY—See Leslie Equipment Company; *U.S. Private*, pg. 2432
LESLIE'S, INC.; *U.S. Public*, pg. 1308
LESLIE'S POOLMART, INC.—See Leonard Green & Partners, L.P.; *U.S. Private*, pg. 2426
LESMAN INSTRUMENT COMPANY—See The Stephens Group, LLC; *U.S. Private*, pg. 4121
LES MENUISERIES FRANCAISES—See Compagnie de Saint-Gobain SA; *Int'l*, pg. 1724
L.E. SMITH CO.; *U.S. Private*, pg. 2365
LES MOTOCYCLES ARDOIN SAINT AMND &CIE SA; *Int'l*, pg. 4468
LES MOULINS DE LA CONCORDE LTTE; *Int'l*, pg. 4468
LESNIK, HIMMELSBACH, WILSON, & HEARL; *U.S. Private*, pg. 2432
LESNINA D.D.; *Int'l*, pg. 4469
LESO INDUSTRIAL SRL—See HORIBA Ltd.; *Int'l*, pg. 3477
LE SOLUZIONI SCARL—See ACEA S.p.A.; *Int'l*, pg. 95

COMPANY NAME INDEX

LESON CHEVROLET COMPANY, INC.; *U.S. Private*, pg. 2432
LESOON EQUIPMENT PTE. LTD.—See SHS Holdings Ltd.; *Int'l*, pg. 6867
LESOTHO FLOUR MILLS LIMITED—See Seaboard Corporation; *U.S. Public*, pg. 1850
LESOTHO TELECOMMUNICATIONS CORPORATION; *Int'l*, pg. 4469
LES OUVRIERS DU PARADIS—See WPP plc; *Int'l*, pg. 8465
LES OUVRIERS DUPARADIS—See WPP plc; *Int'l*, pg. 8467
L ESPACE SAS—See Nexity SA; *Int'l*, pg. 5244
LESPAC NETWORK INC.—See Thoma Bravo, L.P.; *U.S. Private*, pg. 4154
LES PAVAGES DORVAL INC.—See BAUVAL inc.; *Int'l*, pg. 899
LES PAVEURS DE MONTROUGE SAS—See VINCI S.A.; *Int'l*, pg. 8223
LES PECHERIES NORREF QUEBEC INC.—See Colabor Group Inc.; *Int'l*, pg. 1697
LES PETROLES R.L. INC.; *Int'l*, pg. 4468
LE SPHINX ASSURANCES LUXEMBOURG SA—See BNP Paribas SA; *Int'l*, pg. 1091
LES PINKHAM LINCOLN MERCURY, INC.; *U.S. Private*, pg. 2431
LES PLASTIQUES TPI INC.; *Int'l*, pg. 4468
LES PRODUITS CHIMIQUES ERPAC INC.—See Ecolab Inc.; *U.S. Public*, pg. 714
LES PRODUITS PLASTIQUE QUALIPAK INC.; *Int'l*, pg. 4468
LESPROM LLC—See RusForest AB; *Int'l*, pg. 6429
LES QUATRE GLACES (1994) INC—See Canlan Ice Sports Corporation; *Int'l*, pg. 1291
LES RECOLLETS SA—See Clariane SE; *Int'l*, pg. 1643
LES SABLIERES DE LA MEURTHE SAS—See VINCI S.A.; *Int'l*, pg. 8223
LES SALINES DEVELOPMENT LTD.—See Patel Engineering Ltd.; *Int'l*, pg. 5755
LESS ANNOYING SOFTWARE, LLC; *U.S. Private*, pg. 2432
LES SCHWAB HOLDING COMPANY—See Les Schwab Tire Centers of Oregon, Inc.; *U.S. Private*, pg. 2432
LES SCHWAB TIRE CENTERS OF OREGON, INC.; *U.S. Private*, pg. 2432
LES SCHWAB WAREHOUSE CENTER, INC.—See Les Schwab Tire Centers of Oregon, Inc.; *U.S. Private*, pg. 2432
LESS COMMON METALS LIMITED—See Great Western Minerals Group Ltd.; *Int'l*, pg. 3066
LES SENIORIALES DE JUVIGNAC SCI—See Pierre & Vacances SA; *Int'l*, pg. 5864
LES SENIORIALES DE MORDELLES SCCV—See Pierre & Vacances SA; *Int'l*, pg. 5864
LES SENIORIALES EN VILLE DE MARSEILLE - ST LOUP SCI—See Pierre & Vacances SA; *Int'l*, pg. 5864
LES SENIORIALES EN VILLE D'EMERAINVILLE SCI—See Pierre & Vacances SA; *Int'l*, pg. 5864
LES SENIORIALES EN VILLE DE SAINT AVERTIN SCI—See Pierre & Vacances SA; *Int'l*, pg. 5864
LES SENIORIALES EN VILLE MANOSQUE SCI—See Pierre & Vacances SA; *Int'l*, pg. 5864
LES SENIORIALES VILLE DE DIJON SNC—See Pierre & Vacances SA; *Int'l*, pg. 5864
LES SENIORIALES VILLE DE NIMES SCI—See Pierre & Vacances SA; *Int'l*, pg. 5864
LES SENIORIALES VILLE DE RILLIEUX LA PAPE SCI—See Pierre & Vacances SA; *Int'l*, pg. 5864
LES SENIORIALES VILLE DE ST ETIENNE SCI—See Pierre & Vacances SA; *Int'l*, pg. 5864
LES SERVICES G&K—See Cintas Corporation; *U.S. Public*, pg. 496
LES SERVICES MENAGERS ROY LTEE; *Int'l*, pg. 4468
LESSINGS INC.; *U.S. Private*, pg. 2432
LES SITELLES SA—See Clariane SE; *Int'l*, pg. 1643
LESSITER PUBLICATIONS, INC.; *U.S. Private*, pg. 2432
LESS MESS STORAGE INC.—See Metric Capital Partners LLP; *Int'l*, pg. 4856
LES SOLUTIONS VICTRIX INC.—See Alan Allman Associates SA; *Int'l*, pg. 290
LESSON NINE GMBH; *Int'l*, pg. 4469
L'ESSOR SAS—See VINCI S.A.; *Int'l*, pg. 8223
THE LESS PACKAGING COMPANY LTD.—See DS Smith Plc; *Int'l*, pg. 2208
LES SPECIALISTES DE L'ENERGIE SA—See VINCI S.A.; *Int'l*, pg. 8223
LES STANFORD CHEVROLET INC.; *U.S. Private*, pg. 2432
LES STUMPF FORD; *U.S. Private*, pg. 2432
LESTELLE COMMUNICATIONS, LLC; *U.S. Private*, pg. 2432
LESTER BUILDING SUPPLY CO.—See The Lester Group Inc.; *U.S. Private*, pg. 4069
LESTER BUILDING SYSTEMS, LLC; *U.S. Private*, pg. 2432
LESTER DEVELOPMENT CORPORATION—See The Lester Group Inc.; *U.S. Private*, pg. 4069
THE LESTER GROUP INC.; *U.S. Private*, pg. 4069
LESTER INC.; *U.S. Private*, pg. 2433

LESTER INDIA—See Lester Inc.; *U.S. Private*, pg. 2433
LESTER RAINES MAZDA—See Raines Imports, Inc.; *U.S. Private*, pg. 3347
LESTER RAINES MITSUBISHI—See Raines Imports, Inc.; *U.S. Private*, pg. 3347
LES THERMES DE SAUJON SA; *Int'l*, pg. 4468
LES TOQUES BLANCHES DU MONDE SARL; *Int'l*, pg. 4468
LES TOURS JUMPSTREET TOURS, INC.—See TUI AG; *Int'l*, pg. 7965
LES TROIS CHENES SA; *Int'l*, pg. 4468
LE SUEUR INCORPORATED—See Delos Capital, LLC; *U.S. Private*, pg. 1198
LE SUEUR INCORPORATED—See Silverfern Capital Management, LLC; *U.S. Private*, pg. 3663
LES VERANDAS 4 SAISONS; *Int'l*, pg. 4468
LES VIGNERONS DE CALVISSONS; *Int'l*, pg. 4468
LES VIGNERONS D UNI-MEDOC; *Int'l*, pg. 4468
LES VILLAS DE BEL OMBRE LTEE—See ENL Limited; *Int'l*, pg. 2442
LES VINS DE MAEIL CO., LTD.—See Maeil Holdings Co., Ltd.; *Int'l*, pg. 4636
LES ZELLES—See Compagnie de Saint-Gobain SA; *Int'l*, pg. 1724
LETABA DEWATERING—See Set Point Group Limited; *Int'l*, pg. 6730
LETABA GROUP—See Set Point Group Limited; *Int'l*, pg. 6730
LETABA INDUSTRIAL PUMPS (PTY) LTD—See Set Point Group Limited; *Int'l*, pg. 6730
LETA ENTERPRISES INC.; *U.S. Private*, pg. 2433
LETA INFORMATION ENIRO AB—See Eniro Group AB; *Int'l*, pg. 2439
LE TANNEUR & CIE BRUXELLES S.A.—See Le Tanneur & Cie SA; *Int'l*, pg. 4432
LE TANNEUR & CIE SA; *Int'l*, pg. 4432
LETCHWORTH COURIERS LTD.—See CitySprint (UK) Limited; *Int'l*, pg. 1630
LETCHWORTH INVESTMENTS LTD.; *Int'l*, pg. 4469
LETCO MEDICAL, LLC—See Fagron NV; *Int'l*, pg. 2603
LETECH CORPORATION; *Int'l*, pg. 4469
LE TEMPS SA; *Int'l*, pg. 4432
LETENG AS—See Lagercrantz Group AB; *Int'l*, pg. 4394
L'ETE SAS—See VINCI S.A.; *Int'l*, pg. 8223
LET FREEDOM RING, INC.; *U.S. Private*, pg. 2433
LET GROUP HOLDINGS LIMITED; *Int'l*, pg. 4469
LETHAL PERFORMANCE INC.; *U.S. Private*, pg. 2433
LETHEM-VERGEER B.V.—See Headlam Group plc; *Int'l*, pg. 3301
LETHO RESOURCES CORP.; *Int'l*, pg. 4470
LETHUILLIER SA; *Int'l*, pg. 4470
LETICA CORPORATION - LETICA OF ALABAMA FACILITY—See Berry Global Group, Inc; *U.S. Public*, pg. 322
LETICA CORPORATION - LETICA OF DELAWARE FACILITY—See Berry Global Group, Inc; *U.S. Public*, pg. 322
LETICA CORPORATION - LETICA OF GEORGIA FACILITY—See Berry Global Group, Inc; *U.S. Public*, pg. 322
LETICA CORPORATION - LETICA OF INDIANA FACILITY—See Berry Global Group, Inc; *U.S. Public*, pg. 322
LETICA CORPORATION - LETICA OF IOWA FACILITY—See Berry Global Group, Inc; *U.S. Public*, pg. 322
LETICA CORPORATION - LETICA OF KENTUCKY FACILITY—See Berry Global Group, Inc; *U.S. Public*, pg. 322
LETICA CORPORATION - LETICA OF NEVADA FACILITY—See Berry Global Group, Inc; *U.S. Public*, pg. 323
LETICA CORPORATION - LETICA OF OKLAHOMA FACILITY—See Berry Global Group, Inc; *U.S. Public*, pg. 323
LETICA CORPORATION - LETICA OF OREGON FACILITY—See Berry Global Group, Inc; *U.S. Public*, pg. 323
LETICA CORPORATION—See Berry Global Group, Inc; *U.S. Public*, pg. 322
LETICA RESOURCES INC.—See Berry Global Group, Inc; *U.S. Public*, pg. 322
LETISKO KOSICE - AIRPORT KOSICE, A.S.—See Flughafen Wien Aktiengesellschaft; *Int'l*, pg. 2712
LETNES RESTAURANT INC.; *U.S. Private*, pg. 2433
LETONG CHEMICAL CO., LTD.; *Int'l*, pg. 4470
LETO S.A.—See DIAGNOSTIC AND THERAPEUTIC CENTER OF ATHENS-HYGEIA S.A.; *Int'l*, pg. 2103
LE TOTE, INC.; *U.S. Private*, pg. 2405
LETOURNEAU TECHNOLOGIES AMERICA, INC.—See Komatsu Ltd.; *Int'l*, pg. 4236
LETOURNEAU TECHNOLOGIES (DALIAN) CO., LTD.—See Komatsu Ltd.; *Int'l*, pg. 4236
LETOV S.R.O.—See Searchlight Capital Partners, L.P.; *Int'l*, pg. 3588
LE TREMAIL; *Int'l*, pg. 4432
LETRIKA LAB D.O.O.—See MAHLE GmbH; *Int'l*, pg. 4648
LE TRIOMPHE PROPERTY GROUP LLC; *U.S. Private*, pg. 2405

LET'S CONNECT IT SOLUTIONS LIMITED—See Personal Group Holdings plc; *Int'l*, pg. 5820
LET'S DO LUNCH, INC.; *U.S. Private*, pg. 2433
LETSEB, S.A. DE C.V.—See Grupo Televisa, S.A.B.; *Int'l*, pg. 3136
LET'S GO PUBLICATIONS, INC.—See Harvard Student Agencies, Inc.; *U.S. Private*, pg. 1875
LETSHEGO FINANCIAL SERVICES (PTY) LTD.; *Int'l*, pg. 4470
LETS HOLDINGS GROUP CO., LTD.; *Int'l*, pg. 4470
LETS MOVE PROPERTY LIMITED—See LSL Property Services plc; *Int'l*, pg. 4570
LETSOS COMPANY; *U.S. Private*, pg. 2433
LET'S PLAY SPORTS, INC.; *U.S. Private*, pg. 2433
LETSTALK.COM INC.—See Brightstar Capital Partners, L.P.; *U.S. Private*, pg. 653
LETTERBOX MAIL ORDER LIMITED—See Tobar Ltd.; *Int'l*, pg. 7770
LETTERFOLDERS.COM; *U.S. Private*, pg. 2433
LETTERLOGIC, LLC—See GTCR LLC; *U.S. Private*, pg. 1806
LETTERONE HOLDINGS S.A.; *Int'l*, pg. 4470
LETTERONE INVESTMENT HOLDINGS S.A.—See LetterOne Holdings S.A.; *Int'l*, pg. 4470
LETTERONE TELECOM LIMITED—See LetterOne Holdings S.A.; *Int'l*, pg. 4470
LETTERONE TREASURY SERVICES LLP—See LetterOne Holdings S.A.; *Int'l*, pg. 4470
LETTERONE TREASURY SERVICES S.A.—See LetterOne Holdings S.A.; *Int'l*, pg. 4470
LETTERS OF DISTINCTION LIMITED—See The Skipton Building Society; *Int'l*, pg. 7686
LETTERSTREAM, INC.; *U.S. Private*, pg. 2433
LETTS INDUSTRIES, INC.; *U.S. Private*, pg. 2433
LETTUCE ENTERTAIN YOU ENTERPRISES, INC.; *U.S. Private*, pg. 2433
LETTUCE FEED YOU INC.; *U.S. Private*, pg. 2433
LETTUCE INC.—See Intuit Inc.; *U.S. Public*, pg. 1160
LETTUCE SOUPRISE YOU, INC.; *U.S. Private*, pg. 2433
LETUS CAPITAL S.A.; *Int'l*, pg. 4470
LETZIGRABEN GARAGE AG—See Honda Motor Co., Ltd.; *Int'l*, pg. 3463
LEUCADIA ASSET MANAGEMENT LLC—See Jefferies Financial Group Inc.; *U.S. Public*, pg. 1189
LEUCADIA FINANCIAL CORPORATION—See Jefferies Financial Group Inc.; *U.S. Public*, pg. 1189
LEUCADIA LLC—See Jefferies Financial Group Inc.; *U.S. Public*, pg. 1189
LEUCHTSTOFFWERK BREITUNGEN GMBH—See Treibacher Industrie AG; *Int'l*, pg. 7910
LEUCROTTA EXPLORATION INC.—See Vermilion Energy Inc.; *Int'l*, pg. 8172
LEU & GYGAX AG; *Int'l*, pg. 4470
THE LEUKEMIA & LYMPHOMA SOCIETY, INC.; *U.S. Private*, pg. 4069
LEUMI & CO. INVESTMENT HOUSE LTD.—See Bank Leumi Le-Israel B.M.; *Int'l*, pg. 839
LEUMI FINANCE CO., LTD.—See Bank Leumi Le-Israel B.M.; *Int'l*, pg. 839
LEUMI INDUSTRIAL DEVELOPMENT LTD.—See Bank Leumi Le-Israel B.M.; *Int'l*, pg. 839
LEUMI (LATIN AMERICA)—See Bank Leumi Le-Israel B.M.; *Int'l*, pg. 839
LEUMI LEASING AND INVESTMENTS LTD.—See Bank Leumi Le-Israel B.M.; *Int'l*, pg. 839
LEUMI LEASING LTD.—See Bank Leumi Le-Israel B.M.; *Int'l*, pg. 839
LEUMI L.P. LTD.—See Bank Leumi Le-Israel B.M.; *Int'l*, pg. 839
LEUMI MORTGAGE BANK LTD.—See Bank Leumi Le-Israel B.M.; *Int'l*, pg. 839
LEUMI OVERSEAS TRUST CORPORATION LTD—See Bank Leumi Le-Israel B.M.; *Int'l*, pg. 839
LEUMI PARTNERS LTD.—See Bank Leumi Le-Israel B.M.; *Int'l*, pg. 839
LEUMI (SCHWEIZ) AG—See Bank Leumi Le-Israel B.M.; *Int'l*, pg. 839
LEUMITECH LTD.—See Bank Leumi Le-Israel B.M.; *Int'l*, pg. 839
LEUNER INC.; *U.S. Private*, pg. 2433
LEUPOLD & STEVENS, INC.; *U.S. Private*, pg. 2433
LEUSHUIS PROJECTS INTERNATIONAL B.V.—See Pentair plc; *Int'l*, pg. 5789
LEUTEK GMBH—See USU Software AG; *Int'l*, pg. 8099
LEVADURAS Y AVIOS AZTECA, S.A. DE C.V.—See Compagnie des Levures Lesaffre SA; *Int'l*, pg. 1739
LE VAL ENERGIE SARL—See EnBW Energie Baden-Wurttemberg AG; *Int'l*, pg. 2399
LEVANT DISTRIBUTORS—See Thames & Hudson Ltd; *Int'l*, pg. 7607
LEVANTO GSEF (LUX) S.A.R.L.—See ENGIE SA; *Int'l*, pg. 2433
LEVATI FOOD TECH S.R.L.—See ATS Corporation; *Int'l*, pg. 695
LEVCOR, INC.; *U.S. Private*, pg. 2433
LEVCOR INTERNATIONAL INC.; *U.S. Private*, pg. 2433
LE VECKE CORP.; *U.S. Private*, pg. 2405
LEVEE LUMBER INC.; *U.S. Private*, pg. 2434
LEVEL 11; *U.S. Private*, pg. 2434

LEVEL 1, INC.—See ICU Medical, Inc.; *U.S. Public*, pg. 1087
LEVEL 3 ARGENTINA, S.A.—See Lumen Technologies, Inc.; *U.S. Public*, pg. 1346
LEVEL 3 CHILE S.A.—See Lumen Technologies, Inc.; *U.S. Public*, pg. 1347
LEVEL 3 COLOMBIA S.A.—See Lumen Technologies, Inc.; *U.S. Public*, pg. 1347
LEVEL 3 COMMUNICATIONS (ASIA PACIFIC) LIMITED—See Lumen Technologies, Inc.; *U.S. Public*, pg. 1347
LEVEL 3 COMMUNICATIONS AUSTRIA GMBH—See Lumen Technologies, Inc.; *U.S. Public*, pg. 1347
LEVEL 3 COMMUNICATIONS HONG KONG LIMITED—See Lumen Technologies, Inc.; *U.S. Public*, pg. 1347
LEVEL 3 COMMUNICATIONS JAPAN KK—See Lumen Technologies, Inc.; *U.S. Public*, pg. 1347
LEVEL 3 COMMUNICATIONS LIMITED—See Lumen Technologies, Inc.; *U.S. Public*, pg. 1347
LEVEL 3 COMMUNICATIONS, LLC - PITTSBURGH—See Lumen Technologies, Inc.; *U.S. Public*, pg. 1347
LEVEL 3 COMMUNICATIONS, LLC—See Lumen Technologies, Inc.; *U.S. Public*, pg. 1347
LEVEL 3 COMMUNICATIONS PEC IRELAND LIMITED—See Lumen Technologies, Inc.; *U.S. Public*, pg. 1347
LEVEL 3 COMMUNICATIONS PEC LUXEMBOURG II S.A.R.L.—See Lumen Technologies, Inc.; *U.S. Public*, pg. 1347
LEVEL 3 COMMUNICATIONS SINGAPORE PTE. LTD.—See Lumen Technologies, Inc.; *U.S. Public*, pg. 1347
LEVEL 3 MEXICO II, S. DE R.L. DE C.V.—See Lumen Technologies, Inc.; *U.S. Public*, pg. 1347
LEVEL 3 MEXICO LANDING S. DE R.L.—See Lumen Technologies, Inc.; *U.S. Public*, pg. 1347
LEVEL 3 PARENT, LLC—See Lumen Technologies, Inc.; *U.S. Public*, pg. 1347
LEVEL 3 TELECOM OF ARIZONA, LLC—See Lumen Technologies, Inc.; *U.S. Public*, pg. 1347
LEVEL 3 TELECOM OF GEORGIA, LP—See Lumen Technologies, Inc.; *U.S. Public*, pg. 1347
LEVEL 3 TELECOM OF OREGON, LLC—See Lumen Technologies, Inc.; *U.S. Public*, pg. 1347
LEVEL 3 TELECOM OF SOUTH CAROLINA, LLC—See Lumen Technologies, Inc.; *U.S. Public*, pg. 1347
LEVEL 3 TELECOM OF TEXAS, LLC—See Lumen Technologies, Inc.; *U.S. Public*, pg. 1347
LEVEL 3 TELEKOMUNIKACIJSKI STORITVE D.O.O.—See Lumen Technologies, Inc.; *U.S. Public*, pg. 1347
LEVEL 4 TELCOM; *U.S. Private*, pg. 2434
LEVEL5 TOOLS, LLC—See Worthington Industries, Inc.; *U.S. Public*, pg. 2382
LEVEL 8 TECHNOLOGIES, INC.—See SMS Alternatives Inc.; *U.S. Public*, pg. 1896
LEVEL, A ROSETTA CO.—See Publicis Groupe S.A.; *Int'l*, pg. 6107
LEVEL BIOTECHNOLOGY, INC.; *Int'l*, pg. 4470
LEVELBLOX, INC.; *U.S. Public*, pg. 1308
LEVEL ELEVEN, LLC—See The Ascent Group LLC; *U.S. Private*, pg. 3988
LEVEL EQUITY MANAGEMENT, LLC; *U.S. Private*, pg. 2434
LEVELFIELD FINANCIAL, INC.; *U.S. Private*, pg. 2434
LEVELING 8, INC.; *U.S. Private*, pg. 2434
LEVELJUMP HEALTHCARE CORP.; *Int'l*, pg. 4470
LEVEL ONE LLC—See GI Manager L.P.; *U.S. Private*, pg. 1692
LEVEL THREE POST—See Deluxe Corporation; *U.S. Public*, pg. 653
LEVELTWO ADVERTISING; *U.S. Private*, pg. 2434
LEVEL UP! (PHILIPPINES), INC.—See Asphere Innovations Public Company Limited; *Int'l*, pg. 630
LEVELWING MEDIA; *U.S. Private*, pg. 2434
LEVENGER COMPANY; *U.S. Private*, pg. 2434
LEVENSON & HILL, INC.; *U.S. Private*, pg. 2434
LEVERAGED EQUITIES LIMITED—See Bendigo & Adelaide Bank Ltd.; *Int'l*, pg. 970
LEVERAGED TECHNOLOGY INC.; *U.S. Private*, pg. 2435
LEVERAGE INFORMATION SYSTEMS, INC.—See American Securities LLC; *U.S. Private*, pg. 250
LEVERAGE MARKETING GROUP; *U.S. Private*, pg. 2435
LEVERAGE MARKETING, LLC—See Hawke Media, LLC; *U.S. Private*, pg. 1882
LEVER CONSTRUCTION MATERIALS (SHENZHEN) COMPANY LIMITED—See Yau Lee Holdings Limited; *Int'l*, pg. 8571
LEVERE HOLDINGS CORP.; *Int'l*, pg. 4471
LEVER GLOBAL CORPORATION; *U.S. Private*, pg. 2434
LEVER MANUFACTURING CORP.—See Thermwell Products Co., Inc.; *U.S. Private*, pg. 4143
LEVERS ASSOCIATED TRUST LIMITED—See Unilever PLC; *Int'l*, pg. 8044
LEVER STYLE CORPORATION; *Int'l*, pg. 4471
LEVIAT AG—See CRH plc; *Int'l*, pg. 1845
LEVIAT B.V.—See CRH plc; *Int'l*, pg. 1845
LEVIATE AIR GROUP; *U.S. Private*, pg. 2435

LEVIATHAN CORP.; *U.S. Private*, pg. 2435
LEVIATHAN GOLD LTD.; *Int'l*, pg. 4471
LEVIAT PTY LIMITED—See CRH plc; *Int'l*, pg. 1845
LEVICK STRATEGIC COMMUNICATIONS, LP; *U.S. Private*, pg. 2435
LEVI DIS TICARET A.S.—See Suheung Co., Ltd.; *Int'l*, pg. 7255
LEVIKOM EESTI OU; *Int'l*, pg. 4471
LEVIMA ADVANCED MATERIALS CORPORATION—See Legend Holdings Corporation; *Int'l*, pg. 4443
LEVINE COMMUNICATIONS OFFICE; *U.S. Private*, pg. 2435
LEVINE LEICHTMAN CAPITAL PARTNERS, LLC; *U.S. Private*, pg. 2435
LEVINE MANAGEMENT GROUP INC.; *U.S. Private*, pg. 2436
LEVIN ENTERPRISES INC.; *U.S. Private*, pg. 2435
LEVINE PROPERTIES, INC.; *U.S. Private*, pg. 2436
LEVIN FINANCIAL GROUP, INC.; *U.S. Private*, pg. 2435
LEVINGERS DRY CLEANERS (PTY) LTD.—See Excellerate Holdings Ltd.; *Int'l*, pg. 2578
LEVIN PROFESSIONAL SERVICES; *U.S. Private*, pg. 2435
LEV INS AD; *Int'l*, pg. 4470
LEVINSTEIN PROPERTIES LTD.; *Int'l*, pg. 4471
LEV INVEST SPV; *Int'l*, pg. 4470
LEVI, RAY & SHOUP, INC.; *U.S. Private*, pg. 2435
LEVI'S BRAND—See Levi Strauss & Co.; *U.S. Public*, pg. 1309
LEVIS CHEVROLET-CADILLAC; *U.S. Private*, pg. 2436
LEVI'S FOOTWEAR & ACCESSORIES SPAIN S.A.—See Levi Strauss & Co.; *U.S. Public*, pg. 1309
LEVI'S FOOTWEAR & ACCESSORIES (SWITZERLAND) S.A.—See Levi Strauss & Co.; *U.S. Public*, pg. 1309
LEVI STRAUSS (AUSTRALIA) PTY. LTD.—See Levi Strauss & Co.; *U.S. Public*, pg. 1308
LEVI STRAUSS & CO. APD—See Levi Strauss & Co.; *U.S. Public*, pg. 1308
LEVI STRAUSS & CO.—See Levi Strauss & Co.; *U.S. Public*, pg. 1308
LEVI STRAUSS & CO.; *U.S. Public*, pg. 1308
LEVI STRAUSS & CO.—See Levi Strauss & Co.; *U.S. Public*, pg. 1308
LEVI STRAUSS & CO.—See Levi Strauss & Co.; *U.S. Public*, pg. 1308
LEVI STRAUSS & CO.—See Levi Strauss & Co.; *U.S. Public*, pg. 1308
LEVI STRAUSS & CO.—See Levi Strauss & Co.; *U.S. Public*, pg. 1308
LEVI STRAUSS & CO.—See Levi Strauss & Co.; *U.S. Public*, pg. 1308
LEVI STRAUSS & CO.—See Levi Strauss & Co.; *U.S. Public*, pg. 1308
LEVI STRAUSS & CO.—See Levi Strauss & Co.; *U.S. Public*, pg. 1308
LEVI STRAUSS DE ESPANA S.A.—See Levi Strauss & Co.; *U.S. Public*, pg. 1309
LEVI STRAUSS DE MEXICO SA DE CV—See Levi Strauss & Co.; *U.S. Public*, pg. 1309
LEVI STRAUSS DO BRASIL INDUSTRIA E COMERCIO LTDA.—See Levi Strauss & Co.; *U.S. Public*, pg. 1309
LEVI STRAUSS EUROPE—See Levi Strauss & Co.; *U.S. Public*, pg. 1309
LEVI STRAUSS GERMANY GMBH—See Levi Strauss & Co.; *U.S. Public*, pg. 1309
LEVI STRAUSS GLOBAL TRADING COMPANY II, LIMITED—See Levi Strauss & Co.; *U.S. Public*, pg. 1309
LEVI STRAUSS HELLAS SA—See Levi Strauss & Co.; *U.S. Public*, pg. 1309
LEVI STRAUSS (HONG KONG) LIMITED—See Levi Strauss & Co.; *U.S. Public*, pg. 1308
LEVI STRAUSS INTERNATIONAL, INC.—See Levi Strauss & Co.; *U.S. Public*, pg. 1309
LEVI STRAUSS INTERNATIONAL INC.—See Levi Strauss & Co.; *U.S. Public*, pg. 1309
LEVI STRAUSS ISTANBUL KONFEKSIYON SANAYI VE TICARET A.S.—See Levi Strauss & Co.; *U.S. Public*, pg. 1309
LEVI STRAUSS ITALIA SRL—See Levi Strauss & Co.; *U.S. Public*, pg. 1309
LEVI STRAUSS JAPAN K.K.—See Levi Strauss & Co.; *U.S. Public*, pg. 1309
LEVI STRAUSS LISBON—See Levi Strauss & Co.; *U.S. Public*, pg. 1309
LEVI STRAUSS (MALAYSIA) SDN BHD—See Levi Strauss & Co.; *U.S. Public*, pg. 1308
LEVI STRAUSS NEW ZEALAND LIMITED—See Levi Strauss & Co.; *U.S. Public*, pg. 1309
LEVI STRAUSS NORWAY A/S—See Levi Strauss & Co.; *U.S. Public*, pg. 1309
LEVI STRAUSS (PHILIPPINES) INC.—See Levi Strauss & Co.; *U.S. Public*, pg. 1308
LEVI STRAUSS POLAND SP Z.O.O.—See Levi Strauss & Co.; *U.S. Public*, pg. 1309
LEVI STRAUSS PRAHA, SPOL S.R.O.—See Levi Strauss & Co.; *U.S. Public*, pg. 1309
LEVI STRAUSS SA (PTY) LTD—See Levi Strauss & Co.; *U.S. Public*, pg. 1309

LEVI STRAUSS (SUISSE) SA—See Levi Strauss & Co.; *U.S. Public*, pg. 1309
LEVI STRAUSS TRADING KFT—See Levi Strauss & Co.; *U.S. Public*, pg. 1309
LEVI STRAUSS (UK) LIMITED—See Levi Strauss & Co.; *U.S. Public*, pg. 1309
LEVITEC GMBH—See KEBA AG; *Int'l*, pg. 4113
LEVITON INTEGRATED METERING SYSTEMS, INC.—See Leviton Manufacturing Company, Inc.; *U.S. Private*, pg. 2436
LEVITON/LES—See Leviton Manufacturing Company, Inc.; *U.S. Private*, pg. 2437
LEVITON MANUFACTURING COMPANY, INC. - PLANT 05—See Leviton Manufacturing Company, Inc.; *U.S. Private*, pg. 2436
LEVITON MANUFACTURING COMPANY, INC.; *U.S. Private*, pg. 2436
LEVITON MANUFACTURING OF CANADA LTD.—See Leviton Manufacturing Company, Inc.; *U.S. Private*, pg. 2436
LEVITON MANUFACTURING/SOUTHERN DEVICES—See Leviton Manufacturing Company, Inc.; *U.S. Private*, pg. 2436
LEVITON MIDDLE EAST—See Leviton Manufacturing Company, Inc.; *U.S. Private*, pg. 2436
LEVITON NETWORK SOLUTIONS PVT. LTD.—See Leviton Manufacturing Company, Inc.; *U.S. Private*, pg. 2437
LEVITON NETWORK SOLUTIONS—See Leviton Manufacturing Company, Inc.; *U.S. Private*, pg. 2437
LEVITON—See Leviton Manufacturing Company, Inc.; *U.S. Private*, pg. 2436
LEVITON SRL DE C.V.—See Leviton Manufacturing Company, Inc.; *U.S. Private*, pg. 2437
LE VITRAGE DU MIDI—See Compagnie de Saint-Gobain SA; *Int'l*, pg. 1736
LEVITT HOMES CORPORATION; *U.S. Private*, pg. 2437
LEVITTOWN FISH MARKET INC.; *U.S. Private*, pg. 2437
LEVLAD, LLC—See Harvest Partners L.P.; *U.S. Private*, pg. 1876
LEVLANE ADVERTISING, PR & INTERACTIVE; *U.S. Private*, pg. 2437
LEVLANE ADVERTISING/PR/INTERACTIVE-FLORIDA—See LevLane Advertising, PR & Interactive; *U.S. Private*, pg. 2437
LEVOLOR INC.—See 3G Capital Partners L.P.; *U.S. Private*, pg. 13
LEVOLOR, INC.—See 3G Capital Partners L.P.; *U.S. Private*, pg. 13
LEVOLOR KIRSCH WINDOW FASHIONS—See 3G Capital Partners L.P.; *U.S. Private*, pg. 13
LEVOLUX A.T. LIMITED—See Rcapital Partners LLP; *Int'l*, pg. 6227
LEVOLUX LIMITED—See Rcapital Partners LLP; *Int'l*, pg. 6227
LEVONIAN BROTHERS INC.; *U.S. Private*, pg. 2437
LEVON RESOURCES LTD.—See Discovery Metals Corp.; *Int'l*, pg. 2134
LEVOTEC S.R.O.—See Zeppelin GmbH; *Int'l*, pg. 8637
LEVTECH CONSULTING DMCC—See Schneider Electric SE; *Int'l*, pg. 6624
LEVTECH CONSULTING LLC—See Schneider Electric SE; *Int'l*, pg. 6624
LEVTECH CONSULTING SAUDI CO. LTD.—See Schneider Electric SE; *Int'l*, pg. 6625
LEVTECH CONSULTING SERVICES INDIA PRIVATE LTD.—See Schneider Electric SE; *Int'l*, pg. 6625
LEVVEL, LLC—See Endava plc; *Int'l*, pg. 2402
LEVY BEFFORT, LLC—See BGC Group, Inc.; *U.S. Public*, pg. 329
LEVY GROUP, INC.; *U.S. Private*, pg. 2437
LEVY JEWELERS INC.; *U.S. Private*, pg. 2437
LEVY MARKETING & AWARDS; *U.S. Private*, pg. 2437
LEVYPYORA OY—See Nokian Renkaat Oyj; *Int'l*, pg. 5407
LEVY RESTAURANTS FRANCE SAS—See Compass Group PLC; *Int'l*, pg. 1752
LEVY RESTAURANTS, INC.—See Compass Group PLC; *Int'l*, pg. 1751
LEVY RESTAURANTS—See Compass Group PLC; *Int'l*, pg. 1751
LEVY SECURITY CORPORATION; *U.S. Private*, pg. 2437
LEW A. CUMMINGS CO., INC.; *U.S. Private*, pg. 2437
LEWAG HOLDING AG; *Int'l*, pg. 4471
LEWA GMBH—See Nikkiso Co., Ltd.; *Int'l*, pg. 5291
LEWAN & ASSOCIATES, INC.—See Xerox Holdings Corporation; *U.S. Public*, pg. 2388
LEWANDOWSKI ENGINEERS—See Sterling Investment Partners, L.P.; *U.S. Private*, pg. 3806
LEWA-NIKKISO AMERICA, INC.—See Nikkiso Co., Ltd.; *Int'l*, pg. 5291
LEWAN TECHNOLOGY—See Xerox Holdings Corporation; *U.S. Public*, pg. 2388
LEWARE CONSTRUCTION COMPANY OF FLORIDA, INC.; *U.S. Private*, pg. 2437
LEWEKO RESOURCES BERHAD; *Int'l*, pg. 4471
LEWELLYN TECHNOLOGY, LLC—See Align Capital Partners, LLC; *U.S. Private*, pg. 167
L.E. WENTZ GROUP, INC.; *U.S. Private*, pg. 2365

COMPANY NAME INDEX

L.E.W. EQUIPMENT CO. INC.—See L.E.W. Holding Co. Inc.; *U.S. Private*, pg. 2365
LEWER LIFE INSURANCE COMPANY INC.; *U.S. Private*, pg. 2437
L.E.W. HOLDING CO. INC.; *U.S. Private*, pg. 2365
LEWIATAN CZESTOCHOWA SP. Z O.O.—See Emperia Holding S.A; *Int'l*, pg. 2385
LEWIATAN HOLDING S.A.—See Emperia Holding S.A; *Int'l*, pg. 2385
LEWIATAN KUJAWY SP. Z O.O.—See Emperia Holding S.A; *Int'l*, pg. 2385
LEWIATAN OPOLE SP. Z O.O.—See Emperia Holding S.A; *Int'l*, pg. 2386
LEWIATAN-ORBITA SP.Z O.O.—See Emperia Holding S.A; *Int'l*, pg. 2386
LEWIATAN PODKARPACIE SP. Z O.O.—See Eurocash S.A.; *Int'l*, pg. 2533
LEWIATAN PODLASIE SP. Z O.O.—See Eurocash S.A.; *Int'l*, pg. 2533
LEWIATAN POLNOC SP. Z O.O.—See Eurocash S.A.; *Int'l*, pg. 2533
LEWIATAN SLASK SP. Z O.O.—See Emperia Holding S.A; *Int'l*, pg. 2386
LEWIATAN WIELKOPOLSKA SP. Z O.O.—See Emperia Holding S.A; *Int'l*, pg. 2386
LEWIATAN ZACHOD SP. Z O.O.—See Eurocash S.A.; *Int'l*, pg. 2533
LEWICKI MICROELECTRONIC GMBH—See TE Connectivity Ltd.; *Int'l*, pg. 7496
THE LEWIN GROUP—See UnitedHealth Group Incorporated; *U.S. Public*, pg. 2248
LEWINSKY-OFER LTD.; *Int'l*, pg. 4471
LEWIS ADVERTISING, INC.; *U.S. Private*, pg. 2438
LEWIS BAKERIES—See Lewis Brothers Bakeries, Inc.; *U.S. Private*, pg. 2438
THE LEWIS BEAR COMPANY; *U.S. Private*, pg. 4069
LEWIS BRISBOIS BISGAARD & SMITH LLP; *U.S. Private*, pg. 2438
LEWIS BROTHERS BAKERIES, INC.; *U.S. Private*, pg. 2438
LEWIS BROTHERS LEASING CO. INC.—See Lewis Management Inc.; *U.S. Private*, pg. 2439
LEWISBURG ASSOCIATES LIMITED PARTNERSHIP—See Apartment Investment and Management Company; *U.S. Public*, pg. 144
LEWISBURG CONTAINER CO.—See Visy Industries Holdings Pty. Ltd.; *Int'l*, pg. 8256
LEWISBURG PRINTING, INC.—See Radial Equity Partners LP; *U.S. Private*, pg. 3343
LEWIS CELLARS—See The Wonderful Company LLC; *U.S. Private*, pg. 4138
LEWIS CHEMICAL COMPANY; *U.S. Private*, pg. 2438
LEWIS CHEVROLET COMPANY—See Lewis One Plaza Center Corporation; *U.S. Private*, pg. 2439
LEWIS & CLARK BANK; *U.S. Public*, pg. 1309
LEWIS & CLARK CAPITAL LLC; *U.S. Private*, pg. 2437
LEWIS-CLARK KIDNEY CENTER, LLC—See Nautic Partners, LLC; *U.S. Private*, pg. 2870
LEWIS & CLARK PHARMACEUTICALS, INC.—See REBUS HOLDINGS INC.; *U.S. Public*, pg. 1769
LEWIS-CLARK TERMINAL, INC.—See CHS INC.; *U.S. Public*, pg. 492
LEWIS COMMODITIES, INC.; *U.S. Private*, pg. 2438
LEWIS COMMUNICATIONS LIMITED; *Int'l*, pg. 4471
LEWIS COMMUNICATIONS; *U.S. Private*, pg. 2438
LEWIS COMMUNICATIONS—See Lewis Communications; *U.S. Private*, pg. 2438
LEWIS CONTROLS, INC—See Corley Manufacturing Co.; *U.S. Private*, pg. 1050
LEWIS CORP.; *U.S. Private*, pg. 2438
LEWIS COUNTY PRIMARY CARE CENTER; *U.S. Private*, pg. 2438
LEWIS DIGITAL, INC.—See Robert J. Young Company, LLC; *U.S. Private*, pg. 3458
LEWIS DIRECT, INC.; *U.S. Private*, pg. 2438
LEWIS DRUG BRANDON—See Lewis Drug, Inc.; *U.S. Private*, pg. 2438
LEWIS DRUG EASTGATE—See Lewis Drug, Inc.; *U.S. Private*, pg. 2438
LEWIS DRUG HURON—See Lewis Drug, Inc.; *U.S. Private*, pg. 2438
LEWIS DRUG, INC.; *U.S. Private*, pg. 2438
LEWIS DRUG SOUTHEAST—See Lewis Drug, Inc.; *U.S. Private*, pg. 2438
LEWIS DRUG SOUTHGATE—See Lewis Drug, Inc.; *U.S. Private*, pg. 2438
LEWIS DRUG SOUTHWEST—See Lewis Drug, Inc.; *U.S. Private*, pg. 2438
LEWIS DRUG WESTGATE—See Lewis Drug, Inc.; *U.S. Private*, pg. 2438
LEWIS ENERGY GROUP LTD; *U.S. Private*, pg. 2438
LEWIS ENGINEERING COMPANY—See Jabil Inc.; *U.S. Public*, pg. 1181
LEWIS ENTERPRISES; *U.S. Private*, pg. 2438
LEWIS ESTATES GOLF COURSE—See Melcor Developments Ltd.; *Int'l*, pg. 4808
LEWIS FLOOR & HOME; *U.S. Private*, pg. 2438
LEWIS FOODS INC.; *U.S. Private*, pg. 2439
LEWIS FOOD TOWN INC.; *U.S. Private*, pg. 2438

LEWIS FORD—See Lewis Management Inc.; *U.S. Private*, pg. 2439
LEWISGALE HOSPITAL ALLEGHANY—See HCA Healthcare, Inc.; *U.S. Public*, pg. 1001
LEWISGALE HOSPITAL ALLEGHANY—See HCA Healthcare, Inc.; *U.S. Public*, pg. 1001
LEWIS-GALE HOSPITAL, INCORPORATED—See HCA Healthcare, Inc.; *U.S. Public*, pg. 1001
LEWISGALE HOSPITAL MONTGOMERY—See HCA Healthcare, Inc.; *U.S. Public*, pg. 1001
LEWISGALE HOSPITAL MONTGOMERY—See HCA Healthcare, Inc.; *U.S. Public*, pg. 1003
LEWISGALE HOSPITAL-PULASKI—See HCA Healthcare, Inc.; *U.S. Public*, pg. 1001
LEWIS-GALE MEDICAL CENTER, LLC—See HCA Healthcare, Inc.; *U.S. Public*, pg. 1001
LEWIS-GALE PHYSICIANS, LLC—See HCA Healthcare, Inc.; *U.S. Public*, pg. 1001
LEWIS GLASS, INC.; *U.S. Private*, pg. 2439
LEWIS GROUP LIMITED; *Int'l*, pg. 4471
LEWIS HYMAN INC.; *U.S. Private*, pg. 2439
LEWIS HYMANSON SMALL SOLICITORS LLP—See Markel Group Inc.; *U.S. Public*, pg. 1367
LEWIS INDUSTRIAL SERVICES, INC.; *U.S. Private*, pg. 2439
LEWIS INNOVATIVE TECHNOLOGIES, INC.—See Mercury Systems, Inc.; *U.S. Public*, pg. 1422
LEWIS INVESTMENT COMPANIES, LLC—See Lewis Operating Corp.; *U.S. Private*, pg. 2439
LEWIS & LEWIS, INC.—See Summit Materials, Inc.; *U.S. Public*, pg. 1959
LEWIS MANAGEMENT INC.; *U.S. Private*, pg. 2439
LEWIS MARINE SUPPLY INC.; *U.S. Private*, pg. 2439
LEWIS M. CARTER MANUFACTURING CO.; *U.S. Private*, pg. 2439
LEWIS-MCCHORD COMMUNITIES, LLC—See Equity Residential; *U.S. Public*, pg. 792
LEWIS & MICHAEL, INC.; *U.S. Private*, pg. 2437
LEWIS MITTMAN INC.; *U.S. Private*, pg. 2439
LEWIS ONE PLAZA CENTER CORPORATION; *U.S. Private*, pg. 2439
LEWIS OPERATING CORP.; *U.S. Private*, pg. 2439
LEWIS PAPER INTERNATIONAL INC.—See Central National Gottesman Inc.; *U.S. Private*, pg. 823
LEWIS PETROLEUM PRODUCTS CO.; *U.S. Private*, pg. 2439
LEWISPORT TELEPHONE COMPANY INC.—See Telephone & Data Systems, Inc.; *U.S. Public*, pg. 1998
LEWIS PR - BOSTON—See LEWIS Communications Limited; *Int'l*, pg. 4471
LEWIS PR - DUSSELDORF—See LEWIS Communications Limited; *Int'l*, pg. 4471
LEWIS PR - EINDHOVEN—See LEWIS Communications Limited; *Int'l*, pg. 4471
LEWIS-PRICE & ASSOCIATES, INC.; *U.S. Private*, pg. 2440
LEWIS PR INC.—See LEWIS Communications Limited; *Int'l*, pg. 4471
LEWIS PR - MADRID—See LEWIS Communications Limited; *Int'l*, pg. 4471
LEWIS PR - MANCHESTER—See LEWIS Communications Limited; *Int'l*, pg. 4471
LEWIS PR - MILAN—See LEWIS Communications Limited; *Int'l*, pg. 4471
LEWIS PR - MUMBAI—See LEWIS Communications Limited; *Int'l*, pg. 4471
LEWIS PR - MUNICH—See LEWIS Communications Limited; *Int'l*, pg. 4471
LEWIS PROPERTIES INC.; *U.S. Private*, pg. 2439
LEWIS PR - PARIS—See LEWIS Communications Limited; *Int'l*, pg. 4471
LEWIS PR - SAN DIEGO—See LEWIS Communications Limited; *Int'l*, pg. 4471
LEWIS PR - SINGAPORE—See LEWIS Communications Limited; *Int'l*, pg. 4471
LEWIS PR - STOCKHOLM—See LEWIS Communications Limited; *Int'l*, pg. 4471
LEWIS PR - SYDNEY—See LEWIS Communications Limited; *Int'l*, pg. 4471
LEWIS PR - WANCHAI—See LEWIS Communications Limited; *Int'l*, pg. 4471
LEWIS & RAULERSON, INC.; *U.S. Private*, pg. 2437
LEWIS ROCA ROTHGERBER CHRISTIE LLP; *U.S. Private*, pg. 2439
LEWIS & SHERON TEXTILE COMPANY; *U.S. Private*, pg. 2437
LEWIS-SMITH CORPORATION; *U.S. Private*, pg. 2440
LEWIS STAGES INC.; *U.S. Private*, pg. 2439
LEWIS, THOMASON, KING, KRIEG & WALDROP, P.C. - MEMPHIS—See Lewis, Thomason, King, Krieg & Waldrop, P.C.; *U.S. Private*, pg. 2440
LEWIS, THOMASON, KING, KRIEG & WALDROP, P.C.; *U.S. Private*, pg. 2440
LEWISTON DAILY SUN; *U.S. Private*, pg. 2440
LEWISTON SALES INC.; *U.S. Private*, pg. 2440
LEWISTON STATE BANK—See Glacier Bancorp, Inc.; *U.S. Public*, pg. 938

LEXINGTON GOLD LTD.

LEWISTOWN COMPREHENSIVE TREATMENT CENTER, LLC—See Acadia Healthcare Company, Inc.; *U.S. Public*, pg. 29
LEWISTOWN NEWS-ARGUS—See Yellowstone Communications; *U.S. Private*, pg. 4587
LEWIS TOYOTA INC.; *U.S. Private*, pg. 2439
LEWIS TRANSPORTATION SYSTEMS; *U.S. Private*, pg. 2439
LEWIS TRANSPORT INC.; *U.S. Private*, pg. 2439
LEWIS TREE SERVICE INC.; *U.S. Private*, pg. 2440
LEWISVILLE COLLISION, INC.—See AutoNation, Inc.; *U.S. Public*, pg. 236
LEWISVILLE IMPORTS, LTD.—See AutoNation, Inc.; *U.S. Public*, pg. 236
LEWISVILLE LANDFILL TX, LP—See Republic Services, Inc.; *U.S. Public*, pg. 1786
LEWISVILLE MEDICAL CENTER LLC—See Adeptus Health Inc.; *U.S. Private*, pg. 78
LEWISVILLE WOOD PRODUCTS INC.—See Magnolia Forest Products Inc.; *U.S. Private*, pg. 2548
LEWIS VINCENNES, INC.—See Lewis Brothers Bakeries, Inc.; *U.S. Private*, pg. 2438
LEW JAN TEXTILE CORP.; *U.S. Private*, pg. 2437
LEWMAR INC.—See LCI Industries; *U.S. Public*, pg. 1295
LEWMAR LTD.—See LCI Industries; *U.S. Public*, pg. 1295
LEWMAR MARINE LTD.—See LCI Industries; *U.S. Public*, pg. 1295
LEWMAR NORTH EUROPE LTD.—See LCI Industries; *U.S. Public*, pg. 1295
LEW SERVICE & CONSULTING GMBH—See RWE AG; *Int'l*, pg. 6434
LEWTAN TECHNOLOGIES INC.—See Moody's Corporation; *U.S. Public*, pg. 1468
LEW TELNET GMBH—See RWE AG; *Int'l*, pg. 6434
LEW VERTEILNETZ GMBH—See RWE AG; *Int'l*, pg. 6434
LEXAGENE HOLDINGS INC.; *U.S. Public*, pg. 2440
LEXA INTERNATIONAL CORPORATION; *U.S. Private*, pg. 2440
LEXALYTICS, INC.—See Madison Dearborn Partners, LLC; *U.S. Private*, pg. 2541
LEXARIA BIOSCIENCE CORP.; *Int'l*, pg. 4471
LEX AUTOLEASE LTD.—See Lloyds Banking Group plc; *Int'l*, pg. 4536
LEXCEL SOLUTIONS, INC.—See Fidelity National Infor; *U.S. Public*, pg. 833
LEXCOM TELECOMMUNICATIONS; *U.S. Private*, pg. 2440
LEX DALLAS L.P.—See LXP Industrial Trust; *U.S. Public*, pg. 1349
LEXEDIS LIGHTING GMBH—See Toyoda Gosei Co., Ltd.; *Int'l*, pg. 7861
LEXEL AB—See Schneider Electric SE; *Int'l*, pg. 6628
LEXEL BATTERY (JAPAN) CO., LTD.—See Coslight Technology International Group Limited; *Int'l*, pg. 1810
LEXEL FABRIKA SIA—See Schneider Electric SE; *Int'l*, pg. 6628
LEXEL HOLDINGS (UK) LTD—See Schneider Electric SE; *Int'l*, pg. 6628
LEXEL IMAGING SYSTEMS INC.; *U.S. Private*, pg. 2440
LEX ENGINEERING LTD.—See Quanta Services, Inc.; *U.S. Public*, pg. 1751
LEXEO THERAPEUTICS, INC.; *U.S. Public*, pg. 1309
L-EX EQUIPMENTS TRANSPORTS LOGISTICS—See Axel Johnson Gruppen AB; *Int'l*, pg. 764
LEXIA LEARNING SYSTEMS, LLC—See Veritas Capital Fund Management, LLC; *U.S. Private*, pg. 4361
LEXIA SOLUTIONS GROUP LTD; *Int'l*, pg. 4471
LEXIBOOK S.A; *Int'l*, pg. 4472
LEXI CO., LTD.—See JSR Corp.; *Int'l*, pg. 4014
LEXI-COMP, INC.—See Wolters Kluwer n.v.; *Int'l*, pg. 8444
LEXICON COMMUNICATIONS CORP.; *U.S. Private*, pg. 2440
LEXICON CONSULTING, INC.; *U.S. Private*, pg. 2440
LEXICON, INC.; *U.S. Private*, pg. 2440
LEXICON MARKETING CORPORATION—See Golden Gate Capital Management II, LLC; *U.S. Private*, pg. 1731
LEXICON PHARMACEUTICALS, INC.; *U.S. Public*, pg. 1309
LEXICON PHARMACEUTICALS, INC.—See Lexicon Pharmaceuticals, Inc.; *U.S. Public*, pg. 1309
LEXICON RELOCATION LTD.—See The Suddath Companies; *U.S. Private*, pg. 4124
LEXICON RELOCATION—See The Suddath Companies; *U.S. Private*, pg. 4124
LEXINFINTECH HOLDINGS LTD.; *Int'l*, pg. 4472
LEXINGTON BIOSCIENCES, INC.; *Int'l*, pg. 4472
LEXINGTON CENTER CORPORATION; *U.S. Private*, pg. 2440
LEXINGTON-CJD, LLC—See Lithia Motors, Inc.; *U.S. Public*, pg. 1323
LEXINGTON COMPANY AB; *Int'l*, pg. 4472
LEXINGTON FAMILY PHYSICIANS, LLC—See Quorum Health Corporation; *U.S. Private*, pg. 3330
LEXINGTON FINANCE—See LXP Industrial Trust; *U.S. Public*, pg. 1349
LEXINGTON FURNITURE INDUSTRIES, INC.—See Luolai Lifestyle Technology Co., Ltd.; *Int'l*, pg. 4584
LEXINGTON GOLD LTD.; *Int'l*, pg. 4472

1597

LEXINGTON GROUP, INC.   CORPORATE AFFILIATIONS

LEXINGTON GROUP, INC.; *U.S. Private,* pg. 2440
LEXINGTON HERALD-LEADER—See Chatham Asset Management, LLC; *U.S. Private,* pg. 866
LEXINGTON H-L SERVICES, INC.—See Chatham Asset Management, LLC; *U.S. Private,* pg. 866
LEXINGTON HOMES, INC.—See Cavco Industries, Inc.; *U.S. Public,* pg. 455
LEXINGTON HOSPITAL CORPORATION—See Quorum Health Corporation; *U.S. Private,* pg. 3330
LEXINGTON INSURANCE COMPANY—See American International Group, Inc.; *U.S. Public,* pg. 107
LEXINGTON ISS HOLDINGS—See LXP Industrial Trust; *U.S. Public,* pg. 1349
LEXINGTON JEWELERS EXCHANGE; *U.S. Private,* pg. 2440
LEXINGTON KIDNEY CENTER, LLC—See Nautic Partners, LLC; *U.S. Private,* pg. 2870
LEXINGTON KNOXVILLE LLC—See LXP Industrial Trust; *U.S. Public,* pg. 1349
LEXINGTON LAC LENEXA L.P.—See LXP Industrial Trust; *U.S. Public,* pg. 1349
LEXINGTON MANUFACTURING INC.—See Watkins Associated Industries Inc.; *U.S. Private,* pg. 4455
LEXINGTON MEMORIAL HOSPITAL INC.—See Davidson Health Care, Inc.; *U.S. Private,* pg. 1171
LEXINGTON MINUTEMAN—See Gannett Co., Inc.; *U.S. Public,* pg. 902
LEXINGTON NATIONAL LAND SERVICES, LLC—See Blackstone Inc.; *U.S. Public,* pg. 355
LEXINGTON OLIVE BRANCH MANAGER LLC—See LXP Industrial Trust; *U.S. Public,* pg. 1349
LEXINGTON PARTNERS INC.—See Franklin Resources, Inc.; *U.S. Public,* pg. 883
LEXINGTON PRECISION CORPORATION—See Aurora Capital Group, LLC; *U.S. Private,* pg. 393
LEXINGTON REAL ESTATE INCOME TRUST—See LXP Industrial Trust; *U.S. Public,* pg. 1349
LEXINGTON SURGERY CENTER, LTD.—See UnitedHealth Group Incorporated; *U.S. Public,* pg. 2242
LEXINGTON TROTS BREEDERS ASSOCIATION; *U.S. Private,* pg. 2440
LEXINGTON WEALTH MANAGEMENT; *U.S. Private,* pg. 2440
LEXIN RESOURCES LTD.; *Int'l,* pg. 4472
LEXIPOL, LLC—See Riverside Partners, LLC; *U.S. Private,* pg. 3446
LEXIS CHEMICAL SDN. BHD.—See Luxchem Corporation Berhad; *Int'l,* pg. 4588
LEXISNEXIS ASIA PACIFIC—See RELX plc; *Int'l,* pg. 6267
LEXISNEXIS AUSTRALIA—See RELX plc; *Int'l,* pg. 6267
LEXISNEXIS BENELUX BV—See RELX plc; *Int'l,* pg. 6267
LEXISNEXIS BUSINESS INFORMATION SOLUTIONS SA—See RELX plc; *Int'l,* pg. 6268
LEXISNEXIS CANADA INC.—See RELX plc; *Int'l,* pg. 6267
LEXISNEXIS CHINA - BEIJING—See RELX plc; *Int'l,* pg. 6267
LEXISNEXIS CHINA - SHANGHAI—See RELX plc; *Int'l,* pg. 6267
LEXISNEXIS ENTERPRISE SOLUTIONS—See RELX plc; *Int'l,* pg. 6268
LEXISNEXIS ENTERPRISE SOLUTIONS—See RELX plc; *Int'l,* pg. 6268
LEXISNEXIS GMBH—See RELX plc; *Int'l,* pg. 6267
LEXISNEXIS HONG KONG—See RELX plc; *Int'l,* pg. 6267
LEXISNEXIS INDIA—See RELX plc; *Int'l,* pg. 6267
LEXISNEXIS JAPAN CO., LTD—See RELX plc; *Int'l,* pg. 6267
LEXISNEXIS LEGAL & PROFESSIONAL—See RELX plc; *Int'l,* pg. 6267
LEXISNEXIS MALAYSIA SDN. BHD.—See RELX plc; *Int'l,* pg. 6267
LEXISNEXIS NZ LIMITED—See RELX plc; *Int'l,* pg. 6267
LEXIS-NEXIS PHILIPPINES PTE LTD.—See RELX plc; *Int'l,* pg. 6267
LEXISNEXIS (PTY) LIMITED—See RELX plc; *Int'l,* pg. 6267
LEXISNEXIS RISK SOLUTIONS INC. - DAYTON—See RELX plc; *Int'l,* pg. 6267
LEXISNEXIS RISK SOLUTIONS INC. - MINNEAPOLIS—See RELX plc; *Int'l,* pg. 6267
LEXISNEXIS RISK SOLUTIONS INC. - OKLAHOMA CITY—See RELX plc; *Int'l,* pg. 6267
LEXISNEXIS RISK SOLUTIONS INC.—See RELX plc; *Int'l,* pg. 6267
LEXISNEXIS SA—See RELX plc; *Int'l,* pg. 6268
LEXISNEXIS SINGAPORE—See RELX plc; *Int'l,* pg. 6267
LEXISNEXIS SPECIAL SERVICES INC.—See RELX plc; *Int'l,* pg. 6267
LEXISNEXIS UK—See RELX plc; *Int'l,* pg. 6268
LEXISNEXIS VERLAG ARD ORAC GMBH & CO KG—See RELX plc; *Int'l,* pg. 6268
LEXISNEXIS VITALCHEK NETWORK INC.—See RELX plc; *Int'l,* pg. 6267
LEXIS PUBLIC RELATIONS; *Int'l,* pg. 4472
LEX MACHINA, INC.—See RELX plc; *Int'l,* pg. 6267
LEXMARK CANADA, INC.—See PAG Asia Capital Ltd.; *Int'l,* pg. 5696
LEXMARK CANADA, INC.—See Zhuhai Seine Technology Co., Ltd.; *Int'l,* pg. 8678

LEXMARK CARPET MILLS, INC.—See Tarkett S.A.; *Int'l,* pg. 7463
LEXMARK GOVERNMENT SOLUTIONS, LLC—See PAG Asia Capital Ltd.; *Int'l,* pg. 5696
LEXMARK GOVERNMENT SOLUTIONS, LLC—See Zhuhai Seine Technology Co., Ltd.; *Int'l,* pg. 8678
LEXMARK HANDELSGESELLSCHAFT M.B.H.—See PAG Asia Capital Ltd.; *Int'l,* pg. 5696
LEXMARK HANDELSGESELLSCHAFT M.B.H.—See Zhuhai Seine Technology Co., Ltd.; *Int'l,* pg. 8678
LEXMARK INFORMATION TECHNOLOGIES PRODUCTS TIC. LTD. STI.—See PAG Asia Capital Ltd.; *Int'l,* pg. 5696
LEXMARK INFORMATION TECHNOLOGIES PRODUCTS TIC. LTD. STI.—See Zhuhai Seine Technology Co., Ltd.; *Int'l,* pg. 8678
LEXMARK INTERNATIONAL AFRICA SARL—See PAG Asia Capital Ltd.; *Int'l,* pg. 5696
LEXMARK INTERNATIONAL AFRICA SARL—See Zhuhai Seine Technology Co., Ltd.; *Int'l,* pg. 8678
LEXMARK INTERNATIONAL (AUSTRALIA) PTY LTD.—See PAG Asia Capital Ltd.; *Int'l,* pg. 5696
LEXMARK INTERNATIONAL (AUSTRALIA) PTY LTD.—See Zhuhai Seine Technology Co., Ltd.; *Int'l,* pg. 8678
LEXMARK INTERNATIONAL B.V.—See PAG Asia Capital Ltd.; *Int'l,* pg. 5696
LEXMARK INTERNATIONAL B.V.—See Zhuhai Seine Technology Co., Ltd.; *Int'l,* pg. 8678
LEXMARK INTERNATIONAL CRT D.O.O.—See PAG Asia Capital Ltd.; *Int'l,* pg. 5696
LEXMARK INTERNATIONAL CRT D.O.O.—See Zhuhai Seine Technology Co., Ltd.; *Int'l,* pg. 8678
LEXMARK INTERNATIONAL CZECH S.R.O.—See PAG Asia Capital Ltd.; *Int'l,* pg. 5696
LEXMARK INTERNATIONAL CZECH S.R.O.—See Zhuhai Seine Technology Co., Ltd.; *Int'l,* pg. 8678
LEXMARK INTERNATIONAL, INC.—See PAG Asia Capital Ltd.; *Int'l,* pg. 5696
LEXMARK INTERNATIONAL, INC.—See Zhuhai Seine Technology Co., Ltd.; *Int'l,* pg. 8678
LEXMARK INTERNATIONAL LIMITED—See PAG Asia Capital Ltd.; *Int'l,* pg. 5696
LEXMARK INTERNATIONAL LIMITED—See Zhuhai Seine Technology Co., Ltd.; *Int'l,* pg. 8678
LEXMARK INTERNATIONAL POLSKA SP.Z.O.O.—See PAG Asia Capital Ltd.; *Int'l,* pg. 5696
LEXMARK INTERNATIONAL POLSKA SP.Z.O.O.—See Zhuhai Seine Technology Co., Ltd.; *Int'l,* pg. 8678
LEXMARK INTERNATIONAL PUERTO RICO—See PAG Asia Capital Ltd.; *Int'l,* pg. 5696
LEXMARK INTERNATIONAL PUERTO RICO—See Zhuhai Seine Technology Co., Ltd.; *Int'l,* pg. 8678
LEXMARK INTERNATIONAL RS D.O.O.—See PAG Asia Capital Ltd.; *Int'l,* pg. 5696
LEXMARK INTERNATIONAL RS D.O.O.—See Zhuhai Seine Technology Co., Ltd.; *Int'l,* pg. 8678
LEXMARK INTERNATIONAL SASU—See PAG Asia Capital Ltd.; *Int'l,* pg. 5696
LEXMARK INTERNATIONAL SASU—See Zhuhai Seine Technology Co., Ltd.; *Int'l,* pg. 8678
LEXMARK INTERNATIONAL (SINGAPORE) PTE LTD.—See PAG Asia Capital Ltd.; *Int'l,* pg. 5696
LEXMARK INTERNATIONAL (SINGAPORE) PTE LTD.—See Zhuhai Seine Technology Co., Ltd.; *Int'l,* pg. 8678
LEXMARK INTERNATIONAL TECHNOLOGY S.A.—See PAG Asia Capital Ltd.; *Int'l,* pg. 5697
LEXMARK INTERNATIONAL TECHNOLOGY S.A.—See Zhuhai Seine Technology Co., Ltd.; *Int'l,* pg. 8678
LEXMARK MAGYARORSZAG KFT—See PAG Asia Capital Ltd.; *Int'l,* pg. 5697
LEXMARK MAGYARORSZAG KFT—See Zhuhai Seine Technology Co., Ltd.; *Int'l,* pg. 8678
LEXMARK RESEARCH & DEVELOPMENT CORPORATION—See PAG Asia Capital Ltd.; *Int'l,* pg. 5697
LEXMARK RESEARCH & DEVELOPMENT CORPORATION—See Zhuhai Seine Technology Co., Ltd.; *Int'l,* pg. 8678
LEXMARK SCHWEIZ AG—See PAG Asia Capital Ltd.; *Int'l,* pg. 5697
LEXMARK SCHWEIZ AG—See Zhuhai Seine Technology Co., Ltd.; *Int'l,* pg. 8678
LEXMARK SPAIN SL—See PAG Asia Capital Ltd.; *Int'l,* pg. 5697
LEXMARK SPAIN SL—See Zhuhai Seine Technology Co., Ltd.; *Int'l,* pg. 8678
LEXNET LLC—See Visual Edge Technology, Inc.; *U.S. Private,* pg. 4404
LEX NIMBLE SOLUTIONS LTD.; *Int'l,* pg. 4471
LEXOLUTION, LLC—See JLL Partners, LLC; *U.S. Private,* pg. 2213
LEXOS SOLUCAO EM TECNOLOGIA LTDA.—See TOTVS S.A.; *Int'l,* pg. 7846
LEX PHOENIX L.P.—See LXP Industrial Trust; *U.S. Public,* pg. 1349
LEX PRODUCTS CORP.; *U.S. Private,* pg. 2440

LEX PROPERTIES INC.—See Davidson Health Care, Inc.; *U.S. Private,* pg. 1171
LEXSTON LIFE SCIENCES CORP.; *Int'l,* pg. 4472
LEXTAR ELECTRONICS (CHUZHOU) CORP.—See Ennostar Inc.; *Int'l,* pg. 2444
LEXTAR ELECTRONICS CORP.—See Ennostar Inc.; *Int'l,* pg. 2444
LEXTAR ELECTRONICS (SUZHOU) CO., LTD.—See Ennostar Inc.; *Int'l,* pg. 2444
LEXTAR ELECTRONICS (XIAMEN) CORP.—See Ennostar Inc.; *Int'l,* pg. 2444
LEX TERRAE, LTD.—See Old Republic International Corporation; *U.S. Public,* pg. 1569
LEX TERRAE NATIONAL TITLE SERVICES, INC.—See Old Republic International Corporation; *U.S. Public,* pg. 1569
LEXUS DIVISION—See Toyota Motor Corporation; *Int'l,* pg. 7874
LEXUS GRANITO (INDIA) LTD.; *Int'l,* pg. 4472
LEXUS MANILA, INC.—See GT Capital Holdings, Inc.; *Int'l,* pg. 3151
LEXUS OF BELLEVUE—See Michael O'Brien Enterprises, Inc.; *U.S. Private,* pg. 2698
LEXUS OF CERRITOS LIMITED PARTNERSHIP—See AutoNation, Inc.; *U.S. Public,* pg. 236
LEXUS OF MAPLEWOOD—See North American Automotive Services, Inc.; *U.S. Private,* pg. 2940
LEXUS OF NORTH MIAMI; *U.S. Private,* pg. 2440
LEXUS OF SACRAMENTO—See RPM Management Inc.; *U.S. Private,* pg. 3495
LEXUS OF TACOMA—See Michael O'Brien Enterprises, Inc.; *U.S. Private,* pg. 2698
LEXUS OF THOUSAND OAKS; *U.S. Private,* pg. 2441
LEXUS OF TOLEDO; *U.S. Private,* pg. 2441
LEXUS OF VALENCIA; *U.S. Private,* pg. 2441
LEXY ENROBES SAS—See VINCI S.A.; *Int'l,* pg. 8223
LEXYL TRAVEL TECHNOLOGIES LLC; *U.S. Private,* pg. 2441
LEYARD (EUROPE) CO., LTD.—See Leyard Optoelectronic Co., Ltd.; *Int'l,* pg. 4472
LEYARD (JAPAN) CO., LTD.—See Leyard Optoelectronic Co., Ltd.; *Int'l,* pg. 4472
LEYARD OPTOELECTRONIC CO., LTD.; *Int'l,* pg. 4472
LEYBOLD DO BRASIL LTDA.—See Atlas Copco AB; *Int'l,* pg. 683
LEYBOLD FRANCE SAS—See Atlas Copco AB; *Int'l,* pg. 683
LEYBOLD FRANCE S.A.S.—See Atlas Copco AB; *Int'l,* pg. 683
LEYBOLD HISPÁNICA, S.A.—See Atlas Copco AB; *Int'l,* pg. 683
LEYBOLD HISPANICA S.A.—See Atlas Copco AB; *Int'l,* pg. 683
LEYBOLD INDIA PVT LTD.—See Atlas Copco AB; *Int'l,* pg. 683
LEYBOLD IRELAND—See Atlas Copco AB; *Int'l,* pg. 683
LEYBOLD ITALIA S.R.L.—See Atlas Copco AB; *Int'l,* pg. 683
LEYBOLD ITALIA SRL—See Atlas Copco AB; *Int'l,* pg. 683
LEYBOLD JAPAN CO., LTD.—See Atlas Copco AB; *Int'l,* pg. 683
LEYBOLD JAPAN CO., LTD.—See Atlas Copco AB; *Int'l,* pg. 683
LEYBOLD KOREA LTD.—See Atlas Copco AB; *Int'l,* pg. 683
LEYBOLD NEDERLAND B.V.—See Atlas Copco AB; *Int'l,* pg. 683
LEYBOLD OPTICS GMBH—See Buhler AG; *Int'l,* pg. 1212
LEYBOLD SCHWEIZ AG—See Atlas Copco AB; *Int'l,* pg. 683
LEYBOLD SINGAPORE PTE LTD—See Atlas Copco AB; *Int'l,* pg. 683
LEYBOLD TAIWAN LTD—See Atlas Copco AB; *Int'l,* pg. 683
LEYBOLD (TIANJIN) INTERNATIONAL TRADE CO., LTD.—See Atlas Copco AB; *Int'l,* pg. 683
LEYBOLD UK LTD.—See Atlas Copco AB; *Int'l,* pg. 683
LEYBOLD USA INC.—See Atlas Copco AB; *Int'l,* pg. 683
LEY CHOON GROUP HOLDINGS LIMITED; *Int'l,* pg. 4472
LEYLAND TRUCKS LIMITED—See PACCAR Inc.; *U.S. Public,* pg. 1630
LEYOU NEW ENERGY MATERIALS (WUXI) CO., LTD.—See LG Chem Ltd.; *Int'l,* pg. 4474
LEYOU TECHNOLOGIES HOLDINGS LIMITED—See Tencent Holdings Limited; *Int'l,* pg. 7559
LEYSEN JEWELRY INC.; *Int'l,* pg. 4472
LEZAOLA THOMPSON INSURANCE, INC.—See Thompson Insurance Group; *U.S. Private,* pg. 4160
LEZIER TRANSPORTS; *Int'l,* pg. 4472
LEZZER LUMBER, INC.; *U.S. Private,* pg. 2441
LEZZER LUMBER—See Lezzer Lumber, Inc.; *U.S. Private,* pg. 2441
LF ACCESSORIES GROUP LLC—See Li & Fung Limited; *Int'l,* pg. 4480
LFA CELTIC LIMITED—See Compagnie des Levures Lesaffre SA; *Int'l,* pg. 1738
LFA GLOBAL PTE. LTD.—See Mitani Corporation; *Int'l,* pg. 4924

COMPANY NAME INDEX

LFA MACHINES DFW, LLC—See Operio Group, LLC; *U.S. Private*, pg. 3032
LFA MACHINES OXFORD LTD.—See Operio Group, LLC; *U.S. Private*, pg. 3032
LF ASIA INVESTMENTS, LTD.—See King Lun Holdings Limited; *Int'l*, pg. 4169
LF ASIA (MALAYSIA) SDN. BHD.—See Li & Fung Limited; *Int'l*, pg. 4479
LFB BIOMANUFACTURING SASU—See LFB S.A.; *Int'l*, pg. 4473
LF BEAUTY LIMITED—See Li & Fung Limited; *Int'l*, pg. 4479
LF BEAUTY (UK) LIMITED—See Li & Fung Limited; *Int'l*, pg. 4479
LFB HEMODERIVADOS E BIOTECNOLOGIA LTDA.—See LFB S.A.; *Int'l*, pg. 4473
LFB LILLE—See LFB S.A.; *Int'l*, pg. 4473
LFB S.A.; *Int'l*, pg. 4473
LFB USA INC.—See LFB S.A.; *Int'l*, pg. 4473
LF CENTENNIAL PTE. LTD.—See Li & Fung Limited; *Int'l*, pg. 4479
LF CENTENNIAL SERVICES (HONG KONG) LIMITED—See Li & Fung Limited; *Int'l*, pg. 4479
L & F CO., LTD. - GUJI FACTORY—See L & F Co.; *Int'l*, pg. 4369
L & F CO., LTD.; *Int'l*, pg. 4369
L & F CO., LTD. - WAEGWAN FACTORY—See L & F Co., Ltd.; *Int'l*, pg. 4369
LF CORP.; *Int'l*, pg. 4472
L & F DISTRIBUTORS LTD.; *U.S. Private*, pg. 2361
L & F DISTRIBUTORS—See L & F Distributors Ltd.; *U.S. Private*, pg. 2361
LFD, LLC; *U.S. Private*, pg. 2441
L.F. DRISCOLL COMPANY LLC—See STO Building Group Inc.; *U.S. Private*, pg. 3813
LFE CORPORATION BERHAD; *Int'l*, pg. 4473
LFE ENGINEERING (JB) SDN. BHD.—See LFE Corporation Berhad; *Int'l*, pg. 4473
LFE ENGINEERING SDN. BHD.—See LFE Corporation Berhad; *Int'l*, pg. 4473
L. FERIOZZI CONCRETE COMPANY; *U.S. Private*, pg. 2364
LF FINANCE (SUISSE) S.A.—See Banque Libano-Francaise S.A.L.; *Int'l*, pg. 854
LF GEORGE HOLDINGS, INC.; *U.S. Private*, pg. 2441
L.F. GEORGE INC.; *U.S. Private*, pg. 2365
LFG INVESTMENT HOLDINGS LIMITED; *Int'l*, pg. 4473
LFG SPECIALTIES, L.L.C.—See The Shaw Group Inc.; *U.S. Private*, pg. 4117
LFI FORT PIERCE INC.; *U.S. Private*, pg. 2441
LFI GROUP PTY. LTD.—See Liberty Financial Group Limited; *Int'l*, pg. 4484
LF-INTERNATIONAL HOLDINGS LIMITED—See Lifestyle Global Enterprise, Inc.; *Int'l*, pg. 4495
L. FISHMAN & SON INC.; *U.S. Private*, pg. 2364
LFKF, LLC—See Lithia Motors, Inc.; *U.S. Public*, pg. 1323
LFL MADAGASCAR SA—See Livestock Feed Limited; *Int'l*, pg. 4531
LF LOGISTICS (BANGLADESH) LIMITED—See Li & Fung Limited; *Int'l*, pg. 4479
LF LOGISTICS (CAMBODIA) LIMITED—See Li & Fung Limited; *Int'l*, pg. 4479
LF LOGISTICS (CHINA) CO., LTD.—See Li & Fung Limited; *Int'l*, pg. 4479
LF LOGISTICS (HONG KONG) LIMITED—See A.P. Moller-Maersk A/S; *Int'l*, pg. 26
LF LOGISTICS (INDIA) PRIVATE LIMITED—See Li & Fung Limited; *Int'l*, pg. 4479
LF LOGISTICS JAPAN LIMITED—See Li & Fung Limited; *Int'l*, pg. 4480
LF LOGISTICS KOREA LIMITED—See Li & Fung Limited; *Int'l*, pg. 4480
LF LOGISTICS LIMITED—See Li & Fung Limited; *Int'l*, pg. 4479
LF LOGISTICS PAKISTAN (PRIVATE) LIMITED—See Li & Fung Limited; *Int'l*, pg. 4480
LF LOGISTICS SERVICES PTE. LTD.—See Li & Fung Limited; *Int'l*, pg. 4480
LF LOGISTICS (TAIWAN) LIMITED—See Li & Fung Limited; *Int'l*, pg. 4479
LF LOGISTICS (UK) LIMITED—See Li & Fung Limited; *Int'l*, pg. 4479
LF LOGISTICS USA INC.—See Li & Fung Limited; *Int'l*, pg. 4480
LF LOGISTICS (VIETNAM) COMPANY LIMITED—See Li & Fung Limited; *Int'l*, pg. 4479
LFMA AUSTRALIA PTY. LTD.—See Xiamen C&D Inc.; *Int'l*, pg. 8523
L.F. MANUFACTURING INC.; *U.S. Private*, pg. 2365
LFM CAPITAL LLC; *U.S. Private*, pg. 2441
LFM PROPERTIES CORPORATION; *Int'l*, pg. 4473
LFN LIMITED—See Lifestyle Global Enterprise, Inc.; *Int'l*, pg. 4495
LFNT RESOURCES CORP.; *Int'l*, pg. 4473
LFOUNDR S.R.L.; *Int'l*, pg. 4473
LFOUNDRY S.R.L. ZWEIGNIEDERLASSUNG LANDSHUT; *Int'l*, pg. 4473
LFP BROADCASTING, LLC—See L.F.P., Inc.; *U.S. Private*, pg. 2365

LF (PHILIPPINES), INC.—See Li & Fung Limited; *Int'l*, pg. 4479
L.F.P., INC.; *U.S. Private*, pg. 2365
LF-SHANGHAI TRADING LIMITED—See Lifestyle Global Enterprise, Inc.; *Int'l*, pg. 4495
LFS INC.—See Trident Seafoods Corporation; *U.S. Private*, pg. 4230
L.F. SPORTSWEAR INC.; *U.S. Private*, pg. 2365
LFTD PARTNERS INC.; *U.S. Public*, pg. 1309
LF USA INC.—See Li & Fung Limited; *Int'l*, pg. 4480
LG2; *Int'l*, pg. 4477
LGA HOLDINGS, INC.; *U.S. Public*, pg. 1309
LGAI CHILE, S.A.—See I Squared Capital Advisors (US) LLC; *U.S. Private*, pg. 2023
LGAI CHILE, S.A.—See TDR Capital LLP; *Int'l*, pg. 7492
LGA INTERCERT ZERTIFIZIERUNGSGESELLSCHAFT MBH—See TUV Rheinland Berlin-Brandenburg Pfalz e.V.; *Int'l*, pg. 7982
LGAI TECHNOLOGICAL, CENTER, S.A.—See I Squared Capital Advisors (US) LLC; *U.S. Private*, pg. 2023
LGAI TECHNOLOGICAL, CENTER, S.A.—See TDR Capital LLP; *Int'l*, pg. 7492
LG ALINA ELECTRONICS—See LG Corp.; *Int'l*, pg. 4474
L-GAM ADVISERS LLP; *Int'l*, pg. 4381
LGAM PRIVATE CREDIT LLC; *U.S. Private*, pg. 2441
LGANG OPTRONICS TECHNOLOGY CO., LTD.—See The Place Holdings Limited; *Int'l*, pg. 7673
L.G. BALAKRISHNAN & BROS. LTD.; *Int'l*, pg. 4386
LGB FORGE LIMITED—See L.G. Balakrishnan & Bros. Ltd.; *Int'l*, pg. 4386
LGB GMBH—See Systemair AB; *Int'l*, pg. 7391
LGBTQ LOYALTY HOLDINGS, INC.; *U.S. Public*, pg. 1309
LGC ASSOCIATES, LLC; *U.S. Private*, pg. 2441
LGC BIOSEARCH TECHNOLOGIES—See KKR & Co. Inc.; *U.S. Public*, pg. 1258
LG CHEM AUSTRALIA PTY. LTD.—See LG Chem Ltd.; *Int'l*, pg. 4474
LG CHEM BRASIL, LTD.—See LG Chem Ltd.; *Int'l*, pg. 4474
LG CHEM CHINA INVESTMENT CO., LTD.—See LG Chem Ltd.; *Int'l*, pg. 4474
LG CHEM (CHONGQING) ENGINEERING PLASTICS CO., LTD.—See LG Chem Ltd.; *Int'l*, pg. 4473
LG CHEM DISPLAY MATERIALS (BEIJING) CO., LTD.—See LG Chem Ltd.; *Int'l*, pg. 4474
LG CHEM EUROPE GMBH—See LG Chem Ltd.; *Int'l*, pg. 4474
LG CHEM (GUANGZHOU) INFORMATION & ELECTRONICS MATERIALS CO., LTD.—See LG Chem Ltd.; *Int'l*, pg. 4473
LG CHEM HAI PHONG VIETNAM CO., LTD.—See LG Chem Ltd.; *Int'l*, pg. 4474
LG CHEM (HUIZHOU) PETROCHEMICAL CO., LTD.—See LG Chem Ltd.; *Int'l*, pg. 4473
LG CHEMICAL AMERICA INC.—See LG Chem Ltd.; *Int'l*, pg. 4474
LG CHEMICAL CO., LTD.—See LG Chem Ltd.; *Int'l*, pg. 4474
LG CHEMICAL (GUANGZHOU) ENGINEERING PLASTICS CO., LTD.—See LG Chem Ltd.; *Int'l*, pg. 4474
LG CHEMICAL INDIA PRIVATE LTD.—See LG Chem Ltd.; *Int'l*, pg. 4474
LG CHEM JAPAN CO., LTD.—See LG Chem Ltd.; *Int'l*, pg. 4474
LG CHEM LTD.; *Int'l*, pg. 4473
LG CHEM MALAYSIA SDN. BHD.—See LG Chem Ltd.; *Int'l*, pg. 4474
LG CHEM MEXICO S.A. DE C.V.—See LG Chem Ltd.; *Int'l*, pg. 4474
LG CHEM MICHIGAN INC.—See LG Corp.; *Int'l*, pg. 4475
LG CHEM NANJING ENERGY SOLUTION CO., LTD.—See LG Chem Ltd.; *Int'l*, pg. 4474
LG CHEM (NANJING) INFORMATION & ELECTRONICS MATERIALS CO., LTD.—See LG Chem Ltd.; *Int'l*, pg. 4473
LG CHEM POLAND SP. Z O.O.—See LG Chem Ltd.; *Int'l*, pg. 4474
LG CHEM (TAIWAN), LTD.—See LG Chem Ltd.; *Int'l*, pg. 4473
LG CHEM (TIANJIN) ENGINEERING PLASTICS CO., LTD.—See LG Chem Ltd.; *Int'l*, pg. 4474
LG CHEM TK KIMYA SANAYI VE TIC. LTD. STI.—See LG Chem Ltd.; *Int'l*, pg. 4474
LG CHEM WROCLAW ENERGY SP. Z O.O.—See LG Chem Ltd.; *Int'l*, pg. 4474
LGC LIMITED—See KKR & Co. Inc.; *U.S. Public*, pg. 1258
LG CNS CHINA CO., LTD.—See LG Corp.; *Int'l*, pg. 4474
LG CNS EUROPE B.V.—See LG Corp.; *Int'l*, pg. 4474
LG CNS INDIA PVT.—See LG Corp.; *Int'l*, pg. 4474
LG CNS INDIA U.K.—See LG Corp.; *Int'l*, pg. 4474
LG CNS JAPAN CO.—See LG Corp.; *Int'l*, pg. 4474
LG CNS MIDDLE EAST—See LG Corp.; *Int'l*, pg. 4474
LG CNS—See LG Corp.; *Int'l*, pg. 4474
LG CORP.; *Int'l*, pg. 4474
LG PETROCHEMICAL INDIA PRIVATE LTD.—See LG Chem Ltd.; *Int'l*, pg. 4474
LGC PROMOCHEM INDIA PRIVATE LTD.—See Thermo Fisher Scientific Inc.; *U.S. Public*, pg. 2146

LGC WIRELESS COMMUNICATION (SHENZHEN) CO. LTD.—See TE Connectivity Ltd.; *Int'l*, pg. 7495
LGCY POWER, LLC; *U.S. Private*, pg. 2441
LG & DE LIMITED; *Int'l*, pg. 4473
LG DEVELOPMENT GROUP, LLC; *U.S. Private*, pg. 2441
LG DISPLAY GERMANY GMBH—See LG Corp.; *Int'l*, pg. 4475
LG DISPLAY CO., LTD.—See LG Corp.; *Int'l*, pg. 4475
LG DISPLAY JAPAN CO., LTD—See LG Corp.; *Int'l*, pg. 4475
LG DISPLAY SHANGHAI CO., LTD.—See LG Corp.; *Int'l*, pg. 4475
LG DISPLAY SHENZHEN CO., LTD.—See LG Corp.; *Int'l*, pg. 4475
LG DISPLAY SINGAPORE PTE. LTD.—See LG Corp.; *Int'l*, pg. 4475
LG DISPLAY TAIWAN CO., LTD.—See LG Corp.; *Int'l*, pg. 4475
LG DISPLAY YANTAI CO., LTD.—See LG Corp.; *Int'l*, pg. 4475
LG DOW POLYCARBONATE LIMITED—See LG Chem Ltd.; *Int'l*, pg. 4474
LG&E AND KU ENERGY LLC—See PPL Corporation; *U.S. Public*, pg. 1711
LGE COMMUNITY CREDIT UNION; *U.S. Private*, pg. 2441
LG ECONOMIC RESEARCH INSTITUTE—See LG Corp.; *Int'l*, pg. 4475
LG ELECTRONICS ALABAMA, INC.—See LG Corp.; *Int'l*, pg. 4476
LG ELECTRONICS ARGENTINA S.A.—See LG Corp.; *Int'l*, pg. 4475
LG ELECTRONICS AUSTRALIA PTY LTD—See LG Corp.; *Int'l*, pg. 4475
LG ELECTRONICS BENELUX SALES BV—See LG Corp.; *Int'l*, pg. 4475
LG ELECTRONICS CANADA, INC.—See LG Corp.; *Int'l*, pg. 4475
LG ELECTRONICS COLOMBIA LTDA.—See LG Corp.; *Int'l*, pg. 4475
LG ELECTRONICS CZ, S.R.O.—See LG Corp.; *Int'l*, pg. 4475
LG ELECTRONICS DEUTSCHLAND GMBH—See LG Corp.; *Int'l*, pg. 4475
LG ELECTRONICS EGYPT S.A.E.—See LG Corp.; *Int'l*, pg. 4475
LG ELECTRONICS ESPANA S.A.—See LG Corp.; *Int'l*, pg. 4475
LG ELECTRONICS EUROPEAN LOGISTICS & SERVICES B.V.—See LG Corp.; *Int'l*, pg. 4475
LG ELECTRONICS EUROPEAN SHARED SERVICE CENTER B.V.—See LG Corp.; *Int'l*, pg. 4475
LG ELECTRONICS FRANCE S.A.R.L.—See LG Corp.; *Int'l*, pg. 4475
LG ELECTRONICS GULF FZE—See LG Corp.; *Int'l*, pg. 4475
LG ELECTRONICS (HANGZHOU) RECORDING MEDIA CO., LTD.—See LG Corp.; *Int'l*, pg. 4475
LG ELECTRONICS HELLAS S.A.—See LG Corp.; *Int'l*, pg. 4475
LG ELECTRONICS HK LTD.—See LG Corp.; *Int'l*, pg. 4475
LG ELECTRONICS, INC. POLAND—See LG Corp.; *Int'l*, pg. 4476
LG ELECTRONICS, INC.—See LG Corp.; *Int'l*, pg. 4475
LG ELECTRONICS INDIA PVT. LTD.—See LG Corp.; *Int'l*, pg. 4475
LG ELECTRONICS ITALIA S.P.A—See LG Corp.; *Int'l*, pg. 4475
LG ELECTRONICS JAPAN—See LG Corp.; *Int'l*, pg. 4475
LG ELECTRONICS (KUNSHAN) COMPUTER CO., LTD—See LG Corp.; *Int'l*, pg. 4475
LG ELECTRONICS LATVIA, LLC—See LG Corp.; *Int'l*, pg. 4475
LG ELECTRONICS MAGYAR KFT—See LG Corp.; *Int'l*, pg. 4475
LG ELECTRONICS MEXICO S.A. DE C.V—See LG Corp.; *Int'l*, pg. 4475
LG ELECTRONICS MLAWA SP. Z O.O.—See LG Corp.; *Int'l*, pg. 4475
LG ELECTRONICS MONTERREY MEXICO S.A. DE C.V.—See LG Corp.; *Int'l*, pg. 4475
LG ELECTRONICS MOROCCO S.A.R.L.—See LG Corp.; *Int'l*, pg. 4476
LG ELECTRONICS NORDIC AB—See LG Corp.; *Int'l*, pg. 4476
LG ELECTRONICS, PANAMA S.A.—See LG Corp.; *Int'l*, pg. 4476
LG ELECTRONICS PERU S.A.—See LG Corp.; *Int'l*, pg. 4476
LG ELECTRONICS PHILIPPINES, INC.—See LG Corp.; *Int'l*, pg. 4476
LG ELECTRONICS PORTUGAL S.A.—See LG Corp.; *Int'l*, pg. 4476
LG ELECTRONICS QINHUANGDAO INC—See LG Corp.; *Int'l*, pg. 4476
LG ELECTRONICS RUS, LLC—See LG Corp.; *Int'l*, pg. 4476

LGE COMMUNITY CREDIT UNION — CORPORATE AFFILIATIONS

LG ELECTRONICS S.A. (PTY) LTD.—See LG Corp.; *Int'l*, pg. 4476
LG ELECTRONICS SINGAPORE PTE LTD—See LG Corp.; *Int'l*, pg. 4476
LG ELECTRONICS TAIWAN TAIPEI CO., LTD—See LG Corp.; *Int'l*, pg. 4476
LG ELECTRONICS (THAILAND) CO., LTD.—See LG Corp.; *Int'l*, pg. 4475
LG ELECTRONICS TICARET A.S.—See LG Corp.; *Int'l*, pg. 4476
LG ELECTRONICS UKRAINE INC—See LG Corp.; *Int'l*, pg. 4476
LG ELECTRONICS UNITED KINGDOM LTD.—See LG Corp.; *Int'l*, pg. 4476
LG ELECTRONICS U.S.A., INC.—See LG Corp.; *Int'l*, pg. 4476
LG ELECTRONICS VENEZUELA S.A.—See LG Corp.; *Int'l*, pg. 4476
LG ELECTRONICS VIETNAM CO., LTD—See LG Corp.; *Int'l*, pg. 4476
LG ELECTRONICS WROCLAW SP. Z O.O.—See LG Corp.; *Int'l*, pg. 4476
LG ENERGY SOLUTION CO., LTD.—See LG Chem Ltd.; *Int'l*, pg. 4474
L.G. EVERIST INC. - MOUNTAIN DIVISION—See L.G. Everist Inc.; *U.S. Private*, pg. 2366
L.G. EVERIST INC.; *U.S. Private*, pg. 2365
LG&EW INC.—See create restaurants holdings inc.; *Int'l*, pg. 1832
L & G FOREST PRODUCTS LTD.—See Grafton Group plc; *Int'l*, pg. 3051
L.G. GRAPHITE S.R.L.—See Ibiden Co., Ltd.; *Int'l*, pg. 3576
LG HARRIS & CO. LTD.—See Orkla ASA; *Int'l*, pg. 5637
LG HELLOVISION CORP.—See LG Uplus Corp.; *Int'l*, pg. 4477
L.G. HETAGER DRILLING, INC.—See OceanSound Partners, LP; *U.S. Private*, pg. 2991
LG HITACHI LTD.—See Hitachi, Ltd.; *Int'l*, pg. 3423
LG HOUSEHOLD & HEALTH CARE AMERICA INC.—See LG Corp.; *Int'l*, pg. 4476
LG HOUSEHOLD & HEALTH CARE LTD.—See LG Corp.; *Int'l*, pg. 4476
LG HOUSEHOLD & HEALTH CARE (TAIWAN), LTD.—See LG Corp.; *Int'l*, pg. 4476
LG HOUSEHOLD & HEALTH CARE TRADING (SHANGHAI) CO., LTD—See LG Corp.; *Int'l*, pg. 4476
LGI DEVELOPMENT; *U.S. Private*, pg. 2441
LGI HOMES - ARIZONA, LLC—See LGI Homes, Inc.; *U.S. Public*, pg. 1310
LGI HOMES AVONDALE, LLC—See LGI Homes, Inc.; *U.S. Public*, pg. 1310
LGI HOMES AZ SALES, LLC—See LGI Homes, Inc.; *U.S. Public*, pg. 1310
LGI HOMES - DEER CREEK, LLC—See LGI Homes, Inc.; *U.S. Public*, pg. 1310
LGI HOMES - E SAN ANTONIO, LLC—See LGI Homes, Inc.; *U.S. Public*, pg. 1310
LGI HOMES - FLORIDA, LLC—See LGI Homes, Inc.; *U.S. Public*, pg. 1310
LGI HOMES - FW, LLC—See LGI Homes, Inc.; *U.S. Public*, pg. 1310
LGI HOMES GROUP, LLC—See LGI Homes, Inc.; *U.S. Public*, pg. 1310
LGI HOMES, INC.; *U.S. Public*, pg. 1309
LGI HOMES - LUCKEY RANCH, LLC—See LGI Homes, Inc.; *U.S. Public*, pg. 1310
LGI HOMES - MAPLE PARK, LLC—See LGI Homes, Inc.; *U.S. Public*, pg. 1310
LGI HOMES - NC, LLC—See LGI Homes, Inc.; *U.S. Public*, pg. 1310
LGI HOMES - OAK HOLLOW, LLC—See LGI Homes, Inc.; *U.S. Public*, pg. 1310
LGI HOMES - PRESIDENTIAL GLEN, LLC—See LGI Homes, Inc.; *U.S. Public*, pg. 1310
LGI HOMES REALTY LLC—See LGI Homes, Inc.; *U.S. Public*, pg. 1310
LGI HOMES - SC, LLC—See LGI Homes, Inc.; *U.S. Public*, pg. 1310
LGI HOMES - SONTERRA, LLC—See LGI Homes, Inc.; *U.S. Public*, pg. 1310
LGI HOMES - STERLING LAKES PARTNERS, LLC—See LGI Homes, Inc.; *U.S. Public*, pg. 1310
LGI HOMES - WINDMILL FARMS, LLC—See LGI Homes, Inc.; *U.S. Public*, pg. 1310
LGI LIMITED; *Int'l*, pg. 4477
LGI LOGISTICS GROUP INTERNATIONAL GMBH—See Carl Bennet AB; *Int'l*, pg. 1331
LGI LOGISTIKZENTRUM IM GUTERVERKEHRSZENTRUM INGOLSTADT BETREIBERGESELLSCHAFT MBH—See Porsche Automobil Holding SE; *Int'l*, pg. 5929
LGI NETWORK—See The NPD Group, Inc.; *U.S. Private*, pg. 4085
LG INFOCOMM U.S.A., INC.—See LG Corp.; *Int'l*, pg. 4476
LG INNOTEK CO., LTD.—See LG Corp.; *Int'l*, pg. 4476
LG INNOTEK HUIZHOU INC.—See LG Corp.; *Int'l*, pg. 4476

LG INNOTEK YANTAI CO., LTD.—See LG Corp.; *Int'l*, pg. 4476
LG INTERNATIONAL (AMERICA), INC.—See LG Corp.; *Int'l*, pg. 4477
LG INTERNATIONAL (CHINA) CORP.—See LG Corp.; *Int'l*, pg. 4477
LG INTERNATIONAL CORP. DEUTSCHLAND GMBH—See LG Corp.; *Int'l*, pg. 4477
LG INTERNATIONAL CORP. HO CHI MINH CITY OFFICE—See LG Corp.; *Int'l*, pg. 4477
LG INTERNATIONAL CORP.—See LG Corp.; *Int'l*, pg. 4477
LG INTERNATIONAL CORP.—See LG Corp.; *Int'l*, pg. 4477
LG INTERNATIONAL CORP.—See LG Corp.; *Int'l*, pg. 4477
LG INTERNATIONAL DO BRAZIL LTDA—See LG Corp.; *Int'l*, pg. 4477
LG INTERNATIONAL JAPAN LTD.—See LG Corp.; *Int'l*, pg. 4477
LG INTERNATIONAL (SINGAPORE) PTE., LTD.—See LG Corp.; *Int'l*, pg. 4477
L. G. JORDAN OIL CO., INC.; *U.S. Private*, pg. 2364
LGL GERMANY GMBH—See Lennox International Inc.; *U.S. Public*, pg. 1307
THE LGL GROUP, INC.; *U.S. Public*, pg. 2109
LG LIFE SCIENCES (BEIJING) CO., LTD.—See LG Chem Ltd.; *Int'l*, pg. 4474
LG LIFE SCIENCES INDIA PVT. LTD.—See LG Chem Ltd.; *Int'l*, pg. 4474
LG LIFE SCIENCES (THAILAND) LTD.—See LG Chem Ltd.; *Int'l*, pg. 4474
LGL RESOURCES CI SA—See Newmont Corporation; *U.S. Public*, pg. 1517
LGM BELGIUM SPRL—See LGM; *Int'l*, pg. 4477
LGM ENTERPRISES LLC—See flyExclusive, Inc.; *U.S. Public*, pg. 861
LG MICRON (FUJIAN) ELECTRONICS CO., LTD.—See LG Corp.; *Int'l*, pg. 4476
LG MITR ELECTRONICS CO., LTD.—See LG Corp.; *Int'l*, pg. 4476
LG MMA CORP.—See Sumitomo Chemical Company, Limited; *Int'l*, pg. 7264
LGMS BERHAD; *Int'l*, pg. 4477
LGM; *Int'l*, pg. 4477
LG NANOH2O, INC.—See LG Chem Ltd.; *Int'l*, pg. 4474
LG N-SYS INC.—See LG Corp.; *Int'l*, pg. 4474
LGPAC, INC.—See Lithia Motors, Inc.; *U.S. Public*, pg. 1323
LG PHILIPS DISPLAY USA INC—See Koninklijke Philips N.V.; *Int'l*, pg. 4269
L.G. PIKE CONSTRUCTION CO.; *U.S. Private*, pg. 2366
LG POLYMERS INDIA PVT. LTD.—See LG Chem Ltd.; *Int'l*, pg. 4474
LGP OPERATIONS LLC—See CrossAmerica Partners LP; *U.S. Public*, pg. 596
LG SEEDS—See Groupe Limagrain Holding SA; *Int'l*, pg. 3108
LG SEEDS—See KWS SAAT SE & Co. KGaA; *Int'l*, pg. 4352
LGS GROUP INC—See International Business Machines Corporation; *U.S. Public*, pg. 1146
LG SILTRON - FRANCE—See LG Corp.; *Int'l*, pg. 4476
LGS INDUSTRIES, INC.; *U.S. Private*, pg. 2441
LGS INNOVATIONS LLC—See CACI International Inc.; *U.S. Public*, pg. 418
LG SOFT INDIA PRIVATE LIMITED—See LG Corp.; *Int'l*, pg. 4476
LG SPORTS—See LG Corp.; *Int'l*, pg. 4476
LGS SPECIALTY SALES LTD.; *U.S. Private*, pg. 2441
LGSTX DISTRIBUTION SERVICES, INC.—See Air Transport Services Group, Inc.; *U.S. Public*, pg. 67
LGSTX SERVICES, INC.—See Air Transport Services Group, Inc.; *U.S. Public*, pg. 67
LGT BANK IN LIECHTENSTEIN AG—See Liechtenstein Global Trust AG; *Int'l*, pg. 4491
LGT BANK IN SWITZERLAND LTD.—See Liechtenstein Global Trust AG; *Int'l*, pg. 4491
LGT BANK (IRELAND) LIMITED—See Liechtenstein Global Trust AG; *Int'l*, pg. 4491
LGT BANK LTD.—See Liechtenstein Global Trust AG; *Int'l*, pg. 4491
LGT BANK (SINGAPORE) LTD.—See Liechtenstein Global Trust AG; *Int'l*, pg. 4491
LGT BANK SWITZERLAND—See Liechtenstein Global Trust AG; *Int'l*, pg. 4491
LGT CAPITAL MANAGEMENT LIMITED—See Liechtenstein Global Trust AG; *Int'l*, pg. 4491
LGT CAPITAL PARTNERS (ASIA-PACIFIC) LTD.—See Liechtenstein Global Trust AG; *Int'l*, pg. 4491
LGT CAPITAL PARTNERS (AUSTRALIA) PTY LTD.—See Liechtenstein Global Trust AG; *Int'l*, pg. 4491
LGT CAPITAL PARTNERS (IRELAND) LIMITED—See Liechtenstein Global Trust AG; *Int'l*, pg. 4491
LGT CAPITAL PARTNERS (JAPAN) CO. LTD.—See Liechtenstein Global Trust AG; *Int'l*, pg. 4491
LGT CAPITAL PARTNERS (U.K.) LIMITED—See Liechtenstein Global Trust AG; *Int'l*, pg. 4491

LGT CAPITAL PARTNERS (USA) INC.—See Liechtenstein Global Trust AG; *Int'l*, pg. 4491
LGT FINANCIAL SERVICES LTD—See Liechtenstein Global Trust AG; *Int'l*, pg. 4491
LGT FUND MANAGERS (IRELAND) LTD.—See Castle Private Equity AG; *Int'l*, pg. 1357
LGT INVESTMENT CONSULTING (BEIJING) LIMITED—See Liechtenstein Global Trust AG; *Int'l*, pg. 4491
LGT INVESTMENT MANAGEMENT (ASIA) LTD.—See Liechtenstein Global Trust AG; *Int'l*, pg. 4491
LGT INVESTMENT MANAGEMENT (JAPAN) CO. LTD.—See Liechtenstein Global Trust AG; *Int'l*, pg. 4491
LGT INVESTMENT PARTNERS LTD.—See Liechtenstein Global Trust AG; *Int'l*, pg. 4491
LGT LOGISTICS AB—See Litorina Capital Management AB; *Int'l*, pg. 4528
LGT LOGISTICS A/S—See Litorina Capital Management AB; *Int'l*, pg. 4528
LGT (MIDDLE EAST) LTD.—See Liechtenstein Global Trust AG; *Int'l*, pg. 4491
LGT (URUGUAY) LTD.—See Liechtenstein Global Trust AG; *Int'l*, pg. 4491
LG UNICHARM CO., LTD.—See Unicharm Corporation; *Int'l*, pg. 8032
LG UPLUS CORP.; *Int'l*, pg. 4477
LGV CAPITAL LTD.—See Legal & General Group Plc; *Int'l*, pg. 4443
LH ACCESS TECHNOLOGY LIMITED—See Westinghouse Air Brake Technologies Corporation; *U.S. Public*, pg. 2358
L&H AIRCO; *U.S. Private*, pg. 2362
L HARDWARE & SERVICES CO, LTD—See Loxley Public Company Limited; *Int'l*, pg. 4567
L. HARVEY & SON CO.—See Harvey Fertilizer & Gas Co.; *U.S. Private*, pg. 1878
LH ASSET CO., LTD.—See Land & Houses Public Company Limited; *Int'l*, pg. 4403
LH ASSISTED LIVING, LLC—See Brookdale Senior Living Inc.; *U.S. Public*, pg. 394
LHB INDUSTRIES, INC.; *U.S. Private*, pg. 2442
LHB INTERNATIONALE HANDELSBANK AG—See Nova Ljubljanska banka d.d.; *Int'l*, pg. 5451
L.H. CARBIDE CORPORATION—See L.H. Industries Corp.; *U.S. Private*, pg. 2366
LH CARGO HOLDING GMBH—See Deutsche Lufthansa AG; *Int'l*, pg. 2066
LHCG CVIII, LLC—See UnitedHealth Group Incorporated; *U.S. Public*, pg. 2245
LHCG CX, LLC—See UnitedHealth Group Incorporated; *U.S. Public*, pg. 2245
LHCG CXV, LLC—See UnitedHealth Group Incorporated; *U.S. Public*, pg. 2245
LHCG CXXI, LLC—See UnitedHealth Group Incorporated; *U.S. Public*, pg. 2245
LHCG LIX, LLC—See UnitedHealth Group Incorporated; *U.S. Public*, pg. 2245
LHCG LVII, LLC—See UnitedHealth Group Incorporated; *U.S. Public*, pg. 2245
LHCG LXIII, LLC—See UnitedHealth Group Incorporated; *U.S. Public*, pg. 2245
LHCG LXXIX, LLC—See UnitedHealth Group Incorporated; *U.S. Public*, pg. 2245
LHCG LXX, LLC—See UnitedHealth Group Incorporated; *U.S. Public*, pg. 2245
LHC GROUP, INC.—See UnitedHealth Group Incorporated; *U.S. Public*, pg. 2243
LHC GROUP PHARMACEUTICAL SERVICES, LLC—See UnitedHealth Group Incorporated; *U.S. Public*, pg. 2245
LHCG-VI, LLC—See UnitedHealth Group Incorporated; *U.S. Public*, pg. 2245
LHCG-V, L.L.C—See UnitedHealth Group Incorporated; *U.S. Public*, pg. 2245
LHCG XLII, LLC—See UnitedHealth Group Incorporated; *U.S. Public*, pg. 2245
LHCG XL, LLC—See UnitedHealth Group Incorporated; *U.S. Public*, pg. 2245
LHCG XLVII, LLC—See UnitedHealth Group Incorporated; *U.S. Public*, pg. 2245
LHCG XVII, LLC—See UnitedHealth Group Incorporated; *U.S. Public*, pg. 2245
LHCG XXI, LLC—See UnitedHealth Group Incorporated; *U.S. Public*, pg. 2245
LHCG XXXIII, LLC—See UnitedHealth Group Incorporated; *U.S. Public*, pg. 2245
LHCG XXXVII, LLC—See UnitedHealth Group Incorporated; *U.S. Public*, pg. 2245
LHC HOMECARE OF TENNESSEE, LLC—See UnitedHealth Group Incorporated; *U.S. Public*, pg. 2245
L&H COMPANY INC.; *U.S. Private*, pg. 2362
LHC PORTER NOVELLI—See Omnicom Group Inc.; *U.S. Public*, pg. 1591
LHC STRUCTURAL ENGINEERS, PC—See Bennett & Pless, Inc.; *U.S. Private*, pg. 526
LHD GROUP DEUTSCHLAND GMBH—See Lakeland Industries, Inc.; *U.S. Public*, pg. 1288

COMPANY NAME INDEX

LHD LANDHANDEL DREBKAU IMPORT - UND EXPORT GMBH—See BayWa AG; *Int'l*, pg. 918
LHE CO. LTD.—See Alfa Laval AB; *Int'l*, pg. 312
LH FINANCIAL GROUP PLC—See Land & Houses Public Company Limited; *Int'l*, pg. 4403
LH FINANCIAL GROUP PUBLIC COMPANY LIMITED; *Int'l*, pg. 4477
L&H GROUP—See Sonepar S.A.; *Int'l*, pg. 7091
L. H. HAYWARD & CO., LLC; *U.S. Private*, pg. 2364
L.H. HAYWARD & CO., LLC; *U.S. Private*, pg. 2366
LH HOTEL LEASEHOLD REAL ESTATE INVESTMENT TRUST; *Int'l*, pg. 4477
LHH RECRUITMENT SOLUTIONS—See Adecco Group AG; *Int'l*, pg. 136
LHI ACQUISITION CORPORATION; *U.S. Private*, pg. 2442
LHI LEASING GMBH & CO. IMMOBILIEN KG—See Norddeutsche Landesbank Girozentrale; *Int'l*, pg. 5417
LHI LEASING GMBH—See Norddeutsche Landesbank Girozentrale; *Int'l*, pg. 5417
L&H INDUSTRIAL INC; *U.S. Private*, pg. 2362
L.H. INDUSTRIES CORP.; *U.S. Private*, pg. 2366
LHI TECHNOLOGY SHENZEN CO.—See Carlisle Companies Incorporated; *U.S. Public*, pg. 437
L.H. LACY COMPANY; *U.S. Private*, pg. 2366
LHL CO., LTD.—See Nippon Life Insurance Company; *Int'l*, pg. 5322
LH MALL & HOTEL CO., LTD.—See Land & Houses Public Company Limited; *Int'l*, pg. 4403
L&H MANAGEMENT CO., LTD.—See Land & Houses Public Company Limited; *Int'l*, pg. 4403
LH MARTHINUSEN (PTY.) LTD.—See ACTOM (Pty) Ltd.; *Int'l*, pg. 120
LHM SERVICES GMBH—See Stadtwerke Munchen GmbH; *Int'l*, pg. 7162
LH MUANG MAI CO., LTD.—See Land & Houses Public Company Limited; *Int'l*, pg. 4403
LHN LIMITED; *Int'l*, pg. 4477
LHN LOGISTICS LIMITED—See LHN Limited; *Int'l*, pg. 4477
LHN PARKING HK LIMITED—See LHN Limited; *Int'l*, pg. 4477
LHN PARKING PTE. LTD.—See LHN Limited; *Int'l*, pg. 4477
LHO ALEXIS LESSEE, L.L.C.—See Pebblebrook Hotel Trust; *U.S. Public*, pg. 1660
LHOBERGE LESSEE, INC.—See Pebblebrook Hotel Trust; *U.S. Public*, pg. 1660
LHOIST BENELUX—See Lhoist S.A.; *Int'l*, pg. 4478
LHOIST BUKOWA SP. ZO.O.—See Lhoist S.A.; *Int'l*, pg. 4478
LHOIST CHILE LTDA—See Lhoist S.A.; *Int'l*, pg. 4478
LHOIST DO BRASIL LTDA—See Lhoist S.A.; *Int'l*, pg. 4478
LHOIST FRANCE SA—See Lhoist S.A.; *Int'l*, pg. 4478
LHOIST INDIA PVT LTD—See Lhoist S.A.; *Int'l*, pg. 4478
LHOIST INDUSTRIE S.A.—See Lhoist S.A.; *Int'l*, pg. 4478
LHOIST KALK GMBH—See Lhoist S.A.; *Int'l*, pg. 4478
LHOIST (MALAYSIA) SDN. BHD.—See Lhoist S.A.; *Int'l*, pg. 4478
LHOIST NEDERLAND NV—See Lhoist S.A.; *Int'l*, pg. 4478
LHOIST NORTH AMERICA, INC - ALABASTER (MINERALS) PLANT—See Lhoist S.A.; *Int'l*, pg. 4478
LHOIST NORTH AMERICA, INC - ANDERSON PLANT—See Lhoist S.A.; *Int'l*, pg. 4478
LHOIST NORTH AMERICA, INC - ARMAGOSA VALLEY PLANT—See Lhoist S.A.; *Int'l*, pg. 4478
LHOIST NORTH AMERICA, INC - CHARLESTON PLANT—See Lhoist S.A.; *Int'l*, pg. 4478
LHOIST NORTH AMERICA, INC - CLIFTON PLANT—See Lhoist S.A.; *Int'l*, pg. 4478
LHOIST NORTH AMERICA, INC - CRAB ORCHARD PLANT—See Lhoist S.A.; *Int'l*, pg. 4478
LHOIST NORTH AMERICA, INC - CRAWFORD PLANT—See Lhoist S.A.; *Int'l*, pg. 4478
LHOIST NORTH AMERICA, INC - DALTON PLANT—See Lhoist S.A.; *Int'l*, pg. 4478
LHOIST NORTH AMERICA, INC - DOUGLAS PLANT—See Lhoist S.A.; *Int'l*, pg. 4478
LHOIST NORTH AMERICA, INC - HENDERSON PLANT—See Lhoist S.A.; *Int'l*, pg. 4478
LHOIST NORTH AMERICA, INC - LOWELL PLANT—See Lhoist S.A.; *Int'l*, pg. 4478
LHOIST NORTH AMERICA, INC - NATIVIDAD PLANT—See Lhoist S.A.; *Int'l*, pg. 4478
LHOIST NORTH AMERICA, INC - NOLANVILLE PLANT—See Lhoist S.A.; *Int'l*, pg. 4478
LHOIST NORTH AMERICA, INC - O'NEAL PLANT—See Lhoist S.A.; *Int'l*, pg. 4478
LHOIST NORTH AMERICA, INC - SPINKS CLAY PLANT—See Lhoist S.A.; *Int'l*, pg. 4478
LHOIST NORTH AMERICA, INC - STE. GENEVIEVE PLANT—See Lhoist S.A.; *Int'l*, pg. 4478
LHOIST NORTH AMERICA, INC - TENMILE PLANT—See Lhoist S.A.; *Int'l*, pg. 4478
LHOIST POLSKA—See Lhoist S.A.; *Int'l*, pg. 4478
LHOIST S.A.; *Int'l*, pg. 4478
LHOIST S.A. - TEXADA LANGLEY PLANT—See Lhoist S.A.; *Int'l*, pg. 4478

LHOIST SINGAPORE PTE LTD—See Lhoist S.A.; *Int'l*, pg. 4478
LHOIST SRO—See Lhoist S.A.; *Int'l*, pg. 4478
LHOIST TRADING (SHANGHAI) CO. LTD.—See Lhoist S.A.; *Int'l*, pg. 4478
LHOIST UK—See Lhoist S.A.; *Int'l*, pg. 4478
L'HOTELLIER—See RTX Corporation; *U.S. Public*, pg. 1822
LHO VIKING HOTEL, L.L.C.—See Pebblebrook Hotel Trust; *U.S. Public*, pg. 1660
L&H PACKING COMPANY; *U.S. Private*, pg. 2362
L&H PROPERTY CO., LTD.—See Land & Houses Public Company Limited; *Int'l*, pg. 4403
LHP SOFTWARE; *U.S. Private*, pg. 2442
LHPT COLUMBUS THE, LLC—See Ventas, Inc.; *U.S. Public*, pg. 2278
LHP TRANSPORTATION SERVICES—See Prime, Inc.; *U.S. Private*, pg. 3262
LH REAL ESTATE CO., LTD.—See Land & Houses Public Company Limited; *Int'l*, pg. 4403
L&H RETAIL MANAGEMENT CO., LTD.—See Land & Houses Public Company Limited; *Int'l*, pg. 4403
LHRET ASCENSION AUSTIN II, LP—See Ventas, Inc.; *U.S. Public*, pg. 2278
LHRET ASCENSION SJ, LLC—See Ventas, Inc.; *U.S. Public*, pg. 2278
LHRET ASCENSION SV, LLC—See Ventas, Inc.; *U.S. Public*, pg. 2278
LHRET ST. LOUIS, LLC—See Ventas, Inc.; *U.S. Public*, pg. 2278
L&H SATHON CO., LTD.—See Land & Houses Public Company Limited; *Int'l*, pg. 4403
LH SHOPPING CENTERS LEASEHOLD REAL ESTATE INVESTMENT TRUST; *Int'l*, pg. 4477
L.H. STAMPING CORP.—See L.H. Industries Corp.; *U.S. Private*, pg. 2366
LHS (UK) LIMITED—See Ecolab Inc.; *U.S. Public*, pg. 714
L & H SUPPLY CO. INC.—See Mainco Investments Inc.; *U.S. Private*, pg. 2552
L&H TECHNOLOGIES INC.; *U.S. Private*, pg. 2362
LHT HOLDINGS LIMITED; *Int'l*, pg. 4478
THE L.H. THOMSON COMPANY, INC.; *U.S. Private*, pg. 4067
L&H THREADED RODS CORP.—See Gray America Corp.; *U.S. Private*, pg. 1759
LHT MARKETING PTE LTD—See LHT Holdings Limited; *Int'l*, pg. 4479
LH TRADING (HOLDING) AG—See Holcim Ltd.; *Int'l*, pg. 3448
LH TRADING LTD—See Holcim Ltd.; *Int'l*, pg. 3448
LH TRADING PTE. LTD.—See Holcim Ltd.; *Int'l*, pg. 3448
LHV GROUP; *Int'l*, pg. 4479
L.H. VOSS MATERIALS, INC.—See SiteOne Landscape Supply, Inc.; *U.S. Public*, pg. 1889
LI3 LITHIUM CORP.; *Int'l*, pg. 4481
LIA AUTO GROUP; *U.S. Private*, pg. 2442
LIAB INSTRUMENTERINGAR AB—See Instalco AB; *Int'l*, pg. 3722
LIACOM SYSTEMS LTD.—See Advanced Business Software & Solutions Ltd.; *Int'l*, pg. 157
LIA HONDA OF ALBANY—See Lia Auto Group; *U.S. Private*, pg. 2442
LIA HONDA WILLIAMSVILLE—See Lia Auto Group; *U.S. Private*, pg. 2442
LIA INSURANCE SAL—See Saham Group SA; *Int'l*, pg. 6480
LIAISON INTERNATIONAL, INC.; *U.S. Private*, pg. 2442
LIAISON MARKETING COMMUNICATIONS, LTD.; *U.S. Private*, pg. 2442
LIAISON TECHNOLOGIES AB—See Open Text Corporation; *Int'l*, pg. 5597
LIAISON TECHNOLOGIES EUROPE—See Open Text Corporation; *Int'l*, pg. 5597
LIAISON TECHNOLOGIES INC.—See Open Text Corporation; *Int'l*, pg. 5597
LIAISON TECHNOLOGIES NETHERLANDS—See Open Text Corporation; *Int'l*, pg. 5597
LIAISON TECHNOLOGIES UNITED KINGDOM—See Open Text Corporation; *Int'l*, pg. 5597
LIAM VENTURES, INC.; *U.S. Private*, pg. 2442
LIAN BENG ENGINEERING & MACHINERY PTE LTD—See Lian Beng Group Ltd.; *Int'l*, pg. 4481
LIAN BENG GROUP LTD.; *Int'l*, pg. 4481
LIANBIO; *U.S. Public*, pg. 1310
LIANCHUANG ELECTRONIC TECHNOLOGY CO., LTD.; *Int'l*, pg. 4482
LIANDER N.V.—See Alliander N.V.; *Int'l*, pg. 341
LIANDI CLEAN TECHNOLOGY INC.; *Int'l*, pg. 4482
LIANDI (NANJING) INFORMATION SYSTEMS CO., LTD; *Int'l*, pg. 4482
LIANDON B.V.—See Alliander N.V.; *Int'l*, pg. 341
LIANDON MEETBEDRIJF N.V.—See Alliander N.V.; *Int'l*, pg. 341
LIANE AUTOMOBILES; *Int'l*, pg. 4482
LIAN EE HYDRAULICS PTE LTD.; *Int'l*, pg. 4481
LIANFA TEXTILE EUROPE SRL—See Jiangsu Lianfa Textile Co., Ltd.; *Int'l*, pg. 3950
LIANFA TEXTILE (H.K.) LTD.—See Jiangsu Lianfa Textile Co., Ltd.; *Int'l*, pg. 3950

LIAONING ENERGY INDUSTRY CO., LTD.

LIANG JING CO., LTD.—See Sumitomo Mitsui Financial Group, Inc.; *Int'l*, pg. 7294
LIANGSHAN CIMC DONGYUE VEHICLES CO., LTD.—See CIMC Vehicle (Group) Co., Ltd.; *Int'l*, pg. 1608
LIANGSHAN DONGYUE CIMC VEHICLE CO., LTD.—See China International Marine Containers (Group) Co., Ltd.; *Int'l*, pg. 1512
LIANG SHING INDUSTRIES (HK) LIMITED—See Symphony Holdings Limited; *Int'l*, pg. 7379
LI ANG TIMOR, LTDA.—See Bridgestone Corporation; *Int'l*, pg. 1308
LIANG YUAN PTE. LTD.—See Neo Group Limited; *Int'l*, pg. 5196
LIANHE CHEMICAL TECHNOLOGY CO., LTD.; *Int'l*, pg. 4482
LIANHE INVESTMENTS PTE. LTD.—See Singapore Press Holdings Ltd.; *Int'l*, pg. 6942
LIANHE PUBLISHING PTE LTD—See Singapore Press Holdings Ltd.; *Int'l*, pg. 6942
LIANHUA AJINOMOTO CO., LTD.—See Ajinomoto Company, Inc.; *Int'l*, pg. 257
LIANHUA SUPERMARKET HOLDINGS CO., LTD.—See Bailian Group Co., Ltd.; *Int'l*, pg. 802
LIAN HUP PACKAGING INDUSTRIES SDN. BHD.—See LHT Holdings Limited; *Int'l*, pg. 4479
LIAN HWA FOODS CORPORATION; *Int'l*, pg. 4482
LIA NISSAN LTD.—See Lia Auto Group; *U.S. Private*, pg. 2442
LIANNEX CORPORATION (S) PTE. LTD.; *Int'l*, pg. 4482
LIAN SHENG TECHNOLOGY CO., LTD.; *Int'l*, pg. 4482
LIAN TREVAREFABRIKK AS—See VKR Holding A/S; *Int'l*, pg. 8281
LIANTRONICS (HONG KONG) CO. LTD.—See Shenzhen Liantronics Co., Ltd.; *Int'l*, pg. 6816
LIANTS DE L'OUEST SAS—See VINCI S.A.; *Int'l*, pg. 8223
LIANTS DE PICARDIE SAS—See VINCI S.A.; *Int'l*, pg. 8223
LIANTS ROUTIERS DE GARONNE SAS—See VINCI S.A.; *Int'l*, pg. 8223
LIAN VINDUER AS—See VKR Holding A/S; *Int'l*, pg. 8281
LIANYNGANG JUMP PETROLEUM AND CHEMICAL MACHINERY CO.—See Dover Corporation; *U.S. Public*, pg. 681
LIANYUNGANG AJINOMOTO FROZEN FOODS CO., LTD.—See Ajinomoto Company, Inc.; *Int'l*, pg. 257
LIANYUNGANG AJINOMOTO RUYI FOODS CO., LTD.—See Ajinomoto Company, Inc.; *Int'l*, pg. 257
LIANYUNGANG AJINOMOTO RUYI FOODS CO., LTD.—See Grand Industrial Holding Co., Ltd.; *Int'l*, pg. 3055
LIANYUNGANG BENYI NEW MATERIAL TECHNOLOGY CO., LTD.—See Rengo Co., Ltd.; *Int'l*, pg. 6280
LIANYUNGANG CHIA TAI FEED CO., LTD.—See Charoen Pokphand Foods Public Company Limited; *Int'l*, pg. 1453
LIANYUNGANG DIC COLOR CO., LTD.—See DIC Corporation; *Int'l*, pg. 2107
LIANYUNGANG FUSHI FOOD CO., LTD.—See Grand Industrial Holding Co., Ltd.; *Int'l*, pg. 3055
LIANYUNGANG LIFE RUYI FOODS CO., LTD.—See Grand Industrial Holding Co., Ltd.; *Int'l*, pg. 3055
LIANYUNGANG NBTM NEW MATERIALS CO., LTD.—See NBTM New Materials Group Co., Ltd.; *Int'l*, pg. 5179
LIANYUNGANG RUNZHONG PHARMACEUTICAL CO., LTD.—See Sino Biopharmaceutical Limited; *Int'l*, pg. 6946
LIANYUNGANG TAILE CHEMICAL INDUSTRY CO. LTD.—See Tessenderlo Group NV; *Int'l*, pg. 7573
LIANYUNGANG ZAOLING ABRASIVES CO., LTD.—See Resonac Holdings Corporation; *Int'l*, pg. 6298
LIANYUNGANG ZHONGFU LIANZHONG COMPOSITES GROUP CO., LTD.—See China National Building Material Group Co., Ltd.; *Int'l*, pg. 1525
LIANYUNG DONGMUJIANGHE NEW MATERIAL CO., LTD.—See NBTM New Materials Group Co., Ltd.; *Int'l*, pg. 5179
LIAOCHENG LANTIAN COGENERATION PLANT CO., LTD.—See CJ Corporation; *Int'l*, pg. 1634
LIAOHE SOKEN CHEMICAL CO., LTD.—See Soken Chemical & Engineering Co.,Ltd.; *Int'l*, pg. 7066
LIAONING BIRLA CARBON CO., LTD.—See The Aditya Birla Group; *Int'l*, pg. 7610
LIAONING BRINGSPRING FINANCIAL SERVICE CO., LTD—See Bringspring Science & Technology Co., Ltd.; *Int'l*, pg. 1164
LIAONING CHENGDA CO., LTD.; *Int'l*, pg. 4482
LIAONING CIMC VEHICLE LOGISTICS EQUIPMENTS CO., LTD.—See CIMC Vehicle (Group) Co., Ltd.; *Int'l*, pg. 1608
LIAONING DAOHENG TECHNOLOGY CO., LTD—See Cantronic Systems Inc.; *Int'l*, pg. 1300
LIAONING DARE INDUSTRIAL COMPANY LTD.; *Int'l*, pg. 4482
LIAONING EAST SHINE CHEMICAL TECHNOLOGY CO., LTD.—See SK Materials Co., Ltd.; *Int'l*, pg. 6974
LIAONING ENERGY INDUSTRY CO., LTD.; *Int'l*, pg. 4482

LIAONING FU-AN HEAVY INDUSTRY CO., LTD.

LIAONING FU-AN HEAVY INDUSTRY CO., LTD.; *Int'l*, pg. 4483
LIAONING GAOKE ENERGY GROUP COMPANY LIMITED—See A-Power Energy Generation Systems, Ltd.; *Int'l*, pg. 20
LIAONING GOLD MANTIS CURTAIN WALL DECORATION CO., LTD.—See Suzhou Gold Mantis Construction Decoration Co., Ltd.; *Int'l*, pg. 7350
LIAONING HAISCO PHARMACEUTICAL CO., LTD.—See Haisco Pharmaceutical Group Co., Ltd.; *Int'l*, pg. 3217
LIAONING HANKING GREEN BUILDING MATERIALS CO., LTD.—See China Hanking Holdings Limited; *Int'l*, pg. 1506
LIAONING HE EYE HOSPITAL GROUP CO., LTD.; *Int'l*, pg. 4483
LIAONING HEZHAN ENERGY GROUP CO., LTD; *Int'l*, pg. 4483
LIAONING HUAPENG GUANGYUAN GLASS CO., LTD.—See Shangdong Huapeng Glass Co., Ltd.; *Int'l*, pg. 6760
LIAONING KELONG FINE CHEMICAL CO., LTD.; *Int'l*, pg. 4483
LIAONING KINGFA ADVANCED MATERIALS CO. LTD.—See Kingfa Sci &Tech Co., Ltd.; *Int'l*, pg. 4172
LIAONING MIGAO CHEMICAL CO., LTD.—See Migao Corporation; *Int'l*, pg. 4890
LIAONING OXIRANCHEM GROUP CO., LTD.; *Int'l*, pg. 4483
LIAONING POLY ARMOR VEHICLE CO., LTD.—See China Poly Group Corporation; *Int'l*, pg. 1541
LIAONING PORT CO., LTD.; *Int'l*, pg. 4483
LIAONING RHI JINDING MAGNESIA CO., LTD.—See RHI Magnesita N.V.; *Int'l*, pg. 6325
LIAONING SECOM SECURITY CO., LTD.—See SECOM Co., Ltd.; *Int'l*, pg. 6671
LIAONING SG AUTOMOTIVE GROUP CO., LTD.; *Int'l*, pg. 4483
LIAONING SHENGSHENG BIOTECHNOLOGY CO., LTD.; *Int'l*, pg. 4483
LIAONING SHENHUA HOLDINGS CO., LTD.; *Int'l*, pg. 4483
LIAONING SHIDAI WANHENG CO., LTD.; *Int'l*, pg. 4483
LIAONING SHUIYUN QINGHE RICE INDUSTRY CO., LTD.; *Int'l*, pg. 4483
LIAONING XINDE NEW MATERIAL TECHNOLOGY CO., LTD.; *Int'l*, pg. 4483
LIAONING YONGXUETAI AUTO PARTS CO. LTD.—See Shanghai Yongmaotai Automotive Technology Co., Ltd.; *Int'l*, pg. 6782
LIAONING YUANYANG FOOD CO., LTD.—See ORG Technology Co., Ltd.; *Int'l*, pg. 5617
LIAOSHEN INDUSTRIAL GROUP CO., LTD.—See China North Industries Group Corporation; *Int'l*, pg. 1535
LIAOYANG K.S. AUTOMOTIVE SPRING COMPANY LIMITED—See ThyssenKrupp AG; *Int'l*, pg. 7732
LIAT (1974) LTD.; *Int'l*, pg. 4483
LIA TOYOTA OF COLONIE—See Lia Auto Group; *U.S. Private*, pg. 2442
LI AUTO INC.; *Int'l*, pg. 4481
LIAVER GMBH & CO. KG—See Sto SE & Co. KGaA; *Int'l*, pg. 7219
LIAZON CORPORATION—See Willis Towers Watson Public Limited Company; *Int'l*, pg. 8414
LIBAN CABLES SAL - JBEIL FACTORY—See Nexans S.A.; *Int'l*, pg. 5240
LIBAN CABLES SAL—See Nexans S.A.; *Int'l*, pg. 5240
LI BANG INTERNATIONAL CORPORATION INC.; *Int'l*, pg. 4481
LIBANO-FRANCAISE FINANCE S.A.L.—See Banque Libano-Francaise S.A.L.; *Int'l*, pg. 854
LI BAO GE GROUP LIMITED; *Int'l*, pg. 4481
LIBAS CONSUMER PRODUCTS LTD.; *Int'l*, pg. 4483
LIBB CO. INC.; *U.S. Private*, pg. 2442
LIBBEY EUROPE B.V.—See Libbey, Inc.; *U.S. Private*, pg. 2442
LIBBEY, INC.; *U.S. Private*, pg. 2442
LIBBY CARE CENTER OF CASCADIA—See Cascadia Healthcare LLC; *U.S. Private*, pg. 781
LIBCON INC.; *U.S. Private*, pg. 2442
LIBECOM S.A.—See Liberis Publications SA; *Int'l*, pg. 4483
LIBER AB—See SHV Holdings N.V.; *Int'l*, pg. 6872
LIBERA INC.; *U.S. Private*, pg. 2442
LIBERATA UK LTD.—See Bain Capital, LP; *U.S. Private*, pg. 434
LIBERATED SYNDICATION INC.; *U.S. Public*, pg. 1310
LIBERATE LEARNING PTY. LTD.—See MPS Limited; *Int'l*, pg. 5063
LIBERATION EXPLOITATIE, B.V.—See Minor International PCL; *Int'l*, pg. 4911
LIBERATION PROGRAMS INC.; *U.S. Private*, pg. 2442
LIBERATOR HEALTH & WELLNESS, INC.—See Becton, Dickinson & Company; *U.S. Public*, pg. 291
LIBERATOR MEDICAL HOLDINGS, INC.—See Becton, Dickinson & Company; *U.S. Public*, pg. 291
LIBERATOR MEDICAL SUPPLY, INC.—See Becton, Dickinson & Company; *U.S. Public*, pg. 291
LIBER ENTERTAINMENT INC.—See Aeria Inc.; *Int'l*, pg. 179

LIBERIA CEMENT CORPORATION LTD.—See Heidelberg Materials AG; *Int'l*, pg. 3318
LIBERIS PUBLICATIONS SA; *Int'l*, pg. 4483
LIBERIS—See Lone Star Global Acquisitions, LLC; *U.S. Private*, pg. 2487
LIBERIUM GLOBAL RESOURCES PRIVATE LIMITED—See Zee Learn Limited; *Int'l*, pg. 8629
LIBERMAN BROADCASTING CORPORATION; *U.S. Private*, pg. 2442
LIBERO COPPER & GOLD CORPORATION; *Int'l*, pg. 4484
LIBERO IS GMBH—See Knosys Limited; *Int'l*, pg. 4212
LIBERO SYSTEMS PTY. LTD.—See Knosys Limited; *Int'l*, pg. 4212
LIBERTA CO., LTD.; *Int'l*, pg. 4484
LIBERTA PARTNERS HOLDING GMBH; *Int'l*, pg. 4484
LIBERTAS 7, S.A.; *Int'l*, pg. 4484
LIBERTAS COPPER, LLC—See Patriarch Partners, LLC; *U.S. Private*, pg. 3109
LIBERTAS UBE, LTD.—See UBE Corporation; *Int'l*, pg. 8001
LIBERTINE HOLDINGS PLC; *Int'l*, pg. 4484
LIBERTINE; *Int'l*, pg. 4484
LIBERTO OF HARLINGEN INC.—See Liberto Specialty Company Inc.; *U.S. Private*, pg. 2442
LIBERTO SPECIALTY COMPANY INC.; *U.S. Private*, pg. 2442
LIBERTY 77 CAPITAL, L.P.; *U.S. Private*, pg. 2443
LIBERTY AIPO LIMITED PARTNERSHIP—See Prologis, Inc.; *U.S. Public*, pg. 1727
LIBERTY ALLIANCE; *U.S. Private*, pg. 2443
LIBERTY ALL-STAR EQUITY FUND; *U.S. Public*, pg. 1310
LIBERTY AMBULATORY SURGERY CENTER, LLC—See Tenet Healthcare Corporation; *U.S. Public*, pg. 2011
LIBERTY AMBULATORY SURGERY CENTER, L.P.—See Tenet Healthcare Corporation; *U.S. Public*, pg. 2011
LIBERTY AMERICAN INSURANCE GROUP, INC.—See Tokio Marine Holdings, Inc.; *Int'l*, pg. 7782
LIBERTY AUTOMOTIVE LTD.; *U.S. Private*, pg. 2443
LIBERTY AV SOLUTIONS—See WESCO International, Inc.; *U.S. Public*, pg. 2351
LIBERTY BANCSHARES INC.—See Middlefield Banc Corp.; *U.S. Public*, pg. 1445
LIBERTY BANK FOR SAVINGS INC.; *U.S. Private*, pg. 2443
LIBERTY BANK JSC; *Int'l*, pg. 4484
LIBERTY BANK, N.A.—See DMG Bancshares, Inc.; *U.S. Private*, pg. 1248
LIBERTY BANK; *U.S. Private*, pg. 2443
LIBERTY BANK; *U.S. Private*, pg. 2443
LIBERTY BANK & TRUST COMPANY—See Liberty Financial Services, Inc.; *U.S. Private*, pg. 2444
LIBERTY BAY CREDIT UNION; *U.S. Private*, pg. 2443
LIBERTY BELL EQUIPMENT CORP.—See Sycamore Partners Management, LP; *U.S. Private*, pg. 3896
LIBERTY BELL WHOLESALE; *U.S. Private*, pg. 2443
LIBERTY BENEFIT INSURANCE SERVICES, INC.—See Clayton, Dubilier & Rice, LLC; *U.S. Private*, pg. 927
LIBERTY BENEFIT INSURANCE SERVICES, INC.—See Mubadala Investment Company PJSC; *Int'l*, pg. 5076
LIBERTY BENEFIT INSURANCE SERVICES, INC.—See Stone Point Capital LLC; *U.S. Private*, pg. 3826
LIBERTY BILLING & CONSULTING SERVICES, INC.—See Linden LLC; *U.S. Private*, pg. 2460
THE LIBERTY BLUE GROUP LLC; *U.S. Private*, pg. 4069
LIBERTY BROADBAND CORPORATION; *U.S. Public*, pg. 1310
LIBERTY BUICK INC.; *U.S. Private*, pg. 2443
LIBERTY BUSINESS SYSTEMS, INC.; *U.S. Private*, pg. 2443
LIBERTY CABLEVISION OF PUERTO RICO LLC—See Liberty Global plc; *Int'l*, pg. 4485
LIBERTY CAPITAL INC.; *U.S. Private*, pg. 2443
LIBERTY CARTON COMPANY—See Liberty Diversified International Inc.; *U.S. Private*, pg. 2443
LIBERTY CASH-A-CHECK, INC.—See Liberty Bank; *U.S. Private*, pg. 2443
LIBERTY CHEMICALS PRIVATE LIMITED—See Control Print Ltd.; *Int'l*, pg. 1785
LIBERTY COATING COMPANY LLC; *U.S. Private*, pg. 2443
LIBERTYCOM LLC—See ERPSOFT Systems Ltd.; *Int'l*, pg. 2497
THE LIBERTY COMPANY INSURANCE BROKERS, INC.; *U.S. Private*, pg. 4069
LIBERTY DATA PRODUCTS INC.; *U.S. Private*, pg. 2443
LIBERTY DEFENSE HOLDINGS, LTD.; *Int'l*, pg. 4484
LIBERTY DISTRIBUTORS INC.; *U.S. Private*, pg. 2443
LIBERTY DIVERSIFIED INTERNATIONAL INC.; *U.S. Private*, pg. 2443
LIBERTY DURHAM, LLC—See Prologis, Inc.; *U.S. Public*, pg. 1727
LIBERTY ENERGY CORP.; *U.S. Private*, pg. 2444
LIBERTY ENERGY INC.; *U.S. Public*, pg. 1311
LIBERTY EXPEDIA HOLDINGS, INC.—See Expedia Group, Inc.; *U.S. Public*, pg. 809
LIBERTY FINANCIAL GROUP LIMITED; *Int'l*, pg. 4484

LIBERTY FINANCIAL SERVICES, INC.; *U.S. Private*, pg. 2444
LIBERTY FINANCIAL—See Evansville Teachers Federal Credit Union; *U.S. Private*, pg. 1435
LIBERTY FLIGHTS LIMITED—See Supreme Plc; *Int'l*, pg. 7341
LIBERTY FLOUR MILLS, INC.; *Int'l*, pg. 4484
LIBERTY FORD LINCOLN MERCURY—See Jim Herrick Motors Inc.; *U.S. Private*, pg. 2209
LIBERTY FRUIT COMPANY, INC.—See Russ Davis Wholesale; *U.S. Private*, pg. 3506
LIBERTY FUELS COMPANY, LLC—See NACCO Industries, Inc.; *U.S. Public*, pg. 1490
LIBERTY FUNERALS PTY LIMITED—See TPG Capital, L.P.; *U.S. Public*, pg. 2174
LIBERTY FURNITURE INDUSTRIES INC.; *U.S. Private*, pg. 2444
LIBERTY GLOBAL B.V.—See Liberty Global plc; *Int'l*, pg. 4484
LIBERTY GLOBAL EUROPE LTD.—See Liberty Global plc; *Int'l*, pg. 4484
LIBERTY GLOBAL, INC.—See Liberty Global plc; *Int'l*, pg. 4484
LIBERTY GLOBAL INSURANCE COMPANY LIMITED—See Liberty Global plc; *Int'l*, pg. 4484
LIBERTY GLOBAL PLC; *Int'l*, pg. 4484
LIBERTY GLOVE & SAFETY, INC.; *U.S. Private*, pg. 2444
LIBERTY GOLD CORP.; *Int'l*, pg. 4486
LIBERTY GROUP LIMITED—See Abengoa S.A.; *Int'l*, pg. 59
LIBERTY GROUP LIMITED—See Algonquin Power & Utilities Corp.; *Int'l*, pg. 319
LIBERTY GROUP OF COMPANIES; *U.S. Private*, pg. 2444
LIBERTY HALL CAPITAL PARTNERS, L.P.; *U.S. Private*, pg. 2444
LIBERTY HARDWARE MANUFACTURING CORPORATION—See Masco Corporation; *U.S. Public*, pg. 1390
LIBERTY HARDWOODS INC.; *U.S. Private*, pg. 2444
LIBERTY HEALTH SCIENCES INC.—See Ayr Wellness Inc.; *Int'l*, pg. 775
LIBERTY HIGHER EDUCATION, LLC—See Liberty Partners, L.P.; *U.S. Private*, pg. 2447
LIBERTY HOME MORTGAGE CORPORATION; *U.S. Private*, pg. 2444
LIBERTY HOSPITAL; *U.S. Private*, pg. 2444
LIBERTY HOUSE LIMITED—See GFG Alliance Limited; *Int'l*, pg. 2956
LIBERTY IMPORTS INC.; *U.S. Private*, pg. 2444
LIBERTY INDUSTRIAL GROUP, INC.—See Terra Millenium Corporation; *U.S. Private*, pg. 3970
LIBERTY INSURANCE AGENCY INC.—See Liberty Bank for Savings Inc.; *U.S. Private*, pg. 2443
LIBERTY INSURANCE ASSOCIATES; *U.S. Private*, pg. 2444
LIBERTY INSURANCE PTE. LTD.—See Liberty Mutual Holding Company Inc.; *U.S. Private*, pg. 2445
LIBERTY INSURANCE UNDERWRITERS, INC.—See Liberty Mutual Holding Company Inc.; *U.S. Private*, pg. 2445
LIBERTY INTERACTIVE LLC—See Qurate Retail, Inc.; *U.S. Public*, pg. 1758
LIBERTY INTERNATIONAL INSURANCE LTD.—See Liberty Mutual Holding Company Inc.; *U.S. Private*, pg. 2445
LIBERTY INTERNATIONAL UNDERWRITERS—See Liberty Mutual Holding Company Inc.; *U.S. Private*, pg. 2445
LIBERTY INVESTMENT EXCHANGE; *U.S. Private*, pg. 2444
LIBERTY IRON & METAL, INC.; *U.S. Private*, pg. 2444
LIBERTY LANDFILL, L.L.C.—See Waste Management, Inc.; *U.S. Public*, pg. 2331
LIBERTY LANE PARTNERS LLC; *U.S. Private*, pg. 2444
LIBERTY LATIN AMERICA LTD.—See Liberty Global plc; *Int'l*, pg. 4485
LIBERTY LEASING CO.—See BNP Paribas SA; *Int'l*, pg. 1091
LIBERTY LINEHAUL INC.; *Int'l*, pg. 4486
LIBERTY LINES TRANSIT, INC.—See Liberty Systems, Inc.; *U.S. Private*, pg. 2447
LIBERTY LOGISTICS SERVICES, INC.—See RPM Consolidated Services, Inc.; *U.S. Private*, pg. 3495
LIBERTY LTD—See BlueGem Capital Partners LLP; *Int'l*, pg. 1071
LIBERTY LUMBER COMPANY—See Younger Brothers Group Inc.; *U.S. Private*, pg. 4593
LIBERTY MANAGEMENT GROUP, INC.; *U.S. Private*, pg. 2444
LIBERTY MEDIA ACQUISITION CORPORATION; *U.S. Public*, pg. 1311
LIBERTY MEDIA CORPORATION; *U.S. Public*, pg. 1311
LIBERTY MEDIA FOR WOMEN, LLC; *U.S. Private*, pg. 2444
LIBERTY MEDIA INTERNATIONAL, INC.—See Liberty Global plc; *Int'l*, pg. 4485
LIBERTY MEDICAL NZ LIMITED—See Hollister Incorporated; *U.S. Private*, pg. 1966

COMPANY NAME INDEX

LIBERTY MEDICAL PTY. LTD.—See Hollister Incorporated; *U.S. Private*, pg. 1966
LIBERTY MEDICAL (SWITZERLAND) AG—See Hollister Incorporated; *U.S. Private*, pg. 1966
LIBERTY METAL PRODUCTS CO.—See The Handy/Kenlin Group; *U.S. Private*, pg. 4043
LIBERTY MEXICANA S.A. DE C.V.—See AISIN Corporation; *Int'l*, pg. 253
LIBERTY MILLS LIMITED; *Int'l*, pg. 4486
LIBERTY MINING INTERNATIONAL PTY. LTD.; *Int'l*, pg. 4486
LIBERTY MINISTRIES; *U.S. Private*, pg. 2445
LIBERTY MORTGAGE CO. INC.; *U.S. Private*, pg. 2445
LIBERTY MUTUAL AGENCY CORPORATION—See Liberty Mutual Holding Company Inc.; *U.S. Private*, pg. 2446
LIBERTY MUTUAL FIRE INSURANCE CO.—See Liberty Mutual Holding Company Inc.; *U.S. Private*, pg. 2446
LIBERTY MUTUAL GROUP INC.—See Liberty Mutual Holding Company Inc.; *U.S. Private*, pg. 2445
LIBERTY MUTUAL HOLDING COMPANY INC.; *U.S. Private*, pg. 2445
LIBERTY MUTUAL INSURANCE COMPANY—See Liberty Mutual Holding Company Inc.; *U.S. Private*, pg. 2446
LIBERTY MUTUAL MID-ATLANTIC INSURANCE COMPANY—See Liberty Mutual Holding Company Inc.; *U.S. Private*, pg. 2446
LIBERTY NATIONAL BANK; *U.S. Private*, pg. 2446
LIBERTY NATIONAL INSURANCE CO—See Globe Life Inc.; *U.S. Public*, pg. 946
LIBERTY NATIONAL LIFE INSURANCE CO.—See Globe Life Inc.; *U.S. Public*, pg. 946
LIBERTY NORTHWEST INSURANCE CORP.—See Liberty Mutual Holding Company Inc.; *U.S. Private*, pg. 2446
LIBERTY OIL CO. INC.; *U.S. Private*, pg. 2446
LIBERTY OILFIELD SERVICES LLC—See Liberty Energy Inc.; *U.S. Public*, pg. 1311
LIBERTY ORCHARDS CO., INC.; *U.S. Private*, pg. 2446
LIBERTY PAPER, INC.—See Liberty Diversified International Inc.; *U.S. Private*, pg. 2443
LIBERTY PAPER & PRINTING; *U.S. Private*, pg. 2446
LIBERTY PAPER PRODUCTS LLC—See Elm Creek Partners; *U.S. Private*, pg. 1375
LIBERTY PARTNERS, L.P.; *U.S. Private*, pg. 2446
LIBERTY PERSONNEL SERVICES; *U.S. Private*, pg. 2447
LIBERTY PIPELINE GROUP, LLC—See Energy Transfer LP; *U.S. Public*, pg. 763
LIBERTY POCHIN LIMITED—See Pochin's Ltd.; *Int'l*, pg. 5902
LIBERTY POINT BEHAVIORAL HEALTHCARE, LLC—See Universal Health Services, Inc.; *U.S. Public*, pg. 2258
LIBERTY POLYGLAS, INC.; *U.S. Private*, pg. 2447
LIBERTY POWER CORP. LLC; *U.S. Private*, pg. 2447
LIBERTY PREMIUM FINANCE, INC.—See Fosun International Limited; *Int'l*, pg. 2752
LIBERTY PROCUREMENT CO. INC.—See 20230930-DK-Butterfly-1, Inc.; *U.S. Private*, pg. 5
LIBERTY PROPERTY LIMITED PARTNERSHIP; *U.S. Private*, pg. 2447
LIBERTY PROPERTY TRUST—See Prologis, Inc.; *U.S. Public*, pg. 1727
LIBERTY PROPERTY TRUST UK LIMITED—See Prologis, Inc.; *U.S. Public*, pg. 1727
LIBERTY PUMPS; *U.S. Private*, pg. 2447
LIBERTY RAILWAY SERVICES, INC.—See ERS Industries Inc.; *U.S. Private*, pg. 1423
LIBERTY RC, INC.—See DaVita Inc.; *U.S. Public*, pg. 640
LIBERTY RESOURCES ACQUISITION CORP.; *U.S. Public*, pg. 1311
LIBERTY RESOURCES, INC.; *U.S. Private*, pg. 2447
LIBERTY RETAIL LIMITED—See BlueGem Capital Partners LLP; *Int'l*, pg. 1071
LIBERTY RICHTER—See World Finer Foods, Inc.; *U.S. Private*, pg. 4565
LIBERTY SAFE & SECURITY PRODUCTS, INC.—See Compass Diversified Holdings; *U.S. Public*, pg. 560
LIBERTY SAVINGS BANK, F.S.B.—See Liberty Capital Inc.; *U.S. Private*, pg. 2443
LIBERTY SCIENCE CENTER, INC.; *U.S. Private*, pg. 2447
LIBERTY SEGUROS—See Liberty Mutual Holding Company Inc.; *U.S. Private*, pg. 2446
LIBERTY SEGUROS—See Liberty Mutual Holding Company Inc.; *U.S. Private*, pg. 2446
LIBERTY SHIP INC.—See Melco Holdings Inc.; *Int'l*, pg. 4808
LIBERTY SHOES LIMITED; *Int'l*, pg. 4486
LIBERTY STAR URANIUM & METALS CORP.; *U.S. Public*, pg. 1311
LIBERTY STEEL GEORGETOWN, INC.—See GFG Alliance Limited; *Int'l*, pg. 2956
LIBERTY STEEL PRODUCTS INC.; *U.S. Private*, pg. 2447
LIBERTY STREET ADVISORS, LLC; *U.S. Private*, pg. 2447
LIBERTY SUPPLY INC.; *U.S. Private*, pg. 2447
LIBERTY SYSTEMS, INC.; *U.S. Private*, pg. 2447

LIBERTY TAX SERVICE INC.—See B. Riley Financial, Inc.; *U.S. Public*, pg. 261
LIBERTY TAX SERVICE INC.—See Irradiant Partners, LP; *U.S. Private*, pg. 2140
LIBERTY TECHNOLOGIES—See Millwood Inc.; *U.S. Private*, pg. 2738
LIBERTY TELECOMS HOLDINGS, INC.—See Globe Telecom, Inc.; *Int'l*, pg. 3006
LIBERTY TELECOMS HOLDINGS, INC.—See PLDT Inc.; *Int'l*, pg. 5896
LIBERTY TIRE RECYCLING, LLC—See The Carlyle Group Inc.; *U.S. Public*, pg. 2048
LIBERTY TIRE RECYCLING—See The Carlyle Group Inc.; *U.S. Public*, pg. 2048
LIBERTY TIRE SERVICES, LLC—See The Carlyle Group Inc.; *U.S. Public*, pg. 2048
LIBERTY TRANSPORTATION, INC.; *U.S. Private*, pg. 2447
LIBERTY U.S.A., INC.—See Performance Food Group Company; *U.S. Public*, pg. 1674
LIBERTY UTILITIES APPLE VALLEY—See Algonquin Power & Utilities Corp.; *Int'l*, pg. 319
LIBERTY UTILITIES (CANADA) CORP.—See Algonquin Power & Utilities Corp.; *Int'l*, pg. 319
LIBERTY UTILITIES CO.—See Algonquin Power & Utilities Corp.; *Int'l*, pg. 319
LIBERTY UTILITIES ENERGY SOLUTIONS (APPLIANCE) CORP.—See Algonquin Power & Utilities Corp.; *Int'l*, pg. 319
LIBERTY UTILITIES (PINE BLUFF WATER) INC.—See Algonquin Power & Utilities Corp.; *Int'l*, pg. 319
LIBERTY UTILITIES WEST—See Algonquin Power & Utilities Corp.; *Int'l*, pg. 319
LIBERTYBANK & TRUST COMPANY, N.A.—See Wintrust Financial Corporation; *U.S. Public*, pg. 2375
LIBERTYVILLE BUICK, PONTIAC, GMC, INC.; *U.S. Private*, pg. 2447
LIBERTYVILLE LINCOLN SALES INC.; *U.S. Private*, pg. 2447
LIBET SA; *Int'l*, pg. 4486
LIBI PLASTIC COMPOUNDING (SHENZHEN) CO., LTD.—See Toray Industries, Inc.; *Int'l*, pg. 7823
LIBLA COMMUNICATIONS INC.; *U.S. Private*, pg. 2447
LIBLA INDUSTRIES INC.; *U.S. Private*, pg. 2447
THE LIBMAN COMPANY; *U.S. Private*, pg. 4069
LIBNET CO., LTD.—See MIRAIT ONE Corporation; *Int'l*, pg. 4917
LIBORD ADVISORS PVT. LTD.—See Libord Finance Ltd.; *Int'l*, pg. 4486
LIBORD FINANCE LTD.; *Int'l*, pg. 4486
LIBORD SECURITIES LTD.; *Int'l*, pg. 4486
LIBRA AG—See PHOENIX Pharmahandel GmbH & Co. KG; *Int'l*, pg. 5854
LIBRA CAPITAL LIMITED—See Libra Group Limited; *Int'l*, pg. 4486
LIBRA ELECTRIC COMPANY; *U.S. Private*, pg. 2447
LIBRA GROUP LIMITED; *Int'l*, pg. 4486
LIBRA HOLIDAYS GROUP PUBLIC LTD.; *Int'l*, pg. 4486
LIBRA INDUSTRIES, INCORPORATED; *U.S. Private*, pg. 2447
LIBRA INDUSTRIES, INC.; *U.S. Private*, pg. 2447
LIBRA INFUSIONS LIMITED; *Int'l*, pg. 4486
LIBRA INSURANCE SERVICES LIMITED—See Marsh & McLennan Companies, Inc.; *U.S. Public*, pg. 1377
LIBRAIRIE ARTHEME FAYARD S.A.—See Vivendi SE; *Int'l*, pg. 8274
LIBRAIRIE GENERALE FRANCAISE—See Vivendi SE; *Int'l*, pg. 8273
LIBRAIRIE PAPETERIE NATIONALE S.A.—See Vivendi SE; *Int'l*, pg. 8278
LIBRAIRIE PARAGRAPHE BOOKSTORE—See Quebecor Inc.; *Int'l*, pg. 6159
LIBRAMIENTO ICA LA PIEDAD, S.A. DE C.V.—See Empresas ICA S.A.B. de C.V.; *Int'l*, pg. 2391
LIBRARY BINDING SERVICE INC.; *U.S. Private*, pg. 2447
THE LIBRARY CORPORATION; *U.S. Private*, pg. 4069
LIBRARY VIDEO COMPANY; *U.S. Private*, pg. 2447
LIBRA SYSTEMS LTD.; *Int'l*, pg. 4487
LIBRATO, INC.—See Silver Lake Group, LLC; *U.S. Private*, pg. 3661
LIBRATO, INC.—See Thoma Bravo, L.P.; *U.S. Private*, pg. 4153
LIBREDIGITAL, INC.—See Atlas Holdings, LLC; *U.S. Private*, pg. 377
LIBREMAX CAPITAL, LLC; *U.S. Private*, pg. 2447
LIBSTAR HOLDINGS LTD.; *Int'l*, pg. 4487
LIBSYS, INC.; *U.S. Private*, pg. 2448
LIBURNIA RIVIERA HOTELI D.D.; *Int'l*, pg. 4487
LIB WORK CO., LTD.; *Int'l*, pg. 4483
LIBYAN INVESTMENT AUTHORITY; *Int'l*, pg. 4487
LICA PARKING COMPANY LIMITED—See Wang On Group Ltd; *Int'l*, pg. 8341
LICARD OOO—See PJSC Lukoil; *Int'l*, pg. 5881
LIC CO., LTD.—See Bengo4.com, Inc.; *Int'l*, pg. 974
LIC DEER LTD—See Livestock Improvement Corporation Limited; *Int'l*, pg. 4531
LICENSELOGIX, LLC—See Wolters Kluwer n.v.; *Int'l*, pg. 8444

LICENSE MONITOR, INC.—See Vista Equity Partners, LLC; *U.S. Private*, pg. 4400
LICENSE ONLINE, INC.—See TD Synnex Corp; *U.S. Public*, pg. 1984
LICENSE TECHNOLOGIES GROUP, INC.—See Dell Technologies Inc.; *U.S. Public*, pg. 650
THE LICENSING COMPANY GERMANY GMBH—See The Licensing Company Limited; *Int'l*, pg. 7664
THE LICENSING COMPANY LIMITED; *Int'l*, pg. 7664
LIC FIJI—See Life Insurance Corporation of India; *Int'l*, pg. 4493
LICHARZ GMBH; *Int'l*, pg. 4487
LICHARZ LTD—See Licharz GmbH; *Int'l*, pg. 4487
LICHARZ PLASTIQUE TECHNIQUE EURL;—See Licharz GmbH; *Int'l*, pg. 4487
LICHEN CHINA LIMITED; *Int'l*, pg. 4487
LI CHENG ENTERPRISE CO., LTD.; *Int'l*, pg. 4481
LICHER MT GMBH—See L'Air Liquide S.A.; *Int'l*, pg. 4374
LICHFL ASSET MANAGEMENT COMPANY LIMITED—See LIC Housing Finance Ltd; *Int'l*, pg. 4487
LICHFL CARE HOMES LIMITED—See LIC Housing Finance Ltd; *Int'l*, pg. 4487
L.I. CHILD & FAMILY DEVELOPMENT SERVICES, INC.; *U.S. Private*, pg. 2366
LIC HOUSING FINANCE LTD; *Int'l*, pg. 4487
LICHTENERGIEWERKE AG; *Int'l*, pg. 4487
LICHTI BROTHERS OIL COMPANY; *U.S. Private*, pg. 2448
LICHTREKLAME-ERZEUGUNG GMBH; *Int'l*, pg. 4487
LICHT ZENTRALE LICHTGROSSHANDEL GMBH—See Wurth Verwaltungsgesellschaft mbH; *Int'l*, pg. 8506
LI CHUNG SHING TONG (HOLDINGS) LIMITED—See Jacobson Pharma Corporation Limited; *Int'l*, pg. 3866
LI CHUNG SHING TONG (S) PTE LIMITED—See Jacobson Pharma Corporation Limited; *Int'l*, pg. 3866
LIC (INTERNATIONAL) B.S.C.—See Warba Insurance and Reinsurance Company K.S.C.P.; *Int'l*, pg. 8344
LIC IRELAND LIMITED—See Livestock Improvement Corporation Limited; *Int'l*, pg. 4531
LICKING VALLEY OIL CO. INC.; *U.S. Private*, pg. 2448
LIC LATIN AMERICA SA—See Livestock Improvement Corporation Limited; *Int'l*, pg. 4531
LIC MAURITIUS OFFSHORE LTD—See Life Insurance Corporation of India; *Int'l*, pg. 4493
LICOGI 13 JOINT STOCK COMPANY—See Infrastructure Development and Construction Corporation; *Int'l*, pg. 3697
LICOGI 14 JOINT STOCK COMPANY; *Int'l*, pg. 4487
LICOGI 16.6 JOINT STOCK COMPANY—See Infrastructure Development and Construction Corporation; *Int'l*, pg. 3697
LICOGI 16 JOINT STOCK COMPANY; *Int'l*, pg. 4487
LICOGI CONSTRUCTION AND FOUNDATION ENGINEERING JOINT STOCK COMPANY NO.20—See Infrastructure Development and Construction Corporation; *Int'l*, pg. 3697
LI-COR, INC.—See Battery Ventures, L.P.; *U.S. Private*, pg. 489
LICO STEEL, INC.—See Columbus McKinnon Corporation; *U.S. Public*, pg. 536
LICOS TRUCKTEC GMBH—See Concentric AB; *Int'l*, pg. 1764
LIC PENSION FUND LTD.—See Life Insurance Corporation of India; *Int'l*, pg. 4493
LICT CORPORATION; *U.S. Public*, pg. 1311
LIC UK LTD—See Livestock Improvement Corporation Limited; *Int'l*, pg. 4531
LIC USA LTD—See Livestock Improvement Corporation Limited; *Int'l*, pg. 4531
LI-CYCLE CORP.—See Li-Cycle Holdings Corp.; *Int'l*, pg. 4481
LI-CYCLE HOLDINGS CORP.; *Int'l*, pg. 4481
LICYN MERCANTIL INDUSTRIAL LTDA—See F.I.L.A. - Fabbrica Italiana Lapis ed Affini S.p.A.; *Int'l*, pg. 2597
LIDA AUSTRALIA PTY. LTD.—See M&C Saatchi plc; *Int'l*, pg. 4611
LIDA (CHINA) MACHINE EQUIPMENT COMPANY LIMITED—See Lida Holdings Limited; *Int'l*, pg. 4487
LIDA HOLDINGS LIMITED; *Int'l*, pg. 4487
LIDAN MARINE AB—See Robert Bosch GmbH; *Int'l*, pg. 6366
LIDA PLANT RESEARCH, S.L.—See OAT Agrio Co., Ltd.; *Int'l*, pg. 5507
LIDA RESOURCES, INC.; *Int'l*, pg. 4488
LIDA SAS—See Air Products & Chemicals, Inc.; *U.S. Public*, pg. 66
LIDA—See M&C Saatchi plc; *Int'l*, pg. 4611
LIDCO GROUP PLC—See Masimo Corporation; *U.S. Public*, pg. 1392
LIDCO LIMITED—See Masimo Corporation; *U.S. Public*, pg. 1392
LIDDELL BROTHERS, INC.—See Investcorp Holdings B.S.C.; *Int'l*, pg. 3777
LIDDELL BROTHERS, INC.—See Trilantic Capital Management L.P.; *U.S. Private*, pg. 4231
LIDDS AB; *Int'l*, pg. 4488
LIDER FAKTORING AS; *Int'l*, pg. 4488
LIDERGAS S.A. E.S.P.—See Air Products & Chemicals, Inc.; *U.S. Public*, pg. 66

LIDESTRI FOODS, INC.; *U.S. Private*, pg. 2448
LIDINGO ELEKTRISKA AB—See Instalco AB; *Int'l*, pg. 3722
LI DING SEMICONDUCTOR TECHNOLOGY (SHENZHEN) CO., LTD.—See Zhen Ding Technology Holding Limited; *Int'l*, pg. 8669
LIDIS; *Int'l*, pg. 4488
LIDKOEB APS—See NoHo Partners Plc; *Int'l*, pg. 5400
LIDL LIMITED—See Schwarz Unternehmenstreuhand KG; *Int'l*, pg. 6645
LIDL STIFTUNG & CO. KG—See Schwarz Unternehmenstreuhand KG; *Int'l*, pg. 6645
LIDO BEACH RESORT; *U.S. Private*, pg. 2448
LIDOCHEM, INC.; *U.S. Private*, pg. 2448
LIDRONE SPOL S.R.O.—See CEZ, a.s.; *Int'l*, pg. 1429
LID TECHNOLOGIES INC.—See Amphenol Corporation; *U.S. Public*, pg. 130
LIDYE CHEMICAL CO., LTD.—See DIC Corporation; *Int'l*, pg. 2109
LIDYE CHEMICAL CO., LTD.—See Lidye Co., Ltd.; *Int'l*, pg. 4488
LIDYE CO., LTD.; *Int'l*, pg. 4488
LIEBEL-FLARSHEIM COMPANY LLC—See Guerbet SA; *Int'l*, pg. 3172
LIEBEL-FLARSHEIM IRELAND LIMITED—See Guerbet SA; *Int'l*, pg. 3172
LIEBEN LOGISTICS PROPRIETARY LIMITED—See Super Group Limited; *Int'l*, pg. 7334
LIEBERMAN COMPANIES, INC.—See American Vending Sales, Inc.; *U.S. Private*, pg. 258
LIEBERT CANADA—See Emerson Electric Co.; *U.S. Public*, pg. 744
LIEBERT CORPORATION—See Vertiv Holdings Co; *U.S. Public*, pg. 2289
LIEBERT CORPORATION—See Vertiv Holdings Co; *U.S. Public*, pg. 2289
LIEBERT CORPORATION—See Vertiv Holdings Co; *U.S. Public*, pg. 2289
LIEBERT CORPORATION—See Vertiv Holdings Co; *U.S. Public*, pg. 2289
LIEBHERR-AEROSPACE BRASIL LTDA.—See Embraer S.A.; *Int'l*, pg. 2375
LIEBHERR-AEROSPACE BRASIL LTDA.—See Liebherr-International AG; *Int'l*, pg. 4489
LIEBHERR-AEROSPACE LINDENBERG GMBH—See Liebherr-International AG; *Int'l*, pg. 4490
LIEBHERR-AEROSPACE NIZHNY NOVGOROD OOO—See Liebherr-International AG; *Int'l*, pg. 4489
LIEBHERR-AEROSPACE SALINE, INC.—See Liebherr-International AG; *Int'l*, pg. 4489
LIEBHERR-AEROSPACE TOULOUSE S.A.—See Liebherr-International AG; *Int'l*, pg. 4489
LIEBHERR-AEROSPACE & TRANSPORTATION SAS—See Liebherr-International AG; *Int'l*, pg. 4489
LIEBHERR-AFRICA (PTY.) LTD.—See Liebherr-International AG; *Int'l*, pg. 4489
LIEBHERR-AMERICA INC.—See Liebherr-International AG; *Int'l*, pg. 4489
LIEBHERR APPLIANCES KLUANG SDN. BHD.—See Liebherr-International AG; *Int'l*, pg. 4488
LIEBHERR-ARGENTINA S.A—See Liebherr-International AG; *Int'l*, pg. 4489
LIEBHERR-AUSTRALIA PTY. LTD.—See Liebherr-International AG; *Int'l*, pg. 4489
LIEBHERR-AUTOMATION SYSTEMS CO.—See Liebherr-International AG; *Int'l*, pg. 4489
LIEBHERR-AZERI LLC—See Liebherr-International AG; *Int'l*, pg. 4489
LIEBHERR-BAUMASCHINEN AG—See Liebherr-International AG; *Int'l*, pg. 4490
LIEBHERR-BETONPUMPEN GMBH—See Liebherr-International AG; *Int'l*, pg. 4489
LIEBHERR BRASIL GUINDASTES E MAQUINAS OPERATRIZES LTDA.—See Liebherr-International AG; *Int'l*, pg. 4488
LIEBHERR-CANADA LTD.—See Liebherr-International AG; *Int'l*, pg. 4489
LIEBHERR CHILE SPA—See Liebherr-International AG; *Int'l*, pg. 4488
LIEBHERR CMCTEC INDIA PVT. LTD.—See Liebherr-International AG; *Int'l*, pg. 4488
LIEBHERR-COLOMBIA SAS—See Liebherr-International AG; *Int'l*, pg. 4489
LIEBHERR-COMPONENTS AG—See Liebherr-International AG; *Int'l*, pg. 4489
LIEBHERR-COMPONENTS BIBERACH GMBH—See Liebherr-International AG; *Int'l*, pg. 4489
LIEBHERR COMPONENTS (DALIAN) CO. LTD.—See Liebherr-International AG; *Int'l*, pg. 4488
LIEBHERR COMPONENTS NORTH AMERICA CO.—See Liebherr-International AG; *Int'l*, pg. 4488
LIEBHERR-COMPONENT TECHNOLOGIES AG—See Liebherr-International AG; *Int'l*, pg. 4489
LIEBHERR CONCRETE TECHNOLOGY CO.—See Liebherr-International AG; *Int'l*, pg. 4488
LIEBHERR CONSTRUCTION EQUIPMENT CO.—See Liebherr-International AG; *Int'l*, pg. 4489

LIEBHERR-CONSTRUCTION EQUIPMENT IRELAND LIMITED—See Liebherr-International AG; *Int'l*, pg. 4489
LIEBHERR CONTAINER CRANES LTD.—See Liebherr-International AG; *Int'l*, pg. 4488
LIEBHERR-DANMARK APS—See Liebherr-International AG; *Int'l*, pg. 4489
LIEBHERR-ELEKTRONIK GMBH—See Liebherr-International AG; *Int'l*, pg. 4489
LIEBHERR-EMTEC ITALIA S.P.A.—See Liebherr-International AG; *Int'l*, pg. 4489
LIEBHERR EPITOIPARI-GEPEK MAGYARORSZAG KFT.—See Liebherr-International AG; *Int'l*, pg. 4489
LIEBHERR-ETTLINGEN GMBH—See Liebherr-International AG; *Int'l*, pg. 4489
LIEBHERR-EXPORT AG—See Liebherr-International AG; *Int'l*, pg. 4490
LIEBHERR-FINLAND OY AB—See Liebherr-International AG; *Int'l*, pg. 4489
LIEBHERR-FRANCE S.A.—See Liebherr-International AG; *Int'l*, pg. 4489
LIEBHERR-FRANCE SAS—See Liebherr-International AG; *Int'l*, pg. 4490
LIEBHERR-GREAT BRITAIN LTD.—See Liebherr-International AG; *Int'l*, pg. 4490
LIEBHERR GRUES A TOUR SAS—See Liebherr-International AG; *Int'l*, pg. 4489
LIEBHERR GRUES MOBILES SAS—See Liebherr-International AG; *Int'l*, pg. 4489
LIEBHERR-GUTSVERWALTUNG GMBH—See Liebherr-International AG; *Int'l*, pg. 4490
LIEBHERR-HAUSGERATE GMBH—See Liebherr-International AG; *Int'l*, pg. 4490
LIEBHERR-HAUSGERATE LIENZ GMBH—See Liebherr-International AG; *Int'l*, pg. 4490
LIEBHERR-HAUSGERATE MARICA EOOD—See Liebherr-International AG; *Int'l*, pg. 4490
LIEBHERR-HAUSGERATE OCHSENHAUSEN GMBH—See Liebherr-International AG; *Int'l*, pg. 4490
LIEBHERR (HKG) LIMITED—See Liebherr-International AG; *Int'l*, pg. 4488
LIEBHERR-HOLDING GMBH—See Liebherr-International AG; *Int'l*, pg. 4490
LIEBHERR HYDRAULIC EXCAVATORS GMBH—See Liebherr-International AG; *Int'l*, pg. 4490
LIEBHERR-HYDRAULIKBAGGER GMBH—See Liebherr-International AG; *Int'l*, pg. 4490
LIEBHERR IBERICA, S.A.—See Liebherr-International AG; *Int'l*, pg. 4488
LIEBHERR IBERICA, S.L.—See Liebherr-International AG; *Int'l*, pg. 4488
LIEBHERR INDIA PRIVATE LIMITED—See Liebherr-International AG; *Int'l*, pg. 4488
LIEBHERR INDUSTRIAS METALICAS, S.A.—See Liebherr-International AG; *Int'l*, pg. 4488
LIEBHERR-INDUSTRIEANLAGEN AG—See Liebherr-International AG; *Int'l*, pg. 4490
LIEBHERR-INTERNATIONAL AG; *Int'l*, pg. 4488
LIEBHERR-INTERNATIONAL AG—See Liebherr-International AG; *Int'l*, pg. 4491
LIEBHERR INTERNATIONAL AUSTRIA GMBH—See Liebherr-International AG; *Int'l*, pg. 4488
LIEBHERR-INTERTRADING AG—See Liebherr-International AG; *Int'l*, pg. 4491
LIEBHERR (IRELAND) HOLDING LTD.—See Liebherr-International AG; *Int'l*, pg. 4490
LIEBHERR-ITALIA S.P.A.—See Liebherr-International AG; *Int'l*, pg. 4490
LIEBHERR JAPAN CO. LTD.—See Liebherr-International AG; *Int'l*, pg. 4488
LIEBHERR LOGISTIK GMBH—See Liebherr-International AG; *Int'l*, pg. 4490
LIEBHERR MACHINERY (DALIAN) CO., LTD.—See Liebherr-International AG; *Int'l*, pg. 4489
LIEBHERR MACHINERY SERVICE (SHANGHAI) CO. LTD.—See Liebherr-International AG; *Int'l*, pg. 4489
LIEBHERR MACHINES BULLE S.A.—See Liebherr-International AG; *Int'l*, pg. 4490
LIEBHERR MACHINE TOOLS INDIA PVT. LTD.—See Liebherr-International AG; *Int'l*, pg. 4489
LIEBHERR MAKINE TICARET SERVIS LIMITED SIRKETI—See Liebherr-International AG; *Int'l*, pg. 4489
LIEBHERR MALAXAGE & TECHNIQUES SAS—See Liebherr-International AG; *Int'l*, pg. 4490
LIEBHERR-MARITIM BENELUX—See Liebherr-International AG; *Int'l*, pg. 4488
LIEBHERR MARITIME BENELUX B.V.—See Liebherr-International AG; *Int'l*, pg. 4489
LIEBHERR MEXICO S. DE R.L. DE C.V.—See Liebherr-International AG; *Int'l*, pg. 4489
LIEBHERR MIDDLE EAST, FZE.—See Liebherr-International AG; *Int'l*, pg. 4489
LIEBHERR-MIETPARTNER GMBH—See Liebherr-International AG; *Int'l*, pg. 4490
LIEBHERR-MINING EQUIPMENT COLMAR SAS—See Liebherr-International AG; *Int'l*, pg. 4490
LIEBHERR MINING EQUIPMENT CO.—See Liebherr-International AG; *Int'l*, pg. 4489

LIEBHERR-MINING GHANA LIMITED—See Liebherr-International AG; *Int'l*, pg. 4490
LIEBHERR-MISCHTECHNIK GMBH—See Liebherr-International AG; *Int'l*, pg. 4490
LIEBHERR MOBILE CRANES KOREA LTD.—See Liebherr-International AG; *Int'l*, pg. 4489
LIEBHERR MONTERREY, S. DE R.L. DE C. V.—See Liebherr-International AG; *Int'l*, pg. 4489
LIEBHERR-MOZAMBIQUE LDA.—See Liebherr-International AG; *Int'l*, pg. 4490
LIEBHERR-NEDERLAND B.V.—See Liebherr-International AG; *Int'l*, pg. 4490
LIEBHERR NENZING CRANE CO.—See Liebherr-International AG; *Int'l*, pg. 4489
LIEBHERR NENZING CRANE—See Liebherr-International AG; *Int'l*, pg. 4489
LIEBHERR-NENZING EQUIPEMENTS SAS—See Liebherr-International AG; *Int'l*, pg. 4490
LIEBHERR-NENZING SERVICE GMBH—See Liebherr-International AG; *Int'l*, pg. 4490
LIEBHERR-NIGERIA LTD.—See Liebherr-International AG; *Int'l*, pg. 4490
LIEBHERR-NOUVELLE-CALEDONIE SAS—See Liebherr-International AG; *Int'l*, pg. 4490
LIEBHERR-POLSKA SP. Z O.O.—See Liebherr-International AG; *Int'l*, pg. 4490
LIEBHERR-ROMANIA S.R.L.—See Liebherr-International AG; *Int'l*, pg. 4490
LIEBHERR-RUSSLAND O.O.O.—See Liebherr-International AG; *Int'l*, pg. 4490
LIEBHERR SALES KLUANG SDN. BHD.—See Liebherr-International AG; *Int'l*, pg. 4488
LIEBHERR-SERVICE AG—See Liebherr-International AG; *Int'l*, pg. 4491
LIEBHERR-SINGAPORE PTE. LTD.—See Liebherr-International AG; *Int'l*, pg. 4490
LIEBHERR-STAVEBNI STROJE CZ S.R.O.—See Liebherr-International AG; *Int'l*, pg. 4491
LIEBHERR SUNDERLAND WORKS LTD.—See Liebherr-International AG; *Int'l*, pg. 4489
LIEBHERR-SVERIGE AB—See Liebherr-International AG; *Int'l*, pg. 4490
LIEBHERR-SWISSHOLDING AG—See Liebherr-International AG; *Int'l*, pg. 4491
LIEBHERR-THAILAND CO., LTD.—See Liebherr-International AG; *Int'l*, pg. 4491
LIEBHERR-TRANSPORTATION SYSTEMS GMBH—See Liebherr-International AG; *Int'l*, pg. 4491
LIEBHERR-TRANSPORTATION SYSTEMS MANNHEIM GMBH—See Liebherr-International AG; *Int'l*, pg. 4491
LIEBHERR-TRANSPORTATION SYSTEMS MARICA EOOD—See Liebherr-International AG; *Int'l*, pg. 4491
LIEBHERR-UTENSILI S.R.L.—See Liebherr-International AG; *Int'l*, pg. 4491
LIEBHERR-VERKEHRSTECHNIK GMBH—See Liebherr-International AG; *Int'l*, pg. 4488
LIEBHERR VERZAHNTECHNIK GMBH—See Liebherr-International AG; *Int'l*, pg. 4490
LIEBHERR-VERZAHNTECHNIK GMBH—See Liebherr-International AG; *Int'l*, pg. 4490
LIEBHERR-WERK BIBERACH GMBH—See Liebherr-International AG; *Int'l*, pg. 4488
LIEBHERR-WERK BISCHOFSHOFEN GMBH—See Liebherr-International AG; *Int'l*, pg. 4490
LIEBHERR-WERK EHINGEN GMBH—See Liebherr-International AG; *Int'l*, pg. 4490
LIEBHERR-WERK LIENZ GMBH—See Liebherr-International AG; *Int'l*, pg. 4488
LIEBHERR-WERK NENZING GMBH—See Liebherr-International AG; *Int'l*, pg. 4488
LIEBHERR-WERK TELFS GMBH—See Liebherr-International AG; *Int'l*, pg. 4488
LIEBHERR-WUPPER GMBH—See Liebherr-International AG; *Int'l*, pg. 4490
LIEBOVICH BROS., INC.—See Reliance Steel & Aluminum Co.; *U.S. Public*, pg. 1780
LIEBOVICH/PDM STEEL & ALUMINUM COMPANY—See Reliance Steel & Aluminum Co.; *U.S. Public*, pg. 1781
LIECHTENSTEIN GLOBAL TRUST AG; *Int'l*, pg. 4491
LIECHTENSTEINISCHE LANDESBANK AG; *Int'l*, pg. 4491
LIECHTENSTEINISCHE LANDESBANK LTD.—See Liechtensteinische Landesbank AG; *Int'l*, pg. 4492
LIECHTENSTEINISCHE LANDESBANK (OSTERREICH) AG—See Liechtensteinische Landesbank AG; *Int'l*, pg. 4492
LIECHTENSTEINISCHE LANDESBANK (OSTERREICH) AG—See Liechtensteinische Landesbank AG; *Int'l*, pg. 4492
LIECHTENSTEINISCHE LANDESBANK (SCHWEIZ) AG—See Liechtensteinische Landesbank AG; *Int'l*, pg. 4492
LIECHTY FARM EQUIPMENT INC.; *U.S. Private*, pg. 2448
LIEDTKA TRUCKING INCORPORATED; *U.S. Private*, pg. 2448
LIEGENSCHAFTSVERWALTUNGS GMBH—See voestalpine AG; *Int'l*, pg. 8289
LIEGL & DACHSER SZALLITMANYOSZASI ES LOGISZTIKAI KFT.—See Dachser GmbH & Co.; *Int'l*, pg. 1904

COMPANY NAME INDEX

LIEN CHANG ELECTRONIC ENTERPRISE CO., LTD.; *Int'l*, pg. 4492
LIEN FUNG PRECISION TECHNOLOGY DEVELOPMENT CO., LTD—See Linde plc; *Int'l*, pg. 4505
LIENHARD OFFICE GROUP AG; *Int'l*, pg. 4492
LIEN HOE CORPORATION BERHAD; *Int'l*, pg. 4492
LIEN HWA INDUSTRIAL HOLDINGS CORP; *Int'l*, pg. 4492
LIEN JEH TRANSPORTATION CO , LTD.—See MiTAC International Corp.; *Int'l*, pg. 4923
LIENTEH TECHNOLOGY SDN. BHD.—See Eonmetall Group Berhad; *Int'l*, pg. 2458
LIER CHEMICAL CO., LTD.; *Int'l*, pg. 4492
LIERDA SCIENCE AND TECHNOLOGY GROUP CO. LTD.—See STMicroelectronics N.V.; *Int'l*, pg. 7217
LIESCH ASSOCIATES, INC.—See Terracon Consultants, Inc.; *U.S. Private*, pg. 3971
LIETUVOS ENERGIJOS GAMYBA, AB; *Int'l*, pg. 4492
LIETZ DEVELOPMENT, INC.; *U.S. Private*, pg. 2448
LIFAN TECHNOLOGY (GROUP) CO., LTD.; *Int'l*, pg. 4492
LIFCO AB—See Carl Bennet AB; *Int'l*, pg. 1332
LIFCO, LLC—See J.C. Flowers & Co. LLC; *U.S. Private*, pg. 2159
LIFE360, INC.; *U.S. Public*, pg. 1312
LIFE365 PORTRAITS; *U.S. Private*, pg. 2449
LIFE ACTION MINISTRIES; *U.S. Private*, pg. 2448
LIFE ALERT EMERGENCY RESPONSE INC.; *U.S. Private*, pg. 2448
LIFE ANGEL CO., LTD.—See TAKE AND GIVE. NEEDS Co. Ltd.; *Int'l*, pg. 7436
LIFEASSAYS AB; *Int'l*, pg. 4493
LIFE ASSURANCE BANK OF IRELAND LIFE HOLDINGS PLC—See Bank of Ireland Group plc; *Int'l*, pg. 845
LIFE BANC & SPLIT CORP.; *Int'l*, pg. 4492
LIFEBANKUSA—See Human Longevity, Inc.; *U.S. Private*, pg. 2005
LIFE BENEFIT SOLUTIONS INC.—See People Corporation; *Int'l*, pg. 5793
LIFEBOAT DISTRIBUTION, EMEA B.V.—See Climb Global Solutions, Inc.; *U.S. Public*, pg. 515
LIFEBOAT DISTRIBUTION, INC.—See Climb Global Solutions, Inc.; *U.S. Public*, pg. 515
LIFE BOND HOLDING GMBH & CO. KG; *Int'l*, pg. 4492
LIFEBRANDZ LTD.; *Int'l*, pg. 4494
LIFEBRIDGE HEALTH; *U.S. Private*, pg. 2449
LIFE CARD CO., LTD.—See AIFUL Corporation; *Int'l*, pg. 232
LIFECARE ALLIANCE—See Central Ohio Diabetes Association; *U.S. Private*, pg. 824
LIFECARE AMBULANCE, INC.; *U.S. Private*, pg. 2449
LIFECARE AS; *Int'l*, pg. 4494
LIFE CARE CENTER OF CARROLLTON; *U.S. Private*, pg. 2448
LIFE CARE CENTERS OF AMERICA; *U.S. Private*, pg. 2448
LIFE CARE COMPANIES, LLC; *U.S. Private*, pg. 2448
LIFECARE HOLDINGS, INC.—See The Carlyle Group Inc.; *U.S. Public*, pg. 2048
LIFE CARE HOME HEALTH SERVICES CORP—See LCS Holdings Inc.; *U.S. Private*, pg. 2404
LIFECARE HOSPITAL—See Post Acute Medical, LLC; *U.S. Private*, pg. 3234
LIFECARE, INC.—See IAC Inc.; *U.S. Public*, pg. 1082
LIFECARE MEDICAL CENTER; *U.S. Private*, pg. 2449
LIFECARE MEDICAL SERVICES, INC.; *U.S. Private*, pg. 2449
LIFE CARE SERVICES LLC—See LCS Holdings Inc.; *U.S. Private*, pg. 2404
LIFECELL EMEA LIMITED—See AbbVie Inc.; *U.S. Public*, pg. 24
LIFECELL EMEA LIMITED—See AbbVie Inc.; *U.S. Public*, pg. 24
LIFECENTER NORTHWEST; *U.S. Private*, pg. 2449
LIFE CERTAIN WEALTH STRATEGIES, LLC—See Reverence Capital Partners LLC; *U.S. Private*, pg. 3415
LIFECIRCLES; *U.S. Private*, pg. 2449
LIFECLEAN INTERNATIONAL AB; *Int'l*, pg. 4494
LIFE CLIPS, INC.; *U.S. Public*, pg. 1312
LIFECOME BIOCHEMISTRY CO., LTD.; *Int'l*, pg. 4494
LIFE CONCEPTS HOLDINGS LIMITED; *Int'l*, pg. 4492
LIFECORE BIOMEDICAL, INC.; *U.S. Public*, pg. 1312
LIFECORE BIOMEDICAL, INC.—See Lifecore Biomedical, Inc.; *U.S. Public*, pg. 1312
LIFE CORPORATION SERVICES (S) PTE. LTD.—See Global Cord Blood Corporation; *Int'l*, pg. 2994
LIFE CORPORATION; *Int'l*, pg. 4493
LIFECOURSE MANAGEMENT SERVICE; *U.S. Private*, pg. 2449
LIFE CREATE LIMITED—See Fujitsu Limited; *Int'l*, pg. 2834
LIFECYCLE CONSTRUCTION SERVICES INC.; *U.S. Private*, pg. 2449
LIFE DESIGN PARTNERS CO., LTD.—See Aizawa Securities Group Co., Ltd.; *Int'l*, pg. 255
LIFEDESIGNS; *U.S. Private*, pg. 2449
LIFE DESIGN STATION INTERNATIONAL, INC.; *U.S. Public*, pg. 1312
LIFEDNA, INC.—See Nu Skin Enterprises, Inc.; *U.S. Public*, pg. 1551

LIFEDOJO INC.—See Ontrak, Inc.; *U.S. Public*, pg. 1605
LIFEDRINK COMPANY INC.; *Int'l*, pg. 4494
LIFE-EAT CO., LTD.—See Senko Group Holdings Co., Ltd.; *Int'l*, pg. 6710
LIFE ELEX INC.—See Valeo S.A.; *Int'l*, pg. 8113
LIFE EXCHANGE, INC.; *U.S. Public*, pg. 2448
LIFEFACTORY, INC.—See Thermos L.L.C.; *U.S. Private*, pg. 4143
LIFE FITNESS (ATLANTIC) B.V.—See KPS Capital Partners, LP; *U.S. Private*, pg. 2347
LIFE FITNESS BRASIL—See KPS Capital Partners, LP; *U.S. Private*, pg. 2347
LIFE FITNESS EUROPE GMBH—See KPS Capital Partners, LP; *U.S. Private*, pg. 2347
LIFE FITNESS, INC.—See KPS Capital Partners, LP; *U.S. Private*, pg. 2347
LIFE FITNESS ITALIA S.R.L.—See KPS Capital Partners, LP; *U.S. Private*, pg. 2347
LIFE FITNESS JAPAN, LTD.—See KPS Capital Partners, LP; *U.S. Private*, pg. 2347
LIFE FITNESS PHYSICAL THERAPY, LLC—See U.S. Physical Therapy, Inc.; *U.S. Public*, pg. 2215
LIFE FITNESS (U.K.) LIMITED—See KPS Capital Partners, LP; *U.S. Private*, pg. 2347
LIFEFLEET SOUTHEAST, INC.—See KKR & Co. Inc.; *U.S. Public*, pg. 1251
LIFE FOODS CO., LTD.—See Seven & i Holdings Co., Ltd.; *Int'l*, pg. 6731
LIFE FOR RELIEF & DEVELOPMENT; *U.S. Private*, pg. 2448
LIFE FORWARD CO., LTD.—See SAN Holdings, Inc.; *Int'l*, pg. 6521
LIFE GEAR CORPORATION—See Mitsubishi Corporation; *Int'l*, pg. 4939
LIFEGIFT ORGAN DONATION CENTER; *U.S. Private*, pg. 2450
LIFEGLOBAL GROUP LLC—See The Cooper Companies, Inc.; *U.S. Public*, pg. 2066
LIFEGUARD AIR AMBULANCE, INC.; *U.S. Private*, pg. 2450
LIFEGUARD MEDICAL SOLUTIONS, LLC—See Ridgemont Partners Management LLC; *U.S. Private*, pg. 3433
LIFEGUARD TRANSPORTATION SERVICE, INC.; *U.S. Private*, pg. 2450
LIFEGUARD TRANSPORTATION SERVICE, INC.—See Lifeguard Transportation Service, Inc.; *U.S. Private*, pg. 2450
LIFEHEALTHCARE DISTRIBUTION PTY LTD.—See EBOS Group Limited; *Int'l*, pg. 2285
LIFE HEALTHCARE GROUP HOLDINGS LIMITED; *Int'l*, pg. 4493
LIFE HEALTHCARE GROUP LIMITED; *Int'l*, pg. 4493
LIFEHEALTH LIMITED—See Lundbeckfonden; *Int'l*, pg. 4583
LIFEHME, INC.—See AdaptHealth Corp.; *U.S. Public*, pg. 39
LIFEIMAGE, INC.—See HgCapital Trust plc; *Int'l*, pg. 3376
LIFE INSURANCE COMPANIES OF THE SOUTHWEST—See National Life Insurance Company; *U.S. Private*, pg. 2858
LIFE INSURANCE COMPANY FREEDOM FINANCE LIFE JSC; *Int'l*, pg. 4493
LIFE INSURANCE COMPANY OF ALABAMA INC.; *U.S. Private*, pg. 2448
LIFE INSURANCE COMPANY OF BOSTON & NEW YORK—See Boston Mutual Life Insurance Company; *U.S. Private*, pg. 622
LIFE INSURANCE COMPANY OF NORTH AMERICA—See The Cigna Group; *U.S. Public*, pg. 2061
LIFE INSURANCE COMPANY STANDARD LIFE JSC; *Int'l*, pg. 4493
LIFE INSURANCE CORPORATION (LANKA) LTD.—See Life Insurance Corporation of India; *Int'l*, pg. 4493
LIFE INSURANCE CORPORATION (NEPAL) LTD.—See Life Insurance Corporation of India; *Int'l*, pg. 4493
LIFE INSURANCE CORPORATION OF INDIA; *Int'l*, pg. 4493
LIFE INSURANCE CORPORATION (SINGAPORE) PTE. LTD.—See Life Insurance Corporation of India; *Int'l*, pg. 4493
LIFE INTELLIGENT ENTERPRISE HOLDINGS CO., LTD.; *Int'l*, pg. 4493
LIFE INVESTORS INSURANCE COMPANY OF AMERICA—See Aegon N.V.; *Int'l*, pg. 174
LIFE IS HARD S.A.; *Int'l*, pg. 4493
LIFEIST WELLNESS INC.; *Int'l*, pg. 4494
LIFEIT CO., LTD.—See Tea Life Co., Ltd.; *Int'l*, pg. 7499
LIFELABS INC.—See Ontario Municipal Employees Retirement System; *Int'l*, pg. 5583
LIFELAST INC.—See Henkel AG & Co. KGaA; *Int'l*, pg. 3354
LIFELINE AMBULANCE SERVICE, INC.—See KKR & Co. Inc.; *U.S. Public*, pg. 1249
LIFELINE BIOTECHNOLOGIES, INC.; *U.S. Public*, pg. 1312
LIFE LINE EMERGENCY VEHICLES, INC.; *U.S. Private*, pg. 2448

LIFEPICS INC.

LIFELINE HOME HEALTH CARE OF BOWLING GREEN, LLC—See UnitedHealth Group Incorporated; *U.S. Public*, pg. 2245
LIFELINE HOME HEALTH CARE OF FULTON, LLC—See UnitedHealth Group Incorporated; *U.S. Public*, pg. 2245
LIFELINE HOME HEALTH CARE OF HOPKINSVILLE, LLC—See UnitedHealth Group Incorporated; *U.S. Public*, pg. 2245
LIFELINE HOME HEALTH CARE OF LEXINGTON, LLC—See UnitedHealth Group Incorporated; *U.S. Public*, pg. 2245
LIFELINE HOME HEALTH CARE OF RUSSELLVILLE, LLC—See UnitedHealth Group Incorporated; *U.S. Public*, pg. 2246
LIFELINE HOME HEALTH CARE OF SOMERSET, LLC—See UnitedHealth Group Incorporated; *U.S. Public*, pg. 2246
LIFELINE HOME HEALTH CARE OF SPRINGFIELD, LLC—See UnitedHealth Group Incorporated; *U.S. Public*, pg. 2246
LIFELINE OF WEST TENNESSEE, LLC—See UnitedHealth Group Incorporated; *U.S. Public*, pg. 2246
LIFELINE PENSACOLA, LLC—See DaVita Inc.; *U.S. Public*, pg. 640
LIFELINE PRIVATE DUTY SERVICES OF KENTUCKY, LLC—See UnitedHealth Group Incorporated; *U.S. Public*, pg. 2246
LIFELINE ROCKCASTLE HOME HEALTH, LLC—See UnitedHealth Group Incorporated; *U.S. Public*, pg. 2246
LIFELINE SCIENTIFIC, INC.—See Shanghai Genext Medical Technology Co. Ltd.; *Int'l*, pg. 6768
LIFELINE SKINCARE, INC—See International Stem Cell Corporation; *U.S. Public*, pg. 1158
LIFELINE VASCULAR CENTER- ALBANY, LLC—See DaVita Inc.; *U.S. Public*, pg. 640
LIFELINE VASCULAR CENTER OF SOUTH ORLANDO, LLC—See DaVita Inc.; *U.S. Public*, pg. 640
LIFELINE VASCULAR CENTER - ORLANDO, LLC—See DaVita Inc.; *U.S. Public*, pg. 640
LIFELINE YOUTH & FAMILY SERVICES, INC.; *U.S. Private*, pg. 2450
LIFELINK FOUNDATION, INC.; *U.S. Private*, pg. 2450
LIFELOCK, INC.—See Gen Digital Inc.; *U.S. Public*, pg. 910
LIFELOC TECHNOLOGIES, INC.; *U.S. Public*, pg. 1312
LIFE & LONGEVITY LTD.—See Bumrungrad Hospital Public Company Limited; *Int'l*, pg. 1215
LIFELONG MEDICAL CARE; *U.S. Private*, pg. 2450
LIFELONG; *U.S. Private*, pg. 2450
LIFEMAP ASSURANCE COMPANY—See Cambia Health Solutions, Inc.; *U.S. Private*, pg. 726
LIFEMAP SCIENCES, LTD.—See Lineage Cell Therapeutics, Inc.; *U.S. Public*, pg. 1320
LIFEMARK HEALTH CORPORATION—See George Weston Limited; *Int'l*, pg. 2939
LIFEMARK SECURITIES CORP.; *U.S. Private*, pg. 2450
LIFE MASTERY ACADEMY PTE. LTD—See PropNex Limited; *Int'l*, pg. 5998
LIFE MATERIAL TECHNOLOGIES LIMITED—See HeiQ Plc; *Int'l*, pg. 3326
LIFEMATTERS; *U.S. Private*, pg. 2450
LIFEMATTERS—See Lifematters; *U.S. Private*, pg. 2450
LIFEMD, INC.; *U.S. Public*, pg. 1313
LIFEMED ALASKA, LLC—See CVS Health Corporation; *U.S. Public*, pg. 616
LIFE-MEDIC HEALTHCARE SUPPLIES PTE. LTD.—See Singapore Press Holdings Ltd.; *Int'l*, pg. 6942
LIFEMODELER, INC.—See Smith & Nephew plc; *Int'l*, pg. 7009
LIFENET HEALTH, INC.; *U.S. Private*, pg. 2450
LIFENET, INC.; *U.S. Private*, pg. 2450
LIFENET INSURANCE COMPANY; *Int'l*, pg. 4494
LIFE OF THE SOUTH INSURANCE COMPANY—See Tiptree Inc.; *U.S. Public*, pg. 2159
LIFEON ASIA SDN. BHD.—See Texchem Resources Bhd.; *Int'l*, pg. 7583
LIFE ON EARTH, INC.; *U.S. Public*, pg. 1312
LIFE PARTNERS HOLDINGS, INC.; *U.S. Private*, pg. 2448
LIFE PARTNERS, INC.—See Life Partners Holdings, Inc.; *U.S. Private*, pg. 2448
LIFE PARTNERS IRA HOLDER PARTNERSHIP, LLC; *U.S. Private*, pg. 2449
LIFE PARTNERS POSITION HOLDER TRUST; *U.S. Private*, pg. 2449
LIFEPATH; *U.S. Private*, pg. 2450
LIFEPICS INC.; *U.S. Private*, pg. 2450
LIFEPLAN AUSTRALIA BUILDING SOCIETY LIMITED—See Australian Unity Limited; *Int'l*, pg. 723
LIFEPLAN AUSTRALIA FRIENDLY SOCIETY LIMITED—See Australian Unity Limited; *Int'l*, pg. 723
LIFE PLAN CO., LTD.—See Qol Holdings Co., Ltd.; *Int'l*, pg. 6147
LIFEPLANS LLC—See ABRY Partners, LLC; *U.S. Private*, pg. 42
LIFE PLAZA PARTNERS CO., LTD.—See Nippon Life Insurance Company; *Int'l*, pg. 5322

LIFEPLUS EUROPE LTD.—See Lifeplus International; *U.S. Private*, pg. 2450
LIFEPLUS INTERNATIONAL; *U.S. Private*, pg. 2450
LIFE PLUS SP. Z O.O.—See Aviva plc; *Int'l*, pg. 746
LIFEPOINT CORPORATE SERVICES, GENERAL PARTNERSHIP—See Apollo Global Management, Inc.; *U.S. Public*, pg. 158
LIFEPOINT HEALTH, INC.—See Apollo Global Management, Inc.; *U.S. Public*, pg. 154
LIFEPOINT OF LAKE CUMBERLAND, LLC—See Apollo Global Management, Inc.; *U.S. Public*, pg. 158
LIFEQUEST WORLD CORP.; *U.S. Public*, pg. 1313
LIFE QUOTES, INC.—See Bain Capital, LP; *U.S. Private*, pg. 441
LIFE QUOTES, INC.—See Keystone Insurers Group, Inc.; *U.S. Private*, pg. 2300
LIFERAY AUSTRALIA PTY LTD—See Liferay, Inc.; *U.S. Private*, pg. 2450
LIFERAY BRASIL—See Liferay, Inc.; *U.S. Private*, pg. 2450
LIFERAY DALIAN SOFTWARE CO., LTD.—See Liferay, Inc.; *U.S. Private*, pg. 2450
LIFERAY FRANCE—See Liferay, Inc.; *U.S. Private*, pg. 2450
LIFERAY GMBH—See Liferay, Inc.; *U.S. Private*, pg. 2450
LIFERAY HUNGARY KFT.—See Liferay, Inc.; *U.S. Private*, pg. 2451
LIFERAY, INC.; *U.S. Private*, pg. 2450
LIFERAY INDIA PVT. LTD.—See Liferay, Inc.; *U.S. Private*, pg. 2451
LIFERAY IRELAND—See Liferay, Inc.; *U.S. Private*, pg. 2451
LIFERAY JAPAN K. K.—See Liferay, Inc.; *U.S. Private*, pg. 2451
LIFERAY S.L.—See Liferay, Inc.; *U.S. Private*, pg. 2451
LIFERAY UK—See Liferay, Inc.; *U.S. Private*, pg. 2451
LIFE RESEARCH PTY LTD.—See Leading Technology Group Pty Ltd.; *Int'l*, pg. 4433
LIFERIVER BIO-TECH (UNITED STATES) CORP.—See Shanghai ZJ Bio-Tech Co., Ltd.; *Int'l*, pg. 6783
LIFES2GOOD INC.; *U.S. Private*, pg. 2451
LIFESAFE HOLDINGS PLC; *Int'l*, pg. 4494
LIFESAFER, INC; *U.S. Private*, pg. 2451
LIFESAFE TECHNOLOGIES LIMITED—See LifeSafe Holdings Plc; *Int'l*, pg. 4494
LIFE SAFETY COMMERCIAL FIRE & SECURITY SERVICES, INC.; *U.S. Private*, pg. 2449
LIFE SAFETY DISTRIBUTION AG—See Honeywell International Inc.; *U.S. Public*, pg. 1051
LIFE SAFETY SERVICES; *U.S. Private*, pg. 2449
LIFE SALES LLC—See Allianz SE; *Int'l*, pg. 347
LIFESALON CO., LTD.—See Nippon Life Insurance Company; *Int'l*, pg. 5322
LIFESAVING SYSTEMS CORP.—See Arcline Investment Management LP; *U.S. Private*, pg. 315
LIFESCAN CANADA LTD.—See Platinum Equity, LLC; *U.S. Private*, pg. 3205
LIFESCAN, INC.—See Platinum Equity, LLC; *U.S. Private*, pg. 3205
LIFESCAN, LLC—See Platinum Equity, LLC; *U.S. Private*, pg. 3205
LIFESCAN PRODUCTS, LLC—See Johnson & Johnson; *U.S. Public*, pg. 1199
LIFESCAN SCOTLAND LIMITED—See Johnson & Johnson; *U.S. Public*, pg. 1199
LIFESCAN—See Johnson & Johnson; *U.S. Public*, pg. 1199
LIFESCAPE MARKETING CORPORATION—See Dai Nippon Printing Co., Ltd.; *Int'l*, pg. 1915
LIFE SCIENCE ANALYTICS INC—See Informa plc; *Int'l*, pg. 3692
LIFE SCIENCE FACTORY GGMBH—See Sartorius AG; *Int'l*, pg. 6579
LIFE SCIENCE FACTORY MANAGEMENT GMBH—See Sartorius AG; *Int'l*, pg. 6579
LIFE SCIENCE OUTSOURCING, INC.—See Public Pension Capital, LLC; *U.S. Private*, pg. 3300
LIFE SCIENCE REIT PLC; *Int'l*, pg. 4493
LIFE SCIENCES HOLDINGS FRANCE SAS—See Danaher Corporation; *U.S. Public*, pg. 628
LIFE SCIENCES INTERNATIONAL HOLDINGS BV—See Thermo Fisher Scientific Inc.; *U.S. Public*, pg. 2148
LIFE SCIENCES RESEARCH, INC.; *U.S. Private*, pg. 2449
LIFE SCIENCE TECHNOLOGY INC.; *Int'l*, pg. 4493
LIFESCREEN AUSTRALIA PTY LIMITED—See Sonic Healthcare Limited; *Int'l*, pg. 7097
LIFESCRIPT, INC.; *U.S. Private*, pg. 2451
LIFESECURE INSURANCE COMPANY—See Blue Cross Blue Shield of Michigan; *U.S. Private*, pg. 588
LIFE SEMANTICS CORP.; *Int'l*, pg. 4493
LIFE-SEQ, LLC; *U.S. Private*, pg. 2449
LIFESERVE BLOOD CENTER; *U.S. Private*, pg. 2451
LIFE SETTLEMENT ASSETS PLC; *Int'l*, pg. 4493
LIFE SETTLEMENT HOLDING AG; *Int'l*, pg. 4493
LIFESHARE COMMUNITY BLOOD SERVICES; *U.S. Private*, pg. 2451
LIFESHARE MANAGEMENT GROUP, LLC—See Centene Corporation; *U.S. Public*, pg. 469

LIFESHARE TECHNOLOGIES LLC—See The Jordan Company, L.P.; *U.S. Private*, pg. 4062
LIFESIZE COMMUNICATIONS, GMBH—See Logitech International S.A.; *U.S. Public*, pg. 1341
LIFESIZE COMMUNICATIONS, INC.—See Logitech International S.A.; *U.S. Public*, pg. 1341
LIFESIZE COMMUNICATIONS LIMITED—See Logitech International S.A.; *U.S. Public*, pg. 1341
LIFESKILLS, INC.—See Pennyroyal Regional Mental Health, Mental Retardation Board, Inc.; *U.S. Private*, pg. 3138
LIFESOURCE BIOMEDICAL, LLC—See Gold Belt Incorporated; *U.S. Private*, pg. 1727
LIFESOURCE FOODS RESEARCH LIMITED—See Kerry Group plc; *Int'l*, pg. 4139
LIFESPACE COMMUNITIES; *U.S. Private*, pg. 2451
LIFESPAN BRANDS, LLC—See The Bank of New York Mellon Corporation; *U.S. Public*, pg. 2037
LIFESPAN CORP.; *U.S. Private*, pg. 2451
LIFESPAN HOME MEDICAL—See Lifespan Corp.; *U.S. Private*, pg. 2451
LIFESPAN INCORPORATED; *U.S. Private*, pg. 2451
LIFESPAN, INC.—See Community First Solutions; *U.S. Private*, pg. 991
LIFESPAN; *U.S. Private*, pg. 2451
LIFESPEAK, INC.; *Int'l*, pg. 4494
LIFE & SPECIALTY VENTURES, LLC—See USAble Corporation; *U.S. Private*, pg. 4322
LIFESPICE INGREDIENTS, LLC; *U.S. Private*, pg. 2451
LIFE SPORT LTD.—See adidas AG; *Int'l*, pg. 146
LIFESPOT CAPITAL AG; *Int'l*, pg. 4494
LIFESTAGES, SAMARITAN CENTERS FOR WOMEN, LTD.—See Catholic Health Initiatives; *U.S. Private*, pg. 790
LIFESTANCE HEALTH GROUP, INC.; *U.S. Public*, pg. 1313
LIFESTAR AMBULANCE, INC.—See Catholic Healthcare Partners; *U.S. Private*, pg. 792
LIFESTAR CO., LTD.—See RS Public Company Limited; *Int'l*, pg. 6418
LIFESTAR HOLDING PLC; *Int'l*, pg. 4494
LIFESTAR PHARMA LLC—See Mankind Pharma Ltd.; *Int'l*, pg. 4673
LIFESTAR RESPONSE CORP. - HOLTSVILLE—See Lundbeckfonden; *Int'l*, pg. 4582
LIFESTAR RESPONSE CORP.—See Lundbeckfonden; *Int'l*, pg. 4582
LIFESTAR RESPONSE OF ALABAMA, INC.—See Lundbeckfonden; *Int'l*, pg. 4582
LIFESTAR RESPONSE OF MARYLAND, INC—See Lundbeckfonden; *Int'l*, pg. 4582
LIFE'S TILES PTY. LTD.—See Wesfarmers Limited; *Int'l*, pg. 8381
LIFE'S TIME CAPSULE SERVICES, INC.; *U.S. Public*, pg. 1312
LIFE STORAGE, INC.—See Extra Space Storage, Inc.; *U.S. Public*, pg. 813
LIFE STORAGE LP—See Extra Space Storage, Inc.; *U.S. Public*, pg. 813
LIFESTORE FINANCIAL GROUP; *U.S. Public*, pg. 1313
LIFESTREAM BEHAVIORAL CENTER; *U.S. Private*, pg. 2451
LIFESTREAM COMPLETE SENIOR LIVING; *U.S. Private*, pg. 2451
LIFESTREAM; *U.S. Private*, pg. 2451
LIFE STRIDES PHYSICAL THERAPY AND REHABILITATION, LIMITED PARTNERSHIP—See U.S. Physical Therapy, Inc.; *U.S. Public*, pg. 2215
LIFESTYLE CHINA GROUP LIMITED; *Int'l*, pg. 4494
LIFESTYLE COMMUNITIES DEVELOPMENT PTY. LTD.—See Lifestyle Communities Limited; *Int'l*, pg. 4494
LIFESTYLE COMMUNITIES INVESTMENTS CRANBOURNE PTY LTD—See Lifestyle Communities Limited; *Int'l*, pg. 4494
LIFESTYLE COMMUNITIES LIMITED; *Int'l*, pg. 4494
LIFESTYLE COMMUNITIES MANAGEMENT PTY. LTD.—See Lifestyle Communities Limited; *Int'l*, pg. 4494
LIFESTYLE DCG INC.—See Lifestyle Global Enterprise, Inc.; *Int'l*, pg. 4495
LIFESTYLE ENTERPRISE, INC.—See Lifestyle Global Enterprise, Inc.; *Int'l*, pg. 4495
LIFE-STYLE FASHION GMBH—See GERRY WEBER International AG; *Int'l*, pg. 2945
LIFESTYLE FOOTWEAR, INC.—See Rocky Brands, Inc.; *U.S. Public*, pg. 1807
LIFESTYLE GLOBAL ENTERPRISE, INC.; *Int'l*, pg. 4495
LIFESTYLE GURU PTE. LTD.—See Natural Cool Holdings Limited; *Int'l*, pg. 5167
LIFESTYLE INTERNATIONAL HOLDINGS LTD; *Int'l*, pg. 4495
LIFESTYLE INTERNATIONAL PVT. LTD.—See Landmark Retail Holdings 1 Limited; *Int'l*, pg. 4407
LIFESTYLE MAGAZINES PUBLISHING PTE LTD—See Bacui Technologies International Ltd.; *Int'l*, pg. 795
LIFESTYLE MEDICAL NETWORK INC.; *U.S. Public*, pg. 1313

LIFESTYLE PROTECTION AG—See Talanx AG; *Int'l*, pg. 7445
LIFESTYLE PROTECTION LEBENSVERSICHERUNG AG—See Talanx AG; *Int'l*, pg. 7445
LIFESTYLE SEASONS PTY. LTD.—See Lifestyle Communities Limited; *Int'l*, pg. 4494
LIFESTYLE SERVICES GROUP LIMITED—See Assurant, Inc.; *U.S. Public*, pg. 215
LIFESTYLES MARKETING GROUP, INC.—See UBS Group AG; *Int'l*, pg. 8006
LIFE'S WORC; *U.S. Private*, pg. 2449
LIFESYNC CORPORATION—See HealthEdge Investment Partners, LLC; *U.S. Private*, pg. 1896
LIFETECH ENERGY INC.—See Pan Jit International Inc.; *Int'l*, pg. 5714
LIFE-TECH INC.; *U.S. Private*, pg. 2449
LIFE TECHNOLOGIES AUSTRALIA PTY LTD.—See Thermo Fisher Scientific Inc.; *U.S. Public*, pg. 2149
LIFE TECHNOLOGIES CHILE SPA—See Thermo Fisher Scientific Inc.; *U.S. Public*, pg. 2148
LIFE TECHNOLOGIES CLINICAL SERVICES LAB, INC.—See Thermo Fisher Scientific Inc.; *U.S. Public*, pg. 2149
LIFE TECHNOLOGIES CORPORATION—See Thermo Fisher Scientific Inc.; *U.S. Public*, pg. 2148
LIFE TECHNOLOGIES EUROPE B.V. - NEDERLAENDERNA FILIAL SVERIGE - SWEDEN—See Thermo Fisher Scientific Inc.; *U.S. Public*, pg. 2149
LIFE TECHNOLOGIES GMBH—See Thermo Fisher Scientific Inc.; *U.S. Public*, pg. 2149
LIFE TECHNOLOGIES HOLDINGS PTE LTD.—See Thermo Fisher Scientific Inc.; *U.S. Public*, pg. 2149
LIFE TECHNOLOGIES JAPAN LIMITED—See Thermo Fisher Scientific Inc.; *U.S. Public*, pg. 2149
LIFE TECHNOLOGIES KOREA LLC—See Thermo Fisher Scientific Inc.; *U.S. Public*, pg. 2149
LIFE TECHNOLOGIES LIMITED—See Thermo Fisher Scientific Inc.; *U.S. Public*, pg. 2149
LIFE TECHNOLOGIES LIMITED—See Thermo Fisher Scientific Inc.; *U.S. Public*, pg. 2149
LIFE TECHNOLOGIES MAGYARORSZAG KFT.—See Thermo Fisher Scientific Inc.; *U.S. Public*, pg. 2149
LIFE TECHNOLOGIES NEW ZEALAND LTD.—See Thermo Fisher Scientific Inc.; *U.S. Public*, pg. 2149
LIFE TECHNOLOGIES SAS—See Thermo Fisher Scientific Inc.; *U.S. Public*, pg. 2149
LIFETECH SCIENTIFIC CORPORATION; *Int'l*, pg. 4495
LIFETECH SCIENTIFIC INDIA PRIVATE LIMITED—See LifeTech Scientific Corporation; *Int'l*, pg. 4495
LIFETECH SCIENTIFIC (SHENZHEN) CO., LTD.—See LifeTech Scientific Corporation; *Int'l*, pg. 4495
LIFETIME ASSISTANCE INC.; *U.S. Private*, pg. 2451
LIFETIME BRANDS GLOBAL LIMITED—See Lifetime Brands, Inc.; *U.S. Public*, pg. 1313
LIFETIME BRANDS GLOBAL TRADING (SHANGHAI) COMPANY LIMITED—See Lifetime Brands, Inc.; *U.S. Public*, pg. 1313
LIFETIME BRANDS, INC. - BUILT DIVISION—See Lifetime Brands, Inc.; *U.S. Public*, pg. 1313
LIFETIME BRANDS, INC; *U.S. Public*, pg. 1313
LIFETIME DISTRIBUTORS THE BOOK PEOPLE PTY. LIMITED; *Int'l*, pg. 4495
LIFETIME ENTERTAINMENT SERVICES, LLC—See The Hearst Corporation; *U.S. Private*, pg. 4045
LIFETIME ENTERTAINMENT SERVICES, LLC—See The Walt Disney Company; *U.S. Public*, pg. 2137
LIFE TIME FITNESS - BLOOMINGDALE—See Leonard Green & Partners, L.P.; *U.S. Private*, pg. 2426
LIFE TIME FITNESS - BLOOMINGDALE—See TPG Capital, L.P.; *U.S. Public*, pg. 2174
LIFE TIME FITNESS - CHANHASSEN—See Leonard Green & Partners, L.P.; *U.S. Private*, pg. 2426
LIFE TIME FITNESS - CHANHASSEN—See TPG Capital, L.P.; *U.S. Public*, pg. 2174
LIFE TIME FITNESS, INC.—See Leonard Green & Partners, L.P.; *U.S. Private*, pg. 2426
LIFE TIME FITNESS, INC.—See TPG Capital, L.P.; *U.S. Public*, pg. 2174
LIFE TIME GROUP HOLDINGS, INC.; *U.S. Public*, pg. 1312
THE LIFETIME HEALTHCARE COMPANIES; *U.S. Private*, pg. 4069
LIFETIME, INC.; *U.S. Private*, pg. 2451
LIFETIME INDUSTRIES, INC.—See The Goldman Sachs Group, Inc.; *U.S. Public*, pg. 2080
LIFETIME METALS, INC.—See Lifetime Products Inc.; *U.S. Private*, pg. 2451
LIFETIME PARTNERS, INC.—See Mitsubishi Corporation; *Int'l*, pg. 4939
LIFETIME PRODUCTS INC.; *U.S. Private*, pg. 2451
LIFETIME TELEVISION—See The Hearst Corporation; *U.S. Private*, pg. 4045
LIFETIME TELEVISION—See The Walt Disney Company; *U.S. Public*, pg. 2137
LIFETOUCH CANADA INC.—See Apollo Global Management, Inc.; *U.S. Public*, pg. 159
LIFETOUCH CHURCH DIRECTORIES AND PORTRAITS INC.—See Apollo Global Management, Inc.; *U.S. Public*, pg. 159

COMPANY NAME INDEX

LIFETOUCH, INC.—See Apollo Global Management, Inc.; *U.S. Public*, pg. 159
LIFE TRAVEL & TOURIST SERVICE CO., LTD.; *Int'l*, pg. 4493
LIFE UNIFORM COMPANY—See Scrubs & Beyond LLC; *U.S. Private*, pg. 3580
LIFEVANTAGE CANADA LTD.—See LifeVantage Corporation; *U.S. Public*, pg. 1313
LIFEVANTAGE CORPORATION; *U.S. Public*, pg. 1313
LIFEVANTAGE HONG KONG LIMITED—See LifeVantage Corporation; *U.S. Public*, pg. 1313
LIFEVANTAGE THAILAND COMPANY LIMITED—See LifeVantage Corporation; *U.S. Public*, pg. 1313
LIFE VENTURES S.A.—See Nestle S.A.; *Int'l*, pg. 5203
LIFEWATCH AG—See Koninklijke Philips N.V.; *Int'l*, pg. 4267
LIFEWATCH CORP.—See Koninklijke Philips N.V.; *Int'l*, pg. 4267
LIFEWATCH JAPAN, LTD—See Koninklijke Philips N.V.; *Int'l*, pg. 4267
LIFEWATCH SERVICES INC.—See Koninklijke Philips N.V.; *Int'l*, pg. 4267
LIFEWATCH TECHNOLOGIES LTD.—See Koninklijke Philips N.V.; *Int'l*, pg. 4267
LIFEWAVE, INC.; *U.S. Private*, pg. 2452
LIFEWAY FOODS, INC.; *U.S. Public*, pg. 1313
THE LIFEWAY KEFIR SHOP—See Lifeway Foods, Inc.; *U.S. Public*, pg. 1313
LIFEWAY MOBILITY, LLC—See Rockwood Equity Partners, LLC; *U.S. Private*, pg. 3468
LIFEWAYS COMMUNITY CARE LIMITED; *Int'l*, pg. 4495
LIFE WEAR TECHNOLOGIES, INC.—See Modular Thermal Technologies, LLC; *U.S. Private*, pg. 2763
LIFEWELL BEHAVIORAL WELLNESS; *U.S. Private*, pg. 2452
LIFEWHERE, LLC—See Resideo Technologies, Inc.; *U.S. Public*, pg. 1789
LIFEWOOD DATA TECHNOLOGY LIMITED—See China Electronics Corporation; *Int'l*, pg. 1499
LIFE WORKS COMMUNITY LIMITED—See Acadia Healthcare Company, Inc.; *U.S. Public*, pg. 29
LIFEWORKS NW; *U.S. Private*, pg. 2452
LIFEWORKS RESTAURANT GROUP, LLC—See Aramark; *U.S. Public*, pg. 178
LIFEWORKS SERVICES INC.; *U.S. Private*, pg. 2452
LIFEWORKS; *Int'l*, pg. 4495
LIFEZEN HEALTHCARE PRIVATE LIMITED—See Bal Pharma Ltd; *Int'l*, pg. 806
LIFEZONE METALS LIMITED; *Int'l*, pg. 4495
LIFFE (HOLDINGS) LTD.—See Intercontinental Exchange, Inc.; *U.S. Public*, pg. 1143
LIFFEY MILLS LTD.; *Int'l*, pg. 4495
LIFFEY THAMES GROUP LLC—See Lightyear Capital LLC; *U.S. Private*, pg. 2454
LIFIAL - INDUSTRIA METALURGICA DE AGUEDA, LDA.—See NORMA Group SE; *Int'l*, pg. 5430
LIFIS INSURANCE LTD.—See Klakki ehf.; *Int'l*, pg. 4199
LIFOAM INDUSTRIES, LLC—See Newell Brands Inc.; *U.S. Public*, pg. 1514
LIFOCOLOR FARBEN GMBH & CO. KG; *Int'l*, pg. 4495
LIFOCOLOR FARBPLAST SP.Z O.O.—See Lifocolor Farben GmbH & Co. KG; *Int'l*, pg. 4495
LIFOCOLOR S.A.R.L.—See Lifocolor Farben GmbH & Co. KG; *Int'l*, pg. 4495
LIFOCOLOR S.R.O.—See Lifocolor Farben GmbH & Co. KG; *Int'l*, pg. 4495
LI FOOK (QINGDAO) FOODS COMPANY LIMITED—See Four Seas Mercantile Holdings Limited; *Int'l*, pg. 2755
LIFOSA AB—See EuroChem Mineral Chemical Company, OJSC; *Int'l*, pg. 2534
LIFT-ALL CO., INC.; *U.S. Private*, pg. 2452
LIFT-A-LOFT CORPORATION; *U.S. Private*, pg. 2452
LIFT ATLANTA INCORPORATED; *U.S. Private*, pg. 2452
LIFTCO PTY LIMITED—See Wesfarmers Limited; *Int'l*, pg. 8381
LIFTECH EQUIPMENT COMPANIES, INC.—See Alta Equipment Group Inc.; *U.S. Public*, pg. 86
LIFT & ENGINEERING SERVICES LTD.—See ThyssenKrupp AG; *Int'l*, pg. 7724
LIFTEQUIP GMBH—See ThyssenKrupp AG; *Int'l*, pg. 7724
LIFTER CHINA LTD COMPANY—See Generac Holdings Inc.; *U.S. Public*, pg. 912
LIFT GLOBAL VENTURES PLC; *Int'l*, pg. 4495
LIFT INC.; *U.S. Private*, pg. 2452
LIFTKING MANUFACTURING CORP.—See Lanco International Inc.; *U.S. Private*, pg. 2382
LIFT MAINTENANCE LIMITED—See KONE Oyj; *Int'l*, pg. 4250
LIFT MATERIAL AUSTRALIA PTY LTD—See Dewhurst Group plc; *Int'l*, pg. 2091
LIFT MATERIALS AUSTRALIA—See Dewhurst Group plc; *Int'l*, pg. 2091
LIFTOMATIC MATERIAL HANDLING INC.; *U.S. Private*, pg. 2452
LIFTONE LLC—See Carolina Tractor &; *U.S. Private*, pg. 769
LI-FT POWER LTD.; *Int'l*, pg. 4481
LIFT-RITE INC.—See Toyota Industries Corporation; *Int'l*, pg. 7869

LIFTSERVICE UND MONTAGE GMBH—See ThyssenKrupp AG; *Int'l*, pg. 7724
LIFT SOLUTIONS, INC.; *U.S. Private*, pg. 2452
LIFTSTORE LTD.—See Dewhurst Group plc; *Int'l*, pg. 2091
LIFT TECHNOLOGIES, INC.—See Toyota Industries Corporation; *Int'l*, pg. 7869
LIFT-TEK ELECAR S.P.A.—See Toyota Industries Corporation; *Int'l*, pg. 7869
LIFT TRUCK SERVICE CENTER INC.; *U.S. Private*, pg. 2452
LIFTTRUCKS JH—See Jungheinrich AG; *Int'l*, pg. 4029
LIFT TRUCK SPECIALISTS, INC.—See Fairchild Equipment, Inc.; *U.S. Private*, pg. 1462
LIFTUP AS—See Alfa Laval AB; *Int'l*, pg. 312
LIFULL BIZAS CO., LTD.—See LIFULL Co., Ltd.; *Int'l*, pg. 4495
LIFULL CO., LTD.; *Int'l*, pg. 4495
LIFULL FAM CO., LTD.—See LIFULL Co., Ltd.; *Int'l*, pg. 4495
LIFULL INVESTMENT CO., LTD.—See LIFULL Co., Ltd.; *Int'l*, pg. 4495
LIFULL MARKETING PARTNERS CO., LTD.—See LIFULL Co., Ltd.; *Int'l*, pg. 4495
LIFULL MOVE CO., LTD.—See LIFULL Co., Ltd.; *Int'l*, pg. 4495
LIFULL SPACE CO., LTD.—See LIFULL Co., Ltd.; *Int'l*, pg. 4495
LIFULL TECH VIETNAM CO., LTD.—See LIFULL Co., Ltd.; *Int'l*, pg. 4495
LIFU MACHINERY INDUSTRIAL CO., LTD.—See Lelon Electronics Corp.; *Int'l*, pg. 4447
LI & FUNG (BANGLADESH) LIMITED—See Li & Fung Limited; *Int'l*, pg. 4480
LI & FUNG (CAMBODIA) LIMITED—See Li & Fung Limited; *Int'l*, pg. 4480
LI & FUNG (GUATEMALA) S.A.—See Li & Fung Limited; *Int'l*, pg. 4480
LI & FUNG (INDIA) PRIVATE LIMITED—See Li & Fung Limited; *Int'l*, pg. 4480
LI & FUNG (KOREA) LIMITED—See Li & Fung Limited; *Int'l*, pg. 4480
LI & FUNG LIMITED; *Int'l*, pg. 4479
LI & FUNG (MAURITIUS) LIMITED—See Li & Fung Limited; *Int'l*, pg. 4480
LI & FUNG MUMESSILLIK PAZARLAMA LIMITED SIRKETI—See Li & Fung Limited; *Int'l*, pg. 4480
LI & FUNG (PHILIPPINES) INC.—See Li & Fung Limited; *Int'l*, pg. 4480
LI & FUNG (PORTUGAL) LIMITED—See Li & Fung Limited; *Int'l*, pg. 4480
LI & FUNG (SINGAPORE) PTE. LIMITED—See Li & Fung Limited; *Int'l*, pg. 4480
LI & FUNG (TAIWAN) LIMITED—See Li & Fung Limited; *Int'l*, pg. 4480
LI & FUNG (TRADING) LIMITED—See Li & Fung Limited; *Int'l*, pg. 4480
LI & FUNG TRADING (SHANGHAI) LIMITED—See Li & Fung Limited; *Int'l*, pg. 4480
LIG ACE CO. LTD.—See BASF SE; *Int'l*, pg. 884
LIGADO NETWORKS; *U.S. Private*, pg. 2452
LIGA INDEPENDIENTE DE FUTBOL S.A.; *Int'l*, pg. 4496
LIGAND PHARMACEUTICALS INCORPORATED; *U.S. Public*, pg. 1314
LIGAO FOODS CO., LTD.; *Int'l*, pg. 4496
LIGARE LIMITED—See OPUS Group Limited; *Int'l*, pg. 5606
LIGARE PTY LTD—See Lion Rock Group Ltd; *Int'l*, pg. 4519
LIG ASSETS, INC.; *U.S. Public*, pg. 1314
LIGATT SECURITY INTERNATIONAL, INC.; *U.S. Public*, pg. 1314
THE LIGATURE—See Taylor Corporation; *U.S. Private*, pg. 3939
LIG CO.,LTD; *Int'l*, pg. 4495
LIGEANCE AEROSPACE TECHNOLOGY CO., LTD.; *Int'l*, pg. 4496
LIGENTIA AIR LIMITED—See Ligentia Group Ltd.; *Int'l*, pg. 4496
LIGENTIA ASIA LTD—See Ligentia Group Ltd.; *Int'l*, pg. 4496
LIGENTIA CHINA (GUANGZHOU) LTD—See Ligentia Group Ltd.; *Int'l*, pg. 4496
LIGENTIA CHINA (NINGBO) LTD—See Ligentia Group Ltd.; *Int'l*, pg. 4496
LIGENTIA CHINA (QINGDAO) LTD—See Ligentia Group Ltd.; *Int'l*, pg. 4496
LIGENTIA CHINA (SHANGHAI) LTD—See Ligentia Group Ltd.; *Int'l*, pg. 4496
LIGENTIA CHINA (SHENZHEN) LTD—See Ligentia Group Ltd.; *Int'l*, pg. 4496
LIGENTIA CHINA (TIANJIN) LTD—See Ligentia Group Ltd.; *Int'l*, pg. 4496
LIGENTIA CHINA (XIAMEN) LTD—See Ligentia Group Ltd.; *Int'l*, pg. 4496
LIGENTIA GROUP LTD.; *Int'l*, pg. 4496
LIGENTIA LOGISTICS LIMITED—See Ligentia Group Ltd.; *Int'l*, pg. 4496

LIGENTIA (THAILAND) LIMITED—See Ligentia Group Ltd.; *Int'l*, pg. 4496
LIGETVAROS KFT—See Atlas Estates Limited; *Int'l*, pg. 685
LIGGETT GROUP LLC—See Japan Tobacco Inc.; *Int'l*, pg. 3907
LIGGETT VECTOR BRANDS INC.—See Japan Tobacco Inc.; *Int'l*, pg. 3907
LIGHTBAY MANAGEMENT, LLC; *U.S. Private*, pg. 2452
LIGHTBEAM HEALTH SOLUTIONS LLC; *U.S. Private*, pg. 2452
LIGHTBODY EUROPE SARL—See DBAY Advisors Limited; *Int'l*, pg. 1987
LIGHTBODY GROUP LTD.—See DBAY Advisors Limited; *Int'l*, pg. 1987
LIGHTBOX EDUCATION—See RM plc; *Int'l*, pg. 6356
LIGHTBOX JEWELRY INC.—See Anglo American PLC; *Int'l*, pg. 462
LIGHTBOX—See Battery Ventures, L.P.; *U.S. Private*, pg. 489
LIGHTBOX—See Silver Lake Group, LLC; *U.S. Private*, pg. 3658
LIGHTBRIDGE COMMUNICATIONS CORPORATION—See Mahindra & Mahindra Limited; *Int'l*, pg. 4647
LIGHTBRIDGE CORPORATION; *U.S. Public*, pg. 1315
LIGHT BUREAU AS—See AFRY AB; *Int'l*, pg. 194
LIGHT BUREAU LIMITED—See AFRY AB; *Int'l*, pg. 194
LIGHTEDGE SOLUTIONS, INC.—See GI Manager L.P.; *U.S. Private*, pg. 1692
LIGHT ENGINE DESIGN CORP.; *U.S. Public*, pg. 1315
LIGHTEN THE LOAD, INC.; *U.S. Private*, pg. 2452
LIGHT ERA DEVELOPMENT CO., LTD.—See Chunghwa Telecom Co., Ltd.; *Int'l*, pg. 1598
LIGHTERING LLC—See International Seaways, Inc.; *U.S. Public*, pg. 1158
LIGHT EXPRESSIONS—See Shaw Electric Inc.; *U.S. Private*, pg. 3628
LIGHT FANTASTIC REALTY, INC.; *U.S. Private*, pg. 2452
LIGHTHOUSE ADVISORY SERVICES LIMITED—See Quilter plc; *Int'l*, pg. 6163
LIGHTHOUSE BANK; *U.S. Private*, pg. 2452
LIGHTHOUSE BUSINESS INFORMATION SOLUTIONS, LLC—See The Riverside Company; *U.S. Private*, pg. 4109
LIGHTHOUSE CARRWOOD—See Quilter plc; *Int'l*, pg. 6163
LIGHTHOUSE COMPUTER SERVICES, INC.—See Converge Technology Solutions Corp.; *Int'l*, pg. 1787
LIGHTHOUSE CREDIT FOUNDATION; *U.S. Private*, pg. 2452
LIGHTHOUSE DEVELOPMENT GMBH—See Rheinmetall AG; *Int'l*, pg. 6322
LIGHTHOUSE DIGITAL INC.—See Aquarius AI, Inc.; *Int'l*, pg. 528
LIGHTHOUSE DOCUMENT TECHNOLOGIES, INC.—See Lightyear Capital LLC; *U.S. Private*, pg. 2454
LIGHTHOUSE EDISCOVERY—See Lightyear Capital LLC; *U.S. Private*, pg. 2454
LIGHTHOUSE ELECTRONICS, INC.; *U.S. Private*, pg. 2453
LIGHTHOUSE EXPRESS—See Quilter plc; *Int'l*, pg. 6163
LIGHTHOUSE FINANCE LLC—See Greenbacker Renewable Energy Company LLC; *U.S. Private*, pg. 1774
LIGHTHOUSEGEB LIMITED.—See Quilter plc; *Int'l*, pg. 6163
LIGHTHOUSE GLOBAL HOLDINGS, INC.; *U.S. Public*, pg. 1315
LIGHTHOUSE GP LIMITED—See Quilter plc; *Int'l*, pg. 6163
LIGHTHOUSE GROUP PLC—See Quilter plc; *Int'l*, pg. 6162
LIGHTHOUSE GUILD INTERNATIONAL; *U.S. Private*, pg. 2453
LIGHTHOUSE HOLDINGS, INC.—See Pharos Capital Group, LLC; *U.S. Private*, pg. 3166
LIGHTHOUSE HOLDINGS, INC.—See TPG Capital, L.P.; *U.S. Public*, pg. 2174
LIGHTHOUSE IMAGING LLC—See Precision Optics Corporation, Inc.; *U.S. Public*, pg. 1713
LIGHTHOUSE INVESTMENT PARTNERS, LLC—See Navigator Global Investments Limited; *Int'l*, pg. 5174
LIGHTHOUSE LIMITED—See Hadco Limited; *Int'l*, pg. 3205
LIGHTHOUSE LIST COMPANY INC.; *U.S. Private*, pg. 2453
LIGHTHOUSE LOUISIANA; *U.S. Private*, pg. 2453
LIGHTHOUSE PARTNERS LIMITED (HK)—See Navigator Global Investments Limited; *Int'l*, pg. 5174
LIGHTHOUSE PARTNERS NY LLC—See Navigator Global Investments Limited; *Int'l*, pg. 5174
LIGHTHOUSE PARTNERS UK LLC—See Navigator Global Investments Limited; *Int'l*, pg. 5174
LIGHTHOUSE PLACEMENT SERVICES, INC.—See Staffing 360 Solutions, Inc.; *U.S. Public*, pg. 1925
LIGHTHOUSE POINT, LLC—See Caesars Entertainment, Inc.; *U.S. Public*, pg. 421
LIGHTHOUSE POINT MARINA—See Marina Investment Management Inc.; *U.S. Private*, pg. 2574

Company Index
LIGHTHOUSE LOUISIANA CORPORATE AFFILIATIONS

LIGHTHOUSE POINT MARINA—See Miller Yacht Sales, Inc.; *U.S. Private*, pg. 2736
LIGHTHOUSE PROPERTIES, LLC—See Blue Beacon International, Inc.; *U.S. Private*, pg. 585
LIGHTHOUSE PROPERTY INSURANCE CORP.; *U.S. Private*, pg. 2453
LIGHTHOUSE PROPERTY SERVICES LTD.—See The Skipton Building Society; *Int'l*, pg. 7686
LIGHTHOUSE SERVICES LLC—See Ontario Teachers' Pension Plan; *Int'l*, pg. 5586
LIGHTHOUSE TECHNOLOGIES HOLDINGS CORP.—See Lightyear Capital LLC; *U.S. Private*, pg. 2454
LIGHTHOUSE TECHNOLOGIES, INC.; *U.S. Private*, pg. 2453
LIGHTHOUSE WEALTH—See Quilter plc; *Int'l*, pg. 6163
LIGHTICO LTD.; *Int'l*, pg. 4496
LIGHT IMPRESSIONS; *U.S. Private*, pg. 2452
LIGHTING AND EQUIPMENT PUBLIC COMPANY LIMITED; *Int'l*, pg. 4496
LIGHTING AUSTRALIA PTY. LTD.—See A.A.G. STUCCHI s.r.l.; *Int'l*, pg. 23
LIGHTING CORPORATION PTY LTD—See Bain Capital, LP; *U.S. Private*, pg. 439
LIGHTING CORPORATION PTY LTD—See Investec Limited; *Int'l*, pg. 3777
LIGHTING FOR STAFFORDSHIRE LIMITED—See E.ON SE; *Int'l*, pg. 2256
LIGHTING INCORPORATED; *U.S. Private*, pg. 2453
LIGHTING INNOVATIONS AFRICA (PTY) LTD.—See Fagerhult Group AB; *Int'l*, pg. 2602
LIGHTING & LAMP CORP.; *U.S. Private*, pg. 2453
LIGHTING SCIENCE GROUP CORPORATION; *U.S. Private*, pg. 2453
LIGHTING SCIENCES INC.—See Underwriters Laboratories Inc.; *U.S. Private*, pg. 4280
LIGHTING TECHNOLOGY SERVICES, INC.—See Willdan Group, Inc.; *U.S. Public*, pg. 2371
LIGHTINTHEBOX HOLDING CO., LTD.; *Int'l*, pg. 4496
LIGHTJUMP ACQUISITION CORPORATION—See Moolec Science SA; *Int'l*, pg. 5038
LIGHTLIFE FOODS, INC.—See Maple Leaf Foods, Inc.; *Int'l*, pg. 4686
LIGHT MASTER TECHNOLOGY INC.—See Ezconn Corporation; *Int'l*, pg. 2593
LIGHT MEDIA HOLDINGS, INC.; *U.S. Public*, pg. 1315
LIGHT MOBILITY SOLUTIONS GMBH—See Mutares SE & Co. KGaA; *Int'l*, pg. 5105
LIGHTNING AUDIO CORPORATION—See Patrick Industries, Inc.; *U.S. Public*, pg. 1653
LIGHTNING BUG LTD.; *U.S. Private*, pg. 2453
LIGHTNING DIGITAL TECHNOLOGY CO., LTD—See Truly International Holdings Limited; *Int'l*, pg. 7942
LIGHTNING DIVERSION SYSTEMS, INC.—See Ducommun Incorporated; *U.S. Public*, pg. 690
LIGHTNING EMOTORS, INC.; *U.S. Public*, pg. 1315
LIGHTNING ENTERTAINMENT GROUP, INC.—See L.F.P., Inc.; *U.S. Private*, pg. 2365
LIGHTNING GOLF AND PROMOTIONS, INC.—See HH Global Group Limited; *Int'l*, pg. 3379
THE LIGHTNING GROUP, INC.; *U.S. Private*, pg. 4070
LIGHTNING HEALTHCARE, INC.—See The Ensign Group, Inc.; *U.S. Public*, pg. 2071
LIGHTNING HOCKEY LP—See Tampa Bay Sports & Entertainment LLC; *U.S. Private*, pg. 3929
LIGHTNING MINERALS LTD.; *Int'l*, pg. 4496
LIGHTNING PACKAGING SUPPLIES LIMITED—See Bunzl plc; *Int'l*, pg. 1218
LIGHTNING QUICK GAS-N-GO; *U.S. Private*, pg. 2453
LIGHTNING ROD MUTUAL INSURANCE CO.; *U.S. Private*, pg. 2453
LIGHTNING SOURCE, INC.—See Ingram Industries, Inc.; *U.S. Private*, pg. 2076
LIGHTNING TRANSPORTATION INC.; *U.S. Private*, pg. 2453
LIGHTNING VENTURES INC.; *U.S. Private*, pg. 2453
LIGHTOLIER DE MEXICO, S.A. DE C.V.—See Signify N.V.; *Int'l*, pg. 6912
LIGHTOPIA LLC—See L2 Capital Partners; *U.S. Private*, pg. 2367
LIGHTPATH TECHNOLOGIES, INC.; *U.S. Public*, pg. 1315
LIGHT PLUS DESIGN LIMITED—See Allied Sustainability & Environmental Consultants Group Limited; *Int'l*, pg. 358
LIGHTPOWER GMBH; *Int'l*, pg. 4496
LIGHT READING LLC—See Informa plc; *Int'l*, pg. 3692
LIGHTRIDGE SOLUTIONS—See ATL Partners, LLC; *U.S. Private*, pg. 369
LIGHTRIVER TECHNOLOGIES, INC.—See Grain Management, LLC; *U.S. Private*, pg. 1751
LIGHTRONICS B.V.—See F.W. Thorpe plc; *Int'l*, pg. 2597
LIGHTRON, INC.; *Int'l*, pg. 4497
LIGHT S.A.; *Int'l*, pg. 4496
LIGHTSCAPE TECHNOLOGIES (GREATER CHINA) LIMITED—See Lightscape Technologies, Inc.; *Int'l*, pg. 4497
LIGHTSCAPE TECHNOLOGIES, INC.; *Int'l*, pg. 4497
LIGHT SCIENCES ONCOLOGY, INC.; *U.S. Private*, pg. 2452
LIGHT SCIENCE TECHNOLOGIES HOLDINGS PLC; *Int'l*, pg. 4496
LIGHT SCIENCE TECHNOLOGIES LIMITED—See Light Science Technologies Holdings Plc; *Int'l*, pg. 4496
LIGHT SERVICOS DE ELETRICIDADE S.A.—See Companhia Energetica de Minas Gerais - CEMIG; *Int'l*, pg. 1747
LIGHTSHIP SECURITY, INC.—See I Squared Capital Advisors (US) LLC; *U.S. Private*, pg. 2023
LIGHTSHIP SECURITY, INC.—See TDR Capital LLP; *Int'l*, pg. 7492
LIGHTSHIP SECURITY USA, INC.—See I Squared Capital Advisors (US) LLC; *U.S. Private*, pg. 2023
LIGHTSHIP SECURITY USA, INC.—See TDR Capital LLP; *Int'l*, pg. 7492
LIGHTSIDE LABS, LLC—See Advance Publications, Inc.; *U.S. Private*, pg. 87
LIGHTSMYTH TECHNOLOGIES, INC.—See Coherent Corp.; *U.S. Public*, pg. 528
LIGHTS OF AMERICA, INC.; *U.S. Private*, pg. 2453
LIGHTSOURCES, INC.; *U.S. Private*, pg. 2453
LIGHT SOURCE SOLUTIONS NEW ZEALAND LIMITED—See Beacon Lighting Group Ltd; *Int'l*, pg. 932
LIGHTSPEED COMMERCE INC.; *Int'l*, pg. 4497
LIGHTSPEED DISCOVERIES INC.; *Int'l*, pg. 4497
LIGHTSPEED MANAGEMENT COMPANY, LLC; *U.S. Private*, pg. 2453
LIGHTSPEED ONLINE RESEARCH, INC.—See WPP plc; *Int'l*, pg. 8483
LIGHTSPEED SYSTEMS INC.; *U.S. Private*, pg. 2453
LIGHTSPEED TECHNOLOGIES, INC.—See Integra Business Center Inc.; *U.S. Private*, pg. 2098
LIGHTSQUARED COMPANY - CANADA—See Spectrum Brands Holdings, Inc.; *U.S. Public*, pg. 1915
LIGHTSQUARED COMPANY—See Spectrum Brands Holdings, Inc.; *U.S. Public*, pg. 1915
LIGHTSTEP, INC.—See ServiceNow, Inc.; *U.S. Public*, pg. 1872
THE LIGHTSTONE GROUP, LLC; *U.S. Private*, pg. 4070
LIGHTSTONE VALUE PLUS REIT III, INC.—See The Lightstone Group, LLC; *U.S. Private*, pg. 4070
LIGHTSTONE VALUE PLUS REIT II, INC.—See The Lightstone Group, LLC; *U.S. Private*, pg. 4070
LIGHTSTONE VALUE PLUS REIT I, INC.—See The Lightstone Group, LLC; *U.S. Private*, pg. 4070
LIGHTSTONE VALUE PLUS REIT IV, INC.—See The Lightstone Group, LLC; *U.S. Private*, pg. 4070
LIGHTSTONE VALUE PLUS REIT LLC—See The Lightstone Group, LLC; *U.S. Private*, pg. 4070
LIGHTSTONE VALUE PLUS REIT V, INC.—See The Lightstone Group, LLC; *U.S. Private*, pg. 4070
LIGHT & STRONG, LTD.—See Lohia Corp. Limited; *Int'l*, pg. 4543
LIGHT TOWER RENTALS, LLC—See Clearlake Capital Group, L.P.; *U.S. Private*, pg. 935
LIGHTUP SHOPPING CLUB INC.—See TBS Holdings, Inc.; *Int'l*, pg. 7481
LIGHTVIEW CAPITAL LLC; *U.S. Private*, pg. 2453
LIGHTWAVE LOGIC, INC.; *U.S. Public*, pg. 1315
LIGHTWAVERF PLC; *Int'l*, pg. 4497
LIGHTWAVE SOLAR, LLC; *U.S. Private*, pg. 2454
LIGHTWAVE TELECOMMUNICATIONS, INC.; *U.S. Private*, pg. 2454
LIGHTWEDGE LLC; *U.S. Private*, pg. 2454
LIGHTWELL CO., LTD—See Sumitomo Heavy Industries, Ltd.; *Int'l*, pg. 7287
LIGHTWIRE LLC—See Cisco Systems, Inc.; *U.S. Public*, pg. 499
LIGHT & WONDER, INC.; *U.S. Public*, pg. 1314
LIGHTWORKS OPTICAL SYSTEMS, INC.—See Coherent Corp.; *U.S. Public*, pg. 529
LIGHTWORKS OPTICAL SYSTEMS, INC.—See Coherent Corp.; *U.S. Public*, pg. 529
LIGHTYEAR CAPITAL LLC; *U.S. Private*, pg. 2454
LIGITEK ELECTRONICS CO., LTD.; *Int'l*, pg. 4497
LIGITEK PHOTOVOLTAIC CO., LTD.—See Ligitek Electronics Co., Ltd.; *Int'l*, pg. 4497
LIGNAPPS, INC.—See NextGen, Inc.; *Int'l*, pg. 5249
LIGNETICS, INC.—See EagleTree Capital, LP; *U.S. Private*, pg. 1311
LIGNE T SAS—See Bunzl plc; *Int'l*, pg. 1218
LIG NEX1 CO., LTD.; *Int'l*, pg. 4495
LIGNIS GMBH & CO. KG—See UPM-Kymmene Corporation; *Int'l*, pg. 8090
LIGNITIKI MEGALOPOLIS S.A.—See Public Power Corporation S.A.; *Int'l*, pg. 6095
LIGNOL INNOVATIONS LTD.—See Suzano Holding S.A.; *Int'l*, pg. 7348
LIGNUM FOREST PRODUCTS LLP—See The Futura Corporation; *Int'l*, pg. 7647
LIGON ELECTRIC SUPPLY COMPANY INC. OF NC—See Arthur's Enterprises, Inc.; *U.S. Private*, pg. 342
LIGON INDUSTRIES LLC; *U.S. Private*, pg. 2455
LIGON OIL CO. INC.; *U.S. Private*, pg. 2455
LIGO PRODUCTS INC.; *U.S. Private*, pg. 2455
LIG PUNGSHAN PROTECH CO., LTD.—See LIG Nex1 Co., Ltd.; *Int'l*, pg. 4496
LIGUA, INC.; *Int'l*, pg. 4497
LIGUM SPOL. S.R.O.—See Westland Gummiwerke GmbH & Co. KG; *Int'l*, pg. 8390
LIGUNA INC.—See euglena Co., Ltd.; *Int'l*, pg. 2526
LIGURIA FOODS, INC.—See Black Diamond Capital Holdings, LLC; *U.S. Private*, pg. 570
LIGURIA FOODS, INC.—See Massachusetts Mutual Life Insurance Company; *U.S. Private*, pg. 2605
LIHAI INTERNATIONAL SHIPPING CO., LTD.—See COFCO Limited; *Int'l*, pg. 1692
LIHATUKKU HARRI TAMMINEN OY—See HKFoods Plc; *Int'l*, pg. 3429
LI HENG CHEMICAL FIBRE TECHNOLOGIES LIMITED; *Int'l*, pg. 4481
LIHE TECHNOLOGY (HUNAN) CO., LTD.; *Int'l*, pg. 4497
LIH-HSIANG OMYA CORP.—See Omya (Schweiz) AG; *Int'l*, pg. 5570
LIHIT LAB., INC. - SHIZUOKA FACTORY—See Lihit Lab., Inc.; *Int'l*, pg. 4497
LIHIT LAB., INC.; *Int'l*, pg. 4497
LIHNIDA OHRID; *Int'l*, pg. 4497
LIHTAI CONSTRUCTION & DEVELOPMENT CO., LTD.; *Int'l*, pg. 4497
LII HEN FURNITURE SDN BHD—See Lii Hen Industries Bhd.; *Int'l*, pg. 4497
LII HEN INDUSTRIES BHD.; *Int'l*, pg. 4497
LIJIANG CHINA INTERNATIONAL TRAVEL SERVICE CO., LTD.—See China Tourism Group Duty Free Corporation Limited; *Int'l*, pg. 1560
LIJIANG YULONG TOURISM CO., LTD.; *Int'l*, pg. 4497
LI KANG BIOMEDICAL CO., LTD.; *Int'l*, pg. 4481
LIKEABLE MEDIA; *U.S. Private*, pg. 2455
LIKE CARE, INC.—See LIKE Co., Ltd.; *Int'l*, pg. 4497
LIKE CO., LTD.; *Int'l*, pg. 4497
LIKE KIDS,INC.—See LIKE Co., Ltd.; *Int'l*, pg. 4498
LIKE REPLY GMBH—See Reply S.p.A.; *Int'l*, pg. 6291
LIKE REPLY S.R.L.—See Reply S.p.A.; *Int'l*, pg. 6291
LIKE STAFFING, INC.—See LIKE Co., Ltd.; *Int'l*, pg. 4498
LIKEWISE GROUP PLC; *Int'l*, pg. 4498
LIKE WORKS, INC.—See LIKE Co., Ltd.; *Int'l*, pg. 4498
THE LIKHACHOV PLANT PJSC; *Int'l*, pg. 7664
LIKHAMI CONSULTING LIMITED; *Int'l*, pg. 4498
LIKHITHA INFRASTRUCTURE LIMITED; *Int'l*, pg. 4498
LIKO AB—See Baxter International Inc.; *U.S. Public*, pg. 282
LIKOM CASEWORKS USA INC.—See Lion Group Management Services Sdn Bhd; *Int'l*, pg. 4518
LIKOM CMS SDN BHD—See Lion Group Management Services Sdn Bhd; *Int'l*, pg. 4518
LIKOM DE MEXICO S.A. DE C.V.—See Lion Group Management Services Sdn Bhd; *Int'l*, pg. 4518
LIK SHEN SAWMILL SDN. BHD.—See Ta Ann Holdings Berhad; *Int'l*, pg. 7398
LILAMA 10 JSC—See Vietnam Machinery Installation Corporation JSC; *Int'l*, pg. 8200
LILAMA 18 JSC—See Vietnam Machinery Installation Corporation JSC; *Int'l*, pg. 8200
LILAMA 45-1 JSC—See Vietnam Machinery Installation Corporation JSC; *Int'l*, pg. 8200
LILAMA 45-3 JOINT STOCK COMPANY—See Vietnam Machinery Installation Corporation JSC; *Int'l*, pg. 8200
LILAMA 45-4 JOINT STOCK COMPANY—See Vietnam Machinery Installation Corporation JSC; *Int'l*, pg. 8200
LILAMA 5 JOINT STOCK COMPANY—See Vietnam Machinery Installation Corporation JSC; *Int'l*, pg. 8200
LILAMA 69-1 JOINT STOCK COMPANY—See Vietnam Machinery Installation Corporation JSC; *Int'l*, pg. 8200
LILAMA 69-3 JSC—See Vietnam Machinery Installation Corporation JSC; *Int'l*, pg. 8200
LILAMA 7 JOINT STOCK COMPANY—See Vietnam Machinery Installation Corporation JSC; *Int'l*, pg. 8200
LILAMA ERECTION MECHANICAL JOINT STOCK COMPANY—See Vietnam Machinery Installation Corporation JSC; *Int'l*, pg. 8200
LIL' DRUG STORE PRODUCTS, INC.; *U.S. Private*, pg. 2455
LILE INTERNATIONAL COMPANIES; *U.S. Private*, pg. 2455
LILIAL S.A.S.—See Coloplast A/S; *Int'l*, pg. 1704
THE LILIAN RAJI AGENCY; *U.S. Private*, pg. 4070
LILIENTHAL INSULATION COMPANY, LLC—See Masco Corporation; *U.S. Public*, pg. 1391
LILING KIBING SILICON CO., LTD.—See Zhuzhou Kibing Group Co., Ltd.; *Int'l*, pg. 8680
LILIS ENERGY, INC.; *U.S. Private*, pg. 2455
LILIUM GROUP LLC; *U.S. Private*, pg. 2455
LILIUOKALANI TRUST; *U.S. Private*, pg. 2455
LILJA CORP.; *U.S. Private*, pg. 2455
LILJEGRENS MASKINVERKTYG AB—See Indutrade AB; *Int'l*, pg. 3680
LILJEHOLMENS STEARINFABRIKS AB—See Gies Holding GmbH; *Int'l*, pg. 2969
LILJENDALS BRUK AB—See Illinois Tool Works Inc.; *U.S. Public*, pg. 1109
LILKER ASSOCIATES CONSULTING ENGINEERS, PC; *U.S. Private*, pg. 2455
LILLA P LLC; *U.S. Private*, pg. 2455
LILLARD & CLARK CONSTRUCTION COMPANY INC.; *U.S. Private*, pg. 2455

COMPANY NAME INDEX

LILLARD & CLARK-WYOMING—See Lillard & Clark Construction Company Inc.; *U.S. Private*, pg. 2456
LILLEBA & HERREMAN AS—See AcadeMedia AB; *Int'l*, pg. 77
LILLEBORG AS—See Platinum Equity, LLC; *U.S. Private*, pg. 3204
LILLE DIGITAL SOLUTIONS SAS—See VINCI S.A.; *Int'l*, pg. 8223
LILLEHEDEN A/S—See Maj Invest Holding A/S; *Int'l*, pg. 4653
LILLEHEDEN LTD.—See Maj Invest Holding A/S; *Int'l*, pg. 4653
LILLEHEDEN SP. Z O.O.—See Maj Invest Holding A/S; *Int'l*, pg. 4653
LILLE PROCESS SOLUTIONS SAS—See VINCI S.A.; *Int'l*, pg. 8223
LILLIAN VERNON CORPORATION—See Regent, L.P.; *U.S. Private*, pg. 3387
LILLIBRIDGE HEALTHCARE SERVICES, INC.—See Ventas, Inc.; *U.S. Public*, pg. 2278
LILLIPUT (DUNMURRY) LIMITED—See Johnson Service Group PLC; *Int'l*, pg. 3993
LILLO SPA; *Int'l*, pg. 4498
LILLY AND ASSOCIATES INTERNATIONAL; *U.S. Private*, pg. 2456
LILLY ASIA VENTURES; *Int'l*, pg. 4498
THE LILLY COMPANY INC.; *U.S. Private*, pg. 4070
LILLY DEL CARIBE INC.—See Eli Lilly & Company; *U.S. Public*, pg. 733
LILLY DEUTSCHLAND GMBH—See Eli Lilly & Company; *U.S. Public*, pg. 733
LILLY FRANCE S.A.—See Eli Lilly & Company; *U.S. Public*, pg. 733
LILLY HOLDINGS, LLC—See Eli Lilly & Company; *U.S. Public*, pg. 733
LILLY HUNGARIA KFT—See Eli Lilly & Company; *U.S. Public*, pg. 733
LILLY ILAC TICARET LIMITED SIRKETI—See Eli Lilly & Company; *U.S. Public*, pg. 733
LILLY INDUSTRIES (SHANGHAI) LIMITED—See The Sherwin-Williams Company; *U.S. Public*, pg. 2129
LILLY KOREA LIMITED—See Eli Lilly & Company; *U.S. Public*, pg. 732
LILLY NEDERLAND FINANCE B.V.—See Eli Lilly & Company; *U.S. Public*, pg. 733
LILLY-NUS CENTRE FOR CLINICAL PHARMACOLOGY—See Eli Lilly & Company; *U.S. Public*, pg. 733
LILLY PHARMACEUTICALS—See Eli Lilly & Company; *U.S. Public*, pg. 733
LILLY PHARMA HOLDING GMBH—See Eli Lilly & Company; *U.S. Public*, pg. 733
LILLY-PORTUGAL PRODUTOS FARMACEUTICOS, LDA.—See Eli Lilly & Company; *U.S. Public*, pg. 733
LILLY RESEARCH CENTRE LIMITED—See Eli Lilly & Company; *U.S. Public*, pg. 733
LILLY RESEARCH LABORATORIES—See Eli Lilly & Company; *U.S. Public*, pg. 733
LILLY, S.A.—See Eli Lilly & Company; *U.S. Public*, pg. 733
LILLY TIPPECANOE LABORATORIES—See Eli Lilly & Company; *U.S. Public*, pg. 733
LILLY USA, LLC—See Eli Lilly & Company; *U.S. Public*, pg. 733
LILLY VENTURES FUND I LLC—See Eli Lilly & Company; *U.S. Public*, pg. 733
LILLYWHITES LTD.—See Jeronimo Martins SGPS SA; *Int'l*, pg. 3931
LILONTEX CORPORATION; *Int'l*, pg. 4498
LIL PROJECTS PRIVATE LIMITED—See Brightcom Group Ltd.; *Int'l*, pg. 1162
LIL THRIFT FOOD MARTS INC.—See Petroleum Marketing Group Inc.; *U.S. Private*, pg. 3162
LILY AW MEDICAL SERVICES PTE. LTD.—See New Silkroutes Group Limited; *Int'l*, pg. 5227
LILYCOLOR CO., LTD.; *Int'l*, pg. 4498
LILY GROUP CO.,LTD; *Int'l*, pg. 4498
LILY MEDICAL CORPORATION—See Audix Corporation; *Int'l*, pg. 702
LILYPAD INSURANCE COMPANY—See Arbol Inc.; *U.S. Private*, pg. 308
LILYPONS WATER GARDENS INC.; *U.S. Private*, pg. 2456
LILY TEXTILE CO., LTD.; *Int'l*, pg. 4498
LILY TRANSPORTATION CORP.—See ZS Fund L.P.; *U.S. Private*, pg. 4609
LIMA AIRLINES S.A.C—See Macrolink Capital Holdings Limited; *Int'l*, pg. 4632
LIMA AIRPORT PARTNERS S.R.L.—See Fraport AG; *Int'l*, pg. 2764
LIMA AUSTRIA GMBH—See Enovis Corporation; *U.S. Public*, pg. 773
LIMA AUTO MALL INC.; *U.S. Public*, pg. 2456
LIMA COMMUNICATIONS CORP. WLIO TELEVISION—See Block Communications, Inc.; *U.S. Private*, pg. 582
LIMACORPORATE S.P.A.—See Enovis Corporation; *U.S. Public*, pg. 773
LIMA CZ S.R.O.—See Enovis Corporation; *U.S. Public*, pg. 773

LIMA DEUTSCHLAND GMBH—See Enovis Corporation; *U.S. Public*, pg. 773
LIMA FRANCE S.A.S.—See Enovis Corporation; *U.S. Public*, pg. 773
LIMAGAS NATURAL PERU S.A.—See Empresas Lipigas SA; *Int'l*, pg. 2391
LIMA GAS S.A.; *Int'l*, pg. 4498
LIMAGRAIN ARGENTINA S.A.—See Groupe Limagrain Holding SA; *Int'l*, pg. 3107
LIMAGRAIN A/S—See Groupe Limagrain Holding SA; *Int'l*, pg. 3107
LIMAGRAIN BELGIUM NV—See Groupe Limagrain Holding SA; *Int'l*, pg. 3107
LIMAGRAIN BULGARIA LTD—See Groupe Limagrain Holding SA; *Int'l*, pg. 3107
LIMAGRAIN CENTRAL EUROPE CEREALS, S.R.O.—See Groupe Limagrain Holding SA; *Int'l*, pg. 3107
LIMAGRAIN CENTRAL EUROPE S.E.—See Groupe Limagrain Holding SA; *Int'l*, pg. 3107
LIMAGRAIN CEREALES INGREDIENTS—See Groupe Limagrain Holding SA; *Int'l*, pg. 3107
LIMAGRAIN CEREAL SEEDS LLC—See Groupe Limagrain Holding SA; *Int'l*, pg. 3107
LIMAGRAIN CESKA REPUBLIKA, S.R.O.—See Groupe Limagrain Holding SA; *Int'l*, pg. 3107
LIMAGRAIN EUROPE—See Groupe Limagrain Holding SA; *Int'l*, pg. 3107
LIMAGRAIN GENETICS GRANDES CULTURES S.A.—See Groupe Limagrain Holding SA; *Int'l*, pg. 3107
LIMAGRAIN GENETICS INTERNATIONAL—See Groupe Limagrain Holding SA; *Int'l*, pg. 3107
LIMAGRAIN GMBH—See Groupe Limagrain Holding SA; *Int'l*, pg. 3107
LIMAGRAIN IBERICA S.A.—See Groupe Limagrain Holding SA; *Int'l*, pg. 3107
LIMAGRAIN ITALIA SPA—See Groupe Limagrain Holding SA; *Int'l*, pg. 3107
LIMAGRAIN MAGYARORSZAG KFT.—See Groupe Limagrain Holding SA; *Int'l*, pg. 3107
LIMAGRAIN MOLDOVA SRL—See Groupe Limagrain Holding SA; *Int'l*, pg. 3107
LIMAGRAIN NEDERLAND BV—See Groupe Limagrain Holding SA; *Int'l*, pg. 3107
LIMAGRAIN POLSKA SP. Z O.O.—See Groupe Limagrain Holding SA; *Int'l*, pg. 3107
LIMAGRAIN RU LLC—See Groupe Limagrain Holding SA; *Int'l*, pg. 3107
LIMAGRAIN SLOVENSKO, S.R.O.—See Groupe Limagrain Holding SA; *Int'l*, pg. 3107
LIMAGRAIN UK LTD—See Groupe Limagrain Holding SA; *Int'l*, pg. 3107
LIMAGRAIN UKRAINE LLC—See Groupe Limagrain Holding SA; *Int'l*, pg. 3107
LIMA IMPLANTES PORTUGAL S.U. LDA.—See Enovis Corporation; *U.S. Public*, pg. 773
LIMA IMPLANTES S.L.U.—See Enovis Corporation; *U.S. Public*, pg. 773
LIMA JAPAN KK—See Enovis Corporation; *U.S. Public*, pg. 773
LIMAK HOLDING A.S.; *Int'l*, pg. 4498
LIMAKO SUIKER B.V.—See Royal Cosun U.A.; *Int'l*, pg. 6412
LIMA LAND, INC.—See Aboitiz Equity Ventures, Inc.; *Int'l*, pg. 66
THE LIMA NEWS—See Independence Capital Partners, LLC; *U.S. Private*, pg. 2057
LIMANGO GMBH—See Otto GmbH & Co. KG; *Int'l*, pg. 5663
LIMA O.I. D.O.O. ORTOPEDIJA—See Enovis Corporation; *U.S. Public*, pg. 773
LIMA ONE CAPITAL, LLC—See MFA FINANCIAL, INC.; *U.S. Public*, pg. 1434
LIMA ORTHOPAEDICS CANADA INC.—See Enovis Corporation; *U.S. Public*, pg. 773
LIMA ORTHOPAEDICS NEW ZEALAND PTY. LTD.—See Enovis Corporation; *U.S. Public*, pg. 773
LIMA ORTHOPAEDICS UK LTD—See Enovis Corporation; *U.S. Public*, pg. 773
LIMA POLSKA SP. Z O.O.—See Enovis Corporation; *U.S. Public*, pg. 773
LIMA S.A./N.V.—See The Hain Celestial Group, Inc.; *U.S. Public*, pg. 2087
LIMA SK S.R.O.—See Enovis Corporation; *U.S. Public*, pg. 773
LIMA SP. Z O.O.; *Int'l*, pg. 4498
LIMASSOL MEDICAL CENTRE 'ACHILLION' LTD—See DIAGNOSTIC AND THERAPEUTIC CENTER OF ATHENS-HYGEIA S.A.; *Int'l*, pg. 2103
LIMA SWEDEN S.R.O.—See Enovis Corporation; *U.S. Public*, pg. 773
LIMA SWITZERLAND S.A.—See Enovis Corporation; *U.S. Public*, pg. 773
LIMATHERM COMPONENTS SP. Z O.O.—See Introl S.A.; *Int'l*, pg. 3769
LIMATHERM S.A.—See Introl S.A.; *Int'l*, pg. 3769
LIMATHERM SENSOR SP. Z O.O.—See Introl S.A.; *Int'l*, pg. 3769
LIMA TOURS S.A.C.—See TUI AG; *Int'l*, pg. 7965

LIMIN GROUP CO., LTD.

LIMAY GRINDING MILL CORPORATION CO. LTD.—See Heidelberg Materials AG; *Int'l*, pg. 3310
LIMBACH COMPANY LLC—See Limbach Holdings, Inc.; *U.S. Public*, pg. 1316
LIMBACH ENGINEERING & DESIGN SERVICES (LEDS)—See Limbach Holdings, Inc.; *U.S. Public*, pg. 1316
LIMBACH FACILITY SERVICES LLC—See Limbach Holdings, Inc.; *U.S. Public*, pg. 1316
LIMBACH HOLDINGS, INC.; *U.S. Public*, pg. 1315
LIMBURGER LACKFABRIK GMBH—See SWARCO AG; *Int'l*, pg. 7360
LIMBURG RAFFINADERIJ BV—See Koninklijke DSM N.V.; *Int'l*, pg. 4264
LIMBURG VENTURES BV—See Koninklijke DSM N.V.; *Int'l*, pg. 4266
LIMCO AIREPAIR INC.—See First Israel Mezzanine Investors Ltd.; *Int'l*, pg. 2685
LIMCO-PIEDMONT INC.—See First Israel Mezzanine Investors Ltd.; *Int'l*, pg. 2685
LIMEADE, INC.—See KKR & Co. Inc.; *U.S. Public*, pg. 1254
LIME AVENUE RADIOLOGY PTY LTD—See Capitol Health Limited; *Int'l*, pg. 1314
LIME BROKERAGE, LLC—See Wedbush Capital Partners; *U.S. Private*, pg. 4468
LIME CHEMICALS LIMITED; *Int'l*, pg. 4498
LIME CRIME INC.—See Tengram Capital Partners, Limited Partnership; *U.S. Private*, pg. 3967
LIME ENERGY CO.—See Willdan Group, Inc.; *U.S. Public*, pg. 2371
LIMEJUMP LTD.—See Shell plc; *Int'l*, pg. 6795
LIMELIGHT NETWORKS FRANCE SARL—See EDGIO, INC.; *U.S. Public*, pg. 718
LIMELIGHT NETWORKS GERMANY GMBH—See EDGIO, INC.; *U.S. Public*, pg. 718
LIMELIGHT NETWORKS INC.—See EDGIO, INC.; *U.S. Public*, pg. 719
LIMELIGHT NETWORKS INDIA PRIVATE LIMITED—See EDGIO, INC.; *U.S. Public*, pg. 719
LIMELIGHT NETWORKS JAPAN—See EDGIO, INC.; *U.S. Public*, pg. 719
LIMELIGHT NETWORKS KOREA LTD.—See EDGIO, INC.; *U.S. Public*, pg. 719
LIMELIGHT NETWORKS NETHERLANDS B.V.—See EDGIO, INC.; *U.S. Public*, pg. 719
LIMELIGHT NETWORKS SINGAPORE PTE LTD.—See EDGIO, INC.; *U.S. Public*, pg. 719
LIMELIGHT NETWORKS (UK) LIMITED—See EDGIO, INC.; *U.S. Public*, pg. 718
LIMELIGHT WEB TECHNOLOGIES (IL) LTD.—See EDGIO, INC.; *U.S. Public*, pg. 719
LIME PETROLEUM AS—See Rex International Holding Ltd; *Int'l*, pg. 6315
LIMERICK LEADER LTD—See JPIMedia Holdings Limited; *Int'l*, pg. 4006
LIME ROCK MANAGEMENT, L.P.—See Lime Rock Partners, LLC; *U.S. Private*, pg. 2456
LIME ROCK NEW ENERGY GP LP—See Lime Rock Partners, LLC; *U.S. Private*, pg. 2456
LIME ROCK PARTNERS, LLC; *U.S. Private*, pg. 2456
LIMERSTON CAPITAL LLP; *Int'l*, pg. 4498
LIME—See Liberty Global plc; *Int'l*, pg. 4485
LIMES SCHLOSSKLINIKEN AG; *Int'l*, pg. 4499
LIMESTONE BANCORP, INC.—See Peoples Bancorp Inc.; *U.S. Public*, pg. 1667
THE LIMESTONE BOAT COMPANY LIMITED; *Int'l*, pg. 7664
LIMESTONE CAPITAL AG—See 029 Group SE; *Int'l*, pg. 1
LIMESTONE MEDICAL CENTER, LLC—See UnitedHealth Group Incorporated; *U.S. Public*, pg. 2242
LIME & STONE PRODUCTION CO LTD—See CEMEX, S.A.B. de C.V.; *Int'l*, pg. 1398
LIMESTONE PROPERTIES LTD—See Bank of Cyprus Holdings Public Limited Company; *Int'l*, pg. 842
LIMESTONE RESOURCES AUSTRALIA PTY LTD—See Schaffer Corporation Limited; *Int'l*, pg. 6615
LIME STREET INSURANCE PCC LIMITED—See Willis Towers Watson Public Limited Company; *Int'l*, pg. 8414
LIME TECHNOLOGIES AB; *Int'l*, pg. 4498
LIMHAMNS FORSKOLA AB—See AcadeMedia AB; *Int'l*, pg. 77
LIMINAL BIOSCIENCES INC.—See Thomvest Ventures LLC; *U.S. Private*, pg. 4162
LIMINAL COLLECTIVE, INC.—See Logitech International S.A.; *U.S. Public*, pg. 1341
LIMIN CHEMICAL CO., LTD. - INTERNATIONAL BUSINESS UNIT—See Limin Group Co., Ltd.; *Int'l*, pg. 4499
LIMING A.D.; *Int'l*, pg. 4499
LI MING DEVELOPMENT CONSTRUCTION CO., LTD.; *Int'l*, pg. 4481
LIMIN GROUP CO., LTD.; *Int'l*, pg. 4499
LIMIT CORPORATE MEMBERS LIMITED—See QBE Insurance Group Limited; *Int'l*, pg. 6136
LIMITED BRAND & CREATIVE SERVICES—See Bath & Body Works, Inc.; *U.S. Public*, pg. 279
LIMITED DURATION INVESTMENT GRADE PREFERRED SECURITIES FUND—See Purpose Investments Inc.; *Int'l*, pg. 6123

1609

LIMIN GROUP CO., LTD.
CORPORATE AFFILIATIONS

LIMITED EDITION INC.—See Bon Fame Co., Ltd.; *Int'l*, pg. 1105
LIMITED LIABILITY COMPANY BARCLAYS CAPITAL—See Barclays PLC; *Int'l*, pg. 862
LIMITED LIABILITY COMPANY BAUSCH & LOMB—See Bausch Health Companies Inc.; *Int'l*, pg. 897
LIMITED LIABILITY COMPANY BRINK'S—See The Brink's Company; *U.S. Public*, pg. 2043
LIMITED LIABILITY COMPANY CASIO—See Casio Computer Co., Ltd.; *Int'l*, pg. 1353
LIMITED LIABILITY COMPANY CHINA TELECOM—See China Telecommunications Corporation; *Int'l*, pg. 1558
LIMITED LIABILITY COMPANY CYBM VOZNESENKIY HOTEL LEASING—See Marriott International, Inc.; *U.S. Public*, pg. 1370
LIMITED LIABILITY COMPANY EISAI—See Eisai Co., Ltd.; *Int'l*, pg. 2335
LIMITED LIABILITY COMPANY FISHER & PAYKEL HEALTHCARE—See Fisher & Paykel Healthcare Corporation Limited; *Int'l*, pg. 2693
LIMITED LIABILITY COMPANY HEIDELBERGBETON UKRAINE—See Heidelberg Materials AG; *Int'l*, pg. 3318
LIMITED LIABILITY COMPANY HUNTSMAN (UKRAINE)—See Huntsman Corporation; *U.S. Public*, pg. 1075
LIMITED LIABILITY COMPANY INTER RAO EXPORT—See JSC INTER RAO UES; *Int'l*, pg. 4009
LIMITED LIABILITY COMPANY KIRISHIAVTOSERVIS—See Surgutneftegas OAO; *Int'l*, pg. 7344
LIMITED LIABILITY COMPANY MARKETING ASSOCIATION TVERNEFTEPRODUKT—See Surgutneftegas OAO; *Int'l*, pg. 7344
LIMITED LIABILITY COMPANY MICRO FOCUS—See Micro Focus International plc; *Int'l*, pg. 4876
LIMITED LIABILITY COMPANY NGK SPARK PLUGS—See Niterra Co., Ltd.; *Int'l*, pg. 5380
LIMITED LIABILITY COMPANY NISSIN RUS—See Nissin Corporation; *Int'l*, pg. 5375
LIMITED LIABILITY COMPANY NOVGORODNEFTEPRODUKT—See Surgutneftegas OAO; *Int'l*, pg. 7344
LIMITED LIABILITY COMPANY OIL REFINING AND PETROCHEMICAL ENTERPRISES DESIGN INSTITUTE—See Surgutneftegas OAO; *Int'l*, pg. 7344
LIMITED LIABILITY COMPANY OLAINFARM ASIA—See AS Olainfarm; *Int'l*, pg. 591
LIMITED LIABILITY COMPANY OLAINFARM AZERBAIJAN—See AS Olainfarm; *Int'l*, pg. 591
LIMITED LIABILITY COMPANY OLAINFARM OZBAXT—See AS Olainfarm; *Int'l*, pg. 591
LIMITED LIABILITY COMPANY OLAINFARM PHARMACEUTICAL & MEDICAL PRODUCTS INDUSTRY & TRADE—See AS Olainfarm; *Int'l*, pg. 591
LIMITED LIABILITY COMPANY PHILIP MORRIS SALES & DISTRIBUTION—See Philip Morris International Inc.; *U.S. Public*, pg. 1685
LIMITED LIABILITY COMPANY PHILIPS UKRAINE—See Koninklijke Philips N.V.; *Int'l*, pg. 4268
LIMITED LIABILITY COMPANY "ABBOTT UKRAINE"—See Abbott Laboratories; *U.S. Public*, pg. 20
LIMITED LIABILITY COMPANY "CY GRIBOEDOVA HOTEL LEASING"—See Marriott International, Inc.; *U.S. Public*, pg. 1370
LIMITED LIABILITY COMPANY "GROUP" SODRUZHESTVO; *Int'l*, pg. 4499
LIMITED LIABILITY COMPANY ROCHE DIAGNOSTICS RUS—See Roche Holding AG; *Int'l*, pg. 6374
LIMITED LIABILITY COMPANY RYBINSKELEKTROKABEL—See Prysmian S.p.A.; *Int'l*, pg. 6012
LIMITED LIABILITY COMPANY SANOFI-AVENTIS UKRAINE—See Sanofi; *Int'l*, pg. 6550
LIMITED LIABILITY COMPANY SAP CIS—See SAP SE; *Int'l*, pg. 6566
LIMITED LIABILITY COMPANY SAP KAZAKHSTAN—See SAP SE; *Int'l*, pg. 6566
LIMITED LIABILITY COMPANY SAP UKRAINE—See SAP SE; *Int'l*, pg. 6566
LIMITED LIABILITY COMPANY SIEMENS ENERGY—See Siemens Energy AG; *Int'l*, pg. 6902
LIMITED LIABILITY COMPANY VOLGALON LIMITED—See Koninklijke DSM N.V.; *Int'l*, pg. 4263
LIMITED LIABILITY COMPANY VOLGAPLAST COMPOUNDING—See Koninklijke DSM N.V.; *Int'l*, pg. 4263
LIMITED LIABILITY COMPANY YASENSVIT—See Ovostar Union N.V.; *Int'l*, pg. 5673
LIMITED LIABILITY PARTNERSHIP "CREDIT SUISSE (KAZAKHSTAN)"—See UBS Group AG; *Int'l*, pg. 8007
LIMITED PARTNERSHIP FOR INVESTMENT EHIME VENTURE FUND 2013—See The Ehime Bank, Ltd.; *Int'l*, pg. 7638
LIMITED REAL ESTATE—See Bath & Body Works, Inc.; *U.S. Public*, pg. 279
THE LIMITED STORES, INC.—See Sycamore Partners Management, LP; *U.S. Private*, pg. 3898

LIMIT HOLDINGS LIMITED—See QBE Insurance Group Limited; *Int'l*, pg. 6136
LIMITLESS EARTH PLC; *Int'l*, pg. 4499
LIMITLESS INTERNATIONAL INC.; *U.S. Private*, pg. 2456
LIMITLESS PJSC—See Dubai World Corporation; *Int'l*, pg. 2222
LIMITLESS PROJECTS INC.; *U.S. Private*, pg. 2456
LIMITLESS VENTURE GROUP, INC.; *U.S. Public*, pg. 1316
LIMITLESS X HOLDINGS INC.; *U.S. Public*, pg. 1316
LIM JIT FOO COLORECTAL PTE. LTD.—See Alliance Healthcare Group Limited; *Int'l*, pg. 340
LIM KET LENG TIMBER SDN. BHD.—See Classic Scenic Berhad; *Int'l*, pg. 1653
LIM KIM HAI ELECTRIC CO (S) PTE LTD—See Tai Sin Electric Limited; *Int'l*, pg. 7409
LIM KIM HAI ELECTRIC (VN) COMPANY LIMITED—See Tai Sin Electric Limited; *Int'l*, pg. 7409
LIMMATDRUCK AG—See The Federation of Migros Cooperatives; *Int'l*, pg. 7642
L-IMMOBILIEN GMBH—See Landesbank Baden-Wurttemberg; *Int'l*, pg. 4405
LIMNES BOTTLING ACQUISITION CO.; *U.S. Private*, pg. 2456
LIMOLINK, INC.; *U.S. Private*, pg. 2456
LIMONEIRA COMPANY; *U.S. Public*, pg. 1316
LIMONEIRA INTERNATIONAL DIVISION, LLC—See Limoneira Company; *U.S. Public*, pg. 1316
LIMONEIRA LEWIS COMMUNITY BUILDERS, LLC—See Limoneira Company; *U.S. Public*, pg. 1316
LIMON GMBH—See EWE Aktiengesellschaft; *Int'l*, pg. 2575
LIMORES LIMOS; *U.S. Private*, pg. 2456
LIMOS.COM, INC.—See On Demand iCars, Inc.; *U.S. Private*, pg. 3018
LIMOTEC BVBA—See Halma plc; *Int'l*, pg. 3232
LIMOUSIN ADHESIFS; *Int'l*, pg. 4499
LIMOUSINE SERVICE OF WESTCHESTER; *U.S. Private*, pg. 2456
LIM OVIN; *Int'l*, pg. 4498
LIMPAH MEWAH SDN. BHD.—See W T K Holdings Berhad; *Int'l*, pg. 8320
LIMPENS SA—See Eiffage S.A.; *Int'l*, pg. 2330
LIMPEX-KUZBARI & ANAN ENTERPRISES S.A.L.—See VIMPEX Handelsgesellschaft mbH; *Int'l*, pg. 8209
LIMPIEZAS DEYSE, S.L.—See ACS, Actividades de Construccion y Servicios, S.A.; *Int'l*, pg. 115
LIMPIEZAS LAFUENTE, S.L.—See ACS, Actividades de Construccion y Servicios, S.A.; *Int'l*, pg. 115
LIMPOTECNICA SOCIEDADE DE LIMPEZA TECNICA E MECANICA LDA—See OCS Group Limited; *Int'l*, pg. 5521
LIMTECH BIOMETRIC SOLUTIONS (PROPRIETARY) LIMITED—See Hosken Consolidated Investments Limited; *Int'l*, pg. 3485
THE LIMU COMPANY LLC—See NewAge, Inc.; *U.S. Public*, pg. 1513
LIMURU TEA PLC; *Int'l*, pg. 4499
LIM WEN HENG CONSTRUCTION PTE LTD; *Int'l*, pg. 4498
LINACAL S.L.U.—See Brookfield Corporation; *Int'l*, pg. 1188
LINAIR BIO-SCIENCE PTE. LTD.—See Acesian Partners Limited; *Int'l*, pg. 102
LINAIR ENGINEERING PTE. LTD.—See Acesian Partners Limited; *Int'l*, pg. 102
LINAIR TECHNOLOGIES (TAIWAN) CO., LTD—See Acesian Partners Limited; *Int'l*, pg. 102
LINAK ACTUADORES S.L.—See Linak A/S; *Int'l*, pg. 4500
LINAK ACTUATORS SDN. BHD.—See Linak A/S; *Int'l*, pg. 4500
LINAK ACTUATOR-SYSTEMS B.V.—See Linak A/S; *Int'l*, pg. 4500
LINAK ACTUATOR-SYSTEMS NV/SA—See Linak A/S; *Int'l*, pg. 4500
LINAK AG—See Linak A/S; *Int'l*, pg. 4500
LINAK A/S; *Int'l*, pg. 4500
LINAK AUSTRALIA PTY. LTD.—See Linak A/S; *Int'l*, pg. 4500
LINAK BENELUX—See Linak A/S; *Int'l*, pg. 4500
LINAK CANADA INC.—See Linak A/S; *Int'l*, pg. 4500
LINAK C&S S.R.O.—See Linak A/S; *Int'l*, pg. 4500
LINAK DANMARK A/S—See Linak A/S; *Int'l*, pg. 4500
LINAK DO BRASIL COMERCIO DE ATUADORES LTDA—See Linak A/S; *Int'l*, pg. 4500
LINAK FRANCE SARL—See Linak A/S; *Int'l*, pg. 4500
LINAK GMBH—See Linak A/S; *Int'l*, pg. 4500
LINAK ITALIA S.R.L.—See Linak A/S; *Int'l*, pg. 4500
LINAK ITH, IHR, SAN. VE TIC. A.S.—See Linak A/S; *Int'l*, pg. 4500
LINAK K.K.—See Linak A/S; *Int'l*, pg. 4500
LINAK KOREA LTD.—See Linak A/S; *Int'l*, pg. 4500
LINAK NEW ZEALAND LTD.—See Linak A/S; *Int'l*, pg. 4500
LINAK NORGE AS—See Linak A/S; *Int'l*, pg. 4500
LINAK OY—See Linak A/S; *Int'l*, pg. 4500
LINAK POLSKA—See Linak A/S; *Int'l*, pg. 4500
LINAK SCANDINAVIA AB—See Linak A/S; *Int'l*, pg. 4500

LINAK (SHENZHEN) ACTUATOR SYSTEMS LTD.—See Linak A/S; *Int'l*, pg. 4500
LINAK SLOVAKIA S.R.O.—See Linak A/S; *Int'l*, pg. 4500
LINAKS MICROELECTRONICS LTD.; *Int'l*, pg. 4500
LINAK UK LIMITED—See Linak A/S; *Int'l*, pg. 4500
LINAK US INC.—See Linak A/S; *Int'l*, pg. 4500
LINAMAR ANTRIEBSTECHNIK GMBH—See Linamar Corporation; *Int'l*, pg. 4501
LINAMAR AUTOMOTIVE SYSTEMS (WUXI) CO., LTD—See Linamar Corporation; *Int'l*, pg. 4501
LINAMAR CONSUMER PRODUCTS LTD.—See Linamar Corporation; *Int'l*, pg. 4501
LINAMAR CORPORATION - LINAMAR CUSTOMS FACILITY—See Linamar Corporation; *Int'l*, pg. 4501
LINAMAR CORPORATION - LINAMAR GEAR FACILITY—See Linamar Corporation; *Int'l*, pg. 4501
LINAMAR CORPORATION; *Int'l*, pg. 4500
LINAMAR DE MEXICO S.A. DE C.V.—See Linamar Corporation; *Int'l*, pg. 4501
LINAMAR DRIVELINE SYSTEMS GROUP - CORVEX MFG FACILITY—See Linamar Corporation; *Int'l*, pg. 4501
LINAMAR DRIVELINE SYSTEMS GROUP - LINAMAR GEAR FACILITY—See Linamar Corporation; *Int'l*, pg. 4501
LINAMAR DRIVELINE SYSTEMS GROUP—See Linamar Corporation; *Int'l*, pg. 4501
LINAMAR GMBH—See Linamar Corporation; *Int'l*, pg. 4501
LINAMAR HUNGARY ZRT—See Linamar Corporation; *Int'l*, pg. 4501
LINAMAR INDUSTRIAL, COMMERCIAL & ENERGY MANUFACTURING GROUP - CAMTAC MFG FACILITY—See Linamar Corporation; *Int'l*, pg. 4501
LINAMAR INDUSTRIAL, COMMERCIAL & ENERGY MANUFACTURING GROUP - FAMER RIVOIRE FACILITY—See Linamar Corporation; *Int'l*, pg. 4501
LINAMAR INDUSTRIAL, COMMERCIAL & ENERGY MANUFACTURING GROUP - FAMER TRANSMISSION FACILITY—See Linamar Corporation; *Int'l*, pg. 4501
LINAMAR INDUSTRIAL, COMMERCIAL & ENERGY MANUFACTURING GROUP - LINAMAR FLUID PRODUCTS FACILITY—See Linamar Corporation; *Int'l*, pg. 4501
LINAMAR INDUSTRIAL, COMMERCIAL & ENERGY MANUFACTURING GROUP - LINERGY MANUFACTURING FACILITY—See Linamar Corporation; *Int'l*, pg. 4501
LINAMAR INDUSTRIAL, COMMERCIAL & ENERGY MANUFACTURING GROUP - LINEX MANUFACTURING FACILITY—See Linamar Corporation; *Int'l*, pg. 4501
LINAMAR INDUSTRIAL, COMMERCIAL & ENERGY MANUFACTURING GROUP—See Linamar Corporation; *Int'l*, pg. 4501
LINAMAR INDUSTRIAL, COMMERCIAL & ENERGY MANUFACTURING GROUP - TRAXLE MFG FACILITY—See Linamar Corporation; *Int'l*, pg. 4501
LINAMAR JAPAN, INC.—See Linamar Corporation; *Int'l*, pg. 4501
LINAMAR MANUFACTURING GROUP - ARISS MANUFACTURING FACILITY—See Linamar Corporation; *Int'l*, pg. 4501
LINAMAR MANUFACTURING GROUP - AUTOCOM MANUFACTURING FACILITY—See Linamar Corporation; *Int'l*, pg. 4501
LINAMAR MANUFACTURING GROUP - CAMCOR MFG FACILITY—See Linamar Corporation; *Int'l*, pg. 4501
LINAMAR MANUFACTURING GROUP - CEMTOL MFG FACILITY—See Linamar Corporation; *Int'l*, pg. 4501
LINAMAR MANUFACTURING GROUP - COMTECH MFG FACILITY—See Linamar Corporation; *Int'l*, pg. 4501
LINAMAR MANUFACTURING GROUP - ENGICOM FACILITY—See Linamar Corporation; *Int'l*, pg. 4501
LINAMAR MANUFACTURING GROUP - ESTON MANUFACTURING FACILITY—See Linamar Corporation; *Int'l*, pg. 4501
LINAMAR MANUFACTURING GROUP - EXKOR MANUFACTURING FACILITY—See Linamar Corporation; *Int'l*, pg. 4501
LINAMAR MANUFACTURING GROUP - HASTECH MFG FACILITY—See Linamar Corporation; *Int'l*, pg. 4501
LINAMAR MANUFACTURING GROUP - LINAMAR PRODUCTS DIVISION—See Linamar Corporation; *Int'l*, pg. 4501
LINAMAR MANUFACTURING GROUP - OROS DIVISION—See Linamar Corporation; *Int'l*, pg. 4501
LINAMAR MANUFACTURING GROUP - POWERCOR FACILITY—See Linamar Corporation; *Int'l*, pg. 4501
LINAMAR MANUFACTURING GROUP - QUADRAD MANUFACTURING FACILITY—See Linamar Corporation; *Int'l*, pg. 4501
LINAMAR MANUFACTURING GROUP - ROCTEL MANUFACTURING FACILITY—See Linamar Corporation; *Int'l*, pg. 4501
LINAMAR MANUFACTURING GROUP—See Linamar Corporation; *Int'l*, pg. 4501

COMPANY NAME INDEX

LINAMAR MANUFACTURING GROUP - SPINIC MANUFACTURING FACILITY—See Linamar Corporation; *Int'l*, pg. 4501
LINAMAR MANUFACTURING GROUP - TRANSGEAR MANUFACTURING FACILITY—See Linamar Corporation; *Int'l*, pg. 4501
LINAMAR MANUFACTURING GROUP - VEHCOM MANUFACTURING FACILITY—See Linamar Corporation; *Int'l*, pg. 4501
LINAMAR NORTH CAROLINA, INC.—See Linamar Corporation; *Int'l*, pg. 4501
LINAMAR TRANSPORTATION INC.—See Linamar Corporation; *Int'l*, pg. 4502
LINAMAR U.S.A., INC.—See Linamar Corporation; *Int'l*, pg. 4502
LINAS AB; *Int'l*, pg. 4502
LINAS AGRO GROUP AB; *Int'l*, pg. 4502
LINATEX A/S—See Sorensen & Kofoed A/S; *Int'l*, pg. 7111
LINBECK CONSTRUCTION CORPORATION-FT. WORTH—See Linbeck Group LLC; *U.S. Private*, pg. 2456
LINBECK CONSTRUCTION CORPORATION-HOUSTON—See Linbeck Group LLC; *U.S. Private*, pg. 2456
LINBECK GROUP LLC; *U.S. Private*, pg. 2456
LINBECK—See Linbeck Group LLC; *U.S. Private*, pg. 2456
LINC AB; *Int'l*, pg. 4502
LINCARE HOLDINGS INC—See Linde plc; *Int'l*, pg. 4505
LINCARE INC.—See Linde plc; *Int'l*, pg. 4505
LINCARE OF CANADA INC.—See Linde plc; *Int'l*, pg. 4505
LINCARE OF NEW YORK INC.—See Linde plc; *Int'l*, pg. 4505
LINCAT GROUP PLC—See The Middleby Corporation; *U.S. Public*, pg. 2114
LINCAT LIMITED—See The Middleby Corporation; *U.S. Public*, pg. 2115
LIN CHI HYDRAULICS CO., LTD.—See Daikin Industries, Ltd.; *Int'l*, pg. 1936
LINCHRIS HOTEL CORP.; *U.S. Private*, pg. 2457
LINC LIMITED; *Int'l*, pg. 4502
LINC LOGISTICS COMPANY—See Universal Logistics Holdings, Inc.; *U.S. Public*, pg. 2261
LINCLUDEN MANAGEMENT LIMITED; *Int'l*, pg. 4502
LINCOLN ARCHIVES INC.—See Lincoln Securities Corp.; *U.S. Private*, pg. 2459
LINCOLN BENEFIT LIFE COMPANY—See Resolution Capital Limited; *Int'l*, pg. 6297
LINCOLN BENEFITS GROUP, INC.—See Aon plc; *Int'l*, pg. 496
LINCOLN BRASS WORKS, INC.—See Mueller Industries, Inc.; *U.S. Public*, pg. 1484
LINCOLN BRICK AND STONE INC.; *U.S. Private*, pg. 2457
LINCOLN BUILDERS INC.; *U.S. Private*, pg. 2457
LINCOLN CANADA HOLDINGS ULC—See Lincoln Electric Holdings, Inc.; *U.S. Public*, pg. 1317
LINCOLN CASTING LTD.—See Georg Fischer AG; *Int'l*, pg. 2937
LINCOLN CENTER FOR THE PERFORMING ARTS, INC.; *U.S. Private*, pg. 2457
LINCOLN COLLEGE OF TECHNOLOGY—See Lincoln Educational Services Corporation; *U.S. Public*, pg. 1316
LINCOLN CONTRACTING & EQUIPMENT CO. INC—See Riggs Industries, Inc.; *U.S. Private*, pg. 3435
LINCOLN CONTRACTING & EQUIPMENT COMPANY, INC.—See Riggs Industries, Inc.; *U.S. Private*, pg. 3435
LINCOLN CONTRACTORS SUPPLY INC; *U.S. Private*, pg. 2457
LINCOLN COUNTY BANCORP., INC.; *U.S. Private*, pg. 2457
LINCOLN EDUCATIONAL SERVICES CORPORATION; *U.S. Public*, pg. 1316
LINCOLN ELECTRIC BELGIUM—See Lincoln Electric Holdings, Inc.; *U.S. Public*, pg. 1317
LINCOLN ELECTRIC BESTER SP. Z O.O.—See Lincoln Electric Holdings, Inc.; *U.S. Public*, pg. 1317
THE LINCOLN ELECTRIC COMPANY (ASIA PACIFIC) PTE. LTD.—See Lincoln Electric Holdings, Inc.; *U.S. Public*, pg. 1318
THE LINCOLN ELECTRIC COMPANY AUSTRALIA PTY. LTD.—See Lincoln Electric Holdings, Inc.; *U.S. Public*, pg. 1318
LINCOLN ELECTRIC COMPANY (INDIA) PRIVATE LIMITED—See Lincoln Electric Holdings, Inc.; *U.S. Public*, pg. 1317
THE LINCOLN ELECTRIC COMPANY (NEW ZEALAND) LIMITED—See Lincoln Electric Holdings, Inc.; *U.S. Public*, pg. 1318
THE LINCOLN ELECTRIC COMPANY OF CANADA LP—See Lincoln Electric Holdings, Inc.; *U.S. Public*, pg. 1318
THE LINCOLN ELECTRIC COMPANY OF SOUTH AFRICA (PTY) LTD.—See Lincoln Electric Holdings, Inc.; *U.S. Public*, pg. 1318
LINCOLN ELECTRIC CZ S.R.O.—See Lincoln Electric Holdings, Inc.; *U.S. Public*, pg. 1317
LINCOLN ELECTRIC DEUTSCHLAND—See Lincoln Electric Holdings, Inc.; *U.S. Public*, pg. 1317
LINCOLN ELECTRIC DO BRASIL INDUSTRIA E COMERCIO LTDA.—See Lincoln Electric Holdings, Inc.; *U.S. Public*, pg. 1318
LINCOLN ELECTRIC EUROPE B.V.—See Lincoln Electric Holdings, Inc.; *U.S. Public*, pg. 1317
LINCOLN ELECTRIC EUROPE S.L.—See Lincoln Electric Holdings, Inc.; *U.S. Public*, pg. 1317
LINCOLN ELECTRIC FRANCE S.A.S.—See Lincoln Electric Holdings, Inc.; *U.S. Public*, pg. 1317
LINCOLN ELECTRIC HELI (ZHENGZHOU) WELDING MATERIALS COMPANY LTD.—See Lincoln Electric Holdings, Inc.; *U.S. Public*, pg. 1317
LINCOLN ELECTRIC HOLDINGS, INC.; *U.S. Public*, pg. 1316
LINCOLN ELECTRIC IBERIA, S.L.—See Lincoln Electric Holdings, Inc.; *U.S. Public*, pg. 1317
LINCOLN ELECTRIC ITALIA S.R.L.—See Lincoln Electric Holdings, Inc.; *U.S. Public*, pg. 1317
LINCOLN ELECTRIC JAPAN K.K.—See Lincoln Electric Holdings, Inc.; *U.S. Public*, pg. 1317
LINCOLN ELECTRIC LUXEMBOURG S.A.R.L.—See Lincoln Electric Holdings, Inc.; *U.S. Public*, pg. 1317
LINCOLN ELECTRIC MALAYSIA SDN. BHD.—See Lincoln Electric Holdings, Inc.; *U.S. Public*, pg. 1317
LINCOLN ELECTRIC MAQUINAS, S. DE R.L. DE C.V.—See Lincoln Electric Holdings, Inc.; *U.S. Public*, pg. 1317
LINCOLN ELECTRIC MEXICANA S.A. DE C.V.—See Lincoln Electric Holdings, Inc.; *U.S. Public*, pg. 1317
LINCOLN ELECTRIC MIDDLE EAST FZE—See Lincoln Electric Holdings, Inc.; *U.S. Public*, pg. 1317
LINCOLN ELECTRIC PORTUGAL, S.A.—See Lincoln Electric Holdings, Inc.; *U.S. Public*, pg. 1317
LINCOLN ELECTRIC S.A.—See Lincoln Electric Holdings, Inc.; *U.S. Public*, pg. 1317
LINCOLN ELECTRIC SPAIN, S.L.—See Lincoln Electric Holdings, Inc.; *U.S. Public*, pg. 1317
LINCOLN ELECTRIC SVERIGE—See Lincoln Electric Holdings, Inc.; *U.S. Public*, pg. 1318
LINCOLN ELECTRIC SYSTEM; *U.S. Private*, pg. 2457
LINCOLN ELECTRIC (THAILAND) LTD.—See Lincoln Electric Holdings, Inc.; *U.S. Public*, pg. 1317
LINCOLN ELECTRIC (U.K.) LTD.—See Lincoln Electric Holdings, Inc.; *U.S. Public*, pg. 1317
LINCOLN EQUIPMENT, LTD.; *U.S. Private*, pg. 2457
LINCOLN FEDERAL SAVINGS BANK OF NEBRASKA; *U.S. Private*, pg. 2457
LINCOLN FINANCIAL ADVISORS CORPORATION—See Lincoln National Corporation; *U.S. Public*, pg. 1319
LINCOLN FINANCIAL BENEFIT PARTNERS—See Lincoln National Corporation; *U.S. Public*, pg. 1319
LINCOLN FINANCIAL DISTRIBUTORS, INC.—See Lincoln National Corporation; *U.S. Public*, pg. 1319
LINCOLN FINANCIAL LIMITED LIABILITY COMPANY I—See Lincoln National Corporation; *U.S. Public*, pg. 1319
LINCOLN FINANCIAL MEDIA COMPANY OF GEORGIA—See AUDACY, INC.; *U.S. Public*, pg. 227
LINCOLN FINANCIAL MEDIA COMPANY—See Lincoln National Corporation; *U.S. Public*, pg. 1319
LINCOLN FINANCIAL SECURITIES CORPORATION—See Lincoln National Corporation; *U.S. Public*, pg. 1319
LINCOLN FUNERAL HOME, INC.—See Service Corporation International; *U.S. Public*, pg. 1870
LINCOLN GENERAL INSURANCE COMPANY—See Financiere Pinault SCA; *Int'l*, pg. 2669
LINCOLN GENERAL INSURANCE COMPANY—See Kingsway Financial Services Inc.; *U.S. Public*, pg. 1235
LINCOLN GOLD MINING INC.; *Int'l*, pg. 4502
LINCOLN HARRIS CSG—See Lincoln Property Company; *U.S. Private*, pg. 2458
LINCOLN HARRIS, LLC—See Lincoln Property Company; *U.S. Private*, pg. 2458
LINCOLN HEIGHTS FORD SALES; *Int'l*, pg. 4502
LINCOLN HELIOS (INDIA) LTD.—See SKF AB; *Int'l*, pg. 6981
LINCOLN HERITAGE LIFE INSURANCE CO.—See London Insurance Group, Inc.; *U.S. Private*, pg. 2483
LINCOLN HOLDINGS ENTERPRISES, INC.—See SKF AB; *Int'l*, pg. 6985
LINCOLN HOLDINGS LLC; *U.S. Private*, pg. 2457
LINCOLN INDUSTRIES, INC.—See Zoeller Co.; *U.S. Private*, pg. 4607
LINCOLN INDUSTRIES; *U.S. Private*, pg. 2457
LINCOLN INSURANCE—See King Insurance Partners, LLC; *U.S. Private*, pg. 2309
LINCOLN INVESTMENT PLANNING INC.; *U.S. Private*, pg. 2457
LINCOLN JOURNAL, INC.—See HD Media Company, LLC; *U.S. Private*, pg. 1890
LINCOLN JOURNAL—See Gannett Co., Inc.; *U.S. Public*, pg. 902
LINCOLN JOURNAL-STAR—See Lee Enterprises, Incorporated; *U.S. Public*, pg. 1299
LINCOLN LIFE & ANNUITY COMPANY OF NEW YORK—See Lincoln National Corporation; *U.S. Public*, pg. 1319
LINCOLN LUBRICATION (SA) PTY. LTD.—See SKF AB; *Int'l*, pg. 6981
LINCOLN LUMBER COMPANY; *U.S. Private*, pg. 2458
LINCOLN MEDIA SERVICES, INC.; *U.S. Private*, pg. 2458
LINCOLN MEMORIAL PARK—See Service Corporation International; *U.S. Public*, pg. 1870
LINCOLN MINERALS LIMITED; *Int'l*, pg. 4502
THE LINCOLN NATIONAL BANK OF HODGENVILLE—See First Cecilian Bancorp, Inc.; *U.S. Private*, pg. 1515
LINCOLN NATIONAL CORPORATION; *U.S. Public*, pg. 1318
THE LINCOLN NATIONAL LIFE INSURANCE CO.—See Lincoln National Corporation; *U.S. Public*, pg. 1319
LINCOLN NEWS MESSENGER—See Brehm Communications Inc.; *U.S. Private*, pg. 644
LINCOLN OFFICE SUPPLY CO. INCORPORATED; *U.S. Private*, pg. 2458
LINCOLN PARK BANCORP—See Ion Financial, MHC; *U.S. Private*, pg. 2133
LINCOLN PARK DIALYSIS SERVICES, INC.—See DaVita Inc.; *U.S. Public*, pg. 640
LINCOLN PARK KIDNEY CENTER, LLC—See Nautic Partners, LLC; *U.S. Private*, pg. 2870
LINCOLN PARK ZOO; *U.S. Private*, pg. 2458
LINCOLN PEAK CAPITAL MANAGEMENT, LLC; *U.S. Private*, pg. 2458
LINCOLN PHARMACEUTICALS LTD.; *Int'l*, pg. 4503
LINCOLN PRODUCTS—See Ferguson plc; *Int'l*, pg. 2638
LINCOLN PROPERTY COMPANY COMMERCIAL, INC.—See Lincoln Property Company; *U.S. Private*, pg. 2458
LINCOLN PROPERTY COMPANY RESIDENTIAL—See Lincoln Property Company; *U.S. Private*, pg. 2458
LINCOLN PROPERTY COMPANY; *U.S. Private*, pg. 2458
LINCOLN PROVISION, INC.; *U.S. Private*, pg. 2458
LINCOLN RACKHOUSE—See Lincoln Property Company; *U.S. Private*, pg. 2458
LINCOLN RESOURCE GROUP CORPORATION—See Lincoln Gold Mining Inc.; *Int'l*, pg. 4502
LINCOLN ROAD MANAGEMENT LLC—See Vornado Realty Trust; *U.S. Public*, pg. 2310
LINCOLN SAVINGS BANK; *U.S. Private*, pg. 2458
LINCOLN SECURITIES CORP.; *U.S. Private*, pg. 2458
LINCOLN SENTRY GROUP PTY LIMITED—See Nippon Paint Holdings Co., Ltd.; *Int'l*, pg. 5325
LINCOLNSHIRE MANAGEMENT, INC.; *U.S. Private*, pg. 2459
LINCOLNSHIRE NEWSPAPERS LTD—See JPIMedia Holdings Limited; *Int'l*, pg. 4006
LINCOLN SMITWELD BELGIUM S.A.—See Lincoln Electric Holdings, Inc.; *U.S. Public*, pg. 1318
LINCOLN STORES INC.; *U.S. Private*, pg. 2459
LINCOLN STRUCTURAL SOLUTIONS LLC—See Owen Industries, Inc.; *U.S. Private*, pg. 3054
LINCOLN SURGERY CENTER, LLC—See HCA Healthcare, Inc.; *U.S. Public*, pg. 1001
LINCOLN SYMPHONY ORCHESTRA; *U.S. Private*, pg. 2459
LINCOLN TECHNICAL INSTITUTE; *U.S. Private*, pg. 2459
LINCOLN TEXTILE PRODUCTS CO.; *U.S. Private*, pg. 2459
LINCOLNTON DIALYSIS, LLC—See DaVita Inc.; *U.S. Public*, pg. 640
LINCOLN TRIANGLE PARTNERS L.P.—See Millennium Management Inc.; *U.S. Private*, pg. 2731
LINCOLN VARIABLE INSURANCE PRODUCTS TRUST—See Lincoln National Corporation; *U.S. Public*, pg. 1319
LINCOLN VENTURES LTD.; *Int'l*, pg. 4503
LINCOLNVILLE TELEPHONE COMPANY; *U.S. Private*, pg. 2459
LINCOLN WAY COMMUNITY BANK—See LWCBancorp, Inc.; *U.S. Private*, pg. 2518
LINCOLNWAY ENERGY, LLC; *U.S. Private*, pg. 2459
LINCOLN WEST LIMITED—See The Warehouse Group Limited; *Int'l*, pg. 7699
LINCOLN WOOD PRODUCTS, INC.; *U.S. Private*, pg. 2459
LINCOLNWOOD TOWN CENTER, LLC—See Washington Prime Group Inc.; *U.S. Private*, pg. 4448
LINCOM AB—See Instalco AB; *Int'l*, pg. 3722
LINCOTRADE & ASSOCIATES HOLDINGS LIMITED; *Int'l*, pg. 4503
LINC SYSTEMS, INC.; *U.S. Private*, pg. 2456
LINDAB AG—See Lindab International AB; *Int'l*, pg. 4503
LINDAB AS—See Lindab International AB; *Int'l*, pg. 4503
LINDAB A.S.—See Lindab International AB; *Int'l*, pg. 4504
LINDAB AS—See Lindab International AB; *Int'l*, pg. 4503
LINDAB A/S—See Lindab International AB; *Int'l*, pg. 4503
LINDAB-ASTRON GMBH—See Lindab International AB; *Int'l*, pg. 4503
LINDAB-ASTRON S.A.S.—See Lindab International AB; *Int'l*, pg. 4503
LINDAB-ASTRON SP. Z O.O.—See Lindab International AB; *Int'l*, pg. 4503
LINDAB-ASTRON S.R.O.—See Lindab International AB; *Int'l*, pg. 4503

LINC SYSTEMS, INC.

CORPORATE AFFILIATIONS

LINDAB BUILDING SYSTEMS KFT.—See Lindab International AB; *Int'l*, pg. 4503
LINDAB DOOR B.V.—See Lindab International AB; *Int'l*, pg. 4503
LINDAB D.O.O.—See Lindab International AB; *Int'l*, pg. 4504
LINDAB D.O.O.—See Lindab International AB; *Int'l*, pg. 4504
LINDAB EOOD—See Lindab International AB; *Int'l*, pg. 4503
LINDAB FRANCE S.A.S.—See Lindab International AB; *Int'l*, pg. 4503
LINDAB GMBH—See Lindab International AB; *Int'l*, pg. 4503
LINDAB HAVALANDIRMA LTD STI—See Lindab International AB; *Int'l*, pg. 4503
LINDAB HOLDING A/S—See Lindab International AB; *Int'l*, pg. 4503
LINDAB INTERNATIONAL AB; *Int'l*, pg. 4503
LINDAB (IRL) LTD—See Lindab International AB; *Int'l*, pg. 4503
LINDAB KFT.—See Lindab International AB; *Int'l*, pg. 4504
LINDAB LLC—See Lindab International AB; *Int'l*, pg. 4504
LINDAB LTD—See Lindab International AB; *Int'l*, pg. 4504
LINDAB N.V.—See Lindab International AB; *Int'l*, pg. 4503
LINDAB PROFIL AB—See Lindab International AB; *Int'l*, pg. 4504
LINDAB S.A.R.L—See Lindab International AB; *Int'l*, pg. 4504
LINDAB SIA—See Lindab International AB; *Int'l*, pg. 4504
LINDAB SP. Z O.O.—See Lindab International AB; *Int'l*, pg. 4503
LINDAB SP. Z.O.O.—See Lindab International AB; *Int'l*, pg. 4504
LINDAB SRL—See Lindab International AB; *Int'l*, pg. 4504
LINDAB S.R.O.—See Lindab International AB; *Int'l*, pg. 4504
LINDAB STEEL AB—See Lindab International AB; *Int'l*, pg. 4504
LINDAB SVERIGE AB—See Lindab International AB; *Int'l*, pg. 4504
LINDAB TREASURY AB—See Lindab International AB; *Int'l*, pg. 4504
LINDAB VENTILATION AB—See Lindab International AB; *Int'l*, pg. 4504
LINDAHL HEALTHCARE, INC.—See The Ensign Group, Inc.; *U.S. Public*, pg. 2071
LINDA JONES RETIREMENT VILLAGE LIMITED—See Ryman Healthcare Ltd.; *Int'l*, pg. 6439
LINDAL BUILDING PRODUCTS—See Lindal Cedar Homes, Inc.; *U.S. Private*, pg. 2459
LINDAL CEDAR HOMES, INC.; *U.S. Private*, pg. 2459
LINDAL CEDAR HOMES, INC.—See Lindal Cedar Homes, Inc.; *U.S. Private*, pg. 2459
LINDALE MALL, LLC—See Washington Prime Group Inc.; *U.S. Private*, pg. 4448
LINDA NEKTAR AS; *Int'l*, pg. 4503
LINDAU CHEMICALS INC.; *U.S. Private*, pg. 2459
LINDA VISTA S.A.—See Ball Horticultural Company; *U.S. Private*, pg. 460
LINDBERG AS—See Kering S.A.; *Int'l*, pg. 4135
LINDBERGH & ASSOCIATES, LLC—See T.Y. Lin International Group Ltd.; *U.S. Private*, pg. 3913
LINDBERGH S.P.A.; *Int'l*, pg. 4504
LINDBERG/MPH—See Resilience Capital Partners, LLC; *U.S. Private*, pg. 3405
LINDBERG STENBERG ARKITEKTER AB—See Storskogen Group AB; *Int'l*, pg. 7228
LINDBLAD EXPEDITIONS HOLDINGS, INC.; *U.S. Public*, pg. 1319
LINDBLAD EXPEDITIONS, LLC—See Lindblad Expeditions Holdings, Inc.; *U.S. Public*, pg. 1319
LINDCO AS—See ITAB Shop Concept AB; *Int'l*, pg. 3828
LINDE AG - ENGINEERING DIVISION—See Linde plc; *Int'l*, pg. 4505
LINDE AG - GASES DIVISION, HAMBURG—See Linde plc; *Int'l*, pg. 4505
LINDE AG - GASES DIVISION—See Linde plc; *Int'l*, pg. 4505
LINDE AG—See Linde plc; *Int'l*, pg. 4504
LINDE ARABIAN CONTRACTING CO., LTD.—See Linde plc; *Int'l*, pg. 4507
LINDE (AUSTRALIA) PTY. LTD.—See Linde plc; *Int'l*, pg. 4505
LINDE BANGLADESH LIMITED—See Linde plc; *Int'l*, pg. 4507
LINDE BANGLADESH LIMITED—See Linde plc; *Int'l*, pg. 4507
LINDE BRANDMATERIEL APS—See London Security PLC; *Int'l*, pg. 4547
LINDE CANADA INC.—See Linde plc; *Int'l*, pg. 4508
LINDE (CHINA) FORKLIFT TRUCK CORP., LTD.—See KKR & Co. Inc.; *U.S. Public*, pg. 1255
LINDE (CHINA) FORKLIFT TRUCK CORP., LTD.—See The Goldman Sachs Group, Inc.; *U.S. Public*, pg. 2079
LINDE CORPORATION; *U.S. Private*, pg. 2459
LINDE CRYOPLANTS LTD.—See Linde plc; *Int'l*, pg. 4507
LINDE ELECTRONICS B.V.—See Linde plc; *Int'l*, pg. 4507

LINDE ELECTRONICS GMBH—See Linde plc; *Int'l*, pg. 4507
LINDE ELECTRONICS SAS—See Linde plc; *Int'l*, pg. 4505
LINDE ELECTRONICS & SPECIALTY GASES (SUZHOU) CO LTD.—See Linde plc; *Int'l*, pg. 4507
LINDE ENGINEERING (DALIAN) CO. LTD.—See Linde plc; *Int'l*, pg. 4507
LINDE ENGINEERING DRESDEN GMBH—See Linde plc; *Int'l*, pg. 4505
LINDE ENGINEERING (HANGZHOU) CO. LTD.—See Linde plc; *Int'l*, pg. 4507
LINDE ENGINEERING INDIA PRIVATE LIMITED—See Linde plc; *Int'l*, pg. 4507
LINDE ENGINEERING KOREA, LTD.—See Linde plc; *Int'l*, pg. 4505
LINDE ENGINEERING (MALAYSIA) SDN. BHD.—See Linde plc; *Int'l*, pg. 4505
LINDE ENGINEERING MIDDLE EAST LLC—See Linde plc; *Int'l*, pg. 4505
LINDE FINANCE B.V.—See Linde plc; *Int'l*, pg. 4507
LINDE FINANCE—See Linde plc; *Int'l*, pg. 4505
LINDE FORDERTECHNIK GMBH—See KKR & Co. Inc.; *U.S. Public*, pg. 1255
LINDE FORDERTECHNIK GMBH—See The Goldman Sachs Group, Inc.; *U.S. Public*, pg. 2079
LINDE FRANCE S.A.—See Linde plc; *Int'l*, pg. 4507
LINDE GAS AB—See Linde plc; *Int'l*, pg. 4505
LINDE GAS ALGERIE S.P.A.—See Linde plc; *Int'l*, pg. 4506
LINDE GAS ASIA PTE LTD—See Linde plc; *Int'l*, pg. 4506
LINDE GAS A/S—See Linde plc; *Int'l*, pg. 4505
LINDE GAS AS—See Linde plc; *Int'l*, pg. 4506
LINDE GAS A.S.—See Linde plc; *Int'l*, pg. 4506
LINDE GAS BELGIUM N.V.—See Linde plc; *Int'l*, pg. 4506
LINDE GAS BENELUX B.V.—See Linde plc; *Int'l*, pg. 4506
LINDE GAS BULGARIA EOOD—See Linde plc; *Int'l*, pg. 4506
LINDE GAS CHILE S.A.—See Linde plc; *Int'l*, pg. 4506
LINDE GAS CRYOSERVICES B.V.—See Linde plc; *Int'l*, pg. 4506
LINDE GAS CURACAO N.V.—See Linde plc; *Int'l*, pg. 4506
LINDE GAS DEL PERU S.A.—See Linde plc; *Int'l*, pg. 4506
LINDE GAS EHF—See Linde plc; *Int'l*, pg. 4506
LINDE GAS & EQUIPMENT INC.—See Linde plc; *Int'l*, pg. 4508
LINDE GASES (CHANGZHOU) COMPANY LIMITED—See Linde plc; *Int'l*, pg. 4506
LINDE GASES (CHENGDU) CO., LTD.—See Linde plc; *Int'l*, pg. 4506
LINDE GASES (FUSHUN) CO., LTD.—See Linde plc; *Int'l*, pg. 4506
LINDE GASES (NANJING) COMPANY LIMITED—See Linde plc; *Int'l*, pg. 4506
LINDE GAS ESPANA SAU - ALCALA DE HENARES PLANT—See Linde plc; *Int'l*, pg. 4506
LINDE GASES (SHANGHAI) CO., LTD.—See Linde plc; *Int'l*, pg. 4505
LINDE GASES (SUZHOU) COMPANY LIMITED—See Linde plc; *Int'l*, pg. 4506
LINDE GAS GMBH—See Linde plc; *Int'l*, pg. 4506
LINDE GAS (H.K.) LIMITED—See Linde plc; *Int'l*, pg. 4505
LINDE GAS ITALIA S.R.L.—See Linde plc; *Int'l*, pg. 4506
LINDE GAS K. S.—See Linde plc; *Int'l*, pg. 4506
LINDE GAS NORTH AMERICA LLC—See Linde plc; *Int'l*, pg. 4507
LINDE GAS PRODUKTIONSGESELLSCHAFT MBH & CO. KG—See Linde plc; *Int'l*, pg. 4506
LINDE GAS SHENZHEN LTD.—See Linde plc; *Int'l*, pg. 4506
LINDE GAS SIA—See Linde plc; *Int'l*, pg. 4506
LINDE GAS SINGAPORE PTE. LTD.—See Linde plc; *Int'l*, pg. 4506
LINDE GAS SRBIJA INDUSTRIJA GASOVA A.D.—See Linde plc; *Int'l*, pg. 4505
LINDE GAS THERAPEUTICS BENELUX B.V.—See Linde plc; *Int'l*, pg. 4506
LINDE GAS THERAPEUTICS GMBH & CO. KG—See Linde plc; *Int'l*, pg. 4506
LINDE GAS TUNISIE S.A.—See Linde plc; *Int'l*, pg. 4506
LINDE GAS UAB—See Linde plc; *Int'l*, pg. 4506
LINDE GAS ZHENHAI LTD.—See Linde plc; *Int'l*, pg. 4506
LINDE GAZ A.S.—See Linde plc; *Int'l*, pg. 4506
LINDE GAZ MAGYARORSZAG ZRT.—See Linde plc; *Int'l*, pg. 4506
LINDE GAZ POLSKA SPOLKA Z.O.O.—See Linde plc; *Int'l*, pg. 4506
LINDE GAZ ROMANIA S.R.L.—See Linde plc; *Int'l*, pg. 4506
LINDE HADJIKYRIAKOS GAS LIMITED—See Linde plc; *Int'l*, pg. 4505
LINDE HEALTHCARE BENELUX—See Linde plc; *Int'l*, pg. 4506
LINDE HEAVY TRUCK DIVISION LTD.—See KKR & Co. Inc.; *U.S. Public*, pg. 1255
LINDE HEAVY TRUCK DIVISION LTD.—See The Goldman Sachs Group, Inc.; *U.S. Public*, pg. 2079
LINDE HELLAS E.P.E.—See Linde plc; *Int'l*, pg. 4507

LINDE HIGH LIFT CHILE S.A.—See KKR & Co. Inc.; *U.S. Public*, pg. 1255
LINDE HIGH LIFT CHILE S.A.—See The Goldman Sachs Group, Inc.; *U.S. Public*, pg. 2079
LINDE HKO LIMITED—See Linde plc; *Int'l*, pg. 4507
LINDE HOLDINGS NETHERLANDS B.V.—See Linde plc; *Int'l*, pg. 4508
LINDE HOMECARE BENELUX B.V.—See Linde plc; *Int'l*, pg. 4508
LINDE HUACHANG (ZHANGJIAGANG) GAS CO., LTD.—See Linde plc; *Int'l*, pg. 4508
LINDE HYDRAULICS CORPORATION—See Shandong Heavy Industry Group Co., Ltd.; *Int'l*, pg. 6754
LINDE HYDRAULICS LP—See Shandong Heavy Industry Group Co., Ltd.; *Int'l*, pg. 6754
LINDE HYDRAULICS LTD.—See Shandong Heavy Industry Group Co., Ltd.; *Int'l*, pg. 6754
LINDE INDIA LIMITED—See Linde plc; *Int'l*, pg. 4508
LINDE INDUSTRIAL GASES - MALAYSIAN SDN. BHD—See Linde plc; *Int'l*, pg. 4508
LINDE KOREA CO., LTD.—See Linde plc; *Int'l*, pg. 4508
LINDE KRYOTECHNIK AG—See Linde plc; *Int'l*, pg. 4505
LINDE LANSING FORDERTECHNIK AG—See KKR & Co. Inc.; *U.S. Public*, pg. 1255
LINDE LANSING FORDERTECHNIK AG—See The Goldman Sachs Group, Inc.; *U.S. Public*, pg. 2079
LIND ELECTRONICS, INC.—See Main Street Capital Corporation; *U.S. Public*, pg. 1354
LINDELL BANK & TRUST COMPANY—See First Illinois Bancorp, Inc.; *U.S. Private*, pg. 1520
LINDELL PROPERTIES, INC.; *U.S. Private*, pg. 2459
LINDE MALAYSIA SDN. BHD.—See Linde plc; *Int'l*, pg. 4508
LINDE MALAYSIA SDN. BHD.—See Linde plc; *Int'l*, pg. 4508
LINDEMAN ASIA INVESTMENT CORP.; *Int'l*, pg. 4510
LINDEMANS WINES PTY. LTD.—See Treasury Wine Estates Limited; *Int'l*, pg. 7909
LINDE MATERIAL HANDLING (AUSTRALIA) PTY. LTD.—See KKR & Co. Inc.; *U.S. Public*, pg. 1255
LINDE MATERIAL HANDLING (AUSTRALIA) PTY. LTD.—See The Goldman Sachs Group, Inc.; *U.S. Public*, pg. 2079
LINDE MATERIAL HANDLING CESKA REPUBLICA S.R.O.—See KKR & Co. Inc.; *U.S. Public*, pg. 1255
LINDE MATERIAL HANDLING CESKA REPUBLICA S.R.O.—See The Goldman Sachs Group, Inc.; *U.S. Public*, pg. 2079
LINDE MATERIAL HANDLING DO BRASIL LTDA.—See KKR & Co. Inc.; *U.S. Public*, pg. 1255
LINDE MATERIAL HANDLING DO BRASIL LTDA.—See The Goldman Sachs Group, Inc.; *U.S. Public*, pg. 2079
LINDE MATERIAL HANDLING GMBH—See KKR & Co. Inc.; *U.S. Public*, pg. 1254
LINDE MATERIAL HANDLING GMBH—See The Goldman Sachs Group, Inc.; *U.S. Public*, pg. 2079
LINDE MATERIAL HANDLING IBERICA S.A.—See KKR & Co. Inc.; *U.S. Public*, pg. 1255
LINDE MATERIAL HANDLING IBERICA S.A.—See The Goldman Sachs Group, Inc.; *U.S. Public*, pg. 2079
LINDE MATERIAL HANDLING ITALIA S.P.A.—See KKR & Co. Inc.; *U.S. Public*, pg. 1255
LINDE MATERIAL HANDLING ITALIA S.P.A.—See The Goldman Sachs Group, Inc.; *U.S. Public*, pg. 2079
LINDE MATERIAL HANDLING (PTY) LTD.—See KKR & Co. Inc.; *U.S. Public*, pg. 1255
LINDE MATERIAL HANDLING (PTY) LTD.—See The Goldman Sachs Group, Inc.; *U.S. Public*, pg. 2079
LINDE MATERIAL HANDLING (UK) LTD.—See KKR & Co. Inc.; *U.S. Public*, pg. 1255
LINDE MATERIAL HANDLING (UK) LTD.—See The Goldman Sachs Group, Inc.; *U.S. Public*, pg. 2079
LINDE MEDICALE S.R.L.—See Linde plc; *Int'l*, pg. 4508
LINDENBERG TECHNOLOGIES—See Stockell Consulting Inc.; *U.S. Private*, pg. 3815
LINDEN BULK TRANSPORTATION CO., LLC—See KKR & Co. Inc.; *U.S. Public*, pg. 1241
LINDENGROVE, INC.; *U.S. Private*, pg. 2460
LINDENGRUPPEN AB; *Int'l*, pg. 4510
LINDEN HOMES EASTERN LIMITED—See Vistry Group PLC; *Int'l*, pg. 8255
LINDEN HOMES SOUTH-EAST LIMITED—See Vistry Group PLC; *Int'l*, pg. 8255
LINDEN HOMES SOUTHERN LIMITED—See Vistry Group PLC; *Int'l*, pg. 8255
LINDEN HOMES WESTERN LIMITED—See Vistry Group PLC; *Int'l*, pg. 8255
LINDEN LLC; *U.S. Private*, pg. 2459
LINDEN LUMBER, LLC—See H.I.G. Capital, LLC; *U.S. Private*, pg. 1832
LINDENMEYR BOOK PUBLISHING PAPERS—See Central National Gottesman Inc.; *U.S. Private*, pg. 823
LINDENMEYR CENTRAL—See Central National Gottesman Inc.; *U.S. Private*, pg. 823
LINDENMEYR MUNROE—See Central National Gottesman Inc.; *U.S. Private*, pg. 823
LINDEN STREET CAPITAL CORP.; *U.S. Private*, pg. 2460
LINDEN WAREHOUSE & DISTRIBUTION CO., INC.—See KKR & Co. Inc.; *U.S. Public*, pg. 1241

LINDE PHILIPPINES, INC.—See Linde plc; *Int'l*, pg. 4508
LINDE PLC; *Int'l*, pg. 4504
LINDER & ASSOCIATES, INC.; *U.S. Private*, pg. 2460
LINDE REFRIGERATION SYSTEMS LTD.—See Carrier Global Corporation; *U.S. Public*, pg. 441
LINDER INDUSTRIAL MACHINERY COMPANY—See Sumitomo Corporation; *Int'l*, pg. 7273
LINDER'S FURNITURE, INC.; *U.S. Private*, pg. 2460
LINDE RSS LLC—See Linde plc; *Int'l*, pg. 4508
LINDE SCHWEISSTECHNIK GMBH—See Linde plc; *Int'l*, pg. 4508
LINDESNES AS—See Schibsted ASA; *Int'l*, pg. 6617
LINDE SOKOLOVSKA S.R.O.—See Linde plc; *Int'l*, pg. 4508
LINDE (THAILAND) PUBLIC COMPANY LIMITED—See Linde plc; *Int'l*, pg. 4507
LINDE URUGUAY LIMITADA—See Linde plc; *Int'l*, pg. 4506
LINDE VILICARI HRVATSKA D.O.O.—See KKR & Co. Inc.; *U.S. Public*, pg. 1255
LINDE VILICARI HRVATSKA D.O.O.—See The Goldman Sachs Group, Inc.; *U.S. Public*, pg. 2079
LINDEX OU EESTI—See Stockmann plc; *Int'l*, pg. 7220
LINDEX UK FASHION LTD.—See Stockmann plc; *Int'l*, pg. 7220
LINDGREN R.F. ENCLOSURES, INC.—See ESCO Technologies, Inc.; *U.S. Public*, pg. 794
LINDHARDT OG RINGHOF FORLAG A/S—See Egmont Fonden; *Int'l*, pg. 2325
LINDIAN RESOURCES LIMITED; *Int'l*, pg. 4511
LINDI JUMBO LTD.—See Walkabout Resources Ltd; *Int'l*, pg. 8333
LINDLEY FOOD SERVICE CORPORATION—See Charterhouse Capital Partners LLP; *Int'l*, pg. 1455
LINDLEY MOOR MEADOWS (HUDDERSFIELD) MANAGEMENT COMPANY LIMITED—See Persimmon plc; *Int'l*, pg. 5816
LIND MARINE, INC.; *U.S. Private*, pg. 2459
LINDNER GMBH & CO. KG—See Linde plc; *Int'l*, pg. 4506
LINDO/FCB—See The Interpublic Group of Companies, Inc.; *U.S. Public*, pg. 2093
LINDO INDUSTRIPARK A/S—See A.P. Moller-Maersk A/S; *Int'l*, pg. 26
LINDOPHARM GMBH; *Int'l*, pg. 4511
LINDORFF AS—See Intrum AB; *Int'l*, pg. 3771
LINDORFF A/S—See Nordic Capital AB; *Int'l*, pg. 5420
LINDORFF EESTI AS—See Nordic Capital AB; *Int'l*, pg. 5420
LINDORFF NETHERLANDS B.V.—See Nordic Capital AB; *Int'l*, pg. 5420
LINDORFF OY—See Nordic Capital AB; *Int'l*, pg. 5420
LINDORFF SVERIGE AB—See Nordic Capital AB; *Int'l*, pg. 5420
LINDOR INC.; *Int'l*, pg. 4511
LINDPRO A/S—See Kemp & Lauritzen A/S; *Int'l*, pg. 4125
LINDQUIST FORD INC.; *U.S. Private*, pg. 2460
LINDQUIST MACHINE CORPORATION; *U.S. Private*, pg. 2460
LINDQUIST STEELS INCORPORATED; *U.S. Private*, pg. 2460
LINDSAY AMERICA DO SUL LTDA.—See Lindsay Corporation; *U.S. Public*, pg. 1319
LINDSAY AUSTRALIA LIMITED; *Int'l*, pg. 4511
LINDSAY BROTHERS HOLDINGS PTY LTD—See Lindsay Australia Limited; *Int'l*, pg. 4511
LINDSAY CADILLAC COMPANY; *U.S. Private*, pg. 2460
LINDSAY CHEVROLET LLC; *U.S. Private*, pg. 2460
LINDSAY CORPORATION; *U.S. Public*, pg. 1319
LINDSAY EUROPE SA—See Lindsay Corporation; *U.S. Public*, pg. 1319
LINDSAY FORD, LLC; *U.S. Private*, pg. 2460
LINDSAY INTERNATIONAL (ANZ) PTY LTD.—See Lindsay Corporation; *U.S. Public*, pg. 1319
LINDSAY INTERNATIONAL (ANZ) PTY LTD.—See Lindsay Corporation; *U.S. Public*, pg. 1319
LINDSAY MANUFACTURING AFRICA PTY. LTD.—See Lindsay Corporation; *U.S. Public*, pg. 1319
LINDSAY MANUFACTURING COMPANY—See Lindsay Corporation; *U.S. Public*, pg. 1319
LINDSAY MANUFACTURING INC.; *U.S. Private*, pg. 2460
LINDSAY MORGAN ASSOCIATES LTD.—See Empresaria Group Plc; *Int'l*, pg. 2389
LINDSAY SULAMA VE ALTYAPI SANAYI VE TICARCT A.S.—See Lindsay Corporation; *U.S. Public*, pg. 1319
LINDSAY (TIANJIN) INDUSTRY CO., LTD.—See Lindsay Corporation; *U.S. Public*, pg. 1319
LINDSAY TRANSPORTATION, INC.—See Lindsay Corporation; *U.S. Public*, pg. 1320
LINDSAY TRANSPORTATION SOLUTIONS, INC.—See Lindsay Corporation; *U.S. Public*, pg. 1319
LINDSCHULTE + GGL INGENIEURGESELLSCHAFT MBH—See BKW AG; *Int'l*, pg. 1055
LINDSCHULTE INGENIEURGESELLSCHAFT MBH—See BKW AG; *Int'l*, pg. 1055
LINDSCHULTE PLANUNGSGESELLSCHAFT MBH—See BKW AG; *Int'l*, pg. 1055
LINDSCHULTE THILLMANN GMBH—See BKW AG; *Int'l*, pg. 1055

LINDSELL TRAIN INVESTMENT TRUST PLC; *Int'l*, pg. 4511
LINDSTENS ELEKTRISKA AB—See Bravida Holding AB; *Int'l*, pg. 1142
LINDSTROM AIR CONDITIONING & PLUMBING, INC.; *U.S. Private*, pg. 2460
LINDSTROM METRIC, LLC—See Nautic Partners, LLC; *U.S. Private*, pg. 2871
LINDSTROM & SONDEN AB—See BHG Group AB; *Int'l*, pg. 1015
LINDT & SPRUNGLI (ASIA PACIFIC) LTD.—See Chocoladefabriken Lindt & Sprungli AG; *Int'l*, pg. 1576
LINDT & SPRUNGLI (AUSTRALIA) PTY. LTD.—See Chocoladefabriken Lindt & Sprungli AG; *Int'l*, pg. 1576
LINDT & SPRUNGLI (AUSTRIA) GMBH—See Chocoladefabriken Lindt & Sprungli AG; *Int'l*, pg. 1576
LINDT & SPRUNGLI (BRAZIL) HOLDING LTDA.—See Chocoladefabriken Lindt & Sprungli AG; *Int'l*, pg. 1576
LINDT & SPRUNGLI (CANADA), INC.—See Chocoladefabriken Lindt & Sprungli AG; *Int'l*, pg. 1576
LINDT & SPRUNGLI (CEE) S.R.O.—See Chocoladefabriken Lindt & Sprungli AG; *Int'l*, pg. 1576
LINDT & SPRUNGLI (CHINA) LTD.—See Chocoladefabriken Lindt & Sprungli AG; *Int'l*, pg. 1576
LINDT & SPRUNGLI DE MEXICO SA DE CV—See Chocoladefabriken Lindt & Sprungli AG; *Int'l*, pg. 1577
LINDT & SPRUNGLI (ESPANA) SA—See Chocoladefabriken Lindt & Sprungli AG; *Int'l*, pg. 1576
LINDT & SPRUNGLI JAPAN CO., LTD.—See Chocoladefabriken Lindt & Sprungli AG; *Int'l*, pg. 1577
LINDT & SPRUNGLI (NORDIC) AB—See Chocoladefabriken Lindt & Sprungli AG; *Int'l*, pg. 1576
LINDT & SPRUNGLI (NORTH AMERICA) INC.—See Chocoladefabriken Lindt & Sprungli AG; *Int'l*, pg. 1576
LINDT & SPRUNGLI (POLAND) SP. Z OO—See Chocoladefabriken Lindt & Sprungli AG; *Int'l*, pg. 1576
LINDT & SPRUNGLI SA—See Chocoladefabriken Lindt & Sprungli AG; *Int'l*, pg. 1577
LINDT & SPRUNGLI (SOUTH AFRICA) (PTY) LTD.—See Chocoladefabriken Lindt & Sprungli AG; *Int'l*, pg. 1576
LINDT & SPRUNGLI S.P.A.—See Chocoladefabriken Lindt & Sprungli AG; *Int'l*, pg. 1577
LINDT & SPRUNGLI (UK) LTD.—See Chocoladefabriken Lindt & Sprungli AG; *Int'l*, pg. 1576
LINDT & SPRUNGLI (USA) INC.—See Chocoladefabriken Lindt & Sprungli AG; *Int'l*, pg. 1576
THE LINDUM SNACK COMPANY LIMITED—See Raisio PLC; *Int'l*, pg. 6191
LINDUSTRIES LIMITED—See Heidelberg Materials AG; *Int'l*, pg. 3318
LINDY OFFICE PRODUCTS, INC.; *U.S. Private*, pg. 2460
LINDY PAVING, INC.—See P.J. Dick Incorporated; *U.S. Private*, pg. 3060
LINDY SPRINGS; *U.S. Private*, pg. 2460
LINE 6, INC.—See Yamaha Corporation; *Int'l*, pg. 8549
LINEA 12/MCCANN ERICKSON—See The Interpublic Group of Companies, Inc.; *U.S. Public*, pg. 2098
LINEA AMBIENTE S.R.L.—See A2A S.p.A.; *Int'l*, pg. 29
LINEA DE SEGURIDAD S.L.U—See Superhouse Limited; *Int'l*, pg. 7337
LINEAFRESCA LOGISTIC AG—See F. Murpf AG; *Int'l*, pg. 2596
LINEAGE CELL THERAPEUTICS, INC.; *U.S. Public*, pg. 1320
LINEAGE FINANCIAL NETWORK, INC.; *U.S. Private*, pg. 2460
LINEAGE LOGISTICS - ALGONA—See Bay Grove Capital LLC; *U.S. Private*, pg. 492
LINEAGE LOGISTICS HOLDINGS LLC—See Bay Grove Capital LLC; *U.S. Private*, pg. 492
LINEAGE LOGISTICS, LLC—See Bay Grove Capital LLC; *U.S. Private*, pg. 493
LINEAGE LOGISTICS - MIDWEST REGIONAL OFFICE—See Bay Grove Capital LLC; *U.S. Private*, pg. 492
LINEAGEN, INC.—See Bionano Genomics, Inc.; *U.S. Public*, pg. 338
LINEA GESTIONI S.R.L.—See A2A S.p.A.; *Int'l*, pg. 29
LINEA GREEN S.P.A.—See A2A S.p.A.; *Int'l*, pg. 29
LINEA GROUP HOLDING S.P.A.—See A2A S.p.A.; *Int'l*, pg. 29
LINEAL VENEER INC.—See Industrial Ventilation, Inc.; *U.S. Private*, pg. 2069
LINEA PELLE, INC.; *U.S. Private*, pg. 2460
LINEAR COMPOSITES LIMITED—See Societa Esercizi Commerciali Industriali; *Int'l*, pg. 7034
LINEAR ELECTRONICS (SHENZHEN) LIMITED—See Melrose Industries PLC; *Int'l*, pg. 4813
LINEAR INDUSTRIES LIMITED; *Int'l*, pg. 4511
LINEAR INDUSTRIES LTD.; *U.S. Private*, pg. 2460
LINEARIZER TECHNOLOGY, INC.—See MACOM Technology Solutions Holdings, Inc.; *U.S. Public*, pg. 1352
LINEAR LIGHTING CORPORATION; *U.S. Private*, pg. 2460
LINEAR MARITIME MEXICANA S.A. DE C.V.—See Grupo TMM, S.A.B.; *Int'l*, pg. 3137
LINEARMODUL A/S—See Indutrade AB; *Int'l*, pg. 3680
LINEAR MOTION LLC—See UMBRAGROUP S.p.A.; *Int'l*, pg. 8021

LINEAR SPACE TECHNOLOGY, LLC—See MACOM Technology Solutions Holdings, Inc.; *U.S. Public*, pg. 1352
LINEAR TECHNOLOGY AB—See Analog Devices, Inc.; *U.S. Public*, pg. 135
LINEAR TECHNOLOGY CORPORATION LIMITED—See Analog Devices, Inc.; *U.S. Public*, pg. 135
LINEAR TECHNOLOGY GK—See Analog Devices, Inc.; *U.S. Public*, pg. 135
LINEAR TECHNOLOGY GMBH—See Analog Devices, Inc.; *U.S. Public*, pg. 135
LINEAR TECHNOLOGY (ITALY) S.R.L.—See Analog Devices, Inc.; *U.S. Public*, pg. 135
LINEAR TECHNOLOGY K.K.—See Analog Devices, Inc.; *U.S. Public*, pg. 135
LINEAR TECHNOLOGY PTE. LTD.—See Analog Devices, Inc.; *U.S. Public*, pg. 135
LINEAR TECHNOLOGY S.A.R.L.—See Analog Devices, Inc.; *U.S. Public*, pg. 135
LINEAR TECHNOLOGY SEMICONDUCTOR MEXICO S. DE R.L. DE C.V.—See Analog Devices, Inc.; *U.S. Public*, pg. 135
LINEAR TECHNOLOGY (TAIWAN) CORPORATION—See Analog Devices, Inc.; *U.S. Public*, pg. 135
LINEAR TECHNOLOGY (U.K.) LTD.—See Analog Devices, Inc.; *U.S. Public*, pg. 135
LINEARTEC SRL—See THK CO., LTD.; *Int'l*, pg. 7712
LINEAR TITLE & CLOSING, LTD.—See Real Matters, Inc.; *Int'l*, pg. 6233
LINEARX, INC.—See Applied DNA Sciences, Inc.; *U.S. Public*, pg. 170
LINECALL TELECOM GMBH—See 3U Holding AG; *Int'l*, pg. 10
LINE CLEAR EXPRESS (KT) SDN. BHD.—See MMAG Holdings Berhad; *Int'l*, pg. 5005
LINE CLEAR EXPRESS & LOGISTICS SDN. BHD.—See MMAG Holdings Berhad; *Int'l*, pg. 5005
LINE CORPORATION—See NAVER Corporation; *Int'l*, pg. 5174
LINECROSS COMPOSITES LTD; *Int'l*, pg. 4511
LINEDATA CAPITALSTREAM—See Linedata Services SA; *Int'l*, pg. 4511
LINEDATA SERVICES SA; *Int'l*, pg. 4511
LINE DIGITAL LIMITED—See Arsenal Capital Management LP; *U.S. Private*, pg. 338
LINE GAMES CORP.; *Int'l*, pg. 4511
LINEKONG INTERACTIVE GROUP CO., LTD.; *Int'l*, pg. 4511
LINEMARK TRAFFIC CONTROL PTY LTD.—See AVADA Group Limited; *Int'l*, pg. 734
LIN ENGINEERING, INC.—See Shanghai Moons' Electric Co., Ltd.; *Int'l*, pg. 6775
LINEN KING, LLC—See York Capital Management Global Advisors, LLC; *U.S. Private*, pg. 4590
LINENS 'N THINGS, INC.—See The Carlyle Group Inc.; *U.S. Public*, pg. 2048
LINER LLP—See DLA Piper Global; *Int'l*, pg. 2140
LINER PRODUCTS, LLC—See Granite Construction Incorporated; *U.S. Public*, pg. 957
LINESENSE FIRE DETECTION LTD.—See Sdiptech AB; *Int'l*, pg. 6658
LINESETS, INC.—See Mueller Industries, Inc.; *U.S. Public*, pg. 1484
LINESTAR INTEGRITY SERVICES LLC—See First Reserve Management, L.P.; *U.S. Private*, pg. 1526
LINESTAR SERVICES, INC.—See First Reserve Management, L.P.; *U.S. Private*, pg. 1526
LINE SYSTEMS, INC.; *U.S. Private*, pg. 2460
LINETECH HOLDING SA; *Int'l*, pg. 4511
LINE TECHNOLOGY VIETNAM CO., LTD.—See NAVER Corporation; *Int'l*, pg. 5174
LINETEC SERVICES, LLC—See Southwest Gas Holdings, Inc.; *U.S. Public*, pg. 1913
LINETEC—See Apogee Enterprises, Inc.; *U.S. Public*, pg. 145
LINETEK JAPAN CO., LTD.—See Taiwan Line Tek Electronic Co., Ltd.; *Int'l*, pg. 7422
LINETTE QUALITY CHOCOLATES, INC.—See Conagra Brands, Inc.; *U.S. Public*, pg. 564
LINETT & HARRISON; *U.S. Private*, pg. 2461
LINEWELL SOFTWARE CO., LTD.; *Int'l*, pg. 4512
LINEWISE SERVICES AB—See Addnode Group AB; *Int'l*, pg. 130
LINEWIZE LIMITED—See Family Zone Cyber Safety Limited; *Int'l*, pg. 2612
LINEWIZE SERVICES LIMITED—See Family Zone Cyber Safety Limited; *Int'l*, pg. 2612
LINEX MANUFACTURING, INC.—See Linamar Corporation; *Int'l*, pg. 4502
LINFEN BAOZEN AUTOMOBILE SALES AND SERVICES CO., LTD.—See China Yongda Automobiles Services Holdings Limited; *Int'l*, pg. 1564
LINGARO SP Z O.O.; *Int'l*, pg. 4512
LINGBAO GOLD GROUP COMPANY LTD.; *Int'l*, pg. 4512
LINGBAO ZHONGYU GAS CO., LTD.—See Zhongyu Energy Holdings Limited; *Int'l*, pg. 8676
LINGDA GROUP CO., LTD.; *Int'l*, pg. 4512
LING DESIGN LTD—See Swan Mill Paper Company Ltd.; *Int'l*, pg. 7360

LINGDA GROUP CO., LTD.

LINGE NOEL CO., LTD.—See Wacoal Holdings Corp.; *Int'l*, pg. 8326
LINGEN PRECISION MEDICAL PRODUCTS (SHANGHAI) CO., LTD.—See Shenzhen Changhong Technology Co., Ltd.; *Int'l*, pg. 6806
LINGERFELT OFFICE PROPERTIES LLC—See Ladder Capital Corp.; *U.S. Public*, pg. 1288
LINGERIE FIGHTING CHAMPIONSHIPS, INC.; *U.S. Public*, pg. 1320
LINGERING WHO'S CORPORATION—See Ringer Hut Co., Ltd.; *Int'l*, pg. 6343
LINGER LONGER DEVELOPMENT COMPANY; *U.S. Private*, pg. 2461
LINGFIELD PARK LIMITED—See Reuben Brothers SA; *Int'l*, pg. 6311
LINGKARAN TRANS KOTA HOLDINGS BERHAD; *Int'l*, pg. 4512
LINGLE BROS COFFEE INC.; *U.S. Private*, pg. 2461
LINGLONG INTERNATIONAL TIRE (THAILAND) CO., LTD.—See Shandong Linglong Tyre Co., Ltd.; *Int'l*, pg. 6755
LINGNAN ECO&CULTURE-TOURISM CO. LTD.; *Int'l*, pg. 4512
LINGNER GROUP PRODUCTIONS, INC.; *U.S. Private*, pg. 2461
LINGO MANAGEMENT, LLC; *U.S. Private*, pg. 2461
LINGONEER OY—See Panostaja Oyj; *Int'l*, pg. 5729
LINGON GARAGE; *Int'l*, pg. 4512
LINGO STAFFING, INC.; *U.S. Private*, pg. 2461
LINGOTEK, INC.—See Straker Limited; *Int'l*, pg. 7235
LINGOTES ESPECIALES, S.A.; *Int'l*, pg. 4512
LINGSEN PRECISION INDUSTRIES, LTD.; *Int'l*, pg. 4512
LINGUALCARE, INC.—See Solventum Corporation; *U.S. Public*, pg. 1902
LINGUALINX INC.; *U.S. Private*, pg. 2461
LINGUAMATICS LIMITED—See IQVIA Holdings Inc.; *U.S. Public*, pg. 1169
LINGUAPHONE DISTRIBUTORS SDN BHD—See LG & DE Limited; *Int'l*, pg. 4473
LINGUAPHONE EDUCATION PTE LTD—See LG & DE Limited; *Int'l*, pg. 4473
LINGUAPHONE FRANCE S.A.R.L.—See LG & DE Limited; *Int'l*, pg. 4473
LINGUAPHONE IRELAND LTD.—See LG & DE Limited; *Int'l*, pg. 4473
LINGUAPHONE JAPAN LIMITED—See LG & DE Limited; *Int'l*, pg. 4473
LINGUI DEVELOPMENT SDN BERHAD—See Samling Strategic Corporation Sdn. Bhd.; *Int'l*, pg. 6507
LINGYI ITECH (GUANGDONG) COMPANY; *Int'l*, pg. 4512
LINGYOPHONE COMPANY LTD.—See Alkhaleej Training & Education Company; *Int'l*, pg. 331
LINGYUAN IRON & STEEL CO., LTD.; *Int'l*, pg. 4512
LING YUE SERVICES GROUP LIMITED; *Int'l*, pg. 4512
LING YUI HOLDINGS LIMITED; *Int'l*, pg. 4512
LINGYUN INDUSTRIAL CORPORATION LIMITED; *Int'l*, pg. 4513
LING ZHENG INVESTMENT CONSULTING (SHANGHAI) CO., LTD.—See Mitsubishi UFJ Financial Group, Inc.; *Int'l*, pg. 4969
LINHAI BAOZEN AUTOMOBILE SALES AND SERVICES CO., LTD.—See China Yongda Automobiles Services Holdings Limited; *Int'l*, pg. 1564
LINHAI CO., LTD.; *Int'l*, pg. 4513
LINHAI HUANAN CHEMICALS CO., LTD.—See Zhejiang Huahai Pharmaceutical Co., Ltd.; *Int'l*, pg. 8655
LINHART PUBLIC RELATIONS, LLP; *U.S. Private*, pg. 2461
LIN HORN TECHNOLOGY CO., LTD.; *Int'l*, pg. 4499
LINIA PRAVA URANIUM OJSC—See Walkabout Resources Ltd; *Int'l*, pg. 8333
LINIAR LTD.—See Quanex Building Products Corp.; *U.S. Public*, pg. 1749
LINICAL ACCELOVANCE AMERICA, INC.—See Linical Co., Ltd.; *Int'l*, pg. 4513
LINICAL CO., LTD.; *Int'l*, pg. 4513
LINICAL FRANCE SARL—See Linical Co., Ltd.; *Int'l*, pg. 4513
LINICAL HUNGARY KFT.—See Linical Co., Ltd.; *Int'l*, pg. 4513
LINICAL KOREA CO., LTD.—See Linical Co., Ltd.; *Int'l*, pg. 4513
LINICAL NETHERLANDS B.V.—See Linical Co., Ltd.; *Int'l*, pg. 4513
LINICAL POLAND SP. Z O.O.—See Linical Co., Ltd.; *Int'l*, pg. 4513
LINICAL ROMANIA S.R.L.—See Linical Co., Ltd.; *Int'l*, pg. 4513
LINICAL SPAIN, S.L.—See Linical Co., Ltd.; *Int'l*, pg. 4513
LINICAL TAIWAN CO., LTD.—See Linical Co., Ltd.; *Int'l*, pg. 4513
LINICAL U.K. LIMITED—See Linical Co., Ltd.; *Int'l*, pg. 4513
LINICAL USA, INC.—See Linical Co., Ltd.; *Int'l*, pg. 4513
THE LINICK GROUP, INC.; *U.S. Private*, pg. 4070
LINIFICIO E CANAPIFICIO NAZIONALE S.P.A.—See Marzotto S.p.A.; *Int'l*, pg. 4718
LI NING (CHINA) SPORTS GOODS CO., LTD.—See Li Ning Co., Ltd.; *Int'l*, pg. 4481

LI NING CO., LTD.; *Int'l*, pg. 4481
LINING COMPONENTS OY—See Indutrade AB; *Int'l*, pg. 3680
LI NING SPORTS (CHINA) CO., LTD.—See Li Ning Co., Ltd.; *Int'l*, pg. 4481
LINIO COLOMBIA S.A.S.—See Falabella S.A.; *Int'l*, pg. 2610
LINIUS TECHNOLOGIES LIMITED; *Int'l*, pg. 4513
LINIU TECHNOLOGY GROUP; *Int'l*, pg. 4513
LINJEBYGG OFFSHORE AS—See Fortum Oyj; *Int'l*, pg. 2742
LINJE & KABELPLOJNING I BORLANGE AB—See Peab AB; *Int'l*, pg. 5772
LINK2GOV CORP.—See Fidelity National Infor; *U.S. Public*, pg. 833
LINK 51 SHELVING AND STORAGE—See Whittan Storage Systems Ltd.; *Int'l*, pg. 8400
LINK 51 (STORAGE PRODUCTS)—See Whittan Storage Systems Ltd.; *Int'l*, pg. 8400
LINK ACADEMY INC.—See Link & Motivation Inc.; *Int'l*, pg. 4513
LINKAD INC.—See FreeBit Co., Ltd.; *Int'l*, pg. 2769
LINK ADMINISTRATION HOLDINGS LIMITED—See Mitsubishi UFJ Financial Group, Inc.; *Int'l*, pg. 4971
LINK ADVICE PTY LIMITED—See Mitsubishi UFJ Financial Group, Inc.; *Int'l*, pg. 4971
LINKAGE ASSURANCE PLC; *Int'l*, pg. 4514
LINKAGE BIOSCIENCES, INC.—See Thermo Fisher Scientific Inc.; *U.S. Public*, pg. 2149
LINKAGE GLOBAL INC.; *Int'l*, pg. 4514
LINKAGE INC.—See Prospect Partners, LLC; *U.S. Private*, pg. 3288
LINKAGE SOFTWARE CO., LTD.; *Int'l*, pg. 4514
LINK AMERICA INC.; *U.S. Private*, pg. 2461
LINK ARKITEKTUR AS—See Multiconsult ASA; *Int'l*, pg. 5083
LINK-ASIA INTERNATIONAL MEDTECH GROUP LIMITED; *Int'l*, pg. 4514
THE LINK ASSET AND SECURITIES COMPANY LIMITED—See CME Group, Inc.; *U.S. Public*, pg. 518
LINK ASSET SERVICES (FRANCE) SAS—See Mitsubishi UFJ Financial Group, Inc.; *Int'l*, pg. 4971
LINKBAL INC.; *Int'l*, pg. 4515
LINKBANCORP, INC.; *U.S. Public*, pg. 1320
LINKBANK—See LINKBANCORP, Inc.; *U.S. Public*, pg. 1320
LINK-BELT CONSTRUCTION EQUIPMENT CO. - MID ATLANTIC—See Sumitomo Heavy Industries, Ltd.; *Int'l*, pg. 7287
LINK-BELT CONSTRUCTION EQUIPMENT CO.—See Sumitomo Heavy Industries, Ltd.; *Int'l*, pg. 7287
LINK BILGISAYAR SISTEMLERI YAZILIMI VE DONANIMI SANAYI VE TICARET A.S.; *Int'l*, pg. 4513
LINK COMPUTER CORPORATION; *U.S. Private*, pg. 2461
LINK CONSTRUCTION GROUP, INC.; *U.S. Private*, pg. 2461
LINK CORPORATE COMMUNICATIONS INC.—See Link & Motivation Inc.; *Int'l*, pg. 4513
LINK DIGICOM PTY LIMITED—See Mitsubishi UFJ Financial Group, Inc.; *Int'l*, pg. 4971
LINK DIGITAL SOLUTIONS PTY LIMITED—See Mitsubishi UFJ Financial Group, Inc.; *Int'l*, pg. 4971
LINKDOC TECHNOLOGY LTD.; *Int'l*, pg. 4515
LINKEDGE TECHNOLOGIES, INC.; *U.S. Private*, pg. 2462
LINKEDGE TECHNOLOGIES, INC.—See LinkEdge Technologies, Inc.; *U.S. Private*, pg. 2462
LINKEDIN CORPORATION—See Microsoft Corporation; *U.S. Public*, pg. 1441
LINKED TECHNOLOGIES, INC.—See SureTec; *U.S. Private*, pg. 3883
LINK ELECTRIC & SAFETY CONTROL CO.; *U.S. Private*, pg. 2461
LINK ENERGY PTY LTD—See Ampol Limited; *Int'l*, pg. 436
LINK ENGINEERING COMPANY; *U.S. Private*, pg. 2461
LINKERS INDUSTRIES LIMITED; *Int'l*, pg. 4515
LINK EVENT PRODUCE INC.—See Link & Motivation Inc.; *Int'l*, pg. 4513
LINKEX, INC.—See Saia, Inc.; *U.S. Public*, pg. 1835
LINK FUND SOLUTIONS PTY LIMITED—See Mitsubishi UFJ Financial Group, Inc.; *Int'l*, pg. 4971
LINKGENESIS CO., LTD.; *Int'l*, pg. 4515
LINK GLOBAL SOLUTION INC.—See Link & Motivation Inc.; *Int'l*, pg. 4513
LINK GLOBAL TECHNOLOGIES, INC.; *Int'l*, pg. 4513
LINK HOLDINGS LIMITED; *Int'l*, pg. 4513
LINKHOUSE INDUSTRIES LTD.; *Int'l*, pg. 4515
LINKIA, LLC—See Patient Square Capital, L.P.; *U.S. Private*, pg. 3107
LINK-I INC.—See Link & Motivation Inc.; *Int'l*, pg. 4513
LINK INTERAC INC.—See Link & Motivation Inc.; *Int'l*, pg. 4513
LINK INTERNATIONAL—See Whittan Storage Systems Ltd.; *Int'l*, pg. 8400
LINK INTIME INDIA PRIVATE LIMITED—See Mitsubishi UFJ Financial Group, Inc.; *Int'l*, pg. 4971

LINK JAPAN CAREERS INC.—See Link & Motivation Inc.; *Int'l*, pg. 4513
LINKLINE COMMUNICATIONS INC.; *U.S. Private*, pg. 2462
LINK LOCKERS—See Whittan Storage Systems Ltd.; *Int'l*, pg. 8400
LINKLOGIS INC.; *Int'l*, pg. 4515
LINKLOGIS INTERNATIONAL COMPANY LIMITED—See Linklogis Inc.; *Int'l*, pg. 4515
THE LINK MANAGEMENT LIMITED—See The Link Real Estate Investment Trust; *Int'l*, pg. 7664
LINK MANUFACTURING LTD.; *U.S. Private*, pg. 2461
LINK MARKET SERVICES (FRANKFURT) GMBH—See Mitsubishi UFJ Financial Group, Inc.; *Int'l*, pg. 4971
LINK MARKET SERVICES GMBH—See Mitsubishi UFJ Financial Group, Inc.; *Int'l*, pg. 4971
LINK MARKET SERVICES (HONG KONG) PTY LIMITED—See Mitsubishi UFJ Financial Group, Inc.; *Int'l*, pg. 4971
LINK MARKET SERVICES LIMITED—See Mitsubishi UFJ Financial Group, Inc.; *Int'l*, pg. 4972
LINK MARKET SERVICES LTD.—See Pacific Equity Partners Pty. Limited; *Int'l*, pg. 5688
LINK MARKET SERVICES LTD.—See Pacific Equity Partners Pty. Limited; *Int'l*, pg. 5689
LINK MARKET SERVICES SA—See Pacific Equity Partners Pty. Limited; *Int'l*, pg. 5689
LINKMEDIA 360; *U.S. Private*, pg. 2462
LINK MEDIA GEORGIA, LLC—See Boston Omaha Corporation; *U.S. Public*, pg. 372
LINK MOBILITY AS—See Link Mobility Group Holding ASA; *Int'l*, pg. 4514
LINK MOBILITY EAD—See Link Mobility Group Holding ASA; *Int'l*, pg. 4514
LINK MOBILITY GROUP HOLDING ASA; *Int'l*, pg. 4513
LINK MOBILITY HUNGARY KFT.—See Link Mobility Group Holding ASA; *Int'l*, pg. 4513
LINK MOBILITY OY—See Link Mobility Group Holding ASA; *Int'l*, pg. 4514
LINK MOBILITY SAS—See Link Mobility Group Holding ASA; *Int'l*, pg. 4514
LINK MOBILITY SP. Z O.O.—See Link Mobility Group Holding ASA; *Int'l*, pg. 4514
LINK MOTION INC.; *Int'l*, pg. 4514
LINK & MOTIVATION INC.; *Int'l*, pg. 4513
LINKOFFERS, LLC—See Red Ventures, LLC; *U.S. Private*, pg. 3376
LINKOPING CITY AIRPORT AB—See Saab AB; *Int'l*, pg. 6459
LINKOPINGS STAL AB—See SSAB AB; *Int'l*, pg. 7155
LINKOUS CONSTRUCTION COMPANY, INC.; *U.S. Private*, pg. 2462
LINK PETROLEUM INC.—See Gibson Energy Inc.; *Int'l*, pg. 2963
LINK PHARMA CHEM LTD.; *Int'l*, pg. 4514
LINK PROP INVESTMENT AB; *Int'l*, pg. 4514
THE LINK REAL ESTATE INVESTMENT TRUST; *Int'l*, pg. 7664
LINK RESERVATIONS, INC.; *Int'l*, pg. 4513
LINK RING CO., LTD.—See Screen Holdings Co., Ltd.; *Int'l*, pg. 6655
LINKS AT SPRUCE CREEK SOUTH—See Heritage Management Corp.; *U.S. Private*, pg. 1924
THE LINKS AT SPRUCE GROVE—See Melcor Developments Ltd.; *Int'l*, pg. 4808
LINKSCORP LLC; *U.S. Private*, pg. 2462
LINK SECURITIES HONG KONG LIMITED—See CME Group, Inc.; *U.S. Public*, pg. 517
LINKS FREIGHT MANAGEMENT LLC; *U.S. Private*, pg. 2462
LINK SHAREHOLDER SERVICES, LLC—See Pacific Equity Partners Pty. Limited; *Int'l*, pg. 5689
LINKSHARE JAPAN K.K.—See Rakuten Group, Inc.; *Int'l*, pg. 6195
LINKS (LONDON) LIMITED—See Folli Follie S.A.; *Int'l*, pg. 2721
LINKS MARKETING GROUP INC.—See Grossman Marketing Group; *U.S. Private*, pg. 1792
LINKSMART, INC.—See sovrn Holdings, Inc.; *U.S. Private*, pg. 3743
LINK SNACKS, INC. - ANSBACH PLANT—See Link Snacks, Inc.; *U.S. Private*, pg. 2461
LINK SNACKS, INC.; *U.S. Private*, pg. 2461
LINKS OF LONDON, INC.—See Folli Follie S.A.; *Int'l*, pg. 2721
LINKS OF LONDON (INTERNATIONAL) LTD.—See Folli Follie S.A.; *Int'l*, pg. 2721
LINK SOLUTIONS, INC.; *U.S. Private*, pg. 2461
LINKSON INTERNATIONAL LTD.; *Int'l*, pg. 4515
LINKSOURCE TECHNOLOGIES, LLC—See UPSTACK, Inc.; *U.S. Private*, pg. 4312
LINK STAFFING SERVICES, INC.; *U.S. Private*, pg. 2461
LINK SUSPENSIONS OF CANADA, LP; *Int'l*, pg. 4514
LINKSYS—See Hon Hai Precision Industry Co., Ltd.; *Int'l*, pg. 3456
LINK SYSTEMS, INC.—See GI Manager L.P.; *U.S. Private*, pg. 1693
LINK-SYSTEMS INTERNATIONAL, INC.; *U.S. Private*, pg. 2462

COMPANY NAME INDEX

LINK TECHNOLOGIES; *U.S. Private*, pg. 2461
LINKTECH WORLDWIDE; *U.S. Private*, pg. 2462
LINKTEL TECHNOLOGIES CO., LTD.; *Int'l*, pg. 4515
LINKTHINK INC.—See Marvelous Inc.; *Int'l*, pg. 4717
LINK TOOL & DIE—See MNP Corporation; *U.S. Private*, pg. 2756
LINK-U GROUP INC; *Int'l*, pg. 4514
LINKVAST TECHNOLOGIES INC.—See Silicon Integrated Systems Corp.; *Int'l*, pg. 6920
LINKVERSE S.R.L.—See Cosmo Pharmaceuticals N.V.; *Int'l*, pg. 1813
LINKVISUM CONSULTING GROUP; *U.S. Private*, pg. 2462
LINK VUE SYSTEMS PTE. LTD.—See Zicom Group Limited; *Int'l*, pg. 8681
LINK WELD ENGINEERING PTY LTD—See Kempe Engineering Pty. Ltd.; *Int'l*, pg. 4125
LINK WITH HOME TRAVEL INC.—See Home Hardware Stores Limited; *Int'l*, pg. 3454
LINKZ INTERNATIONAL LIMITED—See Time Interconnect Technology Limited; *Int'l*, pg. 7751
LINMARK (HK) LIMITED—See Daohe Global Group Limited; *Int'l*, pg. 1970
LINMARK INTERNATIONAL (HONG KONG) LIMITED—See Daohe Global Group Limited; *Int'l*, pg. 1970
LINMON MEDIA LIMITED; *Int'l*, pg. 4515
LINN AREA CREDIT UNION; *U.S. Private*, pg. 2462
THE LINN CONTRACTING COMPANIES INC.; *U.S. Private*, pg. 4070
LINN COOPERATIVE OIL COMPANY; *U.S. Private*, pg. 2462
LINN COUNTY RURAL ELECTRIC COOPERATIVE ASSOCIATION; *U.S. Private*, pg. 2462
LINNEA YACHT GROUP; *Int'l*, pg. 4515
LINN ENERGY HOLDINGS, LLC—See Citizen Energy Operating LLC; *U.S. Private*, pg. 902
LINN ENERGY, INC.—See Citizen Energy Operating LLC; *U.S. Private*, pg. 902
LINN ENTERPRISES INC.; *U.S. Private*, pg. 2462
LINNIG BRASIL ACOPLAMENTOS LTDA—See Kendrion N.V.; *Int'l*, pg. 4126
LINNIG DE MEXICO, S.A. DE C.V.—See Kendrion N.V.; *Int'l*, pg. 4127
LINNIG DRIVE TECH. (NANJING) CO. LTD—See Kendrion N.V.; *Int'l*, pg. 4127
LINN-MATHES INC.—See The Linn Contracting Companies Inc.; *U.S. Private*, pg. 4070
LINN PAPER STOCK COMPANY; *U.S. Private*, pg. 2462
LINN PRODUCTS, INC.; *U.S. Private*, pg. 2462
LINOCRAFT HOLDINGS LIMITED; *Int'l*, pg. 4515
LINOCRAFT PRINTERS PHILIPPINES INC.—See Linocraft Holdings Limited; *Int'l*, pg. 4515
LINOCRAFT PRINTERS SDN. BHD.—See Linocraft Holdings Limited; *Int'l*, pg. 4515
LINOCRAFT SINGAPORE PTE. LTD.—See Linocraft Holdings Limited; *Int'l*, pg. 4515
LINODE, LLC—See Akamai Technologies, Inc.; *U.S. Public*, pg. 69
LINO HOTEL-LEASING GMBH—See UniCredit S.p.A.; *Int'l*, pg. 8037
LINOLEUMKOMPANIET AB—See BHG Group AB; *Int'l*, pg. 1014
LINOMA SOFTWARE; *U.S. Private*, pg. 2462
LINON HOME DECOR PRODUCTS INC.; *U.S. Private*, pg. 2462
LINPAC GROUP LIMITED—See Strategic Value Partners, LLC; *U.S. Private*, pg. 3836
LINPAC PACKAGING AS—See Strategic Value Partners, LLC; *U.S. Private*, pg. 3836
LINPAC PACKAGING AUSTRALIA PTY LTD—See Strategic Value Partners, LLC; *U.S. Private*, pg. 3836
LINPAC PACKAGING BV—See Strategic Value Partners, LLC; *U.S. Private*, pg. 3836
LINPAC PACKAGING (CHANGZHOU) CO., LTD.—See Strategic Value Partners, LLC; *U.S. Private*, pg. 3836
LINPAC PACKAGING GMBH—See Strategic Value Partners, LLC; *U.S. Private*, pg. 3836
LINPAC PACKAGING HUNGARIA KFT—See Strategic Value Partners, LLC; *U.S. Private*, pg. 3836
LINPAC PACKAGING INFIA ITALY S.R.L.—See Strategic Value Partners, LLC; *U.S. Private*, pg. 3836
LINPAC PACKAGING LIMITED—See Strategic Value Partners, LLC; *U.S. Private*, pg. 3836
LINPAC PACKAGING PONTIVY SAS—See Strategic Value Partners, LLC; *U.S. Private*, pg. 3836
LINPAC PACKAGING PRAVIA, S.A.—See Strategic Value Partners, LLC; *U.S. Private*, pg. 3836
LINPAC PACKAGING PRODUCTION SP Z.O.O.—See Strategic Value Partners, LLC; *U.S. Private*, pg. 3836
LINPAC PACKAGING RIGID GMBH—See Strategic Value Partners, LLC; *U.S. Private*, pg. 3836
LINPAC PACKAGING ROMANIA S.R.L.—See Strategic Value Partners, LLC; *U.S. Private*, pg. 3836
LINPAC PACKAGING RUSSIA OOO—See Strategic Value Partners, LLC; *U.S. Private*, pg. 3836
LINPAC PACKAGING SCANDINAVIA—See Strategic Value Partners, LLC; *U.S. Private*, pg. 3836
LINPAC PACKAGING SPOL. S.R.O.—See Strategic Value Partners, LLC; *U.S. Private*, pg. 3836
LINPAC PACKAGING SRO—See Strategic Value Partners, LLC; *U.S. Private*, pg. 3836
LINPAC PACKAGING VERONA SRL—See Strategic Value Partners, LLC; *U.S. Private*, pg. 3836
LINPEPCO PARTNERSHIP; *U.S. Private*, pg. 2462
LINQ CAPITAL LIMITED; *Int'l*, pg. 4515
THE LINQ HOTEL & CASINO—See Caesars Entertainment, Inc.; *U.S. Public*, pg. 420
LINQ SERVICES; *U.S. Private*, pg. 2462
LINQUEST CORPORATION—See KBR, Inc.; *U.S. Public*, pg. 1216
LINROC COMMUNITY SERVICE CORPORATION; *U.S. Private*, pg. 2462
LIN R. ROGERS ELECTRICAL CONTRACTORS INC.; *U.S. Private*, pg. 2456
LINSALATA CAPITAL PARTNERS, INC.; *U.S. Private*, pg. 2463
LINSHANHAO PLYWOOD (SARAWAK) SDN. BHD.—See W T K Holdings Berhad; *Int'l*, pg. 8320
LINSHINE ENGINEERING PLASTICS (SUZHOU) CO., LTD.—See Chi Mei Group; *Int'l*, pg. 1475
LINSTOL LLC—See The Hoffmann Family of Companies; *U.S. Private*, pg. 4053
LINS TRADING LTD.; *Int'l*, pg. 4515
LINTBELLS LIMITED—See Inflexion Private Equity Partners LLP; *Int'l*, pg. 3689
LINTEC ADVANCED TECHNOLOGIES (EUROPE) GMBH—See LINTEC Corporation; *Int'l*, pg. 4515
LINTEC ADVANCED TECHNOLOGIES (EUROPE) GMBH—See LINTEC Corporation; *Int'l*, pg. 4516
LINTEC ADVANCED TECHNOLOGIES (KOREA), INC.—See LINTEC Corporation; *Int'l*, pg. 4515
LINTEC ADVANCED TECHNOLOGIES (MALAYSIA) SDN. BHD.—See LINTEC Corporation; *Int'l*, pg. 4516
LINTEC ADVANCED TECHNOLOGIES (MALAYSIA) SDN.—See LINTEC Corporation; *Int'l*, pg. 4515
LINTEC ADVANCED TECHNOLOGIES (PHILIPPINES), INC.—See LINTEC Corporation; *Int'l*, pg. 4516
LINTEC ADVANCED TECHNOLOGIES (SHANGHAI), INC.—See LINTEC Corporation; *Int'l*, pg. 4516
LINTEC ADVANCED TECHNOLOGIES (TAIWAN), INC.—See LINTEC Corporation; *Int'l*, pg. 4516
LINTEC ASIA PACIFIC REGIONAL HEADQUARTERS PTE. LTD.—See LINTEC Corporation; *Int'l*, pg. 4516
LINTEC BKK PTE LIMITED—See LINTEC Corporation; *Int'l*, pg. 4516
LINTEC CORPORATION; *Int'l*, pg. 4515
LINTEC CORPORATION—See LINTEC Corporation; *Int'l*, pg. 4516
LINTEC EUROPE B.V.—See LINTEC Corporation; *Int'l*, pg. 4516
LINTEC EUROPE B.V.—See LINTEC Corporation; *Int'l*, pg. 4516
LINTEC EUROPE (UK) LIMITED—See LINTEC Corporation; *Int'l*, pg. 4516
LINTEC HANOI VIETNAM CO., LTD.—See LINTEC Corporation; *Int'l*, pg. 4516
LINTEC HI-TECH (TAIWAN), INC.—See LINTEC Corporation; *Int'l*, pg. 4516
LINTECH S.A.S.—See Komax Holding AG; *Int'l*, pg. 4241
LINTEC INDIA PRIVATE LIMITED—See LINTEC Corporation; *Int'l*, pg. 4516
LINTEC INDUSTRIES (MALAYSIA) SDN. BHD.—See LINTEC Corporation; *Int'l*, pg. 4516
LINTEC INDUSTRIES (SARAWAK) SDN. BHD.—See LINTEC Corporation; *Int'l*, pg. 4516
LINTEC KOREA, INC.—See LINTEC Corporation; *Int'l*, pg. 4516
LINTEC KUALA LUMPUR SDN. BHD.—See LINTEC Corporation; *Int'l*, pg. 4516
LINTEC OF AMERICA, INC.—See LINTEC Corporation; *Int'l*, pg. 4516
LINTEC PHILIPPINES (PEZA), INC.—See LINTEC Corporation; *Int'l*, pg. 4516
LINTEC SINGAPORE PRIVATE LIMITED—See LINTEC Corporation; *Int'l*, pg. 4516
LINTEC SPECIALITY FILMS (KOREA), INC.—See LINTEC Corporation; *Int'l*, pg. 4516
LINTEC SPECIALITY FILMS (TAIWAN), INC.—See LINTEC Corporation; *Int'l*, pg. 4516
LINTEC (SUZHOU) TECH CORPORATION—See LINTEC Corporation; *Int'l*, pg. 4515
LINTEC (THAILAND) CO., LTD.—See LINTEC Corporation; *Int'l*, pg. 4515
LINTEC (TIANJIN) INDUSTRY CO., LTD.—See LINTEC Corporation; *Int'l*, pg. 4515
LINTEC VIETNAM CO., LTD.—See LINTEC Corporation; *Int'l*, pg. 4516
LIN TELEVISION OF TEXAS, INC.—See Nexstar Media Group, Inc.; *U.S. Public*, pg. 1523
LINTEL INC.; *U.S. Private*, pg. 2463
LINTEX CO. INC.; *U.S. Private*, pg. 2463
LINTHICUM CORPORATION; *U.S. Private*, pg. 2463
LINTHICUM CUSTOM BUILDERS, LLC—See Linthicum Corporation; *U.S. Private*, pg. 2463
LINTON ENGINEERING LLC—See Bennett & Pless, Inc.; *U.S. Private*, pg. 527
LINTON FUEL OILS LIMITED—See World Kinect Corporation; *U.S. Public*, pg. 2380
LINTON PARK PLC—See Camellia Plc; *Int'l*, pg. 1271
LINTON STREET PTY. LTD.—See Sigma Healthcare Ltd.; *Int'l*, pg. 6907
LINTON SUPPLY CO.; *U.S. Private*, pg. 2463
LINTORFER EISENGIESSEREI GMBH—See DIHAG Holding GmbH; *Int'l*, pg. 2124
LINTOTT CONTROL SYSTEMS LIMITED—See Galliford Try Holdings plc; *Int'l*, pg. 2874
LINUO GROUP HOLDINGS CO.,LTD.—See Shandong Linuo Technical Glass Co., Ltd.; *Int'l*, pg. 6755
LINUS CADILLAC BUICK GMC; *U.S. Private*, pg. 2463
LINUS DIGITAL FINANCE AG; *Int'l*, pg. 4516
LINUS RELATIONSHIP MANAGEMENT GMBH—See Linus Digital Finance AG; *Int'l*, pg. 4516
LINUX GOLD CORP.; *Int'l*, pg. 4516
LINVATEC BIOMATERIALS, LTD.—See CONMED Corporation; *U.S. Public*, pg. 567
LINVATEC CORPORATION—See CONMED Corporation; *U.S. Public*, pg. 567
LINVATEC EUROPE SPRL—See CONMED Corporation; *U.S. Public*, pg. 567
LINVATEC KOREA LTD.—See CONMED Corporation; *U.S. Public*, pg. 567
LINVATEC SWEDEN AB—See CONMED Corporation; *U.S. Public*, pg. 567
LINVATEC U.K. LTD.—See CONMED Corporation; *U.S. Public*, pg. 567
LINWAVE TECHNOLOGY LIMITED—See Alaris Holdings Limited; *Int'l*, pg. 291
LIN WEN CHIH SUNBOW ENTERPRISES CO., LTD.—See Fulgent Sun International (Holding) Co., Ltd.; *Int'l*, pg. 2842
LINWOOD MINING & MINERALS CORP.—See McCarthy Bush Corporation; *U.S. Private*, pg. 2626
LINWORTH LUMBER INC.—See Strait & Lamp Lumber Co. Inc.; *U.S. Private*, pg. 3833
LINX COMMUNICATIONS CORP.; *U.S. Private*, pg. 2463
LINXENS—See Astorg Partners S.A.S.; *Int'l*, pg. 656
LINX INDUSTRIES, INC.—See Ductmate Industries Inc.; *U.S. Private*, pg. 1284
LINX INTERNATIONAL GROUP LTD.—See MITIE Group Plc; *Int'l*, pg. 4926
LINXIS GROUP—See Hillenbrand, Inc.; *U.S. Public*, pg. 1037
LINXIT LLC—See Amphenol Corporation; *U.S. Public*, pg. 130
LINX LLLP; *U.S. Private*, pg. 2463
LINX PARTNERS, LLC; *U.S. Private*, pg. 2463
LINX PRINTING TECHNOLOGIES LIMITED—See Danaher Corporation; *U.S. Public*, pg. 628
LINX S.A.—See StoneCo Ltd.; *Int'l*, pg. 7222
LINYANG INTERNATIONAL CO., LTD.—See Jiangsu Linyang Energy Co., Ltd.; *Int'l*, pg. 3950
LINYI CNG GLASS COMPANY LIMITED—See China Glass Holdings Limited; *Int'l*, pg. 1504
LINYI HENGXING FRUIT JUICE CO., LTD.—See QAF Limited; *Int'l*, pg. 6132
LINYI KAIYUAN BEARING CO., LTD.; *Int'l*, pg. 4516
LINYI O.R.G PRINTING IRON CAN CO., LTD.—See ORG Technology Co., Ltd.; *Int'l*, pg. 5617
LIN YI SAINT-GOBAIN REFRACTORY CO., LTD—See Compagnie de Saint-Gobain SA; *Int'l*, pg. 1724
LINYI YEHUA COKING CO., LTD.—See Techna-X Berhad; *Int'l*, pg. 7506
LINYI YUBAOHANG AUTOMOBILE SALES AND SERVICE COMPANY LIMITED—See China Yongda Automobiles Services Holdings Limited; *Int'l*, pg. 1564
LINYI ZHONGYU ENERGY CO., LTD.—See Zhongyu Energy Holdings Limited; *Int'l*, pg. 8676
LIN YUAN INVESTMENT CO., LTD.; *Int'l*, pg. 4499
LINZER PRODUCTS CORP.; *U.S. Private*, pg. 2463
LINZHANG ZHONGYU GAS CO., LTD.—See Zhongyu Energy Holdings Limited; *Int'l*, pg. 8676
LINZHOU HEAVY MACHINERY GROUP CO., LTD.; *Int'l*, pg. 4517
LINZ TEXTIL GESELLSCHAFT M.B.H.—See Linz Textil Holding AG; *Int'l*, pg. 4516
LINZ TEXTIL HOLDING AG; *Int'l*, pg. 4516
LIOCHEM, INC.—See Toyo Ink SC Holdings Co., Ltd.; *Int'l*, pg. 7855
LIOHO MACHINERY INDUSTRY (HIANAN) CO.,LTD.—See Universal Cement Corporation; *Int'l*, pg. 8078
LIO-HO MACHINE WORKS LTD.—See Universal Cement Corporation; *Int'l*, pg. 8078
LIO IMMOBILIARE S.R.L.—See Recipharm AB; *Int'l*, pg. 6235
LIOMATIC S.P.A.—See IVS Group S.A.; *Int'l*, pg. 3848
LION AKZO CO., LTD.—See GIC Pte. Ltd.; *Int'l*, pg. 2968
LION AKZO CO., LTD.—See Lion Corporation; *Int'l*, pg. 4517
LION AKZO CO., LTD.—See The Carlyle Group Inc.; *U.S. Public*, pg. 2051
LION APPAREL, INC.—See Lakeland Industries, Inc.; *U.S. Public*, pg. 1288
LION ASIAPAC LIMITED; *Int'l*, pg. 4517

LIONAX INTERNATIONAL INVESTMENT HOLDINGS LIMITED — CORPORATE AFFILIATIONS

LIONAX INTERNATIONAL INVESTMENT HOLDINGS LIMITED; *Int'l*, pg. 4519
LION-BEER, SPIRITS & WINE PTY. LTD.—See Kirin Holdings Company, Limited; *Int'l*, pg. 4189
LION BRAND YARN COMPANY; *U.S. Private*, pg. 2463
THE LION BREWERY, INC.—See Encore Associates Inc.; *U.S. Private*, pg. 1390
LIONBRIDGE (CANADA) INC.—See H.I.G. Capital, LLC; *U.S. Private*, pg. 1830
LIONBRIDGE DENMARK A/S—See H.I.G. Capital, LLC; *U.S. Private*, pg. 1830
LIONBRIDGE DEUTSCHLAND GMBH—See H.I.G. Capital, LLC; *U.S. Private*, pg. 1830
LIONBRIDGE ESPANA S.L.—See H.I.G. Capital, LLC; *U.S. Private*, pg. 1830
LIONBRIDGE FRANCE SAS—See H.I.G. Capital, LLC; *U.S. Private*, pg. 1830
LIONBRIDGE HOLDING GMBH—See H.I.G. Capital, LLC; *U.S. Private*, pg. 1830
LIONBRIDGE IRELAND LIMITED—See H.I.G. Capital, LLC; *U.S. Private*, pg. 1830
LIONBRIDGE JAPAN III K.K.—See H.I.G. Capital, LLC; *U.S. Private*, pg. 1830
LIONBRIDGE JAPAN KK—See H.I.G. Capital, LLC; *U.S. Private*, pg. 1830
LIONBRIDGE KOREA CO. LTD.—See H.I.G. Capital, LLC; *U.S. Private*, pg. 1830
LIONBRIDGE MIDWEST, LLC—See H.I.G. Capital, LLC; *U.S. Private*, pg. 1830
LIONBRIDGE NEDERLAND B.V.—See H.I.G. Capital, LLC; *U.S. Private*, pg. 1830
LIONBRIDGE OY—See H.I.G. Capital, LLC; *U.S. Private*, pg. 1830
LIONBRIDGE POLAND SP. Z O.O.—See H.I.G. Capital, LLC; *U.S. Private*, pg. 1830
LIONBRIDGE SINGAPORE PTE LTD—See H.I.G. Capital, LLC; *U.S. Private*, pg. 1830
LIONBRIDGE (SLOVAKIA) S.R.O.—See H.I.G. Capital, LLC; *U.S. Private*, pg. 1830
LIONBRIDGE SWEDEN AKTIEBOLAG—See H.I.G. Capital, LLC; *U.S. Private*, pg. 1830
LIONBRIDGE TECHNOLOGIES (FRANCE) S.A.R.L.—See H.I.G. Capital, LLC; *U.S. Private*, pg. 1830
LIONBRIDGE TECHNOLOGIES, INC.—See H.I.G. Capital, LLC; *U.S. Private*, pg. 1830
LIONBRIDGE TECHNOLOGIES PRIVATE LIMITED—See H.I.G. Capital, LLC; *U.S. Private*, pg. 1830
LIONBRIDGE TESTING SERVICES OY—See H.I.G. Capital, LLC; *U.S. Private*, pg. 1830
LIONBRIDGE (THAILAND) LIMITED—See H.I.G. Capital, LLC; *U.S. Private*, pg. 1830
LIONBRIDGE (UK) LTD.—See H.I.G. Capital, LLC; *U.S. Private*, pg. 1830
LION BROTHERS COMPANY, INC.—See Avery Dennison Corporation; *U.S. Public*, pg. 244
LION BROTHERS FAR EAST, LTD.—See Avery Dennison Corporation; *U.S. Public*, pg. 244
LION BUSINESS SERVICE CO., LTD.—See Lion Corporation; *Int'l*, pg. 4517
LION CAPITAL LLP; *Int'l*, pg. 4517
LION CHEMICAL CO., LTD.—See Lion Corporation; *Int'l*, pg. 4517
LION CHEMICAL CO., LTD.—See Lion Corporation; *Int'l*, pg. 4517
LION CHEMICAL INDUSTRY (TAIWAN) CO., LTD.—See Lion Corporation; *Int'l*, pg. 4517
LION CHEMTECH CO., LTD.; *Int'l*, pg. 4517
LION COFFEE COMPANY—See Paradise Beverages, Inc.; *U.S. Private*, pg. 3090
LIONCO PHARMACEUTICAL GROUP CO.,LTD.; *Int'l*, pg. 4520
LION COPOLYMER GEISMAR, LLC—See Lion Copolymer Holdings, LLC; *U.S. Private*, pg. 2463
LION COPOLYMER HOLDINGS, LLC; *U.S. Private*, pg. 2463
LION COPPER AND GOLD CORP.; *Int'l*, pg. 4517
LION CORDIAL SUPPORT CO., LTD.—See Lion Corporation; *Int'l*, pg. 4517
LION CORPORATION - AKASHI PLANT—See Lion Corporation; *Int'l*, pg. 4517
LION CORPORATION - CHIBA PLANT—See Lion Corporation; *Int'l*, pg. 4518
LION CORPORATION (HONG KONG) LTD.—See Lion Corporation; *Int'l*, pg. 4517
LION CORPORATION - ODAWARA PLANT—See Lion Corporation; *Int'l*, pg. 4518
LION CORPORATION - OSAKA PLANT—See Lion Corporation; *Int'l*, pg. 4518
LION CORPORATION (SINGAPORE) PTE LTD—See Lion Corporation; *Int'l*, pg. 4517
LION CORPORATION; *Int'l*, pg. 4517
LION CORPORATION—See Lion Corporation; *Int'l*, pg. 4517
LION CORPORATION (THAILAND) LTD.—See Lion Corporation; *Int'l*, pg. 4517
LION COURTS SDN BHD—See Lion Industries Corporation Berhad; *Int'l*, pg. 4519
LION DAILY NECESSITIES CHEMICALS (QINGDAO) CO., LTD.—See Lion Corporation; *Int'l*, pg. 4518

LION DAIRY & DRINKS PTY. LTD. - CHELSEA HEIGHTS PLANT—See Bega Cheese Ltd.; *Int'l*, pg. 940
LION DAIRY & DRINKS PTY. LTD. - PENRITH PLANT—See Bega Cheese Ltd.; *Int'l*, pg. 940
LION DAIRY & DRINKS PTY. LTD. - SALISBURY PLANT—See Bega Cheese Ltd.; *Int'l*, pg. 940
LION DAIRY & DRINKS PTY. LTD. - THEBARTON PLANT—See Bega Cheese Ltd.; *Int'l*, pg. 940
LION DENTAL PRODUCTS CO., LTD.—See Lion Corporation; *Int'l*, pg. 4518
LION DRI SDN. BHD.—See Lion Group Management Services Sdn Bhd; *Int'l*, pg. 4518
LION ELASTOMERS LLC—See Lion Copolymer Holdings, LLC; *U.S. Private*, pg. 2463
THE LION ELECTRIC CO.—See Applied Intuition, Inc.; *U.S. Private*, pg. 299
LIONEL HENDERSON & CO., INC.; *U.S. Private*, pg. 2464
LIONEL LLC; *U.S. Private*, pg. 2464
LION E-MOBILITY AG; *Int'l*, pg. 4518
LION ENERGY LIMITED; *Int'l*, pg. 4518
LION ENGINEERING CO., LTD.—See Lion Corporation; *Int'l*, pg. 4518
LION EQUITY PARTNERS, LLC; *U.S. Private*, pg. 2463
LION EXPERT BUSINESS CO., LTD.—See Lion Corporation; *Int'l*, pg. 4518
LION FIELD MARKETING CO., LTD.—See Lion Corporation; *Int'l*, pg. 4518
LION FINANCE PTY LTD—See Collection House Limited; *Int'l*, pg. 1699
LIONFISH EVEN EMPREENDIMENTOS IMOBILIARIOS LTDA.—See Even Construtora e Incorporadora S.A.; *Int'l*, pg. 2562
LIONFISH LITIGATION FINANCE LIMITED—See RBG Holdings PLC; *Int'l*, pg. 6227
LION FOODS B.V.—See Top Taste Holding BV; *Int'l*, pg. 7813
THE LION FOUNDATION FOR DENTAL HEALTH—See Lion Corporation; *Int'l*, pg. 4518
LIONGATE CAPITAL MANAGEMENT INC.—See Principal Financial Group, Inc.; *U.S. Public*, pg. 1720
LIONGATE CAPITAL MANAGEMENT LLP—See Principal Financial Group, Inc.; *U.S. Public*, pg. 1720
LION GLOBAL INVESTORS LIMITED—See Oversea-Chinese Banking Corporation Limited; *Int'l*, pg. 5671
LION GROUP HOLDING LTD.; *Int'l*, pg. 4518
LION GROUP, INC—See Lakeland Industries, Inc.; *U.S. Public*, pg. 1288
LION GROUP MANAGEMENT SERVICES SDN BHD; *Int'l*, pg. 4518
LIONHEAD TECHNOLOGY DEVELOPMENT CO., LTD.; *Int'l*, pg. 4520
LIONHEART CAPITAL; *U.S. Private*, pg. 2464
LIONHEART VENTURES; *U.S. Private*, pg. 2464
LION HOME PRODUCTS (INTERNATIONAL) LTD.—See Lion Corporation; *Int'l*, pg. 4518
LION HOME PRODUCTS (TAIWAN) CO., LTD.—See Lion Corporation; *Int'l*, pg. 4518
LIONHUB GROUP LIMITED; *Int'l*, pg. 4520
LION HYGIENE CO., LTD.—See Lion Corporation; *Int'l*, pg. 4518
LION IDEMITSU COMPOSITES CO., LTD—See Idemitsu Kosan Co., Ltd.; *Int'l*, pg. 3591
LION IDEMITSU COMPOSITES CO., LTD—See Lion Corporation; *Int'l*, pg. 4518
LION IDEMITSU COMPOSITES (HONG KONG) LIMITED—See Idemitsu Kosan Co., Ltd.; *Int'l*, pg. 3591
LION IDEMITSU COMPOSITES (HONG KONG) LIMITED—See Lion Corporation; *Int'l*, pg. 4518
LION IDEMITSU COMPOSITES (INDIA) PRIVATE LIMITED—See Idemitsu Kosan Co., Ltd.; *Int'l*, pg. 3591
LION IDEMITSU COMPOSITES (INDIA) PRIVATE LIMITED—See Lion Corporation; *Int'l*, pg. 4518
LION IDEMITSU COMPOSITES (SHANGHAI) CO., LTD.—See Idemitsu Kosan Co., Ltd.; *Int'l*, pg. 3591
LION IDEMITSU COMPOSITES (SHANGHAI) CO., LTD.—See Lion Corporation; *Int'l*, pg. 4518
LION IDEMITSU COMPOSITES (THAILAND) CO., LTD.—See Idemitsu Kosan Co., Ltd.; *Int'l*, pg. 3592
LION IDEMITSU COMPOSITES (THAILAND) CO., LTD.—See Lion Corporation; *Int'l*, pg. 4518
LION INDUSTRIES CORPORATION BERHAD; *Int'l*, pg. 4519
LION INDUSTRIES INC.; *U.S. Private*, pg. 2464
LION INTERNATIONAL MANAGEMENT LIMITED—See HSBC Holdings plc; *Int'l*, pg. 3504
LION KALLOL LIMITED—See Lion Corporation; *Int'l*, pg. 4518
LION LABORATORIES LIMITED—See MPD, Inc.; *U.S. Private*, pg. 2803
LION LAM DIAMOND CORP.; *U.S. Private*, pg. 2464
LION LOGISTICS SERVICE CO., LTD.—See Lion Corporation; *Int'l*, pg. 4518
LIONMARK INC.; *U.S. Private*, pg. 2464
LIONMARK INSURANCE COMPANY—See Ameris Bancorp; *U.S. Public*, pg. 114
LIONMESH PRIMA TBK; *Int'l*, pg. 4520
LION METAL WORKS TBK; *Int'l*, pg. 4519

LION OF AFRICA HOLDINGS COMPANY (PTY) LTD—See Brimstone Investment Corporation Ltd.; *Int'l*, pg. 1164
LION OIL COMPANY—See Delek Group Ltd.; *Int'l*, pg. 2012
LION OIL TRADING & TRANSPORTATION, LLC—See Delek Group Ltd.; *Int'l*, pg. 2012
LION ONE AUSTRALIA PTY LTD—See Lion One Metals Limited; *Int'l*, pg. 4519
LION ONE LIMITED—See Lion One Metals Limited; *Int'l*, pg. 4519
LION ONE METALS LIMITED; *Int'l*, pg. 4519
LION PET CO., LTD.—See Lion Corporation; *Int'l*, pg. 4518
LION PETROLEUM PRODUCTS SDN BHD—See Lion Industries Corporation Berhad; *Int'l*, pg. 4519
LION POSIM BERHAD—See Lion Industries Corporation Berhad; *Int'l*, pg. 4519
LION PRINT CORPORATION; *Int'l*, pg. 4519
LION PTY. LTD.—See Kirin Holdings Company, Limited; *Int'l*, pg. 4189
LION RIBBON COMPANY, LLC—See IG Design Group Plc; *Int'l*, pg. 3600
LIONROCK CAPITAL LIMITED; *Int'l*, pg. 4520
LION ROCK GROUP LTD; *Int'l*, pg. 4519
LION ROCK RESOURCES INC.; *Int'l*, pg. 4519
LION RUBBER INDUSTRIES PTE LTD—See Lion Industries Corporation Berhad; *Int'l*, pg. 4519
LIONS BAY CAPITAL INC.; *Int'l*, pg. 4520
LIONSBRIDGE CONTRACTOR GROUP—See CCA Global Partners, Inc.; *U.S. Private*, pg. 799
LION SELECTION GROUP LIMITED; *Int'l*, pg. 4519
LIONS EYE INSTITUTE FOR TRANSPLANT & RESEARCH, INC.; *U.S. Private*, pg. 2464
LIONS GATE ENTERTAINMENT CORP.; *Int'l*, pg. 4520
LIONS GATE ENTERTAINMENT INC.—See Lions Gate Entertainment Corp.; *Int'l*, pg. 4520
LIONSGATE STUDIOS CORP.—See Lions Gate Entertainment Corp.; *Int'l*, pg. 4521
LIONS GATE STUDIOS—See Lions Gate Entertainment Corp.; *Int'l*, pg. 4520
LIONS GATE TELEVISION CORP.—See Lions Gate Entertainment Corp.; *Int'l*, pg. 4520
LIONS GATE TELEVISION DEVELOPMENT LLC—See Lions Gate Entertainment Corp.; *Int'l*, pg. 4520
LIONS GATE UK LTD.—See Lions Gate Entertainment Corp.; *Int'l*, pg. 4521
LION SPECIALTY CHEMICALS CO., LTD.—See Lion Corporation; *Int'l*, pg. 4518
LIONS QUICK MARTS INC.; *U.S. Private*, pg. 2464
LION STEEL SDN BHD—See Lion Industries Corporation Berhad; *Int'l*, pg. 4519
LIONSTONE PARTNERS, LLC—See Ameriprise Financial, Inc.; *U.S. Public*, pg. 114
LION STREET INC.—See Integrity Marketing Group LLC; *U.S. Private*, pg. 2103
LION TELESERVICES CZ AS—See Teleperformance SE; *Int'l*, pg. 7540
LION TELESERVICES SK—See Teleperformance SE; *Int'l*, pg. 7540
LION TOMONI CO., LTD.—See Lion Corporation; *Int'l*, pg. 4518
LIONTOWN RESOURCES LIMITED; *Int'l*, pg. 4521
LION TRADING CO., LTD.—See Lion Corporation; *Int'l*, pg. 4518
LION TRAVEL SERVICE CO., LTD.; *Int'l*, pg. 4519
LIONTREE ADVISORS LLC—See LionTree LLC; *U.S. Private*, pg. 2464
LIONTREE LLC; *U.S. Private*, pg. 2464
LIONTRUST ASSET MANAGEMENT PLC; *Int'l*, pg. 4521
LIONTRUST INVESTMENT MANAGEMENT LIMITED—See Liontrust Asset Management plc; *Int'l*, pg. 4521
LIONVEST CORPORATION (PAHANG) SDN. BHD.—See Minho (M) Berhad; *Int'l*, pg. 4910
LIONVEST TIMBER INDUSTRIES SDN. BHD.—See Minho (M) Berhad; *Int'l*, pg. 4910
LION VICTORIA PTY. LTD.—See Kirin Holdings Company, Limited; *Int'l*, pg. 4189
LIONWELD KENNEDY FLOORING LTD—See Hill & Smith PLC; *Int'l*, pg. 3391
LIORET SA; *Int'l*, pg. 4521
LIOSINTEX S.R.L.—See Recipharm AB; *Int'l*, pg. 6235
LIPA A.D., NOVI PAZAR; *Int'l*, pg. 4521
LIPA A.D., SOMBOR; *Int'l*, pg. 4521
LIPA PHARMACEUTICALS LIMITED—See CK Hutchison Holdings Limited; *Int'l*, pg. 1637
LIPARI ENERGY, INC.; *U.S. Private*, pg. 2464
LIPARI FOODS OPERATING COMPANY, LLC—See Littlejohn & Co., LLC; *U.S. Private*, pg. 2472
LIPARK LEASING GESELLSCHAFT M.B.H.—See UniCredit S.p.A.; *Int'l*, pg. 8036
LIPELLA PHARMACEUTICALS INC.; *U.S. Public*, pg. 1320
LI PENG ENTERPRISE CO., LTD.; *Int'l*, pg. 4481
LIPENWALD INC.; *U.S. Private*, pg. 2464
LIPERS ELECTRONIC (SHENZHEN) CO., LTD.—See Nichidenbo Corporation; *Int'l*, pg. 5268
LIPESA COLOMBIA SA—See Danaher Corporation; *U.S. Public*, pg. 628

COMPANY NAME INDEX

LIPHAM CONSTRUCTION CO. INC.; *U.S. Private*, pg. 2464
LIPHART STEEL COMPANY INC.; *U.S. Private*, pg. 2464
LIPIGON PHARMACEUTICALS AB; *Int'l*, pg. 4521
LIPLA CO., LTD.—See Sony Group Corporation; *Int'l*, pg. 7106
LIPLASTEC S.R.O—See Denso Corporation; *Int'l*, pg. 2032
LIPMAN HEARNE, INC.; *U.S. Private*, pg. 2465
LIPMAN HEARNE, INC. - WASHINGTON, DC—See Lipman Hearne, Inc.; *U.S. Private*, pg. 2465
LIPMAN & LIPMAN, INC.; *U.S. Private*, pg. 2464
LIPMAN-PORTLAND, LLC—See Lipman & Lipman, Inc.; *U.S. Private*, pg. 2465
LIPMAN SERVICES CORP.; *U.S. Private*, pg. 2465
LIPOCINE INC.; *U.S. Public*, pg. 1320
LIPOCINE OPERATING INC.—See Lipocine Inc.; *U.S. Public*, pg. 1320
LIPO CORPORATION BERHAD—See Kobay Technology Bhd.; *Int'l*, pg. 4216
LIPOGENE AB—See BASF SE; *Int'l*, pg. 884
LIPOSCIENCE, INC.—See Laboratory Corporation of America Holdings; *U.S. Public*, pg. 1287
LIPOTEC, S.A.—See Berkshire Hathaway Inc.; *U.S. Public*, pg. 308
LIPOTEC USA, INC.—See Berkshire Hathaway Inc.; *U.S. Public*, pg. 319
LIPPER INC.—See Thomson Reuters Corporation; *Int'l*, pg. 7715
LIPPER INTERNATIONAL INC.; *U.S. Private*, pg. 2465
LIPPERT ADLINK TECHNOLOGY GMBH—See ADLINK Technology, Inc.; *Int'l*, pg. 151
LIPPERT COMPONENTS, INC.—See LCI Industries; *U.S. Public*, pg. 1295
LIPPERT INCORPORATED; *U.S. Private*, pg. 2465
LIPPES MATHIAS WEXLER FRIEDMAN LLP - ALBANY—See Lippes Mathias Wexler Friedman LLP; *U.S. Private*, pg. 2465
LIPPES MATHIAS WEXLER FRIEDMAN LLP; *U.S. Private*, pg. 2465
LIPP GMBH; *Int'l*, pg. 4521
LIPPI & CO. ADVERTISING; *U.S. Private*, pg. 2465
LIPPINCOTT - SAN FRANCISCO—See Marsh & McLennan Companies, Inc.; *U.S. Public*, pg. 1387
LIPPINCOTT—See Marsh & McLennan Companies, Inc.; *U.S. Public*, pg. 1387
LIPPINCOTT WILLIAMS & WILKINS ASIA LTD.—See Wolters Kluwer n.v.; *Int'l*, pg. 8444
LIPPINCOTT WILLIAMS & WILKINS, INC.—See Wolters Kluwer n.v.; *Int'l*, pg. 8444
LIPPINCOTT WILLIAMS & WILKINS PTY, LTD.—See Wolters Kluwer n.v.; *Int'l*, pg. 8444
THE LIPPIN GROUP, INC. - NEW YORK—See The Lippin Group; *U.S. Private*, pg. 4070
THE LIPPIN GROUP; *U.S. Private*, pg. 4070
THE LIPPIN GROUP—See The Lippin Group; *U.S. Private*, pg. 4070
LIPPI SYSTEMS LIMITED; *Int'l*, pg. 4521
LIPPMANN MILWAUKEE, INC.—See Valmet Oyj; *Int'l*, pg. 8118
LIPPO CHINA RESOURCES LIMITED—See Lippo Limited; *Int'l*, pg. 4522
LIPPO INVESTMENTS MANAGEMENT LIMITED—See Lippo Limited; *Int'l*, pg. 4522
LIPPO LIMITED; *Int'l*, pg. 4521
LIPPO MALLS INDONESIA RETAIL TRUST; *Int'l*, pg. 4522
LIPPS MINERALOLE GMBH—See Marquard & Bahls AG; *Int'l*, pg. 4699
LIPPUPISTE OY—See CTS Eventim AG & Co. KGAA; *Int'l*, pg. 1873
LIPRO ELECTRICAL MANUFACTURING SDN. BHD.—See Oriental Holdings Berhad; *Int'l*, pg. 5624
LIPRO (LP) AG—See Schweizerische Nationalbank; *Int'l*, pg. 6646
LIPRO MOLD ENGINEERING SDN. BHD.—See Oriental Holdings Berhad; *Int'l*, pg. 5624
LIPRO TRADING SDN. BHD.—See Oriental Holdings Berhad; *Int'l*, pg. 5624
LIPSCOMB CHEMICAL COMPANY INC—See Omya (Schweiz) AG; *Int'l*, pg. 5572
LIPSCOMB OIL CO. INC.; *U.S. Private*, pg. 2465
LIPSCOMB & PITTS INSURANCE, LLC—See Galiot Insurance Services, Inc.; *U.S. Private*, pg. 1638
LIPSPLUS B.V.; *Int'l*, pg. 4522
LIPSPLUS EMMEN B.V.—See LipsPlus B.V.; *Int'l*, pg. 4522
LIPSPLUS GEMERT B.V.—See LipsPlus B.V.; *Int'l*, pg. 4522
LIPSPLUS GOES B.V.—See LipsPlus B.V.; *Int'l*, pg. 4522
LIPSPLUS RAALTE B.V.—See LipsPlus B.V.; *Int'l*, pg. 4522
LIPSPLUS TIEL B.V.—See LipsPlus B.V.; *Int'l*, pg. 4522
LIPSPLUS VOORBURG B.V.—See LipsPlus B.V.; *Int'l*, pg. 4522
LIPSPLUS WASVERZORGING B.V.—See LipsPlus B.V.; *Int'l*, pg. 4522
LIPSY LIMITED—See NEXT plc; *Int'l*, pg. 5248
LIPTEN COMPANY LLC; *U.S. Private*, pg. 2465

LIPTON CORPORATE CHILDCARE, INC.—See Bain Capital, LP; *U.S. Private*, pg. 437
LIQAL, B.V.—See Dover Corporation; *U.S. Public*, pg. 681
LIQHOBONG MINING DEVELOPMENT CO.(PROPRIETARY) LIMITED—See Firestone Diamonds plc; *Int'l*, pg. 2679
LIQTECH INTERNATIONAL A/S—See LiqTech International, Inc.; *Int'l*, pg. 4522
LIQTECH INTERNATIONAL, INC.; *Int'l*, pg. 4522
LIQUECOLOR INKJET GROUP; *U.S. Private*, pg. 2465
LIQUEFIED NATURAL GAS LIMITED; *Int'l*, pg. 4522
LIQUI-BOX CORPORATION—See Sealed Air Corporation; *U.S. Public*, pg. 1853
LIQUI-BOX CORP.—See Sealed Air Corporation; *U.S. Public*, pg. 1854
LIQUI-BOX GERMANY GMBH—See Sealed Air Corporation; *U.S. Public*, pg. 1853
LIQUICHEM HANDELS GMBH; *Int'l*, pg. 4523
LIQUIDAGENTS HEALTHCARE, LLC; *U.S. Private*, pg. 2466
LIQUID AIR LAB GMBH—See 24 Mobile Advertising Solutions AB; *Int'l*, pg. 4
LIQUID AVATAR TECHNOLOGIES INC.; *Int'l*, pg. 4523
LIQUID CAPITAL CORP.—See Garrington Group of Companies Inc.; *Int'l*, pg. 2886
LIQUID CONTROLS, INC.—See IDEX Corp; *U.S. Public*, pg. 1091
LIQUID CRYSTAL RESOURCES; *U.S. Private*, pg. 2465
LIQUID DEVELOPMENT LLC—See Canada Pension Plan Investment Board; *Int'l*, pg. 1280
LIQUID DEVELOPMENT LLC—See EQT AB; *Int'l*, pg. 2483
LIQUID DEVELOPMENT LLC—See Temasek Holdings (Private) Limited; *Int'l*, pg. 7548
LIQUID DIGITAL LIMITED—See Retec Digital Plc; *Int'l*, pg. 6306
LIQUID DIGITAL MEDIA—See Anderson Companies, Inc.; *U.S. Private*, pg. 276
LIQUID ENVIRONMENTAL SOLUTIONS OF TEXAS, LLC—See Audax Group, Limited Partnership; *U.S. Private*, pg. 388
LIQUID & ENVY PORTSMOUTH—See Luminar Group Holdings Plc; *Int'l*, pg. 4578
LIQUID FENCE CO., INC.—See Spectrum Brands Holdings, Inc.; *U.S. Public*, pg. 1917
LIQUIDFRAMEWORKS, INC.—See Silver Lake Group, LLC; *U.S. Private*, pg. 3658
LIQUID GAS CO.,LTD.—See Osaka Gas Co., Ltd.; *Int'l*, pg. 5645
LIQUID GAS EQUIPMENT LIMITED—See Babcock International Group PLC; *Int'l*, pg. 793
LIQUID HOLDINGS GROUP, INC.; *U.S. Private*, pg. 2465
LIQUIDHUB, INC.; *U.S. Private*, pg. 2466
LIQUIDIA TECHNOLOGIES, INC.; *U.S. Public*, pg. 1320
LIQUID INTELLIGENT TECHNOLOGIES LTD.—See EcoCash Holdings Zimbabwe Limited; *Int'l*, pg. 2294
LIQUID INVESTMENTS, INC.; *U.S. Private*, pg. 2466
LIQUIDITY MANAGEMENT HOUSE FOR INVESTMENT CO. K.S.C.C.—See Kuwait Finance House K.S.C.; *Int'l*, pg. 4345
LIQUIDITY MANAGEMENT HOUSE KSCC—See Kuwait Finance House K.S.C.; *Int'l*, pg. 4345
LIQUIDITY SERVICES, INC.; *U.S. Public*, pg. 1320
LIQUIDITY SERVICES UK LTD—See Liquidity Services, Inc.; *U.S. Public*, pg. 1321
LIQUID MEDIA GROUP LTD.; *Int'l*, pg. 4523
LIQUID MEDIA S.L.—See WPP plc; *Int'l*, pg. 8475
LIQUIDMETAL TECHNOLOGIES, INC.; *U.S. Public*, pg. 1321
LIQUID MINERALS GROUP LTD.—See Pilot Chemical Company; *U.S. Private*, pg. 3181
LIQUID MOTORS INC.; *U.S. Private*, pg. 2466
LIQUIDM TECHNOLOGY GMBH—See Bertelsmann SE & Co. KGaA; *Int'l*, pg. 993
LIQUIDNET ASIA LIMITED—See TP ICAP Finance PLC; *Int'l*, pg. 7881
LIQUIDNET AUSTRALIA PTY LTD.—See TP ICAP Finance PLC; *Int'l*, pg. 7881
LIQUIDNET CANADA INC.—See TP ICAP Finance PLC; *Int'l*, pg. 7881
LIQUIDNET EUROPE LTD.—See TP ICAP Finance PLC; *Int'l*, pg. 7881
LIQUIDNET HOLDINGS, INC.—See TP ICAP Finance PLC; *Int'l*, pg. 7881
LIQUIDNET, INC.—See TP ICAP Finance PLC; *Int'l*, pg. 7881
LIQUIDNET JAPAN, INC.—See TP ICAP Finance PLC; *Int'l*, pg. 7881
LIQUIDO CARBONICO COLOMBIANA S.A.—See Linde plc; *Int'l*, pg. 4509
LIQUIDPLANNER, INC.—See Tempo Software, Inc.; *U.S. Private*, pg. 3964
LIQUIDPOWER SPECIALTY PRODUCTS INC—See Berkshire Hathaway Inc.; *U.S. Public*, pg. 308
LIQUID RESINS INTERNATIONAL, LTD.; *U.S. Private*, pg. 2466
LIQUID ROBOTICS, INC.—See The Boeing Company; *U.S. Public*, pg. 2041

LIQUID TECHNOLOGIES, INC.—See The Pritzker Group - Chicago, LLC; *U.S. Private*, pg. 4099
LIQUID TECHNOLOGY CORPORATION—See CI Capital Partners LLC; *U.S. Private*, pg. 895
LIQUID TECHNOLOGY INC.; *U.S. Private*, pg. 2466
LIQUID THREAD—See Publicis Groupe S.A.; *Int'l*, pg. 6111
LIQUID THREAD—See Publicis Groupe S.A.; *Int'l*, pg. 6111
LIQUID TRANSPORT CORP.—See Dana Transport Inc.; *U.S. Private*, pg. 1152
LIQUID TRANSPORT INC.—See Dana Transport Inc.; *U.S. Private*, pg. 1152
LIQUIDUS MARKETING, INC.; *U.S. Private*, pg. 2466
LIQUID VIOLET LIMITED—See Canada Pension Plan Investment Board; *Int'l*, pg. 1280
LIQUID VIOLET LIMITED—See EQT AB; *Int'l*, pg. 2483
LIQUID VIOLET LIMITED—See Temasek Holdings (Private) Limited; *Int'l*, pg. 7548
LIQUID WEB, INC.; *U.S. Private*, pg. 2466
LIQUIDX, INC.—See Broadridge Financial Solutions, Inc.; *U.S. Public*, pg. 392
LIQUIDYN GMBH—See Nordson Corporation; *U.S. Public*, pg. 1533
LIQUIGAS DISTRIBUIDORA S.A.—See Petroleo Brasileiro S.A. - PETROBRAS; *Int'l*, pg. 5827
LIQUIGAS LIMITED—See Vector Limited; *Int'l*, pg. 8145
LIQUIGAS LIMITED—See Vector Limited; *Int'l*, pg. 8145
LIQUIGAS LIMITED—See Vector Limited; *Int'l*, pg. 8145
LIQUIGAS LIMITED—See Vector Limited; *Int'l*, pg. 8145
LIQUIGAS SPA—See SHV Holdings N.V.; *Int'l*, pg. 6873
LIQUILUX GAS CORP.; *U.S. Private*, pg. 2466
LIQUI - MOLY GESELLSCHAFT MIT BESCHRDNKTER HAFTUNG—See Wurth Verwaltungsgesellschaft mbH; *Int'l*, pg. 8506
LIQUI-MOLY IBERIA, UNIPESSOAL, LDA—See Wurth Verwaltungsgesellschaft mbH; *Int'l*, pg. 8506
LIQUI MOLY SOUTH AFRICA (PTY) LTD.—See Wurth Verwaltungsgesellschaft mbH; *Int'l*, pg. 8506
LIQUIP INTERNATIONAL PTY LIMITED—See Dover Corporation; *U.S. Public*, pg. 681
LIQUIT B.V.—See Recast Software Inc.; *U.S. Private*, pg. 3370
LIQUIVEX D.O.O.—See SHV Holdings N.V.; *Int'l*, pg. 6873
LIQUN COMMERCIAL GROUP CO., LTD.; *Int'l*, pg. 4523
LIQUOR BARN INC.—See SNDL Inc.; *Int'l*, pg. 7027
LIQUORLAND (AUSTRALIA) PTY LTD—See Wesfarmers Limited; *Int'l*, pg. 8382
LIQUOR STORES GP, INC.—See SNDL Inc.; *Int'l*, pg. 7027
LIQUOR TRADERS PTY. LTD.—See Metcash Limited; *Int'l*, pg. 4852
LIQVIS GMBH—See Fortum Oyj; *Int'l*, pg. 2742
LIREBA SERVEIS INTEGRATS, S.L.—See ACS, Actividades de Construccion y Servicios, S.A.; *Int'l*, pg. 115
LIRIK, INC.—See Tecnos Japan Inc.; *Int'l*, pg. 7517
THE LIRO GROUP; *U.S. Private*, pg. 4070
LIR S.R.L.; *Int'l*, pg. 4523
LIRTIX S.A.—See Sundiro Holding Co., Ltd.; *Int'l*, pg. 7312
LISA DRAXLMAIER AUTOPART ROMANIA SRL—See Draexlmaier Gruppe; *Int'l*, pg. 2198
LISA DRAXLMAIER GMBH—See Draexlmaier Gruppe; *Int'l*, pg. 2198
LISA ELIA PUBLIC RELATIONS; *U.S. Private*, pg. 2466
LISA MOTOR LINES, INC.—See Frozen Food Express Industries, Inc.; *U.S. Private*, pg. 1617
LISAM SYSTEMS INC.; *Int'l*, pg. 4523
LI SAN (SHANGHAI) INTERNATIONAL TRADE LTD.—See Laster Tech Co., Ltd.; *Int'l*, pg. 4422
LISANYDIS; *Int'l*, pg. 4523
LISBOAGAS GDL - SOCIEDADE DISTRIBUIDORA DE GAS NATURAL DE LISBOA, S.A.—See Galp Energia SGPS, S.A.; *Int'l*, pg. 2875
LISBON BUILDERS SUPPLY—See D.W. Dickey & Sons Inc.; *U.S. Private*, pg. 1143
LISCA, D.D.; *Int'l*, pg. 4523
LISCA D.O.O - MODNA ODECA—See Lisca, d.d.; *Int'l*, pg. 4523
LISCA GROUP DEUTSCHLAND GMBH—See Lisca, d.d.; *Int'l*, pg. 4523
LISCA MODA D.O.O.—See Lisca, d.d.; *Int'l*, pg. 4523
LISCA MODA S.R.O.—See Lisca, d.d.; *Int'l*, pg. 4523
LISCIO'S ITALIAN BAKERY; *U.S. Private*, pg. 2466
LIS CO., LTD.; *Int'l*, pg. 4523
L.I.S. CUSTOM DESIGNS, INC.; *U.S. Private*, pg. 2366
LISDEN CARE HOME KIRRIEMUIR—See Balhousie Holdings Limited; *Int'l*, pg. 808
LISEGA SOUTH INC.—See US Tech Services Inc.; *U.S. Private*, pg. 4320
LI-S ENERGY LIMITED—See PPK Group Limited; *Int'l*, pg. 5951
LISERTECO LDA—See W.A.G Payment Solutions Plc; *Int'l*, pg. 8321
LISE WATIER COSMETIQUES INC.—See Groupe Marcelle, Inc.; *Int'l*, pg. 3108
LISGRAFICA IMPRESSAO E ARTES GRAFICAS SA; *Int'l*, pg. 4523
LISHENG INDUSTRIAL CO., LTD.—See Transcenta Holding Limited; *Int'l*, pg. 7896

LISHENG SPORTS (SHANGHAI) CO., LTD. — CORPORATE AFFILIATIONS

LISHENG SPORTS (SHANGHAI) CO., LTD.; *Int'l*, pg. 4523
LISHUI JIACHENG AUTOMOBILE SALES CO., LTD.—See China Yongda Automobiles Services Holdings Limited; *Int'l*, pg. 1564
LISHUI POLY GRAND THEATRE MANAGEMENT CORPORATION LIMITED—See Poly Culture Group Corporation Limited; *Int'l*, pg. 5914
LISI AEROSPACE ADDITIVE MANUFACTURING SAS—See LISI S.A.; *Int'l*, pg. 4524
LISI AEROSPACE CANADA CORPORATION—See LISI S.A.; *Int'l*, pg. 4524
LISI AEROSPACE, HI-SHEAR CORP.—See LISI S.A.; *Int'l*, pg. 4524
LISI AEROSPACE NORTH AMERICA, INC.—See LISI S.A.; *Int'l*, pg. 4524
LISI AEROSPACE S.A.S.—See LISI S.A.; *Int'l*, pg. 4524
LISI AUTOMOTIVE FORM A.S—See LISI S.A.; *Int'l*, pg. 4524
LISI AUTOMOTIVE FORMER S.A.S.—See LISI S.A.; *Int'l*, pg. 4524
LISI AUTOMOTIVE HI-VOL INC.—See LISI S.A.; *Int'l*, pg. 4523
LISI AUTOMOTIVE KKP GMBH & CO KG—See LISI S.A.; *Int'l*, pg. 4524
LISI AUTOMOTIVE KKP GMBH—See LISI S.A.; *Int'l*, pg. 4524
LISI AUTOMOTIVE KNIPPING ESPANA S.A.—See LISI S.A.; *Int'l*, pg. 4523
LISI AUTOMOTIVE MECANO GMBH—See LISI S.A.; *Int'l*, pg. 4524
LISI AUTOMOTIVE MOHR UND FRIEDRICH GMBH—See LISI S.A.; *Int'l*, pg. 4524
LISI AUTOMOTIVE NOMEL—See LISI S.A.; *Int'l*, pg. 4523
LISI AUTOMOTIVE RAPID S.A.—See LISI S.A.; *Int'l*, pg. 4524
LISI AUTOMOTIVE SARL—See LISI S.A.; *Int'l*, pg. 4524
LISI AUTOMOTIVE SAS—See LISI S.A.; *Int'l*, pg. 4523
LISI AUTOMOTIVE SHANGHAI CO., LTD—See LISI S.A.; *Int'l*, pg. 4523
LISI COSMETICS S.A.S.—See Pochet S.A.; *Int'l*, pg. 5901
LISI MEDICAL JEROPA INC.—See LISI S.A.; *Int'l*, pg. 4523
LISI MEDICAL ORTHOPAEDICS—See LISI S.A.; *Int'l*, pg. 4523
LISI MEDICAL SAS—See LISI S.A.; *Int'l*, pg. 4524
LISI S.A.; *Int'l*, pg. 4523
LISK CONTROL TECHNOLOGY (SUZHOU) CO., LTD.—See G.W. Lisk Company, Inc.; *U.S. Private*, pg. 1631
LISK IRELAND LTD—See G.W. Lisk Company, Inc.; *U.S. Private*, pg. 1631
LISK TRUCKING INC.; *U.S. Private*, pg. 2466
LISLE CORPORATION; *U.S. Private*, pg. 2466
LISMORE MAZDA PTY. LIMITED—See Peter Warren Automotive Holdings Ltd.; *Int'l*, pg. 5824
LISSAGE LTD.—See Kao Corporation; *Int'l*, pg. 4075
LISTA AG—See GreatStar Group Co., Ltd.; *Int'l*, pg. 3068
LISTA ARNEGG—See Lienhard Office Group AG; *Int'l*, pg. 4492
LISTA AUSTRIA GMBH—See GreatStar Group Co., Ltd.; *Int'l*, pg. 3068
LISTA GMBH—See GreatStar Group Co., Ltd.; *Int'l*, pg. 3068
LISTA HOLDING AG—See GreatStar Group Co., Ltd.; *Int'l*, pg. 3068
LISTA INTERNATIONAL CORPORATION—See Stanley Black & Decker, Inc.; *U.S. Public*, pg. 1935
LISTA ITALIA S.R.L.—See GreatStar Group Co., Ltd.; *Int'l*, pg. 3068
LIST AMERICA—See Market Development Group, Inc.; *U.S. Private*, pg. 2579
LISTA OFFICE AG—See Lienhard Office Group AG; *Int'l*, pg. 4492
LISTA SISTEMAS DE ALMACENAJE, S.A.—See GreatStar Group Co., Ltd.; *Int'l*, pg. 3068
LISTA UK LTD.—See GreatStar Group Co., Ltd.; *Int'l*, pg. 3068
LIST BIOLOGICAL LABORATORIES, INC.—See Genome & Company; *Int'l*, pg. 2925
LISTEN360, INC.; *U.S. Private*, pg. 2466
LIST ENGAGE, INC.—See Broadtree Partners, LLC; *U.S. Private*, pg. 659
LISTEN JAPAN, INC.—See Transcosmos Inc.; *Int'l*, pg. 7898
LISTENLOGIC, LLC—See Guggenheim Partners, LLC; *U.S. Private*, pg. 1811
LISTENUP.COM; *U.S. Private*, pg. 2466
LISTEN UP ESPANOL INC. (LUE); *U.S. Private*, pg. 2466
LISTER FERTILITY AT PORTLAND HOSPITAL LIMITED—See HCA Healthcare, Inc.; *U.S. Public*, pg. 1001
LISTERHILL CREDIT UNION INC.; *U.S. Private*, pg. 2467
LISTER HOSPITAL—See HCA Healthcare, Inc.; *U.S. Public*, pg. 1001
LISTER PETTER AFRICA (PTY) LTD—See Lister-Petter Limited; *Int'l*, pg. 4524
LISTER PETTER AMERICAS INC—See Lister-Petter Limited; *Int'l*, pg. 4524

LISTER PETTER FZE—See Lister-Petter Limited; *Int'l*, pg. 4524
LISTER PETTER GLOBAL HUB—See Lister-Petter Limited; *Int'l*, pg. 4524
LISTER-PETTER INC.—See Lister-Petter Limited; *Int'l*, pg. 4524
LISTER-PETTER LIMITED; *Int'l*, pg. 4524
LISTER PETTER OCEANIA LTD—See Lister-Petter Limited; *Int'l*, pg. 4524
LISTER WILDER LTD; *Int'l*, pg. 4524
L.I.S.T. INC.; *U.S. Private*, pg. 2366
LIST INDUSTRIES, INC.; *U.S. Private*, pg. 2466
LIST INNOVATIVE SOLUTIONS, INC.—See Bridge Growth Partners, LLC; *U.S. Private*, pg. 649
LIST INNOVATIVE SOLUTIONS, INC.—See Frontenac Company LLC; *U.S. Private*, pg. 1614
LIST MANAGEMENT SERVICES, INC.; *U.S. Private*, pg. 2466
LISTO CORPORATION INC.; *U.S. Private*, pg. 2467
LISTON BRICK COMPANY OF CORONA INC.; *U.S. Private*, pg. 2467
LISTOWEL TECHNOLOGY, INC.—See Moriroku Holdings Company, Ltd.; *Int'l*, pg. 5047
LISTRAK, INC.; *U.S. Private*, pg. 2467
LISTRINDO CAPITAL B.V.—See PT Cikarang Listrindo Tbk; *Int'l*, pg. 6034
LIST SERVICES CORPORATION; *U.S. Private*, pg. 2466
LIST SOLUTIONS, INC.; *U.S. Private*, pg. 2466
LISY CORPORATION; *U.S. Private*, pg. 2467
LITALICO, LNC.; *Int'l*, pg. 4524
LITANIA SPORTS GROUP, INC.; *U.S. Private*, pg. 2467
LITASCO CENTRAL ASIA LLP—See PJSC Lukoil; *Int'l*, pg. 5881
LITASCO MIDDLE EAST DMCC—See PJSC Lukoil; *Int'l*, pg. 5881
LITASCO SA—See PJSC Lukoil; *Int'l*, pg. 5881
THE LITCHFIELD COMPANY; *U.S. Private*, pg. 4071
LITCHNEY LAW FIRM; *U.S. Private*, pg. 2467
LITCO PETROLEUM INC.; *U.S. Private*, pg. 2467
LITE ACCESS TECHNOLOGIES INC.; *Int'l*, pg. 4524
LITEC FRANCE S.A.S.—See Crown Holdings, Inc.; *U.S. Public*, pg. 599
LITECONTROL CORPORATION; *U.S. Private*, pg. 2467
LITECURE LLC—See Enovis Corporation; *U.S. Public*, pg. 773
LITEFLEX, LLC—See The Boler Company; *U.S. Private*, pg. 3996
LITEHOUSE FOODS, INC.; *U.S. Private*, pg. 2467
LITEHOUSE PRODUCTS INC.; *U.S. Private*, pg. 2467
LITELAB CORP.; *U.S. Private*, pg. 2467
LITEL PARTICIPACOES S.A.; *Int'l*, pg. 4526
LITEMAX ELECTRONICS, INC.; *Int'l*, pg. 4526
LITEN LOGISTICS SERVICES PTE LTD—See Chasen Holdings Limited; *Int'l*, pg. 1457
LITENORDIC AB—See DistIT AB; *Int'l*, pg. 2136
LITE-ON AUTOMOTIVE CORP.—See Lite-On Technology Corporation; *Int'l*, pg. 4525
LITE-ON AUTOMOTIVE ELECTRONICS EUROPE B.V.—See Lite-On Technology Corporation; *Int'l*, pg. 4525
LITE-ON AUTOMOTIVE ELECTRONICS (GUANG ZHOU) CO., LTD.—See Lite-On Technology Corporation; *Int'l*, pg. 4525
LITE-ON AUTOMOTIVE NORTH AMERICA INC.—See Lite-On Technology Corporation; *Int'l*, pg. 4525
LITE-ON CLEAN ENERGY TECHNOLOGY CORP.—See Lite-On Technology Corporation; *Int'l*, pg. 4525
LITE-ON ELECTRONICS CO., LTD.—See Lite-On Technology Corporation; *Int'l*, pg. 4525
LITE-ON ELECTRONICS (DONGGUAN) CO., LTD.—See Lite-On Technology Corporation; *Int'l*, pg. 4525
LITE-ON ELECTRONICS (EUROPE) LTD.—See Lite-On Technology Corporation; *Int'l*, pg. 4525
LITE-ON ELECTRONICS H.K. LTD.—See Lite-On Technology Corporation; *Int'l*, pg. 4525
LITE-ON ELECTRONICS (THAILAND) CO., LTD.—See Lite-On Technology Corporation; *Int'l*, pg. 4525
LITE-ON ELECTRONICS TIANJIN CO., LTD.—See Lite-On Technology Corporation; *Int'l*, pg. 4525
LITE-ON GREEN TECHNOLOGIES INC.—See Lite-On Technology Corporation; *Int'l*, pg. 4525
LITE-ON, INC.—See Lite-On Technology Corporation; *Int'l*, pg. 4526
LITE-ON IT BV—See Lite-On Technology Corporation; *Int'l*, pg. 4525
LITE-ON IT CORPORATION—See Lite-On Technology Corporation; *Int'l*, pg. 4525
LITE-ON JAPAN (H.K.) LIMITED—See Lite-On Technology Corporation; *Int'l*, pg. 4525
LITE-ON JAPAN LTD.—See Lite-On Technology Corporation; *Int'l*, pg. 4525
LITE-ON JAPAN (THAILAND) CO., LTD.—See Lite-On Technology Corporation; *Int'l*, pg. 4525
LITE-ON LI SHIN TECHNOLOGY (GANZHOU) LTD.—See Lite-On Technology Corporation; *Int'l*, pg. 4525
LITE-ON MOBILE INDUSTRIA E COMERCIO DE PLASTICOS LTDA—See Lite-On Technology Corporation; *Int'l*, pg. 4525

LITE-ON MOBILE OYJ—See Lite-On Technology Corporation; *Int'l*, pg. 4525
LITE-ON OPTO TECHNOLOGY (GUANGZHOU) LTD.—See Lite-On Technology Corporation; *Int'l*, pg. 4525
LITE-ON OVERSEAS TRADING CO., LTD.—See Lite-On Technology Corporation; *Int'l*, pg. 4526
LITE-ON SEMICONDUCTOR CORP - HSINCHU PLANT—See Lite-On Semiconductor Corp.; *Int'l*, pg. 4525
LITE-ON SEMICONDUCTOR CORP. - KEELUNG PLANT—See Lite-On Semiconductor Corp.; *Int'l*, pg. 4525
LITE-ON SEMICONDUCTOR CORP. - PHILIPPINES PLANT—See Lite-On Semiconductor Corp.; *Int'l*, pg. 4525
LITE-ON SEMICONDUCTOR CORP. - SHANGHAI PLANT—See Lite-On Semiconductor Corp.; *Int'l*, pg. 4525
LITE-ON SEMICONDUCTOR CORP.; *Int'l*, pg. 4524
LITE-ON SINGAPORE PTE. LTD.—See Lite-On Technology Corporation; *Int'l*, pg. 4526
LITE-ON TECHNOLOGY (CHANGZHOU) CO., LTD.—See Lite-On Technology Corporation; *Int'l*, pg. 4526
LITE-ON TECHNOLOGY CORPORATION; *Int'l*, pg. 4525
LITE-ON TECHNOLOGY (GUANGZHOU) CO., LTD.—See Lite-On Technology Corporation; *Int'l*, pg. 4525
LITE-ON TRADING USA, INC.—See Lite-On Technology Corporation; *Int'l*, pg. 4526
LITEPANELS INC.—See Videndum plc; *Int'l*, pg. 8190
LITEPOINT CORP.—See Teradyne, Inc.; *U.S. Public*, pg. 2018
LITEPOINT EUROPE A/S—See Teradyne, Inc.; *U.S. Public*, pg. 2018
LITEPOINT JAPAN K.K.—See Teradyne, Inc.; *U.S. Public*, pg. 2018
LITEPOINT TECHNOLOGY (SHANGHAI) COMPANY LTD.—See Teradyne, Inc.; *U.S. Public*, pg. 2018
LITERACY CAPITAL PLC; *Int'l*, pg. 4526
LITERARY CLASSICS OF THE UNITED STATES, INC.; *U.S. Private*, pg. 2467
LITERS QUARRY INC.; *U.S. Private*, pg. 2467
LITESTREAM HOLDINGS, LLC; *U.S. Private*, pg. 2467
LITE TECH INDUSTRIES LLC—See Dubai Investments PJSC; *Int'l*, pg. 2219
LITEXIMP—See Koncernas Achemos Grupe; *Int'l*, pg. 4246
LITEX PROMO SP. Z O.O—See Lubawa S.A.; *Int'l*, pg. 4572
LITEYE SYSTEMS, INC.—See Highlander Partners, LP.; *U.S. Private*, pg. 1939
LITFERT SARL—See Koncernas Achemos Grupe; *Int'l*, pg. 4246
LITGRID AB; *Int'l*, pg. 4526
LITHA HEALTHCARE GROUP LIMITED—See Endo International plc; *Int'l*, pg. 2404
LITHGOW CABLE SERVICES PTY LTD—See Washington H. Soul Pattinson & Company Limited; *Int'l*, pg. 8351
LITHIA ACDM, INC.—See Lithia Motors, Inc.; *U.S. Public*, pg. 1323
LITHIA BNM, INC.—See Lithia Motors, Inc.; *U.S. Public*, pg. 1323
LITHIA BRYAN TEXAS, INC.—See Lithia Motors, Inc.; *U.S. Public*, pg. 1323
LITHIA CDH, INC.—See Lithia Motors, Inc.; *U.S. Public*, pg. 1323
LITHIA CHRYSLER JEEP DODGE OF BILLINGS—See Lithia Motors, Inc.; *U.S. Public*, pg. 1324
LITHIA CJDO, INC.—See Lithia Motors, Inc.; *U.S. Public*, pg. 1323
LITHIA CJDSA, INC.—See Lithia Motors, Inc.; *U.S. Public*, pg. 1323
LITHIA CJDSF, INC.—See Lithia Motors, Inc.; *U.S. Public*, pg. 1323
LITHIA DE, INC.—See Lithia Motors, Inc.; *U.S. Public*, pg. 1324
LITHIA DES MOINES-VW, LLC—See Lithia Motors, Inc.; *U.S. Public*, pg. 1324
LITHIA DMID, INC.—See Lithia Motors, Inc.; *U.S. Public*, pg. 1324
LITHIA DM, INC.—See Lithia Motors, Inc.; *U.S. Public*, pg. 1324
LITHIA DODGE OF TRI-CITIES, INC.—See Lithia Motors, Inc.; *U.S. Public*, pg. 1324
LITHIA FINANCIAL CORPORATION—See Lithia Motors, Inc.; *U.S. Public*, pg. 1324
LITHIA FMF, INC.—See Lithia Motors, Inc.; *U.S. Public*, pg. 1324
LITHIA FORD LINCOLN OF FRESNO; *U.S. Private*, pg. 2467
LITHIA FORD OF BOISE, INC.—See Lithia Motors, Inc.; *U.S. Public*, pg. 1324
LITHIA HGF—See Lithia Motors, Inc.; *U.S. Public*, pg. 1324
LITHIA HMID, INC.—See Lithia Motors, Inc.; *U.S. Public*, pg. 1324
LITHIA IDAHO FALLS-F, INC.—See Lithia Motors, Inc.; *U.S. Public*, pg. 1324

LITHIA JEF, INC.—See Lithia Motors, Inc.; *U.S. Public*, pg. 1324
LITHIA KLAMATH, INC.—See Lithia Motors, Inc.; *U.S. Public*, pg. 1324
LITHIA MBDM, INC.—See Lithia Motors, Inc.; *U.S. Public*, pg. 1324
LITHIA MEDFORD HON, INC.—See Lithia Motors, Inc.; *U.S. Public*, pg. 1324
LITHIA MMF, INC.—See Lithia Motors, Inc.; *U.S. Public*, pg. 1324
LITHIA MONROEVILLE-F, LLC—See Lithia Motors, Inc.; *U.S. Public*, pg. 1324
LITHIA MOON-S, LLC—See Lithia Motors, Inc.; *U.S. Public*, pg. 1324
LITHIA MOON-V, LLC—See Lithia Motors, Inc.; *U.S. Public*, pg. 1324
LITHIA MOTORS, INC.; *U.S. Public*, pg. 1321
LITHIA MTLM, LLC—See Lithia Motors, Inc.; *U.S. Public*, pg. 1324
LITHIA NA, INC.—See Lithia Motors, Inc.; *U.S. Public*, pg. 1324
LITHIA ND ACQUISITION CORP. #3—See Lithia Motors, Inc.; *U.S. Public*, pg. 1324
LITHIA NF, INC.—See Lithia Motors, Inc.; *U.S. Public*, pg. 1324
LITHIA NISSAN OF AMES—See Lithia Motors, Inc.; *U.S. Public*, pg. 1324
LITHIA NSA, INC.—See Lithia Motors, Inc.; *U.S. Public*, pg. 1324
LITHIA OF ABILENE, INC.—See Lithia Motors, Inc.; *U.S. Public*, pg. 1325
LITHIA OF BELLINGHAM, LLC—See Lithia Motors, Inc.; *U.S. Public*, pg. 1325
LITHIA OF BENNINGTON - 1, LLC—See Lithia Motors, Inc.; *U.S. Public*, pg. 1325
LITHIA OF CASPER, LLC—See Lithia Motors, Inc.; *U.S. Public*, pg. 1325
LITHIA OF CLEAR LAKE, LLC—See Lithia Motors, Inc.; *U.S. Public*, pg. 1325
LITHIA OF CONCORD II, INC.—See Lithia Motors, Inc.; *U.S. Public*, pg. 1325
LITHIA OF CONCORD I, INC.—See Lithia Motors, Inc.; *U.S. Public*, pg. 1325
LITHIA OF CORPUS CHRISTI, INC.—See Lithia Motors, Inc.; *U.S. Public*, pg. 1325
LITHIA OF DES MOINES, INC.—See Lithia Motors, Inc.; *U.S. Public*, pg. 1325
LITHIA OF EUGENE, LLC—See Lithia Motors, Inc.; *U.S. Public*, pg. 1325
LITHIA OF EUREKA, INC.—See Lithia Motors, Inc.; *U.S. Public*, pg. 1325
LITHIA OF GREAT FALLS, INC.—See Lithia Motors, Inc.; *U.S. Public*, pg. 1325
LITHIA OF HONOLULUBGMCC, LLC—See Lithia Motors, Inc.; *U.S. Public*, pg. 1325
LITHIA OF HONOLULUV, LLC—See Lithia Motors, Inc.; *U.S. Public*, pg. 1325
LITHIA OF KILLEEN, LLC—See Lithia Motors, Inc.; *U.S. Public*, pg. 1325
LITHIA OF MAUI-H, LLC—See Lithia Motors, Inc.; *U.S. Public*, pg. 1325
LITHIA OF MISSOULA, INC.—See Lithia Motors, Inc.; *U.S. Public*, pg. 1325
LITHIA OF PORTLAND, LLC—See Lithia Motors, Inc.; *U.S. Public*, pg. 1325
LITHIA OF ROSEBURG, INC.—See Lithia Motors, Inc.; *U.S. Public*, pg. 1325
LITHIA OF SANTA ROSA, INC.—See Lithia Motors, Inc.; *U.S. Public*, pg. 1325
LITHIA OF SEATTLE, INC.—See Lithia Motors, Inc.; *U.S. Public*, pg. 1325
LITHIA OF SOUTH CENTRAL AK, INC.—See Lithia Motors, Inc.; *U.S. Public*, pg. 1325
LITHIA OF SPOKANE, INC.—See Lithia Motors, Inc.; *U.S. Public*, pg. 1325
LITHIA OF STOCKTON-V, INC.—See Lithia Motors, Inc.; *U.S. Public*, pg. 1325
LITHIA OF TF, INC.—See Lithia Motors, Inc.; *U.S. Public*, pg. 1325
LITHIA OF UTICA-1, LLC—See Lithia Motors, Inc.; *U.S. Public*, pg. 1325
LITHIA OF WALNUT CREEK, INC.—See Lithia Motors, Inc.; *U.S. Public*, pg. 1325
LITHIA OF WASILLA, LLC—See Lithia Motors, Inc.; *U.S. Public*, pg. 1325
LITHIA OF YORKVILLE-1, LLC—See Lithia Motors, Inc.; *U.S. Public*, pg. 1325
LITHIA OF YORKVILLE-3, LLC—See Lithia Motors, Inc.; *U.S. Public*, pg. 1325
LITHIA PARAMUS-M, LLC—See Lithia Motors, Inc.; *U.S. Public*, pg. 1324
LITHIA RAMSEY-B, LLC—See Lithia Motors, Inc.; *U.S. Public*, pg. 1324
LITHIA RAMSEY-L, LLC—See Lithia Motors, Inc.; *U.S. Public*, pg. 1324
LITHIA RAMSEY-M, LLC—See Lithia Motors, Inc.; *U.S. Public*, pg. 1324
LITHIA RENO-CJ, LLC—See Lithia Motors, Inc.; *U.S. Public*, pg. 1324

LITHIA RENO SUB-HYUN, INC.—See Lithia Motors, Inc.; *U.S. Public*, pg. 1324
LITHIA RENO-VW, LLC—See Lithia Motors, Inc.; *U.S. Public*, pg. 1324
LITHIA ROSE-FT, INC.—See Lithia Motors, Inc.; *U.S. Public*, pg. 1324
LITHIA SALMIR, INC.—See Lithia Motors, Inc.; *U.S. Public*, pg. 1324
LITHIA SEA P, INC.—See Lithia Motors, Inc.; *U.S. Public*, pg. 1325
LITHIA SEASIDE, INC.—See Lithia Motors, Inc.; *U.S. Public*, pg. 1325
LITHIA SOC, INC.—See Lithia Motors, Inc.; *U.S. Public*, pg. 1324
LITHIA SUBARU HYUNDAI GMC BUICK—See Lithia Motors, Inc.; *U.S. Public*, pg. 1325
LITHIA SUBARU OF FRESNO; *U.S. Private*, pg. 2467
LITHIA TA, INC.—See Lithia Motors, Inc.; *U.S. Public*, pg. 1325
LITHIA TR, INC.—See Lithia Motors, Inc.; *U.S. Public*, pg. 1325
LITHIA UNIONTOWN-C, LLC—See Lithia Motors, Inc.; *U.S. Public*, pg. 1325
LITHIA VF, INC.—See Lithia Motors, Inc.; *U.S. Public*, pg. 1325
LITHIONICS BATTERY, LLC—See Winnebago Industries, Inc.; *U.S. Public*, pg. 2374
LITHIUM AMERICAS CORP.; *Int'l*, pg. 4526
LITHIUM AUSTRALIA NL; *Int'l*, pg. 4526
LITHIUM BALANCE A/S—See Sensata Technologies Holding plc; *U.S. Public*, pg. 1865
LITHIUMBANK RESOURCES CORP.; *Int'l*, pg. 4527
LITHIUM & BORON TECHNOLOGY, INC.; *Int'l*, pg. 4526
LITHIUM CHILE INC.; *Int'l*, pg. 4527
LITHIUM CORPORATION; *U.S. Public*, pg. 1326
LITHIUM DEVELOPMENT PTE LTD—See Hong Lai Huat Group Limited; *Int'l*, pg. 3467
LITHIUM ENERGI EXPLORATION INC.; *Int'l*, pg. 4527
LITHIUM ENERGY LIMITED; *Int'l*, pg. 4527
LITHIUM EXPLORATION GROUP, INC.; *U.S. Private*, pg. 2467
LITHIUM-FOR-EARTH INC.; *Int'l*, pg. 4527
LITHIUM IONIC CORP.; *Int'l*, pg. 4527
LITHIUM PLUS MINERALS LTD.; *Int'l*, pg. 4527
LITHIUM POWER INTERNATIONAL LIMITED—See Corporacion Nacional del Cobre de Chile; *Int'l*, pg. 1805
LITHIUM ROYALTY CORP.; *Int'l*, pg. 4527
LITHIUM SOUTH DEVELOPMENT CORPORATION; *Int'l*, pg. 4527
LITHIUM X ENERGY CORP.; *Int'l*, pg. 4527
LITHKO CONTRACTING LLC—See The Pritzker Organization, LLC; *U.S. Private*, pg. 4100
LITHOCRAFT, INC.—See Graphic Packaging Holding Company; *U.S. Public*, pg. 959
LITHO FORMAS, SA; *Int'l*, pg. 4527
LITHOGRAPHICS INC.; *U.S. Private*, pg. 2467
LITHOGRAPHIX, INC.; *U.S. Private*, pg. 2467
LITHO-KROME COMPANY—See Hallmark Cards, Inc.; *U.S. Private*, pg. 1845
LITHOLINK CORPORATION—See Laboratory Corporation of America Holdings; *U.S. Public*, pg. 1287
LITHONIA LIGHTING—See Acuity Brands, Inc.; *U.S. Public*, pg. 37
LITHONPLUS GMBH & CO. KG—See Heidelberg Materials AG; *Int'l*, pg. 3318
LITHORADE PACKAGING SOLUTIONS B.V.; *Int'l*, pg. 4527
LITHOS ENERGY LTD.; *Int'l*, pg. 4527
LITHO SUPPLIES LTD; *Int'l*, pg. 4527
LITHO SUPPLIES (UK) LTD—See Litho Supplies Ltd; *Int'l*, pg. 4527
LITHOTECH AFRIC MAIL PINETOWN (PTY) LIMITED—See The Bidvest Group Limited; *Int'l*, pg. 7624
LITHOTECH GROUP SERVICES (PTY) LIMITED—See The Bidvest Group Limited; *Int'l*, pg. 7624
LITHO TECH, INC.—See Taylor Corporation; *U.S. Private*, pg. 3938
LITHOTECH LABELS (PTY) LIMITED—See The Bidvest Group Limited; *Int'l*, pg. 7624
LITHOTECH MANUFACTURING CAPE (PTY) LIMITED—See The Bidvest Group Limited; *Int'l*, pg. 7625
LITHOTECH MANUFACTURING PINETOWN (PTY) LIMITED—See The Bidvest Group Limited; *Int'l*, pg. 7625
LITHOTECH PRINT ON DEMAND PTY. LTD.—See The Bidvest Group Limited; *Int'l*, pg. 7625
LITHOTECH SALES BLOEMFONTEIN (PTY) LIMITED—See The Bidvest Group Limited; *Int'l*, pg. 7625
LITHOTECH SALES CAPE (PTY) LIMITED—See The Bidvest Group Limited; *Int'l*, pg. 7625
LITHOTECH SALES EAST LONDON (PTY) LIMITED—See The Bidvest Group Limited; *Int'l*, pg. 7625
LITHOTECH SALES KWAZULU-NATAL (PTY) LIMITED—See The Bidvest Group Limited; *Int'l*, pg. 7625

LITHOTECH SALES PORT ELIZABETH (PTY) LIMITED—See The Bidvest Group Limited; *Int'l*, pg. 7625
LITHOTECH SALES PRETORIA (PTY) LIMITED—See The Bidvest Group Limited; *Int'l*, pg. 7625
LITHOTECH SOLUTIONS (PTY) LIMITED—See The Bidvest Group Limited; *Int'l*, pg. 7625
LITHOTONE INC.; *U.S. Private*, pg. 2468
LITHOTYPE COMPANY, INC. - MIDWEST FACILITY—See Lithotype Company, Inc.; *U.S. Private*, pg. 2468
LITHOTYPE COMPANY, INC.; *U.S. Private*, pg. 2468
LITHUANIAN CENTRAL SECURITIES DEPOSITARY—See Nasdaq, Inc.; *U.S. Public*, pg. 1491
LITIAN PICTURES HOLDINGS LIMITED; *Int'l*, pg. 4527
LITIGATION CAPITAL MANAGEMENT LIMITED; *Int'l*, pg. 4527
LITIGATION INSIGHTS, INC.—See IMS Consulting & Expert Services; *U.S. Private*, pg. 2051
LITIGATION SERVICES, LLC; *U.S. Private*, pg. 2468
LITIGATION SOLUTIONS, LLC—See MCMC LLC; *U.S. Private*, pg. 2642
LITI RESEARCH & DEVELOPMENT INC.—See KKR & Co. Inc.; *U.S. Public*, pg. 1259
LITITZ MUTUAL INSURANCE COMPANY; *U.S. Private*, pg. 2468
LITIUM AB; *Int'l*, pg. 4527
LITLAMP COMMUNICATIONS GROUP; *U.S. Private*, pg. 2468
LITMUS SOLUTIONS PTY. LTD.—See HFBG Holding B.V.; *Int'l*, pg. 3375
LITOGRAFIA BYRON ZADIK, S.A.—See Sigma S.A. de C.V.; *Int'l*, pg. 6908
LITOGRAFIA SPADA S.R.L.—See Poligrafica S. Faustino S.p.A.; *Int'l*, pg. 5909
LITON TECHNOLOGY CORP.—See Lelon Electronics Corp.; *Int'l*, pg. 4447
LITORAL GAS SA—See ENGIE SA; *Int'l*, pg. 2434
LITORINA CAPITAL MANAGEMENT AB; *Int'l*, pg. 4527
LITORIUM GROUP CORP.; *Int'l*, pg. 4528
LITOS GMBH—See DZ BANK AG Deutsche Zentral-Genossenschaftsbank; *Int'l*, pg. 2244
LITOTIPOGRAFIA ALCIONE S.R.L.—See Cimpress plc; *Int'l*, pg. 1609
LITRA CO., LTD.—See A&D Co., Ltd.; *Int'l*, pg. 19
LITRO ENERGIE NEDERLAND B.V.—See Delta N.V.; *Int'l*, pg. 2019
LITT DIFFUSION SAS—See SIG plc; *Int'l*, pg. 6906
LITTELFUSE ASIA SALES B.V.—See Littelfuse, Inc.; *U.S. Public*, pg. 1327
LITTELFUSE DO BRASIL—See Littelfuse, Inc.; *U.S. Public*, pg. 1327
LITTELFUSE FAR EAST, PTE. LTD.—See Littelfuse, Inc.; *U.S. Public*, pg. 1327
LITTELFUSE GMBH—See Littelfuse, Inc.; *U.S. Public*, pg. 1327
LITTELFUSE HK LTD.—See Littelfuse, Inc.; *U.S. Public*, pg. 1327
LITTELFUSE, INC.; *U.S. Public*, pg. 1326
LITTELFUSE ITALY S.R.L.—See Littelfuse, Inc.; *U.S. Public*, pg. 1327
LITTELFUSE JAPAN LLC—See Littelfuse, Inc.; *U.S. Public*, pg. 1327
LITTELFUSE LT, UAB—See Littelfuse, Inc.; *U.S. Public*, pg. 1327
LITTELFUSE MEXICO HOLDING LLC—See Littelfuse, Inc.; *U.S. Public*, pg. 1327
LITTELFUSE S. DE R.L. DE C.V.—See Littelfuse, Inc.; *U.S. Public*, pg. 1327
LITTELFUSE SEMICONDUCTOR (WUXI) COMPANY—See Littelfuse, Inc.; *U.S. Public*, pg. 1327
LITTELFUSE STARTCO—See Littelfuse, Inc.; *U.S. Public*, pg. 1327
LITTELFUSE TRIAD, INC.—See Littelfuse, Inc.; *U.S. Public*, pg. 1327
LITTER INDUSTRIES INC.; *U.S. Private*, pg. 2468
LITTER QUALITY PROPANE COMPANY—See Litter Industries, Inc.; *U.S. Private*, pg. 2468
LITTFIN LUMBER COMPANY; *U.S. Private*, pg. 2468
LITTLE AIRPLANE PRODUCTIONS, INC.—See Studio 100 NV; *Int'l*, pg. 7244
LITTLE AMERICA HOTELS—See HF Sinclair Corporation; *U.S. Public*, pg. 1034
LITTLE BEAR ORGANIC FOODS, INC.—See The Hain Celestial Group, Inc.; *U.S. Public*, pg. 2087
LITTLE BIG CAT, INC.; *U.S. Private*, pg. 2468
LITTLE, BROWN BOOK GROUP LTD.—See Vivendi SE; *Int'l*, pg. 8278
LITTLE, BROWN & COMPANY—See Vivendi SE; *Int'l*, pg. 8273
LITTLE BROWNIE PROPERTIES INC.; *U.S. Private*, pg. 2468
LITTLE BULL—See Armando Testa S.p.A.; *Int'l*, pg. 574
LITTLE CAESAR ENTERPRISES, INC.—See Ilitch Holdings, Inc.; *U.S. Private*, pg. 2041
LITTLE CAESARS ENTERPRISES, INC.—See Ilitch Holdings, Inc.; *U.S. Private*, pg. 2042
THE LITTLE CLINIC LLC—See The Kroger Co.; *U.S. Public*, pg. 2109

LITTLE BROWNIE PROPERTIES INC.   CORPORATE AFFILIATIONS

THE LITTLE CLINIC OF ARIZONA LLC—See The Kroger Co.; *U.S. Public*, pg. 2109
THE LITTLE CLINIC OF COLORADO LLC—See The Kroger Co.; *U.S. Public*, pg. 2109
THE LITTLE CLINIC OF IN LLC—See The Kroger Co.; *U.S. Public*, pg. 2109
THE LITTLE CLINIC OF OHIO LLC—See The Kroger Co.; *U.S. Public*, pg. 2109
THE LITTLE CLINIC OF TENNESSEE LLC—See The Kroger Co.; *U.S. Public*, pg. 2109
LITTLE COMPANY OF MARY HEALTH CARE LIMITED; *Int'l*, pg. 4528
LITTLE & COMPANY; *U.S. Private*, pg. 2468
LITTLE CREATURES BREWING PTY LTD—See Kirin Holdings Company, Limited; *Int'l*, pg. 4189
LITTLE CROW FOODS; *U.S. Private*, pg. 2468
LITTLE DIAMOND RV RESORT—See Equity LifeStyle Properties, Inc.; *U.S. Public*, pg. 790
LITTLE DIVERSIFIED ARCHITECTURAL CONSULTING, INC.; *U.S. Private*, pg. 2468
LITTLE DIX BAY—See Chow Tai Fook Enterprises Limited; *Int'l*, pg. 1585
LITTLE DOG AGENCY INC.; *U.S. Private*, pg. 2468
LITTLE EAGLE COAL COMPANY, LLC—See CONSOL Energy Inc.; *U.S. Public*, pg. 569
LITTLE ENTERPRISES, INC.—See OEP Capital Advisors, L.P.; *U.S. Private*, pg. 2999
LITTLE FALLS ALLOYS, INC.; *U.S. Private*, pg. 2468
LITTLE FAMILY SS INSURANCE CO., LTD.—See MS&AD Insurance Group Holdings, Inc.; *Int'l*, pg. 5066
LITTLEFIELD CORPORATION; *U.S. Public*, pg. 1327
LITTLEFIELD ENTERTAINMENT—See Littlefield Corporation; *U.S. Public*, pg. 1327
LITTLEFIELD FEED YARD—See Friona Industries, LP; *U.S. Private*, pg. 1612
LITTLEFIELD, INC.; *U.S. Private*, pg. 2469
LITTLE FRIENDS, INC.; *U.S. Private*, pg. 2468
LITTLE GENERAL STORE, THE; *U.S. Private*, pg. 2468
LITTLE GIANT FARMERS MARKET CORP.—See Mitchell Grocery Corp.; *U.S. Private*, pg. 2750
LITTLE GREEN PHARMA LTD.; *Int'l*, pg. 4528
THE LITTLE GYM INTERNATIONAL, INC.; *U.S. Private*, pg. 4071
LITTLE HAMPTON BOOK SERVICE LTD—See Vivendi SE; *Int'l*, pg. 8273
LITTLE HARPETH BREWING LLC—See R.S. Lipman Brewing Company, LLC; *U.S. Private*, pg. 3339
LITTLE INNOSCENTS PTY. LTD.—See Wattle Health Australia Limited; *Int'l*, pg. 8359
LITTLEJOHN & CO., LLC; *U.S. Private*, pg. 2469
LITTLEJOHN GRAIN INC.; *U.S. Private*, pg. 2472
LITTLE LADY FOODS, INC.; *U.S. Private*, pg. 2469
LITTLE OCMULGEE ELECTRIC CORPORATION; *U.S. Private*, pg. 2469
THE LITTLE OIL COMPANY, INC.; *U.S. Private*, pg. 4071
LITTLE ORBIT EUROPE LTD.—See Little Orbit LLC; *U.S. Private*, pg. 2469
LITTLE ORBIT LLC; *U.S. Private*, pg. 2469
LITTLE PALM ISLAND ASSOCIATES, LTD.—See Noble House Hotels & Resorts, Ltd.; *U.S. Private*, pg. 2932
LITTLE PROJECTS PTY. LIMITED—See Little Real Estate Pty. Ltd.; *Int'l*, pg. 4528
LITTLE RAPIDS CORPORATION; *U.S. Private*, pg. 2469
LITTLE REAL ESTATE PTY. LTD. - COMMERCIAL DIVISION—See Little Real Estate Pty. Ltd.; *Int'l*, pg. 4528
LITTLE REAL ESTATE PTY. LTD. - RESIDENTIAL DIVISION—See Little Real Estate Pty. Ltd.; *Int'l*, pg. 4528
LITTLE REAL ESTATE PTY. LTD.; *Int'l*, pg. 4528
THE LITTLE RED SCHOOL HOUSE, INC.—See Rainbow Rascals Learning Center, Inc.; *U.S. Private*, pg. 3347
LITTLE RED SERVICES, INC.; *U.S. Private*, pg. 2469
LITTLER MENDELSON P.C.; *U.S. Private*, pg. 2472
LITTLE ROCK DIALYSIS CENTERS, LLC—See DaVita Inc.; *U.S. Public*, pg. 640
LITTLE ROCK HMA, INC.—See Community Health Systems, Inc.; *U.S. Public*, pg. 554
LITTLE ROCK TOOLS INC.—See Jasco Tools Inc.; *U.S. Private*, pg. 2189
LITTLE ROCK WASTE WATER UTILITY; *U.S. Private*, pg. 2469
LITTLE SCHOLARS MONTESSORI LEARNING CENTRE INC.—See Ontario Teachers' Pension Plan; *Int'l*, pg. 5587
LITTLESEA S.R.L.—See Doxee S.p.A; *Int'l*, pg. 2187
LITTLE SHEEP GROUP LIMITED—See Yum China Holdings, Inc.; *U.S. Public*, pg. 2399
LITTLE SIOUX CORN PROCESSORS, L.L.C.; *U.S. Public*, pg. 1327
LITTLESOFT CORPORATION—See Systena Corporation; *Int'l*, pg. 7393
LITTLE SPROUTS LLC—See Evancia SAS; *Int'l*, pg. 2560
LITTLE SWITZERLAND, INC.—See NXP Corp.; *U.S. Private*, pg. 2975
THE LITTLE TIKES COMPANY—See MGA Entertainment, Inc.; *U.S. Private*, pg. 2694
LITTLETON CHEVROLET BUICK OLDS PONTIAC; *U.S. Private*, pg. 2472

LITTLETON COIN CO., INC.; *U.S. Private*, pg. 2472
LITTLETON REGIONAL HEALTHCARE; *U.S. Private*, pg. 2472
THE LITTLE TRAVELER INC.; *U.S. Private*, pg. 4071
LITTLE VALLEY HOMES INC.; *U.S. Private*, pg. 2469
LITTLEWOODS SHOP DIRECT HOME SHOPPING LTD.—See Shop Direct Home Shopping Limited; *Int'l*, pg. 6859
LITU HOLDINGS LIMITED; *Int'l*, pg. 4528
LITURGICAL PUBLICATIONS, INC.; *U.S. Private*, pg. 2472
LITWIN PEL LLC—See Nauvata Engineering Pvt. Ltd; *Int'l*, pg. 5173
LIU CHONG HING GODOWN COMPANY, LIMITED—See Liu Chong Hing Investment Limited; *Int'l*, pg. 4528
LIU CHONG HING INVESTMENT LIMITED; *Int'l*, pg. 4528
LIU CHONG HING PROPERTY MANAGEMENT AND AGENCY LIMITED—See Liu Chong Hing Investment Limited; *Int'l*, pg. 4529
LIUGONG CONSTRUCTION MACHINERY N.A., LLC—See Guangxi Liugong Machinery Co., Ltd.; *Int'l*, pg. 3163
LIUGONG DRESSTA MACHINERY SP. Z O.O.—See Guangxi Liugong Machinery Co., Ltd.; *Int'l*, pg. 3163
LIUGONG INDIA PVT. LTD.—See Guangxi Liugong Machinery Co., Ltd.; *Int'l*, pg. 3163
LIUGONG MACHINERY ASIA PACIFIC PTE. LTD.—See Guangxi Liugong Machinery Co., Ltd.; *Int'l*, pg. 3163
LIUGONG MACHINERY EUROPE B.V—See Guangxi Liugong Machinery Co., Ltd.; *Int'l*, pg. 3163
LIUGONG MACHINERY HONG KONG CO., LTD.—See Guangxi Liugong Machinery Co., Ltd.; *Int'l*, pg. 3163
LIUGONG MACHINERY LATIN AMERICA, LTDA—See Guangxi Liugong Machinery Co., Ltd.; *Int'l*, pg. 3163
LIUGONG MACHINERY MIDDLE EAST FZE—See Guangxi Liugong Machinery Co., Ltd.; *Int'l*, pg. 3163
LIUGONG MACHINERY (POLAND) SP. Z O.O.—See Guangxi Liugong Machinery Co., Ltd.; *Int'l*, pg. 3163
LIUGONG MACHINERY RU, LLC—See Guangxi Liugong Machinery Co., Ltd.; *Int'l*, pg. 3163
LIUGONG MACHINERY SOUTH AFRICA (PTY) LTD—See Guangxi Liugong Machinery Co., Ltd.; *Int'l*, pg. 3163
LIUHUA HOTEL GROUP COMPANY LTD.—See Guangzhou Lingnan Group Holdings Company Limited; *Int'l*, pg. 3166
LIULIGONGFANG HONG KONG CO., LTD.—See Coretronic Corporation; *Int'l*, pg. 1800
LIULIGONGFANG SHANGHAI CO., LTD—See Coretronic Corporation; *Int'l*, pg. 1800
LIULI GONG FANG (U.S.A.), INC.—See Coretronic Corporation; *Int'l*, pg. 1800
LIULI OPTOMA TECHNOLOGY CORP.—See Coretronic Corporation; *Int'l*, pg. 1800
LIUNA MIDWEST REGION; *U.S. Private*, pg. 2472
LIUNA PENSION FUND OF CENTRAL AND EASTERN CANADA; *Int'l*, pg. 4529
LIUPANSHUI MAS TECHNOLOGY CO., LTD.—See Chongqing MAS Sci. & Tech. Co., Ltd.; *Int'l*, pg. 1580
LIUYANG FIREWORKS LIMITED; *Int'l*, pg. 4529
LIUYANG MEIBAOHANG AUTO SALES & SERVICES CO., LTD.—See China MeiDong Auto Holdings Limited; *Int'l*, pg. 1519
LIUZHOU CHEMICAL INDUSTRY CO., LTD.; *Int'l*, pg. 4529
LIUZHOU IRON & STEEL CO. LTD.; *Int'l*, pg. 4529
LIUZHOU LIUGONG FORKLIFT CO., LTD.—See Guangxi Liugong Machinery Co., Ltd.; *Int'l*, pg. 3163
LIUZHOU LMZ CO., LTD.; *Int'l*, pg. 4529
LIUZHOU LONGRUN AUTO PARTS MANUFACTURING CO., LTD.—See Changzhou Tenglong Auto Parts Co., Ltd.; *Int'l*, pg. 1445
LIUZHOU RELIABLE AUTO ANALYSIS TESTING LTD.—See I Squared Capital Advisors (US) LLC; *U.S. Private*, pg. 2023
LIUZHOU RELIABLE AUTO ANALYSIS TESTING LTD.—See TDR Capital LLP; *Int'l*, pg. 7492
LIUZHOU SHUANGFEI AUTO ELECTRIC APPLIANCES MANUFACTURING CO., LTD.—See Shenzhen Deren Electronic Co., Ltd.; *Int'l*, pg. 6808
LIUZHOU TECH MACHINERY CO., LTD.—See Atlas Copco AB; *Int'l*, pg. 683
LIUZHOU UNION ZINC INDUSTRY CO., LTD.—See USP Group Limited; *Int'l*, pg. 8099
LIUZHOU ZF MACHINERY CO., LTD.—See ZF Friedrichshafen AG; *Int'l*, pg. 8642
LIVABLE ASSET MANAGEMENT INC.—See Tokyu Fudosan Holdings Corporation; *Int'l*, pg. 7798
LIVA IMMOBILIEN LEASING GESELLSCHAFT M.B.H.—See UniCredit S.p.A.; *Int'l*, pg. 8037
LIVA INSURANCE COMPANY; *Int'l*, pg. 4529
LIVAL OY; *Int'l*, pg. 4529
LIVANIS PUBLICATIONS SA; *Int'l*, pg. 4529
LIVANOVA AUSTRALIA PTY. LIMITED—See LivaNova PLC; *Int'l*, pg. 4529
LIVANOVA AUSTRIA GMBH—See LivaNova PLC; *Int'l*, pg. 4529
LIVANOVA BELGIUM N.V.—See LivaNova PLC; *Int'l*, pg. 4529

LIVANOVA CANADA CORP.—See LivaNova PLC; *Int'l*, pg. 4529
LIVANOVA CHILE S.P.A.—See LivaNova PLC; *Int'l*, pg. 4529
LIVANOVA (CHINA) MEDICAL TECHNOLOGY CO., LTD.—See LivaNova PLC; *Int'l*, pg. 4529
LIVANOVA DEUTSCHLAND GMBH—See LivaNova PLC; *Int'l*, pg. 4529
LIVANOVA ESPANA, S.L.—See LivaNova PLC; *Int'l*, pg. 4529
LIVANOVA FRANCE SAS—See LivaNova PLC; *Int'l*, pg. 4529
LIVANOVA JAPAN K.K.—See LivaNova PLC; *Int'l*, pg. 4529
LIVANOVA PLC; *Int'l*, pg. 4529
LIVANOVA POLSKA SP. Z O.O.—See LivaNova PLC; *Int'l*, pg. 4529
LIVANOVA PORTUGAL LDA.—See LivaNova PLC; *Int'l*, pg. 4529
LIVANOVA S.A.S.—See LivaNova PLC; *Int'l*, pg. 4530
LIVANOVA SCANDINAVIA AB—See LivaNova PLC; *Int'l*, pg. 4530
LIVANOVA SINGAPORE PTE. LTD.—See LivaNova PLC; *Int'l*, pg. 4530
LIVANOVA SWITZERLAND S.A.—See LivaNova PLC; *Int'l*, pg. 4530
LIVANOVA UK LTD.—See LivaNova PLC; *Int'l*, pg. 4530
LIVANOVA USA, INC—See LivaNova PLC; *Int'l*, pg. 4530
LIVANOVA USA, INC.—See LivaNova PLC; *Int'l*, pg. 4530
LIVARNA TITAN, D.O.O.; *Int'l*, pg. 4530
LIVBAG SAS—See Autoliv, Inc.; *U.S. Public*, pg. 730
LIV CAPITAL ACQUISITION CORP.; *U.S. Public*, pg. 4529
LIVEAREALABS, INC.—See GXO Logistics, Inc.; *U.S. Public*, pg. 975
LIVE AUCTIONEERS, LLC—See Auction Technology Group PLC; *Int'l*, pg. 700
LIVEBLOCK AUCTIONS INTERNATIONAL INC—See OPENLANE, Inc.; *U.S. Public*, pg. 1607
LIVE BOARD, INC.—See Dentsu Group Inc.; *Int'l*, pg. 2039
LIVECHAIN, INC.; *U.S. Private*, pg. 2473
LIVECHAT, INC.—See Text S.A.; *Int'l*, pg. 7584
LIVE COMPANY GROUP PLC; *Int'l*, pg. 4530
LIVE CONSULTING, LLC—See Frontenac Company LLC; *U.S. Private*, pg. 1614
LIVE CURRENT MEDIA INC.; *U.S. Public*, pg. 1327
LIVE DAIKOU, LIMITED—See Relo Group, Inc.; *Int'l*, pg. 6265
LIVEDEVICES LTD—See Robert Bosch GmbH; *Int'l*, pg. 6362
LIVEDRIVE INTERNET LIMITED—See Ziff Davis, Inc.; *U.S. Public*, pg. 2403
LIVEHIRE; *Int'l*, pg. 4530
LIVEINTENT, INC.—See Zeta Global Holdings Corp.; *U.S. Public*, pg. 2403
LIVEIT INVESTMENTS, INC.—See Ayala Corporation; *Int'l*, pg. 774
THE LIVEKINDLY COMPANY, INC.; *U.S. Private*, pg. 4071
LIVE LETTING EXCHANGE LIMITED—See First American Financial Corporation; *U.S. Public*, pg. 838
LIVELINE TECHNOLOGIES INC.—See Cooper-Standard Holdings Inc.; *U.S. Public*, pg. 574
LIVELY GROUP, LLC; *U.S. Private*, pg. 2473
LIVE MARKETING, INC.; *U.S. Private*, pg. 2472
LIVE MEDIA GROUP, LLC; *U.S. Private*, pg. 2473
LIVE MICROSYSTEMS, INC.; *U.S. Public*, pg. 1327
LIVE MOTION GAMES SA; *Int'l*, pg. 4530
LIVE MUSIC PRODUCTION SA—See DEAG Deutsche Entertainment AG; *Int'l*, pg. 1998
LIVE NATION AUSTRALIA PTY LTD—See Live Nation Entertainment, Inc.; *U.S. Public*, pg. 1329
LIVE NATION BALTICS OU—See Live Nation Entertainment, Inc.; *U.S. Public*, pg. 1329
LIVE NATION BEC-TERO ENTERTAINMENT CO., LTD—See Live Nation Entertainment, Inc.; *U.S. Public*, pg. 1329
LIVE NATION BRAND PARTNERSHIP & MEDIA GMBH—See Live Nation Entertainment, Inc.; *U.S. Public*, pg. 1329
LIVE NATION DENMARK APS—See Live Nation Entertainment, Inc.; *U.S. Public*, pg. 1329
LIVE NATION DENMARK MANAGEMENT APS—See Live Nation Entertainment, Inc.; *U.S. Public*, pg. 1329
LIVE NATION ENTERTAINMENT, INC.; *U.S. Public*, pg. 1327
LIVE NATION ENTERTAINMENT, INC. - TIMES SQUARE OFFICE—See Live Nation Entertainment, Inc.; *U.S. Public*, pg. 1329
LIVE NATION ESPANA SAU—See Live Nation Entertainment, Inc.; *U.S. Public*, pg. 1329
LIVE NATION FINLAND OY—See Live Nation Entertainment, Inc.; *U.S. Public*, pg. 1329
LIVE NATION (HK) LIMITED—See Live Nation Entertainment, Inc.; *U.S. Public*, pg. 1329
LIVE NATION ITALIA S.R.L.—See Live Nation Entertainment, Inc.; *U.S. Public*, pg. 1329
LIVE NATION LGTOURS (USA), LLC—See Live Nation Entertainment, Inc.; *U.S. Public*, pg. 1329

COMPANY NAME INDEX — LIXIANG EDUCATION HOLDING CO., LTD.

LIVE NATION LUSHINGTON (HONG KONG) LIMITED—See Live Nation Entertainment, Inc.; *U.S. Public*, pg. 1329
LIVE NATION MERCHANDISE INC.—See Live Nation Entertainment, Inc.; *U.S. Public*, pg. 1329
LIVE NATION MIDDLE EAST FZ-LLC—See Live Nation Entertainment, Inc.; *U.S. Public*, pg. 1329
LIVE NATION - MIDWEST DIVISION—See Live Nation Entertainment, Inc.; *U.S. Public*, pg. 1329
LIVE NATION (MUSIC) UK LIMITED—See Live Nation Entertainment, Inc.; *U.S. Public*, pg. 1329
LIVE NATION NORDIC AB—See Live Nation Entertainment, Inc.; *U.S. Public*, pg. 1329
LIVE NATION NORWAY AS—See Live Nation Entertainment, Inc.; *U.S. Public*, pg. 1330
LIVE NATION - SOUTHERN DIVISION—See Live Nation Entertainment, Inc.; *U.S. Public*, pg. 1329
LIVE NATION SP. Z.O.O.—See Live Nation Entertainment, Inc.; *U.S. Public*, pg. 1330
LIVE NATION SWEDEN AB—See Live Nation Entertainment, Inc.; *U.S. Public*, pg. 1330
LIVE NATION VENUES (NETHERLANDS) BV—See Live Nation Entertainment, Inc.; *U.S. Public*, pg. 1330
LIVENGOOD FEEDS INC.; *U.S. Private*, pg. 2473
LIVENGRIN FOUNDATION; *U.S. Private*, pg. 2473
LIVENT CORPORATION; *U.S. Public*, pg. 1332
LIVENTO GROUP, INC.; *U.S. Public*, pg. 1332
LIVENUP GROUP INC.; *Int'l*, pg. 4530
LIVE OAK BANCSHARES CORPORATION; *U.S. Private*, pg. 2473
LIVE OAK BANCSHARES, INC.; *U.S. Public*, pg. 1331
LIVE OAK BANKING COMPANY—See Live Oak Bancshares, Inc.; *U.S. Public*, pg. 1331
LIVE OAK CRESTVIEW CLIMATE ACQUISITION CORP.; *U.S. Public*, pg. 1331
LIVE OAK GAS CO.—See Suburban Propane Partners, L.P.; *U.S. Public*, pg. 1958
LIVE OAK GOTTESMAN, LLC.; *U.S. Private*, pg. 2473
LIVE OAK HMA, LLC—See Community Health Systems, Inc.; *U.S. Public*, pg. 554
LIVE OAK IMMEDIATE CARE CENTER, LLC—See HCA Healthcare, Inc.; *U.S. Public*, pg. 1001
LIVE OAK MOBILITY ACQUISITION CORP.; *U.S. Public*, pg. 1331
LIVE OAK PEST CONTROL INC.—See Thompson Street Capital Manager LLC; *U.S. Private*, pg. 4161
LIVE OAK PRIVATE WEALTH, LLC—See Live Oak Bancshares, Inc.; *U.S. Public*, pg. 1331
LIVEOFFICE LLC—See Gen Digital Inc.; *U.S. Public*, pg. 910
LIVEONE, INC.; *U.S. Public*, pg. 1332
LIVEOPS, INC.; *U.S. Private*, pg. 2473
LIVE-PA LTD.—See InTechnology Plc; *Int'l*, pg. 3729
LIVEPERSON, INC.; *U.S. Public*, pg. 1332
LIVEPERSON NETHERLANDS B.V.—See LivePerson, Inc.; *U.S. Public*, pg. 1332
LIVEPROCESS CORP.; *U.S. Private*, pg. 2473
LIVERAMP HOLDINGS, INC.; *U.S. Public*, pg. 1333
LIVERAMP, INC.—See LiveRamp Holdings, Inc.; *U.S. Public*, pg. 1333
LIVERAMP UK LTD.—See LiveRamp Holdings, Inc.; *U.S. Public*, pg. 1333
LIVERENT CO., LTD.—See PT Bank JTrust Indonesia Tbk.; *Int'l*, pg. 6026
LIVE REPLY GMBH—See Reply S.p.A.; *Int'l*, pg. 6291
LIVERIGHT PUBLISHING CORP.—See W.W. Norton & Company, Inc.; *U.S. Private*, pg. 4423
LIVERINGA PASTORAL COMPANY—See Milne AgriGroup Pty., Ltd.; *Int'l*, pg. 4897
LIVERMORE AUTO GROUP; *U.S. Private*, pg. 2473
LIVERMORE INVESTMENTS GROUP LTD.; *Int'l*, pg. 4530
LIVERMORE SOFTWARE TECHNOLOGY CORP.—See ANSYS, Inc.; *U.S. Public*, pg. 139
LIVERON INC.—See Vector Inc.; *Int'l*, pg. 8144
LIVERPOOL COIL PROCESSING, INCORPORATED—See Shiloh Industries, Inc.; *U.S. Private*, pg. 3636
LIVERPOOL ENTERPRISES INC.; *U.S. Private*, pg. 2473
LIVERPOOL FOOTBALL CLUB & ATHLETIC GROUNDS LTD.—See Fenway Sports Group Holdings, LLC; *U.S. Private*, pg. 1496
LIVERPOOL OS VETS4PETS LIMITED—See Pets at Home Group Plc; *Int'l*, pg. 5834
LIVERPOOL PARTNERS PTY LTD; *Int'l*, pg. 4530
LIVERPOOL VICTORIA FRIENDLY SOCIETY LIMITED—See Allianz SE; *Int'l*, pg. 353
LIVERPOOL VICTORIA INSURANCE COMPANY LIMITED—See Allianz SE; *Int'l*, pg. 353
LIVERS BRONZE CO., INC.—See Sage Capital LLC; *U.S. Private*, pg. 3526
LIVESCRIBE, INC.—See Anoto Group AB; *Int'l*, pg. 474
LIVESENSE CONNECT INC.—See Livesense Inc.; *Int'l*, pg. 4530
LIVESENSE INC.; *Int'l*, pg. 4530
LIVE SMART @ HOME LIMITED—See Home Group Limited; *Int'l*, pg. 3454
LIVE STAGE SAS—See Metropole Television SA; *Int'l*, pg. 4863
LIVESTOCK FEED LIMITED; *Int'l*, pg. 4530
LIVESTOCK FEEDS PLC; *Int'l*, pg. 4531

LIVESTOCK IMPROVEMENT AUSTRALIA PTY LTD—See Livestock Improvement Corporation Limited; *Int'l*, pg. 4531
LIVESTOCK IMPROVEMENT CORPORATION LIMITED; *Int'l*, pg. 4531
LIVESTOCK IMPROVEMENT CORPORATION (UK) LTD—See Livestock Improvement Corporation Limited; *Int'l*, pg. 4531
LIVESTOCK TRANSPORT & TRADING CO. K.S.C.; *Int'l*, pg. 4531
LIVESTREAM LLC—See Vimeo, Inc.; *U.S. Public*, pg. 2298
LIVESTRONG FOUNDATION; *U.S. Private*, pg. 2473
LIVESTYLE, INC.; *U.S. Private*, pg. 2473
LIVESYSTEMS AG—See Die Schweizerische Post AG; *Int'l*, pg. 2113
LIVETILES CORPORATION—See LiveTiles Limited; *U.S. Private*, pg. 2473
LIVETILES LIMITED; *U.S. Private*, pg. 2473
LIVETOBEHAPPY, INC.; *U.S. Public*, pg. 1333
LIVETRAVEL, INC.—See American International Group, Inc.; *U.S. Public*, pg. 106
LIVETV AIRFONE, LLC—See Gogo Inc.; *U.S. Public*, pg. 949
LIVETV, LLC—See Thales S.A.; *Int'l*, pg. 7606
LIVE VENTURES INCORPORATED; *U.S. Public*, pg. 1332
LIVE VENTURES INCORPORATED—See Live Ventures Incorporated; *U.S. Public*, pg. 1332
LIVE VERDURE LTD.; *Int'l*, pg. 4530
LIVEVOL, LLC—See Cboe Global Markets, Inc.; *U.S. Public*, pg. 459
LIVEVOX COLOMBIA SAS—See NICE Ltd.; *Int'l*, pg. 5265
LIVEVOX HOLDINGS, INC.—See NICE Ltd.; *Int'l*, pg. 5265
LIVEVOX, INC.—See NICE Ltd.; *Int'l*, pg. 5265
LIVEWATCH SECURITY, LLC; *U.S. Private*, pg. 2473
LIVEWELL CLINIC, LLC; *U.S. Private*, pg. 2473
LIVEWELL GIYILEBILIR SAGLIK URUN HIZM. A.S.—See Turkiye Is Bankasi A.S.; *Int'l*, pg. 7976
LIVEWIRE ERGOGENICS INC.; *U.S. Private*, pg. 2473
LIVEWIRE ERGOGENICS INC.; *U.S. Public*, pg. 1333
LIVEWIRE GROUP, INC.; *U.S. Public*, pg. 1333
LIVEWIRE KIOSK, INC.—See REDYREF Interactive Kiosks; *U.S. Private*, pg. 3381
LIVEWIRE, LLC—See Xerox Holdings Corporation; *U.S. Public*, pg. 2388
LIVEWORLD, INC.; *U.S. Public*, pg. 1333
LIVFORSAKRINGSAKTIEBOLAGET SKANDIA; *Int'l*, pg. 4531
LIVHOME, INC.—See Bain Capital, LP; *U.S. Private*, pg. 431
LIVIA CORPORATE DEVELOPMENT SE; *Int'l*, pg. 4532
LIVIDA MOLARIS GRUNDSTUCKS-VERMIETUNGSGESELLSCHAFT MBH & CO.—See Landesbank Baden-Württemberg; *Int'l*, pg. 4405
LIVIN AGAIN INC.—See Organicell Regenerative Medicine, Inc.; *U.S. Public*, pg. 1615
LIVING 3D HOLDINGS, INC.; *Int'l*, pg. 4532
LIVING AND LEISURE AUSTRALIA GROUP—See Merlin Entertainments plc; *Int'l*, pg. 4837
LIVING ARATA CO., LTD.—See Arata Corporation; *Int'l*, pg. 536
LIVING AT HOME SENIOR CARE—See Nova Leap Health Corp.; *Int'l*, pg. 5451
LIVING BREATHING; *U.S. Private*, pg. 2473
LIVINGBRIDGE EP LLP; *Int'l*, pg. 4532
LIVINGBRIDGE VC LLP—See Livingbridge EP LLP; *Int'l*, pg. 4532
LIVING CELL TECHNOLOGIES LIMITED; *Int'l*, pg. 4532
LIVING CELL TECHNOLOGIES NEW ZEALAND LTD.—See Living Cell Technologies Limited; *Int'l*, pg. 4532
LIVING CORPORATION, INC.—See Iida Group Holdings Co., Ltd.; *Int'l*, pg. 3607
LIVING DIRECT, INC.; *U.S. Private*, pg. 2474
LIVING EARTH LIMITED—See Capital Environment Holdings Limited; *Int'l*, pg. 1310
LIVING EARTH; *U.S. Private*, pg. 2474
LIVING JUMBO INDUSTRY SA—See ROMCARBON S.A.; *Int'l*, pg. 6395
LIVING LENS ENTERPRISE LIMITED—See Thoma Bravo, L.P.; *U.S. Private*, pg. 4149
LIVING LIGHTING INC.—See Franchise Bancorp Inc.; *Int'l*, pg. 2760
LIVINGLY MEDIA, INC.—See Axel Springer SE; *Int'l*, pg. 766
LIVING PLUS LIMITED—See City of London Group PLC; *Int'l*, pg. 1627
LIVING PROOF, INC.—See Unilever PLC; *Int'l*, pg. 8047
LIVING PRO-SEED, INC.—See Seino Holdings Co., Ltd.; *Int'l*, pg. 6690
LIVING SALA CO., LTD.—See Sala Corporation; *Int'l*, pg. 6490
LIVING SALINAS EMPREENDIMENTOS IMOBILIARIOS LTDA.—See Cyrela Brazil Realty S.A.; *Int'l*, pg. 1897
LIVINGSOCIAL, LLC—See Groupon, Inc.; *U.S. Public*, pg. 972
LIVINGSOCIAL LTD.—See Groupon Inc.; *U.S. Public*, pg. 972

LIVING SOUNDS HEARING CENTRE LTD.—See Amplifon S.p.A.; *Int'l*, pg. 435
LIVINGSTON CARE ASSOCIATES, INC.—See The Ensign Group, Inc.; *U.S. Public*, pg. 2071
LIVINGSTONE HEALTH HOLDINGS LIMITED; *Int'l*, pg. 4532
LIVINGSTON ELECTRONIC SERVICES GMBH—See Livingston Group Ltd.; *Int'l*, pg. 4532
LIVINGSTON ENTERPRISE—See Yellowstone Communications; *U.S. Private*, pg. 4587
LIVINGSTON GROUP LTD.; *Int'l*, pg. 4532
LIVINGSTON HOSPITAL & HEALTHCARE SERVICES, INC.; *U.S. Private*, pg. 2474
LIVINGSTON INDIA PVT. LTD—See Livingston Group Ltd.; *Int'l*, pg. 4532
LIVINGSTON INSURANCE AGENCY, INC.—See World Insurance Associates LLC; *U.S. Private*, pg. 4566
LIVINGSTON INTERNATIONAL INC.—See Platinum Equity, LLC; *U.S. Private*, pg. 3205
LIVINGSTON INTERNATIONAL, INC.—See Platinum Equity, LLC; *U.S. Private*, pg. 3205
LIVINGSTON MACHINERY CO.; *U.S. Private*, pg. 2474
LIVINGSTON MUTUAL INSURANCE COMPANY—See Lititz Mutual Insurance Company; *U.S. Private*, pg. 2468
LIVINGSTON PIPE AND TUBE INC.; *U.S. Private*, pg. 2474
LIVINGSTON REGIONAL HOSPITAL, LLC—See Apollo Global Management, Inc.; *U.S. Public*, pg. 158
LIVINGSTON'S CONCRETE SERVICE, INC.; *U.S. Private*, pg. 2474
LIVINGSTON SERVICES SAS—See Livingston Group Ltd.; *Int'l*, pg. 4532
LIVINGSTON S.P.A.; *Int'l*, pg. 4532
LIVINGSTON T&M B.V.—See Livingston Group Ltd.; *Int'l*, pg. 4532
LIVINGSTON T&M GMBH—See Livingston Group Ltd.; *Int'l*, pg. 4532
LIVINGSTON UK LTD.—See Livingston Group Ltd.; *Int'l*, pg. 4532
LIVING STREAM MINISTRY; *U.S. Private*, pg. 2474
LIVING TECHNOLOGIES, INC.; *Int'l*, pg. 4532
LIVINGVENTURES, INC.; *U.S. Private*, pg. 2474
LIVING WELL DISABILITY SERVICES; *U.S. Private*, pg. 2474
LIVING WELLNESS PARTNERS LLC; *U.S. Private*, pg. 2474
LIVING WHOLE FOODS, INC.; *U.S. Private*, pg. 2474
LIVIN' LITE CORP.—See Thor Industries, Inc.; *U.S. Public*, pg. 2156
LIVISTO GROUP GMBH—See AGRAVIS Raiffeisen AG; *Int'l*, pg. 215
LIVISTO SP. Z O.O.—See AGRAVIS Raiffeisen AG; *Int'l*, pg. 215
LIVIT AG—See Swiss Life Holding; *Int'l*, pg. 7368
LIVIT FM SERVICES AG—See Swiss Life Holding; *Int'l*, pg. 7368
LIV LABORATORIES CO., LTD.—See Ohki Healthcare Holdings Co., Ltd.; *Int'l*, pg. 5532
LIVNICA AD LJUBIJA; *Int'l*, pg. 4533
LIVNICA A.D.—See Palladio Holding SpA; *Int'l*, pg. 5708
LIVNICA D.D.; *Int'l*, pg. 4533
LIVNICA LJIG A.D.; *Int'l*, pg. 4533
LIVNICA PRECIZNIH ODLIVAKA D.O.O.—See Bet Shemesh Engines Holdings (1997) Ltd.; *Int'l*, pg. 1001
LIVNYNASOS JSC—See HMS Hydraulic Machines & Systems Group plc; *Int'l*, pg. 3432
LIVONGO HEALTH, INC.—See Teladoc Health, Inc.; *U.S. Public*, pg. 1992
LIVONIA, AVON & LAKEVILLE RAILROAD CORP.; *U.S. Private*, pg. 2474
LIVORSI MARINE INC.—See Contran Corporation; *U.S. Private*, pg. 1033
LIVRA EUROPE LTD.—See Ipsos S.A.; *Int'l*, pg. 3802
LIVRETECH CO., LTD.—See TOPPAN Holdings Inc.; *Int'l*, pg. 7817
LIVWELL LTD.—See Xaver Fassin GmbH; *Int'l*, pg. 8520
LIVZON NEW NORTH RIVER PHARMACEUTICAL CO., LTD.—See Livzon Pharmaceutical Group Inc.; *Int'l*, pg. 4533
LIVZON PHARMACEUTICAL GROUP INC.; *Int'l*, pg. 4533
LIVZON SYNTPHARM CO., LTD.—See Livzon Pharmaceutical Group Inc.; *Int'l*, pg. 4533
LIWA ENERGY LIMITED LLC—See Mubadala Investment Company PJSC; *Int'l*, pg. 5076
LIWANLI INNOVATION CO., LTD.; *Int'l*, pg. 4533
LIWE ESPANOLA S.A.; *Int'l*, pg. 4533
LIX DETERGENT JOINT STOCK COMPANY; *Int'l*, pg. 4533
LIXIANG EDUCATION HOLDING CO., LTD.; *Int'l*, pg. 4533
LIXIL (CHINA) INVESTMENT CO., LTD.—See LIXIL Group Corporation; *Int'l*, pg. 4534
LIXIL CORPORATION—See LIXIL Group Corporation; *Int'l*, pg. 4534
LIXIL ENERGY CO., LTD.—See LIXIL Group Corporation; *Int'l*, pg. 4534
LIXIL GLOBAL MANUFACTURING VIETNAM COMPANY LIMITED—See LIXIL Group Corporation; *Int'l*, pg. 4534

LIXIL GROUP CORPORATION

LIXIL GROUP CORPORATION; *Int'l*, pg. 4533
LIXIL HOUSING RESEARCH INSTITUTE, LTD.—See LIXIL Group Corporation; *Int'l*, pg. 4534
LIXIL INFORMATION SYSTEMS CORPORATION—See LIXIL Group Corporation; *Int'l*, pg. 4534
LIXIL REALTY, CORP.—See LIXIL Group Corporation; *Int'l*, pg. 4534
LIXIL SANITARY FITTING MANUFACTURING (SUZHOU) CORP.—See LIXIL Group Corporation; *Int'l*, pg. 4534
LIXIL SUZUKI SHUTTER CORPORATION—See Sanwa Holdings Corporation; *Int'l*, pg. 6560
LIXIL VIVA CORPORATION—See LIXIL Group Corporation; *Int'l*, pg. 4535
LIXOFT SAS—See Simulations Plus, Inc.; *U.S. Public*, pg. 1884
LIXTE BIOTECHNOLOGY HOLDINGS, INC.; *U.S. Public*, pg. 1333
LIXUS INDUSTRIE—See LISI S.A.; *Int'l*, pg. 4524
LIYANG RHODIA RARE EARTH NEW MATERIAL CO., LTD—See Solvay S.A.; *Int'l*, pg. 7078
LIYANG SIFANG STAINLESS STEEL PRODUCTS CO., LTD—See Alfa Laval AB; *Int'l*, pg. 308
LIZARD SKINS, LLC—See Fox Factory Holding Corp.; *U.S. Public*, pg. 877
LIZARD'S THICKET INC.; *U.S. Private*, pg. 2474
LIZARDTECH—See Celartem Technology Inc.; *Int'l*, pg. 1391
LIZ EARLE BEAUTY CO. LIMITED—See Walgreens Boots Alliance, Inc.; *U.S. Public*, pg. 2322
LIZEE SAS; *Int'l*, pg. 4535
LIZHAN ENVIRONMENTAL CORPORATION; *Int'l*, pg. 4535
LIZHONG SITONG LIGHT ALLOYS GROUP CO., LTD.; *Int'l*, pg. 4535
LIZHONG WHEEL GROUP LTD; *Int'l*, pg. 4535
LIZ LANGE—See Bluestar Alliance LLC; *U.S. Private*, pg. 598
LIZTON FINANCIAL CORPORATION; *U.S. Private*, pg. 2474
LIZZY LIFT, INC.—See BigRentz, Inc.; *U.S. Private*, pg. 556
LJA ENGINEERING, INC.; *U.S. Private*, pg. 2474
LJC DEVELOPMENT CORP.—See Loews Corporation; *U.S. Public*, pg. 1340
LJ DISTRIBUTORS INC.; *U.S. Private*, pg. 2474
LJECILISTE SLANA BANJA D.D.; *Int'l*, pg. 4535
LJ ENGINEERING & MANUFACTURING INC.—See NGK Insulators, Ltd.; *Int'l*, pg. 5254
L&J ENTERPRISES INC.; *U.S. Private*, pg. 2362
LJF ASSOCIATES, INC.; *U.S. Private*, pg. 2474
L. & J.G. STICKLEY INC.; *U.S. Private*, pg. 2364
L. J. HUGHES & SONS, INC.; *U.S. Private*, pg. 2364
LJ INTERNATIONAL, INC.; *Int'l*, pg. 4535
LJK COMPANIES INC.—See Corpay, Inc.; *U.S. Public*, pg. 580
L.J. KUSHNER & ASSOCIATES, L.L.C.—See BGSF, Inc.; *U.S. Public*, pg. 330
LJ MINOR—See Nestle S.A.; *Int'l*, pg. 5208
LJ NETWORK HOLDING BV—See CalAmp Corp.; *U.S. Public*, pg. 422
LJP ENTERPRISES, INC.; *U.S. Private*, pg. 2474
L.J. SMITH INC.—See Hardwoods Distribution Inc.; *Int'l*, pg. 3273
LJ STEIN & COMPANY INC.—See GTCR LLC; *U.S. Private*, pg. 1803
L.J. STONE INC.; *U.S. Private*, pg. 2366
L&J TECHNOLOGIES; *U.S. Private*, pg. 2362
L.J. THALMANN COMPANY; *U.S. Private*, pg. 2366
L&J TRANSPORTATION COMPANIES, INC.; *U.S. Private*, pg. 2362
LJUBLJANSKA BORZA, D.D.—See Zagrebacka burza d.d.; *Int'l*, pg. 8619
LJUNGBERG GRUPPEN HOLDING AB—See Atrium Ljungberg AB; *Int'l*, pg. 694
LJUNGBYHED PARK AB—See Peab AB; *Int'l*, pg. 5772
LJUNGBYHEDS GOLFCENTER AB—See Peab AB; *Int'l*, pg. 5772
LJUNGHALL S.R.O.—See Gnutti Carlo S.p.A.; *Int'l*, pg. 3017
LJUSGRUPPEN AKTIEBOLAG—See Koninklijke Philips N.V.; *Int'l*, pg. 4268
LKAB BERG & BETONG AB—See Luossavaara-Kiirunavaara AB; *Int'l*, pg. 4584
LKAB FAR EAST PTE LTD—See Luossavaara-Kiirunavaara AB; *Int'l*, pg. 4584
LKAB FASTIGHETER AB—See Luossavaara-Kiirunavaara AB; *Int'l*, pg. 4584
LKAB HOLDINGS LTD—See Luossavaara-Kiirunavaara AB; *Int'l*, pg. 4584
LKAB KIMIT AB—See Luossavaara-Kiirunavaara AB; *Int'l*, pg. 4585
LKAB MALMTRAFIK AB—See Luossavaara-Kiirunavaara AB; *Int'l*, pg. 4585
LKAB MALMTRAFIKK AS—See Luossavaara-Kiirunavaara AB; *Int'l*, pg. 4585
LKAB MEKANISKA AB—See Luossavaara-Kiirunavaara AB; *Int'l*, pg. 4585
LKAB MINERALS ASIA PACIFIC LTD.—See Luossavaara-Kiirunavaara AB; *Int'l*, pg. 4585
LKAB MINERALS B.V.—See Luossavaara-Kiirunavaara AB; *Int'l*, pg. 4585
LKAB MINERALS FRANCE—See Luossavaara-Kiirunavaara AB; *Int'l*, pg. 4585
LKAB MINERALS GMBH—See Luossavaara-Kiirunavaara AB; *Int'l*, pg. 4585
LKAB MINERALS GREECE—See Luossavaara-Kiirunavaara AB; *Int'l*, pg. 4585
LKAB MINERALS, INC.—See Luossavaara-Kiirunavaara AB; *Int'l*, pg. 4585
LKAB MINERALS LTD.—See Luossavaara-Kiirunavaara AB; *Int'l*, pg. 4585
LKAB MINERALS OY—See Luossavaara-Kiirunavaara AB; *Int'l*, pg. 4585
LKAB MINERALS RICHMOND LTD.—See Luossavaara-Kiirunavaara AB; *Int'l*, pg. 4585
LKAB MINERALS SLOVAK REPUBLIC—See Luossavaara-Kiirunavaara AB; *Int'l*, pg. 4585
LKAB MINERALS SPAIN—See Luossavaara-Kiirunavaara AB; *Int'l*, pg. 4585
LKAB MINERALS (TIANJIN) MINERALS CO. LTD.—See Luossavaara-Kiirunavaara AB; *Int'l*, pg. 4585
LKAB S.A—See Luossavaara-Kiirunavaara AB; *Int'l*, pg. 4585
LKAB SCHWEDENERZ GMBH—See Luossavaara-Kiirunavaara AB; *Int'l*, pg. 4585
LKAB TRADING (SHANGHAI) CO. LTD.—See Luossavaara-Kiirunavaara AB; *Int'l*, pg. 4585
LKAB WASSARA AB—See Luossavaara-Kiirunavaara AB; *Int'l*, pg. 4585
L.K. ADVERTISING AGENCY—See The Linick Group, Inc.; *U.S. Private*, pg. 4070
LKA GOLD, INC.; *U.S. Public*, pg. 1333
LKB EXPERT FONDSLEITUNG AG—See Luzerner Kantonalbank; *Int'l*, pg. 4590
LKB INTERNATIONAL; *Int'l*, pg. 4535
L&K BIOMED CO., LTD.; *Int'l*, pg. 4369
L&K BIOMED CO., LTD. - YONGIN-SI FACTORY—See L&K Biomed Co., Ltd.; *Int'l*, pg. 4369
LKCM HEADWATER INVESTMENTS; *U.S. Private*, pg. 2474
L.K. COMSTOCK & COMPANY, INC.—See Wind Point Advisors LLC; *U.S. Private*, pg. 4535
L. KEELEY CONSTRUCTION CO.—See The Keeley Companies; *U.S. Private*, pg. 4064
LKE HAUSTECHNIK AG—See Burkhalter Holding AG; *Int'l*, pg. 1225
L. KELLENBERGER & CO. AG—See Privet Fund Management, LLC; *U.S. Private*, pg. 3269
L & K ENGINEERING CO., LTD.; *Int'l*, pg. 4369
L & K ENGINEERING (SUZHOU) CO., LTD.—See L & K ENGINEERING CO., LTD.; *Int'l*, pg. 4369
LK ESTATE SERVICES, INC.—See Fairway Lawns, LLC; *U.S. Private*, pg. 1465
LKG ELITE (GUANGZHOU) COMPANY LIMITED—See Lee Kee Holdings Limited; *Int'l*, pg. 4440
LKG ELITE (SHENZHEN) COMPANY LIMITED—See Lee Kee Holdings Limited; *Int'l*, pg. 4440
LKG ELITE (WUXI) COMPANY LIMITED—See Lee Kee Holdings Limited; *Int'l*, pg. 4440
L&K GMBH; *Int'l*, pg. 4369
LKG (SINGAPORE) PRIVATE LIMITED—See Lee Kee Holdings Limited; *Int'l*, pg. 4440
LKH ELECTRIC MIDDLE EAST (FZE)—See Tai Sin Electric Limited; *Int'l*, pg. 7409
LKH KUNSTSTOFFWERK HEILIGENROTH GMBH & CO. KG—See Friedhelm Loh Stiftung & Co. KG; *Int'l*, pg. 2791
LKH LEONI KABELGYAR HUNGARIA KFT.—See LEONI AG; *Int'l*, pg. 4463
LKH PRECICON PTE LTD—See Tai Sin Electric Limited; *Int'l*, pg. 7409
LKH PRECICON PTE. LTD.—See Tai Sin Electric Limited; *Int'l*, pg. 7409
LKH PROJECTS DISTRIBUTION PTE LTD—See Tai Sin Electric Limited; *Int'l*, pg. 7409
LKH PROJECTS DISTRIBUTION PTE. LTD.—See Tai Sin Electric Limited; *Int'l*, pg. 7409
LKH&S LOUISVILLE—See LKH&S; *U.S. Private*, pg. 2475
LKH&S; *U.S. Private*, pg. 2475
L-K INDUSTRIES, INC.—See Dorilton Capital Advisors LLC; *U.S. Private*, pg. 1263
L.K. JAPAN CO., LTD.—See L.K. Technology Holdings Limited; *Int'l*, pg. 4386
LKL ADVANCE METALTECH SDN. BHD.—See LKL International Berhad; *Int'l*, pg. 4535
LKL ASSOCIATES INC.; *U.S. Private*, pg. 2475
LKL INTERNATIONAL BERHAD; *Int'l*, pg. 4535
L.K. MACHINERY CORP.—See L.K. Technology Holdings Limited; *Int'l*, pg. 4386
L.K. MACHINERY, INC.—See L.K. Technology Holdings Limited; *Int'l*, pg. 4386
L.K. MACHINERY INDIA PVT. LTD.—See L.K. Technology Holdings Limited; *Int'l*, pg. 4386
L.K. MACHINERY INTERNATIONAL LIMITED—See L.K. Technology Holdings Limited; *Int'l*, pg. 4386
LK MACHINERY RUS LTD.—See L.K. Technology Holdings Limited; *Int'l*, pg. 4386
LKM PERU S.A.—See Advent International Corporation; *U.S. Private*, pg. 103
L. KNIFE & SON INC.; *U.S. Private*, pg. 2364
L-KONZEPT HOLDING AG; *Int'l*, pg. 4381
L-KONZEPT SACHSEN GMBH—See L-KONZEPT Holding AG; *Int'l*, pg. 4381
LKP FINANCE LIMITED; *Int'l*, pg. 4535
L.K. PRECISION MACHINERY (KUNSHAN) CO., LTD.—See L.K. Technology Holdings Limited; *Int'l*, pg. 4386
LKP SECURITIES LTD.; *Int'l*, pg. 4535
LKP WEALTH ADVISORY LIMITED—See LKP Securities Ltd.; *Int'l*, pg. 4535
LKQ 1ST CHOICE AUTO PARTS, LLC—See LKQ Corporation; *U.S. Public*, pg. 1335
LKQ 250 AUTO, INC.—See LKQ Corporation; *U.S. Public*, pg. 1335
LKQ ALL MODELS CORP.—See LKQ Corporation; *U.S. Public*, pg. 1335
LKQ APEX AUTO PARTS, INC.—See LKQ Corporation; *U.S. Public*, pg. 1335
LKQ ATLANTA, L.P.—See LKQ Corporation; *U.S. Public*, pg. 1335
LKQ AUTO PARTS OF NORTH TEXAS, L.P.—See LKQ Corporation; *U.S. Public*, pg. 1335
LKQ AUTO PARTS OF ORLANDO, LLC—See LKQ Corporation; *U.S. Public*, pg. 1335
LKQ BELGIUM BVBA—See LKQ Corporation; *U.S. Public*, pg. 1335
LKQ BEST AUTOMOTIVE CORP.—See LKQ Corporation; *U.S. Public*, pg. 1335
LKQ CANADA AUTO PARTS INC.—See LKQ Corporation; *U.S. Public*, pg. 1335
LKQ CENTRAL, INC.—See LKQ Corporation; *U.S. Public*, pg. 1335
LKQ COPHER SELF SERVICE AUTO PARTS-BRADENTON INC.—See LKQ Corporation; *U.S. Public*, pg. 1335
LKQ COPHER SELF SERVICE AUTO PARTS-ST. PETERSBURG INC.—See LKQ Corporation; *U.S. Public*, pg. 1335
LKQ CORPORATION; *U.S. Public*, pg. 1333
LKQ CRYSTAL RIVER, INC.—See LKQ Corporation; *U.S. Public*, pg. 1335
LKQ CZ S.R.O.—See LKQ Corporation; *U.S. Public*, pg. 1335
LKQ FOSTER AUTO PARTS, INC.—See LKQ Corporation; *U.S. Public*, pg. 1335
LKQ GORHAM AUTO PARTS CORP.—See LKQ Corporation; *U.S. Public*, pg. 1335
LKQ GREAT LAKES CORP.—See LKQ Corporation; *U.S. Public*, pg. 1335
LKQ HEAVY TRUCK-TEXAS BEST DIESEL, L.P.—See LKQ Corporation; *U.S. Public*, pg. 1335
LKQ HUNTS POINT AUTO PARTS CORP.—See LKQ Corporation; *U.S. Public*, pg. 1335
LKQ LAKENOR AUTO & TRUCK SALVAGE, INC.—See LKQ Corporation; *U.S. Public*, pg. 1335
LKQ METRO, INC.—See LKQ Corporation; *U.S. Public*, pg. 1335
LKQ MIDWEST, INC.—See LKQ Corporation; *U.S. Public*, pg. 1335
LKQ OF MICHIGAN, INC.—See LKQ Corporation; *U.S. Public*, pg. 1335
LKQ OF NEVADA, INC.—See LKQ Corporation; *U.S. Public*, pg. 1335
LKQ OF TENNESSEE, INC.—See LKQ Corporation; *U.S. Public*, pg. 1335
LKQ ONLINE CORP.—See LKQ Corporation; *U.S. Public*, pg. 1335
LKQ PENN-MAR, INC.—See LKQ Corporation; *U.S. Public*, pg. 1335
LKQ PLUNKS TRUCK PARTS & EQUIPMENT-JACKSON, INC.—See LKQ Corporation; *U.S. Public*, pg. 1335
LKQ PRECIOUS METALS, INC.—See LKQ Corporation; *U.S. Public*, pg. 1335
LKQ RALEIGH AUTO PARTS CORP.—See LKQ Corporation; *U.S. Public*, pg. 1335
LKQ SELF SERVICE AUTO PARTS-HOLLAND, INC.—See LKQ Corporation; *U.S. Public*, pg. 1335
LKQ SELF SERVICE AUTO PARTS-KALAMAZOO, INC.—See LKQ Corporation; *U.S. Public*, pg. 1335
LKQ SELF SERVICE AUTO PARTS-MEMPHIS LLC—See LKQ Corporation; *U.S. Public*, pg. 1335
LKQ SELF SERVICE AUTO PARTS-TULSA, INC.—See LKQ Corporation; *U.S. Public*, pg. 1335
LKQ SK S.R.O.—See LKQ Corporation; *U.S. Public*, pg. 1335
LKQ SMART PARTS, INC.—See LKQ Corporation; *U.S. Public*, pg. 1335
LKQ SOUTHWICK LLC—See LKQ Corporation; *U.S. Public*, pg. 1335
LKQ TRIPLETT ASAP, INC.—See LKQ Corporation; *U.S. Public*, pg. 1335
LKQ U-PULL-IT AUTO DAMASCUS, INC.—See LKQ Corporation; *U.S. Public*, pg. 1335
LKS CA CARIBE S.A.—See Mondragon Corporation; *Int'l*, pg. 5030

COMPANY NAME INDEX

LKS COLOMBIA—See Mondragon Corporation; *Int'l*, pg. 5030
LKS CORP, S.A.—See Mondragon Corporation; *Int'l*, pg. 5030
LKS IAMM S.L.—See Mondragon Corporation; *Int'l*, pg. 5030
LKS INDIA PVT. LTD.—See Mondragon Corporation; *Int'l*, pg. 5030
LKS INGENIERIA S. COOP.—See Mondragon Corporation; *Int'l*, pg. 5031
LKS OUTSOURCING, S.COOP.—See Mondragon Corporation; *Int'l*, pg. 5031
LKS PERU—See Mondragon Corporation; *Int'l*, pg. 5031
LKS S. COOP.—See Mondragon Corporation; *Int'l*, pg. 5030
LKS SELECCION Y FORMACION S.L.—See Mondragon Corporation; *Int'l*, pg. 5031
LKS TASACIONES S.A.—See Mondragon Corporation; *Int'l*, pg. 5031
LKS TRANSPORTATION, LLC—See Installed Building Products, Inc.; *U.S. Public*, pg. 1133
LK SYSTEMS, INC.—See L.K. Technology Holdings Limited; *Int'l*, pg. 4386
L.K. TECHNOLOGY HOLDINGS LIMITED; *Int'l*, pg. 4386
LK TECHNOLOGY IMPORTACAO E EXPORTACAO LTDA—See Gadsden Properties, Inc.; *U.S. Public*, pg. 894
L.K. TECH (TIANJIN) CO. LTD.—See L.K. Technology Holdings Limited; *Int'l*, pg. 4386
LKT HOLDINGS PTY LTD—See Lee Kim Tah Holdings Ltd.; *Int'l*, pg. 4440
L & K TRADING CO., LTD.—See Japan Logistic Systems Corp.; *Int'l*, pg. 3899
LLADRO USA INC.—See Weil Ceramics & Glass Inc.; *U.S. Private*, pg. 4471
LLAMASOFT INC.—See Thoma Bravo, L.P.; *U.S. Private*, pg. 4147
LLANELLI SAND DREDGING LTD.—See HAL Trust N.V.; *Int'l*, pg. 3225
LLANO DIALYSIS, LLC—See DaVita Inc.; *U.S. Public*, pg. 640
LLANO UTILITY SERVICES INC.; *U.S. Private*, pg. 2475
LLB ASSET MANAGEMENT AG—See Liechtensteinische Landesbank AG; *Int'l*, pg. 4491
L.L. BEAN, INC.; *U.S. Private*, pg. 2366
LLB FONDSLEITUNG AG—See Liechtensteinische Landesbank AG; *Int'l*, pg. 4491
LLB FUND SERVICES AG—See Liechtensteinische Landesbank AG; *Int'l*, pg. 4491
LLB HOLDING (SCHWEIZ) AG—See Liechtensteinische Landesbank AG; *Int'l*, pg. 4491
LLB INVEST AGMVK—See Liechtensteinische Landesbank AG; *Int'l*, pg. 4491
LLB INVESTMENT PARTNERS AG—See Liechtensteinische Landesbank AG; *Int'l*, pg. 4492
LLB LINTH HOLDING AG—See Liechtensteinische Landesbank AG; *Int'l*, pg. 4492
LLB SWISS INVESTMENT AG—See Liechtensteinische Landesbank AG; *Int'l*, pg. 4492
LLB TREUHAND AG—See Liechtensteinische Landesbank AG; *Int'l*, pg. 4492
LL BUILDING PRODUCTS, INC.—See GAF Materials Corporation; *U.S. Private*, pg. 1633
LLC ABZAKOVO—See OJSC Magnitogorsk Iron & Steel Works; *Int'l*, pg. 5539
LLC ADIDAS, LTD.—See adidas AG; *Int'l*, pg. 146
LLC AGORA UKRAINE—See Agora S.A.; *Int'l*, pg. 212
LLC AGROTECHNOLOGY—See Gruppa Kompaniy Rusagro OOO; *Int'l*, pg. 3140
LLC ALLIANCE OIL COMPANY MC—See Alliance Oil Company Ltd.; *Int'l*, pg. 340
LLC A&M ELECTROINSTRUMENTI—See Techtronic Industries Co., Ltd.; *Int'l*, pg. 7512
LLC ANDREX—See Public Joint Stock Company Acron; *Int'l*, pg. 6094
LLC ANDRITZ HYDRO—See ANDRITZ AG; *Int'l*, pg. 456
LLC AQUAPARK—See OJSC Magnitogorsk Iron & Steel Works; *Int'l*, pg. 5540
LLC ASH RUS.—See Aebi Schmidt Holding AG; *Int'l*, pg. 170
LLC ASTROINVEST-ENERGY—See Cadogan Energy Solutions plc; *Int'l*, pg. 1248
LLC ATLAS COPCO UKRAINE—See Atlas Copco AB; *Int'l*, pg. 683
LLC AUDATEX UKRAINE—See Vista Equity Partners, LLC; *U.S. Private*, pg. 4400
LLC BAHMACHREGIONPOSTACH—See Milkiland N.V.; *Int'l*, pg. 4895
LLC BASHKIR GENERATION COMPANY—See JSC INTER RAO UES; *Int'l*, pg. 4009
LLC BELDEN RUS—See Belden, Inc.; *U.S. Public*, pg. 294
LLC BELYE NOCHI—See RussNeft PJSC; *Int'l*, pg. 6432
LLC BEREZKI—See OJSC Magnitogorsk Iron & Steel Works; *Int'l*, pg. 5540
LLC BOEHRINGER INGELHEIM—See C.H. Boehringer Sohn AG & Co. KG; *Int'l*, pg. 1242
LLC BONAVA SAINT-PETERSBURG—See Bonava AB; *Int'l*, pg. 1105

LLC BUSKUL—See OJSC Magnitogorsk Iron & Steel Works; *Int'l*, pg. 5540
LLC CAMOZZI—See Camozzi Group; *Int'l*, pg. 1274
LLC CAPSUGEL—See Lonza Group AG; *Int'l*, pg. 4553
LLC CHERMETINVEST—See OJSC Magnitogorsk Iron & Steel Works; *Int'l*, pg. 5540
LLC CHUBB INSURANCE COMPANY—See Chubb Limited; *Int'l*, pg. 1592
LLC COCA-COLA HBC EURASIA—See Coca-Cola HBC AG; *Int'l*, pg. 1686
LLC CREDIT SUISSE SECURITIES—See UBS Group AG; *Int'l*, pg. 8007
LLC DENTSPLY IH—See DENTSPLY SIRONA Inc.; *U.S. Public*, pg. 655
LLC DENTSPLY RUSSIA—See DENTSPLY SIRONA Inc.; *U.S. Public*, pg. 655
LLC DFDS—See DFDS A/S; *Int'l*, pg. 2095
LLC DHL EXPRESS—See Deutsche Post AG; *Int'l*, pg. 2078
LLC DHL INTERNATIONAL KAZAKHSTAN—See Deutsche Post AG; *Int'l*, pg. 2078
LLC E D & F MAN—See ED&F Man Holdings Limited; *Int'l*, pg. 2303
LLC ELDORADO—See Safmar Industrial & Financial Group; *Int'l*, pg. 6472
LLC ESE SOUTH AMERICA S.R.L.—See Berry Global Group, Inc; *U.S. Public*, pg. 322
LLC EUROPAPIER—See Heinzel Holding GmbH; *Int'l*, pg. 3325
LLC EUROPE HOTEL—See LVMH Moet Hennessy Louis Vuitton SE; *Int'l*, pg. 4591
LLC EXTERRAN VOSTOK—See Enerflex Ltd.; *Int'l*, pg. 2419
LLC FABER-CASTELL ANADOLU—See Faber-Castell AG; *Int'l*, pg. 2599
LLC FURUKAWA UNIC RUS—See Furukawa Co., Ltd.; *Int'l*, pg. 2847
LLC GAZNEFTESERVICE—See Volga Gas plc; *Int'l*, pg. 8302
LLC GC ZEMIK—See Zhonghang Electronic Measuring Instruments Co., Ltd.; *Int'l*, pg. 8673
LLC GENUS ABS RUS—See Genus Plc; *Int'l*, pg. 2930
LLC GEOPHYZSERVIS—See Integra Management LLC; *Int'l*, pg. 3730
LLC GERMAN CENTRE FOR INDUSTRY AND TRADE—See Landesbank Baden-Wurttemberg; *Int'l*, pg. 4405
LLC GLASTON—See Glaston Oyj Abp; *Int'l*, pg. 2989
LLC GLC METALLURG-MAGNITOGORSK—See OJSC Magnitogorsk Iron & Steel Works; *Int'l*, pg. 5540
LLC GLOBAL-FLOT—See OJSC Globalstroy-Engineering; *Int'l*, pg. 5539
LLC GLOBAL-NEFTEGAZSTROY—See OJSC Globalstroy-Engineering; *Int'l*, pg. 5539
LLC GSE GIPROKAUCHUK—See OJSC Globalstroy-Engineering; *Int'l*, pg. 5539
LLC GSE-NEFTECHIM-MONTAZH—See OJSC Globalstroy-Engineering; *Int'l*, pg. 5539
LLC GSE-PERMNEFTE-GAZSTROY—See OJSC Globalstroy-Engineering; *Int'l*, pg. 5539
LLC GSE-SNEMA—See OJSC Globalstroy-Engineering; *Int'l*, pg. 5539
LLC GSE SURGUTNEFTE-CHIMMONTAZH—See OJSC Globalstroy-Engineering; *Int'l*, pg. 5539
LLC GSE VOLGOGRAD FIRM NZM—See OJSC Globalstroy-Engineering; *Int'l*, pg. 5539
LLC GSE-VOLGONEFTE-GAZSTROY—See OJSC Globalstroy-Engineering; *Int'l*, pg. 5539
LLC GSE YUG-STROY—See OJSC Globalstroy-Engineering; *Int'l*, pg. 5539
LLC HANS H. MEYER OOO—See Hyster-Yale Materials Handling, Inc.; *U.S. Public*, pg. 1080
LLC HEIDELBERGCEMENT RUS—See Heidelberg Materials AG; *Int'l*, pg. 3318
L.L.C. HEURTEY PETROCHEM RUS—See Heurtey Petrochem SA; *Int'l*, pg. 3366
LLC HIKVISION TASHKENT—See Hangzhou Hikvision Digital Technology Co., Ltd.; *Int'l*, pg. 3248
LLC IK MMK-FINANCE—See OJSC Magnitogorsk Iron & Steel Works; *Int'l*, pg. 5540
LLC IMC MONTAN—See TUV NORD AG; *Int'l*, pg. 7980
LLC INDUSTRIAL COMPANY GAZVYDOBUVANNYA—See Cadogan Energy Solutions plc; *Int'l*, pg. 1248
LLC INNOVATIVE MEASURING TECHNOLOGIES MOSCOW—See VMT GmbH; *Int'l*, pg. 8283
LLC INTEGRA-DRILLING—See Integra Management LLC; *Int'l*, pg. 3730
LLC IT-PARK UNIVERSITY—See EPAM Systems, Inc.; *U.S. Public*, pg. 783
LLC IZDATELSTVO PANINI RUS—See Panini S.p.A.; *Int'l*, pg. 5727
LLC JVCKENWOOD RUS—See JVCKENWOOD Corporation; *Int'l*, pg. 4034
LLC JV O'ZAUTO-AUSTEM—See Austem Co., Ltd.; *Int'l*, pg. 717
LLC KALININGRADCEMENT—See Heidelberg Materials AG; *Int'l*, pg. 3318
LLC KARPATYGAZ—See Misen Energy AB; *Int'l*, pg. 4920

LLC KATERYNOPILSKY ELEVATOR—See OJSC Myronivsky Hliboprodukt; *Int'l*, pg. 5540
LLC KELLY SERVICES IT SOLUTIONS—See Kelly Services, Inc.; *U.S. Public*, pg. 1219
LLC KIA RUSSIA—See Kia Corporation; *Int'l*, pg. 4157
LLC KRKA KAZAKHSTAN—See Krka, d.d., Novo Mesto; *Int'l*, pg. 4303
LLC KYB EURASIA—See KYB Corporation; *Int'l*, pg. 4354
LLC LEIPURIN—See Aspo Oyj; *Int'l*, pg. 631
LLC LEKSTAR COMMUNICATION—See PJSC Rostelecom; *Int'l*, pg. 5884
LLC LENOVO (EAST EUROPE / ASIA)—See Lenovo Group Limited; *Int'l*, pg. 4453
LLC LMT TOOLS—See LMT GmbH & Co. KG; *Int'l*, pg. 4538
LLC LUKOIL-EKOENERGO—See PJSC Lukoil; *Int'l*, pg. 5881
LLC LUKOIL-ENERGOSETI—See PJSC Lukoil; *Int'l*, pg. 5881
LLC LUKOIL EPU SERVICE—See PJSC Lukoil; *Int'l*, pg. 5881
LLC LUKOIL-GEORGIA—See PJSC Lukoil; *Int'l*, pg. 5881
LLC LUKOIL-KGPZ—See PJSC Lukoil; *Int'l*, pg. 5881
LLC LUKOIL-KMN—See PJSC Lukoil; *Int'l*, pg. 5881
LLC LUKOIL-KOMI—See PJSC Lukoil; *Int'l*, pg. 5881
LLC LUKOIL-KUBANENERGO—See PJSC Lukoil; *Int'l*, pg. 5881
LLC LUKOIL-NIZHEGORODNEFTEORGSINTEZ—See PJSC Lukoil; *Int'l*, pg. 5881
LLC LUKOIL-NIZHEGORODNIINEFTEPROEKT—See PJSC Lukoil; *Int'l*, pg. 5881
LLC LUKOIL-ROSTOVENERGO—See PJSC Lukoil; *Int'l*, pg. 5881
LLC LUKOIL-SEVERO-ZAPADNEFTEPRODUKT—See PJSC Lukoil; *Int'l*, pg. 5881
LLC LUKOIL-WEST SIBERIA—See PJSC Lukoil; *Int'l*, pg. 5881
LLC LUKOIL-YUGNEFTEPRODUKT—See PJSC Lukoil; *Int'l*, pg. 5881
LLC MAGSTORN—See OJSC Magnitogorsk Iron & Steel Works; *Int'l*, pg. 5540
LLC MARCEGAGLIA RU—See Marcegaglia S.p.A.; *Int'l*, pg. 4689
LLC MEKHANOREMONTNY KOMPLEX—See OJSC Magnitogorsk Iron & Steel Works; *Int'l*, pg. 5540
LLC MESSER EUTECTIC CASTOLIN—See MEC Holding GmbH; *Int'l*, pg. 4764
LLC METADYNEA—See Metafrax OJSC; *Int'l*, pg. 4844
LLC MILKILAND-KAZAKHSTAN—See Milkiland N.V.; *Int'l*, pg. 4895
LLC MILKILAND RU—See Milkiland N.V.; *Int'l*, pg. 4895
LLC MILKILAND UKRAINE—See Milkiland N.V.; *Int'l*, pg. 4895
LLC MMK-INFORMSERVICE—See OJSC Magnitogorsk Iron & Steel Works; *Int'l*, pg. 5540
LLC MMK-VTORMET—See OJSC Magnitogorsk Iron & Steel Works; *Int'l*, pg. 5540
LLC MONDI ARAMIL—See Mondi plc; *Int'l*, pg. 5026
LLC MONDI PERESLAVL—See Mondi plc; *Int'l*, pg. 5026
LLC MOTHER & CHILD SAINT-PETERSBURG—See MD Medical Group Investments Plc; *Int'l*, pg. 4761
LLC MPP SALSKY—See PJSC Cherkizovo Group; *Int'l*, pg. 5878
LLC MULTIPURPOSE RELOADING COMPLEX—See Universal Cargo Logistics Holding B.V.; *Int'l*, pg. 8077
LLC NCC-ALABUGA—See Aksa Akrilik Kimya Sanayii A.S.; *Int'l*, pg. 264
LLC NEFTEBYTSERVIS—See RussNeft PJSC; *Int'l*, pg. 6432
LLC NESTE SAINT-PETERSBURG—See Neste Oyj; *Int'l*, pg. 5201
LLC NESTLE UKRAINE—See Nestle S.A.; *Int'l*, pg. 5203
LLC NK RUSSNEFT-BRYANSK—See RussNeft PJSC; *Int'l*, pg. 6432
LLC NLMK-KALUGA—See Novolipetski Metallurgicheski Komb OAO; *Int'l*, pg. 5466
LLC NLMK LONG PRODUCTS—See Novolipetski Metallurgicheski Komb OAO; *Int'l*, pg. 5466
LLC NLMK-METALWARE—See Novolipetski Metallurgicheski Komb OAO; *Int'l*, pg. 5466
LLC NORILSKGEOLOGIYA—See PJSC MMC Norilsk Nickel; *Int'l*, pg. 5882
LLC NOVOSIBIRSK FUEL CORPORATION—See OAO Kuzbasskaya Toplivnaya Company OJSC; *Int'l*, pg. 5506
LLC OBARA RUS—See Obara Group Incorporated; *Int'l*, pg. 5508
LLC OBNEFTEREMONT—See Integra Management LLC; *Int'l*, pg. 3730
LLC OGNEUPOR—See OJSC Magnitogorsk Iron & Steel Works; *Int'l*, pg. 5540
THE L&L COMPANY-BALTIMORE/DELAWARE DIVISION—See The L&L Company; *U.S. Private*, pg. 4066
THE L&L COMPANY-CENTRAL VIRGINIA—See The L&L Company; *U.S. Private*, pg. 4066
THE L&L COMPANY-CERAMIC DIVISION—See The L&L Company; *U.S. Private*, pg. 4066

L.L. BEAN, INC.

CORPORATE AFFILIATIONS

THE L&L COMPANY-CHARLOTTE DIVISION—See The L&L Company; *U.S. Private*, pg. 4066
THE L&L COMPANY-FRANKLIN DIVISION—See The L&L Company; *U.S. Private*, pg. 4066
THE L&L COMPANY-FREDERICK—See The L&L Company; *U.S. Private*, pg. 4066
THE L&L COMPANY-GREENVILLE DIVISION—See The L&L Company; *U.S. Private*, pg. 4066
THE L&L COMPANY-OWINGS MILLS—See The L&L Company; *U.S. Private*, pg. 4066
THE L&L COMPANY - PITTSBURGH DIVISION—See The L&L Company; *U.S. Private*, pg. 4066
THE L&L COMPANY-POINTER RIDGE & BLINDS DIVISIONS—See The L&L Company; *U.S. Private*, pg. 4066
THE L&L COMPANY-RICHMOND—See The L&L Company; *U.S. Private*, pg. 4066
THE L&L COMPANY-SALISBURY DIVISION—See The L&L Company; *U.S. Private*, pg. 4066
THE L&L COMPANY; *U.S. Private*, pg. 4066
THE L&L COMPANY - TIMONIUM DIVISION—See The L&L Company; *U.S. Private*, pg. 4066
LLC PAKRUT—See China Nonferrous Gold Limited; *Int'l*, pg. 1535
LLC PETRORESURS—See Lundin Group of Companies; *Int'l*, pg. 4583
LLC PIK-COMFORT—See OAO Group of Companies PIK; *Int'l*, pg. 5506
LLC POYRY - MANAGEMENT CONSULTING—See Ramboll Gruppen A/S; *Int'l*, pg. 6197
LLC POYRY—See Ramboll Gruppen A/S; *Int'l*, pg. 6197
LLC PRIMORSK TRADE PORT—See PJSC Novorossiysk Commercial Sea Port; *Int'l*, pg. 5883
LLC PROFIT-CENTER—See OJSC Magnitogorsk Iron & Steel Works; *Int'l*, pg. 5540
LLC PROMETEY—See PJSC Rostelecom; *Int'l*, pg. 5884
LLC PROSTOFINANCE—See Societe Generale S.A.; *Int'l*, pg. 7040
LLC "ETALON-INVEST"—See Etalon Group Plc; *Int'l*, pg. 2520
LLC "MARY KAY (MOLDOVA) LIMITED"—See Mary Kay Holding Corporation; *U.S. Private*, pg. 2599
LLC "VEB-CAPITAL"—See VEB.RF; *Int'l*, pg. 8143
LLC "VEB ENGINEERING"—See VEB.RF; *Int'l*, pg. 8143
LLC REAL ESTATE INVESTMENT MANAGEMENT—See Immofinanz AG; *Int'l*, pg. 3628
LLC REGION—See OJSC Magnitogorsk Iron & Steel Works; *Int'l*, pg. 5540
LLC ROCKWOOL NORTH—See ROCKWOOL A/S; *Int'l*, pg. 6380
LLC ROCKWOOL—See ROCKWOOL A/S; *Int'l*, pg. 6380
LLC ROCKWOOL UKRAINE—See ROCKWOOL A/S; *Int'l*, pg. 6380
LLC RPC BRAMLAGE YEKATERINBURG—See Berry Global Group, Inc; *U.S. Public*, pg. 324
LLC RUSSIAN DAIRY COMPANY—See Temasek Holdings (Private) Limited; *Int'l*, pg. 7549
LLC RUSSIAN QUARTZ—See Sumitomo Corporation; *Int'l*, pg. 7269
LLC RUUKKI UKRAINE—See SSAB AB; *Int'l*, pg. 7153
LLC SAARE FARMER—See Agromino A/S; *Int'l*, pg. 220
LLC SANATORII METALLURG—See OJSC Magnitogorsk Iron & Steel Works; *Int'l*, pg. 5540
LLC SANATORII YBILEYNY—See OJSC Magnitogorsk Iron & Steel Works; *Int'l*, pg. 5540
LLC SANDVIK MINING AND CONSTRUCTION REGION CIS—See Sandvik AB; *Int'l*, pg. 6531
LLC SANDVIK - SANDVIK COROMANT DIVISION—See Sandvik AB; *Int'l*, pg. 6529
LLC SANDVIK—See Sandvik AB; *Int'l*, pg. 6529
LLC SAP LABS—See SAP SE; *Int'l*, pg. 6566
LLC SARTORIUS STEDIM—See Sartorius AG; *Int'l*, pg. 6579
LLC SCARTEL—See PJSC Megafon; *Int'l*, pg. 5882
LLC SDL RUS—See RWS Holdings plc; *Int'l*, pg. 6437
LLC SDL UKRAINE—See RWS Holdings plc; *Int'l*, pg. 6437
LLC SHAKHTA CHERTINSKAYA-YUZHNAYA—See OJSC Magnitogorsk Iron & Steel Works; *Int'l*, pg. 5540
LLC SHLAKSERVIS—See OJSC Magnitogorsk Iron & Steel Works; *Int'l*, pg. 5540
LLC SIKA UKRAINA—See Sika AG; *Int'l*, pg. 6915
LLC SKY MOBILE—See VEON Ltd.; *Int'l*, pg. 8164
LLC SMITH DRILLING SERVICES—See Integra Management LLC; *Int'l*, pg. 3730
LLC SOLAR SECURITY—See PJSC Rostelecom; *Int'l*, pg. 5884
LLC SUTK—See OJSC Magnitogorsk Iron & Steel Works; *Int'l*, pg. 5540
LLC TALIS—See Triton Advisers Limited; *Int'l*, pg. 7934
LLC TAMBOVMYASOPROM—See PJSC Cherkizovo Group; *Int'l*, pg. 5878
LLC TAMOZHENNY BROKER—See OJSC Magnitogorsk Iron & Steel Works; *Int'l*, pg. 5540
LLC TAVRIYSKY PLANT—See OJSC Myronivsky Hliboproduct; *Int'l*, pg. 5540
LLC TECHNOCOM—See Nestle SA; *Int'l*, pg. 5203
LLC TELKO CENTRAL ASIA—See Aspo Oyj; *Int'l*, pg. 631
LLC TELKO—See Aspo Oyj; *Int'l*, pg. 631

LLC TFC OF OJSC MMK—See OJSC Magnitogorsk Iron & Steel Works; *Int'l*, pg. 5540
LLC TNS-RU—See OJSC Globalstroy-Engineering; *Int'l*, pg. 5539
LLC TOMSKAYA NEFT—See RussNeft PJSC; *Int'l*, pg. 6432
LLC TORGOVY DOM MMK—See OJSC Magnitogorsk Iron & Steel Works; *Int'l*, pg. 5540
LLC TORGOVY DOM MMK URAL—See OJSC Magnitogorsk Iron & Steel Works; *Int'l*, pg. 5540
LLC TRANSIT—See Petropavlovsk PLC; *Int'l*, pg. 5832
LLC TZK-ARKHANGELSK—See PJSC Lukoil; *Int'l*, pg. 5881
LLC UKRAINIAN INTERMODAL COMPANY—See Hamburger Hafen und Logistik AG; *Int'l*, pg. 3236
LLC URALKONTRAKT—See OJSC Magnitogorsk Iron & Steel Works; *Int'l*, pg. 5540
LLC UROZHAYNA KRAINA—See OJSC Myronivsky Hliboproduct; *Int'l*, pg. 5540
LLC VATECH CORP.—See Vatech Co., Ltd.; *Int'l*, pg. 8135
LLC VIZ-STEEL—See Novolipetski Metallurgicheski Komb OAO; *Int'l*, pg. 5466
LLC VNIIBT-BUROVOY INSTRUMENT—See Integra Management LLC; *Int'l*, pg. 3730
LLC VTORCHERMET NLMK—See Novolipetski Metallurgicheski Komb OAO; *Int'l*, pg. 5466
LLC WACKER CHEMIE RUS—See Wacker Chemie AG; *Int'l*, pg. 8323
LLC WILLIAMS LEA—See Deutsche Post AG; *Int'l*, pg. 2081
LLC WINCOR NIXDORF—See Diebold Nixdorf, Inc.; *U.S. Public*, pg. 661
LLC YIT SERVICE—See YIT Corporation; *Int'l*, pg. 8586
LLC ZHERDEVSKY ELEVATOR—See Gruppa Kompaniy Rusagro OOO; *Int'l*, pg. 3140
LLEIDA CHILE SPA—See Lleidanetworks Serveis Telematics SA; *Int'l*, pg. 4535
LLEIDANETWORKS SERVEIS TELEMATICS SA; *Int'l*, pg. 4535
L & L ENERGY, INC.; *U.S. Private*, pg. 2361
LLET NOSTRA ALIMENTARIA S.L.—See Emmi AG; *Int'l*, pg. 2385
LLEWELLYN WORLDWIDE LIMITED; *U.S. Private*, pg. 2475
LLFLEX, LLC; *U.S. Private*, pg. 2475
LL FLOORING HOLDINGS, INC.; *U.S. Public*, pg. 1337
LLI MANAGEMENT COMPANY, LLC; *U.S. Private*, pg. 2475
LLJ INC.; *U.S. Private*, pg. 2475
LLL SALES CO LLC—See Lithia Motors, Inc.; *U.S. Public*, pg. 1323
LLL TRANSPORT, INC.—See Great Range Capital, LLC; *U.S. Private*, pg. 1767
LL LUCKY GAMES AB; *Int'l*, pg. 4535
L&L MANUFACTURING CO.; *U.S. Private*, pg. 2363
LLM APPLIANCES LIMITED—See Crompton Greaves Consumer Electricals Limited; *Int'l*, pg. 1853
L&L NURSERY SUPPLY, INC.; *U.S. Private*, pg. 2363
LLOG EXPLORATION OFFSHORE, INC.; *U.S. Private*, pg. 2475
L.LOGISTICS INC.—See LOOK INCORPORATED; *Int'l*, pg. 4554
LLORENTE & CUENCA MADRID, S.L.; *Int'l*, pg. 4535
LLOYD ADRIATICO S.P.A.—See Allianz SE; *Int'l*, pg. 354
LLOYD AEREO BOLIVIANO S.A.; *Int'l*, pg. 4535
LLOYD BEDFORD COX, INC.—See Arthur J. Gallagher & Co.; *U.S. Public*, pg. 206
LLOYD BELT AUTOMOTIVE; *U.S. Private*, pg. 2475
LLOYD CAPITAL AG; *Int'l*, pg. 4535
LLOYD COILS EUROPE S.R.O.—See LEEL Electricals Ltd.; *Int'l*, pg. 4441
LLOYD COILS, L.P.—See LEEL Electricals Ltd.; *Int'l*, pg. 4441
LLOYD & CO.; *U.S. Private*, pg. 2475
LLOYD ELECTRIC, INC.; *U.S. Private*, pg. 2475
LLOYD ENTERPRISES INC.; *U.S. Private*, pg. 2475
LLOYD/FLANDERS INDUSTRIES, INC.—See Flanders Industries, Inc.; *U.S. Private*, pg. 1540
LLOYD FONDS GESELLSCHAFT FUR IMMOBILIEN-BETEILIGUNGEN MBH & CO. KG—See Lloyd Capital AG; *Int'l*, pg. 4536
LLOYD FONDS SINGAPORE PTE. LTD.—See Lloyd Capital AG; *Int'l*, pg. 4536
LLOYD FONDS SPECIAL ASSETS GMBH—See Lloyd Capital AG; *Int'l*, pg. 4536
LLOYD GEORGE MANAGEMENT (EUROPE) LIMITED—See Bank of Montreal; *Int'l*, pg. 847
LLOYD GEORGE MANAGEMENT (HONG KONG) LIMITED—See Bank of Montreal; *Int'l*, pg. 847
LLOYD GEORGE MANAGEMENT (SINGAPORE) PTE LTD.—See Bank of Montreal; *Int'l*, pg. 847
LLOYD GERMANICO DE MEXICO, S. DE R.L. DE C.V.—See DNV GL Group AS; *Int'l*, pg. 2150
LLOYD GERMAN IRAN KISH, LTD.—See DNV GL Group AS; *Int'l*, pg. 2150
THE LLOYD GROUP, INC.; *U.S. Private*, pg. 4071
LLOYD MATERIALS TESTING—See AMETEK, Inc.; *U.S. Public*, pg. 117

LLOYD MORGAN CHINA LIMITED—See Ignite Limited; *Int'l*, pg. 3603
LLOYD MORGAN HONG KONG LIMITED—See Ignite Limited; *Int'l*, pg. 3603
LLOYD MORGAN INTERNATIONAL PTY LIMITED—See Ignite Limited; *Int'l*, pg. 3603
LLOYD & PARTNERS LIMITED—See Marsh & McLennan Companies, Inc.; *U.S. Public*, pg. 1377
LLOYD PEST CONTROL COMPANY INCORPORATED; *U.S. Private*, pg. 2476
LLOYDS BANK COMMERCIAL FINANCE LTD.—See Lloyds Banking Group plc; *Int'l*, pg. 4536
LLOYDS BANK GENERAL INSURANCE HOLDINGS LIMITED—See Lloyds Banking Group plc; *Int'l*, pg. 4537
LLOYDS BANK GMBH—See Lloyds Banking Group plc; *Int'l*, pg. 4536
LLOYDS BANKING GROUP PLC; *Int'l*, pg. 4536
LLOYDS BANK INTERNATIONAL LIMITED—See Lloyds Banking Group plc; *Int'l*, pg. 4537
LLOYDS BANK LEASING LIMITED—See Lloyds Banking Group plc; *Int'l*, pg. 4537
LLOYDS BANK PENSIONS PROPERTY (GUERNSEY) LTD.—See Lloyds Banking Group plc; *Int'l*, pg. 4536
LLOYDS BANK PLC - NEW YORK REPRESENTATIVE OFFICE—See Lloyds Banking Group plc; *Int'l*, pg. 4537
LLOYDS BANK PLC—See Lloyds Banking Group plc; *Int'l*, pg. 4536
LLOYDS BANK PRIVATE BANKING LIMITED—See Lloyds Banking Group plc; *Int'l*, pg. 4537
LLOYDS BANK UNIT TRUST MANAGERS LTD.—See Lloyds Banking Group plc; *Int'l*, pg. 4537
LLOYDS BARBEQUE COMPANY, LLC—See Hormel Foods Corporation; *U.S. Public*, pg. 1054
LLOYDS DEVELOPMENT CAPITAL (HOLDINGS) LIMITED—See Lloyds Banking Group plc; *Int'l*, pg. 4537
LLOYDS ENGINEERING CO. L.L.C—See Gulf General Investment Company PSC; *Int'l*, pg. 3180
LLOYD SHIPPING GMBH—See Lloyd Capital AG; *Int'l*, pg. 4536
LLOYDS HYPOTHEKEN B.V.—See Lloyds Banking Group plc; *Int'l*, pg. 4538
LLOYDS KONECRANES PENSION TRUSTEES LTD.—See Konecranes Plc; *Int'l*, pg. 4252
LLOYDS METALS AND ENERGY LIMITED; *Int'l*, pg. 4538
LLOYD'S OF LONDON; *Int'l*, pg. 4536
LLOYDS PHARMACY CLINICAL HOMECARE LIMITED—See McKesson Corporation; *U.S. Public*, pg. 1408
LLOYDS REALTY DEVELOPERS LIMITED—See Shree Global Tradefin Limited; *Int'l*, pg. 6863
LLOYD'S REGISTER AMERICAS, INC.—See Lloyd's Register Foundation; *Int'l*, pg. 4536
LLOYD'S REGISTER FOUNDATION; *Int'l*, pg. 4536
LLOYD'S REGISTER GROUP LIMITED—See Lloyd's Register Foundation; *Int'l*, pg. 4536
LLOYD'S REGISTER GROUP SERVICES LIMITED—See Lloyd's Register Foundation; *Int'l*, pg. 4536
LLOYD'S REGISTER NORTH AMERICA, INC.—See Lloyd's Register Foundation; *Int'l*, pg. 4536
LLOYD'S REGISTER QUALITY ASSURANCE, INC.—See Lloyd's Register Foundation; *Int'l*, pg. 4536
LLOYD'S REGISTER QUALITY ASSURANCE LIMITED—See Lloyd's Register Foundation; *Int'l*, pg. 4536
LLOYD'S REGISTER TECHNICAL SERVICES, INC.—See Lloyd's Register Foundation; *Int'l*, pg. 4536
LLOYDS SECURITIES INC.—See Lloyds Banking Group plc; *Int'l*, pg. 4538
LLOYDS STEELS INDUSTRIES LTD.—See Shree Global Tradefin Limited; *Int'l*, pg. 6863
LLOYD STAFFING INC. - NEW YORK CITY—See Lloyd Staffing Inc.; *U.S. Private*, pg. 2476
LLOYD STAFFING INC.; *U.S. Private*, pg. 2476
LLOYDS TSB COMMERCIAL FINANCE LTD.—See Lloyds Banking Group plc; *Int'l*, pg. 4538
LLOYDS TSB GENERAL INSURANCE LIMITED—See Lloyds Banking Group plc; *Int'l*, pg. 4537
LLOYDS TSB INSURANCE SERVICES LIMITED—See Lloyds Banking Group plc; *Int'l*, pg. 4537
LLOYD TEXTILE TRADING LIMITED—See Li & Fung Limited; *Int'l*, pg. 4480
LLOYD TREUHAND GMBH—See Lloyd Capital AG; *Int'l*, pg. 4536
LLOYD WERFT BREMERHAVEN GMBH—See Genting Hong Kong Limited; *Int'l*, pg. 2929
LLOYD ZWEIMARKT GMBH—See Lloyd Capital AG; *Int'l*, pg. 4536
LL PELLING COMPANY INC.; *U.S. Private*, pg. 2475
LL PLANT ENGINEERING AG—See GEA Group Aktiengesellschaft; *Int'l*, pg. 2903
L&L PLANT SOIL DIVISION—See L&L Nursery Supply, Inc.; *U.S. Private*, pg. 2363
LLP MFO SHINHAN FINANCE—See Shinhan Financial Group Co., Ltd.; *Int'l*, pg. 6843
LLP "ENGINEERING PROCUREMENT SERVICES"—See OGCC KazStroyService JSC; *Int'l*, pg. 5531

COMPANY NAME INDEX

L&L PRODUCTS AUSTRALIA (PTY) LTD.—See L&L Products, Inc.; *U.S. Private*, pg. 2363
L&L PRODUCTS DO BRASIL LTDA.—See L&L Products, Inc.; *U.S. Private*, pg. 2363
L&L PRODUCTS EUROPE SAS—See L&L Products, Inc.; *U.S. Private*, pg. 2363
L&L PRODUCTS, INC.; *U.S. Private*, pg. 2363
L&L PRODUCTS OTOMOTIV LTD STI—See L&L Products, Inc.; *U.S. Private*, pg. 2363
LLP SMC KAZAKHSTAN—See SMC Corporation; *Int'l*, pg. 7003
L. L. ROWE COMPANY—See TE Connectivity Ltd.; *Int'l*, pg. 7495
LLR PARTNERS, INC.—See Independence Capital Partners, LLC; *U.S. Private*, pg. 2056
L & L SPECIAL FURNACE CO., INC.; *U.S. Private*, pg. 2361
L&L STORES INCORPORATED; *U.S. Private*, pg. 2363
LLT BUILDING CORPORATION; *U.S. Private*, pg. 2476
LLTD 1 SARL—See Lazard Ltd.; *Int'l*, pg. 4427
L&L TRANSPORTATION, LLC—See Crestwood Equity Partners LP; *U.S. Public*, pg. 594
L & L VAN LINES INC.—See HI-Boy Group Inc.; *U.S. Private*, pg. 1931
L.L. VANN ELECTRIC INC.; *U.S. Private*, pg. 2366
L&L WINGS INC.; *U.S. Private*, pg. 2363
LLW REPOSITORY LIMITED—See AECOM; *U.S. Public*, pg. 51
LLYR FLOATING WIND LIMITED—See SBM Offshore N.V.; *Int'l*, pg. 6607
LLYS YSTRAD (BRIDGEND) MANAGEMENT COMPANY LIMITED—See Persimmon plc; *Int'l*, pg. 5816
LMACP SA—See Alten S.A.; *Int'l*, pg. 390
LMA RECRUITMENT LIMITED—See Empresaria Group Plc; *Int'l*, pg. 2389
LMA RECRUITMENT SINGAPORE PTE. LIMITED—See Empresaria Group Plc; *Int'l*, pg. 2389
LMA UROLOGY B.V.—See Teleflex Incorporated; *U.S. Public*, pg. 1996
LMA UROLOGY SUISSE SA—See Teleflex Incorporated; *U.S. Public*, pg. 1996
LMBB, LLC—See Lithia Motors, Inc.; *U.S. Public*, pg. 1323
LMBP, LLC—See Lithia Motors, Inc.; *U.S. Public*, pg. 1323
LMC CAHAVAN GMBH & CO. KG—See Thor Industries, Inc.; *U.S. Public*, pg. 2156
LMC CONSTRUCTION, LLC—See Lennar Corporation; *U.S. Public*, pg. 1306
LMC EAST VILLAGE I HOLDINGS, LLC—See Lennar Corporation; *U.S. Public*, pg. 1306
LMC INTERNATIONAL LIMITED—See GlobalData Plc; *Int'l*, pg. 3003
LMC LIVING, LLC—See Lennar Corporation; *U.S. Public*, pg. 1306
LMC MARINE CENTER; *U.S. Private*, pg. 2476
L&M COMPANIES, INC.; *U.S. Private*, pg. 2363
L&M CONSTRUCTION CHEMICALS, INC.—See LATICRETE International, Inc.; *U.S. Private*, pg. 2397
LMC RIGHT START, INC.—See giggle, Inc.; *U.S. Private*, pg. 1697
LMC S.R.O.—See Alma Media Corporation; *Int'l*, pg. 362
LMC TYRE & RUBBER LIMITED—See GlobalData Plc; *Int'l*, pg. 3003
LMD INTEGRATED LOGISTIC SERVICES, INC.; *U.S. Private*, pg. 2476
LME CLEAR LIMITED—See Hong Kong Exchanges & Clearing Limited; *Int'l*, pg. 3466
L & M ELECTRIC, INC.—See Strada Services, LLC; *U.S. Private*, pg. 3832
LM ERICSSON BANGLADESH LIMITED—See Telefonaktiebolaget LM Ericsson; *Int'l*, pg. 7534
LM ERICSSON EGYPT—See Telefonaktiebolaget LM Ericsson; *Int'l*, pg. 7534
LM ERICSSON HOLDINGS LTD.—See Telefonaktiebolaget LM Ericsson; *Int'l*, pg. 7534
LM ERICSSON INTERNATIONAL AB—See Telefonaktiebolaget LM Ericsson; *Int'l*, pg. 7534
LM ERICSSON INTERNATIONAL AB—See Telefonaktiebolaget LM Ericsson; *Int'l*, pg. 7534
LM ERICSSON INTERNATIONAL AB—See Telefonaktiebolaget LM Ericsson; *Int'l*, pg. 7534
LM ERICSSON INTERNATIONAL AB—See Telefonaktiebolaget LM Ericsson; *Int'l*, pg. 7534
LM ERICSSON ISRAEL LTD.—See Telefonaktiebolaget LM Ericsson; *Int'l*, pg. 7534
LM ERICSSON LTD.—See Telefonaktiebolaget LM Ericsson; *Int'l*, pg. 7534
LM ERICSSON (NIGERIA) LTD.—See Telefonaktiebolaget LM Ericsson; *Int'l*, pg. 7534
LM ERICSSON—See Telefonaktiebolaget LM Ericsson; *Int'l*, pg. 7534
LMF COMMERCIAL, LLC—See Lennar Corporation; *U.S. Public*, pg. 1306
L&M FERTILIZER INC.; *U.S. Private*, pg. 2363
L&M FOOTWEAR INC.; *U.S. Private*, pg. 2363
L&M FOUNDATION SPECIALIST PTE. LTD.—See CSC Holdings Limited; *Int'l*, pg. 1862
LM FUNDING AMERICA, INC.; *U.S. Public*, pg. 1337
LMG CORP.; *Int'l*, pg. 4538

LM GEAR COMPANY, INC.—See Anderson-Cook Inc.; *U.S. Private*, pg. 278
LMG INSIGHT & COMMUNICATION—See Aimia Inc.; *Int'l*, pg. 233
LMG, LLC—See Entertainment Technology Partners LLC; *U.S. Private*, pg. 1405
LMG NETHERLANDS II B.V.—See Concentra nv; *Int'l*, pg. 1763
LMG REALTY PTE. LTD.—See BRC Asia Limited; *Int'l*, pg. 1143
L.M.G. S.R.L.—See Monrif S.p.A.; *Int'l*, pg. 5035
LMG STOCKTON, INC.—See Gannett Co., Inc.; *U.S. Public*, pg. 904
LMHC MASSACHUSETTS HOLDINGS INC.—See Liberty Mutual Holding Company Inc.; *U.S. Private*, pg. 2445
LMI AEROSPACE, INC.—See SONACA S.A; *Int'l*, pg. 7088
L.M.I. ASIA PACIFIC (PRIVATE) LIMITED—See SONACA S.A; *Int'l*, pg. 7088
LMI CAPITAL, INC.—See Marcus & Millichap, Inc.; *U.S. Public*, pg. 1365
LMI CONNECTORS—See ABB Ltd.; *Int'l*, pg. 52
LMI CONTRACTORS, LLC—See Lennar Corporation; *U.S. Public*, pg. 1306
LMI EVERETT - MERRILL CREEK—See SONACA S.A; *Int'l*, pg. 7088
LMI FINISHING INC.—See SONACA S.A; *Int'l*, pg. 7088
LMI INNOVATIVE TECHNOLOGIES CENTRE LLC—See Quaser Machine Tools, Inc.; *Int'l*, pg. 6157
LMI PACKAGING SOLUTIONS, INC.; *U.S. Private*, pg. 2476
LMI SAN DIEGO—See SONACA S.A; *Int'l*, pg. 7088
LMI (SHANGHAI) TRADING CO. LTD.—See TKH Group N.V.; *Int'l*, pg. 7764
LMI SUN VALLEY—See SONACA S.A; *Int'l*, pg. 7088
LMI TECHNOLOGIES B.V.—See TKH Group N.V.; *Int'l*, pg. 7764
LMI TECHNOLOGIES CO. LTD.—See TKH Group N.V.; *Int'l*, pg. 7764
LMI TECHNOLOGIES INC.—See TKH Group N.V.; *Int'l*, pg. 7764
LMK AUTO GROUP LTD.; *U.S. Private*, pg. 2476
LMK VEJ A/S—See YIT Corporation; *Int'l*, pg. 8586
LM LAND HOLDINGS, LP—See Forestar Group Inc.; *U.S. Public*, pg. 867
LM LIFTMATERIAL GMBH—See Bain Capital, LP; *U.S. Private*, pg. 452
LM MASKIN AS—See HEINRICH DE FRIES GmbH; *Int'l*, pg. 3324
LM MATERIAUX SA—See Compagnie de Saint-Gobain SA; *Int'l*, pg. 1725
L.M. MCLAMB & SON CONSTRUCTION CO., INC.; *U.S. Private*, pg. 2366
LMNEXT UK LTD.—See Bravofly Rumbo Group N.V.; *Int'l*, pg. 1142
LMN LABORATORIO DE MEDICINA NUCLEAR, UNIPESSOAL, LDA.—See UnitedHealth Group Incorporated; *U.S. Public*, pg. 2242
LM&O ADVERTISING; *U.S. Private*, pg. 2476
LMOOGI FASHIONS PRIVATE LIMITED—See Rupa & Co Limited; *Int'l*, pg. 6428
LMP AUTOMOTIVE HOLDINGS, INC.; *U.S. Public*, pg. 1337
LMP CAPITAL & INCOME FUND, INC.; *U.S. Public*, pg. 1337
LMPI (LES MESSAGERIES DE PRESSE INTERNATIONALE)—See Vivendi SE; *Int'l*, pg. 8276
LMP IMPIANTI SRL—See Owens Corning; *U.S. Public*, pg. 1626
LMP INTERNATIONAL LIMITED—See Harbour Equine Holdings Limited; *Int'l*, pg. 3272
LMP MANAGEMENT GROUP, INC.; *U.S. Private*, pg. 2476
L&M RADIATOR INCORPORATED—See Westinghouse Air Brake Technologies Corporation; *U.S. Public*, pg. 2358
LMR DISPOSAL LLC—See Casella Waste Systems, Inc.; *U.S. Public*, pg. 446
LM RESTAURANTS, INC.; *U.S. Private*, pg. 2476
L.M. SANDLER & SONS; *U.S. Private*, pg. 2366
LMS CAPITAL GROUP LIMITED—See LMS Capital plc; *Int'l*, pg. 4538
LMS CAPITAL HOLDINGS LIMITED—See LMS Capital plc; *Int'l*, pg. 4538
LMS CAPITAL PLC; *Int'l*, pg. 4538
L.M. SCOFIELD COMPANY; *U.S. Private*, pg. 2366
L.M. SCOFIELD COMPANY—See L.M. Scofield Company; *U.S. Private*, pg. 2366
L.M. SCOFIELD COMPANY—See L.M. Scofield Company; *U.S. Private*, pg. 2366
L.M. SCOFIELD COMPANY—See L.M. Scofield Company; *U.S. Private*, pg. 2366
LMS CO. LTD.; *Int'l*, pg. 4538
LMS, INC.—See AptarGroup, Inc.; *U.S. Public*, pg. 174
LMS INTELLIBOUND, INC.; *U.S. Private*, pg. 2476
LMS INVESTMENT COMPANY; *Int'l*, pg. 4538
LMS PROLINK LTD.; *Int'l*, pg. 4538
LMS REINFORCING STEEL GROUP; *Int'l*, pg. 4538
LMS SA—See Headlam Group plc; *Int'l*, pg. 3301
L&M SUPPLY INC.; *U.S. Private*, pg. 2363

LM SYSTEMS B.V.—See THK CO., LTD.; *Int'l*, pg. 7711
LM SYSTEMS B.V.—See THK CO., LTD.; *Int'l*, pg. 7711
LMT ASIA PTE LTD.—See LMT GmbH & Co. KG; *Int'l*, pg. 4538
LMT BELIN S.A.S.—See LMT GmbH & Co. KG; *Int'l*, pg. 4538
LMT CHINA CO. LTD.—See LMT GmbH & Co. KG; *Int'l*, pg. 4539
LMT CZECH REPUBLIC S.R.O.—See LMT GmbH & Co. KG; *Int'l*, pg. 4539
L&M TECHNOLOGIES, INC.; *U.S. Private*, pg. 2363
LMT FETTE WERKZEUGTECHNIK GMBH & CO. KG—See LMT GmbH & Co. KG; *Int'l*, pg. 4539
LMT GMBH & CO. KG; *Int'l*, pg. 4538
LMT (INDIA) PRIVATE LIMITED—See LMT GmbH & Co. KG; *Int'l*, pg. 4538
LMT KIENINGER GMBH—See LMT GmbH & Co. KG; *Int'l*, pg. 4539
LMT KOREA CO. LTD.—See LMT GmbH & Co. KG; *Int'l*, pg. 4539
LMT MEDICAL SYSTEMS GMBH—See Geratherm Medical AG; *Int'l*, pg. 2942
LMT ONSRUD ONSRUD LP—See LMT GmbH & Co. KG; *Int'l*, pg. 4539
L&M TRAFFIC SERVICES PTY LTD—See Traffic Technologies Ltd.; *Int'l*, pg. 7889
L&M TRANSPORTATION SERVICES, INC.; *U.S. Private*, pg. 2363
LMT SURGICAL PTY LTD—See EBOS Group Limited; *Int'l*, pg. 2285
LMT TOOLS BRASIL FERRAMENTAS LTDA—See LMT GmbH & Co. KG; *Int'l*, pg. 4539
LMT TOOLS GMBH & CO. KG—See LMT GmbH & Co. KG; *Int'l*, pg. 4539
LMT TOOLS INDIA PVT. LTD.—See LMT GmbH & Co. KG; *Int'l*, pg. 4539
LMT TOOLS MEXICO, SA DE CV—See LMT GmbH & Co. KG; *Int'l*, pg. 4539
LMT TOOL SYSTEMS GMBH & CO. KG—See LMT GmbH & Co. KG; *Int'l*, pg. 4539
LMT TOOL SYSTEMS GMBH & CO. KG—See LMT GmbH & Co. KG; *Int'l*, pg. 4539
LMT TOOL SYSTEMS GMBH—See LMT GmbH & Co. KG; *Int'l*, pg. 4539
LMT TOOL SYSTEMS RO SRL—See LMT GmbH & Co. KG; *Int'l*, pg. 4539
LMT UK LTD.—See LMT GmbH & Co. KG; *Int'l*, pg. 4539
LMT USA, INC.—See LMT GmbH & Co. KG; *Int'l*, pg. 4539
L & M WASTE SYSTEMS, INC.—See Watts Trucking Service, Inc.; *U.S. Private*, pg. 4456
L&M WELDING SUPPLY, INC.—See CI Capital Partners LLC; *U.S. Private*, pg. 895
LM WIND POWER A/S—See General Electric Company; *U.S. Public*, pg. 920
LM WIND POWER BLADES (POLAND) SP. Z.O.O.—See General Electric Company; *U.S. Public*, pg. 920
LM WIND POWER (SPAIN) SLU—See General Electric Company; *U.S. Public*, pg. 920
LMW RESIDENTIAL PTY LTD—See Acumentis Group Limited; *Int'l*, pg. 121
LMZ (JIANGSU) INDUSTRIES CO., LTD.—See Liuzhou LMZ Co., Ltd.; *Int'l*, pg. 4529
L. NAKAGAWA-JOHNSTON; *U.S. Private*, pg. 2364
L & N BRIDGE, LLC.; *U.S. Private*, pg. 2361
LNC PARTNERS; *U.S. Private*, pg. 2476
LNC TECHNOLOGY CO., LTD—See Pou Chen Corporation; *Int'l*, pg. 5941
L.N. CURTIS & SONS - INTERMOUNTAIN DIVISION—See L.N. Curtis & Sons; *U.S. Private*, pg. 2366
L.N. CURTIS & SONS - NORTHWEST DIVISION—See L.N. Curtis & Sons; *U.S. Private*, pg. 2366
L.N. CURTIS & SONS - PACIFIC SOUTH DIVISION—See L.N. Curtis & Sons; *U.S. Private*, pg. 2367
L.N. CURTIS & SONS; *U.S. Private*, pg. 2366
L.N. CURTIS & SONS - SOUTHWEST DIVISION—See L.N. Curtis & Sons; *U.S. Private*, pg. 2367
LN GARDEN HOTEL COMPANY LTD.—See Guangzhou Lingnan Group Holdings Company Limited; *Int'l*, pg. 3166
LNG HRVATSKA D.O.O.—See Hrvatska elektroprivreda d.d.; *Int'l*, pg. 3502
LNG INTERNATIONAL PTY LTD—See Liquefied Natural Gas Limited; *Int'l*, pg. 4522
LNG SHIPPING SPA—See Eni S.p.A.; *Int'l*, pg. 2438
LNGTOP (JIANGSU) TECHNOLOGY CO., LTD—See Zhangjiagang Furui Special Equipment Co., Ltd.; *Int'l*, pg. 8647
L NISSHO CORPORATION—See Nitto Denko Corporation; *Int'l*, pg. 5384
LNI VERKKO HOLDING OY—See 3i Group plc; *Int'l*, pg. 9
LNI VERKKO HOLDING OY—See The Goldman Sachs Group, Inc.; *U.S. Public*, pg. 2080
LNK GROUP—See MG Baltic UAB; *Int'l*, pg. 4871
LN MAURICE—See FAYAT SAS; *Int'l*, pg. 2625
LNOX WIND ENERGY LIMITED; *Int'l*, pg. 4539
LN PARTICIPACOES LTDA.—See W.W. Grainger, Inc.; *U.S. Public*, pg. 2320

LNR PARTNERS, LLC—See Starwood Property Trust, Inc.; *U.S. Public*, pg. 1939
LNR PROPERTY LLC—See Starwood Property Trust, Inc.; *U.S. Public*, pg. 1939
LNR SCOTTS VALLEY HOTEL LLC—See Starwood Property Trust, Inc.; *U.S. Public*, pg. 1940
LNRS DATA SERVICES B.V.—See RELX plc; *Int'l*, pg. 6266
LNRS DATA SERVICES INC.—See RELX plc; *Int'l*, pg. 6266
LNRS DATA SERVICES LIMITED - ESTATES GAZETTE GROUP—See RELX plc; *Int'l*, pg. 6266
LNRS DATA SERVICES LIMITED - FLIGHT GROUP—See RELX plc; *Int'l*, pg. 6266
LNRS DATA SERVICES LIMITED - ICIS GROUP—See RELX plc; *Int'l*, pg. 6266
LNRS DATA SERVICES LIMITED - PROAGRICA GROUP—See RELX plc; *Int'l*, pg. 6266
LNRS DATA SERVICES LIMITED—See RELX plc; *Int'l*, pg. 6266
LNRS DATA SERVICES PTE. LTD.—See RELX plc; *Int'l*, pg. 6266
L-N SAFETY GLASS, SA DE CV—See Nippon Sheet Glass Co. Ltd.; *Int'l*, pg. 5332
LNS KOMMUNIKATION AB—See Elisa Corporation; *Int'l*, pg. 2361
LNTERQUIM S.A.—See Akzo Nobel N.V.; *Int'l*, pg. 275
L & N TRUCK SERVICE OF ELLENWOOD, LLC—See American Securities LLC; *U.S. Private*, pg. 248
L&N UNIFORM SUPPLY, LLC—See Vestis Corp; *U.S. Public*, pg. 2290
LNV TECHNOLOGY PVT. LTD.—See Sinoma International Engineering Co., Ltd.; *Int'l*, pg. 6952
LOABIRAN COMPANY; *Int'l*, pg. 4539
LOAD CONTROLS SYSTEMS PTE LTD—See Affirma Capital Limited; *Int'l*, pg. 187
LOAD DELIVERED LOGISTICS LLC; *U.S. Private*, pg. 2476
LOAD INDICATOR AB—See Lagercrantz Group AB; *Int'l*, pg. 4394
LOADING AUTOMATION, INC.—See Joloda Hydraroll Limited; *Int'l*, pg. 3996
LOAD KING, LLC—See Utility One Source L.P.; *U.S. Private*, pg. 4326
LOADMATCH LOGISTICS INC.; *U.S. Private*, pg. 2476
LOAD-ONE TRANSPORTATION & LOGISTICS; *U.S. Private*, pg. 2476
LOADPATH, LLC—See Redwire Corporation; *U.S. Public*, pg. 1771
LOADPOINT BEARINGS LIMITED—See GL Tech Co., Ltd.; *Int'l*, pg. 2986
LOADPOINT LIMITED—See GL Tech Co., Ltd.; *Int'l*, pg. 2986
LOADRITE LIMITED—See Trimble, Inc.; *U.S. Public*, pg. 2190
LOADSPRING SOLUTIONS, INC.; *U.S. Private*, pg. 2476
LOADSTAR CAPITAL, K.K.; *Int'l*, pg. 4539
LOADSTAR FUNDING K.K.—See Loadstar Capital, K.K.; *Int'l*, pg. 4539
LOADTEST, INC.—See Fugro N.V.; *Int'l*, pg. 2805
LOADUP TECHNOLOGIES, LLC; *U.S. Private*, pg. 2476
LOANATIK, LLC; *U.S. Private*, pg. 2476
LOAN AVENUE HOLDING PTY. LTD.—See Yellow Brick Road Holdings Ltd.; *Int'l*, pg. 8576
LOANBRIGHT.COM; *U.S. Private*, pg. 2477
LOAN CENTRAL, INC.—See Ohio Valley Banc Corp.; *U.S. Public*, pg. 1565
LOANCORE REALTY TRUST, INC.; *U.S. Private*, pg. 2477
LOANCOS GMBH; *Int'l*, pg. 4539
LOANDEPOT.COM, LLC; *U.S. Private*, pg. 2477
LOANDEPOT, INC.; *U.S. Public*, pg. 1337
LOAN MART OF OKLAHOMA, INC.—See Lone Star Global Acquisitions, LLC; *U.S. Private*, pg. 2487
LOAN RESOLUTION CORPORATION; *U.S. Private*, pg. 2476
LOANS4LESS.COM, INC.; *U.S. Public*, pg. 1337
LOANSOURCE INC.; *U.S. Private*, pg. 2477
LOAR GROUP, INC.; *U.S. Private*, pg. 2477
LOBA FEINCHEMIE GMBH—See Shilpa Medicare Ltd; *Int'l*, pg. 6831
LOBA GMBH & CO. KG; *Int'l*, pg. 4539
LOBA TRADING (SHANGHAI) COMPANY LIMITED—See sam Vertriebs GmbH + Co. KG; *Int'l*, pg. 6500
LOBATSE CLAY WORKS (PTY) LTD—See Botswana Development Corporation Limited; *Int'l*, pg. 1118
LOBA-WAKOL, LLC—See Wakol GmbH; *Int'l*, pg. 8332
LOBA-WAKOL POLSKA SP. Z O.O.—See sam Vertriebs GmbH + Co. KG; *Int'l*, pg. 6500
LOBER DRUCK UND KUVERT GMBH—See Bong AB; *Int'l*, pg. 1107
LOBE SCIENCES LTD.; *Int'l*, pg. 4539
LOBLAW BRANDS LIMITED—See George Weston Limited; *Int'l*, pg. 2938
LOBLAW COMPANIES LIMITED—See George Weston Limited; *Int'l*, pg. 2938
LOBLAW PROPERTIES LIMITED—See George Weston Limited; *Int'l*, pg. 2938

LOBLAW PROPERTIES WEST, INC.—See George Weston Limited; *Int'l*, pg. 2938
LOBSTER POINT PROPERTIES LTD.; *Int'l*, pg. 4539
LOBSTER TRAP CO. INC.; *U.S. Private*, pg. 2477
LOBTEX CO., LTD.; *Int'l*, pg. 4539
LOBUE & MAJDALANY MANAGEMENT GROUP, INC.; *U.S. Private*, pg. 2477
LOCAFY LIMITED; *Int'l*, pg. 4539
LOCAL AUTHORITIES PENSION PLAN—See Alberta Pension Services Corporation; *Int'l*, pg. 298
LOCAL BOUNTI CORPORATION; *U.S. Public*, pg. 1337
LOCAL.CH LTD—See Swisscom AG; *Int'l*, pg. 7374
THE LOCAL CHOICE PROPRIETARY LIMITED—See Dis-Chem Pharmacies Ltd.; *Int'l*, pg. 2131
LOCAL CONCRETE SUPPLY & EQUIPMENT, LLC—See Vulcan Materials Company; *U.S. Public*, pg. 2314
LOCAL CORPORATION; *U.S. Public*, pg. 1337
LOCALEDGE MEDIA, INC.—See The Hearst Corporation; *U.S. Private*, pg. 4047
LOCALEDGE—See The Hearst Corporation; *U.S. Private*, pg. 4047
LOCALIST LIMITED—See New Zealand Post Limited; *Int'l*, pg. 5232
LOCALITY PLANNING ENERGY HOLDINGS LIMITED; *Int'l*, pg. 4539
LOCALIZA RENT A CAR S.A.; *Int'l*, pg. 4540
LOCAL LEADS HQ; *U.S. Private*, pg. 2477
LOCALLOOP, INC.—See InterCloud Systems, Inc.; *U.S. Public*, pg. 1141
LOCAL MARKETING CORP.—See WPP plc; *Int'l*, pg. 8464
LOCAL MARKETING GIANT, LLC; *U.S. Private*, pg. 2477
LOCAL MARKETING SOLUTIONS GROUP, INC.; *U.S. Private*, pg. 2477
LOCAL MATTERS, INC.; *U.S. Private*, pg. 2477
LOCAL MEDIA GROUP, INC.—See Gannett Co., Inc.; *U.S. Public*, pg. 904
LOCAL MEDIA LINK; *U.S. Private*, pg. 2477
LOCAL MERCHAT SERVICES, INC.—See Telenav, Inc.; *U.S. Private*, pg. 3960
LOCALNET CORP.; *U.S. Private*, pg. 2477
LOCAL OIL DISTRIBUTING INC.; *U.S. Private*, pg. 2477
LOCAL PROJECTS, LLC—See Pico Far East Holdings Limited; *Int'l*, pg. 5861
LOCALTAPIOLA ASSET MANAGEMENT LTD.—See LocalTapiola Group; *Int'l*, pg. 4540
LOCALTAPIOLA BANK PLC—See LocalTapiola Group; *Int'l*, pg. 4540
LOCALTAPIOLA GENERAL MUTUAL INSURANCE COMPANY—See LocalTapiola Group; *Int'l*, pg. 4540
LOCALTAPIOLA GROUP; *Int'l*, pg. 4540
LOCALTAPIOLA MUTUAL LIFE INSURANCE COMPANY—See LocalTapiola Group; *Int'l*, pg. 4540
LOCALTAPIOLA MUTUAL PENSION INSURANCE COMPANY—See LocalTapiola Group; *Int'l*, pg. 4540
LOCALTAPIOLA REAL ESTATE ASSET MANAGEMENT LTD.—See LocalTapiola Group; *Int'l*, pg. 4540
LOCAL VIEW MARKETING INC.; *Int'l*, pg. 4539
LOCAL YOKEL MEDIA LLC—See PubSquared LLC; *U.S. Private*, pg. 3301
LOCALYTICS COMPANY; *U.S. Private*, pg. 2477
LOCAPOR - COMPANHIA PORTUGUESA LOCACAO FINANCEIRA MOBILIARIA, S.A.—See Caixa Geral de Depositos S.A.; *Int'l*, pg. 1260
LOCARE SNC—See Gecina S.A.; *Int'l*, pg. 2909
LOCASOLOG SA; *Int'l*, pg. 4540
LOC AT CHELSEA LLP—See HCA Healthcare, Inc.; *U.S. Public*, pg. 1000
LOCAT CROATIA DOO—See UniCredit S.p.A.; *Int'l*, pg. 8036
LOCATEL S.A.—See TCR Capital SAS; *Int'l*, pg. 7485
LOCATIENET B.V.—See Porsche Automobil Holding SE; *Int'l*, pg. 5926
LOCATING, INC.—See Dycom Industries, Inc.; *U.S. Public*, pg. 698
LOCATION BASED TECHNOLOGIES INC.; *U.S. Public*, pg. 1337
LOCATION INC. GROUP CORPORATION—See Insight Venture Management, LLC; *U.S. Private*, pg. 2089
LOCATION INC. GROUP CORPORATION—See Stone Point Capital LLC; *U.S. Private*, pg. 3822
LOCATION LABS, INC.—See Gen Digital Inc.; *U.S. Public*, pg. 910
LOCATION ONE LTD.—See Facilities by ADF Plc; *Int'l*, pg. 2600
LOCATION SERVICES, LLC; *U.S. Private*, pg. 2477
LOCATRICE ITALIANA SPA—See BNP Paribas SA; *Int'l*, pg. 1091
LOCAT S.P.A.—See UniCredit S.p.A.; *Int'l*, pg. 8035
LOC AT THE HARBORNE HOSPITAL LIMITED—See HCA Healthcare, Inc.; *U.S. Public*, pg. 1000
L'OCCITANE AUSTRALIA PTY LTD—See L'Occitane Groupe S.A.; *Int'l*, pg. 4378
L'OCCITANE GMBH—See L'Occitane Groupe S.A.; *Int'l*, pg. 4378
L'OCCITANE GMBH—See L'Occitane Groupe S.A.; *Int'l*, pg. 4378
L'OCCITANE GROUPE S.A.; *Int'l*, pg. 4378
L'OCCITANE INC.—See L'Occitane Groupe S.A.; *Int'l*, pg. 4378

L'OCCITANE INTERNATIONAL S.A.—See L'Occitane Groupe S.A.; *Int'l*, pg. 4378
L'OCCITANE JAPON K.K.—See L'Occitane Groupe S.A.; *Int'l*, pg. 4378
L'OCCITANE (KOREA) LIMITED—See L'Occitane Groupe S.A.; *Int'l*, pg. 4378
L'OCCITANE LTD.—See L'Occitane Groupe S.A.; *Int'l*, pg. 4378
L'OCCITANE (SUISSE) SA—See L'Occitane Groupe S.A.; *Int'l*, pg. 4378
LOCH DUART LTD.; *Int'l*, pg. 4540
LOCHER BROS INC.; *U.S. Private*, pg. 2478
LOCHER EVERS INTERNATIONAL, INC.—See Expolanka Holdings PLC; *Int'l*, pg. 2589
LOCHINVAR LIMITED—See A. O. Smith Corporation; *U.S. Public*, pg. 12
LOCHINVAR, LLC—See A. O. Smith Corporation; *U.S. Public*, pg. 12
LOCHRANE ENGINEERING, INC.—See NV5 Global, Inc.; *U.S. Public*, pg. 1557
LOCHRIDGE-PRIEST INC.; *U.S. Private*, pg. 2478
LOCHTE-OPTIK GMBH—See Fielmann Group AG; *Int'l*, pg. 2659
LOCI CONTROLS, INC.; *U.S. Private*, pg. 2478
LOCIMOBILE, INC.—See MetAlert Inc.; *U.S. Public*, pg. 1427
LOCK AND STORE (GLENMARIE) SDN. BHD.—See Singapore Post Limited; *Int'l*, pg. 6942
LOCKARD DEVELOPMENT INC.—See LLJ Inc.; *U.S. Private*, pg. 2475
LOCKARD & WECHSLER; *U.S. Private*, pg. 2478
LOCK AS—See Nordic Capital AB; *Int'l*, pg. 5420
LOCKBOX LINK INC.; *U.S. Private*, pg. 2478
LOCKE EQUIPMENT SALES CO.; *U.S. Private*, pg. 2478
LOCKE INSULATORS, INC.—See NGK Insulators, Ltd.; *Int'l*, pg. 5254
LOCKE LORD EDWARDS LLP; *U.S. Private*, pg. 2478
LOCKERBIE & HOLE CONTRACTING LIMITED—See Aecon Group Inc.; *Int'l*, pg. 172
LOCKERBIE & HOLE CONTRACTING LIMITED—See Aecon Group Inc.; *Int'l*, pg. 172
LOCKERBIE & HOLE CONTRACTING LIMITED—See Aecon Group Inc.; *Int'l*, pg. 172
LOCKERBIE & HOLE INC.—See Aecon Group Inc.; *Int'l*, pg. 172
LOCKER GROUP HOLDINGS PTY. LTD.—See Valmont Industries, Inc.; *U.S. Public*, pg. 2273
LOCKER INPOST ITALIA S.R.L.—See InPost S.A.; *Int'l*, pg. 3717
LOCKE SUPPLY CO.; *U.S. Private*, pg. 2478
LOCKEY CORP.—See Ingersoll Rand Inc.; *U.S. Public*, pg. 1122
LOCK FOCUS PTY. LTD.—See Safecorp Group Ltd.; *Int'l*, pg. 6469
LOCKFORMER COMPANY—See Mestek, Inc.; *U.S. Public*, pg. 1426
LOCKHART CADILLAC INC.; *U.S. Private*, pg. 2478
LOCKHART CADILLAC SOUTH—See Lockhart Cadillac Inc.; *U.S. Private*, pg. 2478
LOCKHART CATERING EQUIPMENT LIMITED—See Bunzl plc; *Int'l*, pg. 1219
LOCKHART COMPANIES LIMITED; *U.S. Private*, pg. 2478
LOCKHART DIALYSIS, LLC—See DaVita Inc.; *U.S. Public*, pg. 640
THE LOCK HAVEN EXPRESS—See The Nutting Company, Inc.; *U.S. Private*, pg. 4086
LOCK HAVEN HOME CARE SERVICES, LLC—See Community Health Systems, Inc.; *U.S. Public*, pg. 554
LOCKHEED MARTIN ADVANCED PROJECTS—See Lockheed Martin Corporation; *U.S. Public*, pg. 1337
LOCKHEED MARTIN AERONAUTICS COMPANY—See Lockheed Martin Corporation; *U.S. Public*, pg. 1337
LOCKHEED MARTIN AERONAUTICS COMPANY—See Lockheed Martin Corporation; *U.S. Public*, pg. 1338
LOCKHEED MARTIN AERONAUTICS COMPANY—See Lockheed Martin Corporation; *U.S. Public*, pg. 1338
LOCKHEED MARTIN AEROPARTS, INC.—See Lockheed Martin Corporation; *U.S. Public*, pg. 1337
LOCKHEED MARTIN AUSTRALIA PTY. LIMITED—See Lockheed Martin Corporation; *U.S. Public*, pg. 1338
LOCKHEED MARTIN BUSINESS TECHNOLOGY SOLUTIONS LIMITED—See Lockheed Martin Corporation; *U.S. Public*, pg. 1338
LOCKHEED MARTIN CANADA INC.—See Lockheed Martin Corporation; *U.S. Public*, pg. 1338
LOCKHEED MARTIN CANADA—See Lockheed Martin Corporation; *U.S. Public*, pg. 1338
LOCKHEED MARTIN COMMERCIAL SPACE SYSTEMS—See Lockheed Martin Corporation; *U.S. Public*, pg. 1338
LOCKHEED MARTIN CORPORATION; *U.S. Public*, pg. 1337
LOCKHEED MARTIN DESKTOP SOLUTIONS, INC.—See Lockheed Martin Corporation; *U.S. Public*, pg. 1338
LOCKHEED MARTIN ENGINE INVESTMENTS, LLC—See Lockheed Martin Corporation; *U.S. Public*, pg. 1338
LOCKHEED MARTIN GLOBAL, INC. - BELGIUM OFFICE—See Lockheed Martin Corporation; *U.S. Public*, pg. 1338

COMPANY NAME INDEX

LOCKHEED MARTIN GLOBAL, INC.—See Lockheed Martin Corporation; *U.S. Public*, pg. 1338
LOCKHEED MARTIN GLOBAL, INC. - TURKEY OFFICE—See Lockheed Martin Corporation; *U.S. Public*, pg. 1338
LOCKHEED MARTIN GOVERNMENT ELECTRONIC SYSTEMS—See Lockheed Martin Corporation; *U.S. Public*, pg. 1338
LOCKHEED MARTIN INTEGRATED SYSTEMS, INC.—See Lockheed Martin Corporation; *U.S. Public*, pg. 1338
LOCKHEED MARTIN INTEGRATED TECHNOLOGY, LLC—See Lockheed Martin Corporation; *U.S. Public*, pg. 1338
LOCKHEED MARTIN INTERNATIONAL S.A.—See Lockheed Martin Corporation; *U.S. Public*, pg. 1338
LOCKHEED MARTIN INVESTMENTS INC.—See Lockheed Martin Corporation; *U.S. Public*, pg. 1338
LOCKHEED MARTIN MANAGEMENT & DATA SYSTEMS—See Lockheed Martin Corporation; *U.S. Public*, pg. 1338
LOCKHEED MARTIN MARITIME SYSTEMS & SENSORS—See Lockheed Martin Corporation; *U.S. Public*, pg. 1338
LOCKHEED MARTIN MARITIME SYSTEMS & SENSORS—See Lockheed Martin Corporation; *U.S. Public*, pg. 1338
LOCKHEED MARTIN MISSILES & FIRE CONTROL - ORLANDO—See Lockheed Martin Corporation; *U.S. Public*, pg. 1338
LOCKHEED MARTIN MISSILES & FIRE CONTROL—See Lockheed Martin Corporation; *U.S. Public*, pg. 1338
LOCKHEED MARTIN NAVAL & ELECTRONIC SYSTEMS—See Lockheed Martin Corporation; *U.S. Public*, pg. 1338
LOCKHEED MARTIN OPERATIONS SUPPORT, INC.—See Lockheed Martin Corporation; *U.S. Public*, pg. 1338
LOCKHEED MARTIN SERVICES, INC.—See Lockheed Martin Corporation; *U.S. Public*, pg. 1338
LOCKHEED MARTIN SIMULATION, TRAINING & SUPPORT—See Lockheed Martin Corporation; *U.S. Public*, pg. 1338
LOCKHEED MARTIN SIMULATION, TRAINING & SUPPORT—See Lockheed Martin Corporation; *U.S. Public*, pg. 1338
LOCKHEED MARTIN SIPPICAN COUNTERMEASURE SYSTEMS—See Lockheed Martin Corporation; *U.S. Public*, pg. 1338
LOCKHEED MARTIN SIPPICAN, INC.—See Lockheed Martin Corporation; *U.S. Public*, pg. 1338
LOCKHEED MARTIN SPACE SYSTEMS CO. - EL PASO—See Lockheed Martin Corporation; *U.S. Public*, pg. 1338
LOCKHEED MARTIN SPACE SYSTEMS COMPANY—See Lockheed Martin Corporation; *U.S. Public*, pg. 1338
LOCKHEED MARTIN SPACE SYSTEMS CO. - NEW ORLEANS—See Lockheed Martin Corporation; *U.S. Public*, pg. 1339
LOCKHEED MARTIN SPACE SYSTEMS CO. - SUNNYVALE—See Lockheed Martin Corporation; *U.S. Public*, pg. 1339
LOCKHEED MARTIN SYSTEMS INTEGRATION - OWEGO—See Lockheed Martin Corporation; *U.S. Public*, pg. 1338
LOCKHEED MARTIN TACTICAL DEFENSE SYSTEMS—See Lockheed Martin Corporation; *U.S. Public*, pg. 1338
LOCKHEED MARTIN UK AMPTHILL LIMITED—See Lockheed Martin Corporation; *U.S. Public*, pg. 1338
LOCKHEED MARTIN UK LTD.—See Lockheed Martin Corporation; *U.S. Public*, pg. 1338
LOCKHEED MIDDLE EAST SERVICES—See Lockheed Martin Corporation; *U.S. Public*, pg. 1338
LOCK INSPECTION SYSTEMES FRANCE SARL—See Illinois Tool Works Inc.; *U.S. Public*, pg. 1109
LOCK INSPECTION SYSTEMS BV—See Illinois Tool Works Inc.; *U.S. Public*, pg. 1109
LOCK INSPECTION SYSTEMS LIMITED—See Illinois Tool Works Inc.; *U.S. Public*, pg. 1109
LOCK JOINT TUBE INC.; *U.S. Private*, pg. 2478
LOCK&LOCK CO., LTD.; *Int'l*, pg. 4540
LOCK&LOCK GHIDINI SRL—See Lock&Lock Co., Ltd.; *Int'l*, pg. 4540
LOCK&LOCK GMBH—See Lock&Lock Co., Ltd.; *Int'l*, pg. 4540
LOCK & LOCK HCM CO., LTD.—See Lock&Lock Co., Ltd.; *Int'l*, pg. 4540
LOCK&LOCK HN COMPANY LIMITED—See Lock&Lock Co., Ltd.; *Int'l*, pg. 4540
LOCK&LOCK (HONG KONG) COMPANY LIMITED—See Lock&Lock Co., Ltd.; *Int'l*, pg. 4540
LOCK&LOCK INDIA TRADING PRIVATE, LTD.—See Lock&Lock Co., Ltd.; *Int'l*, pg. 4540
LOCK&LOCK JAPAN CO., LTD.—See Lock&Lock Co., Ltd.; *Int'l*, pg. 4540
LOCK&LOCK PHNOM PENH CO., LTD.—See Lock&Lock Co., Ltd.; *Int'l*, pg. 4540

LOCK&LOCK RETAIL CO., LTD.—See Lock&Lock Co., Ltd.; *Int'l*, pg. 4540
LOCK&LOCK (THAILAND) CO., LTD.—See Lock&Lock Co., Ltd.; *Int'l*, pg. 4540
LOCK&LOCK TRADE (SHENZHEN) CO., LTD.—See Lock&Lock Co., Ltd.; *Int'l*, pg. 4540
LOCK LOWER HOLDING AS—See Nordic Capital AB; *Int'l*, pg. 5420
LOCKMAN ELECTRONIC HOLDINGS LIMITED—See Advent International Corporation; *U.S. Private*, pg. 100
LOCKMASTERS, INC.—See Dominus Capital, L.P.; *U.S. Private*, pg. 1256
LOCKNEY & ASSOCIATES, INC.; *U.S. Private*, pg. 2478
LOCK-N-STITCH, INC.—See Wartsila Corporation; *Int'l*, pg. 8346
LOCKON VIETNAM CO., LTD.—See YRGLM Inc.; *Int'l*, pg. 8606
LOCKOO LIMITED—See Hang Lung Group Limited; *Int'l*, pg. 3245
LOCKPATH, INC.—See BC Partners LLP; *Int'l*, pg. 925
LOCKPORT ICE ARENA; *U.S. Private*, pg. 2478
LOCKPORT UNION SUN & JOURNAL—See The Retirement Systems of Alabama; *U.S. Private*, pg. 4105
LOCKSLEY RESOURCES LIMITED; *Int'l*, pg. 4540
LOCK STORE (AYER RAJAH) PTE. LTD.—See Singapore Post Limited; *Int'l*, pg. 6942
LOCK STORE (CHAI CHEE) PTE. LTD.—See Singapore Post Limited; *Int'l*, pg. 6942
LOCK STORE (TANJONG PAGAR) PTE. LTD.—See Singapore Post Limited; *Int'l*, pg. 6942
LOCKTECH INTERNATIONAL SDN. BHD.—See LYC Healthcare Berhad; *Int'l*, pg. 4605
LOCKTON COMPANIES INTERNATIONAL LIMITED—See The Lockton Companies, LLC; *U.S. Private*, pg. 4071
THE LOCKTON COMPANIES, LLC; *U.S. Private*, pg. 4071
LOCKTON COMPANIES LLP - BELFAST—See The Lockton Companies, LLC; *U.S. Private*, pg. 4071
LOCKTON COMPANIES LLP - BIRMINGHAM—See The Lockton Companies, LLC; *U.S. Private*, pg. 4071
LOCKTON COMPANIES LLP - MANCHESTER—See The Lockton Companies, LLC; *U.S. Private*, pg. 4071
LOCKTON COMPANIES LLP—See The Lockton Companies, LLC; *U.S. Private*, pg. 4071
LOCKTON COMPANIES OF COLORADO, INC.—See The Lockton Companies, LLC; *U.S. Private*, pg. 4071
LOCKTON DUNNING BENEFIT COMPANY—See The Lockton Companies, LLC; *U.S. Private*, pg. 4071
THE LOCKTON INSURANCE AGENCY INC.—See The Lockton Companies, LLC; *U.S. Private*, pg. 4071
LOCKTON INSURANCE BROKERS LLC—See The Lockton Companies, LLC; *U.S. Private*, pg. 4071
LOCKTON OVERSEAS LTD.—See The Lockton Companies, LLC; *U.S. Private*, pg. 4071
LOCKWOOD ADVISORS, INC.—See The Bank of New York Mellon Corporation; *U.S. Public*, pg. 2037
LOCKWOOD AGENCY, INC.—See Stone Point Capital LLC; *U.S. Private*, pg. 3819
LOCKWOOD ANDREWS & NEWNAM, INC.—See Leo A. Daly Company; *U.S. Private*, pg. 2422
LOCKWOOD BROADCASTING INC.; *U.S. Private*, pg. 2478
LOCKWOOD BROTHERS, INC.; *U.S. Private*, pg. 2478
LOCKWOOD FINANCIAL GROUP, INC.—See The Bank of New York Mellon Corporation; *U.S. Public*, pg. 2038
LOCKWOOD INDUSTRIES INC.—See Arsenal Capital Management LP; *U.S. Private*, pg. 338
LOCKWOOD KESSLER & BARTLETT, INC.—See Wind Point Advisors LLC; *U.S. Private*, pg. 4536
LOCKWOOD MANUFACTURING, INC.—See Yamabiko Corporation; *Int'l*, pg. 8547
LOCKWOOD MCKINNON CO. INC.; *U.S. Private*, pg. 2479
LOC MANUTENTION—See Manitou BF S.A.; *Int'l*, pg. 4672
LOCOCHEM SP. Z O.O.—See PCC SE; *Int'l*, pg. 5766
LOCOGUIDE, INC.—See Kufu Company Inc.; *Int'l*, pg. 4326
LOCO HONG KONG HOLDINGS LIMITED; *Int'l*, pg. 4540
LOCO, INC.; *U.S. Private*, pg. 2479
LOCOMOTE IP PTY. LTD.—See Elliott Management Corporation; *U.S. Private*, pg. 1373
LOCOMOTE IP PTY. LTD.—See Siris Capital Group, LLC; *U.S. Private*, pg. 3674
LOCOMOTE TECHNOLOGIES TRADING PTY. LTD.—See Elliott Management Corporation; *U.S. Private*, pg. 1373
LOCOMOTE TECHNOLOGIES TRADING PTY. LTD.—See Siris Capital Group, LLC; *U.S. Private*, pg. 3674
LOCONDO, INC.; *Int'l*, pg. 4540
LOCORR FUND MANAGEMENT LLC—See Octavus Group LLC; *U.S. Private*, pg. 2993
LOCOSOCO GROUP PLC; *Int'l*, pg. 4540
LOCRETE INDUSTRIES CO.—See National Real Estate Company K.S.C.; *Int'l*, pg. 5162
LOCTEK ERGONOMIC TECHNOLOGY CORP.; *Int'l*, pg. 4540
LOCTITE INTERNATIONAL B.V.—See Henkel AG & Co. KGaA; *Int'l*, pg. 3351

LOCTITE ITALIA S.P.A.—See Henkel AG & Co. KGaA; *Int'l*, pg. 3352
LOCTITE (OVERSEAS) LTD.—See Henkel AG & Co. KGaA; *Int'l*, pg. 3351
LOCTITE PUERTO RICO, INC.—See Henkel AG & Co. KGaA; *Int'l*, pg. 3353
LOCUM LEADERS; *U.S. Private*, pg. 2479
THE LOCUM PARTNERSHIP LIMITED—See Servoca Plc; *Int'l*, pg. 6726
LOCUS ENERGY, LLC—See Also Energy Inc.; *U.S. Private*, pg. 203
LOCUS TELECOMMUNICATIONS, INC.—See Telrite Holdings, Inc.; *U.S. Private*, pg. 3962
LOCUST GROVE INC.; *U.S. Private*, pg. 2479
LOCUST LUMBER COMPANY, INC.—See Builders FirstSource, Inc.; *U.S. Public*, pg. 410
LOCUST RIDGE CONTRACTORS—See Haines & Kibblehouse Inc.; *U.S. Private*, pg. 1841
LOCUST RIDGE QUARRY—See Haines & Kibblehouse Inc.; *U.S. Private*, pg. 1841
LOCUST WALK ACQUISITION CORP.; *U.S. Public*, pg. 1339
LOCUZ ENTERPRISE SOLUTIONS LTD.—See SHI International Corp.; *U.S. Private*, pg. 3635
LOC VACANCES SARL—See TUI AG; *Int'l*, pg. 7965
LODAL, INC.; *U.S. Private*, pg. 2479
LODAM ELECTRONICS A/S—See BITZER SE; *Int'l*, pg. 1052
L-O DEL MAR HOLDING, INC.; *U.S. Private*, pg. 2363
LODE METALS INC.; *Int'l*, pg. 4541
LODE RESOURCES LTD.; *Int'l*, pg. 4541
LODERS CROKLAAN CANADA INC.—See Bunge Limited; *U.S. Public*, pg. 411
LODERS CROKLAAN FOR OILS S.A.E.—See Bunge Limited; *U.S. Public*, pg. 412
LODERS CROKLAAN USA, LLC—See Bunge Limited; *U.S. Public*, pg. 411
LODESTAR INVESTMENT COUNSEL, LLC—See Canadian Imperial Bank of Commerce; *Int'l*, pg. 1283
LODESTAR INVESTMENT HOLDINGS CORPORATION; *Int'l*, pg. 4541
LODESTAR LOGISTICS CORP.; *Int'l*, pg. 4541
LODESTAR MINERALS LIMITED; *Int'l*, pg. 4541
LODE-STAR MINING INC.; *U.S. Public*, pg. 1339
LODESTAR SEA& AIR CO., LTD.—See Well Biotec Co., Ltd.; *Int'l*, pg. 8372
LODESTONE ADVERTISING; *U.S. Private*, pg. 2479
LODESTONE MANAGEMENT CONSULTANTS AG—See Infosys Limited; *Int'l*, pg. 3696
LODGE AT AMES POND LIMITED PARTNERSHIP—See UDR, Inc.; *U.S. Public*, pg. 2218
THE LODGE AT VAIL—See Vail Resorts, Inc.; *U.S. Public*, pg. 2271
LODGECAP, INC.; *U.S. Private*, pg. 2479
LODGE CONSTRUCTION INC.; *U.S. Private*, pg. 2479
LODGENET STAYONLINE INC.—See SONIFI Solutions, Inc.; *U.S. Private*, pg. 3714
LODGE OF FOUR SEASONS; *U.S. Private*, pg. 2479
LODGEPINE CAPITAL MANAGEMENT LIMITED—See Markel Group Inc.; *U.S. Public*, pg. 1368
LODGES & MOUNTAIN HOTELS SARL—See TUI AG; *Int'l*, pg. 7965
LODGE STOCK & BARREL PROPRIETARY LIMITED—See Steinhoff International Holdings N.V.; *Int'l*, pg. 7194
LODGIAN INC.—See Lone Star Global Acquisitions, LLC; *U.S. Private*, pg. 2489
LODGICO LTD.—See Honkarakenne Oyj; *Int'l*, pg. 3471
LODGING ACCESS SYSTEMS, LLC—See CCL Industries Inc.; *Int'l*, pg. 1367
LODGING ENTERPRISES INC.; *U.S. Private*, pg. 2479
LODGING ENTERPRISES, LLC—See American Hotel Income Properties REIT LP; *Int'l*, pg. 422
LODGING INTERACTIVE; *U.S. Private*, pg. 2479
LODGING MEDIA, INC.; *Int'l*, pg. 4541
LODGING PARTNER SERVICES DENMARK APS—See Expedia Group, Inc.; *U.S. Public*, pg. 809
LODGING RESOURCES, INC.; *U.S. Private*, pg. 2479
LODGING UNLIMITED, INC.; *U.S. Private*, pg. 2479
LODHA GROUP; *Int'l*, pg. 4541
LODIAF S.A.—See Carrefour SA; *Int'l*, pg. 1345
LODIC AS—See Kongsberg Gruppen ASA; *Int'l*, pg. 4256
LODI GAS STORAGE, LLC—See Brookfield Infrastructure Partners L.P.; *Int'l*, pg. 1190
LODIGE AUFZUGE GMBH—See KONE Oyj; *Int'l*, pg. 4248
LODI MOTORS INC.; *U.S. Private*, pg. 2479
LODMOOR SANDS (WEYMOUTH) MANAGEMENT COMPANY LIMITED—See Persimmon plc; *Int'l*, pg. 5816
LODOLCE MACHINE COMPANY, INC.; *U.S. Private*, pg. 2479
LODUR AMAGER A/S—See NIBE Industrier AB; *Int'l*, pg. 5261
LODUR CITY VEST A/S—See NIBE Industrier AB; *Int'l*, pg. 5261
LODZIA-ROTEX INVESTMENT LTD.; *Int'l*, pg. 4541
LOEA COMMUNICATIONS CORP.—See Trex Enterprises Corporation; *U.S. Private*, pg. 4219
THE LOEB ELECTRIC COMPANY, INC.; *U.S. Private*, pg. 4071

LOEB EQUIPMENT & APPRAISAL CO.; *U.S. Private*, pg. 2479
LOEBER MOTORS, INC.; *U.S. Private*, pg. 2480
LOEB ET ASSOCIES—See Publicis Groupe S.A.; *Int'l*, pg. 6102
LOEB HOLDING CORPORATION; *U.S. Private*, pg. 2479
LOEB INDUSTRIES INC.; *U.S. Private*, pg. 2479
LOEB & LOEB LLP; *U.S. Private*, pg. 2479
LOEB PARTNERS CORPORATION—See Loeb Holding Corporation; *U.S. Private*, pg. 2479
LOEB PARTNERS REALTY & DEVELOPMENT—See Loeb Holding Corporation; *U.S. Private*, pg. 2479
LOEB PARTNERS REALTY, LLC; *U.S. Private*, pg. 2480
LOEFFEL STEEL PRODUCTS INC.; *U.S. Private*, pg. 2480
LOEFFLER KETCHUM MOUNTJOY (LKM); *U.S. Private*, pg. 2480
LOEHMANN'S HOLDINGS INC.—See Dubai World Corporation; *Int'l*, pg. 2222
LOEHMANN'S, INC.—See Dubai World Corporation; *Int'l*, pg. 2222
LOEKIE B.V.—See Accell Group N.V.; *Int'l*, pg. 81
LOEKS THEATRES, INC.; *U.S. Private*, pg. 2480
LOENBRO, INC.—See Braemont Capital Management LLC; *U.S. Private*, pg. 633
LOEPFE BROTHERS LTD.—See Alpha Associes Conseil SAS; *Int'l*, pg. 367
LOEWE AUSTRALIA PTY LTD.—See LVMH Moet Hennessy Louis Vuitton SE; *Int'l*, pg. 4601
LOEWE FASHION (M) SDN BHD—See LVMH Moet Hennessy Louis Vuitton SE; *Int'l*, pg. 4598
LOEWE FASHION SDN. BHD—See LVMH Moet Hennessy Louis Vuitton SE; *Int'l*, pg. 4601
LOEWE FRANCE S.A.S.—See Stargate Capital GmbH; *Int'l*, pg. 7176
LOEWE HAWAII INC.—See LVMH Moet Hennessy Louis Vuitton SE; *Int'l*, pg. 4602
LOEWE HERMANOS S.A—See LVMH Moet Hennessy Louis Vuitton SE; *Int'l*, pg. 4602
LOEWE HERMANOS (U.K) LTD—See LVMH Moet Hennessy Louis Vuitton SE; *Int'l*, pg. 4602
LOEWE HERMANOS (U.K) LTD—See LVMH Moet Hennessy Louis Vuitton SE; *Int'l*, pg. 4602
LOEWE HONG KONG LTD.—See LVMH Moet Hennessy Louis Vuitton SE; *Int'l*, pg. 4602
LOEWE JAPAN KK—See LVMH Moet Hennessy Louis Vuitton SE; *Int'l*, pg. 4602
LOEWE MACAO LTD—See LVMH Moet Hennessy Louis Vuitton SE; *Int'l*, pg. 4602
LOEWEN; *Int'l*, pg. 4541
LOEWE OPTA BENELUX N.V./S.A—See Stargate Capital GmbH; *Int'l*, pg. 7176
LOEWE SAIPAN INC.—See LVMH Moet Hennessy Louis Vuitton SE; *Int'l*, pg. 4602
LOEWE S.A.—See LVMH Moet Hennessy Louis Vuitton SE; *Int'l*, pg. 4601
LOEWE TAIWAN LTD.—See LVMH Moet Hennessy Louis Vuitton SE; *Int'l*, pg. 4602
LOEWE TECHNOLOGIES GMBH—See Stargate Capital GmbH; *Int'l*, pg. 7176
LOEWS ANNAPOLIS HOTEL CORP.; *U.S. Private*, pg. 2480
LOEWS CORPORATION; *U.S. Public*, pg. 1339
LOEWS HOTELS HOLDING CORPORATION—See Loews Corporation; *U.S. Public*, pg. 1340
LOEWS SANTA MONICA BEACH HOTEL—See Loews Corporation; *U.S. Public*, pg. 1340
LOEWS VANDERBILT PLAZA HOTEL—See Loews Corporation; *U.S. Public*, pg. 1340
LOFA INDUSTRIES, LLC—See Harbour Group Industries, Inc.; *U.S. Private*, pg. 1860
LOFFLER BUSINESS SYSTEMS INC.; *U.S. Private*, pg. 2480
LOFFLER COMPANIES, INC.; *U.S. Private*, pg. 2480
LOFFREDO FRESH PRODUCE CO., INC.; *U.S. Private*, pg. 2480
LOFO HIGH TECH FILM GMBH—See Shin Kong Group; *Int'l*, pg. 6837
LOFRA GMBH & CO.KG—See Commerzbank AG; *Int'l*, pg. 1718
LOFRA VERWALTUNGS-GESELLSCHAFT MBH—See Commerzbank AG; *Int'l*, pg. 1718
LOFTA, INC.—See Owens & Minor, Inc.; *U.S. Public*, pg. 1625
THE LOFT CO., LTD.—See Seven & i Holdings Co., Ltd.; *Int'l*, pg. 6731
LOFT INC.; *U.S. Private*, pg. 2480
LOFTIS HOME MEDICAL, LLC—See AdaptHealth Corp.; *U.S. Public*, pg. 39
LOFTLEIOIR - ICELANDIC EHF.—See Icelandair Group hf.; *Int'l*, pg. 3579
LOFT MAGAZACILIK INC.—See Eroglu Holding AS; *Int'l*, pg. 2496
LOFTON LABEL, INC.—See Leonard Green & Partners, L.P.; *U.S. Private*, pg. 2428
LOFTS AT CHARLES RIVER LANDING, LLC—See UDR, Inc.; *U.S. Public*, pg. 2218
LOG 607 S.R.L.—See RCS MediaGroup S.p.A.; *Int'l*, pg. 6229

LOGAER MASCHINENBAU GMBH; *Int'l*, pg. 4541
LOG AGGREGATEBAU GMBH—See Weber-Hydraulik GmbH; *Int'l*, pg. 8366
LOGAHOLIC B.V.; *Int'l*, pg. 4541
LOGAH TECHNOLOGY CORPORATION; *Int'l*, pg. 4541
LOGAIR—See Air France-KLM S.A.; *Int'l*, pg. 237
THE LOGAN BANNER—See HD Media Company, LLC; *U.S. Private*, pg. 1890
LOGAN CAMPBELL RETIREMENT VILLAGE LIMITED—See Ryman Healthcare Ltd.; *Int'l*, pg. 6439
LOGAN CIRCLE PARTNERS, L.P.—See MetLife, Inc.; *U.S. Public*, pg. 1340
LOGAN CLAY PRODUCTS CO.; *U.S. Public*, pg. 1340
LOGAN COMMUNITY FINANCIAL SERVICES LIMITED—See Bendigo & Adelaide Bank Ltd.; *Int'l*, pg. 971
LOGAN COMMUNITY RESOURCES, INC.; *U.S. Private*, pg. 2480
LOGAN COPPER INC.; *Int'l*, pg. 4541
LOGAN CORPORATION; *U.S. Private*, pg. 2480
LOGAN COUNTY ELECTRIC COOPERATIVE; *U.S. Private*, pg. 2480
LOGAN COUNTY MINE SERVICES, INC.—See Alpha Natural Resources, Inc.; *U.S. Private*, pg. 199
LOGAN GENERAL HOSPITAL, LLC—See Apollo Global Management, Inc.; *U.S. Public*, pg. 158
LOGAN GROUP COMPANY LIMITED; *Int'l*, pg. 4541
LOGAN HEALTH; *U.S. Private*, pg. 2480
LOGAN INVESTMENT CORPORATION; *U.S. Private*, pg. 2480
LOGAN & KANAWHA COAL COMPANY, INC.—See International Industries, Inc.; *U.S. Private*, pg. 2117
LOGAN LABORATORIES, LLC—See Bain Capital, LP; *U.S. Private*, pg. 445
LOGAN OUTDOOR PRODUCTS, LLC—See Vista Outdoor Inc.; *U.S. Public*, pg. 2305
LOGAN RIDGE FINANCE CORPORATION; *U.S. Public*, pg. 1340
LOGANSPORT FINANCIAL CORP.; *U.S. Public*, pg. 1340
LOGANSPORT SAVINGS BANK—See Logansport Financial Corp.; *U.S. Public*, pg. 1340
LOGAN SQUARE ALUMINUM SUPPLY, INC.; *U.S. Private*, pg. 2480
LOGAN TELEFLEX (FRANCE) S.A.—See Daifuku Co., Ltd.; *Int'l*, pg. 1926
LOGAN TELEFLEX, INC.—See Daifuku Co., Ltd.; *Int'l*, pg. 1925
LOGAN & WHALEY CO.; *U.S. Private*, pg. 2480
LOG CABIN DEMOCRAT, LLC—See Paxton Media Group LLC; *U.S. Private*, pg. 3116
LOG CABIN HOMES LTD.; *U.S. Private*, pg. 2480
LOG COMMERCIAL PROPERTIES E PARTICIPACOES S.A.; *Int'l*, pg. 4541
LOGDIS SAS—See Carrefour SA; *Int'l*, pg. 1345
LOGENIX INTERNATIONAL; *U.S. Private*, pg. 2481
LOGGERHEAD MARINA—See Seven Kings Holdings, Inc.; *U.S. Private*, pg. 3618
LOGGHE STAMPING COMPANY; *U.S. Private*, pg. 2481
LOGGLY, INC.—See Silver Lake Group, LLC; *U.S. Private*, pg. 3661
LOGGLY, INC.—See Thoma Bravo, L.P.; *U.S. Private*, pg. 4153
LOGHMAN PHARMACEUTICAL & HYGIENIC CO.; *Int'l*, pg. 4541
LOG HYDRAULIK GMBH—See Weber-Hydraulik GmbH; *Int'l*, pg. 8366
LOGI ANALYTICS, INC.—See TA Associates, Inc.; *U.S. Private*, pg. 3915
LOGIBEC INC.—See GI Manager L.P.; *U.S. Private*, pg. 1693
LOGICAL DESIGN SOLUTIONS INC.; *U.S. Private*, pg. 2481
LOGICAL IMAGES, INC.; *U.S. Private*, pg. 2481
LOGICALIS ANDINA S.A.C.—See Datatec Limited; *Int'l*, pg. 1980
LOGICALIS ARGENTINA S.A.—See Datatec Limited; *Int'l*, pg. 1980
LOGICALIS AUSTRALIA PTY LIMITED—See Datatec Limited; *Int'l*, pg. 1980
LOGICALIS BRASIL IMPORTACAO EXPORTACAO LTDA—See Datatec Limited; *Int'l*, pg. 1980
LOGICALIS CHILE S.A.—See Datatec Limited; *Int'l*, pg. 1980
LOGICALIS DEUTSCHLAND GMBH—See Datatec Limited; *Int'l*, pg. 1980
LOGICALIS ECUADOR S.A.—See Datatec Limited; *Int'l*, pg. 1980
LOGICALIS GROUP LTD.—See Datatec Limited; *Int'l*, pg. 1980
LOGICALIS GUERNSEY LIMITED—See Datatec Limited; *Int'l*, pg. 1980
LOGICALIS HONG KONG LIMITED—See Datatec Limited; *Int'l*, pg. 1980
LOGICALIS, INC.—See Datatec Limited; *Int'l*, pg. 1980
LOGICALIS IRELAND LIMITED—See Datatec Limited; *Int'l*, pg. 1980
LOGICALIS JERSEY LIMITED—See Datatec Limited; *Int'l*, pg. 1980

LOGICALIS MALAYSIA SDN. BHD.—See Datatec Limited; *Int'l*, pg. 1980
LOGICALIS MEXICO, S. DE R.L. DE C.V.—See Datatec Limited; *Int'l*, pg. 1980
LOGICALIS-MINTERS GMBH—See Datatec Limited; *Int'l*, pg. 1980
LOGICALIS PARAGUAY S.A.—See Datatec Limited; *Int'l*, pg. 1980
LOGICALIS PTE. LIMITED—See Datatec Limited; *Int'l*, pg. 1980
LOGICALIS PUERTO RICO INC.—See Datatec Limited; *Int'l*, pg. 1980
LOGICALIS SA (PTY) LTD—See Datatec Limited; *Int'l*, pg. 1981
LOGICALIS SHANGHAI LIMITED—See Datatec Limited; *Int'l*, pg. 1981
LOGICALIS SINGAPORE PTE. LIMITED—See Datatec Limited; *Int'l*, pg. 1981
LOGICALIS SPAIN SL—See Datatec Limited; *Int'l*, pg. 1980
LOGICALIS UK LIMITED—See Datatec Limited; *Int'l*, pg. 1980
LOGICALIS US—See Datatec Limited; *Int'l*, pg. 1980
LOGICALLY, INC.—See The Riverside Company; *U.S. Private*, pg. 4109
LOGICAL OPERATIONS INC.; *U.S. Private*, pg. 2481
LOGICAL SOLUTION SERVICES INC.; *U.S. Private*, pg. 2481
LOGICAL SYSTEMS, LLC.; *U.S. Private*, pg. 2481
LOGICAL TECHNICAL SERVICES, CORP. (LTS)—See Sentrillion Corporation; *U.S. Private*, pg. 3610
LOGICAL VENTURES INC.; *U.S. Private*, pg. 2481
LOGICAMMS (CENTRAL) PTY LTD—See Verbrec Limited; *Int'l*, pg. 8165
LOGICAMMS CONSULTANTS—See Verbrec Limited; *Int'l*, pg. 8165
LOGICAN TECHNOLOGIES INC.; *Int'l*, pg. 4541
LOGICARE CORPORATION—See Interactivation Health Networks LLC; *U.S. Private*, pg. 2108
LOGICA VENTURES CORP.; *Int'l*, pg. 4541
LOGICBIO THERAPEUTICS, INC.—See AstraZeneca PLC; *Int'l*, pg. 659
LOGIC COMMUNICATIONS LTD.—See One Communications Ltd.; *Int'l*, pg. 5575
LOGIC DEVICES INCORPORATED; *U.S. Private*, pg. 2481
LOGICEASE SOLUTIONS, INC.; *U.S. Private*, pg. 2481
LOGICIELS EASYVISTA INC—See Eurazeo SE; *Int'l*, pg. 2528
LOGIC INFORMATION SYSTEMS, INC.—See Accenture plc; *Int'l*, pg. 87
LOGIC INSTRUMENT DEUTSCHLAND GMBH—See Logic Instrument S.A.; *Int'l*, pg. 4541
LOGIC INSTRUMENT S.A.; *Int'l*, pg. 4541
LOGIC INSTRUMENT USA INC.—See Logic Instrument S.A.; *Int'l*, pg. 4541
LOGIC INTEGRATION INC.; *U.S. Private*, pg. 2481
LOGICJUNCTION INC.—See Purple Wifi Ltd; *Int'l*, pg. 6123
LOGICLINE GMBH—See Lenze SE; *Int'l*, pg. 4455
LOGICMARK, INC.; *U.S. Public*, pg. 1340
LOGICMARK, LLC—See LogicMark, Inc.; *U.S. Public*, pg. 1340
LOGICMONITOR, INC.—See Vista Equity Partners, LLC; *U.S. Public*, pg. 4398
LOGICO DESIGN S.R.L.—See Ningbo Joyson Electronic Corp.; *Int'l*, pg. 5304
LOGICOM DUBAI LLC—See Logicom Public Ltd; *Int'l*, pg. 4542
LOGICOM FZE—See Logicom Public Ltd; *Int'l*, pg. 4542
LOGICOM, INC.—See CRE, Inc.; *U.S. Private*, pg. 1830
LOGICOM ITALIA S.R.L.—See Logicom Public Ltd; *Int'l*, pg. 4542
LOGICOM JORDAN LLC—See Logicom Public Ltd; *Int'l*, pg. 4542
LOGICOM KUWAIT FOR COMPUTER COMPANY W.L.L.—See Logicom Public Ltd; *Int'l*, pg. 4542
LOGICOM LLC—See Logicom Public Ltd; *Int'l*, pg. 4542
LOGICOM (MIDDLE EAST) SAL—See Logicom Public Ltd; *Int'l*, pg. 4542
LOGICOM N.G.—See Vontier Corporation; *U.S. Public*, pg. 2309
LOGICOM PUBLIC LTD; *Int'l*, pg. 4542
LOGICOM SAUDI ARABIA LLC—See Logicom Public Ltd; *Int'l*, pg. 4542
LOGICOM SOLUTIONS LIMITED—See Logicom Public Ltd; *Int'l*, pg. 4542
LOGICOM SYSTEMS INC.; *U.S. Private*, pg. 2481
LOGICON BUILDING SYSTEMS PRIVATE LIMITED—See Nitin Fire Protection Industries Ltd; *Int'l*, pg. 5381
LOGI CO-NET CORP.—See Toyo Ink SC Holdings Co., Ltd.; *Int'l*, pg. 7853
LOGICOOL CO., LTD.—See Logitech International S.A.; *U.S. Public*, pg. 1341
LOGIC PD, INC.—See Compass Group, LLC; *U.S. Private*, pg. 999
LOGIC SOLUTIONS, INC.; *U.S. Private*, pg. 2481
LOGICSYNERGY SP. Z O.O.—See WASKO S.A.; *Int'l*, pg. 8352

COMPANY NAME INDEX

LOGIC WAY B.V.—See Trimble, Inc.; *U.S. Public*, pg. 2190
LOGIDIS LIMITED—See Ireland Blyth Limited; *Int'l*, pg. 3807
LOGI FACTORING CO., LTD.—See Senko Group Holdings Co., Ltd.; *Int'l*, pg. 6710
LOGIGEAR CORPORATION; *U.S. Private*, pg. 2481
LOGIGEAR JAPAN CORPORATION—See Digital Hearts Holdings Co., Ltd.; *Int'l*, pg. 2122
LOGILITY, INC.—See American Software, Inc.; *U.S. Public*, pg. 109
LOGILITY NZ (UC)—See American Software, Inc.; *U.S. Public*, pg. 109
LOGILITY SOLUTIONS PVT. LTD.—See American Software, Inc.; *U.S. Public*, pg. 109
LOGIMAR SRL—See DSV A/S; *Int'l*, pg. 2214
LOGINET JAPAN CO., LTD.; *Int'l*, pg. 4542
LOG-IN LOGISTICA INTERMODAL S.A.; *Int'l*, pg. 4541
LOGIN LOGISTICS LLC—See EPES Carriers Inc.; *U.S. Private*, pg. 1412
LOGIN PEOPLE S.A.; *Int'l*, pg. 4542
LOGIN SA—See PROFILE SYSTEMS & SOFTWARE S.R.L.; *Int'l*, pg. 5989
LOGINTEGRAL 2000 S.A.U.—See RCS MediaGroup S.p.A.; *Int'l*, pg. 6230
LOGINTRADE SA; *Int'l*, pg. 4542
LOGIPAL EXPRESS INC—See BANDAI NAMCO Holdings Inc.; *Int'l*, pg. 829
LOGIQ3 INC.—See Reinsurance Group of America, Inc.; *U.S. Public*, pg. 1777
LOGIQ, INC.; *U.S. Public*, pg. 1341
LOGIS CONFORT SOCIMI, S.A.; *Int'l*, pg. 4542
LOGISCO; *Int'l*, pg. 4542
LOGIS INDUSTRIEDIENSTLEISTUNG GMBH—See Deufol SE; *Int'l*, pg. 2048
LOGISITICS HEALTH, INC.—See UnitedHealth Group Incorporated; *U.S. Public*, pg. 2242
LOGIS IT SERVICE GMBH—See Raiffeisenlandesbank Oberosterreich Aktiengesellschaft; *Int'l*, pg. 6187
LOGISMOS INFORMATION SYSTEMS S.A.; *Int'l*, pg. 4542
LOGISNEXT CHUBU CO., LTD.—See Mitsubishi Heavy Industries, Ltd.; *Int'l*, pg. 4954
LOGISNEXT CHUGOKU CO., LTD.—See Mitsubishi Heavy Industries, Ltd.; *Int'l*, pg. 4954
LOGISNEXT HANDLING SYSTEM CORPORATION—See Hitachi Zosen Corporation; *Int'l*, pg. 3411
LOGISNEXT HOKKAIDO CO., LTD.—See Mitsubishi Heavy Industries, Ltd.; *Int'l*, pg. 4954
LOGISNEXT KINKI CO., LTD.—See Mitsubishi Heavy Industries, Ltd.; *Int'l*, pg. 4954
LOGISNEXT KYUSHU CO., LTD.—See Mitsubishi Heavy Industries, Ltd.; *Int'l*, pg. 4954
LOGISNEXT MANUFACTURING (THAILAND) CO., LTD.—See Mitsubishi Heavy Industries, Ltd.; *Int'l*, pg. 4954
LOGISNEXT SHIKOKU CO., LTD.—See Mitsubishi Heavy Industries, Ltd.; *Int'l*, pg. 4954
LOGISNEXT SHINETSU CO., LTD.—See Mitsubishi Heavy Industries, Ltd.; *Int'l*, pg. 4954
LOGISNEXT SHIZUOKA CO., LTD.—See Mitsubishi Heavy Industries, Ltd.; *Int'l*, pg. 4954
LOGISNEXT TOHOKU CO., LTD.—See Mitsubishi Heavy Industries, Ltd.; *Int'l*, pg. 4954
LOGISNEXT TOKYO CO., LTD.—See Mitsubishi Heavy Industries, Ltd.; *Int'l*, pg. 4954
LOGISNEXT UNICARRIERS CO., LTD.—See Mitsubishi Heavy Industries, Ltd.; *Int'l*, pg. 4954
LOGISOFT COMPUTER PRODUCTS, LLC—See RMK Holdings Corp.; *U.S. Private*, pg. 3452
LOGI SOLUTION CO., LTD.—See Senko Group Holdings Co., Ltd.; *Int'l*, pg. 6710
LOGISOLVE, LLC; *U.S. Private*, pg. 2481
LOGIS PRUMYSLOVE OBALY A.S.—See Deufol SE; *Int'l*, pg. 2048
LOGISTA ITALIA S.P.A.—See Imperial Brands PLC; *Int'l*, pg. 3632
LOGISTAR INTERNATIONAL HOLDING COMPANY LIMITED—See Cal-Comp Electronics (Thailand) pcl; *Int'l*, pg. 1261
LOGISTEA AB; *Int'l*, pg. 4542
LOGISTEC CORPORATION—See Blue Wolf Capital Partners LLC; *U.S. Private*, pg. 594
LOGISTEC GULF COAST LLC—See Blue Wolf Capital Partners LLC; *U.S. Private*, pg. 594
LOGIS-TECH, INC.; *U.S. Private*, pg. 2481
LOGISTEC MARINE AGENCIES INC—See Blue Wolf Capital Partners LLC; *U.S. Private*, pg. 594
LOGISTEC STEVEDORING (ATLANTIC) INC.—See Blue Wolf Capital Partners LLC; *U.S. Private*, pg. 594
LOGISTEC STEVEDORING INC. - CHURCHILL—See Blue Wolf Capital Partners LLC; *U.S. Private*, pg. 595
LOGISTEC STEVEDORING INC. - CONTRECOEUR—See Blue Wolf Capital Partners LLC; *U.S. Private*, pg. 595
LOGISTEC STEVEDORING INC. - MONTREAL, LAURIER TERMINAL—See Blue Wolf Capital Partners LLC; *U.S. Private*, pg. 595
LOGISTEC STEVEDORING INC. - QUEBEC—See Blue Wolf Capital Partners LLC; *U.S. Private*, pg. 595
LOGISTEC STEVEDORING INC. - SEPT-ILES—See Blue Wolf Capital Partners LLC; *U.S. Private*, pg. 595
LOGISTEC STEVEDORING INC.—See Blue Wolf Capital Partners LLC; *U.S. Private*, pg. 594
LOGISTEC STEVEDORING INC. - TROIS-RIVIERES—See Blue Wolf Capital Partners LLC; *U.S. Private*, pg. 595
LOGISTEC STEVEDORING (NEW BRUNSWICK) INC.—See Blue Wolf Capital Partners LLC; *U.S. Private*, pg. 594
LOGISTEC STEVEDORING (NOVA SCOTIA) INC.—See Blue Wolf Capital Partners LLC; *U.S. Private*, pg. 595
LOGISTEC STEVEDORING (NOVA SCOTIA) INC. - SYDNEY—See Blue Wolf Capital Partners LLC; *U.S. Private*, pg. 595
LOGISTEC STEVEDORING (ONTARIO) INC.—See Blue Wolf Capital Partners LLC; *U.S. Private*, pg. 595
LOGISTEC USA INC. - PORT MANATEE—See Blue Wolf Capital Partners LLC; *U.S. Private*, pg. 595
LOGISTEC USA INC.—See Blue Wolf Capital Partners LLC; *U.S. Private*, pg. 595
LOGISTEED, LTD.—See KKR & Co. Inc.; *U.S. Public*, pg. 1258
LOGISTER, S.A.—See Grifols, S.A.; *Int'l*, pg. 3084
LOGISTICA DE QUIMICOS DEL SUR S.A.C.—See Marquard & Bahls AG; *Int'l*, pg. 4700
LOGISTICA GRIFOLS S.A DE C.V—See Grifols, S.A.; *Int'l*, pg. 3085
LOGISTICARE BONDED—See Taavura Holdings, Ltd.; *Int'l*, pg. 7401
LOGISTICARE, LTD.—See Taavura Holdings, Ltd.; *Int'l*, pg. 7401
LOGISTICARE SOLUTIONS LLC—See ModivCare, Inc.; *U.S. Public*, pg. 1455
LOGISTICA SANMIVAL S.L.—See Deutsche Bahn AG; *Int'l*, pg. 2051
LOGISTICA TRAINING LIMITED—See MBH Corporation Plc; *Int'l*, pg. 4752
LOGISTICA TRANSPORTE Y SERVICIOS ASOCIADOS S.A.S.—See Companhia Brasileira de Distribuicao; *Int'l*, pg. 1746
LOGISTIC DYNAMICS, INC.; *U.S. Private*, pg. 2481
LOGISTIC LEASING, LLC.; *U.S. Private*, pg. 2481
LOGISTIC MAO DE MEXICO, S.A. DE C.V.—See Mid-America Overseas Inc.; *U.S. Private*, pg. 2707
LOGISTICS BUSINESS SYSTEMS LIMITED—See PTC Inc.; *U.S. Public*, pg. 1734
LOGISTICS DIRECT LTD.—See Perenti Global Limited; *Int'l*, pg. 5798
LOGISTICS & ENVIRONMENTAL SUPPORT SERVICES CORPORATION; *U.S. Private*, pg. 2482
LOGISTIC SERVICES, INC.—See Hormel Foods Corporation; *U.S. Public*, pg. 1054
LOGISTIC SERVICES INTERNATIONAL INC.; *U.S. Private*, pg. 2481
LOGISTICS HEALTH, INC.—See UnitedHealth Group Incorporated; *U.S. Public*, pg. 2242
LOGISTICS HOLDINGS AUSTRALIA PTY. LTD.—See Singapore Post Limited; *Int'l*, pg. 6942
LOGISTICS HOLDINGS LTD; *Int'l*, pg. 4542
LOGISTICS & INFORMATION TECHNOLOGY (LOGIT) DIVISION—See Management Training & Consulting Inc.; *U.S. Private*, pg. 2561
LOGISTICS INNOVATION TECHNOLOGIES CORP.; *U.S. Public*, pg. 1341
LOGISTICS INTERNATIONAL LTD.—See Nippon Yusen Kabushiki Kaisha; *Int'l*, pg. 5358
LOGISTICS MANAGEMENT INSTITUTE; *U.S. Private*, pg. 2482
LOGISTICS MANAGEMENT RESOURCES INC.; *U.S. Private*, pg. 2482
LOGISTICS MANAGEMENT SERVICES LTD.—See McCollister's Transportation Group Inc.; *U.S. Private*, pg. 2629
LOGISTICS MANAGEMENT SOLUTIONS LLC—See TPG Capital, L.P.; *U.S. Public*, pg. 2177
LOGISTICS MATES CORP.—See Japan Logistic Systems Corp.; *Int'l*, pg. 3899
LOGISTICS NETWORK INC.—See Nichirei Corporation; *Int'l*, pg. 5270
LOGISTIC SOLUTIONS AUSTRALASIA PTY. LTD.—See Rheinmetall AG; *Int'l*, pg. 6322
LOGISTIC SOLUTIONS INC.; *U.S. Private*, pg. 2482
LOGISTICS OPERATION SERVICE CO., LTD.—See Mitsui-Soko Holdings Co., Ltd.; *Int'l*, pg. 4993
LOGISTIC; *U.S. Private*, pg. 2481
THE LOGISTICS PARTNERSHIP LLP; *Int'l*, pg. 7664
LOGISTICS PLANNER INC.—See Nichirei Corporation; *Int'l*, pg. 5270
LOGISTICS PLANNING SERVICES, INC.; *U.S. Private*, pg. 2482
LOGISTICS PLUS, INC.; *U.S. Private*, pg. 2482
LOGISTICS SPECIALTIES, INC.; *U.S. Private*, pg. 2482
LOGISTICS SUPPORT INC.; *U.S. Private*, pg. 2482
LOGISTICS VICEM JOINT STOCK COMPANY; *Int'l*, pg. 4542
LOGISTIKCENTER NORRKOPING—See Lagercrantz Group AB; *Int'l*, pg. 4394
LOGISTIK PHARMA INC.—See KDA Group, Inc.; *Int'l*, pg. 4111
LOGISTIK SERVICE CENTER S.R.O.—See Hubert Burda Media Holding Kommanditgesellschaft; *Int'l*, pg. 3520
LOGISTIK SERVICE GMBH—See voestalpine AG; *Int'l*, pg. 8295
LOGISTIQUES TRANS-WEST INC; *Int'l*, pg. 4542
LOGISTIX—See EMAK Worldwide, Inc.; *U.S. Private*, pg. 1378
LOGISTRA S.A.—See SNCF; *Int'l*, pg. 7026
LOGISTRI FASTIGHETS AB; *Int'l*, pg. 4542
LOGISTYX TECHNOLOGIES, LLC—See Insight Venture Management, LLC; *U.S. Private*, pg. 2091
LOGISYS INC.; *Int'l*, pg. 4542
LOGISZTAR KFT.—See OBB-Holding AG; *Int'l*, pg. 5509
LOGITECH ASIA PACIFIC LIMITED—See Logitech International S.A.; *U.S. Public*, pg. 1341
LOGITECH AUSTRALIA COMPUTER PERIPHERALS PTY, LIMITED—See Logitech International S.A.; *U.S. Public*, pg. 1341
LOGITECH ENGINEERING & DESIGNS INDIA PRIVATE LIMITED—See Logitech International S.A.; *U.S. Public*, pg. 1341
LOGITECH EUROPE SA—See Logitech International S.A.; *U.S. Public*, pg. 1341
LOGITECH FAR EAST LTD.—See Logitech International S.A.; *U.S. Public*, pg. 1341
LOGITECH FRANCE SAS—See Logitech International S.A.; *U.S. Public*, pg. 1341
LOGITECH GMBH—See Logitech International S.A.; *U.S. Public*, pg. 1341
LOGITECH HELLAS MEPE—See Logitech International S.A.; *U.S. Public*, pg. 1341
LOGITECH HONG KONG, LIMITED—See Logitech International S.A.; *U.S. Public*, pg. 1341
LOGITECH INC.—See Logitech International S.A.; *U.S. Public*, pg. 1341
LOGITECH INTERNATIONAL S.A.; *U.S. Public*, pg. 1341
LOGITECH IRELAND SERVICES LIMITED—See Logitech International S.A.; *U.S. Public*, pg. 1341
LOGITECH ITALIA SRL—See Logitech International S.A.; *U.S. Public*, pg. 1341
LOGITECH KOREA LTD.—See Logitech International S.A.; *U.S. Public*, pg. 1341
LOGITECH LIMITED—See Roper Technologies, Inc.; *U.S. Public*, pg. 1812
LOGITECH MIDDLE EAST FZ-LLC—See Logitech International S.A.; *U.S. Public*, pg. 1341
LOGITECH NORDIC AB—See Logitech International S.A.; *U.S. Public*, pg. 1341
LOGITECH SCHWEIZ AG—See Logitech International S.A.; *U.S. Public*, pg. 1341
LOGITECH (STREAMING MEDIA) SA—See Logitech International S.A.; *U.S. Public*, pg. 1341
LOGITECH TECHNOLOGY (SUZHOU) CO., LTD.—See Logitech International S.A.; *U.S. Public*, pg. 1341
LOGITECH UK LTD—See Logitech International S.A.; *U.S. Public*, pg. 1341
LOGITEK INC.—See North Atlantic Industries Inc.; *U.S. Private*, pg. 2942
LOGITEK TECHNOLOGY LTD.—See The Co-operators Group Limited; *Int'l*, pg. 7634
LOGITEM (CAMBODIA) CO., LTD.—See Japan Logistic Systems Corp.; *Int'l*, pg. 3899
LOGITEM ENGINEERING CORP.—See Japan Logistic Systems Corp.; *Int'l*, pg. 3899
LOGITEM HONG KONG CO., LTD.—See Japan Logistic Systems Corp.; *Int'l*, pg. 3899
LOGITEM INTERNATIONAL CORP.—See Japan Logistic Systems Corp.; *Int'l*, pg. 3899
LOGITEM KEIKABIN CORP.—See Japan Logistic Systems Corp.; *Int'l*, pg. 3899
LOGITEM LAOS GLKP CO., LTD.—See Japan Logistic Systems Corp.; *Int'l*, pg. 3899
LOGITEM MYANMAR CO., LTD.—See Japan Logistic Systems Corp.; *Int'l*, pg. 3899
LOGITEM SHANGHAI CORP.—See Japan Logistic Systems Corp.; *Int'l*, pg. 3899
LOGITEM SHANGHAI WAREHOUSE CORP.—See Japan Logistic Systems Corp.; *Int'l*, pg. 3899
LOGITEM TAIWAN CO., LTD.—See Japan Logistic Systems Corp.; *Int'l*, pg. 3899
LOGITEM (THAILAND) CO., LTD.—See Japan Logistic Systems Corp.; *Int'l*, pg. 3899
LOGITEM TRADING (THAILAND) CO., LTD.—See Japan Logistic Systems Corp.; *Int'l*, pg. 3899
LOGITEM TSUMURA CO., LTD.—See Tsumura & Co.; *Int'l*, pg. 7957
LOGITEM VIETNAM CORP. NO. 1—See Japan Logistic Systems Corp.; *Int'l*, pg. 3899
LOGITEM VIETNAM CORP. NO. 2—See Japan Logistic Systems Corp.; *Int'l*, pg. 3899
LOGITEM VIETNAM CORP.—See Japan Logistic Systems Corp.; *Int'l*, pg. 3899
LOGITEM VIETNAM HOLDING & INVESTMENT COMPANY LIMITED—See Japan Logistic Systems Corp.; *Int'l*, pg. 3899
LOGITEM VIETNAM NORTH SERVICE CO., LTD.—See Japan Logistic Systems Corp.; *Int'l*, pg. 3899

LOGITECH INTERNATIONAL S.A.

LOGITEM VIETNAM SOUTH SERVICE CO., LTD.—See Japan Logistic Systems Corp.; *Int'l*, pg. 3899
LOGITEM VIETNAM TRADING CO., LTD.—See Japan Logistic Systems Corp.; *Int'l*, pg. 3899
LOGITERS PORTUGAL, S.A.—See Corpfin Capital SA; *Int'l*, pg. 1802
LOGITRANS A/S; *Int'l*, pg. 4542
LOGITRI HOLDINGS CO., LTD.—See Mitsuuroko Group Holdings Co., Ltd.; *Int'l*, pg. 4993
LOGIT SDN. BHD.—See Salcon Berhad; *Int'l*, pg. 6492
LOGIT S.R.O.—See Radici Partecipazioni S.p.A.; *Int'l*, pg. 6175
LOGIX COMMUNICATIONS, L.P.—See Astra Capital Management LLC; *U.S. Private*, pg. 361
LOGIX HEALTHCARE SEARCH PARTNERS, LLC—See Maxim Healthcare Services, Inc.; *U.S. Private*, pg. 2618
LOGIX S.A.—See Arrow Electronics, Inc.; *U.S. Public*, pg. 199
LOGIXTECH SOLUTIONS, LLC—See TSR, Inc.; *U.S. Public*, pg. 2202
LOGIXX SECURITY INC.—See SSC Security Services Corp.; *Int'l*, pg. 7155
LOGIZARD CO., LTD.; *Int'l*, pg. 4542
LOGJAM PRESENTS, LLC—See Live Nation Entertainment, Inc.; *U.S. Public*, pg. 1330
LOGLIFT JONSERED AB—See Cargotec Corporation; *Int'l*, pg. 1327
LOGLY, INC.; *Int'l*, pg. 4543
LOG MAX INC.—See Komatsu Ltd.; *Int'l*, pg. 4238
LOGMEIN AUS PTY LTD—See Elliott Management Corporation; *U.S. Private*, pg. 1368
LOGMEIN AUS PTY LTD—See Francisco Partners Management, LP; *U.S. Private*, pg. 1590
LOGMEIN EUROPE B.V.—See Elliott Management Corporation; *U.S. Private*, pg. 1368
LOGMEIN EUROPE B.V.—See Francisco Partners Management, LP; *U.S. Private*, pg. 1590
LOGMEIN, INC.—See Elliott Management Corporation; *U.S. Private*, pg. 1368
LOGMEIN, INC.—See Francisco Partners Management, LP; *U.S. Private*, pg. 1590
LOGMEIN SYSTEMS INDIA PRIVATE LIMITED—See Elliott Management Corporation; *U.S. Private*, pg. 1368
LOGMEIN SYSTEMS INDIA PRIVATE LIMITED—See Francisco Partners Management, LP; *U.S. Private*, pg. 1590
LOGMI, INC.—See Sansan, Inc.; *Int'l*, pg. 6555
LOGNET SYSTEMS; *Int'l*, pg. 4543
LOGO INFOSOFT BUSINESS TECHNOLOGY PRIVATE LIMITED—See Logo Yazilim Sanayi ve Ticaret A.S.; *Int'l*, pg. 4543
LOGO KOBI DIJITAL HIZMETLER A.S.—See Logo Yazilim Sanayi ve Ticaret A.S.; *Int'l*, pg. 4543
LOGONATION, INC.; *U.S. Private*, pg. 2482
LOGOPAK B.V.—See L. Possehl & Co. mbH; *Int'l*, pg. 4383
LOGOPAK INTERNATIONAL LTD.—See L. Possehl & Co. mbH; *Int'l*, pg. 4383
LOGOPAK SISTEMAS S.L.—See L. Possehl & Co. mbH; *Int'l*, pg. 4383
LOGOPAK SYSTEME GMBH & CO. KG—See L. Possehl & Co. mbH; *Int'l*, pg. 4383
LOGOPAK SYSTEMS AB—See L. Possehl & Co. mbH; *Int'l*, pg. 4383
LOGOPAK VERTRIEBSGESELLSCHAFT SUD MBH—See L. Possehl & Co. mbH; *Int'l*, pg. 4383
LOGOPAK VERTRIEBSGESELLSCHAFT WEST MBH—See L. Possehl & Co. mbH; *Int'l*, pg. 4383
LOGOPLASTE CANADA INC.—See The Carlyle Group Inc.; *U.S. Public*, pg. 2048
LOGOPLASTE CZECH, S.R.O.—See The Carlyle Group Inc.; *U.S. Public*, pg. 2048
LOGOPLASTE DO BRASIL LTDA—See The Carlyle Group Inc.; *U.S. Public*, pg. 2048
LOGOPLASTE ELST B.V.—See The Carlyle Group Inc.; *U.S. Public*, pg. 2048
LOGOPLASTE INVESTIMENTO, S.G.P.S., S.A.—See The Carlyle Group Inc.; *U.S. Public*, pg. 2048
LOGOPLASTE MEXICO S DE R.L. DE C.V.—See The Carlyle Group Inc.; *U.S. Public*, pg. 2048
LOGOPLASTE (M) KUANTAN SDN BHD—See The Carlyle Group Inc.; *U.S. Public*, pg. 2048
LOGOPLASTE RUSSIA LLC—See The Carlyle Group Inc.; *U.S. Public*, pg. 2048
LOGOPLASTE UKRAINE LLC—See The Carlyle Group Inc.; *U.S. Public*, pg. 2048
LOGOPLASTE USA, INC.—See The Carlyle Group Inc.; *U.S. Public*, pg. 2048
LOGO PLUS LIMITED—See Global Strategic Group Limited; *Int'l*, pg. 3001
LOGORY LOGISTICS TECHNOLOGY CO., LTD.; *Int'l*, pg. 4543
LOGOS COMMUNICATIONS, INC.—See Black Box Limited; *Int'l*, pg. 1058
LOGOS ENGENHARIA S.A.—See ARCADIS N.V.; *Int'l*, pg. 542
LOGOS LOGISTICS, INC.; *U.S. Private*, pg. 2482

LOGOSOFT D.O.O.—See Telekomunikacije Republike Srpske a.d.; *Int'l*, pg. 7538
LOGO—See National Amusements, Inc.; *U.S. Private*, pg. 2841
LOGOSPORTSWEAR.COM; *U.S. Private*, pg. 2482
LOGOTECH, INC.—See Tadbik Group; *Int'l*, pg. 7404
LOGOWORKS—See HP Inc.; *U.S. Public*, pg. 1063
LOGO YAZILIM SANAYI VE TICARET A.S.; *Int'l*, pg. 4543
LOGPAY FINANCIAL SERVICES GMBH—See Porsche Automobil Holding SE; *Int'l*, pg. 5931
LOGPAY FINANCIAL SERVICES GMBH—See Mitsubishi UFJ Financial Group, Inc.; *Int'l*, pg. 4968
LOGRET IMPORT & EXPORT CO. INC.—See John Lenore & Company, Inc.; *U.S. Private*, pg. 2223
LOGRHYTHM, INC.—See Thoma Bravo, L.P.; *U.S. Private*, pg. 4149
LOGSITE APS—See PostNord AB; *Int'l*, pg. 5940
LOGSTOR AB—See Triton Advisers Limited; *Int'l*, pg. 7932
LOGSTOR A/S—See Kingspan Group PLC; *Int'l*, pg. 4178
LOGSTOR A/S—See Triton Advisers Limited; *Int'l*, pg. 7932
LOGSTOR AUSTRIA GMBH—See Kingspan Group PLC; *Int'l*, pg. 4178
LOGSTOR DEUTSCHLAND GMBH—See Kingspan Group PLC; *Int'l*, pg. 4178
LOGSTOR FINLAND OY—See Kingspan Group PLC; *Int'l*, pg. 4178
LOGSTOR FRANCE SA—See Kingspan Group PLC; *Int'l*, pg. 4178
LOGSTOR FREDERICIA A/S—See Kingspan Group PLC; *Int'l*, pg. 4178
LOGSTOR HOLDING A/S—See Kingspan Group PLC; *Int'l*, pg. 4178
LOGSTOR INSULATION (WUXI) CO LTD.—See Kingspan Group PLC; *Int'l*, pg. 4178
LOGSTOR ITALIA SRL—See Kingspan Group PLC; *Int'l*, pg. 4178
LOGSTOR NEDERLAND BV—See Kingspan Group PLC; *Int'l*, pg. 4178
LOGSTOR POLSKA SP. Z O.O.—See Kingspan Group PLC; *Int'l*, pg. 4178
LOGSTOR POLSKA SP. ZO.O.—See Kingspan Group PLC; *Int'l*, pg. 4178
LOGSTOR POLSKA SP. Z.O.O.—See Kingspan Group PLC; *Int'l*, pg. 4178
LOGSTOR SCHWEIZ AG—See Kingspan Group PLC; *Int'l*, pg. 4178
LOGSTOR SVERIGE AB—See Kingspan Group PLC; *Int'l*, pg. 4178
LOGSTOR UAB—See Kingspan Group PLC; *Int'l*, pg. 4178
LOG SYSTEM SARL—See Clasquin S.A.; *Int'l*, pg. 1652
LOGTEK LIMITED—See OEP Capital Advisors, L.P.; *U.S. Private*, pg. 3000
LOGTHAI-HAI LECK ENGINEERING CO., LTD.—See Hai Leck Holdings Limited; *Int'l*, pg. 3208
LOGTRANS SPEDITION UND LOGISTIK GMBH—See Schnellecke Group AG & Co. KG; *Int'l*, pg. 6636
LOGWIN AG—See Delton AG; *Int'l*, pg. 2021
LOGWIN AIR AND OCEAN KENYA LIMITED—See Delton AG; *Int'l*, pg. 2022
LOGWIN AIR AND OCEAN LOJISTIK HIZMETLERI VE TICARET LIMITED SIRKETI—See Delton AG; *Int'l*, pg. 2022
LOGWIN AIR + OCEAN AUSTRALIA PTY. LTD.—See Delton AG; *Int'l*, pg. 2021
LOGWIN AIR + OCEAN AUSTRIA GMBH—See Delton AG; *Int'l*, pg. 2021
LOGWIN AIR + OCEAN BELGIUM N.V.—See Delton AG; *Int'l*, pg. 2021
LOGWIN AIR + OCEAN BRAZIL LTDA—See Delton AG; *Int'l*, pg. 2021
LOGWIN AIR + OCEAN CHILE S.A.—See Delton AG; *Int'l*, pg. 2021
LOGWIN AIR + OCEAN CHINA LTD.—See Delton AG; *Int'l*, pg. 2021
LOGWIN AIR + OCEAN CZECH S.R.O.—See Delton AG; *Int'l*, pg. 2021
LOGWIN AIR + OCEAN DEUTSCHLAND GMBH—See Delton AG; *Int'l*, pg. 2021
LOGWIN AIR & OCEAN FAR EAST LTD.—See Delton AG; *Int'l*, pg. 2021
LOGWIN AIR & OCEAN HUNGARY KFT.—See Delton AG; *Int'l*, pg. 2022
LOGWIN AIR & OCEAN INDIA PVT. LTD.—See Delton AG; *Int'l*, pg. 2021
LOGWIN AIR & OCEAN INDONESIA P.T.—See Delton AG; *Int'l*, pg. 2022
LOGWIN AIR + OCEAN INTERNATIONAL GMBH—See Delton AG; *Int'l*, pg. 2022
LOGWIN AIR + OCEAN ITALY S.R.L.—See Delton AG; *Int'l*, pg. 2022
LOGWIN AIR & OCEAN KOREA CO. LTD.—See Delton AG; *Int'l*, pg. 2021
LOGWIN AIR & OCEAN MIDDLE EAST (LLC)—See Delton AG; *Int'l*, pg. 2021
LOGWIN AIR + OCEAN PHILIPPINES INC.—See Delton AG; *Int'l*, pg. 2022
LOGWIN AIR + OCEAN POLAND SP. Z O.O.—See Delton AG; *Int'l*, pg. 2022

CORPORATE AFFILIATIONS

LOGWIN AIR + OCEAN SHANGHAI LTD.—See Delton AG; *Int'l*, pg. 2022
LOGWIN AIR + OCEAN SINGAPORE PTE. LTD.—See Delton AG; *Int'l*, pg. 2022
LOGWIN AIR + OCEAN SOUTH AFRICA (PTY.) LTD.—See Delton AG; *Int'l*, pg. 2022
LOGWIN AIR & OCEAN SPAIN S.L.—See Delton AG; *Int'l*, pg. 2021
LOGWIN AIR + OCEAN SWITZERLAND AG—See Delton AG; *Int'l*, pg. 2022
LOGWIN AIR + OCEAN TAIWAN LTD.—See Delton AG; *Int'l*, pg. 2022
LOGWIN AIR + OCEAN (THAILAND) LTD.—See Delton AG; *Int'l*, pg. 2021
LOGWIN AIR + OCEAN THE NETHERLANDS B.V.—See Delton AG; *Int'l*, pg. 2022
LOGWIN AIR + OCEAN UK LIMITED—See Delton AG; *Int'l*, pg. 2022
LOGWIN AIR + OCEAN VIETNAM COMPANY LTD.—See Delton AG; *Int'l*, pg. 2022
LOGWIN CROATIA D.O.O.—See Delton AG; *Int'l*, pg. 2022
LOGWIN ROAD + RAIL TRIER GMBH—See Delton AG; *Int'l*, pg. 2022
LOGWIN SOLUTIONS LIECHTENSTEIN AG—See Delton AG; *Int'l*, pg. 2022
LOGWIN SOLUTIONS LOGISTICS SERVICES GMBH—See Delton AG; *Int'l*, pg. 2022
LOGWIN SOLUTIONS MEDIA GMBH—See Ohl Logistik GmbH & Co. KG; *Int'l*, pg. 5532
LOGWIN SOLUTIONS NECKARTENZLINGEN GMBH—See Delton AG; *Int'l*, pg. 2022
LOGWIN SOLUTIONS SPAIN S.A.—See Delton AG; *Int'l*, pg. 2022
LOGYCOM JSC; *Int'l*, pg. 4543
LOHA CO., LTD.; *Int'l*, pg. 4543
LOHAKIT METAL PUBLIC COMPANY LIMITED; *Int'l*, pg. 4543
LOH BOON SIEW EDUCATION SDN. BHD.—See Oriental Holdings Berhad; *Int'l*, pg. 5624
LOHIA CORP. LIMITED; *Int'l*, pg. 4543
LOHIA METALS PRIVATE LIMITED—See Pondy Oxides & Chemicals Limited; *Int'l*, pg. 5919
LOHIA SECURITIES LTD; *Int'l*, pg. 4543
LOHILO FOODS AB; *Int'l*, pg. 4543
LOH & LOH CONSTRUCTION SDN BHD—See Loh & Loh Corporation Berhad; *Int'l*, pg. 4543
LOH & LOH CORPORATION BERHAD; *Int'l*, pg. 4543
LOHMANN ADHESIVE TAPES INDIA PVT. LTD.—See Lohmann GmbH & Co. KG; *Int'l*, pg. 4544
LOHMANN ADHESIVE TAPE TECHNOLOGIES (TIANJIN) CO., LTD—See Lohmann GmbH & Co. KG; *Int'l*, pg. 4544
LOHMANN ANIMAL HEALTH BETEILIGUNGS GMBH—See Eli Lilly & Company; *U.S. Public*, pg. 733
LOHMANN ANIMAL HEALTH GMBH—See Eli Lilly & Company; *U.S. Public*, pg. 733
LOHMANN ANIMAL HEALTH INTERNATIONAL, INC.—See Eli Lilly & Company; *U.S. Public*, pg. 733
LOHMANN ASIA PACIFIC PTE. LTD.—See Lohmann GmbH & Co. KG; *Int'l*, pg. 4544
LOHMANN DANMARK APS—See Lohmann GmbH & Co. KG; *Int'l*, pg. 4544
LOHMANN FRANCE S.A.S.—See Lohmann GmbH & Co. KG; *Int'l*, pg. 4544
LOHMANN GMBH & CO. KG; *Int'l*, pg. 4544
LOHMANN ITALIA S.R.L.—See Lohmann GmbH & Co. KG; *Int'l*, pg. 4544
LOHMANN KLEBEBANDSYSTEME GES.M.B.H.—See Lohmann GmbH & Co. KG; *Int'l*, pg. 4544
LOHMANN-KOESTER ASIA PACIFIC CO. LTD.—See Lohmann GmbH & Co. KG; *Int'l*, pg. 4544
LOHMANN-KOESTER GMBH & CO. KG—See Lohmann GmbH & Co. KG; *Int'l*, pg. 4544
LOHMANN-KOESTER S. DE R.L. DE C.V.—See Lohmann GmbH & Co. KG; *Int'l*, pg. 4544
LOHMANN KOREA CO. LTD.—See Lohmann GmbH & Co. KG; *Int'l*, pg. 4544
LOHMANN NETHERLANDS BV—See Lohmann GmbH & Co. KG; *Int'l*, pg. 4544
LOHMANN NORDIC AB—See Lohmann GmbH & Co. KG; *Int'l*, pg. 4544
LOHMANN POLSKA SP. Z O.O.—See Lohmann GmbH & Co. KG; *Int'l*, pg. 4544
LOHMANN PRECISION DIE CUTTING, LLC—See Lohmann GmbH & Co. KG; *Int'l*, pg. 4544
LOHMANN & RAUSCHER AB—See Lohmann & Rauscher International GmbH & Co. KG; *Int'l*, pg. 4544
LOHMANN & RAUSCHER AG—See Lohmann & Rauscher International GmbH & Co. KG; *Int'l*, pg. 4544
LOHMANN & RAUSCHER A/S—See Lohmann & Rauscher International GmbH & Co. KG; *Int'l*, pg. 4544
LOHMANN & RAUSCHER B.V.—See Lohmann & Rauscher International GmbH & Co. KG; *Int'l*, pg. 4544
LOHMANN & RAUSCHER CHINA MEDICAL PRODUCTS CO., LTD.—See Lohmann & Rauscher International GmbH & Co. KG; *Int'l*, pg. 4544
LOHMANN & RAUSCHER D.O.O.—See Lohmann & Rauscher International GmbH & Co. KG; *Int'l*, pg. 4544

COMPANY NAME INDEX

LOHMANN & RAUSCHER GMBH & CO. KG—See Lohmann & Rauscher International GmbH & Co. KG; *Int'l*, pg. 4544
LOHMANN & RAUSCHER GMBH—See Lohmann & Rauscher International GmbH & Co. KG; *Int'l*, pg. 4544
LOHMANN & RAUSCHER, INC.—See Lohmann & Rauscher International GmbH & Co. KG; *Int'l*, pg. 4544
LOHMANN & RAUSCHER INTERNATIONAL GMBH & CO. KG; *Int'l*, pg. 4543
LOHMANN & RAUSCHER MIDDLE EAST DMCC—See Lohmann & Rauscher International GmbH & Co. KG; *Int'l*, pg. 4544
LOHMANN & RAUSCHER POLSKA SP. Z O. O.—See Lohmann & Rauscher International GmbH & Co. KG; *Int'l*, pg. 4544
LOHMANN & RAUSCHER PTY. LTD.—See Lohmann & Rauscher International GmbH & Co. KG; *Int'l*, pg. 4544
LOHMANN & RAUSCHER S.A.R.L.—See Lohmann & Rauscher International GmbH & Co. KG; *Int'l*, pg. 4544
LOHMANN & RAUSCHER S.A.S.—See Lohmann & Rauscher International GmbH & Co. KG; *Int'l*, pg. 4544
LOHMANN & RAUSCHER, S.L.O.—See Lohmann & Rauscher International GmbH & Co. KG; *Int'l*, pg. 4544
LOHMANN & RAUSCHER S.R.L—See Lohmann & Rauscher International GmbH & Co. KG; *Int'l*, pg. 4544
LOHMANN & RAUSCHER S.R.O.—See Lohmann & Rauscher International GmbH & Co. KG; *Int'l*, pg. 4544
LOHMANN & RAUSCHER, S.R.O.—See Lohmann & Rauscher International GmbH & Co. KG; *Int'l*, pg. 4544
LOHMANN & RAUSCHER TUNISIE S.A.R.L.—See Lohmann & Rauscher International GmbH & Co. KG; *Int'l*, pg. 4544
LOHMANN SPAIN S.A.—See Lohmann GmbH & Co. KG; *Int'l*, pg. 4544
LOHMANN SPECIALTY COATINGS LLC—See Lohmann GmbH & Co. KG; *Int'l*, pg. 4544
LOHMANN TAIWAN CO. LTD., TAIWAN—See Eli Lilly & Company; *U.S. Public*, pg. 733
LOHMANN TECHNOLOGIES CORP.—See Lohmann GmbH & Co. KG; *Int'l*, pg. 4544
LOHMANN TECHNOLOGIES UK LTD.—See Lohmann GmbH & Co. KG; *Int'l*, pg. 4544
LOHMANN TURKEY YAPISTIRICI BANTLAR SANAYI VE TICARET LIMITED SIRKETI—See Lohmann GmbH & Co. KG; *Int'l*, pg. 4544
LOHMANN UKRAINA TOV—See Lohmann GmbH & Co. KG; *Int'l*, pg. 4544
LOHMILLER & COMPANY; *U.S. Private*, pg. 2482
LOHSE GMBH—See Phoenix Mecano AG; *Int'l*, pg. 5852
LOH SERVICES GMBH & CO. KG—See Friedhelm Loh Stiftung & Co. KG; *Int'l*, pg. 2791
LOH & SONS PAINT CO (S) PTE. LTD.—See Natural Cool Holdings Limited; *Int'l*, pg. 5167
LOIBL ALLEN-SHERMAN-HOFF GMBH—See Babcock & Wilcox Enterprises, Inc.; *U.S. Public*, pg. 262
LOIMAAN MAATALOUS- JA RAUTAKAUPPA OY—See Kesko Corporation; *Int'l*, pg. 4142
LOIS GELLER MARKETING GROUP; *U.S. Private*, pg. 2482
LOIS PAUL & PARTNERS—See Omnicom Group Inc.; *U.S. Public*, pg. 1585
LOIS PAUL & PARTNERS—See Omnicom Group Inc.; *U.S. Public*, pg. 1585
LOI THERMPROCESS GMBH—See E.ON SE; *Int'l*, pg. 2255
LOJAC INC.; *U.S. Private*, pg. 2482
LOJACK CORPORATION—See CalAmp Corp.; *U.S. Public*, pg. 422
LOJACK DE MEXICO, S. DE R.L. DE CV—See CalAmp Corp.; *U.S. Public*, pg. 422
LOJACK EQUIPMENT IRELAND LIMITED—See CalAmp Corp.; *U.S. Public*, pg. 422
LOJAS AMERICANAS S.A.—See Americanas S.A.; *Int'l*, pg. 423
LOJAS FRANCAS DE PORTUGAL SA—See VINCI S.A.; *Int'l*, pg. 8223
LOJAS HERING S/A; *Int'l*, pg. 4544
LOJAS RENNER S.A.; *Int'l*, pg. 4545
LOJAS SEB—See SEB S.A.; *Int'l*, pg. 6668
THE LOJETA GROUP; *U.S. Private*, pg. 4071
LOKALBAHN MIXNITZ-ST. ERHARD AG—See RHI Magnesita N.V.; *Int'l*, pg. 6325
LOKALBOLIG A/S—See Svenska Handelsbanken AB; *Int'l*, pg. 7358
LOKAL-NACHRICHTEN MURI-GUMLIGEN AG—See Stampfli AG; *Int'l*, pg. 7166
LOKALTIDNINGEN MITT I STOCKHOLM AB—See Ge-Te Media AB; *Int'l*, pg. 2897
LOKESH MACHINES LTD; *Int'l*, pg. 4545
LOKEY KIA—See Lokey Motor Company; *U.S. Private*, pg. 2482
LOKEY MOTOR COMPANY; *U.S. Private*, pg. 2482
LOKEY NISSAN, INC.—See Lokey Motor Company; *U.S. Private*, pg. 2482
LOKEY SUBARU OF PORT RICHEY—See Lokey Motor Company; *U.S. Private*, pg. 2482
LOKEY VOLKSWAGEN—See Lokey Motor Company; *U.S. Private*, pg. 2482
LOKION; *U.S. Private*, pg. 2482

LOKMAN HEKIM ENGURUSAG SAGLIK TURIZM EGITIM HIZMETLERI VE INSAAT TAAHHUT A.S.; *Int'l*, pg. 4545
LOK'NSTORE LIMITED—See Shurgard Self Storage; *Int'l*, pg. 6870
LOKS PLASMA SERVICES LIMITED—See A. M. Castle & Co.; *U.S. Public*, pg. 11
LOKUM DEWELOPER SA; *Int'l*, pg. 4545
LOK WING GROUP LIMITED—See China Properties Investment Holdings Limited; *Int'l*, pg. 1542
LOLAB CO., LTD.—See KT Corporation; *Int'l*, pg. 4315
LOLA MADRID—See The Interpublic Group of Companies, Inc.; *U.S. Public*, pg. 2091
LOLA MULLENLOWE—See The Interpublic Group of Companies, Inc.; *U.S. Public*, pg. 2091
LOLA TRAVEL CO., INC.; *U.S. Private*, pg. 2483
LOLC HOLDINGS PLC; *Int'l*, pg. 4545
LOLLANDS BANK A/S; *Int'l*, pg. 4545
LOLLAPALOOZA, LLC—See Live Nation Entertainment, Inc.; *U.S. Public*, pg. 1330
LOLLICUP USA, INC.; *U.S. Private*, pg. 2483
LOLLIPOP CORPORATION; *U.S. Private*, pg. 2483
LOLLIPOPS EDUCARE (BIRKENHEAD) LIMITED—See Evolve Education Group Limited; *Int'l*, pg. 2573
LOLLIPROPS INC.; *U.S. Private*, pg. 2483
LOLLYTOGS, LTD.; *U.S. Private*, pg. 2483
LOLLYTOGS—See Lollytogs, Ltd.; *U.S. Private*, pg. 2483
LOLYN FINANCIAL CORPORATION; *U.S. Private*, pg. 2483
LOMAK INDUSTRIAL CO. LTD.; *Int'l*, pg. 4545
LOMA LINDA UNIVERSAL SELF STORAGE—See National Storage Affiliates Trust; *U.S. Public*, pg. 1498
LOMANCO INC.; *U.S. Private*, pg. 2483
LOMA NEGRA CIA INDUSTRIA ARGENTINA SA—See Camargo Correa S.A.; *Int'l*, pg. 1268
LOMA NEGRA COMPANIA INDUSTRIAL ARGENTINA SOCIEDAD ANONIMA; *Int'l*, pg. 4545
LOMAPHARM GMBH—See Daicel Corporation; *Int'l*, pg. 1919
LOMAR DISTRIBUTING—See Hy-Vee, Inc.; *U.S. Private*, pg. 2016
LOMAR MACHINE & TOOL CO.; *U.S. Private*, pg. 2483
LOM ASSET MANAGEMENT LIMITED—See LOM Financial Limited; *Int'l*, pg. 4545
LOMA SYSTEMS BV—See Illinois Tool Works Inc.; *U.S. Public*, pg. 1109
LOMA SYSTEMS (CANADA) INC.—See Illinois Tool Works Inc.; *U.S. Public*, pg. 1109
LOMA SYSTEMS-ILLINOIS—See Illinois Tool Works Inc.; *U.S. Public*, pg. 1109
LOMA SYSTEMS LTD—See Illinois Tool Works Inc.; *U.S. Public*, pg. 1109
LOMA SYSTEMS SRO—See Illinois Tool Works Inc.; *U.S. Public*, pg. 1109
LOMA VISTA MEDICAL, INC.—See Becton, Dickinson & Company; *U.S. Public*, pg. 291
LOMA VISTA NURSERY, INC.—See SiteOne Landscape Supply, Inc.; *U.S. Public*, pg. 1889
LOMBARD ARCHITECTURAL PRECAST PRODUCTS CO., INC.—See The Lombard Investment Co.; *U.S. Private*, pg. 4072
LOMBARD BANK MALTA P.L.C.; *Int'l*, pg. 4545
THE LOMBARD CO., INC.—See The Lombard Investment Co.; *U.S. Private*, pg. 4072
LOMBARD ESTATE HOLDINGS LIMITED—See U City Public Company Limited; *Int'l*, pg. 7996
LOMBARD ET MEDOT SA; *Int'l*, pg. 4545
LOMBARDI BROTHERS MEAT PACKERS, INC.; *U.S. Private*, pg. 2483
LOMBARDINI S.R.L.—See Kohler Company; *U.S. Private*, pg. 2340
LOMBARD INSURANCE COMPANY LIMITED—See Hollard Insurance Company Ltd; *Int'l*, pg. 3451
LOMBARD INTERNATIONAL ADMINISTRATION SERVICES COMPANY, LLC—See Blackstone Inc.; *U.S. Public*, pg. 356
LOMBARD INTERNATIONAL ASSURANCE SA—See Blackstone Inc.; *U.S. Public*, pg. 360
LOMBARD INTERNATIONAL LIFE ASSURANCE COMPANY—See Blackstone Inc.; *U.S. Public*, pg. 356
THE LOMBARD INVESTMENT CO.; *U.S. Private*, pg. 4072
LOMBARDI'S SEAFOOD INC.; *U.S. Private*, pg. 2483
LOMBARD MEDICAL, INC.; *Int'l*, pg. 4545
LOMBARD MEDICAL INC.—See MicroPort Scientific Corporation; *Int'l*, pg. 4880
LOMBARD MEDICAL (SCOTLAND) LIMITED—See Lombard Medical, Inc.; *Int'l*, pg. 4545
LOMBARD MEDICAL TECHNOLOGIES GMBH—See Lombard Medical, Inc.; *Int'l*, pg. 4545
LOMBARD MEDICAL TECHNOLOGIES, INC.—See Lombard Medical, Inc.; *Int'l*, pg. 4546
LOMBARD MEDICAL TECHNOLOGIES PLC—See Lombard Medical, Inc.; *Int'l*, pg. 4546
LOMBARD NORTH CENTRAL PLC—See NatWest Group plc; *Int'l*, pg. 5170
LOMBARDO FUNERAL HOME—See Carriage Services, Inc.; *U.S. Public*, pg. 439

LOMBARDO & LIPE ELECTRICAL CONTRACTORS INC.; *U.S. Private*, pg. 2483
LOMBART BROTHERS, INC.—See Atlantic Street Capital Management LLC; *U.S. Private*, pg. 374
LOM CAPITAL LIMITED—See LOM Financial Limited; *Int'l*, pg. 4545
LOMELLINA ENERGIA S.R.L.—See A2A S.p.A.; *Int'l*, pg. 29
LOME MULTIPURPOSE TERMINAL SA—See Financiere de L'Odet; *Int'l*, pg. 2667
LOM FINANCIAL (BAHAMAS) LIMITED—See LOM Financial Limited; *Int'l*, pg. 4545
LOM FINANCIAL LIMITED; *Int'l*, pg. 4545
LOMIKO METALS INC.; *Int'l*, pg. 4546
LOMIKO TECHNOLOGIES INC.—See Lomiko Metals Inc.; *Int'l*, pg. 4546
LOMONDO, LTD.—See Melia Hotels International, S.A.; *Int'l*, pg. 4809
LOMONT MOLDING LLC; *U.S. Private*, pg. 2483
LOM SECURITIES (BAHAMAS) LTD.—See LOM Financial Limited; *Int'l*, pg. 4545
LOM SECURITIES (BERMUDA) LTD.—See LOM Financial Limited; *Int'l*, pg. 4545
LOMSKO PIVO AD; *Int'l*, pg. 4546
LOM (UK) LIMITED—See LOM Financial Limited; *Int'l*, pg. 4545
LOMY MORINA SPOL, S.R.O.—See CEZ, a.s.; *Int'l*, pg. 1428
LONCIN MOTOR CO., LTD.; *Int'l*, pg. 4546
LONCOR GOLD INC.; *Int'l*, pg. 4546
LONDA HOTEL—See Schoeller Holdings Ltd.; *Int'l*, pg. 6637
LONDEN INSURANCE GROUP, INC.; *U.S. Private*, pg. 2483
LONDEN LAND COMPANY, L.L.C.—See Londen Insurance Group, Inc.; *U.S. Private*, pg. 2483
LONDEN MEDIA GROUP, L.L.C.—See Londen Insurance Group, Inc.; *U.S. Private*, pg. 2483
LONDON AND BIRMINGHAM RAILWAY LIMITED—See GLOBALVIA Inversiones, S.A.U.; *Int'l*, pg. 3005
LONDON AND BIRMINGHAM RAILWAY LIMITED—See Kinetic Group Services Pty Ltd.; *Int'l*, pg. 4168
LONDON AND EDINBURGH INSURANCE COMPANY LIMITED—See Aviva plc; *Int'l*, pg. 746
LONDON AND NORTH WESTERN RAILWAY COMPANY LIMITED—See Deutsche Bahn AG; *Int'l*, pg. 2052
LONDON AND ST. LAWRENCE INVESTMENT COMPANY PLC; *Int'l*, pg. 4546
LONDON & ASSOCIATED PROPERTIES PLC; *Int'l*, pg. 4546
LONDON BAY CAPITAL LLC; *U.S. Private*, pg. 2483
LONDON BIO PACKAGING LIMITED—See Bunzl plc; *Int'l*, pg. 1219
LONDON BISCUITS BERHAD; *Int'l*, pg. 4546
THE LONDON BREAST INSTITUTE UK LTD—See HCA Healthcare, Inc.; *U.S. Public*, pg. 1012
LONDON BRICK ENGINEERING LIMITED—See Heidelberg Materials AG; *Int'l*, pg. 3318
LONDON BRIDGE HOSPITAL—See HCA Healthcare, Inc.; *U.S. Public*, pg. 1001
LONDON BRIDGE HOSPITAL—See HCA Healthcare, Inc.; *U.S. Public*, pg. 1001
LONDON BROADCASTING COMPANY, INC.—See SunTx Capital Partners, L.P.; *U.S. Private*, pg. 3874
LONDON CAPITAL GROUP HOLDINGS PLC; *Int'l*, pg. 4546
LONDON CAPITAL GROUP LIMITED; *Int'l*, pg. 4546
LONDON & CAPITAL GROUP LTD.—See Lovell Minnick Partners LLC; *U.S. Private*, pg. 2503
LONDON CENTRAL—See GLOBALVIA Inversiones, S.A.U.; *Int'l*, pg. 3005
LONDON CENTRAL—See Kinetic Group Services Pty Ltd.; *Int'l*, pg. 4167
LONDON CITY AIRPORT LIMITED—See Alberta Investment Management Corporation; *Int'l*, pg. 297
LONDON CITY AIRPORT LIMITED—See Kuwait Investment Authority; *Int'l*, pg. 4345
LONDON CITY AIRPORT LIMITED—See Ontario Municipal Employees Retirement System; *Int'l*, pg. 5584
LONDON CITY AIRPORT LIMITED—See Ontario Teachers' Pension Plan; *Int'l*, pg. 5590
LONDON CITY EQUITIES LIMITED; *Int'l*, pg. 4546
LONDON CITY PLYMOUTH CHRYSLER (1995) LTD; *Int'l*, pg. 4546
LONDON CLUBS LSQ LIMITED—See Caesars Entertainment, Inc.; *U.S. Public*, pg. 420
LONDON CLUBS MANAGEMENT LIMITED—See Caesars Entertainment, Inc.; *U.S. Public*, pg. 420
LONDON CLUBS (OVERSEAS) LIMITED—See Caesars Entertainment, Inc.; *U.S. Public*, pg. 420
LONDON CLUBS SOUTHEND LIMITED—See Caesars Entertainment, Inc.; *U.S. Public*, pg. 420
LONDON COIN GALLERIES INCORPORATED; *U.S. Private*, pg. 2483
LONDON & COLONIAL (TRUSTEE SERVICES) LIMITED—See STM Group Plc; *Int'l*, pg. 7216
LONDON CONCRETE LTD.—See Holcim Ltd.; *Int'l*, pg. 3446

LONDON COIN GALLERIES INCORPORATED / CORPORATE AFFILIATIONS

LONDON DIAMOND DRILLING SERVICES LTD.—See Robore Holdings Ltd.; *Int'l*, pg. 6371
LONDON DRUGS LIMITED; *Int'l*, pg. 4546
LONDON EASTERN RAILWAY LIMITED—See Mobico Group PLC; *Int'l*, pg. 5008
LONDON & EUROPEAN TITLE INSURANCE SERVICES LIMITED—See Talanx AG; *Int'l*, pg. 7445
LONDON FINANCE & INVESTMENT GROUP P.L.C.; *Int'l*, pg. 4546
LONDON FORFAITING AMERICAS INC.—See FIMBank p.l.c.; *Int'l*, pg. 2664
LONDON FORFAITING A PARIS SA—See FIMBank p.l.c.; *Int'l*, pg. 2664
LONDON FORFAITING COMPANY LTD—See FIMBank p.l.c.; *Int'l*, pg. 2664
LONDON FORFAITING DEUTSCHLAND GMBH—See FIMBank p.l.c.; *Int'l*, pg. 2664
LONDON FORFAITING DO BRASIL LTDA—See FIMBank p.l.c.; *Int'l*, pg. 2664
LONDON FORFAITING POLSKA SP. Z.O.O—See FIMBank p.l.c.; *Int'l*, pg. 2664
THE LONDON FREE PRESS—See Chatham Asset Management, LLC; *U.S. Private*, pg. 861
LONDON FRUIT, INC.—See GrubMarket, Inc.; *U.S. Private*, pg. 1797
THE LONDON GAMMA KNIFE CENTRE LLP—See HCA Healthcare, Inc.; *U.S. Public*, pg. 1012
LONDON GATEWAY PORT LIMITED—See Dubai World Corporation; *Int'l*, pg. 2220
LONDON GENERAL INSURANCE COMPANY LIMITED—See Assurant, Inc.; *U.S. Public*, pg. 215
THE LONDON GENERAL PRACTICE LIMITED—See HCA Healthcare, Inc.; *U.S. Public*, pg. 1012
LONDON GENERAL—See GLOBALVIA Inversiones, S.A.U.; *Int'l*, pg. 3005
LONDON GENERAL—See Kinetic Group Services Pty Ltd.; *Int'l*, pg. 4167
LONDON GENERAL TRANSPORT SERVICES LIMITED—See GLOBALVIA Inversiones, S.A.U.; *Int'l*, pg. 3005
LONDON GENERAL TRANSPORT SERVICES LIMITED—See Kinetic Group Services Pty Ltd.; *Int'l*, pg. 4167
LONDON GROUP, INC.; *U.S. Private*, pg. 2483
LONDON IBT LTD.—See Navitas Limited; *Int'l*, pg. 5176
LONDON INDUSTRIAL LEASING LIMITED—See Deutsche Bank Aktiengesellschaft; *Int'l*, pg. 2061
LONDON INSURANCE GROUP, INC.—See Power Corporation of Canada; *Int'l*, pg. 5944
LONDON LIFE INSURANCE COMPANY—See Power Corporation of Canada; *Int'l*, pg. 5944
LONDON LINEN SUPPLY LIMITED—See Johnson Service Group PLC; *Int'l*, pg. 3993
LONDON LUTON AIRPORT GROUP LIMITED—See Ardian SAS; *Int'l*, pg. 556
LONDON LUTON AIRPORT GROUP LIMITED—See ENAIRE; *Int'l*, pg. 2396
LONDON LUTON AIRPORT OPERATIONS LIMITED—See Ardian SAS; *Int'l*, pg. 556
LONDON LUTON AIRPORT OPERATIONS LIMITED—See ENAIRE; *Int'l*, pg. 2396
LONDON MACHINERY INC.—See Oshkosh Corporation; *U.S. Public*, pg. 1620
LONDON MARINE CONSULTANTS LIMITED—See Ezra Holdings Ltd.; *Int'l*, pg. 2594
LONDONMETRIC PROPERTY PLC; *Int'l*, pg. 4548
LONDON MIDLAND—See GLOBALVIA Inversiones, S.A.U.; *Int'l*, pg. 3005
LONDON MIDLAND—See Kinetic Group Services Pty Ltd.; *Int'l*, pg. 4167
LONDON MINING PLC; *Int'l*, pg. 4546
LONDON (MTL) INC.—See Oshkosh Corporation; *U.S. Public*, pg. 1620
THE LONDON OTOLOGICAL CENTRE LTD—See Amplifon S.p.A.; *Int'l*, pg. 436
LONDON PHILHARMONIC ORCHESTRA; *Int'l*, pg. 4546
LONDON PROPERTY GUIDE LTD.—See Vivendi SE; *Int'l*, pg. 8278
LONDON RADIOTHERAPY CENTRE LTD.—See HCA Healthcare, Inc.; *U.S. Public*, pg. 1001
LONDON & REGIONAL PROPERTIES LIMITED; *Int'l*, pg. 4546
LONDON SECURITY PLC; *Int'l*, pg. 4546
LONDON & SOUTH EASTERN RAILWAY LIMITED—See GLOBALVIA Inversiones, S.A.U.; *Int'l*, pg. 3005
LONDON & SOUTH EASTERN RAILWAY LIMITED—See Kinetic Group Services Pty Ltd.; *Int'l*, pg. 4167
LONDON SOUTHEND AIRPORT COMPANY LIMITED—See Esken Limited; *Int'l*, pg. 2503
LONDON STOCK EXCHANGE GROUP PLC; *Int'l*, pg. 4547
LONDON STOCK EXCHANGE PLC—See London Stock Exchange Group plc; *Int'l*, pg. 4548
LONDON STREET PROJECT COMPANY LIMITED—See Republic Financial Holdings Limited; *Int'l*, pg. 6294
LONDON SYMPHONY ORCHESTRA AMERICAN FOUNDATION—See London Symphony Orchestra Ltd; *Int'l*, pg. 4548
LONDON SYMPHONY ORCHESTRA LTD; *Int'l*, pg. 4548

LONDON SYMPHONY ORCHESTRA ST. LUKE'S—See London Symphony Orchestra Ltd; *Int'l*, pg. 4548
THE LONDON TAXI CORPORATION LIMITED—See Leacy MG Ltd.; *Int'l*, pg. 4432
LONDON UNITED BUSWAYS—See Caisse des Depots et Consignations; *Int'l*, pg. 1259
LONDON VERZEKERINGEN N.V.—See Allianz SE; *Int'l*, pg. 349
THE LONDON WEST HOLLYWOOD HOTEL—See Blackstone Inc.; *U.S. Public*, pg. 351
LONDON WORKWEAR RENTAL LIMITED—See Johnson Service Group PLC; *Int'l*, pg. 3993
LONDON YORK FUND MANAGERS LIMITED—See Walker Crips Group plc; *Int'l*, pg. 8333
LONE FIR CONSULTING, LLC; *U.S. Private*, pg. 2483
LONELY PLANET PUBLICATIONS LIMITED—See NC2 Media, LLC; *U.S. Private*, pg. 2875
LONELY PLANET PUBLICATIONS PTY. LIMITED—See NC2 Media, LLC; *U.S. Private*, pg. 2875
LONE MOUNTAIN EXCAVATION & UTILITIES, LLC—See MDU Resources Group, Inc.; *U.S. Public*, pg. 1411
THE LONE MOUNTAIN RANCH, LLC—See Makar Properties, LLC; *U.S. Private*, pg. 2556
LONE PALM GOLF CLUB, LLC—See Publix Super Markets, Inc.; *U.S. Private*, pg. 3301
LONE PEAK HOSPITAL, INC.—See HCA Healthcare, Inc.; *U.S. Public*, pg. 1001
LONE PINE HOTEL (C) SDN. BHD.—See Eastern & Oriental Berhad; *Int'l*, pg. 2271
LONESOURCE, INC.; *U.S. Private*, pg. 2489
LONE STAR A/C & APPLIANCE REPAIR, LLC—See NRG Energy, Inc.; *U.S. Public*, pg. 1550
LONE STAR AG CREDIT; *U.S. Private*, pg. 2484
LONE STAR AMERICAS ACQUISITIONS, LLC—See Lone Star Funds; *U.S. Private*, pg. 2485
LONE STAR BEEF PROCESSORS, L.P.; *U.S. Private*, pg. 2484
LONE STAR CAPITAL BANK, N.A.; *U.S. Private*, pg. 2484
LONE STAR CIRCLE OF CARE; *U.S. Private*, pg. 2484
LONE STAR CIRCUITS INC.; *U.S. Private*, pg. 2484
LONE STAR COACHES, INC.; *U.S. Private*, pg. 2484
LONE STAR COMPANY INC.; *U.S. Private*, pg. 2484
LONE STAR CONSOLIDATED FOODS; *U.S. Private*, pg. 2484
LONE STAR CONTAINER SALES CORP.—See Lone Star Corrugated Container Corporation; *U.S. Private*, pg. 2484
LONE STAR CORRUGATED CONTAINER CORPORATION; *U.S. Private*, pg. 2484
LONE STAR DISPOSAL, LP—See Waste Connections, Inc.; *Int'l*, pg. 8352
LONESTAR ECOLOGY, LLC—See EQT AB; *Int'l*, pg. 2473
LONE STAR ENDOSCOPY CENTER, LLC—See Tenet Healthcare Corporation; *U.S. Public*, pg. 2011
LONE STAR EQUITIES, INC.; *U.S. Private*, pg. 2484
LONESTAR FASTENERS EUROPE LIMITED—See Trinity Hunt Management, L.P.; *U.S. Private*, pg. 4235
LONE STAR FASTENERS, L.P.—See Trinity Hunt Management, L.P.; *U.S. Private*, pg. 4235
LONE STAR FOUNDRIES, INC.; *U.S. Private*, pg. 2484
LONESTAR FREIGHTLINER GROUP, LTD.; *U.S. Private*, pg. 2489
LONE STAR FUNDS; *U.S. Private*, pg. 2484
LONE STAR GLOBAL ACQUISITIONS, LLC; *U.S. Private*, pg. 2487
LONE STAR HMA, L.P.—See Prime Healthcare Services, Inc.; *U.S. Private*, pg. 3261
LONE STAR HOLDINGS, LLC; *U.S. Private*, pg. 2489
LONE STAR INVESTMENT ADVISORS, LLC; *U.S. Private*, pg. 2489
LONE STAR LEEDS LIMITED—See Trinity Hunt Management, L.P.; *U.S. Private*, pg. 4235
LONE STAR LEGAL AID; *U.S. Private*, pg. 2489
LONESTAR MARINE SHELTERS; *U.S. Private*, pg. 2489
LONE STAR MATERIALS, INC.—See GMS Inc.; *U.S. Public*, pg. 948
LONE STAR MERCEDES-BENZ; *Int'l*, pg. 4548
LONE STAR MOTORSPORTS INCORPORATED; *U.S. Private*, pg. 2489
LONE STAR NATIONAL BANCSHARES-TEXAS, INC.; *U.S. Private*, pg. 2489
LONE STAR NEW MARKETS LP; *U.S. Private*, pg. 2489
LONE STAR NGL HATTIESBURG LLC—See Energy Transfer LP; *U.S. Public*, pg. 763
LONE STAR NGL REFINERY SERVICES LLC—See Energy Transfer LP; *U.S. Public*, pg. 763
LONE STAR PET SUPPLY, INC.—See Summit Partners, L.P.; *U.S. Private*, pg. 3855
LONE STAR PLASTICS, INC.—See Myers Industries, Inc.; *U.S. Public*, pg. 1488
LONESTAR PROVIDER NETWORK—See HCA Healthcare, Inc.; *U.S. Public*, pg. 1001
LONE STAR RACE PARK, LTD.—See Global Gaming Solutions, LLC; *U.S. Private*, pg. 1714
LONESTAR RESOURCES US INC.—See Baytex Energy Corp.; *Int'l*, pg. 915

LONE STAR SPECIAL TEES INC.—See Periodical Management Group International Ltd.; *U.S. Private*, pg. 3150
LONE STAR STATE BANCSHARES, INC.—See Prosperity Bancshares, Inc.; *U.S. Public*, pg. 1728
LONE STAR STATE BANK OF WEST TEXAS—See Prosperity Bancshares, Inc.; *U.S. Public*, pg. 1728
LONE STAR STEAKHOUSE—See Day Star Restaurant Holdings, LLC; *U.S. Private*, pg. 1176
LONESTAR SYLVAN INC.—See Clean Harbors, Inc.; *U.S. Public*, pg. 510
LONE STAR TANK RENTAL INC.—See United Rentals, Inc.; *U.S. Public*, pg. 2235
LONE STAR TRANSPORTATION, LLC—See Daseke, Inc.; *U.S. Private*, pg. 1161
LONESTAR TRANSPORTATION, LLC—See Daseke, Inc.; *U.S. Private*, pg. 1161
LONESTAR WEST INC.—See Clean Harbors, Inc.; *U.S. Public*, pg. 510
LONETREE CAPITAL LLC; *U.S. Private*, pg. 2490
LONE WOLF REAL ESTATE TECHNOLOGIES INC.; *Int'l*, pg. 4548
LONG ACRE (SHINFIELD) MANAGEMENT COMPANY LIMITED—See Bellway plc; *Int'l*, pg. 968
LONG AN BOOK & EDUCATIONAL EQUIPMENT JSC; *Int'l*, pg. 4548
LONG AN FOOD PROCESSING EXPORT JOINT STOCK COMPANY - LONG AN CASHEW FACTORY—See Long An Food Processing Export Joint Stock Company; *Int'l*, pg. 4548
LONG AN FOOD PROCESSING EXPORT JOINT STOCK COMPANY; *Int'l*, pg. 4548
LONG & ASSOCIATES ARCHITECTS/ENGINEERS, INC.; *U.S. Private*, pg. 2490
LONG BEACH AFFORDABLE HOUSING COALITION; *U.S. Private*, pg. 2490
LONG BEACH CONTAINER TERMINAL LLC—See China COSCO Shipping Corporation Limited; *Int'l*, pg. 1495
LONG BEACH DIALYSIS CENTER, LLC—See DaVita Inc.; *U.S. Public*, pg. 640
LONG BEACH MEMORIAL MEDICAL CENTER—See Memorial Health Services; *U.S. Private*, pg. 2664
LONG BEACH MEMORIAL NURSING HOME; *U.S. Private*, pg. 2490
LONG BEACH PUBLIC TRANSPORTATION CO.; *U.S. Private*, pg. 2490
LONG BEACH PUBLISHING COMPANY—See Alden Global Capital LLC; *U.S. Private*, pg. 158
LONG BEACH RESORT LTD.—See CIEL Ltd.; *Int'l*, pg. 1605
LONG BEACH SURGERY CENTER, L.P.—See KKR & Co. Inc.; *U.S. Public*, pg. 1246
LONG BEACH YACHT SALES INC.; *U.S. Private*, pg. 2490
LONG BELL VENTURES LLC; *U.S. Private*, pg. 2490
LONG BIEN TOYOTA CO., LTD—See Saigon General Service Corporation; *Int'l*, pg. 6483
THE LONG BINH INDUSTRIAL ZONE DEVELOPMENT LLC—See Sojitz Corporation; *Int'l*, pg. 7066
LONGBOARD PHARMACEUTICALS, INC.; *U.S. Public*, pg. 1341
LONGBOAT ENERGY PLC; *Int'l*, pg. 4549
LONGBOAT KEY CLUB MOORINGS—See Ocean Properties, Ltd.; *U.S. Private*, pg. 2989
LONG BON INTERNATIONAL CO., LTD; *Int'l*, pg. 4548
LONGBOW REAL ESTATE CAPITAL LLP—See Intermediate Capital Group plc; *Int'l*, pg. 3742
LONG BROTHERS LANDSCAPING, LLC—See Aspen Grove Landscape Companies, LLC; *U.S. Private*, pg. 352
LONG BUILDING TECHNOLOGIES; *U.S. Private*, pg. 2490
LONGBURN WIND FARM LTD.—See ERG S.p.A.; *Int'l*, pg. 2491
LONGCHAMP S.A.S.; *Int'l*, pg. 4550
LONGCHAMP USA INC—See Longchamp S.A.S.; *Int'l*, pg. 4550
LONGCHEER HOLDINGS LTD.; *Int'l*, pg. 4550
LONG CHEN PAPER CO., LTD. - LUZHU PLANT—See Longchen Paper & Packaging Co., Ltd.; *Int'l*, pg. 4550
LONG CHEN PAPER CO., LTD. - SHENGANG PLANT—See Longchen Paper & Packaging Co., Ltd.; *Int'l*, pg. 4550
LONG CHEN PAPER CO., LTD. - YUNLIN PLANT—See Longchen Paper & Packaging Co., Ltd.; *Int'l*, pg. 4550
LONGCHEN PAPER & PACKAGING CO., LTD.; *Int'l*, pg. 4550
THE LONG COMPANY; *U.S. Private*, pg. 4072
LONGDA CONSTRUCTION & DEVELOPMENT CORPORATION; *Int'l*, pg. 4550
LONGDEN COMPANY INC.; *U.S. Private*, pg. 2492
LONGDIS S.A.—See Selectpart Participacoes S.A.; *Int'l*, pg. 6700
LONG DISTANCE DIRECT HOLDINGS; *U.S. Private*, pg. 2490
LONG DISTANCE DIRECT INC.—See Long Distance Direct Holdings; *U.S. Private*, pg. 2490
LONG ELECTRIC COMPANY INC.; *U.S. Private*, pg. 2490

COMPANY NAME INDEX

LONG ENGINEERING, LLC—See GI Manager L.P.; *U.S. Private*, pg. 1691
LONGEVERON INC.; *U.S. Public*, pg. 1342
LONGEVITY ACQUISITION CORPORATION—See 4D Pharma PLC; *Int'l*, pg. 11
LONG FENCE COMPANY INC.; *U.S. Private*, pg. 2490
LONGFIELD CHEMICALS LIMITED; *Int'l*, pg. 4550
LONGFIELD LIMITED—See U10 Corp SA; *Int'l*, pg. 7998
LONGFIN CORP.; *U.S. Public*, pg. 1342
LONG FIOUL; *Int'l*, pg. 4549
LONGFORD & COMPANY INC.—See Great Mill Rock LLC; *U.S. Private*, pg. 1766
THE LONGFORD GROUP, INC.; *U.S. Private*, pg. 4072
LONGFORD LEADER LTD—See JPIMedia Holdings Limited; *Int'l*, pg. 4006
LONGFOR GROUP HOLDINGS LIMITED; *Int'l*, pg. 4550
LONG FORK COAL COMPANY—See Alpha Natural Resources, Inc.; *U.S. Private*, pg. 198
THE LONG & FOSTER COMPANIES, INC. - HARRISON ST—See The Long & Foster Companies, Inc.; *U.S. Private*, pg. 4072
THE LONG & FOSTER COMPANIES, INC.; *U.S. Private*, pg. 4072
LONG & FOSTER REAL ESTATE, INC.—See The Long & Foster Companies, Inc.; *U.S. Private*, pg. 4072
LONG FOUNDATION DRILLING CO.; *U.S. Private*, pg. 2490
LONG FU PAPER (KUNSHAN) CO., LTD.—See Cheng Loong Corp.; *Int'l*, pg. 1466
LONG GIANG INVESTMENT & URBAN DEVELOPMENT JOINT-STOCK COMPANY; *Int'l*, pg. 4549
LONGHAI STEEL, INC.; *Int'l*, pg. 4550
LONG HARBOUR EXPLORATION CORP.; *Int'l*, pg. 4549
LONG HAU CORPORATION; *Int'l*, pg. 4549
THE LONGHORN COUNCIL, BOY SCOUTS OF AMERICA; *U.S. Private*, pg. 4072
LONGHORN GLASS INC.—See Anheuser-Busch InBev SA/NV; *Int'l*, pg. 465
LONGHORN HARLEY DAVIDSON; *U.S. Private*, pg. 2492
LONGHORN, INC.; *U.S. Private*, pg. 2492
LONGHORN INTERNATIONAL TRUCKS; *U.S. Private*, pg. 2492
LONGHORN PRODUCE COMPANY; *U.S. Private*, pg. 2492
LONGHOHN STEEL & FLAMECUTTING, INC.—See Joint Holdings/Basic Metal Industries, Inc.; *U.S. Private*, pg. 2230
LONG HO SCIENCE CO., LTD.—See Hitachi Zosen Corporation; *Int'l*, pg. 3411
LONGHOUSE HOSPITALITY—See J.E. Robert Company; *U.S. Private*, pg. 2162
LONGHUA TECHNOLOGY GROUP LUOYANG CO., LTD.; *Int'l*, pg. 4550
LONGHUI INTERNATIONAL HOLDINGS LIMITED; *Int'l*, pg. 4550
LONGIAL GMBH—See Munchener Ruckversicherungs AG; *Int'l*, pg. 5087
LONGI GREEN ENERGY TECHNOLOGY CO., LTD.; *Int'l*, pg. 4550
LONGINO & CARDENAL LIMITED—See Longino & Cardenal SpA; *Int'l*, pg. 4550
LONGINO & CARDENAL NY LLC—See Longino & Cardenal SpA; *Int'l*, pg. 4550
LONGINO & CARDENAL SPA; *Int'l*, pg. 4550
LONGINO & CARDENAL TRADING LLC—See Longino & Cardenal SpA; *Int'l*, pg. 4550
LONG IRON MEATS (PTY) LIMITED—See Country Bird Holdings Limited; *Int'l*, pg. 1818
LONG ISLAND AUTOMOTIVE GROUP, INC.—See Marubeni Corporation; *Int'l*, pg. 4706
LONG ISLAND BUSINESS NEWS, LLC—See The Dolan Company; *U.S. Private*, pg. 4022
LONG ISLAND CHILDREN'S MUSEUM; *U.S. Private*, pg. 2490
LONG ISLAND COMPOST CORP.; *U.S. Private*, pg. 2490
LONG ISLAND EDUCATIONAL TV COUNCIL, INC.—See WNET; *U.S. Private*, pg. 4553
LONG ISLAND FIREPROOF DOOR INC.; *U.S. Private*, pg. 2490
LONG ISLAND PIPE SUPPLY, INC.—See Core & Main, Inc.; *U.S. Public*, pg. 576
LONG ISLAND POWER AUTHORITY; *U.S. Private*, pg. 2490
LONG ISLAND RAIL ROAD—See Metropolitan Transportation Authority; *U.S. Private*, pg. 2689
LONG ISLAND TENNIS TIME INC.—See Island Tennis LP; *U.S. Private*, pg. 2145
LONGI SOLAR AUSTRALIA PTY. LTD.—See LONGi Green Energy Technology Co., Ltd.; *Int'l*, pg. 4550
LONGI SOLAR TECHNOLOGIE GMBH—See LONGi Green Energy Technology Co., Ltd.; *Int'l*, pg. 4550
LONGI SOLAR TECHNOLOGY CO., LTD.—See LONGi Green Energy Technology Co., Ltd.; *Int'l*, pg. 4550
LONGI SOLAR TECHNOLOGY K.K.—See LONGi Green Energy Technology Co., Ltd.; *Int'l*, pg. 4550
LONGITUDE CAPITAL MANAGEMENT CO., LLC; *U.S. Private*, pg. 2492
LONGITUDE LLC—See Nasdaq, Inc.; *U.S. Public*, pg. 1491

LONGJIANG ENVIRONMENTAL PROTECTION GROUP CO., LTD.—See SIIC Environment Holdings Ltd.; *Int'l*, pg. 6913
LONGJIAN ROAD & BRIDGE CO., LTD.; *Int'l*, pg. 4550
LONG JOHN SILVER'S LLC; *U.S. Private*, pg. 2490
LONG KANG MEDICAL INVESTMENT MANAGEMENT HEBEI CO., LTD.—See Hebei Changshan Biochemical Pharmaceutical Co. Ltd.; *Int'l*, pg. 3305
LONGKLOOF LTD.—See E Media Holdings Limited; *Int'l*, pg. 2246
LONGKOU NANSHAN CDB VILLAGE BANK CO., LTD.—See China Development Bank Corporation; *Int'l*, pg. 1497
LONGKOU O.R.G PACKING CO., LTD.—See ORG Technology Co., Ltd.; *Int'l*, pg. 5617
LONGKOU UNION CHEMICAL CO., LTD.; *Int'l*, pg. 4550
LONGLEAF C&D DISPOSAL FACILITY, INC.—See Waste Management, Inc.; *U.S. Public*, pg. 2331
LONGLEAF SURGERY CENTER, LLC—See Tenet Healthcare Corporation; *U.S. Public*, pg. 2004
LONG-LEWIS HARDWARE CO.—See House-Hasson Hardware Company; *U.S. Private*, pg. 1992
LONG-LEWIS INCORPORATED; *U.S. Private*, pg. 2492
LONGLEY CONCRETE LTD.—See Ibstock plc; *Int'l*, pg. 3577
LONGLEY SUPPLY COMPANY, INC.; *U.S. Private*, pg. 2492
LONGLEY SUPPLY COMPANY, INC.—See Longley Supply Company, Inc.; *U.S. Private*, pg. 2492
LONGLIDE INTELLIGENT TECHNOLOGY CO., LTD.; *Int'l*, pg. 4550
LONGLIDE PACKAGING TECHNOLOGY (SHANGHAI) CO., LTD.—See Longlide Intelligent Technology Co., Ltd.; *Int'l*, pg. 4551
LONGLIFE DINING CO., LTD.—See LONGLIFE HOLDING Co., Ltd.; *Int'l*, pg. 4551
LONGLIFE GLOBAL CONSULTANT CO., LTD.—See LONGLIFE HOLDING Co., Ltd.; *Int'l*, pg. 4551
LONGLIFE HOLDING CO., LTD.; *Int'l*, pg. 4551
LONGLIFE MEDICAL CO., LTD.—See LONGLIFE HOLDING Co., Ltd.; *Int'l*, pg. 4551
LONG LINES, LLC—See Schurz Communications, Inc.; *U.S. Private*, pg. 3571
LONGLI TECHNOLOGY (INDIA) CO., LTD.—See Shenzhen Longli Technology Co., Ltd.; *Int'l*, pg. 6817
LONG-LOK FASTENERS CORPORATION - LOCKING DIVISION WEST—See KKR & Co. Inc.; *U.S. Public*, pg. 1262
LONG-LOK FASTENERS CORPORATION—See KKR & Co. Inc.; *U.S. Public*, pg. 1262
LONGMAN AUSTRALASIA PTY LTD—See Pearson plc; *Int'l*, pg. 5775
LONGMAN GROUP (OVERSEAS) HOLDINGS LTD—See Pearson plc; *Int'l*, pg. 5775
LONGMAN KENYA LTD—See Pearson plc; *Int'l*, pg. 5775
LONGMAN LESOTHO (PTY) LTD—See Pearson plc; *Int'l*, pg. 5776
LONGMAN MALAWI LTD—See Pearson plc; *Int'l*, pg. 5775
LONGMAN NAMIBIA (PTY) LTD—See Pearson plc; *Int'l*, pg. 5775
LONGMAN NIGERIA LTD.—See Pearson plc; *Int'l*, pg. 5776
LONGMAN ZAMBIA LTD—See Pearson plc; *Int'l*, pg. 5775
LONGMAN ZIMBABWE (PTE) LTD.—See Pearson plc; *Int'l*, pg. 5776
LONG MARCH CAPITAL LTD.; *Int'l*, pg. 4549
LONG-MCARTHUR INC.; *U.S. Private*, pg. 2492
LONG MEADOW RANCH WINERY & FARMSTEAD; *U.S. Private*, pg. 2490
LONG MECHANICAL INC.; *U.S. Private*, pg. 2491
LONG MING GREEN ENERGY TECHNOLOGY ENGINEERING CO., LTD.; *Int'l*, pg. 4549
LONGMONT TIMES-CALL—See Alden Global Capital LLC; *U.S. Public*, pg. 157
LONGMONT UNITED HOSPITAL; *U.S. Private*, pg. 2492
LONGMOOR SERVICES LIMITED—See Westminster Group Plc; *Int'l*, pg. 8391
LONG MOTOR CORPORATION; *U.S. Private*, pg. 2491
LONG MOTORS INC.; *U.S. Private*, pg. 2491
LONGNECKER & ASSOCIATES INC.—See Aon plc; *Int'l*, pg. 496
LONGNECK & THUNDERFOOT LLC; *U.S. Private*, pg. 2492
LONGNORTH LIMITED—See Brown-Forman Corporation; *U.S. Public*, pg. 403
THE LONG NOW FOUNDATION; *U.S. Private*, pg. 4072
LONGO BROTHERS FRUIT MARKETS INC.; *Int'l*, pg. 4551
LONGO-DE PUERTO RICO INC.; *U.S. Private*, pg. 2492
LONGO ELECTRICAL-MECHANICAL INC.; *U.S. Private*, pg. 2492
LONG PAINTING COMPANY; *U.S. Private*, pg. 2491
LONG PATH PARTNERS, LP; *U.S. Private*, pg. 2491
LONG POINT CAPITAL LLC; *U.S. Private*, pg. 2491
LONG POWER SYSTEMS (SUZHOU) CO., LTD.—See Sichuan Western Resources Holding Co., Ltd.; *Int'l*, pg. 6881
LONG PRAIRIE PACKING LLC—See Rosens Diversified, Inc.; *U.S. Private*, pg. 3484

LONG QUAN SAFE FOOD JSC—See Malee Group Public Company Limited; *Int'l*, pg. 4662
LONGRANGE CAPITAL LLC; *U.S. Private*, pg. 2492
THE LONGREACH GROUP; *Int'l*, pg. 7664
LONG REACH INC.—See Allied Systems Company; *U.S. Private*, pg. 188
LONGREACH OIL LIMITED; *Int'l*, pg. 4551
LONG REALTY COMPANY—See Berkshire Hathaway Inc.; *U.S. Public*, pg. 306
LONGREN & PARKS; *U.S. Private*, pg. 2493
LONG RIDGE EQUITY PARTNERS, LLC; *U.S. Private*, pg. 2492
LONGROOT (THAILAND) LTD.—See Axion Ventures Inc.; *Int'l*, pg. 769
LONG RUN EXPLORATION LTD.; *Int'l*, pg. 4549
LONG'S DRUGS, INC.—See Tailwind Capital Group, LLC; *U.S. Private*, pg. 3924
LONG'S ELECTRONICS, INC.; *U.S. Private*, pg. 2492
LONGSHINE TECHNOLOGY GROUP CO LTD; *Int'l*, pg. 4551
LONGSHORE CAPITAL PARTNERS; *U.S. Private*, pg. 2493
LONGSHORE REOSURCES LTD.; *Int'l*, pg. 4551
LONG'S JEWELERS LTD.; *U.S. Private*, pg. 2492
LONG SON PETROCHEMICALS CO., LTD.—See The Siam Cement Public Company Limited; *Int'l*, pg. 7682
LONGSTRETH SPORTING GOODS, LLC—See Roebling Management Company, LLC; *U.S. Private*, pg. 3470
LONGSUN TECHNOLOGIES CO., LTD.—See Jung Shing Wire Co., Ltd.; *Int'l*, pg. 4026
LONG TALL SALLY LTD.—See AK Retail Holdings Limited; *Int'l*, pg. 259
LONG TERM CARE GROUP, INC.—See ABRY Partners, LLC; *U.S. Private*, pg. 42
LONG TERM SOLUTIONS INC.—See UnitedHealth Group Incorporated; *U.S. Public*, pg. 2244
LONG-THINK INTERNATIONAL (HONG KONG) LTD.—See WPG Holdings Limited; *Int'l*, pg. 8461
LONG TRAIL BREWING COMPANY—See Massachusetts Bay Brewing Co.; *U.S. Private*, pg. 2603
LONGUEUIL NISSAN INC.; *Int'l*, pg. 4551
LONGUEVUE CAPITAL, LLC; *U.S. Private*, pg. 2493
LONGULF TRRADING (UK) LTD.—See Hayel Saeed Anam Group of Companies; *Int'l*, pg. 3290
LONGUST DISTRIBUTING INC.; *U.S. Private*, pg. 2493
LONGVIEW ASPHALT INC.—See Madden Contracting Company Inc.; *U.S. Private*, pg. 2539
LONGVIEW CABLE TELEVISION INC.—See Wehco Media, Inc.; *U.S. Private*, pg. 4469
LONGVIEW EUROPE GMBH—See TA Associates, Inc.; *U.S. Private*, pg. 3915
LONGVIEW FIBRE PAPER AND PACKAGING, INC.—See WestRock Company; *U.S. Public*, pg. 2361
LONGVIEW NEWS-JOURNAL—See Texas Community Media LLC; *U.S. Private*, pg. 3975
LONGVIEW PARTNERS (GUERNSEY) LTD—See Northill Capital LLP; *Int'l*, pg. 5445
LONGVIEW PLACE, LLC—See Equity Residential; *U.S. Public*, pg. 792
LONGVIEW REGIONAL MEDICAL CENTER—See Community Health Systems, Inc.; *U.S. Public*, pg. 554
LONGVIEW TEA COMPANY LIMITED; *Int'l*, pg. 4551
LONGVIEW TECHNOLOGY INC.—See WPG Holdings Limited; *Int'l*, pg. 8461
LONGWALL SERVICES INC.; *U.S. Private*, pg. 2493
LONGWATER OPPORTUNITIES LLC; *U.S. Private*, pg. 2493
LONG WAVE INCORPORATED; *U.S. Private*, pg. 2492
LONGWAY POLAND SP. Z O.O.—See Shanghai Baolong Automotive Corporation; *Int'l*, pg. 6762
LONGWEI PETROLEUM INVESTMENT HOLDING LIMITED; *Int'l*, pg. 4551
LONGWELL COMPANY; *Int'l*, pg. 4551
LONG WELL INTERNATIONAL HOLDINGS LIMITED; *Int'l*, pg. 4549
LONGWEN GROUP CORP.; *U.S. Public*, pg. 1342
LONG WHOLESALE, INC.; *U.S. Private*, pg. 2492
LONGWOOD CAPITAL GROUP, INC.; *U.S. Private*, pg. 2493
LONGWOOD ELASTOMERS, INC.—See Longwood Industries Holdings, LLC; *U.S. Private*, pg. 2493
LONGWOOD ELASTOMERS, S.A.—See Westinghouse Air Brake Technologies Corporation; *U.S. Public*, pg. 2358
LONGWOOD GATHERING & DISPOSAL SYSTEMS, LP—See Matador Resources Company; *U.S. Public*, pg. 1395
LONGWOOD INDUSTRIES HOLDINGS, LLC; *U.S. Private*, pg. 2493
LONGWOOD INTERNATIONAL, INC.—See Westinghouse Air Brake Technologies Corporation; *U.S. Public*, pg. 2358
LONGWORTH DIALYSIS, LLC—See DaVita Inc.; *U.S. Public*, pg. 640
LONGWORTH INDUSTRIES, INC.—See Stanfield's Limited; *Int'l*, pg. 7169
LONGXING CHEMICAL INDUSTRY CO., LTD.; *Int'l*, pg. 4551
LONGXING CHEMICAL STOCK CO., LTD.; *Int'l*, pg. 4551

1633

LONGXING CHEMICAL STOCK CO., LTD.   CORPORATE AFFILIATIONS

LONGYAN HAIDEXIN AUTOMOBILE CO., LTD—See Tellhow Group Co., Ltd.; *Int'l*, pg. 7545
LONGYAN ITG LONGFENG MOTOR SALES & SERVICE CO., LTD.—See Xiamen ITG Group Corp., Ltd.; *Int'l*, pg. 8524
LONGYAN KAOLIN CLAY CO., LTD.; *Int'l*, pg. 4551
LONGYAN MEIDONG LEXUS AUTO SALES & SERVICES CO., LTD.—See China MeiDong Auto Holdings Limited; *Int'l*, pg. 1519
LONGYAN ZHUOYUE NEW ENERGY CO., LTD.; *Int'l*, pg. 4551
LONGYAO ZHONGYU GAS CO. LTD.—See Zhongyu Energy Holdings Limited; *Int'l*, pg. 8676
LONGYEAR SOUTH AFRICA (PTY) LTD—See Boart Longyear Ltd.; *Int'l*, pg. 1095
LONG YOUNG ELECTRIC (KUNSAN) CO., LTD.—See Long Young Electronic (Kunshan) Co., Ltd.; *Int'l*, pg. 4549
LONG YOUNG ELECTRONIC (KUNSHAN) CO., LTD.; *Int'l*, pg. 4549
LONG YUAN CONSTRUCTION GROUP CO., LTD; *Int'l*, pg. 4549
LONGYUAN MINGCHENG INVESTMENT MANAGEMENT (SHANGHAI) CO., LTD.—See Long Yuan Construction Group Co., Ltd; *Int'l*, pg. 4549
LONGYUAN MINGZHU TECHNOLOGY CO., LTD.—See Long Yuan Construction Group Co., Ltd; *Int'l*, pg. 4549
LONGYUAN MUNICIPAL MAINTENANCE (SHANGHAI) CO., LTD.—See Long Yuan Construction Group Co., Ltd; *Int'l*, pg. 4549
LONGZHU GROUP CO., LTD.; *Int'l*, pg. 4551
LONGZHU OILFIELD SERVICES (S) PTE. LTD.—See Falcon Energy Group Limited; *Int'l*, pg. 2611
LONHAM GROUP LIMITED—See The Hanover Insurance Group, Inc.; *U.S. Public*, pg. 2087
LONKEY INDUSTRIAL CO., LTD.; *Int'l*, pg. 4551
LONKING HOLDINGS LIMITED; *Int'l*, pg. 4551
LONMAR GLOBAL RISKS LIMITED—See Brown & Brown, Inc.; *U.S. Public*, pg. 401
LONMIN PLC—See Sibanye-Stillwater Limited; *Int'l*, pg. 6876
LONNEGAL PROPERTY PTY. LTD.—See Cedar Woods Properties Limited; *Int'l*, pg. 1388
LONNIE MCCURRY'S FOUR WHEEL DRIVE CENTER, INC.; *U.S. Private*, pg. 2493
LON OPERATIONS LLC—See Bread Financial Holdings Inc.; *U.S. Public*, pg. 381
LONRHO LIMITED; *Int'l*, pg. 4551
LONSDALE CAPITAL PARTNERS LLP; *Int'l*, pg. 4552
LONSDALE GROUP; *Int'l*, pg. 4552
LONSDALE MIDLANDS LIMITED—See Sheikh Holdings Group (Investments) Limited; *Int'l*, pg. 6793
LONSDALE OPERATIONS SAS—See Lonsdale Group; *Int'l*, pg. 4552
LONSDALE SAATCHI & SAATCHI—See Publicis Groupe S.A.; *Int'l*, pg. 6108
LONSEAL CORPORATION; *Int'l*, pg. 4552
LONSEN KIRI CHEMICAL INDUSTRIES LTD.—See Zhejiang Longsheng Group Co., Ltd.; *Int'l*, pg. 8659
LONS MEMORIALS—See Family Memorials Inc.; *Int'l*, pg. 2612
LONSTROFF AG—See Sumitomo Rubber Industries, Ltd.; *Int'l*, pg. 7299
LONSTROFF MEDICINSKI ELASTOMERI D.O.O.—See Sumitomo Rubber Industries, Ltd.; *Int'l*, pg. 7299
LONTRUE CO., LTD.; *Int'l*, pg. 4552
LONZA AUSTRALIA PTY LTD—See Lonza Group AG; *Int'l*, pg. 4553
LONZA BENELUX BV—See Lonza Group AG; *Int'l*, pg. 4554
LONZA BIOLOGICS, INC.—See Lonza Group AG; *Int'l*, pg. 4554
LONZA BIOLOGICS LTD.—See Lonza Group AG; *Int'l*, pg. 4554
LONZA BIOLOGICS PLC—See Lonza Group AG; *Int'l*, pg. 4554
LONZA BIOLOGICS PLC—See Lonza Group AG; *Int'l*, pg. 4554
LONZA BIOLOGICS PORRINO, S.L.—See Lonza Group AG; *Int'l*, pg. 4554
LONZA BIOLOGICS TUAS PTE LTD—See Lonza Group AG; *Int'l*, pg. 4554
LONZA BIOPHARMA LTD—See Lonza Group AG; *Int'l*, pg. 4554
LONZA BIOSCIENCE S.A.R.L—See Lonza Group AG; *Int'l*, pg. 4554
LONZA BIOSCIENCE SINGAPORE PTE. LTD.—See Lonza Group AG; *Int'l*, pg. 4554
LONZA BIOTEC S.R.O.—See Lonza Group AG; *Int'l*, pg. 4554
LONZA CANADA INC.—See Lonza Group AG; *Int'l*, pg. 4554
LONZA (CHINA) INVESTMENTS CO LTD—See Lonza Group AG; *Int'l*, pg. 4553
LONZA COLOGNE GMBH—See Lonza Group AG; *Int'l*, pg. 4554
LONZA COPENHAGEN APS—See Lonza Group AG; *Int'l*, pg. 4554
LONZA COSTA RICA, S.A.—See Lonza Group AG; *Int'l*, pg. 4554
LONZA FRANCE S.A.R.L.—See Lonza Group AG; *Int'l*, pg. 4554
LONZA GMBH—See Lonza Group AG; *Int'l*, pg. 4554
LONZA GROUP AG; *Int'l*, pg. 4552
LONZA GUANGZHOU ENGINEERING AND CONSULTING CO LTD—See Lonza Group AG; *Int'l*, pg. 4554
LONZA GUANGZHOU LTD.—See Lonza Group AG; *Int'l*, pg. 4554
LONZA GUANGZHOU NANSHA LTD—See Lonza Group AG; *Int'l*, pg. 4554
LONZA GUANGZHOU RESEARCH AND DEVELOPMENT CENTER LTD.—See Lonza Group AG; *Int'l*, pg. 4554
LONZA HONG KONG LTD.—See Lonza Group AG; *Int'l*, pg. 4554
LONZA IBERICA S.A.—See Lonza Group AG; *Int'l*, pg. 4554
LONZA INC.—See Lonza Group AG; *Int'l*, pg. 4554
LONZA INDIA PRIVATE LIMITED—See Lonza Group AG; *Int'l*, pg. 4554
LONZA JAPAN LTD.—See Lonza Group AG; *Int'l*, pg. 4554
LONZA K.K.—See Lonza Group AG; *Int'l*, pg. 4554
LONZA MICROBIAL CONTROL ASIA PACIFIC PTE. LTD.—See Lonza Group AG; *Int'l*, pg. 4554
LONZA MILANO S.R.L.—See Lonza Group AG; *Int'l*, pg. 4554
LONZA NANJING LTD—See Lonza Group AG; *Int'l*, pg. 4554
LONZA NETHERLANDS B.V.—See Lonza Group AG; *Int'l*, pg. 4554
LONZA NZ LIMITED—See Lonza Group AG; *Int'l*, pg. 4554
LONZA ROCKLAND, INC.—See Lonza Group AG; *Int'l*, pg. 4554
LONZA SALES LTD—See Lonza Group AG; *Int'l*, pg. 4554
LONZA (THAILAND) CO., LTD.—See Lonza Group AG; *Int'l*, pg. 4553
LONZA VERVIERS SPRL—See Lonza Group AG; *Int'l*, pg. 4554
LONZA WALKERSVILLE, INC.—See Lonza Group AG; *Int'l*, pg. 4554
LONZA WAYNEC INC.—See Lonza Group AG; *Int'l*, pg. 4554
LONZA WOOD PROTECTION—See Lonza Group AG; *Int'l*, pg. 4553
LOOK CHINA CO., LTD.—See LOOK INCORPORATED; *Int'l*, pg. 4555
LOOKER DATA SCIENCES INC.—See Alphabet Inc.; *U.S. Public*, pg. 83
LOOKERS BIRMINGHAM LIMITED—See Lookers plc; *Int'l*, pg. 4555
LOOKERS LEASING LIMITED—See Lookers plc; *Int'l*, pg. 4555
LOOKERS MOTOR GROUP LIMITED—See Lookers plc; *Int'l*, pg. 4555
LOOKERS PLC; *Int'l*, pg. 4555
LOOK(H.K)LTD.—See LOOK INCORPORATED; *Int'l*, pg. 4555
LOOK INCORPORATED; *Int'l*, pg. 4554
LOOKINGGLASS CYBER SOLUTIONS, LLC—See Whanau Interests LLC.; *U.S. Private*, pg. 4504
LOOKING GLASS LABS LTD.; *Int'l*, pg. 4555
LOOK MEDIA USA, LLC; *U.S. Private*, pg. 2493
LOOK-O-LOOK INTERNATIONAL BV—See Perfetti Van Melle Holding B.V.; *Int'l*, pg. 5800
LOOKOUT GROUP INC.; *U.S. Private*, pg. 2493
LOOKOUT, INC.; *U.S. Private*, pg. 2493
LOOKOUT MARINE SALES—See OneWater Marine Holdings LLC; *U.S. Private*, pg. 3026
LOOKOUT POINT LIMITED—See British Broadcasting Corporation; *Int'l*, pg. 1169
LOOKS FINLAND OY; *Int'l*, pg. 4555
LOOKS HEALTH SERVICES LIMITED; *Int'l*, pg. 4555
LOOKSMART CANADA LTD—See LookSmart Group, Inc.; *U.S. Public*, pg. 1342
LOOKSMART GROUP, INC.; *U.S. Public*, pg. 1342
LOOKTOURS.COM LLC—See TripAdvisor, Inc.; *U.S. Public*, pg. 2195
LOOMCRAFT TEXTILE & SUPPLY CO.; *U.S. Private*, pg. 2494
LOOM INC.—See Atlassian Corporation; *Int'l*, pg. 686
LOOMIS AB; *Int'l*, pg. 4555
THE LOOMIS AGENCY; *U.S. Private*, pg. 4072
LOOMIS BELGIUM NV—See Loomis AB; *Int'l*, pg. 4555
LOOMIS COMMUNITIES, INC.; *U.S. Private*, pg. 2494
LOOMIS COMPANY; *U.S. Private*, pg. 2494
LOOMIS CZECH REPUBLIC A.S.—See Loomis AB; *Int'l*, pg. 4555
LOOMIS DANMARK A/S—See Loomis AB; *Int'l*, pg. 4555
LOOMIS DIGITAL SOLUTION AB—See Loomis AB; *Int'l*, pg. 4555
LOOMIS D.O.O.—See Loomis AB; *Int'l*, pg. 4556
LOOMIS ESTORE AB—See Loomis AB; *Int'l*, pg. 4556
LOOMIS EXPRESS—See TFI International Inc.; *Int'l*, pg. 7586
LOOMIS FEDERAL SAVINGS & LOAN ASSOCIATION—See Hoyne Financial Corporation; *U.S. Private*, pg. 1996
LOOMIS FOREIGN EXCHANGE AS—See Loomis AB; *Int'l*, pg. 4555
LOOMIS FRANCE S.A.S.—See Loomis AB; *Int'l*, pg. 4555
LOOMIS FX GOLD AND SERVICES SAS—See Loomis AB; *Int'l*, pg. 4555
LOOMIS GUVENLIK HIZMETLERI A.S.—See Loomis AB; *Int'l*, pg. 4555
LOOMIS HOLDER SPAIN SL—See Loomis AB; *Int'l*, pg. 4555
LOOMIS INTERNATIONAL SERVICES GMBH—See Loomis AB; *Int'l*, pg. 4555
LOOMIS & LAPANN, INC.—See Arrow Financial Corporation; *U.S. Public*, pg. 200
LOOMIS NORGE AS—See Loomis AB; *Int'l*, pg. 4555
LOOMIS OSTERREICH GMBH—See Loomis AB; *Int'l*, pg. 4555
LOOMIS PORTUGAL, LDA.—See Loomis AB; *Int'l*, pg. 4555
LOOMIS, SAYLES & COMPANY, L.P.—See Groupe BPCE; *Int'l*, pg. 3096
LOOMIS SAYLES INVESTMENTS ASIA PTE. LTD.—See Groupe BPCE; *Int'l*, pg. 3098
LOOMIS SAYLES INVESTMENTS LTD.—See Groupe BPCE; *Int'l*, pg. 3098
LOOMIS SCHWEIZ AG—See Loomis AB; *Int'l*, pg. 4555
LOOMIS SLOVENSKO, S.R.O.—See Loomis AB; *Int'l*, pg. 4555
LOOMIS SPAIN, S.A.—See Loomis AB; *Int'l*, pg. 4555
LOOMIS SUOMI OY—See Loomis AB; *Int'l*, pg. 4555
LOOMIS SVERIGE AB—See Loomis AB; *Int'l*, pg. 4555
LOOMIS UK LTD.—See Loomis AB; *Int'l*, pg. 4556
LOOMIS US INC.—See Loomis AB; *Int'l*, pg. 4556
LOOMIS VALUE SOLUTIONS OY—See Loomis AB; *Int'l*, pg. 4556
LOOMWORKS APPAREL INC.—See GMM Capital LLC; *U.S. Private*, pg. 1722
LOONEY ADVERTISING AND DESIGN; *U.S. Private*, pg. 2494
LOONG FU PAPER (KUNSAN) CO., LTD.—See Cheng Loong Corp.; *Int'l*, pg. 1466
LOONTJENS AUTOMATEN B.V.—See Novomatic AG; *Int'l*, pg. 5467
LOOP CAPITAL MARKETS; *U.S. Private*, pg. 2494
LOOP GMBH—See Landesbank Baden-Wurttemberg; *Int'l*, pg. 4405
LOOP INDUSTRIES, INC.; *Int'l*, pg. 4556
LOOP, LLC—See Marathon Petroleum Corporation; *U.S. Public*, pg. 1364
LOOP, LLC; *U.S. Private*, pg. 2494
LOOP-LOC LTD.; *U.S. Private*, pg. 2494
LOOP MEDIA, INC.; *U.S. Public*, pg. 1342
LOOPNET, INC.—See CoStar Group, Inc.; *U.S. Public*, pg. 586
LOOP PAPER RECYCLING INC.; *U.S. Private*, pg. 2494
LOOP SECURE PTY. LTD.—See Thales S.A.; *Int'l*, pg. 7601
LOOPSHARE LTD.; *Int'l*, pg. 4556
LOOP TELECOMMUNICATION INTERNATIONAL, INC.; *Int'l*, pg. 4556
LOOP TELECOM NA, INC.—See Loop Telecommunication International, Inc.; *Int'l*, pg. 4556
LOOPUP AUSTRALIA PTY LTD—See LoopUp Group plc; *Int'l*, pg. 4556
LOOPUP GROUP PLC; *Int'l*, pg. 4556
LOOPUP (HK) LIMITED—See LoopUp Group plc; *Int'l*, pg. 4556
LOOS & COMPANY, INC. - CABLEWARE—See Loos & Company, Inc.; *U.S. Private*, pg. 2494
LOOS & COMPANY, INC.; *U.S. Private*, pg. 2494
LOOSTAD BV—See Koninklijke VolkerWessels N.V.; *Int'l*, pg. 4271
LOOTOM TELCO-VIDEO NETWORK(WUXI).CO.,LTD; *Int'l*, pg. 4556
LOPAM; *Int'l*, pg. 4556
LOPAREX BV—See Pamplona Capital Management LLP; *Int'l*, pg. 5711
LOPAREX LLC - IOWA CITY PLANT—See Intermediate Capital Group plc; *Int'l*, pg. 3742
LOPAREX LLC—See Intermediate Capital Group plc; *Int'l*, pg. 3742
LOPEZ FOODS INC.; *U.S. Private*, pg. 2494
LOPEZ HOLDINGS CORPORATION—See Lopez, Inc.; *Int'l*, pg. 4556
LOPEZ, INC.; *Int'l*, pg. 4556
LOPEZ NEGRETE COMMUNICATIONS, INC.; *U.S. Private*, pg. 2494
LOPEZ NEGRETE COMMUNICATIONS WEST, INC.—See Lopez Negrete Communications, Inc.; *U.S. Private*, pg. 2494
LOPEZ TAX SERVICE, INC.; *U.S. Private*, pg. 2494
LOPHOS HOLDINGS INC.; *Int'l*, pg. 4557
LOPHOS PHARMACEUTICALS CORP.—See Lophos Holdings Inc.; *Int'l*, pg. 4557
LOPITO, ILEANA & HOWIE, INC.; *U.S. Private*, pg. 2494
L & O POWER COOPERATIVE; *U.S. Private*, pg. 2361
LOPREST WATER TREATMENT COMPANY—See Water Remediation Technology LLC; *U.S. Private*, pg. 4451
LOPRO CORPORATION—See J Trust Co., Ltd.; *Int'l*, pg. 3852
LOQATE LIMITED—See GB Group plc; *Int'l*, pg. 2892

COMPANY NAME INDEX

LOQUENDO S.P.A.—See Microsoft Corporation; *U.S. Public*, pg. 1442
LOQUS; *Int'l*, pg. 4557
LO-Q VIRTUAL QUEUING INC.—See accesso Technology Group Plc; *Int'l*, pg. 89
LORAIN COUNTY AUTOMOTIVE SYSTEMS INC.—See P&C Group, Inc.; *U.S. Private*, pg. 3059
LORAINE'S ACADEMY, INC.; *U.S. Private*, pg. 2494
THE LORAIN JOURNAL COMPANY-THE MORNING JOURNAL—See Alden Global Capital LLC; *U.S. Private*, pg. 159
LORAIN-MEDINA RURAL ELECTRONIC COOPORATIVE, INC.; *U.S. Private*, pg. 2494
LORAL SPACE & COMMUNICATIONS INC.—See Telesat Corporation; *Int'l*, pg. 7541
LORAMENDI CHINA—See Mondragon Corporation; *Int'l*, pg. 5031
LORAMENDI FRANCE SASU—See Mondragon Corporation; *Int'l*, pg. 5031
LORAMENDI INC—See Mondragon Corporation; *Int'l*, pg. 5031
LORAMENDI S.COOP.—See Mondragon Corporation; *Int'l*, pg. 5031
LORAMENDI SOUTH AFRICA (PTI) LTD—See Mondragon Corporation; *Int'l*, pg. 5031
LORAMENDI VERTRIEBS GMBH—See Mondragon Corporation; *Int'l*, pg. 5031
LORAM MAINTENANCE OF WAY INC.; *U.S. Private*, pg. 2494
L'ORANGE FUEL INJECTION (NINGBO) CO., LTD.—See Woodward, Inc.; *U.S. Public*, pg. 2377
L'ORANGE FUEL INJECTION TRADING (SUZHOU) CO., LTD.—See Woodward, Inc.; *U.S. Public*, pg. 2377
LORAS HOLDING A.S.; *Int'l*, pg. 4557
LORD ABBETT & CO.; *U.S. Private*, pg. 2495
LORD, AECK & SARGENT, INC.; *U.S. Private*, pg. 2495
LORDAE INC.; *U.S. Private*, pg. 2495
LORD ASIA INTERNATIONAL LTD—See Parker Hannifin Corporation; *U.S. Public*, pg. 1641
LORD BALTIMORE CAPITAL CORP.; *U.S. Private*, pg. 2495
LORD BALTIMORE DIALYSIS, LLC—See DaVita Inc.; *U.S. Public*, pg. 640
LORD BUDDHA FINANCE LIMITED—See Global IME Bank Limited; *Int'l*, pg. 2997
LORD CHEMICAL PRODUCTS (MALAYSIA) SDN. BHD.—See Parker Hannifin Corporation; *U.S. Public*, pg. 1641
LORD CHEMICAL (SHANGHAI) CO., LTD.—See Parker Hannifin Corporation; *U.S. Public*, pg. 1641
LORD & COMPANY TECHNOLOGIES, INC.—See Sentinel Capital Partners, L.L.C.; *U.S. Private*, pg. 3609
LORDCO PARTS LTD.; *Int'l*, pg. 4557
LORD CORP. - ERIE—See Parker Hannifin Corporation; *U.S. Public*, pg. 1641
LORD CORPORATION (EUROPE) LTD—See Parker Hannifin Corporation; *U.S. Public*, pg. 1641
LORD CORPORATION MICROSTRAIN SENSING SYSTEMS—See Spectris Plc; *Int'l*, pg. 7131
LORD CORPORATION PRODUCTS AND ENGINEERING, LTD.—See Parker Hannifin Corporation; *U.S. Public*, pg. 1641
LORD CORPORATION SLOVAKIA S.R.O.—See Parker Hannifin Corporation; *U.S. Public*, pg. 1641
LORD CORPORATION—See Parker Hannifin Corporation; *U.S. Public*, pg. 1641
LORD CORP. RESEARCH & DEVELOPMENT—See Parker Hannifin Corporation; *U.S. Public*, pg. 1641
LORD ELECTRIC COMPANY OF PUERTO RICO INC.; *U.S. Private*, pg. 2495
LORDEN OIL CO. INC.; *U.S. Private*, pg. 2495
LORD FAR EAST, INC.—See Parker Hannifin Corporation; *U.S. Public*, pg. 1641
LORD GERMANY GMBH—See Parker Hannifin Corporation; *U.S. Public*, pg. 1641
LORD GLOBAL CORPORATION; *U.S. Public*, pg. 1342
LORD GREEN REAL ESTATE STRATEGIES, INC.—See Blackstone Inc.; *U.S. Public*, pg. 355
LORD INDIA PVT. LTD.—See Parker Hannifin Corporation; *U.S. Public*, pg. 1641
LORD INDUSTRIAL LTDA.—See Parker Hannifin Corporation; *U.S. Public*, pg. 1641
LORD INTERNATIONAL TRADING (SHANGHAI) CO., LTD.—See Parker Hannifin Corporation; *U.S. Public*, pg. 1641
LORD ITALIA S.R.L.—See Parker Hannifin Corporation; *U.S. Public*, pg. 1641
LORD KOREA, LTD.—See Parker Hannifin Corporation; *U.S. Public*, pg. 1641
LORD KOREA, LTD.—See Parker Hannifin Corporation; *U.S. Public*, pg. 1641
LORDOS HOTEL (HOLDINGS) PUBLIC LTD; *Int'l*, pg. 4557
LORDOS HOTELS (HOLDINGS) PUBLIC LTD.; *Int'l*, pg. 4557
LORDOS UNITED PLASTICS PUBLIC LTD; *Int'l*, pg. 4557
LORDS CHLORO ALKALI LIMITED; *Int'l*, pg. 4557
LORDS GROUP TRADING PLC; *Int'l*, pg. 4557
LORDS ISHWAR HOTELS LIMITED; *Int'l*, pg. 4557

LORD SOLUTIONS FRANCE—See Parker Hannifin Corporation; *U.S. Public*, pg. 1641
LORD & SONS INC.; *U.S. Private*, pg. 2494
LORDSTOWN MOTORS CORP.; *U.S. Public*, pg. 1342
LORD SUISSE SARL—See Parker Hannifin Corporation; *U.S. Public*, pg. 1641
LORD & TAYLOR LLC—See Le Tote, Inc.; *U.S. Private*, pg. 2405
LORD TECHNOL, INC.—See Parker Hannifin Corporation; *U.S. Public*, pg. 1641
LORD (THAILAND) LTD.—See Parker Hannifin Corporation; *U.S. Public*, pg. 1641
LORD WEST FORMAL WEAR; *U.S. Private*, pg. 2495
L'OREAL ADRIA D.O.O.—See L'Oreal S.A.; *Int'l*, pg. 4379
L'OREAL ARGENTINA SA—See L'Oreal S.A.; *Int'l*, pg. 4379
L'OREAL AUSTRALIA PTY LTD—See L'Oreal S.A.; *Int'l*, pg. 4379
L'OREAL BALKAN D.O.O.—See L'Oreal S.A.; *Int'l*, pg. 4379
L'OREAL BELGILUX SA—See L'Oreal S.A.; *Int'l*, pg. 4379
L'OREAL BULGARIA EOOD—See L'Oreal S.A.; *Int'l*, pg. 4379
L'OREAL CANADA—See L'Oreal S.A.; *Int'l*, pg. 4380
L'OREAL CESKA REPUBLIKA S.R.O—See L'Oreal S.A.; *Int'l*, pg. 4379
L'OREAL CHILE S.A.—See L'Oreal S.A.; *Int'l*, pg. 4379
L'OREAL CHINA CO LTD—See L'Oreal S.A.; *Int'l*, pg. 4379
L'OREAL COLOMBIA S.A.—See L'Oreal S.A.; *Int'l*, pg. 4379
L'OREAL DENMARK A/S—See L'Oreal S.A.; *Int'l*, pg. 4379
L'OREAL DEUTSCHLAND GMBH—See L'Oreal S.A.; *Int'l*, pg. 4379
L'OREAL ESPANA S.A.—See L'Oreal S.A.; *Int'l*, pg. 4379
L'OREAL FINLAND OY—See L'Oreal S.A.; *Int'l*, pg. 4379
L'OREAL HELLAS S.A.—See L'Oreal S.A.; *Int'l*, pg. 4379
L'OREAL HONG-KONG LTD—See L'Oreal S.A.; *Int'l*, pg. 4379
L'OREAL INDIA PRIVATE LTD—See L'Oreal S.A.; *Int'l*, pg. 4379
L'OREAL ISRAEL LTD—See L'Oreal S.A.; *Int'l*, pg. 4379
L'OREAL ITALIA SPA—See L'Oreal S.A.; *Int'l*, pg. 4379
L'OREAL JAPAN SA—See L'Oreal S.A.; *Int'l*, pg. 4379
L'OREAL KAZAKHSTAN LLP—See L'Oreal S.A.; *Int'l*, pg. 4379
L'OREAL KOREA LTD.—See L'Oreal S.A.; *Int'l*, pg. 4379
L'OREAL LIBAN SAL—See L'Oreal S.A.; *Int'l*, pg. 4379
L'OREAL MAGYARORSZAG KOSMETIKAI KFT—See L'Oreal S.A.; *Int'l*, pg. 4379
L'OREAL MALAYSIA SDN BHD—See L'Oreal S.A.; *Int'l*, pg. 4379
L'OREAL MANUFACTURING MIDRAND (PTY) LTD.—See L'Oreal S.A.; *Int'l*, pg. 4379
L'OREAL MAROC SA—See L'Oreal S.A.; *Int'l*, pg. 4379
L'OREAL MEXICO S. A DE C. V—See L'Oreal S.A.; *Int'l*, pg. 4379
L'OREAL MEXICO SERVICIOS S.A. DE C.V.—See L'Oreal S.A.; *Int'l*, pg. 4379
L'OREAL MIDDLE EAST FZE—See L'Oreal S.A.; *Int'l*, pg. 4379
L'OREAL NEDERLAND B.V.—See L'Oreal S.A.; *Int'l*, pg. 4379
L'OREAL NEW ZEALAND LTD.—See L'Oreal S.A.; *Int'l*, pg. 4379
L'OREAL OSTERREICH GMBH—See L'Oreal S.A.; *Int'l*, pg. 4379
L'OREAL PANAMA S.A.—See L'Oreal S.A.; *Int'l*, pg. 4379
L'OREAL PARFUMS—See L'Oreal S.A.; *Int'l*, pg. 4379
L'OREAL PERU S.A.—See L'Oreal S.A.; *Int'l*, pg. 4379
L'OREAL PHILIPPINES, INC.—See L'Oreal S.A.; *Int'l*, pg. 4379
L'OREAL POLSKA SP. Z.O.O.—See L'Oreal S.A.; *Int'l*, pg. 4379
L'OREAL PORTUGAL LDA—See L'Oreal S.A.; *Int'l*, pg. 4379
L'OREAL PRODUITS DE LUXE FRANCE S.N.C.—See L'Oreal S.A.; *Int'l*, pg. 4380
L'OREAL PRODUITS DE LUXE INTERNATIONAL S.N.C.—See L'Oreal S.A.; *Int'l*, pg. 4379
L'OREAL ROMANIA SRL—See L'Oreal S.A.; *Int'l*, pg. 4380
L'OREAL RUSSIA—See L'Oreal S.A.; *Int'l*, pg. 4380
L'OREAL S.A. - GEMEY DIVISION—See L'Oreal S.A.; *Int'l*, pg. 4379
L'OREAL SAIPO INDUSTRIALE S.P.A.—See L'Oreal S.A.; *Int'l*, pg. 4379
L'OREAL S.A. - LABORATORY DIVISION—See L'Oreal S.A.; *Int'l*, pg. 4379
L'OREAL S.A.; *Int'l*, pg. 4378
L'OREAL SINGAPORE PTE LTD—See L'Oreal S.A.; *Int'l*, pg. 4380
L'OREAL SLOVENIJA KOSMETIKA D.O.O.—See L'Oreal S.A.; *Int'l*, pg. 4380
L'OREAL SLOVENSKO S.R.O.—See L'Oreal S.A.; *Int'l*, pg. 4380
L'OREAL SOUTH AFRICA HOLDINGS PTY LTD—See L'Oreal S.A.; *Int'l*, pg. 4380
L'OREAL SUISSE SA—See L'Oreal S.A.; *Int'l*, pg. 4380
L'OREAL SVERIGE AB—See L'Oreal S.A.; *Int'l*, pg. 4380

LORUSSO CORPORATION

L'OREAL THAILAND LTD—See L'Oreal S.A.; *Int'l*, pg. 4380
L'OREAL TURKIYE KOZMETIK SANAYI VE TICARET ANONIM SIRKETI—See L'Oreal S.A.; *Int'l*, pg. 4380
L'OREAL (UK) LIMITED—See L'Oreal S.A.; *Int'l*, pg. 4378
L'OREAL UKRAINE—See L'Oreal S.A.; *Int'l*, pg. 4380
L'OREAL URUGUAY—See L'Oreal S.A.; *Int'l*, pg. 4380
L'OREAL USA, INC. - DESIGNER FRAGRANCE DIVISION—See L'Oreal S.A.; *Int'l*, pg. 4380
L'OREAL USA, INC. - SAVANNAH—See L'Oreal S.A.; *Int'l*, pg. 4380
L'OREAL USA, INC.—See L'Oreal S.A.; *Int'l*, pg. 4380
L'OREAL VERWALTUNGS GMBH—See L'Oreal S.A.; *Int'l*, pg. 4380
L'OREAL VIETNAM CO., LTD.—See L'Oreal S.A.; *Int'l*, pg. 4380
LOREFCO, INC.—See HF Sinclair Corporation; *U.S. Public*, pg. 1034
LORE IO, INC.—See Clearlake Capital Group, L.P.; *U.S. Private*, pg. 933
LORE IO, INC.—See Insight Venture Management, LLC; *U.S. Private*, pg. 2087
LORELEC SARL—See Alstom S.A.; *Int'l*, pg. 383
LOREL MARKETING GROUP LLC; *U.S. Private*, pg. 2495
LOREN AUTO GROUP; *U.S. Private*, pg. 2495
LOREN BERG CHEVROLET; *U.S. Private*, pg. 2495
LOREN COMMUNICATIONS INTERNATIONAL LTD., INC.; *U.S. Private*, pg. 2495
LOREN COOK COMPANY; *U.S. Private*, pg. 2495
LOREN INDUSTRIES INC.; *U.S. Private*, pg. 2495
LORENSBERGS COMMUNICATION AB—See CompuGroup Medical SE & Co. KGaA; *Int'l*, pg. 1756
LORENTZEN & WAETTRE SKANDINAVIEN AB—See ABB Ltd.; *Int'l*, pg. 49
LORENTZEN & WETTRE AB—See ABB Ltd.; *Int'l*, pg. 49
LORENTZEN & WETTRE INTERNATIONAL AB—See ABB Ltd.; *Int'l*, pg. 50
LORENTZEN & WETTRE LTDA—See ABB Ltd.; *Int'l*, pg. 50
LORENTZEN & WETTRE S.A.R.L.—See ABB Ltd.; *Int'l*, pg. 50
LORENZI LUMBER CO. INC.; *U.S. Private*, pg. 2495
LORENZINI APPARELS LIMITED; *Int'l*, pg. 4557
LORENZ LIGHT TECHNIC SARL—See Lucibel SA; *Int'l*, pg. 4573
LORENZO CRYSTAL LTD.—See LJ International, Inc.; *Int'l*, pg. 4535
LORENZO INTERNATIONAL (KUNSHAN) CO., LTD.—See Lorenzo International Limited; *Int'l*, pg. 4558
LORENZO INTERNATIONAL LIMITED; *Int'l*, pg. 4557
LORENZO JEWELRY LIMITED—See LJ International, Inc.; *Int'l*, pg. 4535
LORENZO (SHENZHEN) CO., LTD.—See LJ International, Inc.; *Int'l*, pg. 4535
LORENZO SHIPPING CORPORATION; *Int'l*, pg. 4558
LORENZ RUBARTH LANDTECHNIK GMBH—See AGRAVIS Raiffeisen AG; *Int'l*, pg. 215
LOREX CORPORATION—See Teledyne Technologies Incorporated; *U.S. Public*, pg. 1993
LOREX TECHNOLOGY INC.—See Teledyne Technologies Incorporated; *U.S. Public*, pg. 1993
LORIC IMPORT & EXPORT CORP., LTD.—See CRRC Corporation Limited; *Int'l*, pg. 1858
LORIEN ENGINEERING SOLUTIONS LIMITED—See NIRAS Gruppen A/S; *Int'l*, pg. 5362
LORIEN ENGINEERING SOLUTIONS SP. Z.O.O.—See NIRAS Gruppen A/S; *Int'l*, pg. 5362
LORIEN RESOURCING LIMITED - LEEDS—See HFBG Holding B.V.; *Int'l*, pg. 3375
LORIEN RESOURCING LIMITED - LONDON—See HFBG Holding B.V.; *Int'l*, pg. 3375
LORIEN RESOURCING LIMITED - MANCHESTER—See HFBG Holding B.V.; *Int'l*, pg. 3375
LORIENT CAPITAL MANAGEMENT LLC; *U.S. Private*, pg. 2495
LORING HOSPITAL; *U.S. Private*, pg. 2495
LORMEDO SAS; *Int'l*, pg. 4558
LORNAMEAD, INC.; *U.S. Private*, pg. 2495
LORNE PARK CAPITAL PARTNERS INC.; *Int'l*, pg. 4558
LORNE STEWART PLC; *Int'l*, pg. 4558
LOROMAN CO. INC.—See Abbott Industries Inc.; *U.S. Private*, pg. 35
LORO PIANA S.P.A.—See LVMH Moet Hennessy Louis Vuitton SE; *Int'l*, pg. 4595
LORO PIANA USA, LLC—See LVMH Moet Hennessy Louis Vuitton SE; *Int'l*, pg. 4595
LORRAINE CAPITAL LLC; *U.S. Private*, pg. 2495
LORRAINE COPPER CORP.—See NorthWest Copper Corp.; *Int'l*, pg. 5446
LORRAINE HOME FASHIONS; *U.S. Private*, pg. 2496
LORRAINE LINENS INC.; *U.S. Private*, pg. 2496
LORRAINE PRECISION MECANIQUE SARL—See Lormedo SAS; *Int'l*, pg. 4558
LORRIE WALKER COMMUNICATIONS INC.; *U.S. Private*, pg. 2495
LORUNSER AUSTRIA GMBH—See Knill Holding GmbH; *Int'l*, pg. 4208
LORUSSO CORPORATION; *U.S. Private*, pg. 2496
LORVAL—See Veolia Environnement S.A.; *Int'l*, pg. 8155

LOS ABRIGADOS RESORT & SPA—See Apollo Global Management, Inc.; *U.S. Public*, pg. 150
LOS ABRIGADOS RESORT & SPA—See Reverence Capital Partners LLC; *U.S. Private*, pg. 3415
LOSA - LADRILLOS OLAVARRIA S.A.—See Techint S.p.A.; *Int'l*, pg. 7503
LOS ALAMITOS MEDICAL CENTER, INC.—See UCI Health; *U.S. Private*, pg. 4274
LOS ALAMOS MONITOR—See Irish Times; *U.S. Private*, pg. 2139
LOS ALAMOS NATIONAL BANK—See Enterprise Financial Services Corp; *U.S. Public*, pg. 778
LOS ALAMOS TECHNICAL ASSOCIATES, INC.; *U.S. Private*, pg. 2496
LOS ANDES COPPER LTD.; *Int'l*, pg. 4558
LOS ANDES SERVICIOS CORPORATIVOS S.A.C.—See China Three Gorges Corporation; *Int'l*, pg. 1558
LOS ANGELES BROADCASTING PARTNERS, LLC—See iHeartMedia, Inc.; *U.S. Public*, pg. 1095
LOS ANGELES CARDIOLOGY & ASSOCIATES—See Presbyterian Intercommunity Hospital, Inc.; *U.S. Private*, pg. 3253
LOS ANGELES CHILD GUIDANCE CLINIC; *U.S. Private*, pg. 2496
THE LOS ANGELES CLIPPERS FOUNDATION—See LA Clippers LLC; *U.S. Private*, pg. 2368
LOS ANGELES COUNTY FAIR ASSOCIATION; *U.S. Private*, pg. 2496
LOS ANGELES COUNTY METROPOLITAN TRANSPORTATION AUTHORITY; *U.S. Private*, pg. 2496
LOS ANGELES COUNTY MUSEUM OF NATURAL HISTORY FOUNDATION; *U.S. Private*, pg. 2496
LOS ANGELES DAILY NEWS PUBLISHING COMPANY—See Alden Global Capital LLC; *U.S. Private*, pg. 158
THE LOS ANGELES DEPARTMENT OF WATER & POWER; *U.S. Private*, pg. 4072
LOS ANGELES DODGERS LLC—See Guggenheim Baseball Management, L.P.; *U.S. Private*, pg. 1811
LOS ANGELES FIREMENS CREDIT UNION; *U.S. Private*, pg. 2496
LOS ANGELES FIREMEN'S RELIEF ASSOCIATION; *U.S. Private*, pg. 2496
LOS ANGELES/INGLEWOOD ENDOSCOPY ASC, LP—See KKR & Co. Inc.; *U.S. Public*, pg. 1249
LOS ANGELES JEWISH HOME; *U.S. Private*, pg. 2496
LOS ANGELES JUNCTION RAILWAY COMPANY—See Berkshire Hathaway Inc.; *U.S. Public*, pg. 303
LOS ANGELES KINGS HOCKEY CLUB L.P.—See The Anschutz Corporation; *U.S. Private*, pg. 3987
THE LOS ANGELES LAKERS, INC.; *U.S. Private*, pg. 4072
LOS ANGELES MAGAZINE, LLC—See Hour Media Group, LLC; *U.S. Private*, pg. 1991
LOS ANGELES MISSION, INC.; *U.S. Private*, pg. 2496
LOS ANGELES OPERA; *U.S. Private*, pg. 2496
LOS ANGELES PAPER BOX, LLC—See Greif Inc.; *U.S. Public*, pg. 966
LOS ANGELES PHILHARMONIC ASSOCIATION; *U.S. Private*, pg. 2496
LOS ANGELES PUBLIC LIBRARY DOCENTS; *U.S. Private*, pg. 2497
THE LOS ANGELES RAMS, LLC; *U.S. Private*, pg. 4072
LOS ANGELES RUBBER COMPANY; *U.S. Private*, pg. 2497
LOS ANGELES TELEVISION STATION KCAL LLC—See National Amusements, Inc.; *U.S. Private*, pg. 2840
LOS ANGELES TIMES COMMUNICATIONS, LLC; *U.S. Private*, pg. 2497
LOS ANGELES TRUCK CENTERS LLC—See Velocity Vehicle Group; *U.S. Private*, pg. 4354
LOS ANGELES TURF CLUB, INCORPORATED—See The Stronach Group Inc.; *Int'l*, pg. 7689
LOS ANGELES WHOLESALE PRODUCE MARKET; *U.S. Private*, pg. 2497
LOS ARQUEROS GOLF & COUNTRY CLUB S.A.—See Taylor Wimpey plc; *Int'l*, pg. 7478
LOSBERGER FRANCE SAS—See Gilde Buy Out Partners B.V.; *Int'l*, pg. 2975
LOSBERGER GMBH—See Gilde Buy Out Partners B.V.; *Int'l*, pg. 2975
LOSBERGER MODULAR SYSTEMS GMBH—See Gilde Buy Out Partners B.V.; *Int'l*, pg. 2975
LOSBERGER RAPID DEPLOYMENT SYSTEMS SAS—See Gilde Buy Out Partners B.V.; *Int'l*, pg. 2975
LOSBERGER SHANGHAI CO., LTD.—See Gilde Buy Out Partners B.V.; *Int'l*, pg. 2975
LOSBERGER UK LTD.—See Gilde Buy Out Partners B.V.; *Int'l*, pg. 2975
LOSBERGER U.S., LLC—See Gilde Buy Out Partners B.V.; *Int'l*, pg. 2975
LOSCALZO ASSOCIATES, LTD.—See Graham Holdings Company; *U.S. Public*, pg. 956
LOSCAM AUSTRALIA PTY LTD.—See China Merchants Group Limited; *Int'l*, pg. 1521
LOSCAM (HONG KONG) LIMITED—See China Merchants Group Limited; *Int'l*, pg. 1521
LOSCAM (MALAYSIA) SDN. BHD.—See China Merchants Group Limited; *Int'l*, pg. 1521

LOSCAM (NEW ZEALAND) LIMITED—See China Merchants Group Limited; *Int'l*, pg. 1521
LOSCAM PACKAGING EQUIPMENT LEASING (SHANGHAI) CO., LTD.—See China Merchants Group Limited; *Int'l*, pg. 1521
LOSCAM (PHILIPPINES), INC—See China Merchants Group Limited; *Int'l*, pg. 1521
LOSCAM (SINGAPORE) PRIVATE LIMITED—See China Merchants Group Limited; *Int'l*, pg. 1521
LOSCAM (THAILAND) LIMITED—See China Merchants Group Limited; *Int'l*, pg. 1521
LOSCAM VIETNAM CO., LTD.—See China Merchants Group Limited; *Int'l*, pg. 1521
LOS CASTILLOS REAL ESTATE, INC.; *Int'l*, pg. 4558
LO'S CLEANING SERVICES LIMITED—See Xinhua News Media Holdings Limited; *Int'l*, pg. 8530
LOSFELD DISTRIBUTION; *Int'l*, pg. 4558
LOS GATOS ACURA; *U.S. Private*, pg. 2497
LOS GATOS BREWING CO.; *U.S. Private*, pg. 2497
LOSINGER HOLDING AG—See Bouygues S.A.; *Int'l*, pg. 1122
LOSINGER MARAZZI AG—See Bouygues S.A.; *Int'l*, pg. 1122
LOSINJSKA PLOVIDBA - HOLDING D.D; *Int'l*, pg. 4558
LOS MEDANOS ENERGY CENTER LLC—See Energy Capital Partners Management, LP; *U.S. Private*, pg. 1394
L.O. SMITH AB—See Constellation Brands, Inc.; *U.S. Public*, pg. 571
LOS OLIVOS PACKAGING INC.; *U.S. Private*, pg. 2497
LO & SON LAND INVESTMENT COMPANY LIMITED—See Cheuk Nang (Holdings) Limited; *Int'l*, pg. 1473
LOS ROBLES REGIONAL MEDICAL CENTER—See HCA Healthcare, Inc.; *U.S. Public*, pg. 1001
LOS ROBLES SURGICENTER, LLC—See HCA Healthcare, Inc.; *U.S. Public*, pg. 1001
LOSS MANAGEMENT GROUP LTD.; *Int'l*, pg. 4558
LOS TIOS LTD.; *U.S. Private*, pg. 2497
THE LOST PARADISE OF DILMUN WATER PARK BSC—See GFH Financial Group B.S.C.; *Int'l*, pg. 2957
LOST PINES BEVERAGE, LLC—See Hyatt Hotels Corporation; *U.S. Public*, pg. 1078
LOST PLANET; *U.S. Private*, pg. 2497
LOST PLANET—See Lost Planet; *U.S. Private*, pg. 2497
LOST SANDS PTY LTD—See Diatreme Resources Limited; *Int'l*, pg. 2107
LOSUGEN PTY LTD—See Tega Industries Limited; *Int'l*, pg. 7521
LOSURDO FOODS, INC.; *U.S. Private*, pg. 2497
LOT78, INC.; *Int'l*, pg. 4558
LOTARIJA NA MAKEDONIJA AD; *Int'l*, pg. 4558
LOT AUTO SERVICES SP. Z O.O.—See LOT Polish Airlines S.A.; *Int'l*, pg. 4558
LOT CATERING SP. Z O.O.—See LOT Polish Airlines S.A.; *Int'l*, pg. 4558
LOTCE LIMITED; *Int'l*, pg. 4558
LOTERIOS S.R.L.—See Mutares SE & Co. KGaA; *Int'l*, pg. 5104
LOTES CO., LTD.; *Int'l*, pg. 4558
LOTES GUANGZHOU CO.,LTD.—See LOTES Co., Ltd.; *Int'l*, pg. 4559
LOTES SUZHOU CO., LTD.—See LOTES Co., Ltd.; *Int'l*, pg. 4559
LOTHBURY INVESTMENT MANAGEMENT LIMITED—See Nomura Real Estate Holdings, Inc.; *Int'l*, pg. 5412
LOTH INC.—See Loth MBI, Inc.; *U.S. Private*, pg. 2497
LOTH MBI, INC.; *U.S. Private*, pg. 2497
LOTITO FOODS LLC—See TINE SA; *Int'l*, pg. 7753
LOTO-QUEBEC; *Int'l*, pg. 4559
LOTOS ASFALT SP. Z O.O.—See Grupa LOTOS S.A.; *Int'l*, pg. 3117
LOTOS CZECHOWICE S.A.—See Grupa LOTOS S.A.; *Int'l*, pg. 3117
LOTOS EXPLORATION AND PRODUCTION NORGE AS—See Grupa LOTOS S.A.; *Int'l*, pg. 3117
LOTOS INFRASTRUKTURA S.A.—See Grupa LOTOS S.A.; *Int'l*, pg. 3117
LOTOS JASLO S.A.—See Grupa LOTOS S.A.; *Int'l*, pg. 3117
LOTOS KOLEJ SP. Z O.O.—See Grupa LOTOS S.A.; *Int'l*, pg. 3117
LOTOS LAB SP. Z O.O.—See Grupa LOTOS S.A.; *Int'l*, pg. 3117
LOTOS OCHRONA SP. Z O.O.—See Grupa LOTOS S.A.; *Int'l*, pg. 3117
LOTOS OIL S.A.—See Grupa LOTOS S.A.; *Int'l*, pg. 3117
LOTOS PALIWA SP. Z O.O.—See Grupa LOTOS S.A.; *Int'l*, pg. 3117
LOTOS PARAFINY SP. Z O.O.—See Grupa LOTOS S.A.; *Int'l*, pg. 3117
LOTOS PETROBALTIC S.A.—See Grupa LOTOS S.A.; *Int'l*, pg. 3117
LOTOS SERWIS SP. Z O.O.—See Grupa LOTOS S.A.; *Int'l*, pg. 3117
LOTOS STRAZ SP. Z O.O.—See Grupa LOTOS S.A.; *Int'l*, pg. 3117

LOTOS TANK SP. Z O.O.—See Grupa LOTOS S.A.; *Int'l*, pg. 3117
LOTOS TERMINALE S.A.—See Grupa LOTOS S.A.; *Int'l*, pg. 3117
LOTOS UPSTREAM SP. Z O.O.—See Grupa LOTOS S.A.; *Int'l*, pg. 3117
LOT POLISH AIRLINES S.A.; *Int'l*, pg. 4558
LOT POLISH AIRLINES SA—See LOT Polish Airlines S.A.; *Int'l*, pg. 4558
LOTS INTERMEDIATE CO.—See Tiptree Inc.; *U.S. Public*, pg. 2159
LOTSOLUTIONS, INC.—See Tiptree Inc.; *U.S. Public*, pg. 2159
LOTSPEICH AND ASSOCIATES, INC.—See Comvest Group Holdings LLC; *U.S. Private*, pg. 1007
LOTSPEICH CO. OF FLORIDA, INC.; *U.S. Private*, pg. 2497
LOTSPEICH CO.; *U.S. Private*, pg. 2497
LOTTE ASAHI CO., LTD.—See Asahi Group Holdings Ltd.; *Int'l*, pg. 594
LOTTE ASSET DEVELOPMENT CO., LTD.—See Lotte Co., Ltd.; *Int'l*, pg. 4559
LOTTE AUTO LEASE CO., LTD.—See Lotte Rental Co., Ltd.; *Int'l*, pg. 4560
LOTTE BOULANGERIE CO., LTD.—See Lotte Co., Ltd.; *Int'l*, pg. 4560
LOTTE CAPITAL CO., LTD.—See Lotte Co., Ltd.; *Int'l*, pg. 4559
LOTTE CHEMICAL CORPORATION—See Lotte Co., Ltd.; *Int'l*, pg. 4559
LOTTE CHEMICAL PAKISTAN LTD.—See Lotte Co., Ltd.; *Int'l*, pg. 4559
LOTTE CHEMICAL TITAN HOLDING BERHAD—See Lotte Co., Ltd.; *Int'l*, pg. 4559
LOTTE CHILSUNG BEVERAGE CO., LTD. - ANSEONG PLANT—See Lotte Co., Ltd.; *Int'l*, pg. 4559
LOTTE CHILSUNG BEVERAGE CO., LTD. - BUPYEONG PLANT—See Lotte Co., Ltd.; *Int'l*, pg. 4559
LOTTE CHILSUNG BEVERAGE CO., LTD. - OPO PLANT—See Lotte Co., Ltd.; *Int'l*, pg. 4559
LOTTE CHILSUNG BEVERAGE CO., LTD.—See Lotte Co., Ltd.; *Int'l*, pg. 4559
LOTTE CHILSUNG BEVERAGE CO., LTD. - YANGSAN PLANT—See Lotte Co., Ltd.; *Int'l*, pg. 4559
LOTTE CHINA FOODS CO., LTD.—See Lotte Co., Ltd.; *Int'l*, pg. 4560
LOTTE CO., LTD.; *Int'l*, pg. 4559
LOTTE.COM INC.—See Lotte Co., Ltd.; *Int'l*, pg. 4560
LOTTE CORP.—See Lotte Co., Ltd.; *Int'l*, pg. 4559
LOTTE DATA COMMUNICATIONS COMPANY—See Lotte Co., Ltd.; *Int'l*, pg. 4559
LOTTE ENGINEERING & CONSTRUCTION CO., LTD.—See Lotte Co., Ltd.; *Int'l*, pg. 4559
LOTTE ENGINEERING & MACHINERY MFG. CO., LTD.—See Lotte Co., Ltd.; *Int'l*, pg. 4559
LOTTE FINE CHEMICAL CO., LTD.—See Lotte Co., Ltd.; *Int'l*, pg. 4559
LOTTE FOODS CO., LTD.—See Lotte Co., Ltd.; *Int'l*, pg. 4560
LOTTE GLOBAL LOGISTICS CO., LTD.—See Lotte Co., Ltd.; *Int'l*, pg. 4559
LOTTE HIMART CO., LTD.—See Lotte Co., Ltd.; *Int'l*, pg. 4560
LOTTE INEOS CHEMICAL CO., LTD.—See INEOS Limited; *Int'l*, pg. 3683
LOTTE INEOS CHEMICAL CO., LTD.—See Lotte Co., Ltd.; *Int'l*, pg. 4559
LOTTE INTERNATIONAL AMERICA CORP.—See Lotte Co., Ltd.; *Int'l*, pg. 4560
LOTTE INTERNATIONAL CO., LTD.—See Lotte Co., Ltd.; *Int'l*, pg. 4560
LOTTE JTB CO., LTD.—See Lotte Co., Ltd.; *Int'l*, pg. 4560
LOTTE LHP CORPORATION—See Lotte Co., Ltd.; *Int'l*, pg. 4559
LOTTE LOGISTICS CO., LTD.—See Lotte Co., Ltd.; *Int'l*, pg. 4560
LOTTEN-EYES OFTALMOLOGIA CLINICA E CIRURGICA LTDA.—See UnitedHealth Group Incorporated; *U.S. Public*, pg. 2242
LOTTE NON-LIFE INSURANCE CO., LTD.—See JKL Partners, Inc.; *Int'l*, pg. 3973
LOTTE PS NET CO., LTD.—See Lotte Co., Ltd.; *Int'l*, pg. 4560
LOTTE REIT CO., LTD.; *Int'l*, pg. 4560
LOTTE RENT-A-CAR (THAILAND) CO., LTD.—See Lotte Rental Co., Ltd.; *Int'l*, pg. 4560
LOTTE RENTAL CO., LTD.; *Int'l*, pg. 4560
LOTTERIA CO., LTD.—See Lotte Co., Ltd.; *Int'l*, pg. 4560
LOTTERS & MIRUNA ARAMES LTD.—See Drahtwerk Friedr. Lotters GmbH & Co. KG; *Int'l*, pg. 2200
LOTTERS POLSKA SP. Z O.O.—See Drahtwerk Friedr. Lotters GmbH & Co. KG; *Int'l*, pg. 2200
LOTTERY.COM INC.; *U.S. Public*, pg. 1342
LOTTE SHOPPING CO., LTD.—See Lotte Co., Ltd.; *Int'l*, pg. 4560
LOTTE SINGAPORE PTE. LTD.—See Lotte Co., Ltd.; *Int'l*, pg. 4560
LOTTE TOUR DEVELOPMENT CO., LTD.; *Int'l*, pg. 4560

COMPANY NAME INDEX

LOTTE UBE SYNTHETIC RUBBER SDN. BHD.—See UBE Corporation; *Int'l*, pg. 8001
LOTTE U.S.A., INC.—See Lotte Co., Ltd.; *Int'l*, pg. 4560
LOTTE VIETNAM CO., LTD.—See Lotte Co., Ltd.; *Int'l*, pg. 4560
LOTTE VINA INTERNATIONAL CO., LTD.—See Lotte Co., Ltd.; *Int'l*, pg. 4560
LOTTE WELLFOOD CO.,LTD—See Lotte Co., Ltd.; *Int'l*, pg. 4560
LOTTO24 AG—See ZEAL Network SE; *Int'l*, pg. 8628
LOTT OIL COMPANY, INC.; *U.S. Private*, pg. 2497
LOTTO SPORT ITALIA S.P.A.; *Int'l*, pg. 4560
LOTTOTECH LTD.; *Int'l*, pg. 4561
LOT TRAVEL LTD.—See LOT Polish Airlines S.A.; *Int'l*, pg. 4558
LOTTVISION (HONG KONG) LIMITED—See NutryFarm International Limited; *Int'l*, pg. 5494
LOTUS ADVERTISING; *U.S. Private*, pg. 2497
LOTUS AGRAR GMBH—See AGRAVIS Raiffeisen AG; *Int'l*, pg. 215
LOTUS BAKERIES CZ S.R.O.—See Lotus Bakeries N.V.; *Int'l*, pg. 4561
LOTUS BAKERIES GMBH—See Lotus Bakeries N.V.; pg. 4561
LOTUS BAKERIES NORTH AMERICA INC.—See Lotus Bakeries N.V.; *Int'l*, pg. 4561
LOTUS BAKERIES N.V.; *Int'l*, pg. 4561
LOTUS BIO-TECHNOLOGY DEVELOPMENT CORP.; *Int'l*, pg. 4561
LOTUS BODY ENGINEERING LIMITED—See Zhejiang Geely Holding Group Co., Ltd.; *Int'l*, pg. 8652
LOTUS BOUTIQUE HOTEL—See NMC Health PLC; *Int'l*, pg. 5392
LOTUS CAPITAL FINANCIAL SERVICES LTD.; *Int'l*, pg. 4561
LOTUS CARS LIMITED—See Zhejiang Geely Holding Group Co., Ltd.; *Int'l*, pg. 8652
LOTUS CHOCOLATE COMPANY LIMITED—See Reliance - ADA Group Limited; *Int'l*, pg. 6262
LOTUS COMMUNICATIONS CORP.; *U.S. Private*, pg. 2497
LOTUS ENGINEERING, INC.—See Zhejiang Geely Holding Group Co., Ltd.; *Int'l*, pg. 8652
LOTUS ENGINEERING LIMITED—See Zhejiang Geely Holding Group Co., Ltd.; *Int'l*, pg. 8652
LOTUS ESTATE CO., LTD.—See Astellas Pharma Inc.; *Int'l*, pg. 653
LOTUS EYE HOSPITAL AND INSTITUTE LTD.; *Int'l*, pg. 4561
LOTUS HEATING SYSTEMS A/S—See NIBE Industrier AB; *Int'l*, pg. 5261
LOTUS HOLDINGS CO LTD; *Int'l*, pg. 4561
LOTUS HORIZON HOLDINGS LIMITED; *Int'l*, pg. 4561
LOTUS HYDRO POWER PLC; *Int'l*, pg. 4561
LOTUS INFRASTRUCTURE PARTNERS LLC; *U.S. Private*, pg. 2497
LOTUS INNOVATIONS LLC; *U.S. Private*, pg. 2497
LOTUS KFM BERHAD; *Int'l*, pg. 4561
LOTUS MARULA PTY. LTD.—See Lotus Resources Limited; *Int'l*, pg. 4561
LOTUS MJYX LLC—See ST Dupont S.A.; *Int'l*, pg. 7158
LOTUS PACIFIC INC.—See TCL Technology Group Corp.; *Int'l*, pg. 7483
LOTUS PARSIAN CONSTRUCTION DEVELOPMENT COMPANY—See Parsian Bank; *Int'l*, pg. 5747
LOTUS PAY JOINT STOCK COMPANY—See PT GoTo Gojek Tokopedia Tbk; *Int'l*, pg. 6041
LOTUS PHARMACEUTICAL CO., LTD.; *Int'l*, pg. 4561
LOTUS PHARMACEUTICALS, INC.; *Int'l*, pg. 4561
LOTUS RESOURCES LIMITED; *Int'l*, pg. 4561
LOTUSSS STORES (MALAYSIA) SDN. BHD.—See C.P. All Public Company Limited; *Int'l*, pg. 1244
LOTUS SUPPLIES SDN. BHD.—See Citra Nusa Holdings Berhad; *Int'l*, pg. 1626
LOTUS TISSUE REPAIR INC—See Takeda Pharmaceutical Company Limited; *Int'l*, pg. 7438
LOTUS TOURS LIMITED—See Corporate Travel Management Limited; *Int'l*, pg. 1805
LOT VACUUM CO., LTD.—See Lot Vacuum Co., Ltd.; *Int'l*, pg. 4558
LOU BACHRODT CHEVROLET INC.; *U.S. Private*, pg. 2498
LOU BACHRODT FREIGHTLINER; *U.S. Private*, pg. 2498
LOUDCLOUD SYSTEMS, INC.—See Barnes & Noble Education, Inc.; *U.S. Public*, pg. 276
LOUDMAC CREATIVE, INC.; *U.S. Private*, pg. 2498
LOUDON COUNTY TRUCKING, LLC—See OEP Capital Advisors, L.P.; *U.S. Private*, pg. 2999
LOUDON PARK FUNERAL HOME, INC.—See Service Corporation International; *U.S. Public*, pg. 1871
LOUDOUN COUNTY SANITATION AUTHORITY; *U.S. Private*, pg. 2498
LOUDOUN ELECTRIC COMPANY; *U.S. Private*, pg. 2498
LOUDSPEAKER COMPONENTS, L.L.C.; *U.S. Private*, pg. 2498
LOUD TECHNOLOGIES INC.; *U.S. Public*, pg. 1342
LOUD TELEVISION, LLC—See ITV plc; *Int'l*, pg. 3845
LOUETTA MEDICAL CENTER LLC—See Adeptus Health Inc.; *U.S. Private*, pg. 78

LOU FUSZ AUTOMOTIVE NETWORK; *U.S. Private*, pg. 2498
LOU FUSZ MOTOR COMPANY—See Lou Fusz Automotive Network; *U.S. Private*, pg. 2498
LOUGEE INSURANCE AGENCY, LLC—See Cross Financial Corporation; *U.S. Private*, pg. 1104
LOUGHBERRY MFG. CORP.—See The Fort Miller Group Inc.; *U.S. Private*, pg. 4030
LOUGHBOROUGH BUILDING SOCIETY; *Int'l*, pg. 4561
LOU GIROUD TREE SERVICE, INC.—See Apax Partners LLP; *Int'l*, pg. 506
LOU HAMMOND & ASSOCIATES, INC.; *U.S. Private*, pg. 2498
LOUIE'S FINER MEATS, INC.; *U.S. Private*, pg. 2498
LOUISA HOME CARE SERVICES, LLC—See Community Health Systems, Inc.; *U.S. Public*, pg. 554
LOUIS A. WILLIAMS & ASSOCIATES; *U.S. Private*, pg. 2498
THE LOUIS BERGER GROUP, INC. - PROVIDENCE—See The Louis Berger Group, Inc.; *U.S. Private*, pg. 4073
THE LOUIS BERGER GROUP, INC.; *U.S. Private*, pg. 4073
LOUIS BERGER SERVICES INC.—See Kingswood Capital Management LLC; *U.S. Private*, pg. 2312
LOUISBOURG INVESTMENTS INC.—See Assumption Mutual Life Insurance Company; *Int'l*, pg. 649
LOUISBOURG INVESTMENTS INC.—See Montrusco Bolton Inc.; *Int'l*, pg. 5037
LOUISBOURG SEAFOODS LTD.; *Int'l*, pg. 4563
LOUISBURG CIDER MILL, INC.; *U.S. Private*, pg. 2499
LOUISBURG HMA, INC.—See Community Health Systems, Inc.; *U.S. Public*, pg. 554
LOUIS CAPITAL MARKETS FRANCE SA—See TP ICAP Finance PLC; *Int'l*, pg. 7881
LOUIS CAPITAL MARKETS ISRAEL LTD.—See TP ICAP Finance PLC; *Int'l*, pg. 7881
LOUIS CAPITAL MARKETS UK LLP—See TP ICAP Finance PLC; *Int'l*, pg. 7881
LOUIS COHEN & SONS, INC.—See Medico Industries, Inc.; *U.S. Private*, pg. 2656
LOUIS DREYFUS ARMATEURS; *Int'l*, pg. 4561
LOUIS DREYFUS CITRUS, INC.—See Louis Dreyfus S.A.S.; *Int'l*, pg. 4562
LOUIS DREYFUS COMMODITIES, LLC—See Louis Dreyfus S.A.S.; *Int'l*, pg. 4562
LOUIS DREYFUS COMPANY AFRICA PTY. LTD.—See Louis Dreyfus Company B.V.; *Int'l*, pg. 4562
LOUIS DREYFUS COMPANY AGRICULTURAL INDUSTRIES LLC—See Louis Dreyfus Company B.V.; *Int'l*, pg. 4562
LOUIS DREYFUS COMPANY BRASIL S.A.—See Raizen S.A.; *Int'l*, pg. 6192
LOUIS DREYFUS COMPANY B.V.; *Int'l*, pg. 4562
LOUIS DREYFUS COMPANY COLOMBIA S.A.S.—See Louis Dreyfus Company B.V.; *Int'l*, pg. 4562
LOUIS DREYFUS COMPANY COTTON LLC—See Louis Dreyfus Company B.V.; *Int'l*, pg. 4562
LOUIS DREYFUS COMPANY DISTRIBUTION FRANCE S.A.S.—See Louis Dreyfus Company B.V.; *Int'l*, pg. 4562
LOUIS DREYFUS COMPANY ESPANA S.A.—See Louis Dreyfus Company B.V.; *Int'l*, pg. 4562
LOUIS DREYFUS COMPANY GRAND JUNCTION LLC—See Louis Dreyfus Company B.V.; *Int'l*, pg. 4562
LOUIS DREYFUS COMPANY KENYA LTD.—See Louis Dreyfus Company B.V.; *Int'l*, pg. 4562
LOUIS DREYFUS COMPANY MEXICO S.A. DE C.V.—See Louis Dreyfus Company B.V.; *Int'l*, pg. 4562
LOUIS DREYFUS COMPANY POLSKA SP. Z.O.O.—See Louis Dreyfus Company B.V.; *Int'l*, pg. 4562
LOUIS DREYFUS COMPANY SUISSE S.A.—See Raizen S.A.; *Int'l*, pg. 6192
LOUIS DREYFUS COMPANY UKRAINE LTD.—See Louis Dreyfus Company B.V.; *Int'l*, pg. 4562
LOUIS DREYFUS COMPANY WITTENBERG GMBH—See Louis Dreyfus Company B.V.; *Int'l*, pg. 4562
LOUIS DREYFUS S.A.S.; *Int'l*, pg. 4562
LOUIS DREYFUS (SHANGHAI) CO. LTD.—See Louis Dreyfus Company B.V.; *Int'l*, pg. 4562
LOUIS DREYFUS TRAVOCEAN—See Louis Dreyfus Armateurs; *Int'l*, pg. 4562
LOUIS DREYFUS (ZHANGJIAGANG) FEED PROTEIN COMPANY LTD.—See Louis Dreyfus Company B.V.; *Int'l*, pg. 4562
LOUISE GOODWIN LIMITED—See Mountview Estates PLC; *Int'l*, pg. 5057
LOUISE PARIS LTD.; *U.S. Private*, pg. 2499
LOUIS FERAUD INC.—See Feraud Sarl; *Int'l*, pg. 2635
LOUIS F. LEEPER COMPANY; *U.S. Private*, pg. 2498
LOUIS HARRIS FRANCE SA—See Bain Capital, LP; *U.S. Private*, pg. 448
LOUIS HORNICK & CO. INC.; *U.S. Private*, pg. 2498
LOUIS HOTELS PUBLIC COMPANY LTD.—See Louis PLC; *Int'l*, pg. 4563
LOUIS HYATT, INC.—See Reliable Contracting Company Inc.; *U.S. Private*, pg. 3394
LOUISIANA ACQUISITIONS CORP.—See InterContinental Hotels Group PLC; *Int'l*, pg. 3738

LOUISIANA QUARTER HORSE BREEDERS ASSOCIATION

LOUISIANA ASSOCIATION FOR THE BLIND; *U.S. Private*, pg. 2499
LOUISIANA CASINO CRUISES, INC.—See Gaming and Leisure Properties, Inc.; *U.S. Public*, pg. 896
LOUISIANA CHEMICAL EQUIPMENT CO., LLC—See Woodvine Group, LLC; *U.S. Private*, pg. 4561
LOUISIANA COMPANIES; *U.S. Private*, pg. 2499
LOUISIANA DEALER SERVICES INSURANCE; *U.S. Private*, pg. 2499
LOUISIANA & DELTA RAILROAD, INC.—See Brookfield Infrastructure Partners L.P.; *Int'l*, pg. 1192
LOUISIANA & DELTA RAILROAD, INC.—See GIC Pte. Ltd.; *Int'l*, pg. 2966
LOUISIANA EDUCATIONAL TELEVISION AUTHORITY; *U.S. Private*, pg. 2499
LOUISIANA ENERGY & POWER AUTHORITY; *U.S. Private*, pg. 2499
LOUISIANA EXTENDED CARE HOSPITAL OF KENNER, LLC—See UnitedHealth Group Incorporated; *U.S. Public*, pg. 2246
LOUISIANA FARM BUREAU CASUALTY INSURANCE COMPANY—See Southern Farm Bureau Casualty Insurance Company; *U.S. Private*, pg. 3731
LOUISIANA FINE FOOD COMPANIES, INC.; *U.S. Private*, pg. 2499
LOUISIANA FISH FRY PRODUCTS LTD.—See Peak Rock Capital LLC; *U.S. Private*, pg. 3124
LOUISIANA FOOD COMPANY; *U.S. Public*, pg. 1342
LOUISIANA GAS DEVELOPMENT CORP.; *U.S. Private*, pg. 2499
LOUISIANA HEALTHCARE CONNECTIONS, INC.—See Centene Corporation; *U.S. Public*, pg. 469
LOUISIANA HEALTH CARE CONNECTIONS, INC.—See Centene Corporation; *U.S. Public*, pg. 469
LOUISIANA HEALTH CARE GROUP, LLC—See UnitedHealth Group Incorporated; *U.S. Public*, pg. 2246
LOUISIANA HEALTH PLAN; *U.S. Private*, pg. 2499
LOUISIANA HEALTH SERVICE & INDEMNITY COMPANY, INC.; *U.S. Private*, pg. 2499
LOUISIANA HEART HOSPITAL, LLC—See Cardiovascular Care Group, Inc.; *U.S. Private*, pg. 751
LOUISIANA HOME BUILDERS ASSOCIATION; *U.S. Private*, pg. 2499
LOUISIANA HOMECARE OF AMITE, LLC—See UnitedHealth Group Incorporated; *U.S. Public*, pg. 2246
LOUISIANA HOMECARE OF DELHI, LLC—See UnitedHealth Group Incorporated; *U.S. Public*, pg. 2246
LOUISIANA HOMECARE OF KENNER, LLC—See UnitedHealth Group Incorporated; *U.S. Public*, pg. 2246
LOUISIANA HOMECARE OF MISS-LOU, LLC—See UnitedHealth Group Incorporated; *U.S. Public*, pg. 2246
LOUISIANA HOMECARE OF MONROE, LLC—See UnitedHealth Group Incorporated; *U.S. Public*, pg. 2246
LOUISIANA HOMECARE OF NORTHWEST LOUISIANA, LLC—See UnitedHealth Group Incorporated; *U.S. Public*, pg. 2246
LOUISIANA HOMECARE OF RACELAND, LLC—See UnitedHealth Group Incorporated; *U.S. Public*, pg. 2246
LOUISIANA HOMECARE OF SLIDELL, LLC—See UnitedHealth Group Incorporated; *U.S. Public*, pg. 2246
LOUISIANA HOSPICE AND PALLIATIVE CARE, LLC—See UnitedHealth Group Incorporated; *U.S. Public*, pg. 2246
LOUISIANA HOSPICE & PALLIATIVE CARE—See UnitedHealth Group Incorporated; *U.S. Public*, pg. 2246
LOUISIANA INTERSTATE LOGOS, L.L.C.—See Lamar Advertising Company; *U.S. Public*, pg. 1291
LOUISIANA LANDSCAPE SPECIALTY, INC.—See Carousel Capital Partners; *U.S. Private*, pg. 769
LOUISIANA LIFT & EQUIPMENT INC.; *U.S. Private*, pg. 2499
LOUISIANA MACHINERY COMPANY INC.; *U.S. Private*, pg. 2499
LOUISIANA MEDIA COMPANY, LLC; *U.S. Private*, pg. 2499
LOUISIANA MEDICAL MUTUAL INSURANCE COMPANY; *U.S. Private*, pg. 2499
LOUISIANA ORGAN PROCUREMENT AGENCY; *U.S. Private*, pg. 2500
LOUISIANA-PACIFIC ARGENTINA S.R.L.—See Louisiana-Pacific Corporation; *U.S. Public*, pg. 1342
LOUISIANA-PACIFIC CHILE S.A.—See Louisiana-Pacific Corporation; *U.S. Public*, pg. 1342
LOUISIANA-PACIFIC COLOMBIA S.A.S.—See Louisiana-Pacific Corporation; *U.S. Public*, pg. 1342
LOUISIANA-PACIFIC CORPORATION; *U.S. Public*, pg. 1342
LOUISIANA-PACIFIC PARAGUAY S.A.—See Louisiana-Pacific Corporation; *U.S. Public*, pg. 1343
LOUISIANA-PACIFIC SOUTHERN DIV.—See Louisiana-Pacific Corporation; *U.S. Public*, pg. 1343
LOUISIANA PHYSICAL THERAPY, LLC—See UnitedHealth Group Incorporated; *U.S. Public*, pg. 2246
LOUISIANA PIGMENT COMPANY L.P.—See Contran Corporation; *U.S. Private*, pg. 1033
LOUISIANA PUBLIC HEALTH INSTITUTE; *U.S. Private*, pg. 2500
LOUISIANA QUARTER HORSE BREEDERS ASSOCIATION; *U.S. Private*, pg. 2500

Company Index
LOUISIANA RICE MILL, LLC. CORPORATE AFFILIATIONS

LOUISIANA RICE MILL, LLC.; *U.S. Private*, pg. 2500
LOUISIANA'S FIRST CHOICE AUTO AUCTION LLC—See E Automotive Inc.; *Int'l*, pg. 2245
LOUISIANA TELEVISION BROADCASTING CORPORATION; *U.S. Private*, pg. 2500
LOUISIANA THOROUGHBRED BREEDERS ASSOCIATION; *U.S. Private*, pg. 2500
LOUISIANA TRANSPORTATION, INC.—See Universal Logistics Holdings, Inc.; *U.S. Public*, pg. 2261
LOUISIANA UTILITIES SUPPLY COMPANY—See Ferguson plc; *Int'l*, pg. 2638
LOUISIANA VALVE SOURCE INC.—See MiddleGround Management, LP; *U.S. Private*, pg. 2712
LOUISIANA WATER COMPANY—See Utility Holdings Inc.; *U.S. Private*, pg. 4326
LOUISIANA WORKERS COMPENSATION CORP.; *U.S. Private*, pg. 2500
LOUIS J. PARADIS INC.; *U.S. Private*, pg. 2498
LOUIS KEMP SEAFOOD COMPANY—See Trident Seafoods Corporation; *U.S. Private*, pg. 4230
LOUIS MAULL COMPANY; *U.S. Private*, pg. 2498
LOUIS M. GERSON CO. INC.; *U.S. Private*, pg. 2498
LOUIS PADNOS IRON & METAL COMPANY - CADILLAC RECYCLING DIVISION—See Louis Padnos Iron & Metal Company; *U.S. Private*, pg. 2498
LOUIS PADNOS IRON & METAL COMPANY - HASTINGS DIVISION—See Louis Padnos Iron & Metal Company; *U.S. Private*, pg. 2498
LOUIS PADNOS IRON & METAL COMPANY - LANSING DIVISION—See Louis Padnos Iron & Metal Company; *U.S. Private*, pg. 2498
LOUIS PADNOS IRON & METAL COMPANY - PERE MARQUETTE DIVISION—See Louis Padnos Iron & Metal Company; *U.S. Private*, pg. 2498
LOUIS PADNOS IRON & METAL COMPANY; *U.S. Private*, pg. 2498
LOUIS PADNOS IRON & METAL COMPANY - WYOMING RECYCLING DIVISION—See Louis Padnos Iron & Metal Company; *U.S. Private*, pg. 2498
LOUIS PAPPAS RESTAURANT GROUP, LLC; *U.S. Private*, pg. 2499
LOUIS P. CIMINELLI CONSTRUCTION CO. INC.—See LPCiminelli Inc.; *U.S. Private*, pg. 2507
LOUIS PLC; *Int'l*, pg. 4562
LOUIS POULSEN AS; *Int'l*, pg. 4563
LOUIS POULSEN UK LIMITED—See Louis Poulsen AS; *Int'l*, pg. 4563
LOUIS ROYER SAS—See Terroirs Distillers; *Int'l*, pg. 7568
LOUIS SHANKS OF TEXAS INC.; *U.S. Private*, pg. 2499
LOUIS T. OLLESHEIMER & SON, INC.—See Leonard Green & Partners, L.P.; *U.S. Private*, pg. 2429
LOUISVILLE BEDDING COMPANY; *U.S. Private*, pg. 2500
LOUISVILLE GAS AND ELECTRIC COMPANY—See PPL Corporation; *U.S. Public*, pg. 1711
LOUISVILLE & JEFFERSON COUNTY METROPOLITAN SEWER DISTRICT; *U.S. Private*, pg. 2500
LOUISVILLE LADDER INC.—See Cuprum S.A. de C.V.; *Int'l*, pg. 1878
LOUISVILLE ORCHESTRA, INC.; *U.S. Private*, pg. 2500
LOUISVILLE PAVING COMPANY, INC.—See LPX, Inc.; *U.S. Private*, pg. 2507
LOUISVILLE PHYSICAL THERAPY, P.S.C.—See Select Medical Holdings Corporation; *U.S. Public*, pg. 1858
LOUISVILLE PLATE GLASS COMPANY, INC.—See Aldora Aluminum & Glass Products, Inc.; *U.S. Private*, pg. 160
LOUISVILLE S.C., LTD.—See UnitedHealth Group Incorporated; *U.S. Public*, pg. 2242
LOUISVILLE TILE DISTRIBUTORS INC.; *U.S. Private*, pg. 2500
LOUISVILLE TRANSPORTATION—See Interlock Industries, Inc.; *U.S. Private*, pg. 2111
LOUISVILLE WATER CO. INC.; *U.S. Private*, pg. 2500
LOUIS VUITTON ARGENTINA S.A.—See LVMH Moet Hennessy Louis Vuitton SE; *Int'l*, pg. 4595
LOUIS VUITTON (ARUBA) N.V—See LVMH Moet Hennessy Louis Vuitton SE; *Int'l*, pg. 4598
LOUIS VUITTON AUSTRALIA PTY LTD.—See LVMH Moet Hennessy Louis Vuitton SE; *Int'l*, pg. 4595
LOUIS VUITTON AUTRICHE—See LVMH Moet Hennessy Louis Vuitton SE; *Int'l*, pg. 4595
LOUIS VUITTON BAHRAIN W.L.L—See LVMH Moet Hennessy Louis Vuitton SE; *Int'l*, pg. 4595
LOUIS VUITTON BELGIUM S.A.—See LVMH Moet Hennessy Louis Vuitton SE; *Int'l*, pg. 4595
LOUIS VUITTON CANADA INC.—See LVMH Moet Hennessy Louis Vuitton SE; *Int'l*, pg. 4595
LOUIS VUITTON CESKA S.R.O.—See LVMH Moet Hennessy Louis Vuitton SE; *Int'l*, pg. 4595
LOUIS VUITTON CHILE LTDA—See LVMH Moet Hennessy Louis Vuitton SE; *Int'l*, pg. 4595
LOUIS VUITTON (CHINA) CO LTD—See LVMH Moet Hennessy Louis Vuitton SE; *Int'l*, pg. 4595
LOUIS VUITTON COLOMBIA S.A.—See LVMH Moet Hennessy Louis Vuitton SE; *Int'l*, pg. 4595
LOUIS VUITTON CYPRUS LIMITED—See LVMH Moet Hennessy Louis Vuitton SE; *Int'l*, pg. 4595
LOUIS VUITTON DANMARK A/S—See LVMH Moet Hennessy Louis Vuitton SE; *Int'l*, pg. 4595
LOUIS VUITTON DEUTSCHLAND GMBH—See LVMH Moet Hennessy Louis Vuitton SE; *Int'l*, pg. 4595
LOUIS VUITTON EAU LLC—See LVMH Moet Hennessy Louis Vuitton SE; *Int'l*, pg. 4598
LOUIS VUITTON ESPANA S.A.—See LVMH Moet Hennessy Louis Vuitton SE; *Int'l*, pg. 4595
LOUIS VUITTON GUAM INC—See LVMH Moet Hennessy Louis Vuitton SE; *Int'l*, pg. 4595
LOUIS VUITTON HAWAII, INC—See LVMH Moet Hennessy Louis Vuitton SE; *Int'l*, pg. 4595
LOUIS VUITTON HELLAS SCA—See LVMH Moet Hennessy Louis Vuitton SE; *Int'l*, pg. 4595
LOUIS VUITTON HONG KONG LTD—See LVMH Moet Hennessy Louis Vuitton SE; *Int'l*, pg. 4595
LOUIS VUITTON HUNGARIA SARL—See LVMH Moet Hennessy Louis Vuitton SE; *Int'l*, pg. 4595
LOUIS VUITTON ITALIA SPA—See LVMH Moet Hennessy Louis Vuitton SE; *Int'l*, pg. 4595
LOUIS VUITTON JAPAN KK—See LVMH Moet Hennessy Louis Vuitton SE; *Int'l*, pg. 4595
LOUIS VUITTON KOREA—See LVMH Moet Hennessy Louis Vuitton SE; *Int'l*, pg. 4593
LOUIS VUITTON KUWAIT—See LVMH Moet Hennessy Louis Vuitton SE; *Int'l*, pg. 4595
LOUIS VUITTON LTD—See LVMH Moet Hennessy Louis Vuitton SE; *Int'l*, pg. 4595
LOUIS VUITTON LUXEMBOURG SARL—See LVMH Moet Hennessy Louis Vuitton SE; *Int'l*, pg. 4595
LOUIS VUITTON MALAYSIA SDN BHD—See LVMH Moet Hennessy Louis Vuitton SE; *Int'l*, pg. 4595
LOUIS VUITTON MALLETIER S.A.—See LVMH Moet Hennessy Louis Vuitton SE; *Int'l*, pg. 4595
LOUIS VUITTON MEXICO SA DE RL DE CV—See LVMH Moet Hennessy Louis Vuitton SE; *Int'l*, pg. 4595
LOUIS VUITTON NEW ZEALAND LTD.—See LVMH Moet Hennessy Louis Vuitton SE; *Int'l*, pg. 4596
LOUIS VUITTON NORGE AS—See LVMH Moet Hennessy Louis Vuitton SE; *Int'l*, pg. 4596
LOUIS VUITTON NORTH AMERICA INC.—See LVMH Moet Hennessy Louis Vuitton SE; *Int'l*, pg. 4596
LOUIS VUITTON OSTERREICH GESMBH—See LVMH Moet Hennessy Louis Vuitton SE; *Int'l*, pg. 4596
LOUIS VUITTON PANAMA INC—See LVMH Moet Hennessy Louis Vuitton SE; *Int'l*, pg. 4596
LOUIS VUITTON (PHILIPPINES) INC—See LVMH Moet Hennessy Louis Vuitton SE; *Int'l*, pg. 4595
LOUIS VUITTON PORTUGAL MALEIRO LIMITADA—See LVMH Moet Hennessy Louis Vuitton SE; *Int'l*, pg. 4596
LOUIS VUITTON SAIPAN INC.—See LVMH Moet Hennessy Louis Vuitton SE; *Int'l*, pg. 4596
LOUIS VUITTON SOUTH AFRICA LTD—See LVMH Moet Hennessy Louis Vuitton SE; *Int'l*, pg. 4596
LOUIS VUITTON SOUTH EUROPE SRL—See LVMH Moet Hennessy Louis Vuitton SE; *Int'l*, pg. 4596
LOUIS VUITTON SUISSE SA—See LVMH Moet Hennessy Louis Vuitton SE; *Int'l*, pg. 4596
LOUIS VUITTON SUOMY OY—See LVMH Moet Hennessy Louis Vuitton SE; *Int'l*, pg. 4596
LOUIS VUITTON TAIWAN LTD.—See LVMH Moet Hennessy Louis Vuitton SE; *Int'l*, pg. 4596
LOUIS VUITTON (THAILAND) LTD.—See LVMH Moet Hennessy Louis Vuitton SE; *Int'l*, pg. 4595
LOUIS VUITTON VENEZUELA SA—See LVMH Moet Hennessy Louis Vuitton SE; *Int'l*, pg. 4596
LOUIS VUITTON VIETNAM COMPANY LTD—See LVMH Moet Hennessy Louis Vuitton SE; *Int'l*, pg. 4596
LOUIS VUITTON VOSTOCK LLC—See LVMH Moet Hennessy Louis Vuitton SE; *Int'l*, pg. 4596
LOUIS WOHL & SON INC.; *U.S. Private*, pg. 2499
LOU LARICHE CHEVROLET INC.—See LaFontaine Automotive Group, LLC; *U.S. Private*, pg. 2373
LOU LEVY & SONS FASHIONS INC.; *U.S. Private*, pg. 2498
LOULIS FOOD INGREDIENTS S.A.; *Int'l*, pg. 4563
LOU MADDALONI JEWELERS INC.; *U.S. Private*, pg. 2498
LOU MITCHELL'S INC.; *U.S. Private*, pg. 2498
LOUNGE CLUB—See The Collinson Group Limited; *Int'l*, pg. 7634
LOUNGEFLY, LLC—See Funko Inc.; *U.S. Public*, pg. 893
LOUNGE PASS—See The Collinson Group Limited; *Int'l*, pg. 7634
LOUNGERS PLC; *Int'l*, pg. 4563
LOUNORA INDUSTRIES INC.; *U.S. Private*, pg. 2500
LOUNOR EXPLORATION INC.; *Int'l*, pg. 4563
LOUP DIALYSIS, LLC—See DaVita Inc.; *U.S. Public*, pg. 640
LOUP RIVER PUBLIC POWER DISTRICT; *U.S. Private*, pg. 2500
LOURD CAPITAL LLC; *U.S. Private*, pg. 2500
LOURDES COUNSELING CENTER—See Ascension Health Alliance; *U.S. Private*, pg. 347
LOURDES DIALYSIS, LLC—See DaVita Inc.; *U.S. Public*, pg. 640
LOURDES HEALTH NETWORK—See Ascension Health Alliance; *U.S. Private*, pg. 347
LOURDES INDUSTRIES INC.; *U.S. Private*, pg. 2500
LOURDES MEDICAL CENTER—See Ascension Health Alliance; *U.S. Private*, pg. 347
LOURDES-NOREEN MCKEEN RESIDENCE; *U.S. Private*, pg. 2500
LOUREIRO ENGINEERING ASSOCIATES INC.; *U.S. Private*, pg. 2501
LOU-RICH, INC.—See Innovance, Inc.; *U.S. Private*, pg. 2081
LOU'S WHOLESALERS (PTY) LIMITED—See The Bidvest Group Limited; *Int'l*, pg. 7625
LOUVRE HOTELS GROUP—See Shanghai Jin Jiang Capital Company Limited; *Int'l*, pg. 6772
LOUWERSHANIQUE B.V.—See IDEX Corp; *U.S. Public*, pg. 1091
LOVABLE ITALIANA INTERNATIONAL LIMITED—See Hanesbrands Inc.; *U.S. Public*, pg. 983
LOVABLE LINGERIE LIMITED; *Int'l*, pg. 4565
LOVAL OY—See NIBE Industrier AB; *Int'l*, pg. 5261
LOVAN INDUSTRIES, INC.—See Bain Capital, LP; *U.S. Private*, pg. 441
LOVCEN AUTO D.O.O.—See Zavarovalnica Triglav, d.d.; *Int'l*, pg. 8626
LOVCEN OSIGURANJE A.D.—See Zavarovalnica Triglav, d.d.; *Int'l*, pg. 8626
LOVCEN ZIVOTNA OSIGURANJA A.D.—See Zavarovalnica Triglav, d.d.; *Int'l*, pg. 8626
LOVE ADVERTISING INC.; *U.S. Private*, pg. 2501
LOVE BOTTLING CO.; *U.S. Private*, pg. 2501
LOVEBUG NUTRITION INC.; *U.S. Private*, pg. 2501
LOVE BUICK GMC, INC.; *U.S. Private*, pg. 2501
LOVECE HOLDING INC.; *U.S. Private*, pg. 2501
LOVE CHEVROLET COMPANY; *U.S. Private*, pg. 2501
LOVE CONTROLS CORPORATION—See Arcline Investment Management LP; *U.S. Private*, pg. 313
LOVE & CO. PTE. LTD.—See SK Jewellery Group Limited; *Int'l*, pg. 6974
LOVE & CO. SDN. BHD.—See SK Jewellery Group Limited; *Int'l*, pg. 6974
LOVEFILM UK LTD.—See Amazon.com, Inc.; *U.S. Public*, pg. 90
LOVE FM INTERNATIONAL BROADCASTING CO., LTD.—See Nishi-Nippon Railroad Co., Ltd.; *Int'l*, pg. 5364
LOVE FUNDING CORPORATION—See Dwight Capital LLC; *U.S. Private*, pg. 1295
LOVE GROUP GLOBAL LTD; *Int'l*, pg. 4565
LOVE HOTEL MANAGEMENT COMPANY—See Love Real Estate Company; *U.S. Private*, pg. 2501
LOVE INTERNATIONAL GROUP, INC.; *Int'l*, pg. 4565
LOVEJOY CURTIS, LLC—See The Timken Company; *U.S. Public*, pg. 2133
LOVEJOY INC.—See The Timken Company; *U.S. Public*, pg. 2133
LOVEJOY INDUSTRIES INC.; *U.S. Private*, pg. 2501
LOVELACE HEALTH SYSTEM—See Ventas, Inc.; *U.S. Public*, pg. 2279
LOVELACE RESPIRATORY RESEARCH INSTITUTE; *U.S. Private*, pg. 2501
LOVELAND PRODUCTS, INC.—See Nutrien Ltd.; *Int'l*, pg. 5492
LOVELAND REPORTER-HERALD—See Alden Global Capital LLC; *U.S. Private*, pg. 157
LOVELESS WEALTH MANAGEMENT LLC—See Dakota Wealth Management LLC; *U.S. Private*, pg. 1148
LOVELL COMMUNICATIONS INC.—See Health Management Associates, Inc.; *U.S. Private*, pg. 1893
LOVELL LATER LIVING LLP—See Morgan Sindall Group Plc; *Int'l*, pg. 5044
LOVELL MINNICK PARTNERS LLC; *U.S. Private*, pg. 2501
LOVELL PARTNERSHIPS LIMITED—See Morgan Sindall Group Plc; *Int'l*, pg. 5044
LOVELL PUBLIC RELATIONS, INC.; *U.S. Private*, pg. 2503
LOVELY DAY (GRANTCHESTER) LIMITED—See LOV Group Invest SAS; *Int'l*, pg. 4565
LOVE MANAGEMENT COMPANY, LLC—See Love Real Estate Company; *U.S. Private*, pg. 2501
LOVEMAN STEEL CORPORATION; *U.S. Private*, pg. 2503
LOVEPAC CONVERTING LTD.—See Nolato AB; *Int'l*, pg. 5407
LOVEPAC CONVERTING PRIVATE LTD—See Nolato AB; *Int'l*, pg. 5407
LOVEPAC TECHNOLOGY (SHENZHEN) CO., LTD.—See Nolato AB; *Int'l*, pg. 5407
LOVE PRODUCTIONS USA, INC.—See Comcast Corporation; *U.S. Public*, pg. 538
LOVE REAL ESTATE COMPANY; *U.S. Private*, pg. 2501
LOVER'S LANE& CO.; *U.S. Private*, pg. 2504
THE LOVESAC COMPANY; *U.S. Public*, pg. 2109
LOVESHAW—See Illinois Tool Works Inc.; *U.S. Public*, pg. 1109
LOVE'S TRAVEL STOPS & COUNTRY STORES, INC.; *U.S. Private*, pg. 2501
LOVE THE 88 LLC—See Vivendi SE; *Int'l*, pg. 8269
LOVETT INC.; *U.S. Private*, pg. 2504
LOVETT MILLER & CO.; *U.S. Private*, pg. 2504
LOVETT, SILVERMAN CONSTRUCTION CONSULTANTS, INC.—See Kelso & Company, L.P.; *U.S. Private*, pg. 2278

COMPANY NAME INDEX

LOVGREN MARKETING GROUP; *U.S. Private*, pg. 2504
LOV GROUP INVEST SAS; *Int'l*, pg. 4563
LOVIK FASTIGHETS AB—See Oy Karl Fazer Ab; *Int'l*, pg. 5677
LOVIN CONSTRUCTION, INC.; *U.S. Private*, pg. 2504
LOVINGER INSURANCE, INC—See Purmort & Martin Insurance Agency, LLC; *U.S. Private*, pg. 3306
LOVING HANDS LTD.; *U.S. Private*, pg. 2504
LOVING PETS CORP.; *U.S. Private*, pg. 2504
LOVIO GEORGE INC.; *U.S. Private*, pg. 2504
LOVISAGRUVAN AB; *Int'l*, pg. 4566
LOVISA HOLDINGS LIMITED; *Int'l*, pg. 4565
LOVITT RESOURCES INC.; *Int'l*, pg. 4566
LOVITT & TOUCHE, INC.—See Marsh & McLennan Companies, Inc.; *U.S. Public*, pg. 1381
LOVOCHEMIE, A.S.—See Agrofert Holding, a.s.; *Int'l*, pg. 219
LOW AND BONAR (NEDERLAND) BV—See Freudenberg SE; *Int'l*, pg. 2789
LOWAN WHOLE FOODS PTY. LIMITED—See Green's General Foods Pty. Limited; *Int'l*, pg. 3073
LOWARA GMBH—See Xylem Inc.; *U.S. Public*, pg. 2396
LOWARA S.R.L.—See Xylem Inc.; *U.S. Public*, pg. 2396
LOW + ASSOCIATES—See Crosby Marketing Communications; *U.S. Private*, pg. 1104
LOW & BONAR HUNGARY KFT—See Waterland Private Equity Investments B.V.; *Int'l*, pg. 8357
LOW & BONAR PLC—See Freudenberg SE; *Int'l*, pg. 2789
LOWCOUNTRY FOOD BANK INC.; *U.S. Private*, pg. 2504
LOW COUNTRY MACHINERY, INC.; *U.S. Private*, pg. 2504
LOW CURRENT - TELECOM JOINT STOCK COMPANY; *Int'l*, pg. 4566
LOWDENS—See Grafton Group plc; *Int'l*, pg. 3051
LOWDER CONSTRUCTION COMPANY, INC.—See Colonial Company; *U.S. Private*, pg. 970
LOWDER NEW HOMES—See Colonial Company; *U.S. Private*, pg. 970
LOWE ADVENTA—See The Interpublic Group of Companies, Inc.; *U.S. Public*, pg. 2091
LOWE AND PARTNERS SA—See The Interpublic Group of Companies, Inc.; *U.S. Public*, pg. 2091
LOWE AVANTA—See The Interpublic Group of Companies, Inc.; *U.S. Public*, pg. 2091
LOWE BOATS—See Brunswick Corporation; *U.S. Public*, pg. 407
LOWE BRINDFORS—See The Interpublic Group of Companies, Inc.; *U.S. Public*, pg. 2091
LOWE CHINA—See The Interpublic Group of Companies, Inc.; *U.S. Public*, pg. 2091
LOWE COMMERCIAL SERVICES LLC—See Lowe Enterprises, Inc.; *U.S. Private*, pg. 2504
LOWE DESTINATION DEVELOPMENT DESERT—See Lowe Enterprises, Inc.; *U.S. Private*, pg. 2504
LOWE DESTINATION DEVELOPMENT, INC.—See Lowe Enterprises, Inc.; *U.S. Private*, pg. 2504
LOWE DESTINATION DEVELOPMENT SOUTHEAST—See Lowe Enterprises, Inc.; *U.S. Private*, pg. 2504
LOWE ELECTRIC SUPPLY COMPANY; *U.S. Private*, pg. 2504
LOWE ENTERPRISES, INC.; *U.S. Private*, pg. 2504
LOWE ENTERPRISES INVESTMENT MANAGEMENT INC.—See The Guardian Life Insurance Company of America; *U.S. Private*, pg. 4040
LOWE ENTERPRISES REAL ESTATE GROUP—See Lowe Enterprises, Inc.; *U.S. Private*, pg. 2504
LOWE ENTERPRISES REAL ESTATE GROUP—See Lowe Enterprises, Inc.; *U.S. Private*, pg. 2504
LOWE ENTERPRISES TEXAS INC.—See Lowe Enterprises, Inc.; *U.S. Private*, pg. 2504
LOWE FMRG—See The Interpublic Group of Companies, Inc.; *U.S. Public*, pg. 2091
LOWE GGK—See The Interpublic Group of Companies, Inc.; *U.S. Public*, pg. 2091
LOWE GGK—See The Interpublic Group of Companies, Inc.; *U.S. Public*, pg. 2091
LOWE GGK—See The Interpublic Group of Companies, Inc.; *U.S. Public*, pg. 2091
LOWE GGK—See The Interpublic Group of Companies, Inc.; *U.S. Public*, pg. 2091
LOWE GGK—See The Interpublic Group of Companies, Inc.; *U.S. Public*, pg. 2091
LOWE GINKGO—See The Interpublic Group of Companies, Inc.; *U.S. Public*, pg. 2091
LOWE HOSPITALITY GROUP—See Lowe Enterprises, Inc.; *U.S. Private*, pg. 2504
LOWE LDB—See The Interpublic Group of Companies, Inc.; *U.S. Public*, pg. 2091
LOWELL CAPITAL LIMITED—See Southern Cross Payments Limited; *Int'l*, pg. 7119
LOWELL COMMUNITY HEALTH CENTER, INC.; *U.S. Private*, pg. 2505
LOWELL FARMS INC.; *U.S. Public*, pg. 1343
LOWELL FINANCIAL LTD.—See Permira Advisers LLP; *Int'l*, pg. 5807
LOWELL FINANCIAL SERVICES GMBH—See Permira Advisers LLP; *Int'l*, pg. 5807

LOWELL FIVE CENT SAVINGS BANK; *U.S. Private*, pg. 2505
LOWELL GFKL COLLECTIONS GMBH—See Permira Advisers LLP; *Int'l*, pg. 5807
LOWELL GFKL PAYPROTECT GMBH—See Permira Advisers LLP; *Int'l*, pg. 5807
LOWELL INKASSO BECKER WUPPERTAL GMBH & CO. KG—See Permira Advisers LLP; *Int'l*, pg. 5807
LOWELL PACKING COMPANY; *U.S. Private*, pg. 2505
LOWELL PROCEED COLLECTION SERVICES GMBH—See Permira Advisers LLP; *Int'l*, pg. 5807
LOWELL SIRIUS INKASSO GMBH—See Permira Advisers LLP; *Int'l*, pg. 5807
LOWELL WOLF INDUSTRIES INC.; *U.S. Private*, pg. 2505
LOWELL ZYKLOP INKASSO DEUTSCHLAND GMBH—See Permira Advisers LLP; *Int'l*, pg. 5807
THE LOWE-MARTIN GROUP; *Int'l*, pg. 7664
LOWE MENA—See The Interpublic Group of Companies, Inc.; *U.S. Public*, pg. 2091
LOWEN CORPORATION - LOWEN CERTIFIED DIVISION—See Lowen Corporation; *U.S. Private*, pg. 2505
LOWEN CORPORATION - LOWEN IT DIVISION—See Lowen Corporation; *U.S. Private*, pg. 2505
LOWEN CORPORATION; *U.S. Private*, pg. 2505
LOWEN ENTERTAINMENT GMBH—See Novomatic AG; *Int'l*, pg. 5467
LOWEN GARAGE AG—See Stellantis N.V.; *Int'l*, pg. 7202
LOWE-NORTH CONSTRUCTION INC.; *U.S. Private*, pg. 2505
LOWENSTEIN SANDLER PC; *U.S. Private*, pg. 2505
LOWENSTEIN SANDLER PC—See Lowenstein Sandler PC; *U.S. Private*, pg. 2505
LOWENSTEIN SANDLER PC—See Lowenstein Sandler PC; *U.S. Private*, pg. 2505
LOWEN VISUAL IMAGING—See Lowen Corporation; *U.S. Private*, pg. 2505
LOWE & PARTNERS—See The Interpublic Group of Companies, Inc.; *U.S. Public*, pg. 2091
LOWE & PARTNERS—See The Interpublic Group of Companies, Inc.; *U.S. Public*, pg. 2091
LOWE & PARTNERS WORLDWIDE LTD—See The Interpublic Group of Companies, Inc.; *U.S. Public*, pg. 2097
LOWE PIRELLA FRONZONI—See The Interpublic Group of Companies, Inc.; *U.S. Public*, pg. 2091
LOWE PORTA—See The Interpublic Group of Companies, Inc.; *U.S. Public*, pg. 2091
LOWE PROFERO (HK) LIMITED—See The Interpublic Group of Companies, Inc.; *U.S. Public*, pg. 2097
LOWE PROFERO IBERIA S.A.—See The Interpublic Group of Companies, Inc.; *U.S. Public*, pg. 2097
LOWE PROFERO LIMITED—See The Interpublic Group of Companies, Inc.; *U.S. Public*, pg. 2097
LOWE PROFERO PTY. LIMITED—See The Interpublic Group of Companies, Inc.; *U.S. Public*, pg. 2097
LOWE PROFERO (SHANGHAI) CO., LTD.—See The Interpublic Group of Companies, Inc.; *U.S. Public*, pg. 2097
LOWER BUCKS HOSPITAL; *U.S. Private*, pg. 2505
LOWER COLORADO RIVER AUTHORITY; *U.S. Private*, pg. 2505
LOWE REAL ESTATE GROUP—See Lowe Enterprises, Inc.; *U.S. Private*, pg. 2504
LOWER EASTSIDE SERVICE CENTER, INC.; *U.S. Private*, pg. 2505
LOWER RENTAL LTD—See Perwyn LLP; *Int'l*, pg. 5822
LOWER GREAT LAKES KENWORTH INC; *U.S. Private*, pg. 2506
LOWER HOLDING COMPANY; *U.S. Private*, pg. 2506
LOWER HUTT VETERINARY SERVICES LTD—See National Veterinary Care Ltd; *Int'l*, pg. 5164
LOWER LAKES TOWING (17) LTD.—See AIP, LLC; *U.S. Private*, pg. 135
LOWER LAKES TOWING LTD.—See AIP, LLC; *U.S. Private*, pg. 135
LOWER MANHATTAN MEDICAL ASSOCIATES P.C.—See Schweiger Dermatology Group; *U.S. Private*, pg. 3572
LOWER MATTAGAMI ENERGY LIMITED PARTNERSHIP—See Ontario Power Generation, Inc.; *Int'l*, pg. 5585
LOWERMYBILLS, INC.—See RockBridge Growth Equity, LLC; *U.S. Private*, pg. 3465
LOWER NECHES VALLEY AUTHORITY; *U.S. Private*, pg. 2506
LOWE ROCHE—See The Interpublic Group of Companies, Inc.; *U.S. Public*, pg. 2091
LOWER VALLEY ENERGY INC.; *U.S. Private*, pg. 2506
LOWER VALLEY HOSPITAL ASSOCIATION; *U.S. Private*, pg. 2506
LOWERY CORPORATION; *U.S. Private*, pg. 2506
LOWE SCANAD—See The Interpublic Group of Companies, Inc.; *U.S. Public*, pg. 2091
LOWE'S COMMERCIAL PAINTING; *U.S. Private*, pg. 2505
LOWE'S COMPANIES, INC.; *U.S. Public*, pg. 1343
LOWE'S FOOD STORES, INC.—See Alex Lee, Inc.; *U.S. Private*, pg. 163

LOXLEY PUBLIC COMPANY LIMITED

LOWE'S HOME CENTERS, LLC—See Lowe's Companies, Inc.; *U.S. Public*, pg. 1343
LOWE'S HOME CENTRES (CANADA) INC.—See Lowe's Companies, Inc.; *U.S. Public*, pg. 1343
LOWE SINGAPORE—See The Interpublic Group of Companies, Inc.; *U.S. Public*, pg. 2091
LOWES MANHATTAN PTY. LTD.; *Int'l*, pg. 4566
LOWE—See The Interpublic Group of Companies, Inc.; *U.S. Public*, pg. 2091
LOWE—See The Interpublic Group of Companies, Inc.; *U.S. Public*, pg. 2091
LOWE—See The Interpublic Group of Companies, Inc.; *U.S. Public*, pg. 2091
LOWE—See The Interpublic Group of Companies, Inc.; *U.S. Public*, pg. 2091
LOWE—See The Interpublic Group of Companies, Inc.; *U.S. Public*, pg. 2091
LOWE—See The Interpublic Group of Companies, Inc.; *U.S. Public*, pg. 2091
LOWE—See The Interpublic Group of Companies, Inc.; *U.S. Public*, pg. 2091
LOWE—See The Interpublic Group of Companies, Inc.; *U.S. Public*, pg. 2091
LOWE—See The Interpublic Group of Companies, Inc.; *U.S. Public*, pg. 2091
LOWE—See The Interpublic Group of Companies, Inc.; *U.S. Public*, pg. 2091
LOWE—See The Interpublic Group of Companies, Inc.; *U.S. Public*, pg. 2091
LOWE'S PAY AND SAVE INC.; *U.S. Private*, pg. 2505
LOWE'S PELLETS & GRAIN, INC.; *U.S. Private*, pg. 2505
LOWE SSPM—See The Interpublic Group of Companies, Inc.; *U.S. Public*, pg. 2091
LOWE STRATEUS—See The Interpublic Group of Companies, Inc.; *U.S. Public*, pg. 2092
LOWE SWING COMMUNICATIONS—See The Interpublic Group of Companies, Inc.; *U.S. Public*, pg. 2092
LOWE TRACTOR & EQUIPMENT, INC.; *U.S. Private*, pg. 2504
LOWE WILD DUNES INVESTORS LP; *U.S. Private*, pg. 2505
LOWHAM-WALSH ENGINEERING & ENVIRONMENT SERVICES, LLC—See WSP Global, Inc.; *Int'l*, pg. 8496
LOW KENG HUAT (SINGAPORE) LIMITED; *Int'l*, pg. 4566
LOWLAND DOORS LIMITED—See BID Group Ltd; *Int'l*, pg. 1019
LOWLAND INVESTMENT COMPANY PLC; *Int'l*, pg. 4566
LOW MOOR MEADOWS (MORLEY) MANAGEMENT COMPANY LIMITED—See Persimmon plc; *Int'l*, pg. 5816
LOWP CO., LTD.—See AJIS Co., Ltd.; *Int'l*, pg. 258
LOWRIE ELECTRIC COMPANY, INC.—See EMCOR Group, Inc.; *U.S. Public*, pg. 737
LOWRIE SHIPPING LLC—See Southern Cross Capital Management SA; *Int'l*, pg. 7118
LOWRY COMPUTER PRODUCTS, INC.—See Lowry Holding Company Inc.; *U.S. Private*, pg. 2506
LOWRY HOLDING COMPANY INC.; *U.S. Private*, pg. 2506
LOWRY OIL COMPANY INCORPORATED; *U.S. Private*, pg. 2506
LOWRY PARK ZOOLOGICAL SOCIETY OF TAMPA INC.; *U.S. Private*, pg. 2506
LOWRY'S INC.—See Beacon Roofing Supply, Inc.; *U.S. Public*, pg. 286
LOWRY'S—See Beacon Roofing Supply, Inc.; *U.S. Public*, pg. 286
LOWRY SURGERY CENTER, LLC—See HCA Healthcare, Inc.; *U.S. Public*, pg. 1001
LOWS OF DUNDEE LTD.; *Int'l*, pg. 4566
LOW VOLATILITY U.S. EQUITY INCOME FUND; *Int'l*, pg. 4566
LOW VOLTAGE CONTRACTORS, INC.; *U.S. Private*, pg. 2504
LOW VOLTAGE INTEGRATED SYSTEMS INC.—See The Carlyle Group Inc.; *U.S. Public*, pg. 2053
LOW VOLTAGE PTY LTD—See Bapcor Limited; *Int'l*, pg. 857
LOWY & DONNATH, INC.—See EJ Electric Installation Co.; *U.S. Private*, pg. 1348
LOXA BEAUTY LLC—See Sally Beauty Holdings, Inc.; *U.S. Public*, pg. 1839
LOXAM SAS; *Int'l*, pg. 4566
LOXBIT PA PLC—See Loxley Public Company Limited; *Int'l*, pg. 4567
LOXBIT PUBLIC CO.LTD—See Loxley Public Company Limited; *Int'l*, pg. 4567
THE LOXCREEN COMPANY, INC.; *U.S. Private*, pg. 4073
LOXDATA COMPANY LIMITED—See Loxley Public Company Limited; *Int'l*, pg. 4567
LOXEO GMBH—See Durr AG; *Int'l*, pg. 2233
LOXITE GMBH—See Aurelius Equity Opportunities SE & Co. KGaA; *Int'l*, pg. 709
LOXLEY INTERTRADE (GUANGZHOU) CO., LTD.—See Loxley Public Company Limited; *Int'l*, pg. 4567
LOXLEY PUBLIC COMPANY LIMITED; *Int'l*, pg. 4567

1639

LOXLEY TRADING CO. LTD.—See Loxley Public Company Limited; *Int'l*, pg. 4567
LOXLEY WIRELESS CO. LTD.—See Loxley Public Company Limited; *Int'l*, pg. 4567
LOXO ONCOLOGY, INC.—See Eli Lilly & Company; *U.S. Public*, pg. 734
LOYAL AMERICAN LIFE INSURANCE COMPANY—See The Cigna Group; *U.S. Public*, pg. 2061
LOYAL CHRISTIAN BENEFIT ASSOCIATION; *U.S. Private*, pg. 2506
LOYAL EQUIPMENTS LIMITED; *Int'l*, pg. 4567
LOYAL FINANCE AG—See Banque Cantonale de Geneve S.A.; *Int'l*, pg. 852
LOYALIST EXPLORATION LIMITED; *Int'l*, pg. 4567
LOYAL SOURCE GOVERNMENT SERVICES, LLC; *U.S. Private*, pg. 2506
LOYAL SOURCE MARKET SERVICES INC; *Int'l*, pg. 4567
LOYAL SPORTS PVT. LTD.—See Loyal Equipments Limited; *Int'l*, pg. 4567
LOYAL TEXTILE MILLS LIMITED; *Int'l*, pg. 4567
LOYALTOUCH SA; *Int'l*, pg. 4567
LOYALTY ALLIANCE ENTERPRISE CORPORATION; *Int'l*, pg. 4567
LOYALTY COMPANY SAS; *Int'l*, pg. 4567
LOYALTYEXPRESS INC.—See Williston Financial Group, LLC; *U.S. Private*, pg. 4528
LOYALTY FOUNDER CO., LTD.; *Int'l*, pg. 4567
LOYALTYONE, INC.—See Bread Financial Holdings Inc.; *U.S. Public*, pg. 381
LOYALTYONE US, INC.—See Bread Financial Holdings Inc.; *U.S. Public*, pg. 381
LOYALTY PARTNER GMBH—See American Express Company; *U.S. Public*, pg. 102
LOYALTY PARTNER SOLUTIONS GMBH—See American Express Company; *U.S. Public*, pg. 102
LOY CLARK PIPELINE CO. INC.; *U.S. Private*, pg. 2506
LOY CLARK PIPELINE CO.—See MDU Resources Group, Inc.; *U.S. Public*, pg. 1410
LOYD'S ELECTRIC SUPPLY INC.; *U.S. Private*, pg. 2506
LOYDS LIBERTY HOMES, INC.—See Centerbridge Partners, L.P.; *U.S. Private*, pg. 813
LOYENS & LOEFF N.V.; *Int'l*, pg. 4567
LOY-LANGE BOX COMPANY; *U.S. Private*, pg. 2506
LOYOLA AMBULATORY SURGERY CENTER AT OAKBROOK, INC.—See UnitedHealth Group Incorporated; *U.S. Public*, pg. 2242
LOYOLA RECOVERY FOUNDATION; *U.S. Private*, pg. 2506
LOYOLA UNIVERSITY HEALTH SYSTEM—See Trinity Health Corporation; *U.S. Private*, pg. 4233
LOYOLA UNIVERSITY MEDICAL CENTER—See Trinity Health Corporation; *U.S. Private*, pg. 4233
LOYTAPE INDUSTRIES SDN. BHD.—See W T K Holdings Berhad; *Int'l*, pg. 8320
LOZANO ENTERPRISES, LP; *U.S. Private*, pg. 2506
LOZ D.O.O.—See KJK Capital Oy; *Int'l*, pg. 4198
LOZIER CORPORATION - SCOTTSBORO PLANT 1—See Lozier Corporation; *U.S. Private*, pg. 2506
LOZIER CORPORATION - SCOTTSBORO PLANT 2—See Lozier Corporation; *U.S. Private*, pg. 2506
LOZIER CORPORATION; *U.S. Private*, pg. 2506
LOZINAK PROFESSIONAL BASEBALL LLC; *U.S. Private*, pg. 2506
LOZ METALPRES D.O.O.—See KJK Capital Oy; *Int'l*, pg. 4198
LOZNICAELEKTRO A.D.; *Int'l*, pg. 4567
L&P AEROSPACE ACQUISITION COMPANY, LLC—See Leggett & Platt, Incorporated; *U.S. Public*, pg. 1302
LPA EXCIL ELECTRONICS LTD—See LPA Group plc; *Int'l*, pg. 4567
LPA GROUP PLC; *Int'l*, pg. 4567
LPA HASWELL ENGINEERS LTD—See LPA Group plc; *Int'l*, pg. 4567
LPA INDUSTRIES LTD—See LPA Group plc; *Int'l*, pg. 4567
LPA NIPHAN LTD—See LPA Group plc; *Int'l*, pg. 4568
L&P AUTOMOTIVE EUROPE HEADQUARTERS GMBH—See Leggett & Platt, Incorporated; *U.S. Public*, pg. 1302
LPC CRUDE OIL MARKETING LLC—See Devon Energy Corporation; *U.S. Public*, pg. 657
L P CIMINELLI CONSTRUCTION COMPANY INC.—See LPCiminelli Inc.; *U.S. Private*, pg. 2507
LPCIMINELLI INC.; *U.S. Private*, pg. 2507
L.P.C SINGLE MEMBER S.A.—See Motor Oil (Hellas) Corinth Refineries S. A.; *Int'l*, pg. 5054
LPC SOUTHEAST—See Lincoln Property Company; *U.S. Private*, pg. 2458
L&P DENMARK APS—See Leggett & Platt, Incorporated; *U.S. Public*, pg. 1302
L. PERRIGO COMPANY—See Perrigo Company plc; *Int'l*, pg. 5813
L.P. EVANS MOTORS, INC.—See AutoNation, Inc.; *U.S. Public*, pg. 236
L.P. EVANS MOTORS, INC.—See AutoNation, Inc.; *U.S. Public*, pg. 236
L.P. EVANS MOTORS WPB, INC.—See AutoNation, Inc.; *U.S. Public*, pg. 236

L.P. EVANS MOTORS WPB, INC.—See AutoNation, Inc.; *U.S. Public*, pg. 236
L&P FINANCIAL SERVICES CO.—See Leggett & Platt, Incorporated; *U.S. Public*, pg. 1302
LP FIRST CAPITAL; *U.S. Private*, pg. 2507
LPG 4 U LIMITED—See UGI Corporation; *U.S. Public*, pg. 2222
LPGA INTERNATIONAL GIRLS GOLF CLUB, INC.—See Fore Golf Services, LP; *U.S. Private*, pg. 1565
LPG AMERICA LATINA SOCIEDAD ANONIMA—See Johnson Controls International plc; *Int'l*, pg. 3987
LP GAS B.V.—See DCC plc; *Int'l*, pg. 1990
L&P GLOBAL BERHAD; *Int'l*, pg. 4369
LPG TECNICAS EN EXTINCION DE INCENDIOS, S.L.—See Johnson Controls International plc; *Int'l*, pg. 3987
LPI CAPITAL BHD; *Int'l*, pg. 4568
LPI CORPORATION—See HEICO Corporation; *U.S. Public*, pg. 1019
LPI, INC.; *U.S. Private*, pg. 2507
LPI, INC.; *U.S. Private*, pg. 2507
LP INNOVATIONS, INC.—See DTIQ Technologies, Inc.; *U.S. Private*, pg. 1282
L&P INTERNATIONAL HOLDINGS COMPANY—See Leggett & Platt, Incorporated; *U.S. Public*, pg. 1302
LPK CO., LTD.; *Int'l*, pg. 4568
LPKF FRANCE S.A.R.L.—See LPKF Laser & Electronics AG; *Int'l*, pg. 4568
LPKF LASER & ELECTRONICS AG; *Int'l*, pg. 4568
LPKF LASER & ELECTRONICS (ASIA) LTD.—See LPKF Laser & Electronics AG; *Int'l*, pg. 4568
LPKF LASER & ELECTRONICS D.O.O.—See LPKF Laser & Electronics AG; *Int'l*, pg. 4568
LPKF LASER & ELECTRONICS INC.—See LPKF Laser & Electronics AG; *Int'l*, pg. 4568
LPKF LASER & ELECTRONICS K.K.—See LPKF Laser & Electronics AG; *Int'l*, pg. 4568
LPKF LASER & ELECTRONICS KOREA LTD.—See LPKF Laser & Electronics AG; *Int'l*, pg. 4568
LPKF MOTION & CONTROL GMBH—See LPKF Laser & Electronics AG; *Int'l*, pg. 4568
LPKF SOLARQUIPMENT GMBH—See LPKF Laser & Electronics AG; *Int'l*, pg. 4568
LPKF TIANJIN CO., LTD.—See LPKF Laser & Electronics AG; *Int'l*, pg. 4568
LPKF WELDINGQUIPMENT GMBH—See LPKF Laser & Electronics AG; *Int'l*, pg. 4568
LPK GMBH FRANKFURT—See LPK; *U.S. Private*, pg. 2507
LPK SARL GENEVA—See LPK; *U.S. Private*, pg. 2507
LPK; *U.S. Private*, pg. 2507
LPL FINANCIAL HOLDINGS INC.; *U.S. Public*, pg. 1343
LPL FINANCIAL LLC—See LPL Financial Holdings Inc.; *U.S. Public*, pg. 1343
LPL INSURANCE AGENCY, INC.—See Inszone Insurance Services, LLC; *U.S. Private*, pg. 2096
LPL INSURANCE ASSOCIATES, INC.—See LPL Financial Holdings Inc.; *U.S. Public*, pg. 1343
LP MANAGEMENT VERWALTUNG GMBH—See American Express Company; *U.S. Public*, pg. 102
L&P MATERIALS MANUFACTURING, INC.—See Leggett & Platt, Incorporated; *U.S. Public*, pg. 1302
LPM FORKLIFT SALES & SERVICE, INC.; *U.S. Private*, pg. 2507
L.P.N. DEVELOPMENT PUBLIC COMPANY LIMITED; *Int'l*, pg. 4386
L. POSSEHL & CO. MBH; *Int'l*, pg. 4381
L. POWELL COMPANY ACQUISITION CORP.; *U.S. Private*, pg. 2364
LPP HUNGARY KFT—See LPP S.A.; *Int'l*, pg. 4568
LPP MANUFACTURING INC.—See Linamar Corporation; *Int'l*, pg. 4500
LPP RETAIL LATVIA LTD—See LPP S.A.; *Int'l*, pg. 4568
L&P PROPERTY MANAGEMENT COMPANY—See Leggett & Platt, Incorporated; *U.S. Public*, pg. 1302
LPP S.A.; *Int'l*, pg. 4568
L.P.R. CONSTRUCTION CO.; *U.S. Private*, pg. 2367
LPR FRANCE—See LPR Logistic Packaging Return S.A.S.; *Int'l*, pg. 4568
LP RISK, INC.—See XPT Group LLC; *U.S. Private*, pg. 4582
LPR LOGISTIC PACKAGING RETURN S.A.S.; *Int'l*, pg. 4568
LPR NETHERLANDS—See LPR Logistic Packaging Return S.A.S.; *Int'l*, pg. 4568
LPR PORTUGAL—See LPR Logistic Packaging Return S.A.S.; *Int'l*, pg. 4568
LPR S.R.L.—See LPR Logistic Packaging Return S.A.S.; *Int'l*, pg. 4568
LPR UK LIMITED—See LPR Logistic Packaging Return S.A.S.; *Int'l*, pg. 4568
LPS BOSSARD PVT. LTD.—See Bossard Holding AG; *Int'l*, pg. 1117
LPS BRASIL - CONSULTORIA DE IMOVEIS SA; *Int'l*, pg. 4568
LPS CORPORATION—See Louisiana-Pacific Corporation; *U.S. Public*, pg. 1342
LPS FIELD SERVICES, INC.—See Fidelity National Financial, Inc.; *U.S. Public*, pg. 831

LPS INDUSTRIES INC.; *U.S. Private*, pg. 2507
LPS INTEGRATION INC.—See Court Square Capital Partners, L.P.; *U.S. Private*, pg. 1068
L&P SOMAPPA COMFORT SYSTEMS (INDIA) PRIVATE LIMITED—See Leggett & Platt, Incorporated; *U.S. Public*, pg. 1302
L&P SPRINGS DENMARK A/S—See Leggett & Platt, Incorporated; *U.S. Public*, pg. 1302
L&P SPRINGS ITALIA S.R.L.—See Leggett & Platt, Incorporated; *U.S. Public*, pg. 1302
LPS RAUL FULGENCIO CONSULTORIA DE IMOVEIS S.A.—See LPS Brasil - Consultoria de Imoveis SA; *Int'l*, pg. 4568
LPS VALUATION SOLUTIONS, LLC—See Fidelity National Financial, Inc.; *U.S. Public*, pg. 831
L&P SWISS HOLDING GMBH—See Leggett & Platt, Incorporated; *U.S. Public*, pg. 1302
LPT D.O.O.—See Leggett & Platt, Incorporated; *U.S. Public*, pg. 1302
L&P TEHNOLOGIJE D.O.O.—See Leggett & Platt, Incorporated; *U.S. Public*, pg. 1302
L.P. THEBAULT COMPANY; *U.S. Private*, pg. 2367
LPT PUBLICIS—See Publicis Groupe S.A.; *Int'l*, pg. 6099
L.P. TRANSBETON PUBLIC LTD.; *Int'l*, pg. 4386
L&P TRANSPORTATION, LLC—See Leggett & Platt, Incorporated; *U.S. Public*, pg. 1302
LPV LEBENSMITTEL PRAXIS VERLAG NEUWIED GMBH—See Management Capital Holding AG; *Int'l*, pg. 4666
LPX, INC.; *U.S. Private*, pg. 2507
LQR HOUSE INC.; *U.S. Public*, pg. 1343
LQWD TECHNOLOGIES CORP.—See TAG Oil Ltd.; *Int'l*, pg. 7407
LR3 ENTERPRISES INC.; *U.S. Private*, pg. 2507
LRA MKP TRS L.P.—See LXP Industrial Trust; *U.S. Public*, pg. 1349
LRA WORLDWIDE, INC.—See Deloitte LLP; *U.S. Private*, pg. 1198
L&R CONSTRUCTION SERVICES, INC.; *U.S. Private*, pg. 2363
LR DEVELOPMENT COMPANY LLC—See The Related Companies, L.P.; *U.S. Private*, pg. 4103
L&R DISTRIBUTORS, INC.—See Platinum Equity, LLC; *U.S. Private*, pg. 3205
LRE GROUND SERVICES, INC.; *U.S. Private*, pg. 2507
LRE MEDICAL GMBH—See TransDigm Group Incorporated; *U.S. Public*, pg. 2180
LRES CORP.; *U.S. Private*, pg. 2507
LRG CATERING LTD.—See Precision Drilling Corporation; *Int'l*, pg. 5957
LRG INVESTOR LLC—See KKR & Co. Inc.; *U.S. Public*, pg. 1259
LRG MARKETING COMMUNICATIONS, INC.; *U.S. Private*, pg. 2507
L.R. GORRELL COMPANY INC.; *U.S. Private*, pg. 2367
L R HEIN CONSTRUCTION CORP.; *U.S. Private*, pg. 2361
LRI HOLDINGS, INC.—See Kelso & Company, L.P.; *U.S. Private*, pg. 2278
LRI INVEST S.A.—See Augur Capital AG; *Int'l*, pg. 703
LRI, LLC—See Xerox Holdings Corporation; *U.S. Public*, pg. 2388
L&R MANUFACTURING COMPANY; *U.S. Private*, pg. 2363
L&R MEDICAL UK LTD.—See Lohmann & Rauscher International GmbH & Co. KG; *Int'l*, pg. 4543
LR MEDIENVERLAG GMBH—See Verlagsgruppe Georg von Holtzbrinck GmbH; *Int'l*, pg. 8170
LRM—See FAYAT SAS; *Int'l*, pg. 2625
LRN CORPORATION; *U.S. Private*, pg. 2508
L. ROBERT KIMBALL & ASSOCIATES, INC.—See Ocean-Sound Partners, LP; *U.S. Private*, pg. 2991
L.R. PAK (PVT) LIMITED—See Landi Renzo S.p.a.; *Int'l*, pg. 4406
L & R PALLET SERVICE, INC.—See Freeman Spogli & Co. Incorporated; *U.S. Private*, pg. 1606
LRP PUBLICATIONS - PENNSYLVANIA—See LRP Publications; *U.S. Private*, pg. 2508
LRP PUBLICATIONS; *U.S. Private*, pg. 2508
LRR ENERGY, L.P.—See Grizzly Energy, LLC; *U.S. Public*, pg. 970
LR SENERGY LIMITED—See Lloyd's Register Foundation; *Int'l*, pg. 4536
LRS HOLDINGS, LLC—See Macquarie Group Limited; *Int'l*, pg. 4628
LRS LUFTHANSA REVENUE SERVICES GMBH—See Deutsche Lufthansa AG; *Int'l*, pg. 2069
LRTDEA - TUV RHEINLAND GRUPA, SIA—See TUV Rheinland Berlin-Brandenburg Pfalz e.V.; *Int'l*, pg. 7982
LRT RECORD SERVICES, INC.—See Fidelity National Financial, Inc.; *U.S. Public*, pg. 831
L&R USA INC.—See Lohmann & Rauscher International GmbH & Co. KG; *Int'l*, pg. 4544
L. R. WILLSON & SONS, INC.; *U.S. Private*, pg. 2364
LRX GROUP, INC.; *U.S. Private*, pg. 2508
LS 2 HOLDINGS LIMITED; *Int'l*, pg. 4568
LS3P ASSOCIATES LTD.; *U.S. Private*, pg. 2508
LS4 RADIO CONTINENTAL, S.A—See Promotora de Informaciones S.A.; *Int'l*, pg. 5995

COMPANY NAME INDEX

LSAB INSTRUMENT SERVICE—See Investment AB Latour; *Int'l*, pg. 3782
LSAB LATVIA SIA—See Investment AB Latour; *Int'l*, pg. 3782
LSAB NORGE AS—See Investment AB Latour; *Int'l*, pg. 3782
LSAB VANDRA AS—See Investment AB Latour; *Int'l*, pg. 3781
LSAB VAXJO AB—See Investment AB Latour; *Int'l*, pg. 3782
LSAB WESTLINGS AB—See Investment AB Latour; *Int'l*, pg. 3782
LSA, LLC—See TE Connectivity Ltd.; *Int'l*, pg. 7495
LS ALSCO CO., LTD.—See LS Corp.; *Int'l*, pg. 4569
LSA LUBES SERVICES GMBH & CO. KG—See Marquard & Bahls AG; *Int'l*, pg. 4699
LSB CHEMICAL LLC—See LSB Industries, Inc.; *U.S. Public*, pg. 1344
LSB INDUSTRIES, INC.; *U.S. Public*, pg. 1344
LSBL COMMERCIAL ARCHITECTURAL DESIGN CO., LTD.—See Moon Environment Technology Co., Ltd.; *Int'l*, pg. 5038
LS CABLE INDIA PVT. LTD.—See LS Corp.; *Int'l*, pg. 4569
LS CABLE LTD. - ANYANG PLANT—See LS Corp.; *Int'l*, pg. 4569
LS CABLE LTD. - DONGHAE PLANT—See LS Corp.; *Int'l*, pg. 4569
LS CABLE LTD. - GUMI PLANT—See LS Corp.; *Int'l*, pg. 4569
LS CABLE LTD. - INDONG PLANT—See LS Corp.; *Int'l*, pg. 4569
LS CABLE LTD.—See LS Corp.; *Int'l*, pg. 4569
LS CABLE & SYSTEM ASIA LTD.; *Int'l*, pg. 4568
LS CABLE & SYSTEM LTD.—See LS Corp.; *Int'l*, pg. 4569
LSC ACQUISITION CORPORATION; *U.S. Private*, pg. 2508
LS CARGO LOGISTICS MIDDLE EAST FZCO—See LS International Cargo GmbH; *Int'l*, pg. 4570
LS CARGO LOGISTICS OY—See LS International Cargo GmbH; *Int'l*, pg. 4570
LSCA—See LS Corp.; *Int'l*, pg. 4569
LSC COMMUNICATIONS INC.—See Atlas Holdings, LLC; *U.S. Private*, pg. 376
LSC COMMUNICATIONS LLC—See Atlas Holdings, LLC; *U.S. Private*, pg. 376
LSCD—See LS Corp.; *Int'l*, pg. 4569
LSC ENVIRONMENTAL PRODUCTS, LLC—See Ancor Holdings, L.P.; *U.S. Private*, pg. 275
LSCG MANAGEMENT, INC.; *U.S. Private*, pg. 2508
LSC GROUP LIMITED—See Babcock International Group PLC; *Int'l*, pg. 792
L SCHERBERICH; *Int'l*, pg. 4369
LSCJ—See LS Corp.; *Int'l*, pg. 4569
LSC LITHIUM CORPORATION—See Pluspetrol Resources Corporation BV; *Int'l*, pg. 5899
L.S.C., LLC—See Komar Company; *U.S. Private*, pg. 2341
LSC MICHIGAN CORP.—See LSC Acquisition Corporation; *U.S. Private*, pg. 2508
LSCM—See LS Corp.; *Int'l*, pg. 4569
LS & COMPANY; *U.S. Private*, pg. 2508
LS CORP.; *Int'l*, pg. 4569
LSCT—See LS Corp.; *Int'l*, pg. 4569
LSCU—See LS Corp.; *Int'l*, pg. 4569
LSCV—See LS Corp.; *Int'l*, pg. 4569
LSCW—See LS Corp.; *Int'l*, pg. 4569
LS DAVOL SQUARE, LLC—See Ventas, Inc.; *U.S. Public*, pg. 2278
LS DEUTSCHLAND GMBH—See Vivendi SE; *Int'l*, pg. 8271
LSEB CREATIVE CORP.; *U.S. Public*, pg. 1344
LSE ELEKTRIK LTD.; *Int'l*, pg. 4570
LS ELECTRIC CO., LTD.; *Int'l*, pg. 4569
L&S ELECTRIC INC. - IRON MOUNTAIN—See L&S Electric Inc.; *U.S. Private*, pg. 2363
L&S ELECTRIC INC.; *U.S. Private*, pg. 2363
L&S ELECTRIC OF CANADA—See L&S Electric Inc.; *U.S. Private*, pg. 2363
LS ENERGY SOLUTIONS LLC—See LS Electric Co., Ltd.; *Int'l*, pg. 4569
LSEQ—See LS Corp.; *Int'l*, pg. 4569
LSE SPACE ENGINEERING & OPERATIONS AG—See GomSpace Group AB; *Int'l*, pg. 3037
LSE SPACE GMBH—See GomSpace Group AB; *Int'l*, pg. 3037
LSE SPACE MIDDLE EAST JLT—See GomSpace Group AB; *Int'l*, pg. 3037
LS EV KOREA LTD.—See LS Corp.; *Int'l*, pg. 4569
LSF LOAN SOLUTIONS FRANKFURT GMBH—See Commerzbank AG; *Int'l*, pg. 1718
L&S FOOD SALES CORP.; *U.S. Private*, pg. 2363
LS-GAON CABLE MYANMAR CO., LTD.—See LS Cable & System Asia Ltd.; *Int'l*, pg. 4568
LSG CATERING CHINA LTD—See Deutsche Lufthansa AG; *Int'l*, pg. 2067
LSG CATERING (THAILAND) LTD.—See Deutsche Lufthansa AG; *Int'l*, pg. 2067
LSG CO., LTD.—See EPS Holdings, Inc.; *Int'l*, pg. 2466
LSG-FOOD & NONFOOD HANDEL GMBH—See Deutsche Lufthansa AG; *Int'l*, pg. 2067

LSG HOLDING ASIA LTD.—See Deutsche Lufthansa AG; *Int'l*, pg. 2067
LSG HYDRO POWER LIMITED—See Korea Electric Power Corporation; *Int'l*, pg. 4284
LSG-HYGIENE INSTITUTE GMBH—See TUV SUD AG; *Int'l*, pg. 7985
LSG INSURANCE PARTNERS, INC.—See Arthur J. Gallagher & Co.; *U.S. Public*, pg. 206
LSG INSURANCE—See Assurant, Inc.; *U.S. Public*, pg. 215
LS GLOBAL INC.—See LS Corp.; *Int'l*, pg. 4569
LSG LUFTHANSA SERVICE ASIA LTD.—See Deutsche Lufthansa AG; *Int'l*, pg. 2067
LSG LUFTHANSA SERVICE CAPE TOWN (PTY) LTD—See Deutsche Lufthansa AG; *Int'l*, pg. 2067
LSG LUFTHANSA SERVICE CATERING- UND DIENSTLEISTUNGSGESELLSCHAFT MBH—See Deutsche Lufthansa AG; *Int'l*, pg. 2067
LSG LUFTHANSA SERVICE EUROPA/AFRIKA GMBH—See Deutsche Lufthansa AG; *Int'l*, pg. 2067
LSG LUFTHANSA SERVICE HOLDING AG—See Deutsche Lufthansa AG; *Int'l*, pg. 2066
LSG LUFTHANSA SERVICE HONG KONG LTD.—See Deutsche Lufthansa AG; *Int'l*, pg. 2067
LSG SKY CHEFS BELGIUM N.V.—See Deutsche Lufthansa AG; *Int'l*, pg. 2067
LSG SKY CHEFS BUILDING AB—See Deutsche Lufthansa AG; *Int'l*, pg. 2068
LSG SKY CHEFS DEUTSCHLAND GMBH—See Deutsche Lufthansa AG; *Int'l*, pg. 2067
LSG SKY CHEFS DE VENEZUELA C.A.—See Deutsche Lufthansa AG; *Int'l*, pg. 2068
LSG/SKY CHEFS EUROPE HOLDINGS LTD.—See Deutsche Lufthansa AG; *Int'l*, pg. 2067
LSG SKY CHEFS/GCC LTD.—See Deutsche Lufthansa AG; *Int'l*, pg. 2068
LSG SKY CHEFS HAVACILIK HIZMETLERI A.S.—See Deutsche Lufthansa AG; *Int'l*, pg. 2067
LSG SKY CHEFS (INDIA) PVT. LTD.—See Deutsche Lufthansa AG; *Int'l*, pg. 2067
LSG SKY CHEFS KOREA CO LTD.—See Deutsche Lufthansa AG; *Int'l*, pg. 2067
LSG SKY CHEFS LOUNGE GMBH—See Deutsche Lufthansa AG; *Int'l*, pg. 2067
LSG SKY CHEFS NEW ZEALAND LIMITED—See Deutsche Lufthansa AG; *Int'l*, pg. 2067
LSG SKY CHEFS NORGE AS—See Deutsche Lufthansa AG; *Int'l*, pg. 2067
LSG SKY CHEFS NORTH AMERICA SOLUTIONS, INC.—See Deutsche Lufthansa AG; *Int'l*, pg. 2067
LSG SKY CHEFS SCHWEIZ AG—See Deutsche Lufthansa AG; *Int'l*, pg. 2067
LSG SKY CHEFS SOLUTIONS ASIA LIMITED—See Deutsche Lufthansa AG; *Int'l*, pg. 2067
LSG SKY CHEFS SOUTH AFRICA (PTY) LTD.—See Deutsche Lufthansa AG; *Int'l*, pg. 2067
LSG SKY CHEFS SUPPLY CHAIN SOLUTIONS, INC.—See Deutsche Lufthansa AG; *Int'l*, pg. 2067
LSG SKY CHEFS SVERIGE AB—See Deutsche Lufthansa AG; *Int'l*, pg. 2068
LSG SKY CHEFS (THAILAND) LTD.—See Deutsche Lufthansa AG; *Int'l*, pg. 2067
LSG SKY CHEFS USA, INC.—See Deutsche Lufthansa AG; *Int'l*, pg. 2067
LSG-SKY FOOD GMBH—See Deutsche Lufthansa AG; *Int'l*, pg. 2067
LSH INDUSTRIAL SOLUTIONS PTE. LTD.—See Bunzl plc; *Int'l*, pg. 1218
LSHQ—See LS Corp.; *Int'l*, pg. 4569
LSI ADAPT INC.—See LSI Industries Inc.; *U.S. Public*, pg. 1344
LSI ADL TECHNOLOGY INC.—See LSI Industries Inc.; *U.S. Public*, pg. 1344
LSI CORPORATION OF AMERICA, INC.—See Stevens Industries, Inc.; *U.S. Private*, pg. 3809
LSIC—See LS Corp.; *Int'l*, pg. 4569
LSI GRAPHIC SOLUTIONS PLUS—See LSI Industries Inc.; *U.S. Public*, pg. 1344
LSI GRAPHIC SOLUTIONS PLUS—See LSI Industries Inc.; *U.S. Public*, pg. 1344
LSI INC.; *U.S. Private*, pg. 2509
LSI INDUSTRIES INC.; *U.S. Public*, pg. 1344
LSI INTEGRATED GRAPHICS L.P.—See LSI Industries Inc.; *U.S. Public*, pg. 1344
LSI KENTUCKY LLC—See LSI Industries Inc.; *U.S. Public*, pg. 1344
LSI LIGHTRON INC.—See LSI Industries Inc.; *U.S. Public*, pg. 1344
LSI MEDIENCE CORPORATION—See PHC Holdings Corporation; *Int'l*, pg. 5843
LSI MIDWEST LIGHTING INC.—See LSI Industries Inc.; *U.S. Public*, pg. 1344
LSI RETAIL GRAPHICS INC.—See LSI Industries Inc.; *U.S. Public*, pg. 1344
LSI SACO TECHNOLOGIES, INC.—See LSI Industries Inc.; *U.S. Public*, pg. 1344
LSI SOFTWARE S.A; *Int'l*, pg. 4570

LSI SOFTWARE S.R.O.—See LSI Software S.A; *Int'l*, pg. 4570
LSL CORPORATE CLIENT SERVICES LIMITED—See LSL Property Services plc; *Int'l*, pg. 4570
L.S. LEE INC.—See REH Holdings Inc.; *U.S. Private*, pg. 3389
LSLI LIMITED—See LSL Property Services plc; *Int'l*, pg. 4570
LSL LAND & NEW HOMES LIMITED—See LSL Property Services plc; *Int'l*, pg. 4570
LSL PHARMA GROUP INC.; *Int'l*, pg. 4570
LSL PROPERTY SERVICES PLC; *Int'l*, pg. 4570
LS MARINE CO., LTD.—See Daeyang Electric Co., Ltd.; *Int'l*, pg. 1911
LSM BRASIL S.A.—See AMG Critical Materials N.V.; *Int'l*, pg. 426
LS MECAPION CO., LTD.—See LS Electric Co., Ltd.; *Int'l*, pg. 4569
LS METAL CO. LTD.—See LS Corp.; *Int'l*, pg. 4569
LSM (JIAXING) CO., LTD.—See AMG Critical Materials N.V.; *Int'l*, pg. 426
LS MTRON LTD. - ENGINE PLANT—See LS Corp.; *Int'l*, pg. 4569
LS MTRON LTD. - JEONJU PLANT—See LS Corp.; *Int'l*, pg. 4569
LS MTRON—See LS Corp.; *Int'l*, pg. 4569
LS NETWORKS CORPORATION LIMITED; *Int'l*, pg. 4570
LS NETWORKS TRADING (BEIJING) CO., LTD.—See LS Networks Corporation Limited; *Int'l*, pg. 4570
LS-NIKKO COPPER INC.—See LS Corp.; *Int'l*, pg. 4569
LS OF SOUTH AFRICA RADIO COMMUNICATION SERVICES (PTY) LTD.—See LS telcom AG; *Int'l*, pg. 4570
L-SOFT INTERNATIONAL, INC.; *U.S. Private*, pg. 2364
L&S PACKING CO., INC.; *U.S. Private*, pg. 2363
LSP COMMUNICATIONS PTY LIMITED—See Aware Super Pty Ltd; *Int'l*, pg. 752
LSP COMMUNICATIONS PTY LIMITED—See Macquarie Group Limited; *Int'l*, pg. 4629
LSP DIGITAL GMBH & CO. KG—See Stroer SE & Co. KGaA; *Int'l*, pg. 7242
LS POWER DEVELOPMENT, LLC; *U.S. Private*, pg. 2508
LS POWER EQUITY ADVISORS, LLC—See LS Power Development, LLC; *U.S. Private*, pg. 2508
LSP PRODUCTS GROUP INC.—See NCH Corporation; *U.S. Private*, pg. 2875
LSP SOLUTIONS B.V.—See WiseTech Global Limited; *Int'l*, pg. 8437
LSP TECHNOLOGIES, INC.; *U.S. Private*, pg. 2509
LSQ FUNDING GROUP, L.C.; *U.S. Private*, pg. 2509
L SQUARED CAPITAL MANAGEMENT LP; *U.S. Private*, pg. 2361
LSR CONSTRUCTION-URALS LTD.—See PJSC LSR Group; *Int'l*, pg. 5881
LS RESEARCH, LLC—See DuPont de Nemours, Inc.; *U.S. Public*, pg. 693
LSR-STROY OOO—See PJSC LSR Group; *Int'l*, pg. 5881
LSR WALL MATERIALS LTD.—See PJSC LSR Group; *Int'l*, pg. 5881
LS SECURITIES CO., LTD.; *Int'l*, pg. 4570
LSS ETIKETTERING A/S—See L. Possehl & Co. mbH; *Int'l*, pg. 4383
LSSM SALES, INC.—See Revolution Capital Group, LLC; *U.S. Private*, pg. 3416
LSSPI SDN. BHD.—See SCGM Berhad; *Int'l*, pg. 6614
THE L.S. STARRETT COMPANY LIMITED—See MiddleGround Management, LP; *U.S. Private*, pg. 2713
THE L.S. STARRETT COMPANY OF AUSTRALIA PTY LTD—See MiddleGround Management, LP; *U.S. Private*, pg. 2713
THE L.S. STARRETT COMPANY OF CANADA LIMITED—See MiddleGround Management, LP; *U.S. Private*, pg. 2713
THE L.S. STARRETT COMPANY OF MEXICO S. DE R.L. DE C.V.—See MiddleGround Management, LP; *U.S. Private*, pg. 2713
L.S. STARRETT COMPANY - SAW DIVISION—See MiddleGround Management, LP; *U.S. Private*, pg. 2713
THE L.S. STARRETT COMPANY—See MiddleGround Management, LP; *U.S. Private*, pg. 2713
LS SYSTEMS, LLC; *U.S. Private*, pg. 2508
LSTA—See LS Corp.; *Int'l*, pg. 4569
LS TECHNOLOGIES, LLC.—See Tetra Tech, Inc.; *U.S. Public*, pg. 2023
LS TELCOM AG MKK—See LS telcom AG; *Int'l*, pg. 4570
LS TELCOM AG; *Int'l*, pg. 4570
LS TELCOM INC.—See LS telcom AG; *Int'l*, pg. 4570
LS TELCOM LTD.—See LS telcom AG; *Int'l*, pg. 4570
LS TELCOM SAS—See LS telcom AG; *Int'l*, pg. 4570
LS TELCOM UK LIMITED—See LS telcom AG; *Int'l*, pg. 4570
L & S TIRE COMPANY; *U.S. Private*, pg. 2361
LST MARKETING, LLC; *U.S. Private*, pg. 2509
LST MIDDLE EAST FZ-LLC—See LS telcom AG; *Int'l*, pg. 4570
LS TRAVEL RETAIL BULGARIA LTD.—See Vivendi SE; *Int'l*, pg. 8271
LS TRAVEL RETAIL DEUTSCHLAND GMBH—See Vivendi SE; *Int'l*, pg. 8276

LST MARKETING, LLC

LS TRAVEL RETAIL MALAYSIA SDN. BHD.—See Vivendi SE; *Int'l*, pg. 8271
LS TR ITALIA SRL—See Vivendi SE; *Int'l*, pg. 8271
LS TR NORTH AMERICA INC.—See Vivendi SE; *Int'l*, pg. 8271
L. STROETMANN GMBH & CO. KG; *Int'l*, pg. 4385
L. STROETMANN GROSSMARKTE GMBH & CO. KG—See L. Stroetmann GmbH & Co. KG; *Int'l*, pg. 4385
L. STROETMANN GROSSVERBRAUCHER GMBH & CO. KG—See L. Stroetmann GmbH & Co. KG; *Int'l*, pg. 4385
L. STROETMANN LEBENSMITTEL GMBH & CO. KG—See L. Stroetmann GmbH & Co. KG; *Int'l*, pg. 4385
L. STROETMANN SAAT GMBH & CO. KG—See L. Stroetmann GmbH & Co. KG; *Int'l*, pg. 4385
L&S TRUCK CENTER OF APPLETON; *U.S. Private*, pg. 2363
L. SUZIO CONCRETE COMPANY INC.; *U.S. Private*, pg. 2364
LS-VINA CABLE & SYSTEM JOINT STOCK CO.—See LS Cable & System Asia Ltd.; *Int'l*, pg. 4569
LSW LANDE-STADTWERKE WOLFSBURG GMBH & CO. KG—See E.ON SE; *Int'l*, pg. 2254
LSW LANDE-STADTWERKE WOLFSBURG VERWALTUNGS-GMBH—See E.ON SE; *Int'l*, pg. 2258
LT ACQUISITION CORP.; *U.S. Private*, pg. 2509
LT APPAREL GROUP; *U.S. Private*, pg. 2509
L&T BIOWATTI OY—See Lassila & Tikanoja plc; *Int'l*, pg. 4421
LTB LEITUNGSBAU GMBH—See BKW AG; *Int'l*, pg. 1055
LTC ADVERTISING LAGOS—See WPP plc; *Int'l*, pg. 8481
LTC BUILDING MATERIALS PTE LTD—See LTC Corporation Limited; *Int'l*, pg. 4571
LTCC MATERIALS CO., LTD.—See YOKOWO Co., Ltd.; *Int'l*, pg. 8595
LTC CO., LTD.; *Int'l*, pg. 4571
LTC CORPORATION LIMITED; *Int'l*, pg. 4571
LTC ENGINEERING ASSOCIATES, INC.—See CACI International Inc.; *U.S. Public*, pg. 418
LTC FINANCIAL PARTNERS, LLC.—See LTC Global, Inc.; *U.S. Private*, pg. 2509
LTC GLOBAL, INC.; *U.S. Private*, pg. 2509
L&T-CHIYODA LIMITED—See Chiyoda Corporation; *Int'l*, pg. 1575
L&T-CHIYODA LIMITED—See Larsen & Toubro Limited; *Int'l*, pg. 4419
LTC, INC.—See PRL Inc.; *U.S. Private*, pg. 3269
LTCI PARTNERS, LLC—See Aon plc; *Int'l*, pg. 496
LTC PERFORMANCE STRATEGIES, INC.—See IMA Financial Group, Inc.; *U.S. Private*, pg. 2043
LTC PROPERTIES, INC.; *U.S. Public*, pg. 1344
LTD BLOMINFO UKRAINE—See NRC Group ASA; *Int'l*, pg. 5473
LTD COMMODITIES LLC; *U.S. Private*, pg. 2509
LT DESIGN STUDIO—See Lerthai Group Limited; *Int'l*, pg. 4466
LTD PARK MV—See Bank of Georgia Group PLC; *Int'l*, pg. 843
L&T ELECTRICAL & AUTOMATION FZE—See Schneider Electric SE; *Int'l*, pg. 6628
L&T EMSYS PRIVATE LIMITED—See Larsen & Toubro Limited; *Int'l*, pg. 4418
L&T FINANCE HOLDINGS LIMITED—See Larsen & Toubro Limited; *Int'l*, pg. 4419
L&T FINANCE LIMITED—See Larsen & Toubro Limited; *Int'l*, pg. 4419
LT FOODS LTD; *Int'l*, pg. 4571
LT GAME AUSTRALIA PTY. LTD.—See PARADISE ENTERTAINMENT LIMITED; *Int'l*, pg. 5735
LT GAME LIMITED—See PARADISE ENTERTAINMENT LIMITED; *Int'l*, pg. 5735
LTG DEVELOPMENT SDN BHD—See United Overseas Australia Ltd; *Int'l*, pg. 8071
LTG DISPLAY AB—See Amplex AB; *Int'l*, pg. 434
LT GROUP, INC.; *Int'l*, pg. 4571
LT GROWTH SDN. BHD.—See Tiong Nam Logistics Holdings Berhad; *Int'l*, pg. 7755
L T HAMPEL CORP.; *U.S. Private*, pg. 2362
L&T HANKINTA KY—See Lassila & Tikanoja plc; *Int'l*, pg. 4421
LTH LOGISTICS (SINGAPORE) PTE. LTD.—See Vibrant Group Limited; *Int'l*, pg. 8184
L. THORN COMPANY INC.; *U.S. Private*, pg. 2364
L & T HOWDEN PRIVATE LTD.—See Chart Industries, Inc.; *U.S. Public*, pg. 482
LTI AUSTRIA GMBH—See Korber AG; *Int'l*, pg. 4281
LTI DEVELOPMENT CO. INC.; *U.S. Private*, pg. 2509
LTI DIRVE SYSTEMS (SHANGHAI) CO. LTD.—See KEBA AG; *Int'l*, pg. 4113
LTI DRIVES CO., LTD.—See KEBA AG; *Int'l*, pg. 4113
LTI DRIVES GMBH—See KEBA AG; *Int'l*, pg. 4113
LTI DRIVES USA LTD.—See KEBA AG; *Int'l*, pg. 4113
LTI DRIVE SYSTEMS CO., LTD.—See KEBA AG; *Int'l*, pg. 4113
LTI DRIVE SYSTEMS (SHANGHAI) CO., LTD.—See KEBA AG; *Int'l*, pg. 4113
LTI ELECTRONICS GMBH—See KEBA AG; *Int'l*, pg. 4113
LTI GMBH—See Korber AG; *Int'l*, pg. 4281
LTI, INC.—See Lynden Incorporated; *U.S. Private*, pg. 2521
LTI, INC.—See Lynden Incorporated; *U.S. Private*, pg. 2521
LTI ITALIA S.R.L.—See Korber AG; *Int'l*, pg. 4281
LTIMINDTREE LIMITED—See Larsen & Toubro Limited; *Int'l*, pg. 4419
LTI MOTION GMBH—See KEBA AG; *Int'l*, pg. 4113
L&T INFRASTRUCTURE DEVELOPMENT PROJECTS LIMITED—See Edelweiss Financial Services Ltd.; *Int'l*, pg. 2306
LTI PORTFOLIO MANAGEMENT CORP.—See Leasing Technologies International Inc.; *U.S. Private*, pg. 2409
LTI POWER SYSTEMS, INC.; *U.S. Private*, pg. 2509
LTI PRINTING, INC.—See Max Solutions Inc.; *U.S. Private*, pg. 2617
LTI REEENERGY CO., LTD.—See Korber AG; *Int'l*, pg. 4281
L&T KALUSTO OY—See Lassila & Tikanoja plc; *Int'l*, pg. 4421
LTK DEVELOPMENT SDN. BHD.—See LTKM Bhd; *Int'l*, pg. 4571
LTK ELECTRIC WIRE (HUIZHOU) LIMITED—See Shenzhen Woer Heat-Shrinkable Material Co., Ltd.; *Int'l*, pg. 6824
LTK INTERNATIONAL LTD.—See Shenzhen Woer Heat-Shrinkable Material Co., Ltd.; *Int'l*, pg. 6824
LT KM BERHAD; *Int'l*, pg. 4571
LTKM BHD; *Int'l*, pg. 4571
LTK (MELAKA) SDN. BHD.—See LTKM Bhd; *Int'l*, pg. 4571
L&T-KOMATSU LIMITED—See Komatsu Ltd.; *Int'l*, pg. 4238
L&T-KOMATSU LIMITED—See Larsen & Toubro Limited; *Int'l*, pg. 4419
LTL HOLDINGS, INC.; *U.S. Private*, pg. 2509
LTL HOME PRODUCTS, INC.; *U.S. Private*, pg. 2509
LTL INC.—See Joe Garrell & Associates Inc.; *U.S. Private*, pg. 2218
L&T MBDA MISSILE SYSTEMS LIMITED—See Larsen & Toubro Limited; *Int'l*, pg. 4419
L&T MEAT CO.; *U.S. Private*, pg. 2363
LT METAL CO., LTD.—See Tanaka Holdings Co., Ltd.; *Int'l*, pg. 7455
L&T - MHI POWER BOILERS PRIVATE LIMITED—See Larsen & Toubro Limited; *Int'l*, pg. 4418
L&T.- MHI POWER TURBINE GENERATORS PRIVATE LIMITED—See Larsen & Toubro Limited; *Int'l*, pg. 4418
LTM INC.; *U.S. Private*, pg. 2509
L.T.M. INDUSTRIE SAS—See Bilfinger SE; *Int'l*, pg. 1028
L&T MUOVIPORTTI OY—See Lassila & Tikanoja plc; *Int'l*, pg. 4421
L&T MUTUAL FUND TRUSTEE LIMITED—See Larsen & Toubro Limited; *Int'l*, pg. 4419
LTN GLOBAL COMMUNICATIONS, INC.; *U.S. Private*, pg. 2509
LT PLAN SERVICES, INC.—See LT Trust Company; *U.S. Private*, pg. 2509
LTP MANAGEMENT GROUP, INC.; *U.S. Private*, pg. 2510
L TRADING CO., LTD.—See THK CO., LTD.; *Int'l*, pg. 7711
L&T-RAMBOLL CONSULTING ENGINEERS LIMITED—See Larsen & Toubro Limited; *Int'l*, pg. 4419
LTRIM TECHNOLOGIES—See Constellation Software Inc.; *Int'l*, pg. 1774
LTR INDUSTRIES S.A.—See Mativ Holdings, Inc.; *U.S. Public*, pg. 1396
LTS ASIA CO., LIMITED—See LTS, Inc.; *Int'l*, pg. 4571
LTS CORPORATION—See Sentrillion Corporation; *U.S. Private*, pg. 3610
L.T. SERVICE CORPORATION—See Old Republic International Corporation; *U.S. Public*, pg. 1569
LTS, INC.; *Int'l*, pg. 4571
LTS LICHT & LEUCHTEN GMBH—See Fagerhult Group AB; *Int'l*, pg. 2602
LTS LOHMANN THERAPIE-SYSTEME AG—See dievini Hopp BioTech holding GmbH & Co. KG; *Int'l*, pg. 2117
LTS LOHMANN THERAPY SYSTEMS CORP.—See dievini Hopp BioTech holding GmbH & Co. KG; *U.S. Public*, pg. 2117
L&T SPECIAL STEELS & HEAVY FORGINGS PRIVATE LIMITED—See Larsen & Toubro Limited; *Int'l*, pg. 4419
LTS SCALE COMPANY, LLC—See Main Street Capital Holdings, LLC; *U.S. Private*, pg. 2551
LTS SHIPPING CORPORATION—See Alliance International Forwarders, Inc.; *U.S. Private*, pg. 183
L&T TECHNOLOGY SERVICES LIMITED—See Larsen & Toubro Limited; *Int'l*, pg. 4419
L&T TOIMI OY—See Lassila & Tikanoja plc; *Int'l*, pg. 4421
LT TRUST COMPANY; *U.S. Private*, pg. 2509
LTU TECHNOLOGIES, INC.—See Nippon Telegraph & Telephone Corporation; *Int'l*, pg. 5346
LTU TECHNOLOGIES S. A. S.—See Nippon Telegraph & Telephone Corporation; *Int'l*, pg. 5346
L&T VALVES ARABIA MANUFACTURING LLC—See Larsen & Toubro Limited; *Int'l*, pg. 4419
L&T VRINDAVAN PROPERTIES LTD.; *Int'l*, pg. 4369
LTW INTRALOGISTICS GMBH—See Doppelmayr Group; *Int'l*, pg. 2175

CORPORATE AFFILIATIONS

LTX-CREDENCE ARMENIA L.L.C.—See Cohu, Inc.; *U.S. Public*, pg. 530
LTX-CREDENCE (DEUTSCHLAND) GMBH—See Cohu, Inc.; *U.S. Public*, pg. 530
LTX-CREDENCE ITALIA S.R.L.—See Cohu, Inc.; *U.S. Public*, pg. 530
LTX-CREDENCE SINGAPORE PTE LTD.—See Cohu, Inc.; *U.S. Public*, pg. 530
LTX-CREDENCE SYSTEMS KK—See Cohu, Inc.; *U.S. Public*, pg. 530
L&T YMPARISTOHUOLTO OY—See Lassila & Tikanoja plc; *Int'l*, pg. 4421
LTZ CHEMNITZ GMBH—See BayWa AG; *Int'l*, pg. 918
LUBAIR AVIATION TECHNOLOGY CO., LTD.; *Int'l*, pg. 4572
LUBA MUTUAL HOLDING COMPANY; *U.S. Private*, pg. 2510
LUBAR & CO., INC.; *U.S. Private*, pg. 2510
LUBATTI LIMITED—See Venture Life Group PLC; *Int'l*, pg. 8152
LUBAWA S.A.; *Int'l*, pg. 4572
LUBAWA USA, INC.—See Lubawa S.A.; *Int'l*, pg. 4572
THE LUBBOCK AVALANCHE-JOURNAL—See Gannett Co., Inc.; *U.S. Public*, pg. 904
LUBBOCK HEART HOSPITAL, LLC—See Bain Capital, LP; *U.S. Private*, pg. 445
LUBBOCK MOTORS-T, INC.—See Group 1 Automotive, Inc.; *U.S. Public*, pg. 971
LUBBOCK SYMPHONY ORCHESTRA; *U.S. Private*, pg. 2510
LUBCO, INC.—See Luby's, Inc.; *U.S. Public*, pg. 1345
LUBCON BULGARIEN LTD—See LUBRICANT CONSULT GMBH; *Int'l*, pg. 4572
LUBCON D.O.O.—See LUBRICANT CONSULT GMBH; *Int'l*, pg. 4573
LUBCON FRANCE S.A.R.L.—See LUBRICANT CONSULT GMBH; *Int'l*, pg. 4572
LUBCON LUBRICANT CONSULT AG—See LUBRICANT CONSULT GMBH; *Int'l*, pg. 4573
LUBCON LUBRICANTS ASIA PACIFIC INC.—See LUBRICANT CONSULT GMBH; *Int'l*, pg. 4572
LUBCON LUBRICANTS UK LTD—See LUBRICANT CONSULT GMBH; *Int'l*, pg. 4573
LUBCON LUBRIFICANTI S.R.L.—See LUBRICANT CONSULT GMBH; *Int'l*, pg. 4573
LUBCON MALAYSIA SDN BHD—See LUBRICANT CONSULT GMBH; *Int'l*, pg. 4573
LUBCON POLSKA SP. Z O.O.—See LUBRICANT CONSULT GMBH; *Int'l*, pg. 4573
LUBCON S.R.O.—See LUBRICANT CONSULT GMBH; *Int'l*, pg. 4573
LUBCON TURMO LUBRICATION, INC.—See LUBRICANT CONSULT GMBH; *Int'l*, pg. 4573
LUBECA VERSICHERUNGSKONTOR GMBH—See L. Possehl & Co. mbH; *Int'l*, pg. 4383
LUBECKER KUNSTSTOFFWERK GMBH—See Alpla-Werke Alwin Lehner GmbH & Co. KG; *Int'l*, pg. 374
LUBECON SYSTEMS, INC.—See BP plc; *Int'l*, pg. 1127
LUBEKONSULT AB—See Eleco Plc; *Int'l*, pg. 2348
LUBELSKI WEGIEL BOGDANKA SPOLKA AKCYJNA; *Int'l*, pg. 4572
LUBE MANAGEMENT CORPORATION—See Greenbriar Equity Group, L.P.; *U.S. Private*, pg. 1776
LUBERSKI INC.; *U.S. Private*, pg. 2510
LUBERT-ADLER MANAGEMENT, LLC—See Independence Capital Partners, LLC; *U.S. Private*, pg. 2056
LUBERT-ADLER PARTNERS, L.P.—See Independence Capital Partners, LLC; *U.S. Private*, pg. 2056
THE LUBE STOP, INC.—See Argonne Capital Group, LLC; *U.S. Private*, pg. 321
LUBEST—See Momar, Inc.; *U.S. Private*, pg. 2768
LUBE-TECH LIQUID RECYCLING, INC.—See Lubrication Technologies, Inc.; *U.S. Private*, pg. 2510
LUBE-TECH & PARTNERS, LLC—See Lubrication Technologies, Inc.; *U.S. Private*, pg. 2510
LUBETECH SDN BHD—See Sime Darby Berhad; *Int'l*, pg. 6930
LUBICOM MARKETING CONSULTING; *U.S. Private*, pg. 2510
LU BISCUITS-BARCELONA—See Mondelez International, Inc.; *U.S. Public*, pg. 1463
LUBMIN-BRANDOV GASTRANSPORT GMBH—See E.ON SE; *Int'l*, pg. 2255
LUBNER GROUP, LLC; *U.S. Private*, pg. 2510
LUBOA GROUP, INC.—See Ultimate Holdings Group, Inc.; *Int'l*, pg. 8018
THE LUBRICANT COMPANY LIMITED—See World Kinect Corporation; *U.S. Public*, pg. 2381
LUBRICANT CONSULT GMBH; *Int'l*, pg. 4572
LUBRICANTES FUCHS DE MEXICO S.A. DE C.V.—See FUCHS SE; *Int'l*, pg. 2804
LUBRICANTS BUSINESS DIVISION—See CPC Corporation; *Int'l*, pg. 1824
LUBRICANT SERVICE KFT—See LUBRICANT CONSULT GMBH; *Int'l*, pg. 4573
LUBRICANTS UK LTD—See BP plc; *Int'l*, pg. 1131
LUBRICATING SPECIALTIES COMPANY INC.—See Amalie Oil Company; *U.S. Private*, pg. 216
LUBRICATION ENGINEERS, INC.; *U.S. Private*, pg. 2510

COMPANY NAME INDEX

LUBRICATION TECHNOLOGIES, INC.; *U.S. Private*, pg. 2510
LUBRICOR, INC.—See Quaker Chemical Corporation; *U.S. Public*, pg. 1746
LUBRICORP, LLC; *U.S. Private*, pg. 2510
LUBRICO WARRANTY INC.—See iA Financial Corporation Inc.; *Int'l*, pg. 3568
LUBRIPLATE LUBRICANTS—See Fiske Brothers Refining Company; *U.S. Private*, pg. 1535
LUBRITECH ARGENTINA, S.R.L—See Enovis Corporation; *U.S. Public*, pg. 773
LUBRITECH CARIBBEAN LIMITED—See Enovis Corporation; *U.S. Public*, pg. 773
LUBRITECH DO BRASIL SERVICOS DE LUBRIFICACAO LTDA.—See Enovis Corporation; *U.S. Public*, pg. 773
LUBRITECH LIMITED—See Sime Darby Berhad; *Int'l*, pg. 6930
LUBRITECH PERU S.A.C.—See Enovis Corporation; *U.S. Public*, pg. 773
LUBRITE TECHNOLOGIES—See U.S. Bronze Foundry & Machine, Inc.; *U.S. Private*, pg. 4270
LUBRIVAL S. A.—See Saudi Arabian Oil Company; *Int'l*, pg. 6589
LUBRIZOL ADVANCED MATERIALS ASIA PACIFIC LIMITED—See Berkshire Hathaway Inc.; *U.S. Public*, pg. 319
LUBRIZOL ADVANCED MATERIALS EUROPE BVBA—See Berkshire Hathaway Inc.; *U.S. Public*, pg. 319
LUBRIZOL ADVANCED MATERIALS, INC. - PASO ROBLES—See Berkshire Hathaway Inc.; *U.S. Public*, pg. 319
LUBRIZOL ADVANCED MATERIALS, INC.—See Berkshire Hathaway Inc.; *U.S. Public*, pg. 319
LUBRIZOL ADVANCED MATERIALS INTERNATIONAL, INC.—See Berkshire Hathaway Inc.; *U.S. Public*, pg. 319
LUBRIZOL AUSTRALIA—See Berkshire Hathaway Inc.; *U.S. Public*, pg. 319
LUBRIZOL CANADA LTD.—See Berkshire Hathaway Inc.; *U.S. Public*, pg. 319
THE LUBRIZOL CORPORATION—See Berkshire Hathaway Inc.; *U.S. Public*, pg. 318
LUBRIZOL DEUTSCHLAND GMBH—See Berkshire Hathaway Inc.; *U.S. Public*, pg. 319
LUBRIZOL DO BRASIL ADITIVOS LTDA.—See Berkshire Hathaway Inc.; *U.S. Public*, pg. 319
LUBRIZOL ESPANOLA, S.A.—See Berkshire Hathaway Inc.; *U.S. Public*, pg. 319
LUBRIZOL FRANCE SAS—See Berkshire Hathaway Inc.; *U.S. Public*, pg. 319
LUBRIZOL GMBH—See Berkshire Hathaway Inc.; *U.S. Public*, pg. 319
LUBRIZOL GROUP, LLP—See Berkshire Hathaway Inc.; *U.S. Public*, pg. 319
LUBRIZOL INDIA PVT. LTD.—See Berkshire Hathaway Inc.; *U.S. Public*, pg. 319
LUBRIZOL ITALIANA, S.P.A.—See Berkshire Hathaway Inc.; *U.S. Public*, pg. 319
LUBRIZOL JAPAN LIMITED—See Berkshire Hathaway Inc.; *U.S. Public*, pg. 319
LUBRIZOL LIMITED—See Berkshire Hathaway Inc.; *U.S. Public*, pg. 319
LUBRIZOL LUXEMBOURG S.A.R.L.—See Berkshire Hathaway Inc.; *U.S. Public*, pg. 319
LUBRIZOL OILFIELD SOLUTIONS, INC.—See Berkshire Hathaway Inc.; *U.S. Public*, pg. 319
LUBRIZOL OVERSEAS TRADING CORPORATION—See Berkshire Hathaway Inc.; *U.S. Public*, pg. 319
LUBRIZOL SOUTHEAST ASIA (PTE.) LTD.—See Berkshire Hathaway Inc.; *U.S. Public*, pg. 319
LUBRIZOL SPECIALTY PRODUCTS LLC—See Berkshire Hathaway Inc.; *U.S. Public*, pg. 319
LUBY'S BEVCO, INC.—See Luby's, Inc.; *U.S. Public*, pg. 1345
LUBY'S FUDDRUCKERS RESTAURANTS, LLC; *U.S. Private*, pg. 2510
LUBY'S HOLDINGS, INC.—See Luby's, Inc.; *U.S. Public*, pg. 1345
LUBY'S, INC.; *U.S. Public*, pg. 1344
LUBY'S LIMITED PARTNER, INC.—See Luby's, Inc.; *U.S. Public*, pg. 1345
LUBY'S MANAGEMENT, INC.—See Luby's, Inc.; *U.S. Public*, pg. 1345
LUBY'S RESTAURANTS LP; *U.S. Private*, pg. 2510
LUCANIA GESTION, S.L.—See Encore Capital Group, Inc.; *U.S. Public*, pg. 759
LUCAPA DIAMOND COMPANY LIMITED; *Int'l*, pg. 4573
LUCARA DIAMOND CORP.; *Int'l*, pg. 4573
LUCARA IMMOBILIENVERWALTUNGS GMBH—See BASF SE; *Int'l*, pg. 884
LUCARDIE BV—See CVC Capital Partners SICAV-FIS S.A.; *Int'l*, pg. 1886
LUCART IBERICA S.L.U.—See Cartiera Lucchese S.p.A.; *Int'l*, pg. 1348
LUCART SAS—See Cartiera Lucchese S.p.A.; *Int'l*, pg. 1348
LUCAS AMERICA INC.—See Maschinenfabrik Harry Lucas GmbH & Co. KG; *Int'l*, pg. 4720

LUCAS ASSOCIATES INC.—See H.I.G. Capital, LLC; *U.S. Private*, pg. 1830
LUCAS AUTOMOTIVE GMBH—See ZF Friedrichshafen AG; *Int'l*, pg. 8646
LUCAS AUTOMOTIVE SDN. BHD.—See ZF Friedrichshafen AG; *Int'l*, pg. 8645
LUCAS BOLS B.V.; *Int'l*, pg. 4573
LUCAS BUSINESS SYSTEMS, INC.—See Xerox Holdings Corporation; *U.S. Public*, pg. 2388
LUCAS ET DEGAND S.A.R.L—See Encore Capital Group, Inc.; *U.S. Public*, pg. 759
LUCASFILM LTD.—See The Walt Disney Company; *U.S. Public*, pg. 2139
LUCAS GROUP—See H.I.G. Capital, LLC; *U.S. Private*, pg. 1830
LUCAS INDIAN SERVICE LIMITED—See Sundaram Brake Linings Limited; *Int'l*, pg. 7312
LUCAS MEYER COSMETICS AUSTRALIA PTY LTD—See International Flavors & Fragrances Inc.; *U.S. Public*, pg. 1153
LUCAS MEYER COSMETICS CANADA INC.—See Clariant AG; *Int'l*, pg. 1648
LUCAS MEYER COSMETICS—See Clariant AG; *Int'l*, pg. 1648
LUCAS-MILHAUPT BRAZING MATERIALS (SUZHOU) CO. LTD.—See Steel Partners Holdings L.P.; *U.S. Public*, pg. 1943
LUCAS-MILHAUPT, INC.—See Steel Partners Holdings L.P.; *U.S. Public*, pg. 1943
LUCAS MILHAUPT RIBERAC SA—See Steel Partners Holdings L.P.; *U.S. Public*, pg. 1943
LUCAS-MILHAUPT WARWICK LLC—See Steel Partners Holdings L.P.; *U.S. Public*, pg. 1943
LUCAS OIL PRODUCTS INC.; *U.S. Private*, pg. 2510
LUCAS PRECISION LLC—See FERMAT Group, a.s.; *Int'l*, pg. 2639
LUCAS SARL—See A.J. Lucas Group Limited; *Int'l*, pg. 24
LUCAS TEXTILMASCHINEN GMBH—See Maschinenfabrik Harry Lucas GmbH & Co. KG; *Int'l*, pg. 4720
LUCAS-TVS LIMITED—See Sundaram Brake Linings Limited; *Int'l*, pg. 7312
LUCASVARITY LANGZHONG BRAKE COMPANY LIMITED—See ZF Friedrichshafen AG; *Int'l*, pg. 8641
LUCASVARITY (M) SDN. BHD.—See ZF Friedrichshafen AG; *Int'l*, pg. 8645
LUCA TECHNOLOGIES INC.; *U.S. Private*, pg. 2510
LUCA WAY S.R.L.; *Int'l*, pg. 4573
LUCCHESE, INC.—See Kainos Capital, LLC; *U.S. Private*, pg. 2254
LUCCHI LTDA.—See A.A.G. STUCCHI s.r.l.; *Int'l*, pg. 23
LUC CORPORATION, LTD.—See Takara Holdings, Inc.; *Int'l*, pg. 7432
LUCECO ELECTRICAL (JIAXING) LIMITED—See Luceco PLC; *Int'l*, pg. 4573
LUCECO PLC; *Int'l*, pg. 4573
LUCECO SOUTHERN EUROPE SL—See Luceco PLC; *Int'l*, pg. 4573
LUCENDRO SA—See Azienda Elettrica Ticinese; *Int'l*, pg. 778
LUCENT INDUSTRIES LIMITED; *Int'l*, pg. 4573
LUCENT PICTURES ENTERTAINMENT, INC.—See Tsuburaya Fields Holdings Inc.; *Int'l*, pg. 7955
LUCENT POLYMERS, INC.; *U.S. Private*, pg. 2510
LUCEPLAN GMBH—See Signify N.V.; *Int'l*, pg. 6912
LUCEPLAN S.A.R.L.—See Signify N.V.; *Int'l*, pg. 6912
LUCEPLAN SCANDINAVIA A/S—See Signify N.V.; *Int'l*, pg. 6912
LUCEPLAN S.P.A—See Signify N.V.; *Int'l*, pg. 6912
LUCEPLAN USA, INC.—See Signify N.V.; *Int'l*, pg. 6912
LUCERA FINANCIAL INFRASTRUCTURES, LLC—See BGC Group, Inc.; *U.S. Public*, pg. 329
LUCERNE APARTMENTS TAMPA, LLC—See Independence Realty Trust, Inc.; *U.S. Public*, pg. 1115
LUCERNE CAPITAL MANAGEMENT, LP.; *U.S. Private*, pg. 2510
LUCERNE FOODS, INC.—See Cerberus Capital Management, L.P.; *U.S. Private*, pg. 836
LUCE SCHWAB & KASE INC.; *U.S. Private*, pg. 2510
LUCEY TRANSPORT LOGISTICS LTD.—See DFDS A/S; *Int'l*, pg. 2095
LUCHTHAVEN LELYSTAD VASTGOED B.V.—See Schiphol Group NV; *Int'l*, pg. 6621
LUCHUAN BOSSCO BIOTECH CO., LTD.—See Guangxi Bossco Environmental Protection Technology Co., Ltd.; *Int'l*, pg. 3163
LUCIAD, INC.—See Hexagon AB; *Int'l*, pg. 3369
LUCIAD NV—See Hexagon AB; *Int'l*, pg. 3369
LUCIA S.A.; *Int'l*, pg. 4573
LUCIBEL MIDDLE EAST FZCO—See Lucibel SA; *Int'l*, pg. 4573
LUCIBEL SA; *Int'l*, pg. 4573
LUCIC PRIGREVICA A.D.; *Int'l*, pg. 4573
LUCID AGENCY, LLC; *U.S. Private*, pg. 2510
LUCID CZECH REPUBLIC S.R.O.—See Cint Group AB; *Int'l*, pg. 1611
LUCID DIAGNOSTICS INC.—See PAVmed Inc.; *U.S. Public*, pg. 1655
LUCID EDGE PTY. LTD.—See NBA Quantum PLC; *Int'l*, pg. 5179

LUCID ENERGY GROUP II, LLC—See Targa Resources Corp.; *U.S. Public*, pg. 1981
LUCID ENERGY GROUP, LLC—See EnCap Investments L.P.; *U.S. Private*, pg. 1390
LUCIDEON; *Int'l*, pg. 4573
LUCID GLOBAL, INC.—See Altaris Capital Partners, LLC; *U.S. Private*, pg. 206
LUCID GROUP, INC.; *U.S. Public*, pg. 1345
LUCID, INC.; *U.S. Public*, pg. 1345
LUCIDITY CONSULTING GROUP LP—See Kelso & Company, L.P.; *U.S. Private*, pg. 2278
LUCID TECHNOLOGY; *U.S. Private*, pg. 2511
LUCIDWORKS INC.; *U.S. Private*, pg. 2511
LUCIDYNE TECHNOLOGIES, INC.—See Microtec s.r.l.; *Int'l*, pg. 4881
LUCIEN GEORGELIN SAS; *Int'l*, pg. 4573
LUCIGEN CORP.—See KKR & Co. Inc.; *U.S. Public*, pg. 1258
LUCILLE MAUD CORPORATION; *U.S. Private*, pg. 2511
LUCINI ITALIA COMPANY—See California Olive Ranch Inc.; *U.S. Private*, pg. 720
LUCION ENVIRONMENTAL LIMITED—See Palatine Private Equity LLP; *Int'l*, pg. 5706
LUCION SERVICES LTD.—See Palatine Private Equity LLP; *Int'l*, pg. 5706
LUCIRA HEALTH, INC.; *U.S. Public*, pg. 1345
LUCISANO MEDIA GROUP S.P.A; *Int'l*, pg. 4573
LUCITEA ATLANTIQUE SAS—See VINCI S.A.; *Int'l*, pg. 8223
LUCITEA OUEST SAS—See VINCI S.A.; *Int'l*, pg. 8223
LUCITE INTERNATIONAL ASIA PACIFIC PTE LIMITED—See Mitsubishi Chemical Group Corporation; *Int'l*, pg. 4930
LUCITE INTERNATIONAL CANADA INC.—See Mitsubishi Chemical Group Corporation; *Int'l*, pg. 4930
LUCITE INTERNATIONAL (CHINA) CHEMICAL INDUSTRY CO., LTD.—See Mitsubishi Chemical Group Corporation; *Int'l*, pg. 4930
LUCITE INTERNATIONAL FRANCE SAS—See Mitsubishi Chemical Group Corporation; *Int'l*, pg. 4930
LUCITE INTERNATIONAL HOLLAND B.V.—See Mitsubishi Chemical Group Corporation; *Int'l*, pg. 4930
LUCITE INTERNATIONAL, INC.—See Mitsubishi Chemical Group Corporation; *Int'l*, pg. 4930
LUCITE INTERNATIONAL JAPAN LIMITED—See Mitsubishi Chemical Group Corporation; *Int'l*, pg. 4930
LUCITE INTERNATIONAL LTD—See Mitsubishi Chemical Group Corporation; *Int'l*, pg. 4930
LUCITE INTERNATIONAL NETHERLANDS B.V.—See Mitsubishi Chemical Group Corporation; *Int'l*, pg. 4930
LUCITE INTERNATIONAL (SHANGHAI) TRADING CO LIMITED—See Mitsubishi Chemical Group Corporation; *Int'l*, pg. 4930
LUCITE INTERNATIONAL SINGAPORE PTE LIMITED—See Mitsubishi Chemical Group Corporation; *Int'l*, pg. 4930
LUCITE INTERNATIONAL SPECIALITY POLYMERS AND RESINS LIMITED—See Mitsubishi Chemical Group Corporation; *Int'l*, pg. 4930
LUCITE INTERNATIONAL UK LIMITED—See Mitsubishi Chemical Group Corporation; *Int'l*, pg. 4930
LUCIX CORP.—See HEICO Corporation; *U.S. Public*, pg. 1020
LUCK BROTHERS INC.; *U.S. Private*, pg. 2511
LUCKCHAI LIQUOR TRADING CO., LTD.—See Thai Beverage Public Company Limited; *Int'l*, pg. 7591
LUCKETT & FARLEY ARCHITECTS, ENGINEERS AND CONSTRUCTION MANAGERS, INC.; *U.S. Private*, pg. 2511
LUCKETTS TRAVEL LIMITED—See Mobico Group PLC; *Int'l*, pg. 5008
LUCKETT TOBACCOS INC.; *U.S. Private*, pg. 2511
LUCKEY FARMERS INC.; *U.S. Private*, pg. 2511
LUCKIE & CO. LTD.; *U.S. Private*, pg. 2511
LUCKINBILL INC.; *U.S. Private*, pg. 2511
LUCKIN COFFEE INC.; *Int'l*, pg. 4573
LUCKLAND CO., LTD.; *Int'l*, pg. 4574
LUCKS FOOD DECORATING COMPANY; *U.S. Private*, pg. 2511
LUCK STONE CORPORATION; *U.S. Private*, pg. 2511
LUCKWEL PHARMACEUTICALS INC.; *U.S. Private*, pg. 2511
LUCKY AIR CO., LTD.—See Hainan Traffic Administration Holding Co., Ltd.; *Int'l*, pg. 3215
LUCKY BRAND DUNGAREES, INC.—See Leonard Green & Partners, L.P.; *U.S. Private*, pg. 2426
LUCKY BRAND DUNGAREES, INC.—See Leonard Green & Partners, L.P.; *U.S. Private*, pg. 2426
LUCKY BUCKS LLC—See Trive Capital Inc.; *U.S. Private*, pg. 4240
LUCKY BUMS LLC; *U.S. Private*, pg. 2511
LUCKY-CAR FRANCHISE & BETEILIGUNGS GMBH; *Int'l*, pg. 4574
LUCKY CEMENT CORPORATION - DONGAO PLANT—See Lucky Cement Corporation; *Int'l*, pg. 4574
LUCKY CEMENT CORPORATION - HOREN PLANT—See Lucky Cement Corporation; *Int'l*, pg. 4574

1643

LUCKY CEMENT CORPORATION - PUXIN PLANT—See Lucky Cement Corporation; *Int'l*, pg. 4574
LUCKY CEMENT CORPORATION; *Int'l*, pg. 4574
LUCKY CEMENT LIMITED; *Int'l*, pg. 4574
LUCKY COMMODITIES (PRIVATE) LIMITED—See Lucky Cement Limited; *Int'l*, pg. 4574
LUCKY CORE INDUSTRIES LIMITED—See Lucky Cement Limited; *Int'l*, pg. 4574
LUCKY CREATION ENTERPRISE (SHANGHAI) LIMITED—See Smartac International Holdings Limited.; *Int'l*, pg. 7001
LUCKY DOLLAR STORES INC.; *U.S. Private*, pg. 2511
LUCKY DUCK INTERNATIONAL FOOD B.V.—See Bangkok Ranch Public Company Limited; *Int'l*, pg. 835
LUCKY ELECTRIC POWER COMPANY LIMITED—See Lucky Cement Limited; *Int'l*, pg. 4574
LUCKY ENERGY (PRIVATE) LIMITED—See Lucky Cement Limited; *Int'l*, pg. 4574
LUCKY FILM CO., LTD.; *Int'l*, pg. 4574
LUCKY FOODS LLC—See Daesang Corporation; *Int'l*, pg. 1909
LUCKY FOODS (PRIVATE) LIMITED—See Lucky Cement Limited; *Int'l*, pg. 4574
LUCKY FRIDAY EXTENSION MINING CO.; *U.S. Public*, pg. 1345
LUCKY HARVEST CO., LTD.; *Int'l*, pg. 4574
LUCKY HOLDINGS LIMITED—See Lucky Cement Limited; *Int'l*, pg. 4574
LUCKY INTERNATIONAL TRADING, INC.; *U.S. Private*, pg. 2511
LUCKY KNITS (PRIVATE) LIMITED—See Lucky Cement Limited; *Int'l*, pg. 4574
LUCKY LANDSCAPE SUPPLY LLC—See SiteOne Landscape Supply, Inc.; *U.S. Public*, pg. 1889
LUCKY MINERALS INC.; *Int'l*, pg. 4574
LUCKY MINMAT LIMITED—See Adani Enterprises Limited; *Int'l*, pg. 125
LUCKY PORT TRADING LIMITED—See Symphony Holdings Limited; *Int'l*, pg. 7379
LUCKY'S LEASE, INC.—See Lucky's Trailer Sales, Inc.; *U.S. Private*, pg. 2511
LUCKY STAR MANAGEMENT LIMITED—See I-Remit, Inc.; *Int'l*, pg. 3564
LUCKY START LTD.; *U.S. Private*, pg. 2511
LUCKY'S TRAILER SALES, INC.; *U.S. Private*, pg. 2511
LUCKY-TEAM BIOTECH DEVELOPMENT (HEPU) LIMITED—See Asian Citrus Holdings Limited; *Int'l*, pg. 617
LUCKYTEX (THAILAND) PUBLIC COMPANY LIMITED—See Toray Industries, Inc.; *Int'l*, pg. 7827
LUCKYVITAMIN LLC—See TSG Consumer Partners LLC; *U.S. Private*, pg. 4253
LUCOAT POWDER COATINGS TLD—See Akzo Nobel N.V.; *Int'l*, pg. 272
LUCOM GMBH ELEKTROKOMPONENTEN UND SYSTEME—see Kontron AG; *Int'l*, pg. 4277
LUCOR, INC.; *U.S. Private*, pg. 2511
LUCOZADE RIBENA SUNTORY LIMITED—See Suntory Holdings Limited; *Int'l*, pg. 7326
LUC-PRODUCT SP. Z O.O.—See Maschinenfabrik Harry Lucas GmbH & Co. KG; *Int'l*, pg. 4720
LUCTA DO BRASIL COMERCIAL LTDA.—See Lucta, S.A.; *Int'l*, pg. 4574
LUCTA GRANCOLOMBIANA, S.A.S.—See Lucta, S.A.; *Int'l*, pg. 4574
LUCTA (GUANGZHOU) FLAVOURS CO., LTD.—See Lucta, S.A.; *Int'l*, pg. 4574
LUCTA MEXICANA S.A. DE C.V.—See Lucta, S.A.; *Int'l*, pg. 4574
LUCTA POLSKA SP. Z O.O.—See Lucta, S.A.; *Int'l*, pg. 4574
LUCTA, S.A.; *Int'l*, pg. 4574
LUCTA USA INC.—See Lucta, S.A.; *Int'l*, pg. 4574
LUCURA RUCKVERSICHERUNGS AG—See BASF SE; *Int'l*, pg. 884
LUCY ACTIVEWEAR, INC.—See V. F. Corporation; *U.S. Public*, pg. 2270
LUCY ASIA PACIFIC SDN BHD—See W. Lucy & Co. Ltd.; *Int'l*, pg. 8321
LUCY ELECTRIC BEIJING COMPANY LTD.—See W. Lucy & Co. Ltd.; *Int'l*, pg. 8321
LUCY ELECTRIC INDIA (PRIVATE) LIMITED—See W. Lucy & Co. Ltd.; *Int'l*, pg. 8321
LUCY ELECTRIC SOUTH AFRICA PTY LTD.—See W. Lucy & Co. Ltd.; *Int'l*, pg. 8321
LUCY ELECTRIC (THAILAND) LTD.—See W. Lucy & Co. Ltd.; *Int'l*, pg. 8321
LUCY MIDDLE EAST FZE—See W. Lucy & Co. Ltd.; *Int'l*, pg. 8321
LUCY SCIENTIFIC DISCOVERY INC.; *Int'l*, pg. 4574
LUCY ZODION LIMITED—See W. Lucy & Co. Ltd.; *Int'l*, pg. 8321
LUDAN ENGINEERING CO., LTD.; *Int'l*, pg. 4575
LUDDEN & MENNEKES ENTSORGUNGS-SYSTEME GMBH; *Int'l*, pg. 4575
LUDENS CO., LTD.—See AOI TYO Holdings Inc.; *Int'l*, pg. 488

LUDERITZ BAY SHIPPING & FORWARDING PROPRIETARY LIMITED—See The Bidvest Group Limited; *Int'l*, pg. 7625
LUDGATE ENGINEERING CORP.; *U.S. Private*, pg. 2512
LUDGATE INVESTMENT HOLDINGS LIMITED—See The British Land Company PLC; *Int'l*, pg. 7628
LUDGATE INVESTMENTS LTD.; *Int'l*, pg. 4575
LUDIA INC.—See Netmarble Corp.; *Int'l*, pg. 5214
LUDICORP RESEARCH & DEVELOPMENT LTD.—See SmugMug, Inc.; *U.S. Private*, pg. 3699
LUDLOW COMPOSITES CORPORATION; *U.S. Private*, pg. 2512
LUDLOW CO-OPERATIVE ELEVATOR COMPANY INC.; *U.S. Private*, pg. 2512
LUDLOW JUTE & SPECIALITIES LIMITED; *Int'l*, pg. 4575
LUDLOW TECHNICAL PRODUCTS CANADA, LTD.—See Medtronic plc; *Int'l*, pg. 4787
LUDLOW TEXTILES COMPANY, INC.; *U.S. Private*, pg. 2512
LUDLUM MEASUREMENTS INC.; *U.S. Private*, pg. 2512
LUDOPARC S.A.—See Burelle S.A.; *Int'l*, pg. 1222
LUDORUM PLC; *Int'l*, pg. 4575
LUDOWICI AUSTRALIA PTY LTD.—See FLSmidth & Co. A/S; *Int'l*, pg. 2711
LUDOWICI (BEIJING) CO., LTD—See FLSmidth & Co. A/S; *Int'l*, pg. 2711
LUDOWICI INDIA PRIVATE LIMITED—See FLSmidth & Co. A/S; *Int'l*, pg. 2711
LUDOWICI LIMITED—See FLSmidth & Co. A/S; *Int'l*, pg. 2711
LUDOWICI LLC—See FLSmidth & Co. A/S; *Int'l*, pg. 2711
LUDOWICI MINING PROCESS INDIA PVT LIMITED—See FLSmidth & Co. A/S; *Int'l*, pg. 2711
LUDOWICI PACKAGING AUSTRALIA PTY LIMITED—See FLSmidth & Co. A/S; *Int'l*, pg. 2711
LUDOWICI ROOF TILE INC.—See LBO France S.a.r.l.; *Int'l*, pg. 4430
LUDOWICI SCREENS LLC—See FLSmidth & Co. A/S; *Int'l*, pg. 2711
LUDOWICI TECHNOLOGIES PTY LTD—See FLSmidth & Co. A/S; *Int'l*, pg. 2711
LUDUSON G INC.; *Int'l*, pg. 4575
LUDVIK ELECTRIC CO., INC.; *U.S. Private*, pg. 2512
LUDVIK HOLDINGS, INC.; *U.S. Private*, pg. 2512
LUDWICK EYE CENTER LTD.—See NMS Capital Services, LLC; *U.S. Private*, pg. 2931
LUDWIG BECK AG; *Int'l*, pg. 4575
LUDWIG BECK VERWALTUNGS GMBH—See Ludwig Beck AG; *Int'l*, pg. 4575
LUDWIG DISTRIBUTING CO., INC.; *U.S. Private*, pg. 2512
LUDWIG ENTERPRISES, INC.; *U.S. Public*, pg. 1345
LUDWIG FRISCHHUT GMBH & CO. KG—See Triton Advisers Limited; *Int'l*, pg. 7934
LUDWIG GORTZ GMBH; *Int'l*, pg. 4575
LUDWIG/MUSSER PERCUSSION INSTRUMENTS—See Paulson & Co. Inc.; *U.S. Private*, pg. 3114
LUEDER CONSTRUCTION COMPANY; *U.S. Private*, pg. 2512
LUEDERS ENVIRONMENTAL, INC.; *U.S. Private*, pg. 2512
LUEKEN'S FOOD STORE INC.; *U.S. Private*, pg. 2512
LUEMME, INC.—See Calida Holding AG; *Int'l*, pg. 1264
LUEN HENG F&B SDN. BHD.; *Int'l*, pg. 4575
LUENMEI QUANTUM CO., LTD.; *Int'l*, pg. 4575
LUEN THAI HOLDINGS LIMITED—See Shangtex Holding Co., Ltd.; *Int'l*, pg. 6784
LUFAPAK MONTAGE VERPACKEN LOGISTIK; *Int'l*, pg. 4575
LUFAX HOLDING LTD.; *Int'l*, pg. 4575
LUFF RESEARCH INC.—See Ironwave Technologies LLC; *U.S. Private*, pg. 2140
LUFKIN ARGENTINA, S.A.—See KPS Capital Partners, LP; *U.S. Private*, pg. 2348
LUFKIN CREOSOTING CO., INC.—See Stella-Jones, Inc.; *Int'l*, pg. 7196
LUFKIN INDUSTRIES - CALGARY—See KPS Capital Partners, LP; *U.S. Private*, pg. 2348
LUFKIN INDUSTRIES LLC - FOUNDRY DIVISION—See KPS Capital Partners, LP; *U.S. Private*, pg. 2347
LUFKIN INDUSTRIES LLC - OILFIELD DIVISION—See KPS Capital Partners, LP; *U.S. Private*, pg. 2347
LUFKIN INDUSTRIES LLC - POWER TRANSMISSION DIVISION—See KPS Capital Partners, LP; *U.S. Private*, pg. 2348
LUFKIN INDUSTRIES LLC - POWER TRANSMISSION DIVISION—See KPS Capital Partners, LP; *U.S. Private*, pg. 2348
LUFKIN INDUSTRIES LLC—See KPS Capital Partners, LP; *U.S. Private*, pg. 2347
LUFKIN INDUSTRIES SRL—See KPS Capital Partners, LP; *U.S. Private*, pg. 2348
LUFKIN & PARTNERS LLC—See KPS Capital Partners, LP; *U.S. Private*, pg. 2348
LUFTHANSA AG—See Deutsche Lufthansa AG; *Int'l*, pg. 2068
LUFTHANSA AIRPLUS SERVICEKARTEN GMBH—See Deutsche Lufthansa AG; *Int'l*, pg. 2068

LUFTHANSA AVIATION TRAINING AUSTRIA GMBH—See Deutsche Lufthansa AG; *Int'l*, pg. 2068
LUFTHANSA AVIATION TRAINING BERLIN GMBH—See Deutsche Lufthansa AG; *Int'l*, pg. 2068
LUFTHANSA AVIATION TRAINING CREW ACADEMY GMBH—See Deutsche Lufthansa AG; *Int'l*, pg. 2068
LUFTHANSA AVIATION TRAINING GERMANY GMBH—See Deutsche Lufthansa AG; *Int'l*, pg. 2068
LUFTHANSA AVIATION TRAINING GMBH—See Deutsche Lufthansa AG; *Int'l*, pg. 2068
LUFTHANSA AVIATION TRAINING OPERATIONS GERMANY GMBH—See Deutsche Lufthansa AG; *Int'l*, pg. 2068
LUFTHANSA AVIATION TRAINING USA INC.—See Deutsche Lufthansa AG; *Int'l*, pg. 2068
LUFTHANSA BOMBARDIER AVIATION SERVICES GMBH—See Bombardier Inc.; *Int'l*, pg. 1104
LUFTHANSA CARGO AG—See Deutsche Lufthansa AG; *Int'l*, pg. 2068
LUFTHANSA CARGO INDIA (PRIV) LTD.—See Deutsche Lufthansa AG; *Int'l*, pg. 2068
LUFTHANSA CARGO—See Deutsche Lufthansa AG; *Int'l*, pg. 2068
LUFTHANSA CARGO—See Deutsche Lufthansa AG; *Int'l*, pg. 2068
LUFTHANSA CITY CENTER INTERNATIONAL GMBH—See Deutsche Lufthansa AG; *Int'l*, pg. 2068
LUFTHANSA CITYLINE GMBH—See Deutsche Lufthansa AG; *Int'l*, pg. 2068
LUFTHANSA COMMERCIAL HOLDING GMBH—See Deutsche Lufthansa AG; *Int'l*, pg. 2069
LUFTHANSA CONSULTING GMBH—See Deutsche Lufthansa AG; *Int'l*, pg. 2069
LUFTHANSA ENGINEERING AND OPERATIONAL SERVICES GMBH—See Deutsche Lufthansa AG; *Int'l*, pg. 2070
LUFTHANSA FLIGHT TRAINING VIENNA GMBH—See Deutsche Lufthansa AG; *Int'l*, pg. 2068
LUFTHANSA GERMAN AIRLINES—See Deutsche Lufthansa AG; *Int'l*, pg. 2068
LUFTHANSA GLOBAL TELE SALES GMBH—See Deutsche Lufthansa AG; *Int'l*, pg. 2069
LUFTHANSA INDUSTRY SOLUTIONS GMBH & CO. KG.—See Deutsche Lufthansa AG; *Int'l*, pg. 2069
LUFTHANSA INNOVATION HUB GMBH—See Deutsche Lufthansa AG; *Int'l*, pg. 2069
LUFTHANSA LEASING GMBH & CO. ECHO-ZULU OHG—See Deutsche Lufthansa AG; *Int'l*, pg. 2068
LUFTHANSA LEASING GMBH—See Commerzbank AG; *Int'l*, pg. 1718
LUFTHANSA LEASING GMBH—See Deutsche Lufthansa AG; *Int'l*, pg. 2069
LUFTHANSA MALTA PENSION HOLDING LTD.—See Deutsche Lufthansa AG; *Int'l*, pg. 2069
LUFTHANSA PROCESS MANAGEMENT GMBH—See Deutsche Lufthansa AG; *Int'l*, pg. 2069
LUFTHANSA SEEHEIM GMBH—See Deutsche Lufthansa AG; *Int'l*, pg. 2069
LUFTHANSA SERVICES (THAILAND) LTD.—See Deutsche Lufthansa AG; *Int'l*, pg. 2069
LUFTHANSA SHENZHEN MANAGEMENT COMPANY LIMITED—See Deutsche Lufthansa AG; *Int'l*, pg. 2069
LUFTHANSA SYSTEMS AG—See Deutsche Lufthansa AG; *Int'l*, pg. 2069
LUFTHANSA SYSTEMS AMERICAS, INC.—See Deutsche Lufthansa AG; *Int'l*, pg. 2069
LUFTHANSA SYSTEMS AS GMBH—See Deutsche Lufthansa AG; *Int'l*, pg. 2069
LUFTHANSA SYSTEMS ASIA PACIFIC PTE. LTD.—See Deutsche Lufthansa AG; *Int'l*, pg. 2069
LUFTHANSA SYSTEMS BERLIN GMBH—See Deutsche Lufthansa AG; *Int'l*, pg. 2069
LUFTHANSA SYSTEMS BUSINESS SOLUTIONS GMBH—See Deutsche Lufthansa AG; *Int'l*, pg. 2069
LUFTHANSA SYSTEMS FLIGHTNAV AG—See Deutsche Lufthansa AG; *Int'l*, pg. 2069
LUFTHANSA SYSTEMS HUNGARIA KFT—See Deutsche Lufthansa AG; *Int'l*, pg. 2069
LUFTHANSA SYSTEMS IS CONSULTING GMBH—See Deutsche Lufthansa AG; *Int'l*, pg. 2069
LUFTHANSA SYSTEMS NETWORK GMBH—See Deutsche Lufthansa AG; *Int'l*, pg. 2069
LUFTHANSA SYSTEMS NETWORK SERVICES GMBH—See Deutsche Lufthansa AG; *Int'l*, pg. 2069
LUFTHANSA SYSTEMS PASSENGER SERVICES GMBH—See Deutsche Lufthansa AG; *Int'l*, pg. 2069
LUFTHANSA SYSTEMS POLAND SP. Z O.O.—See Deutsche Lufthansa AG; *Int'l*, pg. 2069
LUFTHANSA TECHNICAL TRAINING GMBH—See Deutsche Lufthansa AG; *Int'l*, pg. 2069
LUFTHANSA TECHNIK AERO ALZEY GMBH—See Deutsche Lufthansa AG; *Int'l*, pg. 2070
LUFTHANSA TECHNIK AG—See Deutsche Lufthansa AG; *Int'l*, pg. 2069
LUFTHANSA TECHNIK AIRMOTIVE IRELAND HOLDINGS LTD.—See Deutsche Lufthansa AG; *Int'l*, pg. 2070
LUFTHANSA TECHNIK AIRMOTIVE IRELAND LEASING LTD—See Deutsche Lufthansa AG; *Int'l*, pg. 2070

COMPANY NAME INDEX

LUFTHANSA TECHNIK AIRMOTIVE IRELAND LTD.—See Deutsche Lufthansa AG; *Int'l*, pg. 2070
LUFTHANSA TECHNIK BRUSSELS N.V.—See Deutsche Lufthansa AG; *Int'l*, pg. 2070
LUFTHANSA TECHNIK COMPONENT SERVICES LLC—See Deutsche Lufthansa AG; *Int'l*, pg. 2070
LUFTHANSA TECHNIK IMMOBILIEN- UND VERWALTUNGSGESELLSCHAFT MBH—See Deutsche Lufthansa AG; *Int'l*, pg. 2070
LUFTHANSA TECHNIK LOGISTIK OF AMERICA LLC—See Deutsche Lufthansa AG; *Int'l*, pg. 2070
LUFTHANSA TECHNIK LOGISTIK SERVICES GMBH—See Deutsche Lufthansa AG; *Int'l*, pg. 2070
LUFTHANSA TECHNIK MAINTENANCE INTERNATIONAL GMBH—See Deutsche Lufthansa AG; *Int'l*, pg. 2070
LUFTHANSA TECHNIK OBJEKT- UND VERWALTUNGSGESELLSCHAFT MBH—See Deutsche Lufthansa AG; *Int'l*, pg. 2070
LUFTHANSA TECHNIK PHILIPPINES INC.—See Deutsche Lufthansa AG; *Int'l*, pg. 2070
LUFTHANSA TECHNIK PUERTO RICO LLC—See Deutsche Lufthansa AG; *Int'l*, pg. 2070
LUFTHANSA TECHNIK SERVICES INDIA PRIVATE LIMITED—See Deutsche Lufthansa AG; *Int'l*, pg. 2070
LUFTHANSA TECHNIK SWITZERLAND GMBH—See Deutsche Lufthansa AG; *Int'l*, pg. 2070
LUFTHANSA TECHNIK TURBINE SHANNON LIMITED—See Deutsche Lufthansa AG; *Int'l*, pg. 2070
LUFTHANSA TRAINING & CONFERENCE CENTER GMBH—See Deutsche Lufthansa AG; *Int'l*, pg. 2070
LUFTHANSA WORLDSHOP GMBH—See Deutsche Lufthansa AG; *Int'l*, pg. 2070
LUFT+KLIMAKONTOR GMBH—See Oy Halton Group Ltd.; *Int'l*, pg. 5677
LUFT- UND THERMOTECHNIK BAYREUTH GMBH—See Durr AG; *Int'l*, pg. 2233
LUGANO DIAMONDS & JEWELRY, INC.—See Compass Diversified Holdings; *U.S. Public*, pg. 560
LUGA SUMINISTROS MEDICOS, S.L.—See Prim S.A.; *Int'l*, pg. 5973
LU GENERAL BISCUITS BELGIE N.V.—See Mondelez International, Inc.; *U.S. Public*, pg. 1463
LU GENERAL BISCUITS NEDERLAND B.V.—See Mondelez International, Inc.; *U.S. Public*, pg. 1463
LUGER GESELLSCHAFT M.B.H.; *Int'l*, pg. 4575
LUGERINC AB—See Live Nation Entertainment, Inc.; *U.S. Public*, pg. 1330
LUGGAGE AMERICA INCORPORATED; *U.S. Private*, pg. 2512
LUGGAGE FORWARD, INC.; *U.S. Private*, pg. 2512
LU GIA MECHANICAL ELECTRIC JOINT STOCK COMPANY; *Int'l*, pg. 4571
LUGO HERMANOS S.A.—See THK CO., LTD.; *Int'l*, pg. 7712
LU HAI HOLDING CORP.; *Int'l*, pg. 4571
LUHAI INTELLIGENT TECHNOLOGY (KUNSHAN) CO., LTD.—See Lu Hai Holding Corp.; *Int'l*, pg. 4571
LUHARUKA MEDIA & INFRA LIMITED; *Int'l*, pg. 4575
LUHN-MCCAIN INSURANCE AGENCY, LTD.—See Southwest Bancshares, Inc.; *U.S. Private*, pg. 3738
LUHR BROS., INC.; *U.S. Private*, pg. 2512
LUHRING GMBH—See VINCI S.A.; *Int'l*, pg. 8223
LUHRSEN LAW GROUP, P.L.; *U.S. Private*, pg. 2512
LUIDIA, INC.; *U.S. Private*, pg. 2512
LUIDIA UK LTD.—See Luidia, Inc.; *U.S. Private*, pg. 2512
LUIGI LAVAZZA S.P.A.; *Int'l*, pg. 4575
LUIGI UGOLOTTI S.R.L.—See ALFA, S.A.B. de C.V.; *Int'l*, pg. 314
LUIHN FOOD SYSTEMS INC.; *U.S. Private*, pg. 2512
LUIRI GOLD LIMITED; *Int'l*, pg. 4575
LUIS A. AYALA COLON SUCRS INC.—See Albert Ballin KG; *Int'l*, pg. 297
LUIS A. AYALA COLON SUCRS. INC.; *U.S. Private*, pg. 2512
LUIS PALAU ASSOCIATION; *U.S. Private*, pg. 2512
LUITHAGEN NV—See Agfa-Gevaert N.V.; *Int'l*, pg. 209
LUITPOLDPARK-HOTEL BETRIEBS- UND VERMIETUNGSGESELLSCHAFT MBH—See Erste Group Bank AG; *Int'l*, pg. 2499
LUITPOLD PHARMACEUTICALS, INC. - NORRISTOWN OFFICE—See Daiichi Sankyo Co., Ltd.; *Int'l*, pg. 1930
LUIV AMARO—See Lectra SA; *Int'l*, pg. 4438
LUJIAZUI INTERNATIONAL TRUST COMPANY—See Shanghai Lujiazui Finance & Trade Zone Development; *Int'l*, pg. 6774
LUKA BACKA PALANKA D.O.O.—See Victoria Group a.d.; *Int'l*, pg. 8188
LUKA BEOGRAD A.D.; *Int'l*, pg. 4576
LUKA DUNAV A.D.; *Int'l*, pg. 4576
LUK-AFTERMARKET SERVICES, LLC—See INA-Holding Schaeffler GmbH & Co. KG; *Int'l*, pg. 3640
LUKA KOPER D.D.; *Int'l*, pg. 4576
LUKA KOPER INPO D.O.O.—See Luka Koper d.d.; *Int'l*, pg. 4576
LUKA KOPER PRISTAN, D.O.O.—See Luka Koper d.d.; *Int'l*, pg. 4576
LUKA PLOCE D.D.; *Int'l*, pg. 4576
LUKA PRIVEZ - ODVEZ D.O.O.—See Luka Rijeka d.d.; *Int'l*, pg. 4576

LUKA RIJEKA D.D.; *Int'l*, pg. 4576
LUKA SENTA A.D.; *Int'l*, pg. 4576
LUKAS HYDRAULIK GMBH—See IDEX Corp; *U.S. Public*, pg. 1091
LUKA SPED D.O.O.—See Luka Ploce d.d.; *Int'l*, pg. 4576
LUKATIT INVESTMENTS 14 (PTY) LTD.—See Sonova Holding AG; *Int'l*, pg. 7100
LUKA TRANZIT OSIJEK D.O.O.—See Nexe Grupa d.d.; *Int'l*, pg. 5243
LUK CLUTCH SYSTEMS, LLC—See INA-Holding Schaeffler GmbH & Co. KG; *Int'l*, pg. 3640
LUK CRISIS CENTER, INC.; *U.S. Private*, pg. 2512
LUKE & ASSOCIATES, INC.; *U.S. Private*, pg. 2512
LUKE BARNETT LIMITED—See The British United Provident Association Limited; *Int'l*, pg. 7629
LUKE BROTHERS, INC.; *U.S. Private*, pg. 2513
LUKE REIT; *Int'l*, pg. 4576
LUK FOOK HOLDINGS (INTERNATIONAL) LIMITED; *Int'l*, pg. 4575
LUK FOOK JEWELLERY & GOLDSMITH (HK) COMPANY LIMITED—See Luk Fook Holdings (International) Limited; *Int'l*, pg. 4576
LUK FOOK JEWELLERY & GOLDSMITH (MACAO) COMPANY LIMITED—See Luk Fook Holdings (International) Limited; *Int'l*, pg. 4576
LUK GMBH & CO. OHG—See INA-Holding Schaeffler GmbH & Co. KG; *Int'l*, pg. 3640
LUK HING ENTERTAINMENT GROUP HOLDINGS LIMITED; *Int'l*, pg. 4576
LUK HOP GARMENTS LIMITED—See YGM Trading Ltd; *Int'l*, pg. 8580
LUKIE GAMES INC.; *U.S. Private*, pg. 2513
LUK, INC.; *U.S. Private*, pg. 2512
LUK INDIA PRIVATE LIMITED—See INA-Holding Schaeffler GmbH & Co. KG; *Int'l*, pg. 3640
LUKOIL ACCOUNTING & FINANCE EUROPE S.R.O.—See PJSC Lukoil; *Int'l*, pg. 5881
LUKOIL AMERICAS HOLDING LIMITED—See PJSC Lukoil; *Int'l*, pg. 5882
LUKOIL AMERICAS LLC—See PJSC Lukoil; *Int'l*, pg. 5882
LUKOIL ASIA PACIFIC PTE LTD.—See PJSC Lukoil; *Int'l*, pg. 5881
LUKOIL AVIATION BULGARIA EOOD—See PJSC Lukoil; *Int'l*, pg. 5882
LUKOIL BELORUSSIA FLLC—See PJSC Lukoil; *Int'l*, pg. 5882
LUKOIL BENELUX B.V.—See PJSC Lukoil; *Int'l*, pg. 5881
LUKOIL-BULGARIA EOOD—See PJSC Lukoil; *Int'l*, pg. 5881
LUKOIL HAMBURG GMBH—See PJSC Lukoil; *Int'l*, pg. 5881
LUKOIL INFORM COMPANY—See PJSC Rostelecom; *Int'l*, pg. 5884
LUKOIL INTERNATIONAL UPSTREAM WEST INC.—See PJSC Lukoil; *Int'l*, pg. 5882
LUKOIL ITALIA S.R.L.—See PJSC Lukoil; *Int'l*, pg. 5881
LUKOIL LUBRICANTS CENTRAL ASIA LLP—See PJSC Lukoil; *Int'l*, pg. 5882
LUKOIL LUBRICANTS EAST EUROPE S.R.L.—See PJSC Lukoil; *Int'l*, pg. 5882
LUKOIL LUBRICANTS MEXICO S.DE R.L.DE C.V.—See PJSC Lukoil; *Int'l*, pg. 5881
LUKOIL LUBRICANTS MIDDLE EAST MADENI YAG SANAYI VE TICARET LIMITED SIRKETI—See PJSC Lukoil; *Int'l*, pg. 5881
LUKOIL MACEDONIA LTD.—See PJSC Lukoil; *Int'l*, pg. 5882
LUKOIL MARINE LUBRICANTS DMCC—See PJSC Lukoil; *Int'l*, pg. 5882
LUKOIL MARINE LUBRICANTS GERMANY GMBH—See PJSC Lukoil; *Int'l*, pg. 5882
LUKOIL MARINE LUBRICANTS USA INC.—See PJSC Lukoil; *Int'l*, pg. 5882
LUKOIL MID-EAST LIMITED—See PJSC Lukoil; *Int'l*, pg. 5881
LUKOIL-MOLDOVA S.R.L.—See PJSC Lukoil; *Int'l*, pg. 5882
LUKOIL MONTENEGRO DOO—See PJSC Lukoil; *Int'l*, pg. 5882
LUKOIL NEFTOCHIM BURGAS AD—See PJSC Lukoil; *Int'l*, pg. 5882
LUKOIL - NIZHNEVOLZHSKNEFT OOO—See PJSC Lukoil; *Int'l*, pg. 5882
LUKOIL OVERSEAS CYPRUS LIMITED—See PJSC Lukoil; *Int'l*, pg. 5881
LUKOIL - PERMNEFTEORGSINTEZ OOO—See PJSC Lukoil; *Int'l*, pg. 5881
LUKOIL - PERM OOO—See PJSC Lukoil; *Int'l*, pg. 5881
LUKOIL ROMANIA S.R.L.—See PJSC Lukoil; *Int'l*, pg. 5882
LUKOIL SRBIJA A.D.; *Int'l*, pg. 4576
LUKOIL TECHNOLOGY SERVICES GMBH—See PJSC Lukoil; *Int'l*, pg. 5881
LUKOM A.D.; *Int'l*, pg. 4576
LUKOPLAST SPOL.S R.O.—See L&K GmbH; *Int'l*, pg. 4369
LUKOS SA; *Int'l*, pg. 4576
LUK PUEBLA, S. DE R.L. DE C.V.—See INA-Holding Schaeffler GmbH & Co. KG; *Int'l*, pg. 3640

LUMBER KING INC.

LUKRECIJA BBDO—See Omnicom Group Inc.; *U.S. Public*, pg. 1576
LUK SAVARIA KFT.—See INA-Holding Schaeffler GmbH & Co. KG; *Int'l*, pg. 3640
LUKS CEMENT (VIETNAM) LIMITED—See LUKS GROUP (Vietnam Holdings) Company Limited; *Int'l*, pg. 4576
LUKS GROUP (VIETNAM HOLDINGS) COMPANY LIMITED; *Int'l*, pg. 4576
LUKS INDUSTRIAL COMPANY LIMITED—See LUKS GROUP (Vietnam Holdings) Company Limited; *Int'l*, pg. 4576
LUKS KADIFE TICARET VE SANAYII A.S.; *Int'l*, pg. 4576
LUKTA POLSKA SP. Z O.O—See AGRANA Beteiligungs-AG; *Int'l*, pg. 214
LUKTA POLSKA SP. Z O.O—See BayWa AG; *Int'l*, pg. 919
LUK (UK) LIMITED—See INA-Holding Schaeffler GmbH & Co. KG; *Int'l*, pg. 3640
LUK UNNA GMBH & CO. KG—See INA-Holding Schaeffler GmbH & Co. KG; *Int'l*, pg. 3639
LUK USA LLC—See INA-Holding Schaeffler GmbH & Co. KG; *Int'l*, pg. 3640
LULA-WESTFIELD LLC; *U.S. Private*, pg. 2513
LULU INC.; *U.S. Private*, pg. 2513
LULULEMON AHLETICA AUSTRALIA HOLDINGS PTY LTD—See lululemon athletica inc.; *Int'l*, pg. 4577
LULULEMON ATHLETICA CANADA INC.—See lululemon athletica inc.; *Int'l*, pg. 4577
LULULEMON ATHLETICA CH GMBH—See lululemon athletica inc.; *Int'l*, pg. 4577
LULULEMON ATHLETICA INC.; *Int'l*, pg. 4577
LULULEMON ATHLETICA NL BV—See lululemon athletica inc.; *Int'l*, pg. 4577
LULULEMON HONG KONG LIMITED—See lululemon athletica inc.; *Int'l*, pg. 4577
LULULEMON USA INC.—See lululemon athletica inc.; *Int'l*, pg. 4577
LULUMCO INC.; *Int'l*, pg. 4577
LULU'S FASHION LOUNGE HOLDINGS, INC.; *U.S. Public*, pg. 1345
LULU'S; *U.S. Private*, pg. 2513
LULUTRIP INC.—See Woqu.com; *Int'l*, pg. 8455
LUMA INVESTMENTS, LTD.; *Int'l*, pg. 4577
LUMANITY, INC.—See Arsenal Capital Management LP; *U.S. Private*, pg. 338
LUMARA HEALTH INC.—See AMAG Pharmaceuticals, Inc.; *U.S. Private*, pg. 215
LUMARA HEALTH SERVICES LTD.—See AMAG Pharmaceuticals, Inc.; *U.S. Private*, pg. 215
LUMASENSE EQUIPMENT INDIA PVT. LTD. CO.—See Advanced Energy Industries, Inc.; *U.S. Public*, pg. 47
LUMASENSE SENSOR GMBH—See Advanced Energy Industries, Inc.; *U.S. Public*, pg. 47
LUMASENSE TECHNOLOGIES A/S—See Advanced Energy Industries, Inc.; *U.S. Public*, pg. 47
LUMASENSE TECHNOLOGIES BENELUX B.V.—See Advanced Energy Industries, Inc.; *U.S. Public*, pg. 47
LUMASENSE TECHNOLOGIES EUROPE GMBH—See Advanced Energy Industries, Inc.; *U.S. Public*, pg. 47
LUMASENSE TECHNOLOGIES GMBH MERKEZI—See Advanced Energy Industries, Inc.; *U.S. Public*, pg. 47
LUMASENSE TECHNOLOGIES GMBH—See Advanced Energy Industries, Inc.; *U.S. Public*, pg. 47
LUMASENSE TECHNOLOGIES, INC.—See Advanced Energy Industries, Inc.; *U.S. Public*, pg. 47
LUMASENSE TECHNOLOGIES LIMITED—See Advanced Energy Industries, Inc.; *U.S. Public*, pg. 47
LUMASENSE TECHNOLOGIES SARL—See Advanced Energy Industries, Inc.; *U.S. Public*, pg. 47
LUMASENSE, VENDAS BRASIL—See Advanced Energy Industries, Inc.; *U.S. Public*, pg. 47
LUMAS REALTY, INC.; *U.S. Private*, pg. 2513
LUMASTREAM, INC.; *U.S. Private*, pg. 2513
LUMATA AUSTRALASIA PTY. LTD.—See Francisco Partners Management, LP; *U.S. Public*, pg. 1590
LUMATA HOLDINGS LIMITED—See Francisco Partners Management, LP; *U.S. Public*, pg. 1590
LUMATA ITALIA S.R.L.—See Francisco Partners Management, LP; *U.S. Public*, pg. 1590
LUMATA NETHERLANDS B.V.—See Francisco Partners Management, LP; *U.S. Public*, pg. 1590
LUMATA UK LIMITED—See CCUR Holdings Inc.; *U.S. Public*, pg. 461
LUMAX AUTO TECHNOLOGIES LTD.; *Int'l*, pg. 4577
LUMAX INDUSTRIES LTD; *Int'l*, pg. 4577
LUMAX INTERNATIONAL CORP., LTD.; *Int'l*, pg. 4577
LUMAX INTERNATIONAL (SHANGHAI) CO., LTD.—See Lumax International Corp., Ltd.; *Int'l*, pg. 4577
LUMAX TRADING (XIAMEN) LIMITED—See Lumax International Corp., Ltd.; *Int'l*, pg. 4577
LUMBEE GUARANTY BANK; *U.S. Public*, pg. 1345
LUMBEE RIVER ELECTRIC MEMBERSHIP CORP.; *U.S. Private*, pg. 2513
LUMBER GROUP INC.; *U.S. Private*, pg. 2513
LUMBER INSURANCE CO.; *U.S. Private*, pg. 2513
LUMBER INVESTORS LLC; *U.S. Private*, pg. 2513
LUMBERJACK BUILDING CENTERS—See Tyndale Advisors, LLC; *U.S. Private*, pg. 4268
LUMBERJACK'S, INC.; *U.S. Private*, pg. 2513
LUMBER KING INC.; *U.S. Private*, pg. 2513

LUMBER LIQUIDATORS SERVICES, LLC—See LL Flooring Holdings, Inc.; *U.S. Public*, pg. 1337
LUMBER MART INC.; *U.S. Private*, pg. 2513
LUMBERMEN'S BRICK & SUPPLY CO.; *U.S. Private*, pg. 2513
LUMBERMEN'S CREDIT ASSOCIATION OF BROWARD COUNTY INC.; *U.S. Private*, pg. 2513
LUMBERMEN'S INC.; *U.S. Private*, pg. 2513
LUMBERMENS MERCHANDISING CORPORATION; *U.S. Private*, pg. 2514
LUMBERMEN'S MUTUAL CASUALTY COMPANY—See Lumbermens Mutual Group; *U.S. Private*, pg. 2514
LUMBERMENS MUTUAL GROUP; *U.S. Private*, pg. 2514
LUMBERMEN'S UNDERWRITING ALLIANCE; *U.S. Private*, pg. 2513
LUMBER SPECIALTIES LTD.; *U.S. Private*, pg. 2513
LUMBER TECHNOLOGY CORPORATION; *U.S. Private*, pg. 2513
LUMBERYARD SUPPLIERS INC.; *U.S. Private*, pg. 2514
LUM CHANG BUILDING CONTRACTORS PTE LTD—See Lum Chang Holdings Limited; *Int'l*, pg. 4577
LUM CHANG HOLDINGS LIMITED; *Int'l*, pg. 4577
LUMEDX CORP.—See HgCapital Trust plc; *Int'l*, pg. 3376
LUMEDYNE TECHNOLOGIES INCORPORATED—See Alphabet Inc.; *U.S. Public*, pg. 83
LUMENAD INC.; *U.S. Private*, pg. 2514
LUMENA PHARMACEUTICALS, LLC—See Takeda Pharmaceutical Company Limited; *Int'l*, pg. 7438
LUMENATE.COM; *U.S. Private*, pg. 2514
LUMENDATA, INC.—See LumenData, Inc.; *U.S. Private*, pg. 2514
LUMENDATA, INC.; *U.S. Private*, pg. 2514
LUMENE NORTH AMERICA LLC—See Langholm Capital LLP; *Int'l*, pg. 4409
LUMENE OY—See Langholm Capital LLP; *Int'l*, pg. 4409
LUMENERA CORPORATION—See Teledyne Technologies Incorporated; *U.S. Public*, pg. 1992
LUMENERGIA S.P.A.—See A2A S.p.A.; *Int'l*, pg. 29
LUMENE RUSSIA—See Langholm Capital LLP; *Int'l*, pg. 4409
LUMENETIX, INC.—See Angeles Equity Partners, LLC; *U.S. Private*, pg. 282
LUMEN GMBH—See IREKS GmbH; *Int'l*, pg. 3806
LUMENIS (FRANCE) SARL—See Boston Scientific Corporation; *U.S. Public*, pg. 375
LUMENIS (GERMANY) GMBH—See Boston Scientific Corporation; *U.S. Public*, pg. 375
LUMENIS (HK) LIMITED—See Boston Scientific Corporation; *U.S. Public*, pg. 375
LUMENIS HOLDINGS (HOLLAND) B.V.—See Boston Scientific Corporation; *U.S. Public*, pg. 375
LUMENIS INDIA PRIVATE LTD—See Boston Scientific Corporation; *U.S. Public*, pg. 375
LUMENIS (ITALY) SRL—See Boston Scientific Corporation; *U.S. Public*, pg. 375
LUMENIS JAPAN CO. LTD.—See Boston Scientific Corporation; *U.S. Public*, pg. 375
LUMENIS LTD.—See Boston Scientific Corporation; *U.S. Public*, pg. 375
LUMENIS—See Boston Scientific Corporation; *U.S. Public*, pg. 375
LUMENIS (UK), LTD.—See Boston Scientific Corporation; *U.S. Public*, pg. 375
LUMENLAB MALAYSIA SDN. BHD.—See MetLife, Inc.; *U.S. Public*, pg. 1430
LUMENOS—See Elevance Health, Inc.; *U.S. Public*, pg. 730
LUMENPUIES GROUP INC.—See Power Corporation of Canada; *Int'l*, pg. 5943
LUMENPULSE INC.—See Power Corporation of Canada; *Int'l*, pg. 5943
LUMENRADIO AB; *Int'l*, pg. 4577
LUMENS CO., LTD.; *Int'l*, pg. 4577
LUMENS INTEGRATION INC.—See Pegatron Corporation; *Int'l*, pg. 5781
LUMEN—See Sonepar S.A.; *Int'l*, pg. 7091
LUMEN TECHNOLOGIES EUROPE LIMITED—See Lumen Technologies, Inc.; *U.S. Public*, pg. 1347
LUMEN TECHNOLOGIES GERMANY GMBH—See Lumen Technologies, Inc.; *U.S. Public*, pg. 1347
LUMEN TECHNOLOGIES, INC.; *U.S. Public*, pg. 1345
LUMEN TECHNOLOGIES POLAND SP. Z O.O.—See Lumen Technologies, Inc.; *U.S. Public*, pg. 1347
LUMEN TECHNOLOGIES SWITZERLAND AG—See Lumen Technologies, Inc.; *U.S. Public*, pg. 1347
LUMEN TECHNOLOGIES UK LIMITED—See Lumen Technologies, Inc.; *U.S. Public*, pg. 1347
LUMENT FINANCE TRUST, INC.; *U.S. Public*, pg. 1348
LUMENTUM HOLDINGS INC; *U.S. Public*, pg. 1348
LUMENTUM INTERNATIONAL (THAILAND) CO., LTD.—See Lumentum Holdings Inc.; *U.S. Public*, pg. 1348
LUMENTUM OPERATIONS LLC—See Lumentum Holdings Inc.; *U.S. Public*, pg. 1348
LUMENTUM SWITZERLAND AG—See Lumentum Holdings Inc.; *U.S. Public*, pg. 1348
LUMENTUM TAIWAN CO., LTD.—See Lumentum Holdings Inc.; *U.S. Public*, pg. 1348

LUMESIS, INC.—See Solve Advisors Inc.; *U.S. Private*, pg. 3711
LUMESSE, INC.—See Clearlake Capital Group, L.P.; *U.S. Private*, pg. 934
LUMESSE LIMITED—See Clearlake Capital Group, L.P.; *U.S. Private*, pg. 934
LUMETA CORP.—See Insight Venture Management, LLC; *U.S. Private*, pg. 2090
LUMETRICS, INC.; *U.S. Private*, pg. 2514
LUMEX, INC.—See Illinois Tool Works Inc.; *U.S. Public*, pg. 1109
LUMEX LIGHTING LTD.—See A.A.G. STUCCHI s.r.l.; *Int'l*, pg. 23
LUMEX LTD.; *Int'l*, pg. 4578
LUMIBIRD GMBH—See Lumibird Group; *Int'l*, pg. 4578
LUMIBIRD GROUP; *Int'l*, pg. 4578
LUMIBIRD JAPAN CO., LTD.—See Lumibird Group; *Int'l*, pg. 4578
LUMIBIRD LTD.—See Lumibird Group; *Int'l*, pg. 4578
LUMICAN, S.A.—See ACS, Actividades de Construccion y Servicios, S.A.; *Int'l*, pg. 115
LUMICERA HEALTH SERVICES LLC—See SSM Health Care Corporation; *U.S. Private*, pg. 3769
LUMICO LIFE INSURANCE COMPANY—See Swiss Re Ltd.; *Int'l*, pg. 7371
LUMIERA HEALTH INC.; *Int'l*, pg. 4578
LUMIERE CHILDREN'S THERAPY, INC.; *U.S. Private*, pg. 2514
LUMIERE IMAGING FRANCE SAS—See Ilford Imaging Switzerland GmbH; *Int'l*, pg. 3614
LUMIFICIENT CORPORATION—See Revolution Lighting Technologies, Inc.; *U.S. Public*, pg. 1793
LUMIFY LEARN PTY. LTD.—See AWN Holdings Limited; *Int'l*, pg. 753
LUMIGEN, INC—See Danaher Corporation; *U.S. Public*, pg. 625
LUMI GLASS INDUSTRIES LLC—See Dubai Investments PJSC; *Int'l*, pg. 2219
LUMI GRUPPEN AS; *Int'l*, pg. 4578
LUMIKKO TECHNOLOGIES OY—See BITZER SE; *Int'l*, pg. 1052
LUMILEDS LLC—See Apollo Global Management, Inc.; *U.S. Public*, pg. 153
LUMILEDS NETHERLANDS B.V.—See Apollo Global Management, Inc.; *U.S. Public*, pg. 153
LUMINA DATAMATICS, INC.—See Datamatics Global Services Ltd.; *Int'l*, pg. 1979
LUMINA DATAMATICS LIMITED—See Datamatics Global Services Ltd.; *Int'l*, pg. 1979
LUMINA FOUNDATION FOR EDUCATION; *U.S. Private*, pg. 2514
LUMINA GOLD CORP.; *Int'l*, pg. 4578
LUMINA GROUP LIMITED; *Int'l*, pg. 4578
LUMINAIRE METAL UNION SAS—See Sonepar S.A.; *Int'l*, pg. 7091
LUMINANT ENERGY COMPANY, LLC—See Vistra Corp.; *U.S. Public*, pg. 2306
LUMINA POWER, INC.—See HEICO Corporation; *U.S. Public*, pg. 1020
LUMINAR DANCING SCOTLAND LTD.—See Luminar Group Holdings Plc; *Int'l*, pg. 4578
LUMINAR GROUP HOLDINGS PLC; *Int'l*, pg. 4578
LUMINAR LEISURE LIMITED—See Luminar Group Holdings Plc; *Int'l*, pg. 4578
LUMINAR MEDIA GROUP, INC.; *Int'l*, pg. 4578
LUMINAR—See Luminar Group Holdings Plc; *Int'l*, pg. 4578
LUMINAR TECHNOLOGIES, INC.; *U.S. Public*, pg. 1348
LUMINATE CAPITAL MANAGEMENT, INC.; *U.S. Private*, pg. 2514
LUMINATOR HOLDING LP—See Audax Group, Limited Partnership; *U.S. Private*, pg. 389
LUMINE GROUP INC.—See Constellation Software Inc.; *Int'l*, pg. 1773
LUMINESCENT SYSTEMS CANADA, INC.—See Astronics Corporation; *U.S. Public*, pg. 217
LUMINESCENT SYSTEMS, INC.—See Astronics Corporation; *U.S. Public*, pg. 217
LUMINEX (AUSTRALIA) PTY. LTD—See DiaSorin S.p.A.; *Int'l*, pg. 2106
LUMINEX BV—See DiaSorin S.p.A.; *Int'l*, pg. 2106
LUMINEX CORPORATION—See DiaSorin S.p.A.; *Int'l*, pg. 2106
LUMINEX MOLECULAR DIAGNOSTICS—See DiaSorin S.p.A.; *Int'l*, pg. 2106
LUMINEX RESOURCES CORP.—See Silvercorp Metals Inc.; *Int'l*, pg. 6925
LUMINO CARE DENTAL—See BGH Capital Pty Ltd; *Int'l*, pg. 1008
LUMINO CARE DENTAL—See Ontario Teachers' Pension Plan; *Int'l*, pg. 5586
LUMINO DENTAL LIMITED—See BGH Capital Pty Ltd; *Int'l*, pg. 1008
LUMINO DENTAL LIMITED—See Ontario Teachers' Pension Plan; *Int'l*, pg. 5586
LUMINOR FINANCIAL HOLDINGS LIMITED—See GRP Limited; *Int'l*, pg. 3113
LUMINOUS POWER TECHNOLOGIES PRIVATE LTD—See Schneider Electric SE; *Int'l*, pg. 6628

LUMINOUS TOWN ELECTRIC CO., LTD. - DONG GUAN FACTORY—See Man Yue Technology Holdings Limited; *Int'l*, pg. 4665
LUMINOUS TOWN ELECTRIC CO., LTD. - KUNSHAN FACTORY—See Man Yue Technology Holdings Limited; *Int'l*, pg. 4665
LUMINOUS TOWN ELECTRIC CO., LTD.—See Man Yue Technology Holdings Limited; *Int'l*, pg. 4665
LUMINOX PTE. LTD.—See LifeBrandz Ltd.; *Int'l*, pg. 4494
LUMINUS MANAGEMENT, LLC; *U.S. Private*, pg. 2514
LUMINUS SYSTEMS LIMITED; *Int'l*, pg. 4579
LUMIN WEALTH LIMITED—See VZ Holding AG; *Int'l*, pg. 8319
LUMIN WEALTH MANAGEMENT LIMITED—See VZ Holding AG; *Int'l*, pg. 8319
LUMIOTEC INC.—See V-Technology Co., Ltd.; *Int'l*, pg. 8105
LUMIPAPER LTD—See Stora Enso Oyj; *Int'l*, pg. 7224
LUMIPAPER N.V.—See Stora Enso Oyj; *Int'l*, pg. 7223
LUMIRA CAPITAL CORP.; *Int'l*, pg. 4579
LUMIRADX LIMITED; *Int'l*, pg. 4579
LUMI RENTAL COMPANY; *Int'l*, pg. 4578
LUMITEC LLC—See Genstar Capital, LLC; *U.S. Private*, pg. 1676
LUMITEX INC.; *U.S. Private*, pg. 2514
LUMITHERA, INC.; *U.S. Private*, pg. 2514
LUMITRON INC—See Fortive Corporation; *U.S. Public*, pg. 870
LUMLEY GENERAL INSURANCE (NZ) LIMITED—See Insurance Australia Group Limited; *Int'l*, pg. 3725
LUMLEY INSURANCE GROUP LIMITED—See Insurance Australia Group Limited; *Int'l*, pg. 3725
LUMMUS AUSTRALIA PTY. LTD.—See Lummus Corporation; *U.S. Private*, pg. 2514
LUMMUS CORPORATION; *U.S. Private*, pg. 2514
LUMMUS DO BRASIL LTDA.—See Lummus Corporation; *U.S. Private*, pg. 2514
LUMMUS NOVOLEN TECHNOLOGY GMBH—See McDermott International, Inc.; *U.S. Public*, pg. 1405
LUMMUS SUPPLY COMPANY INC.; *U.S. Private*, pg. 2514
LUMMUS TECHNOLOGY HEAT TRANSFER B.V.—See McDermott International, Inc.; *U.S. Public*, pg. 1405
LUMMUS TECHNOLOGY - HEAT TRANSFER—See McDermott International, Inc.; *U.S. Public*, pg. 1405
LUMMUS TECHNOLOGY, INC.—See McDermott International, Inc.; *U.S. Public*, pg. 1405
LUMO ENERGIA OJY—See Genie Energy Ltd.; *U.S. Public*, pg. 931
LUMONICS K. K.—See Kanematsu Corporation; *Int'l*, pg. 4069
LUMOSA THERAPEUTICS CO., LTD.; *Int'l*, pg. 4579
LUMOS DIAGNOSTICS HOLDINGS LIMITED; *Int'l*, pg. 4579
LUMOS DIAGNOSTICS, INC.—See Lumos Diagnostics Holdings Limited; *Int'l*, pg. 4579
LUMOS LABS—See Warner Bros. Discovery, Inc.; *U.S. Public*, pg. 2327
LUMOS NETWORKS CORP.—See EQT AB; *Int'l*, pg. 2480
LUMOS NETWORKS INC.—See EQT AB; *Int'l*, pg. 2480
LUMOS NETWORKS OPERATING COMPANY—See EQT AB; *Int'l*, pg. 2480
LUMOS PHARMA, INC.; *U.S. Public*, pg. 1348
LUMOTECH (PTY) LTD.—See Metair Investments Limited; *Int'l*, pg. 4844
LUMPHUN SHINDENGEN CO., LTD.—See Shindengen Electric Manufacturing Co., Ltd.; *Int'l*, pg. 6842
LUMPI-BERNDORF DRAHT- UND SEILWERK GMBH—See Berndorf AG; *Int'l*, pg. 987
LUM'S AUTO CENTER INC.; *U.S. Private*, pg. 2513
LUMUT MARITIME TERMINAL SDN. BHD.—See Perak Corporation Berhad; *Int'l*, pg. 5796
LUMUT PARK RESORT SDN. BHD.—See Johan Holdings Berhad; *Int'l*, pg. 3977
LUMX GROUP LIMITED; *Int'l*, pg. 4579
LUNA AB—See Bergman & Beving AB; *Int'l*, pg. 980
LUNA CARPET & BLINDS CO., INC.; *U.S. Private*, pg. 2515
THE LUNADA BAY CORPORATION; *U.S. Private*, pg. 4073
LUNA DATA SOLUTIONS, INC.; *U.S. Private*, pg. 2515
LUNA INNOVATIONS INCORPORATED; *U.S. Public*, pg. 1348
LUNAN CORPORATION; *U.S. Private*, pg. 2515
LUNAR BBDO—See Omnicom Group Inc.; *U.S. Public*, pg. 1576
LUNAR CAPITAL MANAGEMENT LTD.; *Int'l*, pg. 4579
LUNARDI'S SUPER MARKET INC.; *U.S. Private*, pg. 2515
LUNAR INVESTMENT, LLC—See Enpro Inc.; *U.S. Public*, pg. 775
LUNARLINE, INC.; *U.S. Private*, pg. 2515
LUNARPAGES INTERNET SOLUTIONS; *U.S. Private*, pg. 2515
LUNA SERVICE S.R.L.—See Gruppo MutuiOnline S.p.A.; *Int'l*, pg. 3141
LUNA TBWA BELGRADE—See Omnicom Group Inc.; *U.S. Public*, pg. 1594

COMPANY NAME INDEX

LUNA TBWA SARAJEVO—See Omnicom Group Inc.; *U.S. Public*, pg. 1594
LUNA TBWA—See Omnicom Group Inc.; *U.S. Public*, pg. 1594
LUNA TECHNOLOGIES, INC.—See Luna Innovations Incorporated; *U.S. Public*, pg. 1348
LUNA TEXTILES—See Camira Fabrics Ltd.; *Int'l*, pg. 1273
LUNCARTY CARE HOME—See Balhousie Holdings Limited; *Int'l*, pg. 808
LUNCH COMMUNICATIONS LIMITED—See Enero Group Limited; *Int'l*, pg. 2424
LUNCHEON TICKETS S.A.—See Sodexo S.A.; *Int'l*, pg. 7045
LUNDA CONSTRUCTION COMPANY—See Tutor Perini Corporation; *U.S. Public*, pg. 2206
LUNDAHL BUILDING SYSTEMS, INC.; *U.S. Private*, pg. 2515
LUNDALOGIK AB—See Ratos AB; *Int'l*, pg. 6217
LUNDALOGIK AS—See Ratos AB; *Int'l*, pg. 6217
LUNDALOGIK FINLAND OY—See Ratos AB; *Int'l*, pg. 6217
LUNDBECK AMERICA CENTRAL S.A.—See Lundbeckfonden; *Int'l*, pg. 4581
LUNDBECK ARGENTINA S.A.—See Lundbeckfonden; *Int'l*, pg. 4581
LUNDBECK AUSTRALIA PTY LTD.—See Lundbeckfonden; *Int'l*, pg. 4581
LUNDBECK AUSTRIA GMBH—See Lundbeckfonden; *Int'l*, pg. 4581
LUNDBECK (BEIJING) PHARMACEUTICALS CONSULTING CO., LTD.—See Lundbeckfonden; *Int'l*, pg. 4581
LUNDBECK BRASIL LTDA.—See Lundbeckfonden; *Int'l*, pg. 4581
LUNDBECK BUSINESS SERVICE CENTRE SP.Z.O.O—See Lundbeckfonden; *Int'l*, pg. 4581
LUNDBECK B.V.—See Lundbeckfonden; *Int'l*, pg. 4581
LUNDBECK CANADA, INC.—See Lundbeckfonden; *Int'l*, pg. 4581
LUNDBECK CHILE FARMACEUTICA LTDA.—See Lundbeckfonden; *Int'l*, pg. 4581
LUNDBECK CROATIA LTD.—See Lundbeckfonden; *Int'l*, pg. 4581
LUNDBECK CZECH REPUBLIC S.R.O.—See Lundbeckfonden; *Int'l*, pg. 4581
LUNDBECK DE VENEZUELA, C.A.—See Lundbeckfonden; *Int'l*, pg. 4582
LUNDBECK EESTI A/S—See Lundbeckfonden; *Int'l*, pg. 4581
LUNDBECK ESPANA S.A.—See Lundbeckfonden; *Int'l*, pg. 4581
LUNDBECK EXPORT A/S-CENTRAL EUROPEAN REGIONAL OFFICE—See Lundbeckfonden; *Int'l*, pg. 4581
LUNDBECK EXPORT A/S—See Lundbeckfonden; *Int'l*, pg. 4581
LUNDBECK EXPORT A/S—See Lundbeckfonden; *Int'l*, pg. 4581
LUNDBECK EXPORT A/S—See Lundbeckfonden; *Int'l*, pg. 4581
LUNDBECK EXPORT A/S—See Lundbeckfonden; *Int'l*, pg. 4581
LUNDBECK EXPORT A/S-SOUTHERN EUROPE REGIONAL OFFICE—See Lundbeckfonden; *Int'l*, pg. 4581
LUNDBECKFONDEN; *Int'l*, pg. 4579
LUNDBECKFOND INVEST A/S—See Lundbeckfonden; *Int'l*, pg. 4579
LUNDBECK GMBH—See Lundbeckfonden; *Int'l*, pg. 4581
LUNDBECK GROUP LIMITED (HOLDING COMPANY)—See Lundbeckfonden; *Int'l*, pg. 4581
LUNDBECK HELLAS S.A.—See Lundbeckfonden; *Int'l*, pg. 4581
LUNDBECK HONG KONG—See Lundbeckfonden; *Int'l*, pg. 4581
LUNDBECK HUNGARIA KFT.—See Lundbeckfonden; *Int'l*, pg. 4581
LUNDBECK ILAC TICARET LIMITED SIRKETI—See Lundbeckfonden; *Int'l*, pg. 4581
LUNDBECK INDIA PRIVATE LIMITED—See Lundbeckfonden; *Int'l*, pg. 4581
LUNDBECK IRAN—See Lundbeckfonden; *Int'l*, pg. 4581
LUNDBECK (IRELAND) LIMITED—See Lundbeckfonden; *Int'l*, pg. 4581
LUNDBECK ISRAEL LTD.—See Lundbeckfonden; *Int'l*, pg. 4581
LUNDBECK ITALIA S.P.A.—See Lundbeckfonden; *Int'l*, pg. 4582
LUNDBECK JAPAN KABUSHIKI KAISHA—See Lundbeckfonden; *Int'l*, pg. 4582
LUNDBECK KOREA CO., LTD.—See Lundbeckfonden; *Int'l*, pg. 4582
LUNDBECK LIMITED—See Lundbeckfonden; *Int'l*, pg. 4582
LUNDBECK, LLC—See Lundbeckfonden; *Int'l*, pg. 4582
LUNDBECK MALAYSIA—See Lundbeckfonden; *Int'l*, pg. 4582
LUNDBECK MEXICO SA DE CV—See Lundbeckfonden; *Int'l*, pg. 4582
LUNDBECK MIDDLE EAST A/S—See Lundbeckfonden; *Int'l*, pg. 4582
LUNDBECK PAKISTAN (PRIVATE) LIMITED—See Lundbeckfonden; *Int'l*, pg. 4582
LUNDBECK PERU S.A.C.—See Lundbeckfonden; *Int'l*, pg. 4582
LUNDBECK PHARMA A/S—See Lundbeckfonden; *Int'l*, pg. 4582
LUNDBECK PHARMACEUTICALS IRELAND LIMITED—See Lundbeckfonden; *Int'l*, pg. 4582
LUNDBECK PHARMACEUTICALS, ITALY S.P.A.—See Lundbeckfonden; *Int'l*, pg. 4582
LUNDBECK PHARMACEUTICALS, ITALY S.P.A.—See Lundbeckfonden; *Int'l*, pg. 4582
LUNDBECK PHARMACEUTICALS LIMITED—See Lundbeckfonden; *Int'l*, pg. 4582
LUNDBECK PHARMACEUTICALS (TIANJIN) CO., LTD.—See Lundbeckfonden; *Int'l*, pg. 4582
LUNDBECK PHARMA D.O.O.—See Lundbeckfonden; *Int'l*, pg. 4582
LUNDBECK POLAND SP.Z.O.O.—See Lundbeckfonden; *Int'l*, pg. 4582
LUNDBECK PORTUGAL - PRODUTOS FARMACEUTICOS UNIPESSOAL LDA.—See Lundbeckfonden; *Int'l*, pg. 4582
LUNDBECK RESEARCH USA INC.—See Lundbeckfonden; *Int'l*, pg. 4582
LUNDBECK RUS OOO—See Lundbeckfonden; *Int'l*, pg. 4582
LUNDBECK SA—See Lundbeckfonden; *Int'l*, pg. 4582
LUNDBECK SA—See Lundbeckfonden; *Int'l*, pg. 4582
LUNDBECK SAS—See Lundbeckfonden; *Int'l*, pg. 4582
LUNDBECK (SCHWEIZ) AG—See Lundbeckfonden; *Int'l*, pg. 4581
LUNDBECK SINGAPORE PTE. LTD.—See Lundbeckfonden; *Int'l*, pg. 4582
LUNDBECK SLOVENSKO S.R.O.—See Lundbeckfonden; *Int'l*, pg. 4582
LUNDBECK SOUTH AFRICA (PTY) LIMITED—See Lundbeckfonden; *Int'l*, pg. 4582
LUNDBERGS PRODUKTER AB—See Ratos AB; *Int'l*, pg. 6220
LUND BOAT COMPANY—See Brunswick Corporation; *U.S. Public*, pg. 407
LUNDE AUTO CENTER; *U.S. Private*, pg. 2515
LUND FOOD HOLDINGS, INC.; *U.S. Private*, pg. 2515
LUND & FRANGIE MOTORS INC.; *U.S. Private*, pg. 2515
LUNDGRENS NORGE AS—See Beijer Alma AB; *Int'l*, pg. 943
LUNDGRENS SVERIGE AB—See Beijer Alma AB; *Int'l*, pg. 943
LUNDIN BANYUMAS BV—See Lundin Group of Companies; *Int'l*, pg. 4583
LUNDIN ENERGY AB—See Lundin Group of Companies; *Int'l*, pg. 4583
LUNDIN GOLD INC.; *Int'l*, pg. 4583
LUNDIN GROUP OF COMPANIES; *Int'l*, pg. 4583
LUNDIN INTERNATIONAL SA—See Lundin Group of Companies; *Int'l*, pg. 4583
LUNDIN MALAYSIA BV—See Lundin Group of Companies; *Int'l*, pg. 4583
LUNDIN MARINE BV—See Lundin Group of Companies; *Int'l*, pg. 4583
LUNDIN MINING CORPORATION; *Int'l*, pg. 4583
LUNDIN MINING UK LTD.—See Lundin Mining Corporation; *Int'l*, pg. 4583
LUNDIN NETHERLANDS FACILITIES BV—See Lundin Group of Companies; *Int'l*, pg. 4583
LUNDIN NORWAY AS—See Lundin Group of Companies; *Int'l*, pg. 4583
LUNDIN OIL & GAS BV—See Lundin Group of Companies; *Int'l*, pg. 4583
LUNDIN PETROLEUM BV—See Lundin Group of Companies; *Int'l*, pg. 4583
LUNDIN PETROLEUM—See Lundin Group of Companies; *Int'l*, pg. 4583
LUNDIN RUSSIA SERVICES BV—See Lundin Group of Companies; *Int'l*, pg. 4583
LUNDIN SAREBA BV—See Lundin Group of Companies; *Int'l*, pg. 4583
LUNDIN SERVICES BV—See Lundin Group of Companies; *Int'l*, pg. 4583
LUND INTERNATIONAL HOLDING COMPANY—See CCMP Capital Advisors, LP; *U.S. Private*, pg. 801
LUND INTERNATIONAL HOLDING COMPANY—See TA Associates, Inc.; *U.S. Private*, pg. 3919
LUNDIN TUNISIA BV—See Lundin Group of Companies; *Int'l*, pg. 4583
LUND-IORIO, INC.—See Forward Solutions; *U.S. Private*, pg. 1578
LUNDMARK ADVERTISING + DESIGN INC.; *U.S. Private*, pg. 2515
LUND'S FISHERIES, INC.; *U.S. Private*, pg. 2515
LUND'S INC.—See Lund Food Holdings, Inc.; *U.S. Private*, pg. 2515
LUND & SORENSEN A/S—See NIBE Industrier AB; *Int'l*, pg. 5261
LUND & SORENSEN ELECTRIC HEATING EQUIPMENT ACCESSORY CO LTD—See NIBE Industrier AB; *Int'l*, pg. 5261
LUND & SORENSEN ELECTRIC HEATING INC—See NIBE Industrier AB; *Int'l*, pg. 5261
LUNDSTROM INSURANCE AGENCY, INC.—See GTCR LLC; *U.S. Private*, pg. 1803
LUNDY CONSTRUCTION CO., INC.; *U.S. Private*, pg. 2515
LUNDY SERVICES INC.; *U.S. Private*, pg. 2515
LUNEHJEM.NO AS—See Europris ASA; *Int'l*, pg. 2557
LUNENG GROUP CO., LTD.—See State Grid Corporation of China; *Int'l*, pg. 7183
LUNEXA, LLC; *U.S. Private*, pg. 2515
LUNG BIOENGINEERING INC.—See United Therapeutics Corporation; *U.S. Public*, pg. 2238
LUNG BIOTECHNOLOGY INC.—See United Therapeutics Corporation; *U.S. Public*, pg. 2238
LUNG BIOTECHNOLOGY PBC—See United Therapeutics Corporation; *U.S. Public*, pg. 2238
LUNGENPRAXIS AM WORDEMANNSWEG GMBH—See Asklepios Kliniken GmbH & Co. KGaA; *Int'l*, pg. 623
LUNG HWA ELECTRONICS CO., LTD.; *Int'l*, pg. 4584
LUNG KEE BERMUDA HOLDINGS LTD.; *Int'l*, pg. 4584
LUNG TEH SHIPBUILDING CO., LTD.; *Int'l*, pg. 4584
LUNGYEN LIFE SERVICE CORPORATION, LTD.; *Int'l*, pg. 4584
LUNIA BIO PTY. LTD.; *Int'l*, pg. 4584
L'UNION CANADIENNE, COMPAGNIE D'ASSURANCES—See Intact Financial Corporation; *Int'l*, pg. 3727
L'UNION CANADIENNE, COMPAGNIE D'ASSURANCES—See Tryg A/S; *Int'l*, pg. 7946
L'UNIQUE, COMPAGNIE D'ASSURANCES GENERALES—See La Capitale Civil Service Mutual; *Int'l*, pg. 4387
LUNIT, INC.; *Int'l*, pg. 4584
LUNNON METALS LIMITED; *Int'l*, pg. 4584
LUNN POLY (JERSEY) LTD.—See TUI AG; *Int'l*, pg. 7965
LUNN POLY LTD.—See TUI AG; *Int'l*, pg. 7965
LUNSEMFWA HYDRO POWER COMPANY LTD—See Statkraft AS; *Int'l*, pg. 7184
LUNSETH PLUMBING AND HEATING CO.; *U.S. Private*, pg. 2515
LUNZ PREBOR FOWLER ARCHITECTS; *U.S. Private*, pg. 2515
LUOHE BUILDING MATERIALS COMPANY—See Dalian Shide Group Co., Ltd.; *Int'l*, pg. 1952
LUOKUNG TECHNOLOGY CORP.; *Int'l*, pg. 4584
LUOLAI LIFESTYLE TECHNOLOGY CO., LTD.; *Int'l*, pg. 4584
LUO LIH-FEN HOLDING CO., LTD.; *Int'l*, pg. 4584
LUONG TAI INVESTMENT & CONSTRUCTION CORPORATION; *Int'l*, pg. 4584
LUONIUSHAN CO., LTD.; *Int'l*, pg. 4584
LUOSSAVAARA-KIIRUNAVAARA AB; *Int'l*, pg. 4584
LUOTSIMAJA OY—See Humana AB; *Int'l*, pg. 3530
LUOXIN PHARMACEUTICALS GROUP STOCK CO., LTD.; *Int'l*, pg. 4585
LUOYANG CIMC LINGYU AUTOMOBILE CO., LTD.—See China International Marine Containers (Group) Co., Ltd.; *Int'l*, pg. 1512
LUOYANG GAOCE PRECISION MACHINERY CO., LTD.—See Qingdao GaoCe Technology Co., Ltd.; *Int'l*, pg. 6143
LUOYANG GLASS COMPANY LIMITED; *Int'l*, pg. 4585
LUOYANG GOLDEN EGRET GEOTOOLS CO., LTD.—See Xiamen Tungsten Co., Ltd.; *Int'l*, pg. 8526
LUOYANG HUIZHONG ANIMAL MEDICINE CO., LTD.—See Pulike Biological Engineering Inc.; *Int'l*, pg. 6116
LUOYANG HUIZHONG BIOLOGICAL TECHNOLOGY CO., LTD.—See Pulike Biological Engineering Inc.; *Int'l*, pg. 6116
LUOYANG HUIZHONG BIOTECHNOLOGY CO., LTD.—See Pulike Biological Engineering Inc.; *Int'l*, pg. 6116
LUOYANG JIANLONG MICRO-NANO NEW MATERIALS CO., LTD.; *Int'l*, pg. 4585
LUOYANG JIASHENG POWER SUPPLY TECHNOLOGY CO., LTD.—See Jiangsu Yinhe Electronics Co., Ltd.; *Int'l*, pg. 3956
LUOYANG LINYU AUTOMOBILE CO., LTD—See China International Marine Containers (Group) Co., Ltd.; *Int'l*, pg. 1512
LUOYANG NORTH GLASS TECHNOLOGY CO., LTD.; *Int'l*, pg. 4585
LUOYANG SUNTECH POWER CO., LTD.—See Suntech Power Holdings Co., Ltd.; *Int'l*, pg. 7325
LUOYANG XINQIANGLIAN SLEWING BEARING CO., LTD.; *Int'l*, pg. 4585
LUPAKA GOLD CORP.; *Int'l*, pg. 4585
LUPATECH S.A.; *Int'l*, pg. 4585
LUPIENT AUTOMOTIVE GROUP, INC.; *U.S. Private*, pg. 2515
LUPIENT CHEVROLET INC.; *U.S. Private*, pg. 2515
LUPIN ATLANTIS HOLDINGS SA—See Lupin Limited; *Int'l*, pg. 4586

LUPIN DIGITAL HEALTH LIMITED—See Lupin Limited; *Int'l*, pg. 4586
LUPIN (EUROPE) LTD.—See Lupin Limited; *Int'l*, pg. 4586
LUPINI CONSTRUCTION INC.—See Valcourt Building Services LLC; *U.S. Private*, pg. 4330
LUPIN INVESTMENTS PVT. LIMITED—See Lupin Limited; *Int'l*, pg. 4586
LUPIN LIMITED; *Int'l*, pg. 4585
LUPIN PHARMA CANADA LTD.—See Lupin Limited; pg. 4586
LUPIN PHARMACEUTICALS, INC.—See Lupin Limited; *Int'l*, pg. 4586
LU POLSKA S.A.—See Mondelez International, Inc.; *U.S. Public*, pg. 1463
LUPPRIANS LTD.—See RETHMANN AG & Co. KG; *Int'l*, pg. 6309
LUPUS FOUNDATION OF AMERICA, INC.; *U.S. Private*, pg. 2515
LUQUAN DONGFANG DINGXIN CEMENT CO., LTD—See BBMG Corporation; *Int'l*, pg. 921
LUQUIRE GEORGE ANDREWS, INC.; *U.S. Private*, pg. 2516
LURA GRUPA DOO; *Int'l*, pg. 4586
LUR BERRI; *Int'l*, pg. 4586
LUREN PRECISION CO., LTD.—See Hiwin Technologies Corp.; *Int'l*, pg. 3427
LURGI AG—See L'Air Liquide S.A.; *Int'l*, pg. 4375
LURGI CARIBBEAN LTD.—See L'Air Liquide S.A.; *Int'l*, pg. 4375
LURGI DO BRASIL INSTALACOES INDUSTRIAIS LTDA.—See L'Air Liquide S.A.; *Int'l*, pg. 4375
LURGI (PTY) LTD.—See L'Air Liquide S.A.; *Int'l*, pg. 4375
LURGI, S.A.—See L'Air Liquide S.A.; *Int'l*, pg. 4375
LURGI SDN. BHD.—See L'Air Liquide S.A.; *Int'l*, pg. 4375
LURGI TURKIYE—See L'Air Liquide S.A.; *Int'l*, pg. 4375
LURI 4, SA—See Banco Santander, S.A.; *Int'l*, pg. 826
THE LURIE COMPANIES; *U.S. Private*, pg. 4073
LURIE GLASS COMPANY—See The Lurie Companies; *U.S. Private*, pg. 4073
LURIE INVESTMENTS, INC; *U.S. Private*, pg. 2516
LURN INC.; *U.S. Private*, pg. 2516
LUSAKA STOCK EXCHANGE; *Int'l*, pg. 4586
LUSARDI CONSTRUCTION CO.; *U.S. Private*, pg. 2516
LUSCOMBE ENGINEERING COMPONENTS CO. INC.; *U.S. Private*, pg. 2516
LUSE COMPANIES, INC.—See Luse Holdings, Inc.; *U.S. Private*, pg. 2516
LUSE HOLDINGS, INC.; *U.S. Private*, pg. 2516
LUSE-STEVENSON CO. INC.—See Luse Holdings, Inc.; *U.S. Private*, pg. 2516
LUSE THERMAL TECHNOLOGIES LLC—See Luse Holdings, Inc.; *U.S. Private*, pg. 2516
LUSHANG HEALTH INDUSTRY DEVELOPMENT CO.,LTD.; *Int'l*, pg. 4587
LUSHANG LIFE SERVICE CO., LTD.; *Int'l*, pg. 4587
LUSH ASIA LIMITED—See Lush Cosmetics Ltd.; *Int'l*, pg. 4586
LUSH AUSTRALIA PTY LIMITED—See Lush Cosmetics Ltd.; *Int'l*, pg. 4586
LUSH BOSNA I HERCEGOVINA—See Lush Cosmetics Ltd.; *Int'l*, pg. 4586
LUSH BULGARIA LTD.—See Lush Cosmetics Ltd.; *Int'l*, pg. 4586
LUSH BV—See Lush Cosmetics Ltd.; *Int'l*, pg. 4586
LUSH CESKA REPUBLIKA—See Lush Cosmetics Ltd.; *Int'l*, pg. 4586
LUSH COSMETICS LTD.; *Int'l*, pg. 4586
LUSH COSMETICS SL—See Lush Cosmetics Ltd.; *Int'l*, pg. 4586
LUSH FINLAND OY—See Lush Cosmetics Ltd.; *Int'l*, pg. 4586
LUSH FRANCE—See Lush Cosmetics Ltd.; *Int'l*, pg. 4586
LUSH FRESH HANDMADE COSMETICS—See Lush Cosmetics Ltd.; *Int'l*, pg. 4587
LUSH GMBH—See Lush Cosmetics Ltd.; *Int'l*, pg. 4586
LUSH GMBH—See Lush Cosmetics Ltd.; *Int'l*, pg. 4586
LUSH HANDMADE COSMETICS LTD—See Lush Cosmetics Ltd.; *Int'l*, pg. 4587
LUSH HRVATSKA—See Lush Cosmetics Ltd.; *Int'l*, pg. 4586
LUSH HUNGARY KFT.—See Lush Cosmetics Ltd.; *Int'l*, pg. 4586
LUSH INTERNET INC.—See Lush Cosmetics Ltd.; *Int'l*, pg. 4586
LUSH IRELAND LIMITED—See Lush Cosmetics Ltd.; *Int'l*, pg. 4587
LUSH ITALIA SRL—See Lush Cosmetics Ltd.; *Int'l*, pg. 4586
LUSH LATVIJA—See Lush Cosmetics Ltd.; *Int'l*, pg. 4586
LUSH LEBANON—See Lush Cosmetics Ltd.; *Int'l*, pg. 4587
LUSH LTD.—See Lush Cosmetics Ltd.; *Int'l*, pg. 4587
LUSH MANUFACTURING LTD.—See Lush Cosmetics Ltd.; *Int'l*, pg. 4587
LUSH NORGE—See Lush Cosmetics Ltd.; *Int'l*, pg. 4587
LUSH RETAIL LTD.—See Lush Cosmetics Ltd.; *Int'l*, pg. 4587
LUSH SAUDI ARABIA—See Lush Cosmetics Ltd.; *Int'l*, pg. 4587

LUSH SINGAPORE—See Lush Cosmetics Ltd.; *Int'l*, pg. 4587
LUSH SLOVENIA—See Lush Cosmetics Ltd.; *Int'l*, pg. 4587
LUSH SOUTH AFRICA—See Lush Cosmetics Ltd.; *Int'l*, pg. 4587
LUSH SWEDEN AB—See Lush Cosmetics Ltd.; *Int'l*, pg. 4587
LUSH (SWITZERLAND) AG—See Lush Cosmetics Ltd.; *Int'l*, pg. 4586
LUSH TICINO SA—See Lush Cosmetics Ltd.; *Int'l*, pg. 4587
LUSH UKRAINE—See Lush Cosmetics Ltd.; *Int'l*, pg. 4586
LUSH UNITED ARAB EMIRATES—See Lush Cosmetics Ltd.; *Int'l*, pg. 4587
LUSIADAS-PARCERIAS CASCAIS, S.A.—See UnitedHealth Group Incorporated; *U.S. Public*, pg. 2242
LUSIADAS, SGPS, S.A.—See UnitedHealth Group Incorporated; *U.S. Public*, pg. 2242
L'USINAGE ELECTRIQUE SARL—See Georg Fischer AG; *Int'l*, pg. 2935
LUSITANIAGAS COMERCIALIZACAO, S.A.—See Galp Energia SGPS, S.A.; *Int'l*, pg. 2875
LUSIVE DECOR; *U.S. Private*, pg. 2516
LUSOCERAM-EMPREENDIMENTOS CERAMICOS, S.A.—See Nefinsa S.A.; *Int'l*, pg. 5192
LUSOMAPEI S.A.—See Mapei SpA; *Int'l*, pg. 4681
LUSOSIDER PROJECTOS SIDERURGICOS S.A.—See Companhia Siderurgica Nacional; *Int'l*, pg. 1748
LUSSIER CABINET D'ASSURANCES & SERVICES FINANCIERS INC; *Int'l*, pg. 4587
LUSTER INDUSTRIES BHD.; *Int'l*, pg. 4587
LUSTER MEKANISKE INDUSTRI AS—See Schlumberger Limited; *U.S. Public*, pg. 1844
LUSTER-ON PRODUCTS, INC.; *U.S. Private*, pg. 2516
LUSTER PRODUCTS INC.; *U.S. Private*, pg. 2516
LUSTICA DEVELOPMENT A.D.—See Orascom Development Holding AG; *Int'l*, pg. 5613
LUSTROS, INC.; *U.S. Private*, pg. 2516
LUSTY EMS PTY LTD—See MaxiPARTS Limited; *Int'l*, pg. 4742
LUTAB AB—See Etteplan Oyj; *Int'l*, pg. 2525
LUTCO, INC.; *U.S. Private*, pg. 2516
LUTECH ADVANCED SOLUTIONS S.P.A.—See Apax Partners LLP; *Int'l*, pg. 501
LUTECH RESOURCES LTD—See ABB Ltd.; *Int'l*, pg. 53
LUTECH SPA—See Apax Partners LLP; *Int'l*, pg. 501
LUTE PLUMBING SUPPLY INC.; *U.S. Private*, pg. 2516
LUTETIA—See Henry Crown & Company; *U.S. Private*, pg. 1917
LUTGEN & ASSOCIATES, INC.; *U.S. Private*, pg. 2516
LU THAI TEXTILE CO., LTD.; *Int'l*, pg. 4571
LUTH-AR, LLC; *U.S. Private*, pg. 2516
LUTHERAN CHURCH MISSOURI SYNOD; *U.S. Private*, pg. 2517
LUTHERAN COMMUNITY SERVICES NORTHWEST; *U.S. Private*, pg. 2517
LUTHERAN FAMILY SERVICES IN THE CAROLINAS; *U.S. Private*, pg. 2517
LUTHERAN FAMILY SERVICES OF VIRGINIA, INC.; *U.S. Private*, pg. 2517
LUTHERAN HOME FOR THE AGED; *U.S. Private*, pg. 2517
THE LUTHERAN HOME, INC.; *U.S. Private*, pg. 4073
LUTHERAN HOMES OF OCONOMOWOC; *U.S. Private*, pg. 2517
LUTHERAN IMMIGRATION AND REFUGEE SERVICE; *U.S. Private*, pg. 2517
LUTHERAN MEDICAL GROUP, LLC—See Community Health Systems, Inc.; *U.S. Public*, pg. 554
LUTHERAN SERVICES FLORIDA INC.; *U.S. Private*, pg. 2517
LUTHERAN SOCIAL SERVICES OF NORTHEAST FLORIDA; *U.S. Private*, pg. 2517
LUTHERAN SOCIAL SERVICES OF THE SOUTH, INC.; *U.S. Private*, pg. 2517
LUTHER BROOKDALE TOYOTA; *U.S. Private*, pg. 2516
LUTHER BURBANK CORPORATION—See WaFd, Inc.; *U.S. Public*, pg. 2321
LUTHER BURBANK MEMORIAL FOUNDATION; *U.S. Private*, pg. 2516
LUTHER BURBANK SAVINGS—See WaFd, Inc.; *U.S. Public*, pg. 2321
LUTHERCARE; *U.S. Private*, pg. 2518
LUTHER HL GMBH & CO. KG—See Zeppelin GmbH; *Int'l*, pg. 8637
LUTHER HOLDING COMPANY; *U.S. Private*, pg. 2516
LUTHER KING CAPITAL MANAGEMENT CORPORATION; *U.S. Private*, pg. 2517
LUTHER P. MILLER, INC.; *U.S. Private*, pg. 2517
LUTHERS RUDY WHITE BEAR MOTORS—See Luther Holding Company; *U.S. Private*, pg. 2517
LUTHI ELEKTRONIK-FEINMECHANIK AG—See AMETEK, Inc.; *U.S. Public*, pg. 120
LUTHIN ASSOCIATES, INC.—See L5E LLC; *U.S. Private*, pg. 2367
LUTH RESEARCH, LLC; *U.S. Private*, pg. 2516
LUTONIX, INC.—See Becton, Dickinson & Company; *U.S. Public*, pg. 291

LUTO RESEARCH LIMITED—See Mawdsley-Brooks & Co. Ltd.; *Int'l*, pg. 4733
LUTOSA SA—See McCain Foods Limited; *Int'l*, pg. 4756
LUTRIJA RS A.D.; *Int'l*, pg. 4587
LUTRONIC CORPORATION—See Hahn & Company; *Int'l*, pg. 3208
LUTRONIC JAPAN CO., LTD.—See Hahn & Company; *Int'l*, pg. 3208
LUTRONIC MEDICAL SYSTEMS GERMANY GMBH—See Hahn & Company; *Int'l*, pg. 3208
LUTSK BEARING PLANT—See SKF AB; *Int'l*, pg. 6981
LUTZ BODENMULLER AG—See BKW AG; *Int'l*, pg. 1055
LUVATA APPLETON LLC—See Mitsubishi Materials Corporation; *Int'l*, pg. 4963
LUVATA CZECH S.R.O.—See Fedders Electric and Engineering Limited; *Int'l*, pg. 2629
LUVATA FRANKLIN, INC.—See Waybill USA Inc.; *U.S. Private*, pg. 4459
LUVATA MALAYSIA SDN BHD—See Mitsubishi Materials Corporation; *Int'l*, pg. 4963
LUVATA OHIO, INC.—See Mitsubishi Materials Corporation; *Int'l*, pg. 4963
LUVATA PORI OY—See Mitsubishi Materials Corporation; *Int'l*, pg. 4963
LUVATA WATERBURY, INC—See Mitsubishi Materials Corporation; *Int'l*, pg. 4963
LUVATA WELYN GARDEN LTD.—See Mitsubishi Materials Corporation; *Int'l*, pg. 4963
LU-VE ASIA PACIFIC LTD.—See LU-VE SpA; *Int'l*, pg. 4572
LU-VE CONTARDO CARIBE S.A.—See LU-VE SpA; *Int'l*, pg. 4572
LU-VE CONTARDO DEUTSCHLAND GMBH—See LU-VE SpA; *Int'l*, pg. 4572
LU-VE CONTARDO FRANCE S.A.R.L.—See LU-VE SpA; *Int'l*, pg. 4572
LU-VE CONTARDO IBERICA S.L.—See LU-VE SpA; *Int'l*, pg. 4572
LU-VE CONTARDO PACIFIC PTY. LTD.—See LU-VE SpA; *Int'l*, pg. 4572
LU-VE HEAT EXCHANGERS (CHANGSHU) LTD—See LU-VE SpA; *Int'l*, pg. 4572
LU-VE INDIA CORPORATION PRIVATE LIMITED—See LU-VE SpA; *Int'l*, pg. 4572
LUVEL DAIRY PRODUCTS, INC.; *U.S. Private*, pg. 2518
LUVERNE TRUCK EQUIPMENT INC.—See LCI Industries; *U.S. Public*, pg. 1295
LU-VE SPA; *Int'l*, pg. 4572
LU-VE SWEDEN AB—See LU-VE SpA; *Int'l*, pg. 4572
LU-VE UK—See LU-VE SpA; *Int'l*, pg. 4572
LUV 'N CARE LTD.; *U.S. Private*, pg. 2518
LUVU BRANDS, INC.; *U.S. Public*, pg. 1349
LUWA AIR ENGINEERING AG—See Nederman Holding AB; *Int'l*, pg. 5190
LUWA AIR ENGINEERING (PTE.) LTD.—See Nederman Holding AB; *Int'l*, pg. 5189
LUWA AIR ENGINEERING (SHANGHAI) CO., LTD.—See Nederman Holding AB; *Int'l*, pg. 5190
LUWA AMERICA, INC.—See Nederman Holding AB; *Int'l*, pg. 5189
LUWA ANLAGENTECHNIK GMBH—See Nederman Holding AB; *Int'l*, pg. 5190
LUWA ENGINEERING (PTE.) LTD.—See Nederman Holding AB; *Int'l*, pg. 5190
LUWA (INDIA) PRIVATE LTD.—See Nederman Holding AB; *Int'l*, pg. 5190
LUWA JAPAN LTD.—See Nederman Holding AB; *Int'l*, pg. 5190
LUWA (UK) LTD.—See Nederman Holding AB; *Int'l*, pg. 5190
LUWOGE CONSULT GMBH—See BASF SE; *Int'l*, pg. 884
LUWOGE GMBH HAUS BREITNAU—See BASF SE; *Int'l*, pg. 884
LUWOGE GMBH HAUS WESTERLAND—See BASF SE; *Int'l*, pg. 884
LUWOGE GMBH—See BASF SE; *Int'l*, pg. 884
LUWOGE GMBH STUDIENHAUS ST. JOHANN—See BASF SE; *Int'l*, pg. 884
LUXAIRCARGO—See Societe Luxembourgeoise de Navigation Aerienne, S.A.; *Int'l*, pg. 7043
LUXAIR COMMUTER S.A.—See Societe Luxembourgeoise de Navigation Aerienne, S.A.; *Int'l*, pg. 7043
LUX AIR JET CENTERS; *U.S. Private*, pg. 2518
LUX AMBER, CORP.; *Int'l*, pg. 4587
LUX APPLIANCE PHILIPPINES, INC—See Vorwerk & Co. KG; *Int'l*, pg. 8307
LUX ASIA PACIFIC PTE LTD.—See Vorwerk & Co. KG; *Int'l*, pg. 8307
LUXAT; *Int'l*, pg. 4587
LUX AUTOMATION GMBH—See SMS Holding GmbH; *Int'l*, pg. 7015
LUXBET PTY. LTD.—See Tabcorp Holdings Limited; *Int'l*, pg. 7401
LUX BOND & GREEN INCORPORATED; *U.S. Private*, pg. 2518
LUXBRIGHT AB; *Int'l*, pg. 4588
LUX CAPITAL, LLC; *U.S. Private*, pg. 2518
LUXCHEM CORPORATION BERHAD; *Int'l*, pg. 4588

COMPANY NAME INDEX

LUXCHEM POLYMER INDUSTRIES SDN BHD—See Luxchem Corporation Berhad; *Int'l*, pg. 4588

LUXCHEM TRADING SDN BHD—See Luxchem Corporation Berhad; *Int'l*, pg. 4588

LUXCHEM VIETNAM COMPANY LIMITED—See Luxchem Corporation Berhad; *Int'l*, pg. 4588

LUXCO CLEVELAND DIVISION - BOTTLING & BLENDING FACILITY—See MGP Ingredients, Inc.; *U.S. Public*, pg. 1436

LUXCO, INC.—See MGP Ingredients, Inc.; *U.S. Public*, pg. 1436

LUX CO., LTD.—See Helios Techno Holding Co., Ltd.; *Int'l*, pg. 3330

L.U.X COMPANY LTD.—See Vorwerk & Co. KG; *Int'l*, pg. 8307

LUX CONSULTING GROUP INC; *U.S. Private*, pg. 2518

LUXCONTROL GMBH—See TUV Rheinland Berlin-Brandenburg Pfalz e.V.; *Int'l*, pg. 7982

LUXCONTROL NEDERLAND B.V.—See TUV Rheinland Berlin-Brandenburg Pfalz e.V.; *Int'l*, pg. 7982

LUXCSD S.A.—See Deutsche Borse AG; *Int'l*, pg. 2064

LUXDESIGN AS—See Amplex AB; *Int'l*, pg. 434

LUX (DEUTSCHLAND) GMBH—See Shapoorji Pallonji & Co. Ltd.; *Int'l*, pg. 6788

LUXE BRANDS, INC.; *U.S. Private*, pg. 2518

LUXE DESTINATION WEDDINGS INC.—See Sunwing Travel Group, Inc.; *Int'l*, pg. 7332

LUXE GREEN ENERGY TECHNOLOGY CO., LTD.; *Int'l*, pg. 4588

LUXE HOLDINGS LIMITED; *Int'l*, pg. 4588

LUXE LIGHTS LIMITED—See Eneraqua Technologies Plc; *Int'l*, pg. 2418

LUXELL TECHNOLOGIES INC; *Int'l*, pg. 4588

LUXEMBOURG AIRPORT COMPANY; *Int'l*, pg. 4588

LUXEMBOURG CONTACT CENTERS SARL—See Teleperformance SE; *Int'l*, pg. 7540

LUXEMBOURG FAMILY OFFICE S.A.—See Deutsche Bank Aktiengesellschaft; *Int'l*, pg. 2061

LUXEMBOURG MEDICINE COMPANY LIMITED—See Wang On Group Ltd; *Int'l*, pg. 8341

LUXEMBOURG MOUNTING CENTER S.A.—See The Goodyear Tire & Rubber Company; *U.S. Public*, pg. 2084

LUXEMPART SA; *Int'l*, pg. 4588

LUXENDO GMBH—See Bruker Corporation; *U.S. Public*, pg. 407

LUXENERGIE S.A.—See Enovos International S.A.; *Int'l*, pg. 2444

LUXE RV, INC.; *U.S. Private*, pg. 2518

LUXE TRAVEL MANAGEMENT, INC.—See Frosch International Travel Inc.; *U.S. Private*, pg. 1616

LUXEY INTERNATIONAL (HOLDINGS) LIMITED; *Int'l*, pg. 4588

LUXFER AUSTRALIA PTY LIMITED—See Luxfer Holdings PLC; *Int'l*, pg. 4588

LUXFER GAS CYLINDERS LIMITED—See Luxfer Holdings PLC; *Int'l*, pg. 4588

LUXFER GAS CYLINDERS S.A.S.—See Luxfer Holdings PLC; *Int'l*, pg. 4588

LUXFER GAS CYLINDERS (SHANGHAI) CO., LIMITED—See Luxfer Holdings PLC; *Int'l*, pg. 4588

LUXFER GROUP LIMITED—See Luxfer Holdings PLC; *Int'l*, pg. 4588

LUXFER HOLDINGS PLC; *Int'l*, pg. 4588

LUXFER, INC.—See Luxfer Holdings PLC; *Int'l*, pg. 4588

LUXFER MAGTECH INC.—See Luxfer Holdings PLC; *Int'l*, pg. 4588

LUXFUEL S.A.—See Marquard & Bahls AG; *Int'l*, pg. 4700

LUX GLOBAL LABEL COMPANY, LLC—See Resilience Capital Partners, LLC; *U.S. Private*, pg. 3405

LUX GROUP HOLDINGS LIMITED; *Int'l*, pg. 4587

LUX HEALTH TECH ACQUISITION CORP.; *U.S. Private*, pg. 2518

LUX HUNGARIA KERESKEDELMI KFT.—See Shapoorji Pallonji & Co. Ltd.; *Int'l*, pg. 6788

LUXI CHEMICAL GROUP CO., LTD.; *Int'l*, pg. 4589

LUXIM CORPORATION—See Luma Investments, Ltd.; *Int'l*, pg. 4577

LUX INDUSTRIES LIMITED; *Int'l*, pg. 4587

LUX INTERNATIONAL AG—See Shapoorji Pallonji & Co. Ltd.; *Int'l*, pg. 6788

LUXIN VENTURE CAPITAL GROUP CO., LTD; *Int'l*, pg. 4589

LUX ISLAND RESORTS LTD; *Int'l*, pg. 4587

LUX ITALIA S.R.L—See Shapoorji Pallonji & Co. Ltd.; *Int'l*, pg. 6788

LUXIUM SOLUTIONS, LLC—See Edgewater Capital Partners, L.P.; *U.S. Private*, pg. 1335

LUXIUM SOLUTIONS, LLC—See SK Capital Partners, LP; *U.S. Private*, pg. 3679

LUXKING GROUP HOLDINGS LIMITED; *Int'l*, pg. 4589

LUXL CO., LTD.; *Int'l*, pg. 4589

LUXLIFE—See Groupama SA; *Int'l*, pg. 3091

LUXLITE (SHENZHEN) CORPORATION LIMITED—See Ennostar Inc.; *Int'l*, pg. 2444

LUX MED SP. Z.O.O—See Abris Capital Partners Sp. z o.o.; *Int'l*, pg. 69

LUXMOBILE GROUP; *U.S. Private*, pg. 2518

LUX NORGE A/S—See Shapoorji Pallonji & Co. Ltd.; *Int'l*, pg. 6788

LUXOFT BULGARIA E.O.O.D.—See DXC Technology Company; *U.S. Public*, pg. 696

LUXOFT GMBH—See DXC Technology Company; *U.S. Public*, pg. 696

LUXOFT HOLDING, INC.—See DXC Technology Company; *U.S. Public*, pg. 696

LUXOFT INDIA LLP—See DXC Technology Company; *U.S. Public*, pg. 696

LUXOFT ITALY S.R.L.—See DXC Technology Company; *U.S. Public*, pg. 696

LUXOFT KOREA LLC—See DXC Technology Company; *U.S. Public*, pg. 696

LUXOFT MALAYSIA SDN. BHD.—See DXC Technology Company; *U.S. Public*, pg. 696

LUXOFT MEXICO S.A. DE C.V.—See DXC Technology Company; *U.S. Public*, pg. 696

LUXOFT SWEDEN AB—See DXC Technology Company; *U.S. Public*, pg. 696

LUXOFT UK LIMITED—See DXC Technology Company; *U.S. Public*, pg. 696

LUXOFT UKRAINE LLC—See DXC Technology Company; *U.S. Public*, pg. 696

LUXOFT VIETNAM COMPANY LIMITED—See DXC Technology Company; *U.S. Public*, pg. 696

LUXON FINANCIAL LLC; *U.S. Private*, pg. 2518

LUXOR CAPITAL GROUP, LP; *U.S. Private*, pg. 2518

LUXOR CORP.—See EBSCO Industries, Inc.; *U.S. Private*, pg. 1325

LUXORO S.R.L.—See Leonhard Kurz GmbH & Co. KG; *Int'l*, pg. 4462

LUXOS SA; *Int'l*, pg. 4589

LUX OSTERREICH GMBH—See Shapoorji Pallonji & Co. Ltd.; *Int'l*, pg. 6788

LUXOTTICA AUSTRALIA PTY. LTD.—See EssilorLuxottica SA; *Int'l*, pg. 2515

LUXOTTICA BELGIUM N.V.—See EssilorLuxottica SA; *Int'l*, pg. 2515

LUXOTTICA CANADA, INC.—See EssilorLuxottica SA; *Int'l*, pg. 2515

LUXOTTICA DO BRASIL LTDA.—See EssilorLuxottica SA; *Int'l*, pg. 2515

LUXOTTICA FASHION BRILLEN VIRTIES GMBH—See EssilorLuxottica SA; *Int'l*, pg. 2515

LUXOTTICA FRANCE S.A.R.L.—See EssilorLuxottica SA; *Int'l*, pg. 2515

LUXOTTICA GROUP S.P.A.—See EssilorLuxottica SA; *Int'l*, pg. 2515

LUXOTTICA HELLAS AE—See EssilorLuxottica SA; *Int'l*, pg. 2515

LUXOTTICA IBERICA S.A.—See EssilorLuxottica SA; *Int'l*, pg. 2515

LUXOTTICA MEXICO SA DE C.V.—See EssilorLuxottica SA; *Int'l*, pg. 2515

LUXOTTICA NEDERLAND B.V.—See EssilorLuxottica SA; *Int'l*, pg. 2515

LUXOTTICA PORTUGAL S.A.—See EssilorLuxottica SA; *Int'l*, pg. 2515

LUXOTTICA RETAIL AUSTRALIA PTY. LIMITED—See EssilorLuxottica SA; *Int'l*, pg. 2515

LUXOTTICA RETAIL NORTH AMERICA INC.—See EssilorLuxottica SA; *Int'l*, pg. 2515

LUXOTTICA—See EssilorLuxottica SA; *Int'l*, pg. 2515

LUXOTTICA SWEDEN A.B.—See EssilorLuxottica SA; *Int'l*, pg. 2515

LUXOTTICA (SWITZERLAND) A.G.—See EssilorLuxottica SA; *Int'l*, pg. 2515

LUXOTTICA U.K. LTD.—See EssilorLuxottica SA; *Int'l*, pg. 2515

LUXOTTICA USA LLC—See EssilorLuxottica SA; *Int'l*, pg. 2515

LUXOTTICA VERTRIEBS GMBH—See EssilorLuxottica SA; *Int'l*, pg. 2515

LUXPET A.G./S.A.—See Plastipak Holdings, Inc.; *U.S. Private*, pg. 3199

LUXPIA CO., LTD - JEONJU PLANT—See Luxpia Co., Ltd; *Int'l*, pg. 4589

LUXPIA CO., LTD; *Int'l*, pg. 4589

LUX PRODUCTS CORP.—See Johnson Controls International plc; *Int'l*, pg. 3985

LUX RESEARCH, INC.—See COFRA Holding AG; *Int'l*, pg. 1694

LUX ROYAL (THAILAND) CO., LTD.—See Vorwerk & Co. KG; *Int'l*, pg. 8307

LUXSCAN TECHNOLOGIES S.A.R.L.—See Michael Weinig AG; *Int'l*, pg. 4874

LUX SCHWEIZ AG—See Shapoorji Pallonji & Co. Ltd.; *Int'l*, pg. 6788

LUX SCIENTIAE, INC.—See Main Capital Partners B.V.; *Int'l*, pg. 4650

LUXSHARE-ICT EUROPE LIMITED—See Luxshare Precision Industry Co., Ltd.; *Int'l*, pg. 4589

LUXSHARE-ICT, INC.—See Luxshare Precision Industry Co., Ltd.; *Int'l*, pg. 4589

LUXSHARE-ICT (JAPAN) LIMITED—See Luxshare Precision Industry Co., Ltd.; *Int'l*, pg. 4589

LUXSHARE PRECISION INDUSTRY CO., LTD.; *Int'l*, pg. 4589

LUXSPACE SARL—See OHB SE; *Int'l*, pg. 5532

LUXTRON SISTEMS FZCO—See A.A.G. STUCCHI s.r.l.; *Int'l*, pg. 23

LUXURBAN HOTELS INC.; *U.S. Public*, pg. 1349

LUXURY BRAND HOLDINGS; *U.S. Public*, pg. 2518

LUXURY BRANDS, LLC; *U.S. Private*, pg. 2518

LUXURY BRANDS (PRIVATE) LIMITED—See Carson Cumberbatch PLC; *Int'l*, pg. 1347

LUXURY CONCEPTS WATCHES & JEWELLERY SDN. BHD.; *Int'l*, pg. 4589

LUXURY FOR LESS LIMITED; *Int'l*, pg. 4589

LUXURY GOODS OPERATIONS SA—See Kering S.A.; *Int'l*, pg. 4135

LUXURY GOODS SPAIN SL—See Kering S.A.; *Int'l*, pg. 4135

LUXURY HOTEL MANAGEMENT OF CZECH REPUBLIC S.R.O.—See Marriott International, Inc.; *U.S. Public*, pg. 1370

LUXURY HOTELS INTERNATIONAL OF SPAIN S.L.U.—See Marriott International, Inc.; *U.S. Public*, pg. 1371

LUXURY LEISURE LTD.—See Novomatic AG; *Int'l*, pg. 5467

LUXURY MORTGAGE CORP.—See Tiptree Inc.; *U.S. Public*, pg. 2159

LUXURY MOUNTAIN HOTELS SARL—See TUI AG; *Int'l*, pg. 7965

LUXURY ORLANDO IMPORTS, INC.—See AutoNation, Inc.; *U.S. Public*, pg. 236

LUXURY TIMEPIECES JAPAN LIMITED—See Kering S.A.; *Int'l*, pg. 4135

LUXURY TRAINS S.R.L.—See LVMH Moet Hennessy Louis Vuitton SE; *Int'l*, pg. 4591

LUXURY WOODLANDS IMPORTS, INC.—See AutoNation, Inc.; *U.S. Public*, pg. 236

LUXVISIONS INNOVATION LIMITED; *Int'l*, pg. 4589

LUXXFOLIO HOLDINGS, INC.; *Int'l*, pg. 4589

LUXXO, INC.; *Int'l*, pg. 4589

LUXXU GROUP LIMITED; *Int'l*, pg. 4589

LUYAN (FUJIAN) PHARMA CO., LTD.; *Int'l*, pg. 4589

LUYANG ENERGY-SAVING MATERIALS CO., LTD.—See Clearlake Capital Group, L.P.; *U.S. Private*, pg. 937

LUYE MEDICAL GROUP; *Int'l*, pg. 4589

LUYE PHARMA AG—See AsiaPharma Holdings Ltd.; *Int'l*, pg. 620

LUYE PHARMA GROUP LTD.—See AsiaPharma Holdings Ltd.; *Int'l*, pg. 620

LUYIN INVESTMENT GROUP CO., LTD.; *Int'l*, pg. 4590

LUYTEN S.A.—See Recochem Inc.; *Int'l*, pg. 6238

LUZ DEL SUR S.A.A—See Sempra; *U.S. Public*, pg. 1863

THE LUZERNE BANK—See Penns Woods Bancorp, Inc.; *U.S. Public*, pg. 1663

LUZERNE COUNTY HEAD START, INC.; *U.S. Private*, pg. 2518

THE LUZERNE FOUNDATION; *U.S. Private*, pg. 4073

LUZERNER KANTONALBANK; *Int'l*, pg. 4590

LUZHOU BANK CO., LTD.; *Int'l*, pg. 4590

LUZHOU BIO-CHEM TECHNOLOGY (LIAONING) CO., LTD.—See Luzhou Bio-Chem Technology Limited; *Int'l*, pg. 4590

LUZHOU BIO-CHEM TECHNOLOGY LIMITED; *Int'l*, pg. 4590

LUZHOU BIO-CHEM TECHNOLOGY (SHAANXI) CO., LTD.—See Luzhou Bio-Chem Technology Limited; *Int'l*, pg. 4590

LUZHOU CHANGJIANG MACHINERY CO., LTD.—See Chengdu Haoneng Technology Co., Ltd.; *Int'l*, pg. 1468

LUZHOU JINCAI PRINTING & PACKAGING CO., LTD.—See MYS Group Co., Ltd.; *Int'l*, pg. 5114

LU ZHOU LAO JIAO CO., LTD.; *Int'l*, pg. 4572

LUZHOU XINGLU WATER (GROUP) CO., LTD.; *Int'l*, pg. 4590

LUZIER PERSONALIZED COSMETICS, INC.; *U.S. Private*, pg. 2518

LUZO FOODSERVICE CORPORATION; *U.S. Private*, pg. 2518

LUZ SAUDE, S.A.—See Fosun International Limited; *Int'l*, pg. 2751

LUZY ENERGIA RENOVABLE, S.L.U.—See Elecnor, S.A.; *Int'l*, pg. 2347

LVAC RESEARCH CENTER SUZHOU CO., LTD.—See ULVAC, Inc.; *Int'l*, pg. 8020

LVB LAWOG-VAMED BAUPLANUNGS- UND ERRICHTUNGS-GMBH—See Fresenius SE & Co. KGaA; *Int'l*, pg. 2780

LV CHARRIERES LIMITED—See Aedifica SA; *Int'l*, pg. 173

L.V. CONTROL MANUFACTURING LIMITED—See Exchange Income Corporation; *Int'l*, pg. 2444

LVCUT ASSOCIATES, LLC—See Las Vegas Sands Corp.; *U.S. Public*, pg. 1293

LVGEM (CHINA) REAL ESTATE INVESTMENT COMPANY LIMITED; *Int'l*, pg. 4590

LVGV, LLC—See PENN Entertainment, Inc.; *U.S. Public*, pg. 1662

L.V.H. INC.—See Butz Enterprises, Inc.; *U.S. Private*, pg. 698

LVI-DAHL OY—See Compagnie de Saint-Gobain SA; *Int'l*, pg. 1724

Company Index

LVGEM (CHINA) REAL ESTATE INVESTMENT COMPANY LIMITED CORPORATE AFFILIATIONS

LVI HELIN OY—See Electricite de France S.A.; *Int'l*, pg. 2351
LV INSURANCE MANAGEMENT LIMITED—See Allianz SE; *Int'l*, pg. 354
LVI-TALO KANNOSTO OY—See Instalco AB; *Int'l*, pg. 3722
LVI-URAKOINTI PAAVOLA OY—See Instalco AB; *Int'l*, pg. 3722
LVJ GROUP KK—See LVMH Moet Hennessy Louis Vuitton SE; *Int'l*, pg. 4592
LVJING HOLDING CO., LTD.; *Int'l*, pg. 4590
LVJI TECHNOLOGY HOLDINGS INC.; *Int'l*, pg. 4590
LVL ENERGY FUND PLC; *Int'l*, pg. 4590
LVL MEDICAL GROUPE S.A.—See L'Air Liquide S.A.; *Int'l*, pg. 4375
L V MARTIN & SON LIMITED—See Smiths City Group Limited; *Int'l*, pg. 7009
LVMC HOLDINGS; *Int'l*, pg. 4590
LVM GROUP, INC.—See Didit.com, Inc.; *U.S. Private*, pg. 1228
LVMH ASIA PACIFIC LTD.—See LVMH Moet Hennessy Louis Vuitton SE; *Int'l*, pg. 4592
LVMH COSMETICS KK—See LVMH Moet Hennessy Louis Vuitton SE; *Int'l*, pg. 4597
LVMH FASHION GROUP BRASIL LTDA—See LVMH Moet Hennessy Louis Vuitton SE; *Int'l*, pg. 4594
LVMH FASHION GROUP FRANCE SNC—See LVMH Moet Hennessy Louis Vuitton SE; *Int'l*, pg. 4592
LVMH FASHION GROUP KOREA—See LVMH Moet Hennessy Louis Vuitton SE; *Int'l*, pg. 4594
LVMH FASHION GROUP MICRONESIA—See LVMH Moet Hennessy Louis Vuitton SE; *Int'l*, pg. 4595
LVMH FASHION GROUP PACIFIC LTD.—See LVMH Moet Hennessy Louis Vuitton SE; *Int'l*, pg. 4595
LVMH FASHION GROUP S.A.—See LVMH Moet Hennessy Louis Vuitton SE; *Int'l*, pg. 4592
LVMH FASHION GROUP SERVICES SAS—See LVMH Moet Hennessy Louis Vuitton SE; *Int'l*, pg. 4598
LVMH FASHION GROUP SINGAPORE—See LVMH Moet Hennessy Louis Vuitton SE; *Int'l*, pg. 4595
LVMH FASHION GROUP SWITZERLAND S.A.—See LVMH Moet Hennessy Louis Vuitton SE; *Int'l*, pg. 4595
LVMH FASHION GROUP THAILAND—See LVMH Moet Hennessy Louis Vuitton SE; *Int'l*, pg. 4595
LVMH FASHION GROUP TRADING KOREA LTD—See LVMH Moet Hennessy Louis Vuitton SE; *Int'l*, pg. 4598
LVMH FASHION GROUP UK LTD—See LVMH Moet Hennessy Louis Vuitton SE; *Int'l*, pg. 4595
LVMH FASHION TRADING CO. LTD—See LVMH Moet Hennessy Louis Vuitton SE; *Int'l*, pg. 4595
LVMH FG BRASIL LTDA—See LVMH Moet Hennessy Louis Vuitton SE; *Int'l*, pg. 4594
LVMH FG SERVICES UK LTD—See LVMH Moet Hennessy Louis Vuitton SE; *Int'l*, pg. 4594
LVMH FINANCE SA—See LVMH Moet Hennessy Louis Vuitton SE; *Int'l*, pg. 4597
LVMH FRAGRANCE BRANDS AUSTRIA—See LVMH Moet Hennessy Louis Vuitton SE; *Int'l*, pg. 4597
LVMH FRAGRANCE BRANDS CANADA LTD—See LVMH Moet Hennessy Louis Vuitton SE; *Int'l*, pg. 4597
LVMH FRAGRANCE BRANDS GMBH—See LVMH Moet Hennessy Louis Vuitton SE; *Int'l*, pg. 4597
LVMH FRAGRANCE BRANDS KK—See LVMH Moet Hennessy Louis Vuitton SE; *Int'l*, pg. 4597
LVMH FRAGRANCE BRANDS LLC—See LVMH Moet Hennessy Louis Vuitton SE; *Int'l*, pg. 4597
LVMH FRAGRANCE BRANDS LTD—See LVMH Moet Hennessy Louis Vuitton SE; *Int'l*, pg. 4597
LVMH FRAGRANCE BRANDS LTD—See LVMH Moet Hennessy Louis Vuitton SE; *Int'l*, pg. 4597
LVMH FRAGRANCE BRANDS SA—See LVMH Moet Hennessy Louis Vuitton SE; *Int'l*, pg. 4597
LVMH FRAGRANCE BRANDS WHD INC—See LVMH Moet Hennessy Louis Vuitton SE; *Int'l*, pg. 4601
LVMH FRAGRANCES & COSMETICS (SINGAPORE) PTE. LTD.—See LVMH Moet Hennessy Louis Vuitton SE; *Int'l*, pg. 4597
LVMH IBERIA SL—See LVMH Moet Hennessy Louis Vuitton SE; *Int'l*, pg. 4598
LVMH INC.—See LVMH Moet Hennessy Louis Vuitton SE; *Int'l*, pg. 4601
LVMH ITALIA S.P.A.—See LVMH Moet Hennessy Louis Vuitton SE; *Int'l*, pg. 4597
LVMH MOET HENNESSY LOUIS VUITTON BV—See LVMH Moet Hennessy Louis Vuitton SE; *Int'l*, pg. 4601
LVMH MOET HENNESSY LOUIS VUITTON INC.—See LVMH Moet Hennessy Louis Vuitton SE; *Int'l*, pg. 4598
LVMH MOET-HENNESSY LOUIS VUITTON (JAPAN) KK—See LVMH Moet Hennessy Louis Vuitton SE; *Int'l*, pg. 4595
LVMH MOET HENNESSY LOUIS VUITTON KK—See LVMH Moet Hennessy Louis Vuitton SE; *Int'l*, pg. 4597
LVMH MOET HENNESSY LOUIS VUITTON SE; *Int'l*, pg. 4590
LVMH MONTRES ET JOAILLERIE—See LVMH Moet Hennessy Louis Vuitton SE; *Int'l*, pg. 4602
LVMH PARFUMS & COSMETIQUES DO BRASIL LTDA—See LVMH Moet Hennessy Louis Vuitton SE; *Int'l*, pg. 4597
LVMH PARFUMS ET COSMETIQUES DO BRASIL LTDA—See LVMH Moet Hennessy Louis Vuitton SE; *Int'l*, pg. 4597
LVMH PARFUMS & KOSMETIK DEUTSCHLAND GMBH—See LVMH Moet Hennessy Louis Vuitton SE; *Int'l*, pg. 4597
LVMH PARTICIPATIONS BV—See LVMH Moet Hennessy Louis Vuitton SE; *Int'l*, pg. 4597
LVMH P&C DE MEXICO SA DE CV—See LVMH Moet Hennessy Louis Vuitton SE; *Int'l*, pg. 4597
LVMH PERFUMES AND COSMETIC OF BRAZIL—See LVMH Moet Hennessy Louis Vuitton SE; *Int'l*, pg. 4594
LVMH PERFUMES & COSMETICOS IBERICA SA—See LVMH Moet Hennessy Louis Vuitton SE; *Int'l*, pg. 4597
LVMH PERFUMES & COSMETICS ASIA PACIFIC LTD—See LVMH Moet Hennessy Louis Vuitton SE; *Int'l*, pg. 4597
LVMH PERFUMES & COSMETICS CHINA LTD—See LVMH Moet Hennessy Louis Vuitton SE; *Int'l*, pg. 4594
LVMH PERFUMES & COSMETICS DE MEXICO S.A. DE C.V.—See LVMH Moet Hennessy Louis Vuitton SE; *Int'l*, pg. 4597
LVMH PERFUMES & COSMETICS DO BRASIL LTDA.—See LVMH Moet Hennessy Louis Vuitton SE; *Int'l*, pg. 4597
LVMH PERFUMES & COSMETICS GMBH—See LVMH Moet Hennessy Louis Vuitton SE; *Int'l*, pg. 4597
LVMH PERFUMES & COSMETICS GROUP PTY LTD—See LVMH Moet Hennessy Louis Vuitton SE; *Int'l*, pg. 4597
LVMH PERFUMES & COSMETICS ITALIA S.P.A.—See LVMH Moet Hennessy Louis Vuitton SE; *Int'l*, pg. 4597
LVMH PERFUMES & COSMETICS (KOREA) LTD.—See LVMH Moet Hennessy Louis Vuitton SE; *Int'l*, pg. 4597
LVMH PERFUMES & COSMETICS (MALAYSIA) SDN. BHD.—See LVMH Moet Hennessy Louis Vuitton SE; *Int'l*, pg. 4597
LVMH PERFUMES & COSMETICS SHANGHAI CO. LTD.—See LVMH Moet Hennessy Louis Vuitton SE; *Int'l*, pg. 4597
LVMH PERFUMES & COSMETICS—See LVMH Moet Hennessy Louis Vuitton SE; *Int'l*, pg. 4597
LVMH PERFUMES & COSMETICS TAIWAN FA HUA FRAGRANCE & COSMETIC CO., LTD.—See LVMH Moet Hennessy Louis Vuitton SE; *Int'l*, pg. 4593
LVMH PERFUMES & COSMETICS (THAILAND) LTD—See LVMH Moet Hennessy Louis Vuitton SE; *Int'l*, pg. 4597
LVMH PERFUMES & COSMETICS THAILAND—See LVMH Moet Hennessy Louis Vuitton SE; *Int'l*, pg. 4597
LVMH PERFUMES & COSMETICS UK—See LVMH Moet Hennessy Louis Vuitton SE; *Int'l*, pg. 4597
LVMH PERFUMES E COSMETICA LDA—See LVMH Moet Hennessy Louis Vuitton SE; *Int'l*, pg. 4598
LVMH P&K GMBH—See LVMH Moet Hennessy Louis Vuitton SE; *Int'l*, pg. 4597
LVMH PUBLICA SA—See LVMH Moet Hennessy Louis Vuitton SE; *Int'l*, pg. 4598
LVMH RELOJERIA & JOYERIA ESPANA SA—See LVMH Moet Hennessy Louis Vuitton SE; *Int'l*, pg. 4602
LVMH RELOJERIA S.A.—See LVMH Moet Hennessy Louis Vuitton SE; *Int'l*, pg. 4602
LVMH SERVICES BV—See LVMH Moet Hennessy Louis Vuitton SE; *Int'l*, pg. 4598
LVMH SWISS MANUFACTURES SA—See LVMH Moet Hennessy Louis Vuitton SE; *Int'l*, pg. 4598
LVMH WATCH AND JEWELRY TAIWAN LTD CORTECH SA—See LVMH Moet Hennessy Louis Vuitton SE; *Int'l*, pg. 4599
LVMH WATCHES & JEWELRY HONG KONG LTD.—See LVMH Moet Hennessy Louis Vuitton SE; *Int'l*, pg. 4602
LVMH WATCHES & JEWELRY LTD.—See LVMH Moet Hennessy Louis Vuitton SE; *Int'l*, pg. 4602
LVMH WATCHES & JEWELRY SINGAPORE PTE. LTD.—See LVMH Moet Hennessy Louis Vuitton SE; *Int'l*, pg. 4603
LVMH WATCHES & JEWELRY (SWITZERLAND)—See LVMH Moet Hennessy Louis Vuitton SE; *Int'l*, pg. 4602
LVMH WATCHES & JEWELRY TAIWAN LTD—See LVMH Moet Hennessy Louis Vuitton SE; *Int'l*, pg. 4603
LVMH WATCH & JEWELLERY AUSTRALIA PTY. LIMITED—See LVMH Moet Hennessy Louis Vuitton SE; *Int'l*, pg. 4602
LVMH WATCH & JEWELLERY UK LTD—See LVMH Moet Hennessy Louis Vuitton SE; *Int'l*, pg. 4602
LVMH WATCH & JEWELRY AUSTRALIA PTY. LTD.—See LVMH Moet Hennessy Louis Vuitton SE; *Int'l*, pg. 4602
LVMH WATCH & JEWELRY CENTRAL EUROPE—See LVMH Moet Hennessy Louis Vuitton SE; *Int'l*, pg. 4602
LVMH WATCH & JEWELRY GMBH—See LVMH Moet Hennessy Louis Vuitton SE; *Int'l*, pg. 4603
LVMH WATCH & JEWELRY HOLDING ITALY S.P.A—See LVMH Moet Hennessy Louis Vuitton SE; *Int'l*, pg. 4602
LVMH WATCH & JEWELRY HONG KONG LTD—See LVMH Moet Hennessy Louis Vuitton SE; *Int'l*, pg. 4602
LVMH WATCH & JEWELRY INDIA PVT LTD—See LVMH Moet Hennessy Louis Vuitton SE; *Int'l*, pg. 4602
LVMH WATCH & JEWELRY ITALY S.P.A.—See LVMH Moet Hennessy Louis Vuitton SE; *Int'l*, pg. 4602
LVMH WATCH & JEWELRY JAPAN KK—See LVMH Moet Hennessy Louis Vuitton SE; *Int'l*, pg. 4602
LVMH WATCH & JEWELRY K.K.—See LVMH Moet Hennessy Louis Vuitton SE; *Int'l*, pg. 4602
LVMH WATCH & JEWELRY MALAYSIA SDN BHD—See LVMH Moet Hennessy Louis Vuitton SE; *Int'l*, pg. 4602
LVMH WATCH & JEWELRY (SHANGHAI) COMMERCIAL CO., LTD.—See LVMH Moet Hennessy Louis Vuitton SE; *Int'l*, pg. 4602
LVMH WATCH & JEWELRY SINGAPORE PTE LTD—See LVMH Moet Hennessy Louis Vuitton SE; *Int'l*, pg. 4602
LVMH WATCH & JEWELRY UK LTD—See LVMH Moet Hennessy Louis Vuitton SE; *Int'l*, pg. 4602
LVMH WATCH & JEWELRY USA INC—See LVMH Moet Hennessy Louis Vuitton SE; *Int'l*, pg. 4602
LVMH WINES & SPIRITS SUISSE SA—See LVMH Moet Hennessy Louis Vuitton SE; *Int'l*, pg. 4599
LVMH W&J SERVICES (SUISSE) SA—See LVMH Moet Hennessy Louis Vuitton SE; *Int'l*, pg. 4602
LVMH W&J USA INC.—See LVMH Moet Hennessy Louis Vuitton SE; *Int'l*, pg. 4602
LVM LIMBURG B.V.—See Tessenderlo Group NV; *Int'l*, pg. 7573
LVM N.V.—See Tessenderlo Group NV; *Int'l*, pg. 7573
LVNV FUNDING, LLC—See Sherman Financial Group LLC; *U.S. Private*, pg. 3634
L V RAWLINSON & ASSOCIATES PTY LTD—See Cleanaway Waste Management Limited; *Int'l*, pg. 1655
L.V.TECHNIK KFT.—See SAF-Holland S.A.; *Int'l*, pg. 6467
L.V. TECHNOLOGY PUBLIC COMPANY LIMITED; *Int'l*, pg. 4386
LV US MANUFACTURING, INC—See LVMH Moet Hennessy Louis Vuitton SE; *Int'l*, pg. 4601
LV YANG OFFSHORE EQUIPMENT CO., LTD.—See AMOS Group Limited; *Int'l*, pg. 430
LVYUAN GREEN BUILDING MATERIAL TECHNOLOGY CORP.; *Int'l*, pg. 4604
LW1, INC.—See Wilhelmina International, Inc.; *U.S. Public*, pg. 2370
LW BOGDANKA SA; *Int'l*, pg. 4604
LWCBANCORP, INC.; *U.S. Private*, pg. 2518
LWC, LLC—See FirstCash Holdings, Inc.; *U.S. Public*, pg. 849
LWD INC.; *U.S. Private*, pg. 2519
LWG ZURN AUSTRALIA PTY LTD.—See Zurn Elkay Water Solutions Corporation; *U.S. Public*, pg. 2413
L&W, INC.—See KPS Capital Partners, LP; *U.S. Private*, pg. 2346
L.W. LAMBOURN NIGERIA LTD.—See Stemcor Holdings Limited; *Int'l*, pg. 7205
LWL-SACHSENKABEL GMBH—See Zech Group SE; *Int'l*, pg. 8628
L.W. MILLER TRANSPORTATION; *U.S. Private*, pg. 2367
L.W.M. SA—See Skandinaviska Enskilda Banken AB; *Int'l*, pg. 6977
L. WOLF COMPANY; *U.S. Private*, pg. 2364
L.W. PACKARD & CO., INC.; *U.S. Private*, pg. 2367
LWP CLAIMS SOLUTIONS, INC.; *U.S. Private*, pg. 2519
LWP TECHNOLOGIES LIMITED; *Int'l*, pg. 4604
L.W. SAFETY LIMITED—See London Security PLC; *Int'l*, pg. 4547
LWS KNITWEAR LIMITED; *Int'l*, pg. 4604
L W SOLUTIONS LTD.—See Metall Zug AG; *Int'l*, pg. 4847
L&W SUPPLY CORPORATION—See Hendricks Holding Company, Inc.; *U.S. Private*, pg. 1915
LWT COMMUNICATIONS; *U.S. Private*, pg. 2519
LXB COMMUNICATIONS MARKETING; *Int'l*, pg. 4604
LXB COMMUNICATIONS MARKETING—See LXB Communications Marketing; *Int'l*, pg. 4604
LXB HOLDINGS LIMITED—See Hammerson plc; *Int'l*, pg. 3238
LXB RETAIL PROPERTIES PLC; *Int'l*, pg. 4604
LX HAUSYS, LTD—See LG Corp.; *Int'l*, pg. 4476
LX HOLDINGS CORP.; *Int'l*, pg. 4604
LX INTERNATIONAL CORP—See LG Corp.; *Int'l*, pg. 4476
LXI REIT PLC—See LondonMetric Property Plc; *Int'l*, pg. 4548
LX MMA CORP.—See Sumitomo Chemical Company, Limited; *Int'l*, pg. 7264
LX PANTOS AUSTRALIA PTY LTD—See LX Holdings Corp.; *Int'l*, pg. 4604
LX PANTOS (CAMBODIA) CO., LTD.—See LX Holdings Corp.; *Int'l*, pg. 4604
LX PANTOS GERMANY GMBH—See LX Holdings Corp.; *Int'l*, pg. 4604
LX PANTOS HUNGARY KFT.—See LX Holdings Corp.; *Int'l*, pg. 4604
LX PANTOS INDIA PRIVATE LIMITED—See LX Holdings Corp.; *Int'l*, pg. 4604
LX PANTOS JAPAN INC.—See LX Holdings Corp.; *Int'l*, pg. 4604
LX PANTOS LOGISTICS (HONG KONG) CO., LTD.—See LX Holdings Corp.; *Int'l*, pg. 4604
LX PANTOS LOGISTICS (SHANGHAI) CO., LTD.—See LX Holdings Corp.; *Int'l*, pg. 4604
LX PANTOS LOGISTICS TAIWAN CO., LTD.—See LX Holdings Corp.; *Int'l*, pg. 4604
LX PANTOS MALAYSIA SDN. BHD.—See LX Holdings Corp.; *Int'l*, pg. 4604

COMPANY NAME INDEX

LX PANTOS MEXICO, S.A.DE C.V.—See LX Holdings Corp.; *Int'l*, pg. 4604
LX PANTOS NETHERLANDS B.V.—See LX Holdings Corp.; *Int'l*, pg. 4604
LX PANTOS PANAMA S.A.—See LX Holdings Corp.; *Int'l*, pg. 4604
LX PANTOS PHILLIPPINES, INC.—See LX Holdings Corp.; *Int'l*, pg. 4604
LX PANTOS POLAND SP. Z O.O.—See LX Holdings Corp.; *Int'l*, pg. 4604
LX PANTOS SINGAPORE PTE. LTD.—See LX Holdings Corp.; *Int'l*, pg. 4604
LX PANTOS SPAIN S.L.—See LX Holdings Corp.; *Int'l*, pg. 4604
LX PANTOS (THAILAND) CO., LTD.—See LX Holdings Corp.; *Int'l*, pg. 4604
LX PANTOS UK LTD.—See LX Holdings Corp.; *Int'l*, pg. 4604
LX PANTOS VIETNAM COMPANY LIMITED—See LX Holdings Corp.; *Int'l*, pg. 4604
LXP INDUSTRIAL TRUST; *U.S. Public*, pg. 1349
LXRANDCO; *Int'l*, pg. 4605
LX SEMICON CO., LTD.; *Int'l*, pg. 4604
LYBARGER OIL INC.; *U.S. Private*, pg. 2519
LYB INTERNATIONAL FINANCE II B.V.—See LyondellBasell Industries N.V.; *Int'l*, pg. 4608
LY BROTHERS CORPORATION; *U.S. Private*, pg. 2519
LYCAMOBILE UK LTD—See Lycatel Group; *Int'l*, pg. 4605
LYCAON RESOURCES LIMITED; *Int'l*, pg. 4605
LYCATEL CANADA INC—See Lycatel Group; *Int'l*, pg. 4605
LYCATEL GMBH—See Lycatel Group; *Int'l*, pg. 4605
LYCATEL GROUP; *Int'l*, pg. 4605
LYCATEL IRELAND LIMITED—See Lycatel Group; *Int'l*, pg. 4605
LYC CHILD CARE CENTRE SDN. BHD.—See LYC Healthcare Berhad; *Int'l*, pg. 4605
LYC HEALTHCARE BERHAD; *Int'l*, pg. 4605
LYCKEGARD FINLAND OY AB—See Lyckegard Group AB; *Int'l*, pg. 4605
LYCKEGARD GROUP AB; *Int'l*, pg. 4605
LYC MEDICARE SDN BHD—See LYC Healthcare Berhad; *Int'l*, pg. 4605
LYC MEDICARE (SINGAPORE) PTE. LTD.—See LYC Healthcare Berhad; *Int'l*, pg. 4605
LYCOMING-CLINTON JOINDER BOARD; *U.S. Private*, pg. 2519
LYCOMING COMMUNITY CARE INC; *U.S. Private*, pg. 2519
LYCON, INC.; *U.S. Private*, pg. 2519
LYCOPODIUM (GHANA) LIMITED—See Lycopodium Limited; *Int'l*, pg. 4605
LYCOPODIUM (GHANA) PTY LTD—See Lycopodium Limited; *Int'l*, pg. 4605
LYCOPODIUM LIMITED; *Int'l*, pg. 4605
LYCOPODIUM (PHILIPPINES) PTY LTD—See Lycopodium Limited; *Int'l*, pg. 4605
LY CORPORATION LIMITED; *Int'l*, pg. 4605
LY CORPORATION—See SoftBank Group Corp.; *Int'l*, pg. 7052
LYCOS ENERGY INC.; *Int'l*, pg. 4605
LYCOS, INC.—See Brightcove Group Ltd.; *Int'l*, pg. 1162
LYC SENIOR LIVING CARE CENTRE SDN. BHD.—See LYC Healthcare Berhad; *Int'l*, pg. 4605
LYC SENIOR LIVING SDN BHD—See LYC Healthcare Berhad; *Int'l*, pg. 4605
LYDALL FILTRATION, INC.—See Lydall, Inc.; *U.S. Public*, pg. 1349
LYDALL FILTRATION/SEPARATION, INC. ROCHESTER OPERATION—See Lydall, Inc.; *U.S. Public*, pg. 1349
LYDALL FILTRATION SEPARATION S.A.S.—See Lydall, Inc.; *U.S. Public*, pg. 1349
LYDALL GUTSCHE GMBH & CO. KG—See Lydall, Inc.; *U.S. Public*, pg. 1349
LYDALL, INC.; *U.S. Public*, pg. 1349
LYDALL INDUSTRIAL FILTRATION (EMEA) LIMITED—See Lydall, Inc.; *U.S. Public*, pg. 1349
LYDALL INDUSTRIAL FILTRATION TEXTILE MANUFACTURING (EMEA) LIMITED—See Lydall, Inc.; *U.S. Public*, pg. 1349
LYDALL INDUSTRIAL TEXTILE MANUFACTURING COMPANY (SHANGHAI) LIMITED—See Lydall, Inc.; *U.S. Public*, pg. 1349
LYDALL INDUSTRIAL TEXTILE MANUFACTURING COMPANY (WUXI) LIMITED—See Lydall, Inc.; *U.S. Public*, pg. 1349
LYDALL PERFORMANCE MATERIALS B.V.—See Lydall, Inc.; *U.S. Public*, pg. 1349
LYDALL PERFORMANCE MATERIALS, INC.—See Lydall, Inc.; *U.S. Public*, pg. 1350
LYDALL PERFORMANCE MATERIALS S.A.S.—See Lydall, Inc.; *U.S. Public*, pg. 1349
LYDALL SOLUTECH B.V.—See Lydall, Inc.; *U.S. Public*, pg. 1350
LYDALL THERMAL/ACOUSTICAL SALES, LLC—See Lydall, Inc.; *U.S. Public*, pg. 1350
LYDALL THERMAL/ACOUSTICAL—See Lydall, Inc.; *U.S. Public*, pg. 1350

LYDALL THERMAL/ACOUSTICAL (TAICANG) COMPANY LIMITED—See Lydall, Inc.; *U.S. Public*, pg. 1350
LYDALL THERMIQUE/ACOUSTIQUE S.A.S.—See Lydall, Inc.; *U.S. Public*, pg. 1350
LYDA SWINERTON BUILDERS, INC.; *U.S. Private*, pg. 2519
LYDEC—See Veolia Environnement S.A.; *Int'l*, pg. 8155
LYDEN OIL COMPANY-LANSING DIVISION—See Lyden Oil Company; *U.S. Private*, pg. 2519
LYDEN OIL COMPANY; *U.S. Private*, pg. 2519
LYDEN OIL COMPANY-YOUNGSTOWN DIVISION—See Lyden Oil Company; *U.S. Private*, pg. 2519
LYDIG CONSTRUCTION INC.; *U.S. Private*, pg. 2519
LYDIS B.V.—See Econocom Group SA; *Int'l*, pg. 2298
THE LYDON COMPANY, LLC.; *U.S. Private*, pg. 4073
LYDROMMET AS—See DistIT AB; *Int'l*, pg. 2136
LYELL IMMUNOPHARMA, INC.; *U.S. Public*, pg. 1350
LYE MANUFACTURING SDN. BHD.—See Engtex Group Berhad; *Int'l*, pg. 2436
LYE MARKETING SDN. BHD.—See Engtex Group Berhad; *Int'l*, pg. 2436
LYERLY AGENCY INC.; *U.S. Private*, pg. 2519
LYFE MARKETING LLC; *U.S. Private*, pg. 2519
LYFT, INC.; *U.S. Public*, pg. 1350
LYF-TYM BUILDING PRODUCTS CO., INC.—See Beacon Roofing Supply, Inc.; *U.S. Public*, pg. 286
LY FURNITURE SDN. BHD.—See LY Corporation Limited; *Int'l*, pg. 4605
LYGEND RESOURCES & TECHNOLOGY CO., LTD.; *Int'l*, pg. 4605
LYKA LABS LIMITED; *Int'l*, pg. 4605
LYKE CORPORATION—See Walsworth Publishing Company, Inc.; *U.S. Private*, pg. 4433
LYKES BROS. INC. - RANCH DIVISION—See Lykes Brothers Inc.; *U.S. Private*, pg. 2519
LYKES BROTHERS INC. - LYKES CITRUS DIVISION—See Lykes Brothers Inc.; *U.S. Private*, pg. 2519
LYKES BROTHERS INC.; *U.S. Private*, pg. 2519
LYKES CARTAGE COMPANY, INC.; *U.S. Private*, pg. 2519
LYKES INSURANCE, INC.—See Lykes Brothers Inc.; *U.S. Private*, pg. 2519
LYKES LAND INVESTMENTS, INC.—See Lykes Brothers Inc.; *U.S. Private*, pg. 2519
LYKINS COMPANIES, INC.; *U.S. Private*, pg. 2519
LYKINS OIL COMPANY—See Lykins Companies, Inc.; *U.S. Private*, pg. 2520
LYKINS TRANSPORTATION—See Lykins Companies, Inc.; *U.S. Private*, pg. 2520
LYKIS LIMITED; *Int'l*, pg. 4605
LYKOS BALKAN METALS D.O.O.—See Lykos Metals Limited; *Int'l*, pg. 4606
LYKOS METALS LIMITED; *Int'l*, pg. 4605
LYKOS PAPERLESS SOLUTIONS S.A.—See INFORM P. LYKOS S.A.; *Int'l*, pg. 3691
LYLE MACHINERY CO.; *U.S. Private*, pg. 2520
LYLES DIVERSIFIED INC.; *U.S. Private*, pg. 2520
LYLE SIGNS INC.; *U.S. Private*, pg. 2520
LYLES MECHANICAL CO.—See Lyles Diversified Inc.; *U.S. Private*, pg. 2520
LYLES UTILITY CONSTRUCTION, LLC—See Lyles Diversified Inc.; *U.S. Private*, pg. 2520
LYLLY CENTRE FOR CLINICAL PHARMACOLOGY PTE. LTD.—See Eli Lilly & Company; *U.S. Public*, pg. 734
LYMA KEMITEKNIK AB—See Indutrade AB; *Int'l*, pg. 3680
LYMAN BROS.; *U.S. Private*, pg. 2520
LYMAN DAVIDSON DOOLEY, INC.; *U.S. Private*, pg. 2520
LYMAN DAVIDSON DOOLEY INC.—See Lyman Davidson Dooley, Inc.; *U.S. Private*, pg. 2520
LYMAN PRODUCTS CORPORATION; *U.S. Private*, pg. 2520
LYMAN-RICHEY CORPORATION; *U.S. Private*, pg. 2520
LYMINGTON PRECISION ENGINEERS CO., LTD.—See Senior plc; *Int'l*, pg. 6708
LYMPIKE PTY LTD—See Gebr. Knauf KG; *Int'l*, pg. 2908
LYMPIKE PTY LTD—See Seven Group Holdings Limited; *Int'l*, pg. 6733
LYMTAL INTERNATIONAL, INC.; *U.S. Private*, pg. 2520
LYNAS MALAYSIA SDN BHD—See Lynas Rare Earths Limited; *Int'l*, pg. 4606
LYNAS RARE EARTHS LIMITED; *Int'l*, pg. 4606
LYNAY HEALTHCARE INC.; *U.S. Private*, pg. 2520
LYNCHBURG HYUNDAI MITSUBISHI INC; *U.S. Private*, pg. 2521
LYNCHBURG STEEL & SPECIALTY CO.—See Beta International & Affiliates; *U.S. Private*, pg. 544
LYNCH FORD MOUNT VERNON INC.; *U.S. Private*, pg. 2520
LYNCH GROUP HOLDINGS LIMITED; *Int'l*, pg. 4606
LYNCH HOLDINGS, LLC; *U.S. Private*, pg. 2520
LYNCH INSULATION OF MONTANA, LLC—See Installed Building Products, Inc.; *U.S. Public*, pg. 1133
LYNCH INSURANCE BROKERS LIMITED—See Marsh & McLennan Companies, Inc.; *U.S. Public*, pg. 1377
LYNCH LIVESTOCK INC.; *U.S. Private*, pg. 2521
LYNCH MATERIAL HANDLING CO.; *U.S. Private*, pg. 2521
LYNC LOGISTICS, LLC; *U.S. Private*, pg. 2520

LYNCO FLANGE & FITTING, INC.; *U.S. Private*, pg. 2521
LYNDALE ENTERPRISES INC.; *U.S. Private*, pg. 2521
LYNDAN, INC.; *U.S. Private*, pg. 2521
THE LYND COMPANY; *U.S. Private*, pg. 4073
LYNDE CREEK MANOR RETIREMENT COMMUNITY INC.—See Extendicare Inc.; *Int'l*, pg. 2591
LYNDEN AIR CARGO, LLC—See Lynden Incorporated; *U.S. Private*, pg. 2521
LYNDEN AIR FREIGHT, INC.—See Lynden Incorporated; *U.S. Private*, pg. 2521
LYNDEN INCORPORATED; *U.S. Private*, pg. 2521
LYNDEN INTERNATIONAL LOGISTICS CO.—See Lynden Incorporated; *U.S. Private*, pg. 2521
LYNDEN INTERNATIONAL—See Lynden Incorporated; *U.S. Private*, pg. 2521
LYNDEN LOGISTICS, INC.—See Lynden Incorporated; *U.S. Private*, pg. 2521
LYNDEN TRANSPORT, INC.—See Lynden Incorporated; *U.S. Private*, pg. 2521
LYNDON PROPERTY INSURANCE COMPANY—See Dai-ichi Life Holdings, Inc.; *Int'l*, pg. 1917
LYNDON SOUTHERN INSURANCE COMPANY—See Tiptree Inc.; *U.S. Public*, pg. 2159
LYNDON STEEL COMPANY LLC; *U.S. Private*, pg. 2521
LYNEER STAFFING SOLUTIONS, LLC; *U.S. Private*, pg. 2521
LYNET KOMMUNIKATION AG—See SPARTA AG; *Int'l*, pg. 7127
LYNGSO GARDEN MATERIALS, INC.; *U.S. Private*, pg. 2521
LYNGSO MARINE A/S—See L3Harris Technologies, Inc.; *U.S. Public*, pg. 1284
LYNK USA, INC.—See B.O.S. Better OnLine Solutions Ltd.; *Int'l*, pg. 790
LYN-LAD GROUP LTD.; *U.S. Private*, pg. 2520
LYNN ASSOCIATES INC.; *U.S. Private*, pg. 2521
LYNN ECONOMIC OPPORTUNITY, INC.; *U.S. Private*, pg. 2521
LYNN ELECTRONICS CORPORATION—See Odyssey Investment Partners, LLC; *U.S. Private*, pg. 2995
LYNN-ETTE & SONS, INC.; *U.S. Private*, pg. 2522
LYNNHAVEN MALL—See Brookfield Corporation; *Int'l*, pg. 1185
LYNNHAVEN MARINE BOATEL INC.; *U.S. Private*, pg. 2522
LYNN LAYTON FORD; *U.S. Private*, pg. 2522
LYNN ROBERTS INTERNATIONAL; *U.S. Private*, pg. 2522
LYNNS MARKET INC.; *U.S. Private*, pg. 2522
LYNNWOOD HEALTH SERVICES, INC.—See The Ensign Group, Inc.; *U.S. Public*, pg. 2071
LYNNWOOD INNS, INC.—See Hilton Worldwide Holdings Inc.; *U.S. Public*, pg. 1041
LYNTEGAR ELECTRIC COOPERATIVE INC.; *U.S. Private*, pg. 2522
LYNWOOD BUILDING MATERIALS, INC.; *U.S. Private*, pg. 2522
LYNX EQUITY LIMITED; *Int'l*, pg. 4606
LYNX EUROPE 2 LIMITED—See Liberty Global plc; *Int'l*, pg. 4485
LYNX FRANCHISING, LLC—See MidOcean Partners, LLP; *U.S. Private*, pg. 2717
LYNX GLOBAL DIGITAL FINANCE CORPORATION; *Int'l*, pg. 4606
LYNX GRILLS, INC.—See The Middleby Corporation; *U.S. Public*, pg. 2114
LYNX HOLDCO INC—See The Middleby Corporation; *U.S. Public*, pg. 2114
LYNX MACHINERY & COMMERCIALS LIMITED; *Int'l*, pg. 4606
LYNX OPERATING COMPANY INCORPORATED; *U.S. Private*, pg. 2522
LYNX PORTER NOVELLI AS—See Omnicom Group Inc.; *U.S. Public*, pg. 1591
LYNX PRODUCT GROUP, LLC.—See Chalmers Group of Companies; *Int'l*, pg. 1438
LYNX PR—See Freshwater UK PLC; *Int'l*, pg. 2782
LYNX RESOURCES (US) INC.—See BHP Group Limited; *Int'l*, pg. 1016
LYNX SERVICES, LLC—See Vista Equity Partners, LLC; *U.S. Private*, pg. 4400
LYNXS HOLDING LLC; *U.S. Private*, pg. 2522
THE LYON & BILLARD CO., INC.; *U.S. Private*, pg. 4073
LYON-COFFEY ELECTRIC COOPERATIVE, INC.; *U.S. Private*, pg. 2522
LYONDELL ASIA PACIFIC, LTD.—See LyondellBasell Industries N.V.; *Int'l*, pg. 4608
LYONDELLBASELL ACETYLS, LLC—See LyondellBasell Industries N.V.; *Int'l*, pg. 4608
LYONDELLBASELL ADVANCED POLYOLEFINS PTY LTD—See LyondellBasell Industries N.V.; *Int'l*, pg. 4607
LYONDELLBASELL ADVANCED POLYOLEFINS USA, INC.—See LyondellBasell Industries N.V.; *Int'l*, pg. 4608
LYONDELLBASELL AUSTRALIA PTY LTD—See Viva Energy Group Limited; *Int'l*, pg. 8264
LYONDELLBASELL BRASIL LTDA.—See LyondellBasell Industries N.V.; *Int'l*, pg. 4608

LYONDELLBASELL EGYPT LLC—See LyondellBasell Industries N.V.; *Int'l*, pg. 4608
LYONDELLBASELL INDUSTRIES N.V.; *Int'l*, pg. 4606
LYONDELLBASELL INDUSTRIES—See LyondellBasell Industries N.V.; *Int'l*, pg. 4608
LYONDELL BRUSSELS—See LyondellBasell Industries N.V.; *Int'l*, pg. 4608
LYONDELL CHEMICAL COMPANY—See LyondellBasell Industries N.V.; *Int'l*, pg. 4608
LYONDELL CHEMICAL EUROPE, INC.—See LyondellBasell Industries N.V.; *Int'l*, pg. 4608
LYONDELL CHEMICAL ITALIA SRL—See LyondellBasell Industries N.V.; *Int'l*, pg. 4608
LYONDELL CHEMIE NEDERLAND B.V.—See LyondellBasell Industries N.V.; *Int'l*, pg. 4608
LYONDELL CHIMIE FRANCE, SAS—See LyondellBasell Industries N.V.; *Int'l*, pg. 4608
LYONDELL CHIMIE FRANCE SNC—See LyondellBasell Industries N.V.; *Int'l*, pg. 4608
LYONDELL GREATER CHINA, LTD.—See LyondellBasell Industries N.V.; *Int'l*, pg. 4608
LYONDELL JAPAN, INC.—See LyondellBasell Industries N.V.; *Int'l*, pg. 4608
LYONDELL QUIMICA DO BRASIL LTDA.—See LyondellBasell Industries N.V.; *Int'l*, pg. 4608
LYONDELL REFINING COMPANY LLC—See LyondellBasell Industries N.V.; *Int'l*, pg. 4608
LYONDELL SOUTH ASIA PTE LTD—See LyondellBasell Industries N.V.; *Int'l*, pg. 4608
LYON & DITTRICH HOLDING COMPANY; *U.S. Private*, pg. 2522
LYON MAINTENANCE—See Air France-KLM S.A.; *Int'l*, pg. 238
LYONNAISE DES EAUX FRANCE—See Veolia Environnement S.A.; *Int'l*, pg. 8155
LYON POCHE PRESSE; *Int'l*, pg. 4606
LYON ROOFING & SUPPLY; *U.S. Private*, pg. 2522
LYONS BANCORP, INC.; *U.S. Public*, pg. 1350
THE LYONS COMPANIES; *U.S. Private*, pg. 4073
LYONS CONSULTING GROUP INC.—See Capgemini SE; *Int'l*, pg. 1307
LYONS CORPORATE MARKET LIMITED; *Int'l*, pg. 4608
LYONS EQUIPMENT COMPANY, INC.—See CJ Logging Equipment LLC; *U.S. Private*, pg. 908
LYONS GAS—See UGI Corporation; *U.S. Public*, pg. 2221
LYONS HR, INC.—See New Mountain Capital, LLC; *U.S. Private*, pg. 2901
LYONS INDUSTRIES, INC.; *U.S. Private*, pg. 2522
THE LYONS NATIONAL BANK—See Lyons Bancorp, Inc.; *U.S. Public*, pg. 1350
LYONS SEAFOODS LIMITED—See Alfesca hf.; *Int'l*, pg. 315
LYON VIDEO, INC.—See Live Media Group, LLC; *U.S. Private*, pg. 2473
LYOPHILIZATION SERVICES OF NEW ENGLAND, INC.—See Kohlberg & Company, LLC; *U.S. Private*, pg. 2339
LYPPARD AUSTRALIA LIMITED; *Int'l*, pg. 4608
LYPRO BIOSCIENCES, INC.—See Abionyx Pharma SA; *Int'l*, pg. 62
LYPSA GEMS & JEWELLERY LIMITED; *Int'l*, pg. 4609
LYRA ASIA PTE LTD—See F.I.L.A. - Fabbrica Italiana Lapis ed Affini S.p.A.; *Int'l*, pg. 2597
LYRA SCANDINAVIA AB—See F.I.L.A. - Fabbrica Italiana Lapis ed Affini S.p.A.; *Int'l*, pg. 2597
LYRASIS INC.; *U.S. Private*, pg. 2522
LYRA THERAPEUTICS, INC.; *U.S. Public*, pg. 1350
LYRECO AUSTRALIA—See Lyreco S.A.S.; *Int'l*, pg. 4609
LYRECO BENELUX SA—See Lyreco S.A.S.; *Int'l*, pg. 4609
LYRECO (CANADA) LIMITED—See Lyreco S.A.S.; *Int'l*, pg. 4609
LYRECO CE/SE—See Lyreco S.A.S.; *Int'l*, pg. 4609
LYRECO DANMARK A/S—See Lyreco S.A.S.; *Int'l*, pg. 4609
LYRECO DEUTSCHLAND GMBH—See Lyreco S.A.S.; *Int'l*, pg. 4609
LYRECO ESPANA, S.A.—See Lyreco S.A.S.; *Int'l*, pg. 4609
LYRECO FINLAND OY—See Lyreco S.A.S.; *Int'l*, pg. 4609
LYRECO (HONG KONG) CO. LTD.—See Lyreco S.A.S.; *Int'l*, pg. 4609
LYRECO IRELAND LTD—See Lyreco S.A.S.; *Int'l*, pg. 4609
LYRECO ITALIA SPA—See Lyreco S.A.S.; *Int'l*, pg. 4609
LYRECO (JAPAN) CO. LTD.—See Lyreco S.A.S.; *Int'l*, pg. 4609
LYRECO (KOREA) CO., LTD.—See Lyreco S.A.S.; *Int'l*, pg. 4609
LYRECO LUXEMBOURG SA—See Lyreco S.A.S.; *Int'l*, pg. 4609
LYRECO NEDERLAND B.V.—See Lyreco S.A.S.; *Int'l*, pg. 4609
LYRECO NORGE AS—See Lyreco S.A.S.; *Int'l*, pg. 4609
LYRECO OFFICE SUPPLIES (M) SDN. BHD.—See Lyreco S.A.S.; *Int'l*, pg. 4609
LYRECO POLSKA SA—See Lyreco S.A.S.; *Int'l*, pg. 4609
LYRECO PORTUGAL, S.A.—See Lyreco S.A.S.; *Int'l*, pg. 4609
LYRECO S.A.S.; *Int'l*, pg. 4609

LYRECO (SINGAPORE) PTE LTD.—See Lyreco S.A.S.; *Int'l*, pg. 4609
LYRECO SVERIGE AB—See Lyreco S.A.S.; *Int'l*, pg. 4609
LYRECO SWITZERLAND AG—See Lyreco S.A.S.; *Int'l*, pg. 4609
LYRECO UK LTD.—See Lyreco S.A.S.; *Int'l*, pg. 4609
LYSAGHT GALVANIZED STEEL BERHAD; *Int'l*, pg. 4609
LYSAGHT MARKETING SDN. BHD.—See Lysaght Galvanized Steel Berhad; *Int'l*, pg. 4609
LYSAGHT MARKETING (S) PTE. LTD.—See Lysaght Galvanized Steel Berhad; *Int'l*, pg. 4609
LYSANDA LTD.—See Tantalum Corporation Limited; *Int'l*, pg. 7460
LYSING LTD.—See Klakki ehf.; *Int'l*, pg. 4199
LYSIS SA—See Kudelski S.A.; *Int'l*, pg. 4323
LYSOGENE; *Int'l*, pg. 4609
LYSSAND TREINDUSTRI AS—See Ratos AB; *Int'l*, pg. 6220
LYSSE—See E&A Industries, Inc.; *U.S. Private*, pg. 1301
LYTAG LTD—See Holcim Ltd.; *Int'l*, pg. 3446
LYTE MALAYSIA SDN. BHD.—See OSK Holdings Berhad; *Int'l*, pg. 5651
LYTRON INCORPORATED—See The Goldman Sachs Group, Inc.; *U.S. Public*, pg. 2080
LYTTELTON PORT COMPANY LIMITED—See Christchurch City Holdings Ltd.; *Int'l*, pg. 1586
LYTTON GARDENS INC.; *U.S. Private*, pg. 2522
LYTUS TECHNOLOGIES HOLDINGS PTV. LTD.; *Int'l*, pg. 4609
LYTX, INC.—See Permira Advisers LLP; *Int'l*, pg. 5807
LYVEN S.A.—See Etablissements J. Soufflet; *Int'l*, pg. 2519
LYVE S.R.L.—See Openjobmetis S.p.A.; *Int'l*, pg. 5599
LZB FURNITURE GALLERIES OF PARAMUS, INC.—See La-Z-Boy Incorporated; *U.S. Public*, pg. 1285
LZB FURNITURE GALLERIES OF ST. LOUIS, INC.—See La-Z-Boy Incorporated; *U.S. Public*, pg. 1285
LZ-CATERING GMBH—See Deutsche Lufthansa AG; *Int'l*, pg. 2068
LZG INTERNATIONAL, INC.—See Genius Group Limited; *Int'l*, pg. 2924
LZ LIFESCIENCE LIMITED—See Cognizant Technology Solutions Corporation; *U.S. Public*, pg. 524
LZ LIFESCIENCE US INC.—See Cognizant Technology Solutions Corporation; *U.S. Public*, pg. 524

M

M1 D.D. LJUBLJANA; *Int'l*, pg. 4617
M1-ENERGY LLC—See E1 Corporation; *Int'l*, pg. 2260
M1 KLINIKEN AG; *Int'l*, pg. 4617
M1 LIMITED; *Int'l*, pg. 4617
M1 MED BEAUTY CROATIA D.O.O.—See M1 Kliniken AG; *Int'l*, pg. 4617
M1 MED BEAUTY HUNGARY KFT.—See M1 Kliniken AG; *Int'l*, pg. 4617
M1 MED BEAUTY NETHERLANDS B.V.—See M1 Kliniken AG; *Int'l*, pg. 4617
M1 MED BEAUTY UK LTD.—See M1 Kliniken AG; *Int'l*, pg. 4617
M1 NET LTD.—See M1 Limited; *Int'l*, pg. 4617
M1 PAY SDN. BHD.—See MobilityOne Limited; *Int'l*, pg. 5011
M247 EUROPE SRL—See Livingbridge EP LLP; *Int'l*, pg. 4532
M247 LIMITED—See Livingbridge EP LLP; *Int'l*, pg. 4532
M2B WORLD ASIA PACIFIC PTE. LTD.—See AMARU, INC.; *Int'l*, pg. 412
M2B WORLD PTE. LTD.—See AMARU, INC.; *Int'l*, pg. 412
M2 COMMANDER PTY. LTD.—See Aware Super Pty Ltd; *Int'l*, pg. 752
M2 COMMANDER PTY. LTD.—See Macquarie Group Limited; *Int'l*, pg. 4629
M2 COMMUNICATIONS LTD; *Int'l*, pg. 4617
M2E LLC; *U.S. Private*, pg. 2530
M2 EQUIPMENT FINANCE, LLC—See QCR Holdings, Inc.; *U.S. Public*, pg. 1742
M2GEN—See H. Lee Moffitt Cancer Center & Research Institute; *U.S. Private*, pg. 1825
M2I CORPORATION; *Int'l*, pg. 4617
M2I FORMATION DIPL SA—See Prologue S.A.; *Int'l*, pg. 5992
M2I FORMATION—See Prologue S.A.; *Int'l*, pg. 5992
M2I LOCATION SA—See Prologue S.A.; *Int'l*, pg. 5992
M2I SA; *Int'l*, pg. 4617
M2I TECH SASU—See Prologue S.A.; *Int'l*, pg. 5992
M2K-LASER GMBH—See Coherent Corp.; *U.S. Public*, pg. 528
M2L2 COMMUNICATIONS; *U.S. Private*, pg. 2530
M2 LEASE FUNDS, LLC—See QCR Holdings, Inc.; *U.S. Public*, pg. 1742
M2L INC.; *U.S. Private*, pg. 2530
M2M COMMUNICATIONS; *U.S. Private*, pg. 2530
M2M DATA CORP.—See Caterpillar, Inc.; *U.S. Public*, pg. 452
M2 MEDIA GROUP, LLC; *U.S. Private*, pg. 2530
M2M EUROPE NETWORK & SOLUTIONS GES.MBH—See OHB SE; *Int'l*, pg. 5532
M2M GROUP SA; *Int'l*, pg. 4617

M2N CO., LTD.; *Int'l*, pg. 4617
M2P MEDIENFABRIK GMBH & CO. KG—See Pearson plc; *Int'l*, pg. 5778
M2S MIDDLE EAST FZE—See BC Partners LLP; *Int'l*, pg. 922
M2S MIDDLE EAST FZE—See The Carlyle Group Inc.; *U.S. Public*, pg. 2044
M2 SYSTEMS CORPORATION—See Digital Payments PLC; *Int'l*, pg. 2123
M2 TECHNOLOGY, INC.; *U.S. Private*, pg. 2530
M2 UNIVERSAL COMMUNICATIONS MANAGEMENT—See The Interpublic Group of Companies, Inc.; *U.S. Public*, pg. 2100
M30 STANDS 2003 S.A.—See Espiga Capital Gestion S.G.E.C.R, S.A.; *Int'l*, pg. 2506
M3 ACCOUNTING SERVICES INC.; *U.S. Private*, pg. 2530
M3-BRIGADE ACQUISITION V CORP.; *U.S. Public*, pg. 1351
M3 CAPITAL PARTNERS LLC; *U.S. Private*, pg. 2530
M3 CAREER, INC.—See SMS Co., Ltd.; *Int'l*, pg. 7014
M3 ELECTRONIC GMBH—See DISA LIMITED; *Int'l*, pg. 2131
M3 FINANCIAL, INC.—See Simplicity Financial Marketing Holdings Inc.; *U.S. Public*, pg. 3667
M3 GLASS TECHNOLOGIES; *U.S. Private*, pg. 2530
M3, INC.—See Sony Group Corporation; *Int'l*, pg. 7102
M3 INSURANCE SOLUTIONS, INC.; *U.S. Private*, pg. 2530
M3 MANAGEMENT CONSULTING GMBH—See msg group GmbH; *Int'l*, pg. 5067
M3 METALS CORP.; *Int'l*, pg. 4617
M3 MIDSTREAM LLC; *U.S. Private*, pg. 2530
M3 MINING LIMITED; *Int'l*, pg. 4617
M3 SAS—See Groupe Dubreuil SA; *Int'l*, pg. 3102
M3 STEEL STRUCTURES LTD.; *Int'l*, pg. 4618
M3 TECHNOLOGIES MIDDLE EAST FZE—See XOX Technology Bhd; *Int'l*, pg. 8537
M3 TECHNOLOGIES PAKISTAN (PRIVATE) LIMITED—See XOX Technology Bhd; *Int'l*, pg. 8536
M3 TECHNOLOGIES (SHENZHEN) COMPANY LIMITED—See XOX Technology Bhd; *Int'l*, pg. 8537
M3 TECHNOLOGIES (THAILAND) CO., LTD.—See XOX Technology Bhd; *Int'l*, pg. 8536
M3 TECHNOLOGIES (XIAMEN) CO., LTD—See XOX Technology Bhd; *Int'l*, pg. 8537
M3 USA CORPORATION—See Sony Group Corporation; *Int'l*, pg. 7102
M45 MARKETING SERVICES; *U.S. Private*, pg. 2530
M4D (JOHOR) SDN. BHD.—See MPHB Capital Berhad; *Int'l*, pg. 5062
M4E AG—See Studio 100 NV; *Int'l*, pg. 7244
M4JAM (PTY) LTD.—See Lesaka Technologies, Inc.; *Int'l*, pg. 4468
M5 MARKETING COMMUNICATIONS INC.—See Group m5; *Int'l*, pg. 3089
M5 MARKETING COMMUNICATIONS, INC.—See Group m5; *Int'l*, pg. 3089
M6 COMMUNICATION SAS—See Metropole Television SA; *Int'l*, pg. 4863
M6 INTERACTIONS SAS—See Metropole Television SA; *Int'l*, pg. 4863
M6 PUBLICITE SAS—See Bertelsmann SE & Co. KGaA; *Int'l*, pg. 993
M6-THEMATIQUE SAS—See Metropole Television SA; *Int'l*, pg. 4863
M6 TOLNA UZEMELTETO KFT—See Groupe Egis S.A.; *Int'l*, pg. 3102
M6 WEB SAS—See Metropole Television SA; *Int'l*, pg. 4863
M7 AEROSPACE LP—See Elbit Systems Limited; *Int'l*, pg. 2344
M7 GROUP SA—See Vivendi SE; *Int'l*, pg. 8278
M7 SERVICES, LLC; *U.S. Private*, pg. 2530
M80—See WPP plc; *Int'l*, pg. 8475
M9 SOLUTIONS; *U.S. Private*, pg. 2530
MAA ARKANSAS REIT, LLC—See Mid-America Apartment Communities, Inc.; *U.S. Public*, pg. 1444
MAABAROT PRODUCTS LTD.; *Int'l*, pg. 4618
MAAF ASSURANCES S.A.—See Covea Groupe S.A.S.; *Int'l*, pg. 1820
MAAG AUTOMATIK GMBH—See Dover Corporation; *U.S. Public*, pg. 681
MAAG AUTOMATIK, INC.—See Dover Corporation; *U.S. Public*, pg. 681
MAAG AUTOMATIK PLASTICS MACHINERY (SHANGHAI) CO., LTD.—See Dover Corporation; *U.S. Public*, pg. 681
MAAG AUTOMATIK SRL—See Dover Corporation; *U.S. Public*, pg. 681
MAA GENERAL ASSURANCE PHILIPPINES, INC.—See MAA Group Berhad; *Int'l*, pg. 4618
MAAGH ADVERTISING & MARKETING SERVICES LIMITED; *Int'l*, pg. 4618
MAAG PUMP SYSTEMS AG—See Dover Corporation; *U.S. Public*, pg. 681
MAAG PUMP SYSTEMS GMBH—See Dover Corporation; *U.S. Public*, pg. 682

MAAG PUMP SYSTEMS PTE. LTD.—See Dover Corporation; *U.S. Public*, pg. 682
MAAG PUMP SYSTEMS SAS—See Dover Corporation; *U.S. Public*, pg. 682
MAAG PUMP SYSTEMS (SWITZERLAND) AG—See Dover Corporation; *U.S. Public*, pg. 682
MAA GROUP BERHAD; *Int'l*, pg. 4618
MAAGTECHNIC AG—See SHV Holdings N.V.; *Int'l*, pg. 6871
MAA JAGDAMBE TRADELINKS LTD.; *Int'l*, pg. 4618
MAALI ENTERPRISES INC.; *U.S. Private*, pg. 2530
MAALI RESTAURANT INC.—See Maali Enterprises Inc.; *U.S. Private*, pg. 2530
MAAN AL SANEA FURNITURE—See SAAD Group; *Int'l*, pg. 6460
MAAN ALUMINIUM LTD.; *Int'l*, pg. 4618
M.A. ANGELIADES INC.; *U.S. Private*, pg. 2527
MA'ANSHAN DALI FOODS CO., LTD.—See Dali Foods Group Co. Ltd.; *Int'l*, pg. 1951
MAANSHAN IRON AND STEEL (AUSTRALIA) PROPRIETARY LIMITED—See China Baowu Steel Group Corp., Ltd.; *Int'l*, pg. 1486
MAANSHAN IRON & STEEL COMPANY LIMITED—See China Baowu Steel Group Corp., Ltd.; *Int'l*, pg. 1485
MAANSHAN IRON & STEEL (HK) LIMITED—See China Baowu Steel Group Corp., Ltd.; *Int'l*, pg. 1486
MA'ANSHAN POLY GRAND THEATRE MANAGEMENT CORPORATION LIMITED—See Poly Culture Group Corporation Limited; *Int'l*, pg. 5914
MAANSHAN YUSHAN METALLURGY NEW MATERIALS CO., LTD.—See Puyang Refractories Group Co., Ltd.; *Int'l*, pg. 6124
MAARUD AS—See Intersnack Group GmbH & Co. KG; *Int'l*, pg. 3761
MAASDOTS SDN. BHD.—See G3 Global Berhad; *Int'l*, pg. 2866
MAAS GROUP HOLDINGS LIMITED; *Int'l*, pg. 4618
MAAS-HANSEN STEEL CORPORATION; *U.S. Private*, pg. 2530
MAAS INTERNATIONAL B.V.—See Miko NV; *Int'l*, pg. 4892
MAASKANT SHIPYARDS BV—See Damen Shipyards Group; *Int'l*, pg. 1956
MAASS CORPORATION; *U.S. Private*, pg. 2530
MAASSEN OIL COMPANY INC.—See Palmdale Oil Company, Inc.; *U.S. Private*, pg. 3080
MAASS FLANGE CORPORATION—See AFG Holdings, Inc.; *U.S. Private*, pg. 123
THE MAASTRICHT FORENSIC INSTITUTE B.V.—See Eurofins Scientific S.E.; *Int'l*, pg. 2552
MAASVLAKTE ENERGIE B.V.—See L'Air Liquide S.A.; *Int'l*, pg. 4372
MAAT PHARMA SA; *Int'l*, pg. 4618
MA AUTOMOTIVE BRAZIL LTD.—See Unipres Corporation; *Int'l*, pg. 8056
MAAX BATH INC. - PLYMOUTH—See American Bath Group; *U.S. Private*, pg. 224
MAAX BATH INC.—See American Bath Group; *U.S. Private*, pg. 224
MAAX CANADA INC.—See American Bath Group; *U.S. Private*, pg. 224
MAAX FACTOR SDN. BHD.—See MAA Group Berhad; *Int'l*, pg. 4618
MAAX INC.-MINNEAPOLIS—See American Bath Group; *U.S. Private*, pg. 224
MAAX INC.-VALDOSTA—See American Bath Group; *U.S. Private*, pg. 224
MAAX SPAS INDUSTRIES CORP.—See American Bath Group; *U.S. Private*, pg. 224
MAAYAN VENTURES LTD.; *Int'l*, pg. 4618
MABANAFT AUSTRIA GMBH & CO. KG—See Marquard & Bahls AG; *Int'l*, pg. 4699
MABANAFT HUNGARY KFT.—See Marquard & Bahls AG; *Int'l*, pg. 4699
MABANAFT LIMITED—See Marquard & Bahls AG; *Int'l*, pg. 4699
MABANAFT MOLDOVA SRL—See Marquard & Bahls AG; *Int'l*, pg. 4699
MABANAFT PTE. LTD.—See Marquard & Bahls AG; *Int'l*, pg. 4699
MABANEE COMPANY S.A.K.; *Int'l*, pg. 4618
MABBETT & ASSOCIATES, INC.; *U.S. Private*, pg. 2531
MABCO CONSTRUCTION S.A.—See The Mabetex Group; *Int'l*, pg. 7665
MAB DEVELOPMENT GROUP B.V.—See Cooperatieve Centrale Raiffeisen-Boerenleenbank B.A.; *Int'l*, pg. 1791
MAB DEVELOPMENT NEDERLAND B.V.—See Cooperatieve Centrale Raiffeisen-Boerenleenbank B.A.; *Int'l*, pg. 1791
MABE CHILE LTDA.—See Maire Tecnimont S.p.A.; *Int'l*, pg. 4652
MABECO NV—See Ackermans & van Haaren NV; *Int'l*, pg. 106
MABEG MACHINERY (SHANGHAI) CO., LTD.—See Koenig & Bauer AG; *Int'l*, pg. 4227
MABELEK SIGNLIGHT—See A.A.G. STUCCHI s.r.l.; *Int'l*, pg. 23
MABEMA AB—See Pomona-Gruppen AB; *Int'l*, pg. 5918

MABE MEXICO, S. DE R.L. DE C.V.—See Panasonic Holdings Corporation; *Int'l*, pg. 5725
MABESA DO BRASIL LTDA—See Hypera Pharma S.A.; *Int'l*, pg. 3553
THE MABETEX GROUP; *Int'l*, pg. 7664
MABETOC—See Compagnie de Saint-Gobain SA; *Int'l*, pg. 1724
MABION SA; *Int'l*, pg. 4618
MAB LTD.; *U.S. Private*, pg. 2531
MAB MANNESMANN GMBH; *Int'l*, pg. 4618
MABO FARMA, S.A.U.—See LURA Grupa doo; *Int'l*, pg. 4586
M.A. BONGIOVANNI INC.; *U.S. Private*, pg. 2527
MABPHARM LIMITED; *Int'l*, pg. 4618
MABREY BANCORPORATION INC.; *U.S. Private*, pg. 2531
MABREY BANK—See Mabrey Bancorporation Inc.; *U.S. Private*, pg. 2531
MABROC TEAS (PVT) LTD.—See Hayleys PLC; *Int'l*, pg. 3292
MABRY IRON CASTINGS, LLC—See Advanced Metals Group, LLC; *U.S. Private*, pg. 91
MABUCHI INDUSTRY CO., LTD.—See Mabuchi Motor Co., Ltd.; *Int'l*, pg. 4619
MABUCHI MOTOR AMERICA CORP.—See Mabuchi Motor Co., Ltd.; *Int'l*, pg. 4619
MABUCHI MOTOR CO., LTD.; *Int'l*, pg. 4619
MABUCHI MOTOR DALIAN CO.,LTD.—See Mabuchi Motor Co., Ltd.; *Int'l*, pg. 4619
MABUCHI MOTOR DANANG LTD.—See Mabuchi Motor Co., Ltd.; *Int'l*, pg. 4619
MABUCHI MOTOR (DONGGUAN) CO., LTD.—See Mabuchi Motor Co., Ltd.; *Int'l*, pg. 4619
MABUCHI MOTOR DONGGUAN DAOJIAO CO., LTD.—See Mabuchi Motor Co., Ltd.; *Int'l*, pg. 4619
MABUCHI MOTOR ELECTROMAG SA—See Mabuchi Motor Co., Ltd.; *Int'l*, pg. 4619
MABUCHI MOTOR (EUROPE) GMBH—See Mabuchi Motor Co., Ltd.; *Int'l*, pg. 4619
MABUCHI MOTOR (JIANGSU) CO., LTD.—See Mabuchi Motor Co., Ltd.; *Int'l*, pg. 4619
MABUCHI MOTOR (JIANGXI) CO., LTD.—See Mabuchi Motor Co., Ltd.; *Int'l*, pg. 4619
MABUCHI MOTOR KOREA CO., LTD.—See Mabuchi Motor Co., Ltd.; *Int'l*, pg. 4619
MABUCHI MOTOR MEXICO S.A. DE C.V.—See Mabuchi Motor Co., Ltd.; *Int'l*, pg. 4619
MABUCHI MOTOR OKEN CO., LTD.—See Mabuchi Motor Co., Ltd.; *Int'l*, pg. 4619
MABUCHI MOTOR POLAND SP. Z O.O.—See Mabuchi Motor Co., Ltd.; *Int'l*, pg. 4619
MABUCHI MOTOR (SHANGHAI) CO., LTD.—See Mabuchi Motor Co., Ltd.; *Int'l*, pg. 4619
MABUCHI MOTOR (SINGAPORE) PTE LTD.—See Mabuchi Motor Co., Ltd.; *Int'l*, pg. 4619
MABUCHI MOTOR TAIWAN LTD.—See Mabuchi Motor Co., Ltd.; *Int'l*, pg. 4619
MABUCHI MOTOR (THAILAND) CO., LTD.—See Mabuchi Motor Co., Ltd.; *Int'l*, pg. 4619
MABUCHI MOTOR TRADING (SHENZHEN) CO., LTD.—See Mabuchi Motor Co., Ltd.; *Int'l*, pg. 4619
MABUCHI MOTOR VIETNAM LTD.—See Mabuchi Motor Co., Ltd.; *Int'l*, pg. 4619
MABUCHI MOTOR WAFANGDIAN CO.,LTD.—See Mabuchi Motor Co., Ltd.; *Int'l*, pg. 4619
MABUCHI TAIWAN CO., LTD.—See Mabuchi Motor Co., Ltd.; *Int'l*, pg. 4619
MABUCHI PRECISION (JIANGMEN) CO., LTD.—See Mabuchi Motor Co., Ltd.; *Int'l*, pg. 4619
M. ABUHAB PARTICIPACOES S.A.; *Int'l*, pg. 4615
MABUHAY HOLDINGS CORPORATION; *Int'l*, pg. 4619
MABUHAY MILES SERVICE CENTER—See PAL Holdings, Inc.; *Int'l*, pg. 5705
MABUHAY PHILIPPINES SATELLITE CORP.—See PLDT Inc.; *Int'l*, pg. 5896
MABUHAY VINYL CORPORATION—See Tosoh Corporation; *Int'l*, pg. 7832
MABUS BROTHERS CONSTRUCTION COMPANY INC.; *U.S. Private*, pg. 2531
MABXIENCE SWITZERLAND—See Insud Pharma, S.L.; *Int'l*, pg. 3725
MABXIENCE URUGUAY—See Insud Pharma, S.L.; *Int'l*, pg. 3725
MACADAM FLOOR & DESIGN; *U.S. Private*, pg. 2531
MACADAMS INTERNATIONAL (PTY) LTD.—See TRG Management LP; *U.S. Private*, pg. 4220
MACADOS INC.; *U.S. Private*, pg. 2531
MACA LIMITED; *Int'l*, pg. 4619
THE MACALLAN DISTILLERS LIMITED—See The Edrington Group; *Int'l*, pg. 7638
MACALLISTER MACHINERY CO. INC.; *U.S. Private*, pg. 2531
MAC ALPHA LIMITED; *Int'l*, pg. 4619
THE MACALUSO GROUP; *U.S. Private*, pg. 4073
MACANDREWS & COMPANY LIMITED—See CMA CGM S.A.; *Int'l*, pg. 1668
MACANDREWS & FORBES INCORPORATED; *U.S. Private*, pg. 2531

MACAO CEMENT MANUFACTURING CO., LTD.—See CITIC Group Corporation; *Int'l*, pg. 1621
MACAO WATER—See Veolia Environnement S.A.; *Int'l*, pg. 8156
M&A CAPITAL PARTNERS CO., LTD.; *Int'l*, pg. 4610
MACARDO LODGE (PTY) LIMITED—See The Bidvest Group Limited; *Int'l*, pg. 7625
M. A. CARGILL TRADING LTD.—See Cargill, Inc.; *U.S. Private*, pg. 759
MACARI-HEALEY PUBLISHING COMPANY, LLC; *U.S. Private*, pg. 2534
MACARTHUR AUSTRALIA LIMITED; *Int'l*, pg. 4619
MACARTHUR CO.; *U.S. Private*, pg. 2534
MACARTHUR CO.—See MacArthur Co.; *U.S. Private*, pg. 2534
MACARTHUR INTERMODAL SHIPPING TERMINAL PTY LTD—See Qube Holdings Limited; *Int'l*, pg. 6158
MACARTHUR MINERALS LIMITED; *Int'l*, pg. 4619
MACARTHUR SHOPPING CENTER LLC—See Simon Property Group, Inc.; *U.S. Public*, pg. 1881
MACARTHYS LABORATORIES LIMITED—See PAI Partners S.A.S.; *Int'l*, pg. 5700
MACARTNEY A/S; *Int'l*, pg. 4620
MACARTNEY AUSTRALIA PTY LTD.—See MacArtney A/S; *Int'l*, pg. 4620
MACARTNEY BENELUX BV—See MacArtney A/S; *Int'l*, pg. 4620
MACARTNEY CANADA LTD.—See MacArtney A/S; *Int'l*, pg. 4620
MACARTNEY FRANCE SAS—See MacArtney A/S; *Int'l*, pg. 4620
MACARTNEY INC.—See MacArtney A/S; *Int'l*, pg. 4620
MACARTNEY NORGE AS—See MacArtney A/S; *Int'l*, pg. 4620
MACARTNEY SINGAPORE PTE. LTD.—See MacArtney A/S; *Int'l*, pg. 4620
MACARTNEY UK LTD.—See MacArtney A/S; *Int'l*, pg. 4620
MACATAWA BANK CORPORATION—See Wintrust Financial Corporation; *U.S. Public*, pg. 2375
MACATAWA BANK—See Wintrust Financial Corporation; *U.S. Public*, pg. 2375
MACAU CAPITAL INVESTMENTS, INC.; *U.S. Public*, pg. 1351
MAC AUDIO ELECTRONIC GMBH—See VOXX International Corporation; *U.S. Public*, pg. 2311
MACAU E&M HOLDING LIMITED; *Int'l*, pg. 4620
MACAU FISHERMAN'S WHARF INTERNATIONAL INVESTMENT LIMITED—See Macau Legend Development Limited; *Int'l*, pg. 4620
MACAU INSURANCE COMPANY LIMITED—See Dah Sing Financial Holdings Limited; *Int'l*, pg. 1913
MACAULAY-BROWN, INC.—See Veritas Capital Fund Management, LLC; *U.S. Private*, pg. 4360
MACAULAY CONTROLS CO—See H.I.G. Capital, LLC; *U.S. Private*, pg. 1834
MACAULAY MOTORS LTD—See The Colonial Motor Company Limited; *Int'l*, pg. 7634
MACAU LEGEND DEVELOPMENT LIMITED; *Int'l*, pg. 4620
MACAU MATTERS COMPANY LIMITED—See Shun Tak Holdings Limited; *Int'l*, pg. 6870
MACAU PENSION FUND MANAGEMENT COMPANY LIMITED—See Tahoe Investment Group Co., Ltd.; *Int'l*, pg. 7408
MACAU PROPERTY OPPORTUNITIES FUND LTD.; *Int'l*, pg. 4620
MACAU RESOURCES GROUP LIMITED; *Int'l*, pg. 4620
MACAUTO GROUP GMBH—See Macauto Industrial Co., Ltd.; *Int'l*, pg. 4620
MACAUTO INDUSTRIAL CO., LTD.; *Int'l*, pg. 4620
MACAUTO MEXICO, S.A. DE C.V.—See Macauto Industrial Co., Ltd.; *Int'l*, pg. 4620
MACAU WEI AN CO., LTD.—See China Security Co., Ltd.; *Int'l*, pg. 1550
MACAWBER BEEKAY PRIVATE LIMITED—See Clyde Blowers Capital IM LLP; *Int'l*, pg. 1665
MACAY HOLDINGS, INC.; *Int'l*, pg. 4620
MACAYO RESTAURANTS LLC; *U.S. Private*, pg. 2534
MAC BAREN TOBACCO COMPANY A/S—See Skandinavisk Holding A/S; *Int'l*, pg. 6976
MACBEATH HARDWOOD COMPANY INC.; *U.S. Private*, pg. 2534
MACBEE PLANET, INC.; *Int'l*, pg. 4620
MACBER INC.; *U.S. Private*, pg. 2534
MACCAFERRI, INC.—See Societa Esercizi Commerciali Industriali; *Int'l*, pg. 7034
MACCARESE S.P.A.—See Edizione S.r.l.; *Int'l*, pg. 2312
MACCARTHY MOTORS (TERRACE) LTD.; *Int'l*, pg. 4620
MAC CASTINGS INC.—See Mac Group Incorporated; *U.S. Private*, pg. 2531
MAC CHAIN CO. LTD.—See Renold plc; *Int'l*, pg. 6284
MAC CHARLES (INDIA) LIMITED—See Blackstone Inc.; *U.S. Public*, pg. 350
MACCHINGRAF SRL—See Sycamore Partners Management, LP; *U.S. Private*, pg. 3897
MACC OF ILLINOIS INC.; *U.S. Private*, pg. 2535
MAC CONSTRUCTION & EXCAVATING, INC.; *U.S. Private*, pg. 2531

MAC CORPORATION
CORPORATE AFFILIATIONS

MAC CORPORATION; *U.S. Private*, pg. 2531
M.A.C. COSMETICS—See The Estee Lauder Companies Inc.; *U.S. Public*, pg. 2073
MACCOUNTING, LLC—See InDinero Inc.; *U.S. Private*, pg. 2064
MACCURA BIOTECHNOLOGY CO., LTD.; *Int'l*, pg. 4620
MACCURA BIOTECHNOLOGY (XINJIANG HONGKANG) CO., LTD.—See Maccura Biotechnology Co., Ltd.; *Int'l*, pg. 4620
MACDERMID ACUMEN INC.—See Element Solutions Inc.; *U.S. Public*, pg. 726
MACDERMID ALPHA ELECTRONICS SOLUTIONS, INC.—See Element Solutions Inc.; *U.S. Public*, pg. 726
MACDERMID AUTOTYPE (ASIA) PTE LTD—See Element Solutions Inc.; *U.S. Public*, pg. 726
MACDERMID AUTOTYPE INC—See Element Solutions Inc.; *U.S. Public*, pg. 727
MACDERMID AUTOTYPE LTD—See Element Solutions Inc.; *U.S. Public*, pg. 727
MACDERMID BENELUX B.V.—See Element Solutions Inc.; *U.S. Public*, pg. 727
MACDERMID CANNING LTD—See Element Solutions Inc.; *U.S. Public*, pg. 727
MACDERMID CANNING—See Element Solutions Inc.; *U.S. Public*, pg. 727
MACDERMID CHEMICALS, INC.—See Element Solutions Inc.; *U.S. Public*, pg. 727
MACDERMID CHEMICAL TAIWAN LTD—See Element Solutions Inc.; *U.S. Public*, pg. 727
MACDERMID DO BRASIL LTDA.—See Element Solutions Inc.; *U.S. Public*, pg. 727
MACDERMID DO BRAZIL LTDA—See Element Solutions Inc.; *U.S. Public*, pg. 728
MACDERMID ENTHONE GMBH—See Element Solutions Inc.; *U.S. Public*, pg. 727
MACDERMID ENTHONE SP. Z.O.O.—See Element Solutions Inc.; *U.S. Public*, pg. 727
MACDERMID ESPANOLA S.A.—See Element Solutions Inc.; *U.S. Public*, pg. 727
MACDERMID FRANCE, S.A.—See Element Solutions Inc.; *U.S. Public*, pg. 727
MACDERMID GMBH—See Element Solutions Inc.; *U.S. Public*, pg. 727
MACDERMID GRAPHIC SOLUTIONS EUROPE SAS—See Element Solutions Inc.; *U.S. Public*, pg. 727
MACDERMID GRAPHIC SOLUTIONS LLC—See Element Solutions Inc.; *U.S. Public*, pg. 727
MACDERMID GROUP, INC.—See Element Solutions Inc.; *U.S. Public*, pg. 726
MACDERMID HONG KONG LTD.—See Element Solutions Inc.; *U.S. Public*, pg. 727
MACDERMID, INC. - CONNECTICUT—See Element Solutions Inc.; *U.S. Public*, pg. 727
MACDERMID, INCORPORATED—See Element Solutions Inc.; *U.S. Public*, pg. 726
MACDERMID INVESTMENT CORP.—See Element Solutions Inc.; *U.S. Public*, pg. 727
MACDERMID ITALIANA SRL—See Element Solutions Inc.; *U.S. Public*, pg. 727
MACDERMID KFT—See Element Solutions Inc.; *U.S. Public*, pg. 727
MACDERMID KOREA LTD.—See Element Solutions Inc.; *U.S. Public*, pg. 727
MACDERMID LTD—See Element Solutions Inc.; *U.S. Public*, pg. 727
MACDERMID MEXICO SA DE CV—See Element Solutions Inc.; *U.S. Public*, pg. 727
MACDERMID NETHERLANDS COOPERATIEF W.A.—See Element Solutions Inc.; *U.S. Public*, pg. 727
MACDERMID OFFSHORE SOLUTIONS LLC—See Element Solutions Inc.; *U.S. Public*, pg. 727
MACDERMID OVERSEAS ASIA LTD—See Element Solutions Inc.; *U.S. Public*, pg. 727
MACDERMID PANYU SPECIALTY CHEMICALS CO LTD—See Element Solutions Inc.; *U.S. Public*, pg. 727
MACDERMID PERFORMANCE HONG KONG LTD.—See Element Solutions Inc.; *U.S. Public*, pg. 726
MACDERMID PERFORMANCE SOLUTIONS ESPANOLA SA—See Element Solutions Inc.; *U.S. Public*, pg. 727
MACDERMID PERFORMANCE SOLUTIONS FRANCE S.A.S—See Element Solutions Inc.; *U.S. Public*, pg. 727
MACDERMID PERFORMANCE SOLUTIONS JAPAN K.K.—See Element Solutions Inc.; *U.S. Public*, pg. 727
MACDERMID PERFORMANCE SOLUTIONS KIMYASAL SANAYI VE TICARET A.S.—See Element Solutions Inc.; *U.S. Public*, pg. 727
MACDERMID PRINTING SOLUTIONS EUROPE—See Element Solutions Inc.; *U.S. Public*, pg. 727
MACDERMID PRINTING SOLUTIONS, LLC - SAN MARCOS—See Element Solutions Inc.; *U.S. Public*, pg. 727
MACDERMID PRINTING SOLUTIONS, LLC—See Element Solutions Inc.; *U.S. Public*, pg. 727
MACDERMID SCANDINAVIA AB—See Element Solutions Inc.; *U.S. Public*, pg. 727
MACDERMID SINGAPORE PTE. LTD.—See Element Solutions Inc.; *U.S. Public*, pg. 727

MACDERMID SUISSE SARL—See Element Solutions Inc.; *U.S. Public*, pg. 727
MACDERMID TAIWAN LTD.—See Element Solutions Inc.; *U.S. Public*, pg. 727
MACDERMID UK LTD—See Element Solutions Inc.; *U.S. Public*, pg. 727
MACD LLC—See The Macerich Company; *U.S. Public*, pg. 2110
THE MACDONALD BROADCASTING COMPANY; *U.S. Private*, pg. 4073
MACDONALD & COMPANY PROPERTY LIMITED—See Prime People Plc; *Int'l*, pg. 5978
MACDONALD, DETTWILER AND ASSOCIATES CORP.—See Advent International Corporation; *U.S. Private*, pg. 103
MACDONALD, DETTWILER & ASSOCIATES INC.—See Advent International Corporation; *U.S. Private*, pg. 103
MACDONALD HOTELS & RESORTS; *Int'l*, pg. 4621
MACDONALD HUMFREY (AUTOMATION) LIMITED—See L3Harris Technologies, Inc.; *U.S. Public*, pg. 1284
MACDONALD HUMFREY (AUTOMATION) SEA PTE. LTD.—See L3Harris Technologies, Inc.; *U.S. Public*, pg. 1284
MACDONALD JOHNSTON LTD.—See Bucher Industries AG; *Int'l*, pg. 1208
MACDONALD MEDIA/LOS ANGELES—See MacDonald Media; *U.S. Private*, pg. 2535
MACDONALD MEDIA; *U.S. Private*, pg. 2535
MACDONALD-MILLER FACILITY SOLUTIONS INC.; *U.S. Private*, pg. 2535
MACDONALD MINES EXPLORATION LTD.; *Int'l*, pg. 4621
MACDONALD & OWEN VENEER & LUMBER CO., INC.; *U.S. Private*, pg. 2535
MACDONALD PONTIAC BUICK GMC LTD; *Int'l*, pg. 4621
MACDONALD REAL ESTATE GROUP INC.; *Int'l*, pg. 4621
MACDONALD STEEL LIMITED; *Int'l*, pg. 4621
MACDON, INC.—See Linamar Corporation; *Int'l*, pg. 4502
MACDON INDUSTRIES LTD—See Linamar Corporation; *Int'l*, pg. 4502
MACDOUGALL BIOMEDICAL COMMUNICATIONS, INC.; *U.S. Private*, pg. 2535
MACDUFF UNDERWRITERS, INC.—See Brown & Brown, Inc.; *U.S. Public*, pg. 401
MACE AUSTRALIA PTY LTD—See Mace Limited; *Int'l*, pg. 4621
MACE (CHINA) LTD.—See Mace Limited; *Int'l*, pg. 4621
MACE DOEL—See Mace Limited; *Int'l*, pg. 4621
MACEDONIAN AIRLINES AD; *Int'l*, pg. 4621
MACEDONIAN STOCK EXCHANGE, INC.—See Zagrebacka burza d.d.; *Int'l*, pg. 8619
MACE D.O.O.—See Mace Limited; *Int'l*, pg. 4621
MACE D.O.O.—See Mace Limited; *Int'l*, pg. 4621
MACE D.O.O.—See Mace Limited; *Int'l*, pg. 4621
MACE EGYPT LLC—See Mace Limited; *Int'l*, pg. 4621
MACE GMBH—See Mace Limited; *Int'l*, pg. 4621
MACE HOLDING LIMITED—See Mace Limited; *Int'l*, pg. 4621
MACE INSAAT YONETIM VE DANISMANLK HIZMETLERI LTD—See Mace Limited; *Int'l*, pg. 4621
MACE INSTRUMENTATION SDN. BHD.—See JHM Consolidation Berhad; *Int'l*, pg. 3941
MACE INTERNATIONAL LIMITED—See Mace Limited; *Int'l*, pg. 4621
MACE INTERNATIONAL LTD—See Mace Limited; *Int'l*, pg. 4621
MACE INTERNATIONAL (VIETNAM) BIDV—See Mace Limited; *Int'l*, pg. 4621
MAC ELECTRIC INC.; *U.S. Private*, pg. 2531
MACE LIMITED; *Int'l*, pg. 4621
MACELROYS INC.; *U.S. Private*, pg. 2535
MACE MANAGEMENT SERVICES LIMITED—See Mace Limited; *Int'l*, pg. 4621
MACE MANAGEMENT SERVICES (PTY) LTD—See Mace Limited; *Int'l*, pg. 4621
MACE MANAGEMENT SERVICES S.A.—See Mace Limited; *Int'l*, pg. 4621
MACE POLSKA SP.O.O.—See Mace Limited; *Int'l*, pg. 4621
MACE PORTUGAL, CONSULMACE LDA—See Mace Limited; *Int'l*, pg. 4621
MACE PROJECT AND COST MANAGEMENT PVT, LTD.—See Mace Limited; *Int'l*, pg. 4621
MACE PROJETS SARL—See Mace Limited; *Int'l*, pg. 4621
MAC EQUIPMENT, LLC—See Herc Holdings Inc.; *U.S. Public*, pg. 1028
MACERICH BROADWAY PLAZA LLC—See The Macerich Company; *U.S. Public*, pg. 2110
THE MACERICH COMPANY—See The Macerich Company; *U.S. Public*, pg. 2111
THE MACERICH COMPANY; *U.S. Public*, pg. 2109
MACERICH DB LLC—See The Macerich Company; *U.S. Public*, pg. 2110
MACERICH DEPTFORD LLC—See The Macerich Company; *U.S. Public*, pg. 2110
MACERICH LAKE SQUARE MALL LLC—See The Macerich Company; *U.S. Public*, pg. 2110

MACERICH LAKEWOOD, LLC—See The Macerich Company; *U.S. Public*, pg. 2110
MACERICH LAKEWOOD LP—See The Macerich Company; *U.S. Public*, pg. 2110
MACERICH LUBBOCK GP CORP.—See The Macerich Company; *U.S. Public*, pg. 2110
MACERICH NORTH PARK MALL LLC—See The Macerich Company; *U.S. Public*, pg. 2110
MACERICH NORTHRIDGE LP—See The Macerich Company; *U.S. Public*, pg. 2110
MACERICH OAKS LLC—See The Macerich Company; *U.S. Public*, pg. 2110
MACERICH PANORAMA LP—See The Macerich Company; *U.S. Public*, pg. 2110
THE MACERICH PARTNERSHIP, L.P.—See The Macerich Company; *U.S. Public*, pg. 2111
MACERICH RIMROCK GP CORP.—See The Macerich Company; *U.S. Public*, pg. 2110
MACERICH SANTA MONICA LP—See The Macerich Company; *U.S. Public*, pg. 2110
MACERICH SANTA MONICA PLACE CORP.—See The Macerich Company; *U.S. Public*, pg. 2110
MACERICH SOUTH PARK MALL LLC—See The Macerich Company; *U.S. Public*, pg. 2110
MACERICH SOUTH PLAINS LP—See The Macerich Company; *U.S. Public*, pg. 2110
MACERICH SOUTHRIDGE MALL LLC—See The Macerich Company; *U.S. Public*, pg. 2110
MACERICH STONEWOOD, LLC—See The Macerich Company; *U.S. Public*, pg. 2110
MACERICH TWENTY NINTH STREET LLC—See The Macerich Company; *U.S. Public*, pg. 2110
MACERICH TYSONS LLC—See The Macerich Company; *U.S. Public*, pg. 2110
MACERICH VALLEY RIVER CENTER LLC—See The Macerich Company; *U.S. Public*, pg. 2110
MACERICH VICTOR VALLEY LLC—See The Macerich Company; *U.S. Public*, pg. 2110
MACERICH VINTAGE FAIRE LIMITED PARTNERSHIP—See The Macerich Company; *U.S. Public*, pg. 2110
MACERICH WESTSIDE GP CORP.—See The Macerich Company; *U.S. Public*, pg. 2110
MACERICH WESTSIDE PAVILION PROPERTY LLC—See The Macerich Company; *U.S. Public*, pg. 2110
MACE (RUSSIA) LIMITED—See Mace Limited; *Int'l*, pg. 4621
MACE SAUDI ARABIA CO. LTD.—See Abdullah Abdul Mohsin Al-Khodari Sons Company; *Int'l*, pg. 59
MACE SECURITY INTERNATIONAL, INC.; *U.S. Public*, pg. 1351
MACEWEN AGRICENTRE INC.; *Int'l*, pg. 4621
MACEWEN PETROLEUM INC.; *Int'l*, pg. 4621
MACEY'S, INC.; *U.S. Private*, pg. 2535
MACFADDEN & ASSOCIATES, INC.—See Amentum Services, Inc.; *U.S. Private*, pg. 219
MACFADDEN COMMUNICATIONS GROUP, LLC; *U.S. Private*, pg. 2535
MACFARLAND PICK & SAVE; *U.S. Private*, pg. 2535
MACFARLANE GROUP PLC; *Int'l*, pg. 4621
MACFARLANE GROUP SWEDEN AB—See Macfarlane Group PLC; *Int'l*, pg. 4621
MACFARLANE GROUP UK LTD—See Macfarlane Group PLC; *Int'l*, pg. 4621
MACFARLANE LABELS (IRELAND) LTD—See Macfarlane Group PLC; *Int'l*, pg. 4621
MACFARLANE LABELS LTD—See Macfarlane Group PLC; *Int'l*, pg. 4621
MACFARLANE PACKAGING LIMITED—See Macfarlane Group PLC; *Int'l*, pg. 4622
MACFARLAN SMITH LIMITED—See Johnson Matthey PLC; *Int'l*, pg. 3993
MACFARMS, LLC—See Health and Plant Protein Group Limited; *Int'l*, pg. 3303
MACFLEURS S.A.R.L.—See Thomas Fleurs SA; *Int'l*, pg. 7714
MAC FOOD SERVICES (MALAYSIA) SDN. BHD.—See Tyson Foods, Inc.; *U.S. Public*, pg. 2210
MACFOS LTD.; *Int'l*, pg. 4622
MAC FUNDING CORPORATION—See Mitsubishi Corporation; *Int'l*, pg. 4939
MAC-GRAY CORPORATION—See Pamplona Capital Management LLP; *Int'l*, pg. 5711
MACGREGOR (ARE) LLC—See Cargotec Corporation; *Int'l*, pg. 1328
MACGREGOR (AUS) PTY. LTD.—See Cargotec Corporation; *Int'l*, pg. 1328
MACGREGOR BELGIUM N.V.—See Cargotec Corporation; *Int'l*, pg. 1328
MACGREGOR BLRT BALTIC OU—See BLRT Grupp AS; *Int'l*, pg. 1066
MACGREGOR BLRT BALTIC OU—See Cargotec Corporation; *Int'l*, pg. 1328
MACGREGOR (CHN) LTD.—See Cargotec Corporation; *Int'l*, pg. 1328
MACGREGOR CONVER GMBH—See Cargotec Corporation; *Int'l*, pg. 1329
MACGREGOR CROATIA D.O.O.—See Cargotec Corporation; *Int'l*, pg. 1328

MACGREGOR (CYPRUS) LTD.—See Cargotec Corporation; *Int'l*, pg. 1328
MACGREGOR (ESP) S.A.—See Cargotec Corporation; *Int'l*, pg. 1328
MACGREGOR FRANCE S.A.S—See Cargotec Corporation; *Int'l*, pg. 1328
MACGREGOR (GBR) LTD.—See Cargotec Corporation; *Int'l*, pg. 1328
MACGREGOR GERMANY GMBH—See Cargotec Corporation; *Int'l*, pg. 1328
MACGREGOR GOLF ASIA LTD.—See Hellman & Friedman LLC; *U.S. Private*, pg. 1907
MACGREGOR (GRC) E.P.E.—See Cargotec Corporation; *Int'l*, pg. 1328
MACGREGOR GREECE LTD—See Cargotec Corporation; *Int'l*, pg. 1328
MACGREGOR GROUP AB—See Cargotec Corporation; *Int'l*, pg. 1328
MACGREGOR (HONG KONG) LTD.—See Cargotec Corporation; *Int'l*, pg. 1328
MACGREGOR (HRV) D.O.O.—See Cargotec Corporation; *Int'l*, pg. 1328
MACGREGOR HYDRAMARINE AS—See Cargotec Corporation; *Int'l*, pg. 1328
MACGREGOR JAPAN LTD.—See Cargotec Corporation; *Int'l*, pg. 1329
MACGREGOR KAYABA LTD.—See Cargotec Corporation; *Int'l*, pg. 1329
MACGREGOR (KOR) LTD.—See Cargotec Corporation; *Int'l*, pg. 1329
MACGREGOR (NOR) A/S—See Cargotec Corporation; *Int'l*, pg. 1328
MACGREGOR OY—See Cargotec Corporation; *Int'l*, pg. 1329
MACGREGOR PARK, INC.—See The AES Corporation; *U.S. Public*, pg. 2032
MACGREGOR PARTNERS, LLC—See Accenture plc; *Int'l*, pg. 87
MACGREGOR PLIMSOLL OFFSHORE SERVICES PTE LTD—See Cargotec Corporation; *Int'l*, pg. 1329
MACGREGOR PLIMSOLL PTE LTD—See Cargotec Corporation; *Int'l*, pg. 1328
MACGREGOR PLIMSOLL SDN BHD—See Cargotec Corporation; *Int'l*, pg. 1329
MACGREGOR PLIMSOLL (TIANJIN) CO., LTD—See Cargotec Corporation; *Int'l*, pg. 1329
MACGREGOR POLAND SP. Z O.O.—See Cargotec Corporation; *Int'l*, pg. 1329
MACGREGOR (POL) SP. Z O.O.—See Cargotec Corporation; *Int'l*, pg. 1329
MACGREGOR (PRT) LDA.—See Cargotec Corporation; *Int'l*, pg. 1328
MACGREGOR (SGP) PTE. LTD.—See Cargotec Corporation; *Int'l*, pg. 1328
MACGREGOR SHANGHAI TRADING CO., LTD.—See Cargotec Corporation; *Int'l*, pg. 1328
MACGREGORS MEAT & SEAFOOD LTD.; *Int'l*, pg. 4622
MACGREGOR (UKR) A.O.—See Cargotec Corporation; *Int'l*, pg. 1328
MAC GROUP INCORPORATED; *U.S. Private*, pg. 2531
MACH1 GLOBAL SERVICES, INC.; *U.S. Private*, pg. 2535
MACH 2 LIBRI S.P.A.—See Fininvest S.p.A.; *Int'l*, pg. 2675
MACH49 LLC—See Next 15 Group plc; *Int'l*, pg. 5246
MACH49 SINGAPORE PTE LTD—See Next 15 Group plc; *Int'l*, pg. 5246
MACH 4 AUTOMATISIERUNGS TECHNIK, GMBH.—See Omnicell, Inc.; *U.S. Public*, pg. 1572
MACH7 TECHNOLOGIES, INC.—See Mach7 Technologies Limited; *U.S. Public*, pg. 1352
MACH7 TECHNOLOGIES LIMITED; *U.S. Public*, pg. 1352
MACHADO/GARCIA-SERRA PUBLICIDAD, INC.; *U.S. Private*, pg. 2535
MACH AERO BRETIGNY RECTIFICATION S.A.S.—See Minebea Mitsumi Inc.; *Int'l*, pg. 4903
MAC HAIK CHEVEROLET; *U.S. Private*, pg. 2531
MACH ENERGY—See Gainline Capital Partners LP; *U.S. Private*, pg. 1635
MACHHAPUCHCHHRE BANK LIMITED; *Int'l*, pg. 4622
MACHHAPUCHCHHRE CAPITAL LIMITED—See Machhapuchchhre Bank Limited; *Int'l*, pg. 4622
MACHIAS SAVINGS BANK; *U.S. Private*, pg. 2535
MACHIDA INCORPORATED—See Investor AB; *Int'l*, pg. 3786
MACHIDA KIKOU CO., LTD.—See Kanamoto Co., Ltd.; *Int'l*, pg. 4064
MACHINAGE PICHE; *Int'l*, pg. 4622
MACHINEFABRIEK GEBRS.FRENCKEN B.V.—See Frencken Group Limited; *Int'l*, pg. 2773
MACHINEFABRIEK GOUDKUIL APELDOORN B.V.; *Int'l*, pg. 4622
MACHINEFABRIEK TECHNOLOGY TWENTE B.V.—See Standard Investment Management B.V.; *Int'l*, pg. 7169
MACHINE INSITE LIMITED—See Vianet Group plc; *Int'l*, pg. 8183
MACHINELOGIC, LLC—See Sourcepass, Inc.; *U.S. Private*, pg. 3719
MACHINE MAINTENANCE, INC.; *U.S. Private*, pg. 2535

MACHINERY FINANCE RESOURCES, LLC—See Morris Group, Inc.; *U.S. Private*, pg. 2787
MACHINERY & INDUSTRIAL SUPPLIES SDN. BHD.—See SMIS Corporation Berhad; *Int'l*, pg. 7007
MACHINERY SALES CO.; *U.S. Private*, pg. 2536
MACHINERY SYSTEMS INC.; *U.S. Private*, pg. 2536
MACHINERY TOOLING & SUPPLY LLC—See Machinery Systems Inc.; *U.S. Private*, pg. 2536
MACHINE SERVICE INC.; *U.S. Private*, pg. 2535
MACHINE SOLUTIONS, INC.—See Forsyth Capital Investors LLC; *U.S. Private*, pg. 1573
THE MACHINE; *U.S. Private*, pg. 4073
MACHINES ROGER INTERNATIONAL INC.; *Int'l*, pg. 4622
THE MACHINES YVONAND SA—See CAPCELLENCE Mittelstandspartner GmbH; *Int'l*, pg. 1302
MACHINE TOOL & GEAR, INC.—See Cie Automotive S.A.; *Int'l*, pg. 1604
MACHINETOOLS.COM; *U.S. Private*, pg. 2536
MACHINE TOOLS INTERNATIONAL SP. Z O.O.—See C Dugard Ltd; *Int'l*, pg. 1238
MACHINE TOOL TECHNOLOGIES INC.; *U.S. Private*, pg. 2535
MACHINE TRADING TEAM OY LTD—See Investment AB Latour; *Int'l*, pg. 3782
MACHINE & WELDING SUPPLY COMPANY; *U.S. Private*, pg. 2535
MACHIN & EWIN PTY. LTD.—See Valmont Industries, Inc.; *U.S. Public*, pg. 2273
MACHINING TIME SAVERS INC.; *U.S. Private*, pg. 2536
MACHINIO CORP.—See Liquidity Services, Inc.; *U.S. Public*, pg. 1321
MACHINISTS INCORPORATED; *U.S. Private*, pg. 2536
MACHINO PLASTICS LTD.; *Int'l*, pg. 4622
MACH MONUMENT AVIATION FUELLING CO. LTD.—See BP plc; *Int'l*, pg. 1131
MACH NATURAL RESOURCES LP; *U.S. Public*, pg. 1352
MAC HOTELS LTD.; *Int'l*, pg. 4619
MAC-HOUSE CO., LTD.; *Int'l*, pg. 4619
MACHTEN, INC.; *U.S. Public*, pg. 1352
MACH USA INC.—See Great Universal Incorporated; *U.S. Private*, pg. 1768
MACHVISION (DONGGUAN) INC.—See Machvision, Inc.; *Int'l*, pg. 4622
MACHVISION, INC.; *Int'l*, pg. 4622
MACIF GESTION; *Int'l*, pg. 4622
MACINTOSH HONG KONG LTD—See Macintosh Retail Group NV; *Int'l*, pg. 4622
MACINTOSH INTERNATIONAL BV—See Macintosh Retail Group NV; *Int'l*, pg. 4622
MACINTOSH INTRAGROUP SERVICES NV—See Macintosh Retail Group NV; *Int'l*, pg. 4622
MACINTOSH LINEN & UNIFORM RENTAL; *U.S. Private*, pg. 2536
MACINTOSH RETAIL GROUP NV; *Int'l*, pg. 4622
MACINTYRE CHEVROLET CADILLAC LIMITED; *Int'l*, pg. 4622
MAC & JACK'S BREWERY, INC.—See Ackley Beverage Group, LLC; *U.S. Private*, pg. 60
MACK AIR LTD.—See John Keells Holdings PLC; *Int'l*, pg. 3978
MACK AIR SERVICES MALDIVES (PTE) LTD.—See John Keells Holdings PLC; *Int'l*, pg. 3978
MACKAY COMMUNICATIONS, INC.; *U.S. Private*, pg. 2536
MACKAYMITCHELL ENVELOPE COMPANY - IOWA MANUFACTURING FACILITY—See MackayMitchell Envelope Company; *U.S. Private*, pg. 2536
MACKAYMITCHELL ENVELOPE COMPANY; *U.S. Private*, pg. 2536
MACKAY SHIELDS LLC—See New York Life Insurance Company; *U.S. Private*, pg. 2911
MACKAY SPECIALIST DAY HOSPITAL PTY LIMITED—See Virtus Health Limited; *Int'l*, pg. 8249
MACKAY & SPOSITO, INC.; *U.S. Private*, pg. 2536
MACKAY SUGAR LIMITED LTD.—See Nordzucker AG; *Int'l*, pg. 5426
MACK BORING & PARTS CO.; *U.S. Private*, pg. 2536
MACK-BROOKS EXHIBITIONS LIMITED—See RELX plc; *Int'l*, pg. 6266
MACK-CALI REALTY, L.P.—See Veris Residential, Inc.; *U.S. Public*, pg. 2281
MACK-CALI WOODBRIDGE L.L.C.—See Veris Residential, Inc.; *U.S. Public*, pg. 2281
MACK CANADA, INC.—See AB Volvo; *Int'l*, pg. 45
MACK ENERGY CORPORATION; *U.S. Private*, pg. 2536
MACKENZIE CAPITAL MANAGEMENT, LP; *U.S. Private*, pg. 2536
MACKENZIE-CHILDS LLC—See EagleTree Capital, LP; *U.S. Private*, pg. 1311
MACKENZIE CUNDILL INVESTMENT MANAGEMENT LTD.—See Power Corporation of Canada; *Int'l*, pg. 5944
MACKENZIE FINANCIAL CORPORATION—See Power Corporation of Canada; *Int'l*, pg. 5944
MACKENZIE GROUP INC.; *U.S. Private*, pg. 2537
MACKENZIE HYDROCARBONS (AUSTRALIA) PTY. LTD.—See Wah Seong Corporation Berhad; *Int'l*, pg. 8330

MACKENZIE INDUSTRIES SDN. BHD.—See Wah Seong Corporation Berhad; *Int'l*, pg. 8329
MACKENZIE MASTER LIMITED PARTNERSHIP; *Int'l*, pg. 4623
MACKENZIE MOTOR CO.; *U.S. Private*, pg. 2537
MACKENZIE NORTHERN RAILWAY—See Canadian National Railway Company; *Int'l*, pg. 1284
MACKENZIE REALTY CAPITAL, INC.; *U.S. Public*, pg. 1352
MACKENZIE TIMES NEWSPAPER—See Chatham Asset Management, LLC; *U.S. Private*, pg. 861
MACKEVISION CG TECHNOLOGY & SERVICE (SHANGHAI) CO. LTD.—See Accenture plc; *Int'l*, pg. 87
MACKEVISION CORPORATION—See Accenture plc; *Int'l*, pg. 87
MACKEVISION JAPAN CO., LTD.—See Accenture plc; *Int'l*, pg. 87
MACKEVISION MEDIEN DESIGN GMBH - STUTTGART—See Accenture plc; *Int'l*, pg. 87
MACKEY BANCO, INC.; *U.S. Private*, pg. 2537
MACK FIRE PROTECTION, LLC—See LiUNA Pension Fund of Central and Eastern Canada; *Int'l*, pg. 4529
MACK FIRE PROTECTION, LLC—See Newlook Capital Inc.; *Int'l*, pg. 5235
MACK GROUP INC.; *U.S. Private*, pg. 2536
MACK GRUBBS MOTORS INC.—See Walt Massey Automotive, Inc.; *U.S. Private*, pg. 4433
MACK HARVEY SALES & SERVICE; *U.S. Private*, pg. 2536
MACK HILS, INC.; *U.S. Private*, pg. 2536
MACKIE DESIGNS S.P.A.—See LOUD Technologies Inc.; *U.S. Private*, pg. 1342
MACKINAC FINANCIAL CORPORATION; *U.S. Public*, pg. 1352
MACKINAC ISLAND REALTY, INC.; *U.S. Private*, pg. 2537
MACKINAW ADMINISTRATORS, LLC—See Fosun International Limited; *Int'l*, pg. 2752
MACKINAW FOOD SERVICE CORP.—See Daland Corporation; *U.S. Private*, pg. 1148
MACK INDUSTRIES INC.; *U.S. Private*, pg. 2536
MACKIN EDUCATIONAL RESOURCES; *U.S. Private*, pg. 2537
MACKINNON & KEELLS FINANCIAL SERVICES LTD.—See John Keells Holdings PLC; *Int'l*, pg. 3978
MACKINNON MACKENZIE AND CO OF CEYLON LTD.—See John Keells Holdings PLC; *Int'l*, pg. 3978
MACKINNON MACKENZIE AND CO (SHIPPING) LTD.—See John Keells Holdings PLC; *Int'l*, pg. 3978
MACKINNON MACKENZIE & CO. OF PAKISTAN (PVT.) LTD.—See Dubai World Corporation; *Int'l*, pg. 2221
MACKINNONS TOURS LTD.—See John Keells Holdings PLC; *Int'l*, pg. 3978
MACKINNONS TRAVELS (PVT) LTD—See John Keells Holdings PLC; *Int'l*, pg. 3978
MACKINNON TRANSPORT INC.; *Int'l*, pg. 4623
MACKIN TECHNOLOGIES; *U.S. Private*, pg. 2537
MACK LEASING SYSTEM—See AB Volvo; *Int'l*, pg. 45
MACKLOWE MANAGEMENT CO., INC.—See Macklowe Properties, L.L.C.; *U.S. Private*, pg. 2537
MACKLOWE MANAGEMENT, LLC—See Macklowe Properties, L.L.C.; *U.S. Private*, pg. 2537
MACKLOWE PROPERTIES, L.L.C.; *U.S. Private*, pg. 2537
MACK MACK & WALTZ INSURANCE GROUP, INC.—See GTCR LLC; *U.S. Private*, pg. 1803
MACK MCBRIDE SALES INC.; *U.S. Private*, pg. 2536
MACK MOLDING COMPANY INC.; *U.S. Private*, pg. 2536
MACKMYRA SVENSK WHISKY AB; *Int'l*, pg. 4623
MACK OIL CO. INC.; *U.S. Private*, pg. 2536
MACK OPERATIONS LLC; *U.S. Private*, pg. 2536
MACKOUL DISTRIBUTORS INC.; *U.S. Private*, pg. 2537
MACK PAPER CO.—See Shorr Packaging Corp.; *U.S. Private*, pg. 3642
MACK REMANUFACTURING CENTER—See AB Volvo; *Int'l*, pg. 45
MACKSON, INC.—See MetalTek International; *U.S. Private*, pg. 2682
MACK STE-FOY INC.; *Int'l*, pg. 4622
MACK TRADING COMPANY LIMITED; *Int'l*, pg. 4622
MACK TRUCKS AUSTRALIA PTY. LTD.—See AB Volvo; *Int'l*, pg. 45
MACK TRUCKS, INC.—See AB Volvo; *Int'l*, pg. 45
MACK TRUCKS-MACUNGIE ASSEMBLY—See AB Volvo; *Int'l*, pg. 45
MACKWELL ELECTRONICS LIMITED; *Int'l*, pg. 4623
MACKWELL HONG KONG—See Mackwell Electronics Limited; *Int'l*, pg. 4623
MACKWELL MIDDLE EAST—See Mackwell Electronics Limited; *Int'l*, pg. 4623
MACKWOODS INTERNATIONAL TOURS & TRAVELS (PVT) LTD.—See Mackwoods Limited; *Int'l*, pg. 4623
MACKWOODS I.T. (PVT) LTD.—See Mackwoods Limited; *Int'l*, pg. 4623
MACKWOODS LIMITED; *Int'l*, pg. 4623
MACKWOODS TEA (PVT) LTD.—See Mackwoods Limited; *Int'l*, pg. 4623
MACLAB ENTERPRISES LTD.; *Int'l*, pg. 4623
MACLAREN MINERALS LTD.; *Int'l*, pg. 4623

MACLAREN MINERALS LTD. CORPORATE AFFILIATIONS

MACLARY—See Sonepar S.A.; *Int'l*, pg. 7091
MACLEAN CURTIS, LLC - CORNELIUS PLANT—See MacLean-Fogg Company; *U.S. Private*, pg. 2537
MACLEAN CURTIS, LLC—See MacLean-Fogg Company; *U.S. Private*, pg. 2537
MACLEAN ELECTRICAL (AUSTRALIA) PTY LTD.—See DNOW Inc.; *U.S. Public*, pg. 671
MACLEAN ELECTRICAL INC.—See DNOW Inc.; *U.S. Public*, pg. 671
MACLEAN FASTENERS, LLC—See MacLean-Fogg Company; *U.S. Private*, pg. 2537
MACLEAN-FOGG COMPANY; *U.S. Private*, pg. 2537
MACLEAN-FOGG COMPONENT SOLUTIONS, LLC—See MacLean-Fogg Company; *U.S. Private*, pg. 2537
MACLEAN-FOGG CO.; *U.S. Private*, pg. 2537
MACLEAN INTERNATIONAL GROUP LIMITED—See DNOW Inc.; *U.S. Public*, pg. 671
MACLEAN INVESTMENT PARTNERS, LLC—See MacLean-Fogg Company; *U.S. Private*, pg. 2537
MACLEAN MAYNARD LLC—See MacLean-Fogg Company; *U.S. Private*, pg. 2537
MACLEAN POWER CANADA—See Centerbridge Partners, L.P.; *U.S. Private*, pg. 815
MACLEAN POWER, LLC—See Centerbridge Partners, L.P.; *U.S. Private*, pg. 815
MAC LEAN PRECISION MACHINE CO.; *U.S. Private*, pg. 2531
MACLEAN SENIOR INDUSTRIES LLC—See Centerbridge Partners, L.P.; *U.S. Private*, pg. 815
MACLEH (CHEVALIER) LIMITED—See Chevalier International Holdings Limited; *Int'l*, pg. 1474
MACLELLAN INTEGRATED SERVICES; *U.S. Private*, pg. 2538
MACLEOD CONSTRUCTION INC.; *U.S. Private*, pg. 2538
MACMAHON CONSTRUCTION PTY. LTD.—See Macmahon Holdings Limited; *Int'l*, pg. 4623
MACMAHON CONTRACTORS PTY LTD—See Macmahon Holdings Limited; *Int'l*, pg. 4623
MACMAHON HOLDINGS LIMITED; *Int'l*, pg. 4623
MACMAHON MINING SERVICES PTY. LTD.—See Macmahon Holdings Limited; *Int'l*, pg. 4623
MACMAHON SDN. BHD.—See Macmahon Holdings Limited; *Int'l*, pg. 4623
MACMASTER CHEVROLET CADILLAC BUICK GMC LTD.; *Int'l*, pg. 4623
MACMILLAN AIDAN LTD—See Verlagsgruppe Georg von Holtzbrinck GmbH; *Int'l*, pg. 8170
MACMILLAN AUDIO—See Verlagsgruppe Georg von Holtzbrinck GmbH; *Int'l*, pg. 8170
MACMILLAN BOLESWA (PTY) LIMITED—See Verlagsgruppe Georg von Holtzbrinck GmbH; *Int'l*, pg. 8170
MACMILLAN BOTSWANA PUBLISHING CO.—See Verlagsgruppe Georg von Holtzbrinck GmbH; *Int'l*, pg. 8170
MACMILLAN CHILDRENS BOOKS LIMITED—See Verlagsgruppe Georg von Holtzbrinck GmbH; *Int'l*, pg. 8170
MACMILLAN COMPANY INC.; *U.S. Private*, pg. 2538
MACMILLAN DISTRIBUTION LTD.—See Verlagsgruppe Georg von Holtzbrinck GmbH; *Int'l*, pg. 8170
MACMILLAN DO BRASIL—See Verlagsgruppe Georg von Holtzbrinck GmbH; *Int'l*, pg. 8170
MACMILLAN EDUCACAO MOZAMBIQUE LIMITADA—See Verlagsgruppe Georg von Holtzbrinck GmbH; *Int'l*, pg. 8170
MACMILLAN EDUCATION AUSTRALIA PTY LIMITED—See Verlagsgruppe Georg von Holtzbrinck GmbH; *Int'l*, pg. 8170
MACMILLAN EDUCATION LIMITED—See Verlagsgruppe Georg von Holtzbrinck GmbH; *Int'l*, pg. 8170
MACMILLAN EDUCATION NAMBIA PUBLISHERS (PTY) LIMITED—See Verlagsgruppe Georg von Holtzbrinck GmbH; *Int'l*, pg. 8170
MACMILLAN HEINEMANN ELT—See Verlagsgruppe Georg von Holtzbrinck GmbH; *Int'l*, pg. 8170
MACMILLAN IBERIA SA—See Verlagsgruppe Georg von Holtzbrinck GmbH; *Int'l*, pg. 8170
MACMILLAN INFORMATION CONSULTING SERVICES (SHANGHAI) CO., LTD—See Verlagsgruppe Georg von Holtzbrinck GmbH; *Int'l*, pg. 8170
MACMILLAN KOREA PUBLISHERS LTD—See Verlagsgruppe Georg von Holtzbrinck GmbH; *Int'l*, pg. 8170
MACMILLAN LANGUAGE HOUSE LTD.—See Verlagsgruppe Georg von Holtzbrinck GmbH; *Int'l*, pg. 8170
MACMILLAN LTD.—See Verlagsgruppe Georg von Holtzbrinck GmbH; *Int'l*, pg. 8170
MACMILLAN MALAWI LTD—See Verlagsgruppe Georg von Holtzbrinck GmbH; *Int'l*, pg. 8171
MACMILLAN NEW VENTURES, LLC—See Verlagsgruppe Georg von Holtzbrinck GmbH; *Int'l*, pg. 8171
MACMILLAN NIGERIA PUBLISHERS LTD.—See Verlagsgruppe Georg von Holtzbrinck GmbH; *Int'l*, pg. 8170
MACMILLAN-PIPER LLC—See GSC Logistics Inc.; *U.S. Private*, pg. 1800
MACMILLAN POLSKA SP ZOO—See Verlagsgruppe Georg von Holtzbrinck GmbH; *Int'l*, pg. 8171
MACMILLAN PRODUCTION (ASIA) LIMITED—See Verlagsgruppe Georg von Holtzbrinck GmbH; *Int'l*, pg. 8171

MACMILLAN PUBLISHERS AUSTRALIA PTY. LTD.—See Verlagsgruppe Georg von Holtzbrinck GmbH; *Int'l*, pg. 8170
MACMILLAN PUBLISHERS (CHINA) LTD.—See Verlagsgruppe Georg von Holtzbrinck GmbH; *Int'l*, pg. 8170
MACMILLAN PUBLISHERS EGYPT LTD—See Verlagsgruppe Georg von Holtzbrinck GmbH; *Int'l*, pg. 8171
MACMILLAN PUBLISHERS INDIA LIMITED—See Verlagsgruppe Georg von Holtzbrinck GmbH; *Int'l*, pg. 8171
MACMILLAN PUBLISHERS NEW ZEALAND LIMITED—See Verlagsgruppe Georg von Holtzbrinck GmbH; *Int'l*, pg. 8171
MACMILLAN PUBLISHERS S.A DE CV—See Verlagsgruppe Georg von Holtzbrinck GmbH; *Int'l*, pg. 8171
MACMILLAN PUBLISHERS SA—See Verlagsgruppe Georg von Holtzbrinck GmbH; *Int'l*, pg. 8171
MACMILLAN PUBLISHERS SAS—See Verlagsgruppe Georg von Holtzbrinck GmbH; *Int'l*, pg. 8171
MACMILLAN PUBLISHERS (ZAMBIA) LTD—See Verlagsgruppe Georg von Holtzbrinck GmbH; *Int'l*, pg. 8171
MACMILLAN PUBLISHING LTD.—See Verlagsgruppe Georg von Holtzbrinck GmbH; *Int'l*, pg. 8170
MACMILLAN REFERENCE USA—See Apax Partners LLP; *Int'l*, pg. 503
MACMILLAN REFERENCE USA—See Apollo Global Management, Inc.; *U.S. Public*, pg. 168
MACMILLAN REFERENCE USA—See KKR & Co. Inc.; *U.S. Public*, pg. 1256
MACMILLAN REFERENCE USA—See Searchlight Capital Partners, L.P.; *U.S. Private*, pg. 3587
MACMILLAN SWAZILAND NATIONAL PUBLISHING CO.—See Verlagsgruppe Georg von Holtzbrinck GmbH; *Int'l*, pg. 8170
MACMILLAN TAIWAN LTD—See Verlagsgruppe Georg von Holtzbrinck GmbH; *Int'l*, pg. 8171
MAC MOLDING COMPANY, INC.—See Tacony Corporation; *U.S. Private*, pg. 3921
MACMOR INDUSTRIES LTD.; *Int'l*, pg. 4623
MACMUNNIS, INC.—See GI Manager L.P.; *U.S. Private*, pg. 1693
MACNAUGHTON BLAIR LIMITED—See Grafton Group plc; *Int'l*, pg. 3051
MACNEAL HEALTH PROVIDERS, INC.—See Tenet Healthcare Corporation; *U.S. Public*, pg. 2014
MACNEAL HOSPITAL—See Trinity Health Corporation; *U.S. Private*, pg. 4233
MACNEIL GEORGE PROPRIETARY LIMITED—See Steinhoff International Holdings N.V.; *Int'l*, pg. 7194
MACNEILL ENGINEERING CO., INC.—See Centre Partners Management LLC; *U.S. Private*, pg. 828
MACNEILL GROUP, INC.; *U.S. Private*, pg. 2538
MACNEIL PROPRIETARY LIMITED—See Steinhoff International Holdings N.V.; *Int'l*, pg. 7194
MACNICA AMERICAS, INC.—See Macnica Holdings, Inc.; *Int'l*, pg. 4624
MACNICA ATD EUROPE GMBH—See Macnica Galaxy, Inc.; *Int'l*, pg. 4623
MACNICA DHW LTDA.—See Macnica Galaxy, Inc.; *Int'l*, pg. 4623
MACNICA GALAXY, INC.; *Int'l*, pg. 4623
MACNICA GMBH—See Macnica Holdings, Inc.; *Int'l*, pg. 4624
MACNICA HOLDINGS, INC.; *Int'l*, pg. 4623
MACNICA, INC.—See Macnica Holdings, Inc.; *Int'l*, pg. 4624
MACNICA KOREA, LIMITED—See Macnica Galaxy, Inc.; *Int'l*, pg. 4623
MACNICA NETWORKS CORP.—See Macnica Holdings, Inc.; *Int'l*, pg. 4624
MACNICA NETWORKS USA, INC.—See Macnica Galaxy, Inc.; *Int'l*, pg. 4623
MACNICA UK LTD.—See Macnica Galaxy, Inc.; *Int'l*, pg. 4623
MACO LITORAL S.A.—See The Brink's Company; *U.S. Public*, pg. 2043
MACOMB COUNTY LEGAL NEWS—See Detroit Legal News Company; *U.S. Public*, pg. 657
THE MACOMB DAILY—See Alden Global Capital LLC; *U.S. Private*, pg. 159
THE MACOMB GROUP, INC.; *U.S. Private*, pg. 4073
MACOMB-OAKLAND REGIONAL CENTER; *U.S. Private*, pg. 2538
MACOMB PIPE & SUPPLY CO. INC.; *U.S. Private*, pg. 2538
MACOM JAPAN LIMITED—See MACOM Technology Solutions Holdings, Inc.; *U.S. Public*, pg. 1352
MACOM TECHNOLOGY SOLUTIONS (BANGALORE) PRIVATE LIMITED—See MACOM Technology Solutions Holdings, Inc.; *U.S. Public*, pg. 1352
MACOM TECHNOLOGY SOLUTIONS CANADA INC.—See MACOM Technology Solutions Holdings, Inc.; *U.S. Public*, pg. 1352
M/ACOM TECHNOLOGY SOLUTIONS (CORK) LIMITED—See MACOM Technology Solutions Holdings, Inc.; *U.S. Public*, pg. 1352
MACOM TECHNOLOGY SOLUTIONS HOLDINGS, INC.; *U.S. Public*, pg. 1352

M/A-COM TECHNOLOGY SOLUTIONS INC.—See MA-COM Technology Solutions Holdings, Inc.; *U.S. Public*, pg. 1352
M/A-COM TECHNOLOGY SOLUTIONS (UK) LIMITED—See MACOM Technology Solutions Holdings, Inc.; *U.S. Public*, pg. 1352
MACON BIBB COUNTY ECONOMIC OPPORTUNITY COUNCIL, INC.; *U.S. Private*, pg. 2538
MACON CIGAR & TOBACCO CO.; *U.S. Private*, pg. 2538
MACON PSYCHIATRIC HOSPITALISTS, LLC—See HCA Healthcare, Inc.; *U.S. Public*, pg. 1001
MACON SRL—See Lone Star Global Acquisitions, LLC; *U.S. Private*, pg. 2489
THE MACON TELEGRAPH PUBLISHING CO.—See Chatham Asset Management, LLC; *U.S. Private*, pg. 867
MACON TRADING POST INC.—See HI-Boy Group Inc.; *U.S. Private*, pg. 1931
MACON WATER AUTHORITY; *U.S. Private*, pg. 2538
MACOPLEX S.A.—See EL. D. MOUZAKIS S.A.; *Int'l*, pg. 2341
MACOTAB—See Imperial Brands PLC; *Int'l*, pg. 3633
MACOUPIN ENERGY LLC—See Foresight Energy LP; *U.S. Public*, pg. 867
MACOY RESOURCE CORPORATION—See Sims Limited; *U.S. Public*, pg. 1883
MACPAC FILMS LIMITED; *Int'l*, pg. 4624
MACPAC NEW ZEALAND LIMITED—See Super Retail Group Limited; *Int'l*, pg. 7335
MAC PAPERS, INC.—See Monomoy Capital Partners LLC; *U.S. Private*, pg. 2772
MAC PAPERS, INC.—See Monomoy Capital Partners LLC; *U.S. Private*, pg. 2772
MACPEK INC; *Int'l*, pg. 4624
MACPHEE FORD SALES; *Int'l*, pg. 4624
MACPHEE PONTIAC BUICK GMC LTD; *Int'l*, pg. 4624
MACPHERSON ENERGY CORP.—See Berry Corporation (Bry); *U.S. Public*, pg. 320
MACPHERSON WESTERN TOOL & SUPPLY CO. INC.; *U.S. Private*, pg. 2538
MACPHERSON WESTERN TOOL & SUPPLY CO. INC. - TOOL & GAGE ASSOCIATES DIVISION—See Macpherson Western Tool & Supply Co. Inc.; *U.S. Private*, pg. 2538
MACPIE PRO SDN BHD—See XOX Networks Berhad; *Int'l*, pg. 8536
MACPOWER CNC MACHINES LTD.; *Int'l*, pg. 4624
MACPRACTICE, INC.—See Valsef Group; *Int'l*, pg. 8123
MACQUARIE AGRICULTURAL FUNDS MANAGEMENT LIMITED—See Macquarie Group Limited; *Int'l*, pg. 4625
MACQUARIE ALTERNATIVE ASSETS MANAGEMENT LIMITED—See Macquarie Group Limited; *Int'l*, pg. 4625
MACQUARIE AMERICAS PARKING CORPORATION—See Macquarie Group Limited; *Int'l*, pg. 4627
MACQUARIE ASSET FINANCE JAPAN LIMITED—See Macquarie Group Limited; *Int'l*, pg. 4625
MACQUARIE ASSET MANAGEMENT, INC.—See Macquarie Group Limited; *Int'l*, pg. 4625
MACQUARIE AVIATION NORTH AMERICA 2 INC.—See Macquarie Group Limited; *Int'l*, pg. 4627
MACQUARIE BANK EUROPE DESIGNATED ACTIVITY COMPANY—See Macquarie Group Limited; *Int'l*, pg. 4624
MACQUARIE BANK INTERNATIONAL LIMITED—See Macquarie Group Limited; *Int'l*, pg. 4625
MACQUARIE BANK LIMITED—See Macquarie Group Limited; *Int'l*, pg. 4624
MACQUARIE CAPITAL ADVISERS KOREA—See Macquarie Group Limited; *Int'l*, pg. 4625
MACQUARIE CAPITAL (AUSTRALIA) LIMITED—See Macquarie Group Limited; *Int'l*, pg. 4625
MACQUARIE CAPITAL (EUROPE) LIMITED—See Macquarie Group Limited; *Int'l*, pg. 4625
MACQUARIE CAPITAL FRANCE SOCIETE ANONYME—See Macquarie Group Limited; *Int'l*, pg. 4630
MACQUARIE CAPITAL GROUP LIMITED—See Macquarie Group Limited; *Int'l*, pg. 4625
MACQUARIE CAPITAL (INDIA) PRIVATE LIMITED—See Macquarie Group Limited; *Int'l*, pg. 4625
MACQUARIE CAPITAL KOREA LIMITED—See Macquarie Group Limited; *Int'l*, pg. 4625
MACQUARIE CAPITAL LIMITED—See Macquarie Group Limited; *Int'l*, pg. 4630
MACQUARIE CAPITAL SECURITIES (INDIA) PRIVATE LIMITED—See Macquarie Group Limited; *Int'l*, pg. 4625
MACQUARIE CAPITAL SECURITIES (JAPAN) LIMITED—See Macquarie Group Limited; *Int'l*, pg. 4625
MACQUARIE CAPITAL SECURITIES (PHILIPPINES) INC.—See Macquarie Group Limited; *Int'l*, pg. 4630
MACQUARIE CAPITAL VENTURE STUDIO—See Macquarie Group Limited; *Int'l*, pg. 4625

COMPANY NAME INDEX

MACQUARIE CAPITAL VENTURE STUDIO—See The Interpublic Group of Companies, Inc.; *U.S. Public*, pg. 2104
MACQUARIE COMMODITIES TRADING SA—See Macquarie Group Limited; *Int'l*, pg. 4630
MACQUARIE COMMODITIES TRADING (SHANGHAI) CO., LTD.—See Macquarie Group Limited; *Int'l*, pg. 4630
MACQUARIE COOK ENERGY CANADA LTD—See Macquarie Group Limited; *Int'l*, pg. 4629
MACQUARIE CORPORATE AND ASSET FINANCE LIMITED—See Macquarie Group Limited; *Int'l*, pg. 4625
MACQUARIE EMERGING MARKETS ASIAN TRADING PTE. LIMITED—See Macquarie Group Limited; *Int'l*, pg. 4630
MACQUARIE ENERGY CANADA LTD.—See Macquarie Group Limited; *Int'l*, pg. 4630
MACQUARIE ENERGY LLC—See Macquarie Group Limited; *Int'l*, pg. 4630
MACQUARIE EQUIPMENT FINANCE—See Macquarie Group Limited; *Int'l*, pg. 4625
MACQUARIE EQUIPMENT LEASING FUND, LLC—See Macquarie Group Limited; *Int'l*, pg. 4625
MACQUARIE EQUITIES LIMITED—See Macquarie Group Limited; *Int'l*, pg. 4625
MACQUARIE EQUITIES NEW ZEALAND LIMITED—See Macquarie Group Limited; *Int'l*, pg. 4625
MACQUARIE ESSENTIAL ASSETS PARTNERSHIP—See Macquarie Group Limited; *Int'l*, pg. 4625
MACQUARIE FINANCE (INDIA) PVT. LTD.—See Macquarie Group Limited; *Int'l*, pg. 4625
MACQUARIE FINANCE KOREA CO., LIMITED—See Macquarie Group Limited; *Int'l*, pg. 4625
MACQUARIE FINANCIAL HOLDINGS LIMITED—See Macquarie Group Limited; *Int'l*, pg. 4625
MACQUARIE FINANCIAL LIMITED—See Macquarie Group Limited; *Int'l*, pg. 4629
MACQUARIE FINANCIAL PRODUCTS MANAGEMENT LIMITED—See Macquarie Group Limited; *Int'l*, pg. 4625
MACQUARIE FIRST SOUTH ADVISERS (PROPRIETARY) LIMITED—See Macquarie Group Limited; *Int'l*, pg. 4625
MACQUARIE/FIRST TRUST GLOBAL INFRASTRUCTURE/UTILITIES DIVIDEND & INCOME FUND; *U.S. Public*, pg. 1352
MACQUARIE GLOBAL INFRASTRUCTURE TOTAL RETURN FUND INC.; *U.S. Public*, pg. 1352
MACQUARIE GLOBAL INVESTMENTS—See Macquarie Group Limited; *Int'l*, pg. 4629
MACQUARIE GLOBAL OPPORTUNITIES PARTNERS, L.P.—See Macquarie Group Limited; *Int'l*, pg. 4626
MACQUARIE GLOBAL SERVICES PRIVATE LIMITED—See Macquarie Group Limited; *Int'l*, pg. 4625
MACQUARIE GROUP BRAZIL—See Macquarie Group Limited; *Int'l*, pg. 4630
MACQUARIE GROUP - FRANKFURT—See Macquarie Group Limited; *Int'l*, pg. 4630
MACQUARIE GROUP - GENEVA—See Macquarie Group Limited; *Int'l*, pg. 4630
MACQUARIE GROUP HONG KONG—See Macquarie Group Limited; *Int'l*, pg. 4630
MACQUARIE GROUP IRELAND—See Macquarie Group Limited; *Int'l*, pg. 4630
MACQUARIE GROUP LIMITED; *Int'l*, pg. 4624
MACQUARIE GROUP - MUNICH—See Macquarie Group Limited; *Int'l*, pg. 4630
MACQUARIE GROUP NETHERLANDS—See Macquarie Group Limited; *Int'l*, pg. 4630
MACQUARIE GROUP PHILIPPINES—See Macquarie Group Limited; *Int'l*, pg. 4630
MACQUARIE GROUP SERVICES AUSTRALIA PTY LIMITED—See Macquarie Group Limited; *Int'l*, pg. 4630
MACQUARIE GROUP SINGAPORE—See Macquarie Group Limited; *Int'l*, pg. 4630
MACQUARIE GROUP - VIENNA—See Macquarie Group Limited; *Int'l*, pg. 4630
MACQUARIE HOLDINGS (USA) INC.—See Macquarie Group Limited; *Int'l*, pg. 4625
MACQUARIE INFRASTRUCTURE CORPORATION—See Macquarie Group Limited; *Int'l*, pg. 4627
MACQUARIE INFRASTRUCTURE PARTNERS INC.—See Macquarie Group Limited; *Int'l*, pg. 4628
MACQUARIE INFRASTRUCTURE & REAL ASSETS (EUROPE) LIMITED—See Macquarie Group Limited; *Int'l*, pg. 4626
MACQUARIE INFRASTRUCTURE & REAL ASSETS INC.—See Macquarie Group Limited; *Int'l*, pg. 4626
MACQUARIE INFRASTRUCTURE & REAL ASSETS LIMITED—See Macquarie Group Limited; *Int'l*, pg. 4626
MACQUARIE INSURANCE FACILITY LUXEMBOURG S.A R.L.—See Macquarie Group Limited; *Int'l*, pg. 4630
MACQUARIE INTERNATIONAL HOUSING AND LAND CONSULTING (SHANGHAI) CO., LTD—See Macquarie Group Limited; *Int'l*, pg. 4629

MACQUARIE INVESTMENT ADVISORY (BEIJING) CO., LTD—See Macquarie Group Limited; *Int'l*, pg. 4629
MACQUARIE INVESTMENT MANAGEMENT AUSTRIA KAPITALANLAGE AG—See Macquarie Group Limited; *Int'l*, pg. 4629
MACQUARIE INVESTMENT MANAGEMENT KOREA CO., LIMITED—See Shinhan Financial Group Co., Ltd.; *Int'l*, pg. 6843
MACQUARIE INVESTMENT MANAGEMENT LIMITED—See Macquarie Group Limited; *Int'l*, pg. 4629
MACQUARIE INVESTMENT SERVICES LIMITED—See Macquarie Group Limited; *Int'l*, pg. 4629
MACQUARIE KOREA ASSET MANAGEMENT CO., LIMITED—See Macquarie Group Limited; *Int'l*, pg. 4629
MACQUARIE LEASING PTY LIMITED; *Int'l*, pg. 4631
MACQUARIE METALS AND ENERGY CAPITAL (CANADA) LTD—See Macquarie Group Limited; *Int'l*, pg. 4629
MACQUARIE NORTH AMERICA LTD.—See Macquarie Group Limited; *Int'l*, pg. 4629
MACQUARIE OFFSHORE SERVICES PTY LTD—See Macquarie Group Limited; *Int'l*, pg. 4630
MACQUARIE RESOURCE CAPITAL CANADA LTD—See Macquarie Group Limited; *Int'l*, pg. 4629
MACQUARIE SECURITIES KOREA LIMITED—See Macquarie Group Limited; *Int'l*, pg. 4629
MACQUARIE SECURITIES (NEW ZEALAND) LIMITED—See Macquarie Group Limited; *Int'l*, pg. 4629
MACQUARIE SECURITIES (NZ) LIMITED—See Macquarie Group Limited; *Int'l*, pg. 4630
MACQUARIE SECURITIES SOUTH AFRICA (PTY) LTD—See Macquarie Group Limited; *Int'l*, pg. 4630
MACQUARIE SECURITIES (THAILAND) LIMITED—See Macquarie Group Limited; *Int'l*, pg. 4629
MACQUARIE SECURITISATION LIMITED—See Macquarie Group Limited; *Int'l*, pg. 4630
MACQUARIE SPECIALISED ASSET MANAGEMENT LIMITED—See Macquarie Group Limited; *Int'l*, pg. 4630
MACQUARIE TECHNOLOGY GROUP PTY. LTD.—See Macquarie Telecom Group Limited; *Int'l*, pg. 4631
MACQUARIE TELECOM GROUP LIMITED; *Int'l*, pg. 4631
MACQUARIE TELECOM PTY LIMITED—See Macquarie Telecom Group Limited; *Int'l*, pg. 4631
MACQUARIUM INTELLIGENT COMMUNICATIONS; *U.S. Private*, pg. 2538
MACQUEEN EQUIPMENT, LLC—See Rotunda Capital Partners LLC; *U.S. Private*, pg. 3488
MACREPORT.NET, INC.; *U.S. Public*, pg. 1353
MAC RISK MANAGEMENT, INC—See Koninklijke Ahold Delhaize N.V.; *Int'l*, pg. 4260
MACRO 4 AG—See UNICOM Global, Inc.; *U.S. Private*, pg. 4281
MACRO 4 (BENELUX) NV/SA—See UNICOM Global, Inc.; *U.S. Private*, pg. 4281
MACRO 4 (FRANCE) SARL—See UNICOM Global, Inc.; *U.S. Private*, pg. 4281
MACRO 4 GMBH—See UNICOM Global, Inc.; *U.S. Private*, pg. 4281
MACRO 4 INC.—See UNICOM Global, Inc.; *U.S. Private*, pg. 4281
MACRO 4 LTD.—See UNICOM Global, Inc.; *U.S. Private*, pg. 4281
MACROASIA AIRPORT SERVICES CORPORATION—See MacroAsia Corporation; *Int'l*, pg. 4631
MACROASIA AIR TAXI SERVICES, INC—See MacroAsia Corporation; *Int'l*, pg. 4631
MACROASIA CATERING SERVICES, INC—See MacroAsia Corporation; *Int'l*, pg. 4631
MACROASIA CORPORATION; *Int'l*, pg. 4631
MACROASIA PROPERTIES DEVELOPMENT CORPORATION—See MacroAsia Corporation; *Int'l*, pg. 4631
MACROASIA SATS FOOD INDUSTRIES CORPORATION—See MacroAsia Corporation; *Int'l*, pg. 4631
MACRO BANK LTD—See Banco Macro S.A.; *Int'l*, pg. 823
MACROBERTS LLP—See Morton Fraser MacRoberts LLP; *Int'l*, pg. 5049
MACRO BLOB SDN. BHD.—See GMO Internet Group, Inc.; *Int'l*, pg. 3014
MACROBLOCK, INC.; *Int'l*, pg. 4631
MACROBRIGHT LLC; *U.S. Private*, pg. 2538
MACRO CONSULTANTS LLC—See Savills plc; *Int'l*, pg. 6598
MACRO ENERGY; *U.S. Private*, pg. 2538
MACRO ENTERPRISES INC.; *Int'l*, pg. 4631
MACROGEN ASIA PACIFIC PTE. LTD.—See Macrogen Inc.; *Int'l*, pg. 4631
MACROGEN CORP.—See Macrogen Inc.; *Int'l*, pg. 4632
MACROGEN CORP.—See Macrogen Inc.; *Int'l*, pg. 4632
MACROGEN CORP.—See Macrogen Inc.; *Int'l*, pg. 4632
MACROGENICS, INC.; *U.S. Public*, pg. 1353
MACROGEN INC.; *Int'l*, pg. 4631
MACROGEN JAPAN CORP.—See Macrogen Inc.; *Int'l*, pg. 4632

MACRO-Z-TECHNOLOGY COMPANY

MACRO INDUSTRIES INC.—See Macro Enterprises Inc.; *Int'l*, pg. 4631
MACRO INTEGRATION SERVICES INC.—See The Graham Group, Inc.; *U.S. Private*, pg. 4036
MACRO INTERNATIONAL INC.—See ICF International, Inc.; *U.S. Public*, pg. 1086
MACRO INTERNATIONAL LIMITED; *Int'l*, pg. 4631
MACRO KIOSK (AUSTRALIA) PTY LTD—See Macro Kiosk Berhad; *Int'l*, pg. 4631
MACRO KIOSK BERHAD; *Int'l*, pg. 4631
MACRO KIOSK CO. LTD.—See Macro Kiosk Berhad; *Int'l*, pg. 4631
MACRO KIOSK FZ-LLC—See Macro Kiosk Berhad; *Int'l*, pg. 4631
MACRO KIOSK (GUANGZHOU) TECHNOLOGY CO. LTD—See Macro Kiosk Berhad; *Int'l*, pg. 4631
MACRO KIOSK (HK) LIMITED—See Macro Kiosk Berhad; *Int'l*, pg. 4631
MACRO KIOSK (INDIA) PRIVATE LIMITED—See Macro Kiosk Berhad; *Int'l*, pg. 4631
MACRO KIOSK JOINT STOCK COMPANY—See Macro Kiosk Berhad; *Int'l*, pg. 4631
MACRO KIOSK LIMITED—See Macro Kiosk Berhad; *Int'l*, pg. 4631
MACRO KIOSK (MYANMAR) CO. LTD.—See GMO Internet Group, Inc.; *Int'l*, pg. 3014
MACRO KIOSK PHILIPPINES, INC.—See Macro Kiosk Berhad; *Int'l*, pg. 4631
MACRO KIOSK PTE LTD—See Macro Kiosk Berhad; *Int'l*, pg. 4631
MACRO KIOSK (TAIWAN) TECHNOLOGY LIMITED—See GMO Internet Group, Inc.; *Int'l*, pg. 3014
MACROLEASE CORPORATION—See Brookline Bancorp, Inc.; *U.S. Public*, pg. 396
MACROLINK CAPITAL HOLDINGS LIMITED; *Int'l*, pg. 4632
MACROLINK CULTURALTAINMENT DEVELOPMENT CO., LTD.; *Int'l*, pg. 4632
MACROLINK, INC.—See RTX Corporation; *U.S. Public*, pg. 1822
MACROLOGIC S.A.—See Asseco Poland S.A.; *Int'l*, pg. 641
MACRO LYNX SDN. BHD.—See IGB Berhad; *Int'l*, pg. 3601
MACROMARKETS LLC; *U.S. Private*, pg. 2538
MACROMERIC—See Saco Polymers Inc.; *U.S. Private*, pg. 3522
MACRO METALS LIMITED; *Int'l*, pg. 4631
MACROMILL CARENET, INC.—See Macromill Embrain Co., Ltd.; *Int'l*, pg. 4632
MACROMILL EMBRAIN CO., LTD.; *Int'l*, pg. 4632
MACROMILL, INC.—See Bain Capital, LP; *U.S. Private*, pg. 442
MACRO-M, S.A. DE C.V.—See Grupo Kuo, S.A.B. de C.V.; *Int'l*, pg. 3131
MACRONIX AMERICA INC.—See Macronix International Co., Ltd.; *Int'l*, pg. 4632
MACRONIX (ASIA) LIMITED—See Macronix International Co., Ltd.; *Int'l*, pg. 4632
MACRONIX (BVI) CO LTD—See Macronix International Co., Ltd.; *Int'l*, pg. 4632
MACRONIX EUROPE NV—See Macronix International Co., Ltd.; *Int'l*, pg. 4632
MACRONIX (HONG KONG) CO., LIMITED—See Macronix International Co., Ltd.; *Int'l*, pg. 4632
MACRONIX INTERNATIONAL CO., LTD.; *Int'l*, pg. 4632
MACRONIX MICROELECTRONICS (SUZHOU) CO., LTD—See Macronix International Co., Ltd.; *Int'l*, pg. 4632
MACRONIX PTE LTD—See Macronix International Co., Ltd.; *Int'l*, pg. 4632
MACRON SAFETY SYSTEMS (UK) LIMITED—See Johnson Controls International plc; *Int'l*, pg. 3987
MACRO OIL COMPANY INC.; *U.S. Private*, pg. 2538
MACROPLAS INDUSTRIES CO., LTD.—See UPA Corporation Berhad; *Int'l*, pg. 8087
MACRO PLASTIC SDN. BHD.—See UPA Corporation Berhad; *Int'l*, pg. 8087
MACROSCOPE INFORMATIQUE, INC.—See Fujitsu Limited; *Int'l*, pg. 2834
MACRO SECURITIES S.A.—See Banco Macro S.A.; *Int'l*, pg. 823
MACROSHARES HOUSING DEPOSITOR, LLC—See MacroMarkets LLC; *U.S. Private*, pg. 2538
MACROS REPLY GMBH—See Reply S.p.A.; *Int'l*, pg. 6291
MACROSTAT (CHINA) CLINICAL RESEARCH CO., LTD—See Hangzhou Tigermed Consulting Co., Ltd.; *Int'l*, pg. 3251
MACROSTIE HISTORIC ADVISORS, LLC—See Ryan, LLC; *U.S. Private*, pg. 3511
MACROVISION KOREA CO., LTD.—See Adeia Inc.; *U.S. Public*, pg. 41
MACROVISION SOLUTIONS NETWORKS—See Adeia Inc.; *U.S. Public*, pg. 41
MACROWELL OMG DIGITAL ENTERTAINMENT CO., LTD.; *Int'l*, pg. 4632
MACRO-Z-TECHNOLOGY COMPANY; *U.S. Private*, pg. 2538

MACSA ID, S.A.
CORPORATE AFFILIATIONS

MACSA ID, S.A.; *Int'l,* pg. 4632
MACSA PORTUGAL LDA.—See MACSA ID, S.A.; *Int'l,* pg. 4632
MAC'S CONVENIENCE STORES, INC.—See Alimentation Couche-Tard Inc.; *Int'l,* pg. 328
MAC'S CONVENIENCE STORES, INC.—See Alimentation Couche-Tard Inc.; *Int'l,* pg. 328
MACS MINIT MART; *U.S. Private,* pg. 2538
MAC SOLUTIONS S.A.—See TXT e-Solutions S.p.A.; *Int'l,* pg. 7993
MAC'S OYSTERS LTD.; *Int'l,* pg. 4619
MACSTEEL HOLDINGS LUXEMBOURG S.A.R.L.; *Int'l,* pg. 4632
MACSTEEL INTERNATIONAL AUSTRALIA PTY LIMITED—See Macsteel Holdings Luxembourg S.a.r.l.; *Int'l,* pg. 4632
MACSTEEL INTERNATIONAL FZCO—See Macsteel Holdings Luxembourg S.a.r.l.; *Int'l,* pg. 4632
MACSTEEL INTERNATIONAL HOLDINGS B.V.—See Macsteel Holdings Luxembourg S.a.r.l.; *Int'l,* pg. 4632
MACSTEEL INTERNATIONAL USA CORP.—See Macsteel Holdings Luxembourg S.a.r.l.; *Int'l,* pg. 4632
MACSTEEL SERVICE CENTERS USA, INC.—See Klockner & Co. SE; *Int'l,* pg. 4203
MACSTEEL SERVICE CENTRES SA (PTY) LTD.—See Macsteel Holdings Luxembourg S.a.r.l.; *Int'l,* pg. 4633
MACTAC DEUTSCHLAND GMBH—See Avery Dennison Corporation; *U.S. Public,* pg. 244
MACTAC EUROPE SPRL—See Avery Dennison Corporation; *U.S. Public,* pg. 244
MACTAC FRANCE SARL—See Avery Dennison Corporation; *U.S. Public,* pg. 244
MACTAC MEXICO, S.A. DE C.V.—See LINTEC Corporation; *Int'l,* pg. 4516
MACTAC POLSKA—See Avery Dennison Corporation; *U.S. Public,* pg. 244
MACTAC SCANDINAVIA AB—See LINTEC Corporation; *Int'l,* pg. 4516
MACTAC U.K. LIMITED—See LINTEC Corporation; *Int'l,* pg. 4516
MACTAN ENERZONE CORPORATION—See Aboitiz Equity Ventures, Inc.; *Int'l,* pg. 67
MACTAN SHANGRI-LA HOTEL & RESORT, INC.—See Shangri-La Asia Limited; *Int'l,* pg. 6783
MACTAN STEEL CENTER INC.—See Sumitomo Corporation; *Int'l,* pg. 7269
MACTECH CO., LTD.—See Wintek Corporation; *Int'l,* pg. 8431
M.A.C. TECHNOLOGY (M) SDN. BHD.—See Abico Group; *Int'l,* pg. 61
MACTEK CORP.—See Pepperl+Fuchs Inc; *U.S. Private,* pg. 3145
MACTER INTERNATIONAL LTD.; *Int'l,* pg. 4633
MAC TOOLS—See Stanley Black & Decker, Inc.; *U.S. Public,* pg. 1933
MACTUS GROUP; *U.S. Private,* pg. 2538
MAC VALVES ASIA, INC.—See MAC Valves, Inc.; *U.S. Private,* pg. 2531
MAC VALVES EUROPE, INC.—See MAC Valves, Inc.; *U.S. Private,* pg. 2531
MAC VALVES, INC.-DUNDEE—See MAC Valves, Inc.; *U.S. Private,* pg. 2531
MAC VALVES, INC.; *U.S. Private,* pg. 2531
MAC VALVES PACIFIC—See MAC Valves, Inc.; *U.S. Private,* pg. 2531
MACWIN STEEL INC; *Int'l,* pg. 4633
MACYS BACKSTAGE, INC.—See Macy's, Inc.; *U.S. Public,* pg. 1353
MACYS.COM, INC.—See Macy's, Inc.; *U.S. Public,* pg. 1353
MACY'S CORPORATE SERVICES, INC.—See Macy's, Inc.; *U.S. Public,* pg. 1353
MACY'S CREDIT AND CUSTOMER SERVICES, INC.—See Macy's, Inc.; *U.S. Public,* pg. 1353
MACY'S FLORIDA STORES, LLC—See Macy's, Inc.; *U.S. Public,* pg. 1353
MACY'S, INC. - FINANCIAL, ADMINISTRATIVE & CREDIT SERVICES GROUP—See Macy's, Inc.; *U.S. Public,* pg. 1353
MACY'S, INC.; *U.S. Public,* pg. 1353
MACY'S LOGISTICS & OPERATIONS—See Macy's, Inc.; *U.S. Public,* pg. 1353
MACY'S LOGISTICS & OPERATIONS—See Macy's, Inc.; *U.S. Public,* pg. 1353
MACY'S MERCHANDISING GROUP, INC.—See Macy's, Inc.; *U.S. Public,* pg. 1353
MACY'S SYSTEMS AND TECHNOLOGY, INC.—See Macy's, Inc.; *U.S. Public,* pg. 1353
MACY'S WEST STORES, INC. - HAWAII—See Macy's, Inc.; *U.S. Public,* pg. 1353
MACY'S WEST STORES, INC.—See Macy's, Inc.; *U.S. Public,* pg. 1353
MACY'S WEST STORES, INC.—See Macy's, Inc.; *U.S. Public,* pg. 1353
MADAD PTY. LTD.—See Dyer Holdings Pty. Ltd.; *Int'l,* pg. 2238
MADAGASCAR AUTOMOBILE SA—See Honda Motor Co., Ltd.; *Int'l,* pg. 3463

MADAGASCAR DAIHO COMPANY LIMITED—See DAIHO CORPORATION; *Int'l,* pg. 1927
MADAGASCAR INTERNATIONAL CONTAINER TERMINAL SERVICES LTD.—See International Container Terminal Services, Inc.; *Int'l,* pg. 3746
MADAH PERKASA SDN BHD—See Far East Holdings Berhad; *Int'l,* pg. 2616
MADALENA ENERGY S.A.—See Centaurus Energy Inc.; *Int'l,* pg. 1402
MADAL PALFINGER S.A.—See Palfinger AG; *Int'l,* pg. 5707
MADA MEDICAL PRODUCTS INC.; *U.S. Private,* pg. 2539
MADAME TUSSAUD LAS VEGAS LLC—See Merlin Entertainments plc; *Int'l,* pg. 4837
MADAME TUSSAUDS AMSTERDAM B.V.—See Merlin Entertainments plc; *Int'l,* pg. 4837
MADAME TUSSAUDS AUSTRIA GMBH—See Merlin Entertainments plc; *Int'l,* pg. 4837
MADAME TUSSAUDS DEUTSCHLAND GMBH—See Merlin Entertainments plc; *Int'l,* pg. 4837
MADAME TUSSAUDS HOLLYWOOD LLC—See Merlin Entertainments plc; *Int'l,* pg. 4838
MADAME TUSSAUDS ORLANDO LLC—See Merlin Entertainments plc; *Int'l,* pg. 4837
MADAME TUSSAUDS WASHINGTON LLC—See Merlin Entertainments plc; *Int'l,* pg. 4837
MADANES INSURANCE AGENCY LTD.—See Harel Insurance Investments & Financial Services Ltd.; *Int'l,* pg. 3274
MADANG PORT SERVICES LIMITED—See Steamships Trading Company Limited; *Int'l,* pg. 7188
MAD ANTHONY'S INCORPORATED; *U.S. Private,* pg. 2538
MADARA COSMETICS AS; *Int'l,* pg. 4633
MADARA EUROPE AD; *Int'l,* pg. 4633
MADA S.P.A.—See CIEM S.p.A.; *Int'l,* pg. 1605
MADATA IT, S.A. DE C.V.—See GCC, S.A.B. de C.V.; *Int'l,* pg. 2895
MADAVOR MEDIA, LLC—See BeBop Channel Corporation; *U.S. Public,* pg. 288
MADBOX CO., LTD.—See Nippon Television Holdings Inc.; *Int'l,* pg. 5356
MAD BY DESIGN LLC; *U.S. Private,* pg. 2538
MADCAP SOFTWARE, INC.—See Battery Ventures, L.P.; *U.S. Private,* pg. 489
MAD CATZ EUROPE LIMITED—See Mad Catz Interactive Inc.; *U.S. Private,* pg. 2538
MAD CATZ GMBH—See Mad Catz Interactive Inc.; *U.S. Private,* pg. 2539
MAD CATZ, INC.—See Mad Catz Interactive Inc.; *U.S. Private,* pg. 2539
MAD CATZ INTERACTIVE ASIA LIMITED—See Mad Catz Interactive Inc.; *U.S. Private,* pg. 2539
MAD CATZ INTERACTIVE INC.; *U.S. Private,* pg. 2538
MAD CATZ SAS—See Mad Catz Interactive Inc.; *U.S. Private,* pg. 2539
MAD CITY WINDOWS & BATHS, LLC—See Florida Home Improvement Associates Inc.; *U.S. Private,* pg. 1549
MADDEN COMMUNICATIONS INC.—See HH Global Group Limited; *Int'l,* pg. 3379
MADDEN COMMUNICATIONS, INC.; *U.S. Private,* pg. 2539
MADDEN CONTRACTING COMPANY INC.; *U.S. Private,* pg. 2539
THE MADDEN CORPORATION; *U.S. Private,* pg. 4074
MADDEN ELEVATOR COMPANY—See American Elevator Group; *U.S. Private,* pg. 231
MADDEN INTERNATIONAL LTD.—See Steven Madden, Ltd.; *U.S. Public,* pg. 1947
MADDEN LINCOLN MERCURY INC.; *U.S. Private,* pg. 2539
MADDEN MANUFACTURING CO., INC.—See Caisse de Depot et Placement du Quebec; *Int'l,* pg. 1254
MADDEN MANUFACTURING CO., INC.—See TorQuest Partners Inc.; *Int'l,* pg. 7830
MADDOCK DOUGLAS, INC.; *U.S. Private,* pg. 2539
MAD DOG DESIGN & CONSTRUCTION CO., INC.; *U.S. Private,* pg. 2539
MADDOX INDUSTRIAL TRANSFORMER, LLC; *U.S. Private,* pg. 2539
MADDOX METAL WORKS INC; *U.S. Private,* pg. 2539
MADE4NET LLC—See Stichting INGKA Foundation; *Int'l,* pg. 7215
M.A. DEATLEY CONSTRUCTION INC.; *U.S. Private,* pg. 2527
MADE BY PROSPER LIMITED—See HAL Trust N.V.; *Int'l,* pg. 3226
MADE.FOR.DIGITAL B.V.—See S4 Capital plc; *Int'l,* pg. 6458
MADE IN JAPAN TERIYAKI EXPERIENCE; *Int'l,* pg. 4633
MADEIRA MINERALS LTD.; *Int'l,* pg. 4633
MADEIRAS PRECIOSAS DE AMAZONIA MANEJO LTDA.—See Precious Woods Holding AG; *Int'l,* pg. 5956
MADEIRAS SL LIMITADA—See WoodBois Ltd.; *Int'l,* pg. 8449
MADEIRA USA LTD.; *U.S. Private,* pg. 2539

MADELAINE CHOCOLATE NOVELTIES, INC.; *U.S. Private,* pg. 2539
MADELEINE MODE GMBH—See Equistone Partners Europe Limited; *Int'l,* pg. 2487
MADEMOISELLE DESSERTS CORBY LTD.; *Int'l,* pg. 4633
MAD ENGINE, LLC—See Platinum Equity, LLC; *U.S. Private,* pg. 3205
MADEN TECH CONSULTING INC.; *U.S. Private,* pg. 2539
MADERA AUTO CENTER; *U.S. Private,* pg. 2539
MADERA KIDNEY CENTER, LLC—See Nautic Partners, LLC; *U.S. Private,* pg. 2870
MADERAS COUNTRY CLUB LLC—See Sunroad Holding Corporation; *U.S. Private,* pg. 3870
MADERAS PRECIOSAS DE COSTA RICA S.A.—See Precious Woods Holding AG; *Int'l,* pg. 5956
MADERAS Y SINTETICOS DEL PERU S.A.C.—See GrupoNueva S.A.; *Int'l,* pg. 3139
MADER CONSTRUCTION CORP; *U.S. Private,* pg. 2539
MADER TECHNIC AG—See Pema Holding AG; *Int'l,* pg. 5784
MADE SA; *Int'l,* pg. 4633
MADE—See Marcegaglia S.p.A.; *Int'l,* pg. 4689
MADE TECH GROUP PLC; *Int'l,* pg. 4633
MADE TECH LIMITED—See Made Tech Group Plc; *Int'l,* pg. 4633
MADETOORDER; *U.S. Private,* pg. 2539
MADEWELL GROUP, INC.; *U.S. Private,* pg. 2539
MADEWELL, INC.—See Leonard Green & Partners, L.P.; *U.S. Private,* pg. 2426
MADEWELL, INC.—See TPG Capital, L.P.; *U.S. Public,* pg. 2174
MADE YA SMILE DENTAL; *U.S. Private,* pg. 2539
MADHAV COPPER LTD.; *Int'l,* pg. 4633
MADHAV INFRA PROJECTS LIMITED; *Int'l,* pg. 4633
MADHAV MARBLES AND GRANITES LIMITED - GRANITE FACTORY—See Madhav Marbles and Granites Limited; *Int'l,* pg. 4633
MADHAV MARBLES AND GRANITES LIMITED; *Int'l,* pg. 4633
MADHOUSE INC.—See Nippon Television Holdings Inc.; *Int'l,* pg. 5356
MADHUCON INFRA LIMITED—See Madhucon Projects Limited; *Int'l,* pg. 4633
MADHUCON PROJECTS LIMITED; *Int'l,* pg. 4633
MADHUR CAPITAL & FINANCE LTD.; *Int'l,* pg. 4633
MADHUR INDUSTRIES LIMITED; *Int'l,* pg. 4633
MADHUSUDAN INDUSTRIES LIMITED; *Int'l,* pg. 4634
MADHUSUDAN SECURITIES LIMITED; *Int'l,* pg. 4634
MADHYA BHARAT AGRO PRODUCTS LTD.; *Int'l,* pg. 4634
MADHYA BHARAT POWER CORPORATION LIMITED—See Sarda Energy & Minerals Ltd; *Int'l,* pg. 6577
MADHYA BHOTEKOSHI JALAVIDHYUT COMPANY LIMITED—See Chilime Hydropower Company Limited; *Int'l,* pg. 1478
MADHYA PRADESH TODAY MEDIA LIMITED; *Int'l,* pg. 4634
MADICOB SA; *Int'l,* pg. 4634
MADICO, INC.—See LINTEC Corporation; *Int'l,* pg. 4516
MADICO WINDOW FILMS INC—See LINTEC Corporation; *Int'l,* pg. 4516
MADIGAN DIALYSIS, LLC—See DaVita Inc.; *U.S. Public,* pg. 640
MADILL MOTORS PTY LTD; *Int'l,* pg. 4634
MADI MINERALS LTD.; *Int'l,* pg. 4634
MADINET NASR FOR HOUSING & DEVELOPMENT; *Int'l,* pg. 4634
MADISON APARTMENT GROUP, LP—See Equus Capital Partners, Ltd.; *U.S. Private,* pg. 1416
MADISON APPROACH STAFFING, INC.; *U.S. Private,* pg. 2539
MADISON AVENUE HOLDINGS, INC.; *U.S. Private,* pg. 2539
MADISON BANK OF MARYLAND—See Bay-Vanguard, M.H.C.; *U.S. Private,* pg. 495
MADISON BEHAVIORAL HEALTH, LLC—See HCA Healthcare, Inc.; *U.S. Public,* pg. 1001
MADISON BLOCK & STONE LLC—See SiteOne Landscape Supply, Inc.; *U.S. Public,* pg. 1889
MADISON COMMUNICATIONS; *Int'l,* pg. 4634
MADISON COMMUNITY HOSPITAL INC.; *U.S. Private,* pg. 2540
MADISON COMPONENTS LLC; *U.S. Private,* pg. 2540
MADISON CONSULTING GROUP, INC.—See FTI Consulting, Inc.; *U.S. Public,* pg. 891
MADISON COUNTY BANK—See Madison County Financial, Inc.; *U.S. Public,* pg. 1353
MADISON COUNTY FINANCIAL, INC.; *U.S. Public,* pg. 1353
MADISON COUNTY MEDICAL EQUIPMENT, INC.—See AdaptHealth Corp.; *U.S. Public,* pg. 39
MADISON COUNTY WOOD PRODUCTS, INC.; *U.S. Private,* pg. 2540
MADISON CREATIVE—See Madison Communications; *Int'l,* pg. 4634
MADISON CREATIVE—See Madison Communications; *Int'l,* pg. 4634

COMPANY NAME INDEX

MADISON DAIRY PRODUCE COMPANY—See Land O'Lakes, Inc.; *U.S. Private*, pg. 2383
MADISON DEARBORN PARTNERS, LLC; *U.S. Private*, pg. 2540
MADISON/EAST TOWNE, LLC—See CBL & Associates Properties, Inc.; *U.S. Public*, pg. 458
MADISON ELECTRIC COMPANY; *U.S. Private*, pg. 2542
MADISON ELECTRIC SERVICE—See Tri-State Armature & Electric Works, Inc.; *U.S. Private*, pg. 4223
MADISON FARMERS ELEVATOR CO.; *U.S. Private*, pg. 2543
MADISON FINANCIAL ADVISORS, LTD.—See Keystone Group, L.P.; *U.S. Private*, pg. 2297
MADISON FOOTWEAR CO. LTD.—See Mercury International Trading Corp.; *U.S. Private*, pg. 2670
MADISON GAS & ELECTRIC COMPANY—See MGE Energy, Inc.; *U.S. Public*, pg. 1434
MADISON/GRAHAM COLORGRAPHICS, INC.—See Cenveo, Inc.; *U.S. Private*, pg. 835
MADISON/GRAHAM COLORGRAPHICS INTERSTATE SERVICES, INC.—See Cenveo, Inc.; *U.S. Private*, pg. 835
THE MADISON GROUP, INC.—See Winged Keel Group, LLC; *U.S. Private*, pg. 4541
MADISON HMA, LLC—See Community Health Systems, Inc.; *U.S. Public*, pg. 555
MADISON HOLDINGS GROUP LIMITED; *Int'l*, pg. 4634
MADISON HOSPITALITY GROUP, LLC; *U.S. Private*, pg. 2543
MADISON HUNTSVILLE COUNTY AIRPORT AUTHORITY; *U.S. Private*, pg. 2543
MADISON, INC.—See John S. Frey Enterprises; *U.S. Private*, pg. 2224
MADISON INDUSTRIES HOLDINGS LLC; *U.S. Private*, pg. 2543
MADISON INDUSTRIES INC. OF ARIZONA—See John S. Frey Enterprises; *U.S. Private*, pg. 2224
MADISON INDUSTRIES INC. OF GEORGIA—See John S. Frey Enterprises; *U.S. Private*, pg. 2224
MADISON INDUSTRIES INC.—See John S. Frey Enterprises; *U.S. Private*, pg. 2224
MADISON INDUSTRIES INC.; *U.S. Private*, pg. 2543
MADISON INDUSTRIES, INC.; *U.S. Private*, pg. 2543
MADISON INTERNAL MEDICINE, LLC—See HCA Healthcare, Inc.; *U.S. Public*, pg. 1001
MADISON INTERNATIONAL REALTY, LLC; *U.S. Private*, pg. 2543
MADISON INVESTMENT ADVISORS, INC.; *U.S. Private*, pg. 2544
MADISON-KIPP CORPORATION; *U.S. Private*, pg. 2544
MADISON LIQUIDITY INVESTORS LLC; *U.S. Private*, pg. 2544
MADISON LOGIC, INC.—See Clarion Capital Partners, LLC; *U.S. Private*, pg. 911
MADISON LUTHERAN HOME; *U.S. Private*, pg. 2544
MADISON MAIDEN; *U.S. Private*, pg. 2544
MADISON MARQUETTE DEVELOPMENT CORPORATION; *U.S. Private*, pg. 2544
MADISON MARQUETTE REALTY SERVICES LLC—See Madison Marquette Development Corporation; *U.S. Private*, pg. 2544
MADISON MEDIA PLUS—See Madison Communications; *Int'l*, pg. 4634
MADISON MEDIA—See Madison Communications; *Int'l*, pg. 4634
MADISON NATIONAL LIFE INSURANCE CO., INC.—See Geneve Holdings Corp.; *U.S. Private*, pg. 1670
MADISON NEWSPAPERS, INC.—See Lee Enterprises, Incorporated; *U.S. Public*, pg. 1299
MADISON NEWSPAPERS, INC.—See The Capital Times Company; *U.S. Private*, pg. 4004
MADISON ONE HOLDINGS; *U.S. Private*, pg. 2544
MADISON PACIFIC PROPERTIES INC.; *Int'l*, pg. 4634
MADISON PARKER CAPITAL; *U.S. Private*, pg. 2544
MADISON PHARMACEUTICALS INC.—See Cipla Ltd.; *Int'l*, pg. 1617
MADISON PR—See Madison Communications; *Int'l*, pg. 4634
MADISON PT OF NEW JERSEY, PC—See U.S. Physical Therapy, Inc.; *U.S. Public*, pg. 2215
MADISON REHABILITATION CENTER, INC.—See Select Medical Holdings Corporation; *U.S. Public*, pg. 1858
MADISON RESEARCH CORPORATION—See Kratos Defense & Security Solutions, Inc.; *U.S. Public*, pg. 1276
MADISON RETAIL PARADIGM PVT. LTD.—See Madison Communications; *Int'l*, pg. 4634
MADISON RIVER COMMUNICATIONS, LLC—See Lumen Technologies, Inc.; *U.S. Public*, pg. 1347
MADISON RIVER HOLDINGS LLC—See Lumen Technologies, Inc.; *U.S. Public*, pg. 1347
MADISON RIVER OAKS MEDICAL CENTER—See Community Health Systems, Inc.; *U.S. Public*, pg. 556
MADISON SENIOR LIVING, INC.—See The Ensign Group, Inc.; *U.S. Public*, pg. 2070
MADISON SPINE, LIMITED PARTNERSHIP—See U.S. Physical Therapy, Inc.; *U.S. Public*, pg. 2215
MADISON SQUARE GARDEN ENTERTAINMENT CORP.; *U.S. Public*, pg. 1353
MADISON SQUARE GARDEN, L.P.—See Madison Square Garden Sports Corp.; *U.S. Public*, pg. 1354
MADISON SQUARE GARDEN NETWORK—See Sphere Entertainment Co.; *U.S. Public*, pg. 1918
MADISON SQUARE GARDEN SPORTS CORP.; *U.S. Public*, pg. 1353
MADISON SYSTEMS, INC.; *Int'l*, pg. 4634
MADISON TAX CAPITAL, LLC—See JPMorgan Chase & Co.; *U.S. Public*, pg. 1210
MADISON TEAMWORKS FP&E—See Madison Communications; *Int'l*, pg. 4634
MADISON TECHNOLOGIES INC.; *U.S. Public*, pg. 1354
MADISON VALLEY BANK—See Jackass Creek Land & Livestock Company; *U.S. Private*, pg. 2175
MADISON WOOD PRESERVERS INC.; *U.S. Private*, pg. 2544
MADIVA SOLUCIONES, S.L.—See Banco Bilbao Vizcaya Argentaria, S.A.; *Int'l*, pg. 818
MADIX INC.; *U.S. Private*, pg. 2544
MAD MAGAZINE/E.C. PUBLICATIONS, INC.—See Warner Bros. Discovery, Inc.; *U.S. Public*, pg. 2328
MADMAN ENTERTAINMENT NZ—See Madman Entertainment Pty. Limited; *Int'l*, pg. 4634
MADMAN ENTERTAINMENT PTY. LIMITED; *Int'l*, pg. 4634
MADMAN PRODUCTION COMPANY PTY. LIMITED—See Madman Entertainment Pty. Limited; *Int'l*, pg. 4634
MAD MOBILE, INC.; *U.S. Private*, pg. 2539
MADONNA ENTERPRISES; *U.S. Private*, pg. 2544
MADORO METALS CORP.; *Int'l*, pg. 4634
MAD PAWS HOLDING LIMITED; *Int'l*, pg. 4633
MADRAS ALUMINUM COMPANY LTD.—See Vedanta Resources Ltd; *Int'l*, pg. 8145
MADRAS FERTILIZERS LIMITED; *Int'l*, pg. 4634
MADRE—See Mother Ltd.; *Int'l*, pg. 5052
MADREX CO., LTD.—See PATH Corporation; *Int'l*, pg. 5756
MADRID DEPORTES Y ESPECTACULOS SA—See Live Nation Entertainment, Inc.; *U.S. Public*, pg. 1329
MADRID ENGINEERING GROUP, INC.; *U.S. Private*, pg. 2544
MADRID HOME COMMUNITIES; *U.S. Private*, pg. 2544
MADRIGALL SA; *Int'l*, pg. 4635
MADRIGAL PHARMACEUTICALS, INC.; *U.S. Public*, pg. 1354
MADRONA SOLUTIONS GROUP; *U.S. Private*, pg. 2544
MADSEN MOTORS LTD.; *Int'l*, pg. 4635
MADSHUS A/S—See Kohlberg & Company, LLC; *U.S. Private*, pg. 2338
MADURA GARMENTS LIFESTYLE RETAIL COMPANY LIMITED—See The Aditya Birla Group; *Int'l*, pg. 7611
MADURA MICRO FINANCE LIMITED—See CreditAccess Grameen Limited; *Int'l*, pg. 1836
MADURO & CURIEL'S BANK (BONAIRE) N.V.—See Maduro & Curiel's Bank N.V.; *Int'l*, pg. 4635
MADURO & CURIEL'S BANK N.V.; *Int'l*, pg. 4635
MADURO & CURIEL'S INSURANCE SERVICES N.V.—See Maduro & Curiel's Bank N.V.; *Int'l*, pg. 4635
MADVERTISE S.A.; *Int'l*, pg. 4635
MAECENAS MINERALS LLP—See Dorchester Minerals, L.P.; *U.S. Public*, pg. 677
MAE.CH GMBH—See Gesco AG; *Int'l*, pg. 2945
MAEDA (BEIJING) BUSINESS CONSULTING CO., LTD.—See Maeda Corporation; *Int'l*, pg. 4635
MAEDA CORPORATION INDIA PRIVATE LTD.—See Maeda Corporation; *Int'l*, pg. 4635
MAEDA CORPORATION; *Int'l*, pg. 4635
MAEDA CORPORATION—See Maeda Corporation; *Int'l*, pg. 4635
MAEDA CORPORATION, U.S.A.—See Maeda Corporation; *Int'l*, pg. 4635
MAEDA KOSEN CO., LTD.; *Int'l*, pg. 4635
MAEDA ROAD CONSTRUCTION CO., LTD.—See Maeda Corporation; *Int'l*, pg. 4635
MAEDA SEISAKUSHO CO., LTD.—See Maeda Corporation; *Int'l*, pg. 4635
MAEDA THIEN DUC CO., LTD.—See Maeda Corporation; *Int'l*, pg. 4635
MAEDA USA LLC—See Maeda Corporation; *Int'l*, pg. 4635
MAEDA VIETNAM CO., LTD.—See Maeda Corporation; *Int'l*, pg. 4635
MAE-EITEL INC.—See Gesco AG; *Int'l*, pg. 2945
MAEIL CO., LTD.—See Zero to Seven Inc.; *Int'l*, pg. 8639
MAEIL DAIRIES CO., LTD. - ASAN PLANT—See Maeil Holdings Co., Ltd.; *Int'l*, pg. 4636
MAEIL DAIRIES CO., LTD. - CHEONGYANG PLANT—See Maeil Holdings Co., Ltd.; *Int'l*, pg. 4636
MAEIL DAIRIES CO., LTD. - GWANGJU PLANT—See Maeil Holdings Co., Ltd.; *Int'l*, pg. 4636
MAEIL DAIRIES CO., LTD. - GYEONGSAN PLANT—See Maeil Holdings Co., Ltd.; *Int'l*, pg. 4636
MAEIL DAIRIES CO., LTD. - PYEONGTAEK PLANT—See Maeil Holdings Co., Ltd.; *Int'l*, pg. 4636
MAEIL DAIRIES CO., LTD. - SANGHA PLANT—See Maeil Holdings Co., Ltd.; *Int'l*, pg. 4636
MAEIL DAIRIES CO., LTD. - YEONGDONG PLANT—See Maeil Holdings Co., Ltd.; *Int'l*, pg. 4636
MAEIL HOLDINGS CO., LTD.; *Int'l*, pg. 4636

M & A EQUITY HOLDINGS BERHAD

MAEKAWA CONSTRUCTION CO., LTD.—See Freesia Macross Corporation; *Int'l*, pg. 2771
MAEKAWA GLASS CO., LTD.—See Nippon Sheet Glass Co. Ltd.; *Int'l*, pg. 5331
MAEKAWA TRANSPORT CO., LTD.—See Konoike Transport Co., Ltd.; *Int'l*, pg. 4275
M & A ELECTRIC POWER COOPERATIVE; *U.S. Private*, pg. 2522
MAE MACHINES (BEIJING) CO., LTD.—See Gesco AG; *Int'l*, pg. 2945
MAE MASCHINEN- UND APPARATEBAU GOTZEN GMBH—See Gesco AG; *Int'l*, pg. 2945
M & A EQUITY HOLDINGS BERHAD; *Int'l*, pg. 4609
MAERSK A/S—See A.P. Moller-Maersk A/S; *Int'l*, pg. 26
MAERSK AUSTRALIA PTY. LTD.—See A.P. Moller-Maersk A/S; *Int'l*, pg. 26
MAERSK BANGLADESH LTD.—See A.P. Moller-Maersk A/S; *Int'l*, pg. 26
MAERSK BENELUX B.V.—See A.P. Moller-Maersk A/S; *Int'l*, pg. 26
MAERSK BRASIL LTDA.—See A.P. Moller-Maersk A/S; *Int'l*, pg. 26
MAERSK BROKER ALBIS SCHIFFAHRT GMBH—See MB Shipbrokers K/S; *Int'l*, pg. 4750
MAERSK BROKER AMERICA INC—See MB Shipbrokers K/S; *Int'l*, pg. 4751
MAERSK BROKER HELLAS LIMITED—See MB Shipbrokers K/S; *Int'l*, pg. 4751
MAERSK BROKER HONG KONG LTD—See MB Shipbrokers K/S; *Int'l*, pg. 4751
MAERSK BROKER KOREA CO., LTD—See MB Shipbrokers K/S; *Int'l*, pg. 4751
MAERSK BROKER MIDDLE EAST DMC EST—See MB Shipbrokers K/S; *Int'l*, pg. 4751
MAERSK BROKER UK LTD—See MB Shipbrokers K/S; *Int'l*, pg. 4751
MAERSK (CHINA) SHIPPING COMPANY LTD.—See A.P. Moller-Maersk A/S; *Int'l*, pg. 26
THE MAERSK COMPANY LIMITED—See A.P. Moller-Maersk A/S; *Int'l*, pg. 28
MAERSK CONTAINER INDUSTRI AS—See A.P. Moller-Maersk A/S; *Int'l*, pg. 26
MAERSK CONTAINER INDUSTRY DONGGUAN LTD.—See A.P. Moller-Maersk A/S; *Int'l*, pg. 26
MAERSK CONTAINER INDUSTRY QINGDAO LTD.—See A.P. Moller-Maersk A/S; *Int'l*, pg. 26
MAERSK DENIZCILIK A.S.—See A.P. Moller-Maersk A/S; *Int'l*, pg. 26
MAERSK DEUTSCHLAND A/S & CO.KG—See A.P. Moller-Maersk A/S; *Int'l*, pg. 26
MAERSK DRILLING A/S—See A.P. Moller-Maersk A/S; *Int'l*, pg. 26
MAERSK DRILLING HOLDINGS SINGAPORE PTE. LTD.—See A.P. Moller-Maersk A/S; *Int'l*, pg. 26
MAERSK DRILLING NORGE AS—See A.P. Moller-Maersk A/S; *Int'l*, pg. 26
MAERSK DRILLING SERVICES A/S—See A.P. Moller-Maersk A/S; *Int'l*, pg. 26
MAERSK DRILLING USA INC.—See A.P. Moller-Maersk A/S; *Int'l*, pg. 26
MAERSK FRANCE S.A.—See A.P. Moller-Maersk A/S; *Int'l*, pg. 26
MAERSK GABON SA—See A.P. Moller-Maersk A/S; *Int'l*, pg. 27
MAERSK GLOBAL SERVICE CENTRES (INDIA) PRIVATE LIMITED—See A.P. Moller-Maersk A/S; *Int'l*, pg. 27
MAERSK HOLDING B.V.—See A.P. Moller-Maersk A/S; *Int'l*, pg. 27
MAERSK (HONG KONG) LTD.—See A.P. Moller-Maersk A/S; *Int'l*, pg. 27
MAERSK INC.—See A.P. Moller-Maersk A/S; *Int'l*, pg. 27
MAERSK INSURANCE A/S—See A.P. Moller-Maersk A/S; *Int'l*, pg. 27
MAERSK ITALIA SPA—See A.P. Moller-Maersk A/S; *Int'l*, pg. 27
MAERSK KENYA LTD.—See A.P. Moller-Maersk A/S; *Int'l*, pg. 27
MAERSK KENYA LTD.—See A.P. Moller-Maersk A/S; *Int'l*, pg. 27
MAERSK K.K.—See A.P. Moller-Maersk A/S; *Int'l*, pg. 27
MAERSK LINE AGENCY HOLDING A/S—See A.P. Moller-Maersk A/S; *Int'l*, pg. 27
MAERSK LINE, LIMITED—See A.P. Moller-Maersk A/S; *Int'l*, pg. 27
MAERSK LINE PERU S.A.C.—See A.P. Moller-Maersk A/S; *Int'l*, pg. 27
MAERSK LOGISTICS & SERVICES INTERNATIONAL A/S—See A.P. Moller-Maersk A/S; *Int'l*, pg. 27
MAERSK LOGISTICS & SERVICES PERU S.A.—See A.P. Moller-Maersk A/S; *Int'l*, pg. 27
MAERSK MALAYSIA SDN BHD—See A.P. Moller-Maersk A/S; *Int'l*, pg. 27
MAERSK NEW ZEALAND LTD.—See A.P. Moller-Maersk A/S; *Int'l*, pg. 27
MAERSK SINGAPORE PTE. LTD.—See A.P. Moller-Maersk A/S; *Int'l*, pg. 27
MAERSK SPAIN, S.L.U.—See A.P. Moller-Maersk A/S; *Int'l*, pg. 27

MAERSK SUPPLY SERVICE APOIO MARITIMO LTDA.—See A.P. Moller-Maersk A/S; *Int'l*, pg. 27
MAERSK SUPPLY SERVICE A/S—See DOF Group ASA; *Int'l*, pg. 2154
MAERSK SUPPLY SERVICE CANADA LTD.—See A.P. Moller-Maersk A/S; *Int'l*, pg. 27
MAERSK SUPPLY SERVICE HOLDINGS UK LIMITED—See A.P. Moller-Maersk A/S; *Int'l*, pg. 27
MAERSK SUPPLY SERVICE UK LIMITED—See A.P. Moller-Maersk A/S; *Int'l*, pg. 27
MAERSK TANKERS A/S—See A.P. Moller Holding A/S; *Int'l*, pg. 25
MAERSK TANKERS SINGAPORE PTE. LTD—See A.P. Moller-Maersk A/S; *Int'l*, pg. 27
MAERSK VIETNAM LTD.—See A.P. Moller-Maersk A/S; *Int'l*, pg. 27
MAERTIENS ROBOTEC GMBH—See Dieffenbacher Holding GmbH & Co. KG; *Int'l*, pg. 2114
MAERZ OFENBAU AG—See ThyssenKrupp AG; *Int'l*, pg. 7732
MAESA HOME—See F&B Group; *Int'l*, pg. 2595
MAESA INC—See F&B Group; *Int'l*, pg. 2595
MAESA SA—See F&B Group; *Int'l*, pg. 2595
MAESA UK LTD—See F&B Group; *Int'l*, pg. 2595
MAE SOD CLEAN ENERGY CO., LTD.—See Padaeng Industry pcl; *Int'l*, pg. 5693
MAESSA TELECOMUNICACIONES, INGENIERIA, INSTALACIONES Y SERVICIOS, S.A.—See ACS, Actividades de Construccion y Servicios, S.A.; *Int'l*, pg. 115
MAESSA TELECOMUNICACIONES, S.A.—See ACS, Actividades de Construccion y Servicios, S.A.; *Int'l*, pg. 115
MAESTRALE GREEN ENERGY SRL—See Electricite de France S.A.; *Int'l*, pg. 2350
MAESTRO FILMWORKS LLC; *U.S. Private*, pg. 2544
MAESTRO HEALTH, INC.—See Marpai, Inc; *U.S. Public*, pg. 1370
MAESTRO LLC; *U.S. Private*, pg. 2544
MAESTRO LOCADORA DE VEICULOS S.A.; *Int'l*, pg. 4636
MAESTRO PRINT MANAGEMENT LLC; *U.S. Private*, pg. 2544
MAESTROSOFT, INC.—See Arreva LLC; *U.S. Private*, pg. 335
MAESTRO TECHNOLOGIES, INC.; *U.S. Private*, pg. 2545
MAESTRO WIRELESS SOLUTIONS LIMITED—See LinkAsia International MedTech Group Limited; *Int'l*, pg. 4514
MAETEC POWER, INC.; *U.S. Private*, pg. 2545
MAETEHNIKA AS—See Eesti Energia AS; *Int'l*, pg. 2317
MAEZAWA INDUSTRIES, INC.; *Int'l*, pg. 4636
MAEZAWA KASEI INDUSTRIES CO., LTD.; *Int'l*, pg. 4636
MAEZAWA KYUSO INDUSTRIES CO., LTD.; *Int'l*, pg. 4636
MAFATLAL INDUSTRIES LIMITED—See Arvind Mafatlal Group; *Int'l*, pg. 587
MAFCO CONSOLIDATED GROUP INC.—See MacAndrews & Forbes Incorporated; *U.S. Private*, pg. 2532
MAFCO NATURAL PRODUCTS—See MacAndrews & Forbes Incorporated; *U.S. Private*, pg. 2532
MAFCOTE INDUSTRIES INC.; *U.S. Private*, pg. 2545
MAFCO WORLDWIDE CORPORATION—See MacAndrews & Forbes Incorporated; *U.S. Private*, pg. 2532
MA FEDERAL INC.; *U.S. Private*, pg. 2530
MAFFEI SARDA SILICATI S.P.A.—See Gruppo Minerali Maffei S.p.A.; *Int'l*, pg. 3140
MAFIA TRENDS LIMITED; *Int'l*, pg. 4636
MA FINANCIAL GROUP LIMITED; *Int'l*, pg. 4618
MAFI SRL—See Clariane SE; *Int'l*, pg. 1643
MAF MAGNESITE BV—See L. Possehl & Co. mbH; *Int'l*, pg. 4383
M.A. FORD MANUFACTURING CO.; *U.S. Private*, pg. 2527
MAFRA, A.S.—See Agrofert Holding, a.s.; *Int'l*, pg. 219
MAFRA HOSPITALAR S/A; *Int'l*, pg. 4636
MAG+ AB—See Bonnier AB; *Int'l*, pg. 1109
MAGADANENERGO OAO; *Int'l*, pg. 4636
MAGA DESIGN GROUP; *U.S. Private*, pg. 2545
MAGAJINE SAPURAI MALAYSIA SDN BHD—See TungJetek Co., Ltd.; *Int'l*, pg. 7971
MAGAL CHINA—See Senstar Technologies Ltd.; *Int'l*, pg. 6714
MAGALDI LIFE S.R.L.—See Mitsubishi Chemical Group Corporation; *Int'l*, pg. 4936
MAGAL-S3 CANADA INC.—See Senstar Technologies Ltd.; *Int'l*, pg. 6714
MAGAL S3 ESPANA, S.L.—See Senstar Technologies Ltd.; *Int'l*, pg. 6714
MAGAL SECURITY SYSTEMS (INDIA) LIMITED—See Senstar Technologies Ltd.; *Int'l*, pg. 6714
MAGANG (GROUP) HOLDING COMPANY LIMITED—See China Baowu Steel Group Corp., Ltd.; *Int'l*, pg. 1486
MAGAN KOREA CO. LTD.—See China National Chemical Corporation; *Int'l*, pg. 1526
MAGAPORT, INC.—See Dentsu Group Inc.; *Int'l*, pg. 2039
MAGA PTY LIMITED—See Sonic Healthcare Limited; *Int'l*, pg. 7097
MAGASEEK CORPORATION—See Nippon Telegraph & Telephone Corporation; *Int'l*, pg. 5343

MAGASINET FASTIGHETSSVERIGE AB—See Byggfakta Group Nordic HoldCo AB; *Int'l*, pg. 1234
MAGA T.E.A.M. S.R.L—See Skandinavisk Holding A/S; *Int'l*, pg. 6977
MAGAZINE LUIZA S.A.; *Int'l*, pg. 4636
MAGAZINES.COM INC.; *U.S. Private*, pg. 2545
MAGAZINES INCORPORATED PTE LTD.—See Singapore Press Holdings Ltd.; *Int'l*, pg. 6942
MAGAZINE SUPPLY CO., LTD.—See Tung-Jetek Co., Ltd.; *Int'l*, pg. 7971
MAGAZINES WORLD SDN BHD—See Singapore Press Holdings Ltd.; *Int'l*, pg. 6942
MAGAZZINI GENERALI DELLE TAGLIATE (M.G.T.) SPA—See Credito Emiliano S.p.A.; *Int'l*, pg. 1836
MAGBEE CONTRACTORS SUPPLY; *U.S. Private*, pg. 2545
MAGBERG MANUFACTURING (PTY) LTD—See MC Mining Limited; *Int'l*, pg. 4755
MAG CAPITAL, LLC—See Mid Western Automotive LLC; *U.S. Private*, pg. 2706
MAG CHEMICAL PTE. LTD.—See Sanli Environmental Limited; *Int'l*, pg. 6546
MAGCO DRILLING, INC.—See Aldridge Construction, Inc.; *U.S. Private*, pg. 160
MAG-CON ENGINEERING—See Badger Magnetics, Inc.; *U.S. Private*, pg. 424
MAGDEBURGER SIGORTA A.S.—See Allianz SE; *Int'l*, pg. 354
MAGDEV LIMITED—See Bunting Magnetics Co.; *U.S. Private*, pg. 686
MAG DS CORP.; *U.S. Private*, pg. 2545
MAGEAN HOLDING PLC; *Int'l*, pg. 4637
MAGEBA A.S.—See Mageba S.A.; *Int'l*, pg. 4637
MAGEBA BRIDGE PRODUCTS LTD.—See Mageba S.A.; *Int'l*, pg. 4637
MAGEBA GMBH—See Mageba S.A.; *Int'l*, pg. 4637
MAGEBA (KOREA) CO. LTD.—See Mageba S.A.; *Int'l*, pg. 4637
MAGEBA S.A.; *Int'l*, pg. 4637
MAGEBA (SHANGHAI) LTD.—See Mageba S.A.; *Int'l*, pg. 4637
MAGEBA USA LLC—See Mageba S.A.; *Int'l*, pg. 4637
MAGEE GENERAL HOSPITAL; *U.S. Private*, pg. 2545
MAGELLAN AEROSPACE, BETHEL, INC.—See Magellan Aerospace Corporation; *Int'l*, pg. 4637
MAGELLAN AEROSPACE CORPORATION; *Int'l*, pg. 4637
MAGELLAN AEROSPACE, GLENDALE, INC.—See Magellan Aerospace Corporation; *Int'l*, pg. 4637
MAGELLAN AEROSPACE, HAVERHILLL, INC.—See Magellan Aerospace Corporation; *Int'l*, pg. 4637
MAGELLAN AEROSPACE LIMITED—See Magellan Aerospace Corporation; *Int'l*, pg. 4637
MAGELLAN AEROSPACE, MIDDLETOWN, INC.—See Magellan Aerospace Corporation; *Int'l*, pg. 4637
MAGELLAN AEROSPACE, NEW YORK, INC.—See Magellan Aerospace Corporation; *Int'l*, pg. 4637
MAGELLAN AEROSPACE (UK) LIMITED—See Magellan Aerospace Corporation; *Int'l*, pg. 4637
MAGELLAN ASSET MANAGEMENT LTD.—See Magellan Financial Group Limited; *Int'l*, pg. 4637
MAGELLAN AVIATION GROUP LLLP—See Marubeni Corporation; *Int'l*, pg. 4706
MAGELLAN BEHAVIORAL HEALTH, INC.—See Centene Corporation; *U.S. Public*, pg. 469
MAGELLAN BEHAVIORAL HEALTH OF FLORIDA, INC.—See Centene Corporation; *U.S. Public*, pg. 469
MAGELLAN BEHAVIORAL HEALTH OF PENNSYLVANIA, INC.—See Centene Corporation; *U.S. Public*, pg. 469
MAGELLAN DIAGNOSTICS, INC.—See Meridian Bioscience Inc.; *U.S. Public*, pg. 1424
MAGELLAN FINANCIAL GROUP LIMITED; *Int'l*, pg. 4637
MAGELLAN GLOBAL TRUST—See Magellan Financial Group Limited; *Int'l*, pg. 4637
MAGELLAN GOLD CORPORATION; *U.S. Public*, pg. 1354
MAGELLAN HEALTHCARE, INC.—See Centene Corporation; *U.S. Public*, pg. 469
MAGELLAN HEALTHCARE PROVIDER GROUP, INC.—See Centene Corporation; *U.S. Public*, pg. 469
MAGELLAN HEALTH, INC.—See Centene Corporation; *U.S. Public*, pg. 469
MAGELLAN HEALTH SERVICES—See Centene Corporation; *U.S. Public*, pg. 469
MAGELLAN HEALTH SERVICES—See Centene Corporation; *U.S. Public*, pg. 469
MAGELLANIC CLOUD LIMITED; *Int'l*, pg. 4637
MAGELLAN JETS LLC.; *U.S. Private*, pg. 2545
MAGELLAN LIFE INSURANCE COMPANY—See Centene Corporation; *U.S. Public*, pg. 470
MAGELLAN METHOD, LLC—See Centene Corporation; *U.S. Public*, pg. 470
MAGELLAN MIDSTREAM PARTNERS, L.P.—See ONEOK, Inc.; *U.S. Public*, pg. 1603
MAGELLAN NAVIGATION, INC.—See Shah Capital Partners, LP; *U.S. Private*, pg. 3623
MAGELLAN PIPELINE COMPANY, L.P.—See ONEOK, Inc.; *U.S. Public*, pg. 1603

MAGELLAN PIPELINE LP—See ONEOK, Inc.; *U.S. Public*, pg. 1603
MAGELLAN PROCESSING, L.P.—See ONEOK, Inc.; *U.S. Public*, pg. 1603
MAGELLAN S.A.—See Banca Farmafactoring S.p.A.; *Int'l*, pg. 814
MAGELLAN SEARCH GROUP, INC.; *U.S. Private*, pg. 2545
MAGENIC TECHNOLOGIES, INC.—See Cognizant Technology Solutions Corporation; *U.S. Public*, pg. 524
MAGENTA MASTER FIBERS CO., LTD.—See Avient Corporation; *U.S. Public*, pg. 247
MAGENTA MASTER FIBERS S.R.L—See Avient Corporation; *U.S. Public*, pg. 247
MAGENTA RESEARCH LTD—See Melrose Industries PLC; *Int'l*, pg. 4813
MAGENTIS B.V.—See Sopra Steria Group S.A.; *Int'l*, pg. 7109
MAGERLE AG MASCHINENFABRIK—See United Grinding Group AG; *Int'l*, pg. 8067
MAGEX CORPORATION; *U.S. Private*, pg. 2545
MAGFIVE CONTENT AB—See LOV Group Invest SAS; *Int'l*, pg. 4565
MAGFORCE AG; *Int'l*, pg. 4637
MAG FRUITS; *Int'l*, pg. 4636
MAGGARD ENTERPRISES INC.; *U.S. Private*, pg. 2545
MAGGIANO'S BEVERAGE COMPANY—See Brinker International, Inc.; *U.S. Public*, pg. 384
MAGGIANO'S, INC.—See Brinker International, Inc.; *U.S. Public*, pg. 384
MAGGIEMOO'S FRANCHISING, LLC—See Fog Cutter Capital Group Inc.; *U.S. Private*, pg. 1557
MAGGIES ENTERPRISES INC.; *U.S. Private*, pg. 2545
MAGGI GMBH—See Nestle S.A.; *Int'l*, pg. 5205
MAGGY LONDON INTERNATIONAL LTD. INC.; *U.S. Private*, pg. 2545
MAG HOLDINGS BERHAD; *Int'l*, pg. 4636
MAGHREBAIL SA—See Bank of Africa; *Int'l*, pg. 839
MAG IAS GMBH—See Fair Friend Group; *Int'l*, pg. 2604
MAG IAS HOLDINGS, INC.; *U.S. Private*, pg. 2545
MAGIC 828 PROPRIETARY LIMITED—See African Equity Empowerment Investmts Limited; *Int'l*, pg. 191
MAGIC 94.9—See Maritime Broadcasting System Ltd.; *Int'l*, pg. 4695
MAGIC ACQUISITION CORP.—See AutoNation, Inc.; *U.S. Public*, pg. 236
MAGIC ACQUISITION CORP.—See AutoNation, Inc.; *U.S. Public*, pg. 236
MAGICAD GROUP OY—See Glodon Co., Ltd.; *Int'l*, pg. 3008
MAGICAL CRUISE COMPANY, LIMITED—See The Walt Disney Company; *U.S. Public*, pg. 2139
MAGICARD LTD.—See Brady Corporation; *U.S. Public*, pg. 379
MAGIC CABIN—See Evergreen Enterprises, Inc.; *U.S. Private*, pg. 1439
MAGIC CIRCLE MANUFACTURING DIVISION—See Acme Foundry, Inc.; *U.S. Private*, pg. 61
MAGIC EMPIRE GLOBAL LIMITED; *Int'l*, pg. 4637
MAGIC FLIGHT FILM GMBH—See ProSiebenSat.1 Media SE; *Int'l*, pg. 6000
MAGIC FUEL INC.—See TruFin plc; *Int'l*, pg. 7941
MAGICGRAND DEVELOPMENT LIMITED—See China Automobile New Retail (Holdings) Limited; *Int'l*, pg. 1484
MAGIC HAT BREWING CO. & PERFORMING ARTS CENTER INC.—See Florida Ice and Farm Co. S.A.; *Int'l*, pg. 2707
MAGIC HAT CONSULTING; *U.S. Private*, pg. 2546
MAGIC HOTELS SA—See TUI AG; *Int'l*, pg. 7965
MAGICIAN INDUSTRIAL COMPANY LIMITED—See China Automobile New Retail (Holdings) Limited; *Int'l*, pg. 1484
MAGICIAN LIFESTYLE LIMITED—See China Automobile New Retail (Holdings) Limited; *Int'l*, pg. 1484
MAGIC ICE USA, INC.—See Everything Ice, Inc.; *U.S. Private*, pg. 1441
MAGICJACK VOCALTEC LTD.—See B. Riley Financial, Inc.; *U.S. Public*, pg. 262
MAGIC JOHNSON ENTERPRISES; *U.S. Private*, pg. 2546
MAGIC LIFE DER CLUB INTERNATIONAL TURIZM HIZMETLERI A.S—See TUI AG; *Int'l*, pg. 7965
MAGIC LIFE EGYPT FOR HOTELS LLC—See TUI AG; *Int'l*, pg. 7965
MAGIC LIFE INTERNATIONAL HOTELBETRIEBS GMBH & CO. KG—See TUI AG; *Int'l*, pg. 7965
MAGIC LOGIX INC.; *U.S. Private*, pg. 2546
MAGICMICRO CO., LTD.; *Int'l*, pg. 4637
MAGIC MOBILE HOMES, INC.—See Style Crest, Inc.; *U.S. Private*, pg. 3846
MAGIC MOMENTS, INC.; *U.S. Private*, pg. 2546
MAGIC PIXEL INC—See Macronix International Co., Ltd.; *Int'l*, pg. 4632
MAGIC POSTER GMBH - MUNICH OFFICE—See WPP plc; *Int'l*, pg. 8472
MAGIC POSTER GMBH—See WPP plc; *Int'l*, pg. 8472
MAGIC SOFTWARE ENTERPRISES FRANCE—See Asseco Poland S.A.; *Int'l*, pg. 642

COMPANY NAME INDEX

MAGIC SOFTWARE ENTERPRISES GMBH—See Asseco Poland S.A.; *Int'l*, pg. 642
MAGIC SOFTWARE ENTERPRISES HUNGARY LTD.—See Asseco Poland S.A.; *Int'l*, pg. 642
MAGIC SOFTWARE ENTERPRISES INC.—See Asseco Poland S.A.; *Int'l*, pg. 642
MAGIC SOFTWARE ENTERPRISES INDIA PVT. LTD.—See Asseco Poland S.A.; *Int'l*, pg. 642
MAGIC SOFTWARE ENTERPRISES LTD.—See Asseco Poland S.A.; *Int'l*, pg. 642
MAGIC SOFTWARE ENTERPRISES NEDERLAND B.V.—See Asseco Poland S.A.; *Int'l*, pg. 642
MAGIC SOFTWARE ENTERPRISES UK LTD.—See Asseco Poland S.A.; *Int'l*, pg. 642
MAGIC SOFTWARE JAPAN KK—See Asseco Poland S.A.; *Int'l*, pg. 642
MAGIC SPORTS MEDIA GMBH—See Highlight Communications AG; *Int'l*, pg. 3388
MAGIC STEEL CORPORATION; *U.S. Private*, pg. 2546
MAGICSTEM GROUP CORP.; *Int'l*, pg. 4638
MAGIC TECHNOLOGIES, INC.—See TDK Corporation; *Int'l*, pg. 7489
MAGIC TILT TRAILERS, INC.; *U.S. Private*, pg. 2546
MAGIC VALLEY ELECTRIC COOPERATIVE; *U.S. Private*, pg. 2546
MAGIC VALLEY FRESH FROZEN, INC.; *U.S. Private*, pg. 2546
MAGIC VALLEY TRUCK BROKERS INC.—See Allen Lund Company, LLC; *U.S. Private*, pg. 179
MAGIC WIRELESS TECHNOLOGY CO., LTD.—See Yageo Corporation; *Int'l*, pg. 8545
MAGID GLOVE SAFETY MANUFACTURING CO. LLC; *U.S. Private*, pg. 2546
MAGIKITCH'N, INC.—See The Middleby Corporation; *U.S. Public*, pg. 2113
MAGIL CONSTRUCTION—See Fayolle et Fils; *Int'l*, pg. 2626
MAGILL CONSTRUCTION COMPANY, INC.; *U.S. Private*, pg. 2546
MAGILLEM DESIGN SERVICES; *Int'l*, pg. 4638
MAGILLEM ISRAEL—See Magillem Design Services; *Int'l*, pg. 4638
MAGILLEM JAPAN—See Magillem Design Services; *Int'l*, pg. 4638
MAGILLEM KOREA—See Magillem Design Services; *Int'l*, pg. 4638
MAGILLEM USA—See Magillem Design Services; *Int'l*, pg. 4638
MAG INDIA INDUSTRIAL AUTOMATION SYSTEMS PVT. LTD.—See MAG IAS Holdings, Inc.; *U.S. Private*, pg. 2545
MAGINET INTERACTIVE LTD.—See Nippon Telegraph & Telephone Corporation; *Int'l*, pg. 5351
MAG INSTRUMENT INC.; *U.S. Private*, pg. 2545
MAG INTERACTIVE AB; *Int'l*, pg. 4636
MAGIQUE GALILEO SOFTWARE LTD.—See Sword Group SE; *Int'l*, pg. 7376
MAGIRUS CAMIVA S.A.S.—See CNH Industrial N.V.; *Int'l*, pg. 1676
MAGIRUS GMBH—See Iveco Group N.V.; *Int'l*, pg. 3847
MAGIRUS LOHR GMBH—See CNH Industrial N.V.; *Int'l*, pg. 1676
MAGIRUS UK LTD—See Avnet, Inc.; *U.S. Public*, pg. 253
MAG ISOVER K.K.—See Compagnie de Saint-Gobain SA; *Int'l*, pg. 1724
MAGIS S.P.A.; *Int'l*, pg. 4638
MAGISTA NETHERLANDS—See Van Keulen Interieurbouw BV; *Int'l*, pg. 8126
MAGISTRALA A.D.; *Int'l*, pg. 4638
MAGISTRAL KAUBANDUSKESKUSE OU—See EfTEN Capital AS; *Int'l*, pg. 2321
MAGIX AG; *Int'l*, pg. 4638
MAGIX DEVELOPMENT GMBH.—See MAGIX AG; *Int'l*, pg. 4638
MAGIX ENTERTAINMENT S. A. R. L.—See MAGIX AG; *Int'l*, pg. 4638
MAGIX MECHATRONICS COMPANY LIMITED—See InnoTek Limited; *Int'l*, pg. 3711
MAGIX MECHATRONICS (DONGGUAN) COMPANY LIMITED—See InnoTek Limited; *Int'l*, pg. 3710
MAGIX ONLINE SERVICES GMBH.—See MAGIX AG; *Int'l*, pg. 4638
MAG JLT SPA—See Marsh & McLennan Companies, Inc.; *U.S. Public*, pg. 1377
MAGLABS (HOLDINGS) LIMITED—See Writtle Holdings Limited; *Int'l*, pg. 8495
MAGLABS LIMITED—See Writtle Holdings Limited; *Int'l*, pg. 8495
MAG LAYERS USA, INC.—See Yageo Corporation; *Int'l*, pg. 8545
MAGLE CHEMOSWED AB—See Magle Chemoswed Holding AB; *Int'l*, pg. 4638
MAGLE CHEMOSWED HOLDING AB; *Int'l*, pg. 4638
MAGLIFICIO ERIKA S.R.L.—See Onward Holdings Co., Ltd.; *Int'l*, pg. 5592
MAGLINE, INC.; *U.S. Private*, pg. 2546
MAGLINER DO BRASIL—See Magline, Inc.; *U.S. Private*, pg. 2546

MAGLINER INTERNATIONAL LLC—See Magline, Inc.; *U.S. Private*, pg. 2546
MAGLINE SANO GMBH—See Magline, Inc.; *U.S. Private*, pg. 2546
MAGLIO BROS INC.; *U.S. Private*, pg. 2546
M&A GLOBAL PARTNERS CO. LTD.—See Striders Corporation; *Int'l*, pg. 7240
MAGMA BILISIM VE TEKNOLOJI HIZMETLERI LTD. STI.—See MAGMA GmbH; *Int'l*, pg. 4638
MAGMA D.D.; *Int'l*, pg. 4638
MAGMA ENERGY ITALIA S.R.L.—See Graziella Green Power S.p.A; *Int'l*, pg. 3063
MAGMA ENERGY ITALIA S.R.L.—See Innergex Renewable Energy Inc.; *Int'l*, pg. 3708
MAGMA ENGENHARIA DO BRASIL LTDA.—See MAGMA GmbH; *Int'l*, pg. 4638
MAGMA ENGINEERING ASIA PACIFIC PTE LTD.—See MAGMA GmbH; *Int'l*, pg. 4638
MAGMA ENGINEERING KOREA CO., LTD.—See MAGMA GmbH; *Int'l*, pg. 4638
MAGMA ENGINEERING (SUZHOU) CO., LTD.—See MAGMA GmbH; *Int'l*, pg. 4638
MAGMA FOUNDRY TECHNOLOGIES INC.—See MAGMA GmbH; *Int'l*, pg. 4638
MAGMA GIESSEREITECHNOLOGIE GMBH—See MAGMA GmbH; *Int'l*, pg. 4638
MAGMAG, INC.; *Int'l*, pg. 4638
MAGMA GLOBAL LTD.—See TechnipFMC plc; *Int'l*, pg. 7507
MAGMA GMBH; *Int'l*, pg. 4638
MAG MAINTENANCE UK LIMITED—See MAG IAS Holdings, Inc.; *U.S. Private*, pg. 2545
MAGMA INTERNATIONAL LTD.—See Magma d.d.; *Int'l*, pg. 4638
MAGMA—See One Stop Systems, Inc.; *U.S. Public*, pg. 1602
MAGMATIC LIMITED—See Heroes Technology Ltd.; *Int'l*, pg. 3364
MAGMATIC RESOURCES LIMITED; *Int'l*, pg. 4638
MAG MUTUAL INSURANCE COMPANY; *U.S. Private*, pg. 2545
MAGNA5 LLC—See NewSpring Capital LLC; *U.S. Private*, pg. 2918
MAGNA BDW TECHNOLOGIES GMBH—See Magna International Inc.; *Int'l*, pg. 4639
MAGNA BDW TECHNOLOGIES HUNGARY KFT.—See Magna International Inc.; *Int'l*, pg. 4639
MAGNA BDW TECHNOLOGIES SOEST GMBH—See Magna International Inc.; *Int'l*, pg. 4639
MAGNABLEND, INC.—See Apollo Global Management, Inc.; *U.S. Public*, pg. 165
MAGNA CARTA COMPANIES; *U.S. Private*, pg. 2546
MAGNA CARTA—See Omnicom Group Inc.; *U.S. Public*, pg. 1597
MAGNACHIP SEMICONDUCTOR CORPORATION; *Int'l*, pg. 4640
MAGNA COLOURS LIMITED—See Avient Corporation; *U.S. Public*, pg. 247
MAGNA DONNELLY CORPORATION—See Magna International Inc.; *Int'l*, pg. 4639
MAGNA DONNELLY ELECTRONICS—See Magna International Inc.; *Int'l*, pg. 4639
MAGNA DONNELLY EUROGLAS SYSTEMS—See Magna International Inc.; *Int'l*, pg. 4639
MAGNADRIVE CORPORATION; *U.S. Private*, pg. 2546
MAGNADYNE CORPORATION; *U.S. Private*, pg. 2546
MAGNA ELECTRO CASTINGS LIMITED; *Int'l*, pg. 4638
MAGNAFLUX—See Illinois Tool Works Inc.; *U.S. Public*, pg. 1109
MAGNAFLUX LIMITED—See Illinois Tool Works Inc.; *U.S. Public*, pg. 1109
MAGNA FOREMOST SDN BHD—See Owens Corning; *U.S. Public*, pg. 1627
MAGNAGHI AERONAUTICA S.P.A.; *Int'l*, pg. 4640
MAGNA GOLD CORP.; *Int'l*, pg. 4638
MAGNAGRIP—See Bidwell Industrial Group, Inc.; *U.S. Private*, pg. 551
MAGNA INDUSTRIAL COMPANY LIMITED—See Illinois Tool Works Inc.; *U.S. Public*, pg. 1109
MAGNA INDUSTRIES & EXPORTS LIMITED; *Int'l*, pg. 4639
MAGNA INTERNATIONAL AG—See Magna International Inc.; *Int'l*, pg. 4639
MAGNA INTERNATIONAL CHINA—See Magna International Inc.; *Int'l*, pg. 4639
MAGNA INTERNATIONAL INC.; *Int'l*, pg. 4639
MAGNA IV; *U.S. Private*, pg. 2546
MAGNA-LASTIC DEVICES—See Methode Electronics, Inc.; *U.S. Public*, pg. 1428
MAGNA LEGAL SERVICES—See Odyssey Investment Partners, LLC; *U.S. Private*, pg. 2995
MAGNA MACHINE CO. INC.; *U.S. Private*, pg. 2546
MAGNA MAKINE SAN. VE TIC. LTD.STI.—See Arcure; *Int'l*, pg. 552
MAGNA MINING NL; *Int'l*, pg. 4640
MAGNANI CARUSO DUTTON; *U.S. Private*, pg. 2546
MAGNANIMOUS TRADE & FINANCE LIMITED; *Int'l*, pg. 4640
MAGNAPLAN CORPORATION; *U.S. Private*, pg. 2546

MAGNAPLAN CORPORATION VISUAL PLANNING DIVISION—See Magnaplan Corporation; *U.S. Private*, pg. 2546
MAGNA POLONIA S.A.; *Int'l*, pg. 4640
MAGNA POWERTRAIN AG & CO. KG—See Magna International Inc.; *Int'l*, pg. 4639
MAGNA POWERTRAIN INC.—See Magna International Inc.; *Int'l*, pg. 4640
MAGNA POWERTRAIN USA, INC.—See Magna International Inc.; *Int'l*, pg. 4640
MAGNA PRIMA BERHAD; *Int'l*, pg. 4640
MAGNA PT B.V. & CO. KG—See Magna International Inc.; *Int'l*, pg. 4639
MAGNA REFRACTARIOS MEXICO SA DE CV—See Grecian Magnesite S.A; *Int'l*, pg. 3068
MAGNA REFRACTORIES INC.—See Grecian Magnesite S.A; *Int'l*, pg. 3068
MAGNA REWARDS (JAMAICA) LIMITED—See Massy Holdings Ltd.; *Int'l*, pg. 4723
MAGNA REWARDS (TRINIDAD) LIMITED—See Massy Holdings Ltd.; *Int'l*, pg. 4723
MAGNA SEATING INC.—See Magna International Inc.; *Int'l*, pg. 4640
MAGNA SEATING OF AMERICA, INC.—See Magna International Inc.; *Int'l*, pg. 4640
MAGNA STEYR AG & CO. KG—See Magna International Inc.; *Int'l*, pg. 4639
MAGNA STEYR ENGINEERING AG & CO. KG—See Magna International Inc.; *Int'l*, pg. 4639
MAGNA STEYR FAHRZEUGTECHNIK AG & CO. KG—See Magna International Inc.; *Int'l*, pg. 4639
MAGNA STEYR HEAVY STAMPING—See Magna International Inc.; *Int'l*, pg. 4640
MAGNA STEYR LLC—See Magna International Inc.; *Int'l*, pg. 4639
MAGNA STRUCTURAL SYSTEMS INC.—See Magna International Inc.; *Int'l*, pg. 4640
MAGNAT AUDIO-PRODUKTE GMBH—See VOXX International Corporation; *U.S. Public*, pg. 2311
MAGNATE CAPITAL PARTNERS, LLC; *U.S. Private*, pg. 2547
MAGNA-TECH MANUFACTURING CORPORATION—See Henkel AG & Co. KGaA; *Int'l*, pg. 3353
MAGNATE COMMUNICATION CORP.—See WSP Global, Inc.; *Int'l*, pg. 8497
MAGNA TERRA MINERALS INC.; *Int'l*, pg. 4640
MAGNECO/METREL, INC.; *U.S. Private*, pg. 2547
MAGNECO/METREL UK LTD.—See Magneco/Metrel, Inc.; *U.S. Private*, pg. 2547
MAGNECO CORPORATION—See InnoTek Limited; *Int'l*, pg. 3710
MAGNECOMP PRECISION TECHNOLOGY PUBLIC COMPANY LIMITED—See TDK Corporation; *Int'l*, pg. 7487
MAGNECOMP TECHNOLOGY LIMITED—See InnoTek Limited; *Int'l*, pg. 3710
MAGNECORP, INC.; *U.S. Private*, pg. 2547
MAGNEGAS ARC APPLIED SOLUTIONS—See BBHC, Inc.; *U.S. Public*, pg. 284
MAGNEMOTION INC.—See Rockwell Automation, Inc.; *U.S. Public*, pg. 1805
MAGNEQUENCH INTERNATIONAL, INC.—See Brookfield Corporation; *Int'l*, pg. 1181
MAGNEQUENCH NEO POWDERS PTE. LTD.—See Brookfield Corporation; *Int'l*, pg. 1181
MAGNEQUENCH (TIANJIN) CO., LTD.—See Brookfield Corporation; *Int'l*, pg. 1181
MAGNER SANBORN; *U.S. Private*, pg. 2547
MAGNESCALE AMERICAS INC.—See DMG MORI Co., Ltd.; *Int'l*, pg. 2145
MAGNESCALE CO., LTD.—See DMG MORI Co., Ltd.; *Int'l*, pg. 2145
MAGNESCALE EUROPE GMBH—See DMG MORI Co., Ltd.; *Int'l*, pg. 2145
MAGNESIT ANONIM SIRKETI (MAS)—See RHI Magnesita N.V.; *Int'l*, pg. 6325
MAGNESIT ANONIM SIRKETI—See RHI Magnesita N.V.; *Int'l*, pg. 6325
MAGNESITA REFRACTORIES GMBH—See RHI Magnesita N.V.; *Int'l*, pg. 6325
MAGNESITA REFRATARIOS S.A.—See RHI Magnesita N.V.; *Int'l*, pg. 6325
MAGNESITAS NAVARRAS S.A.—See Grecian Magnesite S.A; *Int'l*, pg. 3068
MAGNESIUM ELEKTRON LIMITED—See Luxfer Holdings PLC; *Int'l*, pg. 4588
MAGNESIUM ELEKTRON NORTH AMERICA, INC.—See Luxfer Holdings PLC; *Int'l*, pg. 4588
MAGNESIUM PRODUCTS OF AMERICA—See Wanfeng Auto Holding Group Co., Ltd.; *Int'l*, pg. 8340
MAGNESIUM TECHNOLOGIES CORPORATION—See SunOpta Inc.; *Int'l*, pg. 7319
MAGNESS OIL COMPANY INC.; *U.S. Private*, pg. 2547
MAGNET 360, LLC—See Larsen & Toubro Limited; *Int'l*, pg. 4419
MAGNET ADVERTISING; *Int'l*, pg. 4640
MAGNET APPLICATIONS INC.—See Bunting Magnetics Co.; *U.S. Private*, pg. 686
MAGNETAR CAPITAL, LLC; *U.S. Private*, pg. 2547

MAGNETAR CAPITAL, LLC
CORPORATE AFFILIATIONS

MAGNETATION, INC.—See ERP Iron Ore, LLC; *U.S. Private*, pg. 1423
MAGNETEC GMBH; *Int'l*, pg. 4640
MAGNETECH INDUSTRIAL SERVICES, INC.—See IES Holdings, Inc.; *U.S. Public*, pg. 1094
MAGNETEC MAGNETIC DEVICE CO. LTD.—See MAGNETEC GmbH; *Int'l*, pg. 4640
MAGNETEC-UNGARN KFT.—See MAGNETEC GmbH; *Int'l*, pg. 4640
MAGNETEK CANADA ULC—See Columbus McKinnon Corporation; *U.S. Public*, pg. 536
MAGNETEK ELEVATORS—See Columbus McKinnon Corporation; *U.S. Public*, pg. 536
MAGNETEK, INC.—See Columbus McKinnon Corporation; *U.S. Public*, pg. 536
MAGNETEK MATERIAL HANDLING—See Columbus McKinnon Corporation; *U.S. Public*, pg. 536
MAGNETEK MINING—See Columbus McKinnon Corporation; *U.S. Public*, pg. 536
MAGNETEK (UK) LTD.—See Columbus McKinnon Corporation; *U.S. Public*, pg. 536
MAGNET HARLEQUIN HOLDINGS LIMITED—See Writtle Holdings Limited; *Int'l*, pg. 8495
MAGNET HARLEQUIN LTD.—See Writtle Holdings Limited; *Int'l*, pg. 8495
MAGNETIC ANALYSIS AUSTRALIA, PTY. LTD.—See Magnetic Analysis Corporation; *U.S. Private*, pg. 2547
MAGNETIC ANALYSIS CORPORATION; *U.S. Private*, pg. 2547
MAGNETIC ANALYSIS ITALIA, S.R.L.—See Magnetic Analysis Corporation; *U.S. Private*, pg. 2547
MAGNETIC ANALYSIS LTD—See Magnetic Analysis Corporation; *U.S. Private*, pg. 2547
MAGNETIC ANALYSIS NORDIC AB—See Magnetic Analysis Corporation; *U.S. Private*, pg. 2547
MAGNETIC COMPONENT ENGINEERING INC.; *U.S. Private*, pg. 2547
MAGNETIC MEDIA ONLINE, INC.; *U.S. Private*, pg. 2547
MAGNETIC METALS CORP.—See Indel, Inc.; *U.S. Private*, pg. 2055
MAGNETIC NORTH ACQUISITION CORPORATION; *Int'l*, pg. 4640
MAGNETIC POWER SYSTEMS INC.—See Berwind Corporation; *U.S. Private*, pg. 541
MAGNETIC PRODUCTS & SERVICES, INC.; *U.S. Private*, pg. 2547
MAGNETIC RESONANCE IMAGING OF SAN LUIS OBISPO, INC.—See Tenet Healthcare Corporation; *U.S. Public*, pg. 2008
MAGNETIC RESOURCES NL; *Int'l*, pg. 4640
MAGNETICS INTERNATIONAL, INC.—See International Steel Services, Inc.; *U.S. Private*, pg. 2121
MAGNETIC SPRINGS WATER COMPANY; *U.S. Private*, pg. 2547
MAGNETICS—See Spang & Company; *U.S. Private*, pg. 3744
MAGNETIC TICKET & LABEL CORP.; *U.S. Private*, pg. 2547
MAGNETIC VARIATION SERVICES, LLC—See Helmerich & Payne, Inc.; *U.S. Public*, pg. 1024
MAGNETIKA, INC.-GARDENA—See Magnetika, Inc.; *U.S. Private*, pg. 2547
MAGNETIKA, INC.; *U.S. Private*, pg. 2547
MAGNETIKA, INC.—See Magnetika, Inc.; *U.S. Private*, pg. 2547
MAGNETI MARELLI AFTERMARKET GMBH—See KKR & Co. Inc.; *U.S. Public*, pg. 1260
MAGNETI MARELLI AFTER MARKET PARTS AND SERVICES S.P.A.—See KKR & Co. Inc.; *U.S. Public*, pg. 1260
MAGNETI MARELLI AFTERMARKET SP. Z O.O.—See KKR & Co. Inc.; *U.S. Public*, pg. 1260
MAGNETI MARELLI AUTOMOTIVE COMPONENTS (WUHU) CO. LTD.—See KKR & Co. Inc.; *U.S. Public*, pg. 1260
MAGNETI MARELLI DO BRASIL INDUSTRIA E COMERCIO SA—See KKR & Co. Inc.; *U.S. Public*, pg. 1261
MAGNETI MARELLI EXHAUST SYSTEMS POLSKA SP. Z O.O.—See KKR & Co. Inc.; *U.S. Public*, pg. 1260
MAGNETI MARELLI FRANCE S.A.S.—See KKR & Co. Inc.; *U.S. Public*, pg. 1261
MAGNETI MARELLI HOLDING U.S.A. INC.—See KKR & Co. Inc.; *U.S. Public*, pg. 1261
MAGNETI MARELLI JAPAN K.K.—See KKR & Co. Inc.; *U.S. Public*, pg. 1261
MAGNETI MARELLI MOTOPROPULSION FRANCE SAS—See KKR & Co. Inc.; *U.S. Public*, pg. 1261
MAGNETI MARELLI POWERTRAIN (SHANGHAI) CO. LTD.—See KKR & Co. Inc.; *U.S. Public*, pg. 1261
MAGNETI MARELLI POWERTRAIN SLOVAKIA S.R.O.—See KKR & Co. Inc.; *U.S. Public*, pg. 1261
MAGNETI MARELLI REPUESTOS S.A.—See KKR & Co. Inc.; *U.S. Public*, pg. 1260
MAGNETI MARELLI SLOVAKIA S.R.O.—See KKR & Co. Inc.; *U.S. Public*, pg. 1261
MAGNETI MARELLI SUSPENSION SYSTEMS BIELSKO SP. Z.O.O.—See KKR & Co. Inc.; *U.S. Public*, pg. 1261
MAGNET INC.; *U.S. Private*, pg. 2547
MAGNETITE MINES LIMITED; *Int'l*, pg. 4640

MAGNET KITCHENS LTD.—See Nobia AB; *Int'l*, pg. 5395
MAGNET LIMITED—See Nobia AB; *Int'l*, pg. 5395
MAGNET LLC; *U.S. Private*, pg. 2547
MAGNET NETWORKS LTD.—See AMP Limited; *Int'l*, pg. 432
MAGNETO & DIESEL INJECTOR SERVICE, INC.—See Warren Equity Partners, LLC; *U.S. Private*, pg. 4443
MAGNETO EQUIPMENT, INC.—See Ilion Capital Partners; *U.S. Private*, pg. 2041
MAGNETO POWER, LLC—See Power Distributors, LLC; *U.S. Private*, pg. 3238
MAGNETO SPECIAL ANODES B.V.—See Xylem Inc.; *U.S. Public*, pg. 2394
MAGNET RESOURCE COMPANY PTY. LTD.—See White Cliff Minerals Limited; *Int'l*, pg. 8398
MAGNETROL ENVIRONMENTAL, L.P.—See AMETEK, Inc.; *U.S. Public*, pg. 121
MAGNETROL INSTRUMENTATION INDUSTRIAL LTDA.—See AMETEK, Inc.; *U.S. Public*, pg. 121
MAGNETROL INTERNATIONAL INC.—See AMETEK, Inc.; *U.S. Public*, pg. 121
MAGNETROL INTERNATIONAL, INC.—See AMETEK, Inc.; *U.S. Public*, pg. 121
MAGNETROL INTERNATIONAL N.V.—See AMETEK, Inc.; *U.S. Public*, pg. 121
MAGNETROL INTERNATIONAL—See AMETEK, Inc.; *U.S. Public*, pg. 121
MAGNETROL INTERNATIONAL—See AMETEK, Inc.; *U.S. Public*, pg. 121
MAGNETROL INTERNATIONAL—See AMETEK, Inc.; *U.S. Public*, pg. 121
MAGNETROL INTERNATIONAL—See AMETEK, Inc.; *U.S. Public*, pg. 121
MAGNETROL INTERNATIONAL—See AMETEK, Inc.; *U.S. Public*, pg. 121
MAGNI AMERICA DO SUL—See Magni Group Inc.; *U.S. Private*, pg. 2548
MAGNI EUROPE GMBH & CO. KG—See Magni Group Inc.; *U.S. Private*, pg. 2548
MAGNI-FAB SOUTHWEST CO. INC.—See Magni-Power Company Inc.; *U.S. Private*, pg. 2548
MAGNIFAIR COMPANY LIMITED—See Kerry Group Limited; *Int'l*, pg. 4137
MAGNIFICENT HOTEL INVESTMENTS LIMITED; *Int'l*, pg. 4641
MAGNIFICENT INTERNATIONAL HOTEL LIMITED—See Magnificent Hotel Investments Limited; *Int'l*, pg. 4641
MAGNIFI FINANCIAL CREDIT UNION; *U.S. Private*, pg. 2548
MAG-NIF INC.; *U.S. Private*, pg. 2545
MAGNIFIN MAGNESIAPRODUKTE GMBH & CO KG—See J.M. Huber Corporation; *U.S. Private*, pg. 2168
MAGNIFIN MAGNESIAPRODUKTE GMBH & CO KG—See RHI Magnesita N.V.; *Int'l*, pg. 6325
MAGNI GROUP INC.; *U.S. Private*, pg. 2547
MAGNI-INDUSTRIES INC.—See Magni Group Inc.; *U.S. Private*, pg. 2548
MAGNI-POWER COMPANY INC.; *U.S. Private*, pg. 2548
MAGNIS ENERGY TECHNOLOGIES LTD; *Int'l*, pg. 4641
MAGNI-TECH INDUSTRIES BERHAD; *Int'l*, pg. 4640
MAGNITE, INC.; *U.S. Public*, pg. 1354
MAGNITE SINGAPORE PTE. LTD.—See Magnite, Inc.; *U.S. Public*, pg. 1354
MAGNIT PJSC; *Int'l*, pg. 4641
MAGNITUDE GROUP PTY LIMITED—See Westpac Banking Corporation; *Int'l*, pg. 8391
MAGNITUDE SOFTWARE, INC.—See TA Associates, Inc.; *U.S. Private*, pg. 3915
MAGNODE CORPORATION; *U.S. Private*, pg. 2548
MAGNOLIA AMERICAS, INC.—See Genui GmbH; *Int'l*, pg. 2930
MAGNOLIA AUDIO VIDEO—See Best Buy Co., Inc.; *U.S. Public*, pg. 326
MAGNOLIA BAKERY INC.; *U.S. Private*, pg. 2548
MAGNOLIA BANKING CORPORATION; *U.S. Private*, pg. 2548
MAGNOLIA BOSTAD AB; *Int'l*, pg. 4641
MAGNOLIA CAPITAL PARTNERS LTD.; *Int'l*, pg. 4641
MAGNOLIA CREEK—See Nautic Partners, LLC; *U.S. Private*, pg. 2871
MAGNOLIA DIALYSIS, LLC—See DaVita Inc.; *U.S. Public*, pg. 641
MAGNOLIA ENTERTAINMENT LLC; *U.S. Private*, pg. 2548
MAGNOLIA ESPANA SOFTWARE AND COMPUTER APPLICATIONS S.L.—See Genui GmbH; *Int'l*, pg. 2930
MAGNOLIA FOREST PRODUCTS INC.; *U.S. Private*, pg. 2548
MAGNOLIA GAS INC.—See Ergon, Inc.; *U.S. Private*, pg. 1418
MAGNOLIA GREEN DEVELOPMENT PARTNERS LLC—See Safehold Inc.; *U.S. Public*, pg. 1834
MAGNOLIA HEALTH PLAN INC.—See Centene Corporation; *U.S. Public*, pg. 470
MAGNOLIA HEALTH PLAN, INC.—See Centene Corporation; *U.S. Public*, pg. 470
MAGNOLIA HI-FI, LLC—See Best Buy Co., Inc.; *U.S. Public*, pg. 326

MAGNOLIA HOTELS; *U.S. Private*, pg. 2548
MAGNOLIA, INC.—See Top Frontier Investment Holdings, Inc.; *Int'l*, pg. 7812
MAGNOLIA INTERNATIONAL LTD.—See Genui GmbH; *Int'l*, pg. 2930
MAGNOLIA ITALY—See De Agostini S.p.A.; *Int'l*, pg. 1994
MAGNOLIA MARINE TRANSPORT COMPANY—See Ergon, Inc.; *U.S. Private*, pg. 1418
MAGNOLIA METAL CORPORATION; *U.S. Private*, pg. 2548
MAGNOLIA MIDSTREAM GAS SERVICES, L.L.C.—See The Williams Companies, Inc.; *U.S. Public*, pg. 2143
MAGNOLIA OIL & GAS CORPORATION; *U.S. Public*, pg. 1354
MAGNOLIA PETROLEUM PLC; *U.S. Private*, pg. 2548
MAGNOLIA PROPERTIES & INVESTMENTS INC.; *U.S. Private*, pg. 2548
MAGNOLIA RIVER SERVICES, INC.—See Warren Equity Partners, LLC; *U.S. Private*, pg. 4443
MAGNOLIA SOFTWARE & SERVICES CZ S.R.O.—See Genui GmbH; *Int'l*, pg. 2930
MAGNOLIA SOLAR, INC.—See RiskOn International, Inc.; *U.S. Public*, pg. 1799
MAGNOLIA SPAIN—See De Agostini S.p.A.; *Int'l*, pg. 1994
MAGNOLIA SURGERY CENTER LIMITED PARTNERSHIP—See Tenet Healthcare Corporation; *U.S. Public*, pg. 2014
MAGNOLIA VILLAGE—See Formation Capital, LLC; *U.S. Private*, pg. 1571
MAGNORA ASA; *Int'l*, pg. 4641
MAGNO SOUND INC.; *U.S. Private*, pg. 2548
MAGNOTTA BREWERY (VAUGHAN) LTD—See Magnotta Winery Corporation; *Int'l*, pg. 4641
MAGNOTTA CELLARS CORPORATION—See Magnotta Winery Corporation; *Int'l*, pg. 4641
MAGNOTTA DISTILLERY LTD—See Magnotta Winery Corporation; *Int'l*, pg. 4641
MAGNOTTA WINERY CORPORATION; *Int'l*, pg. 4641
MAGNOTTA WINERY ESTATES LIMITED—See Magnotta Winery Corporation; *Int'l*, pg. 4641
MAGNOTTA WINES LTD—See Magnotta Winery Corporation; *Int'l*, pg. 4641
MAGNPOWER CORPORATION—See China Steel Corporation; *Int'l*, pg. 1556
MAGNUM 4D BERHAD—See MPHB Capital Berhad; *Int'l*, pg. 5062
MAGNUM BERHAD; *Int'l*, pg. 4641
MAGNUM BUILDERS OF SARASOTA, INC.; *U.S. Private*, pg. 2548
MAGNUM CONSTRUCTION MANAGEMENT; *U.S. Private*, pg. 2548
MAGNUM CORPORATION; *U.S. Private*, pg. 2548
MAGNUM ENERGY INC.; *Int'l*, pg. 4641
MAGNUM ENERGY SERVICES LTD.—See Corrosion & Abrasion Solutions Ltd.; *Int'l*, pg. 1806
MAGNUM ENTERPRISES INC.; *U.S. Private*, pg. 2549
MAGNUM FEEDYARD, LLC.; *U.S. Private*, pg. 2549
MAGNUM GOLDCORP INC.; *Int'l*, pg. 4641
MAGNUM INDUSTRIAL PARTNERS, S.L.; *Int'l*, pg. 4641
MAGNUM INFORMATION TECHNOLOGY SDN. BHD.—See MPHB Capital Berhad; *Int'l*, pg. 5062
MAGNUM INTEGRATED TECHNOLOGIES, INC.; *Int'l*, pg. 4642
MAGNUM LIMITED; *Int'l*, pg. 4642
MAGNUM LOGISTICS, INC.; *U.S. Private*, pg. 2549
MAGNUM LOGISTICS, INC.—See Magnum, Ltd.; *U.S. Private*, pg. 2549
MAGNUM, LTD.; *U.S. Private*, pg. 2549
MAGNUM LTL, INC.—See Magnum, Ltd.; *U.S. Private*, pg. 2549
MAGNUM MACHINING INCORPORATED; *U.S. Private*, pg. 2549
MAGNUM MAGNETICS CORPORATION; *U.S. Private*, pg. 2549
MAGNUM MINING AND EXPLORATION LIMITED; *Int'l*, pg. 4642
MAGNUM OPUS ACQUISITION LIMITED; *Int'l*, pg. 4642
MAGNUM PRINT SOLUTIONS, INC.; *U.S. Private*, pg. 2549
MAGNUM STAFFING SERVICES INC.; *U.S. Private*, pg. 2549
MAGNUM TECHNICAL SERVICES, INC.—See Southland Industries; *U.S. Private*, pg. 3737
MAGNUM VENTURES LIMITED; *Int'l*, pg. 4642
MAGNUM VENUS PRODUCTS; *U.S. Private*, pg. 2549
MAGNUM WAREHOUSING, INC.—See Magnum, Ltd.; *U.S. Private*, pg. 2549
MAGNUS CONCORDIA GROUP LIMITED; *Int'l*, pg. 4642
MAGNUS ENERGY GROUP LTD.; *Int'l*, pg. 4642
MAGNUS MANAGEMENT GROUP, LLC—See NXTKey Corporation; *U.S. Private*, pg. 2976
MAGNUSON CORPORATION—See Atlas Pacific Engineering Company, Inc.; *U.S. Private*, pg. 379
MAGNUSON - HAGOPIAN ENTERPRISES, INC.—See LKQ Corporation; *U.S. Public*, pg. 1336
MAGNUSON HOTELS; *U.S. Private*, pg. 2549
MAGNUSON SOD/HAAG SERVICES; *U.S. Private*, pg. 2549
MAGNUS POIRIER INC.; *Int'l*, pg. 4642

MAGNUS PRECISION MANUFACTURING INC.—See Floturn Inc.; *U.S. Private*, pg. 1551
MAGNUSSEN HOME FURNISHINGS LTD.; *Int'l*, pg. 4642
MAGNUSSEN'S AUBURN IMPORTS; *U.S. Private*, pg. 2549
MAGNUSSEN'S AUBURN TOYOTA; *U.S. Private*, pg. 2549
MAGNUSSEN'S CAR WEST AUTO BODY; *U.S. Private*, pg. 2549
MAGNUS—See Liam Ventures, Inc.; *U.S. Private*, pg. 2442
MAGOFFIN DIALYSIS, LLC—See DaVita Inc.; *U.S. Public*, pg. 641
MAGONTEC GMBH—See Magontec Limited; *Int'l*, pg. 4642
MAGONTEC LIMITED; *Int'l*, pg. 4642
MAGOR CORPORATION; *Int'l*, pg. 4642
MAGOTTEAUX GROUP S.A.—See Sigdo Koppers S.A.; *Int'l*, pg. 6907
MAGPIE SOFTWARE SERVICES CORP.—See Syncroness, Inc.; *U.S. Private*, pg. 3903
MAGPLUS INC.—See Bonnier AB; *Int'l*, pg. 1108
MAG-PRIM; *Int'l*, pg. 4636
MAGRABAR, LLC—See MUNZING Chemie GmbH; *Int'l*, pg. 5095
MAGRI S.A.S.—See Owens Corning; *U.S. Public*, pg. 1627
MAGRIS RESOURCES INC.; *Int'l*, pg. 4642
MAGRIS SPA; *Int'l*, pg. 4642
MAGROS-METAL D.D.; *Int'l*, pg. 4643
MAGROS VELETRGOVINA D.D.; *Int'l*, pg. 4642
MAGRUDER HOLDINGS INC.; *U.S. Private*, pg. 2549
MAGRUDER HOSPITAL; *U.S. Private*, pg. 2549
MAGRUDERS—See Magruder Holdings Inc.; *U.S. Private*, pg. 2549
MAGSAYSAY MOL MARINE, INC.—See Mitsui O.S.K. Lines, Ltd.; *Int'l*, pg. 4991
MAGSEIS FAIRFIELD ASA—See TGS ASA; *Int'l*, pg. 7587
MAGSEIS FAIRFIELD ASA—See TGS ASA; *Int'l*, pg. 7587
MAG SILVER CORP; *Int'l*, pg. 4636
MAG SPA—See Marsh & McLennan Companies, Inc.; *U.S. Public*, pg. 1377
MAG SPECIALTY VEHICLES—See Mid Western Automotive LLC; *U.S. Private*, pg. 2707
MAGSTIM, INC.—See Telegraph Hill Partners Management Company, LLC; *U.S. Private*, pg. 3900
MAG-TEK INC.; *U.S. Private*, pg. 2545
MAGTICOM LTD.; *Int'l*, pg. 4643
MAG TRANSPORT, LLC—See Mid Western Automotive LLC; *U.S. Private*, pg. 2707
MAGUIRE ASSOCIATES, INC.—See Carnegie Dartlet LLC; *U.S. Private*, pg. 766
MAGUIRE AUTOMOTIVE GROUP; *U.S. Private*, pg. 2549
MAGUIRE AUTOMOTIVE, LLC; *U.S. Private*, pg. 2549
MAGUIRE CHEVROLET-CADILLAC—See Maguire Automotive, LLC; *U.S. Private*, pg. 2549
MAGUIRE FINANCIAL ADVISORS, LLC—See Aon plc; *Int'l*, pg. 496
MAGUIRE IMPORTS—See Maguire Automotive, LLC; *U.S. Private*, pg. 2549
MAGUIRE OIL COMPANY INC.; *U.S. Private*, pg. 2550
MAGUIRE RESOURCES COMPANY INC.; *U.S. Private*, pg. 2550
MAGUIRE'S FORD OF HERSHEY, PA. INC.; *U.S. Private*, pg. 2550
MAGXO SDN. BHD.—See Insas Berhad; *Int'l*, pg. 3718
MAGYAR & ASSOCIATES; *U.S. Private*, pg. 2550
MAGYAR BANCORP, INC.—See Magyar Bancorp, MHC; *U.S. Private*, pg. 2550
MAGYAR BANCORP, MHC; *U.S. Private*, pg. 2550
MAGYAR BANK—See Magyar Bancorp, MHC; *U.S. Private*, pg. 2550
MAGYAR CETELEM BANK ZRT.—See BNP Paribas SA; *Int'l*, pg. 1090
MAGYARCOM HOLDING GMBH—See Deutsche Telekom AG; *Int'l*, pg. 2083
MAGYAR DOKA KFT.—See Umdasch Group AG; *Int'l*, pg. 8023
MAGYAR FOLDGAZKERESKEDO ZRT.—See MVM Magyar Villamos Muvek Zrt.; *Int'l*, pg. 5108
MAGYAR FOLDGAZTAROLO ZRT—See MVM Magyar Villamos Muvek Zrt.; *Int'l*, pg. 5108
MAGYAR GAZ TRANZIT ZRT.—See MOL Magyar Olaj- es Gazipari Nyrt.; *Int'l*, pg. 5020
MAGYAR NEMZETI BANK; *Int'l*, pg. 4643
MAGYAR OPTIKAI MUVEK VIZMERESTECHNIKAI ZARTKORUEN MUKODO RESZVENYTARSASAG—See Diehl Stiftung & Co. KG; *Int'l*, pg. 2115
MAGYARORSZAGI VOLKSBANK ZRT.—See OJSC Sberbank of Russia; *Int'l*, pg. 5542
MAGYAR PLASTIROUTE FORGALOMTECHNIKAI KFT.—See Solix Group AB; *Int'l*, pg. 7073
MAGYAR SUZUKI CORP.—See Suzuki Motor Corporation; *Int'l*, pg. 7354
MAGYAR TELEKOM TELECOMMUNICATIONS PLC—See Deutsche Telekom AG; *Int'l*, pg. 2083
MAGZTER INC.—See VerSe Innovation Private Limited; *U.S. Private*, pg. 4369
MAHAAN FOODS LIMITED; *Int'l*, pg. 4643

MAHABUILDERS SDN. BHD.—See MB World Group Berhad; *Int'l*, pg. 4751
MAHACHAI HOSPITAL PCL; *Int'l*, pg. 4643
MAHA ENERGY AB; *Int'l*, pg. 4643
MAHA ENERGY BRASIL LTDA.—See PetroReconcavo S.A.; *Int'l*, pg. 5832
MAHA ENERGY INC.—See Maha Energy AB; *Int'l*, pg. 4643
MAHAFFEY FABRIC STRUCTURES.; *U.S. Private*, pg. 2550
MAHAJAK INTERNATIONAL ELECTRIC CO., LTD.—See Fuji Electric Co., Ltd.; *Int'l*, pg. 2812
MAHAJAK KYODO CO., LTD.—See Kobe Steel, Ltd.; *Int'l*, pg. 4220
MAHAJAYA BERHAD; *Int'l*, pg. 4643
MAHALAXMI BIKAS BANK LTD.; *Int'l*, pg. 4643
MAHALAXMI RUBTECH LIMITED; *Int'l*, pg. 4643
MAHALAXMI SEAMLESS LTD; *Int'l*, pg. 4643
MAHALO ACQUISITION CORP.—See CRH plc; *Int'l*, pg. 1845
MAHA-MAYANG SDN. BHD.—See Mitrajaya Holdings Berhad; *Int'l*, pg. 4928
MAHAMAYA STEEL INDUSTRIES LIMITED; *Int'l*, pg. 4643
MAHAMERU CONSULTANCY D.O.O.—See Berjaya Corporation Berhad; *Int'l*, pg. 983
MAHANADI COALFIELDS LIMITED—See Coal India Limited; *Int'l*, pg. 1680
MAHANAGAR GAS LIMITED; *Int'l*, pg. 4644
MAHANAGAR TELEPHONE (MAURITIUS) LTD.—See Mahanagar Telephone Nigam Limited; *Int'l*, pg. 4644
MAHANAGAR TELEPHONE NIGAM LIMITED; *Int'l*, pg. 4644
MAHAN AIR PJSC; *Int'l*, pg. 4643
MAHANEY GROUP—See Altas Partners LP; *Int'l*, pg. 386
MAHAN INDUSTRIES LIMITED; *Int'l*, pg. 4643
MAHANIVESH (INDIA) LIMITED; *Int'l*, pg. 4644
MAHARAJA SHREE UMAID MILLS LTD.; *Int'l*, pg. 4644
MAHARAM FABRIC CORPORATION—See MillerKnoll, Inc.; *U.S. Public*, pg. 1447
MAHARANI SPECIALIST HOSPITAL SDN BHD—See KPJ Healthcare Berhad; *Int'l*, pg. 4297
MAHA RASHTRA APEX CORPORATION LIMITED; *Int'l*, pg. 1613
MAHARASHTRA BORDER CHECK POST NETWORK LIMITED—See Sadbhav Infrastructure Projects Ltd.; *Int'l*, pg. 6466
MAHARASHTRA CORPORATION LIMITED; *Int'l*, pg. 4644
THE MAHARASHTRA EXECUTOR & TRUSTEE CO. PVT. LTD.—See The Bank of Maharashtra Limited; *Int'l*, pg. 7616
MAHARASHTRA POLYBUTENES LTD.; *Int'l*, pg. 4644
MAHARASHTRA SCOOTERS LIMITED—See Bajaj Auto Ltd.; *Int'l*, pg. 804
MAHARASHTRA SEAMLESS LTD; *Int'l*, pg. 4644
MAHARD EGG FARM, INC.—See Cal-Maine Foods, Inc.; *U.S. Public*, pg. 421
MAHARD FEED MILL INC.; *U.S. Private*, pg. 2550
MAHAR TOOL SUPPLY COMPANY INC.; *U.S. Private*, pg. 2550
MAHASAGAR TRAVELS LIMITED; *Int'l*, pg. 4644
MAHASHREE TRADING LIMITED; *Int'l*, pg. 4644
MAHASKA BOTTLING COMPANY INC.; *U.S. Private*, pg. 2550
MAHA USAHA SDN. BHD.—See MKH Berhad; *Int'l*, pg. 5002
MAHAVEER INFOWAY LTD.; *Int'l*, pg. 4644
MAHAVIR GREEN CROP LIMITED; *Int'l*, pg. 4644
MAHAVIR INDUSTRIES LIMITED; *Int'l*, pg. 4644
MAHAWELI MARINE CEMENT (PRIVATE) LIMITED—See Siam City Cement Public Company Limited; *Int'l*, pg. 6874
MAHAWELI REACH HOTEL; *Int'l*, pg. 4644
MAHDIA GOLD CORP.; *Int'l*, pg. 4644
MAHE HUBERT SA; *Int'l*, pg. 4644
MAHER BIRD ASSOCIATES—See Omnicom Group Inc.; *U.S. Public*, pg. 1596
MAHER CHEVROLET INC.; *U.S. Private*, pg. 2550
MAHER OIL COMPANY INC.; *U.S. Private*, pg. 2550
MAHER TERMINALS, LLC—See Macquarie Group Limited; *Int'l*, pg. 4630
MAHESH DEVELOPERS LIMITED; *Int'l*, pg. 4644
MAHESHWARI LOGISTICS LIMITED; *Int'l*, pg. 4644
M.A.H. FOOD CONTROLL KFT.—See Eurofins Scientific S.E.; *Int'l*, pg. 2551
MAHICKRA CHEMICALS LIMITED; *Int'l*, pg. 4644
MAHILA SAHAYATRA MICROFINANCE BITTIYA SANSTHA LTD.—See National Laghubitta Bittiya Sanstha Limited; *Int'l*, pg. 5160
MAHINDRA AEROSPACE PRIVATE LIMITED—See Mahindra & Mahindra Limited; *Int'l*, pg. 4645
MAHINDRA AGRI SOLUTIONS LIMITED—See Mahindra & Mahindra Limited; *Int'l*, pg. 4645
MAHINDRA AUTOMOTIVE AUSTRALIA PTY. LTD.—See Mahindra & Mahindra Limited; *Int'l*, pg. 4645
MAHINDRA AUTO STEEL PRIVATE LIMITED—See Mahindra & Mahindra Limited; *Int'l*, pg. 4646

MAHINDRA BANGLADESH PVT. LTD.—See Mahindra & Mahindra Limited; *Int'l*, pg. 4645
MAHINDRA CASTINGS LIMITED—See Mahindra & Mahindra Limited; *Int'l*, pg. 4645
MAHINDRA CONSULTING ENGINEERS LIMITED—See Mahindra & Mahindra Limited; *Int'l*, pg. 4645
MAHINDRA CONVEYOR SYSTEMS PRIVATE LIMITED—See Mahindra & Mahindra Limited; *Int'l*, pg. 4645
MAHINDRA EMIRATES VEHICLE ARMOURING FZ-LLC—See Mahindra & Mahindra Limited; *Int'l*, pg. 4645
MAHINDRA ENGINEERING SERVICES (EUROPE) LIMITED—See Mahindra & Mahindra Limited; *Int'l*, pg. 4645
MAHINDRA ENGINEERING SERVICES LIMITED—See Mahindra & Mahindra Limited; *Int'l*, pg. 4645
MAHINDRA EPC IRRIGATION LIMITED; *Int'l*, pg. 4648
MAHINDRA EUROPE S.R.L.—See Mahindra & Mahindra Limited; *Int'l*, pg. 4645
MAHINDRA FIRST CHOICE SERVICES LIMITED—See TVS Automobile Solutions Pvt. Ltd.; *Int'l*, pg. 7988
MAHINDRA FIRST CHOICE WHEELS LIMITED—See Mahindra & Mahindra Limited; *Int'l*, pg. 4645
MAHINDRA FORGINGS EUROPE AG—See Mahindra & Mahindra Limited; *Int'l*, pg. 4645
MAHINDRA GEARS & TRANSMISSIONS PRIVATE LIMITED—See Mahindra & Mahindra Limited; *Int'l*, pg. 4646
MAHINDRA GRAPHIC RESEARCH DESIGN S.R.L.—See Mahindra & Mahindra Limited; *Int'l*, pg. 4646
MAHINDRA GREENYARD PRIVATE LTD.—See Greenyard N.V.; *Int'l*, pg. 3078
MAHINDRA GUJARAT TRACTOR LIMITED—See Mahindra & Mahindra Limited; *Int'l*, pg. 4646
MAHINDRA HOLIDAYS & RESORTS INDIA, LTD.—See Mahindra & Mahindra Limited; *Int'l*, pg. 4646
MAHINDRA INSURANCE BROKERS LIMITED—See Mahindra & Mahindra Limited; *Int'l*, pg. 4646
MAHINDRA INTERTRADE LIMITED—See Mahindra & Mahindra Limited; *Int'l*, pg. 4646
MAHINDRA LIFESPACE DEVELOPERS LTD.—See Mahindra & Mahindra Limited; *Int'l*, pg. 4646
MAHINDRA LOGISTICS LIMITED—See Mahindra & Mahindra Limited; *Int'l*, pg. 4646
MAHINDRA & MAHINDRA FINANCIAL SERVICES LIMITED—See Mahindra & Mahindra Limited; *Int'l*, pg. 4645
MAHINDRA & MAHINDRA LIMITED - DEFENSE SYSTEMS DIVISION—See Mahindra & Mahindra Limited; *Int'l*, pg. 4645
MAHINDRA & MAHINDRA LIMITED; *Int'l*, pg. 4645
MAHINDRA & MAHINDRA SOUTH AFRICA (PROPRIETARY) LIMITED—See Mahindra & Mahindra Limited; *Int'l*, pg. 4645
MAHINDRA MIDDLEEAST ELECTRICAL STEEL SERVICE CENTRE (FZC)—See Mahindra & Mahindra Limited; *Int'l*, pg. 4646
MAHINDRA NAVISTAR AUTOMOTIVES LIMITED—See Mahindra & Mahindra Limited; *Int'l*, pg. 4646
MAHINDRA NAVISTAR AUTOMOTIVES LIMITED—See Porsche Automobil Holding SE; *Int'l*, pg. 5930
MAHINDRA PUNJAB TRACTORS PRIVATE LIMITED—See Mahindra & Mahindra Limited; *Int'l*, pg. 4646
MAHINDRA RESIDENTIAL DEVELOPERS LIMITED—See Mahindra & Mahindra Limited; *Int'l*, pg. 4646
MAHINDRA RETAIL PRIVATE LIMITED—See Mahindra & Mahindra Limited; *Int'l*, pg. 4646
MAHINDRA RURAL HOUSING FINANCE LIMITED—See Mahindra & Mahindra Limited; *Int'l*, pg. 4645
MAHINDRA SATYAM—See Mahindra & Mahindra Limited; *Int'l*, pg. 4647
MAHINDRA STEEL SERVICE CENTRE LIMITED—See Mahindra & Mahindra Limited; *Int'l*, pg. 4646
MAHINDRA TRACTOR ASSEMBLY INC.—See Mahindra & Mahindra Limited; *Int'l*, pg. 4646
MAHINDRA TSUBAKI CONVEYOR SYSTEMS PRIVATE LIMITED—See Tsubakimoto Chain Co.; *Int'l*, pg. 7953
MAHINDRA TWO WHEELERS LIMITED—See Mahindra & Mahindra Limited; *Int'l*, pg. 4646
MAHINDRA USA INC—See Mahindra & Mahindra Limited; *Int'l*, pg. 4646
MAHINDRA VEHICLE MANUFACTURERS LIMITED—See Mahindra & Mahindra Limited; *Int'l*, pg. 4646
MAHINDRA WORLD CITY DEVELOPERS LIMITED—See Mahindra & Mahindra Limited; *Int'l*, pg. 4646
MAHINDRA WORLD CITY (JAIPUR) LIMITED—See Mahindra & Mahindra Limited; *Int'l*, pg. 4646
MAHIP INDUSTRIES LTD.; *Int'l*, pg. 4648
MAHISOM CO., LTD.—See SCB X Public Company Limited; *Int'l*, pg. 6614
MAHISORN CO., LTD.—See Siam Commercial Bank Public Company Limited; *Int'l*, pg. 6875
MAHKOTA MEDICAL CENTRE SDN. BHD.—See EQT AB; *Int'l*, pg. 2475
MAHLE AFTERMARKET DEUTSCHLAND GMBH—See Food Empire Holdings Limited; *Int'l*, pg. 2727
MAHLE AFTERMARKET FRANCE S.A.S.—See MAHLE GmbH; *Int'l*, pg. 4648

MAHLE AFTERMARKET GMBH—See MAHLE GmbH; Int'l, pg. 4648
MAHLE ARGENTINA S.A.—See Food Empire Holdings Limited; Int'l, pg. 2727
MAHLE BEHR CHARLESTON INC.—See MAHLE GmbH; Int'l, pg. 4648
MAHLE BEHR DAYTON L.L.C.—See MAHLE GmbH; Int'l, pg. 4648
MAHLE BEHR FRANCE HAMBACK S.A.S.—See MAHLE GmbH; Int'l, pg. 4648
MAHLE BEHR FRANCE ROUFFACH S.A.S.—See MAHLE GmbH; Int'l, pg. 4648
MAHLE BEHR GMBH & CO. KG—See MAHLE GmbH; Int'l, pg. 4648
MAHLE BEHR JAPAN K.K.—See MAHLE GmbH; Int'l, pg. 4648
MAHLE BEHR KIRCHBERG GMBH—See MAHLE GmbH; Int'l, pg. 4648
MAHLE BEHR KORNWESTHEIM GMBH—See MAHLE GmbH; Int'l, pg. 4648
MAHLE BEHR SERVICE AMERICA L.L.C.—See MAHLE GmbH; Int'l, pg. 4648
MAHLE BEHR SERVICE GMBH—See MAHLE GmbH; Int'l, pg. 4648
MAHLE BEHR SERVICE GMBH—See MAHLE GmbH; Int'l, pg. 4648
MAHLE CLEVITE INC.—See MAHLE GmbH; Int'l, pg. 4648
MAHLE COMPONENTE DE MOTOR SRL—See Food Empire Holdings Limited; Int'l, pg. 2727
MAHLE ELECTRIC DRIVES JAPAN CORPORATION—See MAHLE GmbH; Int'l, pg. 4648
MAHLE ENGINE COMPONENTS (CHONGQING) CO., LTD.—See Food Empire Holdings Limited; Int'l, pg. 2727
MAHLE ENGINE COMPONENTS JAPAN CORPORATION—See MAHLE GmbH; Int'l, pg. 4648
MAHLE ENGINE COMPONENTS (NANJING) CO., LTD.—See Food Empire Holdings Limited; Int'l, pg. 2727
MAHLE ENGINE COMPONENTS (THAILAND) CO., LTD.—See Food Empire Holdings Limited; Int'l, pg. 2727
MAHLE ENGINE COMPONENTS USA, INC.—See MAHLE GmbH; Int'l, pg. 4648
MAHLE ENGINE COMPONENTS (YINGKOU) CO., LTD.—See Food Empire Holdings Limited; Int'l, pg. 2727
MAHLE ENGINEERING SERVICES INDIA PRIVATE LIMITED—See Food Empire Holdings Limited; Int'l, pg. 2727
MAHLE FILTER SYSTEMS JAPAN CORPORATION—See MAHLE GmbH; Int'l, pg. 4648
MAHLE FILTER SYSTEMS NORTH AMERICA, INC.—See Food Empire Holdings Limited; Int'l, pg. 2727
MAHLE FILTER SYSTEMS PHILIPPINES CORPORATION—See Food Empire Holdings Limited; Int'l, pg. 2727
MAHLE GMBH; Int'l, pg. 4648
MAHLE GUANGZHOU FILTER SYSTEMS CO., LTD.—See Food Empire Holdings Limited; Int'l, pg. 2727
MAHLE INDUSTRIA E COMERCIO LTDA.—See Food Empire Holdings Limited; Int'l, pg. 2727
MAHLE INDUSTRIES, INCORPORATED—See MAHLE GmbH; Int'l, pg. 4648
MAHLE INTERNATIONAL GMBH—See Food Empire Holdings Limited; Int'l, pg. 2727
MAHLE LETRIKA BOVEC D.O.O.—See MAHLE GmbH; Int'l, pg. 4648
MAHLE LETRIKA DEUTSCHLAND GMBH—See MAHLE GmbH; Int'l, pg. 4648
MAHLE LETRIKA D.O.O—See MAHLE GmbH; Int'l, pg. 4648
MAHLE LETRIKA ITALIA S.R.L.—See MAHLE GmbH; Int'l, pg. 4648
MAHLE LETRIKA KOMEN D.O.O.—See MAHLE GmbH; Int'l, pg. 4648
MAHLE LETRIKA LAKTASI D.O.O.—See MAHLE GmbH; Int'l, pg. 4648
MAHLE LETRIKA (SUZHOU) AUTOMOTIVE ELECTRICS CO., LTD.—See MAHLE GmbH; Int'l, pg. 4648
MAHLE LETRIKA UK LTD.—See MAHLE GmbH; Int'l, pg. 4648
MAHLE LETRIKA USA INC.—See MAHLE GmbH; Int'l, pg. 4648
MAHLE METAL LEVE S.A.; Int'l, pg. 4649
MAHLE POWERTRAIN GMBH—See Food Empire Holdings Limited; Int'l, pg. 2727
MAHLE POWERTRAIN LTD.—See MAHLE GmbH; Int'l, pg. 4648
MAHLER BESSE SA; Int'l, pg. 4649
MAHLE SHANGHAI FILTER SYSTEMS CO., LTD.—See Food Empire Holdings Limited; Int'l, pg. 2727
MAHLE SIAM FILTER SYSTEMS CO., LTD.—See Food Empire Holdings Limited; Int'l, pg. 2727
MAHLE TRADING (SHANGHAI) CO., LTD.—See Food Empire Holdings Limited; Int'l, pg. 2727

MAHLO AMERICA INC.—See Mahlo GmbH & Co. KG; Int'l, pg. 4649
MAHLO ASIA LTD.—See Mahlo GmbH & Co. KG; Int'l, pg. 4649
MAHLO DO BRASIL CONTROLE DE PROCESSOS LTDA.—See Mahlo GmbH & Co. KG; Int'l, pg. 4649
MAHLO ESPANA SISTEMAS DE REGULACION Y CONTROL S.L.—See Mahlo GmbH & Co. KG; Int'l, pg. 4649
MAHLO GMBH & CO. KG; Int'l, pg. 4649
MAHLO ITALIA S.R.L.—See Mahlo GmbH & Co. KG; Int'l, pg. 4649
MAHLO OUEST S.A.R.L.—See Mahlo GmbH & Co. KG; Int'l, pg. 4649
MAHMOOD GROUP OF COMPANIES LLC; Int'l, pg. 4649
MAHMOOD POWER GENERATION LIMITED—See Mahmood Group of Companies LLC; Int'l, pg. 4649
MAHMOOD SALEH ABBAR COMPANY; Int'l, pg. 4649
MAHMOOD TEXTILE MILLS LIMITED—See Mahmood Group of Companies LLC; Int'l, pg. 4649
MAHOGANY OY; Int'l, pg. 4649
THE MAHONEY COMPANY; U.S. Private, pg. 4074
MAHONEY DIALYSIS, LLC—See DaVita Inc.; U.S. Public, pg. 641
MAHONEY ENVIRONMENTAL, INC.—See Neste Oyj; Int'l, pg. 5201
MAHONEY ENVIRONMENTAL SOLUTIONS, LLC—See Neste Oyj; Int'l, pg. 5201
MAHONEY'S ROCKY LEDGE FARM GARDEN; U.S. Private, pg. 2550
MAHONEY'S SILVER NUGGET INC.; U.S. Private, pg. 2550
MAHONING LANDFILL, INC.—See Waste Management, Inc.; U.S. Public, pg. 2331
MAHONING & TRUMBULL BUILDING TRADES INSURANCE FUND; U.S. Private, pg. 2550
MAHOPAC BANK—See Tompkins Financial Corporation; U.S. Public, pg. 2162
MAHORASHA CO., LTD.—See Cosmos Machinery Enterprises Limited; Int'l, pg. 1813
MAHOROBA FARM CO., LTD.—See DMG MORI Co., Ltd.; Int'l, pg. 2145
MAHORSKY GROUP, INC—See Kelso & Company, L.P.; U.S. Private, pg. 2280
MAHOU, S.A. - BARCELONA—See Mahou, S.A.; Int'l, pg. 4649
MAHOU, S.A.; Int'l, pg. 4649
MAHOWALD INSURANCE AGENCY, LLC—See Arthur J. Gallagher & Co.; U.S. Public, pg. 206
MAH PHARMACY, LLC—See The Cigna Group; U.S. Public, pg. 2061
MAHR AG—See Carl Mahr Holding GmbH; Int'l, pg. 1333
MAHRAM MFG. GROUP; Int'l, pg. 4649
MAHR AUSTRIA GMBH—See Carl Mahr Holding GmbH; Int'l, pg. 1333
MAHR CHINA LTD.—See Carl Mahr Holding GmbH; Int'l, pg. 1333
MAHR CORPORATION DE MEXICO S.A. DE C.V.—See Carl Mahr Holding GmbH; Int'l, pg. 1333
MAHR DO BRASIL LTDA.—See Carl Mahr Holding GmbH; Int'l, pg. 1333
MAHR FEDERAL, INC.—See Carl Mahr Holding GmbH; Int'l, pg. 1333
MAHR GMBH—See Carl Mahr Holding GmbH; Int'l, pg. 1333
MAHR JAPAN CO., LTD.—See Carl Mahr Holding GmbH; Int'l, pg. 1333
MAHR KOREA LTD.—See Carl Mahr Holding GmbH; Int'l, pg. 1333
MAHR MALAYSIA SDN. BHD.—See Carl Mahr Holding GmbH; Int'l, pg. 1333
MAHR METERING SYSTEMS CORPORATION—See Carl Mahr Holding GmbH; Int'l, pg. 1333
MAHR METERING SYSTEMS GMBH—See Carl Mahr Holding GmbH; Int'l, pg. 1333
MAHR METROLOGY INDIA PRIVATE LTD.—See Carl Mahr Holding GmbH; Int'l, pg. 1333
MAHR POLSKA S.P.O.O.—See Carl Mahr Holding GmbH; Int'l, pg. 1333
MAHR PRECISION METROLOGY SUZHOU LTD.—See Carl Mahr Holding GmbH; Int'l, pg. 1333
MAHR S.E.A. CO. LTD.—See Carl Mahr Holding GmbH; Int'l, pg. 1333
MAHR, SPOL S.R.O.—See Carl Mahr Holding GmbH; Int'l, pg. 1333
MAHR TRADING CO., LTD.—See Carl Mahr Holding GmbH; Int'l, pg. 1333
MAHR U.K. PLC—See Carl Mahr Holding GmbH; Int'l, pg. 1333
MAH SING GROUP BERHAD; Int'l, pg. 4643
MAH SING PLASTICS INDUSTRIES SENDIRIAN BERHAD—See Mah Sing Group Berhad; Int'l, pg. 4643
MAHUBE INFRASTRUCTURE LTD; Int'l, pg. 4649
MAHULI LAGHUBITTA BITTIYA SANSTHA LIMITED; Int'l, pg. 4649
MAHWAH BERGEN RETAIL GROUP, INC.; U.S. Private, pg. 2550
MAHYCO MONSANTO BIOTECH (INDIA) LIMITED—See Bayer Aktiengesellschaft; Int'l, pg. 908

MAIA BIOTECHNOLOGY, INC.; U.S. Public, pg. 1354
MAIB-LEASING SA—See BC Moldova Agroindbank S.A.; Int'l, pg. 922
MAICA LAMINATES SDN. BHD.—See AICA Kogyo Company, Limited; Int'l, pg. 229
MAI CAPITAL MANAGEMENT, LLC—See Keystone Group, L.P.; U.S. Private, pg. 2297
MAICENTRE—See Groupe Limagrain Holding SA; Int'l, pg. 3107
MAICHE DISTRIBUTION SA—See Carrefour SA; Int'l, pg. 1345
MAICO DIAGNOSTIC GMBH—See Demant A/S; Int'l, pg. 2024
MAICO S.R.L.—See Demant A/S; Int'l, pg. 2024
MAIDEN FORGINGS LIMITED; Int'l, pg. 4649
MAIDENFORM BRANDS, LLC—See Hanesbrands Inc.; U.S. Public, pg. 983
MAIDENFORM LLC—See Hanesbrands Inc.; U.S. Public, pg. 983
MAIDEN HOLDINGS, LTD.; Int'l, pg. 4649
MAIDEN HOLDINGS NORTH AMERICA, LTD.—See Maiden Holdings, Ltd.; Int'l, pg. 4649
MAIDEN LANE JEWELRY, LTD.; U.S. Private, pg. 2551
MAIDEN REINSURANCE NORTH AMERICA, INC.—See Enstar Group Limited; Int'l, pg. 2449
MAIDEN RE INSURANCE SERVICES, LLC—See Maiden Holdings, Ltd.; Int'l, pg. 4649
MAIDER MEDICAL INDUSTRY EQUIPMENT CO., LTD.; Int'l, pg. 4650
MAID OF THE MIST CORPORATION; U.S. Private, pg. 2550
MAIDO—See Rubis SCA; Int'l, pg. 6423
MAID-RITE STEAK COMPANY INC.; U.S. Private, pg. 2551
THE MAIDS INTERNATIONAL, LLC—See Gladstone Management Corporation; U.S. Private, pg. 1705
MAIDS MORETON OPERATIONS LIMITED—See Welltower Inc.; U.S. Public, pg. 2348
MAIDSTONE CLUB INC; U.S. Private, pg. 2551
MAIDSTONE INSURANCE COMPANY—See Turning Point Brands, Inc.; U.S. Public, pg. 2205
MAIDSTONE VETS4PETS LIMITED—See Pets at Home Group Plc; Int'l, pg. 5834
MAIER ADVERTISING, INC.; U.S. Private, pg. 2551
MAIER PACKAGING GMBH—See OPTIMA Packaging Group GmbH; Int'l, pg. 5603
MAIER + PARTNER AG; Int'l, pg. 4650
MAIER S. COOP.—See Mondragon Corporation; Int'l, pg. 5031
MAIER SPORTS GMBH & CO. KG—See Findos Investor GmbH; Int'l, pg. 2673
M.A.I. GMBH & CO. KG—See Nanjing Estun Automation Co., Ltd.; Int'l, pg. 5140
MAIHAMA BUILDING MAINTENANCE CO. LTD.—See Oriental Land Co., Ltd.; Int'l, pg. 5625
MAIHAMA CORPORATION CO. LTD.—See Oriental Land Co., Ltd.; Int'l, pg. 5625
MAIHAMA RESORT LINE CO. LTD.—See Oriental Land Co., Ltd.; Int'l, pg. 5625
MAIKE TUBE INDUSTRY HOLDINGS LIMITED; Int'l, pg. 4650
MAIKUBEN WEST HOLDING JSC—See Nova Resources B.V.; Int'l, pg. 5452
MAIL A DOC LIMITED—See Xerox Holdings Corporation; U.S. Public, pg. 2386
MAILBOX MEDIA MBM AB; Int'l, pg. 4650
MAIL CONTRACTORS OF AMERICA, INC.—See Pat Salmon & Sons, Inc.; U.S. Private, pg. 3105
MAIL CUSTOMER CENTER CO., LTD.—See Bain Capital, LP; U.S. Private, pg. 449
MAILENDER, INC.—See Bain Capital, LP; U.S. Private, pg. 441
MAILER MAGIC—See Transcontinental Inc.; Int'l, pg. 7897
MAILERMAILER, LLC—See Khera Communications Inc.; U.S. Private, pg. 2301
MAILER'S CHOICE, INC.—See DNI Corp.; U.S. Private, pg. 1224
MAILHOT INDUSTRIES USA, INC.—See Novacap Management Inc.; Int'l, pg. 5454
MAILIAO HARBOR ADMINISTRATION CORPORATION—See Formosa Petrochemical Corporation; Int'l, pg. 2735
MAI-LIAO POWER CORPORATION—See Formosa Plastics Corporation; Int'l, pg. 2736
MAILIAO POWER CORP.—See Formosa Plastics Corporation; Int'l, pg. 2736
MAILIGEN CHINA—See Pipedrive Inc.; U.S. Private, pg. 3189
MAILIGEN EUROPE—See Pipedrive Inc.; U.S. Private, pg. 3189
MAILIGEN LIMITED—See Pipedrive Inc.; U.S. Private, pg. 3189
MAILIGEN RUSSIA—See Pipedrive Inc.; U.S. Private, pg. 3189
MAILING AND PRINT SERVICES—See AAB Holdings Pty Limited; Int'l, pg. 30
MAILING JAPAN CO., LTD.—See TOSNET Corporation; Int'l, pg. 7832
MAILING LIST SYSTEMS CORP.; U.S. Private, pg. 2551

COMPANY NAME INDEX

MAILING PRODUCTS LIMITED—See Laing O'Rourke Plc; *Int'l*, pg. 4396
MAILING SERVICES OF PITTSBURGH, INC.—See Direct Marketing Solutions, Inc.; *U.S. Private*, pg. 1235
MAILINGS UNLIMITED; *U.S. Private*, pg. 2551
MAILING SYSTEMS, INC.; *U.S. Private*, pg. 2551
MAI LINH CENTRAL JOINT STOCK COMPANY; *Int'l*, pg. 4649
MAI LINH NORTH JOINT STOCK COMPANY; *Int'l*, pg. 4649
MAIL MARKETING (SCOTLAND) LIMITED; *Int'l*, pg. 4650
MAIL.RU GROUP LIMITED; *Int'l*, pg. 4650
MAIL SHARK; *U.S. Private*, pg. 2551
MAILSOUTH, INC.; *U.S. Private*, pg. 2551
MAILSTEP HOLDING A.S.—See Osterreichische Post AG; *Int'l*, pg. 5654
MAILSTORE SOFTWARE GMBH—See Open Text Corporation; *Int'l*, pg. 5596
THE MAIL TRIBUNE, INC.—See Rosebud Media, LLC; *U.S. Private*, pg. 3482
MAILUP INC.—See Growens S.p.A.; *Int'l*, pg. 3112
MAILWORLD AB—See Unifiedpost Group SA; *Int'l*, pg. 8043
MAIMU CO., LTD.—See BELLUNA CO. LTD.; *Int'l*, pg. 967
MAINBRIGHT ENTERPRISES LTD.—See Bright Led Electronics Corp.; *Int'l*, pg. 1161
MAIN BROTHERS OIL COMPANY, INC.; *U.S. Private*, pg. 2551
MAIN CAPITAL PARTNERS B.V.; *Int'l*, pg. 4650
MAINCO INVESTMENTS INC.; *U.S. Private*, pg. 2552
MAIN CO., LTD.—See CMC Corporation; *Int'l*, pg. 1669
MAINCONCEPT GMBH—See William Morris Endeavor Entertainment, LLC; *U.S. Private*, pg. 4523
MAINCONCEPT JAPAN, INC.—See William Morris Endeavor Entertainment, LLC; *U.S. Private*, pg. 4523
MAINCONCEPT LLC—See William Morris Endeavor Entertainment, LLC; *U.S. Private*, pg. 4523
MAINCON CORPORATION—See Datavan International Corp.; *Int'l*, pg. 1981
M.A. INC.—See Midwest Real Estate Development; *U.S. Private*, pg. 2723
M.A.IND. S.R.L.—See Brookfield Corporation; *Int'l*, pg. 1182
M.A. INDUSTRIES, INC.; *U.S. Private*, pg. 2527
MAINE ASSISTED LIVING, L.L.C.—See Apollo Global Management, Inc.; *U.S. Public*, pg. 157
MAINE COAST BOOK SHOP, INC.—See Sherman's Books & Stationery, Inc.; *U.S. Private*, pg. 3634
MAINE COAST REGIONAL HEALTH FACILITIES INC.; *U.S. Private*, pg. 2552
MAINE COMMUNITY BANCORP, MHC; *U.S. Private*, pg. 2552
MAINE COMMUNITY BANK—See Maine Community Bancorp, MHC; *U.S. Private*, pg. 2552
MAINE COMMUNITY FOUNDATION; *U.S. Private*, pg. 2552
MAINE CONSTRUCTION SAS—See Maisons France Confort SA; *Int'l*, pg. 4653
MAINE DRILLING & BLASTING INC. - CENTRAL DIVISION—See Maine Drilling & Blasting Inc.; *U.S. Private*, pg. 2552
MAINE DRILLING & BLASTING INC. - EASTERN DIVISION—See Maine Drilling & Blasting Inc.; *U.S. Private*, pg. 2552
MAINE DRILLING & BLASTING INC. - MID-ATLANTIC DIVISION—See Maine Drilling & Blasting Inc.; *U.S. Private*, pg. 2552
MAINE DRILLING & BLASTING INC. - NORTH DIVISION—See Maine Drilling & Blasting Inc.; *U.S. Private*, pg. 2552
MAINE DRILLING & BLASTING INC.; *U.S. Private*, pg. 2552
MAINE DRILLING & BLASTING INC. - SOUTH DIVISION—See Maine Drilling & Blasting Inc.; *U.S. Private*, pg. 2552
MAINE DRILLING & BLASTING INC. - WESTERN DIVISION—See Maine Drilling & Blasting Inc.; *U.S. Private*, pg. 2552
MAINE ELECTRIC POWER CO., INC.—See Iberdrola, S.A.; *Int'l*, pg. 3570
MAINE EMPLOYERS MUTUAL INSURANCE CO.; *U.S. Private*, pg. 2552
MAINE FINANCE LIMITED—See Watchstone Group plc; *Int'l*, pg. 8356
MAINEGENERAL HEALTH INC.; *U.S. Private*, pg. 2552
MAINEGENERAL MEDICAL CENTER—See MaineGeneral Health Inc.; *U.S. Private*, pg. 2552
MAINEHEALTH; *U.S. Private*, pg. 2552
MAINE INDUSTRIAL TIRE LLC—See The Yokohama Rubber Co., Ltd.; *Int'l*, pg. 7703
MAINE MEDICAL PARTNERS—See MaineHealth; *U.S. Private*, pg. 2553
MAINE NATURAL GAS—See Iberdrola, S.A.; *Int'l*, pg. 3570
MAINE ORNAMENTAL, LLC—See UFP Industries, Inc.; *U.S. Public*, pg. 2219
MAINE OXY-ACETYLENE SUPPLY CO.; *U.S. Private*, pg. 2552

MAINE PHYSICAL THERAPY, LIMITED PARTNERSHIP—See U.S. Physical Therapy, Inc.; *U.S. Public*, pg. 2215
MAINE POINTE LLC—See SGS SA; *Int'l*, pg. 6745
MAINE POTATO GROWERS, INC.; *U.S. Private*, pg. 2552
MAINE SEABOARD REALTY LLC—See Jefferies Financial Group Inc.; *U.S. Public*, pg. 1188
MAINE SECURITIES CORPORATION; *U.S. Private*, pg. 2552
MAINES PAPER & FOOD SERVICE, INC.; *U.S. Private*, pg. 2553
MAINE SPIRITS—See Pine State Trading Co.; *U.S. Private*, pg. 3183
MAINE STATE CREDIT UNION; *U.S. Private*, pg. 2552
MAINETODAY MEDIA, INC.; *U.S. Private*, pg. 2553
MAINETTI SPA—See Mauna N.V.; *Int'l*, pg. 4732
MAINE TURNPIKE AUTHORITY; *U.S. Private*, pg. 2552
MAIN EVENT CATERERS; *U.S. Private*, pg. 2551
MAIN EVENT ENTERTAINMENT LP—See Keystone Group, L.P.; *U.S. Private*, pg. 2297
THE MAINE WATER CO. - BIDDEFORD & SACO—See SJW Group; *U.S. Public*, pg. 1891
THE MAINE WATER CO. - BUCKSPORT—See SJW Group; *U.S. Public*, pg. 1891
THE MAINE WATER CO. - GREENVILLE—See SJW Group; *U.S. Public*, pg. 1891
THE MAINE WATER CO. - KEZAR FALLS—See SJW Group; *U.S. Public*, pg. 1891
THE MAINE WATER CO. - MILLINOCKET—See SJW Group; *U.S. Public*, pg. 1891
THE MAINE WATER COMPANY—See SJW Group; *U.S. Public*, pg. 1891
THE MAINE WATER CO. - SKOWHEGAN—See SJW Group; *U.S. Public*, pg. 1891
MAINFAUCET.COM—See Kenry Home Improvement Network, Inc.; *U.S. Private*, pg. 2287
MAIN FINE INTERNATIONAL, LLC—See Main Fine International Ltd.; *Int'l*, pg. 4650
MAIN FINE INTERNATIONAL LTD.; *Int'l*, pg. 4650
MAINFIRST BANK AG—See Stifel Financial Corp.; *U.S. Public*, pg. 1950
MAINFREIGHT AIR & OCEAN-BRISBANE—See Mainfreight Ltd.; *Int'l*, pg. 4650
MAINFREIGHT BV—See Mainfreight Ltd.; *Int'l*, pg. 4650
MAINFREIGHT CHILE SPA—See Mainfreight Ltd.; *Int'l*, pg. 4650
MAINFREIGHT DISTRIBUTION PTY LTD.—See Mainfreight Ltd.; *Int'l*, pg. 4650
MAINFREIGHT EXPRESS LTD—See Mainfreight Ltd.; *Int'l*, pg. 4650
MAINFREIGHT FORWARDING BELGIUM NV—See Mainfreight Ltd.; *Int'l*, pg. 4650
MAINFREIGHT GLOBAL TAIWAN LTD.—See Mainfreight Ltd.; *Int'l*, pg. 4650
MAINFREIGHT GMBH—See Mainfreight Ltd.; *Int'l*, pg. 4650
MAINFREIGHT HOLDINGS PTY LTD—See Mainfreight Ltd.; *Int'l*, pg. 4651
MAINFREIGHT HONG KONG LTD.—See Mainfreight Ltd.; *Int'l*, pg. 4651
MAINFREIGHT INTERNATIONAL LTD—See Mainfreight Ltd.; *Int'l*, pg. 4651
MAINFREIGHT ITALY SRL—See Mainfreight Ltd.; *Int'l*, pg. 4651
MAINFREIGHT JAPAN CO., LTD.—See Mainfreight Ltd.; *Int'l*, pg. 4651
MAINFREIGHT KOREA LTD.—See Mainfreight Ltd.; *Int'l*, pg. 4651
MAINFREIGHT LOGISTICS (MALAYSIA) SDN. BHD.—See Mainfreight Ltd.; *Int'l*, pg. 4651
MAINFREIGHT LTD.; *Int'l*, pg. 4650
MAINFREIGHT N.V.—See Mainfreight Ltd.; *Int'l*, pg. 4651
MAINFREIGHT POLAND SP Z O.O.—See Mainfreight Ltd.; *Int'l*, pg. 4651
MAINFREIGHT RUSS LLC—See Mainfreight Ltd.; *Int'l*, pg. 4651
MAINFREIGHT SAS—See Mainfreight Ltd.; *Int'l*, pg. 4651
MAINFREIGHT—See Mainfreight Ltd.; *Int'l*, pg. 4650
MAINFREIGHT SPAIN, S.L.U.—See Mainfreight Ltd.; *Int'l*, pg. 4651
MAINFREIGHT SP Z O.O.—See Mainfreight Ltd.; *Int'l*, pg. 4651
MAINFREIGHT (THAILAND) CO., LTD.—See Mainfreight Ltd.; *Int'l*, pg. 4650
MAINFREIGHT UKRAINE LLC—See Mainfreight Ltd.; *Int'l*, pg. 4651
MAINFREIGHT VIETNAM COMPANY LTD.—See Mainfreight Ltd.; *Int'l*, pg. 4651
MAINGEAR INC.; *U.S. Private*, pg. 2553
MAINICHICOMNET CO. LTD.; *Int'l*, pg. 4651
MAINI CORPORATE PVT LTD.; *Int'l*, pg. 4651
MAIN IDEAS; *U.S. Private*, pg. 2551
MAIN INCUBATOR GMBH—See Commerzbank AG; *Int'l*, pg. 1719
MAIN INDUSTRIES, INC.—See Stellex Capital Management LP; *U.S. Private*, pg. 3800
MAINI PRECISION PRODUCTS LTD.—See Raymond Limited; *Int'l*, pg. 6224

MAINSTREAM ENERGY CORPORATION

MAINKRAFTWERK SCHWEINFURT GESELLSCHAFT MIT BESCHRANKTER HAFTUNG—See E.ON SE; *Int'l*, pg. 2258
MAINLAND CONSTRUCTION MATERIALS ULC—See Summit Materials, Inc.; *U.S. Private*, pg. 1959
MAINLAND FUNERAL HOME, INC.—See Service Corporation International; *U.S. Public*, pg. 1870
MAINLAND HEADWEAR HOLDINGS LTD.; *Int'l*, pg. 4651
MAINLAND MUSIC AG—See Live Nation Entertainment, Inc.; *U.S. Public*, pg. 1330
MAINLAND PRIMARY CARE PHYSICIANS, PLLC—See HCA Healthcare, Inc.; *U.S. Public*, pg. 1001
MAINLAND PRODUCTS LIMITED—See Fonterra Co-Operative Group Ltd.; *Int'l*, pg. 2726
MAIN LINE AUDIOLOGY CONSULTANTS, PC—See Alpaca Audiology; *U.S. Private*, pg. 196
MAINLINE DIGITAL COMMUNICATIONS LIMITED—See BT Group plc; *Int'l*, pg. 1203
MAIN LINE EQUITY PARTNERS, LLC; *U.S. Private*, pg. 2551
MAINLINE FIRE PROTECTION, LLC.; *U.S. Private*, pg. 2553
MAINLINE GLOBAL LOGISTICS PTE. LTD.—See Mainfreight Ltd.; *Int'l*, pg. 4651
MAINLINE INFORMATION SYSTEMS, INC.—See H.I.G. Capital, LLC; *U.S. Private*, pg. 1833
MAIN LINE MEDIA NEWS—See Alden Global Capital LLC; *U.S. Private*, pg. 156
THE MAIN LINE PA ENDOSCOPY ASC, L.P.—See KKR & Co. Inc.; *U.S. Public*, pg. 1248
MAINLINE PIPELINES LIMITED—See Valero Energy Corporation; *U.S. Public*, pg. 2272
MAINLINE PRINTING INC.; *U.S. Private*, pg. 2553
MAIN LINE SPINE SURGERY CENTER, LLC—See UnitedHealth Group Incorporated; *U.S. Public*, pg. 2242
MAIN LINE SUPPLY CO. INC.; *U.S. Private*, pg. 2551
MAINLINE SYSTEMS DO BRASIL LTDA.—See H.I.G. Capital, LLC; *U.S. Private*, pg. 1833
MAINLINING SERVICE INC.; *U.S. Private*, pg. 2553
MAINNERVE FEDERAL SERVICES, INC.—See Castellum, Inc.; *U.S. Public*, pg. 447
MAINONE CABLE COMPANY GHANA LTD.—See Equinix, Inc.; *U.S. Public*, pg. 788
MAINONE CABLE COMPANY LTD.—See Equinix, Inc.; *U.S. Public*, pg. 788
MAINONE CABLE COMPANY NIGERIA LIMITED—See Equinix, Inc.; *U.S. Public*, pg. 788
MAINONE CABLE COMPANY PORTUGAL, S.A.—See Equinix, Inc.; *U.S. Public*, pg. 788
MAINOSKENTTA OY; *Int'l*, pg. 4651
MAINOVA AG; *Int'l*, pg. 4651
MAIN PASS OIL GATHERING COMPANY—See ArcLight Capital Holdings, LLC; *U.S. Private*, pg. 312
MAIN POST PARTNERS, L.P.; *U.S. Private*, pg. 2551
MAINPOWER HELLAS LTD.—See Eguana Technologies Inc.; *Int'l*, pg. 2326
MAIN PULZE, INC.; *U.S. Private*, pg. 2551
MAINSAIL LODGING & DEVELOPMENT, LLC; *U.S. Private*, pg. 2553
MAINSAIL MANAGEMENT COMPANY, LLC; *U.S. Private*, pg. 2553
MAINSAIL SUITES HOTEL & CONFERENCE CENTER TAMPA—See Mainsail Lodging & Development, LLC; *U.S. Private*, pg. 2553
MAINSPED BANSE GMBH & CO. KG; *Int'l*, pg. 4651
MAINSPRING, INC.; *U.S. Private*, pg. 2553
MAIN STAGE CO., LTD.—See Nihonwasou Holdings, Inc.; *Int'l*, pg. 5288
MAINSTAR TECHNOLOGIES COMPANY; *Int'l*, pg. 4651
MAINSTAY BUSINESS SOLUTIONS; *U.S. Private*, pg. 2553
MAINSTAY GROUP LIMITED—See Equistone Partners Europe Limited; *Int'l*, pg. 2486
MAINSTAY MACKAY DEFINEDTERM MUNICIPAL OPPORTUNITIES FUND; *U.S. Public*, pg. 1355
MAINSTAY MEDICAL LIMITED; *Int'l*, pg. 4651
MAINSTAY TECHNOLOGIES; *U.S. Private*, pg. 2553
MAIN STEEL, LLC—See Samuel, Son & Co., Limited; *Int'l*, pg. 6516
MAINSTREAM DATA, INC.; *U.S. Private*, pg. 2553
MAINSTREAM ENERGY CORPORATION; *U.S. Private*, pg. 2553
MAINSTREAM FUND SERVICES (CAYMAN) LIMITED—See Apex Fund Services Holdings Ltd.; *Int'l*, pg. 510
MAINSTREAM FUND SERVICES (HK) LIMITED—See Apex Fund Services Holdings Ltd.; *Int'l*, pg. 510
MAINSTREAM FUND SERVICES (IOM) LIMITED—See Apex Fund Services Holdings Ltd.; *Int'l*, pg. 510
MAINSTREAM FUND SERVICES (IRELAND) LIMITED—See Apex Fund Services Holdings Ltd.; *Int'l*, pg. 510
MAINSTREAM FUND SERVICES (MALTA) LIMITED—See Apex Fund Services Holdings Ltd.; *Int'l*, pg. 510
MAINSTREAM FUND SERVICES PTE LTD—See Apex Fund Services Holdings Ltd.; *Int'l*, pg. 510
MAINSTREAM GROUP HOLDINGS LIMITED—See Apex Fund Services Holdings Ltd.; *Int'l*, pg. 510

MAINSTREAM MINERALS CORPORATION / CORPORATE AFFILIATIONS

MAINSTREAM MINERALS CORPORATION; *Int'l*, pg. 4651
MAINSTREAM OUTFITTERS—See Dave's Sports Center, Inc.; *U.S. Private*, pg. 1168
MAINSTREAM PE SERVICES, INC.—See Apex Fund Services Holdings Ltd.; *Int'l*, pg. 510
MAINSTREAM PE SERVICES, INC.—See Apex Fund Services Holdings Ltd.; *Int'l*, pg. 510
MAINSTREAM TECHNOLOGIES, INC; *U.S. Private*, pg. 2553
MAINSTREET 1878 (PTY.) LTD.—See A.P. Moller-Maersk A/S; *Int'l*, pg. 27
THE MAIN STREET AMERICA GROUP—See American Family Mutual Insurance Company; *U.S. Private*, pg. 233
MAINSTREET BANCSHARES, INC.; *U.S. Public*, pg. 1355
MAIN STREET BANK CORP.—See Main Street Financial Services Corp.; *U.S. Public*, pg. 1355
MAINSTREET BANK—See MainStreet Bancshares, Inc.; *U.S. Public*, pg. 1355
MAIN STREET CAPITAL CORPORATION; *U.S. Public*, pg. 1354
MAIN STREET CAPITAL HOLDINGS, LLC; *U.S. Private*, pg. 2551
MAIN STREET CLINICAL LABORATORY, INC.—See Schryver Medical Sales; *U.S. Private*, pg. 3570
MAIN STREET COMPLEX PLC; *Int'l*, pg. 4650
MAIN STREET COMPLEX PLC; *Int'l*, pg. 4650
MAINSTREET COMPUTERS, INC.—See The Beekman Group, LLC; *U.S. Private*, pg. 3992
MAINSTREET CREDIT UNION; *U.S. Private*, pg. 2554
MAINSTREET EQUITY CORP; *Int'l*, pg. 4651
MAIN STREET FINANCIAL SERVICES CORP.; *U.S. Public*, pg. 1355
MAIN STREET HUB INC.—See KKR & Co. Inc.; *U.S. Public*, pg. 1252
MAIN STREET HUB INC.—See Silver Lake Group, LLC; *U.S. Private*, pg. 3657
MAIN STREET HUB INC.—See TCMI, Inc.; *U.S. Private*, pg. 3943
MAIN STREET INGREDIENTS LLC; *U.S. Private*, pg. 2551
MAINSTREET INVESTMENT ADVISORS, LLC—See Fifth Third Bancorp; *U.S. Public*, pg. 834
MAINSTREET INVESTMENT COMPANY, LLC; *U.S. Private*, pg. 2554
MAIN STREET MARKET SQUARE REDEVELOPMENT AUTHORITY; *U.S. Private*, pg. 2552
MAINSTREET PROPERTY GROUP, LLC—See Mainstreet Investment Company, LLC; *U.S. Private*, pg. 2554
MAINSTREET PROPERTY GROUP; *U.S. Private*, pg. 2554
MAIN STREET REAL ESTATE HOLDINGS, LLC—See Waterstone Financial, Inc.; *U.S. Public*, pg. 2336
MAINTAG SAS—See TXCOM S.A.; *Int'l*, pg. 7993
MAINTAINCO INC.; *U.S. Private*, pg. 2554
MAIN TAPE COMPANY, INC.—See Chargeurs SA; *Int'l*, pg. 1449
MAIN-TAUNUS-ZENTRUM KG—See Deutsche EuroShop AG; *Int'l*, pg. 2065
MAINTECH EUROPE LIMITED—See American CyberSystems, Inc.; *U.S. Private*, pg. 230
MAINTECH, INCORPORATED—See Oak Lane Partners, LLC; *U.S. Private*, pg. 2983
MAINTEL EUROPE LIMITED—See Maintel Holdings Plc; *Int'l*, pg. 4652
MAINTEL HOLDINGS PLC; *Int'l*, pg. 4652
MAINTEL SUD-EST SAS—See VINCI S.A.; *Int'l*, pg. 8223
MAINTEL VOICE AND DATA LIMITED—See Maintel Holdings Plc; *Int'l*, pg. 4652
MAINTENANCE DESIGN GROUP LLC—See HDR, Inc.; *U.S. Private*, pg. 1890
MAINTENANCE ENGINEERING; *U.S. Private*, pg. 2554
MAINTENANCE ENTERPRISES LLC—See Bernhard Capital Partners Management, LP; *U.S. Private*, pg. 537
MAINTENANCE ENTERPRISES LLC—See KBR, Inc.; *U.S. Public*, pg. 1216
MAINTENANCENET, INC.—See Cisco Systems, Inc.; *U.S. Public*, pg. 499
MAINTENANCE PARTNERS, NV—See Mitsubishi Heavy Industries, Ltd.; *Int'l*, pg. 4955
MAINTENANCE SOLUTIONS INC.; *U.S. Private*, pg. 2554
MAINTENANCE SUPPLY COMPANY INC.; *U.S. Private*, pg. 2554
MAINTENANCE SUPPLY HEADQUARTERS, LP—See Lowe's Companies, Inc.; *U.S. Public*, pg. 1343
MAINTENANCE & TRAVAUX SPECIAUX—See VINCI S.A.; *Int'l*, pg. 8233
MAINTEQ EUROPE B.V.—See Qisda Corporation; *Int'l*, pg. 6146
MAINTHIA TECHNOLOGIES, INC.; *U.S. Private*, pg. 2554
MAINTPARTNER ASI SP. Z O.O.—See Triton Advisers Limited; *Int'l*, pg. 7935
MAINTPARTNER GROUP OY—See Triton Advisers Limited; *Int'l*, pg. 7935
MAIN & VINE LLC—See The Kroger Co.; *U.S. Public*, pg. 2108

MAIN WATERLINE LLP—See KazTransOil JSC; *Int'l*, pg. 4103
MAINZ BIOMED N.V.; *Int'l*, pg. 4652
MAIOR DOMUS HAUSVERWALTUNGS GMBH—See S IMMO AG; *Int'l*, pg. 6442
MAIQUER GROUP CO., LTD.; *Int'l*, pg. 4652
MAIRA S.P.A.—See Iren S.p.A.; *Int'l*, pg. 3808
MAIRE TECNIMONT S.P.A.; *Int'l*, pg. 4652
MAISEN CO., LTD.—See Kameda Seika Co., Ltd.; *Int'l*, pg. 4061
MAISHA HEALTH FUND (PRIVATE) LIMITED—See Eco-Cash Holdings Zimbabwe Limited; *Int'l*, pg. 2295
MAIS INTERIOR DESIGN LLC—See Alpha Dhabi Holding PJSC; *Int'l*, pg. 367
MAIS MOTORLU ARACLAR IMAL VE SATIS A.S.—See OYAK Cement Group; *Int'l*, pg. 5677
MAISON ANTOINE BAUD SA; *Int'l*, pg. 4652
MAISON BLEUE; *Int'l*, pg. 4652
MAISON CHARLOIS SAS; *Int'l*, pg. 4652
MAISON CLIO BLUE SA; *Int'l*, pg. 4652
MAISON DAUPHINE SAVOIE; *Int'l*, pg. 4652
MAISON DE SAVOIE SAS—See Coop-Gruppe Genossenschaft; *Int'l*, pg. 1790
MAISON DE XX AOUT SA—See Clariane SE; *Int'l*, pg. 1643
MAISON DU CAFE COFFEE SYSTEMS FRANCE SNC—See JAB Holding Company S.a.r.l.; *Int'l*, pg. 3863
MAISON F E TRIMBACH SA; *Int'l*, pg. 4652
MAISON INSURANCE COMPANY—See FedNat Holding Company; *U.S. Public*, pg. 829
MAISON JOHANES BOUBEE SAS—See Carrefour SA; *Int'l*, pg. 1345
MAISON LAZARD S.A.S—See Lazard Ltd.; *Int'l*, pg. 4428
MAISON MOREAU JAPAN CO., LTD.—See Onward Holdings Co., Ltd.; *Int'l*, pg. 5592
MAISONS AQUITAINES SARL; *Int'l*, pg. 4652
MAISONS AXIAL; *Int'l*, pg. 4653
MAISONS COUDRELLE; *Int'l*, pg. 4653
MAISONS DELMAS; *Int'l*, pg. 4653
MAISONS D'EN FRANCE; *Int'l*, pg. 4653
MAISONS DE THE MARIAGE FRERES; *Int'l*, pg. 4653
MAISONS & DOMAINES HENRIOT FRANCE SASU; *Int'l*, pg. 4652
MAISONS DOMINIQUE CHARLES; *Int'l*, pg. 4653
MAISONS DU MARAIS; *Int'l*, pg. 4653
MAISONS DU MONDE SA; *Int'l*, pg. 4653
MAISONS ECUREUIL; *Int'l*, pg. 4653
MAISONS FRANCE CONFORT SA; *Int'l*, pg. 4653
MAISONS LELIEVRE; *Int'l*, pg. 4653
MAISONS LES NATURELLES; *Int'l*, pg. 4653
MAISON SOLUTIONS INC.; *U.S. Public*, pg. 1355
MAISONS PARTOUT; *Int'l*, pg. 4653
MAISON TEXIER SAS—See Renaissance Industries SAS; *Int'l*, pg. 6272
MAISTO INTERNATIONAL, INC.; *U.S. Private*, pg. 2554
MAISTRA D.D.—See Adris Grupa d.d.; *Int'l*, pg. 153
MAISTRO PLC; *Int'l*, pg. 4653
MAITA ENTERPRISES INC.; *U.S. Private*, pg. 2554
MAITA'S NISSAN OF SACRAMENTO; *U.S. Private*, pg. 2554
MAITHAN ALLOYS LTD—See Bhagwati Syndicate Pvt. Ltd.; *Int'l*, pg. 1010
MAITLAND LUXURY IMPORTS, INC.—See AutoNation, Inc.; *U.S. Public*, pg. 236
MAITLAND PRIMROSE GROUP; *U.S. Private*, pg. 2554
MAITLAND-SMITH CEBU, INC.—See Heritage Home Group, LLC; *U.S. Private*, pg. 1924
MAITLAND-SMITH FURNITURE INDUSTRIES, INC.—See Heritage Home Group, LLC; *U.S. Private*, pg. 1924
MAITONG SUNSHINE CULTURAL DEVELOPMENT CO., LIMITED; *Int'l*, pg. 4653
MAITRI ENTERPRISES LTD.; *Int'l*, pg. 4653
MAIWEAVE LLC—See Clearlake Capital Group, L.P.; *U.S. Private*, pg. 935
MAIZE PRODUCTS LIMITED—See Sayaji Industries Limited; *Int'l*, pg. 6603
MAIZORO S.A. DE C.V.—See PepsiCo, Inc.; *U.S. Public*, pg. 1670
MAIZURU KOUSOKU YUSOU CO., LTD.—See Kawasaki Kisen Kaisha, Ltd.; *Int'l*, pg. 4100
MAJA-MASCHINENFABRIK HERMANN SCHILL GMBH—See Marel hf; *Int'l*, pg. 4690
MAJAN COLLEGE (UNIVERSITY COLLEGE) SAOG; *Int'l*, pg. 4653
MAJAN GLASS COMPANY SAOG; *Int'l*, pg. 4654
MAJANI INSURANCE BROKERS LTD.—See Kenya Tea Development Agency Limited; *Int'l*, pg. 4129
MAJAN SHIPPING & TRANSPORT CO. LLC—See Muscat Overseas Co., L.L.C.; *Int'l*, pg. 5102
MAJA-WERK MANFRED JAROSCH GMBH & CO. KG—See Vivonio Furniture GmbH; *Int'l*, pg. 8280
MAJD FOOD COMPANY-K.S.C.—See Al Imtiaz Investment Group Company- K.S.C.; *Int'l*, pg. 279
MAJEDIE INVESTMENTS PLC; *Int'l*, pg. 4654
MAJEK FIRE PROTECTION INC.; *U.S. Private*, pg. 2554
MAJENCIA S.A.; *Int'l*, pg. 4654
MAJESCOMASTEK CANADA LTD—See Mastek Ltd.; *Int'l*, pg. 4724

MAJESCOMASTEK SOFTWARE, INC.—See Mastek Ltd.; *Int'l*, pg. 4724
MAJESCO—See Thoma Bravo, L.P.; *U.S. Private*, pg. 4149
MAJESTIC ATHLETIC LTD.—See V. F. Corporation; *U.S. Public*, pg. 2269
MAJESTIC AUTO LTD.—See Hero Corp.; *Int'l*, pg. 3363
MAJESTIC CONSTRUCTION LLC; *U.S. Private*, pg. 2554
MAJESTIC ENERGY (SINGAPORE) PTE. LTD.—See CBL International Limited; *Int'l*, pg. 1366
MAJESTIC ENGINEERING COMPANY LIMITED—See FSE Services Group Limited; *Int'l*, pg. 2798
MAJESTIC ENGINEERING (MACAO) COMPANY LIMITED—See FSE Services Group Limited; *Int'l*, pg. 2798
MAJESTIC ENGRAVING CORP.—See Schwaab Inc.; *U.S. Private*, pg. 3572
MAJESTIC GOLD CORP.; *Int'l*, pg. 4654
MAJESTIC HORIZON HOLDINGS LTD; *Int'l*, pg. 4654
MAJESTIC INDUSTRIES INC.—See GenNx360 Capital Partners, L.P.; *U.S. Private*, pg. 1672
MAJESTIC LIQUOR STORES INC.; *U.S. Private*, pg. 2554
MAJESTIC MARBLE AND GLASS CO.; *U.S. Private*, pg. 2554
MAJESTIC METALS, INC.—See CORE Industrial Partners, LLC; *U.S. Private*, pg. 1048
MAJESTIC MOTORS INC.; *U.S. Private*, pg. 2554
MAJESTIC OIL CO. INC.; *U.S. Private*, pg. 2554
MAJESTIC PRODUCTS B.V.—See Bunzl plc; *Int'l*, pg. 1219
MAJESTIC PROPERTIES, LLC—See Japan Tobacco Inc.; *Int'l*, pg. 3907
MAJESTIC RESEARCH SERVICES & SOLUTIONS LTD; *Int'l*, pg. 4654
MAJESTIC STAR CASINO & HOTEL; *U.S. Private*, pg. 2554
THE MAJESTIC STAR CASINO II, INC.—See Majestic Star Casino & Hotel; *U.S. Private*, pg. 2554
MAJESTIC STEEL SERVICE, INC.; *U.S. Private*, pg. 2554
MAJESTIC STONE, INC.—See Horizon Stone LLC; *U.S. Private*, pg. 1982
MAJESTIC TRANSPORTATION; *U.S. Private*, pg. 2554
MAJESTIC UNDERWRITERS LLC—See Geneve Holdings Corp.; *U.S. Private*, pg. 1671
MAJESTIC WINE & SPIRITS USA, INC.—See Allied Beverage Group L.L.C.; *U.S. Private*, pg. 185
MAJESTIC WOODS, LLC—See Lennar Corporation; *U.S. Public*, pg. 1306
MAJESTY GOLF & CO., LTD.—See Smart Score Co., Ltd.; *Int'l*, pg. 7001
MAJESTY GOLF KOREA CO., LTD.—See Smart Score Co., Ltd.; *Int'l*, pg. 7001
MAJEVICA A.D.; *Int'l*, pg. 4654
MAJEVICA HOLDING A.D.; *Int'l*, pg. 4654
MAJIC WHEELS, INC.; *U.S. Private*, pg. 2555
MAJILITE CORPORATION—See Meridian Industries, Inc.; *U.S. Private*, pg. 2673
MAJ INVEST EQUITY A/S—See Maj Invest Holding A/S; *Int'l*, pg. 4653
MAJ INVEST HOLDING A/S; *Int'l*, pg. 4653
MAJIQ INC.—See Constellation Software Inc.; *Int'l*, pg. 1772
MAJOR AFFILIATES INC.; *U.S. Private*, pg. 2555
THE MAJOR AUTOMOTIVE COMPANIES, INC.; *U.S. Private*, pg. 4074
MAJOR BRANDS, INC.; *U.S. Private*, pg. 2555
MAJOR BUSINESS SYSTEMS, INC.—See Ennis, Inc.; *U.S. Public*, pg. 769
MAJOR CASH & CARRY INC.—See Ko-Amex General Wholesale Inc.; *U.S. Private*, pg. 2325
MAJOR CINEPLEX GROUP PLC; *Int'l*, pg. 4654
MAJOR CLEAN, INC.—See Warburg Pincus LLC; *U.S. Private*, pg. 4440
MAJOR COMMERCIAL CLEANING INC.—See O2 Investment Partners, LLC; *U.S. Private*, pg. 2982
MAJOR CUSTOM CABLE INC.—See VTG Corp.; *U.S. Private*, pg. 4415
MAJOR DEVELOPMENT PUBLIC COMPANY LIMITED; *Int'l*, pg. 4654
MAJOR DRILLING AMERICA, INC.—See Major Drilling Group International Inc.; *Int'l*, pg. 4654
MAJOR DRILLING CHILE S.A.—See Major Drilling Group International Inc.; *Int'l*, pg. 4654
MAJOR DRILLING DE MEXICO, S.A. DE C.V.—See Major Drilling Group International Inc.; *Int'l*, pg. 4654
MAJOR DRILLING ENVIRONMENTAL, LLC—See Major Drilling Group International Inc.; *Int'l*, pg. 4654
MAJOR DRILLING GROUP AUSTRALASIA PTY LTD—See Major Drilling Group International Inc.; *Int'l*, pg. 4654
MAJOR DRILLING GROUP INTERNATIONAL INC.; *Int'l*, pg. 4654
MAJOR DRILLING INTERNATIONAL INC.—See Major Drilling Group International Inc.; *Int'l*, pg. 4654
MAJOR DRILLING NAMIBIA (PTY) LIMITED—See Major Drilling Group International Inc.; *Int'l*, pg. 4654
MAJOR DRILLING PTY LTD—See Major Drilling Group International Inc.; *Int'l*, pg. 4654

COMPANY NAME INDEX

MAJOR DRILLING SOUTH AFRICA (PTY) LIMITED—See Major Drilling Group International Inc.; *Int'l*, pg. 4654
MAJOR DRILLING TANZANIA LIMITED—See Major Drilling Group International Inc.; *Int'l*, pg. 4654
MAJOREL BERLIN GMBH—See Bertelsmann SE & Co. KGaA; *Int'l*, pg. 993
MAJOREL BRANDENBURG GMBH—See Majorel Group Luxembourg S.A.; *Int'l*, pg. 4655
MAJOREL DORTMUND GMBH—See Bertelsmann SE & Co. KGaA; *Int'l*, pg. 993
MAJOREL GROUP LUXEMBOURG S.A.; *Int'l*, pg. 4655
MAJOREL MUNSTER GMBH—See Majorel Group Luxembourg S.A.; *Int'l*, pg. 4655
MAJOREL NEUBRANDENBURG GMBH—See Bertelsmann SE & Co. KGaA; *Int'l*, pg. 993
MAJOREL NORDHORN GMBH—See Majorel Group Luxembourg S.A.; *Int'l*, pg. 4655
MAJOREL ROSTOCK I GMBH—See Bertelsmann SE & Co. KGaA; *Int'l*, pg. 993
MAJOR HOLDINGS LIMITED; *Int'l*, pg. 4655
MAJORICA JEWELRY, LTD.—See Majorica, S.A.; *Int'l*, pg. 4655
MAJORICA, S.A.; *Int'l*, pg. 4655
MAJOR INTERNATIONAL LTD.—See Givaudan S.A.; *Int'l*, pg. 2981
MAJOR LEAGUE BASEBALL PROPERTIES, INC.—See Major League Baseball; *U.S. Private*, pg. 2555
MAJOR LEAGUE BASEBALL; *U.S. Private*, pg. 2555
MAJOR LEAGUE FOOTBALL, INC.; *U.S. Public*, pg. 1355
MAJOR LEAGUE SOCCER LLC; *U.S. Private*, pg. 2555
MAJOR, LINDSEY & AFRICA, LLC—See Allegis Group, Inc.; *U.S. Private*, pg. 177
MAJOR MARKET, INC.; *U.S. Private*, pg. 2555
MAJOR MEDICAL SUPPLY OF COLORADO SPRINGS, LLC—See AdaptHealth Corp.; *U.S. Public*, pg. 39
MAJOR MEDICAL SUPPLY OF DENVER, LLC—See AdaptHealth Corp.; *U.S. Public*, pg. 39
MAJOR MEDICAL SUPPLY OF FORT COLLINS, LLC—See AdaptHealth Corp.; *U.S. Public*, pg. 39
MAJOR PERFORACIONES S.A.—See Major Drilling Group International Inc.; *Int'l*, pg. 4654
MAJOR PETROLEUM INDUSTRIES INC.; *U.S. Private*, pg. 2555
MAJOR PLAYERS LTD—See Randstad N.V.; *Int'l*, pg. 6202
MAJORPOWER CORPORATION; *U.S. Private*, pg. 2555
MAJORS MANAGEMENT, LLC; *U.S. Private*, pg. 2555
MAJORS PLASTICS INC.; *U.S. Private*, pg. 2555
MAJOR SPV ONE COMPANY LIMITED—See Major Development Public Company Limited; *Int'l*, pg. 4654
MAJORS SCIENTIFIC BOOKS, INC.; *U.S. Private*, pg. 2555
MAJOR SUPPLY INC.; *U.S. Private*, pg. 2555
MAJOR TEAM HOLDINGS BERHAD; *Int'l*, pg. 4655
MAJOR TOOL & MACHINE, INC.; *U.S. Private*, pg. 2555
MAJOR VENOUS JAPAN CO., LTD.—See Rever Holdings Corporation; *Int'l*, pg. 6313
MAJUBA HILL COPPER CORP.; *Int'l*, pg. 4655
MAJULAH INVESTMENT, INC.; *U.S. Private*, pg. 2555
MAJULAH KOKO TAWAU SDN. BHD.—See Teck Guan Perdana Berhad; *Int'l*, pg. 7514
MAJUPERAK HOLDINGS BERHAD; *Int'l*, pg. 4655
MAKAAN.COM PRIVATE LIMITED—See News Corporation; *U.S. Public*, pg. 1519
MAKADAMLABOR SCHWABEN GMBH—See VINCI S.A.; *Int'l*, pg. 8223
MAKADAMWERK SCHWABEN GMBH & CO. KG—See VINCI S.A.; *Int'l*, pg. 8224
MAK AD; *Int'l*, pg. 4655
MAKAI CAPITAL PARTNERS LLC; *U.S. Private*, pg. 2556
MAKALOT GROUP USA—See Informa plc; *Int'l*, pg. 3694
MAKALOT INDUSTRIAL CO., LTD. - EASTERN CHINA FACTORY—See Makalot Industrial Co., Ltd.; *Int'l*, pg. 4655
MAKALOT INDUSTRIAL CO., LTD.; *Int'l*, pg. 4655
MAKAMER HOLDINGS, INC.; *U.S. Public*, pg. 1355
MAKAN CHANNEL SDN. BHD.—See Insas Berhad; *Int'l*, pg. 3718
MAKARONY POLSKIE S.A.; *Int'l*, pg. 4655
MAKAR PROPERTIES, LLC; *U.S. Private*, pg. 2556
MAKAT CANDY TECHNOLOGY GMBH—See Robert Bosch GmbH; *Int'l*, pg. 6361
MAKATI FINANCE CORPORATION; *Int'l*, pg. 4655
MAKATI OY—See Axcel Management A/S; *Int'l*, pg. 762
MAKATI SHANGRI-LA HOTEL & RESORT, INC.—See Shangri-La Asia Limited; *Int'l*, pg. 6783
MAK BETEILIGUNGS GMBH—See Caterpillar, Inc.; *U.S. Public*, pg. 453
MAK BULGARIA LTD.—See Mohammed Abdulmohsin Al-Kharafi & Sons WLL; *Int'l*, pg. 5018
MAK CONTRACTING S.A.R.L.—See Mohammed Abdulmohsin Al-Kharafi & Sons WLL; *Int'l*, pg. 5018
MAKE-A-WISH FOUNDATION OF AMERICA; *U.S. Private*, pg. 2556
MAKE-A-WISH FOUNDATION OF GREATER LOS ANGELES; *U.S. Private*, pg. 2556
MAKEBOT ROBOTIC SOLUTIONS PRIVATE LIMITED—See Globalspace Technologies Limited; *Int'l*, pg. 3004
MAKEDONIJATURIST A.D SKOPJE; *Int'l*, pg. 4655
MAKEDONSKI TELEKOM AD; *Int'l*, pg. 4655
MAKEEZI LTD.—See Vassallo Builders Group Limited; *Int'l*, pg. 8134
MAKEFET FINANCIAL SERVICES - INSURANCE AGENCY LTD.—See Assicurazioni Generali S.p.A.; *Int'l*, pg. 647
MAKE IT CHEAPER LIMITED; *Int'l*, pg. 4655
MAKEMEUP PRIVATE LIMITED—See Touchwood Entertainment Ltd.; *Int'l*, pg. 7847
MAKEMUSIC, INC.—See LaunchEquity Partners, LLC; *U.S. Private*, pg. 2398
MAKEMYTRIP.COM INC.—See Trip.com Group Ltd.; *Int'l*, pg. 7926
MAKEMYTRIP (INDIA) PRIVATE LIMITED—See Trip.com Group Ltd.; *Int'l*, pg. 7926
MAKEMYTRIP LIMITED—See Trip.com Group Ltd.; *Int'l*, pg. 7926
MAKER 1 MARINA—See Coastal Marina Management LLC; *U.S. Private*, pg. 956
MAKERBOT INDUSTRIES, LLC—See SHV Holdings N.V.; *Int'l*, pg. 6872
MAKERS LABORATORIES LIMITED; *Int'l*, pg. 4655
MAKER'S MARK DISTILLERY, INC.—See Suntory Holdings Limited; *Int'l*, pg. 7325
MAKERS NUTRITION, LLC; *U.S. Private*, pg. 2556
MAKER TECHNOLOGIES SDN. BHD—See Kobay Technology Bhd.; *Int'l*, pg. 4216
MAKE THE ROAD NEW YORK; *U.S. Private*, pg. 2556
MAKETOWIN HOLDING PUBLIC CO LTD; *Int'l*, pg. 4656
MAKE UP FOR EVER CANADA LTD—See LVMH Moet Hennessy Louis Vuitton SE; *Int'l*, pg. 4596
MAKE UP FOR EVER LLC—See LVMH Moet Hennessy Louis Vuitton SE; *Int'l*, pg. 4596
MAKE UP FOR EVER PARIS—See LVMH Moet Hennessy Louis Vuitton SE; *Int'l*, pg. 4596
MAKE UP TECHNIQUE INTERNATIONAL CO., LTD.—See Saha Pathanapibul Public Company Limited; *Int'l*, pg. 6479
MAKE YOUR OWN DESIGN IN SCANDINAVIA AB—See New Wave Group AB; *Int'l*, pg. 5229
M.A. KHARAFI CONSTRUCTION (PTY) LTD—See Mohammed Abdulmohsin Al-Kharafi & Sons WLL; *Int'l*, pg. 5018
M.A. KHARAFI & SONS CO. (THE GAMBIA) LTD.—See Mohammed Abdulmohsin Al-Kharafi & Sons WLL; *Int'l*, pg. 5018
MAKHEIA GROUP SA; *Int'l*, pg. 4656
MAKIANSIA ENGINEERING (M) SDN. BHD.—See Taikisha Ltd.; *Int'l*, pg. 7413
MAKIBER, S.A.—See ACS, Actividades de Construccion y Servicios, S.A.; *Int'l*, pg. 115
MAKI CORPORATION; *Int'l*, pg. 4656
MAKI HOME CENTER, INC.—See Maki Corporation; *U.S. Private*, pg. 2556
MAKILALA MINING COMPANY, INC.—See Celsius Resources Limited; *Int'l*, pg. 1395
MAKINA TAKIM ENDUSTRISI AS; *Int'l*, pg. 4656
MAKING EVERLASTING MEMORIES, L.L.C.—See Service Corporation International; *U.S. Public*, pg. 1870
MAKING LIFE EASY - MOBILITY AND INDEPENDENT LIVING SUPERSTORES PTY LTD—See Wesfarmers Limited; *Int'l*, pg. 8380
MAKING MEMORIES WHOLESALE INC.—See Advent International Corporation; *U.S. Private*, pg. 103
MAKING SCIENCE GROUP, S.A.; *Int'l*, pg. 4656
MAKING SENSE LLC—See Internet Cowboy Ventures LLC; *U.S. Private*, pg. 2122
MAKIN METALS LTD.—See Varsteel Ltd.; *Int'l*, pg. 8134
MAKINO ASIA PTE LTD—See Makino Milling Machine Co., Ltd.; *Int'l*, pg. 4656
MAKINO CHINA CO., LTD.—See Makino Milling Machine Co., Ltd.; *Int'l*, pg. 4656
MAKINO-CNC ILERI TEKNOLOJI VE PAZARLAMA LIMITED SIRKETI—See Makino Milling Machine Co., Ltd.; *Int'l*, pg. 4656
MAKINO DO BRASIL LTDA.—See Makino Milling Machine Co., Ltd.; *Int'l*, pg. 4656
MAKINO EUROPE GMBH—See Makino Milling Machine Co., Ltd.; *Int'l*, pg. 4656
MAKINO EUROPE GMBH—See Makino Milling Machine Co., Ltd.; *Int'l*, pg. 4656
MAKINO FRANCE S.A.S.—See Makino Milling Machine Co., Ltd.; *Int'l*, pg. 4656
MAKINO GIKEN CO., LTD.—See Makino Milling Machine Co., Ltd.; *Int'l*, pg. 4656
MAKINO GMBH—See Makino Milling Machine Co., Ltd.; *Int'l*, pg. 4656
MAKINO IBERIA SL—See Makino Milling Machine Co., Ltd.; *Int'l*, pg. 4656
MAKINO INC.—See Makino Milling Machine Co., Ltd.; *Int'l*, pg. 4656
MAKINO INDIA PRIVATE LIMITED—See Makino Milling Machine Co., Ltd.; *Int'l*, pg. 4656
MAKINO ITALIA S.R.L.—See Makino Milling Machine Co., Ltd.; *Int'l*, pg. 4656

MAKITA CORPORATION

MAKINO J CO., LTD.—See Makino Milling Machine Co., Ltd.; *Int'l*, pg. 4656
MAKINO KOREA CO., LTD.—See Makino Milling Machine Co., Ltd.; *Int'l*, pg. 4656
MAKINO LOGISTICS CO., LTD.—See Makino Milling Machine Co., Ltd.; *Int'l*, pg. 4656
MAKINO MEXICO S DE R.L. DE C.V.—See Makino Milling Machine Co., Ltd.; *Int'l*, pg. 4656
MAKINO MILLING MACHINE CO., LTD.; *Int'l*, pg. 4656
MAKINO PHILIPPINES INC.—See Makino Milling Machine Co., Ltd.; *Int'l*, pg. 4656
MAKINO RESOURCE DEVELOPMENT PTE LTD.—See Makino Milling Machine Co., Ltd.; *Int'l*, pg. 4656
MAKINO SAS—See Makino Milling Machine Co., Ltd.; *Int'l*, pg. 4656
MAKINOSATO AGRICULTURAL PRODUCERS COOPERATIVE CORPORATION—See Daiei Kankyo Co., Ltd.; *Int'l*, pg. 1924
MAKINO SP. Z.O.O.—See Makino Milling Machine Co., Ltd.; *Int'l*, pg. 4656
MAKINO S.R.O.—See Makino Milling Machine Co., Ltd.; *Int'l*, pg. 4656
MAKINO TECHNICAL SERVICE CO., LTD.—See Makino Milling Machine Co., Ltd.; *Int'l*, pg. 4656
MAKINO THAILAND CO., LTD.—See Makino Milling Machine Co., Ltd.; *Int'l*, pg. 4656
MAKINO USA INC.—See Makino Milling Machine Co., Ltd.; *Int'l*, pg. 4656
MAKINO VIETNAM CO., LTD.—See Makino Milling Machine Co., Ltd.; *Int'l*, pg. 4656
MAKISHIMA FARM CO., LTD.—See Okaya & Co., Ltd.; *Int'l*, pg. 5546
MAKITA (AUSTRALIA) PTY. LTD.—See Makita Corporation; *Int'l*, pg. 4657
MAKITA BENELUX B.V.—See Makita Corporation; *Int'l*, pg. 4657
MAKITA BULGARIA EOOD—See Makita Corporation; *Int'l*, pg. 4657
MAKITA CANADA, INC.—See Makita Corporation; *Int'l*, pg. 4657
MAKITA CHILE COMERCIAL LTDA.—See Makita Corporation; *Int'l*, pg. 4657
MAKITA (CHINA) CO., LTD.—See Makita Corporation; *Int'l*, pg. 4657
MAKITA COLOMBIA, S.A.—See Makita Corporation; *Int'l*, pg. 4657
MAKITA CORPORATION OF AMERICA—See Makita Corporation; *Int'l*, pg. 4658
MAKITA CORPORATION OF TAIWAN—See Makita Corporation; *Int'l*, pg. 4657
MAKITA CORPORATION - OKAZAKI PLANT—See Makita Corporation; *Int'l*, pg. 4657
MAKITA CORPORATION; *Int'l*, pg. 4657
MAKITA DO BRASIL FERRAMENTAS ELETRICAS LTDA.—See Makita Corporation; *Int'l*, pg. 4658
MAKITA D.O.O.—See Makita Corporation; *Int'l*, pg. 4658
MAKITA ELEKTROMOS KISGEPERTEKESITO KFT.—See Makita Corporation; *Int'l*, pg. 4657
MAKITA ELVAERKTOJ DANMARK—See Makita Corporation; *Int'l*, pg. 4657
MAKITA ENGINEERING GERMANY GMBH—See Makita Corporation; *Int'l*, pg. 4657
MAKITA, F.E.S.U. LDA.—See Makita Corporation; *Int'l*, pg. 4658
MAKITA FRANCE S.A.S.—See Makita Corporation; *Int'l*, pg. 4657
MAKITA GULF FZE—See Makita Corporation; *Int'l*, pg. 4657
MAKITA HELLAS S.A.—See Makita Corporation; *Int'l*, pg. 4657
MAKITA HERRAMIENTAS ELECTRICAS DE ARGENTINA S.A.—See Makita Corporation; *Int'l*, pg. 4657
MAKITA INTERNATIONAL EUROPE LTD.—See Makita Corporation; *Int'l*, pg. 4657
MAKITA KAZAKHSTAN LLP—See Makita Corporation; *Int'l*, pg. 4657
MAKITA KOREA CO., LTD.—See Makita Corporation; *Int'l*, pg. 4657
MAKITA (KUNSHAN) CO., LTD.—See Makita Corporation; *Int'l*, pg. 4657
MAKITA LATIN AMERICA INC.—See Makita Corporation; *Int'l*, pg. 4657
MAKITA LLC—See Makita Corporation; *Int'l*, pg. 4657
MAKITA MANUFACTURING EUROPE LTD.—See Makita Corporation; *Int'l*, pg. 4657
MAKITA MANUFACTURING (THAILAND) CO., LTD.—See Makita Corporation; *Int'l*, pg. 4657
MAKITA MEXICO, S.A. DE C.V.—See Makita Corporation; *Int'l*, pg. 4657
MAKITA NEDERLAND B.V.—See Makita Corporation; *Int'l*, pg. 4657
MAKITA (NEW ZEALAND) LTD.—See Makita Corporation; *Int'l*, pg. 4657
MAKITA NORWAY—See Makita Corporation; *Int'l*, pg. 4657
MAKITA NUMAZU CORPORATION—See Makita Corporation; *Int'l*, pg. 4657
MAKITA OY—See Makita Corporation; *Int'l*, pg. 4657
MAKITA PERU S.A.—See Makita Corporation; *Int'l*, pg. 4657

1667

MAKITA CORPORATION

MAKITA POWER TOOLS (H.K.) LTD.—See Makita Corporation; *Int'l*, pg. 4657
MAKITA POWER TOOLS INDIA PRIVATE LTD.—See Makita Corporation; *Int'l*, pg. 4657
MAKITA POWER TOOLS (MALAYSIA) SDN. BHD.—See Makita Corporation; *Int'l*, pg. 4657
MAKITA ROMANIA S.R.L.—See Makita Corporation; *Int'l*, pg. 4657
MAKITA SA—See Makita Corporation; *Int'l*, pg. 4657
MAKITA, S.A.—See Makita Corporation; *Int'l*, pg. 4658
MAKITA SINGAPORE PTE. LTD.—See Makita Corporation; *Int'l*, pg. 4658
MAKITA S.P.A.—See Makita Corporation; *Int'l*, pg. 4657
MAKITA, SPOL. S R.O.—See Makita Corporation; *Int'l*, pg. 4658
MAKITA SP. Z.O.O.—See Makita Corporation; *Int'l*, pg. 4658
MAKITA S.R.O.—See Makita Corporation; *Int'l*, pg. 4658
MAKITA SWEDEN—See Makita Corporation; *Int'l*, pg. 4658
MAKITA (TAIWAN) LTD.—See Makita Corporation; *Int'l*, pg. 4657
MAKITA (U.K.) LTD.—See Makita Corporation; *Int'l*, pg. 4657
MAKITA UKRAINE LLC—See Makita Corporation; *Int'l*, pg. 4658
MAKITA U.S.A., INC.—See Makita Corporation; *Int'l*, pg. 4658
MAKITA VIETNAM CO., LTD.—See Makita Corporation; *Int'l*, pg. 4658
MAKITA WERKZEUG GMBH—See Makita Corporation; *Int'l*, pg. 4658
MAKITA WERKZEUG GMBH—See Makita Corporation; *Int'l*, pg. 4658
MAKIVIK CORPORATION; *Int'l*, pg. 4658
MAKIYA CO., LTD.; *Int'l*, pg. 4658
MAKKAH CONSTRUCTION & DEVELOPMENT COMPANY; *Int'l*, pg. 4658
MAKKAH MADINAH HOLDINGS LTD; *Int'l*, pg. 4658
MAKKE LLC; *U.S. Private*, pg. 2556
MAKLOC BUILDINGS INC.; *Int'l*, pg. 4658
MAK MEDIA INC.; *U.S. Private*, pg. 2555
MA KNOWLEDGE SERVICES RESEARCH (INDIA) PRIVATE LIMITED—See Moody's Corporation; *U.S. Public*, pg. 1468
MAKO ELEKTRIK SANAYI VE TICARET A.S.—See Stellantis N.V.; *Int'l*, pg. 7200
MAKO GOLD LIMITED; *Int'l*, pg. 4658
THE MAKO GROUP, LLC—See Centric Consulting, LLC; *U.S. Private*, pg. 829
MAKO HYDROCARBONS LIMITED; *Int'l*, pg. 4658
MAKOLAB SA; *Int'l*, pg. 4658
MAKOLIN ELECTRONICS SDN. BHD.—See Tatung Company; *Int'l*, pg. 7475
MAKOMBOKI TEA FACTORY COMPANY LIMITED—See Kenya Tea Development Agency Limited; *Int'l*, pg. 4129
MAKO MEDICAL LABORATORIES, LLC; *U.S. Private*, pg. 2556
MAKO MINING CORP.; *Int'l*, pg. 4658
MAKONJWAAN IMPERIAL MINING COMPANY (PTY). LTD—See Vantage Goldfields Limited; *Int'l*, pg. 8130
MAKO SURGICAL CORP.—See Stryker Corporation; *U.S. Public*, pg. 1955
MAKOTEX A.D.; *Int'l*, pg. 4658
MAKOTO CONSTRUCTION CO., LTD.; *Int'l*, pg. 4658
MAKOTO-FUCHS K.K.—See FUCHS SE; *Int'l*, pg. 2804
MAKOVICH & PUSTI ARCHITECTS INC.—See CPL Architects, Engineers & Landscape Architect D.P.C.; *U.S. Private*, pg. 1080
MAKOVSKY & COMPANY, INC.; *U.S. Private*, pg. 2556
MAKOWSKY RINGEL GREENBERG, LLC.; *U.S. Private*, pg. 2556
MAKPETROL A.D.; *Int'l*, pg. 4658
MAKPROMET AD; *Int'l*, pg. 4659
MAKRIS-GPH LTD.—See Nexans S.A.; *Int'l*, pg. 5240
MAKRO ATACADISTA S.A.—See SHV Holdings N.V.; *Int'l*, pg. 6871
MAKRO AUTOSERVICIO MAYORISTA S. A. U.—See Metro AG; *Int'l*, pg. 4859
MAKRO (CAMBODIA) COMPANY LIMITED—See C.P. All Public Company Limited; *Int'l*, pg. 1244
MAKRO CASH & CARRY BELGIUM NV—See Metro AG; *Int'l*, pg. 4857
MAKRO CASH & CARRY CR S.R.O.—See Metro AG; *Int'l*, pg. 4857
MAKRO CASH & CARRY EGYPT LLC—See Metro AG; *Int'l*, pg. 4859
MAKRO CASH & CARRY POLSKA S.A.—See Metro AG; *Int'l*, pg. 4857
MAKRO CASH & CARRY PORTUGAL, S.A.—See Metro AG; *Int'l*, pg. 4857
MAKRO COMERCIALIZADORA S.A.—See SHV Holdings N.V.; *Int'l*, pg. 6871
MAKRO DE COLOMBIA S.A.—See SHV Holdings N.V.; *Int'l*, pg. 6871
MAKRO DISTRIBUCION MAYORISTA, S.A.U.—See Metro AG; *Int'l*, pg. 4859
MAKRO-HABIB PAKISTAN LTD.—See House of Habib; *Int'l*, pg. 3491
MAKRO MOROCCO S.A.—See Metro AG; *Int'l*, pg. 4857
MAKRO N.V.—See SHV Holdings N.V.; *Int'l*, pg. 6871
MAKRO SELF SERVICE WHOLESALERS LTD.—See Tesco PLC; *Int'l*, pg. 7571
MAKRO SOUTH AMERICA—See SHV Holdings N.V.; *Int'l*, pg. 6871
MAKRO TECHNOLGIES, INC.; *U.S. Private*, pg. 2556
MAKS GMBH—See VINCI S.A.; *Int'l*, pg. 8223
MAKSTEEL—See UPG Enterprises LLC; *U.S. Private*, pg. 4311
MAKSTIL A.D.; *Int'l*, pg. 4659
MAKSUN LIMITED—See Xin Point Holdings Limited; *Int'l*, pg. 8529
MAK TECHNOLOGIES INC.—See Temasek Holdings (Private) Limited; *Int'l*, pg. 7552
MAKUAKE, INC.—See CyberAgent, Inc.; *Int'l*, pg. 1892
MA KUANG HEALTHCARE GROUP PTE. LTD.—See Ma Kuang Healthcare Holdings Ltd.; *Int'l*, pg. 4618
MA KUANG HEALTHCARE HOLDINGS LTD.; *Int'l*, pg. 4618
MAKUHARI TECHNO-GARDEN CO., LTD.—See Shimizu Corporation; *Int'l*, pg. 6835
MAKUS, INC.; *Int'l*, pg. 4659
MALABAR RESOURCES LIMITED; *Int'l*, pg. 4659
MA LABORATORIES, INC.; *U.S. Private*, pg. 2530
MALACCA BRANTAS FINANCE, B.V.—See PT Energi Mega Persada Tbk; *Int'l*, pg. 6038
MALACCA STRAITS ACQUISITION COMPANY LIMITED; *Int'l*, pg. 4659
MALACCA TRUST WUWUNGAN INSURANCE PT; *Int'l*, pg. 4659
MALACO K/S—See Cloetta AB; *Int'l*, pg. 1661
MALAGA BANK FSB—See Malaga Financial Corp.; *U.S. Public*, pg. 1355
MALAGA FINANCIAL CORP.; *U.S. Public*, pg. 1355
MALAGASY COMMUNITY NETWORK SERVICES SA—See SGS SA; *Int'l*, pg. 6743
MALAKOFF CORPORATION BERHAD—See MMC Corporation Berhad; *Int'l*, pg. 5005
MALAM PAYROLL LTD.—See Malam-Team Ltd.; *Int'l*, pg. 4659
MALAM PROVIDENT FUND OPERATION LTD.—See Malam-Team Ltd.; *Int'l*, pg. 4659
MALAM SYSTEMS LTD.; *Int'l*, pg. 4659
MALAM-TEAM LTD.; *Int'l*, pg. 4659
MALANDA DAIRYFOODS PTY. LIMITED—See Bega Cheese Ltd.; *Int'l*, pg. 940
MALANI PADAYACHEE & ASSOCIATES (PTY) LTD.; *Int'l*, pg. 4659
MALANPUR CAPTIVE POWER LIMITED—See Avantha Group; *Int'l*, pg. 735
MALAPUR CAPTIVE POWER LTD—See Avantha Group; *Int'l*, pg. 736
MALARIA RESEARCH COMPANY PTY LTD—See Arovella Therapeutics Limited; *Int'l*, pg. 578
MALARKEY ROOFING PRODUCTS; *U.S. Private*, pg. 2556
MALATH COOPERATIVE INSURANCE COMPANY; *Int'l*, pg. 4659
MALAWI STOCK EXCHANGE; *Int'l*, pg. 4659
MALAYAN ADHESIVE & CHEMICALS SDN BHD—See Kuok Brothers Sdn. Bhd.; *Int'l*, pg. 4335
MALAYAN BANKING BERHAD; *Int'l*, pg. 4659
MALAYAN CEMENT BERHAD—See YTL Corporation Berhad; *Int'l*, pg. 8606
MALAYAN DACHING CO. PTE. LTD.; *Int'l*, pg. 4661
MALAYAN FLOUR MILLS BERHAD; *Int'l*, pg. 4661
MALAYAN INSURANCE COMPANY, INC.—See Yuchengco Group of Companies; *Int'l*, pg. 8609
MALAYAN SUGAR MANUFACTURING COMPANY BERHAD—See FGV Holdings Bhd; *Int'l*, pg. 2649
MALAYAN UNITED INDUSTRIES BERHAD; *Int'l*, pg. 4661
MALAYAN UNITED SECURITY SERVICES SDN BHD—See Malayan United Industries Berhad; *Int'l*, pg. 4661
THE MALAYA PRESS SDN. BHD.—See Sasbadi Holdings Berhad; *Int'l*, pg. 6582
MALAYSIA AIRLINES CARGO SDN. BHD.—See Khazanah Nasional Berhad; *Int'l*, pg. 4153
MALAYSIA AIRPORTS CONSULTANCY SERVICES SDN. BHD.—See Malaysia Airports Holdings Berhad; *Int'l*, pg. 4661
MALAYSIA AIRPORTS HOLDINGS BERHAD; *Int'l*, pg. 4661
MALAYSIA AIRPORTS (NIAGA) SDN. BHD.—See Malaysia Airports Holdings Berhad; *Int'l*, pg. 4661
MALAYSIA AIRPORTS (PROPERTIES) SDN. BHD.—See Malaysia Airports Holdings Berhad; *Int'l*, pg. 4661
MALAYSIA AIRPORTS (SEPANG) SDN. BHD.—See Malaysia Airports Holdings Berhad; *Int'l*, pg. 4661
MALAYSIA AIRPORTS TECHNOLOGIES SDN. BHD.—See Malaysia Airports Holdings Berhad; *Int'l*, pg. 4661
MALAYSIA BUILDING SOCIETY BERHAD; *Int'l*, pg. 4661
MALAYSIA DERIVATIVES EXCHANGE BERHAD—See Bursa Malaysia Berhad; *Int'l*, pg. 1227
MALAYSIAHOSOKAWA MICRON MALAYSIA SDN. BHD.—See Hosokawa Micron Corporation; *Int'l*, pg. 3486

CORPORATE AFFILIATIONS

MALAYSIA INTERNATIONAL AEROSPACE CENTRE SDN. BHD.—See Malaysia Airports Holdings Berhad; *Int'l*, pg. 4661
MALAYSIA LNG DUA SDN. BHD.—See Petroliam Nasional Berhad; *Int'l*, pg. 5830
MALAYSIA LNG SDN. BHD.—See Petroliam Nasional Berhad; *Int'l*, pg. 5830
MALAYSIA LNG TIGA SDN. BHD.—See Petroliam Nasional Berhad; *Int'l*, pg. 5830
MALAYSIA MARINE AND HEAVY ENGINEERING HOLDINGS BERHAD; *Int'l*, pg. 4662
MALAYSIA MARINE & HEAVY ENGINEERING SDN BHD—See Malaysia Marine and Heavy Engineering Holdings Berhad; *Int'l*, pg. 4662
MALAYSIAN AE MODELS HOLDINGS BERHAD; *Int'l*, pg. 4662
MALAYSIAN AGRIFOOD CORPORATION BERHAD—See Khazanah Nasional Berhad; *Int'l*, pg. 4152
MALAYSIAN AIRLINES BERHAD—See Khazanah Nasional Berhad; *Int'l*, pg. 4153
MALAYSIAN AUTOMOTIVE LIGHTING SDN. BHD.—See Stellantis N.V.; *Int'l*, pg. 7196
MALAYSIAN BULK CARRIERS BERHAD; *Int'l*, pg. 4662
MALAYSIAN CENTRAL DEPOSITORY SDN BHD—See Bursa Malaysia Berhad; *Int'l*, pg. 1227
MALAYSIAN ELECTRONICS MATERIALS SDN. BHD—See Sumitomo Metal Mining Co., Ltd.; *Int'l*, pg. 7291
MALAYSIAN ENERGY CHEMICAL & SERVICES SDN. BHD.—See Uzma Berhad; *Int'l*, pg. 8104
MALAYSIAN GENOMICS RESOURCE CENTRE BERHAD; *Int'l*, pg. 4662
MALAYSIAN HOYA LENS SDN. BHD.—See Hoya Corporation; *Int'l*, pg. 3496
MALAYSIAN INDUSTRIAL DEVELOPMENT FINANCE BERHAD—See Malaysia Building Society Berhad; *Int'l*, pg. 4662
MALAYSIAN INTERNATIONAL TRADING CORPORATION SDN. BHD.—See Petroliam Nasional Berhad; *Int'l*, pg. 5830
MALAYSIA & NIPPON INSURANCE BERHAD—See Koperasi Angkatan Tentera Malaysia Berhad; *Int'l*, pg. 4279
MALAYSIAN ISSUING HOUSE SDN. BHD.—See Ranhill Utilities Berhad; *Int'l*, pg. 6207
MALAYSIAN MEGA GALVANISER SDN. BHD.—See Allgreentech International PLC; *Int'l*, pg. 338
MALAYSIAN MOSAICS SDN BHD—See Hap Seng Consolidated Berhad; *Int'l*, pg. 3268
MALAYSIAN PACIFIC INDUSTRIES BERHAD—See Hong Leong Investment Holdings Pte. Ltd.; *Int'l*, pg. 3468
MALAYSIAN PHOSPHATE ADDITIVES (SARAWAK) SDN. BHD.—See Cahya Mata Sarawak Berhad; *Int'l*, pg. 1251
MALAYSIAN PRECISION MANUFACTURING SDN. BHD.—See Nitto Seiko Co., Ltd.; *Int'l*, pg. 5388
MALAYSIAN PRECLSION MANUFACTURING SDN. BHD.—See Sumitomo Electric Industries, Ltd.; *Int'l*, pg. 7285
MALAYSIAN RE (DUBAI) LTD.—See MNRB Holdings Berhad; *Int'l*, pg. 5006
MALAYSIAN REFINING COMPANY SDN BHD—See Petroliam Nasional Berhad; *Int'l*, pg. 5830
MALAYSIAN REINSURANCE BERHAD—See MNRB Holdings Berhad; *Int'l*, pg. 5006
MALAYSIAN RESOURCES CORPORATION BERHAD; *Int'l*, pg. 4662
MALAYSIAN SH ELECTRONICS SDN. BHD.—See Chang Wah Technology Co., Ltd.; *Int'l*, pg. 1441
MALAYSIAN SHIPPING AGENCIES SDN. BHD.—See DRB-HICOM Berhad; *Int'l*, pg. 2201
MALAYSIAN SH PRECISION SDN. BHD.—See Jih Lin Technology Co., Ltd.; *Int'l*, pg. 3963
MALAYSIAN TECHNOLOGY DEVELOPMENT CORPORATION SDN BHD—See Khazanah Nasional Berhad; *Int'l*, pg. 4153
MALAYSIAN TRUCK & BUS SDN. BHD.—See Isuzu Motors Limited; *Int'l*, pg. 3826
MALAYSIAN VENTURES MANAGEMENT INCORPORATED SDN BHD—See AMMB Holdings Berhad; *Int'l*, pg. 429
MALAYSIA SMELTING CORPORATION BERHAD—See Tecity Group; *Int'l*, pg. 7514
MALAYSIA STEEL WORKS (KL) BHD; *Int'l*, pg. 4662
MALAYSIA TRANSFORMER MANUFACTURING SDN. BHD.—See Tenaga Nasional Berhad; *Int'l*, pg. 7557
MALAY-SINO CHEMICAL INDUSTRIES SDN. BHD.—KEMAMAN PLANT—See Batu Kawan Berhad; *Int'l*, pg. 891
MALAY-SINO CHEMICAL INDUSTRIES SDN. BHD.—See Batu Kawan Berhad; *Int'l*, pg. 891
MALBAK LTD.—See Nampak Ltd.; *Int'l*, pg. 5136
MALCO ENTERPRISES NEVADA INC.; *U.S. Private*, pg. 2556
MALCO INTERNATIONAL—See Malco Products, Inc.; *U.S. Private*, pg. 2556
MALCOLM DRILLING COMPANY INC.; *U.S. Private*, pg. 2557
MALCOLM GROUP INC.; *U.S. Private*, pg. 2557

MALCOLM MEATS COMPANY—See Sysco Corporation; *U.S. Public*, pg. 1974
MALCO PRODUCTS, INC.; *U.S. Private*, pg. 2556
MALCO PRODUCTS, INC.; *U.S. Private*, pg. 2556
MALCO PRODUCTS—See Malco Products, Inc.; *U.S. Private*, pg. 2557
MALCO THEATRES INC.; *U.S. Private*, pg. 2557
MALC-THAI CO., LTD.—See Mitsubishi Materials Corporation; *Int'l*, pg. 4963
MALDANER GMBH—See Quaker Chemical Corporation; *U.S. Public*, pg. 1746
MALDEN OBSERVER—See Gannett Co., Inc.; *U.S. Public*, pg. 902
MALDIVES AIRPORT COMPANY LIMITED—See Maldives Transport & Contracting Company Plc; *Int'l*, pg. 4662
MALDIVES TRANSPORT & CONTRACTING COMPANY PLC; *Int'l*, pg. 4662
MALDIVIAN; *Int'l*, pg. 4662
MALECON PHARMACY, INC.—See Omni Health, Inc.; *U.S. Private*, pg. 3016
MALEE ENTERPRISE COMPANY LIMITED.—See Malee Group Public Company Limited; *Int'l*, pg. 4662
MALEE GROUP PUBLIC COMPANY LIMITED; *Int'l*, pg. 4662
MALEK MANAGEMENT CORPORATION; *U.S. Private*, pg. 2557
MALEK SPINNING MILLS LIMITED; *Int'l*, pg. 4662
MALEMA ENGINEERING CORP.—See Dover Corporation; *U.S. Public*, pg. 682
MAL ENTERPRISES, INC.; *U.S. Private*, pg. 2556
MALESELA TAIHAN ELECTRIC CABLE (PTY) LTD.—See Community Investment Holdings (Pty) Ltd.; *Int'l*, pg. 1721
MALESELA TAIHAN ELECTRIC CABLE (PTY) LTD.—See Taihan Cable & Solution Co., Ltd.; *Int'l*, pg. 7410
MALEV LTD.; *Int'l*, pg. 4663
MALEY & WERTZ, INC.; *U.S. Private*, pg. 2557
M. ALFIERI CO. INC.; *U.S. Private*, pg. 2526
MALGOR & CO. INC.; *U.S. Private*, pg. 2557
MALHER S.A.—See Nestle S.A.; *Int'l*, pg. 5203
MALHEUR LUMBER COMPANY—See Ochoco Lumber Company; *U.S. Private*, pg. 2992
MALIBU ACCEPTANCE CORP.—See The Sterling Group, L.P.; *U.S. Private*, pg. 4122
MALIBU BOATS HOLDINGS, LLC See Malibu Boats, Inc.; *U.S. Public*, pg. 1356
MALIBU BOATS, INC.; *U.S. Public*, pg. 1355
MALIBU BOATS PTY LTD.—See Malibu Boats, Inc.; *U.S. Public*, pg. 1356
MALIBU TEXTILES INC.; *U.S. Private*, pg. 2557
MALIKA FARM LLP—See HORIBA Ltd; *Int'l*, pg. 3477
MALIM JAYA (MELAKA) SDN BHD—See Lion Industries Corporation Berhad; *Int'l*, pg. 4519
MALIN CORPORATION PLC; *Int'l*, pg. 4663
MALIN INTEGRATED HANDLING SOLUTIONS & DESIGN; *U.S. Private*, pg. 2557
MALIN LIFE SCIENCES (US) INC.—See Malin Corporation plc; *Int'l*, pg. 4663
MALINTECH S.A.R.L.—See Komax Holding AG; *Int'l*, pg. 4241
MALINTECH W.P.S.—See Komax Holding AG; *Int'l*, pg. 4241
MALION NEW MATERIALS CO., LTD; *Int'l*, pg. 4663
MALI PROTECTION DES CULTURES (MPC) SA—See Element Solutions Inc.; *U.S. Public*, pg. 728
THE MALISH CORP.; *U.S. Private*, pg. 4074
MALITA INVESTMENTS P.L.C.; *Int'l*, pg. 4663
M. ALJANICH ASSOCIATES INC.; *U.S. Private*, pg. 2526
MALKA MEDIA GROUP LLC—See MoneyLion Inc.; *U.S. Public*, pg. 1464
MALKIN PROPERTIES, L.L.C.; *U.S. Private*, pg. 2557
MALKIN SECURITIES CORP.—See Malkin Properties, L.L.C.; *U.S. Private*, pg. 2557
MALKO ELECTRIC COMPANY; *U.S. Private*, pg. 2557
MALKOWSKI-MARTECH S.A.; *Int'l*, pg. 4663
MALLARD ACQUISITION CORP.; *U.S. Public*, pg. 1356
MALLARD HOLDING COMPANY LLC; *U.S. Private*, pg. 2557
MALLARD MANUFACTURING CORP.—See MacLean-Fogg Co.; *U.S. Private*, pg. 2537
MALLARD OIL COMPANY INC.; *U.S. Private*, pg. 2557
MALLATITE LTD—See Hill & Smith PLC; *Int'l*, pg. 3392
MALL AT JEFFERSON VALLEY, LLC—See Washington Prime Group Inc.; *U.S. Private*, pg. 4448
MALL AT JOHNSON CITY REIT, LLC—See Washington Prime Group Inc.; *U.S. Private*, pg. 4448
MALL AT LONGVIEW, LLC—See Washington Prime Group Inc.; *U.S. Private*, pg. 4448
MALL AT VALLE VISTA, LLC—See Washington Prime Group Inc.; *U.S. Private*, pg. 4448
MALL CHEVROLET; *U.S. Private*, pg. 2557
MALL CHRYSLER-SUZUKI; *U.S. Private*, pg. 2557
MALLCOM INDIA LTD.; *Int'l*, pg. 4663
MALL CRAFT INC.; *U.S. Private*, pg. 2557
MALL DEL NORTE, LLC—See CBL & Associates Properties, Inc.; *U.S. Public*, pg. 458
MALLEE RESOURCES LIMITED; *Int'l*, pg. 4663
MALLET & COMPANY, INC.—See H.I.G. Capital, LLC; *U.S. Private*, pg. 1832

MALLETT INC.—See The Stanley Gibbons Group Plc; *Int'l*, pg. 7688
MALLETT PLC—See The Stanley Gibbons Group Plc; *Int'l*, pg. 7688
MALLETT & SON (ANTIQUES) LIMITED—See The Stanley Gibbons Group Plc; *Int'l*, pg. 7688
MALLINCKRODT BELGIUM BVBA—See Curium SAS; *Int'l*, pg. 1879
MALLINCKRODT CB LLC—See Mallinckrodt Public Limited Company; *Int'l*, pg. 4663
MALLINCKRODT DAR SRL—See Medtronic plc; *Int'l*, pg. 4787
MALLINCKRODT HOSPITAL PRODUCTS INC.—See Mallinckrodt Public Limited Company; *Int'l*, pg. 4663
MALLINCKRODT INC.—See Mallinckrodt Public Limited Company; *Int'l*, pg. 4663
MALLINCKRODT LLC—See Mallinckrodt Public Limited Company; *Int'l*, pg. 4663
MALLINCKRODT MEDICAL B.V.—See Curium SAS; *Int'l*, pg. 1878
MALLINCKRODT PUBLIC LIMITED COMPANY; *Int'l*, pg. 4663
MALLINCKRODT SPECIALTY PHARMACEUTICALS IRELAND LIMITED—See Mallinckrodt Public Limited Company; *Int'l*, pg. 4663
MALLINCKRODT UK LTD—See Mallinckrodt Public Limited Company; *Int'l*, pg. 4663
MALLIOUHANA HOTEL & SPA; *Int'l*, pg. 4663
MALLOF, ABRUZINO & NASH MARKETING; *U.S. Private*, pg. 2557
THE MALL OF CYPRUS (MC) PLC; *Int'l*, pg. 7665
THE MALL OF ENGOMI (ME) PLC; *Int'l*, pg. 7665
MALL OF (MAURITIUS) AT BAGATELLE LTD.—See ENL Limited; *Int'l*, pg. 2441
MALLORY ALEXANDER INTERNATIONAL LOGISTICS, LLC; *U.S. Private*, pg. 2557
MALLORY & EVANS INC.; *U.S. Private*, pg. 2557
MALLORY SAFETY & SUPPLY LLC - SAN BERNARDINO—See Mallory Safety & Supply LLC; *U.S. Private*, pg. 2558
MALLORY SAFETY & SUPPLY LLC; *U.S. Private*, pg. 2557
MALLOUPPAS & PAPACOSTAS PUBLIC CO LTD; *Int'l*, pg. 4663
MALLOY AUTOMOTIVE OF WINCHESTER LLC; *U.S. Private*, pg. 2558
MALLOY INC.; *U.S. Private*, pg. 2558
MALL PLAZA COLOMBIA S.A.S.—See Falabella S.A.; *Int'l*, pg. 2610
MALL PLAZA PERU S.A.—See Falabella S.A.; *Int'l*, pg. 2610
MALL & SC DEVELOPMENT INC.—See Seven & i Holdings Co., Ltd.; *Int'l*, pg. 6731
MALL ST. MATTHEWS—See Brookfield Corporation; *Int'l*, pg. 1185
MALL ST. VINCENT, LLC—See Brookfield Corporation; *Int'l*, pg. 1185
MALMBERG B.V.—See Sanoma Oyj; *Int'l*, pg. 6553
MALMBERG-ELEKTRO OY—See Malmbergs Elektriska AB; *Int'l*, pg. 4663
MALMBERGS ELEKTRISKA AB; *Int'l*, pg. 4663
MALMBERGS ELEKTRISKA A/S—See Malmbergs Elektriska AB; *Int'l*, pg. 4663
MALMBERGS ELEKTRISKE AS—See Malmbergs Elektriska AB; *Int'l*, pg. 4663
MALMBERG TRUCK TRAILER EQUIPMENT LTD.; *Int'l*, pg. 4663
MALMO AVIATION AB—See Braganza AS; *Int'l*, pg. 1136
MALMO BORSHUS AB—See Wihlborgs Fastigheter AB; *Int'l*, pg. 8407
MALMO-LIMHAMNS JARNVAGSAKTIEBOLAG—See Heidelberg Materials AG; *Int'l*, pg. 3318
MALNOVE INCORPORATED OF FLORIDA—See Malnove Incorporated; *U.S. Private*, pg. 2558
MALNOVE INCORPORATED OF NEBRASKA—See Malnove Incorporated; *U.S. Private*, pg. 2558
MALNOVE INCORPORATED OF UTAH—See Malnove Incorporated; *U.S. Private*, pg. 2558
MALNOVE INCORPORATED; *U.S. Private*, pg. 2558
MALNOVE PACKAGING SYSTEMS INC.—See Malnove Incorporated; *U.S. Private*, pg. 2558
MALONE FINKLE ECKHARDT & COLLINS, INC.—See RTM & Associates, Inc.; *U.S. Private*, pg. 3498
MALONE'S FOOD STORES, LLC; *U.S. Private*, pg. 2558
MALONE'S LIMITED—See Lippo Limited; *Int'l*, pg. 4522
MALONE WORKFORCE SOLUTIONS; *U.S. Private*, pg. 2558
MALONEY & BELL GENERAL CONTRACTORS, INC. OF CALIFORNIA; *U.S. Private*, pg. 2558
MALONEY & FOX—See Waggener Edstrom; *U.S. Private*, pg. 4425
MALONEY INVESTMENTS LIMITED—See Barclays PLC; *Int'l*, pg. 862
MALONEY METALCRAFT LTD.—See Avingtrans plc; *Int'l*, pg. 744
MALONEY TECHNICAL PRODUCTS, INC.—See S&B Technical Products, Inc.; *U.S. Private*, pg. 3512
MALONY CO., LTD.—See House Foods Group Inc.; *Int'l*, pg. 3490

MALO S.P.A.—See IT Holding S.p.A.; *Int'l*, pg. 3826
MALOUF BUICK-GMC; *U.S. Private*, pg. 2558
MALOUF CONSTRUCTION CORP.; *U.S. Private*, pg. 2558
MALOYTERMINALEN AS—See Caiano AS; *Int'l*, pg. 1252
MALPAC HOLDINGS BERHAD; *Int'l*, pg. 4663
MAL PAKISTAN LTD.—See Army Welfare Trust LLC; *Int'l*, pg. 576
MALPREH A.D.; *Int'l*, pg. 4663
MALTA AIR LIMITED—See Ryanair Holdings PLC; *Int'l*, pg. 6438
MALTA DIRECT TRAVEL INC.—See SMS Group Limited; *Int'l*, pg. 7014
MALTA INFORMATIQUE SASU—See La Cooperative WELCOOP SA; *Int'l*, pg. 4387
MALTA INTERNATIONAL AIRPORT PLC—See Flughafen Wien Aktiengesellschaft; *Int'l*, pg. 2712
MALTAIS GEOMATICS INC.—See Altus Group Limited; *Int'l*, pg. 399
MALTAPOST GROUP P.L.C.—See Lombard Bank Malta p.l.c.; *Int'l*, pg. 4545
MALTAPOST PLC—See Lombard Bank Malta p.l.c.; *Int'l*, pg. 4545
MALTA PROPERTIES COMPANY PLC; *Int'l*, pg. 4664
MALTBIE, INC.; *U.S. Private*, pg. 2558
MALTBY ELECTRIC SUPPLY COMPANY; *U.S. Private*, pg. 2558
MALTCO LOTTERIES LTD.—See INTRALOT S.A.; *Int'l*, pg. 3768
MALTERIES FRANC-BELGES S.A.—See Etablissements J. Soufflet; *Int'l*, pg. 2519
MALTEUROP AUSTRALIA PTY LTD—See Vivescia; *Int'l*, pg. 8279
MALTEUROP (BAODING) MALTING CO., LTD—See Vivescia; *Int'l*, pg. 8279
MALTEUROP CANADA LTD—See Vivescia; *Int'l*, pg. 8279
MALTEUROP DEUTSCHLAND GMBH—See Vivescia; *Int'l*, pg. 8279
MALTEUROP GROUPE S.A.—See Vivescia; *Int'l*, pg. 8279
MALTEUROP NORTH AMERICA INC.—See Vivescia; *Int'l*, pg. 8279
MALTEUROP POLSKA SPOLKA Z O.O.—See Vivescia; *Int'l*, pg. 8279
MALTHA GLASRECYCLAGE BELGIE B.V.—See Renewi plc; *Int'l*, pg. 6278
MALTHA GLASS RECYCLING PORTUGAL LDA.—See Renewi plc; *Int'l*, pg. 6278
MALTHA GROEP B.V.—See Renewi plc; *Int'l*, pg. 6278
MAL/TOKYO—See Omnicom Group Inc.; *U.S. Public*, pg. 1594
MALTON BERHAD; *Int'l*, pg. 4664
MALTON ELECTRIC CO.; *U.S. Private*, pg. 2558
MALT PRODUCTS CORP. OF N.J.; *U.S. Private*, pg. 2558
MALT REALTY & DEVELOPMENT INC.; *U.S. Private*, pg. 2558
MALU PAPER MILLS LIMITED; *Int'l*, pg. 4664
MALUTSA (PTY) LTD—See Veolia Environnement S.A.; *Int'l*, pg. 8162
MALVAUX INDUSTRIES S.A.; *Int'l*, pg. 4664
MALVERN-AIMIL INSTRUMENTS PVT LIMITED—See Spectris Plc; *Int'l*, pg. 7131
MALVERN BANCORP, INC.—See First Bank; *U.S. Public*, pg. 840
MALVERN BANK, NATIONAL ASSOCIATION—See First Bank; *U.S. Public*, pg. 840
MALVERN DAILY RECORD—See Horizon Publications Inc.; *U.S. Private*, pg. 1982
MALVERN INSTRUMENTS LTD—See Spectris Plc; *Int'l*, pg. 7131
MALVERN INSURANCE ASSOCIATES, LLC—See First Bank; *U.S. Public*, pg. 840
THE MALVERN NATIONAL BANK—See MNB Bancshares, Inc.; *U.S. Private*, pg. 2755
MALVERN PANALYTICAL B.V.—See Spectris Plc; *Int'l*, pg. 7131
MALVERN PANALYTICAL GMBH—See Spectris Plc; *Int'l*, pg. 7131
MALVERN PANALYTICAL INC.—See Spectris Plc; *Int'l*, pg. 7131
MALVERN PANALYTICAL LIMITED—See Spectris Plc; *Int'l*, pg. 7131
MALVERN PANALYTICAL NORDIC AB—See Spectris Plc; *Int'l*, pg. 7131
MALVERN PANALYTICAL (PTY.) LIMITED—See Spectris Plc; *Int'l*, pg. 7131
MALVERN PANALYTICAL S.A.S.—See Spectris Plc; *Int'l*, pg. 7131
MALVERN PANALYTICAL SRL—See Spectris Plc; *Int'l*, pg. 7131
MALVERN TUBULAR COMPONENTS LIMITED—See Tricorn Group plc; *Int'l*, pg. 7920
MALVINA MAJOR RETIREMENT VILLAGE LIMITED—See Ryman Healthcare Ltd.; *Int'l*, pg. 6439
MALWA COTTON SPINNING MILLS LTD.; *Int'l*, pg. 4664
MALWATTE VALLEY PLANTATIONS PLC; *Int'l*, pg. 4664
MALY'S WEST, INC.—See L'Oreal S.A.; *Int'l*, pg. 4380
MAMA & COMPANY LIMITED—See Live Nation Entertainment, Inc.; *U.S. Public*, pg. 1330
MAMAC SYSTEMS (ASIA) PTE LIMITED—See Mamac Systems Inc.; *U.S. Private*, pg. 2558

MALWATTE VALLEY PLANTATIONS PLC — CORPORATE AFFILIATIONS

MAMAC SYSTEMS (CANADA) LIMITED—See Mamac Systems Inc.; *U.S. Private*, pg. 2558
MAMAC SYSTEMS INC.; *U.S. Private*, pg. 2558
MAMAC SYSTEMS PTY LIMITED—See Mamac Systems Inc.; *U.S. Private*, pg. 2559
MAMAC SYSTEMS (UK) LIMITED—See Mamac Systems Inc.; *U.S. Private*, pg. 2559
MAMA DEVECHIO'S PIZZERIA, LLC—See UTG, Inc.; *U.S. Public*, pg. 2267
MAMA FU'S—See Raving Brands, Inc.; *U.S. Private*, pg. 3357
MAMA GROUP PLC—See Lloyds Banking Group plc; *Int'l*, pg. 4537
MAMAIA SA; *Int'l*, pg. 4664
MA MANAGED FUTURES FUND, LP; *U.S. Private*, pg. 2530
MAMAN AVIATION LTD.—See Taavura Holdings, Ltd.; *Int'l*, pg. 7401
MAMAN CARGO & SECURITY LTD.—See Taavura Holdings, Ltd.; *Int'l*, pg. 7401
MAMAN CARGO TERMINALS & HANDLING, LTD.—See Taavura Holdings, Ltd.; *Int'l*, pg. 7401
MAMA'S CREATIONS, INC.; *U.S. Public*, pg. 1356
MAMAX LEBENSVERSICHERUNG AG—See UNIQA Insurance Group AG; *Int'l*, pg. 8058
MAMBA EXPLORATION LIMITED; *Int'l*, pg. 4664
MAMBO-PLAK GMBH—See Bertelsmann SE & Co. KGaA; *Int'l*, pg. 993
MAMCO CORPORATION; *U.S. Private*, pg. 2559
MAMEDA INC—See H2O Retailing Corp.; *Int'l*, pg. 3200
MAMESTA B V—See Aalberts N.V.; *Int'l*, pg. 35
MAMEZOU HOLDINGS CO., LTD.—See Integral Corporation; *Int'l*, pg. 3730
MA MICRO AUTOMATION GMBH—See Hitachi, Ltd.; *Int'l*, pg. 3423
MAMIYA-OP CO., LTD; *Int'l*, pg. 4664
MAMIYE SALES, INC.; *U.S. Private*, pg. 2559
MAMMA ILARDO'S CORP.; *U.S. Private*, pg. 2559
MAMMINA CO., LTD.—See Isetan Mitsukoshi Holdings Ltd.; *Int'l*, pg. 3815
MAMMOET DEUTSCHLAND GMBH—See SHV Holdings N.V.; *Int'l*, pg. 6871
MAMMOET HOLDING B.V.—See SHV Holdings N.V.; *Int'l*, pg. 6871
MAMMOET USA, INC.—See SHV Holdings N.V.; *Int'l*, pg. 6871
MAMMOTH DIALYSIS, LLC—See DaVita Inc.; *U.S. Public*, pg. 641
MAMMOTH ENERGY PARTNERS LP—See Wexford Capital Limited Partnership; *U.S. Private*, pg. 4502
MAMMOTH ENERGY SERVICES, INC.—See Wexford Capital Limited Partnership; *U.S. Private*, pg. 4502
MAMMOTH HOLDINGS, LLC—See Red Dog Equity LLC; *U.S. Private*, pg. 3374
MAMMOTH INVESTMENTS INC.; *U.S. Private*, pg. 2559
MAMMOTH MOUNTAIN SKI AREA, LLC—See KSL Capital Partners, LLC; *U.S. Private*, pg. 2354
MAMMOTH PACIFIC LP—See Ormat Technologies, Inc.; *U.S. Public*, pg. 1618
MAMMOTH PROPERTIES, INC.; *U.S. Private*, pg. 2559
MAMMOTH PROPERTY RESERVATIONS—See Mammoth Properties, Inc.; *U.S. Private*, pg. 2559
MAMMOTH RESORTS LLC—See KSL Capital Partners, LLC; *U.S. Private*, pg. 2354
MAMMOTH RESOURCES CORP.; *Int'l*, pg. 4664
MAMMOTH SCREEN LTD.—See ITV plc; *Int'l*, pg. 3845
MAMMUT SPORTS GROUP AG—See Bystronic AG; *Int'l*, pg. 1236
MAMMUT SPORTS GROUP GMBH—See Bystronic AG; *Int'l*, pg. 1236
MAMMUT SPORTS GROUP INC.—See Bystronic AG; *Int'l*, pg. 1236
MAMMY MART CO., LTD.; *Int'l*, pg. 4664
MAMOLO'S CONTINENTAL & BAILEY BAKERIES INC.; *U.S. Private*, pg. 2559
M.A. MORTENSON COMPANY; *U.S. Private*, pg. 2527
MAMOURA DIVERSIFIED GLOBAL HOLDING PJSC—See Mubadala Investment Company PJSC; *Int'l*, pg. 5075
MAMPAEY INSTALLATIETECHNIEK B.V.—See E.ON SE; *Int'l*, pg. 2258
MAM SOFTWARE GROUP INC, —See KKR & Co. Inc.; *U.S. Public*, pg. 1256
MAM SOFTWARE, INC.—See KKR & Co. Inc.; *U.S. Public*, pg. 1257
MAM SOFTWARE LTD.—See KKR & Co. Inc.; *U.S. Public*, pg. 1256
MAMUN AGRO PRODUCTS LTD.; *Int'l*, pg. 4664
MAMUT AB—See Cinven Limited; *Int'l*, pg. 1616
MAMUT AB—See HgCapital Trust plc; *Int'l*, pg. 3377
MAMUT AB—See KKR & Co. Inc.; *U.S. Public*, pg. 1266
MAMUT APS—See Cinven Limited; *Int'l*, pg. 1616
MAMUT APS—See HgCapital Trust plc; *Int'l*, pg. 3377
MAMUT APS—See KKR & Co. Inc.; *U.S. Public*, pg. 1266
MAMUT NORGE AS—See Cinven Limited; *Int'l*, pg. 1616
MAMUT NORGE AS—See HgCapital Trust plc; *Int'l*, pg. 3377
MAMUT NORGE AS—See KKR & Co. Inc.; *U.S. Public*, pg. 1267

MAMUT SOFTWARE LTD.—See Cinven Limited; *Int'l*, pg. 1616
MAMUT SOFTWARE LTD.—See HgCapital Trust plc; *Int'l*, pg. 3377
MAMUT SOFTWARE LTD.—See KKR & Co. Inc.; *U.S. Public*, pg. 1267
MANABI HOLDING S.A.; *Int'l*, pg. 4665
MANAC INCORPORATED - GOBUN FACTORY—See Manac Incorporated; *Int'l*, pg. 4666
MANAC INCORPORATED; *Int'l*, pg. 4665
MANAC INC.—See Placements CMI Inc.; *Int'l*, pg. 5887
MANAC (SHANGHAI) CO., LTD.—See Manac Incorporated; *Int'l*, pg. 4666
MANADIALISIS S.A.—See Fresenius Medical Care AG; *Int'l*, pg. 2776
MANAFAE HOLDING COMPANY K.S.C; *Int'l*, pg. 4666
MANAFORT BROTHERS INCORPORATED; *U.S. Private*, pg. 2559
MANAGED ASSETS CORPORATION—See Hilton Grand Vacations Inc.; *U.S. Public*, pg. 1040
MANAGED BUSINESS SOLUTIONS LLC; *U.S. Private*, pg. 2559
MANAGED CARE ADVISORS, INC.—See The Carlyle Group Inc.; *U.S. Public*, pg. 2053
MANAGED CARE CONSULTANTS LLC—See Aon plc; *Int'l*, pg. 496
MANAGED CARE NETWORK INC.; *U.S. Private*, pg. 2559
MANAGED CARE OF AMERICA INC.; *U.S. Private*, pg. 2559
MANAGED CARE OF NORTH AMERICA, INC.; *U.S. Private*, pg. 2559
MANAGED CHIROPRACTICS INC.—See NCMIC Group Inc.; *U.S. Private*, pg. 2876
MANAGED ENERGY SYSTEMS LLC; *U.S. Private*, pg. 2559
MANAGED FUTURES PREMIER WARRINGTON L.P.; *U.S. Private*, pg. 2559
MANAGED HEALTH CARE ASSOCIATES, INC.—See Roper Technologies, Inc.; *U.S. Public*, pg. 1812
MANAGED HEALTH NETWORK, LLC—See Centene Corporation; *U.S. Public*, pg. 470
MANAGED HEALTH NETWORK—See Centene Corporation; *U.S. Public*, pg. 470
MANAGED HEALTH SERVICES—See Centene Corporation; *U.S. Public*, pg. 470
MANAGED INSURANCE OPERATIONS B.V.—See Allianz SE; *Int'l*, pg. 354
MANAGED LAB SERVICES INC.—See Flagship Facility Services, Inc.; *U.S. Private*, pg. 1539
MANAGED MARKET RESOURCES LLC—See NPG Health LLC; *U.S. Private*, pg. 2969
MANAGED MOBILE, INC.—See Epika Fleet Services, Inc.; *U.S. Private*, pg. 1413
MANAGED OCCUPATIONAL HEALTH LIMITED—See Marlowe Plc; *Int'l*, pg. 4698
MANAGEDSTORAGE INTERNATIONAL, INC.; *U.S. Private*, pg. 2559
MANAGE INC.; *U.S. Private*, pg. 2559
MANAGEMENT ALLIANCE PROGRAMS, INC.; *U.S. Private*, pg. 2560
MANAGEMENT ANALYSIS & UTILIZATION, INC.; *U.S. Private*, pg. 2560
MANAGEMENT ANALYTICS GROUP, LLC; *U.S. Private*, pg. 2560
MANAGEMENT AND ENGINEERING TECHNOLOGIES INTERNATIONAL, INC.; *U.S. Private*, pg. 2560
MANAGEMENT ANGELS GMBH—See Randstad N.V.; *Int'l*, pg. 6202
MANAGEMENT APPLIED PROGRAMMING INC.; *U.S. Private*, pg. 2560
MANAGEMENT (BMG) PTY LTD—See Woolworths Group Limited; *Int'l*, pg. 8451
MANAGEMENT BROKERS, INC.—See Aon plc; *Int'l*, pg. 496
MANAGEMENT CAPITAL HOLDING AG; *Int'l*, pg. 4666
MANAGEMENT CAPITAL, LLC; *U.S. Private*, pg. 2560
MANAGEMENT CENTRE TURKIYE; *Int'l*, pg. 4666
MANAGEMENT CONSULTANCY INTERNATIONAL PTY LTD.—See Madison Dearborn Partners, LLC; *U.S. Private*, pg. 2540
MANAGEMENT CONSULTING GROUP PLC; *Int'l*, pg. 4666
MANAGEMENT CONSULTING, INC.; *U.S. Private*, pg. 2560
MANAGEMENT, CONSULTING & LIST-BROKING SERVICES S.A.; *Int'l*, pg. 4666
MANAGEMENT CONTROL SYSTEMS LIMITED—See Jamaica National Building Society; *Int'l*, pg. 3874
MANAGEMENT DATA SYSTEMS INTERNATIONAL; *U.S. Private*, pg. 2560
MANAGEMENT DIAGNOSTICS LIMITED—See The Arena Group Holdings, Inc; *U.S. Public*, pg. 2035
THE MANAGEMENT EDGE, INC.; *U.S. Private*, pg. 4074
THE MANAGEMENT GROUP LLC—See Centene Corporation; *U.S. Public*, pg. 470
MANAGEMENT MENTORS, INC.—See Engagedly, Inc.; *U.S. Private*, pg. 1397

MANAGEMENT & NETWORK SERVICES LLC—See CVS Health Corporation; *U.S. Public*, pg. 616
MANAGEMENT PARTNERS, INC.—See Baker Tilly US LLP; *U.S. Private*, pg. 457
MANAGEMENT PARTNERS, INC.; *U.S. Private*, pg. 2560
MANAGEMENT RECRUITERS INC. BOSTON; *U.S. Private*, pg. 2560
MANAGEMENT RECRUITERS INTERNATIONAL, INC.; *U.S. Private*, pg. 2560
MANAGEMENT RECRUITERS OF TAMPA-NORTH, INC.; *U.S. Private*, pg. 2560
MANAGEMENT RESOURCES GROUP, INC.—See Emerson Electric Co.; *U.S. Public*, pg. 748
MANAGEMENT RESOURCE SOLUTIONS PLC; *Int'l*, pg. 4666
MANAGEMENT SCIENCE & INNOVATION LLC; *U.S. Private*, pg. 2560
MANAGEMENT SCIENCES FOR HEALTH, INC.; *U.S. Private*, pg. 2561
MANAGEMENT SERVICES NORTHWEST; *U.S. Private*, pg. 2561
MANAGEMENT SEVEN, LLC; *U.S. Private*, pg. 2561
MANAGEMENT SOLUTIONS CO., LTD.; *Int'l*, pg. 4666
MANAGEMENT SOLUTIONS, LLC; *U.S. Private*, pg. 2561
MANAGEMENT SYSTEMS INTERNATIONAL INC.—See Tetra Tech, Inc.; *U.S. Public*, pg. 2023
MANAGEMENT TECHNOLOGY, INC.; *U.S. Private*, pg. 2561
MANAGEMENT TRAINING & CONSULTING INC.; *U.S. Private*, pg. 2561
MANAGEMENT & TRAINING CORPORATION; *U.S. Private*, pg. 2560
MANAGEMENT TRANSPORT & LOGISTIK GMBH—See Jerich International GmbH; *Int'l*, pg. 3931
MANAGEMENT TRUST HOLDING AG; *Int'l*, pg. 4666
MANAGE MOBILITY, LLC—See Sole Source Capital LLC; *U.S. Private*, pg. 3708
MANAGEPAY SYSTEMS BERHAD; *Int'l*, pg. 4666
MANAGER MAGAZIN ONLINE GMBH—See SPIEGEL-Verlag Rudolf Augstein GmbH & Co.; *Int'l*, pg. 7136
MANAGER MAGAZIN VERLAGSGESELLSCHAFT GMBH—See SPIEGEL-Verlag Rudolf Augstein GmbH & Co.; *Int'l*, pg. 7136
MANAGERPLUS SOLUTIONS, LLC—See iOffice, LLC; *U.S. Private*, pg. 2133
MANAGING AUTOMATION—See Thomas Publishing Company LLC; *U.S. Private*, pg. 4157
MANAIRCO, INC.—See Hughey & Phillips, LLC; *U.S. Private*, pg. 2004
MANAJANS THOMPSON ISTANBUL—See WPP plc; *Int'l*, pg. 8481
MANAKSIA ALUMINIUM COMPANY LIMITED—See Manaksia Ltd; *Int'l*, pg. 4667
MANAKSIA COATED METALS & INDUSTRIES LIMITED—See Manaksia Ltd; *Int'l*, pg. 4667
MANAKSIA LTD; *Int'l*, pg. 4667
MANAKSIA STEELS LIMITED—See Manaksia Ltd; *Int'l*, pg. 4667
MANALI PETROCHEMICALS LTD; *Int'l*, pg. 4667
MANALTO LIMITED; *Int'l*, pg. 4667
MANA MINERAL S.A.—See Endeavour Mining plc; *Int'l*, pg. 2402
MAN AND MACHINE AB—See Mensch und Maschine Software SE; *Int'l*, pg. 4817
MAN AND MACHINE BENELUX NV—See Mensch und Maschine Software SE; *Int'l*, pg. 4817
MAN AND MACHINE FRANCE S.A.R.L.—See Mensch und Maschine Software SE; *Int'l*, pg. 4817
MAN AND MACHINE LTD.—See Mensch und Maschine Software SE; *Int'l*, pg. 4817
MAN AND MACHINE ROMANIA SRL—See Mensch und Maschine Software SE; *Int'l*, pg. 4817
MAN AND MACHINE S.A.R.L.—See Mensch und Maschine Software SE; *Int'l*, pg. 4817
MANAPPURAM FINANCE LIMITED; *Int'l*, pg. 4667
MANAPPURAM HOME FINANCE LIMITED—See Manappuram Finance Limited; *Int'l*, pg. 4667
MANA PRODUCTS, INC.—See Marvin Traub Associates, Inc.; *U.S. Private*, pg. 2598
MANAR, INC. - CEW ENTERPRISE DIVISION—See Manar, Inc.; *U.S. Private*, pg. 2561
MANAR, INC. - GTR DIVISION—See Manar, Inc.; *U.S. Private*, pg. 2561
MANAR, INC. - PLASFINCO DIVISION—See Manar, Inc.; *U.S. Private*, pg. 2561
MANAR, INC.; *U.S. Private*, pg. 2561
MANAR, INC. - TENNPLASCO - LAFAYETTE DIVISION—See Manar, Inc.; *U.S. Private*, pg. 2561
MANASIAN INC.; *U.S. Private*, pg. 2561
MANASOTA COMMERCIAL CONSTRUCTION CO., INC.; *U.S. Private*, pg. 2561
MANASOTA FLOORING INC.; *U.S. Private*, pg. 2561
MANASOTA GROUP, INC.; *U.S. Private*, pg. 2561
MANAS PETROLEUM AG—See MNP Petroleum Corporation; *Int'l*, pg. 5006
MANAS PROPERTIES LIMITED; *Int'l*, pg. 4667
MANASQUAN RIVER REGIONAL SEWERAGE AUTHORITY; *U.S. Private*, pg. 2561

COMPANY NAME INDEX

MANASQUAN SAVINGS BANK—See MSB Mutual Holding Company; *U.S. Private*, pg. 2806
MANASSAS ICE & FUEL CO. INC.; *U.S. Private*, pg. 2561
MANASSEN FOODS AUSTRALIA PTY. LTD.—See Bright Food (Group) Co., Ltd.; *Int'l*, pg. 1161
MANATEE CARDIOLOGY ASSOCIATES, LLC—See Universal Health Services, Inc.; *U.S. Public*, pg. 2258
MANATEE COUNTY PORT AUTHORITY; *U.S. Private*, pg. 2561
MANATEE LANES—See Bowlero Corp; *U.S. Public*, pg. 376
MANATEE MEMORIAL HOSPITAL & HEALTH SYSTEM—See Universal Health Services, Inc.; *U.S. Public*, pg. 2260
MANATEE SURGICAL CENTER, LLC—See KKR & Co. Inc.; *U.S. Public*, pg. 1246
MANATEE SURGICARE, LTD.—See HCA Healthcare, Inc.; *U.S. Public*, pg. 1001
MANATI INDUSTRIES, INC.; *U.S. Public*, pg. 1356
MANATT, PHELPS & PHILLIPS LLP; *U.S. Private*, pg. 2561
MANATT'S, INC.; *U.S. Private*, pg. 2561
MANAUS AMBIENTAL S.A.—See Solvi S.A.; *Int'l*, pg. 7082
MANAUS ENERGIA S/A—See Centrais Eletricas Brasileiras S.A.; *Int'l*, pg. 1403
MAN AUTOMOTIVE IMPORTS (NZ) LTD—See Penske Automotive Group, Inc.; *U.S. Public*, pg. 1666
MAN AUTOMOTIVE IMPORTS PTY LTD—See Penske Automotive Group, Inc.; *U.S. Public*, pg. 1666
MANAV INFRA PROJECTS LTD.; *Int'l*, pg. 4667
MANAWA ENERGY LIMITED—See Infratil Limited; *Int'l*, pg. 3698
THE MANAWATU STANDARD LIMITED—See Nine Entertainment Co. Holdings Limited; *Int'l*, pg. 5298
MANAZEL HOLDING CO.; *Int'l*, pg. 4667
MANAZEL REAL ESTATE; *Int'l*, pg. 4667
MANCAN INC.; *U.S. Private*, pg. 2562
MAN CAPITAL CORPORATION—See Porsche Automobil Holding SE; *Int'l*, pg. 5929
MANCARI CHRYSLER JEEP INC.; *U.S. Private*, pg. 2562
MANCARI'S CHRYSLER JEEP INC.; *U.S. Private*, pg. 2562
MANCELLE D'HABITATION SA—See Groupe BPCE; *Int'l*, pg. 3094
MANCHASOL 1 CENTRAL TERMOSOLAR UNO, S.L.—See ACS, Actividades de Construccion y Servicios, S.A.; *Int'l*, pg. 115
MANCHASOL 2 CENTRAL TERMOSOLAR DOS, S.L.—See ACS, Actividades de Construccion y Servicios, S.A.; *Int'l*, pg. 115
MANCHAUG POND FOUNDATION; *U.S. Private*, pg. 2562
MANCHE EST SAS—See VINCI S.A.; *Int'l*, pg. 8224
MANCHES LLP; *Int'l*, pg. 4667
MANCHESTER ACADEMY OF ENGLISH—See TUI AG; *Int'l*, pg. 7965
MANCHESTER ACADEMY TEACHER TRAINING (UK) LIMITED—See TUI AG; *Int'l*, pg. 7965
THE MANCHESTER AIRPORT GROUP PLC; *Int'l*, pg. 7665
MANCHESTER AIRPORT GROUP PROPERTY SERVICES LIMITED—See The Manchester Airport Group plc; *Int'l*, pg. 7665
MANCHESTER AIRPORT PLC—See The Manchester Airport Group plc; *Int'l*, pg. 7665
MANCHESTER AMBULATORY SURGERY CENTER, LP—See Tenet Healthcare Corporation; *U.S. Public*, pg. 2011
MANCHESTER BUILDING SOCIETY—See Newcastle Building Society; *Int'l*, pg. 5233
MANCHESTER COPPERSMITHS LIMITED—See Kingspan Group PLC; *Int'l*, pg. 4178
MANCHESTER DIALYSIS, LLC—See DaVita Inc.; *U.S. Public*, pg. 641
MANCHESTER GRAND RESORTS, INC.—See Host Hotels & Resorts, Inc.; *U.S. Public*, pg. 1055
MANCHESTER HEALTH SERVICES—See VNA & Hospice of the Southwest Region, Inc.; *U.S. Private*, pg. 4408
MANCHESTER HONDA; *U.S. Private*, pg. 2562
MANCHESTER INDUSTRIES, INC. OF VIRGINIA—See Clearwater Paper Corporation; *U.S. Public*, pg. 513
THE MANCHESTER JOURNAL—See Alden Global Capital LLC; *U.S. Private*, pg. 159
MANCHESTER & LONDON INVESTMENT TRUST PLC; *Int'l*, pg. 4667
MANCHESTER MARKETING, INC.; *U.S. Private*, pg. 2562
MANCHESTER MILLS, LLC—See Sysco Corporation; *U.S. Public*, pg. 1974
MANCHESTER ORGANICS LIMITED—See Navin Fluorine International Ltd; *Int'l*, pg. 5175
MANCHESTER SAND, GRAVEL & CEMENT CO. INC.—See Boston Sand & Gravel Company; *U.S. Public*, pg. 373
MANCHESTER SUBARU; *U.S. Private*, pg. 2562
MANCHESTER TANK & EQUIPMENT COMPANY - CHILE PLANT—See McWane, Inc.; *U.S. Private*, pg. 2645
MANCHESTER TANK & EQUIPMENT COMPANY—See McWane, Inc.; *U.S. Private*, pg. 2645

MANCHESTER TANK & EQUIPMENT—See McWane, Inc.; *U.S. Private*, pg. 2645
MANCHESTER TECHNOPARK LIMITED—See Pochin's Ltd.; *Int'l*, pg. 5902
MANCHESTER UNITED LIMITED—See Manchester United plc; *Int'l*, pg. 4668
MANCHESTER UNITED MERCHANDISING LIMITED—See NIKE, Inc.; *U.S. Public*, pg. 1528
MANCHESTER UNITED PLC; *Int'l*, pg. 4667
MANCHESTER WHOLESALE DISTRIBUTORS, INC.; *U.S. Private*, pg. 2562
MANCIL'S TRACTOR SERVICE, INC.—See Construction Partners, Inc.; *U.S. Public*, pg. 572
MANCINI FOODS; *U.S. Private*, pg. 2562
MANCINI'S SLEEPWORLD INC.; *U.S. Private*, pg. 2562
MANCINO HOLDINGS INC.; *U.S. Private*, pg. 2562
MAN COMMERCIAL VEHICLES (THAILAND) CO., LTD.—See Tan Chong International Limited; *Int'l*, pg. 7453
MAN-CON INCORPORATED; *U.S. Private*, pg. 2559
MANCOR CANADA INC.; *Int'l*, pg. 4668
MANCOR OHIO INC.—See Mancor Canada Inc.; *Int'l*, pg. 4668
MANDALA AIRLINES; *Int'l*, pg. 4668
MANDALA COMMUNICATIONS CO., LTD.—See Internet Thailand Public Company Limited; *Int'l*, pg. 3754
MANDALA COMMUNICATIONS, INC.; *U.S. Private*, pg. 2562
MANDALAY BASEBALL PROPERTIES, LLC—See Mandalay Entertainment Group; *U.S. Private*, pg. 2562
MANDALAY BASEBALL PROPERTIES, LLC—See Seaport Capital, LLC; *U.S. Private*, pg. 3586
MANDALAY CAPITAL—See Silk Road Capital Ltd.; *Int'l*, pg. 6921
MANDALAY CORP.—See MGM Resorts International; *U.S. Public*, pg. 1435
MANDALAY ENTERTAINMENT GROUP; *U.S. Private*, pg. 2562
MANDALAY OWNER TEXAS, LLC—See RAIT Financial Trust; *U.S. Private*, pg. 3349
MANDALAY PICTURES, LLC—See Mandalay Entertainment Group; *U.S. Private*, pg. 2562
MANDALAY PLACE—See MGM Resorts International; *U.S. Public*, pg. 1435
MANDALAY RESOURCES CORPORATION; *Int'l*, pg. 4668
MANDALAY SPORTS ENTERTAINMENT LLC—See Mandalay Entertainment Group; *U.S. Private*, pg. 2562
MANDAL'S, INC.; *U.S. Private*, pg. 2562
MANDA PACKING CO. INC.; *U.S. Private*, pg. 2562
MANDARAKE INC.; *Int'l*, pg. 4668
MANDARA SPA ARUBA N.V.—See OneSpaWorld Holdings Limited; *U.S. Public*, pg. 1604
MANDARA SPA ASIA LIMITED—See Catterton Management Company, LLC; *U.S. Private*, pg. 794
MANDARA SPA (BAHAMAS) LIMITED—See OneSpaWorld Holdings Limited; *U.S. Public*, pg. 1604
MANDARA SPA LLC—See Catterton Management Company, LLC; *U.S. Private*, pg. 794
MANDARA SPA PALAU—See OneSpaWorld Holdings Limited; *U.S. Public*, pg. 1604
MANDARA SPA PUERTO RICO, INC.—See OneSpaWorld Holdings Limited; *U.S. Public*, pg. 1604
MANDARIN ADVISORY S.R.L.—See Mandarin Capital Management SA; *Int'l*, pg. 4668
MANDARIN AIRLINES—See China Airlines Ltd.; *Int'l*, pg. 1482
MANDARIN CAPITAL ADVISORY LTD.—See Mandarin Capital Management SA; *Int'l*, pg. 4668
MANDARIN CAPITAL MANAGEMENT II SA—See Mandarin Capital Management SA; *Int'l*, pg. 4668
MANDARIN CAPITAL MANAGEMENT SA; *Int'l*, pg. 4668
MANDARIN FILMS LIMITED—See Keyne Ltd.; *Int'l*, pg. 4146
THE MANDARIN HOTEL B.V.—See PPHE Hotel Group Limited; *Int'l*, pg. 5951
MANDARIN HOTEL PUBLIC COMPANY LIMITED; *Int'l*, pg. 4668
MANDARIN ORIENTAL HOTEL COMPANY, INC. - NEW YORK OFFICE—See Jardine Matheson Holdings Limited; *Int'l*, pg. 3910
MANDARIN ORIENTAL HOTEL COMPANY, INC.—See Jardine Matheson Holdings Limited; *Int'l*, pg. 3910
MANDARIN ORIENTAL HOTEL GROUP INTERNATIONAL LIMITED—See Jardine Matheson Holdings Limited; *Int'l*, pg. 3910
MANDARIN ORIENTAL HOTEL GROUP LIMITED—See Jardine Matheson Holdings Limited; *Int'l*, pg. 3910
MANDARIN ORIENTAL HYDE PARK LIMITED—See Jardine Matheson Holdings Limited; *Int'l*, pg. 3910
MANDARIN ORIENTAL INTERNATIONAL LIMITED—See Jardine Matheson Holdings Limited; *Int'l*, pg. 3910
MANDARIN ORIENTAL TOKYO KK—See Jardine Matheson Holdings Limited; *Int'l*, pg. 3910
MANDATE FILMS, LLC—See Lions Gate Entertainment Corp.; *Int'l*, pg. 4521
MANDATROPA AG—See M.M. Warburg & Co. KGaA; *Int'l*, pg. 4616
MANDATUM AND CO LTD; *Int'l*, pg. 4668

MANDOM CORPORATION

MANDATUM ASSET MANAGEMENT LTD.—See Sampo plc; *Int'l*, pg. 6508
MANDATUM LIFE INSURANCE BALTIC SE LITHUANIAN BRANCH—See Sampo plc; *Int'l*, pg. 6508
MANDATUM LIFE INSURANCE BALTIC SE—See Sampo plc; *Int'l*, pg. 6508
MANDATUM LIFE INSURANCE COMPANY LIMITED—See Sampo plc; *Int'l*, pg. 6508
MAN-DELL FOOD STORES, INC.; *U.S. Private*, pg. 2559
MANDELLI SISTEMI S.P.A.—See Gruppo Riello Sistemi S.p.A.; *Int'l*, pg. 3141
MANDEL METALS INC.; *U.S. Private*, pg. 2562
MANDERE CONSTRUCTION, INC.—See Kodiak Building Partners LLC; *U.S. Private*, pg. 2336
MANDER PORTMAN WOODWARD LIMITED—See Graham Holdings Company; *U.S. Public*, pg. 956
MANDERS AUTOMATION B.V.—See Manders Industries B.V.; *Int'l*, pg. 4668
MANDERS INDUSTRIES B.V.; *Int'l*, pg. 4668
MANDEX INC.—See MTS3 Inc.; *U.S. Private*, pg. 2810
MANDG INVESTMENTS LIFE SOUTH AFRICA (RF) LTD.—See M&G Plc; *Int'l*, pg. 4612
MANDG INVESTMENTS (NAMIBIA) (PTY.) LTD.—See M&G Plc; *Int'l*, pg. 4612
MANDHANA INDUSTRIES LIMITED - MANDHANA DYEING DIVISION—See GB Global Limited; *Int'l*, pg. 2892
MANDHANA INDUSTRIES LIMITED - MANDHANA DYEING UNIT-II—See GB Global Limited; *Int'l*, pg. 2892
MANDHANA INDUSTRIES LTD (EXPORT DIVISION) UNIT I—See GB Global Limited; *Int'l*, pg. 2892
MANDHANA WEAVING HOUSE (SHIRTING DIVISION)—See GB Global Limited; *Int'l*, pg. 2892
MANDIANT AUSTRALIA PTY LTD—See Alphabet Inc.; *U.S. Public*, pg. 84
MANDIANT CORPORATION—See Alphabet Inc.; *U.S. Public*, pg. 84
MANDIANT CYBERSECURITY PRIVATE LIMITED—See Alphabet Inc.; *U.S. Public*, pg. 84
MANDIANT DEUTSCHLAND GMBH—See Alphabet Inc.; *U.S. Public*, pg. 84
MANDIANT, INC.—See Alphabet Inc.; *U.S. Public*, pg. 83
MANDIANT IRELAND LIMITED—See Alphabet Inc.; *U.S. Public*, pg. 84
MANDIANT K.K.—See Alphabet Inc.; *U.S. Public*, pg. 84
MANDIANT KOREA LIMITED—See Alphabet Inc.; *U.S. Public*, pg. 84
MANDIANT SINGAPORE PRIVATE LIMITED—See Alphabet Inc.; *U.S. Public*, pg. 84
MANDIANT UK LTD.—See Alphabet Inc.; *U.S. Public*, pg. 84
MAN DIESEL & TURBO FRANCE SAS—See Porsche Automobil Holding SE; *Int'l*, pg. 5930
MAN DIESEL & TURBO JAPAN LTD.—See Porsche Automobil Holding SE; *Int'l*, pg. 5930
MAN DIESEL & TURBO LTD.—See Porsche Automobil Holding SE; *Int'l*, pg. 5930
MAN DIESEL & TURBO NORGE AS—See Porsche Automobil Holding SE; *Int'l*, pg. 5930
MAN DIESEL & TURBO NORTH AMERICA INC. - BATON ROUGE—See Porsche Automobil Holding SE; *Int'l*, pg. 5930
MAN DIESEL & TURBO NORTH AMERICA INC.—See Porsche Automobil Holding SE; *Int'l*, pg. 5930
MAN DIESEL & TURBO NORTH AMERICA INC. - WOODBRIDGE—See Porsche Automobil Holding SE; *Int'l*, pg. 5930
MAN DIESEL & TURBO SCHWEIZ AG—See Porsche Automobil Holding SE; *Int'l*, pg. 5930
MAN DIESEL & TURBO SE - OBERHAUSEN—See Porsche Automobil Holding SE; *Int'l*, pg. 5930
MAN DIESEL & TURBO SE—See Porsche Automobil Holding SE; *Int'l*, pg. 5929
MAN DIESEL & TURBO—See Porsche Automobil Holding SE; *Int'l*, pg. 5930
MANDIRI INTERNATIONAL REMITTANCE SENDIRIAN BERHAD—See PT Bank Mandiri (Persero) Tbk.; *Int'l*, pg. 6026
MANDIRI SECURITIES PTE. LTD.—See PT Bank Mandiri (Persero) Tbk.; *Int'l*, pg. 6026
M AND J WOODCRAFTS LTD.; *Int'l*, pg. 4610
MANDM DIRECT HOLDINGS PLC; *Int'l*, pg. 4668
MANDO BRAND ASSURANCE LIMITED—See WPP plc; *Int'l*, pg. 8465
MANDO BROSE CORPORATION—See Brose Fahrzeugteile GmbH & Co. KG; *Int'l*, pg. 1196
MANDO CORPORATION - IKSAN DIVISION—See Halla Group; *Int'l*, pg. 3230
MANDO CORPORATION LIMITED—See WPP plc; *Int'l*, pg. 8465
MANDO CORPORATION - WONJU DIVISION—See Halla Group; *Int'l*, pg. 3230
MANDOM CHINA CORPORATION—See Mandom Corporation; *Int'l*, pg. 4668
MANDOM CORPORATION (SINGAPORE) PTE. LTD.—See Mandom Corporation; *Int'l*, pg. 4668
MANDOM CORPORATION; *Int'l*, pg. 4668
MANDOM CORPORATION (THAILAND) LTD.—See Mandom Corporation; *Int'l*, pg. 4668

MANDOM KOREA CORPORATION—See Mandom Corporation; *Int'l*, pg. 4668
MANDOM (MALAYSIA) SDN. BHD.—See Mandom Corporation; *Int'l*, pg. 4668
MANDOM PHILIPPINES CORPORATION—See Mandom Corporation; *Int'l*, pg. 4668
MANDOM TAIWAN CORPORATION—See Mandom Corporation; *Int'l*, pg. 4668
MANDRAKE RESOURCES LIMITED; *Int'l*, pg. 4669
MANDRIVA BRASIL—See Mandriva S.A.; *Int'l*, pg. 4669
MANDRIVA S.A.; *Int'l*, pg. 4669
MANDURIAMBIENTE S.P.A.—See Iren S.p.A.; *Int'l*, pg. 3808
MANDVIWALLA MAUSER PLASTIC INDUSTRIES LIMITED; *Int'l*, pg. 4669
MAN DWE GMBH—See Porsche Automobil Holding SE; *Int'l*, pg. 5930
MANE AROMA VE ESANS SAN. VE TIC. LTD. STI—See V. Mane Fils SA; *Int'l*, pg. 8106
MANE AUSTRIA GMBH—See V. Mane Fils SA; *Int'l*, pg. 8105
MANE CHILE, S.A.—See V. Mane Fils SA; *Int'l*, pg. 8105
MANE DEUTSCHLAND GMBH—See V. Mane Fils SA; *Int'l*, pg. 8105
MANE DO BRASIL INDUSTRIA E COMERCIO LTDA—See V. Mane Fils SA; *Int'l*, pg. 8106
MANE IBERICA S.A.—See V. Mane Fils SA; *Int'l*, pg. 8105
MANEI LIFT SAS—See VINCI S.A.; *Int'l*, pg. 8224
MANE INC.—See V. Mane Fils SA; *Int'l*, pg. 8105
MANE INDIA PRIVATE LIMITED—See V. Mane Fils SA; *Int'l*, pg. 8105
MANE ITALIA S.R.L.—See V. Mane Fils SA; *Int'l*, pg. 8105
MANEKIN LLC—See Colliers International Group Inc.; *Int'l*, pg. 1701
MANE LTD.—See V. Mane Fils SA; *Int'l*, pg. 8105
MANE MEXICO, S.A. DE C.V.—See V. Mane Fils SA; *Int'l*, pg. 8105
MAN ENGINES & COMPONENTS INC.—See Porsche Automobil Holding SE; *Int'l*, pg. 5930
MANE POLSKA SP. Z O.O.—See V. Mane Fils SA; *Int'l*, pg. 8106
MANER BUILDERS SUPPLY CO.—See Bain Capital, LP; *U.S. Private*, pg. 451
MANE SA (PTY) LTD—See V. Mane Fils SA; *Int'l*, pg. 8106
MANE SAS—See V. Mane Fils SA; *Int'l*, pg. 8106
MANE SHANGHAI CO., LTD.—See V. Mane Fils SA; *Int'l*, pg. 8106
MANE TAIWAN FRAGRANCES AND FLAVOURS CO., LTD—See V. Mane Fils SA; *Int'l*, pg. 8106
MANET COMMUNITY HEALTH CENTER, INC.; *U.S. Private*, pg. 2563
MAN (EUROPE) AG—See MAN Group plc; *Int'l*, pg. 4664
MANEVAL CONSTRUCTION CO. INC.; *U.S. Private*, pg. 2563
MANE VOSTOK LLC—See V. Mane Fils SA; *Int'l*, pg. 8106
MANEX & POWER MARINE LTD—See Cullinan Holdings Limited; *Int'l*, pg. 1877
MANEY INTERNATIONAL INC.; *U.S. Private*, pg. 2563
MANFORCE GROUP BHD; *Int'l*, pg. 4669
MANFRED HUCK GMBH; *Int'l*, pg. 4669
MANFREDI OF GREENWICH, LTD.; *U.S. Private*, pg. 2563
MANFRED MAYER MMM MINERALOL VERTRIEBSGESELLSCHAFT M.B.H.—See Marquard & Bahls AG; *Int'l*, pg. 4699
MANFROTTO BAG LIMITED—See Videndum plc; *Int'l*, pg. 8190
MANFROTTO DISTRIBUTION INC.—See Videndum plc; *Int'l*, pg. 8191
MANGA DESIGNERS LAB. CO., LTD.—See KAYAC Inc.; *Int'l*, pg. 4101
MANGALAM ALLOYS LIMITED; *Int'l*, pg. 4669
MANGALAM CEMENT LTD; *Int'l*, pg. 4669
MANGALAM DRUGS & ORGANICS LTD.; *Int'l*, pg. 4669
MANGALAM DRUGS & ORGANICS LTD. - VAPI - UNIT II—See Mangalam Drugs & Organics Ltd.; *Int'l*, pg. 4669
MANGALAM GLOBAL ENTERPRISE LIMITED; *Int'l*, pg. 4669
MANGALAM ORGANICS LIMITED; *Int'l*, pg. 4669
MANGALAM SEEDS LIMITED; *Int'l*, pg. 4669
MANGALAM TIMBER PRODUCTS LTD.; *Int'l*, pg. 4669
MANGALAM VENTURES LIMITED; *Int'l*, pg. 4669
MANGAL COMPUSOLUTION PRIVATE LIMITED—See Mangal Credit & Fincorp Limited; *Int'l*, pg. 4669
MANGAL CREDIT & FINCORP LIMITED; *Int'l*, pg. 4669
MANGAL MINES & MINERALS PVT. LTD.—See Mangal Credit & Fincorp Limited; *Int'l*, pg. 4669
MANGALORE CHEMICALS & FERTILIZERS LTD; *Int'l*, pg. 4669
MANGALORE REFINERY & PETROCHEMICALS LIMITED—See Oil & Natural Gas Corporation Limited; *Int'l*, pg. 5534
MANGALORE SPORTS DATA INDIA PRIVATE LIMITED—See Vista Equity Partners, LLC; *U.S. Private*, pg. 4401
MANGAL PRECISION PRODUCTS LIMITED - WORKS 1—See Amara Raja Energy & Mobility Limited; *Int'l*, pg. 412

MANGALYA SOFT-TECH LIMITED; *Int'l*, pg. 4669
MANGANARO MIDATLANTIC, LLC; *U.S. Private*, pg. 2563
MANGANARO NORTHEAST, LLC—See Manganaro MidAtlantic, LLC; *U.S. Private*, pg. 2563
MANGANESE METAL CO. (PTY.) LTD.—See Valmont Industries, Inc.; *U.S. Public*, pg. 2273
MANGANESE X ENERGY CORP.; *Int'l*, pg. 4670
MANGANESOS ATACAMA S.A.—See CAP S.A.; *Int'l*, pg. 1300
MANGAN HOLCOMB PARTNERS; *U.S. Private*, pg. 2563
MANGAN, INC.; *U.S. Private*, pg. 2563
MANGAR INDUSTRIES INC.; *U.S. Private*, pg. 2563
MANGATA HOLDING S.A.; *Int'l*, pg. 4670
MANGAUNG SUN (PTY) LIMITED—See Sun International Limited; *Int'l*, pg. 7304
MANGAZEYA MINING LTD.; *Int'l*, pg. 4670
MANGELS INDUSTRIAL S.A.; *Int'l*, pg. 4670
MANGIAROTTI S.P.A.—See Brookfield Corporation; *Int'l*, pg. 1186
MANGIN EGLY ENTREPRISES SAS—See VINCI S.A.; *Int'l*, pg. 8237
MANGINO CHEVROLET, INC.—See General Motors Company; *U.S. Public*, pg. 925
MANGINO HOLDING CORP.; *U.S. Private*, pg. 2563
MANG INSURANCE AGENCY, LLC—See NBT Bancorp, Inc.; *U.S. Public*, pg. 1500
MANGISTAUMUNAIGAZ JSC; *Int'l*, pg. 4670
MANGISTAU REGIONAL ELECTRICITY NETWORK CO JSC; *Int'l*, pg. 4670
MAN GLOBAL PRIVATE MARKETS (USA) INC,—See MAN Group plc; *Int'l*, pg. 4664
MANGO AIRLINES SOC LTD—See South African Airways (Pty) Ltd; *Int'l*, pg. 7115
MANGOCEUTICALS, INC.; *U.S. Public*, pg. 1356
MANGO DISTRIBUTING CO. INC.—See Home Service Oil Co. Inc.; *U.S. Private*, pg. 1972
MANGO EXCELLENT MEDIA CO., LTD.; *Int'l*, pg. 4670
MANGO GIDA SANAYI VE TICARET AS; *Int'l*, pg. 4670
MANGO INC.—See Septeni Holdings Co., Ltd.; *Int'l*, pg. 6718
MANGO LANGUAGES; *U.S. Private*, pg. 2563
MANGOLD FONDKOMMISSION AB; *Int'l*, pg. 4670
MANGO.LV SIA—See AS Ekspress Grupp; *Int'l*, pg. 589
MANGOOLA COAL OPERATIONS PTY. LIMITED—See Glencore plc; *Int'l*, pg. 2990
MANGOSPRING INC; *U.S. Private*, pg. 2563
MANGO TREE (HK) LIMITED—See 1957 & Co. (Hospitality) Limited; *Int'l*, pg. 3
MAN GROUP JAPAN LIMITED—See MAN Group plc; *Int'l*, pg. 4664
MAN GROUP PLC; *Int'l*, pg. 4664
MANGROVE COBRASOURCE, LLC—See Asure Software, Inc.; *U.S. Public*, pg. 218
MANGROVE EQUITY PARTNERS, LP; *U.S. Private*, pg. 2563
MANGROVE HOLDINGS PTE LTD.; *Int'l*, pg. 4670
MANGROVE SOFTWARE, INC.—See Asure Software, Inc.; *U.S. Public*, pg. 218
MANHATTAN AMERICAN TERRAZZO STRIP COMPANY INC.—See The Platt Brothers & Company, Inc.; *U.S. Private*, pg. 4096
MANHATTAN ASSOCIATES EUROPE B.V.—See Manhattan Associates, Inc.; *U.S. Public*, pg. 1356
MANHATTAN ASSOCIATES FRANCE SARL—See Manhattan Associates, Inc.; *U.S. Public*, pg. 1356
MANHATTAN ASSOCIATES, INC.; *U.S. Public*, pg. 1356
MANHATTAN ASSOCIATES (INDIA) DEVELOPMENT CENTRE PRIVATE LIMITED—See Manhattan Associates, Inc.; *U.S. Public*, pg. 1356
MANHATTAN ASSOCIATES KK—See Manhattan Associates, Inc.; *U.S. Public*, pg. 1356
MANHATTAN ASSOCIATES LIMITED—See Manhattan Associates, Inc.; *U.S. Public*, pg. 1356
MANHATTAN ASSOCIATES PTY LTD—See Manhattan Associates, Inc.; *U.S. Public*, pg. 1356
MANHATTAN ASSOCIATES SOFTWARE PTE LTD.—See Manhattan Associates, Inc.; *U.S. Public*, pg. 1356
MANHATTAN ASSOCIATES SOFTWARE (SHANGHAI), CO. LTD.—See Manhattan Associates, Inc.; *U.S. Public*, pg. 1356
MANHATTAN AUTOMOBILE COMPANY—See Ford Motor Company; *U.S. Public*, pg. 866
MANHATTAN BAGEL COMPANY, INC.—See JAB Holding Company S.a.r.l.; *Int'l*, pg. 3861
MANHATTAN BEACHWEAR, LLC—See Linsalata Capital Partners, Inc.; *U.S. Private*, pg. 2463
MANHATTAN BEER DISTRIBUTORS LLC; *U.S. Private*, pg. 2563
MANHATTAN BRIDGE CAPITAL, INC.; *U.S. Public*, pg. 1356
MANHATTAN CENTERSTONE, INC.—See Trimble, Inc.; *U.S. Public*, pg. 2190
MANHATTAN CENTER STUDIOS INC.—See Family Federation for World Peace & Unification; *U.S. Private*, pg. 1469
MANHATTAN COMMUNICATIONS (PVT) LTD.—See Publicis Groupe S.A.; *Int'l*, pg. 6102

MANHATTAN COMMUNICATIONS PVT. LTD.—See Publicis Groupe S.A.; *Int'l*, pg. 6102
MANHATTAN CONSTRUCTION COMPANY—See Rooney Holdings, Inc.; *U.S. Private*, pg. 3479
MANHATTAN CONSTRUCTION COMPANY—See Rooney Holdings, Inc.; *U.S. Private*, pg. 3479
MANHATTAN CORPORATION; *Int'l*, pg. 4670
MANHATTAN DATACRAFT LTD—See Trimble, Inc.; *U.S. Public*, pg. 2190
MANHATTAN DERMATOLOGY PA—See Heartland Dermatology and Skin Cancer Center, P.A.; *U.S. Private*, pg. 1899
MANHATTAN DRUG COMPANY, INC.—See Integrated Biopharma, Inc.; *U.S. Public*, pg. 1136
MANHATTAN GROUP LLC—See Crown Crafts, Inc.; *U.S. Public*, pg. 596
THE MANHATTAN INSURANCE GROUP; *U.S. Private*, pg. 4074
MANHATTAN LIFE INSURANCE COMPANY—See The Manhattan Insurance Group; *U.S. Private*, pg. 4074
MANHATTAN MARKETING ENSEMBLE; *U.S. Private*, pg. 2563
MANHATTAN MINI STORAGE—See Edison Properties, LLC; *U.S. Private*, pg. 1337
MANHATTAN MOTORCARS, INC.; *U.S. Private*, pg. 2563
MANHATTAN NATIONAL LIFE INSURANCE COMPANY—See Massachusetts Mutual Life Insurance Company; *U.S. Private*, pg. 2605
MANHATTAN PARKING SYSTEMS GARAGE; *U.S. Private*, pg. 2563
MANHATTAN PARKING SYSTEMS-PARK AVE; *U.S. Private*, pg. 2563
MANHATTAN PARTNERS; *U.S. Private*, pg. 2563
MANHATTAN REVIEW INC.; *U.S. Private*, pg. 2563
MANHATTAN ROAD & BRIDGE CO.—See Rooney Holdings, Inc.; *U.S. Private*, pg. 3479
MANHATTAN ROAD & BRIDGE-MUSKOGEE OFFICE—See Rooney Holdings, Inc.; *U.S. Private*, pg. 3479
MANHATTAN SCIENTIFICS, INC.; *U.S. Public*, pg. 1356
MANHATTAN SPECIAL BOTTLING CORP.; *U.S. Private*, pg. 2564
MANHATTANTECHSUPPORT.COM LLC—See Acrisure, LLC; *U.S. Private*, pg. 65
MANHATTAN THEATRE CLUB, INC.; *U.S. Private*, pg. 2564
MANHATTAN TOY EUROPE LIMITED—See Crown Crafts, Inc.; *U.S. Public*, pg. 596
MANHEIM ALBANY—See Cox Enterprises, Inc.; *U.S. Private*, pg. 1076
MANHEIM ASIA PACIFIC LTD.—See Cox Enterprises, Inc.; *U.S. Private*, pg. 1076
MANHEIM AUCTIONS, INC.—See Cox Enterprises, Inc.; *U.S. Private*, pg. 1076
MANHEIM AUTO AUCTIONS LIMITED—See Cox Enterprises, Inc.; *U.S. Private*, pg. 1076
MANHEIM BALTIMORE-WASHINGTON—See Cox Enterprises, Inc.; *U.S. Private*, pg. 1076
MANHEIM CALIFORNIA—See Cox Enterprises, Inc.; *U.S. Private*, pg. 1076
MANHEIM CINCINNATI—See Cox Enterprises, Inc.; *U.S. Private*, pg. 1076
MANHEIM DARLINGTON—See Cox Enterprises, Inc.; *U.S. Private*, pg. 1076
MANHEIM GEORGIA—See Cox Enterprises, Inc.; *U.S. Private*, pg. 1076
MANHEIM HAWAII—See Cox Enterprises, Inc.; *U.S. Private*, pg. 1077
MANHEIM IMPERIAL FLORIDA—See Cox Enterprises, Inc.; *U.S. Private*, pg. 1077
MANHEIM ITALIA S.R.L.—See Cox Enterprises, Inc.; *U.S. Private*, pg. 1077
MANHEIM LOUISVILLE AUTO AUCTION—See Cox Enterprises, Inc.; *U.S. Private*, pg. 1077
MANHEIM METRO DALLAS—See Cox Enterprises, Inc.; *U.S. Private*, pg. 1077
MANHEIM NEW ENGLAND—See Cox Enterprises, Inc.; *U.S. Private*, pg. 1077
MANHEIM NEW JERSEY—See Cox Enterprises, Inc.; *U.S. Private*, pg. 1077
MANHEIM NEW MEXICO—See Cox Enterprises, Inc.; *U.S. Private*, pg. 1077
MANHEIM NORTHSTAR MINNESOTA—See Cox Enterprises, Inc.; *U.S. Private*, pg. 1077
MANHEIM OF PHOENIX—See Cox Enterprises, Inc.; *U.S. Private*, pg. 1077
MANHEIM OHIO—See Cox Enterprises, Inc.; *U.S. Private*, pg. 1077
MANHEIM ORLANDO—See Cox Enterprises, Inc.; *U.S. Private*, pg. 1077
MANHEIM PHILADELPHIA—See Cox Enterprises, Inc.; *U.S. Private*, pg. 1077
MANHEIM PITTSBURGH—See Cox Enterprises, Inc.; *U.S. Private*, pg. 1077
MANHEIM PORTLAND—See Cox Enterprises, Inc.; *U.S. Private*, pg. 1077
MANHEIM SAN ANTONIO—See Cox Enterprises, Inc.; *U.S. Private*, pg. 1077

COMPANY NAME INDEX

MANHEIM SEATTLE—See Cox Enterprises, Inc.; *U.S. Private*, pg. 1077
MANHEIM'S GREATER PENSACOLA AUCTION—See Cox Enterprises, Inc.; *U.S. Private*, pg. 1077
MANHEIM'S OSHAWA DEALERS EXCHANGE—See Cox Enterprises, Inc.; *U.S. Private*, pg. 1077
MANHEIM SOUTHERN CALIFORNIA—See Cox Enterprises, Inc.; *U.S. Private*, pg. 1077
MANHEIM'S THE MOTOR CITY AUTO AUCTION—See Cox Enterprises, Inc.; *U.S. Private*, pg. 1077
MANHEIM TAMPA—See Cox Enterprises, Inc.; *U.S. Private*, pg. 1077
MANHEIM TORONTO—See Cox Enterprises, Inc.; *U.S. Private*, pg. 1077
MANHO ROPE & WIRE LTD. - BUSAN FACTORY—See Manho Rope & Wire Ltd.; *Int'l*, pg. 4670
MANHO ROPE & WIRE LTD. - CHANGWON FACTORY—See Manho Rope & Wire Ltd.; *Int'l*, pg. 4670
MANHO ROPE & WIRE LTD.; *Int'l*, pg. 4670
MANHO ROPE & WIRE LTD. - YANGSAN FACTORY—See Manho Rope & Wire Ltd.; *Int'l*, pg. 4670
MANICA AFRICA (PTY) LIMITED—See The Bidvest Group Limited; *Int'l*, pg. 7625
MANICA GROUP NAMIBIA (PTY) LIMITED—See The Bidvest Group Limited; *Int'l*, pg. 7625
MANICA (ZAMBIA) LIMITED—See The Bidvest Group Limited; *Int'l*, pg. 7625
MANICA ZIMBABWE LIMITED—See The Bidvest Group Limited; *Int'l*, pg. 7625
MANIFATTURE ASSOCIATE CASHMERE USA INC—See IT Holding S.p.A.; *Int'l*, pg. 3827
MANIFATTURE SIGARO TOSCANO S.R.L.—See Societa Esercizi Commerciali Industriali; *Int'l*, pg. 7034
MANIFEST DIGITAL; *U.S. Private*, pg. 2564
MANIFEST DISCS & TAPES INCORPORATED; *U.S. Private*, pg. 2564
MANIFESTSEVEN HOLDINGS CORPORATION; *U.S. Public*, pg. 1356
MANIFOLD CAPITAL CORP.; *U.S. Private*, pg. 2564
MANIFOLD SERVICES INC.; *U.S. Private*, pg. 2564
MANIILAQ ASSOCIATION; *U.S. Private*, pg. 2564
MANI INC. - KIYOHARA FACTORY—See Mani Inc.; *Int'l*, pg. 4670
MANI INC.; *Int'l*, pg. 4670
MANIKER CO., LTD.; *Int'l*, pg. 4670
MANIKER F&G CO., LTD.; *Int'l*, pg. 4670
MANILA BROADCASTING COMPANY; *Int'l*, pg. 4671
MANILA BULLETIN PUBLISHING CORPORATION; *Int'l*, pg. 4671
MANILA ELECTRIC COMPANY; *Int'l*, pg. 4671
MANILA HARBOR CENTER PORT SERVICES, INC.—See LATAM Airlines Group S.A.; *Int'l*, pg. 4422
MANILA INTERNATIONAL FREIGHT FORWARDERS, INC.—See KKR & Co. Inc.; *U.S. Public*, pg. 1259
MANILA JOCKEY CLUB, INC.; *Int'l*, pg. 4671
MANILA MANDARIN HOTEL INCORPORATED—See Jardine Matheson Holdings Limited; *Int'l*, pg. 3910
MANILA MINING CORPORATION; *Int'l*, pg. 4671
MANILA PENINSULA HOTEL, INC.—See The Hongkong and Shanghai Hotels Limited; *Int'l*, pg. 7653
MANILA WATER COMPANY, INC.; *Int'l*, pg. 4671
THE MANILDRA GROUP; *Int'l*, pg. 7665
MAN IMPORTS PTY LTD—See Penske Automotive Group, Inc.; *U.S. Public*, pg. 1666
MAN INDUSTRIES INDIA LTD.; *Int'l*, pg. 4665
MAN INFRACONSTRUCTION LTD.; *Int'l*, pg. 4665
MAN INFRAPROJECTS LIMITED—See Man Industries India Ltd.; *Int'l*, pg. 4665
MAN INVESTMENT MANAGEMENT (SHANGHAI) CO., LTD.—See MAN Group plc; *Int'l*, pg. 4664
MAN INVESTMENTS AG—See MAN Group plc; *Int'l*, pg. 4664
MAN INVESTMENTS AG—See MAN Group plc; *Int'l*, pg. 4664
MAN INVESTMENTS AUSTRALIA LTD.—See MAN Group plc; *Int'l*, pg. 4664
MAN INVESTMENTS (HONG KONG) LTD.—See MAN Group plc; *Int'l*, pg. 4664
MAN INVESTMENTS INC.—See MAN Group plc; *Int'l*, pg. 4664
MAN INVESTMENTS LTD.—See MAN Group plc; *Int'l*, pg. 4665
MAN INVESTMENTS (LUXEMBOURG) S.A.—See MAN Group plc; *Int'l*, pg. 4665
MAN INVESTMENTS MIDDLE EAST LTD.—See MAN Group plc; *Int'l*, pg. 4665
MAN INVESTMENTS NETHERLANDS B.V.—See MAN Group plc; *Int'l*, pg. 4665
MAN INVESTMENTS SECURITIES JAPAN LTD.—See MAN Group plc; *Int'l*, pg. 4665
MAN INVESTMENTS SGR S.P.A—See MAN Group plc; *Int'l*, pg. 4665
MAN INVESTMENTS (SINGAPORE) PTE. LTD.—See MAN Group plc; *Int'l*, pg. 4664
MAN INVESTMENTS (USA) LLC—See MAN Group plc; *Int'l*, pg. 4664

MANION WILKINS & ASSOCIATES LTD.—See Munchener Ruckversicherungs AG; *Int'l*, pg. 5089
MANIPAL CIGNA HEALTH INSURANCE COMPANY LIMITED—See The Cigna Group; *U.S. Public*, pg. 2062
MANIPAL FINANCE CORPORATION LIMITED; *Int'l*, pg. 4671
MANIPAL HEALTH ENTERPRISES PRIVATE LIMITED—See Temasek Holdings (Private) Limited; *Int'l*, pg. 7548
MANIPAL UNIVERSAL LEARNING (P) LTD.; *Int'l*, pg. 4671
MANIPULACION Y RECUPERACION MAREPA, S.A.—See Fomento de Construcciones y Contratas, S.A.; *Int'l*, pg. 2723
MANISCHEWITZ COMPANY—See R.A.B. Holdings, Inc.; *U.S. Private*, pg. 3334
MANIS LUMBER COMPANY—See Wheeler's Corporation; *U.S. Private*, pg. 4505
MANIS OIL SENDIRIAN BERHAD—See Ta Ann Holdings Berhad; *Int'l*, pg. 7398
THE MANISTEE NEWS ADVOCATE—See The Pioneer Group, Inc.; *U.S. Private*, pg. 4096
MANITEX CAPITAL INC.; *Int'l*, pg. 4672
MANITEX, INC.—See Manitex International, Inc.; *U.S. Public*, pg. 1356
MANITEX INTERNATIONAL, INC.; *U.S. Public*, pg. 1356
MANITEX SABRE, INC.—See Super Steel LLC; *U.S. Private*, pg. 3875
MANITEX VALLA S.R.L.—See Manitex International, Inc.; *U.S. Public*, pg. 1356
MANITOBA CORPORATION; *U.S. Private*, pg. 2564
MANITOBA HVDC RESEARCH CENTRE INC.—See The Manitoba Hydro-Electric Board; *Int'l*, pg. 7665
THE MANITOBA HYDRO-ELECTRIC BOARD; *Int'l*, pg. 7665
MANITOBA HYDRO INTERNATIONAL LTD.—See The Manitoba Hydro-Electric Board; *Int'l*, pg. 7665
MANITOBA HYDRO UTILITY SERVICES, LTD.—See The Manitoba Hydro-Electric Board; *Int'l*, pg. 7665
MANITOBA MOTOR LEAGUE—See CAA Club Group; *Int'l*, pg. 1245
MANITO DIALYSIS, LLC—See DaVita Inc.; *U.S. Public*, pg. 641
MANITOK ENERGY INC.; *Int'l*, pg. 4672
MANITO TRANSIT LLC—See Growmark, Inc.; *U.S. Private*, pg. 1795
MANITOU AMERICAS, INC.—See Manitou BF S.A.; *Int'l*, pg. 4672
MANITOU AMERICAS—See Manitou BF S.A.; *Int'l*, pg. 4672
MANITOU ASIA PTE LTD.—See Manitou BF S.A.; *Int'l*, pg. 4672
MANITOU BENELUX SA—See Manitou BF S.A.; *Int'l*, pg. 4672
MANITOU BF S.A.; *Int'l*, pg. 4672
MANITOU DEUTSCHLAND GMBH—See Manitou BF S.A.; *Int'l*, pg. 4672
MANITOU EQUIPMENT CORP.; *U.S. Private*, pg. 2564
MANITOU EQUIPMENT INDIA PRIVATE LTD—See Manitou BF S.A.; *Int'l*, pg. 4672
MANITOU FINANCE LTD.—See BNP Paribas SA; *Int'l*, pg. 1091
MANITOU GOLD INC.—See Alamos Gold Inc.; *Int'l*, pg. 290
MANITOU INVESTMENT MANAGEMENT LTD.; *Int'l*, pg. 4672
MANITOULIN GROUP OF COMPANIES; *Int'l*, pg. 4672
MANITOU POLSKA SP.Z.O.O.—See Manitou BF S.A.; *Int'l*, pg. 4672
MANITOU PORTUGAL SA—See Manitou BF S.A.; *Int'l*, pg. 4672
MANITOU SOUTHERN AFRICA PTY. LTD.—See Manitou BF S.A.; *Int'l*, pg. 4672
MANITOU UK LTD—See Manitou BF S.A.; *Int'l*, pg. 4672
THE MANITOWOC COMPANY, INC.; *U.S. Public*, pg. 2111
MANITOWOC CRANE CARE - FRANCE—See The Manitowoc Company, Inc.; *U.S. Public*, pg. 2111
MANITOWOC CRANE COMPANIES, INC.—See The Manitowoc Company, Inc.; *U.S. Public*, pg. 2111
MANITOWOC CRANE GROUP ASIA PTE. LTD.—See The Manitowoc Company, Inc.; *U.S. Public*, pg. 2111
MANITOWOC CRANE GROUP AUSTRALIA PTY LTD.—See The Manitowoc Company, Inc.; *U.S. Public*, pg. 2111
MANITOWOC CRANE GROUP COLOMBIA, S.A.S.—See The Manitowoc Company, Inc.; *U.S. Public*, pg. 2111
MANITOWOC CRANE GROUP FRANCE SAS—See The Manitowoc Company, Inc.; *U.S. Public*, pg. 2111
MANITOWOC CRANE GROUP GERMANY GMBH—See The Manitowoc Company, Inc.; *U.S. Public*, pg. 2111
MANITOWOC CRANE GROUP NETHERLANDS B.V.—See The Manitowoc Company, Inc.; *U.S. Public*, pg. 2111
MANITOWOC CRANE GROUP POLAND SP—See The Manitowoc Company, Inc.; *U.S. Public*, pg. 2111
MANITOWOC CRANE GROUP (UK) LTD.—See The Manitowoc Company, Inc.; *U.S. Public*, pg. 2111
MANITOWOC CRANES, INC.—See The Manitowoc Company, Inc.; *U.S. Public*, pg. 2111

MANITOWOC DEBARKING TECHNOLOGY—See Heavy Machines, Inc.; *U.S. Private*, pg. 1902
MANITOWOC FOODSERVICE COMPANIES, LLC—See Ali Holding S.r.l; *Int'l*, pg. 322
MANITOWOC FSG MANUFACTURA MEXICO, S. DE R.L. DE C.V.—See Ali Holding S.r.l; *Int'l*, pg. 322
MANITOWOC FSG OPERATIONS, LLC—See The Manitowoc Company, Inc.; *U.S. Public*, pg. 2111
MANITOWOC GROUP (UK) LIMITED—See The Manitowoc Company, Inc.; *U.S. Public*, pg. 2111
MANITOWOC ICE, INC.—See Ali Holding S.r.l; *Int'l*, pg. 322
MANITOWOC PUBLIC UTILITIES; *U.S. Private*, pg. 2564
MANITOWOC RE-MANUFACTURING, INC.—See The Manitowoc Company, Inc.; *U.S. Public*, pg. 2111
MANITOWOC SENIOR LIVING, INC.—See The Ensign Group, Inc.; *U.S. Public*, pg. 2070
MANITOWOC WESTERN COMPANY, INC.—See The Manitowoc Company, Inc.; *U.S. Public*, pg. 2111
MANIYAR PLAST LTD.; *Int'l*, pg. 4672
MANJEERA CONSTRUCTIONS LTD; *Int'l*, pg. 4672
MANJUSHREE FINANCE LIMITED; *Int'l*, pg. 4672
MANJUSHREE TECHNOPACK LIMITED—See Advent International Corporation; *U.S. Private*, pg. 103
MANKATO FORD ACQUISITION CORP.; *U.S. Private*, pg. 2564
MANKATO MOTOR CO.; *U.S. Private*, pg. 2564
MANKATO REHABILITATION CENTER, INC.; *U.S. Private*, pg. 2564
MANKE LUMBER COMPANY, INC.; *U.S. Private*, pg. 2564
MANKICHI SOFTWARE (VIETNAM) CO., LTD.; *Int'l*, pg. 4672
MANKIND AGRITECH PRIVATE LIMITED—See Mankind Pharma Ltd.; *Int'l*, pg. 4673
MANKIND PHARMA LTD.; *Int'l*, pg. 4673
MANKIND SPECIALITIES—See Mankind Pharma Ltd.; *Int'l*, pg. 4673
MAN KING HOLDINGS LIMITED; *Int'l*, pg. 4665
MANKIN MEDIA SYSTEMS, INC.; *U.S. Private*, pg. 2564
MANKOTA STOCKMEN'S WEIGH CO. LTD; *Int'l*, pg. 4673
MANKO WINDOW SYSTEMS INC.; *U.S. Private*, pg. 2564
MANLI TECHNOLOGY GROUP LIMITED—See PC Partner Group Limited; *Int'l*, pg. 5766
MANLY GMC BUICK HYUNDAI MITSUBISHI; *U.S. Private*, pg. 2564
MAN & MACHINE SOFTWARE SP. Z O.O.—See Mensch und Maschine Software SE; *Int'l*, pg. 4817
MAN & MACHINE SOFTWARE S.R.L.—See Mensch und Maschine Software SE; *Int'l*, pg. 4817
MAN-MACHINES SYSTEMS ASSESSMENT, INC.; *U.S. Private*, pg. 2559
MAN MARKETING, INC.; *U.S. Private*, pg. 2559
MANNA DISTRIBUTION; *U.S. Private*, pg. 2565
MANNA FREIGHT SYSTEMS, INC.—See A.P. Moller-Maersk A/S; *Int'l*, pg. 27
MANNAI CORPORATION QPSC; *Int'l*, pg. 4674
MANNAI MARINE CO. LIMITED—See Mannai Corporation QPSC; *Int'l*, pg. 4675
MANNAI TRADING COMPANY WLL—See Mannai Corporation QPSC; *Int'l*, pg. 4675
MANN AND HUMMEL FILTER PRIVATE LIMITED - PLANT 1—See Mann+Hummel GmbH; *Int'l*, pg. 4673
MANN AND HUMMEL FILTER PRIVATE LIMITED - PLANT 2—See Mann+Hummel GmbH; *Int'l*, pg. 4673
MANN AND HUMMEL FILTER PRIVATE LIMITED—See Mann+Hummel GmbH; *Int'l*, pg. 4673
MANN AND HUMMEL THAILAND LTD.—See Mann+Hummel GmbH; *Int'l*, pg. 4673
MANNA PRO PRODUCTS, LLC—See The Carlyle Group Inc.; *U.S. Public*, pg. 2049
MANNATECH AUSTRALIA PTY LIMITED—See Mannatech, Incorporated; *U.S. Public*, pg. 1357
MANNATECH, INCORPORATED; *U.S. Public*, pg. 1356
MANNATECH JAPAN, INC.—See Mannatech, Incorporated; *U.S. Public*, pg. 1357
MANNATECH TAIWAN CORPORATION—See Mannatech, Incorporated; *U.S. Public*, pg. 1357
MANNATEC, INC.—See Corpay, Inc.; *U.S. Public*, pg. 580
MANNA UNYU CO., LTD.—See Kato Sangyo Co., Ltd.; *Int'l*, pg. 4090
MANN CHRYSLER-PLYMOUTH-DODGE-JEEP; *U.S. Private*, pg. 2564
MANNER HONG KONG LIMITED—See Barnes Group Inc.; *U.S. Public*, pg. 277
MANNER JAPAN CO. LTD.—See Barnes Group Inc.; *U.S. Public*, pg. 278
MANNER METAL A/S—See Wieland-Werke AG; *Int'l*, pg. 8403
MANNER USA, INC.—See Barnes Group Inc.; *U.S. Public*, pg. 277
MANNESMANN GROSSROHR GMBH—See Salzgitter AG; *Int'l*, pg. 6497
MANNESMANN LINE PIPE GMBH—See Salzgitter AG; *Int'l*, pg. 6497
MANNESMANN PRECISION TUBES FRANCE SAS—See Salzgitter AG; *Int'l*, pg. 6497

MANN CHRYSLER-PLYMOUTH-DODGE-JEEP — CORPORATE AFFILIATIONS

MANNESMANN PRECISION TUBES GMBH—See Salzgitter AG; *Int'l*, pg. 6497
MANNESMANN PRECISION TUBES MEXICO S.A. DE C.V.—See Salzgitter AG; *Int'l*, pg. 6497
MANNESMANN PRECISION TUBES NETHERLANDS B.V.—See Salzgitter AG; *Int'l*, pg. 6497
MANNESMANNROHREN-WERKE GMBH—See Salzgitter AG; *Int'l*, pg. 6497
MANNESMANN SOTEP STAINLESS TUBES SAS—See Salzgitter AG; *Int'l*, pg. 6497
MANNESMANN STAINLESS TUBES GMBH—See Salzgitter AG; *Int'l*, pg. 6497
MANNEY'S SHOPPER, INC.; *U.S. Private*, pg. 2565
MANNHEIMER AG HOLDING—See Continentale Holding AG; *Int'l*, pg. 1784
MANNHEIMER KRANKENVERSICHERUNG AG—See Continentale Holding AG; *Int'l*, pg. 1784
MANNHEIMER SERVICE UND VERMOGENSVERWALTUNGS GMBH—See UNIQA Insurance Group AG; *Int'l*, pg. 8058
MANNHEIMER VERSICHERUNG AG—See Continentale Holding AG; *Int'l*, pg. 1784
MANNHEIM HOLDINGS, LLC—See Mannheim, LLC; *U.S. Private*, pg. 2565
MANNHEIM, LLC; *U.S. Private*, pg. 2565
MANN+HUMMEL ADVANCED FILTRATION CONCEPTS, INC.—See Mann+Hummel GmbH; *Int'l*, pg. 4674
MANN+HUMMEL ARGENTINA S.A.—See Mann+Hummel GmbH; *Int'l*, pg. 4674
MANN+HUMMEL ATEX FILTER VERWALTUNGSGESELLSCHAFT MBH—See Mann+Hummel GmbH; *Int'l*, pg. 4673
MANN+HUMMEL BA J.S.C.—See Mann+Hummel GmbH; *Int'l*, pg. 4673
MANN+HUMMEL BRASIL LTDA.—See Mann+Hummel GmbH; *Int'l*, pg. 4674
MANN+HUMMEL BRASIL TECNOLOGIA EM AGUA PARTICIPACOES LTDA.—See Mann+Hummel GmbH; *Int'l*, pg. 4673
MANN+HUMMEL COLOMBIA S.A.S.—See Mann+Hummel GmbH; *Int'l*, pg. 4674
MANN+HUMMEL (CZ) S.R.O.—See Mann+Hummel GmbH; *Int'l*, pg. 4674
MANN+HUMMEL FILTER (CHONGQING) CO., LTD.—See Mann+Hummel GmbH; *Int'l*, pg. 4674
MANN & HUMMEL FILTERS SOUTH AFRICA (PTY) LTD.—See Mann+Hummel GmbH; *Int'l*, pg. 4674
MANN+HUMMEL FILTER TECHNOLOGY (S.E.A.) PTE. LTD.—See Mann+Hummel GmbH; *Int'l*, pg. 4674
MANN+HUMMEL FILTRATION TECHNOLOGY CANADA ULC—See Mann+Hummel GmbH; *Int'l*, pg. 4674
MANN+HUMMEL FILTRATION TECHNOLOGY MEXICO S. DE R.L.DE C.V.—See Mann+Hummel GmbH; *Int'l*, pg. 4674
MANN+HUMMEL FILTRATION TECHNOLOGY US LLC—See Mann+Hummel GmbH; *Int'l*, pg. 4674
MANN+HUMMEL FILTRATION TECHNOLOGY VENEZUELA C.A.—See Mann+Hummel GmbH; *Int'l*, pg. 4674
MANN+HUMMEL FRANCE S.A.S.—See Mutares SE & Co. KGaA; *Int'l*, pg. 5105
MANN+HUMMEL FT POLAND SPOLKA Z OGRANICZONA ODPOWIEDZIALNOSCIA SP.K.—See Mann+Hummel GmbH; *Int'l*, pg. 4673
MANN+HUMMEL GMBH - MARKLKOFEN—See Mann+Hummel GmbH; *Int'l*, pg. 4674
MANN+HUMMEL GMBH - SONNEBERG—See Mutares SE & Co. KGaA; *Int'l*, pg. 5105
MANN+HUMMEL GMBH; *Int'l*, pg. 4673
MANN+HUMMEL GMBH - SPEYER—See Mann+Hummel GmbH; *Int'l*, pg. 4674
MANN+HUMMEL HYDROMATION N.V.—See Mann+Hummel GmbH; *Int'l*, pg. 4674
MANN+HUMMEL IBERICA S.A.—See Mann+Hummel GmbH; *Int'l*, pg. 4674
MANN+HUMMEL, INC.—See Mann+Hummel GmbH; *Int'l*, pg. 4674
MANN+HUMMEL JAPAN K.K.—See Mann+Hummel GmbH; *Int'l*, pg. 4674
MANN+HUMMEL KOREA CO. LTD.—See Mann+Hummel GmbH; *Int'l*, pg. 4673
MANN+HUMMEL MEXICO, S.A. DE C.V.—See Mann+Hummel GmbH; *Int'l*, pg. 4674
MANN+HUMMEL MIDDLE EAST FZE—See Mann+Hummel GmbH; *Int'l*, pg. 4673
MANN+HUMMEL PROTEC GMBH—See Mann+Hummel GmbH; *Int'l*, pg. 4674
MANN+HUMMEL PUROLATOR FILTERS LLC—See Mann+Hummel GmbH; *Int'l*, pg. 4674
MANN+HUMMEL TOGLIATTI OOO—See Mann+Hummel GmbH; *Int'l*, pg. 4674
MANN+HUMMEL TRADING (SHANGHAI) CO., LTD.—See Mann+Hummel GmbH; *Int'l*, pg. 4674
MANN+HUMMEL (UK) LTD.—See Mann+Hummel GmbH; *Int'l*, pg. 4674
MANN+HUMMEL USA, INC.—See Mann+Hummel GmbH; *Int'l*, pg. 4674
MANN+HUMMEL VOKES AIR AB—See Mann+Hummel GmbH; *Int'l*, pg. 4673

MANN+HUMMEL VOKES AIR AS—See Mann+Hummel GmbH; *Int'l*, pg. 4673
MANN+HUMMEL VOKES AIR GMBH—See Mann+Hummel GmbH; *Int'l*, pg. 4673
MANN+HUMMEL VOKES-AIR LIMITED—See Mann+Hummel GmbH; *Int'l*, pg. 4673
MANN+HUMMEL VOKES AIR SAS—See Mann+Hummel GmbH; *Int'l*, pg. 4673
MANN+HUMMEL VOKES AIR SL—See Mann+Hummel GmbH; *Int'l*, pg. 4673
MANN+HUMMEL VOKES AIR SRL—See Mann+Hummel GmbH; *Int'l*, pg. 4673
MANN+HUMMEL VOKES AIR TREATMENT HOLDINGS LIMITED—See SPX Technologies, Inc.; *U.S. Public*, pg. 1921
MANNING BUILDING SUPPLIES, INC.—See Bain Capital, LP; *U.S. Private*, pg. 451
MANNING ENTERPRISES INC.; *U.S. Private*, pg. 2565
MANNING EQUIPMENT, LLC—See Manning Enterprises Inc.; *U.S. Private*, pg. 2565
MANNING FINANCIAL GROUP, INC.; *U.S. Private*, pg. 2565
MANNING FOREST PRODUCTS LTD.—See West Fraser Timber Co., Ltd.; *Int'l*, pg. 8383
MANNING GOTTLIEB OMD; *Int'l*, pg. 4675
MANNING GREAT LAKES MEMORIAL GARDENS PTY LTD—See Propel Funeral Partners Limited; *Int'l*, pg. 5997
MANNING GROSS + MASSENBURG LLP; *U.S. Private*, pg. 2565
MANNINGHAM COMMUNITY ENTERPRISES LIMITED—See Bendigo & Adelaide Bank Ltd.; *Int'l*, pg. 971
MANNINGHAM HOTEL (BMG) PTY LTD—See Woolworths Group Limited; *Int'l*, pg. 8451
MANNING, INC.; *U.S. Private*, pg. 2565
MANNING JAYA TRADING (B) SDN. BHD.—See Biotronik GmbH & Co.; *Int'l*, pg. 1044
MANNING & LEWIS ENGINEERING COMPANY; *U.S. Private*, pg. 2565
MANNING LIGHT TRUCK EQUIPMENT, LLC—See Manning Enterprises Inc.; *U.S. Private*, pg. 2565
MANNING MANAGEMENT CORPORATION; *U.S. Private*, pg. 2565
MANNING & NAPIER ADVISORS, LLC—See Callodine Acquisition Corporation; *U.S. Public*, pg. 424
MANNING & NAPIER BENEFITS, LLC—See Callodine Acquisition Corporation; *U.S. Public*, pg. 424
MANNING & NAPIER, INC.—See Callodine Acquisition Corporation; *U.S. Public*, pg. 424
MANNING REGIONAL HEALTHCARE CENTER; *U.S. Private*, pg. 2565
MANNINGS (ASIA) CONSULTANTS LIMITED—See Boltek Holdings Limited; *Int'l*, pg. 1103
MANNING'S BEEF LLC.; *U.S. Private*, pg. 2565
MANNING SELVAGE & LEE LONDON—See Publicis Groupe S.A.; *Int'l*, pg. 6103
MANNING SELVAGE & LEE—See Publicis Groupe S.A.; *Int'l*, pg. 6103
MANNING SELVAGE & LEE—See Publicis Groupe S.A.; *Int'l*, pg. 6103
MANNING SELVAGE & LEE—See Publicis Groupe S.A.; *Int'l*, pg. 6103
MANNING SELVAGE & LEE—See Publicis Groupe S.A.; *Int'l*, pg. 6103
MANNINGS GUANGDONG RETAIL COMPANY LTD—See Jardine Matheson Holdings Limited; *Int'l*, pg. 3909
MANNING-SQUIRES-HENNIG CO. INC.; *U.S. Private*, pg. 2565
MANNINGTON CARPETS—See Mannington Mills, Inc.; *U.S. Private*, pg. 2566
MANNINGTON MILLS, INC.; *U.S. Private*, pg. 2565
MANNINGTON RESILIENT FLOORS—See Mannington Mills, Inc.; *U.S. Private*, pg. 2566
MANNINGTON WOOD FLOORS—See Mannington Mills, Inc.; *U.S. Private*, pg. 2566
MANNING TRUCK MODIFICATION—See Manning Enterprises Inc.; *U.S. Private*, pg. 2565
MANNING VENTURES, INC.; *Int'l*, pg. 4675
MANNIX MARKETING, INC.; *U.S. Private*, pg. 2566
MANNKIND BIOPHARMACEUTICALS—See MannKind Corporation; *U.S. Public*, pg. 1357
MANNKIND CORPORATION; *U.S. Public*, pg. 1357
MANNKRAFT CORPORATION—See Four M Holdings LLC; *U.S. Private*, pg. 1582
MANN LAKE LTD.—See Grey Mountain Partners, LLC; *U.S. Private*, pg. 1784
MANN PACKING CO., INC.—See Fresh Del Monte Produce Inc.; *U.S. Public*, pg. 886
MANN REALTY COMPANY; *U.S. Private*, pg. 2564
MANN'S INTERNATIONAL MEAT SPECIALTIES INC.; *U.S. Private*, pg. 2565
MANNSTAEDT-WERKE GMBH & CO. KG—See Georgsmarienhutte Holding GmbH; *Int'l*, pg. 2940
MANNS WINE CO., LTD.—See Kikkoman Corporation; *Int'l*, pg. 4161
MANNS WINE PUB CO., LTD.—See Kikkoman Corporation; *Int'l*, pg. 4161
MANN THEATERS INC.; *U.S. Private*, pg. 2564

MANN VE HUMMEL FILTRE SANAYI VE TICARET LIMITED SIRKETI—See Mann+Hummel GmbH; *Int'l*, pg. 4673
MANN WASTE MANAGEMENT PTY LTD—See Cleanaway Waste Management Limited; *Int'l*, pg. 1655
MANN & WATTERS, INC.—See New Mountain Capital, LLC; *U.S. Private*, pg. 2901
MANNY'S TV AND APPLIANCES; *U.S. Private*, pg. 2566
THE MANOFF GROUP, INC.—See John Snow, Inc.; *U.S. Private*, pg. 2224
MANOHAY ARGENTINA SA—See Straumann Holding AG; *Int'l*, pg. 7238
MANOHAY DENTAL SA—See Straumann Holding AG; *Int'l*, pg. 7238
MANOHAY MEXICO SA DE CV—See Straumann Holding AG; *Int'l*, pg. 7238
MANOIR ARCHER INC.—See Welltower Inc.; *U.S. Public*, pg. 2348
MANOIR INDUSTRIES - MANOIR BOUZONVILLE PLANT—See Manoir Industries; *Int'l*, pg. 4675
MANOIR INDUSTRIES - MANOIR ENGRENAGES PLANT—See Manoir Industries; *Int'l*, pg. 4675
MANOIR INDUSTRIES; *Int'l*, pg. 4675
MANOIR INDUSTRIES—See Manoir Industries; *Int'l*, pg. 4675
MANOIR INDUSTRIES—See Manoir Industries; *Int'l*, pg. 4675
MANOIR INDUSTRIES—See Manoir Industries; *Int'l*, pg. 4675
MANOIR INDUSTRIES—See Manoir Industries; *Int'l*, pg. 4675
MANOIR PETRO INDIA LIMITED—See Manoir Industries; *Int'l*, pg. 4675
MANOJ VAIBHAV GEMS N JEWELLERS LIMITED; *Int'l*, pg. 4675
MANOLETE PARTNERS PLC; *Int'l*, pg. 4675
MANOMAY TEX INDIA LIMITED; *Int'l*, pg. 4675
MANOR AG—See Maus Freres S.A.; *Int'l*, pg. 4732
MANORAMA INDUSTRIES LIMITED; *Int'l*, pg. 4675
THE MANOR CLINIC LIMITED—See Acadia Healthcare Company, Inc.; *U.S. Public*, pg. 30
M.A. NORDEN COMPANY INC.; *U.S. Private*, pg. 2527
MANOR ESTATES & INDUSTRIES LIMITED; *Int'l*, pg. 4675
MANOR FRESH LIMITED; *Int'l*, pg. 4675
MANOR GARDENS (SELSEY) MANAGEMENT COMPANY LIMITED—See Persimmon plc; *Int'l*, pg. 5816
MANOR HARDWARE, INC.—See KYOCERA Corporation; *Int'l*, pg. 4355
THE MANOR HOSPITAL OXFORD—See Nuffield Health; *Int'l*, pg. 5487
MANOR HOUSE KITCHENS INC.; *U.S. Private*, pg. 2566
MANOR HOUSE PUBLISHING CO, INC.; *U.S. Private*, pg. 2566
MANOR NATIONAL BANK; *U.S. Public*, pg. 1357
MANOR PARK HEALTHCARE LLC—See The Ensign Group, Inc.; *U.S. Public*, pg. 2071
MANPOWER AB—See ManpowerGroup Inc.; *U.S. Public*, pg. 1360
MANPOWER A/S (DENMARK)—See ManpowerGroup Inc.; *U.S. Public*, pg. 1358
MANPOWER A/S—See ManpowerGroup Inc.; *U.S. Public*, pg. 1360
MANPOWER BULGARIA OOD—See ManpowerGroup Inc.; *U.S. Public*, pg. 1358
MANPOWER BUSINESS CONSULTING (SHANGHAI) CO. LTD.—See ManpowerGroup Inc.; *U.S. Public*, pg. 1358
MANPOWER BUSINESS SOLUTIONS GMBH—See ManpowerGroup Inc.; *U.S. Public*, pg. 1358
MANPOWER BUSINESS SOLUTIONS KFT—See ManpowerGroup Inc.; *U.S. Public*, pg. 1358
MANPOWER BUSINESS SOLUTIONS -RETAIL AS—See ManpowerGroup Inc.; *U.S. Public*, pg. 1360
MANPOWER BUSINESS SOLUTIONS SA—See ManpowerGroup Inc.; *U.S. Public*, pg. 1358
MANPOWER BUSINESS SOLUTIONS SERVICE CENTER AB—See ManpowerGroup Inc.; *U.S. Public*, pg. 1360
MANPOWER BUSINESS SOLUTIONS, S.L.U—See ManpowerGroup Inc.; *U.S. Public*, pg. 1358
MANPOWER B.V.—See ManpowerGroup Inc.; *U.S. Public*, pg. 1360
MANPOWER B.V.—See ManpowerGroup Inc.; *U.S. Public*, pg. 1358
MANPOWER CADEN CHINA CO LTD—See ManpowerGroup Inc.; *U.S. Public*, pg. 1358
MANPOWER CARE LTD.—See ManpowerGroup Inc.; *U.S. Public*, pg. 1358
MANPOWER DEUTSCHLAND GMBH—See ManpowerGroup Inc.; *U.S. Public*, pg. 1358
MANPOWER DE VENEZUELA C.A.—See ManpowerGroup Inc.; *U.S. Public*, pg. 1360
MANPOWER D.O.O.—See ManpowerGroup Inc.; *U.S. Public*, pg. 1360
MANPOWER EL & TELE AB—See ManpowerGroup Inc.; *U.S. Public*, pg. 1360
MANPOWER EUROPE HOLDINGS, APS—See ManpowerGroup Inc.; *U.S. Public*, pg. 1358
MANPOWER FRAMNAES INSTALLASJON AS—See ManpowerGroup Inc.; *U.S. Public*, pg. 1358
MANPOWER FRANCE SAS—See ManpowerGroup Inc.; *U.S. Public*, pg. 1360

COMPANY NAME INDEX

MANPOWER GMBH & CO. KG PERSONALDIENSTLEISTUNGEN—See ManpowerGroup Inc.; *U.S. Public*, pg. 1358
MANPOWERGROUP AB—See ManpowerGroup Inc.; *U.S. Public*, pg. 1360
MANPOWERGROUP AS—See ManpowerGroup Inc.; *U.S. Public*, pg. 1360
MANPOWERGROUP BUSINESS SOLUTIONS LTD.—See ManpowerGroup Inc.; *U.S. Public*, pg. 1360
MANPOWERGROUP CO. LIMITED—See ManpowerGroup Inc.; *U.S. Public*, pg. 1360
MANPOWERGROUP CO., LTD.—See ManpowerGroup Inc.; *U.S. Public*, pg. 1360
MANPOWERGROUP DEUTSCHLAND GMBH—See ManpowerGroup Inc.; *U.S. Public*, pg. 1360
MANPOWERGROUP FRANCE SAS—See ManpowerGroup Inc.; *U.S. Public*, pg. 1360
MANPOWERGROUP GMBH—See ManpowerGroup Inc.; *U.S. Public*, pg. 1360
MANPOWERGROUP GREATER CHINA LIMITED; *Int'l*, pg. 4675
MANPOWERGROUP HOLDING GMBH—See ManpowerGroup Inc.; *U.S. Public*, pg. 1360
MANPOWERGROUP INC.; *U.S. Public*, pg. 1357
MANPOWERGROUP (IRELAND) LIMITED—See ManpowerGroup Inc.; *U.S. Public*, pg. 1360
MANPOWERGROUP KOREA, INC.—See ManpowerGroup Inc.; *U.S. Public*, pg. 1360
MANPOWERGROUP NETHERLANDS B.V.—See ManpowerGroup Inc.; *U.S. Public*, pg. 1360
MANPOWERGROUP OY—See ManpowerGroup Inc.; *U.S. Public*, pg. 1360
MANPOWERGROUP POLSKA SP. Z O.O.—See ManpowerGroup Inc.; *U.S. Public*, pg. 1360
MANPOWERGROUP PORTUGAL - SGPS, S.A.—See ManpowerGroup Inc.; *U.S. Public*, pg. 1360
MANPOWERGROUP PUBLIC SECTOR INC.—See ManpowerGroup Inc.; *U.S. Public*, pg. 1360
MANPOWERGROUP S.A.—See ManpowerGroup Inc.; *U.S. Public*, pg. 1360
MANPOWERGROUP SERVICES INDIA PVT. LTD.—See ManpowerGroup Inc.; *U.S. Public*, pg. 1361
MANPOWERGROUP SLOVENSKO S.R.O.—See ManpowerGroup Inc.; *U.S. Public*, pg. 1361
MANPOWERGROUP SOLUTIONS AS—See ManpowerGroup Inc.; *U.S. Public*, pg. 1361
MANPOWERGROUP SOLUTIONS BELGIUM SA—See ManpowerGroup Inc.; *U.S. Public*, pg. 1362
MANPOWERGROUP SOLUTIONS B.V.—See ManpowerGroup Inc.; *U.S. Public*, pg. 1360
MANPOWERGROUP SOLUTIONS IT AB—See ManpowerGroup Inc.; *U.S. Public*, pg. 1360
MANPOWERGROUP SOLUTIONS LDA—See ManpowerGroup Inc.; *U.S. Public*, pg. 1360
MANPOWERGROUP SOLUTIONS, S.L.U—See ManpowerGroup Inc.; *U.S. Public*, pg. 1361
MANPOWERGROUP SOLUTIONS SRL—See ManpowerGroup Inc.; *U.S. Public*, pg. 1361
MANPOWERGROUP SP. Z O.O.—See ManpowerGroup Inc.; *U.S. Public*, pg. 1361
MANPOWERGROUP S R.O.—See ManpowerGroup Inc.; *U.S. Public*, pg. 1361
MANPOWERGROUP UK LIMITED—See ManpowerGroup Inc.; *U.S. Public*, pg. 1361
MANPOWER GUATEMALA S.A.—See ManpowerGroup Inc.; *U.S. Public*, pg. 1358
MANPOWER HOLDING AG—See ManpowerGroup Inc.; *U.S. Public*, pg. 1358
MANPOWER HOLDING CORP.; *U.S. Private*, pg. 2566
MANPOWER HONDURAS, S.A.—See ManpowerGroup Inc.; *U.S. Public*, pg. 1359
MANPOWER HR MANAGEMENT S.A.—See ManpowerGroup Inc.; *U.S. Public*, pg. 1358
MANPOWER HR SRL—See ManpowerGroup Inc.; *U.S. Public*, pg. 1358
MANPOWER, INC. / CALIFORNIA PENINSULA—See ManpowerGroup Inc.; *U.S. Public*, pg. 1360
MANPOWER, INCORPORATED OF SOUTHERN NEVADA—See Manpower Holding Corp.; *U.S. Private*, pg. 2566
MANPOWER INC. - SAN DIEGO—See ManpowerGroup Inc.; *U.S. Public*, pg. 1359
MANPOWER INSAN KAYNAKLARI LIMITED SIRKETI—See ManpowerGroup Inc.; *U.S. Public*, pg. 1359
MANPOWER (IRELAND) GROUP LIMITED—See ManpowerGroup Inc.; *U.S. Public*, pg. 1358
MANPOWER (IRELAND) LIMITED—See ManpowerGroup Inc.; *U.S. Public*, pg. 1358
MANPOWER (ISRAEL) LTD.—See ManpowerGroup Inc.; *U.S. Public*, pg. 1358
MANPOWER KAZ LLC—See ManpowerGroup Inc.; *U.S. Public*, pg. 1358
MANPOWER KOREA, INC.—See ManpowerGroup Inc.; *U.S. Public*, pg. 1358
MANPOWER LIT UAB—See ManpowerGroup Inc.; *U.S. Public*, pg. 1359
MANPOWER LUXEMBOURG S.A.—See ManpowerGroup Inc.; *U.S. Public*, pg. 1359

MANPOWER MENSAJERIA, S.A. DE C.V.—See ManpowerGroup Inc.; *U.S. Public*, pg. 1359
MANPOWER MIDDLE EAST FZ-LLC—See ManpowerGroup Inc.; *U.S. Public*, pg. 1359
MANPOWER MONACO SAM—See ManpowerGroup Inc.; *U.S. Public*, pg. 1359
MANPOWER NICARUAGUA S.A.—See ManpowerGroup Inc.; *U.S. Public*, pg. 1359
MANPOWER NORWAY HOLDINGS AS—See ManpowerGroup Inc.; *U.S. Public*, pg. 1359
MANPOWER OUTSOURCING SERVICES INC.—See ManpowerGroup Inc.; *U.S. Public*, pg. 1359
MANPOWER OUTSOURCING SERVICES (MACAU) LIMITED—See ManpowerGroup Greater China Limited; *Int'l*, pg. 4675
MANPOWER OY—See ManpowerGroup Inc.; *U.S. Public*, pg. 1359
MANPOWER PANAMA S.A.—See ManpowerGroup Inc.; *U.S. Public*, pg. 1359
MANPOWER PANAMA S.A.—See ManpowerGroup Inc.; *U.S. Public*, pg. 1359
MANPOWER PARAGUAY S.R.L.—See ManpowerGroup Inc.; *U.S. Public*, pg. 1359
MANPOWER PERU S.A.—See ManpowerGroup Inc.; *U.S. Public*, pg. 1359
MANPOWER POLSKA SP. ZO. O—See ManpowerGroup Inc.; *U.S. Public*, pg. 1359
MANPOWER PORTUGAL EMPRESA DE TRABALHO TEMPORARIO S.A.—See ManpowerGroup Inc.; *U.S. Public*, pg. 1359
MANPOWER PROFESSIONAL ENGINEERING AS—See ManpowerGroup Inc.; *U.S. Public*, pg. 1360
MANPOWER ROMANIA SRL—See ManpowerGroup Inc.; *U.S. Public*, pg. 1359
MANPOWER S.A. DE C.V.—See ManpowerGroup Inc.; *U.S. Public*, pg. 1359
MANPOWER, S.A. DE C.V.—See ManpowerGroup Inc.; *U.S. Public*, pg. 1359
MANPOWER SA (PTY) LTD.—See ManpowerGroup Inc.; *U.S. Public*, pg. 1359
MANPOWER S.A.—See ManpowerGroup Inc.; *U.S. Public*, pg. 1359
MANPOWER SAVJETOVANJE DOO—See ManpowerGroup Inc.; *U.S. Public*, pg. 1359
MANPOWER SERVICE INC.—See ManpowerGroup Inc.; *U.S. Public*, pg. 1359
MANPOWER SERVICES (AUSTRALIA) PTY. LTD.—See ManpowerGroup Inc.; *U.S. Public*, pg. 1359
MANPOWER SERVICES CANADA LIMITED—See ManpowerGroup Inc.; *U.S. Public*, pg. 1359
MANPOWER SERVICES (HONG KONG) LIMITED—See ManpowerGroup Inc.; *U.S. Public*, pg. 1359
MANPOWER SERVICES (MACAU) LIMITED—See ManpowerGroup Inc.; *U.S. Public*, pg. 1359
MANPOWER SERVICES (TAIWAN) CO., LTD.—See ManpowerGroup Inc.; *U.S. Public*, pg. 1359
MANPOWER SLOVAKIA SRO—See ManpowerGroup Inc.; *U.S. Public*, pg. 1359
MANPOWER S.R.L—See ManpowerGroup Inc.; *U.S. Public*, pg. 1359
MANPOWER STAFFING (AUSTRALIA) PTY LIMITED—See ManpowerGroup Inc.; *U.S. Public*, pg. 1359
MANPOWER STAFFING SERVICES AS—See ManpowerGroup Inc.; *U.S. Public*, pg. 1360
MANPOWER STAFFING SERVICES (MALAYSIA) SDN BHD—See ManpowerGroup Inc.; *U.S. Public*, pg. 1359
MANPOWER STAFFING SERVICES (SINGAPORE) PTE. LTD.—See ManpowerGroup Inc.; *U.S. Public*, pg. 1359
MANPOWER STUDENT AB—See ManpowerGroup Inc.; *U.S. Public*, pg. 1359
MANPOWER TUNISIE INTERNATIONAL SARL—See ManpowerGroup Inc.; *U.S. Public*, pg. 1359
MANPOWER UK LIMITED—See ManpowerGroup Inc.; *U.S. Public*, pg. 1359
MANRAJ HOUSING FINANCE LIMITED; *Int'l*, pg. 4675
MANROC DEVELOPMENTS INC.; *Int'l*, pg. 4675
MANROLAND ADRIATIC D.O.O.—See Langley Holdings Plc; *Int'l*, pg. 4411
MANROLAND AUSTRALASIA PTY. LTD.—See Langley Holdings Plc; *Int'l*, pg. 4410
MANROLAND BENELUX N.V.—See Langley Holdings Plc; *Int'l*, pg. 4411
MANROLAND BULGARIA EOOD—See Langley Holdings Plc; *Int'l*, pg. 4410
MANROLAND CANADA INC.—See Langley Holdings Plc; *Int'l*, pg. 4411
MANROLAND (CHINA) LTD.—See Langley Holdings Plc; *Int'l*, pg. 4410
MANROLAND CZECH S.R.O.—See Langley Holdings Plc; *Int'l*, pg. 4410
MANROLAND DO BRASIL SERVICOS LTDA—See Langley Holdings Plc; *Int'l*, pg. 4410
MANROLAND D.O.O.—See Langley Holdings Plc; *Int'l*, pg. 4411
MANROLAND FRANCE SAS—See Langley Holdings Plc; *Int'l*, pg. 4411
MANROLAND GOSS WEB SYSTEMS AMERICAS LLC—See L. Possehl & Co. mbH; *Int'l*, pg. 4385

MANROLAND GOSS WEB SYSTEMS AUSTRALASIA PTY. LTD.—See L. Possehl & Co. mbH; *Int'l*, pg. 4385
MANROLAND GOSS WEB SYSTEMS FRANCE S.A.S.—See L. Possehl & Co. mbH; *Int'l*, pg. 4385
MANROLAND GOSS WEB SYSTEMS GMBH—See AIP, LLC; *U.S. Private*, pg. 134
MANROLAND GOSS WEB SYSTEMS (INDIA) PVT. LTD.—See L. Possehl & Co. mbH; *Int'l*, pg. 4385
MANROLAND GOSS WEB SYSTEMS JAPAN CORP—See L. Possehl & Co. mbH; *Int'l*, pg. 4385
MANROLAND GOSS WEB SYSTEMS SINGAPORE PTE. LTD.—See L. Possehl & Co. mbH; *Int'l*, pg. 4385
MANROLAND GOSS WEB SYSTEMS UK LTD.—See L. Possehl & Co. mbH; *Int'l*, pg. 4385
MANROLAND HEUSENSTAMM GMBH—See Langley Holdings Plc; *Int'l*, pg. 4411
MANROLAND IBERICA SISTEMAS S.A.—See Langley Holdings Plc; *Int'l*, pg. 4411
MANROLAND IBERICA SISTEMAS S.L.—See Langley Holdings Plc; *Int'l*, pg. 4411
MANROLAND INC.—See Langley Holdings Plc; *Int'l*, pg. 4411
MANROLAND INDIA PVT. LTD.—See Langley Holdings Plc; *Int'l*, pg. 4410
MANROLAND INDONESIA P.T.—See Langley Holdings Plc; *Int'l*, pg. 4410
MANROLAND IRELAND LTD.—See Langley Holdings Plc; *Int'l*, pg. 4411
MANROLAND ITALIA S.P.A.—See Langley Holdings Plc; *Int'l*, pg. 4410
MANROLAND JAPAN CO., LTD.—See Langley Holdings Plc; *Int'l*, pg. 4411
MANROLAND KOREA LTD.—See Langley Holdings Plc; *Int'l*, pg. 4410
MANROLAND LATINA S.A.C.—See Langley Holdings Plc; *Int'l*, pg. 4410
MANROLAND LATINA SA DE CV—See Langley Holdings Plc; *Int'l*, pg. 4410
MANROLAND LATINA S.A.—See Langley Holdings Plc; *Int'l*, pg. 4410
MANROLAND LATINA S.A.S—See Langley Holdings Plc; *Int'l*, pg. 4410
MANROLAND MAGYARORSZAG KFT.—See Langley Holdings Plc; *Int'l*, pg. 4411
MANROLAND MALAYSIA SDN BHD—See Langley Holdings Plc; *Int'l*, pg. 4410
MANROLAND NORDIC DANMARK A/S—See Langley Holdings Plc; *Int'l*, pg. 4411
MANROLAND NORDIC FINLAND OY—See Langley Holdings Plc; *Int'l*, pg. 4411
MANROLAND NORDIC NORGE AS—See Langley Holdings Plc; *Int'l*, pg. 4411
MANROLAND NORDIC SVERIGE AB—See Langley Holdings Plc; *Int'l*, pg. 4411
MANROLAND OSTERREICH GMBH—See Langley Holdings Plc; *Int'l*, pg. 4410
MANROLAND POLAND SP. Z O.O.—See Langley Holdings Plc; *Int'l*, pg. 4411
MANROLAND PRINTING EQUIPMENT (SHANGHAI) LTD.—See Langley Holdings Plc; *Int'l*, pg. 4411
MANROLAND PRINTING EQUIPMENT (SHENZHEN) CO. LTD.—See Langley Holdings Plc; *Int'l*, pg. 4410
MANROLAND ROMANIA S.R.L.—See Langley Holdings Plc; *Int'l*, pg. 4411
MANROLAND SHEETFED GMBH—See Langley Holdings Plc; *Int'l*, pg. 4410
MANROLAND SHEETFED (UK) LTD—See Langley Holdings Plc; *Int'l*, pg. 4410
MANROLAND SOUTHERN AFRICA (PTY) LTD.—See Langley Holdings Plc; *Int'l*, pg. 4410
MANROLAND SWISS AG—See Langley Holdings Plc; *Int'l*, pg. 4411
MANROLAND (TAIWAN) LTD.—See Langley Holdings Plc; *Int'l*, pg. 4411
MANROLAND THAILAND LTD.—See Langley Holdings Plc; *Int'l*, pg. 4411
MANROLAND VERTRIEB UND SERVICE GMBH—See Langley Holdings Plc; *Int'l*, pg. 4411
MANROLAND WEB SYSTEMS CANADA INC.—See L. Possehl & Co. mbH; *Int'l*, pg. 4385
MANROLAND WEB SYSTEMS FRANCE S.A.S.—See L. Possehl & Co. mbH; *Int'l*, pg. 4385
MANROLAND WEB SYSTEMS INC.—See L. Possehl & Co. mbH; *Int'l*, pg. 4385
MANROLAND WEB SYSTEMS SOUTHERN AFRICA PTY., LTD.—See L. Possehl & Co. mbH; *Int'l*, pg. 4385
MANROLAND WEB SYSTEMS (UK) LTD.—See AIP, LLC; *U.S. Private*, pg. 134
MANROLAND WESTERN EUROPE GROUP B.V.—See Langley Holdings Plc; *Int'l*, pg. 4411
MANROY ENGINEERING LTD.—See Herstal, S.A.; *Int'l*, pg. 3365
MANRY-RAWLS, LLC—See Towne Bank; *U.S. Public*, pg. 2166
MANSA CAPITAL MANAGEMENT, LLC; *U.S. Private*, pg. 2566
MANSAL OFFSHORE LIMITED—See Mannai Corporation QPSC; *Int'l*, pg. 4675

MANSA CAPITAL MANAGEMENT, LLC — CORPORATE AFFILIATIONS

MAN SANG INTERNATIONAL LIMITED—See China Metro-Rural Holdings Limited; *Int'l*, pg. 1524
MAN SANG JEWELLERY COMPANY LIMITED—See Affluent Partners Holdings Limited; *Int'l*, pg. 188
MANSAROVAR ENERGY COLOMBIA LTD.—See China Petrochemical Corporation; *Int'l*, pg. 1540
MANSAROVAR ENERGY COLOMBIA LTD.—See Oil & Natural Gas Corporation Limited; *Int'l*, pg. 5534
MANSEI CORPORATION; *Int'l*, pg. 4676
MANSEI DENKI HK LTD.—See Mansei Corporation; *Int'l*, pg. 4676
MANSEI DENKI SHANGHAI LTD.—See Mansei Corporation; *Int'l*, pg. 4676
MANSELL GROUP, INC.—See The Riverside Company; *U.S. Private*, pg. 4109
MANSELL PLC—See Balfour Beatty plc; *Int'l*, pg. 807
MANSER SAXON ALUMINIUM LTD.—See Ireland Blyth Limited; *Int'l*, pg. 3807
MANSER SAXON CONTRACTING LTD.—See Ireland Blyth Limited; *Int'l*, pg. 3807
MANSER SAXON DUBAI LLC—See Ireland Blyth Limited; *Int'l*, pg. 3807
MANSER SAXON PLUMBING LTD—See Ireland Blyth Limited; *Int'l*, pg. 3807
MAN SE—See Porsche Automobil Holding SE; *Int'l*, pg. 5929
MANSFELDER KUPFER UND MESSING GMBH—See Nova Resources B.V.; *Int'l*, pg. 5452
MANSFELDER METALS LTD.; *Int'l*, pg. 4676
MANSFIELD BUILDING SOCIETY; *Int'l*, pg. 4676
MANSFIELD COOPERATIVE BANK; *U.S. Private*, pg. 2566
MANSFIELD ENERGY CORP.; *U.S. Private*, pg. 2566
MANSFIELD-KING LLC—See The Pritzker Group - Chicago, LLC; *U.S. Private*, pg. 4099
MANSFIELD MANUFACTURING CO., LTD.—See InnoTek Limited; *Int'l*, pg. 3711
MANSFIELD MANUFACTURING (WUHAN) COMPANY LIMITED—See InnoTek Limited; *Int'l*, pg. 3711
MANSFIELD-MARTIN EXPLORATION MINING, INC.; *U.S. Private*, pg. 2566
MANSFIELD MINERA S.A.—See Fortuna Mining Corp.; *Int'l*, pg. 2743
MANSFIELD MOTOR GROUP; *U.S. Private*, pg. 2566
MANSFIELD NEWS JOURNAL—See Gannett Co., Inc.; *U.S. Public*, pg. 898
MANSFIELD NEWS—See Gannett Co., Inc.; *U.S. Public*, pg. 902
MANSFIELD OIL COMPANY OF GAINSVILLE, INC.—See Mansfield Energy Corp.; *U.S. Private*, pg. 2566
MANSFIELD PAPER CO. INC.; *U.S. Private*, pg. 2566
MANSFIELD PHYSICAL THERAPY, LIMITED PARTNERSHIP—See U.S. Physical Therapy, Inc.; *U.S. Public*, pg. 2215
MANSFIELD PLUMBING PRODUCTS LLC; *U.S. Private*, pg. 2566
MANSFIELD SALES PARTNERS, LLC—See JMC Capital Partners LLC; *U.S. Private*, pg. 2215
MANSFIELD (SUZHOU) MANUFACTURING COMPANY LIMITED—See InnoTek Limited; *Int'l*, pg. 3711
MANSFIELD (THAILAND) CO. LTD.—See InnoTek Limited; *Int'l*, pg. 3711
MAN SHING AGRICULTURAL HOLDINGS, INC.; *Int'l*, pg. 4665
MAN SHING CLEANING SERVICE COMPANY LIMITED—See Man Shing Global Holdings Limited; *Int'l*, pg. 4665
MAN SHING GLOBAL HOLDINGS LIMITED; *Int'l*, pg. 4665
MAN SHUN GROUP (HOLDINGS) LIMITED; *Int'l*, pg. 4665
MANSI FINANCE (CHENNAI) LIMITED; *Int'l*, pg. 4676
MANSI GLOBIZ INC.; *U.S. Private*, pg. 2566
MANSI MEDIA; *U.S. Private*, pg. 2566
MANSION HOUSE CONSULTING INC.—See Mansion House Consulting Limited; *Int'l*, pg. 4676
MANSION HOUSE CONSULTING LIMITED; *Int'l*, pg. 4676
MANSION HOUSE RECRUITMENT LTD.—See Empresaria Group Plc; *Int'l*, pg. 2389
MANSION INTERNATIONAL HOLDINGS LIMITED; *Int'l*, pg. 4676
THE MANSION ON TURTLE CREEK—See Chow Tai Fook Enterprises Limited; *Int'l*, pg. 1585
MANSITA LIMITED—See Hang Lung Group Limited; *Int'l*, pg. 3245
MANSKE MATERIAL HANDLING, INC.—See Richards Supply Company; *U.S. Private*, pg. 3429
MANSON CONSTRUCTION CO., INC.; *U.S. Private*, pg. 2566
MANSON GULF LLC—See Manson Construction Co., Inc.; *U.S. Private*, pg. 2566
MANSON WARNER HEALTHCARE LIMITED—See Marsh & McLennan Companies, Inc.; *U.S. Public*, pg. 1377
MANSOON TRADING CO., LTD.; *Int'l*, pg. 4676
MANSOURA POULTRY CO.; *Int'l*, pg. 4676
MANSOUR BANK FOR INVESTMENT—See Qatar National Bank S.A.Q.; *Int'l*, pg. 6135
MANSOUR GROUP; *Int'l*, pg. 4676

MANS-STEEL DIVISION—See Hutchens Industries Inc.; *U.S. Private*, pg. 2014
MANS-STEEL FOUNDRY—See Hutchens Industries Inc.; *U.S. Private*, pg. 2014
MANSUETO VENTURES LLC; *U.S. Private*, pg. 2566
MANTA CORPORATION—See Wipro Limited; *Int'l*, pg. 8432
MANTA ENGINEERING & EQUIPMENT CO. LTD.—See Kaisa Group Holdings Limited; *Int'l*, pg. 4052
MANTA EQUIPMENT (S) PTE LTD—See Kaisa Group Holdings Limited; *Int'l*, pg. 4052
MANTA MEDIA, INC.; *U.S. Private*, pg. 2567
MANTAN PUMPPAUSPALVELU OY—See KSB SE & Co. KGaA; *Int'l*, pg. 4311
MANTA REISEN AG—See REWE-Zentral-Aktiengesellschaft; *Int'l*, pg. 6314
MANTARO PRECIOUS METALS CORP.; *Int'l*, pg. 4676
MANT. AYUDA A LA EXPLOT. Y SERVICIOS, S.A—See ACS, Actividades de Construccion y Servicios, S.A.; *Int'l*, pg. 115
MANTECA FORD MERCURY, INC.; *U.S. Private*, pg. 2567
MANTECH ADVANCED SYSTEMS INTERNATIONAL INC.—See The Carlyle Group Inc.; *U.S. Public*, pg. 2048
MANTECH CO., LTD.—See Abdulla Fouad Holding Co.; *Int'l*, pg. 59
MANTECH COMPUTER & TELECOMMUNICATIONS CO., LTD.—See Abdulla Fouad Holding Co.; *Int'l*, pg. 59
MANTECH ELECTRONICS (CAPE) (PROPRIETARY) LIMITED—See Mobicon Group Limited; *Int'l*, pg. 5009
MANTECH ELECTRONICS (KZN) (PROPRIETARY) LIMITED—See Mobicon Group Limited; *Int'l*, pg. 5009
MANTECH ELECTRONICS (PTY) LTD.—See Mobicon Group Limited; *Int'l*, pg. 5009
MANTECH ENVIRONMENTAL RESEARCH SERVICES CORP.—See The Carlyle Group Inc.; *U.S. Public*, pg. 2048
MANTECH EUROPE SYSTEMS CORPORATION—See The Carlyle Group Inc.; *U.S. Public*, pg. 2048
MANTECH INTERNATIONAL CORPORATION—See The Carlyle Group Inc.; *U.S. Public*, pg. 2048
MANTECH SECURITY & MISSION ASSURANCE—See The Carlyle Group Inc.; *U.S. Public*, pg. 2048
MANTECH SENSOR TECHNOLOGIES, INC.—See The Carlyle Group Inc.; *U.S. Public*, pg. 2048
MANTECH SRS TECHNOLOGIES, INC.—See The Carlyle Group Inc.; *U.S. Public*, pg. 2048
MANTECH TECHNICAL SERVICES INC.—See The Carlyle Group Inc.; *U.S. Public*, pg. 2049
MANTECH TELECOMMUNICATIONS & INFORMATION SYSTEMS CORPORATION—See The Carlyle Group Inc.; *U.S. Public*, pg. 2049
MANTECH TELECOMMUNICATIONS—See The Carlyle Group Inc.; *U.S. Public*, pg. 2049
MANTEK—See NCH Corporation; *U.S. Private*, pg. 2875
MANTEL SA—See Teleperformance SE; *Int'l*, pg. 7540
MANTENIMENT I CONSERVACIO DEL VALLES, S.A.—See ACS, Actividades de Construccion y Servicios, S.A.; *Int'l*, pg. 115
MANTENIMIENTO DE INFRAESTRUCTURAS, S.A.—See Fomento de Construcciones y Contratas, S.A.; *Int'l*, pg. 2723
MANTENIMIENTOS, AYUDA A LA EXPLOTACION Y SERVICIOS, S.A.—See ACS, Actividades de Construccion y Servicios, S.A.; *Int'l*, pg. 115
MANTENIMIENTO Y CONSERVACION DE VIALIDADES, S.A. DE C.V—See Infrastructure Leasing & Financial Services Limited; *Int'l*, pg. 3698
MANTENIMIENTO Y MONTAJES INDUSTRIALES, S.A—See ACS, Actividades de Construccion y Servicios, S.A.; *Int'l*, pg. 115
MANTEQUERIAS ARIAS S. A.—See Savencia Fromage & Dairy; *Int'l*, pg. 6597
MANTEX AB; *Int'l*, pg. 4676
MANTEX SUPPLIES COMPANY LIMITED—See Mansion International Holdings Limited; *Int'l*, pg. 4676
MANTHAN SOFTWARE SERVICES PVT. LTD.; *Int'l*, pg. 4677
MANTH-BROWNELL INC.—See MiddleGround Management, LP; *U.S. Private*, pg. 2711
MANTHEI INC.; *U.S. Private*, pg. 2567
MANTI RESOURCES, INC.; *U.S. Private*, pg. 2567
MANTIS INNOVATION GROUP, LLC—See O2 Investment Partners, LLC; *U.S. Private*, pg. 2982
MANTIS VISION LTD.; *Int'l*, pg. 4677
MANTLE MINERALS LIMITED; *Int'l*, pg. 4677
MANTLE WHITE CABINET GROUP, INC.—See Mantle White Partnership; *U.S. Private*, pg. 2567
MANTLE WHITE PARTNERSHIP; *U.S. Private*, pg. 2567
MANTRAC EGYPT—See Mansour Group; *Int'l*, pg. 4676
MANTRAC GHANA LTD.—See Mansour Group; *Int'l*, pg. 4676
MANTRAC IRAQ—See Mansour Group; *Int'l*, pg. 4676
MANTRAC ITD EGYPT—See Mansour Group; *Int'l*, pg. 4676
MANTRAC KENYA LTD.—See Mansour Group; *Int'l*, pg. 4676
MANTRAC NIGERIA LTD.—See Mansour Group; *Int'l*, pg. 4676

MANTRAC RUSSIA—See Mansour Group; *Int'l*, pg. 4676
MANTRAC SIERRA LEONE LTD.—See Mansour Group; *Int'l*, pg. 4676
MANTRAC TANZANIA LTD.—See Mansour Group; *Int'l*, pg. 4676
MANTRAC UGANDA LTD.—See Mansour Group; *Int'l*, pg. 4676
MANTRA DESIGN SDN. BHD.—See Berjaya Corporation Berhad; *Int'l*, pg. 984
MANTRA GROUP LIMITED—See Accor S.A.; *Int'l*, pg. 91
MANTRA GROUP OPERATIONS PTY. LTD.—See Accor S.A.; *Int'l*, pg. 92
MANTRA PUBLIC RELATIONS, INC.; *U.S. Private*, pg. 2567
MANTROSE-HAEUSER CO.—See RPM International Inc.; *U.S. Public*, pg. 1817
MANTROSE UK LIMITED—See RPM International Inc.; *U.S. Public*, pg. 1817
MAN TRUCK & BUS AG—See Porsche Automobil Holding SE; *Int'l*, pg. 5930
MAN TRUCK & BUS DEUTSCHLAND GMBH - FLENSBURG—See Porsche Automobil Holding SE; *Int'l*, pg. 5930
MAN TRUCK & BUS DEUTSCHLAND GMBH - SALZGITTER—See Porsche Automobil Holding SE; *Int'l*, pg. 5930
MAN TRUCK & BUS OSTERREICH AG—See Porsche Automobil Holding SE; *Int'l*, pg. 5930
MAN TRUCK & BUS OSTERREICH AG - VIENNA—See Porsche Automobil Holding SE; *Int'l*, pg. 5930
MAN TRUCK & BUS POLSKA SP. Z O.O.—See Porsche Automobil Holding SE; *Int'l*, pg. 5930
MAN TRUCK & BUS (S.A.) (PTY) LTD.—See Porsche Automobil Holding SE; *Int'l*, pg. 5930
MAN TRUCK & BUS VERTRIEB OSTERREICH AG—See Porsche Automobil Holding SE; *Int'l*, pg. 5930
MANTUA MANUFACTURING CO. INC.; *U.S. Private*, pg. 2567
MAN TURKIYE A.S.—See Porsche Automobil Holding SE; *Int'l*, pg. 5930
MANTYNUMMEN LAMPO OY—See Fortum Oyj; *Int'l*, pg. 2742
MANTZ AUTOMATION, INC.; *U.S. Private*, pg. 2567
MANUAL TRANSMISSIONS OF MUNCIE—See General Motors Company; *U.S. Public*, pg. 926
MANUAL WOODWORKERS & WEAVERS, INC.; *U.S. Private*, pg. 2567
MANUEL HUERTA TRUCKING INC.; *U.S. Private*, pg. 2567
MANUEL LUJAN INSURANCE, INC.; *U.S. Private*, pg. 2567
MANUEL VILLA ENTERPRISES INC.; *U.S. Private*, pg. 2567
MANUFACT LOGISTICS LTD; *Int'l*, pg. 4677
MANUFACTUM GMBH & CO. KG—See Otto GmbH & Co. KG; *Int'l*, pg. 5663
MANUFACTURA AVANZADA DE COLIMA S.A. DE C.V.—See Yazaki Corporation; *Int'l*, pg. 8572
MANUFACTURAS CIFUNSA, S.A. DE C.V.—See Grupo Industrial Saltillo S.A. de C.V.; *Int'l*, pg. 3130
MANUFACTURAS ELECTRICAS SA—See Schneider Electric SE; *Int'l*, pg. 6628
MANUFACTURAS LOEWE S.L—See LVMH Moet Hennessy Louis Vuitton SE; *Int'l*, pg. 4602
MANUFACTURAS SHAW SOUTH AMERICA, C.A.—See The Shaw Group Inc.; *U.S. Private*, pg. 4117
MANUFACTURAS SONOCO, S.A. DE C.V.—See Sonoco Products Company; *U.S. Public*, pg. 1904
MANUFACTURAS VITROMEX, S.A. DE C.V.—See Grupo Industrial Saltillo S.A. de C.V.; *Int'l*, pg. 3130
MANUFACTURAS Y ACCESORIOS ELECTRICOS S.A.—See Hella GmbH & Co. KGaA; *Int'l*, pg. 3332
MANUFACTURAS ZAPALINAME, S.A. DE C.V.—See Vantage Drilling International; *Int'l*, pg. 8130
MANUFACTURED ASSEMBLIES CORPORATION; *U.S. Private*, pg. 2567
MANUFACTURE DE PANNEAUX BOIS DU SUD SA; *Int'l*, pg. 4677
MANUFACTURE DE SOULIERS LOUIS VUITTON SRL—See LVMH Moet Hennessy Louis Vuitton SE; *Int'l*, pg. 4596
MANUFACTURE DES TAPIS DE COGOLIN SAS—See Tai Ping Carpets International Limited; *Int'l*, pg. 7408
MANUFACTURED HOUSING PROPERTIES INC.; *U.S. Public*, pg. 1362
MANUFACTURED STRUCTURES CORP.; *U.S. Private*, pg. 2567
MANUFACTURED TECHNOLOGIES CORPORATION—See New Mountain Capital, LLC; *U.S. Private*, pg. 2900
MANUFACTURE FAVRE ET PERRET SA—See The Swatch Group Ltd.; *Int'l*, pg. 7691
MANUFACTURE FRANCAISE DES PNEUMATIQUES MICHELIN—See Compagnie Generale des Etablissements Michelin SCA; *Int'l*, pg. 1743
MANUFACTURE JAEGER-LECOULTRE SA—See Compagnie Financiere Richemont S.A.; *Int'l*, pg. 1741
MANUFACTURE JAEGER-LE COULTRE S.A.—See Reinet Investments S.C.A.; *Int'l*, pg. 6257

1676

COMPANY NAME INDEX

MANUFACTURE KERING EYEWEAR SAS—See Kering S.A.; *Int'l*, pg. 4135
MANUFACTURE LA JOUX-PERRET S.A.—See Citizen Watch Co., Ltd.; *Int'l*, pg. 1625
MANUFACTURE ROGER DUBUIS SA—See Compagnie Financiere Richemont S.A.; *Int'l*, pg. 1741
MANUFACTURERS ALLIANCE INSURANCE COMPANY—See Old Republic International Corporation; *U.S. Public*, pg. 1568
MANUFACTURERS BANK—See Sumitomo Mitsui Financial Group, Inc.; *Int'l*, pg. 7293
MANUFACTURERS CAPITAL—See BDT Capital Partners, LLC; *U.S. Private*, pg. 502
MANUFACTURERS CHEMICALS, LLC—See Ascent Industries Co.; *U.S. Public*, pg. 210
MANUFACTURERS DISCOUNT FURNITURE & BEDDING, INC.; *U.S. Private*, pg. 2567
MANUFACTURERS EQUIPMENT AND SUPPLY COMPANY—See TVS Logistics Services Ltd.; *Int'l*, pg. 7989
MANUFACTURERS' JUNCTION RAILWAY, LLC—See The Broe Companies, Inc.; *U.S. Private*, pg. 4001
THE MANUFACTURERS LIFE INSURANCE COMPANY—See Manulife Financial Corporation; *Int'l*, pg. 4678
THE MANUFACTURERS LIFE INSURANCE CO. (PHILS.), INC.—See Manulife Financial Corporation; *Int'l*, pg. 4679
MANUFACTURERS' NEWS, INC.; *U.S. Private*, pg. 2567
MANUFACTURERS P&C LIMITED—See Manulife Financial Corporation; *Int'l*, pg. 4679
MANUFACTURERS PRODUCTS COMPANY; *U.S. Private*, pg. 2567
MANUFACTURERS RAILWAY COMPANY—See Anheuser-Busch InBev SA/NV; *Int'l*, pg. 465
MANUFACTURERS SOAP AND CHEMICALS COMPANY—See Ascent Industries Co.; *U.S. Public*, pg. 210
MANUFACTURERS & TRADERS TRUST COMPANY—See M&T Bank Corporation; *U.S. Public*, pg. 1350
MANUFACTURE RUEDIN SA—See The Swatch Group Ltd.; *Int'l*, pg. 7691
MANUFACTUR FUR GLAS UND SPIEGEL GMBH—See Physiotherm GmbH; *Int'l*, pg. 5858
MANUFACTURIER DE BAS IRIS INC.; *Int'l*, pg. 4677
MANUFACTURING AFFINITY PROGRAM—See TR Cutler, Inc.; *U.S. Private*, pg. 4200
MANUFACTURING ASSEMBLY SOLUTIONS OF MONTERREY, INC.—See Nortech Systems Incorporated; *U.S. Public*, pg. 1536
MANUFACTURING AUTOMATION & SOFTWARE SYSTEM, INC.—See The Brydon Group LLC; *U.S. Private*, pg. 4001
MANUFACTURING INTEGRATION TECHNOLOGY LTD; *Int'l*, pg. 4677
MANUFACTURING NETWORK PTE. LTD.—See New Wave Holdings Ltd.; *Int'l*, pg. 5231
MANUFACTURING RESOURCE GROUP, INC.—See Cerberus Capital Management, L.P.; *U.S. Private*, pg. 838
MANUFACTURING SCIENCES CORPORATION—See The Toronto-Dominion Bank; *Int'l*, pg. 7696
MANUFACTURING SUPPLIERS LIMITED—See STEEL & TUBE Holdings Limited; *Int'l*, pg. 7189
MANUFACTURING SUPPORT INDUSTRIES, INC.—See Craig Technologies, Inc.; *U.S. Private*, pg. 1083
MANUFACTURING TECHNICAL SOLUTIONS INC.; *U.S. Private*, pg. 2567
MANU FRUTA SUR S.L.—See Dole plc; *Int'l*, pg. 2158
MANUGRAPH DGM INC—See Manugraph India Ltd; *Int'l*, pg. 4677
MANUGRAPH INDIA LTD - MANUFACTURING UNIT NO.1—See Manugraph India Ltd; *Int'l*, pg. 4677
MANUGRAPH INDIA LTD - MANUFACTURING UNIT NO.2—See Manugraph India Ltd; *Int'l*, pg. 4677
MANUGRAPH INDIA LTD; *Int'l*, pg. 4677
MANUGRAPH KENYA LIMITED—See Manugraph India Ltd; *Int'l*, pg. 4677
MANUKA RESOURCES LIMITED; *Int'l*, pg. 4677
MANULIFE AFFINITY MARKETS—See Manulife Financial Corporation; *Int'l*, pg. 4678
MANULIFE ASSET MANAGEMENT (EUROPE) LIMITED—See Manulife Financial Corporation; *Int'l*, pg. 4678
MANULIFE ASSET MANAGEMENT (HONG KONG) LIMITED—See Manulife Financial Corporation; *Int'l*, pg. 4679
MANULIFE ASSET MANAGEMENT INTERNATIONAL HOLDINGS LIMITED—See Manulife Financial Corporation; *Int'l*, pg. 4679
MANULIFE ASSET MANAGEMENT LIMITED—See Manulife Financial Corporation; *Int'l*, pg. 4678
MANULIFE ASSET MANAGEMENT LIMITED—See Manulife Financial Corporation; *Int'l*, pg. 4678
MANULIFE ASSET MANAGEMENT (THAILAND) COMPANY LIMITED—See Manulife Financial Corporation; *Int'l*, pg. 4678
MANULIFE BANK OF CANADA—See Manulife Financial Corporation; *Int'l*, pg. 4678
MANULIFE CANADA LTD.—See Manulife Financial Corporation; *Int'l*, pg. 4678
MANULIFE CANADIAN GROUP PENSIONS—See Manulife Financial Corporation; *Int'l*, pg. 4678
MANULIFE FINANCIAL CORPORATION; *Int'l*, pg. 4678
MANULIFE FINANCIAL GROUP BENEFITS—See Manulife Financial Corporation; *Int'l*, pg. 4678
MANULIFE GLOBAL INVESTMENTS—See Manulife Financial Corporation; *Int'l*, pg. 4678
MANULIFE HOLDINGS BERHAD—See Manulife Financial Corporation; *Int'l*, pg. 4679
MANULIFE HOLDINGS (BERMUDA) LIMITED—See Manulife Financial Corporation; *Int'l*, pg. 4678
MANULIFE INSURANCE BERHAD—See Manulife Financial Corporation; *Int'l*, pg. 4678
MANULIFE INSURANCE (THAILAND) PUBLIC COMPANY LIMITED—See Manulife Financial Corporation; *Int'l*, pg. 4679
MANULIFE (INTERNATIONAL) LIMITED—See Manulife Financial Corporation; *Int'l*, pg. 4679
MANULIFE INVESTMENT MANAGEMENT (MALAYSIA) BHD—See Manulife Financial Corporation; *Int'l*, pg. 4678
MANULIFE INVESTMENT MANAGEMENT (SINGAPORE) PTE. LTD.—See Manulife Financial Corporation; *Int'l*, pg. 4678
MANULIFE INVESTMENT MANAGEMENT (US) LLC—See Manulife Financial Corporation; *Int'l*, pg. 4678
MANULIFE LIFE INSURANCE COMPANY—See Manulife Financial Corporation; *Int'l*, pg. 4679
MANULIFE MUTUAL FUNDS—See Manulife Financial Corporation; *Int'l*, pg. 4679
MANULIFE PROVIDENT FUNDS TRUST COMPANY LIMITED—See Manulife Financial Corporation; *Int'l*, pg. 4679
MANULIFE REAL ESTATE—See Manulife Financial Corporation; *Int'l*, pg. 4679
MANULIFE REINSURANCE LIMITED—See Manulife Financial Corporation; *Int'l*, pg. 4679
MANULIFE SECURITIES INCORPORATED—See Manulife Financial Corporation; *Int'l*, pg. 4679
MANULIFE SECURITIES INVESTMENT SERVICES INC.—See Manulife Financial Corporation; *Int'l*, pg. 4670
MANULIFE (SINGAPORE) PTE. LTD.—See Manulife Financial Corporation; *Int'l*, pg. 4679
MANULIFE-SINOCHEM LIFE INSURANCE COMPANY LTD.—See Manulife Financial Corporation; *Int'l*, pg. 4679
MANULIFE-SINOCHEM LIFE INSURANCE COMPANY LTD.—See Sinochem Corporation; *Int'l*, pg. 6950
MANULIFE US REAL ESTATE INVESTMENT TRUST; *Int'l*, pg. 4679
MANULIFE (VIETNAM) LIMITED—See Manulife Financial Corporation; *Int'l*, pg. 4679
MANULI FLUICONNECTO (PTY) LTD.—See Manuli Rubber Industries S.p.A.; *Int'l*, pg. 4677
MANULI HYDRAULICS (AMERICAS) INC.—See Manuli Rubber Industries S.p.A.; *Int'l*, pg. 4677
MANULI HYDRAULICS EUROPE S.R.O—See Manuli Rubber Industries S.p.A.; *Int'l*, pg. 4677
MANULI HYDRAULICS GMBH—See Manuli Rubber Industries S.p.A.; *Int'l*, pg. 4677
MANULI HYDRAULICS KOREA CO. LTD.—See Manuli Rubber Industries S.p.A.; *Int'l*, pg. 4677
MANULI HYDRAULICS LTD.—See Manuli Rubber Industries S.p.A.; *Int'l*, pg. 4677
MANULI HYDRAULICS POLSKA S.A.—See Manuli Rubber Industries S.p.A.; *Int'l*, pg. 4677
MANULI HYDRAULICS (SHANGHAI) CO. LTD.—See Manuli Rubber Industries S.p.A.; *Int'l*, pg. 4677
MANULI HYDRAULICS SUZHOU CO., LTD—See Manuli Rubber Industries S.p.A.; *Int'l*, pg. 4677
MANULI OIL & MARINE (USA) INC.—See Manuli Rubber Industries S.p.A.; *Int'l*, pg. 4677
MANULI OTIM S.A.—See Manuli Rubber Industries S.p.A.; *Int'l*, pg. 4677
MANULI REFRIGERATION CONNECTORS S.P.A.—See Manuli Rubber Industries S.p.A.; *Int'l*, pg. 4677
MANULI RUBBER INDUSTRIES - FLEXMATIC DIVISION—See Manuli Rubber Industries S.p.A.; *Int'l*, pg. 4678
MANULI RUBBER INDUSTRIES - OEM DIVISION—See Manuli Rubber Industries S.p.A.; *Int'l*, pg. 4678
MANULI RUBBER INDUSTRIES S.P.A.; *Int'l*, pg. 4677
MANULOC GROUP; *Int'l*, pg. 4679
MANUS ABRASIVE SYSTEMS, INC—See Ridgemont Partners Management LLC; *U.S. Private*, pg. 3432
MANUS DEI, INC.—See The 20 Msp Group LLC; *U.S. Private*, pg. 3980
MANUS MEDICAL, LLC—See Apiary Medical, Inc.; *U.S. Private*, pg. 294
MANUS PRESSE GMBH—See Verlagsgruppe Georg von Holtzbrinck GmbH; *Int'l*, pg. 8171
MANUTAN B.V.—See Manutan International SA; *Int'l*, pg. 4679
MANUTAN COLLECTIVITES SAS—See Manutan International SA; *Int'l*, pg. 4679
MANUTAN HUNGARIA KFT—See Manutan International SA; *Int'l*, pg. 4679
MANUTAN INTERNATIONAL SA; *Int'l*, pg. 4679
MANUTAN ITALIA SPA—See Manutan International SA; *Int'l*, pg. 4679
MANUTAN LTD—See Eraser Dust, Inc.; *U.S. Private*, pg. 1417
MANUTAN NV—See Manutan International SA; *Int'l*, pg. 4679
MANUTAN O.O.O—See Manutan International SA; *Int'l*, pg. 4680
MANUTAN POLSKA SP Z.O.O—See Manutan International SA; *Int'l*, pg. 4680
MANUTAN SA—See Manutan International SA; *Int'l*, pg. 4680
MANUTAN SLOVAKIA S.R.O—See Manutan International SA; *Int'l*, pg. 4680
MANUTAN S.L.—See Manutan International SA; *Int'l*, pg. 4680
MANUTAN S.R.O.—See Manutan International SA; *Int'l*, pg. 4680
MANUTAN UK LTD.—See Manutan International SA; *Int'l*, pg. 4680
MANUTAN UNIPESSOAL LDA—See Manutan International SA; *Int'l*, pg. 4680
MANUTENCOOP SOCIETA COOPERATIVA; *Int'l*, pg. 4680
MANVIA ESPANA S A—See Mota-Engil SGPS, S.A.; *Int'l*, pg. 5052
MAN WAH FURNITURE MANUFACTURING (HUIZHOU) CO., LTD.—See Man Wah Holdings Limited; *Int'l*, pg. 4665
MAN WAH HOLDINGS LIMITED; *Int'l*, pg. 4665
MANWEIR LIMITED—See Mannai Corporation QPSC; *Int'l*, pg. 4675
MANX FINANCIAL GROUP PLC; *Int'l*, pg. 4680
MANX FX LIMITED—See Manx Financial Group PLC; *Int'l*, pg. 4680
MANX TELECOM PLC—See Colliers International Group Inc.; *Int'l*, pg. 1700
MANYAVAR CREATIONS PRIVATE LIMITED—See Vedant Fashions Limited; *Int'l*, pg. 8145
MANY BRIGHT IDEAS TECHNOLOGIES INC.; *Int'l*, pg. 4680
MANYCORE TECH INC.; *Int'l*, pg. 4680
MANY IDEA CLOUD HOLDINGS LIMITED; *Int'l*, pg. 4680
MANYO FACTORY CO., LTD.; *Int'l*, pg. 4680
MAN YUE ELECTRONICS COMPANY LIMITED—See Man Yue Technology Holdings Limited; *Int'l*, pg. 4665
MAN YUE TECHNOLOGY HOLDINGS LIMITED; *Int'l*, pg. 4665
MANZ AG; *Int'l*, pg. 4680
MANZ AG - TUBINGEN—See Manz AG; *Int'l*, pg. 4681
MAN ZAI INDUSTRIAL CO., LTD.; *Int'l*, pg. 4665
MANZANILLO INTERNATIONAL TERMINAL, PANAMA S.A.—See Carrix, Inc.; *U.S. Private*, pg. 773
MANZANITA SYSTEMS, LLC—See Xperi Inc.; *U.S. Public*, pg. 2392
MANZANO DIALYSIS, LLC—See DaVita Inc.; *U.S. Public*, pg. 641
MANZARDO SPA—See Ferguson plc; *Int'l*, pg. 2638
MANZ AUTOMATION INDIA PRIVATE LIMITED—See Manz AG; *Int'l*, pg. 4681
MANZ AUTOMATION (SHANGHAI) CO. LTD.—See Manz AG; *Int'l*, pg. 4681
MANZ AUTOMATION SPAIN S.L.—See Manz AG; *Int'l*, pg. 4681
MANZ AUTOMATION TAIWAN LTD.—See Manz AG; *Int'l*, pg. 4681
MANZ CHINA SUZHOU LTD.—See Manz AG; *Int'l*, pg. 4681
MANZELLA MARKETING GROUP, INC—See 360 PSG, Inc.; *U.S. Private*, pg. 8
MANZHOULI XIJIAO AIRPORT CO., LTD.—See Hainan Traffic Administration Holding Co., Ltd.; *Int'l*, pg. 3215
MANZ HUNGARY KFT.—See Manz AG; *Int'l*, pg. 4681
MANZI INSURANCE; *U.S. Private*, pg. 2567
MANZI METALS, INC.; *U.S. Private*, pg. 2567
MANZ INTECH MACHINES CO. LTD—See Manz AG; *Int'l*, pg. 4681
MANZ ITALY S.R.L.—See Manz AG; *Int'l*, pg. 4681
MANZO PHARMACEUTICALS, INC.; *U.S. Private*, pg. 2567
MANZ SLOVAKIA S.R.O.—See Manz AG; *Int'l*, pg. 4681
MANZ TAIWAN LTD.—See Manz AG; *Int'l*, pg. 4681
MANZ USA INC.—See Manz AG; *Int'l*, pg. 4681
MAO BAO INC.; *Int'l*, pg. 4681
MAOLA MILK & ICE CREAM COMPANY; *U.S. Private*, pg. 2567
MAOMING HENGDA STEEL CO., LTD.—See General Steel Holdings, Inc.; *Int'l*, pg. 2920
MAOMING PETRO-CHEMICAL SHIHUA CO., LTD.; *Int'l*, pg. 4681
MAOMING SAKATA INX CO., LTD.—See Sakata INX Corporation; *Int'l*, pg. 6487
MAOMING TIANYUAN TERMINAL OPERATION COMPANY LIMITED—See Tian Yuan Group Holdings Limited; *Int'l*, pg. 7737

MAOMING ZHENGYUAN TRADE DEVELOPMENT COMPANY LIMITED—See Tian Yuan Group Holdings Limited; *Int'l*, pg. 7737
MAOYAN ENTERTAINMENT; *Int'l*, pg. 4681
MAOYE COMMERCIAL CO., LTD.; *Int'l*, pg. 4681
MAOYE INTERNATIONAL HOLDING LIMITED; *Int'l*, pg. 4681
MAOYE INTERNATIONAL HOLDINGS LTD.; *Int'l*, pg. 4681
MA PACKAGING CO., LTD.—See Mitsubishi Materials Corporation; *Int'l*, pg. 4963
MAP ACTIVE (THAILAND) LTD.—See PT. Mitra Adiperkasa Tbk; *Int'l*, pg. 6088
MAPA GMBH—See Newell Brands Inc.; *U.S. Public*, pg. 1514
MAPAL COMMUNICATIONS LTD.; *Int'l*, pg. 4681
MAPA MAPPING & PUBLISHING LTD.—See ITURAN Location & Control Ltd.; *Int'l*, pg. 3844
MAPANYTHING, INC.—See Salesforce, Inc.; *U.S. Public*, pg. 1837
MAPA SPONTEX CE S.R.O.—See Newell Brands Inc.; *U.S. Public*, pg. 1514
MAPA SPONTEX ITALIA S.P.A.—See Newell Brands Inc.; *U.S. Public*, pg. 1514
MAPA SPONTEX POLSKA SP. Z.O.O.—See Newell Brands Inc.; *U.S. Public*, pg. 1514
MAPA SPONTEX S.A.—See Newell Brands Inc.; *U.S. Public*, pg. 1514
MAPA SPONTEX UK LIMITED—See Newell Brands Inc.; *U.S. Public*, pg. 1514
M.A. PATOUT & SON LIMITED; *U.S. Private*, pg. 2527
MAPAUTO; *Int'l*, pg. 4681
MAP CARGO INTERNATIONAL INC.; *U.S. Private*, pg. 2568
MAP CARGO S.A.S—See Nippon Express Holdings, Inc.; *Int'l*, pg. 5315
MAPCITY.COM CHILE S.A.—See Equifax Inc.; *U.S. Public*, pg. 786
MAPCITY PERU S.A.C.—See Equifax Inc.; *U.S. Public*, pg. 787
MAPCO EXPRESS, INC.—See Majors Management, LLC; *U.S. Private*, pg. 2555
MAP COMMUNICATIONS INC.; *U.S. Private*, pg. 2568
MAPCOM SYSTEMS, LLC—See Battery Ventures, L.P.; *U.S. Private*, pg. 489
MAPCON MAPPING INC.—See OSI Maritime Systems; *Int'l*, pg. 5650
MAPCON MAPPING LTD.—See OSI Maritime Systems; *Int'l*, pg. 5650
MAPDATA SERVICES PTY LTD—See Boustead Singapore Limited; *Int'l*, pg. 1120
MAPEFIN DEUTSCHLAND GMBH—See Mapei SpA; *Int'l*, pg. 4681
MAPEI AB—See Mapei SpA; *Int'l*, pg. 4682
MAPEI ARGENTINA S.A.—See Mapei SpA; *Int'l*, pg. 4681
MAPEI AS—See Mapei SpA; *Int'l*, pg. 4682
MAPEI AUSTRALIA PTY. LTD.—See Mapei SpA; *Int'l*, pg. 4682
MAPEI BENELUX S.A./N.V.—See Mapei SpA; *Int'l*, pg. 4682
MAPEI BETONTECHNIK G.M.B.H.—See Mapei SpA; *Int'l*, pg. 4682
MAPEI BRASIL CONSTRUCTION MATERIALS LTDA—See Mapei SpA; *Int'l*, pg. 4682
MAPEI CARIBE INC.—See Mapei SpA; *Int'l*, pg. 4682
MAPEI CHINA LTD—See Mapei SpA; *Int'l*, pg. 4682
MAPEI COLOMBIA S.A.S.—See Mapei SpA; *Int'l*, pg. 4682
MAPEI CONSTRUCTION CHEMICALS LLC—See Mapei SpA; *Int'l*, pg. 4682
MAPEI CONSTRUCTION CHEMICALS PANAMA SA—See Mapei SpA; *Int'l*, pg. 4682
MAPEI CONSTRUCTION MATERIALS COMPANY LTD—See Mapei SpA; *Int'l*, pg. 4682
MAPEI CONSTRUCTION PRODUCTS INDIA LTD.—See Mapei SpA; *Int'l*, pg. 4682
MAPEI CORPORATION—See Mapei SpA; *Int'l*, pg. 4681
MAPEI CROATIA D.O.O.—See Mapei SpA; *Int'l*, pg. 4682
MAPEI DE MEXICO, S.A. DE C.V.—See Mapei SpA; *Int'l*, pg. 4682
MAPEI DENMARK A/S—See Mapei SpA; *Int'l*, pg. 4682
MAPEI DE VENEZUELA C.A.—See Mapei SpA; *Int'l*, pg. 4682
MAPEI D.O.O.—See Mapei SpA; *Int'l*, pg. 4683
MAPEI EAST AFRICA LTD.—See Mapei SpA; *Int'l*, pg. 4682
MAPEI EAST CORP—See Mapei SpA; *Int'l*, pg. 4682
MAPEI EGYPT FOR CONSTRUCTION CHEMICALS S.A.E.—See Mapei SpA; *Int'l*, pg. 4682
MAPEI FAR EAST PTE. LTD.—See Mapei SpA; *Int'l*, pg. 4682
MAPEI FRANCE S.A.—See Mapei SpA; *Int'l*, pg. 4682
MAPEI GMBH—See Mapei SpA; *Int'l*, pg. 4682
MAPEI G.M.B.H.—See Mapei SpA; *Int'l*, pg. 4682
MAPEI HELLAS SA—See Mapei SpA; *Int'l*, pg. 4682
MAPEI INC.—See Mapei SpA; *Int'l*, pg. 4682
MAPEI KFT—See Mapei SpA; *Int'l*, pg. 4682
MAPEI KOREA LTD.—See Mapei SpA; *Int'l*, pg. 4682
MAPEI MALAYSIA SDN. BHD.—See Mapei SpA; *Int'l*, pg. 4682
MAPEI NEDERLAND B.V.—See Mapei SpA; *Int'l*, pg. 4682
MAPEI NEW ZEALAND LTD—See Mapei SpA; *Int'l*, pg. 4682
MAPEI OY—See Mapei SpA; *Int'l*, pg. 4682
MAPEI PHILIPPINES INC.—See Mapei SpA; *Int'l*, pg. 4682
MAPEI POLSKA SP.Z O.O.—See Mapei SpA; *Int'l*, pg. 4682
MAPEI ROMANIA S.R.L.—See Mapei SpA; *Int'l*, pg. 4682
MAPEI SK S.R.O.—See Mapei SpA; *Int'l*, pg. 4682
MAPEI SOUTH AFRICA PTY (LTD)—See Mapei SpA; *Int'l*, pg. 4682
MAPEI SPAIN S.A.—See Mapei SpA; *Int'l*, pg. 4682
MAPEI SPA; *Int'l*, pg. 4681
MAPEI, SPOL. S R.O.—See Mapei SpA; *Int'l*, pg. 4682
MAPEI SRB D.O.O.—See Mapei SpA; *Int'l*, pg. 4682
MAPEI SUISSE SA—See Mapei SpA; *Int'l*, pg. 4683
MAPEI UK LTD.—See Mapei SpA; *Int'l*, pg. 4683
MAPEI VIETNAM LTD—See Mapei SpA; *Int'l*, pg. 4683
MAPEI YAPI KIMYASALLARI INS.SAN. VE TIC.A.S.—See Mapei SpA; *Int'l*, pg. 4683
MAPE PERU S.A.C.—See Mapei SpA; *Int'l*, pg. 4683
MAPES 5 & 10 STORES LTD.; *U.S. Private*, pg. 2568
MAPFRE AMERICA, S.A.—See MAPFRE S.A.; *Int'l*, pg. 4683
MAPFRE ARGENTINA S.A.—See MAPFRE S.A.; *Int'l*, pg. 4683
MAPFRE ASISTENCIA CHILE—See MAPFRE S.A.; *Int'l*, pg. 4685
MAPFRE ASISTENCIA CIA. INTERNACIONAL DE SEGUROS Y REASEGUROS, S.A.—See MAPFRE S.A.; *Int'l*, pg. 4684
MAPFRE ASISTENCIA, S.A.—See MAPFRE S.A.; *Int'l*, pg. 4684
MAPFRE CAJA MADRID HOLDING DE ENTIDADES ASEGURADORAS, S.A.—See MAPFRE S.A.; *Int'l*, pg. 4684
MAPFRE CAJA SALUD DE SEGUROS Y REASEGUROS, S.A.—See MAPFRE S.A.; *Int'l*, pg. 4684
MAPFRE CHILE REASEGUROS, S.A.—See MAPFRE S.A.; *Int'l*, pg. 4685
MAPFRE GUANARTEME CIA. DE SEGUROS GENERALES Y REASEGUROS DE CANARIAS, S.A.—See MAPFRE S.A.; *Int'l*, pg. 4685
MAPFRE INDUSTRIAL, S.A. DE SEGUROS—See MAPFRE S.A.; *Int'l*, pg. 4684
MAPFRE INMUEBLES, S.A.—See MAPFRE S.A.; *Int'l*, pg. 4685
MAPFRE INSURANCE COMPANY OF FLORIDA—See MAPFRE S.A.; *Int'l*, pg. 4683
MAPFRE INVERSION DOS, SOCIEDAD GESTORA DE INSTITUCIONES DE INVERSION COLECTIVA, S.A.—See MAPFRE S.A.; *Int'l*, pg. 4685
MAPFRE INVERSION G.I.I.C.—See MAPFRE S.A.; *Int'l*, pg. 4685
MAPFRE INVERSION SOCIEDAD DE VALORES, S.A.—See MAPFRE S.A.; *Int'l*, pg. 4685
MAPFRE MGA, INC.—See MAPFRE S.A.; *Int'l*, pg. 4683
MAPFRE MIDDLESEA P.L.C.—See MAPFRE S.A.; *Int'l*, pg. 4685
MAPFRE PANAMA, S.A.—See MAPFRE S.A.; *Int'l*, pg. 4685
MAPFRE PARAGUAY COMPANIA DE SEGUROS, S.A.—See MAPFRE S.A.; *Int'l*, pg. 4683
MAPFRE PARAGUAY S.A.—See MAPFRE S.A.; *Int'l*, pg. 4685
MAPFRE PUERTO RICO—See MAPFRE S.A.; *Int'l*, pg. 4683
MAPFRE RE CIA. REASEGUROS, S.A.—See MAPFRE S.A.; *Int'l*, pg. 4684
MAPFRE REINSURANCE CO.—See MAPFRE S.A.; *Int'l*, pg. 4685
MAPFRE REINSURANCE—See MAPFRE S.A.; *Int'l*, pg. 4685
MAPFRE R.E.—See MAPFRE S.A.; *Int'l*, pg. 4685
MAPFRE S.A.; *Int'l*, pg. 4683
MAPFRE SEGUROS GENERALES, CIA. DE SEGUROS Y REASEGUROS, S.A.—See MAPFRE S.A.; *Int'l*, pg. 4684
MAPFRE SEGUROS GENERALES DE COLOMBIA, S.A.—See MAPFRE S.A.; *Int'l*, pg. 4684
MAPFRE SEGUROS GERAIS (PORTUGAL)—See MAPFRE S.A.; *Int'l*, pg. 4684
MAPFRE SEGUROS GUATEMALA, S.A.—See MAPFRE S.A.; *Int'l*, pg. 4685
MAPFRE SEGUROS HONDURAS, S.A.—See MAPFRE S.A.; *Int'l*, pg. 4685
MAPFRE SEGUROS NICARAGUA S.A.—See MAPFRE S.A.; *Int'l*, pg. 4685
MAPFRE SERVICIOS DE CAUCION, S.A.—See MAPFRE S.A.; *Int'l*, pg. 4685
MAPFRE SOFT, S.A.—See MAPFRE S.A.; *Int'l*, pg. 4685
MAPFRE TEPEYAC, S.A.—See MAPFRE S.A.; *Int'l*, pg. 4684
MAPFRE U.S.A. CORP.—See MAPFRE S.A.; *Int'l*, pg. 4684
MAPFRE VIDA E PREVIDENCIA, S.A.—See MAPFRE S.A.; *Int'l*, pg. 4684
MAPFRE VIDA PENSIONES ENTIDAD GESTORA DE FONDOS DE PENSIONES, S.A.—See MAPFRE S.A.; *Int'l*, pg. 4685
MAPFRE VIDA, S.A. DE SEGUROS Y REASEGUROS SOBRE LA VIDA HUMANA—See MAPFRE S.A.; *Int'l*, pg. 4684
MAPIDE, S.A.—See ACS, Actividades de Construccion y Servicios, S.A.; *Int'l*, pg. 115
MAPI LIFE SCIENCES SINGAPORE PTE. LTD.—See ICON plc; *Int'l*, pg. 3585
MAPINTEC S.R.L.—See Mapei SpA; *Int'l*, pg. 4682
M.A.P. INTERNATIONAL INC.; *U.S. Private*, pg. 2528
MAPION CO., LTD.—See TOPPAN Holdings Inc.; *Int'l*, pg. 7817
MAPI - PHARMA LTD.; *Int'l*, pg. 4685
MAPIVA PORTO CARRAS S.A.—See Technical Olympic SA; *Int'l*, pg. 7506
MAPLEBEAR INC; *U.S. Public*, pg. 1362
MAPLE BIOSCIENCES INC.—See MedMira Inc.; *Int'l*, pg. 4785
MAPLE BROOK, L.L.C.—See Sun Communities, Inc.; *U.S. Public*, pg. 1961
THE MAPLE CITY ICE COMPANY; *U.S. Private*, pg. 4074
MAPLE CITY RUBBER COMPANY; *U.S. Private*, pg. 2568
MAPLE CITY SAVINGS BANK, FSB—See Maple City Savings, MHC; *U.S. Private*, pg. 2568
MAPLE CITY SAVINGS, MHC; *U.S. Private*, pg. 2568
MAPLE CITY WOODWORKING CORP.—See Patrick Industries, Inc.; *U.S. Public*, pg. 1652
MAPLE CREST DEVELOPMENT LIMITED—See Kerry Group Limited; *Int'l*, pg. 4137
MAPLE ENERGY PLC; *Int'l*, pg. 4685
MAPLE FINANCIAL GROUP INC.; *Int'l*, pg. 4685
MAPLE GATE FREIGHT SYSTEMS INC.; *Int'l*, pg. 4686
MAPLE GOLD MINES LTD.; *Int'l*, pg. 4686
MAPLE GROVE AUTO SERVICE, INC.—See O2 Investment Partners, LLC; *U.S. Private*, pg. 2982
MAPLE GROVE HOSPITAL; *U.S. Private*, pg. 2568
MAPLE HILL AUTO GROUP; *U.S. Private*, pg. 2568
MAPLEHURST BAKERIES, INC.—See George Weston Limited; *Int'l*, pg. 2939
MAPLEHURST FARMS INC.; *U.S. Private*, pg. 2568
MAPLE ISLAND ESTATES, INC.; *U.S. Private*, pg. 2568
MAPLE ISLAND INC.; *U.S. Private*, pg. 2568
MAPLE LAWN SURGERY CENTER, LLC—See Tenet Healthcare Corporation; *U.S. Public*, pg. 2004
MAPLE LEAF CAPITAL LIMITED—See Kohinoor Maple Leaf Group; *Int'l*, pg. 4229
MAPLE LEAF CEMENT FACTORY LIMITED—See Kohinoor Maple Leaf Group; *Int'l*, pg. 4229
MAPLE-LEAF CONSTRUCTION CO, INC; *U.S. Private*, pg. 2568
MAPLE LEAF CONSUMER FOODS—See Maple Leaf Foods, Inc.; *Int'l*, pg. 4686
MAPLE LEAF CONSUMER FOODS—See Maple Leaf Foods, Inc.; *Int'l*, pg. 4686
MAPLE LEAF CONSUMER FOODS—See Maple Leaf Foods, Inc.; *Int'l*, pg. 4686
MAPLE LEAF EDUCATION ASI PACIFIC LTD—See China Maple Leaf Educational Systems Limited; *Int'l*, pg. 1517
MAPLE LEAF EDUCATION NORTH AMERICA LIMITED—See China Maple Leaf Educational Systems Limited; *Int'l*, pg. 1517
MAPLE LEAF FARMS INC.; *U.S. Private*, pg. 2568
MAPLE LEAF FOODS, INC.; *Int'l*, pg. 4686
MAPLE LEAF GREEN WORLD INC.; *Int'l*, pg. 4686
MAPLE LEAF METALS INC.—See Kyoei Steel Ltd.; *Int'l*, pg. 4362
MAPLE LEAF SPORTS & ENTERTAINMENT LTD.—See BCE Inc.; *Int'l*, pg. 927
MAPLE LEAF SPORTS & ENTERTAINMENT LTD.—See Rogers Communications Inc.; *Int'l*, pg. 6383
MAPLE LIFE FINANCIAL, INC.; *U.S. Private*, pg. 2568
MAPLE LODGE FARMS LTD.; *Int'l*, pg. 4686
MAPLE LOGISTICS SOLUTIONS—See The Maple-Vail Book Manufacturing Group; *U.S. Private*, pg. 4074
MAPLE MARKETING (GFTZ) LTD—See Sunstar Suisse S.A .; *Int'l*, pg. 7323
MAPLE MARKETING LTD.—See Sunstar Suisse S.A.; *Int'l*, pg. 7323
MAPLE MOUNTAIN CO-PACKERS LLC—See Ryder System, Inc.; *U.S. Public*, pg. 1828
MAPLE PICTURES CORP.—See Lions Gate Entertainment Corp.; *Int'l*, pg. 4521
THE MAPLE PRESS COMPANY—See The Maple-Vail Book Manufacturing Group; *U.S. Private*, pg. 4074
MAPLE RESOURCES INC.—See Mega Uranium Ltd.; *Int'l*, pg. 4793
MAPLE RIDGE MOBILE HOMES OF CALIFORNIA, INC.; *U.S. Private*, pg. 2568
MAPLE RIVER GRAIN & AGRONOMY, LLC.; *U.S. Private*, pg. 2568
MAPLES DIALYSIS, LLC—See DaVita Inc.; *U.S. Public*, pg. 641
MAPLE SECURITIES (U.K.) LIMITED—See Maple Financial Group Inc.; *Int'l*, pg. 4685
MAPLE SECURITIES U.S.A. INC.—See Maple Financial Group Inc.; *Int'l*, pg. 4685
MAPLE SHADE MOTOR CORP.; *U.S. Private*, pg. 2568

COMPANY NAME INDEX

MAPLES INDUSTRIES INC.; *U.S. Private*, pg. 2568
THE MAPLES (NGP) MANAGEMENT COMPANY LIMITED—See Persimmon plc; *Int'l*, pg. 5817
MAPLESOFT EUROPE GMBH—See FUJISOFT INCORPORATED; *Int'l*, pg. 2830
MAPLESOFT GROUP INC.—See The Co-operators Group Limited; *Int'l*, pg. 7634
MAPLE STAR NEVADA, INC.—See ATAR Capital, LLC; *U.S. Private*, pg. 364
THE MAPLES (WESTON) RESIDENTS MANAGEMENT COMPANY LIMITED—See Persimmon plc; *Int'l*, pg. 5817
MAPLE SYSTEMS, INC.; *U.S. Private*, pg. 2568
MAPLETON COMMUNICATIONS, LLC - RADIO MERCED—See Mapleton Communications, LLC; *U.S. Private*, pg. 2568
MAPLETON COMMUNICATIONS, LLC - RADIO MONTEREY BAY—See Mapleton Communications, LLC; *U.S. Private*, pg. 2568
MAPLETON COMMUNICATIONS, LLC - RADIO SPOKANE—See Mapleton Communications, LLC; *U.S. Private*, pg. 2568
MAPLETON COMMUNICATIONS, LLC; *U.S. Private*, pg. 2568
MAPLE TRADE FINANCE INC.—See Maple Financial Group Inc.; *Int'l*, pg. 4685
MAPLETREE COMMERCIAL TRUST; *Int'l*, pg. 4686
MAPLETREE INDUSTRIAL TRUST; *Int'l*, pg. 4686
MAPLETREE INVESTMENTS PTE LTD.—See Temasek Holdings (Private) Limited; *Int'l*, pg. 7548
MAPLETREE LOGISTICS TRUST; *Int'l*, pg. 4686
MAPLETREE NORTH ASIA COMMERCIAL TRUST MANAGEMENT LTD.; *Int'l*, pg. 4686
THE MAPLE-VAIL BOOK MANUFACTURING GROUP; *U.S. Private*, pg. 4074
MAPLEWAVE HOLDINGS (PTY) LTD.—See Steinhoff International Holdings N.V.; *Int'l*, pg. 7194
MAPLEWOOD BEVERAGE PACKERS, LLC.; *U.S. Private*, pg. 2568
MAPLEWOOD BUILDING SPECIALTIES; *U.S. Private*, pg. 2569
MAPLEWOOD PHYSICAL THERAPY, LIMITED PARTNERSHIP—See U.S. Physical Therapy, Inc.; *U.S. Public*, pg. 2215
MAP LICENSE AS—See Crayon Group AS; *Int'l*, pg. 1020
MAP LIMITED—See Anderson Group Limited; *Int'l*, pg. 450
MAPLIN ELECTRONICS LTD—See Rutland Partners LLP; *Int'l*, pg. 6432
MAPLUX REINSURANCE COMPANY LTD.—See MAPFRE S.A.; *Int'l*, pg. 4685
MAP MARKETING & INCENTIVES, LLC—See Frosch International Travel Inc.; *U.S. Private*, pg. 1616
MAP MISCHSYSTEME GMBH—See WAMGROUP S.p.A.; *Int'l*, pg. 8338
MAPMYFITNESS, INC—See Outside Interactive, Inc.; *U.S. Private*, pg. 3051
MAPNA BOILER & EQUIPMENT ENGINEERING & MANUFACTURING COMPANY—See MAPNA Group; *Int'l*, pg. 4686
MAPNA COMBINED CYCLE POWER PLANTS CONSTRUCTION & DEVELOPMENT COMPANY—See MAPNA Group; *Int'l*, pg. 4686
MAPNA DRILLING COMPANY—See MAPNA Group; *Int'l*, pg. 4686
MAPNA ELECTRIC & CONTROL ENGINEERING & MANUFACTURING COMPANY—See MAPNA Group; *Int'l*, pg. 4686
MAPNA GENERATOR ENGINEERING & MANUFACTURING COMPANY—See MAPNA Group; *Int'l*, pg. 4686
MAPNA GROUP; *Int'l*, pg. 4686
MAPNA HEALTHCARE COMPANY—See MAPNA Group; *Int'l*, pg. 4686
MAPNA LOCOMOTIVE ENGINEERING & MANUFACTURING COMPANY—See MAPNA Group; *Int'l*, pg. 4686
MAPNA MANAGEMENT CONSULTING COMPANY—See MAPNA Group; *Int'l*, pg. 4686
MAPNA OPERATION & MAINTENANCE COMPANY—See MAPNA Group; *Int'l*, pg. 4686
MAPNA POWER PLANTS CONSTRUCTION & DEVELOPMENT COMPANY—See MAPNA Group; *Int'l*, pg. 4686
MAPNA RAILWAY OPERATION DEVELOPMENT & MAINTENANCE COMPANY—See MAPNA Group; *Int'l*, pg. 4687
MAPNA SPECIAL PROJECTS CONSTRUCTION & DEVELOPMENT COMPANY—See MAPNA Group; *Int'l*, pg. 4687
MAPNA STS COMPANY—See MAPNA Group; *Int'l*, pg. 4687
MAPNA TURBINE BLADE ENGINEERING & MANUFACTURING COMPANY—See MAPNA Group; *Int'l*, pg. 4687
MAPNA TURBINE ENGINEERING & MANUFACTURING COMPANY—See MAPNA Group; *Int'l*, pg. 4687
MAP OF EASTON, INC.; *U.S. Private*, pg. 2568
MAP OF MEDICINE LTD.—See The Hearst Corporation; *U.S. Private*, pg. 4048
MAPP CONSTRUCTION, LLC; *U.S. Private*, pg. 2569
MAPP DIGITAL US, LLC—See Marlin Equity Partners, LLC; *U.S. Private*, pg. 2584

MAP PLASTICS PTE LTD—See Min Aik Technology Co., Ltd.; *Int'l*, pg. 4898
MAPPLE, INC.—See Shobunsha Holdings Inc.; *Int'l*, pg. 6857
MAPP TECHONOLOGIES, LLC—See TGP Investments, LLC; *U.S. Private*, pg. 3979
MAPPY S.A.—See Solocal Group; *Int'l*, pg. 7074
MAPQUEST, INC.—See Apollo Global Management, Inc.; *U.S. Public*, pg. 167
MAPR.AGENCY, INC.; *U.S. Private*, pg. 2569
MAP RENTALS, INC.—See The Sterling Group, L.P.; *U.S. Private*, pg. 4123
MAPROM GMBH; *Int'l*, pg. 4687
MAPR TECHNOLOGIES, INC.—See Hewlett Packard Enterprise Company; *U.S. Public*, pg. 1032
MAPSA S. COOP.—See Mondragon Corporation; *Int'l*, pg. 5031
MAPS CREDIT UNION; *U.S. Private*, pg. 2569
MAPSPEOPLE A/S; *Int'l*, pg. 4687
MAPS SPA; *Int'l*, pg. 4687
MAPSYS INC.; *U.S. Private*, pg. 2569
MAP TA PHUT OLEFINS CO., LTD.—See The Siam Cement Public Company Limited; *Int'l*, pg. 7682
MAP TA PHUT TANK TERMINAL CO., LTD.—See The Siam Cement Public Company Limited; *Int'l*, pg. 7683
MAP TECHNOLOGY HOLDINGS PTE. LTD.—See Min Aik Technology Co., Ltd.; *Int'l*, pg. 4898
MAPTELLIGENT INC.; *U.S. Public*, pg. 1363
MAPTEXT, INC.—See Deutsche Lufthansa AG; *Int'l*, pg. 2069
MAPUTO CAR TERMINAL LIMITADA—See Grindrod Limited; *Int'l*, pg. 3086
MAQ ADMINISTRACION URBANAS SOCIMI, SA; *Int'l*, pg. 4687
MAQBOOL TEXTILE MILLS LTD.; *Int'l*, pg. 4687
MAQL EUROPE LIMITED—See Marvelous Inc.; *Int'l*, pg. 4717
MAQRENT S.P.A.—See Monadelphous Group Limited; *Int'l*, pg. 5024
MAQSIMA GMBH—See BASSETTI GROUP SAS; *Int'l*, pg. 888
MAQ SOFTWARE; *U.S. Private*, pg. 2569
MAQUET & ALM BELGIQUE N.V.—See Getinge AB; *Int'l*, pg. 2951
MAQUET AUSTRALIA PTY LTD—See Getinge AB; *Int'l*, pg. 2951
MAQUET BELGIUM NV—See Getinge AB; *Int'l*, pg. 2951
MAQUET BISTRO GMBH.—See Getinge AB; *Int'l*, pg. 2951
MAQUET CARDIOPULMONARY AG—See Getinge AB; *Int'l*, pg. 2951
MAQUET CARDIOPULMONARY DO BRASIL. IND. E COM S.A—See Getinge AB; *Int'l*, pg. 2951
MAQUET CARDIOPULMONARY MEDIKAL TEKNIK SANTIC LTD. STI—See Getinge AB; *Int'l*, pg. 2951
MAQUET CARDIOVASCULAR GMBH—See Getinge AB; *Int'l*, pg. 2951
MAQUET CARDIOVASCULAR LLC—See Getinge AB; *Int'l*, pg. 2951
MAQUET CARDIOVASCULAR US SALES, LLC—See Getinge AB; *Int'l*, pg. 2951
MAQUET CRITICAL CARE AB—See Getinge AB; *Int'l*, pg. 2951
MAQUET DENMARK A/S—See Getinge AB; *Int'l*, pg. 2951
MAQUET DO BRASIL EQUIPAMENTOS. MEDICOS LTDA.—See Getinge AB; *Int'l*, pg. 2952
MAQUET-DYNAMED INC—See Getinge AB; *Int'l*, pg. 2952
MAQUET FINANCIAL SERVICES GMBH.—See Getinge AB; *Int'l*, pg. 2951
MAQUET FINLAND OY—See Getinge AB; *Int'l*, pg. 2951
MAQUET GMBH & CO. KG—See Getinge AB; *Int'l*, pg. 2951
MAQUET HONG KONG LTD.—See Getinge AB; *Int'l*, pg. 2952
MAQUET HOSPITAL SOLUTIONS GMBH.—See Getinge AB; *Int'l*, pg. 2952
MAQUET, INC.—See Getinge AB; *Int'l*, pg. 2951
MAQUET IRELAND LTD—See Getinge AB; *Int'l*, pg. 2952
MAQUET ITALIA S.P.A.—See Getinge AB; *Int'l*, pg. 2951
MAQUET JAPAN KK—See Getinge AB; *Int'l*, pg. 2952
MAQUET LLC—See Getinge AB; *Int'l*, pg. 2952
MAQUET LTD—See Getinge AB; *Int'l*, pg. 2952
MAQUET MEDICAL INDIA PVT LTD—See Getinge AB; *Int'l*, pg. 2952
MAQUET MEDICAL KOREA CO. LTD.—See Getinge AB; *Int'l*, pg. 2952
MAQUET MEDICAL SYSTEMS USA LLC—See Getinge AB; *Int'l*, pg. 2952
MAQUET MEDIZINTECHNIK VERTRIEB UND SERVICE GMBH-O.S—See Getinge AB; *Int'l*, pg. 2952
MAQUET MEXICANA, S.DE R.L.DE CV—See Getinge AB; *Int'l*, pg. 2952
MAQUET MIDDLE EAST FZ-LLC—See Getinge AB; *Int'l*, pg. 2952
MAQUET NETHERLANDS B.V.—See Getinge AB; *Int'l*, pg. 2952
MAQUET POLAND SP.Z.O.O—See Getinge AB; *Int'l*, pg. 2952

MAQUET PORTUGAL LDA—See Getinge AB; *Int'l*, pg. 2952
MAQUET SA—See Getinge AB; *Int'l*, pg. 2951
MAQUET (SHANGHAI) MEDICAL EQUIPMENT CO., LTD.—See Getinge AB; *Int'l*, pg. 2951
MAQUET SOUTH EAST ASIA LTD.—See Getinge AB; *Int'l*, pg. 2952
MAQUET SOUTHERN AFRICA (PTY) LTD.—See Getinge AB; *Int'l*, pg. 2952
MAQUET SPAIN S.L.U.—See Getinge AB; *Int'l*, pg. 2952
MAQUET (SUZHOU) CO. LTD.—See Getinge AB; *Int'l*, pg. 2951
MAQUET VERTRIEB UND SERVICE. DEUTSCHLAND GMBH—See Getinge AB; *Int'l*, pg. 2952
MAQUIA CAPITAL ACQUISITION CORPORATION; *U.S. Public*, pg. 1363
MAQUIASFALT SL—See Bucher Industries AG; *Int'l*, pg. 1209
MAQUILADORA GENERAL DE MATAMOROS S.A. DE C.V.—See Arkema S.A.; *Int'l*, pg. 568
MAQUILA PRODUCTS DEL NOROESTE S.DE R.L. DE C.V.—See Brady Corporation; *U.S. Public*, pg. 379
MAQUILAS PAMI, S.A. DE C.V.—See Premier Brands Group Holdings LLC; *U.S. Private*, pg. 3249
MAQUINADOS DE PRECISION DE MEXICO S. DE R.L. DE C.V.—See Cie Automotive S.A.; *Int'l*, pg. 1604
MAQUINARIA AMECO GUATEMALA, LIMITADA—See OEP Capital Advisors, L.P.; *U.S. Private*, pg. 2998
MAQUINARIA ARTES GRAFICAS HARTMANN SA—See Sycamore Partners Management, LP; *U.S. Private*, pg. 3897
MAQUINARIAS KRONES DE VENEZUELA S.A.—See Krones AG; *Int'l*, pg. 4306
MAQUINAS Y HERRAMIENTAS BLACK & DECKER DE CHILE S.A.—See Stanley Black & Decker, Inc.; *U.S. Public*, pg. 1936
MAQUOKETA VALLEY ELECTRIC COOP; *U.S. Private*, pg. 2569
MARAC ALBANIA SH.P.K—See MARAC ELECTRONICS SA; *Int'l*, pg. 4687
MARAC BULGARIA EOOD—See MARAC ELECTRONICS SA; *Int'l*, pg. 4687
MARAC ELECTRONICS SA; *Int'l*, pg. 4687
MARAC FINANCE & LENDING—See Heartland Bank Limited; *Int'l*, pg. 3304
MARADYNE CORPORATION - POW-R-QUIK DIVISION—See Dreison International, Inc.; *U.S. Private*, pg. 1276
MARADYNE CORPORATION—See Dreison International, Inc.; *U.S. Private*, pg. 1276
MARADYNE CORPORATION - SUPERTRAPP INDUSTRIAL MUFFLERS DIVISION—See Dreison International, Inc.; *U.S. Private*, pg. 1276
MARADYNE MOBILE PRODUCTS—See Dreison International, Inc.; *U.S. Private*, pg. 1276
MARA ESCROW COMPANY—See Old Republic International Corporation; *U.S. Public*, pg. 1569
MARAFEQ AL TASHGHEEL COMPANY—See Abdullah Al-Othaim Markets Company; *Int'l*, pg. 59
MARAFIQ COMPANY—See Abdullah Al-Othaim Markets Company; *Int'l*, pg. 59
MARAGON PRIVATE SCHOOLS AVIANTO (PTY) LTD.—See ADvTECH Limited; *Int'l*, pg. 169
MARAGON PRIVATE SCHOOLS RUIMSIG (PTY) LTD.—See ADvTECH Limited; *Int'l*, pg. 169
MARAGRA ACUCAR SARL—See The Garfield Weston Foundation; *Int'l*, pg. 7648
MARAIS COTE D'IVOIRE SARL—See TESMEC S.p.A.; *Int'l*, pg. 7572
MARAIS GUINEE SARLU—See TESMEC S.p.A.; *Int'l*, pg. 7572
MARAKANA INC.; *U.S. Private*, pg. 2569
MARAKON ASSOCIATES, INC.—See CRA International, Inc.; *U.S. Public*, pg. 588
MARAL OVERSEAS LIMITED; *Int'l*, pg. 4687
THE MARAMONT CORPORATION; *U.S. Private*, pg. 4074
MARANA AEROSPACE SOLUTIONS, INC.; *U.S. Private*, pg. 2569
MARANATHA VOLUNTEERS INTERNATIONAL, INC.; *U.S. Private*, pg. 2569
MARANDA ENTERPRISES, LLC; *U.S. Private*, pg. 2569
MARAND D.O.O.; *Int'l*, pg. 4687
MARANDER ASSURANTIE COMPAGNIE BV—See JAB Holding Company S.a.r.l.; *Int'l*, pg. 3863
MARANELLO CONCESSIONAIRES LIMITED—See Penske Automotive Group, Inc.; *U.S. Public*, pg. 1665
MARANELLO SALES LIMITED—See Penske Automotive Group, Inc.; *U.S. Public*, pg. 1665
MARAN FILM GMBH—See Bavaria Film GmbH; *Int'l*, pg. 899
MARANGONI ARGENTINA SA—See Marangoni S.p.A.; *Int'l*, pg. 4687
MARANGONI DO BRASIL, LTDA—See Marangoni S.p.A.; *Int'l*, pg. 4688
MARANGONI INDUSTRIAL TYRES LANKA PVT LTD—See Marangoni S.p.A.; *Int'l*, pg. 4687
MARANGONI INDUSTRIE MANUTENTION SAS—See Marangoni S.p.A.; *Int'l*, pg. 4687

MARAND D.O.O. — CORPORATE AFFILIATIONS

MARANGONI KAUCUK TICARET A.S.—See Marangoni S.p.A.; *Int'l*, pg. 4687
MARANGONI MECCANICA S.P.A.—See Marangoni S.p.A.; *Int'l*, pg. 4687
MARANGONI PNEUMATICI S.P.A.—See Marangoni S.p.A.; *Int'l*, pg. 4687
MARANGONI RETREADING SYSTEMS DEUTSCHLAND GMBH—See Marangoni S.p.A.; *Int'l*, pg. 4687
MARANGONI SHANGHAI TRADING CO., LTD.—See Marangoni S.p.A.; *Int'l*, pg. 4687
MARANGONI S.P.A.; *Int'l*, pg. 4687
MARANGONI TREAD N.A., INC.—See Borrachas Vipal SA; *Int'l*, pg. 1114
MARANGONI TREAD S.P.A—See Marangoni S.p.A.; *Int'l*, pg. 4688
MARANGONI TREAD (UK) LTD—See Marangoni S.p.A.; *Int'l*, pg. 4688
MARANGONI TYRE GMBH—See Marangoni S.p.A.; *Int'l*, pg. 4688
MARANI BRANDS, INC.; *U.S. Public*, pg. 1363
MARAN INC.; *U.S. Private*, pg. 2569
MARANON & ASSOCIATES ADVERTISING; *U.S. Private*, pg. 2569
MARANON CAPITAL, L.P.—See Eldridge Industries LLC; *U.S. Private*, pg. 1351
MARANTZ AMERICA INC.—See Bain Capital, LP; *U.S. Private*, pg. 438
MARANTZ EUROPE B.V.—See Bain Capital, LP; *U.S. Private*, pg. 438
MARANTZ FRANCE SAS—See Bain Capital, LP; *U.S. Private*, pg. 438
MARANTZ GMBH—See Bain Capital, LP; *U.S. Private*, pg. 438
MARANTZ ITALY SRL—See Bain Capital, LP; *U.S. Private*, pg. 439
MARANTZ JAPAN INC.—See Bain Capital, LP; *U.S. Private*, pg. 438
MARANTZ UK LTD.—See Bain Capital, LP; *U.S. Private*, pg. 439
MARARA SA—See Accor S.A.; *Int'l*, pg. 92
MARASKA D.D—See Saponia d.d.; *Int'l*, pg. 6571
MARASTAR LLC—See AIP, LLC; *U.S. Private*, pg. 137
MARATHON ASSET MANAGEMENT LP; *U.S. Private*, pg. 2569
MARATHON AUTOMOTIVE GROUP LLC—See Marathon Asset Management LP; *U.S. Private*, pg. 2570
MARATHON BANCORP, INC.; *U.S. Public*, pg. 1363
MARATHON CHEESE CORP.; *U.S. Private*, pg. 2570
MARATHON COACH, INC.; *U.S. Private*, pg. 2570
MARATHON CONSTRUCTION CORP.; *U.S. Private*, pg. 2570
MARATHON CONSULTING; *U.S. Private*, pg. 2570
MARATHON DATA SYSTEMS, INC.—See Chicago Growth Partners, LLC; *U.S. Private*, pg. 877
MARATHON DIGITAL HOLDINGS, INC.; *U.S. Public*, pg. 1363
MARATHON ELECTRICAL CONTRACTORS, INC.; *U.S. Private*, pg. 2570
MARATHON ELECTRIC FAR EAST PTE LTD.—See Regal Rexnord Corporation; *U.S. Public*, pg. 1773
MARATHON ENTERPRISES, INC.; *U.S. Private*, pg. 2570
MARATHON EQUIPMENT COMPANY—See Terex Corporation; *U.S. Public*, pg. 2019
MARATHON FLINT OIL COMPANY; *U.S. Private*, pg. 2570
MARATHON GOLD CORPORATION—See Calibre Mining Corp.; *Int'l*, pg. 1264
MARATHON HEALTH, LLC—See General Atlantic Service Company, L.P.; *U.S. Private*, pg. 1663
MARATHON HVAC SERVICES, LLC; *U.S. Private*, pg. 2570
MARATHON INTERNATIONAL OIL COMPANY—See ConocoPhillips; *U.S. Public*, pg. 569
MARATHON INTERNATIONAL PETROLEUM INDONESIA LIMITED—See ConocoPhillips; *U.S. Public*, pg. 569
MARATHON INVESTMENTS LTD.; *Int'l*, pg. 4688
MARATHON MARTINEZ REFINERY—See Marathon Petroleum Corporation; *U.S. Public*, pg. 1363
MARATHON MEDIA LLC; *U.S. Private*, pg. 2570
MARATHON MEDIA—See De Agostini S.p.A.; *Int'l*, pg. 1994
MARATHON METALS LLC—See MNP Corporation; *U.S. Private*, pg. 2756
MARATHON NEXTGEN REALTY LTD.; *Int'l*, pg. 4688
MARATHONNORCO AEROSPACE, INC.—See TransDigm Group Incorporated; *U.S. Public*, pg. 2182
MARATHON OIL CORPORATION—See ConocoPhillips; *U.S. Public*, pg. 568
MARATHON OIL EXPLORATION (U.K.) LIMITED—See ConocoPhillips; *U.S. Public*, pg. 569
MARATHON OIL HOLDINGS U.K. LIMITED—See ConocoPhillips; *U.S. Public*, pg. 569
MARATHON OIL SUPPLY COMPANY (U.S.) LIMITED—See ConocoPhillips; *U.S. Public*, pg. 569
MARATHON PETROLEUM COMPANY CANADA LTD.—See Marathon Petroleum Corporation; *U.S. Public*, pg. 1364
MARATHON PETROLEUM COMPANY LLC—See Marathon Petroleum Corporation; *U.S. Public*, pg. 1364
MARATHON PETROLEUM COMPANY LLC—See Marathon Petroleum Corporation; *U.S. Public*, pg. 1364
MARATHON PETROLEUM COMPANY LLC—See Marathon Petroleum Corporation; *U.S. Public*, pg. 1364
MARATHON PETROLEUM COMPANY LLC—See Marathon Petroleum Corporation; *U.S. Public*, pg. 1364
MARATHON PETROLEUM CORPORATION; *U.S. Public*, pg. 1363
MARATHON PETROLEUM INVESTMENT, LTD.—See ConocoPhillips; *U.S. Public*, pg. 569
MARATHON PIPE LINE LLC—See Marathon Petroleum Corporation; *U.S. Public*, pg. 1364
MARATHON PRODUCTS, INC.—See Harbour Group Industries, Inc.; *U.S. Private*, pg. 1861
MARATHON SENSORS INC.—See Halma plc; *Int'l*, pg. 3231
MARATHON SERVICE (G.B.) LIMITED—See ConocoPhillips; *U.S. Public*, pg. 569
MARATHON SPECIAL PRODUCTS CORP.—See Regal Rexnord Corporation; *U.S. Public*, pg. 1773
MARATHON STRATEGIES, LLC; *U.S. Private*, pg. 2570
MARATHON TRANSPORT, INC.—See Transport Investments, Inc.; *U.S. Private*, pg. 4210
MARATHON TS, INC.; *U.S. Private*, pg. 2570
MARATHON TYRES PTY. LIMITED; *Int'l*, pg. 4688
MARAVAI LIFESCIENCES HOLDINGS, INC.; *U.S. Public*, pg. 1364
MARAVAI LIFESCIENCES, INC.; *U.S. Public*, pg. 2570
MARAWOOD CONSTRUCTION SERVICES; *U.S. Private*, pg. 2570
MARAZZI DEUTSCHLAND G.M.B.H.—See Mohawk Industries, Inc.; *U.S. Public*, pg. 1457
MARAZZI DISTRIBUTION, INC.—See Mohawk Industries, Inc.; *U.S. Public*, pg. 1457
MARAZZI GROUP F.Z.E.—See Mohawk Industries, Inc.; *U.S. Public*, pg. 1457
MARAZZI GROUP S.R.L.—See Mohawk Industries, Inc.; *U.S. Public*, pg. 1457
MARAZZI GROUP TRADING (SHANGHAI) CO. LTD.—See Mohawk Industries, Inc.; *U.S. Public*, pg. 1457
MARAZZI IBERIA S.A.—See Mohawk Industries, Inc.; *U.S. Public*, pg. 1457
MARAZZI JAPAN CO., LTD.—See Mohawk Industries, Inc.; *U.S. Public*, pg. 1458
MARBAISE HANLO LS GMBH—See Emerson Electric Co.; *U.S. Public*, pg. 750
MAR-BAL INC.; *U.S. Private*, pg. 2569
MARBAS MENKUL DEGERLER A.S.—See Gedik Yatirim Menkul Degerler A.S.; *Int'l*, pg. 2910
MARBELLA PELLAMI SPA—See Kering S.A.; *Int'l*, pg. 4135
MARBET MARION & BETTINA WURTH GMBH & CO. KG—See Wurth Verwaltungsgesellschaft mbH; *Int'l*, pg. 8506
MARBET VIAJES ESPANA S.A.—See Wurth Verwaltungsgesellschaft mbH; *Int'l*, pg. 8514
MARBLE ARTS AD; *Int'l*, pg. 4688
MARBLE CITY INDIA LIMITED; *Int'l*, pg. 4688
MARBLE CRAFT DESIGN, INC.; *U.S. Private*, pg. 2570
MARBLE DESIGN FACTORY COMPANY; *Int'l*, pg. 4688
MARBLEGATE ACQUISITION CORP.; *U.S. Public*, pg. 1364
MARBLEHEAD BANK; *U.S. Private*, pg. 2570
MARBLEHEAD REPORTER—See Gannett Co., Inc.; *U.S. Public*, pg. 902
MARBLE POINT LOAN FINANCING LIMITED; *Int'l*, pg. 4688
MARBLE RIVER, L.L.C.—See EDP - Energias de Portugal, S.A.; *Int'l*, pg. 2314
MARBLE SLAB FRANCHISING, LLC—See Fog Cutter Capital Group Inc.; *U.S. Private*, pg. 1557
MARBOB ENERGY CORP.—See ConocoPhillips; *U.S. Public*, pg. 568
MARBODAL AB—See Nobia AB; *Int'l*, pg. 5395
MARBO D.O.O. LAKTASI—See PepsiCo, Inc.; *U.S. Public*, pg. 1669
MARBO PRODUCT D.O.O. BEOGRAD—See PepsiCo, Inc.; *U.S. Public*, pg. 1669
MARBORG INDUSTRIES INC.; *U.S. Private*, pg. 2570
MARBOUR SAS; *Int'l*, pg. 4688
MARBULK CANADA INC.—See Algoma Central Corporation; *Int'l*, pg. 318
MARBULK CANADA INC.—See The CSL Group Inc.; *Int'l*, pg. 7636
MARBULK SHIPPING INC.—See Algoma Central Corporation; *Int'l*, pg. 318
MARBULK SHIPPING INC.—See The CSL Group Inc.; *Int'l*, pg. 7636
MARBURGER IONENSTRAHL-THERAPIE BETRIEBSGESELLSCHAFT MBH—See Asklepios Kliniken GmbH & Co. KGaA; *Int'l*, pg. 624
MARBURG TECHNOLOGY INC.; *U.S. Private*, pg. 2570
MARBURN STORES INC.; *U.S. Private*, pg. 2570
MARC16 EQUIPMENT MANUFACTURING SDN. BHD.—See MSM International Limited; *Int'l*, pg. 5069
MARC1 CARWASH—See Red Dog Equity LLC; *U.S. Private*, pg. 3374
MARCA HISPANIC LLC—See MARC USA, LLC; *U.S. Private*, pg. 2571
MARCALI YACHT BROKERAGE & CONSULTING, LLC; *U.S. Private*, pg. 2571
MARC ANTHONY COSMETICS LTD.—See Nexus Capital Management LP; *U.S. Private*, pg. 2922
MARCA PROTECCION LABORAL, S.L.U.—See Bunzl plc; *Int'l*, pg. 1219
MARCARD FAMILY OFFICE TREUHAND GMBH—See M.M. Warburg & Co. KGaA; *Int'l*, pg. 4616
MARCARD, STEIN & CO. GMBH & CO. KG—See M.M. Warburg & Co. KGaA; *Int'l*, pg. 4616
MARCAS NESTLE, S.A. DE C.V.—See Nestle S.A.; *Int'l*, pg. 5203
MARCATEL S.A. DE C.V.; *Int'l*, pg. 4688
MARCATO CAPITAL MANAGEMENT, LP; *U.S. Private*, pg. 2571
MARC CONLETH INDUSTRIES SDN. BHD.; *Int'l*, pg. 4688
MARCEGAGLIA ALBIGNASEGO—See Marcegaglia S.p.A.; *Int'l*, pg. 4689
MARCEGAGLIA BUILDTECH—See Marcegaglia S.p.A.; *Int'l*, pg. 4689
MARCEGAGLIA CASALMAGGIORE—See Marcegaglia S.p.A.; *Int'l*, pg. 4689
MARCEGAGLIA CHINA CO., LTD.—See Marcegaglia S.p.A.; *Int'l*, pg. 4689
MARCEGAGLIA CONTINO—See Marcegaglia S.p.A.; *Int'l*, pg. 4689
MARCEGAGLIA CORSICO—See Marcegaglia S.p.A.; *Int'l*, pg. 4689
MARCEGAGLIA DEUTSCHLAND—See Marcegaglia S.p.A.; *Int'l*, pg. 4689
MARCEGAGLIA ENGINEERING DIVISION S.P.A.—See Marcegaglia S.p.A.; *Int'l*, pg. 4689
MARCEGAGLIA FINANZIARIA—See Marcegaglia S.p.A.; *Int'l*, pg. 4689
MARCEGAGLIA FORLI—See Marcegaglia S.p.A.; *Int'l*, pg. 4689
MARCEGAGLIA IBERICA—See Marcegaglia S.p.A.; *Int'l*, pg. 4689
MARCEGAGLIA IRELAND—See Marcegaglia S.p.A.; *Int'l*, pg. 4689
MARCEGAGLIA POLAND SP Z O O - PRASZKA PLANT—See Marcegaglia S.p.A.; *Int'l*, pg. 4689
MARCEGAGLIA POLAND SP Z O O—See Marcegaglia S.p.A.; *Int'l*, pg. 4689
MARCEGAGLIA RAVENNA—See Marcegaglia S.p.A.; *Int'l*, pg. 4689
MARCEGAGLIA ROMANIA SRL—See Marcegaglia S.p.A.; *Int'l*, pg. 4689
MARCEGAGLIA S.P.A. - BENELUX PLANT—See Marcegaglia S.p.A.; *Int'l*, pg. 4689
MARCEGAGLIA S.P.A. - BOLTIERE PLANT—See Marcegaglia S.p.A.; *Int'l*, pg. 4689
MARCEGAGLIA S.P.A. - CASTEL MONASTERO PLANT—See Marcegaglia S.p.A.; *Int'l*, pg. 4689
MARCEGAGLIA S.P.A. - ETA DIVISION—See Marcegaglia S.p.A.; *Int'l*, pg. 4689
MARCEGAGLIA S.P.A. - FOGGIA PLANT—See Marcegaglia S.p.A.; *Int'l*, pg. 4689
MARCEGAGLIA S.P.A. - GUARDRAIL DIVISION—See Marcegaglia S.p.A.; *Int'l*, pg. 4689
MARCEGAGLIA S.P.A. - LIMA PLANT—See Marcegaglia S.p.A.; *Int'l*, pg. 4689
MARCEGAGLIA S.P.A. - LOMAGNA PLANT—See Marcegaglia S.p.A.; *Int'l*, pg. 4689
MARCEGAGLIA S.P.A. - LYON PLANT—See Marcegaglia S.p.A.; *Int'l*, pg. 4689
MARCEGAGLIA S.P.A. - MONTECHIARUGOLO PLANT—See Marcegaglia S.p.A.; *Int'l*, pg. 4689
MARCEGAGLIA S.P.A. - SAN GIORGIO DI NOGARO PLANT—See Marcegaglia S.p.A.; *Int'l*, pg. 4689
MARCEGAGLIA S.P.A. - SESTO AL REGHENA PLANT—See Marcegaglia S.p.A.; *Int'l*, pg. 4689
MARCEGAGLIA S.P.A.; *Int'l*, pg. 4688
MARCEGAGLIA S.P.A.—See Marcegaglia S.p.A.; *Int'l*, pg. 4689
MARCEGAGLIA S.P.A. - STINTINO PLANT—See Marcegaglia S.p.A.; *Int'l*, pg. 4689
MARCEGAGLIA S.P.A. - TERAMO PLANT—See Marcegaglia S.p.A.; *Int'l*, pg. 4689
MARCEGAGLIA S.P.A. - TRISIDER DIVISION—See Marcegaglia S.p.A.; *Int'l*, pg. 4689
MARCEGAGLIA UK—See Marcegaglia S.p.A.; *Int'l*, pg. 4689
MARCEGAGLIA USA, INC.—See Marcegaglia S.p.A.; *Int'l*, pg. 4689
MARCEL & HENRI SELECT MEATS, INC.; *U.S. Private*, pg. 2571
MARCEL HUFSCHMID AG—See Burkhalter Holding AG; *Int'l*, pg. 1225
MARCEL JACQUART ET FILS SAS; *Int'l*, pg. 4689
MARCELLINO MARTINS & E JOHNSTON EXPORTADORES LTDA—See ED&F Man Holdings Limited; *Int'l*, pg. 2303
MARCEL RIEBEN INGENIEURE AG—See BKW AG; *Int'l*, pg. 1055
MARC GLASSMAN, INC.; *U.S. Private*, pg. 2571

COMPANY NAME INDEX

MARCHANT CHEVROLET, INC.; *U.S. Private*, pg. 2571
MARCH COMMUNICATIONS, INC.—See Walker Sands, Inc.; *U.S. Private*, pg. 4429
MARCH CONSTRUCTION LTD—See VINCI S.A.; *Int'l*, pg. 8233
MARCH CORREDURIA DE SEGUROS S.A.—See Alba Grupo March; *Int'l*, pg. 292
MARCHE CORPORATION; *Int'l*, pg. 4689
MARCHEL INDUSTRIES, INC.—See Regimen Equity Partners Inc.; *Int'l*, pg. 6253
MARCHESI ANTINORI S.P.A; *Int'l*, pg. 4690
MARCHETTI CONSTRUCTION INC.; *U.S. Private*, pg. 2571
MARCHEX, INC.; *U.S. Public*, pg. 1364
MARCHEX SALES, LLC—See Marchex, Inc.; *U.S. Public*, pg. 1365
MARCHING PHARMACEUTICAL LIMITED—See Jacobson Pharma Corporation Limited; *Int'l*, pg. 3866
MARCHI THERMAL SYSTEMS, INC.—See Ultra Clean Holdings, Inc.; *U.S. Public*, pg. 2223
MARCH-JLT CORREDURIA DE SEGUROS, SA—See Alba Grupo March; *Int'l*, pg. 292
MARCH MANUFACTURING INC.; *U.S. Private*, pg. 2571
MARCH NETWORKS (AUSTRALIA) PTY LIMITED—See Delta Electronics, Inc.; *Int'l*, pg. 2018
MARCH NETWORKS CORPORATION—See Shenzhen Infinova Co., Ltd.; *Int'l*, pg. 6813
MARCH NETWORKS (FRANCE) SAS—See Delta Electronics, Inc.; *Int'l*, pg. 2018
MARCH NETWORKS S.R.L.—See Delta Electronics, Inc.; *Int'l*, pg. 2018
MARCHON EYEWEAR, INC.—See Vision Service Plan; *U.S. Private*, pg. 4391
MARCHON GERMANY GMBH—See Vision Service Plan; *U.S. Private*, pg. 4391
MARCHON HELLAS S.A.—See Vision Service Plan; *U.S. Private*, pg. 4391
MARCHON HISPANIA, SL—See Vision Service Plan; *U.S. Private*, pg. 4391
MARCHON ITALIA S.R.L.—See Vision Service Plan; *U.S. Private*, pg. 4391
MARCHON PORTUGAL UNIPESSOAL LDA—See Vision Service Plan; *U.S. Private*, pg. 4391
MARCH PATRIMONIOS S.A.—See Alba Grupo March; *Int'l*, pg. 292
MARCH PLASMA SYSTEMS, INC. - FLORIDA PCB LAB & CONTRACT SERVICES—See Nordson Corporation; *U.S. Public*, pg. 1533
MARCH PLASMA SYSTEMS, INC.—See Nordson Corporation; *U.S. Public*, pg. 1533
MARCH - UNIPSA CORREDURIA DE SEGUROS, S.A.U—See Alba Grupo March; *Int'l*, pg. 292
MARCH VISION CARE, INC.—See UnitedHealth Group Incorporated; *U.S. Public*, pg. 2242
MAR CITY DEVELOPMENTS LIMITED—See Mar City Plc; *Int'l*, pg. 4687
MAR CITY HOMES LIMITED—See Mar City Plc; *Int'l*, pg. 4687
MAR CITY PLC; *Int'l*, pg. 4687
MARC JACOBS INTERNATIONAL LLC—See LVMH Moet Hennessy Louis Vuitton SE; *Int'l*, pg. 4601
MARCK & ASSOCIATES, INC.; *U.S. Private*, pg. 2571
MARC MILLER BUICK GMC, INC.; *U.S. Private*, pg. 2571
MARC MOTORS INC.; *U.S. Private*, pg. 2571
MARC MOTORS NISSAN—See Marc Motors Inc.; *U.S. Private*, pg. 2571
MARCO 4 SRL—See UNICOM Global, Inc.; *U.S. Private*, pg. 4281
MARCOA PUBLISHING INC.; *U.S. Private*, pg. 2572
MARCO BEACH OCEAN RESORT MANAGEMENT INC.; *U.S. Private*, pg. 2571
MARCO CABLES & CONDUCTORS LIMITED; *Int'l*, pg. 4690
MARCO COLOR LABORATORY, INC.; *U.S. Private*, pg. 2571
MARCO CORPORATION (M) SDN. BHD.—See Marco Holdings Berhad; *Int'l*, pg. 4690
MARCO CRANE & RIGGING CO.; *U.S. Private*, pg. 2571
MARCO DESTIN INC.; *U.S. Private*, pg. 2571
MARCO ENTERPRISES, INC.; *U.S. Private*, pg. 2571
MARCO GLOBAL INC.; *U.S. Private*, pg. 2571
MARCO GROUP INTERNATIONAL, INC.—See Ridgemont Partners Management LLC; *U.S. Private*, pg. 3432
MARCO HOLDINGS BERHAD; *Int'l*, pg. 4690
MARCO ISLAND EAGLE—See Gannett Co., Inc.; *U.S. Public*, pg. 898
MARCOLE ENTERPRISES LLC—See Wilcas Corp.; *U.S. Private*, pg. 4518
MARCOLIN ASIA LTD.—See PAI Partners S.A.S.; *Int'l*, pg. 5701
MARCOLIN BENELUX S.P.R.L—See PAI Partners S.A.S.; *Int'l*, pg. 5701
MARCOLIN (DEUTSCHLAND) GMBH—See PAI Partners S.A.S.; *Int'l*, pg. 5701
MARCOLIN DO BRASIL LTDA—See PAI Partners S.A.S.; *Int'l*, pg. 5701
MARCOLIN FRANCE SARL—See PAI Partners S.A.S.; *Int'l*, pg. 5701
MARCOLIN GMBH—See PAI Partners S.A.S.; *Int'l*, pg. 5701
MARCOLIN IBERICA S.A.—See PAI Partners S.A.S.; *Int'l*, pg. 5701
MARCOLIN JAPAN CO LTD—See PAI Partners S.A.S.; *Int'l*, pg. 5701
MARCOLIN PORTUGAL LDA—See PAI Partners S.A.S.; *Int'l*, pg. 5701
MARCOLIN S.P.A.—See PAI Partners S.A.S.; *Int'l*, pg. 5701
MARCOLIN SWISS GMBH—See PAI Partners S.A.S.; *Int'l*, pg. 5701
MARCOLIN (UK) LTD.—See PAI Partners S.A.S.; *Int'l*, pg. 5701
MARCOLIN USA INC.—See PAI Partners S.A.S.; *Int'l*, pg. 5701
MARCOM CO LTD.—See British American Investment Co. (Mtius) Ltd.; *Int'l*, pg. 1165
MARCOM GROUP; *U.S. Private*, pg. 2572
MARCOM PLASTICS (PTY) LTD—See Berry Global Group, Inc; *U.S. Public*, pg. 324
MARCOM—See The Interpublic Group of Companies, Inc.; *U.S. Public*, pg. 2093
MARCONA GMBH & CO. KG—See Steilmann Holding AG; *Int'l*, pg. 7193
MARCON & BOYER INC.; *U.S. Private*, pg. 2572
MARCON DENSO CO., LTD.—See Denso Corporation; *Int'l*, pg. 2032
MAR-CONE APPLIANCE PARTS CENTER INC.—See Mar-Cone Appliance Parts Co.; *U.S. Private*, pg. 2569
MAR-CONE APPLIANCE PARTS CO.; *U.S. Private*, pg. 2569
MARCONE SUPPLY COMPANY; *U.S. Private*, pg. 2572
MARCON GRUPPEN I SVERIGE AB—See Endur ASA; *Int'l*, pg. 2410
MARCONI COMMUNICATIONS HOLDINGS—See Telent Limited; *Int'l*, pg. 7539
MARCONI COMMUNICATIONS INC.—See Telent Limited; *Int'l*, pg. 7539
MARCONI COMMUNICATIONS INC.—See Telent Limited; *Int'l*, pg. 7539
MARCONI CORP.—See Telent Limited; *Int'l*, pg. 7539
MARCON INTERNATIONAL INC.—See Media Central Corporation Inc.; *Int'l*, pg. 4770
MARCONI—See Telent Limited; *Int'l*, pg. 7539
MARCONI WIRELESS—See Telent Limited; *Int'l*, pg. 7539
MARCONS SA; *Int'l*, pg. 4690
MARCOPOLO AUTO COMPONENTS CO., LTD—See Marcopolo S.A.; *Int'l*, pg. 4690
THE MARCO POLO HOTEL (HONG KONG) LIMITED—See Wheelock & Company Limited; *Int'l*, pg. 8397
MARCO POLO HOTELS MANAGEMENT LIMITED; *Int'l*, pg. 4690
MARCO POLO INDUSTRIES MERCHANDISING COMPANY LIMITED—See Techtronic Industries Co., Ltd.; *Int'l*, pg. 7512
MARC O'POLO INTERNATIONAL GMBH; *Int'l*, pg. 4688
MARCO POLO INTERNATIONAL, INC.; *U.S. Private*, pg. 2572
MARCO POLO MARINE LTD.; *Int'l*, pg. 4690
MARCO POLO PARK S.R.L.—See InfraVia Capital Partners SAS; *Int'l*, pg. 3699
MARCOPOLO S.A.; *Int'l*, pg. 4690
MARCOPOLO SOUTH AFRICA PTY. LTD.—See Marcopolo S.A.; *Int'l*, pg. 4690
MARCOR DEVELOPMENT CORP.—See KODA Enterprises Group, LLC; *U.S. Private*, pg. 2336
MAR COR PURIFICATION CANADA—See STERIS plc; *Int'l*, pg. 7209
MAR COR PURIFICATION, INC.—See STERIS plc; *Int'l*, pg. 7209
MAR COR PURIFICATION—See STERIS plc; *Int'l*, pg. 7209
MARCO RUBBER & PLASTIC PRODUCTS, INC.—See Align Capital Partners, LLC; *U.S. Private*, pg. 167
MARCO'S AUTO BODY, INC.—See Blackstone Inc.; *U.S. Public*, pg. 356
MARCO SEATTLE, INC.—See MARCO Global Inc.; *U.S. Private*, pg. 2572
MARCO'S PIZZA, INC.—See Highland Ventures, Ltd.; *U.S. Private*, pg. 1939
MARCO STEEL & ALUMINUM INC.—See Triple-S Steel Holdings Inc.; *U.S. Private*, pg. 4237
MARCO TECHNOLOGIES, LLC—See Wells Fargo & Company; *U.S. Public*, pg. 2344
MARCOTTE INSURANCE AGENCY, INC.—See Caisse de Depot et Placement du Quebec; *Int'l*, pg. 1256
MARCOTTE INSURANCE AGENCY, INC.—See KKR & Co. Inc.; *U.S. Public*, pg. 1265
MARCOULY SAS—See VINCI S.A.; *Int'l*, pg. 8224
MARCOU TRANSPORTATION GROUP LLC; *U.S. Private*, pg. 2572
MARCO WORLDWIDE SDN. BHD.—See Marco Holdings Berhad; *Int'l*, pg. 4690
MARCRAFT APPAREL GROUP; *U.S. Private*, pg. 2572
M/A/R/C RESEARCH—See Omnicom Group Inc.; *U.S. Public*, pg. 1588
MARC RUTENBERG HOMES INC.; *U.S. Private*, pg. 2571
MARCS DAVID LAWRENCE PTY. LTD.—See Myer Pty Ltd; *Int'l*, pg. 5112
MARC TRUANT & ASSOCIATES, INC.; *U.S. Private*, pg. 2571
MARCUM LLP—See CBIZ, Inc.; *U.S. Public*, pg. 457
MARCUM WEALTH LLC; *U.S. Private*, pg. 2572
MARC USA, LLC - CHICAGO—See MARC USA, LLC; *U.S. Private*, pg. 2571
MARC USA, LLC; *U.S. Private*, pg. 2571
MARCUS BROTHERS TEXTILES, INC.; *U.S. Private*, pg. 2572
THE MARCUS BUCKINGHAM COMPANY, LLC.—See Automatic Data Processing, Inc.; *U.S. Public*, pg. 230
MARCUS CENTER FOR THE PERFORMING ARTS; *U.S. Private*, pg. 2572
THE MARCUS CORPORATION; *U.S. Public*, pg. 2111
MARCUS CORPORATION—See The Marcus Corporation; *U.S. Public*, pg. 2112
MARCUS DAIRY, INC.; *U.S. Private*, pg. 2572
MARCUS DALY MEMORIAL HOSPITAL; *U.S. Private*, pg. 2572
MARCUS FOOD COMPANY, INC.; *U.S. Private*, pg. 2572
MARCUS HOTELS ASSOCIATES, INC.—See The Marcus Corporation; *U.S. Public*, pg. 2112
MARCUS INVESTMENTS, LLC; *U.S. Private*, pg. 2572
MARCUS MADISON, LLC—See The Marcus Corporation; *U.S. Public*, pg. 2112
MARCUS MANAGEMENT LAS VEGAS, LLC—See The Marcus Corporation; *U.S. Public*, pg. 2112
MARCUS & MILLICHAP CAPITAL CORPORATION—See Marcus & Millichap, Inc.; *U.S. Public*, pg. 1365
MARCUS & MILLICHAP, INC.; *U.S. Public*, pg. 1365
MARCUS & MILLICHAP REAL ESTATE INVESTMENT BROKERAGE COMPANY—See Marcus & Millichap, Inc.; *U.S. Public*, pg. 1365
MARCUS & MILLICHAP REAL ESTATE INVESTMENT SERVICES, INC.—See Marcus & Millichap, Inc.; *U.S. Public*, pg. 1365
MARCUS & MILLICHAP REIS OF ATLANTA, INC.—See Marcus & Millichap, Inc.; *U.S. Public*, pg. 1365
MARCUS & MILLICHAP REIS OF CHICAGO, INC.—See Marcus & Millichap, Inc.; *U.S. Public*, pg. 1365
MARCUS & MILLICHAP REIS OF FLORIDA, INC.—See Marcus & Millichap, Inc.; *U.S. Public*, pg. 1365
MARCUS & MILLICHAP REIS OF NEVADA, INC.—See Marcus & Millichap, Inc.; *U.S. Public*, pg. 1365
MARCUS & MILLICHAP REIS OF NORTH CAROLINA, INC.—See Marcus & Millichap, Inc.; *U.S. Public*, pg. 1365
MARCUS & MILLICHAP REIS OF SEATTLE, INC.—See Marcus & Millichap, Inc.; *U.S. Public*, pg. 1365
MARCUS NORTHSTAR, INC.—See The Marcus Corporation; *U.S. Public*, pg. 2112
MARCUS PARTNERS, INC.; *U.S. Private*, pg. 2573
MARCUS THEATRES CORP.—See The Marcus Corporation; *U.S. Public*, pg. 2112
MARCUS THOMAS LLC-PUBLIC RELATIONS—See Marcus Thomas LLC; *U.S. Private*, pg. 2573
MARCUS THOMAS LLC; *U.S. Private*, pg. 2573
MARCVENTURES HOLDINGS, INC.; *Int'l*, pg. 4690
MARDECK LIMITED; *U.S. Private*, pg. 2573
MARDEL INC.; *U.S. Private*, pg. 2573
MARDEN-KANE, INC.; *U.S. Private*, pg. 2573
MARDEN-KANE, INC.—See Marden-Kane, Inc.; *U.S. Private*, pg. 2573
MARDEN'S, INC.; *U.S. Private*, pg. 2573
THE MARDENT GROUP PTY LIMITED—See Consolidated Operations Group Limited; *Int'l*, pg. 1771
MARDER BENEFITS, INC.—See New Mountain Capital, LLC; *U.S. Private*, pg. 2901
MARDER TRAWLING, INC.; *U.S. Private*, pg. 2573
MARDIA SAMYOUNG CAPILLARY TUBES COMPANY LIMITED; *Int'l*, pg. 4690
MARDIN CIMENTO SANAYI VE TICARET A.S.; *Int'l*, pg. 4690
MAREBLU SRL—See Thai Union Group Public Company Limited; *Int'l*, pg. 7596
MARECHALE CAPITAL PLC; *Int'l*, pg. 4690
MAREDO GASTSTATTEN-GMBH & CO. BETRIEBS-KG—See Perusa GmbH; *Int'l*, pg. 5821
MAREDO RESTAURANTS GMBH—See Whitbread PLC; *Int'l*, pg. 8398
MAREDO RESTAURANTS HOLDING GMBH—See Perusa GmbH; *Int'l*, pg. 5821
M.A. REICH & CO., INC.—See Jay Jems Inc.; *U.S. Private*, pg. 2192
MAREK BROTHERS SYSTEMS, INC.; *U.S. Private*, pg. 2573
MAREK LIEBERBERG KONZERTAGENTUR GMBH & CO. KG—See CTS Eventim AG & Co. KGAA; *Int'l*, pg. 1873
MAREK LIEBERBERG KONZERTAGENTUR HOLDING GMBH—See CTS Eventim AG & Co. KGAA; *Int'l*, pg. 1873
MAREL A/S—See Marel hf; *Int'l*, pg. 4690
MAREL AUSTRALIA PTY. LTD.—See Marel hf; *Int'l*, pg. 4690
MAREL BRASIL COMMERCIAL E INDUSTRIAL LTDA—See Marel hf; *Int'l*, pg. 4690

MAREK BROTHERS SYSTEMS, INC. CORPORATE AFFILIATIONS

MAREL CARNITECH (THAILAND) LTD.—See Marel hf; *Int'l*, pg. 4691
MAREL CHILE S.A.—See Marel hf; *Int'l*, pg. 4691
MAREL FOOD SYSTEMS A/S—See Marel hf; *Int'l*, pg. 4691
MAREL FOOD SYSTEMS GB LTD.—See Marel hf; *Int'l*, pg. 4691
MAREL FOOD SYSTEMS GMBH—See Marel hf; *Int'l*, pg. 4691
MAREL FOOD SYSTEMS LLC—See Marel hf; *Int'l*, pg. 4691
MAREL FOOD SYSTEMS SARL—See Marel hf; *Int'l*, pg. 4691
MAREL FOOD SYSTEMS—See Marel hf; *Int'l*, pg. 4691
MAREL FOOD SYSTEMS SP. Z O.O.—See Marel hf; *Int'l*, pg. 4691
MAREL FRANCE S.A.R.L.—See Marel hf; *Int'l*, pg. 4691
MAREL FURTHER PROCESSING B.V.—See Marel hf; *Int'l*, pg. 4691
MAREL GMBH & CO. KG—See Marel hf; *Int'l*, pg. 4691
MAREL GMBH & CO. KG—See Marel hf; *Int'l*, pg. 4691
MAREL HF; *Int'l*, pg. 4690
MAREL HOLDING B.V.—See Marel hf; *Int'l*, pg. 4691
MAREL ICELAND EHF.—See Marel hf; *Int'l*, pg. 4691
MARELICH MECHANICAL CO., INC.—See EMCOR Group, Inc.; *U.S. Public*, pg. 737
MARELICH MECHANICAL CO.—See EMCOR Group, Inc.; *U.S. Public*, pg. 737
MAREL, INC.—See Marel hf; *Int'l*, pg. 4691
MAREL ITALIA S.R.L.—See Marel hf; *Int'l*, pg. 4691
MARELLI ASIA PACIFIC SDN BHD—See The Carlyle Group Inc.; *U.S. Public*, pg. 2049
MARELLI AUTOMOTIVE COMPONENTS (GUANGZHOU) CORPORATION—See KKR & Co. Inc.; *U.S. Public*, pg. 1260
MARELLI AUTOMOTIVE COMPONENTS (WUXI) CORPORATION—See KKR & Co. Inc.; *U.S. Public*, pg. 1260
MARELLI AUTOMOTIVE SYSTEMS EUROPE PLC - FRANCE BRANCH OFFICE—See KKR & Co. Inc.; *U.S. Public*, pg. 1260
MARELLI AUTOMOTIVE SYSTEMS EUROPE PLC—See KKR & Co. Inc.; *U.S. Public*, pg. 1260
MARELLI AUTOMOTIVE SYSTEMS UK LIMITED—See KKR & Co. Inc.; *U.S. Public*, pg. 1260
MARELLI BARCELONA ESPANA S.A.U.—See KKR & Co. Inc.; *U.S. Public*, pg. 1260
MARELLI CENTRAL EUROPE GMBH—See The Carlyle Group Inc.; *U.S. Public*, pg. 2049
MARELLI CHINA HOLDING COMPANY—See KKR & Co. Inc.; *U.S. Public*, pg. 1260
MARELLI CORPORATION—See KKR & Co. Inc.; *U.S. Public*, pg. 1260
MARELLI DO BRASIL INDUSTRIA E COMERCIO LTDA—See KKR & Co, Inc.; *U.S. Public*, pg. 1260
MARELLI ELECTRICAL MACHINES SOUTH AFRICA (PTY) LTD.—See The Carlyle Group Inc.; *U.S. Public*, pg. 2049
MARELLI EUROPE S.P.A.—See KKR & Co. Inc.; *U.S. Public*, pg. 1260
MARELLI HOLDINGS CO., LTD.—See KKR & Co. Inc.; *U.S. Public*, pg. 1260
MARELLI MOTORI CENTRAL EUROPE GMBH—See Langley Holdings Plc; *Int'l*, pg. 4410
MARELLI MOTORI SOUTH AFRICA LTD. (PTY)—See Langley Holdings Plc; *Int'l*, pg. 4410
MARELLI MOTORI S.P.A.—See The Carlyle Group Inc.; *U.S. Public*, pg. 2049
MARELLI NORTH AMERICA, INC.—See KKR & Co. Inc.; *U.S. Public*, pg. 1260
MARELLI NORTH CAROLINA USA LLC—See KKR & Co. Inc.; *U.S. Public*, pg. 1261
MARELLI PLOIESTI ROMANIA S.R.L.—See KKR & Co. Inc.; *U.S. Public*, pg. 1260
MARELLI R&D CO., LIMITED—See KKR & Co. Inc.; *U.S. Public*, pg. 1260
MARELLI TENNESSEE USA LLC—See KKR & Co. Inc.; *U.S. Public*, pg. 1261
MARELLI (THAILAND) CO., LTD—See KKR & Co. Inc.; *U.S. Public*, pg. 1260
MARELLI TOOLING (GUANGZHOU) CORPORATION—See KKR & Co. Inc.; *U.S. Public*, pg. 1260
MARELLI UK LTD.—See The Carlyle Group Inc.; *U.S. Public*, pg. 2049
MARELLI USA, INC.—See The Carlyle Group Inc.; *U.S. Public*, pg. 2049
MARELLI (XIANG YANG) CORPORATION—See KKR & Co. Inc.; *U.S. Public*, pg. 1260
MAREL NEW ZEALAND LTD—See Marel hf; *Int'l*, pg. 4691
MAREL NORGE AS—See Marel hf; *Int'l*, pg. 4691
MAREL POLSKA SP. Z.O.O.—See Marel hf; *Int'l*, pg. 4691
MAREL POULTRY B.V.—See Marel hf; *Int'l*, pg. 4691
MAREL RED MEAT B.V.—See Marel hf; *Int'l*, pg. 4691
MAREL RED MEAT SLAUGHTERING B.V.—See Marel hf; *Int'l*, pg. 4691
MAREL RED MEAT SLAUGHTERING B.V.—See Marel hf; *Int'l*, pg. 4691
MAREL SALMON AS—See Marel hf; *Int'l*, pg. 4691

MAREL SEATTLE INC.—See Marel hf; *Int'l*, pg. 4691
MAREL SINGAPORE PTE. LTD.-FREEZING & TEMPERATURE DIVISION—See Marel hf; *Int'l*, pg. 4691
MAREL SPAIN & PORTUGAL S.L.—See Marel hf; *Int'l*, pg. 4691
MAREL STORK POULTRY PROCESSING B.V.—See Marel hf; *Int'l*, pg. 4691
MAREL SYTEMS AS—See Marel hf; *Int'l*, pg. 4691
MAREL TOWNSEND FURTHER PROCESSING—See Marel hf; *Int'l*, pg. 4691
MAREN ENGINEERING CORPORATION—See Komar Industries, LLC; *U.S. Private*, pg. 2342
MARENO ALI S.P.A.—See Ali Holding S.r.l.; *Int'l*, pg. 321
MARES AMERICA—See Head B.V.; *Int'l*, pg. 3300
MARES ASIA PACIFIC LTD.—See Head B.V.; *Int'l*, pg. 3300
MARESCO INTERNATIONAL CORP.; *U.S. Private*, pg. 2573
MARESCO LIMITED; *Int'l*, pg. 4691
M&A RESEARCH INSTITUTE INC.; *Int'l*, pg. 4610
MARESI AUSTRIA GMBH—See Raiffeisenlandesbank Oberosterreich Aktiengesellschaft; *Int'l*, pg. 6188
MARESI FOODBROKER KFT.—See Raiffeisenlandesbank Oberosterreich Aktiengesellschaft; *Int'l*, pg. 6188
MARESI FOODBROKER S.R.O.—See Raiffeisenlandesbank Oberosterreich Aktiengesellschaft; *Int'l*, pg. 6188
MARES—See Head B.V.; *Int'l*, pg. 3300
MARETERRA GROUP HOLDING SRL; *Int'l*, pg. 4691
MAREVEN FOOD CENTRAL LLC - SERPUKHOV PLANT—See Nissin Foods Holdings Co., Ltd.; *Int'l*, pg. 5376
MAREVEN FOOD CENTRAL LLC—See Nissin Foods Holdings Co., Ltd.; *Int'l*, pg. 5376
MAREVEN FOOD HOLDINGS LIMITED—See Nissin Foods Holdings Co., Ltd.; *Int'l*, pg. 5376
MAREX SPECTRON GROUP LTD.—See JRJ Ventures LLP; *Int'l*, pg. 4008
MARFIN INVESTMENT GROUP HOLDINGS S.A.; *Int'l*, pg. 4691
MARFLEX-M.J.MAILLIS POLAND SP. Z O.O.—See M.J. Maillis S.A.; *Int'l*, pg. 4616
THE MARFO COMPANY INC.; *U.S. Private*, pg. 4074
MARFOGLIA CONSTRUCTION INC.; *Int'l*, pg. 4692
MARFOOD USA, INC.—See Marfrig Global Foods S.A.; *Int'l*, pg. 4692
MARFORK COAL COMPANY, INC.—See Alpha Natural Resources, Inc.; *U.S. Public*, pg. 198
MARFRIG CHILE S.A.—See Marfrig Global Foods S.A.; *Int'l*, pg. 4692
MARFRIG GLOBAL FOODS S.A.; *Int'l*, pg. 4692
MARGA BV—See Unilever PLC; *Int'l*, pg. 8046
MARGANEC ZHAIREMA JSC; *Int'l*, pg. 4692
MARGARET INC.—See BNP Paribas SA; *Int'l*, pg. 1088
MARGARET LAKE DIAMONDS INC.; *Int'l*, pg. 4692
MARGARET MARY COMMUNITY HOSPITAL; *U.S. Private*, pg. 2573
MARGARET O'LEARY INC.; *U.S. Private*, pg. 2573
MARGARET STODDART RETIREMENT VILLAGE LIMITED—See Ryman Healthcare Ltd.; *Int'l*, pg. 6439
MARGATE CAPITAL PARTNERS FUND LP—See The Toronto-Dominion Bank; *Int'l*, pg. 7695
MARGIE KORSHAK INC.; *U.S. Private*, pg. 2573
MARGIE WOOD TRUCKING INC.; *U.S. Private*, pg. 2573
MARG INC.—See Newterra Ltd.; *Int'l*, pg. 5238
MARG LTD; *Int'l*, pg. 4692
MARGO CARIBE, INC.; *U.S. Public*, pg. 1365
MARGO - CSM SCHWEIZ AG—See Rhone Group, LLC; *U.S. Private*, pg. 3423
MARGO FINANCE LIMITED; *Int'l*, pg. 4692
MARGO GARDEN PRODUCTS, INC.—See Margo Caribe, Inc.; *U.S. Public*, pg. 1365
MARGO, INC.—See Altas Partners LP; *Int'l*, pg. 386
MARGOLIN, WINER & EVENS LLP; *U.S. Private*, pg. 2573
MARGO NURSERY FARMS, INC.—See Margo Caribe, Inc.; *U.S. Public*, pg. 1365
MARGRES S.A.—See Panariagroup Industrie Ceramiche S.p.A.; *Int'l*, pg. 5717
MARG TECHNO PROJECTS LIMITED; *Int'l*, pg. 4692
MARIADB CORPORATION AB—See California Technology Ventures, LLC; *U.S. Private*, pg. 721
MARIADB PLC—See K1 Investment Management, LLC; *U.S. Private*, pg. 2252
MARIAGE QUEBEC—See St. Joseph Communications Inc.; *Int'l*, pg. 7159
MARIAH MEDIA INC.; *U.S. Private*, pg. 2573
MARIAK INDUSTRIES, INC.—See AEA Investors LP; *U.S. Private*, pg. 115
MARIAK INDUSTRIES, INC.—See British Columbia Investment Management Corp.; *Int'l*, pg. 1170
MARIA MALLABAND CARE GROUP LTD.; *Int'l*, pg. 4693
MARIAN HEATH GREETING CARDS LLC; *U.S. Private*, pg. 2573
MARIAN HEATH GREETING CARDS—See Marian Heath Greeting Cards LLC; *U.S. Private*, pg. 2573
MARIAN INC.; *U.S. Private*, pg. 2574
MARIANI NUT COMPANY; *U.S. Private*, pg. 2574
MARIANI PACKING COMPANY; *U.S. Private*, pg. 2574

MARIANJOY REHABILITATION HOSPITAL—See Wheaton Franciscan Services Inc.; *U.S. Private*, pg. 4504
MARIAN MEDICAL CENTER—See Catholic Health Initiatives; *U.S. Private*, pg. 789
MARIANNA IMPORTS INC.; *U.S. Private*, pg. 2574
MARIANNA MEMPHIS INC.—See Marianna Imports Inc.; *U.S. Private*, pg. 2574
MARIAN SHIPPING LTD.; *U.S. Private*, pg. 2574
MARIA REGINA RESIDENCE; *U.S. Private*, pg. 2573
MARIA SERVICES LIMITED—See Kindred Group plc; *Int'l*, pg. 4166
MARIBO MEDICO A/S—See ResMed Inc.; *U.S. Public*, pg. 1790
MARIBORSKA LIVARNA MARIBOR, D.D.; *Int'l*, pg. 4693
MARIBO SEED INTERNATIONAL APS—See China National Chemical Corporation; *Int'l*, pg. 1529
MARICO BANGLADESH LIMITED—See Marico Limited; *Int'l*, pg. 4693
MARICO FOR CONSUMER CARE PRODUCTS SAE—See Marico Limited; *Int'l*, pg. 4693
MARICOGEN A/S—See Akzo Nobel N.V.; *Int'l*, pg. 274
MARICO KAYA ENTERPRISES LIMITED; *Int'l*, pg. 4693
MARICO LIMITED; *Int'l*, pg. 4693
MARICO MALAYSIA SDN. BHD.—See Marico Limited; *Int'l*, pg. 4693
MARICO MIDDLE EAST FZE—See Marico Limited; *Int'l*, pg. 4693
MARICO SOUTH AFRICA (PTY) LIMITED—See Marico Limited; *Int'l*, pg. 4693
MARID INDUSTRIES LIMITED; *Int'l*, pg. 4693
MARIDIVE & OIL SERVICES CO.; *Int'l*, pg. 4693
MARIE BRIZARD ESPANA S.A.—See Marie Brizard Wine & Spirits S.A.; *Int'l*, pg. 4693
MARIE BRIZARD & ROGER INTERNATIONAL SAS—See Marie Brizard Wine & Spirits S.A.; *Int'l*, pg. 4693
MARIE BRIZARD WINE & SPIRITS S.A.; *Int'l*, pg. 4693
MARIE CALLENDER PIE SHOPS, LLC—See Marie Callender's, Inc.; *U.S. Private*, pg. 2574
MARIE CALLENDER'S, INC.; *U.S. Private*, pg. 2574
MARIE CLAIRE MAGAZINE—See Meredith Corporation; *U.S. Public*, pg. 1423
MARIE CLAIRE US—See Future plc; *Int'l*, pg. 2857
MARIELLA BURANI FASHION GROUP S.P.A.; *Int'l*, pg. 4694
MARIENIA SA—See Clariane SE; *Int'l*, pg. 1643
MARIE SAS—See LDC SA; *Int'l*, pg. 4431
MARIE'S SALAD DRESSING—See Dean Foods Company; *U.S. Private*, pg. 1184
MARIETTA AREA HEALTH CARE, INC.; *U.S. Private*, pg. 2574
MARIETTA CENTER—See Formation Capital, LLC; *U.S. Private*, pg. 1571
MARIETTA COAL CO.; *U.S. Private*, pg. 2574
MARIETTA CORP. - LOS ANGELES—See Ares Management Corporation; *U.S. Public*, pg. 189
MARIETTA CORP. - OLIVE BRANCH—See Ares Management Corporation; *U.S. Public*, pg. 189
MARIETTA CORPORATION—See Ares Management Corporation; *U.S. Public*, pg. 189
MARIETTA DRAPERY & WINDOW COVERINGS CO., INC.; *U.S. Private*, pg. 2574
MARIETTA HOME HEALTH AND HOSPICE, L.L.C.—See Amedisys, Inc.; *U.S. Public*, pg. 94
MARIETTA INDUSTRIAL ENTERPRISES; *U.S. Private*, pg. 2574
MARIETTA OUTPATIENT SURGERY, LTD.—See HCA Healthcare, Inc.; *U.S. Public*, pg. 1001
MARIETTA SILOS LLC; *U.S. Private*, pg. 2574
MARIETTA SURGICAL CENTER, INC.—See HCA Healthcare, Inc.; *U.S. Public*, pg. 1001
THE MARIETTA TIMES—See The Nutting Company, Inc.; *U.S. Private*, pg. 4086
MARIETTA WRECKER SERVICE LLC; *U.S. Private*, pg. 2574
MARIGNAN GESTION S.A.—See Cerberus Capital Management, L.P.; *U.S. Private*, pg. 839
MARIGOLD FORD LINCOLN SALES; *Int'l*, pg. 4694
MARIGOLD INDUSTRIAL GLOVES IBERIA S.L.—See Ansell Limited; *Int'l*, pg. 478
MARIGOLD INDUSTRIAL GMBH—See Ansell Limited; *Int'l*, pg. 478
MARIGOLD INDUSTRIAL SDN. BHD.—See Ansell Limited; *Int'l*, pg. 478
MARIGOLD INDUSTRIAL USA INC.—See Ansell Limited; *Int'l*, pg. 478
MARIJUANA COMPANY OF AMERICA, INC.; *U.S. Public*, pg. 1365
MARILLAC ST. VINCENT FAMILY SERVICES; *U.S. Private*, pg. 2574
MARILYN MIGLIN, L.P.; *U.S. Private*, pg. 2574
MARIMACA COPPER CORP.; *Int'l*, pg. 4694
MARIMED INC.; *U.S. Public*, pg. 1365
MARIMEKKO AB—See Marimekko Corporation; *Int'l*, pg. 4694
MARIMEKKO AUSTRALIA PTY. LTD.—See Marimekko Corporation; *Int'l*, pg. 4694
MARIMEKKO CORPORATION; *Int'l*, pg. 4694
MARIMEKKO GMBH—See Marimekko Corporation; *Int'l*, pg. 4694

COMPANY NAME INDEX

MARIMEKKO KITEE OY—See Marimekko Corporation; *Int'l*, pg. 4694
MARIMEKKO NORTH AMERICA LLC—See Marimekko Corporation; *Int'l*, pg. 4694
MARIMEKKO TUOTANTO OY—See Marimekko Corporation; *Int'l*, pg. 4694
MARIMEKKO UK LTD—See Marimekko Corporation; *Int'l*, pg. 4694
MARIMO COMMUNITY CO. LTD.—See Tokyu Fudosan Holdings Corporation; *Int'l*, pg. 7798
MARIMO KOUTSU INC.—See Taiheiyo Kouhatsu Incorporated; *Int'l*, pg. 7412
MARIMO REGIONAL REVITALIZATION REIT, INC.; *Int'l*, pg. 4694
MARINA BAY CARNIVAL PTE LTD.—See Pico Far East Holdings Limited; *Int'l*, pg. 5861
MARINA BAY SANDS PTE. LTD.—See Las Vegas Sands Corp.; *U.S. Public*, pg. 1293
MARINA BORIK D.O.O—See Dogus Holding AS; *Int'l*, pg. 2155
MARINA CENTRE HOLDINGS PRIVATE LIMITED—See Singapore Land Group Limited; *Int'l*, pg. 6940
MARINA DALMACIJA D.O.O—See Dogus Holding AS; *Int'l*, pg. 2155
MARINA DISTRICT DEVELOPMENT HOLDING CO., LLC—See MGM Resorts International; *U.S. Public*, pg. 1435
MARINA ENERGY LLC—See JPMorgan Chase & Co.; *U.S. Public*, pg. 1210
MARINA FOR INDUSTRIAL SOLUTIONS CO.—See BERICAP GmbH & Co. KG; *Int'l*, pg. 981
MARINA ICE CREAM CO., INC.; *U.S. Private*, pg. 2574
MARINA, INC.—See Jump Design Group; *U.S. Private*, pg. 2243
MARINA INVESTMENT MANAGEMENT INC.; *U.S. Private*, pg. 2574
MARINA JACK, INC.—See Jack Graham Inc.; *U.S. Private*, pg. 2174
THE MARINA LIMITED PARTNERSHIP; *U.S. Private*, pg. 4074
MARINA PORTO CARRAS SA—See Technical Olympic SA; *Int'l*, pg. 7506
MARINA PORTOROZ D.D.—See Terme Catez, d.d.; *Int'l*, pg. 7565
MARINA SALUD S.A.—See Munchener Ruckversicherungs AG; *Int'l*, pg. 5089
MARINA SP.Z.O.O.—See Munchener Ruckversicherungs AG; *Int'l*, pg. 5089
MARINA TOWER HOLDING GMBH—See Vonovia SE; *Int'l*, pg. 8305
MARINA UROLA, S.A.—See Industry Super Holdings Pty. Ltd.; *Int'l*, pg. 3676
MARINDI METALS PTY. LTD.—See Gascoyne Resources Limited; *Int'l*, pg. 2888
MARINE ACCESSORIES CORPORATION—See Patrick Industries, Inc.; *U.S. Public*, pg. 1652
MARINE ACCESSORIES EUROPE B.V.—See Patrick Industries, Inc.; *U.S. Public*, pg. 1652
MARINE ADVANCED ROBOTICS, INC.—See Ocean Power Technologies, Inc.; *U.S. Public*, pg. 1562
MARINE ATLANTIC INC.; *Int'l*, pg. 4694
MARINE, AVIATION & GENERAL (LONDON) LIMITED—See Marsh & McLennan Companies, Inc.; *U.S. Public*, pg. 1377
MARINE BANCORP, INC.; *U.S. Private*, pg. 2574
MARINE BANCORP OF FLORIDA, INC.; *U.S. Public*, pg. 1366
MARINE BANK—See Marine Bancorp, Inc.; *U.S. Private*, pg. 2575
MARINE BANK & TRUST COMPANY—See Marine Bancorp of Florida, Inc.; *U.S. Public*, pg. 1366
MARINE BIOTECHNOLOGY PRODUCTS LTD.—See Ireland Blyth Limited; *Int'l*, pg. 3807
MARINE CEMENT AG—See Holcim Ltd.; *Int'l*, pg. 3449
MARINE CHEVROLET COMPANY, INC.; *U.S. Private*, pg. 2575
MARINE CHRYSLER DODGE JEEP; *Int'l*, pg. 4694
MARINE CONTAINER SERVICES, INC.—See Saybrook Corporate Opportunity Fund LP; *U.S. Private*, pg. 3558
MARINE CURRENT TURBINES LIMITED—See SIMEC Atlantis Energy Ltd; *Int'l*, pg. 6931
MARINE CYBERNETICS AS—See DNV GL Group AS; *Int'l*, pg. 2151
MARINE DATA SOLUTIONS (PTY.) LTD.—See Kongsberg Gruppen ASA; *Int'l*, pg. 4255
MARINE ELECTRICALS (INDIA) LIMITED; *Int'l*, pg. 4694
MARINE ELECTRIC SYSTEMS, INC.; *U.S. Private*, pg. 2575
MARINE ENGINEERING GALATI—See Damen Shipyards Group; *Int'l*, pg. 1956
MARINE FASTENERS, INC.—See Wurth Verwaltungsgesellschaft mbH; *Int'l*, pg. 8511
THE MARINE FOODS CORPORATION—See NH Foods Ltd.; *Int'l*, pg. 5257
MARINE & GENERAL BERHAD; *Int'l*, pg. 4694
MARINE HARVEST APPETI' MARINE S.A.S.—See Mowi ASA; *Int'l*, pg. 5059
MARINE HARVEST CANADA—See Mowi ASA; *Int'l*, pg. 5058

MARINE HARVEST CHINA—See Mowi ASA; *Int'l*, pg. 5059
MARINE HARVEST FAROES P/F—See Mowi ASA; *Int'l*, pg. 5059
MARINE HARVEST (FORT WILLIAMS) LTD.—See Mowi ASA; *Int'l*, pg. 5058
MARINE HARVEST HOLDING AS—See Mowi ASA; *Int'l*, pg. 5059
MARINE HARVEST KOREA LTD.—See Mowi ASA; *Int'l*, pg. 5059
MARINE HARVEST KRITSEN S.A.S.—See Mowi ASA; *Int'l*, pg. 5059
MARINE HARVEST LORIENT S.A.S.—See Mowi ASA; *Int'l*, pg. 5059
MARINE HARVEST NORWAY AS—See Mowi ASA; *Int'l*, pg. 5059
MARINE HARVEST PIETERS N.V.—See Mowi ASA; *Int'l*, pg. 5059
MARINE HARVEST POLAND SP. Z.O.O.—See Mowi ASA; *Int'l*, pg. 5059
MARINE HARVEST RENNES S.A.S.—See Mowi ASA; *Int'l*, pg. 5059
MARINE HARVEST ROLMER S.A.S.; *Int'l*, pg. 4694
MARINE HARVEST SPAIN II. S.L.—See Mowi ASA; *Int'l*, pg. 5059
MARINE HARVEST TERMINAL AS—See Mowi ASA; *Int'l*, pg. 5059
MARINE HARVEST VAP FRANCE S.A.S.—See Mowi ASA; *Int'l*, pg. 5059
MARINE HARVEST VAP—See Mowi ASA; *Int'l*, pg. 5059
MARINE HOME CENTER; *U.S. Private*, pg. 2575
MARINE HYDRAULICS INTERNATIONAL, INC.—See Stellex Capital Management LP; *U.S. Private*, pg. 3800
MARINE HYDRAULICS INTERNATIONAL, INC.—See The Carlyle Group Inc.; *U.S. Public*, pg. 2056
MARINE INDUSTRIAL DESIGN LIMITED—See Babcock International Group PLC; *Int'l*, pg. 793
MARINE & INDUSTRIAL SUPPLY COMPANY, INC.; *U.S. Private*, pg. 2574
MARINE INDUSTRIES NORTHWEST, INC.—See Stellex Capital Management LP; *U.S. Private*, pg. 3800
MARINE INDUSTRIES NORTHWEST, INC.—See The Carlyle Group Inc.; *U.S. Public*, pg. 2056
MARINE INNOVATION PTE. LTD.—See Jason Marine Group Limited; *Int'l*, pg. 3912
MARINE INSTRUMENTS S.A.—See Grupo Arbulu S.L.; *Int'l*, pg. 3120
MARINE INTERIORS CABINS S.P.A.—See Cassa Depositi e Prestiti S.p.A.; *Int'l*, pg. 1355
MARINE INTERIORS S.P.A.—See Fincantieri S.p.A.; *Int'l*, pg. 2671
MARINELLO SCHOOLS OF BEAUTY—See B&H Education, Inc.; *U.S. Private*, pg. 418
MARINEMAX EAST, INC.—See MarineMax, Inc.; *U.S. Public*, pg. 1366
MARINEMAX, INC.; *U.S. Public*, pg. 1366
MARINEMAX NJ PARTNERS, INC.—See MarineMax, Inc.; *U.S. Public*, pg. 1366
MARINEMAX OF MINNESOTA, INC.—See MarineMax, Inc.; *U.S. Public*, pg. 1366
MARINEMAX OF NEW JERSEY HOLDINGS, INC.—See MarineMax, Inc.; *U.S. Public*, pg. 1366
MARINEMAX OF NORTH CAROLINA, INC.—See MarineMax, Inc.; *U.S. Public*, pg. 1366
MARINEMAX OF OHIO, INC.—See MarineMax, Inc.; *U.S. Public*, pg. 1367
MARINEMAX SERVICES, INC.—See MarineMax, Inc.; *U.S. Public*, pg. 1366
MARINEMAX TX, L.P.—See NXTLVL Marine, LLC; *U.S. Private*, pg. 2976
MARINEMAX VACATIONS, LTD—See MarineMax, Inc.; *U.S. Public*, pg. 1366
MARINE MEDICAL SERVICES—See Polska Zegluga Morska; *Int'l*, pg. 5911
MARINE MOTORS & PUMPS N.V.—See Seika Corporation; *Int'l*, pg. 6685
MARIN ENDOSCOPY CENTER, LLC—See KKR & Co. Inc.; *U.S. Public*, pg. 1246
MARINE OIL CO. INC.; *U.S. Private*, pg. 2575
MARINE PARK COMPUTERS; *U.S. Private*, pg. 2575
MARINE PETROBULK LTD.—See Washington Corporations; *U.S. Private*, pg. 4446
MARINE PETROLEUM TRUST; *U.S. Public*, pg. 1366
MARINE POWER INTERNATIONAL PTY. LTD.—See Brunswick Corporation; *U.S. Public*, pg. 408
MARINE PRODUCE AUSTRALIA LIMITED; *Int'l*, pg. 4694
MARINE PRODUCTS CORPORATION; *U.S. Public*, pg. 1366
MARINE PRODUCTS INTERNATIONAL LLC—See Crawford United Corporation; *U.S. Public*, pg. 592
MARINE RADIO SERVICE, LTD.—See Kawasaki Kisen Kaisha, Ltd.; *Int'l*, pg. 4100
MARINER CAPITAL LTD.—See First Steamship Co., Ltd.; *Int'l*, pg. 2688
MARINER CORPORATION LIMITED; *Int'l*, pg. 4694
MARINER FINANCE, LLC—See Warburg Pincus LLC; *U.S. Private*, pg. 4439
MARINER INTERNATIONAL TRAVEL INC.; *U.S. Private*, pg. 2575

MARIN SOFTWARE INC.

MARINER INVESTMENT GROUP LLC; *U.S. Private*, pg. 2575
MARINERS HOSPITAL—See Baptist Health South Florida, Inc.; *U.S. Private*, pg. 471
MARINERS INSURANCE AGENCY INC.—See Marsh & McLennan Companies, Inc.; *U.S. Public*, pg. 1381
MARINER TRAVEL GMBH—See TUI AG; *Int'l*, pg. 7965
MARINER WEALTH ADVISORS LLC—See Mariner Wealth Advisors, LLC; *U.S. Private*, pg. 2575
MARINER WEALTH ADVISORS, LLC; *U.S. Private*, pg. 2575
MARINESOFT ENTWICKLUNGS- UND LOGISTIKGESELLSCHAFT MBH—See Rheinmetall AG; *Int'l*, pg. 6322
MARINE SPILL RESPONSE CORPORATION; *U.S. Private*, pg. 2575
MARINE SPORTS LLC; *U.S. Private*, pg. 2575
MARINE SUPPLY & ENGINEERING SERVICE JOINT STOCK COMPANY; *Int'l*, pg. 4694
MARINE SYSTEMS, INC.—See Kirby Corporation; *U.S. Public*, pg. 1235
MARINE SYSTEMS, INC.—See Kirby Corporation; *U.S. Public*, pg. 1235
MARINE TECHNOLOGY DEVELOPMENT PTE. LTD.—See Keppel Corporation Limited; *Int'l*, pg. 4132
MARINETEK GROUP OY HAKKILA FACTORY—See Marinetek Group Oy; *Int'l*, pg. 4694
MARINETEK GROUP OY; *Int'l*, pg. 4694
MARINETEK LATVIA SIA—See Marinetek Group Oy; *Int'l*, pg. 4694
MARINETEK MIDDLE EAST AND NORTH AFRICA—See Marinetek Group Oy; *Int'l*, pg. 4694
MARINETEK NCP D.O.O.—See Marinetek Group Oy; *Int'l*, pg. 4694
MARINETEK SOUTH EAST ASIA PTE LTD.—See Marinetek Group Oy; *Int'l*, pg. 4694
MARINETEK SPB ZAO—See Marinetek Group Oy; *Int'l*, pg. 4694
MARINETEK SWEDEN AB—See Marinetek Group Oy; *Int'l*, pg. 4694
MARINE TOWING OF TAMPA, LLC; *U.S. Private*, pg. 2575
MARINE TRADING INTERNATIONAL, INC.—See Miller Yacht Sales, Inc.; *U.S. Private*, pg. 2736
MARINE TRADING LTD.—See Albert Ballin KG; *Int'l*, pg. 295
MARINETRANS INDIA LIMITED; *Int'l*, pg. 4694
MARINE TRANSPORTATION SERVICES, INC.; *U.S. Private*, pg. 2575
MARINE TRANSPORT CORPORATION—See Crowley Maritime Corporation; *U.S. Private*, pg. 1110
MARINE TRANSPORT INC.; *U.S. Private*, pg. 2575
MARINE TRAVELIFT, INC.; *U.S. Private*, pg. 2575
MARINETTE MARINE CORPORATION—See Fincantieri S.p.A.; *Int'l*, pg. 2671
MARINETTI S.A.—See Mayr-Melnhof Karton AG; *Int'l*, pg. 4746
MARINE VENTURES LTD.—See Centerbridge Partners, L.P.; *U.S. Private*, pg. 815
MARINE VIEW BEVERAGE, INC.—See CoHo Distributing LLC; *U.S. Private*, pg. 964
MARINE VIEW BEVERAGE, INC. - SUMNER—See CoHo Distributing LLC; *U.S. Private*, pg. 964
MARINE VIEW BEVERAGE, INC. - TUMWATER—See CoHo Distributing LLC; *U.S. Private*, pg. 964
MARINEX INC.; *U.S. Private*, pg. 2576
MARIN GENERAL HOSPITAL—See Marin Healthcare District; *U.S. Private*, pg. 2574
MARIN HEALTHCARE DISTRICT; *U.S. Private*, pg. 2574
MARINI-ERMONT—See FAYAT SAS; *Int'l*, pg. 2625
MARINI FAYAT LANGFANG CHINA—See FAYAT SAS; *Int'l*, pg. 2625
MARINI INDIA PRIVATE LTD—See FAYAT SAS; *Int'l*, pg. 2625
MARINI MAKINA A.S.—See FAYAT SAS; *Int'l*, pg. 2626
MARINI MANUFACTURING, INC.; *U.S. Private*, pg. 2576
MARIN INDEPENDENT JOURNAL—See Alden Global Capital LLC; *U.S. Private*, pg. 155
MARINI SPA—See FAYAT SAS; *Int'l*, pg. 2625
MARINI UK LIMITED—See FAYAT SAS; *Int'l*, pg. 2625
MARIN LUXURY CARS, LLC.; *U.S. Private*, pg. 2574
MARIN MUNICIPAL WATER DISTRICT; *U.S. Private*, pg. 2574
MARINO CHRYSLER JEEP DODGE; *U.S. Private*, pg. 2576
MARINOMED BIOTECH AG; *Int'l*, pg. 4695
THE MARINO ORGANIZATION, INC.; *U.S. Private*, pg. 4074
MARINO/WARE—See Ware Industries; *U.S. Private*, pg. 4441
MARIN SANITARY SERVICE INC.; *U.S. Private*, pg. 2574
MARIN'S DEUTSCHLAND GMBH—See Quad/Graphics, Inc.; *U.S. Public*, pg. 1744
MARIN SOFTWARE GMBH—See Marin Software Inc.; *U.S. Public*, pg. 1366
MARIN SOFTWARE INC.; *U.S. Public*, pg. 1366
MARIN SOFTWARE K.K.—See Marin Software Inc.; *U.S. Public*, pg. 1366

1683

MARIN SOFTWARE INC.
CORPORATE AFFILIATIONS

MARIN SOFTWARE LIMITED(UK)—See Marin Software Inc.; *U.S. Public*, pg. 1366
MARIN SOFTWARE (SHANGHAI) CO., LTD.—See Marin Software Inc.; *U.S. Public*, pg. 1366
MARIN SUNWISE MOTORS, INC.—See Sojitz Corporation; *Int'l*, pg. 7062
MARINTEK DO BRASIL LTDA.—See SINTEF; *Int'l*, pg. 6957
MARINTEK—See SINTEF; *Int'l*, pg. 6957
MARINTEK (USA), INC.—See SINTEF; *Int'l*, pg. 6957
MARINUS PHARMACEUTICALS INC.; *U.S. Public*, pg. 1367
MARIO CAMACHO FOODS, LLC; *U.S. Private*, pg. 2576
MARIOFF CORPORATION OY—See Carrier Global Corporation; *U.S. Public*, pg. 441
MARIOFF GMBH—See Carrier Global Corporation; *U.S. Public*, pg. 443
MARIOFF HI-FOG S.L.U.—See Carrier Global Corporation; *U.S. Public*, pg. 443
MARIOFF LTD.—See Carrier Global Corporation; *U.S. Public*, pg. 443
MARIOFF SAS—See Carrier Global Corporation; *U.S. Public*, pg. 443
MARIOFF SKANDINAVIEN AB—See Carrier Global Corporation; *U.S. Public*, pg. 443
MARIOFF SRL—See Carrier Global Corporation; *U.S. Public*, pg. 443
MARIO INDUSTRIES OF VIRGINIA; *U.S. Private*, pg. 2576
MARION DAILY REPUBLICAN; *U.S. Private*, pg. 2576
MARION FLUID POWER DIVISION OF MARADYNE CORP—See Dreison International, Inc.; *U.S. Private*, pg. 1276
MARION FOODS, INC.—See Seneca Foods Corporation; *U.S. Public*, pg. 1864
MARION GENERAL HOSPITAL, INC; *U.S. Private*, pg. 2576
MARION GLASS EQUIPMENT & TECHNOLOGY COMPANY—See Ardagh Group S.A.; *Int'l*, pg. 553
MARION HOSPITAL CORPORATION—See Quorum Health Corporation; *U.S. Private*, pg. 3330
MARION LUMBER CO. INC.—See Sequatchie Concrete Service Inc.; *U.S. Private*, pg. 3612
MARION PHYSICIAN SERVICES, LLC—See Community Health Systems, Inc.; *U.S. Public*, pg. 555
MARION PLYWOOD CORPORATION; *U.S. Private*, pg. 2576
MARION-POLK FOOD SHARE; *U.S. Private*, pg. 2576
MARION REGIONAL HOMECARE, LLC—See United Health Group Incorporated; *U.S. Public*, pg. 2246
THE MARION STAR—See Gannett Co., Inc.; *U.S. Public*, pg. 900
MARION SURGERY CENTER, LLC—See Tenet Healthcare Corporation; *U.S. Public*, pg. 2004
MARION TOYOTA; *U.S. Private*, pg. 2576
MARIOS INC.; *U.S. Private*, pg. 2576
MARI PETROLEUM COMPANY LIMITED; *Int'l*, pg. 4693
MARIPOSA MEDSPA; *U.S. Private*, pg. 2576
MARISA LOJAS S.A.; *Int'l*, pg. 4695
MARISAT INC.—See RB Global, Inc.; *Int'l*, pg. 6226
MARISCO LTD.; *U.S. Private*, pg. 2576
MARIS DISTRIBUTING CO. INC.; *U.S. Private*, pg. 2576
MARISOL INTERNATIONAL, LLC—See Roadrunner Transportation Systems, Inc.; *U.S. Public*, pg. 1802
MARIS SPINNERS LIMITED; *Int'l*, pg. 4695
MARIS SPINNERS LIMITED - UNIT I—See Maris Spinners Limited; *Int'l*, pg. 4695
MARIS SUBSEA LTD—See Global Energy (Holdings) Ltd.; *Int'l*, pg. 2995
MARISTAFF INC.; *U.S. Private*, pg. 2576
MARIS-TECH LTD.; *Int'l*, pg. 4695
MARIS, WEST & BAKER, INC.; *U.S. Private*, pg. 2576
MARITECH AS—See Symphony Technology Group, LLC; *U.S. Private*, pg. 3902
MARITECH DYNAMICS LIMITED—See Symphony Technology Group, LLC; *U.S. Private*, pg. 3902
MARITIMA MEXICANA, S.A. DE C.V., MORGAN CITY—See Grupo TMM, S.A.B.; *Int'l*, pg. 3137
MARITIMA MEXICANA, S.A. DE C.V.—See Grupo TMM, S.A.B.; *Int'l*, pg. 3137
MARITIMA MEXICANA, S.A. DE C.V.—See Grupo TMM, S.A.B.; *Int'l*, pg. 3137
MARITIMA SEGUROS S.A.—See Sompo Holdings, Inc.; *Int'l*, pg. 7086
THE MARITIME AQUARIUM AT NORWALK; *U.S. Private*, pg. 4074
MARITIME BANK JSC; *Int'l*, pg. 4695
MARITIME BROADCASTING - SYDNEY—See Maritime Broadcasting System Ltd.; *Int'l*, pg. 4695
MARITIME BROADCASTING SYSTEM LTD.; *Int'l*, pg. 4695
MARITIME COMMUNICATIONS PARTNER AS—See Telenor ASA; *Int'l*, pg. 7539
MARITIME DEDICATED CONTROL N.V.—See Minerva Bunkering; *Int'l*, pg. 4907
MARITIME ELECTRIC COMPANY LIMITED—See Fortis Inc.; *Int'l*, pg. 2740
MARITIME ENERGY, INC.; *U.S. Private*, pg. 2576

MARITIME ENGINEERS PTY LTD—See James Fisher & Sons Public Limited Company; *Int'l*, pg. 3876
MARITIME EXCHANGE FOR THE DELAWARE RIVER AND BAY; *U.S. Private*, pg. 2576
MARITIME HOLDING AD—See Industrial Holding Bulgaria AD; *Int'l*, pg. 3672
MARITIME INTERNATIONAL, INC.—See Trelleborg AB; *Int'l*, pg. 7912
MARITIME & MERCANTILE INTERNATIONAL LLC—See The Emirates Group; *Int'l*, pg. 7639
MARITIME NORTH AMERICA JACKSONVILLE—See DNV GL Group AS; *Int'l*, pg. 2151
MARITIME NORTH AMERICA SEATTLE—See DNV GL Group AS; *Int'l*, pg. 2151
MARITIME ONTARIO FREIGHT LINES LIMITED; *Int'l*, pg. 4695
MARITIME PAPER PRODUCTS LIMITED; *Int'l*, pg. 4695
MARITIME RESOURCES CORP.; *Int'l*, pg. 4695
MARITIMES & NORTHEAST PIPELINE LIMITED PARTNERSHIP—See Enbridge Inc.; *Int'l*, pg. 2397
MARITIME TECHNOLOGIES CORP.—See Pyxis Tankers Inc.; *Int'l*, pg. 6128
MARITIME TRANSPORT SERVICES LIMITED—See CK Hutchison Holdings Limited; *Int'l*, pg. 1638
MARITIME TRAVEL INC; *Int'l*, pg. 4695
MARITSATEX AD; *Int'l*, pg. 4695
MARITZBURG QUARRIES (PTY) LIMITED—See Afrimat Limited; *Int'l*, pg. 193
MARITZ DEALER SOLUTIONS—See Maritz Holdings Inc.; *U.S. Private*, pg. 2577
MARITZ HOLDINGS INC.; *U.S. Private*, pg. 2577
THE MARITZ INSTITUTE—See Maritz Holdings Inc.; *U.S. Private*, pg. 2577
MARITZ MARKETING RESEARCH, INC.—See Maritz Holdings Inc.; *U.S. Private*, pg. 2577
MARITZ MOTIVATION SOLUTIONS INC.—See Maritz Holdings Inc.; *U.S. Private*, pg. 2577
MARITZ PERFORMANCE IMPROVEMENT COMPANY—See Maritz Holdings Inc.; *U.S. Private*, pg. 2577
MARITZ RESEARCH GMBH—See Maritz Holdings Inc.; *U.S. Private*, pg. 2577
MARITZ RESEARCH LTD.—See Maritz Holdings Inc.; *U.S. Private*, pg. 2577
MARITZ RESEARCH—See Maritz Holdings Inc.; *U.S. Private*, pg. 2577
MARITZ TRAVEL CO.—See Maritz Holdings Inc.; *U.S. Private*, pg. 2577
MARIUS HANSEN FACADER A/S—See Hojgaard Holding A/S; *Int'l*, pg. 3442
MARIUS PEDERSEN A/S - AALBORG PLANT—See Marius Pedersen A/S; *Int'l*, pg. 4695
MARIUS PEDERSEN A/S - AARHUS PLANT—See Marius Pedersen A/S; *Int'l*, pg. 4695
MARIUS PEDERSEN A/S - BROBY PLANT—See Marius Pedersen A/S; *Int'l*, pg. 4695
MARIUS PEDERSEN A/S - ESBJERG PLANT—See Marius Pedersen A/S; *Int'l*, pg. 4695
MARIUS PEDERSEN A/S - HERNING PLANT—See Marius Pedersen A/S; *Int'l*, pg. 4695
MARIUS PEDERSEN A/S - KOLDING PLANT—See Marius Pedersen A/S; *Int'l*, pg. 4696
MARIUS PEDERSEN A/S - ODENSE PLANT—See Marius Pedersen A/S; *Int'l*, pg. 4696
MARIUS PEDERSEN A/S - ROEDEKRO PLANT—See Marius Pedersen A/S; *Int'l*, pg. 4696
MARIUS PEDERSEN A/S - ROEDOVRE PLANT—See Marius Pedersen A/S; *Int'l*, pg. 4696
MARIUS PEDERSEN A/S - SAKSKOBING PLANT—See Marius Pedersen A/S; *Int'l*, pg. 4696
MARIUS PEDERSEN A/S; *Int'l*, pg. 4695
MARIUS PEDERSEN A.S.—See Marius Pedersen A/S; *Int'l*, pg. 4696
MARIUS PEDERSEN A.S.—See Marius Pedersen A/S; *Int'l*, pg. 4696
MARIUS PEDERSEN A/S - SVINNINGE PLANT—See Marius Pedersen A/S; *Int'l*, pg. 4696
MARIWASA SIAM CERAMICS, INC.—See The Siam Cement Public Company Limited; *Int'l*, pg. 7682
MARIWASA SIAM HOLDINGS, INC.—See The Siam Cement Public Company Limited; *Int'l*, pg. 7682
MARIX TECHNOLOGIES, INC.—See US Internet Corporation; *U.S. Private*, pg. 4319
MARIZYME, INC.; *U.S. Public*, pg. 1367
MAR-JAC HOLDINGS INC.; *U.S. Private*, pg. 2569
MAR-JAC POULTRY, INC.—See Mar-Jac Holdings Inc.; *U.S. Private*, pg. 2569
MARJAM SUPPLY COMPANY, INC.—See American Securities LLC; *U.S. Private*, pg. 249
MARJAN INC.—See Wieland-Werke AG; *Int'l*, pg. 8403
MARJAN INDUSTRIAL DEVELOPMENT CO.—See Al Fahim Group; *Int'l*, pg. 277
MARJENN TRUCKING COMPANY INC.—See Frank Calandra, Inc.; *U.S. Private*, pg. 1594
MARJON SPECIALTY FOODS, INC.; *U.S. Private*, pg. 2577
MARK 3 SYSTEMS, INC.; *U.S. Private*, pg. 2577
MARK-AIR INC.—See DLVA, Inc.; *U.S. Private*, pg. 1248
MARK ANDY, INC.; *U.S. Private*, pg. 2577

MARKA PJSC; *Int'l*, pg. 4696
MARKA YATIRIM HOLDING AS; *Int'l*, pg. 4696
MARK BBDO—See Omnicom Group Inc.; *U.S. Public*, pg. 1576
MARK BBDO—See Omnicom Group Inc.; *U.S. Public*, pg. 1576
MARK BOULTON DESIGN LIMITED—See HGGC, LLC; *U.S. Public*, pg. 1930
MARK & CHAPPELL (IRELAND) LIMITED—See Bansk Group LLC; *U.S. Private*, pg. 469
MARK & CHAPPELL LIMITED—See Bansk Group LLC; *U.S. Private*, pg. 469
MARK CHEVROLET INC.; *U.S. Private*, pg. 2577
MARK CHRISTOPHER AUTO CENTER; *U.S. Private*, pg. 2577
MARK COLLEGE LIMITED—See Acadia Healthcare Company, Inc.; *U.S. Public*, pg. 29
THE MARK COMPANY / PACIFIC UNION INTERNATIONAL, INC.—See Pacific Union International, Inc.; *U.S. Private*, pg. 3071
MARK CONSTRUCTION CO. INC.; *U.S. Private*, pg. 2577
MARK CORRECTIONAL SYSTEMS—See Kullman Buildings Corp.; *U.S. Private*, pg. 2357
MARK C. POPE ASSOCIATES INC.; *U.S. Private*, pg. 2577
MARK DUNNING INDUSTRIES, INC.; *U.S. Private*, pg. 2577
MARKE CREATIVE MERCHANDISE LTD.—See Sycamore Partners Management, LP; *U.S. Private*, pg. 3897
MARKEDSKRAFT ASA—See Agder Energi AS; *Int'l*, pg. 204
MARKEDSKRAFT ASA—See Arendals Fossekompani ASA; *Int'l*, pg. 559
MARK EDWARD PARTNERS LLC—See GCP Capital Partners Holdings LLC; *U.S. Private*, pg. 1654
MARKEL AMERICAN INSURANCE COMPANY—See Markel Group Inc.; *U.S. Public*, pg. 1368
MARKEL CANADA LIMITED—See Markel Group Inc.; *U.S. Public*, pg. 1368
MARKEL CATCO INVESTMENT MANAGEMENT LTD.—See Markel Group Inc.; *U.S. Public*, pg. 1368
MARKEL CONSULTANCY SERVICES LIMITED—See Markel Group Inc.; *U.S. Public*, pg. 1368
MARKEL CORPORATION; *U.S. Private*, pg. 2578
MARKEL CORP. - WOODLAND HILLS—See Markel Group Inc.; *U.S. Public*, pg. 1368
MARKEL GROUP INC.; *U.S. Public*, pg. 1367
MARKEL INDUSTRIES, INC.—See Mativ Holdings, Inc.; *U.S. Public*, pg. 1397
MARKEL INSURANCE COMPANY—See Markel Group Inc.; *U.S. Public*, pg. 1368
MARKEL INSURANCE S.E.—See Markel Group Inc.; *U.S. Public*, pg. 1368
MARKEL INTERNATIONAL (DUBAI) LIMITED—See Markel Group Inc.; *U.S. Public*, pg. 1368
MARKEL INTERNATIONAL LIMITED—See Markel Group Inc.; *U.S. Public*, pg. 1368
MARKEL INTERNATIONAL SINGAPORE PTE. LIMITED—See Markel Group Inc.; *U.S. Public*, pg. 1368
MARKEL LAW LLP—See Markel Group Inc.; *U.S. Public*, pg. 1368
MARKEL MIDWEST—See Markel Group Inc.; *U.S. Public*, pg. 1368
MARKEL SEGURADORA DO BRASIL, SA—See Markel Group Inc.; *U.S. Public*, pg. 1368
MARKEL SERVICE, INC.—See Markel Group Inc.; *U.S. Public*, pg. 1368
MARKEL SURETY CORPORATION—See Markel Group Inc.; *U.S. Public*, pg. 1368
MARKEL (UK) LIMITED—See Markel Group Inc.; *U.S. Public*, pg. 1368
MARKEL VENTURES, INC.—See Markel Group Inc.; *U.S. Public*, pg. 1368
MARKELYTICS SOLUTIONS INDIA PRIVATE LIMITED—See Cross Marketing Group Inc.; *Int'l*, pg. 1856
MARKEM-IMAJE AG—See Dover Corporation; *U.S. Public*, pg. 680
MARKEM-IMAJE A/S—See Dover Corporation; *U.S. Public*, pg. 680
MARKEM-IMAJE AS—See Dover Corporation; *U.S. Public*, pg. 680
MARKEM-IMAJE BV—See Dover Corporation; *U.S. Public*, pg. 680
MARKEM-IMAJE CO., LTD.—See Dover Corporation; *U.S. Public*, pg. 680
MARKEM-IMAJE CORPORATION—See Dover Corporation; *U.S. Public*, pg. 680
MARKEM-IMAJE CSAT GMBH—See Dover Corporation; *U.S. Public*, pg. 682
MARKEM-IMAJE GMBH - AUSTRIA—See Dover Corporation; *U.S. Public*, pg. 680
MARKEM-IMAJE GMBH—See Dover Corporation; *U.S. Public*, pg. 680
MARKEM-IMAJE HOLDING—See Dover Corporation; *U.S. Public*, pg. 682
MARKEM-IMAJE (HONG KONG) LIMITED—See Dover Corporation; *U.S. Public*, pg. 680

COMPANY NAME INDEX

MARKEM-IMAJE INC.—See Dover Corporation; *U.S. Public*, pg. 680
MARKEM-IMAJE INDIA PRIVATE LIMITED—See Dover Corporation; *U.S. Public*, pg. 680
MARKEM-IMAJE INDUSTRIES LIMITED—See Dover Corporation; *U.S. Public*, pg. 682
MARKEM-IMAJE INDUSTRIES—See Dover Corporation; *U.S. Public*, pg. 682
MARKEM-IMAJE K.K.—See Dover Corporation; *U.S. Public*, pg. 680
MARKEM-IMAJE LIMITED—See Dover Corporation; *U.S. Public*, pg. 682
MARKEM-IMAJE LLC—See Dover Corporation; *U.S. Public*, pg. 680
MARKEM-IMAJE LTD.—See Dover Corporation; *U.S. Public*, pg. 682
MARKEM-IMAJE LTD.—See Dover Corporation; *U.S. Public*, pg. 682
MARKEM-IMAJE LTD.—See Dover Corporation; *U.S. Public*, pg. 680
MARKEM-IMAJE N.V.—See Dover Corporation; *U.S. Public*, pg. 680
MARKEM-IMAJE OY—See Dover Corporation; *U.S. Public*, pg. 680
MARKEM-IMAJE PTE. LTD.—See Dover Corporation; *U.S. Public*, pg. 680
MARKEM-IMAJE PTY LTD.—See Dover Corporation; *U.S. Public*, pg. 680
MARKEM-IMAJE S.A. DE C.V.—See Dover Corporation; *U.S. Public*, pg. 680
MARKEM-IMAJE S.A.—See Dover Corporation; *U.S. Public*, pg. 682
MARKEM-IMAJE SAS—See Dover Corporation; *U.S. Public*, pg. 680
MARKEM-IMAJE SDN BHD—See Dover Corporation; *U.S. Public*, pg. 680
MARKEM-IMAJE SPAIN S.A.—See Dover Corporation; *U.S. Public*, pg. 680
MARKEM-IMAJE SPAIN S.A.U—See Dover Corporation; *U.S. Public*, pg. 682
MARKEM-IMAJE S.R.L A SOCIO UNICO—See Dover Corporation; *U.S. Public*, pg. 680
MARKEM-IMAJE (TAIWAN) LTD.—See Dover Corporation; *U.S. Public*, pg. 680
MARKEM-IMAJE UNIPESSOAL, LDA—See Dover Corporation; *U.S. Public*, pg. 680
MARKEM-IMAJE USA—See Dover Corporation; *U.S. Public*, pg. 680
MARKEM PTE. LTD.—See Dover Corporation; *U.S. Public*, pg. 681
MARKEN LLP—See United Parcel Service, Inc.; *U.S. Public*, pg. 2233
MARKER DALBELLO VOLKL AUSTRIA GMBH—See Kohlberg & Company, LLC; *U.S. Private*, pg. 2338
MARKER FINE FOOD GMBH—See J. Bauer GmbH & Co. KG; *Int'l*, pg. 3854
MARKER GENE TECHNOLOGIES, INC.—See Danaher Corporation; *U.S. Public*, pg. 624
MARKER SEVEN, INC.; *U.S. Private*, pg. 2578
MARKERSTUDY INSURANCE SERVICES LIMITED; *Int'l*, pg. 4696
MARKER THERAPEUTICS, INC.; *U.S. Public*, pg. 1369
MARKER VOLKL (INTERNATIONAL) SALES GMBH—See Kohlberg & Company, LLC; *U.S. Private*, pg. 2338
MARKESFORSAKRING—See Sampo plc; *Int'l*, pg. 6508
MARKET6, INC.—See The Kroger Co.; *U.S. Public*, pg. 2108
MARKET AMERICA REALTY AND INVESTMENTS, INC.; *U.S. Private*, pg. 2578
MARKET AMERICA WORLDWIDE, INC.; *U.S. Private*, pg. 2578
MARKETAXESS CORPORATION—See MarketAxess Holdings Inc.; *U.S. Public*, pg. 1369
MARKETAXESS EUROPE LTD—See MarketAxess Holdings Inc.; *U.S. Public*, pg. 1369
MARKETAXESS HOLDINGS INC.; *U.S. Public*, pg. 1369
MARKETAXESS NL B.V.—See MarketAxess Holdings Inc.; *U.S. Public*, pg. 1369
MARKETAXESS POST-TRADE B.V.—See MarketAxess Holdings Inc.; *U.S. Public*, pg. 1369
MARKETAXESS POST-TRADE LIMITED—See MarketAxess Holdings Inc.; *U.S. Public*, pg. 1369
MARKET BASKET FOOD STORE, INC.; *U.S. Private*, pg. 2578
MARKET BASKET; *U.S. Private*, pg. 2578
MARKET BAYOU HEALTHCARE, INC.—See The Ensign Group, Inc.; *U.S. Public*, pg. 2071
MARKETBOOMER CHINA LIMITED—See Marketboomer Pty. Ltd.; *Int'l*, pg. 4696
MARKETBOOMER INTERNATIONAL LIMITED—See Marketboomer Pty. Ltd.; *Int'l*, pg. 4696
MARKETBOOMER PTY. LTD.; *Int'l*, pg. 4696
MARKET CAFE—See Delaware North Companies, Inc.; *U.S. Public*, pg. 1195
MARKETCAST INC.—See Kohlberg & Company, LLC; *U.S. Private*, pg. 2338
MARKET CITY MANAGEMENT PRIVATE LIMITED—See The Phoenix Mills Limited; *Int'l*, pg. 7673

MARKET CITY RESOURCES PRIVATE LIMITED—See The Phoenix Mills Limited; *Int'l*, pg. 7673
MARKET COMPANY, LTD.—See United Natural Foods, Inc.; *U.S. Public*, pg. 2231
MARKETCOM PUBLIC RELATIONS, LLC; *U.S. Private*, pg. 2579
THE MARKET CONNECTION; *U.S. Private*, pg. 4074
MARKET CONTRACTORS LTD.; *U.S. Private*, pg. 2578
MARKETCOUNSEL; *U.S. Private*, pg. 2579
THE MARKET CREATION GROUP, LLC; *U.S. Private*, pg. 4074
MARKET CREATORS LTD.; *Int'l*, pg. 4696
MARKET DATA RETRIEVAL—See Cannae Holdings, Inc.; *U.S. Public*, pg. 430
MARKET DATA RETRIEVAL—See CC Capital Partners, LLC; *U.S. Private*, pg. 798
MARKET DATA RETRIEVAL—See Intercontinental Exchange, Inc.; *U.S. Public*, pg. 1142
MARKET DATA SERVICE LLC—See Gridiron Capital, LLC; *U.S. Private*, pg. 1786
MARKET DAY CORPORATION; *U.S. Private*, pg. 2579
MARKET DEVELOPMENT GROUP, INC.; *U.S. Private*, pg. 2579
MARKETECH CO., LTD.—See Marketech International Corp.; *Int'l*, pg. 4696
MARKETECH ENGINEERING PTE. LTD.—See Marketech International Corp.; *Int'l*, pg. 4696
MARKETECHING SOLUTIONS, LLC.—See New Mountain Capital, LLC; *U.S. Private*, pg. 2904
MARKETECH INTEGRATED MANUFACTURING COMPANY LIMITED—See Marketech International Corp.; *Int'l*, pg. 4696
MARKETECH INTERNATIONAL CORP. - HUKOU FACTORY—See Marketech International Corp.; *Int'l*, pg. 4696
MARKETECH INTERNATIONAL CORP.; *Int'l*, pg. 4696
MARKETECH NETHERLANDS B.V.—See Marketech International Corp.; *Int'l*, pg. 4696
MARKET ENHANCEMENT GROUP, INC.; *U.S. Private*, pg. 2579
MARKETENTERPRISE CO., LTD.; *Int'l*, pg. 4696
MARKETEX COMPUTER CORP.; *U.S. Private*, pg. 2579
MARKET EXPRESS—See Visy Industries Holdings Pty. Ltd.; *Int'l*, pg. 8256
MARKET FINDERS INSURANCE CORP.; *U.S. Private*, pg. 2579
MARKET FIRST, INC.; *U.S. Private*, pg. 2579
MARKETFISH INC.; *U.S. Private*, pg. 2579
MARKET FORCE INFORMATION, INC.; *U.S. Private*, pg. 2579
MARKETFORCE (UK) LIMITED—See Meredith Corporation; *U.S. Public*, pg. 1423
MARKETFORM HOLDINGS LIMITED—See American Financial Group, Inc.; *U.S. Public*, pg. 103
MARKET FORWARD—See Publicis Groupe S.A.; *Int'l*, pg. 6103
MARKET GROCERY COMPANY, INC.; *U.S. Private*, pg. 2579
MARKET HARBOROUGH BUILDING SOCIETY; *Int'l*, pg. 4696
MARKET HARBOROUGH VETS4PETS LIMITED—See Pets at Home Group Plc; *Int'l*, pg. 5834
MARKET HARDWARE LIMITED—See Grafton Group plc; *Int'l*, pg. 3051
THE MARKET HERALD LIMITED; *Int'l*, pg. 7665
MARKET HORIZONS—See WPP plc; *Int'l*, pg. 8471
MARKET IMPROVEMENT CORPORATION—See United Natural Foods, Inc.; *U.S. Public*, pg. 2232
THE MARKETING AGENCY LLC; *U.S. Private*, pg. 4074
THE MARKETING ALLIANCE, INC.; *U.S. Public*, pg. 2112
MARKETING ALTERNATIVES, INC.; *U.S. Private*, pg. 2580
MARKETING ANALYTICS, INC—See Brookfield Corporation; *Int'l*, pg. 1178
MARKETING ANALYTICS, INC—See Elliott Management Corporation; *U.S. Private*, pg. 1371
MARKETING AND COMMERCIAL AGENCIES COMPANY LTD.—See Dabbagh Group Holding Company Ltd.; *Int'l*, pg. 1902
THE MARKETING ARM—See Omnicom Group Inc.; *U.S. Public*, pg. 1599
THE MARKETING ARM—See Omnicom Group Inc.; *U.S. Public*, pg. 1599
MARKETING ARTS CORPORATION—See Tilt Creative + Production, LLC; *U.S. Private*, pg. 4171
MARKETING BY DESIGN, LLC—See Matthews International Corporation; *U.S. Public*, pg. 1401
THE MARKETING CENTER FOR SOCIAL SECURITY LAW PRACTICES; *U.S. Private*, pg. 4074
MARKETING CONCEPTS GROUP; *U.S. Private*, pg. 2580
MARKETING CONCEPTS OF MINNESOTA, INC.; *U.S. Private*, pg. 2580
THE MARKETING CO PTE LTD—See Metro Holdings Limited; *Int'l*, pg. 4860
MARKETING COUNSELORS LTD.—See WPP plc; *Int'l*, pg. 8484
MARKETING & CREATIVE SERVICES, INC.; *U.S. Private*, pg. 2579
THE MARKETING DEPARTMENT; *Int'l*, pg. 7665

MARKETING DOCTOR, INC.; *U.S. Private*, pg. 2580
MARKETING & ENGINEERING SOLUTIONS INC.; *U.S. Private*, pg. 2580
MARKETING & EVENTS GROUP—See Viad Corp.; *U.S. Public*, pg. 2291
MARKETING EVOLUTION, INC.; *U.S. Private*, pg. 2580
MARKETING FORCE JAPAN, INC.—See The Nisshin OilliO Group, Ltd.; *Int'l*, pg. 7671
MARKETING GARDEN LTD.—See AVIAREPS Marketing Garden Ltd.; *Int'l*, pg. 741
MARKETING GENERAL INC.—See Taylor Corporation; *U.S. Private*, pg. 3938
THE MARKETING GROUP PLC; *Int'l*, pg. 7665
THE MARKETING GROUP; *Int'l*, pg. 7665
MARKETING GROUP; *U.S. Private*, pg. 2580
MARKETING HOUSE SP. ZO.O—See Vivendi SE; *Int'l*, pg. 8269
MARKETING IN COLOR INC.; *U.S. Private*, pg. 2580
MARKETING INFORMATICS, INC.; *U.S. Private*, pg. 2580
MARKETING INNOVATORS INTERNATIONAL, INC.; *U.S. Private*, pg. 2580
MARKETING MANAGEMENT, INC.; *U.S. Private*, pg. 2580
MARKETING MANIACS, INC.; *U.S. Private*, pg. 2580
MARKETING MATTERS; *U.S. Private*, pg. 2580
MARKETING & MEDIA SERVICES, LLC—See Respond2 Cmedia; *U.S. Private*, pg. 3408
MARKETING OPTIONS, LLC; *U.S. Private*, pg. 2580
MARKETING PARTNER CO., LTD.—See SBS Holdings Inc.; *Int'l*, pg. 6607
MARKETING PARTNERS INC.; *U.S. Private*, pg. 2580
MARKETING PERFORMANCE GROUP, INC.; *U.S. Private*, pg. 2580
MARKETINGPLATFORM APS—See Link Mobility Group Holding ASA; *Int'l*, pg. 4514
MARKETING POWER RAPP—See Omnicom Group Inc.; *U.S. Public*, pg. 1592
MARKETING PRODUCTION SYSTEMS, LLC—See Ambassador Programs, Inc.; *U.S. Private*, pg. 217
MARKETINGPROFS, LLC; *U.S. Private*, pg. 2581
MARKETING & RESERVATIONS INTERNATIONAL LTD.; *Int'l*, pg. 4696
MARKETING & RESERVATIONS (USA) INC.—See Marketing & Reservations International Ltd.; *Int'l*, pg. 4696
MARKETING RESOURCE GROUP; *Int'l*, pg. 4696
MARKETING RESOURCE GROUP—See Marketing Resource Group; *Int'l*, pg. 4696
MARKETING RESOURCE GROUP—See Marketing Resource Group; *Int'l*, pg. 4697
MARKETING SOFTWARE COMPANY LLC—See Valid Solucoes S.A.; *Int'l*, pg. 8116
MARKETING SOLUTIONS UNLIMITED, LLC; *U.S. Private*, pg. 2580
THE MARKETING STORE; *U.S. Private*, pg. 4075
THE MARKETING STORE—See The Marketing Store; *U.S. Private*, pg. 4075
THE MARKETING STORE—See The Marketing Store; *U.S. Private*, pg. 4075
THE MARKETING STORE—See The Marketing Store; *U.S. Private*, pg. 4075
THE MARKETING STORE—See The Marketing Store; *U.S. Private*, pg. 4075
THE MARKETING STORE WORLDWIDE (EUROPE) LIMITED—See The Marketing Store; *U.S. Private*, pg. 4075
MARKETING SUPPORT, INC.; *U.S. Private*, pg. 2580
MARKETING SUPPORT SOLUTIONS, INC.—See Integrated Distribution & Logistics Direct LLC; *U.S. Private*, pg. 2099
MARKETING TECHNOLOGY CONCEPTS, INC.; *U.S. Private*, pg. 2580
MARKETING V F LIMITED; *Int'l*, pg. 4697
MARKETING VISIONS, INC.; *U.S. Private*, pg. 2580
MARKETING WERKS, INC.—See Acosta, Inc.; *U.S. Private*, pg. 64
MARKETING WORKSHOP INC.; *U.S. Private*, pg. 2581
MARKETING WORKS, INC.; *U.S. Private*, pg. 2580
MARKETING Y PROMOCIONES S.A.—See Empresaria Group Plc; *Int'l*, pg. 2389
MARKET & JOHNSON, INC.; *U.S. Private*, pg. 2578
MARKETLAB, INC.; *U.S. Private*, pg. 2581
MARKETLAB RESEARCH, INC.—See Schlesinger Group; *U.S. Private*, pg. 3565
MARKET LEADER, INC.—See Constellation Software Inc.; *Int'l*, pg. 1772
MARKETLINE INTERNATIONAL LTD.—See Informa plc; *Int'l*, pg. 3692
MARKET LOGISTICS INC.; *U.S. Private*, pg. 2579
MARKET LOGISTICS SERVICES, LTD.—See Wilson Logistics, Inc.; *U.S. Private*, pg. 4531
MARKET MAKERS INCORPORATED LIMITED—See Centaur Media plc; *Int'l*, pg. 1402
MARKET MATCH MEDIA, INC.; *U.S. Private*, pg. 2579
MARKET METRICS, LLC—See FactSet Research Systems Inc.; *U.S. Public*, pg. 820
MARKET METRIX LLC—See Canada Pension Plan Investment Board; *Int'l*, pg. 1281
MARKET METRIX LLC—See Silver Lake Group, LLC; *U.S. Private*, pg. 3655

MARKET MATCH MEDIA, INC.

CORPORATE AFFILIATIONS

MARKET MORTGAGE LIMITED—See Capita plc; *Int'l*, pg. 1309
MARKET MOTIVE, INC.—See Simplilearn Solutions Pvt Ltd; *Int'l*, pg. 6934
MARKETNET, INC.—See Bridgeline Digital, Inc.; *U.S. Public*, pg. 382
MARKETNET SERVICES, LLC; *U.S. Private*, pg. 2581
MARKET NEWS INTERNATIONAL INC.—See DMEP Corporation; *U.S. Private*, pg. 1248
MARKETO AUSTRALIA PTY LTD.—See Adobe Inc.; *U.S. Public*, pg. 42
MARKETO EMEA LTD.—See Adobe Inc.; *U.S. Public*, pg. 42
MARKETO, INC.—See Adobe Inc.; *U.S. Public*, pg. 42
MARKETOPIA, LLC; *U.S. Private*, pg. 2581
MARKETPATH, INC.; *U.S. Private*, pg. 2581
MARKETPLACE AT CONCORD MILLS, LLC—See Washington Prime Group Inc.; *U.S. Private*, pg. 4448
MARKETPLACE CENTER, INC.—See Regency Centers Corporation; *U.S. Public*, pg. 1774
MARKETPLACE EVENTS LLC—See Sentinel Capital Partners, L.L.C.; *U.S. Private*, pg. 3609
MARKETPLACE FOODS, INC.—See Coborn's Incorporated; *U.S. Private*, pg. 958
MARKETPLACE HOMES; *U.S. Private*, pg. 2581
MARKET PLACE INC.; *U.S. Private*, pg. 2579
MARKETPLACE STRATEGY, LLC—See Graham Holdings Company; *U.S. Public*, pg. 956
MARKETPLACE TECHNOLOGIES PVT LTD.—See Bombay Stock Exchange Limited; *Int'l*, pg. 1104
MARKET PROBE INC.; *U.S. Private*, pg. 2579
MARKET QUEST, INC.—See Bischof + Klein GmbH & Co. KG; *Int'l*, pg. 1048
MARKETRESEARCH.COM; *U.S. Private*, pg. 2581
MARKET RESEARCH FOUNDATION; *U.S. Private*, pg. 2579
MARKET RESOURCE PARTNERS LLC—See FD Technologies PLC; *Int'l*, pg. 2628
MARKETRON BROADCAST SOLUTIONS, LLC—See Diversis Capital, LLC; *U.S. Private*, pg. 1244
MARKETRX INC.—See Cognizant Technology Solutions Corporation; *U.S. Public*, pg. 525
MARKETRX INDIA PRIVATE LIMITED—See Cognizant Technology Solutions Corporation; *U.S. Public*, pg. 525
MARKET SELF CHILE SPA—See Bertelsmann SE & Co. KGaA; *Int'l*, pg. 993
MARKET SELF S.A.—See Bertelsmann SE & Co. KGaA; *Int'l*, pg. 993
MARKET SHARE DEVELOPMENT; *U.S. Private*, pg. 2579
MARKETSHARE PARTNERS, LLC—See TransUnion; *U.S. Public*, pg. 2184
MARKETSHARE PLUS, INC.; *U.S. Private*, pg. 2581
MARKETSHARE PUBLICATIONS, INC.; *U.S. Private*, pg. 2581
THE MARKETS LLC—See Hancock Park Associates, LP; *U.S. Private*, pg. 1852
MARKETSMITH, INC.; *U.S. Private*, pg. 2581
MARKETSOURCE, INC.—See Allegis Group, Inc.; *U.S. Private*, pg. 177
MARKETSPHERE CONSULTING, LLC; *U.S. Private*, pg. 2581
MARKET SQUARE TRAVEL LLC—See Travel Leaders Group, LLC; *U.S. Private*, pg. 4213
MARKET STAFF INC.; *U.S. Private*, pg. 2579
MARKETSTAR CORPORATION—See Wasatch Advantage Group, LLC; *U.S. Private*, pg. 4445
MARKET STREET RECYCLING LLC—See M. Lipsitz & Co., Ltd.; *U.S. Private*, pg. 2527
MARKET STREET SETTLEMENT GROUP LLC—See Anywhere Real Estate Inc.; *U.S. Public*, pg. 142
MARKETSWITCH JAPAN KK—See Transcosmos Inc.; *Int'l*, pg. 7898
MARKET TRACK, LLC—See Vista Equity Partners, LLC; *U.S. Private*, pg. 4398
MARKET TRANSPORT LTD.; *U.S. Private*, pg. 2579
MARKET VANTAGE, LLC; *U.S. Private*, pg. 2579
MARKET VECTORS COMMODITY TRUST—See Van Eck Associates Corp.; *U.S. Private*, pg. 4340
MARKET VECTORS REDEEMABLE GOLD TRUST—See Van Eck Associates Corp.; *U.S. Private*, pg. 4340
MARKET VECTORS REDEEMABLE SILVER TRUST—See Van Eck Associates Corp.; *U.S. Private*, pg. 4340
MARKET VECTORS-RUSSIA EFT—See Van Eck Associates Corp.; *U.S. Private*, pg. 4339
MARKET VELOCITY, INC.—See KKR & Co. Inc.; *U.S. Public*, pg. 1267
MARKETVISION; *U.S. Private*, pg. 2581
MARKETWATCH, INC.—See News Corporation; *U.S. Public*, pg. 1518
MARKETWAY LTD.—See Publicis Groupe S.A.; *Int'l*, pg. 6103
MARKETWIRED CHINA LTD.—See Apollo Global Management, Inc.; *U.S. Public*, pg. 152
MARKETWISE, INC.; *U.S. Public*, pg. 1369
MARKEY MACHINE LLC; *U.S. Private*, pg. 2581
MARKEYS AUDIO VISUAL INC.; *U.S. Private*, pg. 2581
MARK FACEY & COMPANY; *U.S. Private*, pg. 2577
MARKFEST INC.; *U.S. Private*, pg. 2581

MARKFORGED HOLDING CORPORATION; *U.S. Public*, pg. 1369
THE MARK GORDON COMPANY—See Lions Gate Entertainment Corp.; *Int'l*, pg. 4520
MARK GROUP AUSTRALIA PTY LTD—See Anchorage Capital Partners Pty. Limited; *Int'l*, pg. 448
MARK GRUNDFOS LTDA—See The Poul Due Jensen Foundation; *Int'l*, pg. 7676
MARKHAM-B, LP—See Lithia Motors, Inc.; *U.S. Public*, pg. 1325
MARKHAM NORTON MOSTELLER WRIGHT & COMPANY, P.A.; *U.S. Private*, pg. 2581
MARKHAM-P, LP—See Lithia Motors, Inc.; *U.S. Public*, pg. 1325
MARKHAM REAL ESTATE PARTNERS (KSW) PTY. LIMITED—See Talanx AG; *Int'l*, pg. 7445
MARKHAM VINEYARDS—See Kirin Holdings Company, Limited; *Int'l*, pg. 4187
MARKHAM WOODS PRESS PUBLISHING CO., INC.; *U.S. Private*, pg. 2582
MARK HERSHEY FARMS INC.; *U.S. Private*, pg. 2577
MARK III PROPERTIES, LLC—See Sumitomo Forestry Co., Ltd.; *Int'l*, pg. 7286
MARK & INFRA I SVERIGE AB—See Kesko Corporation; *Int'l*, pg. 4142
MARKIN TUBING, INC.; *U.S. Private*, pg. 2582
MARKISCHES MEDIENHAUS GMBH & CO. KG—See Neue Pressegesellschaft mbH & Co. KG; *Int'l*, pg. 5218
MARK-IT SMART INC.; *U.S. Private*, pg. 2582
MARK JACOBSON & ASSOCIATES; *U.S. Private*, pg. 2577
MARK J. BECKER & ASSOCIATES, LLC—See Arthur J. Gallagher & Co.; *U.S. Public*, pg. 206
MARKLAND INDUSTRIES INC.; *U.S. Private*, pg. 2582
MARKLAND MALL, LLC—See Washington Prime Group Inc.; *U.S. Private*, pg. 4448
MARKLAND PLAZA, LLC—See Washington Prime Group Inc.; *U.S. Private*, pg. 4448
MARKLEY MOTORS INC.; *U.S. Private*, pg. 2582
MARK LIGHTING FIXTURE CO., INC.—See Acuity Brands, Inc.; *U.S. Public*, pg. 37
MARK LINE INDUSTRIES; *U.S. Private*, pg. 2577
MARKLINES CO., LTD.; *Int'l*, pg. 4697
MARKLINES EUROPE GMBH—See MarkLines Co., Ltd.; *Int'l*, pg. 4697
MARKLINES MEXICANA S.A. DE C.V.—See MarkLines Co., Ltd.; *Int'l*, pg. 4697
MARKLINES NORTH AMERICA INCORPORATED—See MarkLines Co., Ltd.; *Int'l*, pg. 4697
MARKLIN, INC.—See Gebr. Marklin & Cie. GmbH; *Int'l*, pg. 2909
MARKLIN-VERTRIEBS AG—See Gebr. Marklin & Cie. GmbH; *Int'l*, pg. 2909
MARKLOGIC CORPORATION—See Vector Capital Management, L.P.; *U.S. Private*, pg. 4351
MARKLUND CHILDREN'S HOME; *U.S. Private*, pg. 2582
MARK-LYNN FOODS, INC.—See Hormel Foods Corporation; *U.S. Public*, pg. 1054
MARKMANS DIAMOND BROKERS INC.; *U.S. Private*, pg. 2582
MARKMASTER, INC.; *U.S. Private*, pg. 2582
MARK MITSUBISHI SCOTTSDALE; *U.S. Private*, pg. 2578
MARK MITSUBISHI; *U.S. Private*, pg. 2578
MARK M. JONES & ASSOCIATES P.C.—See Calvetti Ferguson, P.C.; *U.S. Private*, pg. 724
MARKMONITOR INC.—See Clearlake Capital Group, L.P.; *U.S. Private*, pg. 934
MARKMONITOR INC.—See Siris Capital Group, LLC; *U.S. Private*, pg. 3673
MARK MOTORS INC.; *U.S. Private*, pg. 2578
MARKNADSINFORMATION ANALYS MIA AB—See Ratos AB; *Int'l*, pg. 6217
MARKO FOAM PRODUCTS, INC.; *U.S. Private*, pg. 2582
MARKOLINES TRAFFIC CONTROLS LIMITED; *Int'l*, pg. 4697
MARKOM/LEO BURNETT—See Publicis Groupe S.A.; *Int'l*, pg. 6102
MARK ONE CAPITAL, INC.—See Marcus & Millichap, Inc.; *U.S. Public*, pg. 1365
MARKON, INC.—See Sterling Investment Partners, L.P.; *U.S. Private*, pg. 3805
MARKOR INTERNATIONAL HOME FURNISHINGS CO., LTD.; *Int'l*, pg. 4697
MARKOS-MEFAR S.P.A.—See L'Air Liquide S.A.; *Int'l*, pg. 4373
MARKQUART INC.; *U.S. Private*, pg. 2582
MARKQUART TOYOTA—See Markquart Inc.; *U.S. Private*, pg. 2582
MARKRAFT CABINETS INC.—See The Sterling Group, L.P.; *U.S. Private*, pg. 4122
MARKRAY CORP.; *U.S. Public*, pg. 1370
MARK RICHEY WOODWORKING & DESIGN, INC.; *U.S. Private*, pg. 2578
MARK RITE LINES EQUIPMENT CO., INC.—See Federal Signal Corporation; *U.S. Public*, pg. 826
MARKS AND SPENCER 2005 (CHESTER STORE) LIMITED—See Marks & Spencer Group plc; *Int'l*, pg. 4697

MARKS AND SPENCER 2005 (GLASGOW SAUCHIEHALL STORE) LIMITED—See Marks & Spencer Group plc; *Int'l*, pg. 4697
MARKS AND SPENCER 2005 (HEDGE END STORE) LIMITED—See Marks & Spencer Group plc; *Int'l*, pg. 4697
MARKS AND SPENCER 2005 (KENSINGTON STORE) LIMITED—See Marks & Spencer Group plc; *Int'l*, pg. 4697
MARKS AND SPENCER 2005 (KINGSTON-ON-THAMES STORE) LIMITED—See Marks & Spencer Group plc; *Int'l*, pg. 4697
MARKS AND SPENCER 2005 (WARRINGTON GEMINI STORE) LIMITED—See Marks & Spencer Group plc; *Int'l*, pg. 4697
MARKS AND SPENCER (BRADFORD) LIMITED—See Marks & Spencer Group plc; *Int'l*, pg. 4697
MARKS AND SPENCER PENSION TRUST LIMITED—See Marks & Spencer Group plc; *Int'l*, pg. 4697
MARKSANS PHARMA LTD; *Int'l*, pg. 4697
MARKS BROTHERS, INC.; *U.S. Private*, pg. 2582
MARK'S CARD SHOPS INC.; *U.S. Private*, pg. 2578
MARK SCOTT CONSTRUCTION, INC.; *U.S. Private*, pg. 2578
MARKS CRANE & RIGGING CO. LTD.; *U.S. Private*, pg. 2582
MARKS ELECTRICAL GROUP PLC; *Int'l*, pg. 4697
MARKS ELECTRICAL LIMITED—See Marks Electrical Group Plc; *Int'l*, pg. 4697
MARKSERV, B.V.—See Melia Hotels International, S.A.; *Int'l*, pg. 4809
MARK SHALE DIRECT—See Mark Shale; *U.S. Private*, pg. 2578
MARK SHALE; *U.S. Private*, pg. 2578
MARKS INC.—See Mark's Card Shops Inc.; *U.S. Private*, pg. 2578
MARKS-LANDAU CONSTRUCTION, LLC—See Landau Building Company; *U.S. Private*, pg. 2384
MARKSMEN ENERGY INC.; *Int'l*, pg. 4697
MARKS METAL TECHNOLOGY INC.—See Environmental Containment Corporation; *U.S. Private*, pg. 1407
MARKSNELSON LLC; *U.S. Private*, pg. 2582
MARK.—See M&C Saatchi plc; *Int'l*, pg. 4611
MARKS PANETH LLP; *U.S. Private*, pg. 2582
MARKS SATTIN (AUSTRALIA) PTY LIMITED—See ManpowerGroup Inc.; *U.S. Public*, pg. 1361
MARKS & SPENCER FINANCIAL SERVICES PLC—See HSBC Holdings plc; *Int'l*, pg. 3503
MARKS & SPENCER GROUP PLC; *Int'l*, pg. 4697
MARKS & SPENCER (IRELAND) LIMITED—See Marks & Spencer Group plc; *Int'l*, pg. 4697
MARKS & SPENCER PROPERTY DEVELOPMENTS LIMITED—See Marks & Spencer Group plc; *Int'l*, pg. 4697
MARK STEEL CORPORATION; *U.S. Private*, pg. 2578
MARK STEELS LTD.—See Manaksia Ltd; *Int'l*, pg. 4667
MARKSTEIN BEVERAGE CO. UNION CITY; *U.S. Private*, pg. 2582
MARK STEVENS INDUSTRIES INC.; *U.S. Private*, pg. 2578
MARKS TRANSPORT, INC.—See AutoNation, Inc.; *U.S. Public*, pg. 236
MARKS WORK WEARHOUSE LTD.—See Canadian Tire Corporation Limited; *Int'l*, pg. 1286
MARKS WORK WEARHOUSE—See Canadian Tire Corporation Limited; *Int'l*, pg. 1286
MARKTEC CORPORATION—See Alconix Corporation; *Int'l*, pg. 302
MARKTGURU DEUTSCHLAND GMBH—See ProSiebenSat.1 Media SE; *Int'l*, pg. 6001
MARK THOMAS MOTORS INC.; *U.S. Private*, pg. 2578
MARKTKAUF HOLDING GMBH—See EDEKA Zentrale AG & Co. KG; *Int'l*, pg. 2305
MARKTPLAATS B.V.—See eBay Inc.; *U.S. Public*, pg. 709
MARK/TRECE INC.; *U.S. Private*, pg. 2578
MARK TWAIN MEDICAL CENTER—See Catholic Health Initiatives; *U.S. Private*, pg. 790
MARK TWO ENGINEERING, INC.—See CORE Industrial Partners, LLC; *U.S. Private*, pg. 1048
MARKUSSON NEW HOLLAND OF REGINA LTD.; *Int'l*, pg. 4697
MARKUSSON PROFESSIONAL GRINDERS AB—See Emak S.p.A.; *Int'l*, pg. 2373
MARK VII EQUIPMENT INC.—See WashTec AG; *Int'l*, pg. 8351
MARK WESTBY & ASSOCIATES, INC.; *U.S. Private*, pg. 2578
MARKWEST ENERGY PARTNERS, L.P. - CARTHAGE PROCESSING FACILITY—See Marathon Petroleum Corporation; *U.S. Public*, pg. 1364
MARKWEST ENERGY PARTNERS, L.P.—See Marathon Petroleum Corporation; *U.S. Public*, pg. 1364
MARKWEST MICHIGAN PIPELINE COMPANY, L.L.C.—See Marathon Petroleum Corporation; *U.S. Public*, pg. 1364
MARKWEST PINNACLE LP; *U.S. Private*, pg. 2582
MARKWEST POWER TEX, L.L.C.—See Marathon Petroleum Corporation; *U.S. Public*, pg. 1364

COMPANY NAME INDEX

MARKWEST TEXAS LPG PIPELINE, L.L.C.—See Marathon Petroleum Corporation; *U.S. Public*, pg. 1364
MARK WILKINSON FURNITURE LIMITED—See Canburg Limited; *Int'l*, pg. 1288
MARKWINS INTERNATIONAL CORPORATION; *U.S. Private*, pg. 2582
MARK WORLDWIDE COMPANY LIMITED—See City Steel Public Company Limited; *Int'l*, pg. 1628
MARK WRIGHT CONSTRUCTION INC.; *U.S. Private*, pg. 2578
MARLABS, INC.; *U.S. Private*, pg. 2582
MARLABS, INC.—See Marlabs, Inc.; *U.S. Private*, pg. 2583
MARLABS SOFTWARE PRIVATE LTD.—See Marlabs, Inc.; *U.S. Private*, pg. 2582
MARLAND CLUTCH PRODUCTS—See Regal Rexnord Corporation; *U.S. Public*, pg. 1772
MARLBORO HUDSON AMBULANCE & WHEELCHAIR SERVICE, INC.—See KKR & Co. Inc.; *U.S. Public*, pg. 1249
MARLBORO MANUFACTURING, INC.; *U.S. Private*, pg. 2583
MARLBORO PARK HOSPITAL—See McLeod Health; *U.S. Private*, pg. 2641
MARLBOROUGH COMMUNICATIONS LIMITED—See Cohort plc; *Int'l*, pg. 1696
MARLBOROUGH DAY NURSERY LTD.—See Ontario Teachers' Pension Plan; *Int'l*, pg. 5587
THE MARLBOROUGH EXPRESS—See Nine Entertainment Co. Holdings Limited; *Int'l*, pg. 5298
MARLBOROUGH MUSSEL CO LIMITED—See Skeggs Group Limited; *Int'l*, pg. 6980
MARLBOROUGH SAVINGS BANK; *U.S. Private*, pg. 2583
MARLBOROUGH WINE ESTATES GROUP LIMITED; *Int'l*, pg. 4698
MAR-LEE COMPANIES, INC.—See PSB Industries SA; *Int'l*, pg. 6014
MAR-LEE MOLD—See PSB Industries SA; *Int'l*, pg. 6014
MAR-LEE PACKAGING AND CONSUMER PRODUCTS—See PSB Industries SA; *Int'l*, pg. 6014
MARLEN GAS—See UGI Corporation; *U.S. Public*, pg. 2222
MARLEN INTERNATIONAL, INC.—See Warburg Pincus LLC; *U.S. Private*, pg. 4438
MARLEN TEXTILES INC.—See Arsenal Capital Management LP; *U.S. Private*, pg. 338
MARLETTE HOMES, INC.—See Berkshire Hathaway Inc.; *U.S. Public*, pg. 304
MARLETTE REGIONAL HOSPITAL; *U.S. Private*, pg. 2583
MARLEX PHARMACEUTICALS, INC.; *U.S. Private*, pg. 2583
MARLEY ALUTEC LTD.—See Aliaxis S.A./N.V.; *Int'l*, pg. 325
MARLEY CANADIAN INC—See SPX Technologies, Inc.; *U.S. Public*, pg. 1921
MARLEY CONTRACT SERVICES—See Etex SA/NV; *Int'l*, pg. 2522
MARLEY DEUTSCHLAND GMBH—See Aliaxis S.A./N.V.; *Int'l*, pg. 325
MARLEY ENGINEERED PRODUCTS—See SPX Technologies, Inc.; *U.S. Public*, pg. 1921
MARLEY LTD.—See Etex SA/NV; *Int'l*, pg. 2522
MARLEY MAGYARORSZAG RT—See Aliaxis S.A./N.V.; *Int'l*, pg. 325
MARLEY MEXICANA S.A. DE C.V.—See SPX Technologies, Inc.; *U.S. Public*, pg. 1921
MARLEY NEW ZEALAND—See Aliaxis S.A./N.V.; *Int'l*, pg. 325
MARLEY PIPE SYSTEMS PTY LTD—See Aliaxis S.A./N.V.; *Int'l*, pg. 325
MARLEY POLSKA LTD.—See Etex SA/NV; *Int'l*, pg. 2522
MARLEY POLSKA SP. Z.O.O.—See Aliaxis S.A./N.V.; *Int'l*, pg. 325
MARLEY ROOFING (PTY) LTD—See Etex SA/NV; *Int'l*, pg. 2522
MARLEY SPOON GROUP SE; *Int'l*, pg. 4698
MARLIN & ASSOCIATES NEW YORK LLC; *U.S. Private*, pg. 2583
MARLIN BADMOBEL GMBH.—See Nobia AB; *Int'l*, pg. 5395
MARLIN BUSINESS BANK—See HPS Investment Partners, LLC; *U.S. Private*, pg. 1997
MARLIN BUSINESS SERVICES CORP.—See HPS Investment Partners, LLC; *U.S. Private*, pg. 1997
MARLIN COMPANY; *U.S. Private*, pg. 2583
MARLIN COMPRESSION, LLC—See Chesapeake Utilities Corporation; *U.S. Public*, pg. 485
MARLIN EQUITY PARTNERS, LLC; *U.S. Private*, pg. 2583
THE MARLIN FIREARMS COMPANY, INC.—See Cerberus Capital Management, L.P.; *U.S. Private*, pg. 839
MARLIN GAS SERVICES, LLC—See Chesapeake Utilities Corporation; *U.S. Public*, pg. 485
MARLING & EVANS LTD.—See Lanificio Angelico SRL; *Int'l*, pg. 4411
MARLIN GLOBAL LIMITED; *Int'l*, pg. 4698
MARLING LUMBER CO., INC.; *U.S. Private*, pg. 2585

MARLIN INGRAM RV CENTER, LLC—See Redwood Capital Investments, LLC; *U.S. Public*, pg. 3380
MARLINK AS—See Apax Partners LLP; *Int'l*, pg. 504
MARLINK COMMUNICATIONS S.A.—See Apax Partners LLP; *Int'l*, pg. 504
MARLINK, INC.—See Airbus SE; *Int'l*, pg. 245
MARLINK K.K.—See Apax Partners LLP; *Int'l*, pg. 504
MARLINK LTD.—See Apax Partners LLP; *Int'l*, pg. 504
MARLINK PTE. LTD.—See Apax Partners LLP; *Int'l*, pg. 504
MARLINK S.A.—See Apax Partners LLP; *Int'l*, pg. 504
MARLINK SAS—See Apax Partners LLP; *Int'l*, pg. 504
MARLIN LEASING CORPORATION—See HPS Investment Partners, LLC; *U.S. Private*, pg. 1997
THE MARLIN NETWORK, INC.; *U.S. Private*, pg. 4075
MARLIN—See The Marlin Network, Inc.; *U.S. Private*, pg. 4075
MARLIN STEEL WIRE PRODUCTS LLC; *U.S. Private*, pg. 2585
MARLINS TRAINING LIMITED—See Oakley Capital Limited; *Int'l*, pg. 5504
MARLIN TECHNOLOGY CORPORATION; *U.S. Public*, pg. 1370
MARLITE, INC.; *U.S. Private*, pg. 2585
MARLO FURNITURE CO., INC.; *U.S. Private*, pg. 2585
MARLOK AUTOMOTIVE GMBH; *Int'l*, pg. 4698
MARLO MARKETING COMMUNICATIONS; *U.S. Private*, pg. 2585
MARLOWE PLC; *Int'l*, pg. 4698
MARLOW FOODS LTD.—See Monde Nissin Corporation; *Int'l*, pg. 5025
MARLOW INDUSTRIES, INC.—See Coherent Corp.; *U.S. Public*, pg. 529
MARLTON DIALYSIS CENTER, LLC—See DaVita Inc.; *U.S. Public*, pg. 641
MARLUX KLAPS N.V.—See CRH plc; *Int'l*, pg. 1845
MAR-MAC MANUFACTURING COMPANY, INC.; *U.S. Private*, pg. 2569
MARMAGOA STEEL LIMITED; *Int'l*, pg. 4698
MARMALADE LLC; *U.S. Private*, pg. 2586
MARMARIS ALTINYUNUS TURISTIK TESISLERI A.S.; *Int'l*, pg. 4698
MARMAR MEDIA LTD.—See XLMedia PLC; *Int'l*, pg. 8536
MARMAXX OPERATING CORP.—See The TJX Companies, Inc.; *U.S. Public*, pg. 2134
MAR (MD), LLC—See GF Capital Management & Advisors, LLC; *U.S. Private*, pg. 1689
MARMEN, INC.; *Int'l*, pg. 4698
MARMI BIANCHI SRL—See FHL I. KIRIAKIDIS MARBLE - GRANITE SA; *Int'l*, pg. 2650
MARMIC FIRE & SAFETY CO., INC.—See KKR & Co. Inc.; *U.S. Public*, pg. 1261
MARMIE MOTORS INC.; *U.S. Private*, pg. 2586
MARMION INDUSTRIES CORP.; *U.S. Private*, pg. 2586
MARMITE SP. Z O.O.—See The Cranemere Group Limited; *Int'l*, pg. 7635
MARM LIGHTING LTD—See Dionic Industrial & Trading S.A; *Int'l*, pg. 2128
MARMON BUILDING WIRE—See Berkshire Hathaway Inc.; *U.S. Public*, pg. 309
MARMON CRANE SERVICES, INC.—See Berkshire Hathaway Inc.; *U.S. Public*, pg. 309
MARMON DISTRIBUTION SERVICES—See Berkshire Hathaway Inc.; *U.S. Public*, pg. 309
MARMON ENGINEERED WIRE & CABLE—See Berkshire Hathaway Inc.; *U.S. Public*, pg. 309
MARMON FLOW PRODUCTS—See Berkshire Hathaway Inc.; *U.S. Public*, pg. 310
MARMON FOOD SERVICE EQUIPMENT—See Berkshire Hathaway Inc.; *U.S. Public*, pg. 310
THE MARMON GROUP LLC—See Berkshire Hathaway Inc.; *U.S. Public*, pg. 308
MARMON-HERRINGTON—See Berkshire Hathaway Inc.; *U.S. Public*, pg. 310
MARMON HIGHWAY TECHNOLOGIES—See Berkshire Hathaway Inc.; *U.S. Public*, pg. 310
MARMON HOLDINGS, INC.—See Berkshire Hathaway Inc.; *U.S. Public*, pg. 308
MARMON INDUSTRIAL PRODUCTS—See Berkshire Hathaway Inc.; *U.S. Public*, pg. 310
MARMON/KEYSTONE CANADA, INC.—See Berkshire Hathaway Inc.; *U.S. Public*, pg. 309
MARMON/KEYSTONE CORPORATION—See Berkshire Hathaway Inc.; *U.S. Public*, pg. 309
MARMON/KEYSTONE CORPORATION—See Berkshire Hathaway Inc.; *U.S. Public*, pg. 309
MARMON/KEYSTONE LLC—See Berkshire Hathaway Inc.; *U.S. Public*, pg. 309
MARMON RETAIL STORE FIXTURES—See Berkshire Hathaway Inc.; *U.S. Public*, pg. 311
MARMON TRANSPORTATION SERVICES & ENGINEERED PRODUCTS—See Berkshire Hathaway Inc.; *U.S. Public*, pg. 311
MARMON WATER TREATMENT—See Berkshire Hathaway Inc.; *U.S. Public*, pg. 311
MARMOSA PTY LTD—See Auteco Minerals Ltd.; *Int'l*, pg. 724
MARMOTA LTD.—See Auteco Minerals Ltd.; *Int'l*, pg. 724

MARQETA, INC.

MARMOT MOUNTAIN EUROPE GMBH—See Newell Brands Inc.; *U.S. Public*, pg. 1514
MARMUM DAIRY FARM LLC—See Emirates Advanced Investments Group LLC; *Int'l*, pg. 2381
MARNELL CORRAO ASSOCIATES, INC.; *U.S. Private*, pg. 2586
MARNELL SHER GAMING LLC—See Marnell Corrao Associates, Inc.; *U.S. Private*, pg. 2586
MARNIX CORPORATION—See Marubeni Corporation; *Int'l*, pg. 4706
MARNIX EUROPE LTD—See Marubeni Corporation; *Int'l*, pg. 4707
MARNIX REINSURANCE BROKERS PTE. LTD.—See Marubeni Corporation; *Int'l*, pg. 4706
MARNLEN MANAGEMENT LTD; *Int'l*, pg. 4698
MARNOY INTERESTS LTD.; *U.S. Private*, pg. 2586
MAROC DYNAMITE—See Societe Anonyme d'Explosifs et de Produits Chimiques; *Int'l*, pg. 7035
MAROC FACTORING—See Bank of Africa; *Int'l*, pg. 840
MAROC LEASING SA; *Int'l*, pg. 4698
MAROCSTAT S.A.R.L—See Ipsos S.A.; *Int'l*, pg. 3802
MAROC TELECOM S.A.—See Emirates Telecommunications Group Compapny PJSC; *Int'l*, pg. 2382
MARODYNE MEDICAL, LLC; *U.S. Private*, pg. 2586
MAROHN THYSSENKRUPP ELEVATOR CO. LTD.—See ThyssenKrupp AG; *Int'l*, pg. 7725
MAROIS BROTHERS, INC.; *U.S. Private*, pg. 2586
MAROLINE DISTRIBUTING INC.; *Int'l*, pg. 4698
MARO MARKETY SP. Z O.O.—See Emperia Holding S.A; *Int'l*, pg. 2386
MARONDA INC.; *U.S. Private*, pg. 2586
MARON ELECTRIC COMPANY; *U.S. Private*, pg. 2586
MARO N.V.—See Liberty Global plc; *Int'l*, pg. 4485
MAROONE AUTO PLAZA—See AutoNation, Inc.; *U.S. Public*, pg. 236
MAROONE DODGE, LLC—See AutoNation, Inc.; *U.S. Public*, pg. 236
MAROTTA CONTROLS, INC.; *U.S. Private*, pg. 2586
MAROTTE SA—See Rougier S.A.; *Int'l*, pg. 6407
MAROUN OIL & GAS COMPANY—See National Iranian Oil Company; *Int'l*, pg. 5160
MAROX CORP.—See Argosy Capital Group, LLC; *U.S. Private*, pg. 321
MARPAI, INC.; *U.S. Public*, pg. 1370
MARPAN INC.; *U.S. Private*, pg. 2586
MARPEX CHEMICALS LTD.—See Cathay Investments Limited; *Int'l*, pg. 1360
MARPIN 2K4 LTD.; *Int'l*, pg. 4698
MARPLES RIDGWAY LIMITED—See Heidelberg Materials AG; *Int'l*, pg. 3318
MARPLESS COMMUNICATION TECHNOLOGIES (PTY) LTD.—See Marubeni Corporation; *Int'l*, pg. 4707
MARPORT AMERICAS, INC.—See Amphenol Corporation; *U.S. Public*, pg. 131
MARPORT EHF—See Amphenol Corporation; *U.S. Public*, pg. 131
MARPORT FRANCE SAS—See Amphenol Corporation; *U.S. Public*, pg. 131
MARPORT NORGE AS—See Amphenol Corporation; *U.S. Public*, pg. 131
MARPORT SOUTH AFRICA (PTY) LTD.—See Amphenol Corporation; *U.S. Public*, pg. 131
MARPORT SPAIN SL—See Amphenol Corporation; *U.S. Public*, pg. 131
MARPORT UK LTD.—See Amphenol Corporation; *U.S. Public*, pg. 131
MARPOSS AB—See Marposs S.p.A.; *Int'l*, pg. 4698
MARPOSS AG—See Marposs S.p.A.; *Int'l*, pg. 4698
MARPOSS APARELHOS ELETRONICOS DE MEDICAO LTDA.—See Marposs S.p.A.; *Int'l*, pg. 4698
MARPOSS AUSTRALIA PTY. LTD.—See Marposs S.p.A.; *Int'l*, pg. 4698
MARPOSS AUSTRIA GMBH—See Marposs S.p.A.; *Int'l*, pg. 4699
MARPOSS CANADA CORP.—See Marposs S.p.A.; *Int'l*, pg. 4698
MARPOSS COMPANY LIMITED—See Marposs S.p.A.; *Int'l*, pg. 4698
MARPOSS CORPORATION—See Marposs S.p.A.; *Int'l*, pg. 4699
MARPOSS GMBH—See Marposs S.p.A.; *Int'l*, pg. 4698
MARPOSS INDIA PVT. LTD.—See Marposs S.p.A.; *Int'l*, pg. 4698
MARPOSS KABUSHIKI KAISHA—See Marposs S.p.A.; *Int'l*, pg. 4699
MARPOSS LIMITED—See Marposs S.p.A.; *Int'l*, pg. 4699
MARPOSS (NANJING) AUTOMATION CO., LTD.—See Marposs S.p.A.; *Int'l*, pg. 4698
MARPOSS S.A. DE C.V.—See Marposs S.p.A.; *Int'l*, pg. 4699
MARPOSS S.A.—See Marposs S.p.A.; *Int'l*, pg. 4699
MARPOSS SA—See Marposs S.p.A.; *Int'l*, pg. 4699
MARPOSS S.P.A.; *Int'l*, pg. 4698
MARPOSS S.R.O.—See Marposs S.p.A.; *Int'l*, pg. 4699
MARPOSS T&E CO., LTD.—See Marposs S.p.A.; *Int'l*, pg. 4699
MAR PROPERTIES INC.—See Sun Capital Partners, Inc.; *U.S. Public*, pg. 3860
MARQETA, INC.; *U.S. Public*, pg. 1370

MARQETA, INC. — CORPORATE AFFILIATIONS

Company Index

MARQMETRIX, INC.—See Thermo Fisher Scientific Inc.; *U.S. Public*, pg. 2149
MARQUAM GROUP; *U.S. Private*, pg. 2586
MARQUARD & BAHLS AG; *Int'l*, pg. 4699
MARQUARDT BUICK, INC.; *U.S. Private*, pg. 2586
MARQUARDT & ROCHE AND PARTNERS; *U.S. Private*, pg. 2586
MARQUEE BRANDS LLC; *U.S. Private*, pg. 2586
MARQUEE BROADCASTING, INC.; *U.S. Private*, pg. 2586
MARQUEE MANAGED CARE SOLUTIONS, INC.—See Brown & Brown, Inc.; *U.S. Public*, pg. 401
MARQUEE RESOURCES LIMITED; *Int'l*, pg. 4701
MARQUEST ASSET MANAGEMENT INC.; *Int'l*, pg. 4701
MARQUE TDI - TECHNOLLOGIAS DE CODIFICACAO S.A.—See Brother Industries, Ltd.; *Int'l*, pg. 1198
MARQUET INTERNATIONAL LTD.—See Sunblock Systems, Inc.; *U.S. Private*, pg. 3865
MARQUETTE ASSET MANAGEMENT, LLC—See UMB Financial Corporation; *U.S. Public*, pg. 2224
MARQUETTE ASSOCIATES, INC.; *U.S. Private*, pg. 2586
MARQUETTE BANK—See Marquette National Corporation; *U.S. Public*, pg. 1370
MARQUETTE BUSINESS CREDIT, LLC—See UMB Financial Corporation; *U.S. Public*, pg. 2224
MARQUETTE CAPITAL PARTNERS, LLC—See Pohlad Companies; *U.S. Private*, pg. 3220
MARQUETTE COMMERCIAL FINANCE—See UMB Financial Corporation; *U.S. Public*, pg. 2224
MARQUETTE COPPERSMITHING CO., INC.; *U.S. Private*, pg. 2587
MARQUETTE COPPERSMITHING-MANUFACTURING DIVISION—See Marquette Coppersmithing Co., Inc.; *U.S. Private*, pg. 2587
MARQUETTE COPPERSMITHING-PIPING DESIGN DIVISION—See Marquette Coppersmithing Co., Inc.; *U.S. Private*, pg. 2587
MARQUETTE LUMBER CO. INC.; *U.S. Private*, pg. 2587
MARQUETTE LUMBERMENS WAREHOUSE—See Hager Group Inc.; *U.S. Private*, pg. 1839
MARQUETTE NATIONAL CORPORATION; *U.S. Public*, pg. 1370
MARQUETTE RAIL, LLC—See Brookfield Infrastructure Partners L.P.; *Int'l*, pg. 1192
MARQUETTE RAIL, LLC—See GIC Pte. Ltd.; *Int'l*, pg. 2966
MARQUETTE SAGINAW WAREHOUSE—See Hager Group Inc.; *U.S. Private*, pg. 1839
MARQUETTE SAVINGS BANK; *U.S. Public*, pg. 2587
MARQUETTE TOOL & DIE COMPANY; *U.S. Private*, pg. 2587
MARQUETTE TRANSPORTATION CO.; *U.S. Private*, pg. 2587
MARQUETTE TRANSPORTATION FINANCE, LLC—See UMB Financial Corporation; *U.S. Public*, pg. 2224
MARQUEZ BROTHERS ENTERPRISES, INC.—See Marquez Brothers International, Inc.; *U.S. Private*, pg. 2587
MARQUEZ BROTHERS FOODS, INC.—See Marquez Brothers International, Inc.; *U.S. Private*, pg. 2587
MARQUEZ BROTHERS INTERNATIONAL, INC.; *U.S. Private*, pg. 2587
MARQUEZ BROTHERS INTERNATIONAL S.A. DE C.V.—See Marquez Brothers International, Inc.; *U.S. Private*, pg. 2587
MARQUEZ BROTHERS NEVADA, INC.—See Marquez Brothers International, Inc.; *U.S. Private*, pg. 2587
MARQUEZ BROTHERS RENO, INC.—See Marquez Brothers International, Inc.; *U.S. Private*, pg. 2587
MARQUEZ BROTHERS SOUTHERN CALIFORNIA, INC.—See Marquez Brothers International, Inc.; *U.S. Private*, pg. 2587
MARQUEZ BROTHERS SOUTHWEST, INC.—See Marquez Brothers International, Inc.; *U.S. Private*, pg. 2587
MARQUEZ BROTHERS TEXAS, LP—See Marquez Brothers International, Inc.; *U.S. Private*, pg. 2587
MARQUEZ WORLDWIDE—See The Interpublic Group of Companies, Inc.; *U.S. Public*, pg. 2093
THE MARQUIE GROUP, INC.; *U.S. Public*, pg. 2112
MARQUINARIAS INGERSOLL-RAND DE COLOMBIA S.A.—See Ingersoll Rand Inc.; *U.S. Public*, pg. 1122
MARQUIPWARDUNITED, INC.—See Barry-Wehmiller Companies, Inc.; *U.S. Private*, pg. 482
MARQUIPWARDUNITED, INC.—See Barry-Wehmiller Companies, Inc.; *U.S. Private*, pg. 482
MARQUIS AGENCY—See NIP Group, Inc.; *U.S. Private*, pg. 2928
MARQUIS BANCORP, INC.; *U.S. Private*, pg. 2587
MARQUIS BANK—See Marquis Bancorp, Inc.; *U.S. Private*, pg. 2587
MARQUIS BOOK PRINTING INC.—See Atlas Holdings, LLC; *U.S. Private*, pg. 377
MARQUIS CORP.—See Monomoy Capital Partners LLC; *U.S. Private*, pg. 2772
MARQUIS ENERGY LLC - NECEDAH WI PLANT—See Marquis Grain, Inc.; *U.S. Private*, pg. 2587
MARQUIS FURNITURE GALLERY PTE LTD—See Nobel Design Holdings Pte Ltd; *Int'l*, pg. 5394
MARQUIS GRAIN, INC.; *U.S. Private*, pg. 2587
MARQUIS HEALTH SERVICES—See Tryko Partners, LLC; *U.S. Private*, pg. 4252
MARQUIS HNC PTE LTD—See Nobel Design Holdings Pte Ltd; *Int'l*, pg. 5394
MARQUIS HQO PTE LTD—See Nobel Design Holdings Pte Ltd; *Int'l*, pg. 5394
MARQUIS INDUSTRIES, INC.—See Live Ventures Incorporated; *U.S. Public*, pg. 1332
MARQUIS INDUSTRIES, INC.; *U.S. Private*, pg. 2587
MARQUIS INDUSTRIES, INC.; *U.S. Private*, pg. 2587
MARQUIS JET PARTNERS INC.—See Berkshire Hathaway Inc.; *U.S. Public*, pg. 313
MARQUIS-LARSON BOAT GROUP; *U.S. Private*, pg. 2588
MARQUIS PROPERTIES REALTY; *U.S. Private*, pg. 2587
MARQUIS SOFTWARE SOLUTIONS, INC.—See Falfurrias Capital Partners, LP; *U.S. Private*, pg. 1467
MARQUIS WEALTH MANAGEMENT GROUP; *U.S. Private*, pg. 2587
MARQUIS WHO'S WHO, LLC; *U.S. Private*, pg. 2588
MARRAZZO'S THRIFTWAY; *U.S. Private*, pg. 2588
MARR COMPANIES; *U.S. Private*, pg. 2588
M.A.R. REPORTING GROUP, LLC.—See Planet Depos, LLC; *U.S. Private*, pg. 3196
MARRET ASSET MANAGEMENT INC.—See CI Financial Corporation; *Int'l*, pg. 1601
MARRET HIGH YIELD STRATEGIES FUND—See CI Financial Corporation; *Int'l*, pg. 1601
MARRET MULTI-STRATEGY INCOME FUND—See CI Financial Corporation; *Int'l*, pg. 1601
MARR FOODSERVICE IBERICA S.A.—See Cremonini S.p.A.; *Int'l*, pg. 1838
MARRICK MEDICAL; *U.S. Private*, pg. 2588
MARRICKVILLE METRO SHOPPING CENTRE PTY LIMITED—See AMP Limited; *Int'l*, pg. 432
MARRINER MARKETING COMMUNICATIONS, INC.; *U.S. Private*, pg. 2588
MARRIOTT CURACAO N.V.—See Marriott International, Inc.; *U.S. Public*, pg. 1371
MARRIOTT DRYWALL MATERIALS, INC—See American Securities LLC; *U.S. Private*, pg. 249
MARRIOTT EUROPEAN HOTEL OPERATING COMPANY LIMITED—See Marriott International, Inc.; *U.S. Public*, pg. 1371
MARRIOTT HOTEL-BETRIEBSGESELLSCHAFT, MBH—See Marriott International, Inc.; *U.S. Public*, pg. 1371
MARRIOTT HOTEL HOLDING GMBH—See Marriott International, Inc.; *U.S. Public*, pg. 1371
MARRIOTT HOTELMANAGEMENT COLOGNE GMBH—See Marriott International, Inc.; *U.S. Public*, pg. 1371
MARRIOTT HOTELMANAGEMENT GMBH—See Marriott International, Inc.; *U.S. Public*, pg. 1371
MARRIOTT HOTELS AND RESORTS OF CANADA—See Marriott International, Inc.; *U.S. Public*, pg. 1371
MARRIOTT HOTEL SERVICES, INC.—See Marriott International, Inc.; *U.S. Public*, pg. 1371
MARRIOTT HOTELS INTERNATIONAL B.V.—See Marriott International, Inc.; *U.S. Public*, pg. 1371
MARRIOTT HOTELS INTERNATIONAL LIMITED—See Marriott International, Inc.; *U.S. Public*, pg. 1371
MARRIOTT HOTELS LIMITED—See Marriott International, Inc.; *U.S. Public*, pg. 1371
MARRIOTT HOTELS MANAGEMENT FRANCE SAS—See Marriott International, Inc.; *U.S. Public*, pg. 1371
MARRIOTT HOTELS OF AMSTERDAM, B.V.—See Marriott International, Inc.; *U.S. Public*, pg. 1371
MARRIOTT HOTELS OF CANADA LTD.—See Marriott International, Inc.; *U.S. Public*, pg. 1371
MARRIOTT INTERNATIONAL CAPITAL CORPORATION—See Marriott International, Inc.; *U.S. Public*, pg. 1371
MARRIOTT INTERNATIONAL HOTELS—See Marriott International, Inc.; *U.S. Public*, pg. 1371
MARRIOTT INTERNATIONAL, INC.; *U.S. Public*, pg. 1370
MARRIOTT OWNERSHIP RESORTS, INC.—See Marriott Vacations Worldwide Corporation; *U.S. Public*, pg. 1374
MARRIOTT PERU LICENSING COMPANY SAC—See Marriott International, Inc.; *U.S. Public*, pg. 1371
MARRIOTT VACATIONS WORLDWIDE CORPORATION; *U.S. Public*, pg. 1373
MARRON & ASSOCIATES, INC.—See NV5 Global, Inc.; *U.S. Public*, pg. 1557
MARRON CO., LTD.—See Kamei Corporation; *Int'l*, pg. 4061
MARRON STYLE CO., LTD.—See Seven & i Holdings Co., Ltd.; *Int'l*, pg. 6731
MARROQUIN ORGANIC INTERNATIONAL, INC.—See AGRANA Beteiligungs-AG; *Int'l*, pg. 214
MARR RUSSIA L.L.C.—See Cremonini S.p.A.; *Int'l*, pg. 1838
MARRS ELECTRIC INC.; *U.S. Private*, pg. 2588
MARR S.P.A.—See Cremonini S.p.A.; *Int'l*, pg. 1838
MARRYAT & SCOTT EGYPT S.A.E.—See KONE Oyj; *Int'l*, pg. 4250
MARRY MARBLE CO., LTD.—See Polaris Capital Group Co., Ltd.; *Int'l*, pg. 5907
MARS ACQUISITION CORP.; *U.S. Public*, pg. 1374
MARS ADVERTISING GROUP; *U.S. Private*, pg. 2588
MARS AIRCRAFT SERVICES CO. OF NEW JERSEY—See AAR Corp.; *U.S. Public*, pg. 13
MARSA KRAFT JACOBS SUCHARD SABANCI GIDA SANAYI VE TICARET A.S—See Haci Omer Sabanci Holding A.S.; *Int'l*, pg. 3204
MARSA KRAFT JACOBS SUCHARD SABANCI GIDA SANAYI VE TICARET A.S—See Mondelez International, Inc.; *U.S. Public*, pg. 1462
MARSALA BEVERAGE LLC; *U.S. Private*, pg. 2591
MARSALIS BYGG SVERIGE AB; *Int'l*, pg. 4701
MARSAL & SONS, INC.—See The Middleby Corporation; *U.S. Public*, pg. 2114
MARSA MARSA ALAM FOR TOURISM DEVELOPMENT; *Int'l*, pg. 4701
MARSAN FOODS LIMITED; *Int'l*, pg. 4701
MARS AS—See Mars, Incorporated; *U.S. Private*, pg. 2589
MARSA TURKEY B.V.—See Condor Petroleum Inc.; *Int'l*, pg. 1766
MARS AUSTRALIA—See Mars, Incorporated; *U.S. Private*, pg. 2589
MARS AUSTRIA—See Mars, Incorporated; *U.S. Private*, pg. 2589
MARS BANCORP, INC.—See NexTier, Inc.; *U.S. Private*, pg. 2921
MARS BANK—See NexTier, Inc.; *U.S. Private*, pg. 2921
MARS BELGIUM—See Mars, Incorporated; *U.S. Private*, pg. 2589
MARS BRAZIL—See Mars, Incorporated; *U.S. Private*, pg. 2589
MARS BULGARIA—See Mars, Incorporated; *U.S. Private*, pg. 2589
MARS CANADA INC.—See Mars, Incorporated; *U.S. Private*, pg. 2589
MARS CAPITAL FINANCE IRELAND DAC—See Arrow Global Group PLC; *Int'l*, pg. 579
MARS CAPITAL FINANCE LIMITED—See Arrow Global Group PLC; *Int'l*, pg. 579
MARS CARIBBEAN & CENTRAL AMERICA—See Mars, Incorporated; *U.S. Private*, pg. 2589
MARS CHOCOLAT FRANCE—See Mars, Incorporated; *U.S. Private*, pg. 2589
MARS & CO.; *U.S. Private*, pg. 2588
MARS CROATIA—See Mars, Incorporated; *U.S. Private*, pg. 2589
MARS CZECH REPUBLIC—See Mars, Incorporated; *U.S. Private*, pg. 2589
MARSDEN BUILDING MAINTENANCE COMPANY, L.L.C.—See Marsden Holding, L.L.C.; *U.S. Private*, pg. 2591
MARSDEN BUILDING SOCIETY; *Int'l*, pg. 4701
MARSDEN HOLDING, L.L.C.; *U.S. Private*, pg. 2591
MARSDEN MARITIME HOLDINGS LIMITED; *Int'l*, pg. 4701
MARS DENMARK A/S—See Mars, Incorporated; *U.S. Private*, pg. 2589
MARS DRINKS FRANCE—See Mars, Incorporated; *U.S. Private*, pg. 2589
MARS DRINKS—See Mars, Incorporated; *U.S. Private*, pg. 2590
MARSEILLE ETIENNE D'ORVES STATIONNEMENT SA—See Indigo Group S.A.S.; *Int'l*, pg. 3655
MARSEILLE-KLINIK OMEGA GMBH—See MK-Kliniken AG; *Int'l*, pg. 5001
MARS ELECTRIC CO., INC.; *U.S. Private*, pg. 2588
MARS ESPANA—See Mars, Incorporated; *U.S. Private*, pg. 2589
MARS FINLAND OY—See Mars, Incorporated; *U.S. Private*, pg. 2589
MARS FISHCARE, INC.—See Mars, Incorporated; *U.S. Private*, pg. 2589
MARS FOOD (CHINA) CO., LTD.—See Mars, Incorporated; *U.S. Private*, pg. 2589
MARS FOOD EUROPE C.V.—See Mars, Incorporated; *U.S. Private*, pg. 2589
MARS GLOBAL SERVICES—See Mars, Incorporated; *U.S. Private*, pg. 2589
MARS GREECE—See Mars, Incorporated; *U.S. Private*, pg. 2589
MARS GROUP HOLDINGS CORPORATION; *Int'l*, pg. 4701
MARSH AB—See Marsh & McLennan Companies, Inc.; *U.S. Public*, pg. 1379
MARSH ADVANTAGE INSURANCE PTY LTD.—See Marsh & McLennan Companies, Inc.; *U.S. Public*, pg. 1378
MARSH AG—See Marsh & McLennan Companies, Inc.; *U.S. Public*, pg. 1379
MARSHALL ADVERTISING, INC.; *U.S. Private*, pg. 2592
MARSHALL AEROSPACE AUSTRALIA PTY LIMITED—See Marshall of Cambridge (Holdings) Limited; *Int'l*, pg. 4702
MARSHALL AEROSPACE CANADA, INC.—See Marshall of Cambridge (Holdings) Limited; *Int'l*, pg. 4702
MARSHALL AEROSPACE NETHERLANDS B.V.—See Marshall of Cambridge (Holdings) Limited; *Int'l*, pg. 4702
MARSHALL AMPLIFICATION PLC; *Int'l*, pg. 4701

COMPANY NAME INDEX

MARSHALL ASSOCIATES, INC.; *U.S. Private*, pg. 2592
MARSHALL BOYA VE VERNIK SANAYII AS; *Int'l*, pg. 4701
MARSHALL BROTHERS INC.; *U.S. Private*, pg. 2592
MARSHALL CAMBRIDGE PEUGEOT—See Marshall of Cambridge (Holdings) Limited; *Int'l*, pg. 4702
MARSHALL CAVENDISH BUSINESS INFORMATION (HONG KONG) LIMITED—See Thai Beverage Public Company Limited; *Int'l*, pg. 7590
MARSHALL CAVENDISH CORPORATION—See Thai Beverage Public Company Limited; *Int'l*, pg. 7590
MARSHALL CAVENDISH EDUCATION CHILE SPA—See Thai Beverage Public Company Limited; *Int'l*, pg. 7590
MARSHALL CAVENDISH EDUCATION PTE. LTD.—See Thai Beverage Public Company Limited; *Int'l*, pg. 7590
MARSHALL CAVENDISH INTERNATIONAL (S) PTE LTD—See Thai Beverage Public Company Limited; *Int'l*, pg. 7590
MARSHALL CAVENDISH (MALAYSIA) SDN BHD—See Thai Beverage Public Company Limited; *Int'l*, pg. 7590
MARSHALL COMPANY; *U.S. Private*, pg. 2592
MARSHALL CONSTRUCTION LIMITED - SCAFFOLD DIVISION—See Marshall Construction Limited; *Int'l*, pg. 4701
MARSHALL CONSTRUCTION LIMITED; *Int'l*, pg. 4701
MARSHALL COUNTY HMA, LLC—See Community Health Systems, Inc.; *U.S. Public*, pg. 555
MARSHALL COUNTY HMPN, LLC—See Community Health Systems, Inc.; *U.S. Public*, pg. 555
MARSHALL COUNTY HOSPITAL; *U.S. Private*, pg. 2592
MARSHALL DENNEHEY WARNER COLEMAN & GOGGIN, P.C.; *U.S. Private*, pg. 2592
MARSHALL EDITIONS LTD.—See The Quarto Group, Inc.; *Int'l*, pg. 7677
MARSHALL ELECTRIC CORPORATION; *U.S. Private*, pg. 2592
MARSHALL ENGINES, INC.; *U.S. Private*, pg. 2592
MARSHALL EXCELSIOR COMPANY—See Dover Corporation; *U.S. Public*, pg. 679
MARSHALL FENN COMMUNICATIONS LTD.; *Int'l*, pg. 4701
MARSHALL FENN COMMUNICATIONS LTD.—See Marshall Fenn Communications Ltd.; *Int'l*, pg. 4701
MARSHALL FLEET SOLUTIONS LIMITED—See Marshall of Cambridge (Holdings) Limited; *Int'l*, pg. 4702
MARSHALL GROUP PROPERTIES LIMITED—See Marshall of Cambridge (Holdings) Limited; *Int'l*, pg. 4702
MARSHALL INDUSTRIES, INC.; *U.S. Private*, pg. 2592
MARSHALL JUNCTION PARTNERS, LLC; *U.S. Private*, pg. 2592
MARSHALL LAND SYSTEMS LIMITED—See Marshall of Cambridge (Holdings) Limited; *Int'l*, pg. 4702
MARSHALL LEASING LIMITED—See Bank of Ireland Group plc; *Int'l*, pg. 844
MARSHALL LETHLEAN INDUSTRIES PTY LTD—See China International Marine Containers (Group) Co., Ltd.; *Int'l*, pg. 1512
MARSHALL MACHINES LTD.; *Int'l*, pg. 4701
MARSHALL MEDICAL CENTER NORTH—See Marshall Medical Center; *U.S. Private*, pg. 2593
MARSHALL MEDICAL CENTER; *U.S. Private*, pg. 2592
MARSHALL MONTEAGLE PLC; *Int'l*, pg. 4701
MARSHALL MOTOR GROUP LIMITED—See Marshall of Cambridge (Holdings) Limited; *Int'l*, pg. 4702
MARSHALL MUSIC CO.; *U.S. Private*, pg. 2593
THE MARSHALL NEWS MESSENGER—See Texas Community Media LLC; *U.S. Private*, pg. 3975
MARSHALL OF CAMBRIDGE AEROSPACE LIMITED—See Marshall of Cambridge (Holdings) Limited; *Int'l*, pg. 4702
MARSHALL OF CAMBRIDGE (AIRPORT PROPERTIES) LIMITED—See Marshall of Cambridge (Holdings) Limited; *Int'l*, pg. 4702
MARSHALL OF CAMBRIDGE (HOLDINGS) LIMITED; *Int'l*, pg. 4701
MARSHALL OF CAMBRIDGE (MOTOR HOLDINGS) LIMITED—See Marshall of Cambridge (Holdings) Limited; *Int'l*, pg. 4702
MARSHALL OF IPSWICH LIMITED—See General Motors Company; *U.S. Public*, pg. 928
MARSHALL OF PETERBOROUGH LIMITED—See General Motors Company; *U.S. Public*, pg. 928
MARSHALL PIERSON, INC.—See Inszone Insurance Services, LLC; *U.S. Private*, pg. 2096
MARSHALL PLANTATIONS LIMITED—See S.L. Horsford & Company Limited; *Int'l*, pg. 6456
MARSHALL RESOURCES INC.; *U.S. Private*, pg. 2593
MARSHALL RETAIL GROUP LLC—See Brentwood Associates; *U.S. Private*, pg. 646
MARSHALLS BAHRAIN LIMITED—See TP ICAP Finance PLC; *Int'l*, pg. 7881
MARSHALLS (BAHRAIN) WLL—See TP ICAP Finance PLC; *Int'l*, pg. 7881
MARSHALL SCIENTIFIC LLC; *U.S. Private*, pg. 2593
MARSHALLS (EAST AFRICA) LIMITED; *Int'l*, pg. 4702
MARSHALLS HOLDING CO.; *U.S. Private*, pg. 2593
MARSHALLS MONO LIMITED—See Marshalls plc; *Int'l*, pg. 4702
MARSHALLS NV—See Marshalls plc; *Int'l*, pg. 4702
MARSHALLS OF CA, LLC—See The TJX Companies, Inc.; *U.S. Public*, pg. 2134
MARSHALLS OF IL, LLC—See The TJX Companies, Inc.; *U.S. Public*, pg. 2134
MARSHALLS OF MA, INC.—See The TJX Companies, Inc.; *U.S. Public*, pg. 2134
MARSHALLS PLC; *Int'l*, pg. 4702
MARSHALL STEEL, INC.—See Steel Dynamics, Inc.; *U.S. Public*, pg. 1942
MARSHALL & STERLING ENTERPRISES, INC.; *U.S. Private*, pg. 2592
MARSHALL & STERLING, INC.—See Marshall & Sterling Enterprises, Inc.; *U.S. Private*, pg. 2592
MARSHALL & STEVENS INC.; *U.S. Private*, pg. 2592
MARSHALL STONE, INC.—See SiteOne Landscape Supply, Inc.; *U.S. Public*, pg. 1889
MARSHALL STREET CAPITAL, INC.; *U.S. Private*, pg. 2593
MARSHALL SUPPLY CO.; *U.S. Private*, pg. 2593
MARSHALL & SWIFT/BOECKH, LLC—See Insight Venture Management, LLC; *U.S. Private*, pg. 2089
MARSHALL & SWIFT/BOECKH, LLC—See Stone Point Capital LLC; *U.S. Private*, pg. 3822
MARSHALL TOOL & SUPPLY CORP.; *U.S. Private*, pg. 2593
MARSHALLTOWN MEDICAL & SURGICAL CENTER; *U.S. Private*, pg. 2593
MARSHALLTOWN NEWSPAPER INC.—See The Nutting Company, Inc.; *U.S. Private*, pg. 4086
MARSHALLTOWN TROWEL COMPANY; *U.S. Private*, pg. 2593
MARSHALL UNIVERSITY RESEARCH CORP.; *U.S. Private*, pg. 2593
MARSHALL VEHICLE ENGINEERING LIMITED—See Marshall of Cambridge (Holdings) Limited; *Int'l*, pg. 4702
MARSHALL WACE ASIA LIMITED—See Marshall Wace LLP; *Int'l*, pg. 4702
MARSHALL WACE LLP; *Int'l*, pg. 4702
MARSHALL WACE NORTH AMERICA LP—See Marshall Wace LLP; *Int'l*, pg. 4702
MARSHALL & WINSTON INC.; *U.S. Private*, pg. 2592
MARSHALL W NELSON & ASSOCIATES, INC.—See Relevant Industrial LLC; *U.S. Private*, pg. 3393
MARSHALL WOOLDRIDGE LIMITED—See Brown & Brown, Inc.; *U.S. Public*, pg. 401
MARSHAL MIZE FORD, INC.; *U.S. Private*, pg. 2592
MARSHAL OFFSHORE & MARINE ENGINEERING CO. LTD.—See 9R Limited; *Int'l*, pg. 17
MARSHAL OFFSHORE & MARINE ENGRG CO. LTD.—See 9R Limited; *Int'l*, pg. 17
MARSHAL SYSTEMS PTE. LTD.—See 9R Limited; *Int'l*, pg. 17
MARSHA LYNN BUILDING CORP.; *U.S. Private*, pg. 2592
MARSHA SALDANA INC; *U.S. Private*, pg. 2592
MARSH A/S—See Marsh & McLennan Companies, Inc.; *U.S. Public*, pg. 1378
MARSH AS—See Marsh & McLennan Companies, Inc.; *U.S. Public*, pg. 1378
MARSH AUSTRIA G.M.B.H.—See Marsh & McLennan Companies, Inc.; *U.S. Public*, pg. 1379
MARSH (BAHRAIN) COMPANY SPC—See Marsh & McLennan Companies, Inc.; *U.S. Public*, pg. 1378
MARSH (BEIJING) INSURANCE BROKERS CO., LTD.—See Marsh & McLennan Companies, Inc.; *U.S. Public*, pg. 1378
MARSH BELLOFRAM CORPORATION—See Desco Corporation; *U.S. Public*, pg. 1211
MARSH BELLOFRAM EUROPE LTD—See Desco Corporation; *U.S. Private*, pg. 1211
MARSH BELLOFRAM SHANGHAI TRADING CO. LTD.—See Desco Corporation; *U.S. Private*, pg. 1211
MARSH BELLOFRAM—See Desco Corporation; *U.S. Private*, pg. 1211
MARSHBERRY CAPITAL, INC.—See Marsh, Berry & Company, Inc.; *U.S. Private*, pg. 2592
MARSH, BERRY & COMPANY, INC. - NEW YORK—See Marsh, Berry & Company, Inc.; *U.S. Private*, pg. 2592
MARSH, BERRY & COMPANY, INC.; *U.S. Private*, pg. 2591
MARSH BOTSWANA (PROPRIETARY) LIMITED—See Marsh & McLennan Companies, Inc.; *U.S. Public*, pg. 1378
MARSH BROCKMAN Y SCHUH AGENTE DE SEGUROS Y DE FIANZAS, S.A. DE C.V.—See Marsh & McLennan Companies, Inc.; *U.S. Public*, pg. 1378
MARSH BROKER DE ASIGURARE-REASIGURARE S.R.L.—See Marsh & McLennan Companies, Inc.; *U.S. Public*, pg. 1378
MARSH BROKER JAPAN, INC.—See Marsh & McLennan Companies, Inc.; *U.S. Public*, pg. 1379
MARSH BROKERS (HONG KONG) LIMITED—See Marsh & McLennan Companies, Inc.; *U.S. Public*, pg. 1378
MARSH BROKERS LIMITED—See Marsh & McLennan Companies, Inc.; *U.S. Public*, pg. 1380
MARSH BUILDING PRODUCTS, INC.—See Leonard Green & Partners, L.P.; *U.S. Private*, pg. 2429
MARSH B.V.—See Marsh & McLennan Companies, Inc.; *U.S. Public*, pg. 1379
MARSH CANADA LIMITED—See Marsh & McLennan Companies, Inc.; *U.S. Public*, pg. 1379
MARSH (CHINA) INSURANCE BROKERS CO., LTD.—See Marsh & McLennan Companies, Inc.; *U.S. Public*, pg. 1378
MARSH CONSTRUCTION SERVICES, INC.; *U.S. Private*, pg. 2591
MARSH CORRETORA DE SEGUROS LTDA.—See Marsh & McLennan Companies, Inc.; *U.S. Public*, pg. 1378
MARSH D.O.O. BEOGRAD—See Marsh & McLennan Companies, Inc.; *U.S. Public*, pg. 1383
MARSH D.O.O. ZA POSREDOVANJE U OSIGURANJU—See Marsh & McLennan Companies, Inc.; *U.S. Public*, pg. 1383
MARSH ELECTRONICS, INC.; *U.S. Private*, pg. 2591
MARSH EOOD—See Marsh & McLennan Companies, Inc.; *U.S. Public*, pg. 1378
MARSH EUROFINANCE B.V.—See Marsh & McLennan Companies, Inc.; *U.S. Public*, pg. 1378
MARSH EUROPE - ORGANIZACNA ZLOZKA SLOVENSKO—See Marsh & McLennan Companies, Inc.; *U.S. Public*, pg. 1379
MARSH EUROPE S.A.—See Marsh & McLennan Companies, Inc.; *U.S. Public*, pg. 1379
MARSHFIELD CLINIC-MEDICAL RESEARCH FOUNDATION—See Marshfield Clinic; *U.S. Private*, pg. 2593
MARSHFIELD CLINIC; *U.S. Private*, pg. 2593
MARSHFIELD DOORSYSTEMS, INC.—See Owens Corning; *U.S. Public*, pg. 1627
MARSHFIELD MARINER—See Gannett Co., Inc.; *U.S. Public*, pg. 902
MARSH FINANCE B.V.—See Marsh & McLennan Companies, Inc.; *U.S. Public*, pg. 1379
MARSH FOR INSURANCE SERVICES—See Marsh & McLennan Companies, Inc.; *U.S. Public*, pg. 1378
MARSH FURNITURE COMPANY; *U.S. Private*, pg. 2591
MARSH GLOBAL HOLDINGS LTD; *Int'l*, pg. 4701
MARSH GMBH—See Marsh & McLennan Companies, Inc.; *U.S. Public*, pg. 1379
MARSH GMBH—See Marsh & McLennan Companies, Inc.; *U.S. Public*, pg. 1379
MARSH GSC ADMINISTRACAO E CORRETAGEM DE SEGUROS LTDA.—See Marsh & McLennan Companies, Inc.; *U.S. Public*, pg. 1378
MARSH HOLDING AB—See Marsh & McLennan Companies, Inc.; *U.S. Public*, pg. 1378
MARSH HOLDINGS B.V.—See Marsh & McLennan Companies, Inc.; *U.S. Public*, pg. 1378
MARSH (HONG KONG) LIMITED—See Marsh & McLennan Companies, Inc.; *U.S. Public*, pg. 1378
MARSH IAS MANAGEMENT SERVICES (BERMUDA) LTD.—See Marsh & McLennan Companies, Inc.; *U.S. Public*, pg. 1378
MARSH INC.—See Marsh & McLennan Companies, Inc.; *U.S. Public*, pg. 1378
MARSH INDIA INSURANCE BROKERS PVT. LIMITED—See Marsh & McLennan Companies, Inc.; *U.S. Public*, pg. 1383
MARSH INDUSTRIES, INC.—See Industrial Opportunity Partners, LLC; *U.S. Private*, pg. 2067
MARSH INSCO LLC—See Marsh & McLennan Companies, Inc.; *U.S. Public*, pg. 1379
MARSH INSURANCE AND REINSURANCE BROKERS LLC—See Marsh & McLennan Companies, Inc.; *U.S. Public*, pg. 1383
MARSH INSURANCE AND RISK MANAGEMENT CONSULTANTS LTD.—See Marsh & McLennan Companies, Inc.; *U.S. Public*, pg. 1379
MARSH (INSURANCE BROKERS) LLP—See Marsh & McLennan Companies, Inc.; *U.S. Public*, pg. 1378
MARSH INSURANCE BROKERS (MALAYSIA) SDN BHD—See Marsh & McLennan Companies, Inc.; *U.S. Public*, pg. 1383
MARSH INTERNATIONAL HOLDINGS, INC.—See Marsh & McLennan Companies, Inc.; *U.S. Public*, pg. 1383
MARSH INVESTMENT B.V.—See Marsh & McLennan Companies, Inc.; *U.S. Public*, pg. 1383
MARSH IRELAND LIMITED—See Marsh & McLennan Companies, Inc.; *U.S. Public*, pg. 1379
MARSH (ISLE OF MAN) LIMITED—See Marsh & McLennan Companies, Inc.; *U.S. Public*, pg. 1380
MARSH ISRAEL CONSULTANTS LTD.—See Marsh & McLennan Companies, Inc.; *U.S. Public*, pg. 1383
MARSH ISRAEL (HOLDINGS) LTD.—See Marsh & McLennan Companies, Inc.; *U.S. Public*, pg. 1383
MARSH ISRAEL INSURANCE AGENCY LTD.—See Marsh & McLennan Companies, Inc.; *U.S. Public*, pg. 1379
MARSH JAPAN, INC.—See Marsh & McLennan Companies, Inc.; *U.S. Public*, pg. 1379
MARSH JCS INC.—See Marsh & McLennan Companies, Inc.; *U.S. Public*, pg. 1383
MARSH KINDLUSTUSMAAKLER AS—See Marsh & McLennan Companies, Inc.; *U.S. Public*, pg. 1379
MARSH KOREA, INC.—See Marsh & McLennan Companies, Inc.; *U.S. Public*, pg. 1383
MARSH KOREA, INC.—See Marsh & McLennan Companies, Inc.; *U.S. Public*, pg. 1383

MARSH GLOBAL HOLDINGS LTD

MARSHLAND EMERGENCY PHYSICIANS, LLC—See HCA Healthcare, Inc.; *U.S. Public*, pg. 1001
MARSH LANDING MANAGEMENT COMPANY, INC.; *U.S. Private*, pg. 2591
MARSH, LDA.—See Marsh & McLennan Companies, Inc.; *U.S. Public*, pg. 1384
MARSH LIMITED—See Marsh & McLennan Companies, Inc.; *U.S. Public*, pg. 1379
MARSH LIMITED—See Marsh & McLennan Companies, Inc.; *U.S. Public*, pg. 1379
MARSH LIMITED—See Marsh & McLennan Companies, Inc.; *U.S. Public*, pg. 1379
MARSH LIMITED—See Marsh & McLennan Companies, Inc.; *U.S. Public*, pg. 1383
MARSH LLC INSURANCE BROKERS—See Marsh & McLennan Companies, Inc.; *U.S. Public*, pg. 1379
MARSH LLC—See Marsh & McLennan Companies, Inc.; *U.S. Public*, pg. 1379
MARSH LLC—See Marsh & McLennan Companies, Inc.; *U.S. Public*, pg. 1383
MARSH LORANT AGENTE DE SEGUROS Y DE FIANZAS, S.A. DE C.V.—See Marsh & McLennan Companies, Inc.; *U.S. Public*, pg. 1383
MARSH LTD.—See Marsh & McLennan Companies, Inc.; *U.S. Public*, pg. 1383
MARSH LTD. TAIWAN BRANCH—See Marsh & McLennan Companies, Inc.; *U.S. Public*, pg. 1379
MARSH LUXEMBOURG SA—See Marsh & McLennan Companies, Inc.; *U.S. Public*, pg. 1379
MARSH (MALAWI) LIMITED—See Marsh & McLennan Companies, Inc.; *U.S. Public*, pg. 1378
MARSH MANAGEMENT SERVICES (BARBADOS) LTD.—See Marsh & McLennan Companies, Inc.; *U.S. Public*, pg. 1379
MARSH MANAGEMENT SERVICES (BERMUDA) LTD.—See Marsh & McLennan Companies, Inc.; *U.S. Public*, pg. 1379
MARSH MANAGEMENT SERVICES (CAYMAN) LTD.—See Marsh & McLennan Companies, Inc.; *U.S. Public*, pg. 1379
MARSH MANAGEMENT SERVICES (DUBAI) LIMITED—See Marsh & McLennan Companies, Inc.; *U.S. Public*, pg. 1383
MARSH MANAGEMENT SERVICES (DUBLIN) LIMITED—See Marsh & McLennan Companies, Inc.; *U.S. Public*, pg. 1383
MARSH MANAGEMENT SERVICES INC.—See Marsh & McLennan Companies, Inc.; *U.S. Public*, pg. 1383
MARSH MANAGEMENT SERVICES ISLE OF MAN LIMITED—See Marsh & McLennan Companies, Inc.; *U.S. Public*, pg. 1383
MARSH MANAGEMENT SERVICES (LABUAN) LIMITED—See Marsh & McLennan Companies, Inc.; *U.S. Public*, pg. 1383
MARSH MANAGEMENT SERVICES (LUXEMBOURG) SA—See Marsh & McLennan Companies, Inc.; *U.S. Public*, pg. 1379
MARSH MANAGEMENT SERVICES MALTA LIMITED—See Marsh & McLennan Companies, Inc.; *U.S. Public*, pg. 1383
MARSH MANAGEMENT SERVICES SWEDEN AB—See Marsh & McLennan Companies, Inc.; *U.S. Public*, pg. 1383
MARSH MARINE & ENERGY AB—See Marsh & McLennan Companies, Inc.; *U.S. Public*, pg. 1383
MARSH MARINE & ENERGY AS—See Marsh & McLennan Companies, Inc.; *U.S. Public*, pg. 1379
MARSH MARINE NEDERLAND B.V.—See Marsh & McLennan Companies, Inc.; *U.S. Public*, pg. 1383
MARSH & MCLENNAN AGENCIES AS—See Marsh & McLennan Companies, Inc.; *U.S. Public*, pg. 1377
MARSH & MCLENNAN AGENCY AB—See Marsh & McLennan Companies, Inc.; *U.S. Public*, pg. 1377
MARSH & MCLENNAN AGENCY A/S—See Marsh & McLennan Companies, Inc.; *U.S. Public*, pg. 1381
MARSH & MCLENNAN AGENCY LLC - MIDWEST REGION—See Marsh & McLennan Companies, Inc.; *U.S. Public*, pg. 1381
MARSH & MCLENNAN AGENCY LLC—See Marsh & McLennan Companies, Inc.; *U.S. Public*, pg. 1380
MARSH & MCLENNAN AGENCY PTY LTD.—See Marsh & McLennan Companies, Inc.; *U.S. Public*, pg. 1377
MARSH & MCLENNAN COMPANIES, INC.; *U.S. Public*, pg. 1374
MARSH & MCLENNAN COMPANIES UK LIMITED—See Marsh & McLennan Companies, Inc.; *U.S. Public*, pg. 1377
MARSH & MCLENNAN DEUTSCHLAND GMBH—See Marsh & McLennan Companies, Inc.; *U.S. Public*, pg. 1383
MARSH & MCLENNAN, INCORPORATED—See Marsh & McLennan Companies, Inc.; *U.S. Public*, pg. 1378
MARSH & MCLENNAN REAL ESTATE ADVISORS INC.—See Marsh & McLennan Companies, Inc.; *U.S. Public*, pg. 1378
MARSH & MCLENNAN SERVICIOS, S.A. DE C.V.—See Marsh & McLennan Companies, Inc.; *U.S. Public*, pg. 1378

MARSH & MCLENNAN SWEDEN AB—See Marsh & McLennan Companies, Inc.; *U.S. Public*, pg. 1378
MARSH MEDICAL CONSULTING GMBH—See Marsh & McLennan Companies, Inc.; *U.S. Public*, pg. 1383
MARSH-MERCER HOLDINGS (AUSTRALIA) PTY LTD—See Marsh & McLennan Companies, Inc.; *U.S. Public*, pg. 1383
MARSH (NAMIBIA) (PROPRIETARY) LIMITED—See Marsh & McLennan Companies, Inc.; *U.S. Public*, pg. 1378
MARSH NORWAY AS—See Marsh & McLennan Companies, Inc.; *U.S. Public*, pg. 1379
MARSH OMAN LLC—See Marsh & McLennan Companies, Inc.; *U.S. Public*, pg. 1383
MARS HONG KONG—See Mars, Incorporated; *U.S. Private*, pg. 2589
MARS HORSECARE US, INC.—See Mars, Incorporated; *U.S. Private*, pg. 2589
MARSH OY—See Marsh & McLennan Companies, Inc.; *U.S. Public*, pg. 1383
MARSH & PARSONS LIMITED—See LSL Property Services plc; *Int'l*, pg. 4570
MARSH PB CO., LTD.—See Marsh & McLennan Companies, Inc.; *U.S. Public*, pg. 1379
MARSH PERU SA CORREDORES DE SEGUROS—See Marsh & McLennan Companies, Inc.; *U.S. Public*, pg. 1379
MARSH PHILIPPINES, INC.—See Marsh & McLennan Companies, Inc.; *U.S. Public*, pg. 1379
MARSH PRIVATE CLIENT LIFE INSURANCE SERVICES—See Marsh & McLennan Companies, Inc.; *U.S. Public*, pg. 1383
MARSH PTY LTD—See Marsh & McLennan Companies, Inc.; *U.S. Public*, pg. 1379
MARSH (QLD) PTY LTD.—See Marsh & McLennan Companies, Inc.; *U.S. Public*, pg. 1378
MARSH RESOLUTIONS PTY LIMITED—See Marsh & McLennan Companies, Inc.; *U.S. Public*, pg. 1383
MARSH RISK CONSULTING LIMITADA—See Marsh & McLennan Companies, Inc.; *U.S. Public*, pg. 1384
MARSH RISK CONSULTING, S.L.—See Marsh & McLennan Companies, Inc.; *U.S. Public*, pg. 1384
MARSH RISK & INSURANCE SERVICES—See Marsh & McLennan Companies, Inc.; *U.S. Public*, pg. 1382
MARSH S.A. CORREDORES DE SEGUROS—See Marsh & McLennan Companies, Inc.; *U.S. Public*, pg. 1380
MARSH SALDANA INC.—See Marsh & McLennan Companies, Inc.; *U.S. Public*, pg. 1382
MARSH, S.A. MEDIADORES DE SEGUROS—See Marsh & McLennan Companies, Inc.; *U.S. Public*, pg. 1383
MARSH S.A.—See Marsh & McLennan Companies, Inc.; *U.S. Public*, pg. 1379
MARSH SA—See Marsh & McLennan Companies, Inc.; *U.S. Public*, pg. 1380
MARSH SA—See Marsh & McLennan Companies, Inc.; *U.S. Public*, pg. 1384
MARSH SA—See Marsh & McLennan Companies, Inc.; *U.S. Public*, pg. 1384
MARSH S.A.S.—See Marsh & McLennan Companies, Inc.; *U.S. Public*, pg. 1384
MARSH SAUDI ARABIA INSURANCE & REINSURANCE BROKERS—See Marsh & McLennan Companies, Inc.; *U.S. Public*, pg. 1384
MARSH SERVICES SPOLKA Z.O.O.—See Marsh & McLennan Companies, Inc.; *U.S. Public*, pg. 1384
MARSH SIA—See Marsh & McLennan Companies, Inc.; *U.S. Public*, pg. 1380
MARSH SIGORTA VE REASURANS BROKERLIGI, A.S.—See Marsh & McLennan Companies, Inc.; *U.S. Public*, pg. 1380
MARSH SINGAPORE PTE LTD.—See Marsh & McLennan Companies, Inc.; *U.S. Public*, pg. 1380
MARSH—See Marsh & McLennan Companies, Inc.; *U.S. Public*, pg. 1377
MARSH S.P.A.—See Marsh & McLennan Companies, Inc.; *U.S. Public*, pg. 1380
MARSH SPOLKA Z.O.O.—See Marsh & McLennan Companies, Inc.; *U.S. Public*, pg. 1380
MARSH S.R.O.—See Marsh & McLennan Companies, Inc.; *U.S. Public*, pg. 1383
MARSH SUPERMARKETS, INC.—See Sun Capital Partners, Inc.; *U.S. Private*, pg. 3860
MARSH TREASURY SERVICES (DUBLIN) LIMITED—See Marsh & McLennan Companies, Inc.; *U.S. Public*, pg. 1384
MARSH UGANDA LIMITED—See Marsh & McLennan Companies, Inc.; *U.S. Public*, pg. 1384
MARSH UK HOLDINGS LIMITED—See Marsh & McLennan Companies, Inc.; *U.S. Public*, pg. 1380
MARSH UK LIMITED—See Marsh & McLennan Companies, Inc.; *U.S. Public*, pg. 1380
MARSH USA INC. - ALABAMA—See Marsh & McLennan Companies, Inc.; *U.S. Public*, pg. 1382
MARSH USA INC. - ALASKA—See Marsh & McLennan Companies, Inc.; *U.S. Public*, pg. 1382
MARSH USA INC. - CONNECTICUT—See Marsh & McLennan Companies, Inc.; *U.S. Public*, pg. 1382
MARSH USA INC. - IDAHO—See Marsh & McLennan Companies, Inc.; *U.S. Public*, pg. 1382

CORPORATE AFFILIATIONS

MARSH USA INC. - ILLINOIS—See Marsh & McLennan Companies, Inc.; *U.S. Public*, pg. 1382
MARSH USA INC. - INDIANA—See Marsh & McLennan Companies, Inc.; *U.S. Public*, pg. 1382
MARSH USA INC. - KENTUCKY—See Marsh & McLennan Companies, Inc.; *U.S. Public*, pg. 1382
MARSH USA INC. - MICHIGAN—See Marsh & McLennan Companies, Inc.; *U.S. Public*, pg. 1382
MARSH USA INC. - NEVADA—See Marsh & McLennan Companies, Inc.; *U.S. Public*, pg. 1382
MARSH USA INC. - PENNSYLVANIA—See Marsh & McLennan Companies, Inc.; *U.S. Public*, pg. 1382
MARSH USA INC.—See Marsh & McLennan Companies, Inc.; *U.S. Public*, pg. 1380
MARSH USA INC. - TENNESSEE—See Marsh & McLennan Companies, Inc.; *U.S. Public*, pg. 1382
MARSH USA INC. - TEXAS—See Marsh & McLennan Companies, Inc.; *U.S. Public*, pg. 1382
MARSH USA INC. - UTAH—See Marsh & McLennan Companies, Inc.; *U.S. Public*, pg. 1382
MARSH USA INC. - VIRGINIA—See Marsh & McLennan Companies, Inc.; *U.S. Public*, pg. 1382
MARSH USA INC. - WASHINGTON, D.C.—See Marsh & McLennan Companies, Inc.; *U.S. Public*, pg. 1382
MARSH VENTURES INC.; *U.S. Private*, pg. 2591
MARSH WORTHAM—See Marsh & McLennan Companies, Inc.; *U.S. Public*, pg. 1382
MARSH ZAMBIA LIMITED—See Marsh & McLennan Companies, Inc.; *U.S. Public*, pg. 1382
MARSILIO EDITORI S.P.A.—See GEM S.r.l.; *Int'l*, pg. 2915
MARSILLI AUTOMATION TECHNOLOGY (BEIJING) CO., LTD—See Marsilli & Co. S.p.A.; *Int'l*, pg. 4702
MARSILLI AUTOMATION TECHNOLOGY (SUZHOU) CO, LTD.—See Marsilli & Co. S.p.A.; *Int'l*, pg. 4702
MARSILLI & CO. S.P.A.; *Int'l*, pg. 4702
MARSILLI DEUTSCHLAND GMBH—See Marsilli & Co. S.p.A.; *Int'l*, pg. 4702
MARSILLI INDIA PVT. LTD.—See Marsilli & Co. S.p.A.; *Int'l*, pg. 4702
MARSILLI NORTH AMERICA INC.—See Marsilli & Co. S.p.A.; *Int'l*, pg. 4702
MARS, INCORPORATED; *U.S. Private*, pg. 2588
MARS INDONESIA—See Mars, Incorporated; *U.S. Private*, pg. 2589
MARS IRELAND LTD—See Mars, Incorporated; *U.S. Private*, pg. 2589
MARS ITALIA S.P.A.—See Mars, Incorporated; *U.S. Private*, pg. 2589
MARS JAPAN—See Mars, Incorporated; *U.S. Private*, pg. 2589
MARS KOREA—See Mars, Incorporated; *U.S. Private*, pg. 2589
MAR SK, S.R.O.—See Cie Automotive S.A.; *Int'l*, pg. 1604
MARS LATVIA—See Mars, Incorporated; *U.S. Private*, pg. 2589
MARS LIETUVA—See Mars, Incorporated; *U.S. Private*, pg. 2589
MARS MAGYARORSZAG ERTEKESITO BT.—See Mars, Incorporated; *U.S. Private*, pg. 2589
MARS MALAYSIA—See Mars, Incorporated; *U.S. Private*, pg. 2589
MARS NEDERLAND B.V.—See Mars, Incorporated; *U.S. Private*, pg. 2589
MARS NEW ZEALAND LIMITED—See Mars, Incorporated; *U.S. Private*, pg. 2589
MARS NORTH AMERICA—See Mars, Incorporated; *U.S. Private*, pg. 2589
MARS NORWAY—See Mars, Incorporated; *U.S. Private*, pg. 2590
MARSON & MARSON LUMBER, INC.—See TAL Holdings LLC; *U.S. Private*, pg. 3925
MARSONS LTD.; *Int'l*, pg. 4703
MARSOVIN LTD.; *Int'l*, pg. 4703
MARS PETCARE—See Mars, Incorporated; *U.S. Private*, pg. 2590
MARS PETCARE—See Mars, Incorporated; *U.S. Private*, pg. 2590
MARS PF FRANCE—See Mars, Incorporated; *U.S. Private*, pg. 2590
MARS PHILIPPINES—See Mars, Incorporated; *U.S. Private*, pg. 2590
MARS POLSKA SP. Z.O.O.—See Mars, Incorporated; *U.S. Private*, pg. 2590
MARSPRING CORPORATION; *U.S. Private*, pg. 2593
MARSSENGER KITCHENWARE CO., LTD.; *Int'l*, pg. 4703
MARS SINGAPORE—See Mars, Incorporated; *U.S. Private*, pg. 2590
MARS SNACKFOOD—See Mars, Incorporated; *U.S. Private*, pg. 2590
MARS SNACKFOODS U.S.—See Mars, Incorporated; *U.S. Private*, pg. 2590
MARS SOUTHERN CORE—See Mars, Incorporated; *U.S. Private*, pg. 2590
MARS STEEL CORPORATION; *U.S. Private*, pg. 2588
MARS SUPER MARKETS, INC.; *U.S. Private*, pg. 2588
MARS SWITZERLAND—See Mars, Incorporated; *U.S. Private*, pg. 2590
MARS TAIWAN—See Mars, Incorporated; *U.S. Private*, pg. 2590

COMPANY NAME INDEX

MARSTALLER MOTORS, INC.; *U.S. Private*, pg. 2593
MARSTEL-DAY, LLC; *U.S. Private*, pg. 2593
MARSTELLER ADVERTISING—See WPP plc; *Int'l*, pg. 8468
MARSTELLER—See WPP plc; *Int'l*, pg. 8468
MARS THAILAND, INC.—See Mars, Incorporated; *U.S. Private*, pg. 2590
MARSTON IMPORT AGENCIES, INC.; *U.S. Private*, pg. 2593
MARSTON PROPERTIES LIMITED; *Int'l*, pg. 4703
MARSTON'S PLC; *Int'l*, pg. 4703
MARSTON'S PUBS LIMITED—See Marston's plc; *Int'l*, pg. 4703
MARSTON'S TELECOMS LIMITED—See Marston's plc; *Int'l*, pg. 4703
MARSTON TECHNICAL SERVICES—See Belair Instrument Company LLC; *U.S. Private*, pg. 516
MARSTON WEBB INTERNATIONAL; *U.S. Private*, pg. 2593
MARS UK LTD.—See Mars, Incorporated; *U.S. Private*, pg. 2590
MARS VIETNAM—See Mars, Incorporated; *U.S. Private*, pg. 2590
MARTAM CONSTRUCTION, INC.; *U.S. Private*, pg. 2593
MARTAS MARMARA EREGLISI LIMAN TESISLERI A.S.—See Kaptan Demir Celik Endustrisi ve Ticaret A.S.; *Int'l*, pg. 4078
MART BV—See Siris Capital Group, LLC; *U.S. Private*, pg. 3673
MARTCO INC.; *U.S. Private*, pg. 2593
MARTCO LTD PARTNERSHIP—See Roy O. Martin Lumber Company, LLC; *U.S. Private*, pg. 3491
MARTECH MEDIA—See Waud Capital Partners LLC; *U.S. Private*, pg. 4457
MARTEC LIMITED—See Amphenol Corporation; *U.S. Public*, pg. 131
MARTEC PORTER NOVELLI—See Omnicom Group Inc.; *U.S. Public*, pg. 1591
MARTE ENGENHARIA LTDA—See AtkinsRealis Group Inc.; *Int'l*, pg. 671
MARTEGO SDN BHD—See Cheuk Nang (Holdings) Limited; *Int'l*, pg. 1473
MARTEK-MARINE (ASIA PACIFIC) PTE LTD.—See James Fisher & Sons Public Limited Company; *Int'l*, pg. 3876
MARTEK MARINE LIMITED—See James Fisher & Sons Public Limited Company; *Int'l*, pg. 3876
MARTELA AB—See Martela Oyj; *Int'l*, pg. 4703
MARTELA AS—See Martela Oyj; *Int'l*, pg. 4703
MARTELA A/S—See Martela Oyj; *Int'l*, pg. 4703
MARTELA OYJ; *Int'l*, pg. 4703
MARTEL CONSTRUCTION, INC.; *U.S. Private*, pg. 2593
MARTELL & CO. SA—See Pernod Ricard S.A.; *Int'l*, pg. 5810
MARTELL ELECTRIC, LLC; *U.S. Private*, pg. 2593
MARTELL MUMM PERRIER-JOUET—See Pernod Ricard S.A.; *Int'l*, pg. 5810
MARTELLO TECHNOLOGIES GROUP, INC.; *Int'l*, pg. 4703
MARTENS ASPHALT LTD.—See VINCI S.A.; *Int'l*, pg. 8218
MARTENS CARS OF WASHINGTON, INC.; *U.S. Private*, pg. 2594
MARTENS VOLVO; *U.S. Private*, pg. 2594
MARTEN TRANSPORT, LTD.; *U.S. Public*, pg. 1388
MARTES ENTERPRISES, LLC—See DRG Technologies, Inc.; *U.S. Private*, pg. 1277
MAR.TE SRL—See WPP plc; *Int'l*, pg. 8481
MARTEX CO., LTD.—See Holy Stone Enterprise Co., Ltd.; *Int'l*, pg. 3454
MARTEX FIBER SOUTHERN CORPORATION—See Leigh Fibers, Inc.; *U.S. Private*, pg. 2419
MART FINANCIAL GROUP INCORPORATED; *U.S. Private*, pg. 2593
MARTHA & MARY LUTHERAN SERVICES; *U.S. Private*, pg. 2594
MARTHA'S TABLE; *U.S. Private*, pg. 2594
MARTHA STEWART LIVING OMNIMEDIA, INC.—See Marquee Brands LLC; *U.S. Private*, pg. 2586
MARTHA'S VINEYARD FINANCIAL GROUP—See Martha's Vineyard Savings Bank; *U.S. Private*, pg. 2594
MARTHA'S VINEYARD HOSPITAL INC.—See Partners HealthCare System, Inc.; *U.S. Private*, pg. 3102
MARTHA'S VINEYARD SAVINGS BANK; *U.S. Private*, pg. 2594
MARTHA TURNER SOTHEBY'S INTERNATIONAL REALTY—See Anywhere Real Estate Inc.; *U.S. Public*, pg. 141
MARTHINUSEN & COUTTS (PTY.) LTD.—See ACTOM (Pty) Ltd.; *Int'l*, pg. 120
M. ARTHUR GENSLER JR. & ASSOCIATES INC.; *U.S. Private*, pg. 2526
MARTH WOOD SHAVING SUPPLY, INC.—See EagleTree Capital, LP; *U.S. Private*, pg. 1311
MARTIA A.S.—See CEZ, a.s.; *Int'l*, pg. 1428
MARTI FARM LTD.—See Hangzhou Tigermed Consulting Co., Ltd.; *Int'l*, pg. 3251
MARTIFER - CONSTRUCCIONES METALICAS ESPANA, S.A.—See Martifer SGPS S.A.; *Int'l*, pg. 4703
MARTIFER - CONSTRUCOES METALICAS ANGOLA, S.A.—See Martifer SGPS S.A.; *Int'l*, pg. 4703
MARTIFER CONSTRUCTIONS, SAS—See Martifer SGPS S.A.; *Int'l*, pg. 4703
MARTIFER SGPS S.A.; *Int'l*, pg. 4703
MARTI GAYRIMENKUL YATIRIM ORTAKLIGI AS; *Int'l*, pg. 4703
MARTIGNETTI COMPANIES OF NH—See Martignetti Companies; *U.S. Private*, pg. 2594
MARTIGNETTI COMPANIES; *U.S. Private*, pg. 2594
MARTIGNETTI COMPANIES - UNITED LIQUORS DIVISION—See Martignetti Companies; *U.S. Private*, pg. 2594
MARTI ILERI TEKNOLOJI A.S.—See Marti Technologies, Inc.; *U.S. Public*, pg. 1389
THE MARTIN AGENCY, INC. - NEW YORK—See The Interpublic Group of Companies, Inc.; *U.S. Public*, pg. 2102
THE MARTIN AGENCY INC.—See ABRY Partners, LLC; *U.S. Private*, pg. 43
THE MARTIN AGENCY, INC.—See The Interpublic Group of Companies, Inc.; *U.S. Public*, pg. 2102
MARTINAIR HOLLAND N.V.—See Air France-KLM S.A.; *Int'l*, pg. 238
MARTINA MINERALS CORPORATION; *Int'l*, pg. 4704
MARTIN ASPHALT COMPANY—See Martin Resource Management Corporation; *U.S. Private*, pg. 2595
MARTIN ASPHALT COMPANY—See Martin Resource Management Corporation; *U.S. Private*, pg. 2595
MARTINA & TECHNOLOGIES S.A.C.—See Sulzer Ltd.; *Int'l*, pg. 7257
MARTIN AUDIO LTD.—See Focusrite plc; *Int'l*, pg. 2720
MARTIN AUDIO US, LLC—See Focusrite plc; *Int'l*, pg. 2720
MARTIN AUTOMOTIVE, INC.—See General Motors Company; *U.S. Public*, pg. 926
MARTIN-BAKER AIRCRAFT COMPANY LIMITED; *Int'l*, pg. 4704
MARTIN-BAKER AMERICA INC.—See Martin-Baker Aircraft Company Limited; *Int'l*, pg. 4704
MARTIN & BAYLEY, INC.; *U.S. Private*, pg. 2594
MARTIN BOHSUNG GMBH—See Alpiq Holding AG; *Int'l*, pg. 372
MARTIN BRAUN-GRUPPE—See Dr. August Oetker KG; *Int'l*, pg. 2100
MARTIN BROKERS (UK) LTD—See R P Martin Holdings Limited; *Int'l*, pg. 6167
MARTIN BROS./MARCOWALL, INC.; *U.S. Private*, pg. 2594
MARTIN BROTHERS CONSTRUCTION, INC.; *U.S. Private*, pg. 2594
MARTIN BROTHERS DISTRIBUTING COMPANY, INC.; *U.S. Private*, pg. 2594
THE MARTIN-BROWER COMPANY, LLC—See Reyes Holdings, LLC; *U.S. Private*, pg. 3418
MARTIN-BROWER OF CANADA CO.—See Reyes Holdings, LLC; *U.S. Private*, pg. 3418
MARTIN BRUUSGAARD AS—See Addtech AB; *Int'l*, pg. 134
MARTIN BUILDING MATERIALS, LLC—See Lumber Investors LLC; *U.S. Private*, pg. 2513
MARTIN BULK HANDLING SOLUTIONS (PTY) LIMITED—See Martin Engineering; *U.S. Private*, pg. 2595
MARTIN BURN LIMITED; *Int'l*, pg. 4703
MARTIN CADILLAC COMPANY, INC.; *U.S. Private*, pg. 2594
MARTIN CAR FINANCING INC.; *U.S. Private*, pg. 2594
MARTIN CHEVROLET-BUICK, INC.; *U.S. Private*, pg. 2594
MARTIN CHEVROLET SALES, INC.; *U.S. Private*, pg. 2594
MARTIN & CHOCK, INC.—See John A. Martin & Associates, Incorporated; *U.S. Public*, pg. 2220
MARTIN CLINIC CORP.—See Community Health Systems, Inc.; *U.S. Public*, pg. 555
MARTIN COLOR-FI, INC.—See Dimeling, Schreiber & Park; *U.S. Private*, pg. 1232
MARTIN & COMPANY, INC.—See First Horizon Corporation; *U.S. Public*, pg. 845
MARTIN & CO (UK) LTD.; *Int'l*, pg. 4703
MARTIN COUNTY COAL CORPORATION—See Alpha Natural Resources, Inc.; *U.S. Private*, pg. 198
MARTIN COUNTY PETROLEUM & PROPANE; *U.S. Private*, pg. 2594
MARTIN CURRIE GLOBAL PORTFOLIO TRUST PLC; *Int'l*, pg. 4703
MARTIN CURRIE, INC.—See Franklin Resources, Inc.; *U.S. Public*, pg. 882
MARTIN CURRIE INVESTMENT MANAGEMENT LIMITED—See Franklin Resources, Inc.; *U.S. Public*, pg. 882
MARTINDALE, LLC—See KKR & Co. Inc.; *U.S. Public*, pg. 1253
MARTIN DAWES ANALYTICS—See Martin Dawes Systems; *Int'l*, pg. 4703
MARTIN DAWES SYSTEMS; *Int'l*, pg. 4703
MARTIN DOOR MANUFACTURING, INC.; *U.S. Private*, pg. 2594

MARTINO FLYNN LLC

MARTIN DUNITZ LTD.—See Informa plc; *Int'l*, pg. 3692
MARTIN EAGLE OIL COMPANY, INC.; *U.S. Private*, pg. 2594
MARTIN EMPLOYEES, INC.; *U.S. Private*, pg. 2594
MARTIN ENERGY SERVICES LLC—See Martin Resource Management Corporation; *U.S. Private*, pg. 2596
MARTIN ENGINEERING COMPANY INDIA PRIVATE LIMITED—See Martin Engineering; *U.S. Private*, pg. 2595
MARTIN ENGINEERING GMBH—See Martin Engineering; *U.S. Private*, pg. 2595
MARTIN ENGINEERING ITALY SRL—See Martin Engineering; *U.S. Private*, pg. 2595
MARTIN ENGINEERING LIMITED—See Martin Engineering; *U.S. Private*, pg. 2595
MARTIN ENGINEERING LTDA.—See Martin Engineering; *U.S. Private*, pg. 2595
MARTIN ENGINEERING PERU SRL—See Martin Engineering; *U.S. Private*, pg. 2595
MARTIN ENGINEERING SARL—See Martin Engineering; *U.S. Private*, pg. 2595
MARTIN ENGINEERING S. DE R.L. DE C.V.—See Martin Engineering; *U.S. Private*, pg. 2595
MARTIN ENGINEERING; *U.S. Private*, pg. 2595
MARTIN EQUIPMENT OF ILLINOIS; *U.S. Private*, pg. 2595
MARTINEZ & TUREK, INC.; *U.S. Private*, pg. 2596
MARTIN FASTENING SOLUTIONS—See MSCO Inc.; *U.S. Private*, pg. 2806
MARTIN FINANCIAL GROUP; *U.S. Private*, pg. 2595
MARTIN FLETCHER ASSOCIATES HOLDINGS, INC.—See HCA Healthcare, Inc.; *U.S. Public*, pg. 1001
MARTIN FLUID POWER COMPANY, INC.; *U.S. Private*, pg. 2595
MARTIN FLYER INC.; *U.S. Private*, pg. 2595
MARTIN/F. WEBER COMPANY—See Martin Universal Design, Inc.; *U.S. Private*, pg. 2596
MARTINGALE MALTA 2 LIMITED—See Entain PLC; *Int'l*, pg. 2450
MARTIN GOTTLIEB & ASSOCIATES, LLC—See Varsity Management Company, LP; *U.S. Public*, pg. 4347
THE MARTIN GROUP LLC; *U.S. Private*, pg. 4075
MARTIN HEALTH SERVICES, LLC—See CVS Health Corporation; *U.S. Public*, pg. 616
MARTIN HEALTH SYSTEM; *U.S. Private*, pg. 2595
MARTIN HOSPITAL COMPANY, LLC—See Community Health Systems, Inc.; *U.S. Public*, pg. 555
MARTINIC ENGINEERING, INC.—See TriMas Corporation; *U.S. Public*, pg. 2189
MARTINI MEDIA INC.; *U.S. Private*, pg. 2596
MARTINI MEDIA NETWORK, INC.—See Evolve Media, LLC; *U.S. Private*, pg. 1443
MARTIN INDUSTRIAL SUPPLY—See MSCO Inc.; *U.S. Private*, pg. 2806
MARTIN K. EBY CONSTRUCTION COMPANY, INC.—See Eby Corporation; *U.S. Private*, pg. 1326
MARTIN-LAVELL LIMITED—See Smiths News PLC; *Int'l*, pg. 7013
MARTIN LIBRARY ASSOCIATION; *U.S. Private*, pg. 2595
MARTIN LINEN SUPPLY COMPANY—See Federated Linen & Uniform Services; *U.S. Private*, pg. 1491
MARTIN LITHOGRAPH, INC.; *U.S. Private*, pg. 2595
MARTIN-LOGAN, LTD.—See ShoreView Industries, LLC; *U.S. Private*, pg. 3642
MARTIN LP GAS INC.—See Martin Resource Management Corporation; *U.S. Private*, pg. 2596
MARTIN LUTHER KING, JR. COMMUNITY HEALTH FOUNDATION; *U.S. Private*, pg. 2595
MARTIN L WEINER & ASSOCIATES; *U.S. Private*, pg. 2595
MARTIN MARIETTA AGGREGATES—See Martin Marietta Materials, Inc.; *U.S. Public*, pg. 1389
MARTIN MARIETTA MAGNESIA SPECIALTIES, INC.—See Martin Marietta Materials, Inc.; *U.S. Public*, pg. 1389
MARTIN MARIETTA MATERIALS, INC.; *U.S. Public*, pg. 1389
MARTIN MARIETTA MATERIALS SOUTHWEST, INC.—See Martin Marietta Materials, Inc.; *U.S. Public*, pg. 1389
MARTIN/MARTIN INC.—See John A. Martin & Associates, Incorporated; *U.S. Private*, pg. 2220
MARTIN / MARTIN WYOMING, INC.—See John A. Martin & Associates, Incorporated; *U.S. Private*, pg. 2220
MARTIN MATHYS NV—See RPM International Inc.; *U.S. Public*, pg. 1817
MARTIN MIDSTREAM FINANCE CORP—See Martin Midstream Partners LP; *U.S. Public*, pg. 1389
MARTIN MIDSTREAM PARTNERS LP; *U.S. Public*, pg. 1389
MARTIN MILLER NORTH AMERICA, INC.—See voestalpine AG; *Int'l*, pg. 8292
MARTIN MODERN PTE. LTD.—See Hong Leong Investment Holdings Pte. Ltd.; *Int'l*, pg. 3468
MARTIN NEWARK DEALERSHIP, INC.; *U.S. Private*, pg. 2595
MARTINO & BINZER, INC.—See High Road Capital Partners, LLC; *U.S. Private*, pg. 1936
MARTINO FLYNN LLC; *U.S. Private*, pg. 2596

MARTIN OIL COMPANY

MARTIN OIL COMPANY; *U.S. Private*, pg. 2595
MARTIN OLSSON CASHAR AB—See Martin Olsson Handels AB; *Int'l*, pg. 4704
MARTIN OLSSON HANDELS AB; *Int'l*, pg. 4704
MARTIN OPERATING PARTNERSHIP L.P.—See Martin Midstream Partners LP; *U.S. Public*, pg. 1389
MARTIN PALLET, INC.—See Burlington Capital Partners, LLC; *U.S. Private*, pg. 689
MARTIN PETERSEN COMPANY, INC.; *U.S. Private*, pg. 2595
MARTIN PEVZNER ENGINEERING—See I & S Group, Inc.; *U.S. Private*, pg. 2020
MARTIN PLANT SERVICES—See MSCO Inc.; *U.S. Private*, pg. 2806
MARTIN PREFERRED FOODS LP; *U.S. Private*, pg. 2595
MARTIN PRODUCT SALES LLC—See Martin Resource Management Corporation; *U.S. Private*, pg. 2595
MARTIN PROFESSIONAL A/S—See Samsung Group; *Int'l*, pg. 6512
MARTIN PROFESSIONAL PTE. LTD.—See Samsung Group; *Int'l*, pg. 6512
MARTIN-RAY LAUNDRY SYSTEMS, INC.—See EVI Industries, Inc.; *U.S. Public*, pg. 803
MARTINREA AUTOMATIVE SYSTEMS (USA) LLC—See Martinrea International, Inc.; *Int'l*, pg. 4704
MARTINREA DEVELOPMENTS DE MEXICO, S.A. DE C.V.—See Martinrea International, Inc.; *Int'l*, pg. 4704
MARTINREA FABCO AUTOMATIVE STRUCTURES (USA) INC.—See Martinrea International, Inc.; *Int'l*, pg. 4704
MARTINREA FABCO HOT STAMPINGS INC.—See Martinrea International, Inc.; *Int'l*, pg. 4704
MARTINREA FABCO—See ThyssenKrupp AG; *Int'l*, pg. 7729
MARTINREA FABCO—See Martinrea International, Inc.; *Int'l*, pg. 4704
MARTINREA FABCO—See Martinrea International, Inc.; *Int'l*, pg. 4704
MARTINREA FABCO—See Martinrea International, Inc.; *Int'l*, pg. 4704
MARTINREA FABCO—See Martinrea International, Inc.; *Int'l*, pg. 4704
MARTINREA HEAVY STAMPINGS INC.—See Martinrea International, Inc.; *Int'l*, pg. 4704
MARTINREA HONSEL GERMANY GMBH—See Martinrea International, Inc.; *Int'l*, pg. 4704
MARTINREA HOPKINSVILLE LLC—See Martinrea International, Inc.; *Int'l*, pg. 4704
MARTINREA INDUSTRIES, INC.—See Martinrea International, Inc.; *Int'l*, pg. 4704
MARTINREA INTERNATIONAL, INC.; *Int'l*, pg. 4704
MARTINREA JONESVILLE LLC—See Martinrea International, Inc.; *Int'l*, pg. 4704
MARTINREA METAL INDUSTRIES, INC.—See Martinrea International, Inc.; *Int'l*, pg. 4704
MARTIN RESOURCE MANAGEMENT CORPORATION; *U.S. Private*, pg. 2595
MARTIN RESOURCE MANAGEMENT CORP. - PAX DIVISION—See Martin Resource Management Corporation; *U.S. Private*, pg. 2596
MARTIN RESOURCES, INC.—See Martin Resource Management Corporation; *U.S. Private*, pg. 2596
MARTIN RESOURCES, INC.—See Martin Resource Management Corporation; *U.S. Private*, pg. 2596
MARTIN SAFETY SOLUTIONS—See MSCO Inc.; *U.S. Private*, pg. 2806
MARTIN S.A.—See Bobst Group S.A.; *Int'l*, pg. 1096
MARTINSBURG FARMERS ELEVATORS CO; *U.S. Private*, pg. 2597
MARTIN-SCHAFFER, INC.; *U.S. Private*, pg. 2596
MARTINS CONSTRUCTION CORP.—See Posillico, Inc.; *U.S. Private*, pg. 3233
MARTINS COUNTRY MARKET; *U.S. Private*, pg. 2597
MARTINS CREEK SOLAR NC, LLC—See Duke Energy Corporation; *U.S. Public*, pg. 691
MARTIN & SERVERA AB—See Martin Olsson Handels AB; *Int'l*, pg. 4704
MARTIN'S FAMOUS PASTRY SHOPPES - SNACK DIVISION—See Martin's Famous Pastry Shoppes; *U.S. Private*, pg. 2596
MARTIN'S FAMOUS PASTRY SHOPPES; *U.S. Private*, pg. 2596
MARTIN'S FANTASY ISLAND—See Edgewater Services, LLC; *U.S. Private*, pg. 1335
MARTIN'S FARM MARKET, INC.—See Weis Markets, Inc.; *U.S. Public*, pg. 2342
MARTINS INC.; *U.S. Private*, pg. 2597
MARTINS PETERBILT INC.; *U.S. Private*, pg. 2597
MARTINS POTATO CHIPS INC; *U.S. Private*, pg. 2597
MARTIN SPROCKET & GEAR DE MEXICO, S.A. DE C.V.—See Martin Sprocket & Gear, Inc.; *U.S. Private*, pg. 2596
MARTIN SPROCKET & GEAR, INC. - MARTIN TOOLS DIVISION—See Martin Sprocket & Gear, Inc.; *U.S. Private*, pg. 2596
MARTIN SPROCKET & GEAR, INC. - MISSISSAUGA—See Martin Sprocket & Gear, Inc.; *U.S. Private*, pg. 2596
MARTIN SPROCKET & GEAR, INC.; *U.S. Private*, pg. 2596

MARTIN SPROCKET & GEAR (SHANGHAI) CO., LTD.—See Martin Sprocket & Gear, Inc.; *U.S. Private*, pg. 2596
MARTINS RESTAURANT SYSTEMS INC.; *U.S. Private*, pg. 2597
MARTIN STAUD GMBH—See Vivonio Furniture GmbH; *Int'l*, pg. 8280
MARTIN SUPPLY COMPANY INC.—See Martin Supply Company Inc.; *U.S. Private*, pg. 2596
MARTIN SUPPLY COMPANY INC.; *U.S. Private*, pg. 2596
MARTINSVILLE INTERNATIONAL, INC.—See National Association for Stock Car Auto Racing, Inc.; *U.S. Private*, pg. 2845
MARTINSWERK GMBH—See Albemarle Corporation; *U.S. Public*, pg. 73
MARTIN THOMAS, INC.; *U.S. Private*, pg. 2596
MARTIN THOMAS INTERNATIONAL, PUBLIC RELATIONS DIVISION—See Martin Thomas, Inc.; *U.S. Private*, pg. 2596
MARTIN TIRE CO.; *U.S. Private*, pg. 2596
MARTIN TRADING ZHUHAI LTD.—See Samsung Group; *Int'l*, pg. 6512
MARTIN TRANSPORT, INC.—See Martin Resource Management Corporation; *U.S. Private*, pg. 2596
MARTIN UNIVERSAL DESIGN, INC.; *U.S. Private*, pg. 2596
MARTIN WALTER ULTRASONICS AG—See Crest Group Inc.; *U.S. Private*, pg. 1096
MARTIN WARD ANDERSON B.V.—See Randstad N.V.; *Int'l*, pg. 6202
MARTIN WELLS INDUSTRIES; *U.S. Private*, pg. 2596
MARTIN WHALEN OFFICE SOLUTIONS INC.; *U.S. Private*, pg. 2596
MARTIN/WILLIAMS ADVERTISING INC.—See Omnicom Group Inc.; *U.S. Public*, pg. 1588
MARTIN YALE INDUSTRIES, LLC—See Escalade, Incorporated; *U.S. Public*, pg. 793
MARTI OTEL ISLETMELERI A.S.; *Int'l*, pg. 4703
MARTIS CAPITAL, LLC—See SK Inc.; *Int'l*, pg. 6972
MARTIS CAPITAL MANAGEMENT LLC; *U.S. Private*, pg. 2597
MARTI TECHNOLOGIES, INC.; *U.S. Public*, pg. 1389
MARTIVAL TECHNOLOGIE S.A.—See SICC S.p.A.; *Int'l*, pg. 6877
MARTS & LUNDY, INC.; *U.S. Private*, pg. 2597
MARTTIINI OU—See Rapala VMC Oyj; *Int'l*, pg. 6209
MARTTIINI OY—See Rapala VMC Oyj; *Int'l*, pg. 6209
MARTY FELDMAN CHEVROLET, INC.; *U.S. Private*, pg. 2597
MARTY FRANICH FORD LINCOLN MERCURY INC; *U.S. Private*, pg. 2597
MARTY SHOES, INC.; *U.S. Private*, pg. 2597
MARTY SUSSMAN MOTORS INC—See Marty Sussman Organization; *U.S. Private*, pg. 2597
MARTY SUSSMAN ORGANIZATION; *U.S. Private*, pg. 2597
MARTZ COMMUNICATIONS GROUP INC; *U.S. Private*, pg. 2597
MARUBENI AEROSPACE AMERICA CORPORATION—See Marubeni Corporation; *Int'l*, pg. 4706
MARUBENI AEROSPACE CORPORATION—See Marubeni Corporation; *Int'l*, pg. 4706
MARUBENI AG MAKINA TICARET LIMITED SIRKETI—See Marubeni Corporation; *Int'l*, pg. 4705
MARUBENI ALUMINIUM AUSTRALIA PTY. LTD.—See Marubeni Corporation; *Int'l*, pg. 4707
MARUBENI AMERICA CORPORATION - LOS ANGELES—See Marubeni Corporation; *Int'l*, pg. 4706
MARUBENI AMERICA CORPORATION—See Marubeni Corporation; *Int'l*, pg. 4706
MARUBENI ARCH-LOG CO., LTD.—See Marubeni Corporation; *Int'l*, pg. 4707
MARUBENI ARGENTINA S.A.—See Marubeni Corporation; *Int'l*, pg. 4707
MARUBENI ASEAN PTE. LTD.—See Marubeni Corporation; *Int'l*, pg. 4707
MARUBENI ASIAN POWER SINGAPORE PTE. LTD.—See Marubeni Corporation; *Int'l*, pg. 4707
MARUBENI ASSET MANAGEMENT CO., LTD.—See Marubeni Corporation; *Int'l*, pg. 4707
MARUBENI AUSTRALIA LTD.—See Marubeni Corporation; *Int'l*, pg. 4707
MARUBENI AUTO FINANCE, LTDA—See Marubeni Corporation; *Int'l*, pg. 4707
MARUBENI AUTO INVESTMENT (UK) LTD—See Marubeni Corporation; *Int'l*, pg. 4707
MARUBENI AUTO LTDA—See Marubeni Corporation; *Int'l*, pg. 4707
MARUBENI AUTOMOTIVE CORPORATION—See Marubeni Corporation; *Int'l*, pg. 4707
MARUBENI BRASIL S.A.—See Marubeni Corporation; *Int'l*, pg. 4707
MARUBENI BUSINESS MACHINES (AMERICA) INC.—See Marubeni Corporation; *Int'l*, pg. 4706
MARUBENI CEMENT & CONSTRUCTION MATERIALS CO., LTD.—See Marubeni Corporation; *Int'l*, pg. 4707
MARUBENI CHEMIX CORPORATION—See Marubeni Corporation; *Int'l*, pg. 4707

MARUBENI CHILE LIMITADA—See Marubeni Corporation; *Int'l*, pg. 4707
MARUBENI (CHINA) CO., LTD.—See Marubeni Corporation; *Int'l*, pg. 4706
MARUBENI CITIZEN-CINCOM INC.—See Citizen Watch Co., Ltd.; *Int'l*, pg. 1625
MARUBENI CITIZEN-CINCOM INC.—See Marubeni Corporation; *Int'l*, pg. 4706
MARUBENI CLS CORPORATION—See Marubeni Corporation; *Int'l*, pg. 4707
MARUBENI COAL PTY. LTD.—See Marubeni Corporation; *Int'l*, pg. 4707
MARUBENI CONSTRUCTION MATERIAL LEASE CO., LTD. - ASAHIKAWA PLANT—See Marubeni Construction Material Lease Co., Ltd.; *Int'l*, pg. 4704
MARUBENI CONSTRUCTION MATERIAL LEASE CO., LTD. - GIFU PLANT—See Marubeni Construction Material Lease Co., Ltd.; *Int'l*, pg. 4704
MARUBENI CONSTRUCTION MATERIAL LEASE CO., LTD. - ICHIHARA PLANT—See Marubeni Construction Material Lease Co., Ltd.; *Int'l*, pg. 4704
MARUBENI CONSTRUCTION MATERIAL LEASE CO., LTD. - ICHIHARA SECOND PLANT—See Marubeni Construction Material Lease Co., Ltd.; *Int'l*, pg. 4705
MARUBENI CONSTRUCTION MATERIAL LEASE CO., LTD. - INAZAWA PLANT—See Marubeni Construction Material Lease Co., Ltd.; *Int'l*, pg. 4705
MARUBENI CONSTRUCTION MATERIAL LEASE CO., LTD. - NISHIHARA PLANT—See Marubeni Construction Material Lease Co., Ltd.; *Int'l*, pg. 4705
MARUBENI CONSTRUCTION MATERIAL LEASE CO., LTD. - SAPPORO PLANT—See Marubeni Construction Material Lease Co., Ltd.; *Int'l*, pg. 4705
MARUBENI CONSTRUCTION MATERIAL LEASE CO., LTD.; *Int'l*, pg. 4704
MARUBENI CORPORATION; *Int'l*, pg. 4705
MARUBENI EGG CORPORATION—See Marubeni Corporation; *Int'l*, pg. 4707
MARUBENI ELE-NEXT CO., LTD.—See Marubeni Corporation; *Int'l*, pg. 4707
MARUBENI ENEBLE CORPORATION—See Marubeni Corporation; *Int'l*, pg. 4707
MARUBENI ENERGY CORPORATION—See Marubeni Corporation; *Int'l*, pg. 4707
MARUBENI ENERGY EUROPE LIMITED—See Marubeni Corporation; *Int'l*, pg. 4707
MARUBENI ENNEX CORPORATION—See Marubeni Corporation; *Int'l*, pg. 4707
MARUBENI EQUIPMENT FINANCE (OCEANIA) PTY. LTD.—See Marubeni Corporation; *Int'l*, pg. 4707
MARUBENI EUROPE PLC - DUSSELDORF BRANCH—See Marubeni Corporation; *Int'l*, pg. 4707
MARUBENI EUROPE PLC—See Marubeni Corporation; *Int'l*, pg. 4707
MARUBENI EUROPOWER LTD—See Marubeni Corporation; *Int'l*, pg. 4707
MARUBENI FASHION LINK, LTD.—See Marubeni Corporation; *Int'l*, pg. 4708
MARUBENI FASHION PLANNING CORP.—See Marubeni Corporation; *Int'l*, pg. 4708
MARUBENI FINANCIAL SERVICE CORPORATION—See Marubeni Corporation; *Int'l*, pg. 4708
MARUBENI FOODS CORPORATION—See Marubeni Corporation; *Int'l*, pg. 4708
MARUBENI FOOTWEAR INC.—See Marubeni Corporation; *Int'l*, pg. 4708
MARUBENI FOOTWEAR RESOURCES LIMITED—See Marubeni Corporation; *Int'l*, pg. 4708
MARUBENI FOREST LINX CO., LTD.—See Marubeni Corporation; *Int'l*, pg. 4708
MARUBENI HEAVY EQUIPMENT COMPANY LIMITED—See Marubeni Corporation; *Int'l*, pg. 4708
MARUBENI HOLDING LTDA.—See Marubeni Corporation; *Int'l*, pg. 4708
MARUBENI HOSPITAL PARTNERS CORPORATION—See Marubeni Corporation; *Int'l*, pg. 4708
MARUBENI INDIA PRIVATE LTD.—See Marubeni Corporation; *Int'l*, pg. 4708
MARUBENI INFORMATION SYSTEMS CO., LTD.—See Marubeni Corporation; *Int'l*, pg. 4708
MARUBENI INFORMATION SYSTEMS USA CORPORATION—See Marubeni Corporation; *Int'l*, pg. 4708
MARUBENI INTERNATIONAL (EUROPE) GMBH—See Marubeni Corporation; *Int'l*, pg. 4708
MARUBENI INTERNATIONAL PETROLEUM (SINGAPORE) PTE. LTD—See Marubeni Corporation; *Int'l*, pg. 4708
MARUBENI INTEX CO., LTD.—See Marubeni Corporation; *Int'l*, pg. 4708
MARUBENI IRAN CO., LTD.—See Marubeni Corporation; *Int'l*, pg. 4708
MARUBENI ITOCHU PIPE & TUBE, INC.—See ITOCHU Corporation; *Int'l*, pg. 3840
MARUBENI ITOCHU PIPE & TUBE, INC.—See Marubeni Corporation; *Int'l*, pg. 4706
MARUBENI-ITOCHU STEEL AMERICA, INC.—See ITOCHU Corporation; *Int'l*, pg. 3840

COMPANY NAME INDEX

MARUBENI-ITOCHU STEEL AMERICA, INC.—See Marubeni Corporation; *Int'l*, pg. 4709
MARUBENI-ITOCHU STEEL INC. - OSAKA DIVISION—See ITOCHU Corporation; *Int'l*, pg. 3840
MARUBENI-ITOCHU STEEL INC. - OSAKA DIVISION—See Marubeni Corporation; *Int'l*, pg. 4709
MARUBENI-ITOCHU STEEL INC.—See ITOCHU Corporation; *Int'l*, pg. 3840
MARUBENI-ITOCHU STEEL INC.—See Marubeni Corporation; *Int'l*, pg. 4709
MARUBENI-ITOCHU TUBULARS AMERICA, INC.—See ITOCHU Corporation; *Int'l*, pg. 3840
MARUBENI-ITOCHU TUBULARS AMERICA, INC.—See Marubeni Corporation; *Int'l*, pg. 4709
MARUBENI IT SOLUTIONS INC.—See Marubeni Corporation; *Int'l*, pg. 4708
MARUBENI-KOMATSU LTD.—See Marubeni Corporation; *Int'l*, pg. 4708
MARUBENI KOREA CORPORATION—See Marubeni Corporation; *Int'l*, pg. 4708
MARUBENI LOGISTICS CORPORATION—See Marubeni Corporation; *Int'l*, pg. 4708
MARUBENI MAQUINARIAS MEXICO, S.A. DE C.V.—See Marubeni Corporation; *Int'l*, pg. 4708
MARUBENI METALS CORPORATION—See Marubeni Corporation; *Int'l*, pg. 4708
MARUBENI MEXICO S.A. DE C.V.—See Marubeni Corporation; *Int'l*, pg. 4708
MARUBENI-MITSUHASHI RICE, INC.—See Marubeni Corporation; *Int'l*, pg. 4709
MARUBENI MYANMAR FERTILIZER CO., LTD.—See Marubeni Corporation; *Int'l*, pg. 4708
MARUBENI NETWORK SOLUTIONS INC—See Marubeni Corporation; *Int'l*, pg. 4708
MARUBENI NEW ZEALAND LTD.—See Marubeni Corporation; *Int'l*, pg. 4707
MARUBENI NIGERIA LTD.—See Marubeni Corporation; *Int'l*, pg. 4708
MARUBENI NISSHIN FEED CO., LTD.—See Marubeni Corporation; *Int'l*, pg. 4708
MARUBENI NORTH SEA LIMITED—See Marubeni Corporation; *Int'l*, pg. 4707
MARUBENI OFFICE SUPPLY CO., LTD.—See Marubeni Corporation; *Int'l*, pg. 4708
MARUBENI OFFICE SUPPORT CORPORATION—See Marubeni Corporation; *Int'l*, pg. 4708
MARUBENI OIL & GAS (USA) INC.—See Marubeni Corporation; *Int'l*, pg. 4706
MARUBENI OKI NETWORK SOLUTIONS INC—See Oki Electric Industry Co., Ltd.; *Int'l*, pg. 5548
MARUBENI PAPER & PULP LOGISTICS CO., LTD.—See Marubeni Corporation; *Int'l*, pg. 4708
MARUBENI PAPER RECYCLE CO., LTD.—See Marubeni Corporation; *Int'l*, pg. 4708
MARUBENI PERSONNEL MANAGEMENT CORPORATION—See Marubeni Corporation; *Int'l*, pg. 4708
MARUBENI PLANT CONTRACTOR, INC.—See Marubeni Corporation; *Int'l*, pg. 4706
MARUBENI PLANT ENGINEERING CORPORATION—See Marubeni Corporation; *Int'l*, pg. 4708
MARUBENI PLAX CORPORATION—See Marubeni Corporation; *Int'l*, pg. 4708
MARUBENI POWER ASSET MANAGEMENT LTD.—See Marubeni Corporation; *Int'l*, pg. 4708
MARUBENI POWER INTERNATIONAL, INC.—See Marubeni Corporation; *Int'l*, pg. 4706
MARUBENI POWER RETAIL CORPORATION—See Marubeni Corporation; *Int'l*, pg. 4708
MARUBENI POWER SYSTEMS CORPORATION—See Marubeni Corporation; *Int'l*, pg. 4708
MARUBENI PROTECHS CORPORATION—See Marubeni Corporation; *Int'l*, pg. 4708
MARUBENI PULP & PAPER CO., LTD.—See Marubeni Corporation; *Int'l*, pg. 4709
MARUBENI REAL ESTATE CO., LTD.—See Marubeni Corporation; *Int'l*, pg. 4709
MARUBENI REAL ESTATE DEVELOPMENT CO., LTD.—See Marubeni Corporation; *Int'l*, pg. 4709
MARUBENI REAL ESTATE MANAGEMENT CO., LTD.—See Marubeni Corporation; *Int'l*, pg. 4709
MARUBENI SAFENET CO., LTD.—See Marubeni Corporation; *Int'l*, pg. 4709
MARUBENI SERVICE CORPORATION—See Marubeni Corporation; *Int'l*, pg. 4709
MARUBENI SPECIALTY CHEMICALS INC.—See Marubeni Corporation; *Int'l*, pg. 4706
MARUBENI STEEL PROCESSING INC.—See Marubeni Corporation; *Int'l*, pg. 4706
MARUBENI TAIWAN CO., LTD.—See Marubeni Corporation; *Int'l*, pg. 4709
MARUBENI TECHNO RUBBER CORPORATION—See Marubeni Corporation; *Int'l*, pg. 4709
MARUBENI TECHNO-SYSTEMS CORP—See Marubeni Corporation; *Int'l*, pg. 4709
MARUBENI TELECOM CO., LTD.—See Marubeni Corporation; *Int'l*, pg. 4709
MARUBENI TETSUGEN CO., LTD.—See Marubeni Corporation; *Int'l*, pg. 4709

MARUBENI TEXTILE ASIA PACIFIC LTD.—See Marubeni Corporation; *Int'l*, pg. 4709
MARUBENI TRANSPORT ENGINEERING CO., LTD.—See Marubeni Corporation; *Int'l*, pg. 4709
MARUBENI TRANSPORT SERVICE CORP.—See Marubeni Corporation; *Int'l*, pg. 4706
MARUBENI UTILITY SERVICES, LTD—See Marubeni Corporation; *Int'l*, pg. 4709
MARUBENI VENEZUELA C.A.—See Marubeni Corporation; *Int'l*, pg. 4709
MARUBISHI PAPER TEC. CORPORATION—See Daio Paper Corporation; *Int'l*, pg. 1940
MARUBOSHI CO., LTD.—See Yuasa Trading Co., Ltd.; *Int'l*, pg. 8609
MARUBOSHI EUROPE B.V.—See CMC Corporation; *Int'l*, pg. 1669
MARUBOSHI THAILAND CO., LTD.—See CMC Corporation; *Int'l*, pg. 1669
MARUBUN/ARROW (HK) LIMITED—See Arrow Electronics, Inc.; *U.S. Public*, pg. 199
MARUBUN-ARROW MEXICO, S. DE R.L. DE C.V.—See Arrow Electronics, Inc.; *U.S. Public*, pg. 199
MARUBUN/ARROW (M) SDN. BHD—See Arrow Electronics, Inc.; *U.S. Public*, pg. 199
MARUBUN/ARROW (PHILIPPINES) INC.—See Arrow Electronics, Inc.; *U.S. Public*, pg. 199
MARUBUN/ARROW (PHILS), INC.—See MARUBUN CORPORATION; *Int'l*, pg. 4710
MARUBUN/ARROW (SHANGHAI) CO.—See Arrow Electronics, Inc.; *U.S. Public*, pg. 199
MARUBUN/ARROW (S) PTE LTD.—See Arrow Electronics, Inc.; *U.S. Public*, pg. 199
MARUBUN/ARROW (THAILAND) CO., LTD.—See Arrow Electronics, Inc.; *U.S. Public*, pg. 199
MARUBUN/ARROW (THAILAND) CO.—See Arrow Electronics, Inc.; *U.S. Public*, pg. 199
MARUBUN CORPORATION; *Int'l*, pg. 4710
MARUBUN SEMICON CORPORATION—See MARUBUN CORPORATION; *Int'l*, pg. 4710
MARUBUN SEMICON (SHANGHAI) CO., LTD—See MARUBUN CORPORATION; *Int'l*, pg. 4710
MARUBUN TAIWAN, INC.—See MARUBUN CORPORATION; *Int'l*, pg. 4710
MARUBUN TSUSYO CO., LTD.—See MARUBUN CORPORATION; *Int'l*, pg. 4710
MARUBUN WEST CORPORATION—See MARUBUN CORPORATION; *Int'l*, pg. 4710
MARUCCI AND GAFFNEY EXCAVATING CO.; *U.S. Private*, pg. 2597
MARUCCI CLUBHOUSE, LLC—See Compass Diversified Holdings; *U.S. Public*, pg. 560
MARUCCI ELITE TRAINING L.L.C.—See Compass Diversified Holdings; *U.S. Public*, pg. 560
MARUCCI HITTERS HOUSE, LLC—See Compass Diversified Holdings; *U.S. Public*, pg. 560
MARUCCI SPORTS, LLC—See Fox Factory Holding Corp.; *U.S. Public*, pg. 877
MARUC CO., LTD.; *Int'l*, pg. 4710
MARUCHAN AJINOMOTO INDIA PRIVATE LIMITED—See Ajinomoto Company, Inc.; *Int'l*, pg. 257
MARUCHAN DE MEXICO, S.A. DE C.V.—See Toyo Suisan Kaisha, Ltd.; *Int'l*, pg. 7858
MARUCHAN INC.—See Toyo Suisan Kaisha, Ltd.; *Int'l*, pg. 7858
MARUCHAN VIRGINIA, INC.—See Toyo Suisan Kaisha, Ltd.; *Int'l*, pg. 7858
MARUCHIYO YAMAOKAYA CORPORATION; *Int'l*, pg. 4710
MARUDAI CO., LTD.—See Seven & i Holdings Co., Ltd.; *Int'l*, pg. 6731
MARUDAI FOOD CO., LTD.; *Int'l*, pg. 4710
MARUDAI MEAT CO., LTD.—See Marudai Food Co., Ltd.; *Int'l*, pg. 4710
MARUDAS GRAPHICS, INC.; *U.S. Private*, pg. 2597
MARUESU GT CO., LTD.—See GLORY Ltd.; *Int'l*, pg. 3010
THE MARUETSU INC.—See AEON Co., Ltd.; *Int'l*, pg. 178
MARUFUJI CO., LTD.—See Senko Group Holdings Co., Ltd.; *Int'l*, pg. 6710
MARUFUJI CORP.—See Itoham Yonekyu Holdings Inc.; *Int'l*, pg. 3843
MARUFUJI SHEET PILING CO., LTD.; *Int'l*, pg. 4711
MARUFUKU SHOJI CO., LTD.—See Yamano Holdings Corporation; *Int'l*, pg. 8553
MARUGAME SEIMEN INC.—See TORIDOLL Holdings Corporation; *Int'l*, pg. 7828
MARUHA CAPITAL INVESTMENT, INC.—See Maruha Nichiro Corporation; *Int'l*, pg. 4711
MARUHACHI HOLDINGS CO., LTD.; *Int'l*, pg. 4712
MARUHACHI SECURITIES CO., LTD.; *Int'l*, pg. 4712
MARUHACHI WAREHOUSE COMPANY LIMITED; *Int'l*, pg. 4712
MARUHA HOLDINGS (THAILAND) CO., LTD—See Maruha Nichiro Corporation; *Int'l*, pg. 4711
MARUHAN CORPORATION; *Int'l*, pg. 4712
MARUHA NICHIRO ASSET, INC—See Maruha Nichiro Corporation; *Int'l*, pg. 4711
MARUHA NICHIRO CORPORATION; *Int'l*, pg. 4711

MARUHA NICHIRO LOGISTICS, INC.-KYUSYU BRANCH—See Maruha Nichiro Corporation; *Int'l*, pg. 4711
MARUHA NICHIRO LOGISTICS, INC.—See Maruha Nichiro Corporation; *Int'l*, pg. 4711
MARUHA NICHIRO MEAT & PRODUCTS USA, INC.—See Maruha Nichiro Corporation; *Int'l*, pg. 4711
MARUHA (N.Z.) CORPORATION LTD.—See Maruha Nichiro Corporation; *Int'l*, pg. 4711
MARUHA (SHANGHAI) TRADING CORPORATION—See Maruha Nichiro Corporation; *Int'l*, pg. 4711
MARUHO CO., LTD. - HIKONE PLANT—See Maruho Co., Ltd.; *Int'l*, pg. 4712
MARUHO CO., LTD. - NAGAHAMA PLANT—See Maruho Co., Ltd.; *Int'l*, pg. 4712
MARUHO CO., LTD.; *Int'l*, pg. 4712
MARUHO DEUTSCHLAND GMBH—See Maruho Co., Ltd.; *Int'l*, pg. 4712
MARUHO HATSUJYO KOGYO CO., LTD. - KAMEOKA FACTORY—See Maruho Co., Ltd.; *Int'l*, pg. 4712
MARUHO HATSUJYO KOGYO CO., LTD. - SHINKOU-ETSU FACTORY—See Maruho Co., Ltd.; *Int'l*, pg. 4712
MARUHO HATSUJYO KOGYO CO., LTD.—See Maruho Co., Ltd.; *Int'l*, pg. 4712
MARUHON HONMA SUISAN CO., LTD.—See Hanwa Co., Ltd.; *Int'l*, pg. 3263
MARUICHI AMERICAN CORP.—See Mitsubishi Corporation; *Int'l*, pg. 4940
MARUICHI AMERICAN CORP.—See Sojitz Corporation; *Int'l*, pg. 7062
MARUICHI KOHAN LTD.—See Maruichi Steel Tube Ltd; *Int'l*, pg. 4713
MARUICHI KUMA STEEL TUBE PRIVATE LIMITED—See Maruichi Steel Tube Ltd; *Int'l*, pg. 4713
MARUICHI LEAVITT PIPE & TUBE, LLC—See Maruichi Steel Tube Ltd; *Int'l*, pg. 4713
MARUICHI METAL PRODUCT (FOSHAN) CO., LTD.—See Maruichi Steel Tube Ltd; *Int'l*, pg. 4713
MARUICHI METAL PRODUCT (TIANJIN) CO., LTD.—See Maruichi Steel Tube Ltd; *Int'l*, pg. 4713
MARUICHIMEX S.A. DE C.V.—See Maruichi Steel Tube Ltd; *Int'l*, pg. 4714
MARUICHI OREGON STEEL TUBE, LLC—See Maruichi Steel Tube Ltd; *Int'l*, pg. 4713
MARUICHI PHILIPPINES STEEL TUBE INC.—See Maruichi Steel Tube Ltd; *Int'l*, pg. 4713
MARUICHI STAINLESS TUBE CO., LTD.—See Maruichi Steel Tube Ltd; *Int'l*, pg. 4713
MARUICHI STEEL TUBE LTD - KASHIMA POLE PLANT—See Maruichi Steel Tube Ltd; *Int'l*, pg. 4713
MARUICHI STEEL TUBE LTD - NAGOYA PLANT—See Maruichi Steel Tube Ltd; *Int'l*, pg. 4713
MARUICHI STEEL TUBE LTD - OSAKA PLANT—See Maruichi Steel Tube Ltd; *Int'l*, pg. 4713
MARUICHI STEEL TUBE LTD - POLE DIVISION—See Maruichi Steel Tube Ltd; *Int'l*, pg. 4713
MARUICHI STEEL TUBE LTD - SAKAI PLANT—See Maruichi Steel Tube Ltd; *Int'l*, pg. 4713
MARUICHI STEEL TUBE LTD - SAKAI POLE PLANT—See Maruichi Steel Tube Ltd; *Int'l*, pg. 4713
MARUICHI STEEL TUBE LTD; *Int'l*, pg. 4713
MARUICHI STEEL TUBE LTD - TAKUMA PLANT—See Maruichi Steel Tube Ltd; *Int'l*, pg. 4713
MARUICHI STEEL TUBE LTD - TOKYO PLANT—See Maruichi Steel Tube Ltd; *Int'l*, pg. 4714
MARUICHI SUN STEEL (HANOI) COMPANY LIMITED—See Maruichi Steel Tube Ltd; *Int'l*, pg. 4714
MARUICHI SUN STEEL JOINT STOCK COMPANY—See Maruichi Steel Tube Ltd; *Int'l*, pg. 4714
MARUI CO., LTD.—See Marui Group Co., Ltd.; *Int'l*, pg. 4713
MARUI FACILITIES CO., LTD.—See Marui Group Co., Ltd.; *Int'l*, pg. 4713
MARUI GROUP CO., LTD.; *Int'l*, pg. 4712
MARUI HOME SERVICE CO., LTD.—See Marui Group Co., Ltd.; *Int'l*, pg. 4713
MARUI KIT CENTER CO., LTD.—See Marui Group Co., Ltd.; *Int'l*, pg. 4713
MARUI ORIMONO KK; *Int'l*, pg. 4713
MARUISHI CHEMICAL TRADING CO., LTD.—See Inabata & Co. Ltd.; *Int'l*, pg. 3644
MARUKA CORPORATION—See Maruka Furusato Corporation; *Int'l*, pg. 4714
MARUKA ENTERPRISES, INC.—See Maruka Furusato Corporation; *Int'l*, pg. 4714
MARUKA FURUSATO CORPORATION; *Int'l*, pg. 4714
MARUKAI HAWAII CO., LTD.—See Pan Pacific International Holdings Corporation; *Int'l*, pg. 5715
MARUKA INDIA PVT LTD.—See Maruka Furusato Corporation; *Int'l*, pg. 4714
MARUKA MACHINERY CORP.—See Maruka Furusato Corporation; *Int'l*, pg. 4714
MARUKA MACHINERY (THAILAND) CO., LTD.—See Maruka Furusato Corporation; *Int'l*, pg. 4714
MARUKA MEXICO S.A. DE C.V.—See Maruka Furusato Corporation; *Int'l*, pg. 4714
MARUKA (M) SDN.BHD.—See Maruka Furusato Corporation; *Int'l*, pg. 4714

MARUKA FURUSATO CORPORATION / CORPORATE AFFILIATIONS

MARUKA TRADING GUANGZHOU LIMITED—See Maruka Furusato Corporation; *Int'l*, pg. 4714
MARUKA USA INC.—See Maruka Furusato Corporation; *Int'l*, pg. 4714
MARUKA VIETNAM CO., LTD.—See Maruka Furusato Corporation; *Int'l*, pg. 4714
MARUKAWA SHOKUHIN CO., LTD.—See Yoshimura Food Holdings K.K.; *Int'l*, pg. 8600
MARUKEN KISOKOJI CO., LTD.—See Marubeni Construction Material Lease Co., Ltd.; *Int'l*, pg. 4704
MARUKEN SERVICE CO., LTD.—See Yuasa Trading Co., Ltd.; *Int'l*, pg. 8609
MARUKI CHEMICAL IND. CO. LTD.—See Shin-Etsu Chemical Co. Ltd.; *Int'l*, pg. 6838
MARUKO MARINE TRANSPORT CO., LTD.—See Kamigumi Co., Ltd.; *Int'l*, pg. 4062
MARUKOME CO., LTD.; *Int'l*, pg. 4714
MARUKYO TRANSPORTATION CO., LTD.—See Mitsui-Soko Holdings Co., Ltd.; *Int'l*, pg. 4993
MARUKYU SHOKUHIN CO., LTD.—See NICHIMO CO. LTD.; *Int'l*, pg. 5269
MARUMAE CO., LTD.; *Int'l*, pg. 4714
MARUMAN AMERICA, INC.—See Smart Score Co., Ltd.; *Int'l*, pg. 7001
MARUMAN (BEIJING) COMMERCE & TRADE CO., LTD.—See Smart Score Co., Ltd.; *Int'l*, pg. 7001
MARUMAN GOLF CORPORATION—See Smart Score Co., Ltd.; *Int'l*, pg. 7001
MARUMAN (HONG KONG) HOLDING LTD.—See Smart Score Co., Ltd.; *Int'l*, pg. 7001
MARUMANKOREA CO., LTD.—See Smart Score Co., Ltd.; *Int'l*, pg. 7001
MARUMAN SHANGHAI SPORTS GOODS TRADING CO—See Smart Score Co., Ltd.; *Int'l*, pg. 7001
MARUMBI TRANSMISSORA DE ENERGIA S.A.—See Companhia Paranaense de Energia; *Int'l*, pg. 1748
MARUNAKA CO., LTD.—See AEON Co., Ltd.; *Int'l*, pg. 178
MARUNI CHIKIRIYA CO., LTD.—See Japan Pulp and Paper Company Limited; *Int'l*, pg. 3904
MARUNOUCHI CAPITAL INC.—See Mitsubishi Corporation; *Int'l*, pg. 4940
MARUNOUCHI & CO., LTD.—See Mizuho Leasing Company, Limited; *Int'l*, pg. 4999
MARUNOUCHI DIRECT ACCESS CO., LTD.—See Mitsubishi Estate Co., Ltd.; *Int'l*, pg. 4946
MARUNOUCHI HEAT SUPPLY CO., LTD.—See Mitsubishi Estate Co., Ltd.; *Int'l*, pg. 4946
MARUNOUCHI HOTEL CO., LTD.—See Mitsubishi Estate Co., Ltd.; *Int'l*, pg. 4946
MARUNOUCHI INFRASTRUCTURE INC.—See Mitsubishi Corporation; *Int'l*, pg. 4940
MARUO CALCIUM CO., LTD.; *Int'l*, pg. 4714
MARUO CALCIUM CO., LTD. - TSUCHIURA PLANT—See Maruo Calcium Co., Ltd.; *Int'l*, pg. 4714
MARUO CALCIUM CO., LTD. - TSUCHIYAMA PLANT—See Maruo Calcium Co., Ltd.; *Int'l*, pg. 4714
MARUOKA SHOJI CO., LTD.—See Shinyei Kaisha; *Int'l*, pg. 6850
MARUO (SHANGHAI) TRADING CO., LTD.—See Maruo Calcium Co., Ltd.; *Int'l*, pg. 4714
MARUPI LIFETECH CO., LTD.—See Sumitomo Chemical Company, Limited; *Int'l*, pg. 7267
MARUSA CO., LTD.—See Toray Industries, Inc.; *Int'l*, pg. 7823
MARUSAN-AI CO., LTD.; *Int'l*, pg. 4714
MARUSANAI-TOTTORI CO., LTD.—See Marusan-Ai Co., Ltd.; *Int'l*, pg. 4715
MARUSAN PAPER MFG. CO., LTD.—See Rengo Co., Ltd.; *Int'l*, pg. 6280
MARUSAN SECURITIES CO., LTD.; *Int'l*, pg. 4714
MARUSE ENGINEERING (V) CO., LTD.—See Miura Co., Ltd.; *Int'l*, pg. 4994
MARUSHIN CANNERIES (M) SDN. BHD.—See JFE Holdings, Inc.; *Int'l*, pg. 3937
MARUSHO HOTTA CO., LTD.; *Int'l*, pg. 4715
MARUTAI CO., LTD.; *Int'l*, pg. 4715
MARUTA TRANSPORT CO., LTD.—See Daido Steel Co., Ltd.; *Int'l*, pg. 1923
MARUTI INFRASTRUCTURE LIMITED; *Int'l*, pg. 4715
MARUTI INTERIOR PRODUCTS LTD.; *Int'l*, pg. 4715
MARUTI SECURITIES LIMITED; *Int'l*, pg. 4715
MARUTI SUZUKI INDIA LIMITED—See Suzuki Motor Corporation; *Int'l*, pg. 7354
MARUTO SANGYO CO., LTD.; *Int'l*, pg. 4715
MARUUO SUISAN CO.,LTD—See Nissui Corporation; *Int'l*, pg. 5378
MARUWA AMERICA CORPORATION—See Maruwa Co., Ltd.; *Int'l*, pg. 4715
MARUWA CO., LTD.; *Int'l*, pg. 4715
MARUWA ELECTRONICS BEIJING CO., LTD.—See Maruwa Co., Ltd.; *Int'l*, pg. 4715
MARUWA ELECTRONICS HK CO., LTD.—See Maruwa Co., Ltd.; *Int'l*, pg. 4715
MARUWA EUROPE LTD—See Maruwa Co., Ltd.; *Int'l*, pg. 4715
MARUWA KOREA CO., LTD.—See Maruwa Co., Ltd.; *Int'l*, pg. 4715
MARUWA QUARTZ CO.—See Maruwa Co., Ltd.; *Int'l*, pg. 4715
MARUWA SHANGHAI TRADING CO., LTD.—See Maruwa Co., Ltd.; *Int'l*, pg. 4715
MARUWA SHOMEI CO., LTD.—See Maruwa Co., Ltd.; *Int'l*, pg. 4715
MARUWN CORPORATION; *Int'l*, pg. 4715
MARUYAMA EXCELL CO., LTD. - CHIBA FACTORY—See Maruyama Mfg. Co., Inc.; *Int'l*, pg. 4715
MARUYAMA LOGISTICS CO., INC.—See Maruyama Mfg. Co., Inc.; *Int'l*, pg. 4715
MARUYAMA MFG. CO., INC.; *Int'l*, pg. 4715
MARUYAMA MFG (THAILAND) CO., LTD.—See Maruyama Mfg. Co., Inc.; *Int'l*, pg. 4715
MARUYAMA (SHANGHAI) TRADING CO., INC.—See Maruyama Mfg. Co., Inc.; *Int'l*, pg. 4715
MARUYAMA U.S. INC.—See Maruyama Mfg. Co., Inc.; *Int'l*, pg. 4715
MARUYASU SHOKAI LTD.—See SPK Corporation; *Int'l*, pg. 7140
MARUYOSHI CENTER INC.; *Int'l*, pg. 4715
MARUZ CORPORATION; *U.S. Private*, pg. 2597
MARUZEN BOOKMATES CO., LTD.—See Dai Nippon Printing Co., Ltd.; *Int'l*, pg. 1915
MARUZEN BOOKSTORES CO., LTD.—See Dai Nippon Printing Co., Ltd.; *Int'l*, pg. 1915
MARUZEN CHI HOLDINGS CO., LTD.—See Dai Nippon Printing Co., Ltd.; *Int'l*, pg. 1915
MARUZEN CHUBU RYUTSU CO., LTD.—See Maruzen Showa Unyu Co., Ltd.; *Int'l*, pg. 4716
MARUZEN CO., LTD. - LONDON OFFICE—See Dai Nippon Printing Co., Ltd.; *Int'l*, pg. 1915
MARUZEN DENSAN LOGISTICS (PINGHU) CORPORATION—See Maruzen Showa Unyu Co., Ltd.; *Int'l*, pg. 4716
MARUZEN HOKKAIDO UNYU CO., LTD.—See Maruzen Showa Unyu Co., Ltd.; *Int'l*, pg. 4716
MARUZEN IBARAKI RYUTSU CO., LTD.—See Maruzen Showa Unyu Co., Ltd.; *Int'l*, pg. 4716
MARUZEN INTERNATIONAL CO., LTD.—See Dai Nippon Printing Co., Ltd.; *Int'l*, pg. 1915
MARUZEN KANSAI RYUTSU CO., LTD.—See Maruzen Showa Unyu Co., Ltd.; *Int'l*, pg. 4716
MARUZEN KASHIMA BUTSURYU CO., LTD.—See Maruzen Showa Unyu Co., Ltd.; *Int'l*, pg. 4716
MARUZEN KEIYO BUTSURYU CO., LTD.—See Maruzen Showa Unyu Co., Ltd.; *Int'l*, pg. 4716
MARUZEN KYOEI PRINCE—See Dai Nippon Printing Co., Ltd.; *Int'l*, pg. 1915
MARUZEN MEGA PASARAYA—See Dai Nippon Printing Co., Ltd.; *Int'l*, pg. 1915
MARUZEN OF AMERICA, INC.—See Maruzen Showa Unyu Co., Ltd.; *Int'l*, pg. 4716
MARUZEN PASARAYA MANGGARAI—See Dai Nippon Printing Co., Ltd.; *Int'l*, pg. 1916
MARUZEN PETROCHEMICAL CO., LTD.—See Cosmo Energy Holdings Co., Ltd.; *Int'l*, pg. 1812
MARUZEN PUBLISHING CO., LTD.—See Dai Nippon Printing Co., Ltd.; *Int'l*, pg. 1916
MARUZEN RYUTSU SERVICE CO., LTD.—See Maruzen Showa Unyu Co., Ltd.; *Int'l*, pg. 4716
MARUZEN SH LOGISTICS SDN. BHD.—See Maruzen Showa Unyu Co., Ltd.; *Int'l*, pg. 4716
MARUZEN SHOWA (HONG KONG) CO.—See Maruzen Showa Unyu Co., Ltd.; *Int'l*, pg. 4716
MARUZEN SHOWA KOREA CO.—See Maruzen Showa Unyu Co., Ltd.; *Int'l*, pg. 4716
MARUZEN SHOWA LOGISTICS CO., LTD.—See Maruzen Showa Unyu Co., Ltd.; *Int'l*, pg. 4716
MARUZEN SHOWA SINGAPORE PTE LTD.—See Maruzen Showa Unyu Co., Ltd.; *Int'l*, pg. 4716
MARUZEN SHOWA (TAIWAN) CO.—See Maruzen Showa Unyu Co., Ltd.; *Int'l*, pg. 4716
MARUZEN SHOWA UNYU CO., LTD. - PLANT ENGINEERING DIVISION—See Maruzen Showa Unyu Co., Ltd.; *Int'l*, pg. 4716
MARUZEN SHOWA UNYU CO., LTD.; *Int'l*, pg. 4715
MARUZEN SUDAMERICANA LTDA.—See Maruzen Showa Unyu Co., Ltd.; *Int'l*, pg. 4716
MARUZEN SYSTEM SERVICE CO., LTD.—See Dai Nippon Printing Co., Ltd.; *Int'l*, pg. 1916
MARUZEN TRANSPACK CO., LTD.—See Maruzen Showa Unyu Co., Ltd.; *Int'l*, pg. 4716
MARUZEN-YUSHODO COMPANY, LIMITED—See Dai Nippon Printing Co., Ltd.; *Int'l*, pg. 1915
MARVAC ELECTRONICS; *U.S. Private*, pg. 2597
MARVAIR—See Thor Industries, Inc.; *U.S. Public*, pg. 2156
MAR-VAL FOOD STORE 1 INC.; *U.S. Private*, pg. 2569
MARVAL INDUSTRIES, INC.; *U.S. Private*, pg. 2597
MARVDASHT SUGAR COMPANY; *Int'l*, pg. 4716
MARVEL ANIMATION, INC.—See The Walt Disney Company; *U.S. Public*, pg. 2139
MARVEL CAPITAL & FINANCE (INDIA) LIMITED; *Int'l*, pg. 4716
MARVEL DECOR LTD.; *Int'l*, pg. 4716
MARVEL DISCOVERY CORP.; *Int'l*, pg. 4716
MARVEL ENGINEERING COMPANY; *U.S. Private*, pg. 2597
MARVEL ENTERTAINMENT INTERNATIONAL LIMITED—See The Walt Disney Company; *U.S. Public*, pg. 2139
MARVEL ENTERTAINMENT, LLC—See The Walt Disney Company; *U.S. Public*, pg. 2139
MARVEL GOLD LIMITED—See Indiana Resources Limited; *Int'l*, pg. 3655
THE MARVEL GROUP, INC.; *U.S. Private*, pg. 4075
MARVELL ACCEL JAPAN K.K.—See Marvell Technology Group Ltd.; *Int'l*, pg. 4717
MARVELL ASIA PTE, LTD.—See Marvell Technology Group Ltd.; *Int'l*, pg. 4717
MARVELL HONG KONG LIMITED—See Marvell Technology Group Ltd.; *Int'l*, pg. 4717
MARVEL LIFE SCIENCES PVT LTD—See Yifan Pharmaceutical Co., Ltd.; *Int'l*, pg. 8582
MARVELL INDIA PRIVATE LIMITED—See Marvell Technology Group Ltd.; *Int'l*, pg. 4717
MARVELL INTERNATIONAL LTD.—See Marvell Technology Group Ltd.; *Int'l*, pg. 4717
MARVELL ISRAEL (M.I.S.L)—See Marvell Technology Group Ltd.; *Int'l*, pg. 4717
MARVELL ITALIA S.R.L.—See Marvell Technology Group Ltd.; *Int'l*, pg. 4717
MARVELL JAPAN K.K.—See Marvell Technology Group Ltd.; *Int'l*, pg. 4717
MARVELL NETHERLANDS B.V.—See Marvell Technology Group Ltd.; *Int'l*, pg. 4717
MARVELL SEMICONDUCTOR GERMANY GMBH—See Marvell Technology Group Ltd.; *Int'l*, pg. 4717
MARVELL SEMICONDUCTOR, INC.—See Marvell Technology Group Ltd.; *Int'l*, pg. 4717
MARVELL SEMICONDUCTOR ISRAEL, LTD.—See Marvell Technology Group Ltd.; *Int'l*, pg. 4717
MARVELL SEMICONDUCTOR KOREA, LTD.—See Marvell Technology Group Ltd.; *Int'l*, pg. 4717
MARVELL SEMICONDUCTOR SDN. BHD.—See Marvell Technology Group Ltd.; *Int'l*, pg. 4717
MARVELL SEMICONDUCTOR TECHNOLOGY SARL—See Marvell Technology Group Ltd.; *Int'l*, pg. 4717
MARVELL SWEDEN AB—See Marvell Technology Group Ltd.; *Int'l*, pg. 4717
MARVELL SWITZERLAND SARL—See Marvell Technology Group Ltd.; *Int'l*, pg. 4717
MARVELL TAIWAN LTD.—See Marvell Technology Group Ltd.; *Int'l*, pg. 4717
MARVELL TECHNOLOGY (BEIJING), LTD.—See Marvell Technology Group Ltd.; *Int'l*, pg. 4717
MARVELL TECHNOLOGY GROUP LTD.; *Int'l*, pg. 4716
MARVELL TECHNOLOGY, INC.—See Marvell Technology Group Ltd.; *Int'l*, pg. 4717
MARVELL TECHNOLOGY JAPAN Y.K.—See Marvell Technology Group Ltd.; *Int'l*, pg. 4717
MARVELL TECHNOLOGY (NANJING), LTD.—See Marvell Technology Group Ltd.; *Int'l*, pg. 4717
MARVELL TECHNOLOGY SWEDEN AB—See Marvell Technology Group Ltd.; *Int'l*, pg. 4717
MARVELL TECHNOLOGY VIETNAM LIMITED LIABILITY COMPANY—See Marvell Technology Group Ltd.; *Int'l*, pg. 4717
MARVELL TOWER INSURANCE AGENCIES; *U.S. Private*, pg. 2597
MARVELOUS FINLAND—See The Interpublic Group of Companies, Inc.; *U.S. Public*, pg. 2095
MARVELOUS INC.; *Int'l*, pg. 4717
MARVELOUS NORDIC—See The Interpublic Group of Companies, Inc.; *U.S. Public*, pg. 2094
MARVELOUS SVERIGE—See The Interpublic Group of Companies, Inc.; *U.S. Public*, pg. 2095
MARVEL PACKERS PTY. LTD.—See Lamb Weston Holdings, Inc.; *U.S. Public*, pg. 1291
MARVEL PUBLISHING, INC.—See The Walt Disney Company; *U.S. Public*, pg. 2139
MARVEL TECHNOLOGIES, INC.; *U.S. Private*, pg. 2597
MARVEL VINYLS LTD.; *Int'l*, pg. 4716
MARVEL WORLDWIDE, INC.—See The Walt Disney Company; *U.S. Public*, pg. 2139
MARVI ASCENSORES S.L.—See KONE Oyj; *Int'l*, pg. 4250
MARVIL PACKAGE COMPANY; *U.S. Private*, pg. 2597
MARVIN DEVELOPMENT CORP.; *U.S. Private*, pg. 2597
MARVIN ENGINEERING COMPANY, INC.; *U.S. Private*, pg. 2597
MARVIN F. POER & COMPANY; *U.S. Private*, pg. 2598
MARVIN K. BROWN AUTO CENTER, INC.; *U.S. Private*, pg. 2598
MARVIN LAND SYSTEMS—See Marvin Engineering Company, Inc.; *U.S. Private*, pg. 2598
MARVIN'S FOODS; *U.S. Private*, pg. 2598
MARVIN'S FOOD WAREHOUSE, INC.; *U.S. Private*, pg. 2598
MARVIN'S, LLC—See Tyndale Advisors, LLC; *U.S. Private*, pg. 4268
MARVIN TEST SOLUTIONS, INC.—See Marvin Engineering Company, Inc.; *U.S. Private*, pg. 2598
MARVIN TRAUB ASSOCIATES, INC.; *U.S. Private*, pg. 2598
MARVIN WINDOWS & DOORS INC.; *U.S. Private*, pg. 2598
MARVION INC.; *U.S. Public*, pg. 1389
MARVIPOL S.A.; *Int'l*, pg. 4717

COMPANY NAME INDEX

MARV JONES LTD.; *Int'l*, pg. 4716
MARVO FEUERUNGS- UND INDUSTRIEBAU GMBH—See RHI Magnesita N.V.; *Int'l*, pg. 6325
MARV'S INSULATION, INC.—See Installed Building Products, Inc.; *U.S. Public*, pg. 1133
MARVY CORPORATION—See Uchida Yoko Co., Ltd.; *Int'l*, pg. 8012
MARWAY POWER SYSTEMS INC.—See HEICO Corporation; *U.S. Public*, pg. 1021
MARWELL CORPORATION; *U.S. Private*, pg. 2598
MARWEST APARTMENT REAL ESTATE INVESTMENT TRUST; *Int'l*, pg. 4717
MARWEST MANAGEMENT CANADA LTD.—See All in West! Capital Corporation; *Int'l*, pg. 332
THE MARWIN COMPANY, INC.—See Validor Capital LLC; *U.S. Private*, pg. 4332
MARWIT CAPITAL; *U.S. Private*, pg. 2598
MARWYN INVESTMENT MANAGEMENT LLP; *Int'l*, pg. 4718
MARWYN VALUE INVESTORS LIMITED; *Int'l*, pg. 4718
MARX COMPANIES, LLC; *U.S. Private*, pg. 2598
MARX MCCLELLAN THRUN; *U.S. Private*, pg. 2598
MARX/OKUBO ASSOCIATES, INC.; *U.S. Private*, pg. 2598
MARX SPAENLIN SA—See Derichebourg S.A.; *Int'l*, pg. 2041
MARY ANN INDUSTRIES INC.—See Leggett & Platt, Incorporated; *U.S. Public*, pg. 1303
MARY ANN MORSE HEALTHCARE CENTER; *U.S. Private*, pg. 2598
MARY BIRD PERKINS CANCER CENTER; *U.S. Private*, pg. 2598
MARY BLACK HEALTH SYSTEM LLC—See Spartanburg Regional Health Services District, Inc.; *U.S. Private*, pg. 3747
MARY CHIA HOLDINGS LIMITED—See Suki Sushi Pte Ltd.; *Int'l*, pg. 7255
MARY CHOCOLATE CO., LTD.—See Lotte Co., Ltd.; *Int'l*, pg. 4560
MARY FEED & SUPPLIES, INC.; *U.S. Private*, pg. 2598
MARYFIELD, INC.; *U.S. Private*, pg. 2599
MARY FRANCES ACCESSORIES, INC.; *U.S. Private*, pg. 2598
THE MARYGOLD COMPANIES, INC.; *U.S. Public*, pg. 2112
MARYHAVEN CENTER OF HOPE—See Catholic Health Services of Long Island; *U.S. Private*, pg. 791
MARYHAVEN, INC.; *U.S. Private*, pg. 2598
MARYHILL DISPENSARY LIMITED—See Walgreens Boots Alliance, Inc.; *U.S. Public*, pg. 2322
MARY IMMACULATE AMBULATORY SURGERY CENTER, LLC—See Tenet Healthcare Corporation; *U.S. Public*, pg. 2011
THE MARYJANE GROUP, INC.; *U.S. Private*, pg. 4075
MARY JANE'S CBD DISPENSARY, INC.; *U.S. Private*, pg. 2598
MARY KAY ASIA SERVICES LIMITED—See Mary Kay Holding Corporation; *U.S. Private*, pg. 2599
MARY KAY (CHINA) COSMETICS CO., LTD.—See Mary Kay Holding Corporation; *U.S. Private*, pg. 2599
MARY KAY COSMETICOS DE MEXICO, S.A. DE C.V.—See Mary Kay Holding Corporation; *U.S. Private*, pg. 2599
MARY KAY COSMETICOS DO BRAZIL LTDA.—See Mary Kay Holding Corporation; *U.S. Private*, pg. 2599
MARY KAY COSMETICOS, S.A.—See Mary Kay Holding Corporation; *U.S. Private*, pg. 2599
MARY KAY COSMETICOS DE ESPANA, S.A.—See Mary Kay Holding Corporation; *U.S. Private*, pg. 2599
MARY KAY COSMETICS GMBH—See Mary Kay Holding Corporation; *U.S. Private*, pg. 2599
MARY KAY COSMETICS LTD.—See Mary Kay Holding Corporation; *U.S. Private*, pg. 2599
MARY KAY COSMETICS (NEW ZEALAND) INC.—See Mary Kay Holding Corporation; *U.S. Private*, pg. 2599
MARY KAY COSMETICS POLAND SP. Z. O.O—See Mary Kay Holding Corporation; *U.S. Private*, pg. 2599
MARY KAY COSMETICS PTY. LTD.—See Mary Kay Holding Corporation; *U.S. Private*, pg. 2599
MARY KAY COSMETICS (TAIWAN) INC.—See Mary Kay Holding Corporation; *U.S. Private*, pg. 2599
MARY KAY COSMETICS (U.K.) LTD.—See Mary Kay Holding Corporation; *U.S. Private*, pg. 2599
MARY KAY CZECH REPUBLIC S.R.O.—See Mary Kay Holding Corporation; *U.S. Private*, pg. 2599
MARY KAY HOLDING CORPORATION; *U.S. Private*, pg. 2598
MARY KAY (HONG KONG) LIMITED—See Mary Kay Holding Corporation; *U.S. Private*, pg. 2599
MARY KAY INC.—See Mary Kay Holding Corporation; *U.S. Private*, pg. 2599
MARY KAY (KAZAKHSTAN) LLP—See Mary Kay Holding Corporation; *U.S. Private*, pg. 2599
MARY KAY KOREA, LTD.—See Mary Kay Holding Corporation; *U.S. Private*, pg. 2599
MARY KAY LITHUANIA—See Mary Kay Holding Corporation; *U.S. Private*, pg. 2599
MARY KAY (MALAYSIA) SDN BHD—See Mary Kay Holding Corporation; *U.S. Private*, pg. 2599

MARY KAY PHILIPPINES, INC.—See Mary Kay Holding Corporation; *U.S. Private*, pg. 2599
MARY KAY (SINGAPORE) PRIVATE LIMITED—See Mary Kay Holding Corporation; *U.S. Private*, pg. 2599
MARY KRAFT AND ASSOCIATES INC.—See Imagine Staffing Technology, Inc.; *U.S. Private*, pg. 2045
MARYLAND AEROSPACE, INC.—See Redwire Corporation; *U.S. Public*, pg. 1771
MARYLAND-AMERICAN WATER COMPANY—See American Water Works Company, Inc.; *U.S. Public*, pg. 112
MARYLAND AUTOMOBILE INSURANCE FUND; *U.S. Private*, pg. 2600
MARYLAND CASUALTY COMPANY—See Zurich Insurance Group Limited; *Int'l*, pg. 8699
MARYLAND CHEMICAL COMPANY, INC.; *U.S. Private*, pg. 2600
MARYLAND COLLABORATIVE CARE TRANSFORMATION ORGANIZATION, INC.—See Centene Corporation; *U.S. Public*, pg. 471
MARYLAND COMPOSITION—See Chatham Asset Management, LLC; *U.S. Private*, pg. 862
THE MARYLAND & DELAWARE GROUP OF LONG & FOSTER; *U.S. Private*, pg. 4075
MARYLAND ECONOMIC DEVELOPMENT CORPORATION; *U.S. Private*, pg. 2600
MARYLAND ENDOSCOPY ANESTHESIA, LLC—See KKR & Co. Inc.; *U.S. Public*, pg. 1249
MARYLAND ENDOSCOPY CENTER LIMITED LIABILITY COMPANY—See KKR & Co. Inc.; *U.S. Public*, pg. 1246
MARYLAND HEIGHTS CENTER FOR BEHAVIORAL HEALTH, LLC—See National HealthCare Corporation; *U.S. Public*, pg. 1495
MARYLAND JOCKEY CLUB, INC.—See The Stronach Group Inc.; *Int'l*, pg. 7689
MARYLAND MIDLAND RAILWAY, INC.—See Brookfield Infrastructure Partners L.P.; *Int'l*, pg. 1192
MARYLAND MIDLAND RAILWAY, INC.—See GIC Pte. Ltd.; *Int'l*, pg. 2966
MARYLAND ORTHOTICS & PROSTHETICS CO., INC.—See D&J Sales Co. LLC; *U.S. Private*, pg. 1138
MARYLAND PLASTICS, INC.—See Bio Medic Corporation; *U.S. Private*, pg. 561
MARYLAND PRECISION SPRING—See American Securities LLC; *U.S. Private*, pg. 250
MARYLAND STATE EDUCATION ASSOCIATION; *U.S. Private*, pg. 2600
MARYLAND SURGERY CENTER FOR WOMEN, LLC—See KKR & Co. Inc.; *U.S. Public*, pg. 1249
MARYLAND & VIRGINIA MILK PRODUCERS COOP ASSOCIATION INC; *U.S. Private*, pg. 2600
MARYLAND ZOOLOGICAL SOCIETY, INC.; *U.S. Private*, pg. 2600
MARYL CONSTRUCTION, INC.—See Maryl Group, Inc.; *U.S. Private*, pg. 2600
MARY LEE PACKAGING CORPORATION—See Gilster-Mary Lee Corporation; *U.S. Private*, pg. 1701
MARYL GROUP, INC.; *U.S. Private*, pg. 2600
MARY MAC APPAREL INC.—See Easyknit International Holdings Ltd.; *Int'l*, pg. 2277
MARY MAXIM, INC.; *U.S. Private*, pg. 2599
MARY MAXIM, LTD.—See Mary Maxim, Inc.; *U.S. Private*, pg. 2599
MARY ROACH INSURANCE AGENCY, INC.—See Stone Point Capital LLC; *U.S. Private*, pg. 3819
MARY RUTAN HOSPITAL; *U.S. Private*, pg. 2599
MARY'S GONE CRACKERS; *U.S. Private*, pg. 2599
MARY'S GROUP, LTD.—See Rachel Allan, LLC; *U.S. Private*, pg. 3342
MARYS PIZZA SHACK; *U.S. Private*, pg. 2600
MARY'S RIVER LUMBER CO., INC.; *U.S. Private*, pg. 2599
MARYSVILLE DIALYSIS CENTER, LLC—See DaVita Inc.; *U.S. Public*, pg. 641
MARYSVILLE HYDROCARBONS LLC—See Phillips 66 Company; *U.S. Public*, pg. 1688
MARYSVILLE MARINE DISTRIBUTORS; *U.S. Private*, pg. 2600
MARYVALE; *U.S. Private*, pg. 2600
THE MARYVILLE ASC, L.P.—See KKR & Co. Inc.; *U.S. Public*, pg. 1248
MARYVILLE DATA SYSTEMS INC.; *U.S. Private*, pg. 2600
MARYVILLE MARITIME INC.—See EXCEL MARITIME CARRIERS LTD.; *Int'l*, pg. 2577
MARYWILSKA 44 SP Z O.O.—See Mirbud S.A.; *Int'l*, pg. 4919
MARZA ANIMATION PLANET INC—See Sega Sammy Holdings, Inc.; *Int'l*, pg. 6681
MARZETTI FROZEN PASTA—See Lancaster Colony Corporation; *U.S. Public*, pg. 1291
MARZETTO S.P.A DIVISION GUABELLO—See Marzotto S.p.A.; *Int'l*, pg. 4718
MARZOCCHI POMPE S.P.A.; *Int'l*, pg. 4718
MARZOCCHI PUMPS USA CORP.—See Marzocchi Pompe S.p.A.; *Int'l*, pg. 4718
MARZOCCHI (SHANGHAI) TRADING CO., LTD.—See Marzocchi Pompe S.p.A.; *Int'l*, pg. 4718

MASCHINENFABRIK BERTHOLD HERMLE AG

MARZOLI INTERNATIONAL, INC.—See Camozzi Group; *Int'l*, pg. 1274
MARZOLI MACHINES TEXTILE SRL—See Camozzi Group; *Int'l*, pg. 1274
MARZOLI TEXTILE MACHINERY MANUFACTURERS PRIVATE LIMITED—See Camozzi Group; *Int'l*, pg. 1274
MARZOLO & PARTNER AG—See BKW AG; *Int'l*, pg. 1055
MARZOTTO S.P.A. DIVISION MARLANE—See Marzotto S.p.A.; *Int'l*, pg. 4718
MARZOTTO S.P.A. - ESTETHIA/ G.B CONTE DIVISION—See Marzotto S.p.A.; *Int'l*, pg. 4718
MARZOTTO S.P.A.; *Int'l*, pg. 4718
MARZOTTO S.P.A.—See Marzotto S.p.A.; *Int'l*, pg. 4718
MARZOTTO TEXTILE-DIVISIONE FILATI LANEROSSI—See Marzotto S.p.A.; *Int'l*, pg. 4718
MARZOTTO TEXTILE-DIVISIONE TESSUTI DI SONDRIO—See Marzotto S.p.A.; *Int'l*, pg. 4718
MARZOTTO TEXTILE-DIVISIONE TESSUTI LANEROSSI—See Marzotto S.p.A.; *Int'l*, pg. 4718
MARZOTTO TEXTILE—See Marzotto S.p.A.; *Int'l*, pg. 4718
MARZOTTO TEXTILES (U.S.A.) CORP.—See Marzotto S.p.A.; *Int'l*, pg. 4718
MASA ALGECIRAS, S.A.—See ACS, Actividades de Construccion y Servicios, S.A.; *Int'l*, pg. 115
MASA CONCRETE PLANTS INDIA PVT. LTD.—See CGS Management AG; *Int'l*, pg. 1435
THE MASA CORPORATION; *U.S. Private*, pg. 4075
MASA DA AMAZONIA LTDA.—See Flex Ltd.; *Int'l*, pg. 2704
MASADA BAKERY, LLC—See Tennessee Bun Company, LLC; *U.S. Private*, pg. 3967
MASADAR ENERGY COMPANY FOR GENERAL TRADING W.L.L.—See First Investment Company K.S.C.C.; *Int'l*, pg. 2685
MAS ADVISORS, LLC; *U.S. Private*, pg. 2600
MASAFAT SPECIALIZED TRANSPORT COMPANY; *Int'l*, pg. 4718
MASA GALICIA, S.A.—See ACS, Actividades de Construccion y Servicios, S.A.; *Int'l*, pg. 115
MASA GMBH—See CGS Management AG; *Int'l*, pg. 1435
MASA GROUP INC.—See SCA Qualis; *Int'l*, pg. 6610
MASA GROUP S.A.—See SCA Qualis; *Int'l*, pg. 6610
MASAHA HEAVY EQUIPMENT CO.—See Fouad Alghanim & Sons Group of Companies; *Int'l*, pg. 2753
MASA HUELVA, S.A.—See ACS, Actividades de Construccion y Servicios, S.A.; *Int'l*, pg. 115
MAS AIR SYSTEMS, LLC—See The New York Blower Company, Inc.; *U.S. Private*, pg. 4083
MASA MIDDLE EAST FZCO—See CGS Management AG; *Int'l*, pg. 1435
MA SAN CONSUMER CORPORATION—See Masan Consumer Corp.; *Int'l*, pg. 4719
MASAN CONSUMER CORP.; *Int'l*, pg. 4718
MA SAN HORIZON CORPORATION—See Masan Consumer Corp.; *Int'l*, pg. 4719
MASA NORTE, S.A.—See ACS, Actividades de Construccion y Servicios, S.A.; *Int'l*, pg. 115
MASAN PLANT OF SHINSUNG AUTOMOTIVE CO.,LTD.—See Shinsung Delta Tech Co., Ltd.; *Int'l*, pg. 6848
MA SANTE FACILE S.A.—See Swiss Life Holding; *Int'l*, pg. 7368
MASANTO CONTAINERS PRIVATE LIMITED—See Bhagyanagar Properties Limited; *Int'l*, pg. 1010
MASA PUERTOLLANO, S.A.—See ACS, Actividades de Construccion y Servicios, S.A.; *Int'l*, pg. 115
MASARU CORPORATION; *Int'l*, pg. 4719
MASA SERVICIOS, S.A.—See ACS, Actividades de Construccion y Servicios, S.A.; *Int'l*, pg. 115
MASA TENERIFE, S.A.—See ACS, Actividades de Construccion y Servicios, S.A.; *Int'l*, pg. 115
MASA TIANJIN BUILDING MATERIAL MACHINERY CO., LTD.—See CGS Management AG; *Int'l*, pg. 1435
MASA-USA, LLC—See CGS Management AG; *Int'l*, pg. 1435
MAS AUSTRALASIA PTY LTD—See AusGroup Limited; *Int'l*, pg. 716
MAS AUTOMATION CORP.—See Chroma ATE Inc.; *Int'l*, pg. 1588
MASAWARA PLC; *Int'l*, pg. 4719
MAS-BE TRAVEL SERVICES SDN BHD—See Jiankun International Berhad; *Int'l*, pg. 3961
MASCAL ELECTRIC, INC.; *U.S. Private*, pg. 2600
MASCAREN INTERNATIONAL INC; *Int'l*, pg. 4720
MASCARO CONSTRUCTION CO. LP; *U.S. Private*, pg. 2600
MASCHHOFF FAMILY FOODS, LLC; *U.S. Private*, pg. 2600
THE MASCHHOFFS, LLC—See Maschhoff Family Foods, LLC; *U.S. Private*, pg. 2601
MASCHINENFABRIIK GERD MOSCA AG—See Mosca AG; *Int'l*, pg. 5050
MASCHINENFABRIK BERNER GMBH & CO. KG—See INDUS Holding AG; *Int'l*, pg. 3663
MASCHINENFABRIK BERTHOLD HERMLE AG; *Int'l*, pg. 4720

MASCHINENFABRIK GUSTAV EIRICH GMBH & CO KG — CORPORATE AFFILIATIONS

MASCHINENFABRIK GUSTAV EIRICH GMBH & CO KG; *Int'l*, pg. 4720
MASCHINENFABRIK HARRY LUCAS GMBH & CO. KG; *Int'l*, pg. 4720
MASCHINENFABRIK HEID AKTIENGESELLSCHAFT; *Int'l*, pg. 4720
MASCHINENFABRIK KBA-MODLING AG—See Koenig & Bauer AG; *Int'l*, pg. 4227
MASCHINENFABRIK MOENNINGHOFF GMBH & CO. KG—See Miki Pulley Co., Ltd.; *Int'l*, pg. 4891
MASCHINENFABRIK MOENNINGHOFF GMBH & CO. KG—See Miki Pulley Co., Ltd.; *Int'l*, pg. 4891
MASCHINENFABRIK OTTO BAIER GMBH; *Int'l*, pg. 4720
MASCHINENFABRIK RIETER AG—See Rieter Holding Ltd.; *Int'l*, pg. 6338
MASCHINENFABRIK WAGNER GMBH & CO. KG; *Int'l*, pg. 4721
MASCHINEN RITTER WICKELTECHNIK GMBH—See Jagenberg AG; *Int'l*, pg. 3870
MASCHINEN UND APPARATEBAU GOTZEN GMBH—See Gesco AG; *Int'l*, pg. 2945
MASCHINO HUDELSON & ASSOCIATES LLC—See Aon plc; *U.S. Public*, pg. 496
MASCIONI S.P.A.—See Vincenzo Zucchi S.p.A.; *Int'l*, pg. 8211
MASCIONI USA LTD.—See Vincenzo Zucchi S.p.A.; *Int'l*, pg. 8211
MASCO ASIA (SHENZHEN) CO. LTD.—See Masco Corporation; *U.S. Public*, pg. 1390
MASCO BATH CORPORATION—See Masco Corporation; *U.S. Public*, pg. 1390
MASCO BATH—See Masco Corporation; *U.S. Public*, pg. 1390
MASCO BETEILIGUNGSGESELLSCHAFT MBH—See Masco Corporation; *U.S. Public*, pg. 1390
MASCO BUILDER CABINET GROUP-MERILLAT, ATKINS PANEL PLANT—See AIP, LLC; *U.S. Private*, pg. 133
MASCO BUILDER CABINET GROUP-MERILLAT, JACKSON PLANT—See AIP, LLC; *U.S. Private*, pg. 133
MASCO BUILDER CABINET GROUP-MERILLAT, LAS VEGAS PLANT—See AIP, LLC; *U.S. Private*, pg. 133
MASCO BUILDER CABINET GROUP-MERILLAT, MOUNT JACKSON PLANT—See AIP, LLC; *U.S. Private*, pg. 133
MASCO CABINETRY, LLC—See AIP, LLC; *U.S. Private*, pg. 133
MASCO CANADA LIMITED—See Masco Corporation; *U.S. Public*, pg. 1390
MASCO CHILE LIMITADA—See Masco Corporation; *U.S. Public*, pg. 1391
MASCO CORPORATION LIMITED—See Masco Corporation; *U.S. Public*, pg. 1391
MASCO CORPORATION OF INDIANA—See Masco Corporation; *U.S. Public*, pg. 1391
MASCO CORPORATION; *U.S. Public*, pg. 1389
MASCO EUROPE S.A.R.L.—See Masco Corporation; *U.S. Public*, pg. 1391
MASCO GERMANY HOLDING GMBH—See Masco Corporation; *U.S. Public*, pg. 1391
MASCOLA ADVERTISING; *U.S. Private*, pg. 2601
MASCOMA CORPORATION; *U.S. Private*, pg. 2601
MASCOMA MUTUAL FINANCIAL SERVICES CORPORATION; *U.S. Private*, pg. 2601
MASCOMA SAVINGS BANK—See Mascoma Mutual Financial Services Corporation; *U.S. Private*, pg. 2601
MASCOMEX S.A. DE C.V.—See Masco Corporation; *U.S. Public*, pg. 1392
MASCO MIDEAST AIRCRAFT SERVICES COMPANY—See Middle East Airlines Airliban S.A.L.; *Int'l*, pg. 4883
MASCOM WIRELESS BOTSWANA (PTY) LIMITED—See MTN Group Limited; *Int'l*, pg. 5071
MASCO INCORPORATED; *U.S. Private*, pg. 2601
MASCO PETROLEUM, INC—See Bristol Bay Native Corporation; *U.S. Private*, pg. 656
MASCO PRODUCT DESIGN, INC.—See Masco Corporation; *U.S. Public*, pg. 1391
MASCO RETAIL CABINET GROUP, LLC—See Masco Corporation; *U.S. Public*, pg. 1391
MASCO RETAIL SALES SUPPORT, INC.—See Masco Corporation; *U.S. Public*, pg. 1391
MASCO SERVICES GROUP CORP.—See Masco Corporation; *U.S. Public*, pg. 1391
MASCO SERVICES, INC.—See Masco Corporation; *U.S. Public*, pg. 1391
MASCOT-CHEMICAL PAPER CO., LTD.—See Marubeni Corporation; *Int'l*, pg. 4709
MASCOTT CORPORATION; *U.S. Private*, pg. 2601
MASCO UK WINDOW GROUP LIMITED—See Masco Corporation; *U.S. Public*, pg. 1391
MASCUS A/S—See Alma Media Corporation; *Int'l*, pg. 362
MASCUS BENELUX—See RB Global, Inc.; *Int'l*, pg. 6226
MASCUS USA INC.—See RB Global, Inc.; *Int'l*, pg. 6226
MASDA CORPORATION; *U.S. Private*, pg. 2601
MASDAR AL HAYAT FOR FOOD INDUSTRIES, LTD.—See Ali Abdullah Al Tamimi Company; *Int'l*, pg. 319
MAS DISTRIBUTION COMPANY—See MAS Economic Group; *Int'l*, pg. 4718

MAS ECONOMIC GROUP; *Int'l*, pg. 4718
M & A SECURITIES SDN. BHD.—See M & A Equity Holdings Berhad; *Int'l*, pg. 4609
MASELLE & ASSOCIATES, INC.; *U.S. Private*, pg. 2601
MASER AND QUARTZELEC SERVICE SDN. BHD.—See Quartzelec Ltd.; *Int'l*, pg. 6156
MASERATI DEUTSCHLAND GMBH—See Stellantis N.V.; *Int'l*, pg. 7200
MASERATI GB LTD.—See Stellantis N.V.; *Int'l*, pg. 7200
MASERATI JAPAN KK—See Stellantis N.V.; *Int'l*, pg. 7200
MASERATI NORTH AMERICA, INC.—See Stellantis N.V.; *Int'l*, pg. 7200
MASERATI S.P.A.—See Stellantis N.V.; *Int'l*, pg. 7200
MASER CONSULTING—See Colliers International Group Inc.; *Int'l*, pg. 1700
MASER CONSULTING—See Colliers International Group Inc.; *Int'l*, pg. 1700
MASER CONSULTING—See Colliers International Group Inc.; *Int'l*, pg. 1700
MASER CONSULTING—See Colliers International Group Inc.; *Int'l*, pg. 1700
MASER CONSULTING—See Colliers International Group Inc.; *Int'l*, pg. 1700
MASER CONSULTING—See Colliers International Group Inc.; *Int'l*, pg. 1700
MASER CONSULTING—See Colliers International Group Inc.; *Int'l*, pg. 1700
MASER CONSULTING—See Colliers International Group Inc.; *Int'l*, pg. 1700
MASER CONSULTING—See Colliers International Group Inc.; *Int'l*, pg. 1700
MASER CONSULTING—See Colliers International Group Inc.; *Int'l*, pg. 1700
MASER CONSULTING—See Colliers International Group Inc.; *Int'l*, pg. 1700
MASER CONSULTING—See Colliers International Group Inc.; *Int'l*, pg. 1700
MASER CONSULTING—See Colliers International Group Inc.; *Int'l*, pg. 1700
MASER CONSULTING—See Colliers International Group Inc.; *Int'l*, pg. 1700
MASER ENGINEERING SA—See Groupe Crit, S.A.; *Int'l*, pg. 3101
MASERGY COMMUNICATIONS, INC.—See Berkshire Partners LLC; *U.S. Private*, pg. 535
MASERGY COMMUNICATIONS UK LIMITED—See Berkshire Partners LLC; *U.S. Private*, pg. 535
MASFALT S.A.—See Eiffage S.A.; *Int'l*, pg. 2331
MASFALT SP. Z O.O.—See CRH plc; *Int'l*, pg. 1845
MAS FINANCIAL SERVICES LIMITED; *Int'l*, pg. 4718
MAS FOR METAL ENDS COMPANY—See MAS Economic Group; *Int'l*, pg. 4718
MAS GLOBAL CONSULTING, LLC; *U.S. Private*, pg. 2600
MAS GOLD CORP.; *Int'l*, pg. 4718
MASHAER HOLDING COMPANY (K.S.C.P); *Int'l*, pg. 4721
MASHANTUCKET PEQUOT GAMING ENTERPRISE INC.; *U.S. Private*, pg. 2601
MASHBURN CONSTRUCTION COMPANY; *U.S. Private*, pg. 2601
MASHELL, INC.—See Palisade Investment Partners Limited; *Int'l*, pg. 5708
MASHELL TELECOM, INC.—See Palisade Investment Partners Limited; *Int'l*, pg. 5708
MASHHAD CARTON INDUSTRIES COMPANY; *Int'l*, pg. 4721
MASH HEALTH LIMITED—See Arsenal Capital Management LP; *U.S. Private*, pg. 338
MASHITA HOLDINGS SDN. BHD.—See Pappajack Berhad; *Int'l*, pg. 5734
MASHONALAND HOLDINGS LIMITED; *Int'l*, pg. 4721
MASHONALAND TOBACCO COMPANY—See Pyxus International, Inc.; *U.S. Public*, pg. 1740
MASHONALAND TOBACCO HOLDINGS (PVT) LTD.—See Pyxus International, Inc.; *U.S. Public*, pg. 1740
MASHPEE ACQUISITION LLC—See The Royal Health Group LLC; *U.S. Private*, pg. 4113
MASHREQBANK P.S.C - MASHREQ AL ISLAMI DIVISION—See Mashreqbank P.S.C; *Int'l*, pg. 4721
MASHREQBANK P.S.C - NEW YORK—See Mashreqbank P.S.C; *Int'l*, pg. 4721
MASHREQBANK P.S.C; *Int'l*, pg. 4721
MASHREQBANK P.S.C. - UK—See Mashreqbank P.S.C; *Int'l*, pg. 4721
MASHREQ SECURITIES WLL—See Mashreqbank P.S.C; *Int'l*, pg. 4721
MASHSTROY JSC; *Int'l*, pg. 4721
MASI AGRICOLA S.P.A.; *Int'l*, pg. 4721
MASIDEF S.R.L.—See Wurth Verwaltungsgesellschaft mbH; *Int'l*, pg. 8506
MASIF LATEX PRODUCTS SDN BHD—See Kuala Lumpur Kepong Berhad; *Int'l*, pg. 4318
MASIMBA HOLDINGS LIMITED; *Int'l*, pg. 4721
MASIMO AMERICAS, INC.—See Masimo Corporation; *U.S. Public*, pg. 1392
MASIMO ASIA PACIFIC PTE. LTD.—See Masimo Corporation; *U.S. Public*, pg. 1392
MASIMO CORPORATION; *U.S. Public*, pg. 1392

MASIMO EUROPE LIMITED, SUCURSAL EN ESPANA—See Masimo Corporation; *U.S. Public*, pg. 1392
MASIMO EUROPE LTD.—See Masimo Corporation; *U.S. Public*, pg. 1392
MASIMO GULF, LLC—See Masimo Corporation; *U.S. Public*, pg. 1392
MASIMO INTERNATIONAL SARL - DUBAI, U.A.E.—See Masimo Corporation; *U.S. Public*, pg. 1392
MASIMO KOREA, LLC—See Masimo Corporation; *U.S. Public*, pg. 1392
MASIMO MEDIKAL URUNLER TICARET LIMITED SIRKETI ISTANBUL SUBESI—See Masimo Corporation; *U.S. Public*, pg. 1392
MASIMO SEMICONDUCTOR, INC.—See Masimo Corporation; *U.S. Public*, pg. 1392
MASIMO SWEDEN AB—See Masimo Corporation; *U.S. Public*, pg. 1392
MASIMO UK LTD.—See Masimo Corporation; *U.S. Public*, pg. 1392
MAS, INC.; *U.S. Private*, pg. 2600
MASINOPROJEKT KOPRING A.D.; *Int'l*, pg. 4721
MASINSKI CENTAR A.D.; *Int'l*, pg. 4721
MASINSKI SERVIS UPP A.D.; *Int'l*, pg. 4721
MASISA ARGENTINA S.A.—See Fritz Egger GmbH & Co.; *Int'l*, pg. 2793
MASISA CHILE S.A.—See GrupoNueva S.A.; *Int'l*, pg. 3139
MASISA COMPONENTES SPA—See GrupoNueva S.A.; *Int'l*, pg. 3139
MASISA DO BRASIL LTDA.—See AntarChile S.A.; *Int'l*, pg. 481
MASISA MANUFACTURA S.A. DE C.V.—See AntarChile S.A.; *Int'l*, pg. 481
MASISA PLC S.A.S.—See GrupoNueva S.A.; *Int'l*, pg. 3139
MASISA S.A.—See GrupoNueva S.A.; *Int'l*, pg. 3139
MASISA USA, INC.—See GrupoNueva S.A.; *Int'l*, pg. 3140
MASIUS LONDON—See Publicis Groupe S.A.; *Int'l*, pg. 6102
MASIVO SILVER CORP.; *Int'l*, pg. 4721
MASI WINE BAR MUNICH GMBH—See MASI Agricola S.p.A.; *Int'l*, pg. 4721
MASKA POWER TRANSMISSION (CHANGZHOU) CO. LTD.—See ABB Ltd.; *Int'l*, pg. 49
MASKARGO LOGISTICS SDN. BHD.—See Khazanah Nasional Berhad; *Int'l*, pg. 4153
MASKELIYA PLANTATIONS PLC; *Int'l*, pg. 4721
MASKELIYA TEA GARDENS (CEYLON) LIMITED—See Richard Pieris & Co. Ltd.; *Int'l*, pg. 6330
MASKELL PIPE & SUPPLY, INC.—See Core & Main, Inc.; *U.S. Public*, pg. 576
MASKEW MILLER LONGMAN (PTY) LTD.—See Pearson plc; *Int'l*, pg. 5775
MASKIMI POLYOL SDN. BHD.—See Bina Puri Holdings Bhd; *Int'l*, pg. 1032
MASKINCENTRUM I ORNSKOLDSVIK AB—See Investment AB Latour; *Int'l*, pg. 3783
MASKINERING OG SVEISESERVICE AS—See Schlumberger Limited; *U.S. Public*, pg. 1844
MASKINKLIPPET AB—See BHG Group AB; *Int'l*, pg. 1015
MASK INVESTMENTS LIMITED; *Int'l*, pg. 4721
MASLACK SUPPLY LTD.—See LKQ Corporation; *U.S. Public*, pg. 1336
MASLAND CARPETS—See The Dixie Group, Inc.; *U.S. Public*, pg. 2067
MASLANSKY, LUNTZ & PARTNERS—See Omnicom Group Inc.; *U.S. Public*, pg. 1588
MASLAVI CONSTRUCTION CO., LTD.; *Int'l*, pg. 4722
MASLOW LUMIA BARTORILLO ADVERTISING; *U.S. Private*, pg. 2601
THE MASLOW MEDIA GROUP, INC.—See Reliability Incorporated; *U.S. Public*, pg. 1778
MASMEDIA B.V.—See ITV plc; *Int'l*, pg. 3845
MAS MEDICAL STAFFING; *U.S. Private*, pg. 2600
MAS METAMAP (BEIJING) SOFTWARE TECHNOLOGY CO., LTD.—See Chongqing MAS Sci. & Tech. Co., Ltd.; *Int'l*, pg. 1580
MASMOVIL IBERCOM, S.A.—See Orange S.A.; *Int'l*, pg. 5609
MASNOVA QUIMICA S.A. DE C.V.—See AntarChile S.A.; *Int'l*, pg. 481
MASODIK PHN 2007. KFT—See PHOENIX Pharmahandel GmbH & Co. KG; *Int'l*, pg. 5854
MASON BANCSHARES, INC.; *U.S. Private*, pg. 2601
MASON BANK—See Mason Bancshares, Inc.; *U.S. Private*, pg. 2601
MASON BLAU & ASSOCIATES, INC.—See Godspeed Capital Management LP; *U.S. Private*, pg. 1725
MASON CAPITAL CORP; *Int'l*, pg. 4722
MASON CHEMICAL COMPANY—See Pilot Chemical Company; *U.S. Private*, pg. 3181
MASON CITY FORD; *U.S. Private*, pg. 2601
MASON CLAIM SERVICES, INC.; *U.S. Private*, pg. 2601
MASON COMPANIES, INC.; *U.S. Private*, pg. 2602
THE MASON COMPANY, LLC—See Midmark Corporation; *U.S. Private*, pg. 2716
MASON CORPORATION; *U.S. Private*, pg. 2602

COMPANY NAME INDEX

MASON COUNTY GARBAGE CO., INC.—See Waste Connections, Inc.; *Int'l*, pg. 8353
MASON COUNTY PUBLIC UTILITY DISTRICT 3; *U.S. Private*, pg. 2602
MASON DISTRIBUTORS, INC.; *U.S. Private*, pg. 2602
MASON DIXON INTERMODAL, INC.—See Universal Logistics Holdings, Inc.; *U.S. Public*, pg. 2261
MASON ELECTRIC CO.—See TransDigm Group Incorporated; *U.S. Public*, pg. 2181
MASON FOREST PRODUCTS INC.; *U.S. Private*, pg. 2602
MASON GROUP HOLDINGS LIMITED; *Int'l*, pg. 4722
MASON GROUP LTD.—See Datatec Limited; *Int'l*, pg. 1980
THE MASON & HANGER GROUP INC.—See The Day & Zimmermann Group, Inc.; *U.S. Private*, pg. 4019
MASONIC HOME OF VIRGINIA; *U.S. Private*, pg. 2602
MASONIC HOMES OF CALIFORNIA, INC.; *U.S. Private*, pg. 2602
MASON, INC.; *U.S. Private*, pg. 2602
MASON INDUSTRIAL TECHNOLOGY, INC.; *U.S. Public*, pg. 1392
MASON INDUSTRIES; *U.S. Private*, pg. 2602
MASONITE BEAMS AB—See Byggma ASA; *Int'l*, pg. 1235
MASONITE CANADA CORPORATION—See Owens Corning; *U.S. Public*, pg. 1627
MASONITE CANADA CORP. - YARROW—See Owens Corning; *U.S. Public*, pg. 1627
MASONITE CHILE HOLDINGS—See Owens Corning; *U.S. Public*, pg. 1627
MASONITE CHILE S.A.—See Owens Corning; *U.S. Public*, pg. 1627
MASONITE CORP. - CORNING—See Owens Corning; *U.S. Public*, pg. 1627
MASONITE CORP. - DICKSON—See Owens Corning; *U.S. Public*, pg. 1627
MASONITE CORP. - GREENVILLE—See Owens Corning; *U.S. Public*, pg. 1627
MASONITE CORP. - NORTH PLATTE—See Owens Corning; *U.S. Public*, pg. 1627
MASONITE CORPORATION—See Owens Corning; *U.S. Public*, pg. 1627
MASONITE CORP. - STANLEY—See Owens Corning; *U.S. Public*, pg. 1627
MASONITE CORP. - WEST CHICAGO—See Owens Corning; *U.S. Public*, pg. 1627
MASONITE CZ SPOL S.R.O.—See Owens Corning; *U.S. Public*, pg. 1627
MASONITE DOORS PRIVATE LTD.—See Owens Corning; *U.S. Public*, pg. 1627
MASONITE INTERNATIONAL CORPORATION—See Owens Corning; *U.S. Public*, pg. 1626
MASONITE IRELAND—See Owens Corning; *U.S. Public*, pg. 1627
MASON & MASON INSURANCE AGENCY, INC.—See The Baldwin Insurance Group, Inc.; *U.S. Public*, pg. 2035
MASON & MASON TECHNOLOGY INSURANCE SERVICES, INC.—See The Baldwin Insurance Group, Inc.; *U.S. Public*, pg. 2035
MASON-McDUFFIE MORTGAGE CORP.; *U.S. Private*, pg. 2602
MASON METAL INDUSTRY CO., LTD.—See Sumitomo Corporation; *Int'l*, pg. 7269
MASON PARK, LTD—See American Realty Investors, Inc.; *U.S. Public*, pg. 108
MASON PRIVATBANK LIECHTENSTEIN AG—See Mason Group Holdings Limited; *Int'l*, pg. 4722
MASONPRO, INC.—See The Sterling Group, L.P.; *U.S. Private*, pg. 4122
MASON RESOURCES INC.; *Int'l*, pg. 4722
MASONRYARTS, INC.; *U.S. Private*, pg. 2603
MASONRY BUILDERS, INC.; *U.S. Private*, pg. 2603
MASONRY REINFORCING CORPORATION AMERICA; *U.S. Private*, pg. 2603
MASON SELKOWITZ MARKETING, INC; *U.S. Private*, pg. 2602
MASON'S MILL & LUMBER CO., INC.; *U.S. Private*, pg. 2602
MASON STRUCTURAL STEEL, INC.; *U.S. Private*, pg. 2602
MASON VITAMINS, INC.—See Mason Distributors, Inc.; *U.S. Private*, pg. 2602
MASON WELLS, INC.; *U.S. Private*, pg. 2602
MASON WEST INC.—See Gladstone Management Corporation; *U.S. Private*, pg. 1705
MASOOD TEXTILE MILLS LIMITED - APPAREL FACTORY—See Masood Textile Mills Limited; *Int'l*, pg. 4722
MASOOD TEXTILE MILLS LIMITED - APPAREL-III FACTORY—See Masood Textile Mills Limited; *Int'l*, pg. 4722
MASOOD TEXTILE MILLS LIMITED - FALCON FACTORY—See Masood Textile Mills Limited; *Int'l*, pg. 4722
MASOOD TEXTILE MILLS LIMITED - LEOPARD FACTORY—See Masood Textile Mills Limited; *Int'l*, pg. 4722

MASOOD TEXTILE MILLS LIMITED - PANTHER FACTORY—See Masood Textile Mills Limited; *Int'l*, pg. 4722
MASOOD TEXTILE MILLS LIMITED; *Int'l*, pg. 4722
MASOVAL AS; *Int'l*, pg. 4722
MASPETH FEDERAL SAVINGS & LOAN ASSOCIATION; *U.S. Private*, pg. 2603
MAS P.L.C; *Int'l*, pg. 4718
MASPORT INC—See Skellerup Holdings Limited; *Int'l*, pg. 6980
MASQUE SOUND & RECORDING CORP.; *U.S. Private*, pg. 2603
MASRAF AL RAYAN (Q.S.C.); *Int'l*, pg. 4722
MASSACHUSETTS AVENUE SURGERY CENTER, LLC—See UnitedHealth Group Incorporated; *U.S. Public*, pg. 2242
MASSACHUSETTS BAY BREWING CO.; *U.S. Private*, pg. 2603
MASSACHUSETTS BAY HEALTH CARE TRUST FUND; *U.S. Private*, pg. 2603
MASSACHUSETTS BAY INSURANCE CO.—See The Hanover Insurance Group, Inc.; *U.S. Public*, pg. 2087
MASSACHUSETTS BEHAVIORAL HEALTH PARTNERSHIP, LLP—See Elevance Health, Inc.; *U.S. Public*, pg. 730
MASSACHUSETTS BUSINESS DEVELOPMENT CORP.; *U.S. Public*, pg. 1392
MASSACHUSETTS CAPITAL RESOURCE COMPANY; *U.S. Private*, pg. 2603
MASSACHUSETTS CONTAINER CORPORATION—See Connecticut Container Corporation; *U.S. Private*, pg. 1016
MASSACHUSETTS CONVENTION CENTER AUTHORITY; *U.S. Private*, pg. 2603
MASSACHUSETTS FINANCIAL SERVICES COMPANY—See Sun Life Financial Inc.; *Int'l*, pg. 7305
THE MASSACHUSETTS GENERAL HOSPITAL—See Partners HealthCare System, Inc.; *U.S. Private*, pg. 3102
MASSACHUSETTS GENERAL PHYSICIANS ORGANIZATION, INC.—See Partners HealthCare System, Inc.; *U.S. Private*, pg. 3102
MASSACHUSETTS GREEN HIGH PERFORMANCE COMPUTING CENTER INC.; *U.S. Private*, pg. 2603
MASSACHUSETTS HOSPITAL ASSOCIATION, INC.; *U.S. Private*, pg. 2604
MASSACHUSETTS INSTITUTE OF TECHNOLOGY; *U.S. Private*, pg. 2604
MASSACHUSETTS INSTITUTE OF TECHNOLOGY; *U.S. Private*, pg. 2604
MASSACHUSETTS LABORERS BENEFIT FUNDS; *U.S. Private*, pg. 2604
MASSACHUSETTS LAWYERS WEEKLY, INC.—See The Dolan Company; *U.S. Private*, pg. 4022
MASSACHUSETTS LEAGUE OF COMMUNITY HEALTH CENTERS; *U.S. Private*, pg. 2604
THE MASSACHUSETTS LEGAL ASSISTANCE CORPORATION; *U.S. Private*, pg. 4075
MASSACHUSETTS MEDICAL SOCIETY; *U.S. Private*, pg. 2604
MASSACHUSETTS MENTOR, LLC—See Centerbridge Partners, L.P.; *U.S. Private*, pg. 813
MASSACHUSETTS MUNICIPAL WHOLESALE ELECTRIC CO.; *U.S. Private*, pg. 2604
MASSACHUSETTS MUTUAL LIFE INSURANCE COMPANY; *U.S. Private*, pg. 2604
MASSACHUSETTS PORT AUTHORITY; *U.S. Private*, pg. 2606
MASSACHUSETTS SOCIETY FOR THE PREVENTION OF CRUELTY TO CHILDREN; *U.S. Private*, pg. 2606
MASS ADVERTISING AGENCY LTD.—See Hayel Saeed Anam Group of Companies; *Int'l*, pg. 3290
MASSAGE ENVY FRANCHISING, LLC; *U.S. Private*, pg. 2606
MASSAGE ENVY LIMITED, LLC—See Roark Capital Group Inc.; *U.S. Private*, pg. 3455
MASSAGE HEIGHTS; *U.S. Private*, pg. 2606
MASSAGE THERAPY CONNECTIONS LLC; *U.S. Private*, pg. 2606
MASSALIN PARTICULARES S.A.—See Philip Morris International Inc.; *U.S. Public*, pg. 1685
MASSA MINERALI S.R.L.—See Omya (Schweiz) AG; *Int'l*, pg. 5570
MASSARELLA CATERING GROUP LTD.; *Int'l*, pg. 4722
MASS AUDUBON; *U.S. Private*, pg. 2603
MASS CONNECTIONS, INC.; *U.S. Private*, pg. 2603
MASS CONSULTANTS LIMITED—See Cohort plc; *Int'l*, pg. 1696
MASS DESIGN, INC.; *U.S. Private*, pg. 2603
MASS. ELECTRIC CONSTRUCTION CO., INC.—See Peter Kiewit Sons', Inc.; *U.S. Private*, pg. 3158
MASSELIN COMMUNICATION SAS—See VINCI S.A.; *Int'l*, pg. 8224
MASSELIN ENERGIE S.A.S—See VINCI S.A.; *Int'l*, pg. 8237
MASSENA PARTNERS S.A—See Groupe BPCE; *Int'l*, pg. 3098
MASSENA PARTNERS SA—See Groupe BPCE; *Int'l*, pg. 3098

MASSIMO ZANETTI BEVERAGE GROUP SPA

MASSENBERG GMBH—See DPE Deutsche Private Equity GmbH; *Int'l*, pg. 2188
MASSENGILL TIRE CO. INC.; *U.S. Private*, pg. 2606
MASSEY BUILDERS' SUPPLY CORP.—See Bain Capital, LP; *U.S. Public*, pg. 451
MASSEY CADILLAC, INC.—See Sonic Automotive, Inc.; *U.S. Public*, pg. 1902
MASSEY-CHESSON, INC.—See Applied Industrial Technologies, Inc.; *U.S. Public*, pg. 171
MASSEY COAL SERVICES, INC.—See Alpha Natural Resources, Inc.; *U.S. Private*, pg. 198
MASSEY COMMUNICATIONS, INC.—See Massey Services, Inc.; *U.S. Private*, pg. 2606
MASSEY CONSTRUCTION INC.; *U.S. Private*, pg. 2606
MASSEY FERGUSON CORP.—See AGCO Corporation; *U.S. Public*, pg. 59
MASSEY FERGUSON TARIM MAKINELERI LTD—See AGCO Corporation; *U.S. Public*, pg. 59
MASSEY FERGUSON WORKS PENSION TRUST LTD.—See AGCO Corporation; *U.S. Public*, pg. 59
MASSEY MOTORS INC.; *U.S. Private*, pg. 2606
MASSEY QUICK SIMON & CO., LLC; *U.S. Private*, pg. 2606
MASSEY SERVICES, INC. - PORT CHARLOTTE—See Massey Services, Inc.; *U.S. Private*, pg. 2606
MASSEY SERVICES, INC.; *U.S. Private*, pg. 2606
MASSEY SERVICES INC.—See Massey Services, Inc.; *U.S. Private*, pg. 2606
MASSEY; *U.S. Private*, pg. 2606
MASSEY'S PLATE GLASS & ALUMINUM, INC.; *U.S. Private*, pg. 2606
MASSEY WOOD & WEST INC.; *U.S. Private*, pg. 2606
MASS FIDELITY ASSET MANAGEMENT LIMITED—See WLS Holdings Limited; *Int'l*, pg. 8440
MASS FINISHING, INC.—See Innovance, Inc.; *U.S. Private*, pg. 2081
MASS FOOD SAE—See Kellanova; *U.S. Public*, pg. 1218
MASSFORD (HONG KONG) LIMITED—See E. Bon Holdings Ltd; *Int'l*, pg. 2250
MASS GENERAL BRIGHAM INCORPORATED; *U.S. Private*, pg. 2603
MASS HISPANIC; *U.S. Private*, pg. 2603
MASS HYSTERIA ENTERTAINMENT COMPANY, INC.; *U.S. Private*, pg. 2603
MASSILLON CABLE TV, INC.; *U.S. Private*, pg. 2606
MASSILLON CONTAINER CO., INC.—See Vail Industries, Inc.; *U.S. Private*, pg. 4329
MASSIMO DUTTI DANMARK A/S—See Industria de Diseno Textil, S.A.; *Int'l*, pg. 3666
MASSIMO DUTTI DEUTSCHLAND GMBH—See Industria de Diseno Textil, S.A.; *Int'l*, pg. 3666
MASSIMO DUTTI DISENO, S.L—See Industria de Diseno Textil, S.A.; *Int'l*, pg. 3666
MASSIMO DUTTI FRANCE S.A.R.L.—See Industria de Diseno Textil, S.A.; *Int'l*, pg. 3666
MASSIMO DUTTI GIYIM ITHALAT IH.VE TIC. LTD—See Industria de Diseno Textil, S.A.; *Int'l*, pg. 3666
MASSIMO DUTTI HELLAS S.A—See Industria de Diseno Textil, S.A.; *Int'l*, pg. 3666
MASSIMO DUTTI HONG KONG LTD—See Industria de Diseno Textil, S.A.; *Int'l*, pg. 3666
MASSIMO DUTTI IRELAND LTD.—See Industria de Diseno Textil, S.A.; *Int'l*, pg. 3666
MASSIMO DUTTI KOREA, LTD.—See Industria de Diseno Textil, S.A.; *Int'l*, pg. 3666
MASSIMO DUTTI LOGISTICA S.A—See Industria de Diseno Textil, S.A.; *Int'l*, pg. 3666
MASSIMO DUTTI MAGYARORXZAG KFT.—See Industria de Diseno Textil, S.A.; *Int'l*, pg. 3666
MASSIMO DUTTI MEXICO S.A. DE C.V.—See Industria de Diseno Textil, S.A.; *Int'l*, pg. 3666
MASSIMO DUTTI NEDERLAND, B.V.—See Industria de Diseno Textil, S.A.; *Int'l*, pg. 3666
MASSIMO DUTTI NORGE AS.—See Industria de Diseno Textil, S.A.; *Int'l*, pg. 3666
MASSIMO DUTTI POLSKA SP Z.O.O.—See Industria de Diseno Textil, S.A.; *Int'l*, pg. 3666
MASSIMO DUTTI PORTUGAL - COMERCIO E INDUSTRIA TEXTIL, S.A.—See Industria de Diseno Textil, S.A.; *Int'l*, pg. 3666
MASSIMO DUTTI RO, SRL—See Industria de Diseno Textil, S.A.; *Int'l*, pg. 3666
MASSIMO DUTTI SLOVAKIA, S.R.O.—See Industria de Diseno Textil, S.A.; *Int'l*, pg. 3666
MASSIMO DUTTI SVERIGE AB—See Industria de Diseno Textil, S.A.; *Int'l*, pg. 3666
MASSIMO DUTTI UK LTD—See Industria de Diseno Textil, S.A.; *Int'l*, pg. 3666
MASSIMO DUTTI UKRAINE, LLC—See Industria de Diseno Textil, S.A.; *Int'l*, pg. 3666
MASSIMO DUTTI USA, LTD.—See Industria de Diseno Textil, S.A.; *Int'l*, pg. 3666
MASSIMO GROUP; *U.S. Public*, pg. 1392
MASSIMO ZANETTI BEVERAGE GROUP SPA; *Int'l*, pg. 4722
MASSIMO ZANETTI BEVERAGE IBERIA S.A.—See Massimo Zanetti Beverage Group SpA; *Int'l*, pg. 4722
MASSIMO ZANETTI BEVERAGE MEXICO, S.A. DE C.V.—See Segafredo Zanetti S.p.A.; *Int'l*, pg. 6682

MASSIMO ZANETTI BEVERAGE GROUP SPA — CORPORATE AFFILIATIONS

MASSIMO ZANETTI BEVERAGE S.A.—See Segafredo Zanetti S.p.A.; *Int'l*, pg. 6682
MASSIMO ZANETTI BEVERAGE USA, INC.—See Segafredo Zanetti S.p.A.; *Int'l*, pg. 6682
MASSIMO ZANETTI BEVERAGE VIETNAM COMPANY LTD.—See Massimo Zanetti Beverage Group SpA; *Int'l*, pg. 4723
MASS INTEGRATED SYSTEMS; *U.S. Private*, pg. 2603
MASS INTERNATIONAL CO. LLC—See Schindler Holding AG; *Int'l*, pg. 6619
MASS INTERNATIONAL (PRIVATE) LIMITED—See The Kuwait Company for Process Plant Construction & Contracting K.S.C.; *Int'l*, pg. 7663
MASSIVE DYNAMICS, INC.; *U.S. Private*, pg. 2606
MASSIVE INTERACTIVE, INC.—See Bruins Sports Capital, LLC; *U.S. Private*, pg. 671
MASSIVE MEDIA MATCH NV—See IAC Inc.; *U.S. Public*, pg. 1082
MASSIVE TELECOM—See I.T. Source; *U.S. Private*, pg. 2027
MASSIVIT 3D EUROPE BV—See Massivit 3D Printing Technologies Ltd.; *Int'l*, pg. 4723
MASSIVIT 3D PRINTING TECHNOLOGIES LTD.; *Int'l*, pg. 4723
MASS LEASE—See Panta Holdings B.V.; *Int'l*, pg. 5730
MASSMAN AUTOMATION DESIGNS, LLC—See Granite Equity Partners LLC; *U.S. Private*, pg. 1755
MASSMAN CONSTRUCTION CO.; *U.S. Private*, pg. 2606
MASSMART HOLDINGS, LTD.—See Walmart Inc.; *U.S. Public*, pg. 2325
MASSMEDIA CORPORATE COMMUNICATIONS; *U.S. Private*, pg. 2606
MASS MEDIA MARKETING; *U.S. Private*, pg. 2603
MASS MEDICAL STORAGE, LLC—See Levine Leichtman Capital Partners, LLC; *U.S. Private*, pg. 2435
MASS MEGAWATTS WIND POWER, INC.; *U.S. Public*, pg. 1392
MASSMUTUAL INTERNATIONAL LLC—See Massachusetts Mutual Life Insurance Company; *U.S. Private*, pg. 2605
THE MASSMUTUAL TRUST COMPANY, FSB—See Massachusetts Mutual Life Insurance Company; *U.S. Private*, pg. 2606
MASS NAZCA SAATCHI & SAATCHI—See Publicis Groupe S.A.; *Int'l*, pg. 6107
MASSO ENTERPRISES; *U.S. Private*, pg. 2607
MASS PRECISION SHEETMETAL; *U.S. Private*, pg. 2603
MASS PUBLICIDAD S.R.L.—See Publicis Groupe S.A.; *Int'l*, pg. 6102
MASS RESPONSE DEUTSCHLAND GMBH—See America Movil, S.A.B. de C.V.; *Int'l*, pg. 421
MASS RESPONSE SERVICE GMBH; *Int'l*, pg. 4722
MASS SYSTEMS AMERON GLOBAL, INC.—See AMETEK, Inc.; *U.S. Public*, pg. 117
MASS TELECOM INNOVATION PLC; *Int'l*, pg. 4722
MASSTOCK ARABLE (UK) LTD—See ARYZTA AG; *Int'l*, pg. 589
MASSULLO MOTORS LTD; *Int'l*, pg. 4723
MASSY DISTRIBUTION (BARBADOS) LTD.—See Massy Holdings Ltd.; *Int'l*, pg. 4723
MASSY DISTRIBUTION (GUYANA) INC.—See Massy Holdings Ltd.; *Int'l*, pg. 4723
MASSY DISTRIBUTION (ST. LUCIA) LTD.—See Massy Holdings Ltd.; *Int'l*, pg. 4723
MASSY ENERGY COLOMBIA S.A.S.—See Massy Holdings Ltd.; *Int'l*, pg. 4723
MASSY ENERGY (TRINIDAD) LTD.—See Massy Holdings Ltd.; *Int'l*, pg. 4723
MASSY FINANCE GFC LIMITED—See Massy Holdings Ltd.; *Int'l*, pg. 4723
MASSY GAS PRODUCTS (GUYANA) LTD.—See Massy Holdings Ltd.; *Int'l*, pg. 4723
MASSY GAS PRODUCTS (JAMAICA) LIMITED—See Massy Holdings Ltd.; *Int'l*, pg. 4723
MASSY GAS PRODUCTS (TRINIDAD) LIMITED—See Massy Holdings Ltd.; *Int'l*, pg. 4723
MASSY HOLDINGS LTD.; *Int'l*, pg. 4723
MASSY MACHINERY LIMITED—See Massy Holdings Ltd.; *Int'l*, pg. 4723
MASSY MOTORS LTD.—See Massy Holdings Ltd.; *Int'l*, pg. 4723
MASSY PROPERTIES (BARBADOS) LTD.—See Massy Holdings Ltd.; *Int'l*, pg. 4723
MASSY PROPERTIES (TRINIDAD) LTD.—See Massy Holdings Ltd.; *Int'l*, pg. 4723
MASSY SECURITY (GUYANA) INC.—See Amalgamated Security Services Limited; *Int'l*, pg. 409
MASSY STORES (BARBADOS) LTD.—See Massy Holdings Ltd.; *Int'l*, pg. 4723
MASSY STORES (GUYANA) INC.—See Massy Holdings Ltd.; *Int'l*, pg. 4723
MASSY STORES (SLU) LTD.—See Massy Holdings Ltd.; *Int'l*, pg. 4723
MASSY STORES (SVG) LTD.—See Massy Holdings Ltd.; *Int'l*, pg. 4723
MASSY UNITED INSURANCE LTD.—See Massy Holdings Ltd.; *Int'l*, pg. 4723
MAST BAU GMBH—See PORR AG; *Int'l*, pg. 5923

MASTEC CANADA, INC.—See MasTec, Inc.; *U.S. Public*, pg. 1393
MASTECH DIGITAL, INC.; *U.S. Public*, pg. 1393
MASTECH INFOTRELLIS, INC.—See Mastech Digital, Inc.; *U.S. Public*, pg. 1394
MASTECH STAFFING SERVICES PVT. LTD.—See Mastech Digital, Inc.; *U.S. Public*, pg. 1394
MASTEC, INC.; *U.S. Public*, pg. 1392
MASTEC NORTH AMERICA, INC.—See MasTec, Inc.; *U.S. Public*, pg. 1393
MA STEEL INTERNATIONAL TRADE AND ECONOMIC CORPORATION—See China Baowu Steel Group Corp., Ltd.; *Int'l*, pg. 1486
MA STEEL OCI CHEMICAL CO., LTD.—See OCI Holdings Co., Ltd.; *Int'l*, pg. 5519
MA STEEL (WUHU) PROCESSING AND DISTRIBUTION CO., LTD.—See China Baowu Steel Group Corp., Ltd.; *Int'l*, pg. 1486
MASTEK DIGITAL INC.—See Mastek Ltd.; *Int'l*, pg. 4724
MASTEK ENTERPRISE SOLUTIONS PRIVATE LIMITED—See Mastek Ltd.; *Int'l*, pg. 4724
MASTEK LTD.; *Int'l*, pg. 4724
MASTEK MSC SDN. BHD.—See Mastek Ltd.; *Int'l*, pg. 4724
MASTEK MSC (THAILAND) CO. LTD.—See Mastek Ltd.; *Int'l*, pg. 4724
MASTEK (UK) LIMITED—See Mastek Ltd.; *Int'l*, pg. 4724
MASTEN ENTERPRISES LLC; *U.S. Private*, pg. 2607
MAST ENERGY DEVELOPMENTS PLC; *Int'l*, pg. 4724
MASTEN-WRIGHT, INC.; *U.S. Private*, pg. 2607
MASTERANK INC.; *U.S. Private*, pg. 2608
MASTER APPLIANCE CORP.; *U.S. Private*, pg. 2607
MASTER AUTOMATIC MACHINE COMPANY, INC.—See MacLean-Fogg Company; *U.S. Private*, pg. 2537
MASTER-BILT PRODUCTS—See Ten Oaks Group; *U.S. Private*, pg. 3964
MASTERBLASTERS INDUSTRIAL COATINGS INC.—See Corrosion & Abrasion Solutions Ltd.; *Int'l*, pg. 1806
MASTER BLEND FEEDS LIMITED—See Jamaica Broilers Group Limited; *Int'l*, pg. 3874
MASTER BOND INC.; *U.S. Private*, pg. 2607
MASTERBRAND CABINET NHB INDUSTRIES LTD.—See MasterBrand, Inc.; *U.S. Public*, pg. 1394
MASTERBRAND CABINETS LLC - DECORA CABINETS—See MasterBrand, Inc.; *U.S. Public*, pg. 1394
MASTERBRAND CABINETS LLC—See MasterBrand, Inc.; *U.S. Public*, pg. 1394
MASTERBRAND, INC.; *U.S. Public*, pg. 1394
MASTER BUILDERS SOLUTIONS BELGIUM N.V.—See BASF SE; *Int'l*, pg. 884
MASTER BUILDERS SOLUTIONS NEDERLAND B.V.—See BASF SE; *Int'l*, pg. 884
MASTER BUILDERS SOLUTIONS POLSKA SP. Z O.O.—See BASF SE; *Int'l*, pg. 884
MASTER BUILDERS SOLUTIONS YAPI KIMYASALLARI SANAYI VE TICARET LIMITED SIRKETI—See BASF SE; *Int'l*, pg. 884
MASTERBUILT MANUFACTURING, LLC—See The Middleby Corporation; *U.S. Public*, pg. 2114
MASTER CANADA INC. - FORT ST. JOHN—See MasTec, Inc.; *U.S. Public*, pg. 1393
MASTERCARD ASIA/PACIFIC (AUSTRALIA) PTY. LTD.—See Mastercard Incorporated; *U.S. Public*, pg. 1394
MASTERCARD ASIA/PACIFIC PTE. LTD.—See Mastercard Incorporated; *U.S. Public*, pg. 1394
MASTERCARD CANADA, INC.—See Mastercard Incorporated; *U.S. Public*, pg. 1394
MASTERCARD EUROPE SA—See Mastercard Incorporated; *U.S. Public*, pg. 1394
MASTERCARD INCORPORATED; *U.S. Public*, pg. 1394
MASTERCARD INTERNATIONAL INCORPORATED - IRELAND—See Mastercard Incorporated; *U.S. Public*, pg. 1394
MASTERCARD INTERNATIONAL INCORPORATED—Mastercard Incorporated; *U.S. Public*, pg. 1394
MASTERCARD PAYMENT GATEWAY SERVICES LTD.—See Mastercard Incorporated; *U.S. Public*, pg. 1394
MASTER CHANNEL COMMUNITY NETWORK PRIVATE LIMITED—See Essel Corporate Resources Pvt. Ltd.; *Int'l*, pg. 2509
MASTER CHEMICAL CORPORATION; *U.S. Private*, pg. 2607
MASTER CHEMICAL EUROPE LTD.—See Master Chemical Corporation; *U.S. Private*, pg. 2607
MASTER CHEMICAL (SHANGHAI) CO., LTD.—See Master Chemical Corporation; *U.S. Private*, pg. 2607
MASTER CHEMICAL SIAM CO., LTD.—See Master Chemical Corporation; *U.S. Private*, pg. 2607
MASTER CHEMICALS LIMITED; *Int'l*, pg. 4724
MASTER CHEMICALS OOO—See Ecolab Inc.; *U.S. Public*, pg. 714
MASTER CHEMICAL (TIANJIN) CO., LTD.—See Master Chemical Corporation; *U.S. Private*, pg. 2607
MASTER CHEMICAL VIETNAM CO., LTD.—See Master Chemical Corporation; *U.S. Private*, pg. 2607

MASTERCHEM INDUSTRIES, LLC—See Masco Corporation; *U.S. Public*, pg. 1392
MASTER CLEAN SERVICE LIMITED—See ISP Holdings Limited; *Int'l*, pg. 3821
MASTERCLEAN TECHNOLOGIES (M) SDN BHD—See Careplus Group Berhad; *Int'l*, pg. 1325
MASTER COATING TECHNOLOGIES, INC.—See Audax Group, Limited Partnership; *U.S. Private*, pg. 388
MASTERCODI INDUSTRIAL LTDA.—See Vesuvius plc; *Int'l*, pg. 8179
MASTER COMPONENTS LIMITED; *Int'l*, pg. 4724
MASTERCONTROL, INC.; *U.S. Private*, pg. 2608
MASTERCORP INC.; *U.S. Private*, pg. 2608
MASTERCRAFT BOAT COMPANY, LLC—See MasterCraft Boat Holdings, Inc.; *U.S. Public*, pg. 1395
MASTERCRAFT BOAT HOLDINGS, INC.; *U.S. Public*, pg. 1394
MASTERCRAFT CABINETS, INC.—See Zurn Elkay Water Solutions Corporation; *U.S. Public*, pg. 2412
MASTERCRAFT FLOORING DISTRIBUTORS, INC.—See Gilford-Johnson Flooring LLC; *U.S. Private*, pg. 1700
MASTERCRAFT INDUSTRIES, INC.; *U.S. Private*, pg. 2608
MASTERCRAFT INTERNATIONAL LIMITED—See China Baofeng (International) Ltd.; *Int'l*, pg. 1485
MASTER CROWN ELECTRONICS (WUZHOU) LTD.—See Citizen Watch Co., Ltd.; *Int'l*, pg. 1625
MASTER CURRENCY (PTY) LIMITED—See The Bidvest Group Limited; *Int'l*, pg. 7625
MASTERCUT TOOL CORP.; *U.S. Private*, pg. 2608
MASTER DESIGN LLC; *U.S. Private*, pg. 2607
MASTER DRILLING BRASIL LTDA—See Master Drilling Group Limited; *Int'l*, pg. 4724
MASTER DRILLING CHANGZHOU CO., LTD.—See Master Drilling Group Limited; *Int'l*, pg. 4724
MASTER DRILLING CHILE SA—See Master Drilling Group Limited; *Int'l*, pg. 4724
MASTER DRILLING EGYPT LIMITED—See Master Drilling Group Limited; *Int'l*, pg. 4724
MASTER DRILLING EUROPE AB—See Master Drilling Group Limited; *Int'l*, pg. 4724
MASTER DRILLING GROUP LIMITED; *Int'l*, pg. 4724
MASTER DRILLING MEXICO SA DE CV—See Master Drilling Group Limited; *Int'l*, pg. 4724
MASTER DRILLING USA LLC—See Master Drilling Group Limited; *Int'l*, pg. 4724
MASTERDUCT BRAZIL LTDA—See Masterflex SE; *Int'l*, pg. 4725
MASTERDUCT INC.—See Masterflex SE; *Int'l*, pg. 4725
MASTER ELECTRIC CO. INC.; *U.S. Private*, pg. 2607
MASTER ELECTRONICS—See Master International Corp.; *U.S. Private*, pg. 2607
MASTER FARM SERVICES (GB) LTD.—See Mitsubishi Heavy Industries, Ltd.; *Int'l*, pg. 4956
MASTERFEEDS INC.—See Alltech, Inc.; *U.S. Private*, pg. 194
MASTER FIBERS INCORPORATED; *U.S. Private*, pg. 2607
MASTERFIX POLAND LTD. SP.Z.O.O—See Stanley Black & Decker, Inc.; *U.S. Public*, pg. 1934
MASTERFIX PRODUCTS U.K. LTD.—See Stanley Black & Decker, Inc.; *U.S. Public*, pg. 1933
MASTER FLEET, LLC; *U.S. Private*, pg. 2607
MASTERFLEX ASIA PTE. LTD.—See Masterflex SE; *Int'l*, pg. 4725
MASTERFLEX BRENNSTOFFZELLENTECHNIK GMBH—See Masterflex SE; *Int'l*, pg. 4725
MASTERFLEX CESKO S. R. O.—See Masterflex SE; *Int'l*, pg. 4725
MASTERFLEX HANDELSGESELLSCHAFT MBH—See Masterflex SE; *Int'l*, pg. 4725
MASTERFLEX HOSES (KUNSHAN) CO. LTD.—See Masterflex SE; *Int'l*, pg. 4725
MASTERFLEX LLC—See Avantor, Inc.; *U.S. Public*, pg. 242
MASTERFLEX MOBILITY GMBH—See Masterflex SE; *Int'l*, pg. 4725
MASTERFLEX RUS OOO—See Masterflex SE; *Int'l*, pg. 4725
MASTERFLEX S.A.R.L.—See Masterflex SE; *Int'l*, pg. 4725
MASTERFLEX SCANDINAVIA AB—See Masterflex SE; *Int'l*, pg. 4725
MASTERFLEX SE; *Int'l*, pg. 4725
MASTERFLEX TECHNICAL HOSES, LTD.—See Masterflex SE; *Int'l*, pg. 4725
MASTERFLEX VERTRIEBS GMBH—See Masterflex SE; *Int'l*, pg. 4725
MASTERFLIGHT FOUNDATION INC.; *U.S. Private*, pg. 2608
MASTERFLOW LTD—See International Building Products Ltd.; *Int'l*, pg. 3744
MASTER FLUID SOLUTIONS (INDIA) PRIVATE LIMITED—See Master Chemical Corporation; *U.S. Private*, pg. 2607
MASTERFORM SPOLKA Z O.O.—See Mangata Holding S.A.; *Int'l*, pg. 4670
THE MASTER GROUP, INC—See Novacap Management Inc.; *Int'l*, pg. 5454

COMPANY NAME INDEX

MASTERGUARD FABRIC PROTECTION AFRICA (PTY) LIMITED—See The Bidvest Group Limited; *Int'l*, pg. 7625
MASTERGUARD GMBH—See Emerson Electric Co.; *U.S. Public*, pg. 750
MASTER HALCO, INC.—See ITOCHU Corporation; *Int'l*, pg. 3838
MASTER HALCO—See ITOCHU Corporation; *Int'l*, pg. 3838
MASTER INTERNATIONAL CORP.; *U.S. Private*, pg. 2607
MASTER KEY RESOURCES LLC; *U.S. Private*, pg. 2607
MASTER KONG (TAIWAN) FOODS CO. LTD.—See Tingyi (Cayman Islands) Holding Corp.; *Int'l*, pg. 7754
MASTERKOOL INTERNATIONAL PUBLIC COMPANY LIMITED; *Int'l*, pg. 4725
MASTER LAUNDRY CO., LTD.—See Panjawattana Plastic Public Company Limited; *Int'l*, pg. 5728
MASTERLIFT; *Int'l*, pg. 4725
MASTER LINE SHIPPING CO.; *U.S. Private*, pg. 2607
MASTERLINK FUTURES CO., LTD.—See Shin Kong Group; *Int'l*, pg. 6837
THE MASTERLINK GROUP, INC.; *U.S. Private*, pg. 4075
MASTERLINK SECURITIES CORPORATION—See Shin Kong Group; *Int'l*, pg. 6837
MASTERLINK SECURITIES (HK) CORP., LTD.—See Shin Kong Group; *Int'l*, pg. 6837
MASTERLINK SECURITIES INVESTMENT ADVISORY CORP.—See Shin Kong Group; *Int'l*, pg. 6837
MASTER LOCK COMPANY LLC—See Fortune Brands Innovations, Inc.; *U.S. Public*, pg. 873
MASTER LOCK EUROPE, S.A.S.—See Fortune Brands Innovations, Inc.; *U.S. Public*, pg. 873
MASTER MAGNETICS INC.—See Factor 89 Partners, LLC; *U.S. Private*, pg. 1460
MASTER MECHANIC MFG. CO.—See Brinkmere Capital Partners LLC; *U.S. Private*, pg. 655
MASTERMIND MARKETING; *U.S. Private*, pg. 2608
MASTERMINDS; *U.S. Private*, pg. 2608
MASTER MIX, LLC—See Vulcan Materials Company; *U.S. Public*, pg. 2314
MASTER MIX OF TRINIDAD LIMITED—See Archer-Daniels-Midland Company; *U.S. Public*, pg. 185
MASTER MOLDED PRODUCTS CORPORATION; *U.S. Private*, pg. 2607
MASTER MOLD—See The Plastek Group; *U.S. Private*, pg. 4096
MASTERNAUT AB—See Compagnie Generale des Etablissements Michelin SCA; *Int'l*, pg. 1743
MASTERNAUT B.V.—See Corpay, Inc.; *U.S. Public*, pg. 580
MASTERNAUT DEUTSCHLAND GMBH—See Compagnie Generale des Etablissements Michelin SCA; *Int'l*, pg. 1743
MASTERNAUT GMBH—See Compagnie Generale des Etablissements Michelin SCA; *Int'l*, pg. 1743
MASTERNAUT IBERICA SL—See Corpay, Inc.; *U.S. Public*, pg. 580
MASTERNAUT INTERNATIONAL S.A.S.—See Compagnie Generale des Etablissements Michelin SCA; *Int'l*, pg. 1743
MASTERNAUT LIMITED—See Compagnie Generale des Etablissements Michelin SCA; *Int'l*, pg. 1743
MASTERPAC CORP.—See Cameron Holdings Corporation; *U.S. Private*, pg. 729
MASTER-PACK GROUP BERHAD; *Int'l*, pg. 4724
MASTER-PACK SARAWAK SDN. BHD.—See Master-Pack Group Berhad; *Int'l*, pg. 4725
MASTER-PACK SDN. BHD.—See Master-Pack Group Berhad; *Int'l*, pg. 4725
MASTERPAVE SDN. BHD.—See Gamuda Berhad; *Int'l*, pg. 2879
MASTERPAYMENT A.G.—See Lesaka Technologies, Inc.; *Int'l*, pg. 4469
MASTERPET AUSTRALIA PTY LTD—See EBOS Group Limited; *Int'l*, pg. 2285
MASTERPIECE INTERNATIONAL LIMITED—See Littlejohn & Co., LLC; *U.S. Private*, pg. 2470
MASTERPIECE LONDON LIMITED—See MCH Group AG; *Int'l*, pg. 4758
MASTERPIECE MACHINE & MANUFACTURING COMPANY—See Sanmina Corporation; *U.S. Public*, pg. 1840
MASTERPIECE STUDIOS, INC.—See Taylor Corporation; *U.S. Private*, pg. 3938
MASTERPLAST D.O.O.—See Masterplast Nyrt.; *Int'l*, pg. 4725
MASTERPLAST HUNGARIA KFT.—See Masterplast Nyrt.; *Int'l*, pg. 4725
MASTERPLAST INTERNATIONAL KFT.—See Masterplast Nyrt.; *Int'l*, pg. 4725
MASTERPLAST ITALIA S.R.L.—See Masterplast Nyrt.; *Int'l*, pg. 4725
MASTERPLAST MEDICAL KFT.—See Masterplast Nyrt.; *Int'l*, pg. 4725
MASTERPLAST NONWOVEN GMBH—See Masterplast Nyrt.; *Int'l*, pg. 4725
MASTERPLAST NYRT.; *Int'l*, pg. 4725
MASTERPLAST ROMANIA S.R.L.—See Masterplast Nyrt.; *Int'l*, pg. 4725

MASTERPLAST SP. Z O.O.—See Masterplast Nyrt.; *Int'l*, pg. 4725
MASTER PLAST S.R.O.—See Masterplast Nyrt.; *Int'l*, pg. 4725
MASTERPLAST YU D.O.O.—See Masterplast Nyrt.; *Int'l*, pg. 4725
MASTER PROTECTION CORPORATION; *U.S. Private*, pg. 2607
MASTER PROTECTION, LP—See Johnson Controls International plc; *Int'l*, pg. 3987
MASTER PUBLICIDADE S/A—See WPP plc; *Int'l*, pg. 8481
MASTER PUMPS & EQUIPMENT CORPORATION; *U.S. Private*, pg. 2607
MASTER PYROSERVE SDN BHD—See FITTERS Diversified Berhad; *Int'l*, pg. 2695
MASTERRACKCROWN—See Leggett & Platt, Incorporated; *U.S. Public*, pg. 1303
MASTER RISK, INC.—See Marshall & Sterling Enterprises, Inc.; *U.S. Private*, pg. 2592
MASTERS CRAFT CORPORATION; *U.S. Private*, pg. 2608
MASTERS ENERGY INC.—See Zargon Oil & Gas Ltd.; *Int'l*, pg. 8625
MASTERS GALLERY FOODS, INC.; *U.S. Private*, pg. 2608
MASTERS, INC.—See NRG Energy, Inc.; *U.S. Public*, pg. 1549
MASTERS MANNA INC.; *U.S. Private*, pg. 2608
MASTERS OF DESIGN, INC.—See Bain Capital, LP; *U.S. Private*, pg. 452
THE MASTERSON COMPANY, INC.; *U.S. Private*, pg. 4075
MASTER SPORTS; *U.S. Private*, pg. 2607
MASTER'S SUPPLY, INC.; *U.S. Private*, pg. 2608
MASTER STYLE PUBLIC COMPANY LIMITED; *Int'l*, pg. 4724
MASTER TEK INTERNATIONAL, INC.—See Minol USA; *U.S. Private*, pg. 2744
MASTER TOOL CORP.—See Sumitomo Electric Industries, Ltd.; *Int'l*, pg. 7282
MASTERTRADE LTD.—See Sonepar S.A.; *Int'l*, pg. 7090
MASTER TRANSPORTATION BUS MANUFACTURING LTD.—See Young An Hat Co., Ltd.; *Int'l*, pg. 8602
MASTER TRIM DE ARGENTINA S.R.I.—See Toyota Boshoku Corporation; *Int'l*, pg. 7864
THE MASTER TRUST BANK OF JAPAN, LTD.—See Mitsubishi UFJ Financial Group, Inc.; *Int'l*, pg. 4972
MASTER TRUST LIMITED; *Int'l*, pg. 4724
MASTERWORK ELECTRONICS INC.; *U.S. Private*, pg. 2608
MASTERWORK GROUP CO.,LTD.; *Int'l*, pg. 4725
MASTER WORK-HOLDING, INC.—See Rohm Products of America; *U.S. Private*, pg. 3473
MASTER YACHTING GMBH—See Sailogy S.A.; *Int'l*, pg. 6483
MASTERYWORKS, INC.—See Adecco Group AG; *Int'l*, pg. 139
M. A. STEWART & SONS LTD.; *Int'l*, pg. 4615
MAST GENERAL STORE INCORPORATED; *U.S. Private*, pg. 2607
MASTHEAD INDUSTRIES INC.—See Bridgestone Corporation; *Int'l*, pg. 1160
MASTHEAD INTERNATIONAL, INC.—See Performance Contracting Group; *U.S. Private*, pg. 3148
MASTHERCELL GLOBAL, INC.—See Catalent, Inc.; *U.S. Public*, pg. 448
MASTHERCELL, S.A.—See Catalent, Inc.; *U.S. Public*, pg. 448
MASTHERCELL U.S., LLC—See Catalent, Inc.; *U.S. Public*, pg. 448
MASTIFF NORWAY—See De Agostini S.p.A.; *Int'l*, pg. 1995
MASTIMBER INDUSTRIES SDN. BHD.—See EG Industries Berhad; *Int'l*, pg. 2322
MAST INVESTMENTS LTD.; *Int'l*, pg. 4724
MASTIX MEDICA, LLC—See GelStat Corporation; *U.S. Public*, pg. 910
MAST-JAGERMEISTER SE; *Int'l*, pg. 4724
MAST LOGISTICS SERVICES, INC.—See Bath & Body Works, Inc.; *U.S. Public*, pg. 279
MAST MICROWAVE—See Advent International Corporation; *U.S. Private*, pg. 100
MASTODON DESIGN LLC—See CACI International Inc.; *U.S. Public*, pg. 418
MASTORAN RESTAURANT INC.; *U.S. Private*, pg. 2608
MASTRA CORPORATION PTY. LTD.—See Nufarm Limited; *Int'l*, pg. 5486
MASTRAD SA; *Int'l*, pg. 4725
MASTRAK SDN BHD—See Heidelberg Materials AG; *Int'l*, pg. 3315
MASTRAN SNC—See VINCI S.A.; *Int'l*, pg. 8224
MASTRAPASQUA ASSET MANAGEMENT, INC.—See Sequoia Financial Group, LLC; *U.S. Private*, pg. 3612
MASTRIA BUICK-PONTIAC-GMC TRUCK; *U.S. Private*, pg. 2608
MASTRO LUXE PTE. LTD.—See Polaris Ltd.; *Int'l*, pg. 5907
MASTRONARDI PRODUCE LIMITED; *Int'l*, pg. 4726

MASTRO PROPERTIES; *U.S. Private*, pg. 2608
MASTRY ENGINE CENTER LLC—See Yanmar Co., Ltd.; *Int'l*, pg. 8564
MASTRY MANAGEMENT LLC; *U.S. Private*, pg. 2608
MASTSYSTEM INTERNATIONAL OY—See Advent International Corporation; *U.S. Private*, pg. 100
MAST TECHNOLOGIES, INC.—See Arcline Investment Management LP; *U.S. Private*, pg. 314
MAST TECHNOLOGY SERVICES, INC.—See Bath & Body Works, Inc.; *U.S. Public*, pg. 279
MASTUBARA TECHNO CO., LTD.—See Yamato Kogyo Co. Ltd.; *Int'l*, pg. 8555
MAST UTILITY BARNS; *U.S. Private*, pg. 2607
(MASUDA) DAIICHI TRAFFIC CO., LTD.—See Daiichi Koutsu Sangyo Co., Ltd.; *Int'l*, pg. 1928
MASUDA ECO CREATION—See Mitsubishi Heavy Industries, Ltd.; *Int'l*, pg. 4955
MASUDA FLOUR MILLING CO., LTD.—See Mitsubishi Corporation; *Int'l*, pg. 4942
MASUKA BINA SDN. BHD.—See Hunza Properties Berhad; *Int'l*, pg. 3537
M&A SUPPLY COMPANY INC.; *U.S. Private*, pg. 2524
MAS (USA) LTD.—See M. A. Stewart & Sons Ltd.; *Int'l*, pg. 4615
MASUZEN CO., LTD.—See Kobe Bussan Co., Ltd.; *Int'l*, pg. 4217
MASY BIOSERVICES, INC.; *U.S. Private*, pg. 2608
MAS ZHONGTAI (BEIJING) TECHNOLOGY CO., LTD.—See Chongqing MAS Sci. & Tech. Co., Ltd.; *Int'l*, pg. 1580
MATABELELAND INNS (PVT) LTD—See Innscor Africa Ltd.; *Int'l*, pg. 3713
MATACHEWAN CONSOLIDATED MINES, LIMITED; *Int'l*, pg. 4726
MATA DE SANTA GENEBRA TRANSMISSAO S.A.—See Companhia Paranaense de Energia; *Int'l*, pg. 1748
MATADOR PRODUCTION COMPANY—See Matador Resources Company; *U.S. Public*, pg. 1395
MATADOR RESOURCES COMPANY; *U.S. Public*, pg. 1395
MATAGA OF STOCKTON; *U.S. Private*, pg. 2608
MATAGORDA COMPLEX EQUISTAR CHEMICALS, LP—See LyondellBasell Industries N.V.; *Int'l*, pg. 4608
MATAI RESOURCE CO., LTD.—See Rengo Co., Ltd.; *Int'l*, pg. 6280
MATAI SHIKO CO., LTD.—See Rengo Co., Ltd.; *Int'l*, pg. 6280
MATAI (VIETNAM) CO., LTD.—See Rengo Co., Ltd.; *Int'l*, pg. 6280
MATALAN RETAIL LTD.; *Int'l*, pg. 4726
MATANG BERHAD; *Int'l*, pg. 4726
MATANUSKA ELECTRIC ASSOCIATION, INC.; *U.S. Private*, pg. 2608
MATANZAS CREEK WINERY—See Jackson Family Wines, Inc.; *U.S. Private*, pg. 2176
MATARI ADVERTISING—See WPP plc; *Int'l*, pg. 8491
MATARIKI FORESTRY GROUP—See Rayonier Inc.; *U.S. Public*, pg. 1765
MATARIKI FORESTS—See Rayonier Inc.; *U.S. Public*, pg. 1765
MATAS A/S; *Int'l*, pg. 4726
MATASSA CONSTRUCTION INC.; *U.S. Private*, pg. 2609
MATASSA INCORPORATED; *Int'l*, pg. 4726
MATAS SVERIGE AB—See Matas A/S; *Int'l*, pg. 4726
MATCHBOX PICTURES PTY LTD.—See Comcast Corporation; *U.S. Public*, pg. 538
MATCH.COM CANADA LTD.—See IAC Inc.; *U.S. Public*, pg. 1082
MATCH.COM NORDIC AB—See IAC Inc.; *U.S. Public*, pg. 1082
MATCHCOM TELECOMMUNICATIONS INC.—See Mexedia S.p.A.; *Int'l*, pg. 4869
MATCHCRAFT, INC.—See Advance Local LLC; *U.S. Private*, pg. 83
MATCHES, INC.; *Int'l*, pg. 4726
THE MATCHETT GROUP LIMITED—See Wilmington plc; *Int'l*, pg. 8422
MATCH GROUP, INC.—See IAC Inc.; *U.S. Public*, pg. 1082
MATCHING BROADCAST CO., LTD.—See Bangkok Broadcasting & TV Co., Ltd.; *Int'l*, pg. 833
MATCHING ENTERTAINMENT CO., LTD.—See Bangkok Broadcasting & TV Co., Ltd.; *Int'l*, pg. 833
MATCHING MAXIMIZE SOLUTION PLC—See Bangkok Broadcasting & TV Co., Ltd.; *Int'l*, pg. 833
MATCHING MOTION PICTURES CO., LTD.—See Bangkok Broadcasting & TV Co., Ltd.; *Int'l*, pg. 833
MATCHING MOVIE TOWN CO., LTD.—See Bangkok Broadcasting & TV Co., Ltd.; *Int'l*, pg. 833
MATCHING SERVICE JAPAN CO., LTD.; *Int'l*, pg. 4726
MATCHLESS METAL POLISH COMPANY—See Jason Industries, Inc.; *U.S. Public*, pg. 2189
MATCHMAKER SERVICES LIMITED—See Scottish Enterprise; *Int'l*, pg. 6652
MATCH MEDIA AUSTRALIA LTD.—See Publicis Groupe S.A.; *Int'l*, pg. 6103
MATCHPOINT; *U.S. Private*, pg. 2609
MATCHTECH GROUP UK LTD—See Gattaca plc; *Int'l*, pg. 2890

MATCHPOINT — CORPORATE AFFILIATIONS

MATCHWORK DANMARK A/S—See North Media A/S; *Int'l*, pg. 5441
MATCHWORK UK LTD.—See North Media A/S; *Int'l*, pg. 5441
MATC INFRAESTRUCTURA, S. DE R.L. DE C.V.—See American Tower Corporation; *U.S. Public*, pg. 111
MATCO ELECTRIC CORPORATION; *U.S. Private*, pg. 2609
MATCO FINANCIAL INC.; *Int'l*, pg. 4726
THE MATCO GROUP, INC.; *U.S. Private*, pg. 4075
MATCO INVESTMENTS LTD.—See Matco Financial Inc.; *Int'l*, pg. 4726
MATCON CONSTRUCTION SERVICES, INC.; *U.S. Private*, pg. 2609
MATCON LIMITED—See IDEX Corp.; *U.S. Public*, pg. 1091
MATCO-NORCA, LLC—See NIBCO Inc.; *U.S. Private*, pg. 2924
MATCOR AUTOMOTIVE INC.—See Matcor-Matsu Group Inc.; *Int'l*, pg. 4726
MATCOR AUTOMOTIVE (MICHIGAN) INC. - MICHIGAN PLANT—See Matcor-Matsu Group Inc.; *Int'l*, pg. 4726
MATCOR AUTOMOTIVE (MICHIGAN) INC.—See Matcor-Matsu Group Inc.; *Int'l*, pg. 4726
MATCOR AUTOMOTIVE (MOGREEN) INC.—See Matcor-Matsu Group Inc.; *Int'l*, pg. 4726
MATCO RAVARY INC.—See Groupe B.M.R. Inc.; *Int'l*, pg. 3092
MATCOR, INC.—See Brand Industrial Services, Inc.; *U.S. Private*, pg. 636
MATCOR-MATSU GROUP INC.; *Int'l*, pg. 4726
MATCOR MATSU—See Matcor-Matsu Group Inc.; *Int'l*, pg. 4726
MATCOR METAL FABRICATION, INC.—See Matcor-Matsu Group Inc.; *Int'l*, pg. 4726
MATCOR METAL FABRICATION, INC.—See Matcor-Matsu Group Inc.; *Int'l*, pg. 4726
MATCOR METAL FABRICATION, INC.—See Matcor-Matsu Group Inc.; *Int'l*, pg. 4726
MATCOR METAL FABRICATION (WELCOME) INC.—See Matcor-Matsu Group Inc.; *Int'l*, pg. 4726
MATCO SERVICES, INC.—See Valmont Industries, Inc.; *U.S. Public*, pg. 2274
MATCO SEVICES, INC.—See Valmont Industries, Inc.; *U.S. Public*, pg. 2274
MATCO TOOLS CORPORATION—See Vontier Corporation; *U.S. Public*, pg. 2309
MAT CRAIOVA; *Int'l*, pg. 4726
MATC TECHNOLOGY (M) SDN BHD.—See Min Aik Technology Co., Ltd.; *Int'l*, pg. 4898
MATEBAT SAS—See La Financiere Patrimoniale d'Investissement S.A.S.; *Int'l*, pg. 4387
MATEC APPLIED SCIENCES—See Matec Instrument Companies, Inc.; *U.S. Private*, pg. 2609
MATEC CONSTRUCTION MACHINERY CO., LTD.—See Hoa Binh Construction Group JSC; *Int'l*, pg. 3435
MATECH, INC.; *U.S. Private*, pg. 2609
M&A TECHNOLOGY, INC.; *U.S. Private*, pg. 2524
M.A.TECHNOLOGY, INC.—See MITACHI Co., LTD.; *Int'l*, pg. 4924
MATECH SYSTEMS A/S—See Komax Holding AG; *Int'l*, pg. 4241
MATEC INSTRUMENT COMPANIES, INC.; *U.S. Private*, pg. 2609
MATEC INSTRUMENTS NDT—See Matec Instrument Companies, Inc.; *U.S. Private*, pg. 2609
MATECO GMBH—See Group Thermote & Vanhalst; *Int'l*, pg. 3090
MATECO LOCATION DE NACELLES SA—See Group Thermote & Vanhalst; *Int'l*, pg. 3089
MATECO PODESTY RUCHOME SP Z OO—See Group Thermote & Vanhalst; *Int'l*, pg. 3089
MATECRA GMBH—See Berner SE; *Int'l*, pg. 988
MATEER & HARBERT, P.A.—See Dinsmore & Shohl LLP; *U.S. Private*, pg. 1234
MATEJKA & PARTNER ASSET MANAGEMENT GMBH—See Wiener Privatbank SE; *Int'l*, pg. 8404
MATENAER CORPORATION; *U.S. Private*, pg. 2609
MATEN PETROLEUM JSC; *Int'l*, pg. 4727
MATEOMATEO COMUNICACIONES, S.L.U.—See Vocento, S.A.; *Int'l*, pg. 8284
MATE PRECISION TOOLING INC.; *U.S. Private*, pg. 2609
MATERA PAPER COMPANY, INC.—See Ferguson plc; *Int'l*, pg. 2638
MATEREALITY, LLC—See I Squared Capital Advisors (US) LLC; *U.S. Private*, pg. 2023
MATEREALITY, LLC—See TDR Capital LLP; *Int'l*, pg. 7492
MATERIA AB—See Kinnarps AB; *Int'l*, pg. 4181
MATERIA, INC.; *U.S. Private*, pg. 2609
MATERIALAB CONSULTANTS LTD.—See Fugro N.V.; *Int'l*, pg. 2808
MATERIAL AUTOMATION (THAILAND) CO., LTD.—See Amiya Corporation; *Int'l*, pg. 428
MATERIAL BUSINESS SUPPORT CORP.—See Mitsubishi Materials Corporation; *Int'l*, pg. 4964
MATERIAL CHANGE LIMITED—See Heathpatch Ltd.; *Int'l*, pg. 3305
MATERIAL CONNEXION, INC.—See Sandow Media LLC; *U.S. Private*, pg. 3544

MATERIAL CONNEXION MILANO—See Sandow Media LLC; *U.S. Private*, pg. 3544
MATERIAL CONTROL SYSTEMS INC.; *U.S. Private*, pg. 2609
MATERIAL DE AIREACION S.A.—See Aliaxis S.A./N.V.; *Int'l*, pg. 325
MATERIAL DELIVERY SERVICE INC.—See TFI International Inc.; *Int'l*, pg. 7586
MATERIALES SIDERURGICOS S.A.—See Klockner & Co. SE; *Int'l*, pg. 4202
MATERIAL HANDLING INC; *U.S. Private*, pg. 2609
MATERIAL HANDLING INDUSTRY; *U.S. Private*, pg. 2609
MATERIAL HANDLING PRODUCTS CORP; *U.S. Private*, pg. 2609
MATERIAL HANDLING SERVICES, LLC; *U.S. Private*, pg. 2609
MATERIAL HANDLING SUPPLY, INC.; *U.S. Private*, pg. 2609
MATERIAL HANDLING SYSTEMS, INC.—See Thomas H. Lee Partners, L.P.; *U.S. Private*, pg. 4156
MATERIAL HANDLING TECHNOLOGIES; *U.S. Private*, pg. 2609
MATERIAL HOLDINGS, LLC—See Tailwind Capital Group, LLC; *U.S. Private*, pg. 3924
MATERIALISE IBERIA N.V.—See Materialise NV; *Int'l*, pg. 4727
MATERIALISE NV; *Int'l*, pg. 4727
MATERIALISE UKRAINE LLC—See Materialise NV; *Int'l*, pg. 4727
MATERIALISE USA, LLC—See Materialise NV; *Int'l*, pg. 4727
MATERIALISTEN SOLROD/CENTRET APS—See Matas A/S; *Int'l*, pg. 4726
MATERIAL.ONE AG—See adesso SE; *Int'l*, pg. 144
MATERIAL RECLAMATION, LLC—See BC Partners LLP; *Int'l*, pg. 924
MATERIAL ANALYSIS TECHNOLOGY INC.; *Int'l*, pg. 4727
MATERIAL SCIENCES CORPORATION - OHIO FACILITY—See Sky Island Capital LLC; *U.S. Private*, pg. 3684
MATERIAL SCIENCES CORPORATION—See Sky Island Capital LLC; *U.S. Private*, pg. 3684
MATERIAL SCIENCES CORPORATION - TORONTO FACILITY—See Sky Island Capital LLC; *U.S. Private*, pg. 3684
MATERIALS CONVERTING, INC.—See ADDEV Material SAS; *Int'l*, pg. 128
MATERIALS ECO RECYCLE CO., LTD.—See Mitsubishi Materials Corporation; *Int'l*, pg. 4964
MATERIALS ECO-REFINING CO., LTD.—See Mitsubishi Materials Corporation; *Int'l*, pg. 4964
MATERIAL SERVICES COMPANY, INC.—See American Airlines Group Inc.; *U.S. Public*, pg. 96
MATERIALS' FINANCE CO., LTD.—See Mitsubishi Materials Corporation; *Int'l*, pg. 4964
MATERIALS HANDLING EQUIPMENT CORP.; *U.S. Private*, pg. 2609
MATERIALS HANDLING SOLUTIONS LLC—See Energy Transfer LP; *U.S. Public*, pg. 764
MATERIALS MARKETING CORP.; *U.S. Private*, pg. 2610
MATERIALS PETROLEUM JOINT STOCK COMPANY; *Int'l*, pg. 4727
MATERIALS PROCESSING INC.; *U.S. Private*, pg. 2610
MATERIALS RESEARCH SOCIETY; *U.S. Private*, pg. 2610
MATERIALS SCIENCE INTERNATIONAL, INC.; *U.S. Private*, pg. 2610
MATERIALS SCIENCES CORPORATION—See Seemann Composites, Inc.; *U.S. Private*, pg. 3598
MATERIALS SOLUTIONS LIMITED—See Siemens Energy AG; *Int'l*, pg. 6902
MATERIALS TECHNOLOGIES; *Int'l*, pg. 4727
MATERIALS TECHNOLOGY EDUCATION SDN. BHD.—See Serba Dinamik Holdings Berhad; *Int'l*, pg. 6721
MATERIALS TECHNOLOGY SOLUTIONS, LLC—See Scope Metals Group Ltd.; *Int'l*, pg. 6650
MATERIALS TOHOKU CORPORATION—See Mitsubishi Materials Corporation; *Int'l*, pg. 4964
MATERIALS TRANSPORTATION CO.; *U.S. Private*, pg. 2610
MATERIAL TECHNOLOGY & LOGISTICS, INC.; *U.S. Private*, pg. 2609
MATERIAL TECHNOLOGY SOLUTIONS LLC—See Scope Metals Group Ltd.; *Int'l*, pg. 6650
MATERIAL TRANSFER, INC.—See LPX, Inc.; *U.S. Private*, pg. 2507
MATERIAL US, INC.—See Tailwind Capital Group, LLC; *U.S. Private*, pg. 3924
MATERIAUX BAIE DE SEINE SAS—See VINCI S.A.; *Int'l*, pg. 8224
MATERIAUX COUPAL INC; *Int'l*, pg. 4727
MATERIAUX ROUTIERS DU LITTORAL SAS—See VINCI S.A.; *Int'l*, pg. 8224
MATERIAUX S.A.—See Buzzi SpA; *Int'l*, pg. 1230
MATERION ADVANCED CHEMICALS INC—See Materion Corporation; *U.S. Public*, pg. 1395

MATERION ADVANCED MATERIALS GERMANY GMBH—See Materion Corporation; *U.S. Public*, pg. 1395
MATERION ADVANCED MATERIALS TECHNOLOGIES AND SERVICES INC.—See Materion Corporation; *U.S. Public*, pg. 1395
MATERION ADVANCED MATERIALS TECHNOLOGIES AND SERVICES (SUZHOU) LTD.—See Materion Corporation; *U.S. Public*, pg. 1395
MATERION ADVANCED MATERIALS TECHNOLOGIES & SERVICES FAR EAST PHILIPPINES PTD LTD.—See Materion Corporation; *U.S. Public*, pg. 1395
MATERION BREWSTER LLC—See Materion Corporation; *U.S. Public*, pg. 1395
MATERION BRUSH GMBH—See Materion Corporation; *U.S. Public*, pg. 1395
MATERION BRUSH INTERNATIONAL, INC.—See Materion Corporation; *U.S. Public*, pg. 1395
MATERION BRUSH INTERNATIONAL—See Materion Corporation; *U.S. Public*, pg. 1395
MATERION BRUSH INTERNATIONAL—See Materion Corporation; *U.S. Public*, pg. 1395
MATERION BRUSH (JAPAN) LTD.—See Materion Corporation; *U.S. Public*, pg. 1395
MATERION BRUSH PERFORMANCE ALLOYS—See Materion Corporation; *U.S. Public*, pg. 1395
MATERION BRUSH (SINGAPORE) PTE LTD.—See Materion Corporation; *U.S. Public*, pg. 1395
MATERION BRUSH SINGAPORE SHANGHAI—See Materion Corporation; *U.S. Public*, pg. 1395
MATERION CERAMICS INC.—See Materion Corporation; *U.S. Public*, pg. 1395
MATERION CORPORATION; *U.S. Public*, pg. 1395
MATERION HOLDINGS LIMITED—See Materion Corporation; *U.S. Public*, pg. 1395
MATERION IRELAND LTD.—See Materion Corporation; *U.S. Public*, pg. 1395
MATERION JAPAN LTD.—See Materion Corporation; *U.S. Public*, pg. 1395
MATERION KOREA LTD.—See Materion Corporation; *U.S. Public*, pg. 1395
MATERION MICROELECTRONICS & SERVICES—See Materion Corporation; *U.S. Public*, pg. 1396
MATERION MICROELECTRONICS & SERVICES—See Materion Corporation; *U.S. Public*, pg. 1396
MATERION PRECISION OPTICS AND THIN FILM COATINGS CORPORATION—See Materion Corporation; *U.S. Public*, pg. 1395
MATERION PRECISION OPTICS AND THIN FILM COATINGS INC.—See Materion Corporation; *U.S. Public*, pg. 1396
MATERION PRECISION OPTICS (SHANGHAI) LIMITED—See Materion Corporation; *U.S. Public*, pg. 1395
MATERION PRECISION OPTICS (U.K.) LIMITED—See Materion Corporation; *U.S. Public*, pg. 1395
MATERION SINGAPORE PTE. LTD.—See Materion Corporation; *U.S. Public*, pg. 1395
MATERION TAIWAN CO. LTD.—See Materion Corporation; *U.S. Public*, pg. 1395
MATERION TECHNICAL MATERIALS, INC.—See Materion Corporation; *U.S. Public*, pg. 1396
MATERION UK LIMITED—See Materion Corporation; *U.S. Public*, pg. 1396
MATERIS PAINTS ITALIA S.P.A. DIVISIONE VIERO—See Wendel S.A.; *Int'l*, pg. 8376
MATERIS PAINTS ITALIA S.P.A.—See Wendel S.A.; *Int'l*, pg. 8376
MATERIS PEINTURES S.A.S.—See Wendel S.A.; *Int'l*, pg. 8376
MATERNE INDUSTRIES—See Unibel SA; *Int'l*, pg. 8031
MATERNE S.A.S.—See Unibel SA; *Int'l*, pg. 8031
MATERRA, LLC; *U.S. Private*, pg. 2610
MATEWAN REALTY CORPORATION—See Truist Financial Corporation; *U.S. Public*, pg. 2200
MATEX A.D.; *Int'l*, pg. 4727
MATEX BANGLADESH LIMITED—See Apex Holding Limited; *Int'l*, pg. 511
MATEX CHEMICALS (TAIXING) CO., LTD.—See Matex International Limited; *Int'l*, pg. 4727
MATEX CO., LTD.—See Nippon Sheet Glass Co. Ltd.; *Int'l*, pg. 5331
MATEX INC.—See Morito Co., Ltd.; *Int'l*, pg. 5048
MATEX INTERNATIONAL LIMITED; *Int'l*, pg. 4727
MATEX KAKOH CORPORATION—See Nitto Denko Corporation; *Int'l*, pg. 5384
MATEX PLANETARY DRIVE INTERNATIONAL, INC.—See Nippon Sheet Glass Co. Ltd.; *Int'l*, pg. 5331
MATHAND, INC.; *U.S. Private*, pg. 2610
MATHEMATICA INC.; *U.S. Private*, pg. 2610
MATHEMATICAL ASSOCIATION OF AMERICA, INCORPORATED; *U.S. Private*, pg. 2610
MATHEMATICA POLICY RESEARCH INC.—See Mathematica Inc.; *U.S. Private*, pg. 2610
MATHEMATICA POLICY RESEARCH INC.—See Mathematica Inc.; *U.S. Private*, pg. 2610
MATHEMATICA POLICY RESEARCH INC.—See Mathematica Inc.; *U.S. Private*, pg. 2610

1700

COMPANY NAME INDEX

MATHEMATICA POLICY RESEARCH INC.—See Mathematica Inc.; *U.S. Private*, pg. 2610
MATHEMATICA POLICY RESEARCH INC.—See Mathematica Inc.; *U.S. Private*, pg. 2610
MATHEMATICA POLICY RESEARCH INC.—See Mathematica Inc.; *U.S. Private*, pg. 2610
MATHENA, INC.—See The Weir Group PLC; *Int'l*, pg. 7699
MATHENY MEDICAL AND EDUCATIONAL CENTER; *U.S. Private*, pg. 2610
MATHER & CO., CPAS, LLC; *U.S. Private*, pg. 2610
MATHER COMMUNICATIONS S.R.O.—See WPP plc; *Int'l*, pg. 8484
THE MATHER GROUP, LLC; *U.S. Private*, pg. 4075
MATHER LIFEWAYS; *U.S. Private*, pg. 2610
MATHER & PLATT IRELAND LIMITED—See Johnson Controls International plc; *Int'l*, pg. 3988
MATHER & PLATT (K) LTD.—See Olympia Capital Holdings Limited; *Int'l*, pg. 5555
MATHER + PLATT (PTY) LIMITED—See WPIL Limited; *Int'l*, pg. 8462
MATHERS FOUNDRY LIMITED—See WPIL Limited; *Int'l*, pg. 8462
MATHERS SHOES PTY LTD.—See Fusion Retail Brands, Pty. Ltd.; *Int'l*, pg. 2849
MATHES MANAGEMENT ENTERPRISES; *U.S. Private*, pg. 2610
MATHESON & CO., LTD.—See Jardine Matheson Holdings Limited; *Int'l*, pg. 3909
MATHESON GAS PRODUCTS KOREA, CO., LTD.—See Mitsubishi Chemical Group Corporation; *Int'l*, pg. 4936
MATHESON K-AIR INDIA PRIVATE LIMITED—See Mitsubishi Chemical Group Corporation; *Int'l*, pg. 4936
MATHESON TRI-GAS, INC.—See Mitsubishi Chemical Group Corporation; *Int'l*, pg. 4936
MATHESON TRUCKING, INC.; *U.S. Private*, pg. 2610
MATHESON VALVES; *Int'l*, pg. 4727
MATHEW EASOW RESEARCH SECURITIES LIMITED; *Int'l*, pg. 4727
MATHEW HALL LUMBER CO; *U.S. Private*, pg. 2610
MATHEWS ASSOCIATES, INC.; *U.S. Private*, pg. 2611
MATHEW'S DODGE CHRYSLER JEEP, INC.; *U.S. Private*, pg. 2611
MATHEWS FORD SANDUSKY, INC.; *U.S. Private*, pg. 2611
MATHEWS INC.; *U.S. Private*, pg. 2611
MATHEWS KENNEDY FORD LINCOLN-MERCURY INC.; *U.S. Private*, pg. 2611
MATHEWS READYMIX LLC—See Teichert, Inc.; *U.S. Private*, pg. 3958
MATHEW ZAHERI CORPORATION; *U.S. Private*, pg. 2610
MATHEY DEARMAN, INC.—See Gladstone Management Corporation; *U.S. Private*, pg. 1705
MATH FOR AMERICA; *U.S. Private*, pg. 2610
MATHIAS BANCSHARES, INC.; *U.S. Private*, pg. 2611
MATHIEU—See FAYAT SAS; *Int'l*, pg. 2626
MATHIOS AD—See MATHIOS REFRACTORY S.A.; *Int'l*, pg. 4727
MATHIOS REFRACTORY S.A.; *Int'l*, pg. 4727
MATHIOWETZ CONSTRUCTION COMPANY; *U.S. Private*, pg. 2611
MATHIS BROS. FURNITURE CO. INC.; *U.S. Private*, pg. 2611
MATHIS EXTERMINATING; *U.S. Private*, pg. 2611
MATHIS-KELLEY CONSTRUCTION SUPPLY CO.; *U.S. Private*, pg. 2611
MATHNASIUM LLC—See Roark Capital Group Inc.; *U.S. Private*, pg. 3455
MAT HOLDING, INC.—See Shandong Heavy Industry Group Co., Ltd.; *Int'l*, pg. 6753
MATHS FOR MORE SL; *Int'l*, pg. 4727
THE MATHWORKS AUSTRALIA PTY LTD—See The Mathworks, Inc.; *U.S. Private*, pg. 4075
THE MATHWORKS, INC.; *U.S. Private*, pg. 4075
THE MATHWORKS KOREA, LLC—See The Mathworks, Inc.; *U.S. Private*, pg. 4076
THE MATHWORKS S.A.S.—See The Mathworks, Inc.; *U.S. Private*, pg. 4076
MATHY CONSTRUCTION CO; *U.S. Private*, pg. 2611
MAT'HYGIENE SAS—See Bunzl plc; *Int'l*, pg. 1219
MATHYS AG—See Enovis Corporation; *U.S. Public*, pg. 773
MATHYS ORTHOPADIE GMBH—See Enovis Corporation; *U.S. Public*, pg. 773
MATHYS ORTHOPAEDICS BV—See Enovis Corporation; *U.S. Public*, pg. 773
MATHYS ORTHOPAEDICS LTD.—See Enovis Corporation; *U.S. Public*, pg. 773
MATHYS ORTHOPAEDICS PTY. LTD.—See Enovis Corporation; *U.S. Public*, pg. 773
MATHYS ORTHOPEDIE SAS—See Enovis Corporation; *U.S. Public*, pg. 773
MATHYS ORTOPEDIA SRL—See Enovis Corporation; *U.S. Public*, pg. 773
MATICA BIOTECHNOLOGY, INC.—See Chabiotech Co., Ltd.; *Int'l*, pg. 1436
MATICA ENTERPRISES INC.; *Int'l*, pg. 4727

MATICA FINTEC S.P.A.—See Matica Technologies AG; *Int'l*, pg. 4727
MATICA TECHNOLOGIES AG; *Int'l*, pg. 4727
MATICH CORPORATION - CABAZON ASPHALT PLANT—See Matich Corporation; *U.S. Private*, pg. 2611
MATICH CORPORATION - REDLANDS ASPHALT PLANT—See Matich Corporation; *U.S. Private*, pg. 2611
MATICH CORPORATION - RIALTO ASPHALT PLANT—See Matich Corporation; *U.S. Private*, pg. 2611
MATICH CORPORATION; *U.S. Private*, pg. 2611
MATICHON PUBLIC COMPANY LIMITED; *Int'l*, pg. 4728
MATICMIND SPA—See Ascom Holding AG; *Int'l*, pg. 603
MATIKA S.P.A.—See WIIT SpA; *Int'l*, pg. 8408
MATILA NOMINEES PTY LIMITED—See COCA-COLA EUROPACIFIC PARTNERS PLC; *Int'l*, pg. 1684
MATILA ROHR PRODUCTIONS (MRP)—See Egmont Fonden; *Int'l*, pg. 2326
MATINA GMBH—See Hubert Burda Media Holding Kommanditgesellschaft; *Int'l*, pg. 3520
MATINAS BIOPHARMA HOLDINGS, INC.; *U.S. Public*, pg. 1396
MATIN SPINNING MILLS LTD.; *Int'l*, pg. 4728
MATIPU EMPREENDIMENTOS IMOBILIARIOS LTDA—See PDG Realty S.A. Empreendimentos e Participacoes; *Int'l*, pg. 5770
MATISSART NORD SA; *Int'l*, pg. 4728
MATIV HOLDINGS, INC.; *U.S. Public*, pg. 1396
MATLINPATTERSON GLOBAL ADVISERS LLC; *U.S. Private*, pg. 2611
MATLOCK ADVERTISING & PUBLIC RELATIONS-NY—See Matlock Advertising & Public Relations; *U.S. Private*, pg. 2611
MATLOCK ADVERTISING & PUBLIC RELATIONS; *U.S. Private*, pg. 2611
MATLOCK MEDICAL CENTER LLC—See Adeptus Health Inc.; *U.S. Private*, pg. 78
MAT MASCHINENTECHNIK GMBH—See Hormann Holding GmbH & Co. KG; *Int'l*, pg. 3480
MAT MISCHANLAGENTECHNIK GMBH.—See BAUER Aktiengesellschaft; *Int'l*, pg. 893
MATMOWN, INC.; *U.S. Public*, pg. 1397
MAT NUWOOD, LLC.—See Ancor Holdings, L.P.; *U.S. Private*, pg. 275
MATO AUSTRALIA PTY. LTD.—See Mato GmbH & Co., KG; *Int'l*, pg. 4728
MATO BELT MAINTENANCE EQUIPMENT (LANGFANG) CO., LTD.—See Mato GmbH & Co., KG; *Int'l*, pg. 4728
MAT OCH UPPLEVELSER I KUNGSBACK AB—See Mackmyra Svensk Whisky AB; *Int'l*, pg. 4623
MATO FRANCE S.A.R.L.—See Mato GmbH & Co., KG; *Int'l*, pg. 4728
MATO GMBH & CO., KG; *Int'l*, pg. 4728
MATO IBERICA S.L.U.—See Mato GmbH & Co., KG; *Int'l*, pg. 4728
MATO INDUSTRIES LTD.—See Mato GmbH & Co., KG; *Int'l*, pg. 4728
MATOMY MEDIA GROUP LTD.; *Int'l*, pg. 4728
MATO PRODUCTS PTY. LTD—See Mato GmbH & Co., KG; *Int'l*, pg. 4728
MATOR AS—See Magnora ASA; *Int'l*, pg. 4641
MATORIT DATA AB—See LKQ Corporation; *U.S. Public*, pg. 1335
MATOS GREY—See WPP plc; *Int'l*, pg. 8472
MATO SUISSE GMBH—See Mato GmbH & Co., KG; *Int'l*, pg. 4728
MATOT INC.; *U.S. Private*, pg. 2611
MAT-PAC INC.—See HCI Equity Management, L.P.; *U.S. Private*, pg. 1889
M A T PARCEL EXPRESS, INC.; *U.S. Private*, pg. 2523
MA TRADING CO., LTD.—See Mitsubishi Materials Corporation; *Int'l*, pg. 4963
MA-TRA FIDUCIARIA SRL—See Mittel S.p.A.; *Int'l*, pg. 4994
MATRAH COLD STORES LLC—See W.J. Towell & Co. LLC; *Int'l*, pg. 8322
MATRA HOLDING GMBH—See Airbus SE; *Int'l*, pg. 242
MATRAI EROMU ZARTKORUEN MUKODO RESZVENYTARSASAG—See RWE AG; *Int'l*, pg. 6434
MATRA KAUSHAL ENTERPRISE LIMITED; *Int'l*, pg. 4728
MATRA MANUFACTURING & SERVICES SAS—See MGF Easybike SAS; *Int'l*, pg. 4872
MA TRANSTECNO S.A.P.I. DE C.V.—See Interpump Group S.p.A.; *Int'l*, pg. 3756
MATRA PRODUCTS—See International Business Machines Corporation; *U.S. Public*, pg. 1149
MATRA REALTY LIMITED; *Int'l*, pg. 4728
MATRA—See SKion GmbH; *Int'l*, pg. 6987
MATRATZEN CONCORD GMBH; *Int'l*, pg. 4728
MATRA-WERKE GMBH—See Prima Industrie SpA; *Int'l*, pg. 5974
MATREX MOLD & TOOL, INC.—See Shandong Weigao Group Medical Polymer Company Limited; *Int'l*, pg. 6759
MATREYA LLC—See Cayman Chemical Company, Inc.; *U.S. Private*, pg. 795

MATRICA LIMITED—See CK Asset Holdings Limited; *Int'l*, pg. 1635
MATRICELF; *Int'l*, pg. 4728
MATRICERIA DEUSTO, S.L.—See Acek Desarrollo y Gestion Industrial SL; *Int'l*, pg. 98
MATRIJZENMAKERIJ MARO B.V.—See Pema Holding AG; *Int'l*, pg. 5784
MATRIKON DEUTSCHLAND AG—See Honeywell International Inc.; *U.S. Public*, pg. 1051
MATRIKON INC.—See Honeywell International Inc.; *U.S. Public*, pg. 1051
MATRIKON INTERNATIONAL INC.—See Honeywell International Inc.; *U.S. Public*, pg. 1051
MATRIKON MIDDLE EAST CO WLL—See Honeywell International Inc.; *U.S. Public*, pg. 1051
MATRIKS FINANSAL TEKNOLOJILER A.S.; *Int'l*, pg. 4728
MATRIMONY.COM LIMITED; *Int'l*, pg. 4728
MATRIMONY DMCC—See Matrimony.Com Limited; *Int'l*, pg. 4728
MATRITA SA; *Int'l*, pg. 4728
MATRIX ABSENCE MANAGEMENT, INC.—See Tokio Marine Holdings, Inc.; *Int'l*, pg. 7782
MATRIX APPLIED TECHNOLOGIES, LTD.—See Matrix Service Company; *U.S. Public*, pg. 1397
MATRIX APPLIED TECHNOLOGIES, PTY. LTD.—See Matrix Service Company; *U.S. Public*, pg. 1397
MATRIX ASSET MANAGEMENT INC.; *Int'l*, pg. 4728
MATRIX AVIATION, INC.—See Greenwich AeroGroup, Inc.; *U.S. Private*, pg. 1781
MATRIX BUSINESS SERVICES INDIA PRIVATE LIMITED—See Updater Services Limited; *Int'l*, pg. 8087
MATRIX CAPITAL ADVISORS LLC—See CI Financial Corporation; *Int'l*, pg. 1601
MATRIXCARE, INC.—See ResMed Inc.; *U.S. Public*, pg. 1790
MATRIX COMMUNICATIONS INC.; *U.S. Private*, pg. 2611
THE MATRIX COMPANIES; *U.S. Private*, pg. 4076
MATRIX COMPOSITES & ENGINEERING LIMITED; *Int'l*, pg. 4729
MATRIX COMPOSITES, INC.—See ITT Inc.; *U.S. Public*, pg. 1178
MATRIX CONCEPTS HOLDINGS BERHAD; *Int'l*, pg. 4729
MATRIX CONCEPTS SDN. BHD.—See Matrix Concepts Holdings Berhad; *Int'l*, pg. 4729
MATRIX CONSULTING, LLC.—See The Climatic Corporation; *U.S. Private*, pg. 4010
MATRIX DATA LTD—See FactSet Research Systems Inc.; *U.S. Public*, pg. 820
MATRIX DESIGN CO., LTD.; *Int'l*, pg. 4729
MATRIX DESIGN GROUP, LLC—See Alliance Holdings GP, L.P.; *U.S. Private*, pg. 183
MATRIX DEVELOPMENT GROUP INC.; *U.S. Private*, pg. 2611
MATRIX DISTRIBUTION GMBH—See L'Oreal S.A.; *Int'l*, pg. 4381
MATRIX ENERGY SERVICES INC.; *U.S. Private*, pg. 2612
MATRIX ESSENTIALS, INC.—See L'Oreal S.A.; *Int'l*, pg. 4380
MATRIX-FOCALSPOT, INC.—See Nordson Corporation; *U.S. Public*, pg. 1533
MATRIX GOLF & HOSPITALITY—See Matrix Development Group Inc.; *U.S. Private*, pg. 2612
MATRIX GROUP (AUSTRALIA) PTY. LTD.; *Int'l*, pg. 4729
MATRIX HEALTHCARE SERVICES, INC.—See The Cigna Group; *U.S. Public*, pg. 2061
MATRIX HEALTH MANAGEMENT CORP.—See GIC Pte. Ltd.; *Int'l*, pg. 2964
MATRIX HEALTH MANAGEMENT CORP.—See Leonard Green & Partners, L.P.; *U.S. Private*, pg. 2425
MATRIX HOLDINGS LIMITED; *Int'l*, pg. 4729
MATRIX HUMAN SERVICES; *U.S. Private*, pg. 2612
MATRIX INFORMATION CONSULTING, INC.; *U.S. Private*, pg. 2612
MATRIX INSPECTION SYSTEMS, PTE. LTD.—See Nordson Corporation; *U.S. Public*, pg. 1533
MATRIX INSURANCE & REINSURANCE BROKERS S.A.—See Howden Group Holdings Limited; *Int'l*, pg. 3494
MATRIX INTEGRATION LLC; *U.S. Private*, pg. 2612
MATRIX INTERNATIONAL LTD.; *U.S. Private*, pg. 2612
MATRIX IT LTD.—See Asseco Poland S.A.; *Int'l*, pg. 642
MATRIX IV INC.; *U.S. Private*, pg. 2612
MATRIX LABORATORIES (XIAMEN) LTD.—See Viatris Inc.; *U.S. Public*, pg. 2293
MATRIX LOGISTICS SERVICES LTD.—See Deutsche Post AG; *Int'l*, pg. 2081
MATRIX MACHINE TOOL (COVENTRY) LIMITED—See Hiwin Technologies Corp.; *Int'l*, pg. 3427
MATRIX MANAGEMENT SOLUTIONS, LLC—See Thoma Bravo, L.P.; *U.S. Private*, pg. 4150
MATRIX MANUFACTURING VIETNAM COMPANY LIMITED—See Matrix Holdings Limited; *Int'l*, pg. 4729
MATRIX MARINE FUELS L LC—See Marquard & Bahls AG; *Int'l*, pg. 4699
MATRIX MEDIA SERVICES, INC.; *U.S. Private*, pg. 2612
MATRIX MEDICAL NETWORK OF ARIZONA, L.L.C.—See Frazier & Company, Inc.; *U.S. Private*, pg. 1599

MATRIX MEDICAL NETWORK OF ARIZONA, L.L.C.—See ModivCare, Inc.; *U.S. Public*, pg. 1455
MATRIX METALS LLC—See Sanmar Holdings Ltd.; *Int'l*, pg. 6546
MATRIX NORTH AMERICAN CONSTRUCTION, INC.—See Matrix Service Company; *U.S. Public*, pg. 1397
MATRIX OIL CORP.—See Royale Energy, Inc.; *U.S. Public*, pg. 1816
MATRIXONESOURCE, LLC—See GPB Capital Holdings, LLC; *U.S. Private*, pg. 1748
MATRIX PACKAGING MACHINERY, LLC—See Leonard Green & Partners, L.P.; *U.S. Private*, pg. 2428
MATRIX PARTNERS; *U.S. Private*, pg. 2612
MATRIX PDM ENGINEERING, INC.—See Matrix Service Company; *U.S. Public*, pg. 1397
MATRIX PLANNING SOLUTIONS LIMITED—See ClearView Wealth Limited; *Int'l*, pg. 1657
MATRIX REFRACTORIES DIVISION—See Allied Mineral Products, Inc.; *U.S. Private*, pg. 187
MATRIX RESOURCES, INC.—See Littlejohn & Co., LLC; *U.S. Private*, pg. 2471
MATRIX RISK CONSULTANTS, INC.—See Equitable Holdings, Inc.; *U.S. Public*, pg. 790
MATRIX SERVICE CANADA ULC—See Matrix Service Company; *U.S. Public*, pg. 1397
MATRIX SERVICE COMPANY - FABRICATION DIVISION—See Matrix Service Company; *U.S. Public*, pg. 1397
MATRIX SERVICE COMPANY; *U.S. Public*, pg. 1397
MATRIX SERVICE COMPANY - TANK CONSTRUCTION DIVISION—See Matrix Service Company; *U.S. Public*, pg. 1397
MATRIX SERVICE, INC.—See Matrix Service Company; *U.S. Public*, pg. 1397
MATRIX SERVICE, INC.—See Matrix Service Company; *U.S. Public*, pg. 1397
MATRIX SERVICE, INC.—See Matrix Service Company; *U.S. Public*, pg. 1397
MATRIX SERVICE, INC.—See Matrix Service Company; *U.S. Public*, pg. 1397
MATRIX SERVICE, INC.—See Matrix Service Company; *U.S. Public*, pg. 1397
MATRIX SERVICE INDUSTRIAL CONTRACTORS INC.—See Matrix Service Company; *U.S. Public*, pg. 1397
MATRIX S.P.A.—See TIM S.p.A.; *Int'l*, pg. 7749
MATRIX (SUZHOU) TRADING CO., LTD.—See Nordson Corporation; *U.S. Public*, pg. 1533
MATRIX SYSTEMS, INC.; *U.S. Private*, pg. 2612
MATRIX TECHNOLOGIES GMBH—See Nordson Corporation; *U.S. Public*, pg. 1533
MATRIX TECHNOLOGIES INCORPORATED; *U.S. Private*, pg. 2612
MATRIX TECHNOLOGIES, INC.—See Matrix Technologies Incorporated; *U.S. Private*, pg. 2612
MATRIX TECHNOLOGIES, INC.—See Matrix Technologies Incorporated; *U.S. Private*, pg. 2612
MATRIX TELECOM, LLC—See Blue Casa Communications, Inc.; *U.S. Private*, pg. 586
MATRIX TELECOM, LLC—See Garrison Investment Group LP; *U.S. Private*, pg. 1646
MATRIX TRUST COMPANY—See Broadridge Financial Solutions, Inc.; *U.S. Public*, pg. 392
MATRIX VEHICLE TRACKING—See PowerFleet, Inc.; *U.S. Public*, pg. 1706
MATRIX VISUAL SOLUTIONS, INC.—See Westminster Capital Inc.; *U.S. Private*, pg. 4499
MATRIX WIRE, INC.; *U.S. Private*, pg. 2612
MATRIXX INITIATIVES, INC.—See Gryphon Investors, LLC; *U.S. Private*, pg. 1799
MATROT EQUIPEMENTS SAS—See Exel Industries SA; *Int'l*, pg. 2582
MATROT UK LTD—See Exel Industries SA; *Int'l*, pg. 2582
MATROX ELECTRONIC SYSTEMS GMBH—See Zebra Technologies Corporation; *U.S. Public*, pg. 2401
MATROX ELECTRONIC SYSTEMS LTD—See Zebra Technologies Corporation; *U.S. Public*, pg. 2401
MATROX EUROPE LTD—See Zebra Technologies Corporation; *U.S. Public*, pg. 2401
MATROX GRAPHICS, INC.—See Zebra Technologies Corporation; *U.S. Public*, pg. 2401
MATROX VIDEO AND IMAGING TECHNOLOGY EUROPE LIMITED—See Zebra Technologies Corporation; *U.S. Public*, pg. 2401
MATRX BY MIDMARK—See Midmark Corporation; *U.S. Private*, pg. 2716
MATSA RESOURCES LIMITED; *Int'l*, pg. 4729
MATSCHEL OF FLAGLER INC.; *U.S. Private*, pg. 2612
MATS, INC.—See Moran Transportation Corp.; *U.S. Private*, pg. 2782
MATSON ALASKA, INC.—See Matson, Inc.; *U.S. Public*, pg. 1398
MATSON DISTRIBUTING, INC.; *U.S. Private*, pg. 2612
MATSON, DRISCOLL & DAMICO; *U.S. Private*, pg. 2612
MATSON, INC.; *U.S. Public*, pg. 1397
MATSON, LLC—See Central Garden & Pet Company; *U.S. Public*, pg. 473

MATSON LOGISTICS, INC.—See Matson, Inc.; *U.S. Public*, pg. 1398
MATSON NAVIGATION COMPANY, INC.—See Matson, Inc.; *U.S. Public*, pg. 1398
MATSON TERMINALS, INC.—See Matson, Inc.; *U.S. Public*, pg. 1398
MAT SP. Z O.O.—See Grupa SMT S.A.; *Int'l*, pg. 3117
MATSU ALABAMA INC.—See Matcor-Matsu Group Inc.; *Int'l*, pg. 4726
MATSU BARRIE INC.—See Matcor-Matsu Group Inc.; *Int'l*, pg. 4726
MATSUBO CORPORATION—See Kobe Steel, Ltd.; *Int'l*, pg. 4221
MATSUBO GMBH—See Kobe Steel, Ltd.; *Int'l*, pg. 4221
MATSUDA ECOLOGY CO., LTD.—See Matsuda Sangyo Co., Ltd.; *Int'l*, pg. 4729
MATSUDA MANUFACTURING (THAILAND) CO., LTD.—See Kawakin Holdings Co., Ltd.; *Int'l*, pg. 4094
MATSUDA RYUTSU CO., LTD.—See Matsuda Sangyo Co., Ltd.; *Int'l*, pg. 4729
MATSUDA SANGYO CO. LTD. - IRUMA PLANT II—See Matsuda Sangyo Co., Ltd.; *Int'l*, pg. 4729
MATSUDA SANGYO CO. LTD. - IRUMA PLANT—See Matsuda Sangyo Co., Ltd.; *Int'l*, pg. 4729
MATSUDA SANGYO CO. LTD. - MUSASHI FACTORY—See Matsuda Sangyo Co., Ltd.; *Int'l*, pg. 4729
MATSUDA SANGYO CO., LTD.; *Int'l*, pg. 4729
MATSUDA SANGYO CO. LTD. - URBAN RECYCLE BUSINESS DEPT.—See Matsuda Sangyo Co., Ltd.; *Int'l*, pg. 4729
MATSUDA SANGYO (PHILIPPINES) CORPORATION—See Matsuda Sangyo Co., Ltd.; *Int'l*, pg. 4729
MATSUDA SANGYO (SINGAPORE) PTE. LTD.—See Matsuda Sangyo Co., Ltd.; *Int'l*, pg. 4729
MATSUDA SANGYO (THAILAND) CO., LTD.—See Matsuda Sangyo Co., Ltd.; *Int'l*, pg. 4729
MATSUDA SEISAKUSHO CO., LTD.—See Kawakin Holdings Co., Ltd.; *Int'l*, pg. 4094
MATSUDO KOUSAN CO., LTD.—See Mitsui Fudosan Co., Ltd.; *Int'l*, pg. 4988
MATSUDO MEDICAL LABORATORIES, INC.—See BML, Inc.; *Int'l*, pg. 1076
MATSUE BIOMASS POWER CO., LTD.—See Japan Pulp and Paper Company Limited; *Int'l*, pg. 3904
MATSUE DAI-ICHI SEIKO CO., LTD—See I-PEX Inc.; *Int'l*, pg. 3564
MATSUE DAIICHI TRAFFIC LTD—See Daiichi Koutsu Sangyo Co., Ltd.; *Int'l*, pg. 1928
MATSUI CHEMICAL CO., LTD.—See Toyo Ink SC Holdings Co., Ltd.; *Int'l*, pg. 7853
MATSUI CONSTRUCTION CO., LTD.; *Int'l*, pg. 4729
MATSUI SECURITIES CO., LTD.; *Int'l*, pg. 4729
MATSUKEN CO., LTD.—See MORESCO Corporation; *Int'l*, pg. 5040
MATSUKIYA CO., LTD.—See Yamaha Corporation; *Int'l*, pg. 8549
MATSUKIYOCOCOKARA & CO.; *Int'l*, pg. 4729
MATSU MANUFACTURING (BARRIE) INC.—See Matcor-Matsu Group Inc.; *Int'l*, pg. 4726
(MATSUMOTO) DAIICHI TRAFFIC CO., LTD.—See Daiichi Koutsu Sangyo Co., Ltd.; *Int'l*, pg. 1928
MATSUMOTO INC.; *Int'l*, pg. 4730
MATSUMOTOKIYOSHI CHU-SHIKOKU CO., LTD.—See MatsukiyoCocokara & Co.; *Int'l*, pg. 4730
MATSUMOTOKIYOSHI CO., LTD.—See MatsukiyoCocokara & Co.; *Int'l*, pg. 4730
MATSUMOTOKIYOSHI EAST CO., LTD.—See MatsukiyoCocokara & Co.; *Int'l*, pg. 4730
MATSUMOTOKIYOSHI KOU-SHIN-ETSU CO., LTD.—See MatsukiyoCocokara & Co.; *Int'l*, pg. 4730
MATSUMOTOKIYOSHI KYUSYU CO., LTD.—See MatsukiyoCocokara & Co.; *Int'l*, pg. 4730
MATSUMOTOKIYOSHI PHARMACIES CO., LTD.—See MatsukiyoCocokara & Co.; *Int'l*, pg. 4730
MATSUMOTO KOSAN CO., LTD.—See Matsumoto Yushi-Seiyaku Co.,Ltd; *Int'l*, pg. 4730
MATSUMOTO YUSHI-SEIYAKU CO.,LTD - OSAKA FACTORY—See Matsumoto Yushi-Seiyaku Co.,Ltd; *Int'l*, pg. 4730
MATSUMOTO YUSHI-SEIYAKU CO.,LTD - SHIZUOKA FACTORY—See Matsumoto Yushi-Seiyaku Co.,Ltd; *Int'l*, pg. 4730
MATSUMOTO YUSHI-SEIYAKU CO.,LTD; *Int'l*, pg. 4730
MATSUMOTO YUSHI-SEIYAKU CO.,LTD - YAO FACTORY—See Matsumoto Yushi-Seiyaku Co.,Ltd; *Int'l*, pg. 4730
MATSUO ELECTRIC CO., LTD.—See Stanley Electric Co., Ltd.; *Int'l*, pg. 7170
MATSU OHIO INC.—See Matcor-Matsu Group Inc.; *Int'l*, pg. 4726
MATSUOKA CORPORATION, LTD.; *Int'l*, pg. 4730
MATSUOKA KOZAI CO., LTD.—See Hanwa Co., Ltd.; *Int'l*, pg. 3263
MATSUSAKA COUNTRY CLUB CO., LTD.—See Mie Kotsu Group Holdings, Inc.; *Int'l*, pg. 4888
MATSUSAKA PLANT SAKAI MANUFACTURING—See Central Glass Co., Ltd.; *Int'l*, pg. 1407

MAT-SU SERVICES FOR CHILDREN AND ADULTS INC.; *U.S. Private*, pg. 2608
MATSUSHIMA WAKABA DAIICHI TRAFFIC LTD.—See Daiichi Koutsu Sangyo Co., Ltd.; *Int'l*, pg. 1928
MATSUSHITA AVIONICS SYSTEMS CORPORATION—See Panasonic Holdings Corporation; *Int'l*, pg. 5720
MATSUSHITA AVIONICS SYSTEMS CORPORATION—See Panasonic Holdings Corporation; *Int'l*, pg. 5720
MATSUSHITA BATTERY INDUSTRIAL CO., LTD.—See Panasonic Holdings Corporation; *Int'l*, pg. 5717
MATSUSHITA COMMUNICATION INDUSTRIAL CORP.—See Panasonic Holdings Corporation; *Int'l*, pg. 5720
MATSUSHITA ELECTRIC CORPORATION OF AMERICA—See Panasonic Holdings Corporation; *Int'l*, pg. 5720
MATSUSHITA ELECTRIC CORPORATION OF AMERICA—See Panasonic Holdings Corporation; *Int'l*, pg. 5720
MATSUSHITA ELECTRIC CORPORATION OF AMERICA—See Panasonic Holdings Corporation; *Int'l*, pg. 5720
MATSUSHITA ELECTRIC CORPORATION OF AMERICA—See Panasonic Holdings Corporation; *Int'l*, pg. 5720
MATSUYA CO., LTD. - ASAKUSA—See ALPICO Holdings Co., Ltd.; *Int'l*, pg. 371
MATSUYA CO., LTD. - GINZA—See ALPICO Holdings Co., Ltd.; *Int'l*, pg. 371
MATSUYA CO., LTD.—See ALPICO Holdings Co., Ltd.; *Int'l*, pg. 371
MATSUYA FLOUR MILLS CO., LTD.—See NIPPN Corporation; *Int'l*, pg. 5309
MATSUYA FOODS, CO., LTD. - MT. FUJI FACTORY—See Matsuya Foods Holdings Co., Ltd.; *Int'l*, pg. 4730
MATSUYA FOODS, CO., LTD. - RANZAN FACTORY—See Matsuya Foods Holdings Co., Ltd.; *Int'l*, pg. 4730
MATSUYA FOODS HOLDINGS CO., LTD.; *Int'l*, pg. 4730
MATSUYAMA ENVIRONMENT TECHNOLOGY CO., LTD.—See Hitachi Zosen Corporation; *Int'l*, pg. 3411
MATSUYAMA MITSUKOSHI LTD.—See Isetan Mitsukoshi Holdings Ltd.; *Int'l*, pg. 3815
MATSUYA R&D TRADING (SHANGHAI) CO., LTD.—See Matsuya Research & Development Co., Ltd.; *Int'l*, pg. 4730
MATSUYA R&D (VIETNAM) CO., LTD.—See Matsuya Research & Development Co., Ltd.; *Int'l*, pg. 4730
MATSUYA RESEARCH & DEVELOPMENT CO., LTD.; *Int'l*, pg. 4730
MATSUZAKAYA - NAGOYA—See J. Front Retailing Co., Ltd.; *Int'l*, pg. 3855
THE MATTAMY CORPORATION; *Int'l*, pg. 7665
MATT BLATT INC.; *U.S. Private*, pg. 2612
MATT CASTRUCCI, LLC; *U.S. Private*, pg. 2613
MATTCO FORGE, INC.—See Blue Point Capital Partners, LLC; *U.S. Private*, pg. 590
MATT CONSTRUCTION CORPORATION; *U.S. Private*, pg. 2613
MATT CONSTRUCTION SERVICES INC.—See Columbia National Group Inc; *U.S. Private*, pg. 977
MATTEI COMPRESSORS INC.; *U.S. Private*, pg. 2613
MATTEK CORPORATION—See BICO Group AB; *Int'l*, pg. 1019
MATTEL ASIA LTD.—See Mattel, Inc.; *U.S. Public*, pg. 1398
MATTEL AUSTRALIA PTY. LTD.—See Mattel, Inc.; *U.S. Public*, pg. 1398
MATTEL B.V. (NETHERLANDS)—See Mattel, Inc.; *U.S. Public*, pg. 1398
MATTEL CANADA, INC.—See Mattel, Inc.; *U.S. Public*, pg. 1398
MATTEL ESPANA, S.A.—See Mattel, Inc.; *U.S. Public*, pg. 1398
MATTEL EUROPA BV—See Mattel, Inc.; *U.S. Public*, pg. 1398
MATTEL EUROPE HOLDINGS B.V.—See Mattel, Inc.; *U.S. Public*, pg. 1398
MATTEL FOREIGN HOLDINGS, LTD.—See Mattel, Inc.; *U.S. Public*, pg. 1398
MATTEL GAMES/PUZZLES—See Mattel, Inc.; *U.S. Public*, pg. 1398
MATTEL GMBH—See Mattel, Inc.; *U.S. Public*, pg. 1398
MATTEL GMBH—See Mattel, Inc.; *U.S. Public*, pg. 1399
MATTEL HOLDING, INC.—See Mattel, Inc.; *U.S. Public*, pg. 1399
MATTEL, INC.; *U.S. Public*, pg. 1398
MATTEL INTERNATIONAL FINANCE B.V.—See Mattel, Inc.; *U.S. Public*, pg. 1399
MATTEL (MALAYSIA) SDN. BHD.—See Mattel, Inc.; *U.S. Public*, pg. 1398
MATTEL OVERSEAS, INC.—See Mattel, Inc.; *U.S. Public*, pg. 1399
MATTEL PTY. LTD.—See Mattel, Inc.; *U.S. Public*, pg. 1399
MATTEL S.R.L.—See Mattel, Inc.; *U.S. Public*, pg. 1399
MATTEL TOYS (H.K.) LTD.—See Mattel, Inc.; *U.S. Public*, pg. 1399

COMPANY NAME INDEX

MATTEL (UK) LTD.—See Mattel, Inc.; *U.S. Public*, pg. 1398
MATTEO ALUMINUM, INC.; *U.S. Private*, pg. 2613
MATTER COMMUNICATIONS INC.; *U.S. Private*, pg. 2613
MATTERMARK, INC.—See FullContact, Inc.; *U.S. Private*, pg. 1621
MATTERPORT, INC.; *U.S. Public*, pg. 1399
MATTERPORT OPERATING, LLC—See Matterport, Inc.; *U.S. Public*, pg. 1399
MATTERSIGHT CORPORATION—See NICE Ltd.; *Int'l*, pg. 5265
MATTERSOFT OY—See init innovation in traffic systems SE; *Int'l*, pg. 3704
MATTER; *U.S. Private*, pg. 2613
MATTHEW 25 MINISTRIES, INC; *U.S. Private*, pg. 2613
MATTHEW BENDER & COMPANY, INC.—See RELX plc; *Int'l*, pg. 6267
MATTHEW CLARK BIBENDUM LIMITED—See C&C Group Plc; *Int'l*, pg. 1238
MATTHEW F MCCARTY M D PLLC—See Iron Path Capital, L.P.; *U.S. Private*, pg. 2139
MATTHEW JOHNSON MARSHALL LTD.; *Int'l*, pg. 4731
MATTHEWS AUTO GROUP; *U.S. Private*, pg. 2613
MATTHEWS BRONZE PTY. LTD.—See Matthews International Corporation; *U.S. Public*, pg. 1399
MATTHEWS BUSES INC.—See The Matthews Group Inc.; *U.S. Private*, pg. 4076
MATTHEWS CANADA LTD.—See Matthews International Corporation; *U.S. Public*, pg. 1400
MATTHEWS CONSTRUCTION CO., INC.; *U.S. Private*, pg. 2613
MATTHEWS-DANIEL COMPANY—See Bureau Veritas S.A.; *Int'l*, pg. 1222
MATTHEWS-DANIEL INTERNATIONAL (LONDON) LIMITED—See Bureau Veritas S.A.; *Int'l*, pg. 1222
MATTHEWSDANIEL LIMITED—See Bureau Veritas S.A.; *Int'l*, pg. 1222
MATTHEWS DESIGN GROUP, LLC—See White Wolf Capital LLC; *U.S. Private*, pg. 4510
MATTHEWS ENVIRONMENTAL SOLUTIONS LIMITED—See Matthews International Corporation; *U.S. Public*, pg. 1399
MATTHEWS EUROPE GMBH—See Matthews International Corporation; *U.S. Public*, pg. 1399
MATTHEWS, EVANS & ALBERTAZZI; *U.S. Private*, pg. 2614
MATTHEWS GIBRALTAR MAUSOLEUM & CONSTRUCTION COMPANY—See Matthews International Corporation; *U.S. Public*, pg. 1399
THE MATTHEWS GROUP INC.; *U.S. Private*, pg. 4076
MATTHEWS HARGREAVES CHEVROLET; *U.S. Private*, pg. 2613
MATTHEWS INSTORE SOLUTIONS EUROPE GMBH—See Matthews International Corporation; *U.S. Public*, pg. 1399
MATTHEWS INTERNATIONAL CAPITAL MANAGEMENT, LLC; *U.S. Private*, pg. 2613
MATTHEWS INTERNATIONAL CORP. - BRONZE—See Matthews International Corporation; *U.S. Public*, pg. 1400
MATTHEWS INTERNATIONAL CORP. - CASKET DIVISION DISTRIBUTION CENTER—See Matthews International Corporation; *U.S. Public*, pg. 1400
MATTHEWS INTERNATIONAL CORP. - GRAPHICS IMAGING—See Matthews International Corporation; *U.S. Public*, pg. 1400
MATTHEWS INTERNATIONAL CORP. - MARKING PRODUCTS—See Matthews International Corporation; *U.S. Public*, pg. 1400
MATTHEWS INTERNATIONAL CORPORATION; *U.S. Public*, pg. 1399
MATTHEWS INTERNATIONAL (EFN) GMBH—See Matthews International Corporation; *U.S. Public*, pg. 1399
MATTHEWS INTERNATIONAL GMBH—See Matthews International Corporation; *U.S. Public*, pg. 1400
MATTHEWS INTERNATIONAL SARL—See Matthews International Corporation; *U.S. Public*, pg. 1400
MATTHEWS INTERNATIONAL S.P.A.—See Matthews International Corporation; *U.S. Public*, pg. 1400
MATTHEWS KODIERSYSTEME GMBH—See Matthews International Corporation; *U.S. Public*, pg. 1400
MATTHEWS MARKING SYSTEMS SWEDEN AB—See Matthews International Corporation; *U.S. Public*, pg. 1400
MATTHEWS PACKAGING GRAPHICS & DESIGN—See Matthews International Corporation; *U.S. Public*, pg. 1400
MATTHEWS PACKAGING GRAPHICS—See Matthews International Corporation; *U.S. Public*, pg. 1400
MATTHEWS REAL ESTATE INVESTMENT SERVICES; *U.S. Private*, pg. 2613
MATTHEWS STEER PTY. LTD.—See Azimut Holding SpA; *Int'l*, pg. 779
MATTHEWS STUDIO EQUIPMENT, INC.; *U.S. Private*, pg. 2613
MATTHEWS SWEDOT AB—See Matthews International Corporation; *U.S. Public*, pg. 1400

MATTHEW THORNTON HEALTH PLAN, INC.—See Elevance Health, Inc.; *U.S. Public*, pg. 730
MATTHEW WARREN SPRING—See American Securities LLC; *U.S. Private*, pg. 250
MATTHEW WILLIAMSON LTD.; *Int'l*, pg. 4731
MATTH. HOHNER AG; *Int'l*, pg. 4730
MATTHIAS PAPER CORPORATION; *U.S. Private*, pg. 2614
MATTHIAS SCHERNIKAU GMBH—See KONE Oyj; *Int'l*, pg. 4250
MATTHIESSEN ASSURANS AB—See Marsh & McLennan Companies, Inc.; *U.S. Public*, pg. 1384
MATT INDUSTRIES INC.; *U.S. Private*, pg. 2613
MATTINGLY FOODS INC.—See Creation Gardens, Inc.; *U.S. Private*, pg. 1087
MATTING TECHNOLOGY CORPORATION; *Int'l*, pg. 4731
MATTIOLI WOODS PLC—See Pollen Street Limited; *Int'l*, pg. 5910
MATTI-OVI OY—See Panostaja Oyj; *Int'l*, pg. 5729
MATTIS INSURANCE AGENCY—See Inszone Insurance Services, LLC; *U.S. Private*, pg. 2096
MATT MANAGEMENT INC.; *U.S. Private*, pg. 2613
MATT MARTIN REAL ESTATE MANAGEMENT LLC; *U.S. Private*, pg. 2613
MATTONI 1873 A.S.; *Int'l*, pg. 4731
MATTORSOFT OY—See init innovation in traffic systems SE; *Int'l*, pg. 3704
MAT TOURS & TRAVEL (CAMBODIA) PTE. LTD.—See Warisan TC Holdings Berhad; *Int'l*, pg. 8345
MATTRESS DEPOT USA; *U.S. Private*, pg. 2614
MATTRESS DIRECT, INC.; *U.S. Private*, pg. 2614
MATTRESS DISCOUNTERS CORP; *U.S. Private*, pg. 2614
MATTRESS FIRM GROUP INC.—See Steinhoff International Holdings N.V.; *Int'l*, pg. 7194
MATTRESS FIRM, INC.—See Steinhoff International Holdings N.V.; *Int'l*, pg. 7195
MATTRESS HOLDINGS INTERNATIONAL B.V.—See Tempur Sealy International, Inc.; *U.S. Public*, pg. 1999
MATTRESS KING, INC.—See Tempur Sealy International, Inc.; *U.S. Public*, pg. 1999
MATTRESS LAND SLEEPFIT; *U.S. Private*, pg. 2614
MATTS CASH & CARRY BUILDING MATERIALS; *U.S. Private*, pg. 2614
MATTSCO SUPPLY CO.; *U.S. Private*, pg. 2614
MATT SLAP SUBARU; *U.S. Private*, pg. 2613
MATTSON TECHNOLOGY, INC.—See Beijing E-Town International Investment & Development Co., Ltd.; *Int'l*, pg. 949
MATTSON TECHNOLOGY SINGAPORE PTE. LTD.—See Beijing E-Town International Investment & Development Co., Ltd.; *Int'l*, pg. 949
MATTSON THERMAL PRODUCTS GMBH—See Beijing E-Town International Investment & Development Co., Ltd.; *Int'l*, pg. 949
MATTSON TRADING (SHANGHAI) CO., LTD.—See Beijing E-Town International Investment & Development Co., Ltd.; *Int'l*, pg. 949
MATTSSON METAL AB; *Int'l*, pg. 4731
MATTY CO., LTD.—See YAMAICHI ELECTRONICS Co Ltd; *Int'l*, pg. 8552
MATULAITIS NURSING HOME; *U.S. Private*, pg. 2614
MATUSSIERE & FOREST S.A.—See MatlinPatterson Global Advisers LLC; *U.S. Private*, pg. 2611
MATUTANO-SOCIEDADE DE PRODUTOS ALIMENTARES, UNIPESOAL LDA.—See PepsiCo, Inc.; *U.S. Public*, pg. 1669
MATVAREEXPRESSEN AS; *Int'l*, pg. 4731
MATVAREHUSET AS—See TINE SA; *Int'l*, pg. 7753
MATVEST INC.; *U.S. Private*, pg. 2614
MATYS HEALTHY PRODUCTS LLC—See Bayer Aktiengesellschaft; *Int'l*, pg. 908
MATZEN & TIMM GMBH—See Masterflex SE; *Int'l*, pg. 4725
MATZ-ERREKA, S.COOP.—See Mondragon Corporation; *Int'l*, pg. 5031
MAUCH CHUNK TRUST COMPANY; *U.S. Private*, pg. 2614
MAUDLIN INTERNATIONAL TRUCKS, INC.; *U.S. Private*, pg. 2614
MAUDLIN & SON MANUFACTURING CO., INC.—See American Securities LLC; *U.S. Private*, pg. 250
MAUDORE MINERALS LTD.; *Int'l*, pg. 4731
MAUGEL ARCHITECTS INC; *U.S. Private*, pg. 2614
MAUGER & COMPANY, INC.; *U.S. Private*, pg. 2614
MAUGHAN THIEM GROUP; *Int'l*, pg. 4731
MAUI CAPITAL LTD.; *Int'l*, pg. 4731
MAUI CHEMICAL & PAPER PRODUCTS, INC.; *U.S. Private*, pg. 2614
MAUI CLOTHING CO. INC.; *U.S. Private*, pg. 2614
MAUI DIVERS OF HAWAII, LTD.; *U.S. Private*, pg. 2614
MAUI ELDORADO KAANAPALI BY OUTRIGGER—See KSL Capital Partners, LLC; *U.S. Private*, pg. 2355
MAUI ELECTRIC COMPANY, LIMITED—See Hawaiian Electric Industries, Inc.; *U.S. Public*, pg. 989
MAUI ESTATES INTERNATIONAL, LLC—See Hawaii Life; *U.S. Private*, pg. 1881
MAUIGROWN COFFEE DISTRIBUTORS, LLC—See Kaanapali Land, LLC; *U.S. Public*, pg. 1212

MAUI JIM ASIA LIMITED—See Kering S.A.; *Int'l*, pg. 4135
MAUI JIM AUSTRALIA PTY., LTD.—See Kering S.A.; *Int'l*, pg. 4135
MAUI JIM CANADA ULC—See Kering S.A.; *Int'l*, pg. 4135
MAUI JIM GERMANY, GMBH—See Kering S.A.; *Int'l*, pg. 4135
MAUI JIM, INC.—See Kering S.A.; *Int'l*, pg. 4134
MAUI JIM - ITALY S.R.L.—See Kering S.A.; *Int'l*, pg. 4135
MAUI JIM MIDDLE EAST FZE—See Kering S.A.; *Int'l*, pg. 4135
MAUI JIM NORDIC AB—See Kering S.A.; *Int'l*, pg. 4135
MAUI JIM SOUTH AFRICA (PTY.) LTD.—See Kering S.A.; *Int'l*, pg. 4136
MAUI JIM SPAIN, S.L.—See Kering S.A.; *Int'l*, pg. 4136
MAUI JIM SUNGLASSES DE MEXICO S DE R.L. DE C.V.—See Kering S.A.; *Int'l*, pg. 4136
MAUI JIM SUN OPTICS INDIA PRIVATE LIMITED—See Kering S.A.; *Int'l*, pg. 4136
MAUI JIM UK LTD.—See Kering S.A.; *Int'l*, pg. 4136
MAUI LAND & PINEAPPLE COMPANY, INC.; *U.S. Public*, pg. 1401
MAUI LEONES LLC; *U.S. Private*, pg. 2614
MAUI MAGNETS INC.; *U.S. Private*, pg. 2614
MAUI PAVING, LLC—See Alexander & Baldwin, Inc.; *U.S. Public*, pg. 75
MAUI PINEAPPLE COMPANY, LTD.—See Maui Land & Pineapple Company, Inc.; *U.S. Public*, pg. 1402
MAUI RESORT RENTALS INC.; *U.S. Private*, pg. 2614
MAUI ROOFING—See Petersen-Dean Inc.; *U.S. Private*, pg. 3160
MAUI TACOS INTERNATIONAL, INC.—See Blimpie International Inc.; *U.S. Private*, pg. 581
MAUI TOYS, INC.—See JAKKS Pacific, Inc.; *U.S. Public*, pg. 1187
MAUI VARIETIES, LTD.; *U.S. Private*, pg. 2615
MAUI WOWI FRANCHISING, INC.; *U.S. Private*, pg. 2615
MAUJI TRIP LIMITED—See SBC Exports Ltd.; *Int'l*, pg. 6603
MAUL + CO - CHR. BELSER GMBH—See Bertelsmann SE & Co. KGaA; *Int'l*, pg. 996
MAULDIN CORPORATION; *U.S. Private*, pg. 2615
MAULDIN-DORFMEIER CONSTRUCTION; *U.S. Private*, pg. 2615
MAULDIN & JENKINS, LLC; *U.S. Private*, pg. 2615
MAUL ELECTRIC INC.; *U.S. Private*, pg. 2615
MAULTECH CORPORATION—See Denso Corporation; *Int'l*, pg. 2032
MAUM.AI, INC; *Int'l*, pg. 4731
MAUNA KEA AGRIBUSINESS CO., INC.—See C. Brewer & Co. Ltd.; *U.S. Private*, pg. 705
MAUNA KEA RESORT SERVICE LLC.—See Seibu Holdings Inc.; *Int'l*, pg. 6685
MAUNA KEA TECHNOLOGIES INC.—See Mauna Kea Technologies SA; *Int'l*, pg. 4732
MAUNA KEA TECHNOLOGIES SA; *Int'l*, pg. 4732
MAUNA LOA MACADAMIA NUT CORPORATION—See Hawaiian Host Inc.; *U.S. Private*, pg. 1882
MAUNA N.V.; *Int'l*, pg. 4732
MAUPINTOUR INC.; *U.S. Private*, pg. 2615
MAURER ELECTRONICS GMBH—See Bundesdruckerei GmbH; *Int'l*, pg. 1215
MAURER SUPPLY INC.; *U.S. Private*, pg. 2615
MAUREXCO INTERNATIONAL—See Maurice Electrical Supply Company; *U.S. Private*, pg. 2615
MAUREY MANUFACTURING CORPORATION; *U.S. Private*, pg. 2615
MAURIA UDYOG LTD.; *Int'l*, pg. 4732
MAURICE ELECTRICAL SUPPLY COMPANY; *U.S. Private*, pg. 2615
MAURICE J. MARKELL SHOE CO., INC.; *U.S. Private*, pg. 2615
MAURICE LACROIX S.A.; *Int'l*, pg. 4732
MAURICE PINCOFF COMPANY INC.; *U.S. Private*, pg. 2615
MAURICE PUBLICITE LTD.—See WPP plc; *Int'l*, pg. 8484
MAURICES INCORPORATED—See OpCapita LLP; *Int'l*, pg. 5595
MAURICE SPORTING GOODS, INC.—See Peak Global Holdings, LLC; *U.S. Private*, pg. 3123
MAURICE TAYLOR INSURANCE BROKERS INC.—See Inszone Insurance Services, LLC; *U.S. Private*, pg. 2096
MAURIGO PTE.LTD.—See Gokul Refoils and Solvent Limited; *Int'l*, pg. 3023
MAURI MAYA SANAYI A.S.—See The Garfield Weston Foundation; *Int'l*, pg. 7648
MAURIN-OGDEN PROPERTIES; *U.S. Private*, pg. 2615
MAURITEL SA—See Emirates Telecommunications Group Compapy PJSC; *Int'l*, pg. 2382
THE MAURITIUS CHEMICAL & FERTILIZER INDUSTRY LIMITED—See Harel Mallac & Co. Ltd.; *Int'l*, pg. 3274
THE MAURITIUS COMMERCIAL BANK LTD.; *Int'l*, pg. 7665
MAURITIUS COMMERCIAL BANK - MADAGASCAR (ANTANANARIVO) S.A.—See The Mauritius Commercial Bank Ltd.; *Int'l*, pg. 7666
THE MAURITIUS COMMERCIAL BANK (MOCAMBIQUE) S.A.—See The Mauritius Commercial Bank Ltd.; *Int'l*, pg. 7666

THE MAURITIUS COMMERCIAL BANK LTD.

CORPORATE AFFILIATIONS

THE MAURITIUS COMMERCIAL BANK (SEYCHELLES) LTD—See The Mauritius Commercial Bank Ltd.; *Int'l*, pg. 7666
THE MAURITIUS DEVELOPMENT INVESTMENT TRUST COMPANY LIMITED; *Int'l*, pg. 7666
MAURITIUS FREEPORT DEVELOPMENT CO., LTD.; *Int'l*, pg. 4732
MAURITIUS HELICOPTER LTD.—See Air Mauritius Limited; *Int'l*, pg. 238
MAURITIUS MOLASSES COMPANY LTD—See Taylor Smith Group; *Int'l*, pg. 7478
MAURITIUS OIL REFINERIES LIMITED; *Int'l*, pg. 4732
MAURITIUS TELECOM LTD.; *Int'l*, pg. 4732
THE MAURITIUS UNION ASSURANCE COMPANY LIMITED; *Int'l*, pg. 7666
MAURI YEAST AUSTRALIA PTY. LTD.—See The Garfield Weston Foundation; *Int'l*, pg. 7648
MAURO DEMETRIO S.P.A.; *Int'l*, pg. 4732
MAURY, DONNELLY & PARR, INC.; *U.S. Private*, pg. 2615
MAURY MICROWAVE INC.—See Artemis Capital Partners Management Co., LLC; *U.S. Private*, pg. 340
MAURY S.A.S.—See SIG plc; *Int'l*, pg. 6906
MAUSER GROUP N.V.—See Stone Canyon Industries, LLC; *U.S. Private*, pg. 3817
MAUSER PACKAGING SOLUTIONS—See Stone Canyon Industries, LLC; *U.S. Private*, pg. 3817
MAUSER USA, LLC—See Stone Canyon Industries, LLC; *U.S. Private*, pg. 3817
MAUSER-WERKE GMBH—See Stone Canyon Industries, LLC; *U.S. Private*, pg. 3817
MAUS FRERES S.A.; *Int'l*, pg. 4732
MAU-SHERWOOD SUPPLY CO; *U.S. Private*, pg. 2614
MAUS & HOFFMAN, INC.; *U.S. Private*, pg. 2615
MAUST CORPORATION; *U.S. Private*, pg. 2615
MAUTILUS S.R.O.—See Aferian plc; *Int'l*, pg. 185
MAUTNER MARKHOF FEINKOST GMBH—See PAI Partners S.A.S.; *Int'l*, pg. 5700
MAUTOURCO LTD.—See New Mauritius Hotels Limited; *Int'l*, pg. 5226
MAU WORKFORCE SOLUTIONS; *U.S. Private*, pg. 2614
M. A. V. 7., BANK AUSTRIA LEASING BAUTRAGER GMBH & CO.OHG.—See UniCredit S.p.A.; *Int'l*, pg. 8038
MAVADKARAN COMPANY—See MAPNA Group; *Int'l*, pg. 4687
MAVAL INDUSTRIES LLC—See Torque Capital Group, LLC; *U.S. Private*, pg. 4189
MAV BEAUTY BRANDS, INC.—See Nexus Capital Management LP; *U.S. Private*, pg. 2922
MAVEC CORPORATION—See Merck & Co., Inc.; *U.S. Public*, pg. 1418
MAVECOM PALVELUT OY—See Wulff Yhtiot Oyj; *Int'l*, pg. 8502
MAVEN BRANDS INC.; *Int'l*, pg. 4732
MAVEN CAPITAL PARTNERS UK LLP—See Pollen Street Limited; *Int'l*, pg. 5910
MAVENHILL CAPITAL; *U.S. Private*, pg. 2615
MAVEN INCOME & GROWTH VCT 4 PLC; *Int'l*, pg. 4732
MAVEN INCOME & GROWTH VCT 5 PLC; *Int'l*, pg. 4733
MAVEN INCOME & GROWTH VCT PLC; *Int'l*, pg. 4733
MAVENIR AUSTRALASIA PTY LTD.—See Siris Capital Group, LLC; *U.S. Private*, pg. 3673
MAVENIR (NZ) LIMITED—See Siris Capital Group, LLC; *U.S. Private*, pg. 3673
MAVENIR SPAIN SL—See Siris Capital Group, LLC; *U.S. Private*, pg. 3673
MAVENIR SYSTEMS, INC.—See Siris Capital Group, LLC; *U.S. Private*, pg. 3673
MAVENS BIOTECH LIMITED; *Int'l*, pg. 4733
MAVENS CONSULTING SERVICES, INC.—See Komodo Health, Inc.; *U.S. Private*, pg. 2342
MAVEN SYSTEMS PRIVATE LIMITED—See Moschip Technologies Limited; *Int'l*, pg. 5050
MAVEN WAVE PARTNERS, LLC—See Atos SE; *Int'l*, pg. 692
MAVEN WIRELESS SWEDEN AB; *Int'l*, pg. 4733
MAVEPCELL KFT.—See Swietelsky Baugesellschaft m.b.H.; *Int'l*, pg. 7367
MAVERICK ADVERTISING & DESIGN; *Int'l*, pg. 4733
MAVERICK AIR CENTER LLC—See Sanford Health; *U.S. Private*, pg. 3545
MAVERICK ARMS, INC.—See Mossberg Corporation; *U.S. Private*, pg. 2794
MAVERICK BOAT CO. INC.; *U.S. Private*, pg. 2615
MAVERICK BOAT GROUP, INC.—See Malibu Boats, Inc.; *U.S. Public*, pg. 1356
MAVERICK BUILDING SYSTEMS, LLC—See Zeeland Lumber & Supply Co.; *U.S. Private*, pg. 4599
MAVERICK CONSTRUCTION CORPORATION; *U.S. Private*, pg. 2615
MAVERICK DENTAL, LLC; *U.S. Private*, pg. 2616
MAVERICK DRILLING & EXPLORATION LIMITED; *Int'l*, pg. 4733
MAVERICK ENERGY GROUP, LTD.; *U.S. Public*, pg. 1402
MAVERICK FRAMING, INC.; *U.S. Private*, pg. 2616
MAVERICK GOLD LLC; *U.S. Private*, pg. 2616
MAVERICK HARDWARE—See Richelieu Hardware Ltd.; *Int'l*, pg. 6331

MAVERICK INFOTEC—See Bhoruka Aluminium Ltd.; *Int'l*, pg. 1015
MAVERICK INTERACTIVE, INC.; *U.S. Private*, pg. 2616
MAVERICK LEASING, LLC—See Maverick USA, Inc.; *U.S. Private*, pg. 2616
MAVERICK MEDIA LIMITED—See Canada Pension Plan Investment Board; *Int'l*, pg. 1280
MAVERICK MEDIA LIMITED—See EQT AB; *Int'l*, pg. 2483
MAVERICK MEDIA LIMITED—See Temasek Holdings (Private) Limited; *Int'l*, pg. 7548
MAVERICK MOTORS, LLC; *U.S. Private*, pg. 2616
MAVERICK NATURAL RESOURCES, LLC; *U.S. Private*, pg. 2616
MAVERICK NETWORKS, INC.; *U.S. Private*, pg. 2616
MAVERICK TECHNOLOGIES, LLC—See Rockwell Automation, Inc.; *U.S. Public*, pg. 1805
MAVERICK USA, INC. - NC FACILITY—See Maverick USA, Inc.; *U.S. Private*, pg. 2616
MAVERICK USA, INC.; *U.S. Private*, pg. 2616
MAVERIC MINI MARTS INC.; *U.S. Private*, pg. 2615
MAVERIK COUNTRY STORES, INC.; *U.S. Private*, pg. 2616
MAVERIK LACROSSE—See Fairfax Financial Holdings Limited; *Int'l*, pg. 2605
MAVERIK LACROSSE—See Power Corporation of Canada; *Int'l*, pg. 5944
MAVERIX METALS, INC.—See Triple Flag Precious Metals Corp.; *Int'l*, pg. 7926
MAVESA, S.A.—See Empresas Polar; *Int'l*, pg. 2391
MAVIC, INC.—See ANTA Sports Products Limited; *Int'l*, pg. 480
MAVIC S.A.S.—See ANTA Sports Products Limited; *Int'l*, pg. 480
MAVI EUROPE AG—See Mavi Giyim Sanayi ve Ticaret AS; *Int'l*, pg. 4733
MAVIFLEX SAS—See Hormann KG Verkaufsgesellschaf; *Int'l*, pg. 3481
MAVIGA EAST AFRICA LIMITED—See ED&F Man Holdings Limited; *Int'l*, pg. 2303
MAVIGA GHANA LIMITED—See ED&F Man Holdings Limited; *Int'l*, pg. 2303
MAVI GIYIM SANAYI VE TICARET AS; *Int'l*, pg. 4733
MAVI HOSPITAL SAGLIK HIZMETLERI A.S.—See Verusa Holding A.S.; *Int'l*, pg. 8175
MAVIK CAPITAL MANAGEMENT, LP; *U.S. Private*, pg. 2616
MAVILOR MOTORS SA—See Perrot Duval Holding S.A.; *Int'l*, pg. 5814
MAVIR HUNGARIAN INDEPENDENT TRANSMISSION OPERATOR COMPANY LTD.—See MVM Magyar Villamos Muvek Zrt.; *Int'l*, pg. 5107
MAVIS TIRE EXPRESS SERVICES CORP.—See Golden Gate Capital Management II, LLC; *U.S. Private*, pg. 1731
MAV KELHEIM GMBH—See STRABAG SE; *Int'l*, pg. 7231
MAV LUNEN GMBH—See STRABAG SE; *Int'l*, pg. 7231
MAV MINERALSTOFF - AUFBEREITUNG UND - VERWERTUNG GMBH—See STRABAG SE; *Int'l*, pg. 7231
MAV MINERALSTOFF - AUFBEREITUNG UND VERWERTUNG LUNEN GMBH—See STRABAG SE; *Int'l*, pg. 7231
MAVO SYSTEMS, INC.—See Arctic Slope Regional Corporation; *U.S. Private*, pg. 316
MAVOTRANS B.V.—See CRH plc; *Int'l*, pg. 1845
MAVSHACK AB; *Int'l*, pg. 4733
MAWANA SUGARS LIMITED—See Siddharth Shriram Group; *Int'l*, pg. 6883
MAWARID HOLDING INVESTMENT LLC—See Alpha Dhabi Holding PJSC; *Int'l*, pg. 367
MAWARID HOTELS AND HOSPITALITY LLC—See Alpha Dhabi Holding PJSC; *Int'l*, pg. 367
MAWARID MINING LLC—See MB Holding Company LLC; *Int'l*, pg. 4750
MAWDSLEY-BROOKS & CO. LTD.; *Int'l*, pg. 4733
MAWENZI COFFEE EXPORTERS LTD.—See Ecom Agroindustrial Corporation Ltd.; *Int'l*, pg. 2296
MAWISTA GMBH—See Allianz SE; *Int'l*, pg. 354
MAWI-THERM TEMPERATUR-PROZESSTECHNIK GMBH—See CHINO Corporation; *Int'l*, pg. 1571
MAWLAMYINE CEMENT LIMITED—See The Siam Cement Public Company Limited; *Int'l*, pg. 7682
MAW MANSFELDER ALUMINIUMWERKE GMBH—See Mansfelder Metals Ltd.; *Int'l*, pg. 4676
MAWSON ENERGI AB—See Mawson Gold Limited; *Int'l*, pg. 4733
MAWSON GOLD LIMITED; *Int'l*, pg. 4733
MAWSON INFRASTRUCTURE GROUP INC.; *Int'l*, pg. 4733
MAWSON & MAWSON INC.; *U.S. Private*, pg. 2616
MAWSON SWEDEN AB—See Mawson Gold Limited; *Int'l*, pg. 4733
MAWSON WEST LTD.; *Int'l*, pg. 4733
MAX 21 AG; *Int'l*, pg. 4733
MAX ADVERTISING; *U.S. Private*, pg. 2616
MAXAGO AB—See Investment AB Latour; *Int'l*, pg. 3784
MAX ALERT SYSTEMS LIMITED; *Int'l*, pg. 4733
MAXAL INTERNATIONAL, INC.—See Illinois Tool Works Inc.; *U.S. Public*, pg. 1109
MAXAM CAPITAL CORP.; *Int'l*, pg. 4736

MAXAMCORP HOLDING, S.L.; *Int'l*, pg. 4736
MAXAMTECH DIGITAL VENTURES PRIVATE LIMITED—See QYOU Media, Inc.; *Int'l*, pg. 6167
MAXAM TIRE NORTH AMERICA INC.—See Sailun Co. Ltd.; *Int'l*, pg. 6484
MAX ARNOLD & SONS, INC.; *U.S. Private*, pg. 2617
MAXA ROCKDRILLS LIMITED—See Yuk Wing Group Holdings Limited; *Int'l*, pg. 8612
MAXAR TECHNOLOGIES INC.—See Advent International Corporation; *U.S. Private*, pg. 103
MAX ASIA CO., LTD.—See Thai Beverage Public Company Limited; *Int'l*, pg. 7591
MAX ASSET MANAGEMENT COMPANY LIMITED—See Thanachart Capital PCL; *Int'l*, pg. 7607
MAX-ATLAS EQUIPMENT INTERNATIONAL INC.; *Int'l*, pg. 4736
MAXAUTO COMPANY LIMITED—See Shenzhen Maxonic Automation Control Co., Ltd.; *Int'l*, pg. 6817
MAX AUTOMATION SE; *Int'l*, pg. 4733
MAX AUTO SUPPLY CO.; *U.S. Private*, pg. 2617
MAX BALZ GMBH & CO.—See H. Geiger GmbH; *Int'l*, pg. 3194
MAX BAUM STAHL SERVICE GMBH—See Knauf Interfer SE; *Int'l*, pg. 4205
MAXBIZ CORPORATION BERHAD; *Int'l*, pg. 4736
MAX BORGES AGENCY; *U.S. Private*, pg. 2617
MAX BRENNER SECOND AVENUE LLC—See Strauss Group Ltd.; *Int'l*, pg. 7238
MAX BUPA HEALTH INSURANCE COMPANY LIMITED—See Max India Limited; *Int'l*, pg. 4734
MAXBURG CAPITAL PARTNERS GMBH; *Int'l*, pg. 4736
MAX BUSINESS CO., LTD.—See MAX Co., Ltd.; *Int'l*, pg. 4734
MAX CARD CO., LTD.—See PTG Energy Public Company Limited; *Int'l*, pg. 6090
MAXCESS INTERNATIONAL CORPORATION—See Berwind Corporation; *U.S. Private*, pg. 541
MAXCLEAN HOLDINGS LTD; *Int'l*, pg. 4736
MAX COCHIUS GMBH—See ThyssenKrupp AG; *Int'l*, pg. 7725
MAX CO (HK) LTD.—See MAX Co., Ltd.; *Int'l*, pg. 4734
MAX CO., LTD.; *Int'l*, pg. 4734
MAXCOM INC.—See Relia, Inc.; *Int'l*, pg. 6260
MAXCOM S.A.; *Int'l*, pg. 4736
MAXCOM SERVICES DIVISION—See Platinum Equity, LLC; *U.S. Private*, pg. 3210
MAXCOM TELECOMUNICACIONES, S.A.B. DE C.V.—See Transtelco Holding, Inc.; *U.S. Private*, pg. 4211
MAXCO SUPPLY INC., BOX DIVISION—See Maxco Supply Inc.; *U.S. Private*, pg. 2617
MAXCO SUPPLY INC., MACHINERY DIVISION—See Maxco Supply Inc.; *U.S. Private*, pg. 2617
MAXCO SUPPLY INC.; *U.S. Private*, pg. 2617
MAX CREDIT UNION; *U.S. Private*, pg. 2617
MAXCY DEVELOPMENT GROUP—See Latt Maxcy Corporation; *U.S. Private*, pg. 2397
MAXCYTE, INC.; *U.S. Public*, pg. 1402
MAX DAETWYLER CORP.—See Daetwyler Global Tec Holding AG; *Int'l*, pg. 1909
MAXDATA (SCHWEIZ) AG—See Kontron AG; *Int'l*, pg. 4277
MAX DAVIS ASSOCIATES INC.—See Adams Remco Inc.; *U.S. Private*, pg. 75
MAX DEVELOPMENT LLC—See Englander Knabe & Allen; *U.S. Private*, pg. 1399
MAX DIGITAL, LLC—See ACV Auctions Inc.; *U.S. Public*, pg. 37
MAXDOME GMBH—See ProSiebenSat.1 Media SE; *Int'l*, pg. 6000
MAXDOME GMBH—See Warner Bros. Discovery, Inc.; *U.S. Public*, pg. 2327
MAX EASE INTERNATIONAL LIMITED—See Tien Wah Press Holdings Berhad; *Int'l*, pg. 7744
MAXEDA B.V.—See KKR & Co. Inc.; *U.S. Public*, pg. 1261
MAXELER TECHNOLOGIES, INC.—See Groq, Inc.; *U.S. Private*, pg. 1792
MAXELL ASIA, LTD.—See Maxell, Ltd.; *Int'l*, pg. 4736
MAXELL ASIA (SINGAPORE) PTE LTD.—See Maxell, Ltd.; *Int'l*, pg. 4736
MAXELL CANADA—See Maxell, Ltd.; *Int'l*, pg. 4736
MAXELL CORPORATION OF AMERICA—See Maxell, Ltd.; *Int'l*, pg. 4736
MAXELL DEUTSCHLAND GMBH—See Maxell, Ltd.; *Int'l*, pg. 4736
MAXELL DIGITAL PRODUCTS CHINA CO., LTD.—See Maxell, Ltd.; *Int'l*, pg. 4736
MAXELLE SA—See LVMH Moet Hennessy Louis Vuitton SE; *Int'l*, pg. 4596
MAXELL EUROPE LTD.—See Maxell, Ltd.; *Int'l*, pg. 4736
MAXELL FRONTIER CO., LTD.—See Maxell, Ltd.; *Int'l*, pg. 4737
MAXELL HUNGARY KFT.—See Maxell, Ltd.; *Int'l*, pg. 4737
MAXELL IZUMI CO., LTD.—See Maxell, Ltd.; *Int'l*, pg. 4737
MAXELL KUREHA CO., LTD.—See Maxell, Ltd.; *Int'l*, pg. 4737
MAXELL LATIN AMERICA S.A.—See Maxell, Ltd.; *Int'l*, pg. 4737

COMPANY NAME INDEX

MAXELL, LTD.; *Int'l*, pg. 4736
MAXELL (SHANGHAI) TRADING CO., LTD.—See Maxell, Ltd.; *Int'l*, pg. 4736
MAXELL (SHENZHEN) TRADING CO., LTD.—See Maxell, Ltd.; *Int'l*, pg. 4736
MAXELL SPAIN S.A.—See Maxell, Ltd.; *Int'l*, pg. 4737
MAXELL TAIWAN, LTD.—See Maxell, Ltd.; *Int'l*, pg. 4737
MAXENE WEINBERG AGENCY—See Huseby, LLC; *U.S. Private*, pg. 2013
MAX ENGINEERING LLC—See AYRO, Inc.; *U.S. Public*, pg. 256
MAXEON SOLAR TECHNOLOGIES, LTD.; *Int'l*, pg. 4737
MAX & ERMA'S RESTAURANTS, INC.—See Glacier Restaurant Group LLC; *U.S. Private*, pg. 1704
MAXETA AS—See Addtech AB; *Int'l*, pg. 134
MAX EUROPE B.V.—See MAX Co., Ltd.; *Int'l*, pg. 4734
MAX EUROPE GMBH—See MAX Co., Ltd.; *Int'l*, pg. 4734
MAXEY ENERGY CO.; *U.S. Private*, pg. 2617
MAXEY LOGISTICS, INC; *U.S. Private*, pg. 2617
MAXEY TRAILERS MFG., INC.; *U.S. Private*, pg. 2618
MAXFAIR TECHNOLOGIES HOLDINGS LTD.—See Computer & Technologies Holdings Limited; *Int'l*, pg. 1758
MAX FASHIONS—See Landmark Retail Holdings 1 Limited; *Int'l*, pg. 4407
MAX FASTENERS (M) SDN. BHD.—See MAX Co., Ltd.; *Int'l*, pg. 4734
MAX FASTENING SYSTEMS CO., LTD.—See MAX Co., Ltd.; *Int'l*, pg. 4734
MAXFASTIGHETER I SVERIGE AB; *Int'l*, pg. 4737
MAXFIELD ENTERPRISES INC.; *U.S. Private*, pg. 2618
MAX FINANCIAL SERVICES LIMITED; *Int'l*, pg. 4734
MAX FINKELSTEIN INC.; *U.S. Private*, pg. 2617
MAXFLOW MEMBRAN FILTRATION GMBH—See EnviTec Biogas AG; *Int'l*, pg. 2455
MAX FOOTE CONSTRUCTION COMPANY, INC.; *U.S. Private*, pg. 2618
MAXFORD TECHNOLOGY LIMITED—See CN Innovations Holdings Limited; *Int'l*, pg. 1673
MAXFORD TECHNOLOGY, LLC—See CN Innovations Holdings Limited; *Int'l*, pg. 1673
MAXGAMING NSW PTY LTD—See Tabcorp Holdings Limited; *Int'l*, pg. 7401
MAXGAMING QLD PTY LTD—See Tabcorp Holdings Limited; *Int'l*, pg. 7401
MAXGEAR SP. Z O.O. SP. KOMANDYTOWA—See Auto Partner SA; *Int'l*, pg. 725
MAXGEN ENERGY SERVICES CORP.—See Willcrest Partners; *U.S. Private*, pg. 4521
MAXGRAND SDN BHD—See IOI Corporation Berhad; *Int'l*, pg. 3792
MAX GRIGSBY CO. INC.; *U.S. Private*, pg. 2617
MAX GROUP CORPORATION; *U.S. Private*, pg. 2617
MAXGROW INDIA LTD.; *Int'l*, pg. 4737
MAX HEALTHCARE INSTITUTE LIMITED; *Int'l*, pg. 4734
MAX HEIGHTS INFRASTRUCTURE LIMITED; *Int'l*, pg. 4734
MAX HOLDER GMBH; *Int'l*, pg. 4734
MAXHOME, LLC—See York Capital Management Global Advisors, LLC; *U.S. Private*, pg. 4590
MAX HOTEL CO., LTD.—See Mida Assets Public Co,.Ltd.; *Int'l*, pg. 4883
MAX HYPERMARKETS INDIA PVT. LTD—See Landmark Retail Holdings 1 Limited; *Int'l*, pg. 4407
MAXI CANADA INC.—See Altamont Capital Partners; *U.S. Private*, pg. 205
MAXI-CASH (CLEMENTI) PTE. LTD.—See Aspial Lifestyle Limited; *Int'l*, pg. 630
MAXICITY HOLDINGS LIMITED; *Int'l*, pg. 4737
MAXI DRUG SOUTH, L.P.—See New Rite Aid, LLC; *U.S. Private*, pg. 2905
MAXI FOODS LLC; *U.S. Private*, pg. 2618
MAXIFY SOLUTIONS INC.; *U.S. Private*, pg. 2618
MAXIGEN BIOTECH INC.; *Int'l*, pg. 4737
MAXIGRAF, S.A.; *Int'l*, pg. 4737
MAXIKARTY.PL. SP. Z O.O—See Egmont Fonden; *Int'l*, pg. 2326
MAXIL TECHNOLOGY SOLUTIONS, INC.; *U.S. Private*, pg. 2618
MAXIMA AIR SEPARATION CENTER LTD.—See IDB Development Corporation Ltd.; *Int'l*, pg. 3588
MAXIMAA PROYURVEDA LTD.—See MAXIMAA SYSTEMS LIMITED; *Int'l*, pg. 4737
MAXIMAA SYSTEMS LIMITED; *Int'l*, pg. 4737
MAXIMAL NEWS TELEVISION—See Vivendi SE; *Int'l*, pg. 8275
MAXIMAL PRODUCTIONS—See Vivendi SE; *Int'l*, pg. 8275
MAXIMATECC AB—See Enerpac Tool Group Corp.; *U.S. Public*, pg. 766
MAXIMA TECHNOLOGIES & SYSTEMS LLC—See Enerpac Tool Group Corp.; *U.S. Public*, pg. 766
MAXIM AUTOMOTIVE PRODUCTS LLC; *U.S. Private*, pg. 2618
MAXIM CRANE WORKS, L.P. - SEATTLE—See Apollo Global Management, Inc.; *U.S. Public*, pg. 153
MAXIM CRANE WORKS, L.P.—See Apollo Global Management, Inc.; *U.S. Public*, pg. 153
MAXIM DIRECT—See Analog Devices, Inc.; *U.S. Public*, pg. 135

MAXIM ENTERPRISES, INC; *U.S. Private*, pg. 2618
MAXIMET—See Karsten Manufacturing Corporation; *U.S. Private*, pg. 2263
MAXIM EXCAVATING LTD—See K-Rite Construction Ltd.; *Int'l*, pg. 4042
MAXIM FIRE SYSTEMS LLC—See Highview Capital, LLC; *U.S. Private*, pg. 1942
MAXIM GLOBAL BERHAD; *Int'l*, pg. 4737
MAXIM HEALTHCARE SERVICES, INC.; *U.S. Private*, pg. 2618
MAXIM HEALTHCARE SERVICES INC.—See Maxim Healthcare Services, Inc.; *U.S. Private*, pg. 2618
MAXIM HEALTH INFORMATION SERVICES—See Maxim Healthcare Services, Inc.; *U.S. Private*, pg. 2618
MAXIM HOME HEALTH RESOURCES, INC.—See Maxim Healthcare Services, Inc.; *U.S. Private*, pg. 2618
MAXI MILIAAN B.V—See Dorel Industries, Inc.; *Int'l*, pg. 2176
MAXIMILIAN ONLINE MEDIA GMBH—See ProSiebenSat.1 Media SE; *Int'l*, pg. 6001
MAXIM INC.—See Biglari Holdings Inc.; *U.S. Public*, pg. 331
MAXIM INDIA INTEGRATED CIRCUIT DESIGN PVT LTD—See Analog Devices, Inc.; *U.S. Public*, pg. 135
MAXIM INSURANCE AGENCY INC.; *U.S. Private*, pg. 2618
MAXIM INTEGRATED PRODUCTS GMBH—See Analog Devices, Inc.; *U.S. Public*, pg. 135
MAXIM INTEGRATED PRODUCTS, INC.—See Analog Devices, Inc.; *U.S. Public*, pg. 135
MAXIM INTEGRATED PRODUCTS INDIA SALES PVT LTD.—See Analog Devices, Inc.; *U.S. Public*, pg. 135
MAXIM INTEGRATED PRODUCTS INTERNATIONAL SALES JAPAN GK—See Analog Devices, Inc.; *U.S. Public*, pg. 135
MAXIM INTEGRATED PRODUCTS INTERNATIONAL SALES LIMITED—See Analog Devices, Inc.; *U.S. Public*, pg. 135
MAXIM INTEGRATED PRODUCTS (IRELAND) HOLDINGS LIMITED—See Analog Devices, Inc.; *U.S. Public*, pg. 135
MAXIM INTEGRATED PRODUCTS NETHERLANDS B.V.—See Analog Devices, Inc.; *U.S. Public*, pg. 135
MAXIM INTEGRATED PRODUCTS (THAILAND) CO., LTD.—See Analog Devices, Inc.; *U.S. Public*, pg. 135
MAXIM INTEGRATED PRODUCTS UK LIMITED—See Analog Devices, Inc.; *U.S. Public*, pg. 135
MAXIM INTEGRATED S.A.—See Analog Devices, Inc.; *U.S. Public*, pg. 136
MAXIMIZER ASIA LIMITED—See Maximizer Software, Inc.; *Int'l*, pg. 4737
MAXIMIZER SOFTWARE, INC.; *Int'l*, pg. 4737
MAXIMIZER SOFTWARE LTD.—See Maximizer Software, Inc.; *Int'l*, pg. 4737
MAXIMIZER SOFTWARE SOLUTIONS PTY., LTD.—See Maximizer Software, Inc.; *Int'l*, pg. 4737
MAXIM JAPAN CO., LTD.—See Analog Devices, Inc.; *U.S. Public*, pg. 136
MAXIMO MARINA; *U.S. Private*, pg. 2618
MAXIM PHILIPPINES OPERATING CORPORATION—See Analog Devices, Inc.; *U.S. Public*, pg. 136
MAXIM PHYSICIAN RESOURCES, LLC—See Maxim Healthcare Services, Inc.; *U.S. Private*, pg. 2618
MAXIM POWER (AUSTRIA) GMBH—See Maxim Power Corp.; *Int'l*, pg. 4737
MAXIM POWER CORP.; *Int'l*, pg. 4737
MAXIM POWER EUROPE BV—See Maxim Power Corp.; *Int'l*, pg. 4737
MAXIM RESOURCES INC.; *Int'l*, pg. 4737
MAXIM'S CATERERS LTD.—See Jardine Matheson Holdings Limited; *Int'l*, pg. 3909
MAXIM STAFFING SOLUTIONS - TRAVELMAX DIVISION—See Maxim Healthcare Services, Inc.; *U.S. Private*, pg. 2618
MAXIMUM ALARM & SECURITY INC.—See Co-op Atlantic; *Int'l*, pg. 1679
MAXIMUM CORPORATION; *U.S. Private*, pg. 2618
MAXIMUM DESIGN & ADVERTISING; *U.S. Private*, pg. 2618
MAXIMUM ENTERTAINMENT AB; *Int'l*, pg. 4737
MAXIMUM GAMES LLC—See Maximum Entertainment AB; *Int'l*, pg. 4737
MAXIMUM GRAPHICS—See Chatham Asset Management, LLC; *U.S. Private*, pg. 862
MAXIMUM IMPACT INC.; *U.S. Private*, pg. 2618
MAXIMUM IMPACT PHYSICAL THERAPY SERVICES, LLC—See Athletico Ltd.; *U.S. Private*, pg. 368
MAXIMUM MEDIA ENTERPRISES, INC.; *U.S. Private*, pg. 2619
MAXIMUM ONE REALTY; *U.S. Private*, pg. 2619
MAXIMUM QUALITY FOODS; *U.S. Private*, pg. 2619
MAXIMUM SOLUTIONS, LLC—See Global Payments Inc.; *U.S. Public*, pg. 943
MAXIMUM TALENT AGENCY—See The Block Agency, Inc.; *U.S. Private*, pg. 3995
MAXIMUS AIR L.L.C.—See Abu Dhabi Aviation; *Int'l*, pg. 70
MAXIMUS ASIA PTE. LTD.—See MAXIMUS, Inc.; *U.S. Public*, pg. 1402

MAXIMUS CANADA, INC.—See MAXIMUS, Inc.; *U.S. Public*, pg. 1402
MAXIMUS COFFEE GROUP, LLC.; *U.S. Private*, pg. 2619
MAXIMUS CONSULTING (HONG KONG) LTD.—See Future Data Group Limited; *Int'l*, pg. 2854
MAXIMUS EMPLOYMENT & TRAINING LIMITED—See MAXIMUS, Inc.; *U.S. Public*, pg. 1402
MAXIMUS FEDERAL SERVICES, INC.—See MAXIMUS, Inc.; *U.S. Public*, pg. 1402
MAXIMUS HEALTH & HUMAN SERVICES LIMITED—See MAXIMUS, Inc.; *U.S. Public*, pg. 1402
MAXIMUS HEALTH SERVICES, INC.—See MAXIMUS, Inc.; *U.S. Public*, pg. 1402
MAXIMUS, INC.; *U.S. Public*, pg. 1402
MAXIMUS INTERNATIONAL LIMITED; *Int'l*, pg. 4738
MAXIMUS LUBRICANT LLC—See Maximus International Limited; *Int'l*, pg. 4738
MAXIMUS PROPERTIES LLC—See MAXIMUS, Inc.; *U.S. Public*, pg. 1402
MAXIMUS RESOURCES LIMITED; *Int'l*, pg. 4738
MAXIMUS SECURITIES LIMITED—See Hybrid Financial Services Limited; *Int'l*, pg. 3544
MAX INDIA LIMITED; *Int'l*, pg. 4734
MAXINE OF HOLLYWOOD, INC.; *U.S. Private*, pg. 2619
MAX INFORMATION—See Armando Testa S.p.A.; *Int'l*, pg. 574
MAXINGVEST AG; *Int'l*, pg. 4738
MAX INTERACTIVE PTY LTD.—See Brightcom Group Ltd.; *Int'l*, pg. 1162
MAX INTERNATIONAL CONVERTERS, INC.—See PT Sinar Mas Group; *Int'l*, pg. 6073
MAXION COMPONENTES AUTOMOTIVOS S.A.—See Iochpe-Maxion S.A.; *Int'l*, pg. 3791
MAXION COMPONENTES ESTRUTURAIS LTDA.—See Iochpe-Maxion S.A.; *Int'l*, pg. 3791
MAXION INCI JANT SANAYI, A.S.—See Iochpe-Maxion S.A.; *Int'l*, pg. 3791
MAXION JANTAS JANT SANAYI VE TICARET A.S.—See Iochpe-Maxion S.A.; *Int'l*, pg. 3791
MAXION (NANTONG) WHEELS CO., LTD.—See Iochpe-Maxion S.A.; *Int'l*, pg. 3791
MAXION WHEELS AKRON LLC—See Iochpe-Maxion S.A.; *Int'l*, pg. 3791
MAXION WHEELS ALUMINUM INDIA PVT. LTD.—See Iochpe-Maxion S.A.; *Int'l*, pg. 3791
MAXION WHEELS CZECH S.R.O.—See Iochpe-Maxion S.A.; *Int'l*, pg. 3791
MAXION WHEELS DE MEXICO, S. DE R.L.DE C.V.—See Iochpe-Maxion S.A.; *Int'l*, pg. 3791
MAXION WHEELS ESPANA S.L.—See Iochpe-Maxion S.A.; *Int'l*, pg. 3791
MAXION WHEELSHOLDING GMBH—See Iochpe-Maxion S.A.; *Int'l*, pg. 3791
MAXION WHEELS ITALIA S.R.L.—See Iochpe-Maxion S.A.; *Int'l*, pg. 3791
MAXION WHEELS JAPAN K.K.—See Iochpe-Maxion S.A.; *Int'l*, pg. 3791
MAXION WHEELS SEDALIA LLC—See Iochpe-Maxion S.A.; *Int'l*, pg. 3791
MAXION WHEELS SOUTH AFRICA (PTY) LTD.—See Iochpe-Maxion S.A.; *Int'l*, pg. 3791
MAXION WHEELS (THAILAND) CO. LTD.—See Iochpe-Maxion S.A.; *Int'l*, pg. 3791
MAXION WHEELS WERKE GMBH—See Iochpe-Maxion S.A.; *Int'l*, pg. 3791
MAXIPARTS LIMITED; *Int'l*, pg. 4742
MAXIPRINT GRAFICA E EDITORA LTDA—See Cogna Educacao S.A.; *Int'l*, pg. 1695
MAXISAVER GROUP, INC.; *U.S. Private*, pg. 2619
MAXIS BERHAD; *Int'l*, pg. 4742
MAXIS BROADBAND SDN.BHD.—See Maxis Berhad; *Int'l*, pg. 4742
MAXIS GBN S.A.S.—See AXA S.A.; *Int'l*, pg. 759
MAXIS GBN S.A.S.—See MetLife, Inc.; *U.S. Public*, pg. 1430
MAXIS GIRISIM SERMAYESI PORTFOY YONETIMI A.S.—See Turkiye Is Bankasi A.S.; *Int'l*, pg. 7976
MAXIS INTERNATIONAL SDN. BHD.—See Maxis Berhad; *Int'l*, pg. 4742
MAXIS INVESTMENTS LTD.—See Turkiye Is Bankasi A.S.; *Int'l*, pg. 7976
MAXIS MOBILE SDN. BHD.—See Maxis Berhad; *Int'l*, pg. 4742
MAXIS STUDIO—See Electronic Arts Inc.; *U.S. Public*, pg. 724
MAXITRANS AUSTRALIA PTY LTD—See MaxiPARTS Limited; *Int'l*, pg. 4742
MAXITRANS INDUSTRIES (N.Z.) PTY LTD—See MaxiPARTS Limited; *Int'l*, pg. 4742
MAXITRANS SERVICES PTY LTD—See MaxiPARTS Limited; *Int'l*, pg. 4742
MAXITROL COMPANY - BLISSFIELD DIVISION—See Maxitrol Company; *U.S. Private*, pg. 2619
MAXITROL COMPANY - COLON DIVISION—See Maxitrol Company; *U.S. Private*, pg. 2619
MAXITROL COMPANY - MAXITROL ELECTRONICS DIVISION—See Maxitrol Company; *U.S. Private*, pg. 2619
MAXITROL COMPANY; *U.S. Private*, pg. 2619

MAXIUM TECHNOLOGIES (SHANGHAI) INC.—See Hiyes International Co., Ltd.; *Int'l*, pg. 3427
MAX JANTZ EXCAVATING, LLC; *U.S. Private*, pg. 2617
MAX J. KUNEY CONSTRUCTION COMPANY; *U.S. Private*, pg. 2617
MAX KAHAN INC.; *U.S. Private*, pg. 2617
MAX KURAGANO CO., LTD.—See MAX Co., Ltd.; *Int'l*, pg. 4734
MAXLAV LAVANDERIA ESPECIALIZADA S.A.—See Servizi Italia SpA; *Int'l*, pg. 6726
MAX LEATHER GROUP—See Li & Fung Limited; *Int'l*, pg. 4480
MAX LEVY AUTOGRAPH, INC.—See Coherent Corp.; *U.S. Public*, pg. 529
MAX LIFE INSURANCE COMPANY LIMITED—See Max Financial Services Limited; *Int'l*, pg. 4734
MAXLINEAR ASIA SINGAPORE PTE. LTD.—See MaxLinear, Inc.; *U.S. Public*, pg. 1403
MAXLINEAR HISPANIA, S.L.—See MaxLinear, Inc.; *U.S. Public*, pg. 1403
MAXLINEAR, INC.; *U.S. Public*, pg. 1402
MAXLINEAR JAPAN GK—See MaxLinear, Inc.; *U.S. Public*, pg. 1403
MAXLINEAR SHANGHAI LIMITED—See MaxLinear, Inc.; *U.S. Public*, pg. 1403
MAXLINEAR TECHNOLOGIES PRIVATE LIMITED—See MaxLinear, Inc.; *U.S. Public*, pg. 1403
MAXLIN GARMENTS SDN. BHD.—See Baneng Holdings Bhd.; *Int'l*, pg. 831
MAX LORNE S.A.—See PAUL HARTMANN AG; *Int'l*, pg. 5761
MAX MADSEN IMPORTS INC.; *U.S. Private*, pg. 2617
MAX MATTHIESSEN AB—See Nordic Capital AB; *Int'l*, pg. 5420
MAX ME CORP CO., LTD.—See PTG Energy Public Company Limited; *Int'l*, pg. 6090
MAX METAL CORPORATION PUBLIC COMPANY LIMITED; *Int'l*, pg. 4734
MAXMIND PHARMACEUTICAL S.L.; *Int'l*, pg. 4742
MAXNERVA TECHNOLOGY SERVICES LTD.; *Int'l*, pg. 4742
MAX OIL COMPANY INC.; *U.S. Private*, pg. 2617
MAXON B.V.—See Honeywell International Inc.; *U.S. Public*, pg. 1048
MAXON COMBUSTION EQUIPMENT SHANGHAI CO. LTD.—See Honeywell International Inc.; *U.S. Public*, pg. 1048
MAXON COMBUSTION SYSTEMS AB—See Honeywell International Inc.; *U.S. Public*, pg. 1048
MAXON COMBUSTION SYSTEMS A/S—See Honeywell International Inc.; *U.S. Public*, pg. 1048
MAXON COMBUSTION SYSTEMS LTD.—See Honeywell International Inc.; *U.S. Public*, pg. 1048
MAXON COMPETENCE CENTER—See Nemetschek SE; *Int'l*, pg. 5194
MAXON COMPUTER GMBH—See Nemetschek SE; *Int'l*, pg. 5194
MAXON COMPUTER INC—See Nemetschek SE; *Int'l*, pg. 5194
MAXON COMPUTER JAPAN—See Nemetschek SE; *Int'l*, pg. 5194
MAXON COMPUTER LTD—See Nemetschek SE; *Int'l*, pg. 5194
MAXON CORPORATION—See Honeywell International Inc.; *U.S. Public*, pg. 1048
MAXON FURNITURE, INC—See HNI Corporation; *U.S. Public*, pg. 1043
MAXON GMBH—See Honeywell International Inc.; *U.S. Public*, pg. 1048
MAXON GMBH—See Honeywell International Inc.; *U.S. Public*, pg. 1048
MAXON INDUSTRIES, S.A. DE C.V.—See Maxon Lift Corp.; *U.S. Private*, pg. 2619
MAXON INTERNATIONAL B.V.B.A.—See Honeywell International Inc.; *U.S. Public*, pg. 1048
MAXON LIFT CORP.; *U.S. Private*, pg. 2619
MAX ONLINE LIMITED—See Novacon Technology Group Limited; *Int'l*, pg. 5454
MAXON PROJECT SUPPORT—See Randstad N.V.; *Int'l*, pg. 6202
MAXON S.A.R.L.—See Honeywell International Inc.; *U.S. Public*, pg. 1048
MAXONS RESTORATIONS, INC.—See FirstService Corporation; *Int'l*, pg. 2691
MAXOR NATIONAL PHARMACY SERVICES CORPORATION; *U.S. Private*, pg. 2619
MAXO TELECOMMUNICATIONS PTY. LTD.; *Int'l*, pg. 4742
MAXPAX LLC; *U.S. Private*, pg. 2619
MAX PETROLEUM PLC; *Int'l*, pg. 4735
MAX PLANCK FLORIDA CORPORATION; *U.S. Private*, pg. 2617
MAXPOINT INTERACTIVE INC.—See MacAndrews & Forbes Incorporated; *U.S. Private*, pg. 2532
MAXPOWER AUTOMOTIVE LIMITED—See Tricorn Group plc; *Int'l*, pg. 7920
MAX POWER MINING CORP.; *Int'l*, pg. 4735
MAXPRO CAPITAL ACQUISITION CORP.; *Int'l*, pg. 4742
MAX PROCESS GMBH—See Rotork Plc; *Int'l*, pg. 6405

MAXQ AI LTD.; *Int'l*, pg. 4742
MAXRAY OPTICAL TECHNOLOGY CO. LTD.; *Int'l*, pg. 4742
MAX-REALTY INC.—See XYMAX Corporation; *Int'l*, pg. 8542
MAX RECOVERY LIMITED—See JPMorgan Chase & Co.; *U.S. Public*, pg. 1210
MAX RESOURCE CORP.; *Int'l*, pg. 4735
MAXRISE INC.—See Macronix International Co., Ltd.; *Int'l*, pg. 4632
MAXROTEC CO., LTD. - SEONGJU FACTORY—See Maxrotec Co., Ltd.; *Int'l*, pg. 4742
MAXROTEC CO., LTD.; *Int'l*, pg. 4742
MAXSCEND MICROELECTRONICS COMPANY LIMITED; *Int'l*, pg. 4742
MAXSEC GROUP LIMITED—See Ava Risk Group Limited; *Int'l*, pg. 733
MAX SECURITY SERVICE CORPORATION—See XYMAX Corporation; *Int'l*, pg. 8542
MAXSENT INC.—See CDA Incorporated; *U.S. Private*, pg. 802
MAX'S GROUP, INC.; *Int'l*, pg. 4736
MAXSHINWA CO.,LTD.—See MAX Co., Ltd.; *Int'l*, pg. 4734
MAX SIGHT GROUP HOLDINGS LTD.; *Int'l*, pg. 4735
MAXS OF SAN FRANCISCO INC.; *U.S. Private*, pg. 2619
MAX SOLUTIONS INC.; *U.S. Private*, pg. 2617
MAX SOLUTIONS PTY LIMITED—See MAXIMUS, Inc.; *U.S. Public*, pg. 1402
MAXSON INDUSTRIES LIMITED—See Gold Peak Technology Group Limited; *Int'l*, pg. 3025
MAX SOUND CORPORATION; *U.S. Public*, pg. 1402
MAX SOURCE HOLDING LTD—See Brookfield Corporation; *Int'l*, pg. 1181
MAXST CO., LTD.; *Int'l*, pg. 4742
MAX STOCK LTD.; *Int'l*, pg. 4735
MAXSYS FUEL SYSTEMS LTD.—See Lionheart Ventures; *U.S. Private*, pg. 2464
MAX TECHNICAL TRAINING; *U.S. Private*, pg. 2617
MAXTEC LLC—See Halma plc; *Int'l*, pg. 3232
MAXTEK COMPONENTS CORPORATION—See Fortive Corporation; *U.S. Public*, pg. 871
MAXTEK INTERNATIONAL (HK) LIMITED—See WT Microelectronics Co., Ltd.; *Int'l*, pg. 8498
MAXTEK TECHNOLOGY CO., LTD.—See WT Microelectronics Co., Ltd.; *Int'l*, pg. 8498
MAXTER CATHETERS SAS—See Avanos Medical, Inc.; *U.S. Public*, pg. 241
MAXTER HEALTHCARE PTE. LTD.—See Supermax Corporation Berhad; *Int'l*, pg. 7339
MAX THAILAND CO., LTD.—See MAX Co., Ltd.; *Int'l*, pg. 4734
MAXTON MOTORS INC.; *U.S. Private*, pg. 2619
MAX-TORQUE LTD.—See Schlumberger Limited; *U.S. Public*, pg. 1844
MAX-TRAC TIRE CO., INC.—See The Goodyear Tire & Rubber Company; *U.S. Public*, pg. 2083
MAXTRAL INDUSTRY BERHAD; *Int'l*, pg. 4742
MAX TRANS LOGISTICS OF CHATTANOOGA, LLC; *U.S. Private*, pg. 2617
MAXUM ENERGY LOGISTICS PARTNERS, LP; *U.S. Private*, pg. 2619
MAXUM PETROLEUM, INC.—See Berkshire Hathaway Inc.; *U.S. Public*, pg. 313
MAX USA CORP.—See MAX Co., Ltd.; *Int'l*, pg. 4734
MAXUS COMMUNICATIONS (UK) LIMITED—See WPP plc; *Int'l*, pg. 8475
MAXUS GLOBAL—See WPP plc; *Int'l*, pg. 8475
MAXUS REALTY TRUST, INC.; *U.S. Public*, pg. 1403
MAXUS—See WPP plc; *Int'l*, pg. 8475
MAXUS—See WPP plc; *Int'l*, pg. 8475
MAXUS—See WPP plc; *Int'l*, pg. 8475
MAXUS—See WPP plc; *Int'l*, pg. 8475
MAXUS—See WPP plc; *Int'l*, pg. 8475
MAXUS—See WPP plc; *Int'l*, pg. 8475
MAXUS—See WPP plc; *Int'l*, pg. 8475
MAXUS—See WPP plc; *Int'l*, pg. 8475
MAXUS—See WPP plc; *Int'l*, pg. 8475
MAXUS—See WPP plc; *Int'l*, pg. 8475
MAXUS—See WPP plc; *Int'l*, pg. 8475
MAXUS—See WPP plc; *Int'l*, pg. 8475
MAXUS—See WPP plc; *Int'l*, pg. 8475
MAXUS—See WPP plc; *Int'l*, pg. 8475
MAXUS—See WPP plc; *Int'l*, pg. 8475
MAXUS—See WPP plc; *Int'l*, pg. 8475
MAXVALU HOKKAIDO CO., LTD.—See AEON Co., Ltd.; *Int'l*, pg. 178
MAXVALU HOKURIKU CO., LTD.—See AEON Co., Ltd.; *Int'l*, pg. 178
MAXVALU KANTO CO., LTD.—See AEON Co., Ltd.; *Int'l*, pg. 178
MAXVALU KYUSHU CO., LTD.—See AEON Co., Ltd.; *Int'l*, pg. 178
MAXVALU MINAMI TOHOKU CO., LTD.—See AEON Co., Ltd.; *Int'l*, pg. 178
MAXVALU NISHINIHON CO., LTD.—See Fuji Co., Ltd.; *Int'l*, pg. 2809

MAXVALU TOHOKU CO., LTD.—See AEON Co., Ltd.; *Int'l*, pg. 178
MAXVALU TOKAI CO., LTD.—See AEON Co., Ltd.; *Int'l*, pg. 178
MAXVANTAGE LLC—See Dart Appraisal.com, Inc.; *U.S. Private*, pg. 1159
MAXVISION TECHNOLOGY CORP.; *Int'l*, pg. 4742
MAXVIVA TECHNOLOGIES AG—See Unister Holding GmbH; *Int'l*, pg. 8062
MAX-VIZ, INC.—See Astronics Corporation; *U.S. Public*, pg. 217
MAXWAY INDUSTRIES, INC.; *Int'l*, pg. 4742
MAX WEISHAUPT A/S—See Max Weishaupt GmbH; *Int'l*, pg. 4735
MAX WEISHAUPT GMBH; *Int'l*, pg. 4735
MAXWELL CHASE TECHNOLOGIES, LLC.—See AptarGroup, Inc.; *U.S. Public*, pg. 174
MAXWELL ELECTRONICS LTD.; *Int'l*, pg. 4743
MAXWELL FOODS, LLC; *U.S. Private*, pg. 2619
MAXWELL FORD, INC.—See Group 1 Automotive, Inc.; *U.S. Public*, pg. 971
MAXWELL GLOVE MANUFACTURING BERHAD—See Supermax Corporation Berhad; *Int'l*, pg. 7339
MAXWELL INDUSTRIES LTD - STITCHING UNITS, 2—See VIP Clothing Limited; *Int'l*, pg. 8245
MAXWELL & MILLER MARKETING COMMUNICATIONS; *U.S. Private*, pg. 2619
MAXWELL-NII, INC.—See Group 1 Automotive, Inc.; *U.S. Public*, pg. 971
MAXWELL PAPER CANADA, INC.; *Int'l*, pg. 4743
MAXWELL PRODUCTS, INC.; *U.S. Private*, pg. 2619
MAXWELL-REDDICK & ASSOCIATES, INC.—See Palm Beach Capital Partners LLC; *U.S. Private*, pg. 3079
MAXWELL RESOURCES, INC.; *U.S. Private*, pg. 2619
MAXWELL STATE BANK—See Dentel Bancorporation; *U.S. Private*, pg. 1206
MAXWELL TECHNOLOGIES GMBH—See Tesla, Inc.; *U.S. Public*, pg. 2021
MAXWELL TECHNOLOGIES, INC.—See Tesla, Inc.; *U.S. Public*, pg. 2021
MAXWELL TECHNOLOGIES KOREA CO., LTD—See Tesla, Inc.; *U.S. Public*, pg. 2021
MAXWELL TECHNOLOGIES SA—See Renaissance Management SA; *Int'l*, pg. 6272
MAXXAM, INC.; *U.S. Private*, pg. 2620
MAXXAM PROPERTY COMPANY—See Maxxam, Inc.; *U.S. Private*, pg. 2620
MAXXESS SYSTEMS EUROPE, LTD.—See MAXxess Systems, Inc.; *U.S. Private*, pg. 2620
MAXXESS SYSTEMS, INC.; *U.S. Private*, pg. 2620
MAXX HD SUNGLASSES; *U.S. Private*, pg. 2619
MAXX HOTEL GMBH—See H World Group Limited; *Int'l*, pg. 3191
MAXXIA FLEET LIMITED—See McMillan Shakespeare Limited; *Int'l*, pg. 4760
MAXXIA LTD.—See McMillan Shakespeare Limited; *Int'l*, pg. 4760
MAXXIME PTY LTD—See McMillan Shakespeare Limited; *Int'l*, pg. 4760
MAXXIM REBUILD CO., LLC—See Alpha Natural Resources, Inc.; *U.S. Private*, pg. 199
MAXXIM REBUILD COMPANY, INC.—See The Brink's Company; *U.S. Public*, pg. 2043
MAXXIS INTERNATIONAL - UK PLC—See Cheng Shin Rubber (Xiamen) Ind., Ltd.; *Int'l*, pg. 1466
MAXXIS TECH CENTER EUROPE B.V.—See Cheng Shin Rubber (Xiamen) Ind., Ltd.; *Int'l*, pg. 1466
MAXXIUM ESPANA S.L.—See Suntory Holdings Limited; *Int'l*, pg. 7325
MAXXIUM SHANGHAI LTD.—See Suntory Holdings Limited; *Int'l*, pg. 7325
MAXXIUM UK LTD.—See Suntory Holdings Limited; *Int'l*, pg. 7325
MAXX MANUFACTURING LLC—See HTC Purenergy Inc.; *Int'l*, pg. 3508
MAXX MARKETING INC.—See WPP plc; *Int'l*, pg. 8484
MAXX MARKETING LTD.—See WPP plc; *Int'l*, pg. 8484
MAXX MARKETING LTD.—See WPP plc; *Int'l*, pg. 8484
MAXX MARKETING LTD.—See WPP plc; *Int'l*, pg. 8484
MAXX MARKETING—See WPP plc; *Int'l*, pg. 8484
MAXX MARKETING—See WPP plc; *Int'l*, pg. 8484
MAXX MARKETING—See WPP plc; *Int'l*, pg. 8484
MAXXON LOGISTICS LLC—See Legend Oil and Gas, Ltd.; *U.S. Public*, pg. 1301
MAXXSOUTH BROADBAND—See Block Communications, Inc.; *U.S. Private*, pg. 582
MAXXTEC AG; *Int'l*, pg. 4743
MAXXTON B.V.—See Choice Hotels International, Inc.; *U.S. Public*, pg. 490
MAXXTON US CORP.—See Choice Hotels International, Inc.; *U.S. Public*, pg. 490
MAXXVISION GMBH—See Indutrade AB; *Int'l*, pg. 3680
MAX YIELD COOPERATIVE; *U.S. Private*, pg. 2617
MAXYMILLIAN TECHNOLOGIES INC.; *U.S. Private*, pg. 2620
MAXYMISER GMBH—See Maxymiser Inc.; *U.S. Private*, pg. 2620
MAXYMISER INC.; *U.S. Private*, pg. 2620

COMPANY NAME INDEX

MAXYMISER TECHNICAL CENTER—See Maxymiser Inc.; *U.S. Private*, pg. 2620
MAXZI THE GOOD FOOD RESTAURANT & CAFE L.L.C.—See C.P. All Public Company Limited; *Int'l*, pg. 1244
MAXZONE AUTO PARTS CORP.—See DEPO AUTO PARTS IND. CO., LTD.; *Int'l*, pg. 2041
MAXZONE VEHICLE LIGHTING INC.; *U.S. Private*, pg. 2620
MAYA DESIGN, INC.—See The Boston Consulting Group, Inc.; *U.S. Private*, pg. 3997
MAYADO PHARMACEUTICAL CO., LTD.—See Rohto Pharmaceutical Co. Ltd.; *Int'l*, pg. 6295
MAYA ENERJI YATIRIMLARI A.S.—See EnBW Energie Baden-Wurttemberg AG; *Int'l*, pg. 2399
MAYAGUEZ SA; *Int'l*, pg. 4743
MAYA INTERNATIONAL GMBH—See Messe Munchen GmbH; *Int'l*, pg. 4841
MAYAIR GROUP PLC; *Int'l*, pg. 4743
MAYANOT TAMDA LTD.; *Int'l*, pg. 4743
MAYA STEELS FABRICATION, INC.; *U.S. Private*, pg. 2620
MAY & BAKER NIGERIA PLC.; *Int'l*, pg. 4743
MAYBAN INTERNATIONAL TRUST (LABUAN) BHD—See Malayan Banking Berhad; *Int'l*, pg. 4660
MAYBAN INVESTMENT MANAGEMENT SDN. BHD—See Malayan Banking Berhad; *Int'l*, pg. 4660
MAYBAN-JAIC CAPITAL MANAGEMENT SDN. BHD—See Malayan Banking Berhad; *Int'l*, pg. 6387
MAYBANK ASSET MANAGEMENT GROUP BERHAD—See Malayan Banking Berhad; *Int'l*, pg. 4660
MAYBANK ASSET MANAGEMENT SINGAPORE PTE LTD.—See Malayan Banking Berhad; *Int'l*, pg. 4660
MAYBANK ATR KIM ENG CAPITAL PARTNERS, INC.—See Malayan Banking Berhad; *Int'l*, pg. 4660
MAYBANK ATR KIM ENG SECURITIES, INC.—See Malayan Banking Berhad; *Int'l*, pg. 4660
MAY BANK (CAMBODIA) PLC.—See National Bank of Cambodia; *Int'l*, pg. 5152
MAYBANK INTERNATIONAL ISLAMIC BANKING OPERATIONS—See Malayan Banking Berhad; *Int'l*, pg. 4660
MAYBANK INTERNATIONAL (L) LIMITED—See Malayan Banking Berhad; *Int'l*, pg. 4660
MAYBANK INVESTMENT BANK BERHAD—See Malayan Banking Berhad; *Int'l*, pg. 4660
MAYBANK ISLAMIC ASSET MANAGEMENT SDN BHD—See Malayan Banking Berhad; *Int'l*, pg. 4660
MAYBANK KIM ENG HOLDINGS LIMITED—See Malayan Banking Berhad; *Int'l*, pg. 4660
MAYBANK KIM ENG SECURITIES JSC—See Malayan Banking Berhad; *Int'l*, pg. 4660
MAYBANK KIM ENG SECURITIES (LONDON) LTD.—See Malayan Banking Berhad; *Int'l*, pg. 4660
MAYBANK KIM ENG SECURITIES PTE. LTD.—See Malayan Banking Berhad; *Int'l*, pg. 4660
MAYBANK KIM ENG SECURITIES (THAILAND) PUBLIC COMPANY LIMITED—See Malayan Banking Berhad; *Int'l*, pg. 4660
MAYBANK KIM ENG SECURITIES USA INC.—See Malayan Banking Berhad; *Int'l*, pg. 4660
MAYBANK NOMINEES (SINGAPORE) PRIVATE LIMITED—See Malayan Banking Berhad; *Int'l*, pg. 4660
MAYBANK PHILIPPINES, INCORPORATED—See Malayan Banking Berhad; *Int'l*, pg. 4660
MAYBANK SECURITIES, INC.—See Malayan Banking Berhad; *Int'l*, pg. 4661
MAYBANK SECURITIES (LONDON) LIMITED—See Malayan Banking Berhad; *Int'l*, pg. 4660
MAYBANK SECURITIES PTE LTD.—See Malayan Banking Berhad; *Int'l*, pg. 4661
MAYBANK SECURITIES (THAILAND) PUBLIC COMPANY LIMITED—See Malayan Banking Berhad; *Int'l*, pg. 4661
MAYBANK SECURITIES USA INC.—See Malayan Banking Berhad; *Int'l*, pg. 4661
MAYBAN LIFE INTERNATIONAL (LABUAN) LTD.—See Malayan Banking Berhad; *Int'l*, pg. 4660
MAYBAN NOMINEES (ASING) SDN. BHD.—See Malayan Banking Berhad; *Int'l*, pg. 4660
MAYBAN (NOMINEES) SDN BHD—See Malayan Banking Berhad; *Int'l*, pg. 4660
MAYBAN (NOMINEES) SENDIRIAN BERHAD—See Malayan Banking Berhad; *Int'l*, pg. 4660
MAYBAN TRUSTEES BERHAD—See Malayan Banking Berhad; *Int'l*, pg. 4660
MAYBAN VENTURES SDN. BHD.—See Malayan Banking Berhad; *Int'l*, pg. 4660
MAYBARU SHIPPING & TRADING PTE. LTD.—See Meiji Shipping Co., Ltd.; *Int'l*, pg. 4802
MAYBELLINE, INC.—See L'Oreal S.A.; *Int'l*, pg. 4380
MAYBELLINE PRODUCTS CO. INC.—See L'Oreal S.A.; *Int'l*, pg. 4380
MAYBERRY INVESTMENTS LTD.; *Int'l*, pg. 4743
MAYBERRY JAMAICAN EQUITIES LTD.; *Int'l*, pg. 4743
MAYBERRY RESOURCES PLC; *Int'l*, pg. 4743

MAY, BONEE & CLARK INSURANCE—See Kelso & Company, L.P.; *U.S. Private*, pg. 2280
MAYBORN GROUP LIMITED—See Ping An Insurance (Group) Company of China, Ltd.; *Int'l*, pg. 5869
MAYBORN MOROCCO SARL—See Ping An Insurance (Group) Company of China, Ltd.; *Int'l*, pg. 5870
MAYBORN USA INC.—See Ping An Insurance (Group) Company of China, Ltd.; *Int'l*, pg. 5870
MAYBOURNE HOTELS LIMITED; *Int'l*, pg. 4744
MAYBROOK DAIRY LIMITED—See Donegal Investment Group Plc; *Int'l*, pg. 2163
MAYCO INDUSTRIES, LLC; *U.S. Private*, pg. 2620
MAYCO INDUSTRIES—See Metalico Inc.; *U.S. Private*, pg. 2681
MAYCO MIX LTD.—See Heidelberg Materials AG; *Int'l*, pg. 3318
MAY CONSTRUCTION CO.; *U.S. Private*, pg. 2620
MAYDAY MANUFACTURING CO.—See ESCO Technologies, Inc.; *U.S. Public*, pg. 794
MAYDENKI SDN. BHD.—See ACO Group Berhad; *Int'l*, pg. 107
MAYEGAWA CHILE S.A.C.—See Mayekawa Mfg. Co. Ltd.; *Int'l*, pg. 4743
MAYEKAWA ARGENTINA S.A.—See Mayekawa Mfg. Co. Ltd.; *Int'l*, pg. 4743
MAYEKAWA AUSTRALIA PTY. LTD.—See Mayekawa Mfg. Co. Ltd.; *Int'l*, pg. 4744
MAYEKAWA CANADA, INC.—See Mayekawa Mfg. Co. Ltd.; *Int'l*, pg. 4744
MAYEKAWA CENTROAMERICA S.A.—See Mayekawa Mfg. Co. Ltd.; *Int'l*, pg. 4744
MAYEKAWA CHINA INDUSTRIES CO. LTD.—See Mayekawa Mfg. Co. Ltd.; *Int'l*, pg. 4744
MAYEKAWA COLOMBIA S.A.S.—See Mayekawa Mfg. Co. Ltd.; *Int'l*, pg. 4744
MAYEKAWA DEUTSCHLAND GMBH—See Mayekawa Mfg. Co. Ltd.; *Int'l*, pg. 4744
MAYEKAWA DO BRASIL EUIPAMENTOS INDUSTRIAIS LTDA.—See Mayekawa Mfg. Co. Ltd.; *Int'l*, pg. 4744
MAYEKAWA ECUADOR S.A.—See Mayekawa Mfg. Co. Ltd.; *Int'l*, pg. 4744
MAYEKAWA FRANCE SARL—See Mayekawa Mfg. Co. Ltd.; *Int'l*, pg. 4744
MAYEKAWA HOLDING (THAILAND) CO., LTD—See Mayekawa Mfg. Co. Ltd.; *Int'l*, pg. 4743
MAYEKAWA INDIA PVT. LTD.—See Mayekawa Mfg. Co. Ltd.; *Int'l*, pg. 4744
MAYEKAWA INTERTECH A.G.—See Mayekawa Mfg. Co. Ltd.; *Int'l*, pg. 4744
MAYEKAWA ITALIA S.R.L.—See Mayekawa Mfg. Co. Ltd.; *Int'l*, pg. 4744
MAYEKAWA MEXICO SA DE CV—See Mayekawa Mfg. Co. Ltd.; *Int'l*, pg. 4744
MAYEKAWA MFG. CO. LTD. (CHINA)—See Mayekawa Mfg. Co. Ltd.; *Int'l*, pg. 4744
MAYEKAWA MFG. CO. LTD. (RUSSIA)—See Mayekawa Mfg. Co. Ltd.; *Int'l*, pg. 4744
MAYEKAWA MFG. CO. LTD.; *Int'l*, pg. 4743
MAYEKAWA MIDDLE EAST FZCO, DUBAI - U.A.E.—See Mayekawa Mfg. Co. Ltd.; *Int'l*, pg. 4744
MAYEKAWA (M) SDN. BHD.—See Mayekawa Mfg. Co. Ltd.; *Int'l*, pg. 4743
MAYEKAWA PHILIPPINES CORP.—See Mayekawa Mfg. Co. Ltd.; *Int'l*, pg. 4744
MAYEKAWA SINGAPORE PTE. LTD.—See Mayekawa Mfg. Co. Ltd.; *Int'l*, pg. 4744
MAYEKAWA S.L.—See Mayekawa Mfg. Co. Ltd.; *Int'l*, pg. 4744
MAYEKAWA SOUTH AFRICA (PTY) LTD.—See Mayekawa Mfg. Co. Ltd.; *Int'l*, pg. 4743
MAYEKAWA-SVEDAN SP. Z O.O.—See Mayekawa Mfg. Co. Ltd.; *Int'l*, pg. 4743
MAYEKAWA (TAIWAN) CO. LTD.—See Mayekawa Mfg. Co. Ltd.; *Int'l*, pg. 4743
MAYEKAWA (THAILAND) CO. LTD.—See Mayekawa Mfg. Co. Ltd.; *Int'l*, pg. 4743
MAYEKAWA TURKEY SOGUTMA SANAYI VE TICARET LIMITED SIRKETI—See Mayekawa Mfg. Co. Ltd.; *Int'l*, pg. 4744
MAYEKAWA U.S.A., INC.—See Mayekawa Mfg. Co. Ltd.; *Int'l*, pg. 4744
MAYEKAWA VIETNAM ONE MEMBER CO., LIMITED—See Mayekawa Mfg. Co. Ltd.; *Int'l*, pg. 4743
MAYER/BERKSHIRE CORPORATION; *U.S. Private*, pg. 2621
MAYER BROS. APPLE PRODUCTS, INC.; *U.S. Private*, pg. 2621
MAYER BROTHERS CONSTRUCTION CO.; *U.S. Private*, pg. 2621
MAYER BROWN LLP; *U.S. Private*, pg. 2621
MAYER & CO BESCHLAGE GMBH—See Guangdong Kinlong Hardware Prdcts Co., Ltd.; *Int'l*, pg. 3157
MAYER ELECTRIC FINANCIAL CORPORATION—See Mayer Electric Supply Company Inc.; *U.S. Private*, pg. 2621
MAYER ELECTRIC SUPPLY COMPANY INC.; *U.S. Private*, pg. 2621
MAYER ELECTRIC SUPPLY COMPANY, INC.—See Mayer Electric Supply Company Inc.; *U.S. Private*, pg. 2621

MAYER ELECTRIC SUPPLY SERVICE CO. INC.—See Mayer Electric Supply Company Inc.; *U.S. Private*, pg. 2621
MAYERHOFER ARGENTINA S.A.—See Leonhard Kurz GmbH & Co. KG; *Int'l*, pg. 4462
MAYER HOFFMAN MCCANN, P.C.; *U.S. Private*, pg. 2621
MAYER HOLDINGS LIMITED; *Int'l*, pg. 4744
MAYER INTERNATIONAL CORPORATION—See Mayer Steel Pipe Corporation; *Int'l*, pg. 4744
MAYER-JOHNSON LLC—See Tobii AB; *Int'l*, pg. 7771
MAYER MALAYSIA SDN. BHD.—See Khind Holdings Berhad; *Int'l*, pg. 4155
MAYER MARKETING PTE. LTD.—See Khind Holdings Berhad; *Int'l*, pg. 4155
MAYER MASCHINENBAUGESELLSCHAFT MBH; *Int'l*, pg. 4744
MAYER/MCCANN-ERICKSON S.R.O.—See The Interpublic Group of Companies, Inc.; *U.S. Public*, pg. 2099
MAYER-MCCANN—See The Interpublic Group of Companies, Inc.; *U.S. Public*, pg. 2099
MAYER RAMOT GENERAL INSURANCE AGENCY (2009) LTD.—See Mayer's Cars & Trucks Co. Ltd.; *Int'l*, pg. 4744
MAYER'S CARS & TRUCKS CO. LTD.; *Int'l*, pg. 4744
MAYER STEEL PIPE CORPORATION - PU-HSIN FACTORY—See Mayer Steel Pipe Corporation; *Int'l*, pg. 4744
MAYER STEEL PIPE CORPORATION; *Int'l*, pg. 4744
MAYER STEEL PIPE CORPORATION - YOUTH-SHIH FACTORY—See Mayer Steel Pipe Corporation; *Int'l*, pg. 4744
MAYER TEXTILE MACHINE CORP.—See KARL MAYER Textilmaschinenfabrik GmbH; *Int'l*, pg. 4082
MAYES COUNTY HMA, LLC—See Community Health Systems, Inc.; *U.S. Public*, pg. 555
MAYES COUNTY HMPN, LLC—See Community Health Systems, Inc.; *U.S. Public*, pg. 555
MAYESH WHOLESALE FLORIST, INC.; *U.S. Private*, pg. 2621
MAYES TESTING ENGINEERS, INC.—See Terracon Consultants, Inc.; *U.S. Private*, pg. 3971
MAYET PIERRE DE BRESSE—See PSB Industries SA; *Int'l*, pg. 6015
MAYEX USA, INC.; *Int'l*, pg. 4744
MAYFAIR CAPITAL INVESTMENT MANAGEMENT LIMITED—See Swiss Life Holding; *Int'l*, pg. 7368
MAYFAIR CONSTRUCTION GROUP, LLC.; *U.S. Private*, pg. 2621
MAYFAIR EQUITY PARTNERS LLP; *Int'l*, pg. 4744
MAYFAIRE TOWN CENTER, LP—See CBL & Associates Properties, Inc.; *U.S. Public*, pg. 458
MAYFAIR GOLD CORP.; *Int'l*, pg. 4745
MAYFAIR HOLDING GMBH & CO. SINGAPUR KG—See Munchener Ruckversicherungs AG; *Int'l*, pg. 5089
MAYFAIR LUMBER SALES LTD; *Int'l*, pg. 4745
MAYFAIR PHILATELICS LIMITED—See Scholium Group plc; *Int'l*, pg. 6638
MAYFAIR RENT-A-CAR, LLC - WAUKESHA—See Ewald Automotive Group, LLC; *U.S. Private*, pg. 1444
MAYFIELD CHILDCARE LIMITED; *Int'l*, pg. 4745
MAYFIELD DAIRY FARMS, LLC—See Dean Foods Company; *U.S. Private*, pg. 1183
MAYFIELD DAIRY FARMS—See Dean Foods Company; *U.S. Private*, pg. 1183
MAYFIELD EQUIPMENT CO.; *U.S. Private*, pg. 2621
MAYFIELD FUND; *U.S. Private*, pg. 2621
MAYFIELD GRAIN COMPANY INC.; *U.S. Private*, pg. 2621
MAYFIELD PAPER CO. INC.; *U.S. Private*, pg. 2621
MAYFIELD PLASTICS, INC.—See Wembly Enterprises LLC; *U.S. Private*, pg. 4480
MAYFIELD SPINE SURGERY CENTER, LLC—See Tenet Healthcare Corporation; *U.S. Public*, pg. 2004
MAYFIELD TOYOTA; *Int'l*, pg. 4745
MAYFIELD TRANSFER COMPANY INCORPORATED; *U.S. Private*, pg. 2621
MAYFLOWER CAR RENTAL SDN BHD—See Warisan TC Holdings Berhad; *Int'l*, pg. 8345
MAYFLOWER CORPORATE TRAVEL SERVICES SDN BHD—See Warisan TC Holdings Berhad; *Int'l*, pg. 8345
MAYFLOWER ENGINEERING LTD; *Int'l*, pg. 4745
MAYFLOWER FOOD STORES INC.; *U.S. Private*, pg. 2622
MAYFLOWER GMBH; *Int'l*, pg. 4745
MAYFLOWER HOLIDAYS SDN BHD—See Warisan TC Holdings Berhad; *Int'l*, pg. 8345
MAYFLOWER INN & SPA; *U.S. Private*, pg. 2622
MAYFLOWER INTERNATIONAL FORWARDING INC.—See UniGroup, Inc.; *U.S. Private*, pg. 4283
MAYFLOWER MILITARY MOVERS, LLC—See UniGroup, Inc.; *U.S. Private*, pg. 4283
MAYFLOWER SALES CO., LLC—See Gen Cap America, Inc.; *U.S. Private*, pg. 1660
MAYFLOWER TRANSIT, LLC—See UniGroup, Inc.; *U.S. Private*, pg. 4283
MAYFRAN FRANCE S.A.R.L.—See Tsubakimoto Chain Co.; *Int'l*, pg. 7953
MAYFRAN GMBH—See Tsubakimoto Chain Co.; *Int'l*, pg. 7953

MAYFLOWER INN & SPA

CORPORATE AFFILIATIONS

MAYFRAN INTERNATIONAL, B.V.—See Mayfran International, Inc.; *U.S. Private*, pg. 2622
MAYFRAN INTERNATIONAL, INC.; *U.S. Private*, pg. 2622
MAYFRAN LIMBURG B.V.—See Tsubakimoto Chain Co.; *Int'l*, pg. 7953
MAYFRAN U.K. LIMITED—See Tsubakimoto Chain Co.; *Int'l*, pg. 7953
MAYHEW STEEL PRODUCTS INC.; *U.S. Private*, pg. 2622
MAYHILL BEHAVIORAL HEALTH, LLC—See Universal Health Services, Inc.; *U.S. Public*, pg. 2258
MAYHOOLA FOR INVESTMENTS LLC; *Int'l*, pg. 4745
MAYHUGH REALTY, INC.; *U.S. Private*, pg. 2622
MAYINGLONG PHARMACEUTICAL GROUP CO., LTD.; *Int'l*, pg. 4745
MAY INSTITUTE, INC.; *U.S. Private*, pg. 2620
MAY INSURANCE SERVICES, INC.—See Emerson Reid LLC; *U.S. Private*, pg. 1382
MAYLANDS INVESTMENT PTE LTD—See Tuan Sing Holdings Limited; *Int'l*, pg. 7962
MAYLINE COMPANY, LLC—See Liberty Diversified International Inc.; *U.S. Private*, pg. 2444
MAYMEDIC TECHNOLOGY SDN. BHD.—See BCM Alliance Berhad; *Int'l*, pg. 928
MAYMONT FOUNDATION; *U.S. Private*, pg. 2622
MAYNARD, COOPER & GALE, P.C.; *U.S. Private*, pg. 2622
MAYNARD & HARRIS PLASTICS—See Berry Global Group, Inc; *U.S. Public*, pg. 324
MAYNARD OIL CO.—See Plantation Petroleum Holdings IV, LLC (PPH); *U.S. Private*, pg. 3197
MAYNARDS ELECTRIC SUPPLY, INC.; *U.S. Private*, pg. 2622
MAYNARDS EUROPE GMBH—See Maynards Industries, Ltd.; *Int'l*, pg. 4745
MAYNARDS INDUSTRIES, LTD.; *Int'l*, pg. 4745
MAYNARD STEEL CASTING COMPANY; *U.S. Private*, pg. 2622
MAYNE PHARMA GROUP LIMITED; *Int'l*, pg. 4745
MAYNE PHARMA INC.—See Mayne Pharma Group Limited; *Int'l*, pg. 4745
MAYNE PHARMA INTERNATIONAL PTY. LTD.—See Mayne Pharma Group Limited; *Int'l*, pg. 4745
MAYO CLINIC ARIZONA—See Mayo Clinic; *U.S. Private*, pg. 2622
MAYO CLINIC FLORIDA—See Mayo Clinic; *U.S. Private*, pg. 2622
MAYO CLINIC; *U.S. Private*, pg. 2622
MAYO ECUADOR—See The Interpublic Group of Companies, Inc.; *U.S. Public*, pg. 2093
MAYO FOUNDATION FOR MEDICAL EDUCATION & RESEARCH; *U.S. Private*, pg. 2622
MAYO KNITTING MILL INC.; *U.S. Private*, pg. 2622
MAYOLY SPINDLER; *Int'l*, pg. 4745
MAYO PERFORMING ARTS CENTER; *U.S. Private*, pg. 2622
MAYO PUBLICIDAD—See The Interpublic Group of Companies, Inc.; *U.S. Public*, pg. 2093
MAYORGA COFFEE INC.; *U.S. Private*, pg. 2622
THE MAYOR'S FUND TO ADVANCE NEW YORK CITY; *U.S. Private*, pg. 4076
MAYOR'S JEWELERS, INC.—See Apollo Global Management, Inc.; *U.S. Public*, pg. 167
MAYOR'S JEWELERS OF FLORIDA, INC.—See Apollo Global Management, Inc.; *U.S. Public*, pg. 167
MAYOSEITZ MEDIA; *U.S. Private*, pg. 2622
MAYOSON, S.A. DE C.V.—See Invecture Group, S.A. de C.V.; *Int'l*, pg. 3772
MAYO—See The Interpublic Group of Companies, Inc.; *U.S. Public*, pg. 2093
MAYPLAS LIMITED—See SIG plc; *Int'l*, pg. 6906
MAYPOLE CHEVROLET INC.; *U.S. Private*, pg. 2622
MAYPORT C&C FISHERIES INC.; *U.S. Private*, pg. 2622
MAYPORT FARMERS CO-OP; *U.S. Private*, pg. 2622
MAYR CORP.—See Christian Mayr GmbH & Co. KG; *Int'l*, pg. 1586
MAYR FRANCE S.A.—See Christian Mayr GmbH & Co. KG; *Int'l*, pg. 1586
MAYR ITALIA S.R.L.—See Christian Mayr GmbH & Co. KG; *Int'l*, pg. 1586
MAY RIVER CAPITAL, LLC; *U.S. Private*, pg. 2620
MAYR KOREA CO. LTD.—See Christian Mayr GmbH & Co. KG; *Int'l*, pg. 1586
MAYR KUPPLUNGEN AG—See Christian Mayr GmbH & Co. KG; *Int'l*, pg. 1586
MAYR-MELLNHOF CARTONBOARD UK LIMITED—See Mayr-Melnhof Karton AG; *Int'l*, pg. 4746
MAYR-MELNHOF BELGIUM N.V. / S.A.—See Mayr-Melnhof Karton AG; *Int'l*, pg. 4746
MAYR-MELNHOF BENELUX B.V.—See Mayr-Melnhof Karton AG; *Int'l*, pg. 4746
MAYR-MELNHOF CARTONBOARD INTERNATIONAL GMBH—See Mayr-Melnhof Karton AG; *Int'l*, pg. 4746
MAYR-MELNHOF CARTONBOARD UK LIMITED—See Mayr-Melnhof Karton AG; *Int'l*, pg. 4746
MAYR-MELNHOF EERBEEK B.V.—See Mayr-Melnhof Karton AG; *Int'l*, pg. 4746
MAYR-MELNHOF FRANCE SARL—See Mayr-Melnhof Karton AG; *Int'l*, pg. 4746

MAYR-MELNHOF GERNSBACH GMBH—See Mayr-Melnhof Karton AG; *Int'l*, pg. 4746
MAYR-MELNHOF GRAPHIA IZMIR KARTON SANAYI VE TICARET A.S.—See Mayr-Melnhof Karton AG; *Int'l*, pg. 4746
MAYR-MELNHOF GRAVURE GMBH—See Mayr-Melnhof Karton AG; *Int'l*, pg. 4746
MAYR-MELNHOF HOLDINGS N.V.—See Mayr-Melnhof Karton AG; *Int'l*, pg. 4746
MAYR-MELNHOF ITALIA SRL—See Mayr-Melnhof Karton AG; *Int'l*, pg. 4746
MAYR-MELNHOF KARTON AG; *Int'l*, pg. 4745
MAYR-MELNHOF KARTON GESELLSCHAFT M.B.H.—See Mayr-Melnhof Karton AG; *Int'l*, pg. 4746
MAYR-MELNHOF KARTON GESELLSCHAFT M.B.H.—See Mayr-Melnhof Karton AG; *Int'l*, pg. 4746
MAYR-MELNHOF KARTON POLSKA SP. Z O.O.—See Mayr-Melnhof Karton AG; *Int'l*, pg. 4746
MAYR-MELNHOF KARTON SCHWEIZ GMBH—See Mayr-Melnhof Karton AG; *Int'l*, pg. 4746
MAYR-MELNHOF MEDITERRA SARL—See Mayr-Melnhof Karton AG; *Int'l*, pg. 4746
MAYR-MELNHOF NEDERLAND B.V.—See Mayr-Melnhof Karton AG; *Int'l*, pg. 4746
MAYR-MELNHOF PACKAGING AUSTRIA GMBH—See Mayr-Melnhof Karton AG; *Int'l*, pg. 4747
MAYR-MELNHOF PACKAGING GMBH—See Mayr-Melnhof Karton AG; *Int'l*, pg. 4747
MAYR-MELNHOF PACKAGING IBERICA SL—See Mayr-Melnhof Karton AG; *Int'l*, pg. 4747
MAYR-MELNHOF PACKAGING INTERNATIONAL GMBH—See Mayr-Melnhof Karton AG; *Int'l*, pg. 4747
MAYR-MELNHOF PACKAGING MARINETTI LIMITADA—See Mayr-Melnhof Karton AG; *Int'l*, pg. 4747
MAYR-MELNHOF PACKAGING ROMANIA SA—See Mayr-Melnhof Karton AG; *Int'l*, pg. 4747
MAYR-MELNHOF PACKAGING UK LIMITED—See Mayr-Melnhof Karton AG; *Int'l*, pg. 4747
MAYR-MELNHOF PAPIERRESIDU VERWERKING B.V.—See Mayr-Melnhof Karton AG; *Int'l*, pg. 4747
MAYR-MELNHOF PRINTING & PACKAGING TEHRAN COMPANY, PRIVATE JOINT STOCK—See Mayr-Melnhof Karton AG; *Int'l*, pg. 4747
MAYR-MELNHOF UK LTD.—See Mayr-Melnhof Karton AG; *Int'l*, pg. 4747
MAYR POLSKA SP. Z O.O.—See Christian Mayr GmbH & Co. KG; *Int'l*, pg. 1586
MAYR POWER TRANSMISSION (ZHANGJIAGANG) CO., LTD.—See Christian Mayr GmbH & Co. KG; *Int'l*, pg. 1586
MAYR TRANSMISSIONS LTD.—See Christian Mayr GmbH & Co. KG; *Int'l*, pg. 1586
MAYR TRANSMISSION (S) PTE LTD.—See Christian Mayr GmbH & Co. KG; *Int'l*, pg. 1586
MAYS CAPTREE—See Mays Chemical Company; *U.S. Private*, pg. 2623
MAYS CHEMICAL COMPANY - MAYS LIFE SCIENCES DIVISON—See Mays Chemical Company; *U.S. Private*, pg. 2623
MAYS CHEMICAL COMPANY; *U.S. Private*, pg. 2623
MAYS CHEMICAL COMPANY—See Mays Chemical Company; *U.S. Private*, pg. 2623
MAYS DISTRIBUTING COMPANY; *U.S. Private*, pg. 2623
MAYSE AUTOMOTIVE GROUP; *U.S. Private*, pg. 2623
MAY SHYH CORPORATION—See Nippon Telegraph & Telephone Corporation; *Int'l*, pg. 5351
MAY+SPIES GESELLSCHAFT M.B.H. + CO KG—See MAY+SPIES GMBH; *Int'l*, pg. 4743
MAY+SPIES GMBH; *Int'l*, pg. 4743
MAYSTA INTERNATIONAL LTD.—See Jiangsu Maysta Chemical Co., Ltd.; *Int'l*, pg. 3951
MAYSTAR FOOTWEAR COMPANY LIMITED—See Kingmaker Footwear Holdings Limited; *Int'l*, pg. 4174
MAYSTEEL INDUSTRIES, LLC—See Littlejohn & Co., LLC; *U.S. Private*, pg. 2471
MAY STREET SURGI CENTER, LLC—See KKR & Co. Inc.; *U.S. Public*, pg. 1246
MAY SUPPLY COMPANY—See Winsupply, Inc.; *U.S. Private*, pg. 4545
MAYTAG AIRCRAFT CORP.—See Mercury Air Group Inc.; *U.S. Private*, pg. 2670
MAYTAG COMERCIAL, S. DE R.L. DE C.V.—See Whirlpool Corporation; *U.S. Public*, pg. 2367
MAYTEX MILLS, INC.—See ONEX Corporation; *Int'l*, pg. 5578
MAYTRONICS AUSTRALIA PTY. LTD.—See Maytronics Ltd.; *Int'l*, pg. 4747
MAYTRONICS LTD.; *Int'l*, pg. 4747
MAYTRONICS US INC.—See Maytronics Ltd.; *Int'l*, pg. 4747
MAY TRUCKING COMPANY INC.; *U.S. Private*, pg. 2620
MAYU GLOBAL GROUP BERHAD; *Int'l*, pg. 4747
MAYUKH DEALTRADE LTD.; *Int'l*, pg. 4748
MAYUR FLOORINGS LIMITED; *Int'l*, pg. 4748
MAYUR LEATHER PRODUCTS LTD.; *Int'l*, pg. 4748
MAYUR RESOURCES LIMITED; *Int'l*, pg. 4748
MAYUR UNIQUOTERS LIMITED; *Int'l*, pg. 4748

MAYVILLE ENGINEERING COMPANY, INC. - BYRON CENTER—See Mayville Engineering Company, Inc.; *U.S. Public*, pg. 1403
MAYVILLE ENGINEERING COMPANY, INC.; *U.S. Public*, pg. 1403
MAYWA KOMUTEN, LTD.—See ShinMaywa Industries, Ltd.; *Int'l*, pg. 6846
MAYWA KOUMUTEN, LTD.—See ShinMaywa Industries, Ltd.; *Int'l*, pg. 6846
MAYWO KUNSTSTOFF GMBH—See Rochling SE & Co. KG; *Int'l*, pg. 6376
MAYWOOD ACRES HEALTHCARE—See Apollo Global Management, Inc.; *U.S. Public*, pg. 157
MAYWOOD PARK TROTTING ASSOCIATION, INC.; *U.S. Private*, pg. 2623
MAYWUFA COMPANY LIMITED; *Int'l*, pg. 4748
MAYZO, INC.; *U.S. Private*, pg. 2623
MAZAGON DOCK SHIPBUILDERS LIMITED; *Int'l*, pg. 4748
MAZAKA ENDUSTRIYEL URUNLER SAN TIC VE TEKNOLOJI A.S.—See Phoenix Mecano AG; *Int'l*, pg. 5852
MAZAK CORPORATION—See Yamazaki Mazak Corporation; *Int'l*, pg. 8557
MAZAK MEXICO S.A. DE C.V.—See Yamazaki Mazak Corporation; *Int'l*, pg. 8557
MAZAK OPTONICS CORPORATION—See Yamazaki Mazak Corporation; *Int'l*, pg. 8557
MAZAK SULAMERICANA LTDA—See Yamazaki Mazak Corporation; *Int'l*, pg. 8557
MAZAK (THAILAND) CO., LTD.—See Yamazaki Mazak Corporation; *Int'l*, pg. 8557
MAZARIN INC.; *Int'l*, pg. 4748
MAZARO N.V.; *Int'l*, pg. 4748
MAZAYA QATAR REAL ESTATE DEVELOPMENT Q.S.C.; *Int'l*, pg. 4748
MAZDA ACE CO., LTD.—See Mazda Motor Corporation; *Int'l*, pg. 4749
MAZDA AUSTRALIA PTY. LTD.—See Mazda Motor Corporation; *Int'l*, pg. 4749
MAZDA AUSTRIA GMBH—See Mazda Motor Corporation; *Int'l*, pg. 4749
MAZDA AUTOMOBILES FRANCE SAS—See Mazda Motor Corporation; *Int'l*, pg. 4749
MAZDA AUTOMOVILES ESPANA, S.A.—See Mazda Motor Corporation; *Int'l*, pg. 4749
MAZDA CANADA, INC.—See Mazda Motor Corporation; *Int'l*, pg. 4749
MAZDA CHUHAN CO., LTD.—See Mazda Motor Corporation; *Int'l*, pg. 4749
MAZDA COLOMBIA S.A.S.—See Mazda Motor Corporation; *Int'l*, pg. 4749
MAZDA COMPUTING; *U.S. Private*, pg. 2623
MAZDA KNOXVILLE; *U.S. Private*, pg. 2623
MAZDA LTD; *Int'l*, pg. 4748
MAZDA LTD - UNIT 1—See Mazda Ltd; *Int'l*, pg. 4748
MAZDA LTD - UNIT 2—See Mazda Ltd; *Int'l*, pg. 4748
MAZDA MOBILITY NIIGATA CO., LTD.—See Nippon Seiki Co., Ltd.; *Int'l*, pg. 5329
MAZDA MOTOR CORPORATION; *Int'l*, pg. 4748
MAZDA MOTOR DE MEXICO, S. DE R.L. DE C.V.—See Mazda Motor Corporation; *Int'l*, pg. 4749
MAZDA MOTOR DE PORTUGAL LDA—See Mazda Motor Corporation; *Int'l*, pg. 4749
MAZDA MOTOR EUROPE GMBH—See Mazda Motor Corporation; *Int'l*, pg. 4749
MAZDA MOTOR ITALIA S.P.A.—See Mazda Motor Corporation; *Int'l*, pg. 4749
MAZDA MOTOR LOGISTICS EUROPE N.V.—See Mazda Motor Corporation; *Int'l*, pg. 4749
MAZDA MOTOR RUSSIA, OOO—See Mazda Motor Corporation; *Int'l*, pg. 4749
MAZDA MOTORS (DEUTSCHLAND) G.M.B.H.—See Mazda Motor Corporation; *Int'l*, pg. 4749
MAZDA MOTORS OF NEW ZEALAND LIMITED—See Mazda Motor Corporation; *Int'l*, pg. 4749
MAZDA MOTORS UK LTD.—See Mazda Motor Corporation; *Int'l*, pg. 4749
MAZDA NORTH AMERICAN OPERATIONS—See Mazda Motor Corporation; *Int'l*, pg. 4749
MAZDA NORTH AMERICAN OPERATIONS—See Mazda Motor Corporation; *Int'l*, pg. 4749
MAZDA NORTH AMERICAN OPERATIONS—See Mazda Motor Corporation; *Int'l*, pg. 4749
MAZDA NORTH AMERICAN OPERATIONS-WESTERN REGION—See Mazda Motor Corporation; *Int'l*, pg. 4749
MAZDA OF MESQUITE; *U.S. Private*, pg. 2623
MAZDA OF WEST RIDGE—See West Herr Automotive Group, Inc.; *U.S. Private*, pg. 4485
MAZDA PARTS CO., LTD.—See Mazda Motor Corporation; *Int'l*, pg. 4749
MAZDA SALES (THAILAND) CO., LTD.—See Mazda Motor Corporation; *Int'l*, pg. 4749
MAZDA SOUTHERN AFRICA (PTY.) LTD.—See Mazda Motor Corporation; *Int'l*, pg. 4749
MAZDA STEEL CO., LTD.—See Sumitomo Corporation; *Int'l*, pg. 7269

COMPANY NAME INDEX

MAZDA (SUISSE) S.A.—See Mazda Motor Corporation; *Int'l*, pg. 4749
MAZEL & COMPANY INCORPORATED; *U.S. Private*, pg. 2623
MAZE LUMBER—See W.H. Maze Company; *U.S. Private*, pg. 4420
THE MAZER CORPORATION; *U.S. Private*, pg. 4076
THE MAZEROV GROUP; *U.S. Private*, pg. 4076
MAZER'S DISCOUNT HOME CENTERS; *U.S. Private*, pg. 2623
MAZHAR ZORLU HOLDING A.S.; *Int'l*, pg. 4749
MAZIK GLOBAL, INC.—See Quisitive Technology Solutions, Inc.; *Int'l*, pg. 6165
MAZ MIKROELEKTRONIK-ANWENDUNGSZENTRUM GMBH IM LAND BRANDENBURG—See ELMOS Semiconductor AG; *Int'l*, pg. 2368
MAZ & MORE TV-PRODUKTION GMBH—See Axel Springer SE; *Int'l*, pg. 766
MAZONIA DIALYSIS, LLC—See DaVita Inc.; *U.S. Public*, pg. 641
MAZOON PRINTING, PUBLISHING & ADVERTISING (L.L.C)—See W.J. Towell & Co. LLC; *Int'l*, pg. 8322
MAZOR ALUMINIUM (PTY) LTD.—See Mazor Group Limited; *Int'l*, pg. 4749
MAZOR GROUP LIMITED; *Int'l*, pg. 4749
MAZOR ROBOTICS LTD.—See Medtronic plc; *Int'l*, pg. 4787
MAZOWIECKA SPOLKA GAZOWNICTWA SP. Z O.O.—See Polskie Gornictwo Naftowe i Gazownictwo S.A.; *Int'l*, pg. 5912
MAZRI INC.—See AOI TYO Holdings Inc.; *Int'l*, pg. 488
MAZU ALLIANCE LIMITED; *Int'l*, pg. 4750
MAZUR PARKPLATZ GMBH—See Flughafen Wien Aktiengesellschaft; *Int'l*, pg. 2712
MAZU SHIPPING (PVT) LTD.—See Hemas Holdings PLC; *Int'l*, pg. 3340
MAZZARO'S ITALIAN MARKET, LLC; *U.S. Private*, pg. 2623
MAZZELLA LIFTING TECHNOLOGIES; *U.S. Private*, pg. 2623
MAZZIO'S CORPORATION; *U.S. Private*, pg. 2623
MAZZIO'S PIZZA—See Mazzio's Corporation; *U.S. Private*, pg. 2623
MAZZI SONEPAR S.P.A.—See Sonepar S.A.; *Int'l*, pg. 7092
MAZZOLA FINANCIAL SERVICES; *U.S. Private*, pg. 2623
MAZZONE HOSPITALITY, LLC—See Compass Group PLC; *Int'l*, pg. 1752
MAZZONE MANAGEMENT GROUP LTD, INC.; *U.S. Private*, pg. 2623
MAZZUCCHELLI 1849 S.P.A.; *Int'l*, pg. 4750
MB2 DENTAL SOLUTIONS LLC; *U.S. Private*, pg. 2624
MBA AG—See CNH Industrial N.V.; *Int'l*, pg. 1674
MBAC BRAZIL HOLDINGS B.V.—See Itafos; *U.S. Public*, pg. 1175
MB AEROSPACE HOLDINGS INC.—See Barnes Group Inc.; *U.S. Public*, pg. 277
MB AEROSPACE LIMITED—See Barnes Group Inc.; *U.S. Public*, pg. 277
MB AEROSPACE STERLING HEIGHTS, INC.—See Barnes Group Inc.; *U.S. Public*, pg. 277
MB AEROSPACE WARREN, LLC—See Barnes Group Inc.; *U.S. Public*, pg. 277
MBA HEALTHGROUP; *U.S. Private*, pg. 2624
M.B.A. HOLDINGS, INC.; *U.S. Private*, pg. 2528
MB AIR SYSTEMS LIMITED—See Ingersoll Rand Inc.; *U.S. Public*, pg. 1122
MBA LAZARD ARGENTINA—See Lazard Ltd.; *Int'l*, pg. 4428
MBA LAZARD CHILE S.A.—See Lazard Ltd.; *Int'l*, pg. 4428
MBA LAZARD COLOMBIA S.A.S.—See Lazard Ltd.; *Int'l*, pg. 4428
MBA LAZARD PANAMA S.A.—See Lazard Ltd.; *Int'l*, pg. 4428
MBA LAZARD PERU S.A.C.—See Lazard Ltd.; *Int'l*, pg. 4428
MBA LAZARD URUGUAY—See Lazard Ltd.; *Int'l*, pg. 4428
MBANK HIPOTECZNY S.A.—See Commerzbank AG; *Int'l*, pg. 1719
MBANK S.A.—See Commerzbank AG; *Int'l*, pg. 1719
MBANK—See Mackinac Financial Corporation; *U.S. Public*, pg. 1352
MBA TULSA BEVERAGE COMPANY; *U.S. Private*, pg. 2624
MB AUTOMAXI UK LTD—See Accent Equity Partners AB; *Int'l*, pg. 81
MB BANCORP, INC.—See Bay-Vanguard, M.H.C.; *U.S. Private*, pg. 495
MB BARTER SINGAPORE PTE LTD.—See REHAU Verwaltungszentrale AG; *Int'l*, pg. 6255
MB BARTER & TRADING D.O.O.—See REHAU Verwaltungszentrale AG; *Int'l*, pg. 6255
MB BARTER & TRADING (PTY) LTD.—See REHAU Verwaltungszentrale AG; *Int'l*, pg. 6255
MB BARTER & TRADING SA SHANGHAI—See REHAU Verwaltungszentrale AG; *Int'l*, pg. 6255
MB BARTER & TRADING SA—See REHAU Verwaltungszentrale AG; *Int'l*, pg. 6255

MB BARTER & TRADING SA—See REHAU Verwaltungszentrale AG; *Int'l*, pg. 6255
MB BARTER & TRADING SPAIN, S.L.—See REHAU Verwaltungszentrale AG; *Int'l*, pg. 6255
MB BARTER (USA) INC.—See REHAU Verwaltungszentrale AG; *Int'l*, pg. 6255
MBB HUBFIX S.R.O.—See Palfinger AG; *Int'l*, pg. 5707
MBB INTERLIFT N.V.—See Palfinger AG; *Int'l*, pg. 5707
MBB PALFINGER GMBH—See Palfinger AG; *Int'l*, pg. 5707
MBB SE; *Int'l*, pg. 4751
MB BUSINESS CAPITAL CANADA INC.—See Fifth Third Bancorp; *U.S. Public*, pg. 833
MBCA BANK LIMITED; *Int'l*, pg. 4751
MB CENTURY DRILLING LIMITED—See MB Holding Company LLC; *Int'l*, pg. 4750
MB CENTURY DRILLING PTY LTD.—See MB Holding Company LLC; *Int'l*, pg. 4750
MBC HOLDINGS, INC.; *U.S. Private*, pg. 2624
MBC IMMOBILIEN LEASING GESELLSCHAFT M.B.H.—See UniCredit S.p.A.; *Int'l*, pg. 8037
M-B COMPANIES, INC. - AIRPORT SNOW REMOVAL DIVISION—See M-B Companies, Inc.; *U.S. Private*, pg. 2525
M-B COMPANIES, INC. - PAVEMENT MARKING EQUIPMENT DIVISION—See M-B Companies, Inc.; *U.S. Private*, pg. 2525
M-B COMPANIES, INC.; *U.S. Private*, pg. 2525
MB CONSULTANTS LTD.; *U.S. Private*, pg. 2623
M&B CORPORATION; *U.S. Private*, pg. 2524
MBCREDIT SOLUTIONS S.P.A.—See Mediobanca S.P.A.; *Int'l*, pg. 4778
MBC S.A.—See TPG Capital, L.P.; *U.S. Public*, pg. 2174
MBC UNITED WHOLESALE LLC—See Unistan Inc.; *U.S. Private*, pg. 4287
MBDA DEUTSCHLAND GMBH—See Airbus SE; *Int'l*, pg. 247
MBDA DEUTSCHLAND GMBH—See BAE Systems plc; *Int'l*, pg. 798
MBDA DEUTSCHLAND GMBH—See Leonardo S.p.A.; *Int'l*, pg. 4460
MBDA FRANCE SAS—See Airbus SE; *Int'l*, pg. 247
MBDA FRANCE SAS—See BAE Systems plc; *Int'l*, pg. 798
MBDA FRANCE SAS—See Leonardo S.p.A.; *Int'l*, pg. 4460
MBDA HOLDINGS S.A.S.—See Airbus SE; *Int'l*, pg. 247
MBDA HOLDINGS S.A.S.—See BAE Systems plc; *Int'l*, pg. 798
MBDA HOLDINGS S.A.S.—See Leonardo S.p.A.; *Int'l*, pg. 4460
MBDA ITALIA SPA—See Airbus SE; *Int'l*, pg. 247
MBDA ITALIA SPA—See BAE Systems plc; *Int'l*, pg. 798
MBDA ITALIA SPA—See Leonardo S.p.A.; *Int'l*, pg. 4460
MBDA UK LTD.—See Airbus SE; *Int'l*, pg. 247
MBDA UK LTD.—See BAE Systems plc; *Int'l*, pg. 798
MBDA UK LTD.—See Leonardo S.p.A.; *Int'l*, pg. 4460
MBDA UK—See Airbus SE; *Int'l*, pg. 247
MBDA UK—See BAE Systems plc; *Int'l*, pg. 798
MBDA UK—See Leonardo S.p.A.; *Int'l*, pg. 4460
MBD CONSTRUCTION COMPANY, INC.; *U.S. Private*, pg. 2624
MB DEUTSCHLAND GMBH—See MB Holding Company LLC; *Int'l*, pg. 4750
MB DEVELOPMENT, LLC—See Icahn Enterprises L.P.; *U.S. Public*, pg. 1084
MB DRILLING CO. LTD.—See MB Holding Company LLC; *Int'l*, pg. 4750
MB DRILLING OVERSEAS LTD—See MB Holding Company LLC; *Int'l*, pg. 4750
MB DRILLING OVERSEAS—See MB Holding Company LLC; *Int'l*, pg. 4750
MBE CONTROL SOLUTIONS—See Riber S.A.; *Int'l*, pg. 6328
MBE CPAS LLP; *U.S. Private*, pg. 2624
MB ELECTRONIQUE S.A.—See Yokogawa Electric Corporation; *Int'l*, pg. 8592
M. BELMONT VER STANDIG, INC.—See Saga Communications, Inc.; *U.S. Public*, pg. 1835
MBE TECHNOLOGY PTE LTD—See IQE plc; *Int'l*, pg. 3803
MBE WORLDWIDE S.P.A.; *Int'l*, pg. 4751
MBEYA CEMENT COMPANY LIMITED—See Holcim Ltd.; *Int'l*, pg. 3449
MB FACTA S.P.A.—See Mediobanca-Banca de Credito Finanziario S.p.A.; *Int'l*, pg. 4778
MB FAMILY HOLDINGS, INC.—See Winsupply, Inc.; *U.S. Private*, pg. 4545
MBF CARDS (MSIA) SDN. BHD.—See AMMB Holdings Berhad; *Int'l*, pg. 429
MBF CARPENTERS SHIPPING LTD.—See MBf Holdings Berhad; *Int'l*, pg. 4752
MBF EMBALAGENS LTDA.—See AptarGroup, Inc.; *U.S. Public*, pg. 174
MBF HEALTHCARE PARTNERS, L.P.; *U.S. Private*, pg. 2624
MBF HOLDINGS BERHAD; *Int'l*, pg. 4751
MB FINANCIAL BANK, N.A.—See Fifth Third Bancorp; *U.S. Public*, pg. 833

MBM RESOURCES BERHAD

MB FINANCIAL, INC.—See Fifth Third Bancorp; *U.S. Public*, pg. 833
MBF INDUSTRIES, INC.; *U.S. Private*, pg. 2624
MBF MANAGEMENT SDN. BHD.—See MBf Holdings Berhad; *Int'l*, pg. 4752
MB FOOD SERVICE INC.; *U.S. Private*, pg. 2623
MBF PRINTING INDUSTRY SDN. BHD.—See MBf Holdings Berhad; *Int'l*, pg. 4752
MBF WOOD TERRACE CAPITAL CORPORATION—See MBf Holdings Berhad; *Int'l*, pg. 4752
MBG BRUGGE—See Ackermans & van Haaren NV; *Int'l*, pg. 105
MBG DALLGOW GMBH & CO. KG—See ADLER Group SA; *Int'l*, pg. 150
MBG GROUP JOINT STOCK COMPANY; *Int'l*, pg. 4752
MBG HOLDINGS, INC.; *U.S. Public*, pg. 1403
MB GLOBAL ADVISERS, LLC; *U.S. Private*, pg. 2623
MBG SACHSEN GMBH—See ADLER Group SA; *Int'l*, pg. 150
MB GTC GMBH MERCEDES-BENZ GEBRAUCHTTEILE CENTER—See Mercedes-Benz Group AG; *Int'l*, pg. 4825
MBG WILRIJK—See Ackermans & van Haaren NV; *Int'l*, pg. 105
MB HAYNES CORPORATION; *U.S. Private*, pg. 2623
MBH BANK NYRT.; *Int'l*, pg. 4752
MBH CORPORATION PLC; *Int'l*, pg. 4752
MB HOLDING COMPANY LLC; *Int'l*, pg. 4750
MB HOLDING GMBH—See BayernLB Holding AG; *Int'l*, pg. 914
MBIA INC.; *U.S. Public*, pg. 1403
MBIA INSURANCE CORPORATION—See MBIA Inc.; *U.S. Public*, pg. 1403
MBIA MEXICO, S.A. DE C.V.—See MBIA Inc.; *U.S. Public*, pg. 1403
MBIA—See MBIA Inc.; *U.S. Public*, pg. 1403
MBI, INC.; *U.S. Private*, pg. 2624
MBI INTERNATIONAL HOLDINGS LIMITED—See MBI & Partners U.K. Limited; *Int'l*, pg. 4752
M BILAR GROUP AB—See Bilia AB; *Int'l*, pg. 1029
MBILLS D.O.O.—See Petrol, Slovenska energetska druzba, d.d.; *Int'l*, pg. 5827
MB INFORMATICS INDIA LTD.—See MB Holding Company LLC; *Int'l*, pg. 4750
MB INVESTMENTS, INC.; *U.S. Private*, pg. 2623
MBI & PARTNERS U.K. LIMITED; *Int'l*, pg. 4752
MBI PUBLISHING COMPANY LLC—See The Quarto Group, Inc.; *Int'l*, pg. 7677
MBJ CHEMICAL CORPORATION—See Mitsui & Co., Ltd.; *Int'l*, pg. 4974
M.B. JONES OIL COMPANY INC.; *U.S. Private*, pg. 2528
M.B. KAHN CONSTRUCTION CO., INC.; *U.S. Private*, pg. 2528
MBK CO., LTD.; *Int'l*, pg. 4752
MBK LIFE ASSURANCE PLC—See Thanachart Capital PCL; *Int'l*, pg. 7607
MBK NIGERIA LTD.—See Mitsui & Co., Ltd.; *Int'l*, pg. 4973
MBK PARTNERS LTD.; *Int'l*, pg. 4753
MBK PUBLIC COMPANY LIMITED; *Int'l*, pg. 4754
MBK REAL ESTATE LTD.; *U.S. Private*, pg. 2624
MBL ANTRIEBSTECHNIK DEUTSCHLAND GMBH.—See Mitsuboshi Belting Ltd.; *Int'l*, pg. 4972
MBL BEIJING BIOTECH CO., LTD.—See JSR Corp.; *Int'l*, pg. 4014
MBL-BION—See JSR Corp.; *Int'l*, pg. 4014
MB LEASING CORP.—See Mercedes-Benz of Coral Gables; *U.S. Private*, pg. 2668
MBL HANGZHOU BIOTECH CO., LTD.—See JSR Corp.; *Int'l*, pg. 4014
MBL INDUSTRIES LIMITED—See Marico Limited; *Int'l*, pg. 4693
MBL INFRASTRUCTURES LTD; *Int'l*, pg. 4754
MBL INTERNATIONAL CORPORATION—See AESKU.Diagnostics GmbH & Co. KG; *Int'l*, pg. 182
M. BLOCK & SONS, INC.; *U.S. Private*, pg. 2526
MBL SHANGHAI INTERNATIONAL TRADING CO., LTD.—See Mitsuboshi Belting Ltd.; *Int'l*, pg. 4972
MBL TECHNOLOGIES; *U.S. Private*, pg. 2624
MBL (USA) CORPORATION—See Mitsuboshi Belting Ltd.; *Int'l*, pg. 4972
MBL VENTURE CAPITAL CO., LTD.—See JSR Corp.; *Int'l*, pg. 4014
MBM ADVISORS, INC.—See BOK Financial Corporation; *U.S. Public*, pg. 367
MBM CORPORATION; *U.S. Private*, pg. 2624
M&B METAL PRODUCTS CO. INC.; *U.S. Private*, pg. 2524
M&BM EXPRESS OOD—See Osterreichische Post AG; *Int'l*, pg. 5653
MBMI RESOURCES INC.; *Int'l*, pg. 4754
MBM RESOURCES BERHAD; *Int'l*, pg. 4754
MBNA LIMITED—See Bank of America Corporation; *U.S. Public*, pg. 271
MBNA MARKETING SYSTEMS, INC.—See Bank of America Corporation; *U.S. Public*, pg. 271
MBN CORPORATION—See Middlefield Group Limited; *Int'l*, pg. 4884
M&B OF TAMPA INC.—See M&B Products Inc.; *U.S. Private*, pg. 2524

MBM RESOURCES BERHAD

CORPORATE AFFILIATIONS

MBO, LLC—See Waste Connections, Inc.; *Int'l*, pg. 8353
M. BOOTH & ASSOCIATES—See Next 15 Group plc; *Int'l*, pg. 5246
MBO PARTNERS; *U.S. Private*, pg. 2624
MBO POSTPRESS SOLUTIONS GMBH—See Komori Corporation; *Int'l*, pg. 4243
MB PAPELES ESPECIALES S.A.—See Miquel y Costas & Miquel, S.A.; *Int'l*, pg. 4915
MBP BELTING PHIL. CORPORATION; *Int'l*, pg. 4754
MB PETROLEUM DEUTSCHLAND GMBH—See MB Holding Company LLC; *Int'l*, pg. 4750
MB PETROLEUM SERVICES LLC—See MB Holding Company LLC; *Int'l*, pg. 4750
MB PETROLEUM SERVICES LLC—See MB Holding Company LLC; *Int'l*, pg. 4750
MB PETROLEUM SERVICES LLC—See MB Holding Company LLC; *Int'l*, pg. 4750
MB PETROLEUM SERVICES LLC—See MB Holding Company LLC; *Int'l*, pg. 4750
MB PETROLEUM SERVICES LLC—See MB Holding Company LLC; *Int'l*, pg. 4750
MB PETROLEUM SERVICES LTD.—See MB Holding Company LLC; *Int'l*, pg. 4750
MBP (NZ) LTD.—See Mapei SpA; *Int'l*, pg. 4682
M&B PRODUCTS INC.; *U.S. Private*, pg. 2524
MBP SOLUTIONS SDN. BHD.—See TFP Solutions Berhad; *Int'l*, pg. 7587
MB RAHASTOT OY; *Int'l*, pg. 4750
M & B RAILROAD L.L.C.—See Brookfield Infrastructure Partners L.P.; *Int'l*, pg. 1192
M & B RAILROAD L.L.C.—See GIC Pte. Ltd.; *Int'l*, pg. 2966
M-BRAIN AB—See M-Brain Oy; *Int'l*, pg. 4614
M-BRAIN GMBH—See M-Brain Oy; *Int'l*, pg. 4614
M-BRAIN INFORMATION AB—See M-Brain Oy; *Int'l*, pg. 4614
M-BRAIN INFORMATION SDN. BHD.—See M-Brain Oy; *Int'l*, pg. 4614
M-BRAIN INSIGHT OY—See M-Brain Oy; *Int'l*, pg. 4614
M-BRAIN LIMITED—See M-Brain Oy; *Int'l*, pg. 4614
M-BRAIN MEDIA OY—See M-Brain Oy; *Int'l*, pg. 4614
M-BRAIN OY; *Int'l*, pg. 4614
M. BRAUN INCORPORATED—See INDUS Holding AG; *Int'l*, pg. 3663
M. BRAUN-INERTGAS-SYSTEME GMBH—See INDUS Holding AG; *Int'l*, pg. 3663
M. BRAUN INERTGAS SYSTEMS (SHANGHAI) CO. LTD.—See INDUS Holding AG; *Int'l*, pg. 3663
M. BRAUN UK LTD.—See INDUS Holding AG; *Int'l*, pg. 3663
MBR CONSTRUCTION SERVICES INC.—See MBR Construction Services Inc.; *U.S. Private*, pg. 2624
MBR CONSTRUCTION SERVICES INC.; *U.S. Private*, pg. 2624
MB REAL ESTATE; *U.S. Private*, pg. 2624
M.B.R. INDUSTRIES, INC., *U.S. Private*, pg. 2528
MBR MEDICAL BILLING INC.—See Radiation Billing Solutions, Inc.; *U.S. Private*, pg. 3343
MBR TARGETING GMBH—See Stroer SE & Co. KGaA; *Int'l*, pg. 7242
M. BRUENGER & CO., INC.—See Roadrunner Transportation Systems, Inc.; *U.S. Public*, pg. 1802
MBS CORPORATION—See Mandom Corporation; *Int'l*, pg. 4668
MBS DIRECT, LLC—See Barnes & Noble Education, Inc.; *U.S. Public*, pg. 276
MB SECURITIES JOINT STOCK COMPANY—See Military Commercial Joint Stock Bank; *Int'l*, pg. 4895
MB SERVICE JAPAN CO., LTD.—See Kamigumi Co., Ltd.; *Int'l*, pg. 4062
MB SERVICES PTE. LTD—See Meyer Burger Technology AG; *Int'l*, pg. 4869
MB SHIPBROKERS K/S; *Int'l*, pg. 4754
MB SHOP DESIGN AB—See ITAB Shop Concept AB; *Int'l*, pg. 3828
MBS, INC.; *Int'l*, pg. 4754
MBS INSURANCE SERVICES INC.; *U.S. Private*, pg. 2625
MBSL INSURANCE COMPANY LIMITED—See Bank of Ceylon; *Int'l*, pg. 841
MBSL SAVINGS BANK LIMITED—See Bank of Ceylon; *Int'l*, pg. 841
MBS (MANPOWER BUSINESS SOLUTIONS) LTD.—See ManpowerGroup Inc.; *U.S. Public*, pg. 1358
MBS/NET, INC.—See Medsphere Systems Corp.; *U.S. Private*, pg. 2658
MBS NURNBERG GMBH—See Bertelsmann SE & Co. KGaA; *Int'l*, pg. 997
MBS—See Montagne et Neige Developpement SA; *Int'l*, pg. 5035
MBS SYSTEMS, LLC—See Sealaska Corporation; *U.S. Private*, pg. 3585
MBS TEXTBOOK EXCHANGE, LLC—See Barnes & Noble Education, Inc.; *U.S. Public*, pg. 276
MBS VALUE PARTNERS, LLC; *U.S. Private*, pg. 2625
MBS WEST—See Media Buying Services, Inc.; *U.S. Private*, pg. 2651
MB SYSTEMS CO. LTD—See Meyer Burger Technology AG; *Int'l*, pg. 4869

MBT EAST AFRICA LTD.—See REHAU Verwaltungszentrale AG; *Int'l*, pg. 6255
MBTECH AUTO TESTING PROPERTIES LLC—See Adecco Group AG; *Int'l*, pg. 140
MBTECH BOHEMIA S.R.O.—See Adecco Group AG; *Int'l*, pg. 140
MBTECH CONSULTING GMBH—See Adecco Group AG; *Int'l*, pg. 140
MBTECH GROUP GMBH & CO. KGAA—See Adecco Group AG; *Int'l*, pg. 140
MB TECHNOLOGY HOLDINGS, LLC; *U.S. Private*, pg. 2624
MB-TECHNOLOGY NA LLC—See Adecco Group AG; *Int'l*, pg. 140
MBTECH POLSKA SP. Z O.O.—See Adecco Group AG; *Int'l*, pg. 140
MBT EGYPT LTD.—See REHAU Verwaltungszentrale AG; *Int'l*, pg. 6255
MBT (FAR EAST) LTD.—See REHAU Verwaltungszentrale AG; *Int'l*, pg. 6255
MBT INA POLIMER—See REHAU Verwaltungszentrale AG; *Int'l*, pg. 6255
MBT INDIA—See REHAU Verwaltungszentrale AG; *Int'l*, pg. 6255
MBT KUNSTSTOFFE GMBH—See REHAU Verwaltungszentrale AG; *Int'l*, pg. 6255
MBT MARKETING; *U.S. Private*, pg. 2625
MBT PET IMPORT D.O.O.—See REHAU Verwaltungszentrale AG; *Int'l*, pg. 6255
MBT POLSKA SP.Z.O.O.—See REHAU Verwaltungszentrale AG; *Int'l*, pg. 6255
MBT POLYMERS BENELUX N.V.—See REHAU Verwaltungszentrale AG; *Int'l*, pg. 6255
MBT POLYMERS (BULGARIA) D.O.O.—See REHAU Verwaltungszentrale AG; *Int'l*, pg. 6255
MBT POLYMERS GENERAL TRADING LLC—See REHAU Verwaltungszentrale AG; *Int'l*, pg. 6256
MBT POLYMERS GMBH—See REHAU Verwaltungszentrale AG; *Int'l*, pg. 6256
MBT POLYMERS HUNGARY KFT. (LTD.)—See REHAU Verwaltungszentrale AG; *Int'l*, pg. 6256
MBT POLYMERS SRL—See REHAU Verwaltungszentrale AG; *Int'l*, pg. 6256
MBT POLYTAPES GMBH—See REHAU Verwaltungszentrale AG; *Int'l*, pg. 6255
MBTS BROKING SERVICES COMPANY LIMITED—See MS&AD Insurance Group Holdings, Inc.; *Int'l*, pg. 5066
MBT SYSTEMS LTD—See Meyer Burger Technology AG; *Int'l*, pg. 4869
MBT UK—See REHAU Verwaltungszentrale AG; *Int'l*, pg. 6256
M. BURSTEIN CO, INC.—See BMH Corp.; *U.S. Private*, pg. 600
MBV INTERNATIONAL LIMITED; *Int'l*, pg. 4754
MB WEB S.A.S.—See IVS Group S.A.; *Int'l*, pg. 3848
MB WESTFIELD, INC.—See Insight Equity Holdings LLC; *U.S. Private*, pg. 2086
M-B-W INC.; *U.S. Private*, pg. 2525
MBW MATERIALBEWIRTSCHAFTUNG MITHOLZ AG—See Vicat S.A.; *Int'l*, pg. 8186
MBW METALLBEARBEITUNG WERTHEIM GMBH - BAIERSDORF PLANT—See Kurtz Holding GmbH & Co. Beteiligungs KG; *Int'l*, pg. 4343
MBW METALLBEARBEITUNG WERTHEIM GMBH—See Kurtz Holding GmbH & Co. Beteiligungs KG; *Int'l*, pg. 4343
MB WORLD BUILDERS SDN. BHD.—See MB World Group Berhad; *Int'l*, pg. 4751
MB WORLD GROUP BERHAD; *Int'l*, pg. 4751
MBX SYSTEMS—See Berkshire Partners LLC; *U.S. Private*, pg. 534
M&B ZEITSCHRIFTENPRODUKTIONS GMBH; *Int'l*, pg. 4610
MC2 CONSULTING SERVICES, INC.—See The Graham Group, Inc.; *U.S. Private*, pg. 4037
MC2 DESIGN GROUP, INC.—See Lone Fir Consulting, LLC; *U.S. Private*, pg. 2484
MC2 MARKETING INC.—See Mass Connections, Inc.; *U.S. Private*, pg. 2603
MC2 PACIFIC PTY. LTD.—See WSP Global, Inc.; *Int'l*, pg. 8497
MC2 SECURITY INC.; *U.S. Private*, pg. 2625
MC2—See Dominique Dutscher SAS; *Int'l*, pg. 2161
MC2—See MCH Group AG; *Int'l*, pg. 4758
MCABEE CONSTRUCTION, INC.; *U.S. Private*, pg. 2625
MCA COMMUNICATIONS INC.; *U.S. Private*, pg. 2625
MCA COMMUNICATIONS, LLC; *U.S. Private*, pg. 2625
MCAD DESIGN, INC.; *U.S. Private*, pg. 2625
MCAFEE CO., LTD.—See Advent International Corporation; *U.S. Private*, pg. 104
MCAFEE CO., LTD.—See Crosspoint Capital Partners LP; *U.S. Private*, pg. 1107
MCAFEE CO., LTD.—See Permira Advisers LLP; *Int'l*, pg. 5807
MCAFEE HENDERSON SOLUTIONS, INC.—See Alfred Benesch & Company; *U.S. Private*, pg. 165
MCAFEE INSTITUTE, INC.; *U.S. Private*, pg. 2625
MCAFEE INTERNATIONAL BV—See Advent International Corporation; *U.S. Private*, pg. 104

MCAFEE INTERNATIONAL BV—See Crosspoint Capital Partners LP; *U.S. Private*, pg. 1107
MCAFEE INTERNATIONAL BV—See Permira Advisers LLP; *Int'l*, pg. 5807
MCAFEE, LLC—See Advent International Corporation; *U.S. Private*, pg. 104
MCAFEE, LLC—See Crosspoint Capital Partners LP; *U.S. Private*, pg. 1107
MCAFEE, LLC—See Permira Advisers LLP; *Int'l*, pg. 5807
MC AGRI ALLIANCE LTD.—See Mitsubishi Corporation; *Int'l*, pg. 4939
MC AGRO-CHEMICALS CO., LTD.—See Thai Central Chemical Public Company Limited; *Int'l*, pg. 7592
MC&A INC.; *U.S. Private*, pg. 2625
MCAIRLAID'S INC—See McAirlaid's Vliesstoffe GmbH & Co. KG; *Int'l*, pg. 4755
MCAIRLAID'S NORDIC OU—See McAirlaid's Vliesstoffe GmbH & Co. KG; *Int'l*, pg. 4755
MCAIRLAID'S VLIESSTOFFE GMBH & CO. KG; *Int'l*, pg. 4755
MCALESTER NEWS-CAPITAL & DEMOCRAT—See The Retirement Systems of Alabama; *U.S. Private*, pg. 4105
MCALISTER DESIGN, INC.—See Wauseon Machine and Manufacturing, Inc.; *U.S. Private*, pg. 4457
MCALISTER ENGINEERING SDN BHD—See Yanlord Land Group Limited; *Int'l*, pg. 8562
MCALISTER'S CORPORATION—See Roark Capital Group Inc.; *U.S. Private*, pg. 3455
MCALISTER'S DELI—See Four Corners Property Trust, Inc.; *U.S. Public*, pg. 875
MCALLEN HEART HOSPITAL, L.P.—See Universal Health Services, Inc.; *U.S. Public*, pg. 2258
MCALLEN MEDICAL CENTER—See Universal Health Services, Inc.; *U.S. Public*, pg. 2260
M. CALL, S.A.—See APG Asset Management NV; *Int'l*, pg. 512
M. CALL, S.A.—See National Pension Service of Korea; *Int'l*, pg. 5162
M. CALL, S.A.—See Swiss Life Holding; *Int'l*, pg. 7369
MCALPINE FORD LINCOLN SALES; *Int'l*, pg. 4755
M, C & A MEDIAVEST—See Publicis Groupe S.A.; *Int'l*, pg. 6111
MCANALLY WILKINS LLC—See Stone Point Capital LLC; *U.S. Private*, pg. 3819
MCANINCH CORPORATION; *U.S. Private*, pg. 2625
MCAN MORTGAGE CORPORATION; *Int'l*, pg. 4755
MCAP EUROPE LIMITED—See Mitsubishi Corporation; *Int'l*, pg. 4939
MCAP INC; *Int'l*, pg. 4755
M.CAPITAL, S.A.—See Sacyr, S.A.; *Int'l*, pg. 6466
MCARA PRINTING—See Canadian Bank Note Company Limited; *Int'l*, pg. 1282
MCARDLE LTD.; *U.S. Private*, pg. 2625
MCARDLE PRINTING CO., INC.—See Bloomberg L.P.; *U.S. Private*, pg. 584
MCARE SOLUTIONS, LLC—See New Mountain Capital, LLC; *U.S. Private*, pg. 2904
MCARTHUR DAIRY, LLC—See Dean Foods Company; *U.S. Private*, pg. 1183
MCARTHUR FARMS, INC.; *U.S. Private*, pg. 2625
MCARTHUR RIVER MINING PTY. LTD.—See Glencore plc; *Int'l*, pg. 2991
MCA SOLUTIONS BVBA—See PTC Inc.; *U.S. Public*, pg. 1734
MCASPHALT INDUSTRIES LIMITED—See Bouygues S.A.; *Int'l*, pg. 1122
MCASPHALT, LLC—See Natural Resource Partners L.P.; *U.S. Public*, pg. 1499
M. CASSAB COM. IND. LTDA—See Husqvarna AB; *Int'l*, pg. 3539
M-CAST, INC—See Mitsubishi HC Capital Inc.; *Int'l*, pg. 4951
MC AUTOS DEL PERU, S.A.—See Mitsubishi Corporation; *Int'l*, pg. 4939
MC AVIATION PARTNERS INC.—See Mitsubishi Corporation; *Int'l*, pg. 4939
M C BANCSHARES, INC.; *U.S. Private*, pg. 2523
MC BANK RUS JSC; *Int'l*, pg. 4755
M C BANK & TRUST COMPANY—See M C Bancshares, Inc.; *U.S. Private*, pg. 2523
MCB-ARIF HABIB SAVINGS AND INVESMENTS LIMITED—See MCB Bank Limited; *Int'l*, pg. 4755
MCB - ARIF HABIB SAVINGS & INVESTMENTS LIMITED—See MCB Bank Limited; *Int'l*, pg. 4755
MCBARSCOT COMPANY; *U.S. Private*, pg. 2625
MCB BANK LIMITED; *Int'l*, pg. 4755
MCB CAPITAL PARTNERS LTD—See The Mauritius Commercial Bank Ltd.; *Int'l*, pg. 7665
MCB CONSULTING SERVICES LTD—See The Mauritius Commercial Bank Ltd.; *Int'l*, pg. 7665
MCBEE ASSOCIATES INC.—See GI Manager L.P.; *U.S. Private*, pg. 1693
MCBEE ASSOCIATES INC.—See TA Associates, Inc.; *U.S. Private*, pg. 3916
MCBEE OPERATING COMPANY LLC; *U.S. Private*, pg. 2625
MCBEE STRATEGIC CONSULTING, LLC—See Wiley Rein LLP; *U.S. Private*, pg. 4520

COMPANY NAME INDEX

MCB FACTORS LTD—See The Mauritius Commercial Bank Ltd.; *Int'l*, pg. 7665
MCB INVESTMENT MANAGEMENT CO. LTD—See The Mauritius Commercial Bank Ltd.; *Int'l*, pg. 7666
MCB ISLAMIC BANK LIMITED—See MCB Bank Limited; *Int'l*, pg. 4755
MC BITOR LIMITED—See Petroleos de Venezuela S.A.; *Int'l*, pg. 5828
MCB (MALDIVES) PRIVATE LTD—See The Mauritius Commercial Bank Ltd.; *Int'l*, pg. 7665
MCB NON-BANK CREDIT ORGANISATION CLOSED JOINT STOCK COMPANY—See MCB Bank Limited; *Int'l*, pg. 4755
MCB NON-BANK CREDIT ORGANIZATION CLOSED JOINT STOCK COMPANY—See MCB Bank Limited; *Int'l*, pg. 4755
MCB PROPERTIES LTD—See The Mauritius Commercial Bank Ltd.; *Int'l*, pg. 7666
MCBRAYER INSURANCE CENTER—See Platte Valley Financial Service Companies Inc.; *U.S. Private*, pg. 3211
MCB REGISTRY & SECURITIES LIMITED—See The Mauritius Commercial Bank Ltd.; *Int'l*, pg. 7666
MCBRIDE AUSTRALIA PTY. LTD.—See McBride plc; *Int'l*, pg. 4755
MCBRIDE (CARIBBEAN) LIMITED—See Goddard Enterprises Limited; *Int'l*, pg. 3019
MCBRIDE CONSTRUCTION RESOURCES, INC.; *U.S. Private*, pg. 2625
MCBRIDE DENMARK A/S—See McBride plc; *Int'l*, pg. 4756
MCBRIDE DOOR & HARDWARE, INC.—See Platinum Equity, LLC; *U.S. Private*, pg. 3209
MCBRIDE ELECTRIC INC.; *U.S. Private*, pg. 2625
MCBRIDE HONG KONG HOLDINGS LIMITED—See McBride plc; *Int'l*, pg. 4756
MCBRIDE MALAYSIA SDN. BHD.—See McBride plc; *Int'l*, pg. 4756
MCBRIDE PLC - BARROW FACTORY—See McBride plc; *Int'l*, pg. 4756
MCBRIDE PLC - BURNLEY FACTORY—See McBride plc; *Int'l*, pg. 4756
MCBRIDE PLC - ESTAIMPUIS FACTORY—See McBride plc; *Int'l*, pg. 4756
MCBRIDE PLC - FOETZ FACTORY—See McBride plc; *Int'l*, pg. 4756
MCBRIDE PLC - HULL FACTORY—See McBride plc; *Int'l*, pg. 4756
MCBRIDE PLC - IEPER PERSONAL CARE FACTORY—See 3i Group plc; *Int'l*, pg. 9
MCBRIDE PLC - MIDDLETON FACTORY—See McBride plc; *Int'l*, pg. 4756
MCBRIDE PLC - MOYAUX FACTORY—See McBride plc; *Int'l*, pg. 4756
MCBRIDE PLC - ROSPORDEN FACTORY—See McBride plc; *Int'l*, pg. 4756
MCBRIDE PLC; *Int'l*, pg. 4755
MCBRIDE PLC - ST. HELENS FACTORY—See McBride plc; *Int'l*, pg. 4756
MCBRIDE S.A.—See McBride plc; *Int'l*, pg. 4756
MCBRIDE S.A.S.—See McBride plc; *Int'l*, pg. 4756
MCBRIDE S.A.U.—See McBride plc; *Int'l*, pg. 4756
MCBRIDE & SON ENTERPRISES INC.; *U.S. Private*, pg. 2625
MCBRYDE RESOURCES, INC.—See Alexander & Baldwin, Inc.; *U.S. Public*, pg. 75
MCB SEYCHELLES LTD—See The Mauritius Commercial Bank Ltd.; *Int'l*, pg. 7666
MCB STOCKBROKERS LIMITED—See The Mauritius Commercial Bank Ltd.; *Int'l*, pg. 7666
THE MCBURNEY CORPORATION; *U.S. Private*, pg. 4076
MC BUSINESS SUPPORT, LTD.—See Mitsui Chemicals, Inc.; *Int'l*, pg. 4981
MCCABE HAMILTON & RENNY COMPANY LTD.—See JBG Corporation; *U.S. Private*, pg. 2193
MCCAFFERTY FORD SALES INC.; *U.S. Private*, pg. 2626
MCCAIN ALIMENTAIRE S.A.—See McCain Foods Limited; *Int'l*, pg. 4756
MCCAIN ALIMENTARI (ITALIA) SRL—See McCain Foods Limited; *Int'l*, pg. 4756
MCCAIN ARGENTINA S.A.—See McCain Foods Limited; *Int'l*, pg. 4756
MCCAIN BINDERY SYSTEMS, INC.—See Numerical Concepts, Inc.; *U.S. Private*, pg. 2973
MCCAIN-ELLIOS FOOD INC.—See McCain Foods Limited; *Int'l*, pg. 4757
MCCAIN ESPANA S.A. (SPAIN)—See McCain Foods Limited; *Int'l*, pg. 4756
MCCAIN FERTILIZERS—See McCain Foods Limited; *Int'l*, pg. 4756
MCCAIN FOODS (CANADA) INC.—See McCain Foods Limited; *Int'l*, pg. 4756
MCCAIN FOODS DENMARK—See McCain Foods Limited; *Int'l*, pg. 4756
MCCAIN FOODS (GB) LIMITED—See McCain Foods Limited; *Int'l*, pg. 4756
MCCAIN FOODS GMBH—See McCain Foods Limited; *Int'l*, pg. 4756

MCCAIN FOODS HOLLAND B.V.—See McCain Foods Limited; *Int'l*, pg. 4757
MCCAIN FOODS (INDIA) PVT. LTD.—See McCain Foods Limited; *Int'l*, pg. 4756
MCCAIN FOODS (JAPAN) LIMITED—See McCain Foods Limited; *Int'l*, pg. 4756
MCCAIN FOODS LIMITED; *Int'l*, pg. 4756
MCCAIN FOODS NORDIC—See McCain Foods Limited; *Int'l*, pg. 4757
MCCAIN FOODS USA INC.—See McCain Foods Limited; *Int'l*, pg. 4757
MCCAIN FOODS USA INC.—See McCain Foods Limited; *Int'l*, pg. 4757
MCCAIN FOODS USA—See McCain Foods Limited; *Int'l*, pg. 4757
MCCAIN GMBH (GERMANY)—See McCain Foods Limited; *Int'l*, pg. 4757
MCCAIN, INC.—See SWARCO AG; *Int'l*, pg. 7361
MCCAIN POLAND SP Z.O.O.—See McCain Foods Limited; *Int'l*, pg. 4757
MCCAIN PORTUGAL LDA.—See McCain Foods Limited; *Int'l*, pg. 4757
MCCAIN SNACK FOODS—See McCain Foods Limited; *Int'l*, pg. 4757
MCCALL & ALMY, INC.—See Newmark Group, Inc.; *U.S. Public*, pg. 1515
MCCALL-F, INC.—See Group 1 Automotive, Inc.; *U.S. Public*, pg. 971
MCCALL HANDLING CO.; *U.S. Private*, pg. 2626
MCCALLIE ASSOCIATES INC.—See Afognak Native Corporation; *U.S. Private*, pg. 124
MCCALLION STAFFING; *U.S. Private*, pg. 2626
MCCALL LIMITED—See Empresaria Group Plc; *Int'l*, pg. 2389
MCCALL OIL & CHEMICAL CORP.; *U.S. Private*, pg. 2626
THE MCCALL PATTERN COMPANY, INC.—See IG Design Group Plc; *Int'l*, pg. 3600
MCCALL PATTERN COMPANY LIMITED—See IG Design Group Plc; *Int'l*, pg. 3600
MCCALLS INC.; *U.S. Private*, pg. 2626
MCCALL-THOMAS ENGINEERING COMPANY, INC.; *U.S. Private*, pg. 2626
MCCALL-TII, INC.—See Group 1 Automotive, Inc.; *U.S. Public*, pg. 971
MCCALLUM GROUP, LLC—See Acadia Healthcare Company, Inc.; *U.S. Public*, pg. 29
MCCALL WINERIES & DISTILLERS—See E. & J. Gallo Winery; *U.S. Private*, pg. 1303
MCCAMBRIDGE LIMITED; *Int'l*, pg. 4757
MCCAMLY PLAZA HOTEL—See Grand Heritage Hotel Group, LLC; *U.S. Private*, pg. 1752
MCCANN AS—See The Interpublic Group of Companies, Inc.; *U.S. Public*, pg. 2099
MCCANN ERICKSON ADVERTISING LTD.—See The Interpublic Group of Companies, Inc.; *U.S. Public*, pg. 2100
MCCANN ERICKSON ADVERTISING PTY. LTD. - BRISBANE—See The Interpublic Group of Companies, Inc.; *U.S. Public*, pg. 2100
MCCANN ERICKSON ADVERTISING PTY. LTD. - MELBOURNE—See The Interpublic Group of Companies, Inc.; *U.S. Public*, pg. 2100
MCCANN ERICKSON ADVERTISING PTY. LTD.—See The Interpublic Group of Companies, Inc.; *U.S. Public*, pg. 2100
MCCANN ERICKSON ATHENS—See The Interpublic Group of Companies, Inc.; *U.S. Public*, pg. 2100
MCCANN ERICKSON AZERBAIJAN—See The Interpublic Group of Companies, Inc.; *U.S. Public*, pg. 2099
MCCANN ERICKSON BRAND COMMUNICATIONS AGENCY—See The Interpublic Group of Companies, Inc.; *U.S. Public*, pg. 2100
MCCANN ERICKSON BRISTOL—See The Interpublic Group of Companies, Inc.; *U.S. Public*, pg. 2100
MCCANN ERICKSON BUDAPEST—See The Interpublic Group of Companies, Inc.; *U.S. Public*, pg. 2099
MCCANN ERICKSON CAMEROON—See The Interpublic Group of Companies, Inc.; *U.S. Public*, pg. 2099
MCCANN-ERICKSON CENTRAL LIMITED—See The Interpublic Group of Companies, Inc.; *U.S. Public*, pg. 2102
MCCANN ERICKSON CENTRAL—See The Interpublic Group of Companies, Inc.; *U.S. Public*, pg. 2099
MCCANN ERICKSON CENTROAMERICANA (COSTA RICA) S.A.—See The Interpublic Group of Companies, Inc.; *U.S. Public*, pg. 2100
MCCANN ERICKSON CENTROAMERICANA (HONDURAS) S. DE R.L.—See The Interpublic Group of Companies, Inc.; *U.S. Public*, pg. 2100
MCCANN ERICKSON COMMUNICATIONS GROUP—See The Interpublic Group of Companies, Inc.; *U.S. Public*, pg. 2100
MCCANN ERICKSON COMMUNICATIONS HOUSE M.E.C.H.—See The Interpublic Group of Companies, Inc.; *U.S. Public*, pg. 2100
MCCANN ERICKSON CORP. PUBLICIDAD S.A.—See The Interpublic Group of Companies, Inc.; *U.S. Public*, pg. 2099

MCCANN ERICKSON CORP. PUBLICIDAD S.A.—See The Interpublic Group of Companies, Inc.; *U.S. Public*, pg. 2100
MCCANN ERICKSON CORP. S.A.—See The Interpublic Group of Companies, Inc.; *U.S. Public*, pg. 2100
MCCANN ERICKSON CORP. (S.A.)—See The Interpublic Group of Companies, Inc.; *U.S. Public*, pg. 2102
MCCANN-ERICKSON DEUTSCHLAND GMBH & CO MANAGEMENT PROPERTY KG—See The Interpublic Group of Companies, Inc.; *U.S. Public*, pg. 2102
MCCANN ERICKSON DEUTSCHLAND GMBH—See The Interpublic Group of Companies, Inc.; *U.S. Public*, pg. 2099
MCCANN ERICKSON DEUTSCHLAND—See The Interpublic Group of Companies, Inc.; *U.S. Public*, pg. 2100
MCCANN ERICKSON DUBLIN—See The Interpublic Group of Companies, Inc.; *U.S. Public*, pg. 2100
MCCANN ERICKSON EL SALVADOR—See The Interpublic Group of Companies, Inc.; *U.S. Public*, pg. 2101
MCCANN ERICKSON GEORGIA—See The Interpublic Group of Companies, Inc.; *U.S. Public*, pg. 2099
MCCANN ERICKSON GESELLSCHAFT M.B.H.—See The Interpublic Group of Companies, Inc.; *U.S. Public*, pg. 2101
MCCANN ERICKSON GROUP—See The Interpublic Group of Companies, Inc.; *U.S. Public*, pg. 2099
MCCANN ERICKSON GUANGMING LTD.—See The Interpublic Group of Companies, Inc.; *U.S. Public*, pg. 2099
MCCANN ERICKSON GUANGMING LTD.—See The Interpublic Group of Companies, Inc.; *U.S. Public*, pg. 2099
MCCANN ERICKSON HONG KONG LTD.—See The Interpublic Group of Companies, Inc.; *U.S. Public*, pg. 2101
MCCANN ERICKSON/HORA—See The Interpublic Group of Companies, Inc.; *U.S. Public*, pg. 2101
MCCANN ERICKSON, INC.—See The Interpublic Group of Companies, Inc.; *U.S. Public*, pg. 2101
MCCANN ERICKSON INC.—See The Interpublic Group of Companies, Inc.; *U.S. Public*, pg. 2101
MCCANN ERICKSON INDIA—See The Interpublic Group of Companies, Inc.; *U.S. Public*, pg. 2099
MCCANN ERICKSON INDIA—See The Interpublic Group of Companies, Inc.; *U.S. Public*, pg. 2099
MCCANN ERICKSON INDIA—See The Interpublic Group of Companies, Inc.; *U.S. Public*, pg. 2099
MCCANN ERICKSON ITALIANA S.P.A.—See The Interpublic Group of Companies, Inc.; *U.S. Public*, pg. 2101
MCCANN ERICKSON ITALIANA S.P.A.—See The Interpublic Group of Companies, Inc.; *U.S. Public*, pg. 2101
MCCANN ERICKSON (JAMAICA) LTD.—See The Interpublic Group of Companies, Inc.; *U.S. Public*, pg. 2099
MCCANN ERICKSON JAPAN INC.—See The Interpublic Group of Companies, Inc.; *U.S. Public*, pg. 2101
MCCANN ERICKSON KAZAKHSTAN—See The Interpublic Group of Companies, Inc.; *U.S. Public*, pg. 2099
MCCANN ERICKSON (KENYA) LTD.—See The Interpublic Group of Companies, Inc.; *U.S. Public*, pg. 2101
MCCANN ERICKSON/LOS ANGELES—See The Interpublic Group of Companies, Inc.; *U.S. Public*, pg. 2102
MCCANN ERICKSON MACEDONIA—See The Interpublic Group of Companies, Inc.; *U.S. Public*, pg. 2099
MCCANN ERICKSON (MALAYSIA) SDN. BHD.—See The Interpublic Group of Companies, Inc.; *U.S. Public*, pg. 2100
MCCANN ERICKSON MEXICO—See The Interpublic Group of Companies, Inc.; *U.S. Public*, pg. 2100
MCCANN ERICKSON (NEDERLAND) B.V.—See The Interpublic Group of Companies, Inc.; *U.S. Public*, pg. 2100
MCCANN ERICKSON/NEW YORK—See The Interpublic Group of Companies, Inc.; *U.S. Public*, pg. 2102
MCCANN ERICKSON NORTH AMERICA—See The Interpublic Group of Companies, Inc.; *U.S. Public*, pg. 2102
MCCANN ERICKSON PARIS—See The Interpublic Group of Companies, Inc.; *U.S. Public*, pg. 2101
MCCANN ERICKSON (PERU) PUBLICIDAD S.A.—See The Interpublic Group of Companies, Inc.; *U.S. Public*, pg. 2100
MCCANN ERICKSON PRAGUE—See The Interpublic Group of Companies, Inc.; *U.S. Public*, pg. 2099
MCCANN ERICKSON PUBLICIDADE LTDA.—See The Interpublic Group of Companies, Inc.; *U.S. Public*, pg. 2100
MCCANN ERICKSON PUBLICIDAD—See The Interpublic Group of Companies, Inc.; *U.S. Public*, pg. 2099
MCCANN ERICKSON RIGA—See The Interpublic Group of Companies, Inc.; *U.S. Public*, pg. 2099
MCCANN ERICKSON ROMANIA—See The Interpublic Group of Companies, Inc.; *U.S. Public*, pg. 2099
MCCANN ERICKSON S.A. DE PUBLICIDAD—See The Interpublic Group of Companies, Inc.; *U.S. Public*, pg. 2101
MCCANN ERICKSON/SALT LAKE CITY—See The Interpublic Group of Companies, Inc.; *U.S. Public*, pg. 2101
MCCANN ERICKSON SARAJEVO—See The Interpublic Group of Companies, Inc.; *U.S. Public*, pg. 2099
MCCANN ERICKSON S.A.—See The Interpublic Group of Companies, Inc.; *U.S. Public*, pg. 2101
MCCANN ERICKSON SEATTLE—See The Interpublic Group of Companies, Inc.; *U.S. Public*, pg. 2102

MCCANN ERICKSON (SINGAPORE) PRIVATE LIMITED—See The Interpublic Group of Companies, Inc.; *U.S. Public*, pg. 2099
MCCANN ERICKSON SOFIA—See The Interpublic Group of Companies, Inc.; *U.S. Public*, pg. 2099
MCCANN ERICKSON—See The Interpublic Group of Companies, Inc.; *U.S. Public*, pg. 2099
MCCANN ERICKSON—See The Interpublic Group of Companies, Inc.; *U.S. Public*, pg. 2099
MCCANN ERICKSON—See The Interpublic Group of Companies, Inc.; *U.S. Public*, pg. 2100
MCCANN ERICKSON—See The Interpublic Group of Companies, Inc.; *U.S. Public*, pg. 2102
MCCANN ERICKSON / SP—See The Interpublic Group of Companies, Inc.; *U.S. Public*, pg. 2100
MCCANN ERICKSON SWITZERLAND—See The Interpublic Group of Companies, Inc.; *U.S. Public*, pg. 2101
MCCANN ERICKSON (TRINIDAD) LTD.—See The Interpublic Group of Companies, Inc.; *U.S. Public*, pg. 2100
MCCANN ERICKSON URUGUAY—See The Interpublic Group of Companies, Inc.; *U.S. Public*, pg. 2101
MCCANN-ERICKSON USA, INC.—See The Interpublic Group of Companies, Inc.; *U.S. Public*, pg. 2102
MCCANN ERICKSON UZBEKISTAN/TASHKENT—See The Interpublic Group of Companies, Inc.; *U.S. Public*, pg. 2099
MCCANN ERICKSON VIETNAM—See The Interpublic Group of Companies, Inc.; *U.S. Public*, pg. 2099
MCCANN ERICKSON WORLDGROUP/PANAMA, S.A.—See The Interpublic Group of Companies, Inc.; *U.S. Public*, pg. 2099
MCCANN ERICKSON WORLDGROUP TURKEY—See The Interpublic Group of Companies, Inc.; *U.S. Public*, pg. 2101
MCCANN ERICKSON WORLDWIDE—See The Interpublic Group of Companies, Inc.; *U.S. Public*, pg. 2099
MCCANN HEALTHCARE MELBOURNE—See The Interpublic Group of Companies, Inc.; *U.S. Public*, pg. 2101
MCCANN HEALTHCARE—See The Interpublic Group of Companies, Inc.; *U.S. Public*, pg. 2100
MCCANN HEALTHCARE SYDNEY—See The Interpublic Group of Companies, Inc.; *U.S. Public*, pg. 2101
MCCANN HEALTH SINGAPORE—See The Interpublic Group of Companies, Inc.; *U.S. Public*, pg. 2101
MCCANN HELSINKI—See The Interpublic Group of Companies, Inc.; *U.S. Public*, pg. 2101
MCCANN INDUSTRIES INC.; *U.S. Private*, pg. 2626
MCCANN JOHANNESBURG—See The Interpublic Group of Companies, Inc.; *U.S. Public*, pg. 2101
MCCANN MANCHESTER LIMITED—See The Interpublic Group of Companies, Inc.; *U.S. Public*, pg. 2101
MCCANN MANCHESTER LTD.—See The Interpublic Group of Companies, Inc.; *U.S. Public*, pg. 2100
MCCANN PLASTICS LLC—See HEXPOL AB; *Int'l*, pg. 3372
MCCANN WORLDGROUP INDONESIA—See The Interpublic Group of Companies, Inc.; *U.S. Public*, pg. 2101
MCCANN WORLDGROUP, LLC—See The Interpublic Group of Companies, Inc.; *U.S. Public*, pg. 2097
MCCANN WORLDGROUP PHILIPPINES, INC.—See The Interpublic Group of Companies, Inc.; *U.S. Public*, pg. 2101
MCCANN WORLDGROUP (SINGAPORE) PTE LTD—See The Interpublic Group of Companies, Inc.; *U.S. Public*, pg. 2101
MCCANN WORLDGROUP—See The Interpublic Group of Companies, Inc.; *U.S. Public*, pg. 2101
MCCANN WORLDGROUP—See The Interpublic Group of Companies, Inc.; *U.S. Public*, pg. 2102
MCCANN WORLDGROUP SOUTH AFRICA (PTY) LTD—See The Interpublic Group of Companies, Inc.; *U.S. Public*, pg. 2102
MCCANN WORLDGROUP THAILAND—See The Interpublic Group of Companies, Inc.; *U.S. Public*, pg. 2101
MCCANN YEREVAN—See The Interpublic Group of Companies, Inc.; *U.S. Public*, pg. 2102
MC CAPITAL INC.—See Mitsubishi Corporation; *Int'l*, pg. 4939
MCCARL'S, INC.—See Riverstone Holdings LLC; *U.S. Private*, pg. 3447
THE MCCARRON GROUP; *U.S. Private*, pg. 4076
MCCARTER & ENGLISH LLP; *U.S. Private*, pg. 2626
MCCARTHY AUTO GROUP; *U.S. Private*, pg. 2626
MCCARTHY BUILDING COMPANIES, INC. - CENTRAL DIVISION—See McCarthy Holdings, Inc.; *U.S. Private*, pg. 2627
MCCARTHY BUILDING COMPANIES, INC. - NEVADA/UTAH DIVISION—See McCarthy Holdings, Inc.; *U.S. Private*, pg. 2627
MCCARTHY BUILDING COMPANIES, INC. - NORTHERN PACIFIC DIVISION-SACRAMENTO—See McCarthy Holdings, Inc.; *U.S. Private*, pg. 2627
MCCARTHY BUILDING COMPANIES, INC. - NORTHERN PACIFIC DIVISION—See McCarthy Holdings, Inc.; *U.S. Private*, pg. 2627
MCCARTHY BUILDING COMPANIES, INC.—See McCarthy Holdings, Inc.; *U.S. Private*, pg. 2627
MCCARTHY BUILDING COMPANIES, INC. - SOUTHEAST DIVISION—See McCarthy Holdings, Inc.; *U.S. Private*, pg. 2627
MCCARTHY BUILDING COMPANIES, INC. - SOUTHERN CALIFORNIA DIVISION—See McCarthy Holdings, Inc.; *U.S. Private*, pg. 2627
MCCARTHY BUILDING COMPANIES, INC. - SOUTHWEST DIVISION—See McCarthy Holdings, Inc.; *U.S. Private*, pg. 2627
MCCARTHY BUILDING COMPANIES, INC. - TEXAS DIVISION—See McCarthy Holdings, Inc.; *U.S. Private*, pg. 2627
MCCARTHY BUSH CORPORATION; *U.S. Private*, pg. 2626
MCCARTHY CAPITAL CORPORATION—See McCarthy Group, LLC; *U.S. Private*, pg. 2627
MCCARTHY FORD INC.—See Harold Zeigler Auto Group, Inc.; *U.S. Private*, pg. 1867
MCCARTHY GROUP, LLC; *U.S. Private*, pg. 2626
MCCARTHY HOLDINGS, INC.; *U.S. Private*, pg. 2627
MCCARTHY HYUNDAI; *U.S. Private*, pg. 2627
MCCARTHY IMPROVEMENT COMPANY—See McCarthy Bush Corporation; *U.S. Private*, pg. 2626
MCCARTHY LIMITED—See The Bidvest Group Limited; *Int'l*, pg. 7625
MCCARTHY & STONE (DEVELOPMENTS) LTD.—See Lloyds Banking Group plc; *Int'l*, pg. 4537
MCCARTHY TIRE AND AUTOMOTIVE CENTER—See McCarthy Tire Service Company; *U.S. Private*, pg. 2628
MCCARTHY TIRE SERVICE COMPANY; *U.S. Private*, pg. 2627
MCCARTNEY CONSTRUCTION CO. INC.—See Vulcan Materials Company; *U.S. Public*, pg. 2314
MCCARTY CONSTRUCTION INC.; *U.S. Private*, pg. 2628
MCCARTY CORPORATION; *U.S. Private*, pg. 2628
MCCARTY EQUIPMENT CO., LTD.—See Clayton, Dubilier & Rice, LLC; *U.S. Private*, pg. 926
MCCARTY-HULL INC.; *U.S. Private*, pg. 2628
MCCAULEY LUMBER COMPANY INCORPORATED; *U.S. Private*, pg. 2628
MCCAULEY PROPELLER SYSTEMS—See Textron Inc.; *U.S. Public*, pg. 2028
MCCAULOU'S, INC.; *U.S. Private*, pg. 2628
MCC COMPOSITE PRODUCTS CO., LTD.—See Mitsubishi Chemical Group Corporation; *Int'l*, pg. 4931
MCC CONTRACTS (PTY) LIMITED—See eXtract Group Limited; *Int'l*, pg. 2592
MCC ELECTRIC, L.L.C.—See The MCC Group, LLC; *U.S. Private*, pg. 4076
MCC ENERGY PLC; *Int'l*, pg. 4756
MCCF—See VINCI S.A.; *Int'l*, pg. 8234
MCC GLOBAL NV; *Int'l*, pg. 4756
MCCGRAPHICS S. COOP.—See Mondragon Corporation; *Int'l*, pg. 5031
THE MCC GROUP, LLC; *U.S. Private*, pg. 4076
MCCHIP RESOURCES INC.; *Int'l*, pg. 4757
MCCHORD PIPELINE COMPANY—See Par Pacific Holdings, Inc.; *U.S. Public*, pg. 1636
MCCI, LLC—See Century Park Capital Partners, LLC; *U.S. Private*, pg. 834
MCC INCORPORATED; *U.S. Private*, pg. 2626
MCC INDUSTRY COMPANY LIMITED—See Chori Co., Ltd.; *Int'l*, pg. 1583
MCC INTERNATIONAL, INC.; *U.S. Private*, pg. 2626
MCC INVESTMENT SA.—See Enka Insaat ve Sanayi A.S.; *Int'l*, pg. 2440
MCCLAIN INTERNATIONAL, INC.—See HEICO Corporation; *U.S. Public*, pg. 1020
MCCLAINS RV INC.; *U.S. Private*, pg. 2628
MCCLANCY SEASONING CO.; *U.S. Private*, pg. 2628
MCCLARIN PLASTICS, LLC; *U.S. Private*, pg. 2628
MCCLASKEY ENTERPRISES; *U.S. Private*, pg. 2628
THE MCCLATCHY COMPANY—See Chatham Asset Management, LLC; *U.S. Private*, pg. 866
MCCLATCHY INTERACTIVE—See Chatham Asset Management, LLC; *U.S. Private*, pg. 866
MCCLATCHY MANAGEMENT SERVICES, INC.—See Chatham Asset Management, LLC; *U.S. Private*, pg. 866
MCCLATCHY NEWSPAPERS, INC.—See Chatham Asset Management, LLC; *U.S. Private*, pg. 866
MCCLATCHY NEWSPRINT COMPANY—See Chatham Asset Management, LLC; *U.S. Private*, pg. 867
MCCLATCHY SHARED SERVICES, INC.—See Chatham Asset Management, LLC; *U.S. Private*, pg. 867
MCCLATCHY-TRIBUNE INFORMATION SERVICES—See Chatham Asset Management, LLC; *U.S. Private*, pg. 867
MCCLATCHY-TRIBUNE INFORMATION SERVICES—See Tribune Publishing Company; *U.S. Private*, pg. 4228
MCCLEARY INC.; *U.S. Private*, pg. 2628
MCCLELLAND HEALTH SYSTEMS; *U.S. Private*, pg. 2628
MCCLELLAND & HINE—See AmWINS Group, Inc.; *U.S. Private*, pg. 270
MCCLELLAND OILFIELD RENTALS LIMITED; *Int'l*, pg. 4757
MCCLELLAN WHEATON CHEVROLET BUICK GMC LTD.; *Int'l*, pg. 4757
MCCLENAHAN BRUER COMMUNICATIONS; *U.S. Private*, pg. 2628
MCCLENDON, LLC—See BAE Systems plc; *Int'l*, pg. 797
MCCLENDON RESOURCES INC.; *U.S. Private*, pg. 2628
MCCLESKEY MILLS, INC.—See Temasek Holdings (Private) Limited; *Int'l*, pg. 7549
MCCLINTOCK ELECTRIC, INC.; *U.S. Private*, pg. 2628
MCCLONE CONSTRUCTION COMPANY, INC.; *U.S. Private*, pg. 2628
MCCLONE CONSTRUCTION COMPANY-NORTHWEST REGIONAL OFFICE—See McClone Construction Company, Inc.; *U.S. Private*, pg. 2628
MCCLONE CONSTRUCTION COMPANY-SOUTHWEST REGIONAL OFFICE—See McClone Construction Company, Inc.; *U.S. Private*, pg. 2628
MCCLOSKEY INTERNATIONAL LIMITED—See Valmet Oyj; *Int'l*, pg. 8118
MCCLOSKEY INTERNATIONAL LTD.—See Metso Oyj; *Int'l*, pg. 4865
MCCLOSKEY MOTORS INC.; *U.S. Private*, pg. 2628
MCCLOSKEY SURPLUS & EXCESS, INC.—See Arthur J. Gallagher & Co.; *U.S. Public*, pg. 207
MCCLUNG-LOGAN EQUIPMENT COMPANY, INC.; *U.S. Private*, pg. 2628
MCCLURE ASSOCIATES INC.; *U.S. Private*, pg. 2629
MCCLURE COMPANY—See Riverstone Holdings LLC; *U.S. Private*, pg. 3447
MCCLURE ENGINEERING CO.; *U.S. Private*, pg. 2629
MCCLURE OIL CORPORATION; *U.S. Private*, pg. 2629
MCCLURE PROPERTIES LTD.; *U.S. Private*, pg. 2629
MCCLURE & ZIMMERMAN—See J.W. Jung Seed Company; *U.S. Private*, pg. 2172
MCCLUSKEY CHEVROLET INC.; *U.S. Private*, pg. 2629
MCCLYMONDS SUPPLY & TRANSIT CO. INC.; *U.S. Private*, pg. 2629
MCC MAGAZINES, LLC—See Shivers Trading & Operating Company; *U.S. Private*, pg. 3638
MCC MECHANICAL LLC—See The MCC Group, LLC; *U.S. Private*, pg. 4076
MCC MECHANICAL OF THE CAROLINAS, L.L.C. - BENNER & FIELDS DIVISION—See The MCC Group, LLC; *U.S. Private*, pg. 4076
MCC MECHANICAL OF THE CAROLINAS, L.L.C.—See The MCC Group, LLC; *U.S. Private*, pg. 4076
MCC MEILI CLOUD COMPUTING INDUSTRY INVESTMENT CO., LTD.; *Int'l*, pg. 4756
MCC-NORWAY, LLC—See Platinum Equity, LLC; *U.S. Private*, pg. 3206
MCCOLLA ENTERPRISES LTD.; *U.S. Private*, pg. 2629
MCCOLLISTER MOVING & STORAGE OF NEW YORK—See McCollister's Transportation Group Inc.; *U.S. Private*, pg. 2629
MCCOLLISTER'S TRANSPORTATION GROUP INC.; *U.S. Private*, pg. 2629
MCCOLL'S RETAIL GROUP PLC; *Int'l*, pg. 4757
MCCOMB COCA-COLA BOTTLING COMPANY—See Coca-Cola Bottling Co. United, Inc.; *U.S. Public*, pg. 958
MCCOMBIE GROUP, LLC; *U.S. Private*, pg. 2629
MCCOMBS ENTERPRISES; *U.S. Private*, pg. 2629
MCCOMBS PARTNERS—See McCombs Enterprises; *U.S. Private*, pg. 2629
MCCOMBS WEST FORD; *U.S. Private*, pg. 2629
MCCOM, LTD.—See Hexatronic Group AB; *Int'l*, pg. 3371
M.C. COMMUNICATION, INC.; *U.S. Private*, pg. 2528
MC COMMUNICATIONS INC.; *U.S. Private*, pg. 2625
MCCON BUILDING & PETROLEUM SERVICES, INC.—See MidOcean Partners, LLP; *U.S. Private*, pg. 2716
MCCONNELL AUTOMOTIVE; *U.S. Private*, pg. 2629
MCCONNELL CABINETS, INC.; *U.S. Private*, pg. 2629
MCCONNELL DOWELL CONSTRUCTORS (AUST.) PTY LIMITED—See Aveng Limited; *Int'l*, pg. 738
MCCONNELL DOWELL CONSTRUCTORS LIMITED—See Aveng Limited; *Int'l*, pg. 738
MCCONNELL DOWELL CONSTRUCTORS THAI LIMITED—See Aveng Limited; *Int'l*, pg. 738
MCCONNELL DOWELL CORPORATION LIMITED—See Aveng Limited; *Int'l*, pg. 738
MCCONNELL DOWELL PHILIPPINES INC.—See Aveng Limited; *Int'l*, pg. 738
MCCONNELL DOWELL SOUTH EAST ASIA PRIVATE LIMITED—See Aveng Limited; *Int'l*, pg. 738
MCCONNELL GOLF LLC; *U.S. Private*, pg. 2629
MCCONNELLS ADVERTISING SERVICE LTD.; *Int'l*, pg. 4757
MCCONNELL SEATS AUSTRALIA PTY. LTD.—See APM Automotive Holdings Berhad; *Int'l*, pg. 516
MCCONNEL LTD.—See Alamo Group Inc.; *U.S. Public*, pg. 70
MC CONSULTING PTE. LTD.—See Saksoft Ltd; *Int'l*, pg. 6488
MCCONVILLE OMNI INSURANCE BROKERS LIMITED; *Int'l*, pg. 4757
MCCONWAY & TORLEY, LLC—See Arcosa, Inc.; *U.S. Public*, pg. 186
MCCORD BROS INC.; *U.S. Private*, pg. 2629

COMPANY NAME INDEX

MCCORMACK BARON MANAGEMENT SERVICES—See McCormack Baron Salazar, Inc.; *U.S. Private*, pg. 2630
MCCORMACK BARON SALAZAR, INC.; *U.S. Private*, pg. 2629
MCCORMACK CONSTRUCTION CO. INC.—See Emerick Construction Co. Inc.; *U.S. Private*, pg. 1381
MCCOR MANAGEMENT; *Int'l*, pg. 4757
MCCOR MANAGEMENT—See McCOR Management; *Int'l*, pg. 4757
MCCOR MANAGEMENT—See McCOR Management; *Int'l*, pg. 4757
MCCOR MANAGEMENT—See McCOR Management; *Int'l*, pg. 4757
MCCOR MANAGEMENT - WEST—See McCOR Management; *Int'l*, pg. 4757
MCCORMICK ARMSTRONG CO. INC.; *U.S. Private*, pg. 2630
MCCORMICK & COMPANY, INCORPORATED; *U.S. Public*, pg. 1403
MCCORMICK COMPANY; *U.S. Private*, pg. 2630
MCCORMICK COMPANY—See McCormick Company; *U.S. Private*, pg. 2630
MCCORMICK COMPANY—See McCormick Company; *U.S. Private*, pg. 2630
MCCORMICK COMPANY-SOUTH BEND—See McCormick & Company, Incorporated; *U.S. Public*, pg. 1404
MCCORMICK CONDIMENT PLANT—See McCormick & Company, Incorporated; *U.S. Public*, pg. 1404
MCCORMICK DE CENTRO AMERICA, S.A. DE C.V.—See McCormick & Company, Incorporated; *U.S. Public*, pg. 1404
MCCORMICK DE MEXICO, S.A. DE C.V.—See Grupo Herdez, S.A.B. de C.V.; *Int'l*, pg. 3130
MCCORMICK DE MEXICO, S.A. DE C.V.—See McCormick & Company, Incorporated; *U.S. Public*, pg. 1404
MCCORMICK DISTILLING CO., INC.; *U.S. Private*, pg. 2630
MCCORMICK EUROPE LTD.—See McCormick & Company, Incorporated; *U.S. Public*, pg. 1404
MCCORMICK FARMS, LLC—See WesBanco, Inc.; *U.S. Public*, pg. 2349
MCCORMICK FLAVOR DIVISION—See McCormick & Company, Incorporated; *U.S. Public*, pg. 1404
MCCORMICK FOODS AUSTRALIA PTY. LTD.—See McCormick & Company, Incorporated; *U.S. Public*, pg. 1404
MCCORMICK FOOD SERVICE DIVISION—See McCormick & Company, Incorporated; *U.S. Public*, pg. 1404
MCCORMICK FRANCE, S.A.S.—See McCormick & Company, Incorporated; *U.S. Public*, pg. 1404
MCCORMICK GLENTHAM (PROPRIETARY) LIMITED—See McCormick & Company, Incorporated; *U.S. Public*, pg. 1404
MCCORMICK (GUANGZHOU) FOOD COMPANY LIMITED—See McCormick & Company, Incorporated; *U.S. Public*, pg. 1404
MCCORMICK-HUNT VALLEY PLANT—See McCormick & Company, Incorporated; *U.S. Public*, pg. 1404
MCCORMICK INCORPORATED; *U.S. Private*, pg. 2630
MCCORMICK INGREDIENTS SOUTHEAST ASIA PRIVATE LIMITED—See McCormick & Company, Incorporated; *U.S. Public*, pg. 1404
MCCORMICK INSULATION SUPPLY; *U.S. Private*, pg. 2630
MCCORMICK INTERNATIONAL HOLDINGS LTD.—See McCormick & Company, Incorporated; *U.S. Public*, pg. 1404
MCCORMICK-LION LTD.—See Lion Corporation; *Int'l*, pg. 4518
MCCORMICK MARKETING INC.; *U.S. Private*, pg. 2630
MCCORMICK PAINT WORKS COMPANY; *U.S. Private*, pg. 2630
MCCORMICK PESA, S.A. DE C.V.—See McCormick & Company, Incorporated; *U.S. Public*, pg. 1404
MCCORMICK PHILIPPINES, INC.—See McCormick & Company, Incorporated; *U.S. Public*, pg. 1404
MCCORMICK PHILIPPINES, INC.—See SYSU International, Inc.; *Int'l*, pg. 7394
MCCORMICK POLSKA S.A.—See McCormick & Company, Incorporated; *U.S. Public*, pg. 1404
MCCORMICK-SALINAS PLANT—See McCormick & Company, Incorporated; *U.S. Public*, pg. 1404
MCCORMICK & SCHMICK'S SEAFOOD RESTAURANTS, INC.—See Fertitta Entertainment, Inc.; *U.S. Private*, pg. 1499
MCCORMICK SOUTH AFRICA PTY LIMITED—See McCormick & Company, Incorporated; *U.S. Public*, pg. 1404
MCCORMICK SPICE MILL—See McCormick & Company, Incorporated; *U.S. Public*, pg. 1404
MCCORMICK STEVENSON CORP.; *U.S. Private*, pg. 2630
MCCORMICK SWITZERLAND GMBH—See McCormick & Company, Incorporated; *U.S. Public*, pg. 1404
MCCORMICK SYSTEMS, INC.—See Thoma Bravo, L.P.; *U.S. Private*, pg. 4148
MCCORMICK TAYLOR; *U.S. Private*, pg. 2630
MCCORMICK (UK) LTD.—See McCormick & Company, Incorporated; *U.S. Public*, pg. 1404

MCCORMIX CORP.; *U.S. Private*, pg. 2630
MCCOURT CONSTRUCTION CO. INC.; *U.S. Private*, pg. 2630
MCCOURT LABEL COMPANY; *U.S. Private*, pg. 2630
MCCOWAN AND ASSOCIATES LTD.; *Int'l*, pg. 4757
MCCOY ELKHORN COAL CORPORATION—See James River Coal Company; *U.S. Private*, pg. 2185
MCCOY FIRE & SAFETY, INC.—See Capital Alignment Partners, Inc.; *U.S. Private*, pg. 738
MCCOY FIRE & SAFETY, INC.—See Lynch Holdings, LLC; *U.S. Private*, pg. 2521
MCCOY FREIGHTLINER—See Penske Automotive Group, Inc.; *U.S. Public*, pg. 1665
MCCOY GLOBAL CANADA CORP.—See McCoy Global Inc.; *Int'l*, pg. 4757
MCCOY GLOBAL INC.; *Int'l*, pg. 4757
MCCOY GLOBAL S.A.R.L—See McCoy Global Inc.; *Int'l*, pg. 4757
MCCOY GLOBAL USA, INC. - BROUSSARD—See McCoy Global Inc.; *Int'l*, pg. 4757
MCCOY GROUP, INC.; *U.S. Private*, pg. 2630
MCCOY MOTORS INC.; *U.S. Private*, pg. 2630
MCCOY NATIONALEASE, INC.—See McCoy Group, Inc.; *U.S. Private*, pg. 2630
MCCOY'S BUILDING SUPPLY CENTERS; *U.S. Private*, pg. 2630
MCC POLSKA SA—See Platinum Equity, LLC; *U.S. Private*, pg. 3206
MCC PTA ASIA PACIFIC PTE. LTD.—See Mitsubishi Chemical Group Corporation; *Int'l*, pg. 4931
MCCRACKEN FINANCIAL SOLUTIONS CORP.; *U.S. Private*, pg. 2630
MC CRAFTSMAN MACHINERY PVT. LTD.—See Mitsubishi Corporation; *Int'l*, pg. 4941
MCCRANEY PROPERTY COMPANY; *U.S. Private*, pg. 2630
MCCRARY DANIELS INSURANCE AGENCY—See PointeNorth Insurance Group LLC; *U.S. Private*, pg. 3222
MCCRAW OIL CO. INC.; *U.S. Private*, pg. 2631
MCCRAY LUMBER COMPANY - MCCRAY LUMBER & MILLWORK DIVISION—See McCray Lumber Company; *U.S. Private*, pg. 2631
MCCRAY LUMBER COMPANY; *U.S. Private*, pg. 2631
MCCREADY FOUNDATION, INC.; *U.S. Private*, pg. 2631
MCCREA HEATING AND AIR CONDITIONING; *U.S. Private*, pg. 2631
MCCREARY MODERN INC.; *U.S. Private*, pg. 2631
MCCREE GENERAL CONTRACTORS & ARCHITECTS; *U.S. Private*, pg. 2631
MCCRILLIS & ELDREDGE INSURANCE, INC.—See Michaud & Sammon Insurance, Inc.; *U.S. Private*, pg. 2699
MCCROMETER INC.—See Danaher Corporation; *U.S. Public*, pg. 628
MCCRORY CONSTRUCTION CO., LLC; *U.S. Private*, pg. 2631
MCCRORY'S PHARMACY, INC.—See Dougherty's Pharmacy, Inc.; *U.S. Private*, pg. 1266
MCC SERVICES, L.L.C.—See The MCC Group, LLC; *U.S. Private*, pg. 4076
MCCTELECOM S. COOP.—See Mondragon Corporation; *Int'l*, pg. 5031
MCC TRADING INTERNATIONAL GMBH—See Metro AG; *Int'l*, pg. 4857
MCC TRANSPORT PHILIPPINES, INC.—See SM Investments Corporation; *Int'l*, pg. 6998
MCCUBBIN HOSIERY, LLC—See Guardian Capital Partners, LLC; *U.S. Private*, pg. 1810
MCCUE CORPORATION; *U.S. Private*, pg. 2631
MCCULLOUGH COMMUNICATIONS & MARKETING; *U.S. Private*, pg. 2631
MCCULLOUGH HYDE MEMORIAL HOSPITAL, INC.—See Catholic Health Initiatives; *U.S. Private*, pg. 790
MCCULLOUGH INDUSTRIES, INC.—See Olympic Steel Inc.; *U.S. Public*, pg. 1570
MCCULLOUGH PUBLIC RELATIONS, INC.; *U.S. Private*, pg. 2631
MCCUNE CYCLE WORLD, INC.—See Iron Pony Motorsports Group, Inc.; *U.S. Private*, pg. 2139
MCCUNE TECHNOLOGY; *U.S. Private*, pg. 2631
MCC UNITEC CO., LTD.—See Mitsubishi Chemical Group Corporation; *Int'l*, pg. 4931
MCCURDY & COMPANY INC; *U.S. Private*, pg. 2631
MCCURDY-WALDEN, INC.—See Shoreline Equity Partners, LLC; *U.S. Private*, pg. 3641
MC CURRY-DECK MOTORS, INC.; *U.S. Private*, pg. 2625
MCCURTAIN MEMORIAL MEDICAL MANAGEMENT, INC.; *U.S. Private*, pg. 2631
MCCUSKER & COMPANY, INC.—See MHHC Enterprises Inc; *U.S. Private*, pg. 1436
MCCUTCHEON ENTERPRISES, INC.; *U.S. Private*, pg. 2631
MCDANEL ADVANCED MATERIAL TECHNOLOGIES LLC—See Artemis Capital Partners Management Co., LLC; *U.S. Private*, pg. 341
MCDANIEL CELLULAR TELEPHONE COMPANY—See Telephone & Data Systems, Inc.; *U.S. Public*, pg. 1998
MCDANIEL FOOD MANAGEMENT INC.; *U.S. Private*, pg. 2631

MCDONALDS OF SIOUX CITY

MCDANIEL KNUTSON FINIANICAL, INC.—See Lightyear Capital LLC; *U.S. Private*, pg. 2454
MCDANIEL KNUTSON FINIANICAL, INC.—See Ontario Teachers' Pension Plan; *Int'l*, pg. 5586
MCDANIEL MACHINERY, INC.; *U.S. Private*, pg. 2631
MCDANIEL MOTOR CO.; *U.S. Private*, pg. 2631
MCDASH ANALYTICS, LLC—See Fidelity National Financial, Inc.; *U.S. Public*, pg. 831
MC DATA PLUS, INC.—See Mitsubishi Corporation; *Int'l*, pg. 4939
MCDAVID AUSTIN-ACRA, LLC—See Asbury Automotive Group, Inc.; *U.S. Public*, pg. 209
MCDAVID HONDA—See David McDavid Automotive Group; *U.S. Private*, pg. 1171
MCDAVID, INC.—See Wells Fargo & Company; *U.S. Public*, pg. 2344
M.C. DEAN, INC.; *U.S. Private*, pg. 2528
MCDECAUX INC.—See JCDecaux S.A.; *Int'l*, pg. 3923
MCDERMOTT AUTO GROUP; *U.S. Private*, pg. 2631
MCDERMOTT CENTER; *U.S. Private*, pg. 2631
MCDERMOTT-COSTA CO., INC.; *U.S. Private*, pg. 2632
MCDERMOTT INTERNATIONAL, INC.; *U.S. Public*, pg. 1404
MCDERMOTT LABORATORIES LTD.—See Viatris Inc.; *U.S. Public*, pg. 2293
MCDERMOTT MARINE CONSTRUCTION LIMITED—See McDermott International, Inc.; *U.S. Public*, pg. 1405
MCDERMOTT & WIEDEMANN, LLC—See Health Carousel, LLC; *U.S. Private*, pg. 1892
MCDERMOTT WILL & EMERY LLP; *U.S. Private*, pg. 2631
MCDEVITT TRUCKS INC; *U.S. Private*, pg. 2632
MCD GASKETS INC.—See Alfa Laval AB; *Int'l*, pg. 312
MCDONALD AUTOMOTIVE GROUP; *U.S. Private*, pg. 2632
MCDONALD EQUIPMENT COMPANY; *U.S. Private*, pg. 2632
MCDONALD FORD INC.; *U.S. Private*, pg. 2632
MCDONALD INDUSTRIAL LAND CO.—See McDonald Steel Corporation; *U.S. Private*, pg. 2632
MCDONALD INDUSTRIES, INC.—See World Micro, Inc.; *U.S. Private*, pg. 4566
MCDONALD LUMBER CO. INC.; *U.S. Private*, pg. 2632
MCDONALD PONTIAC-CADILLAC-GMC-OLDS INC.; *U.S. Private*, pg. 2632
MCDONALD'S AMUSEMENTS INC.; *U.S. Private*, pg. 2632
MCDONALD'S AUSTRALIA LIMITED—See McDonald's Corporation; *U.S. Public*, pg. 1406
MCDONALD'S COMPANY (JAPAN), LTD.—See McDonald's Corporation; *U.S. Public*, pg. 1406
MCDONALD'S CORPORATION; *U.S. Public*, pg. 1405
MCDONALD'S DEUTSCHLAND GMBH—See McDonald's Corporation; *U.S. Public*, pg. 1406
MCDONALD'S FRANCE SA—See McDonald's Corporation; *U.S. Public*, pg. 1406
MCDONALD'S FRANCE SERVICES SARL—See McDonald's Corporation; *U.S. Public*, pg. 1406
MCDONALD'S FRANCHISE GMBH (AUSTRIA)—See McDonald's Corporation; *U.S. Public*, pg. 1406
MCDONALD'S GMBH—See McDonald's Corporation; *U.S. Public*, pg. 1406
MCDONALD'S HOLDINGS CO. (JAPAN), LTD.—See McDonald's Corporation; *U.S. Public*, pg. 1406
MCDONALD'S IMMOBILIEN GMBH—See McDonald's Corporation; *U.S. Public*, pg. 1406
MCDONALD'S INTERNATIONAL—See McDonald's Corporation; *U.S. Public*, pg. 1406
MCDONALD'S ITALIA S.R.L.—See McDonald's Corporation; *U.S. Public*, pg. 1406
MCDONALD'S LIEGENSCHAFTSVERWALTUNGS GESELLSCHAFT M.B.H.—See McDonald's Corporation; *U.S. Public*, pg. 1406
MCDONALD'S LIME - OTOROHANGA PLANT—See Graymont Limited; *Int'l*, pg. 3063
MCDONALD'S NEDERLAND B.V.—See McDonald's Corporation; *U.S. Public*, pg. 1406
MCDONALDS OF CALHOUN INC.; *U.S. Private*, pg. 2632
MCDONALDS OF SCOTTSDALE; *U.S. Private*, pg. 2632
MCDONALDS OF SIOUX CITY; *U.S. Private*, pg. 2632
MCDONALD'S PANAMA—See McDonald's Corporation; *U.S. Public*, pg. 1406
MCDONALD'S POLSKA SP. Z O.O—See McDonald's Corporation; *U.S. Public*, pg. 1406
MCDONALD'S RESTAURANTS (HONG KONG) LTD.—See McDonald's Corporation; *U.S. Public*, pg. 1406
MCDONALD'S RESTAURANTS LIMITED—See McDonald's Corporation; *U.S. Public*, pg. 1406
MCDONALD'S RESTAURANTS (NEW ZEALAND) LIMITED—See McDonald's Corporation; *U.S. Public*, pg. 1406
MCDONALD'S RESTAURANTS (NEW ZEALAND) LIMITED—See McDonald's Corporation; *U.S. Public*, pg. 1406
MCDONALD'S RESTAURANTS OF CANADA LTD.—See McDonald's Corporation; *U.S. Public*, pg. 1406
MCDONALD'S RESTAURANTS OF ILLINOIS, INC.—See McDonald's Corporation; *U.S. Public*, pg. 1406

MCDONALDS OF SIOUX CITY / CORPORATE AFFILIATIONS

MCDONALD'S RESTAURANTS OF IRELAND LIMITED (IRELAND)—See McDonald's Corporation; *U.S. Public*, pg. 1406
MCDONALD'S RESTAURANTS OF MARYLAND, INC.—See McDonald's Corporation; *U.S. Public*, pg. 1406
MCDONALD'S RESTAURANTS PTE., LTD.—See McDonald's Corporation; *U.S. Public*, pg. 1406
MCDONALD'S SUISSE FRANCHISE SARL—See McDonald's Corporation; *U.S. Public*, pg. 1406
MCDONALD STEEL CORPORATION; *U.S. Private*, pg. 2632
MCDONALD'S USA, LLC—See McDonald's Corporation; *U.S. Public*, pg. 1406
MCDONALD TECHNOLOGIES INTERNATIONAL INC.; *U.S. Private*, pg. 2632
MCDONALD TRANSIT ASSOCIATES INC—See Regie Autonome des Transports Parisiens; *Int'l*, pg. 6253
MCDONALD WHOLESALE CO.; *U.S. Private*, pg. 2632
MCDONALD YORK BUILDING COMPANY; *U.S. Private*, pg. 2632
MCDONALD ZARING INSURANCE, INC.—See Marsh & McLennan Companies, Inc.; *U.S. Public*, pg. 1381
MCDONNELL & MILLER DIVISION—See Xylem Inc.; *U.S. Public*, pg. 2396
MC DONNELL PILING & FOUNDATIONS—See VINCI S.A.; *Int'l*, pg. 8234
MCDONOUGH BOLYARD PECK, INC.; *U.S. Private*, pg. 2632
MCDONOUGH CONTRACTING SERVICES—See Wm. F. McDonough Plumbing, Inc.; *U.S. Private*, pg. 4552
MCDONOUGH CORPORATION; *U.S. Private*, pg. 2632
MCDONOUGH ELEVATOR SALES & RENTALS INC—See McDonough Corporation; *U.S. Private*, pg. 2632
MCDONOUGH FIRE SERVICE—See Wm. F. McDonough Plumbing, Inc.; *U.S. Private*, pg. 4552
MCDONOUGH MANUFACTURING COMPANY; *U.S. Private*, pg. 2633
MCDONOUGH MARINE SERVICE, INC.—See McDonough Corporation; *U.S. Private*, pg. 2632
MCDONOUGH PLUMBING SERVICE—See Wm. F. McDonough Plumbing, Inc.; *U.S. Private*, pg. 4552
MCDOUGAL COMPANIES; *U.S. Private*, pg. 2633
MCDOWALL COMPANY; *U.S. Private*, pg. 2633
MCDOWELL HOLDINGS LIMITED; *Int'l*, pg. 4757
MCDOWELL HOME HEALTH AGENCY—See Ephraim McDowell Health, Inc.; *U.S. Private*, pg. 1412
MCDOWELL MOUNTAIN ARIZONA, LLC—See RAIT Financial Trust; *U.S. Private*, pg. 3349
MCDOWELL SUPPLY COMPANY; *U.S. Private*, pg. 2633
MCDOWELL & WALKER INC.; *U.S. Private*, pg. 2633
MCD PRODUCTIONS LIMITED—See Live Nation Entertainment, Inc.; *U.S. Public*, pg. 1330
M&C DRUGSTORE LTD.—See Arthur J. Gallagher & Co.; *U.S. Public*, pg. 206
MCD S.A.S.—See Alfa Laval AB; *Int'l*, pg. 312
MCDT AG—See SRG SSR Idee Suisse; *Int'l*, pg. 7149
MCE ASCHERSLEBEN GMBH; *Int'l*, pg. 4758
MCE BANK GMBH—See Mitsubishi Corporation; *Int'l*, pg. 4939
MCE CORPORATION; *U.S. Private*, pg. 2633
MC EDICIONES S.A.; *Int'l*, pg. 4755
MCE DISTRIBUTING AND SUPPLY; *U.S. Private*, pg. 2633
MCE GMBH—See HABAU Hoch- und Tiefbaugesellschaft m.b.H.; *Int'l*, pg. 3202
MCE HOLDINGS BERHAD; *Int'l*, pg. 4758
MC EKONIVA-APK HOLDING—See Ekosem-Agrar GmbH; *Int'l*, pg. 2339
MC ELECTRONICS LLC—See Volex plc; *Int'l*, pg. 8301
MCELENEY MOTORS INC.; *U.S. Private*, pg. 2633
MC ELEVATOR (MYANMAR) LTD.—See Mitsubishi Corporation; *Int'l*, pg. 4939
MCELROY, DEUTSCH, MULVANEY & CARPENTER, LLP; *U.S. Private*, pg. 2633
MCELROY MANUFACTURING, INC.; *U.S. Private*, pg. 2633
MCELROY METAL MILL, INC.; *U.S. Private*, pg. 2633
MCELROY'S, INC.; *U.S. Private*, pg. 2633
MCELROY TRUCK LINES INC.; *U.S. Private*, pg. 2633
MCELVAIN OIL & GAS PROPERTIES INC; *U.S. Private*, pg. 2633
MCELWAIN CHEVROLET & OLDSMOBILE; *U.S. Private*, pg. 2633
MCEMOTION—See The Interpublic Group of Companies, Inc.; *U.S. Public*, pg. 2101
MCENANY ROOFING & CONTRACTING INC.; *U.S. Private*, pg. 2633
MC ENDEAVORS, INC.; *U.S. Public*, pg. 1403
MCENEARNEY ASSOCIATES INC.; *U.S. Private*, pg. 2633
MCENEARNEY BUSINESS MACHINES LIMITED—See ANSA McAL Limited; *Int'l*, pg. 477
MCENEARNEY MOTORS LIMITED—See ANSA McAL Limited; *Int'l*, pg. 477
MCENEARNEY QUALITY, INC.—See ANSA McAL Limited; *Int'l*, pg. 476
M&C ENERGY GROUP LTD.—See Schneider Electric SE; *Int'l*, pg. 6634

M&C ENGINEERING & TRADING SDN. BHD.—See AWC Berhad; *Int'l*, pg. 752
MCESSY INVESTMENTS CO.; *U.S. Private*, pg. 2633
MCE TECHNOLOGIES (SUZHOU) CO., LTD; *Int'l*, pg. 4758
MC EUROPE B.V.—See TRACOE medical GmbH; *Int'l*, pg. 7887
MCEWEN MINING INC.; *Int'l*, pg. 4758
MC FACILITIES CO., LTD.—See Mitsubishi Corporation; *Int'l*, pg. 4939
MCFADDEN FORD, INC.—See Shults Management Group, Inc.; *U.S. Private*, pg. 3644
MCFADDEN & MILLER CONSTRUCTION; *U.S. Private*, pg. 2633
MCFA LLC; *U.S. Private*, pg. 2633
MCFARLAND CASCADE HOLDINGS, INC.—See Stella-Jones, Inc.; *Int'l*, pg. 7196
MCFARLAND CASCADE POLE & LUMBER COMPANY—See Stella-Jones, Inc.; *Int'l*, pg. 7196
MCFARLAND CASCADE - SHERIDAN—See Stella-Jones, Inc.; *Int'l*, pg. 7196
MCFARLAND CASCADE - SILVER SPRINGS—See Stella-Jones, Inc.; *Int'l*, pg. 7196
MCFARLAND & COMPANY, INC.; *U.S. Private*, pg. 2633
MCFARLAND-DYER & ASSOCIATES INC.—See Bowman Consulting Group Ltd.; *U.S. Public*, pg. 376
THE MCFARLAND GROUP, INC.; *U.S. Private*, pg. 4076
MCFARLAND JOHNSON INC.; *U.S. Private*, pg. 2633
MCFARLANE AGENCIES (1967 LTD)—See Mouvement des caisses Desjardins; *Int'l*, pg. 5058
MCFARLANE MANUFACTURING COMPANY INC.; *U.S. Private*, pg. 2633
MCFARLANE MEDICAL, INC.—See Jacsten Holdings, LLC; *U.S. Private*, pg. 2181
MCFARLANE TOYS—See TMP International, Inc.; *U.S. Private*, pg. 4179
MCFARLING FOODS, INC.; *U.S. Private*, pg. 2634
MCF CONTROLS INC.—See IMI plc; *Int'l*, pg. 3626
MCF CORPORATE FINANCE GMBH; *Int'l*, pg. 4758
MCFEELY'S—See W.W. Grainger, Inc.; *U.S. Public*, pg. 2320
MCF ENERGY LTD.; *Int'l*, pg. 4758
MC FERTICOM CO., LTD.—See Mitsubishi Corporation; *Int'l*, pg. 4939
MCFI (AFRICA) LTD.—See Saudi Arabian Mining Company - Ma'aden; *Int'l*, pg. 6589
MC FINANCE & CONSULTING ASIA PTE. LTD.—See Mitsubishi Corporation; *Int'l*, pg. 4939
MCGF INVESTISSEMENT SA—See A.S. Creation Tapeten AG; *Int'l*, pg. 28
MCFLY ROBOT TECHNOLOGIES A.S.—See Kontrolmatik Teknoloji Enerji ve Muhendislik A.S.; *Int'l*, pg. 4276
MCFRANK & WILLIAMS ADVERTISING AGENCY, INC.; *U.S. Private*, pg. 2634
MCGARD INC.; *U.S. Private*, pg. 2634
MCGARRAH JESSEE; *U.S. Private*, pg. 2634
MCGARVEY DEVELOPMENT COMPANY; *U.S. Private*, pg. 2634
MCGEAN-ROHCO, INC.; *U.S. Private*, pg. 2634
MCGEAN-ROHCO SINGAPORE PTE LTD—See McGean-Rohco, Inc.; *U.S. Private*, pg. 2634
MCGEAN ROHCO (UK) LTD.—See McGean-Rohco, Inc.; *U.S. Private*, pg. 2634
MCGEARY ORGANICS, INC.; *U.S. Private*, pg. 2634
MCGEE AIR SERVICES, INC.—See Alaska Air Group, Inc.; *U.S. Public*, pg. 72
MCGEE BROTHERS CO. INC. - CONCRETE PLANT—See McGee Brothers Co. Inc.; *U.S. Private*, pg. 2634
MCGEE BROTHERS CO. INC.; *U.S. Private*, pg. 2634
MCGEE COMPANY; *U.S. Private*, pg. 2634
MCGEE CO.; *U.S. Private*, pg. 2634
MCGEE GROUP; *U.S. Private*, pg. 2634
MCGEE-HUNTLEY CONSTRUCTION CO. INC.—See McGee Brothers Co. Inc.; *U.S. Private*, pg. 2634
MCGEE STORAGE & HANDLING, INC.—See Atlanta Forklifts, Inc.; *U.S. Private*, pg. 370
MCGEE & THIELEN INSURANCE BROKERS; *U.S. Private*, pg. 2634
MCGEE TIRE STORES INC.; *U.S. Private*, pg. 2634
M&C GENERAL INSURANCE CO. LTD.—See Arthur J. Gallagher & Co.; *U.S. Public*, pg. 206
MCGEORGE CONTRACTING CO., INC.; *U.S. Private*, pg. 2634
MCGEORGES ROLLING HILLS RV; *U.S. Private*, pg. 2634
MCGEOUGH LAMACCHIA REALTY INC.; *U.S. Private*, pg. 2634
MCG GLOBAL, LLC; *U.S. Private*, pg. 2634
MCG HEALTH, LLC—See The Hearst Corporation; *U.S. Private*, pg. 4045
MCGHEE RISK CAPITAL LLC; *U.S. Private*, pg. 2634
MCG HOLDINGS NETHERLANDS BV—See Management Consulting Group PLC; *Int'l*, pg. 4666
MCGILL AIRCLEAN CORP.—See The McGill Corporation; *U.S. Private*, pg. 4076
MCGILL AIRFLOW CORP.—See The McGill Corporation; *U.S. Private*, pg. 4076

MCGILL AIRPRESSURE CORP.—See The McGill Corporation; *U.S. Private*, pg. 4076
MCGILL AIRSEAL LLC—See The McGill Corporation; *U.S. Private*, pg. 4076
MCGILL AIRSILENCE LLC—See The McGill Corporation; *U.S. Private*, pg. 4076
M.C. GILL CORPORATION; *U.S. Private*, pg. 2528
THE MCGILL CORPORATION; *U.S. Private*, pg. 4076
M.C. GILL EUROPE LTD.—See M.C. Gill Corporation; *U.S. Private*, pg. 2528
THE MCGILL GROUP LIMITED—See Pinewood Technologies Group PLC; *Int'l*, pg. 5869
MCGILL MAINTENANCE LLP; *U.S. Private*, pg. 2634
MCGINLEY & ASSOCIATES, INC.—See Universal Engineering Sciences, LLC; *U.S. Private*, pg. 4304
MCGINNIS & MARX MUSIC PUBLISHERS; *U.S. Private*, pg. 2634
MCGINNIS SISTERS SPECIAL FOOD STORES; *U.S. Private*, pg. 2635
MCGINTY-GORDON & ASSOCIATES; *U.S. Private*, pg. 2635
MCG KINGSPORT, INC.—See Moog Inc.; *U.S. Public*, pg. 1469
MCG MARLINK COMM GMBH—See Airbus SE; *Int'l*, pg. 242
MCG METRIC COMPONENTS GMBH—See Metric & Multistandard Components Corporation; *U.S. Private*, pg. 2684
MCGOLDRICK CONSTRUCTION SERVICES CORPORATION; *U.S. Private*, pg. 2635
MCGOUGH CONSTRUCTION CO. INC.; *U.S. Private*, pg. 2635
MCGOVERN AUTO GROUP CORP SERVICES, INC.; *U.S. Private*, pg. 2635
MC GOWAN BUILDERS, INC.; *U.S. Private*, pg. 2625
MCGOWAN & CO. (CONTRACTORS) LIMITED—See J. Smart & Co. (Contractors) PLC; *Int'l*, pg. 3857
MCGOWAN INSURANCE GROUP INC.; *U.S. Private*, pg. 2635
MCGOWAN WORKING PARTNERS INC.; *U.S. Private*, pg. 2635
MCGRADY LIMITED—See Brown & Brown, Inc.; *U.S. Public*, pg. 401
MCGRATH AUTOMOTIVE GROUP INC.; *U.S. Private*, pg. 2635
MCGRATH AUTOMOTIVE, INC.; *U.S. Private*, pg. 2635
MCGRATH CITY HYUNDAI—See McGrath Automotive, Inc.; *U.S. Private*, pg. 2635
MCGRATH HONDA—See McGrath Automotive, Inc.; *U.S. Private*, pg. 2635
MCGRATH LEXUS OF WESTMONT—See McGrath Automotive, Inc.; *U.S. Private*, pg. 2635
MCGRATH LIMITED—See Bayleys Corporation Limited; *Int'l*, pg. 914
MCGRATH LIMITED—See Knight Frank LLP; *Int'l*, pg. 4207
MCGRATH NISSAN; *U.S. Private*, pg. 2635
MCGRATH RENTCORP.; *U.S. Public*, pg. 1406
MCGRATH SALES PADDINGTON PTY LTD—See Bayleys Corporation Limited; *Int'l*, pg. 914
MCGRATH SALES PADDINGTON PTY LTD—See Knight Frank LLP; *Int'l*, pg. 4207
MCGRATH'S PUBLICK FISH HOUSE; *U.S. Private*, pg. 2635
MCGRATH SYSTEMS; *U.S. Private*, pg. 2635
MCGRAW COMMUNICATIONS, INC.; *U.S. Private*, pg. 2635
THE MCGRAW GROUP; *U.S. Private*, pg. 4076
MCGRAW HILL AUSTRALIA PTY LTD—See S&P Global Inc.; *U.S. Public*, pg. 1830
MCGRAW-HILL BOOK PUBLISHING COMPANY—See S&P Global Inc.; *U.S. Public*, pg. 1830
THE MCGRAW-HILL COMPANIES, S.R.L.—See S&P Global Inc.; *U.S. Public*, pg. 1832
MCGRAW-HILL EDUCATION, INC.—See Platinum Equity, LLC; *U.S. Private*, pg. 3205
MCGRAW-HILL EDUCATION INDIA PRIVATE LIMITED—See Platinum Equity, LLC; *U.S. Private*, pg. 3205
MCGRAW-HILL FINANCE (UK) LTD.—See S&P Global Inc.; *U.S. Public*, pg. 1830
MCGRAW-HILL FINANCIAL JAPAN K.K.—See S&P Global Inc.; *U.S. Public*, pg. 1830
MCGRAW-HILL FINANCIAL SINGAPORE PTE. LIMITED—See S&P Global Inc.; *U.S. Public*, pg. 1830
MCGRAW-HILL (GERMANY) GMBH—See S&P Global Inc.; *U.S. Public*, pg. 1830
MCGRAW-HILL HIGHER EDUCATION—See Platinum Equity, LLC; *U.S. Private*, pg. 3205
MCGRAW-HILL INDICES U.K. LIMITED—See S&P Global Inc.; *U.S. Public*, pg. 1830
MCGRAW-HILL/INTERAMERICANA DE CHILE LIMITADA—See S&P Global Inc.; *U.S. Public*, pg. 1831
MCGRAW-HILL INTERAMERICANA DO BRASIL LTDA.—See S&P Global Inc.; *U.S. Public*, pg. 1830
MCGRAW-HILL/INTERAMERICANA, S.A.—See S&P Global Inc.; *U.S. Public*, pg. 1831
MCGRAW-HILL INTERNATIONAL (U.K.) LIMITED—See S&P Global Inc.; *U.S. Public*, pg. 1830

COMPANY NAME INDEX

MCGRAW-HILL KOREA, INC.—See S&P Global Inc.; *U.S. Public*, pg. 1830
MCGRAW-HILL PROFESSIONAL—See S&P Global Inc.; *U.S. Public*, pg. 1830
MCGRAW-HILL RYERSON LIMITED—See Platinum Equity, LLC; *U.S. Private*, pg. 3206
MCGRAW-HILL—See Platinum Equity, LLC; *U.S. Private*, pg. 3205
MCGRAW INSURANCE, INC.—See The McGraw Group; *U.S. Private*, pg. 4077
MCGRAW/KOKOSING, INC.—See Kokosing Construction Company, Inc.; *U.S. Private*, pg. 2341
MCGRAW WENTWORTH, INC.; *U.S. Private*, pg. 2635
MCGREGOR & ASSOCIATES, INC.; *U.S. Private*, pg. 2635
MCGREGOR & ASSOCIATES, INC.; *U.S. Private*, pg. 2635
MCGREGOR COMPANY; *U.S. Private*, pg. 2635
MCGREGOR INDUSTRIES INC.; *U.S. Private*, pg. 2635
MCGRIFF INDUSTRIES INC.; *U.S. Private*, pg. 2635
MCGRIFF INSURANCE SERVICES, INC.—See Truist Financial Corporation; *U.S. Public*, pg. 2199
MCGRIFF, SEIBELS AND WILLIAMS OF TEXAS, INC.—See Truist Financial Corporation; *U.S. Public*, pg. 2201
MCGRIFF SEIBELS OF TEXAS, INC.—See Truist Financial Corporation; *U.S. Public*, pg. 2201
MCGRIFF, SEIBELS & WILLIAMS, INC.—See Truist Financial Corporation; *U.S. Public*, pg. 2200
MCGRIFF, SEIBELS & WILLIAMS OF GEORGIA, INC.—See Truist Financial Corporation; *U.S. Public*, pg. 2201
MC GROUP PUBLIC COMPANY LIMITED; *Int'l*, pg. 4755
MC GROUP—See Fayolle et Fils; *Int'l*, pg. 2626
THE MC GROUP—See WPP plc; *Int'l*, pg. 8488
MC GROUP; *U.S. Private*, pg. 2625
MCGUFFEY'S RESTAURANTS, INC.; *U.S. Private*, pg. 2636
MCGUIGAN TOMBS & CO.—See WithumSmith+Brown PC; *U.S. Private*, pg. 4551
MCGUIRE & ASSOCIATES; *U.S. Private*, pg. 2636
MCGUIRE BEARING COMPANY, INC.; *U.S. Private*, pg. 2636
MCGUIRE CADILLAC; *U.S. Private*, pg. 2636
MCGUIRE DEVELOPMENT COMPANY, LLO; *U.S. Private*, pg. 2636
MCGUIRE FAMILY FURNITURE MAKERS; *U.S. Private*, pg. 2636
THE MCGUIRE FURNITURE COMPANY—See Kohler Company; *U.S. Private*, pg. 2340
THE MCGUIRE GROUP, INC.; *U.S. Private*, pg. 4077
MCGUIRE HARLEY-DAVIDSON LLC; *U.S. Private*, pg. 2636
MCGUIRE MANUFACTURING—See Bead Industries Inc.; *U.S. Private*, pg. 505
MCGUIRE REAL ESTATE SERVICES GROUP—See McGuire Development Company, LLC; *U.S. Private*, pg. 2636
MCGUIREWOODS LLP; *U.S. Private*, pg. 2636
MCGUYER HOMEBUILDERS INC.; *U.S. Private*, pg. 2636
MCHAL CORPORATION—See Victory of West Virginia, Inc.; *U.S. Private*, pg. 4379
MCH BEAULIEU LAUSANNE SA—See MCH Group AG; *Int'l*, pg. 4758
MCH CORP.; *U.S. Private*, pg. 2636
MCHD CYPRESS CREEK CORP.—See Sunburst Hospitality Corporation; *U.S. Private*, pg. 3865
MCHD FORT LAUDERDALE CORP.—See Sunburst Hospitality Corporation; *U.S. Private*, pg. 3865
MCHENRY BANCORP, INC.; *U.S. Public*, pg. 1407
MCHENRY BANK & TRUST—See Wintrust Financial Corporation; *U.S. Public*, pg. 2374
MCHENRY METALS GOLF CORP.; *U.S. Public*, pg. 1407
MCHENRY SAVINGS BANK—See McHenry Bancorp, Inc.; *U.S. Public*, pg. 1407
MCH GROUP AG; *Int'l*, pg. 4758
MCH, INC.; *U.S. Private*, pg. 2636
MCH MANAGEMENT INC.—See Sunburst Hospitality Corporation; *U.S. Private*, pg. 3865
MC HOLDING GMBH & CO. KG—See Giesecke & Devrient GmbH; *Int'l*, pg. 2970
MC HOLOGRAM INC—See MicroCloud Hologram Inc.; *U.S. Public*, pg. 1437
M&C HOME DEPOT LTD.—See Arthur J. Gallagher & Co.; *U.S. Public*, pg. 206
MCH PRIVATE EQUITY ASESORES, S.L.—See Groupe BPCE; *Int'l*, pg. 3095
MCH SWISS EXHIBITION (BASEL) LTD.—See MCH Group AG; *Int'l*, pg. 4758
MCH SWISS EXHIBITION (ZURICH) LTD.—See MCH Group AG; *Int'l*, pg. 4758
MCHUGH ENTERPRISES INC.; *U.S. Private*, pg. 2636
MCHUGH FUNERAL HOME, INC.—See Service Corporation International; *U.S. Public*, pg. 1870
MC HUMANETS CORPORATION—See Mitsubishi Chemical Group Corporation; *Int'l*, pg. 4931
MCH US CORP.—See MCH Group AG; *Int'l*, pg. 4758
MCI CAPITAL ALTERNATYWNA SPOLKA IN-WESTYCYJNA S.A.; *Int'l*, pg. 4758

MCI-EXPERIAN CO., LTD.—See Experian plc; *Int'l*, pg. 2588
MCI GANDALF AKTYWNEJ ALOKACJI SFIO—See MCI Capital Alternatywna Spolka Inwestycyjna S.A.; *Int'l*, pg. 4758
MCI GROUP HOLDING SA; *Int'l*, pg. 4758
MCI INC.; *U.S. Private*, pg. 2636
MCI INSTITUTE PTY LTD.—See Madison Dearborn Partners, LLC; *U.S. Private*, pg. 2540
MCI INTERNATIONAL, INC.—See Verizon Communications Inc.; *U.S. Public*, pg. 2285
MCI, LC; *U.S. Private*, pg. 2636
MCILHENNY COMPANY; *U.S. Private*, pg. 2636
MCI, LLC—See Verizon Communications Inc.; *U.S. Public*, pg. 2285
MCI LOGISTICS (EAST), INC.—See Mitsui Chemicals, Inc.; *Int'l*, pg. 4982
MCI LOGISTICS (WEST), INC.—See Mitsui Chemicals, Inc.; *Int'l*, pg. 4982
MCILROY & KING COMMUNICATIONS INC.; *Int'l*, pg. 4758
MCILVAINE TRUCKING INC.; *U.S. Private*, pg. 2637
MC IMPACTS METALS—See Commercial Metals Company; *U.S. Public*, pg. 547
MC INDUSTRIAL CHEMICAL CO., LTD.—See Thai Central Chemical Public Company Limited; *Int'l*, pg. 7592
MC INDUSTRIAL, INC.—See McCarthy Holdings, Inc.; *U.S. Private*, pg. 2627
M-C INDUSTRIES INC.; *U.S. Private*, pg. 2525
MC INDUSTRIES, LTD.—See Mitsui Chemicals, Inc.; *Int'l*, pg. 4981
MCINERNEY & ASSOCIATES, INC.; *U.S. Private*, pg. 2637
MCINERNEY HOLDINGS PLC.; *Int'l*, pg. 4759
MCINERNEY INC.; *U.S. Private*, pg. 2637
MCINERNEY'S WOODHAVEN CHRYSLER JEEP; *U.S. Private*, pg. 2637
MCINNES ROLLED RINGS—See TSK Partners, Inc.; *U.S. Private*, pg. 4253
MCINNIS BUILDERS, LLC.; *U.S. Private*, pg. 2637
MC INTERNATIONAL GROUP, INC.; *Int'l*, pg. 4755
MCINTOSH BOX & PALLET CO. INC.; *U.S. Private*, pg. 2637
MCINTOSH CONSTRUCTION COMPANY, LLC—See Natural Resource Partners L.P.; *U.S. Public*, pg. 1499
MCINTOSH LABORATORY, INC.—See Fine Sounds S.p.A.; *Int'l*, pg. 2673
MCINTYRE & ASSOCIATES INC.; *U.S. Private*, pg. 2637
THE MCINTYRE COMPANY; *U.S. Private*, pg. 4077
MCINTYRE DODD MARKETING LTD—See DM plc; *Int'l*, pg. 2142
MCINTYRE ELWELL & STRAMMER GENERAL CONTRACTORS, INC.; *U.S. Private*, pg. 2637
MCINTYRE GROUP OFFICE SERVICES INC.; *Int'l*, pg. 4759
MCINTYRE, PANZARELLA, THANASIDES, BRINGGOLD & TODD, P.A.; *U.S. Private*, pg. 2637
MCINTYRE TILE COMPANY INC.—See Elgin-Butler Brick Company; *U.S. Private*, pg. 1359
MC IONIC SOLUTIONS UK, LTD.—See Mitsubishi Chemical Group Corporation; *Int'l*, pg. 4931
MC IONIC SOLUTIONS US, INC.—See Mitsubishi Chemical Group Corporation; *Int'l*, pg. 4932
MCIS INSURANCE BHD.—See Sanlam Limited; *Int'l*, pg. 6545
MCIS SAFETY GLASS SDN. BHD.—See AGC Inc.; *Int'l*, pg. 204
MCIVER CLINIC; *U.S. Private*, pg. 2637
MCI WORLDCOM NETWORK SERVICES, INC.—See Verizon Communications Inc.; *U.S. Public*, pg. 2285
MCI WORLDCOM—See Verizon Communications Inc.; *U.S. Public*, pg. 2285
MCJ CO., LTD.; *Int'l*, pg. 4759
MCJP INC.—See NexTone, Inc.; *Int'l*, pg. 5249
MCKAFKA DEVELOPMENT GROUP, LLC; *U.S. Private*, pg. 2637
MCKAMISH CHESAPEAKE INC.; *U.S. Private*, pg. 2637
MCK AUTOMACAO INDUSTRIAL LTDA—See Mondragon Corporation; *Int'l*, pg. 5031
MCKAY AUTO PARTS INCORPORATED; *U.S. Private*, pg. 2637
MCKAY-COCKER CONSTRUCTION LIMITED—See Fayolle et Fils; *Int'l*, pg. 2626
MCKAY MANAGEMENT CORPORATION—See Associations, Inc.; *U.S. Private*, pg. 359
THE MCKAY PRESS, INC.—See Chatham Asset Management, LLC; *U.S. Private*, pg. 863
MCKAY ROOFING COMPANY, INC.—See Solar Integrated Roofing Corporation; *U.S. Public*, pg. 1899
MCKAY'S CHRYSLER JEEP DODGE; *U.S. Private*, pg. 2637
MCKAY SECURITIES OVERSEAS LIMITED—See Workspace Group Plc; *Int'l*, pg. 8456
MCKAY SECURITIES PLC—See Workspace Group Plc; *Int'l*, pg. 8456
MCK BUILDING ASSOCIATES INC.; *U.S. Private*, pg. 2637
M-CKD PRECISION SDN. BHD.—See CKD Corporation; *Int'l*, pg. 1639

MCKEVITT TRUCKING LIMITED

MCKEAN DEFENSE GROUP LLC; *U.S. Private*, pg. 2637
MCKECHNIE AEROSPACE DE, INC.—See TransDigm Group Incorporated; *U.S. Public*, pg. 2182
MCKECHNIE ALUMINIUM SOLUTIONS LIMITED; *Int'l*, pg. 4759
MCKECHNIE TOOLING & ENGINEERING—See MVC Holdings LLC; *U.S. Private*, pg. 2821
MCKECHNIE VEHICLE COMPONENTS—See MVC Holdings LLC; *U.S. Private*, pg. 2821
MCKEE ASSET MANAGEMENT; *U.S. Private*, pg. 2637
MCKEE AUTO CENTER INC.; *U.S. Private*, pg. 2637
MCKEE FOODS CORPORATION; *U.S. Private*, pg. 2637
MCKEE FOODS TRANSPORTATION, LLC—See McKee Foods Corporation; *U.S. Private*, pg. 2637
MCKEE GROUP REALTY, LLC; *U.S. Private*, pg. 2638
MCKEEVER ENTERPRISES INC.; *U.S. Private*, pg. 2638
MCKEE WALLWORK & COMPANY; *U.S. Private*, pg. 2638
MCKEIL MARINE LIMITED—See Astatine Investment Partners LLC; *U.S. Public*, pg. 360
MCKELVEY HOMES, LLC.; *U.S. Private*, pg. 2638
MCKENNA ENGINEERING & EQUIPMENT CO., INC.—See Wynnchurch Capital, L.P.; *U.S. Private*, pg. 4577
MCKENNA FUNERALS LIMITED—See Co-operative Group Limited; *Int'l*, pg. 1679
MCKENNA HAWAII INC.; *U.S. Private*, pg. 2638
MCKENNA MOTOR COMPANY INC.; *U.S. Private*, pg. 2638
MCKENNA MOTORS INC.; *U.S. Private*, pg. 2638
MCKENNEY CHEVROLET, INC.; *U.S. Private*, pg. 2638
MCKENNEY'S INC.; *U.S. Private*, pg. 2638
MCKENZIE BUYING COMPANY—See Western Family Holding Co., Inc.; *U.S. Private*, pg. 4493
MCKENZIE CHECK ADVANCE OF OHIO, LLC—See Grupo Salinas, S.A. de C.V.; *Int'l*, pg. 3135
MCKENZIE COUNTRY CLASSICS—See Kayem Foods, Inc.; *U.S. Private*, pg. 2266
MCKENZIE ELECTRIC COOPERATIVE, INC.; *U.S. Private*, pg. 2638
MCKENZIE LAIRD OTTINGER LEACH, PLLC—See Maynard, Cooper & Gale, P.C.; *U.S. Private*, pg. 2622
MCKENZIE MEMORIAL HOSPITAL; *U.S. Private*, pg. 2638
MCKENZIE OIL CO. INC.; *U.S. Private*, pg. 2638
MCKENZIE PHYSICIAN SERVICES, LLC—See Quorum Health Corporation; *U.S. Private*, pg. 3330
MCKENZIE PROPERTIES INC.—See Wildish Land Company; *U.S. Private*, pg. 4519
THE MCKENZIE RIVER CORPORATION; *U.S. Private*, pg. 4077
MCKENZIE SPORTS PRODUCTS LLC—See Gridiron Capital, LLC; *U.S. Private*, pg. 1786
MCKENZIE SUPPLY COMPANY; *U.S. Private*, pg. 2638
MCKENZIE TANK LINES, INC.—See Groendyke Transport, Inc.; *U.S. Private*, pg. 1791
MCKENZIE-WILLAMETTE REGIONAL MEDICAL CENTER ASSOCIATES, LLC—See Quorum Health Corporation; *U.S. Private*, pg. 3330
MCKEON DOOR OF NEVADA, INC.—See McKeon Rolling Steel Door Company, Inc.; *U.S. Private*, pg. 2638
MCKEON DOOR OF WASHINGTON DC—See McKeon Rolling Steel Door Company, Inc.; *U.S. Private*, pg. 2638
MCKEON DOOR WEST, INC.—See McKeon Rolling Steel Door Company, Inc.; *U.S. Private*, pg. 2638
MCKEON ROLLING STEEL DOOR COMPANY, INC.; *U.S. Private*, pg. 2638
MCKESSON CANADA—See McKesson Corporation; *U.S. Public*, pg. 1408
MCKESSON CORPORATION; *U.S. Public*, pg. 1407
MCKESSON EUROPE AG—See McKesson Corporation; *U.S. Public*, pg. 1408
MCKESSON EUROPE AG—See McKesson Corporation; *U.S. Public*, pg. 1408
MCKESSON HEALTH SOLUTIONS LLC—See McKesson Corporation; *U.S. Public*, pg. 1408
MCKESSON INFORMATION SOLUTIONS HOLDINGS LIMITED—See McKesson Corporation; *U.S. Public*, pg. 1408
MCKESSON MEDICAL IMAGING GROUP—See McKesson Corporation; *U.S. Public*, pg. 1408
MCKESSON MEDICAL-SURGICAL INC.—See McKesson Corporation; *U.S. Public*, pg. 1408
MCKESSON MEDICAL-SURGICAL—See McKesson Corporation; *U.S. Public*, pg. 1408
MCKESSON PHARMACEUTICAL—See McKesson Corporation; *U.S. Public*, pg. 1408
MCKESSON PHARMACY SYSTEMS—See McKesson Corporation; *U.S. Public*, pg. 1408
MCKESSON PLASMA AND BIOLOGICS, LLC—See McKesson Corporation; *U.S. Public*, pg. 1408
MCKESSON PROVIDER TECHNOLOGIES—See McKesson Corporation; *U.S. Public*, pg. 1408
MCKESSON PROVIDER TECHNOLOGIES—See McKesson Corporation; *U.S. Public*, pg. 1408
MCKESSON SPECIALTY HEALTH—See McKesson Corporation; *U.S. Public*, pg. 1408
MCKEVITT TRUCKING LIMITED; *Int'l*, pg. 4759

MCKEVITT TRUCKING LIMITED

MCKEY FOOD SERVICES LIMITED—See Tyson Foods, Inc.; *U.S. Public*, pg. 2210
MCKEY FOOD SERVICES (THAILAND) LIMITED—See Tyson Foods, Inc.; *U.S. Public*, pg. 2210
MCKEY PERFORATING CO., INC.—See Reliance Steel & Aluminum Co.; *U.S. Public*, pg. 1780
MCKIBBON HOTEL MANAGEMENT, INC.; *U.S. Private*, pg. 2638
MCKIE FORD INC.; *U.S. Private*, pg. 2638
MCKIE FORD LINCOLN MERCURY; *U.S. Private*, pg. 2638
MCKIM & CREED, INC.; *U.S. Private*, pg. 2638
MCKINLEY ASSOCIATES INC.; *U.S. Private*, pg. 2638
MCKINLEY CAPITAL MANAGEMENT; *U.S. Private*, pg. 2638
MCKINLEY CONSULTING, INC.—See McKinley Group, Inc.; *U.S. Private*, pg. 2639
MCKINLEY EQUIPMENT CORP.; *U.S. Private*, pg. 2638
MCKINLEY FINANCE, INC.—See McKinley Group, Inc.; *U.S. Private*, pg. 2639
MCKINLEY FINANCIAL SERVICES, INC.; *U.S. Private*, pg. 2639
MCKINLEY GROUP, INC.; *U.S. Private*, pg. 2639
MCKINLEY MARKETING PARTNERS, INC.—See 24 Seven, LLC; *U.S. Private*, pg. 6
MCKINNEY BEDDING COMPANY—See Restonic Mattress Corporation; *U.S. Private*, pg. 3409
MCKINNEY CHICAGO; *U.S. Private*, pg. 2639
MCKINNEY DOOR AND HARDWARE, INC.—See Bee Street Holdings LLC; *U.S. Private*, pg. 513
MCKINNEY DRILLING COMPANY—See Keller Group plc; *Int'l*, pg. 4121
MCKINNEY PETROLEUM EQUIPMENT, INC.—See Kian Capital Partners, LLC; *U.S. Private*, pg. 2302
MCKINNEY PETROLEUM EQUIPMENT, INC.—See RFE Investment Partners; *U.S. Private*, pg. 3419
MCKINNEY PRODUCTS COMPANY—See ASSA ABLOY AB; *Int'l*, pg. 636
MCKINNEY & SILVER LLC—See Samsung Group; *Int'l*, pg. 6511
MCKINNEY SURGEONS, PLLC—See HCA Healthcare, Inc.; *U.S. Public*, pg. 1001
MCKINNEY TRAILERS & CONTAINERS; *U.S. Private*, pg. 2639
MCKINNEY TRAILERS & CONTAINERS—See Mckinney Trailers & Containers; *U.S. Private*, pg. 2639
MCKINNEY VENTURES LLC—See Samsung BioLogics Co., Ltd.; *Int'l*, pg. 6510
MCKINNIS CONSULTING SERVICES, LLC.—See Bain Capital, LP; *U.S. Private*, pg. 432
MCKINNON MICRO DISTRIBUTING LTD; *Int'l*, pg. 4759
MCKINSEY & COMPANY, INC. - MIDWEST—See McKinsey & Company, Inc.; *U.S. Private*, pg. 2639
MCKINSEY & COMPANY, INC.; *U.S. Private*, pg. 2639
MCKINSEY MOTOR FORD; *U.S. Private*, pg. 2639
MCKINSTRY CO., LLC; *U.S. Private*, pg. 2639
MCKINSTRY ESSENTION, INC.—See McKinstry Co., LLC; *U.S. Private*, pg. 2639
MCKINZIE MECHANICAL HEATING & AIR CONDITIONING, L.L.C.—See Hiller Plumbing, Heating & Cooling Company; *U.S. Private*, pg. 1946
MCKISSICK PRODUCTS CO.—See KKR & Co. Inc.; *U.S. Public*, pg. 1264
MCKIT SYSTEMS LTD.—See Malam-Team Ltd.; *Int'l*, pg. 4659
MCKNIGHT'S LONG TERM CARE NEWS & ASSISTED LIVING—See Haymarket Group Limited; *Int'l*, pg. 3293
MCLABS, LLC—See The Riverside Company; *U.S. Private*, pg. 4108
MCLAGAN PARTNERS, INC.—See Aon plc; *Int'l*, pg. 491
MCLAIN PLUMBING & ELECTRIC SERVICE; *U.S. Private*, pg. 2639
MCLANAHAN CORPORATION; *U.S. Private*, pg. 2640
MCLANE ADVANCED TECHNOLOGIES, LLC; *U.S. Private*, pg. 2640
MCLANE COMPANY, INC.—See Berkshire Hathaway Inc.; *U.S. Public*, pg. 312
MCLANE FOODSERVICE, INC.—See Berkshire Hathaway Inc.; *U.S. Public*, pg. 312
MCLANE GROUP LP; *U.S. Private*, pg. 2640
MCLANE LIVESTOCK TRANSPORT; *U.S. Private*, pg. 2640
MCLAREN CONSTRUCTION GROUP; *Int'l*, pg. 4759
MCLAREN CONSTRUCTION LTD.—See McLaren Construction Group; *Int'l*, pg. 4759
MCLAREN HEALTH CARE CORPORATION; *U.S. Private*, pg. 2640
MCLAREN PERFORMANCE TECHNOLOGIES INC.—See Linamar Corporation; *Int'l*, pg. 4502
MCLAREN PROPERTY BV—See McLaren Construction Group; *Int'l*, pg. 4759
MCLAREN RESOURCES INC.; *Int'l*, pg. 4759
MCLARENS, INC.; *U.S. Private*, pg. 2640
MCLARENS YOUNG INTERNATIONAL PANAMA—See UBS Group AG; *Int'l*, pg. 8007
MCLARENS YOUNG INTERNATIONAL—See McLarens, Inc.; *U.S. Private*, pg. 2640
MCLAREN TECHNOLOGY ACQUISITION CORP.; *U.S. Public*, pg. 1409

MCLARTY CAPITAL PARTNERS UK LLP; *U.S. Private*, pg. 2640
MCLAUGHLIN BODY CO.; *U.S. Private*, pg. 2640
MCLAUGHLIN BRUNSON INSURANCE AGENCY, LLP—See Kelso & Company, L.P.; *U.S. Private*, pg. 2280
THE MCLAUGHLIN COMPANY; *U.S. Private*, pg. 4077
MCLAUGHLIN, DELVECCHIO & CASEY, INC.; *U.S. Private*, pg. 2640
MCLAUGHLIN GORMLEY KING COMPANY—See Sumitomo Chemical Company, Limited; *Int'l*, pg. 7265
MCLAUGHLIN & HARVEY LTD.; *Int'l*, pg. 4759
MCLAUGHLIN MOTORS; *U.S. Private*, pg. 2640
MCLAUGHLIN PAPER CO. INC.; *U.S. Private*, pg. 2640
MCLAUGHLIN RESEARCH CORPORATION; *U.S. Private*, pg. 2640
MCLAURIN PARKING COMPANY INC.; *U.S. Private*, pg. 2640
MCLAURIN'S FUNERAL HOME, LLC—See Service Corporation International; *U.S. Public*, pg. 1871
MCL COMPANIES; *U.S. Private*, pg. 2639
MCLEAN CAPITAL MANAGEMENT; *U.S. Private*, pg. 2640
MCLEAN COMMUNICATIONS—See Yankee Publishing Inc.; *U.S. Private*, pg. 4586
MCLEAN COMPANY; *U.S. Private*, pg. 2640
MCLEAN CONSTRUCTION LTD.; *U.S. Private*, pg. 2641
MCLEAN CONTRACTING COMPANY INC.; *U.S. Private*, pg. 2641
MCLEAN COUNTY ASPHALT & CONCRETE COMPANY, INC.; *U.S. Private*, pg. 2641
MCLEAN ENGINEERING COMPANY, INC.—See EQT AB; *Int'l*, pg. 2479
MCLEAN FAULCONER INC.; *U.S. Private*, pg. 2641
THE MCLEAN HOSPITAL CORPORATION—See Partners HealthCare System, Inc.; *U.S. Private*, pg. 3102
MCLEAN IMPLEMENT INCORPORATED; *U.S. Private*, pg. 2641
MCLEAN INCORPORATED; *U.S. Private*, pg. 2641
MCLEAN INSURANCE AGENCY—See Arthur J. Gallagher & Co.; *U.S. Public*, pg. 206
MCLEAN MEATS INC.—See Premium Brands Holdings Corporation; *Int'l*, pg. 5963
MCLEAN PACKAGING CORPORATION - CORRUGATED DIVISION—See McLean Packaging Corporation; *U.S. Private*, pg. 2641
MCLEAN PACKAGING CORPORATION - RIGID PAPER BOX DIVISION—See McLean Packaging Corporation; *U.S. Private*, pg. 2641
MCLEAN PACKAGING CORPORATION; *U.S. Private*, pg. 2641
MCLEAN & PARTNERS WEALTH MANAGEMENT LTD.—See Canadian Western Bank; *Int'l*, pg. 1287
MCLEAN TECHNOLOGIES BERHAD; *Int'l*, pg. 4759
MCLEAN TECHNOLOGIES PTE LTD—See MClean Technologies Berhad; *Int'l*, pg. 4759
MCLEAN TECHNOLOGIES PTE. LTD.—See MClean Technologies Berhad; *Int'l*, pg. 4759
MCLEA'S TIRE & AUTOMOTIVE CENTERS; *U.S. Private*, pg. 2640
MCLEMORE BUILDING MAINTENANCE INC.; *U.S. Private*, pg. 2641
MCLEMORE MARKETS; *U.S. Private*, pg. 2641
MCLENDON HARDWARE, INC.—See Tyndale Advisors, LLC; *U.S. Private*, pg. 4268
MCLEOD ACCESSORIES PTY. LTD.—See Bridgestone Corporation; *Int'l*, pg. 1160
MCLEOD ADDICTIVE DISEASE CENTER, INC.; *U.S. Private*, pg. 2641
MCLEOD BANCSHARES, INC.; *U.S. Private*, pg. 2641
MCLEOD COOPERATIVE POWER ASSOCIATION; *U.S. Private*, pg. 2641
MCLEOD COOPERATIVE POWER TRUST—See McLeod Cooperative Power Association; *U.S. Private*, pg. 2641
MCLEODD OPTICAL COMPANY INC.—See EssilorLuxottica SA; *Int'l*, pg. 2513
MCLEOD HEALTH; *U.S. Private*, pg. 2641
MCLEOD OIL COMPANY INC.; *U.S. Private*, pg. 2641
MCLEOD RUSSEL AFRICA LIMITED—See McLeod Russel India Limited; *Int'l*, pg. 4759
MCLEOD RUSSEL INDIA LIMITED; *Int'l*, pg. 4759
MCLEOD RUSSEL MIDDLE EAST DMCC—See McLeod Russel India Limited; *Int'l*, pg. 4759
MCLEOD RUSSEL UGANDA LIMITED—See McLeod Russel India Limited; *Int'l*, pg. 4759
MCLEODUSA INFORMATION SERVICES LLC—See Windstream Holdings, Inc.; *U.S. Public*, pg. 2373
MCLIFE ASSURANCE COMPANY LIMITED—See The Bidvest Group Limited; *Int'l*, pg. 7625
MC-LINK S.P.A.; *Int'l*, pg. 4755
MCL LAND LIMITED—See Jardine Matheson Holdings Limited; *Int'l*, pg. 3910
MCL LAND (MALAYSIA) SDN. BHD.—See Hong Kong Land Holdings Ltd.; *Int'l*, pg. 3467
MCL LAND (PANTAI VIEW) SDN. BHD.—See Jardine Matheson Holdings Limited; *Int'l*, pg. 3910
MCL MCCANN—See The Interpublic Group of Companies, Inc.; *U.S. Public*, pg. 2098

CORPORATE AFFILIATIONS

MCL MOTOR CARS (1992) INC.—See Dilawri Group of Companies; *Int'l*, pg. 2125
MCLON JEWELLERY CO., LTD.; *Int'l*, pg. 4759
MCLOONE METAL GRAPHICS, INC.—See JSJ Corporation; *U.S. Private*, pg. 2241
MCLOUD D.O.O.—See DHH.SpA; *Int'l*, pg. 2099
MCLOUD TECHNOLOGIES CORP.; *Int'l*, pg. 4759
MCLOUD TECHNOLOGIES SERVICES INC.—See mCloud Technologies Corp.; *Int'l*, pg. 4760
MCLOUGHLIN ENTERPRISES INC.; *U.S. Private*, pg. 2641
MCL RESTAURANT & BAKERY; *U.S. Private*, pg. 2639
MCL SAATCHI & SAATCHI—See Publicis Groupe S.A.; *Int'l*, pg. 6108
MCLS ASIA CO., LTD.—See Mitsubishi Corporation; *Int'l*, pg. 4941
MCLURES HONEY & MAPLE PRODUCTS—See Dutch Gold Honey Inc.; *U.S. Private*, pg. 1294
MCLYMONT MINES INC.—See Romios Gold Resources Inc.; *Int'l*, pg. 6395
MC MACHINERY SYSTEMS DE MEXICO S.A. DE C.V.—See Mitsubishi Corporation; *Int'l*, pg. 4941
MC MACHINERY SYSTEMS DO BRASIL LTDA.—See Mitsubishi Corporation; *Int'l*, pg. 4941
MC MACHINERY SYSTEMS, INC.—See Mitsubishi Corporation; *Int'l*, pg. 4939
MCM ADVISERS, LP—See Mackenzie Capital Management, LP; *U.S. Private*, pg. 2537
MCMAHON CONTRACTING, L.P.; *U.S. Private*, pg. 2642
MCMAHON FORD, LLC; *U.S. Private*, pg. 2642
MCMAHON FORD; *U.S. Private*, pg. 2642
MCMAHON INSURANCE INC.; *U.S. Private*, pg. 2642
MCMAHON PUBLISHING COMPANY; *U.S. Private*, pg. 2642
MCMAHON TIRE, INC.; *U.S. Private*, pg. 2642
MCMANGA FOODS, INC.; *U.S. Private*, pg. 2642
MC MARKETING & SALES (HONG KONG) LIMITED—See Nissin Foods Holdings Co., Ltd.; *Int'l*, pg. 5376
MCM ASIA LIMITED—See ChinLink International Holdings Limited; *Int'l*, pg. 1570
MCMASTER-CARR SUPPLY COMPANY; *U.S. Private*, pg. 2642
MCMASTERS-KOSS CO.; *U.S. Private*, pg. 2642
MCM AUTOS PTY LTD—See Eagers Automotive Limited; *Int'l*, pg. 2263
MCM CAPITAL GROUP INCORPORATED; *U.S. Private*, pg. 2641
MCM CAPITAL PARTNERS, LP; *U.S. Private*, pg. 2641
M-C MCLANE GROUP INTERNATIONAL—See McLane Group LP; *U.S. Private*, pg. 2640
MCMC LLC; *U.S. Private*, pg. 2642
MCM CONSTRUCTION, INC.; *U.S. Private*, pg. 2642
MCM CORPORATION; *U.S. Private*, pg. 2642
MCM CORP.; *U.S. Private*, pg. 2642
MC MEDIACOMPANY BUDAPEST—See WPP plc; *Int'l*, pg. 8465
MCM ELECTRONICS INC.—See Avnet, Inc.; *U.S. Public*, pg. 254
MCMENAMINS INC.; *U.S. Private*, pg. 2642
MCM ENTERTAINMENT GROUP LIMITED; *Int'l*, pg. 4760
MCM ENTERTAINMENT PTY LTD—See mcm Entertainment Group Limited; *Int'l*, pg. 4760
MCM GROUP—See EBSCO Industries, Inc.; *U.S. Private*, pg. 1325
MCMILLAN BROTHERS ELECTRIC SERVICE; *U.S. Private*, pg. 2642
MCMILLAN ELECTRIC COMPANY; *U.S. Private*, pg. 2642
MCMILLAN SHAKESPEARE AUSTRALIA PTY LIMITED—See McMillan Shakespeare Limited; *Int'l*, pg. 4760
MCMILLAN SHAKESPEARE LIMITED; *Int'l*, pg. 4760
MCMILLION RESEARCH; *U.S. Private*, pg. 2642
MC MINING LIMITED; *Int'l*, pg. 4755
MC MINING LIMITED—See MC Mining Limited; *Int'l*, pg. 4755
MCMINN, INC.—See CRH plc; *Int'l*, pg. 1847
MCMINN'S ASPHALT CO., INC.—See CRH plc; *Int'l*, pg. 1847
MCM INTEGRATED TECHNOLOGIES, LTD.—See Occidental Development Group, Inc.; *U.S. Private*, pg. 2988
MCM MEDIA PTY LTD—See mcm Entertainment Group Limited; *Int'l*, pg. 4760
MCM-MENEDZSER KERESKEDELMI ES SZOLGALTATO KORLATOLT FELELOSSEGU TARSASAG; *Int'l*, pg. 4760
MCMORAN EXPLORATION CO.—See Freeport-McMoRan Inc.; *U.S. Public*, pg. 884
MCMORAN OIL & GAS LLC—See Freeport-McMoRan Inc.; *U.S. Public*, pg. 884
MCM PAVING & CONSTUCTION; *U.S. Private*, pg. 2642
MCM S.A.—See Metropole Television SA; *Int'l*, pg. 4863
M.C.M. TECHNOLOGIES, INC.; *U.S. Private*, pg. 2528
MCM (TN) LLC—See W.P. Carey Inc.; *U.S. Private*, pg. 2316
MCMULLAN EQUIPMENT COMPANY, INC.; *U.S. Private*, pg. 2642
MCMULLEN OIL CO. INC.; *U.S. Private*, pg. 2643

COMPANY NAME INDEX

MCMUNN & YATES BUILDING SUPPLIES LTD.; *Int'l*, pg. 4760
MCMURDO, INC.—See Eurazeo SE; *Int'l*, pg. 2528
MCMURRAY FABRICS INC.; *U.S. Private*, pg. 2643
MCMURRAY SERV-U EXPEDITING LTD.—See TFI International Inc.; *Int'l*, pg. 7586
MCMURRAY STERN INC.—See Grays Peak Capital LP; *U.S. Private*, pg. 1761
MCMURRAY STERN INC.—See Valore Ventures, Inc.; *U.S. Private*, pg. 4337
MCMURREY PIPE LINE COMPANY—See Rosemore Inc.; *U.S. Private*, pg. 3483
MCMURRY READY MIX CO.—See MDU Resources Group, Inc.; *U.S. Public*, pg. 1410
MCM VACCINE B.V.1—See Merck & Co., Inc.; *U.S. Public*, pg. 1417
MCNABB CHEVROLET, OLDS, CADILLAC; *U.S. Private*, pg. 2643
MCNA HEALTH CARE HOLDINGS, LLC—See Managed Care of North America, Inc.; *U.S. Private*, pg. 2559
MCNA INSURANCE COMPANY—See Managed Care of North America, Inc.; *U.S. Private*, pg. 2559
MCNAIR LAW FIRM P.A.—See Burr & Forman LLP; *U.S. Private*, pg. 691
MCNAIRY HOSPITAL CORPORATION—See Community Health Systems, Inc.; *U.S. Public*, pg. 555
MCNALLY BHARAT ENGINEERING CO. LTD.; *Int'l*, pg. 4760
MCNALLY CAPITAL, LLC; *U.S. Private*, pg. 2643
MCNALLY CONTRACTORS LTD—See Koninklijke Volker-Wessels N.V.; *Int'l*, pg. 4272
MCNALLY ENTERPRISES, INC—See Moark Productions Inc.; *U.S. Private*, pg. 2756
MCNALLY INDUSTRIES, LLC; *U.S. Private*, pg. 2643
MCNALLY INTERNATIONAL INC.—See Kiewit Corp.; *U.S. Private*, pg. 2304
MCNALLY OPERATIONS LLC; *U.S. Private*, pg. 2643
MCNALLY SAYAJI ENGINEERING LIMITED—See Tega Industries Limited; *Int'l*, pg. 7521
MCNAMARA, CO.—See Brown & Brown, Inc.; *U.S. Public*, pg. 401
MCNAUGHTON GARDINER INSURANCE BROKERS PTY. LTD.—See AUB Group Limited; *Int'l*, pg. 698
MCNAUGHTON & GUNN, INC.; *U.S. Private*, pg. 2643
MCNAUGHTON-MCKAY ELECTRIC COMPANY; *U.S. Private*, pg. 2643
MCNB BANK AND TRUST CO.—See MCNB Banks, Inc.; *U.S. Public*, pg. 1409
MCNB BANKS, INC.; *U.S. Public*, pg. 1409
MCN DISTRIBUTORS INC.; *U.S. Private*, pg. 2643
MCNEECE BROTHERS OIL CO. INC.; *U.S. Private*, pg. 2643
MCNEEL INTERNATIONAL CORPORATION; *U.S. Private*, pg. 2643
MCNEELY, PIGOTT & FOX; *U.S. Private*, pg. 2643
MCNEELY PLASTIC PRODUCTS INC.—See Alpha Industries, Inc.; *U.S. Private*, pg. 197
MCNEIL AB—See Kenvue Inc.; *U.S. Public*, pg. 1224
MCNEIL COMPANY, INC.; *U.S. Private*, pg. 2643
MCNEIL & COMPANY, INC.—See Arch Capital Group Ltd.; *Int'l*, pg. 547
MCNEIL CONSUMER HEALTHCARE GMBH—See Kenvue Inc.; *U.S. Public*, pg. 1224
MCNEIL CONSUMER NUTRITIONALS LTD.—See Kenvue Inc.; *U.S. Public*, pg. 1224
MCNEIL CONSUMER PHARMACEUTICALS CO.—See Kenvue Inc.; *U.S. Public*, pg. 1224
MCNEIL DENMARK APS—See Kenvue Inc.; *U.S. Public*, pg. 1224
MCNEIL GMBH & CO. OHG—See Kenvue Inc.; *U.S. Public*, pg. 1224
MCNEIL, GRAY & RICE; *U.S. Private*, pg. 2643
MCNEIL HEALTHCARE LLC—See Kenvue Inc.; *U.S. Public*, pg. 1224
MCNEIL HEALTHCARE (UK) LIMITED—See Kenvue Inc.; *U.S. Public*, pg. 1224
MCNEILL COMMUNICATIONS GROUP INC.—See Steinreich Communications, LLC; *U.S. Private*, pg. 3798
MCNEIL & NRM INC.; *U.S. Private*, pg. 2643
MCNEIL NUTRITIONALS, LLC—See Kenvue Inc.; *U.S. Public*, pg. 1224
MCNEIL SWEDEN AB—See Kenvue Inc.; *U.S. Public*, pg. 1224
MCNEILUS COMPANIES, INC.—See Oshkosh Corporation; *U.S. Public*, pg. 1620
MCNEILUS STEEL INC.; *U.S. Private*, pg. 2644
MCNEILUS TRUCK & MANUFACTURING, INC.—See Oshkosh Corporation; *U.S. Public*, pg. 1621
MCNERNEY MANAGEMENT GROUP, INC.—See Integrity Marketing Group LLC; *U.S. Private*, pg. 2103
MCNETT EUROPE—See GEAR AID, Inc.; *U.S. Private*, pg. 1654
MCNEX CO., LTD.; *Int'l*, pg. 4760
MCNICHOLS COMPANY; *U.S. Private*, pg. 2644
MCNICHOLS PLC; *Int'l*, pg. 4760
MCNICOLL VEHICLE HIRE LTD.—See Avis Budget Group, Inc.; *U.S. Public*, pg. 249
MCNICOLL VEHICLE SALES LTD.—See Avis Budget Group, Inc.; *U.S. Public*, pg. 249

MCNS POLYURETHANES MALAYSIA SDN. BHD.—See Mitsui Chemicals, Inc.; *Int'l*, pg. 4981
MCNULTY KOREA CO., LTD; *Int'l*, pg. 4760
MCO HEALTH B.V—See Nestle S.A.; *Int'l*, pg. 5206
M. COHEN & SONS INC.; *U.S. Private*, pg. 2526
M COMMERCE CO., LTD.—See Mitsubishi Chemical Group Corporation; *Int'l*, pg. 4931
THE M. CONLEY COMPANY; *U.S. Private*, pg. 4073
MC ONLINE PTE LTD—See Thai Beverage Public Company Limited; *Int'l*, pg. 7590
M. COOPER WINSUPPLY—See Winsupply Inc.; *U.S. Private*, pg. 4544
MC OPERATION SUPPORT, LTD.—See Mitsui Chemicals, Inc.; *Int'l*, pg. 4981
MCO PROPERTIES INC.—See Maxxam, Inc.; *U.S. Private*, pg. 2620
MCOR CO., LTD.—See CDS Co., Ltd.; *Int'l*, pg. 1371
MCORE TECHNOLOGY CORP.—See Sitronix Technology Corporation; *Int'l*, pg. 6965
MCORPORATE FINANCE S.A.—See Commerzbank AG; *Int'l*, pg. 1719
M CORP; *U.S. Private*, pg. 2523
MCO SAUDI ARABIA LIMITED—See Mitsubishi Heavy Industries, Ltd.; *Int'l*, pg. 4954
MCOT PUBLIC COMPANY LIMITED; *Int'l*, pg. 4760
MCO TRANSPORT, INC.; *U.S. Private*, pg. 2644
MC PACK (MALAYSIA) SDN. BHD.—See Muda Holdings Berhad; *Int'l*, pg. 5076
MC PARTNERS CORPORATION—See Mitsubishi Chemical Group Corporation; *Int'l*, pg. 4931
MC PARTNERS INC.; *U.S. Private*, pg. 2625
MCPC INC.; *U.S. Private*, pg. 2644
THE MCPHERSON COMPANIES, INC.—See MidMark Capital; *U.S. Private*, pg. 2716
MCPHERSON'S CONSUMER PRODUCTS (HK) LIMITED—See McPherson's Limited; *Int'l*, pg. 4761
MCPHERSON'S CONSUMER PRODUCTS (NZ) LIMITED—See McPherson's Limited; *Int'l*, pg. 4760
MCPHERSON'S CONSUMER PRODUCTS PTE. LTD.—See McPherson's Limited; *Int'l*, pg. 4760
MCPHERSON'S CONSUMER PRODUCTS PTY. LTD.—See McPherson's Limited; *Int'l*, pg. 4761
MCPHERSON'S HONG KONG LIMITED—See McPherson's Limited; *Int'l*, pg. 4761
MCPHERSON'S LIMITED; *Int'l*, pg. 4760
MCPHERSON'S PRINTING PTY. LTD.—See Knox Investment Partners Limited; *Int'l*, pg. 4214
MCPHERSON'S (UK) LIMITED—See McPherson's Limited; *Int'l*, pg. 4760
MCPHILLIPS FORD LINCOLN SALES LTD.; *Int'l*, pg. 4761
MCPHILLIPS (WELLINGTON) LTD; *Int'l*, pg. 4761
MCPHY ENERGY DEUTSCHLAND GMBH—See McPhy Energy S.A.; *Int'l*, pg. 4761
MCPHY ENERGY ITALIA SRL—See McPhy Energy S.A.; *Int'l*, pg. 4761
MCPHY ENERGY S.A.; *Int'l*, pg. 4761
MCP, INC.—See Hillenbrand, Inc.; *U.S. Public*, pg. 1035
MCP INDUSTRIES INC.; *U.S. Private*, pg. 2644
MCPI PRIVATE LIMITED—See The Chatterjee Group; *U.S. Private*, pg. 4007
MC PLASTICS TRADING DE MEXICO SA—See Mitsubishi Corporation; *Int'l*, pg. 4939
MCP OF CALIFORNIA, INC.—See Xerox Holdings Corporation; *U.S. Public*, pg. 2388
MCPP FRANCE S.A.S.—See Mitsubishi Chemical Group Corporation; *Int'l*, pg. 4931
MCPP POLAND SP. Z O.O.—See Mitsubishi Chemical Group Corporation; *Int'l*, pg. 4931
MCP PROPERTY MANAGEMENT, LLC—See MetLife, Inc.; *U.S. Public*, pg. 1430
MCQUADE & BANNIGAN, INC.; *U.S. Private*, pg. 2644
MCQUAID & COMPANY; *U.S. Private*, pg. 2644
MCQUAY INTERNATIONAL-CHILLER PRODUCTS—See Daikin Industries, Ltd.; *Int'l*, pg. 1936
THE MCRAE AGENCY; *U.S. Private*, pg. 4077
MCRAE AMERICAN CORP.—See VINCI S.A.; *Int'l*, pg. 8224
MCRAE AVIATION SERVICES INC—See Abrams International LLP; *U.S. Private*, pg. 40
MCRAE COCA-COLA BOTTLING COMPANY—See Coca-Cola Bottling Co. United, Inc.; *U.S. Public*, pg. 958
MCRAE FOOTWEAR DIVISION—See McRae Industries, Inc.; *U.S. Public*, pg. 1409
MCRAE INDUSTRIES, INC.; *U.S. Public*, pg. 1409
MCRAE INTEGRATION LTD.—See VINCI S.A.; *Int'l*, pg. 8224
MCRAY CORPORATION—See Ray Corporation; *Int'l*, pg. 6223
MCR DEVELOPMENT LLC; *U.S. Private*, pg. 2644
MCREL INTERNATIONAL; *U.S. Private*, pg. 2644
MCR, LLC—See Arlington Capital Partners LLC; *U.S. Private*, pg. 328
MCROBERTS PROTECTIVE AGENCY, INC.—See Allied Universal Manager LLC; *U.S. Private*, pg. 191
MCROLLS OY; *Int'l*, pg. 4761
MCROSKEY MATTRESS COMPANY—See Pleasant Mattress, Inc.; *U.S. Private*, pg. 3213

M CROSSING CO., LTD.—See Nissha Co., Ltd.; *Int'l*, pg. 5371
MC RYOKKA CO., LTD.—See Mitsui Chemicals, Inc.; *Int'l*, pg. 4981
M&C SAATCHI CONNECT (PTY.) LIMITED—See M&C Saatchi plc; *Int'l*, pg. 4611
M&C SAATCHI FLUENCY LIMITED—See M&C Saatchi plc; *Int'l*, pg. 4611
M&C SAATCHI LA INC.—See M&C Saatchi plc; *Int'l*, pg. 4611
M&C SAATCHI LITTLE STORIES SAS—See M&C Saatchi plc; *Int'l*, pg. 4611
M&C SAATCHI MADRID SL—See M&C Saatchi plc; *Int'l*, pg. 4611
M&C SAATCHI PLC; *Int'l*, pg. 4611
M&C SAATCHI S.A. DE. C.V—See M&C Saatchi plc; *Int'l*, pg. 4611
M&C SAATCHI SOCIAL LTD.—See M&C Saatchi plc; *Int'l*, pg. 4611
M&C SAATCHI—See M&C Saatchi plc; *Int'l*, pg. 4611
M&C SAATCHI—See M&C Saatchi plc; *Int'l*, pg. 4611
M&C SAATCHI—See M&C Saatchi plc; *Int'l*, pg. 4611
M&C SAATCHI—See M&C Saatchi plc; *Int'l*, pg. 4611
M&C SAATCHI—See M&C Saatchi plc; *Int'l*, pg. 4611
M&C SAATCHI—See M&C Saatchi plc; *Int'l*, pg. 4611
M&C SAATCHI—See M&C Saatchi plc; *Int'l*, pg. 4611
M&C SAATCHI—See M&C Saatchi plc; *Int'l*, pg. 4611
M&C SAATCHI—See M&C Saatchi plc; *Int'l*, pg. 4611
M&C SAATCHI—See M&C Saatchi plc; *Int'l*, pg. 4611
M&C SAATCHI—See M&C Saatchi plc; *Int'l*, pg. 4611
M&C SAATCHI—See M&C Saatchi plc; *Int'l*, pg. 4611
M&C SAATCHI—See M&C Saatchi plc; *Int'l*, pg. 4611
M&C SAATCHI SPA—See M&C Saatchi plc; *Int'l*, pg. 4611
M&C SAATCHI SPORT & ENTERTAINMENT—See M&C Saatchi plc; *Int'l*, pg. 4611
M&C SAATCHI (S) PTE. LTD.—See M&C Saatchi plc; *Int'l*, pg. 4611
M&C SAATCHI (SWITZERLAND) SA—See M&C Saatchi plc; *Int'l*, pg. 4611
M&C SAATCHI TALK LIMITED—See M&C Saatchi plc; *Int'l*, pg. 4611
MCS ADVANTAGE, INC.—See JLL Partners, LLC; *U.S. Private*, pg. 2213
MCSA, L.L.C.—See Community Health Systems, Inc.; *U.S. Public*, pg. 554
MCSAM HOTEL GROUP LLC; *U.S. Private*, pg. 2644
MCS CHASSIS INC.—See Marubeni Corporation; *Int'l*, pg. 4706
MCS CO., LTD.—See Kamei Corporation; *Int'l*, pg. 4061
MC SERVICE GMBH—See Asklepios Kliniken GmbH & Co. KGaA; *Int'l*, pg. 623
M & C SERVICES PRIVATE LIMITED; *Int'l*, pg. 4609
MCS ET ASSOCIES, S.A.; *Int'l*, pg. 4761
MCS EUROPE GROUP B.V.—See Addtech AB; *Int'l*, pg. 134
MCS (EUROPE) LTD.—See Micro Contact Solution Co., Ltd.; *Int'l*, pg. 4876
MCS GROUP INC.; *U.S. Private*, pg. 2644
MCSHARES, INC.; *U.S. Private*, pg. 2644
MCS HEALTHCARE PUBLIC RELATIONS; *U.S. Private*, pg. 2644
MCS HEALTH MANAGEMENT OPTIONS, INC.—See JLL Partners, LLC; *U.S. Private*, pg. 2213
M.C. SHEET METAL LTD.—See Rieter Holding Ltd.; *Int'l*, pg. 6338
M&C SHIPPING DEPARTMENT—See Arthur J. Gallagher & Co.; *U.S. Public*, pg. 206
MC SHIPPING, INC.—See Irving Place Capital Management, L.P.; *U.S. Private*, pg. 2141
MC SHIPPING LTD.—See Irving Place Capital Management, L.P.; *U.S. Private*, pg. 2142
MC SHIPPING PTE LTD—See Irving Place Capital Management, L.P.; *U.S. Private*, pg. 2142
MC SHIPPING S.A.M.—See Irving Place Capital Management, L.P.; *U.S. Private*, pg. 2141
MC SIGN COMPANY—See Arcapita Group Holdings Limited; *Int'l*, pg. 542
M.C.S. INDUSTRIES INC.; *U.S. Private*, pg. 2528
MCS INTERNATIONAL GMBH; *Int'l*, pg. 4761
MCS LIFE INSURANCE CO.—See JLL Partners, LLC; *U.S. Private*, pg. 2213
MCS OF TAMPA, INC.; *U.S. Private*, pg. 2644
MC SOLUTION CO., LTD.—See Soulbrain Holdings Co., Ltd.; *Int'l*, pg. 7114
M&C S.P.A.; *Int'l*, pg. 4610
M&C SPECIALTIES COMPANY—See Illinois Tool Works Inc.; *U.S. Public*, pg. 1109
M&C SPECIALTIES (IRELAND) LIMITED—See Illinois Tool Works Inc.; *U.S. Public*, pg. 1109
M C SPINNERS PVT LTD; *Int'l*, pg. 4610
MC SQUARED ENERGY SERVICES, LLC; *U.S. Private*, pg. 2625
MCS SERVICER CO., LTD.—See Sumitomo Mitsui Financial Group, Inc.; *Int'l*, pg. 7293
MCS SERVICES LIMITED; *Int'l*, pg. 4761
MCS SP. Z O.O.—See Mangata Holding S.A.; *Int'l*, pg. 4670
M.C.S. STEEL PUBLIC COMPANY LIMITED; *Int'l*, pg. 4615

M.C.S. STEEL - XIAMEN CO., LTD.—See M.C.S. Steel Public Company Limited; *Int'l,* pg. 4615
MCSTAIN ENTERPRISES; *U.S. Private,* pg. 2644
MCSWAIN CARPETS INC.; *U.S. Private,* pg. 2644
MCSWEENEY RICCI INSURANCE AGENCY INC.; *U.S. Private,* pg. 2644
M & C SYSTEMS CO., LTD.—See Marui Group Co., Ltd.; *Int'l,* pg. 4713
MCT ASIA (PENANG) SDN BHD—See Cohu, Inc.; *U.S. Public,* pg. 530
MCT CREDIT UNION; *U.S. Private,* pg. 2644
MCTEC B.V.—See Merit Medical Systems, Inc.; *U.S. Public,* pg. 1425
M&C TECH INDIANA CORPORATION—See Moriroku Holdings Company, Ltd.; *Int'l,* pg. 5047
MC TECHNOS (THAILAND) CO., LTD.—See Mitsubishi Corporation; *Int'l,* pg. 4941
MC TERMINAL CO., LTD.—See Mitsubishi Corporation; *Int'l,* pg. 4939
MC TEST SERVICE, INC. - BOSTON—See H.I.G. Capital, LLC; *U.S. Private,* pg. 1833
MC TEST SERVICE, INC. - MEXICO—See H.I.G. Capital, LLC; *U.S. Private,* pg. 1833
MC TEST SERVICE, INC.—See H.I.G. Capital, LLC; *U.S. Private,* pg. 1833
MCTHAI COMPANY LTD.—See McDonald's Corporation; *U.S. Public,* pg. 1406
MCT HOLDINGS LLC—See Macquarie Group Limited; *Int'l,* pg. 4624
MCT INDUSTRIES INCORPORATED; *U.S. Private,* pg. 2644
MCTISH KUNKEL & ASSOCIATES INC.—See CDR Maguire Inc.; *U.S. Private,* pg. 803
MCT LUXEMBOURG MANAGEMENT S.A.R.L.—See Valartis Group AG; *Int'l,* pg. 8111
MC TOHCELLO (MALAYSIA) SDN. BHD.—See Mitsui Chemicals, Inc.; *Int'l,* pg. 4981
MCT REMAN LTD.—See Hasgo Group Ltd.; *Int'l,* pg. 3283
MCT (THAILAND) CO., LTD.—See Meta Health Limited; *Int'l,* pg. 4843
MCT TRADING, INC; *U.S. Private,* pg. 2645
MCTURBINE, INC.—See Textron Inc.; *U.S. Public,* pg. 2029
MCT WORLDWIDE LLC - MALAYSIA FACILITY—See Cohu, Inc.; *U.S. Public,* pg. 530
MCT WORLDWIDE LLC—See Cohu, Inc.; *U.S. Public,* pg. 530
MCTYRE TRUCKING COMPANY, INC.—See ACI Capital Co. LLC; *U.S. Private,* pg. 59
M-CUBED INFORMATION SYSTEMS, INC.—See Transformation Advisors Group, LLC; *U.S. Private,* pg. 4208
M CUBED TECHNOLOGIES, INC.—See Coherent Corp.; *U.S. Public,* pg. 529
MCUBE, INC.—See Kinduct Technologies, Inc.; *Int'l,* pg. 4166
MCU POWER LIMITED—See Mobicon Group Limited; *Int'l,* pg. 5009
MCV COMPANIES INC.; *U.S. Private,* pg. 2645
MCVEIGH ASSOCIATES LTD.—See InteleTravel.com; *U.S. Private,* pg. 2104
MCVEIGH GLOBAL MEETINGS & EVENTS, LLC—See InteleTravel.com; *U.S. Private,* pg. 2104
M/C VENTURE PARTNERS, LLC—See TAC Partners, Inc.; *U.S. Private,* pg. 3920
MCVICAR INDUSTRIES INC.; *Int'l,* pg. 4761
MCWANE, INC. - AB&I FOUNDRY DIVISION—See McWane, Inc.; *U.S. Private,* pg. 2645
MCWANE, INC. - AMERICAN R/D DIVISION—See McWane, Inc.; *U.S. Private,* pg. 2645
MCWANE, INC. - ANACO DIVISION—See McWane, Inc.; *U.S. Private,* pg. 2645
MCWANE, INC. - MCWANE POLES DIVISION—See McWane, Inc.; *U.S. Private,* pg. 2645
MCWANE, INC.; *U.S. Private,* pg. 2645
MCWANE, INC. - TYLER PIPE & COUPLING DIVISION—See McWane, Inc.; *U.S. Private,* pg. 2645
MCWANE, INC. - TYLER UNION COMPANY DIVISION—See McWane, Inc.; *U.S. Private,* pg. 2645
MCWANE SERVICES PRIVATE LTD—See McWane, Inc.; *U.S. Private,* pg. 2645
MCWHORTER CAPITAL PARTNERS, LLC; *U.S. Private,* pg. 2645
MCWILLIAMS ELECTRIC CO. INC.; *U.S. Private,* pg. 2645
MCWILLIAMS FORGE CO.; *U.S. Private,* pg. 2645
MCX EXPLORATION (USA) LTD.—See Mitsubishi Corporation; *Int'l,* pg. 4939
MC XPEDX, S. DE R.L. DE C.V.—See Clayton, Dubilier & Rice, LLC; *U.S. Private,* pg. 928
MCX TECHNOLOGIES CORPORATION; *U.S. Public,* pg. 1409
MDA CONSEIL SA—See Television Francaise 1 S.A.; *Int'l,* pg. 7542
MDA HUB LIMITED—See Advent International Corporation; *U.S. Private,* pg. 103
MDA INFORMATION PRODUCTS LTD.—See Advent International Corporation; *U.S. Private,* pg. 103
MDA INFORMATIONS SYSTEMS LLC—See Advent International Corporation; *U.S. Private,* pg. 103

MDA PROPERTIES LTD.—See ENL Limited; *Int'l,* pg. 2441
MDA SPACE & ROBOTICS LIMITED—See Advent International Corporation; *U.S. Private,* pg. 103
MDA SYSTEMS INC.—See Advent International Corporation; *U.S. Private,* pg. 103
MDA SYSTEMS LTD.—See Advent International Corporation; *U.S. Private,* pg. 103
M. DAVID PAUL & ASSOCIATES; *U.S. Private,* pg. 2526
M. DAVIS & SONS INC.; *U.S. Private,* pg. 2526
MDB CAPITAL HOLDINGS, LLC; *U.S. Public,* pg. 1409
MDB COMMUNICATIONS, INC.—See Hart Associates, Inc.; *U.S. Private,* pg. 1872
MD BENELUX, N.V.—See Industria de Diseno Textil, S.A.; *Int'l,* pg. 3666
MD BIOSCIENCES, INC.—See Great Point Partners, LLC; *U.S. Private,* pg. 1767
M-D BUILDING PRODUCTS, INC.; *U.S. Private,* pg. 2525
MD BUSINESS PARTNER CO., LTD.—See Mitsubishi Research Institute, Inc.; *Int'l,* pg. 4968
MD BUYLINE, INC.—See Clearlake Capital Group, L.P.; *U.S. Private,* pg. 937
MD BUYLINE, INC.—See SkyKnight Capital LLC; *U.S. Private,* pg. 3685
MD CARLISLE CONSTRUCTION CORP; *U.S. Private,* pg. 2646
MDCC MAGDEBURG-CITY-COM GMBH—See Morgan Stanley; *U.S. Public,* pg. 1473
MDC CORPORATE (US) INC.—See Stagwell, Inc.; *U.S. Public,* pg. 1927
MDCGROUP, INC.—See Argo Graphics Inc.; *Int'l,* pg. 562
M.D.C. HOLDINGS, INC.—See Sekisui House, Ltd.; *Int'l,* pg. 6697
M.D.C. LAND CORPORATION—See Sekisui House, Ltd.; *Int'l,* pg. 6697
M.D.C. LTD—See Africa Israel Investments Ltd.; *Int'l,* pg. 190
MD CONNECT, INC.—See Intellibright Corporation; *U.S. Private,* pg. 2105
MDC PARTNERS INC.—See Stagwell, Inc.; *U.S. Public,* pg. 1927
MDCP, LLC—See BioCryst Pharmaceuticals, Inc.; *U.S. Public,* pg. 335
MDC TECHNOLOGY GMBH—See Mercedes-Benz Group AG; *Int'l,* pg. 4825
MDC VACUUM PRODUCTS, LLC; *U.S. Private,* pg. 2646
MD-DE-DC AD PLACEMENT SERVICE; *U.S. Private,* pg. 2646
M.D. DESCANT, INC.; *U.S. Private,* pg. 2528
MD DRINKS, INC.—See Sunsweet Growers, Inc.; *U.S. Private,* pg. 3873
MDECHEM, INC.; *U.S. Public,* pg. 1409
MD&E CLARITY; *U.S. Private,* pg. 2646
MD ENTERPRISES INC.; *U.S. Private,* pg. 2646
MD ESTHETICS, LLC; *U.S. Private,* pg. 2646
M DEVELOPMENT LTD.; *Int'l,* pg. 4610
MDEVERYWHERE, INC.—See Marlin Equity Partners, LLC; *U.S. Private,* pg. 2584
MDEX AG; *Int'l,* pg. 4761
MD EXPRESS, LLC—See Nippon Express Holdings, Inc.; *Int'l,* pg. 5315
MDF COMMERCE, INC.—See KKR & Co. Inc.; *U.S. Public,* pg. 1267
MD FINANCIAL MANAGEMENT INC.—See The Bank of Nova Scotia; *Int'l,* pg. 7617
MDF LA BAIE INC.—See Compagnie de Saint-Gobain SA; *Int'l,* pg. 1723
MDG CONNECTED SOLUTIONS, INC.; *U.S. Private,* pg. 2646
MDG—See Freeman Decorating Co.; *U.S. Private,* pg. 1605
MDH ACQUISITION CORP; *U.S. Public,* pg. 1409
MD HELICOPTERS, INC.—See MB Global Advisers, LLC; *U.S. Private,* pg. 2623
MD HELICOPTERS, INC.—See MBIA Inc.; *U.S. Public,* pg. 1403
MDH ENGINEERED SOLUTIONS CORP.—See AtkinsRealis Group Inc.; *Int'l,* pg. 671
MDH INVESTMENT MANAGEMENT, INC.—See Farmers National Banc Corp.; *U.S. Public,* pg. 822
MDI ACCESS; *U.S. Private,* pg. 2646
M.DIAS BRANCO S.A. IND COM DE ALIMENTOS - FORTALEZA PLANT—See M. Dias Branco S.A. Industria e Comercio de Alimentos; *Int'l,* pg. 4615
M. DIAS BRANCO S.A. INDUSTRIA E COMERCIO DE ALIMENTOS - GORDURAS E MARGARINAS ESPECIAIS PLANT—See M. Dias Branco S.A. Industria e Comercio de Alimentos; *Int'l,* pg. 4615
M. DIAS BRANCO S.A. INDUSTRIA E COMERCIO DE ALIMENTOS - GRANDE MOINHO ARATU PLANT—See M. Dias Branco S.A. Industria e Comercio de Alimentos; *Int'l,* pg. 4615
M. DIAS BRANCO S.A. INDUSTRIA E COMERCIO DE ALIMENTOS - GRANDE MOINHO POTIGUAR PLANT—See M. Dias Branco S.A. Industria e Comercio de Alimentos; *Int'l,* pg. 4615
M. DIAS BRANCO S.A. INDUSTRIA E COMERCIO DE ALIMENTOS - GRANDE MOINHO TAMBAU PLANT—See M. Dias Branco S.A. Industria e Comercio de Alimentos; *Int'l,* pg. 4615

M. DIAS BRANCO S.A. INDUSTRIA E COMERCIO DE ALIMENTOS - MOINHO DIAS BRANCO PLANT—See M. Dias Branco S.A. Industria e Comercio de Alimentos; *Int'l,* pg. 4615
M. DIAS BRANCO S.A. INDUSTRIA E COMERCIO DE ALIMENTOS - MOINHO DIAS BRANCO ROLANDIA PLANT—See M. Dias Branco S.A. Industria e Comercio de Alimentos; *Int'l,* pg. 4615
M. DIAS BRANCO S.A. INDUSTRIA E COMERCIO DE ALIMENTOS; *Int'l,* pg. 4615
MDI ENERGIA SA; *Int'l,* pg. 4761
MDI ENTERTAINMENT LLC—See Light & Wonder, Inc.; *U.S. Public,* pg. 1314
MDI FRANCE SA—See MDI Worldwide; *U.S. Private,* pg. 2646
MDI GROUP, INC.—See Littlejohn & Co., LLC; *U.S. Private,* pg. 2471
MDI MANAGEMENT INC.—See Alex Lee, Inc.; *U.S. Private,* pg. 163
MDINR, LLC—See Linde plc; *Int'l,* pg. 4505
M & D INSULATION, LLC—See Installed Building Products, Inc.; *U.S. Public,* pg. 1133
MDI SDN. BHD.—See I-PEX Inc.; *Int'l,* pg. 3564
MDI SOLUTIONS; *Int'l,* pg. 4761
MDI WORLDWIDE; *U.S. Private,* pg. 2646
MDI WORLDWIDE UK LTD—See MDI Worldwide; *U.S. Private,* pg. 2646
MDJ INCORPORATED; *U.S. Private,* pg. 2646
MDJM LTD; *Int'l,* pg. 4761
MDL DISTRIBUCION Y LOGISTICA S.A.—See Deutsche Bahn AG; *Int'l,* pg. 2051
MDL DOORS INC.; *Int'l,* pg. 4761
MDL MEDICAL ADMINISTRATION LIMITED—See Watchstone Group plc; *Int'l,* pg. 8356
MD LOGISTICS, INC.—See Nippon Express Holdings, Inc.; *Int'l,* pg. 5317
M.D MACHINERY INC. - AICHI FACTORY—See Meiji Electric Industries Co., Ltd.; *Int'l,* pg. 4800
M.D MACHINERY INC.—See Meiji Electric Industries Co., Ltd.; *Int'l,* pg. 4800
MD MALIND PROMET A.D.; *Int'l,* pg. 4761
M & D MASONRY, INC.; *U.S. Private,* pg. 2522
MDM COMMERCIAL ENTERPRISES, INC.; *U.S. Private,* pg. 2646
MDM CONSTRUCTION CO. LTD.; *Int'l,* pg. 4761
MD MEDICAL GROUP INVESTMENT PLC; *Int'l,* pg. 4761
MD MEDICAL GROUP INVESTMENTS PLC; *Int'l,* pg. 4761
MDM ENGINEERING GROUP LIMITED—See John Wood Group PLC; *Int'l,* pg. 3983
MDM PERMIAN, INC.; *U.S. Public,* pg. 1409
MDM SUPPLY INCORPORATED; *U.S. Private,* pg. 2646
MD NOW MEDICAL CENTERS, INC.—See Brockway Moran & Partners, Inc.; *U.S. Private,* pg. 661
MDNX GROUP LTD.—See Kelso Place Asset Management LLP; *Int'l,* pg. 4122
MDNX—See Kelso Place Asset Management LLP; *Int'l,* pg. 4122
MD ON-LINE INC.; *U.S. Private,* pg. 2646
MD OPS, INC.—See UnitedHealth Group Incorporated; *U.S. Public,* pg. 2242
MD ORTHOPAEDICS, INC.; *U.S. Private,* pg. 2646
MDR LIMITED; *Int'l,* pg. 4761
M.D. SASS ASSOCIATES, INC.—See M.D. Sass Holdings, Inc.; *U.S. Private,* pg. 2528
M.D. SASS HOLDINGS, INC.; *U.S. Private,* pg. 2528
M.D. SASS INVESTORS SERVICES, INC.—See M.D. Sass Holdings, Inc.; *U.S. Private,* pg. 2528
MDS AUTOMATIKA D.O.O.—See Yokogawa Electric Corporation; *Int'l,* pg. 8592
MDSAVE, INC.—See Tendo Systems Inc.; *U.S. Private,* pg. 3966
MDS CHINA HOLDING CO., LTD.—See Hancom, Inc.; *Int'l,* pg. 3243
MDS CIRCUIT TECHNOLOGY, INC.—See Meiko Electronics Co., Ltd.; *Int'l,* pg. 4802
MDS COLLIVERY PROPRIETARY LIMITED—See Super Group Limited; *Int'l,* pg. 7334
MDS CO. LTD.—See CMIC Holdings Co., Ltd.; *Int'l,* pg. 1670
MDSCRIPTS, INC.; *U.S. Private,* pg. 2646
MDSINE, LLC—See KKR & Co. Inc.; *U.S. Public,* pg. 1246
MDS LOGISTICS LIMITED—See Dubai World Corporation; *Int'l,* pg. 2221
MDS MEDICAL SOFTWARE; *U.S. Private,* pg. 2646
MDSOL EUROPE LTD.—See Dassault Systemes S.A.; *Int'l,* pg. 1975
MDS PACIFIC INDIA PVT., LTD.—See Hancom, Inc.; *Int'l,* pg. 3243
MDS PACIFIC PTE., LTD.—See MDS Tech Inc.; *Int'l,* pg. 4762
MDS PACIFIC PTY LTD.—See MDS Tech Inc.; *Int'l,* pg. 4762
MD SPECIALIST HEALTHCARE PTE. LTD.—See Pacific Healthcare Holdings Ltd.; *Int'l,* pg. 5689
M.D. SP. Z O.O.—See Safwood S.p.A.; *Int'l,* pg. 6477
MDS TECH INC.; *Int'l,* pg. 4762
MDSTRATEGIES, INC.—See Aquiline Capital Partners LLC; *U.S. Private,* pg. 304

COMPANY NAME INDEX

MD SYSTEMS CO., LTD.—See Meiko Electronics Co., Ltd.; *Int'l*, pg. 4802
MDT ARMOR CORPORATION—See Greenbriar Equity Group, L.P.; *U.S. Private*, pg. 1775
MD TECH PHILS., INC.—See Hokuriku Electric Industry Co., Ltd.; *Int'l*, pg. 3445
MDT INTERNATIONAL INC.—See Medy-Tox Inc.; *Int'l*, pg. 4790
MDT INT'L SA—See Holy Stone Enterprise Co., Ltd.; *Int'l*, pg. 3454
M/D TOTCO—See NOV, Inc.; *U.S. Public*, pg. 1545
MDT SOFTWARE—See Desco Corporation; *U.S. Private*, pg. 1211
MDTVISION—See International Business Machines Corporation; *U.S. Public*, pg. 1149
MDU CONSTRUCTION SERVICES GROUP, INC.—See MDU Resources Group, Inc.; *U.S. Public*, pg. 1410
MDU RESOURCES GROUP, INC.; *U.S. Public*, pg. 1409
MD VERRE, S.A.—See Vidrala S.A.; *Int'l*, pg. 8192
MDVIP, LLC—See Charlesbank Capital Partners, LLC; *U.S. Private*, pg. 855
MDVIP, LLC—See The Goldman Sachs Group, Inc.; *U.S. Public*, pg. 2081
MDWERKS, INC.; *U.S. Public*, pg. 1411
MDW GOLD ROCK LLP—See Midway Gold Corp.; *U.S. Private*, pg. 2718
MDW MULDENDIENST WEST GMBH—See MVV Energie AG; *Int'l*, pg. 5108
MDXHEALTH B.V.—See MDxHealth S.A.; *Int'l*, pg. 4762
MDXHEALTH, INC.—See MDxHealth S.A.; *Int'l*, pg. 4762
MDXHEALTH S.A.; *Int'l*, pg. 4762
MDX PUBLIC COMPANY LIMITED; *Int'l*, pg. 4762
MDY HEALTHCARE LIMITED; *Int'l*, pg. 4762
ME2ON CO., LTD; *Int'l*, pg. 4763
MEAD CLARK LUMBER COMPANY INCORPORATED; *U.S. Private*, pg. 2646
MEADE COUNTY RURAL ELECTRIC COOP; *U.S. Private*, pg. 2646
MEADE ELECTRIC COMPANY, INC.—See L&H Company Inc.; *U.S. Private*, pg. 2362
MEADE GROUP INC.; *U.S. Private*, pg. 2647
MEADE INSTRUMENTS CORPORATION—See Ningbo Sunny Electronic Co. Ltd.; *Int'l*, pg. 5306
MEADE-KING ROBINSON & CO., LTD.; *Int'l*, pg. 4763
MEADE LEXUS OF LAKESIDE—See Meade Group Inc.; *U.S. Private*, pg. 2647
MEADEN SCREW PRODUCTS COMPANY; *U.S. Private*, pg. 2647
MEADERS FEEDS LTD—See Innodis Ltd; *Int'l*, pg. 3709
MEADE TRACTOR - LOUISVILLE—See Meade Tractor; *U.S. Private*, pg. 2647
MEADE TRACTOR; *U.S. Private*, pg. 2647
MEAD GILMAN & ASSOCIATES—See Atwell, LLC; *U.S. Private*, pg. 384
MEAD & HUNT, INC.; *U.S. Private*, pg. 2646
MEAD JOHNSON JAMAICA LTD.—See Bristol-Myers Squibb Company; *U.S. Public*, pg. 386
MEAD JOHNSON NUTRITION (INDIA) PRIVATE LIMITED—See Reckitt Benckiser Group plc; *Int'l*, pg. 6236
MEAD JOHNSON NUTRITION (PHILIPPINES), INC.—See Reckitt Benckiser Group plc; *Int'l*, pg. 6236
MEAD JOHNSON NUTRITION (VIETNAM) COMPANY LIMITED—See Reckitt Benckiser Group plc; *Int'l*, pg. 6236
MEADOR CHRYSLER JEEP; *U.S. Private*, pg. 2647
MEADORS CONSTRUCTION CO., INC.—See Reynolds Construction, LLC; *U.S. Private*, pg. 3418
MEADOR STAFFING SERVICES INC.; *U.S. Private*, pg. 2647
MEADOW BAY GOLD CORP.—See Mountain Valley MD Holdings, Inc.; *Int'l*, pg. 5057
MEADOW BROOK DAIRY COMPANY—See Dean Foods Company; *U.S. Private*, pg. 1183
MEADOWBROOK, INC.—See Fosun International Limited; *Int'l*, pg. 2752
MEADOWBROOK INSURANCE AGENCY FLORIDA—See Fosun International Limited; *Int'l*, pg. 2752
MEADOWBROOK INSURANCE AGENCY, INC.—See Arthur J. Gallagher & Co.; *U.S. Public*, pg. 206
MEADOWBROOK INSURANCE GROUP, INC.—See Fosun International Limited; *Int'l*, pg. 2751
MEADOWBROOK INSURANCE, INC.—See Fosun International Limited; *Int'l*, pg. 2752
MEADOWBROOK MEAT COMPANY, INC.—See Berkshire Hathaway Inc.; *U.S. Public*, pg. 312
MEADOW BURKE—See CRH plc; *Int'l*, pg. 1845
MEADOW BURKE—See CRH plc; *Int'l*, pg. 1845
MEADOW CHEESE CO. LTD.—See Ornua Co-operative Limited; *Int'l*, pg. 5642
MEADOWCRAFT, INC.; *U.S. Private*, pg. 2647
MEADOW FEED MAURITIUS—See Astral Foods Limited; *Int'l*, pg. 658
MEADOW FEEDS CAPE—See Astral Foods Limited; *Int'l*, pg. 658
MEADOW FEEDS DELMAS—See Astral Foods Limited; *Int'l*, pg. 658
MEADOW FEEDS EASTERN CAPE (PTY) LIMITED—See Astral Foods Limited; *Int'l*, pg. 658

MEADOW FEEDS KWA-ZULU NATAL—See Astral Foods Limited; *Int'l*, pg. 658
MEADOW FEEDS PORT ELIZABETH—See Astral Foods Limited; *Int'l*, pg. 658
MEADOW FEEDS PTY. LTD.—See Astral Foods Limited; *Int'l*, pg. 658
MEADOW FEEDS RANDFONTEIN—See Astral Foods Limited; *Int'l*, pg. 658
MEADOW FEEDS ZAMBIA—See Astral Foods Limited; *Int'l*, pg. 658
MEADOWFIELD SDN. BHD.—See Ireka Corporation Berhad; *Int'l*, pg. 3806
MEADOWFILL LANDFILL, INC.—See Waste Management, Inc.; *U.S. Public*, pg. 2331
MEADOW FOODS LIMITED; *Int'l*, pg. 4763
MEADOWFRESH DIARY CORPORATION—See Agrifoods International Cooperative LTD; *Int'l*, pg. 217
MEADOWHALL CENTRE LIMITED—See The British Land Company PLC; *Int'l*, pg. 7628
MEADOW INGREDIENTS USA, LLC—See Ornua Co-operative Limited; *Int'l*, pg. 5642
MEADOWKIRK RETREAT DELTA FARM; *U.S. Private*, pg. 2647
MEADOW LAKE OSB LIMITED PARTNERSHIP—See Tolko Industries Ltd.; *Int'l*, pg. 7798
MEADOW LAKE WIND FARM IV, L.L.C.—See EDP - Energias de Portugal, S.A.; *Int'l*, pg. 2314
MEADOW LAKE WIND FARM, L.L.C.—See EDP - Energias de Portugal, S.A.; *Int'l*, pg. 2314
MEADOWLAND FARMERS CO-OP INC.; *U.S. Private*, pg. 2647
MEADOWLANDS FIRE PROTECTION CORP.—See EMCOR Group, Inc.; *U.S. Public*, pg. 738
MEADOWLANDS NISSAN; *U.S. Private*, pg. 2647
THE MEADOWLARK GROUP, LLC—See Roadrunner Transportation Systems, Inc.; *U.S. Public*, pg. 1802
MEADOW MOCAMBIQUE LIMITADA—See Astral Foods Limited; *Int'l*, pg. 658
MEADOW MOZAMBIQUE LDA—See Astral Foods Limited; *Int'l*, pg. 658
MEADOW RIVER HARDWOOD, LLC.; *U.S. Private*, pg. 2647
MEADOWS CRA-B1, LLC—See Independence Realty Trust, Inc.; *U.S. Public*, pg. 1115
MEADOWS DIALYSIS, LLC—See DaVita Inc.; *U.S. Public*, pg. 641
MEADOWS FARMS INC.; *U.S. Private*, pg. 2647
MEADOWS HOMES INC; *U.S. Private*, pg. 2647
MEADOWS OFFICE FURNITURE COMPANY INC.; *U.S. Private*, pg. 2647
THE MEADOWS STANDARDBRED OWNERS ASSOCIATION; *U.S. Private*, pg. 4077
MEADOWS SURGERY CENTER, LLC—See KKR & Co. Inc.; *U.S. Public*, pg. 1246
MEADOWS URQUHART ACREE & COOK, LLP; *U.S. Private*, pg. 2647
MEADOW VALLEY CONTRACTORS INC.—See Insight Equity Holdings LLC; *U.S. Private*, pg. 2086
MEADOW VALLEY CORPORATION—See Insight Equity Holdings LLC; *U.S. Private*, pg. 2086
MEADVILLE FORGING COMPANY INC.—See Keller Group Inc.; *U.S. Private*, pg. 2275
MEADVILLE MEDICAL CENTER; *U.S. Private*, pg. 2647
MEAG CASH MANAGEMENT GMBH—See Munchener Ruckversicherungs AG; *Int'l*, pg. 5089
MEAG HONG KONG LIMITED—See Munchener Ruckversicherungs AG; *Int'l*, pg. 5089
MEAG LUXEMBOURG S.A.R.L.—See Munchener Ruckversicherungs AG; *Int'l*, pg. 5089
MEAG MUNICH ERGO ASSET MANAGEMENT GMBH—See Munchener Ruckversicherungs AG; *Int'l*, pg. 5089
MEAG MUNICH ERGO KAPITALANLAGEGESELLSCHAFT MBH—See Munchener Ruckversicherungs AG; *Int'l*, pg. 5089
MEAG PROPERTY MANAGEMENT GMBH—See Munchener Ruckversicherungs AG; *Int'l*, pg. 5089
MEAG VA-SYSTEM AB—See Heidelberg Materials AG; *Int'l*, pg. 3315
MEALEYS FURNITURE—See Parallel Investment Partners LLC; *U.S. Private*, pg. 3092
MEAL MART INCORPORATED; *U.S. Private*, pg. 2647
MEALPORT USA LLC—See Just Eat Takeaway.com N.V.; *Int'l*, pg. 4030
MEALS MERCADEO DE ALIMENTOS DE COLOMBIA S.A.S.—See Grupo Nutresa S.A.; *Int'l*, pg. 3133
MEALSUITE, INC.; *U.S. Private*, pg. 2647
MEAL TICKET; *U.S. Private*, pg. 2647
MEAL WORKS CO., LTD.—See Arclands Corp; *Int'l*, pg. 549
MEANS INDUSTRIES, INC.—See AMSTED Industries Incorporated; *U.S. Private*, pg. 2647
MEANS NURSERY INC.; *U.S. Private*, pg. 2647
MEANTIME BREWING COMPANY LTD.—See Asahi Group Holdings Ltd.; *Int'l*, pg. 594
MEARS CANADA CORP.—See Quanta Services, Inc.; *U.S. Public*, pg. 1752
MEARS CARE LIMITED—See Mears Group PLC; *Int'l*, pg. 4763

MEARS GROUP INC.—See Quanta Services, Inc.; *U.S. Public*, pg. 1752
MEARS GROUP PLC; *Int'l*, pg. 4763
MEARS INLINE INSPECTION SERVICES—See Quanta Services, Inc.; *U.S. Public*, pg. 1752
MEARS LIMITED—See Mears Group PLC; *Int'l*, pg. 4763
MEARS MOTOR LIVERY CORPORATION; *U.S. Private*, pg. 2647
MEARS NEW HOMES LIMITED—See Mears Group PLC; *Int'l*, pg. 4763
MEARS TRANSPORTATION GROUP, LLC—See Palm Beach Capital Partners LLC; *U.S. Private*, pg. 3079
MEARTHANE PRODUCTS CORPORATION; *U.S. Private*, pg. 2647
MEAS ASIA LIMITED—See TE Connectivity Ltd.; *Int'l*, pg. 7495
MEASAT BROADBAND (INTERNATIONAL) LTD—See MEASAT Global Berhad; *Int'l*, pg. 4763
MEASAT BROADCAST NETWORK SYSTEMS (BVI) LTD—See Astro All Asia Networks plc; *Int'l*, pg. 662
MEASAT GLOBAL BERHAD; *Int'l*, pg. 4763
MEASAT RADIO COMMUNICATIONS SDN. BHD.—See Astro All Asia Networks plc; *Int'l*, pg. 662
MEASAT SATELLITE SYSTEMS SDN BHD—See MEASAT Global Berhad; *Int'l*, pg. 4763
MEASE COUNTRYSIDE HOSPITAL—See BayCare Health System Inc.; *U.S. Private*, pg. 495
MEASE DUNEDIN HOSPITAL—See BayCare Health System Inc.; *U.S. Private*, pg. 495
MEAS FRANCE SAS—See TE Connectivity Ltd.; *Int'l*, pg. 7495
MEAS IRELAND (BETATHERM) LIMITED—See TE Connectivity Ltd.; *Int'l*, pg. 7495
MEAS NORWAY AS—See TE Connectivity Ltd.; *Int'l*, pg. 7495
MEAS SWITZERLAND S.A.R.L.—See TE Connectivity Ltd.; *Int'l*, pg. 7495
MEASURABL, INC.; *U.S. Private*, pg. 2648
MEASURED PROGRESS INC.; *U.S. Private*, pg. 2648
MEASUREFUL INC.—See Chirpify, Inc.; *U.S. Private*, pg. 887
MEASUREMENT ANALYSIS CORP.; *U.S. Private*, pg. 2648
MEASUREMENT COMPUTING CORPORATION—See National Instruments Corporation; *U.S. Private*, pg. 2856
MEASUREMENT INNOVATIONS CORP.; *U.S. Private*, pg. 2648
MEASUREMENT SPECIALTIES - ADVANCED THERMAL PRODUCTS OPERATIONS—See TE Connectivity Ltd.; *Int'l*, pg. 7495
MEASUREMENT SPECIALTIES (CHINA) LTD.—See TE Connectivity Ltd.; *Int'l*, pg. 7495
MEASUREMENT SPECIALTIES, INC.—See TE Connectivity Ltd.; *Int'l*, pg. 7495
MEASUREMENT SPECIALTIES - PRECISION INERTIAL PRODUCTS OPERATIONS—See TE Connectivity Ltd.; *Int'l*, pg. 7495
MEASUREMENT SYSTEMS INTERNATIONAL, INC.—See Rice Lake Weighing Systems, Inc.; *U.S. Private*, pg. 3425
MEASUREMENT TECHNOLOGY LIMITED—See Eaton Corporation plc; *Int'l*, pg. 2278
MEASUREMENT & VERIFICATION PTE. LTD.—See Furniweb Holdings Limited; *Int'l*, pg. 2846
MEAT BARNS AUSTRALIA PTY LTD—See Midfield Meat International Pty. Ltd.; *Int'l*, pg. 4886
MEATEOR FOODS LIMITED—See Scales Corporation Limited; *Int'l*, pg. 6611
THE MEAT FACTORY LIMITED—See Premium Brands Holdings Corporation; *Int'l*, pg. 5963
MEATHEAD MOVERS; *U.S. Private*, pg. 2648
MEATHEADS; *U.S. Private*, pg. 2648
THE MEAT MARKET INC.; *U.S. Private*, pg. 4077
MEAT ONE CORPORATION—See Sojitz Corporation; *Int'l*, pg. 7062
MEATPAK AUSTRALIA PTY. LTD.; *Int'l*, pg. 4763
MEBACS CO., LTD.—See Screen Holdings Co., Ltd.; *Int'l*, pg. 6655
ME BATH EXPERIENCE INC.—See Yellow Wood Partners LLC; *U.S. Private*, pg. 4587
MEB CONSTRUCTION SDN. BHD.—See Muhibbah Engineering (M) Bhd.; *Int'l*, pg. 5078
MEBEL24 OOD—See BHG Group AB; *Int'l*, pg. 1015
MEBELSYSTEM AD; *Int'l*, pg. 4763
MEB FLEET SDN BHD—See Muhibbah Engineering (M) Bhd.; *Int'l*, pg. 5078
MEBIN B.V.—See Heidelberg Materials AG; *Int'l*, pg. 3309
MEBIN LEEUWARDEN B.V.—See Heidelberg Materials AG; *Int'l*, pg. 3318
MEBIUS CO., LTD.—See Tokai Tokyo Financial Holdings, Inc.; *Int'l*, pg. 7781
MEBIUS PACKAGING CO., LTD.—See Toyo Seikan Group Holdings, Ltd.; *Int'l*, pg. 7856
MEBIX, INC.—See Sony Group Corporation; *Int'l*, pg. 7102
MEBLE POLONIA LTD.—See Fabryki Mebli Forte S.A.; *Int'l*, pg. 2600
MEB MARKETING SDN. BHD.—See Muhibbah Engineering (M) Bhd.; *Int'l*, pg. 5078

MEBELSYSTEM AD — CORPORATE AFFILIATIONS

MEB ON FIRST, INC.—See Ark Restaurants Corp.; *U.S. Public*, pg. 193

MEB SAFETY SERVICES GMBH—See PNE AG; *Int'l*, pg. 5900

MEBTEL, INC.—See Lumen Technologies, Inc.; *U.S. Public*, pg. 1347

MEBUKI FINANCIAL GROUP, INC.; *Int'l*, pg. 4763

MEBUKI LEASE CO., LTD.—See Mebuki Financial Group, Inc.; *Int'l*, pg. 4763

MEC3 OPTIMA SRL—See The Riverside Company; *U.S. Private*, pg. 4109

MECA BILVERKSTAD TUNBY AB—See MEKO AB; *Int'l*, pg. 4805

MECABRIVE IND. SAS—See Figeac-Aero SA; *Int'l*, pg. 2660

MECACHROME CANADA—See Mecachrome International Inc.; *Int'l*, pg. 4765

MECACHROME INTERNATIONAL INC.; *Int'l*, pg. 4765

MECACHROME TANGIER—See Mecachrome International Inc.; *Int'l*, pg. 4765

MECAER AMERICA INC.—See Mecaer S.p.A; *Int'l*, pg. 4765

MECAER S.P.A; *Int'l*, pg. 4765

MECAFRANCE (DEUTSCHLAND) GMBH—See Pentair plc; *Int'l*, pg. 5789

MECAHERS AERONAUTICA, LDA—See Mecachrome International Inc.; *Int'l*, pg. 4765

MECA INC.; *U.S. Private*, pg. 2648

MECAIR S.R.L.—See Pentair plc; *Int'l*, pg. 5789

MECALAB-M. BRAUN AG—See INDUS Holding AG; *Int'l*, pg. 3663

MECALAC BAUMASCHINEN GMBH—See Groupe Mecalac S.A.; *Int'l*, pg. 3108

MECALAC IDF, S.A.S—See Groupe Mecalac S.A.; *Int'l*, pg. 3108

MECALUX ARGENTINA, S.A.—See Acerolux SL; *Int'l*, pg. 101

MECALUX BELGIUM S.A.—See Acerolux SL; *Int'l*, pg. 101

MECALUX DO BRASIL SISTEMAS DE ARMAZENAGEM LTDA.—See Acerolux SL; *Int'l*, pg. 102

MECALUX ESMENA—See Acerolux SL; *Int'l*, pg. 101

MECALUX FRANCE S.A.R.L.—See Acerolux SL; *Int'l*, pg. 101

MECALUX GMBH—See Acerolux SL; *Int'l*, pg. 101

MECALUX MILANO, S.R.L.—See Acerolux SL; *Int'l*, pg. 102

MECALUX SA—See Acerolux SL; *Int'l*, pg. 102

MECALUX, S.A.—See Acerolux SL; *Int'l*, pg. 101

MECALUX SERVIS, S.A.—See Acerolux SL; *Int'l*, pg. 102

MECALUX SP. Z O.O.—See Acerolux SL; *Int'l*, pg. 102

MECALUX (UK) LTD.—See Acerolux SL; *Int'l*, pg. 101

MECANA UMWELTTECHNIK GMBH—See METAWATER Co., Ltd.; *Int'l*, pg. 4851

MECANICA CODLEA SA—See Transilvania Investments Alliance S.A.; *Int'l*, pg. 7900

MECANICA FINA SA; *Int'l*, pg. 4765

MECANISMOS DE MATAMORES S.A. DE C.V.—See TransDigm Group Incorporated; *U.S. Public*, pg. 2183

MECANIZACIONES DEL SUR-MECASUR, S.A.—See Cie Automotive S.A.; *Int'l*, pg. 1604

MECANO COMPONENTS (SHANGHAI) CO. LTD.—See Phoenix Mecano AG; *Int'l*, pg. 5852

MECANOR-RUMANIA S.R.L.—See Corpfin Capital SA; *Int'l*, pg. 1802

MECA NORWAY AS—See MEKO AB; *Int'l*, pg. 4805

MECAPLAST INDIA PVT LTD.—See Equistone Partners Europe Limited; *Int'l*, pg. 2486

MECAPLAST SERBIA D.O.O.—See Equistone Partners Europe Limited; *Int'l*, pg. 2486

MECAPLAST SHANGHAI—See Equistone Partners Europe Limited; *Int'l*, pg. 2487

MECAPLAST SHENYANG CAR COMPONENTS CO., LTD.—See Equistone Partners Europe Limited; *Int'l*, pg. 2487

MECARO CO., LTD.; *Int'l*, pg. 4765

MECAR S.A.—See GIAT Industries S.A.; *Int'l*, pg. 2962

MECA SCANDINAVIA AB—See MEKO AB; *Int'l*, pg. 4805

MECA SERVICE AS—See MEKO AB; *Int'l*, pg. 4805

MECAS ESI S.R.O.—See Keysight Technologies, Inc.; *U.S. Public*, pg. 1227

MECASET N.V.; *Int'l*, pg. 4765

MECASONIC ESPANA SA—See Crest Group Inc.; *U.S. Private*, pg. 1096

MECASONIC SA—See Crest Group Inc.; *U.S. Private*, pg. 1096

MECASONIC UK LTD—See Crest Group Inc.; *U.S. Private*, pg. 1096

MECA SPORTSWEAR INC.; *U.S. Private*, pg. 2648

MEC A/S—See IDEC Corporation; *Int'l*, pg. 3589

MEC & TECHNOLOGY MACHINE, INC.—See May River Capital, LLC; *U.S. Private*, pg. 2620

MECATISS—See VINCI S.A.; *Int'l*, pg. 8233

MECATOOL AG—See Georg Fischer AG; *Int'l*, pg. 2935

MECA VERKSTADSDRIFT AB—See MEKO AB; *Int'l*, pg. 4805

MECCA BINGO LIMITED—See The Rank Group Plc; *Int'l*, pg. 7678

MECCANICA HOLDINGS USA, INC.—See Leonardo S.p.A.; *Int'l*, pg. 4459

MECCANO SA—See Spin Master Corp.; *Int'l*, pg. 7136

MEC CHINA SPECIALTY PRODUCTS (SUZHOU) CO., LTD.—See MEC COMPANY LTD.; *Int'l*, pg. 4764

MEC COMPANY LTD. - NAGAOKA FACTORY—See MEC COMPANY LTD.; *Int'l*, pg. 4764

MEC COMPANY LTD. - NISHINOMIYA FACTORY—See MEC COMPANY LTD.; *Int'l*, pg. 4764

MEC COMPANY LTD.; *Int'l*, pg. 4764

M-E-C COMPANY; *U.S. Private*, pg. 2526

MECCON, INC.; *U.S. Private*, pg. 2648

MECCON INDUSTRIES INC.—See Monico Inc.; *U.S. Private*, pg. 2770

MECCOR INDUSTRIES, LTD.; *U.S. Private*, pg. 2648

MECCS SUPPORT CO., LTD.—See Nippon Telegraph & Telephone Corporation; *Int'l*, pg. 5343

MECCS TECHNO KYUSHU CO., LTD.—See Nippon Telegraph & Telephone Corporation; *Int'l*, pg. 5343

MECCS TECHNO NISHINIHON CO., LTD.—See Nippon Telegraph & Telephone Corporation; *Int'l*, pg. 5343

MECCS TECHNO TOHOKU CO., LTD.—See Nippon Telegraph & Telephone Corporation; *Int'l*, pg. 5343

MECCS TECHNO TOKAI CO., LTD.—See Nippon Telegraph & Telephone Corporation; *Int'l*, pg. 5343

MEC DELACHAUX S.R.L.—See CVC Capital Partners SICAV-FIS S.A.; *Int'l*, pg. 1887

MEC DESIGN INTERNATIONAL CORPORATION—See Mitsubishi Estate Co., Ltd.; *Int'l*, pg. 4946

MECELEC COMPOSITES SA; *Int'l*, pg. 4765

MECER INTER-ED PROPRIETARY LIMITED—See Mustek Limited; *Int'l*, pg. 5103

MEC EUROPE N.V.—See MEC COMPANY LTD.; *Int'l*, pg. 4764

MEC FINE CHEMICAL (ZHUHAI) LTD.—See MEC COMPANY LTD.; *Int'l*, pg. 4764

MECHADYNE INTERNATIONAL LTD.—See Rheinmetall AG; *Int'l*, pg. 6322

MECHALESS GMBH—See ELMOS Semiconductor AG; *Int'l*, pg. 2368

MECHALESS SYSTEMS GMBH—See ELMOS Semiconductor AG; *Int'l*, pg. 2368

MECHANICAL CONSTRUCTION SERVICES; *U.S. Private*, pg. 2648

MECHANICAL CONTRACTING & SERVICES CO. WLL—See Mohammed Jalal & Sons WLL; *Int'l*, pg. 5018

MECHANICAL CONTRACTING SERVICES INC.; *U.S. Private*, pg. 2648

MECHANICAL CONTRACTORS, INC.; *U.S. Private*, pg. 2648

MECHANICAL DATA INC—See Trimble, Inc.; *U.S. Public*, pg. 2192

MECHANICAL DYNAMICS & ANALYSIS LLC—See Mitsubishi Heavy Industries, Ltd.; *Int'l*, pg. 4956

MECHANICAL ENGINEERING & CONSTRUCTION CORPORATION—See Ares Management Corporation; *U.S. Public*, pg. 189

MECHANICAL EQUIPMENT CO. INC.—See Mingledorff's Inc.; *U.S. Private*, pg. 2742

MECHANICAL EQUIPMENT COMPANY INC.; *U.S. Private*, pg. 2648

MECHANICAL, INC.—See The Helm Group; *U.S. Private*, pg. 4051

MECHANICAL INDUSTRIES, LLC; *U.S. Private*, pg. 2648

MECHANICAL LLOYD COMPANY LTD; *Int'l*, pg. 4765

MECHANICAL MAINTENANCE INCORPORATED; *U.S. Private*, pg. 2648

MECHANICAL PRODUCTS INC.; *U.S. Private*, pg. 2649

MECHANICAL REPS INC.—See Mechanical Reps Inc.; *U.S. Private*, pg. 2649

MECHANICAL REPS INC.; *U.S. Private*, pg. 2649

MECHANICAL SERVANTS, LLC—See Lil' Drug Store Products, Inc.; *U.S. Private*, pg. 2455

MECHANICAL SERVICES INC.; *U.S. Private*, pg. 2649

MECHANICAL SERVICES LTD.—See Daikin Industries, Ltd.; *Int'l*, pg. 1936

MECHANICAL SIMULATION CORP.—See Applied Intuition, Inc.; *U.S. Private*, pg. 299

MECHANICAL SOLUTIONS, INC.—See ABM Industries, Inc.; *U.S. Public*, pg. 26

MECHANICAL SUPPLY—See Northern Machining & Repair, Inc.; *U.S. Private*, pg. 2953

MECHANICAL SYSTEMS INC.; *U.S. Private*, pg. 2649

MECHANICAL TECHNICAL SERVICES, INC.—See Comfort Systems USA, Inc.; *U.S. Public*, pg. 544

MECHANICAL TOOL & ENGINEERING CO.; *U.S. Private*, pg. 2649

THE MECHANIC GROUP, INC.—See Hellman & Friedman LLC; *U.S. Private*, pg. 1909

MECHANICNET GROUP, INC.—See Clayton, Dubilier & Rice, LLC; *U.S. Private*, pg. 923

MECHANICS BANC HOLDING COMPANY; *U.S. Private*, pg. 2649

MECHANICS BANK—See Ford Financial Fund II, L.P.; *U.S. Private*, pg. 1564

MECHANICS BANK—See Mechanics Banc Holding Company; *U.S. Private*, pg. 2649

MECHANICS BUILDING MATERIAL CO.; *U.S. Private*, pg. 2649

MECHANICSBURG FARMERS GRAIN CO.; *U.S. Private*, pg. 2649

MECHANICS CONSTRUCTION & FOODSTUFF JOINT STOCK COMPANY; *Int'l*, pg. 4765

MECHANICS SAVINGS BANK NA; *U.S. Private*, pg. 2649

MECHANICSVILLE CONCRETE, INC.—See Titan Cement Company S.A.; *Int'l*, pg. 7759

MECHANIK CENTER ERLANGEN GMBH—See Siemens Aktiengesellschaft; *Int'l*, pg. 6887

MECHANISED FARMING (PTY) LTD.—See Sefalana Holdings Company Limited; *Int'l*, pg. 6679

MECHANIZATION COMPANY LIMITED—See United Investments Ltd.; *Int'l*, pg. 8070

MECHANIZED ENGINEERING COMPANY—See Shaanxi Construction Machinery Co., Ltd.; *Int'l*, pg. 6747

MECHANOS CO., LTD—See Trancom Co., Ltd.; *Int'l*, pg. 7891

MECHANOVENT CORPORATION—See The New York Blower Company, Inc.; *U.S. Private*, pg. 4083

MECHATRONIC AG; *Int'l*, pg. 4765

MECHATRONICS CONTROLS SYSTEMS YANGZHOU CO., LTD.—See Addtech AB; *Int'l*, pg. 134

MECHATRONICS INC.; *U.S. Private*, pg. 2649

MECHATRONICS SYSTEMS WALES LTD.—See JTEKT Corporation; *Int'l*, pg. 4019

MECHDYNE CANADA—See Mechdyne Corp.; *U.S. Private*, pg. 2649

MECHDYNE CORP.; *U.S. Private*, pg. 2649

MECHEL BLUESTONE INC.; *U.S. Private*, pg. 2649

MECHEL CARBON AG—See Mechel PAO; *Int'l*, pg. 4766

MECHEL CARBON SINGAPORE PTE. LTD.—See Mechel PAO; *Int'l*, pg. 4766

MECHEL COKE OOO—See Mechel PAO; *Int'l*, pg. 4766

MECHEL ENERGO OOO—See Mechel PAO; *Int'l*, pg. 4766

MECHEL ENGINEERING OOO—See Mechel PAO; *Int'l*, pg. 4766

MECHELEN RIGID PAPER—See Sonoco Products Company; *U.S. Public*, pg. 1904

MECHEL HARDWARE OOO—See Mechel PAO; *Int'l*, pg. 4766

MECHEL MATERIALS OOO—See Mechel PAO; *Int'l*, pg. 4766

MECHEL MINING OAO—See Mechel PAO; *Int'l*, pg. 4766

MECHEL MINING TRADING HOUSE OOO—See Mechel PAO; *Int'l*, pg. 4766

MECHEL PAO; *Int'l*, pg. 4765

MECHEL SERVICE GLOBAL B.V.—See Mechel PAO; *Int'l*, pg. 4766

MECHEL SERVICE—See Mechel PAO; *Int'l*, pg. 4766

MECHEL SERVICE STAHLHANDEL AUSTRIA GMBH—See Mechel PAO; *Int'l*, pg. 4766

MECHEL-STEEL MANAGEMENT OOO—See Mechel PAO; *Int'l*, pg. 4766

MECHEL TRADING AG—See Mechel PAO; *Int'l*, pg. 4766

MECHEL TRADING LTD—See Mechel PAO; *Int'l*, pg. 4766

MECHEL TRADING LTD., ZUG—See Mechel PAO; *Int'l*, pg. 4766

MECHEL TRANS AUTO OOO—See Mechel PAO; *Int'l*, pg. 4766

MECHELTRANS MANAGEMENT OOO—See Mechel PAO; *Int'l*, pg. 4766

MECHEMA CHEMICALS INTERNATIONAL CORP.; *Int'l*, pg. 4766

MECHMAR BOILERS SDN. BHD.—See Mechmar Corporation (Malaysia) Berhad; *Int'l*, pg. 4766

MECHMAR CAPITAL SDN. BHD.—See Mechmar Corporation (Malaysia) Berhad; *Int'l*, pg. 4766

MECHMAR COCHRAN BOILERS (M) SDN. BHD.—See Mechmar Corporation (Malaysia) Berhad; *Int'l*, pg. 4766

MECHMAR CORPORATION (MALAYSIA) BERHAD; *Int'l*, pg. 4766

MECHMAR (HK) LTD.—See Mechmar Corporation (Malaysia) Berhad; *Int'l*, pg. 4766

MEC HOLDING GMBH; *Int'l*, pg. 4764

MEC (HONG KONG) LTD.—See MEC COMPANY LTD.; *Int'l*, pg. 4764

MECH-POWER GENERATOR PTE. LTD.—See XMH Holdings Ltd.; *Int'l*, pg. 8536

MECHPUMP SDN. BHD.—See Dancomech Holdings Berhad; *Int'l*, pg. 1959

MECHTRONICS CORPORATION; *U.S. Private*, pg. 2649

MECHTRONIX TEXTRON CANADA INC.—See Textron Inc.; *U.S. Public*, pg. 2029

MEC HUMAN RESOURCES, INC.—See Mitsubishi Estate Co., Ltd.; *Int'l*, pg. 4946

MECHWORKS S.R.L.—See Wipro Limited; *Int'l*, pg. 8432

MEC INFORMATION DEVELOPMENT CO., LTD.—See Mitsubishi Estate Co., Ltd.; *Int'l*, pg. 4946

MEC INTERACTION—See WPP plc; *Int'l*, pg. 8473

MEC INTERACTION—See WPP plc; *Int'l*, pg. 8473

MEC INTERACTION—See WPP plc; *Int'l*, pg. 8473

MEC INTERACTION—See WPP plc; *Int'l*, pg. 8473

MEC INTERACTION—See WPP plc; *Int'l*, pg. 8473

MEC INTERACTION—See WPP plc; *Int'l*, pg. 8473

MEC JAPAN—See WPP plc; *Int'l*, pg. 8474

M. ECKER & CO. OF FLORIDA, INC.—See Ecker Enterprises Inc.; *U.S. Private*, pg. 1328

COMPANY NAME INDEX

M. ECKER & CO. OF ILLINOIS, INC.—See Ecker Enterprises Inc.; *U.S. Private*, pg. 1328
MECKLENBURG COMMUNICATIONS SERVICES, INC.—See Mecklenburg Electric Cooperative; *U.S. Private*, pg. 2649
MECKLENBURG ELECTRIC COOPERATIVE; *U.S. Private*, pg. 2649
MECKLENBURGER LANDTECHNIK GMBH—See Claas KGaA mbH; *Int'l*, pg. 1641
MECKLENBURGER METALLGUSS GMBH—See DIHAG Holding GmbH; *Int'l*, pg. 2124
MECKLERMEDIA CORPORATION; *U.S. Private*, pg. 2649
MECKLEYS LIMESTONE PRODUCTS; *U.S. Private*, pg. 2649
MEC - LATIN AMERICAN HQ—See WPP plc; *Int'l*, pg. 8473
MECNO SERVICES S.R.L.—See Sdiptech AB; *Int'l*, pg. 6659
MECO CORPORATION; *U.S. Private*, pg. 2649
MECO ENGINEERING LTD.—See Meco Holdings Co. Ltd.; *Int'l*, pg. 4767
MECO EQUIPMENT ENGINEERS B.V—See BE Semiconductor Industries N.V.; *Int'l*, pg. 931
MECO HOLDINGS CO. LTD. - LOUISIANA PLANT—See Meco Holdings Co. Ltd.; *Int'l*, pg. 4767
MECO HOLDINGS CO. LTD.; *Int'l*, pg. 4766
MECO INC.; *U.S. Private*, pg. 2649
MECO, INC.—See Dubai Holding LLC; *Int'l*, pg. 2218
MECOMB MALAYSIA SDN. BHD.—See Sime Darby Berhad; *Int'l*, pg. 6929
MECOMB SINGAPORE LIMITED—See Sime Darby Berhad; *Int'l*, pg. 6929
MECOMB (THAILAND) LTD.—See Fuji Corporation; *Int'l*, pg. 2810
MECOM FINANCE LIMITED—See DPG Media Group NV; *Int'l*, pg. 2189
MECOM GROUP PLC—See DPG Media Group NV; *Int'l*, pg. 2188
MECOM LTD.; *U.S. Private*, pg. 2650
M-E COMPANIES, INC.; *U.S. Private*, pg. 2525
MECOM POWER & CONSTRUCTION LIMITED; *Int'l*, pg. 4767
MECO NORTH FLORIDA INC.—See Meco of Atlanta Incorporated; *U.S. Private*, pg. 2040
ME CONSTRUCTION LTD.; *Int'l*, pg. 4762
MECO OF ATLANTA INCORPORATED; *U.S. Private*, pg. 2649
MECO OF SAVANNAH INC.—See Meco of Atlanta Incorporated; *U.S. Private*, pg. 2649
MECO S.A.—See The Swatch Group Ltd.; *Int'l*, pg. 7691
MECO U.K.—See Mechanical Equipment Company Inc.; *U.S. Private*, pg. 2648
MECO WATER PURIFICATION (ASIA) PTE LTD—See Meco Holdings Co. Ltd.; *Int'l*, pg. 4767
MEC RESOURCES LIMITED; *Int'l*, pg. 4765
MECS AFRICA (PROPRIETARY) LIMITED—See Sebata Holdings; *Int'l*, pg. 6669
MECS CORPORATION—See Kinden Corporation; *Int'l*, pg. 4166
MEC SERVICES PTY LIMITED—See BSA Limited; *Int'l*, pg. 1201
MECS EUROPE/AFRICA BVBA—See DuPont de Nemours, Inc.; *U.S. Public*, pg. 694
MECS, INC.—See DuPont de Nemours, Inc.; *U.S. Public*, pg. 694
MEC—See WPP plc; *Int'l*, pg. 8473
MEC—See WPP plc; *Int'l*, pg. 8473
MEC—See WPP plc; *Int'l*, pg. 8473
MEC—See WPP plc; *Int'l*, pg. 8473
MEC—See WPP plc; *Int'l*, pg. 8473
MEC—See WPP plc; *Int'l*, pg. 8473
MEC—See WPP plc; *Int'l*, pg. 8473
MEC—See WPP plc; *Int'l*, pg. 8473
MEC—See WPP plc; *Int'l*, pg. 8473
MEC—See WPP plc; *Int'l*, pg. 8473
MEC—See WPP plc; *Int'l*, pg. 8474
MEC—See WPP plc; *Int'l*, pg. 8474
MEC—See WPP plc; *Int'l*, pg. 8474
MEC—See WPP plc; *Int'l*, pg. 8474
MEC SPECIALTY CHEMICAL (THAILAND) CO., LTD.—See MEC COMPANY LTD.; *Int'l*, pg. 4764
MEC TAIWAN COMPANY LTD.—See MEC COMPANY LTD.; *Int'l*, pg. 4764
MEC TECHNO CO., LTD.—See Mitsubishi Chemical Group Corporation; *Int'l*, pg. 4931
MEC TECHNOLOGY CO., LTD.—See WPG Holdings Limited; *Int'l*, pg. 8461
MEC-TRACK S.R.L.—See Caterpillar, Inc.; *U.S. Public*, pg. 451
MECTRON JAPAN, INC.—See Citizen Watch Co., Ltd.; *Int'l*, pg. 1624
MEC UK LIMITED—See Mitsubishi Estate Co., Ltd.; *Int'l*, pg. 4947
MECUM AUCTION, INC.; *U.S. Private*, pg. 2650
MEC USA, INC.—See Mitsubishi Estate Co., Ltd.; *Int'l*, pg. 4947
MEC/Y&R MEDIA—See WPP plc; *Int'l*, pg. 8474

MED3000 GROUP, INC. - OLDSMAR—See McKesson Corporation; *U.S. Public*, pg. 1407
MED3000 GROUP, INC. - SCOTTSDALE—See McKesson Corporation; *U.S. Public*, pg. 1408
MED3000 GROUP, INC.—See McKesson Corporation; *U.S. Public*, pg. 1407
MEDA AB—See Viatris Inc.; *U.S. Public*, pg. 2293
MEDA AS—See Viatris Inc.; *U.S. Public*, pg. 2293
MEDA A/S—See Viatris Inc.; *U.S. Public*, pg. 2293
MEDACIST SOLUTION GROUP, LLC—See Thoma Bravo, L.P.; *U.S. Private*, pg. 4146
MEDAC PHARMA, INC.—See Medexus Pharmaceuticals Inc.; *Int'l*, pg. 4769
MEDACS HEALTHCARE AUSTRALIA (PTY) LIMITED—See HFBG Holding B.V.; *Int'l*, pg. 3375
MEDACS HEALTHCARE LIMITED—See HFBG Holding B.V.; *Int'l*, pg. 3375
MEDACS HEALTHCARE PLC—See HFBG Holding B.V.; *Int'l*, pg. 3375
MEDACTA AUSTRALIA PTY LTD—See Medacta Group SA; *Int'l*, pg. 4767
MEDACTA AUSTRIA GMBH—See Medacta Group SA; *Int'l*, pg. 4767
MEDACTA BELGIUM SPRL—See Medacta Group SA; *Int'l*, pg. 4767
MEDACTA CANADA INC.—See Medacta Group SA; *Int'l*, pg. 4767
MEDACTA ESPANA S.L.—See Medacta Group SA; *Int'l*, pg. 4767
MEDACTA FRANCE SAS—See Medacta Group SA; *Int'l*, pg. 4767
MEDACTA GERMANY GMBH—See Medacta Group SA; *Int'l*, pg. 4767
MEDACTA GROUP SA; *Int'l*, pg. 4767
MEDACTA ITALIA S.R.L.—See Medacta Group SA; *Int'l*, pg. 4767
MEDACTA JAPAN CO. LTD.—See Medacta Group SA; *Int'l*, pg. 4767
MEDACTA UK LTD.—See Medacta Group SA; *Int'l*, pg. 4767
MEDACTA USA INC—See Medacta Group SA; *Int'l*, pg. 4767
MEDADVISOR LIMITED; *Int'l*, pg. 4767
MEDAES LIMITED—See Atlas Copco AB; *Int'l*, pg. 681
MEDAFOR, INC.—See Becton, Dickinson & Company; *U.S. Public*, pg. 291
MEDAG AB—See Viatris Inc.; *U.S. Public*, pg. 2294
MEDA GERMANY HOLDING GMBH—See Viatris Inc.; *U.S. Public*, pg. 2293
MEDA HEALTH SALES IRELAND LTD—See Viatris Inc.; *U.S. Public*, pg. 2293
MEDAIRE INC.; *U.S. Private*, pg. 2650
MEDAIRE LTD.—See MedAire Inc.; *U.S. Private*, pg. 2650
MEDA LIMITED; *Int'l*, pg. 4767
MEDALIST DIVERSIFIED REIT, INC.; *U.S. Public*, pg. 1411
MEDALIST PARTNERS, LP; *U.S. Private*, pg. 2650
MEDALIST VILLAGE CLUB, INC.—See Great White Shark Enterprises, Inc.; *U.S. Private*, pg. 1768
MEDALLIA ARGENTINA—See Thoma Bravo, L.P.; *U.S. Private*, pg. 4149
MEDALLIA AUSTRALIA PTY. LTD.—See Thoma Bravo, L.P.; *U.S. Private*, pg. 4149
MEDALLIA DIGITAL LTD.—See Thoma Bravo, L.P.; *U.S. Private*, pg. 4149
MEDALLIA FRANCE SARL—See Thoma Bravo, L.P.; *U.S. Private*, pg. 4149
MEDALLIA GMBH—See Thoma Bravo, L.P.; *U.S. Private*, pg. 4149
MEDALLIA, INC.—See Thoma Bravo, L.P.; *U.S. Private*, pg. 4149
MEDALLIA SINGAPORE PTE. LTD.—See Thoma Bravo, L.P.; *U.S. Private*, pg. 4149
MEDALLIA SPAIN S.L.U.—See Thoma Bravo, L.P.; *U.S. Private*, pg. 4149
MEDALLIA UK—See Thoma Bravo, L.P.; *U.S. Private*, pg. 4149
MEDALLIC ART COMPANY, LTD.; *U.S. Private*, pg. 2650
MEDALLION AUTO MANAGEMENT LLC—See Ameritrans Capital Corporation; *U.S. Public*, pg. 115
MEDALLION BANK—See Medallion Financial Corp.; *U.S. Public*, pg. 1411
MEDALLION BUSINESS CREDIT, LLC—See Medallion Financial Corp.; *U.S. Public*, pg. 1411
MEDALLION CABINETRY—See Zurn Elkay Water Solutions Corporation; *U.S. Public*, pg. 2412
MEDALLION CAPITAL, INC.—See Medallion Financial Corp.; *U.S. Public*, pg. 1411
MEDALLION FINANCIAL CORP.; *U.S. Public*, pg. 1411
MEDALLION FOODS, INC.—See Conagra Brands, Inc.; *U.S. Public*, pg. 564
MEDALLION FUNDING LLC—See Medallion Financial Corp.; *U.S. Public*, pg. 1411
MEDALLION HOMES GULF COAST, INC.; *U.S. Private*, pg. 2650
MEDALLION INDUSTRIES INC.; *U.S. Private*, pg. 2650
MEDALLION INSTRUMENTATION SYSTEMS LLC.; *U.S. Private*, pg. 2650

MEDALLION LABORATORIES—See General Mills, Inc.; *U.S. Public*, pg. 922
MEDALLION METALS LIMITED; *Int'l*, pg. 4767
MEDALLION PLASTICS INC.—See Patrick Industries, Inc.; *U.S. Public*, pg. 1652
MEDALLION RESOURCES LTD.; *Int'l*, pg. 4767
MEDALLION SPORTS MEDIA, INC.—See Medallion Financial Corp.; *U.S. Public*, pg. 1411
MEDALLIST DEVELOPMENTS INC.—See Great White Shark Enterprises, Inc.; *U.S. Private*, pg. 1768
MEDALLIST DEVELOPMENTS INC.—See Macquarie Group Limited; *Int'l*, pg. 4630
MEDALLIST DEVELOPMENTS PTY. LIMITED—See Great White Shark Enterprises, Inc.; *U.S. Private*, pg. 1768
MEDALLIST DEVELOPMENTS PTY. LIMITED—See Macquarie Group Limited; *Int'l*, pg. 4630
MEDALTUS, LLC—See HealthEdge Investment Partners, LLC; *U.S. Private*, pg. 1896
MEDA MANUFACTURING GMBH—See Viatris Inc.; *U.S. Public*, pg. 2293
MEDA MANUFACTURING SAS—See Viatris Inc.; *U.S. Public*, pg. 2293
MEDAN PRESTASI SDN. BHD.—See M K Land Holdings Berhad; *Int'l*, pg. 4610
MEDA OY—See Viatris Inc.; *U.S. Public*, pg. 2293
MEDA PHARMA B.V.—See Viatris Inc.; *U.S. Public*, pg. 2293
MEDA PHARMACEUTICALS A.E.—See Viatris Inc.; *U.S. Public*, pg. 2293
MEDA PHARMACEUTICALS INC.—See Viatris Inc.; *U.S. Public*, pg. 2293
MEDA PHARMACEUTICALS LIMITED—See Viatris Inc.; *U.S. Public*, pg. 2293
MEDA PHARMACEUTICALS LTD—See Viatris Inc.; *U.S. Public*, pg. 2294
MEDA PHARMACEUTICALS MEA FZ-LLC—See Viatris Inc.; *U.S. Public*, pg. 2294
MEDA PHARMA GMBH & CO. KG—See Viatris Inc.; *U.S. Public*, pg. 2293
MEDA PHARMA GMBH—See Viatris Inc.; *U.S. Public*, pg. 2293
MEDA PHARMA GMBH—See Viatris Inc.; *U.S. Public*, pg. 2293
MEDA PHARMA HUNGARY KFT.—See Viatris Inc.; *U.S. Public*, pg. 2293
MEDA PHARMA ILAC SANAYI VE TICARET LIMITED SIRKETI—See Viatris Inc.; *U.S. Public*, pg. 2293
MEDA PHARMA ILAC SAN VE TIC LTD. STI—See Viatris Inc.; *U.S. Public*, pg. 2293
MEDA PHARMA PRODUTOS FARMACEUTICOS, S.A.—See Viatris Inc.; *U.S. Public*, pg. 2293
MEDA PHARMA S.A.—See Viatris Inc.; *U.S. Public*, pg. 2293
MEDA PHARMA SIA—See Viatris Inc.; *U.S. Public*, pg. 2293
MEDA PHARMA SOUTH AFRICA (PTY) LIMITED—See Viatris Inc.; *U.S. Public*, pg. 2293
MEDA PHARMA S.P.A.—See Viatris Inc.; *U.S. Public*, pg. 2293
MEDA PHARMA S.R.O.—See Viatris Inc.; *U.S. Public*, pg. 2293
MEDAPP HOLDING B.V.—See Shop Apotheke Europe N.V.; *Int'l*, pg. 6859
MEDAPP NEDERLAND B.V.—See Shop Apotheke Europe N.V.; *Int'l*, pg. 6859
MEDAPTUS, INC.—See Constellation Software Inc.; *Int'l*, pg. 1775
MEDARO MINING CORP.; *Int'l*, pg. 4767
MEDART INC.; *U.S. Private*, pg. 2650
MEDARTIS AUSTRALIA & NEW ZEALAND PTY. LTD.—See Medartis Holding AG; *Int'l*, pg. 4768
MEDARTIS CO., LTD.—See Medartis Holding AG; *Int'l*, pg. 4768
MEDARTIS GMBH—See Medartis Holding AG; *Int'l*, pg. 4768
MEDARTIS GMBH—See Medartis Holding AG; *Int'l*, pg. 4768
MEDARTIS HOLDING AG; *Int'l*, pg. 4768
MEDARTIS IBERIA S.L.—See Medartis Holding AG; *Int'l*, pg. 4768
MEDARTIS INC.—See Medartis Holding AG; *Int'l*, pg. 4768
MEDARTIS LTD.—See Medartis Holding AG; *Int'l*, pg. 4768
MEDARTIS S.A. DE C.V.—See Medartis Holding AG; *Int'l*, pg. 4768
MEDARTIS S.A.R.L.—See Medartis Holding AG; *Int'l*, pg. 4768
MEDARTIS SP.Z.O.O—See Medartis Holding AG; *Int'l*, pg. 4768
MEDASCEND LLC—See The Advanced Group of Companies; *U.S. Private*, pg. 3982
MEDASSIST, INC.—See Firstsource Solutions Limited; *Int'l*, pg. 2691
MEDASYS SA; *Int'l*, pg. 4768
MEDATA INC.—See The Carlyle Group Inc.; *U.S. Public*, pg. 2049
MEDAVAIL HOLDINGS, INC.; *Int'l*, pg. 4768
MEDAVAIL TECHNOLOGIES, INC.—See MedAvail Holdings, Inc.; *Int'l*, pg. 4768

MEDAVAIL HOLDINGS, INC.   CORPORATE AFFILIATIONS

MEDAVANTE-PROPHASE, INC.—See Leonard Green & Partners, L.P.; *U.S. Private*, pg. 2430
MEDAVIE BLUE CROSS; *Int'l*, pg. 4768
MEDAXIO INSURANCE MEDICAL SERVICES LP—See Laboratory Corporation of America Holdings; *U.S. Public*, pg. 1287
MEDBASE AG—See The Federation of Migros Cooperatives; *Int'l*, pg. 7642
MEDBASE SOFTWARE INC.—See WELL Health Technologies Corp.; *Int'l*, pg. 8372
MEDBIO, INC; *U.S. Private*, pg. 2650
MEDBLOC, INC.—See Invacare Corporation; *U.S. Private*, pg. 2131
MEDBRIDGE HEALTHCARE, LLC—See Vicente Capital Partners, LLC; *U.S. Private*, pg. 4376
MEDBRIDGE HOME MEDICAL LLC—See AdaptHealth Corp.; *U.S. Public*, pg. 39
MEDBY AS—See Instalco AB; *Int'l*, pg. 3722
MEDCAL SALES LLC—See Medline Industries, LP; *U.S. Private*, pg. 2657
MEDCAMP S.A.; *Int'l*, pg. 4768
MEDCAP AB; *Int'l*, pg. 4768
MEDCARE AMBULANCE—See Ohio Medical Transportation; *U.S. Private*, pg. 3004
MEDCARE EQUIPMENT COMPANY, LLC; *U.S. Private*, pg. 2650
MED-CARE MANAGEMENT, INC.—See Medical Cost Management Corp.; *U.S. Private*, pg. 2654
MEDCAW INVESTMENTS PLC; *Int'l*, pg. 4768
MED CELL MEDICAL CO. K.S.C.C.—See Al-Mazaya Holding Company K.S.C.P.; *Int'l*, pg. 287
MEDCEN COMMUNITY HEALTH FOUNDATION INC.—See Central Georgia Health System Inc.; *U.S. Private*, pg. 821
MEDCERTS LLC; *U.S. Private*, pg. 2651
MEDCO ASIA INVESTMENT CORP.—See Medco Holdings, Inc.; *Int'l*, pg. 4768
MEDCO CONSTRUCTION, LLC—See The Christman Company LLC; *U.S. Private*, pg. 4009
MEDCO HEALTH SOLUTIONS, INC.—See The Cigna Group; *U.S. Public*, pg. 2061
MEDCO HEALTH SOLUTIONS OF LAS VEGAS, LLC—See The Cigna Group; *U.S. Public*, pg. 2062
MEDCO HEALTH SOLUTIONS OF RICHMOND, LLC—See The Cigna Group; *U.S. Public*, pg. 2062
MEDCO HEALTH SOLUTIONS OF TEXAS, LLC—See The Cigna Group; *U.S. Public*, pg. 2062
MEDCO HOLDINGS, INC.; *Int'l*, pg. 4768
MEDCOLCANNA ORGANICS, INC.; *Int'l*, pg. 4768
MEDCOM CARE MANAGEMENT, INC.—See Gilsbar Inc.; *U.S. Private*, pg. 1701
MEDCOM INC—See Chicago City Capitol Group; *U.S. Private*, pg. 877
MEDCOMM SOLUTIONS, LLC—See Dohmen Co.; *U.S. Private*, pg. 1254
MEDCOM TECH, S.A.; *Int'l*, pg. 4768
MEDCONX, INC.—See ATL Technology, Inc.; *U.S. Private*, pg. 370
MEDCORE AB—See EQT AB; *Int'l*, pg. 2478
MEDCO RESPIRATORY INSTRUMENTS INC; *U.S. Private*, pg. 2651
MEDCO SUPPLY CO.—See Patterson Companies, Inc.; *U.S. Public*, pg. 1653
MEDCO TOOL OF OHIO, INC—See Sycamore Partners Management, LP; *U.S. Private*, pg. 3896
MEDCO TOOL OF ST. LOUIS, INC.—See Sycamore Partners Management, LP; *U.S. Private*, pg. 3896
MEDDATA GROUP, LLC—See IQVIA Holdings Inc.; *U.S. Public*, pg. 1169
MEDDATA, INC.—See MEDNAX, Inc.; *U.S. Public*, pg. 1413
MEDDIUS, LLC—See Premier, Inc.; *U.S. Public*, pg. 1715
MEDEANALYTICS, INC.—See Thoma Bravo, L.P.; *U.S. Private*, pg. 4150
MEDEANALYTICS, INC.—See Thoma Bravo, L.P.; *U.S. Private*, pg. 4149
MEDEA S.P.A.—See Italgas S.p.A.; *Int'l*, pg. 3828
MEDECIN DIRECT—See Teladoc Health, Inc.; *U.S. Public*, pg. 1992
MEDECISION, INC.—See Health Care Service Corporation; *U.S. Private*, pg. 1892
MEDECO HIGH SECURITY LOCKS, INC.—See ASSA ABLOY AB; *Int'l*, pg. 636
MEDECO SA/NV—See Advent International Corporation; *U.S. Private*, pg. 104
MEDECO SECURITY LOCKS INC—See ASSA ABLOY AB; *Int'l*, pg. 640
MEDEC SYSTEMS GMBH; *Int'l*, pg. 4768
MEDEFIS, INC.—See AMN Healthcare Services, Inc.; *U.S. Public*, pg. 125
MEDELA AUSTRALIA PTY LTD.—See Medela Holding AG; *Int'l*, pg. 4768
MEDELA BENELUX B.V.—See Medela Holding AG; *Int'l*, pg. 4768
MEDELA CANADA INC—See Medela Holding AG; *Int'l*, pg. 4768
MEDELA DANMARK—See Medela Holding AG; *Int'l*, pg. 4768
MEDELA HOLDING AG; *Int'l*, pg. 4768

MEDELA INC.—See Medela Holding AG; *Int'l*, pg. 4768
MEDELA INDIA PRIVATE LIMITED—See Medela Holding AG; *Int'l*, pg. 4768
MEDELA ITALIA S.R.L.—See Medela Holding AG; *Int'l*, pg. 4768
MEDELA MEDICAL AB—See Medela Holding AG; *Int'l*, pg. 4768
MEDELA MEDICAL NORGE FILIAL AV MEDELA MEDICAL AB—See Medela Holding AG; *Int'l*, pg. 4768
MEDELA MEDIZINTECHNIK GMBH & CO HANDELS KG—See Medela Holding AG; *Int'l*, pg. 4769
MEDELA S.A.R.L—See Medela Holding AG; *Int'l*, pg. 4769
MEDELA UK LTD.—See Medela Holding AG; *Int'l*, pg. 4769
MED-EL CORPORATION—See MED-EL GmbH; *Int'l*, pg. 4767
MED-EL DEUTSCHLAND GMBH—See MED-EL GmbH; *Int'l*, pg. 4767
MED-EL GMBH; *Int'l*, pg. 4767
MED-EL GMBH—See MED-EL GmbH; *Int'l*, pg. 4767
MED-EL HEARING IMPLANT TECHNOLOGY SERVICE BEIJING CO. LTD.—See MED-EL GmbH; *Int'l*, pg. 4767
MED-EL IMPLANT SYSTEMS AUSTRALASIA PTY LTD—See MED-EL GmbH; *Int'l*, pg. 4767
MED-EL INDIA PRIVATE LTD.—See MED-EL GmbH; *Int'l*, pg. 4767
MEDELIS, INC.—See Altasciences Company Inc.; *Int'l*, pg. 387
MEDELITA, LLC; *U.S. Private*, pg. 2651
MEDELLA THERAPEUTICS LIMITED—See IP Group plc; *Int'l*, pg. 3795
MED-EL LATINO AMERICA S.R.L.—See MED-EL GmbH; *Int'l*, pg. 4767
MED-EL MIDDLE EAST FZE—See MED-EL GmbH; *Int'l*, pg. 4767
MED-EL UK LTD—See MED-EL GmbH; *Int'l*, pg. 4767
MED-EMERG INTERNATIONAL INC.—See Imperial Capital Group Ltd.; *Int'l*, pg. 3634
MEDEM, INC.; *U.S. Private*, pg. 2651
MED-ENG, LLC—See Kanders & Company, Inc.; *U.S. Private*, pg. 2259
MED-ENG SYSTEMS INC.—See Kanders & Company, Inc.; *U.S. Private*, pg. 2259
MEDENTEX GMBH—See Rentokil Initial plc; *Int'l*, pg. 6287
MEDENTIKA GMBH—See Straumann Holding AG; *Int'l*, pg. 7238
MEDENTIS MEDICAL GMBH—See Henry Schein, Inc.; *U.S. Public*, pg. 1027
MEDEOLOGIX, INC.—See Medeon Biodesign, Inc.; *Int'l*, pg. 4769
MEDEON BIODESIGN, INC.; *Int'l*, pg. 4769
MEDEONBIO, INC.—See Medeon Biodesign, Inc.; *Int'l*, pg. 4769
MEDEON FASTIGHETER AB—See Wihlborgs Fastigheter AB; *Int'l*, pg. 8407
MEDERGY HEALTHGROUP INC—See Arsenal Capital Management LP; *U.S. Private*, pg. 338
MEDERI CARETENDERS VS OF BROWARD, LLC—See UnitedHealth Group Incorporated; *U.S. Public*, pg. 2244
MEDERI CARETENDERS VS OF SE FL, LLC—See UnitedHealth Group Incorporated; *U.S. Public*, pg. 2244
MEDERI CARETENDERS VS OF SW FL, LLC—See UnitedHealth Group Incorporated; *U.S. Public*, pg. 2244
MEDERMICA LIMITED—See Plutus PowerGen plc; *Int'l*, pg. 5899
MEDESIS PHARMA S.A.; *Int'l*, pg. 4769
MEDEXACT SAS—See Cegedim S.A.; *Int'l*, pg. 1390
MEDEXA DIAGNOSTISK SERVICE AB—See Indutrade AB; *Int'l*, pg. 3680
MEDEX HEALTHCARE, INC.—See PACIFIC HEALTH CARE ORGANIZATION, INC.; *U.S. Public*, pg. 1632
MEDEX INSURANCE SERVICES, INC.—See UnitedHealth Group Incorporated; *U.S. Public*, pg. 2242
MEDEXIS S.A—See Gerolymatos Group of Companies; *Int'l*, pg. 2943
MEDEX-MEDIA—See Clayton, Dubilier & Rice, LLC; *U.S. Private*, pg. 928
MEDEX MEDICAL GMBH—See ICU Medical, Inc.; *U.S. Public*, pg. 1087
MEDEXPRESS JSIC—See Allianz SE; *Int'l*, pg. 354
MEDEXPRESS PHARMACY, LTD; *U.S. Private*, pg. 2651
MEDEXPRESS URGENT CARE OF BOYNTON BEACH, LLC—See UnitedHealth Group Incorporated; *U.S. Public*, pg. 2242
MEDEXPRESS URGENT CARE—See General Atlantic Service Company, L.P.; *U.S. Private*, pg. 1663
MEDEXPRESS URGENT CARE—See Sequoia Capital Operations, LLC; *U.S. Private*, pg. 3612
MEDEX SA—See Guerbet SA; *Int'l*, pg. 3172
MEDEXUS PHARMACEUTICALS INC.; *Int'l*, pg. 4769
MED-FARE DRUG & PHARMACEUTICAL COMPOUNDING, LLC—See Parkview Capital Credit, Inc.; *U.S. Private*, pg. 3098
MEDFIRST HEALTHCARE SERVICES INC.; *Int'l*, pg. 4769
MEDFORCE LLC—See Eureka Equity Partners, L.P.; *U.S. Private*, pg. 1433

MEDFORD CO-OPERATIVE INC.; *U.S. Private*, pg. 2651
MEDFORD FABRICATION, CSC INC.; *U.S. Private*, pg. 2651
MEDFORD NURSERY, INC.—See The Robert Baker Companies; *U.S. Private*, pg. 4111
MED FUSION, LLC—See Quest Diagnostics, Inc.; *U.S. Public*, pg. 1755
MEDGATE DEUTSCHLAND GMBH—See Asklepios Kliniken GmbH & Co. KGaA; *Int'l*, pg. 624
MEDGAZ, S.A.; *Int'l*, pg. 4769
MEDGEL PRIVATE LIMITED—See Medi Caps Ltd.; *Int'l*, pg. 4769
MEDGENICS MEDICAL (ISRAEL) LIMITED—See Avalo Therapeutics, Inc.; *U.S. Public*, pg. 239
MEDGENIX BENELUX NV—See Perrigo Company plc; *Int'l*, pg. 5813
MEDGINEERING GMBH—See adesso SE; *Int'l*, pg. 144
MEDGLUV INC; *U.S. Private*, pg. 2651
MEDGOLD RESOURCES CORP.; *Int'l*, pg. 4769
MEDGULF CONSTRUCTION COMPANY W.L.L.—See Sacyr, S.A.; *Int'l*, pg. 6465
MEDHA SERVICES INC.—See Saven Technologies Limited; *Int'l*, pg. 6597
MEDHEALTH PTY LIMITED—See GIC Pte. Ltd.; *Int'l*, pg. 2964
MEDHEALTH PTY LIMITED—See Leonard Green & Partners, L.P.; *U.S. Private*, pg. 2425
MEDHELP CARE AKTIEBOLAG; *Int'l*, pg. 4769
MEDHOK HEALTHCARE SOLUTIONS, LLC; *U.S. Private*, pg. 2651
MEDHUB, LLC—See Blackstone Inc.; *U.S. Public*, pg. 348
MEDHUB, LLC—See Canada Pension Plan Investment Board; *Int'l*, pg. 1279
MEDI1ONE MEDICAL GMBH—See Fresenius SE & Co. KGaA; *Int'l*, pg. 2780
MEDI24 AG—See Allianz SE; *Int'l*, pg. 354
MEDIA 100—See Optibase Ltd.; *Int'l*, pg. 5602
MEDIA24 PROPRIETARY LIMITED—See Naspers Limited; *Int'l*, pg. 5148
MEDIA2U COMPANY LIMITED—See Media Chinese International Limited; *Int'l*, pg. 4770
MEDIA 3.14—See WPP plc; *Int'l*, pg. 8475
MEDIA3, INC.; *U.S. Private*, pg. 2651
MEDIA 4 (UK) LIMITED—See Retec Digital Plc; *Int'l*, pg. 6306
MEDIA6 DESIGN—See Media 6 SA; *Int'l*, pg. 4770
MEDIA 6 SA; *Int'l*, pg. 4770
MEDIAADVANTAGE CONSULTING L.D.A.—See Ebiquity plc; *Int'l*, pg. 2285
MEDIA AGENCY MIDDLE EAST (MAME)—See Percept Holdings Pvt. Ltd.; *Int'l*, pg. 5796
MEDIAALPHA, INC.; *U.S. Public*, pg. 1411
MEDIA ASIA GROUP HOLDINGS LIMITED—See Lai Sun Group; *Int'l*, pg. 4396
MEDIA ASSURANCES S.A.—See Bertelsmann SE & Co. KGaA; *Int'l*, pg. 993
MEDIA ATLANTIC; *U.S. Private*, pg. 2651
MEDIA BASE SPORT SL—See WPP plc; *Int'l*, pg. 8475
MEDIA BASICS BV—See WPP plc; *Int'l*, pg. 8465
MEDIA BITES, UAB; *Int'l*, pg. 4770
MEDIABRAINS, INC.; *U.S. Private*, pg. 2653
MEDIABRANDS BELGIUM S.A—See The Interpublic Group of Companies, Inc.; *U.S. Public*, pg. 2103
MEDIABRANDS EMEA LTD.—See The Interpublic Group of Companies, Inc.; *U.S. Public*, pg. 2100
MEDIA BREAKAWAY, LLC; *U.S. Private*, pg. 2651
MEDIA BROADCAST GMBH—See freenet AG; *Int'l*, pg. 2770
MEDIA BROKERS INTERNATIONAL, INC.; *U.S. Private*, pg. 2651
MEDIA BUSINESS INSIGHT LIMITED—See GlobalData Plc; *Int'l*, pg. 3003
MEDIA BUYING DECISIONS; *U.S. Private*, pg. 2651
MEDIA BUYING SERVICES, INC.; *U.S. Private*, pg. 2651
MEDIA BY DESIGN—See Hakuhodo DY Holdings Incorporated; *Int'l*, pg. 3222
MEDIA CAMPING CENTER INC.; *U.S. Private*, pg. 2651
MEDIA CANDO LLC; *U.S. Private*, pg. 2651
MEDIACAP SA; *Int'l*, pg. 4771
MEDIA CENTRAL CORPORATION INC.; *Int'l*, pg. 4770
MEDIA CHINESE INTERNATIONAL LIMITED; *Int'l*, pg. 4770
MEDIA CITY ATELIER (MCA) GMBH—See Bavaria Film GmbH; *Int'l*, pg. 899
MEDIACLE GROUP AB; *Int'l*, pg. 4771
MEDIACO HOLDING INC.; *U.S. Public*, pg. 1411
MEDIACOLOR SPAIN S.A—See Media 6 SA; *Int'l*, pg. 4770
MEDIACOM AGENTUR FUR MEDIA-BERATUNG GMBH—See WPP plc; *Int'l*, pg. 8465
MEDIACOM AMSTERDAM—See WPP plc; *Int'l*, pg. 8465
MEDIACOM ARGENTINA—See WPP plc; *Int'l*, pg. 8465
MEDIACOM AS—See WPP plc; *Int'l*, pg. 8465
MEDIACOM ATHENS—See WPP plc; *Int'l*, pg. 8465
MEDIACOM AUSTRALIA PTY. LTD.—See WPP plc; *Int'l*, pg. 8465
MEDIACOM BEIJING—See WPP plc; *Int'l*, pg. 8465
MEDIACOM BELGIUM SA—See WPP plc; *Int'l*, pg. 8465

COMPANY NAME INDEX

MEDIACOM BROADBAND CORPORATION—See Mediacom Communications Corporation; *U.S. Private*, pg. 2653

MEDIACOM BROADBAND LLC—See Mediacom Communications Corporation; *U.S. Private*, pg. 2653

MEDIACOM BUCURESTI—See WPP plc; *Int'l*, pg. 8465

MEDIACOM COLOMBIA—See WPP plc; *Int'l*, pg. 8466

MEDIACOM COMMUNICATIONS CORPORATION; *U.S. Private*, pg. 2653

MEDIACOM COMPANY LTD.—See WPP plc; *Int'l*, pg. 8465

MEDIACOM DENMARK—See WPP plc; *Int'l*, pg. 8465

MEDIACOM DE PUERTO RICO, INC.—See WPP plc; *Int'l*, pg. 8466

MEDIACOM DHAKA—See WPP plc; *Int'l*, pg. 8465

MEDIACOM EDINBURGH—See WPP plc; *Int'l*, pg. 8465

MEDIACOM FINLAND—See WPP plc; *Int'l*, pg. 8465

MEDIACOM GHANA—See WPP plc; *Int'l*, pg. 8465

MEDIACOM GUANGZHOU—See WPP plc; *Int'l*, pg. 8465

MEDIACOM HOLDINGS LTD.—See WPP plc; *Int'l*, pg. 8465

MEDIACOM HONG KONG—See WPP plc; *Int'l*, pg. 8465

MEDIACOM IBERIA—See WPP plc; *Int'l*, pg. 8465

MEDIACOM IBERIA—See WPP plc; *Int'l*, pg. 8465

MEDIACOM INDONESIA—See WPP plc; *Int'l*, pg. 8465

MEDIACOM INTERACTION—See WPP plc; *Int'l*, pg. 8472

MEDIACOM INTERACTION—See WPP plc; *Int'l*, pg. 8472

MEDIACOM INTERACTION—See WPP plc; *Int'l*, pg. 8472

MEDIACOM IOWA LLC—See Mediacom Communications Corporation; *U.S. Private*, pg. 2653

MEDIACOM ISTANBUL—See WPP plc; *Int'l*, pg. 8465

MEDIACOM ITALY—See WPP plc; *Int'l*, pg. 8465

MEDIACOM JAPAN—See WPP plc; *Int'l*, pg. 8465

MEDIACOM KOREA—See WPP plc; *Int'l*, pg. 8465

MEDIACOM LLC—See Mediacom Communications Corporation; *U.S. Private*, pg. 2653

MEDIACOM LLC—See WPP plc; *Int'l*, pg. 8466

MEDIACOM LONDON—See WPP plc; *Int'l*, pg. 8466

MEDIACOM LOS ANGELES—See WPP plc; *Int'l*, pg. 8466

MEDIACOM MENA—See WPP plc; *Int'l*, pg. 8466

MEDIACOM MEXICO—See WPP plc; *Int'l*, pg. 8466

MEDIA COMMUNICATIONS GROUP; *U.S. Private*, pg. 2651

MEDIA & COMMUNICATION SYSTEMS (MCS) GMBH—See Bavaria Film GmbH; *Int'l*, pg. 899

MEDIACOM OUTDOOR—See WPP plc; *Int'l*, pg. 8466

THE MEDIA COMPANY—See WPP plc; *Int'l*, pg. 8466

MEDIACOM PARIS—See WPP plc; *Int'l*, pg. 8466

MEDIACOMPETE MALAYSIA—See WPP plc; *Int'l*, pg. 8466

MEDIACOMPETE SINGAPORE—See WPP plc; *Int'l*, pg. 8466

MEDIA COMPETE—See WPP plc; *Int'l*, pg. 8465

MEDIACOMP, INC.; *U.S. Private*, pg. 2653

MEDIACOM PRAHA—See WPP plc; *Int'l*, pg. 8466

MEDIACOM SANTIAGO—See WPP plc; *Int'l*, pg. 8466

MEDIACOM SHANGHAI—See WPP plc; *Int'l*, pg. 8466

MEDIACOM—See WPP plc; *Int'l*, pg. 8465

MEDIACOM—See WPP plc; *Int'l*, pg. 8465

MEDIACOM—See WPP plc; *Int'l*, pg. 8465

MEDIACOM—See WPP plc; *Int'l*, pg. 8465

MEDIACOM—See WPP plc; *Int'l*, pg. 8465

MEDIACOM—See WPP plc; *Int'l*, pg. 8465

MEDIACOM SOUTH AFRICA—See WPP plc; *Int'l*, pg. 8466

MEDIACOM SVERIGE AB—See WPP plc; *Int'l*, pg. 8466

MEDIACOM SWITZERLAND—See WPP plc; *Int'l*, pg. 8466

MEDIACOM SYDNEY—See WPP plc; *Int'l*, pg. 8466

MEDIACOM VANCOUVER—See WPP plc; *Int'l*, pg. 8466

MEDIACOM VIENNA—See WPP plc; *Int'l*, pg. 8466

MEDIACOM WARSZAWA—See WPP plc; *Int'l*, pg. 8466

MEDIACOM WORLDWIDE INC.—See WPP plc; *Int'l*, pg. 8465

MEDIA CORPORATION PUBLISHING (M)—See Apax Partners LLP; *Int'l*, pg. 507

MEDIA CORPORATION PUBLISHING (M)—See The Scott Trust Limited; *Int'l*, pg. 7681

MEDIACORP PRESS LTD—See Temasek Holdings (Private) Limited; *Int'l*, pg. 7548

MEDIACORP PRIVATE LTD—See Temasek Holdings (Private) Limited; *Int'l*, pg. 7548

MEDIACORP PUBLISHING PTE LTD—See Temasek Holdings (Private) Limited; *Int'l*, pg. 7548

MEDIACORP RADIO SINGAPORE PTE LTD—See Temasek Holdings (Private) Limited; *Int'l*, pg. 7548

MEDIACORP RAINTREE PICTURES PTE LTD—See Temasek Holdings (Private) Limited; *Int'l*, pg. 7548

MEDIACORP STUDIOS PTE LTD—See Temasek Holdings (Private) Limited; *Int'l*, pg. 7548

MEDIACORP TECHNOLOGIES PTE LTD—See Temasek Holdings (Private) Limited; *Int'l*, pg. 7548

MEDIACORP TV12 SINGAPORE PTE LTD—See Temasek Holdings (Private) Limited; *Int'l*, pg. 7548

MEDIACORP TV SINGAPORE PTE LTD—See Temasek Holdings (Private) Limited; *Int'l*, pg. 7548

THE MEDIA CREW; *U.S. Private*, pg. 4077

MEDIACROSSING, INC.; *U.S. Private*, pg. 2653

MEDIACURRENT INTERACTIVE SOLUTIONS LLC—See Stagwell, Inc.; *U.S. Public*, pg. 1927

MEDIA CYBERNETICS INC.—See Roper Technologies, Inc.; *U.S. Public*, pg. 1812

MEDIA DEPARTMENT II, INC.; *U.S. Private*, pg. 2652

MEDIA DESIGN SCHOOL LIMITED—See Strategic Education, Inc.; *U.S. Public*, pg. 1954

MEDIA DESIGN; *U.S. Private*, pg. 2652

MEDIA DIRECT, INC.; *U.S. Private*, pg. 2652

MEDIA DIRECTIONS ADVERTISING, INC.; *U.S. Private*, pg. 2652

MEDIA DIRECTION—See Omnicom Group Inc.; *U.S. Public*, pg. 1575

MEDIA DIRECT NORGE AS—See Egmont Fonden; *Int'l*, pg. 2326

MEDIA-DIREKTSERVICE GMBH—See Stroer SE & Co. KGaA; *Int'l*, pg. 7242

MEDIA DO CO., LTD.; *Int'l*, pg. 4770

MEDIA DREAM; *U.S. Private*, pg. 2652

MEDIA DRIVE CORPORATION—See Nippon Telegraph & Telephone Corporation; *Int'l*, pg. 5346

MEDIAEDGE:CIA WORLDWIDE LTD.—See WPP plc; *Int'l*, pg. 8472

MEDIA EDGE, INC.; *U.S. Private*, pg. 2652

MEDIA ENTERPRISES—See The Interpublic Group of Companies, Inc.; *U.S. Public*, pg. 2102

MEDIA ETC.; *U.S. Private*, pg. 2652

MEDIA EXPERTS—See The Interpublic Group of Companies, Inc.; *U.S. Public*, pg. 2095

MEDIA EXPERTS—See The Interpublic Group of Companies, Inc.; *U.S. Public*, pg. 2095

MEDIA FACTORY, INC.—See Recruit Holdings Co., Ltd.; *Int'l*, pg. 6240

MEDIA FIRST PUBLIC RELATIONS; *U.S. Private*, pg. 2652

MEDIA FIVE CO.; *Int'l*, pg. 4770

MEDIAFLAG OKINAWA INC.—See Bain Capital, LP; *U.S. Private*, pg. 433

MEDIAFLY, INC.—See Boathouse Capital Management, LLC; *U.S. Private*, pg. 603

MEDIA FOCUS SCHWEIZ GMBH—See Brookfield Corporation; *Int'l*, pg. 1178

MEDIA FOCUS SCHWEIZ GMBH—See Elliott Management Corporation; *U.S. Private*, pg. 1371

MEDIAFON, UAB—See MG Baltic UAB; *Int'l*, pg. 4871

MEDIAFORGE; *U.S. Private*, pg. 2653

THE MEDIA FOUNDRY INTERNATIONAL LIMITED—See Cubo Communications Group Plc; *Int'l*, pg. 1875

MEDIA FRANKFURT GMBH—See Fraport AG; *Int'l*, pg. 2764

MEDIA FUSION, INC.; *U.S. Private*, pg. 2652

MEDIAFY AB—See Bonnier AB; *Int'l*, pg. 1109

MEDIAFY MAGAZINES AS—See Bonnier AB; *Int'l*, pg. 1109

MEDIAG3, INC.; *U.S. Public*, pg. 1411

MEDIA GARDEN INC.—See AOI TYO Holdings Inc.; *Int'l*, pg. 488

MEDIAGATE PTE LTD.—See Shinvest Holding Limited; *Int'l*, pg. 6849

MEDIA GLOBE CO., LTD.—See istyle Inc.; *Int'l*, pg. 3825

THE MEDIA GLOBO CORPORATION; *U.S. Public*, pg. 2113

MEDIA GRAPHICS INC.; *U.S. Private*, pg. 2652

MEDIA GROW CO., LTD.—See Septeni Holdings Co., Ltd.; *Int'l*, pg. 6718

MEDIAHEADS 360 PROPRIETARY LIMITED—See African Media Entertainment Limited; *Int'l*, pg. 192

MEDIAHOLDING OAO; *Int'l*, pg. 4771

MEDIAHOUSE LIMITED; *Int'l*, pg. 4772

MEDIAHUB MINNEAPOLIS, LLC—See The Interpublic Group of Companies, Inc.; *U.S. Public*, pg. 2103

MEDIAHUIS NEDERLAND B.V.—See Mediahuis Partners NV; *Int'l*, pg. 4772

MEDIAHUIS NEDERLAND B.V.—See VP Exploitatie N.V.; *Int'l*, pg. 8311

MEDIAHUIS NV—See Mediahuis Partners NV; *Int'l*, pg. 4772

MEDIAHUIS NV—See VP Exploitatie N.V.; *Int'l*, pg. 8311

MEDIAHUIS PARTNERS NV; *Int'l*, pg. 4772

MEDIAID, INC.—See Opto Circuits (India) Limited; *Int'l*, pg. 5605

MEDIAID SINGAPORE PTE LTD.—See Opto Circuits (India) Limited; *Int'l*, pg. 5605

MEDIA IMPACT INC.—See Axel Springer SE; *Int'l*, pg. 766

MEDIA & INCOME TRUST PLC; *Int'l*, pg. 4770

MEDIA IN PR—See WPP plc; *Int'l*, pg. 8469

MEDIA INSIGHT; *U.S. Private*, pg. 2652

MEDIA INTELLIGENCE CO., LTD.—See Hakuhodo DY Holdings Incorporated; *Int'l*, pg. 3222

THE MEDIA INVESTMENT GROUP—See The Interpublic Group of Companies, Inc.; *U.S. Public*, pg. 2102

MEDIA ITALIA HQ—See Armando Testa S.p.A.; *Int'l*, pg. 574

MEDIAKIX, LLC—See Stadiumred Group; *U.S. Private*, pg. 3774

MEDIA KOBO INC.; *Int'l*, pg. 4771

MEDIA LAB S.P.A.; *Int'l*, pg. 4771

MEDIALINK GROUP LIMITED; *Int'l*, pg. 4772

MEDIA LINKS CO., LTD.; *Int'l*, pg. 4771

MEDIA-MAKER S.P.A.

MEDIA LINKS, INC.—See Media Links Co., Ltd.; *Int'l*, pg. 4771

MEDIALIVE INTERNATIONAL INC.; *U.S. Private*, pg. 2653

MEDIA LOGIC USA, LLC; *U.S. Private*, pg. 2652

MEDIA LOGISTIK GMBH—See Bertelsmann SE & Co. KGaA; *Int'l*, pg. 993

MEDIALON INC.—See 7thSense Design Limited; *Int'l*, pg. 15

MEDIALYTICS INC.—See Samsung BioLogics Co., Ltd.; *Int'l*, pg. 6510

MEDIAMAKER LTD.; *Int'l*, pg. 4772

MEDIA-MAKER S.P.A.; *Int'l*, pg. 4771

MEDIA MANAGEMENT, LLC—See Ebiquity plc; *Int'l*, pg. 2285

MEDIAMARKET S.P.A.CON SOCIO UNICO—See Ceconomy AG; *Int'l*, pg. 1385

MEDIAMARKET S. P. A.—See Ceconomy AG; *Int'l*, pg. 1385

MEDIA MARKT 14 - PRODUTOS ELECTRONICOS LDA—See Ceconomy AG; *Int'l*, pg. 1375

MEDIA MARKT 3 DE MAYO SANTA CRUZ DE TENERIFE S.A.—See Ceconomy AG; *Int'l*, pg. 1375

MEDIA MARKT AIGLE SA—See Ceconomy AG; *Int'l*, pg. 1375

MEDIA MARKT ALACANT VIDEO-TV-HIFI-ELEKTRO-COMPUTER-FOTO, S.A.—See Ceconomy AG; *Int'l*, pg. 1373

MEDIA MARKT ALCALA DE GUADAIRA VIDEO-TV-HIFI-ELEKTRO-COMPUTER-FOTO S.A.—See Ceconomy AG; *Int'l*, pg. 1373

MEDIA MARKT ALCALA DE HENARES VIDEO-TV-HIFI-ELEKTRO-COMPUTER-FOTO, S.A.—See Ceconomy AG; *Int'l*, pg. 1373

MEDIA MARKT ALCORCON VIDEO-TV-HIFI-ELEKTRO-COMPUTER-FOTO, S.A.—See Ceconomy AG; *Int'l*, pg. 1373

MEDIA MARKT ALEXANDRIUM B.V.—See Ceconomy AG; *Int'l*, pg. 1375

MEDIA MARKT ALFAFAR VIDEO-TV-HIFI-ELEKTRO-COMPUTER-FOTO, S.A.—See Ceconomy AG; *Int'l*, pg. 1373

MEDIA MARKT ALFRAGIDE - PRODUTOS INFORMATICOS E ELECTRONICOS, LDA—See Ceconomy AG; *Int'l*, pg. 1373

MEDIA MARKT ALKMAAR B.V.—See Ceconomy AG; *Int'l*, pg. 1375

MEDIA MARKT ALMERE B.V.—See Ceconomy AG; *Int'l*, pg. 1375

MEDIA MARKT ALPHEN AAN DEN RIJN B.V.—See Ceconomy AG; *Int'l*, pg. 1375

MEDIA MARKT AMERSFOORT B.V.—See Ceconomy AG; *Int'l*, pg. 1375

MEDIA MARKT AMSTERDAM CENTRUM B.V.—See Ceconomy AG; *Int'l*, pg. 1375

MEDIA MARKT AMSTERDAM NOORD B.V.—See Ceconomy AG; *Int'l*, pg. 1375

MEDIA MARKT AMSTERDAM WEST B.V.—See Ceconomy AG; *Int'l*, pg. 1375

MEDIA MARKT AMSTETTEN TV-HIFI-ELEKTRO GMBH—See Ceconomy AG; *Int'l*, pg. 1375

MEDIA MARKT APELDOORN B.V.—See Ceconomy AG; *Int'l*, pg. 1375

MEDIA MARKT ARENA B.V.—See Ceconomy AG; *Int'l*, pg. 1375

MEDIA MARKT ARNHEM B.V.—See Ceconomy AG; *Int'l*, pg. 1375

MEDIA MARKT ASSEN B.V.—See Ceconomy AG; *Int'l*, pg. 1375

MEDIA MARKT AUGSBURG-OBERHAUSEN—See Ceconomy AG; *Int'l*, pg. 1375

MEDIA MARKT AVEIRO - PRODUTOS INFORMATICOS E ELECTRONICOS, LDA—See Ceconomy AG; *Int'l*, pg. 1375

MEDIA MARKT BADAJOZ S.A.—See Ceconomy AG; *Int'l*, pg. 1375

MEDIA MARKT BADEN-BADEN—See Ceconomy AG; *Int'l*, pg. 1375

MEDIA MARKT BASEL AG—See Ceconomy AG; *Int'l*, pg. 1375

MEDIA MARKT BASILIX NV—See Ceconomy AG; *Int'l*, pg. 1373

MEDIA MARKT BEKESCSABA VIDEO TV HIFI ELEKTRO PHOTO COMPUTER KERESKEDELMI KFT.—See Ceconomy AG; *Int'l*, pg. 1375

MEDIA MARKT BENFICA - PRODUTOS INFORMATICOS E ELECTRONICOS, LDA—See Ceconomy AG; *Int'l*, pg. 1375

MEDIA MARKT BERGEN OP ZOOM B.V.—See Ceconomy AG; *Int'l*, pg. 1376

MEDIA MARKT BIEL-BRUGG AG—See Ceconomy AG; *Int'l*, pg. 1376

MEDIA MARKT BILBAO - ZUBIARTE, S.A.—See Ceconomy AG; *Int'l*, pg. 1376

MEDIA MARKT BORAS TV-HIFI-ELEKTRO AB—See Ceconomy AG; *Int'l*, pg. 1376

MEDIA MARKT BRAGA - PRODUTOS INFORMATICOS E ELECTRONICOS, LDA—See Ceconomy AG; *Int'l*, pg. 1376

MEDIA-MAKER S.P.A.

MEDIA MARKT BRAINE-L'ALLEUD SA—See Ceconomy AG; *Int'l*, pg. 1373
MEDIA MARKT BREDA B.V.—See Ceconomy AG; *Int'l*, pg. 1376
MEDIA MARKT BRUGGE NV—See Ceconomy AG; *Int'l*, pg. 1376
MEDIA MARKT BRUSSEL DOCKS NV—See Ceconomy AG; *Int'l*, pg. 1376
MEDIA MARKT BRUXELLES RUE NEUVE - MEDIA MARKT BRUSSEL NIEUWSTRAAT SA—See Ceconomy AG; *Int'l*, pg. 1373
MEDIA MARKT - BUDAORS VIDEO TV HIFI ELEKTRO FOTO COMPUTER KERESKEDELMI KFT.—See Ceconomy AG; *Int'l*, pg. 1373
MEDIA MARKT BURS TV-HIFI-ELEKTRO GMBH—See Ceconomy AG; *Int'l*, pg. 1376
MEDIA MARKT CARTAGENA VIDEO-TV-ELEKTRO-COMPUTER-FOTO, S.A.—See Ceconomy AG; *Int'l*, pg. 1373
MEDIA MARKT CASTELLO DE LA PLANA VIDEO-TV-HIFI-ELEKTRO-COMPUTER-FOTO, S.A.—See Ceconomy AG; *Int'l*, pg. 1373
MEDIAMARKT CENTRAL WAREHOUSE N.V.—See Ceconomy AG; *Int'l*, pg. 1385
MEDIA MARKT CENTURY CENTER NV—See Ceconomy AG; *Int'l*, pg. 1373
MEDIA MARKT CHUR AG—See Ceconomy AG; *Int'l*, pg. 1376
MEDIA MARKT COLLADO VILLALBA, S.A.—See Ceconomy AG; *Int'l*, pg. 1376
MEDIA MARKT CONTHEY SA—See Ceconomy AG; *Int'l*, pg. 1376
MEDIA MARKT CORDOBA VIDEO-TV-ELEKTRO-COMPUTER-FOTO, S.A.—See Ceconomy AG; *Int'l*, pg. 1373
MEDIA MARKT CRISSIER SA—See Ceconomy AG; *Int'l*, pg. 1376
MEDIA MARKT CRUQUIUS B.V.—See Ceconomy AG; *Int'l*, pg. 1376
MEDIA MARKT CXXIX TV-HIFI-ELEKTRO GMBH INGOLSTADT—See Ceconomy AG; *Int'l*, pg. 1376
MEDIA MARKT DEBRECEN VIDEO-TV-HIFI-ELEKTRO-PHOTO-COMPUTER-KERESKEDELMI KFT.—See Ceconomy AG; *Int'l*, pg. 1373
MEDIA MARKT DEN BOSCH B.V.—See Ceconomy AG; *Int'l*, pg. 1376
MEDIA MARKT DEN HAAG B.V.—See Ceconomy AG; *Int'l*, pg. 1376
MEDIA MARKT DEURNE NV—See Ceconomy AG; *Int'l*, pg. 1376
MEDIA MARKT DEVENTER B.V.—See Ceconomy AG; *Int'l*, pg. 1376
MEDIA MARKT DIAGONAL MAR-BARCELONA VIDEO-TV-HIFI-ELEKTRO-COMPUTER-FOTO S.A.—See Ceconomy AG; *Int'l*, pg. 1376
MEDIA MARKT DOETINCHEM B.V.—See Ceconomy AG; *Int'l*, pg. 1376
MEDIA MARKT DONOSTI VIDEO-TV-HIFI-ELEKTRO-COMPUTER-FOTO, S.A.—See Ceconomy AG; *Int'l*, pg. 1373
MEDIA MARKT DORDRECHT B.V.—See Ceconomy AG; *Int'l*, pg. 1376
MEDIA MARKT DRACHTEN B.V.—See Ceconomy AG; *Int'l*, pg. 1376
MEDIA MARKT DUIVEN B.V.—See Ceconomy AG; *Int'l*, pg. 1376
MEDIA MARKT E-COMMERCE AG—See Ceconomy AG; *Int'l*, pg. 1376
MEDIA MARKT EDE B.V.—See Ceconomy AG; *Int'l*, pg. 1376
MEDIA MARKT EINDHOVEN B.V.—See Ceconomy AG; *Int'l*, pg. 1376
MEDIA MARKT EINDHOVEN EKKERSRIJT B.V.—See Ceconomy AG; *Int'l*, pg. 1376
MEDIA MARKT EMMEN B.V.—See Ceconomy AG; *Int'l*, pg. 1376
MEDIA MARKT ENSCHEDE B.V.—See Ceconomy AG; *Int'l*, pg. 1376
MEDIA MARKT ESKILSTUNA TV-HIFI-ELEKTRO AB—See Ceconomy AG; *Int'l*, pg. 1376
MEDIA MARKT ESPLUGUES, S.A.—See Ceconomy AG; *Int'l*, pg. 1376
MEDIA MARKT FELDKIRCH TV-HIFI-ELEKTRO GMBH—See Ceconomy AG; *Int'l*, pg. 1376
MEDIA MARKT FERROL, SA—See Ceconomy AG; *Int'l*, pg. 1376
MEDIA MARKT FINESTRAT S.A.U.—See Ceconomy AG; *Int'l*, pg. 1376
MEDIA MARKT GAIA - PRODUTOS INFORMATICOS E ELECTRONICOS, LDA—See Ceconomy AG; *Int'l*, pg. 1376
MEDIA MARKT GANDIA S.A.—See Ceconomy AG; *Int'l*, pg. 1376
MEDIA MARKT GAVA VIDEO-TV-HIFI-ELEKTRO-COMPUTER-FOTO S.A.—See Ceconomy AG; *Int'l*, pg. 1373
MEDIA MARKT GAVLE TV-HIFI-ELEKTRO AB—See Ceconomy AG; *Int'l*, pg. 1376

MEDIA MARKT GIRONA VIDEO-TV-HIFI-ELEKTRO-COMPUTER-FOTO, S.A.—See Ceconomy AG; *Int'l*, pg. 1373
MEDIA MARKT GOSSELIES/CHARLEROI N.V.—See Ceconomy AG; *Int'l*, pg. 1373
MEDIA MARKT GOTEBORG-BACKEBOL TV-HIFI-ELEKTRO AB—See Ceconomy AG; *Int'l*, pg. 1376
MEDIA MARKT GOTEBORG-HOGSBO TV-HIFI-ELEKTRO AB—See Ceconomy AG; *Int'l*, pg. 1376
MEDIA MARKT GOTEBORG-TORPAVALLEN TV-HIFI-ELEKTRO AB—See Ceconomy AG; *Int'l*, pg. 1376
MEDIA MARKT GRANADA - NEVADA, S.A.—See Ceconomy AG; *Int'l*, pg. 1376
MEDIA MARKT GRANCIA SA—See Ceconomy AG; *Int'l*, pg. 1376
MEDIA MARKT GRANGES-PACCOT AG—See Ceconomy AG; *Int'l*, pg. 1376
MEDIA MARKT GRONINGEN B.V.—See Ceconomy AG; *Int'l*, pg. 1376
MEDIA MARKT GRONINGEN SONTPLEIN B.V.—See Ceconomy AG; *Int'l*, pg. 1376
MEDIA MARKT GYOR VIDEO TV HIFI ELEKTRO PHOTO COMPUTER KERESKEDELMI KFT.—See Ceconomy AG; *Int'l*, pg. 1376
MEDIA MARKT HEERLEN B.V.—See Ceconomy AG; *Int'l*, pg. 1376
MEDIA MARKT HELSINGBORG TV-HIFI-ELEKTRO AB—See Ceconomy AG; *Int'l*, pg. 1376
MEDIA MARKT HENGELO B.V.—See Ceconomy AG; *Int'l*, pg. 1377
MEDIA MARKT HERSTAL SA—See Ceconomy AG; *Int'l*, pg. 1377
MEDIA MARKT HOOFDDORP B.V.—See Ceconomy AG; *Int'l*, pg. 1377
MEDIA MARKT HOORN B.V.—See Ceconomy AG; *Int'l*, pg. 1377
MEDIA MARKT IMST TV-HIFI-ELEKTRO GMBH—See Ceconomy AG; *Int'l*, pg. 1377
MEDIA MARKT JEMAPPES/MONS SA—See Ceconomy AG; *Int'l*, pg. 1377
MEDIA MARKT JONKOPING TV-HIFI- ELEKTRO AB—See Ceconomy AG; *Int'l*, pg. 1377
MEDIA MARKT KALMAR TV-HIFI-ELEKTRO AB—See Ceconomy AG; *Int'l*, pg. 1377
MEDIA MARKT KECSKEMET VIDEO TV HIFI ELEKTRO PHOTO COMPUTER KERESKEDELMI KFT.—See Ceconomy AG; *Int'l*, pg. 1377
MEDIA MARKT KISPEST VIDEO TV HIFI ELEKTRO PHOTO COMPUTER KERESKEDELMI KFT.—See Ceconomy AG; *Int'l*, pg. 1377
MEDIA MARKT KORTRIJK NV—See Ceconomy AG; *Int'l*, pg. 1377
MEDIA MARKT KRISTIANSTAD TV-HIFI-ELEKTRO AB—See Ceconomy AG; *Int'l*, pg. 1377
MEDIA MARKT LAS ARENAS S.A.—See Ceconomy AG; *Int'l*, pg. 1377
MEDIA MARKT LAS PALMAS DE GRAN CANARIA VIDEO-TV-HIFI-ELEKTRO-COMPUTER-FOTO, S.A.—See Ceconomy AG; *Int'l*, pg. 1373
MEDIA MARKT LEEUWARDEN B.V.—See Ceconomy AG; *Int'l*, pg. 1377
MEDIA MARKT LEGANES VIDEO-TV- HIFI-ELEKTRO-COMPUTER-FOTO, S.A.—See Ceconomy AG; *Int'l*, pg. 1373
MEDIA MARKT LEIDSCHENDAM B.V.—See Ceconomy AG; *Int'l*, pg. 1377
MEDIA MARKT LEIRIA - PRODUTOS INFORMATICOS E ELECTRONICOS, LDA—See Ceconomy AG; *Int'l*, pg. 1377
MEDIA MARKT LEOBEN TV-HIFI-ELEKTRO GMBH—See Ceconomy AG; *Int'l*, pg. 1377
MEDIA MARKT LEON VIDEO-TV-HIFI-ELEKTRO-COMPUTER-FOTO, S.A.—See Ceconomy AG; *Int'l*, pg. 1373
MEDIA MARKT L HOSPITALET VIDEO-TV-HIFI-ELEKTRO-COMPUTER-FOTO S.A.—See Ceconomy AG; *Int'l*, pg. 1373
MEDIA MARKT LIEGE MEDIACITE SA—See Ceconomy AG; *Int'l*, pg. 1377
MEDIA MARKT LIEGE PLACE SAINT-LAMBERT SA—See Ceconomy AG; *Int'l*, pg. 1377
MEDIA MARKT LIEZEN TV-HIFI-ELEKTRO GMBH—See Ceconomy AG; *Int'l*, pg. 1377
MEDIA MARKT LINZ TV-HIFI-ELEKTRO GMBH—See Ceconomy AG; *Int'l*, pg. 1377
MEDIA MARKT LLEIDA, SA—See Ceconomy AG; *Int'l*, pg. 1377
MEDIA MARKT LOGRONO VIDEO-TV-HIFI-ELEKTRO-COMPUTER-FOTO, S.A.U.—See Ceconomy AG; *Int'l*, pg. 1373
MEDIA MARKT LORCA S.A.—See Ceconomy AG; *Int'l*, pg. 1377
MEDIA MARKT LUND TV-HIFI-ELEKTRO AB—See Ceconomy AG; *Int'l*, pg. 1377
MEDIA MARKT MAASTRICHT B.V.—See Ceconomy AG; *Int'l*, pg. 1377
MEDIA MARKT MACHELEN NV—See Ceconomy AG; *Int'l*, pg. 1377

CORPORATE AFFILIATIONS

MEDIA MARKT MADRID BENLLIURE SA—See Ceconomy AG; *Int'l*, pg. 1377
MEDIA MARKT MADRID CASTELLANA SA—See Ceconomy AG; *Int'l*, pg. 1377
MEDIA MARKT MADRID - PLAZA DEL CARMEN, S.A.U.—See Ceconomy AG; *Int'l*, pg. 1377
MEDIA MARKT MADRID PLENILUNIO VIDEO-TV-HIFI-ELEKTRO-COMPUTER-FOTO S.A.—See Ceconomy AG; *Int'l*, pg. 1377
MEDIA MARKT MADRID. - VALLECAS S.A.—See Ceconomy AG; *Int'l*, pg. 1377
MEDIA MARKT MALAGA-CENTRO VFDEO-TV-HIFI-ELEKTRO-COMPUTER-FOTO, SA—See Ceconomy AG; *Int'l*, pg. 1377
MEDIA MARKT MALAGA-CENTRO VIDEO-TV-HIFI-ELEKTRO-COMPUTER-FOTO, S.A.—See Ceconomy AG; *Int'l*, pg. 1373
MEDIA MARKT MALAGA - PLAZA MAYOR S.A.—See Ceconomy AG; *Int'l*, pg. 1377
MEDIA MARKT MALMO-SVAGERTORP TV-HIFI-ELEKTRO AB—See Ceconomy AG; *Int'l*, pg. 1377
MEDIA MARKT MASSALFASSAR S.A.—See Ceconomy AG; *Int'l*, pg. 1377
MEDIA MARKT MATARO VIDEO-TV-HIFI-ELEKTRO-COMPUTER-FOTO, S.A.—See Ceconomy AG; *Int'l*, pg. 1373
MEDIA MARKT MEGAPARK VIDEO TV HIFI ELEKTRO PHOTO COMPUTER KERESKEDELMI KFT.—See Ceconomy AG; *Int'l*, pg. 1374
MEDIA MARKT MEYRIN SA—See Ceconomy AG; *Int'l*, pg. 1377
MEDIA MARKT MIDDELBURG B.V.—See Ceconomy AG; *Int'l*, pg. 1377
MEDIA MARKT MISKOLC VIDEO TV HIFI ELEKTRO PHOTO COMPUTER KERESKEDELMIT KFT—See Ceconomy AG; *Int'l*, pg. 1374
MEDIA MARKT MOLLET VIDEO-TV-HIFI-ELEKTRO-COMPUTER-FOTO, S.A.U.—See Ceconomy AG; *Int'l*, pg. 1374
MEDIA MARKT MURCIA NUEVA CONDOMINA VIDEO-TV-HIFI-ELEKTRO-COMPUTER-FOTO S.A.—See Ceconomy AG; *Int'l*, pg. 1377
MEDIA MARKT NIEUWEGEIN B.V.—See Ceconomy AG; *Int'l*, pg. 1377
MEDIA MARKT NORRKOPING TV-HIFI-ELEKTRO AB—See Ceconomy AG; *Int'l*, pg. 1377
MEDIA MARKT NYIREGYHAZA VIDEO TV HIFI ELEKTRO PHOTO COMPUTER KERESKEDELMI KFT—See Ceconomy AG; *Int'l*, pg. 1377
MEDIA MARKT OBERWART TV-HIFI-ELEKTRO GMBH—See Ceconomy AG; *Int'l*, pg. 1377
MEDIA MARKT OFTRINGEN AG—See Ceconomy AG; *Int'l*, pg. 1377
MEDIA MARKT OOSTAKKER NV—See Ceconomy AG; *Int'l*, pg. 1377
MEDIA MARKT OOSTENDE NV—See Ceconomy AG; *Int'l*, pg. 1377
MEDIA MARKT OREBRO TV-HIFI-ELEKTRO AB—See Ceconomy AG; *Int'l*, pg. 1377
MEDIA MARKT ORIHUELA SA—See Ceconomy AG; *Int'l*, pg. 1378
MEDIA MARKT PALMA DE MALLORCA FAN SAU—See Ceconomy AG; *Int'l*, pg. 1378
MEDIA MARKT PALMA DE MALLORCA S.A.—See Ceconomy AG; *Int'l*, pg. 1378
MEDIA MARKTPARETS DEL VALLES SA—See Ceconomy AG; *Int'l*, pg. 1385
MEDIA MARKT PECS VIDEO TV HIFI ELEKTRO PHOTO COMPUTER KERESKEDELMIT KFT.—See Ceconomy AG; *Int'l*, pg. 1378
MEDIA MARKT PLACA DE CATALUNYA, S.A.U.—See Ceconomy AG; *Int'l*, pg. 1378
MEDIA MARKT POLSKA BIS SPOFKA Z OGRANICZONA ODPOWIEDZIALNOSCIA BYDGOSZCZ II SPOFKA KOMANDYTOWA—See Ceconomy AG; *Int'l*, pg. 1378
MEDIA MARKT POLSKA BIS SPOFKA Z OGRANICZONA ODPOWIEDZIALNOSCIA GDANSK IV SPOFKA KOMANDYTOWA—See Ceconomy AG; *Int'l*, pg. 1378
MEDIA MARKT POLSKA BIS SPOFKA Z OGRANICZONA ODPOWIEDZIALNOSCIA KATOWICE III SPOFKA KOMANDYTOWA—See Ceconomy AG; *Int'l*, pg. 1378
MEDIA MARKT POLSKA BIS SPOFKA Z OGRANICZONA ODPOWIEDZIALNOSCIA LUBIN SPOFKA KOMANDYTOWA—See Ceconomy AG; *Int'l*, pg. 1378
MEDIA MARKT POLSKA BIS SPOFKA Z OGRANICZONA ODPOWIEDZIALNOSCIA POZNAN III SPOFKA KOMANDYTOWA—See Ceconomy AG; *Int'l*, pg. 1378
MEDIA MARKT POLSKA BIS SPOFKA Z OGRANICZONA ODPOWIEDZIALNOSCIA POZNAN IV SPOFKA KOMANDYTOWA—See Ceconomy AG; *Int'l*, pg. 1378
MEDIA MARKT POLSKA BIS SPOFKA Z OGRANICZONA ODPOWIEDZIALNOSCIA SZCZECIN III SPOFKA KOMANDYTOWA—See Ceconomy AG; *Int'l*, pg. 1378
MEDIA MARKT POLSKA BIS SPOFKA Z OGRANICZONA ODPOWIEDZIALNOSCIA TYCHY SPOFKA KOMANDYTOWA—See Ceconomy AG; *Int'l*, pg. 1378
MEDIA MARKT POLSKA BIS SP. Z O.O. WROCLAW V SPOFKA KOMANDYTOWA—See Ceconomy AG; *Int'l*, pg. 1378

COMPANY NAME INDEX

MEDIA MARKT POLSKA SP. Z O.O. BIAFYSTOK SPOFKA KOMANDYTOWA—See Ceconomy AG; *Int'l*, pg. 1378
MEDIA MARKT POLSKA SP. Z O.O. BIELSKO-BIAFA SPOLKA KOMANDYTOWA—See Ceconomy AG; *Int'l*, pg. 1378
MEDIA MARKT POLSKA SP. Z O.O. BIELSKO-BIALA SPOLKA KOMANDYTOWA—See Ceconomy AG; *Int'l*, pg. 1379
MEDIA MARKT POLSKA SP. Z O.O. CHORZOW SPOFKA KOMANDYTOWA—See Ceconomy AG; *Int'l*, pg. 1378
MEDIA MARKT POLSKA SP. Z O.O. CHORZOW SPOLKA KOMANDYTOWA—See Ceconomy AG; *Int'l*, pg. 1378
MEDIA MARKT POLSKA SP. Z O.O. CZELADZ SPOFKA KOMANDYTOWA—See Ceconomy AG; *Int'l*, pg. 1379
MEDIA MARKT POLSKA SP. Z O.O. CZESTOCHOWA SPOFKA KOMANDYTOWA—See Ceconomy AG; *Int'l*, pg. 1379
MEDIA MARKT POLSKA SP. Z O.O. ELBLAG SPOFKA KOMANDYTOWA—See Ceconomy AG; *Int'l*, pg. 1378
MEDIA MARKT POLSKA SP. Z O.O. GDANSK II SPOFKA KOMANDYTOWA—See Ceconomy AG; *Int'l*, pg. 1378
MEDIA MARKT POLSKA SP. Z O.O. GDANSK I SPOFKA KOMANDYTOWA—See Ceconomy AG; *Int'l*, pg. 1378
MEDIA MARKT POLSKA SP. Z O.O. GDANSK I SPOLKA KOMANDYTOWA—See Ceconomy AG; *Int'l*, pg. 1379
MEDIA MARKT POLSKA SP. Z O.O. GDYNIA I SPOFKA KOMANDYTOWA—See Ceconomy AG; *Int'l*, pg. 1378
MEDIA MARKT POLSKA SP. Z O.O. GFOGOW SPOFKA KOMANDYTOWA—See Ceconomy AG; *Int'l*, pg. 1378
MEDIA MARKT POLSKA SP. Z O.O. GLIWICE SPOFKA KOMANDYTOWA—See Ceconomy AG; *Int'l*, pg. 1378
MEDIA MARKT POLSKA SP. Z O.O. GORZOW WIELKO-POLSKI SPOFKA KOMANDYTOWA—See Ceconomy AG; *Int'l*, pg. 1378
MEDIA MARKT POLSKA SP. Z O.O. KALISZ SPOFKA KOMANDYTOWA—See Ceconomy AG; *Int'l*, pg. 1378
MEDIA MARKT POLSKA SP. Z O.O. KATOWICE I SPOFKA KOMANDYTOWA—See Ceconomy AG; *Int'l*, pg. 1379
MEDIA MARKT POLSKA SP. Z O.O. KATOWICE I SPOLKA KOMANDYTOWA—See Ceconomy AG; *Int'l*, pg. 1379
MEDIA MARKT POLSKA SP. Z O.O. KIELCE SPOFKA KOMANDYTOWA—See Ceconomy AG; *Int'l*, pg. 1379
MEDIA MARKT POLSKA SP. Z O.O. KONIN SPOFKA KOMANDYTOWA—See Ceconomy AG; *Int'l*, pg. 1378
MEDIA MARKT POLSKA SP. Z O.O. KONIN SPOLKA KOMANDYTOWA—See Ceconomy AG; *Int'l*, pg. 1378
MEDIA MARKT POLSKA SP. Z O.O. KOSZALIN SPOFKA KOMANDYTOWA—See Ceconomy AG; *Int'l*, pg. 1378
MEDIA MARKT POLSKA SP. Z O.O. KRAKOW II SPOFKA KOMANDYTOWA—See Ceconomy AG; *Int'l*, pg. 1378
MEDIA MARKT POLSKA SP. Z O.O. KRAKOW II SPOLKA KOMANDYTOWA—See Ceconomy AG; *Int'l*, pg. 1378
MEDIA MARKT POLSKA SP. Z O.O. KRAKOW I SPOFKA KOMANDYTOWA—See Ceconomy AG; *Int'l*, pg. 1379
MEDIA MARKT POLSKA SP. Z O.O. LEGNICA SPOFKA KOMANDYTOWA—See Ceconomy AG; *Int'l*, pg. 1378
MEDIA MARKT POLSKA SP. Z O.O. LUBLIN SPOFKA KOMANDYTOWA—See Ceconomy AG; *Int'l*, pg. 1379
MEDIA MARKT POLSKA SP. Z O.O. NOWY SACZ SPOFKA KOMANDYTOWA—See Ceconomy AG; *Int'l*, pg. 1378
MEDIA MARKT POLSKA SP. Z O.O. NOWY SACZ SPOLKA KOMANDYTOWA—See Ceconomy AG; *Int'l*, pg. 1378
MEDIA MARKT POLSKA SP. Z O.O. OLSZTYN SPOFKA KOMANDYTOWA—See Ceconomy AG; *Int'l*, pg. 1379
MEDIA MARKT POLSKA SP. Z O.O. OPOLE SPOFKA KOMANDYTOWA—See Ceconomy AG; *Int'l*, pg. 1379
MEDIA MARKT POLSKA SP. Z O.O. PFOCK SPOFKA KOMANDYTOWA—See Ceconomy AG; *Int'l*, pg. 1378
MEDIA MARKT POLSKA SP. Z O.O. PIOTRKOW TRYBU-NALSKI SPOLKA KOMANDYTOWA—See Ceconomy AG; *Int'l*, pg. 1378
MEDIA MARKT POLSKA SP. Z O.O. POZNAN II SPOFKA KOMANDYTOWA—See Ceconomy AG; *Int'l*, pg. 1378
MEDIA MARKT POLSKA SP. Z O.O. RADOM SPOFKA KOMANDYTOWA—See Ceconomy AG; *Int'l*, pg. 1378
MEDIA MARKT POLSKA SP. Z O.O. RYBNIK SPOFKA KOMANDYTOWA—See Ceconomy AG; *Int'l*, pg. 1378
MEDIA MARKT POLSKA SP. Z O.O. RZESZOW SPOFKA KOMANDYTOWA—See Ceconomy AG; *Int'l*, pg. 1379
MEDIA MARKT POLSKA SP. Z O.O. SFUPSK SPOFKA KOMANDYTOWA—See Ceconomy AG; *Int'l*, pg. 1378
MEDIA MARKT POLSKA SP. Z O.O.—See Ceconomy AG; *Int'l*, pg. 1378
MEDIA MARKT POLSKA SP. Z O.O. TARNOW SPOFKA KOMANDYTOWA—See Ceconomy AG; *Int'l*, pg. 1378
MEDIA MARKT POLSKA SP. Z O.O. TODZ II SPOFKA KOMANDYTOWA—See Ceconomy AG; *Int'l*, pg. 1378
MEDIA MARKT POLSKA SP. Z O.O. TODZ I SPOFKA KOMANDYTOWA—See Ceconomy AG; *Int'l*, pg. 1379
MEDIA MARKT POLSKA SP. Z O.O. TORUN SPOFKA KOMANDYTOWA—See Ceconomy AG; *Int'l*, pg. 1379
MEDIA MARKT POLSKA SP. Z O.O. WAFBRZYCH SPOFKA KOMANDYTOWA—See Ceconomy AG; *Int'l*, pg. 1378

MEDIA MARKT POLSKA SP. Z.O.O. WARSCHAU III SPOFKA KOMANDYTOWA—See Ceconomy AG; *Int'l*, pg. 1379
MEDIA MARKT POLSKA SP. Z.O.O. WARSCHAU II SPOFKA KOMANDYTOWA—See Ceconomy AG; *Int'l*, pg. 1379
MEDIA MARKT POLSKA SP. Z.O.O. WARSCHAU IV SPOFKA KOMANDYTOWA—See Ceconomy AG; *Int'l*, pg. 1379
MEDIA MARKT POLSKA SP. Z.O.O. WROCLAW II SPOLKA KOMANDYTOWA—See Ceconomy AG; *Int'l*, pg. 1379
MEDIA MARKT POLSKA SP. Z.O.O. WROCLAW I SPOLKA KOMANDYTOWA—See Ceconomy AG; *Int'l*, pg. 1379
MEDIA MARKT POLSKA SP. Z.O.O. ZABRZE SPOFKA KOMANDYTOWA—See Ceconomy AG; *Int'l*, pg. 1379
MEDIA MARKT POLSKA SP. Z.O.O. ZAMOSC SPOFKA KOMANDYTOWA—See Ceconomy AG; *Int'l*, pg. 1378
MEDIA MARKT POLUS CENTER VIDEO TV HIFI PHOTO COMPUTER KERESKEDELMI KFT—See Ceconomy AG; *Int'l*, pg. 1379
MEDIA MARKT PUERTO REAL VIDEO-TV-HIFI-ELECTRO-COMPUTER-FOTO, S.A.—See Ceconomy AG; *Int'l*, pg. 1379
MEDIA MARKT QUART DE POBLET, S.A.—See Ceconomy AG; *Int'l*, pg. 1379
MEDIA MARKT REGION BERN AG—See Ceconomy AG; *Int'l*, pg. 1379
MEDIA MARKT RIED TV-HIFI-ELEKTRO GMBH—See Ceconomy AG; *Int'l*, pg. 1379
MEDIA MARKT RIJSWIJK B.V.—See Ceconomy AG; *Int'l*, pg. 1379
MEDIA MARKT RIVAS-VACIAMADRID VIDEO-TV-HIFI-ELEKTRO-COMPUTER-FOTO S.A.—See Ceconomy AG; *Int'l*, pg. 1379
MEDIA MARKT ROERMOND B.V—See Ceconomy AG; *Int'l*, pg. 1379
MEDIA MARKT ROESELARE NV—See Ceconomy AG; *Int'l*, pg. 1379
MEDIA MARKT ROTTERDAM BEIJERLANDSELAAN B.V.—See Ceconomy AG; *Int'l*, pg. 1379
MEDIA MARKT SALAMANCA VIDEO-TV-HIFI-COMPUTER FOTO, S.A.—See Ceconomy AG; *Int'l*, pg. 1374
MEDIA MARKT SAN JUAN DE AZNALFARACHE VIDEO-TV-HIFI-ELECTRO-COMPUTER-FOTO, S.A.—See Ceconomy AG; *Int'l*, pg. 1379
MEDIA MARKT SAN SEBASTIAN DE LOS REYES VIDEO-TV-HIFI-ELEKTRO-COMPUTER-FOTO, S.A.—See Ceconomy AG; *Int'l*, pg. 1374
MEDIA MARKT SANTANDER VIDEO-TV-HIFI-COMPUTER-FOTO, SA—See Ceconomy AG; *Int'l*, pg. 1379
MEDIA MARKT SANT CUGAT DEL VALLES VIDEO-TV-HIFI-ELEKTRO-COMPUTER-FOTO, S.A.—See Ceconomy AG; *Int'l*, pg. 1374
MEDIA MARKT SANTIAGO DE COMPOSTELA S.A.—See Ceconomy AG; *Int'l*, pg. 1379
MEDIA MARKT SATURN ADMINISTRACION ESPANA, S.A.U.—See Ceconomy AG; *Int'l*, pg. 1374
MEDIA MARKT-SATURN BELGIUM N.V—See Ceconomy AG; *Int'l*, pg. 1375
MEDIA MARKT SATURN HOLDING MAGYARORSZAG KFT.—See Ceconomy AG; *Int'l*, pg. 1379
MEDIA MARKT SATURN HOLDING NEDERLAND B.V.—See Ceconomy AG; *Int'l*, pg. 1379
MEDIA MARKT SATURN, S.A.—See Ceconomy AG; *Int'l*, pg. 1374
MEDIA MARKT SCHOTEN NV—See Ceconomy AG; *Int'l*, pg. 1379
MEDIA MARKT SETUBAL - PRODUTOS INFORMATICOS E ELECTRONICOS, LDA.—See Ceconomy AG; *Int'l*, pg. 1374
MEDIA MARKT SEVILLA-SANTA JUSTA VIDEO-TV-HIFII-ELEKTRO-COMPUTER-FOTO, S.A.—See Ceconomy AG; *Int'l*, pg. 1374
MEDIA MARKT SIERO VIDEO-TV-HIFI-ELEKTRO-COMPUTER-FOTO, S.A.—See Ceconomy AG; *Int'l*, pg. 1374
MEDIA MARKT SINGEN GMBH—See Ceconomy AG; *Int'l*, pg. 1379
MEDIA MARKT SINT-PIETERS-LEEUW N.V.—See Ceconomy AG; *Int'l*, pg. 1374
MEDIA MARKT SINTRA - PRODUTOS INFORMATICOS E ELECTRONICOS, LDA—See Ceconomy AG; *Int'l*, pg. 1374
MEDIA MARKT SKOVDE TV-HIFI-ELEKTRO AB—See Ceconomy AG; *Int'l*, pg. 1379
MEDIA MARKT SOROKSAR VIDEO TV HIFI ELEKTRO PHOTO COMPUTER KERESKEDELMI KFT.—See Ceconomy AG; *Int'l*, pg. 1379
MEDIA MARKT SPITTAL TV-HIFI-ELEKTRO GMBH—See Ceconomy AG; *Int'l*, pg. 1379
MEDIA MARKT STEYR TV-HIFI-ELEKTRO GMBH—See Ceconomy AG; *Int'l*, pg. 1379
MEDIA MARKT ST. GALLEN AG—See Ceconomy AG; *Int'l*, pg. 1379

MEDIA-MAKER S.P.A.

MEDIA MARKT ST. LORENZEN TV-HIFI-ELEKTRO GMBH—See Ceconomy AG; *Int'l*, pg. 1379
MEDIA MARKT STOCKHOLM-BARKARBY TV-HIFI-ELEKTRO AB—See Ceconomy AG; *Int'l*, pg. 1380
MEDIA MARKT STOCKHOLM-GALLERIAN TV-HIFI-ELEKTRO AB—See Ceconomy AG; *Int'l*, pg. 1380
MEDIA MARKT STOCKHOLM-HERON CITY TV-HIFI-ELEKTRO AB—See Ceconomy AG; *Int'l*, pg. 1380
MEDIA MARKT STOCKHOLM-LANNA TV-HIFI-ELEKTRO AB—See Ceconomy AG; *Int'l*, pg. 1380
MEDIA MARKT STOCKHOLM-NACKA TV-HIFI-ELEKTRO AB—See Ceconomy AG; *Int'l*, pg. 1380
MEDIA MARKT STOCKHOLM-TABY TV-HIFI-ELEKTRO AB—See Ceconomy AG; *Int'l*, pg. 1380
MEDIA MARKT STOP SHOP VIDEO TV HIFI ELEKTRO PHOTO COMPUTER KERESKEDELMI KFT.—See Ceconomy AG; *Int'l*, pg. 1374
MEDIA MARKT SUNDSVALL TV-HIFI-ELEKTRO AB—See Ceconomy AG; *Int'l*, pg. 1380
MEDIA MARKT SZEGED VIDEO-TV-HIFI-ELEKTRO-PHOTO-COMPUTER-KERESKEDELMI KFT.—See Ceconomy AG; *Int'l*, pg. 1374
MEDIA MARKT SZEKESFEHERVAR VIDEO TV HIFI ELEKTRO PHOTO COMPUTER KERESKEDELMI KFT.—See Ceconomy AG; *Int'l*, pg. 1374
MEDIA MARKT SZOLNOK VIDEO TV HIFI ELEKTRO PHOTO COMPUTER KERESKEDELMI KFT.—See Ceconomy AG; *Int'l*, pg. 1380
MEDIA MARKT SZOMBATHELY VIDEO-TV-HIFI-ELEKTRO-PHOTO-COMPUTER-KERESKEDELMI KFT.—See Ceconomy AG; *Int'l*, pg. 1380
MEDIA MARKT TARRAGONA VIDEO-TV-HIFI-ELEKTRO-COMPUTER-FOTO S.A.—See Ceconomy AG; *Int'l*, pg. 1374
MEDIA MARKT TATABANYA VIDEO TV HIFI ELEKTRO PHOTO COMPUTER KERESKEDELMI KFT.—See Ceconomy AG; *Int'l*, pg. 1384
MEDIA MARKT TELDE VFDEO-TV- HIFI- ELEKTRO-COMPUTER- FOTO, SA—See Ceconomy AG; *Int'l*, pg. 1384
MEDIA MARKT TENERIFE VIDEO-TV-HIFI-ELEKTRO-COMPUTER-FOTO, SA—See Ceconomy AG; *Int'l*, pg. 1384
MEDIA MARKT TERRASSA SA—See Ceconomy AG; *Int'l*, pg. 1384
MEDIA MARKT THE CORNER B.V.—See Ceconomy AG; *Int'l*, pg. 1384
MEDIA MARKT TOLEDO S.A.—See Ceconomy AG; *Int'l*, pg. 1384
MEDIA MARKT TURNHOUT NV—See Ceconomy AG; *Int'l*, pg. 1384
MEDIA MARKT TV-HIFI-ELEKTRO ATHENS I COMMER-CIAL ANONYMI ETERIA—See Ceconomy AG; *Int'l*, pg. 1380
MEDIA MARKT TV-HIFI-ELEKTRO ATHENS II COMMER-CIAL ANONYMI ETERIA—See Ceconomy AG; *Int'l*, pg. 1380
MEDIA-MARKT TV-HIFI-ELEKTRO GMBH AACHEN—See Ceconomy AG; *Int'l*, pg. 1375
MEDIA MARKT TV-HIFI-ELEKTRO GMBH AALEN—See Ceconomy AG; *Int'l*, pg. 1380
MEDIA MARKT TV-HIFI-ELEKTRO GMBH ALBSTADT—See Ceconomy AG; *Int'l*, pg. 1380
MEDIA MARKT TV-HIFI-ELEKTRO GMBH ALZEY—See Ceconomy AG; *Int'l*, pg. 1380
MEDIA MARKT TV-HIFI-ELEKTRO GMBH AMBERG—See Ceconomy AG; *Int'l*, pg. 1380
MEDIA MARKT TV-HIFI-ELEKTRO GMBH ANSBACH—See Ceconomy AG; *Int'l*, pg. 1380
MEDIA MARKT TV-HIFI-ELEKTRO GMBH ASCHAFFENBURG—See Ceconomy AG; *Int'l*, pg. 1375
MEDIA MARKT TV-HIFI-ELEKTRO GMBH AUGSBURG-GOGGINGEN—See Ceconomy AG; *Int'l*, pg. 1380
MEDIA MARKT TV-HIFI-ELEKTRO GMBH BAD KREUZNACH—See Ceconomy AG; *Int'l*, pg. 1374
MEDIA MARKT TV-HIFI-ELEKTRO GMBH BAYREUTH—See Ceconomy AG; *Int'l*, pg. 1375
MEDIA MARKT TV-HIFI-ELEKTRO GMBH BERLIN-BIESDORF—See Ceconomy AG; *Int'l*, pg. 1375
MEDIA MARKT TV-HIFI-ELEKTRO GMBH BERLIN-CHARLOTTENBURG—See Ceconomy AG; *Int'l*, pg. 1380
MEDIA MARKT TV-HIFI-ELEKTRO GMBH BERLIN-GROPIUSSTADT—See Ceconomy AG; *Int'l*, pg. 1375
MEDIA MARKT TV-HIFI-ELEKTRO GMBH BERLIN-HOHENSCHONHAUSEN—See Cecoriomy AG; *Int'l*, pg. 1374
MEDIA MARKT TV-HIFI-ELEKTRO GMBH BERLIN-MITTE—See Ceconomy AG; *Int'l*, pg. 1380
MEDIA MARKT TV-HIFI-ELEKTRO GMBH BERLIN-NEUKOLLN—See Ceconomy AG; *Int'l*, pg. 1375
MEDIA MARKT TV-HIFI-ELEKTRO GMBH BERLIN-PRENZLAUER BERG—See Ceconomy AG; *Int'l*, pg. 1380
MEDIA MARKT TV-HIFI-ELEKTRO GMBH BERLIN-SCHONEWEIDE—See Ceconomy AG; *Int'l*, pg. 1380
MEDIA MARKT TV-HIFI-ELEKTRO GMBH BERLIN-SPANDAU—See Ceconomy AG; *Int'l*, pg. 1374

MEDIA-MAKER S.P.A. — CORPORATE AFFILIATIONS

MEDIA MARKT TV-HIFI-ELEKTRO GMBH BERLIN-STEGLITZ—See Ceconomy AG; *Int'l*, pg. 1380
MEDIA MARKT TV-HIFI-ELEKTRO GMBH BERLIN-TEGEL—See Ceconomy AG; *Int'l*, pg. 1380
MEDIA MARKT TV-HIFI-ELEKTRO GMBH BERLIN-TEMPELHOF—See Ceconomy AG; *Int'l*, pg. 1380
MEDIA MARKT TV-HIFI-ELEKTRO GMBH BERLIN-WEDDING—See Ceconomy AG; *Int'l*, pg. 1374
MEDIA MARKT TV-HIFI-ELEKTRO GMBH BIELEFELD—See Ceconomy AG; *Int'l*, pg. 1380
MEDIA MARKT TV-HIFI-ELEKTRO GMBH BISCHOFSHEIM—See Ceconomy AG; *Int'l*, pg. 1380
MEDIA MARKT TV-HIFI-ELEKTRO GMBH BOCHUM-RUHRPARK—See Ceconomy AG; *Int'l*, pg. 1380
MEDIA MARKT TV-HIFI-ELEKTRO GMBH BOCHUM—See Ceconomy AG; *Int'l*, pg. 1380
MEDIA MARKT TV-HIFI-ELEKTRO GMBH BONN—See Ceconomy AG; *Int'l*, pg. 1380
MEDIA MARKT TV-HIFI-ELEKTRO GMBH BRANDENBURG AN DER HAVEL—See Ceconomy AG; *Int'l*, pg. 1380
MEDIA MARKT TV-HIFI-ELEKTRO GMBH BRAUNSCHWEIG—See Ceconomy AG; *Int'l*, pg. 1380
MEDIA MARKT TV-HIFI-ELEKTRO GMBH BREMEN—See Ceconomy AG; *Int'l*, pg. 1380
MEDIA MARKT TV-HIFI-ELEKTRO GMBH BREMEN-WATERFRONT—See Ceconomy AG; *Int'l*, pg. 1380
MEDIA MARKT TV-HIFI-ELEKTRO GMBH BUCHHOLZ IN DER NORDHEIDE—See Ceconomy AG; *Int'l*, pg. 1380
MEDIA MARKT TV-HIFI-ELEKTRO GMBH BUXTEHUDE—See Ceconomy AG; *Int'l*, pg. 1380
MEDIA MARKT TV-HIFI-ELEKTRO GMBH CASTROP-RAUXEL—See Ceconomy AG; *Int'l*, pg. 1374
MEDIA MARKT TV-HIFI-ELEKTRO GMBH CHEMNITZ-ROHRSDORF—See Ceconomy AG; *Int'l*, pg. 1380
MEDIA MARKT TV-HIFI-ELEKTRO GMBH CHEMNITZ—See Ceconomy AG; *Int'l*, pg. 1380
MEDIA MARKT TV-HIFI-ELEKTRO GMBH COBURG—See Ceconomy AG; *Int'l*, pg. 1380
MEDIA MARKT TV-HIFI-ELEKTRO GMBH & CO. KG BRUCHSAL—See Ceconomy AG; *Int'l*, pg. 1380
MEDIA MARKT TV-HIFI-ELEKTRO GMBH COTTBUS/GROB GAGLOW—See Ceconomy AG; *Int'l*, pg. 1380
MEDIA MARKT TV-HIFI-ELEKTRO GMBH DEGGENDORF—See Ceconomy AG; *Int'l*, pg. 1380
MEDIA MARKT TV-HIFI-ELEKTRO GMBH DESSAU—See Ceconomy AG; *Int'l*, pg. 1380
MEDIA MARKT TV-HIFI-ELEKTRO GMBH DIETZENBACH—See Ceconomy AG; *Int'l*, pg. 1374
MEDIA MARKT TV-HIFI-ELEKTRO GMBH DONAUWORTH—See Ceconomy AG; *Int'l*, pg. 1380
MEDIA MARKT TV-HIFI-ELEKTRO GMBH DORSTEN—See Ceconomy AG; *Int'l*, pg. 1380
MEDIA MARKT TV-HIFI-ELEKTRO GMBH DORTMUND-HORDE—See Ceconomy AG; *Int'l*, pg. 1380
MEDIA MARKT TV-HIFI-ELEKTRO GMBH DORTMUND-OESPEL—See Ceconomy AG; *Int'l*, pg. 1380
MEDIA MARKT TV-HIFI-ELEKTRO GMBH DRESDEN CENTRUM—See Ceconomy AG; *Int'l*, pg. 1380
MEDIA MARKT TV-HIFI-ELEKTRO GMBH DRESDEN-MICKTEN—See Ceconomy AG; *Int'l*, pg. 1374
MEDIA MARKT TV-HIFI-ELEKTRO GMBH DUISBURG-GROBENBAUM—See Ceconomy AG; *Int'l*, pg. 1381
MEDIA MARKT TV-HIFI-ELEKTRO GMBH DUISBURG—See Ceconomy AG; *Int'l*, pg. 1381
MEDIA MARKT TV-HIFI-ELEKTRO GMBH DUSSELDORF BILK—See Ceconomy AG; *Int'l*, pg. 1380
MEDIA MARKT TV-HIFI-ELEKTRO GMBH DUSSELDORF—See Ceconomy AG; *Int'l*, pg. 1381
MEDIA MARKT TV-HIFI-ELEKTRO GMBH EGELSBACH—See Ceconomy AG; *Int'l*, pg. 1381
MEDIA MARKT TV-HIFI-ELEKTRO GMBH EICHE—See Ceconomy AG; *Int'l*, pg. 1381
MEDIA MARKT TV-HIFI-ELEKTRO GMBH EISENACH—See Ceconomy AG; *Int'l*, pg. 1381
MEDIA MARKT TV-HIFI-ELEKTRO GMBH EISLINGEN—See Ceconomy AG; *Int'l*, pg. 1381
MEDIA MARKT TV-HIFI-ELEKTRO GMBH ELMSHORN—See Ceconomy AG; *Int'l*, pg. 1381
MEDIA MARKT TV-HIFI-ELEKTRO GMBH EMDEN—See Ceconomy AG; *Int'l*, pg. 1381
MEDIA MARKT TV-HIFI-ELEKTRO GMBH ERDING—See Ceconomy AG; *Int'l*, pg. 1381
MEDIA MARKT TV-HIFI-ELEKTRO GMBH ERFURT-DABERSTEDT—See Ceconomy AG; *Int'l*, pg. 1381
MEDIA MARKT TV-HIFI-ELEKTRO GMBH ERFURT THURINGEN-PARK—See Ceconomy AG; *Int'l*, pg. 1381
MEDIA MARKT TV-HIFI-ELEKTRO GMBH ERLANGEN—See Ceconomy AG; *Int'l*, pg. 1381
MEDIA MARKT TV-HIFI-ELEKTRO GMBH ESCHWEILER—See Ceconomy AG; *Int'l*, pg. 1381
MEDIA MARKT TV-HIFI-ELEKTRO GMBH ESSEN—See Ceconomy AG; *Int'l*, pg. 1381
MEDIA MARKT TV-HIFI-ELEKTRO GMBH ESSLINGEN—See Ceconomy AG; *Int'l*, pg. 1381
MEDIA MARKT TV-HIFI-ELEKTRO GMBH FELLBACH—See Ceconomy AG; *Int'l*, pg. 1381
MEDIA MARKT TV-HIFI-ELEKTRO GMBH FLENSBURG—See Ceconomy AG; *Int'l*, pg. 1381
MEDIA MARKT TV-HIFI-ELEKTRO GMBH FRANKFURT BORSIGALLEE—See Ceconomy AG; *Int'l*, pg. 1374
MEDIA MARKT TV-HIFI-ELEKTRO GMBH FRANKFURT—See Ceconomy AG; *Int'l*, pg. 1381
MEDIA MARKT TV-HIFI-ELEKTRO GMBH FREIBURG—See Ceconomy AG; *Int'l*, pg. 1381
MEDIA MARKT TV-HIFI-ELEKTRO GMBH FRIEDRICHSHAFEN—See Ceconomy AG; *Int'l*, pg. 1374
MEDIA MARKT TV-HIFI-ELEKTRO GMBH FULDA—See Ceconomy AG; *Int'l*, pg. 1381
MEDIA MARKT TV-HIFI-ELEKTRO GMBH GIFHORN—See Ceconomy AG; *Int'l*, pg. 1381
MEDIA MARKT TV-HIFI-ELEKTRO GMBH GOSLAR—See Ceconomy AG; *Int'l*, pg. 1384
MEDIA MARKT TV-HIFI-ELEKTRO GMBH GOTTINGEN—See Ceconomy AG; *Int'l*, pg. 1381
MEDIA MARKT TV-HIFI-ELEKTRO GMBH GREIFSWALD—See Ceconomy AG; *Int'l*, pg. 1381
MEDIA MARKT TV-HIFI-ELEKTRO GMBH GRUNDAU-LIEBLOS—See Ceconomy AG; *Int'l*, pg. 1381
MEDIA MARKT TV-HIFI-ELEKTRO GMBH GUNTHERSDORF—See Ceconomy AG; *Int'l*, pg. 1381
MEDIA MARKT TV-HIFI-ELEKTRO GMBH GUTERSLOH—See Ceconomy AG; *Int'l*, pg. 1374
MEDIA MARKT TV-HIFI-ELEKTRO GMBH HALBERSTADT—See Ceconomy AG; *Int'l*, pg. 1381
MEDIA MARKT TV-HIFI-ELEKTRO GMBH HALSTENBEK—See Ceconomy AG; *Int'l*, pg. 1381
MEDIA MARKT TV-HIFI-ELEKTRO GMBH HAMBURG-ALTONA—See Ceconomy AG; *Int'l*, pg. 1381
MEDIA MARKT TV-HIFI-ELEKTRO GMBH HAMBURG-BILLSTEDT—See Ceconomy AG; *Int'l*, pg. 1381
MEDIA MARKT TV-HIFI-ELEKTRO GMBH HAMBURG-HARBURG—See Ceconomy AG; *Int'l*, pg. 1381
MEDIA MARKT TV-HIFI-ELEKTRO GMBH HAMBURG-HUMMELSBUTTEL—See Ceconomy AG; *Int'l*, pg. 1381
MEDIA MARKT TV-HIFI-ELEKTRO GMBH HAMBURG-NEDDERFELD—See Ceconomy AG; *Int'l*, pg. 1381
MEDIA MARKT TV-HIFI-ELEKTRO GMBH HAMBURG-WANDSBEK—See Ceconomy AG; *Int'l*, pg. 1381
MEDIA MARKT TV-HIFI-ELEKTRO GMBH HAMELN—See Ceconomy AG; *Int'l*, pg. 1381
MEDIA MARKT TV-HIFI-ELEKTRO GMBH HANNOVER-VAHRENHEIDE—See Ceconomy AG; *Int'l*, pg. 1381
MEDIA MARKT TV-HIFI-ELEKTRO GMBH HANNOVER-WULFEL—See Ceconomy AG; *Int'l*, pg. 1374
MEDIA MARKT TV-HIFI-ELEKTRO GMBH HEIDELBERG-ROHRBACH—See Ceconomy AG; *Int'l*, pg. 1381
MEDIA MARKT TV-HIFI-ELEKTRO GMBH HEIDELBERG—See Ceconomy AG; *Int'l*, pg. 1375
MEDIA MARKT TV-HIFI-ELEKTRO GMBH HEIDE—See Ceconomy AG; *Int'l*, pg. 1381
MEDIA MARKT TV-HIFI-ELEKTRO GMBH HEILBRONN—See Ceconomy AG; *Int'l*, pg. 1381
MEDIA MARKT TV-HIFI-ELEKTRO GMBH HENSTEDT-ULZBURG—See Ceconomy AG; *Int'l*, pg. 1381
MEDIA MARKT TV-HIFI-ELEKTRO GMBH HEPPENHEIM—See Ceconomy AG; *Int'l*, pg. 1381
MEDIA MARKT TV-HIFI-ELEKTRO GMBH HILDESHEIM—See Ceconomy AG; *Int'l*, pg. 1381
MEDIA MARKT TV-HIFI-ELEKTRO GMBH HOF—See Ceconomy AG; *Int'l*, pg. 1381
MEDIA MARKT TV-HIFI-ELEKTRO GMBH HOLZMINDEN—See Ceconomy AG; *Int'l*, pg. 1381
MEDIA MARKT TV-HIFI-ELEKTRO GMBH HOMBURG/SAAR—See Ceconomy AG; *Int'l*, pg. 1381
MEDIA MARKT TV-HIFI-ELEKTRO GMBH HUCKELHOVEN—See Ceconomy AG; *Int'l*, pg. 1382
MEDIA MARKT TV-HIFI-ELEKTRO GMBH IDAR-OBERSTEIN—See Ceconomy AG; *Int'l*, pg. 1382
MEDIA MARKT TV-HIFI-ELEKTRO GMBH ITZEHOE—See Ceconomy AG; *Int'l*, pg. 1382
MEDIA MARKT TV-HIFI-ELEKTRO GMBH JENA—See Ceconomy AG; *Int'l*, pg. 1382
MEDIA MARKT TV-HIFI-ELEKTRO GMBH KAISERSLAUTERN—See Ceconomy AG; *Int'l*, pg. 1382
MEDIA MARKT TV-HIFI-ELEKTRO GMBH KARLSFELD—See Ceconomy AG; *Int'l*, pg. 1382
MEDIA MARKT TV-HIFI-ELEKTRO GMBH KARLSRUHE-ETTLINGER TOR—See Ceconomy AG; *Int'l*, pg. 1382
MEDIA MARKT TV-HIFI-ELEKTRO GMBH KARLSRUHE—See Ceconomy AG; *Int'l*, pg. 1382
MEDIA MARKT TV-HIFI-ELEKTRO GMBH KASSEL—See Ceconomy AG; *Int'l*, pg. 1382
MEDIA MARKT TV-HIFI-ELEKTRO GMBH KEMPTEN—See Ceconomy AG; *Int'l*, pg. 1382
MEDIA MARKT TV-HIFI-ELEKTRO GMBH KIEL—See Ceconomy AG; *Int'l*, pg. 1382
MEDIA MARKT TV-HIFI-ELEKTRO GMBH KIRCHHEIM—See Ceconomy AG; *Int'l*, pg. 1382
MEDIA MARKT TV-HIFI-ELEKTRO GMBH KOBLENZ—See Ceconomy AG; *Int'l*, pg. 1382
MEDIA MARKT TV-HIFI-ELEKTRO GMBH KOLN-CHORWEILER—See Ceconomy AG; *Int'l*, pg. 1382
MEDIA MARKT TV-HIFI-ELEKTRO GMBH KOLN HOHE STRASSE—See Ceconomy AG; *Int'l*, pg. 1382
MEDIA MARKT TV-HIFI-ELEKTRO GMBH KOLN-KALK—See Ceconomy AG; *Int'l*, pg. 1382
MEDIA MARKT TV-HIFI-ELEKTRO GMBH KOLN-MARSDORF—See Ceconomy AG; *Int'l*, pg. 1382
MEDIA MARKT TV-HIFI-ELEKTRO GMBH KONSTANZ—See Ceconomy AG; *Int'l*, pg. 1382
MEDIA MARKT TV-HIFI-ELEKTRO GMBH KREFELD—See Ceconomy AG; *Int'l*, pg. 1382
MEDIA MARKT TV-HIFI-ELEKTRO GMBH KULMBACH—See Ceconomy AG; *Int'l*, pg. 1382
MEDIA MARKT TV-HIFI-ELEKTRO GMBH LAHR—See Ceconomy AG; *Int'l*, pg. 1382
MEDIA MARKT TV-HIFI-ELEKTRO GMBH LANDAU/PFALZ—See Ceconomy AG; *Int'l*, pg. 1382
MEDIA MARKT TV-HIFI-ELEKTRO GMBH LANDSBERG/LECH—See Ceconomy AG; *Int'l*, pg. 1382
MEDIA MARKT TV-HIFI-ELEKTRO GMBH LANDSHUT—See Ceconomy AG; *Int'l*, pg. 1382
MEDIA MARKT TV-HIFI-ELEKTRO GMBH LEIPZIG HOFE AM BRUHL—See Ceconomy AG; *Int'l*, pg. 1382
MEDIA MARKT TV-HIFI-ELEKTRO GMBH LEIPZIG PAUNSDORF—See Ceconomy AG; *Int'l*, pg. 1382
MEDIA MARKT TV-HIFI-ELEKTRO GMBH LIMBURG—See Ceconomy AG; *Int'l*, pg. 1374
MEDIA MARKT TV-HIFI-ELEKTRO GMBH LINGEN—See Ceconomy AG; *Int'l*, pg. 1382
MEDIA MARKT TV-HIFI-ELEKTRO GMBH LUBECK—See Ceconomy AG; *Int'l*, pg. 1382
MEDIA MARKT TV-HIFI-ELEKTRO GMBH LUDWIGSBURG—See Ceconomy AG; *Int'l*, pg. 1382
MEDIA MARKT TV-HIFI-ELEKTRO GMBH LUDWIGSHAFEN—See Ceconomy AG; *Int'l*, pg. 1382
MEDIA MARKT TV-HIFI-ELEKTRO GMBH MAGDEBURG-BORDEPARK—See Ceconomy AG; *Int'l*, pg. 1382
MEDIA MARKT TV-HIFI-ELEKTRO GMBH MAGDEBURG—See Ceconomy AG; *Int'l*, pg. 1374
MEDIA MARKT TV-HIFI-ELEKTRO GMBH MAIN-TAUNUS-ZENTRUM—See Ceconomy AG; *Int'l*, pg. 1382
MEDIA MARKT TV-HIFI-ELEKTRO GMBH MAINZ—See Ceconomy AG; *Int'l*, pg. 1382
MEDIA MARKT TV-HIFI-ELEKTRO GMBH MANNHEIM-SANDHOFEN—See Ceconomy AG; *Int'l*, pg. 1382
MEDIA MARKT TV-HIFI-ELEKTRO GMBH MANNHEIM—See Ceconomy AG; *Int'l*, pg. 1382
MEDIA MARKT TV-HIFI-ELEKTRO GMBH MARBURG—See Ceconomy AG; *Int'l*, pg. 1374
MEDIA MARKT TV-HIFI-ELEKTRO GMBH MARKTREDWITZ—See Ceconomy AG; *Int'l*, pg. 1382
MEDIA MARKT TV-HIFI-ELEKTRO GMBH MEERANE—See Ceconomy AG; *Int'l*, pg. 1382
MEDIA MARKT TV-HIFI-ELEKTRO GMBH MEMMINGEN—See Ceconomy AG; *Int'l*, pg. 1382
MEDIA MARKT TV-HIFI-ELEKTRO GMBH MONCHENGLADBACH—See Ceconomy AG; *Int'l*, pg. 1382
MEDIA MARKT TV-HIFI-ELEKTRO GMBH MUHLDORF/INN—See Ceconomy AG; *Int'l*, pg. 1382
MEDIA MARKT TV-HIFI-ELEKTRO GMBH MULHEIM—See Ceconomy AG; *Int'l*, pg. 1382
MEDIA MARKT TV-HIFI-ELEKTRO GMBH MUNCHEN-HAIDHAUSEN—See Ceconomy AG; *Int'l*, pg. 1382
MEDIA MARKT TV-HIFI-ELEKTRO GMBH MUNCHEN-PASING—See Ceconomy AG; *Int'l*, pg. 1382
MEDIA MARKT TV-HIFI-ELEKTRO GMBH MUNCHEN-SOLLN—See Ceconomy AG; *Int'l*, pg. 1382
MEDIA MARKT TV-HIFI-ELEKTRO GMBH MUNSTER—See Ceconomy AG; *Int'l*, pg. 1382
MEDIA MARKT TV-HIFI-ELEKTRO GMBH NAGOLD—See Ceconomy AG; *Int'l*, pg. 1384
MEDIA MARKT TV-HIFI-ELEKTRO GMBH NEUBRANDENBURG—See Ceconomy AG; *Int'l*, pg. 1383
MEDIA MARKT TV-HIFI-ELEKTRO GMBH NEUBURG AN DER DONAU—See Ceconomy AG; *Int'l*, pg. 1383
MEDIA MARKT TV-HIFI-ELEKTRO GMBH NEUMUNSTER—See Ceconomy AG; *Int'l*, pg. 1383
MEDIA MARKT TV-HIFI-ELEKTRO GMBH NEUNKIRCHEN—See Ceconomy AG; *Int'l*, pg. 1383
MEDIA MARKT TV-HIFI-ELEKTRO GMBH NEUSS—See Ceconomy AG; *Int'l*, pg. 1383
MEDIA MARKT TV-HIFI-ELEKTRO GMBH NEUSTADT AN DER WEINSTRASSE—See Ceconomy AG; *Int'l*, pg. 1383
MEDIA MARKT TV-HIFI-ELEKTRO GMBH NEU-ULM—See Ceconomy AG; *Int'l*, pg. 1383
MEDIA MARKT TV-HIFI-ELEKTRO GMBH NEUWIED—See Ceconomy AG; *Int'l*, pg. 1383
MEDIA MARKT TV-HIFI-ELEKTRO GMBH NIENBURG—See Ceconomy AG; *Int'l*, pg. 1374
MEDIA MARKT TV-HIFI-ELEKTRO GMBH NORDHAUSEN—See Ceconomy AG; *Int'l*, pg. 1383
MEDIA MARKT TV-HIFI-ELEKTRO GMBH NORDHORN—See Ceconomy AG; *Int'l*, pg. 1383
MEDIA MARKT TV-HIFI-ELEKTRO GMBH NURNBERG-KLEINREUTH—See Ceconomy AG; *Int'l*, pg. 1375

MEDIA MARKT TV-HIFI-ELEKTRO GMBH NURNBERG-LANGWASSER—See Ceconomy AG; *Int'l*, pg. 1374
MEDIA MARKT TV-HIFI-ELEKTRO GMBH NURNBERG-SCHOPPERSHOF—See Ceconomy AG; *Int'l*, pg. 1374
MEDIA MARKT TV-HIFI-ELEKTRO GMBH OFFENBURG—See Ceconomy AG; *Int'l*, pg. 1383
MEDIA MARKT TV-HIFI-ELEKTRO GMBH OLDENBURG—See Ceconomy AG; *Int'l*, pg. 1383
MEDIA MARKT TV-HIFI-ELEKTRO GMBH OSTSTEINBEK—See Ceconomy AG; *Int'l*, pg. 1383
MEDIA MARKT TV-HIFI-ELEKTRO GMBH PADERBORN—See Ceconomy AG; *Int'l*, pg. 1383
MEDIA MARKT TV-HIFI-ELEKTRO GMBH PAPENBURG—See Ceconomy AG; *Int'l*, pg. 1383
MEDIA MARKT TV-HIFI-ELEKTRO GMBH PASSAU—See Ceconomy AG; *Int'l*, pg. 1383
MEDIA MARKT TV-HIFI-ELEKTRO GMBH PEINE—See Ceconomy AG; *Int'l*, pg. 1383
MEDIA MARKT TV-HIFI-ELEKTRO GMBH PFORZHEIM—See Ceconomy AG; *Int'l*, pg. 1383
MEDIA MARKT TV-HIFI-ELEKTRO GMBH PIRMASENS—See Ceconomy AG; *Int'l*, pg. 1383
MEDIA MARKT TV-HIFI-ELEKTRO GMBH PLAUEN—See Ceconomy AG; *Int'l*, pg. 1383
MEDIA MARKT TV-HIFI-ELEKTRO GMBH POTSDAM—See Ceconomy AG; *Int'l*, pg. 1383
MEDIA MARKT TV-HIFI-ELEKTRO GMBH RAVENSBURG—See Ceconomy AG; *Int'l*, pg. 1383
MEDIA MARKT TV-HIFI-ELEKTRO GMBH RECKLINGHAUSEN—See Ceconomy AG; *Int'l*, pg. 1383
MEDIA MARKT TV-HIFI-ELEKTRO GMBH REGENSBURG—See Ceconomy AG; *Int'l*, pg. 1383
MEDIA MARKT TV-HIFI-ELEKTRO GMBH RENDSBURG—See Ceconomy AG; *Int'l*, pg. 1383
MEDIA MARKT TV-HIFI-ELEKTRO GMBH REUTLINGEN—See Ceconomy AG; *Int'l*, pg. 1383
MEDIA MARKT TV-HIFI-ELEKTRO GMBH RHEINE—See Ceconomy AG; *Int'l*, pg. 1374
MEDIA MARKT TV-HIFI-ELEKTRO GMBH RODENTAL—See Ceconomy AG; *Int'l*, pg. 1374
MEDIA MARKT TV-HIFI-ELEKTRO GMBH ROSENHEIM—See Ceconomy AG; *Int'l*, pg. 1374
MEDIA MARKT TV-HIFI-ELEKTRO GMBH ROSTOCK-BRINCKMANSDORF—See Ceconomy AG; *Int'l*, pg. 1383
MEDIA MARKT TV-HIFI-ELEKTRO GMBH ROSTOCK—See Ceconomy AG; *Int'l*, pg. 1383
MEDIA MARKT TV-HIFI-ELEKTRO GMBH SAARBRUCKEN-SAARTERRASSEN—See Ceconomy AG; *Int'l*, pg. 1383
MEDIA MARKT TV-HIFI-ELEKTRO GMBH SAARBRUCKEN—See Ceconomy AG; *Int'l*, pg. 1374
MEDIA MARKT TV-HIFI-ELEKTRO GMBH SAARLOUIS—See Ceconomy AG; *Int'l*, pg. 1383
MEDIA MARKT TV-HIFI-ELEKTRO GMBH SCHIFFDORF-SPADEN—See Ceconomy AG; *Int'l*, pg. 1383
MEDIA MARKT TV-HIFI-ELEKTRO GMBH SCHWABACH—See Ceconomy AG; *Int'l*, pg. 1383
MEDIA MARKT TV-HIFI-ELEKTRO GMBH SCHWEDT—See Ceconomy AG; *Int'l*, pg. 1383
MEDIA MARKT TV-HIFI-ELEKTRO GMBH SCHWEINFURT—See Ceconomy AG; *Int'l*, pg. 1383
MEDIA MARKT TV-HIFI-ELEKTRO GMBH SCHWERIN—See Ceconomy AG; *Int'l*, pg. 1383
MEDIA MARKT TV-HIFI-ELEKTRO GMBH SIEGEN—See Ceconomy AG; *Int'l*, pg. 1383
MEDIA MARKT TV-HIFI-ELEKTRO GMBH SINDELFINGEN—See Ceconomy AG; *Int'l*, pg. 1383
MEDIA MARKT TV-HIFI-ELEKTRO GMBH SINGEN—See Ceconomy AG; *Int'l*, pg. 1374
MEDIA MARKT TV-HIFI-ELEKTRO GMBH SINSHEIM—See Ceconomy AG; *Int'l*, pg. 1383
MEDIA MARKT TV-HIFI-ELEKTRO GMBH—See Ceconomy AG; *Int'l*, pg. 1375
MEDIA MARKT TV-HIFI-ELEKTRO GMBH SPEYER—See Ceconomy AG; *Int'l*, pg. 1383
MEDIA MARKT TV-HIFI-ELEKTRO GMBH STADE—See Ceconomy AG; *Int'l*, pg. 1383
MEDIA MARKT TV-HIFI-ELEKTRO GMBH STRALSUND—See Ceconomy AG; *Int'l*, pg. 1383
MEDIA MARKT TV-HIFI-ELEKTRO GMBH STRAUBING—See Ceconomy AG; *Int'l*, pg. 1383
MEDIA MARKT TV-HIFI-ELEKTRO GMBH STUHR—See Ceconomy AG; *Int'l*, pg. 1374
MEDIA MARKT TV-HIFI-ELEKTRO GMBH STUTTGART-FEUERBACH—See Ceconomy AG; *Int'l*, pg. 1383
MEDIA MARKT TV-HIFI-ELEKTRO GMBH STUTTGART-VAIHINGEN—See Ceconomy AG; *Int'l*, pg. 1383
MEDIA MARKT TV-HIFI-ELEKTRO GMBH TRAUNREUT—See Ceconomy AG; *Int'l*, pg. 1384
MEDIA MARKT TV-HIFI-ELEKTRO GMBH TRAUNSTEIN—See Ceconomy AG; *Int'l*, pg. 1384
MEDIA MARKT TV-HIFI-ELEKTRO GMBH TRIER—See Ceconomy AG; *Int'l*, pg. 1374
MEDIA MARKT TV-HIFI-ELEKTRO GMBH ULM—See Ceconomy AG; *Int'l*, pg. 1374
MEDIA MARKT TV-HIFI-ELEKTRO GMBH VELBERT—See Ceconomy AG; *Int'l*, pg. 1384
MEDIA MARKT TV-HIFI-ELEKTRO GMBH VIERNHEIM—See Ceconomy AG; *Int'l*, pg. 1384
MEDIA MARKT TV-HIFI-ELEKTRO GMBH WALTERSDORF BEI BERLIN—See Ceconomy AG; *Int'l*, pg. 1384
MEDIA MARKT TV-HIFI-ELEKTRO GMBH WEIDEN—See Ceconomy AG; *Int'l*, pg. 1384
MEDIA MARKT TV-HIFI-ELEKTRO GMBH WEILHEIM—See Ceconomy AG; *Int'l*, pg. 1384
MEDIA MARKT TV-HIFI-ELEKTRO GMBH WEITERSTADT—See Ceconomy AG; *Int'l*, pg. 1384
MEDIA MARKT TV-HIFI-ELEKTRO GMBH WETZLAR—See Ceconomy AG; *Int'l*, pg. 1384
MEDIA MARKT TV-HIFI-ELEKTRO GMBH WIESBADEN-APPELALLEE—See Ceconomy AG; *Int'l*, pg. 1384
MEDIA MARKT TV-HIFI-ELEKTRO GMBH WIESBADEN—See Ceconomy AG; *Int'l*, pg. 1384
MEDIA MARKT TV-HIFI-ELEKTRO GMBH WOLFSBURG—See Ceconomy AG; *Int'l*, pg. 1384
MEDIA MARKT TV-HIFI-ELEKTRO GMBH WORMS—See Ceconomy AG; *Int'l*, pg. 1384
MEDIA MARKT TV-HIFI-ELEKTRO GMBH WUPPERTAL—See Ceconomy AG; *Int'l*, pg. 1384
MEDIA MARKT TV-HIFI-ELEKTRO GMBH WURZBURG - ALFRED-NOBEL-STRASSE—See Ceconomy AG; *Int'l*, pg. 1384
MEDIA MARKT TV-HIFI-ELEKTRO GMBH WURZBURG—See Ceconomy AG; *Int'l*, pg. 1384
MEDIA MARKT TV-HIFI-ELEKTRO GMBH ZELLA-MEHLIS—See Ceconomy AG; *Int'l*, pg. 1375
MEDIA MARKT TV-HIFI-ELEKTRO GMBH ZWICKAU—See Ceconomy AG; *Int'l*, pg. 1384
MEDIA MARKT TV-HIFI-ELEKTRO LICHT GMBH INGOLSTADT—See Ceconomy AG; *Int'l*, pg. 1375
MEDIA MARKT TV-HIFI-ELEKTRO WIEN XI GESELLSCHAFT M.B.H.—See Ceconomy AG; *Int'l*, pg. 1375
MEDIA MARKT TV-HIFI-ELEKTRO WIEN XIII GMBH—See Ceconomy AG; *Int'l*, pg. 1384
MEDIA MARKT TV-HIFI-ELEKTRO WIEN XXI GESELLSCHAFT M.B.H.—See Ceconomy AG; *Int'l*, pg. 1384
MEDIA MARKT TWEE TORENS HASSELT NV—See Ceconomy AG; *Int'l*, pg. 1375
MEDIA MARKT UMEA TV-HIFI-ELEKTRO AB—See Ceconomy AG; *Int'l*, pg. 1384
MEDIA MARKT UPPSALA TV-HIFI-ELEKTRO AB—See Ceconomy AG; *Int'l*, pg. 1384
MEDIA MARKT UTRECHT B.V.—See Ceconomy AG; *Int'l*, pg. 1384
MEDIA MARKT UTRECHT THE WALL B.V.—See Ceconomy AG; *Int'l*, pg. 1384
MEDIA MARKT VALENCIA COLON SA—See Ceconomy AG; *Int'l*, pg. 1384
MEDIA MARKT VALLADOLID VFDEO-TV-HIFI-ELEKTRO-COMPUTER-FOTO, SA—See Ceconomy AG; *Int'l*, pg. 1384
MEDIA MARKT VASTERAS TV-HIFI-ELEKTRO AB—See Ceconomy AG; *Int'l*, pg. 1384
MEDIA MARKT VENLO B.V.—See Ceconomy AG; *Int'l*, pg. 1384
MEDIA MARKT VIDEO-TV-HIFI-ELEKTRO-COMPUTER-FOTO GRANCIA AG—See Ceconomy AG; *Int'l*, pg. 1384
MEDIA MARKT VIGO VIDEO-TV-HIFI-ELEKTRO-COMPUTER-FOTO S.A.—See Ceconomy AG; *Int'l*, pg. 1384
MEDIA MARKT VITORIA-GASTEIZ VIDEO-TV-HIFI-ELEKTRO-COMPUTER-FOTO, S.A.—See Ceconomy AG; *Int'l*, pg. 1384
MEDIA MARKT VOCKLABRUCK TV-HIFI-ELEKTRO GMBH—See Ceconomy AG; *Int'l*, pg. 1384
MEDIA MARKT WELS TV-HIFI-ELEKTRO GMBH—See Ceconomy AG; *Int'l*, pg. 1384
MEDIA MARKT- WEST END VIDEO TV HIFI ELEKTRO PHOTO COMPUTER KERESKEDELMI KFT.—See Ceconomy AG; *Int'l*, pg. 1375
MEDIA MARKT WIEN III TV-HIFI-ELEKTRO GMBH—See Ceconomy AG; *Int'l*, pg. 1384
MEDIA MARKT WIEN XV TV-HIFI-ELEKTRO GMBH—See Ceconomy AG; *Int'l*, pg. 1384
MEDIA MARKT WIEN XXII TV-HIFI-ELEKTRO GMBH—See Ceconomy AG; *Int'l*, pg. 1384
MEDIA MARKT WORGL TV-HIFI-ELEKTRO GMBH—See Ceconomy AG; *Int'l*, pg. 1375
MEDIA MARKT ZAANDAM B.V.—See Ceconomy AG; *Int'l*, pg. 1385
MEDIA MARKT ZARAGOZA PUERTO VENECIA VIDEO-TV-HIFI-ELEKTRO-COMPUTER-FOTO, S.A.—See Ceconomy AG; *Int'l*, pg. 1375
MEDIA MARKT ZELL AM SEE TV-HIFI-ELEKTRO GMBH—See Ceconomy AG; *Int'l*, pg. 1385
MEDIA MARKT ZOETERMEER B.V.—See Ceconomy AG; *Int'l*, pg. 1385
MEDIA MARKT ZURICH AG—See Ceconomy AG; *Int'l*, pg. 1385
MEDIA MARKT ZWEI TV-HIFI-ELEKTRO GMBH DRESDEN-PROHLIS—See Ceconomy AG; *Int'l*, pg. 1385
MEDIA MARKT ZWIJNAARDE NV—See Ceconomy AG; *Int'l*, pg. 1385
MEDIA MARKT ZWOLLE B.V.—See Ceconomy AG; *Int'l*, pg. 1385
MEDIAMATH, INC.—See PaeDae, Inc.; *U.S. Private*, pg. 3074
MEDIAMATICS, INC.—See Texas Instruments Incorporated; *U.S. Public*, pg. 2025
MEDIA MATRIX WORLDWIDE LIMITED; *Int'l*, pg. 4771
MEDIA MATTERS FOR AMERICA; *U.S. Private*, pg. 2652
MEDIA MEN GROUP ISRAEL LTD—See Universal Music Group N.V.; *Int'l*, pg. 8079
MEDIAMENTE CONSULTING S.R.L.—See Sesa S.p.A.; *Int'l*, pg. 6728
MEDIA MG CO LTD—See Toyota Motor Corporation; *Int'l*, pg. 7873
MEDIAMISER LTD.—See Innodata, Inc.; *U.S. Public*, pg. 1125
MEDIA MIX JAPAN CO., LTD.—See TV Asahi Holdings Corporation; *Int'l*, pg. 7986
MEDIAMONKS BUENOS AIRES SRL—See S4 Capital plc; *Int'l*, pg. 6458
MEDIAMONKS B.V.—See S4 Capital plc; *Int'l*, pg. 6458
MEDIAMONKS FZ-LLC—See S4 Capital plc; *Int'l*, pg. 6458
MEDIAMONKS INFORMATION TECHNOLOGY (SHANGHAI) CO. LTD.—See S4 Capital plc; *Int'l*, pg. 6458
MEDIAMONKS LONDON LTD.—See S4 Capital plc; *Int'l*, pg. 6458
MEDIAMONKS MEXICO CITY S. DE R.L. DE C.V.—See S4 Capital plc; *Int'l*, pg. 6458
MEDIAMONKS SAO PAOLO SERV. DE INTERNET PARA PUBLICIDADE LTDA.—See S4 Capital plc; *Int'l*, pg. 6458
MEDIAMONKS SINGAPORE PTE. LTD.—See S4 Capital plc; *Int'l*, pg. 6458
MEDIAMONKS STOCKHOLM AB—See S4 Capital plc; *Int'l*, pg. 6458
MEDIA & MORE, INC.; *U.S. Private*, pg. 2651
MEDIAMORPHOSIS INC.; *U.S. Private*, pg. 2653
MEDIAMORPHOSIS—See MediaMorphosis Inc.; *U.S. Private*, pg. 2653
MEDIAMOTION—See Chepri Holding B.V.; *Int'l*, pg. 1471
MEDIANA CO., LTD.; *Int'l*, pg. 4772
MEDIANA USA, INC.—See Mediana Co., Ltd.; *Int'l*, pg. 4772
MEDIAN DIAGNOSTICS, INC.; *Int'l*, pg. 4772
MEDIANE INGENIERIE—See Industrielle De Controle Et D Equipement; *Int'l*, pg. 3675
MEDIANE SYSTEME S.A.—See Industrielle De Controle Et D Equipement; *Int'l*, pg. 3675
MEDIANET—See Australian Associated Press Pty Ltd; *Int'l*, pg. 721
MEDIA NETWORKS LATIN AMERICA, S.A.C.—See Telefonica, S.A.; *Int'l*, pg. 7535
MEDIANEWS GROUP, INC.—See Alden Global Capital LLC; *U.S. Private*, pg. 155
MEDIANEWS GROUP INTERACTIVE, INC.—See Alden Global Capital LLC; *U.S. Private*, pg. 156
MEDIAN GROUP INC.; *Int'l*, pg. 4772
MEDIA NIUGINI PTY. LIMITED—See Nine Entertainment Co. Holdings Limited; *Int'l*, pg. 5299
MEDIANO LTD.—See MTI Ltd.; *Int'l*, pg. 5070
MEDIA NORGE AS—See Schibsted ASA; *Int'l*, pg. 6617
MEDIA NORGE TRYKK OSLO AS—See Schibsted ASA; *Int'l*, pg. 6617
MEDIANT COMMUNICATIONS LLC—See Clearlake Capital Group, L.P.; *U.S. Private*, pg. 936
MEDIAN TECHNOLOGIES SA; *Int'l*, pg. 4772
MEDIAOCEAN LLC - LOS ANGELES—See Vista Equity Partners, LLC; *U.S. Private*, pg. 4398
MEDIAOCEAN LLC—See Vista Equity Partners, LLC; *U.S. Private*, pg. 4398
MEDIA ONE GLOBAL ENTERTAINMENT LIMITED; *Int'l*, pg. 4771
MEDIAONE OF UTAH; *U.S. Private*, pg. 2653
MEDIA PALETTE (TAIWAN) INC.—See Dentsu Group Inc.; *Int'l*, pg. 2037
MEDIA PAL HOLDINGS, CORP.; *U.S. Public*, pg. 1411
MEDIA PARTNERSHIP CORPORATION—See The Interpublic Group of Companies, Inc.; *U.S. Public*, pg. 2096
MEDIA PARTNERS INC.—See Advantage Marketing, Inc.; *U.S. Private*, pg. 94
MEDIA PLANNING CANADA, INC.—See Vivendi SE; *Int'l*, pg. 8270
MEDIA PLATFORM LIMITED—See Emperor Culture Group Limited; *Int'l*, pg. 2386
MEDIAPLEX EAST COAST SALES & SUPPORT—See Publicis Groupe S.A.; *Int'l*, pg. 6099
MEDIAPLEX, INC.—See Publicis Groupe S.A.; *Int'l*, pg. 6099
MEDIAPLEX—See Publicis Groupe S.A.; *Int'l*, pg. 6099
MEDIAPLEX—See Publicis Groupe S.A.; *Int'l*, pg. 6099
MEDIAPLEX SYSTEMS, INC. HOME OFFICE—See Publicis Groupe S.A.; *Int'l*, pg. 6099
MEDIAPLEX SYSTEMS, INC.—See Bread Financial Holdings Inc.; *U.S. Public*, pg. 381
MEDIA PLUS A/S; *Int'l*, pg. 4771
MEDIAPOINT GMBH—See REWE-Zentral-Aktiengesellschaft; *Int'l*, pg. 6315
MEDIAPOLIS S.P.A.—See Quantum Blockchain Technologies Plc; *Int'l*, pg. 6154

MEDIA PLUS A/S — CORPORATE AFFILIATIONS

MEDIAPOST GROUP—See La Poste S.A.; *Int'l*, pg. 4388
MEDIA POST INC.—See ProFromGo Internet Marketing, LLC; *U.S. Private*, pg. 3277
MEDIA POWER ADVERTISING; *U.S. Private*, pg. 2652
MEDIA-PRESS.TV AG—See The European Metadata Group; *Int'l*, pg. 7640
MEDIA-PRESS.TV S.A.—See The European Metadata Group; *Int'l*, pg. 7641
MEDIA PRIMA BERHAD; *Int'l*, pg. 4771
MEDIA PRIMA DIGITAL SDN. BHD.—See Media Prima Berhad; *Int'l*, pg. 4771
MEDIA PRINTING CORPORATION; *U.S. Private*, pg. 2652
MEDIAPRODUCCION S.L.U.—See Orient Securities Company Limited; *Int'l*, pg. 5622
MEDIAPRO USA, INC.—See WPP plc; *Int'l*, pg. 8483
MEDIARADAR, INC.—See Thompson Street Capital Manager LLC; *U.S. Private*, pg. 4161
MEDIA RAIN LLC; *U.S. Private*, pg. 2652
MEDIA RECOVERY, INC.—See Capital Southwest Corporation; *U.S. Public*, pg. 432
MEDIA RELATIONS, INC.; *U.S. Private*, pg. 2652
MEDIA RESEARCH CONSULTANTS PTE LTD—See Temasek Holdings (Private) Limited; *Int'l*, pg. 7548
MEDIA RESEARCH, INC.—See Honyaku Center Inc.; *Int'l*, pg. 3472
MEDIA RESOURCES, LTD.; *U.S. Private*, pg. 2652
MEDIA RESOURCES, LTD.—See Media Resources, Ltd.; *U.S. Private*, pg. 2652
MEDIA RESPONSE, INC.; *U.S. Private*, pg. 2652
MEDIA RIGHTS CAPITAL II L.P.—See Valence Media Group; *U.S. Private*, pg. 4330
MEDIARING.COM (SHANGHAI) LIMITED—See Digilife Technologies Limited; *Int'l*, pg. 2119
MEDIA - SATURN BETEILIGUNGSGES .M.B.H.—See Ceconomy AG; *Int'l*, pg. 1375
MEDIA-SATURN DEUTSCHLAND GMBH—See Ceconomy AG; *Int'l*, pg. 1385
MEDIA-SATURN-E-BUSINESS GMBH—See Ceconomy AG; *Int'l*, pg. 1385
MEDIA-SATURN HELLAS COMPANY ADMINISTRATION ANONYMI ETERIA—See Ceconomy AG; *Int'l*, pg. 1385
MEDIA-SATURN-HOLDING GMBH—See Ceconomy AG; *Int'l*, pg. 1385
MEDIA SATURN HOLDING POLSKA SP. Z. O. O.—See Ceconomy AG; *Int'l*, pg. 1385
MEDIA-SATURN HOLDING SWEDEN AB—See Ceconomy AG; *Int'l*, pg. 1385
MEDIA SATURN MULTICHANNEL SAU MADRID-ISLAZUL—See Ceconomy AG; *Int'l*, pg. 1385
MEDIA-SATURN (PORTUGAL), SGPS, UNIPESSOAL LDA—See Ceconomy AG; *Int'l*, pg. 1375
MEDIA SATURN - SERVICOS DE APOIO ADMINSTRATIVO, LDA.—See Ceconomy AG; *Int'l*, pg. 1385
MEDIA-SATURN VERWALTUNG DEUTSCHLAND GMBH—See Ceconomy AG; *Int'l*, pg. 1385
MEDIASCORE GESELLSCHAFT FUR MEDIEN- UND KOMMUNIKATIONSFORSCHUNG MBH—See Bertelsmann SE & Co. KGaA; *Int'l*, pg. 995
MEDIASEEK, INC.—See Solvvy Inc.; *Int'l*, pg. 7082
MEDIA SENTIMENT, INC.; *U.S. Public*, pg. 1411
MEDIASET ESPANA COMUNICACION, S.A.—See Mediaset S.p.A.; *Int'l*, pg. 4773
MEDIASET INVESTMENT S.A.R.L.—See Mediaset S.p.A.; *Int'l*, pg. 4773
MEDIASET S.P.A.; *Int'l*, pg. 4773
MEDIASHIFT, INC.; *U.S. Private*, pg. 2653
MEDIASITE KK—See Enghouse Systems Limited; *Int'l*, pg. 2427
MEDIASKOPAS, UAB—See UP Invest OU; *Int'l*, pg. 8087
MEDIASMACK INC.—See Scorpion Design LLC; *U.S. Private*, pg. 3575
MEDIASMART MOBILE S.L.—See Affle (India) Limited; *Int'l*, pg. 188
MEDIASMITH INC.; *U.S. Private*, pg. 2653
MEDIA SOLUTIONS GMBH—See Publicis Groupe S.A.; *Int'l*, pg. 6103
MEDIA SOLUTIONS, INC.; *U.S. Private*, pg. 2652
MEDIA SOLUTIONS—See Brookfield Corporation; *Int'l*, pg. 1178
MEDIA SOLUTIONS—See Elliott Management Corporation; *U.S. Private*, pg. 1371
MEDIASOURCE FZC—See News Group International Holding; *Int'l*, pg. 5238
MEDIA SOURCE, INC.; *U.S. Private*, pg. 2652
MEDIASPACE SOLUTIONS; *U.S. Private*, pg. 2653
MEDIA SPADE, INC.; *U.S. Private*, pg. 2652
MEDIASPORTS DIGITAL GMBH—See Vista Equity Partners, LLC; *U.S. Private*, pg. 4401
MEDIASPOT, INC.; *U.S. Private*, pg. 2654
MEDI ASSIST HEALTHCARE SERVICES PRIVATE LIMITED; *Int'l*, pg. 4769
MEDIASSOCIATES, INC.; *U.S. Private*, pg. 2654
MEDIAS & SUPPORTS—See Omnicom Group Inc.; *U.S. Public*, pg. 1596
MEDIASTAY FRANCE—See Key Performance Group S.A.S.; *Int'l*, pg. 4145
MEDIA STORM LLC; *U.S. Private*, pg. 2653
MEDIA STRATEGIES & RESEARCH; *U.S. Private*, pg. 2653

MEDIASTREAM VIERTE MEDIEN GMBH—See Munchener Ruckversicherungs AG; *Int'l*, pg. 5090
MEDIASTREET, INC.; *U.S. Private*, pg. 2654
MEDIATEAM LTD.—See China Oceanwide Holdings Group Co., Ltd.; *Int'l*, pg. 1538
MEDIATEAM LTD.—See IDG Capital; *Int'l*, pg. 3594
MEDIATEC BROADCAST SWEDEN AB—See STENA AB; *Int'l*, pg. 7206
MEDIATECH, INC.—See Corning Incorporated; *U.S. Public*, pg. 578
MEDIA TECH INC.—See Daiwa House Industry Co., Ltd.; *Int'l*, pg. 1947
MEDIA TECHNOLOGY CORPORATION—See TDK Corporation; *Int'l*, pg. 7487
MEDIA TECHNOLOGY JAPAN CO., LTD.—See Screen Holdings Co., Ltd.; *Int'l*, pg. 6655
MEDIATEC SOLUTIONS SWEDEN AB—See STENA AB; *Int'l*, pg. 7206
MEDIATEK (BEIJING) INC.—See MediaTek Inc.; *Int'l*, pg. 4773
MEDIATEK DENMARK APS—See MediaTek Inc.; *Int'l*, pg. 4773
MEDIATEK GERMANY GMBH—See MediaTek Inc.; *Int'l*, pg. 4773
MEDIATEK (HEFEI) INC.—See MediaTek Inc.; *Int'l*, pg. 4773
MEDIATEK INC.; *Int'l*, pg. 4773
MEDIATEK INDIA TECHNOLOGY PVT. LTD.—See MediaTek Inc.; *Int'l*, pg. 4773
MEDIATEK JAPAN INC.—See MediaTek Inc.; *Int'l*, pg. 4773
MEDIATEK KOREA INC.—See MediaTek Inc.; *Int'l*, pg. 4773
MEDIATEK (SHANGHAI) INC.—See MediaTek Inc.; *Int'l*, pg. 4773
MEDIATEK (SHENZHEN) INC.—See MediaTek Inc.; *Int'l*, pg. 4773
MEDIATEK SINGAPORE PTE LTD.—See MediaTek Inc.; *Int'l*, pg. 4773
MEDIATEK SWEDEN AB—See MediaTek Inc.; *Int'l*, pg. 4773
MEDIATEK USA INC.—See MediaTek Inc.; *Int'l*, pg. 4773
MEDIATEK WIRELESS FINLAND OY—See MediaTek Inc.; *Int'l*, pg. 4773
MEDIATEK WIRELESS FZ-LLC—See MediaTek Inc.; *Int'l*, pg. 4773
MEDIATEK WIRELESS, INC.—See MediaTek Inc.; *Int'l*, pg. 4773
MEDIATEL S.A.; *Int'l*, pg. 4774
MEDIA TEMPLE, INC.—See KKR & Co. Inc.; *U.S. Public*, pg. 1252
MEDIA TEMPLE, INC.—See Silver Lake Group, LLC; *U.S. Private*, pg. 3657
MEDIA TEMPLE, INC.—See TCMI, Inc.; *U.S. Private*, pg. 3943
MEDIA TIMES LIMITED; *Int'l*, pg. 4771
MEDIATIVE—See Yellow Pages Limited; *Int'l*, pg. 8576
MEDIATORS MARKETING—See Messe Munchen GmbH; *Int'l*, pg. 4841
MEDIA TRANS ASIA LIMITED—See China Oceanwide Holdings Group Co., Ltd.; *Int'l*, pg. 1538
MEDIA TRANS ASIA LIMITED—See IDG Capital; *Int'l*, pg. 3594
MEDIA TRANSCONTINENTAL—See Vivendi SE; *Int'l*, pg. 8278
MEDIA TRAVEL & LOGISTICS—See WPP plc; *Int'l*, pg. 8475
MEDIATRUST; *U.S. Private*, pg. 2654
MEDIATRYKK AS—See Schibsted ASA; *Int'l*, pg. 6617
MEDIA UTILITIES B.V—See Transition Evergreen; *Int'l*, pg. 7901
MEDIAVALET INC.—See Symphony Technology Group, LLC; *U.S. Private*, pg. 3902
MEDIAVEST (MANCHESTER) LTD.—See Publicis Groupe S.A.; *Int'l*, pg. 6111
MEDIAVEST UK LONDON—See Publicis Groupe S.A.; *Int'l*, pg. 6111
MEDIAVEST USA—See Publicis Groupe S.A.; *Int'l*, pg. 6111
MEDIAVEST USA—See Publicis Groupe S.A.; *Int'l*, pg. 6111
MEDIAVEST WORLDWIDE—See Publicis Groupe S.A.; *Int'l*, pg. 6111
MEDIAVEST WORLDWIDE—See Publicis Groupe S.A.; *Int'l*, pg. 6111
MEDIA VISION (1994) CO. LTD.—See GMM Grammy Public Company Limited; *Int'l*, pg. 3013
MEDIA VISTA GROUP, LLC; *U.S. Private*, pg. 2653
MEDIA WALES—See Reach PLC; *Int'l*, pg. 6231
MEDIAWAN SA; *Int'l*, pg. 4774
MEDIA WATCH MIDDLE EAST—See News Group International Holding; *Int'l*, pg. 5237
MEDIA WHIZ HOLDINGS, LLC; *U.S. Private*, pg. 2653
MEDIAWHIZ; *U.S. Private*, pg. 2654
MEDIA WORKS CHARLOTTE—See M Rogers Design, Inc.; *U.S. Private*, pg. 2523
MEDIAWORKS HOLDINGS LIMITED—See Brookfield Corporation; *Int'l*, pg. 1181

MEDIA WORKS, LTD.—See M Rogers Design, Inc.; *U.S. Private*, pg. 2523
MEDIAZEN, INC.; *Int'l*, pg. 4774
MEDIAZEST PLC; *Int'l*, pg. 4774
MEDIAZEST—See MediaZest PLC; *Int'l*, pg. 4774
MEDIBA INC.—See KDDI Corporation; *Int'l*, pg. 4112
MEDIBALLOON, INC.—See Medeon Biodesign, Inc.; *Int'l*, pg. 4769
MEDIBANK PRIVATE LIMITED; *Int'l*, pg. 4774
MEDIBIO LIMITED; *Int'l*, pg. 4774
MEDIBIO LIMITED—See Medibio Limited; *Int'l*, pg. 4774
MEDICA AD—See Sopharma AD; *Int'l*, pg. 7108
MEDICA ARZTEBEDARF AG—See Sonic Healthcare Limited; *Int'l*, pg. 7097
MEDICA GROUP PLC—See IK Investment Partners Limited; *Int'l*, pg. 3609
MEDICA HEALTHCARE PLANS, INC.—See UnitedHealth Group Incorporated; *U.S. Public*, pg. 2251
MEDICA HEALTH PLANS OF FLORIDA, INC.—See UnitedHealth Group Incorporated; *U.S. Public*, pg. 2251
MEDICA HEALTHWORLD/BRNO—See WPP plc; *Int'l*, pg. 8489
MEDICA, INC.; *U.S. Private*, pg. 2654
MEDICAL 3 IMPORTACION SERVICE IBERICA S.L.—See DENTSPLY SIRONA Inc.; *U.S. Public*, pg. 655
MEDICAL ACADEMIC & SCIENTIFIC COMMUNITY ORGANIZATION, INC.; *U.S. Private*, pg. 2654
MEDICAL ACTION INDUSTRIES INC.—See Owens & Minor, Inc.; *U.S. Public*, pg. 1625
MEDICAL AIRPORT SERVICE GMBH—See Fraport AG; *Int'l*, pg. 2764
MEDICAL ANESTHESIA CONSULTANTS MEDICAL GROUP, INC.—See KKR & Co. Inc.; *U.S. Public*, pg. 1246
MEDICAL AREA TOTAL ENERGY PLANT, LLC—See Morgan Stanley; *U.S. Public*, pg. 1474
MEDICAL AREA TOTAL ENERGY PLANT, LLC—See Veolia Environnement S.A.; *Int'l*, pg. 8158
THE MEDICAL ASSURANCE COMPANY, INC.—See ProAssurance Corporation; *U.S. Public*, pg. 1723
THE MEDICAL ASSURANCE COMPANY—See ProAssurance Corporation; *U.S. Public*, pg. 1723
MEDICAL AUSTRALIA LIMITED—See ICU Medical, Inc.; *U.S. Public*, pg. 1087
MEDICAL BENEFITS ADMINISTRATORS INC—See Medical Benefits Mutual Life Insurance Co. Inc.; *U.S. Private*, pg. 2654
MEDICAL BENEFITS MUTUAL LIFE INSURANCE CO. INC.; *U.S. Private*, pg. 2654
MEDICAL BILLING CHOICES, INC.—See Rennova Health, Inc.; *U.S. Public*, pg. 1783
MEDICAL BILLING MANAGEMENT EAST; *U.S. Private*, pg. 2654
MEDICAL BILLING SOLUTIONS, LLC—See Bain Capital, LP; *U.S. Private*, pg. 445
MEDICAL & BIOLOGICAL LABORATORIES CO., LTD.—See JSR Corp.; *Int'l*, pg. 4014
MEDICAL BUSINESS SERVICE INC.; *U.S. Private*, pg. 2654
MEDICAL CARD SYSTEM, INC.—See JLL Partners, LLC; *U.S. Private*, pg. 2212
MEDICAL CARE DEVELOPMENT INC.; *U.S. Private*, pg. 2654
MEDICAL CARE SERVICE CO., LTD.—See Gakken Holdings Co., Ltd.; *Int'l*, pg. 2869
MEDICAL CARE TECHNOLOGIES INC.; *Int'l*, pg. 4774
MEDICAL CENTER ALLIANCE—See HCA Healthcare, Inc.; *U.S. Public*, pg. 1004
THE MEDICAL CENTER COMPANY; *U.S. Private*, pg. 4077
MEDICAL CENTER ENTERPRISE—See Community Health Systems, Inc.; *U.S. Public*, pg. 552
MEDICAL CENTER HOME HEALTH, LLC—See UnitedHealth Group Incorporated; *U.S. Public*, pg. 2246
MEDICAL CENTER OF ARLINGTON—See HCA Healthcare, Inc.; *U.S. Public*, pg. 1001
THE MEDICAL CENTER OF AURORA—See HCA Healthcare, Inc.; *U.S. Public*, pg. 1012
MEDICAL CENTER OF BATON ROUGE, INC.—See HCA Healthcare, Inc.; *U.S. Public*, pg. 1001
THE MEDICAL CENTER OF CENTRAL GEORGIA, INC.—See Central Georgia Health System Inc.; *U.S. Private*, pg. 821
MEDICAL CENTER OF GARDEN GROVE, INC.—See Tenet Healthcare Corporation; *U.S. Public*, pg. 2004
MEDICAL CENTER OF LEWISVILLE—See HCA Healthcare, Inc.; *U.S. Public*, pg. 1001
MEDICAL CENTER OF MCKINNEY—See HCA Healthcare, Inc.; *U.S. Public*, pg. 1001
MEDICAL CENTER OF PLANO—See HCA Healthcare, Inc.; *U.S. Public*, pg. 1001
MEDICAL CENTER OF SANTA ROSA, INC.—See HCA Healthcare, Inc.; *U.S. Public*, pg. 1001
MEDICAL CENTER OF TRINITY—See HCA Healthcare, Inc.; *U.S. Public*, pg. 1002
MEDICAL CENTERS HOMECARE, LLC—See UnitedHealth Group Incorporated; *U.S. Public*, pg. 2246

COMPANY NAME INDEX

MEDICAL CITY DALLAS AMBULATORY SURGERY CENTER—See HCA Healthcare, Inc.; *U.S. Public*, pg. 1002
MEDICAL CITY HOSPITAL—See HCA Healthcare, Inc.; *U.S. Public*, pg. 1002
MEDICAL CITY SURGERY CENTER OF ALLEN, LLC—See HCA Healthcare, Inc.; *U.S. Public*, pg. 1002
MEDICAL CITY SURGERY CENTER OF ALLIANCE, LLC—See HCA Healthcare, Inc.; *U.S. Public*, pg. 1002
MEDICAL CITY SURGERY CENTER OF FRISCO, LLC—See HCA Healthcare, Inc.; *U.S. Public*, pg. 1002
MEDICAL CITY SURGERY CENTER SOUTHLAKE, LLC—See HCA Healthcare, Inc.; *U.S. Public*, pg. 1002
MEDICAL COACHES INCORPORATED; *U.S. Private*, pg. 2654
MEDICAL COMPRESSION SYSTEM (D.B.N) LTD.; *Int'l*, pg. 4774
MEDICAL COMPRESSION SYSTEMS, INC.—See Zimmer Biomet Holdings, Inc.; *U.S. Public*, pg. 2406
MEDICAL CONNECTIONS HOLDINGS, INC.; *U.S. Public*, pg. 1411
MEDICAL COST MANAGEMENT CORP.; *U.S. Private*, pg. 2654
MEDICAL CULTURE INC.—See Roche Holding AG; *Int'l*, pg. 6372
MEDICAL DATA MANAGEMENT, INC.—See IQVIA Holdings Inc.; *U.S. Public*, pg. 1169
MEDICAL DATA SYSTEMS INC.; *U.S. Private*, pg. 2654
MEDICAL DATA VISION CO., LTD.; *Int'l*, pg. 4774
MEDICAL DELIVERY SERVICES, INC.—See HCI Equity Management, L.P.; *U.S. Private*, pg. 1889
MEDICAL DEPOT, INC.; *U.S. Private*, pg. 2654
MEDICAL DEVELOPMENTS INTERNATIONAL LIMITED; *Int'l*, pg. 4774
MEDICAL DEVICES INTERNATIONAL LLC—See Johnson & Johnson; *U.S. Public*, pg. 1199
MEDICAL DEVICES VENTURE SA; *Int'l*, pg. 4775
MEDICAL DIAGNOSTIC EXCHANGE CORP—See DXStorm.com Inc.; *Int'l*, pg. 2237
MEDICAL DIRECT CLUB LLC; *U.S. Private*, pg. 2655
MEDICAL DOCTOR ASSOCIATES INC.; *U.S. Private*, pg. 2655
MEDICALE CORP.; *Int'l*, pg. 4775
MEDICAL EDUCATION AND RESEARCH FOUNDATION—See Saturday Evening Post Society; *U.S. Private*, pg. 3553
MEDICAL EDUCATION BROADCAST NETWORK; *U.S. Private*, pg. 2655
MEDICAL EDUCATION TECHNOLOGIES, INC.—See CAE Inc.; *Int'l*, pg. 1248
MEDICAL EMERGENCY PROFESSIONALS; *U.S. Private*, pg. 2655
MEDICAL ENGINEERING & DEVELOPMENT INSTITUTE, INC.—See Cook Group Incorporated; *U.S. Private*, pg. 1037
MEDICAL ENGINEERS (I) PVT. LTD.—See Everest Kanto Cylinder Limited; *Int'l*, pg. 2564
MEDICAL EQUIPMENT DISTRIBUTORS, INC.—See Roper Technologies, Inc.; *U.S. Public*, pg. 1812
MEDICAL EQUIPMENT TECHNOLOGIES, INC.—See Avista Capital Partners, L.P.; *U.S. Private*, pg. 408
MEDICAL EXPRESS—See AMN Healthcare Services, Inc.; *U.S. Public*, pg. 125
MEDICALEX SARL—See HORIBA Ltd; *Int'l*, pg. 3477
MEDICAL FACILITIES CORPORATION; *Int'l*, pg. 4775
MEDICAL FINANCIAL GROUP, LLC—See LawFinance Ltd.; *Int'l*, pg. 4425
MEDICALGORITHMICS S.A.; *Int'l*, pg. 4775
MEDICAL GRAPHICS CORP.—See Niterra Co., Ltd.; *Int'l*, pg. 5380
THE MEDICAL GROUP OF KANSAS CITY, LLC—See HCA Healthcare, Inc.; *U.S. Public*, pg. 1012
MEDICAL GROUP - SOUTHERN HILLS OF BRENTWOOD, LLC—See HCA Healthcare, Inc.; *U.S. Public*, pg. 1002
MEDICAL GROUP - STONECREST, INC.—See HCA Healthcare, Inc.; *U.S. Public*, pg. 1002
MEDICAL GURADIAN, LLC—See Water Street Healthcare Partners, LLC; *U.S. Private*, pg. 4452
MEDICAL HUMAN RESOURCES (PROPRIETARY) LIMITED—See Remgro Limited; *Int'l*, pg. 6270
MEDICAL IKKOU CO., LTD.; *Int'l*, pg. 4775
MEDICAL IMAGING CENTER OF OCALA, LLP—See Community Health Systems, Inc.; *U.S. Public*, pg. 555
MEDICAL IMAGING CORP.; *U.S. Public*, pg. 1411
MEDICAL IMAGING RESOURCES, INC.—See Oxford Instruments Plc; *Int'l*, pg. 5674
MEDICAL IMAGING SYSTEMS, INC.—See Radon Medical Imaging Corp.; *U.S. Private*, pg. 3345
MEDICAL IMAGING TECHNOLOGIES, INC.; *U.S. Private*, pg. 2655
MEDICAL INDICATORS, INC.—See Progress Equity Partners, LLC; *U.S. Private*, pg. 3278
MEDICAL INDUSTRIAL PLASTICS; *U.S. Private*, pg. 2655
MEDICAL INFORMATION PROFESSIONAL SYSTEMS NV—See Roper Technologies, Inc.; *U.S. Public*, pg. 1812

MEDICAL INFORMATION TECHNOLOGY, INC.; *U.S. Private*, pg. 2655
MEDICAL INNOVATIONS (PROPRIETARY) LIMITED—See Remgro Limited; *Int'l*, pg. 6270
MEDICAL INSTRUMENT DEVELOPMENT (MID) LABS, INC.—See Hoya Corporation; *Int'l*, pg. 3498
MEDICAL INTELLIGENCE MEDIZINTECHNIK GMBH—See 3C-Carbon Group AG; *Int'l*, pg. 7
MEDICAL INTERNATIONAL TECHNOLOGY, INC.; *Int'l*, pg. 4775
MEDICAL LABORATORY WELLINGTON—See BGH Capital Pty Ltd; *Int'l*, pg. 1008
MEDICAL LABORATORY WELLINGTON—See Ontario Teachers' Pension Plan; *Int'l*, pg. 5586
MEDICAL-LATEX (DUA) SDN. BHD.—See Karex Berhad; *Int'l*, pg. 4081
MEDICAL LIABILITY MUTUAL INSURANCE CO. - LATHAM—See Berkshire Hathaway Inc.; *U.S. Public*, pg. 312
MEDICAL LIABILITY MUTUAL INSURANCE COMPANY—See Berkshire Hathaway Inc.; *U.S. Public*, pg. 312
MEDICAL LOGISTIC SOLUTIONS, INC.—See United Parcel Service, Inc.; *U.S. Public*, pg. 2233
MEDICAL MANAGEMENT INTERNATIONAL INC.—See Mars, Incorporated; *U.S. Private*, pg. 2590
MEDICAL MANAGEMENT RESOURCES, INC.—See Blackstone Inc.; *U.S. Public*, pg. 359
MEDICAL MANAGEMENT SYSTEMS INC.; *U.S. Private*, pg. 2655
MEDICAL MARIJUANA INC.; *U.S. Public*, pg. 1412
MEDICAL MARKETING SERVICE INC.; *U.S. Private*, pg. 2655
MEDICAL MART SUPPLIES LIMITED—See Medline Industries, LP; *U.S. Private*, pg. 2657
MEDICAL MEASUREMENT SYSTEMS B.V.—See Investor AB; *Int'l*, pg. 3786
MEDICAL MEASUREMENT SYSTEMS USA, INC.—See Investor AB; *Int'l*, pg. 3786
MEDICAL MEDIA TELEVISION, INC.; *U.S. Private*, pg. 2655
MEDICAL MIME, INC.—See Rennova Health, Inc.; *U.S. Public*, pg. 1783
MEDICAL MODELING INC.—See 3D Systems Corporation; *U.S. Public*, pg. 1
MEDICAL MUTUAL LIABILITY INSURANCE SOCIETY OF MARYLAND; *U.S. Private*, pg. 2655
MEDICAL MUTUAL OF OHIO; *U.S. Private*, pg. 2655
MEDICAL MUTUAL SERVICES, LLC—See Medical Mutual of Ohio; *U.S. Private*, pg. 2655
MEDICAL NET, INC.; *Int'l*, pg. 4775
MEDICAL NET SAS—See CompuGroup Medical SE & Co. KGaA; *Int'l*, pg. 1757
MEDICAL NOTE, INC.—See Aflac Incorporated; *U.S. Public*, pg. 57
MEDICAL NUMERICS, INC.—See Textron Inc.; *U.S. Public*, pg. 2028
MEDICAL ONCOLOGY ASSOCIATES, LLC—See HCA Healthcare, Inc.; *U.S. Public*, pg. 1002
MEDICAL OUTCOMES RESEARCH ANALYTICS, LLC—See Forian Inc.; *U.S. Public*, pg. 868
MEDICAL PACKAGING COMPANY; *Int'l*, pg. 4775
MEDICAL PACKAGING, INC.—See The Zabel Companies, LLC; *U.S. Private*, pg. 4140
MEDICAL PARK DIAGNOSTIC CENTER—See HCA Healthcare, Inc.; *U.S. Public*, pg. 1002
MEDICAL PARK TOWER SURGERY CENTER, LLC—See Tenet Healthcare Corporation; *U.S. Public*, pg. 2011
MEDICAL PAYMENT CORP.—See Fuyo General Lease Co., Ltd.; *Int'l*, pg. 2859
MEDICAL PILOT INC.—See Sony Group Corporation; *Int'l*, pg. 7102
MEDICAL POSITIONING, INC.—See Rockwood Equity Partners, LLC; *U.S. Private*, pg. 3468
MEDICAL PREPARATORY SCHOOL OF ALLIED HEALTH, LLC—See UnitedHealth Group Incorporated; *U.S. Public*, pg. 2242
MEDICAL PRINCIPLE CO., LTD.—See CREEK & RIVER Co., Ltd.; *Int'l*, pg. 1837
MEDICAL PRODUCTS INC.; *U.S. Private*, pg. 2655
MEDICAL PROGNOSIS INSTITUTE A/S; *Int'l*, pg. 4775
MEDICAL PROPERTIES TRUST, INC.; *U.S. Public*, pg. 1412
THE MEDICAL PROTECTIVE COMPANY—See Berkshire Hathaway Inc.; *U.S. Public*, pg. 302
MEDICAL PROTECTIVE CORPORATION—See Berkshire Hathaway Inc.; *U.S. Public*, pg. 312
MEDICAL QOL CO., LTD.—See Qol Holdings Co., Ltd.; *Int'l*, pg. 6147
MEDICAL RECORD ASSOCIATES INC—See ChrysCapital Management Co.; *Int'l*, pg. 1588
MEDICAL RECRUITMENT SPECIALISTS—See Bain Capital, LP; *U.S. Private*, pg. 433
MEDICAL RECRUITMENT STRATEGIES, LLC—See Empresaria Group Plc; *Int'l*, pg. 2389
MEDICAL REIMBURSEMENTS OF AMERICA, INC.—See GrowthCurve Capital LP; *U.S. Private*, pg. 1796
MEDICAL REIMBURSEMENTS OF AMERICA, INC.—See Riverside Partners, LLC; *U.S. Private*, pg. 3446

MEDICCOMM CONSULTANTS, INC.

MEDICAL RESEARCH CONSULTANTS, INC.; *U.S. Private*, pg. 2655
MEDICAL RESOURCE ASSOCIATION, INC.; *U.S. Private*, pg. 2655
MEDICAL RESOURCES CO., LTD.—See Nihon Chouzai Co., Ltd.; *Int'l*, pg. 5283
MEDICAL & SCIENTIFIC SUPPLIES LLC—See Omar Zawawi Establishment LLC; *Int'l*, pg. 5561
MEDICAL SCOPE, S.A.DE C.V.—See Mauna Kea Technologies SA; *Int'l*, pg. 4732
MEDICAL SEARCH SOLUTIONS, INC.—See Subsidium Healthcare, LLC; *U.S. Private*, pg. 3847
MEDICAL SECURITY CARD COMPANY, LLC—See MedImpact Healthcare Systems, Inc.; *U.S. Private*, pg. 2657
MEDICAL SERVICE GMBH—See Teleflex Incorporated; *U.S. Public*, pg. 1996
MEDICAL SERVICES INTERNATIONAL LIMITED—See The British United Provident Association Limited; *Int'l*, pg. 7629
MEDICAL SERVICES OF AMERICA, INC.; *U.S. Private*, pg. 2655
MEDICAL SERVICES PROJECTS COMPANY LTD—See Kingdom Holding Company; *Int'l*, pg. 4172
MEDICAL SOLUTIONS LLC—See TPG Capital, L.P.; *U.S. Public*, pg. 2176
MEDICAL SPECIALISTS OF THE PALM BEACHES, INC.; *U.S. Private*, pg. 2655
MEDICAL SPECIALTIES DISTRIBUTORS LLC—See McKesson Corporation; *U.S. Public*, pg. 1408
MEDICAL SPECIALTIES, INC.—See HCA Healthcare, Inc.; *U.S. Public*, pg. 1002
MEDICAL STAFFING OPTIONS—See Health Carousel, LLC; *U.S. Private*, pg. 1893
THE MEDICAL SUPPLY DEPOT, INC.; *U.S. Private*, pg. 4077
MEDICAL SUPPLY INTERNATIONAL USA, INC.; *U.S. Public*, pg. 1412
MEDICALSYSTEM BIOTECHNOLOGY CO., LTD.; *Int'l*, pg. 4775
MEDICALSYSTEM CO.,LTD; *Int'l*, pg. 4775
MEDICAL SYSTEM NETWORK CO., LTD.; *Int'l*, pg. 4775
MEDICAL TEAMS INTERNATIONAL; *U.S. Private*, pg. 2656
MEDICAL TECHNOLOGIES LIMITED—See Deson Development International Holdings Ltd; *Int'l*, pg. 2045
MEDICAL TECHNOLOGIES OF GEORGIA, INC.—See HR Pharmaceuticals, Inc.; *U.S. Private*, pg. 1998
MEDICAL TECHNOLOGY ASSOCIATES, LLC; *U.S. Private*, pg. 2656
MEDICAL TECHNOLOGY MANAGEMENT INSTITUTE, LLC—See The College of Health Care Professions; *U.S. Private*, pg. 4011
MEDICAL TOUKEI CO., LTD.—See TIS Inc.; *Int'l*, pg. 7757
MEDICAL TOURISM JAPAN CO., LTD.—See Ship Healthcare Holdings, Inc.; *Int'l*, pg. 6852
MEDICAL TRADING INTERNATIONAL LTD—See Ireland Blyth Limited; *Int'l*, pg. 3807
MEDICAL TRANSCRIPTION EDUCATION CENTER, INC.—See Microsoft Corporation; *U.S. Public*, pg. 1442
MEDICAL TRIBUNE VERLAGSGESELLSCHAFT MBH—See Sudwestdeutsche Medienholding GmbH; *Int'l*, pg. 7252
MEDICAL ULTRASONICS LTD—See Getinge AB; *Int'l*, pg. 2952
MEDICAL UNION PHARMACEUTICALS; *Int'l*, pg. 4775
MEDICAL UNIVERSITY OF SOUTH CAROLINA; *U.S. Private*, pg. 2656
MEDICAL & WELFARE INFORMATION CENTER OF SHOWA-OTA INC.—See Business Brain Showa-Ota Inc.; *Int'l*, pg. 1228
MEDICA MEDIZINISCHE LABORATORIEN DR. F. KAPPELI AG—See Sonic Healthcare Limited; *Int'l*, pg. 7097
MEDICAMEN BIOTECH LIMITED; *Int'l*, pg. 4775
MEDICAN CONSTRUCTION LTD; *Int'l*, pg. 4775
MEDICAN ENTERPRISES, INC.; *U.S. Public*, pg. 1412
MEDICANIMAL LIMITED; *Int'l*, pg. 4775
MEDICAPITAL BANK PLC—See Bank of Africa; *Int'l*, pg. 840
MEDI CAPS LTD.; *Int'l*, pg. 4769
MEDICARE ADVANTAGE SPECIALISTS, LLC—See Integrity Marketing Group LLC; *U.S. Private*, pg. 2103
MEDICARE SUPPLY CENTERS INC—See Arcadian Healthcare Inc.; *U.S. Private*, pg. 310
MEDICAROID CORPORATION—See Kawasaki Heavy Industries, Ltd.; *Int'l*, pg. 4098
MEDICAROID, INC.—See Sysmex Corporation; *Int'l*, pg. 7388
MEDICASA ITALIA S.P.A.—See L'Air Liquide S.A.; *Int'l*, pg. 4375
MEDICA S.P.A.; *Int'l*, pg. 4774
MEDICA SUR, S.A.B. DE C.V.; *Int'l*, pg. 4774
MEDICAT LLC—See Banyan Software, Inc.; *U.S. Private*, pg. 470
MEDICA US, INC.—See IK Investment Partners Limited; *Int'l*, pg. 3609
MEDICCOMM CONSULTANTS, INC.; *U.S. Private*, pg. 2656
MEDICEL AG—See Halma plc; *Int'l*, pg. 3232

MEDICENNA THERAPEUTICS CORP.

MEDICENNA THERAPEUTICS CORP.; *Int'l*, pg. 4775
MEDICEO CORPORATION—See Medipal Holdings Corporation; *Int'l*, pg. 4779
MEDICEO MEDICAL CO., LTD.—See Medipal Holdings Corporation; *Int'l*, pg. 4779
MEDICHEMIE BIOLINE AG—See CSL Limited; *Int'l*, pg. 1866
MEDI-CHEM SYSTEMS SDN. BHD.—See Excelsior Medical Co., Ltd.; *Int'l*, pg. 2579
MEDICIA HOLDINGS LLC—See Joshua Partners, LLC; *U.S. Private*, pg. 2237
MEDICIM NV—See Danaher Corporation; *U.S. Public*, pg. 628
MEDICINA CORPORATIVA DE DIALISIS SA—See Baxter International Inc.; *U.S. Public*, pg. 284
MEDICINAL CHEMISTRY PHARMACEUTICAL CO., LTD.—See Trans Genic Inc.; *Int'l*, pg. 7894
MEDICINA NOVE ZAMKY S.R.O.—See Centene Corporation; *U.S. Public*, pg. 470
MEDICINE HAT NEWS—See Glacier Media Inc.; *Int'l*, pg. 2987
MEDICINE MAN TECHNOLOGIES, INC.; *U.S. Public*, pg. 1412
MEDI CINE MEDIENPRODUKTIONS GMBH; *Int'l*, pg. 4769
MEDICINENET, INC.—See KKR & Co. Inc.; *U.S. Public*, pg. 1254
MEDICINES 360; *U.S. Private*, pg. 2656
THE MEDICINES COMPANY (AUSTRALIA) PTY LIMITED—See Novartis AG; *Int'l*, pg. 5460
THE MEDICINES COMPANY (BELGIUM) SPRL/BVBA—See Novartis AG; *Int'l*, pg. 5460
THE MEDICINES COMPANY (DEUTSCHLAND) GMBH—See Novartis AG; *Int'l*, pg. 5460
THE MEDICINES COMPANY -INDIANAPOLIS—See Novartis AG; *Int'l*, pg. 5460
THE MEDICINES COMPANY -MONTREAL—See Novartis AG; *Int'l*, pg. 5460
THE MEDICINES COMPANY (NETHERLANDS) BV—See Novartis AG; *Int'l*, pg. 5460
THE MEDICINES COMPANY -QUEBEC—See Novartis AG; *Int'l*, pg. 5461
THE MEDICINES COMPANY -SAINT LAURENT—See Novartis AG; *Int'l*, pg. 5461
THE MEDICINES COMPANY (SCHWEIZ) GMBH—See Novartis AG; *Int'l*, pg. 5460
THE MEDICINES COMPANY—See Novartis AG; *Int'l*, pg. 5460
THE MEDICINES COMPANY (SPAIN) S.L.—See Novartis AG; *Int'l*, pg. 5460
THE MEDICINES COMPANY UK LIMITED—See Novartis AG; *Int'l*, pg. 5461
MEDICINES DEVELOPMENT FOR GLOBAL HEALTH LIMITED; *Int'l*, pg. 4776
MEDICINE SHOPPE CANADA, INC.—See McKesson Corporation; *U.S. Public*, pg. 1408
MEDICINE SHOPPE INTERNATIONAL, INC.—See Cardinal Health, Inc.; *U.S. Public*, pg. 434
MEDICINE TODAY POLAND SP. Z O.O.—See Bonnier AB; *Int'l*, pg. 1108
MEDICINOVA, INC.; *U.S. Public*, pg. 1412
MEDIC INTERNATIONAL LIMITED; *Int'l*, pg. 4774
MEDICIS AESTHETICS CANADA, LTD.—See Bausch Health Companies Inc.; *Int'l*, pg. 898
MEDICIS AESTHETICS INC.—See Bausch Health Companies Inc.; *Int'l*, pg. 898
MEDICIS GLOBAL SERVICES CORPORATION—See Bausch Health Companies Inc.; *Int'l*, pg. 898
MEDICIS PHARMACEUTICAL CORPORATION—See Bausch Health Companies Inc.; *Int'l*, pg. 898
MEDICITY, INC.—See Health Catalyst, Inc.; *U.S. Public*, pg. 1014
MEDICLIN AKTIENGESELLSCHAFT—See Asklepios Kliniken GmbH & Co. KGaA; *Int'l*, pg. 623
MEDICLIN A LA CARTE GMBH—See Asklepios Kliniken GmbH & Co. KGaA; *Int'l*, pg. 623
MEDICLIN CATERING GMBH—See Asklepios Kliniken GmbH & Co. KGaA; *Int'l*, pg. 623
MEDICLIN GESCHAFTSFUHRUNGS-GMBH—See Asklepios Kliniken GmbH & Co. KGaA; *Int'l*, pg. 623
MEDICLIN GMBH & CO. KG—See Asklepios Kliniken GmbH & Co. KGaA; *Int'l*, pg. 623
MEDICLINIC BLOEMFONTEIN INVESTMENTS (PTY.) LTD.—See Remgro Limited; *Int'l*, pg. 6269
MEDICLINIC BRITS (PTY.) LTD.—See Remgro Limited; *Int'l*, pg. 6270
MEDICLINIC CAPE GATE DAY CLINIC INVESTMENTS (PTY.) LTD.—See Remgro Limited; *Int'l*, pg. 6270
MEDICLINIC DURBANVILLE DAY CLINIC (PTY.) LTD.—See Remgro Limited; *Int'l*, pg. 6270
MEDICLINIC ERMELO (PTY.) LTD.—See Remgro Limited; *Int'l*, pg. 6270
MEDICLINIC GEORGE INVESTMENTS (PTY.) LTD.—See Remgro Limited; *Int'l*, pg. 6270
MEDICLINIC HERMANUS (PTY.) LTD.—See Remgro Limited; *Int'l*, pg. 6270
MEDICLINIC HIGHVELD INVESTMENTS (PTY.) LTD.—See Remgro Limited; *Int'l*, pg. 6270

MEDICLINIC HOOGLAND INVESTMENTS (PTY.) LTD.—See Remgro Limited; *Int'l*, pg. 6270
MEDICLINIC INTERNATIONAL LIMITED—See Remgro Limited; *Int'l*, pg. 6270
MEDICLINIC INTERNATIONAL PLC—See Remgro Limited; *Int'l*, pg. 6269
MEDICLINIC KIMBERLEY—See Remgro Limited; *Int'l*, pg. 6270
MEDICLINIC KLEIN KAROO INVESTMENTS (PTY.) LTD.—See Remgro Limited; *Int'l*, pg. 6270
MEDICLINIC LEGAE INVESTMENTS (PTY.) LTD.—See Remgro Limited; *Int'l*, pg. 6270
MEDICLINIC LEPHALALE (PTY.) LTD.—See Remgro Limited; *Int'l*, pg. 6270
MEDICLINIC LOUIS LEIPOLDT INVESTMENTS (PTY.) LTD.—See Remgro Limited; *Int'l*, pg. 6270
MEDICLINIC MILNERTON INVESTMENTS (PTY.) LTD.—See Remgro Limited; *Int'l*, pg. 6270
MEDICLINIC MORNINGSIDE INVESTMENTS (PTY.) LTD.—See Remgro Limited; *Int'l*, pg. 6270
MEDICLINIC NELSPRUIT DAY CLINIC INVESTMENTS (PTY.) LTD.—See Remgro Limited; *Int'l*, pg. 6270
MEDICLINIC OTJIWARONGO (PTY.) LTD.—See Remgro Limited; *Int'l*, pg. 6270
MEDICLINIC PAARL (PTY.) LTD.—See Remgro Limited; *Int'l*, pg. 6270
MEDICLINIC PANORAMA INVESTMENTS (PTY.) LTD.—See Remgro Limited; *Int'l*, pg. 6270
MEDICLINIC PIETERMARITZBURG INVESTMENTS (PTY.) LTD.—See Remgro Limited; *Int'l*, pg. 6270
MEDICLINIC PLETTENBERG BAY INVESTMENTS (PTY.) LTD.—See Remgro Limited; *Int'l*, pg. 6270
MEDICLINIC SANDTON INVESTMENTS (PTY.) LTD.—See Remgro Limited; *Int'l*, pg. 6270
MEDICLINIC STELLENBOSCH (PTY.) LTD.—See Remgro Limited; *Int'l*, pg. 6270
MEDICLINIC SWAKOPMUND (PTY.) LTD.—See Remgro Limited; *Int'l*, pg. 6270
MEDICLINIC THABAZIMBI (PTY.) LTD.—See Remgro Limited; *Int'l*, pg. 6270
MEDICLINIC VEREENIGING INVESTMENTS (PTY.) LTD.—See Remgro Limited; *Int'l*, pg. 6270
MEDICLINIC VERGELEGEN INVESTMENTS (PTY.) LTD.—See Remgro Limited; *Int'l*, pg. 6270
MEDICLINIC WELKOM INVESTMENTS (PTY.) LTD.—See Remgro Limited; *Int'l*, pg. 6270
MEDICLINIC WINDHOEK (PTY.) LTD.—See Remgro Limited; *Int'l*, pg. 6270
MEDICLINIC WORCESTER INVESTMENTS (PTY.) LTD.—See Remgro Limited; *Int'l*, pg. 6270
MEDICLIN IMMOBILIEN VERWALTUNG GMBH—See Asklepios Kliniken GmbH & Co. KGaA; *Int'l*, pg. 623
MEDICLIN KRAKENHAUS AM CRIVITZER SEE—See Asklepios Kliniken GmbH & Co. KGaA; *Int'l*, pg. 623
MEDICLIN KRANKENHAUS AM CRIVITZER SEE GMBH—See Asklepios Kliniken GmbH & Co. KGaA; *Int'l*, pg. 623
MEDICLIN MEDIZINISCHES VERSORGUNGSZENTRUM GMBH—See Asklepios Kliniken GmbH & Co. KGaA; *Int'l*, pg. 624
MEDICLIN MURITZ-KLINIKUM GMBH & CO. KG—See Asklepios Kliniken GmbH & Co. KGaA; *Int'l*, pg. 623
MEDICLIN MVZ ACHERN GMBH—See Asklepios Kliniken GmbH & Co. KGaA; *Int'l*, pg. 624
MEDICLIN PFLEGE GMBH—See Asklepios Kliniken GmbH & Co. KGaA; *Int'l*, pg. 623
MEDICLIN THERAPIE GMBH—See Asklepios Kliniken GmbH & Co. KGaA; *Int'l*, pg. 623
MEDICO INDUSTRIES, INC.; *U.S. Private*, pg. 2656
MEDICO INSURANCE COMPANY—See American Enterprise Mutual Holding Company; *U.S. Private*, pg. 232
MEDICO INTERCONTINENTAL LIMITED; *Int'l*, pg. 4776
MEDICO INTERNATIONAL INC.; *U.S. Private*, pg. 2656
MEDICOLEGAL SERVICES, LLC—See GIC Pte. Ltd.; *Int'l*, pg. 2964
MEDICOLEGAL SERVICES, LLC—See Leonard Green & Partners, L.P.; *U.S. Private*, pg. 2425
MEDICOM HEALTHCARE B.V.—See A.R. Medicom Inc.; *Int'l*, pg. 28
MEDICOMP, INC.—See United Therapeutics Corporation; *U.S. Public*, pg. 2238
MEDICOM-UKRAINE LLC—See A.R. Medicom Inc.; *Int'l*, pg. 28
MEDICOM USA, INC.—See A.R. Medicom Inc.; *Int'l*, pg. 28
MEDICON HELLAS S.A.; *Int'l*, pg. 4776
MEDICONSTANT HOLDING SDN. BHD.—See Bioalpha Holdings Berhad; *Int'l*, pg. 1036
MEDICONSTANT PHARMACY (AMPANG) SDN. BHD.—See Bioalpha Holdings Berhad; *Int'l*, pg. 1036
MEDICONSTANT PHARMACY (KLANG) SDN. BHD.—See Bioalpha Holdings Berhad; *Int'l*, pg. 1036
MEDICOPACK A/S—See SP Group A/S; *Int'l*, pg. 7122
MEDI-COPY SERVICES INC.—See PCP Enterprise, L.P.; *U.S. Private*, pg. 3121
MEDICO REMEDIES LIMITED; *Int'l*, pg. 4776
MEDI CORP, INC.—See Aquiline Capital Partners LLC; *U.S. Private*, pg. 304
MEDICOVER AB; *Int'l*, pg. 4776

CORPORATE AFFILIATIONS

MEDICOVER HOLDING S.A.; *Int'l*, pg. 4776
MEDICOVER HUNGARY—See Medicover Holding S.A.; *Int'l*, pg. 4776
MEDICOVER ROMBEL SRL—See Medicover Holding S.A.; *Int'l*, pg. 4776
MEDICOVER SLOVAKIA S.R.O.—See Medicover Holding S.A.; *Int'l*, pg. 4776
MEDICOVER SP Z O O—See Medicover Holding S.A.; *Int'l*, pg. 4776
MEDICOVER SRL—See Medicover Holding S.A.; *Int'l*, pg. 4776
MEDICOX CO., LTD.; *Int'l*, pg. 4776
MEDICREA INTERNATIONAL SA—See Medtronic plc; *Int'l*, pg. 4787
MEDICREA POLAND SP. Z.O.O.—See Medtronic plc; *Int'l*, pg. 4788
MEDICREA TECHNOLOGIES—See Medtronic plc; *Int'l*, pg. 4788
MEDICREA USA CORP.—See Medtronic plc; *Int'l*, pg. 4788
MEDICREDIT, INC.—See HCA Healthcare, Inc.; *U.S. Public*, pg. 1001
MEDICROSS HEALTHCARE GROUP PTY LTD—See Netcare Limited; *Int'l*, pg. 5213
MEDICS AMBULANCE SERVICE, INC.—See KKR & Co. Inc.; *U.S. Public*, pg. 1249
MEDICS EMERGENCY SERVICES OF PALM BEACH COUNTY, INC.—See KKR & Co. Inc.; *U.S. Public*, pg. 1250
MEDICS ENTERPIRSES; *U.S. Private*, pg. 2656
MEDICSKIN HOLDINGS LIMITED; *Int'l*, pg. 4776
MEDICUM HAMBURG MVZ GMBH—See Asklepios Kliniken GmbH & Co. KGaA; *Int'l*, pg. 624
MEDICURE INC.; *Int'l*, pg. 4776
MEDICURE INTERNATIONAL, INC.—See Medicure Inc.; *Int'l*, pg. 4776
MEDICURE PHARMA, INC.—See Medicure Inc.; *Int'l*, pg. 4776
THE MEDICUS FIRM LLC—See Sony Group Corporation; *Int'l*, pg. 7102
MEDICUS GMBH—See PAUL HARTMANN AG; *Int'l*, pg. 5761
MEDICUS HOMECARE INC.; *Int'l*, pg. 4776
MEDICUS LIFE BRANDS—See Publicis Groupe S.A.; *Int'l*, pg. 6103
MEDICUS SCIENCES ACQUISITION CORP.; *U.S. Public*, pg. 1412
MEDICUS SOLUTIONS, LLC; *U.S. Private*, pg. 2656
MEDIC WEST AMBULANCE, INC.—See KKR & Co. Inc.; *U.S. Public*, pg. 1251
MEDICX FUND LIMITED—See Primary Health Properties Plc; *Int'l*, pg. 5975
MEDIDATA SOLUTIONS, INC.—See Dassault Systemes S.A.; *Int'l*, pg. 1975
MEDIDATA SOLUTIONS K.K.—See Dassault Systemes S.A.; *Int'l*, pg. 1975
MEDIDORES INTERNACIONALES ROCHESTER S.A. DE C.V.—See Gas Equipment Company, Inc.; *U.S. Private*, pg. 1647
MEDI-DYNE HEALTHCARE PRODUCTS LTD.; *U.S. Private*, pg. 2651
MEDIE CO., LTD.—See Medipal Holdings Corporation; *Int'l*, pg. 4779
MEDIENART AG; *Int'l*, pg. 4776
MEDIENCE CO., LTD.; *Int'l*, pg. 4776
MEDIENFABRIK GUTERSLOH GMBH—See Bertelsmann SE & Co. KGaA; *Int'l*, pg. 995
MEDIENGRUPPE MAIN-POST GMBH—See Verlagsgruppe Georg von Holtzbrinck GmbH; *Int'l*, pg. 8171
MEDIEN.ZUSTELL GMBH—See Osterreichische Post AG; *Int'l*, pg. 5654
MEDIES; *Int'l*, pg. 4777
MEDIEVAL DINNER & TOURNAMENT, INC.; *U.S. Private*, pg. 2656
MEDIEVAL TIMES MANAGEMENT INC.—See Medieval Dinner & Tournament, Inc.; *U.S. Private*, pg. 2656
MEDIFARM A.D.; *Int'l*, pg. 4777
MEDIFAST (HONG KONG) LIMITED—See iKang Healthcare Group, Inc.; *Int'l*, pg. 3610
MEDIFAST, INC.; *U.S. Public*, pg. 1412
MEDIFIRST SOLUTIONS, INC.; *U.S. Public*, pg. 1412
MEDIFIT CORPORATE SERVICES INC.—See Athletes' Performance, Inc.; *U.S. Private*, pg. 368
MEDIFLEET, INC.—See Harbour Group Industries, Inc.; *U.S. Private*, pg. 1860
MEDIFOCUS, INC.; *U.S. Public*, pg. 1412
MEDIFORCE HEALTHCARE PRIVATE LIMITED—See Mankind Pharma Ltd.; *Int'l*, pg. 4673
MEDIFOX GMBH—See ECM Equity Capital Management GmbH; *Int'l*, pg. 2291
MEDIGAIN, INC.—See CareCloud, Inc.; *U.S. Public*, pg. 435
MEDIGARD LIMITED; *Int'l*, pg. 4777
MEDIGAS ITALIA S.R.L.—See Mitsubishi Chemical Group Corporation; *Int'l*, pg. 4937
MEDIGAS SERVICE & TESTING CO., INC.—See Atlas Copco AB; *Int'l*, pg. 681
MEDIGEN BIOTECHNOLOGY CORP.; *Int'l*, pg. 4777
MEDIGENE AG; *Int'l*, pg. 4777

COMPANY NAME INDEX

MEDIGEN VACCINE BIOLOGICS CORP.; *Int'l*, pg. 4777
MEDIGEST CONSULTORES S.L.—See CompuGroup Medical SE & Co. KGaA; *Int'l*, pg. 1757
MEDI GLASS LIMITED; *Int'l*, pg. 4769
MEDIGOLD; *U.S. Private*, pg. 2656
MEDI HUB CO., LTD.—See Birmingham Sports Holdings Limited; *Int'l*, pg. 1048
MEDI IP, LLC; *U.S. Private*, pg. 2651
MEDIKA D.D.; *Int'l*, pg. 4777
MEDIKE, INC.; *U.S. Private*, pg. 2656
MEDIKIT CO., LTD.; *Int'l*, pg. 4777
MEDIKIT EUROPE GMBH—See Medikit Co., Ltd.; *Int'l*, pg. 4777
MEDIKIT VIETNAM CO., LTD.—See Medikit Co., Ltd.; *Int'l*, pg. 4777
MEDIKOMERC D.D. SARAJEVO; *Int'l*, pg. 4777
MEDIKOMP GMBH—See Getinge AB; *Int'l*, pg. 2952
MEDIKREDIT INTEGRATED HEALTHCARE SOLUTIONS (PROPRIETARY) LIMITED—See Lesaka Technologies, Inc.; *Int'l*, pg. 4469
MEDIKUMPPANI OY—See Empresaria Group Plc; *Int'l*, pg. 2389
MEDILEAD INC.—See Cross Marketing Group Inc.; *Int'l*, pg. 1856
MEDI LIFESTYLE LIMITED; *Int'l*, pg. 4769
MEDI LIFESTYLE LIMITED; *Int'l*, pg. 4769
MEDILINES DISTRIBUTORS INCORPORATED; *Int'l*, pg. 4777
MEDI-LYNX CARDIAC MONITORING, LLC—See Medicalgorithmics S.A.; *Int'l*, pg. 4775
MEDILYS LABORGESELLSCHAFT MBH—See Asklepios Kliniken GmbH & Co. KGaA; *Int'l*, pg. 623
MEDIMARK SCIENTIFIC LIMITED—See Byotrol Limited; *Int'l*, pg. 1235
MEDIMAX ONLINE GMBH—See ElectronicPartner Handel SE; *Int'l*, pg. 2354
MEDIMET PRECISION CASTING & IMPLANTS TECHNOLOGY GMBH; *Int'l*, pg. 4777
MEDIMMUNE LIMITED—See AstraZeneca PLC; *Int'l*, pg. 661
MEDIMMUNE LLC—See AstraZeneca PLC; *Int'l*, pg. 660
MEDIMMUNE PHARMA B.V.—See AstraZeneca PLC; *Int'l*, pg. 661
MEDIMMUNE VENTURES, INC.—See AstraZeneca PLC; *Int'l*, pg. 661
MEDIMONDI AG—See CENTROTEC SE; *Int'l*, pg. 1415
MEDIMPACT HEALTHCARE SYSTEMS, INC.; *U.S. Private*, pg. 2657
MEDIMPEX FRANCE S.A.RL.—See Gedeon Richter Plc.; *Int'l*, pg. 2910
MEDIMPEX JAMAICA LTD—See Gedeon Richter Plc.; *Int'l*, pg. 2910
MEDIMPEX OFFICE BLOCK LTD.—See Les Laboratoires Servier SAS; *Int'l*, pg. 4468
MEDIMPEX TRADING CLOSE CO. LTD—See Les Laboratoires Servier SAS; *Int'l*, pg. 4468
MEDIMPEX UK LTD.—See Gedeon Richter Plc.; *Int'l*, pg. 2910
MEDIMPEX WEST INDIES LTD—See Gedeon Richter Plc.; *Int'l*, pg. 2910
MEDINA BELZIG GMBH—See MK-Kliniken AG; *Int'l*, pg. 5001
MEDINA BLANKING, INC.—See Shiloh Industries, Inc.; *U.S. Private*, pg. 3636
MEDINA CAPITAL PARTNERS, INC; *U.S. Private*, pg. 2657
MEDINA ELECTRIC CO-OPERATIVE; *U.S. Private*, pg. 2657
MEDINA GOLF & COUNTRY CLUB—See Apollo Global Management, Inc.; *U.S. Public*, pg. 150
MEDINAH MINERALS, INC.; *U.S. Public*, pg. 1413
MEDINA MANAGEMENT COMPANY, LLC; *U.S. Private*, pg. 2657
MEDINA MEDICAL, INC.—See Medtronic plc; *Int'l*, pg. 4788
MEDINA SOZIALE BEHINDERTENBETREUUNG GMBH—See MK-Kliniken AG; *Int'l*, pg. 5001
MEDINA/TURGUL DDB—See Omnicom Group Inc.; *U.S. Public*, pg. 1582
MEDINAVI AG; *Int'l*, pg. 4777
MEDINCELL S.A.; *Int'l*, pg. 4777
MED, INC.; *U.S. Private*, pg. 2650
MEDINE LIMITED; *Int'l*, pg. 4777
MEDINEOS S.R.L.—See IQVIA Holdings Inc.; *U.S. Public*, pg. 1170
MEDINET CO., LTD.; *Int'l*, pg. 4777
MEDINET GROUP LTD; *Int'l*, pg. 4777
MEDINET HEALTH CENTRE LIMITED—See MediNet Group Ltd; *Int'l*, pg. 4777
MEDINET INTERNATIONAL BV—See Eurofins Scientific S.E.; *Int'l*, pg. 2551
MEDINET SYSTEMY INFORMATYCZNE SP. Z O.O.—See Simple S.A.; *Int'l*, pg. 6933
MEDINEX LIMITED; *Int'l*, pg. 4777
MEDINEX PROFESSIONAL SERVICES PTE. LTD.—See Medinex Limited; *Int'l*, pg. 4777
MEDIN GMBH & CO. KG—See Laurens Spethmann Holding Aktiengesellschaft & Co. KG; *Int'l*, pg. 4424
MEDINICE SA; *Int'l*, pg. 4778

MEDINOTEC INC.; *Int'l*, pg. 4778
MEDINOVA AG—See Diethelm Keller Holding Limited; *Int'l*, pg. 2117
MEDINOVA DIAGNOSTIC SERVICES LIMITED - BANSDRONI UNIT—See Vijaya Diagnostic Centre Pvt. Ltd.; *Int'l*, pg. 8205
MEDINOVA DIAGNOSTIC SERVICES LIMITED—See Vijaya Diagnostic Centre Pvt. Ltd.; *Int'l*, pg. 8205
MEDINSIGHTS, INC.—See Arthur J. Gallagher & Co.; *U.S. Public*, pg. 206
MEDIN TECHNOLOGIES, INC.—See Seven Point Equity Partners, LLC; *U.S. Private*, pg. 3619
MEDI-NUCLEAR CORP.; *U.S. Private*, pg. 2651
MEDIOBANCA-BANCA DE CREDITO FINANZIARIO S.P.A.; *Int'l*, pg. 4778
MEDIOBANCA INTERNATIONAL (LUXEMBOURG) S.A.—See Mediobanca S.P.A.; *Int'l*, pg. 4778
MEDIOBANCA MANAGEMENT COMPANY—See Mediobanca S.P.A.; *Int'l*, pg. 4778
MEDIOBANCA SECURITIES USA LLC—See Mediobanca-Banca de Credito Finanziario S.p.A.; *Int'l*, pg. 4778
MEDIOBANCA SGR S.P.A.—See Mediobanca-Banca de Credito Finanziario S.p.A.; *Int'l*, pg. 4778
MEDIOBANCA S.P.A.; *Int'l*, pg. 4778
MEDIOCREDITO CENTRALE S.P.A.—See UniCredit S.p.A.; *Int'l*, pg. 8035
MEDIOCREDITO EUROPEO SPA—See Argiletum Merchant S.p.A.; *Int'l*, pg. 561
MEDIOCREDITO ITALIANO S.P.A.—See Intesa Sanpaolo S.p.A.; *Int'l*, pg. 3766
MEDIOFACTORING S.P.A.—See Intesa Sanpaolo S.p.A.; *Int'l*, pg. 3766
MEDIOINSURANCE S.R.L.—See Duna House Holding Public Company Limited; *Int'l*, pg. 2225
MEDIOLANUM ASSET MANAGEMENT LTD—See Banca Mediolanum S.p.A.; *Int'l*, pg. 815
MEDIOLANUM COMUNICAZIONE S.P.A.—See Banca Mediolanum S.p.A.; *Int'l*, pg. 815
MEDIOLANUM CORPORATE UNIVERSITY S.P.A.—See Banca Mediolanum S.p.A.; *Int'l*, pg. 815
MEDIOLANUM DISTRIBUZIONE FINANZIARIA S.P.A.—See Banca Mediolanum S.p.A.; *Int'l*, pg. 815
MEDIOLANUM FARMACEUTICI SPA; *Int'l*, pg. 4778
MEDIOLANUM GESTIONE FONDI SGRPA—See Banca Mediolanum S.p.A.; *Int'l*, pg. 815
MEDIOLANUM INTERNATIONAL FUNDS LTD—See Banca Mediolanum S.p.A.; *Int'l*, pg. 815
MEDIOLANUM INTERNATIONAL LIFE—See Banca Mediolanum S.p.A.; *Int'l*, pg. 815
MEDIOLANUM VITA SPA—See Banca Mediolanum S.p.A.; *Int'l*, pg. 815
MEDION AG—See Lenovo Group Limited; *Int'l*, pg. 4454
MEDION ELECTRONICS LIMITED—See Lenovo Group Limited; *Int'l*, pg. 4454
MEDION GRIFOLS DIAGNOSTIC AG—See Grifols, S.A.; *Int'l*, pg. 3085
MEDION IBERIA, S.L.—See Lenovo Group Limited; *Int'l*, pg. 4454
MEDION NORDIC A/S—See Lenovo Group Limited; *Int'l*, pg. 4454
MEDION SCHWEIZ ELECTRONICS AG—See Lenovo Group Limited; *Int'l*, pg. 4454
MEDION USA, INC.—See Lenovo Group Limited; *Int'l*, pg. 4454
MEDIOS AG; *Int'l*, pg. 4778
MEDIOS DIGITAL GMBH—See Medios AG; *Int'l*, pg. 4778
MEDIOS INDIVIDUAL GMBH—See Medios AG; *Int'l*, pg. 4778
MEDIOS MANUFAKTUR GMBH—See Medios AG; *Int'l*, pg. 4778
MEDIOS PHARMA GMBH—See Medios AG; *Int'l*, pg. 4778
MEDIPAL FOODS CORPORATION—See Medipal Holdings Corporation; *Int'l*, pg. 4779
MEDIPAL HOLDINGS CORPORATION; *Int'l*, pg. 4779
MEDIPAL INSURANCE SERVICE CO., LTD.—See Medipal Holdings Corporation; *Int'l*, pg. 4779
MEDIPASS CO., LTD.—See Medley, Inc.; *Int'l*, pg. 4784
MEDIPHARM AB; *Int'l*, pg. 4779
MEDIPHARMA LTD—See Hikal Limited; *Int'l*, pg. 3389
MEDIPHARM HUNGARY KFT—See Novonesis A/S; *Int'l*, pg. 5468
MEDIPHARM LABS CORP.; *Int'l*, pg. 4779
MEDIPHARM USA—See Novonesis A/S; *Int'l*, pg. 5468
MEDIPLAST AB—See AddLife AB; *Int'l*, pg. 129
MEDIPLAST A/S—See AddLife AB; *Int'l*, pg. 129
MEDIPLAST AS—See AddLife AB; *Int'l*, pg. 129
MEDIPLAST BENELUX B.V.—See AddLife AB; *Int'l*, pg. 129
MEDIPLAST GMBH—See AddLife AB; *Int'l*, pg. 130
MEDIPLAST S.R.L.—See AddLife AB; *Int'l*, pg. 130
MEDIPLUS (ECONOMIC ZONE) N.V.—See Gedeon Richter Plc.; *Int'l*, pg. 2910
MEDIPOLIS GMP OY—See BIOTON S.A.; *Int'l*, pg. 1043
MEDIPORT VENTURE FONDS ZWEI GMBH—See BayernLB Holding AG; *Int'l*, pg. 914
MEDIPOST CO., LTD. - CELL DRUG GMP FACTORY—See MEDIPOST Co., Ltd.; *Int'l*, pg. 4780
MEDIPOST CO., LTD.; *Int'l*, pg. 4779

MEDISOUTH, INC.

MEDIPOWER (OVERSEAS) PUBLIC CO. LIMITED; *Int'l*, pg. 4780
MEDIPURE HOLDINGS INC.; *Int'l*, pg. 4780
MEDIQ B.V.—See Advent International Corporation; *U.S. Private*, pg. 104
MEDIQ DANMARK A/S—See Advent International Corporation; *U.S. Private*, pg. 104
MEDIQ DIRECT DIABETES B.V.—See Advent International Corporation; *U.S. Private*, pg. 104
MEDIQ DIREKT DIABETES GMBH—See Advent International Corporation; *U.S. Private*, pg. 104
MEDIQ DIREKT KFT.—See Advent International Corporation; *U.S. Private*, pg. 104
MEDIQ EESTI OU—See Advent International Corporation; *U.S. Private*, pg. 104
MEDIQ FRANCE SA—See Novomed Group; *Int'l*, pg. 5467
MEDIQ LIETUVA UAB—See Advent International Corporation; *U.S. Private*, pg. 104
MEDIQ MEDECO—See Advent International Corporation; *U.S. Private*, pg. 104
MEDIQ MEDISOURCE B.V.—See Advent International Corporation; *U.S. Private*, pg. 104
MEDIQ NORGE AS—See Advent International Corporation; *U.S. Private*, pg. 104
MEDI-QOL INC.—See Polaris Capital Group Co., Ltd.; *Int'l*, pg. 5907
MEDIQON GROUP AG; *Int'l*, pg. 4780
MEDIQ PHARMA SERVICES—See Advent International Corporation; *U.S. Private*, pg. 104
MEDIQ/PRN LIFE SUPPORT SYSTEMS, LLC—See Baxter International Inc.; *U.S. Public*, pg. 283
MEDIQ SUISSE AG—See Advent International Corporation; *U.S. Private*, pg. 104
MEDIQ SUOMI OY—See Advent International Corporation; *U.S. Private*, pg. 104
MEDIQ SVERIGE AB—See Advent International Corporation; *U.S. Private*, pg. 104
MEDIQ TEFA B.V.—See Advent International Corporation; *U.S. Private*, pg. 104
MEDIQUAL SYSTEMS, INC.—See Quantros, Inc.; *U.S. Private*, pg. 3322
MEDIQUANT, INC.; *U.S. Private*, pg. 2657
MEDIQUIP SDN. BHD.—See Medtronic plc; *Int'l*, pg. 4787
MEDIRADIX OY—See Empresaria Group Plc; *Int'l*, pg. 2389
MEDIRECT LATINO, INC.; *U.S. Public*, pg. 1413
MEDIREST GMBH & CO OHG—See Compass Group PLC; *Int'l*, pg. 1750
MEDIREVV INC.; *U.S. Private*, pg. 2657
MEDIROM HEALTHCARE TECHNOLOGIES INC.; *Int'l*, pg. 4780
MEDIS ADRIA D.O.O.—See Medis, d.o.o.; *Int'l*, pg. 4780
MEDISA SHINYAKU INC.—See Sawai Group Holdings Co., Ltd.; *Int'l*, pg. 6602
MEDISCAN DIAGNOSTIC SERVICES, LLC—See Cross Country Healthcare, Inc.; *U.S. Public*, pg. 595
MEDISCAN GMBH & CO. KG—See Greiner Holding AG; *Int'l*, pg. 3079
MEDISCH LABO VAN WAES D. B.V. C.V.B.A.—See Sonic Healthcare Limited; *Int'l*, pg. 7097
MEDISCIENCE PLANNING INC.—See Sony Group Corporation; *Int'l*, pg. 7102
MEDIS, D.O.O.; *Int'l*, pg. 4780
MEDISEAL GMBH—See Korber AG; *Int'l*, pg. 4280
MEDIS EHF.—See Teva Pharmaceutical Industries, Ltd.; *Int'l*, pg. 7579
MEDISELL RWANDA LTD.—See HORIBA Ltd; *Int'l*, pg. 3477
MEDISELL UG LTD.—See HORIBA Ltd; *Int'l*, pg. 3477
MEDISERV GMBH—See Asklepios Kliniken GmbH & Co. KGaA; *Int'l*, pg. 623
MEDISERV SP. ZOO—See ResMed Inc.; *U.S. Public*, pg. 1790
MEDIS GMBH—See Medis, d.o.o.; *Int'l*, pg. 4780
MEDIS HUNGARY KFT.—See Medis, d.o.o.; *Int'l*, pg. 4780
MEDISIGN GMBH—See Deutsche Apotheker- und Arztebank eG; *Int'l*, pg. 2049
MEDIS INTERNATIONAL D.O.O.—See Medis, d.o.o.; *Int'l*, pg. 4780
MEDISIZE B.V.—See Flexicare (Group) Limited; *Int'l*, pg. 2705
MEDISIZE ITALIA SRL—See Flexicare (Group) Limited; *Int'l*, pg. 2705
MEDISIZE OY—See Flexicare (Group) Limited; *Int'l*, pg. 2705
MEDISIZE SCHWEIZ AG—See Flexicare (Group) Limited; *Int'l*, pg. 2705
MEDISKED LLC—See Symphony Technology Group, LLC; *U.S. Private*, pg. 3901
MEDISOFT SA—See Niterra Co., Ltd.; *Int'l*, pg. 5380
MEDISOLUTION LTD.—See Brookfield Corporation; *Int'l*, pg. 1189
MEDISOLUTION PTE. LTD.—See Boustead Singapore Limited; *Int'l*, pg. 1121
MEDISOURCE IRELAND LIMITED—See DCC plc; *Int'l*, pg. 1991
MEDISOUTH, INC.; *U.S. Private*, pg. 2657
MEDI-SPAN—See Wolters Kluwer n.v.; *Int'l*, pg. 8444

MEDIS PHARMA D.O.O.—See Medis, d.o.o.; *Int'l*, pg. 4780
MEDIS PHARMA PTY LTD—See Teva Pharmaceutical Industries, Ltd.; *Int'l*, pg. 7579
MEDISTAR ARZNEIMITTELVERTRIEB GMBH—See Schneider Schreibgerate GmbH; *Int'l*, pg. 6636
MEDISTAR, INC.; *U.S. Private*, pg. 2657
MEDISTAR PRAXISCOMPUTER GMBH—See Compu-Group Medical SE & Co. KGaA; *Int'l*, pg. 1757
MEDISTA S.R.O.; *Int'l*, pg. 4780
MEDISTIM ASA; *Int'l*, pg. 4780
MEDISTIM DANMARK APS—See Medistim ASA; *Int'l*, pg. 4781
MEDISTIM DEUTSCHLAND GMBH—See Medistim ASA; *Int'l*, pg. 4781
MEDISTIM KIROP AS—See Medistim ASA; *Int'l*, pg. 4781
MEDISTIM NORGE AS—See Medistim ASA; *Int'l*, pg. 4781
MEDISTIM SPAIN S.L.—See Medistim ASA; *Int'l*, pg. 4781
MEDISTIM UK LTD.—See Medistim ASA; *Int'l*, pg. 4781
MEDISTIM USA INC.—See Medistim ASA; *Int'l*, pg. 4781
MEDISUITE, LLC—See ADDvise Group AB; *Int'l*, pg. 136
MEDISUN PRECISION MEDICINE LTD.; *Int'l*, pg. 4781
MEDISUPPORT SA—See Sonic Healthcare Limited; *Int'l*, pg. 7097
MEDISURE INDEMNITY AUSTRALIA PTY LTD—See PSC Insurance Group Limited; *Int'l*, pg. 6016
MEDISWITCH NAMIBIA PROPRIETARY LIMITED—See Altron Limited; *Int'l*, pg. 399
MEDISYS HEALTH COMMUNICATIONS, LLC; *U.S. Private*, pg. 2657
MEDISYSTEM PHARMACY—See George Weston Limited; *Int'l*, pg. 2939
MEDITAL COMOTECH LTD.—See THK CO., LTD.; *Int'l*, pg. 7712
MEDITAL NOVELTY LTD.—See THK CO., LTD.; *Int'l*, pg. 7712
MEDITE CANCER DIAGNOSTICS INC.; *U.S. Public*, pg. 1413
MEDI-TECH INTERNATIONAL CORPORATION—See MarketLab, Inc.; *U.S. Private*, pg. 2581
MEDITECHNIK GMBH—See Getinge AB; *Int'l*, pg. 2952
MEDITECHNIK HOLDING GMBH—See Getinge AB; *Int'l*, pg. 2952
MEDITECNA S.R.L.; *Int'l*, pg. 4781
MEDITEC PLASTSTOBNING A/S—See SP Group A/S; *Int'l*, pg. 7122
MEDITEC—See Sartorius AG; *Int'l*, pg. 6579
MEDITE EUROPE LTD.—See Coillte Ltd.; *Int'l*, pg. 1696
MEDITERRA CAPITAL MANAGEMENT LIMITED; *Int'l*, pg. 4781
THE MEDITERRANEAN AND GULF INSURANCE COMPANY P.L.C.; *Int'l*, pg. 7666
MEDITERRANEAN BANK PLC—See AnaCap Financial Partners LLP; *Int'l*, pg. 445
MEDITERRANEAN CARRIERS, INC.—See Heidelberg Materials AG; *Int'l*, pg. 3318
MEDITERRANEAN CORPORATE BANK LIMITED—See AnaCap Financial Partners LLP; *Int'l*, pg. 445
THE MEDITERRANEAN & GULF INSURANCE & REINSURANCE COMPANY S.A.L—See Mediterranean & Gulf Insurance & Reinsurance Company S.J.S.C.; *Int'l*, pg. 4781
MEDITERRANEAN & GULF INSURANCE & REINSURANCE COMPANY S.J.S.C.; *Int'l*, pg. 4781
MEDITERRANEAN MARITIME HUB FINANCE PLC; *Int'l*, pg. 4781
MEDITERRANEAN NAUTILUS GREECE S.A.—See TIM S.p.A.; *Int'l*, pg. 7749
MEDITERRANEAN NAUTILUS ISRAEL LTD—See TIM S.p.A.; *Int'l*, pg. 7749
MEDITERRANEAN NAUTILUS TELEKOMUNIKASYON HIZMETLERI TICARET ANONIM SIRKETI—See TIM S.p.A.; *Int'l*, pg. 7749
MEDITERRANEAN SEEDS LTD.—See Bayer Aktiengesellschaft; *Int'l*, pg. 908
MEDITERRANEAN SHIPPING COMPANY (AUST) PTY LIMITED—See Mediterranean Shipping Company, S.A.; *Int'l*, pg. 4782
MEDITERRANEAN SHIPPING COMPANY (AUST) PTY LIMITED—See Mediterranean Shipping Company, S.A.; *Int'l*, pg. 4782
MEDITERRANEAN SHIPPING COMPANY (AUST) PTY LIMITED—See Mediterranean Shipping Company, S.A.; *Int'l*, pg. 4783
MEDITERRANEAN SHIPPING COMPANY (AUST) PTY LIMITED—See Mediterranean Shipping Company, S.A.; *Int'l*, pg. 4783
MEDITERRANEAN SHIPPING COMPANY (AUST) PTY LIMITED—See Mediterranean Shipping Company, S.A.; *Int'l*, pg. 4783
MEDITERRANEAN SHIPPING COMPANY (AUSTRIA) GMBH—See Mediterranean Shipping Company, S.A.; *Int'l*, pg. 4783
MEDITERRANEAN SHIPPING COMPANY BENIN, S.A.—See Mediterranean Shipping Company, S.A.; *Int'l*, pg. 4783
MEDITERRANEAN SHIPPING COMPANY BOLIVIA—See Mediterranean Shipping Company, S.A.; *Int'l*, pg. 4783

MEDITERRANEAN SHIPPING COMPANY BULGARIA LTD.—See Mediterranean Shipping Company, S.A.; *Int'l*, pg. 4783
MEDITERRANEAN SHIPPING COMPANY CAMEROUN S.A.—See Mediterranean Shipping Company, S.A.; *Int'l*, pg. 4783
MEDITERRANEAN SHIPPING COMPANY CHILE S.A.—See Mediterranean Shipping Company, S.A.; *Int'l*, pg. 4783
MEDITERRANEAN SHIPPING COMPANY COLOMBIA SA.—See Mediterranean Shipping Company, S.A.; *Int'l*, pg. 4783
MEDITERRANEAN SHIPPING COMPANY COSTA RICA S.R.L—See Mediterranean Shipping Company, S.A.; *Int'l*, pg. 4783
MEDITERRANEAN SHIPPING COMPANY DEL PERU S.A.C.—See Mediterranean Shipping Company, S.A.; *Int'l*, pg. 4784
MEDITERRANEAN SHIPPING COMPANY DE VENEZUELA C.A.—See Mediterranean Shipping Company, S.A.; *Int'l*, pg. 4783
MEDITERRANEAN SHIPPING COMPANY (HONG KONG) LIMITED—See Mediterranean Shipping Company, S.A.; *Int'l*, pg. 4783
MEDITERRANEAN SHIPPING COMPANY (LEBANON) S.A.R.L.—See Mediterranean Shipping Company, S.A.; *Int'l*, pg. 4783
MEDITERRANEAN SHIPPING COMPANY LTD.—See Mediterranean Shipping Company, S.A.; *Int'l*, pg. 4783
MEDITERRANEAN SHIPPING COMPANY MADAGASCAR S.A.—See Mediterranean Shipping Company, S.A.; *Int'l*, pg. 4783
MEDITERRANEAN SHIPPING COMPANY (MALAYSIA) SDN. BHD.—See Mediterranean Shipping Company, S.A.; *Int'l*, pg. 4783
MEDITERRANEAN SHIPPING COMPANY (MAROC) SARL—See Mediterranean Shipping Company, S.A.; *Int'l*, pg. 4783
MEDITERRANEAN SHIPPING COMPANY MEXICO SA DE CV—See Mediterranean Shipping Company, S.A.; *Int'l*, pg. 4781
MEDITERRANEAN SHIPPING COMPANY MSC (MALTA) LTD—See Mediterranean Shipping Company, S.A.; *Int'l*, pg. 4783
MEDITERRANEAN SHIPPING COMPANY (NETHERLANDS) B.V.—See Mediterranean Shipping Company, S.A.; *Int'l*, pg. 4783
MEDITERRANEAN SHIPPING COMPANY NEW ZEALAND LIMITED—See Mediterranean Shipping Company, S.A.; *Int'l*, pg. 4783
MEDITERRANEAN SHIPPING COMPANY NEW ZEALAND LIMITED—See Mediterranean Shipping Company, S.A.; *Int'l*, pg. 4783
MEDITERRANEAN SHIPPING COMPANY NEW ZEALAND LIMITED—See Mediterranean Shipping Company, S.A.; *Int'l*, pg. 4783
MEDITERRANEAN SHIPPING COMPANY (PORTUGAL) S.A—See Mediterranean Shipping Company, S.A.; *Int'l*, pg. 4783
MEDITERRANEAN SHIPPING COMPANY (QATAR), WLL.—See Mediterranean Shipping Company, S.A.; *Int'l*, pg. 4783
MEDITERRANEAN SHIPPING COMPANY RUS, LLC—See Mediterranean Shipping Company, S.A.; *Int'l*, pg. 4783
MEDITERRANEAN SHIPPING COMPANY, S.A.; *Int'l*, pg. 4781
MEDITERRANEAN SHIPPING COMPANY SH.P.K.—See Mediterranean Shipping Company, S.A.; *Int'l*, pg. 4782
MEDITERRANEAN SHIPPING COMPANY SPAIN S.A.—See Mediterranean Shipping Company, S.A.; *Int'l*, pg. 4783
MEDITERRANEAN SHIPPING COMPANY S.R.L—See Mediterranean Shipping Company, S.A.; *Int'l*, pg. 4783
MEDITERRANEAN SHIPPING COMPANY TRINIDAD AND TOBAGO LTD—See Mediterranean Shipping Company, S.A.; *Int'l*, pg. 4783
MEDITERRANEAN SHIPPING COMPANY (U.A.E.) L.L.C.—See Mediterranean Shipping Company, S.A.; *Int'l*, pg. 4783
MEDITERRANEAN SHIPPING COMPANY (UK) LTD—See Mediterranean Shipping Company, S.A.; *Int'l*, pg. 4783
MEDITERRANEAN SHIPPING COMPANY URUGUAY SA—See Mediterranean Shipping Company, S.A.; *Int'l*, pg. 4783
MEDITERRANEAN SHIPPING COMPANY USA INC.—See Mediterranean Shipping Company, S.A.; *Int'l*, pg. 4783
MEDITERRANEAN SHIPPING COMPANY W.L.L.—See Mediterranean Shipping Company, S.A.; *Int'l*, pg. 4783
MEDITERRANEAN SHIPPING COMPANY (ZAMBIA) LTD.—See Mediterranean Shipping Company, S.A.; *Int'l*, pg. 4783
MEDITERRANEAN SHIPPING CRUISES LTD.—See Mediterranean Shipping Company, S.A.; *Int'l*, pg. 4784
MEDITERRANEAN SHIPPING (KUWAIT) COMPANY W.L.L—See Mediterranean Shipping Company, S.A.; *Int'l*, pg. 4783

MEDITERRANEAN SHIPPING (THAILAND) CO., LTD.—See Mediterranean Shipping Company, S.A.; *Int'l*, pg. 4782
MEDITERRANEAN TEXTILE COMPANY—See Saif Holdings Limited; *Int'l*, pg. 6482
MEDITERRANEAN TOURISM INVESTMENT COMPANY; *Int'l*, pg. 4784
MEDITERRANEAN VILLAGES S.A—See Kiriacoulis Mediterranean Cruises Shipping S.A.; *Int'l*, pg. 4186
MEDITERRANEO VIDA S.A.—See Banco de Sabadell, S.A.; *Int'l*, pg. 821
M:EDITERRAN POWER GMBH & CO. KG—See Munchener Ruckversicherungs AG; *Int'l*, pg. 5092
MEDITERRA - SEDLCANY, S.R.O.—See Fresenius SE & Co. KGaA; *Int'l*, pg. 2780
MEDITERRA S.R.O.—See Fresenius SE & Co. KGaA; *Int'l*, pg. 2780
MEDITRUST PHARMACY—See McKesson Corporation; *U.S. Public*, pg. 1408
MEDITTS MEDITERRANEAN HEALTHY SNACKS S.L.—See Dole plc; *Int'l*, pg. 2158
MEDIUM BLUE MULTIMEDIA GROUP LLC; *U.S. Private*, pg. 2657
MEDIUM GMBH—See Droege Group AG; *Int'l*, pg. 2205
MEDIUSA, LP.; *U.S. Private*, pg. 2657
MEDIUS HOLDINGS CO., LTD.; *Int'l*, pg. 4784
MEDIUS SVERIGE AB; *Int'l*, pg. 4784
MEDIVAC LIMITED; *Int'l*, pg. 4784
MEDIVANCE, INC.—See Becton, Dickinson & Company; *U.S. Public*, pg. 291
MEDIVATE PARTNERS, LLC; *Int'l*, pg. 4784
MEDIVATORS B.V.—See STERIS plc; *Int'l*, pg. 7209
MEDIVATORS, INC.—See STERIS plc; *Int'l*, pg. 7209
MEDIVIE THERAPEUTIC LTD.; *Int'l*, pg. 4784
MEDIVIR AB; *Int'l*, pg. 4784
MEDIVIR UK LTD—See Medivir AB; *Int'l*, pg. 4784
MEDIVISION, INC.—See HCA Healthcare, Inc.; *U.S. Public*, pg. 1001
MEDIVISION MEDICAL IMAGING LTD.; *Int'l*, pg. 4784
MEDIVO, INC.; *U.S. Private*, pg. 2657
MEDIVOLVE INC.; *Int'l*, pg. 4784
MEDIWARE CONSULTING & ANALYTICS—See Leonard Green & Partners, L.P.; *U.S. Private*, pg. 2430
MEDIWARE CONSULTING & ANALYTICS—See TPG Capital, L.P.; *U.S. Public*, pg. 2177
MEDIWARE REIMBURSEMENT SERVICES—See Leonard Green & Partners, L.P.; *U.S. Private*, pg. 2430
MEDIWARE REIMBURSEMENT SERVICES—See TPG Capital, L.P.; *U.S. Public*, pg. 2177
MEDIWATCH BIOMEDICAL LIMITED—See Investor AB; *Int'l*, pg. 3786
MEDIWATCH UK LTD.—See Investor AB; *Int'l*, pg. 3786
MEDIWELCOME HEALTHCARE MANAGEMENT & TECHNOLOGY INC.; *Int'l*, pg. 4784
MEDIWEST NORWAY AS—See Bayer Aktiengesellschaft; *Int'l*, pg. 908
MEDIWOUND LTD.—See Access Industries, Inc.; *U.S. Private*, pg. 51
MEDIXALL GROUP, INC.—See TBG Holdings Corp.; *U.S. Private*, pg. 3941
MEDIX I.C.S.A.—See ArchiMed SAS; *Int'l*, pg. 548
MEDIX SPECIALTY VEHICLES, INC.—See Caisse de Depot et Placement du Quebec; *Int'l*, pg. 1254
MEDIX SPECIALTY VEHICLES, INC.—See Clearspring Capital Partners; *Int'l*, pg. 1657
MEDIX STAFFING SOLUTIONS INC.; *U.S. Private*, pg. 2657
MEDIZEN HUMANCARE INC.; *Int'l*, pg. 4784
MEDIZINISCHE LABORATORIEN DR. TOGGWEILER AG—See Sonic Healthcare Limited; *Int'l*, pg. 7097
MEDIZONE INTERNATIONAL, INC.; *U.S. Public*, pg. 1413
MEDKINETICS, LLC—See Clearlake Capital Group, L.P.; *U.S. Private*, pg. 937
MEDKINETICS, LLC—See SkyKnight Capital LLC; *U.S. Private*, pg. 3685
MEDKLINN INTERNATIONAL SDN. BHD.—See Esthetics International Group Berhad; *Int'l*, pg. 2518
MEDLAB CENTRAL LIMITED—See Sonic Healthcare Limited; *Int'l*, pg. 7097
MEDLAB CLINICAL LIMITED; *Int'l*, pg. 4784
MED-LAB GMBH—See Sonic Healthcare Limited; *Int'l*, pg. 7097
MEDLAB PATHOLOGY LIMITED—See Sonic Healthcare Limited; *Int'l*, pg. 7097
MEDLAB RESEARCH LTD.—See Medlab Clinical Limited; *Int'l*, pg. 4784
MEDLAB SOUTH LIMITED—See Sonic Healthcare Limited; *Int'l*, pg. 7097
MED-LAB SUPPLY COMPANY, INC.; *U.S. Private*, pg. 2650
MEDLER ELECTRIC COMPANY INC.; *U.S. Private*, pg. 2657
MEDLEVANT SHIPPING S.A.E.—See Albert Ballin KG; *Int'l*, pg. 295
MEDLEY GLOBAL ADVISORS—See Nikkei Inc.; *Int'l*, pg. 5290
MEDLEY, INC.; *Int'l*, pg. 4784
MEDLEY LLC; *U.S. Public*, pg. 1413
MEDLEY MANAGEMENT INC.; *U.S. Public*, pg. 1413

COMPANY NAME INDEX

MEDLEY MATERIAL HANDLING CO.; *U.S. Private*, pg. 2657
MEDLEY S.A. INDUSTRIA FARMACEUTICA LTDA—See Sanofi; *Int'l*, pg. 6548
MEDLIANCE, LLC—See Nautic Partners, LLC; *U.S. Private*, pg. 2871
MEDLIFE S.A.; *Int'l*, pg. 4784
MEDLINE ACCUCARE DIVISION—See Medline Industries, LP; *U.S. Private*, pg. 2657
MEDLINE DERMAL MANAGEMENT SYSTEMS—See Medline Industries, LP; *U.S. Private*, pg. 2657
MEDLINE DYNACOR DIVISION—See Medline Industries, LP; *U.S. Private*, pg. 2657
MEDLINE HEALTHCARE GROUP—See ESAS Holding A.S.; *Int'l*, pg. 2501
MEDLINE INDUSTRIES HOLDINGS, L.P.—See Medline Industries, LP; *U.S. Private*, pg. 2657
MEDLINE INDUSTRIES, LP; *U.S. Private*, pg. 2657
MEDLINE INDUSTRIES LTD.—See Medline Industries, LP; *U.S. Private*, pg. 2658
MEDLINE INTERNATIONAL BELGIUM BVBA—See Medline Industries, LP; *U.S. Private*, pg. 2658
MEDLINE INTERNATIONAL DENMARK APS—See Medline Industries, LP; *U.S. Private*, pg. 2658
MEDLINE INTERNATIONAL FRANCE SAS—See Medline Industries, LP; *U.S. Private*, pg. 2658
MEDLINE INTERNATIONAL GERMANY GMBH—See Medline Industries, LP; *U.S. Private*, pg. 2658
MEDLINE INTERNATIONAL IBERIA S.L.U—See Medline Industries, LP; *U.S. Private*, pg. 2658
MEDLINE INTERNATIONAL ITALY S.R.L.—See Medline Industries, LP; *U.S. Private*, pg. 2658
MEDLINE INTERNATIONAL NETHERLANDS BV—See Medline Industries, LP; *U.S. Private*, pg. 2658
MEDLINE INTERNATIONAL SWITZERLAND SARL—See Medline Industries, LP; *U.S. Private*, pg. 2658
MEDLINE INTERNATIONAL TWO AUSTRALIA PTY LTD—See Medline Industries, LP; *U.S. Private*, pg. 2658
MEDLINE MEDCREST DIVISION—See Medline Industries, LP; *U.S. Private*, pg. 2658
MEDLIT SOLUTIONS, LLC—See Ares Management Corporation; *U.S. Public*, pg. 190
MEDLIVE TECHNOLOGY CO., LTD.; *Int'l*, pg. 4785
MED-LOZ LEASE SERVICE INC.; *U.S. Private*, pg. 2650
MEDMAL DIRECT INSURANCE COMPANY—See Basler Sachversicherungs-AG; *Int'l*, pg. 887
MEDMARC CASUALTY INSURANCE COMPANY—See ProAssurance Corporation; *U.S. Public*, pg. 1723
MEDMARK SERVICES, INC.; *U.S. Private*, pg. 2658
MEDMATICA CONSULTING ASSOCIATES, INC.—See CareCloud, Inc.; *U.S. Public*, pg. 435
MEDMEDIA—See K I Lipton LLC; *U.S. Private*, pg. 2249
MEDMEN ENTERPRISES, INC.; *Int'l*, pg. 4785
MEDMIRA INC.; *Int'l*, pg. 4785
MEDMIRA LABORATORIES INC.—See MedMira Inc.; *Int'l*, pg. 4785
MEDMIX SYSTEMS AG—See Sulzer Ltd.; *Int'l*, pg. 7256
MEDMIX US INC.—See Sulzer Ltd.; *Int'l*, pg. 7256
MED-NAP LLC—See Acme United Corporation; *U.S. Public*, pg. 35
MEDNATION AG; *Int'l*, pg. 4785
MEDNAX, INC.; *U.S. Public*, pg. 1413
MEDNAX SERVICES, INC.—See MEDNAX, Inc.; *U.S. Public*, pg. 1413
MEDNET BAHRAIN W.L.L. MANAMA—See Munchener Ruckversicherungs AG; *Int'l*, pg. 5089
MEDNET GREECE S.A.—See Munchener Ruckversicherungs AG; *Int'l*, pg. 5089
MEDNET HOLDING GMBH—See Munchener Ruckversicherungs AG; *Int'l*, pg. 5089
MEDNET SOLUTIONS, INC.; *U.S. Private*, pg. 2658
MEDNET S.R.O.—See Fresenius SE & Co. KGaA; *Int'l*, pg. 2780
MEDNET TECHNOLOGIES, INC.—See Advice Media LLC; *U.S. Private*, pg. 110
MEDNET UAE FZ L.L.C.—See Munchener Ruckversicherungs AG; *Int'l*, pg. 5089
MEDO INDUSTRIES CO., LTD.—See NITTO KOHKI Co., Ltd.; *Int'l*, pg. 5388
MEDONDO AG—See medondo Holding AG; *Int'l*, pg. 4785
MEDONDO HOLDING AG; *Int'l*, pg. 4785
MED ONE CAPITAL INCORPORATED; *U.S. Private*, pg. 2650
MEDOPTIONS, INC.; *U.S. Private*, pg. 2658
MEDORA HOTELS & RESORTS LTD.; *Int'l*, pg. 4785
MEDOS AG—See Ortivus AB; *Int'l*, pg. 5644
MEDOS INTERNATIONAL SARL—See Johnson & Johnson; *U.S. Public*, pg. 1199
MEDOS MEDIZINTECHNIK AG—See Vorndran Mannheims Capital Advisors GmbH; *Int'l*, pg. 8307
MEDOSWEET FARMS INC.; *U.S. Private*, pg. 2658
MEDOTECH CO., LTD.—See NITTO KOHKI Co.; *Int'l*, pg. 5388
MEDO USA, INC.—See NITTO KOHKI Co., Ltd.; *Int'l*, pg. 5388
MEDOVATIONS, INC.; *U.S. Private*, pg. 2658
MEDPACE AUSTRALIA PTY. LTD.—See Cinven Limited; *Int'l*, pg. 1612
MEDPACE BELGIUM BVBA—See Cinven Limited; *Int'l*, pg. 1612
MEDPACE BRAZIL LTDA.—See Cinven Limited; *Int'l*, pg. 1612
MEDPACE CLINICAL PHARMACOLOGY LLC—See Medpace Holdings, Inc.; *U.S. Public*, pg. 1414
MEDPACE CLINICAL RESEARCH INDIA PVT. LTD.—See Cinven Limited; *Int'l*, pg. 1612
MEDPACE EUROPE B.V.—See Cinven Limited; *Int'l*, pg. 1612
MEDPACE GERMANY GMBH—See Cinven Limited; *Int'l*, pg. 1612
MEDPACE HOLDINGS, INC.; *U.S. Public*, pg. 1414
MEDPACE HONG KONG LTD.—See Cinven Limited; *Int'l*, pg. 1612
MEDPACE HUNGARY KFT.—See Cinven Limited; *Int'l*, pg. 1612
MEDPACE, INC.—See Cinven Limited; *Int'l*, pg. 1612
MEDPACE ITALY SRL—See Cinven Limited; *Int'l*, pg. 1612
MEDPACE REFERENCE LABORATORIES LLC—See Cinven Limited; *Int'l*, pg. 1612
MEDPACE RUSSIA LLC—See Cinven Limited; *Int'l*, pg. 1612
MEDPACE SOUTH AFRICA PTY. LTD.—See Cinven Limited; *Int'l*, pg. 1612
MEDPACE TAIWAN LTD.—See Cinven Limited; *Int'l*, pg. 1612
MED PACKAGING SARL—See International Paper Company; *U.S. Public*, pg. 1157
MEDPACTO INC.; *Int'l*, pg. 4785
MEDPAGES INTERNATIONAL PROPRIETARY LIMITED—See IQVIA Holdings Inc.; *U.S. Public*, pg. 1170
MEDPAGE TODAY, LLC—See Ziff Davis, Inc.; *U.S. Public*, pg. 2404
MED PAPER SA; *Int'l*, pg. 4767
MEDPARTNERS HIM, LLC—See AMN Healthcare Services, Inc.; *U.S. Public*, pg. 125
MEDPASS INTERNATIONAL SAS—See ICON plc; *Int'l*, pg. 3585
MEDPEER, INC.; *Int'l*, pg. 4785
MED-PHARMEX, INC.—See EQT AB; *Int'l*, pg. 2475
MEDPHARMICS, LLC—See GHO Capital Partners LLP; *Int'l*, pg. 2959
MEDPLEX OUTPATIENT SURGERY CENTER, LTD.—See Tenet Healthcare Corporation; *U.S. Public*, pg. 2008
MEDPLUS HEALTH SERVICES LIMITED; *Int'l*, pg. 4785
MEDPRICER.COM, INC.—See Premier, Inc.; *U.S. Public*, pg. 1715
MEDPRIN REGENERATIVE MEDICAL TECHNOLOGIES CO., LTD.; *Int'l*, pg. 4785
MEDPRO GROUP INC—See Berkshire Hathaway Inc.; *U.S. Public*, pg. 312
MEDPROPERTIES HOLDINGS, LLC; *U.S. Private*, pg. 2658
MEDPRO TECHNOLOGIES, LLC—See Bristol Bay Native Corporation; *U.S. Private*, pg. 656
MEDQUIMECA INDUSTRIA FARMACEUTICA LTDA—See Lupin Limited; *Int'l*, pg. 4586
MEDQUIMICA INDUSTRIA FARMACEUTICA LTDA.—See Lupin Limited; *Int'l*, pg. 4586
MEDRA CORP.; *Int'l*, pg. 4785
MEDRAVE SOFTWARE AB—See Carasent ASA; *Int'l*, pg. 1319
MEDRAVE SOFTWARE AS—See Carasent ASA; *Int'l*, pg. 1319
MEDRECS, INC.—See U.S. Legal Support, Inc.; *U.S. Private*, pg. 4271
MEDREICH LIMITED—See Meiji Holdings Co., Ltd.; *Int'l*, pg. 4800
MEDRISK, LLC—See The Carlyle Group Inc.; *U.S. Public*, pg. 2049
MEDRON, LLC—See New Mountain Capital, LLC; *U.S. Private*, pg. 2902
MEDRX CO., LTD.; *Int'l*, pg. 4785
MEDRX USA INC.—See MEDRx Co., Ltd.; *Int'l*, pg. 4785
MEDSANA SRL—See Athens Medical Centers SA; *Int'l*, pg. 670
MEDSCAN TERMINAL COMPANY LIMITED—See Saudi Company For Hardware SJSC; *Int'l*, pg. 6593
MEDSCAPE, LLC—See KKR & Co. Inc.; *U.S. Public*, pg. 1254
MEDSCI HEALTHCARE HOLDINGS LIMITED; *Int'l*, pg. 4785
MEDSCRIBE INFORMATION SYSTEMS, INC.; *U.S. Private*, pg. 2658
MEDSERV KFT.—See Eurofins Scientific S.E.; *Int'l*, pg. 2551
MEDSERV P.L.C.; *Int'l*, pg. 4785
MEDSHOP GARDEN PHARMACY LLC—See Aster DM Healthcare Ltd.; *Int'l*, pg. 654
MEDSHOP SINGAPORE PTE. LTD.—See Bunzl plc; *Int'l*, pg. 1219
MEDSIGN INTERNATIONAL CORPORATION; *U.S. Private*, pg. 2658
MEDSMART GROUP INC.; *Int'l*, pg. 4786
MEDSN, INC—See Indegene Lifesystems Pvt. Ltd.; *Int'l*, pg. 3649
MEDSOLAR S.P.A.—See Meridie S.p.A.; *Int'l*, pg. 4836
MEDSOLL CYPRUS LTD—See Biotronik GmbH & Co.; *Int'l*, pg. 1044
MEDSOURCE; *U.S. Private*, pg. 2658
MEDSOURCE TECHNOLOGIES, LLC—See Integer Holdings Corporation; *U.S. Public*, pg. 1135
MEDSOURCE UK LTD.—See Permira Advisers LLP; *Int'l*, pg. 5804
MEDSPHERE SYSTEMS CORP.; *U.S. Private*, pg. 2658
MEDSTAFF, INC.; *U.S. Private*, pg. 2658
MED-STAFF, INC.—See Cross Country Healthcare, Inc.; *U.S. Public*, pg. 595
MEDSTAR HEALTH; *U.S. Private*, pg. 2659
MED STAR SURGICAL & BREATHING EQUIPMENT, INC.; *U.S. Private*, pg. 2650
MEDSTAT, LLC—See Community Health Systems, Inc.; *U.S. Public*, pg. 554
MED-STAT USA LLC; *U.S. Private*, pg. 2650
MEDSTREAM ANESTHESIA PLLC—See Assured Guaranty Ltd.; *Int'l*, pg. 650
MEDSTREAMING, LLC; *U.S. Private*, pg. 2659
MEDSURGE ADVANCES—See MedSurge Holdings, Inc.; *U.S. Private*, pg. 2659
MEDSURGE HOLDINGS, INC.; *U.S. Private*, pg. 2659
MEDSYNERGIES, INC.—See UnitedHealth Group Incorporated; *U.S. Public*, pg. 2248
MEDSYNERGIES NORTH TEXAS, INC.—See UnitedHealth Group Incorporated; *U.S. Public*, pg. 2242
MEDSYS GROUP CONSULTING; *U.S. Private*, pg. 2659
MED SYSTEMS ASSOCIATES LP; *U.S. Private*, pg. 2650
MEDTEC AMBULANCE CORP.—See Oshkosh Corporation; *U.S. Public*, pg. 1621
MEDTECH GLOBAL LIMITED; *Int'l*, pg. 4786
MEDTECH HOLDINGS, INC.—See Prestige Consumer Healthcare Inc.; *U.S. Public*, pg. 1716
MEDTECH LTD.—See Medtech Global Limited; *Int'l*, pg. 4786
MEDTECH SA—See Zimmer Biomet Holdings, Inc.; *U.S. Public*, pg. 2406
MEDTECH SERVICES OF DADE, INC.—See Apollo Global Management, Inc.; *U.S. Public*, pg. 157
MED TECH SERVICES OF PALM BEACH, INC.—See Apollo Global Management, Inc.; *U.S. Public*, pg. 157
MED. TECH. SERVICES OF SOUTH FLORIDA, INC.—See Apollo Global Management, Inc.; *U.S. Public*, pg. 157
MED TECH SOLUTIONS; *U.S. Private*, pg. 2650
MEDTECH SURGICAL, INC.—See Zimmer Biomet Holdings, Inc.; *U.S. Public*, pg. 2406
MEDTEC, INC.—See Roper Technologies, Inc.; *U.S. Public*, pg. 1812
MEDTECS (ASIA PACIFIC) PTD. LTD.—See Medtecs International Corporation Limited; *Int'l*, pg. 4786
MEDTECS (CAMBODIA) CORPORATION LIMITED—See Medtecs International Corporation Limited; *Int'l*, pg. 4786
MEDTECS INTERNATIONAL CORPORATION LIMITED; *Int'l*, pg. 4786
MEDTECS (TAIWAN) CORPORATION—See Medtecs International Corporation Limited; *Int'l*, pg. 4786
MEDTEK DEVICES, INC.—See Madison Industries Holdings LLC; *U.S. Private*, pg. 2543
MEDTEK MEDIZINTECHNIK GMBH—See SOL S.p.A.; *Int'l*, pg. 7067
MED-TEL.COM INC; *U.S. Private*, pg. 2650
MEDTELL LTD—See MedTel Services, LLC; *U.S. Private*, pg. 2659
MEDTEL PTY. LTD.; *Int'l*, pg. 4786
MEDTEL SERVICES, LLC; *U.S. Private*, pg. 2659
MEDTEST DX, INC.; *U.S. Private*, pg. 2659
MEDTEX CORPORATION—See Medtecs International Corporation Limited; *Int'l*, pg. 4786
MEDTEXX MANUFACTURING SDN. BHD.—See Semperit AG Holding; *Int'l*, pg. 6706
MEDTHINK COMMUNICATIONS; *U.S. Private*, pg. 2659
MEDTON LTD.—See Demant A/S; *Int'l*, pg. 2024
MEDTOUCH LLC—See EQT AB; *Int'l*, pg. 2483
MEDTOX DIAGNOSTICS, INC.—See Laboratory Corporation of America Holdings; *U.S. Public*, pg. 1287
MEDTOX LABORATORIES, INC.—See Laboratory Corporation of America Holdings; *U.S. Public*, pg. 1287
MEDTOX SCIENTIFIC, INC.—See Laboratory Corporation of America Holdings; *U.S. Public*, pg. 1287
MEDTRAK SERVICES, LLC—See New Rite Aid, LLC; *U.S. Private*, pg. 2905
MEDTRAN DIRECT, INC.—See Leonard Green & Partners, L.P.; *U.S. Private*, pg. 2430
MEDTRAN DIRECT, INC.—See TPG Capital, L.P.; *U.S. Public*, pg. 2177
MED-TRANS CORPORATION—See KKR & Co. Inc.; *U.S. Public*, pg. 1252
MED TRENDS, INC.; *U.S. Private*, pg. 2650
MEDTRONIC ABLATION FRONTIERS LLC—See Medtronic plc; *Int'l*, pg. 4788
MEDTRONIC ADRIATIC D.O.O—See Medtronic plc; *Int'l*, pg. 4788
MEDTRONIC ADVANCED ENERGY LLC—See Medtronic plc; *Int'l*, pg. 4788
MEDTRONIC (AFRICA) (PROPRIETARY) LIMITED—See Medtronic plc; *Int'l*, pg. 4788

MED TRENDS, INC.

MEDTRONIC AG—See Medtronic plc; *Int'l*, pg. 4788
MEDTRONIC AKTIEBOLAG—See Medtronic plc; *Int'l*, pg. 4789
MEDTRONIC A/S—See Medtronic plc; *Int'l*, pg. 4788
MEDTRONIC AUSTRALASIA PTY. LTD.—See Medtronic plc; *Int'l*, pg. 4788
MEDTRONIC BAKKEN RESEARCH CENTER B.V.—See Medtronic plc; *Int'l*, pg. 4788
MEDTRONIC BANGLADESH PVT. LTD.—See Medtronic plc; *Int'l*, pg. 4788
MEDTRONIC BELGIUM S.A./N.V.—See Medtronic plc; *Int'l*, pg. 4789
MEDTRONIC B.V.—See Medtronic plc; *Int'l*, pg. 4789
MEDTRONIC CARDIAC RHYTHM & HEART FAILURE MANAGEMENT—See Medtronic plc; *Int'l*, pg. 4788
MEDTRONIC CARE MANAGEMENT SERVICES, LLC—See Medtronic plc; *Int'l*, pg. 4788
MEDTRONIC CHILE SPA—See Medtronic plc; *Int'l*, pg. 4788
MEDTRONIC CHINA KANGHUI HOLDINGS—See Medtronic plc; *Int'l*, pg. 4788
MEDTRONIC COMERCIAL LTDA.—See Medtronic plc; *Int'l*, pg. 4788
MEDTRONIC CZECHIA S.R.O.—See Medtronic plc; *Int'l*, pg. 4789
MEDTRONIC DANMARK A/S—See Medtronic plc; *Int'l*, pg. 4789
MEDTRONIC ENERGY & COMPONENT CENTER—See Medtronic plc; *Int'l*, pg. 4788
MEDTRONIC ENGINEERING & INNOVATION CENTER PRIVATE LIMITED—See Medtronic plc; *Int'l*, pg. 4788
MEDTRONIC EUROPE SARL—See Medtronic plc; *Int'l*, pg. 4788
MEDTRONIC FINLAND OY—See Medtronic plc; *Int'l*, pg. 4789
MEDTRONIC FRANCE S.A.S.—See Medtronic plc; *Int'l*, pg. 4789
MEDTRONIC G.M.B.H.—See Medtronic plc; *Int'l*, pg. 4789
MEDTRONIC HOLDING B.V.—See Medtronic plc; *Int'l*, pg. 4788
MEDTRONIC HONG KONG MEDICAL LIMITED—See Medtronic plc; *Int'l*, pg. 4787
MEDTRONIC HUNGARIA KERESKEDELMI KFT—See Medtronic plc; *Int'l*, pg. 4789
MEDTRONIC IBERICA S.A.—See Medtronic plc; *Int'l*, pg. 4789
MEDTRONIC, INC.—See Medtronic plc; *Int'l*, pg. 4788
MEDTRONIC INTERNATIONAL LTD.—See Medtronic plc; *Int'l*, pg. 4788
MEDTRONIC INTERNATIONAL, LTD.—See Medtronic plc; *Int'l*, pg. 4789
MEDTRONIC INTERNATIONAL TECHNOLOGY, INC.—See Medtronic plc; *Int'l*, pg. 4789
MEDTRONIC INTERNATIONAL TRADING SARL—See Medtronic plc; *Int'l*, pg. 4789
MEDTRONIC INTERVENTIONAL VASCULAR INC.—See Medtronic plc; *Int'l*, pg. 4789
MEDTRONIC IRELAND LIMITED—See Medtronic plc; *Int'l*, pg. 4789
MEDTRONIC ISRAEL—See Medtronic plc; *Int'l*, pg. 4789
MEDTRONIC ITALIA S.P.A.—See Medtronic plc; *Int'l*, pg. 4789
MEDTRONIC JAPAN CO., LTD.—See Medtronic plc; *Int'l*, pg. 4789
MEDTRONIC KAZAKHSTAN LIMITED LIABILITY PARTNERSHIP—See Medtronic plc; *Int'l*, pg. 4790
MEDTRONIC KOREA LTD.—See Medtronic plc; *Int'l*, pg. 4789
MEDTRONIC LIMITED—See Medtronic plc; *Int'l*, pg. 4789
MEDTRONIC LOGISTICS LLC—See Medtronic plc; *Int'l*, pg. 4790
MEDTRONIC MEDICAL APPLIANCE TECHNOLOGY & SERVICE (SHANGHAI) CO., LTD.—See Medtronic plc; *Int'l*, pg. 4788
MEDTRONIC MEDIKAL TEKNOLOJILERI SAN. VE TIC. A.S.—See Medtronic plc; *Int'l*, pg. 4788
MEDTRONIC MEDITERRANEAN SAL—See Medtronic plc; *Int'l*, pg. 4790
MEDTRONIC MEXICO S. DE R.L. DE C.V.—See Medtronic plc; *Int'l*, pg. 4790
MEDTRONIC MICROELECTRONICS CENTER—See Medtronic plc; *Int'l*, pg. 4790
MEDTRONIC MINIMED, INC.—See Medtronic plc; *Int'l*, pg. 4790
MEDTRONIC NAVIGATION, INC.—See Medtronic plc; *Int'l*, pg. 4790
MEDTRONIC NEW ZEALAND LIMITED—See Medtronic plc; *Int'l*, pg. 4788
MEDTRONIC NORGE AS—See Medtronic plc; *Int'l*, pg. 4789
MEDTRONIC OESTERREICH G.M.B.H.—See Medtronic plc; *Int'l*, pg. 4789
MEDTRONIC OF CANADA LTD.—See Medtronic plc; *Int'l*, pg. 4790
MEDTRONIC PLC; *Int'l*, pg. 4786
MEDTRONIC POLAND SP. Z O.O.—See Medtronic plc; *Int'l*, pg. 4789
MEDTRONIC PORTUGAL, LDA—See Medtronic plc; *Int'l*, pg. 4789

MEDTRONIC PS MEDICAL, INC.—See Medtronic plc; *Int'l*, pg. 4790
MEDTRONIC PUERTO RICO OPERATIONS CO.—See Medtronic plc; *Int'l*, pg. 4790
MEDTRONIC ROMANIA SRL—See Medtronic plc; *Int'l*, pg. 4788
MEDTRONIC S.A.I.C.—See Medtronic plc; *Int'l*, pg. 4790
MEDTRONIC (SCHWEIZ) AG—See Medtronic plc; *Int'l*, pg. 4788
MEDTRONIC SERBIA D.O.O.—See Medtronic plc; *Int'l*, pg. 4788
MEDTRONIC (SHANGHAI) MANAGEMENT CO. LTD.—See Medtronic plc; *Int'l*, pg. 4788
MEDTRONIC SLOVAKIA S.R.O.—See Medtronic plc; *Int'l*, pg. 4789
MEDTRONIC SOFAMOR DANEK DEGGENDORF GMBH—See Medtronic plc; *Int'l*, pg. 4789
MEDTRONIC SOFAMOR DANEK, INC.—See Medtronic plc; *Int'l*, pg. 4790
MEDTRONIC SOFAMOR DANEK USA, INC.—See Medtronic plc; *Int'l*, pg. 4790
MEDTRONIC SPINE LLC—See Medtronic plc; *Int'l*, pg. 4790
MEDTRONIC (TAIWAN) LTD.—See Medtronic plc; *Int'l*, pg. 4788
MEDTRONIC (THAILAND) LIMITED—See Medtronic plc; *Int'l*, pg. 4788
MEDTRONIC TRADING NL BV—See Medtronic plc; *Int'l*, pg. 4789
MEDTRONIC VASCULAR GALWAY—See Medtronic plc; *Int'l*, pg. 4789
MEDTRONIC VASCULAR—See Medtronic plc; *Int'l*, pg. 4790
MEDTRONIC XOMED, INC.—See Integra LifeSciences Holdings Corporation; *U.S. Public*, pg. 1136
MEDTRONIC XOMED, INC.—See Medtronic plc; *Int'l*, pg. 4790
MEDULLAN, INC.—See ZS Associates, Inc.; *U.S. Private*, pg. 4609
MEDUSA LABS—See Viavi Solutions Inc.; *U.S. Public*, pg. 2295
MED-USE S.R.L.—See GFT Technologies SE; *Int'l*, pg. 2957
MEDUSPLUS GMBH—See Asklepios Kliniken GmbH & Co. KGaA; *Int'l*, pg. 623
MEDUS TECHNOLOGY INC.—See ASUSTeK Computer Inc.; *Int'l*, pg. 664
MEDVAL, LLC—See Brown & Brown, Inc.; *U.S. Public*, pg. 397
MEDVANTX, INC.; *U.S. Private*, pg. 2659
MEDVED AUTOPLEX; *U.S. Private*, pg. 2659
MEDVENTURE TECHNOLOGY CORPORATION—See Freudenberg SE; *Int'l*, pg. 2789
MEDVESEK PUSNIK BORZNO POSREDNISKA HISA D.D. LJUBLJANA—See ALTA Skupina d.d.; *Int'l*, pg. 384
MEDVET BV—See Sonic Healthcare Limited; *Int'l*, pg. 7098
MEDVIEW AIRLINE PLC; *Int'l*, pg. 4790
MEDWAY MEDICAL EQUIPMENT, LLC—See AdaptHealth Corp.; *U.S. Public*, pg. 39
MED WAY MEDICAL, INC.—See AdaptHealth Corp.; *U.S. Public*, pg. 39
MEDWEL, INC.—See Posiflex Technology Inc.; *Int'l*, pg. 5938
MEDWING.COM INC.; *U.S. Private*, pg. 2659
MEDWIRE—See Sigmund Cohn Corp.; *U.S. Private*, pg. 3649
MEDWISH INTERNATIONAL; *U.S. Private*, pg. 2659
MEDWORK GMBH—See FUJIFILM Holdings Corporation; *Int'l*, pg. 2826
MEDXCEL, LLC—See Ascension Health Alliance; *U.S. Private*, pg. 346
MED X CHANGE INC.—See Novanta Inc.; *U.S. Public*, pg. 1548
MEDX ELECTRONICS INC—See MedX Health Corp.; *Int'l*, pg. 4790
MEDX HEALTH CORP.; *Int'l*, pg. 4790
MED-X, INC.; *U.S. Private*, pg. 2650
MEDXPERT HEALTHCARE SSOLUTIONS GMBH—See CompuGroup Medical SE & Co. KGaA; *Int'l*, pg. 1757
MEDX PUBLISHING INC.; *U.S. Private*, pg. 2659
MEDYSSEY CO LTD—See DONG WHA PHARM CO., LTD.; *Int'l*, pg. 2164
MEDYSSEY USA, INC.—See DONG WHA PHARM CO., LTD.; *Int'l*, pg. 2164
MEDYTOX DIAGNOSTICS, INC.—See Rennova Health, Inc.; *U.S. Public*, pg. 1783
MEDY-TOX INC.; *Int'l*, pg. 4790
MEDYTOX KOREA INC.—See Medy-Tox Inc.; *Int'l*, pg. 4790
MEDYTOX (THAILAND) CO., LTD.—See Medy-Tox Inc.; *Int'l*, pg. 4790
MEECA TECHNOLOGY (SUZHOU INDUSTRIAL PARK) CO., LTD.—See Catcher Technology Co., Ltd.; *Int'l*, pg. 1359
MEECA TECHNOLOGY (TAIZHOU) CO., LTD.—See Catcher Technology Co., Ltd.; *Int'l*, pg. 1359
MEEDER EQUIPMENT COMPANY; *U.S. Private*, pg. 2659
MEED MEDIA FZ LLC—See GlobalData Plc; *Int'l*, pg. 3003

CORPORATE AFFILIATIONS

MEE ENTERPRISES INC.; *U.S. Private*, pg. 2659
MEEHAN AUTOMOBILES INC.; *U.S. Private*, pg. 2659
MEE INC.—See Avex Inc.; *Int'l*, pg. 740
MEEKA METALS LIMITED; *Int'l*, pg. 4790
MEEKRONE FISCH-FEINKOST GMBH—See Thai Union Group Public Company Limited; *Int'l*, pg. 7596
MEEK'S, INC.—See Angeles Equity Partners, LLC; *U.S. Private*, pg. 282
MEEK'S, INC.—See Clearlake Capital Group, L.P.; *U.S. Private*, pg. 936
MEEK'S LUMBER COMPANY—See Angeles Equity Partners, LLC; *U.S. Private*, pg. 282
MEEK'S LUMBER COMPANY—See Clearlake Capital Group, L.P.; *U.S. Private*, pg. 936
ME ELECMETAL COMERCIAL PERU S.A.C.—See Compania Electro Metalurgica S.A.; *Int'l*, pg. 1749
MEEMEE MEDIA INC.; *U.S. Public*, pg. 1414
MEEMIC INSURANCE COMPANY—See The American Automobile Association, Inc.; *U.S. Private*, pg. 3985
MEENAKSHI STEEL INDUSTRIES LIMITED; *Int'l*, pg. 4791
MEENAN HOLDINGS LOVE-EFFRON DIVISION—See Star Group, L.P.; *U.S. Public*, pg. 1937
MEENAN HOLDINGS OF NEW YORK, INC.—See Star Group, L.P.; *U.S. Public*, pg. 1937
MEENAN OIL CO., INC.—See Star Group, L.P.; *U.S. Public*, pg. 1938
MEENAN OIL CO., LP—See Star Group, L.P.; *U.S. Public*, pg. 1937
MEENAN OIL PENNSYLVANIA DIVISION—See Star Group, L.P.; *U.S. Public*, pg. 1937
ME ENGINEERING GMBH—See VINCI S.A.; *Int'l*, pg. 8224
M/E ENGINEERING, P.C.; *U.S. Private*, pg. 2529
M-E ENGINEERS, INC.; *U.S. Private*, pg. 2525
MEEPOS & CO.—See CPAmerica, Inc.; *U.S. Private*, pg. 1080
MEERA INDUSTRIES LIMITED; *Int'l*, pg. 4791
MEERANER DAMPFKESSELBAU GMBH—See Mitsubishi Heavy Industries, Ltd.; *Int'l*, pg. 4956
MEERE COMPANY INC.; *Int'l*, pg. 4791
MEERKAT PRECISION SDN. BHD.—See SAM Engineering & Equipment (M) Berhad; *Int'l*, pg. 6500
MEERKRONE FISCH-FEINKOST GMBH—See Thai Union Group Public Company Limited; *Int'l*, pg. 7597
MEERS ADVERTISING; *U.S. Private*, pg. 2659
MEESA DIALYSIS, LLC—See DaVita Inc.; *U.S. Public*, pg. 641
MEES DISTRIBUTORS INC.; *U.S. Private*, pg. 2659
MEESE INC.—See Olympus Partners; *U.S. Private*, pg. 3013
MEESHAA INC.; *U.S. Private*, pg. 2659
MEESPIERSON (CURACAO) N.V.—See ABN AMRO Group N.V.; *Int'l*, pg. 64
MEET GROUP, INC.; *U.S. Public*, pg. 1414
MEETIC SA—See IAC Inc.; *U.S. Public*, pg. 1082
MEETING ALLIANCE, LLC.; *U.S. Private*, pg. 2660
THE MEETINGHOUSE COMPANIES, INC.—See SBR Events Group; *U.S. Private*, pg. 3560
MEETING OF THE MINDS, INC.—See MBH Corporation Plc; *Int'l*, pg. 4752
MEETING PROFESSIONALS INTERNATIONAL (MPI); *U.S. Private*, pg. 2660
MEETING PROFESSIONALS INTERNATIONAL (MPI)—See Meeting Professionals International (MPI); *U.S. Private*, pg. 2660
MEETINGS & EVENTS INTERNATIONAL INC.; *U.S. Private*, pg. 2660
MEETINGS & EVENTS UK LIMITED—See TUI AG; *Int'l*, pg. 7965
MEETINGS & INCENTIVES; *U.S. Private*, pg. 2660
MEETING TOMORROW, INC.; *U.S. Private*, pg. 2660
MEETINGZONE GMBH—See LoopUp Group plc; *Int'l*, pg. 4556
MEETINGZONE LTD.—See LoopUp Group plc; *Int'l*, pg. 4556
MEETIO AB—See Logitech International S.A.; *U.S. Public*, pg. 1341
MEETIO INC.—See Logitech International S.A.; *U.S. Public*, pg. 1341
MEET THE PEOPLE LLC.—See Innovatus Capital Partners LLC; *U.S. Private*, pg. 2083
MEETUP, INC.—See Bending Spoons S.p.A.; *Int'l*, pg. 971
MEETZE PLUMBING CO, INC.—See Ontario Municipal Employees Retirement System; *Int'l*, pg. 5585
MEEZAN BANK LIMITED; *Int'l*, pg. 4791
MEEZ—See Donnerwood Media, Inc.; *U.S. Private*, pg. 1261
MEFCOM CAPITAL MARKETS LTD.; *Int'l*, pg. 4791
MEFIAG B.V.—See CECO Environmental Corp.; *U.S. Public*, pg. 464
MEFIAG USA—See CECO Environmental Corp.; *U.S. Public*, pg. 464
M.E. FIELDS INC.; *U.S. Private*, pg. 2528
MEFIN S.A.; *Int'l*, pg. 4791
MEFRO RADERWERK RONNEBURG GMBH—See Crestview Partners, L.P.; *U.S. Private*, pg. 1097
MEFRO WHEELS CHINA CO., LTD.—See Crestview Partners, L.P.; *U.S. Private*, pg. 1097

COMPANY NAME INDEX

MEFRO WHEELS FRANCE S.A.S.—See Crestview Partners, L.P.; *U.S. Private*, pg. 1098
MEFRO WHEELS PANAMERICA S.A.—See Crestview Partners, L.P.; *U.S. Private*, pg. 1098
MEFRO WHEELS RUSSIA PLANT TOGLIATTI OOO—See Crestview Partners, L.P.; *U.S. Private*, pg. 1098
MEFRO WHEELS TURKEY JANT SANAYI A.S.—See Crestview Partners, L.P.; *U.S. Private*, pg. 1097
MEFRO WHEELS US SERVICES, INC.—See Crestview Partners, L.P.; *U.S. Private*, pg. 1098
MEF S.R.L.—See Wurth Verwaltungsgesellschaft mbH; *Int'l*, pg. 8506
MEGA ALLIANCE BUILDER SUPPLIES SDN. BHD.—See Engtex Group Berhad; *Int'l*, pg. 2436
MEGA ASSET MANAGEMENT CO., LTD.—See Mega Financial Holding Co., Ltd.; *Int'l*, pg. 4791
MEGA BANK NEPAL LIMITED; *Int'l*, pg. 4791
MEGA BILLS FINANCE CO., LTD.—See Mega Financial Holding Co., Ltd.; *Int'l*, pg. 4791
MEGABOX DEVELOPMENT COMPANY LIMITED—See Kerry Group Limited; *Int'l*, pg. 4137
MEGABOX MANAGEMENT SERVICES LIMITED—See Kerry Group Limited; *Int'l*, pg. 4137
MEGA BRANDS AMERICA INC.—See Mattel, Inc.; *U.S. Public*, pg. 1398
MEGA BRANDS AUSTRALIA PTY. LTD.—See Mattel, Inc.; *U.S. Public*, pg. 1398
MEGA BRANDS EUROPE NV—See Mattel, Inc.; *U.S. Public*, pg. 1398
MEGA BRANDS INC.—See Mattel, Inc.; *U.S. Public*, pg. 1398
MEGA BRANDS ITALY SPA—See Mattel, Inc.; *U.S. Public*, pg. 1398
MEGA BRANDS LATINOAMERICA SA DE CV—See Mattel, Inc.; *U.S. Public*, pg. 1398
MEGA BRANDS SPAIN & PORTUGAL SRL—See Mattel, Inc.; *U.S. Public*, pg. 1398
MEGA BRANDS UNITED KINGDOM LTD.—See Mattel, Inc.; *U.S. Public*, pg. 1398
MEGA BROADBAND INVESTMENTS, LLC—See GTCR LLC; *U.S. Private*, pg. 1805
MEGABYTE LTD.—See United Investments Ltd.; *Int'l*, pg. 8070
MEGACABLE HOLDINGS, S. A. B. DE C. V.; *Int'l*, pg. 4793
MEGA CAPITAL (ASIA) CO., LTD—See Mega Financial Holding Co., Ltd.; *Int'l*, pg. 4791
MEGA CENTER MANAGEMENT JSC; *Int'l*, pg. 4791
MEGACHEM AUSTRALIA PTY. LTD.—See Megachem Limited; *Int'l*, pg. 4793
MEGACHEM INTERNATIONAL TRADING (BEIJING) CO. LTD.—See Megachem Limited; *Int'l*, pg. 4793
MEGACHEM INTERNATIONAL TRADING (SHANGHAI) CO., LTD.—See Megachem Limited; *Int'l*, pg. 4793
MEGACHEM LIMITED; *Int'l*, pg. 4793
MEGACHEM MANUFACTURING PTE LTD—See Megachem Limited; *Int'l*, pg. 4793
MEGACHEM MIDDLE EAST FZE—See Megachem Limited; *Int'l*, pg. 4793
MEGACHEM PHILS., INC—See Megachem Limited; *Int'l*, pg. 4793
MEGACHEM (SHANGHAI) PTE. LTD.—See Megachem Limited; *Int'l*, pg. 4793
MEGACHEM SPECIALTY CHEMICALS (I) PRIVATE LIMITED—See Megachem Limited; *Int'l*, pg. 4793
MEGA CHEM (THAILAND) PUBLIC COMPANY LIMITED; *Int'l*, pg. 4791
MEGACHEM (UK) LTD—See Megachem Limited; *Int'l*, pg. 4793
MEGACHEM VIETNAM COMPANY LIMITED—See Megachem Limited; *Int'l*, pg. 4793
MEGACHIPS CORPORATION; *Int'l*, pg. 4793
MEGACHIPS LSI USA CORPORATION—See MegaChips Corporation; *Int'l*, pg. 4793
MEGA CONSTRUCTION CORP. OF NJ; *U.S. Private*, pg. 2660
MEGA COPPER LTD.; *Int'l*, pg. 4791
MEGA CORPORATION LIMITED; *Int'l*, pg. 4791
MEGA CTB VENTURE CAPITAL CO., LTD.—See Mega Financial Holding Co., Ltd.; *Int'l*, pg. 4791
MEGACUBE MINING (PROPRIETARY) LIMITED—See Unicorn Capital Partners Limited; *Int'l*, pg. 8033
MEGA DATATECH LIMITED—See Vodatel Networks Holdings Limited; *Int'l*, pg. 8286
MEGADIAMOND, INC.—See Schlumberger Limited; *U.S. Public*, pg. 1844
MEGADO MINERALS LIMITED; *Int'l*, pg. 4793
MEGADOOR AB—See ASSA ABLOY AB; *Int'l*, pg. 635
MEGADOOR INC.—See ASSA ABLOY AB; *Int'l*, pg. 635
MEGADYNE MEDICAL PRODUCTS INC.—See Johnson & Johnson; *U.S. Public*, pg. 1196
MEGA ENTERTAINMENT & FAIR (HONG KONG) LIMITED—See NOVA Group Holdings Limited; *Int'l*, pg. 5450
MEGAFAB ENGINEERING PTE. LTD.—See Union Steel Holdings Limited; *Int'l*, pg. 8053
MEGA FINANCIAL HOLDING CO., LTD.; *Int'l*, pg. 4791
MEGA FIN (INDIA) LIMITED; *Int'l*, pg. 4791
MEGA FIRST CORPORATION BERHAD; *Int'l*, pg. 4792

MEGA FIRST HOUSING DEVELOPMENT SDN. BHD.—See Mega First Corporation Berhad; *Int'l*, pg. 4792
MEGA FIRST POWER INDUSTRIES SDN. BHD.—See Mega First Corporation Berhad; *Int'l*, pg. 4792
MEGA FIRST POWER SERVICES SDN. BHD.—See Mega First Corporation Berhad; *Int'l*, pg. 4792
MEGA GENOMICS LIMITED; *Int'l*, pg. 4792
MEGAH CAPITAL SDN. BHD.—See Gamuda Berhad; *Int'l*, pg. 2879
MEGA HERTZ TECHNOLOGIES SDN. BHD.—See Aiphone Co., Ltd.; *Int'l*, pg. 235
MEGA HINDMARSH PTY LTD—See Mega Uranium Ltd.; *Int'l*, pg. 4793
MEGAH MANAGEMENT SERVICES SDN. BHD.—See Gamuda Berhad; *Int'l*, pg. 2879
MEGA HOME CENTER COMPANY LIMITED—See Home Product Center Public Company Limited; *Int'l*, pg. 3455
MEGA HOME CO., LTD.—See Home Product Center Public Company Limited; *Int'l*, pg. 3455
MEGAHOUSE CORPORATION—See BANDAI NAMCO Holdings Inc.; *Int'l*, pg. 829
MEGAH PORT MANAGEMENT SDN. BHD.; *Int'l*, pg. 4793
MEGAH SEWA SDN. BHD.—See Gamuda Berhad; *Int'l*, pg. 2879
MEGAHUB LEHRTE BETREIBERGESELLSCHAFT MBH—See Deutsche Bahn AG; *Int'l*, pg. 2052
MEGAHUNT TECHNOLOGIES INC.—See Hi Sun Technology (China) Limited; *Int'l*, pg. 3380
MEGA IMAGE SRL—See Koninklijke Ahold Delhaize N.V.; *Int'l*, pg. 4261
MEGA-INFO MEDIA CO., LTD.; *Int'l*, pg. 4793
MEGAIN HOLDING (CAYMAN) CO., LTD.; *Int'l*, pg. 4793
MEGA INTERNATIONAL COMMERCIAL BANK (CANADA)—See Mega Financial Holding Co., Ltd.; *Int'l*, pg. 4791
MEGA INTERNATIONAL COMMERCIAL BANK CO., LTD.—See Mega Financial Holding Co., Ltd.; *Int'l*, pg. 4791
MEGA INTERNATIONAL COMMERCIAL BANK PUBLIC CO., LTD.—See Mega Financial Holding Co., Ltd.; *Int'l*, pg. 4792
MEGA INTERNATIONAL DEVELOPMENT CO LTD; *Int'l*, pg. 4792
MEGA INTERNATIONAL INVESTMENT TRUST CO., LTD.—See Mega Financial Holding Co., Ltd.; *Int'l*, pg. 4792
MEGA INTERNATIONAL RESOURCES COMPANY LIMITED—See Lee Kee Holdings Limited; *Int'l*, pg. 4440
MEGA INTERNATIONAL S.A.; *Int'l*, pg. 4792
MEGA JOHNSONS VINA DEL MAR S.A.—See Cencosud S.A.; *Int'l*, pg. 1401
MEGA LABEL (MALAYSIA) SDN. BHD.—See PCCS Group Berhad; *Int'l*, pg. 5767
MEGA LABELS & STICKERS SDN. BHD.—See PCCS Group Berhad; *Int'l*, pg. 5767
MEGALABS—See PJSC Megafon; *Int'l*, pg. 5882
MEGAL A.D.; *Int'l*, pg. 4793
THE MEGA LIFE AND HEALTH INSURANCE COMPANY—See Blackstone Inc.; *U.S. Public*, pg. 354
MEGA LIFE INSURANCE AGENCY CO., LTD.—See Mega Financial Holding Co., Ltd.; *Int'l*, pg. 4792
MEGA LIFESCIENCES (AUSTRALIA) PTY. LIMITED—See Mega Lifesciences Public Company Limited; *Int'l*, pg. 4792
MEGA LIFESCIENCES PTY. LIMITED—See Mega Lifesciences Public Company Limited; *Int'l*, pg. 4792
MEGA LIFESCIENCES PUBLIC COMPANY LIMITED; *Int'l*, pg. 4792
MEGA LIFESCIENCES SDN. BHD.—See Mega Lifesciences Public Company Limited; *Int'l*, pg. 4792
MEGALIFT PTY LTD—See Lampson International, LLC; *U.S. Private*, pg. 2381
MEGALITH PHARMACEUTICALS INC.—See CSPC Pharmaceutical Group Limited; *Int'l*, pg. 1867
MEGALIT SUMNIK A.D.; *Int'l*, pg. 4793
MEGAL MITTEL-EUROPAISCHE-GASLEITUNGSGESELLSCHAFT MBH & CO. KG—See British Columbia Investment Management Corp.; *Int'l*, pg. 1169
MEGAL MITTEL-EUROPAISCHE-GASLEITUNGSGESELLSCHAFT MBH & CO. KG—See ENGIE SA; *Int'l*, pg. 2431
MEGAL MITTEL-EUROPAISCHE-GASLEITUNGSGESELLSCHAFT MBH & CO. KG—See Macquarie Group Limited; *Int'l*, pg. 4626
MEGALOS CO., LTD.—See Nomura Real Estate Holdings, Inc.; *Int'l*, pg. 5412
MEGAL VERWALTUNGS-GMBH—See E.ON SE; *Int'l*, pg. 2258
MEGA MANUFACTURING INC. - BERTSCH DIVISION—See Mega Manufacturing Inc.; *U.S. Private*, pg. 2660
MEGA MANUFACTURING INC.; *U.S. Private*, pg. 2660
MEGA MANUFACTURING INC. - WHITNEY DIVISION—See Mega Manufacturing Inc.; *U.S. Private*, pg. 2660

MEGA MATRIX CORP.; *U.S. Public*, pg. 1414
MEGAMD CO., LTD.—See Megastudy Co., Ltd.; *Int'l*, pg. 4794
MEGAMEIOS - PUBLICIDADE E MEIOS, A.C.E.—See The Interpublic Group of Companies, Inc.; *U.S. Public*, pg. 2103
MEGA METALS, INC.—See Audax Group, Limited Partnership; *U.S. Private*, pg. 390
MEGAMET INDUSTRIES, INC.—See ASSA ABLOY AB; *Int'l*, pg. 640
MEGAMEX FOODS, LLC—See Grupo Herdez, S.A.B. de C.V.; *Int'l*, pg. 3130
MEGAMEX FOODS, LLC—See Hormel Foods Corporation; *U.S. Public*, pg. 1054
MEGA MEX, L.P.; *U.S. Private*, pg. 2660
MEGAMIC ELECTRONICS PRIVATE LIMITED—See Refex Renewables & Infrastructure Limited; *Int'l*, pg. 6250
MEGAMIX (PROPRIETARY) LIMITED—See ARGENT INDUSTRIAL LIMITED; *Int'l*, pg. 560
MEGAMOBILE INC.—See Millennium Global Holdings, Inc.; *Int'l*, pg. 4896
MEGA NA, INC.—See MEGA International S.A.; *Int'l*, pg. 4792
MEGAN DRISCOLL, LLC; *U.S. Private*, pg. 2660
MEGANESUPER CO., LTD.; *Int'l*, pg. 4794
MEGANET CORPORATION; *U.S. Public*, pg. 1414
MEGANET D. O. O.—See Telekom Slovenije, d.d.; *Int'l*, pg. 7538
MEGA NIRMAN & INDUSTRIES LIMITED; *Int'l*, pg. 4792
MEGANTIC METAL—See Russel Metals Inc.; *Int'l*, pg. 6430
MEGA OR HOLDINGS LTD.; *Int'l*, pg. 4792
MEGA PACIFIC NZ PTY. LTD.—See Interpump Group S.p.A.; *Int'l*, pg. 3756
MEGA PACIFIC PTY. LTD.—See Interpump Group S.p.A.; *Int'l*, pg. 3756
MEGA PAK ZIMBABWE (PVT) LTD—See Delta Corporation Limited; *Int'l*, pg. 2016
MEGAPHARM GMBH PHARMAZEUTISCHE ERZEUGNISSE—See Walgreens Boots Alliance, Inc.; *U.S. Public*, pg. 2322
MEGAPHONE, LLC—See Spotify Technology S.A.; *Int'l*, pg. 7143
MEGAPLAS ITALIA, S.P.A.—See Fomento de Construcciones y Contratas, S.A.; *Int'l*, pg. 2723
MEGAPLAS, S.A.—See Fomento de Construcciones y Contratas, S.A.; *Int'l*, pg. 2723
MEGAPOLITAN MANAGEMENT SERVICES SDN. BHD.—See Insas Berhad; *Int'l*, pg. 3718
MEGAPORT LIMITED; *Int'l*, pg. 4794
MEGA POWER CO., LTD.—See Lu Hai Holding Corp.; *Int'l*, pg. 4571
MEGAPRO MARKETING (PTY) LTD—See Primedia Limited; *Int'l*, pg. 5978
MEGARON S.A.; *Int'l*, pg. 4794
MEGASA SIDERURGICA S.L.—See Bipadosa SA; *Int'l*, pg. 1045
MEGA SECURITIES CO., LTD.—See Mega Financial Holding Co., Ltd.; *Int'l*, pg. 4792
MEGASEN CO., LTD.—See TSE Co., Ltd.; *Int'l*, pg. 7949
MEGASERWIS SP. Z O.O.—See PGE Polska Grupa Energetyczna S.A.; *Int'l*, pg. 5837
MEGASIDER ZARAGOZA S.A.U.—See Bipadosa SA; *Int'l*, pg. 1045
MEGAS, INC.; *U.S. Private*, pg. 2660
MEGASOFT CONSULTANTS PTE LTD—See Megasoft Ltd.; *Int'l*, pg. 4794
MEGASOFT CONSULTANTS SDN BHD—See Megasoft Ltd.; *Int'l*, pg. 4794
MEGASOFT LTD.; *Int'l*, pg. 4794
MEGA SPIELGERATE ENTWICKLUNGS- UND VERTRIEBSGESELLSCHAFT MBH & CO. KG—See Gauselmann AG; *Int'l*, pg. 2890
MEGA SPORTS CO., LTD—See AEON Co., Ltd.; *Int'l*, pg. 178
MEGA SPRINT GUARD S.A.; *Int'l*, pg. 4793
MEGASTAR FOODS LIMITED; *Int'l*, pg. 4794
MEGASTRENGTH SECURITY SERVICES COMPANY LIMITED—See Henderson Land Development Co. Ltd.; *Int'l*, pg. 3345
MEGASTUDY CO., LTD.; *Int'l*, pg. 4794
MEGASTUDYEDU CO., LTD.—See Megastudy Co., Ltd.; *Int'l*, pg. 4794
MEGATECH A.Q. INC.—See MiddleGround Management, LP; *U.S. Private*, pg. 2712
MEGATECH CORPORATION; *U.S. Public*, pg. 1414
MEGATECH SCIENTIFIC PTE. LTD.; *Int'l*, pg. 4794
MEGATOUCH CO., LTD.—See TSE Co., Ltd.; *Int'l*, pg. 7949
MEGATRAN INDUSTRIES INC.—See American Superconductor Corporation; *U.S. Public*, pg. 110
MEGATRAX PRODUCTION MUSIC, INC.; *U.S. Private*, pg. 2660
MEGATREND D.O.O. SARAJEVO—See ASBISc Enterprises Plc; *Int'l*, pg. 600
MEGATRON ELECTRONICS & CONTROLS LTD—See MEGATRON Elektronik AG & Co.; *Int'l*, pg. 4794
MEGATRON ELEKTRONIK AG & CO.; *Int'l*, pg. 4794

MEGATRON ELEKTRONIK AG & CO. CORPORATE AFFILIATIONS

MEGATRON HOLDINGS (PTY) LTD.—See Ellies Holdings Limited; *Int'l*, pg. 2366
MEGATRON S.A.R.L.—See MEGATRON Elektronik AG & Co.; *Int'l*, pg. 4794
MEGATRON S.R.O.—See MEGATRON Elektronik AG & Co.; *Int'l*, pg. 4794
MEGA URANIUM LTD.; *Int'l*, pg. 4793
MEGA VENTURE CAPITAL CO., LTD.—See Mega Financial Holding Co., Ltd.; *Int'l*, pg. 4792
MEGA VIEW DIGITAL ENTERTAINMENT CORP.; *Int'l*, pg. 4793
MEGA-VISION PICTURES LIMITED—See Emperor Culture Group Limited; *Int'l*, pg. 2386
MEGAWATT LITHIUM AND BATTERY METALS CORP.; *Int'l*, pg. 4794
MEGAWELL GROUP CO. LTD.—See Texwinca Holdings Limited; *Int'l*, pg. 7584
MEGAWIDE CONSTRUCTION CORPORATION; *Int'l*, pg. 4794
MEGAWIN TECHNOLOGY CO., LTD.; *Int'l*, pg. 4794
MEGAWIN TECHNOLOGY (SHENZHEN) CO., LTD.—See Megawin Technology Co., Ltd.; *Int'l*, pg. 4794
MEGAWORLD CORPORATION—See Alliance Global Group, Inc.; *Int'l*, pg. 339
MEGAZEC SP. Z O.O.—See PGE Polska Grupa Energetyczna S.A.; *Int'l*, pg. 5837
MEGAZYME, LTD.—See Neogen Corporation; *U.S. Public*, pg. 1505
THE MEG & BENNETT GOODMAN FAMILY FOUNDATION; *U.S. Private*, pg. 4077
MEG ENERGY CORP.; *Int'l*, pg. 4791
MEGGER CANADA LTD.—See Megger Group Limited; *Int'l*, pg. 4795
MEGGER CHINA—See Megger Group Limited; *Int'l*, pg. 4795
MEGGER ESPANA—See Megger Group Limited; *Int'l*, pg. 4795
MEGGER GMBH—See Megger Group Limited; *Int'l*, pg. 4795
MEGGER GROUP LIMITED; *Int'l*, pg. 4794
MEGGER HONG KONG LIMITED—See Megger Group Limited; *Int'l*, pg. 4795
MEGGER (INDIA) PVT LIMITED—See Megger Group Limited; *Int'l*, pg. 4795
MEGGER INDONESIA—See Megger Group Limited; *Int'l*, pg. 4795
MEGGER INSTRUMENTS LIMITED—See Megger Group Limited; *Int'l*, pg. 4795
MEGGER LIMITED—See Megger Group Limited; *Int'l*, pg. 4795
MEGGER MANAMA—See Megger Group Limited; *Int'l*, pg. 4795
MEGGER MIDDLE EAST—See Megger Group Limited; *Int'l*, pg. 4795
MEGGER PAKISTAN LIMITED—See Megger Group Limited; *Int'l*, pg. 4795
MEGGER PTY LIMITED—See Megger Group Limited; *Int'l*, pg. 4795
MEGGER SA—See Megger Group Limited; *Int'l*, pg. 4795
MEGGER SOUTH AFRICA—See Megger Group Limited; *Int'l*, pg. 4795
MEGGER SWEDEN AB—See Megger Group Limited; *Int'l*, pg. 4795
MEGGITT ADVANCED COMPOSITES LTD.—See Parker Hannifin Corporation; *U.S. Public*, pg. 1641
MEGGITT AEROSPACE ASIA PACIFIC PTE LIMITED—See Parker Hannifin Corporation; *U.S. Public*, pg. 1641
MEGGITT AEROSPACE LIMITED—See Parker Hannifin Corporation; *U.S. Public*, pg. 1642
MEGGITT AIRCRAFT BRAKING SYSTEMS CORPORATION - DANVILLE FACILITY—See Parker Hannifin Corporation; *U.S. Public*, pg. 1642
MEGGITT AIRCRAFT BRAKING SYSTEMS CORPORATION—See Parker Hannifin Corporation; *U.S. Public*, pg. 1642
MEGGITT AIRDYNAMICS, INC.—See Parker Hannifin Corporation; *U.S. Public*, pg. 1642
MEGGITT AVIONICS—See Parker Hannifin Corporation; *U.S. Public*, pg. 1642
MEGGITT AVIONICS—See Parker Hannifin Corporation; *U.S. Public*, pg. 1642
MEGGITT (BALTIMORE) INC.—See Parker Hannifin Corporation; *U.S. Public*, pg. 1641
MEGGITT CONTROL SYSTEMS - SAN DIEGO—See Parker Hannifin Corporation; *U.S. Public*, pg. 1642
MEGGITT CONTROL SYSTEMS—See Parker Hannifin Corporation; *U.S. Public*, pg. 1642
MEGGITT DEFENCE SYSTEMS LTD.—See Parker Hannifin Corporation; *U.S. Public*, pg. 1642
MEGGITT DEFENSE SYSTEMS, INC.—See Parker Hannifin Corporation; *U.S. Public*, pg. 1642
MEGGITT DEFENSE SYSTEMS—See Parker Hannifin Corporation; *U.S. Public*, pg. 1642
MEGGITT DEFENSE SYSTEMS—See Parker Hannifin Corporation; *U.S. Public*, pg. 1642
MEGGITT (FRANCE) SAS—See Parker Hannifin Corporation; *U.S. Public*, pg. 1641

MEGGITT INDIA PVT LTD—See Parker Hannifin Corporation; *U.S. Public*, pg. 1642
MEGGITT (NEW HAMPSHIRE), INC—See Parker Hannifin Corporation; *U.S. Public*, pg. 1642
MEGGITT (NORTH HOLLYWOOD), INC.—See Parker Hannifin Corporation; *U.S. Public*, pg. 1642
MEGGITT (ORANGE COUNTY), INC.—See Amphenol Corporation; *U.S. Public*, pg. 131
MEGGITT PLC - ANGOULEME FACILITY—See Parker Hannifin Corporation; *U.S. Public*, pg. 1642
MEGGITT PLC - ARCHAMPS FACILITY—See Parker Hannifin Corporation; *U.S. Public*, pg. 1642
MEGGITT PLC - BASINGSTOKE FACILITY—See Parker Hannifin Corporation; *U.S. Public*, pg. 1642
MEGGITT PLC - FRIBOURG FACILITY—See Parker Hannifin Corporation; *U.S. Public*, pg. 1642
MEGGITT PLC - HCL - MEGGITT ODC FACTORY—See Parker Hannifin Corporation; *U.S. Public*, pg. 1642
MEGGITT PLC - KVISTGAARD FACILITY—See Parker Hannifin Corporation; *U.S. Public*, pg. 1642
MEGGITT PLC - MEGGITT SHANGHAI FACILITY—See Parker Hannifin Corporation; *U.S. Public*, pg. 1642
MEGGITT PLC - RUGBY FACILITY—See Parker Hannifin Corporation; *U.S. Public*, pg. 1642
MEGGITT PLC—See Parker Hannifin Corporation; *U.S. Public*, pg. 1641
MEGGITT POLYMER SOLUTIONS—See Parker Hannifin Corporation; *U.S. Public*, pg. 1641
MEGGITT (ROCKMART), INC.—See Parker Hannifin Corporation; *U.S. Public*, pg. 1642
MEGGITT SAFETY SYSTEMS, INC.—See Parker Hannifin Corporation; *U.S. Public*, pg. 1642
MEGGITT SA—See Parker Hannifin Corporation; *U.S. Public*, pg. 1642
MEGGITT (SENSOREX) SAS—See Parker Hannifin Corporation; *U.S. Public*, pg. 1641
MEGGITT-USA HOLDINGS LLC—See Parker Hannifin Corporation; *U.S. Public*, pg. 1642
MEGGITT-USA, INC. - GERMANTOWN FACILITY—See Parker Hannifin Corporation; *U.S. Public*, pg. 1642
MEGGITT-USA, INC.—See Parker Hannifin Corporation; *U.S. Public*, pg. 1642
MEGGITT (XIAMEN) SENSORS & CONTROLS CO LIMITED—See Parker Hannifin Corporation; *U.S. Public*, pg. 1641
MEGHE GROUP OF INSTITUTIONS; *Int'l*, pg. 4795
MEGHMANI EUROPE BVBA—See Meghmani Organics Ltd; *Int'l*, pg. 4795
MEGHMANI FINECHEM LIMITED; *Int'l*, pg. 4795
MEGHMANI ORGANICS LTD - AGRO DIVISION - III—See Meghmani Organics Ltd; *Int'l*, pg. 4795
MEGHMANI ORGANICS LTD - AGRO DIVISION - II—See Meghmani Organics Ltd; *Int'l*, pg. 4795
MEGHMANI ORGANICS LTD - AGRO DIVISION - I—See Meghmani Organics Ltd; *Int'l*, pg. 4795
MEGHMANI ORGANICS LTD - PIGMENT BLUE DIVISION—See Meghmani Organics Ltd; *Int'l*, pg. 4795
MEGHMANI ORGANICS LTD - POWER PLANT—See Meghmani Organics Ltd; *Int'l*, pg. 4795
MEGHMANI ORGANICS LTD; *Int'l*, pg. 4795
MEGH MAYUR INFRA LIMITED; *Int'l*, pg. 4795
MEGHNA CEMENT MILLS LIMITED; *Int'l*, pg. 4795
MEGHNA CONDENSED MILK INDUSTRIES LIMITED; *Int'l*, pg. 4795
MEGHNA LIFE INSURANCE CO. LTD.; *Int'l*, pg. 4795
MEGHNA PETROLEUM LIMITED; *Int'l*, pg. 4795
THE MEGILL-STEPHENSON COMPANY LTD.; *Int'l*, pg. 7666
MEGLAB ELECTRONIQUE INC.—See Epiroc AB; *Int'l*, pg. 2463
MEGLADON MANUFACTURING GROUP—See TyRex Group, Ltd.; *U.S. Private*, pg. 4269
MEGLIOQUESTO S.P.A.; *Int'l*, pg. 4796
MEGLOBAL CANADA INC.—See Dow Inc.; *U.S. Public*, pg. 683
MEGLOBAL CANADA INC.—See Kuwait Petroleum Corporation; *Int'l*, pg. 4346
MEGLON INFRA-REAL (INDIA) LIMITED; *Int'l*, pg. 4796
MEGMEET GERMANY GMBH—See Shenzhen Megmeet Electrical Co.,Ltd; *Int'l*, pg. 6817
MEGMEET SWEDEN AB—See Shenzhen Megmeet Electrical Co.,Ltd; *Int'l*, pg. 6817
MEGMEET USA, INC.—See Shenzhen Megmeet Electrical Co.,Ltd; *Int'l*, pg. 6817
M.E.G. MIKROBIOLOGISCHE ERDDEKONTAMINATION GMBH—See PORR AG; *Int'l*, pg. 5923
MEGMILK SNOW BRAND CO., LTD.; *Int'l*, pg. 4796
MEGOLA INC.—See Acordy Invest S.A.; *Int'l*, pg. 108
MEGRISOFT LIMITED; *Int'l*, pg. 4796
MEGRISOFT LIMITED - SYRACUSE BRANCH—See MegriSoft Limited; *Int'l*, pg. 4796
ME GROUP INTERNATIONAL PLC; *Int'l*, pg. 4762
MEGROUP LTD.; *Int'l*, pg. 4796
MEG—See Hirsh Industries, Inc.; *U.S. Private*, pg. 1951
MEGTEC SYSTEMS AB—See Durr AG; *Int'l*, pg. 2231
MEGTEC SYSTEMS AUSTRALIA, INC.—See Durr AG; *Int'l*, pg. 2231
MEGTEC SYSTEMS, INC.—See Durr AG; *Int'l*, pg. 2231
MEGTEC SYSTEMS SAS—See Durr AG; *Int'l*, pg. 2231

MEGTEC SYSTEMS SHANGHAI LTD—See Durr AG; *Int'l*, pg. 2231
MEGTEC TURBOSONIC, INC.—See Durr AG; *Int'l*, pg. 2231
MEGUIAR'S, INC.—See 3M Company; *U.S. Public*, pg. 5
MEGUIN GMBH & CO. KG MINERALOELWERKE—See Wurth Verwaltungsgesellschaft mbH; *Int'l*, pg. 8506
MEGUMAGOLD CORP.; *Int'l*, pg. 4796
MEGUREIT ISRAEL LTD.; *Int'l*, pg. 4796
MEHADRIN DAIRY CORP.; *U.S. Private*, pg. 2660
MEHADRIN LTD.; *Int'l*, pg. 4796
MEHAFFY & WEBER, A PROFESSIONAL CORPORATION; *U.S. Private*, pg. 2660
MEHAI TECHNOLOGY LIMITED; *Int'l*, pg. 4796
MEHANIZACIJA CACAK A.D.; *Int'l*, pg. 4796
MEHEEN MANUFACTURING, INC.—See Wild Goose Canning Technologies Inc.; *U.S. Private*, pg. 4518
MEHERRIN AGRICULTURE & CHEMICAL CO.; *U.S. Private*, pg. 2660
MEHILAINEN OY; *Int'l*, pg. 4796
MEHLER ENGINEERED PRODUCTS INC.—See KAP Beteiligungs-AG; *Int'l*, pg. 4076
MEHLER ENGINEERED PRODUCTS INDIA PRIVATE LIMITED—See KAP Beteiligungs-AG; *Int'l*, pg. 4076
MEHLER ENGINEERED PRODUCTS S.R.O.—See KAP Beteiligungs-AG; *Int'l*, pg. 4076
MEHLER ENGINEERING CORD (SUZHOU) CO., LTD.—See KAP Beteiligungs-AG; *Int'l*, pg. 4076
MEHLER TEXNOLOGIES GMBH—See Freudenberg SE; *Int'l*, pg. 2789
MEHLER TEXNOLOGIES INC—See Freudenberg SE; *Int'l*, pg. 2789
MEHLER TEXNOLOGIES LOGISTICS GMBH—See Freudenberg SE; *Int'l*, pg. 2789
MEHLER TEXNOLOGIES LTD.—See Freudenberg SE; *Int'l*, pg. 2789
MEHLER TEXNOLOGIES S.A.R.L.—See Freudenberg SE; *Int'l*, pg. 2789
MEHLER TEXNOLOGIES S.I.A—See Freudenberg SE; *Int'l*, pg. 2789
MEHLER TEXNOLOGIES S.P.A—See Freudenberg SE; *Int'l*, pg. 2789
MEHLER TEXNOLOGIES S.R.L—See Freudenberg SE; *Int'l*, pg. 2789
MEHLER TEXNOLOGIES S.R.O—See Freudenberg SE; *Int'l*, pg. 2789
MEHOW INNOVATIVE (HUIZHOU) LTD.—See Mehow Innovative Ltd.; *Int'l*, pg. 4797
MEHOW INNOVATIVE LTD.; *Int'l*, pg. 4796
MEHOW MEDICAL IRELAND LTD.—See Indutrade AB; *Int'l*, pg. 3680
MEHOW MEDICAL (M) SDN. BHD.—See Mehow Innovative Ltd.; *Int'l*, pg. 4797
MEHRABAD INDUSTRIAL CO.; *Int'l*, pg. 4797
MEHRA EYETECH PVT. LTD.—See Topcon Corporation; *Int'l*, pg. 7814
MEHRAN SUGAR MILLS LIMITED; *Int'l*, pg. 4797
MEHRAN SUGAR MILLS LIMITED - TANDO ALLAHYAR MILL—See Mehran Sugar Mills Limited; *Int'l*, pg. 4797
MEHRAVISTA HEALTH; *U.S. Private*, pg. 2660
MEHRCAM PARS COMPANY; *Int'l*, pg. 4797
MEHR DASTGIR TEXTILE MILLS LIMITED; *Int'l*, pg. 4797
MEHREN RUBBER AS—See Trelleborg AB; *Int'l*, pg. 7910
MEHR GOSTAR TAMIN DAROO; *Int'l*, pg. 4797
MEHRING AG—See Alfred Raith GmbH; *Int'l*, pg. 317
MEHR PETROCHEMICAL CO.—See Persian Gulf Petrochemical Industry Commercial Company; *Int'l*, pg. 5815
MEHTA HOUSING FINANCE LIMITED; *Int'l*, pg. 4797
MEHTA INTEGRATED FINANCE LIMITED; *Int'l*, pg. 4797
MEHTA SECUREITIES LIMITED; *Int'l*, pg. 4797
MEI AH CINEPLEX—See Mei Ah Entertainment Group Limited; *Int'l*, pg. 4797
MEI AH ENTERTAINMENT DEVELOPMENT INC.—See Mei Ah Entertainment Group Limited; *Int'l*, pg. 4797
MEI AH ENTERTAINMENT GROUP LIMITED; *Int'l*, pg. 4797
MEI AH (HK) COMPANY LIMITED—See Mei Ah Entertainment Group Limited; *Int'l*, pg. 4797
MEI-AN AUTOLIV CO., LTD.—See Autoliv, Inc.; *Int'l*, pg. 730
MEI AUTO PAYMENT SYSTEM (SHANGHAI) LTD.—See Crane NXT, Co.; *U.S. Public*, pg. 591
MEIBAN GROUP LTD.; *Int'l*, pg. 4797
MEIBAN INTERNATIONAL PTE. LTD.—See Meiban Group Ltd.; *Int'l*, pg. 4797
MEIBAN INVESTMENT PTE LTD—See Meiban Group Ltd.; *Int'l*, pg. 4797
MEIBAN TECHNOLOGIES (MALAYSIA) SDN. BHD.—See Meiban Group Ltd.; *Int'l*, pg. 4797
MEIBAN TECHNOLOGIES (ZHONGSHAN) CO., LTD.—See Meiban Group Ltd.; *Int'l*, pg. 4797
MEIBAN TECHNOLOGY PTE LTD—See Meiban Group Ltd.; *Int'l*, pg. 4797
MEIBES METALL-TECHNIK SP. Z.O.O.—See Aalberts N.V.; *Int'l*, pg. 35
MEIBES RUS OOO—See Aalberts N.V.; *Int'l*, pg. 35
MEIBES SK S.R.O.—See Aalberts N.V.; *Int'l*, pg. 35
MEIBES S.R.O.—See Aalberts N.V.; *Int'l*, pg. 35

COMPANY NAME INDEX

MEIBES SYSTEM-TECHNIK GMBH—See Aalberts N.V.; *Int'l*, pg. 35
M.E /IBI GROUP—See ARCADIS N.V.; *Int'l*, pg. 542
MEICHALEY ZAHAV PACKAGES LTD.—See Bunzl plc; *Int'l*, pg. 1219
MEIDEN AMERICA, INC.—See Meidensha Corporation; *Int'l*, pg. 4798
MEIDEN AMERICA SWITCHGEAR, INC.—See Meidensha Corporation; *Int'l*, pg. 4798
MEIDEN AQUA BUSINESS COMPANY—See Meidensha Corporation; *Int'l*, pg. 4798
MEIDEN ASIA PTE. LTD.—See Meidensha Corporation; *Int'l*, pg. 4798
MEIDEN ASIA PTE. LTD.—See Meidensha Corporation; *Int'l*, pg. 4798
MEIDEN CERAMICS CORPORATION—See Meidensha Corporation; *Int'l*, pg. 4798
MEIDEN CHEMICAL CO., LTD.—See Meidensha Corporation; *Int'l*, pg. 4798
MEIDEN ENGINEERING CORPORATION—See Meidensha Corporation; *Int'l*, pg. 4798
MEIDEN EUROPE GMBH—See Meidensha Corporation; *Int'l*, pg. 4798
MEIDEN FACILITY SERVICE CORPORATION—See Meidensha Corporation; *Int'l*, pg. 4798
MEIDEN FOUNDRY INDUSTRIAL CO., LTD.—See Meidensha Corporation; *Int'l*, pg. 4798
MEIDEN HANGZHOU DRIVE SYSTEMS CO., LTD.—See Meidensha Corporation; *Int'l*, pg. 4797
MEIDEN INDIA PVT. LTD.—See Meidensha Corporation; *Int'l*, pg. 4797
MEIDEN KANKYO SERVICE CO., LTD.—See Meidensha Corporation; *Int'l*, pg. 4798
MEIDEN KIDEN KOGYO CO., LTD.—See Meidensha Corporation; *Int'l*, pg. 4798
MEIDEN KOHSAN CO., LTD.—See Meidensha Corporation; *Int'l*, pg. 4798
MEIDEN KOREA CO., LTD.—See Meidensha Corporation; *Int'l*, pg. 4798
MEIDEN MALAYSIA SDN. BHD.—See Meidensha Corporation; *Int'l*, pg. 4798
MEIDEN MEDIAFRONT CORPORATION—See Meidensha Corporation; *Int'l*, pg. 4798
MEIDEN METAL ENGINEERING SDN. BHD.—See Meidensha Corporation; *Int'l*, pg. 4798
MEIDEN PACIFIC (CHINA) LTD.—See Meidensha Corporation; *Int'l*, pg. 4798
MEIDEN PLANT ENGINEERING & CONSTRUCTION CO LTD—See Meidensha Corporation; *Int'l*, pg. 4798
MEIDEN PLANT SYSTEMS CORPORATION—See Meidensha Corporation; *Int'l*, pg. 4798
MEIDENSHA CORPORATION; *Int'l*, pg. 4797
MEIDEN SHANGHAI CO., LTD.—See Meidensha Corporation; *Int'l*, pg. 4798
MEIDENSHA (SHANGHAI) CORPORATE MANAGEMENT CO., LTD.—See Meidensha Corporation; *Int'l*, pg. 4798
MEIDENSHA SHOJI CO., LTD.—See Meidensha Corporation; *Int'l*, pg. 4798
MEIDEN SHEET METAL PRODUCTS CORPORATION—See Meidensha Corporation; *Int'l*, pg. 4798
MEIDEN SHOJI CO., LTD.—See Meidensha Corporation; *Int'l*, pg. 4798
MEIDEN SINGAPORE PTE LTD.—See Meidensha Corporation; *Int'l*, pg. 4798
MEIDEN SOFTWARE CORPORATION—See Meidensha Corporation; *Int'l*, pg. 4798
MEIDEN SYSCON CO., LTD.—See Meidensha Corporation; *Int'l*, pg. 4798
MEIDEN SYSTEM ENGINEERING CO., LTD.—See Meidensha Corporation; *Int'l*, pg. 4798
MEIDEN SYSTEM MANUFACTURING CORPORATION—See Meidensha Corporation; *Int'l*, pg. 4798
MEIDEN SYSTEM SOLUTIONS CORPORATION—See Meidensha Corporation; *Int'l*, pg. 4798
MEIDEN SYSTEM TECHNOLOGY CO., LTD.—See Meidensha Corporation; *Int'l*, pg. 4798
MEIDEN TECHNO SYSTEM CO., LTD.—See Meidensha Corporation; *Int'l*, pg. 4798
MEIDEN UNIVERSAL SERVICE LTD.—See Meidensha Corporation; *Int'l*, pg. 4798
MEIDEN ZHENGZHOU ELECTRIC CO., LTD.—See Meidensha Corporation; *Int'l*, pg. 4798
MEIDI-YA CORPORATION—See Mitsubishi Corporation; *Int'l*, pg. 4940
MEIDOH CO., LTD; *Int'l*, pg. 4799
MEIDU ENERGY CORPORATION; *Int'l*, pg. 4799
MEIER CAPITAL AG; *Int'l*, pg. 4799
MEIER; *U.S. Private*, pg. 2660
MEIER'S WINE CELLARS, INC.—See MGP Ingredients, Inc.; *U.S. Public*, pg. 1436
MEIER TOBLER GROUP AG—See Meier Capital AG; *Int'l*, pg. 4799
MEIER VERPACKUNGEN GMBH—See Bunzl plc; *Int'l*, pg. 1219
MEIGHS CASTINGS LTD—See MetalTek International; *U.S. Private*, pg. 2682
MEIG SMART TECHNOLOGY CO., LTD.; *Int'l*, pg. 4799

MEIHAN KINTETSU BUS CO., LTD.—See Mie Kotsu Group Holdings, Inc.; *Int'l*, pg. 4888
MEIHAN KINTETSU TRAVEL CO., LTD.—See Mie Kotsu Group Holdings, Inc.; *Int'l*, pg. 4888
MEIHAN SHINKU KOGYO CO., LTD.—See Mitsubishi Gas Chemical Company, Inc.; *Int'l*, pg. 4949
MEIHAO MEDICAL GROUP CO., LTD.; *Int'l*, pg. 4799
MEIHO ENTERPRISE CO., LTD.; *Int'l*, pg. 4799
MEIHO FACILITY WORKS LIMITED; *Int'l*, pg. 4799
MEIHO KOGEN KAIHATSU CO., LTD.—See Nippon Ski Resort Development Co., Ltd.; *Int'l*, pg. 5334
MEIHOKU UOICHIBA CO., LTD.—See Maruha Nichiro Corporation; *Int'l*, pg. 4711
MEIHUA HOLDINGS GROUP CO., LTD.; *Int'l*, pg. 4799
MEIHUA INTERNATIONAL MEDICAL TECHNOLOGIES CO., LTD.; *Int'l*, pg. 4799
MEIJER, INC.; *U.S. Private*, pg. 2660
MEIJI AMERICA INC.—See Meiji Holdings Co., Ltd.; *Int'l*, pg. 4800
MEIJI BUSINESS SUPPORT CO., LTD.—See Meiji Holdings Co., Ltd.; *Int'l*, pg. 4800
MEIJI CHEWING GUM CO., LTD.—See Meiji Holdings Co., Ltd.; *Int'l*, pg. 4800
MEIJI CO., LTD.—See Meiji Holdings Co., Ltd.; *Int'l*, pg. 4800
MEIJI CONSULTANT CO., LTD.—See Japan Asia Group Limited; *Int'l*, pg. 3885
MEIJI CORPORATION—See Meiji Electric Industries Co., Ltd.; *Int'l*, pg. 4800
MEIJI DAIRIES (SUZHOU) CO., LTD.—See Meiji Holdings Co., Ltd.; *Int'l*, pg. 4800
MEIJI DAIRY AUSTRALASIA PTY. LTD—See Meiji Holdings Co., Ltd.; *Int'l*, pg. 4800
MEIJI ELECTRIC INDUSTRIES CO., LTD. - ENGINEERING DIVISION—See Meiji Electric Industries Co., Ltd.; *Int'l*, pg. 4800
MEIJI ELECTRIC INDUSTRIES CO., LTD.; *Int'l*, pg. 4799
MEIJI ELECTRIC INDUSTRIES (SHANGHAI) CO., LTD.—See Meiji Electric Industries Co., Ltd.; *Int'l*, pg. 4800
MEIJI FEED CO., LTD. - KAKOGAWA FACTORY—See Meiji Holdings Co., Ltd.; *Int'l*, pg. 4800
MEIJI FEED CO., LTD. - KASHIMA FACTORY—See Meiji Holdings Co., Ltd.; *Int'l*, pg. 4800
MEIJI FEED CO., LTD.—See Meiji Holdings Co., Ltd.; *Int'l*, pg. 4800
MEIJI FOOD MATERIA CO., LTD.—See Meiji Holdings Co., Ltd.; *Int'l*, pg. 4800
MEIJI FOOD MATERIAL CORP.—See Meiji Holdings Co., Ltd.; *Int'l*, pg. 4800
MEIJI HOLDINGS CO., LTD.; *Int'l*, pg. 4800
MEIJI ICE CREAM (GUANGZHOU) CO., LTD.—See Meiji Holdings Co., Ltd.; *Int'l*, pg. 4801
MEIJI INDIA PRIVATE LIMITED—See Meiji Holdings Co., Ltd.; *Int'l*, pg. 4801
MEIJI KENKO HAM CO., LTD.—See Meiji Holdings Co., Ltd.; *Int'l*, pg. 4800
MEIJI LOGITECH CO., LTD.—See Meiji Holdings Co., Ltd.; *Int'l*, pg. 4800
MEIJI MACHINE CO., LTD.; *Int'l*, pg. 4801
MEIJI MACHINE (DEZHOU) CO., LTD.—See Meiji Machine Co., Ltd.; *Int'l*, pg. 4801
MEIJIN ENERGY GROUP CO. LTD.; *Int'l*, pg. 4802
MEIJI OILS & FATS CO., LTD.—See Meiji Holdings Co., Ltd.; *Int'l*, pg. 4800
MEIJI PHARMA SPAIN, S.A.—See Meiji Holdings Co., Ltd.; *Int'l*, pg. 4801
MEIJI REAL ESTATE CO., LTD.—See Meiji Shipping Co., Ltd.; *Int'l*, pg. 4802
MEIJI RICE DELICA CORPORATION—See Meiji Holdings Co., Ltd.; *Int'l*, pg. 4800
MEIJI SANGYO CO., LTD.—See Meiji Holdings Co., Ltd.; *Int'l*, pg. 4800
MEIJI SEIKA FOOD INDUSTRY (SHANGHAI) CO., LTD.—See Meiji Holdings Co., Ltd.; *Int'l*, pg. 4800
MEIJI SEIKA PHARMA CO., LTD.—See Meiji Holdings Co., Ltd.; *Int'l*, pg. 4801
MEIJI SEIKA (SHANGHAI) CO.—See Meiji Holdings Co., Ltd.; *Int'l*, pg. 4800
MEIJI SEIKA (SINGAPORE) PTE. LTD.—See Meiji Holdings Co., Ltd.; *Int'l*, pg. 4800
MEIJI SEISHI CO., LTD.—See Tokushu Tokai Paper Co., Ltd.; *Int'l*, pg. 7786
MEIJI SHIPPING CO., LTD.; *Int'l*, pg. 4801
MEIJI SHOKUHIN KAISHA, LTD.—See Meiji Holdings Co., Ltd.; *Int'l*, pg. 4801
MEIJI SPORTS PLAZA CO., LTD.—See Central Sports Co., Ltd.; *Int'l*, pg. 1410
MEIJI TECHNO-SERVICE INC.—See Meiji Holdings Co., Ltd.; *Int'l*, pg. 4801
MEIJI (THAILAND) CO., LTD.—See Meiji Electric Industries Co., Ltd.; *Int'l*, pg. 4800
MEIJI UK LTD.—See Meiji Electric Industries Co., Ltd.; *Int'l*, pg. 4800
MEIJI YASUDA AMERICA, INC.—See Meiji Yasuda Life Insurance Company; *Int'l*, pg. 4802
MEIJI YASUDA ASIA LTD.—See Meiji Yasuda Life Insurance Company; *Int'l*, pg. 4802

MEILI AUTO HOLDINGS LIMITED

MEIJI YASUDA EUROPE LTD.—See Meiji Yasuda Life Insurance Company; *Int'l*, pg. 4802
MEIJI YASUDA GENERAL INSURANCE CO., LTD.—See Meiji Yasuda Life Insurance Company; *Int'l*, pg. 4802
MEIJI YASUDA LIFE INSURANCE COMPANY - BEIJING OFFICE—See Meiji Yasuda Life Insurance Company; *Int'l*, pg. 4802
MEIJI YASUDA LIFE INSURANCE COMPANY - FRANKFURT OFFICE—See Meiji Yasuda Life Insurance Company; *Int'l*, pg. 4802
MEIJI YASUDA LIFE INSURANCE COMPANY - SEOUL OFFICE—See Meiji Yasuda Life Insurance Company; *Int'l*, pg. 4802
MEIJI YASUDA LIFE INSURANCE COMPANY; *Int'l*, pg. 4802
MEIJI YASUDA REALTY USA INC.—See Meiji Yasuda Life Insurance Company; *Int'l*, pg. 4802
MEIJI YASUDA SYSTEM TECHNOLOGY COMPANY LIMITED—See Meiji Yasuda Life Insurance Company; *Int'l*, pg. 4802
MEIKAI KOSAN K.K.—See Meiji Shipping Co., Ltd.; *Int'l*, pg. 4802
MEIKAN HONCHOSHA PFI CO., LTD.—See Sumitomo Forestry Co., Ltd.; *Int'l*, pg. 7285
MEIKIKOU CO., LTD.—See Sintokogio Ltd.; *Int'l*, pg. 6958
MEIKLES LIMITED; *Int'l*, pg. 4802
MEIKO AMERICA, INC.—See Meiko Trans Co. Ltd.; *Int'l*, pg. 4803
MEIKO ASIA CO., LTD.—See Meiko Trans Co. Ltd.; *Int'l*, pg. 4803
MEIKO ELEC. HONG KONG. CO., LTD.—See Meiko Electronics Co., Ltd.; *Int'l*, pg. 4803
MEIKO ELECTRONICS AMERICA, INC.—See Meiko Electronics Co., Ltd.; *Int'l*, pg. 4803
MEIKO ELECTRONICS CO., LTD. - FUKUSHIMA FACTORY—See Meiko Electronics Co., Ltd.; *Int'l*, pg. 4803
MEIKO ELECTRONICS CO., LTD. - ISHINOMAKI FACTORY—See Meiko Electronics Co., Ltd.; *Int'l*, pg. 4803
MEIKO ELECTRONICS CO., LTD.; *Int'l*, pg. 4802
MEIKO ELECTRONICS EUROPE GMBH—See Meiko Electronics Co., Ltd.; *Int'l*, pg. 4803
MEIKO ELECTRONICS (GUANGZHOU NANSHA) CO., LTD.—See Meiko Electronics Co., Ltd.; *Int'l*, pg. 4803
MEIKO ELECTRONICS THANG LONG CO., LTD.—See Meiko Electronics Co., Ltd.; *Int'l*, pg. 4803
MEIKO ELECTRONICS VIETNAM CO., LTD.—See Meiko Electronics Co., Ltd.; *Int'l*, pg. 4803
MEIKO ELECTRONICS (WUHAN) CO., LTD.—See Meiko Electronics Co., Ltd.; *Int'l*, pg. 4803
MEIKO EUROEXPRESS N.V.—See Meiko Trans Co. Ltd.; *Int'l*, pg. 4803
MEIKO EUROPE N.V.—See Meiko Trans Co. Ltd.; *Int'l*, pg. 4803
MEIKO KAIUN KOSAN CO., LTD.—See Meiko Trans Co. Ltd.; *Int'l*, pg. 4803
MEIKO LOGISTICS (INDIA) PVT., LTD.—See Meiko Trans Co. Ltd.; *Int'l*, pg. 4803
MEIKO NETWORK JAPAN CO., LTD.; *Int'l*, pg. 4803
MEIKO RIKUUN CO., LTD.—See Meiko Trans Co. Ltd.; *Int'l*, pg. 4803
MEIKO SHANGHAI TRADING CO., LTD.—See Meiko Trans Co. Ltd.; *Int'l*, pg. 4803
MEIKO TECH CO., LTD.—See Meiko Electronics Co., Ltd.; *Int'l*, pg. 4803
MEIKO TECHNO CO., LTD.—See Meiko Electronics Co., Ltd.; *Int'l*, pg. 4803
MEIKO TOWADA VIETNAM CO., LTD.—See Meiko Electronics Co., Ltd.; *Int'l*, pg. 4803
MEIKO TRANS CO., LTD.—See Meiko Trans Co. Ltd.; *Int'l*, pg. 4803
MEIKO TRANS CO. LTD.; *Int'l*, pg. 4803
MEIKO TRANS DE MEXICO, S. DE R.L. DE C.V.—See Meiko Trans Co. Ltd.; *Int'l*, pg. 4803
MEIKO TRANS (GUANGZHOU) CO., LTD.—See Meiko Trans Co. Ltd.; *Int'l*, pg. 4803
MEIKO TRANS (HONG KONG) CO., LTD.—See Meiko Trans Co. Ltd.; *Int'l*, pg. 4803
MEIKO TRANS POLSKA SP. Z O.O.—See Meiko Trans Co. Ltd.; *Int'l*, pg. 4803
MEIKO TRANS (SINGAPORE) PTE. LTD.—See Meiko Trans Co. Ltd.; *Int'l*, pg. 4803
MEIKO TRANS (THAILAND) CO., LTD.—See Meiko Trans Co. Ltd.; *Int'l*, pg. 4803
MEILI AUTO HOLDINGS LIMITED; *Int'l*, pg. 4803
MEI LLC—See S&P Global Inc.; *U.S. Public*, pg. 1830
MEILLERGHP AB—See Osterreichische Post AG; *Int'l*, pg. 5653
MEILLERGHP A.S.—See Osterreichische Post AG; *Int'l*, pg. 5654
MEILLERGHP CZ S.R.O.—See Osterreichische Post AG; *Int'l*, pg. 5653
MEILLERGHP GMBH—See Osterreichische Post AG; *Int'l*, pg. 5654
MEILLERGHP SARL—See Osterreichische Post AG; *Int'l*, pg. 5654
MEILLERGHP SP. Z. O. O.—See Osterreichische Post AG; *Int'l*, pg. 5654

MEILI AUTO HOLDINGS LIMITED

MEILLER LITHOREX AB—See Paragon Group Limited; *Int'l*, pg. 5737
MEILLER LITHOREX FINLAND OY—See Paragon Group Limited; *Int'l*, pg. 5737
MEILLEURE HEALTH INTERNATIONAL INDUSTRY GROUP LIMITED; *Int'l*, pg. 4803
MEILLEURTAUX SA—See Equistone Partners Europe Limited; *Int'l*, pg. 2486
MEILOON INDUSTRIAL CO., LTD.; *Int'l*, pg. 4803
MEIMON TAIYO FERRY CO., LTD.—See Mitsui O.S.K. Lines, Ltd.; *Int'l*, pg. 4991
MEINECKE-JOHNSON COMPANY, INC.; *U.S. Private*, pg. 2660
MEINEKE CAR CARE CENTERS, INC.—See Roark Capital Group Inc.; *U.S. Private*, pg. 3454
MEINESTADT.DE GMBH—See Axel Springer SE; *Int'l*, pg. 767
MEINHARDT FINE FOODS, INC.—See The Jim Pattison Group; *Int'l*, pg. 7660
MEINIAN ONEHEALTH HEALTHCARE HOLDINGS CO., LTD.; *Int'l*, pg. 4804
MEINL BANK AG—See Julius Meinl Industrieholding GmbH; *Int'l*, pg. 4025
MEINL INTERNET COMMERCE GMBH—See Julius Meinl Industrieholding GmbH; *Int'l*, pg. 4025
MEI PHARMA, INC.; *U.S. Public*, pg. 1414
MEIP INTERNATIONAL, S.L.—See Fluidra SA; *Int'l*, pg. 2714
MEI QUERETARO S. DE R.L. DE CV—See Crane NXT, Co.; *U.S. Public*, pg. 591
MEIRA EESTI OU—See Segafredo Zanetti S.p.A.; *Int'l*, pg. 6682
MEIRAGTX HOLDINGS PLC; *U.S. Public*, pg. 1414
MEIRA, INC.; *Int'l*, pg. 4804
MEIRA OY LTD.—See Segafredo Zanetti S.p.A.; *Int'l*, pg. 6682
MEI RIGGING & CRATING, LLC—See Olympus Partners; *U.S. Private*, pg. 3013
MEIRXRS; *U.S. Private*, pg. 2660
MEIRYO KIGYO CO.,LTD.—See Mitsubishi Logistics Corporation; *Int'l*, pg. 4962
MEI SARL—See Crane NXT, Co.; *U.S. Public*, pg. 591
MEISEI CORRESPONDENCE CO., LTD.—See MIRAIT ONE Corporation; *Int'l*, pg. 4917
MEISEI ELECTRIC CO., LTD.—See IHI Corporation; *Int'l*, pg. 3606
MEISEI INDUSTRIAL CO., LTD.; *Int'l*, pg. 4804
MEISEI INTERNATIONAL CO., LTD.—See Meisei Industrial Co., Ltd.; *Int'l*, pg. 4804
MEISEI INTERNATIONAL PTE. LTD.—See Meisei Industrial Co., Ltd.; *Int'l*, pg. 4804
MEISEI KENKO CO., LTD.—See Meisei Industrial Co., Ltd.; *Int'l*, pg. 4804
MEISEI MATSUYAMA KOJI CO., LTD.—See Meisei Industrial Co., Ltd.; *Int'l*, pg. 4804
MEISEI NIGERIA LTD.—See Meisei Industrial Co., Ltd.; *Int'l*, pg. 4804
MEISE MACHINE CO., LTD.—See SIMPAC Holdings Co., Ltd; *Int'l*, pg. 6933
MEISHENG CULTURAL & CREATIVE CORP., LTD.; *Int'l*, pg. 4804
MEISHO CO., LTD.—See Alfresa Holdings Corporation; *Int'l*, pg. 317
MEISINGER CONSTRUCTION COMPANY; *U.S. Private*, pg. 2661
MEISNER ELECTRIC, INC.; *U.S. Private*, pg. 2661
MEISNER GALLERY, INC.; *U.S. Private*, pg. 2661
MEISSEN KERAMIK VERTRIEBS GMBH & CO. KG—See Deutsche Steinzeug Cremer & Breuer AG; *Int'l*, pg. 2083
MEISTER FEINES FLEISCH - FEINE WURST GMBH—See Metro AG; *Int'l*, pg. 4859
MEISTER FRANCE S.A.S.—See Wurth Verwaltungsgesellschaft mbH; *Int'l*, pg. 8506
MEISTERHAUS LABORATORIO OPTICO LTDA.—See Carl-Zeiss-Stiftung; *Int'l*, pg. 1336
MEISTERLABS GMBH; *Int'l*, pg. 4804
MEISTER LOGISTICS CORPORATION AMERICA—See Halla Group; *Int'l*, pg. 3229
MEISTER LOG & LUMBER CO.—See Midwest Hardwood Corporation; *U.S. Private*, pg. 2721
MEISTER MEDIA WORLDWIDE INC.; *U.S. Private*, pg. 2661
MEISTER TOOLS TRADING (SHANGHAI) CO., LTD.—See Wurth Verwaltungsgesellschaft mbH; *Int'l*, pg. 8506
MEISTER WERKZEUGE GMBH—See Wurth Verwaltungsgesellschaft mbH; *Int'l*, pg. 8506
MEITANHOMPO CO., LTD.—See Kobayashi Pharmaceutical Co., Ltd.; *Int'l*, pg. 4216
MEITAN TRADITION CO. LTD—See Viel & Compagnie SA; *Int'l*, pg. 8192
MEITAV INVESTMENT HOUSE LTD.; *Int'l*, pg. 4804
MEITEC BUSINESS SERVICE CORPORATION—See Meitec Corporation; *Int'l*, pg. 4804
MEITEC CAE CORPORATION—See Meitec Corporation; *Int'l*, pg. 4804
MEITEC CAST INC.—See Meitec Corporation; *Int'l*, pg. 4804

MEITEC CORPORATION; *Int'l*, pg. 4804
MEITEC EX CORPORATION—See Meitec Corporation; *Int'l*, pg. 4804
MEITEC FIELDERS INC—See Meitec Corporation; *Int'l*, pg. 4804
MEI TECHNOLOGIES, INC.; *U.S. Private*, pg. 2660
MEITECH OFFSHORE ENGINEERING PTE. LTD.; *Int'l*, pg. 4804
MEITEC INC.; *U.S. Private*, pg. 2661
MEITEC NEXT CORPORATION—See Meitec Corporation; *Int'l*, pg. 4804
MEITEK TECHNOLOGY (QINGDAO) CO., LTD.—See Synutra International, Inc.; *U.S. Private*, pg. 3905
MEITETSU DEPARTMENT STORE CO., LTD.—See Nagoya Railroad Co., Ltd.; *Int'l*, pg. 5129
MEITETSU KYOSHO CO LTD—See Nagoya Railroad Co., Ltd.; *Int'l*, pg. 5129
MEITETSU TRANSPORT CO., LTD.—See Nagoya Railroad Co., Ltd.; *Int'l*, pg. 5129
MEITO SANGYO CO., LTD.; *Int'l*, pg. 4804
MEITO TRANSPORTATION CO., LTD.—See Chilled & Frozen Logis; *Int'l*, pg. 1479
MEITO WAREHOUSE CO., LTD.—See Meiji Holdings Co., Ltd.; *Int'l*, pg. 4801
MEITUAN; *Int'l*, pg. 4804
MEITU INC.; *Int'l*, pg. 4804
MEIVAC, INC.—See Ferrotec Holdings Corporation; *Int'l*, pg. 2643
MEIWA CORPORATION; *Int'l*, pg. 4804
MEIWA (DALIAN) CORPORATION—See Meiwa Corporation; *Int'l*, pg. 4805
MEIWA DENGYO CO., LTD.—See Sumitomo Densetsu Co., Ltd.; *Int'l*, pg. 7276
MEIWA ESTATE CO., LTD.; *Int'l*, pg. 4805
MEIWA INDUSTRY CO., LTD.; *Int'l*, pg. 4805
MEIWA INDUSTRY NORTH AMERICA, INC.—See Meiwa Industry Co., Ltd.; *Int'l*, pg. 4805
MEIWA INDUSTRY (THAILAND) CO., LTD.—See Meiwa Industry Co., Ltd.; *Int'l*, pg. 4805
MEIWA SALES CO., LTD.—See Meiwa Corporation; *Int'l*, pg. 4805
MEIWA SANGYO CO., LTD.—See Namura Shipbuilding Co., Ltd.; *Int'l*, pg. 5136
MEIWA (SHANGHAI) CORPORATION—See Meiwa Corporation; *Int'l*, pg. 4805
MEIWA SHOUKO CO., LTD.—See JTEKT Corporation; *Int'l*, pg. 4019
MEIWA (THAILAND) CO., LTD.—See Meiwa Corporation; *Int'l*, pg. 4805
MEIWA VIETNAM CO., LTD.—See Meiwa Corporation; *Int'l*, pg. 4805
MEIWU TECHNOLOGY COMPANY LIMITED; *Int'l*, pg. 4805
MEIYO ELECTRIC CO., LTD.—See CHINO Corporation; *Int'l*, pg. 1571
MEIYU-GIKEN CO., LTD.—See Japan Aviation Electronics Industry, Ltd.; *Int'l*, pg. 3887
MEIYU KIKO CO., LTD.—See Toyota Motor Corporation; *Int'l*, pg. 7871
MEIZHOU AUCHAN HYPERMARKETS CO., LTD.—See Alibaba Group Holding Limited; *Int'l*, pg. 326
MEIZHOU CHAOHUA CNC TECHNOLOGY CO., LTD.—See Guangdong Chaohua Technology Co., Ltd.; *Int'l*, pg. 3153
MEIZHOU HONGFUHAN TECHNOLOGY CO., LTD.—See Shenzhen Hongfuhan Technology Co., Ltd.; *Int'l*, pg. 6812
MEIZHOU TAIHUA PRINTED CIRCUIT BOARD CO., LTD.—See Guangdong Chaohua Technology Co., Ltd.; *Int'l*, pg. 3153
MEJANA, S.A.—See Nefinsa S.A.; *Int'l*, pg. 5192
MEJERIANDELSLAGET MILKA MEIJERIOSUUSKUNTA; *Int'l*, pg. 4805
MEJERIFORENINGEN—See Arla Foods amba; *Int'l*, pg. 573
MEJORAMIENTO DE SUELOS MENARD MEXICO S.A. DE C.V.—See VINCI S.A.; *Int'l*, pg. 8224
MEKANISM, INC.; *U.S. Private*, pg. 2661
MEK CO., LTD.—See MICRONICS JAPAN CO., LTD.; *Int'l*, pg. 4880
MEKETA INVESTMENT GROUP, INC.; *U.S. Private*, pg. 2661
MEKHA TECHNOLOGY CO., LTD.—See PTT Public Company Limited; *Int'l*, pg. 6092
MEKHONG DISTILLERY LIMITED—See Thai Beverage Public Company Limited; *Int'l*, pg. 7591
MEKICS CO., LTD; *Int'l*, pg. 4805
MEKO AB; *Int'l*, pg. 4805
MEKO ENERGY COMPANY LTD.—See Electricite de France S.A.; *Int'l*, pg. 2352
MEKONG FISHERIES JOINT STOCK COMPANY; *Int'l*, pg. 4807
MEKONG FLOUR MILLS LTD.—See Malayan Flour Mills Berhad; *Int'l*, pg. 4661
MEKONOMEN ALINGSAS AB—See MEKO AB; *Int'l*, pg. 4806
MEKONOMEN ARVIKA AB—See MEKO AB; *Int'l*, pg. 4806
MEKONOMEN AS—See MEKO AB; *Int'l*, pg. 4806

CORPORATE AFFILIATIONS

MEKONOMEN BACKAPLAN AB—See MEKO AB; *Int'l*, pg. 4806
MEKONOMEN BILLIVET ALBYBERG AB—See MEKO AB; *Int'l*, pg. 4806
MEKONOMEN BILLIVET ALMHULT AB—See MEKO AB; *Int'l*, pg. 4806
MEKONOMEN BILLIVET BACKAPLAN AB—See MEKO AB; *Int'l*, pg. 4806
MEKONOMEN BILLIVET BORAS AB—See MEKO AB; *Int'l*, pg. 4806
MEKONOMEN BILLIVET BROMMA AB—See MEKO AB; *Int'l*, pg. 4806
MEKONOMEN BILLIVET EKLANDA AB—See MEKO AB; *Int'l*, pg. 4806
MEKONOMEN BILLIVET FOSIE AB—See MEKO AB; *Int'l*, pg. 4806
MEKONOMEN BILLIVET GARDET AB—See MEKO AB; *Int'l*, pg. 4806
MEKONOMEN BILLIVET GAVLE AB—See MEKO AB; *Int'l*, pg. 4806
MEKONOMEN BILLIVET GISLAVED AB—See MEKO AB; *Int'l*, pg. 4806
MEKONOMEN BILLIVET HARNOSAND AB—See MEKO AB; *Int'l*, pg. 4806
MEKONOMEN BILLIVET HEDEMORA AB—See MEKO AB; *Int'l*, pg. 4806
MEKONOMEN BILLIVET INFRA CITY AB—See MEKO AB; *Int'l*, pg. 4806
MEKONOMEN BILLIVET JOHANNESHOV AB—See MEKO AB; *Int'l*, pg. 4806
MEKONOMEN BILLIVET KARLSHAMN AB—See MEKO AB; *Int'l*, pg. 4806
MEKONOMEN BILLIVET KATRINELUND AB—See MEKO AB; *Int'l*, pg. 4806
MEKONOMEN BILLIVET KIRUNA AB—See MEKO AB; *Int'l*, pg. 4806
MEKONOMEN BILLIVET LIDINGO AB—See MEKO AB; *Int'l*, pg. 4806
MEKONOMEN BILLIVET LJUNGBY AB—See MEKO AB; *Int'l*, pg. 4806
MEKONOMEN BILLIVET NODINGE AB—See MEKO AB; *Int'l*, pg. 4806
MEKONOMEN BILLIVET NORREMARK AB—See MEKO AB; *Int'l*, pg. 4806
MEKONOMEN BILLIVET NYBRO AB—See MEKO AB; *Int'l*, pg. 4806
MEKONOMEN BILLIVET SKELLEFTEA AB—See MEKO AB; *Int'l*, pg. 4806
MEKONOMEN BILLIVET SODERTALJE AB—See MEKO AB; *Int'l*, pg. 4806
MEKONOMEN BILLIVET STROMSTAD AB—See MEKO AB; *Int'l*, pg. 4806
MEKONOMEN BILLIVET TABY AB—See MEKO AB; *Int'l*, pg. 4806
MEKONOMEN BILLIVET VARNAMO AB—See MEKO AB; *Int'l*, pg. 4806
MEKONOMEN BILLIVET VAXJO AB—See MEKO AB; *Int'l*, pg. 4806
MEKONOMEN BILVERKSTAD AB—See MEKO AB; *Int'l*, pg. 4806
MEKONOMEN BOLLNAS AB—See MEKO AB; *Int'l*, pg. 4806
MEKONOMEN EKLANDA AB—See MEKO AB; *Int'l*, pg. 4806
MEKONOMEN ENKOPING AB—See MEKO AB; *Int'l*, pg. 4806
MEKONOMEN ESKILSTUNA AB—See MEKO AB; *Int'l*, pg. 4806
MEKONOMEN FALKENBERG AB—See MEKO AB; *Int'l*, pg. 4806
MEKONOMEN FALUN AB—See MEKO AB; *Int'l*, pg. 4806
MEKONOMEN FLEN AB—See MEKO AB; *Int'l*, pg. 4806
MEKONOMEN GAVLE AB—See MEKO AB; *Int'l*, pg. 4806
MEKONOMEN HALLSBERG AB—See MEKO AB; *Int'l*, pg. 4806
MEKONOMEN HARNOSAND AB—See MEKO AB; *Int'l*, pg. 4806
MEKONOMEN JARFALLA AB—See MEKO AB; *Int'l*, pg. 4806
MEKONOMEN KRISTIANSTAD AB—See MEKO AB; *Int'l*, pg. 4806
MEKONOMEN KUNGSHAMN AB—See MEKO AB; *Int'l*, pg. 4806
MEKONOMEN MARIESTAD AB—See MEKO AB; *Int'l*, pg. 4806
MEKONOMEN MJOLBY AB—See MEKO AB; *Int'l*, pg. 4806
MEKONOMEN NORDIC—See MEKO AB; *Int'l*, pg. 4806
MEKONOMEN OY—See MEKO AB; *Int'l*, pg. 4806
MEKONOMEN SKELLEFTEA AB—See MEKO AB; *Int'l*, pg. 4806
MEKONOMEN SODERTALJE AB—See MEKO AB; *Int'l*, pg. 4806
MEKONOMEN SOLLEFTEA AB—See MEKO AB; *Int'l*, pg. 4806
MEKONOMEN STROMSTAD AB—See MEKO AB; *Int'l*, pg. 4806
MEKONOMEN SUNDSVALL BIRSTA AB—See MEKO AB; *Int'l*, pg. 4806

COMPANY NAME INDEX

MEKONOMEN TONSBERG AS—See MEKO AB; *Int'l*, pg. 4806
MEKONOMEN TRANAS AB—See MEKO AB; *Int'l*, pg. 4806
MEKONOMEN TROLLHATTAN AB—See MEKO AB; *Int'l*, pg. 4806
MEKONOMEN VANERSBORG AB—See MEKO AB; *Int'l*, pg. 4806
MEKONOMEN VERKSTADSCENTER ALVSJO AB—See MEKO AB; *Int'l*, pg. 4807
MEKONOMEN VETLANDA AB—See MEKO AB; *Int'l*, pg. 4807
MEKON SCIENCE NETWORKS GMBH—See BRAIN Biotech AG; *Int'l*, pg. 1137
MEKOPRINT A/S; *Int'l*, pg. 4807
MEKOPRINT CHEMIGRAPHICS—See Mekoprint A/S; *Int'l*, pg. 4807
MEKOPRINT ELECTRONICS—See Mekoprint A/S; *Int'l*, pg. 4807
MEKOPRINT GRAPHICS—See Mekoprint A/S; *Int'l*, pg. 4807
MEKOPRINT MECHANICS—See Mekoprint A/S; *Int'l*, pg. 4807
MEKO SERVICE NORDIC—See MEKO AB; *Int'l*, pg. 4805
MEKSTER AB—See MEKO AB; *Int'l*, pg. 4807
MEKTEC CORPORATION (H.K.) LIMITED—See NOK Corporation; *Int'l*, pg. 5402
MEKTEC CORPORATION KOREA, LTD.—See NOK Corporation; *Int'l*, pg. 5402
MEKTEC CORPORATION (SHENZHEN) LTD.—See NOK Corporation; *Int'l*, pg. 5402
MEKTEC CORPORATION (SINGAPORE) PTE LTD.—See NOK Corporation; *Int'l*, pg. 5402
MEKTEC CORPORATION (TAIWAN) LTD. - KAOHSIUNG PLANT—See NOK Corporation; *Int'l*, pg. 5402
MEKTEC CORPORATION (TAIWAN) LTD.—See NOK Corporation; *Int'l*, pg. 5402
MEKTEC EUROPE GMBH—See NOK Corporation; *Int'l*, pg. 5402
MEKTEC INTERNATIONAL CORPORATION—See NOK Corporation; *Int'l*, pg. 5402
MEKTEC MANUFACTURING CORPORATION EUROPE HU KFT.—See NOK Corporation; *Int'l*, pg. 5402
MEKTEC MANUFACTURING CORPORATION (SUZHOU) LTD.—See NOK Corporation; *Int'l*, pg. 5402
MEKTEC MANUFACTURING CORPORATION (THAILAND). LTD.—See NOK Corporation; *Int'l*, pg. 5402
MEKTEC MANUFACTURING CORPORATION (VIETNAM) LTD.—See NOK Corporation; *Int'l*, pg. 5402
MEKTEC MANUFACTURING CORPORATION (ZHUHAI) LTD.—See NOK Corporation; *Int'l*, pg. 5402
MEKTEC PRECISION COMPONENT (THAILAND) LTD.—See NOK Corporation; *Int'l*, pg. 5402
MEKTEC TRADING (SHANGHAI) CO., LTD.—See NOK Corporation; *Int'l*, pg. 5402
MEKTEC TRADING TAIWAN CO., LTD.—See NOK Corporation; *Int'l*, pg. 5402
MELAKA STRAITS MEDICAL CENTRE SDN. BHD.—See Oriental Holdings Berhad; *Int'l*, pg. 5624
MELALEUCA INC.; *U.S. Private*, pg. 2661
MELAMEDRILEY ADVERTISING, LLC; *U.S. Private*, pg. 2661
MELAMIN D.D.; *Int'l*, pg. 4807
MELANOMA RESEARCH ALLIANCE; *U.S. Private*, pg. 2661
THE MELANSON COMPANY INC—See Altas Partners LP; *Int'l*, pg. 387
MELATI EHSAN HOLDINGS BERHAD; *Int'l*, pg. 4807
MELAT INVESTMENT COMPANY; *Int'l*, pg. 4807
MELAWATI DEVELOPMENT SDN. BHD.—See Sime Darby Berhad; *Int'l*, pg. 6930
MELBANA ENERGY LIMITED; *Int'l*, pg. 4807
MEL BERNIE & COMPANY INC.; *U.S. Private*, pg. 2661
MELBORNE CITY AUTOS (2012) PTY LTD—See Eagers Automotive Limited; *Int'l*, pg. 2263
THE MELBOURNE ASC, L.P.—See KKR & Co. Inc.; *U.S. Public*, pg. 1248
MELBOURNE CONCRETE PTY. LTD.—See Heidelberg Materials AG; *Int'l*, pg. 3318
MELBOURNE CRICKET CLUB FOUNDATION LTD.—See Tabcorp Holdings Limited; *Int'l*, pg. 7401
MELBOURNE ENTERPRISES LIMITED; *Int'l*, pg. 4807
MELBOURNE GOLF ACADEMY PTY LTD—See Blackstone Inc.; *U.S. Public*, pg. 353
MELBOURNE INDEPENDENT NEWSPAPERS PTY LTD—See ARN Media Limited; *Int'l*, pg. 576
MELBOURNE INSTITUTE OF BUSINESS AND TECHNOLOGY PTY LTD.—See Navitas Limited; *Int'l*, pg. 5176
MELBOURNE IT GP HOLDINGS PTY. LTD.—See 5G Networks Limited; *Int'l*, pg. 13
MELBOURNE IVF HOLDINGS PTY LTD—See Virtus Health Limited; *Int'l*, pg. 8249
MELBOURNE PATHOLOGY PTY LIMITED—See Sonic Healthcare Limited; *Int'l*, pg. 7098
MELBOURNE PATHOLOGY SERVICES PTY LIMITED—See Sonic Healthcare Limited; *Int'l*, pg. 7098
MELBOURNE SQUARE, LLC—See Washington Prime Group Inc.; *U.S. Private*, pg. 4448

MELBOURNE SYMPHONY ORCHESTRA; *Int'l*, pg. 4807
MELBOURNE UNDERWATER WORLD PTY LTD—See Merlin Entertainments plc; *Int'l*, pg. 4837
MELBOURNE ZOO—See Zoological Parks and Gardens Board; *Int'l*, pg. 8689
MELBU FRYSELAGER AS—See Austevoll Seafood ASA; *Int'l*, pg. 717
MELBYE SKANDINAVIA AS; *Int'l*, pg. 4807
MELBYE SKANDINAVIA NORGE AS—See Melbye Skandinavia AS; *Int'l*, pg. 4807
MELBYE SKANDINAVIA SVERIGE AB—See Melbye Skandinavia AS; *Int'l*, pg. 4807
MELCARA CORP.—See Property Resources Corp.; *U.S. Private*, pg. 3285
MEL CHEMICALS, INC.—See Luxfer Holdings PLC; *Int'l*, pg. 4588
MELCHER & FRENZEN ARMATUREN GMBH—See Aalberts N.V.; *Int'l*, pg. 35
MELCHER & PRESCOTT INSURANCE; *U.S. Private*, pg. 2662
MELCHIONI SPA; *Int'l*, pg. 4807
MELCHIORRE S.R.L.—See Obara Group Incorporated; *Int'l*, pg. 5508
MELCO DISPLAY TECHNOLOGY INC.—See Mitsubishi Electric Corporation; *Int'l*, pg. 4944
MELCO HOLDINGS INC.; *Int'l*, pg. 4807
MELCO INDUSTRIAL SUPPLIES CO., LIMITED—See Cosmos Machinery Enterprises Limited; *Int'l*, pg. 1813
MELCO INDUSTRIAL SUPPLIES (SHANGHAI) CO., LTD—See Cosmos Machinery Enterprises Limited; *Int'l*, pg. 1813
MELCO INTERNATIONAL DEVELOPMENT, LTD.; *Int'l*, pg. 4808
MELCO INTERNATIONAL LLC; *U.S. Private*, pg. 2662
MELCO PERSONNEL SUPPORT INC.—See Melco Holdings Inc.; *Int'l*, pg. 4808
MELCO POWER DEVICE CORPORATION—See Mitsubishi Electric Corporation; *Int'l*, pg. 4944
MELCOR DEVELOPMENTS ARIZONA INC.—See Melcor Developments Ltd.; *Int'l*, pg. 4808
MELCOR DEVELOPMENTS LTD.; *Int'l*, pg. 4808
MELCO RESORTS AND ENTERTAINMENT (PHILIPPINES) CORPORATION—See Melco International Development, Ltd.; *Int'l*, pg. 4808
MELCO RESORTS & ENTERTAINMENT LIMITED—See Melco International Development, Ltd.; *Int'l*, pg. 4808
MELCOR REAL ESTATE INVESTMENT TRUST; *Int'l*, pg. 4808
MELCO SEMICONDUCTOR ENGINEERING CORPORATION—See Mitsubishi Electric Corporation; *Int'l*, pg. 4944
MELCO TRADING (THAILAND) CO., LTD.—See Mitsubishi Electric Corporation; *Int'l*, pg. 4945
MELDAS SYSTEM ENGINEERING CORPORATION—See Mitsubishi Electric Corporation; *Int'l*, pg. 4944
MEL DAWSON INC.—See Chevron Corporation; *U.S. Public*, pg. 487
MELDERTSE PLAFONNEERARTIKELEN N.V.—See SIG plc; *Int'l*, pg. 6906
MELDRUM LIMITED—See VINCI S.A.; *Int'l*, pg. 8224
MELE COMPANIES, INC.; *U.S. Private*, pg. 2662
MELEEO, LLC—See Platform Partners LLC; *U.S. Private*, pg. 3200
MELEFIN NV—See Melexis N.V.; *Int'l*, pg. 4809
MELETIO ELECTRICAL SUPPLY CO.; *U.S. Private*, pg. 2662
MELETT LIMITED—See Westinghouse Air Brake Technologies Corporation; *U.S. Public*, pg. 2358
MELETT NORTH AMERICA, INC—See Westinghouse Air Brake Technologies Corporation; *U.S. Public*, pg. 2358
MELEWAR INDUSTRIAL GROUP BERHAD; *Int'l*, pg. 4808
MELEWAR STEEL MILLS SDN BHD—See Melewar Industrial Group Berhad; *Int'l*, pg. 4808
MELEWAR STEEL TUBE SDN BHD—See Melewar Industrial Group Berhad; *Int'l*, pg. 4808
MELEXA S.A.S.—See Sonepar S.A.; *Int'l*, pg. 7091
MELEXIS BULGARIA LTD—See Melexis N.V.; *Int'l*, pg. 4809
MELEXIS DRESDEN GMBH—See Melexis N.V.; *Int'l*, pg. 4809
MELEXIS ELECTRONIC TECHNOLOGY CO.LTD—See Melexis N.V.; *Int'l*, pg. 4809
MELEXIS FRANCE SAS—See Melexis N.V.; *Int'l*, pg. 4809
MELEXIS GMBH—See Melexis N.V.; *Int'l*, pg. 4809
MELEXIS, INC.—See Melexis N.V.; *Int'l*, pg. 4809
MELEXIS JAPAN KK—See Melexis N.V.; *Int'l*, pg. 4809
MELEXIS N.V.; *Int'l*, pg. 4808
MELEXIS TECHNOLOGIES SA—See Melexis N.V.; *Int'l*, pg. 4809
MELEXIS TESSENDERLO NV—See Melexis N.V.; *Int'l*, pg. 4809
MELEXIS UKRAINE—See Melexis N.V.; *Int'l*, pg. 4809
MELFAS INC. - ANSEONG PLANT—See MELFAS Inc.; *Int'l*, pg. 4809
MELFAS INC.; *Int'l*, pg. 4809
MEL FOSTER CO. INC.; *U.S. Private*, pg. 2661
MEL FOSTER CO. INC.; *U.S. Private*, pg. 2661
MEL HAMBELTON FORD INC.; *U.S. Private*, pg. 2661

MELLANO & COMPANY

MELHUS SPAREBANK; *Int'l*, pg. 4809
MELIA HOTELS INTERNATIONAL, S.A.; *Int'l*, pg. 4809
MELIA INVERSIONES AMERICANAS, N.V.—See Melia Hotels International, S.A.; *Int'l*, pg. 4809
MELIA LUXEMBOURG, S.A.R.L.—See Melia Hotels International, S.A.; *Int'l*, pg. 4809
MELIAN; *Int'l*, pg. 4810
MELIBOKUS INDUSTRIE-ELEKTRONIK GMBH—See Mettler-Toledo International, Inc.; *U.S. Public*, pg. 1432
MELIES SRL—See MOL Magyar Olaj- es Gazipari Nyrt.; *Int'l*, pg. 5020
MELIFE CO., LTD.—See Sinanen Holdings Co., Ltd.; *Int'l*, pg. 6936
MELIFE-EAST CO., LTD.—See Sinanen Holdings Co., Ltd.; *Int'l*, pg. 6936
MELIFE-WEST CO., LTD.—See Sinanen Holdings Co., Ltd.; *Int'l*, pg. 6936
MELI KASZEK PIONEER CORP.; *U.S. Public*, pg. 1414
MELILLO CONSULTING INC.; *U.S. Private*, pg. 2662
MELINK CORPORATION; *U.S. Private*, pg. 2662
MELINS PLATSLAGERI AB—See Instalco AB; *Int'l*, pg. 3722
ME LIN STEEL JOINT STOCK COMPANY; *Int'l*, pg. 4763
MELINTA SUBSIDIARY CORP.—See Deerfield Management Company L.P.; *U.S. Private*, pg. 1190
MELINTA THERAPEUTICS, INC.—See Deerfield Management Company L.P.; *U.S. Private*, pg. 1190
MELIN TOOL COMPANY, INC.—See Sandvik AB; *Int'l*, pg. 6534
MEL INVEST HOLDING AD; *Int'l*, pg. 4807
MELIORCONSULTING SPA—See BPER BANCA S.p.A; *Int'l*, pg. 1132
MELIORFACTOR SPA—See BPER BANCA S.p.A; *Int'l*, pg. 1132
MELIOR TRUST SPA—See BPER BANCA S.p.A; *Int'l*, pg. 1132
MELISRON LTD.; *Int'l*, pg. 4810
MELISSA CORPORATION; *U.S. Private*, pg. 2662
MELISSA DEVOLENTINE PUBLIC RELATIONS; *U.S. Private*, pg. 2662
MELISSA & DOUG, LLC—See Spin Master Corp.; *Int'l*, pg. 7136
MELITA CAPITAL PLC—See EQT AB; *Int'l*, pg. 2478
MELITA LTD.—See EQT AB; *Int'l*, pg. 2478
MELITE FINANCE PLC; *Int'l*, pg. 4810
MELITE PROPERTIES S.R.L.—See Melite Finance PLC; *Int'l*, pg. 4810
MELITRON CORPORATION; *Int'l*, pg. 4810
MELITTA BELGIE N.V.—See Eckes AG; *Int'l*, pg. 2291
MELITTA BERATUNGS- UND VERWALTUNGS GMBH & CO.KG—See Melitta Unternehmensgruppe Bentz KG; *Int'l*, pg. 4810
MELITTA CANADA INC.—See Melitta Unternehmensgruppe Bentz KG; *Int'l*, pg. 4810
MELITTA CR S.R.O.—See Melitta Unternehmensgruppe Bentz KG; *Int'l*, pg. 4810
MELITTA DO BRASIL INDUSTRIA E COMERCIO LTDA.—See Melitta Unternehmensgruppe Bentz KG; *Int'l*, pg. 4811
MELITTA FRANCE S.A.S.—See Melitta Unternehmensgruppe Bentz KG; *Int'l*, pg. 4810
MELITTA GES.MBH—See Melitta Unternehmensgruppe Bentz KG; *Int'l*, pg. 4810
MELITTA GMBH—See Melitta Unternehmensgruppe Bentz KG; *Int'l*, pg. 4810
MELITTA HAUSHALTSPRODUKTE GMBH & CO. KG—See Melitta Unternehmensgruppe Bentz KG; *Int'l*, pg. 4810
MELITTA-NEDERLAND B.V.—See Melitta Unternehmensgruppe Bentz KG; *Int'l*, pg. 4811
MELITTA NORDIC AB—See Melitta Unternehmensgruppe Bentz KG; *Int'l*, pg. 4810
MELITTA NORDIC A/S—See Melitta Unternehmensgruppe Bentz KG; *Int'l*, pg. 4810
MELITTA PROFESSIONAL COFFEE SOLUTIONS UK LTD.—See Melitta Unternehmensgruppe Bentz KG; *Int'l*, pg. 4810
MELITTA PROFESSIONAL COFFEE SOLUTIONS USA INC.—See Melitta Unternehmensgruppe Bentz KG; *Int'l*, pg. 4811
MELITTA SYSTEMSERVICE GMBH & CO. KG—See Melitta Unternehmensgruppe Bentz KG; *Int'l*, pg. 4810
MELITTA UNTERNEHMENSGRUPPE BENTZ KG; *Int'l*, pg. 4810
MELITTA USA INC.—See Melitta Unternehmensgruppe Bentz KG; *Int'l*, pg. 4811
MEL-JEN; *U.S. Private*, pg. 2661
MELKER SCHORLING AB; *Int'l*, pg. 4811
MELKIOR RESOURCES INC.; *Int'l*, pg. 4811
MELLACE FAMILY BRANDS, INC.; *U.S. Private*, pg. 2662
MELLA HOTEL, INC.—See Vista Land & Lifescapes, Inc.; *Int'l*, pg. 8254
MELLANO & COMPANY; *U.S. Private*, pg. 2662
MELLANOX FEDERAL SYSTEMS, LLC—See NVIDIA Corporation; *U.S. Public*, pg. 1558
MELLANOX TECHNOLOGIES DENMARK A/S—See NVIDIA Corporation; *U.S. Public*, pg. 1558
MELLANOX TECHNOLOGIES, INC.—See NVIDIA Corporation; *U.S. Public*, pg. 1558

MELLANO & COMPANY

MELLANOX TECHNOLOGIES JAPAN K.K.—See NVIDIA Corporation; *U.S. Public*, pg. 1558
MELLANOX TECHNOLOGIES, LTD.—See NVIDIA Corporation; *U.S. Public*, pg. 1558
MELLAT INSURANCE COMPANY; *Int'l*, pg. 4811
MELLBY GARD HOLDING AB; *Int'l*, pg. 4811
MELLE DACHBAUSTOFFE GMBH—See SIG plc; *Int'l*, pg. 6906
MELLER FLOW TRANS LIMITED—See Axel Johnson Gruppen AB; *Int'l*, pg. 763
MELLES GRIOT AB—See IDEX Corp; *U.S. Public*, pg. 1091
MELLES GRIOT B.V.—See IDEX Corp; *U.S. Public*, pg. 1091
MELLING INDUSTRIES INC.—See Melling Tool Company Inc.; *U.S. Private*, pg. 2662
MELLING PRODUCTS CORPORATION—See Melling Tool Company Inc.; *U.S. Private*, pg. 2662
MELLING TOOL COMPANY INC. - AC FOUNDRY DIVISION—See Melling Tool Company Inc.; *U.S. Private*, pg. 2662
MELLING TOOL COMPANY INC. - MELLING CYLINDER SLEEVES DIVISION—See Melling Tool Company Inc.; *U.S. Private*, pg. 2662
MELLING TOOL COMPANY INC. - MELLING ENGINE PARTS DIVISION—See Melling Tool Company Inc.; *U.S. Private*, pg. 2662
MELLING TOOL COMPANY INC. - MELLING SELECT PERFORMANCE DIVISION—See Melling Tool Company Inc.; *U.S. Private*, pg. 2662
MELLING TOOL COMPANY INC. - MELLING SINTERED METALS DIVISION—See Melling Tool Company Inc.; *U.S. Private*, pg. 2662
MELLING TOOL COMPANY INC.; *U.S. Private*, pg. 2662
MELLING TOOL COMPANY INC—See Melling Tool Company Inc.; *U.S. Private*, pg. 2662
MELLON BANK, N.A.—See The Bank of New York Mellon Corporation; *U.S. Public*, pg. 2037
MELLON FUNDING CORPORATION—See The Bank of New York Mellon Corporation; *U.S. Public*, pg. 2037
MELLON INVESTMENTS CORPORATION—See The Bank of New York Mellon Corporation; *U.S. Public*, pg. 2037
MELLON TECHNOLOGY PTE LTD—See Digilife Technologies Limited; *Int'l*, pg. 2119
MELLOW INDUSTRIAL SERVICES, INC.—See PCL Employees Holdings Ltd.; *Int'l*, pg. 5769
MELLOY BROTHERS ENTERPRISES; *U.S. Private*, pg. 2662
MEL MICRON EUROPE LTD.—See Micron Technology, Inc.; *U.S. Public*, pg. 1437
MELNICKA ZDRAVOTNI, A.S.—See Fresenius SE & Co. KGaA; *Int'l*, pg. 2780
MELNICK EVEN DESENVOLVIMENTO IMOBILIARIO S.A.—See Even Construtora e Incorporadora S.A.; *Int'l*, pg. 2562
MELOCHE MONNEX INC.—See The Toronto-Dominion Bank; *Int'l*, pg. 7695
MELO CONTRACTORS, INC.; *U.S. Private*, pg. 2662
MEL-O-CREAM DONUTS INTERNATIONAL, INC.; *U.S. Private*, pg. 2661
MELODIOL GLOBAL HEALTH LIMITED; *Int'l*, pg. 4812
MELODY INVESTMENT ADVISORS LP; *U.S. Private*, pg. 2662
MELOTTE NV—See Tessenderlo Group NV; *Int'l*, pg. 7573
MEL RAPTON HONDA; *U.S. Private*, pg. 2661
MELROB-CHEMIPLUS LIMITED—See Melrob Limited; *Int'l*, pg. 4812
MELROB-EUROLABS LIMITED—See Melrob Limited; *Int'l*, pg. 4812
MELROB EUROPE GMBH—See Melrob Limited; *Int'l*, pg. 4812
MELROB IBERIA S.L.U—See Melrob Limited; *Int'l*, pg. 4812
MELROB KOREA LIMITED—See Melrob Limited; *Int'l*, pg. 4812
MELROB LIMITED; *Int'l*, pg. 4812
MELROB NUTRITION LIMITED—See Melrob Limited; *Int'l*, pg. 4812
MELROB SINGAPORE PTE. LTD—See Melrob Limited; *Int'l*, pg. 4812
MELROB US INC.—See Melrob Limited; *Int'l*, pg. 4812
MELROSE BANCORP, INC.; *U.S. Private*, pg. 2663
MELROSE COOPERATIVE BANK—See Melrose Bancorp, Inc.; *U.S. Private*, pg. 2663
MELROSE DAIRY PROTEINS, LLC; *U.S. Private*, pg. 2663
MELROSE FREE PRESS—See Gannett Co., Inc.; *U.S. Public*, pg. 902
MELROSE INDUSTRIES PLC; *Int'l*, pg. 4812
MELROSEMAC, INC.; *U.S. Private*, pg. 2663
MELROSE NORTH AMERICA INC—See Melrose Industries PLC; *Int'l*, pg. 4813
MELSOL MANAGEMENT, B.V.—See Melia Hotels International, S.A.; *Int'l*, pg. 4809
MELSPRING AGRO INDIA PVT. LTD.—See Olmix S.A.; *Int'l*, pg. 5554
MELSPRING FRANCE SARL—See Olmix S.A.; *Int'l*, pg. 5554

MELSPRING GMBH—See Olmix S.A.; *Int'l*, pg. 5554
MELSPRING INTERNATIONAL B.V.—See Olmix S.A.; *Int'l*, pg. 5554
MELSPRING ROMANIA SRL—See Olmix S.A.; *Int'l*, pg. 5554
MELSTACORP PLC; *Int'l*, pg. 4813
MELSTA LABORATORIES (PVT) LTD.—See Melstacorp PLC; *Int'l*, pg. 4813
MELSTAR INFORMATION TECHNOLOGIES LTD—See The Yash Birla Group; *Int'l*, pg. 7702
MELSTA TECHNOLOGY (PVT) LIMITED—See Melstacorp PLC; *Int'l*, pg. 4813
MEL STEVENSON & ASSOCIATES, INC.; *U.S. Private*, pg. 2661
MELTEC CO., LTD.—See Dowa Holdings Co., Ltd.; *Int'l*, pg. 2183
MELTEC IWAKI CO., LTD.—See Dowa Holdings Co., Ltd.; *Int'l*, pg. 2184
MELTEC S.A.—See Gewiss S.p.A.; *Int'l*, pg. 2955
MELTEMI KASTRI S.A.—See Technical Olympic SA; *Int'l*, pg. 7506
MELTEX ASIA PACIFIC CO., LTD.—See Astena Holdings Co., Ltd.; *Int'l*, pg. 653
MELTEX ASIA (THAILAND) CO., LTD.—See Astena Holdings Co., Ltd.; *Int'l*, pg. 653
MELTEX (HK) LTD.—See Astena Holdings Co., Ltd.; *Int'l*, pg. 653
MELTEX INC. - KUMAGAYA FACTORY—See Astena Holdings Co., Ltd.; *Int'l*, pg. 653
MELTEX INC.—See Astena Holdings Co., Ltd.; *Int'l*, pg. 653
MELTEX KOREA CO., LTD.—See Astena Holdings Co., Ltd.; *Int'l*, pg. 653
MELTEX TAIWAN INC.—See Astena Holdings Co., Ltd.; *Int'l*, pg. 653
MELTEX (TIANJIN) LTD.—See Astena Holdings Co., Ltd.; *Int'l*, pg. 653
THE MELTING POT RESTAURANTS INC.—See Front Burner Brands, Inc.; *U.S. Private*, pg. 1613
MELTMEDIA; *U.S. Private*, pg. 2663
MELTON COMPANY, INC.—See Matthews International Corporation; *U.S. Public*, pg. 1400
MELTON FOODS LIMITED—See Samworth Brothers Ltd.; *Int'l*, pg. 6519
MELTON MANAGEMENT INC.; *U.S. Private*, pg. 2663
MELTON MOWBRAY BUILDING SOCIETY; *Int'l*, pg. 4813
MELTON SALES, INC.; *U.S. Private*, pg. 2663
MELTON TRUCK LINES INC.; *U.S. Private*, pg. 2663
MELTRONIX, INC.; *U.S. Public*, pg. 1414
MELTWATER AUSTRALIA PTY. LTD.—See Meltwater N.V.; *Int'l*, pg. 4814
MELTWATER DEUTSCHLAND GMBH—See Meltwater N.V.; *Int'l*, pg. 4814
MELTWATER FINLAND OY—See Meltwater N.V.; *Int'l*, pg. 4814
MELTWATER JAPAN KK—See Meltwater N.V.; *Int'l*, pg. 4814
MELTWATER NEWS US INC.; *U.S. Private*, pg. 2663
MELTWATER N.V.; *Int'l*, pg. 4814
MELTWATER SINGAPORE PTE. LTD.—See Meltwater N.V.; *Int'l*, pg. 4814
MELTWATER SOUTH AFRICA (PTY.) LTD.—See Meltwater N.V.; *Int'l*, pg. 4814
MELTWATER SWEDEN AB—See Meltwater N.V.; *Int'l*, pg. 4814
MELTWATER THE NETHERLANDS B.V.—See Meltwater N.V.; *Int'l*, pg. 4814
MELUN AUTO; *Int'l*, pg. 4814
MELVILLE AUTOS PTY LTD—See Eagers Automotive Limited; *Int'l*, pg. 2263
MELVILLE LOGISTICS GMBH—See Viad Corp.; *U.S. Public*, pg. 2291
MELVILLE SHIPPING LIMITED—See Massy Holdings Ltd.; *Int'l*, pg. 4723
MELVILLE SURGERY CENTER, LLC—See North Shore Lij Health Systems; *U.S. Private*, pg. 2946
MELVIN CAPITAL MANAGEMENT LP; *U.S. Private*, pg. 2663
MELVIN L. DAVIS OIL CO. INC.; *U.S. Private*, pg. 2663
MEL WHEELER, INC.; *U.S. Private*, pg. 2661
MELZER'S FUEL SERVICE INC.—See BP plc; *Int'l*, pg. 1127
MEMAC OGILVY & MATHER W.L.L.—See WPP plc; *Int'l*, pg. 8484
MEMAC OGILVY PR—See WPP plc; *Int'l*, pg. 8490
MEMAC OGILVY—See WPP plc; *Int'l*, pg. 8484
MEMAC OGILVY—See WPP plc; *Int'l*, pg. 8484
MEMAC OGILVY—See WPP plc; *Int'l*, pg. 8484
MEMAC OGILVY—See WPP plc; *Int'l*, pg. 8484
MEMAC OGILVY—See WPP plc; *Int'l*, pg. 8484
MEMA PANASONIC—See Panasonic Holdings Corporation; *Int'l*, pg. 5720
MEM BAUCHEMIE GMBH—See Arkema S.A.; *Int'l*, pg. 571
MEMBERCLICKS LLC—See Pamlico Capital Management, L.P.; *U.S. Private*, pg. 3083
MEMBERHEALTH LLC—See CVS Health Corporation; *U.S. Public*, pg. 616
MEMBERS 1ST CREDIT UNION; *U.S. Private*, pg. 2663

CORPORATE AFFILIATIONS

MEMBERS CO., LTD.; *Int'l*, pg. 4814
MEMBERS COOPERATIVE CREDIT UNION; *U.S. Private*, pg. 2663
MEMBERS EQUITY BANK LIMITED—See Industry Super Holdings Pty. Ltd.; *Int'l*, pg. 3676
THE MEMBERS INSURANCE COMPANY—See Carolina Motor Club, Inc.; *U.S. Public*, pg. 768
MEMBERS LIFE INSURANCE COMPANY—See CMFG Life Insurance Company; *U.S. Private*, pg. 950
MEMBERS NET INC.—See Vision, Inc; *Int'l*, pg. 8253
MEMBERS TRUST COMPANY; *U.S. Private*, pg. 2663
MEMBERWORKS CANADA CORPORATION—See Vertrue Inc.; *U.S. Private*, pg. 4370
MEMBRATEK (PTY) LTD—See Veolia Environnement S.A.; *Int'l*, pg. 8163
MEMC ELECTRONIC MATERIALS SDN. BHD.—See Sino-American Silicon Products Inc.; *Int'l*, pg. 6948
MEMC ELECTRONIC MATERIALS S.P.A.—See Sino-American Silicon Products Inc.; *Int'l*, pg. 6948
MEMCINE PHARMACEUTICALS—See Spotlight Innovation Inc.; *U.S. Public*, pg. 3762
MEMC JAPAN LTD.—See Sino-American Silicon Products Inc.; *Int'l*, pg. 6948
MEMC KOREA COMPANY—See Sino-American Silicon Products Inc.; *Int'l*, pg. 6948
MEMC KUCHING SDN. BHD.—See SunEdison, Inc.; *U.S. Private*, pg. 3866
MEMCO ENGINEERING PRIVATE LIMITED—See Precision Camshafts Limited; *Int'l*, pg. 5957
MEMCO INC.; *U.S. Private*, pg. 2663
MEMCO LIMITED—See Halma plc; *Int'l*, pg. 3232
MEM CONSUMER FINANCE LIMITED—See Lone Star Global Acquisitions, LLC; *U.S. Private*, pg. 2487
MEMC PASADENA, INC.—See SunEdison, Inc.; *U.S. Private*, pg. 3866
MEMDATA, LLC—See Premier, Inc.; *U.S. Public*, pg. 1715
MEMEC GROUP LIMITED—See Avnet, Inc.; *U.S. Public*, pg. 253
MEMERY CRYSTAL LLP—See RBG Holdings PLC; *Int'l*, pg. 6227
MEMEX INC.; *Int'l*, pg. 4814
MEMG SECURITIES LTD.; *Int'l*, pg. 4814
MEMIONTEC HOLDINGS LTD.; *Int'l*, pg. 4814
MEMO EXPRESS SERVICES LLC—See Aramex PJSC; *Int'l*, pg. 535
MEMOMETAL UK LIMITED—See Stryker Corporation; *U.S. Public*, pg. 1956
MEMORA SERVICIOS FUNERARIOS S.L.—See 3i Group plc; *Int'l*, pg. 9
MEMORIALCARE SURGICAL CENTER AT ORANGE COAST, LLC—See Memorial Health Services; *U.S. Private*, pg. 2664
MEMORIALCARE SURGICAL CENTER AT SADDLEBACK, LLC—See Memorial Health Services; *U.S. Private*, pg. 2664
MEMORIAL COMMUNITY HEALTH, INC.; *U.S. Private*, pg. 2663
MEMORIAL DIALYSIS CENTER, L.P.—See DaVita Inc.; *U.S. Public*, pg. 641
MEMORIAL ENDOSCOPY CENTER—See HCA Healthcare, Inc.; *U.S. Public*, pg. 1002
MEMORIAL ESTATES, INC.—See Security National Financial Corporation; *U.S. Public*, pg. 1856
MEMORIAL GUARDIAN PLAN PTY LIMITED—See TPG Capital, L.P.; *U.S. Public*, pg. 2174
MEMORIAL HEALTHCARE GROUP, INC.—See HCA Healthcare, Inc.; *U.S. Public*, pg. 1002
MEMORIAL HEALTH CARE SYSTEMS; *U.S. Private*, pg. 2663
MEMORIAL HEALTH SERVICES; *U.S. Private*, pg. 2663
MEMORIAL HERMANN BAY AREA ENDOSCOPY CENTER, LLC—See Tenet Healthcare Corporation; *U.S. Public*, pg. 2011
MEMORIAL HERMANN ENDOSCOPY CENTER NORTH FREEWAY, LLC—See Tenet Healthcare Corporation; *U.S. Public*, pg. 2011
MEMORIAL HERMANN ENDOSCOPY & SURGERY CENTER NORTH HOUSTON, L.L.C.—See Tenet Healthcare Corporation; *U.S. Public*, pg. 2011
MEMORIAL HERMANN FOUNDATION; *U.S. Private*, pg. 2664
MEMORIAL HERMANN HEALTHCARE SYSTEM; *U.S. Private*, pg. 2664
MEMORIAL HERMANN SPECIALTY HOSPITAL KINGWOOD, L.L.C.—See Tenet Healthcare Corporation; *U.S. Public*, pg. 2011
MEMORIAL HERMANN SURGERY CENTER KATY, LLP—See Tenet Healthcare Corporation; *U.S. Public*, pg. 2011
MEMORIAL HERMANN SURGERY CENTER KINGSLAND, LLC—See Tenet Healthcare Corporation; *U.S. Public*, pg. 2011
MEMORIAL HERMANN SURGERY CENTER MEMORIAL CITY, L.L.C.—See Tenet Healthcare Corporation; *U.S. Public*, pg. 2011
MEMORIAL HERMANN SURGERY CENTER PINECROFT, LLC—See Tenet Healthcare Corporation; *U.S. Public*, pg. 2011

COMPANY NAME INDEX

MEMORIAL HERMANN SURGERY CENTER RICHMOND, LLC—See Tenet Healthcare Corporation; *U.S. Public*, pg. 2011
MEMORIAL HERMANN SURGERY CENTER SOUTHWEST, LLP—See Tenet Healthcare Corporation; *U.S. Public*, pg. 2011
MEMORIAL HERMANN SURGERY CENTER SUGAR LAND, LLP—See Tenet Healthcare Corporation; *U.S. Public*, pg. 2011
MEMORIAL HERMANN SURGERY CENTER TEXAS MEDICAL CENTER, LLP—See Tenet Healthcare Corporation; *U.S. Public*, pg. 2004
MEMORIAL HERMANN SURGERY CENTER - THE WOODLANDS, LLP—See Tenet Healthcare Corporation; *U.S. Public*, pg. 2011
MEMORIAL HERMANN SURGERY CENTER WOODLANDS PARKWAY, LLC—See Tenet Healthcare Corporation; *U.S. Public*, pg. 2011
MEMORIAL HERMANN TEXAS INTERNATIONAL ENDOSCOPY CENTER, LLC—See Tenet Healthcare Corporation; *U.S. Public*, pg. 2011
MEMORIAL HIGHWAY CHEVROLET, INC.—See General Motors Company; *U.S. Public*, pg. 926
MEMORIAL HOSPITAL, INC.; *U.S. Private*, pg. 2664
MEMORIAL HOSPITAL OF MARTINSVILLE & HENRY COUNTY AMBULATORY SURGERY CENTER, LLC—See Apollo Global Management, Inc.; *U.S. Public*, pg. 158
MEMORIAL HOSPITAL OF SOUTH BEND, INC.—See Beacon Health System, Inc.; *U.S. Private*, pg. 504
MEMORIAL HOSPITAL OF TAMPA—See HCA Healthcare, Inc.; *U.S. Public*, pg. 1002
MEMORIAL HOSPITAL—See HCA Healthcare, Inc.; *U.S. Public*, pg. 1002
MEMORIAL MANAGEMENT, INC.—See Quorum Health Corporation; *U.S. Private*, pg. 3330
MEMORIAL NEUROSURGERY GROUP, LLC—See HCA Healthcare, Inc.; *U.S. Public*, pg. 1002
MEMORIAL PARK CEMETERY ASSOCIATION OF MISSOURI, INC.—See Birch Hill Equity Partners Management Inc.; *Int'l*, pg. 1046
MEMORIAL PARK CEMETERY ASSOCIATION OF MISSOURI, INC.—See Homesteaders Life Co. Inc.; *U.S. Private*, pg. 1974
MEMORIAL REGIONAL HOSPITAL SOUTH—See South Broward Hospital District; *U.S. Private*, pg. 3720
MEMORIAL SATILLA SPECIALISTS, LLC—See HCA Healthcare, Inc.; *U.S. Public*, pg. 1002
MEMORIAL SLOAN-KETTERING CANCER CENTER INC.; *U.S. Private*, pg. 2664
MEMORIAL SPECIALTY HOSPITAL; *U.S. Private*, pg. 2664
MEMORIAL SURGERY CENTER, LLC—See Tenet Healthcare Corporation; *U.S. Public*, pg. 2011
MEMORIES CARIBE BEACH RESORT—See Sunwing Travel Group, Inc.; *Int'l*, pg. 7331
MEMORIES FLAMENCO BEACH RESORT—See Sunwing Travel Group, Inc.; *Int'l*, pg. 7331
MEMORIES HOLGUIN BEACH RESORT—See Sunwing Travel Group, Inc.; *Int'l*, pg. 7331
MEMORIES JIBACAO RESORT—See Sunwing Travel Group, Inc.; *Int'l*, pg. 7331
MEMORIES MIRAMAR HAVANA—See Sunwing Travel Group, Inc.; *Int'l*, pg. 7331
MEMORIES PARAISO BEACH RESORT—See Sunwing Travel Group, Inc.; *Int'l*, pg. 7332
MEMORIES TRINIDAD DEL MAR—See Sunwing Travel Group, Inc.; *Int'l*, pg. 7332
MEMORIES VARADERO BEACH RESORT—See Sunwing Travel Group, Inc.; *Int'l*, pg. 7332
MEMORIJA TURIZEM D.O.O.—See Novomatic AG; *Int'l*, pg. 5467
MEMORY 4 LESS; *U.S. Private*, pg. 2664
MEMORY GARDENS MANAGEMENT CORPORATION; *U.S. Private*, pg. 2664
MEMORY LANE CAKES LIMITED—See DBAY Advisors Limited; *Int'l*, pg. 1987
MEMORY-TECH CORPORATION; *Int'l*, pg. 4814
MEMOSUN, INC.; *U.S. Private*, pg. 2664
MEMOTEC INC.—See Comtech Telecommunications Corp.; *U.S. Public*, pg. 562
MEMPHIS AREA TRANSIT AUTHORITY; *U.S. Private*, pg. 2664
MEMPHIS BASKETBALL, LLC; *U.S. Private*, pg. 2664
MEMPHIS BUSINESS INTERIORS, LLC; *U.S. Private*, pg. 2664
MEMPHIS CITY EMPLOYEES CREDIT UNION; *U.S. Private*, pg. 2664
MEMPHIS DEVELOPMENT FOUNDATION; *U.S. Private*, pg. 2664
MEMPHIS EQUIPMENT COMPANY; *U.S. Private*, pg. 2664
MEMPHIS INVEST GP; *U.S. Private*, pg. 2664
MEMPHIS LIGHT, GAS & WATER; *U.S. Private*, pg. 2664
MEMPHIS PHARMACEUTICAL & CHEMICAL INDUSTRIES; *Int'l*, pg. 4814
MEMPHIS PUBLISHING COMPANY—See Gannett Co., Inc.; *U.S. Public*, pg. 898
MEMPHIS SCALE WORKS INC.; *U.S. Private*, pg. 2665

MEMPHIS SHELBY COUNTY AIRPORT AUTHORITY, INC.; *U.S. Private*, pg. 2665
MEMPHIS URGENT CARE #2, L.L.C.—See Tenet Healthcare Corporation; *U.S. Public*, pg. 2005
MEM PROPERTY MANAGEMENT CORPORATION; *U.S. Private*, pg. 2663
MEMRB PULS PANEL TRGOVINA DOO—See Brookfield Corporation; *Int'l*, pg. 1178
MEMRB PULS PANEL TRGOVINA DOO—See Elliott Management Corporation; *U.S. Private*, pg. 1371
MEMRY CORPORATION—See SAES Getters S.p.A.; *Int'l*, pg. 6467
MEMRY GMBH—See SAES Getters S.p.A.; *Int'l*, pg. 6467
MEMSENSING MICROSYSTEMS SUZHOU CHINA CO., LTD.; *Int'l*, pg. 4814
MEMSIC, INC.—See China Oceanwide Holdings Group Co., Ltd.; *Int'l*, pg. 1538
MEMSIC, INC.—See IDG Capital; *Int'l*, pg. 3594
MEMSSTAR LIMITED; *Int'l*, pg. 4814
MEMSTAR (MIANYANG) CO., LTD.—See Memstar Technology Ltd.; *Int'l*, pg. 4814
MEMSTAR PTE. LTD.—See CITIC Group Corporation; *Int'l*, pg. 1620
MEMSTAR TECHNOLOGY LTD.; *Int'l*, pg. 4814
MEMSTAR USA, INC.—See Memstar Technology Ltd.; *Int'l*, pg. 4814
MEMTECH INTERNATIONAL LTD; *Int'l*, pg. 4814
MEMTECH TECHNOLOGIES HOLDINGS CO., LTD.—See Memtech International Ltd; *Int'l*, pg. 4814
MEMTRON TECHNOLOGIES CO.—See TransDigm Group Incorporated; *U.S. Public*, pg. 2180
MENA DIALYSIS CENTER, LLC—See DaVita Inc.; *U.S. Public*, pg. 641
MENAFACTORS LIMITED—See FIMBank p.l.c.; *Int'l*, pg. 2664
MENAFN.COM—See The Middle East North Africa Financial Network, Inc.; *Int'l*, pg. 7666
MENA FOR TOURISTIC & REAL ESTATE INVESTMENT; *Int'l*, pg. 4815
MENAGE SELECTION VALNET S.A.S; *Int'l*, pg. 4815
MENA HYDROCARBONS INC.; *Int'l*, pg. 4815
MENA INTERNATIONAL PETROLEUM COMPANY LIMITED—See Public Investment Corporation (SOC) Limited; *Int'l*, pg. 6094
MENA MANI INDUSTRIES LIMITED; *Int'l*, pg. 4815
MENA MEDICAL CENTER HOME HEALTH, LLC—See UnitedHealth Group Incorporated; *U.S. Public*, pg. 2246
MENANG CONSTRUCTION (M) SDN. BHD.—See Menang Corporation (M) Berhad; *Int'l*, pg. 4815
MENANG CORPORATION (M) BERHAD; *Int'l*, pg. 4815
MENANG DEVELOPMENT (M) SDN. BHD.—See Menang Corporation (M) Berhad; *Int'l*, pg. 4815
MENAPHI; *Int'l*, pg. 4815
MENARA HAP SENG SDN. BHD.—See Hap Seng Consolidated Berhad; *Int'l*, pg. 3268
MENARA KUALA LUMPUR SDN. BHD.—See Telekom Malaysia Berhad; *Int'l*, pg. 7537
MENARA NETWORKS, INC.—See IPG Photonics Corporation; *U.S. Public*, pg. 1167
MENARA VENTURES; *Int'l*, pg. 4815
MENARD AUTOMOBILES—See Toyota Tsusho Corporation; *Int'l*, pg. 7876
MENARD BACHY PTY LTD—See VINCI S.A.; *Int'l*, pg. 8233
MENARD CANADA INC.—See VINCI S.A.; *Int'l*, pg. 8224
MENARD ELECTRIC COOPERATIVE; *U.S. Private*, pg. 2665
MENARD FREYSSINET EGYPT—See VINCI S.A.; *Int'l*, pg. 8233
MENARD GEOSYSTEMS SDN BHD—See VINCI S.A.; *Int'l*, pg. 8233
MENARD GEOSYSTEMS SINGAPORE PTE. LTD.—See VINCI S.A.; *Int'l*, pg. 8224
MENARDI-CRISWELL—See Hosokawa Micron Corporation; *Int'l*, pg. 3486
MENARDI FILTERS EUROPE A/S—See Nederman Holding AB; *Int'l*, pg. 5189
MENARD, INC.; *U.S. Private*, pg. 2665
MENARD (MADRID)—See VINCI S.A.; *Int'l*, pg. 8232
MENARD MIDDLE EAST CONTRACTING LLC—See VINCI S.A.; *Int'l*, pg. 8224
MENARD OIL CO.; *U.S. Private*, pg. 2665
MENARD POLSKA SP. Z O.O.—See VINCI S.A.; *Int'l*, pg. 8233
MENARD—See VINCI S.A.; *Int'l*, pg. 8233
MENARD THAILAND—See VINCI S.A.; *Int'l*, pg. 8233
MENARD VIBRO—See VINCI S.A.; *Int'l*, pg. 8232
MENARD VIETNAM—See VINCI S.A.; *Int'l*, pg. 8233
MENA REAL ESTATE COMPANY - KPSC; *Int'l*, pg. 4815
MENA RE UNDERWRITERS LTD.—See Doha Insurance Group QPSC; *Int'l*, pg. 2155
MENASHA CORPORATION; *U.S. Private*, pg. 2665
MENASHA CORP., POLY HI SOLIDUR—See Menasha Corporation; *U.S. Private*, pg. 2665
MENASHA CORP., TRAEX DIVISION—See Menasha Corporation; *U.S. Private*, pg. 2665
MENASHA ELECTRIC & WATER UTILITIES; *U.S. Private*, pg. 2666

MENASHA PACKAGING COMPANY, LLC - AURORA FACILITY—See Menasha Corporation; *U.S. Private*, pg. 2665
MENASHA PACKAGING COMPANY, LLC - BETHLEHEM FACILITY—See Menasha Corporation; *U.S. Private*, pg. 2665
MENASHA PACKAGING COMPANY, LLC - BROOKLYN PARK PLANT—See Menasha Corporation; *U.S. Private*, pg. 2665
MENASHA PACKAGING COMPANY, LLC - CINCINNATI FACILITY—See Menasha Corporation; *U.S. Private*, pg. 2665
MENASHA PACKAGING COMPANY, LLC - COLOMA—See Menasha Corporation; *U.S. Private*, pg. 2665
MENASHA PACKAGING COMPANY, LLC - EDWARDSVILLE FACILITY—See Menasha Corporation; *U.S. Private*, pg. 2665
MENASHA PACKAGING COMPANY, LLC - ERIE—See Menasha Corporation; *U.S. Private*, pg. 2665
MENASHA PACKAGING COMPANY, LLC - FANFOLD PLANT—See Menasha Corporation; *U.S. Private*, pg. 2665
MENASHA PACKAGING COMPANY, LLC - HARTFORD PLANT—See Menasha Corporation; *U.S. Private*, pg. 2665
MENASHA PACKAGING COMPANY, LLC - HODGKINS FACILITY—See Menasha Corporation; *U.S. Private*, pg. 2665
MENASHA PACKAGING COMPANY, LLC - LAKEVILLE PLANT—See Menasha Corporation; *U.S. Private*, pg. 2665
MENASHA PACKAGING COMPANY, LLC - MINOOKA FACILITY—See Menasha Corporation; *U.S. Private*, pg. 2665
MENASHA PACKAGING COMPANY, LLC - MUSCATINE PLANT—See Menasha Corporation; *U.S. Private*, pg. 2665
MENASHA PACKAGING COMPANY, LLC - ONTARIO FACILITY—See Menasha Corporation; *U.S. Private*, pg. 2665
MENASHA PACKAGING COMPANY, LLC - PHILADELPHIA PLANT—See Menasha Corporation; *U.S. Private*, pg. 2665
MENASHA PACKAGING COMPANY, LLC - ROCK ISLAND FACILITY—See Menasha Corporation; *U.S. Private*, pg. 2665
MENASHA PACKAGING COMPANY, LLC - SANTA FE SPRINGS PLANT—See Menasha Corporation; *U.S. Private*, pg. 2665
MENASHA PACKAGING COMPANY, LLC—See Menasha Corporation; *U.S. Private*, pg. 2665
MENASHA PACKAGING COMPANY, LLC - ST. CLOUD PLANT—See Menasha Corporation; *U.S. Private*, pg. 2665
MENASHA PACKAGING COMPANY, LLC - YUKON PLANT—See Menasha Corporation; *U.S. Private*, pg. 2665
MENATH INSURANCE, AN ALERA GROUP AGENCY, LLC—See Genstar Capital, LLC; *U.S. Private*, pg. 1674
MENCAST HOLDINGS LTD.; *Int'l*, pg. 4815
MENCAST MARINE PTE. LTD.—See Mencast Holdings Ltd.; *Int'l*, pg. 4815
MENCK GMBH—See Buckthorn Partners LLP; *Int'l*, pg. 1210
MENCK GMBH—See OEP Capital Advisors, L.P.; *U.S. Private*, pg. 2997
MEND CONSULTING PTY. LTD.—See Duratec Limited; *Int'l*, pg. 2228
THE MENDED HEARTS, INC.; *U.S. Private*, pg. 4077
MENDELEY LTD.—See RELX plc; *Int'l*, pg. 6268
MENDELL MACHINE AND MANUFACTURING, LLC—See Frazier & Company, Inc.; *U.S. Private*, pg. 1599
MENDEL PLUMBING & HEATING, INC.; *U.S. Private*, pg. 2666
MENDELSON INFRASTRUCTURES & INDUSTRIES LTD.; *Int'l*, pg. 4815
MENDERES TEKSTIL SANAYI VE TICARET AS; *Int'l*, pg. 4815
MENDES JUNIOR TRADING E ENGENHARIA S.A.; *Int'l*, pg. 4815
MENDES MOTORS LIMITED; *Int'l*, pg. 4815
MENDES SA; *Int'l*, pg. 4815
MENDEZ & CO. INC.; *U.S. Private*, pg. 2666
MENDEZ INTERNATIONAL TROPICAL FOODS, INC.—See GrubMarket, Inc.; *U.S. Private*, pg. 1797
MENDIP MEDIA GROUP LIMITED—See Appen Limited; *Int'l*, pg. 519
MENDIX TECHNOLOGY B.V.—See Siemens Aktiengesellschaft; *Int'l*, pg. 6887
THE MENDOCINO BEACON—See Alden Global Capital LLC; *U.S. Private*, pg. 159
MENDOCINO DIALYSIS, LLC—See DaVita Inc.; *U.S. Public*, pg. 641
MENDOCINO REDWOOD COMPANY, LLC; *U.S. Private*, pg. 2666
MENDO MILL & LUMBER CO.; *U.S. Private*, pg. 2666
MENDON LEASING CORPORATION—See Groupe Petit Forestier SAS; *Int'l*, pg. 3109

MENDO MILL & LUMBER CO.

MENDOTA INSURANCE COMPANY—See Centene Corporation; *U.S. Public*, pg. 470
MENDOTA PUBLISHING CORPORATION—See News Media Corporation; *U.S. Private*, pg. 2916
MENDUS AB; *Int'l*, pg. 4815
MENEBA BV—See Nimbus B.V.; *Int'l*, pg. 5296
MENE INC.; *Int'l*, pg. 4815
MENEMSHA; *U.S. Private*, pg. 2666
MENERGA AS—See Systemair AB; *Int'l*, pg. 7391
MENERGA GMBH—See Systemair AB; *Int'l*, pg. 7391
MENERGA NV—See Systemair AB; *Int'l*, pg. 7391
MENERGA POLSKA SP. Z O.O.—See Systemair AB; *Int'l*, pg. 7391
MENERGIA INC.—See Aucnet Inc.; *Int'l*, pg. 700
MENGALI ACCOUNTANCY—See Moss Adams LLP; *U.S. Private*, pg. 2793
MENGER HOTEL—See Gal-Tex Hotel Corporation; *U.S. Private*, pg. 1635
MENGNIU DAIRY (DENGKOU BAYAN GAOLE) CO., LTD.—See China Mengniu Dairy Company Limited; *Int'l*, pg. 1520
MENHADEN RESOURCE EFFICIENCY PLC; *Int'l*, pg. 4816
MENICON AMERICA, INC.—See Menicon Co., Ltd.; *Int'l*, pg. 4816
MENICON AUSTRALIA PTY LTD.—See Menicon Co., Ltd.; *Int'l*, pg. 4816
MENICON BUSINESS ASSIST CO., LTD.—See Menicon Co., Ltd.; *Int'l*, pg. 4816
MENICON B.V.—See Menicon Co., Ltd.; *Int'l*, pg. 4816
MENICON CO., LTD.; *Int'l*, pg. 4816
MENICON ESPANA S.L.—See Menicon Co., Ltd.; *Int'l*, pg. 4816
MENICON GMBH—See Menicon Co., Ltd.; *Int'l*, pg. 4816
MENICON KOREA CO., LTD.—See Menicon Co., Ltd.; *Int'l*, pg. 4816
MENICON LTD.—See Menicon Co., Ltd.; *Int'l*, pg. 4816
MENICON NECT CO., LTD.—See Menicon Co., Ltd.; *Int'l*, pg. 4816
MENICON PHARMA SAS—See Menicon Co., Ltd.; *Int'l*, pg. 4816
MENICON SAS—See Menicon Co., Ltd.; *Int'l*, pg. 4816
MENICON SINGAPORE SALES PTE. LTD.—See Menicon Co., Ltd.; *Int'l*, pg. 4816
MENICO TUCK PARRISH FINANCIAL SERVICES PTY. LTD.—See Azimut Holding SpA; *Int'l*, pg. 779
MENIF FINANCIAL SERVICES LTD.; *Int'l*, pg. 4816
MENIGO FOODSERVICE AB—See Sysco Corporation; *U.S. Public*, pg. 1973
M.E. NIKKISO CO., LTD.—See Nikkiso Co., Ltd.; *Int'l*, pg. 5291
MENIN HOTELS, INC.; *U.S. Private*, pg. 2666
MENI-ONE CO., LTD.—See Menicon Co., Ltd.; *Int'l*, pg. 4816
MENIVIM THE NEW REIT LTD.; *Int'l*, pg. 4816
MENKE AGRAR GMBH—See AGRAVIS Raiffeisen AG; *Int'l*, pg. 215
MENKE AGRAR POLSKA SP. Z O.O.—See AGRAVIS Raiffeisen AG; *Int'l*, pg. 215
MENKEN ORLANDO B.V.—See Intersnack Group GmbH & Co. KG; *Int'l*, pg. 3761
THE MENKITI GROUP; *U.S. Private*, pg. 4077
MENLO EQUITIES LLC; *U.S. Private*, pg. 2666
MENLO INNOVATIONS LLC; *U.S. Private*, pg. 2666
MENLO TECHNOLOGIES, INC.—See Quisitive Technology Solutions, Inc.; *Int'l*, pg. 6165
MEN MIKRO ELEKTRONIK GMBH—See Deutsche Beteiligungs AG; *Int'l*, pg. 2063
MENNA DEVELOPMENT & MANAGEMENT, INC.; *U.S. Private*, pg. 2666
MENNELLA'S POULTRY CO. INC.; *U.S. Private*, pg. 2666
THE MENNEL MILLING COMPANY - BUCYRUS FLOUR MILL—See The Mennel Milling Company; *U.S. Private*, pg. 4077
THE MENNEL MILLING COMPANY OF ILLINOIS INC.—See The Mennel Milling Company; *U.S. Private*, pg. 4077
THE MENNEL MILLING COMPANY OF INDIANA INC.—See The Mennel Milling Company; *U.S. Private*, pg. 4077
THE MENNEL MILLING COMPANY OF MICHIGAN INC.—See The Mennel Milling Company; *U.S. Private*, pg. 4077
THE MENNEL MILLING COMPANY OF VIRGINIA, INC.—See The Mennel Milling Company; *U.S. Private*, pg. 4077
THE MENNEL MILLING COMPANY; *U.S. Private*, pg. 4077
THE MENNEL MILLING COMPANY - VALLEY GRAIN DIVISION—See The Mennel Milling Company; *U.S. Private*, pg. 4077
MENNEL MILLING LOGAN; *U.S. Private*, pg. 2666
MENNEN MEDICAL CORP.—See Mennen Medical Ltd.; *Int'l*, pg. 4816
MENNEN MEDICAL LTD.; *Int'l*, pg. 4816
MENNENS AMSTERDAM BV—See Axel Johnson Gruppen AB; *Int'l*, pg. 764
MENNENS BELGIUM—See Axel Johnson Gruppen AB; *Int'l*, pg. 764
MENNENS DONGEN BV—See Axel Johnson Gruppen AB; *Int'l*, pg. 764
MENNENS GRONINGEN BV—See Axel Johnson Gruppen AB; *Int'l*, pg. 764
MENNENS HENGELO BV—See Axel Johnson Gruppen AB; *Int'l*, pg. 764
MENNENS SCHIEDAM BV—See Axel Johnson Gruppen AB; *Int'l*, pg. 764
MENNICA INVEST SP. Z O.O.—See Mennica Polska S.A.; *Int'l*, pg. 4816
MENNICA-METALE SZLACHETNE S.A.—See Mennica Polska S.A.; *Int'l*, pg. 4816
MENNICA POLSKA S.A.; *Int'l*, pg. 4816
MENNMEDIA, INC.; *U.S. Private*, pg. 2666
MENNONITE FRIENDSHIP COMMUNITIES; *U.S. Private*, pg. 2666
MENNONITE GENERAL HOSPITAL, INC.; *U.S. Private*, pg. 2666
MENNO TRAVEL SERVICE, INC.; *U.S. Private*, pg. 2666
MENON AND MENON LIMITED—See Menon Pistons Ltd.; *Int'l*, pg. 4816
MENON BEARINGS LTD.—See Menon Pistons Ltd.; *Int'l*, pg. 4816
MENONO, INC.; *U.S. Private*, pg. 2666
MENON PISTON RINGS PVT LIMITED—See Menon Pistons Ltd.; *Int'l*, pg. 4816
MENON PISTONS LTD. - PLANT 2—See Menon Pistons Ltd.; *Int'l*, pg. 4816
MENON PISTONS LTD. - PLANT 3—See Menon Pistons Ltd.; *Int'l*, pg. 4816
MENON PISTONS LTD.; *Int'l*, pg. 4816
MENORAH CAMPUS, INC.; *U.S. Private*, pg. 2666
MENORAH MANOR; *U.S. Private*, pg. 2666
MENORAH MEDICAL GROUP, LLC—See HCA Healthcare, Inc.; *U.S. Public*, pg. 1002
MENORAH PARK CENTER FOR SENIOR LIVING; *U.S. Private*, pg. 2667
MENORA MIVTACHIM HOLDINGS LTD.; *Int'l*, pg. 4816
MENSA SINAI TICARI VE MALI YATIRIMLAR AS; *Int'l*, pg. 4817
MENSCHICK TROCKENSYSTEME GMBH—See Heidelberger Druckmaschinen AG; *Int'l*, pg. 3322
MENSCH UND MASCHINE ACADGRAPH GMBH—See Mensch und Maschine Software SE; *Int'l*, pg. 4817
MENSCH UND MASCHINE AT WORK GMBH—See Mensch und Maschine Software SE; *Int'l*, pg. 4817
MENSCH UND MASCHINE AUSTRIA GMBH—See Mensch und Maschine Software SE; *Int'l*, pg. 4817
MENSCH UND MASCHINE BENCON 3D GMBH—See Mensch und Maschine Software SE; *Int'l*, pg. 4817
MENSCH UND MASCHINE DEUTSCHLAND GMBH—See Mensch und Maschine Software SE; *Int'l*, pg. 4817
MENSCH UND MASCHINE HABERZETTL GMBH—See Mensch und Maschine Software SE; *Int'l*, pg. 4817
MENSCH UND MASCHINE HUNGARY KFT.—See Mensch und Maschine Software SE; *Int'l*, pg. 4817
MENSCH UND MASCHINE INFRASTRUKTUR GMBH—See Mensch und Maschine Software SE; *Int'l*, pg. 4817
MENSCH UND MASCHINE SCHOLLE GMBH—See Mensch und Maschine Software SE; *Int'l*, pg. 4817
MENSCH UND MASCHINE SCHWEIZ AG—See Mensch und Maschine Software SE; *Int'l*, pg. 4817
MENSCH UND MASCHINE SOFTWARE SE; *Int'l*, pg. 4817
MENSCH UND MASCHINE TEDIKON GMBH—See Mensch und Maschine Software SE; *Int'l*, pg. 4817
MENSENLINQ BV—See DPG Media Group NV; *Int'l*, pg. 2189
MENSI, S.A.—See Trimble, Inc.; *U.S. Public*, pg. 2190
MEN'S JOURNAL—See Penske Media Corporation; *U.S. Private*, pg. 3139
MEN'S SHELTER OF CHARLOTTE, INC.—See Urban Ministry Center; *U.S. Private*, pg. 4314
THE MENS WEARHOUSE, INC—See Tailored Brands, Inc.; *U.S. Public*, pg. 1979
MENTAL HEALTH ASSOCIATION OF CONNECTICUT INC.; *U.S. Private*, pg. 2667
MENTAL HEALTH ASSOCIATION OF NEW YORK CITY; *U.S. Private*, pg. 2667
MENTAL HEALTH CARE, INC.; *U.S. Private*, pg. 2667
THE MENTAL HEALTH CENTER OF GREATER MANCHESTER; *U.S. Private*, pg. 4078
MENTAL HEALTH CONNECTICUT, INC.; *U.S. Private*, pg. 2667
MENTAL HEALTH PARTNERS; *U.S. Private*, pg. 2667
MENTAL HEALTH SERVICES FOR CLARK AND MADISON COUNTIES, INC.; *U.S. Private*, pg. 2667
MENTAL HEALTH TECHNOLOGIES CO., LTD.—See Vector Inc.; *Int'l*, pg. 8144
MENTER, RUDIN & TRIVELPIECE, P.C.—See Barclay Damon, LLP; *U.S. Private*, pg. 473
MENTHOLATUM (AP) LTD.—See Rohto Pharmaceutical Co. Ltd.; *Int'l*, pg. 6387
MENTHOLATUM (ASIA PACIFIC) LTD.—See Rohto Pharmaceutical Co. Ltd.; *Int'l*, pg. 6387
MENTHOLATUM AUSTRALASIA PTY. LTD.—See Rohto Pharmaceutical Co. Ltd.; *Int'l*, pg. 6387

CORPORATE AFFILIATIONS

MENTHOLATUM (CHINA) PHARMACEUTICALS COMPANY LIMITED—See Rohto Pharmaceutical Co. Ltd.; *Int'l*, pg. 6387
THE MENTHOLATUM COMPANY LIMITED—See Rohto Pharmaceutical Co. Ltd.; *Int'l*, pg. 6387
THE MENTHOLATUM COMPANY OF CANADA, LIMITED—See Rohto Pharmaceutical Co. Ltd.; *Int'l*, pg. 6387
THE MENTHOLATUM COMPANY—See Rohto Pharmaceutical Co. Ltd.; *Int'l*, pg. 6387
MENTHOLATUM DE MEXICO, SOCIEDAD ANNIMA DE CAPITAL VARIABLE—See Rohto Pharmaceutical Co. Ltd.; *Int'l*, pg. 6387
MENTHOLATUM SOUTH AFRICA (PTY) LTD.—See Rohto Pharmaceutical Co. Ltd.; *Int'l*, pg. 6387
MENTHOLATUM TAIWAN LIMITED—See Rohto Pharmaceutical Co. Ltd.; *Int'l*, pg. 6387
THE MENTHOLATUM (ZHONGSHAN) PHARMACEUTICALS CO., LTD.—See Rohto Pharmaceutical Co. Ltd.; *Int'l*, pg. 6387
MENTICE AB; *Int'l*, pg. 4818
MENTIGA CORPORATION BERHAD; *Int'l*, pg. 4818
MENTIGA PLANTATION SDN BHD—See Mentiga Corporation Berhad; *Int'l*, pg. 4818
MENTIS NEURO EL PASO, LLC—See Centerbridge Partners, L.P.; *U.S. Private*, pg. 813
MENTIS NEURO HOUSTON, LLC—See Centerbridge Partners, L.P.; *U.S. Private*, pg. 813
MENTIS NEURO SAN ANTONIO, LLC—See Centerbridge Partners, L.P.; *U.S. Private*, pg. 813
MENTOLATUM (ASIA-PACIFIC) LIMITED—See Rohto Pharmaceutical Co. Ltd.; *Int'l*, pg. 6387
MENTOR ABI GROUP—See Centerbridge Partners, L.P.; *U.S. Private*, pg. 813
MENTOR ABI, LLC—See Centerbridge Partners, L.P.; *U.S. Private*, pg. 814
MENTORA GROUP, INC.—See CDW Corporation; *U.S. Public*, pg. 463
MENTOR BUSINESS SYSTEMS LIMITED—See Carrier Global Corporation; *U.S. Public*, pg. 443
MENTOR B.V.—See Johnson & Johnson; *U.S. Public*, pg. 1199
MENTOR CAPITAL, INC.; *U.S. Public*, pg. 1414
MENTORCLIQ, INC.; *U.S. Private*, pg. 2667
MENTOR CORPORATION—See Johnson & Johnson; *U.S. Public*, pg. 1196
MENTOR DEUTSCHLAND GMBH—See Johnson & Johnson; *U.S. Public*, pg. 1196
MENTOR EMULATION DIVISION—See Siemens Aktiengesellschaft; *Int'l*, pg. 6890
MENTOR GRAPHICS ASIA PTE LTD.—See Siemens Aktiengesellschaft; *Int'l*, pg. 6890
MENTOR GRAPHICS (CANADA) LIMITED—See Siemens Aktiengesellschaft; *Int'l*, pg. 6890
MENTOR GRAPHICS CORP. - EMBEDDED SOFTWARE DIVISION—See Siemens Aktiengesellschaft; *Int'l*, pg. 6890
MENTOR GRAPHICS CORPORATION—See Siemens Aktiengesellschaft; *Int'l*, pg. 6890
MENTOR GRAPHICS (DEUTSCHLAND) GMBH—See Siemens Aktiengesellschaft; *Int'l*, pg. 6890
MENTOR GRAPHICS (DEUTSCHLAND) GMBH—See Siemens Aktiengesellschaft; *Int'l*, pg. 6890
MENTOR GRAPHICS DEVELOPMENT (SHENZHEN)—See Siemens Aktiengesellschaft; *Int'l*, pg. 6890
MENTOR GRAPHICS EGYPT COMPANY—See Siemens Aktiengesellschaft; *Int'l*, pg. 6890
MENTOR GRAPHICS (ESPANA) S.L.—See Siemens Aktiengesellschaft; *Int'l*, pg. 6890
MENTOR GRAPHICS (FINLAND) OY—See Siemens Aktiengesellschaft; *Int'l*, pg. 6890
MENTOR GRAPHICS (FRANCE) SARL—See Siemens Aktiengesellschaft; *Int'l*, pg. 6890
MENTOR GRAPHICS GERMANY GMBH—See Siemens Aktiengesellschaft; *Int'l*, pg. 6890
MENTOR GRAPHICS (INDIA) PRIVATE LIMITED—See Siemens Aktiengesellschaft; *Int'l*, pg. 6890
MENTOR GRAPHICS (IRELAND) LIMITED—See Siemens Aktiengesellschaft; *Int'l*, pg. 6890
MENTOR GRAPHICS JAPAN CO., LTD. - NAGOYA BRANCH—See Siemens Aktiengesellschaft; *Int'l*, pg. 6890
MENTOR GRAPHICS JAPAN CO., LTD. - OSAKA BRANCH—See Siemens Aktiengesellschaft; *Int'l*, pg. 6890
MENTOR GRAPHICS JAPAN CO. LTD.—See Siemens Aktiengesellschaft; *Int'l*, pg. 6890
MENTOR GRAPHICS (KOREA) LLC—See Siemens Aktiengesellschaft; *Int'l*, pg. 6890
MENTOR GRAPHICS MAGYARORSZAG KFT—See Siemens Aktiengesellschaft; *Int'l*, pg. 6890
MENTOR GRAPHICS-MECHANICAL ANALYSIS DIVISION—See Siemens Aktiengesellschaft; *Int'l*, pg. 6890
MENTOR GRAPHICS (NETHERLANDS) B.V.—See Siemens Aktiengesellschaft; *Int'l*, pg. 6890

COMPANY NAME INDEX

MENTOR GRAPHICS PAKISTAN DEVELOPMENT (PRIVATE) LIMITED—See Siemens Aktiengesellschaft; *Int'l*, pg. 6890
MENTOR GRAPHICS (SALES AND SERVICES) PRIVATE LIMITED—See Siemens Aktiengesellschaft; *Int'l*, pg. 6890
MENTOR GRAPHICS SARL—See Siemens Aktiengesellschaft; *Int'l*, pg. 6890
MENTOR GRAPHICS (SCANDINAVIA) AB—See Siemens Aktiengesellschaft; *Int'l*, pg. 6890
MENTOR GRAPHICS (SCHWEIZ) AG—See Siemens Aktiengesellschaft; *Int'l*, pg. 6890
MENTOR GRAPHICS (SHANGHAI) ELECTRONIC TECHNOLOGY CO., LTD.—See Siemens Aktiengesellschaft; *Int'l*, pg. 6890
MENTOR GRAPHICS—See Siemens Aktiengesellschaft; *Int'l*, pg. 6890
MENTOR GRAPHICS—See Siemens Aktiengesellschaft; *Int'l*, pg. 6890
MENTOR GRAPHICS—See Siemens Aktiengesellschaft; *Int'l*, pg. 6890
MENTOR GRAPHICS (TAIWAN) LIMITED—See Siemens Aktiengesellschaft; *Int'l*, pg. 6890
MENTOR GRAPHICS (UK) LIMITED—See Siemens Aktiengesellschaft; *Int'l*, pg. 6890
MENTOR IMC (AUSTRALIA) PTY. LTD.—See VINCI S.A.; *Int'l*, pg. 8224
MENTOR IMC GROUP LTD.—See VINCI S.A.; *Int'l*, pg. 8224
MENTOR IMC (SINGAPORE) PTE. LTD.—See VINCI S.A.; *Int'l*, pg. 8224
MENTOR IMC (USA) INC.—See VINCI S.A.; *Int'l*, pg. 8224
MENTORING MINDS LP; *U.S. Private*, pg. 2667
THE MENTOR LUMBER & SUPPLY CO., INC.; *U.S. Private*, pg. 4078
MENTOR MANAGEMENT, INC.—See Centerbridge Partners, L.P.; *U.S. Private*, pg. 814
MENTOR MANAGEMENT LIMITED—See CBRE Group, Inc.; *U.S. Public*, pg. 460
MENTOR MARYLAND, INC.—See Centerbridge Partners, L.P.; *U.S. Private*, pg. 814
MENTORMATE, INC.—See TietoEVRY Oyj; *Int'l*, pg. 7745
MENTOR MEDIA CBZ (CHONGQING) CO., LTD—See Carl Bennet AB; *Int'l*, pg. 1332
MENTOR MEDIA (CHONGQING) CO., LTD—See Carl Bennet AB; *Int'l*, pg. 1332
MENTOR MEDIA CZECH S.R.O—See Carl Bennet AB; *Int'l*, pg. 1332
MENTOR MEDIA JAPAN GODOGAISHA—See Carl Bennet AB; *Int'l*, pg. 1332
MENTOR MEDIA JUAREZ S.A. DE C.V—See Carl Bennet AB; *Int'l*, pg. 1332
MENTOR MEDIA (KUNSHAN) CO., LTD—See Carl Bennet AB; *Int'l*, pg. 1332
MENTOR MEDIA LTD—See Carl Bennet AB; *Int'l*, pg. 1332
MENTOR MEDIA (SHENZHEN) CO., LTD—See Carl Bennet AB; *Int'l*, pg. 1332
MENTOR MEDIA (SONGJIANG) CO., LTD—See Carl Bennet AB; *Int'l*, pg. 1332
MENTOR MEDIA (SUZHOU) CO., LTD—See Carl Bennet AB; *Int'l*, pg. 1332
MENTOR MEDIA (USA) SUPPLY CHAIN MANAGEMENT INC—See Carl Bennet AB; *Int'l*, pg. 1332
MENTOR MEDIA (XIAMEN) CO., LTD—See Carl Bennet AB; *Int'l*, pg. 1332
MENTOR MEDICAL SYSTEMS B.V.—See Johnson & Johnson; *U.S. Public*, pg. 1196
MENTOR MEDICAL SYSTEMS LTD.—See Johnson & Johnson; *U.S. Public*, pg. 1196
MENTOR MEDICAL SYSTEMS PTY. LTD.—See Johnson & Johnson; *U.S. Public*, pg. 1196
MENTOR MITSUBISHI; *U.S. Private*, pg. 2667
THE MENTOR NETWORK; *U.S. Private*, pg. 4078
MENTORN INTERNATIONAL—See Vitruvian Partners LLP; *Int'l*, pg. 8263
MENTOR ONLINE AB; *Int'l*, pg. 4818
MENTOR PARTNERS LLC; *U.S. Private*, pg. 2667
MENTOR TEXAS L.P.—See Johnson & Johnson; *U.S. Public*, pg. 1199
MENTOR TEXAS—See Johnson & Johnson; *U.S. Public*, pg. 1196
MENTOR WORLDWIDE LLC—See Johnson & Johnson; *U.S. Public*, pg. 1199
MENTZENDORFF & CO LTD; *Int'l*, pg. 4818
MENUETT GRUNDSTUCKSVERWALTUNGSGESELLSCHAFT M.B.H.—See UniCredit S.p.A.; *Int'l*, pg. 8037
MENU FOODS MIDWEST CORPORATION, INC—See Simmons Foods, Inc.; *U.S. Private*, pg. 3665
MENUISERIE DES PINS LTD.—See Richelieu Hardware Ltd.; *Int'l*, pg. 6331
MENUISERIE DU CENTRE—See Compagnie de Saint-Gobain SA; *Int'l*, pg. 1724
MENUISERIE G. DUBOIS; *Int'l*, pg. 4818
MENULOG PTY. LTD.—See Just Eat Takeaway.com N.V.; *Int'l*, pg. 4030
MENU MAKER FOODS INC.; *U.S. Private*, pg. 2667
MENY AS—See NorgesGruppen ASA; *Int'l*, pg. 5427
MENZEL INC.; *U.S. Private*, pg. 2667

MENZIES AVIATION GROUP—See Agility; *Int'l*, pg. 210
MENZIES CHRYSLER INC.; *Int'l*, pg. 4818
MENZIES DISTRIBUTION LIMITED—See Endless LLP; *Int'l*, pg. 2403
MENZIES GROUP LIMITED; *Int'l*, pg. 4818
MENZIS—See Allianz SE; *Int'l*, pg. 354
MENZIS—See Munchener Ruckversicherungs AG; *Int'l*, pg. 5087
MENZNER LUMBER AND SUPPLY CO.; *U.S. Private*, pg. 2667
MENZOLIT GMBH—See senata GmbH; *Int'l*, pg. 6707
MENZOLIT LTD. (UK)—See senata GmbH; *Int'l*, pg. 6707
MENZOLIT S.R.L.—See senata GmbH; *Int'l*, pg. 6707
MENZOLIT VITROPLAST S.L.—See senata GmbH; *Int'l*, pg. 6707
MEON VERWALTUNGS GMBH—See E.ON SE; *Int'l*, pg. 2258
MEON WAY GARDENS MANAGEMENT COMPANY LIMITED—See Persimmon plc; *Int'l*, pg. 5816
MEP ACQUISITION CORP—See Patrick Industries, Inc.; *U.S. Public*, pg. 1652
M & E PAINTING, LLC.; *U.S. Private*, pg. 2522
MEPC LTD.—See Federated Hermes, Inc.; *U.S. Public*, pg. 827
MEPET METRO PETROL VE TESISLERI SANAYI TICARET AS; *Int'l*, pg. 4818
MEPHA PHARMA AG—See Teva Pharmaceutical Industries, Ltd.; *Int'l*, pg. 7579
MEP INFRASTRUCTURE DEVELOPERS LTD; *Int'l*, pg. 4818
MEP INSTRUMENTS PTY LTD—See Anton Paar GmbH; *Int'l*, pg. 485
MEP INSTRUMENTS PTY LTD—See Metrohm AG; *Int'l*, pg. 4862
MEPLAN GMBH—See Messe Munchen GmbH; *Int'l*, pg. 4841
MEPLUSYOU; *U.S. Private*, pg. 2667
MEPLUSYOU—See MEplusYou; *U.S. Private*, pg. 2667
MEPPELER BETONCENTRALE B.V.—See Heidelberg Materials AG; *Int'l*, pg. 3318
MEPPS SNC—See Sheldons' Inc.; *U.S. Private*, pg. 3631
MEPS DEVICES SDN. BHD.—See AWC Berhad; *Int'l*, pg. 752
MEPT 501, INC.; *U.S. Private*, pg. 2667
MEP TECHNOLOGIES, INC.; *Int'l*, pg. 4818
MEPU OY. - PYHARANTA FACTORY—See Ag Growth International Inc.; *Int'l*, pg. 198
MEPU OY—See Ag Growth International Inc.; *Int'l*, pg. 198
MEPURA METALLPULVERGESELLSCHAFT M. B. H.—See Palladium Equity Partners, LLC; *U.S. Private*, pg. 3078
MEQASA LIMITED—See Frontier Digital Ventures Limited; *Int'l*, pg. 2795
MERAFE FERROCHROME & MINING (PROPRIETARY) LIMITED—See Merafe Resources Limited; *Int'l*, pg. 4818
MERAFE RESOURCES LIMITED; *Int'l*, pg. 4818
MERAGE INVESTMENT GROUP; *U.S. Private*, pg. 2667
MERAGE JEWISH COMMUNITY CENTER OF ORANGE COUNTY; *U.S. Private*, pg. 2668
MERAKI LLC—See Cisco Systems, Inc.; *U.S. Public*, pg. 499
MERAKI NETWORKS AUSTRALIA PTY. LTD.—See Cisco Systems, Inc.; *U.S. Public*, pg. 499
MERAK JINXIN AIR CONDITIONING SYSTEMS (WUXI) CO., LTD.—See Knorr-Bremse AG; *Int'l*, pg. 4212
MERAK KNORR CLIMATIZACION S.A.—See Knorr-Bremse AG; *Int'l*, pg. 4212
MERAK SISTEMAS INTEGRADOS DE CLIMATIZACION S.A.—See Knorr-Bremse AG; *Int'l*, pg. 4212
MERALCO ENERGY, INC.—See Manila Electric Company; *Int'l*, pg. 4671
MERALCO FINANCIAL SERVICES CORPORATION—See Manila Electric Company; *Int'l*, pg. 4671
MERALCO INDUSTRIAL ENGINEERING SERVICES CORP.—See Manila Electric Company; *Int'l*, pg. 4671
MERALCO MILLENNIUM FOUNDATION, INC.—See Manila Electric Company; *Int'l*, pg. 4671
MERALCO POWERGEN CORPORATION—See Manila Electric Company; *Int'l*, pg. 4671
MERALLIANCE ARMORIC SAS—See Thai Union Group Public Company Limited; *Int'l*, pg. 7596
MERALLIANCE POLAND SP. Z.O.O—See Thai Union Group Public Company Limited; *Int'l*, pg. 7596
MERALLIANCE SAS—See Thai Union Group Public Company Limited; *Int'l*, pg. 7596
MERAMEC INSTRUMENT TRANSFORMER COMPANY—See Hubbell Incorporated; *U.S. Public*, pg. 1067
MERA PHARMACEUTICALS, INC.; *U.S. Private*, pg. 2667
MERAS ENGINEERING, INC.; *U.S. Private*, pg. 2668
MERASTAR INSURANCE CO.—See Kemper Corporation; *U.S. Public*, pg. 1221
MERATECH RUS GROUP LLC—See Ecolab Inc.; *U.S. Public*, pg. 714
MERCADO ABIERTO ELECTRONICO S.A.; *Int'l*, pg. 4819
MERCADO DE VALORES DE BUENOS AIRES S.A.; *Int'l*, pg. 4819
MERCADO LATINO INC.; *U.S. Private*, pg. 2668

MERCADOLIBRE.COM ATIVIDADES DE INTERNET LTDA.—See MercadoLibre, Inc.; *Int'l*, pg. 4819
MERCADOLIBRE, INC.; *Int'l*, pg. 4819
MERCADONA, S.A.; *Int'l*, pg. 4819
MERCA LEASING GMBH & CO. KG; *Int'l*, pg. 4818
MERCALIN AB; *Int'l*, pg. 4819
MERCANTIL, C.A. BANCO UNIVERSAL—See Mercantil Servicios Financieros, C.A.; *Int'l*, pg. 4819
MERCANTIL DE PISOS Y BANOS, S.A. DE C.V.—See Grupo Lamosa S.A. de C.V.; *Int'l*, pg. 3132
MERCANTIL DO BRASIL FINANCEIRA S.A.—See Banco Mercantil do Brasil S.A.; *Int'l*, pg. 823
MERCANTILE BANK CORPORATION; *U.S. Public*, pg. 1414
MERCANTILE BANK HOLDINGS LIMITED—See Capitec Bank Holdings Limited; *Int'l*, pg. 1314
MERCANTILE BANK - MORTGAGE CENTER—See United Community Bancorp, Inc.; *U.S. Private*, pg. 4289
MERCANTILE BANK OF MICHIGAN—See Mercantile Bank Corporation; *U.S. Public*, pg. 1414
MERCANTILE BANK PLC; *Int'l*, pg. 4819
MERCANTILE BANK SECURITIES LIMITED—See Mercantile Bank PLC; *Int'l*, pg. 4819
MERCANTILE BANK—See United Community Bancorp, Inc.; *U.S. Private*, pg. 4289
MERCANTILE CAPITAL CORPORATION—See First Horizon Corporation; *U.S. Public*, pg. 845
MERCANTILE CREDIT COMPANY LIMITED—See Barclays PLC; *Int'l*, pg. 862
MERCANTILE DISCOUNT BANK LTD—See IDB Development Corporation Ltd.; *Int'l*, pg. 3588
MERCANTILE EXCHANGE HOUSE (UK) LIMITED—See Mercantile Bank PLC; *Int'l*, pg. 4819
MERCANTILE INDUSTRIAL LEASING LIMITED—See Barclays PLC; *Int'l*, pg. 862
MERCANTILE INFORMATION & TELECOMMUNICATION TECHNOLOGY CO. LLC—See Suhail Bahwan Group (Holding) LLC; *Int'l*, pg. 7254
MERCANTILE INSURANCE COMPANY LIMITED; *Int'l*, pg. 4819
MERCANTILE INVESTMENT COMPANY LTD.—See Sandon Capital Investments Limited; *Int'l*, pg. 6526
MERCANTILE LEASING S.P.A.—See Banco BPM S.p.A.; *Int'l*, pg. 819
MERCANTILE OY AB—See Helvar Merca Oy AB; *Int'l*, pg. 3339
MERCANTILE PORTS & LOGISTICS LIMITED; *Int'l*, pg. 4819
MERCANTILE SHIPPING COMPANY PLC; *Int'l*, pg. 4819
MERCANTILE SOUTHERN MARYLAND BANK—See The PNC Financial Services Group, Inc.; *U.S. Public*, pg. 2119
MERCANTILE VENTURES LIMITED; *Int'l*, pg. 4819
MERCANTIL MERINVEST CASA DE BOLSA, C.A.—See Mercantil Servicios Financieros, C.A.; *Int'l*, pg. 4819
MERCANTIL SEGUROS, C.A.—See Mercantil Servicios Financieros, C.A.; *Int'l*, pg. 4819
MERCANTIL SERVICIOS DE INVERSION, C.A.—See Mercantil Servicios Financieros, C.A.; *Int'l*, pg. 4819
MERCANTIL SERVICIOS FINANCIEROS, C.A.; *Int'l*, pg. 4819
MERCANTIL SERVICIOS FINANCIEROS INTERNACIONAL, S.A.; *Int'l*, pg. 4819
MERCANTIL SOCIEDAD ADMINISTRADORA DE ENTIDADES DE INVERSION COLECTIVA, C.A.—See Mercantil Servicios Financieros, C.A.; *Int'l*, pg. 4819
MERCARD INTERCARD BV—See HAL Trust N.V.; *Int'l*, pg. 3224
MERCARD INTERCARD SA—See HAL Trust N.V.; *Int'l*, pg. 3224
MERCAREON GMBH—See Trimble, Inc.; *U.S. Public*, pg. 2193
MERCARI, INC.; *Int'l*, pg. 4819
MERCARI PTY. LTD.—See Financial & Energy Exchange Limited; *Int'l*, pg. 2665
MERCARIS COMPANY—See General Atlantic Service Company, L.P.; *U.S. Private*, pg. 1662
MERCARIS COMPANY—See HgCapital Trust plc; *Int'l*, pg. 3376
MERCATO PARTNERS ACQUISITION CORP.; *U.S. Public*, pg. 1414
MERCATOR ARGENTINA S.A.—See Mercator Transport Group Corporation; *Int'l*, pg. 4820
MERCATOR BH D.O.O.—See Fortenova Group d.d.; *Int'l*, pg. 2738
MERCATOR CANADA INC.—See Mercator Transport Group Corporation; *Int'l*, pg. 4820
MERCATOR-EMBA D.D.—See Fortenova Group d.d.; *Int'l*, pg. 2738
MERCATOR ENERGY, LLC—See The Southern Company; *U.S. Public*, pg. 2131
MERCATOR GHANA LIMITED—See Mercator Transport Group Corporation; *Int'l*, pg. 4820
MERCATOR - H, D.O.O.—See Fortenova Group d.d.; *Int'l*, pg. 2738
MERCATOR INTERNATIONAL AB—See Axel Johnson Gruppen AB; *Int'l*, pg. 765

MERCATO PARTNERS ACQUISITION CORP.

MERCATOR INTERNATIONAL PTE. LTD.—See Mercator Limited; *Int'l*, pg. 4820
MERCATOR LIMITED; *Int'l*, pg. 4820
MERCATOR MAKEDONIJA D.O.O.E.L.—See Fortenova Group d.d.; *Int'l*, pg. 2738
MERCATOR MEDICAL S.A.; *Int'l*, pg. 4820
MERCATOR - MEX, D.O.O.—See Fortenova Group d.d.; *Int'l*, pg. 2738
MERCATOR OIL & GAS LTD.—See Mercator Limited; *Int'l*, pg. 4820
MERCATOR-S, D.O.O.—See Fortenova Group d.d.; *Int'l*, pg. 2738
MERCATOR SOLUTIONS FZE—See Warburg Pincus LLC; *U.S. Private*, pg. 4439
MERCATOR TRANSPORT FRANCE INC.—See Mercator Transport Group Corporation; *Int'l*, pg. 4820
MERCATOR TRANSPORT GROUP CORPORATION; *Int'l*, pg. 4820
MERCATOR TRANSPORT INTERNATIONAL INC.—See Mercator Transport Group Corporation; *Int'l*, pg. 4820
MERCED AMBULATORY SURGERY CENTER, LLC—See Tenet Healthcare Corporation; *U.S. Public*, pg. 2004
MERCED CHEVROLET, INC.—See General Motors Company; *U.S. Public*, pg. 926
MERCEDES-AMG GMBH—See Mercedes-Benz Group AG; *Int'l*, pg. 4825
MERCEDES AMG HIGH PERFORMANCE POWERTRAINS LIMITED—See Mercedes-Benz Group AG; *Int'l*, pg. 4825
MERCEDES-BENZ ACCESSORIES GMBH—See Mercedes-Benz Group AG; *Int'l*, pg. 4825
MERCEDES-BENZ ADVANCED DESIGN OF NORTH AMERICA, INC.—See Mercedes-Benz Group AG; *Int'l*, pg. 4825
MERCEDES-BENZ AG & CO. GRUNDSTUCKSVERMIETUNG OBJEKTE LEIPZIG UND MAGDEBURG KG—See Mercedes-Benz Group AG; *Int'l*, pg. 4825
MERCEDES-BENZ AG—See Mercedes-Benz Group AG; *Int'l*, pg. 4825
MERCEDES-BENZ - ALUGUER DE VEICULOS, UNIPESSOAL LDA.—See Mercedes-Benz Group AG; *Int'l*, pg. 4825
MERCEDES-BENZ ARGENTINA S.A.—See Mercedes-Benz Group AG; *Int'l*, pg. 4825
MERCEDES-BENZ ASIA GMBH—See Mercedes-Benz Group AG; *Int'l*, pg. 4825
MERCEDES-BENZ AUSTRALIA/PACIFIC PTY. LTD.—See Mercedes-Benz Group AG; *Int'l*, pg. 4825
MERCEDES-BENZ AUTO FINANCE LTD.—See Mercedes-Benz Group AG; *Int'l*, pg. 4821
MERCEDES-BENZ BANK AG—See Mercedes-Benz Group AG; *Int'l*, pg. 4821
MERCEDES-BENZ BANKING SERVICE GMBH—See Mercedes-Benz Group AG; *Int'l*, pg. 4825
MERCEDES-BENZ BANK POLSKA S.A.—See Mercedes-Benz Group AG; *Int'l*, pg. 4825
MERCEDES-BENZ BANK RUS OOO—See Mercedes-Benz Group AG; *Int'l*, pg. 4825
MERCEDES-BENZ BANK SERVICE CENTER GMBH—See Mercedes-Benz Group AG; *Int'l*, pg. 4825
MERCEDES-BENZ BELGIUM LUXEMBOURG S.A.—See Mercedes-Benz Group AG; *Int'l*, pg. 4825
MERCEDES-BENZ BORDEAUX SAS—See Mercedes-Benz Group AG; *Int'l*, pg. 4825
MERCEDES-BENZ BROKER BIZTOSITASI ALKUSZ HUNGARY KFT.—See Mercedes-Benz Group AG; *Int'l*, pg. 4825
MERCEDES-BENZ BROOKLANDS LIMITED—See Mercedes-Benz Group AG; *Int'l*, pg. 4827
MERCEDES-BENZ CANADA INC.—See Mercedes-Benz Group AG; *Int'l*, pg. 4825
MERCEDES-BENZ CANADA INC.—See Mercedes-Benz Group AG; *Int'l*, pg. 4825
MERCEDES BENZ CANADA INC.—See Mercedes-Benz Group AG; *Int'l*, pg. 4825
MERCEDES-BENZ CANADA INC.—See Mercedes-Benz Group AG; *Int'l*, pg. 4825
MERCEDES-BENZ CAPITAL SERVICES (DEBIS) UK LTD.—See Mercedes-Benz Group AG; *Int'l*, pg. 4825
MERCEDES-BENZ CESKA REPUBLIKA S.R.O.—See Mercedes-Benz Group AG; *Int'l*, pg. 4825
MERCEDES-BENZ CHARTERWAY ESPANA, S.A.—See Mercedes-Benz Group AG; *Int'l*, pg. 4825
MERCEDES-BENZ CHARTERWAY GMBH—See Mercedes-Benz Group AG; *Int'l*, pg. 4825
MERCEDES-BENZ CHARTERWAY LTD.—See Mercedes-Benz Group AG; *Int'l*, pg. 4825
MERCEDES-BENZ CHARTERWAY SAS—See Mercedes-Benz Group AG; *Int'l*, pg. 4825
MERCEDES-BENZ CHARTERWAY S.P.A.—See Mercedes-Benz Group AG; *Int'l*, pg. 4825
MERCEDES-BENZ (CHINA) LTD.—See Mercedes-Benz Group AG; *Int'l*, pg. 4825
MERCEDES-BENZ COMERCIAL, LDA.—See Mercedes-Benz Group AG; *Int'l*, pg. 4825
MERCEDES-BENZ COMERCIAL VALENCIA, S.A.—See Mercedes-Benz Group AG; *Int'l*, pg. 4825
MERCEDES-BENZ COMPANIA FINANCIERA ARGENTINA S.A.—See Mercedes-Benz Group AG; *Int'l*, pg. 4825

MERCEDES-BENZ CONSULT GRAZ GMBH—See Mercedes-Benz Group AG; *Int'l*, pg. 4825
MERCEDES-BENZ CREDIT—See Mercedes-Benz Group AG; *Int'l*, pg. 4827
MERCEDES-BENZ CUSTOMER SERVICE CORP.—See Mercedes-Benz Group AG; *Int'l*, pg. 4828
MERCEDES-BENZ DANMARK AS—See Mercedes-Benz Group AG; *Int'l*, pg. 4826
MERCEDES-BENZ DEALER BEDRIJVEN B.V.—See Mercedes-Benz Group AG; *Int'l*, pg. 4826
MERCEDES-BENZ DESARROLLO DE MERCADOS, S. DE R.L. DE C.V.—See Mercedes-Benz Group AG; *Int'l*, pg. 4826
MERCEDES-BENZ DO BRASIL S.A.—See Mercedes-Benz Group AG; *Int'l*, pg. 4828
MERCEDES-BENZ EGYPT S.A.E.—See Mercedes-Benz Group AG; *Int'l*, pg. 4826
MERCEDES-BENZ ESCH S.A.—See Mercedes-Benz Group AG; *Int'l*, pg. 4826
MERCEDES-BENZ ESPANA, S.A.—See Mercedes-Benz Group AG; *Int'l*, pg. 4826
MERCEDES-BENZ FINANCIAL SERVICES AUSTRALIA PTY. LTD.—See Mercedes-Benz Group AG; *Int'l*, pg. 4821
MERCEDES-BENZ FINANCIAL SERVICES AUSTRIA GMBH—See Mercedes-Benz Group AG; *Int'l*, pg. 4821
MERCEDES-BENZ FINANCIAL SERVICES BELUX N.V.—See Mercedes-Benz Group AG; *Int'l*, pg. 4821
MERCEDES-BENZ FINANCIAL SERVICES CANADA—See Mercedes-Benz Group AG; *Int'l*, pg. 4821
MERCEDES-BENZ FINANCIAL SERVICES CESKA REPUBLIKA S.R.O.—See Mercedes-Benz Group AG; *Int'l*, pg. 4821
MERCEDES-BENZ FINANCIAL SERVICES ESPANA E. F. C., S.A.U.—See Mercedes-Benz Group AG; *Int'l*, pg. 4822
MERCEDES-BENZ FINANCIAL SERVICES FRANCE S.A.—See Mercedes-Benz Group AG; *Int'l*, pg. 4822
MERCEDES-BENZ FINANCIAL SERVICES HELLAS AE—See Mercedes-Benz Group AG; *Int'l*, pg. 4822
MERCEDES-BENZ FINANCIAL SERVICES HONG KONG LTD.—See Mercedes-Benz Group AG; *Int'l*, pg. 4822
MERCEDES-BENZ FINANCIAL SERVICES ITALIA S.P.A—See Mercedes-Benz Group AG; *Int'l*, pg. 4822
MERCEDES-BENZ FINANCIAL SERVICES NEDERLAND B.V.—See Mercedes-Benz Group AG; *Int'l*, pg. 4822
MERCEDES-BENZ FINANCIAL SERVICES NEW ZEALAND LTD.—See Mercedes-Benz Group AG; *Int'l*, pg. 4822
MERCEDES-BENZ FINANCIAL SERVICES PORTUGAL - INSTITUICAO FINANCEIRA DE CREDITO S.A.—See Mercedes-Benz Group AG; *Int'l*, pg. 4822
MERCEDES-BENZ FINANCIAL SERVICES RUS OOO—See Mercedes-Benz Group AG; *Int'l*, pg. 4822
MERCEDES-BENZ FINANCIAL SERVICES SCHWEIZ AG—See Mercedes-Benz Group AG; *Int'l*, pg. 4822
MERCEDES-BENZ FINANCIAL SERVICES SLOVAKIA S.R.O.—See Mercedes-Benz Group AG; *Int'l*, pg. 4822
MERCEDES-BENZ FINANCIAL SERVICES SOUTH AFRICA (PTY) LTD.—See Mercedes-Benz Group AG; *Int'l*, pg. 4822
MERCEDES-BENZ FINANCIAL SERVICES TAIWAN LTD.—See Mercedes-Benz Group AG; *Int'l*, pg. 4822
MERCEDES-BENZ FINANCIAL SERVICES UK LIMITED—See Mercedes-Benz Group AG; *Int'l*, pg. 4822
MERCEDES-BENZ FINANCIAL SERVICES USA LLC—See Mercedes-Benz Group AG; *Int'l*, pg. 4822
MERCEDES-BENZ FINANCIAL—See Mercedes-Benz Group AG; *Int'l*, pg. 4828
MERCEDES-BENZ FINANSAL KIRALAMA TURK A.S.—See Mercedes-Benz Group AG; *Int'l*, pg. 4826
MERCEDES-BENZ FINANS DANMARK A/S—See Mercedes-Benz Group AG; *Int'l*, pg. 4826
MERCEDES-BENZ FINANSMAN TURK A.S.—See Mercedes-Benz Group AG; *Int'l*, pg. 4826
MERCEDES-BENZ FINANS SVERIGE AB—See Mercedes-Benz Group AG; *Int'l*, pg. 4826
MERCEDES-BENZ FINANZIERUNGSVERMITTLUNGS GMBH—See Mercedes-Benz Group AG; *Int'l*, pg. 4826
MERCEDES-BENZ FORSALJNINGS AB—See Mercedes-Benz Group AG; *Int'l*, pg. 4826
MERCEDES-BENZ FRANCE S.A.—See Mercedes-Benz Group AG; *Int'l*, pg. 4826
MERCEDES-BENZ GASTROSERVICE GMBH—See Mercedes-Benz Group AG; *Int'l*, pg. 4826
MERCEDES-BENZ GENT N.V.—See Mercedes-Benz Group AG; *Int'l*, pg. 4826
MERCEDES-BENZ GLOBAL TRAINING NEDERLAND B.V.—See Mercedes-Benz Group AG; *Int'l*, pg. 4826
MERCEDES-BENZ GRAND PRIX LTD.—See Mercedes-Benz Group AG; *Int'l*, pg. 4826
MERCEDES-BENZ GROUP AG; *Int'l*, pg. 4820
MERCEDES-BENZ HELLAS S.A.—See Mercedes-Benz Group AG; *Int'l*, pg. 4826
MERCEDES-BENZ HONG KONG LIMITED—See Mercedes-Benz Group AG; *Int'l*, pg. 4826

CORPORATE AFFILIATIONS

MERCEDES-BENZ INDIA PRIVATE LIMITED—See Mercedes-Benz Group AG; *Int'l*, pg. 4826
MERCEDES-BENZ INSURANCE BROKER SRL—See Mercedes-Benz Group AG; *Int'l*, pg. 4826
MERCEDES-BENZ.IO GMBH—See Mercedes-Benz Group AG; *Int'l*, pg. 4828
MERCEDES-BENZ ITALIA S.P.A.—See Mercedes-Benz Group AG; *Int'l*, pg. 4826
MERCEDES-BENZ JAPAN CO., LTD.—See Mercedes-Benz Group AG; *Int'l*, pg. 4826
MERCEDES-BENZ LEASING DO BRASIL ARRENDAMENTO MERCANTIL S.A.—See Mercedes-Benz Group AG; *Int'l*, pg. 4826
MERCEDES-BENZ LEASING GMBH—See Mercedes-Benz Group AG; *Int'l*, pg. 4822
MERCEDES-BENZ LEASING HRVATSKA D.O.O.—See Mercedes-Benz Group AG; *Int'l*, pg. 4826
MERCEDES-BENZ LEASING IFN SA—See Mercedes-Benz Group AG; *Int'l*, pg. 4826
MERCEDES-BENZ LEASING KFT.—See Mercedes-Benz Group AG; *Int'l*, pg. 4826
MERCEDES-BENZ LEASING POLSKA SP. Z.O.O.—See Mercedes-Benz Group AG; *Int'l*, pg. 4826
MERCEDES-BENZ LEASING (THAILAND) CO., LTD.—See Mercedes-Benz Group AG; *Int'l*, pg. 4826
MERCEDES-BENZ LEASING TREUHAND GMBH—See Mercedes-Benz Group AG; *Int'l*, pg. 4826
MERCEDES-BENZ LEUDELANGE S.A.—See Mercedes-Benz Group AG; *Int'l*, pg. 4826
MERCEDES-BENZ LILLE SAS—See Mercedes-Benz Group AG; *Int'l*, pg. 4826
MERCEDES-BENZ LUDWIGSFELDE GMBH—See Mercedes-Benz Group AG; *Int'l*, pg. 4826
MERCEDES-BENZ LUXEMBOURG-CENTRE S.A.—See Mercedes-Benz Group AG; *Int'l*, pg. 4826
MERCEDES-BENZ LUXEMBOURG S.A.—See Mercedes-Benz Group AG; *Int'l*, pg. 4826
MERCEDES-BENZ LYON SAS—See Chopard Automobiles SAS; *Int'l*, pg. 1582
MERCEDES-BENZ MANHATTAN INC.—See Mercedes-Benz Group AG; *Int'l*, pg. 4828
MERCEDES-BENZ MANUFACTURING HUNGARY KFT.—See Mercedes-Benz Group AG; *Int'l*, pg. 4826
MERCEDES-BENZ MEXICO, S. DE R.L. DE C.V.—See Mercedes-Benz Group AG; *Int'l*, pg. 4826
MERCEDES-BENZ MILANO S.P.A.—See Mercedes-Benz Group AG; *Int'l*, pg. 4827
MERCEDES-BENZ MINIBUS GMBH—See Mercedes-Benz Group AG; *Int'l*, pg. 4820
MERCEDES-BENZ MITARBEITER-FAHRZEUGE LEASING GMBH—See Mercedes-Benz Group AG; *Int'l*, pg. 4827
MERCEDES-BENZ MOLSHEIM SAS—See Mercedes-Benz Group AG; *Int'l*, pg. 4827
MERCEDES-BENZ MUSEUM GMBH—See Mercedes-Benz Group AG; *Int'l*, pg. 4827
MERCEDES-BENZ NEDERLAND B.V.—See Mercedes-Benz Group AG; *Int'l*, pg. 4827
MERCEDES-BENZ NEW ZEALAND LTD.—See Mercedes-Benz Group AG; *Int'l*, pg. 4827
MERCEDES-BENZ NINOVE N.V.—See Mercedes-Benz Group AG; *Int'l*, pg. 4827
MERCEDES-BENZ OF BROOKLYN; *U.S. Private*, pg. 2668
MERCEDES-BENZ OF CALDWELL; *U.S. Private*, pg. 2668
MERCEDES-BENZ OF CORAL GABLES; *U.S. Private*, pg. 2668
MERCEDES BENZ OF HAGERSTOWN; *U.S. Private*, pg. 2668
MERCEDES-BENZ OF NANUET; *U.S. Private*, pg. 2668
MERCEDES-BENZ OF NAPLES; *U.S. Private*, pg. 2668
MERCEDES-BENZ OF NORTHWEST ARKANSAS—See Superior Auto Group; *U.S. Private*, pg. 3876
MERCEDES BENZ OF NOVI; *U.S. Private*, pg. 2668
MERCEDES-BENZ OF PORTSMOUTH—See Kaplan Auto Group; *U.S. Private*, pg. 2261
MERCEDES-BENZ OF SARASOTA—See AutoNation, Inc.; *U.S. Public*, pg. 236
MERCEDES-BENZ OF SEATTLE; *U.S. Private*, pg. 2668
MERCEDES-BENZ OF SOUTH AFRICA (PTY.) LTD.—See Mercedes-Benz Group AG; *Int'l*, pg. 4828
MERCEDES-BENZ OF SOUTH BAY—See AutoNation, Inc.; *U.S. Public*, pg. 236
MERCEDES-BENZ OF SPOKANE; *U.S. Private*, pg. 2669
MERCEDES-BENZ OF TRAVERSE CITY—See DP Fox Ventures, LLC; *U.S. Private*, pg. 1270
MERCEDES-BENZ OSTERREICH VERTRIEBSGESELLSCHAFT MBH—See Mercedes-Benz Group AG; *Int'l*, pg. 4827
MERCEDES-BENZ PARIS SAS—See Mercedes-Benz Group AG; *Int'l*, pg. 4827
MERCEDES-BENZ POLSKA SP. Z.O.O.—See Mercedes-Benz Group AG; *Int'l*, pg. 4827
MERCEDES-BENZ PORTUGAL-COMERCIO DE AUTOMOVEIS, S.A.—See Mercedes-Benz Group AG; *Int'l*, pg. 4827
MERCEDES-BENZ PORTUGAL, S.A.—See Mercedes-Benz Group AG; *Int'l*, pg. 4827

COMPANY NAME INDEX

MERCEDES-BENZ PROJECT CONSULT GMBH—See Mercedes-Benz Group AG; *Int'l*, pg. 4827
MERCEDES-BENZ RENTING, S.A.—See Mercedes-Benz Group AG; *Int'l*, pg. 4827
MERCEDES-BENZ RESEARCH & DEVELOPMENT INDIA PVT LTD.—See Mercedes-Benz Group AG; *Int'l*, pg. 4827
MERCEDES-BENZ RESEARCH & DEVELOPMENT NORTH AMERICA, INC.—See Mercedes-Benz Group AG; *Int'l*, pg. 4827
MERCEDES-BENZ RETAIL GROUP UK LIMITED—See Mercedes-Benz Group AG; *Int'l*, pg. 4827
MERCEDES-BENZ ROMANIA S.R.L.—See Mercedes-Benz Group AG; *Int'l*, pg. 4827
MERCEDES-BENZ ROMA S.P.A.—See Mercedes-Benz Group AG; *Int'l*, pg. 4827
MERCEDES-BENZ RUSSIA SAO—See Avtodom OAO; *Int'l*, pg. 751
MERCEDES-BENZ SCHWEIZ AG—See Mercedes-Benz Group AG; *Int'l*, pg. 4827
MERCEDES-BENZ SERVICE CORP.—See Mercedes-Benz Group AG; *Int'l*, pg. 4828
MERCEDES-BENZ SERVICE LEASING SRL—See Mercedes-Benz Group AG; *Int'l*, pg. 4827
MERCEDES-BENZ SERVICES CORREDURIA DE SEGUROS, S.A.—See Mercedes-Benz Group AG; *Int'l*, pg. 4827
MERCEDES-BENZ SERVIZI ASSICURATIVI ITALIA S.P.A.—See Mercedes-Benz Group AG; *Int'l*, pg. 4827
MERCEDES-BENZ SIGORTA ARACILIK HIZMETLERI A.S.—See Mercedes-Benz Group AG; *Int'l*, pg. 4827
MERCEDES-BENZ SLOVAKIA S.R.O.—See Mercedes-Benz Group AG; *Int'l*, pg. 4827
MERCEDES-BENZ SOSNOWIEC SP. Z O.O.—See Mercedes-Benz Group AG; *Int'l*, pg. 4827
MERCEDES-BENZ SOUTH AFRICA LTD.—See Mercedes-Benz Group AG; *Int'l*, pg. 4827
MERCEDES-BENZ SRBIJA I CRNA GORA D.O.O.—See Mercedes-Benz Group AG; *Int'l*, pg. 4827
MERCEDES-BENZ SURREY; *Int'l*, pg. 4829
MERCEDES-BENZ SVERIGE AB—See Mercedes-Benz Group AG; *Int'l*, pg. 4827
MERCEDES-BENZ TAIWAN LTD.—See Mercedes-Benz Group AG; *Int'l*, pg. 4827
MERCEDES-BENZ TAMWORTH—See Mercedes-Benz Group AG; *Int'l*, pg. 4827
MERCEDES-BENZ TASIT TICARET VE SERVIS A.S.—See Mercedes-Benz Group AG; *Int'l*, pg. 4827
MERCEDES-BENZ TECHNICAL CENTER NEDERLAND B.V.—See Mercedes-Benz Group AG; *Int'l*, pg. 4827
MERCEDES-BENZ (THAILAND) LIMITED—See Mercedes-Benz Group AG; *Int'l*, pg. 4825
MERCEDES-BENZ TRUCKS OSTERREICH GMBH—See Mercedes-Benz Group AG; *Int'l*, pg. 4827
MERCEDES-BENZ TURK A.S.—See Mercedes-Benz Group AG; *Int'l*, pg. 4827
MERCEDES-BENZ UK LIMITED—See Mercedes-Benz Group AG; *Int'l*, pg. 4827
MERCEDES-BENZ USA INC.—See Mercedes-Benz Group AG; *Int'l*, pg. 4828
MERCEDES-BENZ USA INC.—See Mercedes-Benz Group AG; *Int'l*, pg. 4828
MERCEDES-BENZ USA INC.—See Mercedes-Benz Group AG; *Int'l*, pg. 4828
MERCEDES-BENZ USA, LLC—See Mercedes-Benz Group AG; *Int'l*, pg. 4827
MERCEDES-BENZ USA LLC—See Mercedes-Benz Group AG; *Int'l*, pg. 4828
MERCEDES-BENZ USA LLC—See Mercedes-Benz Group AG; *Int'l*, pg. 4828
MERCEDES-BENZ USA LOS ANGELES REGIONAL CORPORATE OFFICE—See Mercedes-Benz Group AG; *Int'l*, pg. 4828
MERCEDES-BENZ U.S. INTERNATIONAL, INC.—See Mercedes-Benz Group AG; *Int'l*, pg. 4828
MERCEDES-BENZ VERTRIEBSGESELLSCHAFT MBH—See Mercedes-Benz Group AG; *Int'l*, pg. 4828
MERCEDES-BENZ V.I. LILLE SAS—See Mercedes-Benz Group AG; *Int'l*, pg. 4828
MERCEDES-BENZ V.I. LYON SAS—See Mercedes-Benz Group AG; *Int'l*, pg. 4828
MERCEDES-BENZ V.I. PARIS ILE DE FRANCE SAS—See Mercedes-Benz Group AG; *Int'l*, pg. 4828
MERCEDES-BENZ V.I. TOULOUSE SAS—See Mercedes-Benz Group AG; *Int'l*, pg. 4828
MERCEDES-BENZ WARSZAWA SP. Z O.O.—See Mercedes-Benz Group AG; *Int'l*, pg. 4828
MERCEDES-BENZ WAVRE S.A.—See Mercedes-Benz Group AG; *Int'l*, pg. 4828
MERCEDES ELECTRIC SUPPLY, INC.; *U.S. Private*, pg. 2668
MERCEDES HOMES INC.; *U.S. Private*, pg. 2668
MERCEDES HOMES OF TEXAS LTD.—See Mercedes Homes Inc.; *U.S. Private*, pg. 2668
MERCEDES MEDICAL INC.; *U.S. Private*, pg. 2668
MERCEDES PORSCHE AUDI OF MELBOURNE; *U.S. Private*, pg. 2668
MERCEDES SALAZAR JOYERIA S.A.; *Int'l*, pg. 4820

MERCEDESSERVICE CARD BETEILIGUNGSGESELLSCHAFT MBH—See Mercedes-Benz Group AG; *Int'l*, pg. 4828
MERCEDESSERVICE CARD GMBH & CO. KG—See Mercedes-Benz Group AG; *Int'l*, pg. 4828
MERCED IRRIGATION DISTRICT; *U.S. Private*, pg. 2668
MERCELL HOLDING AS; *Int'l*, pg. 4829
MERCER ADVISORS INC.—See Genstar Capital, LLC; *U.S. Private*, pg. 1677
MERCER ADVISORS INC.—See Keystone Group, L.P.; *U.S. Private*, pg. 2298
MERCER, AGENTE DE SEGUROS, S.A. DE C.V.—See Marsh & McLennan Companies, Inc.; *U.S. Public*, pg. 1386
MERCER (ARGENTINA) S.A.—See Marsh & McLennan Companies, Inc.; *U.S. Public*, pg. 1384
MERCER (AUSTRALIA) PTY LTD—See Marsh & McLennan Companies, Inc.; *U.S. Public*, pg. 1384
MERCER (AUSTRIA) GMBH—See Marsh & McLennan Companies, Inc.; *U.S. Public*, pg. 1384
MERCER BANCORP, INC.; *U.S. Public*, pg. 1415
MERCER (BELGIUM) SA-NV—See Marsh & McLennan Companies, Inc.; *U.S. Public*, pg. 1384
MERCER BENEFIT SERVICES PTY LTD—See Marsh & McLennan Companies, Inc.; *U.S. Public*, pg. 1385
MERCER (CANADA) LIMITED—See Marsh & McLennan Companies, Inc.; *U.S. Public*, pg. 1384
MERCER CELGAR LIMITED—See Mercer International Inc.; *Int'l*, pg. 4829
MERCER CERTIFICERING B.V.—See Marsh & McLennan Companies, Inc.; *U.S. Public*, pg. 1385
MERCER (CHINA) LIMITED—See Marsh & McLennan Companies, Inc.; *U.S. Public*, pg. 1384
MERCER (COLOMBIA) LTDA.—See Marsh & McLennan Companies, Inc.; *U.S. Public*, pg. 1384
MERCER COMPANY—See Columbia National Group Inc; *U.S. Private*, pg. 977
MERCER CONSULTING (AUSTRALIA) PTY LTD—See Marsh & McLennan Companies, Inc.; *U.S. Public*, pg. 1385
MERCER CONSULTING B.V.—See Marsh & McLennan Companies, Inc.; *U.S. Public*, pg. 1385
MERCER CONSULTING (CHILE) LTDA.—See Marsh & McLennan Companies, Inc.; *U.S. Public*, pg. 1385
MERCER CONSULTING (CHINA) LTD.—See Marsh & McLennan Companies, Inc.; *U.S. Public*, pg. 1385
MERCER CONSULTING (FRANCE) SAS—See Marsh & McLennan Companies, Inc.; *U.S. Public*, pg. 1385
MERCER CONSULTING GROUP, INC.—See Marsh & McLennan Companies, Inc.; *U.S. Public*, pg. 1384
MERCER CONSULTING (INDIA) PRIVATE LTD.—See Marsh & McLennan Companies, Inc.; *U.S. Public*, pg. 1385
MERCER CONSULTING LIMITED—See Marsh & McLennan Companies, Inc.; *U.S. Public*, pg. 1385
MERCER CONSULTING, S.L.U.—See Marsh & McLennan Companies, Inc.; *U.S. Public*, pg. 1384
MERCER CORREDORES DE SEGUROS LTDA.—See Marsh & McLennan Companies, Inc.; *U.S. Public*, pg. 1385
MERCER COUNTY STATE BANCORP; *U.S. Private*, pg. 2669
MERCER COUNTY STATE BANK—See Mercer County State Bancorp; *U.S. Private*, pg. 2669
MERCER COUNTY SURGERY CENTER, LLC—See KKR & Co. Inc.; *U.S. Public*, pg. 1246
MERCER (CZECH) A.S.—See Marsh & McLennan Companies, Inc.; *U.S. Public*, pg. 1384
MERCER (DANMARK) A/S—See Marsh & McLennan Companies, Inc.; *U.S. Public*, pg. 1384
MERCER DEUTSCHLAND GMBH—See Marsh & McLennan Companies, Inc.; *U.S. Public*, pg. 1385
MERCER EMPLOYEE BENEFITS LIMITED—See Marsh & McLennan Companies, Inc.; *U.S. Public*, pg. 1385
MERCER EMPLOYEE BENEFITS - MEDIACAO DE SEGUROS, LDA.—See Marsh & McLennan Companies, Inc.; *U.S. Public*, pg. 1385
MERCER EMPLOYEE BENEFITS OY—See Marsh & McLennan Companies, Inc.; *U.S. Public*, pg. 1385
MERCER FINANCIAL ADVICE (AUSTRALIA) PTY LTD—See Marsh & McLennan Companies, Inc.; *U.S. Public*, pg. 1385
MERCER FINLAND—See Marsh & McLennan Companies, Inc.; *U.S. Public*, pg. 1385
MERCER FOODS LLC—See The Graham Group, Inc.; *U.S. Private*, pg. 4037
MERCER FORESTRY SERVICES LTD.—See Mercer International Inc.; *Int'l*, pg. 4829
MERCER FORGE CORPORATION; *U.S. Private*, pg. 2669
MERCER (FRANCE) SAS—See Marsh & McLennan Companies, Inc.; *U.S. Public*, pg. 1384
MERCER FRASER COMPANY; *U.S. Private*, pg. 2669
MERCER GLOBAL ADVISORS INC.—See Genstar Capital, LLC; *U.S. Private*, pg. 1677
MERCER GLOBAL ADVISORS INC.—See Keystone Group, L.P.; *U.S. Private*, pg. 2298
MERCER HEALTH & BENEFITS ADMINISTRATION LLC—See Marsh & McLennan Companies, Inc.; *U.S. Public*, pg. 1385

MERCER LANDMARK INC.

MERCER HEALTH & BENEFITS LLC—See Marsh & McLennan Companies, Inc.; *U.S. Public*, pg. 1385
MERCER HEALTH & BENEFITS (SINGAPORE) PTE. LTD.—See Marsh & McLennan Companies, Inc.; *U.S. Public*, pg. 1385
MERCER HOLZ GMBH—See Mercer International Inc.; *Int'l*, pg. 4829
MERCER (HONG KONG) LIMITED—See Marsh & McLennan Companies, Inc.; *U.S. Public*, pg. 1384
MERCER HUMAN RESOURCE CONSULTING AND INSURANCE BROKERS LIMITED—See Marsh & McLennan Companies, Inc.; *U.S. Public*, pg. 1385
MERCER HUMAN RESOURCE CONSULTING A/S—See Marsh & McLennan Companies, Inc.; *U.S. Public*, pg. 1385
MERCER HUMAN RESOURCE CONSULTING AS—See Marsh & McLennan Companies, Inc.; *U.S. Public*, pg. 1385
MERCER HUMAN RESOURCE CONSULTING GMBH—See Marsh & McLennan Companies, Inc.; *U.S. Public*, pg. 1385
MERCER HUMAN RESOURCE CONSULTING LIMITED—See Marsh & McLennan Companies, Inc.; *U.S. Public*, pg. 1385
MERCER HUMAN RESOURCE CONSULTING LTDA—See Marsh & McLennan Companies, Inc.; *U.S. Public*, pg. 1385
MERCER HUMAN RESOURCE CONSULTING LTD.—See Marsh & McLennan Companies, Inc.; *U.S. Public*, pg. 1385
MERCER HUMAN RESOURCE CONSULTING OF KENTUCKY, INC.—See Marsh & McLennan Companies, Inc.; *U.S. Public*, pg. 1385
MERCER HUMAN RESOURCE CONSULTING OF MASSACHUSETTS, INC.—See Marsh & McLennan Companies, Inc.; *U.S. Public*, pg. 1385
MERCER HUMAN RESOURCE CONSULTING OF TEXAS, INC.—See Marsh & McLennan Companies, Inc.; *U.S. Public*, pg. 1385
MERCER HUMAN RESOURCE CONSULTING OF VIRGINIA, INC.—See Marsh & McLennan Companies, Inc.; *U.S. Public*, pg. 1385
MERCER HUMAN RESOURCE CONSULTING PTY LTD—See Marsh & McLennan Companies, Inc.; *U.S. Public*, pg. 1385
MERCER HUMAN RESOURCE CONSULTING S.A. DE C.V.—See Marsh & McLennan Companies, Inc.; *U.S. Public*, pg. 1385
MERCER HUMAN RESOURCE CONSULTING S.A.—See Marsh & McLennan Companies, Inc.; *U.S. Public*, pg. 1385
MERCER HUMAN RESOURCE CONSULTING SA—See Marsh & McLennan Companies, Inc.; *U.S. Public*, pg. 1385
MERCER HUMAN RESOURCE CONSULTING, S.L.—See Marsh & McLennan Companies, Inc.; *U.S. Public*, pg. 1386
MERCER HUMAN RESOURCE CONSULTING—See Marsh & McLennan Companies, Inc.; *U.S. Public*, pg. 1385
MERCER HUMAN RESOURCE CONSULTING (S) PTE LTD—See Marsh & McLennan Companies, Inc.; *U.S. Public*, pg. 1385
MERCER HUMAN RESOURCE CONSULTING SRL—See Marsh & McLennan Companies, Inc.; *U.S. Public*, pg. 1385
MERCER INDIA PRIVATE LIMITED—See Marsh & McLennan Companies, Inc.; *U.S. Public*, pg. 1385
MERCER INSURANCE COMPANY OF NEW JERSEY, INC.—See United Fire Group, Inc.; *U.S. Public*, pg. 2231
MERCER INSURANCE GROUP, INC.—See United Fire Group, Inc.; *U.S. Public*, pg. 2230
MERCER INTERNATIONAL INC.; *Int'l*, pg. 4829
MERCER INVESTMENT CONSULTING, INC.—See Marsh & McLennan Companies, Inc.; *U.S. Public*, pg. 1385
MERCER INVESTMENT MANAGEMENT, INC.—See Marsh & McLennan Companies, Inc.; *U.S. Public*, pg. 1385
MERCER INVESTMENTS (KOREA) CO., LTD.—See Marsh & McLennan Companies, Inc.; *U.S. Public*, pg. 1386
MERCER (IRELAND) LIMITED—See Marsh & McLennan Companies, Inc.; *U.S. Public*, pg. 1384
MERCER ITALIA SRL—See Marsh & McLennan Companies, Inc.; *U.S. Public*, pg. 1386
MERCER ITALIA SRL—See Marsh & McLennan Companies, Inc.; *U.S. Public*, pg. 1386
MERCER JAPAN LTD—See Marsh & McLennan Companies, Inc.; *U.S. Public*, pg. 1386
MERCER JAPAN LTD—See Marsh & McLennan Companies, Inc.; *U.S. Public*, pg. 1386
MERCER KOREA CO. LTD.—See Marsh & McLennan Companies, Inc.; *U.S. Public*, pg. 1386
MERCER LANDMARK INC.; *U.S. Private*, pg. 2669
MERCER LESTISHARAT ALAMAL LP—See Marsh & McLennan Companies, Inc.; *U.S. Public*, pg. 1386
MERCER LIMITED—See Marsh & McLennan Companies, Inc.; *U.S. Public*, pg. 1386

MERCER LANDMARK INC.

MERCER LLC—See Marsh & McLennan Companies, Inc.; *U.S. Public*, pg. 1384
MERCER LLC—See Marsh & McLennan Companies, Inc.; *U.S. Public*, pg. 1384
MERCER (MALAYSIA) SDN. BHD.—See Marsh & McLennan Companies, Inc.; *U.S. Public*, pg. 1384
MERCER MASS TIMBER LLC—See Mercer International Inc.; *Int'l*, pg. 4829
MERCER (NEDERLAND) B.V.—See Marsh & McLennan Companies, Inc.; *U.S. Public*, pg. 1384
MERCER (NEDERLAND) B.V.—See Marsh & McLennan Companies, Inc.; *U.S. Public*, pg. 1384
MERCER (NORGE) AS—See Marsh & McLennan Companies, Inc.; *U.S. Public*, pg. 1384
MERCER (N.Z.) LIMITED—See Marsh & McLennan Companies, Inc.; *U.S. Public*, pg. 1384
MERCER PEACE RIVER PULP LTD.—See Mercer International Inc.; *Int'l*, pg. 4829
MERCER PHILIPPINES, INC.—See Marsh & McLennan Companies, Inc.; *U.S. Public*, pg. 1386
MERCER PHILIPPINES, INC.—See Marsh & McLennan Companies, Inc.; *U.S. Public*, pg. 1386
MERCER (POLSKA) SP.Z O.O.—See Marsh & McLennan Companies, Inc.; *U.S. Public*, pg. 1384
MERCER (PORTUGAL) LDA—See Marsh & McLennan Companies, Inc.; *U.S. Public*, pg. 1384
MERCER (PORTUGAL) LDA—See Marsh & McLennan Companies, Inc.; *U.S. Public*, pg. 1384
MERCER PRIVATE MARKETS AG—See Marsh & McLennan Companies, Inc.; *U.S. Public*, pg. 1386
MERCER PULP SALES GMBH—See Mercer International Inc.; *Int'l*, pg. 4829
THE MERCER RUBBER COMPANY—See Mason Industries; *U.S. Private*, pg. 2602
MERCER SIGORTA BROKERLIGI ANONIM SIRKETI—See Marsh & McLennan Companies, Inc.; *U.S. Public*, pg. 1386
MERCER (SINGAPORE) PTE LTD—See Marsh & McLennan Companies, Inc.; *U.S. Public*, pg. 1384
MERCER—See Marsh & McLennan Companies, Inc.; *U.S. Public*, pg. 1384
MERCER SOUTH AFRICA (PTY) LTD.—See Marsh & McLennan Companies, Inc.; *U.S. Public*, pg. 1386
MERCER STAINLESS LIMITED—See KKR & Co. Inc.; *U.S. Public*, pg. 1241
MERCER STENDAL GMBH—See Mercer International Inc.; *Int'l*, pg. 4829
MERCER SUPERANNUATION (AUSTRALIA) LIMITED—See Marsh & McLennan Companies, Inc.; *U.S. Public*, pg. 1386
MERCER (SWEDEN) AB—See Marsh & McLennan Companies, Inc.; *U.S. Public*, pg. 1384
MERCER (SWITZERLAND) SA—See Marsh & McLennan Companies, Inc.; *U.S. Public*, pg. 1384
MERCER (SWITZERLAND) SA—See Marsh & McLennan Companies, Inc.; *U.S. Public*, pg. 1385
MERCER (TAIWAN) LTD.—See Marsh & McLennan Companies, Inc.; *U.S. Public*, pg. 1385
MERCER (THAILAND) LTD.—See Marsh & McLennan Companies, Inc.; *U.S. Public*, pg. 1385
MERCER TIMBER PRODUCTS GMBH—See Mercer International Inc.; *Int'l*, pg. 4829
MERCER TORGAU GMBH & CO. KG—See Mercer International Inc.; *Int'l*, pg. 4829
MERCER TRANSPORTATION COMPANY; *U.S. Private*, pg. 2669
MERCER TREUHAND GMBH—See Marsh & McLennan Companies, Inc.; *U.S. Public*, pg. 1386
MERCER (US) INC.—See Marsh & McLennan Companies, Inc.; *U.S. Public*, pg. 1385
MERCFUEL, INC.—See Mercury Air Group Inc.; *U.S. Private*, pg. 2670
MERCHANDISE, INC.; *U.S. Private*, pg. 2669
MERCHANDISE MANIA LIMITED—See HH Global Group Limited; *Int'l*, pg. 3379
MERCHANDISE PARTNERS, LLC; *U.S. Private*, pg. 2669
MERCHANDISE VENDING COMPANY, INC.—See Freeman Spogli & Co. Incorporated; *U.S. Private*, pg. 1606
MERCHANDISING PRAGUE, S.R.O.—See ProSiebenSat.1 Media SE; *Int'l*, pg. 6000
MERCHANDISING WORKSHOP, INC.; *U.S. Private*, pg. 2669
MERCHANDIZE LIQUIDATORS, LLC; *U.S. Private*, pg. 2669
MERCHANT AVIATION LLC—See Aeroports de Paris S.A.; *Int'l*, pg. 181
MERCHANT BANK OF SRI LANKA & FINANCE PLC—See Bank of Ceylon; *Int'l*, pg. 841
MERCHANT BANK OF SRI LANKA LTD—See Bank of Ceylon; *Int'l*, pg. 841
MERCHANT CAPITAL SOLUTIONS LLC—See KKR & Co. Inc.; *U.S. Public*, pg. 1261
MERCHANT CREDIT OF SRI LANKA LTD—See Bank of Ceylon; *Int'l*, pg. 841
MERCHANT EQUIPMENT STORE; *U.S. Private*, pg. 2669
MERCHANT E-SOLUTIONS, INC.—See Cielo S.A.; *Int'l*, pg. 1605
MERCHANT & EVANS, INC.; *U.S. Private*, pg. 2669
MERCHANT FACTORS CORP.; *U.S. Private*, pg. 2669

MERCHANT FINANCE PTE LIMITED—See Fijian Holdings Limited; *Int'l*, pg. 2662
MERCHANT FUNDS MANAGEMENT PTY LTD—See Merchant Group Pty Ltd; *Int'l*, pg. 4830
MERCHANT GROUP PTY LTD; *Int'l*, pg. 4830
MERCHANT HOUSE INTERNATIONAL LIMITED; *Int'l*, pg. 4830
MERCHANT INDUSTRY LLC; *U.S. Private*, pg. 2669
MERCHANT INVESTMENT MANAGEMENT, LLC; *U.S. Private*, pg. 2669
MERCHANT LETTINGS LIMITED—See The Skipton Building Society; *Int'l*, pg. 7686
MERCHANT LOGO GOLDONI KEESTRACK S.R.L.—See Tym Corporation; *Int'l*, pg. 7995
MERCHANT MEDICINE, LLC—See Urgent Care Partners, Inc.; *U.S. Private*, pg. 4315
MERCHANT ONE; *U.S. Private*, pg. 2669
MERCHANT PROCESSING SERVICES, INC.; *U.S. Private*, pg. 2669
MERCHANTRY, INC.—See Tradeshift Inc.; *U.S. Private*, pg. 4202
MERCHANTS AUTOMOTIVE GROUP, LLC—See Abu Dhabi Investment Authority; *Int'l*, pg. 72
MERCHANTS BANCORP; *U.S. Public*, pg. 1415
MERCHANTS BANK OF COMMERCE—See Bank of Commerce Holdings; *U.S. Public*, pg. 272
MERCHANTS BANK OF INDIANA—See Merchants Bancorp; *U.S. Public*, pg. 1415
MERCHANTS BANK; *U.S. Private*, pg. 2669
MERCHANTS BONDING COMPANY; *U.S. Private*, pg. 2669
MERCHANTS BUILDING MAINTENANCE CO.; *U.S. Private*, pg. 2670
THE MERCHANTS COMPANY INC.—See Tatum Development Corp.; *U.S. Private*, pg. 3936
MERCHANTS' CREDIT GUIDE CO.; *U.S. Private*, pg. 2670
MERCHANTS DISTRIBUTORS, INC.—See Alex Lee, Inc.; *U.S. Private*, pg. 163
MERCHANT SERVICES DIRECT LLC; *U.S. Private*, pg. 2669
MERCHANT SERVICES LTD.; *U.S. Private*, pg. 2669
MERCHANTS EXPORT INC.; *U.S. Private*, pg. 2670
MERCHANTS & FARMERS BANK—See M&F Bancorp, Inc.; *U.S. Private*, pg. 2524
MERCHANTS FOODSERVICE—See Tatum Development Corp.; *U.S. Private*, pg. 3936
MERCHANTS FOODSERVICE—See Tatum Development Corp.; *U.S. Private*, pg. 3936
MERCHANTS GROUP, INC.—See American European Group, Inc.; *U.S. Private*, pg. 232
MERCHANTS JAPAN COMPANY LIMITED—See China Merchants Group Limited; *Int'l*, pg. 1521
MERCHANTS LTD.—See Nippon Telegraph & Telephone Corporation; *Int'l*, pg. 5342
MERCHANTS & MARINE BANCORP, INC.; *U.S. Public*, pg. 1415
MERCHANTS & MARINE BANK—See Merchants & Marine Bancorp, Inc.; *U.S. Public*, pg. 1415
MERCHANTS METALS, INC.—See The Sterling Group, L.P.; *U.S. Private*, pg. 4123
MERCHANTS METALS RECYCLING II CD, LLC; *U.S. Private*, pg. 2670
MERCHANTS MORTGAGE & TRUST CORPORATION, LLC—See KKR & Co. Inc.; *U.S. Public*, pg. 1261
MERCHANTS MUTUAL INSURANCE COMPANY—See American European Group, Inc.; *U.S. Private*, pg. 232
THE MERCHANTS NATIONAL BANK; *U.S. Private*, pg. 4078
MERCHANTS OFFICE FURNITURE COMPANY; *U.S. Private*, pg. 2670
MERCHANTS PAPER COMPANY; *Int'l*, pg. 4830
MERCHANTS SA (PTY.) LTD.—See Nippon Telegraph & Telephone Corporation; *Int'l*, pg. 5343
MERCHANTS SAVINGS & LOAN ASSOCIATION INC.—See Yuchengco Group of Companies; *Int'l*, pg. 8610
MERCHANTS TRANSPORT OF HICKORY—See Alex Lee, Inc.; *U.S. Private*, pg. 163
THE MERCHANTS TRUST PLC; *Int'l*, pg. 7666
MERCHAVIA HOLDINGS AND INVESTMENTS LTD; *Int'l*, pg. 4830
MERCHSOURCE, LLC—See AEA Investors LP; *U.S. Private*, pg. 116
MERCIA ASSET MANAGEMENT PLC; *Int'l*, pg. 4830
MERCIA GROUP LIMITED—See Wilmington plc; *Int'l*, pg. 8422
MERCIA IRELAND LIMITED—See Wilmington plc; *Int'l*, pg. 8422
MERCIALYS; *Int'l*, pg. 4830
MERCIAN CHEMICAL CORPORATION—See Kirin Holdings Company, Limited; *Int'l*, pg. 4187
MERCIAN CLEANTEC CORPORATION—See Kirin Holdings Company, Limited; *Int'l*, pg. 4187
MERCIAN CORPORATION—See Kirin Holdings Company, Limited; *Int'l*, pg. 4187
MERCIA NI LIMITED—See Wilmington plc; *Int'l*, pg. 8422
MERCIA WASTE MANAGEMENT LTD.—See Fomento de Construcciones y Contratas, S.A.; *Int'l*, pg. 2723

CORPORATE AFFILIATIONS

MERCIER & KOSINSKI INSURANCE, INC.—See Thompson Insurance Group; *U.S. Private*, pg. 4160
MERCIER—See VINCI S.A.; *Int'l*, pg. 8237
MERCI GMBH & CO KG—See Storck GmbH & Co.; *Int'l*, pg. 7225
MERCITALIA INTERMODAL S.P.A.—See Ferrovie dello Stato Italiane S.p.A.; *Int'l*, pg. 2645
MERCITALIA SHUNTING & TERMINAL S.R.L.—See Ferrovie dello Stato Italiane S.p.A.; *Int'l*, pg. 2645
MERCK BIOLOGICS RESEARCH CENTER—See Merck & Co., Inc.; *U.S. Public*, pg. 1419
MERCK CANADA INC.—See Merck & Co., Inc.; *U.S. Public*, pg. 1419
MERCK CANADA—See Merck & Co., Inc.; *U.S. Public*, pg. 1419
MERCK CHEMICALS AND LIFE SCIENCE, S.A.—See Merck KGaA; *Int'l*, pg. 4830
MERCK CHEMICALS GMBH—See Merck KGaA; *Int'l*, pg. 4830
MERCK & CO., INC. - MANUFACTURING DIVISION—See Merck & Co., Inc.; *U.S. Public*, pg. 1419
MERCK & CO. INC.—See Merck & Co., Inc.; *U.S. Public*, pg. 1419
MERCK & CO. INC.—See Merck & Co., Inc.; *U.S. Public*, pg. 1418
MERCK & CO. INC.—See Merck & Co., Inc.; *U.S. Public*, pg. 1419
MERCK & CO., INC.; *U.S. Public*, pg. 1415
MERCK & CO. INC.—See Merck & Co., Inc.; *U.S. Public*, pg. 1418
MERCK & CO. INC.—See Merck & Co., Inc.; *U.S. Public*, pg. 1418
MERCK & CO., INC. - SPRINGFIELD—See Merck & Co., Inc.; *U.S. Public*, pg. 1419
MERCK & CO., INC. - VACCINE DIVISION—See Merck & Co., Inc.; *U.S. Public*, pg. 1419
MERCK & CO. RESEARCH & DEVELOPMENT—See Merck & Co., Inc.; *U.S. Public*, pg. 1419
MERCK & CO. RESEARCH & DEVELOPMENT—See Merck & Co., Inc.; *U.S. Public*, pg. 1419
MERCK ELECTRONIC MATERIALS LTD.—See Merck KGaA; *Int'l*, pg. 4831
MERCK ELECTRONICS KGAA—See Merck KGaA; *Int'l*, pg. 4831
MERCK FINCK & CO.—See KBL European Private Bankers S.A.; *Int'l*, pg. 4107
MERCK HEALTHCARE PRODUCTS—See Merck & Co., Inc.; *U.S. Public*, pg. 1419
MERCK KGAA; *Int'l*, pg. 4830
MERCKLE RECORDATI GMBH—See Recordati S.p.A.; *Int'l*, pg. 6239
MERCK LIFE SCIENCE AB—See Merck KGaA; *Int'l*, pg. 4831
MERCK LIFE SCIENCE AS—See Merck KGaA; *Int'l*, pg. 4831
MERCK LIFE SCIENCE B.V.—See Merck KGaA; *Int'l*, pg. 4831
MERCK LIFE SCIENCE GMBH—See Merck KGaA; *Int'l*, pg. 4831
MERCK LIFE SCIENCE KGAA—See Merck KGaA; *Int'l*, pg. 4831
MERCK LIFE SCIENCE LLC—See Merck KGaA; *Int'l*, pg. 4831
MERCK LIFE SCIENCE N.V.—See Merck KGaA; *Int'l*, pg. 4831
MERCK LIFE SCIENCE OY—See Merck KGaA; *Int'l*, pg. 4831
MERCK LIFE SCIENCE (PTY.) LTD.—See Merck KGaA; *Int'l*, pg. 4831
MERCK LIFE SCIENCE SPOL. S R.O.—See Merck KGaA; *Int'l*, pg. 4831
MERCK LIFE SCIENCE SP. Z O.O.—See Merck KGaA; *Int'l*, pg. 4831
MERCK LIFE SCIENCE S.R.L.—See Merck KGaA; *Int'l*, pg. 4831
MERCK LIFE SCIENCE UK LIMITED—See Merck KGaA; *Int'l*, pg. 4831
MERCK LUMIRA BIOSCIENCES FUND L.P.—See Merck & Co., Inc.; *U.S. Public*, pg. 1419
MERCK MILLIPORE LTD.—See Merck KGaA; *Int'l*, pg. 4830
MERCK MILLIPORE—See Merck KGaA; *Int'l*, pg. 4830
MERCK PERFORMANCE MATERIALS G.K.—See Merck KGaA; *Int'l*, pg. 4831
MERCK PERFORMANCE MATERIALS PVT. LTD.—See Merck KGaA; *Int'l*, pg. 4831
MERCK PERFORMANCE MATERIALS (SUISSE) S.A.—See Merck KGaA; *Int'l*, pg. 4831
MERCK PHARMA GMBH—See Merck KGaA; *Int'l*, pg. 4831
MERCK RESEARCH LABORATORIES—See Merck & Co., Inc.; *U.S. Public*, pg. 1419
MERCK S.A.—See Merck KGaA; *Int'l*, pg. 4831
MERCK SERONO GMBH—See Merck KGaA; *Int'l*, pg. 4831
MERCK SERONO ISRAEL LTD.—See Merck KGaA; *Int'l*, pg. 4831
MERCK SERONO SA—See Merck KGaA; *Int'l*, pg. 4831

COMPANY NAME INDEX

MERCK SERONO S.A.S.—See Merck KGaA; *Int'l*, pg. 4831
MERCK SERONO S.P.A.—See Merck KGaA; *Int'l*, pg. 4831
MERCK SHARP & DOHME ANIMAL HEALTH, S.L.—See Merck & Co., Inc.; *U.S. Public*, pg. 1419
MERCK SHARP & DOHME (ARGENTINA) INC.—See Merck & Co., Inc.; *U.S. Public*, pg. 1419
MERCK SHARP & DOHME ASIA PACIFIC SERVICES PTE. LTD.—See Merck & Co., Inc.; *U.S. Public*, pg. 1419
MERCK SHARP & DOHME (AUSTRALIA) PTY. LIMITED—See Merck & Co., Inc.; *U.S. Public*, pg. 1419
MERCK SHARP & DOHME BV—See Merck & Co., Inc.; *U.S. Public*, pg. 1420
MERCK SHARP & DOHME BV—See Merck & Co., Inc.; *U.S. Public*, pg. 1419
MERCK SHARP & DOHME-CHIBRET AG—See Merck & Co., Inc.; *U.S. Public*, pg. 1420
MERCK SHARP & DOHME-CHIBRET - MIRABEL—See Merck & Co., Inc.; *U.S. Public*, pg. 1420
MERCK SHARP & DOHME (CHILE) LTDA.—See Merck & Co., Inc.; *U.S. Public*, pg. 1419
MERCK SHARP & DOHME (CHINA) LTD.—See Merck & Co., Inc.; *U.S. Public*, pg. 1419
MERCK SHARP & DOHME COLOMBIA S.A.S.—See Merck & Co., Inc.; *U.S. Public*, pg. 1420
MERCK SHARP & DOHME CYPRUS LIMITED—See Merck & Co., Inc.; *U.S. Public*, pg. 1420
MERCK SHARP & DOHME DE ESPANA, S.A.—See Merck & Co., Inc.; *U.S. Public*, pg. 1420
MERCK SHARP & DOHME DE ESPANA SAU—See Merck & Co., Inc.; *U.S. Public*, pg. 1420
MERCK SHARP & DOHME DE MEXICO S.A. DE C.V.—See Merck & Co., Inc.; *U.S. Public*, pg. 1420
MERCK SHARP & DOHME DE VENEZUELA SRL—See Merck & Co., Inc.; *U.S. Public*, pg. 1420
MERCK SHARP & DOHME D.O.O. BELGRADE—See Merck & Co., Inc.; *U.S. Public*, pg. 1420
MERCK SHARP & DOHME D.O.O.—See Merck & Co., Inc.; *U.S. Public*, pg. 1420
MERCK SHARP & DOHME D.O.O.—See Merck & Co., Inc.; *U.S. Public*, pg. 1420
MERCK SHARP & DOHME (EUROPE) INC.—See Merck & Co., Inc.; *U.S. Public*, pg. 1419
MERCK SHARP & DOHME FARMACEUTICA LTDA—See Merck & Co., Inc.; *U.S. Public*, pg. 1420
MERCK SHARP & DOHME GESELLSCHAFT M.B.H.—See Merck & Co., Inc.; *U.S. Public*, pg. 1420
MERCK SHARP & DOHME (HOLDINGS) LIMITED—See Merck & Co., Inc.; *U.S. Public*, pg. 1419
MERCK SHARP & DOHME (HOLDINGS) PTY LTD—See Merck & Co., Inc.; *U.S. Public*, pg. 1419
MERCK SHARP & DOHME (I.A) CORP.—See Merck & Co., Inc.; *U.S. Public*, pg. 1419
MERCK SHARP & DOHME (I.A.) CORP.—See Merck & Co., Inc.; *U.S. Public*, pg. 1419
MERCK SHARP & DOHME (I.A.) CORP.—See Merck & Co., Inc.; *U.S. Public*, pg. 1419
MERCK SHARP & DOHME (I.A.) CORP.—See Merck & Co., Inc.; *U.S. Public*, pg. 1419
MERCK SHARP & DOHME (I.A.) CORP.—See Merck & Co., Inc.; *U.S. Public*, pg. 1419
MERCK SHARP & DOHME (I.A.) LLC—See Merck & Co., Inc.; *U.S. Public*, pg. 1419
MERCK SHARP & DOHME ILACLARI LIMITED SIRKETI—See Merck & Co., Inc.; *U.S. Public*, pg. 1420
MERCK SHARP & DOHME ILACLARI LIMITED SIRKETI—See Merck & Co., Inc.; *U.S. Public*, pg. 1420
MERCK SHARP & DOHME INOVATIVNA ZDRAVILA D.O.O.—See Merck & Co., Inc.; *U.S. Public*, pg. 1420
MERCK SHARP & DOHME IRELAND (HUMAN HEALTH) LTD—See Merck & Co., Inc.; *U.S. Public*, pg. 1420
MERCK SHARP & DOHME (IRELAND) LTD.—See Merck & Co., Inc.; *U.S. Public*, pg. 1419
MERCK SHARP & DOHME (ITALIA) S.P.A.—See Merck & Co., Inc.; *U.S. Public*, pg. 1419
MERCK SHARP & DOHME LATVIJA—See Merck & Co., Inc.; *U.S. Public*, pg. 1420
MERCK SHARP & DOHME, LIMITADA—See Merck & Co., Inc.; *U.S. Public*, pg. 1420
MERCK SHARP & DOHME LIMITED—See Merck & Co., Inc.; *U.S. Public*, pg. 1420
MERCK SHARP & DOHME (MALAYSIA) SDN. BHD.—See Merck & Co., Inc.; *U.S. Public*, pg. 1419
MERCK SHARP & DOHME (NEW ZEALAND) LIMITED—See Merck & Co., Inc.; *U.S. Public*, pg. 1419
MERCK SHARP & DOHME OU—See Merck & Co., Inc.; *U.S. Public*, pg. 1420
MERCK SHARP & DOHME PERU SRL—See Merck & Co., Inc.; *U.S. Public*, pg. 1420
MERCK SHARP & DOHME QUIMICA DE PUERTO RICO, INC.—See Merck & Co., Inc.; *U.S. Public*, pg. 1419
MERCK SHARP & DOHME RESEARCH GMBH—See Merck & Co., Inc.; *U.S. Public*, pg. 1420
MERCK SHARP & DOHME ROMANIA SRL—See Merck & Co., Inc.; *U.S. Public*, pg. 1420

MERCK SHARP & DOHME SAUDE ANIMAL LTDA.—See Merck & Co., Inc.; *U.S. Public*, pg. 1420
MERCK SHARP & DOHME S. DE R.L. DE C.V.—See Merck & Co., Inc.; *U.S. Public*, pg. 1420
MERCK SHARP & DOHME, S.R.O.—See Merck & Co., Inc.; *U.S. Public*, pg. 1420
MERCK SHARP & DOHME S.R.O.—See Merck & Co., Inc.; *U.S. Public*, pg. 1420
MERCK SHARP & DOHME (SWEDEN) AB—See Merck & Co., Inc.; *U.S. Public*, pg. 1419
MERCK, S.L.U.—See Merck KGaA; *Int'l*, pg. 4832
MERCK SP. Z O.O.—See Merck KGaA; *Int'l*, pg. 4831
MERCK S.R.L.—See Merck KGaA; *Int'l*, pg. 4831
MERCK TBK; *Int'l*, pg. 4833
MERCK VIETNAM COMPANY LIMITED—See Merck KGaA; *Int'l*, pg. 4831
THE MERCO GROUP INC.; *U.S. Private*, pg. 4078
MERCOID DIV.—See Arcline Investment Management LP; *U.S. Private*, pg. 313
MERCOM CAPITAL PLC; *Int'l*, pg. 4833
MERCOM CORPORATION; *U.S. Private*, pg. 2670
MERCON GRAPHIC FZC—See Manugraph India Ltd; *Int'l*, pg. 4677
MERCON HOLDING B.V.; *Int'l*, pg. 4833
MERCON STEEL STRUCTURES B.V.—See Mercon Holding B.V.; *Int'l*, pg. 4833
MERCO PTE. LTD.—See Rich Capital Holdings Limited; *Int'l*, pg. 6329
MERCOR FIRE PROTECTION SYSTEMS S.C. S.R.L.—See Mercor S.A.; *Int'l*, pg. 4833
MERCOR FIRE PROTECTION SYSTEMS S.R.L.—See Mercor S.A.; *Int'l*, pg. 4833
MERCOR-PROOF LLC—See Mercor S.A.; *Int'l*, pg. 4833
MERCOR S.A.; *Int'l*, pg. 4833
MERCOR UKRAINA SP. Z O.O.—See Mercor S.A.; *Int'l*, pg. 4833
MERCOTRADE AGENCIA MARITIMA LTDA.—See Ultramar Ltda.; *Int'l*, pg. 8018
MERCURA S.A.S—See Pomona-Gruppen AB; *Int'l*, pg. 5918
MERCURE—See Accor S.A.; *Int'l*, pg. 92
MERCURIA ENERGY AMERICA, INC.—See Mercuria Energy Group Holding SA; *Int'l*, pg. 4833
MERCURIA ENERGY GROUP HOLDING SA; *Int'l*, pg. 4833
MERCURIA ENERGY TRADING, INC—See Mercuria Energy Group Holding SA; *Int'l*, pg. 4833
MERCURIA ENERGY TRADING S.A.—See Mercuria Energy Group Holding SA; *Int'l*, pg. 4833
MERCURIA HOLDINGS CO., LTD.; *Int'l*, pg. 4833
MERCURIA INVESTMENT CO., LTD.; *Int'l*, pg. 4833
MERCURIA LOGISTICS CO., LTD.—See Qingdao Port International Co., Ltd.; *Int'l*, pg. 6144
MERCURIES & ASSOCIATES, HOLDING LTD.; *Int'l*, pg. 4833
MERCURIES DATA SYSTEMS LTD.; *Int'l*, pg. 4833
MERCURIES LIFE INSURANCE CO., LTD.; *Int'l*, pg. 4833
MERCURI INTERNATIONAL GROUP AB—See Bure Equity AB; *Int'l*, pg. 1221
MERCURITY FINTECH HOLDING INC.; *Int'l*, pg. 4834
MERCURIUS GROEP B.V.—See HAL Trust N.V.; *Int'l*, pg. 3224
MERCURIUS HEALTH SA; *Int'l*, pg. 4834
MERCUR SA; *Int'l*, pg. 4833
MERCURY ADVISORS LLC; *U.S. Private*, pg. 2670
MERCURY AIR CARGO, INC.—See Mercury Air Group Inc.; *U.S. Private*, pg. 2670
MERCURY AIR CENTER-RENO, LLC—See Macquarie Group Limited; *Int'l*, pg. 4630
MERCURY AIR CENTERS, INC.—See Macquarie Group Limited; *Int'l*, pg. 4627
MERCURY AIR CENTER-TULSA, LLC—See Macquarie Group Limited; *Int'l*, pg. 4627
MERCURY AIRCRAFT INC.; *U.S. Private*, pg. 2670
MERCURY AIRCRAFT, MEXICO S. DE R.L. DE C.V.—See Mercury Aircraft Inc.; *U.S. Private*, pg. 2670
MERCURY AIR GROUP INC.; *U.S. Private*, pg. 2670
MERCURY APPLIANCES LIMITED—See The Middleby Corporation; *U.S. Public*, pg. 2114
MERCURY ASCENSORE CO.,LTD.—See Otis Worldwide Corporation; *U.S. Public*, pg. 1623
MERCURY CAPITAL CORP.; *U.S. Private*, pg. 2670
MERCURY CAPITAL INVESTMENTS PTY LIMITED; *Int'l*, pg. 4834
MERCURY CAPITAL PARTNERS, L.P.; *U.S. Private*, pg. 2670
MERCURY CAPITAL TRUST LTD; *Int'l*, pg. 4834
MERCURY CASUALTY COMPANY—See Mercury General Corporation; *U.S. Public*, pg. 1421
MERCURY COMMERCIAL ELECTRONICS, INC.—See Mercury Systems, Inc.; *U.S. Public*, pg. 1422
MERCURY COMMUNICATIONS, INC.—See Warren Equity Partners, LLC; *U.S. Private*, pg. 4443
MERCURY COMPUTER SYSTEMS LTD.—See Mercury Systems, Inc.; *U.S. Public*, pg. 1422
MERCURY COUNTY MUTUAL INSURANCE COMPANY—See Mercury General Corporation; *U.S. Public*, pg. 1421
MERCURYCSC; *U.S. Private*, pg. 2671

MERCURY PARTNERS 90 BI INC.

MERCURY DEFENSE SYSTEMS, INC.—See Mercury Systems, Inc.; *U.S. Public*, pg. 1422
MERCURY ELECTRONICS & PLASTICS MANUFACTURING—See Brunswick Corporation; *U.S. Public*, pg. 408
MERCURY ENERGY LIMITED—See Mercury NZ Limited; *Int'l*, pg. 4834
MERCURY ENGINEERING LTD.; *Int'l*, pg. 4834
MERCURY ENGINEERING MOSCOW—See Mercury Engineering Ltd.; *Int'l*, pg. 4834
MERCURY ENGINEERING POLSKA SP. Z O.O.—See Mercury Engineering Ltd.; *Int'l*, pg. 4834
MERCURY ENGINEERING SERVICES LLC—See Mercury Engineering Ltd.; *Int'l*, pg. 4834
MERCURY ENGINEERING UK—See Mercury Engineering Ltd.; *Int'l*, pg. 4834
MERCURY ENTERPRISES, INC.; *U.S. Private*, pg. 2670
MERCURY EQUIPMENT FINANCE GROUP; *U.S. Private*, pg. 2670
MERCURY FUEL SERVICE INC.; *U.S. Private*, pg. 2670
MERCURY GENERAL CORPORATION; *U.S. Public*, pg. 1421
THE MERCURY GROUP—See Ackerman McQueen, Inc.; *U.S. Private*, pg. 60
MERCURY HIMALAYAN EXPLORATIONS LTD.—See Ebix Inc.; *U.S. Public*, pg. 710
MERCURY INDEMNITY COMPANY OF AMERICA—See Mercury General Corporation; *U.S. Public*, pg. 1421
MERCURY INDUSTRIES BERHAD; *Int'l*, pg. 4834
MERCURY INSTRUMENTS LLC—See Honeywell International Inc.; *U.S. Public*, pg. 1049
MERCURY INSURANCE COMPANY—See Mercury General Corporation; *U.S. Public*, pg. 1421
MERCURY INSURANCE SERVICES, LLC—See Mercury General Corporation; *U.S. Public*, pg. 1421
MERCURY INTELLIGENCE SYSTEMS, INC.—See Mercury Systems, Inc.; *U.S. Public*, pg. 1422
MERCURY INTERNATIONAL CO., LTD.—See Japan Airlines Co., Ltd.; *Int'l*, pg. 3884
MERCURY INTERNATIONAL ELECTRO-MECHANICAL CONTRACTING LLC—See Mercury Engineering Ltd.; *Int'l*, pg. 4834
MERCURY INTERNATIONAL TRADING CORP.; *U.S. Private*, pg. 2670
MERCURY LABORATORIES LIMITED; *Int'l*, pg. 4834
MERCURY LUGGAGE/SEWARD TRUNK; *U.S. Private*, pg. 2670
MERCURY LUGGAGE/SEWARD TRUNK—See Mercury; *U.S. Private*, pg. 2671
MERCURY LUGGAGE/SEWARD TRUNK—See Mercury; *U.S. Private*, pg. 2671
MERCURY MANUFACTURING CO. LTD.—See Godrej & Boyce Mfg. Co. Ltd.; *Int'l*, pg. 3021
MERCURY MANUFACTURING COMPANY—See O2 Investment Partners, LLC; *U.S. Private*, pg. 2982
MERCURY MARINE GROUP—See Brunswick Corporation; *U.S. Public*, pg. 408
MERCURY MARINE LTD.—See Brunswick Corporation; *U.S. Public*, pg. 408
MERCURY MARINE SINGAPORE PTE LTD—See Brunswick Corporation; *U.S. Public*, pg. 408
MERCURY MEDIA - BOSTON—See Mercury Media Holding Corp.; *U.S. Private*, pg. 2671
MERCURY MEDIA HOLDING CORP.; *U.S. Private*, pg. 2671
MERCURY MEDIA - PRINCETON—See Mercury Media Holding Corp.; *U.S. Private*, pg. 2671
MERCURY MEDIA -SANTA MONICA—See Mercury Media Holding Corp.; *U.S. Private*, pg. 2671
MERCURY MESSENGERS PTY LTD—See CTI Logistics Limited; *Int'l*, pg. 1871
MERCURY MIDDLE EAST W.L.L—See Mercury Engineering Ltd.; *Int'l*, pg. 4834
MERCURY MINNESOTA INC.—See Mercury Aircraft Inc.; *U.S. Private*, pg. 2670
MERCURY MISSION SYSTEMS INTERNATIONAL, SA—See Mercury Systems, Inc.; *U.S. Public*, pg. 1422
MERCURY MISSION SYSTEMS SPAIN, SL—See Mercury Systems, Inc.; *U.S. Public*, pg. 1422
MERCURY MOSAICS & TILE, INC.; *U.S. Private*, pg. 2671
MERCURY MUSIC CORPORATION—See Theodore Presser Co.; *U.S. Private*, pg. 4141
MERCURY NETWORK, LLC—See Insight Venture Management, LLC; *U.S. Private*, pg. 2089
MERCURY NETWORK, LLC—See Stone Point Capital LLC; *U.S. Private*, pg. 3822
MERCURY NEW MEDIA, INC.; *U.S. Private*, pg. 2671
MERCURY NZ LIMITED; *Int'l*, pg. 4834
MERCURY PAINT CORP.; *U.S. Private*, pg. 2671
MERCURY PAINTS FACTORY SDN. BHD.—See Mercury Industries Berhad; *Int'l*, pg. 4834
MERCURY PARTNERS 90 BI INC.; *U.S. Private*, pg. 2671
MERCURY PAYMENT SERVICES S.P.A.—See Advent International Corporation; *U.S. Public*, pg. 105
MERCURY PAYMENT SERVICES S.P.A.—See Bain Capital, LP; *U.S. Private*, pg. 442
MERCURY PAYMENT SERVICES S.P.A.—See Italmobiliare S.p.A.; *Int'l*, pg. 3829

MERCURY PAYMENT SYSTEMS, LLC—See GTCR LLC; *U.S. Private*, pg. 1806
MERCURY PHARMACEUTICALS (IRELAND) LIMITED—See ADVANZ PHARMA Corp. Limited; *Int'l*, pg. 166
MERCURY PLASTICS INC.; *U.S. Private*, pg. 2671
MERCURY PLASTICS, INC.; *U.S. Private*, pg. 2671
MERCURY PRINTING COMPANY, LLC—See Chatham Asset Management, LLC; *U.S. Private*, pg. 863
MERCURY PRINTING, INC.—See Chatham Asset Management, LLC; *U.S. Private*, pg. 863
MERCURY PROCESSING SERVICES INTERNATIONAL LLC—See Advent International Corporation; *U.S. Private*, pg. 105
MERCURY PROCESSING SERVICES INTERNATIONAL LLC—See Bain Capital, LP; *U.S. Private*, pg. 442
MERCURY PROCESSING SERVICES INTERNATIONAL LLC—See Italmobiliare S.p.A.; *Int'l*, pg. 3829
MERCURY PROCESSING SERVICES INTERNATIONAL PAYMENT CARD PROCESSING & DEVELOPMENT LTD.—See Advent International Corporation; *U.S. Private*, pg. 105
MERCURY PROCESSING SERVICES INTERNATIONAL PAYMENT CARD PROCESSING & DEVELOPMENT LTD.—See Bain Capital, LP; *U.S. Private*, pg. 442
MERCURY PROCESSING SERVICES INTERNATIONAL PAYMENT CARD PROCESSING & DEVELOPMENT LTD.—See Italmobiliare S.p.A.; *Int'l*, pg. 3829
MERCURY PRODUCTS CORP.; *U.S. Private*, pg. 2671
MERCURY PROMOTIONS & FULFILLMENT, INC.; *U.S. Private*, pg. 2671
MERCURY QATAR—See Mercury Engineering Ltd.; *Int'l*, pg. 4834
MERCURY RECORDS LTD.—See Universal Music Group N.V.; *Int'l*, pg. 8080
MERCURY REFUELING, INC.—See Mercury Air Group Inc.; *U.S. Private*, pg. 2670
MERCURY STAFFING CO., LTD.—See FUJISOFT INCORPORATED; *Int'l*, pg. 2830
MERCURY SYSTEMS, INC. - RF INTEGRATED SOLUTIONS—See Mercury Systems, Inc.; *U.S. Public*, pg. 1422
MERCURY SYSTEMS, INC.; *U.S. Public*, pg. 1422
MERCURY SYSTEMS SARL—See Mercury Systems, Inc.; *U.S. Public*, pg. 1422
MERCURY SYSTEMS - TRUSTED MISSION SOLUTIONS, INC.—See Mercury Systems, Inc.; *U.S. Public*, pg. 1422
MERCURY TECHNOLOGIES, INC.; *U.S. Private*, pg. 2671
MERCURY TECHNOLOGY GROUP, INC.—See Accenture plc; *Int'l*, pg. 87
MERCURY TITLE LLC—See Anywhere Real Estate Inc.; *U.S. Public*, pg. 142
MERCURY TRADE FINANCE SOLUTIONS, S.L.—See Banco Santander, S.A.; *Int'l*, pg. 826
MERCURY TUBE PRODUCTS LLC—See Washington Equity Partners L.L.C.; *U.S. Private*, pg. 4447
MERCUS YRKESKLADER AB—See Nordstjernan AB; *Int'l*, pg. 5425
MERCY COLLEGE OF OHIO—See Catholic Healthcare Partners; *U.S. Private*, pg. 792
MERCY FLIGHTS INC.; *U.S. Private*, pg. 2671
MERCY GENERAL HEALTH PARTNERS—See Trinity Health Corporation; *U.S. Private*, pg. 4233
MERCY GENERAL HOSPITAL—See Catholic Health Initiatives; *U.S. Private*, pg. 790
MERCY HEALTHCARE SACRAMENTO INC.—See Catholic Health Initiatives; *U.S. Private*, pg. 790
MERCY HEALTH SERVICES; *U.S. Private*, pg. 2671
MERCY HEALTH—See Bon Secours Mercy Health, Inc.; *U.S. Private*, pg. 612
MERCY HEALTH SUPPORT SERVICES; *Int'l*, pg. 4834
MERCY HOSPITAL, A CAMPUS OF PLANTATION GENERAL HOSPITAL—See HCA Healthcare, Inc.; *U.S. Public*, pg. 1006
MERCY HOSPITAL & HEALTH SERVICES—See Catholic Health Initiatives; *U.S. Private*, pg. 790
MERCY HOSPITAL OF BUFFALO—See Catholic Health System, Inc.; *U.S. Private*, pg. 791
MERCY HOSPITAL OF FOLSOM—See Catholic Health Initiatives; *U.S. Private*, pg. 790
MERCY MARICOPA INTEGRATED CARE; *U.S. Private*, pg. 2671
MERCY MEDICAL CENTER MT. SHASTA—See Catholic Health Initiatives; *U.S. Private*, pg. 790
MERCY MEDICAL CENTER - NORTH IOWA—See Trinity Health Corporation; *U.S. Private*, pg. 4233
MERCY MEDICAL CENTER REDDING—See Catholic Health Initiatives; *U.S. Private*, pg. 790
MERCY MEDICAL CENTER - SIOUX CITY—See Trinity Health Corporation; *U.S. Private*, pg. 4233
MERCY MEDICAL CENTER—See Catholic Health Services of Long Island; *U.S. Private*, pg. 791
MERCY MEMORIAL HOSPITAL SYSTEM; *U.S. Private*, pg. 2671
MERCY SAN JUAN HOSPITAL—See Catholic Health Initiatives; *U.S. Private*, pg. 790
MERCY SENIOR HOUSING, INC.—See Catholic Health Initiatives; *U.S. Private*, pg. 790

MERCY SOUTHWEST HOSPITAL—See Catholic Health Initiatives; *U.S. Private*, pg. 790
MERCY WESTSIDE HOSPITAL—See Catholic Health Initiatives; *U.S. Private*, pg. 789
MERDEKA AIRCRAFT LEASING (LABUAN) LIMITED—See Marubeni Corporation; *Int'l*, pg. 4705
MERDEKA AIRCRAFT LEASING (LABUAN) LIMITED—See Mizuho Leasing Company, Limited; *Int'l*, pg. 4999
MEREDIAN HOLDINGS GROUP INC.—See Danimer Scientific, Inc.; *U.S. Public*, pg. 632
MEREDITH CORPORATION; *U.S. Public*, pg. 1422
MEREDITH DIGITAL; *U.S. Private*, pg. 2671
MEREDITH DISTRIBUTION (NSW) PTY LTD—See Wesfarmers Limited; *Int'l*, pg. 8381
MEREDITH DISTRIBUTION PTY LTD—See Westarmers Limited; *Int'l*, pg. 8381
MEREDITH EXELERATED MARKETING—See Meredith Corporation; *U.S. Public*, pg. 1423
MEREDITH INTEGRATED MARKETING—See Meredith Corporation; *U.S. Public*, pg. 1423
MEREDITH LIST MARKETING—See Meredith Corporation; *U.S. Public*, pg. 1423
MEREDITH LODGING LLC; *U.S. Private*, pg. 2671
THE MEREDITH PROPERTY GROUP PLC; *Int'l*, pg. 7666
MEREDITH VILLAGE SAVINGS BANK; *U.S. Private*, pg. 2672
MEREDITH-WEBB PRINTING CO. INC.; *U.S. Private*, pg. 2672
MEREEN-JOHNSON MACHINE COMPANY—See North Central Equity LLC; *U.S. Private*, pg. 2943
MEREFA GLASS COMPANY LTD.—See Turkiye Sise ve Cam Fabrikalari A.S.; *Int'l*, pg. 7977
ME RENEWABLE POWER CORPORATION; *Int'l*, pg. 4763
MEREO BIOPHARMA GROUP PLC; *Int'l*, pg. 4834
MEREX AIRCRAFT COMPANY, INCORPORATED—See Merex Holding Corporation; *U.S. Private*, pg. 2672
MEREX FOOD CORP.—See Baldor Specialty Foods Inc.; *U.S. Private*, pg. 458
MEREX HOLDING CORPORATION; *U.S. Private*, pg. 2672
MERFISH PIPE & SUPPLY, CO.—See Reliance Steel & Aluminum Co.; *U.S. Public*, pg. 1780
MERFORD ACOUSTIC MATERIALS B.V.—See Merford Holding B.V.; *Int'l*, pg. 4834
MERFORD HOLDING B.V.; *Int'l*, pg. 4834
MERGANSER CAPITAL MANAGEMENT, INC.—See Annaly Capital Management, Inc.; *U.S. Public*, pg. 138
MERGE DESIGN & INTERACTIVE, INC.—See Keystone Capital, Inc.; *U.S. Private*, pg. 2295
MERGE HEALTHCARE INCORPORATED—See International Business Machines Corporation; *U.S. Public*, pg. 1149
MERGE HOUSING BHD; *Int'l*, pg. 4834
MERGENCE CORP.; *U.S. Public*, pg. 1424
MERGENTHALER TRANSFER & STORAGE CO.—See Mesa Systems, Inc.; *U.S. Private*, pg. 2678
MERGENT, INC.—See London Stock Exchange Group plc; *Int'l*, pg. 4548
MERGENT JAPAN K.K.—See London Stock Exchange Group plc; *Int'l*, pg. 4548
MERGERMARKET LIMITED—See ION Investment Group Ltd.; *Int'l*, pg. 3794
MERGERMARKET (U.S.) LTD.—See ION Investment Group Ltd.; *Int'l*, pg. 3794
MERGER MINES CORP.; *U.S. Public*, pg. 1424
THE MERGIS GROUP—See Randstad N.V.; *Int'l*, pg. 6206
MER GROUP; *Int'l*, pg. 4818
MERIAM INSTRUMENT—See Berkshire Hathaway Inc.; *U.S. Public*, pg. 300
MERIAN GLOBAL INVESTORS; *Int'l*, pg. 4835
MERIBEL ALPINA SAS—See Compagnie des Alpes S.A.; *Int'l*, pg. 1738
MERICAL LLC; *U.S. Private*, pg. 2672
MERICHEM CHEMICALS & REFINING SERVICES LLC—See Merichem Company; *U.S. Private*, pg. 2672
MERICHEM COMPANY - MERICHEM CATALYST PLANT—See Merichem Company; *U.S. Private*, pg. 2672
MERICHEM COMPANY; *U.S. Private*, pg. 2672
MERICHEM HONG KONG LTD.—See Merichem Company; *U.S. Private*, pg. 2672
MERICKEL LUMBER MILLS INC.; *U.S. Private*, pg. 2672
MERICLE COMMERCIAL REAL ESTATE SERVICES; *U.S. Private*, pg. 2672
MERICO ABATEMENT CONTRACTORS, INC.; *U.S. Private*, pg. 2672
MERICSSON ACQUISITION CORPORATION; *Int'l*, pg. 4835
MERIDA BENELUX B.V.—See Merida Industry Co., Ltd.; *Int'l*, pg. 4835
MERIDA & CENTURION GERMANY GMBH—See Merida Industry Co., Ltd.; *Int'l*, pg. 4835
MERIDA INDUSTRY CO., LTD.; *Int'l*, pg. 4835
MERIDA POLSKA SP. Z.O.O—See Merida Industry Co., Ltd.; *Int'l*, pg. 4835
MERIDA SVERIGE AB—See Merida Industry Co., Ltd.; *Int'l*, pg. 4835

MERIDELL ACHIEVEMENT CENTER—See Universal Health Services, Inc.; *U.S. Public*, pg. 2260
MERIDIA CO., LTD.; *Int'l*, pg. 4835
MERIDIAM INFRASTRUCTURE PARTNERS SAS; *Int'l*, pg. 4835
MERIDIAN ADHESIVES GROUP LLC—See Arsenal Capital Management LP; *U.S. Private*, pg. 339
MERIDIAN A.D.; *Int'l*, pg. 4835
MERIDIANA FLY S.P.A.—See Meridiana S.p.A.; *Int'l*, pg. 4835
MERIDIAN AMERICA INC.—See Meridian Audio Ltd; *Int'l*, pg. 4835
MERIDIANA S.P.A.; *Int'l*, pg. 4835
MERIDIAN ASSET SERVICES, LLC—See Stone Point Capital LLC; *U.S. Private*, pg. 3825
MERIDIAN AUDIO LTD; *Int'l*, pg. 4835
MERIDIAN BANCORP, INC.; *U.S. Public*, pg. 1424
MERIDIAN BANK—See Meridian Corporation; *U.S. Public*, pg. 1424
MERIDIAN BEHAVIORAL HEALTHCARE, INC.; *U.S. Private*, pg. 2672
MERIDIAN BIOSCIENCE CORPORATION—See Meridian Bioscience Inc.; *U.S. Public*, pg. 1424
MERIDIAN BIOSCIENCE EUROPE B.V.—See Meridian Bioscience Inc.; *U.S. Public*, pg. 1424
MERIDIAN BIOSCIENCE EUROPE FRANCE—See Meridian Bioscience Inc.; *U.S. Public*, pg. 1424
MERIDIAN BIOSCIENCE EUROPE S.A.—See Meridian Bioscience Inc.; *U.S. Public*, pg. 1424
MERIDIAN BIOSCIENCE EUROPE S.R.L.—See Meridian Bioscience Inc.; *U.S. Public*, pg. 1424
MERIDIAN BIOSCIENCE INC.; *U.S. Public*, pg. 1424
MERIDIAN BIOSCIENCE ISRAEL HOLDING LTD.—See Meridian Bioscience Inc.; *U.S. Public*, pg. 1424
MERIDIAN BIOSCIENCE S.A.—See Meridian Bioscience Inc.; *U.S. Public*, pg. 1424
MERIDIAN BIOSCIENCE UK LTD.—See Meridian Bioscience Inc.; *U.S. Public*, pg. 1424
MERIDIAN BL D.O.O.—See Meridian A.D.; *Int'l*, pg. 4835
MERIDIAN BL D.O.O.—See Meridian A.D.; *Int'l*, pg. 4835
MERIDIAN BRICK LLC - ATHENS—See Wienerberger AG; *Int'l*, pg. 8405
MERIDIAN BRICK LLC - COLUMBIA—See Wienerberger AG; *Int'l*, pg. 8405
MERIDIAN BRICK LLC—See Wienerberger AG; *Int'l*, pg. 8405
MERIDIAN BUSINESS DEVELOPMENT—See Wanfeng Auto Holding Group Co., Ltd.; *Int'l*, pg. 8340
MERIDIAN BUSINESS SUPPORT LTD.; *Int'l*, pg. 4835
MERIDIAN CAPITAL GROUP, LLC—See Banco Santander, S.A.; *Int'l*, pg. 826
MERIDIAN CAPITAL, LLC; *U.S. Private*, pg. 2672
MERIDIAN CAPITAL; *Int'l*, pg. 4835
MERIDIAN CITIZENS MUTUAL INSURANCE COMPANY—See State Automobile Mutual Insurance Company; *U.S. Private*, pg. 3791
MERIDIAN CLINICAL RESEARCH, LLC—See GHO Capital Partners LLP; *Int'l*, pg. 2959
MERIDIAN COCA-COLA BOTTLING CO.; *U.S. Private*, pg. 2672
MERIDIAN CO., LTD.; *Int'l*, pg. 4835
MERIDIAN CONSULTING GROUP, LLC—See HOV Services Limited; *Int'l*, pg. 3492
MERIDIAN CORPORATION; *U.S. Public*, pg. 1424
MERIDIAN CREATIVE ALLIANCE LLC; *U.S. Private*, pg. 2672
MERIDIAN ENERGY LIMITED; *Int'l*, pg. 4835
MERIDIAN ENTERPRISES CORPORATION; *U.S. Private*, pg. 2672
MERIDIAN FINANCIAL SERVICES, INC.—See Marriott Vacations Worldwide Corporation; *U.S. Public*, pg. 1373
MERIDIAN FINANCIAL SERVICES, INC.—See Marriott Vacations Worldwide Corporation; *U.S. Public*, pg. 1373
MERIDIAN FINANCIAL SERVICES, INC.—See Marriott Vacations Worldwide Corporation; *U.S. Public*, pg. 1373
MERIDIAN FINANCIAL SERVICES, INC.—See Marriott Vacations Worldwide Corporation; *U.S. Public*, pg. 1374
MERIDIAN GENERAL, LLC; *U.S. Private*, pg. 2672
MERIDIAN GOLD HOLDINGS MEXICO S.A. DE C.V.—See Equinox Gold Corp.; *Int'l*, pg. 2485
MERIDIAN GOLD INC.—See Pan American Silver Corp.; *Int'l*, pg. 5713
MERIDIAN GROUP INC.; *U.S. Private*, pg. 2673
MERIDIAN GROUP INTERNATIONAL, INC.; *U.S. Private*, pg. 2673
MERIDIAN GROUP SERVICES LIMITED—See Saudi Arabian Mining Company - Ma'aden; *Int'l*, pg. 6589
THE MERIDIAN GROUP; *U.S. Private*, pg. 4078
MERIDIAN HEALTH SERVICES; *U.S. Private*, pg. 2673
MERIDIAN HOME MORTGAGE CORP.; *U.S. Private*, pg. 2673
MERIDIAN IMAGING SOLUTIONS, INC.—See Konica Minolta, Inc.; *Int'l*, pg. 4258
MERIDIAN INDUSTRIES, INC.; *U.S. Private*, pg. 2673

MERIDIAN INSURANCE SERVICE, INC.; *U.S. Private*, pg. 2673
MERIDIAN INTERNATIONAL GROUP, INC.; *U.S. Private*, pg. 2673
MERIDIANI S.R.L.—See Dexelance S.p.A.; *Int'l*, pg. 2092
MERIDIAN IT, INC.—See Meridian Group International, Inc.; *U.S. Private*, pg. 2673
MERIDIAN IT LIMITED—See Meridian Group International, Inc.; *U.S. Private*, pg. 2673
MERIDIAN IT PTY LTD.—See Meridian Group International, Inc.; *U.S. Private*, pg. 2673
MERIDIAN IT SINGAPORE—See Meridian Group International, Inc.; *U.S. Private*, pg. 2673
MERIDIAN LAND SETTLEMENT SERVICES, LLC—See Meridian Corporation; *U.S. Public*, pg. 1424
MERIDIAN LEASING—See Meridian Group International, Inc.; *U.S. Private*, pg. 2673
MERIDIAN LIFE SCIENCE, INC.—See Meridian Bioscience Inc.; *U.S. Public*, pg. 1424
MERIDIAN LIGHTWEIGHT TECHNOLOGIES DEUTSCHLAND GMBH—See Wanfeng Auto Holding Group Co., Ltd.; *Int'l*, pg. 8340
MERIDIAN LIGHTWEIGHT TECHNOLOGIES HOLDINGS INC.—See Wanfeng Auto Holding Group Co., Ltd.; *Int'l*, pg. 8340
MERIDIAN LIGHTWEIGHT TECHNOLOGIES INC.—See Wanfeng Auto Holding Group Co., Ltd.; *Int'l*, pg. 8340
MERIDIAN LIGHTWEIGHT TECHNOLOGIES UK LIMITED—See Wanfeng Auto Holding Group Co., Ltd.; *Int'l*, pg. 8340
MERIDIANLINK, INC.—See Thoma Bravo, L.P.; *U.S. Private*, pg. 4150
MERIDIAN LOGISTICS LLC—See Gryphon Investors, LLC; *U.S. Private*, pg. 1799
MERIDIAN MALL COMPANY, INC.—See CBL & Associates Properties, Inc.; *U.S. Public*, pg. 458
MERIDIAN MANUFACTURING, INC.—See WGI Westman Group, Inc.; *Int'l*, pg. 8394
MERIDIAN MANUFACTURING, INC. - STORM LAKE—See WGI Westman Group, Inc.; *Int'l*, pg. 8394
MERIDIAN MAPLESTAR SDN. BHD.—See Pan-United Corporation Ltd.; *Int'l*, pg. 5716
MERIDIAN MEDICAL MANAGEMENT—See The Gores Group, LLC; *U.S. Private*, pg. 4035
MERIDIAN MEDICAL TECHNOLOGIES, INC.—See Altaris Capital Partners, LLC; *U.S. Private*, pg. 206
MERIDIAN MEDICAL TECHNOLOGIES - WESTPORT—See Altaris Capital Partners, LLC; *U.S. Private*, pg. 206
MERIDIAN MINING SE; *Int'l*, pg. 4835
MERIDIAN OUTDOOR ADVERTISING—See Publicis Groupe S.A.; *Int'l*, pg. 6112
MERIDIAN PACIFIC PROPERTIES INC.; *U.S. Private*, pg. 2673
MERIDIAN PJSC; *Int'l*, pg. 4835
MERIDIAN PLACE (HERTFORD) RESIDENTS MANAGEMENT COMPANY LIMITED—See Persimmon plc; *Int'l*, pg. 5816
MERIDIAN RACK & PINION, INC.—See Gladstone Management Corporation; *U.S. Private*, pg. 1705
MERIDIAN RAIL ACQUISITION CORP.—See The Greenbrier Companies, Inc.; *U.S. Public*, pg. 2086
MERIDIAN RESOURCE COMPANY, LLC—See Elevance Health, Inc.; *U.S. Public*, pg. 730
MERIDIANRX, LLC—See Centene Corporation; *U.S. Public*, pg. 471
MERIDIAN SA—See Karelia Tobacco Company Inc.; *Int'l*, pg. 4080
MERIDIAN SPECIALTY YARN GROUP, INC.—See Meridian Industries, Inc.; *U.S. Private*, pg. 2673
MERIDIAN SPEEDWAY, LLC—See Canadian Pacific Kansas City Limited; *Int'l*, pg. 1285
MERIDIAN SYSTEMS—See Trimble, Inc.; *U.S. Public*, pg. 2190
MERIDIAN TECHNOLOGIES - GLOBAL TECHNOLOGY CENTER—See Wanfeng Auto Holding Group Co., Ltd.; *Int'l*, pg. 8340
MERIDIAN TECHNOLOGIES, INC.; *U.S. Private*, pg. 2673
MERIDIAN TECHNOLOGIES MEXICO, S. DE R.L. DE C.V.—See Wanfeng Auto Holding Group Co., Ltd.; *Int'l*, pg. 8340
MERIDIAN TECHNOLOGY GROUP; *U.S. Private*, pg. 2673
MERIDIAN TRANSPORTATION RESOURCES, LLC; *U.S. Private*, pg. 2673
MERIDIAN VENTURE PARTNERS; *U.S. Private*, pg. 2673
MERIDIAN WASTE ACQUISITIONS, LLC—See Warren Equity Partners, LLC; *U.S. Private*, pg. 4443
MERIDIAN WEALTH PARTNERS, LLC—See Meridian Corporation; *U.S. Public*, pg. 1424
MERIDIAN WORLDWIDE TRANSPORTATION GROUP; *U.S. Private*, pg. 2674
MERIDIENNE CORPORATION; *U.S. Private*, pg. 2674
MERIDIEN RESEARCH; *U.S. Private*, pg. 2674
MERIDIE S.P.A.; *Int'l*, pg. 4836
MERIDIN EAST SDN. BHD.—See Mah Sing Group Berhad; *Int'l*, pg. 4643
MERIDIUM, INC.—See General Electric Company; *U.S. Public*, pg. 920

MERIEUX EQUITY PARTNERS; *Int'l*, pg. 4836
MERIEUX NUTRISCIENCES CORP.; *U.S. Private*, pg. 2674
MERIMEN ONLINE SDN. BHD.—See Silverlake Axis Ltd.; *Int'l*, pg. 6926
MERIMEN TECHNOLOGIES - FZE—See Silverlake Axis Ltd.; *Int'l*, pg. 6926
MERIMEN TECHNOLOGIES HONG KONG LIMITED—See Silverlake Axis Ltd.; *Int'l*, pg. 6926
MERIMEN TECHNOLOGIES JAPAN K.K.—See Silverlake Axis Ltd.; *Int'l*, pg. 6926
MERIMEN TECHNOLOGIES PHILIPPINES INC.—See Silverlake Axis Ltd.; *Int'l*, pg. 6926
MERIMEN TECHNOLOGIES (SINGAPORE) PTE. LTD.—See Silverlake Axis Ltd.; *Int'l*, pg. 6926
MERIMEN TECHNOLOGIES (THAILAND) CO. LTD.—See Silverlake Axis Ltd.; *Int'l*, pg. 6926
MERINAT S.A.—See Burkhalter Holding AG; *Int'l*, pg. 1225
MERING & ASSOCIATES; *U.S. Private*, pg. 2674
MERINGCARSON—See Mering & Associates; *U.S. Private*, pg. 2674
MERINO-ODD SDN. BHD.—See DAI-DAN Co Ltd; *Int'l*, pg. 1917
MERIPLEX COMMUNICATIONS LTD.—See Vitruvian Partners LLP; *Int'l*, pg. 8263
MERISANT AUSTRALIA PTY LTD—See MacAndrews & Forbes Incorporated; *U.S. Private*, pg. 2532
MERISANT COMPANY—See MacAndrews & Forbes Incorporated; *U.S. Private*, pg. 2532
MERISANT CORP.—See MacAndrews & Forbes Incorporated; *U.S. Private*, pg. 2532
MERISANT FRANCE SAS—See MacAndrews & Forbes Incorporated; *U.S. Private*, pg. 2532
MERISANT INDIA PRIVATE LIMITED—See MacAndrews & Forbes Incorporated; *U.S. Private*, pg. 2532
MERISANT UK, LTD.—See MacAndrews & Forbes Incorporated; *U.S. Private*, pg. 2532
MERISANT US, INC.—See MacAndrews & Forbes Incorporated; *U.S. Private*, pg. 2532
MERIS D.O.O.—See Endress+Hauser (International) Holding AG; *Int'l*, pg. 2408
MERISEL, INC.—See Saints Capital, LLC; *U.S. Private*, pg. 3530
MERICOL ANTIOXIDANTS LLC—See Merichem Company; *U.S. Private*, pg. 2672
MERISON (AUSTRALIA) PTY. LTD.—See Bread Financial Holdings Inc.; *U.S. Public*, pg. 381
MERISON RETAIL B.V.—See Bread Financial Holdings Inc.; *U.S. Public*, pg. 381
MERISON RETAIL (HK) LTD.—See Bread Financial Holdings Inc.; *U.S. Public*, pg. 381
MERISTATION MAGAZINE, S.L.—See Promotora de Informaciones S.A.; *Int'l*, pg. 5995
MERITAGE HOMES CORPORATION; *U.S. Public*, pg. 1425
MERITAGE HOMES OF ARIZONA, INC.—See Meritage Homes Corporation; *U.S. Public*, pg. 1425
MERITAGE HOMES OF FLORIDA REALTY LLC—See Meritage Homes Corporation; *U.S. Public*, pg. 1425
MERITAGE HOMES OF THE CAROLINAS, INC.—See Meritage Homes Corporation; *U.S. Public*, pg. 1425
MERITAGE HOSPITALITY GROUP INC.; *U.S. Public*, pg. 1425
MERITAGE MIDSTREAM SERVICES II, LLC—See Western Midstream Partners, LP; *U.S. Public*, pg. 2356
MERITAIN HEALTH, INC.—See CVS Health Corporation; *U.S. Public*, pg. 615
MERIT BENEFITS GROUP, INC.—See Group RHI; *U.S. Private*, pg. 1794
MERIT BRASS COMPANY INC.; *U.S. Private*, pg. 2674
MERIT CAPITAL ADVANCE, LLC—See Island Capital Group LLC; *U.S. Private*, pg. 2144
MERIT CAPITAL PARTNERS; *U.S. Private*, pg. 2674
MERIT CHEVROLET COMPANY; *U.S. Private*, pg. 2674
MERIT CONSULTANTS INTERNATIONAL INC.—See Murray & Roberts Holdings Ltd.; *Int'l*, pg. 5100
MERIT CONTRACTORS NIAGARA; *Int'l*, pg. 4836
MERITDIRECT, LLC; *U.S. Private*, pg. 2674
MERITDIRECT UK—See MeritDirect, LLC; *U.S. Private*, pg. 2674
THE MERIT DISTRIBUTION GROUP, LLC—See Centre Lane Partners, LLC; *U.S. Private*, pg. 827
MERITECH INC.; *U.S. Private*, pg. 2675
MERITEC—See Ohio Associated Enterprises; *U.S. Private*, pg. 3003
MERIT ELECTRIC COMPANY, INC.; *U.S. Private*, pg. 2674
MERIT ELECTRIC INC.; *U.S. Private*, pg. 2674
MERIT ELECTRIC OF SPOKANE; *U.S. Private*, pg. 2674
MERIT ENDS INC—See Viking Processing Corporation; *U.S. Private*, pg. 4382
MERIT ENERGY COMPANY INC.; *U.S. Private*, pg. 2674
MERIT ENTERPRISES, INC.—See Brookfield Corporation; *Int'l*, pg. 1175
MERITEX TECHNOLOGY (SUZHOU) CO. LTD.—See Illinois Tool Works Inc.; *U.S. Public*, pg. 1109
MERIT FINANCIAL GROUP, LLC; *U.S. Private*, pg. 2674
MERIT GROUP PLC; *Int'l*, pg. 4836

MERIT INSURANCE SERVICES, INC.—See Integrity Marketing Group LLC; *U.S. Private*, pg. 2103
MERIT INTERACTIVE CO., LTD.; *Int'l*, pg. 4836
MERIT INTERNATIONAL TURISTIK ISLETMELER VE HIZMETLER A.S.—See Net Holding A.S.; *Int'l*, pg. 5211
MERIT MEDICAL CANADA LTD.—See Merit Medical Systems, Inc.; *U.S. Public*, pg. 1425
MERIT MEDICAL DENMARK A/S—See Merit Medical Systems, Inc.; *U.S. Public*, pg. 1425
MERIT MEDICAL IRELAND, LIMITED—See Merit Medical Systems, Inc.; *U.S. Public*, pg. 1425
MERIT MEDICAL KOREA CO., LTD.—See Merit Medical Systems, Inc.; *U.S. Public*, pg. 1425
MERIT MEDICAL MALAYSIA SDN. BHD—See Merit Medical Systems, Inc.; *U.S. Public*, pg. 1425
MERIT MEDICAL NEDERLAND B.V.—See Merit Medical Systems, Inc.; *U.S. Public*, pg. 1425
MERIT MEDICAL NORWAY AS—See Merit Medical Systems, Inc.; *U.S. Public*, pg. 1425
MERIT MEDICAL SYSTEMS, INC.; *U.S. Public*, pg. 1424
MERIT MEDICAL SYSTEMS INDIA PRIVATE LIMITED—See Merit Medical Systems, Inc.; *U.S. Public*, pg. 1425
MERITOR AFTERMARKET SPAIN, S.A.—See Cummins Inc.; *U.S. Public*, pg. 608
MERITOR AFTERMARKET SWITZERLAND AG—See Cummins Inc.; *U.S. Public*, pg. 608
MERITOR AUTOMOTIVE B.V.—See Cummins Inc.; *U.S. Public*, pg. 608
MERITOR BRAKE HOLDINGS, INC.—See Cummins Inc.; *U.S. Public*, pg. 608
MERITOR HEAVY VEHICLE SYSTEMS CAMERI SPA—See Cummins Inc.; *U.S. Public*, pg. 608
MERITOR HEAVY VEHICLE SYSTEMS, LLC—See Cummins Inc.; *U.S. Public*, pg. 608
MERITOR HOLDINGS NETHERLANDS B.V.—See Cummins Inc.; *U.S. Public*, pg. 609
MERITOR HUAYANG VEHICLE BRAKING COMPANY, LTD.—See Cummins Inc.; *U.S. Public*, pg. 609
MERITOR HVS AB—See Cummins Inc.; *U.S. Public*, pg. 608
MERITOR HVS INDIA LTD.—See Cummins Inc.; *U.S. Public*, pg. 608
MERITOR HVS—See Cummins Inc.; *U.S. Public*, pg. 608
MERITOR, INC.—See Cummins Inc.; *U.S. Public*, pg. 609
MERITOR, INC.—See Cummins Inc.; *U.S. Public*, pg. 608
MERITOR JAPAN K.K.—See Cummins Inc.; *U.S. Public*, pg. 609
MERITOR LIGHT VEHICLE TECHNOLOGY, LLC—See Cummins Inc.; *U.S. Public*, pg. 608
MERITOR LVS ZHENJIANG CO. LTD.—See Cummins Inc.; *U.S. Public*, pg. 608
MERITOR MANAGEMENT CORP.—See Cummins Inc.; *U.S. Public*, pg. 609
MERITOR MEXICANA, S.A. DE C.V.—See Cummins Inc.; *U.S. Public*, pg. 609
MERITOR SUSPENSION SYSTEMS COMPANY—See Cummins Inc.; *U.S. Public*, pg. 609
MERITOR SUSPENSION SYSTEMS COMPANY—See Mitsubishi Steel Mfg. Co., Ltd.; *Int'l*, pg. 4968
MERIT PACKAGING LIMITED; *Int'l*, pg. 4836
MERIT PHARMACEUTICALS; *U.S. Private*, pg. 2674
MERIT RESOURCES, INC. - MERIT SENIOR LIVING DIVISION—See Iowa Network Services Inc.; *U.S. Private*, pg. 2135
MERIT RESOURCES, INC.—See Iowa Network Services Inc.; *U.S. Private*, pg. 2135
MERITRUST CREDIT UNION; *U.S. Private*, pg. 2675
MERITS & BENEFITS NV—See Edenred S.A.; *Int'l*, pg. 2308
MERIT SENSOR SYSTEMS, INC.—See Merit Medical Systems, Inc.; *U.S. Public*, pg. 1425
MERIT SERVICE SOLUTIONS—See Eureka Equity Partners, L.P.; *U.S. Private*, pg. 1433
MERIT TURIZM YATIRIM VE ISLETME A.S.—See Net Holding A.S.; *Int'l*, pg. 5211
MERIT TURIZM YATIRIM VE ISLETMELERI A.S.; *Int'l*, pg. 4836
MERITUM ENERGY HOLDINGS, LP; *U.S. Private*, pg. 2675
MERITURN PARTNERS, LLC - SAN FRANCISCO—See Meriturn Partners, LLC; *U.S. Private*, pg. 2675
MERITURN PARTNERS, LLC; *U.S. Private*, pg. 2675
MERITUS HOTELS & RESORTS—See OUE Limited; *Int'l*, pg. 5666
MERITUS PRIME DISTRIBUTIONS INC.—See Cosco Capital, Inc.; *Int'l*, pg. 1809
MERIT WISE INTERNATIONAL LIMITED—See Enterex International Limited; *Int'l*, pg. 2451
MERITZ ALTERNATIVE INVESTMENT MANAGEMENT CO., LTD.—See Meritz Financial Group Inc.; *Int'l*, pg. 4836
MERITZ ASSET MANAGEMENT CO. LTD.—See Meritz Financial Group Inc.; *Int'l*, pg. 4836
MERITZ FINANCIAL GROUP INC.; *Int'l*, pg. 4836
MERITZ FIRE & MARINE INSURANCE CO., LTD.—See Meritz Financial Group Inc.; *Int'l*, pg. 4836
MERITZ SECURITIES CO., LTD.; *Int'l*, pg. 4836

MERITZ SECURITIES CO., LTD.

CORPORATE AFFILIATIONS

MERIVAARA AB—See Merivaara Oy; *Int'l*, pg. 4836
MERIVAARA AS—See Merivaara Oy; *Int'l*, pg. 4836
MERIVAARA OY; *Int'l*, pg. 4836
MERIWETHER LEWIS ELECTRIC COOPERATIVE; *U.S. Private*, pg. 2675
MERIWETHER READY MIX, INC.—See Heidelberg Materials AG; *Int'l*, pg. 3318
MERIZON GROUP INCORPORATED—See Xerox Holdings Corporation; *U.S. Public*, pg. 2389
MERKANTI BANK LIMITED—See Merkanti Holding PLC; *Int'l*, pg. 4836
MERKANTI HOLDING PLC; *Int'l*, pg. 4836
MERKANTIL BANK LTD.—See OTP Bank Plc; *Int'l*, pg. 5657
MERKANTIL BERLET LTD.—See OTP Bank Plc; *Int'l*, pg. 5657
MERKAVIM TRANSPORTATION TECHNOLOGIES LTD.—See AB Volvo; *Int'l*, pg. 42
MERKAVIM TRANSPORTATION TECHNOLOGIES LTD.—See Mayer's Cars & Trucks Co. Ltd.; *Int'l*, pg. 4744
MERKBURN HOLDINGS LIMITED; *Int'l*, pg. 4836
MERKEL BROTHERS INC.; *U.S. Private*, pg. 2675
MERKEL FREUDENBERG FLUIDTECHNIC GMBH—See Freudenberg SE; *Int'l*, pg. 2789
MERKEL NOK-FREUDENBERG CO. LTD.—See Freudenberg SE; *Int'l*, pg. 2789
MERKER AG—See NIBE Industrier AB; *Int'l*, pg. 5262
MERKLE INC.—See Dentsu Group Inc.; *Int'l*, pg. 2036
MERKLE-KORFF INDUSTRIES INC.—See Nidec Corporation; *Int'l*, pg. 5275
MERKLE RESPONSE MANAGEMENT GROUP—See Moore DM Group, LLC; *U.S. Private*, pg. 2780
MERKLEY + PARTNERS/HEALTHWORKS—See Omnicom Group Inc.; *U.S. Public*, pg. 1588
MERKLEY + PARTNERS—See Omnicom Group Inc.; *U.S. Public*, pg. 1588
MERKO B.V.—See Merck & Co., Inc.; *U.S. Public*, pg. 1420
MERKO GIDA SANAYI VE TICARET A.S.; *Int'l*, pg. 4836
MERKO NV—See Merck & Co., Inc.; *U.S. Public*, pg. 1420
MERKUR 09 SP.Z.O.O—See Orkla ASA; *Int'l*, pg. 5638
MERKUR A.D.; *Int'l*, pg. 4836
MERKUR BANK KGAA; *Int'l*, pg. 4836
MERKUR CASINO LIMITED—See Gauselmann AG; *Int'l*, pg. 2890
MERKUR, D.D.; *Int'l*, pg. 4837
MERKUR D.D.; *Int'l*, pg. 4836
MERKUR DOSNIHA S.L.—See Gauselmann AG; *Int'l*, pg. 2890
MERKUR FREIZEIT LEASING GMBH—See Gauselmann AG; *Int'l*, pg. 2890
MERKUR GMBH—See VIB Vermogen AG; *Int'l*, pg. 8184
MERKUR GRUNDSTUCKS- UND BETEILIGUNGS- GESELLSCHAFT MIT BESCHRANKTER HAFTUNG—See Munchener Ruckversicherungs AG; *Int'l*, pg. 5090
MERKUR HRVATSKA, D. O. O.—See Merkur, d.d.; *Int'l*, pg. 4837
MERKUR IMMOBILIEN- UND BETEILIGUNGS GMBH—See Gauselmann AG; *Int'l*, pg. 2890
MERKUR INTERACTIVE SERVICES GMBH—See Gauselmann AG; *Int'l*, pg. 2890
MERKUR INTERNATIONAL, D.O.O.—See Merkur, d.d.; *Int'l*, pg. 4837
MERKUR INTERNATIONAL PRAHA, SPOL. S.R.O.—See Merkur, d.d.; *Int'l*, pg. 4837
MERKUR MAKEDONIJA, D. O. O.—See Merkur, d.d.; *Int'l*, pg. 4837
MERKUR MI HANDELS, GMBH—See Merkur, d.d.; *Int'l*, pg. 4837
MERKUR NEKRETNINE ZAGREB, D.O.O.—See Merkur, d.d.; *Int'l*, pg. 4837
MERKUR OSIGURANJE D.D.—See Merkur, d.d.; *Int'l*, pg. 4837
MERKUR SPIELBANKEN SACHSEN-ANHALT GMBH & CO. KG—See Gauselmann AG; *Int'l*, pg. 2890
MERKUR SPORTWETTEN GMBH—See Gauselmann AG; *Int'l*, pg. 2890
MERLE BOES INC.; *U.S. Private*, pg. 2675
MERLE NORMAN COSMETICS, INC.; *U.S. Private*, pg. 2675
MERLE S.A.S.—See VINCI S.A.; *Int'l*, pg. 8223
MERLES AUTOMOTIVE SUPPLY, INC.—See Genuine Parts Company; *U.S. Public*, pg. 933
MERLE STONE CHEVROLET CADILLAC; *U.S. Private*, pg. 2675
MERLIN ADVISORS, LLC—See BGC Group, Inc.; *U.S. Public*, pg. 329
MERLIN BUSINESS SOFTWARE LIMITED—See TA Associates, Inc.; *U.S. Private*, pg. 3914
MERLIN DIAGNOSTIKA GMBH—See Bruker Corporation; *U.S. Public*, pg. 405
MERLIN ENTERTAINMENTS GROUP LTD.—See Merlin Entertainments plc; *Int'l*, pg. 4837
MERLIN ENTERTAINMENTS PLC; *Int'l*, pg. 4837
MERLIN GERIN ALES SAS—See Schneider Electric SE; *Int'l*, pg. 6628

MERLIN GERIN ALPES SAS—See Schneider Electric SE; *Int'l*, pg. 6628
MERLIN GERIN LOIRE SAS—See Schneider Electric SE; *Int'l*, pg. 6628
MERLIN MEDICAL SUPPLY—See Laboratory Services MSO LLC; *U.S. Private*, pg. 2370
MERLINONE, INC.—See Canto Software, Inc.; *U.S. Private*, pg. 735
MERLIN PRODUCTIONS, SAS—See Vivendi SE; *Int'l*, pg. 8278
MERLIN PROPERTIES, SOCIMI, S.A.; *Int'l*, pg. 4838
MERLIN SOLAR TECHNOLOGIES, INC.—See Ayala Corporation; *Int'l*, pg. 774
MERLIN TECHNICAL SOLUTIONS, INC.; *U.S. Private*, pg. 2675
MERLION SP. Z O.O.; *Int'l*, pg. 4838
MERMAID DRILLING LTD.—See Thoresen Thai Agencies Public Company Limited; *Int'l*, pg. 7718
MERMAID MARINE VESSEL OPERATIONS PTY. LTD.—See MMA Offshore Limited; *Int'l*, pg. 5005
MERMAID MARITIME PUBLIC COMPANY LIMITED—See Thoresen Thai Agencies Public Company Limited; *Int'l*, pg. 7718
MERMAID MARITIME VIETNAM COMPANY LTD.—See Erria A/S; *Int'l*, pg. 2497
MERMAID SUBSEA SERVICES SAUDI ARABIA CO., LTD.—See Thoresen Thai Agencies Public Company Limited; *Int'l*, pg. 7718
MERMAID SUBSEA SERVICES (THAILAND) LTD.—See Thoresen Thai Agencies Public Company Limited; *Int'l*, pg. 7718
MERMAID SUBSEA SERVICES (UK) LIMITED—See Thoresen Thai Agencies Public Company Limited; *Int'l*, pg. 7718
MERMAID SUPPLY BASE PTY. LTD.—See MMA Offshore Limited; *Int'l*, pg. 5005
MERMAID TRAINING & TECHNICAL SERVICES LTD.—See Thoresen Thai Agencies Public Company Limited; *Int'l*, pg. 7718
MERMER A.D.; *Int'l*, pg. 4838
MERMEREN KOMBINAT AD; *Int'l*, pg. 4838
MERMIER LEMARCHAND SAS—See Monin SAS; *Int'l*, pg. 5034
MERMOZ BASTIE S.C.I.—See DEKRA e.V.; *Int'l*, pg. 2009
MEROLLIS CHEVROLET SALES & SERVICE INC.; *U.S. Private*, pg. 2675
MERO MICROFINANCE BITTIYA SANSTHA LTD.; *Int'l*, pg. 4838
MEROPA LEISURE AND ENTERTAINMENT (PTY) LIMITED—See Sun International Limited; *Int'l*, pg. 7304
MERPRO AMERICAS, INC.—See NOV, Inc.; *U.S. Public*, pg. 1545
MERPRO LIMITED—See NOV, Inc.; *U.S. Public*, pg. 1545
MERQUE FINANCIAL SERVICES PROPRIETARY LIMITED—See Barclays PLC; *Int'l*, pg. 862
MERREDIN RURAL SUPPLIES PTY LIMITED—See Nutrien Ltd.; *Int'l*, pg. 5493
MERRELL-BENCO AGENCY LLC; *U.S. Private*, pg. 2675
MERRIAM-WEBSTER, INC.—See Encyclopaedia Britannica, Inc.; *U.S. Private*, pg. 1391
MERRICK ADVANCED PHOTOGRAMMETRY OF THE AMERICAS, S. DE. R.L. DE C.V.—See Merrick & Company Inc.; *U.S. Private*, pg. 2675
MERRICK ANIMAL NUTRITION, INC.; *U.S. Private*, pg. 2675
MERRICK BANK CORPORATION—See CardWorks, Inc.; *U.S. Private*, pg. 751
MERRICK & COMPANY INC. - DECATUR—See Merrick & Company Inc.; *U.S. Private*, pg. 2675
MERRICK & COMPANY INC.; *U.S. Private*, pg. 2675
MERRICK CONSTRUCTION COMPANIES, INC.—See Merrick Industries Incorporated; *U.S. Private*, pg. 2675
MERRICK ENGINEERING, INC.; *U.S. Private*, pg. 2675
MERRICK ENVIRONMENTAL TECHNOLOGIES—See Tannehill International Industries; *U.S. Private*, pg. 3931
MERRICK INDUSTRIES, INCORPORATED; *U.S. Private*, pg. 2675
MERRICK INDUSTRIES INC—See Tannehill International Industries; *U.S. Private*, pg. 3931
MERRICK INDUSTRIES PVT. LTD.—See Tannehill International Industries; *U.S. Private*, pg. 3931
MERRICK - KEMPER—See Merrick Industries Incorporated; *U.S. Private*, pg. 2675
MERRICK PET CARE, INC.—See Nestle S.A.; *Int'l*, pg. 5203
THE MERRICK PRINTING COMPANY INC.—See Merrick Industries Incorporated; *U.S. Private*, pg. 2675
MERRICK'S ANIMAL HEALTH, LLC—See Vets Plus, Inc.; *U.S. Private*, pg. 4374
MERRICKS CAPITAL PTY LTD.—See Regal Partners Limited; *Int'l*, pg. 6251
MERRICK SYSTEMS, INC.—See HitecVision AS; *Int'l*, pg. 3426
MERRICK TOWLE COMMUNICATIONS; *U.S. Private*, pg. 2676
MERRIDELL ACHIEVEMENT CENTER, INC.—See Universal Health Services, Inc.; *U.S. Public*, pg. 2258
MERRIFIELD GARDEN CENTER CORP.; *U.S. Private*, pg. 2676

MERRILD KAFFE APS—See Luigi Lavazza S.p.A.; *Int'l*, pg. 4575
MERRILL COMPANY; *U.S. Private*, pg. 2676
MERRILL CORPORATION CANADA—See aPriori Capital Partners L.P.; *U.S. Private*, pg. 302
MERRILL CORPORATION CANADA—See aPriori Capital Partners L.P.; *U.S. Private*, pg. 302
MERRILL CORPORATION - CHICAGO OFFICE—See aPriori Capital Partners L.P.; *U.S. Private*, pg. 301
MERRILL CORPORATION - DENVER OFFICE—See aPriori Capital Partners L.P.; *U.S. Private*, pg. 301
MERRILL CORPORATION - HOUSTON OFFICE—See aPriori Capital Partners L.P.; *U.S. Private*, pg. 301
MERRILL CORPORATION - IRVINE OFFICE—See aPriori Capital Partners L.P.; *U.S. Private*, pg. 301
MERRILL CORPORATION - LA MIRADA OFFICE—See aPriori Capital Partners L.P.; *U.S. Private*, pg. 301
MERRILL CORPORATION LIMITED—See aPriori Capital Partners L.P.; *U.S. Private*, pg. 302
MERRILL CORPORATION - LOS ANGELES (SOUTH GRAND) OFFICE—See aPriori Capital Partners L.P.; *U.S. Private*, pg. 301
MERRILL CORPORATION - MONROE OFFICE—See aPriori Capital Partners L.P.; *U.S. Private*, pg. 301
MERRILL CORPORATION—See aPriori Capital Partners L.P.; *U.S. Private*, pg. 301
MERRILL CORPORATION - ST. CLOUD OFFICE—See aPriori Capital Partners L.P.; *U.S. Private*, pg. 301
MERRILL CORPORATION - WASHINGTON, DC OFFICE—See aPriori Capital Partners L.P.; *U.S. Private*, pg. 302
MERRILL/DANIELS, INC.—See aPriori Capital Partners L.P.; *U.S. Private*, pg. 302
MERRILL DISTRIBUTING INC.; *U.S. Private*, pg. 2676
MERRILL FRANCE S.A.R.L.—See aPriori Capital Partners L.P.; *U.S. Private*, pg. 302
MERRILL GARDENS LLC—See RD Merrill Company; *U.S. Private*, pg. 3362
MERRILL GERMANY GMBH—See aPriori Capital Partners L.P.; *U.S. Private*, pg. 302
MERRILL LYNCH CANADA INC.—See Bank of America Corporation; *U.S. Public*, pg. 272
MERRILL LYNCH & CO., INC.—See Bank of America Corporation; *U.S. Public*, pg. 272
MERRILL LYNCH DERIVATIVE PRODUCTS AG—See Bank of America Corporation; *U.S. Public*, pg. 272
MERRILL LYNCH JAPAN SECURITIES CO., LTD.—See Bank of America Corporation; *U.S. Public*, pg. 272
MERRILL LYNCH, KINGDOM OF SAUDI ARABIA COMPANY—See Bank of America Corporation; *U.S. Public*, pg. 272
MERRILL LYNCH MEXICO, S.A. DE C.V., CASA DE BOLSA—See Bank of America Corporation; *U.S. Public*, pg. 272
MERRILL LYNCH PROFESSIONAL CLEARING CORP.—See Bank of America Corporation; *U.S. Public*, pg. 272
MERRILL LYNCH S.A. CORRETORA DE TITULOS E VALORES MOBILIARIOS—See Bank of America Corporation; *U.S. Public*, pg. 272
MERRILL LYNCH YATIRIM BANK A.S.—See Bank of America Corporation; *U.S. Public*, pg. 272
MERRILL PHYSICAL THERAPY, LIMITED PARTNERSHIP—See U.S. Physical Therapy, Inc.; *U.S. Public*, pg. 2215
MERRILL & RING; *U.S. Private*, pg. 2676
MERRILL TOOL & MACHINE INC.; *U.S. Private*, pg. 2676
MERRIMAC INDUSTRIAL SALES INC; *U.S. Private*, pg. 2676
MERRIMAC INDUSTRIES INC.—See Crane NXT, Co.; *U.S. Public*, pg. 591
MERRIMACK BUILDING SUPPLY, INC.—See Hendricks Holding Company, Inc.; *U.S. Private*, pg. 1915
MERRIMACK COUNTY TELEPHONE COMPANY, INC.—See Telephone & Data Systems, Inc.; *U.S. Public*, pg. 1998
MERRIMACK MUTUAL FIRE INSURANCE CO.—See The Andover Companies; *U.S. Private*, pg. 3986
MERRIMACK PHARMACEUTICALS, INC.; *U.S. Public*, pg. 1425
MERRIMACK RIVER PRECISION INDUSTRIAL CORPORATION—See CX Technology Corporation; *Int'l*, pg. 1891
MERRIMACK STREET GARAGE INC.; *U.S. Private*, pg. 2676
MERRIMAN CAPITAL, INC.—See Merriman Holdings, Inc.; *U.S. Private*, pg. 2676
MERRIMAN HOLDINGS, INC.; *U.S. Private*, pg. 2676
MERRION FLEET MANAGEMENT LIMITED—See ALD Automotive; *Int'l*, pg. 303
MERRION PHARMACEUTICALS, LLC—See Merrion Pharmaceuticals plc; *Int'l*, pg. 4838
MERRION PHARMACEUTICALS PLC; *Int'l*, pg. 4838
MERRION SHOPPING CENTRE LIMITED—See Tesco PLC; *Int'l*, pg. 7571
MERRITHEW CORPORATION; *Int'l*, pg. 4838
MERRITHEW HEALTH & FITNESS GROUP—See Merrithew Corporation; *Int'l*, pg. 4838

COMPANY NAME INDEX

MERRITT CONSTRUCTION SERVICES—See Merritt Management Corporation; *U.S. Private*, pg. 2676
MERRITT ESTATE WINERY; *U.S. Private*, pg. 2676
MERRITT GROUP; *U.S. Private*, pg. 2676
MERRITT & HARRIS, INC.—See Jones Lang LaSalle Incorporated; *U.S. Public*, pg. 1205
MERRITT, HAWKINS & ASSOCIATES—See AMN Healthcare Services, Inc.; *U.S. Public*, pg. 125
MERRITT ISLAND ASC, LLC—See Community Health Systems, Inc.; *U.S. Public*, pg. 555
MERRITT ISLAND RHF HOUSING INC; *U.S. Private*, pg. 2676
MERRITT ISLAND SURGERY CENTER—See HCA Healthcare, Inc.; *U.S. Public*, pg. 1002
MERRITT MANAGEMENT CORPORATION; *U.S. Private*, pg. 2676
MERRITT OIL CO. INC.; *U.S. Private*, pg. 2676
MERRITT PLASTICS LTD.—See Tessenderlo Group NV; *Int'l*, pg. 7574
MERRITT PROPERTIES, LLC—See Merritt Management Corporation; *U.S. Private*, pg. 2676
MERRITT RESEARCH SERVICES LLC—See Investortools Inc.; *U.S. Private*, pg. 2132
MERRITT SAFETY ENVIRONMENTAL MANAGEMENT—See Gregg Industries Inc.; *U.S. Private*, pg. 1782
MERRITT VETERINARY SUPPLIES INC.—See Clayton, Dubilier & Rice, LLC; *U.S. Private*, pg. 921
MERRITT VETERINARY SUPPLIES INC.—See TPG Capital, L.P.; *U.S. Public*, pg. 2170
MERROW MACHINE COMPANY; *U.S. Private*, pg. 2676
MERRYCHEF LIMITED—See Ali Holding S.r.l.; *Int'l*, pg. 323
MERRYCK AND CO LIMITED—See Robert Walters plc; *Int'l*, pg. 6368
MERRY ELECTRONICS CO., LTD.; *Int'l*, pg. 4838
MERRY ELECTRONICS (HK) CO., LTD.—See Merry Electronics Co., Ltd.; *Int'l*, pg. 4838
MERRY ELECTRONICS NORTH AMERICA INC.—See Merry Electronics Co., Ltd.; *Int'l*, pg. 4838
MERRY ELECTRONICS (SHENZHEN) CO., LTD.—See Merry Electronics Co., Ltd.; *Int'l*, pg. 4838
MERRY ELECTRONICS (SINGAPORE) PTE. LTD.—See Merry Electronics Co., Ltd.; *Int'l*, pg. 4838
MERRY ELECTRONICS USA—See Merry Electronics Co., Ltd.; *Int'l*, pg. 4838
MERRY GARDEN (US) INC.—See China Environmental Technology & Bioenergy Holdings Limited; *Int'l*, pg. 1500
MERRYHILL ELEMENTARY SCHOOL—See Investcorp Holdings B.S.C.; *Int'l*, pg. 3776
MERRY MAIDS LIMITED PARTNERSHIP—See Roark Capital Group Inc.; *U.S. Private*, pg. 3456
MERRYMANN-FARR, LLC; *U.S. Private*, pg. 2676
MERRYMEETING, INC.; *U.S. Private*, pg. 2676
MERRYWEATHER FOAM INC.; *U.S. Private*, pg. 2677
MERRY X-RAY CORPORATION; *U.S. Private*, pg. 2676
MERSANA THERAPEUTICS, INC; *U.S. Public*, pg. 1425
MERSCHMAN SEEDS INC.; *U.S. Private*, pg. 2677
MERSCORP HOLDINGS, INC.—See Intercontinental Exchange, Inc.; *U.S. Public*, pg. 1143
MERSEN BENELUX B.V.—See Mersen S.A.; *Int'l*, pg. 4838
MERSEN CANADA TORONTO INC.—See Mersen S.A.; *Int'l*, pg. 4838
MERSEN CORPORATE SERVICES SAS—See Mersen S.A.; *Int'l*, pg. 4838
MERSEN FRANCE AMIENS S.A.S.—See Mersen S.A.; *Int'l*, pg. 4839
MERSEN FRANCE GENNEVILLIERS SAS—See Mersen S.A.; *Int'l*, pg. 4839
MERSEN FRANCE PY SAS—See Mersen S.A.; *Int'l*, pg. 4839
MERSEN INDIA PVT. LTD.—See Mersen S.A.; *Int'l*, pg. 4839
MERSEN ITALIA S.P.A.—See Mersen S.A.; *Int'l*, pg. 4839
MERSEN NORDIC AB—See Mersen S.A.; *Int'l*, pg. 4839
MERSEN OCEANIA PTY LTD—See Mersen S.A.; *Int'l*, pg. 4839
MERSEN S.A.; *Int'l*, pg. 4838
MERSEN SOUTH AFRICA PTY LTD—See Mersen S.A.; *Int'l*, pg. 4839
MERSEN UK HOLDINGS LTD.—See Mersen S.A.; *Int'l*, pg. 4839
MERSEN USA BN CORP.—See Mersen S.A.; *Int'l*, pg. 4839
MERSEN USA NEWBURYPORT-MA LLC—See Mersen S.A.; *Int'l*, pg. 4839
THE MERSEY DOCKS & HARBOUR COMPANY—See Peel Holdings Ltd.; *Int'l*, pg. 5779
THE MERSEYSIDE COMMUNITY REHABILITATION COMPANY LTD.—See Interserve Plc; *Int'l*, pg. 3760
MERSION (M) SDN. BHD.—See Kato Sangyo Co., Ltd.; *Int'l*, pg. 4090
MERSIVE TECHNOLOGIES, INC.—See OpenGate Capital Management, LLC; *U.S. Private*, pg. 3031
MERS/MISSOURI GOODWILL INDUSTRIES; *U.S. Private*, pg. 2677
MERSTEEL, D. O. O.—See Merkur, d.d.; *Int'l*, pg. 4837

MERSTEEL, D. O. O.—See Merkur, d.d.; *Int'l*, pg. 4837
THE MERTEN COMPANY—See Champion Industries, Inc.; *U.S. Public*, pg. 478
MERTEN CZECH S.R.O.—See Schneider Electric SE; *Int'l*, pg. 6628
MERTEN GMBH—See Schneider Electric SE; *Int'l*, pg. 6628
MERTEN HOLDING GMBH—See Schneider Electric SE; *Int'l*, pg. 6628
MERTENS B.V.—See Marubeni Corporation; *Int'l*, pg. 4708
MER-TERRE CONTRACTING COMPANY FOR MARINE AND DEVELOPMENT WORK LTD.—See Rimon Group; *Int'l*, pg. 6342
MERTES CONTRACTING CORPORATION; *U.S. Private*, pg. 2677
MERTIK MAXITROL GMBH & CO., KG—See Maxitrol Company; *U.S. Private*, pg. 2619
MERTIK MAXITROL GMBH & CO., KG—See Maxitrol Company; *U.S. Private*, pg. 2619
MERTIVA AB—See Arbona AB; *Int'l*, pg. 537
MERUELO CAPITAL INVESTMENTS, INC.—See Meruelo Group LLC; *U.S. Private*, pg. 2677
MERUELO CONSTRUCTION—See Meruelo Group LLC; *U.S. Private*, pg. 2677
MERUELO ENTERPRISES, INC.—See Meruelo Group LLC; *U.S. Private*, pg. 2677
MERUELO FOODS, INC.—See Meruelo Group LLC; *U.S. Private*, pg. 2677
MERUELO GROUP LLC; *U.S. Private*, pg. 2677
MERUELO PROPERTIES, INC.—See Meruelo Group LLC; *U.S. Private*, pg. 2677
MERU NETWORKS, INC.—See Fortinet, Inc.; *U.S. Public*, pg. 869
MERUS N.V.; *Int'l*, pg. 4839
MERUS POWER OYJ; *Int'l*, pg. 4839
MERUS REFRESHMENT SERVICES INC.—See Castik Capital S.a.r.l.; *Int'l*, pg. 1356
MERUS US, INC.—See Merus N.V.; *Int'l*, pg. 4839
MERU UTAMA SDN. BHD.—See Ancom Nylex Berhad; *Int'l*, pg. 449
MERVIN MANUFACTURING, INC.—See Extreme Holdings, Inc.; *U.S. Private*, pg. 1452
MERVIS INDUSTRIES INC.; *U.S. Private*, pg. 2677
MERWIN, LLC—See Konecranes Plc; *Int'l*, pg. 4252
MERWIN-STOLTZ CO., INC.—See DoALL Company; *U.S. Private*, pg. 1250
MERX TRUCK & TRAILER, INC.; *U.S. Private*, pg. 2677
MERYLLION RESOURCES CORPORATION; *Int'l*, pg. 4839
MERYX, INC.; *U.S. Private*, pg. 2677
MERZ AESTHETICS—See Merz Pharma GmbH & Co. KGaA; *Int'l*, pg. 4839
MERZ ASIA PACIFIC PTE. LTD.—See Merz Pharma GmbH & Co. KGaA; *Int'l*, pg. 4839
MERZ AUSTRALIA PTY LTD—See Merz Pharma GmbH & Co. KGaA; *Int'l*, pg. 4839
MERZ, INC.—See Merz Pharma GmbH & Co. KGaA; *Int'l*, pg. 4839
MERZ & MCLELLAN BOTSWANA (PTY) LIMITED—See Mott MacDonald Group Ltd.; *Int'l*, pg. 5055
MERZ NORTH AMERICA—See Merz Pharma GmbH & Co. KGaA; *Int'l*, pg. 4839
MERZ PHARMA AUSTRIA GMBH—See Merz Pharma GmbH & Co. KGaA; *Int'l*, pg. 4839
MERZ PHARMA BENELUX B.V.—See Merz Pharma GmbH & Co. KGaA; *Int'l*, pg. 4839
MERZ PHARMA CANADA LTD.—See Merz Pharma GmbH & Co. KGaA; *Int'l*, pg. 4839
MERZ PHARMACEUTICALS LLC—See Merz Pharma GmbH & Co. KGaA; *Int'l*, pg. 4839
MERZ PHARMA CHINA LTD.—See Merz Pharma GmbH & Co. KGaA; *Int'l*, pg. 4839
MERZ PHARMA ESPANA S.L.—See Merz Pharma GmbH & Co. KGaA; *Int'l*, pg. 4839
MERZ PHARMA FRANCE S.A.S.—See Merz Pharma GmbH & Co. KGaA; *Int'l*, pg. 4839
MERZ PHARMA GMBH & CO. KGAA; *Int'l*, pg. 4839
MERZ PHARMA ITALIA S.R.L.—See Merz Pharma GmbH & Co. KGaA; *Int'l*, pg. 4839
MERZ PHARMA, S.A DE C.V.—See Merz Pharma GmbH & Co. KGaA; *Int'l*, pg. 4839
MERZ PHARMA (SCHWEIZ) AG—See Merz Pharma GmbH & Co. KGaA; *Int'l*, pg. 4839
MERZ PHARMA UK LTD.—See Merz Pharma GmbH & Co. KGaA; *Int'l*, pg. 4839
MESA ACQUIRER LLC—See Repay Holdings Corporation; *U.S. Public*, pg. 1784
MESA AIR GROUP, INC.; *U.S. Public*, pg. 1425
MESA AIRLINES, INC.—See Mesa Air Group, Inc.; *U.S. Public*, pg. 1425
MESA AIRLINES PILOT DEVELOPMENT, INC.—See Mesa Air Group, Inc.; *U.S. Public*, pg. 1425
MESA BEVERAGE CO., INC.—See Liquid Investments, Inc.; *U.S. Private*, pg. 2466
MESABI CONTROL ENGINEERING, LTD.—See L. Possehl & Co. mbH; *Int'l*, pg. 4383
MESABI NUGGET DELAWARE, LLC—See Steel Dynamics, Inc.; *U.S. Public*, pg. 1942
MESABI TRUST; *U.S. Public*, pg. 1426

MESA/BOOGIE LIMITED; *U.S. Private*, pg. 2678
MESA CANADA, INC.—See Mesa Laboratories, Inc.; *U.S. Public*, pg. 1426
MESAC CORPORATION—See Trinity Industrial Corporation; *Int'l*, pg. 7924
MESA COLLISION, INC.—See AutoNation, Inc.; *U.S. Public*, pg. 236
MESA ENERGY SYSTEMS, INC.—See EMCOR Group, Inc.; *U.S. Public*, pg. 738
MESA EQUIPMENT & SUPPLY COMPANY; *U.S. Private*, pg. 2677
MESA FOODS, LLC—See TruArc Partners, L.P.; *U.S. Private*, pg. 4246
MESA FRANCE SAS—See Mesa Laboratories, Inc.; *U.S. Public*, pg. 1426
MES AFTY CORPORATION—See Mitsui E&S Holdings Co., Ltd.; *Int'l*, pg. 4984
MESA FULLY FORMED INC.; *U.S. Private*, pg. 2677
MESA GERMANY GMBH—See Mesa Laboratories, Inc.; *U.S. Public*, pg. 1426
MESAIEED PETROCHEMICAL HOLDING COMPANY Q.S.C.—See Qatar Petroleum; *Int'l*, pg. 6135
MESA INDUSTRIES, INC.—See Avient Corporation; *U.S. Public*, pg. 247
MESA INDUSTRIES INC.; *U.S. Private*, pg. 2677
MESA LABORATORIES, INC. - BIOLOGICAL INDICATOR FACILITY—See Mesa Laboratories, Inc.; *U.S. Public*, pg. 1426
MESA LABORATORIES, INC. - NORTH BAY BIOSCIENCE—See Mesa Laboratories, Inc.; *U.S. Public*, pg. 1426
MESA LABORATORIES, INC.; *U.S. Public*, pg. 1425
ME SALVE ISABELA INC.; *U.S. Private*, pg. 2646
MESA MANUFACTURING INC—See The Weir Group PLC; *Int'l*, pg. 7699
MESA MINERALS LIMITED—See Mineral Resources Limited; *Int'l*, pg. 4906
MESAN KILIT A.S.—See Essentra plc; *Int'l*, pg. 2511
MESA OIL INC.; *U.S. Private*, pg. 2677
MESA OMAHA (OMF) BIOLOGICAL INDICATOR MANUFACTURING FACILITY—See Mesa Laboratories, Inc.; *U.S. Public*, pg. 1426
MESA PARTS GMBH; *Int'l*, pg. 4839
MESAR BERATUNG—See BVE Holding SE; *Int'l*, pg. 1231
MESA ROYALTY TRUST; *U.S. Public*, pg. 1426
MESA SAFE COMPANY, INC.; *U.S. Private*, pg. 2678
MESASIX, LLC; *U.S. Private*, pg. 2678
MESA SYSTEMS, INC.; *U.S. Private*, pg. 2678
MESA UNDERWRITERS SPECIALTY INSURANCE COMPANY—See Selective Insurance Group, Inc.; *U.S. Public*, pg. 1862
MESA VERDE COMPANY—See Aramark; *U.S. Public*, pg. 176
MESA VIEW PT, LLC—See Quorum Health Corporation; *U.S. Public*, pg. 3330
MESA VINEYARD MANAGEMENT, INC.; *U.S. Private*, pg. 2678
MESB BERHAD; *Int'l*, pg. 4839
MESCA FREIGHT SERVICES; *U.S. Private*, pg. 2678
MESCHINO BANANA COMPANY—See Dominion Holding Corporation; *Int'l*, pg. 2161
MESCO BUILDINGS SOLUTIONS—See Clayton, Dubilier & Rice, LLC; *U.S. Private*, pg. 921
MESCOENG (M) SDN. BHD.—See MESCO Inc; *Int'l*, pg. 4840
MESCO INC - OITA PIPE PLANT—See MESCO Inc; *Int'l*, pg. 4840
MESCO INC; *Int'l*, pg. 4840
MESCO PHARMACEUTICALS LIMITED; *Int'l*, pg. 4840
MESCO (USA) INC.—See MESCO Inc; *Int'l*, pg. 4840
MESEA SAS—See VINCI S.A.; *Int'l*, pg. 8224
MES ENVIRONMENTAL LTD.—See CNIM Constructions Industrielles de la Mediterranee SA; *Int'l*, pg. 1677
MESERCO, S.L.—See Banco de Sabadell, S.A.; *Int'l*, pg. 821
MES FERROTEC CHINA CO., LTD.—See Mitsui E&S Holdings Co., Ltd.; *Int'l*, pg. 4984
MESGO ASIA KAUCUK A.S.—See HEXPOL AB; *Int'l*, pg. 3372
MESGO ASIA KAUCUK SAN. VE TIC. LTD.—See HEXPOL AB; *Int'l*, pg. 3372
MESGO IRIDE COLORS SRL—See HEXPOL AB; *Int'l*, pg. 3372
MESGO SPA—See HEXPOL AB; *Int'l*, pg. 3372
MESH ARCHITECTURE + FABRICATION; *U.S. Private*, pg. 2678
MESHEK ENERGY-RENEWABLE ENERGIES LTD.; *Int'l*, pg. 4840
MESH PACK GMBH—See KARATZIS S.A.; *Int'l*, pg. 4079
MESHULAM LEVINSTEIN CONSTRUCTING & ENGINEERING LTD.; *Int'l*, pg. 4840
MESILLA DIALYSIS, LLC—See DaVita Inc.; *U.S. Public*, pg. 641
MESILLA VALLEY TRANSPORTATION SERVICES INC.; *U.S. Private*, pg. 2678
MESINIAGA BERHAD; *Int'l*, pg. 4840
MESINIAGA MSC SDN. BHD.—See Mesiniaga Berhad; *Int'l*, pg. 4840

MESINIAGA BERHAD

MESINIAGA SERVICES SDN. BHD.—See Mesiniaga Berhad; *Int'l*, pg. 4840
MESINIAGA TECHNIQUES SDN. BHD.—See Mesiniaga Berhad; *Int'l*, pg. 4840
MESIROW ADVANCED STRATEGIES, INC.—See Navigator Global Investments Limited; *Int'l*, pg. 5174
MESIROW FINANCIAL ADMINISTRATIVE CORPORATION—See Mesirow Financial Holdings, Inc.; *U.S. Private*, pg. 2678
MESIROW FINANCIAL AGRICULTURE MANAGEMENT, LLC—See Mesirow Financial Holdings, Inc.; *U.S. Private*, pg. 2678
MESIROW FINANCIAL COMMODITIES MANAGEMENT, LLC—See Mesirow Financial Holdings, Inc.; *U.S. Private*, pg. 2678
MESIROW FINANCIAL CONSULTING, LLC—See Mesirow Financial Holdings, Inc.; *U.S. Private*, pg. 2678
MESIROW FINANCIAL HOLDINGS, INC.; *U.S. Private*, pg. 2678
MESIROW FINANCIAL HONG KONG, LIMITED—See Mesirow Financial Holdings, Inc.; *U.S. Private*, pg. 2678
MESIROW FINANCIAL, INC. - DETROIT—See Mesirow Financial Holdings, Inc.; *U.S. Private*, pg. 2678
MESIROW FINANCIAL, INC. - FORT LAUDERDALE—See Mesirow Financial Holdings, Inc.; *U.S. Private*, pg. 2678
MESIROW FINANCIAL, INC. - HIGHLAND PARK—See Mesirow Financial Holdings, Inc.; *U.S. Private*, pg. 2679
MESIROW FINANCIAL, INC. - NEW YORK CITY—See Mesirow Financial Holdings, Inc.; *U.S. Private*, pg. 2679
MESIROW FINANCIAL, INC. - OAKBROOK—See Mesirow Financial Holdings, Inc.; *U.S. Private*, pg. 2679
MESIROW FINANCIAL, INC. - PITTSBURGH—See Mesirow Financial Holdings, Inc.; *U.S. Private*, pg. 2679
MESIROW FINANCIAL, INC.—See Mesirow Financial Holdings, Inc.; *U.S. Private*, pg. 2678
MESIROW FINANCIAL, INC. - TAMPA—See Mesirow Financial Holdings, Inc.; *U.S. Private*, pg. 2679
MESIROW FINANCIAL INTERIM MANAGEMENT, LLC—See Mesirow Financial Holdings, Inc.; *U.S. Private*, pg. 2678
MESIROW FINANCIAL INTERNATIONAL UK, LIMITED—See Mesirow Financial Holdings, Inc.; *U.S. Private*, pg. 2678
MESIROW FINANCIAL INVESTMENT MANAGEMENT, INC.—See Mesirow Financial Holdings, Inc.; *U.S. Private*, pg. 2678
MESIROW FINANCIAL PRIVATE EQUITY ADVISORS, INC.—See Mesirow Financial Holdings, Inc.; *U.S. Private*, pg. 2678
MESIROW FINANCIAL PRIVATE EQUITY, INC.—See Mesirow Financial Holdings, Inc.; *U.S. Private*, pg. 2678
MESIROW FINANCIAL REAL ESTATE BROKERAGE, INC.—See Mesirow Financial Holdings, Inc.; *U.S. Private*, pg. 2678
MESIROW FINANCIAL SERVICES, INC.—See Mesirow Financial Holdings, Inc.; *U.S. Private*, pg. 2678
MESIROW FINANCIAL STRUCTURED SETTLEMENTS, LLC—See Mesirow Financial Holdings, Inc.; *U.S. Private*, pg. 2678
MESIROW REAL ESTATE INVESTMENTS, INC.—See Mesirow Financial Holdings, Inc.; *U.S. Private*, pg. 2679
MESIROW REALTY SERVICES, INC.—See Mesirow Financial Holdings, Inc.; *U.S. Private*, pg. 2679
MESKER DOOR, LLC—See dormakaba Holding AG; *Int'l*, pg. 2177
MESKER SOUTHEAST—See dormakaba Holding AG; *Int'l*, pg. 2177
MES-KHI YURA DOCK CO., LTD.—See Kawasaki Heavy Industries, Ltd.; *Int'l*, pg. 4098
MES-KHI YURA DOCK CO., LTD.—See Mitsui E&S Holdings Co., Ltd.; *Int'l*, pg. 4985
MESKO GLASS AND MIRROR CO.; *U.S. Private*, pg. 2679
MESL GROUP LTD.—See VINCI S.A.; *Int'l*, pg. 8239
MESLO LTD.—See HORIBA Ltd; *Int'l*, pg. 3477
MESM, LLC—See Avantor, Inc.; *U.S. Public*, pg. 242
MESNAC CO., LTD.; *Int'l*, pg. 4840
MESNA INDUSTRIJA BRACA PIVAC D.O.O.; *Int'l*, pg. 4840
MESOBLAST, INC.—See Mesoblast Limited; *Int'l*, pg. 4840
MESOBLAST LIMITED; *Int'l*, pg. 4840
MESOCOAT INC.—See ABAKAN INC.; *U.S. Private*, pg. 34
MESOMATIC MESSTECHNIK AG—See Yokogawa Electric Corporation; *Int'l*, pg. 8592
MESON AB—See Indutrade AB; *Int'l*, pg. 3680
MESO NUMISMATICS, INC.; *U.S. Public*, pg. 1426
MESOS GESTION Y SERVICIOS S.L.—See Brookfield Corporation; *Int'l*, pg. 1188
MESQUITE GAMING, LLC; *U.S. Private*, pg. 2679
MESSAGEBIRD BV; *Int'l*, pg. 4840
MESSAGEBROADCAST, LLC—See Link Mobility Group Holding ASA; *Int'l*, pg. 4514
MESSAGEGEARS, LLC—See Long Ridge Equity Partners, LLC; *U.S. Private*, pg. 2492

MESSAGE MOBILE GMBH—See MIND C.T.I. Ltd.; *Int'l*, pg. 4900
MESSAGE PROCESSING INTERNATIONAL, INC.; *U.S. Public*, pg. 1426
MESSAGE SYSTEMS - ASIA PACIFIC—See MessageBird BV; *Int'l*, pg. 4841
MESSAGE SYSTEMS - CHINA—See MessageBird BV; *Int'l*, pg. 4841
MESSAGE SYSTEMS - EMEA—See MessageBird BV; *Int'l*, pg. 4841
MESSAGE SYSTEMS, INC.—See MessageBird BV; *Int'l*, pg. 4840
MESSAGE SYSTEMS - JAPAN—See MessageBird BV; *Int'l*, pg. 4841
MESSAGING TECHNOLOGIES HONG KONG LTD.—See XOX Technology Bhd; *Int'l*, pg. 8537
MESSE CONSULT SRL—See Messe Munchen GmbH; *Int'l*, pg. 4841
MESSE ESANG CO LTD.; *Int'l*, pg. 4841
MESSE MUENCHEN JAPAN CO., LTD.—See Messe Munchen GmbH; *Int'l*, pg. 4841
MESSE MUNCHEN GMBH; *Int'l*, pg. 4841
MESSENGER ASSOCIATES, INC.—See Adecco Group AG; *Int'l*, pg. 139
MESSENGER SERVICES LIMITED—See Freightways Group Limited; *Int'l*, pg. 2771
MESSER ALBAGAZ SH.P.K.—See Messer Group GmbH; *Int'l*, pg. 4842
MESSER ALGERIE SPA—See Messer Group GmbH; *Int'l*, pg. 4842
MESSER ALIGAZ SANAYI GAZLARI A.S.—See Messer Group GmbH; *Int'l*, pg. 4842
MESSER AUSTRIA GMBH—See Messer Group GmbH; *Int'l*, pg. 4842
MESSER BELGIUM N.V.—See Messer Group GmbH; *Int'l*, pg. 4842
MESSER BINH PHUOC INDUSTRIAL GASES CO., LTD.—See Messer Group GmbH; *Int'l*, pg. 4842
MESSER BULGARIA EOOD—See Messer Group GmbH; *Int'l*, pg. 4842
MESSER B.V.—See Messer Group GmbH; *Int'l*, pg. 4842
MESSER CONSTRUCTION CO.; *U.S. Private*, pg. 2679
MESSER CROATIA PLIN D.O.O.—See Messer Group GmbH; *Int'l*, pg. 4842
MESSER CUTTING SYSTEMS (CHINA) LTD.—See MEC Holding GmbH; *Int'l*, pg. 4764
MESSER CUTTING SYSTEMS GMBH—See MEC Holding GmbH; *Int'l*, pg. 4764
MESSER CUTTING SYSTEMS, INC.—See MEC Holding GmbH; *Int'l*, pg. 4765
MESSER CUTTING SYSTEMS INDIA PRIVATE LTD.—See MEC Holding GmbH; *Int'l*, pg. 4764
MESSER CUTTING SYSTEMS KOREA LTD.—See MEC Holding GmbH; *Int'l*, pg. 4764
MESSER CUTTING & WELDING CO., LTD.—See MEC Holding GmbH; *Int'l*, pg. 4764
MESSER DANMARK A/S—See Messer Group GmbH; *Int'l*, pg. 4842
MESSER ENERGO GAZ SRL—See Messer Group GmbH; *Int'l*, pg. 4842
MESSE REPS. & TRAVEL—See Messe Munchen GmbH; *Int'l*, pg. 4841
MESSER EUTECTIC CASTOLIN BENELUX NV/SA—See MEC Holding GmbH; *Int'l*, pg. 4764
MESSER EUTECTIC CASTOLIN EGYPT LLC—See MEC Holding GmbH; *Int'l*, pg. 4764
MESSER EUTECTIC CASTOLIN S.A.R.L.—See MEC Holding GmbH; *Int'l*, pg. 4765
MESSER EUTECTIC CASTOLIN SLOVENSKO, S.R.O.—See MEC Holding GmbH; *Int'l*, pg. 4765
MESSER EUTECTIC CASTOLIN SPOL.S.R.O.—See MEC Holding GmbH; *Int'l*, pg. 4765
MESSER EUTECTIC CASTOLIN (S) PTE LTD—See MEC Holding GmbH; *Int'l*, pg. 4764
MESSER EUTECTIC CASTOLIN SP.Z.O.O.—See MEC Holding GmbH; *Int'l*, pg. 4765
MESSER EUTECTIC CASTOLIN SWITZERLAND S.A.—See MEC Holding GmbH; *Int'l*, pg. 4765
MESSER EUTECTIC SOUTH AFRICA (PTY) LTD.—See MEC Holding GmbH; *Int'l*, pg. 4765
MESSER FRANCE S.A.S.—See Messer Group GmbH; *Int'l*, pg. 4842
MESSERGAS, DISTRIBUICAO DE GASES INDUSTRIAIS LDA—See Messer Group GmbH; *Int'l*, pg. 4843
MESSER GASES DEL PERU S.A.—See Messer Group GmbH; *Int'l*, pg. 4842
MESSER GAS LLC—See CVC Capital Partners SICAV-FIS S.A.; *Int'l*, pg. 1885
MESSER GAS LLC—See Messer Group GmbH; *Int'l*, pg. 4842
MESSER GAS PUERTO RICO, INC.—See CVC Capital Partners SICAV-FIS S.A.; *Int'l*, pg. 1885
MESSER GAS PUERTO RICO, INC.—See Messer Group GmbH; *Int'l*, pg. 4842
MESSER GRIESHEIM (CHINA) INVESTMENT CO. LTD.—See Messer Group GmbH; *Int'l*, pg. 4842
MESSER GRIESHEIM LTD.—See MEC Holding GmbH; *Int'l*, pg. 4765

MESSER GRIESHEIM SALDATURA S.R.L.—See MEC Holding GmbH; *Int'l*, pg. 4765
MESSER GROUP GMBH; *Int'l*, pg. 4842
MESSER HUNGAROGAZ KFT.—See Messer Group GmbH; *Int'l*, pg. 4842
MESSER IBERICA DE GASES S.A.—See Messer Group GmbH; *Int'l*, pg. 4842
MESSER INDUSTRIES USA, INC.—See CVC Capital Partners SICAV-FIS S.A.; *Int'l*, pg. 1885
MESSER INDUSTRIES USA, INC.—See Messer Group GmbH; *Int'l*, pg. 4842
MESSER INFORMATION SERVICES GMBH—See Messer Group GmbH; *Int'l*, pg. 4842
MESSER LLC—See Messer Group GmbH; *Int'l*, pg. 4842
MESSER MOSTAR PLIN D.O.O—See Messer Group GmbH; *Int'l*, pg. 4765
MESSER POLSKA SP. Z O.O.—See Messer Group GmbH; *Int'l*, pg. 4842
MESSER ROMANIA GAZ SRL—See Messer Group GmbH; *Int'l*, pg. 4842
MESSERSCHMID ENERGIESYSTEME GMBH—See EnBW Energie Baden-Wurttemberg AG; *Int'l*, pg. 2399
MESSER SCHWEIZ AG—See Messer Group GmbH; *Int'l*, pg. 4842
MESSER SLOVENIJA D.O.O.—See Messer Group GmbH; *Int'l*, pg. 4843
MESSER SLOVNAFT S.R.O.—See Messer Group GmbH; *Int'l*, pg. 4843
MESSER TATRAGAS S.R.O.—See Messer Group GmbH; *Int'l*, pg. 4843
MESSER TECHNOGAS S.R.O.—See Messer Group GmbH; *Int'l*, pg. 4843
MESSER TEHNOGAS AD; *Int'l*, pg. 4843
MESSER TEHNOGAS AD—See Messer Group GmbH; *Int'l*, pg. 4843
MESSER TEHNOPLIN D.O.O.—See Messer Group GmbH; *Int'l*, pg. 4843
MESSER VARDAR TEHNOGAS D.O.O.E.L.—See Messer Group GmbH; *Int'l*, pg. 4843
MESSER VIETNAM INDUSTRIAL GASES CO., LTD.—See Messer Group GmbH; *Int'l*, pg. 4843
MES SHIPPING CO., LTD.—See Mitsui E&S Holdings Co., Ltd.; *Int'l*, pg. 4985
MESSICK FARM EQUIPMENT INC.; *U.S. Private*, pg. 2679
MESSIER-DOWTY INC.—See Safran SA; *Int'l*, pg. 6475
MESSIER DOWTY INTERNATIONAL LTD.—See Safran SA; *Int'l*, pg. 6474
MESSIER-DOWTY LTD.—See Safran SA; *Int'l*, pg. 6475
MESSIER DOWTY MEXICO SA DE CV—See Safran SA; *Int'l*, pg. 6474
MESSIER-DOWTY (SINGAPORE) PTE LTD—See Safran SA; *Int'l*, pg. 6475
MESSIER-DOWTY (SUZHOU) CO., LTD—See Safran SA; *Int'l*, pg. 6475
MESSIER SERVICES LTD.—See Safran SA; *Int'l*, pg. 6474
MESSIER SERVICES MEXICO S.A. DE C.V.—See Safran SA; *Int'l*, pg. 6474
MESSINA DIAMOND MINE (PTY) LTD—See Petra Diamonds Limited; *Int'l*, pg. 5824
MESSINA PLATINUM MINES LTD.—See Sibanye-Stillwater Limited; *Int'l*, pg. 6876
MESSINA WILDLIFE MANAGEMENT; *U.S. Private*, pg. 2679
MESSMER GMBH—See LKQ Corporation; *U.S. Public*, pg. 1335
MESSNER INC.—See Nassco, Inc.; *U.S. Private*, pg. 2837
MES SOLUTIONS—See GIC Pte. Ltd.; *Int'l*, pg. 2964
MES SOLUTIONS—See Leonard Green & Partners, L.P.; *U.S. Private*, pg. 2425
MESS- UND REGELTECHNIK JUCKER GMBH—See MAX Automation SE; *Int'l*, pg. 4734
MESTA ELECTRONICS INC—See Hammond Power Solutions Inc.; *Int'l*, pg. 3239
MES TECHNO SERVICE CO., LTD.—See Mitsui E&S Holdings Co., Ltd.; *Int'l*, pg. 4985
MES TECHNOSERVICE MACHINERY CONSTRUCTION LOGISTICS INDUSTRY & TRADE CORPORATION—See Mitsui E&S Holdings Co., Ltd.; *Int'l*, pg. 4985
MES TECHNOSERVICE MIDDLE EAST W.L.L.—See Mitsui E&S Holdings Co., Ltd.; *Int'l*, pg. 4985
MES TECHNOSERVICE (SHANGHAI) CO., LTD.—See Mitsui E&S Holdings Co., Ltd.; *Int'l*, pg. 4985
MESTEK CANADA INC.—See Mestek, Inc.; *U.S. Public*, pg. 1426
MESTEK, INC.; *U.S. Public*, pg. 1426
MESTERGRUPPEN AS—See Ferd AS; *Int'l*, pg. 2636
MES TESTING & RESEARCH CENTER CO., LTD.—See Mitsui E&S Holdings Co., Ltd.; *Int'l*, pg. 4985
MES (THAILAND) LTD.—See Mitsui E&S Holdings Co., Ltd.; *Int'l*, pg. 4984
MES TOKKI & ENGINEERING CO., LTD.—See Mitsui E&S Holdings Co., Ltd.; *Int'l*, pg. 4985
MESTRELAB RESEARCH S.L.—See Bruker Corporation; *U.S. Public*, pg. 404
MESTRO AB; *Int'l*, pg. 4843
MESTRON HOLDINGS BERHAD; *Int'l*, pg. 4843

COMPANY NAME INDEX

MESUTRONIC GERATEBAU GMBH—See INDUS Holding AG; *Int'l*, pg. 3663
MET2PLASTIC LLC—See Dedienne Multiplasturgy Group SAS; *Int'l*, pg. 2002
METAAGE CORPORATION; *Int'l*, pg. 4844
METAAPES GMBH—See Ardian SAS; *Int'l*, pg. 554
METABANK, N.A.—See Pathward Financial, Inc.; *U.S. Public*, pg. 1652
META BIOMED (CAMBODIA) CO., LTD.—See Meta Biomed Co., Ltd.; *Int'l*, pg. 4843
META BIOMED CO., LTD.; *Int'l*, pg. 4843
META BIOMED INC.—See Meta Biomed Co., Ltd.; *Int'l*, pg. 4843
META BIOMED VINA CO., LTD.—See Meta Biomed Co., Ltd.; *Int'l*, pg. 4843
METABO CORPORATION; *U.S. Private*, pg. 2679
METABOLIC EXPLORER S.A.; *Int'l*, pg. 4844
METABOLIC EXPLORER S.A.—See METabolic EXplorer S.A.; *Int'l*, pg. 4844
METABOLON, INC; *U.S. Private*, pg. 2679
META BRIGHT GROUP BERHAD; *Int'l*, pg. 4843
METACHEM, LLC—See PJSC PhosAgro; *Int'l*, pg. 5883
METACLAY CJSC—See RUSNANO JSC; *Int'l*, pg. 6429
METACOM INC.; *U.S. Private*, pg. 2679
METACON AB; *Int'l*, pg. 4844
METACORP BERHAD—See MTD Capital Bhd.; *Int'l*, pg. 5070
META CORPORATION PUBLIC COMPANY LIMITED; *Int'l*, pg. 4843
METACORP PROPERTIES SDN. BHD.—See MTD Capital Bhd.; *Int'l*, pg. 5070
METACRINE, INC.; *U.S. Public*, pg. 1427
META DATA LTD.; *Int'l*, pg. 4843
META DATA SOFTWARE, INC.; *U.S. Private*, pg. 2679
METADESIGN AG—See Publicis Groupe S.A.; *Int'l*, pg. 6111
METADESIGN CHINA LIMITED—See Publicis Groupe S.A.; *Int'l*, pg. 6111
METADYNEA AUSTRIA GMBH—See Metafrax OJSC; *Int'l*, pg. 4844
METADYNEA TRADING S.A.—See Metafrax OJSC; *Int'l*, pg. 4844
METAFORM LANGUES SARL—See CDS Co., Ltd.; *Int'l*, pg. 1371
METAFORM LTD—See Panasonic Holdings Corporation; *Int'l*, pg. 5725
METAFRAX OJSC; *Int'l*, pg. 4844
METAGENICS INCORPORATED—See Alticor Inc.; *U.S. Private*, pg. 209
META GROUP S.R.L.; *Int'l*, pg. 4843
METAGURU CORPORATION—See MetaAge Corporation; *Int'l*, pg. 4844
META HEALTH LIMITED; *Int'l*, pg. 4843
META HEALTH TECHNOLOGY, INC.—See Streamline Health Solutions, Inc.; *U.S. Public*, pg. 1954
METAHELIX LIFE SCIENCES LIMITED—See Rallis India Limited; *Int'l*, pg. 6196
METAIRIE BANK & TRUST CO.; *U.S. Public*, pg. 1427
METAIRIE PHYSICIAN SERVICES, INC.; *U.S. Private*, pg. 2679
METAIR INVESTMENTS LIMITED; *Int'l*, pg. 4844
METALABS CO., LTD.; *Int'l*, pg. 4845
METALAC A.D.; *Int'l*, pg. 4845
METALAC BOJLER D.O.O.—See Metalac a.d.; *Int'l*, pg. 4845
METALAC FAD D.O.O.—See Metalac a.d.; *Int'l*, pg. 4845
METALAC INKO LTD—See Metalac a.d.; *Int'l*, pg. 4845
METALAC MARKET D.O.O.—See Metalac a.d.; *Int'l*, pg. 4845
METALAC MARKET PODGORICA D.O.O.—See Metalac a.d.; *Int'l*, pg. 4845
METALAC METALURGIJA A.D.; *Int'l*, pg. 4845
METALAC POSUDJE D.O.O.—See Metalac a.d.; *Int'l*, pg. 4845
METALAC PRINT D.O.O.—See Metalac a.d.; *Int'l*, pg. 4845
METALAC PROLETER A.D.; *Int'l*, pg. 4845
METALAC SPS INDUSTRIA E COMERCIO LTDA.—See Berkshire Hathaway Inc.; *U.S. Public*, pg. 315
METAL ACT CO., LTD.—See Sato shoji Corporation; *Int'l*, pg. 6586
METALAC TRADE D.O.O.—See Metalac a.d.; *Int'l*, pg. 4845
METALADE N.Y., INC.; *U.S. Private*, pg. 2680
METAL A.D.; *Int'l*, pg. 4845
METAL AGENCIES LIMITED—See Viohalco SA/NV; *Int'l*, pg. 8243
METALAIRE, INC.—See J.T. Walker Industries, Inc.; *U.S. Private*, pg. 2171
METALART CORPORATION—See Sojitz Corporation; *Int'l*, pg. 7062
METAL ART OF CALIFORNIA, INC.; *U.S. Private*, pg. 2679
METAL ARTS COMPANY, INC.; *U.S. Public*, pg. 1427
METALAST S.A.—See Fluidra SA; *Int'l*, pg. 2714
METAL BANK LIMITED; *Int'l*, pg. 4845
METAL BUILDING COMPONENTS INC.—See Clayton, Dubilier & Rice, LLC; *U.S. Private*, pg. 921

METAL BULLETIN JAPAN—See Astorg Partners S.A.S.; *Int'l*, pg. 656
METAL BULLETIN JAPAN—See Epiris Managers LLP; *Int'l*, pg. 2461
METAL BULLETIN LIMITED—See Astorg Partners S.A.S.; *Int'l*, pg. 656
METAL BULLETIN LIMITED—See Epiris Managers LLP; *Int'l*, pg. 2460
METAL BULLETIN SINGAPORE—See Astorg Partners S.A.S.; *Int'l*, pg. 656
METAL BULLETIN SINGAPORE—See Epiris Managers LLP; *Int'l*, pg. 2461
METAL CASTELLO S.P.A—See Mahindra & Mahindra Limited; *Int'l*, pg. 4646
METAL CASTING TECHNOLOGY, INC.—See General Motors Company; *U.S. Public*, pg. 926
METALCENTER, INC.—See Reliance Steel & Aluminum Co.; *U.S. Public*, pg. 1780
METALCLAD INSULATION CORPORATION—See Entrprize Corporation; *U.S. Private*, pg. 1406
METAL COATERS - HOUSTON PLANT—See Clayton, Dubilier & Rice, LLC; *U.S. Private*, pg. 921
METAL COATERS LP—See Clayton, Dubilier & Rice, LLC; *U.S. Private*, pg. 921
METAL COATERS OF GEORGIA—See Clayton, Dubilier & Rice, LLC; *U.S. Private*, pg. 921
METAL COATERS OF MISSISSIPPI—See Clayton, Dubilier & Rice, LLC; *U.S. Private*, pg. 921
METALCOAT INC. OF FLORIDA; *U.S. Private*, pg. 2680
METAL COATINGS (INDIA) LIMITED; *Int'l*, pg. 4845
METAL COATINGS (INDIA) LIMITED - WORKS -I I—See METAL COATINGS (INDIA) LIMITED; *Int'l*, pg. 4845
METALCOLOUR ASIA PTE LTD—See Metalcolour A/S; *Int'l*, pg. 4846
METALCOLOUR A/S; *Int'l*, pg. 4845
METALCOLOUR SVERIGE AB—See Metalcolour A/S; *Int'l*, pg. 4846
METAL COMPONENTS LLC.; *U.S. Private*, pg. 2680
METAL COMPONENT TECHNOLOGIES (WUXI) CO., LTD—See Meta Health Limited; *Int'l*, pg. 4843
METAL CONTAINER CORPORATION—See Anheuser-Busch InBev SA/NV; *Int'l*, pg. 465
METALCORP LIMITED—See Palladium One Mining Inc.; *Int'l*, pg. 5708
METALCO SA—See Descours & Cabaud SA; *Int'l*, pg. 2044
METALCRAFT INDUSTRIES, INC.; *U.S. Private*, pg. 2680
METALCRAFT OF MAYVILLE, INC.; *U.S. Private*, pg. 2680
METALCRAFT TECHNOLOGIES, INC.—See Madison Dearborn Partners, LLC; *U.S. Private*, pg. 2540
METALCRAFT TECHNOLOGY INC.; *Int'l*, pg. 4846
METALDYNE INTERNATIONAL FRANCE SAS—See American Axle & Manufacturing Holdings, Inc.; *U.S. Public*, pg. 97
METALDYNE INTERNATIONAL (UK) LTD.—See American Axle & Manufacturing Holdings, Inc.; *U.S. Public*, pg. 97
METALDYNE, LLC—See American Axle & Manufacturing Holdings, Inc.; *U.S. Public*, pg. 96
METALDYNE NURNBERG GMBH—See American Axle & Manufacturing Holdings, Inc.; *U.S. Public*, pg. 97
METALDYNE OSLAVANY, SPOL. S.R.O.—See American Axle & Manufacturing Holdings, Inc.; *U.S. Public*, pg. 97
METALDYNE PERFORMANCE GROUP INC.—See American Axle & Manufacturing Holdings, Inc.; *U.S. Public*, pg. 96
METALDYNE POWERTRAIN MEXICO, S. DE R.L. DE C.V.—See American Axle & Manufacturing Holdings, Inc.; *U.S. Public*, pg. 97
METALDYNE SINTERED COMPONENTS, INC. - ST. MARYS—See American Axle & Manufacturing Holdings, Inc.; *U.S. Public*, pg. 97
METALDYNE SINTERED RIDGWAY, LLC—See American Axle & Manufacturing Holdings, Inc.; *U.S. Public*, pg. 97
METALDYNE SINTERFORGED PRODUCTS, LLC—See American Axle & Manufacturing Holdings, Inc.; *U.S. Public*, pg. 97
METALEACH LIMITED—See eEnergy Group Plc; *Int'l*, pg. 2317
METALERT INC.; *U.S. Public*, pg. 1427
METALES DE OLYMPIC, S. DE R. L. DE C.V.—See Olympic Steel Inc.; *U.S. Public*, pg. 1571
METALES INTERAMERICANOS S.A. DE C.V.—See Endeavour Silver Corp.; *Int'l*, pg. 2403
METALES PELAZ, S.L.; *Int'l*, pg. 4846
METAL EXCHANGE CORPORATION; *U.S. Private*, pg. 2680
METALEX LLC—See UPG Enterprises LLC; *U.S. Private*, pg. 4311
METALEX MANUFACTURING INC.; *U.S. Private*, pg. 2680
METALEX VENTURES LTD.; *Int'l*, pg. 4846
METALFAB, INC.; *U.S. Private*, pg. 2681
METAL FABRICATORS AND WELDING LTD.; *Int'l*, pg. 4845

METAL FABRICATORS OF ZAMBIA LTD.—See Prysmian S.p.A.; *Int'l*, pg. 6011
METALFIL S.A.—See Saarstahl AG; *Int'l*, pg. 6461
METAL FINISHING TECHNOLOGIES, INC.—See Battle Investment Group LLC; *U.S. Public*, pg. 489
METALFLEX PTY LTD—See Reece Limited; *Int'l*, pg. 6249
METALFLEX (S.A.) PTY LTD—See Reece Limited; *Int'l*, pg. 6249
METALFLEX (W.A.) PTY LTD—See Reece Limited; *Int'l*, pg. 6249
METAL FORMING & COINING CORP.—See Vickers Engineering, Inc.; *U.S. Private*, pg. 4377
METAL FORM MANUFACTURING, INC.—See S&P Sistemas de Ventilación, S.L.U.; *Int'l*, pg. 6445
METALFRIO SOLUTIONS S.A.; *Int'l*, pg. 4846
METAL FX—See Montage Partners, Inc.; *U.S. Private*, pg. 2774
METALFX TECHNOLOGY LTD.—See BASF SE; *Int'l*, pg. 884
METAL GAYRIMENKUL A.S.; *Int'l*, pg. 4845
METAL GLOBE D.O.O.—See Viohalco SA/NV; *Int'l*, pg. 8243
METALGRAFICA IGUACU S.A.—See Companhia Siderurgica Nacional; *Int'l*, pg. 1748
METAL HAWK LIMITED; *Int'l*, pg. 4845
METALICA SA; *Int'l*, pg. 4846
METALICITY LIMITED; *Int'l*, pg. 4846
METALICO AKRON, INC.—See Metalico Inc.; *U.S. Private*, pg. 2681
METALICO ALUMINUM RECOVERY, INC.—See Metalico Inc.; *U.S. Private*, pg. 2681
METALICO ANNACO—See Metalico Inc.; *U.S. Private*, pg. 2681
METALICO BUFFALO, INC.—See Metalico Inc.; *U.S. Private*, pg. 2681
METALICO INC.; *U.S. Private*, pg. 2681
METALICO NIAGARA, INC.—See Metalico Inc.; *U.S. Private*, pg. 2681
METALICO ROCHESTER, INC.—See Metalico Inc.; *U.S. Private*, pg. 2681
METALICO YOUNGSTOWN, INC.—See Metalico Inc.; *U.S. Private*, pg. 2681
METAL IMPACT LLC—See Thunderbird LLC; *U.S. Private*, pg. 4166
METAL IMPROVEMENT COMPANY, LLC—See Curtiss-Wright Corporation; *U.S. Public*, pg. 612
METALINE CONTACT MINES CO.; *U.S. Public*, pg. 1427
METALINK LTD.; *Int'l*, pg. 4846
METALINOX BILBAO, S.A.—See Acerinox, S.A.; *Int'l*, pg. 101
METALIS HOLDING SAS—See Aalberts N.V.; *Int'l*, pg. 35
METALIS HPS S.A.S.—See Aalberts N.V.; *Int'l*, pg. 35
METALIS POLSKA SP. Z.O.O.—See Aalberts N.V.; *Int'l*, pg. 35
METALIS S.A.S.—See Aalberts N.V.; *Int'l*, pg. 35
METALIS USA, INC.—See Aalberts N.V.; *Int'l*, pg. 35
METALITE AVIATION LIGHTING—See HWH Investments Limited; *Int'l*, pg. 3543
METALITE RESOURCES INC; *Int'l*, pg. 4846
METALIX METALLHANDEL AG—See Wieland-Werke AG; *Int'l*, pg. 8403
METALKRAFT INDUSTRIES, INC.; *U.S. Private*, pg. 2681
METALLA ROYALTY & STREAMING LTD.; *Int'l*, pg. 4847
METALLFABRIKEN LJUNGHALL AB—See Gnutti Carlo S.p.A.; *Int'l*, pg. 3017
METALLFORM, S.R.O.—See Enco spol. s r.o.; *Int'l*, pg. 2401
METALLIANCE SA; *Int'l*, pg. 4847
METALLICA MINERALS LIMITED—See Diatreme Resources Limited; *Int'l*, pg. 2107
METALLICA STAHL- UND FASSADENTECHNIK GMBH—See STRABAG SE; *Int'l*, pg. 7231
METALLIC BUILDING COMPANY—See Clayton, Dubilier & Rice, LLC; *U.S. Private*, pg. 921
METALLIC BUILDING SYSTEMS, LLC; *U.S. Private*, pg. 2681
METALLIC GROUP OF COMPANIES; *Int'l*, pg. 4847
METALLIC MINERALS CORP.; *Int'l*, pg. 4848
METALLICS, INC.; *U.S. Private*, pg. 2681
METALLINVESTBANK PJSC SCB; *Int'l*, pg. 4848
METALLIS RESOURCES INC.; *Int'l*, pg. 4848
METALLIX INC.; *U.S. Private*, pg. 2681
METALLOINVEST JSC; *Int'l*, pg. 4848
METALLOY FIBRES (PTY) LTD—See MC Mining Limited; *Int'l*, pg. 4755
METALLOY INDUSTRIES INC.; *U.S. Private*, pg. 2681
METALLOY METALLE-LEGIERUNGEN GMBH—See CRONIMET Holding GmbH; *Int'l*, pg. 1855
METALL + PLASTIC GMBH—See OPTIMA Packaging Group GmbH; *Int'l*, pg. 5603
METALL SERVICE MENZIKEN AG—See Klockner & Co. SE; *Int'l*, pg. 4202
METALLTECHNIK (UK) LTD—See INDUS Holding AG; *Int'l*, pg. 3664
METALL-TREAT INDUSTRIES PTE. LTD.—See Malayan Daching Co. Pte. Ltd.; *Int'l*, pg. 4661
METALLUM RESOURCES INC.; *Int'l*, pg. 4848
METALL- UND KUNSTSTOFFTECHNIK BARCHFELD GMBH; *Int'l*, pg. 4847

METALL- UND KUNSTSTOFFTECHNIK BARCHFELD GMBH

CORPORATE AFFILIATIONS

METALL- UND SERVICE-CENTER GES.M.B.H. NFG. KG—See Klockner & Co. SE; *Int'l*, pg. 4203
METALLURG HOLDINGS CORPORATION—See AMG Critical Materials N.V.; *Int'l*, pg. 426
METALLURGICA BRESCIANA S.P.A.—See Sterlite Technologies Limited; *Int'l*, pg. 7212
METALLURGICAL CORPORATION OF CHINA LIMITED—See China Rare Earth Resources And Technology Co., Ltd.; *Int'l*, pg. 1545
METALLURGICAL & ENVIRONMENTAL TESTING LABORATORIES INC.—See Miller Consolidated Industries Inc.; *U.S. Private*, pg. 2733
METALLURGICAL INDUSTRIES COMPANY (EJSC); *Int'l*, pg. 4848
METALLURGICAL SERVICE INC.—See Miller Consolidated Industries Inc.; *U.S. Private*, pg. 2733
METALLURG, INC.—See AMG Critical Materials N.V.; *Int'l*, pg. 426
METALLURGISCHE GESELLSCHAFT SAAR GMBH—See Saarstahl AG; *Int'l*, pg. 6461
METALLURG SERVICIOS S.A. DE R.L. DE C.V.—See AMG Critical Materials N.V.; *Int'l*, pg. 426
METALLUS INC.; *U.S. Public*, pg. 1427
METALLVERARBEITUNG OSTALB GMBH—See Georgsmarienhutte Holding GmbH; *Int'l*, pg. 2940
METALLWARENFABRIK GEMMINGEN GMBH—See Rubicon Partners Limited; *Int'l*, pg. 6422
METALLWERK MOLLERSDORF HANDELSGESELLSCHAFT M.B.H.—See Wieland-Werke AG; *Int'l*, pg. 8403
METALL ZUG AG; *Int'l*, pg. 4846
METAL MANAGEMENT CONNECTICUT, INC.—See Sims Limited; *U.S. Public*, pg. 1883
METAL MANAGEMENT, INC.—See Sims Limited; *U.S. Public*, pg. 1883
METAL MANAGEMENT MIDWEST, INC.—See Sims Limited; *U.S. Public*, pg. 1883
METAL MANAGEMENT NORTHEAST, INC.—See Sims Limited; *U.S. Public*, pg. 1883
METAL MANAGEMENT OHIO, INC.—See Sims Limited; *U.S. Public*, pg. 1883
METALMAN INDUSTRIES LIMITED; *Int'l*, pg. 4848
METAL MANUFACTURES PTY LIMITED—See Blackfriars Corp.; *U.S. Private*, pg. 575
METALMARK CAPITAL HOLDINGS LLC; *U.S. Private*, pg. 2681
METAL MARKETPLACE INTERNATIONAL; *U.S. Private*, pg. 2680
METALMARK MANAGEMENT LLC—See Metalmark Capital Holdings LLC; *U.S. Private*, pg. 2681
METAL MASTER SALES CORPORATION; *U.S. Private*, pg. 2680
METAL-MATIC, INC. - BEDFORD PARK PLANT—See Metal-Matic, Inc.; *U.S. Private*, pg. 2680
METAL-MATIC, INC. - OHIO PLANT—See Metal-Matic, Inc.; *U.S. Private*, pg. 2680
METAL-MATIC, INC.; *U.S. Private*, pg. 2680
METAL MOULDING CORP.—See Patrick Industries, Inc.; *U.S. Public*, pg. 1653
METALNA INDUSTRIJA PRIJEDOR A.D.; *Int'l*, pg. 4848
METALNO D.D.—See Almy d.o.o.; *Int'l*, pg. 364
METALNRG ECO LIMITED—See MetalNRG PLC; *Int'l*, pg. 4848
METALNRG PLC; *Int'l*, pg. 4848
METALOCAUCHO, S.L.—See Westinghouse Air Brake Technologies Corporation; *U.S. Public*, pg. 2358
METALO MANUFACTURING INC.; *Int'l*, pg. 4848
METALO MEISTRAI UAB—See Panevezio statybos trestas AB; *Int'l*, pg. 5727
METAL ONE CORPORATION—See Mitsubishi Corporation; *Int'l*, pg. 4940
METAL ONE CORPORATION—See Sojitz Corporation; *Int'l*, pg. 7062
METAL ONE HOLDINGS AMERICA, INC.—See Mitsubishi Corporation; *Int'l*, pg. 4940
METAL ONE SUMISHO TUBULAR PRODUCTS CO., LTD.—See Maruichi Steel Tube Ltd; *Int'l*, pg. 4714
METALOPACK AD; *Int'l*, pg. 4848
METALOPLASTIKA A.D.; *Int'l*, pg. 4848
METALOPLASTIKA A.D.; *Int'l*, pg. 4848
METALOPRERADA A.D. UZICE; *Int'l*, pg. 4848
METALOR ELECTROTECHNICS (PUERTO RICO) LLC—See Tanaka Holdings Co., Ltd.; *Int'l*, pg. 7455
METALOR ELECTROTECHNICS (U.S.A.) CORP.—See Tanaka Holdings Co., Ltd.; *Int'l*, pg. 7455
METALORE RESOURCES LIMITED; *Int'l*, pg. 4848
METALOR FINANCE SA—See Tanaka Holdings Co., Ltd.; *Int'l*, pg. 7455
METALOR TECHNOLOGIES (DEUTSCHLAND) GMBH—See Tanaka Holdings Co., Ltd.; *Int'l*, pg. 7455
METALOR TECHNOLOGIES (FRANCE) S.A.S.—See Tanaka Holdings Co., Ltd.; *Int'l*, pg. 7455
METALOR TECHNOLOGIES (HONG KONG) LTD.—See Tanaka Holdings Co., Ltd.; *Int'l*, pg. 7455
METALOR TECHNOLOGIES (IBERICA) SA—See Tanaka Holdings Co., Ltd.; *Int'l*, pg. 7455
METALOR TECHNOLOGIES (ITALIA) S.R.L.—See Tanaka Holdings Co., Ltd.; *Int'l*, pg. 7455

METALOR TECHNOLOGIES - MARIN—See Tanaka Holdings Co., Ltd.; *Int'l*, pg. 7455
METALOR TECHNOLOGIES SA—See Tanaka Holdings Co., Ltd.; *Int'l*, pg. 7455
METALOR TECHNOLOGIES SA—See Tanaka Holdings Co., Ltd.; *Int'l*, pg. 7455
METALOR TECHNOLOGIES (SINGAPORE) PTE. LTD.—See Tanaka Holdings Co., Ltd.; *Int'l*, pg. 7455
METALOR TECHNOLOGIES (SUZHOU) LTD.—See Tanaka Holdings Co., Ltd.; *Int'l*, pg. 7455
METALOR TECHNOLOGIES (SWEDEN) AB—See Tanaka Holdings Co., Ltd.; *Int'l*, pg. 7455
METALOR TECHNOLOGIES (UK) LTD.—See Tanaka Holdings Co., Ltd.; *Int'l*, pg. 7455
METALOR TECHNOLOGIES USA CORPORATION—See Tanaka Holdings Co., Ltd.; *Int'l*, pg. 7455
METALOR USA REFINING CORPORATION—See Tanaka Holdings Co., Ltd.; *Int'l*, pg. 7455
METALOR USA REFINING CORPORATION SUCCURSAL DEL PERU—See Tanaka Holdings Co., Ltd.; *Int'l*, pg. 7455
METALOTEHNA D.D. TUZLA; *Int'l*, pg. 4848
METALOTEHNA TRADE A.D.; *Int'l*, pg. 4848
METAL-PAK (MALAYSIA) SDN. BHD.—See Can-One Berhad; *Int'l*, pg. 1277
METAL PERFORATORS (MALAYSIA) SDN. BHD.—See Mayu Global Group Berhad; *Int'l*, pg. 4747
METALPHA TECHNOLOGY HOLDING LIMITED; *Int'l*, pg. 4848
METALPLAST-CZESTOCHOWA SP. Z O.O.—See Groupe SFPI SA; *Int'l*, pg. 3111
METAL POWDER PRODUCTS - FORD ROAD DIVISION—See Guggenheim Partners, LLC; *U.S. Private*, pg. 1812
METAL POWDER PRODUCTS, LLC—See Guggenheim Partners, LLC; *U.S. Private*, pg. 1812
METAL PREP TECHNOLOGY, INC.—See Aterian Investment Management, L.P.; *U.S. Private*, pg. 366
METAL PRODUCTS COMPANY; *U.S. Private*, pg. 2680
METAL PROVING SERVICES LIMITED—See Goodwin PLC; *Int'l*, pg. 3042
METAL-QAYNAQ-SINAQ JSC; *Int'l*, pg. 4845
METALQUEST MINING INC; *Int'l*, pg. 4848
METALRAX ENGINEERING SUPPORT SERVICES LIMITED—See Metalrax Group PLC; *Int'l*, pg. 4849
METALRAX GROUP PLC; *Int'l*, pg. 4849
METALRAX SPECIALIST APPLICATIONS LIMITED—See Metalrax Group PLC; *Int'l*, pg. 4849
METAL RECLAMATION BHD.; *Int'l*, pg. 4845
METAL RECLAMATION (INDUSTRIES) SDN. BHD.—See Metal Reclamation Bhd.; *Int'l*, pg. 4845
METAL & RECYCLING COMPANY K.S.C.C.—See Agility; *Int'l*, pg. 210
METAL RESOURCE SOLUTIONS; *U.S. Private*, pg. 2680
METALS ACQUISITION CORP.; *U.S. Public*, pg. 1427
METAL SALES MANUFACTURING CORPORATION—See Interlock Industries, Inc.; *U.S. Private*, pg. 2111
METALS & ALLOYS INTERNATIONAL LTD.—See CRONIMET Holding GmbH; *Int'l*, pg. 1855
METALS AND ADDITIVES CORPORATION, INC.; *U.S. Private*, pg. 2681
METALSA, S.A. DE C.V.—See Grupo Proeza, S.A.P.I. de C.V.; *Int'l*, pg. 3134
METALS AUSTRALIA LIMITED; *Int'l*, pg. 4849
METALS CREEK RESOURCES CORP.; *Int'l*, pg. 4849
METAL SEAL & PRODUCTS, INC.; *U.S. Private*, pg. 2680
METAL SECTIONS LIMITED—See voestalpine AG; *Int'l*, pg. 8293
METALS ENGINEERING, INC.; *U.S. Private*, pg. 2682
METALS EXPLORATION PLC; *Int'l*, pg. 4849
METALSGROVE MINING LIMITED; *Int'l*, pg. 4849
METALS INC.; *U.S. Private*, pg. 2682
METAL SKY STAR ACQUISITION CORPORATION; *U.S. Public*, pg. 1427
METALSPAND, INC.—See NMC Metals Inc.; *U.S. Private*, pg. 2931
METAL SPINNERS INC.; *U.S. Private*, pg. 2680
METALS PLUS INCOME CORP.; *Int'l*, pg. 4849
METALS RECYCLING, L.L.C.—See Radius Recycling, Inc.; *U.S. Public*, pg. 1760
METALS SERVICE CENTER INSTITUTE; *U.S. Private*, pg. 2682
METAL STAMPING SUPPORT GROUP, LLC—See Nidec Corporation; *Int'l*, pg. 5280
METAL STAR KOGYO CO., LTD.—See MK SEIKO CO., LTD.; *Int'l*, pg. 5001
METALSTECH LIMITED; *Int'l*, pg. 4849
METAL SUPERMARKETS (CANADA) LTD.; *Int'l*, pg. 4845
METAL SURFACES INC.; *U.S. Private*, pg. 2680
METALS USA BUILDING PRODUCTS, CANADA INC.—See Reliance Steel & Aluminum Co.; *U.S. Public*, pg. 1780
METALS USA CARBON FLAT ROLLED, INC.—See Reliance Steel & Aluminum Co.; *U.S. Public*, pg. 1780
METALS USA HOLDINGS CORP.—See Reliance Steel & Aluminum Co.; *U.S. Public*, pg. 1780
METALS USA, INC.—See Reliance Steel & Aluminum Co.; *U.S. Public*, pg. 1780

METALS USA PLATE PROCESSING L.L.C.—See Reliance Steel & Aluminum Co.; *U.S. Public*, pg. 1780
METALS USA PLATES AND SHAPES NORTHEAST, L.P.—See Reliance Steel & Aluminum Co.; *U.S. Public*, pg. 1781
METALS USA PLATES AND SHAPES SOUTHEAST, INC.—See Reliance Steel & Aluminum Co.; *U.S. Public*, pg. 1781
METALS USA SPECIALTY METALS NORTHCENTRAL, INC.—See Reliance Steel & Aluminum Co.; *U.S. Public*, pg. 1781
METALS X LIMITED; *Int'l*, pg. 4849
METALTECH CO., LTD.—See Hanwa Co., Ltd.; *Int'l*, pg. 3263
METAL TECHNOLOGIES, INC.; *U.S. Private*, pg. 2680
METAL TECHNOLOGIES THREE RIVERS—See Metal Technologies, Inc.; *U.S. Private*, pg. 2680
METAL TECHNOLOGIES WEST ALLIS DUCTILE IRON—See Metal Technologies, Inc.; *U.S. Private*, pg. 2680
METAL TECHNOLOGIES WOODSTOCK—See Metal Technologies, Inc.; *U.S. Private*, pg. 2680
METALTECH SERVICE CENTER INC.—See Ironwood Capital Management LLC; *U.S. Private*, pg. 2140
METALTEK INTERNATIONAL - METALTEK ENERGY PRODUCTS DIVISION—See MetalTek International; *U.S. Private*, pg. 2682
METALTEK INTERNATIONAL - METALTEK ENERGY SOLUTIONS DIVISION—See MetalTek International; *U.S. Private*, pg. 2682
METALTEK INTERNATIONAL - METALTEK - EUROPE DIVISION—See MetalTek International; *U.S. Private*, pg. 2682
METALTEK INTERNATIONAL; *U.S. Private*, pg. 2682
METAL TEXTILES CORPORATION—See United Capital Corp.; *U.S. Private*, pg. 4288
METAL TIGER PLC; *Int'l*, pg. 4845
METAL TRADES, LLC—See Arlington Capital Partners LLC; *U.S. Private*, pg. 328
METAL TRADING CORPORATION; *U.S. Private*, pg. 2680
METAL TRANSPORT LTD.—See Topy Industries, Ltd.; *Int'l*, pg. 7822
METALUBIA—See BIA Overseas S.A.; *Int'l*, pg. 1017
METALUL MESA SA; *Int'l*, pg. 4849
METALUMEN MANUFACTURING INC; *Int'l*, pg. 4849
METALURGICA DUQUE S.A.; *Int'l*, pg. 4849
METALURGICA GERDAU S.A.; *Int'l*, pg. 4849
METALURGICA GOLDEN ARTS LTDA.—See KITZ CORPORATION; *Int'l*, pg. 4196
METALURGICA NAKAYONE, LTDA.—See Cie Automotive S.A.; *Int'l*, pg. 1604
METALURGICA RIOSULENSE S.A.; *Int'l*, pg. 4850
METALURGICA SA; *Int'l*, pg. 4850
METALURSKO KEMICNA INDUSTRIJA CELJE, D.D.; *Int'l*, pg. 4850
METALUS INC. - METAL GRENIER DIVISION—See Metalus inc.; *Int'l*, pg. 4851
METALUS INC.; *Int'l*, pg. 4850
METALUX—See Groupe SFPI SA; *Int'l*, pg. 3111
METAL WANG PTE LTD—See AnnAik Limited; *Int'l*, pg. 473
THE METAL WARE CORP.; *U.S. Private*, pg. 4078
METAL WARE—See The Metal Ware Corp.; *U.S. Private*, pg. 4078
METALWORKING GROUP HOLDINGS, INC.; *U.S. Private*, pg. 2682
METALWORKING LUBRICANTS COMPANY, INC.; *U.S. Private*, pg. 2682
METAL WORKS INC.; *U.S. Private*, pg. 2680
METALYST FORGINGS LTD.—See Amtek Auto Limited; *Int'l*, pg. 441
METAMAP, INC.—See Incode Technologies, Inc.; *U.S. Private*, pg. 2054
METAMATERIAL INC.—See Meta Materials Inc.; *Int'l*, pg. 4843
META MATERIALS INC.; *Int'l*, pg. 4843
METAMATERIAL TECHNOLOGIES INC.—See Meta Materials Inc.; *Int'l*, pg. 4844
META MEDIA HOLDINGS LIMITED; *Int'l*, pg. 4844
METAMEND SOFTWARE & DESIGN LTD.; *Int'l*, pg. 4851
METAMETRICS, INC.—See Pamlico Capital Management, L.P.; *U.S. Private*, pg. 3083
METAMETRIX, INC.—See Levine Leichtman Capital Partners, LLC; *U.S. Private*, pg. 2436
METAMORPHIC VENTURES; *U.S. Private*, pg. 2682
METANETICS CORPORATION—See Zebra Technologies Corporation; *U.S. Public*, pg. 2401
METANET, INC.; *Int'l*, pg. 4851
METANOIA COMMUNICATIONS INC.—See ELAN Microelectronic Corp.; *Int'l*, pg. 2343
METANOLSKO-SIRCETNI KOMPLEKS KIKINDA; *Int'l*, pg. 4851
METANOMICS GMBH—See BASF SE; *Int'l*, pg. 884
METANOMICS HEALTH GMBH—See BIOCRATES Life Sciences AG; *Int'l*, pg. 1037
METAPACK FAR EAST LIMITED—See Thoma Bravo, L.P.; *U.S. Private*, pg. 4154
METAPACK FRANCE SAS—See Thoma Bravo, L.P.; *U.S. Private*, pg. 4154

COMPANY NAME INDEX

METAPACK GERMANY GMBH—See Thoma Bravo, L.P.; *U.S. Private*, pg. 4154
METAPACK HOLDINGS USA, INC.—See Thoma Bravo, L.P.; *U.S. Private*, pg. 4154
METAPACK LTD—See Thoma Bravo, L.P.; *U.S. Private*, pg. 4153
METAPACK POLAND SP. Z O.O.—See Thoma Bravo, L.P.; *U.S. Private*, pg. 4154
METAPACK SOFTWARE SAS—See Thoma Bravo, L.P.; *U.S. Private*, pg. 4154
METAPAR USINAGEM LTDA.—See Robert Bosch GmbH; *Int'l*, pg. 6361
METAPEOPLE GMBH—See Ardian SAS; *Int'l*, pg. 554
META PLATFORMS, INC.; *U.S. Public*, pg. 1426
METAPOINT PARTNERS LP; *U.S. Private*, pg. 2682
META POWER INTERNATIONAL, INC.; *U.S. Public*, pg. 1427
META PRODUCTIONS GMBH—See LOV Group Invest SAS; *Int'l*, pg. 4564
METAPS INC.; *Int'l*, pg. 4851
METAPS PTE LTD.—See Metaps Inc.; *Int'l*, pg. 4851
METAQUIP TC INDUSTRIAL PTE. LTD.—See Tan Chong International Limited; *Int'l*, pg. 7453
METARCH ARCHITECTURAL PANELS S.A.—See Metecno S.p.A.; *Int'l*, pg. 4852
METAREAL CORPORATION; *Int'l*, pg. 4851
METARESPONSE GROUP, INC.; *U.S. Private*, pg. 2682
METARIS CORP.—See Clearlake Capital Group, L.P.; *U.S. Private*, pg. 933
METARIS, INC.—See Clearlake Capital Group, L.P.; *U.S. Private*, pg. 933
METAROCK GROUP LIMITED; *Int'l*, pg. 4851
METASKIL GROUP LIMITED—See Watchstone Group plc; *Int'l*, pg. 8356
METASOURCE, LLC—See Longshore Capital Partners; *U.S. Private*, pg. 2493
METASPACE (BEIJING) AIR DOME CORP.—See Beijing Sports & Entertainment Industry Group Limited; *Int'l*, pg. 957
METASTAT, INC.; *U.S. Private*, pg. 2682
METASTORM, INC.—See Open Text Corporation; *Int'l*, pg. 5597
META STSTEMS CO., LTD.—See Meta Biomed Co., Ltd.; *Int'l*, pg. 4843
МЕТАЗУЗ ТЕСHNOLOGIES, INC.; *U.S. Private*, pg. 2682
META SYSTEM (CHONGQING) CO., LTD.—See Shenzhen Deren Electronic Co., Ltd.; *Int'l*, pg. 6808
META SYSTEM S.P.A.—See Shenzhen Deren Electronic Co., Ltd.; *Int'l*, pg. 6808
METATECH (AP), INC.; *Int'l*, pg. 4851
METATECH LTD.—See MetaTech (AP), Inc.; *Int'l*, pg. 4851
METATECH (SHENZHEN) LTD.—See MetaTech (AP), Inc.; *Int'l*, pg. 4851
METATECH (S) PTE. LTD.—See MetaTech (AP), Inc.; *Int'l*, pg. 4851
METATHERM 74 S.A.S.—See Aalberts N.V.; *Int'l*, pg. 35
METATHERM S.A.S.—See Aalberts N.V.; *Int'l*, pg. 35
METATRON APPS, INC.; *U.S. Public*, pg. 1427
METATRON CONTROL SYSTEM (SHANGHAI) CO. LTD.—See Landi Renzo S.p.a.; *Int'l*, pg. 4406
METATRON S.P.A.—See Landi Renzo S.p.a.; *Int'l*, pg. 4406
METAULLICS SYSTEMS CO. LP - SANBORN—See Pyrotek Incorporated; *U.S. Private*, pg. 3310
METAULLICS SYSTEMS CO. LP - SOLON—See Pyrotek Incorporated; *U.S. Private*, pg. 3311
METAURUS EQUITY COMPONENT TRUST; *U.S. Public*, pg. 1427
METAUSEL SAS—See BRENNTAG SE; *Int'l*, pg. 1149
METAUX BILLITON CANADA INCORPORATED—See BHP Group Limited; *Int'l*, pg. 1016
METAUX INOX SERVICES, S.A.S.—See Tubacex S.A.; *Int'l*, pg. 7962
METAUX RUSSEL INC.—See Russel Metals Inc.; *Int'l*, pg. 6430
METAUX RUSSEL PRODUITS SPECIALISES—See Russel Metals Inc.; *Int'l*, pg. 6430
METAVAC LLC—See Thermo Fisher Scientific Inc.; *U.S. Public*, pg. 2149
METAVATION, LLC—See MW Universal Inc.; *U.S. Private*, pg. 2822
METAVERSE CAPITAL CORP.; *Int'l*, pg. 4851
METAVERSE CORPORATION; *U.S. Private*, pg. 2683
METAVERSE YUNJI TECHNOLOGY GROUP COMPANY LIMITED; *Int'l*, pg. 4851
METAVESCO, INC.; *U.S. Public*, pg. 1428
METAVIDEOTEX—See Imperial Brands PLC; *Int'l*, pg. 3633
META VISION SYSTEMS LIMITED—See Stanley Black & Decker, Inc.; *U.S. Public*, pg. 1933
METAWATER CO., LTD.; *Int'l*, pg. 4851
METAWATER SERVICE CO., LTD.—See Fuji Electric Co., Ltd.; *Int'l*, pg. 2812
METAWATER SERVICES CO., LTD.—See METAWATER Co., Ltd.; *Int'l*, pg. 4851
METAWATER TECH CO., LTD.—See METAWATER Co., Ltd.; *Int'l*, pg. 4851
METAWATER USA, INC.—See METAWATER Co., Ltd.; *Int'l*, pg. 4851

METAWORKS PLATFORMS, INC.; *U.S. Public*, pg. 1428
METAXA GREECE—See Remy Cointreau S.A.; *Int'l*, pg. 6272
METCALF BROTHERS LLC—See Hyman Brickle & Son, Inc.; *U.S. Private*, pg. 2019
METCALFE INC.; *U.S. Private*, pg. 2683
METCALFE PLANT HIRE LIMITED—See CorpAcq Holdings Limited; *Int'l*, pg. 1802
METCAP SP ZOO; *Int'l*, pg. 4851
METCARE OF FLORIDA, INC.—See Humana, Inc.; *U.S. Public*, pg. 1070
METCASH EXPORT SERVICES PTY. LTD.—See eCargo Holdings Limited; *Int'l*, pg. 2287
METCASH HOLDINGS PTY. LTD.—See Metcash Limited; *Int'l*, pg. 4852
METCASH LIMITED; *Int'l*, pg. 4852
METCASH STORAGE PTY LIMITED—See Metcash Limited; *Int'l*, pg. 4852
METCASH TRADING AFRICA (PTY) LTD—See Metcash Limited; *Int'l*, pg. 4852
METCHEM, INC.—See Ascent Industries Co.; *U.S. Public*, pg. 210
METCO ENVIRONMENTAL, INC.—See H.I.G. Capital, LLC; *U.S. Private*, pg. 1831
METCOE SKYLIGHT SPECIALTIES—See Weiss Sheet Metal Company; *U.S. Private*, pg. 4473
MET CO., LTD. - AMAGASAKI FACTORY—See Sumitomo Corporation; *Int'l*, pg. 7275
MET CO., LTD.—See Sumitomo Corporation; *Int'l*, pg. 7275
MET-CON CONSTRUCTION INC.; *U.S. Private*, pg. 2679
METCON INC.; *U.S. Private*, pg. 2683
MET/CON METALLURGICAL PLANT & PROCESS CONSULTING GMBH—See SMS Holding GmbH; *Int'l*, pg. 7015
METCOR INC; *Int'l*, pg. 4852
METCO SERVICES, LTD.—See Emerson Electric Co.; *U.S. Public*, pg. 748
METCRAFT INC.; *U.S. Private*, pg. 2683
METEC ASSET MANAGEMENT, LC; *U.S. Private*, pg. 2683
METEC GMBH—See uesa GmbH; *Int'l*, pg. 8014
METECH CO., LTD.—See MITACHI Co., LTD.; *Int'l*, pg. 4924
METECH INTERNATIONAL LIMITED; *Int'l*, pg. 4852
METECH RECYCLING, INC.—See Metech International Limited; *Int'l*, pg. 4852
METECH RECYCLING, INC.—See Metech International Limited; *Int'l*, pg. 4852
METECH RECYCLING (SINGAPORE) PTE. LTD.—See Metech International Limited; *Int'l*, pg. 4852
METECH RECYCLING (UK) LTD.; *Int'l*, pg. 4852
METECH REVERSLOG PTE. LTD.—See Metech International Limited; *Int'l*, pg. 4852
METEC INC.—See Metecno S.p.A.; *Int'l*, pg. 4853
METECNO BAUSYSTEME GMBH—See Metecno S.p.A.; *Int'l*, pg. 4853
METECNO BULGARIA AD—See Metecno S.p.A.; *Int'l*, pg. 4853
METECNO DE CHILE S.A.—See Metecno S.p.A.; *Int'l*, pg. 4853
METECNO DE COLOMBIA S.A.—See Metecno S.p.A.; *Int'l*, pg. 4853
METECNO ESPANA S.A.—See Metecno S.p.A.; *Int'l*, pg. 4853
METECNO FRANCE S.A.R.L.—See Metecno S.p.A.; *Int'l*, pg. 4853
METECNO (INDIA) PVT LTD - CHENNAI-SPR-FACTORY—See Metecno S.p.A.; *Int'l*, pg. 4852
METECNO (INDIA) PVT LTD—See Metecno S.p.A.; *Int'l*, pg. 4852
METECNO INTERNATIONAL BV—See Metecno S.p.A.; *Int'l*, pg. 4853
METECNO LANKA (PVT.) LTD.—See Metecno S.p.A.; *Int'l*, pg. 4853
METECNO PORTUGAL S.A.—See Metecno S.p.A.; *Int'l*, pg. 4853
METECNO S.P.A.; *Int'l*, pg. 4852
METECNO (THAILAND) LTD.—See Metecno S.p.A.; *Int'l*, pg. 4852
METECNO TRADING GMBH—See Metecno S.p.A.; *Int'l*, pg. 4853
METECNO TRADING ROMANIA SRL—See Metecno S.p.A.; *Int'l*, pg. 4853
METECNO TRADING S.A.—See Metecno S.p.A.; *Int'l*, pg. 4853
METECNO (VIETNAM) LTD—See Metecno S.p.A.; *Int'l*, pg. 4853
METEHE OY; *Int'l*, pg. 4853
METELEC LTD—See Umcor AG; *Int'l*, pg. 8022
METEM CORPORATION—See General Electric Company; *U.S. Public*, pg. 918
METEMTEKS SENTETIK IPLIK SAN. TIC. A.S.—See Nigbas Nigde Beton Sanayi ve Ticaret A.S.; *Int'l*, pg. 5282
METEMTUR OTELCILIK VE TURIZM ISLETMELERI AS; *Int'l*, pg. 4853
METEN INTERNATIONAL EDUCATION GROUP; *Int'l*, pg. 4853

METENOVA AB—See Repligen Corporation; *U.S. Public*, pg. 1784
METEOCONTROL GMBH—See Shunfeng International Clean Energy Ltd.; *Int'l*, pg. 6870
METEORA CAPITAL LLC; *U.S. Public*, pg. 2683
METEOR COMMUNICATIONS CORPORATION, INC.—See Berkshire Hathaway Inc.; *U.S. Public*, pg. 303
METEOR EDUCATION LLC—See Bain Capital, LP; *U.S. Private*, pg. 431
METEOR EXPRESS, INC.; *U.S. Private*, pg. 2683
METEORIC RESOURCES NL; *Int'l*, pg. 4853
METEOR INKJET LIMITED—See Hybrid Software Group PLC; *Int'l*, pg. 3544
METEORITE CAPITAL, INC.; *Int'l*, pg. 4853
METEOR PARKING LTD.—See Fundacion Bancaria Caixa d'Estalvis i Pensions de Barcelona, la Caixa; *Int'l*, pg. 2845
METEOR PLANT JSC—See Russian Technologies State Corporation; *Int'l*, pg. 6432
METER INSTRUMENTS CO., LTD.; *Int'l*, pg. 4853
METEROLOGY DATA PRIVATE LIMITED—See Brookfield Corporation; *Int'l*, pg. 1178
METEROLOGY DATA PRIVATE LIMITED—See Elliott Management Corporation; *U.S. Private*, pg. 1371
METER SYSTEMS TRADING (PTY) LTD—See Set Point Group Limited; *Int'l*, pg. 6730
METERTEK SDN BHD—See Itron, Inc.; *U.S. Public*, pg. 1176
METER TELEVISION AB—See LOV Group Invest SAS; *Int'l*, pg. 4565
METER-U LIMITED—See Grovepoint Capital LLP; *Int'l*, pg. 3112
METER-U LIMITED—See Rubicon Partners Limited; *Int'l*, pg. 6422
METEX STEEL SDN BHD—See Chin Hin Group Berhad; *Int'l*, pg. 1480
METFOILS AB—See PAI Partners S.A.S.; *Int'l*, pg. 5702
METFORM, LLC—See MacLean-Fogg Company; *U.S. Private*, pg. 2537
METGASCO LIMITED; *Int'l*, pg. 4853
METGLAS, INC—See Proterial, Ltd.; *Int'l*, pg. 6005
M.E.T GMBH—See Tarkett S.A.; *Int'l*, pg. 7462
METHA-METHANHANDEL GMBH—See E.ON SE; *Int'l*, pg. 2258
METHANERGY SA—See TotalEnergies SE; *Int'l*, pg. 7837
METHANEX ASIA PACIFIC LIMITED—See Methanex Corporation; *Int'l*, pg. 4853
METHANEX CHILE S.A.—See Methanex Corporation; *Int'l*, pg. 4853
METHANEX CORPORATION; *Int'l*, pg. 4853
METHANEX EUROPE SA/NV—See Methanex Corporation; *Int'l*, pg. 4853
METHANEX JAPAN LIMITED—See Methanex Corporation; *Int'l*, pg. 4853
METHANEX MOTUNUI LIMITED—See Methanex Corporation; *Int'l*, pg. 4853
METHANEX NEW ZEALAND—See Methanex Corporation; *Int'l*, pg. 4853
METHANEX SERVICES (SHANGHAI) CO., LTD.—See Methanex Corporation; *Int'l*, pg. 4853
METHANOL CHEMICALS COMPANY; *Int'l*, pg. 4853
METHANOR SCA; *Int'l*, pg. 4854
METHAQ REAL ESTATE INVESTMENT P.L.C.; *Int'l*, pg. 4854
METHAQ TAKAFUL INSURANCE COMPANY P.S.C.; *Int'l*, pg. 4854
METHEC BV—See VINCI S.A.; *Int'l*, pg. 8224
METHENY CONCRETE PRODUCTS INC.; *U.S. Private*, pg. 2683
ME THERAPEUTICS HOLDINGS INC.; *Int'l*, pg. 4763
METHES ENERGIES INTERNATIONAL LTD.; *U.S. Public*, pg. 1428
METHOD3, INC.; *U.S. Private*, pg. 2683
METHOD ARCHITECTURE, PLLC; *U.S. Private*, pg. 2683
METHOD COMMUNICATIONS, INC.—See Providence Equity Partners L.L.C.; *U.S. Private*, pg. 3292
MET/HODDER INC.; *U.S. Private*, pg. 2679
METHODE DATAMATE PRODUCTS—See Methode Electronics, Inc.; *U.S. Public*, pg. 1429
METHODE DEVELOPMENT COMPANY—See Methode Electronics, Inc.; *U.S. Public*, pg. 1428
METHODE ELECTRONICS ASIA PTE, LTD.—See Methode Electronics, Inc.; *U.S. Public*, pg. 1428
METHODE ELECTRONICS CONNECTIVITY TECHNOLOGIES, INC.—See Methode Electronics, Inc.; *U.S. Public*, pg. 1428
METHODE ELECTRONICS EUROPE LTD.—See Methode Electronics, Inc.; *U.S. Public*, pg. 1428
METHODE ELECTRONICS FAR EAST PTE., LTD.—See Methode Electronics, Inc.; *U.S. Public*, pg. 1428
METHODE ELECTRONICS, INC.; *U.S. Public*, pg. 1428
METHODE ELECTRONICS INDIA, PRIVATE LTD.—See Methode Electronics, Inc.; *U.S. Public*, pg. 1428
METHODE ELECTRONICS INTERNATIONAL GMBH—See Methode Electronics, Inc.; *U.S. Public*, pg. 1428
METHODE ELECTRONICS IRELAND, LTD.—See Methode Electronics, Inc.; *U.S. Public*, pg. 1428

METHODE ELECTRONICS, INC.   CORPORATE AFFILIATIONS

METHODE ELECTRONICS MALTA HOLDINGS LTD.—See Methode Electronics, Inc.; *U.S. Public*, pg. 1428
METHODE ELECTRONICS MALTA LTD.—See Methode Electronics, Inc.; *U.S. Public*, pg. 1428
METHODE ELECTRONICS (SHANGHAI) CO. LTD.—See Methode Electronics, Inc.; *U.S. Public*, pg. 1428
METHODE ELECTRONICS—See Methode Electronics, Inc.; *U.S. Public*, pg. 1428
METHODE MEXICO, S.A. DE C.V.—See Methode Electronics, Inc.; *U.S. Public*, pg. 1428
METHODE POWER SOLUTIONS GROUP—See Methode Electronics, Inc.; *U.S. Public*, pg. 1428
METHODFACTORY, INC.; *U.S. Private*, pg. 2683
METHODICAL INC.; *U.S. Private*, pg. 2683
METHOD INC.—See Hitachi, Ltd.; *Int'l*, pg. 3313
METHODIST AMBULATORY SURGERY CENTER OF BOERNE, LLC—See HCA Healthcare, Inc.; *U.S. Public*, pg. 1002
METHODIST AMBULATORY SURGERY CENTER OF LANDMARK, LLC—See HCA Healthcare, Inc.; *U.S. Public*, pg. 1002
METHODIST AMBULATORY SURGERY HOSPITAL - NORTHWEST—See HCA Healthcare, Inc.; *U.S. Public*, pg. 1002
METHODIST AMBULATORY SURGERY HOSPITAL - NORTHWEST—See Methodist Healthcare Ministries of South Texas, Inc.; *U.S. Private*, pg. 2683
METHODIST CARENOW URGENT CARE, PLLC—See HCA Healthcare, Inc.; *U.S. Public*, pg. 1002
METHODIST HEALTHCARE MINISTRIES OF SOUTH TEXAS, INC.; *U.S. Private*, pg. 2683
METHODIST HEALTHCARE; *U.S. Private*, pg. 2683
METHODIST HEALTHCARE SYSTEM OF SAN ANTONIO, LTD.—See HCA Healthcare, Inc.; *U.S. Public*, pg. 1002
METHODIST HEALTHCARE SYSTEM OF SAN ANTONIO, LTD.—See Methodist Healthcare Ministries of South Texas, Inc.; *U.S. Private*, pg. 2683
METHODIST HEALTH SYSTEM; *U.S. Private*, pg. 2683
METHODIST HOME OF THE DISTRICT OF COLUMBIA; *U.S. Private*, pg. 2684
METHODIST HOMES OF ALABAMA & NORTHWEST FLORIDA; *U.S. Private*, pg. 2684
METHODIST HOSPITAL FOUNDATION; *U.S. Private*, pg. 2684
METHODIST HOSPITAL HILL COUNTRY—See HCA Healthcare, Inc.; *U.S. Public*, pg. 1002
METHODIST HOSPITAL HILL COUNTRY—See Methodist Healthcare Ministries of South Texas, Inc.; *U.S. Private*, pg. 2683
METHODIST HOSPITAL OF SACRAMENTO—See Catholic Health Initiatives; *U.S. Private*, pg. 790
METHODIST HOSPITAL OF SOUTHERN CALIFORNIA; *U.S. Private*, pg. 2684
THE METHODIST HOSPITALS, INC.; *U.S. Private*, pg. 4078
METHODIST HOSPITAL; *U.S. Private*, pg. 2684
METHODIST HOSPITAL—See HCA Healthcare, Inc.; *U.S. Public*, pg. 1002
METHODIST HOSPITAL SOUTH—See HCA Healthcare, Inc.; *U.S. Public*, pg. 1002
METHODIST HOSPITAL SOUTH—See Methodist Healthcare Ministries of South Texas, Inc.; *U.S. Private*, pg. 2683
METHODIST HOSPITAL UNION COUNTY—See Methodist Hospital; *U.S. Private*, pg. 2684
METHODIST INPATIENT MANAGEMENT GROUP—See HCA Healthcare, Inc.; *U.S. Public*, pg. 1002
METHODIST INPATIENT MANAGEMENT GROUP—See Methodist Healthcare Ministries of South Texas, Inc.; *U.S. Private*, pg. 2683
METHODIST MEDICAL CENTER ASC, L.P.—See HCA Healthcare, Inc.; *U.S. Public*, pg. 1002
METHODIST MEDICAL CENTER ASC, L.P.—See Methodist Healthcare Ministries of South Texas, Inc.; *U.S. Private*, pg. 2683
METHODIST PHYSICIAN ALLIANCE—See HCA Healthcare, Inc.; *U.S. Public*, pg. 1002
METHODIST PHYSICIAN ALLIANCE—See Methodist Healthcare Ministries of South Texas, Inc.; *U.S. Private*, pg. 2683
METHODIST PHYSICIAN PRACTICES, PLLC—See HCA Healthcare, Inc.; *U.S. Public*, pg. 1002
METHODIST REHABILITATION CENTER; *U.S. Private*, pg. 2684
METHODIST SERVICES INC.; *U.S. Private*, pg. 2684
METHODIST SOUTHLAKE HOSPITAL, LLC—See Methodist Health System; *U.S. Private*, pg. 2683
METHODIST STONE OAK HOSPITAL—See HCA Healthcare, Inc.; *U.S. Public*, pg. 1002
METHODIST STONE OAK HOSPITAL—See Methodist Healthcare Ministries of South Texas, Inc.; *U.S. Private*, pg. 2683
METHOD LONDON—See Hitachi, Ltd.; *Int'l*, pg. 3313
METHOD PRODUCTS, INC.—See Ecover Belgium NV; *Int'l*, pg. 2300
METHODS MACHINE TOOLS INC.; *U.S. Private*, pg. 2684
METHVEN CARE HOME PERTH—See Balhousie Holdings Limited; *Int'l*, pg. 808

METHVEN LIMITED—See GWA Group Limited; *Int'l*, pg. 3190
METIA LIMITED; *Int'l*, pg. 4854
METI CAPITAL SPA; *Int'l*, pg. 4854
METIER, LTD.; *U.S. Private*, pg. 2684
METIER MIXED CONCRETE PROPRIETARY LIMITED—See Sephaku Holdings Ltd.; *Int'l*, pg. 6718
METIER OEC AS—See RPS Group plc; *Int'l*, pg. 6415
METI HOLDING SARL; *Int'l*, pg. 4854
MET II OFFICE LLC—See MetLife, Inc.; *U.S. Public*, pg. 1430
METIMPEX SP. Z O.O.—See INDUS Holding AG; *Int'l*, pg. 3664
METINDUSTRIAL (PTY) LTD.—See Metair Investments Limited; *Int'l*, pg. 4844
METISA - METALURGICA TIMBOENSE S.A.; *Int'l*, pg. 4854
METIS BILGISAYAR SISTEMLIRI SANAYI VE TICARET A.S.—See Teleperformance SE; *Int'l*, pg. 7540
METIS B.V.—See Zehnder Group AG; *Int'l*, pg. 8630
METIS ENERGY LIMITED; *Int'l*, pg. 4854
METIS ENGENHARIA, LDA.—See CONDURIL, Engenharia S.A.; *Int'l*, pg. 1767
METISENTRY LLC; *U.S. Private*, pg. 2684
METIS LEVAGE S.A.S—See KSB SE & Co. KGaA; *Int'l*, pg. 4313
METIS SOLUTIONS LLC—See Amentum Services, Inc.; *U.S. Private*, pg. 219
METITO HOLDINGS LTD.; *Int'l*, pg. 4854
METITO INTERNATIONAL, INC.—See Metito Holdings Ltd.; *Int'l*, pg. 4854
METITO LIBYA GENERAL CONTRACTING CO.—See Metito Holdings Ltd.; *Int'l*, pg. 4854
METITO LLC—See Metito Holdings Ltd.; *Int'l*, pg. 4854
METITO (OVERSEAS) QATAR WLL—See Metito Holdings Ltd.; *Int'l*, pg. 4854
METITO POLLUTION CONTROL INDIA PVT. LTD—See Metito Holdings Ltd.; *Int'l*, pg. 4854
METITO SAUDI LIMITED—See Metito Holdings Ltd.; *Int'l*, pg. 4854
METITO UTILITIES LIMITED—See Metito Holdings Ltd.; *Int'l*, pg. 4854
METITO WATER TREATMENT SAE—See Metito Holdings Ltd.; *Int'l*, pg. 4854
METIX (PTY) LTD.—See SMS Holding GmbH; *Int'l*, pg. 7015
METIZI J.S.CO.; *Int'l*, pg. 4854
METKA BRAZI SRL—See Metlen Energy & Metals S.A.; *Int'l*, pg. 4855
METKA-EGM CHILE SPA—See Metlen Energy & Metals S.A.; *Int'l*, pg. 4855
METKA-EGN LIMITED—See Metlen Energy & Metals S.A.; *Int'l*, pg. 4855
METKA EGN MEXICO S. DE R.L. C.V.—See Metlen Energy & Metals S.A.; *Int'l*, pg. 4855
METKA INDUSTRIAL - CONSTRUCTION S.A.—See Metlen Energy & Metals S.A.; *Int'l*, pg. 4855
METKA POWER WEST AFRICA LIMITED—See Metlen Energy & Metals S.A.; *Int'l*, pg. 4855
METKO HUTTENES ALBERTUS KIMYA SANAYI VE TICARET A.S.—See Huettenes-Albertus Chemische Werke GmbH; *Int'l*, pg. 3523
METKOMBANK PJSC; *Int'l*, pg. 4854
MET KOREA, LTD.—See Eurofins Scientific S.E.; *Int'l*, pg. 2551
METKOTE LAMINATED PRODUCTS INC.—See FlashCo Manufacturing, Inc.; *U.S. Private*, pg. 1540
MET LABORATORIES INC.; *U.S. Private*, pg. 2679
METLASE LIMITED—See Rolls-Royce Holdings plc; *Int'l*, pg. 6392
METLEN ENERGY & METALS S.A.; *Int'l*, pg. 4854
METLIFE ADMINISTRADORA DE FUNDOS MULTIPATROCINADOS LTDA.—See MetLife, Inc.; *U.S. Public*, pg. 1430
METLIFE - AIG - ANB COOPERATIVE INSURANCE COMPANY—See Walaa Cooperative Insurance Company; *Int'l*, pg. 8332
METLIFE ALICO CYPRUS—See MetLife, Inc.; *U.S. Public*, pg. 1429
METLIFE ALICO MUTUAL FUNDS COMPANY—See MetLife, Inc.; *U.S. Public*, pg. 1429
METLIFE AMERICAN INTERNATIONAL GROUP AND ARAB NATIONAL BANK COOPERATIVE INSURANCE COMPANY—See MetLife, Inc.; *U.S. Public*, pg. 1430
METLIFE AUTO & HOME INSURANCE AGENCY, INC.—See MetLife, Inc.; *U.S. Public*, pg. 1430
METLIFECARE 7 SAINT VINCENT LIMITED—See Metlifecare Limited; *Int'l*, pg. 4855
METLIFECARE BAYSWATER LIMITED—See Metlifecare Limited; *Int'l*, pg. 4855
METLIFECARE COASTAL VILLAS LIMITED—See Metlifecare Limited; *Int'l*, pg. 4855
METLIFECARE CRESTWOOD LIMITED—See Metlifecare Limited; *Int'l*, pg. 4855
METLIFECARE GREENWOOD PARK LIMITED—See Metlifecare Limited; *Int'l*, pg. 4855
METLIFECARE HIGHLANDS LIMITED—See Metlifecare Limited; *Int'l*, pg. 4855

METLIFECARE KAPITI LIMITED—See Metlifecare Limited; *Int'l*, pg. 4855
METLIFECARE LIMITED; *Int'l*, pg. 4855
METLIFECARE MERIVALE LIMITED—See Metlifecare Limited; *Int'l*, pg. 4855
METLIFECARE OAKWOODS LIMITED—See Metlifecare Limited; *Int'l*, pg. 4855
METLIFECARE PAKURANGA LIMITED—See Metlifecare Limited; *Int'l*, pg. 4855
METLIFECARE PINESONG LIMITED—See Metlifecare Limited; *Int'l*, pg. 4855
METLIFECARE POHUTUKAWA LANDING LIMITED—See Metlifecare Limited; *Int'l*, pg. 4855
METLIFECARE POWLEY LIMITED—See Metlifecare Limited; *Int'l*, pg. 4855
METLIFECARE SOMERVALE LIMITED—See Metlifecare Limited; *Int'l*, pg. 4855
METLIFECARE THE AVENUES LIMITED—See Metlifecare Limited; *Int'l*, pg. 4855
METLIFECARE WAIRARAPA LIMITED—See Metlifecare Limited; *Int'l*, pg. 4855
METLIFE COLOMBIA SEGUROS DE VIDA S.A.—See MetLife, Inc.; *U.S. Public*, pg. 1430
METLIFE COMMERCIAL MORTGAGE INCOME FUND GP, LLC—See MetLife, Inc.; *U.S. Public*, pg. 1430
METLIFE CORE PROPERTY REIT, LLC—See MetLife, Inc.; *U.S. Public*, pg. 1430
METLIFE DIRECT CO., LTD.—See MetLife, Inc.; *U.S. Public*, pg. 1431
METLIFE EUROPE INSURANCE LIMITED—See MetLife, Inc.; *U.S. Public*, pg. 1430
METLIFE GENERAL INSURANCE LIMITED—See MetLife, Inc.; *U.S. Public*, pg. 1430
METLIFE, INC.; *U.S. Public*, pg. 1429
METLIFE INDIA INSURANCE COMPANY PRIVATE LIMITED—See MetLife, Inc.; *U.S. Public*, pg. 1429
METLIFE INSURANCE COMPANY OF CONNECTICUT—See MetLife, Inc.; *U.S. Public*, pg. 1431
METLIFE INSURANCE K.K.—See MetLife, Inc.; *U.S. Public*, pg. 1430
METLIFE INSURANCE LIMITED—See MetLife, Inc.; *U.S. Public*, pg. 1430
METLIFE INSURANCE LIMITED—See MetLife, Inc.; *U.S. Public*, pg. 1431
METLIFE INTERNATIONAL HOLDINGS, LLC—See MetLife, Inc.; *U.S. Public*, pg. 1431
METLIFE INVESTMENT MANAGEMENT LIMITED—See MetLife, Inc.; *U.S. Public*, pg. 1430
METLIFE INVESTMENT MANAGEMENT, LLC—See MetLife, Inc.; *U.S. Public*, pg. 1430
METLIFE INVESTMENTS ASIA LIMITED—See MetLife, Inc.; *U.S. Public*, pg. 1430
METLIFE INVESTORS DISTRIBUTION COMPANY—See MetLife, Inc.; *U.S. Public*, pg. 1431
METLIFE, LIFE INSURANCE COMPANY—See MetLife, Inc.; *U.S. Public*, pg. 1430
METLIFE LIMITED—See MetLife, Inc.; *U.S. Public*, pg. 1431
METLIFE MAS, S.A. DE C.V.—See MetLife, Inc.; *U.S. Public*, pg. 1430
METLIFE MEXICO S.A.—See MetLife, Inc.; *U.S. Public*, pg. 1431
METLIFE POJISTOVNA A.S.—See MetLife, Inc.; *U.S. Public*, pg. 1430
METLIFE POLICYHOLDER TRUST—See MetLife, Inc.; *U.S. Public*, pg. 1431
METLIFE PROPERTIES VENTURES, LLC—See MetLife, Inc.; *U.S. Public*, pg. 1430
METLIFE SAENGMYOUNG INSURANCE CO. LTD.—See MetLife, Inc.; *U.S. Public*, pg. 1431
METLIFE SECURITIES, INC.—See MetLife, Inc.; *U.S. Public*, pg. 1431
METLIFE SEGUROS S.A.—See MetLife, Inc.; *U.S. Public*, pg. 1430
METLIFE SEGUROS S.A.—See MetLife, Inc.; *U.S. Public*, pg. 1430
METLIFE SERVICES CYPRUS LIMITED—See MetLife, Inc.; *U.S. Public*, pg. 1430
METLIFE SLOVAKIA S.R.O.—See MetLife, Inc.; *U.S. Public*, pg. 1430
METLIFE UK LIMITED—See MetLife, Inc.; *U.S. Public*, pg. 1431
METLIFE WORLDWIDE HOLDINGS, INC.—See MetLife, Inc.; *U.S. Public*, pg. 1430
METLITE ALLOYS PROPRIETARY LIMITED—See Insimbi Industrial Holdings Limited; *Int'l*, pg. 3719
METL-SPAN LLC—See Clayton, Dubilier & Rice, LLC; *U.S. Private*, pg. 921
M.E.T. MOTION (ALOR STAR) SDN. BHD.—See UNIMECH Group Berhad; *Int'l*, pg. 8049
M.E.T. MOTION (KL) SDN. BHD.—See UNIMECH Group Berhad; *Int'l*, pg. 8049
MET NEWEN S.P.A.—See Maire Tecnimont S.p.A.; *Int'l*, pg. 4652
METNOR CONSTRUCTION LIMITED—See Metnor Group Plc; *Int'l*, pg. 4855
METNOR (GREAT YARMOUTH) LIMITED—See Metnor Group Plc; *Int'l*, pg. 4855

COMPANY NAME INDEX

METNOR GROUP PLC; *Int'l*, pg. 4855
METODIKA AB—See Carasent ASA; *Int'l*, pg. 1319
METO FENIX HANDELS GMBH—See CCL Industries Inc.; *Int'l*, pg. 1368
METO INTERNATIONAL GMBH—See CCL Industries Inc.; *Int'l*, pg. 1368
METOKOTE CANADA LTD.—See PPG Industries, Inc.; *U.S. Public*, pg. 1707
METOKOTE CORPORATION, INC.—See PPG Industries, Inc.; *U.S. Public*, pg. 1707
METOKOTE DEUTSCHLAND GMBH—See PPG Industries, Inc.; *U.S. Public*, pg. 1707
METOKOTE U.K. LIMITED—See PPG Industries, Inc.; *U.S. Public*, pg. 1707
METON GMBH—See Zeppelin GmbH; *Int'l*, pg. 8637
METOOL PRODUCTS LTD.—See Tsubakimoto Chain Co.; *Int'l*, pg. 7954
ME TOO MARK TUCKER INC.; *U.S. Private*, pg. 2646
METOREX LIMITED - CONSOLIDATED MURCHISON DIVISION—See Jinchuan Group Limited; *Int'l*, pg. 3966
METOREX LIMITED—See Jinchuan Group Limited; *Int'l*, pg. 3965
METOREX (PROPRIETARY) LIMITED—See Jinchuan Group International Resources Co. Ltd.; *Int'l*, pg. 3965
METOREX SP. Z.O.O.—See PBG S.A.; *Int'l*, pg. 5765
METOVA, INC.; *U.S. Private*, pg. 2684
METPAR CORP.; *U.S. Private*, pg. 2684
MET-PRO TECHNOLOGIES LLC—See CECO Environmental Corp.; *U.S. Public*, pg. 463
METQ PROPRIETARY LIMITED—See Tharisa Plc; *Int'l*, pg. 7609
METRA AKDENIZ DIS TICARET A.S.—See Enka Insaat ve Sanayi A.S.; *Int'l*, pg. 2440
METRACLARK SOUTH AFRICA PROPRIETY LTD.—See Beijer Ref AB; *Int'l*, pg. 944
METRACLARK TANZANIA (PTY.) LTD.—See Beijer Ref AB; *Int'l*, pg. 944
METRAC- METALHANDELSGESELLSCHAFT IMPORT-EXPORT MBH; *Int'l*, pg. 4855
METRACOMP, INC.—See CVS Health Corporation; *U.S. Public*, pg. 615
METRADIS S.L.—See Indra Sistemas, S.A.; *Int'l*, pg. 3661
METRA ELECTRONICS CORPORATION; *U.S. Private*, pg. 2684
METRALITE INDUSTRIES INC.; *U.S. Private*, pg. 2684
METRANACO PUBLIC COMPANY LTD.; *Int'l*, pg. 4855
METRANS ADRIA D.O.O.—See Hamburger Hafen und Logistik AG; *Int'l*, pg. 3237
METRANS A.S.—See Hamburger Hafen und Logistik AG; *Int'l*, pg. 3237
METRANS (DANUBIA) A.S.—See Hamburger Hafen und Logistik AG; *Int'l*, pg. 3237
METRANS (DANUBIA) KFT.—See Hamburger Hafen und Logistik AG; *Int'l*, pg. 3237
METRANS DYKO RAIL REPAIR SHOP S.R.O.—See Hamburger Hafen und Logistik AG; *Int'l*, pg. 3237
METRANS RAIL (DEUTSCHLAND) GMBH—See Hamburger Hafen und Logistik AG; *Int'l*, pg. 3237
METRANS RAILPROFI AUSTRIA GMBH—See Hamburger Hafen und Logistik AG; *Int'l*, pg. 3237
METRAWATT INTERNATIONAL GMBH; *Int'l*, pg. 4855
METRAX GMBH—See OSI Systems, Inc.; *U.S. Public*, pg. 1621
METREX RESEARCH, LLC—See Danaher Corporation; *U.S. Public*, pg. 628
METRICA INC.; *U.S. Private*, pg. 2685
METRIC ASSET MANAGEMENT LP; *Int'l*, pg. 4856
METRIC CAPITAL PARTNERS LLP; *Int'l*, pg. 4856
METRIC ENGINEERING INC.; *U.S. Private*, pg. 2684
METRIC GROUP LTD.—See Dutech Holdings Limited; *Int'l*, pg. 2235
METRIC INDUSTRIAL AB—See Addtech AB; *Int'l*, pg. 134
METRIC INDUSTRIAL AS—See Addtech AB; *Int'l*, pg. 134
METRIC INDUSTRIAL A/S—See Addtech AB; *Int'l*, pg. 134
METRIC INDUSTRIAL OY—See Addtech AB; *Int'l*, pg. 134
METRIC MACHINING; *U.S. Private*, pg. 2684
METRIC MOBILITY SOLUTIONS AG; *Int'l*, pg. 4856
METRIC & MULTISTANDARD COMPONENTS CORPORATION; *U.S. Private*, pg. 2684
METRICS IN BALANCE N.V.; *Int'l*, pg. 4856
METRICS MASTER INCOME TRUST; *Int'l*, pg. 4856
METRICSTREAM-ASIA REGIONAL OFFICE—See MetricStream, Inc.; *U.S. Private*, pg. 2685
METRICSTREAM-ATLANTA REGIONAL OFFICE—See MetricStream, Inc.; *U.S. Private*, pg. 2685
METRICSTREAM, INC.; *U.S. Private*, pg. 2685
METRIC TEST EQUIPMENT, INC.; *U.S. Private*, pg. 2685
METRIE CANADA LIMITED; *Int'l*, pg. 4856
METRIE, INC.—See Metrie Canada Limited; *Int'l*, pg. 4856
METRIGUARD, INC.—See Raute Oyj; *Int'l*, pg. 6221
METRIKA BUSINESS INTELLIGENCE CONSULTING, INC.—See IQVIA Holdings Inc.; *U.S. Public*, pg. 1170
METRIS SP. Z O.O.—See Per Aarsleff Holding A/S; *Int'l*, pg. 5796
METRIX4MEDIA, LLC—See The Hearst Corporation; *U.S. Private*, pg. 4047
METRIX INC.; *U.S. Private*, pg. 2685
METRIX INSTRUMENT CO., LP—See Roper Technologies, Inc.; *U.S. Public*, pg. 1812

METRIXLAB BV—See Verlinvest S.A.; *Int'l*, pg. 8172
METRIX—See Publicis Groupe S.A.; *Int'l*, pg. 6113
METRIX—See Sibelga s.c.r.l.; *Int'l*, pg. 6876
METRO 29TH STREET ASSOCIATES, LLC—See KSL Capital Partners, LLC; *U.S. Public*, pg. 2355
METRO ACCIDENT & HEALTH AGENCY, INC.—See Principal Financial Group, Inc.; *U.S. Public*, pg. 1721
METRO ACQUISITION 2004, INC.—See Sangetsu Co., Ltd.; *Int'l*, pg. 6537
METRO AD AGENCY CO., LTD.—See Tokyo Metro Co., Ltd.; *Int'l*, pg. 7793
METRO ADVERTISING GMBH—See Metro AG; *Int'l*, pg. 4857
METRO AGOO WATERWORKS, INC.—See Jolliville Holdings Corporation; *Int'l*, pg. 3996
METRO AG; *Int'l*, pg. 4856
METRO ALLIANCE HOLDINGS & EQUITIES CORP.; *Int'l*, pg. 4860
METRO APPLIANCES & MORE; *U.S. Private*, pg. 2685
METRO APPLIANCES & MORE—See Metro Appliances & More; *U.S. Private*, pg. 2685
METRO APPRAISAL, INC.—See The Carlyle Group Inc.; *U.S. Public*, pg. 2053
METRO ATLANTA PROPERTIES—See Fischbach & Dougherty, Inc.; *U.S. Private*, pg. 1532
METRO AVIATION, INC.; *U.S. Private*, pg. 2685
METRO BANK HOLDINGS PLC; *Int'l*, pg. 4860
METRO BETEILIGUNGSMANAGEMENT DUSSELDORF GMBH & CO. KG—See Metro AG; *Int'l*, pg. 4857
METROBILT CONSTRUCTION PTE LTD—See Metro Holdings Limited; *Int'l*, pg. 4860
METROBILT PTE LTD—See Metro Holdings Limited; *Int'l*, pg. 4860
METRO BRANDS LIMITED; *Int'l*, pg. 4860
METRO BROADCAST LTD.—See WPP plc; *Int'l*, pg. 8466
METROBUILD ASSOCIATES PTY LIMITED—See Metroland Australia Limited; *Int'l*, pg. 4862
METROBUS LIMITED—See GLOBALVIA Inversiones, S.A.U.; *Int'l*, pg. 3005
METROBUS LIMITED—See Kinetic Group Services Pty Ltd.; *Int'l*, pg. 4168
METRO CARPETS, LLC—See The Sterling Group, L.P.; *U.S. Private*, pg. 4122
METRO CASH & CARRY BULGARIA EOOD—See Metro AG; *Int'l*, pg. 1867
METRO CASH & CARRY CHINA HOLDING GMBH—See Metro AG; *Int'l*, pg. 4857
METRO CASH & CARRY DEUTSCHLAND GMBH—See Metro AG; *Int'l*, pg. 4857
METRO CASH & CARRY D.O.O.—See Metro AG; *Int'l*, pg. 4858
METRO CASH & CARRY D.O.O.—See Metro AG; *Int'l*, pg. 4858
METRO CASH & CARRY FRANCE ET CIE—See Metro AG; *Int'l*, pg. 4857
METRO CASH & CARRY FRANCE S.A.S.—See Metro AG; *Int'l*, pg. 4857
METRO CASH & CARRY INDIA PRIVATE LIMITED—See Reliance - ADA Group Limited; *Int'l*, pg. 6262
METRO CASH & CARRY INTERNATIONAL GMBH—See Metro AG; *Int'l*, pg. 4857
METRO CASH & CARRY INTERNATIONAL HOLDING B.V.—See Metro AG; *Int'l*, pg. 4857
METRO CASH & CARRY INTERNATIONAL HOLDING GMBH—See Metro AG; *Int'l*, pg. 4857
METRO CASH & CARRY INTERNATIONAL MANAGEMENT GMBH—See Metro AG; *Int'l*, pg. 4857
METRO CASH & CARRY JAPAN HOLDING GMBH—See Metro AG; *Int'l*, pg. 4857
METRO CASH & CARRY JAPAN KK—See Metro AG; *Int'l*, pg. 4857
METRO CASH & CARRY NEDERLAND B.V.—See Metro AG; *Int'l*, pg. 4859
METRO CASH & CARRY OOO—See Metro AG; *Int'l*, pg. 4857
METRO CASH & CARRY OSTERREICH GMBH—See Metro AG; *Int'l*, pg. 4857
METRO CASH & CARRY ROMANIA SRL—See Metro AG; *Int'l*, pg. 4857
METRO CASH & CARRY SR S.R.O.—See Metro AG; *Int'l*, pg. 4857
METRO CASH & CARRY TOO—See Metro AG; *Int'l*, pg. 4857
METROCAST COMMUNICATIONS—See Gestion Audem, Inc.; *Int'l*, pg. 2946
METRO CENTRAL EAST EUROPE GMBH—See Metro AG; *Int'l*, pg. 4858
METRO CHINA HOLDINGS PTE LTD—See Metro Holdings Limited; *Int'l*, pg. 4860
METRO CHRYSLER LTD.; *Int'l*, pg. 4860
METROCITY BANKSHARES, INC.; *U.S. Public*, pg. 1431
METRO CITY BANK—See MetroCity Bankshares, Inc.; *U.S. Public*, pg. 1431
METROCLEAN EXPRESS CORP.—See GTJ REIT, Inc.; *U.S. Public*, pg. 1807
METRO COMBINED LOGISTICS SOLUTIONS, INC.—See Metro Alliance Holdings & Equities Corp.; *Int'l*, pg. 4860
METRO COMMERCE CO., LTD.—See Tokyo Metro Co., Ltd.; *Int'l*, pg. 7793

METRO-GOLDWYN-MAYER INC.

METRO COMPUTER FACILITIES CLEANING CORP.—See Paris Maintenance Co. Inc.; *U.S. Private*, pg. 3095
METROCONTROL AG—See Zumbach Electronic AG; *Int'l*, pg. 8695
METROCORP CORPORATION—See Metrocorp Holdings Inc.; *U.S. Private*, pg. 2687
METROCORP HOLDINGS INC.; *U.S. Private*, pg. 2687
METRO CREATOR LIMITED—See Link-Asia International MedTech Group Limited; *Int'l*, pg. 4514
METRO CREDIT UNION; *U.S. Private*, pg. 2685
METROCREST SURGERY CENTER, L.P.—See Tenet Healthcare Corporation; *U.S. Public*, pg. 2011
METRO CYCLES OF ATLANTA INC.; *U.S. Private*, pg. 2685
METRO CZESTOCHOWA SP. Z O.O.—See Metro AG; *Int'l*, pg. 4858
METRO DANMARK HOLDING APS—See Metro AG; *Int'l*, pg. 4858
METRO DEUTSCHLAND GMBH—See Metro AG; *Int'l*, pg. 4858
METRO DEVELOPMENT GROUP, LLC; *U.S. Private*, pg. 2685
METROD FLAT PRODUCTS SDN BHD—See Metrod (Malaysia) Berhad; *Int'l*, pg. 4861
METROD HOLDINGS BHD; *Int'l*, pg. 4861
METRO DISTRIBUTIE NEDERLAND B. V.—See Metro AG; *Int'l*, pg. 4858
METROD (MALAYSIA) BERHAD; *Int'l*, pg. 4861
METROD (OFHC) SDN BHD—See Metrod (Malaysia) Berhad; *Int'l*, pg. 4861
METRO DOLOMITI SPA—See Metro AG; *Int'l*, pg. 4858
METRO DOORS LTD.—See ASSA ABLOY AB; *Int'l*, pg. 638
METRO ELECTRIC INC.; *U.S. Private*, pg. 2685
METRO ENGINEERING SRL—See Metropolitana Milanese S.P.A.; *Int'l*, pg. 4864
METRO ENGINES CO., LTD.—See Vector Inc.; *Int'l*, pg. 8144
METRO FIBERNET, LLC—See Keystone Group, L.P.; *U.S. Private*, pg. 2299
METROFILE HOLDINGS LIMITED; *Int'l*, pg. 4861
METROFILE MOZAMBIQUE LDA—See Metrofile Holdings Limited; *Int'l*, pg. 4862
METROFILE RECORDS & INFORMATION MANAGEMENT BOTSWANA (PTY) LTD—See Metrofile Holdings Limited; *Int'l*, pg. 4862
METROFILE RECORDS MANAGEMENT (KENYA) LTD.—See Metrofile Holdings Limited; *Int'l*, pg. 4862
METROFILE VYSION (PTY.) LTD.—See Metrofile Holdings Limited; *Int'l*, pg. 4862
METRO FILM EXPRESS INC.; *U.S. Private*, pg. 2685
METRO FINANCE B.V.—See Metro AG; *Int'l*, pg. 4858
METRO FINANCE LTD—See Metro AG; *Int'l*, pg. 4858
METRO FINANCIAL SERVICES GMBH—See Metro AG; *Int'l*, pg. 4858
METRO FIRE SAFETY, INC.—See Paris Maintenance Co. Inc.; *U.S. Private*, pg. 3095
METRO FOOD SERVICE CO., LTD.—See Tokyo Metro Co., Ltd.; *Int'l*, pg. 7793
METRO FOODS, INC.—See United Natural Foods, Inc.; *U.S. Public*, pg. 2232
METRO FORD, INC.; *U.S. Private*, pg. 2685
METRO FORD-LINCOLN-MERCURY; *U.S. Private*, pg. 2685
METRO FORD SALES, INC.; *U.S. Private*, pg. 2685
METRO FRANCE S.A.S.—See Metro AG; *Int'l*, pg. 4858
METRO FUEL INC.; *U.S. Private*, pg. 2685
METROFUNKKABEL UNION GMBH—See Nexans S.A.; *Int'l*, pg. 5241
METROFUSER LLC; *U.S. Private*, pg. 2687
ACERTUS—See Tailwind Capital Group, LLC; *U.S. Private*, pg. 3924
METRO GLOBAL BUSINESS SERVICES PRIVATE LIMITED—See Metro AG; *Int'l*, pg. 4858
METRO GLOBAL HOLDINGS CORPORATION; *Int'l*, pg. 4860
METROGLOBAL LIMITED; *Int'l*, pg. 4862
METRO GLOBAL SOLUTION CENTER SPOLKA Z OGRANICZONA ODPOWIEDZIALNOSCIA—See Metro AG; *Int'l*, pg. 4858
METRO-GOLDWYN-MAYER DISTRIBUTION CO.—See Amazon.com, Inc.; *U.S. Public*, pg. 90
METRO-GOLDWYN-MAYER HOME ENTERTAINMENT LLC—See Amazon.com, Inc.; *U.S. Public*, pg. 91
METRO-GOLDWYN-MAYER INC.; *U.S. Private*, pg. 2687
METRO-GOLDWYN-MAYER PICTURES INC.—See Amazon.com, Inc.; *U.S. Public*, pg. 91
METRO-GOLDWYN-MAYER STUDIOS, INC.—See Amazon.com, Inc.; *U.S. Public*, pg. 90
METRO GOTEBORG—See Kinnevik AB; *Int'l*, pg. 4182
METRO GROSMARKET BAKIRKOY ALISVERIS HIZMETLERI TICARET LTD. SIRKETI—See Metro AG; *Int'l*, pg. 4858
METRO GROUP ASSET MANAGEMENT B.V.—See Metro AG; *Int'l*, pg. 4858
METRO GROUP ASSET MANAGEMENT EMLAK YONETIM A.S.—See Metro AG; *Int'l*, pg. 4859

METRO-GOLDWYN-MAYER INC. — CORPORATE AFFILIATIONS

METRO GROUP ASSET MANAGEMENT GMBH & CO. KG—See Metro AG; *Int'l*, pg. 4859
METRO GROUP ASSET MANAGEMENT INGATLAN KFT.—See Metro AG; *Int'l*, pg. 4858
METRO GROUP ASSET MANAGEMENT OOO—See Metro AG; *Int'l*, pg. 4859
METRO GROUP ASSET MANAGEMENT POLSKA SP. Z O.O.—See Metro AG; *Int'l*, pg. 4859
METRO GROUP ASSET MANAGEMENT SERVICES GMBH—See Metro AG; *Int'l*, pg. 4858
METRO GROUP, INC.—See Strategic Publications, LLC; *U.S. Private*, pg. 3835
METRO GROUP RETAIL REAL ESTATE GMBH—See Metro AG; *Int'l*, pg. 4858
METRO GROUP SETTLEMENT AG—See Metro AG; *Int'l*, pg. 4859
METRO GROUP WHOLESALE REAL ESTATE GMBH—See Metro AG; *Int'l*, pg. 4858
THE METROHEALTH FOUNDATION, INC.; *U.S. Private*, pg. 4078
METROHM AG; *Int'l*, pg. 4862
METROHM ANALYTICS ROMANIA SRL—See Metrohm AG; *Int'l*, pg. 4862
METROHM APPLIKON B.V.—See Metrohm AG; *Int'l*, pg. 4862
METROHM AUTOLAB B.V.—See Metrohm AG; *Int'l*, pg. 4862
METROHM BELGIUM N.V.—See Metrohm AG; *Int'l*, pg. 4862
METROHM CANADA, INC.—See Metrohm AG; *Int'l*, pg. 4862
METROHM FRANCE SAS—See Metrohm AG; *Int'l*, pg. 4862
METROHM IRELAND LTD—See Metrohm AG; *Int'l*, pg. 4862
METROHM MALAYSIA SDN BHD—See Metrohm AG; *Int'l*, pg. 4862
METROHM MIDDLE EAST FZC—See Metrohm AG; *Int'l*, pg. 4862
METROHM NIRSYSTEMS—See Metrohm AG; *Int'l*, pg. 4862
METROHM NORDIC AB—See Metrohm AG; *Int'l*, pg. 4862
METROHM NORDIC APS—See Metrohm AG; *Int'l*, pg. 4862
METROHM POLSKA SP. Z O.O.—See Metrohm AG; *Int'l*, pg. 4862
METROHM SIAM LTD.—See Metrohm AG; *Int'l*, pg. 4862
METROHM SINGAPORE PTE LTD—See Metrohm AG; *Int'l*, pg. 4862
METROHM UK LTD—See Metrohm AG; *Int'l*, pg. 4862
METROHM USA INC.—See Metrohm AG; *Int'l*, pg. 4862
METRO HOLDINGS LIMITED; *Int'l*, pg. 4860
METRO HOLLAND B.V.—See Mediahuis Partners NV; *Int'l*, pg. 4772
METRO HOLLAND B.V.—See VP Exploitatie N.V.; *Int'l*, pg. 8311
METRO HOME INSULATION, LLC—See Installed Building Products, Inc.; *U.S. Public*, pg. 1133
METRO IMPORTS, INC.; *U.S. Private*, pg. 2685
METRO INC.; *Int'l*, pg. 4860
METRO INDUSTRIES, INC.—See Emerson Electric Co.; *U.S. Public*, pg. 750
METRO INFINITI, INC.—See HGreg.com; *U.S. Private*, pg. 1931
METRO INSURANCE SERVICES, INC.—See Stone Point Capital LLC; *U.S. Private*, pg. 3819
METRO INTERNATIONAL AB—See Kinnevik AB; *Int'l*, pg. 4181
METRO INTERNATIONAL AG—See Metro AG; *Int'l*, pg. 4858
METRO INTERNATIONAL S.A.—See Kinnevik AB; *Int'l*, pg. 4181
METRO INTERNATIONAL SWEDEN AB—See Kinnevik AB; *Int'l*, pg. 4182
METRO INTERNATIONAL TRADE SERVICES LLC—See Reuben Brothers SA; *Int'l*, pg. 6311
METRO INTER PLY CO LTD; *Int'l*, pg. 4860
METRO ITALIA CASH AND CARRY S. P. A.—See Metro AG; *Int'l*, pg. 4858
METRO ITALIA S.P.A—See Metro AG; *Int'l*, pg. 4858
METROJAYA BERHAD—See Pan Malaysian Industries Berhad; *Int'l*, pg. 5715
METRO JINJIANG CASH & CARRY CO., LTD.—See Metro AG; *Int'l*, pg. 4858
METRO JONERGIN, INC.—See Metro Label Group, Inc.; *Int'l*, pg. 4860
METRO KAJANG CONSTRUCTION SDN. BHD.—See MKH Berhad; *Int'l*, pg. 5002
METRO KERESKEDELMI KFT.—See Metro AG; *Int'l*, pg. 4858
METRO KNOXVILLE HMA, LLC—See Community Health Systems, Inc.; *U.S. Public*, pg. 555
METRO LABEL CORP.; *U.S. Private*, pg. 2685
METRO LABEL GROUP, INC.; *Int'l*, pg. 4860
METRO LABEL PACIFIC LTD.—See Metro Label Group, Inc.; *Int'l*, pg. 4860
METROLAND AUSTRALIA LIMITED; *Int'l*, pg. 4862
METRO LAND CORPORATION LTD.; *Int'l*, pg. 4860

METROLAND MEDIA GROUP LTD.—See Torstar Corporation; *Int'l*, pg. 7831
METRO LEASING GMBH—See Metro AG; *Int'l*, pg. 4858
METRO LEO BURNETT ADVERTISING—See Publicis Groupe S.A.; *Int'l*, pg. 6102
METRO LIGERO OESTE, S.A.—See Industry Super Holdings Pty. Ltd.; *Int'l*, pg. 3676
METROLINA PLASTICS, INC.—See Falfurrias Capital Partners, LP; *U.S. Private*, pg. 1467
METROLINA STEEL INC.; *U.S. Private*, pg. 2687
METROLINE INC.; *U.S. Private*, pg. 2687
METROLINE LIMITED—See ComfortDelGro Corporation Limited; *Int'l*, pg. 1713
METROLINK RATP DEV UK—See Regie Autonome des Transports Parisiens; *Int'l*, pg. 6253
METROLITHO—See Transcontinental Inc.; *Int'l*, pg. 7897
METROLOGIC ASIA (PTE) LTD.—See Honeywell International Inc.; *U.S. Public*, pg. 1050
METROLOGIC DO BRASIL LTDA.—See Honeywell International Inc.; *U.S. Public*, pg. 1050
METROLOGIC GROUP GMBH—See Sandvik AB; *Int'l*, pg. 6529
METROLOGIC GROUP ITALIA S.R.L.—See Sandvik AB; *Int'l*, pg. 6529
METROLOGIC GROUP S.A.S.—See Sandvik AB; *Int'l*, pg. 6531
METROLOGIC GROUP SERVICES, INC.—See Sandvik AB; *Int'l*, pg. 6531
METROLOGIC GROUP SPAIN S.L.—See Sandvik AB; *Int'l*, pg. 6530
METROLOGIC INSTRUMENTS GMBH—See Honeywell International Inc.; *U.S. Public*, pg. 1050
METROLOGIC INSTRUMENTS, INC.—See Honeywell International Inc.; *U.S. Public*, pg. 1050
METROLOGIC JAPAN CO., LTD.—See Honeywell International Inc.; *U.S. Public*, pg. 1050
METRO LOGISTICS GERMANY GMBH—See Metro AG; *Int'l*, pg. 4858
METROLOG SP. Z O.O.—See CEZ, a.s.; *Int'l*, pg. 1428
METROLOGY HELLAS S.A.—See SPACE HELLAS SA; *Int'l*, pg. 7123
METROL SPRINGS LTD.—See Beijer Alma AB; *Int'l*, pg. 943
METRO LUMBER WHOLESALE CO. INC.; *U.S. Private*, pg. 2685
METRO MACHINE CORP.—See General Dynamics Corporation; *U.S. Public*, pg. 916
METRO MACHINE & ENGINEERING CORP.—See Doering Company, LLC; *U.S. Private*, pg. 1253
METROMAIL LIMITED—See Saga plc; *Int'l*, pg. 6477
METRO MAINTENANCE SERVICE SYSTEMS, INC.—See Paris Maintenance Co. Inc.; *U.S. Private*, pg. 3095
METRO MALMO—See Kinnevik AB; *Int'l*, pg. 4182
METROMAP PTY. LTD.—See Aerometrex Limited; *Int'l*, pg. 181
METRO MARKETS GMBH—See Metro AG; *Int'l*, pg. 4858
METROMEDIA COMPANY; *U.S. Private*, pg. 2687
METRO MEDIA PUBLISHING PTY LTD—See Nine Entertainment Co. Holdings Limited; *Int'l*, pg. 5298
METRO MEDICAL CENTER L.L.C.—See Aster DM Healthcare Ltd.; *Int'l*, pg. 654
METRO MEDICAL SUPPLY INC.; *U.S. Private*, pg. 2686
METRO METALS NORTHWEST INC.; *U.S. Private*, pg. 2686
METRO MILWAUKEE AUTO AUCTION—See Cox Enterprises, Inc.; *U.S. Private*, pg. 1077
METRO MINING LIMITED; *Int'l*, pg. 4860
METROMIX PTY. LTD.—See Heidelberg Materials AG; *Int'l*, pg. 3311
METROMIX PTY. LTD.—See Holcim Ltd.; *Int'l*, pg. 3446
METRO MOLD & DESIGN - ICM PLASTICS—See Metro Mold & Design, Inc.; *U.S. Private*, pg. 2686
METRO MOLD & DESIGN, INC.; *U.S. Private*, pg. 2686
METROMONT CORPORATION; *U.S. Private*, pg. 2687
METRO MORDYC SWEDEN—See Modern Times Group MTG AB; *Int'l*, pg. 5015
METRO MOTOR GROUP; *U.S. Private*, pg. 2686
METRON-ATHENE, INC.—See Metron Technology Ltd.; *Int'l*, pg. 4862
METRONATIONAL CORPORATION; *U.S. Private*, pg. 2687
METRON AVIATION, INC.—See Airbus SE; *Int'l*, pg. 244
METRON CONSTRUCTION CO. INC.; *U.S. Private*, pg. 2687
METRONET HOLDINGS, LLC—See Keystone Group, L.P.; *U.S. Private*, pg. 2299
METRONET (UK) LTD.—See Livingbridge EP LLP; *Int'l*, pg. 4532
METRO NEWSPAPER ADVERTISING SERVICES, INC.—See Gemini Communications; *U.S. Public*, pg. 1657
METRO NEWSPAPER ADVERTISING SERVICES, INC.—See Gemini Communications; *U.S. Private*, pg. 1657
METRO NEWSPAPERS—See Metro Publishing, Inc.; *U.S. Private*, pg. 2686
METRO NEWS SERVICE INC.; *U.S. Private*, pg. 2686
METRONIC ENGINEERING SDN. BHD.—See Metronic Global Berhad; *Int'l*, pg. 4863

METRONIC GLOBAL BERHAD; *Int'l*, pg. 4862
METRONIC ICARES SDN. BHD.—See Metronic Global Berhad; *Int'l*, pg. 4863
METRONIC SAS—See HF Company; *Int'l*, pg. 3374
METRONICS, INC.—See The Carlyle Johnson Machine Company, LLC; *U.S. Private*, pg. 4005
METRON INSTRUMENTS D.O.O.—See HORIBA Ltd; *Int'l*, pg. 3477
METRON MEDICAL AUSTRALIA PTY LIMITED—See Patterson Companies, Inc.; *U.S. Public*, pg. 1653
METRONOM AUTOMATION GMBH—See Atlas Copco AB; *Int'l*, pg. 683
METRONOME, INC.—See WAVE Technology Solutions Group; *U.S. Private*, pg. 4458
METRONOM EISENBAHNGESELLSCHAFT MBH—See Ferrovie dello Stato Italiane S.p.A.; *Int'l*, pg. 2645
METRONOME, LLC—See LOV Group Invest SAS; *Int'l*, pg. 4565
METRONOME POST AB—See LOV Group Invest SAS; *Int'l*, pg. 4565
METRONOME PRODUCTIONS A/S—See LOV Group Invest SAS; *Int'l*, pg. 4565
METRO-NOM GMBH—See Metro AG; *Int'l*, pg. 4858
METRON SUSTAINABLE SERVICES INC.—See Caisse de Depot et Placement du Quebec; *Int'l*, pg. 1255
METRON SUSTAINABLE SERVICES INC.—See Ontario Teachers' Pension Plan; *Int'l*, pg. 5590
METRON SUSTAINABLE SERVICES INC.—See Partners Group Holding AG; *Int'l*, pg. 5750
METRON TECHNOLOGY LTD.; *Int'l*, pg. 4862
METRON U.S., INC.—See Fortive Corporation; *U.S. Public*, pg. 871
METRO N.V.—See Vandemoortele N.V.; *Int'l*, pg. 8128
METRO ONE TELECOMMUNICATIONS, INC.; *U.S. Public*, pg. 1431
METRO ORLEANS DODGE CHRYSLER JEEP RAM; *Int'l*, pg. 4861
METRO PACIFIC INVESTMENTS CORPORATION; *Int'l*, pg. 4861
METRO PACIFIC TOLLWAYS CORPORATION—See Metro Pacific Investments Corporation; *Int'l*, pg. 4861
METRO PAKISTAN (PVT.) LIMITED—See Metro AG; *Int'l*, pg. 4858
METRO PAPER INDUSTRIES INC—See Kruger Inc.; *Int'l*, pg. 4308
METROPARENT WEST MAGAZINE—See Gannett Co., Inc.; *U.S. Public*, pg. 898
METRO PARK I, L.L.C.—See Blackstone Inc.; *U.S. Public*, pg. 356
METRO PARKING MANAGEMENT (PHILIPPINES) INC.—See Damansara Realty Berhad; *Int'l*, pg. 1955
METRO PARKING (M) SDN. BHD.—See Damansara Realty Berhad; *Int'l*, pg. 1955
METRO PARKING (S) PTE. LTD.—See Damansara Realty Berhad; *Int'l*, pg. 1955
METRO PARKING SYSTEMS INC—See Metropolitan Properties Systems; *U.S. Private*, pg. 2689
METROPARK USA, INC.; *U.S. Private*, pg. 2687
METRO PARK V, LLC—See Blackstone Inc.; *U.S. Public*, pg. 356
METRO PAVIA HEALTH SYSTEM, INC.; *U.S. Private*, pg. 2686
METRO PAVING CORPORATION; *U.S. Private*, pg. 2686
METRO PERFORMANCE GLASS LIMITED; *Int'l*, pg. 4861
METRO PHILADELPHIA—See Metro USA Inc.; *U.S. Private*, pg. 2686
METRO PHOENIX BANK; *U.S. Public*, pg. 1431
METROPLAST SA—See Burelle S.A.; *Int'l*, pg. 1222
METROPLEX ECONOMIC DEVELOPMENT CORP.; *U.S. Private*, pg. 2687
METROPLEX HARRIMAN CORP.—See Metroplex Holdings Inc.; *U.S. Private*, pg. 2687
METROPLEX HOLDINGS INC.; *U.S. Private*, pg. 2687
METROPLEX LONG ISLAND CORPORATION—See Metroplex Holdings Inc.; *U.S. Private*, pg. 2687
METROPLEX SURGICARE PARTNERS, LTD.—See Tenet Healthcare Corporation; *U.S. Public*, pg. 2011
METROPOL (CYPRUS) LIMITED—See METROPOL Group of Companies; *Int'l*, pg. 4863
METROPOLE TELEVISION SA; *Int'l*, pg. 4863
METROPOL GROUP D.D.—See NFD Holding d.d.; *Int'l*, pg. 5252
METROPOL GROUP OF COMPANIES; *Int'l*, pg. 4863
METROPOL INVESTMENT FINANCIAL COMPANY LTD.—See METROPOL Group of Companies; *Int'l*, pg. 4863
METROPOLIS BRAMSER LAB SERVICES (MTIUS) LIMITED—See Metropolis Healthcare Ltd.; *Int'l*, pg. 4863
METROPOLIS CAPITAL HOLDINGS LTD.; *Int'l*, pg. 4863
METROPOLIS HEALTHCARE GHANA LTD.—See Metropolis Healthcare Ltd.; *Int'l*, pg. 4863
METROPOLIS HEALTHCARE LANKA (PVT.) LIMITED—See Metropolis Healthcare Ltd.; *Int'l*, pg. 4863
METROPOLIS HEALTHCARE LTD.; *Int'l*, pg. 4863
METROPOLIS HEALTHCARE (TANZANIA) LTD.—See Metropolis Healthcare Ltd.; *Int'l*, pg. 4863

COMPANY NAME INDEX

METROPOLIS LABEL CORP.—See Metro Label Group, Inc.; *Int'l*, pg. 4860
METROPOLIS TECHNOLOGIES, INC.—See Eldridge Industries LLC; *U.S. Private*, pg. 1351
METROPOLITAN ALLOYS CORPORATION—See Mac Group Incorporated; *U.S. Private*, pg. 2531
METROPOLITANA MILANESE S.P.A.; *Int'l*, pg. 4864
METROPOLITAN AREA AGENCY ON AGING, INC.; *U.S. Private*, pg. 2687
METROPOLITAN ASPHALT, INC.—See Peter A. Basile Sons, Inc.; *U.S. Private*, pg. 3157
METROPOLITAN ASSOCIATION FOR RETARDED CITIZENS, INC.; *U.S. Private*, pg. 2688
METROPOLITAN ATLANTA RAPID TRANSIT AUTHORITY; *U.S. Private*, pg. 2688
METROPOLITAN BAKING COMPANY; *U.S. Private*, pg. 2688
METROPOLITAN BANK HOLDING CORP.; *U.S. Public*, pg. 1431
METROPOLITAN BANK & TRUST COMPANY; *Int'l*, pg. 4863
METROPOLITAN BRICK COMPANY PTY LTD—See Brickworks Limited; *Int'l*, pg. 1152
METROPOLITAN CABINET DISTRIBUTORS; *U.S. Private*, pg. 2688
METROPOLITAN CAPITAL ADVISORS, LTD.—See Marcus & Millichap, Inc.; *U.S. Public*, pg. 1365
METROPOLITAN CARD OPERATIONS (PTY) LTD.—See Momentum Group Limited; *Int'l*, pg. 5023
METROPOLITAN CASUALTY INSURANCE CO.—See MetLife, Inc.; *U.S. Public*, pg. 1431
METROPOLITAN CENTRAL KITCHEN LIMITED—See Century City International Holdings Ltd; *Int'l*, pg. 1418
METROPOLITAN CLUB; *U.S. Private*, pg. 2688
METROPOLITAN COLLECTIVE INVESTMENTS LTD.—See Momentum Group Limited; *Int'l*, pg. 5023
METROPOLITAN COMMITTEE ON ANTI-POVERTY OF SAN DIEGO COUNTY, INC.; *U.S. Private*, pg. 2687
METROPOLITAN CONTRACT CARPETS; *U.S. Private*, pg. 2688
METROPOLITAN CORPORATION; *U.S. Private*, pg. 2688
METROPOLITAN CRANIOFACIAL CENTER, P.A.—See Riverside Oral Surgery; *U.S. Private*, pg. 3445
THE METROPOLITAN DISTRICT; *U.S. Private*, pg. 4078
METROPOLITAN EDISON COMPANY—See FirstEnergy Corp.; *U.S. Public*, pg. 849
METROPOLITAN EMPLOYEES BENEFITS ASSOCIATION; *U.S. Private*, pg. 2688
METROPOLITAN ENTERTAINMENT & CONVENTION AUTHORITY; *U.S. Private*, pg. 2688
METROPOLITAN ENVIRONMENTAL SERVICES, INC.—See Carylon Corporation; *U.S. Private*, pg. 777
METROPOLITAN EUROPEAN TRANSPORT LIMITED; *Int'l*, pg. 4864
METROPOLITAN FOODS INC.; *U.S. Private*, pg. 2688
METROPOLITAN FOODS, INC.; *U.S. Private*, pg. 2688
METROPOLITAN FOODS—See Metropolitan Foods, Inc.; *U.S. Private*, pg. 2688
METROPOLITAN GENERAL INSURANCE CO.—See MetLife, Inc.; *U.S. Public*, pg. 1431
METROPOLITAN HEALTH CARE, INC.; *U.S. Private*, pg. 2688
METROPOLITAN HEALTH CORPORATE (PTY) LTD.—See Momentum Group Limited; *Int'l*, pg. 5023
METROPOLITAN HEALTH CORPORATE (PTY) LTD.—See Momentum Group Limited; *Int'l*, pg. 5023
METROPOLITAN HEALTH CORPORATE (PTY) LTD.—See Momentum Group Limited; *Int'l*, pg. 5023
METROPOLITAN HEALTH CORPORATE (PTY) LTD.—See Momentum Group Limited; *Int'l*, pg. 5023
METROPOLITAN HEALTH GROUP (PTY) LTD.—See Momentum Group Limited; *Int'l*, pg. 5023
METROPOLITAN HEALTH HOLDINGS (PTY) LTD.—See Momentum Group Limited; *Int'l*, pg. 5023
METROPOLITAN HEALTH NETWORKS, INC.—See Humana, Inc.; *U.S. Public*, pg. 1070
METROPOLITAN HEALTH (PTY) LTD.—See Momentum Group Limited; *Int'l*, pg. 5023
METROPOLITAN INDUSTRIES, INC.; *U.S. Private*, pg. 2688
METROPOLITAN INTERACTIVE, LTD.; *U.S. Private*, pg. 2688
METROPOLITAN JEWISH HEALTH SYSTEM; *U.S. Private*, pg. 2688
METROPOLITAN KNOXVILLE AIRPORT AUTHORITY; *U.S. Private*, pg. 2688
METROPOLITAN LESOTHO LTD.—See Momentum Group Limited; *Int'l*, pg. 5023
METROPOLITAN LESOTHO LTD.—See Momentum Group Limited; *Int'l*, pg. 5023
METROPOLITAN LESOTHO LTD.—See Momentum Group Limited; *Int'l*, pg. 5023
METROPOLITAN LESOTHO LTD.—See Momentum Group Limited; *Int'l*, pg. 5023
METROPOLITAN LIFE INSURANCE COMPANY OF HONG KONG LIMITED—See Pacific Century Group Holdings Limited; *Int'l*, pg. 5686
METROPOLITAN LIFE INSURANCE GHANA LTD.—See Momentum Group Limited; *Int'l*, pg. 5023
METROPOLITAN LIFE INSURANCE KENYA LIMITED—See Momentum Group Limited; *Int'l*, pg. 5023
METROPOLITAN LIFE LTD.—See Momentum Group Limited; *Int'l*, pg. 5023
METROPOLITAN LIFE (NAMIBIA) LTD.—See Momentum Group Limited; *Int'l*, pg. 5023
METROPOLITAN LIFE OF BOTSWANA LTD.—See Momentum Group Limited; *Int'l*, pg. 5024
METROPOLITAN LIFE SEGUROS DE VIDA, S.A.—See MetLife, Inc.; *U.S. Public*, pg. 1431
METROPOLITAN LIFE SEGUROS E PREVIDENCIA PRIVADA S.A.—See MetLife, Inc.; *U.S. Public*, pg. 1431
METROPOLITAN LIFE SOCIETATE DE ADMINISTRARE A UNUI FOND DE PENSII ADMINISTRAT PRIVAT S—See MetLife, Inc.; *U.S. Public*, pg. 1431
METROPOLITAN LIGHTING FIXTURE CO.—See Minka Lighting Inc.; *U.S. Private*, pg. 2742
METROPOLITAN LIMOUSINE, INC.—See Marcou Transportation Group LLC; *U.S. Private*, pg. 2572
METROPOLITAN LOGISTIC SERVICES INC.—See Mangino Holding Corp.; *U.S. Private*, pg. 2563
METROPOLITAN LOOSE LEAF—See The Union Group; *U.S. Private*, pg. 4129
METROPOLITAN LUMBER & HARDWARE; *U.S. Private*, pg. 2688
METROPOLITAN MARKET LLC; *U.S. Private*, pg. 2688
METROPOLITAN MECHANICAL CONTRACTORS, INC.—See APi Group Corporation; *Int'l*, pg. 514
METROPOLITAN MEDICAL PARTNERS, LLC—See UnitedHealth Group Incorporated; *U.S. Public*, pg. 2242
METROPOLITAN MEDICAL PRACTICE PLAN PC; *U.S. Private*, pg. 2688
METROPOLITAN METHODIST HOSPITAL, A METHODIST HOSPITAL FACILITY—See HCA Healthcare, Inc.; *U.S. Public*, pg. 1002
METROPOLITAN METHODIST HOSPITAL, A METHODIST HOSPITAL FACILITY—See Methodist Healthcare Ministries of South Texas, Inc.; *U.S. Private*, pg. 2684
METROPOLITAN METHODIST HOSPITAL—See HCA Healthcare, Inc.; *U.S. Public*, pg. 1002
METROPOLITAN METHODIST HOSPITAL—See Methodist Healthcare Ministries of South Texas, Inc.; *U.S. Private*, pg. 2684
METROPOLITAN METRO ASIA (MA ON SHAN) LIMITED—See Century City International Holdings Ltd; *Int'l*, pg. 1417
METROPOLITAN MOVING & STORAGE; *U.S. Private*, pg. 2688
THE METROPOLITAN MUSEUM OF ART; *U.S. Private*, pg. 4078
METROPOLITAN NEW JERSEY, LLC—See Tenet Healthcare Corporation; *U.S. Public*, pg. 2011
METROPOLITAN ODYSSEY LTD.—See Momentum Group Limited; *Int'l*, pg. 5024
METROPOLITAN OPERA ASSOCIATION, INC.; *U.S. Private*, pg. 2689
METROPOLITAN PAPER RECYCLING INC.; *U.S. Private*, pg. 2689
METROPOLITAN PIER & EXPOSITION AUTHORITY; *U.S. Private*, pg. 2689
METROPOLITAN POLICE SERVICE; *Int'l*, pg. 4864
METROPOLITAN PRINTING SERVICES, LLC—See Chatham Asset Management, LLC; *U.S. Private*, pg. 863
METROPOLITAN PROPERTIES AMERICA INCORPORATED; *U.S. Private*, pg. 2689
METROPOLITAN PROPERTIES SYSTEMS; *U.S. Private*, pg. 2689
METROPOLITAN-SAINT LOUIS SEWER DISTRICT INC.; *U.S. Private*, pg. 2690
METROPOLITAN SALES DISTRIBUTORS INCORPORATED; *U.S. Private*, pg. 2689
METROPOLITAN SIDING & WINDOWS; *U.S. Private*, pg. 2689
METROPOLITAN STEEL CORPORATION LIMITED; *Int'l*, pg. 4864
METROPOLITAN STEEL INDUSTRIES INC.; *U.S. Private*, pg. 2689
METROPOLITAN TELECOMMUNICATIONS, INC.; *U.S. Private*, pg. 2689
METROPOLITAN THEATRES CORPORATION; *U.S. Private*, pg. 2689
METROPOLITAN TRANSIT AUTHORITY OF HARRIS COUNTY; *U.S. Private*, pg. 2689
METROPOLITAN TRANSIT SYSTEM; *U.S. Private*, pg. 2689
METROPOLITAN TRANSPORTATION AUTHORITY; *U.S. Private*, pg. 2689
METROPOLITAN TRUCKING, INC.—See P.A.M. Transportation Services, Inc.; *U.S. Public*, pg. 1629
METROPOLITAN TRUCKING INC.—See P.A.M. Transportation Services, Inc.; *U.S. Public*, pg. 1629
METROPOLITAN TV SDN BHD—See Media Prima Berhad; *Int'l*, pg. 4771
METROPOLITAN UTILITIES DISTRICT; *U.S. Private*, pg. 2689
METROPOLITAN VALUATION SERVICES, INC.—See Jones Lang LaSalle Incorporated; *U.S. Public*, pg. 1205
METROPOLITAN WASHINGTON AIRPORTS AUTHORITY; *U.S. Private*, pg. 2689
THE METROPOLITAN WATER DISTRICT OF SOUTHERN CALIFORNIA INC.; *U.S. Private*, pg. 4078
METROPOLITAN WHOLESALE & RETAIL BEER; *U.S. Private*, pg. 2690
METROPOLITAN WINE CELLAR LIMITED—See Star Group Company Limited; *Int'l*, pg. 7174
METROPOLITAN WIRE CANADA, LTD.—See Emerson Electric Co.; *U.S. Public*, pg. 750
METROPOL (UK) LIMITED—See METROPOL Group of Companies; *Int'l*, pg. 4863
METROPOULOS & CO.; *U.S. Private*, pg. 2690
METROPOWER INC.; *U.S. Private*, pg. 2691
METRO PRINTED PRODUCTS, INC.; *U.S. Private*, pg. 2686
METRO (PRIVATE) LIMITED—See Metro Holdings Limited; *Int'l*, pg. 4860
METRO PROFESSIONAL PRODUCTS CO., LTD.—See Metro Systems Corporation Public Company Limited; *Int'l*, pg. 4861
METRO PROPERTIES CR S.R.O.—See Metro AG; *Int'l*, pg. 4858
METRO PROPERTIES GAYRIMENKUL YATIRIM A.S.—See Metro AG; *Int'l*, pg. 4858
METRO PROPERTY MANAGEMENT (CHANGZHOU) CO. LTD.—See Metro AG; *Int'l*, pg. 4859
METRO PUBLIC ADJUSTMENT, INC.; *U.S. Private*, pg. 2686
METRO PUBLISHING HONG KONG LIMITED—See Kinnevik AB; *Int'l*, pg. 4182
METRO PUBLISHING, INC.; *U.S. Private*, pg. 2686
METRO-PUCK COMICS NETWORK—See Gemini Communications; *U.S. Private*, pg. 1657
METRO RADIO—See Heinrich Bauer Verlag KG; *Int'l*, pg. 3324
METRO REALTY; *U.S. Private*, pg. 2686
METRO REINSURANCE N.V.—See Metro AG; *Int'l*, pg. 4859
METRO RETAIL STORES GROUP, INC.; *Int'l*, pg. 4861
METRO ROD LIMITED—See Franchise Brands plc; *Int'l*, pg. 2760
METRO SALES, INC.; *U.S. Private*, pg. 2686
METRO SERVICE GMBH—See Metro AG; *Int'l*, pg. 4858
METRO SERVICES PL SPOTKA Z OGRANICZONQ ODPOWIEDZIALNOSCIQ—See Metro AG; *Int'l*, pg. 4858
METRO SIGN & AWNING; *U.S. Private*, pg. 2686
METRO—See Northern Ireland Transport Holding Company; *Int'l*, pg. 5444
METROSOURCE PUBLISHING, INC.—See Davler Media Group, LLC; *U.S. Private*, pg. 1175
METRO SOURCING INTERNATIONAL LIMITED—See Metro AG; *Int'l*, pg. 4858
METRO SOURCING (SHANGHAI) CO., LTD.—See Metro AG; *Int'l*, pg. 4858
METROSPACES, INC.; *U.S. Public*, pg. 1431
METRO SPECIALTY SURGERY CENTER, LLC—See Tenet Healthcare Corporation; *U.S. Public*, pg. 2004
METROSPEC TECHNOLOGY LLC; *U.S. Private*, pg. 2691
METRO SPINNING LIMITED; *Int'l*, pg. 4861
METROSTAR SYSTEMS; *U.S. Private*, pg. 2691
METRO ST. LOUIS DIALYSIS - FLORISSANT, LLC—See Nautic Partners, LLC; *U.S. Private*, pg. 2870
METRO STOCKHOLM—See Kinnevik AB; *Int'l*, pg. 4182
METROSTUDY, INC.—See MidOcean Partners, LLP; *U.S. Private*, pg. 2717
METRO SUNDAY NEWSPAPERS—See Gemini Communications; *U.S. Private*, pg. 1657
METRO SUPPLY CHAIN GROUP INC.; *Int'l*, pg. 4861
METRO SURGERY CENTER, LLC—See Tenet Healthcare Corporation; *U.S. Public*, pg. 2011
METRO SYSTEMS CORPORATION PUBLIC COMPANY LIMITED; *Int'l*, pg. 4861
METRO SYSTEMS GMBH—See Metro AG; *Int'l*, pg. 4858
METRO SYSTEMS INC.—See Great Mill Rock LLC; *U.S. Private*, pg. 1766
METRO SYSTEMS ROMANIA S.R.L.—See Metro AG; *Int'l*, pg. 4858
METROT D.O.O.—See Metalac a.d.; *Int'l*, pg. 4845
METRO THERAPY, INC.—See Revelstoke Capital Partners LLC; *U.S. Private*, pg. 3413
METRO THERM AB—See NIBE Industrier AB; *Int'l*, pg. 5261
METRO THERM A/S—See NIBE Industrier AB; *Int'l*, pg. 5261
METRO TICARI VE MALI YATIRIMLAR HOLDING A.S.; *Int'l*, pg. 4861
METRO TINT—See Solar Art Window Film, Inc.; *U.S. Private*, pg. 3707
METRO TITLE, LLC—See D.R. Horton, Inc.; *U.S. Public*, pg. 620
METRO TOOL & DIE LIMITED; *Int'l*, pg. 4861
METRO TRAILER LEASING INC.; *U.S. Private*, pg. 2686
METRO TRAINING SERVICES LTD.—See The Colonial Motor Company Limited; *Int'l*, pg. 7635

METRO TRAILER LEASING INC.

CORPORATE AFFILIATIONS

METRO TRAINS MELBOURNE PTY. LTD.—See MTR Corporation Limited; *Int'l*, pg. 5072
METRO USA INC.; *U.S. Private*, pg. 2686
METROVACESA, S.A.; *Int'l*, pg. 4864
METRO VALLEY PAINTING CORP.; *U.S. Private*, pg. 2686
METRO VENDING SERVICE, INC.—See Continental Services, Inc.; *U.S. Private*, pg. 1031
METRO WAREHOUSE MANAGEMENT (HANGZHOU) CO. LTD.—See Metro AG; *Int'l*, pg. 4858
METRO WAREHOUSE MANAGEMENT (TAIZHOU) CO. LTD.—See Metro AG; *Int'l*, pg. 4859
METRO WAREHOUSE MANAGEMENT (YANTAI) CO., LIMITED—See Metro AG; *Int'l*, pg. 4858
METRO WAREHOUSE MANAGEMENT (ZIBO) CO., LTD.—See Metro AG; *Int'l*, pg. 4858
METRO WASTE AUTHORITY; *U.S. Private*, pg. 2686
METRO WASTEWATER RECLAMATION DISTRICT; *U.S. Private*, pg. 2687
METRO WELLNESS AND COMMUNITY CENTERS; *U.S. Private*, pg. 2687
METROWEST DAILY NEWS—See Gannett Co., Inc.; *U.S. Public*, pg. 902
METROWEST HOMECARE & HOSPICE, LLC—See Tenet Healthcare Corporation; *U.S. Public*, pg. 2004
METROWEST IMAGING CENTER, LLC—See Akumin, Inc.; *U.S. Public*, pg. 70
METRO WHOLESALE MYANMAR LTD.—See Metro AG; *Int'l*, pg. 4858
METRO WIRE & CABLE CO; *U.S. Private*, pg. 2687
METROXPRESS DENMARK A/S—See TX Group AG; *Int'l*, pg. 7991
METRO YATIRIM ORTAKLIGI AS; *Int'l*, pg. 4861
METRUM RESEARCH GROUP LLC; *U.S. Private*, pg. 2691
METRYX, LTD.—See Lam Research Corporation; *U.S. Public*, pg. 1290
METSA BOARD AANEKOSKI—See Metsaliitto Osuuskunta; *Int'l*, pg. 4864
METSA BOARD BENELUX B.V.—See Metsaliitto Osuuskunta; *Int'l*, pg. 4864
METSA BOARD BENELUX N.V./S.A.—See Metsaliitto Osuuskunta; *Int'l*, pg. 4864
METSA BOARD CORPORATION—See Metsaliitto Osuuskunta; *Int'l*, pg. 4864
METSA BOARD OYJ—See Metsaliitto Osuuskunta; *Int'l*, pg. 4865
METSA BOARD SWEDEN AB—See Metsaliitto Osuuskunta; *Int'l*, pg. 4864
METSA FOREST EESTI AS—See Metsaliitto Osuuskunta; *Int'l*, pg. 4865
METSA FOREST LATVIA SIA—See Metsaliitto Osuuskunta; *Int'l*, pg. 4865
METSA FOREST OY—See Metsaliitto Osuuskunta; *Int'l*, pg. 4865
METSA FOREST SVERIGE AB—See Metsaliitto Osuuskunta; *Int'l*, pg. 4865
METSA GROUP FINANCIAL SERVICES LTD.—See Metsaliitto Osuuskunta; *Int'l*, pg. 4865
METSALIITTO OSUUSKUNTA; *Int'l*, pg. 4864
METSA TISSUE A/S—See Metsaliitto Osuuskunta; *Int'l*, pg. 4865
METSA TISSUE CORPORATION—See Metsaliitto Osuuskunta; *Int'l*, pg. 4865
METSA TISSUE LTD.—See Metsaliitto Osuuskunta; *Int'l*, pg. 4865
METSA WOOD BACO PRODUCTION S.R.L.—See Metsaliitto Osuuskunta; *Int'l*, pg. 4865
METSA WOOD CZ S.R.O.—See Metsaliitto Osuuskunta; *Int'l*, pg. 4865
METSA WOOD DEUTSCHLAND GMBH—See Metsaliitto Osuuskunta; *Int'l*, pg. 4865
METSA WOOD HOLLAND B.V.—See Metsaliitto Osuuskunta; *Int'l*, pg. 4865
METSA WOOD IBERICA S.L.U.—See Metsaliitto Osuuskunta; *Int'l*, pg. 4865
METSA WOOD OSTERREICH GESMBH—See Metsaliitto Osuuskunta; *Int'l*, pg. 4865
METSA WOOD SCHWEIZ AG—See Metsaliitto Osuuskunta; *Int'l*, pg. 4865
METSA WOOD SLOVENSKO S.R.O.—See Metsaliitto Osuuskunta; *Int'l*, pg. 4865
METSA WOOD—See Metsaliitto Osuuskunta; *Int'l*, pg. 4865
METSA WOOD USA INC.—See Metsaliitto Osuuskunta; *Int'l*, pg. 4865
METSEC PLC—See voestalpine AG; *Int'l*, pg. 8293
METSO AUTOMATION CANADA LTD—See Valmet Oyj; *Int'l*, pg. 8119
METSO AUTOMATION PORTUGAL LDA—See Valmet Oyj; *Int'l*, pg. 8119
METSO AUTOMATION S.A./N.V.—See Valmet Oyj; *Int'l*, pg. 8119
METSO AUTOMATION USA INC.—See Valmet Oyj; *Int'l*, pg. 8119
METSO BRASIL INDUSTRIA E COMERCIO LTDA.—See Valmet Oyj; *Int'l*, pg. 8119
METSO BRAZIL INDUSTRIA E COMERCIO LTDA.—See Metso Oyj; *Int'l*, pg. 4865

METSO BULGARIA EOOD—See Metso Oyj; *Int'l*, pg. 4865
METSO CAPITAL OY—See Valmet Oyj; *Int'l*, pg. 8119
METSO CHILE—See Valmet Oyj; *Int'l*, pg. 8119
METSO COPPERSTATE INC.—See Metso Oyj; *Int'l*, pg. 4867
METSO CORPORATION STOCK PREPARATION—See Valmet Oyj; *Int'l*, pg. 8119
METSO DENMARK A/S—See Valmet Oyj; *Int'l*, pg. 8119
METSO ENDRESS+HAUSER OY—See Endress+Hauser (International) Holding AG; *Int'l*, pg. 2408
METSO ENDRESS+HAUSER OY—See Valmet Oyj; *Int'l*, pg. 8119
METSO FRANCE SAS—See Valmet Oyj; *Int'l*, pg. 8119
METSO FZE (DUBAI)—See Valmet Oyj; *Int'l*, pg. 8119
METSO GERMANY GMBH - DUSSELDORF—See Metso Oyj; *Int'l*, pg. 4865
METSO GERMANY GMBH—See Metso Oyj; *Int'l*, pg. 4865
METSO INDIA PRIVATE LTD—See Metso Oyj; *Int'l*, pg. 4865
METSO INDIA PVT. LTD.—See Valmet Oyj; *Int'l*, pg. 8119
METSO MADEN TEKNOLOJILERI ANONIM SIRKETI—See Metso Oyj; *Int'l*, pg. 4865
METSO MEXICO S.A. DE C.V.—See Valmet Oyj; *Int'l*, pg. 8119
METSO MINERALS (ALGERIE) EURL—See Metso Oyj; *Int'l*, pg. 4865
METSO MINERALS (ARGENTINA) S.A.—See Metso Oyj; *Int'l*, pg. 4865
METSO MINERALS (AUSTRALIA) LIMITED - ARNDELL PARK—See Metso Oyj; *Int'l*, pg. 4865
METSO MINERALS (AUSTRALIA) LIMITED - CARRINGTON—See Metso Oyj; *Int'l*, pg. 4866
METSO MINERALS (AUSTRALIA) LIMITED - EAGLE FARM—See Metso Oyj; *Int'l*, pg. 4866
METSO MINERALS (AUSTRALIA) LIMITED—See Metso Oyj; *Int'l*, pg. 4865
METSO MINERALS AUSTRIA—See Metso Oyj; *Int'l*, pg. 4866
METSO MINERALS (BRASIL) LTDA.—See Metso Oyj; *Int'l*, pg. 4866
METSO MINERALS (BRASIL) LTDA.—See Metso Oyj; *Int'l*, pg. 4866
METSO MINERALS CANADA INC.—See Metso Oyj; *Int'l*, pg. 4866
METSO MINERALS CANADA INC.—See Metso Oyj; *Int'l*, pg. 4866
METSO MINERALS CANADA INC.—See Metso Oyj; *Int'l*, pg. 4866
METSO MINERALS (CHILE) SA—See Metso Oyj; *Int'l*, pg. 4866
METSO MINERALS CISA S.A.—See Metso Oyj; *Int'l*, pg. 4867
METSO MINERALS (CZECH REPUBLIC) S.R.O—See Metso Oyj; *Int'l*, pg. 4866
METSO MINERALS DIS TICARET LIMITED SIRKETI—See Metso Oyj; *Int'l*, pg. 4866
METSO MINERALS (DORDRECHT) B.V.—See Metso Oyj; *Int'l*, pg. 4866
METSO MINERALS ESPANA SA—See Metso Oyj; *Int'l*, pg. 4866
METSO MINERALS FINLAND OY AB—See Metso Oyj; *Int'l*, pg. 4866
METSO MINERALS FINLAND OY—See Metso Oyj; *Int'l*, pg. 4866
METSO MINERALS FINLAND OY—See Metso Oyj; *Int'l*, pg. 4866
METSO MINERALS FRANCE—See Metso Oyj; *Int'l*, pg. 4866
METSO MINERALS GHANA LTD.—See Metso Oyj; *Int'l*, pg. 4867
METSO MINERALS (INDIA) PVT. LTD. - HYDERABAD—See Metso Oyj; *Int'l*, pg. 4865
METSO MINERALS (INDIA) PVT. LTD. - KOLKATA—See Metso Oyj; *Int'l*, pg. 4865
METSO MINERALS INDUSTRIES, INC. - BIRMINGHAM—See Metso Oyj; *Int'l*, pg. 4867
METSO MINERALS INDUSTRIES, INC. - CANONSBURG—See Metso Oyj; *Int'l*, pg. 4867
METSO MINERALS INDUSTRIES, INC. - COLORADO SPRINGS—See Metso Oyj; *Int'l*, pg. 4867
METSO MINERALS INDUSTRIES, INC. - DANVILLE—See Metso Oyj; *Int'l*, pg. 4867
METSO MINERALS INDUSTRIES, INC.—See Metso Oyj; *Int'l*, pg. 4867
METSO MINERALS INDUSTRIES, INC. - YORK—See Metso Oyj; *Int'l*, pg. 4867
METSO MINERALS (ITALY) SPA—See Metso Oyj; *Int'l*, pg. 4866
METSO MINERALS JAPAN CO. LTD—See Metso Oyj; *Int'l*, pg. 4867
METSO MINERALS (JOHANNESBURG) (PTY) LTD.—See Metso Oyj; *Int'l*, pg. 4866
METSO MINERALS (MEXICO) SA DE CV—See Metso Oyj; *Int'l*, pg. 4866
METSO MINERALS (NORWAY) AS—See Metso Oyj; *Int'l*, pg. 4866
METSO MINERALS OY—See Metso Oyj; *Int'l*, pg. 4865
METSO MINERALS (PHILIPPINES) INC.—See Metso Oyj; *Int'l*, pg. 4866

METSO MINERALS (POLAND) SP. Z O.O.—See Metso Oyj; *Int'l*, pg. 4866
METSO MINERALS (PORTUGAL) LDA—See Metso Oyj; *Int'l*, pg. 4866
METSO MINERALS S.A.—See Metso Oyj; *Int'l*, pg. 4867
METSO MINERALS (SINGAPORE) PTE LTD—See Metso Oyj; *Int'l*, pg. 4866
METSO MINERALS (SOUTH AFRICA) PTY. LTD.—See Metso Oyj; *Int'l*, pg. 4866
METSO MINERALS S.R.O.—See Metso Oyj; *Int'l*, pg. 4867
METSO MINERALS (SWEDEN) AB - ERSMARK—See Metso Oyj; *Int'l*, pg. 4866
METSO MINERALS (SWEDEN) AB - KIRUNA—See Metso Oyj; *Int'l*, pg. 4866
METSO MINERALS (SWEDEN) AB - MOLNLYCKE—See Metso Oyj; *Int'l*, pg. 4866
METSO MINERALS (SWEDEN) AB—See Metso Oyj; *Int'l*, pg. 4866
METSO MINERALS (THAILAND) CO. LTD—See Metso Oyj; *Int'l*, pg. 4866
METSO MINERALS (TIANJIN) CO., LTD.—See Metso Oyj; *Int'l*, pg. 4866
METSO MINERALS (TIANJIN) INTERNATIONAL TRADE CO., LTD.—See Metso Oyj; *Int'l*, pg. 4866
METSO MINERALS (UK) LTD. - SHEPTON MALLET—See Metso Oyj; *Int'l*, pg. 4866
METSO MINERALS (UK) LTD.—See Metso Oyj; *Int'l*, pg. 4866
METSO MINERALS (ZAMBIA) LTD.—See Metso Oyj; *Int'l*, pg. 4866
METSO MINERALS (ZIMBABWE) (PTY.) LTD.—See Metso Oyj; *Int'l*, pg. 4866
METSO MONGOLIA LLC—See Metso Oyj; *Int'l*, pg. 4867
METSO ND ENGINEERING (PTY) LTD—See Valmet Oyj; *Int'l*, pg. 8119
METSO OUTOTEC MOROCCO LLC—See Metso Oyj; *Int'l*, pg. 4867
METSO OUTOTEC NEW MATERIAL TECHNOLOGY (SHANGHAI) CO., LTD.—See Metso Oyj; *Int'l*, pg. 4867
METSO OYJ; *Int'l*, pg. 4865
METSO PERU SA—See Valmet Oyj; *Int'l*, pg. 8119
METSO ROMANIA S.R.L.—See Metso Oyj; *Int'l*, pg. 4867
METSO SHARED SERVICES OY—See Valmet Oyj; *Int'l*, pg. 8119
METSO SVENSKA AB—See Valmet Oyj; *Int'l*, pg. 8119
METSO SWEDEN AB—See Valmet Oyj; *Int'l*, pg. 8119
METSO (UKRAINE) LLC—See Valmet Oyj; *Int'l*, pg. 8118
METSO VIETNAM CO. LTD—See Valmet Oyj; *Int'l*, pg. 8119
METSOVO BAKING COMPANY; *U.S. Private*, pg. 2691
METSS LTD.—See Cakovecki Milinovi d.d.; *Int'l*, pg. 1260
METSUN JACKSON NJ SENIOR LIVING, LLC—See Welltower Inc.; *U.S. Public*, pg. 2348
METSUN LEAWOOD KS SENIOR LIVING, LLC—See Welltower Inc.; *U.S. Public*, pg. 2348
METTE MUNK A/S—See ARYZTA AG; *Int'l*, pg. 589
METTER & CO.—See Baratz & Associates, PA; *U.S. Private*, pg. 471
METTERS INDUSTRIES, INC.; *U.S. Private*, pg. 2691
METTEXIN SA; *Int'l*, pg. 4868
THE METT GROUP; *Int'l*, pg. 7666
METTLER-TOLEDO AB—See Mettler-Toledo International, Inc.; *U.S. Public*, pg. 1432
METTLER-TOLEDO AG-ANALYTICAL INSTRUMENTS—See Mettler-Toledo International, Inc.; *U.S. Public*, pg. 1432
METTLER-TOLEDO AG—See Mettler-Toledo International, Inc.; *U.S. Public*, pg. 1432
METTLER-TOLEDO (ALBSTADT) GMBH—See Mettler-Toledo International, Inc.; *U.S. Public*, pg. 1432
METTLER TOLEDO ANALYSE INDUSTRIELLE S.A.R.L.—See Mettler-Toledo International, Inc.; *U.S. Public*, pg. 1432
METTLER-TOLEDO A/S—See Mettler-Toledo International, Inc.; *U.S. Public*, pg. 1432
METTLER-TOLEDO A/S—See Mettler-Toledo International, Inc.; *U.S. Public*, pg. 1432
METTLER-TOLEDO AUTOCHEM, INC.—See Mettler-Toledo International, Inc.; *U.S. Public*, pg. 1432
METTLER-TOLEDO B.V.—See Mettler-Toledo International, Inc.; *U.S. Public*, pg. 1432
METTLER-TOLEDO CARGOSCAN AS—See Mettler-Toledo International, Inc.; *U.S. Public*, pg. 1432
METTLER-TOLEDO (CHANGZHOU) PRECISION INSTRUMENTS LTD.—See Mettler-Toledo International, Inc.; *U.S. Public*, pg. 1432
METTLER-TOLEDO (CHANGZHOU) SCALE & SYSTEM LTD.—See Mettler-Toledo International, Inc.; *U.S. Public*, pg. 1432
METTLER-TOLEDO D.O.O.—See Mettler-Toledo International, Inc.; *U.S. Public*, pg. 1433
METTLER-TOLEDO GARVENS GMBH—See Mettler-Toledo International, Inc.; *U.S. Public*, pg. 1432
METTLER-TOLEDO GES.M.B.H.—See Mettler-Toledo International, Inc.; *U.S. Public*, pg. 1432
METTLER-TOLEDO GMBH—See Mettler-Toledo International, Inc.; *U.S. Public*, pg. 1432

COMPANY NAME INDEX MEXICAN GOVERNMENT TOURISM OFFICES

Company Index

METTLER-TOLEDO (HK) LTD.—See Mettler-Toledo International, Inc.; *U.S. Public*, pg. 1432
METTLER-TOLEDO HOLDING AG—See Mettler-Toledo International, Inc.; *U.S. Public*, pg. 1432
METTLER-TOLEDO INC.—See Mettler-Toledo International, Inc.; *U.S. Public*, pg. 1432
METTLER-TOLEDO INC.—See Mettler-Toledo International, Inc.; *U.S. Public*, pg. 1432
METTLER-TOLEDO IND. E COM. LTDA.—See Mettler-Toledo International, Inc.; *U.S. Public*, pg. 1432
METTLER-TOLEDO INDIA PRIVATE LIMITED—See Mettler-Toledo International, Inc.; *U.S. Public*, pg. 1432
METTLER-TOLEDO INGOLD, INC.—See Mettler-Toledo International, Inc.; *U.S. Public*, pg. 1432
METTLER-TOLEDO INGOLD INC.—See Mettler-Toledo International, Inc.; *U.S. Public*, pg. 1432
METTLER TOLEDO INSTRUMENTS (SHANGHAI) LTD.—See Mettler-Toledo International, Inc.; *U.S. Public*, pg. 1432
METTLER-TOLEDO INTERNATIONAL FINANCE, INC.—See Mettler-Toledo International, Inc.; *U.S. Public*, pg. 1432
METTLER-TOLEDO INTERNATIONAL, INC.; *U.S. Public*, pg. 1432
METTLER-TOLEDO INTERNATIONAL TRADING (SHANGHAI) CO., LTD.—See Mettler-Toledo International, Inc.; *U.S. Public*, pg. 1432
METTLER-TOLEDO (KOREA) LTD.—See Mettler-Toledo International, Inc.; *U.S. Public*, pg. 1432
METTLER-TOLEDO LOGISTIK GMBH—See Mettler-Toledo International, Inc.; *U.S. Public*, pg. 1433
METTLER-TOLEDO LTD.—See Mettler-Toledo International, Inc.; *U.S. Public*, pg. 1433
METTLER-TOLEDO LTD.—See Mettler-Toledo International, Inc.; *U.S. Public*, pg. 1433
METTLER-TOLEDO MANAGEMENT HOLDING DEUTSCHLAND GMBH—See Mettler-Toledo International, Inc.; *U.S. Public*, pg. 1433
METTLER-TOLEDO (M) SDN. BHD.—See Mettler-Toledo International, Inc.; *U.S. Public*, pg. 1432
METTLER-TOLEDO ONLINE GMBH—See Mettler-Toledo International, Inc.; *U.S. Public*, pg. 1433
METTLER-TOLEDO PHILIPPINES INC.—See Mettler-Toledo International, Inc.; *U.S. Public*, pg. 1433
METTLER-TOLEDO PROCESS ANALYTICS, INC.—See Mettler-Toledo International, Inc.; *U.S. Public*, pg. 1433
METTLER-TOLEDO PRODUCT INSPECTION B.V.—See Mettler-Toledo International, Inc.; *U.S. Public*, pg. 1433
METTLER-TOLEDO - PRODUCT INSPECTION—See Mettler-Toledo International, Inc.; *U.S. Public*, pg. 1432
METTLER-TOLEDO S.A. DE C.V.—See Mettler-Toledo International, Inc.; *U.S. Public*, pg. 1433
METTLER-TOLEDO SAE—See Mettler-Toledo International, Inc.; *U.S. Public*, pg. 1433
METTLER-TOLEDO SAFELINE LIMITED—See Mettler-Toledo International, Inc.; *U.S. Public*, pg. 1433
METTLER-TOLEDO SAFELINE X-RAY LIMITED—See Mettler-Toledo International, Inc.; *U.S. Public*, pg. 1433
METTLER-TOLEDO SALES INTERNATIONAL GMBH—See Mettler-Toledo International, Inc.; *U.S. Public*, pg. 1433
METTLER-TOLEDO S.A.S.—See Mettler-Toledo International, Inc.; *U.S. Public*, pg. 1433
METTLER-TOLEDO (SCHWEIZ) GMBH—See Mettler-Toledo International, Inc.; *U.S. Public*, pg. 1432
METTLER-TOLEDO S.P.A.—See Mettler-Toledo International, Inc.; *U.S. Public*, pg. 1433
METTLER-TOLEDO SPOL. S.R.O.—See Mettler-Toledo International, Inc.; *U.S. Public*, pg. 1433
METTLER-TOLEDO (S) PTE LTD.—See Mettler-Toledo International, Inc.; *U.S. Public*, pg. 1432
METTLER-TOLEDO SP. Z.O.O.—See Mettler-Toledo International, Inc.; *U.S. Public*, pg. 1433
METTLER-TOLEDO S.R.O.—See Mettler-Toledo International, Inc.; *U.S. Public*, pg. 1433
METTLER-TOLEDO TECHNOLOGIES (CHINA) CO., LTD.—See Mettler-Toledo International, Inc.; *U.S. Public*, pg. 1433
METTLER-TOLEDO (THAILAND) LTD.—See Mettler-Toledo International, Inc.; *U.S. Public*, pg. 1432
METTLER-TOLEDO THORNTON INC.—See Mettler-Toledo International, Inc.; *U.S. Public*, pg. 1433
METTLER-TOLEDO TR OLCUM ALETLERI TICARET SATIS VS SERVIS HIZMETLERI ANONIM SIRKETI—See Mettler-Toledo International, Inc.; *U.S. Public*, pg. 1433
METTLER-TOLEDO UK HOLDINGS LIMITED—See Mettler-Toledo International, Inc.; *U.S. Public*, pg. 1433
METTLER-TOLEDO (XINJIANG) ELECTRONIC SCALE LTD.—See Mettler-Toledo International, Inc.; *U.S. Public*, pg. 1432
METTON AMERICA, INC.—See Sojitz Corporation; *Int'l*, pg. 7064
METTOWEE LUMBER & PLASTIC CO., INC.—See Telescope Casual Furniture Inc.; *U.S. Private*, pg. 3961
METTRUM HEALTH CORP.—See Canopy Growth Corporation; *Int'l*, pg. 1298
METTS CORPORATION—See Honda Motor Co., Ltd.; *Int'l*, pg. 3463
MET T&S LTD.—See Maire Tecnimont S.p.A.; *Int'l*, pg. 4652
METUCHEN COMMUNITY SERVICES CORPORATION; *U.S. Private*, pg. 2691
METUCHEN SAVINGS BANK; *U.S. Private*, pg. 2691
METUS D.O.O.—See Sdiptech AB; *Int'l*, pg. 6659
METWEST REALTY ADVISORS LLC; *U.S. Private*, pg. 2691
METWOOD, INC.; *U.S. Public*, pg. 1433
METZ AERIALS GMBH & CO. KG—See Rosenbauer International AG; *Int'l*, pg. 6399
METZ AERIALS MANAGEMENT GMBH—See Rosenbauer International AG; *Int'l*, pg. 6400
METZ AND ASSOCIATES, LLC—See Comvest Group Holdings LLC; *U.S. Private*, pg. 1007
METZ & ASSOCIATES, LTD.—See Metz Enterprises Inc.; *U.S. Private*, pg. 2691
METZELER AUTOMOTIVE PROFILES INDIA PVT. LTD.—See Toyoda Gosei Co., Ltd.; *Int'l*, pg. 7862
METZELER AUTOMOTIVE PROFILE SYSTEMS GMBH—See Cooper-Standard Holdings Inc.; *U.S. Public*, pg. 574
METZEN S.A R.L—See OSWALD METZEN GmbH; *Int'l*, pg. 5655
METZ ENTERPRISES INC.; *U.S. Private*, pg. 2691
METZGAR CONVEYOR COMPANY; *U.S. Private*, pg. 2691
METZGER ASSOCIATES; *U.S. Private*, pg. 2691
METZGERMEISTER & RESEARCH CORP.; *U.S. Private*, pg. 2691
METZGER & WILLARD, INC.—See V & A Consulting Engineers, Inc.; *U.S. Private*, pg. 4327
METZLER ASSET MANAGEMENT (JAPAN) LTD.—See B. Metzler seel. Sohn & Co. Holding AG; *Int'l*, pg. 788
METZLER GMBH & CO. KG—See Wurth Verwaltungsgesellschaft mbH; *Int'l*, pg. 8506
METZLER GMBH—See Wurth Verwaltungsgesellschaft mbH; *Int'l*, pg. 8506
METZLER IRELAND LIMITED—See B. Metzler seel. Sohn & Co. Holding AG; *Int'l*, pg. 788
METZLER NORTH AMERICA CORPORATION—See B. Metzler seel. Sohn & Co. Holding AG; *Int'l*, pg. 788
METZ WOIPPY CEDEO—See Compagnie de Saint-Gobain SA; *Int'l*, pg. 1724
MEUNIER PROMOTION—See BNP Paribas SA; *Int'l*, pg. 1092
MEURAL, INC.—See NETGEAR, Inc.; *U.S. Public*, pg. 1508
MEURER VERPACKUNGSSYSTEME GMBH—See Illinois Tool Works Inc.; *U.S. Public*, pg. 1109
MEUSELWITZ GUSS EISENGIESSEREI GMBH—See DIHAG Holding GmbH; *Int'l*, pg. 2124
MEVACO GMBH; *Int'l*, pg. 4868
MEVACO S.A.; *Int'l*, pg. 4868
MEVANAH REAL ESTATE KD LTD.; *Int'l*, pg. 4868
MEVAS BANK LIMITED—See Dah Sing Financial Holdings Limited; *Int'l*, pg. 1913
MEVION MEDICAL SYSTEMS, INC.; *U.S. Private*, pg. 2691
MEVIS MEDICAL SOLUTIONS AG—See Siemens Aktiengesellschaft; *Int'l*, pg. 6894
MEWAH COMMODITIES PTE LTD—See Mewah International Inc.; *Int'l*, pg. 4868
MEWAH DAIRIES SDN BHD—See Mewah International Inc.; *Int'l*, pg. 4868
MEWAH DATU SDN. BHD.—See Mewah International Inc.; *Int'l*, pg. 4868
MEWAH INTERNATIONAL INC.; *Int'l*, pg. 4868
MEWAH MARKETING PTE LTD.—See Mewah International Inc.; *Int'l*, pg. 4868
MEWAH OILS & FATS PTE LTD—See Mewah International Inc.; *Int'l*, pg. 4868
MEWAH-OILS SDN BHD—See Mewah International Inc.; *Int'l*, pg. 4868
MEWAHOLEO INDUSTRIES SDN BHD—See Mewah International Inc.; *Int'l*, pg. 4868
MEWAHOLEO MARKETING SDN BHD—See Mewah International Inc.; *Int'l*, pg. 4868
MEWAR HI-TECH ENGINEERING LIMITED; *Int'l*, pg. 4869
MEWAR POLYTEX LIMITED; *Int'l*, pg. 4869
MEWA S.A.; *Int'l*, pg. 4868
MEWBOURNE HOLDINGS INC.; *U.S. Private*, pg. 2691
MEWBOURNE OIL CO. INC.—See Mewbourne Holdings Inc.; *U.S. Private*, pg. 2691
MEWES ENTERTAINMENT GROUP GMBH—See DEAG Deutsche Entertainment AG; *Int'l*, pg. 1998
MEWESTA HYDRAULIK GMBH & CO. KG—See INDUS Holding AG; *Int'l*, pg. 3663
THE M.E. WILSON COMPANY, INC.; *U.S. Private*, pg. 4073
MEXALIT—See Grupo Empresarial Kaluz S.A. de C.V.; *Int'l*, pg. 3127
MEXAN LIMITED; *Int'l*, pg. 4869
MEXATRONIKA-TES LTD.—See Endress+Hauser (International) Holding AG; *Int'l*, pg. 2408
MEXCO ENERGY CORPORATION; *U.S. Public*, pg. 1433
MEXCOMM SDN. BHD.; *Int'l*, pg. 4869
MEXEDIA S.P.A.; *Int'l*, pg. 4869
MEXESS CO., LTD.—See Cresco, Ltd.; *Int'l*, pg. 1840
MEX HOLDINGS CO. LTD.; *Int'l*, pg. 4869
MEXIA PRINCIPAL HEALTHCARE LIMITED PARTNERSHIP—See Apollo Global Management, Inc.; *U.S. Public*, pg. 158
MEXICAN ACCENT, LLC—See Hormel Foods Corporation; *U.S. Public*, pg. 1054
MEXICANA DE AVIACION S.A. DE C.V.—See Grupo Posadas S.A.B. de C.V.; *Int'l*, pg. 3134
MEXICANA DE CALES, S.A. DE C.V.—See Promotora y Operadora de Infraestructura, S.A.B. de C.V.; *Int'l*, pg. 5996
MEXICANA DE COBRE, S.A. DE C.V.—See Grupo Mexico, S.A.B. de C.V.; *Int'l*, pg. 3133
MEXICANA DE GESTION DE AGUA S.A. DE C.V.—See Promotora y Operadora de Infraestructura, S.A.B. de C.V.; *Int'l*, pg. 5996
MEXICANA DE PAQUETERIA URGENTE, S.A.DE C.V.—See Senko Group Holdings Co., Ltd.; *Int'l*, pg. 6710
MEXICANA LOGISTICS, S.A. DE C.V.—See TFI International Inc.; *Int'l*, pg. 7586
MEXICAN AMERICAN OPPORTUNITY FOUNDATION; *U.S. Private*, pg. 2692
MEXICAN CHEESE PRODUCERS, INC.—See ALFA, S.A.B. de C.V.; *Int'l*, pg. 314
MEXICAN GOLD MINING CORP.; *Int'l*, pg. 4869
MEXICAN GOVERNMENT TOURISM OFFICES; *U.S. Private*, pg. 2692
MEXICAN RESTAURANTS, INC.—See Williston Holding Co., Inc.; *U.S. Public*, pg. 2372
MEXICAN SILICATES S.A. DE C.V.—See Gruppo Minerali Maffei S.p.A.; *Int'l*, pg. 3140
MEXICAN TOWN REAL ESTATE CO.—See CenTra, Inc.; *U.S. Private*, pg. 818
MEXICHEM AMERICA, INC.—See Grupo Empresarial Kaluz S.A. de C.V.; *Int'l*, pg. 3127
MEXICHEM ARGENTINA, S.A.—See Grupo Empresarial Kaluz S.A. de C.V.; *Int'l*, pg. 3127
MEXICHEM CID, S.A. DE C.V.—See Grupo Empresarial Kaluz S.A. de C.V.; *Int'l*, pg. 3127
MEXICHEM COLOMBIA, S.A.—See Grupo Empresarial Kaluz S.A. de C.V.; *Int'l*, pg. 3127
MEXICHEM COMPUESTOS, S.A. DE C.V.—See Grupo Empresarial Kaluz S.A. de C.V.; *Int'l*, pg. 3127
MEXICHEM COSTA RICA, S.A.—See Grupo Empresarial Kaluz S.A. de C.V.; *Int'l*, pg. 3127
MEXICHEM DERIVADOS COLOMBIA, S.A.—See Grupo Empresarial Kaluz S.A. de C.V.; *Int'l*, pg. 3127
MEXICHEM DERIVADOS, S.A. DE C.V.—See Grupo Empresarial Kaluz S.A. de C.V.; *Int'l*, pg. 3127
MEXICHEM EL SALVADOR, S.A.—See Grupo Empresarial Kaluz S.A. de C.V.; *Int'l*, pg. 3127
MEXICHEM FLUOR JAPAN LTD.—See Grupo Empresarial Kaluz S.A. de C.V.; *Int'l*, pg. 3127
MEXICHEM FLUOR LTD.—See Grupo Empresarial Kaluz S.A. de C.V.; *Int'l*, pg. 3127
MEXICHEM FLUOR, S.A. DE C.V.—See Grupo Empresarial Kaluz S.A. de C.V.; *Int'l*, pg. 3127
MEXICHEM FLUOR—See Grupo Empresarial Kaluz S.A. de C.V.; *Int'l*, pg. 3127
MEXICHEM FLUOR TAIWAN LIMITED—See Grupo Empresarial Kaluz S.A. de C.V.; *Int'l*, pg. 3127
MEXICHEM GUATEMALA, S.A.—See Grupo Empresarial Kaluz S.A. de C.V.; *Int'l*, pg. 3127
MEXICHEM HONDURAS, S.A.—See Grupo Empresarial Kaluz S.A. de C.V.; *Int'l*, pg. 3127
MEXICHEM NICARAGUA, S.A.—See Grupo Empresarial Kaluz S.A. de C.V.; *Int'l*, pg. 3127
MEXICHEM PANAMA, S.A.—See Grupo Empresarial Kaluz S.A. de C.V.; *Int'l*, pg. 3128
MEXICHEM QUIMIR—See Grupo Empresarial Kaluz S.A. de C.V.; *Int'l*, pg. 3128
MEXICHEM RESINAS COLOMBIA S.A.—See Grupo Empresarial Kaluz S.A. de C.V.; *Int'l*, pg. 3127
MEXICHEM RESINAS VINILICAS, S.A. DE C.V.—See Grupo Empresarial Kaluz S.A. de C.V.; *Int'l*, pg. 3128
MEXICHEM SALINERA DEL SUR, S.A. DE C.V.—See Grupo Empresarial Kaluz S.A. de C.V.; *Int'l*, pg. 3128
MEXICHEM SERVICIOS ADMINISTRATIVOS, S.A. DE C.V.—See Grupo Empresarial Kaluz S.A. de C.V.; *Int'l*, pg. 3128
MEXICHEM UK LTD—See Grupo Empresarial Kaluz S.A. de C.V.; *Int'l*, pg. 3128
MEXICO ASISTENCIA, S.A.—See MAPFRE S.A.; *Int'l*, pg. 4684
MEXICO BOTTLING SERVICES, S.A. DE C.V.—See Primo Water Corporation; *U.S. Public*, pg. 1718
THE MEXICO CITY PALM—See Palm Restaurant Group; *U.S. Private*, pg. 3080
MEXICO CORPORATION OF SHINSUNG AUTOMOTIVE CO,LTD.—See Shinsung Delta Tech Co., Ltd.; *Int'l*, pg. 6849
MEXICOHOSOKAWA MICRON DE MEXICO S.A. DE C.V.—See Hosokawa Micron Corporation; *Int'l*, pg. 3486
MEXICO KIN LONG S.A. DE C.A.—See Guangdong Kinlong Hardware Prdcts Co., Ltd.; *Int'l*, pg. 3157

MEXICAN GOVERNMENT TOURISM OFFICES

MEXICO MARINE CORPORATION OF SHINSUNG DELTATECH CO., LTD.—See Shinsung Delta Tech Co., Ltd.; *Int'l*, pg. 6849
MEXICO MONTERREY CORPORATION OF SHINSUNG DELTATECH CO., LTD.—See Shinsung Delta Tech Co., Ltd.; *Int'l*, pg. 6849
MEXICO SALES MADE EASY, INC.; *U.S. Private*, pg. 2692
MEXICO SONAVOX ELECTRONICS CO. S. DE R.L. DE C.V.—See Suzhou Sonavox Electronics Co., Ltd.; *Int'l*, pg. 7352
MEXICO TOURISM BOARD-LOS ANGELES—See Mexican Government Tourism Offices; *U.S. Private*, pg. 2692
MEXINOX TRADING S.A. DE C.V.—See ThyssenKrupp AG; *Int'l*, pg. 7730
MEX POLSKA S.A.; *Int'l*, pg. 4869
MEXPOL-TRADING SP. Z.O.O.—See Quaser Machine Tools, Inc.; *Int'l*, pg. 6157
MEXPOL WERKZEUGMASCHINEN GMBH—See A-TEC Industries AG; *Int'l*, pg. 21
MEXTAL B.V.—See TKH Group N.V.; *Int'l*, pg. 7764
MEXTYPSA—See Tecnica Y Proyectos S.A.; *Int'l*, pg. 7515
MEXUS GOLD US; *U.S. Public*, pg. 1433
MEXX PAZARLAMA INC.—See Eroglu Holding AS; *Int'l*, pg. 2496
MEY ALKOLLU ICKILER SANAYI VE TICARET A.S.—See Diageo plc; *Int'l*, pg. 2102
MEYCAR AUTOMOTIVE S.L.—See Wulf Gaertner Autoparts AG; *Int'l*, pg. 8502
MEYCO PRODUCTS INC.; *U.S. Private*, pg. 2692
MEYDA STAINED GLASS STUDIO & LIGHTING CORP.; *U.S. Private*, pg. 2692
MEY EDEN IL—See Eden International SA; *Int'l*, pg. 2307
MEYER APPAREL LTD; *Int'l*, pg. 4869
MEYER BROTHERS AUTOMOTIVE CO.; *U.S. Private*, pg. 2692
MEYER BURGER AG—See Meyer Burger Technology AG; *Int'l*, pg. 4869
MEYER BURGER AUTOMATION GMBH—See Meyer Burger Technology AG; *Int'l*, pg. 4869
MEYER BURGER CO. LTD—See Meyer Burger Technology AG; *Int'l*, pg. 4869
MEYER BURGER GLOBAL LTD—See Meyer Burger Technology AG; *Int'l*, pg. 4869
MEYER BURGER INDIA PRIVATE LTD—See Meyer Burger Technology AG; *Int'l*, pg. 4869
MEYER BURGER KK—See Meyer Burger Technology AG; *Int'l*, pg. 4869
MEYER BURGER TECHNOLOGY AG; *Int'l*, pg. 4869
MEYER BURGER TRADING (SHANGHAI) CO. LTD.—See Meyer Burger Technology AG; *Int'l*, pg. 4869
MEYER BURGER TRADING SHANGHAI CO. LTD.—See Meyer Burger Technology AG; *Int'l*, pg. 4869
MEYER CANADA INC.—See Meyer Tool Inc.; *U.S. Private*, pg. 2693
MEYERCORD REVENUE INC.—See SICPA Holding SA; *Int'l*, pg. 6882
MEYER DEVELOPMENT PTE. LTD.—See Sing Holdings Limited; *Int'l*, pg. 6938
MEYER EQUIPMENT, CO.; *U.S. Private*, pg. 2692
MEYER GMBH—See Hyster-Yale Materials Handling, Inc.; *U.S. Public*, pg. 1080
MEYER INDUSTRIES INC.; *U.S. Private*, pg. 2692
MEYER JABARA HOTELS, LLC; *U.S. Private*, pg. 2692
MEYER LABORATORY, INC.—See TruArc Partners, L.P.; *U.S. Private*, pg. 4245
MEYER LAMINATES, INC.—See Compagnie de Saint-Gobain SA; *Int'l*, pg. 1730
MEYER MANSION PTE. LTD.—See Hong Leong Investment Holdings Pte. Ltd.; *Int'l*, pg. 3468
MEYER MATERIAL COMPANY, LLC—See Holcim Ltd.; *Int'l*, pg. 3446
MEYER MAYOR AG—See Getzner Textil AG; *Int'l*, pg. 2954
MEYER & NAJEM INC.; *U.S. Private*, pg. 2692
MEYER NATURAL ANGUS, LLC; *U.S. Private*, pg. 2692
MEYER OIL CO.; *U.S. Private*, pg. 2692
MEYER PLASTICS INC.; *U.S. Private*, pg. 2692
MEYER PLC; *Int'l*, pg. 4870
MEYER PRODUCTS LLC—See Aebi Schmidt Holding AG; *Int'l*, pg. 170
MEYER PROPERTIES CORP.; *U.S. Private*, pg. 2692
MEYERS COLOUR COMPOUNDS LIMITED; *Int'l*, pg. 4870
MEYER SERVICE, INC.; *U.S. Private*, pg. 2692
MEYERS NORRIS PENNY LLP; *Int'l*, pg. 4870
MEYER SOUND LABORATORIES INC.; *U.S. Private*, pg. 2692
MEYERS PRINTING COMPANY INC.; *U.S. Private*, pg. 2693
MEYERS RESEARCH, LLC—See MidOcean Partners, LLP; *U.S. Private*, pg. 2717
MEYERS-REYNOLDS & ASSOCIATES, INC.—See Arthur J. Gallagher & Co.; *U.S. Public*, pg. 206
MEYER STEEL DRUM INC.; *U.S. Private*, pg. 2692
MEYERS TRANSPORT INC.; *Int'l*, pg. 4870
MEYER TOOL INC.; *U.S. Private*, pg. 2692

MEYER TOOL POLAND SP. Z. O. O.—See Meyer Tool Inc.; *U.S. Private*, pg. 2693
MEYER TURKU OY—See MEYER WERFT GmbH; *Int'l*, pg. 4870
MEYER VASTUS AB, OY—See NIBE Industrier AB; *Int'l*, pg. 5261
MEYER & WALLIS, INC.; *U.S. Private*, pg. 2692
MEYER & WALLIS, INC.—See Meyer & Wallis, Inc.; *U.S. Private*, pg. 2692
MEYER WERFT GMBH; *Int'l*, pg. 4870
MEYER WIRE & CABLE COMPANY, LLC; *U.S. Private*, pg. 2693
MEY ICKI SANAYI VE TICARET A.S.—See Diageo plc; *Int'l*, pg. 2102
MEYLE FRANCE S.A.R.L—See Wulf Gaertner Autoparts AG; *Int'l*, pg. 8502
MEYLER LLC—See MJ Hudson Group Plc; *Int'l*, pg. 5000
MEYLE UK LTD.—See Wulf Gaertner Autoparts AG; *Int'l*, pg. 8502
MEYLE USA—See Wulf Gaertner Autoparts AG; *Int'l*, pg. 8502
MEYN AMERICA, LLC—See Berkshire Hathaway Inc.; *U.S. Public*, pg. 303
MEYN FOOD PROCESSING TECHNOLOGY B.V.—See Berkshire Hathaway Inc.; *U.S. Public*, pg. 303
THE MEYOCKS GROUP; *U.S. Private*, pg. 4078
MEZ CRAFTS HUNGARY KFT.—See Aurelius Equity Opportunities SE & Co. KGaA; *Int'l*, pg. 709
MEZ CRAFTS LITHUANIA UAB—See Aurelius Equity Opportunities SE & Co. KGaA; *Int'l*, pg. 709
MEZ CRAFTS PORTUGAL LDA.—See Aurelius Equity Opportunities SE & Co. KGaA; *Int'l*, pg. 709
MEZ CRAFTS TEKSTIL ANONIM SIRKET—See Aurelius Equity Opportunities SE & Co. KGaA; *Int'l*, pg. 709
MEZ CRAFTS UK LTD.—See Aurelius Equity Opportunities SE & Co. KGaA; *Int'l*, pg. 709
MEZ FABRA SPAIN S.A.—See Aurelius Equity Opportunities SE & Co. KGaA; *Int'l*, pg. 709
MEZGER HEFTSYSTEME GMBH—See Illinois Tool Works Inc.; *U.S. Public*, pg. 1109
MEZ GMBH—See Aurelius Equity Opportunities SE & Co. KGaA; *Int'l*, pg. 709
MEZON STAINLESS STEEL FZCO—See Sumitomo Corporation; *Int'l*, pg. 7269
MEZOON CARGO—See Omar Zawawi Establishment LLC; *Int'l*, pg. 5561
MEZOON TRAVEL LLC—See Omar Zawawi Establishment LLC; *Int'l*, pg. 5561
MEZZAN HOLDING CO KSC; *Int'l*, pg. 4870
MEZZANINE CORPORATION—See Houlihan Lokey, Inc.; *U.S. Public*, pg. 1055
MEZZANINE WARE PROPRIETARY LIMITED—See Vodafone Group Plc; *Int'l*, pg. 8284
MEZZANINE FINANZIERUNGS AG—See UniCredit S.p.A.; *Int'l*, pg. 8040
MEZZAN SECURITY W.L.L—See Mezzan Holding Co KSC; *Int'l*, pg. 4870
MEZZION PHARMA CO., LTD.; *Int'l*, pg. 4870
MEZZOMEDIA INC.—See CJ Corporation; *Int'l*, pg. 1634
MEZZO S.A.—See LVMH Moet Hennessy Louis Vuitton SE; *Int'l*, pg. 4592
MEZZO S.A.—See Vivendi SE; *Int'l*, pg. 8266
MF.1 ADVERTISING BRANDING STRATEGY; *Int'l*, pg. 4870
M. FABRIKANT & SONS, INC.; *U.S. Private*, pg. 2526
MFA ENTERPRISES, INC.—See MFA Incorporated; *U.S. Private*, pg. 2693
MFA FINANCIAL, INC.; *U.S. Public*, pg. 1433
MFA INCORPORATED; *U.S. Private*, pg. 2693
MFA OIL BIOMASS LLC—See MFA Oil Company; *U.S. Private*, pg. 2693
MFA OIL COMPANY; *U.S. Private*, pg. 2693
M&F BANCORP, INC.; *U.S. Private*, pg. 2524
M&F BANCORP, INC.; *U.S. Public*, pg. 1350
MF BANKA A.D.; *Int'l*, pg. 4870
M&F BANK—See M&F Bancorp, Inc.; *U.S. Public*, pg. 1350
MFC ASSET MANAGEMENT PUBLIC COMPANY LTD.; *Int'l*, pg. 4870
MFC INSURANCE COMPANY LIMITED—See Manulife Financial Corporation; *Int'l*, pg. 4678
MFC PATONG HERITAGE PROPERTY FUND; *Int'l*, pg. 4870
MFC REAL ESTATE LLC—See Erste Abwicklungsanstalt AoR; *Int'l*, pg. 2497
MFC RESOURCES INC.—See Scully Royalty Ltd.; *Int'l*, pg. 6656
MF DOW JONES NEWS S.R.L.—See Class Editori S.p.A.; *Int'l*, pg. 1652
MFEC PUBLIC COMPANY LIMITED; *Int'l*, pg. 4870
MFF CAPITAL INVESTMENTS LIMITED; *Int'l*, pg. 4871
M.F. FOLEY COMPANY; *U.S. Private*, pg. 2528
MFG CHEMICAL, LLC—See Platte River Ventures, LLC; *U.S. Private*, pg. 3211
MFG.COM CHINA—See MFG.com, Inc.; *U.S. Private*, pg. 2693
MFG.COM, INC.; *U.S. Private*, pg. 2693
MFG DE MEXICO—See Molded Fiber Glass Companies; *U.S. Private*, pg. 2766

CORPORATE AFFILIATIONS

M.F.G. EUROPE S.R.L.—See Cevital S.p.A.; *Int'l*, pg. 1425
MFG PARTNERS LLC; *U.S. Private*, pg. 2693
MFG SPA—See Cevital S.p.A.; *Int'l*, pg. 1425
(MFG) TECH GROUP PUERTO RICO, LLC—See West Pharmaceutical Services, Inc.; *U.S. Public*, pg. 2352
MFG TUNISIA—See Cevital S.p.A.; *Int'l*, pg. 1425
MF HOLDINGS (PTY) LTD.—See Sefalana Holdings Company Limited; *Int'l*, pg. 6679
MF HOUSING SERVICE CHUGOKU CO., LTD.—See Mitsui Fudosan Co., Ltd.; *Int'l*, pg. 4986
MF HOUSING SERVICE KYUSHU CO., LTD.—See Mitsui Fudosan Co., Ltd.; *Int'l*, pg. 4986
MFI COMPANIES, LLC—See GTCR LLC; *U.S. Private*, pg. 1803
MFI HOLDING CORPORATION—See Post Holdings, Inc.; *U.S. Public*, pg. 1703
MFINANCE FRANCE S.A.—See Commerzbank AG; *Int'l*, pg. 1719
M-FINANCE LIMITED—See DTXS Silk Road Investment Holdings Company Limited; *Int'l*, pg. 2217
M FINANCIAL GROUP; *U.S. Private*, pg. 2523
M FINANCIAL HOLDINGS INCORPORATED; *U.S. Private*, pg. 2523
M.F. INOX SRL—See Vimi Fasteners S.p.A.; *Int'l*, pg. 8208
MF INTERNATIONAL LIMITED; *Int'l*, pg. 4870
MFJ ENTERPRISES INC.; *U.S. Private*, pg. 2693
MFL INDIA LIMITED; *Int'l*, pg. 4871
MFM DELAWARE INC.; *U.S. Private*, pg. 2693
MFM KOREA CO., LTD.; *Int'l*, pg. 4871
MFM METRO GROUP FACILITY MANAGEMENT GMBH—See Metro AG; *Int'l*, pg. 4858
MFM WINTER PARK, LLC—See Fertitta Entertainment, Inc.; *U.S. Private*, pg. 1499
M FORCE STAFFING; *U.S. Private*, pg. 2523
MFORMATION TECHNOLOGIES, INC.; *U.S. Private*, pg. 2693
MFO S.A.; *Int'l*, pg. 4871
MFOUNDRY, INC.—See Fidelity National Infor.; *U.S. Public*, pg. 833
MFP PLASTICS LIMITED—See Grafton Group plc; *Int'l*, pg. 3051
MFP SALES LTD.—See Grafton Group plc; *Int'l*, pg. 3051
MFP SOLAR SDN BHD—See Mehran Sugar Mills Limited; *Int'l*, pg. 4797
MFP TECHNOLOGY SERVICES (UK) LTD.—See Renasant Financial Partners Ltd.; *Int'l*, pg. 6273
M. FREDRIC; *U.S. Private*, pg. 2526
MFS CHARTER INCOME TRUST; *U.S. Public*, pg. 1434
MFS CONSULTING ENGINEERS & SURVEYOR CORPORATION; *U.S. Private*, pg. 2693
MF SERVICES S.R.L.—See Sesa S.p.A.; *Int'l*, pg. 6728
MFS FUND DISTRIBUTORS, INC.—See Sun Life Financial Inc.; *Int'l*, pg. 7305
MFS GOVERNMENT MARKETS INCOME TRUST; *U.S. Public*, pg. 1434
MFS HIGH INCOME MUNICIPAL TRUST; *U.S. Public*, pg. 1434
MFS HIGH YIELD MUNICIPAL TRUST; *U.S. Public*, pg. 1434
MFS, INC.; *U.S. Private*, pg. 2693
MFS INSTITUTIONAL TRUST—See Sun Life Financial Inc.; *Int'l*, pg. 7305
MFS INTERCORP LIMITED; *Int'l*, pg. 4871
MFS INTERMEDIATE HIGH INCOME FUND; *U.S. Public*, pg. 1434
MFS INTERMEDIATE INCOME TRUST; *U.S. Public*, pg. 1434
MFS INTERNATIONAL (U.K.) LIMITED—See Sun Life Financial Inc.; *Int'l*, pg. 7305
MFS INVESTMENT GRADE MUNICIPAL TRUST; *U.S. Public*, pg. 1434
MFS INVESTMENT MANAGEMENT COMPANY (LUX) S.A.R.L.—See Sun Life Financial Inc.; *Int'l*, pg. 7305
MFS INVESTMENT MANAGEMENT K.K.—See Sun Life Financial Inc.; *Int'l*, pg. 7305
MFS INVESTMENT MANAGEMENT—See Guggenheim Partners, LLC; *U.S. Private*, pg. 1812
MFS MULTIMARKET INCOME TRUST; *U.S. Public*, pg. 1434
MFS MUNICIPAL INCOME TRUST; *U.S. Public*, pg. 1434
MFS SERVICE CENTER INC.—See Guggenheim Partners, LLC; *U.S. Private*, pg. 1812
MFS SPECIAL VALUE TRUST; *U.S. Public*, pg. 1434
MFS SUPPLY, LLC; *U.S. Private*, pg. 2693
MFS TECHNOLOGY EUROPE UG—See MFS Technology (S) Pte Ltd; *Int'l*, pg. 4871
MFS TECHNOLOGY (HUNAN) CO., LTD.—See MFS Technology (S) Pte Ltd; *Int'l*, pg. 4871
MFS TECHNOLOGY (M) SDN BHD—See MFS Technology (S) Pte Ltd; *Int'l*, pg. 4871
MFS TECHNOLOGY (PCB) CO., LTD.—See MFS Technology (S) Pte Ltd; *Int'l*, pg. 4871
MFS TECHNOLOGY (S) PTE LTD; *Int'l*, pg. 4871
MFS TECHNOLOGY (YIYANG) CO., LTD.—See MFS Technology (S) Pte Ltd; *Int'l*, pg. 4871
MFT MOTOREN UND FAHRZEUGTECHNIK GMBH—See Precision Camshafts Limited; *Int'l*, pg. 5957
M&F WESTERN PRODUCTS INC.; *U.S. Private*, pg. 2524

COMPANY NAME INDEX

M & F WORLDWIDE CORP.—See MacAndrews & Forbes Incorporated; *U.S. Private*, pg. 2532
M.G. ABBOTT, INC.; *U.S. Private*, pg. 2529
MG ABLE MOTORS COMPANY LIMITED—See AAPICO Hitech plc; *Int'l*, pg. 37
MGA CONSULTANTS, INC.—See Aquiline Capital Partners LLC; *U.S. Private*, pg. 304
MGA CONSULTANTS, INC.—See Genstar Capital, LLC; *U.S. Private*, pg. 1675
MGA EMPLOYEE SERVICES INC.; *U.S. Private*, pg. 2694
MGA ENTERTAINMENT, INC.; *U.S. Private*, pg. 2694
MGA ENTERTAINMENT (UK) LTD.—See MGA Entertainment, Inc.; *U.S. Private*, pg. 2694
MG AGRI FOODS (PVT) LTD.—See Mahmood Group of Companies LLC; *Int'l*, pg. 4649
M&G ALTERNATIVES INVESTMENT MANAGEMENT LIMITED—See M&G Group Limited; *Int'l*, pg. 4612
MG ALTERSVERSORGUNG GMBH—See GEA Group Aktiengesellschaft; *Int'l*, pg. 2904
MGAME CORP.; *Int'l*, pg. 4871
MGA METRO GROUP ADVERTISING GMBH—See Metro AG; *Int'l*, pg. 4859
MGA METRO GROUP ADVERTISING POLSKA SP. Z O.O.—See Metro AG; *Int'l*, pg. 4859
MG ASIA LIMITED—See Marposs S.p.A.; *Int'l*, pg. 4699
MGA SYSTEMS, INC.—See Roper Technologies, Inc.; *U.S. Public*, pg. 1814
MGA TRADING EST.—See Al-Osais International Holding Company; *Int'l*, pg. 287
MGA ZAPF CREATION GMBH—See MGA Entertainment, Inc.; *U.S. Private*, pg. 2694
MG BALTIC INVESTMENT—See MG Baltic UAB; *Int'l*, pg. 4871
MG BALTIC UAB; *Int'l*, pg. 4871
MGB BANCSHARES, INC.; *U.S. Private*, pg. 2694
MGB BERHAD—See LBS Bina Group Berhad; *Int'l*, pg. 4430
MGB METRO GROUP BUYING HK LIMITED—See Metro AG; *Int'l*, pg. 4859
MGB PLASTICS LTD.—See Madison Dearborn Partners, LLC; *U.S. Private*, pg. 2541
MG BUILDING MATERIALS; *U.S. Private*, pg. 2693
MG BUILDING MATERIALS - TRUSS DIVISION—See MG Building Materials; *U.S. Private*, pg. 2693
MGC ADVANCE CO., LTD.—See Mitsubishi Gas Chemical Company, Inc.; *Int'l*, pg. 4949
MGC ADVANCED POLYMERS, INC.—See Mitsubishi Gas Chemical Company, Inc.; *Int'l*, pg. 4949
MGC AGELESS CO., LTD.—See Mitsubishi Gas Chemical Company, Inc.; *Int'l*, pg. 4949
MG CAPITAL GMBH—See GEA Group Aktiengesellschaft; *Int'l*, pg. 2904
MGC COMPUTER SERVICE CO., LTD.—See Mitsubishi Gas Chemical Company, Inc.; *Int'l*, pg. 4949
MGC DERMA D.O.O; *Int'l*, pg. 4872
MGC DIAGNOSTICS CORPORATION—See Niterra Co., Ltd.; *Int'l*, pg. 5380
MGC ELECTROTECHNO CO., LTD.—See Mitsubishi Gas Chemical Company, Inc.; *Int'l*, pg. 4949
MGC ELECTROTECHNO (THAILAND) CO., LTD.—See Mitsubishi Gas Chemical Company, Inc.; *Int'l*, pg. 4949
MGC ENERGY COMPANY LIMITED—See Mitsubishi Gas Chemical Company, Inc.; *Int'l*, pg. 4949
M.G.C ENGINEERING CO., INC.—See Mitsubishi Gas Chemical Company, Inc.; *Int'l*, pg. 4949
MGC FARMIX CO., LTD.—See Mitsubishi Gas Chemical Company, Inc.; *Int'l*, pg. 4949
MGC FILSHEET CO., LTD.—See Mitsubishi Gas Chemical Company, Inc.; *Int'l*, pg. 4949
MG CHEMICALS (AUSTRALIA) PTY LTD—See Megachem Limited; *Int'l*, pg. 4793
MG CHINA TRADING LTD.—See Mohawk Industries, Inc.; *U.S. Public*, pg. 1457
MGC INSURANCE SERVICE, INC.—See Mitsubishi Gas Chemical Company, Inc.; *Int'l*, pg. 4949
MG CLEANERS LLC—See SMG Industries Inc.; *U.S. Public*, pg. 1896
MGC LOGISTICS SERVICE MIZUSHIMA CO., LTD.—See Mitsubishi Gas Chemical Company, Inc.; *Int'l*, pg. 4949
MGC LOGISTICS YAMAKITA CO., LTD.—See Mitsubishi Gas Chemical Company, Inc.; *Int'l*, pg. 4949
MGC NIIGATA SERVICE CO., LTD.—See Mitsubishi Gas Chemical Company, Inc.; *Int'l*, pg. 4949
MGC PHARMACEUTICALS LTD.; *Int'l*, pg. 4872
MGC PURE CHEMICALS AMERICA, INC.—See Mitsubishi Gas Chemical Company, Inc.; *Int'l*, pg. 4949
MGC PURE CHEMICALS SINGAPORE PTE. LTD.—See Mitsubishi Gas Chemical Company, Inc.; *Int'l*, pg. 4949
MGC PURE CHEMICALS TAIWAN, INC.—See Mitsubishi Gas Chemical Company, Inc.; *Int'l*, pg. 4949
MGC SPECIALTY CHEMICALS NETHERLANDS B.V.—See Mitsubishi Gas Chemical Company, Inc.; *Int'l*, pg. 4949
MGC TERMINAL COMPANY, INC.—See Mitsubishi Gas Chemical Company, Inc.; *Int'l*, pg. 4949
MGC TRADING (THAILAND) LTD.—See Mitsubishi Gas Chemical Company, Inc.; *Int'l*, pg. 4949
MGC WOODCHEM CORPORATION—See Mitsubishi Gas Chemical Company, Inc.; *Int'l*, pg. 4949

MGDC S.C.—See Tata Sons Limited; *Int'l*, pg. 7468
MG DESIGN ASSOCIATES CORP.; *U.S. Private*, pg. 2693
MGDL DISTRIBUTION PTY LTD—See Movado Group, Inc.; *U.S. Public*, pg. 1479
MGDM HOLDINGS CO.; *U.S. Private*, pg. 2694
M. G. DYESS, INC.—See Quanta Services, Inc.; *U.S. Public*, pg. 1751
MGE ENERGY, INC.; *U.S. Public*, pg. 1434
MGE EQUIPAMENTOS E SERVICOS FERROVIARIOS LTDA.—See Caterpillar, Inc.; *U.S. Public*, pg. 452
MG ELECTRIC SERVICE COMPANY; *U.S. Private*, pg. 2694
M&G ELECTRONICS CORP.; *U.S. Private*, pg. 2524
MGE MANAGEMENT EXPERTS, INC.; *U.S. Private*, pg. 2694
MGEN SOLUTIONS CO., LTD.; *Int'l*, pg. 4872
MGE POWER LLC—See MGE Energy, Inc.; *U.S. Public*, pg. 1434
MGE USV-SYSTEME GMBH—See Schneider Electric SE; *Int'l*, pg. 6628
MG EXEO NETWORK INC.—See EXEO Group Inc.; *Int'l*, pg. 2583
MGF EASYBIKE SAS; *Int'l*, pg. 4872
MG FINANCIAL LLC—See JRJ Ventures LLP; *Int'l*, pg. 4008
M.G.F. LOGISTIQUE S.A.—See G7 Entreprises; *Int'l*, pg. 2867
MGG BLERICK—See Parcom Capital Management B.V.; *Int'l*, pg. 5740
MGG GROUP B.V.—See Parcom Capital Management B.V.; *Int'l*, pg. 5740
MGG INVESTMENT GROUP, LP; *U.S. Private*, pg. 2694
MGG MICRO-GLUHLAMPEN-GESELLSCHAFT MENZEL GMBH—See L. Possehl & Co. mbH; *Int'l*, pg. 4383
MG GOLF INC.; *U.S. Private*, pg. 2694
M&G GROUP LIMITED; *Int'l*, pg. 4611
MGG SCHWABISCH GMUND—See Parcom Capital Management B.V.; *Int'l*, pg. 5741
MGG TREST—See Parcom Capital Management B.V.; *Int'l*, pg. 5741
MGH, INC.; *U.S. Private*, pg. 2694
MGH INSTITUTE OF HEALTH PROFESSIONS—See Partners HealthCare System, Inc.; *U.S. Private*, pg. 3102
MGIC ASSURANCE CORPORATION—See MGIC Investment Corporation; *U.S. Public*, pg. 1434
MGIC CREDIT ASSURANCE CORPORATION—See MGIC Investment Corporation; *U.S. Public*, pg. 1434
MGI CHEMICALS PRIVATE LIMITED—See Megachem Limited; *Int'l*, pg. 4793
MGIC INVESTMENT CORPORATION; *U.S. Public*, pg. 1434
MGI COUTIER UK LTD.—See AKWEL; *Int'l*, pg. 268
MGI & DACHSER, INC.—See Dachser GmbH & Co.; *Int'l*, pg. 1904
MGI DIGITAL TECHNOLOGY SA; *Int'l*, pg. 4872
MGIE - CEV—See Sonepar S.A.; *Int'l*, pg. 7091
MGI INSURANCE BROKERAGE INC.—See iA Financial Corporation Inc.; *Int'l*, pg. 3567
MGI LUXURY ASIA PACIFIC LTD.—See Movado Group, Inc.; *U.S. Public*, pg. 1479
MGI LUXURY GROUP G.M.B.H.—See Movado Group, Inc.; *U.S. Public*, pg. 1479
MGI LUXURY GROUP, S.A.—See Movado Group, Inc.; *U.S. Public*, pg. 1479
MGI METRO GROUP ILETISIM VE ENFORMASYON TICARET LIMITED SIRKETI—See Metro AG; *Int'l*, pg. 4859
MGI METRO GROUP INFORMATION TECHNOLOGY GMBH—See Metro AG; *Int'l*, pg. 4859
MGI METRO GROUP INFORMATION TECHNOLOGY LLC—See Metro AG; *Int'l*, pg. 4859
MGI METRO GROUP INFORMATION TECHNOLOGY ROMANIA SRL—See Metro AG; *Int'l*, pg. 4859
MGI METRO GROUP INFORMATION TECHNOLOGY UKRAINE LLC—See Metro AG; *Int'l*, pg. 4859
MGI-MINAS GERAIS PARTICIPACOES S.A.; *Int'l*, pg. 4859
M-G INC.; *U.S. Private*, pg. 2526
M&G INTERNATIONAL INVESTMENTS SWITZERLAND AG—See M&G Plc; *Int'l*, pg. 4612
MG INTERNATIONAL SA; *Int'l*, pg. 4871
M. G. INTERNATIONAL TRANSPORTS GMBH; *Int'l*, pg. 4615
M&G INVESTMENT MANAGEMENT LIMITED—See M&G Group Limited; *Int'l*, pg. 4612
M&G INVESTMENTS (HONG KONG) LIMITED—See M&G Plc; *Int'l*, pg. 4612
M&G INVESTMENTS (SINGAPORE) PTE. LTD.—See M&G Plc; *Int'l*, pg. 4612
MGI SECURITIES INC.—See iA Financial Corporation Inc.; *Int'l*, pg. 3567
MG LEASING CORPORATION—See Marubeni Corporation; *Int'l*, pg. 4709
MG, LLC—See Willis Towers Watson Public Limited Company; *Int'l*, pg. 8414
MGL METRO GROUP LOGISTICS GMBH—See Metro AG; *Int'l*, pg. 4859
MGL METRO GROUP LOGISTICS WAREHOUSING BETEILIGUNGS GMBH—See Metro AG; *Int'l*, pg. 4859

MGL METRO GROUP LOGISTICS WAREHOUSING GMBH—See Metro AG; *Int'l*, pg. 4859
M. GLOSSER & SONS INC.; *U.S. Private*, pg. 2526
MGM BRAKES DIVISION—See Indian Head Industries, Inc.; *U.S. Private*, pg. 2061
MGM CHINA HOLDINGS LIMITED—See MGM Resorts International; *U.S. Public*, pg. 1435
MGM ELECTRIC LIMITED—See Sonepar S.A.; *Int'l*, pg. 7091
MGM FINANCE CORP.—See MGM Resorts International; *U.S. Public*, pg. 1435
MGM FORD LINCOLN SALES LTD.; *Int'l*, pg. 4872
MGM GOLD COMMUNICATIONS; *U.S. Private*, pg. 2694
MGM GRAND DETROIT, LLC—See MGM Resorts International; *U.S. Public*, pg. 1435
MGM GRAND HOTEL, LLC—See MGM Resorts International; *U.S. Public*, pg. 1435
MGM GRAND (INTERNATIONAL), PTE—See MGM Resorts International; *U.S. Public*, pg. 1435
MGM GRAND (MACAO) LIMITED—See MGM Resorts International; *U.S. Public*, pg. 1435
MGM GROWTH PROPERTIES LLC—See VICI Properties Inc.; *U.S. Public*, pg. 2295
MGM GROWTH PROPERTIES OPERATING PARTNERSHIP LP—See VICI Properties Inc.; *U.S. Public*, pg. 2295
MGM INDUSTRIES, INC.; *U.S. Private*, pg. 2694
MGM INTEGRATION PARTNERS GMBH—See Allgeier SE; *Int'l*, pg. 338
MGM INTERNATIONAL, LLC—See MGM Resorts International; *U.S. Public*, pg. 1435
MGM LIMITED—See Northern Bear Plc; *Int'l*, pg. 5443
MGM MIRAGE ADVERTISING, INC.—See MGM Resorts International; *U.S. Public*, pg. 1435
MGM NATIONAL HARBOR, LLC—See MGM Resorts International; *U.S. Public*, pg. 1435
MGM NETWORKS INC.—See Amazon.com, Inc.; *U.S. Public*, pg. 90
MG MOTOR UK LIMITED—See Shanghai Automotive Industry Corporation; *Int'l*, pg. 6762
MGM RESORTS INTERNATIONAL MARKETING, LTD—See MGM Resorts International; *U.S. Public*, pg. 1435
MGM RESORTS INTERNATIONAL; *U.S. Public*, pg. 1435
MGM RESORTS MISSISSIPPI, INC.—See Cherokee Nation Businesses; *U.S. Private*, pg. 873
MGM SECURITY PARTNERS GMBH—See Allgeier SE; *Int'l*, pg. 337
MGM SPRINGFIELD, LLC—See MGM Resorts International; *U.S. Public*, pg. 1435
MGM TECHNOLOGY PARTNERS EURL—See Allgeier SE; *Int'l*, pg. 337
MGM TECHNOLOGY PARTNERS GMBH—See Allgeier SE; *Int'l*, pg. 338
MGM TECHNOLOGY PARTNERS PORTUGAL, UNIPESSOAL LDA.—See Allgeier SE; *Int'l*, pg. 337
MGM TECHNOLOGY PARTNERS SCHWEIZ AG—See Allgeier SE; *Int'l*, pg. 337
MGM TECHNOLOGY PARTNERS S.R.O.—See Allgeier SE; *Int'l*, pg. 338
MGM TECHNOLOGY PARTNERS USA CORP.—See Allgeier SE; *Int'l*, pg. 337
MGM TECHNOLOGY PARTNERS VIETNAM CO., LTD.—See Allgeier SE; *Int'l*, pg. 337
MGM TELEVISION ENTERTAINMENT INC.—See Amazon.com, Inc.; *U.S. Public*, pg. 90
MGMTREE GMBH—See EnBW Energie Baden-Wurttemberg AG; *Int'l*, pg. 2400
MGM WINE & SPIRITS INC.; *U.S. Private*, pg. 2694
MGN & ASSOCIATES INC.; *U.S. Private*, pg. 2695
M.G. NEWELL CORPORATION; *U.S. Private*, pg. 2529
MGN LIMITED—See Reach PLC; *Int'l*, pg. 6231
MG ODRA GAS, SPOL. S.R.O.—See Messer Group GmbH; *Int'l*, pg. 4842
MGO GLOBAL INC.; *U.S. Public*, pg. 1435
MG OIL INC.; *U.S. Private*, pg. 2694
MGP FINANCE CO-ISSUER INC.—See VICI Properties Inc.; *U.S. Public*, pg. 2296
MG PHARMA INC.—See Rohto Pharmaceutical Co. Ltd.; *Int'l*, pg. 6387
MGP INGREDIENTS, INC.; *U.S. Public*, pg. 1435
M&G PLC; *Int'l*, pg. 4612
M&G POLYMERS USA LLC—See The Far Eastern Group; *Int'l*, pg. 7642
MG PRECISION CO., LTD.—See The Japan Steel Works, Ltd.; *Int'l*, pg. 7659
MG PRODUCTS COMPANY; *U.S. Private*, pg. 2694
MG PRODUKT KFT—See Ameropa AG; *Int'l*, pg. 424
M-GRASS ECOLOGY AND ENVIRONMENT (GROUP) CO., LTD.; *Int'l*, pg. 4614
MGR CONSULTING CO., LTD.—See Pasona Group Inc.; *Int'l*, pg. 5753
M&G REAL ESTATE KOREA CO., LTD.—See M&G Plc; *Int'l*, pg. 4612
MGR EQUIPMENT CORP.; *U.S. Private*, pg. 2695
M. GRIFFITH INVESTMENT SERVICES, INC.—See Baird Financial Group, Inc.; *U.S. Private*, pg. 454
MG ROHSTOFFHANDEL GMBH—See GEA Group Aktiengesellschaft; *Int'l*, pg. 2903

Company Index

MGR EQUIPMENT CORP. CORPORATE AFFILIATIONS

M GROUP INC.—See Penns Woods Bancorp, Inc.; *U.S. Public*, pg. 1663
MGSCOMM - MEXICO CITY—See Machado/Garcia-Serra Publicidad, Inc.; *U.S. Private*, pg. 2535
MGSCOMM - NEW YORK CITY—See Machado/Garcia-Serra Publicidad, Inc.; *U.S. Private*, pg. 2535
M&G SECURITIES LIMITED—See M&G Group Limited; *Int'l*, pg. 4612
THE MGS GROUP; *U.S. Private*, pg. 4078
MGS LANGUAGE SERVICES—See ManpowerGroup Inc.; *U.S. Public*, pg. 1358
MGS MACHINE CORPORATION; *U.S. Private*, pg. 2695
MGS MANUFACTURING GROUP, INC.; *U.S. Private*, pg. 2695
MG SOGO SERVICE CO., LTD.—See VT Holdings Co., Ltd.; *Int'l*, pg. 8315
MG S.P.A.—See Marposs S.p.A.; *Int'l*, pg. 4699
MGT CAPITAL INVESTMENTS, INC.; *U.S. Public*, pg. 1436
M.G.T. INDUSTRIES INC.; *U.S. Private*, pg. 2529
MGTI SNEV S.A.S.—See ThyssenKrupp AG; *Int'l*, pg. 7724
MGT OF AMERICA CONSULTING LLC—See The Vistria Group, LP; *U.S. Private*, pg. 4132
MGT OF AMERICA, LLC—See The Vistria Group, LP; *U.S. Private*, pg. 4132
MG TRADING AND DEVELOPMENT GMBH—See China Baowu Steel Group Corp., Ltd.; *Int'l*, pg. 1486
M/G TRANSPORT SERVICES, INC.—See Auxo Investment Partners, LLC; *U.S. Private*, pg. 402
MGT SWEDEN AB—See MGT Capital Investments, Inc.; *U.S. Public*, pg. 1436
MG UNIT TRUST; *Int'l*, pg. 4871
MGV DISTRI-HIPER S.A. AUCHAN—See Auchan Holding S.A.; *Int'l*, pg. 699
MG VENTURE CAPITAL AG—See GEA Group Aktiengesellschaft; *Int'l*, pg. 2904
MGVV PROJEKTENTWICKLUNG DAIMLERSTRASSE GMBH & CO. KG—See GEA Group Aktiengesellschaft; *Int'l*, pg. 2904
MGVV PROJEKTENTWICKLUNG DAIMLERSTRASSE VERWALTUNGS GMBH—See GEA Group Aktiengesellschaft; *Int'l*, pg. 2904
MG WEST COMPANY; *U.S. Private*, pg. 2694
MGW HOTELS PTY LTD—See Woolworths Group Limited; *Int'l*, pg. 8451
MGX EQUIPMENT SERVICES, LLC—See The Manitowoc Company, Inc.; *U.S. Public*, pg. 2111
MGX MINERALS INC.; *Int'l*, pg. 4872
MGX RENEWABLES INC.—See MGX Minerals Inc.; *Int'l*, pg. 4872
THE MHA GROUP, INC.—See AMN Healthcare Services, Inc.; *U.S. Public*, pg. 125
MHAISKAR INFRASTRUCTURE PVT. LTD.—See IRB Infrastructure Developers Ltd.; *Int'l*, pg. 3805
M.H. ALSHAYA CO. W.L.L.; *Int'l*, pg. 4615
MH ANGEL MEDICAL CENTER, LLLP—See HCA Healthcare, Inc.; *U.S. Public*, pg. 1001
M.HART DO BRASIL LTDA.—See Stanley Black & Decker, Inc.; *U.S. Public*, pg. 1933
MHA-STOPFORD LIMITED—See L3Harris Technologies, Inc.; *U.S. Public*, pg. 1284
MH AVIATION SERVICES (PTY) LTD—See World Kinect Corporation; *U.S. Public*, pg. 2380
M HAYES & ASSOCIATES, LLC—See Stone Point Capital LLC; *U.S. Private*, pg. 3823
MH-BETEILIGUNGS GMBH; *Int'l*, pg. 4872
MHBT, INC.—See Marsh & McLennan Companies, Inc.; *U.S. Public*, pg. 1377
MHCC - MARSEILLE HEALTH CARE CONSULTING GMBH—See MK-Kliniken AG; *Int'l*, pg. 5001
MHC ECO SOLUTIONS CO., LTD.—See Mitsubishi HC Capital Inc.; *Int'l*, pg. 4951
MHC FINANCIAL SERVICES—See Murphy-Hoffman Company; *U.S. Private*, pg. 2816
MHC FORD—See Murphy-Hoffman Company; *U.S. Private*, pg. 2816
MHCG, INC.—See Hitachi, Ltd.; *Int'l*, pg. 3423
MHCG, INC.—See Mitsubishi Heavy Industries, Ltd.; *Int'l*, pg. 4960
MH CHAMPAGNES AND WINES KOREA LTD—See LVMH Moet Hennessy Louis Vuitton SE; *Int'l*, pg. 4599
MHC HOLDING, LTD.; *Int'l*, pg. 4872
MHC JOINT STOCK COMPANY; *Int'l*, pg. 4872
MHC KENWORTH CO. INC.—See Murphy-Hoffman Company; *U.S. Private*, pg. 2816
MHC KENWORTH-OKLAHOMA CITY—See Murphy-Hoffman Company; *U.S. Private*, pg. 2816
MHC MOBILITY B.V.—See Mitsubishi HC Capital Inc.; *Int'l*, pg. 4951
MHC MOBILITY GMBH—See Mitsubishi HC Capital Inc.; *Int'l*, pg. 4951
MHC MOBILITY SP. Z O.O.—See Mitsubishi HC Capital Inc.; *Int'l*, pg. 4951
MH CONNECTORS GROUP LIMITED; *Int'l*, pg. 4872
MHC PLANTATIONS BHD; *Int'l*, pg. 4872
MHC REUSE SERVICES CORPORATION—See Mitsubishi HC Capital Inc.; *Int'l*, pg. 4951
MHC SOFTWARE LLC—See Strattam Capital, LLC; *U.S. Private*, pg. 3837
MHC SYSTEMS, LLC; *U.S. Private*, pg. 2695
MHC TRIPLE WIN CORPORATION—See Mitsubishi HC Capital Inc.; *Int'l*, pg. 4951
MHC TRUCK LEASING INC.—See Murphy-Hoffman Company; *U.S. Private*, pg. 2816
MHC TRUCK SOURCE INC.—See Murphy-Hoffman Company; *U.S. Private*, pg. 2816
M.H. DADABHOY GROUP OF COMPANIES; *Int'l*, pg. 4615
MHD ENTERPRISES; *U.S. Private*, pg. 2695
MHD MOET HENNESSY DIAGEO K.K.—See LVMH Moet Hennessy Louis Vuitton SE; *Int'l*, pg. 4599
M.H. EBY INC.; *U.S. Private*, pg. 2529
MH ECKERD LIVING CENTER, LLLP—See HCA Healthcare, Inc.; *U.S. Public*, pg. 1001
MHE-DEMAG AUSTRALIA PTY LTD—See Jebsen & Jessen (SEA) Pte Ltd; *Int'l*, pg. 3926
MHE-DEMAG MALAYSIA SDN BHD—See Jebsen & Jessen (SEA) Pte Ltd; *Int'l*, pg. 3926
MHE-DEMAG (P) INC—See Jebsen & Jessen (SEA) Pte Ltd; *Int'l*, pg. 3926
MHE-DEMAG (S) PTE. LTD.—See Konecranes Oyj; *Int'l*, pg. 4251
MHE-DEMAG TAIWAN COMPANY LIMITED—See Jebsen & Jessen (SEA) Pte Ltd; *Int'l*, pg. 3926
MHE-DEMAG VIETNAM COMPANY LIMITED—See Jebsen & Jessen (SEA) Pte Ltd; *Int'l*, pg. 3926
M&H ELEKTRO AG—See Burkhalter Holding AG; *Int'l*, pg. 1225
MH EQUIPMENT COMPANY; *U.S. Private*, pg. 2695
MH EQUIPMENT—See MH Equipment Company; *U.S. Private*, pg. 2695
MH EQUIPMENT—See MH Equipment Company; *U.S. Private*, pg. 2695
MHE RENTALS INDIA PRIVATE LIMITED—See Josts Engineering Company Limited; *Int'l*, pg. 4001
MH ETHANOL CO., LTD.; *Int'l*, pg. 4872
MHF INC.; *U.S. Private*, pg. 2695
MHG GLASS PTY LTD; *Int'l*, pg. 4872
MHG MEDIA HOLDINGS AG—See The Jordan Company, L.P.; *U.S. Private*, pg. 4061
M.H. GROUP LTD.—See Kengoo Group Co., Ltd.; *Int'l*, pg. 4127
MHHC ENTERPRISES INC; *U.S. Public*, pg. 1436
MHH FRANCE S.A.S—See BayWa AG; *Int'l*, pg. 918
MH HIGHLANDS-CASHIERS MEDICAL CENTER, LLLP—See HCA Healthcare, Inc.; *U.S. Public*, pg. 1001
MHI ACCOUNTING SERVICE, LTD.—See Mitsubishi Heavy Industries, Ltd.; *Int'l*, pg. 4954
MHI AERO ENGINE SERVICE CO., LTD.—See Mitsubishi Heavy Industries, Ltd.; *Int'l*, pg. 4954
MHI AEROSPACE LOGITEM CO., LTD.—See Mitsubishi Heavy Industries, Ltd.; *Int'l*, pg. 4954
MHI AEROSPACE PRODUCTION, LTD.—See Mitsubishi Heavy Industries, Ltd.; *Int'l*, pg. 4954
MHI AEROSPACE SYSTEMS CORP.—See Mitsubishi Heavy Industries, Ltd.; *Int'l*, pg. 4954
MHI AEROSPACE VIETNAM CO., LTD.—See Mitsubishi Heavy Industries, Ltd.; *Int'l*, pg. 4954
MHIA INC CORRUGATING MACHINERY DIVISION—See Mitsubishi Heavy Industries, Ltd.; *Int'l*, pg. 4956
MHI AIRPORT ENVIRONMENT CO., LTD.—See Mitsubishi Heavy Industries, Ltd.; *Int'l*, pg. 4954
MHI AUSTRALIA, PTY. LTD.—See Mitsubishi Heavy Industries, Ltd.; *Int'l*, pg. 4954
MHI AUTOMOTIVE CAPITAL LLC—See Mitsubishi Heavy Industries, Ltd.; *Int'l*, pg. 4954
MHI BUSINESS RISK SUPPORT, LTD.—See Mitsubishi Heavy Industries, Ltd.; *Int'l*, pg. 4954
MHI CANADA AEROSPACE, INC.—See Mitsubishi Heavy Industries, Ltd.; *Int'l*, pg. 4954
MHI CAPITAL AMERICA, INC.—See Mitsubishi Heavy Industries, Ltd.; *Int'l*, pg. 4954
MHI CAPITAL ASIA PACIFIC PTE. LTD.—See Mitsubishi Heavy Industries, Ltd.; *Int'l*, pg. 4954
MHI COMPRESSOR DO BRAZIL LTDA.—See Mitsubishi Heavy Industries, Ltd.; *Int'l*, pg. 4954
M HIDARY & COMPANY INC.; *U.S. Private*, pg. 2523
MHI DIESEL SERVICE ENGINEERING CO., LTD.—See Mitsubishi Heavy Industries, Ltd.; *Int'l*, pg. 4954
MHIEC ENVIRONMENT (BEIJING) CO., LTD.—See Mitsubishi Heavy Industries, Ltd.; *Int'l*, pg. 4955
MHI ENERGY & SERVICE CO., LTD.—See Mitsubishi Heavy Industries, Ltd.; *Int'l*, pg. 4954
MHI ENGINEERING & INDUSTRIAL PROJECTS INDIA PRIVATE LIMITED—See Mitsubishi Heavy Industries, Ltd.; *Int'l*, pg. 4954
MHI ENGINE SYSTEM HONG KONG LTD.—See Mitsubishi Heavy Industries, Ltd.; *Int'l*, pg. 4954
MHI ENGINE SYSTEM MIDDLE EAST FZE—See Mitsubishi Heavy Industries, Ltd.; *Int'l*, pg. 4954
MHI ENGINE SYSTEM PHILIPPINES, INC.—See Mitsubishi Heavy Industries, Ltd.; *Int'l*, pg. 4954
MHI ENGINE SYSTEM (SHENZHEN) CO., LTD.—See Mitsubishi Heavy Industries, Ltd.; *Int'l*, pg. 4954
MHI ENGINE SYSTEM VIETNAM CO., LTD.—See Mitsubishi Heavy Industries, Ltd.; *Int'l*, pg. 4954
MHI EQUIPMENT ALSACE S.A.S (MEA)—See Mitsubishi Heavy Industries, Ltd.; *Int'l*, pg. 4954
MHI EQUIPMENT EUROPE B.V.—See Mitsubishi Heavy Industries, Ltd.; *Int'l*, pg. 4954
MHI EXECUTIVE EXPERTS CO., LTD.—See Mitsubishi Heavy Industries, Ltd.; *Int'l*, pg. 4955
MHI FACILITY SERVICE CO., LTD.—See Mitsubishi Heavy Industries, Ltd.; *Int'l*, pg. 4955
MHI FINANCE CO., LTD.—See Mitsubishi Heavy Industries, Ltd.; *Int'l*, pg. 4955
MHI GENERAL SERVICES CO., LTD.—See Mitsubishi Heavy Industries, Ltd.; *Int'l*, pg. 4955
MHI HASEG CO., LTD.—See Mitsubishi Heavy Industries, Ltd.; *Int'l*, pg. 4955
MHI HOSPITALITY TRS HOLDING, INC.—See Sotherly Hotels Inc.; *U.S. Public*, pg. 1910
MHI HOTELS LLC; *U.S. Private*, pg. 2695
MHI INFORMATION SYSTEMS CO., LTD.—See Mitsubishi Heavy Industries, Ltd.; *Int'l*, pg. 4955
MHI INTERNATIONAL INVESTMENT B.V.—See Mitsubishi Heavy Industries, Ltd.; *Int'l*, pg. 4955
MHI INVESTMENTS, LLC—See Healthpeak Properties, Inc.; *U.S. Public*, pg. 1016
MHI LOGITEC COMPANY LIMITED—See Mitsubishi Heavy Industries, Ltd.; *Int'l*, pg. 4955
MHI MACHINE TOOL ENGINEERING CO., LTD.—See Mitsubishi Heavy Industries, Ltd.; *Int'l*, pg. 4955
MHI MACHINE TOOL U.S.A. INC.—See Mitsubishi Heavy Industries, Ltd.; *Int'l*, pg. 4956
MHI MARINE ENGINEERING, LTD.—See Mitsubishi Heavy Industries, Ltd.; *Int'l*, pg. 4955
MHI MARITECH, CO., LTD.—See Mitsubishi Heavy Industries, Ltd.; *Int'l*, pg. 4955
MHI NS ENGINEERING CO., LTD.—See Mitsubishi Heavy Industries, Ltd.; *Int'l*, pg. 4955
MH INSTRUMENT OU—See Endress+Hauser (International) Holding AG; *Int'l*, pg. 2408
MHI NUCLEAR ENGINEERING CO. LTD.—See Mitsubishi Heavy Industries, Ltd.; *Int'l*, pg. 4955
MHI OCEANINCS CO., LTD.—See Mitsubishi Heavy Industries, Ltd.; *Int'l*, pg. 4955
MHI PARTNERSHIP LTD.; *U.S. Private*, pg. 2695
MHI PERSONNEL, LTD.—See Mitsubishi Heavy Industries, Ltd.; *Int'l*, pg. 4955
MHI PLANT CORPORATION—See Mitsubishi Heavy Industries, Ltd.; *Int'l*, pg. 4955
MHI POWER AMERICA LATINA EIRELI—See Mitsubishi Heavy Industries, Ltd.; *Int'l*, pg. 4955
MHI POWER CONTROL SYSTEMS CO., LTD.—See Mitsubishi Heavy Industries, Ltd.; *Int'l*, pg. 4955
MHI POWER ENGINEERING CO., LTD.—See Mitsubishi Heavy Industries, Ltd.; *Int'l*, pg. 4955
MHI POWER MIDDLE EAST FOR MANUFACTURING PARTS & MACHINERY, LLC—See Mitsubishi Heavy Industries, Ltd.; *Int'l*, pg. 4955
MHI POWER PROJECT (THAILAND) CO., LTD.—See Mitsubishi Heavy Industries, Ltd.; *Int'l*, pg. 4955
MHI POWER ROMANIA SRL—See Mitsubishi Heavy Industries, Ltd.; *Int'l*, pg. 4955
MHI POWER SYSTEMS INSPECTION TECHNOLOGIES, LTD.—See Mitsubishi Heavy Industries, Ltd.; *Int'l*, pg. 4955
MHI POWER TECHNICAL SERVICES CORPORATION—See Mitsubishi Heavy Industries, Ltd.; *Int'l*, pg. 4955
MHI PRO STAFF CORPORATION—See Mitsubishi Heavy Industries, Ltd.; *Int'l*, pg. 4955
MHI RESIDENTIAL AIR-CONDITIONERS (SHANGHAI) CO., LTD.—See Mitsubishi Heavy Industries, Ltd.; *Int'l*, pg. 4955
MHIRJ AVIATION INC.—See Mitsubishi Heavy Industries, Ltd.; *Int'l*, pg. 4955
MHIRJ AVIATION ULC—See Mitsubishi Heavy Industries, Ltd.; *Int'l*, pg. 4955
MHI RUSSIA LLC—See Mitsubishi Heavy Industries, Ltd.; *Int'l*, pg. 4955
MHI SAGAMI HIGH-TECH LTD.—See Mitsubishi Heavy Industries, Ltd.; *Int'l*, pg. 4955
MHI SEATEC LTD.—See Mitsubishi Heavy Industries, Ltd.; *Int'l*, pg. 4955
MHI SHENYANG PUMP ENGINEERING CO., LTD.—See Mitsubishi Heavy Industries, Ltd.; *Int'l*, pg. 4955
MHI SOLUTION TECHNOLOGIES CO., LTD.—See Mitsubishi Heavy Industries, Ltd.; *Int'l*, pg. 4955
MHI SPACEJET AMERICA, INC.—See Mitsubishi Heavy Industries, Ltd.; *Int'l*, pg. 4955
MHI SPECIAL VEHICLES PARTS SUPPLY & TECHNICAL SERVICE CO., LTD.—See Mitsubishi Heavy Industries, Ltd.; *Int'l*, pg. 4955
MHI STEEL MACHINERY ENGINEERING & SERVICE CO., LTD.—See Mitsubishi Heavy Industries, Ltd.; *Int'l*, pg. 4955
MHI SUL AMERICANA DISTRIBUIDORA DE MOTORES LTDA—See Mitsubishi Heavy Industries, Ltd.; *Int'l*, pg. 4955
MHJ GROUP INC.; *U.S. Private*, pg. 2695
M.H. KING COMPANY INC.; *U.S. Private*, pg. 2529

COMPANY NAME INDEX

MHKW ROTHENSEE GMBH—See Beijing Enterprises Holdings Limited; *Int'l*, pg. 950
MHM AUTOMATION LIMITED—See KKR & Co. Inc.; *U.S. Public*, pg. 1241
MHM INNOVATIONS, INC.—See Integrity Management Consulting, Inc.; *U.S. Private*, pg. 2103
MH MISSION HOSPITAL, LLLP—See HCA Healthcare, Inc.; *U.S. Public*, pg. 1001
MH MISSION HOSPITAL MCDOWELL, LLLP—See HCA Healthcare, Inc.; *U.S. Public*, pg. 1001
MHM SERVICES, INC.—See Centene Corporation; *U.S. Public*, pg. 469
MHN SERVICES—See Centene Corporation; *U.S. Public*, pg. 469
MHOLDING 3 A/S—See Matas A/S; *Int'l*, pg. 4726
MHOLDING 5 APS—See Matas A/S; *Int'l*, pg. 4726
MHOLDING 6 APS—See Matas A/S; *Int'l*, pg. 4726
M. HOLLAND COMPANY; *U.S. Private*, pg. 2526
MHPHILS REALTY CORPORATION—See Mitsubishi Heavy Industries, Ltd.; *Int'l*, pg. 4956
M&H PLASTICS INC.—See Berry Global Group, Inc; *U.S. Public*, pg. 324
M.H. PODELL COMPANY; *U.S. Private*, pg. 2529
M+H POWER PACIFIC LIMITED—See Mpower Group Limited; *Int'l*, pg. 5062
MH POWER SYSTEMS KOREA, LTD.—See Mitsubishi Heavy Industries, Ltd.; *Int'l*, pg. 4954
MH POWER SYSTEMS MIDDLE EAST, LLC—See Mitsubishi Heavy Industries, Ltd.; *Int'l*, pg. 4954
MH PRIVATE EQUITY FUND, LLC; *U.S. Private*, pg. 2695
M&H PROPERTIES LTD.—See American Motel Management; *U.S. Private*, pg. 241
MHPS DALIAN ELECTRICITY EQUIPMENT CO., LTD.—See Mitsubishi Heavy Industries, Ltd.; *Int'l*, pg. 4955
MHP SE; *Int'l*, pg. 4872
MHPS (HANGZHOU) ENVIRONMENTAL EQUIPMENT CO., LTD.—See Mitsubishi Heavy Industries, Ltd.; *Int'l*, pg. 4955
MHPS PLANT SERVICES PTY LTD.—See Hitachi, Ltd.; *Int'l*, pg. 3423
MHPS PLANT SERVICES PTY LTD.—See Mitsubishi Heavy Industries, Ltd.; *Int'l*, pg. 4960
MHPT ENGINEERING SDN. BHD.—See Hitachi, Ltd.; *Int'l*, pg. 3423
MHR FUND MANAGEMENT LLC; *U.S. Private*, pg. 2695
M.H. RHODES CRAMER, LLC—See CapitalWorks, LLC; *U.S. Private*, pg. 742
MHR MANAGEMENT, LLC—See Expand Energy Corporation; *U.S. Public*, pg. 808
MHR MANAGEMENT LLC; *U.S. Private*, pg. 2695
MH ROBOT & AUTOMATION CO., LTD.; *Int'l*, pg. 4872
MHS AVIATION BERHAD—See Lembaga Tabung Angkatan Tentera; *Int'l*, pg. 4448
MHS DISTRIBUTION & FULFILLMENT, LLC—See Thomas H. Lee Partners, L.P.; *U.S. Private*, pg. 4156
MHSI PTY. LTD.—See Medibank Private Limited; *Int'l*, pg. 4774
MHS SURGERY CENTERS, L.P.—See HCA Healthcare, Inc.; *U.S. Public*, pg. 1002
MHS SURGERY CENTERS, L.P.—See Methodist Healthcare Ministries of South Texas, Inc.; *U.S. Private*, pg. 2683
MH SWEDEN AB—See MH Connectors Group Limited; *Int'l*, pg. 4872
MHT ELEKTRONIK TASARIM VE TICARET A.S.—See Exceptional Innovation BV; *Int'l*, pg. 2579
MHT HOLDING AG—See Krones AG; *Int'l*, pg. 4306
MHT HOUSING, INC.; *U.S. Private*, pg. 2695
MHT OPTIC RESEARCH AG—See DENTSPLY SIRONA Inc.; *U.S. Public*, pg. 655
MHT PROPERTIES VII INC.—See MHT Housing, Inc.; *U.S. Private*, pg. 2695
MH TRANSYLVANIA REGIONAL HOSPITAL, LLLP—See HCA Healthcare, Inc.; *U.S. Public*, pg. 1001
MHT S.R.L.—See DENTSPLY SIRONA Inc.; *U.S. Private*, pg. 655
MHT TAKENTREPRENOREN I MALMO AB—See Trelleborg AB; *Int'l*, pg. 7910
MHT USA LLC—See Krones AG; *Int'l*, pg. 4306
M&H VALVE CO.—See McWane, Inc.; *U.S. Private*, pg. 2645
MHWIRTH AS—See Akastor ASA; *Int'l*, pg. 260
MHWIRTH AS—See Akastor ASA; *Int'l*, pg. 260
MHWIRTH AZERBAIJAN—See Akastor ASA; *Int'l*, pg. 260
MHWIRTH CANADA INC.—See Akastor ASA; *Int'l*, pg. 260
MHWIRTH DO BRASIL EQUIPAMENTOS LTDA—See Akastor ASA; *Int'l*, pg. 260
MHWIRTH GMBH—See Akastor ASA; *Int'l*, pg. 260
MHWIRTH INDIA PVT. LTD.—See Akastor ASA; *Int'l*, pg. 260
MHWIRTH LLC—See Akastor ASA; *Int'l*, pg. 260
MHWIRTH OFFSHORE PETROLEUM ENGINEERING (SHANGHAI) CO. LTD.—See Akastor ASA; *Int'l*, pg. 260
MHWIRTH PTY LTD—See Akastor ASA; *Int'l*, pg. 260
MHWIRTH (SINGAPORE) PTE. LTD.—See Akastor ASA; *Int'l*, pg. 260
MHWIRTH UK LTD.—See Akastor ASA; *Int'l*, pg. 260

MHW LTD.; *U.S. Private*, pg. 2695
MHZ DESIGN COMMUNICATIONS INC.; *Int'l*, pg. 4873
MHZ NETWORKS; *U.S. Private*, pg. 2695
MI5 PRINT & DIGITAL COMMUNICATIONS; *U.S. Private*, pg. 2696
MI9 NEW ZEALAND LIMITED—See Nine Entertainment Co. Holdings Limited; *Int'l*, pg. 5299
MI9 RETAIL, INC.; *U.S. Private*, pg. 2696
MIACO MEDIA INC.; *U.S. Private*, pg. 2696
MIA CORPORATION (PVT) LTD.—See Daikin Industries, Ltd.; *Int'l*, pg. 1936
MIAD UK LIMITED—See STRONTIUM PLC; *Int'l*, pg. 7243
MIA DYNAMICS MOTORS LTD.; *Int'l*, pg. 4873
MIAG B.V.—See Metro AG; *Int'l*, pg. 4859
MIAHELSA CORPORATION; *Int'l*, pg. 4873
MIAHELSA HOLDINGS CORPORATION; *Int'l*, pg. 4873
MIAMI AIR INTERNATIONAL, INC.—See TSI Holding Company; *U.S. Private*, pg. 4253
MIAMI-ARA LLC—See Nautic Partners, LLC; *U.S. Private*, pg. 2870
MIAMI AUTOMOTIVE RETAIL, INC.; *U.S. Private*, pg. 2696
MIAMI BEACH COMMUNITY HEALTH CENTER, INC.; *U.S. Private*, pg. 2696
MIAMI BEACH GOLF CLUB—See Professional Course Management, Inc.; *U.S. Private*, pg. 3274
MIAMI BEEF COMPANY INC.—See Trivest Partners, LP; *U.S. Private*, pg. 4240
MIAMI BREEZE CAR CARE, INC.; *U.S. Public*, pg. 1436
MIAMI CHILDREN'S HOSPITAL; *U.S. Private*, pg. 2696
MIAMI CITY BALLET, INC.; *U.S. Private*, pg. 2696
MIAMI CORP.; *U.S. Private*, pg. 2696
MIAMI-DADE CARDIOLOGY CONSULTANTS, LLC—See HCA Healthcare, Inc.; *U.S. Public*, pg. 1002
MIAMI DIVER LLC—See GenNx360 Capital Partners, L.P.; *U.S. Private*, pg. 1672
MIAMI DOLPHINS, LTD.—See Dolphins Enterprises, LLC; *U.S. Private*, pg. 1255
MIAMI DOWNTOWN DEVELOPMENT AUTHORITY; *U.S. Private*, pg. 2696
MIAMI FOUNDATION; *U.S. Private*, pg. 2696
MIAMI GARDENS-S, LLC—See Lithia Motors, Inc.; *U.S. Public*, pg. 1325
MIAMI GARDENS SQUARE ONE, INC.—See BGI Hospitality Holdings, Inc.; *U.S. Public*, pg. 1767
MIAMI HEAT LIMITED PARTNERSHIP—See FBA II, Inc.; *U.S. Private*, pg. 1485
THE MIAMI HERALD MEDIA COMPANY—See Chatham Asset Management, LLC; *U.S. Private*, pg. 867
THE MIAMI HERALD—See Chatham Asset Management, LLC; *U.S. Private*, pg. 867
MIAMI INDUSTRIAL TRUCKS INC.; *U.S. Private*, pg. 2696
MIAMI INDUSTRIAL TRUCKS INC.—See Miami Industrial Trucks Inc.; *U.S. Private*, pg. 2696
MIAMI INTERNATIONAL AIRPORT; *U.S. Private*, pg. 2696
MIAMI INTERNATIONAL COMMERCE CENTER—See Blackstone Inc.; *U.S. Public*, pg. 356
MIAMI INTERNATIONAL HOLDINGS, INC.; *U.S. Private*, pg. 2697
MIAMI INTERNATIONAL UNIVERSITY OF ART & DESIGN—See Dream Center Foundation, a California Nonprofit Corp.; *U.S. Private*, pg. 1274
MIAMI LAKES SURGERY CENTER, LTD.—See HCA Healthcare, Inc.; *U.S. Public*, pg. 1002
MIAMI-LUKEN INC.; *U.S. Private*, pg. 2697
MIAMI NEWSPAPERS, INC.—See American Consolidated Media LP; *U.S. Private*, pg. 228
MIAMI NEW TIMES, LLC—See Village Voice Media Holdings, LLC; *U.S. Private*, pg. 4384
MIAMI REGIONAL DIALYSIS CENTER WEST, LLC—See Nautic Partners, LLC; *U.S. Private*, pg. 2870
MIAMI SHORES COUNTRY CLUB—See Professional Course Management, Inc.; *U.S. Private*, pg. 3274
MIAMI SUBS CAPITAL PARTNERS I, INC.; *U.S. Private*, pg. 2697
MIAMI SUBS CORPORATION—See Miami Subs Capital Partners I, Inc.; *U.S. Private*, pg. 2697
MIAMI SUBS USA, INC.—See Miami Subs Capital Partners I, Inc.; *U.S. Private*, pg. 2697
MIAMI SURGICAL SUITES, LLC—See Tenet Healthcare Corporation; *U.S. Public*, pg. 2004
MIAMI VALLEY BROADCASTING CORPORATION—See Apollo Global Management, Inc.; *U.S. Public*, pg. 164
MIAMI VALLEY CHILD DEVELOPMENT CENTERS, INC.; *U.S. Private*, pg. 2697
MIAMI VALLEY GAMING & RACING, LLC—See Churchill Downs, Inc.; *U.S. Public*, pg. 493
MIAMI VALLEY LIGHTING, LLC—See The AES Corporation; *U.S. Public*, pg. 2031
MIAMI VALLEY STEEL SERVICE INC.—See Polen Capital Management, LLC; *U.S. Private*, pg. 3224
MIAN ELECTRONICS CORPORATION; *Int'l*, pg. 4873
MIANYANG CHENGHONG ELECTRONIC CHEMICALS CO., LTD.—See Nagase & Co., Ltd.; *Int'l*, pg. 5126
MIANYANG FULIN PARKSON PLAZA CO. LTD—See Parkson Holdings Berhad; *Int'l*, pg. 5744
MIANYANG FULIN PRECISION CO., LTD.; *Int'l*, pg. 4873

MIANYANG HONGREN ELECTRONIC CO., LTD.—See Shenzhen Deren Electronic Co., Ltd.; *Int'l*, pg. 6808
MIANYANG SCHLEMMER AUTOMOTIVE PARTS CO., LTD.—See Ningbo Huaxiang Electronic Co., Ltd.; *Int'l*, pg. 5302
MIANYANG SCIENCE TECHNOLOGY CITY DEVELOPMENT INVESTMENT (GROUP) CO., LTD.—See China Metal Resources Utilization Ltd.; *Int'l*, pg. 1524
MIANYANG XINCHEN ENGINE CO., LTD.—See Xinchen China Power Holdings Limited; *Int'l*, pg. 8529
MIANYANG XINJINCHENG AUTOMOBILE SALES & SERVICES CO., LTD.—See China Yongda Automobiles Services Holdings Limited; *Int'l*, pg. 1564
MIANZHU JINCAI PRINTING & PACKAGING CO., LTD.—See MYS Group Co., Ltd.; *Int'l*, pg. 5114
MIAOJIAN PR (SINO PR) CONSULTING CO., LTD.; *Int'l*, pg. 4873
MIAS HUNGARY KFT.—See Jungheinrich AG; *Int'l*, pg. 4029
MIAS INC.—See Jungheinrich AG; *Int'l*, pg. 4029
MIAS MASCHINENBAU, INDUSTRIEANLAGEN & SERVICE GMBH—See Jungheinrich AG; *Int'l*, pg. 4029
MIAS MATERIALS HANDLING (KUNSHAN) CO., LTD.—See Jungheinrich AG; *Int'l*, pg. 4029
MIAS OC SPOL. S R.O.; *Int'l*, pg. 4873
MIASOLE, INC.—See Hanergy Holding Group Limited; *Int'l*, pg. 3244
MIATA HOLDINGS INC.—See Miata Metals Corp.; *Int'l*, pg. 4873
MIATA METALS CORP.; *Int'l*, pg. 4873
MIAXIS BIOMETRICS CO., LTD.—See Shanghai Belling Co., Ltd.; *Int'l*, pg. 6762
MIBA AG; *Int'l*, pg. 4873
MIBA AUTOMATION SYSTEMS GES.M.B.H.—See Miba AG; *Int'l*, pg. 4874
MIBA BEARINGS US LLC—See Miba AG; *Int'l*, pg. 4874
MIBA DEUTSCHLAND GMBH—See Miba AG; *Int'l*, pg. 4874
MIBA FAR EAST PTE LTD—See Miba AG; *Int'l*, pg. 4874
MIBA FRICTEC GMBH—See Miba AG; *Int'l*, pg. 4874
MIBA GLEITLAGER AUSTRIA GMBH—See Miba AG; *Int'l*, pg. 4874
MIBA GLEITLAGER GMBH—See Miba AG; *Int'l*, pg. 4874
MIBA HYDRA MECHANICA CORP.—See Miba AG; *Int'l*, pg. 4874
MIBA INDUSTRIAL BEARINGS BRASIL LTDA.—See Miba AG; *Int'l*, pg. 4874
MIBA INDUSTRIAL BEARINGS GERMANY GMBH—See Miba AG; *Int'l*, pg. 4874
MIBA INDUSTRIAL BEARINGS GERMANY OSTERODE GMBH—See Miba AG; *Int'l*, pg. 4874
MIBANCO-BANCO DE LA MICRO EMPRESA S.A.; *Int'l*, pg. 4874
MIBA PRECISION COMPONENTS (CHINA) CO. LTD.—See Miba AG; *Int'l*, pg. 4874
MIBA SINTER AUSTRIA GMBH—See Miba AG; *Int'l*, pg. 4874
MIBA SINTER BRASIL LTDA.—See Miba AG; *Int'l*, pg. 4874
MIBA SINTER HOLDING GMBH & CO. KG—See Miba AG; *Int'l*, pg. 4874
MIBA SINTER SLOVAKIA S.R.O.—See Miba AG; *Int'l*, pg. 4874
MIBA STEELTEC S.R.O.—See Miba AG; *Int'l*, pg. 4874
MIBAU BAUSTOFFHANDEL GMBH—See Heidelberg Materials AG; *Int'l*, pg. 3318
MIBAU HOLDING GMBH—See Heidelberg Materials AG; *Int'l*, pg. 3318
MIBE GMBH ARZNEIMITTEL—See Dermapharm Holding SE; *Int'l*, pg. 2043
MIBELLE AG—See The Federation of Migros Cooperatives; *Int'l*, pg. 7642
MIBE PHARMACEUTICALS D.O.O—See Dermapharm Holding SE; *Int'l*, pg. 2043
MIBE PHARMA ITALIA SRL—See Dermapharm Holding SE; *Int'l*, pg. 2043
MIBE PHARMA UK LTD.—See Dermapharm Holding SE; *Int'l*, pg. 2043
MIBE UKRAINE LLC—See Dermapharm Holding SE; *Int'l*, pg. 2043
MIB GROUP INC.; *U.S. Private*, pg. 2697
MIB INSURANCE BROKERS PTY LTD—See Wesfarmers Limited; *Int'l*, pg. 8382
MIB METRO GROUP INSURANCE BROKER GMBH—See Metro AG; *Int'l*, pg. 4859
MIB SECURITIES INDIA PRIVATE LIMITED—See Malayan Banking Berhad; *Int'l*, pg. 4660
MIB SUISSE SA—See ITS Group SA; *Int'l*, pg. 3844
MIBU CORPORATION CO., LTD.—See Takamatsu Construction Group Co., Ltd.; *Int'l*, pg. 7430
MIBUGAWA POWER COMPANY—See Marubeni Corporation; *Int'l*, pg. 4709
MICA CORPORATION; *U.S. Private*, pg. 2697
MICAH GROUP ENERGY AND ENVIRONMENTAL; *U.S. Private*, pg. 2697
MICAMP SOLUTIONS, LLC; *U.S. Private*, pg. 2697
MICARNA S.A.—See The Federation of Migros Cooperatives; *Int'l*, pg. 7642

MICAMP SOLUTIONS, LLC

MICCO CONSTRUCTION LLC.—See National Construction Enterprises Inc.; *U.S. Private,* pg. 2851

MICCO LLC—See National Construction Enterprises Inc.; *U.S. Private,* pg. 2851

MIC CO, LTD.—See Medipal Holdings Corporation; *Int'l,* pg. 4779

MIC ELECTRONICS INC.—See MIC Electronics Limited; *Int'l,* pg. 4874

MIC ELECTRONICS LIMITED; *Int'l,* pg. 4874

MICELI DAIRY PRODUCTS CO.; *U.S. Private,* pg. 2697

MICELLO, INC.; *U.S. Private,* pg. 2697

M.I. CEMENT FACTORY LIMITED; *Int'l,* pg. 4615

MIC GROUP—See J.B. Poindexter & Co., Inc.; *U.S. Private,* pg. 2158

THE MICHAEL ALAN GROUP—See BDS Marketing, LLC; *U.S. Private,* pg. 502

MICHAEL ALLEN COMPANY, LLC—See Sony Group Corporation; *Int'l,* pg. 7102

THE MICHAEL-ANN RUSSELL JEWISH COMMUNITY CENTER; *U.S. Private,* pg. 4079

MICHAEL ANTHONY JEWELERS, INC.—See Berkshire Hathaway Inc.; *U.S. Public,* pg. 316

MICHAEL AUTO PARTS, INCORPORATED—See LKQ Corporation; *U.S. Public,* pg. 1335

MICHAEL BAKER INTERNATIONAL, LLC—See D.C. Capital Partners, LLC; *U.S. Private,* pg. 1141

MICHAEL B. BAYLESS & ASSOCIATES, LLC—See Centene Corporation; *U.S. Public,* pg. 470

MICHAEL, BEST & FRIEDRICH LLP; *U.S. Private,* pg. 2699

MICHAEL BLACKMAN & ASSOCIATES, INC.—See The Dickler Corp.; *U.S. Private,* pg. 4021

MICHAEL CADILLAC INC.; *U.S. Private,* pg. 2697

MICHAEL C. FINA CO. INC.; *U.S. Private,* pg. 2697

MICHAEL COLLARD PROPERTIES INC.; *U.S. Private,* pg. 2697

MICHAEL DUNN CENTER; *U.S. Private,* pg. 2697

MICHAEL ELECTRIC, INC.—See Black Box Limited; *Int'l,* pg. 1058

MICHAEL FLORA & ASSOCIATES INC.; *U.S. Private,* pg. 2697

MICHAEL FOODS GROUP, INC.—See Post Holdings, Inc.; *U.S. Public,* pg. 1703

MICHAEL FOODS, INC.—See Post Holdings, Inc.; *U.S. Public,* pg. 1703

MICHAEL FOODS OF DELAWARE, INC.—See Post Holdings, Inc.; *U.S. Public,* pg. 1703

MICHAEL FRIESS GMBH—See Knauf Interfer SE; *Int'l,* pg. 4205

MICHAEL GERALD LTD. INC.; *U.S. Private,* pg. 2697

MICHAEL G. HAAS, M.D., LLC—See Panorama Eye Care LLC; *U.S. Private,* pg. 3087

MICHAEL GLATT MASCHINENBAU GMBH—See Buechl Handels-und Beteiligungs-KG; *Int'l,* pg. 1211

MICHAEL GRAVES & ASSOCIATES, INC.; *U.S. Private,* pg. 2698

MICHAEL G. RUDELSON AND COMPANY—See Aon plc; *Int'l,* pg. 496

MICHAEL HILL INTERNATIONAL INC.—See Michael Hill New Zealand Limited; *Int'l,* pg. 4874

MICHAEL HILL JEWELLER (AUSTRALIA) PTY LIMITED—See Michael Hill New Zealand Limited; *Int'l,* pg. 4874

MICHAEL HILL JEWELLER (CANADA) PTY. LIMITED—See Michael Hill New Zealand Limited; *Int'l,* pg. 4874

MICHAEL HILL JEWELLER LIMITED—See Michael Hill New Zealand Limited; *Int'l,* pg. 4874

MICHAEL HILL NEW ZEALAND LIMITED; *Int'l,* pg. 4874

MICHAEL HOERAUF MASCHINENFABRIK GMBH & CO. KG; *Int'l,* pg. 4874

MICHAEL HOHL MOTOR COMPANY; *U.S. Private,* pg. 2698

MICHAEL HYATT & COMPANY LLC; *U.S. Private,* pg. 2698

MICHAEL JACKSON MOTOR SALES LIMITED; *Int'l,* pg. 4874

MICHAEL J. HALL & CO,—See GTCR LLC; *U.S. Private,* pg. 1803

MICHAEL J. LONDON & ASSOCIATES; *U.S. Private,* pg. 2698

MICHAELKATE INTERIORS AND GALLERY; *U.S. Private,* pg. 2699

MICHAEL KORS (AUSTRIA) GMBH—See Capri Holdings Limited; *Int'l,* pg. 1316

MICHAEL KORS BELGIUM BVBA—See Capri Holdings Limited; *Int'l,* pg. 1316

MICHAEL KORS (BUCHAREST STORE) S.R.L.—See Capri Holdings Limited; *Int'l,* pg. 1316

MICHAEL KORS (CANADA) CO.—See Capri Holdings Limited; *Int'l,* pg. 1316

MICHAEL KORS (CZECH REPUBLIC) S.R.O.—See Capri Holdings Limited; *Int'l,* pg. 1316

MICHAEL KORS (GERMANY) GMBH—See Capri Holdings Limited; *Int'l,* pg. 1316

MICHAEL KORS ITALY S.R.L.—See Capri Holdings Limited; *Int'l,* pg. 1316

MICHAEL KORS JAPAN K.K.—See Capri Holdings Limited; *Int'l,* pg. 1316

MICHAEL KORS LIMITED—See Capri Holdings Limited; *Int'l,* pg. 1316

MICHAEL KORS, LLC—See Capri Holdings Limited; *Int'l,* pg. 1316

MICHAEL KORS (NETHERLANDS) B.V.—See Capri Holdings Limited; *Int'l,* pg. 1316

MICHAEL KORS RETAIL, INC.—See Capri Holdings Limited; *Int'l,* pg. 1316

MICHAEL KORS SPAIN, S.L.—See Capri Holdings Limited; *Int'l,* pg. 1316

MICHAEL KORS STORES (CALIFORNIA), INC.—See Capri Holdings Limited; *Int'l,* pg. 1316

MICHAEL KORS STORES, LLC—See Capri Holdings Limited; *Int'l,* pg. 1316

MICHAEL KORS (SWITZERLAND) GMBH—See Capri Holdings Limited; *Int'l,* pg. 1316

MICHAEL KORS (UK) LIMITED—See Capri Holdings Limited; *Int'l,* pg. 1316

MICHAEL KORS (USA), INC.—See Capri Holdings Limited; *Int'l,* pg. 1316

MICHAEL L. CROSS & CO LTD.—See Herbein + Company, Inc.; *U.S. Private,* pg. 1920

MICHAEL LEWIS COMPANY; *U.S. Private,* pg. 2698

MICHAEL MALTZAN ARCHITECTURE, INC.; *U.S. Private,* pg. 2698

MICHAEL O'BRIEN ENTERPRISES, INC.; *U.S. Private,* pg. 2698

MICHAEL PAGE AFRICA (SA) (PTY) LIMITED—See PageGroup plc; *Int'l,* pg. 5697

MICHAEL PAGE (BEIJING) RECRUITMENT CO., LTD.—See PageGroup plc; *Int'l,* pg. 5697

MICHAEL PAGE DO INTERNATIONAL (BRASIL) RECRUTAMENTO ESPECIALIZADO LTDA—See PageGroup plc; *Int'l,* pg. 5697

MICHAEL PAGE HOLDINGS LIMITED—See PageGroup plc; *Int'l,* pg. 5697

MICHAEL PAGE INTERNATIONAL ARGENTINA SA—See PageGroup plc; *Int'l,* pg. 5698

MICHAEL PAGE INTERNATIONAL (AUSTRALIA) PTY LIMITED—See PageGroup plc; *Int'l,* pg. 5697

MICHAEL PAGE INTERNATIONAL AUSTRIA GMBH—See PageGroup plc; *Int'l,* pg. 5698

MICHAEL PAGE INTERNATIONAL (BELGIUM) NV—See PageGroup plc; *Int'l,* pg. 5697

MICHAEL PAGE INTERNATIONAL CANADA LIMITED—See PageGroup plc; *Int'l,* pg. 5698

MICHAEL PAGE INTERNATIONAL CHILE LTDA—See PageGroup plc; *Int'l,* pg. 5698

MICHAEL PAGE INTERNATIONAL (DEUTSCHLAND) GMBH—See PageGroup plc; *Int'l,* pg. 5697

MICHAEL PAGE INTERNATIONAL EMPRESA DE TRABALHO TEMPORARIO E SERVICOS DE CONSULTADORIA LDA—See PageGroup plc; *Int'l,* pg. 5698

MICHAEL PAGE INTERNATIONAL (ESPANA) SA—See PageGroup plc; *Int'l,* pg. 5697

MICHAEL PAGE INTERNATIONAL (FRANCE) SAS—See PageGroup plc; *Int'l,* pg. 5697

MICHAEL PAGE INTERNATIONAL HOLDINGS LIMITED—See PageGroup plc; *Int'l,* pg. 5698

MICHAEL PAGE INTERNATIONAL (HONG KONG) LIMITED—See PageGroup plc; *Int'l,* pg. 5697

MICHAEL PAGE INTERNATIONAL INC—See PageGroup plc; *Int'l,* pg. 5698

MICHAEL PAGE INTERNATIONAL (IRELAND) LIMITED—See PageGroup plc; *Int'l,* pg. 5697

MICHAEL PAGE INTERNATIONAL ITALIA SRL—See PageGroup plc; *Int'l,* pg. 5698

MICHAEL PAGE INTERNATIONAL (JAPAN) K.K.—See PageGroup plc; *Int'l,* pg. 5697

MICHAEL PAGE INTERNATIONAL (MALAYSIA) SDN. BHD.—See PageGroup plc; *Int'l,* pg. 5697

MICHAEL PAGE INTERNATIONAL (MAROC) SARL AU—See PageGroup plc; *Int'l,* pg. 5698

MICHAEL PAGE INTERNATIONAL (MAURITIUS) LIMITED—See PageGroup plc; *Int'l,* pg. 5698

MICHAEL PAGE INTERNATIONAL MEXICO RECLUTAMIENTO ESPECIALIZADO, S.A. DE C.V.—See PageGroup plc; *Int'l,* pg. 5698

MICHAEL PAGE INTERNATIONAL (NEDERLAND) B.V.—See PageGroup plc; *Int'l,* pg. 5698

MICHAEL PAGE INTERNATIONAL NEM ISTIHDAM DANISMANLIGI LIMITED SIRKETI—See PageGroup plc; *Int'l,* pg. 5698

MICHAEL PAGE INTERNATIONAL (NZ) LIMITED.—See PageGroup plc; *Int'l,* pg. 5698

MICHAEL PAGE INTERNATIONAL PERU SRL—See PageGroup plc; *Int'l,* pg. 5698

MICHAEL PAGE INTERNATIONAL (POLAND) SP.Z.O.O—See PageGroup plc; *Int'l,* pg. 5698

MICHAEL PAGE INTERNATIONAL PORTUGAL - EMPRESSA DE TRABALHO TEMPORARIO E SERVICOS DE CONSULTADORIA LDA—See PageGroup plc; *Int'l,* pg. 5698

MICHAEL PAGE INTERNATIONAL PTE LIMITED—See PageGroup plc; *Int'l,* pg. 5698

MICHAEL PAGE INTERNATIONAL RECRUITMENT LIMITED—See PageGroup plc; *Int'l,* pg. 5698

MICHAEL PAGE INTERNATIONAL RECRUITMENT PVT. LTD.—See PageGroup plc; *Int'l,* pg. 5698

CORPORATE AFFILIATIONS

MICHAEL PAGE INTERNATIONAL RECRUITMENT (THAILAND) LIMITED—See PageGroup plc; *Int'l,* pg. 5698

MICHAEL PAGE INTERNATIONAL RU LLC—See PageGroup plc; *Int'l,* pg. 5698

MICHAEL PAGE INTERNATIONAL (SA) (PTY) LIMITED—See PageGroup plc; *Int'l,* pg. 5698

MICHAEL PAGE INTERNATIONAL (SHANGHAI) CONSULTING LTD—See PageGroup plc; *Int'l,* pg. 5698

MICHAEL PAGE INTERNATIONAL (SWEDEN) AB—See PageGroup plc; *Int'l,* pg. 5698

MICHAEL PAGE INTERNATIONAL (SWITZERLAND) SA—See PageGroup plc; *Int'l,* pg. 5698

MICHAEL PAGE INTERNATIONAL (UAE) LIMITED—See PageGroup plc; *Int'l,* pg. 5698

MICHAEL PAGE INTERNATIONAL (VIETNAM) CO. LIMITED—See PageGroup plc; *Int'l,* pg. 5698

MICHAEL PAGE LIMITED—See PageGroup plc; *Int'l,* pg. 5698

MICHAEL PAGE RECRUITMENT GROUP LIMITED—See PageGroup plc; *Int'l,* pg. 5698

MICHAEL PAGE (SHANGHAI) RECRUITMENT CO. LTD—See PageGroup plc; *Int'l,* pg. 5697

MICHAEL PAGE UK LIMITED—See PageGroup plc; *Int'l,* pg. 5698

MICHAEL RAYMOND NIGERIA LTD.—See Haulotte Group SA; *Int'l,* pg. 3285

MICHAEL RIESZ & CO. INC.; *U.S. Private,* pg. 2698

MICHAEL SAUNDERS & COMPANY; *U.S. Private,* pg. 2698

MICHAEL'S CARPET INC.; *U.S. Private,* pg. 2699

THE MICHAELS COMPANIES, INC.—See Apollo Global Management, Inc.; *U.S. Public,* pg. 164

THE MICHAEL'S DEVELOPMENT COMPANY INC.; *U.S. Private,* pg. 4078

MICHAELS ENTERPRISES INC.; *U.S. Private,* pg. 2699

MICHAEL'S FINER MEATS, LLC—See The Chefs' Warehouse, Inc.; *U.S. Public,* pg. 2059

MICHAELS GROUP, LLC; *U.S. Private,* pg. 2699

MICHAEL SIMON INC.; *U.S. Private,* pg. 2698

MICHAELS INC.—See Michaels Enterprises Inc.; *U.S. Private,* pg. 2699

MICHAEL SKURNIK WINES, INC.; *U.S. Private,* pg. 2698

MICHAELS MILITARY HOUSING, LLC—See The Michael's Development Company Inc.; *U.S. Private,* pg. 4079

MICHAELSON, CONNOR & BOUL, INC.; *U.S. Private,* pg. 2699

MICHAELSON GROUP REAL ESTATE, LLC; *U.S. Private,* pg. 2699

MICHAELS STORES, INC.—See Apollo Global Management, Inc.; *U.S. Public,* pg. 164

MICHAEL STARS, INC.; *U.S. Private,* pg. 2698

MICHAEL STEADS HILLTOP FORD KIA; *U.S. Private,* pg. 2698

MICHAELSWILDER; *U.S. Private,* pg. 2699

MICHAEL THOMAS FURNITURE INC.; *U.S. Private,* pg. 2698

MICHAEL THRASHER TRUCKING CO.; *U.S. Private,* pg. 2698

MICHAEL WALTERS ADVERTISING; *U.S. Private,* pg. 2699

MICHAEL WEINIG AG—See Michael Weinig AG; *Int'l,* pg. 4875

MICHAEL WEINIG AG; *Int'l,* pg. 4874

MICHAEL WEINIG ASIA PTE. LTD.—See Michael Weinig AG; *Int'l,* pg. 4875

MICHAEL WEINIG AUSTRALIA PTY. LTD.—See Michael Weinig AG; *Int'l,* pg. 4875

MICHAEL WEINIG, INC.—See Michael Weinig AG; *Int'l,* pg. 4875

MICHAEL WEINIG SA—See Michael Weinig AG; *Int'l,* pg. 4875

MICHAEL WEINIG (UK) LTD.—See Michael Weinig AG; *Int'l,* pg. 4875

MICHAEL WEINIG (YANTAI) MACHINERY CO LTD.—See Michael Weinig AG; *Int'l,* pg. 4874

MICHANG OIL IND. CO., LTD.; *Int'l,* pg. 4875

MICHAUD & SAMMON INSURANCE, INC.; *U.S. Private,* pg. 2699

MICHCON PIPELINE COMPANY—See DTE Energy Company; *U.S. Public,* pg. 689

MICHEL & CO AG SAND-UND KIESWERKE—See Vicat S.A.; *Int'l,* pg. 8186

MICHELDEVER TYRE SERVICES LTD.—See Sumitomo Rubber Industries, Ltd.; *Int'l,* pg. 7299

MICHELETTI & ASSOCIATES INC.; *U.S. Private,* pg. 2699

MICHELIN AIM FZCO—See Compagnie Generale des Etablissements Michelin SCA; *Int'l,* pg. 1743

MICHELIN AIRCRAFT TIRE CORPORATION—See Compagnie Generale des Etablissements Michelin SCA; *Int'l,* pg. 1743

MICHELIN AIR SERVICES—See Compagnie Generale des Etablissements Michelin SCA; *Int'l,* pg. 1743

MICHELIN ALGERIE SPA—See Compagnie Generale des Etablissements Michelin SCA; *Int'l,* pg. 1743

MICHELIN AMERICA DO SUL—See Compagnie Generale des Etablissements Michelin SCA; *Int'l,* pg. 1743

COMPANY NAME INDEX

MICHELIN AMERICAS RESEARCH & DEVELOPMENT—See Compagnie Generale des Etablissements Michelin SCA; *Int'l*, pg. 1744
MICHELIN ARGENTINA SOCIEDAD ANONIMA, INDUSTRIAL, COMERCIAL Y FINANCIERA—See Compagnie Generale des Etablissements Michelin SCA; *Int'l*, pg. 1743
MICHELIN ASIA (HONG KONG) LIMITED—See Compagnie Generale des Etablissements Michelin SCA; *Int'l*, pg. 1743
MICHELIN ASIA-PACIFIC PTE LTD—See Compagnie Generale des Etablissements Michelin SCA; *Int'l*, pg. 1743
MICHELIN ASIA (SINGAPORE) CO. PTE. LTD.—See Compagnie Generale des Etablissements Michelin SCA; *Int'l*, pg. 1743
MICHELIN AUSTRALIA PTY LTD—See Compagnie Generale des Etablissements Michelin SCA; *Int'l*, pg. 1743
MICHELIN BELUX S.A.—See Compagnie Generale des Etablissements Michelin SCA; *Int'l*, pg. 1743
MICHELIN CHILE LTDA.—See Compagnie Generale des Etablissements Michelin SCA; *Int'l*, pg. 1743
MICHELIN CHUN SHIN LTD.—See Compagnie Generale des Etablissements Michelin SCA; *Int'l*, pg. 1743
MICHELIN CORPORATION—See Compagnie Generale des Etablissements Michelin SCA; *Int'l*, pg. 1743
MICHELIN ESPANA PORTUGAL, S.A.—See Compagnie Generale des Etablissements Michelin SCA; *Int'l*, pg. 1744
MICHELIN FINANCE (PAYS-BAS) B.V.—See Compagnie Generale des Etablissements Michelin SCA; *Int'l*, pg. 1744
MICHELIN FINANZ GESELLSCHAFT FUR BETEILIGUNGEN AG & CO. OHG—See Compagnie Generale des Etablissements Michelin SCA; *Int'l*, pg. 1744
MICHELIN HUNGARIA TYRE MANUFACTURE LTD.—See Compagnie Generale des Etablissements Michelin SCA; *Int'l*, pg. 1744
MICHELIN INDIA PRIVATE LIMITED—See Compagnie Generale des Etablissements Michelin SCA; *Int'l*, pg. 1744
MICHELIN INDIA TAMILNADU TYRES PRIVATE LIMITED—See Compagnie Generale des Etablissements Michelin SCA; *Int'l*, pg. 1744
MICHELIN INDIA TYRES PRIVATE LIMITED—See Compagnie Generale des Etablissements Michelin SCA; *Int'l*, pg. 1744
MICHELIN KOREA COMPANY LIMITED—See Compagnie Generale des Etablissements Michelin SCA; *Int'l*, pg. 1743
MICHELIN LASTIKLERI TICARET A.S.—See Compagnie Generale des Etablissements Michelin SCA; *Int'l*, pg. 1744
MICHELIN MALAYSIA SDN. BHD.—See Compagnie Generale des Etablissements Michelin SCA; *Int'l*, pg. 1744
MICHELIN NEDERLAND N.V.—See Compagnie Generale des Etablissements Michelin SCA; *Int'l*, pg. 1744
MICHELIN NORDIC AB—See Compagnie Generale des Etablissements Michelin SCA; *Int'l*, pg. 1744
MICHELIN NORTH AMERICA (CANADA) INC.—See Compagnie Generale des Etablissements Michelin SCA; *Int'l*, pg. 1744
MICHELIN NORTH AMERICA, INC.—See Compagnie Generale des Etablissements Michelin SCA; *Int'l*, pg. 1743
MICHELIN POLSKA S.A.—See Compagnie Generale des Etablissements Michelin SCA; *Int'l*, pg. 1744
MICHELIN RECHERCHE ET TECHNIQUE S.A.—See Compagnie Generale des Etablissements Michelin SCA; *Int'l*, pg. 1744
MICHELIN REIFENWERKE KGAA—See Compagnie Generale des Etablissements Michelin SCA; *Int'l*, pg. 1744
MICHELIN ROMANIA S.A.—See Compagnie Generale des Etablissements Michelin SCA; *Int'l*, pg. 1744
MICHELIN SIAM CO., LTD. - NONGKHAE PLANT—See Compagnie Generale des Etablissements Michelin SCA; *Int'l*, pg. 1743
MICHELIN SIAM CO., LTD. - SI RACHA PLANT—See Compagnie Generale des Etablissements Michelin SCA; *Int'l*, pg. 1743
MICHELIN SIAM CO., LTD.—See Compagnie Generale des Etablissements Michelin SCA; *Int'l*, pg. 1743
MICHELIN SIAM GROUP CO., LTD.—See Compagnie Generale des Etablissements Michelin SCA; *Int'l*, pg. 1743
MICHELIN SUISSE S.A.—See Compagnie Generale des Etablissements Michelin SCA; *Int'l*, pg. 1744
MICHELIN THAI HOLDING CO., LTD.—See Compagnie Generale des Etablissements Michelin SCA; *Int'l*, pg. 1743
MICHELIN TYRE COMPANY SOUTH AFRICA (PROPRIETARY) LIMITED—See Compagnie Generale des Etablissements Michelin SCA; *Int'l*, pg. 1744
MICHELIN TYRE P.L.C.—See Compagnie Generale des Etablissements Michelin SCA; *Int'l*, pg. 1744
MICHELIN TYRE SERVICES COMPANY LTD.—See Compagnie Generale des Etablissements Michelin SCA; *Int'l*, pg. 1745
MICHELIN UKRAINE LLC—See Compagnie Generale des Etablissements Michelin SCA; *Int'l*, pg. 1745
MICHELIN VIETNAM COMPANY LIMITED—See Compagnie Generale des Etablissements Michelin SCA; *Int'l*, pg. 1743
MICHELL BEARINGS LTD—See British Engines Ltd.; *Int'l*, pg. 1171
MICHELL INSTRUMENTS, INC.—See Battery Ventures, L.P.; *U.S. Private*, pg. 489
MICHELL INSTRUMENTS LIMITED—See Battery Ventures, L.P.; *U.S. Private*, pg. 489
MICHELL Y CIA. S.A.; *Int'l*, pg. 4875
MICHELMAN ASIA-PACIFIC PTE. LTD.—See Michelman Inc.; *U.S. Private*, pg. 2699
MICHELMAN-CANCELLIERE IRON WORKS, INC.; *U.S. Private*, pg. 2699
MICHELMAN CHEMICALS PVT. LTD.—See Michelman Inc.; *U.S. Private*, pg. 2699
MICHELMAN INC.; *U.S. Private*, pg. 2699
MICHELMAN SARL—See Michelman Inc.; *U.S. Private*, pg. 2699
MICHELMAN (SHANGHAI) CHEMICAL TRADING CO., LTD.—See Michelman Inc.; *U.S. Private*, pg. 2699
MICHELMERSH BRICK HOLDINGS PLC; *Int'l*, pg. 4875
MICHELMERSH BRICK & TILE COMPANY LTD.—See Michelmersh Brick Holdings PLC; *Int'l*, pg. 4875
MICHEL RENE LIMITED—See YGM Trading Ltd; *Int'l*, pg. 8580
MICHEL RIME SA—See BKW AG; *Int'l*, pg. 1055
MICHEL-SCHLUMBERGER WINES—See Adams Wine Group, LLC; *U.S. Private*, pg. 75
MICHELS CORPORATION; *U.S. Private*, pg. 2700
MICHEL SEMEGEN HOLDINGS LTD.; *Int'l*, pg. 4875
MICHELSEN BENEFITS GROUP, INC.—See Aon plc; *Int'l*, pg. 496
MICHELSEN PACKAGING CO. INC.; *U.S. Private*, pg. 2700
MICHELSEN PACKAGING OF CALIFORNIA INC.—See Michelsen Packaging Co. Inc.; *U.S. Private*, pg. 2700
THE MICHEL'S GROUP AUSTRALIA PTY LTD—See Retail Food Group Limited; *Int'l*, pg. 6305
MICHELSON DIAGNOSTICS DEUTSCHLAND GMBH—See Michelson Diagnostics Limited; *Int'l*, pg. 4875
MICHELSON DIAGNOSTICS INC.—See Michelson Diagnostics Limited; *Int'l*, pg. 4875
MICHELSON DIAGNOSTICS LIMITED; *Int'l*, pg. 4875
MICHELSON ENERGY COMPANY; *U.S. Private*, pg. 2700
MICHELSON JEWELERS; *U.S. Private*, pg. 2700
MICHEL S PATISSERIE (SA) PTY LTD.—See Retail Food Group Limited; *Int'l*, pg. 6305
MICHIANA RECYCLING & DISPOSAL, LLC—See Macquarie Group Limited; *Int'l*, pg. 4628
MICHIGAN AIR PRODUCTS CO.; *U.S. Private*, pg. 2700
MICHIGAN-AMERICAN WATER COMPANY—See American Water Works Company, Inc.; *U.S. Public*, pg. 112
MICHIGAN ARC PRODUCTS; *U.S. Private*, pg. 2700
MICHIGAN AUTOMOTIVE COMPRESSOR, INC.—See Toyota Industries Corporation; *Int'l*, pg. 7869
MICHIGAN BASIC PROPERTY INSURANCE ASSOCIATION; *U.S. Private*, pg. 2700
MICHIGAN BELL TELEPHONE COMPANY—See AT&T Inc.; *U.S. Public*, pg. 219
MICHIGAN BOX COMPANY; *U.S. Private*, pg. 2700
MICHIGAN BRUSH MANUFACTURING COMPANY, INC.—See Gordon Brush Mfg Co, Inc.; *U.S. Private*, pg. 1742
MICHIGAN CATASTROPHIC CLAIMS ASSOCIATION; *U.S. Private*, pg. 2700
MICHIGAN CHANDELIER COMPANY, LLC—See Seneca Partners Inc.; *U.S. Private*, pg. 3606
MICHIGAN CHANDELIER COMPANY, LLC—See Uniprop, Inc.; *U.S. Private*, pg. 4286
MICHIGAN COMMUNITY ACTION AGENCY ASSOCIATION; *U.S. Private*, pg. 2700
MICHIGAN COMMUNITY DENTAL CLINICS, INC.; *U.S. Private*, pg. 2700
MICHIGAN COMPLETE HEALTH—See Centene Corporation; *U.S. Public*, pg. 470
MICHIGAN CRYSTAL FLASH PETRO; *U.S. Private*, pg. 2700
MICHIGAN CUSTOM MACHINES, INC.; *U.S. Private*, pg. 2700
MICHIGAN DAIRY, L.L.C.—See The Kroger Co.; *U.S. Public*, pg. 2108
MICHIGAN DISPOSAL, INC.—See Republic Services, Inc.; *U.S. Public*, pg. 1788
MICHIGAN DRILL CORPORATION; *U.S. Private*, pg. 2700
MICHIGAN EDUCATION ASSOCIATION; *U.S. Private*, pg. 2700
MICHIGAN ELECTRICAL EMPLOYEES HEALTH PLAN; *U.S. Private*, pg. 2700
MICHIGAN ELECTRIC SUPPLY CO.; *U.S. Private*, pg. 2700
MICHIGAN ELECTRIC TRANSMISSION COMPANY, LLC—See Fortis Inc.; *Int'l*, pg. 2740
MICHIGAN ENGINEERING AND TEST CENTER—See Resilience Capital Partners, LLC; *U.S. Private*, pg. 3405
MICHIGAN ENGINEERS PRIVATE LIMITED—See Welspun Group; *Int'l*, pg. 8375
MICHIGAN FAMILY RESOURCES; *U.S. Private*, pg. 2700
MICHIGAN GAS UTILITIES CORPORATION—See WEC Energy Group, Inc.; *U.S. Public*, pg. 2342
MICHIGAN HISTORIC PRESERVATION NETWORK; *U.S. Private*, pg. 2700
MICHIGAN IMPLEMENT INC. - DEVILS LAKE—See Michigan Implement Inc.; *U.S. Private*, pg. 2701
MICHIGAN IMPLEMENT INC.; *U.S. Private*, pg. 2701
MICHIGAN INDUSTRIAL SHOE CO.—See Saf-Gard Safety Shoe Co.; *U.S. Private*, pg. 3523
MICHIGAN INSURANCE COMPANY—See Donegal Group Inc.; *U.S. Public*, pg. 676
MICHIGAN INTERNATIONAL SPEEDWAY, INC.—See National Association for Stock Car Auto Racing, Inc.; *U.S. Private*, pg. 2845
MICHIGAN JOBBER BROKER EQUIPMENT & SUPPLIES CO. INC.—See CenTra, Inc.; *U.S. Private*, pg. 818
MICHIGAN KENWORTH, INC.; *U.S. Private*, pg. 2701
MICHIGAN LABORERS FRINGE BENEFIT FUNDS; *U.S. Private*, pg. 2701
MICHIGAN LOGOS, INC.—See Lamar Advertising Company; *U.S. Public*, pg. 1291
MICHIGAN MATERIALS & AGGREGATES COMPANY—See CRH plc; *Int'l*, pg. 1847
MICHIGAN METAL COATINGS CO.—See NOF Corporation; *Int'l*, pg. 5399
MICHIGAN MULTI-KING INC.; *U.S. Private*, pg. 2701
MICHIGAN OFFICE SOLUTIONS; *U.S. Private*, pg. 2701
MICHIGAN ORNAMENTAL METALS—See Western Construction Group; *U.S. Private*, pg. 4492
MICHIGAN OUTPATIENT SURGICAL SOLUTIONS, LLC—See Tenet Healthcare Corporation; *U.S. Public*, pg. 2004
MICHIGAN PACKAGING CO.—See Greif Inc.; *U.S. Public*, pg. 967
MICHIGAN PAVING & MATERIALS CO.—See CRH plc; *Int'l*, pg. 1847
MICHIGAN PETROLEUM TECHNOLOGIES, INC.—See AIP, LLC; *U.S. Private*, pg. 136
MICHIGAN PIONEER ACO, LLC—See Tenet Healthcare Corporation; *U.S. Public*, pg. 2015
MICHIGAN PIZZA HUT INC.; *U.S. Private*, pg. 2701
MICHIGAN PROPERTY & CASUALTY GUARANTY ASSOCIATION; *U.S. Private*, pg. 2701
MICHIGAN PUBLIC HEALTH INSTITUTE; *U.S. Private*, pg. 2701
MICHIGAN ROD PRODUCTS INC.; *U.S. Private*, pg. 2701
MICHIGAN'S ADVENTURE—See Six Flags Entertainment Corporation; *U.S. Public*, pg. 1890
MICHIGAN SEAMLESS TUBE LLC—See Optima Specialty Steel, Inc.; *U.S. Private*, pg. 3034
MICHIGAN SHORE RAILROAD—See Brookfield Infrastructure Partners L.P.; *Int'l*, pg. 1192
MICHIGAN SHORE RAILROAD—See GIC Pte. Ltd.; *Int'l*, pg. 2966
MICHIGAN SPORTING GOODS DISTRIBUTORS INC.; *U.S. Private*, pg. 2701
MICHIGAN SPRING & STAMPING LLC—See Hines Corporation; *U.S. Private*, pg. 1949
MICHIGAN STATE UNIVERSITY FEDERAL CREDIT UNION; *U.S. Private*, pg. 2701
MICHIGAN SUGAR COMPANY; *U.S. Private*, pg. 2701
MICHIGAN SUGAR COMPANY—See Michigan Sugar Company; *U.S. Private*, pg. 2701
MICHIGAN SUGAR COMPANY—See Michigan Sugar Company; *U.S. Private*, pg. 2701
MICHIGAN SURGERY SPECIALISTS PC.; *U.S. Private*, pg. 2701
MICHIGAN TRACTOR & MACHINERY CO.; *U.S. Private*, pg. 2701
MICHIGAN TRAILER SERVICE INC.—See Trudell Trailers of Grand Rapids, Inc.; *U.S. Private*, pg. 4247
MICHIGAN TUBE SWAGERS SEATING; *U.S. Private*, pg. 2701
MICHIGAN WEST SHORE NURSERY, LLC.; *U.S. Private*, pg. 2701
MICHIGAN WHEEL OPERATIONS, LLC—See The Anderson Group, LLC; *U.S. Private*, pg. 3986
MICHIGAN WIRE DIE COMPANY—See MNP Corporation; *U.S. Private*, pg. 2756
THE MICHINOKU BANK LIMITED; *Int'l*, pg. 7666
MICHINOKU COCA-COLA BOTTLING CO., LTD.; *Int'l*, pg. 4875
MICHINOKU FINANCE (HONG KONG) LTD.—See The Michinoku Bank Limited; *Int'l*, pg. 7666
MICHINOKU, LTD.—See DyDo Group Holdings, Inc.; *Int'l*, pg. 2238
MICHINOKU MILK CO., LTD.—See MEGMILK SNOW BRAND Co., Ltd.; *Int'l*, pg. 4796
MICHINOKU SERVICE CO., LTD.—See Hitachi Zosen Corporation; *Int'l*, pg. 3411
MICHINORI HOLDINGS, INC.—See Industrial Growth Platform, Inc.; *Int'l*, pg. 3672
MICHLIG AGRICENTER INC.; *U.S. Private*, pg. 2701

MICHLOL FINANCE LTD.

MICHLOL FINANCE LTD.; *Int'l*, pg. 4875
MICHMAN FINANCE LTD; *Int'l*, pg. 4875
MICHONG METAVERSE (CHINA) HOLDINGS GROUP LIMITED; *Int'l*, pg. 4876
MICH RESOURCES LTD; *Int'l*, pg. 4874
MIC INDUSTRIES INC.; *U.S. Private*, pg. 2697
MICKAN GENERALBAUGESELLSCHAFT AMBERG MBH & CO. KG—See L. Possehl & Co. mbH; *Int'l*, pg. 4383
MICKELBERRY COMMUNICATIONS INC.; *U.S. Private*, pg. 2701
MICKEY FINN STORES INC.; *U.S. Private*, pg. 2701
MICKEYS ENTERPRISES INC.; *U.S. Private*, pg. 2702
MICKEYS LINEN & TOWEL SUPPLY; *U.S. Private*, pg. 2702
MICKEY TRUCK BODIES INC.; *U.S. Private*, pg. 2701
MICK RADIO-NUCLEAR INSTRUMENT, INC.—See Eckert & Ziegler Strahlen- und Medizintechnik AG; *Int'l*, pg. 2290
MICKS EXTERMINATING; *U.S. Private*, pg. 2702
MIC LATIN AMERICA BV—See Millicom International Cellular S.A.; *Int'l*, pg. 4896
MICLYN EXPRESS OFFSHORE LIMITED—See CHAMP Private Equity Pty. Ltd.; *Int'l*, pg. 1439
MIC MEDICAL CORPORATION—See Sony Group Corporation; *Int'l*, pg. 7102
MICOBE INC.; *U.S. Private*, pg. 2702
MICO BIOMED CO., LTD.; *Int'l*, pg. 4876
MICO DMC S.R.L.—See Fiera Milano SpA; *Int'l*, pg. 2660
MICO ELECTRONICS (WUXI) LTD.—See MiCo Ltd.; *Int'l*, pg. 4876
MICO, INCORPORATED—See ZF Friedrichshafen AG; *Int'l*, pg. 8641
MICO INSURANCE COMPANY—See Motorists Mutual Insurance Co.; *U.S. Private*, pg. 2797
MICO LTD.; *Int'l*, pg. 4876
M&I CO., LTD.—See CL Holdings Inc.; *Int'l*, pg. 1640
MICOM AMERICA, INC.—See Japan Airlines Co., Ltd.; *Int'l*, pg. 3884
MICONTROLS INC.—See The Stephens Group, LLC; *U.S. Private*, pg. 4121
MICOPOWER CO., LTD.—See MiCo Ltd.; *Int'l*, pg. 4876
MICOR AB—See Duroc AB; *Int'l*, pg. 2230
MICO SERVICES LIMITED—See Carillion plc; *Int'l*, pg. 1330
MICOS TELCOM S.R.O.—See Preformed Line Products Company; *U.S. Public*, pg. 1714
MICREED CO., LTD.; *Int'l*, pg. 4876
MICREX DEVELOPMENT CORPORATION; *Int'l*, pg. 4876
MICRIUM, INC.—See Silicon Laboratories Inc.; *U.S. Public*, pg. 1879
MICRO 2000, INC.; *U.S. Private*, pg. 2702
MICRO2NANO INC.; *Int'l*, pg. 4878
MICROAD, INC.—See CyberAgent, Inc.; *Int'l*, pg. 1892
MICROAGE, INC.—See Frontier Technology LLC; *U.S. Private*, pg. 1616
MICROAIRE SURGICAL INSTRUMENTS INC.—See Berkshire Hathaway Inc.; *U.S. Public*, pg. 308
MICRO-AIR (TIANJIN) TECHNOLOGY CO., LTD.—See Frencken Group Limited; *Int'l*, pg. 2773
MICROALGO INC.; *Int'l*, pg. 4878
MICROALLIANCE GROUP INC; *Int'l*, pg. 4878
MICROALLOYING INTERNATIONAL, INC.—See Stanley Black & Decker, Inc.; *U.S. Public*, pg. 1933
MICROANALYTICS—See Volatile Analysis Corporation; *U.S. Private*, pg. 4410
MICROARRAYS, INC.—See Spectrum Solutions L.L.C.; *U.S. Private*, pg. 3753
MICRO AUTOMATION LLC—See MAX Automation SE; *Int'l*, pg. 4734
MICRO AUTOMATION LLP—See MAX Automation SE; *Int'l*, pg. 4734
MICROBAC LABORATORIES, INC.; *U.S. Private*, pg. 2702
MICROBA LIFE SCIENCE LIMITED; *Int'l*, pg. 4878
MICROBE INOTECH LABORATORIES—See Pluton Biosciences LLC; *U.S. Private*, pg. 3215
MICROBILT COLLECTION AGENCY, INC.—See Bristol Investments, Ltd.; *U.S. Private*, pg. 657
MICROBILT CORPORATION—See Bristol Investments, Ltd.; *U.S. Private*, pg. 657
MICROBIO CO., LTD.; *Int'l*, pg. 4878
MICROBIOLOGY & QUALITY ASSOCIATES, INC.—See Microbiology Research Associates, Inc.; *U.S. Private*, pg. 2702
MICROBIOLOGY RESEARCH ASSOCIATES, INC.; *U.S. Private*, pg. 2702
MICRO BIOPHARM JAPAN CO., LTD.—See Mitsui & Co., Ltd.; *Int'l*, pg. 4974
MICROBIX BIOSYSTEMS INC.; *Int'l*, pg. 4879
MICROBOARDS TECHNOLOGY, LLC; *U.S. Private*, pg. 2703
MICROBOT MEDICAL INC.; *U.S. Public*, pg. 1436
MICRO CAD CO., LTD.—See Future Corporation; *Int'l*, pg. 2853
MICROCARE, LLC; *U.S. Private*, pg. 2703
MICROCAST TECHNOLOGIES INC.; *U.S. Private*, pg. 2703
MICROCHEM CORP.—See Nippon Kayaku Co., Ltd.; *Int'l*, pg. 5320

MICROCHIP TECHNOLOGY INCORPORATED; *U.S. Public*, pg. 1436
MICROCHIP TECHNOLOGY (THAILAND) CO., LTD.—See Microchip Technology Incorporated; *U.S. Public*, pg. 1436
MICRO-CLEAN INC.; *U.S. Private*, pg. 2702
MICROCLOUD HOLOGRAM INC.; *U.S. Public*, pg. 1437
MICRO-COAX, INC.—See Amphenol Corporation; *U.S. Public*, pg. 129
MICROCODE SARL—See Groupe Industriel Marcel Dassault S.A.; *Int'l*, pg. 3105
MICROCOM TECHNOLOGIES, INC.; *U.S. Private*, pg. 2703
MICROCONNEX CORPORATION—See Amphenol Corporation; *U.S. Public*, pg. 129
MICROCONSULT INC.—See Certified Laboratories, Inc.; *U.S. Private*, pg. 841
MICRO CONTACT SOLUTION CO., LTD.; *Int'l*, pg. 4876
MICRO-CONTROLE SPECTRA-PHYSICS S.A.S.—See MKS Instruments, Inc.; *U.S. Public*, pg. 1453
MICRO CONTROL MANUFACTURING INC.—See Stack Electronics; *U.S. Private*, pg. 3774
MICRO CONTROL SYSTEMS INC.; *U.S. Private*, pg. 2702
MICROCORP, LLC—See Cloud Service Partners, Inc.; *U.S. Private*, pg. 947
MICROCOSM, INC.; *U.S. Private*, pg. 2703
MICROCOSM TECHNOLOGY CO., LTD.; *Int'l*, pg. 4879
MICRO CRAFT INC.; *U.S. Private*, pg. 2702
MICROCRAFT K.K.—See Infinite Graphics Incorporated; *U.S. Public*, pg. 1117
MICRO CREDIT NATIONAL S.A.—See Unibank S.A.; *Int'l*, pg. 8030
MICRO CRYSTAL AG—See The Swatch Group Ltd.; *Int'l*, pg. 7691
MICRODATA; *Int'l*, pg. 4879
MICRODENTAL, INC.—See Modern Dental Group Limited; *Int'l*, pg. 5013
MICRODESK LLC—See Addnode Group AB; *Int'l*, pg. 130
MICRODIGITAL CO., LTD.; *Int'l*, pg. 4879
MICRODOC COMPUTERSYSTEME GMBH—See Adecco Group AG; *Int'l*, pg. 140
MICRO DRAINAGE LIMITED—See Cardno Limited; *Int'l*, pg. 1322
MICRODYNAMICS GROUP; *U.S. Private*, pg. 2703
MICRODYNE PLASTICS, INC.; *U.S. Private*, pg. 2703
MICRODYN-NADIR GMBH—See Mann+Hummel GmbH; *Int'l*, pg. 4673
MICRODYN-NADIR OLTREMARE S.P.A.—See Mann+Hummel GmbH; *Int'l*, pg. 4674
MICRODYN-NADIR SINGAPORE PTE LTD.—See Mann+Hummel GmbH; *Int'l*, pg. 4673
MICRODYN-NADIR (XIAMEN) CO., LTD.—See CDH China Management Company Limited; *Int'l*, pg. 1370
MICROEDGE, LLC—See Blackbaud, Inc.; *U.S. Public*, pg. 341
MICROELECTRONICA S.A.; *Int'l*, pg. 4879
MICROELECTRONIC NH GMBH; *Int'l*, pg. 4879
MICRO ELECTRONICS, INC.; *U.S. Private*, pg. 2702
MICROELECTRONICS RESEARCH & DEVELOPMENT LTD—See Siemens Aktiengesellschaft; *Int'l*, pg. 6890
MICROELECTRONICS TECHNOLOGY COMPANY; *U.S. Private*, pg. 2703
MICROELECTRONICS TECHNOLOGY INC. (MTI)—See Microelectronics Technology Company; *U.S. Private*, pg. 2703
MICROELETTRICA HEINE (SUZHOU) CO., LTD.—See Knorr-Bremse AG; *Int'l*, pg. 4212
MICROELETTRICA SCIENTIFICA (PTY.) LTD.—See Knorr-Bremse AG; *Int'l*, pg. 4212
MICROELETTRICA SCIENTIFICA S.P.A.—See Knorr-Bremse AG; *Int'l*, pg. 4212
MICROELETTRICA-USA LLC—See Knorr-Bremse AG; *Int'l*, pg. 4212
MICROEMISSIVE DISPLAYS LTD.; *Int'l*, pg. 4879
MICRO ENGINEERING, INC.—See Solitron Devices, Inc.; *U.S. Public*, pg. 1901
MICROEQUITIES ASSET MANAGEMENT GROUP LIMITED; *Int'l*, pg. 4879
MICROEXCEL, INC.; *U.S. Private*, pg. 2703
MICROFAB, INC.—See Edgewater Capital Partners, L.P.; *U.S. Private*, pg. 1335
MICROFIBRES EUROPE N.V.—See Acasa Group BVBA; *Int'l*, pg. 78
MICROFIBRES INC.; *U.S. Private*, pg. 2703
MICROFINANCIAL INCORPORATED—See SoftBank Group Corp.; *Int'l*, pg. 7053
MICROFITS (BEIJING) TECHNOLOGY CO., LTD.—See Advanced Systems Automation Limited; *Int'l*, pg. 162
MICROFITS PTE LTD; *Int'l*, pg. 4879
MICROFLEX INC.; *U.S. Private*, pg. 2703
MICROFLUIDICS INTERNATIONAL CORPORATION—See IDEX Corp.; *U.S. Public*, pg. 1091
MICROFLUIDIC SYSTEMS—See PositiveID Corporation; *U.S. Public*, pg. 3233
MICRO FOCUS AS—See Micro Focus International plc; *Int'l*, pg. 4877
MICROFOCUS BEIJING—See Micro Focus International plc; *Int'l*, pg. 4877

MICROFOCUS BENGALURU—See Micro Focus International plc; *Int'l*, pg. 4877
MICRO FOCUS BRAZIL—See Micro Focus International plc; *Int'l*, pg. 4876
MICRO FOCUS B.V.—See Micro Focus International plc; *Int'l*, pg. 4877
MICRO FOCUS - COSTA MESA—See Micro Focus International plc; *Int'l*, pg. 4876
MICRO FOCUS CZECHIA S.R.O.—See Micro Focus International plc; *Int'l*, pg. 4877
MICRO FOCUS GMBH—See Micro Focus International plc; *Int'l*, pg. 4877
MICRO FOCUS GMBH—See Micro Focus International plc; *Int'l*, pg. 4877
MICRO FOCUS HOLDINGS LIMITED—See Micro Focus International plc; *Int'l*, pg. 4877
MICRO FOCUS INTERNATIONAL PLC; *Int'l*, pg. 4876
MICRO FOCUS ISRAEL LIMITED—See Micro Focus International plc; *Int'l*, pg. 4877
MICRO FOCUS KK—See Micro Focus International plc; *Int'l*, pg. 4877
MICRO FOCUS KOREA LIMITED—See Micro Focus International plc; *Int'l*, pg. 4877
MICRO FOCUS LIMITED—See Micro Focus International plc; *Int'l*, pg. 4877
MICRO FOCUS LLC—See Micro Focus International plc; *Int'l*, pg. 4877
MICROFOCUS MALAYSIA—See Micro Focus International plc; *Int'l*, pg. 4877
MICRO FOCUS PTE LIMITED—See Micro Focus International plc; *Int'l*, pg. 4877
MICRO FOCUS PTY LIMITED—See Micro Focus International plc; *Int'l*, pg. 4877
MICRO FOCUS SAS—See Micro Focus International plc; *Int'l*, pg. 4877
MICRO FOCUS SL—See Micro Focus International plc; *Int'l*, pg. 4877
MICRO FOCUS SOFTWARE DENMARK APS—See Micro Focus International plc; *Int'l*, pg. 4877
MICRO FOCUS SOFTWARE HK LIMITED—See Micro Focus International plc; *Int'l*, pg. 4877
MICRO FOCUS SOFTWARE (IRELAND) LIMITED—See Micro Focus International plc; *Int'l*, pg. 4877
MICRO FOCUS SOFTWARE ROMANIA SRL—See Micro Focus International plc; *Int'l*, pg. 4877
MICRO FOCUS SOFTWARE SOLUTIONS INDIA PRIVATE LIMITED—See Micro Focus International plc; *Int'l*, pg. 4877
MICRO FOCUS—See Micro Focus International plc; *Int'l*, pg. 4876
MICRO FOCUS SOUTH AFRICA (PTY.) LTD.—See Micro Focus International plc; *Int'l*, pg. 4877
MICRO FOCUS SVERIGE AB—See Micro Focus International plc; *Int'l*, pg. 4877
MICROFOCUS SYDNEY—See Micro Focus International plc; *Int'l*, pg. 4877
MICROFOCUS TAIWAN—See Micro Focus International plc; *Int'l*, pg. 4877
MICRO FOCUS UKRAINE, LLC—See Micro Focus International plc; *Int'l*, pg. 4877
MICRO FOCUS (US) INC.—See Micro Focus International plc; *Int'l*, pg. 4876
MICROFUZZY INDUSTRIE-ELEKTRONIK GMBH—See KRIT Technologies Ltd; *Int'l*, pg. 4296
MICROGAME S.P.A.—See Monitor Clipper Partners, LLC; *U.S. Private*, pg. 2770
MICROGAMING SYSTEMS (UK) LTD.; *Int'l*, pg. 4879
MICRO GAUGE INC.—See Mueller Industries, Inc.; *U.S. Public*, pg. 1484
MICROGEN APTITUDE LIMITED—See Aptitude Software Group Plc; *Int'l*, pg. 523
MICROGEN BANKING SYSTEMS LIMITED—See Aptitude Software Group Plc; *Int'l*, pg. 523
MICROGEN BIOPRODUCTS LTD.—See Novacyt SA; *Int'l*, pg. 5454
MICROGENICS CORPORATION—See Thermo Fisher Scientific Inc.; *U.S. Public*, pg. 2149
MICROGENICS GMBH—See Thermo Fisher Scientific Inc.; *U.S. Public*, pg. 2149
MICROGEN LIMITED—See Aptitude Software Group Plc; *Int'l*, pg. 523
MICROGEN MANAGEMENT SERVICES LIMITED—See Aptitude Software Group Plc; *Int'l*, pg. 523
MICROGEN POLAND SP. Z.O.O.—See Aptitude Software Group Plc; *Int'l*, pg. 524
MICROGEN SOLUTIONS INC—See Aptitude Software Group Plc; *Int'l*, pg. 524
MICROGEN—See Russian Technologies State Corporation; *Int'l*, pg. 6431
MICROGEN (SOUTH AFRICA) LIMITED—See Aptitude Software Group Plc; *Int'l*, pg. 523
MICROGEN UK LIMITED—See Aptitude Software Group Plc; *Int'l*, pg. 524
MICROGEO S.A.—See SONDA S.A.; *Int'l*, pg. 7089
MICROGLEIT SPEZIALSCHMIERSTOFFE, GMBH—See Element Solutions Inc.; *U.S. Public*, pg. 728
MICROGROUP, INC.—See TE Connectivity Ltd.; *Int'l*, pg. 7495

COMPANY NAME INDEX

MICRO IMAGING TECHNOLOGY, INC.; *U.S. Public,* pg. 1436
MICRO INDUSTRIES CORPORATION; *U.S. Private,* pg. 2702
MICROJENICS INC.—See Japan Resistor Mfg Co., Ltd.; *Int'l,* pg. 3905
MICROLAB/FXR LLC—See RF Industries, Ltd.; *U.S. Public,* pg. 1796
MICROLAB LLC—See Artemis Capital Partners Management Co., LLC; *U.S. Private,* pg. 341
MICROLAND ELECTRONICS CORP.; *U.S. Private,* pg. 2703
MICROLEAD PRECISION TECHNOLOGY SDN. BHD.—See MQ Technology Berhad; *Int'l,* pg. 5063
MICROLEASE FRANCE—See Platinum Equity, LLC; *U.S. Private,* pg. 3203
MICROLEASE LIMITED—See Platinum Equity, LLC; *U.S. Private,* pg. 3202
MICROLEASE S.R.L.—See Platinum Equity, LLC; *U.S. Private,* pg. 3203
MICRO LEASING PUBLIC COMPANY LIMITED; *Int'l,* pg. 4877
MICROLIFE AG SWISS CORPORATION—See Microlife Corporation; *Int'l,* pg. 4879
MICROLIFE CORPORATION; *Int'l,* pg. 4879
MICROLIFE USA, INC.—See Microlife Corporation; *Int'l,* pg. 4879
MICROLINE B.V.—See Hoya Corporation; *Int'l,* pg. 3498
MICROLINE SURGICAL INC.—See Hoya Corporation; *Int'l,* pg. 3497
MICROLINK ESTONIA—See Telia Company AB; *Int'l,* pg. 7543
MICROLINK INNOVATION SDN BHD—See Omesti Berhad; *Int'l,* pg. 5562
MICROLINK SOFTWARE SDN BHD—See Omesti Berhad; *Int'l,* pg. 5562
MICROLINK SOLUTIONS BERHAD—See Omesti Berhad; *Int'l,* pg. 5562
MICROLINK SYSTEMS SDN BHD—See Omesti Berhad; *Int'l,* pg. 5562
MICROLISE GROUP PLC; *Int'l,* pg. 4879
MICROLISE S.A.S.—See Microlise Group Plc; *Int'l,* pg. 4879
MICRO-LITE, LLC—See Clarkson Construction Company; *U.S. Private,* pg. 915
MICROLOGIC BUSINESS SYSTEMS, INC.; *U.S. Private,* pg. 2703
MICROLUMEN, INC.; *U.S. Private,* pg. 2703
MICRO MACHINING HOLDING B.V.—See Standard Investment Management B.V.; *Int'l,* pg. 7169
MICRO-MACINAZIONE SA—See Lonza Group AG; *Int'l,* pg. 4554
MICRO MAN DISTRIBUTORS, INC.; *U.S. Private,* pg. 2702
MICROMANIA GROUP SAS—See GameStop Corp.; *U.S. Public,* pg. 896
MICROMAN, INC.; *U.S. Private,* pg. 2703
MICROMASS COMMUNICATIONS, INC.—See Clayton, Dubilier & Rice, LLC; *U.S. Private,* pg. 928
MICROMASS HOLDINGS LTD.—See Waters Corporation; *U.S. Public,* pg. 2334
MICROMASS UK LIMITED—See Waters Corporation; *U.S. Public,* pg. 2334
MICROMATES CORP.—See TIS Inc.; *Int'l,* pg. 7757
MICROMATIC, LLC; *U.S. Private,* pg. 2703
MICROMATIC SPRING STAMPING CO.; *U.S. Private,* pg. 2703
MICRO MATIC USA, INC.; *U.S. Private,* pg. 2702
MICROMAX, INC.—See Danlaw, Inc.; *U.S. Private,* pg. 1157
MICROMAX INFORMATICS LIMITED; *Int'l,* pg. 4879
MICRO-MECHANICS (HOLDINGS) LTD; *Int'l,* pg. 4878
MICRO-MECHANICS INC—See Micro-Mechanics (Holdings) Ltd; *Int'l,* pg. 4878
MICRO-MECHANICS PTE LTD—See Micro-Mechanics (Holdings) Ltd; *Int'l,* pg. 4878
MICRO-MECHANICS TECHNOLOGY INTERNATIONAL, INC.—See Micro-Mechanics (Holdings) Ltd; *Int'l,* pg. 4878
MICRO-MECHANICS TECHNOLOGY SDN. BHD.—See Micro-Mechanics (Holdings) Ltd; *Int'l,* pg. 4878
MICRO-MECHANICS TECHNOLOGY (SUZHOU) CO. LTD.—See Micro-Mechanics (Holdings) Ltd; *Int'l,* pg. 4878
MICRO-MECH INC.—See Ibiden Co., Ltd.; *Int'l,* pg. 3576
MICROMEDICA BACAU SRL—See MedLife S.A.; *Int'l,* pg. 4785
MICROMEDICA ROMAN SRL—See MedLife S.A.; *Int'l,* pg. 4785
MICROMEDICA TARGU NEAMT SRL—See MedLife S.A.; *Int'l,* pg. 4785
MICROMEGA NATIONAL CERTIFICATION AUTHORITY (PROPRIETARY) LIMITED—See Sebata Holdings; *Int'l,* pg. 6669
MICROMEGA TECHNOLOGIES (PROPRIETARY) LIMITED—See Sebata Holdings; *Int'l,* pg. 6669
MICROMEGA TRAEASURY SOLUTIONS (PROPRIETARY) LIMITED—See Sebata Holdings; *Int'l,* pg. 6669

MICROMEM TECHNOLOGIES INC.; *Int'l,* pg. 4879
MICROMENDERS INC.; *U.S. Private,* pg. 2703
MICROMERITICS CHINA—See Micromeritics Instrument Corporation, Inc.; *U.S. Private,* pg. 2703
MICROMERITICS FRANCE S.A.—See Micromeritics Instrument Corporation, Inc.; *U.S. Private,* pg. 2703
MICROMERITICS GERMANY GMBH—See Micromeritics Instrument Corporation, Inc.; *U.S. Private,* pg. 2704
MICROMERITICS INSTRUMENT CORPORATION, INC.; *U.S. Private,* pg. 2703
MICROMERITICS ITALY SRL—See Micromeritics Instrument Corporation, Inc.; *U.S. Private,* pg. 2704
MICROMERITICS JAPAN, G.K.—See Micromeritics Instrument Corporation, Inc.; *U.S. Private,* pg. 2704
MICROMERITICS NV/SA—See Micromeritics Instrument Corporation, Inc.; *U.S. Private,* pg. 2704
MICROMERITICS U.K. LTD.—See Micromeritics Instrument Corporation, Inc.; *U.S. Private,* pg. 2704
MICROMETAL GMBH—See Wickeder Westfalenstahl GmbH; *Int'l,* pg. 8401
MICROMETALS INC.; *U.S. Private,* pg. 2704
MICROMETICS COMERCIO E REPRESENTACOES LTDA—See Micromeritics Instrument Corporation, Inc.; *U.S. Private,* pg. 2704
MICROMETL CORP.; *U.S. Private,* pg. 2704
MICROMICR CORPORATION; *U.S. Private,* pg. 2704
MICROMIDAS, INC.—See Origin Materials, Inc.; *U.S. Public,* pg. 1617
MICROMILL ELECTRONICS LIMITED—See Advent International Corporation; *U.S. Private,* pg. 100
MICROM INTERNATIONAL GMBH—See Thermo Fisher Scientific Inc.; *U.S. Public,* pg. 2149
MICROMOBILITY.COM INC.; *U.S. Public,* pg. 1437
MICRO-MODE PRODUCTS, INC.—See ITT Inc.; *U.S. Public,* pg. 1178
MICROMO ELECTRONICS, INC.—See Dr. Fritz Faulhaber GmbH & Co. KG; *Int'l,* pg. 2191
MICROMOLD, INC.; *U.S. Private,* pg. 2704
MICRO MOLDING, INC.—See Frazier & Company, Inc.; *U.S. Private,* pg. 1599
MICROMOTION GMBH—See Harmonic Drive Systems Inc.; *Int'l,* pg. 3277
MICRO MOTION INC.—See Emerson Electric Co.; *U.S. Public,* pg. 750
MICRO MOTION INC.—See Emerson Electric Co.; *U.S. Public,* pg. 750
MICRON AKITA, INC.—See Micron Technology, Inc.; *U.S. Public,* pg. 1437
MICRONCLEAN IRELAND LTD.—See Franz Haniel & Cie. GmbH; *Int'l,* pg. 2763
MICRON CLEANROOM (PHILIPPINES) INC.—See Channel Micron Holdings Company Limited; *Int'l,* pg. 1446
MICRON CONSUMER PRODUCTS GROUP, INC.—See Micron Technology, Inc.; *U.S. Public,* pg. 1437
MICRON CONSUMER PRODUCTS GROUP—See Micron Technology, Inc.; *U.S. Public,* pg. 1437
MICRON CONSUMER PRODUCTS—See Micron Technology, Inc.; *U.S. Public,* pg. 1437
MICRON CORPORATION; *U.S. Private,* pg. 2704
MICRONESIAN HOSPITALITY, INC.—See Japan Airlines Co., Ltd.; *Int'l,* pg. 3884
MICRONET LTD.—See Tingo Group, Inc.; *U.S. Public,* pg. 2159
MICRONET TECHNOLOGY—See BNL Technologies Inc.; *U.S. Public,* pg. 602
MICRON EUROPE LIMITED—See Micron Technology, Inc.; *U.S. Public,* pg. 1437
MIC-RON GENERAL CONTRACTORS INC.; *U.S. Private,* pg. 2697
MICRONIC HOLDING B.V.—See INTEGRA Holding AG; *Int'l,* pg. 3729
MICRONIC JAPAN K.K.—See Mycronic AB; *Int'l,* pg. 5112
MICRONIC LASER SYSTEMS, INC—See Mycronic AB; *Int'l,* pg. 5112
MICRONIC MANUFACTURING USA LLC—See INTEGRA Holding AG; *Int'l,* pg. 3729
MICRONICS FILTRATION LTD.—See Vance Street Capital LLC; *U.S. Private,* pg. 4342
MICRONICS FILTRATION PTY. LTD.—See Vance Street Capital LLC; *U.S. Private,* pg. 4342
MICRONICS, INC.—See Vance Street Capital LLC; *U.S. Private,* pg. 4342
MICRONICS JAPAN CO., LTD. - AOMORI MATSUZAKI PLANT—See MICRONICS JAPAN CO., LTD.; *Int'l,* pg. 4880
MICRONICS JAPAN CO., LTD. - AOMORI PLANT—See MICRONICS JAPAN CO., LTD.; *Int'l,* pg. 4880
MICRONICS JAPAN CO., LTD.; *Int'l,* pg. 4879
MICRON INDUSTRIES CORP.—See Hammond Power Solutions, Inc.; *U.S. Private,* pg. 1850
MICRON JAPAN, LTD.—See Micron Technology, Inc.; *U.S. Public,* pg. 1437
MICRON MACHINERY CO., LTD. - MIHARASHI FACTORY—See MICRON MACHINERY CO., LTD.; *Int'l,* pg. 4879
MICRON MACHINERY CO., LTD.; *Int'l,* pg. 4879
MICRON MACHINERY (THAILAND) CO., LTD.—See MICRON MACHINERY CO., LTD.; *Int'l,* pg. 4879

MICRON MEMORY JAPAN - HIROSHIMA PLANT—See Micron Technology, Inc.; *U.S. Public,* pg. 1437
MICRON MEMORY JAPAN, INC.—See Micron Technology, Inc.; *U.S. Public,* pg. 1437
MICRON MEMORY TAIWAN CO., LTD.—See Micron Technology, Inc.; *U.S. Public,* pg. 1437
MICRON METROPOLIS HEALTHCARE PRIVATE LIMITED—See Metropolis Healthcare Ltd.; *Int'l,* pg. 4863
MICRON (M) SDN. BHD.—See Channel Micron Holdings Company Limited; *Int'l,* pg. 1446
MICRONNEXUS GMBH—See Canada Pension Plan Investment Board; *Int'l,* pg. 1279
MICRONNEXUS GMBH—See Cinven Limited; *Int'l,* pg. 1612
MICRON PRODUCTS, INC.—See Micron Solutions, Inc.; *U.S. Public,* pg. 1437
MICRON SEMICONDUCTOR ASIA OPERATIONS PTE. LTD.—See Micron Technology, Inc.; *U.S. Public,* pg. 1438
MICRON SEMICONDUCTOR ASIA PTE. LTD.—See Micron Technology, Inc.; *U.S. Public,* pg. 1438
MICRON SEMICONDUCTOR (DEUTSCHLAND) GMBH—See Micron Technology, Inc.; *U.S. Public,* pg. 1437
MICRON SEMICONDUCTOR ITALIA S.R.L.—See Micron Technology, Inc.; *U.S. Public,* pg. 1438
MICRON SEMICONDUCTOR KOREA CO., LTD.—See Micron Technology, Inc.; *U.S. Public,* pg. 1438
MICRON SEMICONDUCTOR MALAYSIA SDN. BHD.—See Micron Technology, Inc.; *U.S. Public,* pg. 1438
MICRON SEMICONDUCTOR PRODUCTS, INC.—See Micron Technology, Inc.; *U.S. Public,* pg. 1438
MICRON SEMICONDUCTOR (XIAMEN) CO., LTD.—See Micron Technology, Inc.; *U.S. Public,* pg. 1438
MICRON SEMICONDUCTOR (XI'AN) CO., LTD.—See Micron Technology, Inc.; *U.S. Public,* pg. 1438
MICRON SOLUTIONS, INC.; *U.S. Public,* pg. 1437
MICRON SYSTEMS INTEGRATION, INC.—See Micron Technology, Inc.; *U.S. Public,* pg. 1438
MICRON TECHNOLOGIES, INC.—See Arlington Capital Partners LLC; *U.S. Private,* pg. 328
MICRON TECHNOLOGIES LIMITED—See Catalent, Inc.; *U.S. Public,* pg. 449
MICRON TECHNOLOGY ASIA PACIFIC, INC.—See Micron Technology, Inc.; *U.S. Public,* pg. 1438
MICRON TECHNOLOGY, INC. - CRUCIAL DIVISION—See Micron Technology, Inc.; *U.S. Public,* pg. 1438
MICRON TECHNOLOGY, INC.; *U.S. Public,* pg. 1437
MICRON TECHNOLOGY OF VIRGINIA—See Micron Technology, Inc.; *U.S. Public,* pg. 1438
MICRON TECHNOLOGY SERVICES, INC.—See Micron Technology, Inc.; *U.S. Public,* pg. 1438
MICRON TECHNOLOGY TAIWAN, INC.—See Micron Technology, Inc.; *U.S. Public,* pg. 1438
MICRON TECHNOLOGY TEXAS, LLC—See Micron Technology, Inc.; *U.S. Public,* pg. 1438
MICRON-U.S.A., INC.—See MICRON MACHINERY CO., LTD.; *Int'l,* pg. 4879
MICRONX CO., LTD.; *Int'l,* pg. 4880
MICRO OFFICE SYSTEMS, INC.—See Medsphere Systems Corp.; *U.S. Private,* pg. 2658
MICRO-OHM CORPORATION; *U.S. Private,* pg. 2702
MICROPAC INDUSTRIES INC.; *U.S. Public,* pg. 1438
MICROPACT, INC.—See Tyler Technologies, Inc.; *U.S. Public,* pg. 2208
MICROPAY (PTY) LTD—See The Sage Group plc; *Int'l,* pg. 7679
MICROPHASE CORPORATION—See Ault Alliance, Inc.; *U.S. Public,* pg. 227
MICROPHONICS, INC.; *U.S. Public,* pg. 1438
MICROPHOR—See Westinghouse Air Brake Technologies Corporation; *U.S. Public,* pg. 2358
MICROPLACE INC.—See eBay Inc.; *U.S. Public,* pg. 709
MICROPLAN FINANCIAL SERVICES (PRIVATE) LIMITED—See FBC Holdings Limited; *Int'l,* pg. 2627
MICRO PLASTICS, INC.—See Essentra plc; *Int'l,* pg. 2511
MICRO PLASTICS INTERNATIONAL LIMITED—See Essentra plc; *Int'l,* pg. 2511
MICRO PLASTICS INTERNATIONAL S.A. DE C.V. DE R.L.—See Essentra plc; *Int'l,* pg. 2511
MICRO PNEUMATICS PVT. LTD.—See KITZ CORPORATION; *Int'l,* pg. 4196
MICRO-POISE INDUSTRIAL EQUIPMENT (BEIJING) CO., LTD—See AMETEK, Inc.; *U.S. Public,* pg. 118
MICROPOISE MEASUREMENT SYSTEMS EUROPE GMBH—See AMETEK, Inc.; *U.S. Public,* pg. 118
MICRO-POISE MEASUREMENT SYSTEMS, LLC—See AMETEK, Inc.; *U.S. Public,* pg. 118
MICROPOLE SA; *Int'l,* pg. 4880
MICROPOLE UNIVERS CONSULTING SAS—See Micropole SA; *Int'l,* pg. 4880
MICROPOLE UNIVERS INSTITUT SA—See Micropole SA; *Int'l,* pg. 4880
MICROPOLE UNIVERS SUISSE SA—See Micropole SA; *Int'l,* pg. 4880

MICROPOLITAN, LLC—See Psomas; *U.S. Private*, pg. 3297
MICROPOROUS PRODUCTS, LLC—See Seven Mile Capital Partners, LLC; *U.S. Private*, pg. 3618
MICROPORT CARDIAC RHYTHM B.V.—See MicroPort Scientific Corporation; *Int'l*, pg. 4880
MICROPORT CARDIOFLOW MEDTECH CORP.; *Int'l*, pg. 4880
MICROPORT CRM B.V.—See MicroPort Scientific Corporation; *Int'l*, pg. 4880
MICROPORT CRM SARL—See MicroPort Scientific Corporation; *Int'l*, pg. 4880
MICROPORT MEDICAL B.V.—See MicroPort Scientific Corporation; *Int'l*, pg. 4880
MICROPORT MEDICAL (SHANGHAI) CO., LTD.—See MicroPort Scientific Corporation; *Int'l*, pg. 4880
MICROPORT NEUROTECH (SHANGHAI) CO., LTD.—See MicroPort Scientific Corporation; *Int'l*, pg. 4880
MICROPORT ORTHOPEDICS INC.—See MicroPort Scientific Corporation; *Int'l*, pg. 4881
MICROPORT ORTHOPEDICS JAPAN K.K.—See MicroPort Scientific Corporation; *Int'l*, pg. 4880
MICROPORT SCIENTIFIC CORPORATION; *Int'l*, pg. 4880
MICROPORT SCIENTIFIC GMBH—See MicroPort Scientific Corporation; *Int'l*, pg. 4880
MICROPORT SORIN CRM (SHANGHAI) CO., LTD.—See MicroPort Scientific Corporation; *Int'l*, pg. 4880
MICRO PRECISION GEAR TECHNOLOGY LIMITED—See Zurn Elkay Water Solutions Corporation; *U.S. Public*, pg. 2413
MICROPRECISION INC.; *U.S. Private*, pg. 2704
MICRO PRODUCTS COMPANY; *U.S. Private*, pg. 2702
MICROPROSS SAS—See National Instruments Corporation; *U.S. Private*, pg. 2856
MICROPUMP, INC.—See IDEX Corp; *U.S. Public*, pg. 1091
MICROQUAL TECHNO LTD.; *Int'l*, pg. 4881
MICRORAM ELECTRONICS INC.; *U.S. Private*, pg. 2704
MICROSAIC SYSTEMS PLC; *Int'l*, pg. 4881
MICRO SAPPORO COMPANY—See Star Micronics Co Ltd; *Int'l*, pg. 7174
MICROSEC AB—See Amplex AB; *Int'l*, pg. 434
MICRO SECURITY SOLUTIONS INC.—See Dunes Point Capital, LLC; *U.S. Private*, pg. 1289
MICROSEISMIC, INC.; *U.S. Private*, pg. 2704
MICROSEMI COMMUNICATIONS, INC.—See Microchip Technology Incorporated; *U.S. Public*, pg. 1436
MICROSEMI CORP. - ANALOG MIXED SIGNAL GROUP—See Microchip Technology Incorporated; *U.S. Public*, pg. 1436
MICROSEMI CORP. - MASSACHUSETTS—See Microchip Technology Incorporated; *U.S. Public*, pg. 1436
MICROSEMI CORPORATION—See Microchip Technology Incorporated; *U.S. Public*, pg. 1436
MICROSEMI CORP. - POWER MANAGEMENT GROUP—See Microchip Technology Incorporated; *U.S. Public*, pg. 1436
MICROSEMI CORP. - POWER PRODUCTS GROUP—See Microchip Technology Incorporated; *U.S. Public*, pg. 1436
MICROSEMI CORP. - RF POWER PRODUCTS—See Microchip Technology Incorporated; *U.S. Public*, pg. 1436
MICROSEMI CORP. - SCOTTSDALE—See Microchip Technology Incorporated; *U.S. Public*, pg. 1436
MICROSEMI FREQUENCY & TIME CORPORATION—See Microchip Technology Incorporated; *U.S. Public*, pg. 1436
MICROSEMI FREQUENCY & TIME GMBH—See Microchip Technology Incorporated; *U.S. Public*, pg. 1436
MICROSEMI IRELAND, LTD.—See Microchip Technology Incorporated; *U.S. Public*, pg. 1437
MICROSEMI ISRAEL, LTD.—See Microchip Technology Incorporated; *U.S. Public*, pg. 1437
MICROSEMI SEMICONDUCTOR CORPORATION A/S—See Microchip Technology Incorporated; *U.S. Public*, pg. 1436
MICROSEMI SEMICONDUCTOR GMBH & CO. KG—See Microchip Technology Incorporated; *U.S. Public*, pg. 1436
MICROSEMI SEMICONDUCTOR ULC—See Microchip Technology Incorporated; *U.S. Public*, pg. 1437
MICROSEMI SEMICONDUCTOR (U.S.) INC.—See Microchip Technology Incorporated; *U.S. Public*, pg. 1437
MICROSEMI STORAGE SOLUTIONS, INC.—See Microchip Technology Incorporated; *U.S. Public*, pg. 1437
MICROSENSE, LLC—See KLA Corporation; *U.S. Public*, pg. 1268
MICROSENS GMBH & CO. KG—See Zech Group SE; *Int'l*, pg. 8628
MICROSENS SP. Z O.O.—See Zech Group SE; *Int'l*, pg. 8628
MICROSEP (PTY) LTD—See Waters Corporation; *U.S. Public*, pg. 2334
MICROSERVE LTD.; *Int'l*, pg. 4881
MICROS-FIDELIO AUSTRALIA PTY LTD.—See Oracle Corporation; *U.S. Public*, pg. 1611
MICROS-FIDELIO HONG KONG LTD.—See Oracle Corporation; *U.S. Public*, pg. 1612

MICROS-FIDELIO SWEDEN AB—See Oracle Corporation; *U.S. Public*, pg. 1613
MICROS-FIDELIO U.K. LTD.—See Oracle Corporation; *U.S. Public*, pg. 1612
MICROSKIN PLC; *Int'l*, pg. 4881
MICRO SMART INC.; *U.S. Private*, pg. 2702
MICROSOFT AB—See Microsoft Corporation; *U.S. Public*, pg. 1439
MICROSOFT BELGIUM & LUXEMBOURG—See Microsoft Corporation; *U.S. Public*, pg. 1439
MICROSOFT BILGISAYAR YAZILIM HIZMETLERI LIMITED SIRKETI—See Microsoft Corporation; *U.S. Public*, pg. 1439
MICROSOFT BUSINESS DIVISION—See Microsoft Corporation; *U.S. Public*, pg. 1439
MICROSOFT B.V.—See Microsoft Corporation; *U.S. Public*, pg. 1439
MICROSOFT CANADA CO.—See Microsoft Corporation; *U.S. Public*, pg. 1439
MICROSOFT CHILE S.A.—See Microsoft Corporation; *U.S. Public*, pg. 1440
MICROSOFT (CHINA) CO., LTD.—See Microsoft Corporation; *U.S. Public*, pg. 1439
MICROSOFT CO., LTD.—See Microsoft Corporation; *U.S. Public*, pg. 1440
MICROSOFT CORP. - BOISE OFFICE—See Microsoft Corporation; *U.S. Public*, pg. 1439
MICROSOFT CORP. - DENVER OFFICE—See Microsoft Corporation; *U.S. Public*, pg. 1439
MICROSOFT CORP. - FARGO OFFICE—See Microsoft Corporation; *U.S. Public*, pg. 1439
MICROSOFT CORPORATION (I) PVT. LTD.—See Microsoft Corporation; *U.S. Public*, pg. 1439
MICROSOFT CORPORATION; *U.S. Public*, pg. 1438
MICROSOFT COSTA RICA—See Microsoft Corporation; *U.S. Public*, pg. 1440
MICROSOFT DANMARK APS—See Microsoft Corporation; *U.S. Public*, pg. 1439
MICROSOFT DEUTSCHLAND GMBH—See Microsoft Corporation; *U.S. Public*, pg. 1439
MICROSOFT D.O.O., LJUBLJANA—See Microsoft Corporation; *U.S. Public*, pg. 1440
MICROSOFT DYNAMICS DANMARK—See Microsoft Corporation; *U.S. Public*, pg. 1439
MICROSOFT EMEA—See Microsoft Corporation; *U.S. Public*, pg. 1439
MICROSOFT ENTERTAINMENT & DEVICES DIVISION—See Microsoft Corporation; *U.S. Public*, pg. 1440
MICROSOFT FRANCE S.A.R.L.—See Microsoft Corporation; *U.S. Public*, pg. 1440
MICROSOFT GULF FZ LLC—See Microsoft Corporation; *U.S. Public*, pg. 1440
MICROSOFT - HAIFA R&D CENTER—See Microsoft Corporation; *U.S. Public*, pg. 1440
MICROSOFT HELLAS S.A.—See Microsoft Corporation; *U.S. Public*, pg. 1440
MICROSOFT - HERZLIYYA R&D CENTER—See Microsoft Corporation; *U.S. Public*, pg. 1440
MICROSOFT HUNGARY—See Microsoft Corporation; *U.S. Public*, pg. 1440
MICROSOFT IBERICA S.R.L.—See Microsoft Corporation; *U.S. Public*, pg. 1440
MICROSOFT INFORMATICA LTDA.—See Microsoft Corporation; *U.S. Public*, pg. 1441
MICROSOFT IRELAND OPERATIONS LIMITED—See Microsoft Corporation; *U.S. Public*, pg. 1440
MICROSOFT ISRAEL LTD.—See Microsoft Corporation; *U.S. Public*, pg. 1440
MICROSOFT KOREA—See Microsoft Corporation; *U.S. Public*, pg. 1440
MICROSOFT LATIN AMERICA—See Microsoft Corporation; *U.S. Public*, pg. 1440
MICROSOFT LICENSING, GP—See Microsoft Corporation; *U.S. Public*, pg. 1441
MICROSOFT LIMITED—See Microsoft Corporation; *U.S. Public*, pg. 1440
MICROSOFT (MALAYSIA) SDN. BHD.—See Microsoft Corporation; *U.S. Public*, pg. 1439
MICROSOFT MEXICO, S.A. DE C.V.—See Microsoft Corporation; *U.S. Public*, pg. 1441
MICROSOFT MOBILE DEUTSCHLAND GMBH - DUSSELDORF—See Microsoft Corporation; *U.S. Public*, pg. 1441
MICROSOFT MOBILE DEUTSCHLAND GMBH—See Microsoft Corporation; *U.S. Public*, pg. 1441
MICROSOFT MOBILE INC.—See Microsoft Corporation; *U.S. Public*, pg. 1441
MICROSOFT MOBILE OY—See Microsoft Corporation; *U.S. Public*, pg. 1441
MICROSOFT NEW ZEALAND LIMITED—See Microsoft Corporation; *U.S. Public*, pg. 1441
MICROSOFT NIGERIA LIMITED—See Microsoft Corporation; *U.S. Public*, pg. 1441
MICROSOFT NORGE AS—See Microsoft Corporation; *U.S. Public*, pg. 1440
MICROSOFT ONLINE, INC.—See Microsoft Corporation; *U.S. Public*, pg. 1441

MICROSOFT ONLINE SERVICES DIVISION—See Microsoft Corporation; *U.S. Public*, pg. 1441
MICROSOFT OPERATIONS PTE LTD—See Microsoft Corporation; *U.S. Public*, pg. 1441
MICROSOFT OSTERREICH GMBH—See Microsoft Corporation; *U.S. Public*, pg. 1440
MICROSOFT OY SUOMI—See Microsoft Corporation; *U.S. Public*, pg. 1440
MICROSOFT PHILIPPINES, INC.—See Microsoft Corporation; *U.S. Public*, pg. 1441
MICROSOFT PTY. LIMITED—See Microsoft Corporation; *U.S. Public*, pg. 1441
MICROSOFT PUERTO RICO S.A.—See Microsoft Corporation; *U.S. Public*, pg. 1441
MICROSOFT RUSSIA—See Microsoft Corporation; *U.S. Public*, pg. 1440
MICROSOFT SCHWEIZ GMBH—See Microsoft Corporation; *U.S. Public*, pg. 1440
MICROSOFT SERVER & TOOLS DIVISION—See Microsoft Corporation; *U.S. Public*, pg. 1441
MICROSOFT SLOVAKIA S.R.O.—See Microsoft Corporation; *U.S. Public*, pg. 1440
MICROSOFT SOUTH AFRICA—See Microsoft Corporation; *U.S. Public*, pg. 1440
MICROSOFT SP. Z O.O.—See Microsoft Corporation; *U.S. Public*, pg. 1440
MICROSOFT S.R.L.—See Microsoft Corporation; *U.S. Public*, pg. 1440
MICROSOFT S.R.O.—See Microsoft Corporation; *U.S. Public*, pg. 1440
MICROSOFT TAIWAN CORPORATION—See Microsoft Corporation; *U.S. Public*, pg. 1441
MICROSOFT (THAILAND) LIMITED—See Microsoft Corporation; *U.S. Public*, pg. 1439
MICROSOFT VENEZUELA S.A.—See Microsoft Corporation; *U.S. Public*, pg. 1441
MICROSOFT WINDOWS & WINDOWS LIVE DIVISION—See Microsoft Corporation; *U.S. Public*, pg. 1441
MICROSOL INTERNATIONAL LL FZE; *Int'l*, pg. 4881
MICROSON S.A.—See Amplifon S.p.A.; *Int'l*, pg. 435
MICROSPACE COMMUNICATIONS CORPORATION—See Capitol Broadcasting Company, Inc.; *U.S. Private*, pg. 743
MICROSPORE S.P.A.; *Int'l*, pg. 4881
THE MICRO SPRING & PRESSWORK COMPANY LTD.—See Indutrade AB; *Int'l*, pg. 3681
MICROS RETAIL SERVICES UK LIMITED—See Oracle Corporation; *U.S. Public*, pg. 1612
MICROSS COMPONENTS, INC. - ELECTRO-MECHANICAL SERVICES, HATFIELD—See Behrman Brothers Management Corp.; *U.S. Private*, pg. 515
MICROSS COMPONENTS, INC.—See Behrman Brothers Management Corp.; *U.S. Private*, pg. 515
MICROSS MANCHESTER—See Behrman Brothers Management Corp.; *U.S. Private*, pg. 515
MICROS SOUTH AFRICA (PTY) LTD—See Constellation Software Inc.; *Int'l*, pg. 1775
MICROS SYSTEMS UK LIMITED - BOLTON—See Oracle Corporation; *U.S. Public*, pg. 1612
MICROS SYSTEMS UK LIMITED—See Oracle Corporation; *U.S. Public*, pg. 1612
MICRO STAMPING CORP. - FLORIDA FACILITY—See Micro Stamping Corp.; *U.S. Private*, pg. 2702
MICRO STAMPING CORP.; *U.S. Private*, pg. 2702
MICRO-STAR INTERNATIONAL CO., LTD.; *Int'l*, pg. 4878
MICROSTAR KEG MANAGEMENT LLC—See Freeman Spogli & Co. Incorporated; *U.S. Private*, pg. 1606
MICRO-STAR NETHERLANDS HOLDING B.V.—See Micro-Star International Co., Ltd; *Int'l*, pg. 4878
MICROSTART SCRL—See BNP Paribas SA; *Int'l*, pg. 1092
MICRO STRATEGIES INC.—See Micro Strategies Inc.; *U.S. Private*, pg. 2702
MICRO STRATEGIES INC.; *U.S. Private*, pg. 2702
MICROSTRATEGY AUSTRIA GMBH—See MicroStrategy, Inc.; *U.S. Public*, pg. 1443
MICROSTRATEGY BELGIUM BVBA—See MicroStrategy, Inc.; *U.S. Public*, pg. 1443
MICROSTRATEGY BENELUX B.V.—See MicroStrategy, Inc.; *U.S. Public*, pg. 1443
MICROSTRATEGY BRASIL LTDA.—See MicroStrategy, Inc.; *U.S. Public*, pg. 1443
MICROSTRATEGY CANADA INC.—See MicroStrategy, Inc.; *U.S. Public*, pg. 1443
MICROSTRATEGY DEUTSCHLAND GMBH—See MicroStrategy, Inc.; *U.S. Public*, pg. 1443
MICROSTRATEGY FRANCE SARL—See MicroStrategy, Inc.; *U.S. Public*, pg. 1443
MICROSTRATEGY IBERICA, S.L.U.—See MicroStrategy, Inc.; *U.S. Public*, pg. 1443
MICROSTRATEGY, INC.; *U.S. Public*, pg. 1443
MICROSTRATEGY INDIA PRIVATE LIMITED—See MicroStrategy, Inc.; *U.S. Public*, pg. 1443
MICROSTRATEGY ITALY S.R.L.—See MicroStrategy, Inc.; *U.S. Public*, pg. 1443
MICROSTRATEGY JAPAN KABUSHIKI KAISHA—See MicroStrategy, Inc.; *U.S. Public*, pg. 1444

COMPANY NAME INDEX

MICROSTRATEGY KOREA CO., LTD.—See MicroStrategy, Inc.; *U.S. Public*, pg. 1443
MICROSTRATEGY LIMITED—See MicroStrategy, Inc.; *U.S. Public*, pg. 1444
MICROSTRATEGY MIDDLE EAST FZ-LLC—See MicroStrategy, Inc.; *U.S. Public*, pg. 1444
MICROSTRATEGY POLAND SP. Z O. O.—See MicroStrategy, Inc.; *U.S. Public*, pg. 1444
MICROSTRATEGY PORTUGAL, LDA.—See MicroStrategy, Inc.; *U.S. Public*, pg. 1444
MICROSTRATEGY PTY. LTD.—See MicroStrategy, Inc.; *U.S. Public*, pg. 1444
MICROSTRATEGY SCHWEIZ AG—See MicroStrategy, Inc.; *U.S. Public*, pg. 1444
MICROSTRATEGY SINGAPORE PTE. LTD.—See MicroStrategy, Inc.; *U.S. Public*, pg. 1444
MICROSTRATEGY SWEDEN AB—See MicroStrategy, Inc.; *U.S. Public*, pg. 1444
MICROSTRATEGY SWITZERLAND GMBH—See MicroStrategy, Inc.; *U.S. Public*, pg. 1444
MICROSTRATEGY UK LIMITED—See MicroStrategy, Inc.; *U.S. Public*, pg. 1444
MICROSTRATEGY YAZILIM HIZMETLERI VE URUNLERI LIMITED SIRKETI—See MicroStrategy, Inc.; *U.S. Public*, pg. 1444
MICRO SURFACE TREATMENT SDN. BHD.—See Kobay Technology Bhd.; *Int'l*, pg. 4216
MICROSURGICAL TECHNOLOGY, INC.—See Halma plc; *Int'l*, pg. 3232
MICRO-SWISS LIMITED—See Kulicke & Soffa Industries, Inc.; *Int'l*, pg. 4329
MICRO SYSTEMATION AB; *Int'l*, pg. 4877
MICRO SYSTEMATION CANADA INC.—See Micro Systemation AB; *Int'l*, pg. 4878
MICRO SYSTEMATION INC.—See Micro Systemation AB; *Int'l*, pg. 4878
MICRO SYSTEMATION LTD—See Micro Systemation AB; *Int'l*, pg. 4878
MICRO SYSTEMATION—See Micro Systemation AB; *Int'l*, pg. 4878
MICROSYSTEMS AUTOMATION GROUP; *U.S. Private*, pg. 2704
MICRO SYSTEMS, INC.—See Kratos Defense & Security Solutions, Inc.; *U.S. Public*, pg. 1276
MICROSYSTEM SRL—See 3D Systems Corporation; *U.S. Public*, pg. 4
MICROSYSTEMS; *U.S. Private*, pg. 2704
MICROTEC ENTERPRISES, INC.—See Stanley Black & Decker, Inc.; *U.S. Public*, pg. 1935
MICROTECH COMPUTERS INC.; *U.S. Private*, pg. 2704
MICRO-TECH ENDOSCOPY USA INC.—See Micro-Tech (Nanjing) Co., Ltd.; *Int'l*, pg. 4878
MICRO-TECH EUROPE GMBH—See Micro-Tech (Nanjing) Co., Ltd.; *Int'l*, pg. 4878
MICROTECH MEDICAL (HANGZHOU) CO., LTD.; *Int'l*, pg. 4881
MICRO-TECH (NANJING) CO., LTD.; *Int'l*, pg. 4878
MICRO-TECH NEDERLAND B.V.—See Micro-Tech (Nanjing) Co., Ltd.; *Int'l*, pg. 4878
MICROTECHNOLOGIES LLC; *U.S. Private*, pg. 2704
MICROTECH STAFFING GROUP INC.; *U.S. Private*, pg. 2704
MICROTECH SYSTEMS, INC.—See Middough, Inc.; *U.S. Private*, pg. 2714
MICROTEC S.R.L.; *Int'l*, pg. 4881
MICROTEK COMPUTER TECHNOLOGY (WU JIANG) CO., LTD—See Microtek International, Inc.; *Int'l*, pg. 4881
MICROTEK INTERNATIONAL DEVELOPMENT SYSTEMS DIVISION INC—See Microtek International, Inc.; *Int'l*, pg. 4881
MICROTEK INTERNATIONAL, INC.; *Int'l*, pg. 4881
MICROTEK LAB INC—See Microtek International, Inc.; *Int'l*, pg. 4881
MICROTEK MEDICAL BV—See Ecolab Inc.; *U.S. Public*, pg. 715
MICROTEK MEDICAL, INC.—See Ecolab Inc.; *U.S. Public*, pg. 715
MICROTEK MEDICAL MALTA LIMITED—See Ecolab Inc.; *U.S. Public*, pg. 715
MICROTEK; *U.S. Private*, pg. 2704
MICROTEL LLC—See Arlington Capital Partners LLC; *U.S. Private*, pg. 328
MICROTEST LABORATORIES, INC.—See Ampersand Management LLC; *U.S. Private*, pg. 265
MICRO THERAPEUTICS, INC.—See Medtronic plc; *Int'l*, pg. 4787
MICROTHERM ENGINEERED SOLUTIONS N.V.—See Etex SA/NV; *Int'l*, pg. 2522
MICROTIPS INC—See Microtips Technology Inc.; *Int'l*, pg. 4881
MICROTIPS TECHNOLOGY INC.; *Int'l*, pg. 4881
MICROTIPS TECHNOLOGY LLC—See Microtips Technology Inc.; *Int'l*, pg. 4881
MICROTRACBEL CORP.—See Nikkiso Co., Ltd.; *Int'l*, pg. 5291
MICROTRAC INC.—See Verder International B.V.; *Int'l*, pg. 8166

MICROTRONICA LTD.—See Arrow Electronics, Inc.; *U.S. Public*, pg. 199
MICRO-TUBE FABRICATORS INC.—See Steel Partners Holdings L.P.; *U.S. Public*, pg. 1943
MICROTURBO, INC.—See Safran SA; *Int'l*, pg. 6476
MICROTURBO SA—See Safran SA; *Int'l*, pg. 6476
MICRO TYPING SYSTEMS, INC.—See Johnson & Johnson; *U.S. Public*, pg. 1200
MICROVAST HOLDINGS, INC.; *U.S. Public*, pg. 1444
MICROVAST POWER SYSTEMS CO., LTD.—See Microvast Holdings, Inc.; *U.S. Public*, pg. 1444
MICROVENTION DEUTSCHLAND G.M.B.H.—See Terumo Corporation; *Int'l*, pg. 7569
MICROVENTION EUROPE—See Terumo Corporation; *Int'l*, pg. 7569
MICROVENTION, INC.—See Terumo Corporation; *Int'l*, pg. 7569
MICROVENTION UK LTD.—See Terumo Corporation; *Int'l*, pg. 7569
MICRO VIDEO INSTRUMENTS INC.; *U.S. Private*, pg. 2702
MICROVISION, INC.; *U.S. Public*, pg. 1444
MICROVISION TECHNOLOGIES SRL—See ViTrox Corporation Berhad; *Int'l*, pg. 8262
MICROVIVE LTD.—See Inoapps Limited; *Int'l*, pg. 3715
MICRO VOICE APPLICATIONS, INC.; *U.S. Private*, pg. 2702
MICROWAREHOUSE BV—See Insight Enterprises, Inc.; *U.S. Public*, pg. 1130
MICROWARE LIMITED; *Int'l*, pg. 4881
MICROWAVE FILTER COMPANY, INC.; *U.S. Public*, pg. 1444
MICROWAVE MEASUREMENT DIVISION—See Anritsu Corporation; *Int'l*, pg. 475
MICROWAVE RADIO COMMUNICATIONS—See Pebble Beach Systems Group PLC; *Int'l*, pg. 5778
MICROWAVE SPECIALTY COMPANY—See Rantec Microwave Systems, Inc.; *U.S. Private*, pg. 3355
MICROWAVE TECHNOLOGY, INC.—See CML Microsystems Plc; *Int'l*, pg. 1671
MICROWAVE TRANSMISSION SYSTEMS, INC.; *U.S. Private*, pg. 2704
MICROWAVE VISION SA; *Int'l*, pg. 4881
MICROWAY, INC.; *U.S. Private*, pg. 2705
MICRO-WORLD, INC.; *U.S. Private*, pg. 2702
MICRO-X LIMITED; *Int'l*, pg. 4878
MICROZERO CO., LTD.—See Hisaka Works, Ltd.; *Int'l*, pg. 3406
MICS CHEMICAL CO.,LTD.; *Int'l*, pg. 4882
MIC TANZANIA PUBLIC LIMITED COMPANY—See Millicom International Cellular S.A.; *Int'l*, pg. 4896
MIC-TECH ELECTRONICS ENGINEERING CORP.—See Marketech International Corp.; *Int'l*, pg. 4696
MIC TECHNOLOGIES AUSTRALIA (PTY.) LTD.—See MIC Electronics Limited; *Int'l*, pg. 4696
MIC-TECH(WUXI)CO., LTD.—See Marketech International Corp.; *Int'l*, pg. 4696
MICUBE SOLUTION, INC.; *Int'l*, pg. 4882
MICURA PFLEGEDIENSTE BERLIN GMBH—See Munchener Ruckversicherungs AG; *Int'l*, pg. 5092
MICURA PFLEGEDIENSTE BREMEN GMBH—See Munchener Ruckversicherungs AG; *Int'l*, pg. 5092
MICURA PFLEGEDIENSTE DUSSELDORF GMBH—See Munchener Ruckversicherungs AG; *Int'l*, pg. 5092
MICURA PFLEGEDIENSTE GMBH NIEDERLASSUNG KOLN—See Munchener Ruckversicherungs AG; *Int'l*, pg. 5092
MICURA PFLEGEDIENSTE HAMBURG GMBH—See Munchener Ruckversicherungs AG; *Int'l*, pg. 5092
MICURA PFLEGEDIENSTE KREFELD GMBH—See Munchener Ruckversicherungs AG; *Int'l*, pg. 5092
MICURA PFLEGEDIENSTE MUNCHEN GMBH—See Munchener Ruckversicherungs AG; *Int'l*, pg. 5092
MICURA PFLEGEDIENSTE MUNCHEN OST GMBH—See Munchener Ruckversicherungs AG; *Int'l*, pg. 5092
MICURA PFLEGEDIENSTE MUNSTER GMBH—See Munchener Ruckversicherungs AG; *Int'l*, pg. 5092
MICURA PFLEGEDIENSTE NURNBERG GMBH—See Munchener Ruckversicherungs AG; *Int'l*, pg. 5092
MICWARE CO. LTD.; *Int'l*, pg. 4882
MIDA ASSETS PUBLIC CO.,LTD.; *Int'l*, pg. 4883
MIDAF FUJINOMIYA CO., LTD.—See Takuma Co., Ltd.; *Int'l*, pg. 7442
MIDAC HOLDINGS CO., LTD.; *Int'l*, pg. 4883
MIDAC KONAN CO., LTD.—See Midac Holdings Co., Ltd.; *Int'l*, pg. 4883
MIDAC LINER CO., LTD.—See Midac Holdings Co., Ltd.; *Int'l*, pg. 4883
MIDAH INDUSTRIES SDN BHD—See Chin Hin Group Berhad; *Int'l*, pg. 1480
MIDA HOTEL AND RESORT CO., LTD—See Mida Assets Public Co.,Ltd.; *Int'l*, pg. 4883
MIDA LEASING PUBLIC COMPANY LIMITED—See Mída Assets Public Co.,Ltd.; *Int'l*, pg. 4883
MID-AM BUILDING SUPPLY, INC.—See Hardwoods Distribution Inc.; *Int'l*, pg. 3273
MID-AMERICA APARTMENT COMMUNITIES, INC.; *U.S. Public*, pg. 1444

MID-AMERICA APARTMENTS, L.P.—See Mid-America Apartment Communities, Inc.; *U.S. Public*, pg. 1444
MID-AMERICA CABINETS INC.; *U.S. Private*, pg. 2707
MID-AMERICA CAPITAL RESOURCES, INC.—See The AES Corporation; *U.S. Public*, pg. 2032
MID AMERICA COMPUTER CORP.—See Constellation Software Inc.; *Int'l*, pg. 1774
MID AMERICA CONTRACTORS, L.L.C.—See Republic Services, Inc.; *U.S. Public*, pg. 1786
MID AMERICA CORP.; *U.S. Private*, pg. 2705
MIDAMERICA DIVISION, INC.—See HCA Healthcare, Inc.; *U.S. Public*, pg. 1003
MID-AMERICA FEED YARD; *U.S. Private*, pg. 2707
MID-AMERICA FITTINGS, INC.—See Gemspring Capital Management, LLC; *U.S. Private*, pg. 1659
MID AMERICA HARDWOODS INC.; *U.S. Private*, pg. 2705
MIDAMERICA HOTELS CORPORATION; *U.S. Private*, pg. 2710
MID-AMERICA ISOTOPES, INC.—See Webster Equity Partners, LLC; *U.S. Private*, pg. 4467
MIDAMERICA JET, INC.—See The Hines Group, Inc.; *U.S. Private*, pg. 4053
MID AMERICA MORTGAGE, INC.; *U.S. Private*, pg. 2705
MID AMERICA MOTORWORKS; *U.S. Private*, pg. 2705
MIDAMERICA NATIONAL BANCSHARES, INC.; *U.S. Private*, pg. 2710
MIDAMERICA NATIONAL BANK—See MidAmerica National Bancshares, Inc.; *U.S. Private*, pg. 2710
MID-AMERICAN CLEANING CONTRACTORS; *U.S. Private*, pg. 2707
MID-AMERICAN ELEVATOR EQUIPMENT CO., INC.; *U.S. Private*, pg. 2707
MIDAMERICAN ENERGY COMPANY—See Berkshire Hathaway Inc.; *U.S. Public*, pg. 300
MIDAMERICAN FUNDING, LLC—See Berkshire Hathaway Inc.; *U.S. Public*, pg. 300
MID-AMERICAN MACHINE & EQUIPMENT, LLC.; *U.S. Private*, pg. 2707
MID AMERICAN NATURAL RESOURCES, LLC—See Emkey Energy, LLC; *U.S. Private*, pg. 1383
MID-AMERICAN RESTAURANTS INC.; *U.S. Private*, pg. 2707
MIDAMERICAN TRUCK MAINTENANCE—See Murphy-Hoffman Company; *U.S. Private*, pg. 2816
MIDAMERICA ONCOLOGY, LLC—See HCA Healthcare, Inc.; *U.S. Public*, pg. 1003
MIDAMERICA ONCOLOGY, LLC—See HCA Healthcare, Inc.; *U.S. Public*, pg. 1003
MID-AMERICA OVERSEAS (CHINA) LTD.—See Mid-America Overseas Inc.; *U.S. Private*, pg. 2707
MID-AMERICA OVERSEAS DE VENEZUELA, C.A.—See Mid-America Overseas Inc.; *U.S. Private*, pg. 2707
MID-AMERICA OVERSEAS DO BRASIL LOGISTICA LTDA.—See Mid-America Overseas Inc.; *U.S. Private*, pg. 2707
MID-AMERICA OVERSEAS INC.; *U.S. Private*, pg. 2707
MID-AMERICA OVERSEAS, LTD.—See Mid-America Overseas Inc.; *U.S. Private*, pg. 2707
MID-AMERICA OVERSEAS (M) SDN. BHD.—See Mid-America Overseas Inc.; *U.S. Private*, pg. 2707
MID-AMERICA OVERSEAS (S) PTE. LTD.—See Mid-America Overseas Inc.; *U.S. Private*, pg. 2707
MID-AMERICA OVERSEAS (THE NETHERLANDS) B.V.—See Mid-America Overseas Inc.; *U.S. Private*, pg. 2707
MID AMERICA PET FOOD LLC.; *U.S. Private*, pg. 2705
MID AMERICA PIPELINE CO., LLC—See Enterprise Products Partners L.P.; *U.S. Public*, pg. 779
MID-AMERICA PIPELINE CO., LLC—See Enterprise Products Partners L.P.; *U.S. Public*, pg. 779
MID-AMERICA PIPELINE CO., LLC—See Enterprise Products Partners L.P.; *U.S. Public*, pg. 779
MID-AMERICA PIPELINE CO., LLC—See Enterprise Products Partners L.P.; *U.S. Public*, pg. 779
MID-AMERICA PIPELINE CO., LLC—See Enterprise Products Partners L.P.; *U.S. Public*, pg. 779
MID-AMERICA PIPELINE CO., LLC—See Enterprise Products Partners L.P.; *U.S. Public*, pg. 779
MID-AMERICA PIPELINE CO., LLC—See Enterprise Products Partners L.P.; *U.S. Public*, pg. 779
MID-AMERICA PLASTICS—See Activar, Inc.; *U.S. Private*, pg. 68
MID-AMERICA RISK MANAGERS, LLC—See Warburg Pincus LLC; *U.S. Private*, pg. 4438
MID-AMERICA STEEL CORP.; *U.S. Private*, pg. 2707
MID AMERICA STEEL, INC.; *U.S. Private*, pg. 2705
MID-AMERICA SURGERY CENTER, LLC—See HCA Healthcare, Inc.; *U.S. Public*, pg. 1002
MID-AMERICA SURGERY INSTITUTE, LLC—See HCA Healthcare, Inc.; *U.S. Public*, pg. 1002
MID-AMERICA TILE, INC.—See Louisville Tile Distributors Inc.; *U.S. Private*, pg. 2500
MID-AMERICA WHOLESALE INCORPORATED; *U.S. Private*, pg. 2707
MIDA PROPERTY CO., LTD.—See Mida Assets Public Co.,Ltd.; *Int'l*, pg. 4883
MID ARCTIC TRANSPORTATION CO. LTD—See Manitoulin Group of Companies; *Int'l*, pg. 4672
MIDAS AI CO., LTD.; *Int'l*, pg. 4883

MIDAS AI CO., LTD.

CORPORATE AFFILIATIONS

MIDAS ASIA PACIFIC PTY. LTD.—See Sumitomo Corporation; *Int'l*, pg. 7274
MIDAS AUSTRALIA PTY LTD—See Bapcor Limited; *Int'l*, pg. 857
MIDAS AUTOSERVICE GMBH—See Lucky-Car Franchise & Beteiligungs GmbH; *Int'l*, pg. 4574
MIDAS AUTO SYSTEMS EXPERTS INC.; *U.S. Private*, pg. 2710
MIDAS BELGIQUE—See Sumitomo Corporation; *Int'l*, pg. 7274
MIDAS CANADA INC.—See Sumitomo Corporation; *Int'l*, pg. 7274
MIDASCO CAPITAL CORP.; *Int'l*, pg. 4883
MIDAS COMPANIES; *U.S. Private*, pg. 2710
MIDAS ESPANA—See Sumitomo Corporation; *Int'l*, pg. 7274
MIDAS EUROPE SAM—See Sumitomo Corporation; *Int'l*, pg. 7274
MIDAS FINANCING LIMITED; *Int'l*, pg. 4883
MIDAS FRANCE SAS—See Sumitomo Corporation; *Int'l*, pg. 7274
MIDAS GOLD, INC.—See Perpetua Resources Corp.; *U.S. Public*, pg. 1677
MIDAS GROUP (PTY) LTD; *Int'l*, pg. 4883
MIDAS, INC.—See Sumitomo Corporation; *Int'l*, pg. 7274
MIDAS INFRA TRADE LTD.; *Int'l*, pg. 4883
MIDAS INTERNATIONAL, INC.—See Sumitomo Corporation; *Int'l*, pg. 7274
MIDAS INVESTMENT LTD.—See MIDAS Financing Limited; *Int'l*, pg. 4883
MIDAS ITALIA S.P.A.—See Sumitomo Corporation; *Int'l*, pg. 7274
MIDAS MANAGEMENT CORPORATION—See Winmill & Co., Incorporated; *U.S. Private*, pg. 2374
MIDAS MINERALS LTD.; *Int'l*, pg. 4883
MIDAS OPCO HOLDINGS LLC—See Stagwell, Inc.; *U.S. Public*, pg. 1925
MIDAS PAINTS (PTY) LIMITED—See Kansai Paint Co., Ltd.; *Int'l*, pg. 4072
MIDASPLAYER AB—See Microsoft Corporation; *U.S. Public*, pg. 1439
MIDAS POLSKA—See Sumitomo Corporation; *Int'l*, pg. 7274
MIDAS PORTUGAL—See Sumitomo Corporation; *Int'l*, pg. 7274
MIDAS PROPERTIES—See Sumitomo Corporation; *Int'l*, pg. 7274
MIDAS S.A.—See Cyfrowy Polsat S.A.; *Int'l*, pg. 1895
MIDAS TOUCH OY—See Ina Group Ltd Oy; *Int'l*, pg. 3639
MIDATECH PHARMA US INC.—See Massachusetts Mutual Life Insurance Company; *U.S. Private*, pg. 2605
MID ATLANTIC BOOK BINDERY INC.—See The HF Group LLC; *U.S. Private*, pg. 4052
MID ATLANTIC CAPITAL CORPORATION—See Mid Atlantic Capital Group, Inc.; *U.S. Private*, pg. 2705
MID ATLANTIC CAPITAL GROUP, INC.; *U.S. Private*, pg. 2705
MID-ATLANTIC COCA-COLA CO.—See The Coca-Cola Company; *U.S. Public*, pg. 2065
MID-ATLANTIC COLLABORATIVE CARE, LLC—See Centene Corporation; *U.S. Public*, pg. 471
MID ATLANTIC COLLISION CENTER—See R.F. Inc.; *U.S. Private*, pg. 3336
MID ATLANTIC CONSTRUCTION GROUP INC.; *U.S. Private*, pg. 2705
MID ATLANTIC CONTRACTING INC.; *U.S. Private*, pg. 2705
MID-ATLANTIC CONVENIENCE STORES, LLC—See Sunoco LP; *U.S. Public*, pg. 1965
MID-ATLANTIC DENTAL SERVICE HOLDINGS LLC—See New Mountain Capital, LLC; *U.S. Private*, pg. 2904
MID ATLANTIC ENDOSCOPY CENTER, LLC—See KKR & Co. Inc.; *U.S. Public*, pg. 1246
MID-ATLANTIC ENDOSCOPY, LLC—See KKR & Co. Inc.; *U.S. Public*, pg. 1250
MID-ATLANTIC FASTENERS INC.—See Carlson Holdings, Inc.; *U.S. Private*, pg. 765
MID ATLANTIC FRAMING, LLC—See UFP Industries, Inc.; *U.S. Public*, pg. 2219
MID ATLANTIC GI CONSULTANTS—See Johnson Controls International plc; *Int'l*, pg. 3986
MID-ATLANTIC HEALTH CARE, LLC; *U.S. Private*, pg. 2707
MID-ATLANTIC HOME HEALTH NETWORK, INC.; *U.S. Public*, pg. 1445
MID-ATLANTIC INDUSTRIAL TEXTILE INC.—See Yanpai Filtration Technology Co., Ltd.; *Int'l*, pg. 8564
MID-ATLANTIC INDUSTRIAL TEXTILES CO., LTD.—See Yanpai Filtration Technology Co., Ltd.; *Int'l*, pg. 8564
MIDATLANTIC MEDEVAC, L.L.C.—See KKR & Co. Inc.; *U.S. Public*, pg. 1252
MID-ATLANTIC PERMANENTE MEDICAL GROUP, P.C.—See Kaiser Permanente; *U.S. Private*, pg. 2256
MID ATLANTIC PETROLEUM PROPERTIES LLC; *U.S. Private*, pg. 2705
MID-ATLANTIC PRINTERS LTD.; *U.S. Private*, pg. 2707
MID-ATLANTIC SETTLEMENT SERVICES LLC—See Anywhere Real Estate Inc.; *U.S. Public*, pg. 142

MID ATLANTIC STATES INVESTMENT COMPANY—See Old Republic International Corporation; *U.S. Public*, pg. 1568
MID ATLANTIC STORAGE SYSTEMS; *U.S. Private*, pg. 2705
MID-ATLANTIC TECHNOLOGY, RESEARCH & INNOVATION CENTER, INC.—See AVN Corporation; *U.S. Private*, pg. 409
MID-ATLANTIC TERMINAL LLC—See Wallenius Wilhelmsen ASA; *Int'l*, pg. 8334
MID-ATLANTIC TOWER MANAGEMENT, LLC—See American Tower Corporation; *U.S. Public*, pg. 111
MID-ATLANTIC TRANSPORTATION SERVICES, LLC—See Russel Metals Inc.; *Int'l*, pg. 6430
MIDBEC AB—See Dainichiseika Color & Chemicals Mfg. Co., Ltd.; *Int'l*, pg. 1939
MIDBORO MANAGEMENT, INC.—See FirstService Corporation; *Int'l*, pg. 2691
MID CAL AG AVIATION INC.—See TORtec Group Corp.; *U.S. Public*, pg. 2164
MIDCAP FINANCIAL INVESTMENT CORPORATION—See Apollo Global Management, Inc.; *U.S. Public*, pg. 153
MIDCAP FINANCIAL SERVICES, LLC; *U.S. Private*, pg. 2710
MID-CAROLINA ELECTRIC COOPERATIVE, INC.; *U.S. Private*, pg. 2707
MIDCENTRAL ENERGY SERVICES, LLC; *U.S. Private*, pg. 2710
MID CENTRAL ICE, LLC—See H.I.G. Capital, LLC; *U.S. Private*, pg. 1829
MID-CENTRAL PRODUCTS LLC—See United Animal Health, Inc.; *U.S. Private*, pg. 4287
MID CITY FOUNDRY CO.; *U.S. Private*, pg. 2705
MID-CITY IRON & METAL CORPORATION—See Sims Limited; *U.S. Public*, pg. 1883
MID-CITY LUMBER COMPANY LTD.; *U.S. Private*, pg. 2707
MID CITY STEEL CORP.; *U.S. Private*, pg. 2705
MID-CITY SUPPLY CO. INC.; *U.S. Private*, pg. 2707
MID COAST ELECTRIC SUPPLY INC.; *U.S. Private*, pg. 2705
MIDCOAST ENERGY PARTNERS, L.P.—See ArcLight Capital Holdings, LLC; *U.S. Private*, pg. 312
MID COAST HOSPITAL—See MaineHealth; *U.S. Private*, pg. 2553
MIDCOAST MARINE GROUP LLC—See MarineMax, Inc.; *U.S. Public*, pg. 1367
MIDCO-BAY INSULATION INC.—See Bay Industries Inc.; *U.S. Private*, pg. 493
MID-CO COMMODITIES, INC.—See Growmark, Inc.; *U.S. Private*, pg. 1795
MIDCO CONSTRUCTION CORPORATION; *U.S. Private*, pg. 2710
MIDCO INC.—See Securitas AB; *Int'l*, pg. 6675
MIDCO INTERNATIONAL, INC.; *U.S. Private*, pg. 2710
MIDCO LLC—See Kinder Morgan, Inc.; *U.S. Public*, pg. 1233
MID COLUMBIA ENGINEERING INC.; *U.S. Private*, pg. 2705
MID COLUMBIA FORKLIFT, INC.; *U.S. Private*, pg. 2705
MID-COLUMBIA MEDICAL CENTER; *U.S. Private*, pg. 2707
MID COLUMBIA PRODUCERS, INC.; *U.S. Private*, pg. 2706
MID COLUMBIA PRODUCERS, INC. - WASCO SEED PLANT—See Mid Columbia Producers, Inc.; *U.S. Private*, pg. 2706
MIDCOM WORKFORCE SOLUTIONS—See Cenergy Partners LLC; *U.S. Private*, pg. 808
MIDCON CABLES LLC; *U.S. Private*, pg. 2710
MIDCON COMPRESSION, L.L.C.—See Rock Hill Capital Group, LLC; *U.S. Private*, pg. 3464
MIDCON DATA SERVICES LLC; *U.S. Private*, pg. 2710
MID-CON ENERGY PARTNERS, LP—See KKR & Co. Inc.; *U.S. Public*, pg. 1244
MIDCON INVESTORS INC.; *U.S. Private*, pg. 2710
MIDCON MIDSTREAM, LP—See SandRidge Energy, Inc.; *U.S. Public*, pg. 1839
MID CONTINENT AIRCRAFT CORP.; *U.S. Private*, pg. 2706
MID-CONTINENTAL RESTORATION CO.; *U.S. Private*, pg. 2708
MID-CONTINENT ASSURANCE COMPANY—See American Financial Group, Inc.; *U.S. Public*, pg. 102
MIDCONTINENT BUSINESS SYSTEMS INC.—See Midcontinent Media Inc.; *U.S. Private*, pg. 2711
MID CONTINENT CABINETRY INC.—See MasterBrand, Inc.; *U.S. Public*, pg. 1394
MIDCONTINENT CABLE CO. INC.—See Midcontinent Media Inc.; *U.S. Private*, pg. 2711
MID-CONTINENT CAPITAL LLC—See Royal Bank of Canada; *Int'l*, pg. 6409
MID-CONTINENT CASUALTY CO.—See American Financial Group, Inc.; *U.S. Public*, pg. 102
MID-CONTINENT COAL & COKE COMPANY—See Mid-Continent Minerals Corporation; *U.S. Private*, pg. 2708
MIDCONTINENT COMMUNICATIONS INVESTOR LLC—See Midcontinent Media Inc.; *U.S. Private*, pg. 2711

MIDCONTINENT COMMUNICATIONS—See Comcast Corporation; *U.S. Public*, pg. 538
MIDCONTINENT COMMUNICATIONS—See Midcontinent Media Inc.; *U.S. Private*, pg. 2711
MID-CONTINENT CONCRETE CO.—See GCC, S.A.B. de C.V.; *Int'l*, pg. 2895
MID-CONTINENT ENVIRONMENTAL PROJECT PTE. LTD.—See Magnus Energy Group Ltd.; *Int'l*, pg. 4642
MID-CONTINENT EQUIPMENT (AUSTRALIA) PTY LTD—See Magnus Energy Group Ltd.; *Int'l*, pg. 4642
MID-CONTINENT EQUIPMENT GROUP PTE LTD—See Magnus Energy Group Ltd.; *Int'l*, pg. 4642
MID-CONTINENT EQUIPMENT, INC.—See Magnus Energy Group Ltd.; *Int'l*, pg. 4642
MID-CONTINENT EXCESS AND SURPLUS INSURANCE COMPANY—See American Financial Group, Inc.; *U.S. Public*, pg. 103
MIDCONTINENT EXPRESS PIPELINE LLC—See Energy Transfer LP; *U.S. Public*, pg. 764
MIDCONTINENT INDEPENDENT SYSTEM OPERATOR, INC.; *U.S. Private*, pg. 2710
MID-CONTINENT INSTRUMENT CO., INC.; *U.S. Private*, pg. 2708
MIDCONTINENT MEDIA INC.—See Midcontinent Media Inc.; *U.S. Private*, pg. 2711
MIDCONTINENT MEDIA INC.; *U.S. Private*, pg. 2710
MID-CONTINENT MINERALS CORPORATION; *U.S. Private*, pg. 2708
MID-CONTINENT PAPER & DISTRIBUTING COMPANY, INC.—See Bain Capital, LP; *U.S. Private*, pg. 440
MID-CONTINENT SAFETY LLC—See DXP Enterprises, Inc.; *U.S. Public*, pg. 697
MIDCO OF SOUTH DAKOTA, INC.—See Midcontinent Media Inc.; *U.S. Private*, pg. 2711
MIDCO SUPPLY AND EQUIPMENT CORPORATION—See Peabody Energy Corporation; *U.S. Public*, pg. 1659
MID COUNTIES CO-OPERATIVE; *Int'l*, pg. 4882
MIDCOUNTRY ACQUISITION CORP.; *U.S. Private*, pg. 2711
MIDCOUNTRY BANK—See MidCountry Acquisition Corp.; *U.S. Private*, pg. 2711
MIDCOUNTRY FINANCIAL CORP.; *U.S. Private*, pg. 2711
MID DEL CONSULTING NETWORK; *U.S. Private*, pg. 2706
MIDDENDORP ELECTRIC CO., PTY. LTD.; *Int'l*, pg. 4883
MID DEVON TYRES LIMITED—See Sumitomo Rubber Industries, Ltd.; *Int'l*, pg. 7299
MIDDLE ATLANTIC PRODUCTS INC.—See Legrand S.A.; *Int'l*, pg. 4445
MIDDLE ATLANTIC WHOLESALE LUMBER COMPANY—See Sherwood Lumber Corporation; *U.S. Private*, pg. 3635
MIDDLEBURG INVESTMENT GROUP, INC.—See Atlantic Union Bankshares Corporation; *U.S. Public*, pg. 223
MIDDLEBURG TRUST COMPANY—See Atlantic Union Bankshares Corporation; *U.S. Public*, pg. 223
MIDDLEBURG TRUST COMPANY—See Atlantic Union Bankshares Corporation; *U.S. Public*, pg. 223
MIDDLEBURG TRUST COMPANY—See Atlantic Union Bankshares Corporation; *U.S. Public*, pg. 223
MIDDLEBURG TRUST COMPANY—See Atlantic Union Bankshares Corporation; *U.S. Public*, pg. 223
MIDDLEBURY HARDWOOD PRODUCTS—See Patrick Industries, Inc.; *U.S. Public*, pg. 1653
MIDDLEBURY INTERACTIVE LANGUAGES LLC—See Stride, Inc.; *U.S. Public*, pg. 1955
MIDDLEBURY NATIONAL CORP.; *U.S. Public*, pg. 1445
MIDDLEBY AUSTRALIA PTY LTD—See The Middleby Corporation; *U.S. Public*, pg. 2114
MIDDLEBY CELFROST INNOVATIONS PVT LTD—See The Middleby Corporation; *U.S. Public*, pg. 2114
MIDDLEBY CHINA CORPORATION—See The Middleby Corporation; *U.S. Public*, pg. 2114
THE MIDDLEBY CORPORATION; *U.S. Public*, pg. 2113
MIDDLEBY COZZINI BRASIL EQUIPAMENTOS, LTDA—See The Middleby Corporation; *U.S. Public*, pg. 2114
MIDDLEBY ESPANA SLU—See The Middleby Corporation; *U.S. Public*, pg. 2114
MIDDLEBY INDIA ENGINEERING PVT LTD—See The Middleby Corporation; *U.S. Public*, pg. 2114
MIDDLEBY KOREA CORPORATION—See The Middleby Corporation; *U.S. Public*, pg. 2114
MIDDLEBY MARSHALL, INC.—See The Middleby Corporation; *U.S. Public*, pg. 2114
MIDDLEBY MEXICO SA DE CV—See The Middleby Corporation; *U.S. Public*, pg. 2114
MIDDLEBY PACKAGING SOLUTIONS, LLC—See The Middleby Corporation; *U.S. Public*, pg. 2114
MIDDLEBY PHILIPPINES CORPORATION—See The Middleby Corporation; *U.S. Public*, pg. 2114
MIDDLEBY UK LTD—See The Middleby Corporation; *U.S. Public*, pg. 2114
THE MIDDLEBY WORLDWIDE EUROPE—See The Middleby Corporation; *U.S. Public*, pg. 2114
MIDDLEBY WORLDWIDE MEXICO SA DE CV—See The Middleby Corporation; *U.S. Public*, pg. 2115
MIDDLE EAST AIRLINE GROUND HANDLING S.A.L.—See Middle East Airlines Airliban S.A.L.; *Int'l*, pg. 4883

COMPANY NAME INDEX

MIDDLE EAST AIRLINES AIRLIBAN S.A.L.; *Int'l*, pg. 4883
MIDDLE EAST AIRPORTS SERVICES (MEAS) SAL—See Middle East Airlines Airliban S.A.L.; *Int'l*, pg. 4883
MIDDLE EAST COMMUNICATION NETWORKS - MCN—See The Interpublic Group of Companies, Inc.; *U.S. Public*, pg. 2103
MIDDLE EAST DIAMOND RESOURCES LIMITED; *Int'l*, pg. 4883
MIDDLE EAST EQUIPMENT & TRADING—See Al Jaber Group; *Int'l*, pg. 280
MIDDLE EAST GLASS MANUFACTURING; *Int'l*, pg. 4883
MIDDLE EAST HEALTHCARE CO; *Int'l*, pg. 4883
MIDDLE EAST INSURANCE CO. PLC; *Int'l*, pg. 4884
MIDDLE EAST INVESTMENT INITIATIVE; *U.S. Private*, pg. 2711
MIDDLE EAST MARKETING CORPORATION FZC—See Max Weishaupt GmbH; *Int'l*, pg. 4735
MIDDLE EAST MARKETING GROUP; *U.S. Private*, pg. 2711
THE MIDDLE EAST NORTH AFRICA FINANCIAL NETWORK, INC.; *Int'l*, pg. 7666
MIDDLE EAST PAPER COMPANY; *Int'l*, pg. 4884
MIDDLE EAST PRODUCING & MARKETING FISH; *Int'l*, pg. 4884
MIDDLE EAST RESOURCES CO.—See Al-Osais International Holding Company; *Int'l*, pg. 288
MIDDLE EAST SHIPPING COMPANY LTD.—See Hayel Saeed Anam Group of Companies; *Int'l*, pg. 3290
MIDDLE EAST SPECIALIZED CABLES CO; *Int'l*, pg. 4884
MIDDLE EAST TRADING CO.—See Hayel Saeed Anam Group of Companies; *Int'l*, pg. 3290
THE MIDDLE EAST TUBE COMPANY LTD.—See Gaon Group Ltd; *Int'l*, pg. 2882
MIDDLE EAST TUBULAR SERVICES (GULF) LIMITED—See Medserv p.l.c.; *Int'l*, pg. 4785
MIDDLE EAST TUBULAR SERVICES (IRAQ) LTD.—See Medserv p.l.c.; *Int'l*, pg. 4786
MIDDLE EAST TUBULAR SERVICES LLC—See Medserv p.l.c.; *Int'l*, pg. 4786
MIDDLE EAST WORLD FACTORIES EQUIPMENT L.L.C—See Gulf General Investment Company PSC; *Int'l*, pg. 3180
MIDDLEFIELD BANC CORP.; *U.S. Public*, pg. 1445
THE MIDDLEFIELD BANKING COMPANY—See Middlefield Banc Corp.; *U.S. Public*, pg. 1445
MIDDLEFIELD CANADIAN INCOME PCC; *Int'l*, pg. 4884
MIDDLEFIELD CAN-GLOBAL REIT INCOME FUND—See Middlefield Group Limited; *Int'l*, pg. 4884
MIDDLEFIELD CAPITAL CORPORATION—See Middlefield Group Limited; *Int'l*, pg. 4884
MIDDLEFIELD FINANCIAL SERVICES INC.—See Middlefield Group Limited; *Int'l*, pg. 4884
MIDDLEFIELD GROUP LIMITED; *Int'l*, pg. 4884
MIDDLEFIELD INTERNATIONAL LIMITED—See Middlefield Group Limited; *Int'l*, pg. 4884
MIDDLEFIELD LIMITED—See Middlefield Group Limited; *Int'l*, pg. 4884
MIDDLEFIELD REALTY SERVICES LIMITED—See Middlefield Group Limited; *Int'l*, pg. 4884
MIDDLEFIELD REIT INDEXPLUS ETF—See Middlefield Group Limited; *Int'l*, pg. 4884
MIDDLEGROUND MANAGEMENT, LP; *U.S. Private*, pg. 2711
MIDDLEGROUND TECHNOLOGIES LLC—See Southfield Capital Advisors, LLC; *U.S. Private*, pg. 3736
MIDDLE ISLAND RESOURCES LIMITED; *Int'l*, pg. 4884
MIDDLEKAUFF AUTOMOTIVE INC.; *U.S. Private*, pg. 2713
MIDDLEMOUNT COAL PTY LTD—See Peabody Energy Corporation; *U.S. Public*, pg. 1659
MIDDLEPORT FAMILY HEALTH CENTER; *U.S. Private*, pg. 2713
MIDDLEPORT TERMINAL, INC.—See CRH plc; *Int'l*, pg. 1847
MIDDLESBORO COCA-COLA BOTTLING; *U.S. Private*, pg. 2713
MIDDLESEA VALLETTA LIFE ASSURANCE COMPANY LTD.—See MAPFRE S.A.; *Int'l*, pg. 4685
MIDDLESEX BANCORP, MHC; *U.S. Private*, pg. 2714
THE MIDDLESEX CORPORATION; *U.S. Private*, pg. 4079
MIDDLESEX COUNTY UTILITIES AUTHORITY; *U.S. Private*, pg. 2714
MIDDLESEX FEDERAL SAVINGS F.A.; *U.S. Private*, pg. 2714
MIDDLESEX INSURANCE CO.—See Sentry Insurance Group; *U.S. Private*, pg. 3611
MIDDLESEX LLC.; *U.S. Private*, pg. 2714
MIDDLESEX MUTUAL ASSURANCE COMPANY—See COUNTRY Financial; *U.S. Private*, pg. 1067
MIDDLESEX SAVINGS BANK—See Middlesex Bancorp, MHC; *U.S. Private*, pg. 2714
MIDDLESEX WATER COMPANY; *U.S. Public*, pg. 1445
MIDDLE TENNESSEE AMBULATORY SURGERY CENTER, L.P.—See Tenet Healthcare Corporation; *U.S. Public*, pg. 2011
MIDDLE TENNESSEE ELECTRIC MEMBERSHIP CORPORATION; *U.S. Private*, pg. 2711

MIDDLE TENNESSEE NATURAL GAS UTILITY DISTRICT INC.; *U.S. Private*, pg. 2711
MIDDLE TENNESSEE NEUROLOGY LLC—See HCA Healthcare, Inc.; *U.S. Public*, pg. 1003
MIDDLETON BUILDING SUPPLY INC.; *U.S. Private*, pg. 2714
MIDDLETON FORD INC.; *U.S. Private*, pg. 2714
MIDDLETON INC.; *U.S. Private*, pg. 2714
MIDDLETON OIL CO. INC.; *U.S. Private*, pg. 2714
MIDDLETON RAINES + ZAPATA LLP—See Baker Tilly US, LLP; *U.S. Private*, pg. 457
MIDDLETON TECHNOLOGY LIMITED—See Thoma Bravo, L.P.; *U.S. Private*, pg. 4149
THE MIDDLETOWN ENDOSCOPY ASC, LLC—See KKR & Co. Inc.; *U.S. Public*, pg. 1248
MIDDLETOWN FORD SALES INC.; *U.S. Private*, pg. 2714
MIDDLETOWN FORD; *U.S. Private*, pg. 2714
MIDDLETOWN HOME SALES; *U.S. Private*, pg. 2714
THE MIDDLETOWN PRESS—See Alden Global Capital LLC; *U.S. Private*, pg. 159
MIDDLETOWN VALLEY BANK—See Community Heritage Financial, Inc.; *U.S. Public*, pg. 558
MIDDLE & WEST DELTA FLOUR MILLS; *Int'l*, pg. 4883
MIDDOUGH CONSULTING, ILLINIOS—See Middough, Inc.; *U.S. Private*, pg. 2714
MIDDOUGH CONSULTING, INC—See Middough, Inc.; *U.S. Private*, pg. 2714
MIDDOUGH CONSULTING, KENTUCKY—See Middough, Inc.; *U.S. Private*, pg. 2714
MIDDOUGH CONSULTING, WEST VIRGINIA—See Middough, Inc.; *U.S. Private*, pg. 2714
MIDDOUGH, INC.; *U.S. Private*, pg. 2714
MIDEA AMERICA (CANADA) CORP.—See Midea Group Co., Ltd.; *Int'l*, pg. 4885
MIDEA AMERICA CORP.—See Midea Group Co., Ltd.; *Int'l*, pg. 4885
MIDEA EUROPE GMBH—See Midea Group Co., Ltd.; *Int'l*, pg. 4886
MIDEA GERMANY MHA HAUSHALTSWAREN GMBH—See Midea Group Co., Ltd.; *Int'l*, pg. 4886
MIDEA GROUP CO., LTD.; *Int'l*, pg. 4884
MIDEA REAL ESTATE HOLDING LTD.; *Int'l*, pg. 4886
MIDEA REFRIGERATING(HONG KONG) CO., LTD.—See Midea Group Co., Ltd.; *Int'l*, pg. 4886
MIDEAST AREA COUNCIL—See Dairy Farmers of America, Inc.; *U.S. Private*, pg. 1146
MIDEAST CONSTRUCTORS LIMITED (MECON)—See Mannai Corporation QPSC; *Int'l*, pg. 4675
MID EASTERN BUILDERS, INC.; *U.S. Private*, pg. 2706
MID-EASTERN INDUSTRIES, INC.—See Technology Dynamics, Inc.; *U.S. Private*, pg. 3955
MIDEAST INTEGRATED STEELS LIMITED; *Int'l*, pg. 4886
MIDEAST PORTFOLIO MANAGEMENT LTD.; *Int'l*, pg. 4886
MIDEAST SHIP MANAGEMENT LTD.—See National Shipping Company of Saudi Arabia; *Int'l*, pg. 5163
MIDER-HELM METHANOL VERTRIEBS GMBH—See HELM AG; *Int'l*, pg. 3338
MIDE TECHNOLOGY CORPORATION—See TotalEnergies SE; *Int'l*, pg. 7837
MIDEUROPA FUND MANAGEMENT LIMITED—See Mid Europa Partners LLP; *Int'l*, pg. 4882
MIDEUROPA FUND MANAGEMENT LUXEMBOURG SARL—See Mid Europa Partners LLP; *Int'l*, pg. 4882
MID EUROPA PARTNERS KFT—See Mid Europa Partners LLP; *Int'l*, pg. 4882
MID EUROPA PARTNERS LLP; *Int'l*, pg. 4882
MID EUROPA PARTNERS SP. Z O.O.—See Mid Europa Partners LLP; *Int'l*, pg. 4882
MIDEUROPA SRL—See Mid Europa Partners LLP; *Int'l*, pg. 4882
MIDFIELD CO-PRODUCTS PTY LTD—See Midfield Meat International Pty. Ltd.; *Int'l*, pg. 4886
MIDFIELD MEAT INTERNATIONAL PTY. LTD.; *Int'l*, pg. 4886
MIDFIELD TRADING PTY LTD—See Midfield Meat International Pty. Ltd.; *Int'l*, pg. 4886
MIDFIRST BANK—See Midland Financial Co.; *U.S. Private*, pg. 2715
MIDFIRST TRUST CO.—See Midland Financial Co.; *U.S. Private*, pg. 2715
MID-FLORIDA AREA AGENCY ON AGING, INC.; *U.S. Private*, pg. 2708
MIDFLORIDA CREDIT UNION; *U.S. Private*, pg. 2714
MID-FLORIDA FREEZER WAREHOUSES, LTD.; *U.S. Private*, pg. 2708
MIDFLOW SERVICES, LLC—See Profire Energy, Inc.; *U.S. Public*, pg. 1724
MIDGLEY-HUBER INC.; *U.S. Private*, pg. 2714
MIDI ATLANTIQUE FONDATIONS SAS—See VINCI S.A.; *Int'l*, pg. 8224
MIDI AUTO 19; *Int'l*, pg. 4886
MIDI AUTO 56; *Int'l*, pg. 4886
MIDI AUTO CAVAILLON; *Int'l*, pg. 4886
MIDI INGENIERIE S.A.S.—See HENSOLDT AG; *Int'l*, pg. 3356
MID-ILLINOIS CONCRETE INC.; *U.S. Private*, pg. 2708
MIDI MUSIC CENTER INC.—See Kawai Musical Instruments Mfg. Co., Ltd.; *Int'l*, pg. 4094

MID INDIA INDUSTRIES LIMITED; *Int'l*, pg. 4882
MID INDUSTRY CAPITAL S.P.A.—See Palladio Holding SpA; *Int'l*, pg. 5708
MID-IOWA COOPERATIVE INC.; *U.S. Private*, pg. 2708
MID IOWA TOOLS INCORPORATED; *U.S. Private*, pg. 2706
MIDI P.L.C.; *Int'l*, pg. 4886
MID ISLAND ELECTRICAL SALES CORP.—See Turtle & Hughes, Inc.; *U.S. Private*, pg. 4262
MID-ISLAND PRIMARY & URGENT CARE, L.L.C.—See Tenet Healthcare Corporation; *U.S. Public*, pg. 2008
MIDI S.R.L.—See Unipol Gruppo S.p.A.; *Int'l*, pg. 8056
MID-KANSAS CO-OP ASSOCIATION; *U.S. Private*, pg. 2708
MID-KANSAS COOP—See Mid-Kansas Co-op Association; *U.S. Private*, pg. 2708
MIDLAND ATLANTIC PROPERTIES, LLC; *U.S. Private*, pg. 2714
MIDLAND ATLANTIC PROPERTIES, LLC—See Midland Atlantic Properties, LLC; *U.S. Private*, pg. 2714
MIDLAND ATLANTIC PROPERTIES, LLC—See Midland Atlantic Properties, LLC; *U.S. Private*, pg. 2714
MIDLAND BRICK LIMITED—See Seven Group Holdings Limited; *Int'l*, pg. 6732
MIDLAND CAPITAL HOLDINGS CORP.; *U.S. Private*, pg. 2714
MIDLAND CARE CONNECTION, INC.; *U.S. Private*, pg. 2715
MIDLAND CHANDLERS LIMITED—See LKQ Corporation; *U.S. Public*, pg. 1335
THE MIDLAND COMPANY—See Munchener Ruckversicherungs AG; *Int'l*, pg. 5090
MIDLAND COMPUTER INC.; *U.S. Private*, pg. 2715
MIDLAND CONTAINER CORPORATION—See Arbor Private Investment Company, LLC; *U.S. Private*, pg. 309
MIDLAND CREDIT MANAGEMENT, INC.—See Encore Capital Group, Inc.; *U.S. Public*, pg. 759
MIDLAND DAILY NEWS—See The Hearst Corporation; *U.S. Private*, pg. 4047
MIDLAND DAVIS CORPORATION—See Peoria Disposal Company/Area Disposal Service, Inc.; *U.S. Private*, pg. 3143
MIDLAND DESIGN SERVICE INC.—See American Tooling Center, Inc.; *U.S. Private*, pg. 257
MIDLAND ENGINEERING COMPANY; *U.S. Private*, pg. 2715
MIDLAND ENGINEERING SERVICES LTD.—See THK CO., LTD.; *Int'l*, pg. 7712
MIDLAND EXPLORATION INC.; *Int'l*, pg. 4886
MIDLAND FEDERAL SAVINGS AND LOAN ASSOCIATION—See Midland Capital Holdings Corp.; *U.S. Private*, pg. 2714
MIDLAND FINANCIAL ADVISORS, INC.—See Midland States Bancorp, Inc.; *U.S. Public*, pg. 1445
MIDLAND FINANCIAL CO.; *U.S. Private*, pg. 2715
MIDLAND FOOD SERVICES; *U.S. Private*, pg. 2715
MIDLAND GIS SOLUTIONS, LLC—See Peak Rock Capital LLC; *U.S. Private*, pg. 3124
MIDLAND-GUARDIAN CO.—See Munchener Ruckversicherungs AG; *Int'l*, pg. 5090
MIDLAND HOLDINGS LIMITED; *Int'l*, pg. 4886
MIDLAND IC&I SURVEYORS LIMITED—See Legend Upstar Holdings Limited; *Int'l*, pg. 4444
MIDLAND IMMIGRATION CONSULTANCY LIMITED—See Midland Holdings Limited; *Int'l*, pg. 4886
MIDLAND IMPLEMENT COMPANY, INC.; *U.S. Private*, pg. 2715
MIDLAND INDUSTRIES. CO., INC.—See Gemspring Capital Management, LLC; *U.S. Private*, pg. 1659
MIDLAND INFORMATION RESOURCES INC.—See Carl Bennet AB; *Int'l*, pg. 1332
MIDLAND MACAU LIMITED—See Midland Holdings Limited; *Int'l*, pg. 4886
MIDLAND MAP COMPANY, LLC—See Hellman & Friedman LLC; *U.S. Private*, pg. 1908
MIDLAND MARKETING COOP, INC.; *U.S. Private*, pg. 2715
MIDLAND METAL MFG. CO., INC.—See Gemspring Capital Management, LLC; *U.S. Private*, pg. 1659
MIDLAND MICROFIN LTD.; *Int'l*, pg. 4886
MIDLAND MORTGAGE CO.—See Midland Financial Co.; *U.S. Private*, pg. 2715
MIDLAND NATIONAL LIFE INSURANCE CO.—See Sammons Enterprises, Inc.; *U.S. Private*, pg. 3537
MIDLAND OPTICAL CHICAGO LABS, INC.—See EssilorLuxottica SA; *Int'l*, pg. 2513
MIDLAND PAPER COMPANY; *U.S. Private*, pg. 2715
MIDLAND PAPER CO.—See Midland Paper Company; *U.S. Private*, pg. 2715
MIDLAND PAPER CO.—See Midland Paper Company; *U.S. Private*, pg. 2715
MIDLAND PAPER CO.—See Midland Paper Company; *U.S. Private*, pg. 2715
MIDLAND PAPER CO.—See Midland Paper Company; *U.S. Private*, pg. 2715
MIDLAND PAPER—See Midland Paper Company; *U.S. Private*, pg. 2715
MIDLAND PLASTICS INC.; *U.S. Private*, pg. 2715

MIDLAND POWDER COMPANY—See Incitec Pivot Limited; *Int'l*, pg. 3648
MIDLAND PRECISION EQUIPMENT CO LTD—See Waters Corporation; *U.S. Public*, pg. 2335
MIDLAND QUARRY PRODUCTS LTD.—See Anglo American PLC; *Int'l*, pg. 462
MIDLAND QUARRY PRODUCTS LTD.—See Heidelberg Materials AG; *Int'l*, pg. 3314
MIDLAND REALTY (COMM. & IND.)LIMITED—See Legend Upstar Holdings Limited; *Int'l*, pg. 4444
MIDLAND REALTY (COMM.) LIMITED—See Legend Upstar Holdings Limited; *Int'l*, pg. 4444
MIDLAND REALTY (GLOBAL) LIMITED—See Midland Holdings Limited; *Int'l*, pg. 4886
MIDLAND REALTY INTERNATIONAL LIMITED—See Midland Holdings Limited; *Int'l*, pg. 4886
MIDLAND REALTY (SHOPS) LIMITED—See Legend Upstar Holdings Limited; *Int'l*, pg. 4444
MIDLAND REPORTER-TELEGRAM—See The Hearst Corporation; *U.S. Private*, pg. 4047
MIDLANDS MANAGEMENT CORPORATION—See Tokio Marine Holdings, Inc.; *Int'l*, pg. 7782
MIDLANDS MECHANICAL INC.; *U.S. Private*, pg. 2715
MIDLANDS ORTHOPAEDICS SURGERY CENTER, LLC; *U.S. Private*, pg. 2715
MIDLANDS POWER (UK) LIMITED—See E.ON SE; *Int'l*, pg. 2256
MIDLAND STATES BANCORP, INC.; *U.S. Public*, pg. 1445
MIDLAND STATES BANK—See Midland States Bancorp, Inc.; *U.S. Public*, pg. 1445
MIDLAND STEEL COMPANY; *U.S. Private*, pg. 2715
MIDLANDS TRUCK & VAN LTD—See Ballyvesey Holdings Limited; *Int'l*, pg. 809
MIDLAND TECHNICAL CRAFTS, INC.—See MDU Resources Group, Inc.; *U.S. Public*, pg. 1411
MIDLAND TECHNOLOGIES, INC.—See Innovance, Inc.; *U.S. Private*, pg. 2081
MIDLAND TEXAS SURGICAL CENTER, LLC—See Tenet Healthcare Corporation; *U.S. Public*, pg. 2011
MIDLAND TOOL & DESIGN LIMITED—See TT Electronics plc; *Int'l*, pg. 7959
MIDLAND TRUST COMPANY—See Midland States Bancorp, Inc.; *U.S. Public*, pg. 1445
MIDLAND WEALTH ADVISORS LLP—See Midland States Bancorp, Inc.; *U.S. Public*, pg. 1445
MIDLAND WEEKLY MEDIA LTD—See Reach PLC; *Int'l*, pg. 6231
MIDLANTIC MACHINERY COMPANY—See ITOCHU Corporation; *Int'l*, pg. 3838
MID-LINK M7/M8 LTD.—See Groupe Egis S.A.; *Int'l*, pg. 3102
MIDLOTHIAN CAPITAL PARTNERS LIMITED; *Int'l*, pg. 4886
MIDLOTHIAN CEMENT PLANT—See Martin Marietta Materials, Inc.; *U.S. Public*, pg. 1389
MIDLOTHIAN ENERGY LIMITED PARTNERSHIP—See ENGIE SA; *Int'l*, pg. 2433
MIDMARK ANIMAL HEALTH—See Midmark Corporation; *U.S. Private*, pg. 2716
MIDMARK CAPITAL; *U.S. Private*, pg. 2715
MIDMARK CORPORATION; *U.S. Private*, pg. 2716
MIDMARK DIAGNOSTICS GROUP—See Midmark Corporation; *U.S. Private*, pg. 2716
MID-MICHIGAN DERMATOLOGY, PLLC—See Harvest Partners L.P.; *U.S. Private*, pg. 1876
MID-MICHIGAN RAILROAD, INC.—See Brookfield Infrastructure Partners L.P.; *Int'l*, pg. 1192
MID-MICHIGAN RAILROAD, INC.—See GIC Pte. Ltd.; *Int'l*, pg. 2966
MID-MICHIGAN RECYCLING, L.C.—See CMS Energy Corporation; *U.S. Public*, pg. 518
MID-MINNESOTA LEGAL AID; *U.S. Private*, pg. 2708
MID-MISSOURI HOLDING COMPANY, INC.; *U.S. Private*, pg. 2708
MID-MISSOURI LIMESTONE, LLC—See Summit Materials, Inc.; *U.S. Public*, pg. 1959
MID MOUNTAIN CONTRACTORS, INC.—See Koninklijke VolkerWessels N.V.; *Int'l*, pg. 4272
MIDNIGHT GAMING CORP.; *U.S. Private*, pg. 2716
MIDNIGHT OIL CREATIVE; *U.S. Private*, pg. 2716
MIDNIGHT SUN MINING CORP.; *Int'l*, pg. 4887
MIDNITE AIR CORP.—See United Parcel Service, Inc.; *U.S. Public*, pg. 2233
MIDNITE EXPRESS INC.—See MME Inc; *U.S. Private*, pg. 2754
MIDNITE EXPRESS INC.—See The Riverside Company; *U.S. Private*, pg. 4109
MID NORTH MOTORS (SUDBURY) LTD.; *Int'l*, pg. 4882
MID OAKS INVESTMENTS LLC; *U.S. Private*, pg. 2706
MIDOCEAN PARTNERS, LLP - LONDON OFFICE—See MidOcean Partners, LLP; *U.S. Private*, pg. 2717
MIDOCEAN PARTNERS, LLP; *U.S. Private*, pg. 2716
MID-OHIO MECHANICAL, INC. - SHEETMETAL DIVISION—See Mid-Ohio Mechanical, Inc.; *U.S. Private*, pg. 2708
MID-OHIO MECHANICAL, INC.; *U.S. Private*, pg. 2708
THE MIDONG CO,. LTD.; *Int'l*, pg. 7666

MIDOR AG—See The Federation of Migros Cooperatives; *Int'l*, pg. 7642
MIDORI INDUSTRIES CO., LTD.—See Aso Co., Ltd.; *Int'l*, pg. 628
MIDORI SERVICES CO., LTD.—See Mie Kotsu Group Holdings, Inc.; *Int'l*, pg. 4888
MIDORI SHOJI CO., LTD.—See Lotte Co., Ltd.; *Int'l*, pg. 4560
MIDORIYAMA STUDIO CITY, INC—See TBS Holdings, Inc.; *Int'l*, pg. 7481
MIDO, SA—See The Swatch Group Ltd.; *Int'l*, pg. 7692
MIDO UNIFORMS PTE. LTD.—See PT Trisula International Tbk; *Int'l*, pg. 6080
MIDPAC AUTO CENTER, INC.; *U.S. Private*, pg. 2717
MID PAC CS, LLC—See Par Pacific Holdings, Inc.; *U.S. Public*, pg. 1636
MID-PARK INC.; *U.S. Private*, pg. 2708
MIDPEN HOUSING CORPORATION; *U.S. Private*, pg. 2717
MID PENN BANCORP, INC.; *U.S. Public*, pg. 1444
MID PENN BANK—See Mid Penn Bancorp, Inc.; *U.S. Public*, pg. 1444
MIDPOINT PROPERTIES LIMITED—See Allgreen Properties Ltd.; *Int'l*, pg. 338
MIDPOINT & TRANSFER LTD.; *Int'l*, pg. 4887
MIDRAND GRADUATE INSTITUTE PTY LTD—See Pearson plc; *Int'l*, pg. 5776
MIDRANGE SUPPORT & SERVICE, INC.—See CDW Corporation; *U.S. Public*, pg. 462
MIDREX INTERNATIONAL B.V.—See Kobe Steel, Ltd.; *Int'l*, pg. 4220
MIDREX METALLURGY TECHNOLOGY SERVICES (SHANGHAI) LTD.—See Kobe Steel, Ltd.; *Int'l*, pg. 4220
MIDREX TECHNOLOGIES GULF SERVICES FZCO—See Kobe Steel, Ltd.; *Int'l*, pg. 4220
MIDREX TECHNOLOGIES INC.—See Kobe Steel, Ltd.; *Int'l*, pg. 4218
MIDREX TECHNOLOGIES INDIA PVT. LTD.—See Kobe Steel, Ltd.; *Int'l*, pg. 4220
MIDREX UK, LTD.—See Kobe Steel, Ltd.; *Int'l*, pg. 4220
MID RIVERS AMBULATORY SURGERY CENTER, L.P.—See Tenet Healthcare Corporation; *U.S. Public*, pg. 2011
MID-RIVERS TELEPHONE COOPERATIVE; *U.S. Private*, pg. 2708
MID ROCKLAND IMAGING PARTNERS, INC.—See RadNet, Inc.; *U.S. Public*, pg. 1761
MIDROOG LTD.—See Moody's Corporation; *U.S. Public*, pg. 1468
MID SEVEN TRANSPORTATION CO.—See Daseke, Inc.; *U.S. Private*, pg. 1161
MID-SHIP GROUP LLC—See Kinder Morgan, Inc.; *U.S. Public*, pg. 1233
MIDSONA AB; *Int'l*, pg. 4887
MIDSONA DEUTSCHLAND GMBH—See Midsona AB; *Int'l*, pg. 4887
MIDSONA NORGE AS—See Midsona AB; *Int'l*, pg. 4887
MID-SOUTH BUILDING SUPPLY CO., INC.; *U.S. Private*, pg. 2708
MID SOUTH BUILDING SUPPLY, COMMERCIAL DIVISION—See Mid South Building Supply; *U.S. Private*, pg. 2706
MID SOUTH BUILDING SUPPLY; *U.S. Private*, pg. 2706
MID SOUTH CONSTRUCTION AND BUILDING PRODUCTS, INC.—See Installed Building Products, Inc.; *U.S. Public*, pg. 1133
MID SOUTH CONTRACTORS LTD.—See Motor City Electric Co., Inc.; *U.S. Private*, pg. 2796
MID-SOUTH ELECTRONICS, INC.—See Mid-South Industries, Inc.; *U.S. Private*, pg. 2708
MID SOUTH ENGINE & POWER SYSTEMS, LLC—See Atlas Copco AB; *Int'l*, pg. 683
MID-SOUTHERN BANCORP, INC.; *U.S. Public*, pg. 1445
MID-SOUTHERN SAVINGS BANK, FSB—See Mid-Southern Bancorp, Inc.; *U.S. Public*, pg. 1445
MIDSOUTH FARMERS CO-OP; *U.S. Private*, pg. 2717
MID-SOUTH INDUSTRIES, INC.; *U.S. Private*, pg. 2708
MID-SOUTH LUMBER AND SUPPLY; *U.S. Private*, pg. 2708
MID-SOUTH LUMBER COMPANY OF GEORGIA INC.; *U.S. Private*, pg. 2709
MID SOUTH MACHINERY INC.; *U.S. Private*, pg. 2706
MID-SOUTH MAINTENANCE, INC.; *U.S. Private*, pg. 2709
MID-SOUTH MANAGEMENT CO. INC.; *U.S. Private*, pg. 2709
MID-SOUTH MILLING COMPANY, INC. - KANSAS PLANT—See Mid-South Milling Company, Inc.; *U.S. Private*, pg. 2709
MID-SOUTH MILLING COMPANY, INC.; *U.S. Private*, pg. 2709
MID-SOUTH PRODUCTS ENGINEERING, INC.—See Mid-South Industries, Inc.; *U.S. Private*, pg. 2708
MID SOUTH RADIOLOGY PARTNERS, LLC; *U.S. Private*, pg. 2709
MID-SOUTH RESTAURANTS INC.; *U.S. Private*, pg. 2709
MID SOUTH SALES, INC.; *U.S. Private*, pg. 2706
MID-SOUTH STEEL INC.; *U.S. Private*, pg. 2709
MID-SOUTH SYNERGY; *U.S. Private*, pg. 2709

MID SOUTH TRANSPORT INC.; *U.S. Private*, pg. 2706
MID-SOUTH WIRE COMPANY, INC.; *U.S. Private*, pg. 2709
MIDSTATE AIR COMPRESSOR, INC.—See Atlas Copco AB; *Int'l*, pg. 680
MIDSTATE BANCORP, INC.; *U.S. Public*, pg. 2717
MID-STATE BOLT & NUT CO., INC.; *U.S. Private*, pg. 2709
MID-STATE COMMUNICATIONS & ELECTRONICS, INC.; *U.S. Private*, pg. 2709
MID-STATE CONSULTANTS, INC.—See John Staurulakis, LLC; *U.S. Private*, pg. 2224
MID-STATE CONTRACTING LLC; *U.S. Private*, pg. 2709
MIDSTATE CREDITCOLLECT PTY LTD—See Collection House Limited; *Int'l*, pg. 1699
MID STATE DISTRIBUTING COMPANY; *U.S. Private*, pg. 2706
MIDSTATE ELECTRIC COOPERATIVE, INC.; *U.S. Private*, pg. 2718
MID-STATE ENDOSCOPY CENTER, LLC—See Tenet Healthcare Corporation; *U.S. Public*, pg. 2011
MID-STATE ENERGY INCORPORATED; *U.S. Private*, pg. 2709
MID-STATE LUMBER CORP.—See Specialty Building Products, LLC; *U.S. Private*, pg. 3749
MID-STATE MACHINE & FABRICATING INC—See CenterGate Capital, LP; *U.S. Private*, pg. 816
MID-STATE MACHINE PRODUCTS, INC.—See Insight Equity Holdings LLC; *U.S. Private*, pg. 2086
MIDSTATE ORTHOPAEDIC AND SPORTS MEDICINE CENTER, INC.—See FFL Partners, LLC; *U.S. Private*, pg. 1500
MID-STATE PETROLEUM INC.; *U.S. Private*, pg. 2709
MIDSTATE RADIOLOGY ASSOCIATES LLC; *U.S. Private*, pg. 2718
MID-STATE RV CENTER, INC.—See Redwood Capital Investments, LLC; *U.S. Private*, pg. 3380
MID-STATES ALUMINUM CORP.—See Mayville Engineering Company, Inc.; *U.S. Public*, pg. 1403
MID-STATES BOLT & SCREW CO.—See MPE Partners, LLC; *U.S. Private*, pg. 2803
MID STATES CONSTRUCTION INC.; *U.S. Private*, pg. 2706
MIDSTATES CONTAINER COMPANY—See Cleveland Steel Container Corporation; *U.S. Private*, pg. 941
MID-STATES DISTRIBUTORS; *U.S. Private*, pg. 2709
MIDSTATE SECURITY COMPANY LLC—See Allied Universal Manager LLC; *U.S. Private*, pg. 190
MID-STATES ENERGY WORKS, INC.; *U.S. Private*, pg. 2709
MID-STATES FORGING DIE & TOOL CO.—See Modern Drop Forge Co.; *U.S. Private*, pg. 2760
MID-STATES GENERAL & MECHANICAL CONTRACTING; *U.S. Private*, pg. 2709
MIDSTATES GROUP COMPANY; *U.S. Private*, pg. 2718
MIDSTATES PRINTING INC.; *U.S. Private*, pg. 2718
MID-STATES SUPPLY COMPANY, INC.; *U.S. Private*, pg. 2709
MID STATE SUPPLY CO., LLC—See Crest Industries, LLC; *U.S. Private*, pg. 1096
MID STATES UTILITY TRAILER SALES, INC.; *U.S. Private*, pg. 2709
MID-STATE TELEPHONE CO.—See Telephone & Data Systems, Inc.; *U.S. Public*, pg. 1998
MID-STATE TRUCK SERVICE INC.; *U.S. Private*, pg. 2709
MIDSTREAM LOGISTICS, LLC—See Energy Transfer LP; *U.S. Public*, pg. 764
MIDSUMMER AB; *Int'l*, pg. 4887
MIDTECH PARTNERS, INC.—See PipelineRx; *U.S. Private*, pg. 3189
MID-TEX OF MIDLAND, INC.; *U.S. Private*, pg. 2709
MIDTEX OIL, LP; *U.S. Private*, pg. 2718
MIDT FACTORING A/S—See Groupe BPCE; *Int'l*, pg. 3098
MIDT-NORSK HAVBRUK AS; *Int'l*, pg. 4887
MIDTOWN BAY PTE. LTD.—See Hong Leong Investment Holdings Pte. Ltd.; *Int'l*, pg. 3468
MIDTOWN CONSULTING GROUP, INC.; *U.S. Private*, pg. 2718
MIDTOWN ELECTRIC SUPPLY CORP.; *U.S. Private*, pg. 2718
MIDTOWN EXPRESS, LLC—See Dycom Industries, Inc.; *U.S. Public*, pg. 698
MIDTOWN FOOD STORES INCORPORATION; *U.S. Private*, pg. 2718
MID-TOWN FORD SALES LIMITED; *Int'l*, pg. 4883
MIDTOWN INSURANCE COMPANY—See The New York Times Company; *U.S. Public*, pg. 2116
MIDTOWN PARTNERS & CO., LLC; *U.S. Private*, pg. 2718
MIDTOWN SURGERY CENTER J.V.—See Campbell Clinic Orthopaedics; *U.S. Private*, pg. 730
MIDTOWN TOYOTA; *U.S. Private*, pg. 2718
MID-TRONIC WIESAUPLAST GMBH—See INDUS Holding AG; *Int'l*, pg. 3664
MIDUHO INDUSTRY CO., LTD.—See Toyota Industries Corporation; *Int'l*, pg. 7866
MID URBAN DEVELOPMENT CO., LTD.; *Int'l*, pg. 4882

COMPANY NAME INDEX

MID-USA CYCLE PARTS INC.; *U.S. Private*, pg. 2709
MIDVALE TRUCK SALES & SERVICE INC.; *U.S. Private*, pg. 2718
MID VALLEY AGRICULTURAL SERVICES, INC.; *U.S. Private*, pg. 2706
MID-VALLEY COMMUNITY ACTION AGENCY; *U.S. Private*, pg. 2709
MIDVALLEY ENTERTAINMENT LIMITED; *Int'l*, pg. 4887
MIDVALLEY HEALTHCARE; *U.S. Private*, pg. 2718
MID VALLEY INDUSTRIES, LLC—See Goldner Hawn Johnson & Morrison Inc.; *U.S. Private*, pg. 1735
MID-VALLEY PIPELINE COMPANY—See Energy Transfer LP; *U.S. Public*, pg. 764
MID-VALLEY TITLE AND ESCROW COMPANY—See First American Financial Corporation; *U.S. Public*, pg. 837
THE MID VALLEY TOWN CRIER—See AIM Media Texas, LLC; *U.S. Private*, pg. 132
MID-VOL COAL SALES, INC.—See ArcelorMittal S.A.; *Int'l*, pg. 546
MIDWAY AIRCRAFT INSTRUMENT CORP.—See Groupe Industriel Marcel Dassault S.A.; *Int'l*, pg. 3105
MIDWAY AIRLINES' TERMINAL CONSORTIUM; *U.S. Private*, pg. 2718
MIDWAY AMUSEMENT GAMES LLC—See Midway Games Inc.; *U.S. Private*, pg. 2718
MIDWAY APPLIANCE CENTER, INC.—See Howard's Appliances, Inc.; *U.S. Private*, pg. 1995
MIDWAY CHEVROLET COMPANY; *U.S. Private*, pg. 2718
MIDWAY COOP INC.; *U.S. Private*, pg. 2718
MIDWAY DENTAL SUPPLY, INC.—See Henry Schein, Inc.; *U.S. Public*, pg. 1027
MIDWAY DIE, LLC—See Auxo Investment Partners, LLC; *U.S. Private*, pg. 402
MIDWAY DODGE INC.; *U.S. Private*, pg. 2718
MIDWAY FORD TRUCK CENTER INC.; *U.S. Private*, pg. 2718
MIDWAY GAMES INC.; *U.S. Private*, pg. 2718
MIDWAY GOLD CORP.; *U.S. Private*, pg. 2718
MIDWAY INC.; *U.S. Private*, pg. 2718
MIDWAY INDUSTRIAL SUPPLY, INC.—See Genstar Capital, LLC; *U.S. Private*, pg. 1678
MIDWAY INDUSTRIES INC.; *U.S. Private*, pg. 2719
MIDWAY METALS PTY. LTD.; *Int'l*, pg. 4887
MIDWAY NISSAN; *Int'l*, pg. 4887
MIDWAY OIL CORP.; *U.S. Private*, pg. 2719
MIDWAY PETROLEUM CO. INC.; *U.S. Private*, pg. 2719
MIDWAY PRODUCTS GROUP, INC.; *U.S. Private*, pg. 2719
MIDWAY PTY LTD; *Int'l*, pg. 4887
MIDWAY RENT-A-CAR INC.; *U.S. Private*, pg. 2719
MIDWAY SALES & DISTRIBUTING, INC.; *U.S. Private*, pg. 2719
MIDWAY SHOPPING CENTER, L.P.—See Regency Centers Corporation; *U.S. Public*, pg. 1774
MIDWAY STAFFING, INC.; *U.S. Private*, pg. 2719
MIDWAY-SUNSET COGENERATION COMPANY—See Edison International; *U.S. Public*, pg. 719
MID-WAY SUPPLY INC.; *U.S. Private*, pg. 2709
MIDWAY TRAILERS, INC.; *U.S. Private*, pg. 2719
MIDWAY TRUCK PARTS INC.; *U.S. Private*, pg. 2719
MIDWAYUSA FOUNDATION, INC.; *U.S. Private*, pg. 2719
MIDWAY U.S.A. INC.—See Midway Ford Truck Center Inc.; *U.S. Private*, pg. 2718
MIDWESCO FILTER RESOURCES, INC.—See Perma-Pipe International Holdings, Inc.; *U.S. Public*, pg. 1676
MIDWESCO INDUSTRIES INC.; *U.S. Private*, pg. 2719
MIDWESCO MECHANICAL AND ENERGY, INC.—See Perma-Pipe International Holdings, Inc.; *U.S. Public*, pg. 1676
MIDWEST ACOUST-A-FIBER INC.; *U.S. Private*, pg. 2719
MIDWEST AGENCIES, INC.—See Peter Kiewit Sons', Inc.; *U.S. Private*, pg. 3158
MIDWEST AGRI-COMMODITIES—See American Crystal Sugar Company; *U.S. Public*, pg. 98
MIDWEST AGRI-COMMODITIES—See Michigan Sugar Company; *U.S. Private*, pg. 2701
MIDWEST AGRI-COMMODITIES—See Minn-Dak Farmers Cooperative; *U.S. Private*, pg. 2742
MIDWEST AGRI-COMMODITIES—See Southern Minnesota Beet Sugar Cooperative; *U.S. Private*, pg. 3733
MIDWEST AG SUPPLEMENTS, LLC—See CHS INC.; *U.S. Public*, pg. 492
MIDWEST AIR TECHNOLOGIES INC.; *U.S. Private*, pg. 2719
MIDWEST AIR TRAFFIC CONTROL SERVICE; *U.S. Private*, pg. 2719
MIDWEST ALARM SERVICES INC.—See Per Mar Security Services; *U.S. Private*, pg. 3146
MIDWEST ALUMINUM SUPPLY INC.—See Richards Building Supply Company; *U.S. Private*, pg. 3428
MIDWEST AORTIC & VASCULAR INSTITUTE, P.C.; *U.S. Private*, pg. 2719
MIDWEST APPAREL GROUP INC.; *U.S. Private*, pg. 2719
MIDWEST ASPHALT CORP.; *U.S. Private*, pg. 2720
MIDWEST AUTOMATION INC.; *U.S. Private*, pg. 2720
MIDWEST BANCO CORPORATION; *U.S. Private*, pg. 2720
MIDWEST BANCORPORATION, INC.; *U.S. Private*, pg. 2720

MIDWEST BANKCENTRE, INC.—See Stupp Bros., Inc.; *U.S. Private*, pg. 3844
MIDWEST BANKCENTRE—See Stupp Bros., Inc.; *U.S. Private*, pg. 3844
MIDWEST BANK NATIONAL ASSOCIATION; *U.S. Private*, pg. 2720
MIDWEST BANK—See Western Illinois Bancshares, Inc.; *U.S. Private*, pg. 4493
MIDWEST BLOCK & BRICK INC.; *U.S. Private*, pg. 2720
MIDWEST BOTTLE GAS COMPANY—See Consolidated Midwest, Inc.; *U.S. Private*, pg. 1021
MIDWEST BOX COMPANY, INC.—See Jamestown Container Corporation; *U.S. Private*, pg. 2185
MIDWEST BUS SALES INC.; *U.S. Private*, pg. 2720
MIDWEST CAR CORPORATION; *U.S. Private*, pg. 2720
MIDWEST CARDIOVASCULAR & THORACIC SURGEONS OF KANSAS, LLC—See HCA Healthcare, Inc.; *U.S. Public*, pg. 1003
MIDWEST CARDIOVASCULAR & THORACIC SURGERY, LLC—See HCA Healthcare, Inc.; *U.S. Public*, pg. 1003
MIDWEST CARDIOVASCULAR & THORACIC SURGERY, LLC—See HCA Healthcare, Inc.; *U.S. Public*, pg. 1003
MIDWEST CARRIERS, LLC—See Roadrunner Transportation Systems, Inc.; *U.S. Public*, pg. 1802
MIDWEST CENTER FOR DAY SURGERY, LLC—See UnitedHealth Group Incorporated; *U.S. Public*, pg. 2242
MIDWEST CENTER FOR STRESS & ANXIETY, LLC—See Transom Capital Group, LLC; *U.S. Private*, pg. 4209
MIDWEST COMMUNICATIONS, INC.; *U.S. Private*, pg. 2720
MIDWEST COMMUNICATIONS & MEDIA; *U.S. Private*, pg. 2720
MIDWEST COMMUNITY BANCSHARES, INC.; *U.S. Private*, pg. 2720
MIDWEST COMMUNITY BANK; *U.S. Private*, pg. 2720
MIDWEST COMPOSITE TECHNOLOGIES, LLC—See CORE Industrial Partners, LLC; *U.S. Private*, pg. 1049
MIDWEST COMPUTER REGISTER CORP.—See FEI, Inc; *U.S. Private*, pg. 1493
MIDWEST CONNECTIONS, INC.—See Midwest Energy Cooperative Inc.; *U.S. Private*, pg. 2721
MIDWEST CONTROL PRODUCTS CORP.; *U.S. Private*, pg. 2720
MIDWEST CONTROLS INC.; *U.S. Private*, pg. 2720
MIDWEST COOLING TOWER SERVICES INC.—See Hastings Equity Partners, LLC; *U.S. Private*, pg. 1879
MIDWEST COOLING TOWER SERVICES INC.—See ORIX Corporation; *Int'l*, pg. 5636
MIDWEST COOPERATIVES; *U.S. Private*, pg. 2720
MIDWEST CORPORATE AVIATION, INC.—See Clemens Aviation LLC; *U.S. Private*, pg. 939
MIDWEST DAIRY ASSOCIATION; *U.S. Private*, pg. 2720
MIDWEST DESIGNER SUPPLY, INC.; *U.S. Private*, pg. 2720
MIDWEST DEVELOPMENT CO. INC.—See Skogman Construction Company of Iowa Inc.; *U.S. Private*, pg. 3683
MIDWEST DIGESTIVE HEALTH CENTER, LLC—See Tenet Healthcare Corporation; *U.S. Public*, pg. 2011
MIDWEST DIRECT; *U.S. Private*, pg. 2720
MIDWEST DISPOSALS LTD.—See Capital Environment Holdings Limited; *Int'l*, pg. 1310
MIDWEST DIVISION - ACH, LLC—See HCA Healthcare, Inc.; *U.S. Public*, pg. 1003
MIDWEST DIVISION - OPRMC, LLC—See HCA Healthcare, Inc.; *U.S. Public*, pg. 1003
MIDWEST DRYWALL CO., INC.; *U.S. Private*, pg. 2720
MIDWEST ELECTRIC COOP CORP.; *U.S. Private*, pg. 2721
MIDWEST ELECTRIC PRODUCTS INC.—See General Electric Company; *U.S. Public*, pg. 919
MIDWEST ELECTRIC; *U.S. Private*, pg. 2721
MIDWEST EMPLOYER'S CASUALTY COMPANY—See W.R. Berkley Corporation; *U.S. Public*, pg. 2318
MIDWEST ENERGY COOPERATIVE INC.; *U.S. Private*, pg. 2721
MIDWEST ENERGY EMISSIONS CORP.; *U.S. Public*, pg. 1445
MIDWEST ENERGY INC.; *U.S. Private*, pg. 2721
MIDWEST ENERGY RESOURCES COMPANY—See DTE Energy Company; *U.S. Public*, pg. 689
MIDWEST ENERGY SERVICES, INC.—See Dakota Electric Association; *U.S. Private*, pg. 1147
MIDWEST ENTERPRISES, INC.—See Munchener Ruckversicherungs AG; *Int'l*, pg. 5090
MIDWEST EQUIPMENT LEASING CORP.—See Midco Construction Corporation; *U.S. Private*, pg. 2710
MID WESTERN AUTOMOTIVE LLC; *U.S. Private*, pg. 2706
MIDWESTERN BIOAG, INC.; *U.S. Private*, pg. 2724
MIDWESTERN CONNECTICUT COUNCIL OF ALCOHOLISM; *U.S. Private*, pg. 2724
MIDWESTERN GAS TRANSMISSION COMPANY—See ONEOK, Inc.; *U.S. Public*, pg. 1603
MIDWESTERN INDUSTRIES INC.; *U.S. Private*, pg. 2724
MIDWESTERN MACHINE & HYDRAULICS, INC.; *U.S. Private*, pg. 2724

MIDWESTERN MANUFACTURING CO. INC.—See Midwesco Industries Inc.; *U.S. Private*, pg. 2719
MIDWESTERN OIL & GAS COMPANY LIMITED; *Int'l*, pg. 4887
MIDWESTERN PIPE LINE PRODUCTS CO. INC.—See Midwesco Industries Inc.; *U.S. Private*, pg. 2719
MIDWESTERN RUST PROOF CO.; *U.S. Private*, pg. 2724
MIDWESTERN WHEELS INC.; *U.S. Private*, pg. 2724
MID WEST FABRICATING COMPANY, INC.; *U.S. Private*, pg. 2706
MIDWEST FARMERS COOPERATIVE—See Frontier Cooperative Company, Inc.; *U.S. Private*, pg. 1615
MIDWEST FARM MANAGEMENT, INC.; *U.S. Private*, pg. 2721
MIDWEST FASTENER CORPORATION; *U.S. Private*, pg. 2721
MID-WEST FERTILIZER INC.; *U.S. Private*, pg. 2709
MIDWEST FLOOR COVERINGS; *U.S. Private*, pg. 2721
MIDWEST FOLDING PRODUCTS—See Sagus International LLC; *U.S. Private*, pg. 3528
MIDWEST FOOD BANK; *U.S. Private*, pg. 2721
MIDWEST FOOD & POULTRY INC.; *U.S. Private*, pg. 2721
MIDWEST FORESTREE LLC; *U.S. Private*, pg. 2721
MID-WEST FORGE CORPORATION; *U.S. Private*, pg. 2709
MIDWEST FOUNDATION CORPORATION—See Midco Construction Corporation; *U.S. Private*, pg. 2710
MIDWEST GENERATION EME, LLC—See NRG Energy, Inc.; *U.S. Public*, pg. 1550
MIDWEST GENERATION, LLC—See NRG Energy, Inc.; *U.S. Public*, pg. 1550
MIDWEST GLASS FABRICATORS, INC.—See KPS Capital Partners, LP; *U.S. Private*, pg. 2348
MIDWEST GLASS, INC.; *U.S. Private*, pg. 2721
MIDWEST GOLD LIMITED; *Int'l*, pg. 4887
MIDWEST GRANITE PVT LTD—See Midwest Gold Limited; *Int'l*, pg. 4887
MIDWEST GROWTH PARTNERS, LLLP; *U.S. Private*, pg. 2721
MIDWEST HARDWOOD CORPORATION - LITTLE RIVER HARDWOODS FACILITY—See Midwest Hardwood Corporation; *U.S. Private*, pg. 2721
MIDWEST HARDWOOD CORPORATION - PARK FALLS HARDWOODS FACILITY—See Midwest Hardwood Corporation; *U.S. Private*, pg. 2721
MIDWEST HARDWOOD CORPORATION - REEDSBURG HARDWOODS FACILITY—See Midwest Hardwood Corporation; *U.S. Private*, pg. 2721
MIDWEST HARDWOOD CORPORATION; *U.S. Private*, pg. 2721
MIDWEST HARDWOOD CORPORATION - WESTBY HARDWOOD PRODUCTS FACILITY—See Midwest Hardwood Corporation; *U.S. Private*, pg. 2721
MIDWEST HEART & VASCULAR SPECIALISTS, LLC—See HCA Healthcare, Inc.; *U.S. Public*, pg. 1003
MIDWEST HEME MANAGEMENT, INC.; *U.S. Private*, pg. 2721
MIDWEST HERITAGE BANK—See Hy-Vee, Inc.; *U.S. Private*, pg. 2016
MIDWEST HOLDING INC.—See Antarctica Capital, LLC; *U.S. Private*, pg. 286
MIDWEST HOLDINGS, INC.—See HCA Healthcare, Inc.; *U.S. Public*, pg. 1003
MIDWEST HOME DISTRIBUTORS INC—See Skogman Construction Company of Iowa Inc.; *U.S. Private*, pg. 3683
MIDWEST ICE CREAM COMPANY, LLC—See Dean Foods Company; *U.S. Private*, pg. 1184
MIDWEST IMPRESSIONS INC.; *U.S. Private*, pg. 2721
MIDWEST INDUSTRIAL METALS CORPORATION; *U.S. Private*, pg. 2721
MIDWEST INDUSTRIAL PACKAGING, INC.—See Illinois Tool Works Inc.; *U.S. Public*, pg. 1109
MIDWEST INDUSTRIAL RUBBER INC.—See Advent International Corporation; *U.S. Private*, pg. 98
MIDWEST INDUSTRIAL SUPPLY, INC.; *U.S. Private*, pg. 2722
MIDWEST INDUSTRIES, INC.; *U.S. Private*, pg. 2722
MIDWEST INFECTIOUS DISEASE SPECIALISTS, LLC—See HCA Healthcare, Inc.; *U.S. Public*, pg. 1003
MIDWEST INSPECTION SERVICES, INC.—See ShawCor Ltd.; *Int'l*, pg. 6791
MIDWEST INTERNATIONAL STANDARD PRODUCTS, INC.; *U.S. Private*, pg. 2722
MIDWEST LEMFORDER LTD.—See ZF Friedrichshafen AG; *Int'l*, pg. 8641
MIDWEST LIVING MAGAZINE—See Meredith Corporation; *U.S. Public*, pg. 1423
MIDWEST LUMBER MINNESOTA, INC.—See Specialty Building Products, LLC; *U.S. Private*, pg. 3749
MID-WEST MANAGEMENT INC.; *U.S. Private*, pg. 2710
MIDWEST MANUFACTURING RESOURCES, INC.—HAAS FACTORY OUTLET MIDWEST DIVISION—See Morris Group, Inc.; *U.S. Private*, pg. 2787
MIDWEST MANUFACTURING RESOURCES, INC.—See Morris Group, Inc.; *U.S. Private*, pg. 2787
MID-WEST MATERIALS, INC.; *U.S. Private*, pg. 2710

MID-WEST MATERIALS, INC. CORPORATE AFFILIATIONS

MIDWEST MECHANICAL CONTRACTORS, INC.—See MMC Corp.; *U.S. Private*, pg. 2754
MIDWEST MECHANICAL CONTRACTORS, INC.—See MMC Corp.; *U.S. Private*, pg. 2754
MIDWEST MEDIA GROUP INC.; *U.S. Private*, pg. 2722
MIDWEST MEDICAL INSURANCE COMPANY—See Curi Holdings, Inc.; *U.S. Private*, pg. 1125
MID-WEST MERCHANDISING CORP.—See Printers' Service, Inc.; *U.S. Private*, pg. 3265
MID-WEST METAL PRODUCTS COMPANY INC.; *U.S. Private*, pg. 2710
MIDWEST METALS CORPORATION; *U.S. Private*, pg. 2722
MIDWEST METALS, INC.—See McCarthy Bush Corporation; *U.S. Private*, pg. 2626
MIDWEST METER INC.—See FEI, Inc; *U.S. Private*, pg. 1493
MIDWEST METROPOLITAN PHYSICIANS GROUP, LLC—See HCA Healthcare, Inc.; *U.S. Public*, pg. 1003
MIDWEST MICROWAVE SOLUTIONS, INC.—See HEICO Corporation; *U.S. Public*, pg. 1020
MIDWEST MINNESOTA COMMUNITY DEVELOPMENT CORPORATION; *U.S. Private*, pg. 2722
MIDWEST MONITORING & SURVEILLANCE INC.; *U.S. Private*, pg. 2722
MIDWEST MOTOR EXPRESS INC.—See MME Inc.; *U.S. Private*, pg. 2754
MIDWEST MOTOR SUPPLY CO.; *U.S. Private*, pg. 2722
MID-WEST NATIONAL LIFE INSURANCE COMPANY OF TENNESSEE—See Blackstone Inc.; *U.S. Public*, pg. 354
MIDWEST NATURAL GAS CORP.; *U.S. Private*, pg. 2722
MID-WEST OIL COMPANY INCORPORATED; *U.S. Private*, pg. 2710
MIDWEST ONCOLOGY ASSOCIATES, LLC—See HCA Healthcare, Inc.; *U.S. Public*, pg. 1003
MIDWESTONE BANK—See MidWestOne Financial Group, Inc.; *U.S. Public*, pg. 1446
MIDWESTONE FINANCIAL GROUP, INC.; *U.S. Public*, pg. 1445
MIDWESTONE INSURANCE SERVICES, INC.—See MidWestOne Financial Group, Inc.; *U.S. Public*, pg. 1446
MIDWESTONE INSURANCE SERVICES—See MidWestOne Financial Group, Inc.; *U.S. Public*, pg. 1446
MIDWEST PACKAGING SOLUTIONS; *U.S. Private*, pg. 2722
MIDWEST PALLIATIVE & HOSPICE CARECENTER; *U.S. Private*, pg. 2722
MIDWEST PAPER GROUP—See Industrial Assets Corp.; *U.S. Private*, pg. 2064
MIDWEST PARATRANSIT SERVICES INC.—See Audax Group, Limited Partnership; *U.S. Private*, pg. 386
MIDWEST PERINATAL ASSOCIATES, P.A.—See MEDNAX, Inc.; *U.S. Public*, pg. 1413
MIDWEST PERISHABLES INC.; *U.S. Private*, pg. 2722
MIDWEST PETROLEUM CO.; *U.S. Private*, pg. 2722
MIDWEST PHARMACIES, INC.—See Tenet Healthcare Corporation; *U.S. Public*, pg. 2014
MIDWEST PIPE COATING INC.—See C.S. McCrossan, Inc.; *U.S. Private*, pg. 709
MIDWEST PIPE & STEEL INC.; *U.S. Private*, pg. 2722
MIDWEST PMS; *U.S. Private*, pg. 2722
MIDWEST POLY—See Custom-Pak, Inc.; *U.S. Private*, pg. 1130
MIDWEST PRECISION LLC—See Shorehill Capital LLC; *U.S. Private*, pg. 3641
MIDWEST PREFINISHING INCORPORATED—See Building Industry Partners LLC; *U.S. Private*, pg. 683
MIDWEST PRIDE INC.—See J&B Group, Inc.; *U.S. Private*, pg. 2153
MIDWEST PRODUCTS & ENGINEERING, INC.; *U.S. Private*, pg. 2722
MIDWEST PROFITS SDN. BHD.—See Bandar Raya Developments Berhad; *Int'l*, pg. 829
MIDWEST PROPERTIES LLC—See Abbott Laboratories; *U.S. Public*, pg. 20
MIDWEST PROTOTYPING LLC; *U.S. Private*, pg. 2722
MIDWEST PUBLISHING, INC.; *U.S. Private*, pg. 2722
MIDWEST QUALITY GLOVES, INC.; *U.S. Private*, pg. 2722
MIDWEST RAILCAR CORPORATION—See Marubeni Corporation; *Int'l*, pg. 4706
MIDWEST RAILROAD TIE SALES; *U.S. Private*, pg. 2722
MIDWEST REAL ESTATE DEVELOPMENT; *U.S. Private*, pg. 2723
MIDWEST REGIONAL MEDICAL CENTER, LLC—See Community Health Systems, Inc.; *U.S. Public*, pg. 555
MIDWEST REMEDIATION INC.; *U.S. Private*, pg. 2723
MIDWEST ROLL FORMING & MANUFACTURING, INC.—See The Ohio Moulding Corporation; *U.S. Private*, pg. 2348
MIDWEST ROOFING SUPPLY INC—See Leonard Green & Partners, L.P.; *U.S. Private*, pg. 2429
MIDWEST RUBBER COMPANY; *U.S. Private*, pg. 2723
MIDWEST SIDING SUPPLY INC.—See Richards Building Supply Company; *U.S. Private*, pg. 3428
MIDWEST SIGN & SCREEN PRINTING SUPPLY COMPANY, INC.; *U.S. Private*, pg. 2723
MIDWEST SINGLE SOURCE INC.; *U.S. Private*, pg. 2723

MIDWEST SPECIALIZED TRANSPORTATION, INC.; *U.S. Private*, pg. 2723
MIDWEST SPECIALTY SURGERY CENTER, LLC—See Tenet Healthcare Corporation; *U.S. Public*, pg. 2004
MID-WEST SPRING & STAMPING, INC.; *U.S. Private*, pg. 2710
MIDWEST STEEL & ALLOY, INC.—See AMG Resources Corp.; *U.S. Private*, pg. 262
MIDWEST STEEL INC.; *U.S. Private*, pg. 2723
MIDWEST SUBURBAN PUBLISHING—See Chicago Public Media, Inc.; *U.S. Private*, pg. 879
MIDWEST SUBURBAN PUBLISHING—See Chicago Public Media, Inc.; *U.S. Private*, pg. 879
MIDWEST SUPERSTORE; *U.S. Private*, pg. 2723
MIDWEST SUPPLY & DISTRIBUTING—See Animart Inc.; *U.S. Private*, pg. 283
MIDWEST TELEMARK INTERNATIONAL INC; *U.S. Private*, pg. 2723
MIDWEST TIRE & MUFFLER, INC.; *U.S. Private*, pg. 2723
MIDWEST TOOL AND CUTLERY CO.; *U.S. Private*, pg. 2723
MIDWEST TOWERS INC.; *U.S. Private*, pg. 2723
MIDWEST TRADING GROUP, INC.—See Dawn Patrol Partners, LLC; *U.S. Private*, pg. 1175
MIDWEST TRAILER SALES INC.; *U.S. Private*, pg. 2723
MIDWEST TRANSIT EQUIPMENT, INC.; *U.S. Private*, pg. 2723
MIDWEST TRANSIT, INC.—See Roadrunner Transportation Systems, Inc.; *U.S. Public*, pg. 1802
MIDWEST TRANSPLANT NETWORK; *U.S. Private*, pg. 2723
MIDWEST UNCUTS, INC.—See Bain Capital, LP; *U.S. Private*, pg. 445
MIDWEST UNDERGROUND TECHNOLOGIES, INC.; *U.S. Private*, pg. 2723
MIDWEST VALVE PARTS SUPPLY COMPANY, INC.—See Wynnchurch Capital, L.P.; *U.S. Private*, pg. 4577
MIDWEST VETERINARY SUPPLY, INC.; *U.S. Private*, pg. 2723
MIDWEST WALNUT COMPANY; *U.S. Private*, pg. 2723
MIDWEST WAREHOUSE & DISTRIBUTION SYSTEMS; *U.S. Private*, pg. 2723
MIDWEST WHEEL COMPANY; *U.S. Private*, pg. 2723
MID-WEST WHOLESALE HARDWARE CO.—See High Road Capital Partners, LLC; *U.S. Private*, pg. 1936
MID-WEST WHOLESALE LIGHTING CORP.; *U.S. Private*, pg. 2710
MIDWEST WOODWORKING & FIXTURE CORP.; *U.S. Private*, pg. 2724
MIDWICH AUSTRALIA PTY LIMITED—See Midwich Group Plc; *Int'l*, pg. 4887
MIDWICH GROUP PLC; *Int'l*, pg. 4887
MIDWICH LIMITED—See Midwich Group Plc; *Int'l*, pg. 4887
MID-WOOD INC.; *U.S. Private*, pg. 2710
MID WYND INTERNATIONAL INVESTMENT TRUST PLC; *Int'l*, pg. 4882
THE MIE BANK, LTD—See San ju San Financial Group, Inc.; *Int'l*, pg. 6521
MIE BROTHER PRECISION INDUSTRIES, LTD.—See Brother Industries, Ltd.; *Int'l*, pg. 1198
MIE CHUO KAIHATSU CO., LTD.—See Daiei Kankyo Co., Ltd.; *Int'l*, pg. 1924
MIECO CHIPBOARD BERHAD; *Int'l*, pg. 4888
MIECO INC.—See Marubeni Corporation; *Int'l*, pg. 4706
MIECO MANUFACTURING SDN. BHD. - PAHANG FACTORY—See Mieco Chipboard Berhad; *Int'l*, pg. 4888
MIECO MANUFACTURING SDN. BHD.—See Mieco Chipboard Berhad; *Int'l*, pg. 4888
MIECO MARKETING SDN BHD—See Mieco Chipboard Berhad; *Int'l*, pg. 4888
MIE COUNTRY CLUB CO., LTD.—See Mie Kotsu Group Holdings, Inc.; *Int'l*, pg. 4888
MIE DATA CRAFT CO., LTD.—See JFE Holdings, Inc.; *Int'l*, pg. 3935
MIE FUJI CO., LTD.—See Fuji Electric Co., Ltd.; *Int'l*, pg. 2812
THE MIEGIN CARD CO., LTD.—See San ju San Financial Group, Inc.; *Int'l*, pg. 6521
THE MIEGIN COMPUTER SERVICE CO., LTD.—See San ju San Financial Group, Inc.; *Int'l*, pg. 6521
THE MIEGIN SHINYO-HOSHO CO., LTD.—See San ju San Financial Group, Inc.; *Int'l*, pg. 6521
THE MIEGIN SOGO LEASE CO., LTD.—See San ju San Financial Group, Inc.; *Int'l*, pg. 6521
MIE GLASS INDUSTRY CO., LTD.—See Central Glass Co., Ltd.; *Int'l*, pg. 1407
MIE HITACHI CO., LTD.—See Hitachi, Ltd.; *Int'l*, pg. 3423
MIE HOLDINGS CORPORATION; *Int'l*, pg. 4888
MIE INDUSTRIAL SDN.BHD.—See CTCI Corporation; *Int'l*, pg. 1870
MIE ISUZU MOTOR CO., LTD.—See Mie Kotsu Group Holdings, Inc.; *Int'l*, pg. 4888
MIEJSKA ENERGETYKA CIEPLNA SP. Z O.O.—See ENEA S.A.; *Int'l*, pg. 2410

MIEJSKIE PRZEDSIEBIORSTWO GOSPODARKI KOMUNALNEJ SP. Z.O.O.—See Fomento de Construcciones y Contratas, S.A.; *Int'l*, pg. 2723
MIE KASAI CO., LTD. - SHIGA PLANT—See Kasai Kogyo Co., Ltd.; *Int'l*, pg. 4086
MIE KASAI CO., LTD.—See Kasai Kogyo Co., Ltd.; *Int'l*, pg. 4086
MIEKEN KANKO KAIHATSU CO., LTD.—See Mie Kotsu Group Holdings, Inc.; *Int'l*, pg. 4888
MIE KOGYO CO., LTD.—See Seiwa Holdings Co., Ltd.; *Int'l*, pg. 6692
MIE KOTSU CO., LTD.—See Mie Kotsu Group Holdings, Inc.; *Int'l*, pg. 4888
MIE KOTSU GROUP HOLDINGS, INC.; *Int'l*, pg. 4888
MIE KYUKO JIDOSHA CO., LTD.—See Mie Kotsu Group Holdings, Inc.; *Int'l*, pg. 4888
MIELE AB—See Miele & Cie KG; *Int'l*, pg. 4889
MIELE AG—See Miele & Cie KG; *Int'l*, pg. 4889
MIELE APPLIANCES LTD.—See Miele & Cie KG; *Int'l*, pg. 4889
MIELE APPLIANCES SRL—See Miele & Cie KG; *Int'l*, pg. 4889
MIELE A/S—See Miele & Cie KG; *Int'l*, pg. 4889
MIELE AS—See Miele & Cie KG; *Int'l*, pg. 4889
MIELE AUSTRALIA PTY. LTD.—See Miele & Cie KG; *Int'l*, pg. 4888
MIELE & CIE KG - ARNSBERG PLANT—See Miele & Cie KG; *Int'l*, pg. 4888
MIELE & CIE KG - BIELEFELD PLANT—See Miele & Cie KG; *Int'l*, pg. 4888
MIELE & CIE KG - BUNDE PLANT—See Miele & Cie KG; *Int'l*, pg. 4888
MIELE & CIE KG -BURMOOS PLANT—See Miele & Cie KG; *Int'l*, pg. 4889
MIELE & CIE KG - EUSKIRCHEN PLANT—See Miele & Cie KG; *Int'l*, pg. 4889
MIELE & CIE KG - LEHRTE PLANT—See Miele & Cie KG; *Int'l*, pg. 4889
MIELE & CIE KG - OELDE PLANT—See Miele & Cie KG; *Int'l*, pg. 4889
MIELE & CIE KG; *Int'l*, pg. 4888
MIELE COMPANY LIMITED—See Miele & Cie KG; *Int'l*, pg. 4889
MIELE COSMED GROUP S.A.; *Int'l*, pg. 4890
M&I ELECTRIC FAR EAST PTE LTD—See STABILIS SOLUTIONS, INC.; *U.S. Public*, pg. 1924
M&I ELECTRIC INDUSTRIES, INC.—See STABILIS SOLUTIONS, INC.; *U.S. Public*, pg. 1924
MIELE D.O.O.—See Miele & Cie KG; *Int'l*, pg. 4889
MIELE ELECTRODOMESTICOS LTDA.—See Miele & Cie KG; *Int'l*, pg. 4889
MIELE ELEKTRIKLI ALETLER DIS TIC. VE PAZ. LTD. STI—See Miele & Cie KG; *Int'l*, pg. 4889
MIELE GES.M.B.H.—See Miele & Cie KG; *Int'l*, pg. 4889
MIELE HELLAS E.P.E.—See Miele & Cie KG; *Int'l*, pg. 4889
MIELE (HONG KONG) LTD.—See Miele & Cie KG; *Int'l*, pg. 4889
MIELE INC.—See Miele & Cie KG; *Int'l*, pg. 4889
MIELE INDIA PVT. LTD.—See Miele & Cie KG; *Int'l*, pg. 4889
MIELE IRELAND LTD—See Miele & Cie KG; *Int'l*, pg. 4889
MIELE ITALIA S.R.L.—See Miele & Cie KG; *Int'l*, pg. 4889
MIELE JAPAN CORP.—See Miele & Cie KG; *Int'l*, pg. 4889
MIELE KFT.—See Miele & Cie KG; *Int'l*, pg. 4889
MIELE KOREA LIMITED—See Miele & Cie KG; *Int'l*, pg. 4889
MIELE LIMITED—See Miele & Cie KG; *Int'l*, pg. 4889
MIELE LLC—See Miele & Cie KG; *Int'l*, pg. 4889
MIELE NEDERLAND B.V.—See Miele & Cie KG; *Int'l*, pg. 4889
MIELE NEW ZEALAND LIMITED—See Miele & Cie KG; *Int'l*, pg. 4889
MIELE OY—See Miele & Cie KG; *Int'l*, pg. 4889
MIELE PORTUGUESA, LDA—See Miele & Cie KG; *Int'l*, pg. 4889
MIELE PTE LTD—See Miele & Cie KG; *Int'l*, pg. 4889
MIELE (PTY) LTD.—See Miele & Cie KG; *Int'l*, pg. 4889
MIELE, S.A. DE C.V.—See Miele & Cie KG; *Int'l*, pg. 4889
MIELE S.A R.L.—See Miele & Cie KG; *Int'l*, pg. 4889
MIELE S.A.S.—See Miele & Cie KG; *Int'l*, pg. 4889
MIELE S.A.U.—See Miele & Cie KG; *Int'l*, pg. 4889
MIELE SDN BHD—See Miele & Cie KG; *Int'l*, pg. 4889
MIELE (SHANGHAI) TRADING LTD.—See Miele & Cie KG; *Int'l*, pg. 4889
MIELE SIA EESTI FILIAAL—See Miele & Cie KG; *Int'l*, pg. 4889
MIELE, SPQL. S R.O.—See Miele & Cie KG; *Int'l*, pg. 4889
MIELE SP. Z O.O.—See Miele & Cie KG; *Int'l*, pg. 4889
MIELE S.R.O.—See Miele & Cie KG; *Int'l*, pg. 4889
MIELE TRGOVINA I SERVIS D.O.O.—See Miele & Cie KG; *Int'l*, pg. 4889
MIELLE ORGANICS, LLC—See The Procter & Gamble Company; *U.S. Public*, pg. 2120
MIELPARQUE CORPORATION—See Kowa Co., Ltd.; *Int'l*, pg. 4294

COMPANY NAME INDEX

MIE NARUMI CORPORATION—See Ishizuka Glass Co., Ltd.; *Int'l*, pg. 3818
MIEN DONG JOINT STOCK COMPANY; *Int'l*, pg. 4890
MIE NITTO DENKO CORPORATION—See Nitto Denko Corporation; *Int'l*, pg. 5384
MIEN TRUNG POWER INVESTMENT & DEVELOPMENT JOINT STOCK COMPANY; *Int'l*, pg. 4890
MIE PROPERTIES INC.; *U.S. Private*, pg. 2724
MI EQUIPMENT KOREA CO., LTD.—See Mi Technovation Berhad; *Int'l*, pg. 4873
MI EQUIPMENT (M) SDN BHD—See Mi Technovation Berhad; *Int'l*, pg. 4873
MI EQUIPMENT (TAIWAN) CO., LTD.—See Mi Technovation Berhad; *Int'l*, pg. 4873
MIERKA DONAUHAFEN KREMS GESELLSCHAFT M.B.H. & CO KG; *Int'l*, pg. 4890
MIESCHKE HOFMANN UND PARTNER GESELLSCHAFT FUR MANAGEMENT- UND IT-BERATUNG MBH—See Porsche Automobil Holding SE; *Int'l*, pg. 5927
MIESCHKE HOFMANN UND PARTNER (SCHWEIZ) AG—See Porsche Automobil Holding SE; *Int'l*, pg. 5928
MIESCOR BUILDERS, INC.—See Manila Electric Company; *Int'l*, pg. 4671
MIESCOR LOGISTICS INC.—See Manila Electric Company; *Int'l*, pg. 4671
MIE SEINO TRANSPORTATION CO., LTD.—See Seino Holdings Co., Ltd.; *Int'l*, pg. 6690
MIE SENKO LOGISTICS CO., LTD.—See Senko Group Holdings Co., Ltd.; *Int'l*, pg. 6710
MIETHER BEARING PRODUCTS, LLC—See Dunes Point Capital, LLC; *U.S. Private*, pg. 1288
MIETHO & BAR KABELKOM KABELKOMMUNIKATIONS-BETRIEBS GMBH—See Morgan Stanley; *U.S. Public*, pg. 1473
MI EUROPEAN HOLDINGS CV—See Koch Industries, Inc.; *U.S. Private*, pg. 2333
MIEUX PRODUCTS CO., LTD.—See Unicharm Corporation; *Int'l*, pg. 8032
MIEV CO LTD; *Int'l*, pg. 4890
MIEXACT LIMITED; *Int'l*, pg. 4890
MIFA AG—See The Federation of Migros Cooperatives; *Int'l*, pg. 7642
MIFA ALUMINIUM B V—See Aalberts N.V.; *Int'l*, pg. 35
MIFAH CO. LTD.—See GMM Grammy Public Company Limited; *Int'l*, pg. 3013
MIF CONSTRUCTION, INC.; *U.S. Private*, pg. 2724
MIFFI LOGISTICS, CO. INC.—See KKR & Co. Inc.; *U.S. Public*, pg. 1259
MIFFLINBURG BANCORP, INC.; *U.S. Private*, pg. 2724
MIFFLINBURG BANK & TRUST CO.—See Mifflinburg Bancorp, Inc.; *U.S. Private*, pg. 2724
M/I FINANCIAL CORP.—See M/I Homes, Inc.; *U.S. Public*, pg. 1351
MIF, L.L.C.—See Marriott International, Inc.; *U.S. Public*, pg. 1371
MIFROMA FRANCE S.A.—See The Federation of Migros Cooperatives; *Int'l*, pg. 7642
MIFROMA S.A.—See The Federation of Migros Cooperatives; *Int'l*, pg. 7642
MI FULFILLMENT SERVICES, LLC—See Marriott International, Inc.; *U.S. Public*, pg. 1371
MIG ABSOLUTE RETURN—See Merage Investment Group; *U.S. Private*, pg. 2667
MIGAO CORPORATION; *Int'l*, pg. 4890
MIGATRONIC CZ A.S—See Svejsemaskinefabrikken Migatronic A/S; *Int'l*, pg. 7356
MIGATRONIC EQUIPEMENT DE SOUDURE S.A.R.L.—See Svejsemaskinefabrikken Migatronic A/S; *Int'l*, pg. 7356
MIGATRONIC INDIA PRIVATE LTD.—See Svejsemaskinefabrikken Migatronic A/S; *Int'l*, pg. 7356
MIGATRONIC KERESKEDELMI KFT.—See Svejsemaskinefabrikken Migatronic A/S; *Int'l*, pg. 7356
MIGATRONIC NEDERLAND B.V.—See Svejsemaskinefabrikken Migatronic A/S; *Int'l*, pg. 7356
MIGATRONIC NORGE AS—See Svejsemaskinefabrikken Migatronic A/S; *Int'l*, pg. 7356
MIGATRONIC OY—See Svejsemaskinefabrikken Migatronic A/S; *Int'l*, pg. 7356
MIGATRONIC SCHWEISSMASCHINEN GMBH—See Svejsemaskinefabrikken Migatronic A/S; *Int'l*, pg. 7356
MIGATRONIC S.R.L.—See Svejsemaskinefabrikken Migatronic A/S; *Int'l*, pg. 7356
MIGATRONIC SVETSMASKINER AB—See Svejsemaskinefabrikken Migatronic A/S; *Int'l*, pg. 7356
MIGATRONIC WELDING EQUIPMENT LTD.—See Svejsemaskinefabrikken Migatronic A/S; *Int'l*, pg. 7356
MIG BUILDING SYSTEMS, LLC—See Installed Building Products, Inc.; *U.S. Public*, pg. 1133
MIGC, LLC—See Western Midstream Partners, LP; *U.S. Public*, pg. 2356
MIG & CO.; *U.S. Private*, pg. 2724
MIGDAL INSURANCE AND FINANCIAL HOLDINGS LTD.—See Shlomo Eliahu Holdings Ltd.; *Int'l*, pg. 6857
MIGDAL INSURANCE COMPANY LTD.—See Shlomo Eliahu Holdings Ltd.; *Int'l*, pg. 6857

MIGDAL INVESTMENT PORTFOLIO MANAGEMENT (1998) LTD—See Shlomo Eliahu Holdings Ltd.; *Int'l*, pg. 6857
MIGDALOR ALTERNATIVE INVESTMENT; *Int'l*, pg. 4890
MIGDAL STOCK EXCHANGE SERVICES (N.E.) LTD.—See Assicurazioni Generali S.p.A.; *Int'l*, pg. 647
MIGDAL UNDERWRITING BUSINESS—See Assicurazioni Generali S.p.A.; *Int'l*, pg. 647
MIGHTY CARD CORPORATION—See Takachiho Koheki Co., Ltd.; *Int'l*, pg. 7429
THE MIGHTY COMPANY LIMITED—See International Flavors & Fragrances Inc.; *U.S. Public*, pg. 1154
MIGHTY CRAFT LIMITED; *Int'l*, pg. 4890
MIGHTY DISTRIBUTING SYSTEM OF AMERICA; *U.S. Private*, pg. 2724
MIGHTYHIVE INC.—See S4 Capital plc; *Int'l*, pg. 6458
MIGHTY LEAF TEA COMPANY—See JAB Holding Company S.a.r.l.; *Int'l*, pg. 3863
MIGHTY OCEAN COMPANY LTD—See Aurelius Equity Opportunities SE & Co. KGaA; *Int'l*, pg. 710
MIGHTY USA, INC.; *U.S. Private*, pg. 2724
MIG II REALTY ADVISORS INC.—See Brookfield Corporation; *Int'l*, pg. 1175
MIGLIARA S.A.—See Lakeland Industries, Inc.; *U.S. Public*, pg. 1289
MIGLIORE SONEPAR S.P.A.—See Sonepar S.A.; *Int'l*, pg. 7092
MIG MEDIA NEURONS LIMITED; *Int'l*, pg. 4890
MIGOM GLOBAL CORP.; *U.S. Public*, pg. 1446
MIG PRIVATE EQUITY—See Merage Investment Group; *U.S. Private*, pg. 2667
MIG PRODUCTION COMPANY LIMITED—See Linde plc; *Int'l*, pg. 4508
MIG REAL ESTATE—See Merage Investment Group; *U.S. Private*, pg. 2668
MIGROL S.A.—See The Federation of Migros Cooperatives; *Int'l*, pg. 7642
MIGROS BANK—See The Federation of Migros Cooperatives; *Int'l*, pg. 7642
MIGROS BETRIEBE BIRSFELDEN AG—See The Federation of Migros Cooperatives; *Int'l*, pg. 7642
MIGROS COOPERATIVE—See The Federation of Migros Cooperatives; *Int'l*, pg. 7642
MIGROS RAARE COOPERATIVE—See The Federation of Migroa Cooperatives; *Int'l*, pg. 7642
MIGROS TICARET A.S.—See AG Anadolu Grubu Holding A.S.; *Int'l*, pg. 197
MIGROS TICARET A.S.—See BC Partners LLP; *Int'l*, pg. 925
MIGROS VALAIS—See The Federation of Migros Cooperatives; *Int'l*, pg. 7643
MIGROS VAUD—See The Federation of Migros Cooperatives; *Int'l*, pg. 7643
MIGROS-VERTEILBETRIEB NEUENDORF AG—See The Federation of Migros Cooperatives; *Int'l*, pg. 7643
MIGRO SWITZERLAND—See The Federation of Migros Cooperatives; *Int'l*, pg. 7642
MIGROS ZURICH—See The Federation of Migros Cooperatives; *Int'l*, pg. 7643
MI-GSO GMBH—See Alten S.A.; *Int'l*, pg. 390
MI-GSO SA—See Alten S.A.; *Int'l*, pg. 390
MIGUA FUGENSYSTEME GMBH & CO. KG—See INDUS Holding AG; *Int'l*, pg. 3663
MIGWANG CONTACT LENS CO., LTD.; *Int'l*, pg. 4890
MIHARU COMMUNICATIONS INC.—See The Furukawa Electric Co., Ltd.; *Int'l*, pg. 7646
MIHARU ELECTRONICS CO., LTD.—See Shibaura Electronics Co., Ltd.; *Int'l*, pg. 6827
MIHG MASCHINEN- INSTANDSETZUNGS- UND HANDELS GMBH; *Int'l*, pg. 4891
MIHIJAM VANASPATI LIMITED; *Int'l*, pg. 4891
MIHIKA INDUSTRIES LTD.; *Int'l*, pg. 4891
MIHLFELD & ASSOCIATES INC.; *U.S. Private*, pg. 2724
M-I HOLDINGS BV—See Schlumberger Limited; *U.S. Public*, pg. 1844
M/I HOMES, INC.; *U.S. Public*, pg. 1351
M/I HOMES OF AUSTIN, LLC—See M/I Homes, Inc.; *U.S. Public*, pg. 1351
M/I HOMES OF CHARLOTTE, LLC—See M/I Homes, Inc.; *U.S. Public*, pg. 1351
M/I HOMES OF INDIANA, L.P.—See M/I Homes, Inc.; *U.S. Public*, pg. 1351
MI HOMES OF MICHIGAN, LLC—See M/I Homes, Inc.; *U.S. Public*, pg. 1351
MI HOMES OF MINNEAPOLISST. PAUL, LLC—See M/I Homes, Inc.; *U.S. Public*, pg. 1351
M/I HOMES OF RALEIGH, LLC—See M/I Homes, Inc.; *U.S. Public*, pg. 1351
MI HYDRONIC ENGINEERING HYDRAULIC SYSTEMS LTD.—See IMI plc; *Int'l*, pg. 3626
MIIKE DYES WORKS, LTD.—See Mitsui Chemicals, Inc.; *Int'l*, pg. 4982
MIILD A/S—See Matas A/S; *Int'l*, pg. 4726
MIINC, LP—See SubSplit Services Group, L.P.; *U.S. Private*, pg. 3847
M/I INSURANCE AGENCY, LLC—See M/I Homes, Inc.; *U.S. Public*, pg. 1351
MI INTERNATIONAL PTE LTD—See Mi Technovation Berhad; *Int'l*, pg. 4873

MI-JACK CANADA, INC.—See Lanco International Inc.; *U.S. Private*, pg. 2382
MI-JACK PRODUCTS, INC.—See Lanco International Inc.; *U.S. Private*, pg. 2382
MIJEM NEWCOMM TECH INC.; *Int'l*, pg. 4891
MIJIN SYSTEM CO. LTD.; *Int'l*, pg. 4891
MIJU CO., LTD.; *Int'l*, pg. 4891
MIJULAND CO., LTD.—See DHSteel; *Int'l*, pg. 2100
MIKA ALAS A.D.; *Int'l*, pg. 4891
MIKADO CHEMICAL M.F.G. CO—See Watanabe Pipe Co., Ltd.; *Int'l*, pg. 8355
MIKADO S.A.—See Publicis Groupe S.A.; *Int'l*, pg. 6103
MIKAGE DAIICHI CO., LTD.—See Daiichi Koutsu Sangyo Co., Ltd.; *Int'l*, pg. 1928
MIKA METAL FABRICATING, CO.—See Weybridge, LLC; *U.S. Private*, pg. 4503
MIKARA CORPORATION; *U.S. Private*, pg. 2724
MIKART INC.; *U.S. Private*, pg. 2724
MIKASA RIKUUN CO. LTD.—See Tradia Corporation; *Int'l*, pg. 7889
MIKAWA NISSAN AUTO CO., LTD.—See VT Holdings Co., Ltd.; *Int'l*, pg. 8315
MIKAWAWAN GAS TERMINAL CO., LTD.—See Sala Corporation; *Int'l*, pg. 6490
MIKAWAYA LLC—See Lakeview Capital, Inc.; *U.S. Private*, pg. 2378
M.I.K. CORP.—See Nippon Steel Corporation; *Int'l*, pg. 5337
MIKE ALBERT LEASING, INC.; *U.S. Private*, pg. 2724
MIKE ANDERSON CHEVROLET BUICK GMC TRUCK, INC.; *U.S. Private*, pg. 2724
MIKE BARNEY NISSAN; *U.S. Private*, pg. 2724
MIKE BROWN ELECTRIC CO.; *U.S. Private*, pg. 2724
MIKE BURKART FORD MERCURY INC.; *U.S. Private*, pg. 2725
MIKE CARTER CONSTRUCTION INC.; *U.S. Private*, pg. 2725
MIKE CASTRUCCI CHEVROLET SALES, INC.—See Mike Castrucci, LLC; *U.S. Private*, pg. 2725
MIKE CASTRUCCI, LLC; *U.S. Private*, pg. 2725
MIKE D. DIMICH & SONS, INC.; *U.S. Private*, pg. 2725
MIKE DUMAN AUTO SALES, INC.; *U.S. Private*, pg. 2725
MIKE ERDMAN MOTORS INC.; *U.S. Private*, pg. 2725
MIKE FINNIN MOTORS INC.; *U.S. Private*, pg. 2725
MIKE GARCIA MERCHANT SECURITY, INC.; *U.S. Private*, pg. 2725
MIKE GATTO INC; *U.S. Private*, pg. 2725
MIKE HALL CHEVROLET, INC.—See AutoNation, Inc.; *U.S. Public*, pg. 236
MIKE JORDAN CO. INC.; *U.S. Private*, pg. 2725
MIKELE INTERNATIONAL GROUP, LLC; *U.S. Private*, pg. 2726
MIKE MURPHY FORD INC.; *U.S. Private*, pg. 2725
MIKE MYERS REALTY INC.; *U.S. Private*, pg. 2725
MIKEN BUILDERS, INC.; *U.S. Private*, pg. 2726
MIKEN SALES INC.; *U.S. Private*, pg. 2726
MIKEN SPECIALTIES, LTD; *U.S. Private*, pg. 2726
MIKE PATTERSON PLUMBING INC.—See Lovett Inc.; *U.S. Private*, pg. 2504
MIKE PATTON AUTO; *U.S. Private*, pg. 2725
MIKE PERRY MOTOR CO.; *U.S. Private*, pg. 2725
MIKE PIAZZA HONDA; *U.S. Private*, pg. 2725
MIKE PILE BMW; *U.S. Private*, pg. 2725
MIKE REICHENBACH CHEVROLET, INC.—See General Motors Company; *U.S. Public*, pg. 926
MIKE REICHENBACH FORD LINCOLN MERCURY; *U.S. Private*, pg. 2725
MIKE ROCHE INC.; *U.S. Private*, pg. 2725
MIKE RYAN TREE SERVICE INC.; *U.S. Private*, pg. 2725
MIKE'S AUTO GLASS INC.; *U.S. Private*, pg. 2726
MIKE SAVOIE CHEVROLET INC.; *U.S. Private*, pg. 2725
MIKE'S CAMERA INC.; *U.S. Private*, pg. 2726
MIKE'S CIGARS DISTRIBUTORS, INC.; *U.S. Private*, pg. 2726
MIKES COLLIERVILLE BIG STAR 52; *U.S. Private*, pg. 2726
MIKESELL'S POTATO CHIP CO.; *U.S. Private*, pg. 2726
MIKE'S FLOORING COMPANIES; *U.S. Private*, pg. 2726
MIKE SHAD FORD, INC.—See AutoNation, Inc.; *U.S. Public*, pg. 236
MIKE SHAW BUICK GMC; *U.S. Private*, pg. 2725
MIKE SHAW SUBARU, INC.—See Asbury Automotive Group, Inc.; *U.S. Public*, pg. 209
MIKE'S INC.; *U.S. Private*, pg. 2726
MIKE SMITH AUTOPLEX DODGE, INC.—See Group 1 Automotive, Inc.; *U.S. Public*, pg. 971
MIKE SMITH TOYOTA MITSUBISHI KIA; *U.S. Private*, pg. 2725
MIKE STEVEN AUTO GROUP INC; *U.S. Private*, pg. 2725
MIKE THOMPSON'S RECREATIONAL VEHICLES; *U.S. Private*, pg. 2725
MIKE VAIL TRUCKING LTD.; *Int'l*, pg. 4891
MIKEVA OY—See Attendo AB; *Int'l*, pg. 696
MIKE VASILINDA PRODUCTIONS, INC.; *U.S. Private*, pg. 2725
MIKE WILSON PUBLIC RELATIONS, INC.; *U.S. Private*, pg. 2726
MIKHAIL DARAFEEV INC.; *U.S. Private*, pg. 2726

MIKI AGENCIA DE VIAGENS LDA—See Miki Travel Ltd; *Int'l*, pg. 4891
MIKI BELTEC CO., LTD.—See Miki Pulley Co., Ltd.; *Int'l*, pg. 4891
MIKIKOGYO CO., LTD.; *Int'l*, pg. 4892
MIKIMOTO (AMERICA) CO., LTD.—See K. Mikimoto & Co., Ltd.; *Int'l*, pg. 4043
MIKIMOTO JEWELRY MFG. CO., LTD.—See K. Mikimoto & Co., Ltd.; *Int'l*, pg. 4043
MIKIMOTO PEARL ISLAND CO., LTD.; *Int'l*, pg. 4892
MIKIMOTO PHARMACEUTICAL CO., LTD.—See K. Mikimoto & Co., Ltd.; *Int'l*, pg. 4043
MIKI POWER CONTROL CO., LTD.—See Miki Pulley Co., Ltd.; *Int'l*, pg. 4891
MIKI PULLEY CO., LTD.; *Int'l*, pg. 4891
MIKI PULLEY (EUROPE) AG—See Miki Pulley Co., Ltd.; *Int'l*, pg. 4891
MIKI PULLEY (HONG KONG) CO., LTD.—See Miki Pulley Co., Ltd.; *Int'l*, pg. 4891
MIKI PULLEY (INDIA) PVT. LTD.—See Miki Pulley Co., Ltd.; *Int'l*, pg. 4891
MIKI PULLEY (KOREA) CO., LTD—See Miki Pulley Co., Ltd.; *Int'l*, pg. 4891
MIKI PULLEY (TRAINING) CO., LTD.—See Miki Pulley Co., Ltd.; *Int'l*, pg. 4891
MIKI RA HANBAI CO., LTD.—See Miki Pulley Co., Ltd.; *Int'l*, pg. 4891
MIKI REISEN GMBH—See Miki Travel Ltd; *Int'l*, pg. 4891
MIKI REISEN GMBH WARSZAWA SP.ZO.O—See Miki Travel Ltd; *Int'l*, pg. 4891
MIKI SIMPLA CO., LTD.—See Miki Pulley Co., Ltd.; *Int'l*, pg. 4891
MIKI TOURIST BELGIUM S.P.R.L.—See Miki Travel Ltd; *Int'l*, pg. 4891
MIKI TOURIST K.K.—See Miki Travel Ltd; *Int'l*, pg. 4891
MIKI TOURIST NAGOYA—See Miki Travel Ltd; *Int'l*, pg. 4892
MIKI TRAVEL AGENCY APS—See Miki Travel Ltd; *Int'l*, pg. 4892
MIKI TRAVEL AGENCY E.U.R.L.—See Miki Travel Ltd; *Int'l*, pg. 4892
MIKI TRAVEL AGENCY GMBH—See Miki Travel Ltd; *Int'l*, pg. 4892
MIKI TRAVEL AGENCY ITALIA SRL—See Miki Travel Ltd; *Int'l*, pg. 4892
MIKI TRAVEL AGENCY S.A.—See Miki Travel Ltd; *Int'l*, pg. 4892
MIKI TRAVEL AGENCY S.A.U.—See Miki Travel Ltd; *Int'l*, pg. 4892
MIKI TRAVEL AS—See Miki Travel Ltd; *Int'l*, pg. 4892
MIKI TRAVEL CONSULTANCY LIMITED—See Miki Travel Ltd; *Int'l*, pg. 4892
MIKI TRAVEL HAWAII INC.—See Miki Travel Ltd; *Int'l*, pg. 4892
MIKI TRAVEL (HONG KONG) LIMITED—See Miki Travel Ltd; *Int'l*, pg. 4892
MIKI TRAVEL IDEGENFORGALMI KFT—See Miki Travel Ltd; *Int'l*, pg. 4892
MIKI TRAVEL LIMITED—See Miki Travel Ltd; *Int'l*, pg. 4892
MIKI TRAVEL LTD; *Int'l*, pg. 4891
MIKI TRAVEL LTD—See Miki Travel Ltd; *Int'l*, pg. 4892
MIKI TRAVEL PRAGUE SPOL S.R.O.—See Miki Travel Ltd; *Int'l*, pg. 4892
MIKI YOKAWA COUNTRY CLUB CO., LTD.—See Tokyu Fudosan Holdings Corporation; *Int'l*, pg. 7798
MIKKELIN MATKATOIMISTO OY—See Finnair Plc; *Int'l*, pg. 2676
MIKOBEAUTE INTERNATIONAL CO., LTD.; *Int'l*, pg. 4892
MIKO CAFE SERVICE S.A.S.—See Miko NV; *Int'l*, pg. 4892
MIKO COFFEE DENMARK APS—See Miko NV; *Int'l*, pg. 4892
MIKO COFFEE (SCOTLAND) LTD.—See Miko NV; *Int'l*, pg. 4892
MIKOH CORPORATION—See Kollakorn Corporation Limited; *Int'l*, pg. 4233
MIKO INTERNATIONAL HOLDINGS LIMITED; *Int'l*, pg. 4892
MIKO KAVA S.R.O.—See Miko NV; *Int'l*, pg. 4892
MIKOM D.O.O.—See Komax Holding AG; *Int'l*, pg. 4241
MIKOM ELECTRONIC D.O.O.—See Komax Holding AG; *Int'l*, pg. 4241
MIKO NV; *Int'l*, pg. 4892
MIKROCOZE INC.; *U.S. Private*, pg. 2726
MIKROELEKTRONIKA A.D.; *Int'l*, pg. 4892
MIKROELEKTRONIK AR-GE TASARIM VE TICARET LTD. CO.—See Aselsan Elektronik Sanayi Ve Ticaret AS; *Int'l*, pg. 605
MIKROFIN OSIGURANJE A.D; *Int'l*, pg. 4892
MIKRO KONTROL D.O.O.—See Yokogawa Electric Corporation; *Int'l*, pg. 8592
MIKRO MSC BERHAD; *Int'l*, pg. 4892
MIKRON ASSEMBLY TECHNOLOGY-NORDIC REG. OFFICE—See Mikron Holding AG; *Int'l*, pg. 4893
MIKRON ASSEMBLY TECHNOLOGY—See Mikron Holding AG; *Int'l*, pg. 4893

MIKRON ASSEMBLY TECHNOLOGY-UK & IRELAND—See Mikron Holding AG; *Int'l*, pg. 4893
MIKRON CORP. DENVER—See Mikron Holding AG; *Int'l*, pg. 4893
MIKRON CORP. MONROE—See Mikron Holding AG; *Int'l*, pg. 4893
MIKRON GMBH—See Mikron Holding AG; *Int'l*, pg. 4893
MIKRON HOLDING AG; *Int'l*, pg. 4892
MIKRON INDUSTRIAL EQUIPMENT (SHANGHAI) CO., LTD.—See Mikron Holding AG; *Int'l*, pg. 4893
MIKRON INDUSTRIES, INC.—See Quanex Building Products Corp.; *U.S. Public*, pg. 1749
MIKRON JSC—See Sistema PJSFC; *Int'l*, pg. 6963
MIKRON MACHINING TECHNOLOGY-INDIA OFFICE—See Mikron Holding AG; *Int'l*, pg. 4893
MIKRON MANAGEMENT AG—See Mikron Holding AG; *Int'l*, pg. 4892
MIKRON S.A. AGNO—See Mikron Holding AG; *Int'l*, pg. 4893
MIKRON S.A. BOUDRY—See Mikron Holding AG; *Int'l*, pg. 4893
MIKRON SAS NERVIANO—See Mikron Holding AG; *Int'l*, pg. 4893
MIKRON SINGAPORE PTE LTD—See Mikron Holding AG; *Int'l*, pg. 4893
MIKRON TOOL S.A. AGNO—See Mikron Holding AG; *Int'l*, pg. 4893
MIKRON TOOL (SHANGHAI) CO., LTD.—See Mikron Holding AG; *Int'l*, pg. 4893
MIKRON TUNSBERG AS—See Mikron Holding AG; *Int'l*, pg. 4893
MIKROP AG—See INDUS Holding AG; *Int'l*, pg. 3663
MIKROPUL AUSTRALIA PTY LTD.—See Nederman Holding AB; *Int'l*, pg. 5188
MIKROPUL CANADA, INC.—See Nederman Holding AB; *Int'l*, pg. 5188
MIKROPUL CHATHAM—See Nederman Holding AB; *Int'l*, pg. 5188
MIKROPUL GMBH—See Nederman Holding AB; *Int'l*, pg. 5188
MIKROPUL LLC—See Nederman Holding AB; *Int'l*, pg. 5188
MIKROPUL PITTSBURGH—See Nederman Holding AB; *Int'l*, pg. 5188
MIKROPUL (PTY) LIMITED—See Nederman Holding AB; *Int'l*, pg. 5188
MIKROPUL S DE RL DE CV—See Nederman Holding AB; *Int'l*, pg. 5188
MIKROS IMAGE S.A.—See Vantiva SA; *Int'l*, pg. 8130
MIKROS SYSTEMS CORPORATION—See McKean Defense Group LLC; *U.S. Private*, pg. 2637
MIKROTRON GMBH—See TKH Group N.V.; *Int'l*, pg. 7764
MIKROVERKTYG AB—See XANO Industri AB; *Int'l*, pg. 8519
MIK SMART LIGHTING NETWORK CORPORATION—See IWASAKI ELECTRIC Co., Ltd.; *Int'l*, pg. 3849
MIK SMART LIGHTING NETWORK CORPORATION—See KOIZUMI Lighting Technology Corp.; *Int'l*, pg. 4231
MIK SMART LIGHTING NETWORK CORPORATION—See Minebea Mitsumi Inc.; *Int'l*, pg. 4902
MIKUNI AMERICAN CORPORATION—See Mikuni Corporation; *Int'l*, pg. 4893
MIKUNI CORPORATION; *Int'l*, pg. 4893
MIKUNI GREEN SERVICE CO., LTD.—See Mikuni Corporation; *Int'l*, pg. 4893
MIKUNI INDIA PRIVATE LIMITED—See Mikuni Corporation; *Int'l*, pg. 4893
MIKUNI LIFE & AUTO CO., LTD.—See Mikuni Corporation; *Int'l*, pg. 4893
MIKUNI PARTEC CORPORATION—See Mikuni Corporation; *Int'l*, pg. 4893
MIKUNI PLASTICS CO. LTD.—See Toagosei Co. Ltd.; *Int'l*, pg. 7769
MIKUNISHIKO CO., LTD.—See Japan Pulp and Paper Company Limited; *Int'l*, pg. 3904
MIKUNI TAIWAN CORPORATION—See Mikuni Corporation; *Int'l*, pg. 4893
MIKUNI (THAILAND) CO., LTD.—See Mikuni Corporation; *Int'l*, pg. 4893
MILACRON B.V.—See Hillenbrand, Inc.; *U.S. Public*, pg. 1037
MILACRON CZECH REPUBLIC SPOL S.R.O.—See Hillenbrand, Inc.; *U.S. Public*, pg. 1037
MILACRON HOLDINGS CORP.—See Hillenbrand, Inc.; *U.S. Public*, pg. 1037
MILACRON LLC—See Hillenbrand, Inc.; *U.S. Public*, pg. 1037
MILACRON MOLD-MASTERS SISTEMAS DE PROCESSAMENTO DE PLASTICOS LTDA.—See Hillenbrand, Inc.; *U.S. Public*, pg. 1037
MILACRON PLASTICS TECHNOLOGIES GROUP LLC—See Hillenbrand, Inc.; *U.S. Public*, pg. 1037
MILAE BIORESOURCES CO., LTD.; *Int'l*, pg. 4893
MILAEGERS INC.; *U.S. Private*, pg. 2726
MILAE RESOURCES ML, LTD.—See Milae Bioresources Co., Ltd.; *Int'l*, pg. 4893
MILAGRO EXPLORATION, LLC; *U.S. Private*, pg. 2726
MILAGRO PACKAGING, LLC; *U.S. Private*, pg. 2726

MILAMAR COATINGS, LLC—See PPG Industries, Inc.; *U.S. Public*, pg. 1707
MILAM OIL CORPORATION; *U.S. Private*, pg. 2726
MILAN BLAGOJEVIC A.D.; *Int'l*, pg. 4893
MILAN BLAGOJEVIC INTERTRANS A.D.; *Int'l*, pg. 4893
MILAN EXPRESS CO., INC.; *U.S. Private*, pg. 2726
MILAN LASER INC.; *U.S. Public*, pg. 1446
MILANO BROTHERS INTERNATIONAL CORPORATION; *U.S. Private*, pg. 2726
MILANO DESIGN STUDIO S.R.L.—See National Amusements, Inc.; *U.S. Private*, pg. 2842
MILANOS HOTEL (BMG) PTY LTD—See Woolworths Group Limited; *Int'l*, pg. 8451
MILAN PREMASUNAC A.D.; *Int'l*, pg. 4893
MILAN RESOURCES SDN. BHD.—See Ekovest Berhad; *Int'l*, pg. 2339
MILAN STATION (CAUSEWAY BAY) LIMITED—See Milan Station Holdings Limited; *Int'l*, pg. 4894
MILAN STATION FASHION (CAUSEWAY BAY) LIMITED—See Milan Station Holdings Limited; *Int'l*, pg. 4894
MILAN STATION FASHION (HONG KONG) LIMITED—See Milan Station Holdings Limited; *Int'l*, pg. 4894
MILAN STATION FASHION (TST) LIMITED—See Milan Station Holdings Limited; *Int'l*, pg. 4894
MILAN STATION HOLDINGS LIMITED; *Int'l*, pg. 4893
MILAN STATION (TSUEN WAN) LIMITED—See Milan Station Holdings Limited; *Int'l*, pg. 4894
MILAN STATION (YUEN LONG) LIMITED—See Milan Station Holdings Limited; *Int'l*, pg. 4894
MILAN SUPPLY COMPANY—See Franklin Electric Co., Inc.; *U.S. Public*, pg. 878
MILA RESOURCES PLC; *Int'l*, pg. 4893
MILAR, S.A. DE C.V.—See Grupo Televisa, S.A.B.; *Int'l*, pg. 3136
MILA S.A.—See Eurocash S.A.; *Int'l*, pg. 2533
MILAVITSA SP ZAO—See Silvano Fashion Group AS; *Int'l*, pg. 6922
MILBANK MANUFACTURING COMPANY INC. - CONCORDIA FACILITY—See Milbank Manufacturing Company Inc.; *U.S. Private*, pg. 2726
MILBANK MANUFACTURING COMPANY INC.—See Milbank Manufacturing Company Inc.; *U.S. Private*, pg. 2726
MILBANK MANUFACTURING COMPANY INC.; *U.S. Private*, pg. 2726
MILBANK MANUFACTURING COMPANY INC.—See Milbank Manufacturing Company Inc.; *U.S. Private*, pg. 2726
MILBANK, TWEED, HADLEY & MCCLOY LLP; *U.S. Private*, pg. 2727
MILBERG FACTORS, INC.; *U.S. Private*, pg. 2727
MILBON CO., LTD. - AOYAMA PLANT—See Milbon Co., Ltd.; *Int'l*, pg. 4894
MILBON CO., LTD.; *Int'l*, pg. 4894
MILBON CO., LTD. - YUMEGAOKA PLANT—See Milbon Co., Ltd.; *Int'l*, pg. 4894
MILBON EUROPE GMBH—See Milbon Co., Ltd.; *Int'l*, pg. 4894
MILBON KOREA CO., LTD.—See Milbon Co., Ltd.; *Int'l*, pg. 4894
MILBON MALAYSIA SDN. BHD.—See Milbon Co., Ltd.; *Int'l*, pg. 4894
MILBON (THAILAND) CO., LTD.—See Milbon Co., Ltd.; *Int'l*, pg. 4894
MILBON TRADING (SHANGHAI) CO., LTD.—See Milbon Co., Ltd.; *Int'l*, pg. 4894
MILBON USA, INC.—See Milbon Co., Ltd.; *Int'l*, pg. 4894
MILBON VIETNAM CO., LTD.—See Milbon Co., Ltd.; *Int'l*, pg. 4894
MILBRO, INC.—See Sycamore Partners Management, LP; *U.S. Private*, pg. 3897
MILBURN DAIRY LIMITED—See Donegal Investment Group Plc; *Int'l*, pg. 2163
MILBURY SYSTEMS LIMITED—See Eleco Plc; *Int'l*, pg. 2348
MILCO INDUSTRIES INC.; *U.S. Private*, pg. 2727
MILCOM COMMUNICATIONS PTY LTD—See Service Stream Limited; *Int'l*, pg. 6725
MILCO NATIONAL CONSTRUCTORS, INC.—See INNOVATE Corp.; *U.S. Public*, pg. 1126
MIL CONTROLS LIMITED—See KSB SE & Co. KGaA; *Int'l*, pg. 4313
MIL CORPORATION; *U.S. Private*, pg. 2726
MILDEF AS—See MilDef Group AB; *Int'l*, pg. 4894
MILDEF CRETE, INC.; *Int'l*, pg. 4894
MILDEF GROUP AB; *Int'l*, pg. 4894
MILDEF, INC.—See MilDef Group AB; *Int'l*, pg. 4894
MILDEF INTEGRATION SWEDEN AB—See MilDef Group AB; *Int'l*, pg. 4894
MILDEF OY—See MilDef Group AB; *Int'l*, pg. 4894
MILDEF SWEDEN AB—See MilDef Group AB; *Int'l*, pg. 4894
MILDEW BV—See Carrefour SA; *Int'l*, pg. 1345
MILDEX OPTICAL, INC.; *Int'l*, pg. 4894
MILDEX OPTICAL USA, INC.—See Mildex Optical, Inc.; *Int'l*, pg. 4894
MILDOLA OY—See Apetit Plc; *Int'l*, pg. 509

COMPANY NAME INDEX

MILDURA FINANCE PTY LIMITED—See Consolidated Operations Group Limited; *Int'l*, pg. 1771
MILE 9; *U.S. Private*, pg. 2727
MILEAGE COMMUNICATIONS PTE. LTD.; *Int'l*, pg. 4894
THE MILEAGE COMPANY LIMITED—See International Consolidated Airlines Group S.A.; *Int'l*, pg. 3746
MILEAGE PLUS, INC.—See United Airlines Holdings, Inc.; *U.S. Public*, pg. 2229
MILEA TRUCK SALES CORP.; *U.S. Private*, pg. 2727
MILE HI FROZEN FOODS CO.; *U.S. Private*, pg. 2727
MILE HIGH EQUIPMENT LLC—See Ali Holding S.r.l; *Int'l*, pg. 321
MILE HIGH INSIGHTS, LLC—See IAC Inc.; *U.S. Public*, pg. 1082
MILE HIGH SURGICENTER, LLC—See UnitedHealth Group Incorporated; *U.S. Public*, pg. 2242
MILEI GMBH—See Morinaga Milk Industry Co., Ltd.; *Int'l*, pg. 5046
MILE MARKER INC.—See Mile Marker International Inc.; *U.S. Private*, pg. 2727
MILE MARKER INTERNATIONAL INC.; *U.S. Private*, pg. 2727
MILENDER WHITE CONSTRUCTION CO.; *U.S. Private*, pg. 2727
MILEND, INC.; *U.S. Private*, pg. 2727
MILENIJUM OSIGURANJE A.D.—See Adris Grupa d.d.; *Int'l*, pg. 153
MILENIUM ESPACIO SOFT, S.A.—See Brookfield Corporation; *Int'l*, pg. 1178
MILENIUM ESPACIO SOFT, S.A.—See Elliott Management Corporation; *U.S. Private*, pg. 1371
MILEPOST CREDIT UNION—See Sound Credit Union; *U.S. Private*, pg. 3717
MILEPOST INDUSTRIES; *U.S. Private*, pg. 2727
MILES 33 INTERNATIONAL LTD—See Vista Equity Partners, LLC; *U.S. Private*, pg. 4399
MILES 33 LIMITED—See Vista Equity Partners, LLC; *U.S. Private*, pg. 4399
MILES 33 SERVICOS EM INFORMATICA LTDA—See Vista Equity Partners, LLC; *U.S. Private*, pg. 4399
MILES 33—See Vista Equity Partners, LLC; *U.S. Private*, pg. 4399
MILESBRAND, INC.; *U.S. Private*, pg. 2728
MILESBRAND SALES—See Milesbrand, Inc.; *U.S. Private*, pg. 2728
MILES CAPITAL, INC.—See PMA Financial Network, LLC; *U.S. Private*, pg. 3217
MILES CHEVROLET INC.; *U.S. Private*, pg. 2727
MILES CITY STAR—See Yellowstone Communications; *U.S. Private*, pg. 4587
MILES CONSULTING CORP.; *U.S. Private*, pg. 2727
MILES DATA TECHNOLOGIES, LLC—See Sole Source Capital LLC; *U.S. Private*, pg. 3708
MILES ENTERPRISES, INC.; *U.S. Private*, pg. 2727
MILES FASHION GMBH—See Li & Fung Limited; *Int'l*, pg. 4480
MILES FASHION GROUP FRANCE EURL—See Li & Fung Limited; *Int'l*, pg. 4480
MILES FIBERGLASS & COMPOSITES, INC.; *U.S. Private*, pg. 2727
MILES GMBH—See Li & Fung Limited; *Int'l*, pg. 4480
THE MILES GROUP, LLC; *U.S. Private*, pg. 4079
MILES-MCCLELLAN CONSTRUCTION COMPANY; *U.S. Private*, pg. 2728
MILES MEDIA GROUP, LLLP; *U.S. Private*, pg. 2727
MILES & MORE INTERNATIONAL GMBH—See Deutsche Lufthansa AG; *Int'l*, pg. 2070
MILES PROPERTIES INC.; *U.S. Private*, pg. 2727
MILES SAND & GRAVEL COMPANY; *U.S. Private*, pg. 2727
MILES SOFTWARE SOLUTIONS FZ - LLC—See Ebix Inc.; *U.S. Public*, pg. 710
MILES SOFTWARE SOLUTIONS INC.—See Ebix Inc.; *U.S. Public*, pg. 710
MILES SOFTWARE SOLUTIONS PVT. LTD.—See Ebix Inc.; *U.S. Public*, pg. 710
MILES SOFTWARE SOLUTIONS UK LIMITED—See Ebix Inc.; *U.S. Public*, pg. 710
MILES SOUTH PACIFIC—See Miles Media Group, LLLP; *U.S. Private*, pg. 2727
MILES TECHNOLOGIES, INC.; *U.S. Private*, pg. 2727
MILESTONE AVIATION GROUP LIMITED—See General Electric Company; *U.S. Public*, pg. 919
MILESTONE AVIATION GROUP LLC—See General Electric Company; *U.S. Public*, pg. 919
MILESTONE BROADCAST; *U.S. Private*, pg. 2728
MILESTONE CAPITAL, INC.; *U.S. Private*, pg. 2728
MILESTONE CAPITAL PARTNERS LLP; *Int'l*, pg. 4894
MILESTONE CENTERS, INC.; *U.S. Private*, pg. 2728
MILESTONE COMMUNITY BUILDERS LLC; *U.S. Private*, pg. 2728
MILESTONE CONSTRUCTION SERVICES, INC.; *U.S. Private*, pg. 2728
MILESTONE CONTRACTORS, LP; *U.S. Private*, pg. 2728
MILESTONE DISTRIBUTORS INC.; *U.S. Private*, pg. 2728
MILESTONE EDUCATION LLC—See Milestone Scientific Inc.; *U.S. Public*, pg. 1446
MILESTONE EHF.; *Int'l*, pg. 4894

MILESTONE ELECTRIC & SECURITY; *U.S. Private*, pg. 2728
MILESTONE EQUIPMENT HOLDINGS, LLC—See Massachusetts Mutual Life Insurance Company; *U.S. Private*, pg. 2605
MILESTONE FURNITURE LIMITED; *Int'l*, pg. 4894
MILESTONE GLOBAL LIMITED; *Int'l*, pg. 4894
MILESTONE HEALTH SYSTEMS, LLC—See American Healthcare Systems Corp., Inc.; *U.S. Private*, pg. 236
MILESTONE HOME LENDING, LLC—See Rithm Capital Corp.; *U.S. Public*, pg. 1800
MILESTONE INSURANCE BROKERS, LLC—See ABRY Partners, LLC; *U.S. Private*, pg. 42
MILESTONE MANAGEMENT—See Olympus Real Estate Corp.; *U.S. Private*, pg. 3014
MILESTONE MARKETING ASSOCIATES, INC.; *U.S. Private*, pg. 2728
MILESTONE MEDICAL INC.—See Milestone Scientific Inc.; *U.S. Public*, pg. 1446
MILESTONE METALS INC.; *U.S. Private*, pg. 2728
MILESTONE PARTNERS LTD.; *U.S. Private*, pg. 2728
MILESTONE PHARMACEUTICALS INC.; *Int'l*, pg. 4894
MILESTONE PROPERTIES INC.; *U.S. Private*, pg. 2729
MILESTONE PROPERTY MANAGEMENT, INC—See Milestone Properties Inc.; *U.S. Private*, pg. 2729
MILESTONE SCIENTIFIC INC.; *U.S. Public*, pg. 1446
MILESTONE SISTEMAS DO BRASIL—See Canon Inc.; *Int'l*, pg. 1297
MILESTONE SYSTEMS A/S—See Canon Inc.; *Int'l*, pg. 1297
MILESTONE SYSTEMS (AUSTRALIA) PTY LIMITED—See Canon Inc.; *Int'l*, pg. 1297
MILESTONE SYSTEMS BULGARIA—See Canon Inc.; *Int'l*, pg. 1297
MILESTONE SYSTEMS FRANCE SARL—See Canon Inc.; *Int'l*, pg. 1297
MILESTONE SYSTEMS GERMANY GMBH—See Canon Inc.; *Int'l*, pg. 1297
MILESTONE SYSTEMS INC.—See Canon Inc.; *Int'l*, pg. 1297
MILESTONE SYSTEMS ITALIA S.R.L.—See Canon Inc.; *Int'l*, pg. 1297
MILESTONE SYSTEMS K.K.—See Canon Inc.; *Int'l*, pg. 1298
MILESTONE SYSTEMS PTE. LTD.—See Canon Inc.; *Int'l*, pg. 1298
MILESTONE SYSTEMS SPAIN S.L.—See Canon Inc.; *Int'l*, pg. 1298
MILESTONE SYSTEMS UAE—See Canon Inc.; *Int'l*, pg. 1298
MILESTONE SYSTEMS UK LTD.—See Canon Inc.; *Int'l*, pg. 1298
MILESTONE TECHNOLOGIES INC.—See H.I.G. Capital, LLC; *U.S. Private*, pg. 1831
MILETA A.S.—See Reliance - ADA Group Limited; *Int'l*, pg. 6261
MILEX PUERTO RICO—See The Cooper Companies, Inc.; *U.S. Public*, pg. 2066
THE MILFORD AGENCY; *U.S. Private*, pg. 4079
MILFORD ASSET MANAGEMENT LIMITED; *Int'l*, pg. 4895
MILFORD AUSTRALIA PTY LTD—See Milford Asset Management Limited; *Int'l*, pg. 4895
MILFORD BANK; *U.S. Private*, pg. 2729
MILFORD CHRONICLE—See Independent Newspapers, Inc.; *U.S. Private*, pg. 2060
MILFORD FEDERAL SAVINGS & LOAN ASSOCIATION; *U.S. Private*, pg. 2729
MILFORD ICE PAVILION—See Blackstreet Capital Holdings LLC; *U.S. Private*, pg. 576
MILFORD MARKETPLACE, LLC—See CBL & Associates Properties, Inc.; *U.S. Private*, pg. 458
MILFORD REGIONAL MEDICAL CENTER, INC.; *U.S. Private*, pg. 2729
MILFORD REGIONAL PHYSICIAN GROUP; *U.S. Private*, pg. 2729
MILFORD SUPPLY CO. INC.; *U.S. Private*, pg. 2729
MILFORD TEA GMBH & CO. KG—See Laurens Spethmann Holding Aktiengesellschaft & Co. KG; *Int'l*, pg. 4424
MILFORD TEE AUSTRIA GESELLSCHAFT M.B.H.—See Laurens Spethmann Holding Aktiengesellschaft & Co. KG; *Int'l*, pg. 4424
MILGARD MANUFACTURING INCORPORATED—See Koch Industries, Inc.; *U.S. Private*, pg. 2332
MILGREY FINANCE & INVESTMENTS LIMITED; *Int'l*, pg. 4895
MILHOLLAND ELECTRIC, INC.—See Solar Integrated Roofing Corporation; *U.S. Public*, pg. 1900
MILHOUSE ENGINEERING & CONSTRUCTION, INC.; *U.S. Private*, pg. 2729
MILIAL RESORT HOTELS CO., LTD.—See Oriental Land Co., Ltd.; *Int'l*, pg. 5625
MILIAN SA—See Dominique Dutscher SAS; *Int'l*, pg. 2161
MILIAN USA—See Dominique Dutscher SAS; *Int'l*, pg. 2161
MILIBOO SA; *Int'l*, pg. 4895
MILIMEWA SUPERSTORE SDN. BHD.—See The Store Corporation Berhad; *Int'l*, pg. 7689

MILLCRAFT INDUSTRIES INC.

MILITARY ADVANTAGE, INC.—See Ontario Teachers' Pension Plan; *Int'l*, pg. 5588
MILITARY BOOK CLUB—See Bertelsmann SE & Co. KGaA; *Int'l*, pg. 992
MILITARY COMMERCIAL JOINT STOCK BANK; *Int'l*, pg. 4895
MILITARY CONSTRUCTION CORPORATION; *U.S. Private*, pg. 2729
MILITARY FAMILY HOME LOANS, LLC—See Wells Fargo & Company; *U.S. Public*, pg. 2344
MILITARY PARK PARTNERSHIP; *U.S. Private*, pg. 2729
MILITARY PRODUCTS GROUP, INC.; *U.S. Private*, pg. 2729
MILITARY WARRIORS SUPPORT FOUNDATION; *U.S. Private*, pg. 2729
MILITTA LLC—See Onexim Group Limited; *Int'l*, pg. 5581
MILJOCENTER I MALMO AB—See Volati AB; *Int'l*, pg. 8300
MILJOCO CORP.—See Arcline Investment Management LP; *U.S. Private*, pg. 313
MILKCO, INC.—See Ingles Markets, Incorporated; *U.S. Public*, pg. 1122
MILK+CO—See Omnicom Group Inc.; *U.S. Public*, pg. 1582
MILKFOOD LIMITED—See Jagatjit Industries Limited; *Int'l*, pg. 3870
MILK + HONEY DAY SPA; *U.S. Private*, pg. 2729
MILKILAND EU SP. Z.O.O.—See Milkiland N.V.; *Int'l*, pg. 4895
MILKILAND INTERMARKET (CY) LTD.—See Milkiland N.V.; *Int'l*, pg. 4895
MILKILAND N.V.; *Int'l*, pg. 4895
MILK INDUSTRY MANAGEMENT CORP.; *U.S. Private*, pg. 2729
MILKO SVERIGE AB—See Arla Foods amba; *Int'l*, pg. 572
MILK PRODUCTS, L.P.—See Capitol Peak Partners, LLC; *U.S. Private*, pg. 744
MILK PRODUCTS, L.P.—See KKR & Co. Inc.; *U.S. Public*, pg. 1242
MILKRON GMBH—See Krones AG; *Int'l*, pg. 4306
MILK SPECIALITIES LTD.; *Int'l*, pg. 4895
MILK SPECIALTIES COMPANY—See American Securities LLC; *U.S. Private*, pg. 250
MILKY JSC—See HighCo S.A.; *Int'l*, pg. 3387
MILKYWAY CHEMICAL SUPPLY CHAIN SERVICE CO., LTD.; *Int'l*, pg. 4895
MILKY WAY INTERNATIONAL TRADING; *U.S. Private*, pg. 2729
MILKY WAY—See Lynden Incorporated; *U.S. Private*, pg. 2521
MILLAR & BRYCE LIMITED—See Daily Mail & General Trust plc; *Int'l*, pg. 1937
MILLARD BOWEN COMMUNITIES, LLC; *U.S. Private*, pg. 2729
THE MILLARD GROUP; *U.S. Private*, pg. 4079
MILLARD LUMBER INC.; *U.S. Private*, pg. 2730
MILLARD MAINTENANCE SERVICE COMPANY INC.—See The Millard Group; *U.S. Private*, pg. 4079
MILLARD TRUCKING LTD.—See Enerchem International, Inc.; *Int'l*, pg. 2418
MILLAR WESTERN FOREST PRODUCTS LTD.—See Atlas Holdings, LLC; *U.S. Private*, pg. 377
MILLAT TRACTORS LIMITED; *Int'l*, pg. 4895
MILLBECK GRANGE (BOWBURN) MANAGEMENT COMPANY LIMITED—See Persimmon plc; *Int'l*, pg. 5816
MILLBROOK CAPITAL MANAGEMENT, INC.; *U.S. Private*, pg. 2730
MILLBROOK, INC.—See Guidewire Software, Inc.; *U.S. Public*, pg. 974
MILLBROOK POWER LIMITED—See Drax Group plc; *Int'l*, pg. 2200
MILLBROOK PROVING GROUND LIMITED—See Union Technique de L'Automobile, du Motocycle et du SASU; *Int'l*, pg. 8054
MILLBROOK REVOLUTIONARY ENGINEERING GMBH—See Spectris Plc; *Int'l*, pg. 7131
MILLBROOK REVOLUTIONARY ENGINEERING INC.—See Union Technique de L'Automobile, du Motocycle et du SASU; *Int'l*, pg. 8054
MILLBROOK SPECIAL VEHICLES LIMITED—See Spectris Plc; *Int'l*, pg. 7131
MILLBURN MULTI-MARKETS FUND L.P.—See Millburn Ridgefield Corporation; *U.S. Private*, pg. 2731
MILLBURN RIDGEFIELD CORPORATION; *U.S. Private*, pg. 2730
MILLBURY NATIONAL BANK; *U.S. Private*, pg. 2731
MILLCHEM ZAMBIA LIMITED—See Cambria Africa Plc; *Int'l*, pg. 1269
MILL CITY CAPITAL, L.P.; *U.S. Private*, pg. 2729
MILL CITY VENTURES III, LTD.; *U.S. Public*, pg. 1446
MILLCON EURAPA COMPANY LIMITED—See Millcon Steel Public Company Limited; *Int'l*, pg. 4895
MILLCON STEEL PUBLIC COMPANY LIMITED; *Int'l*, pg. 4895
MILLCRAFT INDUSTRIES INC.; *U.S. Private*, pg. 2731
MILLCRAFT INVESTMENTS INC.—See Millcraft Industries Inc.; *U.S. Private*, pg. 2731

MILLCRAFT INDUSTRIES INC.

MILLCRAFT PAPER - CINCINNATI SALES & DISTRIBUTION CENTER—See The Millcraft Paper Company Inc.; *U.S. Private*, pg. 4079
THE MILLCRAFT PAPER COMPANY INC.; *U.S. Private*, pg. 4079
MILLCRAFT-SMS SERVICES LLC—See SMS Holding GmbH; *Int'l*, pg. 7016
MILL CREEK DOLOMITE LLC—See United States Lime & Minerals, Inc.; *U.S. Public*, pg. 2236
MILL CREEK LIFE SCIENCES, LLC—See Level Biotechnology, Inc.; *Int'l*, pg. 4470
MILLCREEK MANAGEMENT CORPORATION—See Acadia Healthcare Company, Inc.; *U.S. Public*, pg. 29
MILL CREEK MOTOR FREIGHT L.P.—See Mullen Group Ltd.; *Int'l*, pg. 5080
MILLCREST PRODUCTS CORPORATION—See Pacific Choice Brands, Inc.; *U.S. Private*, pg. 3065
MILLEA ASIA PTE LTD.—See Tokio Marine Holdings, Inc.; *Int'l*, pg. 7782
MILLE LACS BANCORPORATION, INC.; *U.S. Private*, pg. 2731
MILLENIA 3 COMMUNICATIONS, INC.—See YANGAROO Inc.; *Int'l*, pg. 8560
MILLENIA 700, LLC—See Independence Realty Trust, Inc.; *U.S. Public*, pg. 1115
MILLENIA SURGERY CENTER, L.L.C.—See Bain Capital, LP; *U.S. Private*, pg. 445
MILLEN INDUSTRIES INCORPORATED; *U.S. Private*, pg. 2731
MILLENIUM BILLBOARDS L.L.C.—See OUTFRONT Media Inc.; *U.S. Public*, pg. 1625
MILLENIUM BROKERAGE GROUP, LLC; *U.S. Private*, pg. 2731
MILLENIUM FREIGHT SERVICES—See H.H.V. Whitchurch & Co. Ltd; *Int'l*, pg. 3195
MILLENIUM HOME HEALTH CARE, INC.—See Formation Capital, LLC; *U.S. Private*, pg. 1571
MILLENIUM MILLWORK CORP.; *U.S. Private*, pg. 2731
MILLENIUM PROPERTIES, INC.—See First Busey Corporation; *U.S. Public*, pg. 840
MILLENMIN VENTURES INC.; *Int'l*, pg. 4895
THE MILLENNIA DESIGN—See Millennia Group Inc.; *U.S. Private*, pg. 2731
MILLENNIA GROUP INC.; *U.S. Private*, pg. 2731
MILLENNIAL LITHIUM CORP.—See Lithium Americas Corp.; *Int'l*, pg. 4526
MILLENNIAL MEDIA LLC—See Apollo Global Management, Inc.; *U.S. Public*, pg. 167
MILLENNIAL POTASH CORP; *Int'l*, pg. 4895
MILLENNITEK LLC—See MS Technology, Inc.; *U.S. Private*, pg. 2806
MILLENNIUM 3 MANAGEMENT INC.; *U.S. Private*, pg. 2731
MILLENNIUM ACCOUNT SERVICES, LLC—See Exelon Corporation; *U.S. Public*, pg. 807
THE MILLENNIUM ALLIANCE LLC; *U.S. Private*, pg. 4079
MILLENNIUM AUTOMOTIVE LOGISTICS INC.; *U.S. Private*, pg. 2731
MILLENNIUM BCP GESTAO DE ACTIVOS - SOCIEDADE GESTORA DE FUNDOS DE INVESTIMENTO, S.A.—See Banco Comercial Portugues, S.A.; *Int'l*, pg. 820
MILLENNIUM BUILDERS, INC.—See Riverstone Holdings LLC; *U.S. Private*, pg. 3447
MILLENNIUM BUSINESS SYSTEMS, LLC; *U.S. Private*, pg. 2731
MILLENNIUM CELL, INC.; *U.S. Public*, pg. 1446
MILLENNIUM CLEANING (NSW) PTY LIMITED—See SoftBank Group Corp.; *Int'l*, pg. 7051
MILLENNIUM CLEANING (QLD) PTY LIMITED—See SoftBank Group Corp.; *Int'l*, pg. 7051
MILLENNIUM COMMUNICATIONS GROUP LLC; *U.S. Private*, pg. 2731
MILLENNIUM COMMUNICATIONS, INC.; *U.S. Private*, pg. 2731
MILLENNIUM & COPTHORNE HOTELS LIMITED—See Hong Leong Investment Holdings Pte. Ltd.; *Int'l*, pg. 3468
MILLENNIUM, CORP.; *U.S. Private*, pg. 2732
MILLENNIUM ENERGY CORPORATION; *U.S. Public*, pg. 1446
MILLENNIUM ENGINEERING & INTEGRATION COMPANY; *U.S. Private*, pg. 2731
MILLENNIUM ENGINEERING & INTEGRATION COMPANY—See Millennium Engineering & Integration Company; *U.S. Private*, pg. 2731
MILLENNIUM FILMS, INC.—See Nu Image, Inc.; *U.S. Private*, pg. 2971
MILLENNIUM FOODS (PTY) LTD.—See Libstar Holdings Ltd.; *Int'l*, pg. 4487
MILLENNIUM GLOBAL HOLDINGS, INC.; *Int'l*, pg. 4895
MILLENNIUM GROUP INTERNATIONAL HOLDINGS LIMITED; *Int'l*, pg. 4896
THE MILLENNIUM GROUP; *U.S. Private*, pg. 4079
MILLENNIUM HI-TECH (SA) PTY LIMITED—See SoftBank Group Corp.; *Int'l*, pg. 7051
MILLENNIUM IMPORT LLC—See LVMH Moet Hennessy Louis Vuitton SE; *Int'l*, pg. 4599

MILLENNIUM INDUSTRIAL TIRES LLC.; *U.S. Private*, pg. 2731
MILLENNIUM INFORMATION TECHNOLOGIES (PRIVATE) LIMITED—See London Stock Exchange Group plc; *Int'l*, pg. 4548
MILLENNIUM INTEGRATED MARKETING; *U.S. Private*, pg. 2731
MILLENNIUM IT SOFTWARE (PRIVATE) LIMITED—See London Stock Exchange Group plc; *Int'l*, pg. 4548
MILLENNIUM LIMITED; *Int'l*, pg. 4896
MILLENNIUM MANAGEMENT INC.; *U.S. Private*, pg. 2731
MILLENNIUM MANAGEMENT LLC; *U.S. Private*, pg. 2732
MILLENNIUM MANUFACTURING, INC.—See Bracalente Manufacturing Co., Inc.; *U.S. Private*, pg. 630
MILLENNIUM MARKETING CONSULTANTS, INC.; *U.S. Private*, pg. 2732
MILLENNIUM MARKETING GROUP, LLC; *U.S. Private*, pg. 2732
THE MILLENNIUM MAT COMPANY, LLC—See Cintas Corporation; *U.S. Public*, pg. 496
MILLENNIUM MEDICAL MEDICAL PRODUCTS INC.; *U.S. Private*, pg. 2732
MILLENNIUM MINERALS LIMITED; *Int'l*, pg. 4896
MILLENNIUM ONLINE SOLUTIONS (INDIA) LIMITED; *Int'l*, pg. 4896
MILLENNIUM PACIFIC GROUP HOLDINGS LTD; *Int'l*, pg. 4896
MILLENNIUM PHARMACEUTICALS, INC.—See Takeda Pharmaceutical Company Limited; *Int'l*, pg. 7437
MILLENNIUM PHYSICIAN GROUP LLC; *U.S. Private*, pg. 2732
MILLENNIUM PIPELINE COMPANY, LLC—See DT Midstream, Inc.; *U.S. Public*, pg. 689
MILLENNIUM PRIME, INC.; *U.S. Public*, pg. 1446
MILLENNIUM PRINT GROUP—See The Pokemon Company; *Int'l*, pg. 7674
MILLENNIUM PROCESS GROUP, INC.—See Nippon Telegraph & Telephone Corporation; *Int'l*, pg. 5343
MILLENNIUM RISK MANAGEMENT LLC—See Bilfinger SE; *Int'l*, pg. 1028
MILLENNIUM SERVICES GROUP LIMITED—See SoftBank Group Corp.; *Int'l*, pg. 7051
MILLENNIUM SETTLEMENTS, INC.—See Sage Settlement Consulting, LLC; *U.S. Private*, pg. 3527
MILLENNIUM SILVER CORP.; *Int'l*, pg. 4896
MILLENNIUM SOFTWARE DEVELOPERS, INC.—See AccuTitle LLC; *U.S. Private*, pg. 55
MILLENNIUM SOFTWARE SAL—See Softlab S.p.A.; *Int'l*, pg. 7055
MILLENNIUM—See VINCI S.A.; *Int'l*, pg. 8233
MILLENNIUM SPACE SYSTEMS, INC.—See The Boeing Company; *U.S. Public*, pg. 2041
MILLENNIUM STEEL SERVICE LLC.; *U.S. Private*, pg. 2732
MILLENNIUM SURGICAL CENTER, LLC—See Tenet Healthcare Corporation; *U.S. Public*, pg. 2011
MILLENNIUM SURGICAL CORP—See Arlington Capital Partners LLC; *U.S. Private*, pg. 327
MILLENNIUM SUSTAINABLE VENTURES CORP.; *U.S. Public*, pg. 1446
MILLENNIUM TECHNOLOGY GROUP LLC—See Rosen Hotels & Resorts, Inc.; *U.S. Private*, pg. 3483
MILLENNIUM TELCOM, LLC—See Ubiquity Management, L.P.; *U.S. Private*, pg. 4273
MILLENNIUM TITLE AGENCY, LTD.—See Hovnanian Enterprises, Inc.; *U.S. Public*, pg. 1060
MILLENNIUM TITLE OF HOUSTON, LC—See Stewart Information Services Corporation; *U.S. Public*, pg. 1947
MILLENNIUM TOURS; *U.S. Private*, pg. 2732
MILLENNIUM TOYOTA; *U.S. Private*, pg. 2732
MILLENNIUM TRANSPORTATION PVT LTD—See Hayleys PLC; *Int'l*, pg. 3292
MILLENNIUM TRUST COMPANY, LLC—See ABRY Partners, LLC; *U.S. Private*, pg. 42
MILLENNIUM VENTURES LIMITED PARTNERSHIP, L.L.P.—See The Goodman Group, Inc.; *U.S. Private*, pg. 4034
MILLENNIUM WASTE INCORPORATED—See Waste Connections, Inc.; *Int'l*, pg. 8353
MILLENNIUM WASTE INCORPORATED—See Waste Connections, Inc.; *Int'l*, pg. 8353
MILLENNIUM WEAVERS N.V.—See Victoria Plc; *Int'l*, pg. 8189
MILLENWORKS—See Textron Inc.; *U.S. Public*, pg. 2029
MILLER ADAMS ELECTRIC INC.—See Garber Electrical Contractors Inc.; *U.S. Private*, pg. 1642
MILLER ADVERTISING AGENCY INC. CHICAGO—See Miller Advertising Agency Inc.; *U.S. Private*, pg. 2732
MILLER ADVERTISING AGENCY INC.; *U.S. Private*, pg. 2732
MILLER ADVERTISING AGENCY INC.—See Miller Advertising Agency Inc.; *U.S. Private*, pg. 2732
MILLER ADVISORS INC—See MFG Partners LLC; *U.S. Private*, pg. 2693
MILLER ADVISORS INC—See The PNC Financial Services Group, Inc.; *U.S. Public*, pg. 2119

CORPORATE AFFILIATIONS

MILLER ADV.—See Miller Advertising Agency Inc.; *U.S. Private*, pg. 2732
MILLER ALL LINE LEASING INC.—See Miller Enterprises; *U.S. Private*, pg. 2734
MILLER & ANDERSON INC.; *U.S. Private*, pg. 2732
MILLER & ANDERSON—See Miller & Anderson Inc.; *U.S. Private*, pg. 2732
MILLER AND SMITH HOMES, INC.—See Miller & Smith Holding Company Inc.; *U.S. Private*, pg. 2732
MILLER AUTO CLUB—See Miller Enterprises; *U.S. Private*, pg. 2734
MILLER AUTO GROUP; *U.S. Private*, pg. 2733
MILLER AUTOMOBILE CORPORATION; *U.S. Private*, pg. 2733
MILLER AUTO SALES INC.; *U.S. Private*, pg. 2733
MILLER BEARINGS DIVISION - MIAMI—See Genuine Parts Company; *U.S. Public*, pg. 933
MILLER BEARINGS DIVISION - WESTMORELAND—See Genuine Parts Company; *U.S. Public*, pg. 933
MILLERBERND MANUFACTURING CO.; *U.S. Private*, pg. 2736
MILLER-BOWIE SUPPLY CO.; *U.S. Private*, pg. 2736
MILLER-BRADFORD & RISBERG, INC.; *U.S. Private*, pg. 2736
MILLER BREWING COMPANY—See Molson Coors Beverage Company; *U.S. Public*, pg. 1459
MILLER BROS. CONSTRUCTION—See MBC Holdings, Inc.; *U.S. Private*, pg. 2624
MILLER BROTHERS EXPRESS LLC; *U.S. Private*, pg. 2733
MILLER BROTHERS GROCERY INC.; *U.S. Private*, pg. 2733
MILLER BUCKFIRE & CO., LLC; *U.S. Private*, pg. 2733
MILLER BUICK-PONTIAC-GMC CO.; *U.S. Private*, pg. 2733
MILLER BUILDINGS INC.; *U.S. Private*, pg. 2733
MILLER, CANFIELD, PADDOCK AND STONE, P.L.C.; *U.S. Private*, pg. 2736
MILLER & CARTER GASTSTATTEN BETRIEBSGESELLSCHAFT MBH—See Mitchells & Butlers Plc; *Int'l*, pg. 4925
MILLER CHEMICAL & FERTILIZER, LLC—See J.M. Huber Corporation; *U.S. Private*, pg. 2169
MILLER & COMPANY, INC.; *U.S. Private*, pg. 2732
THE MILLER COMPANY—See Wieland-Werke AG; *Int'l*, pg. 8403
MILLER COMPRESSING CO., INC.; *U.S. Private*, pg. 2733
MILLER CONSOLIDATED INDUSTRIES INC.; *U.S. Private*, pg. 2733
MILLER CONSTRUCTION COMPANY; *U.S. Private*, pg. 2733
MILLER CONTAINER CORPORATION - CLINTON DIVISION—See Miller Container Corporation; *U.S. Private*, pg. 2733
MILLER CONTAINER CORPORATION; *U.S. Private*, pg. 2733
MILLER-COOPER PRINTING INK COMPANY LLC—See Grand Rapids Printing Ink Company; *U.S. Private*, pg. 1753
MILLERCOORS LLC—See Molson Coors Beverage Company; *U.S. Public*, pg. 1459
MILLER CURTAIN CO., INC.; *U.S. Private*, pg. 2733
MILLER-DAVIS COMPANY INC.; *U.S. Private*, pg. 2736
MILLER DEVELOPMENTS LIMITED—See Bridgepoint Group Plc; *Int'l*, pg. 1154
MILLER-DIPPEL FUNERAL HOME, INC.—See Service Corporation International; *U.S. Public*, pg. 1870
MILLER DISTRIBUTING INC.; *U.S. Private*, pg. 2733
MILLER DIVERSIFIED INC.; *U.S. Private*, pg. 2733
MILLER-DM, INC.—See Group 1 Automotive, Inc.; *U.S. Public*, pg. 971
MILLER DRUG; *U.S. Private*, pg. 2733
MILLER - EDWARDS BUICK GMC; *U.S. Private*, pg. 2732
MILLER ELECTRIC COMPANY; *U.S. Private*, pg. 2733
MILLER ELECTRIC CONSTRUCTION INC.; *U.S. Private*, pg. 2733
MILLER ELECTRIC CONSTRUCTION—See Miller Electric Construction Inc.; *U.S. Private*, pg. 2734
MILLER ELECTRIC MANUFACTURING CO.—See Illinois Tool Works Inc.; *U.S. Public*, pg. 1109
MILLER ENTERPRISES, INC.; *U.S. Private*, pg. 2734
MILLER ENTERPRISES OF MANATEE, INC.; *U.S. Private*, pg. 2734
MILLER ENTERPRISES; *U.S. Private*, pg. 2734
MILLER ENVIRONMENTAL GROUP, INC.—See GenNx360 Capital Partners, L.P.; *U.S. Private*, pg. 1672
MILLER FABRICATION & CONSTRUCTION, INC.; *U.S. Private*, pg. 2734
MILLER FELPAX CORPORATION; *U.S. Private*, pg. 2734
MILLER FORD SALES INC.; *U.S. Private*, pg. 2734
MILLER-GREEN FINANCIAL SERVICES, INC.—See Lee Equity Partners LLC; *U.S. Public*, pg. 2412
THE MILLER GROUP INC.—See Bouygues S.A.; *Int'l*, pg. 1122
THE MILLER GROUP, INC. (USA)—See Bouygues S.A.; *Int'l*, pg. 1122

COMPANY NAME INDEX

THE MILLER GROUP LTD.—See Bridgepoint Group Plc; *Int'l*, pg. 1154
THE MILLER GROUP; *U.S. Private*, pg. 4079
THE MILLER GROUP; *U.S. Private*, pg. 4079
MILLER HARDWARE COMPANY; *U.S. Private*, pg. 2734
MILLER HEIMAN EUROPE GMBH—See Korn Ferry; *U.S. Public*, pg. 1274
MILLER HEIMAN GROUP (ASIA) PTE. LTD.—See Korn Ferry; *U.S. Public*, pg. 1275
MILLER HEIMAN GROUP, INC.—See Korn Ferry; *U.S. Public*, pg. 1274
MILLER HEIMAN GROUP (UK) LIMITED—See Korn Ferry; *U.S. Public*, pg. 1274
MILLER HOLDING CORP.; *U.S. Private*, pg. 2734
MILLER & HOLMES INC.; *U.S. Private*, pg. 2732
MILLER HOMES LIMITED—See Bridgepoint Group Plc; *Int'l*, pg. 1154
MILLER/HOWARD HIGH INCOME EQUITY FUND; *U.S. Public*, pg. 1446
MILLER HUGHES FORD SALES; *Int'l*, pg. 4896
MILLER INDUSTRIAL FLUIDS, LLC—See PetroChoice LLC; *U.S. Private*, pg. 3162
MILLER INDUSTRIES, INC.; *U.S. Public*, pg. 1446
MILLER INDUSTRIES, INC.; *U.S. Private*, pg. 2734
MILLER INSULATION CO. INC.; *U.S. Private*, pg. 2734
MILLER INSURANCE, INC.—See Keystone Insurers Group, Inc.; *U.S. Private*, pg. 2300
MILLER INSURANCE SERVICES LLP—See GIC Pte. Ltd.; *Int'l*, pg. 2967
MILLER INSURANCE SERVICES (SINGAPORE) PTE. LIMITED—See Willis Towers Watson Public Limited Company; *Int'l*, pg. 8414
MILLER INTERMODAL LOGISTICS SERVICES, INC.—See Dewey Corporation; *U.S. Private*, pg. 1219
MILLER INTERNATIONAL, INC. - CINCH JEANS AND SHIRTS DIVISION—See Miller International, Inc.; *U.S. Private*, pg. 2734
MILLER INTERNATIONAL, INC.; *U.S. Private*, pg. 2734
MILLER INVESTMENT MANAGEMENT, LLC; *U.S. Private*, pg. 2734
MILLERKNOLL, INC.; *U.S. Public*, pg. 1446
MILLER LAW GROUP; *U.S. Private*, pg. 2734
MILLER LEASING MIETE GMBH; *Int'l*, pg. 4896
MILLER LEGAL SERVICES—See Miller Advertising Agency Inc.; *U.S. Private*, pg. 2702
MILLER LEGG & ASSOCIATES INC.; *U.S. Private*, pg. 2734
MILLER LIVESTOCK MARKETS INC.; *U.S. Private*, pg. 2734
MILLER & LONG COMPANY, INC.; *U.S. Private*, pg. 2732
MILLER & LOUGHRY, INC.—See Pinnacle Financial Partners, Inc.; *U.S. Public*, pg. 1692
MILLER MANUFACTURING COMPANY—See Frandsen Corporation; *U.S. Private*, pg. 1593
MILLER MANUFACTURING, INC.; *U.S. Private*, pg. 2735
MILLER MANUFACTURING, INC.; *U.S. Private*, pg. 2735
MILLER MARINE—See Miller Enterprises; *U.S. Private*, pg. 2734
MILLER MCASPHALT CORPORATION—See Bouygues S.A.; *Int'l*, pg. 1122
MILLER MECHANICAL SERVICES, INC.; *U.S. Private*, pg. 2735
MILLER MFG, CO.; *U.S. Private*, pg. 2735
MILLER, MILLER & MCLACHLAN CONSTRUCTION, INC.; *U.S. Private*, pg. 2736
MILLER MILLING COMPANY—See Nisshin Seifun Group, Inc.; *Int'l*, pg. 5372
MILLER MOTOR CAR CORP.; *U.S. Private*, pg. 2735
MILLER MOTORCARS INC.; *U.S. Private*, pg. 2735
MILLER MULTIPLEX DISPLAY FIXTURE CO.—See Miller Manufacturing, Inc.; *U.S. Private*, pg. 2735
MILLER OF DENTON LTD.; *U.S. Private*, pg. 2735
MILLER OIL CO., INC.; *U.S. Private*, pg. 2735
MILLER PAINT COMPANY, INC.—See Cloverdale Paint Inc.; *Int'l*, pg. 1663
MILLER PAPER COMPANY—See GVH Management; *U.S. Private*, pg. 1820
MILLER PATTISON LIMITED—See Brookfield Corporation; *Int'l*, pg. 1188
MILLER PAVING LIMITED—See Bouygues S.A.; *Int'l*, pg. 1122
MILLER PERSONNEL INC.—See Miller Resources International, Inc.; *U.S. Private*, pg. 2735
MILLER PIPELINE, LLC—See CenterPoint Energy, Inc.; *U.S. Public*, pg. 472
MILLER PLASTERING & STUCCO, INC.; *U.S. Private*, pg. 2735
MILLER PONTIAC-BUICK-GMC INC—See Miller Enterprises; *U.S. Private*, pg. 2734
MILLER POWDER COATING—See Miller Manufacturing, Inc.; *U.S. Private*, pg. 2735
MILLER PROCTOR NICKOLAS INC.; *U.S. Private*, pg. 2735
MILLER PRODUCTS COMPANY, INC.; *U.S. Private*, pg. 2735
MILLER PRODUCTS INC.—See Quoin Inc.; *U.S. Private*, pg. 3329
MILLER PRODUCTS, INC.—See GHM Industries, Inc.; *U.S. Private*, pg. 1691

MILLER PUBLISHING GROUP, LLC; *U.S. Private*, pg. 2735
MILLER & RAVED INC.; *U.S. Private*, pg. 2732
MILLER REAL ESTATE INVESTMENTS, LLC—See Kimco Realty Corporation; *U.S. Public*, pg. 1232
MILLER REALTY INVESTMENT PARTNERS, INC.—See Henry S. Miller Management Corp.; *U.S. Private*, pg. 1919
MILLER-REID, INC.; *U.S. Private*, pg. 2736
MILLER RESOURCES INTERNATIONAL, INC.; *U.S. Private*, pg. 2735
MILLER RUBBER PRODUCTS COMPANY—See Miller Products Company, Inc.; *U.S. Private*, pg. 2735
MILLER/RUSSELL & ASSOCIATES LLC; *U.S. Private*, pg. 2736
MILLER'S ALE HOUSE, INC.—See Ale House Management, Inc.; *U.S. Private*, pg. 160
MILLERS CAPITAL INSURANCE CO.; *U.S. Private*, pg. 2736
THE MILLERSCHIN GROUP, INC.—See French/West/Vaughan, LLC; *U.S. Private*, pg. 1609
MILLER'S CHRYSLER-PLYMOUTH JEEP; *U.S. Private*, pg. 2736
MILLER SELLNER IMPLEMENT INC.; *U.S. Private*, pg. 2735
MILLERS FASHION CLUB (QLD) PTY LIMITED—See City Chic Collective Limited; *Int'l*, pg. 1626
MILLERS FASHION CLUB (VIC) PTY LIMITED—See City Chic Collective Limited; *Int'l*, pg. 1626
MILLERS FASHION CLUB (WA) PTY LIMITED—See City Chic Collective Limited; *Int'l*, pg. 1626
MILLERS FORGE INC.; *U.S. Private*, pg. 2736
MILLER SHINGLE COMPANY INC.; *U.S. Private*, pg. 2735
MILLERS INC.; *U.S. Private*, pg. 2736
MILLER & SMITH CO.—See Miller & Smith Holding Company Inc.; *U.S. Private*, pg. 2732
MILLER & SMITH HOLDING COMPANY INC.; *U.S. Private*, pg. 2732
MILLER'S OF COLUMBIA; *U.S. Private*, pg. 2736
MILLERS OILS LTD.; *Int'l*, pg. 4896
MILLER & SON PAVING CO. INC.; *U.S. Private*, pg. 2732
MILLER SPORTS GROUP—See Miller Publishing Group, LLC; *U.S. Private*, pg. 2735
MILLER'S PRESORT, INC.—See Pitney Bowes Inc.; *U.S. Public*, pg. 1694
MILLERS PUBLICATIONS LTD.—See Vivendi SE; *Int'l*, pg. 8274
MILLER-STEPHENSON CHEMICAL COMPANY, INC.; *U.S. Private*, pg. 2736
MILLER-ST. NAZIANZ, INC.—See CNH Industrial N.V.; *Int'l*, pg. 1674
MILLER SUPPLY OF WEST VIRGINIA INCORPORATED; *U.S. Private*, pg. 2735
MILLER SURFACE GALLERY; *U.S. Private*, pg. 2735
MILLER'S VANGUARD LTD.—See Ali Holding S.r.l.; *Int'l*, pg. 322
MILLER TECHNICAL SERVICE—See Honeywell International Inc.; *U.S. Public*, pg. 1049
MILLER TECHNOLOGIES INTERNATIONAL; *U.S. Private*, pg. 2735
MILLER TRANSPORTERS, INC.—See Dewey Corporation; *U.S. Private*, pg. 1219
MILLER TRUCK LINES INC.—See Miller Holding Corp.; *U.S. Private*, pg. 2734
MILLER TRUCK LINES INC. - TULSA—See Miller Holding Corp.; *U.S. Private*, pg. 2734
MILLER WASTE MILLS, INC.; *U.S. Private*, pg. 2735
MILLER.WHITERUNKLE—See Ascentium Corporation; *U.S. Private*, pg. 348
MILLER YACHT SALES, INC.; *U.S. Private*, pg. 2735
MILLERY ENTREPRISE; *Int'l*, pg. 4896
MILLER/ZELL, INC.; *U.S. Private*, pg. 2736
MILLETERRA GESELLSCHAFT FUR IMMOBILIENVERWALTUNG MBH—See UniCredit S.p.A.; *Int'l*, pg. 8038
MILLET INNOVATION SA; *Int'l*, pg. 4896
MILLET MOUNTAIN GROUP SAS; *Int'l*, pg. 4896
MILLET—See Calida Holding AG; *Int'l*, pg. 1264
MILLETT INDUSTRIES—See Vista Outdoor Inc.; *U.S. Public*, pg. 2305
THE MILL (FACILITY) LIMITED—See Vantiva SA; *Int'l*, pg. 8131
MILLFIELD GROUP; *Int'l*, pg. 4896
MILL GARDENS (CULLOMPTON) MANAGEMENT COMPANY LIMITED—See Persimmon plc; *Int'l*, pg. 5816
MILLGATE DEVELOPMENTS LIMITED—See Vistry Group PLC; *Int'l*, pg. 8255
THE MILL GROUP INC. - LOS ANGELES—See Vantiva SA; *Int'l*, pg. 8131
THE MILL GROUP INC.—See Vantiva SA; *Int'l*, pg. 8131
MILL HARDWARE & FOOD SERVICE, INC.—See New Mountain Capital, LLC; *U.S. Private*, pg. 2901
MILLHAVEN COMPANY INC—See Shivers Trading & Operating Company; *U.S. Private*, pg. 3638
MILLHOUSE GROUP, INC.; *U.S. Private*, pg. 2736
MILLHOUSE, INC. PLC; *Int'l*, pg. 4896
MILLIAN AIR CORP.—See Baton Rouge Jet Center LLC; *U.S. Private*, pg. 487

MILLMAN SURVEYING, INC.

MILLICAN NURSERIES, INC.—See SiteOne Landscape Supply, Inc.; *U.S. Public*, pg. 1889
MILLICANSOLUTIONS, LLC—See AMN Healthcare Services, Inc.; *U.S. Public*, pg. 125
MILLICOM HOLDING BV—See Millicom International Cellular S.A.; *Int'l*, pg. 4896
MILLICOM INTERNATIONAL CELLULAR S.A.; *Int'l*, pg. 4896
MILLICOM TELECOMMUNICATIONS BV—See Millicom International Cellular S.A.; *Int'l*, pg. 4896
MILLIE'S COMPANY LIMITED—See Hillhouse Investment Management Limited; *Int'l*, pg. 3393
MILLIE & SEVERSON INC.—See Severson Group Incorporated; *U.S. Private*, pg. 3619
MILLIF INDUSTRIES SDN BHD—See QAF Limited; *Int'l*, pg. 6132
MILLIKEN (AUSTRALIA) P/L—See Milliken & Company; *U.S. Private*, pg. 2737
MILLIKEN & COMPANY; *U.S. Private*, pg. 2736
MILLIKEN FINE GOODS DIV.—See Milliken & Company; *U.S. Private*, pg. 2737
MILLIKEN FINISHED APPAREL DIV.—See Milliken & Company; *U.S. Private*, pg. 2737
MILLIKEN INDUSTRIAL DIV.—See Milliken & Company; *U.S. Private*, pg. 2737
MILLIKEN INTERIOR FURNISHINGS DIV.—See Milliken & Company; *U.S. Private*, pg. 2737
MILLIKEN MILLWORK INC.—See ONEX Corporation; *Int'l*, pg. 5579
MILLIKIN VALVE, LLC—See Mueller Water Products, Inc.; *U.S. Public*, pg. 1485
MILLIMAGES S.A.; *Int'l*, pg. 4896
MILLIMAN GMBH—See Milliman, Inc.; *U.S. Private*, pg. 2737
MILLIMAN, INC.—See Milliman, Inc.; *U.S. Private*, pg. 2737
MILLIMAN, INC.; *U.S. Private*, pg. 2737
MILLING TECHNIKS (PTY) LIMITED—See Raubex Group Limited; *Int'l*, pg. 6221
MILLINGTON BANK—See Kearny Financial Corp.; *U.S. Public*, pg. 1217
MILLINGTON LOCKWOOD INC.; *U.S. Private*, pg. 2737
MILLION CHAMP TRADING LIMITED—See Steed Oriental (Holdings) Company Limited; *Int'l*, pg. 7189
MILLION CHEMICALS CO., LTD.—See Nihon Parkerizing Co., Ltd.; *Int'l*, pg. 5286
MILLION CITIES HOLDINGS LIMITED; *Int'l*, pg. 4896
MILLION DOLLAR BABY; *U.S. Private*, pg. 2737
MILLION DOLLAR ROUND TABLE THE PREMIER ASSOCIATION OF FINANCIAL PROFESSIONALS; *U.S. Private*, pg. 2737
MILLION HOPE INDUSTRIES HOLDINGS LIMITED; *Int'l*, pg. 4896
MILLION HOPE INDUSTRIES LIMITED—See Hanison Construction Holdings Limited; *Int'l*, pg. 3252
MILLION HOPE NEW-TECH BUILDING SUPPLIES (HUIZHOU) LIMITED—See Million Hope Industries; *Int'l*, pg. 4897
MILLION RANK (HK) LIMITED—See Shanghai XNG Holdings Limited; *Int'l*, pg. 6781
MILLION STARS HOLDINGS LIMITED; *Int'l*, pg. 4897
MILLION WEALTH ENTERPRISES LIMITED—See Yau Lee Holdings Limited; *Int'l*, pg. 8571
MILLIPORE AB—See Merck KGaA; *Int'l*, pg. 4830
MILLIPORE AG—See Merck KGaA; *Int'l*, pg. 4830
MILLIPORE A/S—See Merck KGaA; *Int'l*, pg. 4830
MILLIPORE B.V.—See Merck KGaA; *Int'l*, pg. 4830
MILLIPORE CHINA LTD.—See Merck KGaA; *Int'l*, pg. 4830
MILLIPORE CIDRA, INC.—See Merck KGaA; *Int'l*, pg. 4830
MILLIPORE CORPORATION - BIOSCIENCE DIVISION—See Merck KGaA; *Int'l*, pg. 4830
MILLIPORE GMBH—See Merck KGaA; *Int'l*, pg. 4830
MILLIPORE IRELAND B.V.—See Merck KGaA; *Int'l*, pg. 4830
MILLIPORE KOREA, LTD.—See Merck KGaA; *Int'l*, pg. 4830
MILLIPORE OY—See Merck KGaA; *Int'l*, pg. 4831
MILLIPORE S.A./N.V.—See Merck KGaA; *Int'l*, pg. 4831
MILLIPORE S.A.S.—See Merck KGaA; *Int'l*, pg. 4831
MILLIPORESIGMA CANADA LTD.—See Merck KGaA; *Int'l*, pg. 4832
MILLIPORE S.P.A.—See Merck KGaA; *Int'l*, pg. 4831
MILLIPORE UK LTD—See Merck KGaA; *Int'l*, pg. 4831
MILLIS INDUSTRIES, INC.—See Radius Recycling, Inc.; *U.S. Public*, pg. 1760
MILLIS TRANSFER INC.—See Heartland Express, Inc.; *U.S. Public*, pg. 1017
MILL-LOG EQUIPMENT CO., INC.—See Palmer Johnson Enterprises, Inc.; *U.S. Private*, pg. 3081
MILL-LOG WILSON EQUIPMENT LTD.—See Palmer Johnson Enterprises, Inc.; *U.S. Private*, pg. 3081
MILLMAN LUMBER COMPANY; *U.S. Private*, pg. 2737
MILLMAN SURVEYING, INC.; *U.S. Private*, pg. 2737
MILLOG OY—See Patria Oyj; *Int'l*, pg. 5757
MILLPACK COMPANY LIMITED—See Panjawattana Plastic Public Company Limited; *Int'l*, pg. 5728

MILLMAN SURVEYING, INC. CORPORATE AFFILIATIONS

MILL POINT CAPITAL LLC—See Guggenheim Partners, LLC; *U.S. Private*, pg. 1811
MILL POND HOLDINGS LLC; *U.S. Private*, pg. 2730
THE MILL POND PRESS COMPANIES, INC.—See Mill Pond Holdings LLC; *U.S. Private*, pg. 2730
MILL-RITE WOODWORKING COMPANY, INC.; *U.S. Private*, pg. 2730
MILL ROAD CAPITAL MANAGEMENT LLC; *U.S. Private*, pg. 2730
MILLROCK EXPLORATION CORP.—See Alaska Energy Metals Corporation; *Int'l*, pg. 291
MILL ROCK PACKAGING PARTNERS LLC—See Great Mill Rock LLC; *U.S. Private*, pg. 1766
MILL-ROSE CLEAN-FIT—See Mill-Rose Company; *U.S. Private*, pg. 2730
MILL-ROSE COMPANY; *U.S. Private*, pg. 2730
MILL-RUN TOURS INC.; *U.S. Private*, pg. 2730
MILLS & ASSOCIATES, INC.—See Pennoni Associates Inc.; *U.S. Private*, pg. 3136
THE MILLS AT JERSEY GARDENS—See Simon Property Group, Inc.; *U.S. Public*, pg. 1882
MILLS AUTO ENTERPRISES, INC.—See Mills Fleet Farm, Inc.; *U.S. Private*, pg. 2737
MILLS AUTO GROUP, INC.—See Mills Fleet Farm, Inc.; *U.S. Private*, pg. 2737
MILLS CHEVROLET CO., INC.; *U.S. Private*, pg. 2737
MILLS ESTRUTURAS E SERVICOS DE ENGENHARIA, S.A.; *Int'l*, pg. 4897
MILLS FENCE CO. INC.; *U.S. Private*, pg. 2737
MILLS FLEET FARM, INC.; *U.S. Private*, pg. 2737
MILLS FORD OF WILLMAR; *U.S. Private*, pg. 2737
MILLS GROUP INC.; *U.S. Private*, pg. 2738
MILLS MEDICAL PRACTICES, LLC—See Apollo Global Management, Inc.; *U.S. Public*, pg. 157
MILLS MOTOR, INC.—See Mills Fleet Farm, Inc.; *U.S. Private*, pg. 2737
MILLS MUSIC TRUST; *U.S. Public*, pg. 1448
MILLS & PARTNERS—See Kainos Capital, LLC; *U.S. Private*, pg. 2255
MILLS-PENINSULA MEDICAL CENTER—See Sutter Health; *U.S. Private*, pg. 3887
MILLSPORT—See Omnicom Group Inc.; *U.S. Public*, pg. 1588
MILLSPORT—See Omnicom Group Inc.; *U.S. Public*, pg. 1588
MILLS PRODUCTS INC.; *U.S. Private*, pg. 2738
THE MILLS PROPERTIES—See Simon Property Group, Inc.; *U.S. Public*, pg. 1882
MILLS TALBOT COMPANY—See Flynn & Reynolds Agency Inc.; *U.S. Private*, pg. 1553
MILLSTAR LLC—See Galaxy Technologies Corp.; *U.S. Private*, pg. 1636
THE MILL STEEL CO., INC.; *U.S. Public*, pg. 4079
MILLSTEIN & CO., L.P.—See Guggenheim Partners, LLC; *U.S. Private*, pg. 1811
MILLSTONE WEBER, LLC—See Fred Weber, Inc.; *U.S. Private*, pg. 1601
MILLSTREAM MINES LTD.; *Int'l*, pg. 4897
MILLSTREAM UNDERWRITING LIMITED—See Brown & Brown, Inc.; *U.S. Public*, pg. 401
MILLSTREET CAPITAL ACQUISITION CORP.; *U.S. Public*, pg. 1448
MILL STREET PARTNERS LLC; *U.S. Private*, pg. 2730
MILL SUPPLIES INC.; *U.S. Private*, pg. 2730
MILLTECH PRECISION ENGINEERING LTD.—See Indutrade AB; *Int'l*, pg. 3680
MILLTEC MACHINERY PRIVATE LIMITED—See Ag Growth International Inc.; *Int'l*, pg. 198
MILL & TIMBER PRODUCTS LTD - PORT HARDY DIVISION—See Mill & Timber Products Ltd; *Int'l*, pg. 4895
MILL & TIMBER PRODUCTS LTD; *Int'l*, pg. 4895
MILLTRONICS EUROPE B.V.—See Hurco Companies, Inc.; *U.S. Public*, pg. 1076
MILLTRONICS USA, INC.—See Hurco Companies, Inc.; *U.S. Public*, pg. 1076
MILLUX B.V.—See IDEX Corp; *U.S. Public*, pg. 1091
MILL VALLEY MOTORS, INC.—See Sojitz Corporation; *Int'l*, pg. 7062
MILLWALL HOLDINGS PLC; *Int'l*, pg. 4897
MILLWARD BROWN AUSTRALIA—See Bain Capital, LP; *U.S. Private*, pg. 449
MILLWARD BROWN BRAZIL—See Bain Capital, LP; *U.S. Private*, pg. 449
MILLWARD BROWN CANADA—See Bain Capital, LP; *U.S. Private*, pg. 449
MILLWARD BROWN/CENTRUM—See Bain Capital, LP; *U.S. Private*, pg. 449
MILLWARD BROWN CHINA—See Bain Capital, LP; *U.S. Private*, pg. 449
MILLWARD BROWN COLUMBIA—See Bain Capital, LP; *U.S. Private*, pg. 449
MILLWARD BROWN CZECH REPUBLIC—See Bain Capital, LP; *U.S. Private*, pg. 449
MILLWARD BROWN DELFO—See Bain Capital, LP; *U.S. Private*, pg. 449
MILLWARD BROWN DENMARK—See Bain Capital, LP; *U.S. Private*, pg. 449

MILLWARD BROWN FRANCE—See Bain Capital, LP; *U.S. Private*, pg. 449
MILLWARD BROWN GERMANY GMBH—See Bain Capital, LP; *U.S. Private*, pg. 449
MILLWARD BROWN HUNGARY—See Bain Capital, LP; *U.S. Private*, pg. 449
MILLWARD BROWN IMS—See Bain Capital, LP; *U.S. Private*, pg. 449
MILLWARD BROWN, INC.—See Bain Capital, LP; *U.S. Private*, pg. 449
MILLWARD BROWN INC.—See Bain Capital, LP; *U.S. Private*, pg. 448
MILLWARD BROWN MARKET RESEACH SERVICES—See Bain Capital, LP; *U.S. Private*, pg. 449
MILLWARD BROWN MEDIA RESEARCH—See Bain Capital, LP; *U.S. Private*, pg. 449
MILLWARD BROWN MEXICO—See Bain Capital, LP; *U.S. Private*, pg. 449
MILLWARD BROWN PHILIPPINES—See Bain Capital, LP; *U.S. Private*, pg. 449
MILLWARD BROWN PORTUGAL—See Bain Capital, LP; *U.S. Private*, pg. 449
MILLWARD BROWN SINGAPORE—See Bain Capital, LP; *U.S. Private*, pg. 449
MILLWARD BROWN SMG/KRC—See Bain Capital, LP; *U.S. Private*, pg. 449
MILLWARD BROWN—See Bain Capital, LP; *U.S. Private*, pg. 448
MILLWARD BROWN—See Bain Capital, LP; *U.S. Private*, pg. 448
MILLWARD BROWN—See Bain Capital, LP; *U.S. Private*, pg. 449
MILLWARD BROWN—See Bain Capital, LP; *U.S. Private*, pg. 448
MILLWARD BROWN SOUTH AFRICA—See Bain Capital, LP; *U.S. Private*, pg. 449
MILLWARD BROWN SPAIN—See Bain Capital, LP; *U.S. Private*, pg. 449
MILLWARD BROWN SWEDEN—See Bain Capital, LP; *U.S. Private*, pg. 449
MILLWARD BROWN TAIWAN—See Bain Capital, LP; *U.S. Private*, pg. 449
MILLWARD BROWN THAILAND—See Bain Capital, LP; *U.S. Private*, pg. 449
MILLWARD BROWN TURKEY—See Bain Capital, LP; *U.S. Private*, pg. 449
MILLWARD BROWN UK LTD.—See WPP plc; *Int'l*, pg. 8466
MILLWARD BROWN ULSTER—See Bain Capital, LP; *U.S. Private*, pg. 449
MILLWOOD DESIGNER HOMES LIMITED—See Places for People Group Limited; *Int'l*, pg. 5888
MILLWOOD HOSPITAL—See Universal Health Services, Inc.; *U.S. Public*, pg. 2258
MILLWOOD INC.; *U.S. Private*, pg. 2738
MILLWORK 360 LLC—See Validor Capital LLC; *U.S. Private*, pg. 4332
THE MILLWORK, CO.; *U.S. Private*, pg. 4079
MILLWORK DISTRIBUTORS INC.; *U.S. Private*, pg. 2738
MILLWRIGHT HOLDINGS LLC; *U.S. Private*, pg. 2738
MIL MADEIRAS PRECIOSAS LTDA—See Precious Woods Holding AG; *Int'l*, pg. 5956
MILMAN INDUSTRIES INC.; *Int'l*, pg. 4897
MILMEGA LIMITED—See AMETEK, Inc.; *U.S. Public*, pg. 121
MILNE AGRIGROUP PTY., LTD.; *Int'l*, pg. 4897
MILNE CONSTRUCTION CO.; *U.S. Private*, pg. 2738
MILNE FRUITS PRODUCTS, INC.—See Wyckoff Farms, Incorporated; *U.S. Private*, pg. 4575
MILNER CONSOLIDATED SILVER MINES LTD.; *Int'l*, pg. 4897
MILNER DOCUMENT PRODUCTS, INC.—See Milner Document Products, Inc.; *U.S. Private*, pg. 2738
MILNER DOCUMENT PRODUCTS, INC.; *U.S. Private*, pg. 2738
MILNER ELECTRICAL COMPANY; *U.S. Private*, pg. 2738
MILNER-FENWICK, INC.—See Interactivation Health Networks LLC; *U.S. Private*, pg. 2108
MILNER POWER INC.—See Maxim Power Corp.; *Int'l*, pg. 4737
MILNER POWER LIMITED PARTNERSHIP—See Maxim Power Corp.; *Int'l*, pg. 4737
MILNE RUSS FORD INC.; *U.S. Private*, pg. 2738
MI LNG COMPANY, LTD.—See Mitsubishi Heavy Industries, Ltd.; *Int'l*, pg. 4955
MILOC BIOTECHNOLOGY LIMITED—See MiLOC Group Limited; *Int'l*, pg. 4897
MILO C. COCKERHAM INC.; *U.S. Private*, pg. 2738
MILOC GROUP LIMITED; *Int'l*, pg. 4897
MILO GORDON CHRYSLER ISUZU MITSUBISHI; *U.S. Private*, pg. 2738
MILONE & MAC BROOM—See Charterhouse Capital Partners LLP; *Int'l*, pg. 1456
MILON GRUNDSTUCKS-VERWALTUNGSGESELLSCHAFT MBH & CO. KG—See Mercedes-Benz Group AG; *Int'l*, pg. 4825
MILO PETERSON FORD; *U.S. Private*, pg. 2738
MILOSI, INC.; *U.S. Private*, pg. 2738

MILPA TICARI VE SINAI URUNLER PAZARLAMA SANAYI VE TICARET A.S.—See Adil Bey Holding A.S.; *Int'l*, pg. 148
MILPERRA DEVELOPMENTS PTY LIMITED—See Pentair plc; *Int'l*, pg. 5789
MILPHARM LIMITED—See Aurobindo Pharma Ltd.; *Int'l*, pg. 713
MILPITAS POST—See Alden Global Capital LLC; *U.S. Private*, pg. 155
MILROD ENTERPRISES; *U.S. Private*, pg. 2738
MILSAT SERVICES GMBH—See Airbus SE; *Int'l*, pg. 243
MILSCO DE MEXICO, S.A. DE C.V.—See Jason Industries, Inc.; *U.S. Private*, pg. 2189
MILSCO DE MEXICO S. DE R.L. DE C.V.—See Jason Industries, Inc.; *U.S. Private*, pg. 2190
MILSCO EUROPE—See Jason Industries, Inc.; *U.S. Private*, pg. 2189
MILSCO MANUFACTURING COMPANY - JACKSON—See Jason Industries, Inc.; *U.S. Private*, pg. 2189
MILSCO MANUFACTURING COMPANY—See Jason Industries, Inc.; *U.S. Private*, pg. 2189
MILSOFT UTILITY SOLUTIONS, INC.; *U.S. Private*, pg. 2738
MILSO INDUSTRIES CORPORATION—See Matthews International Corporation; *U.S. Public*, pg. 1401
MILSPEC STRAPPING SYSTEMS—See Russel Metals Inc.; *Int'l*, pg. 6430
MILSY A.S.; *Int'l*, pg. 4897
MILTAS TURIZM INSAAT TICARET A.S.—See Turkiye Is Bankasi A.S.; *Int'l*, pg. 7976
MILTEC UV; *U.S. Private*, pg. 2738
MILTE ITALIA SPA—See DMK Deutsches Milchkontor GmbH; *Int'l*, pg. 2146
MILTIMORE SALES, INC.; *U.S. Private*, pg. 2738
MILTON AUSTRALIA PTY. LTD.—See Pyridam Farma Tbk; *Int'l*, pg. 6127
MILTON CAPITAL PLC; *Int'l*, pg. 4897
MILTON CAT—See Southworth-Milton Inc.; *U.S. Private*, pg. 3743
MILTON CHRYSLER DODGE LIMITED; *Int'l*, pg. 4897
MILTON CORPORATION LIMITED—See Washington H. Soul Pattinson & Company Limited; *Int'l*, pg. 8351
MILTON EDU, INC.—See Openbase Inc.; *Int'l*, pg. 5599
MILTON INDUSTRIES, INC.—See Levine Leichtman Capital Partners, LLC; *U.S. Private*, pg. 2436
MILTON INDUSTRIES LIMITED; *Int'l*, pg. 4897
MILTON J. WOOD COMPANY; *U.S. Private*, pg. 2738
MILTON MANUFACTURING INC.—See Align Capital Partners, LLC; *U.S. Private*, pg. 167
MILTON MANUFACTURING, INC.; *U.S. Private*, pg. 2738
MILTON ROY EUROPE—See BC Partners LLP; *Int'l*, pg. 922
MILTON ROY EUROPE—See The Carlyle Group Inc.; *U.S. Public*, pg. 2044
MILTON ROY - HARTELL DIVISION—See BC Partners LLP; *Int'l*, pg. 922
MILTON ROY - HARTELL DIVISION—See The Carlyle Group Inc.; *U.S. Public*, pg. 2044
MILTON ROY INDUSTRIAL (SHANGHAI) CO., LTD.—See Ingersoll Rand Inc.; *U.S. Public*, pg. 1122
MILTON ROY LIQUID METRONICS INCORPORATED—See BC Partners LLP; *Int'l*, pg. 922
MILTON ROY LIQUID METRONICS INCORPORATED—See The Carlyle Group Inc.; *U.S. Public*, pg. 2044
MILTON ROY, LLC—See BC Partners LLP; *Int'l*, pg. 922
MILTON ROY, LLC—See The Carlyle Group Inc.; *U.S. Public*, pg. 2044
MILTON RUBEN CHEVROLET; *U.S. Private*, pg. 2738
MILTON RUBEN LEASING COMPANY—See Milton Ruben Chevrolet; *U.S. Private*, pg. 2738
MILTON RUBEN MOTORS, INC.—See Milton Ruben Chevrolet; *U.S. Private*, pg. 2738
THE MILTON S. HERSHEY MEDICAL CENTER—See Penn State Health; *U.S. Private*, pg. 3135
MILTONS INC.; *U.S. Private*, pg. 2739
MILTON STREET CAPITAL, LLC; *U.S. Private*, pg. 2739
MILTON TRANSPORTATION INC.; *U.S. Private*, pg. 2739
MILTON ULLADULLA PUBLISHING CO. PTY LTD—See Nine Entertainment Co. Holdings Limited; *Int'l*, pg. 5299
MILTOPE GROUP, INC.—See Temasek Holdings (Private) Limited; *Int'l*, pg. 7552
MILUO CDB VILLAGE BANK CO., LTD.—See China Development Bank Corporation; *Int'l*, pg. 1497
MILUPA COMMERCIAL S.A.—See Danone; *Int'l*, pg. 1966
MILUPA GMBH—See Danone; *Int'l*, pg. 1966
MILUPA GMBH—See Danone; *Int'l*, pg. 1966
MILUPA N.V.—See Danone; *Int'l*, pg. 1966
MILUPA S.A.—See Danone; *Int'l*, pg. 1967
MILUX CORPORATION BERHAD; *Int'l*, pg. 4897
MILUX HOME APPLIANCES (INDIA) PRIVATE LIMITED—See Milux Corporation Berhad; *Int'l*, pg. 4897
MILUX SALES & SERVICE SDN. BHD.—See Milux Corporation Berhad; *Int'l*, pg. 4897
MIL-VER METAL COMPANY LTD—See Amalgamated Metal Corporation PLC; *Int'l*, pg. 408

COMPANY NAME INDEX

MILVERTON LTD.—See Alphatec Holdings, Inc.; *U.S. Public*, pg. 84
MILWAUKEE AREA WORKFORCE INVESTMENT BOARD INC.; *U.S. Private*, pg. 2739
MILWAUKEE BREWERS BASEBALL CLUB, INC.; *U.S. Private*, pg. 2739
MILWAUKEE BUCKS, INC.; *U.S. Private*, pg. 2739
MILWAUKEE BULK TERMINALS LLC—See Kinder Morgan, Inc.; *U.S. Public*, pg. 1233
MILWAUKEE CENTER FOR INDEPENDENCE, INC.; *U.S. Private*, pg. 2739
MILWAUKEE CITY CENTER, LLC—See The Marcus Corporation; *U.S. Public*, pg. 2112
MILWAUKEE COUNTY TRANSIT SYSTEM; *U.S. Private*, pg. 2739
MILWAUKEE CYLINDER—See Enerpac Tool Group Corp.; *U.S. Public*, pg. 766
MILWAUKEE ELECTRIC TOOL (CANADA) LTD.—See Techtronic Industries Co., Ltd.; *Int'l*, pg. 7513
MILWAUKEE ELECTRIC TOOL CORP.—See Techtronic Industries Co., Ltd.; *Int'l*, pg. 7513
MILWAUKEE FORGE, INC.; *U.S. Private*, pg. 2739
MILWAUKEE GEAR COMPANY—See Regal Rexnord Corporation; *U.S. Public*, pg. 1773
MILWAUKEE INSULATION CO., INC.—See MacArthur Co.; *U.S. Private*, pg. 2534
MILWAUKEE JEWISH FEDERATION, INC.; *U.S. Private*, pg. 2739
MILWAUKEE METROPOLITAN SEWERAGE DISTRICT; *U.S. Private*, pg. 2739
MILWAUKEE PC INC.; *U.S. Private*, pg. 2739
MILWAUKEE REGIONAL MEDICAL CENTER, INC.; *U.S. Private*, pg. 2739
MILWAUKEE SLIDE AND SPINDLE—See Belco Industries, Inc.; *U.S. Private*, pg. 517
MILWAUKEE SYMPHONY ORCHESTRA INC.; *U.S. Private*, pg. 2739
MILWAUKEE VALVE COMPANY, INC.; *U.S. Private*, pg. 2739
MILWAUKIE LUMBER COMPANY; *U.S. Private*, pg. 2739
MILWHITE INC.; *U.S. Private*, pg. 2740
MILX CORPORATION—See Shimizu Corporation; *Int'l*, pg. 6835
MILYONI, INC.—See Photobucket Corporation; *U.S. Private*, pg. 3174
MIMA FILMS SPRL—See Illinois Tool Works Inc.; *U.S. Public*, pg. 1109
MIMAKI AUSTRALIA PTY LTD—See MIMAKI ENGINEERING CO., LTD.; *Int'l*, pg. 4897
MIMAKI BOMPAN TEXTILE S.R.L.—See MIMAKI ENGINEERING CO., LTD.; *Int'l*, pg. 4898
MIMAKI BRASIL COMERCIO E IMPORTACAO LTDA—See MIMAKI ENGINEERING CO., LTD.; *Int'l*, pg. 4898
MIMAKI DEUTSCHLAND GMBH—See MIMAKI ENGINEERING CO., LTD.; *Int'l*, pg. 4898
MIMAKI ENGINEERING CO., LTD. - KAZAWA FACTORY—See MIMAKI ENGINEERING CO., LTD.; *Int'l*, pg. 4898
MIMAKI ENGINEERING CO., LTD.; *Int'l*, pg. 4897
MIMAKI ENGINEERING (TAIWAN) CO., LTD.—See MIMAKI ENGINEERING CO., LTD.; *Int'l*, pg. 4898
MIMAKI EURASIA DIJITAL BASKI TEKNOLOJILERI PAZARLAMA VE TICARET LIMITED SIRKETI—See MIMAKI ENGINEERING CO., LTD.; *Int'l*, pg. 4898
MIMAKI EUROPE B.V.—See MIMAKI ENGINEERING CO., LTD.; *Int'l*, pg. 4898
MIMAKI IJ TECHNOLOGY (ZHEJIANG) CO., LTD.—See MIMAKI ENGINEERING CO., LTD.; *Int'l*, pg. 4898
MIMAKI INDIA PRIVATE LIMITED—See MIMAKI ENGINEERING CO., LTD.; *Int'l*, pg. 4898
MIMAKI LITHUANIA, UAB—See MIMAKI ENGINEERING CO., LTD.; *Int'l*, pg. 4898
MIMAKI PRECISION CO., LTD.—See MIMAKI ENGINEERING CO., LTD.; *Int'l*, pg. 4898
MIMAKI SINGAPORE PTE. LTD.—See MIMAKI ENGINEERING CO., LTD.; *Int'l*, pg. 4898
MIMAKI (THAILAND) CO., LTD.—See MIMAKI ENGINEERING CO., LTD.; *Int'l*, pg. 4898
MIMAKI USA, INC.—See MIMAKI ENGINEERING CO., LTD.; *Int'l*, pg. 4898
MIMASU SEMICONDUCTOR INDUSTRY CO., LTD.—See Shin-Etsu Chemical Co. Ltd.; *Int'l*, pg. 6838
MIMECAST LTD.; *Int'l*, pg. 4898
MIMECAST NORTH AMERICA, INC.—See Mimecast Ltd.; *Int'l*, pg. 4898
MIMEDIA HOLDINGS INC.; *Int'l*, pg. 4898
MI-MED SUPPLY CO. INC.; *U.S. Private*, pg. 2695
MIMEDX GROUP, INC.; *U.S. Public*, pg. 1448
MIMEDX TISSUE SERVICES, LLC—See MiMedx Group, Inc.; *U.S. Public*, pg. 1448
MIMEO.COM, INC.; *U.S. Private*, pg. 2740
MIMIC TECHNOLOGIES INC.—See Surgical Science Sweden AB; *Int'l*, pg. 7344
MI MING MART HOLDINGS LIMITED; *Int'l*, pg. 4873
MIMIR, INC.—See Uzabase, Inc.; *Int'l*, pg. 8103
MIMIR INVEST AB; *Int'l*, pg. 4898
MIMI'S CAFE KANSAS, INC—See Holding Le Duff SA; *Int'l*, pg. 3450

MIMI'S CAFE OF ROGERS, INC—See Holding Le Duff SA; *Int'l*, pg. 3450
MIMI'S ROCK CORP.—See FitLife Brands, Inc.; *U.S. Public*, pg. 851
MIMIX BROADBAND, INC.—See MACOM Technology Solutions Holdings, Inc.; *U.S. Public*, pg. 1352
MIMO TECH COMPANY LIMITED—See Advanced Info Service Plc; *Int'l*, pg. 160
MIMOTOPES PTY. LTD.—See Leading Technology Group Pty Ltd.; *Int'l*, pg. 4433
MIMS JAPAN CO., LTD.—See SMS Co., Ltd.; *Int'l*, pg. 7014
MIM SOFTWARE INC.—See GE HealthCare Technologies Inc.; *U.S. Public*, pg. 909
MIMS PTE. LTD.—See SMS Co., Ltd.; *Int'l*, pg. 7014
MINACT INC.; *U.S. Private*, pg. 2740
MIN-AD, INC.—See Inter-Rock Minerals Inc.; *Int'l*, pg. 3735
MINAEAN (GHANA) LIMITED—See Minaean SP Construction Corp.; *Int'l*, pg. 4899
MINAEAN HABITAT INDIA (PVT) LTD.—See Minaean SP Construction Corp.; *Int'l*, pg. 4899
MINAEAN POWER STRUCTURES INC.—See Minaean SP Construction Corp.; *Int'l*, pg. 4899
MINAEAN SP CONSTRUCTION CORP.; *Int'l*, pg. 4899
MINAFIN SARL; *Int'l*, pg. 4899
MIN AIK INTERNATIONAL DEVELOPMENT PTE. LTD.—See Min Aik Technology Co., Ltd.; *Int'l*, pg. 4898
MIN AIK PRECISION INDUSTRIAL CO., LTD.—See Min Aik Technology Co., Ltd.; *Int'l*, pg. 4898
MIN AIK TECHNOLOGY CO., LTD.; *Int'l*, pg. 4898
MIN AIK TECHNOLOGY (M) SDN BHD.—See Min Aik Technology Co., Ltd.; *Int'l*, pg. 4898
MIN AIK TECHNOLOGY (SUZHOU) CO., LTD.—See Min Aik Technology Co., Ltd.; *Int'l*, pg. 4898
MIN AIK TECHNOLOGY (THAILAND) CO., LTD.—See Min Aik Technology Co., Ltd.; *Int'l*, pg. 4898
MIN AIK TECHNOLOGY USA INC.—See Min Aik Technology Co., Ltd.; *Int'l*, pg. 4898
MIN AIK THAILAND(MATH) CO., LTD.—See Min Aik Technology Co., Ltd.; *Int'l*, pg. 4898
MINAKEM BEUVRY PRODUCTION SASU—See Minafin Sarl; *Int'l*, pg. 4899
MINAKEM HIGH POTENT—See Minafin Sarl; *Int'l*, pg. 4899
MINAKEM, LLC—See Minafin Sarl; *Int'l*, pg. 4899
MINAKEM SAS—See Minafin Sarl; *Int'l*, pg. 4899
MINAL MEDICAL CENTRE LLC; *Int'l*, pg. 4899
MINAL SPECIALISED CLINIC DERMATOLOGY LLC—See Kaya Limited; *Int'l*, pg. 4101
MINAMATA DENSHI CO., LTD.—See SUMCO Corporation; *Int'l*, pg. 7260
MINAM DIALYSIS, LLC—See DaVita Inc.; *U.S. Public*, pg. 641
MINAMIFUJI PIPELINE CO., LTD.—See INPEX CORPORATION; *Int'l*, pg. 3717
MINAMI KYUSHU COCA-COLA BOTTLING CO., LTD.; *Int'l*, pg. 4899
MINAMI KYUSHU MARINE SERVICE CO., LTD.—See Mitsui O.S.K. Lines, Ltd.; *Int'l*, pg. 4991
MINAMI KYUSHU MAZDA CO., LTD.—See Mazda Motor Corporation; *Int'l*, pg. 4749
MINAMI KYUSHU SENKO CO., LTD.—See Senko Group Holdings Co., Ltd.; *Int'l*, pg. 6710
MINAMI-KYUSHU YAMADA DENKI CO., LTD.—See Yamada Holdings Co., Ltd.; *Int'l*, pg. 8548
THE MINAMI-NIPPON BANK LTD.; *Int'l*, pg. 7666
MINAMI NIPPON SHIPBUILDING CO., LTD.—See Mitsui E&S Holdings Co., Ltd.; *Int'l*, pg. 4985
MINAMI NUTRITION HEALTH BVBA—See Nestle S.A.; *Int'l*, pg. 5206
MINAMI NUTRITION NV-SA—See Nestle S.A.; *Int'l*, pg. 5206
MINAMIOSAKA COMPUTING CENTER CO., LTD.—See Cyberlinks Co., Ltd.; *Int'l*, pg. 1893
MINAMI OSAKA SENKO TRANSPORT CO., LTD.—See Senko Group Holdings Co., Ltd.; *Int'l*, pg. 6710
MINAPHARM PHARMACEUTICALS; *Int'l*, pg. 4899
MINARA RESOURCES HOLDINGS PTY LTD—See Glencore plc; *Int'l*, pg. 2991
MINARA RESOURCES LIMITED—See Glencore plc; *Int'l*, pg. 2991
MINARDOS CONSTRUCTION & ASSOCIATES; *U.S. Private*, pg. 2740
MINARD RUN OIL COMPANY; *U.S. Private*, pg. 2740
MINA REAL MEXICO S.A. DE C.V.—See Rockhaven Resources Ltd.; *Int'l*, pg. 6379
MINARIK CORPORATION—See Littlejohn & Co., LLC; *U.S. Private*, pg. 2471
MINAS DE ORO NACIONAL S.A. DE C.V.—See Zacatecas Silver Corp.; *Int'l*, pg. 8619
MINAS GARGALLO SL—See Enel S.p.A.; *Int'l*, pg. 2414
MINASMAQUINAS S.A.; *Int'l*, pg. 4899
MINASOLVE SASU—See Minafin Sarl; *Int'l*, pg. 4899
MINAS SANTA MARIA DE MORIS, S.A. DE C.V.—See Hochschild Mining plc; *Int'l*, pg. 3438
MINATO ADVANCED TECHNOLOGIES INC.—See Minato Holdings Inc.; *Int'l*, pg. 4899
THE MINATO BANK, LTD.—See Resona Holdings, Inc.; *Int'l*, pg. 6297

MINDCHAMPS PRESCHOOL LIMITED

MINATO CAPITAL CO., LTD.—See Resona Holdings, Inc.; *Int'l*, pg. 6297
MINATO CARD CO., LTD.—See Resona Holdings, Inc.; *Int'l*, pg. 6297
MINATO DAIICHI TRAFFIC CO., LTD.—See Daiichi Koutsu Sangyo Co., Ltd.; *Int'l*, pg. 1928
MINATO FINANCIAL PARTNERS INC.—See Minato Holdings Inc.; *Int'l*, pg. 4899
MINATO HOLDINGS INC.; *Int'l*, pg. 4899
MINATO MIRAI 21 D.H.C. CO., LTD.—See Mitsubishi Estate Co., Ltd.; *Int'l*, pg. 4946
MINATSU, LTD.—See Koito Manufacturing Co., Ltd.; *Int'l*, pg. 4230
MINAT TEGUH SDN BHD—See IJM Corporation Berhad; *Int'l*, pg. 3609
MINAURUM GOLD INC.; *Int'l*, pg. 4899
MINAXI TEXTILES LIMITED; *Int'l*, pg. 4899
MINBOS RESOURCES LIMITED; *Int'l*, pg. 4899
MINCE MASTER—See 2M Tool Company, Inc.; *U.S. Private*, pg. 7
MINCO CAPITAL CORP.; *Int'l*, pg. 4899
MINCO EC AG—See Minco Products, Inc.; *U.S. Private*, pg. 2740
MINCO GMBH—See Minco Products, Inc.; *U.S. Private*, pg. 2740
THE MINCO GROUP; *U.S. Private*, pg. 4079
MINCO, INC.—See 3M Company; *U.S. Public*, pg. 8
MINCO LTD—See Minco Products, Inc.; *U.S. Private*, pg. 2740
MINCO MANUFACTURING, LLC; *U.S. Private*, pg. 2740
MINCO MINING (CHINA) CO. LTD—See Minco Capital Corp.; *Int'l*, pg. 4899
MINCON CARBIDE LTD.—See Mincon Group PLC; *Int'l*, pg. 4900
MINCON CHILE SA—See Mincon Group PLC; *Int'l*, pg. 4900
MINCON GROUP PLC; *Int'l*, pg. 4900
MINCON INTERNATIONAL LIMITED—See Mincon Group PLC; *Int'l*, pg. 4900
MINCON NAMIBIA PTY LTD—See Mincon Group PLC; *Int'l*, pg. 4900
MINCON SWEDEN AB—See Mincon Group PLC; *Int'l*, pg. 4900
MINCON WEST AFRICA SL—See Mincon Group PLC; *Int'l*, pg. 4900
MINCO PRODUCTS, INC.; *U.S. Private*, pg. 2740
MINCOR OPERATIONS PTY LIMITED—See Tattarang Pty. Ltd.; *Int'l*, pg. 7475
MINCOR RESOURCES NL—See Tattarang Pty. Ltd.; *Int'l*, pg. 7475
MINCO SA—See Minco Products, Inc.; *U.S. Private*, pg. 2740
MINCO SILVER CORPORATION; *Int'l*, pg. 4900
MINDA CORPORATION LIMITED; *Int'l*, pg. 4900
MINDA FINANCE LIMITED; *Int'l*, pg. 4900
MINDA INDUSTRIEANLAGEN GMBH; *Int'l*, pg. 4900
MINDA KTSN PLASTIC SOLUTIONS GMBH & CO. KG.—See Minda Corporation Limited; *Int'l*, pg. 4900
MINDA MANAGEMENT SERVICES LIMITED—See Minda Corporation Limited; *Int'l*, pg. 4900
MINDA NABTESCO AUTOMOTIVE PVT. LTD.—See Minda Finance Limited; *Int'l*, pg. 4900
MINDA NABTESCO AUTOMOTIVE PVT. LTD.—See Nabtesco Corporation; *Int'l*, pg. 5120
MINDANAO INTERNATIONAL CONTAINER TERMINAL SERVICES INC.—See International Container Terminal Services, Inc.; *Int'l*, pg. 3746
MINDA RINDER PRIVATE LIMITED—See Uno Minda Limited; *Int'l*, pg. 8084
MINDA SILCA ENGINEERING PVT. LTD.—See dormakaba Holding AG; *Int'l*, pg. 2177
MINDA STONERIDGE INSTRUMENTS LIMITED—See Stoneridge, Inc.; *U.S. Public*, pg. 1951
MINDA VIETNAM AUTOMOTIVE COMPANY LIMITED—See Minda Corporation Limited; *Int'l*, pg. 4900
MINDAX LIMITED; *Int'l*, pg. 4900
MINDBALANCED INC.—See nDatalyze Corp.; *Int'l*, pg. 5182
MINDBANK CONSULTING GROUP OF VIRGINIA, INC.; *U.S. Private*, pg. 2740
MINDBIO THERAPEUTICS CORP.; *Int'l*, pg. 4900
MINDBODY, INC.—See Vista Equity Partners, LLC; *U.S. Private*, pg. 4398
MINDBREEZE CORPORATION—See Fabasoft AG; *Int'l*, pg. 2598
MINDBREEZE GMBH—See Fabasoft AG; *Int'l*, pg. 2598
MIND CANDY LTD.; *Int'l*, pg. 4900
MINDCHAMPION LEARNING SYSTEMS LIMITED—See NIIT Limited; *Int'l*, pg. 5289
MINDCHAMPS AUSTRALIA CORPORATE PTY. LIMITED—See MindChamps PreSchool Limited; *Int'l*, pg. 4901
MINDCHAMPS PRESCHOOL BUANGKOK PRIVATE LIMITED—See MindChamps PreSchool Limited; *Int'l*, pg. 4901
MINDCHAMPS PRESCHOOL CHANGI BUSINESS PARK PTE. LTD.; *Int'l*, pg. 4901
MINDCHAMPS PRESCHOOL LIMITED; *Int'l*, pg. 4901

1783

MINDCHAMPS PRESCHOOL @ MARINA SQUARE PTE. LIMITED—See MindChamps PreSchool Limited; *Int'l*, pg. 4901
MINDCHAMPS PRESCHOOL PARAGON PTE. LIMITED—See MindChamps PreSchool Limited; *Int'l*, pg. 4901
MINDCHAMPS PRESCHOOL TPY PTE. LIMITED—See MindChamps PreSchool Limited; *Int'l*, pg. 4901
MINDCHAMPS PRESCHOOL WOODLANDS PTE. LTD.—See MindChamps PreSchool Limited; *Int'l*, pg. 4901
MINDCHAMPS PRESCHOOL ZHONGSHAN PARK PTE. LTD.—See MindChamps PreSchool Limited; *Int'l*, pg. 4901
MINDCOMET CORPORATION; *U.S. Private*, pg. 2740
MINDCOMET—See MindComet Corporation; *U.S. Private*, pg. 2740
MINDCOMET—See MindComet Corporation; *U.S. Private*, pg. 2740
MIND C.T.I. LTD.; *Int'l*, pg. 4900
MIND CURE HEALTH, INC.; *Int'l*, pg. 4900
MINDDISTRICT B.V.—See Asklepios Kliniken GmbH & Co. KGaA; *Int'l*, pg. 624
MINDDISTRICT GMBH—See Asklepios Kliniken GmbH & Co. KGaA; *Int'l*, pg. 624
MINDDISTRICT LTD.—See Asklepios Kliniken GmbH & Co. KGaA; *Int'l*, pg. 624
MINDEN PHYSICIAN PRACTICES, LLC—See Apollo Global Management, Inc.; *U.S. Public*, pg. 158
MINDFACTORY AG; *Int'l*, pg. 4901
MINDFIRE ENTERTAINMENT; *U.S. Private*, pg. 2740
MINDFLAIR PLC; *Int'l*, pg. 4901
MINDFLASH TECHNOLOGIES, INC.—See Ontario Teachers' Pension Plan; *Int'l*, pg. 5586
MINDFLOW DESIGN LLC—See Midwest Products & Engineering, Inc.; *U.S. Private*, pg. 2722
MIND GYM PLC; *Int'l*, pg. 4900
MIND GYM (USA) INC.—See Mind Gym plc; *Int'l*, pg. 4900
MINDLANCE, INC.; *U.S. Private*, pg. 2740
MINDLEAF TECHNOLOGIES, INC.; *U.S. Private*, pg. 2740
MIND MEDICINE (MINDMED) INC.; *Int'l*, pg. 4900
MIND-NRG SA—See Minerva Neurosciences, Inc.; *U.S. Public*, pg. 1449
MINDORO RESOURCES LTD.; *Int'l*, pg. 4901
MIND OVER MACHINES, INC.; *U.S. Private*, pg. 2740
MINDPATH CARE CENTERS PLLC; *U.S. Private*, pg. 2740
MINDPETAL SOFTWARE SOLUTIONS, INC.; *U.S. Private*, pg. 2741
MINDPOOL TECHNOLOGIES LTD.; *Int'l*, pg. 4901
MINDPOWER INC; *U.S. Private*, pg. 2741
MINDRAY - DISTRIBUTION AND COMMERCIALIZATION OF MEDICAL EQUIPMENT BRAZIL LTDA.—See Mindray Medical International Ltd.; *Int'l*, pg. 4901
MINDRAY DS USA, INC.—See Mindray Medical International Ltd.; *Int'l*, pg. 4901
MINDRAY MEDICAL CANADA LIMITED—See Mindray Medical International Ltd.; *Int'l*, pg. 4901
MINDRAY MEDICAL COLUMBIA SAS—See Mindray Medical International Ltd.; *Int'l*, pg. 4901
MINDRAY MEDICAL ESPANA S.L.—See Mindray Medical International Ltd.; *Int'l*, pg. 4901
MINDRAY MEDICAL FRANCE SARL—See Mindray Medical International Ltd.; *Int'l*, pg. 4901
MINDRAY MEDICAL GERMANY GMBH—See Mindray Medical International Ltd.; *Int'l*, pg. 4901
MINDRAY MEDICAL INDIA PRIVATE LIMITED—See Mindray Medical International Ltd.; *Int'l*, pg. 4901
MINDRAY MEDICAL INTERNATIONAL LTD.; *Int'l*, pg. 4901
MINDRAY MEDICAL MEXICO S DE R. L. DE C. V.—See Mindray Medical International Ltd.; *Int'l*, pg. 4901
MINDRAY MEDICAL NETHERLANDS B.V.—See Mindray Medical International Ltd.; *Int'l*, pg. 4901
MINDRAY MEDICAL RUS LIMITED—See Mindray Medical International Ltd.; *Int'l*, pg. 4901
MINDRAY MEDICAL SWEDEN AB—See Mindray Medical International Ltd.; *Int'l*, pg. 4901
MINDRAY MEDICAL TECHNOLOGY ISTANBUL LIMITED LIABILITY COMPANY—See Mindray Medical International Ltd.; *Int'l*, pg. 4901
MINDRAY MEDICAL THAILAND LIMITED—See Mindray Medical International Ltd.; *Int'l*, pg. 4901
MINDRAY MEDICAL USA CORP.—See Mindray Medical International Ltd.; *Int'l*, pg. 4901
MINDRAY (UK) LIMITED—See Mindray Medical International Ltd.; *Int'l*, pg. 4901
MIND RESEARCH INSTITUTE; *U.S. Private*, pg. 2740
MINDSCAPE INFORMATION TECHNOLOGY—See Mashreqbank P.S.C; *Int'l*, pg. 4721
MINDS CO., LTD.—See Crestec Inc.; *Int'l*, pg. 1841
MINDSEED CORPORATION; *U.S. Private*, pg. 2741
MINDSEEKER, INC.; *U.S. Private*, pg. 2741
MINDSET PHARMA INC.—See Otsuka Holdings Co., Ltd.; *Int'l*, pg. 5660
MINDSEYE SOLUTIONS LLC—See K1 Investment Management, LLC; *U.S. Private*, pg. 2252
MINDS-EYE-VIEW, INC.; *U.S. Private*, pg. 2741

MINDS FCB—See The Interpublic Group of Companies, Inc.; *U.S. Public*, pg. 2093
MINDSHARE GROUP LLC—See WPP plc; *Int'l*, pg. 8475
MINDSHARE—See WPP plc; *Int'l*, pg. 8475
MINDSHARE—See WPP plc; *Int'l*, pg. 8475
MINDSHARE—See WPP plc; *Int'l*, pg. 8475
MINDSHARE—See WPP plc; *Int'l*, pg. 8475
MINDSHARE—See WPP plc; *Int'l*, pg. 8475
MINDSHARE—See WPP plc; *Int'l*, pg. 8475
MINDSHARE—See WPP plc; *Int'l*, pg. 8475
MINDSHARE—See WPP plc; *Int'l*, pg. 8475
MINDSHARE—See WPP plc; *Int'l*, pg. 8475
MINDSHARE—See WPP plc; *Int'l*, pg. 8475
MINDSHARE—See WPP plc; *Int'l*, pg. 8476
MINDSHARE—See WPP plc; *Int'l*, pg. 8476
MINDSHARE—See WPP plc; *Int'l*, pg. 8476
MINDSHARE—See WPP plc; *Int'l*, pg. 8476
MINDSHARE—See WPP plc; *Int'l*, pg. 8476
MINDSHARE—See WPP plc; *Int'l*, pg. 8476
MINDSHARE—See WPP plc; *Int'l*, pg. 8476
MINDSHARE—See WPP plc; *Int'l*, pg. 8476
MINDSHARE—See WPP plc; *Int'l*, pg. 8476
MINDSHARE—See WPP plc; *Int'l*, pg. 8476
MINDSHARE—See WPP plc; *Int'l*, pg. 8476
MINDSHARE—See WPP plc; *Int'l*, pg. 8476
MINDSHARE—See WPP plc; *Int'l*, pg. 8476
MINDSHARE—See WPP plc; *Int'l*, pg. 8476
MINDSHARE—See WPP plc; *Int'l*, pg. 8477
MINDSHARE—See WPP plc; *Int'l*, pg. 8475
MINDSHARE—See WPP plc; *Int'l*, pg. 8475
MINDSHARE—See WPP plc; *Int'l*, pg. 8475
MINDSHARE—See WPP plc; *Int'l*, pg. 8475
MINDSHARE—See WPP plc; *Int'l*, pg. 8475
MINDSHARE—See WPP plc; *Int'l*, pg. 8475
MINDSHARE—See WPP plc; *Int'l*, pg. 8475
MINDSHARE—See WPP plc; *Int'l*, pg. 8476
MINDSHARE—See WPP plc; *Int'l*, pg. 8476
MINDSHARE—See WPP plc; *Int'l*, pg. 8476
MINDSHARE—See WPP plc; *Int'l*, pg. 8476
MINDSHARE—See WPP plc; *Int'l*, pg. 8476
MINDSHARE—See WPP plc; *Int'l*, pg. 8476
MINDSHARE—See WPP plc; *Int'l*, pg. 8476
MINDSHARE—See WPP plc; *Int'l*, pg. 8476
MINDSHARE—See WPP plc; *Int'l*, pg. 8476
MINDSHARE—See WPP plc; *Int'l*, pg. 8476
MINDSHARE—See WPP plc; *Int'l*, pg. 8476
MINDSHARE—See WPP plc; *Int'l*, pg. 8476
MINDSHARE—See WPP plc; *Int'l*, pg. 8476
MINDSHARE—See WPP plc; *Int'l*, pg. 8476
MINDSHARE—See WPP plc; *Int'l*, pg. 8476
MINDSHARE—See WPP plc; *Int'l*, pg. 8476
MINDSHARE—See WPP plc; *Int'l*, pg. 8476
MINDSHARE—See WPP plc; *Int'l*, pg. 8476
MINDSHARE—See WPP plc; *Int'l*, pg. 8476
MINDSHARE—See WPP plc; *Int'l*, pg. 8476
MINDSHARE—See WPP plc; *Int'l*, pg. 8476
MINDSHARE—See WPP plc; *Int'l*, pg. 8476
MINDSHARE—See WPP plc; *Int'l*, pg. 8476
MINDSHARE—See WPP plc; *Int'l*, pg. 8476
MINDSHARE—See WPP plc; *Int'l*, pg. 8476
MINDSHARE—See WPP plc; *Int'l*, pg. 8477
MINDSHARE—See WPP plc; *Int'l*, pg. 8477
MINDSHARE—See WPP plc; *Int'l*, pg. 8477
MINDSHARE—See WPP plc; *Int'l*, pg. 8477
MINDSHARE TEAM DETROIT—See WPP plc; *Int'l*, pg. 8477
MINDSHARE TECHNOLOGIES, INC.; *U.S. Private*, pg. 2741
MINDSHIFT TECHNOLOGIES, INC.—See Ricoh Company, Ltd.; *Int'l*, pg. 6336
MINDSHIFT TECHNOLOGIES - SOUTHWEST—See Ricoh Company, Ltd.; *Int'l*, pg. 6336
MINDS + MACHINES GROUP LIMITED; *Int'l*, pg. 4902
MINDS + MACHINES—See Minds + Machines Group Limited; *Int'l*, pg. 4902
MINDSMACK; *U.S. Private*, pg. 2741
MIND SOFTWARE SRL—See MIND C.T.I. Ltd.; *Int'l*, pg. 4900
MIND SOLUTIONS, INC.; *U.S. Public*, pg. 1448
MINDSPACE BUSINESS PARKS REIT; *Int'l*, pg. 4902
MINDSPACE SERVICES INC.—See Numinus Wellness Inc.; *Int'l*, pg. 5489
MINDSPACE; *U.S. Private*, pg. 2741
MINDSPARK INTERNATIONAL INC.; *U.S. Private*, pg. 2741
MINDSPEED TECHNOLOGIES, INC.—See MACOM Technology Solutions Holdings, Inc.; *U.S. Public*, pg. 1352
MINDSPEED TECHNOLOGIES INDIA PRIVATE LTD.—See MACOM Technology Solutions Holdings, Inc.; *U.S. Public*, pg. 1352
MINDSPEED TECHNOLOGIES (K.K.)—See MACOM Technology Solutions Holdings, Inc.; *U.S. Public*, pg. 1352

MINDSTORM COMMUNICATIONS GROUP, INC.; *U.S. Private*, pg. 2741
MINDSTREAM MEDIA, LLC—See Eastport Holdings, Inc.; *U.S. Private*, pg. 1322
MINDTECH EDUCATION SDN. BHD.—See Sasbadi Holdings Berhad; *Int'l*, pg. 6582
MIND TECHNOLOGY, INC.; *U.S. Public*, pg. 1448
MINDTECK INDIA LTD; *Int'l*, pg. 4902
MINDTECK NETHERLANDS B.V.—See Mindteck India Ltd; *Int'l*, pg. 4902
MINDTECK SINGAPORE PTE. LIMITED—See Mindteck India Ltd; *Int'l*, pg. 4902
MINDTECK SOFTWARE MALAYSIA SDN. BHD.—See Mindteck India Ltd; *Int'l*, pg. 4902
MINDTELL TECHNOLOGY LIMITED; *Int'l*, pg. 4902
MINDTOUCH, INC.—See NICE Ltd.; *Int'l*, pg. 5265
MINDTREE LTD.—See Larsen & Toubro Limited; *Int'l*, pg. 4419
MINDTREE LTD.—See Larsen & Toubro Limited; *Int'l*, pg. 4419
MINDTREE LTD.—See Larsen & Toubro Limited; *Int'l*, pg. 4419
MINDTREE LTD.—See Larsen & Toubro Limited; *Int'l*, pg. 4419
MINDTREE LTD.—See Larsen & Toubro Limited; *Int'l*, pg. 4419
MINDTREE LTD.—See Larsen & Toubro Limited; *Int'l*, pg. 4419
MINDTREE LTD.—See Larsen & Toubro Limited; *Int'l*, pg. 4419
MINDTREE LTD.—See Larsen & Toubro Limited; *Int'l*, pg. 4419
MINDTREE LTD.—See Larsen & Toubro Limited; *Int'l*, pg. 4419
MINDTREE LTD.—See Larsen & Toubro Limited; *Int'l*, pg. 4419
MINDTREE SOFTWARE CO., LTD.—See Larsen & Toubro Limited; *Int'l*, pg. 4419
MINDUS (M) SDN. BHD.—See Tracoma Holdings Berhad; *Int'l*, pg. 7887
MINDWARE, INC.—See Berkshire Hathaway Inc.; *U.S. Public*, pg. 313
MINDWAY APS—See Better Collective A/S; *Int'l*, pg. 1003
MINDWIRE SYSTEMS LIMITED—See Quess Corp Limited; *Int'l*, pg. 6160
MINDWISE INNOVATIONS—See Riverside Community Care, Inc.; *U.S. Private*, pg. 3445
MIND YOUR BUSINESS, INC.; *U.S. Private*, pg. 2740
MINE ARNAUD INC.—See Investissement Quebec; *Int'l*, pg. 3780
MINE ASSIST PTY LIMITED—See The Environmental Group Limited; *Int'l*, pg. 7640
MINEBEA ACCESS SOLUTIONS INC.—See Minebea Mitsumi Inc.; *Int'l*, pg. 4903
MINEBEA (CAMBODIA) CO., LTD.—See Minebea Mitsumi Inc.; *Int'l*, pg. 4903
MINEBEA CO., LTD. - BANG PA-IN PLANT—See Minebea Mitsumi Inc.; *Int'l*, pg. 4905
MINEBEA ELECTRONIC DEVICES (SUZHOU) LTD.—See Minebea Mitsumi Inc.; *Int'l*, pg. 4903
MINEBEA ELECTRONICS & HI-TECH COMPONENTS (SHANGHAI) LTD., - SHANGHAI PLANT—See Minebea Mitsumi Inc.; *Int'l*, pg. 4903
MINEBEA ELECTRONICS & HI-TECH COMPONENTS (SHANGHAI) LTD.—See Minebea Mitsumi Inc.; *Int'l*, pg. 4903
MINEBEA ELECTRONICS & HI-TECH COMPONENTS (SHANGHAI) LTD., - XICEN PLANT—See Minebea Mitsumi Inc.; *Int'l*, pg. 4903
MINEBEA ELECTRONICS MOTOR (MALAYSIA) SDN. BHD.—See Minebea Mitsumi Inc.; *Int'l*, pg. 4903
MINEBEA ELECTRONICS MOTOR (ZHUHAI) CO., LTD.—See Minebea Mitsumi Inc.; *Int'l*, pg. 4903
MINEBEA (HONG KONG) LTD.—See Minebea Mitsumi Inc.; *Int'l*, pg. 4903
MINEBEA INTEC AACHEN GMBH & CO. KG—See Minebea Mitsumi Inc.; *Int'l*, pg. 4903
MINEBEA INTEC AUSTRIA GMBH—See Minebea Mitsumi Inc.; *Int'l*, pg. 4903
MINEBEA INTEC BELGIUM BVBA—See Minebea Mitsumi Inc.; *Int'l*, pg. 4903
MINEBEA INTEC BOVENDEN GMBH & CO. KG—See Minebea Mitsumi Inc.; *Int'l*, pg. 4903
MINEBEA INTEC FRANCE S.A.S.—See Minebea Mitsumi Inc.; *Int'l*, pg. 4903
MINEBEA INTEC GMBH—See Minebea Mitsumi Inc.; *Int'l*, pg. 4903
MINEBEA INTEC INDIA PVT. LTD.—See Minebea Mitsumi Inc.; *Int'l*, pg. 4903
MINEBEA INTEC INDUSTRIAL WEIGHING EQUIPMENT (BEIJING) CO., LTD.—See Minebea Mitsumi Inc.; *Int'l*, pg. 4903
MINEBEA INTEC ITALY S.R.L.—See Minebea Mitsumi Inc.; *Int'l*, pg. 4903
MINEBEA INTEC NETHERLANDS B.V.—See Minebea Mitsumi Inc.; *Int'l*, pg. 4903

COMPANY NAME INDEX

MINEBEA INTEC POLAND SP. Z O.O.—See Minebea Mitsumi Inc.; *Int'l*, pg. 4903
MINEBEA INTEC RUSSIA—See Minebea Mitsumi Inc.; *Int'l*, pg. 4903
MINEBEA INTEC SPAIN S.L.—See Minebea Mitsumi Inc.; *Int'l*, pg. 4903
MINEBEA INTEC SWITZERLAND AG—See Minebea Mitsumi Inc.; *Int'l*, pg. 4903
MINEBEA INTEC UK LTD.—See Minebea Mitsumi Inc.; *Int'l*, pg. 4903
MINEBEA INTEC USA, INC.—See Minebea Mitsumi Inc.; *Int'l*, pg. 4903
MINEBEA MITSUMI INC. - FUJISAWA PLANT—See Minebea Mitsumi Inc.; *Int'l*, pg. 4903
MINEBEA MITSUMI INC.; *Int'l*, pg. 4902
MINEBEAMITSUMI TECHNICAL SERVICE (SUZHOU) LTD.—See Minebea Mitsumi Inc.; *Int'l*, pg. 4903
MINEBEAMITSUMI TECHNOLOGY CENTER EUROPE GMBH—See Minebea Mitsumi Inc.; *Int'l*, pg. 4903
MINEBEA POWER SEMICONDUCTOR DEVICE, INC—See Minebea Mitsumi Inc.; *Int'l*, pg. 4903
MINEBEA PRECISION CO., LTD.—See Minebea Mitsumi Inc.; *Int'l*, pg. 4903
MINEBEA (SHENZHEN) LTD.—See Minebea Mitsumi Inc.; *Int'l*, pg. 4903
MINEBEA SLOVAKIA S.R.O.—See Minebea Mitsumi Inc.; *Int'l*, pg. 4903
MINEBEA TECHNOLOGIES PTE. LTD.-HONG KONG BRANCH—See Minebea Mitsumi Inc.; *Int'l*, pg. 4904
MINEBEA TECHNOLOGIES TAIWAN CO., LTD.—See Minebea Mitsumi Inc.; *Int'l*, pg. 4903
MINEBEA TECHNOLOGIES TAIWAN CO., LTD. TAIPEI BRANCH—See Minebea Mitsumi Inc.; *Int'l*, pg. 4904
MINEBEA THAI LIMITED—See Minebea Mitsumi Inc.; *Int'l*, pg. 4903
MINEBEA TRADING (SHANGHAI) LTD.—See Minebea Mitsumi Inc.; *Int'l*, pg. 4903
MINEEX SA—See Societe Anonyme d'Explosifs et de Produits Chimiques; *Int'l*, pg. 7035
MINEHUB TECHNOLOGIES INC.; *Int'l*, pg. 4905
MINELAB AMERICAS INC.—See Codan Limited; *Int'l*, pg. 1688
MINELAB DE MEXICO SA DE CV—See Codan Limited; *Int'l*, pg. 1688
MINELAB ELECTRONICS PTY LTD—See Codan Limited; *Int'l*, pg. 1688
MINELAB INTERNATIONAL LTD—See Codan Limited; *Int'l*, pg. 1688
MINELCO AB—See Luossavaara-Kiirunavaara AB; *Int'l*, pg. 4585
MINELCO LTD.—See Luossavaara-Kiirunavaara AB; *Int'l*, pg. 4585
MINEL KONCERN A.D.; *Int'l*, pg. 4905
MINELLA CAPITAL MANAGEMENT LLC; *U.S. Private*, pg. 2741
MINELLI CONSTRUCTION CO., INC.; *U.S. Private*, pg. 2741
MINELL KFT.—See TUV Rheinland Berlin-Brandenburg Pfalz e.V.; *Int'l*, pg. 7982
MINEL RASTAVLJACI A.D.; *Int'l*, pg. 4906
MINEMAKERS AUSTRALIA PTY LTD—See Avenira Limited; *Int'l*, pg. 738
MINE MOBILITY CORPORATION CO., LTD.—See Energy Absolute Public Company Limited; *Int'l*, pg. 2422
MINEOLA COMMUNITY BANK SSB—See Texas Community Bancshares, Inc.; *U.S. Public*, pg. 2025
MINE & QUARRY SUPPLIES (PTY.) LTD.—See Sandvik AB; *Int'l*, pg. 6530
MINERA AGUA RICA LLC—See Pan American Silver Corp.; *Int'l*, pg. 5713
MINERA AGUILA DE ORO SAC—See Peruvian Metals Corp.; *Int'l*, pg. 5822
MINERA AGUILA PLATEADA S.A. DE C.V.—See IMPACT Silver Corp.; *Int'l*, pg. 3630
MINERA AGUILA S.L.U—See Pan Global Resources Inc.; *Int'l*, pg. 5714
MINERA ALAMOS DE SONORA S.A. DE C.V.—See Minera Alamos Inc.; *Int'l*, pg. 4906
MINERA ALAMOS INC.; *Int'l*, pg. 4906
MINERA ALTA VISTA S.A. DE C.V.—See Global UAV Technologies Ltd.; *Int'l*, pg. 3002
MINERA ALUMBRERA LIMITED—See Glencore plc; *Int'l*, pg. 2991
MINERA ANDES—See McEwen Mining Inc.; *Int'l*, pg. 4758
MINERA ANDINA DE EXPLORACIONES S.A.A.; *Int'l*, pg. 4906
MINERA ANTUCOYA SCM—See Antofagasta plc; *Int'l*, pg. 484
MINERA ARGENTA S.A.—See Pan American Silver Corp.; *Int'l*, pg. 5713
MINERA BARRICK MISQUICHILCA S.A.—See Barrick Gold Corporation; *Int'l*, pg. 869
MINERA BATEAS S.A.C.—See Fortuna Mining Corp.; *Int'l*, pg. 2743
MINERA CALIPUY S.A.C.—See Pan American Silver Corp.; *Int'l*, pg. 5713
MINERA CANASIL, S.A. DE C.V.—See Canasil Resources Inc.; *Int'l*, pg. 1288

MINERACAO BURITIRAMA SA; *Int'l*, pg. 4906
MINERACAO RIO DO NORTE S.A.; *Int'l*, pg. 4906
MINERACAO SERRAS DO OESTE LTDA.—See Jaguar Mining Inc.; *Int'l*, pg. 3870
MINERACAO VALE VERDE LTDA—See Northwestern Enterprises Ltd.; *Int'l*, pg. 5447
MINERA CERRO QUEMA S.A.—See Orla Mining Ltd.; *Int'l*, pg. 5639
MINERACOES BRASILEIRAS REUNIDAS S.A.—See Vale S.A.; *Int'l*, pg. 8111
MINERA CORNER BAY S.A. DE C.V.—See Pan American Silver Corp.; *Int'l*, pg. 5713
MINERA COSALA S.A. DE C.V.—See Americas Gold and Silver Corporation; *Int'l*, pg. 423
MINERA CUORO S.A.S.—See Eat Well Investment Group Inc.; *Int'l*, pg. 2277
MINERA DEL ALTIPLANO SA—See FMC Corporation; *U.S. Public*, pg. 862
MINERA DEL NORTE—See Grupo Acerero del Norte S.A. de C.V.; *Int'l*, pg. 3118
MINERA DELTA S.A. DE C.V.—See Golden Goliath Resources Ltd.; *Int'l*, pg. 3029
MINERA DE RIO ALAGON, S.L.—See Berkeley Energia Limited; *Int'l*, pg. 985
MINERA DYNACOR DEL PERU, S.A.C.—See Dynacor Group Inc.; *Int'l*, pg. 2239
MINERA EL PORVENIR DE ZACUALPAN S.A. DE C.V.—See IMPACT Silver Corp.; *Int'l*, pg. 3630
MINERA ESPERANZA LTDA.—See Antofagasta plc; *Int'l*, pg. 484
MINERA EVRIM S.A. DE C.V.—See Orogen Royalties Inc.; *Int'l*, pg. 5642
MINERA EXAR S. A.—See Jiangxi Ganfeng Lithium Co., Ltd.; *Int'l*, pg. 3959
MINERA EXAR S.A.—See Lithium Americas Corp.; *Int'l*, pg. 4526
MINERA FOCUS, S.A.C.—See Metallum Resources Inc.; *Int'l*, pg. 4848
MINERA FRESNILLO, S.A. DE C.V.—See Fresnillo PLC; *Int'l*, pg. 2782
MINERA FRISCO, S.A.B. DE C.V.; *Int'l*, pg. 4906
MINERA GOLD FIELDS PERU SA—See Gold Fields Limited; *Int'l*, pg. 3024
MINERA GRENVILLE S.A.C.—See Sierra Grande Minerals Inc.; *Int'l*, pg. 6904
MINERA HIERRO ATACAMA S.A.—See CAP S.A.; *Int'l*, pg. 1300
MINERA HOCHSCHILD MEXICO, S.A. DE C.V.—See Hochschild Mining plc; *Int'l*, pg. 3438
MINERA IRL LIMITED; *Int'l*, pg. 4906
MINERAIS U.S. LLC—See Assore Limited; *Int'l*, pg. 649
MINERA JULCANI S.A.DE C.V—See Compania de Minas Buenaventura SAA; *Int'l*, pg. 1748
MINERAL ABBAU GMBH—See STRABAG SE; *Int'l*, pg. 7231
MINERAL AND MECHANICAL JSC; *Int'l*, pg. 4906
MINERA LA ZANJA S.R.L.—See Compania de Minas Buenaventura SAA; *Int'l*, pg. 1748
MINERALBRUNNEN UBERKINGEN-TEINACH GMBH & CO.; *Int'l*, pg. 4907
MINERAL COMMODITIES LIMITED; *Int'l*, pg. 4906
MINERAL DAILY NEWS TRIBUNE, INC.—See Gannett Co., Inc.; *U.S. Public*, pg. 904
MINERAL DEPOSITS LIMITED—See Eramet SA; *Int'l*, pg. 2489
MINERALES EL PRADO S.A. DE C.V.—See Chesapeake Gold Corporation; *Int'l*, pg. 1472
MINERALES VANE S.A. DE C.V.—See Zephyr Energy Plc; *Int'l*, pg. 8636
MINERALES Y PRODUCTOS DERIVADOS, S. A.; *Int'l*, pg. 4907
MINERAL FEED, S.L.—See Huntsman Corporation; *U.S. Public*, pg. 1075
MINERAL & FINANCIAL INVESTMENTS LIMITED; *Int'l*, pg. 4906
MINERAL FUSION NATURAL BRANDS LLC—See BWX Limited; *Int'l*, pg. 1233
MINERAL GRINDING MILLS LIMITED; *Int'l*, pg. 4906
MINERAL HECLA, S.A. DE C.V.—See Hecla Mining Company; *U.S. Public*, pg. 1019
MINERAL HILL INDUSTRIES LTD.; *Int'l*, pg. 4906
MINERAL IGM D.O.O.—See STRABAG SE; *Int'l*, pg. 7231
MINERALI INDUSTIALI TUNISIA SA—See Gruppo Minerali Maffei S.p.A.; *Int'l*, pg. 3140
MINERALI INDUSTRIALI EOOD, BULGARIA.—See Gruppo Minerali Maffei S.p.A.; *Int'l*, pg. 3140
MINERALI INDUSTRIALI S.P.A.—See Gruppo Minerali Maffei S.p.A.; *Int'l*, pg. 3140
MINERALLAC CO.; *U.S. Private*, pg. 2741
MINERALMAHLWERK C. WELSCH GMBH—See L. Possehl & Co. mbH; *Int'l*, pg. 4384
MINERAL MIDRANGE S.A; *Int'l*, pg. 4906
MINERAL MOUNTAIN RESOURCES LTD.; *Int'l*, pg. 4906
MINERALOGY PTY. LTD.; *Int'l*, pg. 4907
MINERALOLVERTRIEB BRAKEL GMBH & CO. KG—See Marquard & Bahls AG; *Int'l*, pg. 4699
MINERA LOMA DE NIQUEL, CA—See Anglo American PLC; *Int'l*, pg. 462

MINERA LOS LAGARTOS, S.A. DE C.V.—See MAG Silver Corp.; *Int'l*, pg. 4636
MINERA LOS PELAMBRES LTDA.—See Antofagasta plc; *Int'l*, pg. 484
MINERA LOS PELAMBRES SCM—See Antofagasta plc; *Int'l*, pg. 484
MINERALPLUS GMBH—See Asterion Industrial Partners SGEIC SA; *Int'l*, pg. 654
MINERAL POLSKA SP. Z O.O.—See STRABAG SE; *Int'l*, pg. 7231
MINERAL PROCESSING COMPANY—See The Andersons Incorporated; *U.S. Public*, pg. 2034
MINERAL RESEARCH & DEVELOPMENT—See Huntsman Corporation; *U.S. Public*, pg. 1073
MINERAL RESOURCES DE GUATEMALA S.A.—See Gruppo Minerali Maffei S.p.A.; *Int'l*, pg. 3140
MINERAL RESOURCES LIMITED; *Int'l*, pg. 4906
MINERAL-RIGHT INC—See A. O. Smith Corporation; *U.S. Public*, pg. 12
MINERAL ROM SRL—See STRABAG SE; *Int'l*, pg. 7231
MINERALS 260 LIMITED; *Int'l*, pg. 4907
MINERALS AND METALS RECOVERING - MIRECO AKTIEBOLAG—See RHI Magnesita N.V.; *Int'l*, pg. 6325
MINERAL SAN SEBASTIAN, S.A. DE C.V.—See Commerce Group Corp.; *U.S. Public*, pg. 545
MINERALS GANZHOU RARE EARTH CO., LTD—See China Rare Earth Resources And Technology Co., Ltd.; *Int'l*, pg. 1546
MINERAL SPRINGS CENTER—See Formation Capital, LLC; *U.S. Private*, pg. 1571
MINERALS TECHNOLOGIES EUROPE N.V.—See Minerals Technologies, Inc.; *U.S. Public*, pg. 1449
MINERALS TECHNOLOGIES HOLDINGS LTD.—See Minerals Technologies, Inc.; *U.S. Public*, pg. 1449
MINERALS TECHNOLOGIES, INC.; *U.S. Public*, pg. 1448
MINERALS TECHNOLOGIES INDIA PRIVATE LIMITED—See Minerals Technologies, Inc.; *U.S. Public*, pg. 1449
MINERALTECH GULF COAST ABRASIVES, LLC; *U.S. Private*, pg. 2741
MINERAL TECHNOLOGIES, INC.—See Downer EDI Limited; *Int'l*, pg. 2186
MINERAL TECHNOLOGIES PTY. LTD.—See Downer EDI Limited; *Int'l*, pg. 2186
MINERAL WELLS INDEX INC.—See The Retirement Systems of Alabama; *U.S. Private*, pg. 4105
MINERALYS THERAPEUTICS, INC.; *U.S. Public*, pg. 1449
MINERALZ B.V.—See Renewi plc; *Int'l*, pg. 6278
MINERALZ ES TREATMENT N.V.—See Renewi plc; *Int'l*, pg. 6278
MINERALZ MAASVLAKTE B.V.—See Renewi plc; *Int'l*, pg. 6278
MINERALZ ZWEEKHORST B.V.—See Renewi plc; *Int'l*, pg. 6278
MINERA MAJAZ SA—See Zijin Mining Group Company Limited; *Int'l*, pg. 8683
MINERA MARIANA ARGENTINA S.A.—See Capella Minerals Limited; *Int'l*, pg. 1303
MINERA MEXICO S.A. DE C.V.—See Grupo Mexico, S.A.B. de C.V.; *Int'l*, pg. 3133
MINERA MH CHILE LTDA.—See Hochschild Mining plc; *Int'l*, pg. 3438
MINERA MINASNIOC S.A.C.—See Hochschild Mining plc; *Int'l*, pg. 3438
MINERA MIRASOL CHILE LIMITADA—See Mirasol Resources Ltd.; *Int'l*, pg. 4918
MINERA NUEVA VICTORIA S.A.—See Sociedad Quimica y Minera de Chile S.A.; *Int'l*, pg. 7032
MINERA PANAMA S.A.—See First Quantum Minerals Ltd.; *Int'l*, pg. 2687
MINERA PENASQUITO S.A. DE C.V.—See Newmont Corporation; *U.S. Public*, pg. 1516
MINERA PENDER S.A DE C.V.—See Garibaldi Resources Corp.; *Int'l*, pg. 2884
MINERA PIEDRA AZUL, S.A. DE C.V.—See Hancock Prospecting Pty. Ltd.; *Int'l*, pg. 3242
MINERA PIEDRA AZUL, S.A. DE C.V.—See Sociedad Quimica y Minera de Chile S.A.; *Int'l*, pg. 7032
MINERA PLATTE RIVER GOLD S.A. DE RL DE C.V.—See Americas Gold and Silver Corporation; *Int'l*, pg. 423
MINERA QUELLAVECO S.A.—See Anglo American PLC; *Int'l*, pg. 462
MINERA REAL DE ANGELES, S.A. DE C.V.—See Minera Frisco, S.A.B. de C.V.; *Int'l*, pg. 4906
MINERA ROCA RODANDO S. DE R.L. DE C.V.—See RCF Management LLC; *U.S. Private*, pg. 3362
MINERA SAN CRISTOBAL S.A.—See San Cristobal Mining Inc.; *Int'l*, pg. 6520
MINERA SAN FRANCISCO DEL ORO, S.A. DE C.V.—See Minera Frisco, S.A.B. de C.V.; *Int'l*, pg. 4906
MINERA SANTA CRUZ S.A.—See Hochschild Mining plc; *Int'l*, pg. 3438
MINERA SANTA CRUZ Y GARIBALDI SA DE CV—See Endeavour Silver Corp.; *Int'l*, pg. 2403
MINERA SANTA RITA, S. DE R.L. DE C.V.—See Alamos Gold Inc.; *Int'l*, pg. 290

MINERALYS THERAPEUTICS, INC.   CORPORATE AFFILIATIONS

MINERAS HEMISFERIO SUR S.C.M.—See Southern Hemisphere Mining Limited; *Int'l*, pg. 7119
MINERA SOLITARIO PERU, S.A.—See Solitario Zinc Corp.; *U.S. Public*, pg. 1901
MINERA SUD ARGENTINA S.A.—See South32 Limited; *Int'l*, pg. 7117
MINERA TARTISAN PERU S.A.C.—See Tartisan Nickel Corp.; *Int'l*, pg. 7464
MINERA TAYAHUA, S.A. DE C.V.—See Minera Frisco, S.A.B. de C.V.; *Int'l*, pg. 4906
MINERA TERRANOVA S.A. DE C.V.—See Jervois Global Limited; *Int'l*, pg. 3932
MINERA TERRANOVA, S.A. DE C.V.—See Sunshine Silver Mines Corporation; *U.S. Private*, pg. 3872
MINERA TIZAPA, S.A. DE C.V.—See Dowa Holdings Co., Ltd.; *Int'l*, pg. 2184
MINERA TRITON ARGENTINA S.A.—See Pan American Silver Corp.; *Int'l*, pg. 5713
MINERA UAB—See Siauliu bankas AB; *Int'l*, pg. 6876
MINERA VALLE CENTRAL S.A.—See Amerigo Resources Ltd.; *Int'l*, pg. 423
MINERA VALPARAISO S.A.; *Int'l*, pg. 4906
MINER CENTRAL TEXAS—See On-Point Group, LLC; *U.S. Private*, pg. 3019
MINERCONSULT ENGENHARIA LTDA.—See AtkinsRealis Group Inc.; *Int'l*, pg. 672
THE MINER CORPORATION—See On-Point Group, LLC; *U.S. Private*, pg. 3018
MINER DALLAS—See On-Point Group, LLC; *U.S. Private*, pg. 3019
THE MINER-DEDERICK COMPANIES INC.; *U.S. Private*, pg. 4079
MINER ELASTOMER PRODUCTS CORP.—See Miner Enterprises, Inc.; *U.S. Private*, pg. 2741
MINER EL PASO—See On-Point Group, LLC; *U.S. Private*, pg. 3019
MINER ENTERPRISES, INC.; *U.S. Private*, pg. 2741
MINER FLEET MANAGEMENT GROUP—See On-Point Group, LLC; *U.S. Private*, pg. 3019
MINER HOUSTON—See On-Point Group, LLC; *U.S. Private*, pg. 3019
MINEROS SA; *Int'l*, pg. 4907
MINERP CANADA LIMITED—See Epiroc AB; *Int'l*, pg. 2463
MINERP—See FirstRand Limited; *Int'l*, pg. 2690
MINERP—See Hasso Plattner Ventures Africa (Pty) Ltd.; *Int'l*, pg. 3283
MINERP—See Shalamuka Capital (Pty) Ltd.; *Int'l*, pg. 6750
MINERS AND MERCHANTS BANCORP, INC.; *U.S. Private*, pg. 2742
MINERS CONSTRUCTION CO.LTD.; *Int'l*, pg. 4907
MINER'S INCORPORATED; *U.S. Private*, pg. 2741
MINER SOUTHWEST, LLC—See On-Point Group, LLC; *U.S. Private*, pg. 3019
MINERVA ASSOCIATES, INC.—See Connell Limited Partnership; *U.S. Private*, pg. 1017
MINERVA BUNKERING PTE. LTD.; *Int'l*, pg. 4908
MINERVA BUNKERING; *Int'l*, pg. 4907
MINERVA DATA LIMITED—See Waltech plc; *Int'l*, pg. 8336
MINERVA FUNDS MANAGEMENT LIMITED—See Liberty Financial Group Limited; *Int'l*, pg. 4484
MINERVAGRANDIR CO., LTD.; *Int'l*, pg. 4908
MINERVA GROUP HOLDING LIMITED; *Int'l*, pg. 4908
MINERVA INSURANCE COMPANY PUBLIC LTD.; *Int'l*, pg. 4908
MINERVA INTELLIGENCE INC.; *Int'l*, pg. 4908
MINERVA KNITWEAR S.A.; *Int'l*, pg. 4908
MINERVA LTD.—See Delancey Real Estate Asset Management Ltd.; *Int'l*, pg. 2010
MINERVA NEUROSCIENCES, INC.; *U.S. Public*, pg. 1449
MINERVA S.A. EDIBLE OILS & FOOD ENTERPRISES—See DECA Investments AIFM; *Int'l*, pg. 1999
MINERVA S.A.—See Compagnie Financiere Richemont S.A.; *Int'l*, pg. 1741
MINERVA S.A.—See FIERATEX S.A.; *Int'l*, pg. 2660
MINE SAFETY APPLIANCES COMPANY-INSTRUMENT DIVISION—See MSA Safety Incorporated; *U.S. Public*, pg. 1482
MINE SAFETY APPLIANCES COMPANY, LLC—See MSA Safety Incorporated; *U.S. Public*, pg. 1482
MINE SAFETY APPLIANCES COMPANY-SAFETY PRODUCTS DIVISION—See MSA Safety Incorporated; *U.S. Public*, pg. 1482
MINE SAFETY APPLIANCES COMPANY-SAFETY PRODUCTS DIVISION—See MSA Safety Incorporated; *U.S. Public*, pg. 1482
MINE SERVICE COMPANY INC.; *U.S. Private*, pg. 2741
MINE SERVICE INC.; *U.S. Private*, pg. 2741
MINESTO AB; *Int'l*, pg. 4908
MINESTO UK LTD.—See Minesto AB; *Int'l*, pg. 4908
MINE SUPPLY COMPANY INC.; *U.S. Private*, pg. 2741
MINET BOTSWANA—See Aon plc; *Int'l*, pg. 495
MINETECH KOREA PETROLEUM INDUSTRIAL SDN. BHD.—See Minetech Resources Berhad; *Int'l*, pg. 4908
MINETECH RESOURCES BERHAD; *Int'l*, pg. 4908
MINETEC PTY LTD.—See Codan Limited; *Int'l*, pg. 1688
MINET INC.—See Aon plc; *Int'l*, pg. 495

MINETTA LIVE, LLC—See Reading International, Inc.; *U.S. Public*, pg. 1768
MINERACAO RIO DO NORTE—See (?)
MINEWARE PTY LTD—See Komatsu Ltd.; *Int'l*, pg. 4238
MINEXFOR SA; *Int'l*, pg. 4908
MINEX ROMANIA SRL—See Munters AB; *Int'l*, pg. 5093
MINFENG SPECIAL PAPER CO., LTD.; *Int'l*, pg. 4908
MIN FU INTERNATIONAL HOLDING LIMITED; *Int'l*, pg. 4898
MINGARI BV—See Zublin Immobilien Holding AG; *Int'l*, pg. 8692
MING CHENG INTEGRATION TECHNOLOGY CO., LTD.—See ViTrox Corporation Berhad; *Int'l*, pg. 8262
MINGCHEN HEALTH CO., LTD.; *Int'l*, pg. 4909
MING CORPORATION; *U.S. Private*, pg. 2742
MING COURT HOTEL (VANCOUVER) LTD—See Malayan United Industries Berhad; *Int'l*, pg. 4661
MING D.O.O.; *Int'l*, pg. 4908
MINGFA GROUP COMPANY LIMITED—See Mingfa Group (International) Company Limited; *Int'l*, pg. 4909
MINGFA GROUP (INTERNATIONAL) COMPANY LIMITED; *Int'l*, pg. 4909
MINGFA GROUP NANJING REAL ESTATE CO., LTD.—See Mingfa Group (International) Company Limited; *Int'l*, pg. 4909
MING FAI ASIA PACIFIC COMPANY LIMITED—See Ming Fai International Holdings Limited; *Int'l*, pg. 4908
MING FAI ENTERPRISE INTERNATIONAL COMPANY LIMITED—See Ming Fai International Holdings Limited; *Int'l*, pg. 4908
MING FAI INDUSTRIAL (SHENZHEN) COMPANY LIMITED—See Ming Fai International Holdings Limited; *Int'l*, pg. 4908
MING FAI INTERNATIONAL HOLDINGS LIMITED; *Int'l*, pg. 4908
MING FONG PLASTIC (DONG GUAN) CO., LTD.—See Cheng Loong Corp.; *Int'l*, pg. 1466
MING FUNG CONTAINER LIMITED—See Eng Kong Holdings Pte Ltd.; *Int'l*, pg. 2426
MING HING WATERWORKS ENGINEERING (RRC) LIMITED—See China Water Affairs Group Ltd; *Int'l*, pg. 1563
MING HOP COMPANY LIMITED—See Yau Lee Holdings Limited; *Int'l*, pg. 8571
MINGHUA DE MEXICO S.A. DE C.V.—See Jiangnan Mould & Plastic Technology Co., Ltd.; *Int'l*, pg. 3942
MINGHUA USA, INC.—See Jiangnan Mould & Plastic Technology Co., Ltd.; *Int'l*, pg. 3943
MING KOVACNICA AD—See MING d.o.o.; *Int'l*, pg. 4908
MINGLEDORFF'S INC.; *U.S. Private*, pg. 2742
MINGLE, LLC; *U.S. Private*, pg. 2742
MING LE SPORTS AG; *Int'l*, pg. 4908
MINGOS COFFEE D.O.O.—See Studen & Co. Holding GmbH; *Int'l*, pg. 7244
MINGOT S.R.L.—See KONE Oyj; *Int'l*, pg. 4250
MINGPAO.COM LIMITED—See Media Chinese International Limited; *Int'l*, pg. 4770
MING PAO EDUCATION PUBLICATIONS LIMITED—See Media Chinese International Limited; *Int'l*, pg. 4770
MING PAO HOLDINGS (CANADA) LIMITED—See Media Chinese International Limited; *Int'l*, pg. 4770
MING PAO HOLDINGS LIMITED—See Media Chinese International Limited; *Int'l*, pg. 4770
MING PAO INVESTMENT (USA) L.P.—See Media Chinese International Limited; *Int'l*, pg. 4770
MING PAO MAGAZINES LIMITED—See Media Chinese International Limited; *Int'l*, pg. 4770
MING PAO NEWSPAPERS (CANADA) LIMITED—See Media Chinese International Limited; *Int'l*, pg. 4770
MING PAO NEWSPAPERS LIMITED—See Media Chinese International Limited; *Int'l*, pg. 4770
MING PAO PUBLICATIONS LIMITED—See Media Chinese International Limited; *Int'l*, pg. 4770
MINGSHENG (XIAMEN) INVESTMENT & MANAGEMENT CO., LTD.—See Mingfa Group (International) Company Limited; *Int'l*, pg. 4909
MINGS SUPERMARKET INC.; *U.S. Private*, pg. 2742
MING SUN ENTERPRISES (CHINA) LIMITED—See Cosmos Machinery Enterprises Limited; *Int'l*, pg. 1813
MING SURVEYORS, INC.—See Hoffman Corporation; *U.S. Private*, pg. 1960
MING TAI CONSTRUCTION ENGINEERING COMPANY LIMITED—See Royal Deluxe Holdings Limited; *Int'l*, pg. 6412
MINGTENG INTERNATIONAL CORPORATION INC.; *Int'l*, pg. 4909
MINGUS CONSTRUCTORS INCORPORATED; *U.S. Private*, pg. 2742
MING WIN ELECTRONICS LIMITED—See IDT International Limited; *Int'l*, pg. 3596
MINGXIN AUTOMOTIVE LEATHER CO., LTD.; *Int'l*, pg. 4909
MING YANG SMART ENERGY GROUP LIMITED; *Int'l*, pg. 4909
MINGYANG SMART ENERGY GROUP LTD.; *Int'l*, pg. 4909
MING YUAN CLOUD GROUP HOLDINGS LIMITED; *Int'l*, pg. 4909
MINGYUAN MEDICARE DEVELOPMENT COMPANY LIMITED; *Int'l*, pg. 4909

MINGYUE OPTICAL LENS CO., LTD.; *Int'l*, pg. 4909
MINGZHI TECHNOLOGY LEIPZIG GMBH—See Suzhou Mingzhi Technology Co., Ltd.; *Int'l*, pg. 7351
MINGZHU LOGISTICS HOLDINGS LIMITED; *Int'l*, pg. 4909
MIN HAGOREN DEVELOPMENT LTD.—See SolarEdge Technologies, Inc.; *Int'l*, pg. 7069
MINH HUU LIEN JSC; *Int'l*, pg. 4909
MINHO (M) BERHAD; *Int'l*, pg. 4909
MINH PHAT SEAFOOD PROCESSING CO., LTD.—See Minh Phu Seafood Joint Stock Company; *Int'l*, pg. 4909
MINH PHONG TRANSPORTATION JOINT STOCK COMPANY; *Int'l*, pg. 4909
MINH PHU BIOLOGICAL PRODUCTS PROCESSING CO., LTD.—See Minh Phu Seafood Joint Stock Company; *Int'l*, pg. 4909
MINH PHU KIEN GIANG SEAFOOD CO., LTD.—See Minh Phu Seafood Joint Stock Company; *Int'l*, pg. 4909
MINH PHU SEAFOOD JOINT STOCK COMPANY; *Int'l*, pg. 4909
MINH QUI SEAFOOD PROCESSING CO., LTD.—See Minh Phu Seafood Joint Stock Company; *Int'l*, pg. 4909
MINH THANH CONTAINER COMPANY LIMITED—See TCO Holdings Joint Stock Company; *Int'l*, pg. 7485
MINIATURE PRECISION COMPONENTS, INC.—See Equistone Partners Europe Limited; *Int'l*, pg. 2487
THE MINIBUS & COACH CLUB LIMITED—See QBE Insurance Group Limited; *Int'l*, pg. 6138
MINI-CAM LIMITED—See Halma plc; *Int'l*, pg. 3232
MINI CENTER OF SAN ANTONIO; *U.S. Private*, pg. 2742
MINICENTRALES DEL TAJO, S.A.—See Iberdrola, S.A.; *Int'l*, pg. 3573
MINICHAMP B.V.—See Red Light Holland Corp.; *Int'l*, pg. 6244
MINICUT INTERNATIONAL. INC.—See YG-1 Co., Ltd; *Int'l*, pg. 8579
MINI DIAMONDS (INDIA) LIMITED; *Int'l*, pg. 4910
MINI GEARS (STOCKPORT) LTD; *Int'l*, pg. 4910
MINI GEORGIAN—See Georgian International Limited; *Int'l*, pg. 2939
MINI-GOLF, INC.; *U.S. Private*, pg. 2742
MINIGRIP, LLC—See Illinois Tool Works Inc.; *U.S. Public*, pg. 1109
MINIGRIP/ZIP-PAK—See Illinois Tool Works Inc.; *U.S. Public*, pg. 1109
MINILEC SERVICE INCORPORATED; *U.S. Private*, pg. 2742
MINILOGIC DEVICE CORPORATION LIMITED—See New Western Group Limited; *Int'l*, pg. 5231
MINILUXE HOLDING CORP.; *U.S. Public*, pg. 1449
MINILUXE, INC.—See MiniLuxe Holding Corp.; *U.S. Public*, pg. 1449
MINIMALLY INVASIVE SURGERY CENTER OF NE, LLC—See Tenet Healthcare Corporation; *U.S. Public*, pg. 2004
MINIMALLY INVASIVE SURGICENTER LLC—See Tenet Healthcare Corporation; *U.S. Public*, pg. 2004
MINIMALLY INVASIVE SURGICENTER OF DELRAY, LLC—See Tenet Healthcare Corporation; *U.S. Public*, pg. 2004
MINI MART, INC.—See The Kroger Co.; *U.S. Public*, pg. 2108
MINI MART, INC.—See TDR Capital LLP; *Int'l*, pg. 7494
MINI MART, INC. - WYOMING—See TDR Capital LLP; *Int'l*, pg. 7494
MINIMAX GMBH & CO. KG—See Intermediate Capital Group plc; *Int'l*, pg. 3742
MINIMAX GMBH & CO. KG—See Kirkbi A/S; *Int'l*, pg. 4190
MINIMAX IMPLANT PTY LTD—See Dentium Co., Ltd; *Int'l*, pg. 2034
MINIMAX VIKING GMBH—See Intermediate Capital Group plc; *Int'l*, pg. 3742
MINIMAX VIKING GMBH—See Kirkbi A/S; *Int'l*, pg. 4190
MINI MEALS LIMITED—See Restaurant Brands International Inc.; *Int'l*, pg. 6304
MINJ MEDIA SWEDEN AB—See Schibsted ASA; *Int'l*, pg. 6617
MINIMEL A.D.; *Int'l*, pg. 4910
MINI MELTS INC.; *U.S. Private*, pg. 2742
MINIM, INC.; *U.S. Public*, pg. 1449
MINING CONTROLS, LLC—See Brookfield Corporation; *Int'l*, pg. 1181
MINING DEVELOPMENT CORPORATION N.V.—See Rudisa Holdingmaatschappij N.V.; *Int'l*, pg. 6424
MINING EQUIPMENT SUB-CO.—See Taiyuan Heavy Industry Co., Ltd.; *Int'l*, pg. 7427
MINING GREEN METALS LIMITED; *Int'l*, pg. 4910
MINING INFORMATION SYSTEMS, INC.—See Trimble, Inc.; *U.S. Public*, pg. 2190
MINING INVESTMENTS JERSEY LTD—See Barrick Gold Corporation; *Int'l*, pg. 869
MINING MACHINERY INC.; *U.S. Private*, pg. 2742
MINING REMEDIAL RECOVERY COMPANY—See Mueller Industries, Inc.; *U.S. Public*, pg. 1484
MINING, ROCK EXCAVATION & CONSTRUCTION LLC—See Atlas Copco AB; *Int'l*, pg. 681
MINING SERVICES LIMITED—See Harworth Group plc; *Int'l*, pg. 3282

COMPANY NAME INDEX

MINING TAG S.A.—See Epiroc AB; *Int'l*, pg. 2463
MINI-PAC INC.—See Decurion Corp.; *U.S. Private*, pg. 1188
MINISCALCO CONSTRUCTION, L.L.C.—See Haines & Kibblehouse Inc.; *U.S. Private*, pg. 1841
MINISO GROUP HOLDING LIMITED; *Int'l*, pg. 4910
MINISTER DONUT TAIWAN CO., LTD.—See Duskin Co., Ltd.; *Int'l*, pg. 2234
MINISTOP CO., LTD.—See AEON Co., Ltd.; *Int'l*, pg. 178
MINISTOP VIETNAM COMPANY LIMITED—See Sojitz Corporation; *Int'l*, pg. 7062
MINISTRY OF CAKE LTD—See Mademoiselle Desserts Corby Ltd.; *Int'l*, pg. 4633
MINI-SYSTEMS, INC. - ELECTRONIC PACKAGE DIVISION—See Mini-Systems, Inc.; *U.S. Private*, pg. 2742
MINI-SYSTEMS, INC.; *U.S. Private*, pg. 2742
MINIT ASIA PACIFIC CO., LTD.—See AOYAMA TRADING Co. Ltd.; *Int'l*, pg. 498
MINIT AUSTRALIA PTY LIMITED—See AOYAMA TRADING Co. Ltd.; *Int'l*, pg. 498
MINITEL - SOCIEDADE DE FOMENTO DE APLICACOES INFORMATICAS, L.DA.; *Int'l*, pg. 4910
MINIT STOP; *U.S. Private*, pg. 2742
MINJARD S.A.S.—See Vivescia; *Int'l*, pg. 8279
MINKABU THE INFONOID, INC.; *Int'l*, pg. 4910
MINKABU WEB3 WALLET, INC.—See Minkabu The Infonoid, Inc.; *Int'l*, pg. 4910
MINKA LIGHTING INC.; *U.S. Private*, pg. 2742
MINKOFF COMPANY INC.; *U.S. Private*, pg. 2742
MINK THERAPEUTICS, INC.; *U.S. Public*, pg. 1449
MIN MAW PRECISION INDUSTRY CORP.—See Walsin Lihwa Corporation; *Int'l*, pg. 8335
MINMETALS AUSTRALIA PTY. LTD.—See China Rare Earth Resources And Technology Co., Ltd.; *Int'l*, pg. 1546
MINMETALS CAPITAL CO., LTD.—See China Rare Earth Resources And Technology Co., Ltd.; *Int'l*, pg. 1546
MINMETALS CAPITALS & SECURITIES, INC.—See China Rare Earth Resources And Technology Co., Ltd.; *Int'l*, pg. 1546
MINMETALS DEVELOPMENT CO., LTD.—See China Rare Earth Resources And Technology Co., Ltd.; *Int'l*, pg. 1546
MINMETALS ENGINEERING CO. LTD.—See China Rare Earth Resources And Technology Co., Ltd.; *Int'l*, pg. 1546
MINMETALS ENVIRONMENTAL TECHNOLOGY CO., LTD—See China Rare Earth Resources And Technology Co., Ltd.; *Int'l*, pg. 1546
MINMETALS FINANCE COMPANY—See China Rare Earth Resources And Technology Co., Ltd.; *Int'l*, pg. 1546
MINMETALS GERMANY GMBH—See China Rare Earth Resources And Technology Co., Ltd.; *Int'l*, pg. 1546
MINMETALS (GUIZHOU) FERRO-ALLOYS CO. LTD.—See China Rare Earth Resources And Technology Co., Ltd.; *Int'l*, pg. 1546
MINMETALS (HUNAN) FERROALLOYS CO. LTD.—See China Rare Earth Resources And Technology Co., Ltd.; *Int'l*, pg. 1546
MINMETALS, INC. (L.A.)—See China Rare Earth Resources And Technology Co., Ltd.; *Int'l*, pg. 1546
MINMETALS, INC.—See China Rare Earth Resources And Technology Co., Ltd.; *Int'l*, pg. 1546
MINMETALS INTERNATIONAL TENDERING CO., LTD.—See China Rare Earth Resources And Technology Co., Ltd.; *Int'l*, pg. 1546
MINMETALS JAPAN CORPORATION—See China Rare Earth Resources And Technology Co., Ltd.; *Int'l*, pg. 1546
MINMETALS KOREA CO., LTD.—See China Rare Earth Resources And Technology Co., Ltd.; *Int'l*, pg. 1546
MINMETALS LAND LIMITED—See China Rare Earth Resources And Technology Co., Ltd.; *Int'l*, pg. 1546
MINMETALS MATERIALS (CHANGSHU) MANAGEMENT CO., LTD.—See China Rare Earth Resources And Technology Co., Ltd.; *Int'l*, pg. 1546
MINMETALS NANJING INTERNATIONAL TRADING CO., LTD.—See China Rare Earth Resources And Technology Co., Ltd.; *Int'l*, pg. 1546
MINMETALS NORTH EUROPE AB—See China Rare Earth Resources And Technology Co., Ltd.; *Int'l*, pg. 1546
MINMETALS REAL ESTATE COMPANY—See China Rare Earth Resources And Technology Co., Ltd.; *Int'l*, pg. 1546
MINMETAL S.R.L.—See Archer-Daniels-Midland Company; *U.S. Public*, pg. 185
MINMETALS R.S.A. (PTY) LTD.—See China Rare Earth Resources And Technology Co., Ltd.; *Int'l*, pg. 1546
MINMETALS SANTOKU (GANZHOU) RARE EARTH MATERIAL CO., LTD.—See Hitachi, Ltd.; *Int'l*, pg. 3423
MINMETALS SECURITIES BROKERAGE CO. LTD.—See China Rare Earth Resources And Technology Co., Ltd.; *Int'l*, pg. 1546
MINMETALS SHIPPING (SINGAPORE) PTE. LTD.—See China Rare Earth Resources And Technology Co., Ltd.; *Int'l*, pg. 1546

MINMETALS SOUTH-EAST ASIA CORPORATION PTE. LTD.—See China Rare Earth Resources And Technology Co., Ltd.; *Int'l*, pg. 1546
MINMETALS SPAIN S.A.—See China Rare Earth Resources And Technology Co., Ltd.; *Int'l*, pg. 1546
MINMETALS TONGLING GEM STONE CO., LTD.—See China Rare Earth Resources And Technology Co., Ltd.; *Int'l*, pg. 1546
MINMETALS (UK) LTD.—See China Rare Earth Resources And Technology Co., Ltd.; *Int'l*, pg. 1546
MINMETALS XIAMEN ENTERPRISES CO., LTD.—See China Rare Earth Resources And Technology Co., Ltd.; *Int'l*, pg. 1546
MINMETALS XINJIANG ALA-SHANKOU TRADING CO., LTD.—See China Rare Earth Resources And Technology Co., Ltd.; *Int'l*, pg. 1546
MINMETALS YANTAI CO., LTD.—See China Rare Earth Resources And Technology Co., Ltd.; *Int'l*, pg. 1546
MINMETALS YINGKOU MEDIUM-HEAVY PLATE CO., LTD.—See China Rare Earth Resources And Technology Co., Ltd.; *Int'l*, pg. 1546
MINMETALS ZHEJIANG INTERNATIONAL TRADING CO., LTD.—See China Rare Earth Resources And Technology Co., Ltd.; *Int'l*, pg. 1546
MINMETALS ZHENJIANG IMPORT AND EXPORT TRADING CO., LTD.—See China Rare Earth Resources And Technology Co., Ltd.; *Int'l*, pg. 1546
MINMET OPERATIONS PTY LIMITED—See Hydromet Corporation Limited; *Int'l*, pg. 3548
MINMOR INDUSTRIES LLC; *U.S. Private*, pg. 2742
MINNANO WEDDING CO., LTD.—See Kufu Company Inc.; *Int'l*, pg. 4326
MINNAT RESOURCES PTE. LTD.—See China Rare Earth Resources And Technology Co., Ltd.; *Int'l*, pg. 1546
MINN-DAK FARMERS COOPERATIVE; *U.S. Private*, pg. 2742
MINN-DAK GROWERS, LTD.; *U.S. Private*, pg. 2742
MINN-DAK INC.; *U.S. Private*, pg. 2742
MINN-DAK YEAST COMPANY INC.—See Minn-Dak Farmers Cooperative; *U.S. Private*, pg. 2742
MINNEAPOLIS AUTO AUCTION—See Cox Enterprises, Inc.; *U.S. Private*, pg. 1077
MINNEAPOLIS GRAIN EXCHANGE, INC.—See Miami International Holdings, Inc.; *U.S. Private*, pg. 2697
MINNEAPOLIS MEDICAL RESEARCH FOUNDATION, INC.—See Hennepin Healthcare System, Inc.; *U.S. Private*, pg. 1916
THE MINNEAPOLIS OPHTHALMOLOGY ASC, LLC—See KKR & Co. Inc.; *U.S. Public*, pg. 1248
MINNEAPOLIS PUBLIC HOUSING AUTHORITY; *U.S. Private*, pg. 2743
MINNEAPOLIS RAG STOCK CO. INC.; *U.S. Private*, pg. 2743
MINNEAPOLIS-SAINT PAUL INTERNATIONAL AIRPORT; *U.S. Private*, pg. 2743
MINNEAPOLIS SOCIETY OF FINE ARTS; *U.S. Private*, pg. 2743
MINNESOTA AG GROUP INC.; *U.S. Private*, pg. 2743
MINNESOTA BANK & TRUST—See Heartland Financial USA, Inc.; *U.S. Public*, pg. 1018
THE MINNESOTA CHEMICAL COMPANY; *U.S. Private*, pg. 4080
MINNESOTA COMMERCIAL RAILWAY CO.; *U.S. Private*, pg. 2743
MINNESOTA COMPUTERS CORPORATION—See Dynamic Recycling; *U.S. Private*, pg. 1298
MINNESOTA CORRUGATED BOX, INC.—See Visy Industries Holdings Pty. Ltd.; *Int'l*, pg. 8256
MINNESOTA DEHYDRATED VEGETABLES, INC.; *U.S. Private*, pg. 2743
MINNESOTA DIVERSIFIED INDUSTRIES; *U.S. Private*, pg. 2743
MINNESOTA ELEVATOR INC.; *U.S. Private*, pg. 2743
MINNESOTA ENERGY RESOURCES CORPORATION—See WEC Energy Group, Inc.; *U.S. Public*, pg. 2342
MINNESOTA EQUIPMENT, INC.; *U.S. Private*, pg. 2743
MINNESOTA FLEXIBLE CORP.; *U.S. Private*, pg. 2743
MINNESOTA HISTORICAL SOCIETY; *U.S. Private*, pg. 2743
MINNESOTA HOCKEY VENTURES GROUP, LP; *U.S. Private*, pg. 2743
MINNESOTA LAKES BANK—See Wilcox Bancshares, Inc.; *U.S. Private*, pg. 4518
THE MINNESOTA LIFE INSURANCE COMPANY—See Securian Financial Group, Inc.; *U.S. Private*, pg. 3594
MINNESOTA LIMITED, LLC—See CenterPoint Energy, Inc.; *U.S. Public*, pg. 472
MINNESOTA LOGOS, INC.—See Lamar Advertising Company; *U.S. Public*, pg. 1291
MINNESOTA OFFICE TECHNOLOGY GROUP, INC.—See Xerox Holdings Corporation; *U.S. Public*, pg. 2388
MINNESOTA PIPE LINE COMPANY, LLC—See Marathon Petroleum Corporation; *U.S. Public*, pg. 1364
MINNESOTA POWER—See ALLETE, Inc.; *U.S. Public*, pg. 79
MINNESOTA PUBLIC RADIO INC.—See American Public Media Group; *U.S. Private*, pg. 244

MINNESOTA RUBBER & PLASTICS ASIA PACIFIC PTE. LTD.—See KKR & Co. Inc.; *U.S. Public*, pg. 1263
MINNESOTA/SELECT SIRES CO-OP INC.—See Select Sires Inc.; *U.S. Private*, pg. 3601
MINNESOTA SUPPLY COMPANY; *U.S. Private*, pg. 2743
MINNESOTA TEEN CHALLENGE INC; *U.S. Private*, pg. 2743
MINNESOTA THERMAL SCIENCE, LLC—See Platinum Equity, LLC; *U.S. Private*, pg. 3207
MINNESOTA TIMBERWOLVES BASKETBALL LIMITED PARTNERSHIP; *U.S. Private*, pg. 2744
MINNESOTA TWINS, LLC—See Pohlad Companies; *U.S. Private*, pg. 3221
MINNESOTA VIKINGS FOOTBALL LLC; *U.S. Private*, pg. 2744
MINNESOTA VISITING NURSE AGENCY; *U.S. Private*, pg. 2744
MINNESOTA WILD HOCKEY CLUB, LP—See Minnesota Hockey Ventures Group, LP; *U.S. Private*, pg. 2743
MINNESOTA WIRE & CABLE COMPANY; *U.S. Private*, pg. 2744
MINNIE HAMILTON HEALTH CARE CENTER INC.; *U.S. Private*, pg. 2744
MINN-KOTA AG PRODUCTS, INC.; *U.S. Private*, pg. 2743
MINNKOTA POWER COOPERATIVE, INC.; *U.S. Private*, pg. 2744
MINNOTTE MANUFACTURING CORPORATION; *U.S. Private*, pg. 2744
MINNOVA CORP.; *Int'l*, pg. 4910
MINNOW ENVIRONMENTAL, INC.—See Keystone Group, L.P.; *U.S. Private*, pg. 2299
MINNTRONIX, INC.—See Standex International; *U.S. Public*, pg. 1930
MINNWEST BANK—See Minnwest Corporation; *U.S. Private*, pg. 2744
MINNWEST CORPORATION; *U.S. Private*, pg. 2744
MINOAN GROUP PLC; *Int'l*, pg. 4910
MINOAN LINES SHIPPING S.A.—See Grimaldi Group SpA; *Int'l*, pg. 3085
MINO CERAMIC CO., LTD.; *Int'l*, pg. 4910
MINO CERAMICS SHOJI CO., LTD.—See Mino Ceramic Co., Ltd.; *Int'l*, pg. 4910
MINOLTA FINANCE LTD.; *Int'l*, pg. 4910
MINOL USA; *U.S. Private*, pg. 2744
MINOPEX—See DRA Group Holdings Proprietary Limited; *Int'l*, pg. 2196
MINOR CORPORATION PCL—See Minor International PCL; *Int'l*, pg. 4911
MINOR DKL FOOD GROUP PTY. LTD.—See Minor International PCL; *Int'l*, pg. 4911
MINOR FOOD GROUP PCL—See Minor International PCL; *Int'l*, pg. 4911
MINOR FOOD GROUP (SINGAPORE) PTE. LTD.—See Minor International PCL; *Int'l*, pg. 4911
MINOR HOTEL GROUP LIMITED—See Minor International PCL; *Int'l*, pg. 4911
MINOR INTERNATIONAL PCL; *Int'l*, pg. 4910
MINORI SOLUTIONS CO., LTD.; *Int'l*, pg. 4913
MINORITY EQUALITY OPPORTUNITIES ACQUISITION INC.; *U.S. Public*, pg. 1449
MINOR RUBBER CO., INC.; *U.S. Private*, pg. 2744
MINOR RUBBER CO.—See Minor Rubber Co., Inc.; *U.S. Private*, pg. 2744
MINOS A.D.; *Int'l*, pg. 4913
MINOSHA INDIA LTD.—See Ricoh Company, Ltd.; *Int'l*, pg. 6333
MINOTAUR EXPLORATION LTD.—See Andromeda Metals Limited; *Int'l*, pg. 457
MINOT AUTOMOTIVE CENTER; *U.S. Private*, pg. 2744
MINOT BUILDERS SUPPLY ASSOCIATION; *U.S. Private*, pg. 2744
MINOT DAILY NEWS—See The Nutting Company, Inc.; *U.S. Private*, pg. 4086
MINOVA HOLDING GMBH—See Orica Limited; *Int'l*, pg. 5619
MINOVA INTERNATIONAL LIMITED—See Aurelius Equity Opportunities SE & Co. KGaA; *Int'l*, pg. 709
MINOVA KAZAKHSTAN LIMITED LIABILITY PARTNERSHIP—See Orica Limited; *Int'l*, pg. 5619
MINOVA MINING SERVICES S.A.—See Orica Limited; *Int'l*, pg. 5619
MINOX INTERNATIONAL GROUP BERHAD; *Int'l*, pg. 4913
MINPLUS-CDEM GROUP B.V.—See Mayr-Melnhof Karton AG; *Int'l*, pg. 4747
MINPLY CONSTRUCTION & ENGINEERING SDN. BHD.—See TWL Holdings Bhd; *Int'l*, pg. 7991
MINPRO AB—See Nordic Elements AB; *Int'l*, pg. 5421
MINPRO SP. Z O.O.—See VINCI S.A.; *Int'l*, pg. 8224
MINRAD INTERNATIONAL, INC.—See Piramal Enterprises Ltd.; *Int'l*, pg. 5874
MINRAV GROUP LTD.; *Int'l*, pg. 4913
MINREX RESOURCES LIMITED; *Int'l*, pg. 4913
MINSAL LIMITED—See Hysan Development Company Limited; *Int'l*, pg. 3554
MINSEN MACHINERY CO., LTD.—See Nicolas Correa S.A.; *Int'l*, pg. 5273
MINSHANG CREATIVE TECHNOLOGY HOLDINGS LIMITED; *Int'l*, pg. 4913

MINSHENG EDUCATION GROUP COMPANY LIMITED — CORPORATE AFFILIATIONS

MINSHENG EDUCATION GROUP COMPANY LIMITED; *Int'l*, pg. 4913
MINSHENG FINANCIAL LEASING CO., LTD.—See China Minsheng Banking Corporation Ltd.; *Int'l*, pg. 1524
MINSHENG HOLDINGS CO., LTD.; *Int'l*, pg. 4913
MINSHENG ROYAL FUND MANAGEMENT CO., LTD.—See China Minsheng Banking Corporation Ltd.; *Int'l*, pg. 1524
MINSHENG SECURITIES CO., LTD.; *Int'l*, pg. 4913
MINSON CORPORATION; *U.S. Private*, pg. 2744
MINSTER BANK; *U.S. Private*, pg. 2744
MINSTRELL RECRUITMENT LIMITED; *Int'l*, pg. 4913
MINSUD RESOURCES CORP.; *Int'l*, pg. 4913
MINSUR S.A.; *Int'l*, pg. 4913
MINT ADVERTISING; *U.S. Private*, pg. 2744
MINTAILS SA (PTY) LTD—See Labyrinth Resources Limited; *Int'l*, pg. 4391
MINTAKA FINANCIAL, LLC; *U.S. Private*, pg. 2745
MINT (AUST) PTY LIMITED—See Mint Payments Limited; *Int'l*, pg. 4914
MINTECH—See Momar, Inc.; *U.S. Private*, pg. 2768
MINTEC, INC.—See Hexagon AB; *Int'l*, pg. 3368
MINTED LLC; *U.S. Private*, pg. 2745
MINTEL (CONSULTING) INDIA PRIVATE LIMITED—See Mintel Group Ltd.; *Int'l*, pg. 4914
MINTEL CONSULTING (MALAYSIA) SDN. BHD.—See Mintel Group Ltd.; *Int'l*, pg. 4914
MINTEL (CONSULTING) SINGAPORE PTE. LTD.—See Mintel Group Ltd.; *Int'l*, pg. 4914
MINTEL GERMANY GMBH—See Mintel Group Ltd.; *Int'l*, pg. 4914
MINTEL GROUP LTD.; *Int'l*, pg. 4914
MINTEL GROUP LTD—See Mintel Group Ltd.; *Int'l*, pg. 4914
MINTEL GROUP LTD—See Mintel Group Ltd.; *Int'l*, pg. 4914
MINTEL GROUP LTD—See Mintel Group Ltd.; *Int'l*, pg. 4914
MINTEL INFORMATION CONSULTING (SHANGHAI) CO., LTD—See Mintel Group Ltd.; *Int'l*, pg. 4914
MINTEL JAPAN INC—See Mintel Group Ltd.; *Int'l*, pg. 4914
MINTEL PESQUISAS DE MERCADO BRASIL LTDA—See Mintel Group Ltd.; *Int'l*, pg. 4914
MINTEQ AUSTRALIA PTY LTD.—See Minerals Technologies, Inc.; *U.S. Public*, pg. 1449
MINTEQ B.V.—See Minerals Technologies, Inc.; *U.S. Public*, pg. 1449
MINTEQ EUROPE LIMITED.—See Minerals Technologies, Inc.; *U.S. Public*, pg. 1449
MINTEQ INTERNATIONAL GMBH—See Minerals Technologies, Inc.; *U.S. Public*, pg. 1449
MINTEQ INTERNATIONAL, INC.—See Minerals Technologies, Inc.; *U.S. Public*, pg. 1449
MINTEQ ITALIANA S.P.A.—See Minerals Technologies, Inc.; *U.S. Public*, pg. 1449
MINTEQ SHAPES AND SERVICES INC.—See Minerals Technologies, Inc.; *U.S. Public*, pg. 1449
MINTEQ UK LIMITED.—See Minerals Technologies, Inc.; *U.S. Public*, pg. 1449
M INTERNATIONAL INC.; *U.S. Private*, pg. 2523
MINTH AAPICO (THAILAND) CO., LTD.—See Minth Group Limited; *Int'l*, pg. 4914
MINTH AUTOMOTIVE (UK) COMPANY LTD.—See Minth Group Limited; *Int'l*, pg. 4914
MINTH GMBH—See Minth Group Limited; *Int'l*, pg. 4914
MINTH GROUP LIMITED; *Int'l*, pg. 4914
MINTH JAPAN LTD.—See Minth Group Limited; *Int'l*, pg. 4914
MINTH MEXICO, S.A. DE C.V—See Minth Group Limited; *Int'l*, pg. 4914
MINTH NORTH AMERICA, INC.—See Minth Group Limited; *Int'l*, pg. 4914
MINT INCOME FUND; *Int'l*, pg. 4914
MINT MEDICAL PHYSICIAN STAFFING, LP—See Cross Country Healthcare, Inc.; *U.S. Public*, pg. 595
MINTO APARTMENT REIT; *Int'l*, pg. 4914
MINTO BUILDERS FLORIDA INC.—See The Minto Group Inc.; *Int'l*, pg. 7667
MINTO COMMERCIAL PROPERTIES INC.—See The Minto Group Inc.; *Int'l*, pg. 7667
MINTO COMMUNITIES INC.—See The Minto Group Inc.; *Int'l*, pg. 7667
MINTO COMMUNITIES LLC—See The Minto Group Inc.; *Int'l*, pg. 7667
THE MINTO GROUP INC.; *Int'l*, pg. 7666
MINTOLOGY LIMITED—See Edgewell Personal Care Company; *U.S. Public*, pg. 718
MINTON-JONES CO. INC.; *U.S. Private*, pg. 2745
MINT PAYMENTS LIMITED; *Int'l*, pg. 4914
MINTRA HOLDING AS—See Ferd AS; *Int'l*, pg. 2636
MINTRA HOLDING AS—See P/F Tjaldur; *Int'l*, pg. 5683
MINTRA LTD.—See Ferd AS; *Int'l*, pg. 2636
MINTRA LTD.—See P/F Tjaldur; *Int'l*, pg. 5683
MINTRA TRAININGPORTAL AS—See Ferd AS; *Int'l*, pg. 2636
MINTRA TRAININGPORTAL AS—See P/F Tjaldur; *Int'l*, pg. 5684

MINT RESIDENTIAL PTY. LTD.—See Minor International PCL; *Int'l*, pg. 4911
MINT SA; *Int'l*, pg. 4914
MINT SOFTWARE SP. Z O.O.—See Pragma Inkaso S.A.; *Int'l*, pg. 5953
MINTTULIP LTD.—See Sword Group SE; *Int'l*, pg. 7376
MINT TURBINES LLC—See M International Inc.; *U.S. Private*, pg. 2523
MINTWAVE CO., LTD.—See Takaoka Toko Co., Ltd.; *Int'l*, pg. 7431
MINTYE CHEMICALS SDN. BHD.—See Mintye Industries Bhd.; *Int'l*, pg. 4914
MINTYE INDUSTRIES BHD.; *Int'l*, pg. 4914
MINTYE METAL PRODUCTS SDN. BHD.—See Mintye Industries Bhd.; *Int'l*, pg. 4914
MINTZ & HOKE, INC.; *U.S. Private*, pg. 2745
MINTZ, LEVIN, COHN, FERRIS, GLOVSKY & POPEO, P.C.; *U.S. Private*, pg. 2745
MINUANO NORDESTE S.A.—See Natuzzi S.p.A.; *Int'l*, pg. 5170
MINUPAR PARTICIPACOES S.A.; *Int'l*, pg. 4914
MIN UPPLYSNING SVERIGE AB—See Ratos AB; *Int'l*, pg. 6220
MINUS5 D.O.O.—See Entain PLC; *Int'l*, pg. 2450
MINUTE KEY, INC.; *U.S. Private*, pg. 2745
MINUTE MAID COMPANY CANADA INC.—See The Coca-Cola Company; *U.S. Public*, pg. 2064
THE MINUTE MAID COMPANY—See The Coca-Cola Company; *U.S. Public*, pg. 2065
MINUTEMAN CANADA, INC.—See L. Possehl & Co. mbH; *Int'l*, pg. 4383
MINUTEMAN DISTRIBUTORS INC.; *U.S. Private*, pg. 2745
MINUTEMAN INTERNATIONAL, INC.—See L. Possehl & Co. mbH; *Int'l*, pg. 4383
MINUTEMAN POWERBOSS INC.—See L. Possehl & Co. mbH; *Int'l*, pg. 4383
MINUTEMAN PRESS INTERNATIONAL, INC.; *U.S. Private*, pg. 2745
MINUTEMAN TRUCKS, LLC—See Allegiance Trucks, LLC; *U.S. Private*, pg. 176
MINUTE MUFFLER & BRAKE—See Prime Carcare Group, Inc.; *Int'l*, pg. 5976
MINUTI-OGLE CO. INC.; *U.S. Private*, pg. 2745
MINVALCO, INC.—See Building Controls & Solutions; *U.S. Private*, pg. 682
MINVIELLE & CHASTANET INSURANCE BROKERS LIMITED—See Arthur J. Gallagher & Co.; *U.S. Public*, pg. 206
MINWAX COMPANY—See The Sherwin-Williams Company; *U.S. Public*, pg. 2128
MIN XIN HOLDINGS LIMITED; *Int'l*, pg. 4898
MIN XIN INSURANCE COMPANY LIMITED—See Min Xin Holdings Limited; *Int'l*, pg. 4899
MINYARD FOOD STORES, INC.; *U.S. Private*, pg. 2745
MIO TECHNOLOGY BENELUX N.V.—See MiTAC International Corp.; *Int'l*, pg. 4923
MIO TECHNOLOGY CORP.—See MiTAC International Corp.; *Int'l*, pg. 4923
MIO TECHNOLOGY GMBH—See MiTAC International Corp.; *Int'l*, pg. 4923
MIO TECHNOLOGY KOREA—See MiTAC International Corp.; *Int'l*, pg. 4923
MIO TECHNOLOGY LTD.—See MiTAC International Corp.; *Int'l*, pg. 4923
MIOVISION TECHNOLOGIES, INC.; *Int'l*, pg. 4915
MIOX CORPORATION—See Industrie De Nora S.p.A.; *Int'l*, pg. 3674
MIPAC AB—See Berry Global Group, Inc; *U.S. Public*, pg. 323
MIPAK POLYMERS LIMITED—See Hitech Corporation Ltd.; *Int'l*, pg. 3425
MI-PAY GROUP PLC; *Int'l*, pg. 4873
MIPC, LLC—See Delta Air Lines, Inc.; *U.S. Public*, pg. 652
MIPCO SEAMLESS RINGS (GUJARAT) LIMITED; *Int'l*, pg. 4915
MIP D.D.; *Int'l*, pg. 4915
MIPEL IND. E COM. DE VALVULAS LTDA.—See Lupatech S.A.; *Int'l*, pg. 4585
MIPIEN S.P.A; *Int'l*, pg. 4915
MIP METRO GROUP INTELLECTUAL PROPERTY GMBH & CO. KG—See Metro AG; *Int'l*, pg. 4859
MIP MULTIMEDIA INTERNET PARK GMBH—See United Internet AG; *Int'l*, pg. 8069
MI POLYMER CONCRETE PIPES SDN BHD—See Chin Hin Group Berhad; *Int'l*, pg. 1480
MIPOX ABRASIVES INDIA PVT. LTD.—See Mipox Corporation; *Int'l*, pg. 4915
MIPOX CORPORATION; *Int'l*, pg. 4915
MIPOX INTERNATIONAL CORP.—See Mipox Corporation; *Int'l*, pg. 4915
MIPOX MALAYSIA SDN. BHD.—See Mipox Corporation; *Int'l*, pg. 4915
MIPOX (SHANGHAI) TRADING CO., LTD.—See Mipox Corporation; *Int'l*, pg. 4915
MIPRO CONSULTING, LLC.; *U.S. Private*, pg. 2745
M/I PROPERTIES, LLC—See M/I Homes, Inc.; *U.S. Public*, pg. 1351
MIPS AB; *Int'l*, pg. 4915

MIPS AUSTRIA GESMBH—See Roper Technologies, Inc.; *U.S. Public*, pg. 1812
MIPS—See Roper Technologies, Inc.; *U.S. Public*, pg. 1810
MI PUBLISHING SDN BHD—See Singapore Press Holdings Ltd.; *Int'l*, pg. 6942
MIQUEL Y COSTAS ARGENTINA S.A.—See Miquel y Costas & Miquel, S.A.; *Int'l*, pg. 4915
MIQUEL Y COSTAS & MIQUEL, S.A.; *Int'l*, pg. 4915
MIQUEL Y COSTAS TECNOLOGIAS S.A.—See Miquel y Costas & Miquel, S.A.; *Int'l*, pg. 4915
MIRA A.D.—See MESNA INDUSTRIJA BRACA PIVAC d.o.o.; *Int'l*, pg. 4840
MIRABEAU B.V.—See Cognizant Technology Solutions Corporation; *U.S. Public*, pg. 524
MIRABELL FOOTWEAR LIMITED—See Hillhouse Investment Management Limited; *Int'l*, pg. 3393
MIRABELL INTERNATIONAL HOLDINGS LIMITED—See Hillhouse Investment Management Limited; *Int'l*, pg. 3393
MIRABILE INVESTMENT CORP.; *U.S. Private*, pg. 2745
MIRABITO FUEL GROUP; *U.S. Private*, pg. 2745
MIRAC CO., LTD. - WAKAYAMA FACTORY—See Taiyo Technolex Co.,Ltd.; *Int'l*, pg. 7426
MIRACHEM, LLC—See J.F. Lehman & Company, Inc.; *U.S. Private*, pg. 2163
MIRACH ENERGY LIMITED; *Int'l*, pg. 4915
MIRA CHINA LTD.—See HORIBA Ltd; *Int'l*, pg. 3477
MIRACLE AUTOMATION ENGINEERING CO., LTD.; *Int'l*, pg. 4915
MIRACLE CITY HOSPICE, LLC—See Addus HomeCare Corporation; *U.S. Public*, pg. 40
MIRACLECORP PRODUCTS—See Alvarez & Marsal, Inc.; *U.S. Private*, pg. 212
MIRACLE-EAR, INC.—See Amplifon S.p.A.; *Int'l*, pg. 435
MIRACLE ENTERTAINMENT, INC.; *U.S. Public*, pg. 1450
MIRACLE FLIGHTS; *U.S. Private*, pg. 2745
MIRACLE-GRO LAWN PRODUCTS, INC.—See The Scotts Miracle-Gro Company; *U.S. Public*, pg. 2127
MIRACLE INDUSTRIES, INC—See Icahn Enterprises L.P.; *U.S. Public*, pg. 1084
MIRACLE INDUSTRIES LIMITED; *Int'l*, pg. 4915
MIRACLE LINUX CORPORATION—See SoftBank Group Corp.; *Int'l*, pg. 7051
MIRACLE MILE ADVISORS, LLC; *U.S. Private*, pg. 2745
MIRACLE PARTNERS, INC.—See Icahn Enterprises L.P.; *U.S. Public*, pg. 1085
MIRACLE RECREATION EQUIPMENT COMPANY—See Littlejohn & Co., LLC; *U.S. Private*, pg. 2471
MIRACLE SEALANTS COMPANY, LLC—See RPM International Inc.; *U.S. Public*, pg. 1817
MIRACLE SIGNS, INC.; *U.S. Private*, pg. 2745
MIRACLE SOFTWARE SYSTEMS INC.; *U.S. Private*, pg. 2745
MIRACLE SOUND OULU OY—See Warner Bros. Discovery, Inc.; *U.S. Public*, pg. 2327
MIRACLE SOUND OY—See Warner Bros. Discovery, Inc.; *U.S. Public*, pg. 2327
MIRACLE SUPPLY CO. INC.; *U.S. Private*, pg. 2745
MIRACLE TRANSPORTATION, INC.; *U.S. Private*, pg. 2746
MIRACLL CHEMICALS CO., LTD.; *Int'l*, pg. 4915
MIRAC NETWORKS (DONGGUAN) CO., LTD.—See Alpha Networks Inc.; *Int'l*, pg. 369
MIRACOOL CO., LTD.—See Kanematsu Corporation; *Int'l*, pg. 4069
MIRACORP INC.; *U.S. Private*, pg. 2746
MIRACULUM S.A.; *Int'l*, pg. 4915
MIRADA PLC; *Int'l*, pg. 4915
MIRADRY, INC.—See 1315 Capital LLC; *U.S. Private*, pg. 3
MIRAE ASSET CAPITAL MARKETS (INDIA) PVT LTD—See Mirae Asset Financial Group; *Int'l*, pg. 4916
MIRAE ASSET FINANCIAL GROUP; *Int'l*, pg. 4916
MIRAE ASSET GLOBAL INVESTMENTS (BRAZIL) LIMITED—See Mirae Asset Financial Group; *Int'l*, pg. 4916
MIRAE ASSET GLOBAL INVESTMENTS (CHINA)—See Mirae Asset Financial Group; *Int'l*, pg. 4916
MIRAE ASSET GLOBAL INVESTMENTS CO., LTD.—See Mirae Asset Financial Group; *Int'l*, pg. 4916
MIRAE ASSET GLOBAL INVESTMENTS (HK) LIMITED—See Mirae Asset Financial Group; *Int'l*, pg. 4916
MIRAE ASSET GLOBAL INVESTMENTS (INDIA) PVT. LTD.—See Mirae Asset Financial Group; *Int'l*, pg. 4916
MIRAE ASSET GLOBAL INVESTMENTS (UK) LTD.—See Mirae Asset Financial Group; *Int'l*, pg. 4916
MIRAE ASSET GLOBAL INVESTMENTS (USA) LLC—See Mirae Asset Financial Group; *Int'l*, pg. 4916
MIRAE ASSET LIFE INSURANCE CO., LTD.; *Int'l*, pg. 4916
MIRAEASSET NO. 3 SPECIAL PURPOSE ACQUISITION CO., LTD.; *Int'l*, pg. 4916
MIRAE ASSET SECURITIES CO., LTD.—See Mirae Asset Financial Group; *Int'l*, pg. 4916
MIRAE ASSET SECURITIES (USA) INC.—See Mirae Asset Financial Group; *Int'l*, pg. 4916

COMPANY NAME INDEX

MIRAECELLBIO CO., LTD.—See BYON Co., Ltd.; *Int'l*, pg. 1235
MIRAE CORPORATION—See Intops Co., Ltd.; *Int'l*, pg. 3767
MIRAE ING CO., LTD.; *Int'l*, pg. 4916
MIRAE JOINT STOCK COMPANY; *Int'l*, pg. 4916
MIRAE SCI CO., LTD.; *Int'l*, pg. 4916
MIRAE TECHNOLOGY CO., LTD.; *Int'l*, pg. 4916
MIRAFLORES COMPANIA MINERA SAS—See LCL Resources Limited; *Int'l*, pg. 4430
MIRAGE ENERGY CORPORATION; *U.S. Public*, pg. 1450
MIRAGE LEISURE & DEVELOPMENT INC.—See Emaar Properties PJSC; *Int'l*, pg. 2373
MIRAGE PARK OTELCILIK A.S.—See Parsan Makina Parcalari Sanayii AS; *Int'l*, pg. 5747
MIRAGE RESORTS INCORPORATED—See MGM Resorts International; *U.S. Public*, pg. 1435
MIRA GMBH & CO. KG—See Deutsche Bank Aktiengesellschaft; *Int'l*, pg. 2061
MIRAIAL CO., LTD.; *Int'l*, pg. 4917
MIRAIAL TOHOKU CO., LTD.—See Miraial Co., Ltd.; *Int'l*, pg. 4917
MIRAI CONSTRUCTION CO., LTD.—See Takamatsu Construction Group Co., Ltd.; *Int'l*, pg. 7430
MIRAI CORPORATION; *Int'l*, pg. 4916
MIRAI INDUSTRY CO., LTD.; *Int'l*, pg. 4916
MIRAI INTELLECTUAL PROPERTY & TECHNOLOGY RESEARCH CENTER CO., LTD.—See Striders Corporation; *Int'l*, pg. 7240
MIRAI KASEI INC.—See Mitani Sangyo Co., Ltd.; *Int'l*, pg. 4924
MIRAI KOSEN CO., LTD.—See Maeda Kosen Co., Ltd.; *Int'l*, pg. 4635
MIRAIT CORPORATION—See MIRAIT ONE Corporation; *Int'l*, pg. 4917
MIRAIT INFORMATION SYSTEMS CO., LTD.—See MIRAIT ONE Corporation; *Int'l*, pg. 4917
MIRAIT ONE CORPORATION; *Int'l*, pg. 4917
MIRAIT PHILIPPINES INC.—See MIRAIT ONE Corporation; *Int'l*, pg. 4917
MIRAI TRANSLATE, INC.—See Nippon Telegraph & Telephone Corporation; *Int'l*, pg. 5343
MIRAIT SERVICE DESIGN CO. LTD.—See Pole To Win Holdings, Inc.; *Int'l*, pg. 5908
MIRAIT TECHNOLOGIES AUSTRALIA PTY LIMITED—See MIRAIT ONE Corporation; *Int'l*, pg. 4917
MIRAIT TECHNOLOGIES CORPORATION—See MIRAIT ONE Corporation; *Int'l*, pg. 4917
MIRAIT-X CORPORATION—See MIRAIT ONE Corporation; *Int'l*, pg. 4917
MIRAI WORKS, INC.; *Int'l*, pg. 4916
MIRAIYA SHOTEN CO., LTD.—See AEON Co., Ltd.; *Int'l*, pg. 178
MIRAJ ACADEMY SDN BHD—See JM Education Group; *Int'l*, pg. 3974
MIRAK CHEVROLET-HYUNDAI, INC.; *U.S. Private*, pg. 2746
MIRAMAR BOBCAT, INC.—See Brightstar Capital Partners, L.P.; *U.S. Private*, pg. 653
MIRAMAR EVENTS; *U.S. Private*, pg. 2746
MIRAMAR HOTEL AND INVESTMENT COMPANY, LIMITED—See Henderson Land Development Co. Ltd.; *Int'l*, pg. 3345
MIRAMAR RESOURCES LIMITED; *Int'l*, pg. 4918
MIRAMAR UNDERWRITING AGENCY PTY LTD—See Steadfast Group Limited; *Int'l*, pg. 7187
MIRANDA ASIA K.K.—See Belden, Inc.; *U.S. Public*, pg. 294
MIRANDA GOLD U.S.A., INC.—See Outcrop Silver & Gold Corporation; *Int'l*, pg. 5667
MIRANDA MINERALS HOLDINGS LIMITED; *Int'l*, pg. 4918
MIRANDA SPOLKA Z O.O.—See Lubawa S.A.; *Int'l*, pg. 4572
MIRANDA TECHNOLOGIES ASIA LTD.—See Belden, Inc.; *U.S. Public*, pg. 294
MIRANDA TECHNOLOGIES FRANCE SAS—See Belden, Inc.; *U.S. Public*, pg. 294
MIRANDA TOOLS PVT. LTD.—See Sandvik AB; *Int'l*, pg. 6534
MIRANDA WINES PTY. LTD.—See Australian Vintage Ltd.; *Int'l*, pg. 723
MIRANTIS, INC.; *U.S. Private*, pg. 2746
MIRA PHARMACEUTICALS, INC.; *U.S. Public*, pg. 1449
MIRA POWER LIMITED—See Korea Electric Power Corporation; *Int'l*, pg. 4284
MIRARI JAPAN LTD—See EssilorLuxottica SA; *Int'l*, pg. 2515
MIRARTH HOLDINGS, INC.; *Int'l*, pg. 4918
MIRASOL RESOURCES LTD.; *Int'l*, pg. 4918
MIRASSOL S/A SANEAMENTO DE MIRASSOL—See Igua Saneamento SA; *Int'l*, pg. 3603
MIRATECDRONE CORP.—See MIRAIT ONE Corporation; *Int'l*, pg. 4917
MIRATECH CORP.—See Argonaut Private Equity, LLC; *U.S. Private*, pg. 321
MIRATECH LTD.; *Int'l*, pg. 4918

MIRATI THERAPEUTICS, INC.—See Bristol-Myers Squibb Company; *U.S. Public*, pg. 386
MIRATORG HOLDING; *Int'l*, pg. 4918
MIRATO S.P.A.; *Int'l*, pg. 4918
MIRAVAL GROUP, LLC—See Hyatt Hotels Corporation; *U.S. Public*, pg. 1078
MIRAVAL RESORT ARIZONA, LLC—See Hyatt Hotels Corporation; *U.S. Public*, pg. 1078
MIRA VISTA GOLF CLUB, L.C.—See Goff Capital, Inc.; *U.S. Private*, pg. 1726
MIRAXS CO., LTD.—See ZIGExN Co., Ltd.; *Int'l*, pg. 8682
MIRBUD S.A.; *Int'l*, pg. 4918
MIRC ELECTRONICS LTD.; *Int'l*, pg. 4919
MIRCH TECHNOLOGIES INDIA LIMITED; *Int'l*, pg. 4919
MIRCOM TECHNOLOGIES LTD.; *Int'l*, pg. 4919
MIREC B.V.—See Sims Limited; *U.S. Public*, pg. 1884
MIRELIS HOLDING SA; *Int'l*, pg. 4919
MIRENCO, INC.; *U.S. Private*, pg. 2746
MIRESBALL; *U.S. Private*, pg. 2746
MIREX AQUAPURE SOLUTIONS, LP—See BDT Capital Partners, LLC; *U.S. Private*, pg. 502
MIRGOR S.A.C.I.F.I.A.; *Int'l*, pg. 4919
MIRIAM CORBAN RETIREMENT VILLAGE LIMITED—See Ryman Healthcare Ltd.; *Int'l*, pg. 6439
MIRIA SYSTEMS, INC.—See Aquiline Capital Partners LLC; *U.S. Private*, pg. 304
MIRICOR ENTERPRISES HOLDINGS LIMITED; *Int'l*, pg. 4919
MIRIFEX SYSTEMS, LLC; *U.S. Private*, pg. 2746
MIRI INTERNATIONAL LIMITED—See Kingmaker Footwear Holdings Limited; *Int'l*, pg. 4174
MIRION TECHNOLOGIES (CANBERRA BNLS) NV/SA—See Mirion Technologies, Inc.; *U.S. Public*, pg. 1450
MIRION TECHNOLOGIES (CANBERRA), INC.—See Mirion Technologies, Inc.; *U.S. Public*, pg. 1450
MIRION TECHNOLOGIES (CANBERRA) SAS—See Mirion Technologies, Inc.; *U.S. Public*, pg. 1450
MIRION TECHNOLOGIES (CANBERRA UK) LIMITED—See Mirion Technologies, Inc.; *U.S. Public*, pg. 1450
MIRION TECHNOLOGIES (CONAX NUCLEAR), INC.—See Mirion Technologies, Inc.; *U.S. Public*, pg. 1450
MIRION TECHNOLOGIES, INC.; *U.S. Public*, pg. 1450
MIRION TECHNOLOGIES (IST) CORPORATION—See Mirion Technologies, Inc.; *U.S. Public*, pg. 1450
MIRION TECHNOLOGIES (US), INC.—See Mirion Technologies, Inc.; *U.S. Public*, pg. 1450
MIRIS HOLDING AB; *Int'l*, pg. 4919
MIRIXA CORPORATION—See Cardinal Health, Inc.; *U.S. Public*, pg. 434
MIRLAND DEVELOPMENT CORPORATION PLC; *Int'l*, pg. 4919
MIRLE AUTOMATION CORPORATION; *Int'l*, pg. 4919
MIRLE AUTOMATION CORPORATION - TAICHUNG FACTORY—See Mirle Automation Corporation; *Int'l*, pg. 4919
MIRLE AUTOMATION CORPORATION - TAINAN FACTORY—See Mirle Automation Corporation; *Int'l*, pg. 4919
MIRLE AUTOMATION INTER CO., LTD.—See Mirle Automation Corporation; *Int'l*, pg. 4919
MIRLE AUTOMATION (KUNSHAN) CO., LTD.—See Mirle Automation Corporation; *Int'l*, pg. 4919
MIRLE AUTOMATION TECHNOLOGY (SHANGHAI) CO., LTD.—See Mirle Automation Corporation; *Int'l*, pg. 4919
MIRLEX PTY. LTD.; *Int'l*, pg. 4919
MIRMIRE LAGHUBITTA BITTIYA SANSTHA LIMITED; *Int'l*, pg. 4919
MIR, MITCHELL & COMPANY, LLP; *U.S. Private*, pg. 2745
MIRNA D.D.—See Podravka d.d.; *Int'l*, pg. 5903
MIROC A.D.; *Int'l*, pg. 4919
MIRO CONSULTING, INC.; *U.S. Private*, pg. 2746
MIROITERIE DU RHIN—See Compagnie de Saint-Gobain SA; *Int'l*, pg. 1724
MIROITERIES DE L'OUEST ARMORIQUE—See Compagnie de Saint-Gobain SA; *Int'l*, pg. 1736
MIROITERIES DE L'OUEST ATLANTIQUE—See Compagnie de Saint-Gobain SA; *Int'l*, pg. 1724
MIROITERIES DE L'OUEST SEMIVER CLIMAVER—See Compagnie de Saint-Gobain SA; *Int'l*, pg. 1724
MIROKU CORPORATION; *Int'l*, pg. 4919
MIROKU JYOHO SERVICE CO., LTD.; *Int'l*, pg. 4919
MIROKU MACHINE TOOL, INC.—See Miroku Corporation; *Int'l*, pg. 4919
MIROKU MACHINE TOOL, INC.—See Miroku Corporation; *Int'l*, pg. 4919
MIROMAR DEVELOPMENT CORPORATION; *U.S. Private*, pg. 2746
MIROMAR OUTLET EAST, LLC—See Miromar Development Corporation; *U.S. Private*, pg. 2746
MIROMATRIX MEDICAL INC.—See United Therapeutics Corporation; *U.S. Public*, pg. 2238
MIRON CONSTRUCTION CO. INC.; *U.S. Private*, pg. 2746
MIRON ENTERPRISES LLC; *U.S. Private*, pg. 2746

MIRO TECHNOLOGIES, INC.—See The Boeing Company; *U.S. Public*, pg. 179
MIROVA S.A.—See Groupe BPCE; *Int'l*, pg. 3096
MIROVA US LLC—See Groupe BPCE; *Int'l*, pg. 3098
MIRPURKHAS SUGAR MILLS LTD - MIRPURKHAS FACTORY—See Mirpurkhas Sugar Mills Ltd; *Int'l*, pg. 4920
MIRPURKHAS SUGAR MILLS LTD; *Int'l*, pg. 4920
MIRRABOOKA INVESTMENTS LIMITED; *Int'l*, pg. 4920
MIRREN (AUSTRALIA) PTY. LTD.—See Metcash Limited; *Int'l*, pg. 4852
MIRREN (PTY) LTD.—See Cipla Ltd.; *Int'l*, pg. 1617
MIRRIAD ADVERTISING PLC; *Int'l*, pg. 4920
MIRROR IMAGE INTERNET, INC.—See Xcelera Inc.; *Int'l*, pg. 8520
MIRROR IMAGE INTERNET (UK) LTD.—See Xcelera Inc.; *Int'l*, pg. 8520
MIRRORMAX OY—See Yamauchi Corp., Ltd.; *Int'l*, pg. 8556
MIRROR PLUS TECHNOLOGIES, INC.—See ARC DOCUMENT SOLUTIONS, INC.; *U.S. Public*, pg. 179
MIRSA MANUFACTURING LLC; *U.S. Private*, pg. 2746
MIRS COMMUNICATIONS LIMITED—See Motorola Solutions, Inc.; *U.S. Public*, pg. 1478
MIRTEC CORP; *U.S. Private*, pg. 2746
MIRTH INCORPORATED; *U.S. Private*, pg. 2746
MIRTH, LLC—See Thoma Bravo, L.P.; *U.S. Private*, pg. 4150
MIRUCA CORPORATION—See DTS Corporation; *Int'l*, pg. 2217
MIRUM PHARMACEUTICALS, INC.; *U.S. Public*, pg. 1450
MIRUS BIO, LLC—See Merck KGaA; *Int'l*, pg. 4831
MIRUS INTERNATIONAL BV—See Intrum AB; *Int'l*, pg. 3771
MIRVAC FUNDS MANAGEMENT LIMITED—See Mirvac Group Ltd.; *Int'l*, pg. 4920
MIRVAC GROUP LTD.; *Int'l*, pg. 4920
MIRYANG AGAR-AGAR CO., LTD.—See MSC Co., Ltd.; *Int'l*, pg. 5067
MIRZA INTERNATIONAL LTD; *Int'l*, pg. 4920
MIRZA SUGAR MILLS LIMITED; *Int'l*, pg. 4920
MIRZA UK LIMITED—See Mirza International Ltd; *Int'l*, pg. 4920
MISAB SPRINKLER & VVS AB—See Triton Advisers Limited; *Int'l*, pg. 7935
MISAWA & CO., LTD.; *Int'l*, pg. 4920
MISAWA HABITA & CO., LTD.; *Int'l*, pg. 4920
MISAWA HOMES CERAMICS CO., LTD—See Toyota Motor Corporation; *Int'l*, pg. 7873
MISAWA HOMES CHUGOKU CO., LTD.—See Toyota Motor Corporation; *Int'l*, pg. 7873
MISAWA HOMES CO., LTD.—See Toyota Motor Corporation; *Int'l*, pg. 7873
MISAWA HOMES HIGASHIKANTO CO., LTD—See Toyota Motor Corporation; *Int'l*, pg. 7873
MISAWA HOMES HOKKAIDO CO., LTD.—See Toyota Motor Corporation; *Int'l*, pg. 7873
MISAWA HOMES INSTITUTE OF RESEARCH AND DEVELOPMENT CO LTD—See Toyota Motor Corporation; *Int'l*, pg. 7873
MISAWA HOMES KINKI CO., LTD—See Toyota Motor Corporation; *Int'l*, pg. 7873
MISAWA HOMES SHIN-ETSU CO., LTD.—See Toyota Motor Corporation; *Int'l*, pg. 7873
MISAWA HOMES SHIZUOKA CO., LTD.—See Toyota Motor Corporation; *Int'l*, pg. 7873
MISAWA HOMES TOKAI CO., LTD.—See Toyota Motor Corporation; *Int'l*, pg. 7873
MISAWA HOMES TOKYO CO., LTD.—See Toyota Motor Corporation; *Int'l*, pg. 7873
MISAWA MEDICAL INDUSTRY CO., LTD.—See Air Water Inc.; *Int'l*, pg. 240
MISAWA TRADING CO., LTD.—See Sumitomo Electric Industries, Ltd.; *Int'l*, pg. 7278
MISC AGENCIES (AUSTRALIA) PTY LTD—See Petroliam Nasional Berhad; *Int'l*, pg. 5829
MISC BERHAD—See Petroliam Nasional Berhad; *Int'l*, pg. 5829
MISCELLANEOUS METALS INC.; *U.S. Private*, pg. 2746
MISCHEK BAUTRAGER SERVICE GMBH—See STRABAG SE; *Int'l*, pg. 7231
MISCHEK LEASING EINS GESELLSCHAFT M.B.H.—See STRABAG SE; *Int'l*, pg. 7231
MISCHEK SYSTEMBAU GMBH—See STRABAG SE; *Int'l*, pg. 7231
MISCO ITALY COMPUTER SUPPLIES S.P.A.—See Computacenter plc; *Int'l*, pg. 1758
MISCO SOLUTIONS B.V.—See Computacenter plc; *Int'l*, pg. 1758
MISEN ENERGY AB; *Int'l*, pg. 4920
MISENGE ENVIRONMENTAL & TECHNICAL SERVICES LIMITED—See ZCCM Investments Holdings Plc.; *Int'l*, pg. 8627
MISERICORDIA; *U.S. Private*, pg. 2746
M&I SERVICING CORP.—See Bank of Montreal; *Int'l*, pg. 846
MISFIT, INC.—See Axon Enterprise, Inc.; *U.S. Public*, pg. 256

MISHA CONSULTING GROUP INC. CORPORATE AFFILIATIONS

MISHA CONSULTING GROUP INC.; *U.S. Private*, pg. 2746
MISHAWAKA MANUFACTURING CAMPUS—See MacAndrews & Forbes Incorporated; *U.S. Private*, pg. 2532
MISHAWAKA MANUFACTURING CAMPUS—See The Renco Group Inc.; *U.S. Private*, pg. 4104
MISHAWAKA SHEET METAL, INC.—See Patrick Industries, Inc.; *U.S. Public*, pg. 1658
MISH DESIGNS LIMITED; *Int'l*, pg. 4920
MISHIMA FOODS CO., LTD.; *Int'l*, pg. 4920
MISHIMA FOODS USA INC.—See Mishima Foods Co., Ltd.; *Int'l*, pg. 4920
MISHIMA OLYMPUS CO., LTD.—See Olympus Corporation; *Int'l*, pg. 5556
MISHIMA SEIKI CO., LTD.—See MISUMI Group Inc.; *Int'l*, pg. 4922
MISHKA EXIM LIMITED; *Int'l*, pg. 4920
MISHKA FINANCE & TRADING LIMITED; *Int'l*, pg. 4920
MISHO ECOLOGY AND LANDSCAPE CO., LTD.; *Int'l*, pg. 4920
MISHORIM REAL ESTATE INVESTMENTS LTD.; *Int'l*, pg. 4920
MISHRA DHATU NIGAM LTD.; *Int'l*, pg. 4920
MISHTANN FOODS LTD.; *Int'l*, pg. 4920
MISICOM, INC.—See Nippon Telegraph & Telephone Corporation; *Int'l*, pg. 5348
MISKELLY FURNITURE WAREHOUSE INC.; *U.S. Private*, pg. 2746
MISKOLC 2002 KFT.—See BNP Paribas SA; *Int'l*, pg. 1092
MISMAK PROPERTIES CO. LLC—See First Abu Dhabi Bank P.J.S.C.; *Int'l*, pg. 2681
MISO FILM APS—See Bertelsmann SE & Co. KGaA; *Int'l*, pg. 995
MISO FILM NORGE AS—See Bertelsmann SE & Co. KGaA; *Int'l*, pg. 995
MISO FILM SVERIGE AB—See Bertelsmann SE & Co. KGaA; *Int'l*, pg. 995
MISONIX, INC.—See Bioventus Inc.; *U.S. Public*, pg. 339
MISOURCE INC.; *U.S. Private*, pg. 2746
M.I.S. OUTSOURCING COMPANY LIMITED—See MFEC Public Company Limited; *Int'l*, pg. 4871
MIS QUALITY MANAGEMENT CORP.—See Moody's Corporation; *U.S. Public*, pg. 1468
MISQUITA ENGINEERING LIMITED; *Int'l*, pg. 4921
MISR BENI-SUEF CEMENT COMPANY; *Int'l*, pg. 4921
MISR CEMENT COMPANY; *Int'l*, pg. 4921
MISR CO. FOR AROMATIC PRODUCTS (MARP) S.A.E.—See International Flavors & Fragrances Inc.; *U.S. Public*, pg. 1154
MISR FOR CENTRAL CLEARING, DEPOSITORY & REGISTRY SAE—See Cairo & Alexandria Stock Exchanges; *Int'l*, pg. 1253
MISR GULF OIL PROCESSING CO.—See Ajwa Group for Food Industries Holding Ltd. Co.; *Int'l*, pg. 259
MISR HOTELS COMPANY; *Int'l*, pg. 4921
MISRIMPEX FOR PAPER TRADING L.L.C.—See VIMPEX Handelsgesellschaft mbH; *Int'l*, pg. 8209
MISR NATIONAL STEEL SAE; *Int'l*, pg. 4921
MISR OILS & SOAP; *Int'l*, pg. 4921
MISR PIONEER SEEDS COMPANY S.A.E.—See Corteva, Inc.; *U.S. Public*, pg. 582
MISR REFRIGERATION & AIR CONDITIONING MANUFACTURING COMPANY S.A.E—See Carrier Global Corporation; *U.S. Public*, pg. 443
MISR REFRIGERATION & AIR CONDITIONING; *Int'l*, pg. 4921
MISSCO CONTRACT SALES; *U.S. Private*, pg. 2747
MISS ELAINE INC.; *U.S. Private*, pg. 2746
MISSFRESH LTD.; *Int'l*, pg. 4921
MISSILE RANGER—See Gannett Co., Inc.; *U.S. Public*, pg. 900
THE MISSING LINK B.V.—See Sopra Steria Group S.A.; *Int'l*, pg. 7110
MISSION ADVANCEMENT CORP.; *U.S. Public*, pg. 1450
MISSION BANCORP; *U.S. Public*, pg. 1450
MISSION BANK—See Mission Bancorp; *U.S. Public*, pg. 1450
MISSION BIOFUELS INDIA PRIVATE LIMITED—See Mission NewEnergy Limited; *Int'l*, pg. 4921
MISSION BIOTECHNOLOGIES SDN. BHD.—See Mission NewEnergy Limited; *Int'l*, pg. 4921
MISSION BROADCASTING, INC.; *U.S. Private*, pg. 2747
MISSION CAPITAL ADVISORS, LLC—See Marcus & Millichap, Inc.; *U.S. Public*, pg. 1365
MISSION CLOUD SERVICES INC.—See CDW Corporation; *U.S. Public*, pg. 462
MISSION CONSUMER CAPITAL; *U.S. Private*, pg. 2747
MISSION CRITICAL ELECTRONICS, LLC—See Windjammer Capital Investors, LLC; *U.S. Private*, pg. 4538
MISSION CRITICAL FACILITIES INTERNATIONAL LLC—See Mission Critical Group; *U.S. Private*, pg. 2747
MISSION CRITICAL GROUP; *U.S. Private*, pg. 2747
MISSION CRITICAL PARTNERS; *U.S. Private*, pg. 2747
MISSION DATA LLC—See Growth Acceleration Partners, LLC; *U.S. Private*, pg. 1796
MISSION DEVELOPMENT BANK LIMITED; *Int'l*, pg. 4921

MISSION DIALYSIS SERVICES, LLC—See DaVita Inc.; *U.S. Public*, pg. 641
MISSION ESSENTIAL PERSONNEL, LLC; *U.S. Private*, pg. 2747
MISSION FEDERAL CREDIT UNION; *U.S. Private*, pg. 2747
MISSION FOODS (MALAYSIA) SDN. BHD.—See Gruma, S.A.B. de C.V.; *Int'l*, pg. 3114
MISSION FOODS (SHANGHAI) CO., LTD.—See Gruma, S.A.B. de C.V.; *Int'l*, pg. 3114
MISSION FOODS UK, LTD.—See Gruma, S.A.B. de C.V.; *Int'l*, pg. 3114
THE MISSION GROUP PUBLIC LIMITED COMPANY; *Int'l*, pg. 7667
MISSION HEALTH PARTNERS, INC.—See HCA Healthcare, Inc.; *U.S. Public*, pg. 1003
MISSION HEALTH SERVICES; *U.S. Public*, pg. 2747
MISSION HILLS CAPITAL PARTNERS INC—See iA Financial Corporation Inc.; *Int'l*, pg. 3567
MISSION HILLS COUNTRY CLUB—See Apollo Global Management, Inc.; *U.S. Public*, pg. 150
MISSION HILLS-H, INC.—See Lithia Motors, Inc.; *U.S. Public*, pg. 1325
MISSION HILLS, S.A. DE C.V.—See Colgate-Palmolive Company; *U.S. Public*, pg. 533
MISSION INN RESORTS INC.; *U.S. Private*, pg. 2747
MISSION MANAGEMENT & TRUST, CO.—See Notre Dame Federal Credit Union; *U.S. Private*, pg. 2965
MISSION MOUNTAIN RAILROAD—See Kinder Morgan, Inc.; *U.S. Public*, pg. 1233
MISSION NEIGHBORHOOD HEALTH CENTER; *U.S. Private*, pg. 2747
MISSION NEWENERGY LIMITED; *Int'l*, pg. 4921
MISSION PETROLEUM CARRIERS, INC.—See TETCO, Inc.; *U.S. Private*, pg. 3973
MISSION PHARMACAL COMPANY INC.; *U.S. Private*, pg. 2748
MISSION PLASTICS OF ARKANSAS, INC.—See Peterson Manufacturing Company Inc.; *U.S. Private*, pg. 3160
MISSION POOLS OF ESCONDIDO; *U.S. Private*, pg. 2748
MISSION PRODUCE EUROPE B.V.—See Mission Produce, Inc.; *U.S. Public*, pg. 1450
MISSION PRODUCE, INC.; *U.S. Public*, pg. 1450
MISSION READY SOLUTIONS INC.; *Int'l*, pg. 4921
MISSION REHABILITATION AND SPORTS MEDICINE LIMITED PARTNERSHIP—See U.S. Physical Therapy, Inc.; *U.S. Public*, pg. 2215
MISSION SOLAR ENERGY LLC—See OCI Holdings Co., Ltd.; *Int'l*, pg. 5519
MISSION SOLUTIONS, LLC—See Arctic Slope Regional Corporation; *U.S. Public*, pg. 316
MISSION TRAILS HEALTHCARE, INC.—See The Ensign Group, Inc.; *U.S. Public*, pg. 2071
MISSION TUITION, INC.—See Cardiff Lexington Corporation; *U.S. Public*, pg. 433
MISSION WEALTH MANAGEMENT, LLC; *U.S. Private*, pg. 2748
THE MISSISQUOI INSURANCE COMPANY—See The Economical Insurance Group; *Int'l*, pg. 7637
MISSISSAUGA TOYOTA INC.; *Int'l*, pg. 4921
MISSISSIPPI ARTS AND ENTERTAINMENT CENTER; *U.S. Private*, pg. 2748
MISSISSIPPI AUTO AUCTION INC.—See Cox Enterprises, Inc.; *U.S. Private*, pg. 1077
MISSISSIPPI BLENDING COMPANY, INC.—See Arsenal Capital Management LP; *U.S. Private*, pg. 337
MISSISSIPPI BLOOD SERVICES; *U.S. Private*, pg. 2748
MISSISSIPPI CHILDREN'S HOME SERVICES; *U.S. Private*, pg. 2748
MISSISSIPPI COAST ENDOSCOPY AND AMBULATORY SURGERY CENTER, INC.—See KKR & Co. Inc.; *U.S. Public*, pg. 1250
MISSISSIPPI COMPREHENSIVE HEALTH INSURANCE RISK POOL ASSOCIATION; *U.S. Private*, pg. 2748
MISSISSIPPI COUNTY, ARKANSAS, ECONOMIC OPPORTUNITY COMMISSION, INC.; *U.S. Private*, pg. 2748
MISSISSIPPI DISTRIBUTORS; *U.S. Private*, pg. 2748
MISSISSIPPI FARM BUREAU CASUALTY INSURANCE COMPANY—See Southern Farm Bureau Casualty Insurance Group; *U.S. Private*, pg. 3731
MISSISSIPPI FARM BUREAU INSURANCE COMPANIES; *U.S. Private*, pg. 2748
MISSISSIPPI HMA DME, LLC—See Community Health Systems, Inc.; *U.S. Public*, pg. 555
MISSISSIPPI HMA HOSPITALISTS, LLC—See Community Health Systems, Inc.; *U.S. Public*, pg. 555
MISSISSIPPI HOMECARE, LLC—See UnitedHealth Group Incorporated; *U.S. Public*, pg. 2246
MISSISSIPPI INDUSTRIES FOR THE BLIND; *U.S. Private*, pg. 2748
MISSISSIPPI LIGNITE MINING COMPANY—See NACCO Industries, Inc.; *U.S. Public*, pg. 1490
MISSISSIPPI LIME COMPANY—See HBM Holdings Company; *U.S. Private*, pg. 1887
MISSISSIPPI LOGOS, L.L.C.—See Lamar Advertising Company; *U.S. Public*, pg. 1291

MISSISSIPPI MARINE CORPORATION; *U.S. Private*, pg. 2748
MISSISSIPPI METHODIST SENIOR SERVICES; *U.S. Private*, pg. 2748
MISSISSIPPI OIL INC.—See Smith Petroleum Inc.; *U.S. Private*, pg. 3695
MISSISSIPPI ORGAN RECOVERY AGENCY; *U.S. Private*, pg. 2748
MISSISSIPPI PHYSICAL THERAPY SERVICES OF BILOXI, LLC—See UnitedHealth Group Incorporated; *U.S. Public*, pg. 2246
MISSISSIPPI POLYMERS, INC.; *U.S. Private*, pg. 2748
MISSISSIPPI POLYMERS—See Mississippi Polymers, Inc.; *U.S. Private*, pg. 2748
MISSISSIPPI POWER COMPANY—See The Southern Company; *U.S. Public*, pg. 2131
MISSISSIPPI PRECISION CAST PARTS—See Parrish Enterprises, Ltd.; *U.S. Private*, pg. 3100
MISSISSIPPI PRESS SERVICES; *U.S. Private*, pg. 2748
MISSISSIPPI RIVER BANK—See Merchants & Marine Bancorp, Inc.; *U.S. Public*, pg. 1415
MISSISSIPPI TANK COMPANY—See TerraVest Industries, Inc.; *Int'l*, pg. 7568
MISSISSIPPI TANK & MANUFACTURING CO., INC.—See TerraVest Industries, Inc.; *Int'l*, pg. 7568
MISSISSIPPI TV, LLC—See Entertainment Studios, Inc.; *U.S. Private*, pg. 1405
MISSISSIPPI VALLEY COMPANY—See U.S. Bancorp; *U.S. Public*, pg. 2212
MISSISSIPPI VALLEY REGIONAL BLOOD CENTER; *U.S. Private*, pg. 2748
MISSISSIPPI VALLEY TITLE INSURANCE COMPANY—See Old Republic International Corporation; *U.S. Public*, pg. 1569
MISSISSIPPI WELDERS SUPPLY CO.; *U.S. Private*, pg. 2748
MISSONI S.P.A.; *Int'l*, pg. 4921
MISSON SOLAR LIMITED—See Foresight Solar Fund Limited; *Int'l*, pg. 2732
M.I.S.S. OPHTHALMICS LIMITED—See Bausch Health Companies Inc.; *Int'l*, pg. 897
MISSOULA CARTAGE CO. INC.; *U.S. Private*, pg. 2748
MISSOULA ELECTRIC CO-OP INC.; *U.S. Private*, pg. 2749
MISSOULA RADIOLOGY, P.C.—See Inland Imaging Associates, P.S.; *U.S. Private*, pg. 2078
THE MISSOULIAN—See Lee Enterprises, Incorporated; *U.S. Public*, pg. 1300
MISSOURI AGRICULTURAL MARKETING ASSOCIATION—See Missouri Farm Bureau; *U.S. Private*, pg. 2749
MISSOURI-AMERICAN WATER COMPANY—See American Water Works Company, Inc.; *U.S. Public*, pg. 112
MISSOURI ATHLETIC CLUB; *U.S. Private*, pg. 2749
MISSOURI BASIN WELL SERVICE, INC.; *U.S. Private*, pg. 2749
MISSOURI BOTANICAL GARDEN; *U.S. Private*, pg. 2749
MISSOURI CARE, INC.—See Centene Corporation; *U.S. Public*, pg. 471
MISSOURI COLLEGE, INC.—See Perdoceo Education Corporation; *U.S. Public*, pg. 1673
MISSOURI COOPERAGE CO. INC.—See Isco Holding Company Inc.; *U.S. Private*, pg. 2143
MISSOURI DELTA MEDICAL CENTER; *U.S. Private*, pg. 2749
MISSOURI DEPARTMENT OF TRANSPORTATION; *U.S. Private*, pg. 2749
MISSOURI DRYWALL SUPPLY, INC.—See GMS Inc.; *U.S. Public*, pg. 948
MISSOURI EAGLE LLC; *U.S. Private*, pg. 2749
MISSOURI EMPLOYERS MUTUAL INSURANCE CO., INC.; *U.S. Private*, pg. 2749
MISSOURI FARM BUREAU SERVICES—See Missouri Farm Bureau; *U.S. Private*, pg. 2749
MISSOURI FARM BUREAU; *U.S. Private*, pg. 2749
MISSOURI FURNITURE INC.; *U.S. Private*, pg. 2749
THE MISSOURI GAMING COMPANY, LLC—See PENN Entertainment, Inc.; *U.S. Public*, pg. 1662
MISSOURI GAS ENERGY EMPLOYEES' ASSOCIATION—See Energy Transfer LP; *U.S. Public*, pg. 763
MISSOURI GAS ENERGY INC.—See Spire, Inc; *U.S. Public*, pg. 1918
MISSOURI GREAT DANE—See Midway Trailers, Inc.; *U.S. Private*, pg. 2719
MISSOURI HOMECARE LLC—See UnitedHealth Group Incorporated; *U.S. Public*, pg. 2246
MISSOURI LAWYERS MEDIA, INC.—See The Dolan Company; *U.S. Private*, pg. 4022
MISSOURI LOGOS, LLC—See Lamar Advertising Company; *U.S. Public*, pg. 1291
MISSOURI METAL RECYCLING INC.—See Yaffe Iron & Metal Company Inc.; *U.S. Private*, pg. 4584
MISSOURI & NORTHERN ARKANSAS RAILROAD COMPANY, INC.—See Brookfield Infrastructure Partners L.P.; *Int'l*, pg. 1192
MISSOURI & NORTHERN ARKANSAS RAILROAD COMPANY, INC.—See GIC Pte. Ltd.; *Int'l*, pg. 2966

COMPANY NAME INDEX

MISSOURI-PACIFIC LUMBER COMPANY; *U.S. Private*, pg. 2749
MISSOURI PETROLEUM PRODUCTS CO., INC.—See Lionmark Inc.; *U.S. Private*, pg. 2464
MISSOURI POWER TRANSMISSION, INC.—See Genuine Parts Company; *U.S. Public*, pg. 933
MISSOURI SLOPE LUTHERAN CARE CENTER; *U.S. Private*, pg. 2749
MISSOURI TOOLING & AUTOMATION, LLC; *U.S. Private*, pg. 2749
MISSOURI VALLEY INC.; *U.S. Private*, pg. 2749
MISSOURI VALLEY PETROLEUM, INC.—See Parkland Corporation; *Int'l*, pg. 5743
MISSOURI VALLEY STEEL CO.—See Owen Industries, Inc.; *U.S. Private*, pg. 3054
MISS PAIGE LTD.; *U.S. Private*, pg. 2746
MISSRY ASSOCIATES INC.; *U.S. Private*, pg. 2749
MISS SPORTSWEAR INC.; *U.S. Private*, pg. 2746
MISS UNIVERSE, L.P.—See Silver Lake Group, LLC; *U.S. Private*, pg. 3657
MISS UNIVERSE, L.P.—See William Morris Endeavor Entertainment, LLC; *U.S. Private*, pg. 4524
MISSY FARREN & ASSOCIATES LTD.—See Finn Partners, Inc.; *U.S. Private*, pg. 1510
MISTAMERICA CORPORATION; *U.S. Private*, pg. 2749
MISTANGO RIVER RESOURCES INC.; *Int'l*, pg. 4921
MISTCO, INC.—See Rhode Island Novelty, Inc.; *U.S. Private*, pg. 3422
MISTEQUAY GROUP LTD. - BAY ROAD PLANT—See Mistequay Group Ltd.; *U.S. Private*, pg. 2749
MISTEQUAY GROUP LTD.; *U.S. Private*, pg. 2749
MISTEQUAY GROUP LTD. - STANDISH PLANT—See Mistequay Group Ltd.; *U.S. Private*, pg. 2749
MISTEQUAY INTERNATIONAL (PVT) LIMITED—See Mistequay Group Ltd.; *U.S. Private*, pg. 2749
MISTEQUAY—See Mistequay Group Ltd.; *U.S. Private*, pg. 2749
MISTER AUTO SAS—See Stellantis N.V.; *Int'l*, pg. 7202
MISTER CAR WASH, INC; *U.S. Public*, pg. 1450
MISTER CAR WASH—See Car Wash Partners, Inc.; *U.S. Private*, pg. 747
MISTER CAR WASH—See Car Wash Partners, Inc.; *U.S. Private*, pg. 748
MISTER SPEX SE; *Int'l*, pg. 4921
MISTER TWISTER, L.L.C.—See Sheldons' Inc.; *U.S. Private*, pg. 3631
MISTICO ACQUISITION CORP.; *U.S. Private*, pg. 2750
MISTLIN HONDA INC.; *U.S. Private*, pg. 2750
MIS TRAINING INSTITUTE, LLC—See Astorg Partners S.A.S.; *Int'l*, pg. 656
MIS TRAINING INSTITUTE, LLC—See Epiris Managers LLP; *Int'l*, pg. 2460
MISTRAL AIR SRL—See Poste Italiane S.p.A.; *Int'l*, pg. 5939
MISTRAL EQUITY PARTNERS LLC; *U.S. Private*, pg. 2750
MISTRAL GAYRIMENKUL YATIRIM ORTAKLIGI AS; *Int'l*, pg. 4921
MISTRAL (SINGAPORE) PTE. LTD.—See Khind Holdings Berhad; *Int'l*, pg. 4155
MISTRAS CAMBRIDGE—See Mistras Group, Inc.; *U.S. Public*, pg. 1451
MISTRAS CANADA, INC.—See Mistras Group, Inc.; *U.S. Public*, pg. 1451
MISTRAS GROUP BVBA—See Mistras Group, Inc.; *U.S. Public*, pg. 1451
MISTRAS GROUP B.V.—See Mistras Group, Inc.; *U.S. Public*, pg. 1451
MISTRAS GROUP GMBH—See Mistras Group, Inc.; *U.S. Public*, pg. 1451
MISTRAS GROUP HELLAS A.B.E.E.—See Mistras Group, Inc.; *U.S. Public*, pg. 1451
MISTRAS GROUP, INC.; *U.S. Public*, pg. 1451
MISTRAS GROUP LIMITED—See Mistras Group, Inc.; *U.S. Public*, pg. 1451
MISTRAS GROUP SAS—See Mistras Group, Inc.; *U.S. Public*, pg. 1451
MISTRAS HELLAS A.B.E.E.—See Mistras Group, Inc.; *U.S. Public*, pg. 1451
MISTRAS METALTEC INC.—See Mistras Group, Inc.; *U.S. Public*, pg. 1451
MISTRAS ROPEWORKS TRAINING CORP.—See Mistras Group, Inc.; *U.S. Public*, pg. 1451
MIST TECHNOLOGIES INC.—See Adways Inc.; *Int'l*, pg. 169
MISTY MOUNTAIN SPRING WATER CO. LLC—See K-VA-T Food Stores, Inc.; *U.S. Private*, pg. 2251
MISUMI (CHINA) PRECISION MACHINERY TRADING CO., LTD.—See MISUMI Group Inc.; *Int'l*, pg. 4922
MISUMI CORPORATION—See MISUMI Group Inc.; *Int'l*, pg. 4922
MISUMI E.A. HK LIMITED—See MISUMI Group Inc.; *Int'l*, pg. 4922
MISUMI EUROPA GMBH—See MISUMI Group Inc.; *Int'l*, pg. 4922
MISUMI GROUP INC.; *Int'l*, pg. 4921
MISUMI INDIA PVT LTD.—See MISUMI Group Inc.; *Int'l*, pg. 4922

MISUMI KOREA CORP.—See MISUMI Group Inc.; *Int'l*, pg. 4922
MISUMI MALAYSIA SDN. BHD.—See MISUMI Group Inc.; *Int'l*, pg. 4922
MISUMI MEXICO S. DE R.L. DE C.V—See MISUMI Group Inc.; *Int'l*, pg. 4922
MISUMI SOUTH EAST ASIA PTE. LTD.—See MISUMI Group Inc.; *Int'l*, pg. 4922
MISUMI TAIWAN CORP.—See MISUMI Group Inc.; *Int'l*, pg. 4922
MISUMI (THAILAND) CO., LTD.—See MISUMI Group Inc.; *Int'l*, pg. 4922
MISUMI USA, INC.—See MISUMI Group Inc.; *Int'l*, pg. 4922
MISUMI VIETNAM CO., LTD.—See MISUMI Group Inc.; *Int'l*, pg. 4922
MISUNG POLYTECH CO., LTD.; *Int'l*, pg. 4922
MISUZU CO., LTD.—See RIZAP GROUP, Inc.; *Int'l*, pg. 6354
MISUZU ERIE CO., LTD.—See Mitsubishi Chemical Group Corporation; *Int'l*, pg. 4931
MISUZU MACHINERY CO., LTD.—See Kawasaki Kisen Kaisha, Ltd.; *Int'l*, pg. 4100
MISYD CORP.; *U.S. Private*, pg. 2750
MISYS INTERNATIONAL BANKING SYSTEMS (CIS) LIMITED—See Vista Equity Partners, LLC; *U.S. Private*, pg. 4397
MISYS INTERNATIONAL BANKING SYSTEMS GMBH—See Vista Equity Partners, LLC; *U.S. Private*, pg. 4397
MISYS INTERNATIONAL BANKING SYSTEMS INC.—See Vista Equity Partners, LLC; *U.S. Private*, pg. 4397
MISYS INTERNATIONAL BANKING SYSTEMS K.K—See Vista Equity Partners, LLC; *U.S. Private*, pg. 4397
MISYS INTERNATIONAL BANKING SYSTEMS LIMITED—See Vista Equity Partners, LLC; *U.S. Private*, pg. 4397
MISYS INTERNATIONAL BANKING SYSTEMS LIMITED—See Vista Equity Partners, LLC; *U.S. Private*, pg. 4397
MISYS INTERNATIONAL BANKING SYSTEMS LIMITED—See Vista Equity Partners, LLC; *U.S. Private*, pg. 4397
MISYS INTERNATIONAL BANKING SYSTEMS MEXICO S.A. DE CV—See Vista Equity Partners, LLC; *U.S. Private*, pg. 4397
MISYS INTERNATIONAL BANKING SYSTEMS PTY LIMITED—See Vista Equity Partners, LLC; *U.S. Private*, pg. 4397
MISYS INTERNATIONAL BANKING SYSTEMS (RISK) LLC—See Vista Equity Partners, LLC; *U.S. Private*, pg. 4397
MISYS INTERNATIONAL BANKING SYSTEMS SA—See Vista Equity Partners, LLC; *U.S. Private*, pg. 4397
MISYS INTERNATIONAL BANKING SYSTEMS SA—See Vista Equity Partners, LLC; *U.S. Private*, pg. 4397
MISYS INTERNATIONAL FINANCIAL SYSTEMS PTE LIMITED—See Vista Equity Partners, LLC; *U.S. Private*, pg. 4397
MISYS INTERNATIONAL FINANCIAL SYSTEMS (PTY) LIMITED—See Vista Equity Partners, LLC; *U.S. Private*, pg. 4397
MISYS INTERNATIONAL FINANCIAL SYSTEMS S.L.—See Vista Equity Partners, LLC; *U.S. Private*, pg. 4397
MISYS INTERNATIONAL SYSTEMS SDN BHD—See Vista Equity Partners, LLC; *U.S. Private*, pg. 4397
MISYS IQ LLC—See Vista Equity Partners, LLC; *U.S. Private*, pg. 4397
MISYS NETHERLANDS BV—See Vista Equity Partners, LLC; *U.S. Private*, pg. 4397
MISYS PHILIPPINES INC—See Vista Equity Partners, LLC; *U.S. Private*, pg. 4397
MISYS RETAIL BANKING SYSTEMS LTD—See Vista Equity Partners, LLC; *U.S. Private*, pg. 4397
MISYS RISK MANAGEMENT SYSTEMS LTD—See Vista Equity Partners, LLC; *U.S. Private*, pg. 4397
MISYS SERVICES LIMITED—See Vista Equity Partners, LLC; *U.S. Private*, pg. 4397
MISYS SOFTWARE SOLUTIONS (INDIA) PRIVATE LIMITED—See Vista Equity Partners, LLC; *U.S. Private*, pg. 4397
MISYS WHOLESALE BANKING SYSTEMS—See Vista Equity Partners, LLC; *U.S. Private*, pg. 4397
MITAC AUSTRALIA PTY LTD.—See MiTAC International Corp.; *Int'l*, pg. 4923
MITAC BENELUX N.V.—See MiTAC Holdings Corporation; *Int'l*, pg. 4923
MITAC COMMUNICATIONS CO., LTD.—See MiTAC International Corp.; *Int'l*, pg. 4923
MITAC COMPUTER (BEIJING) LTD.—See MiTAC International Corp.; *Int'l*, pg. 4923
MITAC COMPUTER (KUNSHAN) LTD.—See MiTAC International Corp.; *Int'l*, pg. 4923
MITAC COMPUTER (SHANGHAI), LTD.—See MiTAC International Corp.; *Int'l*, pg. 4923
MITAC COMPUTERS (SHUNDE) LTD.—See MiTAC International Corp.; *Int'l*, pg. 4923

MITAC DIGITAL CORP.—See MiTAC Holdings Corporation; *Int'l*, pg. 4923
MITAC DIGITAL TECHNOLOGY CORPORATION—See MiTAC Holdings Corporation; *Int'l*, pg. 4923
MITAC EUROPE LTD.—See MiTAC International Corp.; *Int'l*, pg. 4923
MITACHI CO., LTD.; *Int'l*, pg. 4924
MITACHI ELECTRONICS (SH) CO., LTD.—See MITACHI Co., LTD.; *Int'l*, pg. 4924
MITACHI ELECTRONICS (SZ) CO., LTD.—See MITACHI Co., LTD.; *Int'l*, pg. 4924
MITACHI (HK) CO., LTD.—See MITACHI Co., LTD.; *Int'l*, pg. 4924
MITACHI (THAILAND) CO., LTD.—See MITACHI Co., LTD.; *Int'l*, pg. 4924
MITAC HOLDINGS CORPORATION; *Int'l*, pg. 4923
MITAC INC.—See MiTAC International Corp.; *Int'l*, pg. 4923
MITAC INTERNATIONAL CORP. - HSIN-CHU FACTORY—See MiTAC International Corp.; *Int'l*, pg. 4923
MITAC INTERNATIONAL CORP.; *Int'l*, pg. 4923
MITAC JAPAN CORP.—See MiTAC International Corp.; *Int'l*, pg. 4923
MITAC RESEARCH (SHANGHAI) LTD.—See MiTAC International Corp.; *Int'l*, pg. 4923
MITAC SERVICE (SHANGHAI) CO., LTD.—See MiTAC International Corp.; *Int'l*, pg. 4923
MITAC TECHNOLOGY CORP.—See MiTAC International Corp.; *Int'l*, pg. 4923
MITA GROUP SAATCHI & SAATCHI/PUBLICIS—See Publicis Groupe S.A.; *Int'l*, pg. 6108
MITAKE INFORMATION CORP.; *Int'l*, pg. 4924
MITANI COMPUTER CORP.—See Mitani Corporation; *Int'l*, pg. 4924
MITANI CORPORATION; *Int'l*, pg. 4924
MITANI ENGINEERING CO., LTD.—See Mitani Sekisan Co., Ltd.; *Int'l*, pg. 4925
MITANI SANGYO ADONIS CO., LTD.—See Mitani Sangyo Co., Ltd.; *Int'l*, pg. 4925
MITANI SANGYO CO., LTD.; *Int'l*, pg. 4924
MITANI SANGYO CONSTRUCTIONS CO., LTD.—See Mitani Sangyo Co., Ltd.; *Int'l*, pg. 4925
MITANI SANGYO EC CO., LTD.—See Mitani Sangyo Co., Ltd.; *Int'l*, pg. 4925
MITANI SEKISAN CO., LTD.; *Int'l*, pg. 4925
MITAS D.O.O. RUMA—See Trelleborg AB; *Int'l*, pg. 7910
M.I.T.A.—See Publicis Groupe S.A.; *Int'l*, pg. 6102
MITA-TEKNIK A/S—See Axcel Management A/S; *Int'l*, pg. 762
MITA-TEKNIK LLC—See Axcel Management A/S; *Int'l*, pg. 762
MITA-TEKNIK (NINGBO) CO. LTD.—See Axcel Management A/S; *Int'l*, pg. 762
MITA-TEKNIK TECHNOLOGY PRIVATE LTD—See Axcel Management A/S; *Int'l*, pg. 762
MITCHAM CANADA LTD.—See MIND Technology, Inc.; *U.S. Public*, pg. 1448
MITCHAM CANADA ULC—See MIND Technology, Inc.; *U.S. Public*, pg. 1448
MITCHAM SEISMIC EURASIA, LLC—See MIND Technology, Inc.; *U.S. Public*, pg. 1448
MITCHCO INTERNATIONAL INC.; *U.S. Private*, pg. 2750
MITCH CRAWFORD'S HOLIDAY MOTORS CO.; *U.S. Private*, pg. 2750
MITCHELL AUTOMOTIVE, INC.; *U.S. Private*, pg. 2750
MITCHELL BEVERAGE, LLC—See Mitchell Companies; *U.S. Private*, pg. 2750
MITCHELL COMMUNICATIONS GROUP; *U.S. Private*, pg. 2750
MITCHELL COMPANIES; *U.S. Private*, pg. 2750
THE MITCHELL COMPANY, INC.; *U.S. Private*, pg. 4080
MITCHELL DIESEL LIMITED - CENTRAL DIESEL DIVISION—See Turner & Co. (Glasgow) Limited; *Int'l*, pg. 7978
MITCHELL DIESEL LIMITED - CENTRAL DRIVELINE DIVISION—See Turner & Co. (Glasgow) Limited; *Int'l*, pg. 7978
MITCHELL DISTRIBUTING COMPANY, INC.—See Mitchell Companies; *U.S. Private*, pg. 2750
MITCHELL ELECTRIC MEMBERSHIP CORPORATION; *U.S. Private*, pg. 2750
MITCHELL ENTERPRISES INC.; *U.S. Private*, pg. 2750
MITCHELL GOLD & BOB WILLIAMS—See Wafra Investment Advisory Group, Inc.; *U.S. Private*, pg. 4425
MITCHELL GROCERY CORP.; *U.S. Private*, pg. 2750
MITCHEL-LINCOLN PACKAGING LTD; *Int'l*, pg. 4925
MITCHELL INDUSTRIAL CONTRACTORS, INC.; *U.S. Private*, pg. 2750
MITCHELL INTERNATIONAL, INC.—See Stone Point Capital LLC; *U.S. Private*, pg. 3823
MITCHELL LEWIS & STAVER CO.; *U.S. Private*, pg. 2750
MITCHELL, LINDBERG & TAYLOR, INC.; *U.S. Private*, pg. 2751
MITCHELL MANNING ASSOCIATES, LTD.; *U.S. Private*, pg. 2750
MITCHELL MARTIN, INC.; *U.S. Private*, pg. 2750
MITCHELL MILL SYSTEMS USA INC—See Ag Growth International Inc.; *Int'l*, pg. 198

MITCHELL MARTIN, INC.

MITCHELL & MORONESO INSURANCE SERVICES INC.—See Aon plc; *Int'l*, pg. 496
MITCHELL MOTORS INC.; *U.S. Private*, pg. 2751
MITCHELL & NESS NOSTALGIA COMPANY—See Juggernaut Management, LLC; *U.S. Private*, pg. 2243
MITCHELL ONE—See Snap-on Incorporated; *U.S. Public*, pg. 1897
MITCHELL PONTIAC INC.; *U.S. Private*, pg. 2751
MITCHELL POWERSYSTEMS LTD—See Turner & Co. (Glasgow) Limited; *Int'l*, pg. 7978
MITCHELL, REED & SCHMITTEN INSURANCE, INC.—See Cashmere Valley Bank; *U.S. Public*, pg. 446
MITCHELL REPAIR INFORMATION COMPANY, LLC—See Snap-on Incorporated; *U.S. Public*, pg. 1897
MITCHELL & RESNIKOFF; *U.S. Private*, pg. 2750
MITCHELL RUBBER PRODUCTS INC.; *U.S. Private*, pg. 2751
MITCHELLS & BUTLERS GERMANY GMBH—See Mitchells & Butlers Plc; *Int'l*, pg. 4925
MITCHELLS & BUTLERS LEISURE RETAIL LTD.—See Mitchells & Butlers Plc; *Int'l*, pg. 4925
MITCHELLS & BUTLERS PLC; *Int'l*, pg. 4925
MITCHELLS & BUTLERS RETAIL LTD.—See Mitchells & Butlers Plc; *Int'l*, pg. 4925
MITCHELLS & BUTLERS RETAIL (NO 2) LTD.—See Mitchells & Butlers Plc; *Int'l*, pg. 4925
MITCHELL SERVICES LIMITED; *Int'l*, pg. 4925
MITCHELL'S FRUIT FARMS LIMITED; *Int'l*, pg. 4925
MITCHELL SILBERBERG & KNUPP LLP; *U.S. Private*, pg. 2751
MITCHELLS SALON & DAY SPA; *U.S. Private*, pg. 2751
MITCHELL & STARK CONSTRUCTION CO. INC.; *U.S. Private*, pg. 2750
MITCHELL & TITUS LLP; *U.S. Private*, pg. 2750
MITCHEL & SCOTT MACHINE COMPANY, INC.; *U.S. Private*, pg. 2750
MITCO GROUP LTD.—See CIEL Ltd.; *Int'l*, pg. 1605
MITCON CONSULTANCY & ENGINEERING SERVICES LTD.; *Int'l*, pg. 4925
MITCON TRUSTEESHIP SERVICES LIMITED—See MITCON Consultancy & Engineering Services Ltd.; *Int'l*, pg. 4925
MITECH LIMITED; *Int'l*, pg. 4925
MI TECHNOLOGIES, INC.; *U.S. Private*, pg. 2695
MI TECHNOLOGY GROUP LTD.—See CSA Group; *Int'l*, pg. 1861
MI TECHNOVATION BERHAD; *Int'l*, pg. 4873
MITEC INC.—See TIS Inc.; *Int'l*, pg. 7757
MITEK CANADA, INC.—See Berkshire Hathaway Inc.; *U.S. Public*, pg. 313
MITEK CORPORATION - MONROE FACILITY—See MiTek Corporation; *U.S. Private*, pg. 2751
MITEK CORPORATION; *U.S. Private*, pg. 2751
MITEK INDUSTRIES, INC.—See Berkshire Hathaway Inc.; *U.S. Public*, pg. 312
MITEKS A.D.; *Int'l*, pg. 4925
MITEK SYSTEMS B.V.—See Mitek Systems, Inc.; *U.S. Public*, pg. 1452
MITEK SYSTEMS, INC.; *U.S. Public*, pg. 1451
MITEK SYSTEMS PRIVATE LIMITED—See Mitek Systems, Inc.; *U.S. Public*, pg. 1452
MITEK USA, INC.—See Berkshire Hathaway Inc.; *U.S. Public*, pg. 313
MITEL BELGIUM SA—See Searchlight Capital Partners, L.P.; *U.S. Private*, pg. 3589
MITEL BUSINESS SYSTEMS, INC.—See Searchlight Capital Partners, L.P.; *U.S. Private*, pg. 3589
MITEL COMMUNICATIONS AB—See Searchlight Capital Partners, L.P.; *U.S. Private*, pg. 3588
MITEL COMMUNICATIONS FINLAND AB—See Searchlight Capital Partners, L.P.; *U.S. Private*, pg. 3589
MITEL COMMUNICATIONS INC—See Searchlight Capital Partners, L.P.; *U.S. Private*, pg. 3589
MITEL COMMUNICATIONS PRIVATE LIMITED—See Searchlight Capital Partners, L.P.; *U.S. Private*, pg. 3589
MITEL DANMARK A/S—See Searchlight Capital Partners, L.P.; *U.S. Private*, pg. 3588
MITEL DEUTSCHLAND GMBH—See Searchlight Capital Partners, L.P.; *U.S. Private*, pg. 3589
MITEL FRANCE SAS—See Searchlight Capital Partners, L.P.; *U.S. Private*, pg. 3589
MITEL INCORPORATED MEXICO S.A. DE C.V.—See Searchlight Capital Partners, L.P.; *U.S. Private*, pg. 3589
MITEL ITALIA S.P.A.—See Searchlight Capital Partners, L.P.; *U.S. Private*, pg. 3589
MITEL LEASE SA—See Searchlight Capital Partners, L.P.; *U.S. Private*, pg. 3589
MITEL LEASING, INC.—See Searchlight Capital Partners, L.P.; *U.S. Private*, pg. 3589
MITEL MOBILITY INC—See Searchlight Capital Partners, L.P.; *U.S. Private*, pg. 3589
MITEL NETHERLANDS B.V.—See Searchlight Capital Partners, L.P.; *U.S. Private*, pg. 3589
MITEL NETSOLUTIONS, INC.—See Searchlight Capital Partners, L.P.; *U.S. Private*, pg. 3589
MITEL NETWORKS ASIA PACIFIC LTD.—See Searchlight Capital Partners, L.P.; *U.S. Private*, pg. 3589
MITEL NETWORKS CORPORATION—See Searchlight Capital Partners, L.P.; *U.S. Private*, pg. 3588
MITEL NETWORKS HOLDINGS LIMITED—See Searchlight Capital Partners, L.P.; *U.S. Private*, pg. 3589
MITEL NETWORKS, INC.—See Searchlight Capital Partners, L.P.; *U.S. Private*, pg. 3589
MITEL NETWORKS LTD.—See Searchlight Capital Partners, L.P.; *U.S. Private*, pg. 3589
MITEL NETWORKS LTD.—See Searchlight Capital Partners, L.P.; *U.S. Private*, pg. 3589
MITEL NETWORKS (NEW ZEALAND) LIMITED—See Searchlight Capital Partners, L.P.; *U.S. Private*, pg. 3589
MITEL NETWORKS SOLUTIONS INC—See Searchlight Capital Partners, L.P.; *U.S. Private*, pg. 3589
MITEL NETWORKS SOUTH AFRICA (PTY) LIMITED—See Searchlight Capital Partners, L.P.; *U.S. Private*, pg. 3589
MITEL NORWAY AS—See Searchlight Capital Partners, L.P.; *U.S. Private*, pg. 3589
MITEL PORTUGAL S.A.—See Searchlight Capital Partners, L.P.; *U.S. Private*, pg. 3589
MITEL SCHWEIZ AG—See Searchlight Capital Partners, L.P.; *U.S. Private*, pg. 3589
MITEL SOUTH AFRICA—See Searchlight Capital Partners, L.P.; *U.S. Private*, pg. 3589
MITEL SOUTH PACIFIC PTY. LIMITED—See Searchlight Capital Partners, L.P.; *U.S. Private*, pg. 3589
MITEL SPAIN, S.L.—See Searchlight Capital Partners, L.P.; *U.S. Private*, pg. 3589
MITEL SWEDEN AB—See Searchlight Capital Partners, L.P.; *U.S. Private*, pg. 3589
MITEL TECHNOLOGIES, INC.—See Searchlight Capital Partners, L.P.; *U.S. Private*, pg. 3589
MITEM CORPORATION; *U.S. Private*, pg. 2751
MITEMO CO., LTD.—See Insource Co., Ltd.; *Int'l*, pg. 3719
MITENI S.P.A.—See International Chemical Investors S.E.; *Int'l*, pg. 3745
MITERA S.A.—See DIAGNOSTIC AND THERAPEUTIC CENTER OF ATHENS-HYGEIA S.A.; *Int'l*, pg. 2103
MITERI DEVELOPMENT BANK LTD.; *Int'l*, pg. 4925
MITESCO, INC.; *U.S. Public*, pg. 1452
MITEX INTERNATIONAL (H.K.) LTD.—See Mitsui-Soko Holdings Co., Ltd.; *Int'l*, pg. 4992
MITEX INTERNATIONAL (HONG KONG) LTD.—See Mitsui-Soko Holdings Co., Ltd.; *Int'l*, pg. 4992
MITEX LOGISTICS (SHANGHAI) CO., LTD.—See Mitsui-Soko Holdings Co., Ltd.; *Int'l*, pg. 4992
MITEX MULTIMODAL EXPRESS LTD.—See Mitsui-Soko Holdings Co., Ltd.; *Int'l*, pg. 4992
MITEX SHENZHEN LOGISTICS CO., LTD.—See Mitsui-Soko Holdings Co., Ltd.; *Int'l*, pg. 4992
MITEX (TIANJIN) CO., LTD.—See Mitsui-Soko Holdings Co., Ltd.; *Int'l*, pg. 4992
MITGAS MITTELDEUTSCHE GASVERSORGUNG GMBH—See RWE AG; *Int'l*, pg. 6434
MITHOFF BURTON PARTNERS; *U.S. Private*, pg. 2751
MIT HOLDINGS CO., LTD.; *Int'l*, pg. 4922
MITHRA PHARMACEUTICALS CDMO SA—See Mithra Pharmaceuticals S.A.; *Int'l*, pg. 4925
MITHRA PHARMACEUTICALS S.A.; *Int'l*, pg. 4925
MITHRAS UNDERWRITING EUROPE S.R.L.—See Brown & Brown, Inc.; *U.S. Public*, pg. 401
MITHRAS UNDERWRITING ITALIA S.R.L.—See Brown & Brown, Inc.; *U.S. Public*, pg. 401
MITHRAS UNDERWRITING LTD.—See Brown & Brown, Inc.; *U.S. Public*, pg. 401
MITHRIL BERHAD; *Int'l*, pg. 4925
MITHRIL RESOURCES LTD; *Int'l*, pg. 4925
MITHRIL SAFERAY SDN. BHD.—See Mithril Berhad; *Int'l*, pg. 4925
MITHUN INC.; *U.S. Private*, pg. 2751
MITIE ASSET MANAGEMENT LTD—See MITIE Group Plc; *Int'l*, pg. 4926
MITIE AVIATION SECURITY LTD.—See MITIE Group Plc; *Int'l*, pg. 4926
MITIE BUSINESS SERVICES LTD.—See MITIE Group Plc; *Int'l*, pg. 4926
MITIE CATERING SERVICE (LONDON) LTD.—See MITIE Group Plc; *Int'l*, pg. 4926
MITIE CATERING SERVICES LTD.—See MITIE Group Plc; *Int'l*, pg. 4926
MITIE CLEANING SERVICES LTD.—See MITIE Group Plc; *Int'l*, pg. 4926
MITIE CLEANING & SUPPORT SERVICES LIMITED—See MITIE Group Plc; *Int'l*, pg. 4926
MITIE CLIENT SERVICES LIMITED—See MITIE Group Plc; *Int'l*, pg. 4926
MITIE ENERGY LTD.—See MITIE Group Plc; *Int'l*, pg. 4926
MITIE ENGINEERING MAINTENANCE (CALEDONIA) LTD.—See MITIE Group Plc; *Int'l*, pg. 4926
MITIE ENGINEERING MAINTENANCE LTD.—See MITIE Group Plc; *Int'l*, pg. 4926
MITIE ENGINEERING MAINTENANCE (NORTH) LTD.—See MITIE Group Plc; *Int'l*, pg. 4926
MITIE ENGINEERING PROJECTS LTD.—See MITIE Group Plc; *Int'l*, pg. 4926

CORPORATE AFFILIATIONS

MITIE ENGINEERING SERVICES (BRISTOL) LTD.—See MITIE Group Plc; *Int'l*, pg. 4926
MITIE ENGINEERING SERVICES (EDINBURGH) LTD.—See MITIE Group Plc; *Int'l*, pg. 4926
MITIE ENGINEERING SERVICES (GUERNSEY) LTD.—See MITIE Group Plc; *Int'l*, pg. 4926
MITIE ENGINEERING SERVICES LTD.—See MITIE Group Plc; *Int'l*, pg. 4926
MITIE ENGINEERING SERVICES (NORTH EAST) LTD.—See MITIE Group Plc; *Int'l*, pg. 4926
MITIE ENGINEERING SERVICES (SCOTLAND) LTD.—See MITIE Group Plc; *Int'l*, pg. 4926
MITIE ENGINEERING SERVICES (SE REGION) LTD.—See MITIE Group Plc; *Int'l*, pg. 4926
MITIE ENGINEERING SERVICES (SOUTH EAST) LTD.—See MITIE Group Plc; *Int'l*, pg. 4926
MITIE ENGINEERING SERVICES (SOUTH WEST) LTD.—See MITIE Group Plc; *Int'l*, pg. 4926
MITIE ENGINEERING SERVICES (SWANSEA) LTD.—See MITIE Group Plc; *Int'l*, pg. 4926
MITIE ENGINEERING SERVICES (WEST MIDLANDS) LTD.—See MITIE Group Plc; *Int'l*, pg. 4927
MITIE FACILITIES SERVICES LTD—See MITIE Group Plc; *Int'l*, pg. 4927
MITIE GROUP PLC; *Int'l*, pg. 4926
MITIE INTERIORS LTD.—See MITIE Group Plc; *Int'l*, pg. 4927
MITIE LYNDHURST SERVICES LIMITED—See MITIE Group Plc; *Int'l*, pg. 4927
MITIE PEST CONTROL LTD.—See Rentokil Initial plc; *Int'l*, pg. 6287
MITIE PFI LTD.—See MITIE Group Plc; *Int'l*, pg. 4927
MITIE PROPERTY SERVICES - AIRDRIE—See MITIE Group Plc; *Int'l*, pg. 4927
MITIE PROPERTY SERVICES - CIRENCESTER—See MITIE Group Plc; *Int'l*, pg. 4927
MITIE PROPERTY SERVICES (EASTERN) LTD.—See MITIE Group Plc; *Int'l*, pg. 4927
MITIE PROPERTY SERVICES (NORTH EAST) LTD.—See MITIE Group Plc; *Int'l*, pg. 4927
MITIE PROPERTY SERVICES (SCOTLAND) LTD.—See MITIE Group Plc; *Int'l*, pg. 4927
MITIE PROPERTY SERVICES (UK) LTD.—See MITIE Group Plc; *Int'l*, pg. 4927
MITIE SCOTGATE LTD.—See MITIE Group Plc; *Int'l*, pg. 4927
MITIE SECURITY HOLDINGS LTD.—See MITIE Group Plc; *Int'l*, pg. 4927
MITIE SECURITY (LONDON) LTD.—See MITIE Group Plc; *Int'l*, pg. 4927
MITIE SECURITY LTD.—See MITIE Group Plc; *Int'l*, pg. 4927
MITIE SECURITY (NORTH) LTD.—See MITIE Group Plc; *Int'l*, pg. 4927
MITIE SECURITY (SCOTLAND) LTD.—See MITIE Group Plc; *Int'l*, pg. 4927
MITIE SECURITY SYSTEMS LTD.—See MITIE Group Plc; *Int'l*, pg. 4927
MITIE SERVICES (RETAIL) LIMITED—See MITIE Group Plc; *Int'l*, pg. 4926
MITIE TECHNOLOGY & INFRASTRUCTURE LTD.—See MITIE Group Plc; *Int'l*, pg. 4927
MITIE TRANSPORT SERVICES LIMITED—See MITIE Group Plc; *Int'l*, pg. 4926
MITIM S.R.L.—See Recipharm AB; *Int'l*, pg. 6235
M/I TITLE AGENCY LTD.—See M/I Homes, Inc.; *U.S. Public*, pg. 1351
MI-T-M CORPORATION; *U.S. Private*, pg. 2696
MIT NATIONAL LAND SERVICES LLC—See Newmark Group, Inc.; *U.S. Public*, pg. 1515
MITOBIT S.R.L.—See Tas Tecnologia Avanzata Dei Sistemi Spa; *Int'l*, pg. 7464
MITO CORPORATION; *U.S. Private*, pg. 2751
MITOMO BRAKE CO., LTD.—See Tokai Carbon Co., Ltd.; *Int'l*, pg. 7778
MI TOMONOKAI CO., LTD.—See Isetan Mitsukoshi Holdings Ltd.; *Int'l*, pg. 3815
MITOMO SEMICON ENGINEERING CO., LTD.—See Tanaka Holdings Co., Ltd.; *Int'l*, pg. 7455
MITON GROUP LIMITED—See Premier Miton Group plc; *Int'l*, pg. 5961
MITON UK MICROCAP TRUST PLC; *Int'l*, pg. 4927
MITO PHARMACY CO., LTD.—See Kamei Corporation; *Int'l*, pg. 4061
MITORIZ CO., LTD.—See Softbrain Co., Ltd.; *Int'l*, pg. 7054
MITOSCIENCES INC.—See Danaher Corporation; *U.S. Public*, pg. 624
MITO SECURITIES CO., LTD.; *Int'l*, pg. 4927
MIT PATHANA HOMESHOPPING CO., LTD.—See Saha Pathanapibul Public Company Limited; *Int'l*, pg. 6479
MIT POWER CANADA LP INC.—See Mitsui & Co., Ltd.; *Int'l*, pg. 4973
MITRA BINTANG SDN. BHD.—See TSA Industries Sdn. Bhd.; *Int'l*, pg. 7949
MITRACO LIVESTOCK JOINT STOCK COMPANY; *Int'l*, pg. 4927
MITRADIOPHARMA S.R.L.—See Deutsche Post AG; *Int'l*, pg. 2081

COMPANY NAME INDEX

MITRAIS PTE. LTD.—See CAC Holdings Corporation; *Int'l*, pg. 1247
MITRAJAYA DEVELOPMENT SA (PTY) LTD.—See Mitrajaya Holdings Berhad; *Int'l*, pg. 4928
MITRAJAYA HOLDINGS BERHAD; *Int'l*, pg. 4927
MITRAJAYA HOMES SDN. BHD.—See Mitrajaya Holdings Berhad; *Int'l*, pg. 4928
MITRAS AUTOMOTIVE (UK) LTD.—See senata GmbH; *Int'l*, pg. 6707
MITRAS COMPOSITES SYSTEMS GMBH—See senata GmbH; *Int'l*, pg. 6707
MITRAS MATERIALS GMBH—See senata GmbH; *Int'l*, pg. 6707
MITRASTAR TECHNOLOGY CORPORATION—See Unizyx Holding Corporation; *Int'l*, pg. 8084
MITRATECH HOLDINGS, INC.—See Ontario Teachers' Pension Plan; *Int'l*, pg. 5586
THE MITRE CORPORATION; *U.S. Private*, pg. 4080
THE MITRE CORPORATION; *U.S. Private*, pg. 4080
MITRONIC GMBH—See Dr. Honle AG; *Int'l*, pg. 2192
MITROSREM A.D.; *Int'l*, pg. 4928
MITR PHOL SUGARCANE RESEARCH CENTRE CO., LTD.—See Mitr Phol Sugar Corporation Limited; *Int'l*, pg. 4927
MITR PHOL SUGAR CORPORATION LIMITED; *Int'l*, pg. 4927
MIT (SHANGHAI) CO. LTD.—See Manufacturing Integration Technology Ltd; *Int'l*, pg. 4677
MITSHI INDIA LIMITED; *Int'l*, pg. 4928
MITSIAM INTERNATIONAL, LTD.—See Mitsui & Co., Ltd.; *Int'l*, pg. 4974
MITSIAM MOTORS CO., LTD.—See Mitsui & Co., Ltd.; *Int'l*, pg. 4974
MITSIB LEASING PUBLIC COMPANY LIMITED; *Int'l*, pg. 4928
MITSIDES PUBLIC COMPANY LTD; *Int'l*, pg. 4928
MIT SIM S.P.A.; *Int'l*, pg. 4923
MITS LOGISTICS (THAILAND) CO., LTD.—See Mitsui-Soko Holdings Co., Ltd.; *Int'l*, pg. 4992
MITS TRANSPORT (THAILAND) CO., LTD.—See Mitsui-Soko Holdings Co., Ltd.; *Int'l*, pg. 4992
MITSUBA ABILITY STAFF CORPORATION—See MITSUBA Corporation; *Int'l*, pg. 4928
MITSUBA ASIA R&D CO., LTD.—See MITSUBA Corporation; *Int'l*, pg. 4928
MITSUBA AUTOMOTIVE SYSTEMS OF EUROPE KFT.—See MITSUBA Corporation; *Int'l*, pg. 4928
MITSUBA AUTOMOTIVE TECHNOLOGY (SHANGHAI) CO., LTD.—See MITSUBA Corporation; *Int'l*, pg. 4929
MITSUBA AUTOPARTS DO BRASIL INDUSTRIA LTDA.—See MITSUBA Corporation; *Int'l*, pg. 4929
MITSUBA BARDSTOWN, INC.—See MITSUBA Corporation; *Int'l*, pg. 4929
MITSUBA CHINA (HONG KONG) LTD.—See MITSUBA Corporation; *Int'l*, pg. 4929
MITSUBA CORP. - FUKUSHIMA PLANT—See MITSUBA Corporation; *Int'l*, pg. 4928
MITSUBA CORP. - NIIGATA PLANT—See MITSUBA Corporation; *Int'l*, pg. 4928
MITSUBA CORP. - NIISATO PLANT—See MITSUBA Corporation; *Int'l*, pg. 4928
MITSUBA CORP. - ONISHI PLANT—See MITSUBA Corporation; *Int'l*, pg. 4928
MITSUBA CORPORATION; *Int'l*, pg. 4928
MITSUBA CORP. - TOMIOKA PLANT—See MITSUBA Corporation; *Int'l*, pg. 4928
MITSUBA CORP. - TONE PLANT—See MITSUBA Corporation; *Int'l*, pg. 4928
MITSUBA DO BRASIL LTDA.—See MITSUBA Corporation; *Int'l*, pg. 4929
MITSUBA ELECTRIC (DALIAN) CO., LTD.—See MITSUBA Corporation; *Int'l*, pg. 4929
MITSUBA ENVIRONMENTAL ANALYSIS AND RESEARCH CORPORATION—See MITSUBA Corporation; *Int'l*, pg. 4929
MITSUBA GERMANY GMBH—See MITSUBA Corporation; *Int'l*, pg. 4929
MITSUBA HARVEST CO., LTD.—See MITSUBA Corporation; *Int'l*, pg. 4929
MITSUBA INDIA PVT. LTD.—See MITSUBA Corporation; *Int'l*, pg. 4929
MITSUBA ITALIA S.P.A.—See MITSUBA Corporation; *Int'l*, pg. 4929
MITSUBA LOGISTICS CO., LTD.—See MITSUBA Corporation; *Int'l*, pg. 4929
MITSUBA MANUFACTURING FRANCE S.A.—See MITSUBA Corporation; *Int'l*, pg. 4929
MITSUBA MANUFACTURING MOROCCO SARL AU—See MITSUBA Corporation; *Int'l*, pg. 4929
MITSUBA MITSUBA TURKEY OTOMOTIV A.S.—See MITSUBA Corporation; *Int'l*, pg. 4929
MITSUBA M-TECH VIETNAM CO., LTD.—See MITSUBA Corporation; *Int'l*, pg. 4929
MITSUBA PHILIPPINES CORP.—See MITSUBA Corporation; *Int'l*, pg. 4929
MITSUBA PHILIPPINES TECHNICAL CENTER CORPORATION—See MITSUBA Corporation; *Int'l*, pg. 4929
MITSUBA RUS LLC—See MITSUBA Corporation; *Int'l*, pg. 4929
MITSUBA SANKOWA CORPORATION—See MITSUBA Corporation; *Int'l*, pg. 4929
MITSUBA SHIHLIN ELECTRIC (WUHAN) CO., LTD.—See MITSUBA Corporation; *Int'l*, pg. 4929
MITSUBA VIETNAM CO., LTD.—See MITSUBA Corporation; *Int'l*, pg. 4929
MITSUBA VIETNAM TECHNICAL CENTER CO., LTD.—See MITSUBA Corporation; *Int'l*, pg. 4929
MITSUBISHI AGRICULTURAL MACHINERY CO., LTD.—See Mitsubishi Heavy Industries, Ltd.; *Int'l*, pg. 4956
MITSUBISHI AIRCRAFT CORPORATION AMERICA, INC.—See Mitsubishi Heavy Industries, Ltd.; *Int'l*, pg. 4956
MITSUBISHI ALUMINUM CO., LTD.—See Mitsubishi Materials Corporation; *Int'l*, pg. 4964
MITSUBISHI AUSTRALIA LTD.—See Mitsubishi Corporation; *Int'l*, pg. 4940
MITSUBISHI AUTO LEASING CORPORATION—See Mitsubishi HC Capital Inc.; *Int'l*, pg. 4952
MITSUBISHI AUTOMOTIVE ACCESSORIES & PRODUCTS CO., LTD.—See Mitsubishi Motors Corporation; *Int'l*, pg. 4966
MITSUBISHI AUTOMOTIVE LOGISTICS TECHNOLOGY CO., LTD.—See Mitsubishi Motors Corporation; *Int'l*, pg. 4966
MITSUBISHI CABLE AMERICA, INC.—See Mitsubishi Materials Corporation; *Int'l*, pg. 4964
MITSUBISHI CABLE INDUSTRIES, LTD.—See Mitsubishi Materials Corporation; *Int'l*, pg. 4964
MITSUBISHI CANADA LIMITED—See Mitsubishi Corporation; *Int'l*, pg. 4941
MITSUBISHI CATERPILLAR FORKLIFT AMERICA INC.—See Mitsubishi Heavy Industries, Ltd.; *Int'l*, pg. 4959
MITSUBISHI CATERPILLAR FORKLIFT ASIA PTE. LTD.—See Mitsubishi Heavy Industries, Ltd.; *Int'l*, pg. 4959
MITSUBISHI CATERPILLAR FORKLIFT EUROPE B.V.—See Mitsubishi Heavy Industries, Ltd.; *Int'l*, pg. 1069
MITSUBISHI CEMENT CORPORATION—See Mitsubishi Materials Corporation; *Int'l*, pg. 4964
MITSUBISHI CHEMICAL ADVANCED MATERIALS AG—See Mitsubishi Chemical Group Corporation; *Int'l*, pg. 4930
MITSUBISHI CHEMICAL ADVANCED MATERIALS INC.—See Mitsubishi Chemical Group Corporation; *Int'l*, pg. 4930
MITSUBISHI CHEMICAL AGRI DREAM CO., LTD.—See Mitsubishi Chemical Group Corporation; *Int'l*, pg. 4931
MITSUBISHI CHEMICAL CHINA COMMERCE LIMITED—See Mitsubishi Chemical Group Corporation; *Int'l*, pg. 4931
MITSUBISHI CHEMICAL CLEANSUI CORPORATION—See Mitsubishi Chemical Group Corporation; *Int'l*, pg. 4932
MITSUBISHI CHEMICAL CORPORATION - KASHIMA PLANT—See Mitsubishi Chemical Group Corporation; *Int'l*, pg. 4932
MITSUBISHI CHEMICAL CORPORATION - KUROSAKI PLANT—See Mitsubishi Chemical Group Corporation; *Int'l*, pg. 4932
MITSUBISHI CHEMICAL CORPORATION - MIZUSHIMA PLANT—See Mitsubishi Chemical Group Corporation; *Int'l*, pg. 4932
MITSUBISHI CHEMICAL CORPORATION - SAKAIDE PLANT—See Mitsubishi Chemical Group Corporation; *Int'l*, pg. 4932
MITSUBISHI CHEMICAL CORPORATION—See Mitsubishi Chemical Group Corporation; *Int'l*, pg. 4930
MITSUBISHI CHEMICAL CORPORATION - TSUKUBA PLANT—See Mitsubishi Chemical Group Corporation; *Int'l*, pg. 4932
MITSUBISHI CHEMICAL CORPORATION - YOKKAICHI PLANT—See Mitsubishi Chemical Group Corporation; *Int'l*, pg. 4932
MITSUBISHI CHEMICAL ENGINEERING CORPORATION - KASHIMA DIVISION—See Mitsubishi Chemical Group Corporation; *Int'l*, pg. 4932
MITSUBISHI CHEMICAL ENGINEERING CORPORATION - KUROSAKI DIVISION—See Mitsubishi Chemical Group Corporation; *Int'l*, pg. 4932
MITSUBISHI CHEMICAL ENGINEERING CORPORATION - MIZUSHIMA DIVISION—See Mitsubishi Chemical Group Corporation; *Int'l*, pg. 4932
MITSUBISHI CHEMICAL ENGINEERING CORPORATION - OTAKE DIVISION—See Mitsubishi Chemical Group Corporation; *Int'l*, pg. 4932
MITSUBISHI CHEMICAL ENGINEERING CORPORATION - SAKAIDE DIVISION—See Mitsubishi Chemical Group Corporation; *Int'l*, pg. 4932
MITSUBISHI CHEMICAL ENGINEERING CORPORATION—See Mitsubishi Chemical Group Corporation; *Int'l*, pg. 4932

MITSUBISHI CORPORATION

MITSUBISHI CHEMICAL ENGINEERING CORPORATION - TOYAMA DIVISION—See Mitsubishi Chemical Group Corporation; *Int'l*, pg. 4932
MITSUBISHI CHEMICAL ENGINEERING CORPORATION - TOYOHASHI DIVISION—See Mitsubishi Chemical Group Corporation; *Int'l*, pg. 4932
MITSUBISHI CHEMICAL ENGINEERING CORPORATION - YOKKAICHI DIVISION—See Mitsubishi Chemical Group Corporation; *Int'l*, pg. 4932
MITSUBISHI CHEMICAL EUROPE GMBH—See Mitsubishi Chemical Group Corporation; *Int'l*, pg. 4932
MITSUBISHI-CHEMICAL FOODS CORPORATION—See Mitsubishi Chemical Group Corporation; *Int'l*, pg. 4933
MITSUBISHI CHEMICAL GROUP CORPORATION; *Int'l*, pg. 4930
MITSUBISHI CHEMICAL HOLDINGS (BEIJING) CO., LTD.—See Mitsubishi Chemical Group Corporation; *Int'l*, pg. 4935
MITSUBISHI CHEMICAL HOLDINGS EUROPE GMBH—See Mitsubishi Chemical Group Corporation; *Int'l*, pg. 4935
MITSUBISHI CHEMICAL HONG KONG LTD.—See Mitsubishi Chemical Group Corporation; *Int'l*, pg. 4932
MITSUBISHI CHEMICAL INDIA PRIVATE LTD.—See Mitsubishi Chemical Group Corporation; *Int'l*, pg. 4932
MITSUBISHI CHEMICAL INFONICS PTE LTD—See Mitsubishi Chemical Group Corporation; *Int'l*, pg. 4932
MITSUBISHI CHEMICAL INFRATEC CO., LTD.—See Mitsubishi Chemical Group Corporation; *Int'l*, pg. 4932
MITSUBISHI CHEMICAL LOGISTICS CORPORATION—See Mitsubishi Chemical Group Corporation; *Int'l*, pg. 4932
MITSUBISHI CHEMICAL MEDIA CO., LTD.—See Mitsubishi Chemical Group Corporation; *Int'l*, pg. 4932
MITSUBISHI CHEMICAL PERFORMANCE POLYMERS, INC.—See Mitsubishi Chemical Group Corporation; *Int'l*, pg. 4932
MITSUBISHI CHEMICAL SINGAPORE PTE. LTD.—See Mitsubishi Chemical Group Corporation; *Int'l*, pg. 4932
MITSUBISHI CHEMICAL SYSTEMS, INC.—See Mitsubishi Chemical Group Corporation; *Int'l*, pg. 4932
MITSUBISHI CHEMICAL (THAILAND) CO., LTD.—See Mitsubishi Chemical Group Corporation; *Int'l*, pg. 4931
MITSUBISHI CHEMICAL USA, INC. (MCUSA)—See Mitsubishi Chemical Group Corporation; *Int'l*, pg. 4932
MITSUBISHI COMPANY (THAILAND), LTD.—See Mitsubishi Corporation; *Int'l*, pg. 4940
MITSUBISHI CORPORATION ASSET MANAGEMENT LTD.—See Mitsubishi Corporation; *Int'l*, pg. 4940
MITSUBISHI CORPORATION CAPITAL LTD.—See Mitsubishi Corporation; *Int'l*, pg. 4940
MITSUBISHI CORPORATION (CHINA) INVESTMENT CO., LTD.—See Mitsubishi Corporation; *Int'l*, pg. 4940
MITSUBISHI CORPORATION ENERGY CO., LTD.—See Mitsubishi Corporation; *Int'l*, pg. 4940
MITSUBISHI CORPORATION FINANCIAL & MANAGEMENT SERVICES (JAPAN) LTD.—See Mitsubishi Corporation; *Int'l*, pg. 4940
MITSUBISHI CORPORATION (HONG KONG) LTD.—See Mitsubishi Corporation; *Int'l*, pg. 4940
MITSUBISHI CORPORATION INTERNATIONAL (EUROPE) PLC.—See Mitsubishi Corporation; *Int'l*, pg. 4940
MITSUBISHI CORPORATION (KOREA) LTD.—See Mitsubishi Corporation; *Int'l*, pg. 4940
MITSUBISHI CORPORATION LIFE SCIENCES HOLDINGS LIMITED—See Mitsubishi Corporation; *Int'l*, pg. 4941
MITSUBISHI CORPORATION LIFE SCIENCES LIMITED - FUJI FACTORY—See Mitsubishi Corporation; *Int'l*, pg. 4941
MITSUBISHI CORPORATION LIFE SCIENCES LIMITED—See Mitsubishi Corporation; *Int'l*, pg. 4941
MITSUBISHI CORPORATION LT, INC.—See Mitsubishi Corporation; *Int'l*, pg. 4940
MITSUBISHI CORPORATION LT SINGAPORE PTE., LTD.—See Mitsubishi Corporation; *Int'l*, pg. 4940
MITSUBISHI CORPORATION LT TAIWAN CO., LTD.—See Mitsubishi Corporation; *Int'l*, pg. 4940
MITSUBISHI CORPORATION MACHINERY, INC.—See Mitsubishi Corporation; *Int'l*, pg. 4941
MITSUBISHI CORPORATION OPERATIONS LIMITED—See Mitsubishi Corporation; *Int'l*, pg. 4941
MITSUBISHI CORPORATION POWER SYSTEMS, INC.—See Mitsubishi Corporation; *Int'l*, pg. 4941
MITSUBISHI CORPORATION RTM INTERNATIONAL PTE. LTD.—See Mitsubishi Corporation; *Int'l*, pg. 4941
MITSUBISHI CORPORATION RTM JAPAN LTD.—See Mitsubishi Corporation; *Int'l*, pg. 4941
MITSUBISHI CORPORATION RTM (MIDDLE EAST & CENTRAL ASIA)—See Mitsubishi Corporation; *Int'l*, pg. 4941
MITSUBISHI CORPORATION SERVICES—See The Yokohama Rubber Co., Ltd.; *Int'l*, pg. 7702
MITSUBISHI CORPORATION (SHANGHAI) LTD.—See Mitsubishi Corporation; *Int'l*, pg. 4940
MITSUBISHI CORPORATION; *Int'l*, pg. 4937
MITSUBISHI CORPORATION (TAIWAN) LTD.—See Mitsubishi Corporation; *Int'l*, pg. 4940

MITSUBISHI CORPORATION

CORPORATE AFFILIATIONS

MITSUBISHI CORPORATION TECHNOS CO., LTD.—See Mitsubishi Corporation; *Int'l*, pg. 4941
MITSUBISHI CORPORATION TECHNOS—See Mitsubishi Corporation; *Int'l*, pg. 4941
MITSUBISHI CORPORATION URBAN DEVELOPMENT, INC.—See Mitsubishi Corporation; *Int'l*, pg. 4941
MITSUBISHI DEVELOPMENT PTY LTD—See Mitsubishi Corporation; *Int'l*, pg. 4941
MITSUBISHI DIGITAL ELECTRONICS AMERICA, INC.—See Mitsubishi Electric Corporation; *Int'l*, pg. 4944
MITSUBISHI ELECTRIC AIR CONDITIONING & REFRIGERATION EQUIPMENT SALES CO., LTD.—See Mitsubishi Electric Corporation; *Int'l*, pg. 4944
MITSUBISHI ELECTRIC AIR CONDITIONING & REFRIGERATION SYSTEMS CO., LTD.—See Mitsubishi Electric Corporation; *Int'l*, pg. 4944
MITSUBISHI ELECTRIC AIR CONDITIONING SYSTEMS EUROPE LTD.—See Mitsubishi Electric Corporation; *Int'l*, pg. 4944
MITSUBISHI ELECTRIC ASIA PTE. LTD.—See Mitsubishi Electric Corporation; *Int'l*, pg. 4944
MITSUBISHI ELECTRIC AUSTRALIA PTY. LTD.—See Mitsubishi Electric Corporation; *Int'l*, pg. 4944
MITSUBISHI ELECTRIC AUTOMATION (CHINA) LTD.—See Mitsubishi Electric Corporation; *Int'l*, pg. 4944
MITSUBISHI ELECTRIC AUTOMATION (HONG KONG) LTD.—See Mitsubishi Electric Corporation; *Int'l*, pg. 4944
MITSUBISHI ELECTRIC AUTOMATION, INC. - INDUSTRIAL SEWING EQUIPMENT—See Mitsubishi Electric Corporation; *Int'l*, pg. 4944
MITSUBISHI ELECTRIC AUTOMATION, INC.—See Mitsubishi Electric Corporation; *Int'l*, pg. 4944
MITSUBISHI ELECTRIC AUTOMATION KOREA CO., LTD.—See Mitsubishi Electric Corporation; *Int'l*, pg. 4944
MITSUBISHI ELECTRIC AUTOMATION (THAILAND) CO., LTD.—See Mitsubishi Electric Corporation; *Int'l*, pg. 4944
MITSUBISHI ELECTRIC AUTOMOTIVE AMERICA, INC.—See Mitsubishi Electric Corporation; *Int'l*, pg. 4944
MITSUBISHI ELECTRIC AUTOMOTIVE (CHINA) CO., LTD.—See Mitsubishi Electric Corporation; *Int'l*, pg. 4944
MITSUBISHI ELECTRIC AUTOMOTIVE CZECH S.R.O. - AUTOMATION FACTORY—See Mitsubishi Electric Corporation; *Int'l*, pg. 4944
MITSUBISHI ELECTRIC AUTOMOTIVE CZECH S.R.O.—See Mitsubishi Electric Corporation; *Int'l*, pg. 4944
MITSUBISHI ELECTRIC AUTOMOTIVE INDIA PVT. LTD.—See Mitsubishi Electric Corporation; *Int'l*, pg. 4944
MITSUBISHI ELECTRIC BUSINESS SYSTEMS CO., LTD.—See Mitsubishi Electric Corporation; *Int'l*, pg. 4945
MITSUBISHI ELECTRIC CONSUMER PRODUCTS (THAILAND) CO., LTD.—See Mitsubishi Electric Corporation; *Int'l*, pg. 4945
MITSUBISHI ELECTRIC CONTROL SOFTWARE CORPORATION—See Mitsubishi Electric Corporation; *Int'l*, pg. 4945
MITSUBISHI ELECTRIC CORPORATION; *Int'l*, pg. 4943
MITSUBISHI ELECTRIC CREDIT CORPORATION—See Mitsubishi HC Capital Inc.; *Int'l*, pg. 4952
MITSUBISHI ELECTRIC DALIAN INDUSTRIAL PRODUCTS CO., LTD.—See Mitsubishi Electric Corporation; *Int'l*, pg. 4945
MITSUBISHI ELECTRIC DE MEXICO S.A. DE C.V. - SAN JUAN DEL RIO FACTORY—See Mitsubishi Electric Corporation; *Int'l*, pg. 4945
MITSUBISHI ELECTRIC DE MEXICO S.A. DE C.V.—See Mitsubishi Electric Corporation; *Int'l*, pg. 4945
MITSUBISHI ELECTRIC & ELECTRONICS (SHANGHAI) CO., LTD.—See Mitsubishi Electric Corporation; *Int'l*, pg. 4944
MITSUBISHI ELECTRIC & ELECTRONICS USA, INC.—See Mitsubishi Electric Corporation; *Int'l*, pg. 4944
MITSUBISHI ELECTRIC ENGINEERING CO., LTD.—See Mitsubishi Electric Corporation; *Int'l*, pg. 4944
MITSUBISHI ELECTRIC EUROPE B.V.—See Mitsubishi Electric Corporation; *Int'l*, pg. 4944
MITSUBISHI ELECTRIC FINANCE AMERICA, INC.—See Mitsubishi Electric Corporation; *Int'l*, pg. 4944
MITSUBISHI ELECTRIC FINANCE EUROPE PLC—See Mitsubishi Electric Corporation; *Int'l*, pg. 4945
MITSUBISHI ELECTRIC FINANCIAL SOLUTIONS CORPORATION—See Mitsubishi HC Capital Inc.; *Int'l*, pg. 4952
MITSUBISHI ELECTRIC (H.K.) LTD.—See Mitsubishi Electric Corporation; *Int'l*, pg. 4944
MITSUBISHI ELECTRIC HOME APPLIANCE CO., LTD.—See Mitsubishi Electric Corporation; *Int'l*, pg. 4945
MITSUBISHI ELECTRIC HONG KONG GROUP LTD.—See Mitsubishi Electric Corporation; *Int'l*, pg. 4945
MITSUBISHI ELECTRIC INDIA PVT. LTD.—See Mitsubishi Electric Corporation; *Int'l*, pg. 4945
MITSUBISHI ELECTRIC INFORMATION NETWORK CORPORATION—See Mitsubishi Electric Corporation; *Int'l*, pg. 4945
MITSUBISHI ELECTRIC INFORMATION SYSTEMS CORPORATION—See Mitsubishi Electric Corporation; *Int'l*, pg. 4945
MITSUBISHI ELECTRIC KANG YONG WATANA CO., LTD.—See Mitsubishi Electric Corporation; *Int'l*, pg. 4945
MITSUBISHI ELECTRIC LIFE NETWORK CO., LTD.—See Mitsubishi Electric Corporation; *Int'l*, pg. 4945
MITSUBISHI ELECTRIC LIFE SERVICE CORPORATION—See Mitsubishi Electric Corporation; *Int'l*, pg. 4945
MITSUBISHI ELECTRIC LIGHTING CO., LTD.—See Mitsubishi Electric Corporation; *Int'l*, pg. 4945
MITSUBISHI ELECTRIC LOGISTICS CORPORATION—See Seino Holdings Co., Ltd.; *Int'l*, pg. 6690
MITSUBISHI ELECTRIC (MALAYSIA) SDN. BHD.—See Mitsubishi Electric Corporation; *Int'l*, pg. 4944
MITSUBISHI ELECTRIC MICRO-COMPUTER APPLICATION SOFTWARE CO., LTD.—See Mitsubishi Electric Corporation; *Int'l*, pg. 4945
MITSUBISHI ELECTRIC PLANT ENGINEERING CORPORATION—See Mitsubishi Electric Corporation; *Int'l*, pg. 4945
MITSUBISHI ELECTRIC POWER PRODUCTS, INC.—See Hyosung Heavy Industries Corp.; *Int'l*, pg. 3552
MITSUBISHI ELECTRIC RESEARCH LABORATORIES—See Mitsubishi Electric Corporation; *Int'l*, pg. 4944
MITSUBISHI ELECTRIC RYODEN AIR-CONDITIONING & VISUAL INFORMATION SYSTEMS (HONG KONG) LTD.—See Mitsubishi Electric Corporation; *Int'l*, pg. 4945
MITSUBISHI ELECTRIC SALES CANADA, INC.—See Mitsubishi Electric Corporation; *Int'l*, pg. 4945
MITSUBISHI ELECTRIC (SHANGHAI) CO., LTD.—See Ryoden Corporation; *Int'l*, pg. 6440
MITSUBISHI ELECTRIC SYSTEM & SERVICE CO., LTD.—See Mitsubishi Electric Corporation; *Int'l*, pg. 4945
MITSUBISHI ELECTRIC TAIWAN CO., LTD.—See Mitsubishi Electric Corporation; *Int'l*, pg. 4945
MITSUBISHI ELECTRIC THAI AUTO-PARTS CO., LTD.—See Mitsubishi Electric Corporation; *Int'l*, pg. 4945
MITSUBISHI ELECTRIC TOKKI SYSTEMS CORPORATION—See Mitsubishi Electric Corporation; *Int'l*, pg. 4945
MITSUBISHI ELECTRIC TRADING CORPORATION—See Mitsubishi Electric Corporation; *Int'l*, pg. 4945
MITSUBISHI ELECTRIC VIETNAM COMPANY LIMITED—See Mitsubishi Electric Corporation; *Int'l*, pg. 4945
MITSUBISHI ELECTRIC VISUAL SOLUTIONS AMERICA, INC.—See Mitsubishi Electric Corporation; *Int'l*, pg. 4944
MITSUBISHI ELEVATOR ASIA CO., LTD.—See Mitsubishi Electric Corporation; *Int'l*, pg. 4945
MITSUBISHI ELEVATOR EUROPE B.V.—See Mitsubishi Electric Corporation; *Int'l*, pg. 4945
MITSUBISHI ELEVATOR HONG KONG CO., LTD.—See Mitsubishi Electric Corporation; *Int'l*, pg. 4945
MITSUBISHI ELEVATOR INDIA PVT. LTD.—See Mitsubishi Corporation; *Int'l*, pg. 4941
MITSUBISHI ELEVATOR KOREA CO., LTD.—See Mitsubishi Electric Corporation; *Int'l*, pg. 4945
MITSUBISHI ELEVATOR MALAYSIA SDN. BHD.—See Mitsubishi Electric Corporation; *Int'l*, pg. 4946
MITSUBISHI ELEVATOR (SINGAPORE) PTE LTD—See Mitsubishi Electric Corporation; *Int'l*, pg. 4945
MITSUBISHI ELEVATOR (THAILAND) CO., LTD.—See Mitsubishi Electric Corporation; *Int'l*, pg. 4945
MITSUBISHI ENGINEERING-PLASTICS CORPORATION—See Mitsubishi Chemical Group Corporation; *Int'l*, pg. 4935
MITSUBISHI ENGINEERING-PLASTICS CORPORATION—See Mitsubishi Gas Chemical Company, Inc.; *Int'l*, pg. 4949
MITSUBISHI ENGINE NORTH AMERICA INC—See Mitsubishi Heavy Industries, Ltd.; *Int'l*, pg. 4956
MITSUBISHI ESPANA S.A.—See Mitsubishi Corporation; *Int'l*, pg. 4941
MITSUBISHI ESTATE BUILDING MANAGEMENT CO., LTD.—See Mitsubishi Estate Co., Ltd.; *Int'l*, pg. 4946
MITSUBISHI ESTATE CO., LTD.; *Int'l*, pg. 4946
MITSUBISHI ESTATE HOUSING COMPONENTS CO., LTD.—See Mitsubishi Estate Co., Ltd.; *Int'l*, pg. 4946
MITSUBISHI ESTATE LOGISTICS REIT INVESTMENT CORPORATION; *Int'l*, pg. 4948
MITSUBISHI ESTATE NEW YORK, INC.—See Mitsubishi Estate Co., Ltd.; *Int'l*, pg. 4946
MITSUBISHI ESTATE PARKS CO., LTD.—See Mitsubishi Estate Co., Ltd.; *Int'l*, pg. 4946
MITSUBISHI FBR SYSTEMS, INC.—See Mitsubishi Heavy Industries, Ltd.; *Int'l*, pg. 4956
MITSUBISHI FUSO TRUCK AND BUS AUSTRALIA PTY. LTD.—See Mercedes-Benz Group AG; *Int'l*, pg. 4828
MITSUBISHI FUSO TRUCK & BUS CORP.—See Mercedes-Benz Group AG; *Int'l*, pg. 4828
MITSUBISHI FUSO TRUCK EUROPE, S. A.—See Mercedes-Benz Group AG; *Int'l*, pg. 4828
MITSUBISHI FUSO TRUCK OF AMERICA, INC.—See Mercedes-Benz Group AG; *Int'l*, pg. 4824
MITSUBISHI GAS CHEMICAL AMERICA, INC.—See Mitsubishi Gas Chemical Company, Inc.; *Int'l*, pg. 4949
MITSUBISHI GAS CHEMICAL COMPANY, INC. - KASHIMA PLANT—See Mitsubishi Gas Chemical Company, Inc.; *Int'l*, pg. 4949
MITSUBISHI GAS CHEMICAL COMPANY, INC. - MIZUSHIMA PLANT—See Mitsubishi Gas Chemical Company, Inc.; *Int'l*, pg. 4949
MITSUBISHI GAS CHEMICAL COMPANY, INC. - NANIWA PLANT—See Mitsubishi Gas Chemical Company, Inc.; *Int'l*, pg. 4949
MITSUBISHI GAS CHEMICAL COMPANY, INC. - NIIGATA PLANT—See Mitsubishi Gas Chemical Company, Inc.; *Int'l*, pg. 4949
MITSUBISHI GAS CHEMICAL COMPANY, INC. - SAGA PLANT—See Mitsubishi Gas Chemical Company, Inc.; *Int'l*, pg. 4949
MITSUBISHI GAS CHEMICAL COMPANY, INC.; *Int'l*, pg. 4948
MITSUBISHI GAS CHEMICAL COMPANY, INC. - YAMAKITA PLANT—See Mitsubishi Gas Chemical Company, Inc.; *Int'l*, pg. 4949
MITSUBISHI GAS CHEMICAL COMPANY, INC. - YOKKAICHI PLANT—See Mitsubishi Gas Chemical Company, Inc.; *Int'l*, pg. 4949
MITSUBISHI GAS CHEMICAL ENGINEERING-PLASTICS (SHANGHAI) CO., LTD.—See Mitsubishi Gas Chemical Company, Inc.; *Int'l*, pg. 4949
MITSUBISHI GAS CHEMICAL EUROPE GMBH—See Mitsubishi Gas Chemical Company, Inc.; *Int'l*, pg. 4949
MITSUBISHI GAS CHEMICAL SHANGHAI COMMERCE LTD.—See Mitsubishi Gas Chemical Company, Inc.; *Int'l*, pg. 4949
MITSUBISHI GAS CHEMICAL SINGAPORE PTE. LTD.—See Mitsubishi Gas Chemical Company, Inc.; *Int'l*, pg. 4949
MITSUBISHI GAS CHEMICAL TRADING, INC.—See Mitsubishi Gas Chemical Company, Inc.; *Int'l*, pg. 4949
MITSUBISHI HC BUSINESS LEASE CORPORATION—See Mitsubishi HC Capital Inc.; *Int'l*, pg. 4952
MITSUBISHI HC CAPITAL AMERICA, INC.—See Mitsubishi HC Capital Inc.; *Int'l*, pg. 4951
MITSUBISHI HC CAPITAL ASIA PACIFIC PTE. LTD.—See Mitsubishi HC Capital Inc.; *Int'l*, pg. 4952
MITSUBISHI HC CAPITAL CANADA, INC.—See Mitsubishi HC Capital Inc.; *Int'l*, pg. 4952
MITSUBISHI HC CAPITAL COMMUNITY CORPORATION—See Mitsubishi HC Capital Inc.; *Int'l*, pg. 4952
MITSUBISHI HC CAPITAL ENERGY INC.—See Mitsubishi HC Capital Inc.; *Int'l*, pg. 4952
MITSUBISHI HC CAPITAL ESTATE PLUS INC.—See Mitsubishi HC Capital Inc.; *Int'l*, pg. 4952
MITSUBISHI HC CAPITAL (HONG KONG) LIMITED—See Mitsubishi HC Capital Inc.; *Int'l*, pg. 4952
MITSUBISHI HC CAPITAL INC.; *Int'l*, pg. 4950
MITSUBISHI HC CAPITAL MALAYSIA SDN. BHD.—See Mitsubishi HC Capital Inc.; *Int'l*, pg. 4952
MITSUBISHI HC CAPITAL MANAGEMENT (CHINA) LIMITED—See Mitsubishi HC Capital Inc.; *Int'l*, pg. 4952
MITSUBISHI HC CAPITAL PROPERTY INC.—See Mitsubishi HC Capital Inc.; *Int'l*, pg. 4952
MITSUBISHI HC CAPITAL SERVICER CORPORATION—See Mitsubishi HC Capital Inc.; *Int'l*, pg. 4952
MITSUBISHI HC CAPITAL (THAILAND) CO., LTD.—See Mitsubishi HC Capital Inc.; *Int'l*, pg. 4952
MITSUBISHI HC CAPITAL TRUST CORPORATION—See Mitsubishi HC Capital Inc.; *Int'l*, pg. 4952
MITSUBISHI HC CAPITAL UK PLC—See Mitsubishi HC Capital Inc.; *Int'l*, pg. 4952
MITSUBISHI HEAVY INDUSTRIES AERO ENGINES, LTD.—See Mitsubishi Heavy Industries, Ltd.; *Int'l*, pg. 4956
MITSUBISHI HEAVY INDUSTRIES AIR-CONDITIONERS AUSTRALIA, PTY. LTD.—See Mitsubishi Heavy Industries, Ltd.; *Int'l*, pg. 4957
MITSUBISHI HEAVY INDUSTRIES AIR-CONDITIONERS (SHANGHAI) CO., LTD.—See Mitsubishi Heavy Industries, Ltd.; *Int'l*, pg. 4956
MITSUBISHI HEAVY INDUSTRIES AIR-CONDITIONING EUROPE, LTD.—See Mitsubishi Heavy Industries, Ltd.; *Int'l*, pg. 4956

COMPANY NAME INDEX — MITSUBISHI HEAVY INDUSTRIES, LTD.

MITSUBISHI HEAVY INDUSTRIES AIR-CONDITIONING & REFRIGERATION CORPORATION—See Mitsubishi Heavy Industries, Ltd. *Int'l*, pg. 4956
MITSUBISHI HEAVY INDUSTRIES AIR-CONDITIONING & THERMAL SYSTEMS CORPORATION—See Mitsubishi Heavy Industries, Ltd.; *Int'l*, pg. 4956
MITSUBISHI HEAVY INDUSTRIES AMERICA, INC. - AIRCRAFT PRODUCT SUPPORT DIVISION—See Mitsubishi Heavy Industries, Ltd.; *Int'l*, pg. 4956
MITSUBISHI HEAVY INDUSTRIES AMERICA, INC. - ENVIRONMENTAL SYSTEMS DIVISION—See Mitsubishi Heavy Industries, Ltd.; *Int'l*, pg. 4956
MITSUBISHI HEAVY INDUSTRIES AMERICA, INC. - INJECTION MOLDING MACHINERY DIVISION—See Mitsubishi Heavy Industries, Ltd.; *Int'l*, pg. 4956
MITSUBISHI HEAVY INDUSTRIES AMERICA, INC. - MACHINE TOOL DIVISION—See Mitsubishi Heavy Industries, Ltd.; *Int'l*, pg. 4956
MITSUBISHI HEAVY INDUSTRIES AMERICA, INC.—See Mitsubishi Heavy Industries, Ltd.; *Int'l*, pg. 4956
MITSUBISHI HEAVY INDUSTRIES ASIA PACIFIC PTE. LTD.—See Mitsubishi Heavy Industries, Ltd.; *Int'l*, pg. 4957
MITSUBISHI HEAVY INDUSTRIES AUSTRALIA, PTY. LTD.—See Mitsubishi Heavy Industries, Ltd.; *Int'l*, pg. 4957
MITSUBISHI HEAVY INDUSTRIES BFG GAS TURBINE SERVICE (NANJING) CO., LTD.—See Mitsubishi Heavy Industries, Ltd.; *Int'l*, pg. 4957
MITSUBISHI HEAVY INDUSTRIES (CHANGSHU) MACHINERY CO., LTD.—See Mitsubishi Heavy Industries, Ltd.; *Int'l*, pg. 4956
MITSUBISHI HEAVY INDUSTRIES (CHINA) CO., LTD.—See Mitsubishi Heavy Industries, Ltd.; *Int'l*, pg. 4956
MITSUBISHI HEAVY INDUSTRIES CLIMATE CONTROL INC.—See Mitsubishi Heavy Industries, Ltd.; *Int'l*, pg. 4956
MITSUBISHI HEAVY INDUSTRIES COMPRESSOR CORPORATION—See Mitsubishi Heavy Industries, Ltd.; *Int'l*, pg. 4957
MITSUBISHI HEAVY INDUSTRIES COMPRESSOR INTERNATIONAL CORPORATION—See Mitsubishi Corporation; *Int'l*, pg. 4941
MITSUBISHI HEAVY INDUSTRIES DE MEXICO, S.A. DE C.V.—See Mitsubishi Heavy Industries, Ltd.; *Int'l*, pg. 4958
MITSUBISHI HEAVY INDUSTRIES DONGFANG GAS TURBINE (GUANGZHOU) CO., LTD.—See Mitsubishi Heavy Industries, Ltd.; *Int'l*, pg. 4957
MITSUBISHI HEAVY INDUSTRIES ENGINEERING, LTD.—See Mitsubishi Heavy Industries, Ltd.; *Int'l*, pg. 4957
MITSUBISHI HEAVY INDUSTRIES ENGINE SYSTEM ASIA PTE. LTD.—See Mitsubishi Heavy Industries, Ltd.; *Int'l*, pg. 4957
MITSUBISHI HEAVY INDUSTRIES ENGINE SYSTEM ASIA PTE. LTD.—See Mitsubishi Heavy Industries, Ltd.; *Int'l*, pg. 4957
MITSUBISHI HEAVY INDUSTRIES ENGINE SYSTEMS CO., LTD.—See Mitsubishi Heavy Industries, Ltd.; *Int'l*, pg. 4957
MITSUBISHI HEAVY INDUSTRIES ENGINE & TURBOCHARGER, LTD.—See Mitsubishi Heavy Industries, Ltd.; *Int'l*, pg. 4957
MITSUBISHI HEAVY INDUSTRIES ENVIRONMENTAL & CHEMICAL ENGINEERING CO., LTD. - ENGINEERING DIVISION—See Mitsubishi Heavy Industries, Ltd.; *Int'l*, pg. 4957
MITSUBISHI HEAVY INDUSTRIES ENVIRONMENTAL & CHEMICAL ENGINEERING CO., LTD. - O&M DIVISION—See Mitsubishi Heavy Industries, Ltd.; *Int'l*, pg. 4957
MITSUBISHI HEAVY INDUSTRIES ENVIRONMENTAL & CHEMICAL ENGINEERING CO., LTD. - PLANT ENGINEERING DIVISION—See Mitsubishi Heavy Industries, Ltd.; *Int'l*, pg. 4957
MITSUBISHI HEAVY INDUSTRIES ENVIRONMENTAL & CHEMICAL ENGINEERING CO., LTD.—See Mitsubishi Heavy Industries, Ltd.; *Int'l*, pg. 4957
MITSUBISHI HEAVY INDUSTRIES EUROPE, LTD. - CORRUGATING MACHINERY DIVISION—See Mitsubishi Heavy Industries, Ltd.; *Int'l*, pg. 4957
MITSUBISHI HEAVY INDUSTRIES EUROPE, LTD.—See Mitsubishi Heavy Industries, Ltd.; *Int'l*, pg. 4957
MITSUBISHI HEAVY INDUSTRIES FOOD & PACKAGING MACHINERY CO., LTD.—See Mitsubishi Heavy Industries, Ltd.; *Int'l*, pg. 4957
MITSUBISHI HEAVY INDUSTRIES FORKLIFT (DALIAN) CO., LTD.—See Mitsubishi Heavy Industries, Ltd.; *Int'l*, pg. 4957
MITSUBISHI HEAVY INDUSTRIES FORKLIFT & ENGINE TURBOCHARGER HOLDINGS, LTD.—See Mitsubishi Heavy Industries, Ltd.; *Int'l*, pg. 4957
MITSUBISHI HEAVY INDUSTRIES FRANCE S.A.S.—See Mitsubishi Heavy Industries, Ltd.; *Int'l*, pg. 4957
MITSUBISHI HEAVY INDUSTRIES-HAIER (QINGDAO) AIR-CONDITIONERS CO., LTD.—See Mitsubishi Heavy Industries, Ltd.; *Int'l*, pg. 4958
MITSUBISHI HEAVY INDUSTRIES, (HONG KONG) LTD.—See Mitsubishi Heavy Industries, Ltd.; *Int'l*, pg. 4958
MITSUBISHI HEAVY INDUSTRIES INDIA PRECISION TOOLS, LTD.—See Mitsubishi Heavy Industries, Ltd.; *Int'l*, pg. 4957
MITSUBISHI HEAVY INDUSTRIES INDIA PRIVATE LTD. - POWER SYSTEMS ENGINEERING DIVISION—See Mitsubishi Heavy Industries, Ltd.; *Int'l*, pg. 4957
MITSUBISHI HEAVY INDUSTRIES INDIA PRIVATE LTD.—See Mitsubishi Heavy Industries, Ltd.; *Int'l*, pg. 4957
MITSUBISHI HEAVY INDUSTRIES-JINLING AIR-CONDITIONERS CO., LTD.—See Mitsubishi Heavy Industries, Ltd.; *Int'l*, pg. 4958
MITSUBISHI HEAVY INDUSTRIES KOREA LTD.—See Mitsubishi Heavy Industries, Ltd.; *Int'l*, pg. 4957
MITSUBISHI HEAVY INDUSTRIES LTD.-AIR-CONDITIONING & REFRIGERATION DIVISION—See Mitsubishi Heavy Industries, Ltd.; *Int'l*, pg. 4957
MITSUBISHI HEAVY INDUSTRIES, LTD. - EBA PLANT—See Mitsubishi Heavy Industries, Ltd.; *Int'l*, pg. 4958
MITSUBISHI HEAVY INDUSTRIES, LTD. - FUTAMI PLANT—See Mitsubishi Heavy Industries, Ltd.; *Int'l*, pg. 4958
MITSUBISHI HEAVY INDUSTRIES, LTD. - HIROSHIMA MACHINERY WORKS—See Mitsubishi Heavy Industries, Ltd.; *Int'l*, pg. 4958
MITSUBISHI HEAVY INDUSTRIES, LTD. - HONMOKU PLANT—See Mitsubishi Heavy Industries, Ltd.; *Int'l*, pg. 4958
MITSUBISHI HEAVY INDUSTRIES, LTD. - ISAHAYA PLANT—See Mitsubishi Heavy Industries, Ltd.; *Int'l*, pg. 4958
MITSUBISHI HEAVY INDUSTRIES, LTD. - IWANAI PLANT—See Mitsubishi Heavy Industries, Ltd.; *Int'l*, pg. 4958
MITSUBISHI HEAVY INDUSTRIES, LTD. - IWATSUKA PLANT—See Mitsubishi Heavy Industries, Ltd.; *Int'l*, pg. 4958
MITSUBISHI HEAVY INDUSTRIES, LTD. - KOMAKI MINAMI PLANT—See Mitsubishi Heavy Industries, Ltd.; *Int'l*, pg. 4958
MITSUBISHI HEAVY INDUSTRIES, LTD. - MATSUSAKA PLANT—See Mitsubishi Heavy Industries, Ltd.; *Int'l*, pg. 4958
MITSUBISHI HEAVY INDUSTRIES, LTD. - MIHARA MACHINERY WORKS—See Mitsubishi Heavy Industries, Ltd.; *Int'l*, pg. 4958
MITSUBISHI HEAVY INDUSTRIES, LTD. - NAGOYA AIR-CONDITIONING & REFRIGERATION MACHINERY WORKS—See Mitsubishi Heavy Industries, Ltd.; *Int'l*, pg. 4958
MITSUBISHI HEAVY INDUSTRIES, LTD. - NAGOYA GUIDANCE & PROPULSION SYSTEMS WORKS—See Mitsubishi Heavy Industries, Ltd.; *Int'l*, pg. 4958
MITSUBISHI HEAVY INDUSTRIES, LTD. - RITTO MACHINERY WORKS—See Mitsubishi Heavy Industries, Ltd.; *Int'l*, pg. 4958
MITSUBISHI HEAVY INDUSTRIES, LTD. - SAGAMIHARA MACHINERY WORKS—See Mitsubishi Heavy Industries, Ltd.; *Int'l*, pg. 4958
MITSUBISHI HEAVY INDUSTRIES, LTD. - SAIWAIMACHI PLANT—See Mitsubishi Heavy Industries, Ltd.; *Int'l*, pg. 4958
MITSUBISHI HEAVY INDUSTRIES, LTD.; *Int'l*, pg. 4953
MITSUBISHI HEAVY INDUSTRIES LTD—See Mitsubishi Heavy Industries, Ltd.; *Int'l*, pg. 4958
MITSUBISHI HEAVY INDUSTRIES, LTD. - TAKASAGO PLANT—See Mitsubishi Heavy Industries, Ltd.; *Int'l*, pg. 4958
MITSUBISHI HEAVY INDUSTRIES, LTD. - TOBISHIMA PLANT—See Mitsubishi Heavy Industries, Ltd.; *Int'l*, pg. 4958
MITSUBISHI HEAVY INDUSTRIES, LTD. - YAMATO-MACHI PLANT—See Mitsubishi Heavy Industries, Ltd.; *Int'l*, pg. 4958
MITSUBISHI HEAVY INDUSTRIES MACHINERY SYSTEMS, LTD.—See Mitsubishi Heavy Industries, Ltd.; *Int'l*, pg. 4957
MITSUBISHI HEAVY INDUSTRIES MACHINERY TECHNOLOGY CORPORATION—See Mitsubishi Heavy Industries, Ltd.; *Int'l*, pg. 4957
MITSUBISHI HEAVY INDUSTRIES MACHINE TOOL CO., LTD.—See Mitsubishi Heavy Industries, Ltd.; *Int'l*, pg. 4957
MITSUBISHI HEAVY INDUSTRIES MACHINE TOOL SALES CO., LTD.—See Mitsubishi Heavy Industries, Ltd.; *Int'l*, pg. 4957
MITSUBISHI HEAVY INDUSTRIES-MAHAJAK AIR CONDITIONERS CO., LTD—See Mitsubishi Heavy Industries, Ltd.; *Int'l*, pg. 4958
MITSUBISHI HEAVY INDUSTRIES MARINE MACHINERY & EQUIPMENT CO., LTD.—See Mitsubishi Heavy Industries, Ltd.; *Int'l*, pg. 4957
MITSUBISHI HEAVY INDUSTRIES MARINE STRUCTURE, CO., LTD.—See Mitsubishi Heavy Industries, Ltd.; *Int'l*, pg. 4957
MITSUBISHI HEAVY INDUSTRIES MECHATRONICS SYSTEMS, LTD.—See Mitsubishi Heavy Industries, Ltd.; *Int'l*, pg. 4957
MITSUBISHI HEAVY INDUSTRIES MEIKI ENGINES CO., LTD.—See Mitsubishi Heavy Industries, Ltd.; *Int'l*, pg. 4958
MITSUBISHI HEAVY INDUSTRIES NETHERLANDS—See Mitsubishi Heavy Industries, Ltd.; *Int'l*, pg. 4958
MITSUBISHI HEAVY INDUSTRIES PHILIPPINES, INC.—See Mitsubishi Heavy Industries, Ltd.; *Int'l*, pg. 4958
MITSUBISHI HEAVY INDUSTRIES PRECISION CASTING CO., LTD.—See Mitsubishi Heavy Industries, Ltd.; *Int'l*, pg. 4958
MITSUBISHI HEAVY INDUSTRIES PRINTING & PACKAGING MACHINERY, LTD.—See Mitsubishi Heavy Industries, Ltd.; *Int'l*, pg. 4958
MITSUBISHI HEAVY INDUSTRIES (SHANGHAI) CO., LTD.—See Mitsubishi Heavy Industries, Ltd.; *Int'l*, pg. 4956
MITSUBISHI HEAVY INDUSTRIES SINGAPORE PRIVATE LTD.—See Mitsubishi Heavy Industries, Ltd.; *Int'l*, pg. 4958
MITSUBISHI HEAVY INDUSTRIES (THAILAND) LTD—See Mitsubishi Heavy Industries, Ltd.; *Int'l*, pg. 4956
MITSUBISHI HEAVY INDUSTRIES THERMAL SYSTEMS, LTD.—See Mitsubishi Heavy Industries, Ltd.; *Int'l*, pg. 4958
MITSUBISHI HEAVY INDUSTRIES THERMAL TRANSPORT EUROPE GMBH—See Mitsubishi Heavy Industries, Ltd.; *Int'l*, pg. 4958
MITSUBISHI HEAVY INDUSTRIES TRANSPORTATION & CONSTRUCTION ENGINEERING, LTD.—See Mitsubishi Heavy Industries, Ltd.; *Int'l*, pg. 4958
MITSUBISHI HEAVY INDUSTRIES TRANSPORTATION EQUIPMENT ENGINEERING & SERVICE CO., LTD.—See Mitsubishi Heavy Industries, Ltd.; *Int'l*, pg. 4958
MITSUBISHI HEAVY INDUSTRIES-VST DIESEL ENGINES PRIVATE LIMITED—See Mitsubishi Heavy Industries, Ltd.; *Int'l*, pg. 4958
MITSUBISHI-HITACHI METALS MACHINERY, INC.—See Hitachi, Ltd.; *Int'l*, pg. 3423
MITSUBISHI-HITACHI METALS MACHINERY, INC.—See Mitsubishi Heavy Industries, Ltd.; *Int'l*, pg. 4960
MITSUBISHI-HITACHI METALS MACHINERY (SHANGHAI), INC.—See Hitachi, Ltd.; *Int'l*, pg. 3423
MITSUBISHI-HITACHI METALS MACHINERY (SHANGHAI), INC.—See Mitsubishi Heavy Industries, Ltd.; *Int'l*, pg. 4960
MITSUBISHI-HITACHI METALS MACHINERY USA, INC.—See Hitachi, Ltd.; *Int'l*, pg. 3423
MITSUBISHI-HITACHI METALS MACHINERY USA, INC.—See Mitsubishi Heavy Industries, Ltd.; *Int'l*, pg. 4960
MITSUBISHI HITACHI POWER SYSTEMS AFRICA (PTY) LTD.—See Hitachi, Ltd.; *Int'l*, pg. 3423
MITSUBISHI HITACHI POWER SYSTEMS AFRICA (PTY) LTD.—See Mitsubishi Heavy Industries, Ltd.; *Int'l*, pg. 4960
MITSUBISHI HITACHI POWER SYSTEMS (CHINA) CO., LTD.—See Mitsubishi Heavy Industries, Ltd.; *Int'l*, pg. 4958
MITSUBISHI HITACHI POWER SYSTEMS EUROPE GMBH—See Hitachi, Ltd.; *Int'l*, pg. 3423
MITSUBISHI HITACHI POWER SYSTEMS EUROPE GMBH—See Mitsubishi Heavy Industries, Ltd.; *Int'l*, pg. 4960
MITSUBISHI HITACHI POWER SYSTEMS GAS TURBINE SERVICE (NANJING) CO., LTD.—See Mitsubishi Heavy Industries, Ltd.; *Int'l*, pg. 4958
MITSUBISHI HITACHI POWER SYSTEMS JIENENG (QINGDAO) STEAM TURBINE CO., LTD.—See Mitsubishi Heavy Industries, Ltd.; *Int'l*, pg. 4958
MITSUBISHI HITACHI TOOL ENGINEERING, LTD.—See Mitsubishi Materials Corporation; *Int'l*, pg. 4964
MITSUBISHI HITEC PAPER BIELEFELD GMBH—See Mitsubishi Paper Mills Limited; *Int'l*, pg. 4967
MITSUBISHI HITEC PAPER EUROPE GMBH—See Mitsubishi Paper Mills Limited; *Int'l*, pg. 4967
MITSUBISHI HITEC PAPER FLENSBURG GMBH—See Mitsubishi Paper Mills Limited; *Int'l*, pg. 4967
MITSUBISHI IMAGING (MPM), INC.—See Mitsubishi Corporation; *Int'l*, pg. 4941
MITSUBISHI INDUSTRIAS PESADAS DO BRASIL LTDA.—See Mitsubishi Heavy Industries, Ltd.; *Int'l*, pg. 4958
MITSUBISHI INTERNATIONAL CORPORATION—See Mitsubishi Corporation; *Int'l*, pg. 4941
MITSUBISHI INTERNATIONAL FOOD INGREDIENTS, INC.—See Mitsubishi Corporation; *Int'l*, pg. 4941
MITSUBISHI INTERNATIONAL G.M.B.H.—See Mitsubishi Corporation; *Int'l*, pg. 4941
MITSUBISHI INTERNATIONAL POLYMER TRADE CORPORATION—See Mitsubishi Corporation; *Int'l*, pg. 4941

MITSUBISHI HEAVY INDUSTRIES, LTD. CORPORATE AFFILIATIONS
Company Index

MITSUBISHI JISHO COMMUNITY CO., LTD.—See Mitsubishi Estate Co., Ltd.; *Int'l*, pg. 4946
MITSUBISHI JISHO HOUSE NET CO., LTD.—See Mitsubishi Estate Co., Ltd.; *Int'l*, pg. 4947
MITSUBISHI JISHO INVESTMENT ADVISORS, INC.—See Mitsubishi Estate Co., Ltd.; *Int'l*, pg. 4947
MITSUBISHI JISHO PROPERTY MANAGEMENT CO., LTD.—See Mitsubishi Estate Co., Ltd.; *Int'l*, pg. 4947
MITSUBISHI JISHO RESIDENCE CO., LTD.—See Mitsubishi Estate Co., Ltd.; *Int'l*, pg. 4947
MITSUBISHI JISHO RETAIL PROPERTY MANAGEMENT CO., LTD.—See Mitsubishi Estate Co., Ltd.; *Int'l*, pg. 4947
MITSUBISHI JISHO SEKKEI INC.—See Mitsubishi Estate Co., Ltd.; *Int'l*, pg. 4947
MITSUBISHI JISHO TOWA COMMUNITY CO., LTD.—See Mitsubishi Estate Co., Ltd.; *Int'l*, pg. 4947
MITSUBISHI KAGAKU IMAGING CORPORATION—See Mitsubishi Chemical Group Corporation; *Int'l*, pg. 4932
MITSUBISHI KAKOKI KAISHA, LTD.—See Mitsubishi Corporation; *Int'l*, pg. 4941
MITSUBISHI LOGISNEXT ASIA PACIFIC PTE. LTD.—See Mitsubishi Heavy Industries, Ltd.; *Int'l*, pg. 4958
MITSUBISHI LOGISNEXT CO., LTD.—See Mitsubishi Heavy Industries, Ltd.; *Int'l*, pg. 4958
MITSUBISHI LOGISNEXT FORKLIFT (SHANGHAI) CO., LTD.—See Mitsubishi Heavy Industries, Ltd.; *Int'l*, pg. 4959
MITSUBISHI LOGISTICS AMERICA CORP.—See Mitsubishi Logistics Corporation; *Int'l*, pg. 4962
MITSUBISHI LOGISTICS CHINA CO., LTD.—See Mitsubishi Logistics Corporation; *Int'l*, pg. 4962
MITSUBISHI LOGISTICS CORPORATION; *Int'l*, pg. 4962
MITSUBISHI LOGISTICS EUROPE B.V.—See Mitsubishi Logistics Corporation; *Int'l*, pg. 4962
MITSUBISHI LOGISTICS HONG KONG LTD.—See Mitsubishi Logistics Corporation; *Int'l*, pg. 4962
MITSUBISHI LOGISTICS SINGAPORE PTE. LTD.—See Mitsubishi Logistics Corporation; *Int'l*, pg. 4962
MITSUBISHI LOGISTICS THAILAND CO., LTD.—See Mitsubishi Logistics Corporation; *Int'l*, pg. 4962
MITSUBISHI MATERIALS (AUSTRALIA) PTY. LTD.—See Mitsubishi Materials Corporation; *Int'l*, pg. 4964
MITSUBISHI MATERIALS CORPORATION - AKASHI PLANT—See Mitsubishi Materials Corporation; *Int'l*, pg. 4964
MITSUBISHI MATERIALS CORPORATION - GIFU PLANT—See Mitsubishi Materials Corporation; *Int'l*, pg. 4964
MITSUBISHI MATERIALS CORPORATION; *Int'l*, pg. 4963
MITSUBISHI MATERIALS CORPORATION - TSUKUBA PLANT—See Mitsubishi Materials Corporation; *Int'l*, pg. 4964
MITSUBISHI MATERIALS ELECTRONIC CHEMICALS CO., LTD. - KASHIMA PLANT—See Mitsubishi Materials Corporation; *Int'l*, pg. 4964
MITSUBISHI MATERIALS ELECTRONIC CHEMICALS CO., LTD.—See Mitsubishi Materials Corporation; *Int'l*, pg. 4964
MITSUBISHI MATERIALS ESPANA S.A.—See Mitsubishi Materials Corporation; *Int'l*, pg. 4964
MITSUBISHI MATERIALS KENZAI CORPORATION—See Mitsubishi Materials Corporation; *Int'l*, pg. 4964
MITSUBISHI MATERIALS (SHANGHAI) CORP.—See Mitsubishi Materials Corporation; *Int'l*, pg. 4964
MITSUBISHI MATERIALS SOUTHEAST ASIA CO., LTD.—See Mitsubishi Materials Corporation; *Int'l*, pg. 4965
MITSUBISHI MATERIALS TECHNO CORPORATION—See Mitsubishi Materials Corporation; *Int'l*, pg. 4965
MITSUBISHI MATERIALS TRADING CORP.—See Mitsubishi Materials Corporation; *Int'l*, pg. 4965
MITSUBISHI MATERIALS USA CORPORATION - ELECTRONIC COMPONENTS—See Mitsubishi Materials Corporation; *Int'l*, pg. 4965
MITSUBISHI MATERIALS U.S.A. CORPORATION—See Mitsubishi Materials Corporation; *Int'l*, pg. 4965
MITSUBISHI MOTOR EUROPE B.V.—See Mitsubishi Motors Corporation; *Int'l*, pg. 4966
MITSUBISHI MOTOR SALES NETHERLANDS B.V.—See Mitsubishi Motors Corporation; *Int'l*, pg. 4966
MITSUBISHI MOTOR SALES OF CANADA, INC.—See Mitsubishi Motors Corporation; *Int'l*, pg. 4966
MITSUBISHI MOTOR SALES OF CARIBBEAN INC.—See Mitsubishi Motors Corporation; *Int'l*, pg. 4966
MITSUBISHI MOTORS AUSTRALIA LTD.—See Mitsubishi Motors Corporation; *Int'l*, pg. 4966
MITSUBISHI MOTORS BELGIUM NV—See Mitsubishi Motors Corporation; *Int'l*, pg. 4966
MITSUBISHI MOTORS CORPORATION - POWER TRAIN PLANT—See Mitsubishi Motors Corporation; *Int'l*, pg. 4966
MITSUBISHI MOTORS CORPORATION; *Int'l*, pg. 4966
MITSUBISHI MOTORS CREDIT OF AMERICA, INC.—See Mitsubishi Motors Corporation; *Int'l*, pg. 4966
MITSUBISHI MOTORS DANMARK A/S—See Mitsubishi Motors Corporation; *Int'l*, pg. 4966
MITSUBISHI MOTORS DE PORTUGAL, S.A.—See Mitsubishi Motors Corporation; *Int'l*, pg. 4966
MITSUBISHI MOTORS DEUTSCHLAND GMBH—See Mitsubishi Motors Corporation; *Int'l*, pg. 4966
MITSUBISHI MOTORS EUROPE B.V.—See Mitsubishi Motors Corporation; *Int'l*, pg. 4966
MITSUBISHI MOTORS FRANCE S.A.S—See Mitsubishi Motors Corporation; *Int'l*, pg. 4966
MITSUBISHI MOTORS MALAYSIA SDN. BHD.—See Mitsubishi Corporation; *Int'l*, pg. 4941
MITSUBISHI MOTORS MIDDLE EAST & AFRICA FZE—See Mitsubishi Motors Corporation; *Int'l*, pg. 4966
MITSUBISHI MOTORS NEW ZEALAND LTD.—See Mitsubishi Motors Corporation; *Int'l*, pg. 4966
MITSUBISHI MOTORS NORTH AMERICA, INC.—See Mitsubishi Motors Corporation; *Int'l*, pg. 4966
MITSUBISHI MOTORS NORTH AMERICA, INC.—See Mitsubishi Motors Corporation; *Int'l*, pg. 4966
MITSUBISHI MOTORS PARTS SALES CO., LTD.—See Mitsubishi Motors Corporation; *Int'l*, pg. 4966
MITSUBISHI MOTORS PHILIPPINES CORPORATION—See Mitsubishi Motors Corporation; *Int'l*, pg. 4966
MITSUBISHI MOTORS R&D EUROPE GMBH—See Mitsubishi Motors Corporation; *Int'l*, pg. 4966
MITSUBISHI MOTORS R&D OF AMERICA, INC.—See Mitsubishi Motors Corporation; *Int'l*, pg. 4966
MITSUBISHI MOTORS (THAILAND) CO., LTD.—See Mitsubishi Motors Corporation; *Int'l*, pg. 4966
MITSUBISHI MOTORS VIETNAM CO., LTD.—See Mitsubishi Corporation; *Int'l*, pg. 4941
MITSUBISHI NAGASAKI MACHINERY MFG. CO., LTD—See Mitsubishi Steel Mfg. Co., Ltd.; *Int'l*, pg. 4968
MITSUBISHI NUCLEAR ENERGY SYSTEMS, INC.—See Mitsubishi Heavy Industries, Ltd.; *Int'l*, pg. 4956
MITSUBISHI NUCLEAR FUEL CO., LTD.—See Mitsubishi Materials Corporation; *Int'l*, pg. 4965
MITSUBISHI ORE TRANSPORT CO., LTD.—See Mitsubishi Corporation; *Int'l*, pg. 4941
MITSUBISHI PAPER ENGINEERING CO., LTD.—See Mitsubishi Paper Mills Limited; *Int'l*, pg. 4967
MITSUBISHI PAPER GMBH—See Mitsubishi Paper Mills Limited; *Int'l*, pg. 4967
MITSUBISHI PAPER HOLDING (EUROPE) GMBH—See Mitsubishi Paper Mills Limited; *Int'l*, pg. 4967
MITSUBISHI PAPER MILLS LIMITED; *Int'l*, pg. 4967
MITSUBISHI PENCIL CO., LTD. - GUNMA FACTORY—See Mitsubishi Pencil Co., Ltd.; *Int'l*, pg. 4967
MITSUBISHI PENCIL CO., LTD.; *Int'l*, pg. 4967
MITSUBISHI PENCIL CO., LTD. - YAMAGATA FACTORY—See Mitsubishi Pencil Co., Ltd.; *Int'l*, pg. 4967
MITSUBISHI PENCIL CO., LTD. - YOKOHAMA FACTORY—See Mitsubishi Pencil Co., Ltd.; *Int'l*, pg. 4967
MITSUBISHI PENCIL CORP. OF AMERICA—See Mitsubishi Pencil Co., Ltd.; *Int'l*, pg. 4967
MITSUBISHI PENCIL CO. U.K. LTD.—See Mitsubishi Pencil Co., Ltd.; *Int'l*, pg. 4967
MITSUBISHI PENCIL ESPANA S.A.—See Mitsubishi Pencil Co., Ltd.; *Int'l*, pg. 4967
MITSUBISHI PENCIL FRANCE SA—See Mitsubishi Pencil Co., Ltd.; *Int'l*, pg. 4967
MITSUBISHI PENCIL KOREA SALES CO., LTD.—See Mitsubishi Pencil Co., Ltd.; *Int'l*, pg. 4967
MITSUBISHI PENCIL (TAIWAN) CO., LTD.—See Mitsubishi Pencil Co., Ltd.; *Int'l*, pg. 4967
MITSUBISHI PENCIL (THAILAND) CO., LTD.—See Mitsubishi Pencil Co., Ltd.; *Int'l*, pg. 4967
MITSUBISHI PENCIL VIETNAM CO., LTD.—See Mitsubishi Pencil Co., Ltd.; *Int'l*, pg. 4967
MITSUBISHI PHARMA DEUTSCHLAND GMBH—See Mitsubishi Chemical Group Corporation; *Int'l*, pg. 4935
MITSUBISHI PHARMA EUROPE LTD.—See Mitsubishi Chemical Group Corporation; *Int'l*, pg. 4935
MITSUBISHI PHARMA (GUANGZHOU) CO., LTD.—See Mitsubishi Chemical Group Corporation; *Int'l*, pg. 4935
MITSUBISHI PHARMA RESEARCH & DEVELOPMENT (BEIJING) CO., LTD.—See Mitsubishi Chemical Group Corporation; *Int'l*, pg. 4935
MITSUBISHI PLASTICS ASIA PACIFIC PTE. LTD.—See Mitsubishi Chemical Group Corporation; *Int'l*, pg. 4932
MITSUBISHI PLASTICS COMPOSITES AMERICA, INC.—See Mitsubishi Chemical Group Corporation; *Int'l*, pg. 4933
MITSUBISHI PLASTICS EURO ASIA LTD.—See Mitsubishi Chemical Group Corporation; *Int'l*, pg. 4933
MITSUBISHI PLASTICS, INC. - AZAI PLANT—See Mitsubishi Chemical Group Corporation; *Int'l*, pg. 4933
MITSUBISHI PLASTICS, INC. - HANYU PLANT—See Mitsubishi Chemical Group Corporation; *Int'l*, pg. 4933
MITSUBISHI PLASTICS, INC. - KORIYAMA PLANT—See Mitsubishi Chemical Group Corporation; *Int'l*, pg. 4933
MITSUBISHI PLASTICS, INC. - MINE PLANT—See Mitsubishi Chemical Group Corporation; *Int'l*, pg. 4933
MITSUBISHI PLASTICS, INC. - MIZUSHIMA PLANT—See Mitsubishi Chemical Group Corporation; *Int'l*, pg. 4933
MITSUBISHI PLASTICS, INC. - NAGAHAMA PLANT—See Mitsubishi Chemical Group Corporation; *Int'l*, pg. 4933
MITSUBISHI PLASTICS, INC. - SAKAIDE PLANT—See Mitsubishi Chemical Group Corporation; *Int'l*, pg. 4933
MITSUBISHI PLASTICS, INC. - SANTO PLANT—See Mitsubishi Chemical Group Corporation; *Int'l*, pg. 4933
MITSUBISHI PLASTICS, INC. - TOKYO PLANT—See Mitsubishi Chemical Group Corporation; *Int'l*, pg. 4933
MITSUBISHI PLASTICS, INC. - TSUKUBA PLANT—See Mitsubishi Chemical Group Corporation; *Int'l*, pg. 4933
MITSUBISHI PLASTICS, INC. - UEDA PLANT—See Mitsubishi Chemical Group Corporation; *Int'l*, pg. 4933
MITSUBISHI PLASTICS TRADING SHANGHAI CO., LTD.—See Mitsubishi Chemical Group Corporation; *Int'l*, pg. 4933
MITSUBISHI POLYESTER FILM GMBH—See Mitsubishi Chemical Group Corporation; *Int'l*, pg. 4933
MITSUBISHI POLYESTER FILM, INC.—See Mitsubishi Chemical Group Corporation; *Int'l*, pg. 4933
MITSUBISHI POLYESTER FILM SUZHOU CO., LTD.—See Mitsubishi Chemical Group Corporation; *Int'l*, pg. 4933
MITSUBISHI POLYSILICON AMERICA CORPORATION—See Mitsubishi Materials Corporation; *Int'l*, pg. 4965
MITSUBISHI POWER AERO—See Mitsubishi Heavy Industries, Ltd.; *Int'l*, pg. 4959
MITSUBISHI POWER AMERICAS, INC.—See Mitsubishi Heavy Industries, Ltd.; *Int'l*, pg. 4956
MITSUBISHI POWER ASIA PACIFIC PTE. LTD.—See Mitsubishi Heavy Industries, Ltd.; *Int'l*, pg. 4959
MITSUBISHI POWER AUSTRALIA PTY. LTD.—See Mitsubishi Heavy Industries, Ltd.; *Int'l*, pg. 4959
MITSUBISHI POWER CANADA, LTD.—See Mitsubishi Heavy Industries, Ltd.; *Int'l*, pg. 4959
MITSUBISHI POWER DE MEXICO, S.A. DE C.V.—See Mitsubishi Heavy Industries, Ltd.; *Int'l*, pg. 4960
MITSUBISHI POWER EGYPT, L.L.C.—See Mitsubishi Heavy Industries, Ltd.; *Int'l*, pg. 4959
MITSUBISHI POWER ENVIRONMENTAL SOLUTIONS, LTD.—See Mitsubishi Heavy Industries, Ltd.; *Int'l*, pg. 4959
MITSUBISHI POWER INDIA PRIVATE LIMITED—See Mitsubishi Heavy Industries, Ltd.; *Int'l*, pg. 4959
MITSUBISHI POWER INDUSTRIES CO., LTD.—See Mitsubishi Heavy Industries, Ltd.; *Int'l*, pg. 4959
MITSUBISHI POWER, LTD.—See Hitachi, Ltd.; *Int'l*, pg. 3423
MITSUBISHI POWER, LTD.—See Mitsubishi Heavy Industries, Ltd.; *Int'l*, pg. 4960
MITSUBISHI POWER MAINTENANCE SERVICE CO., LTD.—See Mitsubishi Heavy Industries, Ltd.; *Int'l*, pg. 4959
MITSUBISHI POWER (PHILIPPINES) INC.—See Mitsubishi Heavy Industries, Ltd.; *Int'l*, pg. 4959
MITSUBISHI POWER PRECISION CASTING CO., LTD.—See Mitsubishi Heavy Industries, Ltd.; *Int'l*, pg. 4959
MITSUBISHI POWER SAUDI ARABIA LIMITED, CO.—See Mitsubishi Heavy Industries, Ltd.; *Int'l*, pg. 4959
MITSUBISHI POWER SYSTEMS (ASIA PACIFIC) PTE LTD.—See Mitsubishi Heavy Industries, Ltd.; *Int'l*, pg. 4960
MITSUBISHI POWER SYSTEMS EUROPE, LTD.—See Mitsubishi Heavy Industries, Ltd.; *Int'l*, pg. 4960
MITSUBISHI POWER SYSTEMS INC.—See Mitsubishi Heavy Industries, Ltd.; *Int'l*, pg. 4956
MITSUBISHI POWER SYSTEMS (THAILAND) LTD.—See Mitsubishi Heavy Industries, Ltd.; *Int'l*, pg. 4960
MITSUBISHI POWER (THAILAND) LTD.—See Mitsubishi Heavy Industries, Ltd.; *Int'l*, pg. 4959
MITSUBISHI PRECISION CO., LTD.—See Mitsubishi Electric Corporation; *Int'l*, pg. 4946
MITSUBISHI RAYON AMERICA, INC.—See Mitsubishi Chemical Group Corporation; *Int'l*, pg. 4933
MITSUBISHI RAYON CARBON FIBER AND COMPOSITES, INC.—See Mitsubishi Chemical Group Corporation; *Int'l*, pg. 4933
MITSUBISHI RAYON CO., LTD.—See Mitsubishi Chemical Group Corporation; *Int'l*, pg. 4933
MITSUBISHI RAYON POLYMER NANTONG CO., LTD.—See Mitsubishi Chemical Group Corporation; *Int'l*, pg. 4933
MITSUBISHI RAYON (SHANGHAI) CO., LTD.—See Mitsubishi Chemical Group Corporation; *Int'l*, pg. 4933
MITSUBISHI REAL ESTATE SERVICES CO., LTD.—See Mitsubishi Estate Co., Ltd.; *Int'l*, pg. 4947
MITSUBISHI REAL ESTATE STRATEGIES—See Mitsubishi Estate Co., Ltd.; *Int'l*, pg. 4947
MITSUBISHI RESEARCH INSTITUTE, INC.; *Int'l*, pg. 4967
MITSUBISHI SHINDOH CO, LTD.—See Mitsubishi Materials Corporation; *Int'l*, pg. 4965
MITSUBISHI SHIPBUILDING CO., LTD.—See Mitsubishi Heavy Industries, Ltd.; *Int'l*, pg. 4960
MITSUBISHI SHOJI AGRI-SERVICE CORPORATION—See Mitsubishi Corporation; *Int'l*, pg. 4942
MITSUBISHI SHOJI CHEMICAL CORP.—See Mitsubishi Corporation; *Int'l*, pg. 4942

COMPANY NAME INDEX

MITSUBISHI SHOJI CONSTRUCTION MATERIALS CORPORATION—See Mitsubishi Corporation; *Int'l*, pg. 4942
MITSUBISHI SHOJI PACKAGING CORPORATION—See Mitsubishi Corporation; *Int'l*, pg. 4942
MITSUBISHI SHOJI PLASTICS CORP.—See Mitsubishi Corporation; *Int'l*, pg. 4942
MITSUBISHI SHOKUHIN CO., LTD.—See Mitsubishi Corporation; *Int'l*, pg. 4942
MITSUBISHI SPACE SOFTWARE CO., LTD.—See Mitsubishi Electric Corporation; *Int'l*, pg. 4946
MITSUBISHI STEEL MFG. CO., LTD.; *Int'l*, pg. 4968
MITSUBISHI STEEL MURORAN INC.—See Mitsubishi Steel Mfg. Co., Ltd.; *Int'l*, pg. 4968
MITSUBISHI TANABE PHARMA AMERICA, INC.—See Mitsubishi Chemical Group Corporation; *Int'l*, pg. 4935
MITSUBISHI TANABE PHARMA CORPORATION—See Mitsubishi Chemical Group Corporation; *Int'l*, pg. 4935
MITSUBISHI TANABE PHARMA DEVELOPMENT AMERICA, INC.—See Mitsubishi Chemical Group Corporation; *Int'l*, pg. 4935
MITSUBISHI TANABE PHARMA FACTORY LTD.—See Mitsubishi Chemical Group Corporation; *Int'l*, pg. 4935
MITSUBISHI TANABE PHARMA HOLDINGS AMERICA, INC.—See Mitsubishi Chemical Group Corporation; *Int'l*, pg. 4935
MITSUBISHI TANABE PHARMA KOREA CO., LTD.—See Mitsubishi Chemical Group Corporation; *Int'l*, pg. 4935
MITSUBISHI TURBOCHARGER ASIA CO.—See Mitsubishi Heavy Industries, Ltd.; *Int'l*, pg. 4960
MITSUBISHI TURBOCHARGER & ENGINE AMERICA, INC.—See Mitsubishi Heavy Industries, Ltd.; *Int'l*, pg. 4960
MITSUBISHI TURBOCHARGER & ENGINE EUROPE B.V.—See Mitsubishi Heavy Industries, Ltd.; *Int'l*, pg. 4960
MITSUBISHI UFJ ASSET MANAGEMENT CO., LTD.—See Mitsubishi UFJ Financial Group, Inc.; *Int'l*, pg. 4970
MITSUBISHI UFJ CAPITAL CO., LTD—See Mitsubishi UFJ Financial Group, Inc.; *Int'l*, pg. 4970
MITSUBISHI UFJ FACTORS LIMITED—See Mitsubishi UFJ Financial Group, Inc.; *Int'l*, pg. 4970
MITSUBISHI UFJ FINANCIAL GROUP, INC., *Int'l*, pg. 4968
MITSUBISHI UFJ GLOBAL CUSTODY S.A.—See Mitsubishi UFJ Financial Group, Inc.; *Int'l*, pg. 4970
MITSUBISHI UFJ INFORMATION TECHNOLOGY, LTD—See Mitsubishi UFJ Financial Group, Inc.; *Int'l*, pg. 4970
MITSUBISHI UFJ INVESTMENT SERVICES (HK) LIMITED—See Mitsubishi UFJ Financial Group, Inc.; *Int'l*, pg. 4970
MITSUBISHI UFJ INVESTOR SERVICES & BANKING (LUXEMBOURG) S.A.—See Mitsubishi UFJ Financial Group, Inc.; *Int'l*, pg. 4970
MITSUBISHI UFJ LEASE & FINANCE (CHINA) CO., LTD.—See Mitsubishi HC Capital Inc.; *Int'l*, pg. 4952
MITSUBISHI UFJ LEASE & FINANCE (HONG KONG) LIMITED—See Mitsubishi HC Capital Inc.; *Int'l*, pg. 4952
MITSUBISHI UFJ LEASE & FINANCE (IRELAND) LIMITED—See Mitsubishi HC Capital Inc.; *Int'l*, pg. 4952
MITSUBISHI UFJ LEASE (SINGAPORE) PTE. LTD—See Mitsubishi HC Capital Inc.; *Int'l*, pg. 4952
MITSUBISHI UFJ LOAN BUSINESS—See Mitsubishi UFJ Financial Group, Inc.; *Int'l*, pg. 4970
MITSUBISHI UFJ MERRILL LYNCH PB SECURITIES CO., LTD.—See Mitsubishi UFJ Financial Group, Inc.; *Int'l*, pg. 4971
MITSUBISHI UFJ MORGAN STANLEY SECURITIES CO., LTD.—See Mitsubishi UFJ Financial Group, Inc.; *Int'l*, pg. 4971
MITSUBISHI UFJ MORGAN STANLEY SECURITIES CO., LTD.—See Morgan Stanley; *U.S. Public*, pg. 1473
MITSUBISHI UFJ NICOS CO., LTD.—See Mitsubishi UFJ Financial Group, Inc.; *Int'l*, pg. 4970
MITSUBISHI UFJ PERSONAL FINANCIAL ADVISERS CO., LTD.—See Mitsubishi UFJ Financial Group, Inc.; *Int'l*, pg. 4970
MITSUBISHI UFJ REAL ESTATE SERVICES CO., LTD.—See Mitsubishi UFJ Financial Group, Inc.; *Int'l*, pg. 4971
MITSUBISHI UFJ RESEARCH AND CONSULTING LTD—See Mitsubishi UFJ Financial Group, Inc.; *Int'l*, pg. 4971
MITSUBISHI UFJ SECURITIES (HK), LIMITED—See Mitsubishi UFJ Financial Group, Inc.; *Int'l*, pg. 4971
MITSUBISHI UFJ SECURITIES HOLDINGS CO., LTD.—See Mitsubishi UFJ Financial Group, Inc.; *Int'l*, pg. 4971
MITSUBISHI UFJ SECURITIES INTERNATIONAL PLC—See Mitsubishi UFJ Financial Group, Inc.; *Int'l*, pg. 4971
MITSUBISHI UFJ TRUST & BANKING CORPORATION - NEW YORK BRANCH—See Mitsubishi UFJ Financial Group, Inc.; *Int'l*, pg. 4972

MITSUBISHI UFJ TRUST & BANKING CORPORATION—See Mitsubishi UFJ Financial Group, Inc.; *Int'l*, pg. 4971
MITSUBISHI UFJ TRUST INTERNATIONAL LIMITED—See Mitsubishi UFJ Financial Group, Inc.; *Int'l*, pg. 4972
MITSUBISHI UFJ TRUST INVESTMENT TECHNOLOGY INSTITUTE—See Mitsubishi UFJ Financial Group, Inc.; *Int'l*, pg. 4972
MITSUBISHI WAREHOUSE CALIFORNIA CORP.—See Mitsubishi Logistics Corporation; *Int'l*, pg. 4963
MITSUBISHI WIRELESS COMMUNICATIONS, INC.—See Hyosung Heavy Industries Corp.; *Int'l*, pg. 3552
MITSUBOSHI BELTING EUROPE GMBH—See Mitsuboshi Belting Ltd.; *Int'l*, pg. 4972
MITSUBOSHI BELTING-INDIA PRIVATE LIMITED—See Mitsuboshi Belting Ltd.; *Int'l*, pg. 4972
MITSUBOSHI BELTING LTD. - KOBE PLANT—See Mitsuboshi Belting Ltd.; *Int'l*, pg. 4972
MITSUBOSHI BELTING LTD. - NAGOYA PLANT—See Mitsuboshi Belting Ltd.; *Int'l*, pg. 4972
MITSUBOSHI BELTING LTD. - SHIGA PLANT—See Mitsuboshi Belting Ltd.; *Int'l*, pg. 4972
MITSUBOSHI BELTING LTD. - SHIKOKU PLANT—See Mitsuboshi Belting Ltd.; *Int'l*, pg. 4972
MITSUBOSHI BELTING LTD.; *Int'l*, pg. 4972
MITSUBOSHI BELTING VIETNAM CO., LTD.—See Mitsuboshi Belting Ltd.; *Int'l*, pg. 4972
MITSUBOSHI CO., LTD.; *Int'l*, pg. 4972
MITSUBOSHI METAL INDUSTRY CO., LTD.—See Godo Steel, Ltd.; *Int'l*, pg. 3020
MITSUBOSHI OVERSEAS HEADQUARTERS PRIVATE LIMITED—See Mitsuboshi Belting Ltd.; *Int'l*, pg. 4972
MITSUBOSHI PHILIPPINES CORPORATION—See MITSUBOSHI CO., LTD.; *Int'l*, pg. 4972
MITSUBOSHI POLAND SP. Z O.O.—See Mitsuboshi Belting Ltd.; *Int'l*, pg. 4972
MITSUBOSHI TECHNO CO., LTD.—See COMSYS Holdings Corporation; *Int'l*, pg. 1761
MITSU CHEM PLAST LIMITED; *Int'l*, pg. 4928
MITSUCHI CORPORATION OF AMERICA—See Mitsuchi Corporation; *Int'l*, pg. 4972
MITSUCHI CORPORATION; *Int'l*, pg. 4972
MITSUCHI MANUFACTURING, INC.—See Mitsuchi Corporation; *Int'l*, pg. 4972
MITSUCHI SEISAKUSHO CO., LTD.—See Mitsuchi Corporation; *Int'l*, pg. 4972
MITSUCHI SUZHOU CORPORATION—See Mitsuchi Corporation; *Int'l*, pg. 4972
MITSUI ADVANCED COMPOSITES (ZHONGSHAN) CO., LTD.—See Mitsui Chemicals, Inc.; *Int'l*, pg. 4982
MITSUI AGRISCIENCE INTERNATIONAL SA/NV—See Mitsui & Co., Ltd.; *Int'l*, pg. 4977
MITSUI ALIMENTOS LTDA.—See Mitsui & Co., Ltd.; *Int'l*, pg. 4977
MITSUI ARGENTINA S.A.—See Mitsui & Co., Ltd.; *Int'l*, pg. 4977
MITSUI AUTO FINANCE PERU S.A.; *Int'l*, pg. 4980
MITSUI BUSSAN AEROSPACE CO., LTD.—See Mitsui & Co., Ltd.; *Int'l*, pg. 4977
MITSUI BUSSAN AEROSPACE CORPORATION—See Mitsui & Co., Ltd.; *Int'l*, pg. 4977
MITSUI BUSSAN AGRO BUSINESS CO., LTD.—See Mitsui & Co., Ltd.; *Int'l*, pg. 4978
MITSUI BUSSAN AUTOMOTIVE INC.—See Mitsui & Co., Ltd.; *Int'l*, pg. 4978
MITSUI BUSSAN AUTOMOTIVE (THAILAND) CO., LTD.—See Mitsui & Co., Ltd.; *Int'l*, pg. 4978
MITSUI BUSSAN BUSINESS PARTNERS CO., LTD.—See Mitsui & Co., Ltd.; *Int'l*, pg. 4978
MITSUI BUSSAN CHEMICALS CO., LTD.—See Mitsui & Co., Ltd.; *Int'l*, pg. 4978
MITSUI BUSSAN COMMODITIES LTD.—See Mitsui & Co., Ltd.; *Int'l*, pg. 4978
MITSUI BUSSAN COPPER INVESTMENT & CO., LTD.—See Mitsui & Co., Ltd.; *Int'l*, pg. 4978
MITSUI BUSSAN CREDIT CONSULTING CO., LTD.—See Mitsui & Co., Ltd.; *Int'l*, pg. 4978
MITSUI BUSSAN E-FILM (HONG KONG) MFG. CO. LTD.—See Mitsui & Co., Ltd.; *Int'l*, pg. 4978
MITSUI BUSSAN FINANCIAL MANAGEMENT LTD.—See Mitsui & Co., Ltd.; *Int'l*, pg. 4978
MITSUI BUSSAN FRONTIER CO., LTD.—See Mitsui & Co., Ltd.; *Int'l*, pg. 4978
MITSUIBUSSAN INSURANCE CO., LTD.—See Mitsui & Co., Ltd.; *Int'l*, pg. 4979
MITSUI BUSSAN INTER-FASHION LTD.—See Mitsui & Co., Ltd.; *Int'l*, pg. 4978
MITSUI BUSSAN KOZAI HANBAI CO., LTD.—See Mitsui & Co., Ltd.; *Int'l*, pg. 4973
MITSUI BUSSAN MACHINE TEC CO., LTD.—See Mitsui & Co., Ltd.; *Int'l*, pg. 4973
MITSUI BUSSAN METALS CO., LTD. - CHUBU NON-FERROUS METALS SALES DIVISION—See Mitsui & Co., Ltd.; *Int'l*, pg. 4973
MITSUI BUSSAN METALS CO., LTD. - CHUGOKU AND SHIKOKU BUSINESS DIVISION—See Mitsui & Co., Ltd.; *Int'l*, pg. 4974

MITSUI BUSSAN METALS CO., LTD. - HOKKAIDO BUSINESS DIVISION—See Mitsui & Co., Ltd.; *Int'l*, pg. 4974
MITSUI BUSSAN METALS CO., LTD. - HOKURIKU BUSINESS DIVISION—See Mitsui & Co., Ltd.; *Int'l*, pg. 4974
MITSUI BUSSAN METALS CO., LTD. - IRON MAKING RAW MATERIALS UNIT—See Mitsui & Co., Ltd.; *Int'l*, pg. 4974
MITSUI BUSSAN METALS CO., LTD. - IRON ORE DIVISION—See Mitsui & Co., Ltd.; *Int'l*, pg. 4974
MITSUI BUSSAN METALS CO., LTD. - KYUSHU BUSINESS DIVISION—See Mitsui & Co., Ltd.; *Int'l*, pg. 4974
MITSUI BUSSAN METALS CO., LTD. - METALLURGICAL COAL DIVISION—See Mitsui & Co., Ltd.; *Int'l*, pg. 4974
MITSUI BUSSAN METALS CO., LTD. - NIIGATA BUSINESS DIVISION—See Mitsui & Co., Ltd.; *Int'l*, pg. 4974
MITSUI BUSSAN METALS CO., LTD. - OSAKA NON-FERROUS METALS SALES DIVISION—See Mitsui & Co., Ltd.; *Int'l*, pg. 4974
MITSUI BUSSAN METALS CO., LTD. - OSAKA SCRAP & FERRO ALLOY DIVISION—See Mitsui & Co., Ltd.; *Int'l*, pg. 4974
MITSUI BUSSAN METALS CO., LTD. - SAKAI WORKS—See Mitsui & Co., Ltd.; *Int'l*, pg. 4974
MITSUI BUSSAN METALS CO., LTD.—See Mitsui & Co., Ltd.; *Int'l*, pg. 4973
MITSUI BUSSAN PACKAGING CO., LTD—See Mitsui & Co., Ltd.; *Int'l*, pg. 4974
MITSUI BUSSAN PLASTICS TRADE CO., LTD.—See Mitsui & Co., Ltd.; *Int'l*, pg. 4978
MITSUI BUSSAN PRECIOUS METALS (HONG KONG) LIMITED—See Mitsui & Co., Ltd.; *Int'l*, pg. 4978
MITSUI BUSSAN SECURE DIRECTIONS, INC.—See Mitsui & Co., Ltd.; *Int'l*, pg. 4978
MITSUI BUSSAN STEEL TRADE CO., LTD.—See Mitsui & Co., Ltd.; *Int'l*, pg. 4974
MITSUI BUSSAN TECHNO PRODUCTS CO., LTD.—See Mitsui & Co., Ltd.; *Int'l*, pg. 4974
MITSUI BUSSAN TRADE SERVICES LTD.—See Mitsui & Co., Ltd.; *Int'l*, pg. 4978
MITSUI BUSSAN WOODCHIP OCEANIA PTY. LTD.—See Mitsui & Co., Ltd.; *Int'l*, pg. 4974
MITSUI CHEMICAL ANALYSIS & CONSULTING SERVICE, INC.—See Mitsui Chemicals, Inc.; *Int'l*, pg. 4982
MITSUI CHEMICAL LOGISTICS, INC.—See Mitsui Chemicals, Inc.; *Int'l*, pg. 4982
MITSUI CHEMICALS AGRO, INC.—See Mitsui Chemicals, Inc.; *Int'l*, pg. 4982
MITSUI CHEMICALS AMERICA, INC.—See Mitsui Chemicals, Inc.; *Int'l*, pg. 4982
MITSUI CHEMICALS ASIA PACIFIC, LTD.—See Mitsui Chemicals, Inc.; *Int'l*, pg. 4982
MITSUI CHEMICALS DO BRASIL COMERCIO LTDA.—See Mitsui Chemicals, Inc.; *Int'l*, pg. 4982
MITSUI CHEMICALS ENGINEERING CO., LTD.—See Mitsui Chemicals, Inc.; *Int'l*, pg. 4982
MITSUI CHEMICALS EUROPE GMBH—See Mitsui Chemicals, Inc.; *Int'l*, pg. 4982
MITSUI CHEMICALS FUNCTIONAL COMPOSITES (SHANGHAI) CO., LTD.—See Mitsui Chemicals, Inc.; *Int'l*, pg. 4982
MITSUI CHEMICALS, INC. - ELASTOMERS DIVISION—See Mitsui Chemicals, Inc.; *Int'l*, pg. 4982
MITSUI CHEMICALS, INC. - FINE & PERFORMANCE CHEMICALS DIVISION—See Mitsui Chemicals, Inc.; *Int'l*, pg. 4983
MITSUI CHEMICALS, INC. - FUNCTIONAL FILM DIVISION—See Mitsui Chemicals, Inc.; *Int'l*, pg. 4983
MITSUI CHEMICALS, INC. - HEALTH CARE MATERIALS DIVISION—See Mitsui Chemicals, Inc.; *Int'l*, pg. 4983
MITSUI CHEMICALS, INC. - ICHIHARA WORKS—See Mitsui Chemicals, Inc.; *Int'l*, pg. 4983
MITSUI CHEMICALS, INC. - INDUSTRIAL CHEMICALS DIV.—See Mitsui Chemicals, Inc.; *Int'l*, pg. 4983
MITSUI CHEMICALS, INC. - IWAKUNI-OHTAKE WORKS—See Mitsui Chemicals, Inc.; *Int'l*, pg. 4983
MITSUI CHEMICALS, INC. - LICENSING DIVISION—See Mitsui Chemicals, Inc.; *Int'l*, pg. 4983
MITSUI CHEMICALS, INC. - MOBARA BRANCH FACTORY—See Mitsui Chemicals, Inc.; *Int'l*, pg. 4983
MITSUI CHEMICALS, INC. - NAGOYA WORKS—See Mitsui Chemicals, Inc.; *Int'l*, pg. 4983
MITSUI CHEMICALS, INC. - NONWOVENS FABRIC DIVISION—See Mitsui Chemicals, Inc.; *Int'l*, pg. 4983
MITSUI CHEMICALS, INC. - OMUTA WORKS—See Mitsui Chemicals, Inc.; *Int'l*, pg. 4983
MITSUI CHEMICALS, INC. - OSAKA WORKS—See Mitsui Chemicals, Inc.; *Int'l*, pg. 4983
MITSUI CHEMICALS, INC. - PERFORMANCE COMPOUND DIVISION—See Mitsui Chemicals, Inc.; *Int'l*, pg. 4983
MITSUI CHEMICALS, INC. - PERFORMANCE POLYMERS DIVISION—See Mitsui Chemicals, Inc.; *Int'l*, pg. 4983

MITSUI AUTO FINANCE PERU S.A. CORPORATE AFFILIATIONS

MITSUI CHEMICALS, INC. - PETROCHEMICAL FEEDSTOCKS DIVISION—See Mitsui Chemicals, Inc.; *Int'l*, pg. 4983
MITSUI CHEMICALS, INC. - PHENOLS DIVISION—See Mitsui Chemicals, Inc.; *Int'l*, pg. 4983
MITSUI CHEMICALS, INC. - PLANNING & COORDINATION DIVISION—See Mitsui Chemicals, Inc.; *Int'l*, pg. 4983
MITSUI CHEMICALS, INC. - POLYURETHANE DIVISION—See Mitsui Chemicals, Inc.; *Int'l*, pg. 4983
MITSUI CHEMICALS, INC. - PTA PET DIVISION—See Mitsui Chemicals, Inc.; *Int'l*, pg. 4983
MITSUI CHEMICALS, INC.; *Int'l*, pg. 4980
MITSUI CHEMICALS, INC. - TOKUYAMA BRANCH FACTORY—See Mitsui Chemicals, Inc.; *Int'l*, pg. 4983
MITSUI CHEMICALS INDIA, PVT. LTD.—See Mitsui Chemicals, Inc.; *Int'l*, pg. 4982
MITSUI CHEMICALS INDUSTRIAL PRODUCTS LTD—See Mitsui Chemicals, Inc.; *Int'l*, pg. 4982
MITSUI CHEMICALS KOREA, INC.—See Mitsui Chemicals, Inc.; *Int'l*, pg. 4982
MITSUI CHEMICALS MC, LTD.—See Mitsui Chemicals, Inc.; *Int'l*, pg. 4982
MITSUI CHEMICALS OPERATION SERVICES CO. LTD.—See Mitsui Chemicals, Inc.; *Int'l*, pg. 4982
MITSUI CHEMICALS SCIENTEX SDN. BHD.—See Mitsui Chemicals, Inc.; *Int'l*, pg. 4982
MITSUI CHEMICALS (SHANGHAI) CO., LTD.—See Mitsui Chemicals, Inc.; *Int'l*, pg. 4982
MITSUI CHEMICALS SINGAPORE R&D CENTRE PTE. LTD.—See Mitsui Chemicals, Inc.; *Int'l*, pg. 4982
MITSUI CHEMICALS & SKC POLYURETHANES INC.—See Mitsui Chemicals, Inc.; *Int'l*, pg. 4982
MITSUI CHEMICALS SUN ALLOYS CO., LTD.—See Mitsui Chemicals, Inc.; *Int'l*, pg. 4982
MITSUI CHEMICALS (THAILAND) CO., LTD.—See Mitsui Chemicals, Inc.; *Int'l*, pg. 4982
MITSUI CHEMICALS TOHCELLO, INC. - ANJO WORKS—See Mitsui Chemicals, Inc.; *Int'l*, pg. 4982
MITSUI CHEMICALS TOHCELLO, INC. - FUNCTIONAL SHEET BUSINESS DIVISION—See Mitsui Chemicals, Inc.; *Int'l*, pg. 4982
MITSUI CHEMICALS TOHCELLO, INC. - HAMAMATSU WORKS—See Mitsui Chemicals, Inc.; *Int'l*, pg. 4982
MITSUI CHEMICALS TOHCELLO, INC. - IBARAKI WORKS—See Mitsui Chemicals, Inc.; *Int'l*, pg. 4982
MITSUI CHEMICALS TOHCELLO, INC. - INDUSTRIAL FILM BUSINESS DIVISION—See Mitsui Chemicals, Inc.; *Int'l*, pg. 4982
MITSUI CHEMICALS TOHCELLO, INC. - KATSUTA WORKS—See Mitsui Chemicals, Inc.; *Int'l*, pg. 4982
MITSUI CHEMICALS TOHCELLO, INC. - KOGA WORKS—See Mitsui Chemicals, Inc.; *Int'l*, pg. 4982
MITSUI CHEMICALS TOHCELLO, INC. - NAGOYA WORKS—See Mitsui Chemicals, Inc.; *Int'l*, pg. 4982
MITSUI CHEMICALS TOHCELLO, INC. - PACKAGING FILM BUSINESS DIVISION—See Mitsui Chemicals, Inc.; *Int'l*, pg. 4982
MITSUI CHEMICALS TOHCELLO, INC.—See Mitsui Chemicals, Inc.; *Int'l*, pg. 4982
MITSUI CHILI LTDA.—See Mitsui & Co., Ltd.; *Int'l*, pg. 4978
MITSUI COAL HOLDINGS PTY. LTD.—See Mitsui & Co., Ltd.; *Int'l*, pg. 4978
MITSUI & CO. ALTERNATIVE INVESTMENTS LIMITED—See Mitsui & Co., Ltd.; *Int'l*, pg. 4976
MITSUI & CO. (ARGENTINA) S.A.—See Mitsui & Co., Ltd.; *Int'l*, pg. 4974
MITSUI & CO. (ASIA PACIFIC) PTE. LTD. - KUALA LUMPUR BRANCH—See Mitsui & Co., Ltd.; *Int'l*, pg. 4974
MITSUI & CO. (ASIA PACIFIC) PTE. LTD. - MANILA BRANCH—See Mitsui & Co., Ltd.; *Int'l*, pg. 4974
MITSUI & CO. (ASIA PACIFIC) PTE. LTD.—See Mitsui & Co., Ltd.; *Int'l*, pg. 4974
MITSUI & CO. ASSET MANAGEMENT HOLDINGS LTD.—See Mitsui & Co., Ltd.; *Int'l*, pg. 4976
MITSUI & CO. (AUSTRALIA) LTD.—See Mitsui & Co., Ltd.; *Int'l*, pg. 4974
MITSUI & CO. (AUSTRALIA) LTD.—See Mitsui & Co., Ltd.; *Int'l*, pg. 4974
MITSUI & CO. (AUSTRALIA) LTD.—See Mitsui & Co., Ltd.; *Int'l*, pg. 4974
MITSUI & CO. (AUSTRALIA) LTD.—See Mitsui & Co., Ltd.; *Int'l*, pg. 4974
MITSUI & CO. (BEIJING), LTD.—See Mitsui & Co., Ltd.; *Int'l*, pg. 4974
MITSUI & CO. BENELUX S.A./N.V.—See Mitsui & Co., Ltd.; *Int'l*, pg. 4976
MITSUI & CO. (BRASIL) S.A.—See Mitsui & Co., Ltd.; *Int'l*, pg. 4974
MITSUI & CO. (BRASIL) S.A.—See Mitsui & Co., Ltd.; *Int'l*, pg. 4975
MITSUI & CO. (BRASIL) S.A.—See Mitsui & Co., Ltd.; *Int'l*, pg. 4974
MITSUI & CO. (CANADA) LTD.—See Mitsui & Co., Ltd.; *Int'l*, pg. 4975
MITSUI & CO. (CANADA)—See Mitsui & Co., Ltd.; *Int'l*, pg. 4975
MITSUI & CO. (CANADA)—See Mitsui & Co., Ltd.; *Int'l*, pg. 4975
MITSUI & CO. (CANADA)—See Mitsui & Co., Ltd.; *Int'l*, pg. 4975
MITSUI & CO. (CHILE) LTDA.—See Mitsui & Co., Ltd.; *Int'l*, pg. 4975
MITSUI & CO. (COLOMBIA) LTDA.—See Mitsui & Co., Ltd.; *Int'l*, pg. 4975
MITSUI & CO. COMMODITY RISK MANAGEMENT LTD.—See Mitsui & Co., Ltd.; *Int'l*, pg. 4976
MITSUI & CO. DEUTSCHLAND GMBH - BUCHAREST OFFICE—See Mitsui & Co., Ltd.; *Int'l*, pg. 4976
MITSUI & CO. DEUTSCHLAND GMBH - CZECH REPUBLIC OFFICE—See Mitsui & Co., Ltd.; *Int'l*, pg. 4976
MITSUI & CO. DEUTSCHLAND GMBH - HUNGARY OFFICE—See Mitsui & Co., Ltd.; *Int'l*, pg. 4976
MITSUI & CO. DEUTSCHLAND GMBH—See Mitsui & Co., Ltd.; *Int'l*, pg. 4976
MITSUI & CO. DEUTSCHLAND GMBH-WARSAW—See Mitsui & Co., Ltd.; *Int'l*, pg. 4976
MITSUI & CO. (EGYPT) S.S.C.—See Mitsui & Co., Ltd.; *Int'l*, pg. 4977
MITSUI & CO. ENERGY MARKETING & SERVICES (USA), INC.—See Mitsui & Co., Ltd.; *Int'l*, pg. 4976
MITSUI & CO. EUROPE (ESPANA) S.A.—See Mitsui & Co., Ltd.; *Int'l*, pg. 4976
MITSUI & CO. EUROPE (ESPANA) S.A.—See Mitsui & Co., Ltd.; *Int'l*, pg. 4976
MITSUI & CO. EUROPE HOLDINGS PLC—See Mitsui & Co., Ltd.; *Int'l*, pg. 4976
MITSUI & CO. EUROPE PLC - ATHENS BRANCH—See Mitsui & Co., Ltd.; *Int'l*, pg. 4976
MITSUI & CO. EUROPE PLC - DUBLIN BRANCH—See Mitsui & Co., Ltd.; *Int'l*, pg. 4976
MITSUI & CO. EUROPE PLC - ISTANBUL BRANCH—See Mitsui & Co., Ltd.; *Int'l*, pg. 4976
MITSUI & CO. EUROPE PLC—See Mitsui & Co., Ltd.; *Int'l*, pg. 4976
MITSUI & CO. EUROPE PLC—See Mitsui & Co., Ltd.; *Int'l*, pg. 4976
MITSUI & CO. EUROPE PLC—See Mitsui & Co., Ltd.; *Int'l*, pg. 4976
MITSUI & CO. EUROPE (PORTUGAL) LDA.—See Mitsui & Co., Ltd.; *Int'l*, pg. 4976
MITSUI & CO. EUROPE S.A.—See Mitsui & Co., Ltd.; *Int'l*, pg. 4976
MITSUI & CO. FINANCIAL SERVICES (ASIA) LTD.—See Mitsui & Co., Ltd.; *Int'l*, pg. 4976
MITSUI & CO. GLOBAL INVESTMENT LTD.—See Mitsui & Co., Ltd.; *Int'l*, pg. 4976
MITSUI & CO. GLOBAL LOGISTICS (ASIA) PTE. LTD.—See Mitsui & Co., Ltd.; *Int'l*, pg. 4976
MITSUI & CO. GLOBAL LOGISTICS, LTD.—See Mitsui & Co., Ltd.; *Int'l*, pg. 4976
MITSUI & CO. (GUANGDONG) LTD.—See Mitsui & Co., Ltd.; *Int'l*, pg. 4975
MITSUI & CO., (HONG KONG) LTD.—See Mitsui & Co., Ltd.; *Int'l*, pg. 4975
MITSUI & CO. INDIA PVT. LTD.-CHENNAI BRANCH—See Mitsui & Co., Ltd.; *Int'l*, pg. 4976
MITSUI & CO. INDIA PVT. LTD.—See Mitsui & Co., Ltd.; *Int'l*, pg. 4976
MITSUI & CO. INDIA PVT. LTD.—See Mitsui & Co., Ltd.; *Int'l*, pg. 4976
MITSUI & CO. INDIA PVT. LTD.—See Mitsui & Co., Ltd.; *Int'l*, pg. 4976
MITSUI & CO., IRAN LTD.—See Mitsui & Co., Ltd.; *Int'l*, pg. 4977
MITSUI & CO. (ITALIA) S.P.A.—See Mitsui & Co., Ltd.; *Int'l*, pg. 4975
MITSUI & CO. KOREA LTD.—See Mitsui & Co., Ltd.; *Int'l*, pg. 4979
MITSUI & CO. KUWAIT W.L.L.—See Mitsui & Co., Ltd.; *Int'l*, pg. 4976
MITSUI & CO., LOGISTICS PARTNERS LTD.—See Mitsui & Co., Ltd.; *Int'l*, pg. 4977
MITSUI & CO., LTD. - INDONESIA—See Mitsui & Co., Ltd.; *Int'l*, pg. 4977
MITSUI & CO., LTD. KOREA—See Mitsui & Co., Ltd.; *Int'l*, pg. 4976
MITSUI & CO., LTD.—See Mitsui & Co., Ltd.; *Int'l*, pg. 4977
MITSUI & CO., LTD.—See Mitsui & Co., Ltd.; *Int'l*, pg. 4977
MITSUI & CO., LTD—See Mitsui & Co., Ltd.; *Int'l*, pg. 4977
MITSUI & CO., LTD—See Mitsui & Co., Ltd.; *Int'l*, pg. 4977
MITSUI & CO., LTD—See Mitsui & Co., Ltd.; *Int'l*, pg. 4977
MITSUI & CO., LTD—See Mitsui & Co., Ltd.; *Int'l*, pg. 4977
MITSUI & CO., LTD—See Mitsui & Co., Ltd.; *Int'l*, pg. 4977
MITSUI & CO., LTD—See Mitsui & Co., Ltd.; *Int'l*, pg. 4977
MITSUI & CO., LTD—See Mitsui & Co., Ltd.; *Int'l*, pg. 4977
MITSUI & CO., LTD—See Mitsui & Co., Ltd.; *Int'l*, pg. 4977
MITSUI & CO., LTD.; *Int'l*, pg. 4973
MITSUI & CO. MACHINE TECH LTD.—See Mitsui & Co., Ltd.; *Int'l*, pg. 4976
MITSUI & CO. (MALAYSIA) SDN. BHD.—See Mitsui & Co., Ltd.; *Int'l*, pg. 4975
MITSUI & CO., (MIDDLE EAST) B.S.C.(C)—See Mitsui & Co., Ltd.; *Int'l*, pg. 4973
MITSUI & CO., MIDDLE EAST LTD.—See Mitsui & Co., Ltd.; *Int'l*, pg. 4977
MITSUI & CO., MIDDLE EAST LTD.—See Mitsui & Co., Ltd.; *Int'l*, pg. 4977
MITSUI & CO., MIDDLE EAST LTD.—See Mitsui & Co., Ltd.; *Int'l*, pg. 4977
MITSUI & CO. MOSCOW LLC—See Mitsui & Co., Ltd.; *Int'l*, pg. 4976
MITSUI & COMPANY (U.S.A.), INC. - SEATTLE OFFICE—See Mitsui & Co., Ltd.; *Int'l*, pg. 4975
MITSUI CONCRETE INDUSTRIES CO., LTD.—See Mitsui & Co., Ltd.; *Int'l*, pg. 4978
MITSUI & CO. NORWAY A/S—See Mitsui & Co., Ltd.; *Int'l*, pg. 4976
MITSUI & CO. (N.Z.) LTD.—See Mitsui & Co., Ltd.; *Int'l*, pg. 4975
MITSUI & CO., (PANAMA INTERNATIONAL, S.A.)—See Mitsui & Co., Ltd.; *Int'l*, pg. 4977
MITSUI & CO. (PERU) S.A.—See Mitsui & Co., Ltd.; *Int'l*, pg. 4975
MITSUI & CO. PLANT SYSTEMS, LTD.—See Mitsui & Co., Ltd.; *Int'l*, pg. 4976
MITSUI & CO. PLASTICS LTD.—See Mitsui & Co., Ltd.; *Int'l*, pg. 4977
MITSUI & CO. POWER & INFRASTRUCTURE DEVELOPMENT LTD.—See Mitsui & Co., Ltd.; *Int'l*, pg. 4977
MITSUI & CO., PRINCIPAL INVESTMENTS LTD.—See Mitsui & Co., Ltd.; *Int'l*, pg. 4977
MITSUI & CO., REALTY MANAGEMENT LTD.—See Mitsui & Co., Ltd.; *Int'l*, pg. 4977
MITSUI & CO. SCANDINAVIA AB—See Mitsui & Co., Ltd.; *Int'l*, pg. 4977
MITSUI & CO. (SHANGHAI) LTD.—See Mitsui & Co., Ltd.; *Int'l*, pg. 4975
MITSUI & CO. STEEL LTD.—See Mitsui & Co., Ltd.; *Int'l*, pg. 4977
MITSUI & CO. STEEL LTD.—See Mitsui & Co., Ltd.; *Int'l*, pg. 4977
MITSUI & CO. (TAIWAN), LTD.—See Mitsui & Co., Ltd.; *Int'l*, pg. 4975
MITSUI & CO. (TAIWAN), LTD.—See Mitsui & Co., Ltd.; *Int'l*, pg. 4975
MITSUI & CO. (THAILAND) LTD.—See Mitsui & Co., Ltd.; *Int'l*, pg. 4975
MITSUI & CO. (TIANJIN) LTD.—See Mitsui & Co., Ltd.; *Int'l*, pg. 4975
MITSUI & CO. (TURKEY) LTD.—See Mitsui & Co., Ltd.; *Int'l*, pg. 4975
MITSUI & CO. (U.S.A.), INC.—See Mitsui & Co., Ltd.; *Int'l*, pg. 4975
MITSUI & CO. VENEZUELA C.A.—See Mitsui & Co., Ltd.; *Int'l*, pg. 4977
MITSUI & CO. VIETNAM LTD.—See Mitsui & Co., Ltd.; *Int'l*, pg. 4977
MITSUI DE COLOMBIA S.A.—See Mitsui & Co., Ltd.; *Int'l*, pg. 4979
MITSUI DEL PERU S.A.—See Mitsui & Co., Ltd.; *Int'l*, pg. 4979
MITSUI DE MEXICO, S.A.R.L. DE C.V.—See Mitsui & Co., Ltd.; *Int'l*, pg. 4979
MITSUI DE MEXICO, S. DE R.L. DE C. V.—See Mitsui & Co., Ltd.; *Int'l*, pg. 4979
MITSUI DESIGNTEC CO., LTD.—See Mitsui Fudosan Co., Ltd.; *Int'l*, pg. 4987
MITSUI DE VENEZUELA C.A.—See Mitsui & Co., Ltd.; *Int'l*, pg. 4979
MITSUI DIRECT GENERAL INSURANCE CO., LTD.—See MS&AD Insurance Group Holdings, Inc.; *Int'l*, pg. 5066
MITSUI DM SUGAR HOLDINGS CO LTD; *Int'l*, pg. 4984
MITSUI ELASTOMERS SINGAPORE PTE LTD—See Mitsui Chemicals, Inc.; *Int'l*, pg. 4983
MITSUI ELECTRONICS INC.—See Mitsui & Co., Ltd.; *Int'l*, pg. 4978
MITSUI E&P AUSTRALIA PTY. LIMITED—See Mitsui & Co., Ltd.; *Int'l*, pg. 4978
MITSUI E&P USA LLC—See Mitsui & Co., Ltd.; *Int'l*, pg. 4975
MITSUI E&S ASIA PTE. LTD.—See Mitsui E&S Holdings Co., Ltd.; *Int'l*, pg. 4985
MITSUI E&S BUSINESS SERVICE CO., LTD.—See Mitsui E&S Holdings Co., Ltd.; *Int'l*, pg. 4985
MITSUI E&S (CHINA) CO., LTD.—See Mitsui E&S Holdings Co., Ltd.; *Int'l*, pg. 4985
MITSUI E&S ENGINEERING CO., LTD.—See Mitsui E&S Holdings Co., Ltd.; *Int'l*, pg. 4985
MITSUI E&S HOLDINGS CO., LTD.; *Int'l*, pg. 4984
MITSUI E&S MACHINERY CO., LTD.—See Mitsui E&S Holdings Co., Ltd.; *Int'l*, pg. 4985
MITSUI E&S MACHINERY EUROPE LIMITED—See Mitsui E&S Holdings Co., Ltd.; *Int'l*, pg. 4985
MITSUI E&S POWER SYSTEMS INC.—See Mitsui E&S Holdings Co., Ltd.; *Int'l*, pg. 4985

COMPANY NAME INDEX

MITSUI E&S SHIPBUILDING CO., LTD.—See Mitsui E&S Holdings Co., Ltd.; *Int'l*, pg. 4985
MITSUI E&S SYSTEMS RESEARCH INC.—See Mitsui E&S Holdings Co., Ltd.; *Int'l*, pg. 4985
MITSUI E&S TECHNICAL RESEARCH CO., LTD.—See Mitsui E&S Holdings Co., Ltd.; *Int'l*, pg. 4985
MITSUI FINE CHEMICALS, INC.—See Mitsui Chemicals, Inc.; *Int'l*, pg. 4983
MITSUI FOODS CO., LTD.—See Mitsui & Co., Ltd.; *Int'l*, pg. 4978
MITSUI FUDOSAN ACCOMMODATIONS FUND MANAGEMENT CO., LTD.—See Mitsui Fudosan Co., Ltd.; *Int'l*, pg. 4987
MITSUI FUDOSAN AMERICA, INC.—See Mitsui Fudosan Co., Ltd.; *Int'l*, pg. 4987
MITSUI FUDOSAN ARCHITECTURAL ENGINEERING CO., LTD.—See Mitsui Fudosan Co., Ltd.; *Int'l*, pg. 4987
MITSUI FUDOSAN (ASIA) MALAYSIA SDN. BHD.—See Mitsui Fudosan Co., Ltd.; *Int'l*, pg. 4986
MITSUI FUDOSAN (ASIA) PTE. LTD.—See Mitsui Fudosan Co., Ltd.; *Int'l*, pg. 4987
MITSUI FUDOSAN ASIA (THAILAND) CO., LTD.—See Mitsui Fudosan Co., Ltd.; *Int'l*, pg. 4987
MITSUI FUDOSAN AUSTRALIA PTY. LTD.—See Mitsui Fudosan Co., Ltd.; *Int'l*, pg. 4987
MITSUI FUDOSAN BUILDING MANAGEMENT CO., LTD.—See Mitsui Fudosan Co., Ltd.; *Int'l*, pg. 4987
MITSUI FUDOSAN CO., LTD.; *Int'l*, pg. 4986
MITSUI FUDOSAN CO., LTD.—See Mitsui Fudosan Co., Ltd.; *Int'l*, pg. 4987
MITSUI FUDOSAN CONSULTING (BEIJING) CO., LTD.—See Mitsui Fudosan Co., Ltd.; *Int'l*, pg. 4987
MITSUI FUDOSAN CONSULTING (GUANGZHOU) CO., LTD.—See Mitsui Fudosan Co., Ltd.; *Int'l*, pg. 4987
MITSUI FUDOSAN ENGINEERING ADVISORS INC.—See Mitsui Fudosan Co., Ltd.; *Int'l*, pg. 4987
MITSUI FUDOSAN FACILITIES CO., LTD.—See Mitsui Fudosan Co., Ltd.; *Int'l*, pg. 4987
MITSUI FUDOSAN FRONTIER REIT MANAGEMENT INC.—See Mitsui Fudosan Co., Ltd.; *Int'l*, pg. 4987
MITSUI FUDOSAN HOTEL MANAGEMENT CO., LTD.—See Mitsui Fudosan Co., Ltd.; *Int'l*, pg. 4987
MITSUI FUDOSAN HOUSING LEASE CO., LTD.—See Mitsui Fudosan Co., Ltd.; *Int'l*, pg. 4987
MITSUI FUDOSAN HOUSING SERVICE KANSAI CO.,LTD.—See Mitsui Fudosan Co., Ltd.; *Int'l*, pg. 4987
MITSUI FUDOSAN INVESTMENT ADVISORS, INC.—See Mitsui Fudosan Co., Ltd.; *Int'l*, pg. 4987
MITSUI FUDOSAN LOGISTICS PARK, INC.; *Int'l*, pg. 4988
MITSUI FUDOSAN LOGISTICS REIT MANAGEMENT CO., LTD.—See Mitsui Fudosan Co., Ltd.; *Int'l*, pg. 4987
MITSUI FUDOSAN REALTY CO., LTD.—See Mitsui Fudosan Co., Ltd.; *Int'l*, pg. 4987
MITSUI FUDOSAN RESIDENTIAL CO., LTD.—See Mitsui Fudosan Co., Ltd.; *Int'l*, pg. 4987
MITSUI FUDOSAN RESIDENTIAL LEASE CO., LTD.—See Mitsui Fudosan Co., Ltd.; *Int'l*, pg. 4987
MITSUI FUDOSAN RESIDENTIAL SERVICE CHUGOKU CO., LTD.—See Mitsui Fudosan Co., Ltd.; *Int'l*, pg. 4987
MITSUI FUDOSAN RESIDENTIAL SERVICE CO., LTD.—See Mitsui Fudosan Co., Ltd.; *Int'l*, pg. 4987
MITSUI FUDOSAN RESIDENTIAL SERVICE CO., LTD.—See Mitsui Fudosan Co., Ltd.; *Int'l*, pg. 4987
MITSUI FUDOSAN RESIDENTIAL SERVICE KANSAI CO., LTD.—See Mitsui Fudosan Co., Ltd.; *Int'l*, pg. 4987
MITSUI FUDOSAN RESIDENTIAL SERVICE KYUSHU CO., LTD.—See Mitsui Fudosan Co., Ltd.; *Int'l*, pg. 4987
MITSUI FUDOSAN RESIDENTIAL SERVICE TOHOKU CO., LTD.—See Mitsui Fudosan Co., Ltd.; *Int'l*, pg. 4987
MITSUI FUDOSAN RESIDENTIAL WELLNESS CO., LTD.—See Mitsui Fudosan Co., Ltd.; *Int'l*, pg. 4987
MITSUI FUDOSAN RETAIL MANAGEMENT CO., LTD. - LALAPORT KOSHIEN—See Mitsui Fudosan Co., Ltd.; *Int'l*, pg. 4987
MITSUI FUDOSAN RETAIL MANAGEMENT CO., LTD. - MITSUI OUTLET PARK MAKUHARI—See Mitsui Fudosan Co., Ltd.; *Int'l*, pg. 4987
MITSUI FUDOSAN (SHANGHAI) CONSULTING CO., LTD.—See Mitsui Fudosan Co., Ltd.; *Int'l*, pg. 4987
MITSUI FUDOSAN TAIWAN CO., LTD.—See Mitsui Fudosan Co., Ltd.; *Int'l*, pg. 4987
MITSUI FUDOSAN (U.K.) LTD.—See Mitsui Fudosan Co., Ltd.; *Int'l*, pg. 4987
MITSUI GAS E ENERGIA DO BRASIL LTDA.—See Mitsui & Co., Ltd.; *Int'l*, pg. 4978
MITSUI HIGH-TEC (CANADA), INC.—See Mitsui High-tec Inc.; *Int'l*, pg. 4988
MITSUI HIGH-TEC (EUROPE) SP. Z O.O.—See Mitsui High-tec Inc.; *Int'l*, pg. 4988
MITSUI HIGH-TEC (GUANG DONG) CO., LTD.—See Mitsui High-tec Inc.; *Int'l*, pg. 4988
MITSUI HIGH-TEC (HONG KONG), LTD.—See Mitsui High-tec Inc.; *Int'l*, pg. 4988

MITSUI HIGH-TEC INC. - IC PLANT—See Mitsui High-tec Inc.; *Int'l*, pg. 4988
MITSUI HIGH-TEC INC. - KIBITA PLANT—See Mitsui High-tec Inc.; *Int'l*, pg. 4988
MITSUI HIGH-TEC INC. - KUMAMOTO PLANT—See Mitsui High-tec Inc.; *Int'l*, pg. 4988
MITSUI HIGH-TEC INC. - NOGATA PLANT—See Mitsui High-tec Inc.; *Int'l*, pg. 4988
MITSUI HIGH-TEC INC.; *Int'l*, pg. 4988
MITSUI HIGH-TEC INC. - TOOLING PLANT—See Mitsui High-tec Inc.; *Int'l*, pg. 4988
MITSUI HIGH-TEC (MALAYSIA) SDN. BHD.—See Mitsui High-tec Inc.; *Int'l*, pg. 4988
MITSUI HIGH-TEC (PHILIPPINES), INC.—See Mitsui High-tec Inc.; *Int'l*, pg. 4988
MITSUI HIGH-TEC (SHANGHAI) CO., LTD.—See Mitsui High-tec Inc.; *Int'l*, pg. 4988
MITSUI HIGH-TEC (SINGAPORE) PTE. LTD.—See Mitsui High-tec Inc.; *Int'l*, pg. 4988
MITSUI HIGH-TEC (TAIWAN) CO., LTD.—See Mitsui High-tec Inc.; *Int'l*, pg. 4988
MITSUI HIGH-TEC (THAILAND) CO., LTD.—See Mitsui High-tec Inc.; *Int'l*, pg. 4988
MITSUI HIGH-TEC (TIANJIN) CO., LTD.—See Mitsui High-tec Inc.; *Int'l*, pg. 4988
MITSUI HIGH-TEC TRADING CO., LTD.—See Mitsui High-tec Inc.; *Int'l*, pg. 4988
MITSUI HIGH-TEC (USA), INC.—See Mitsui High-tec Inc.; *Int'l*, pg. 4988
MITSUI HOME CO., LTD.—See Mitsui Fudosan Co., Ltd.; *Int'l*, pg. 4987
MITSUI HOME ESTATE CO., LTD.—See Mitsui Fudosan Co., Ltd.; *Int'l*, pg. 4988
MITSUI HOME REMODELING CO., LTD.—See Mitsui Fudosan Co., Ltd.; *Int'l*, pg. 4988
MITSUI HYGIENE MATERIALS (THAILAND) CO., LTD.—See Mitsui Chemicals, Inc.; *Int'l*, pg. 4983
MITSUI IRON ORE DEVELOPMENT PTY. LTD.—See Mitsui & Co., Ltd.; *Int'l*, pg. 4978
MITSUI KINKAI KISEN CO., LTD.—See Mitsui O.S.K. Lines, Ltd.; *Int'l*, pg. 4991
MITSUI KNOWLEDGE INDUSTRY CO., LTD.—See Mitsui & Co., Ltd.; *Int'l*, pg. 4978
MITSUI LUMBER CO., LTD.—See Mitsui & Co., Ltd.; *Int'l*, pg. 4978
MITSUI MATSUSHIMA HOLDINGS CO., LTD.; *Int'l*, pg. 4988
MITSUI MEEHANITE METAL CO., LTD.—See Mitsui E&S Holdings Co., Ltd.; *Int'l*, pg. 4985
MITSUI MIIKE MACHINERY CO., LTD.—See Mitsui & Co., Ltd.; *Int'l*, pg. 4978
MITSUI MINING & SMELTING CO., LTD.—See Mitsui & Co., Ltd.; *Int'l*, pg. 4978
MITSUI MUTUAL LIFE INSURANCE COMPANY—See Mitsui & Co., Ltd.; *Int'l*, pg. 4978
MITSUI-NO-MORI CO., LTD.—See Mitsui Fudosan Co., Ltd.; *Int'l*, pg. 4988
MITSUI NORIN CO., LTD.—See Mitsui & Co., Ltd.; *Int'l*, pg. 4978
MITSUI OIL EXPLORATION CO., LTD.—See Mitsui & Co., Ltd.; *Int'l*, pg. 4979
MITSUI OIL & GAS CO., LTD.—See Mitsui & Co., Ltd.; *Int'l*, pg. 4978
MITSUI O.S.K. BULK SHIPPING (ASIA OCEANIA) PTE LTD.—See Mitsui O.S.K. Lines, Ltd.; *Int'l*, pg. 4991
MITSUI O.S.K. BULK SHIPPING (EUROPE) LTD.—See Mitsui O.S.K. Lines, Ltd.; *Int'l*, pg. 4991
MITSUI O.S.K. CAREER SUPPORT LTD.—See Mitsui O.S.K. Lines, Ltd.; *Int'l*, pg. 4991
MITSUI O.S.K. HOLDINGS (BENELUX) B.V.—See Mitsui O.S.K. Lines, Ltd.; *Int'l*, pg. 4991
MITSUI O.S.K. KINKAI, LTD.—See Mitsui O.S.K. Lines, Ltd.; *Int'l*, pg. 4991
MITSUI O.S.K. LINES (AUSTRALLIA) PTY .LTD.—See Mitsui O.S.K. Lines, Ltd.; *Int'l*, pg. 4991
MITSUI O.S.K. LINES (JAPAN) LTD.—See Mitsui O.S.K. Lines, Ltd.; *Int'l*, pg. 4991
MITSUI O.S.K. LINES, LTD.; *Int'l*, pg. 4988
MITSUI O.S.K. PASSENGER LINE, LTD.—See Mitsui O.S.K. Lines, Ltd.; *Int'l*, pg. 4991
MITSUI PHENOLS SINGAPORE PTE LTD.—See INEOS Limited; *Int'l*, pg. 3683
MITSUI PLASTICS, INC.—See Mitsui & Co., Ltd.; *Int'l*, pg. 4979
MITSUI PLASTICS TRADING (SHANGHAI) CO., LTD.—See Mitsui & Co., Ltd.; *Int'l*, pg. 4979
MITSUI POWER VENTURES LIMITED—See Mitsui & Co., Ltd.; *Int'l*, pg. 4979
MITSUI PRIME ADVANCED COMPOSITES DO BRASIL INDUSTRIA E COMERCIO DE COMPOSTOS PLASTICOS S.A.—See Mitsui Chemicals, Inc.; *Int'l*, pg. 4983
MITSUI PRIME ADVANCED COMPOSITES INDIA PVT LTD.—See Mitsui Chemicals, Inc.; *Int'l*, pg. 4983
MITSUI RAIL CAPITAL HOLDINGS, INC.—See Mitsui & Co., Ltd.; *Int'l*, pg. 4975
MITSUI RAIL CAPITAL PARTICIPACOES LTDA.—See Mitsui & Co., Ltd.; *Int'l*, pg. 4979
MITSUI SECURITIES CO., LTD.—See Mizuho Financial Group, Inc.; *Int'l*, pg. 4998

MITSUI-SOKO HOLDINGS CO., LTD.

MITSUI SEIKI USA INC.—See Mitsui & Co., Ltd.; *Int'l*, pg. 4975
MITSUI-SOKO AGENCIES (MALAYSIA) SDN. BHD.—See Mitsui-Soko Holdings Co., Ltd.; *Int'l*, pg. 4993
MITSUI-SOKO BUSINESS PARTNERS CO., LTD.—See Mitsui-Soko Holdings Co., Ltd.; *Int'l*, pg. 4993
MITSUI-SOKO (CHIANGMAI) CO., LTD.—See Mitsui-Soko Holdings Co., Ltd.; *Int'l*, pg. 4992
MITSUI-SOKO (EUROPE) S.R.O.—See Mitsui-Soko Holdings Co., Ltd.; *Int'l*, pg. 4992
MITSUI-SOKO EXPRESS CO., LTD.—See Mitsui-Soko Holdings Co., Ltd.; *Int'l*, pg. 4993
MITSUI-SOKO HOLDINGS CO., LTD.; *Int'l*, pg. 4992
MITSUI-SOKO (KOREA) CO., LTD.—See Mitsui-Soko Holdings Co., Ltd.; *Int'l*, pg. 4992
MITSUI-SOKO KYUSHU CO., LTD.—See Mitsui-Soko Holdings Co., Ltd.; *Int'l*, pg. 4993
MITSUI-SOKO LOGISTICS CO., LTD.—See Mitsui-Soko Holdings Co., Ltd.; *Int'l*, pg. 4993
MITSUI-SOKO (MALAYSIA) SDN. BHD.—See Mitsui-Soko Holdings Co., Ltd.; *Int'l*, pg. 4993
MITSUI-SOKO (SINGAPORE) PTE. LTD.—See Mitsui-Soko Holdings Co., Ltd.; *Int'l*, pg. 4992
MITSUI-SOKO SUPPLY CHAIN SOLUTIONS, INC.—See Mitsui-Soko Holdings Co., Ltd.; *Int'l*, pg. 4993
MITSUI-SOKO (TAIWAN) CO., LTD.—See Mitsui-Soko Holdings Co., Ltd.; *Int'l*, pg. 4992
MITSUI-SOKO (THAILAND) CO., LTD.—See Mitsui-Soko Holdings Co., Ltd.; *Int'l*, pg. 4992
MITSUI-SOKO TRANSPORT CO., LTD.—See Mitsui-Soko Holdings Co., Ltd.; *Int'l*, pg. 4993
MITSUI-SOKO (U.S.A.) INC.—See Mitsui-Soko Holdings Co., Ltd.; *Int'l*, pg. 4992
MITSUI-SOKO (U.S.A.) INC.—See Mitsui-Soko Holdings Co., Ltd.; *Int'l*, pg. 4993
MITSUI-SOKO VIETNAM CO., LTD.—See Mitsui-Soko Holdings Co., Ltd.; *Int'l*, pg. 4993
MITSUI STAMPING CO., LTD.—See Mitsui High-tec Inc.; *Int'l*, pg. 4988
MITSUI SUMITOMO AIOI LIFE INSURANCE CO., LTD.—See MS&AD Insurance Group Holdings, Inc.; *Int'l*, pg. 5066
MITSUI SUMITOMO INSURANCE (CHINA) COMPANY LIMITED—See MS&AD Insurance Group Holdings, Inc.; *Int'l*, pg. 5066
MITSUI SUMITOMO INSURANCE CLAIMS ADJUSTING COMPANY LIMITED—See MS&AD Insurance Group Holdings, Inc.; *Int'l*, pg. 5066
MITSUI SUMITOMO INSURANCE CO., LTD.—See MS&AD Insurance Group Holdings, Inc.; *Int'l*, pg. 5066
MITSUI SUMITOMO INSURANCE COMPANY (EUROPE) LIMITED—See MS&AD Insurance Group Holdings, Inc.; *Int'l*, pg. 5066
MITSUI SUMITOMO INSURANCE (LONDON MANAGEMENT) LTD—See MS&AD Insurance Group Holdings, Inc.; *Int'l*, pg. 5066
MITSUI SUMITOMO INSURANCE (MALAYSIA) BHD.—See MS&AD Insurance Group Holdings, Inc.; *Int'l*, pg. 5066
MITSUI SUMITOMO MARINE MANAGEMENT (USA), INC.—See MS&AD Insurance Group Holdings, Inc.; *Int'l*, pg. 5066
MITSUI SUMITOMO METLIFE INSURANCE CO., LTD.—See MS&AD Insurance Group Holdings, Inc.; *Int'l*, pg. 5066
MITSUI SUMITOMO PRIMARY LIFE INSURANCE CO., LTD.—See MS&AD Insurance Group Holdings, Inc.; *Int'l*, pg. 5067
MITSUI TAKEDA CHEMICALS, INC.—See Mitsui Chemicals, Inc.; *Int'l*, pg. 4983
MITSUI TAKEDA CHEMICALS, INC.—See Takeda Pharmaceutical Company Limited; *Int'l*, pg. 7437
MITSUI THANG LONG STEEL CONSTRUCTION CO., LTD.—See Mitsui E&S Holdings Co., Ltd.; *Int'l*, pg. 4985
MITSUI WAREHOUSE TERMINAL SERVICE CO., LTD.—See Mitsui-Soko Holdings Co., Ltd.; *Int'l*, pg. 4992
MITSUI WHARF CO., LTD.—See Taiheiyo Cement Corporation; *Int'l*, pg. 7411
MITSUI ZOSEN CHIBA KIKO ENGINEERING INC.—See Mitsui E&S Holdings Co., Ltd.; *Int'l*, pg. 4985
MITSUI ZOSEN ENVIRONMENT ENGINEERING CORPORATION—See Mitsui E&S Holdings Co., Ltd.; *Int'l*, pg. 4985
MITSUI ZOSEN EUROPE LIMITED—See Mitsui E&S Holdings Co., Ltd.; *Int'l*, pg. 4985
MITSUI ZOSEN PLANT ENGINEERING INC.—See Mitsui E&S Holdings Co., Ltd.; *Int'l*, pg. 4985
MITSUI ZOSEN SYSTEMS RESEARCH INC.—See Mitsui E&S Holdings Co., Ltd.; *Int'l*, pg. 4985
MITSUIZOSEN TECHNOSERVICE HONGKONG LIMITED—See Mitsui E&S Holdings Co., Ltd.; *Int'l*, pg. 4985
MITSUIZOSEN TECHNOSERVICE TAIWAN CO., LTD.—See Mitsui E&S Holdings Co., Ltd.; *Int'l*, pg. 4985
MITSUI ZOSEN (U.S.A.) INC.—See Mitsui E&S Holdings Co., Ltd.; *Int'l*, pg. 4985

MITSUI-SOKO HOLDINGS CO., LTD. CORPORATE AFFILIATIONS

MITSUKOSHI ENTERPRISES CO., LTD.—See Isetan Mitsukoshi Holdings Ltd.; *Int'l*, pg. 3815
MITSUKOSHI ESPANA S.A.—See Isetan Mitsukoshi Holdings Ltd.; *Int'l*, pg. 3815
MITSUKOSHI FRANCE S.A.—See Isetan Mitsukoshi Holdings Ltd.; *Int'l*, pg. 3815
MITSUKOSHI ISETAN IM FACILITIES CO., LTD.—See Isetan Mitsukoshi Holdings Ltd.; *Int'l*, pg. 3815
MITSUKOSHI ISETAN NIKKO TRAVEL, LTD.—See Isetan Mitsukoshi Holdings Ltd.; *Int'l*, pg. 3815
MITSUKOSHI ITALIA S.P.A.—See Isetan Mitsukoshi Holdings Ltd.; *Int'l*, pg. 3815
MITSUKOSHI KANKYO BUILDING MANAGEMENT CO., LTD.—See Isetan Mitsukoshi Holdings Ltd.; *Int'l*, pg. 3815
MITSUKOSHI KANKYO DESIGN CO., LTD.—See Isetan Mitsukoshi Holdings Ltd.; *Int'l*, pg. 3815
MITSUKOSHI, LTD.—See Isetan Mitsukoshi Holdings Ltd.; *Int'l*, pg. 3815
MITSUKOSHI (UK) LTD.—See Isetan Mitsukoshi Holdings Ltd.; *Int'l*, pg. 3815
MITSUKOSHI (U.S.A.) INC.-ORLANDO BRANCH—See Isetan Mitsukoshi Holdings Ltd.; *Int'l*, pg. 3815
MITSUKOSHI (U.S.A.) INC.—See Isetan Mitsukoshi Holdings Ltd.; *Int'l*, pg. 3815
MITSUMI AUTOMOTIVE DE MEXICO, S.A. DE C.V.—See Minebea Mitsumi Inc.; *Int'l*, pg. 4903
MITSUMI CO., LTD.—See Minebea Mitsumi Inc.; *Int'l*, pg. 4903
MITSUMI ELECTRIC CO., LTD. - AKITA BUSINESS DIVISION—See Minebea Mitsumi Inc.; *Int'l*, pg. 4903
MITSUMI ELECTRIC CO., LTD. - ATSUGI DIVISION—See Minebea Mitsumi Inc.; *Int'l*, pg. 4903
MITSUMI ELECTRIC CO., LTD. - CHITOSE BUSINESS DIVISION—See Minebea Mitsumi Inc.; *Int'l*, pg. 4903
MITSUMI ELECTRIC CO., LTD. - KYUSHU BUSINESS DIVISION—See Minebea Mitsumi Inc.; *Int'l*, pg. 4904
MITSUMI ELECTRIC CO., LTD.—See Minebea Mitsumi Inc.; *Int'l*, pg. 4903
MITSUMI ELECTRIC CO., LTD. - YAMAGATA BUSINESS DIVISION—See Minebea Mitsumi Inc.; *Int'l*, pg. 4904
MITSUMI PHILIPPINES, INC.—See Minebea Mitsumi Inc.; *Int'l*, pg. 4904
MITSUMI (SHANGHAI) ELECTRIC CO., LTD.—See Minebea Mitsumi Inc.; *Int'l*, pg. 4903
MITSUMI TECHNOLOGY (M.) SDN.BHD.—See Minebea Mitsumi Inc.; *Int'l*, pg. 4904
MITSUMI (THAILAND) CO., LTD.—See Minebea Mitsumi Inc.; *Int'l*, pg. 4903
MITSUMOTO SHOJI CO., LTD.—See Kamei Corporation; *Int'l*, pg. 4061
MITSUMURA PRINTING CO., LTD.; *Int'l*, pg. 4993
MITSUNORI CORPORATION—See Mitsui-Soko Holdings Co., Ltd.; *Int'l*, pg. 4993
MITSUSHIBA INTERNATIONAL INC.; *U.S. Private*, pg. 2751
MITSUTEC CO., LTD.—See Optex Group Co., Ltd.; *Int'l*, pg. 5601
MITSUUROKO BEVERAGE CO., LTD.—See Mitsuuroko Group Holdings Co., Ltd.; *Int'l*, pg. 4993
MITSUUROKO CO., LTD.—See Mitsuuroko Group Holdings Co., Ltd.; *Int'l*, pg. 4993
MITSUUROKO CREATIVE SOLUTIONS CO., LTD.—See Mitsuuroko Group Holdings Co., Ltd.; *Int'l*, pg. 4994
MITSUUROKO ENERGY FORCE CO., LTD.—See Mitsuuroko Group Holdings Co., Ltd.; *Int'l*, pg. 4994
MITSUUROKO GREEN ENERGY CO., LTD.—See Mitsuuroko Group Holdings Co., Ltd.; *Int'l*, pg. 4994
MITSUUROKO GROUP HOLDINGS CO., LTD.; *Int'l*, pg. 4993
MITSUUROKO LEASE CO., LTD.—See Mitsuuroko Group Holdings Co., Ltd.; *Int'l*, pg. 4994
MITSUUROKO VESSEL CO., LTD.—See Mitsuuroko Group Holdings Co., Ltd.; *Int'l*, pg. 4994
MITSUUROKO VOYAGERS CO., LTD.—See Mitsuuroko Group Holdings Co., Ltd.; *Int'l*, pg. 4994
MITSUWA CORPORATION—See Wanoba Group Inc.; *U.S. Private*, pg. 4436
MITSUWA ELECTRIC CO., LTD. - MOBARA PLANT—See Mitsuwa Electric Co., Ltd.; *Int'l*, pg. 4994
MITSUWA ELECTRIC CO., LTD.; *Int'l*, pg. 4994
MITSUWA ELECTRIC INDUSTRY CO., LTD.; *Int'l*, pg. 4994
MITSUWA TEKKEN CORPORATION—See JFE Holdings, Inc.; *Int'l*, pg. 3937
MITTAG SPO.S. R.O.—See STRABAG SE; *Int'l*, pg. 7231
MITTAL CORP. LIMITED—See Shyam Metalics & Energy Ltd.; *Int'l*, pg. 6873
MITTAL LIFE STYLE LTD.; *Int'l*, pg. 4994
MITTANBUD.NO AS—See Schibsted ASA; *Int'l*, pg. 6618
MITT AUSTRALIA PTY. LTD.—See Atlassian Corporation; *Int'l*, pg. 686
MITTBYGGE AB—See Addnode Group AB; *Int'l*, pg. 130
MIT TECHNOLOGIES PTE. LTD.—See Manufacturing Integration Technology Ltd; *Int'l*, pg. 4677
MITTEL ADVISORY SPA—See Mittel S.p.A.; *Int'l*, pg. 4994
MITTELBRANDENBURGISCHE SPARKASSE IN POTSDAM; *Int'l*, pg. 4994

MITTEL CAPITAL MARKETS SPA—See Mittel S.p.A.; *Int'l*, pg. 4994
MITTELDEUTSCHE BRAUNKOHLENGESELLSCHAFT MBH—See CEZ, a.s.; *Int'l*, pg. 1428
MITTELDEUTSCHE BRAUNKOHLENGESELLSCHAFT MBH—See Energeticky a Prumyslovy Holding, a.s.; *Int'l*, pg. 2420
MITTELDEUTSCHE EISENBAHN GMBH—See Deutsche Bahn AG; *Int'l*, pg. 2051
MITTELDEUTSCHE NETZGESELLSCHAFT GAS MBH—See RWE AG; *Int'l*, pg. 6434
MITTEL GENERALE INVESTIMENTI S.P.A.—See Mittel S.p.A.; *Int'l*, pg. 4994
MITTEL INVESTIMENTI IMMOBILIARI SRL—See Mittel S.p.A.; *Int'l*, pg. 4994
MITTEL PARTECIPAZIONI STABILI SRL—See Mittel S.p.A.; *Int'l*, pg. 4994
MITTELRHEINISCHE ERDGASTRANSPORTLEITUNGSGESELLSCHAFT MBH—See British Columbia Investment Management Corp.; *Int'l*, pg. 1169
MITTELRHEINISCHE ERDGASTRANSPORTLEITUNGSGESELLSCHAFT MBH—See Macquarie Group Limited; *Int'l*, pg. 4626
MITTEL S.P.A.—See Mittel S.p.A.; *Int'l*, pg. 4994
MITTEL S.P.A.; *Int'l*, pg. 4994
MITTELWESER KLINIKEN GMBH KRANKENHAUS HOYA—See Asklepios Kliniken GmbH & Co. KGaA; *Int'l*, pg. 624
MITTELWESER KLINIKEN GMBH NIENBURG HOYA STOLZENAU—See Asklepios Kliniken GmbH & Co. KGaA; *Int'l*, pg. 624
MITTEN FLUIDPOWER INC.; *U.S. Private*, pg. 2751
MITTERA GROUP, INC.; *U.S. Private*, pg. 2751
MITTERNIGHT, INC.; *U.S. Private*, pg. 2752
MITT HJEM NORGE AS—See Fortum Oyj; *Int'l*, pg. 2742
MITTLERE DONAU KRAFTWERKE AKTIENGESELLSCHAFT—See Fortum Oyj; *Int'l*, pg. 2742
MITTONMEDIA—See The Company of Others; *U.S. Private*, pg. 4013
MITTRIC SYSTEMS SDN. BHD.—See Mikro Msc Berhad; *Int'l*, pg. 4892
MITULA GROUP LIMITED; *Int'l*, pg. 4994
MITUTOYO AMERICA CORPORATION; *U.S. Private*, pg. 2752
MIT WATER TECHNOLOGY CHENGDU CO. LTD.—See Memiontec Holdings Ltd.; *Int'l*, pg. 4814
MITY ENTERPRISES, INC.—See Sorenson Capital Partners; *U.S. Private*, pg. 3715
MIURA AMERICA CO., LTD.—See Miura Co., Ltd.; *Int'l*, pg. 4994
MIURA BANGLADESH CO., LTD.—See Miura Co., Ltd.; *Int'l*, pg. 4994
MIURA BOILER BRAZIL LTD.—See Miura Co., Ltd.; *Int'l*, pg. 4994
MIURA BOILER CO., LTD.—See Miura Co., Ltd.; *Int'l*, pg. 4994
MIURA BOILER CO., LTD.—See Miura Co., Ltd.; *Int'l*, pg. 4994
MIURA BOILER MALAYSIA SDN. BHD.—See Miura Co., Ltd.; *Int'l*, pg. 4995
MIURA BOILER MEXICO S.A. DE C.V.—See Miura Co., Ltd.; *Int'l*, pg. 4995
MIURA BOILER WEST INC.—See Miura Co., Ltd.; *Int'l*, pg. 4995
MIURA CANADA CO., LTD.—See Miura Co., Ltd.; *Int'l*, pg. 4995
MIURA CO., LTD.; *Int'l*, pg. 4994
MIURA ENVIRONMENTAL MANAGEMENT CO. LTD—See Miura Co., Ltd.; *Int'l*, pg. 4995
MIURA INDUSTRIES (SUZHOU) CO., LTD.—See Miura Co., Ltd.; *Int'l*, pg. 4995
MIURA INDUSTRIES (CHINA) CO., LTD.—See Miura Co., Ltd.; *Int'l*, pg. 4995
MIURA INDUSTRIES (THAILAND) CO., LTD.—See Miura Co., Ltd.; *Int'l*, pg. 4995
MIURA INSTITUTE OF RESEARCH & DEVELOPMENT—See Miura Co., Ltd.; *Int'l*, pg. 4995
MIURA KOUKI CO. LTD.—See Miura Co., Ltd.; *Int'l*, pg. 4995
MIURA MACHINE CO LTD—See Miura Co., Ltd.; *Int'l*, pg. 4995
MIURA MACHINE VIDER CO., LTD.—See Miura Co., Ltd.; *Int'l*, pg. 4995
MIURA MANUFACTURING AMERICA CO., LTD.—See Miura Co., Ltd.; *Int'l*, pg. 4994
MIURA NETHERLANDS B.V.—See Miura Co., Ltd.; *Int'l*, pg. 4995
MIURA PRINTING CORPORATION; *Int'l*, pg. 4995
MIURA SEIKI CO., LTD.—See Miura Co., Ltd.; *Int'l*, pg. 4995
MIURA SINGAPORE CO PTE. LTD.—See Miura Co., Ltd.; *Int'l*, pg. 4995
MIURA SOUTH EAST ASIA PTE. LTD.—See Miura Co., Ltd.; *Int'l*, pg. 4995
MIURA TAIWAN ENG CO., LTD.—See Miura Co., Ltd.; *Int'l*, pg. 4995
MIURA TECHNO CO., LTD.—See Miura Co., Ltd.; *Int'l*, pg. 4995

MIURA TURKEY HEATING SYSTEMS INDUSTRY CO., LTD.—See Miura Co., Ltd.; *Int'l*, pg. 4995
MIVA MERCHANT, INC.; *U.S. Private*, pg. 2752
MIVAN DEPA CONTRACTING L.L.C.—See Depa PLC; *Int'l*, pg. 2041
MIVENT AS—See AF Gruppen ASA; *Int'l*, pg. 184
MIVEPA GMBH—See DS Smith Plc; *Int'l*, pg. 2209
MIVIN ENGINEERING TECHNOLOGIES PRIVATE LTD.—See Robert Bosch GmbH; *Int'l*, pg. 6361
MIVISA ENVASES S.A.U.—See Crown Holdings, Inc.; *U.S. Public*, pg. 598
MIVISA HUNGARY KFT.—See Crown Holdings, Inc.; *U.S. Public*, pg. 598
MIVISA MAROC, S.A.—See Crown Holdings, Inc.; *U.S. Public*, pg. 598
MIVTACH SHAMIR HOLDINGS LTD.; *Int'l*, pg. 4995
MIVTACH-SIMON INSURANCE AGENCIES LTD.—See Assicurazioni Generali S.p.A.; *Int'l*, pg. 647
MIWA KOZAI CO., LTD.—See Okaya & Co., Ltd.; *Int'l*, pg. 5546
MIWD HOLDING COMPANY LLC—See Koch Industries, Inc.; *U.S. Private*, pg. 2332
MIWEL CONSTRUCTION LIMITED—See Aecon Group Inc.; *Int'l*, pg. 172
MI WINDOWS AND DOORS, LLC—See Koch Industries, Inc.; *U.S. Private*, pg. 2332
MIWON AUSTRIA GMBH—See Miwon Holdings Co.,Ltd.; *Int'l*, pg. 4995
MIWON CHEMICALS CO., LTD.; *Int'l*, pg. 4995
MIWON COMMERCIAL CO LTD - BANWOL FACTORY—See Miwon Commercial Co., Ltd.; *Int'l*, pg. 4995
MIWON COMMERCIAL CO., LTD.; *Int'l*, pg. 4995
MIWON EUROPE GMBH—See Miwon Holdings Co.,Ltd.; *Int'l*, pg. 4995
MIWON GUANGZHOU CHEMICAL CO., LTD.—See Miwon Holdings Co.,Ltd.; *Int'l*, pg. 4995
MIWON HOLDINGS CO.,LTD.; *Int'l*, pg. 4995
MIWON NANTONG CHEMICAL CO., LTD.—See Miwon Holdings Co.,Ltd.; *Int'l*, pg. 4995
MIWON NORTH AMERICA INC.—See Miwon Holdings Co.,Ltd.; *Int'l*, pg. 4995
MIWON (SHENZHEN) CHEMICAL CO., LTD.—See Miwon Holdings Co.,Ltd.; *Int'l*, pg. 4995
MIWON SPAIN SLU—See Miwon Holdings Co.,Ltd.; *Int'l*, pg. 4995
MIWON SPECIALTY CHEMICAL INDIA PVT. LTD.—See Miwon Holdings Co.,Ltd.; *Int'l*, pg. 4995
MIWON SPECIALTY CHEMICAL USA, INC.—See Miwon Holdings Co.,Ltd.; *Int'l*, pg. 4995
MIWON VIETNAM CO., LTD.—See Daesang Corporation; *Int'l*, pg. 1909
MIWON VIETNAM CO., LTD. - TAY NINH TAPIOCA STARCH FACTORY—See Daesang Corporation; *Int'l*, pg. 1909
MIWON VIETNAM CO., LTD. - VIET TRI FACTORY—See Daesang Corporation; *Int'l*, pg. 1909
MIX 1 LIFE INC.; *U.S. Public*, pg. 1452
MIXAMO, INC.—See Adobe Inc.; *U.S. Public*, pg. 42
MIXBOOK INC.; *U.S. Private*, pg. 2752
MIXCOR AGGREGATES INC.; *Int'l*, pg. 4995
MIXER SYSTEMS INC.; *U.S. Private*, pg. 2752
MIXI, INC.; *Int'l*, pg. 4995
MIXING SOLUTIONS LIMITED—See Lone Star Funds; *U.S. Private*, pg. 2485
MIX MEGAPOL.SE AB—See Warner Bros. Discovery, Inc.; *U.S. Public*, pg. 2326
MIXON FRUIT FARMS, INC.; *U.S. Private*, pg. 2752
MIXON-NOLLNER OIL CO.; *U.S. Private*, pg. 2752
MIXON SEED CO., INC.; *U.S. Private*, pg. 2752
MIXONSITE USA, INC.—See Cematrix Corporation; *Int'l*, pg. 1396
MIXPO, INC.—See Netsertive, Inc.; *U.S. Private*, pg. 2888
MIXSON OIL CO. INC.; *U.S. Private*, pg. 2752
MIX TELEMATICS INTERNATIONAL (PTY) LTD.—See PowerFleet, Inc.; *U.S. Public*, pg. 1706
MIX TELEMATICS LIMITED—See PowerFleet, Inc.; *U.S. Public*, pg. 1706
MIXT SOLUTIONS LLC; *U.S. Private*, pg. 2752
MIXTURA 36 BT.—See PHOENIX Pharmahandel GmbH & Co. KG; *Int'l*, pg. 5854
MIXTURA BT.—See PHOENIX Pharmahandel GmbH & Co. KG; *Int'l*, pg. 5854
MIYACHI CORPORATION—See Amada Holdings Co., Ltd.; *Int'l*, pg. 404
MIYAGI DYNAPAC CO., LTD. - FURUKAWA PLANT—See Dynapac Co., Ltd.; *Int'l*, pg. 2241
MIYAGI DYNAPAC CO., LTD.—See Dynapac Co., Ltd.; *Int'l*, pg. 2241
MIYAGI MARINE SERVICE CO., LTD.—See Tokyo Kisen Co., Ltd.; *Int'l*, pg. 7793
MIYAGIN BUSINESS SERVICE CO., LTD—See The Miyazaki Bank, Ltd.; *Int'l*, pg. 7667
MIYAGIN CARD CO. LTD.—See The Miyazaki Bank, Ltd.; *Int'l*, pg. 7667
MIYAGIN COMPUTER SERVICE CO. LTD.—See The Miyazaki Bank, Ltd.; *Int'l*, pg. 7667
MIYAGI NIKON PRECISION CO., LTD.—See Nikon Corporation; *Int'l*, pg. 5292

COMPANY NAME INDEX

MIYAGIN LEASE CO. LTD.—See The Miyazaki Bank, Ltd.; *Int'l*, pg. 7667
MIYAGI NOK CORPORATION—See NOK Corporation; *Int'l*, pg. 5402
MIYAGIN STAFF SERVICE CO.LTD.—See The Miyazaki Bank, Ltd.; *Int'l*, pg. 7667
MIYAGIN VENTURE CAPITAL CO. LTD.—See The Miyazaki Bank; Ltd.; *Int'l*, pg. 7667
MIYAGISEIFUN CO., LTD.—See Kobe Bussan Co., Ltd.; *Int'l*, pg. 4217
MIYAGI SEINO TRANSPORTATION CO., LTD.—See Seino Holdings Co., Ltd.; *Int'l*, pg. 6690
MIYAGI SUBARU INC.—See SUBARU CO., LTD.; *Int'l*, pg. 7246
MIYAGI TOYO KAISHA, LTD.—See Toyo Suisan Kaisha, Ltd.; *Int'l*, pg. 7858
MIYAIRI VALVE MFG. CO., LTD. - KOFU FACTORY—See Miyairi Valve Mfg. Co., Ltd.; *Int'l*, pg. 4996
MIYAIRI VALVE MFG. CO., LTD.; *Int'l*, pg. 4996
MIYAJI ENGINEERING GROUP INC.; *Int'l*, pg. 4996
MIYAKE CONCRETE ACCESSORIES, INC.—See Hawaii Planing Mill Ltd.; *U.S. Private*, pg. 1881
MIYAKO, INC.; *Int'l*, pg. 4996
MIYAKO KAGAKU CO., LTD.—See Chori Co., Ltd.; *Int'l*, pg. 1583
MIYAKOSHI HOLDINGS INC.; *Int'l*, pg. 4996
MIYA LUXEMBURG HOLDINGS S.A.R.L—See Bridgepoint Group Plc; *Int'l*, pg. 1155
MIYAMA KOGYO CO., LTD.—See Maeda Corporation; *Int'l*, pg. 4635
MIYAMOTO INTERNATIONAL, INC.; *U.S. Private*, pg. 2752
MIYASHITA KOUMUTEN CO., LTD.—See Sala Corporation; *Int'l*, pg. 6490
MIYATA CO., LTD.—See Hong Kong Food Investment Holdings Limited; *Int'l*, pg. 3466
MIYATA CYCLE CO., LTD.—See Merida Industry Co., Ltd.; *Int'l*, pg. 4835
MIYATA INDUSTRY CO., LTD.—See Morita Holdings Corporation; *Int'l*, pg. 5048
MIYAZAKI ASMO CO., LTD.—See Denso Corporation; *Int'l*, pg. 2032
THE MIYAZAKI BANK, LTD.; *Int'l*, pg. 7667
MIYAZAKI CANON INC.—See Canon Inc.; *Int'l*, pg. 1298
MIYAZAKI DAISHIN CANON CO., LTD.—See Canon Inc.; *Int'l*, pg. 1298
MIYAZAKI FUJITSU COMPONENTS LIMITED—See FUJITSU COMPONENT LIMITED; *Int'l*, pg. 2832
MIYAZAKI JAMCO CORPORATION—See JAMCO Corporation; *Int'l*, pg. 3874
MIYAZAKI KOGYO CO., LTD.—See NOK Corporation; *Int'l*, pg. 5402
MIYAZAKI MITSUBA CORPORATION—See MITSUBA Corporation; *Int'l*, pg. 4929
MIYAZAKI PRECON CO., LTD.—See Yamau Holdings Co., Ltd.; *Int'l*, pg. 8555
MIYAZAKI SENKO APOLLO CO., LTD.—See Senko Group Holdings Co., Ltd.; *Int'l*, pg. 6710
MIYAZAKI SENKO TRANSPORT CO., LTD.—See Senko Group Holdings Co., Ltd.; *Int'l*, pg. 6710
THE MIYAZAKI TAIYO BANK, LTD.; *Int'l*, pg. 7668
MIYAZAWA CORPORATION—See Rengo Co., Ltd.; *Int'l*, pg. 6280
MIYOSHI ELECTRONICS CORPORATION—See Mitsubishi Electric Corporation; *Int'l*, pg. 4946
MIYOSHI HI-TECH CO., LTD.—See Miyoshi Limited; *Int'l*, pg. 4996
MIYOSHI INDUSTRIES CO., LTD.—See Kurita Water Industries Ltd.; *Int'l*, pg. 4341
MIYOSHI LIMITED; *Int'l*, pg. 4996
MIYOSHI OIL & FAT CO., LTD.; *Int'l*, pg. 4996
MIYOSHI PRECISION HUIZHOU CO., LTD.—See Miyoshi Limited; *Int'l*, pg. 4996
MIYOSHI PRECISION (MALAYSIA) SDN. BHD.—See Miyoshi Limited; *Int'l*, pg. 4996
MIYOSHI PRECISION (THAILAND) CO., LTD.—See Miyoshi Limited; *Int'l*, pg. 4996
MIYOSHI TECHNOLOGIES PHILS., INC.—See Miyoshi Limited; *Int'l*, pg. 4996
MIYOSHI VALVE CO., LTD.—See KITZ CORPORATION; *Int'l*, pg. 4196
MIYOTA DEVELOPMENT CENTER OF AMERICA, INC.—See Citizen Watch Co., Ltd.; *Int'l*, pg. 1623
MIYUKI BUILDING CO., LTD; *Int'l*, pg. 4996
MIYUKIKEORI CO., LTD.—See Toyobo Co., Ltd.; *Int'l*, pg. 7860
MIZAR MOTORS, INC.—See Centaur, Inc.; *U.S. Private*, pg. 809
MIZE HOUSER & CO., P.A.; *U.S. Private*, pg. 2752
MIZE INC.; *U.S. Private*, pg. 2752
MIZELL MEMORIAL HOSPITAL HOMECARE, LLC—See UnitedHealth Group Incorporated; *U.S. Public*, pg. 2246
MIZHUO TRUST & BANKING (LUXEMBOURG) S.A.—See T&D Holdings, Inc.; *Int'l*, pg. 7395
MIZIA-96 AD; *Int'l*, pg. 4996
MIZKAN AMERICAS, INC. - BORDER FOODS PLANT—See Mizkan Holdings Co., Ltd.; *Int'l*, pg. 4996

MIZKAN AMERICAS, INC. - BORDER PRODUCTS DIVISION—See Mizkan Holdings Co., Ltd.; *Int'l*, pg. 4996
MIZKAN AMERICAS, INC.—See Mizkan Holdings Co., Ltd.; *Int'l*, pg. 4996
MIZKAN ASIA PACIFIC PTE. LTD—See Mizkan Holdings Co., Ltd.; *Int'l*, pg. 4996
MIZKAN CHINA CO., LTD.—See Mizkan Holdings Co., Ltd.; *Int'l*, pg. 4996
MIZKAN CO., LTD.—See Mizkan Holdings Co., Ltd.; *Int'l*, pg. 4996
MIZKAN EURO LTD.—See Mizkan Holdings Co., Ltd.; *Int'l*, pg. 4996
MIZKAN HOLDINGS CO., LTD.; *Int'l*, pg. 4996
MIZKAN (THAILAND) CO.,LTD.—See Mizkan Holdings Co., Ltd.; *Int'l*, pg. 4996
MIZNER COUNTRY CLUB, INC.; *U.S. Private*, pg. 2752
MIZONOKUCHISHINTOSHI CO., LTD.—See Marui Group Co., Ltd.; *Int'l*, pg. 4713
MIZRAHI CAPITAL MARKETS—See Mizrahi Tefahot Bank Ltd.; *Int'l*, pg. 4997
MIZRAHI ENTERPRISES INC.; *U.S. Private*, pg. 2752
MIZRAHI TEFAHOT BANK LTD. - LOS ANGELES—See Mizrahi Tefahot Bank Ltd.; *Int'l*, pg. 4997
MIZRAHI TEFAHOT BANK LTD.; *Int'l*, pg. 4996
MIZRAHI-TEFAHOT FACTORING LTD.—See Mizrahi Tefahot Bank Ltd.; *Int'l*, pg. 4997
MIZRAHI TEFAHOT TRUST COMPANY LTD.—See Mizrahi Tefahot Bank Ltd.; *Int'l*, pg. 4997
MIZRAHI TEFAHOT TECHNOLOGY DIVISION LTD.—See Mizrahi Tefahot Bank Ltd.; *Int'l*, pg. 4997
MIZRHAI TEFAHOT TECHNOLOGY DIVISION LTD—See Mizrahi Tefahot Bank Ltd.; *Int'l*, pg. 4997
MIZUHO ALTERNATIVE INVESTMENTS, LLC—See Mizuho Financial Group, Inc.; *Int'l*, pg. 4997
MIZUHO AMERICAS LLC—See Mizuho Financial Group, Inc.; *Int'l*, pg. 4997
MIZUHO BANK (CANADA)—See Mizuho Financial Group, Inc.; *Int'l*, pg. 4997
MIZUHO BANK EUROPE N.V.—See Mizuho Financial Group, Inc.; *Int'l*, pg. 4997
MIZUHO BANK EUROPE N.V.—See Mizuho Financial Group, Inc.; *Int'l*, pg. 4997
MIZUHO BANK, LTD.—See Mizuho Financial Group, Inc.; *Int'l*, pg. 4997
MIZUHO BANK, LTD.—See Mizuho Financial Group, Inc.; *Int'l*, pg. 4998
MIZUHO BANK (SWITZERLAND) LTD.—See Mizuho Financial Group, Inc.; *Int'l*, pg. 4998
MIZUHO CAPITAL CO., LTD.; *Int'l*, pg. 4997
MIZUHO CAPITAL MARKETS CORPORATION—See Mizuho Financial Group, Inc.; *Int'l*, pg. 4998
MIZUHO CAPITAL MARKETS (HK) LIMITED—See Mizuho Financial Group, Inc.; *Int'l*, pg. 4998
MIZUHO CAPITAL MARKETS (UK) LIMITED—See Mizuho Financial Group, Inc.; *Int'l*, pg. 4998
MIZUHO CAPITAL PARTNERS CO., LTD.—See Mizuho Financial Group, Inc.; *Int'l*, pg. 4998
MIZUHO CORPORATE BANK-BA INVESTMENT CONSULTING GMBH—See Mizuho Financial Group, Inc.; *Int'l*, pg. 4998
MIZUHO CORPORATE BANK (CHINA), LTD.—See Mizuho Financial Group, Inc.; *Int'l*, pg. 4998
MIZUHO CORPORATE BANK NEDERLAND N.V.—See Mizuho Financial Group, Inc.; *Int'l*, pg. 4998
MIZUHO CORPORATE BANK OF CALIFORNIA—See Mizuho Financial Group, Inc.; *Int'l*, pg. 4998
MIZUHO CREDIT GUARANTEE CO., LTD.—See Mizuho Financial Group, Inc.; *Int'l*, pg. 4998
MIZUHO FACTORS, LIMITED—See Mizuho Financial Group, Inc.; *Int'l*, pg. 4998
MIZUHO FINANCIAL GROUP, INC.; *Int'l*, pg. 4997
MIZUHO FINANCIAL STRATEGY—See Mizuho Financial Group, Inc.; *Int'l*, pg. 4998
MIZUHO INDUSTRIAL CO., LTD.—See Sanoyas Holdings Corporation; *Int'l*, pg. 6554
MIZUHO INFORMATION & RESEARCH INSTITUTE INC.—See Mizuho Financial Group, Inc.; *Int'l*, pg. 4998
MIZUHO INTERNATIONAL PLC—See Mizuho Financial Group, Inc.; *Int'l*, pg. 4998
MIZUHO INVESTMENT CONSULTING (SHANGHAI) CO., LTD.—See Mizuho Financial Group, Inc.; *Int'l*, pg. 4998
MIZUHO LEASING (CHINA) LTD.—See Mizuho Leasing Company, Limited; *Int'l*, pg. 4999
MIZUHO LEASING COMPANY, LIMITED; *Int'l*, pg. 4999
MIZUHO LEASING (SINGAPORE) PTE. LTD.—See Mizuho Leasing Company, Limited; *Int'l*, pg. 4999
MIZUHO LEASING (UK) LIMITED—See Mizuho Leasing Company, Limited; *Int'l*, pg. 4999
MIZUHO MACHINERY (WUXI) CO., LTD.—See Sanoyas Holdings Corporation; *Int'l*, pg. 6554
MIZUHO MARUBENI LEASING CORPORATION—See Mizuho Leasing Company, Limited; *Int'l*, pg. 4999
MIZUHO MEDY CO., LTD.; *Int'l*, pg. 4999
MIZUHO PRIVATE WEALTH MANAGEMENT CO., LTD.—See Mizuho Financial Group, Inc.; *Int'l*, pg. 4998
MIZUHO RESEARCH INSTITUTE LTD.—See Mizuho Financial Group, Inc.; *Int'l*, pg. 4998

MIZUHO SAUDI ARABIA COMPANY—See Mizuho Financial Group, Inc.; *Int'l*, pg. 4998
MIZUHO SECURITIES ASIA LIMITED—See Mizuho Financial Group, Inc.; *Int'l*, pg. 4998
MIZUHO SECURITIES CO., LTD.—See Mizuho Financial Group, Inc.; *Int'l*, pg. 4998
MIZUHO SECURITIES EUROPE GMBH—See Mizuho Financial Group, Inc.; *Int'l*, pg. 4998
MIZUHO SECURITIES INDIA PRIVATE LIMITED—See Mizuho Financial Group, Inc.; *Int'l*, pg. 4998
MIZUHO SECURITIES PROPERTY MANAGEMENT CO., LTD—See Mizuho Financial Group, Inc.; *Int'l*, pg. 4998
MIZUHO SECURITIES SINGAPORE PTE. LIMITED—See Mizuho Financial Group, Inc.; *Int'l*, pg. 4998
MIZUHO SECURITIES (SINGAPORE) PTE. LTD.—See Mizuho Financial Group, Inc.; *Int'l*, pg. 4998
MIZUHO SECURITIES USA INC.—See Mizuho Financial Group, Inc.; *Int'l*, pg. 4998
MIZUHO-TOSHIBA LEASING COMPANY, LIMITED—See Mizuho Leasing Company, Limited; *Int'l*, pg. 4999
MIZUHO TRUST & BANKING CO., LTD.—See Mizuho Financial Group, Inc.; *Int'l*, pg. 4998
MIZUHO TRUST & BANKING (LUXEMBOURG) S.A.—See Mizuho Financial Group, Inc.; *Int'l*, pg. 4998
MIZUHO UNYU CO., LTD—See Taiheiyo Cement Corporation; *Int'l*, pg. 7412
MIZUMA RAILWAY CO., LTD.—See Gourmet Kineya Co., Ltd.; *Int'l*, pg. 3044
MIZUNO CANADA LIMITED—See Mizuno Corporation; *Int'l*, pg. 4999
MIZUNO (CHINA) CORPORATION—See Mizuno Corporation; *Int'l*, pg. 4999
MIZUNO CORPORATION AUSTRALIA PTY. LTD.—See Mizuno Corporation; *Int'l*, pg. 4999
MIZUNO CORPORATION FRANCE—See Mizuno Corporation; *Int'l*, pg. 4999
MIZUNO CORPORATION (GERMANY)—See Mizuno Corporation; *Int'l*, pg. 4999
MIZUNO CORPORATION NIEDERLASSUNG DEUTSCHLAND—See Mizuno Corporation; *Int'l*, pg. 4999
MIZUNO CORPORATION OF HONG KONG LTD.—See Mizuno Corporation; *Int'l*, pg. 4999
MIZUNO CORPORATION; *Int'l*, pg. 4999
MIZUNO CORPORATION—See Mizuno Corporation; *Int'l*, pg. 4999
MIZUNO CORPORATION—See Mizuno Corporation; *Int'l*, pg. 4999
MIZUNO CORPORATION—See Mizuno Corporation; *Int'l*, pg. 4999
MIZUNO CORPORATION (UK) LTD.—See Mizuno Corporation; *Int'l*, pg. 4999
MIZUNO IBERIA S.L.—See Mizuno Corporation; *Int'l*, pg. 4999
MIZUNO ITALIA S.R.L.—See Mizuno Corporation; *Int'l*, pg. 4999
MIZUNO KOREA LTD.—See Mizuno Corporation; *Int'l*, pg. 5000
MIZUNO NORGE AS—See Mizuno Corporation; *Int'l*, pg. 5000
MIZUNO SINGAPORE PTE LTD—See Mizuno Corporation; *Int'l*, pg. 5000
MIZUNO SPORTS SERVICE CO. LTD.—See Mizuno Corporation; *Int'l*, pg. 5000
MIZUNO (TAIWAN) CORPORATION—See Mizuno Corporation; *Int'l*, pg. 4999
MIZUNO USA, INC.—See Mizuno Corporation; *Int'l*, pg. 5000
MIZUSAWA INDUSTRIAL CHEMICALS, LTD.—See Takeda Pharmaceutical Company Limited; *Int'l*, pg. 7437
MIZUSHIMA ECO-WORKS CO., LTD.—See JFE Holdings, Inc.; *Int'l*, pg. 3938
MIZUSHIMA FERROALLOY CO., LTD.—See JFE Holdings, Inc.; *Int'l*, pg. 3938
MIZUSHIMA GAS CO., LTD.—See Toho Gas Co., Ltd.; *Int'l*, pg. 7775
MIZUSHIMA KASOZAI CO., LTD.—See Mitsubishi Gas Chemical Company, Inc.; *Int'l*, pg. 4950
MIZUSHIMA METAL PRODUCTS CORPORATION—See JFE Holdings, Inc.; *Int'l*, pg. 3937
MIZUSHIMA PARAXYLENE CO., LTD.—See Mitsubishi Gas Chemical Company, Inc.; *Int'l*, pg. 4950
MIZUSHIMA PLASTICIZER CO., LTD.—See Adeka Corporation; *Int'l*, pg. 142
MIZUSHIMA RIVERMENT CORP.—See JFE Holdings, Inc.; *Int'l*, pg. 3939
MIZUSHIMA STEEL CORPORATION—See JFE Holdings, Inc.; *Int'l*, pg. 3937
MJARDIN GROUP, INC.; *U.S. Public*, pg. 1452
M.J. BAKER FOODSERVICE LIMITED—See Kitwave Group Plc; *Int'l*, pg. 4196
MJ BASKETBALL HOLDINGS, LLC; *U.S. Private*, pg. 2752
MJ BIOPHARM PVT LTD—See BIOTON S.A.; *Int'l*, pg. 1043
MJ BIOTECH, INC.; *U.S. Private*, pg. 2752
MJB REALTY INC.; *U.S. Private*, pg. 2752
MJB WOOD GROUP INC.; *U.S. Private*, pg. 2753

MJB WOOD GROUP INC.
CORPORATE AFFILIATIONS

MJC ACQUISITION, LLC—See Webster Equity Partners, LLC; *U.S. Private*, pg. 4467
MJC CITY DEVELOPMENT SDN. BHD.—See Mudajaya Group Berhad; *Int'l*, pg. 5077
MJC ELECTRONICS ASIA PTE. LTD.—See MICRONICS JAPAN CO., LTD.; *Int'l*, pg. 4880
MJC ELECTRONICS CORPORATION—See MICRONICS JAPAN CO., LTD.; *Int'l*, pg. 4880
MJC EUROPE GMBH—See MICRONICS JAPAN CO., LTD.; *Int'l*, pg. 4880
MJC INVESTMENTS CORPORATION—See Manila Jockey Club, Inc.; *Int'l*, pg. 4671
MJC MICROELECTRONICS (KUNSHAN) CO., LTD.—See MICRONICS JAPAN CO., LTD.; *Int'l*, pg. 4880
MJC MICROELECTRONICS (SHANGHAI) CO., LTD.—See MICRONICS JAPAN CO., LTD.; *Int'l*, pg. 4880
M.J. DALY LLC—See Arden Engineering Constructors LLC; *U.S. Private*, pg. 317
MJ ECOPOWER HYBRID SYSTEMS, INC.—See Lanco International Inc.; *U.S. Private*, pg. 2382
M. J. EDWARDS FUNERAL HOME, INC.—See Service Corporation International; *U.S. Public*, pg. 1870
M.J. ELECTRIC, LLC—See Quanta Services, Inc.; *U.S. Public*, pg. 1751
MJE MARKETING SERVICES; *U.S. Private*, pg. 2753
M & J ENGINEERING, P.C.; *U.S. Private*, pg. 2522
M & J ENGINEERS LIMITED—See Gallagher Holdings Ltd.; *Int'l*, pg. 2873
MJ FREEWAY LLC—See Gryphon Digital Mining, Inc.; *U.S. Public*, pg. 973
M & J GAS COMPANY—See UGI Corporation; *U.S. Public*, pg. 2222
MJG CORPORATION; *U.S. Private*, pg. 2753
M&J GENERAL CONTRACTORS INC.; *U.S. Private*, pg. 2524
M. & J. GLEESON INVESTMENTS LTD.—See C&C Group Plc; *Int'l*, pg. 1238
MJ GLEESON PLC; *Int'l*, pg. 5000
M.J. HARRIS INC.; *U.S. Private*, pg. 2529
MJ HARVEST, INC.; *U.S. Public*, pg. 1452
MJ HOLDINGS, INC.; *U.S. Public*, pg. 1452
MJ HUDSON ALLENBRIDGE HOLDINGS LIMITED—See MJ Hudson Group Plc; *Int'l*, pg. 5000
MJ HUDSON GROUP PLC; *Int'l*, pg. 5000
M.J. INTERNATIONAL CO., LTD.; *Int'l*, pg. 4615
MJI UNIVERSAL PTE. LTD.—See Mitani Corporation; *Int'l*, pg. 4924
MJK AUTOMATION APS—See Xylem Inc.; *U.S. Public*, pg. 2394
MJKI INDIA PVT. LTD.—See Digilife Technologies Limited; *Int'l*, pg. 2119
MJL BANGLADESH LIMITED; *Int'l*, pg. 5000
M.J.MAILLIS CZECH S.R.O.—See M.J. Maillis S.A.; *Int'l*, pg. 4615
M.J. MAILLIS ESPANA, S.L.—See M.J. Maillis S.A.; *Int'l*, pg. 4615
M.J. MAILLIS FRANCE SAS—See M.J. Maillis S.A.; *Int'l*, pg. 4615
M.J. MAILLIS HUNGARY PACKING SYSTEMS LTD.—See M.J. Maillis S.A.; *Int'l*, pg. 4615
M.J. MAILLIS ROMANIA S.A.—See M.J. Maillis S.A.; *Int'l*, pg. 4615
M.J. MAILLIS S.A.; *Int'l*, pg. 4615
M&J MANAGEMENT CORPORATION; *U.S. Private*, pg. 2524
MJM ASSOCIATES, LLC; *U.S. Private*, pg. 2753
M&J MATERIALS INC.; *U.S. Private*, pg. 2524
MJ MECHANICAL SERVICES, INC.—See Comfort Systems USA, Inc.; *U.S. Public*, pg. 544
MJM ELECTRIC COOPERATIVE, INC.; *U.S. Private*, pg. 2753
MJM ELECTRIC, INC.; *U.S. Private*, pg. 2753
MJM HOLDINGS INC.; *U.S. Private*, pg. 2753
M&J MOTORS INC.; *U.S. Private*, pg. 2524
MJN SERVICES INC.; *U.S. Private*, pg. 2753
M.J.O. HOLDING BV—See Koninklijke VolkerWessels N.V.; *Int'l*, pg. 4271
MJO INDUSTRIES, INC.; *U.S. Private*, pg. 2753
MJOLBY HANDELSSTAL AB—See SSAB AB; *Int'l*, pg. 7153
MJ ONE COMPANY LIMITED—See Major Development Public Company Limited; *Int'l*, pg. 4654
MJ OPTICAL INC.; *U.S. Private*, pg. 2752
MJOY GAMES CO. LTD—See Youzu Interactive Co., Ltd.; *Int'l*, pg. 8605
MJ PROMOTIONS, INC.—See Lanco International Inc.; *U.S. Private*, pg. 2382
MJ ROOFING & SUPPLY LTD.; *Int'l*, pg. 5000
MJS COMMUNICATIONS; *U.S. Private*, pg. 2753
M&J SEAFOOD HOLDINGS LIMITED—See Sysco Corporation; *U.S. Public*, pg. 1974
M&J SEAFOOD LIMITED—See Sysco Corporation; *U.S. Public*, pg. 1973
MJ SIMPSON CORPORATION; *U.S. Private*, pg. 2752
MJS M&A PARTNERS CO., LTD.—See Miroku Jyoho Service Co., Ltd.; *Int'l*, pg. 4919
M.J. SMITH & ASSOCIATES, INC.—See Genstar Capital, LLC; *U.S. Private*, pg. 1677

M.J. SMITH & ASSOCIATES, INC.—See Keystone Group, L.P.; *U.S. Private*, pg. 2298
M. J. SOFFE, LLC—See Delta Apparel, Inc.; *U.S. Public*, pg. 652
MJT ENTERPRISES INC.; *U.S. Private*, pg. 2753
M&J TRIMMING COMPANY INC.; *U.S. Private*, pg. 2524
MJUNCTION SERVICES LIMITED—See Steel Authority of India Limited; *Int'l*, pg. 7189
MJUNCTION SERVICES LIMITED—See Tata Sons Limited; *Int'l*, pg. 7473
MJV2 COMPANY LIMITED—See Major Development Public Company Limited; *Int'l*, pg. 4654
MJV3 COMPANY LIMITED—See Major Development Public Company Limited; *Int'l*, pg. 4654
MJV4 COMPANY LIMITED—See Major Development Public Company Limited; *Int'l*, pg. 4654
MJV HOLDINGS, LLC; *U.S. Private*, pg. 2753
MJW HAKUHODO—See Hakuhodo DY Holdings Incorporated; *Int'l*, pg. 3222
MJW HAKUHODO—See Hakuhodo DY Holdings Incorporated; *Int'l*, pg. 3222
M/K ADVERTISING PARTNERS, LTD.; *U.S. Private*, pg. 2530
MK AERO LIMITED—See Mecachrome International Inc.; *Int'l*, pg. 4765
MKANGO RESOURCES LTD.; *Int'l*, pg. 5002
MK APPARELS LIMITED—See MATSUOKA Corporation, Ltd.; *Int'l*, pg. 4730
MK ATLANTIQUE, SA—See Mecachrome International Inc.; *Int'l*, pg. 4765
MK AUTOMOTIVE SAS—See Mecachrome International Inc.; *Int'l*, pg. 4765
MKB ALTALANOS BIZTOSITO ZRT.—See MBH Bank Nyrt.; *Int'l*, pg. 4752
MK BATTERY ASIA PACIFIC PTY LIMITED—See East Penn Manufacturing Co., Inc.; *U.S. Private*, pg. 1317
MK BATTERY INTERNATIONAL LTD—See East Penn Manufacturing Co., Inc.; *U.S. Private*, pg. 1317
MK BATTERY—See East Penn Manufacturing Co., Inc.; *U.S. Private*, pg. 1317
MKB AUTOPARK OOD—See MBH Bank Nyrt.; *Int'l*, pg. 4752
MKB - EUROLEASING AUTOLIZING ZRT.—See MBH Bank Nyrt.; *Int'l*, pg. 4752
MKB-EUROLEASING AUTOPARK ZRT.—See Societe Generale S.A.; *Int'l*, pg. 7038
MKB MITTELRHEINISCHE BANK GMBH—See Landesbank Baden-Wurttemberg; *Int'l*, pg. 4405
MKB NYUGDIJPENZTART ES EGESZSEGPENZTART KISZOLGALO KFT.—See MBH Bank Nyrt.; *Int'l*, pg. 4752
MK CHAMBERS COMPANY; *U.S. Private*, pg. 2753
MK-DELTA GMBH—See MK-Kliniken AG; *Int'l*, pg. 5001
MK DENSHI CO., LTD.—See MK SEIKO CO., LTD.; *Int'l*, pg. 5001
MK DIAMOND PRODUCTS, INC.; *U.S. Private*, pg. 2753
MK DISTRIBUTORS INC.; *U.S. Private*, pg. 2753
MK ELECTRIC LIMITED—See Honeywell International Inc.; *U.S. Public*, pg. 1049
M.K. ELECTRONICS LIMITED—See Daikin Industries, Ltd.; *Int'l*, pg. 1936
MK ELECTRON (KUNSHAN) CO., LTD.—See MK Electron Co., Ltd.; *Int'l*, pg. 5000
MK ELECTRON CO., LTD.; *Int'l*, pg. 5000
M&K ENTERPRISE LLC; *U.S. Private*, pg. 2524
MK EXIM (INDIA) LTD.; *Int'l*, pg. 5000
MKF-ERGIS SP. Z O.O.—See Ergis S.A.; *Int'l*, pg. 2491
MK FIRE LIMITED—See London Security PLC; *Int'l*, pg. 4547
MKF-SCHIMANSKI-ERGIS GMBH—See Ergis S.A.; *Int'l*, pg. 2491
MKG CHICAGO—See Acceleration Community of Companies; *U.S. Private*, pg. 49
MKG GLOBAL TECHNOLOGY, INC.—See NSD CO., LTD.; *Int'l*, pg. 5476
MKG PRODUCTIONS, LLC—See Acceleration Community of Companies; *U.S. Private*, pg. 49
MK GROUP DOO; *Int'l*, pg. 5000
MKGS MORGAN KARBON GRAFIT SANAYI ANONIM SIRKETI—See Morgan Advanced Materials plc; *Int'l*, pg. 5041
MKG WEST—See Acceleration Community of Companies; *U.S. Private*, pg. 49
MKH BERHAD; *Int'l*, pg. 5002
MKH BUILDING MATERIALS SDN. BHD.—See MKH Berhad; *Int'l*, pg. 5002
MK HOLETOWN (BARBADOS) INC.—See Capri Holdings Limited; *Int'l*, pg. 1316
MKH—See Accord Group Limited; *Int'l*, pg. 93
MKH—See Accord Group Limited; *Int'l*, pg. 93
MKH—See Accord Group Limited; *Int'l*, pg. 93
M & K INDUSTRIES LIMITED, CO.—See New America Energy Corp.; *U.S. Public*, pg. 1511
M. KINGSBURY CONCRETE INC.; *U.S. Private*, pg. 2526
MKI TECHNOLOGIES CO., LTD.—See Mitsui & Co., Ltd.; *Int'l*, pg. 4978
MK IT-ENTWICKLUNGS GMBH—See MK-Kliniken AG; *Int'l*, pg. 5001
MKI (U.K.), LTD—See Mitsui & Co., Ltd.; *Int'l*, pg. 4978

MK KASHIYAMA CORP.; *Int'l*, pg. 5000
MK KAZSILICON LLP—See Canadian Solar Inc.; *Int'l*, pg. 1286
MK KAZSILICON LLP—See ECM Technologies SAS; *Int'l*, pg. 2292
MK KAZSILICON LLP—See Kasen International Holdings Limited; *Int'l*, pg. 4087
MK KAZSILICON LLP—See Yadran-Oil Group; *Int'l*, pg. 8544
M.K.K. INDUSTRIES SDN. BHD.—See Maxbiz Corporation Berhad; *Int'l*, pg. 4736
MK-KLINIKEN AG; *Int'l*, pg. 5001
MK KOSAN CO., LTD.—See MK SEIKO CO., LTD.; *Int'l*, pg. 5001
M K LAND HOLDINGS BERHAD; *Int'l*, pg. 4610
MKM FRANCE S.A.R.L.—See Nova Resources B.V.; *Int'l*, pg. 5452
MKM ITALIA S.R.L.—See Nova Resources B.V.; *Int'l*, pg. 5452
MKM MANSFELDER COPPER UK LTD.—See Nova Resources B.V.; *Int'l*, pg. 5452
MKM NORTH AMERICA CORPORATION—See Nova Resources B.V.; *Int'l*, pg. 5452
MKM PARTNERS—See Roth Capital Partners LLC; *U.S. Private*, pg. 3487
MKP MOBILITY LIMITED; *Int'l*, pg. 5002
M.K. PRINTPACK (P) LTD.—See Warburg Pincus LLC; *U.S. Private*, pg. 4439
MK PROSTHETIC & ORTHOTIC SERVICES INC.—See Patient Square Capital, L.P.; *U.S. Private*, pg. 3107
M.K. PROTEINS LTD.; *Int'l*, pg. 4616
M.K. REAL ESTATE DEVELOPMENT PUBLIC COMPANY LIMITED—See Bangkok Bank Public Company Limited; *Int'l*, pg. 833
MK RESTAURANT GROUP PUBLIC COMPANY LIMITED; *Int'l*, pg. 5000
MKS ASTEX PRODUCTS—See MKS Instruments, Inc.; *U.S. Public*, pg. 1452
MKSD ARCHITECTS; *U.S. Private*, pg. 2753
MKS DENMARK APS—See MKS Instruments, Inc.; *U.S. Public*, pg. 1452
MK SEIKO CO., LTD.; *Int'l*, pg. 5000
MK SEIKO (VIETNAM) CO., LTD.—See MK SEIKO CO., LTD.; *Int'l*, pg. 5001
MKS ENI PRODUCTS—See MKS Instruments, Inc.; *U.S. Public*, pg. 1452
MKS GERMAN HOLDING GMBH—See MKS Instruments, Inc.; *U.S. Public*, pg. 1452
MKS GERMANY HOLDING GMBH—See MKS Instruments, Inc.; *U.S. Public*, pg. 1452
MKS INDUSTRIES INCORPORATED; *U.S. Private*, pg. 2753
MKS INSTRUMENTS AB—See MKS Instruments, Inc.; *U.S. Public*, pg. 1452
MKS INSTRUMENTS DEUTSCHLAND GMBH—See MKS Instruments, Inc.; *U.S. Public*, pg. 1453
MKS INSTRUMENTS, INC.; *U.S. Public*, pg. 1452
MKS INSTRUMENTS UK LTD.—See MKS Instruments, Inc.; *U.S. Public*, pg. 1453
MKS ION SYSTEMS—See MKS Instruments, Inc.; *U.S. Public*, pg. 1453
MKS JAPAN, INC.—See MKS Instruments, Inc.; *U.S. Public*, pg. 1453
MKS MATERIALS DELIVERY PRODUCTS—See MKS Instruments, Inc.; *U.S. Public*, pg. 1453
MKS MSC, INC.—See MKS Instruments, Inc.; *U.S. Public*, pg. 1453
MKS TAIWAN TECHNOLOGY LTD.—See MKS Instruments, Inc.; *U.S. Public*, pg. 1453
MKS UMETRICS AB—See MKS Instruments, Inc.; *U.S. Public*, pg. 1453
MKSYSTEM CORPORATION; *Int'l*, pg. 5002
MK TECHNOLOGY CO., LTD.—See P-Duke Technology Co., Ltd.; *Int'l*, pg. 5681
MK TECHNOLOGY TRADING LIMITED—See ViTrox Corporation Berhad; *Int'l*, pg. 8262
MKTG INC.; *U.S. Private*, pg. 2753
MKT METALL-KUNSTSTOFF-TECHNIK GMBH & CO KG—See Wurth Verwaltungsgesellschaft mbH; *Int'l*, pg. 8506
MKT PRINT D.D.; *Int'l*, pg. 5003
MKT PRINT NETHERLANDS B.V.—See MKT Print d.d.; *Int'l*, pg. 5003
M&K TRAILER CENTERS—See M & K Truck & Trailer, LLC; *U.S. Private*, pg. 2523
M & K TRUCK & TRAILER, LLC; *U.S. Private*, pg. 2523
MKTWORKS, INC.; *U.S. Private*, pg. 2753
M. KUNZ AG—See Burkhalter Holding AG; *Int'l*, pg. 1225
MKVENTURES CAPITAL LIMITED; *Int'l*, pg. 5003
MLABS SYSTEMS BERHAD; *Int'l*, pg. 5003
MLADINSKA KNJIGA BEOGRAD—See Mladinska knjiga Zalozba, d.d.; *Int'l*, pg. 5003
MLADINSKA KNJIGA SARAJEVO—See Mladinska knjiga Zalozba, d.d.; *Int'l*, pg. 5003
MLADINSKA KNJIGA SKOPJE—See Mladinska knjiga Zalozba, d.d.; *Int'l*, pg. 5003
MLADINSKA KNJIGA TRGOVINA, D.O.O.—See Mladinska knjiga Zalozba, d.d.; *Int'l*, pg. 5003
MLADINSKA KNJIGA ZALOZBA, D.D.; *Int'l*, pg. 5003

MLADOST A.D.; *Int'l*, pg. 5003
MLADOST A.D.; *Int'l*, pg. 5003
M LAKHAMSI INDUSTRIES LIMITED; *Int'l*, pg. 4610
M.L. ALBRIGHT & SONS, INC.; *U.S. Private*, pg. 2529
ML AU PTY LTD.—See Media Links Co., Ltd.; *Int'l*, pg. 4771
MLAVA A.D.; *Int'l*, pg. 5003
M. LAVINE DESIGN WORKSHOP; *U.S. Private*, pg. 2526
MLB ADVANCED MEDIA, L.P.—See Major League Baseball; *U.S. Private*, pg. 2555
M.L. BALL CO. INC.; *U.S. Private*, pg. 2529
MLB CAPITAL PARTNERS, LLC; *U.S. Private*, pg. 2753
M.L.B. CONSTRUCTION SERVICES, LLC; *U.S. Private*, pg. 2529
ML BOVIS HOLDINGS LIMITED—See Lendlease Corporation Limited; *Int'l*, pg. 4453
ML BREADWORKS SDN BHD—See BreadTalk Group Pte Ltd.; *Int'l*, pg. 1143
ML CAMPBELL & FABULON—See The Sherwin-Williams Company; *U.S. Public*, pg. 2128
MLC INVESTMENTS LIMITED—See National Australia Bank Limited; *Int'l*, pg. 5151
MLC ITL LOGISTICS CO., LTD.—See Mitsubishi Logistics Corporation; *Int'l*, pg. 4962
MLC LIMITED—See Nippon Life Insurance Company; *Int'l*, pg. 5322
MLD SA; *Int'l*, pg. 5003
ML DYEING LTD.; *Int'l*, pg. 5003
MLECZARNIA TUREK SP. Z O.O.—See Savencia Fromage & Dairy; *Int'l*, pg. 6597
M LEGO—See Aurea, S.A.; *Int'l*, pg. 707
MLEKARA LOZNICA A.D.; *Int'l*, pg. 5003
MLEKARA PLANA A.D.; *Int'l*, pg. 5003
MLEKARNA HLINSKO, A.S.—See Agrofert Holding, a.s.; *Int'l*, pg. 219
MLEKARNA PRAGOLAKTOS A.S.—See Unternehmensgruppe Theo Muller S.e.c.s.; *Int'l*, pg. 8085
M&L ENGINEERING & MATERIALS PTE LIMITED—See M&L Holdings Group Limited; *Int'l*, pg. 4612
MLE S.R.L.—See 3F Filippi SpA; *Int'l*, pg. 7
M. LEVIN & COMPANY HOLDINGS, INC.; *U.S. Private*, pg. 2527
M. LEVIN & COMPANY, INC.—See M. Levin & Company Holdings, Inc.; *U.S. Private*, pg. 2527
MLEX LIMITED—See RELX plc; *Int'l*, pg. 6268
M.L.F. & ASSOCIATES, INC.; *U.S. Private*, pg. 2529
MLG COMMERCIAL, LLC—See Newmark Group, Inc.; *U.S. Public*, pg. 1515
MLG OZ LIMITED; *Int'l*, pg. 5003
M&L HOLDINGS GROUP LIMITED; *Int'l*, pg. 4612
MLIN A.D.; *Int'l*, pg. 5003
M&L INDUSTRIES INC.; *U.S. Private*, pg. 2524
MLIN I PEKARA D.D.; *Int'l*, pg. 5003
MLINK TECHNOLOGIES INC.—See Sweetview Partners, Inc.; *U.S. Private*, pg. 3892
MLINOVI A.D.; *Int'l*, pg. 5003
MLINPEK D.D. BUGOJNO; *Int'l*, pg. 5003
MLINPEK-ZITAR D.D.; *Int'l*, pg. 5003
M. LIPSITZ & CO., LTD.; *U.S. Private*, pg. 2527
M.L. KISHIGO MANUFACTURING COMPANY, LLC—See Bunzl plc; *Int'l*, pg. 1219
MLM ARMAL, D.O.O—See Mariborska livarna Maribor, d.d.; *Int'l*, pg. 4693
M.L. MCDONALD SALES CO., INC.; *U.S. Private*, pg. 2529
MLMIC INSURANCE COMPANY—See Berkshire Hathaway Inc.; *U.S. Public*, pg. 308
MLM INFORMATION SERVICES, LLC—See Corporation Service Company; *U.S. Private*, pg. 1058
MLM MEDICAL LABS GMBH—See Great Point Partners, LLC; *U.S. Private*, pg. 1767
MLM SAS—See Manitou BF S.A.; *Int'l*, pg. 4672
MLM STORITV D.O.O.—See Mariborska livarna Maribor, d.d.; *Int'l*, pg. 4693
ML MULTISERVICE EXPRESS, INC.; *U.S. Private*, pg. 2753
MLM VERTRIEBS GMBH—See Mariborska livarna Maribor, d.d.; *Int'l*, pg. 4693
MLO MARITIME LOGISTICS UND OPERATIONS GMBH; *Int'l*, pg. 5003
MLO PRODUCTS INCORPORATED; *U.S. Private*, pg. 2754
MLP BANKING AG—See MLP SE; *Int'l*, pg. 5004
MLP BUSINESS PARK POZNAN SP. Z O.O.—See MLP Group S.A.; *Int'l*, pg. 5004
MLP CANADA LIMITED—See Mitsubishi Heavy Industries, Ltd.; *Int'l*, pg. 4955
MLPC INTERNATIONAL SA—See Arkema S.A.; *Int'l*, pg. 571
M&L PETROLEUM INC.; *U.S. Private*, pg. 2524
MLP FINANZBERATUNG SE—See MLP SE; *Int'l*, pg. 5004
MLP GROUP S.A.; *Int'l*, pg. 5004
MLP HONG KONG LTD.—See Mitsubishi Heavy Industries, Ltd.; *Int'l*, pg. 4955
ML PRODUKTION S.R.O.—See Knill Holding GmbH; *Int'l*, pg. 4208
M&L PROPERTY & ASSETS PLC; *Int'l*, pg. 4612
MLP SAGLIK HIZMETLERI AS; *Int'l*, pg. 5004
MLP SE; *Int'l*, pg. 5004

MLP STEEL COMPANY; *U.S. Private*, pg. 2754
MLP UK LTD.—See Mitsubishi Heavy Industries, Ltd.; *Int'l*, pg. 4955
MLP UNIT PLEDGE L.P.—See LXP Industrial Trust; *U.S. Public*, pg. 1349
MLP U.S.A. INC.—See Mitsubishi Heavy Industries, Ltd.; *Int'l*, pg. 4956
M&L ROSE ENTERPRISES INC.; *U.S. Private*, pg. 2524
MLS CO., LTD.; *Int'l*, pg. 5004
MLS DATA MANAGEMENT SOLUTIONS INC.—See Mailing List Systems Corp.; *U.S. Private*, pg. 2551
MLS GROUP OF COMPANIES, LLC—See GIC Pte. Ltd.; *Int'l*, pg. 2964
MLS GROUP OF COMPANIES, LLC—See Leonard Green & Partners, L.P.; *U.S. Private*, pg. 2425
M.L.S. HOLICE SPOL. S.R.O.—See Emerson Electric Co.; *U.S. Public*, pg. 750
MLS INNOVATION INC.; *Int'l*, pg. 5004
M. L. SMITH, JR., INC.; *U.S. Private*, pg. 2526
M&L SUPPLY COMPANY INCORPORATED; *U.S. Private*, pg. 2524
ML SYSTEM SA; *Int'l*, pg. 5003
MLT AIKINS LLP; *Int'l*, pg. 5004
MLT CREATIVE; *U.S. Private*, pg. 2754
MLT VACATIONS, INC.—See Delta Air Lines, Inc.; *U.S. Public*, pg. 652
M. LUIS CONSTRUCTION CO., INC.; *U.S. Private*, pg. 2527
M. LUKAS COMPANY—See APi Group Corporation; *Int'l*, pg. 514
MLYNY A.S.—See NEPI Rockcastle N.V.; *Int'l*, pg. 5200
MM2 ASIA LTD.; *Int'l*, pg. 5004
MM2 ENTERTAINMENT HONG KONG LIMITED—See mm2 Asia Ltd.; *Int'l*, pg. 5004
MM2 ENTERTAINMENT SDN. BHD.—See mm2 Asia Ltd.; *Int'l*, pg. 5004
MM2 ENTERTAINMENT USA, INC.—See mm2 Asia Ltd.; *Int'l*, pg. 5005
MM2 SCREEN MANAGEMENT SDN. BHD.—See mm2 Asia Ltd.; *Int'l*, pg. 5005
MMA CAPITAL HOLDINGS, LLC—See Fundamental Advisors LP; *U.S. Private*, pg. 1622
MMA ENERGY CAPITAL, LLC—See Fundamental Advisors LP; *U.S. Private*, pg. 1622
MMA FINANCIAL TC, LLC—See Fundamental Advisors LP; *U.S. Private*, pg. 1622
MMAG DIGITAL SDN. BHD.—See MMAG Holdings Berhad; *Int'l*, pg. 5005
MMAG HOLDINGS BERHAD; *Int'l*, pg. 5005
MMA HOLDINGS UK PLC—See Covea Groupe S.A.S.; *Int'l*, pg. 1820
M.M.A. (MANUFACTURA DE MOTORES ARGENTINOS) S.R.L.—See Johnson Electric Holdings Limited; *Int'l*, pg. 3990
MMA OFFSHORE ASIA PTE. LTD—See MMA Offshore Limited; *Int'l*, pg. 5005
MMA OFFSHORE LIMITED; *Int'l*, pg. 5005
MMA OFFSHORE SHIPYARD AND ENGINEERING SERVICES PTE. LTD.—See MMA Offshore Limited; *Int'l*, pg. 5005
MMA REALTY CAPITAL, INC.—See Fundamental Advisors LP; *U.S. Private*, pg. 1622
MMA RENEWABLE VENTURES, LLC—See Fundamental Advisors LP; *U.S. Private*, pg. 1623
MMAR MEDICAL GROUP, INC.—See Patient Square Capital, L.P.; *U.S. Private*, pg. 3107
MMARTAN TEXTIL LTDA.—See Coteminas Companhia de Tecidos Norte de Minas; *Int'l*, pg. 1817
M-MART, INC.; *Int'l*, pg. 4614
MMA S.A.—See Covea Groupe S.A.S.; *Int'l*, pg. 1820
MMA SECURITIES LLC—See Marsh & McLennan Companies, Inc.; *U.S. Public*, pg. 1377
M&M BEVERAGES LLC; *U.S. Private*, pg. 2524
MM BRIDGE CO., LTD.—See Miyaji Engineering Group Inc.; *Int'l*, pg. 4996
M & M BROKERAGE SERVICES, INC.—See Aon plc; *Int'l*, pg. 496
MMB; *U.S. Private*, pg. 2754
MM CAPITAL PARTNERS CO., LTD.—See Marubeni Corporation; *Int'l*, pg. 4705
M&M CARTAGE CO. INC.; *U.S. Private*, pg. 2524
MM CARTON - AUSTRIA CARTON, S.A.—See Mayr-Melnhof Karton AG; *Int'l*, pg. 4745
MMC AUTOMOVILES ESPANA, S.A.—See Berge y Cia SA; *Int'l*, pg. 979
MMC CAR POLAND SP. Z O.O.—See Mitsubishi Corporation; *Int'l*, pg. 4939
MMC CONTRACTORS NORTHEAST, INC.—See MMC Corp.; *U.S. Private*, pg. 2754
MMC CONTRACTORS WEST, INC.—See MMC Corp.; *U.S. Private*, pg. 2754
MMC CORPORATION BERHAD; *Int'l*, pg. 5005
MMC CORP.; *U.S. Private*, pg. 2754
MMC DIAMOND FINANCE CORPORATION—See Mitsubishi Motors Corporation; *Int'l*, pg. 4966
MMC ELECTRONIC MATERIALS TAIWAN CO., LTD.—See Mitsubishi Materials Corporation; *Int'l*, pg. 4963

MMC ELECTRONICS AMERICA INC.—See Mitsubishi Materials Corporation; *Int'l*, pg. 4965
MMC ELECTRONICS (BANGKOK) CO., LTD.—See Mitsubishi Materials Corporation; *Int'l*, pg. 4963
MMC ELECTRONICS (HK) LTD.—See Mitsubishi Materials Corporation; *Int'l*, pg. 4965
MMC ELECTRONICS KOREA INC.—See Mitsubishi Materials Corporation; *Int'l*, pg. 4964
MMC ELECTRONICS LAO CO., LTD.—See Mitsubishi Materials Corporation; *Int'l*, pg. 4964
MMC ELECTRONICS (M) SDN. BHD.—See Mitsubishi Materials Corporation; *Int'l*, pg. 4964
MMC ENCOMPASS HEALTH REHABILITATION HOSPITAL, LLC—See Encompass Health Corporation; *U.S. Public*, pg. 758
MMC ENGINEERING & CONSTRUCTION SDN. BHD.—See MMC Corporation Berhad; *Int'l*, pg. 5005
MMC ENGINEERING SDN. BHD.—See MMC Corporation Berhad; *Int'l*, pg. 5005
MMC HARDMETAL (HOLDINGS) EUROPE GMBH—See Mitsubishi Materials Corporation; *Int'l*, pg. 4964
MMC HARDMETAL INDIA PVT. LTD.—See Mitsubishi Materials Corporation; *Int'l*, pg. 4964
MMC HARDMETAL OOO—See Mitsubishi Materials Corporation; *Int'l*, pg. 4964
MMC HARDMETAL POLAND, SP.ZO.O—See Mitsubishi Materials Corporation; *Int'l*, pg. 4964
MMC HARDMETAL RUSSIA LTD.—See Mitsubishi Materials Corporation; *Int'l*, pg. 4964
MMC HARDMETAL THAILAND CO., LTD.—See Mitsubishi Materials Corporation; *Int'l*, pg. 4964
MMC HARD METAL U.K. LTD.—See Mitsubishi Materials Corporation; *Int'l*, pg. 4964
MMC HARTMETALL GMBH—See Mitsubishi Materials Corporation; *Int'l*, pg. 4964
MMC HITACHI TOOL ENGINEERING EUROPE GMBH—See Mitsubishi Materials Corporation; *Int'l*, pg. 4964
MMC HITACHI TOOL ENGINEERING EUROPE—See Mitsubishi Materials Corporation; *Int'l*, pg. 4964
MMC HITACHI TOOL ENGINEERING (SHANGHAI) LTD.—See Mitsubishi Materials Corporation; *Int'l*, pg. 4964
MMC HOLDING (THAILAND) CO., LTD.—See Mitsubishi Motors Corporation; *Int'l*, pg. 4966
MMC INC.—See New-Com Inc.; *U.S. Private*, pg. 2913
M.M.C., INC.; *U.S. Private*, pg. 2529
MMC ITALIA S.R.L.—See Mitsubishi Materials Corporation; *Int'l*, pg. 4964
MMC LIMITED; *Int'l*, pg. 5005
MMC MECHANICAL CONTRACTORS NORTH CENTRAL, INC.—See MMC Corp.; *U.S. Private*, pg. 2754
MMC METAL DE MEXICO S.A.—See Mitsubishi Materials Corporation; *Int'l*, pg. 4964
MMC METAL FRANCE S.A.R.L.—See Mitsubishi Materials Corporation; *Int'l*, pg. 4964
MMC METAL SINGAPORE PTE. LTD.—See Mitsubishi Materials Corporation; *Int'l*, pg. 4964
MMC OF NEVADA, LLC—See Quorum Health Corporation; *U.S. Private*, pg. 3330
MMC OIL & GAS ENGINEERING SDN. BHD.—See MMC Corporation Berhad; *Int'l*, pg. 5005
MM COMPOSITE A/S—See SP Group A/S; *Int'l*, pg. 7122
M&M CONCRETE—See Lycon, Inc.; *U.S. Private*, pg. 2519
MM CONFERENCES; *Int'l*, pg. 5004
MM CORPORATION—See Medipal Holdings Corporation; *Int'l*, pg. 4779
MMC SANAYI VE TICARI YATIRIMLAR AS; *Int'l*, pg. 5005
MMC SAUDI ARABIA LIMITED—See MMC Corporation Berhad; *Int'l*, pg. 5005
MMC SECURITIES CORP.—See Marsh & McLennan Companies, Inc.; *U.S. Public*, pg. 1377
MMC SHANGHAI CO., LTD.—See Mitsubishi Materials Corporation; *Int'l*, pg. 4964
MMC SYSTEMS INC.; *U.S. Private*, pg. 2754
MMC TAISHIN TOOL CO., LTD.—See Mitsubishi Materials Corporation; *Int'l*, pg. 4964
MMC TOOLING CO., LTD.—See Mitsubishi Materials Corporation; *Int'l*, pg. 4964
MMC TOOLS (THAILAND), CO., LTD.—See Mitsubishi Materials Corporation; *Int'l*, pg. 4964
MMC TRANSPORT, INC.—See The Mennel Milling Company; *U.S. Private*, pg. 4077
MMC TRANSPORT OF VIRGINIA, INC.—See The Mennel Milling Company; *U.S. Private*, pg. 4077
MMC UK GROUP LIMITED—See Marsh & McLennan Companies, Inc.; *U.S. Public*, pg. 1378
MMC UK PENSION FUND TRUSTEE LIMITED—See Marsh & McLennan Companies, Inc.; *U.S. Public*, pg. 1378
M & M DIRECT LIMITED—See Bestseller A/S; *Int'l*, pg. 1000
M & M DODGE HYUNDAI, INC; *U.S. Private*, pg. 2523
M & M / D & R LOWE—See The Bidvest Group Limited; *Int'l*, pg. 7625
MMD SAS—See Groupe SFPI SA; *Int'l*, pg. 3111
MMEC MANNESMANN GMBH—See MAB Mannesmann GmbH; *Int'l*, pg. 4618

MME INC.
CORPORATE AFFILIATIONS

MME INC.; *U.S. Private*, pg. 2754
MMEX RESOURCES CORPORATION; *U.S. Public*, pg. 1453
MMF CAPITAL MANAGEMENT LLC; *U.S. Private*, pg. 2754
MM FORGINGS LIMITED; *Int'l*, pg. 5004
M.M. FOWLER INC.; *U.S. Private*, pg. 2529
MMFX TECHNOLOGIES CORP.—See Commercial Metals Company; *U.S. Public*, pg. 545
M&M GASES LIMITED—See Air Products & Chemicals, Inc.; *U.S. Public*, pg. 66
MMG AUSTRALIA LIMITED—See China Rare Earth Resources And Technology Co., Ltd.; *Int'l*, pg. 1545
MMG CANADA, LTD.; *Int'l*, pg. 5005
MMG CANADA—See China Rare Earth Resources And Technology Co., Ltd.; *Int'l*, pg. 1545
MMG CORPORATION; *U.S. Private*, pg. 2754
MMG INDIA PVT LTD—See Delta Manufacturing Ltd; *Int'l*, pg. 2019
MMG INSURANCE COMPANY; *U.S. Private*, pg. 2754
MMG LIMITED - CORPORATE OFFICE—See China Rare Earth Resources And Technology Co., Ltd.; *Int'l*, pg. 1545
MMG LIMITED—See China Rare Earth Resources And Technology Co., Ltd.; *Int'l*, pg. 1545
MMG MANUFACTURAS DE SALTILLO, S. DE R.L. DE C.V.—See Matcor-Matsu Group Inc.; *Int'l*, pg. 4726
MMG MITTELDEUTSCHE MONTAN GMBH.—See BAUER Aktiengesellschaft; *Int'l*, pg. 893
MMG NORTH AMERICA INC.—See TT Electronics plc; *Int'l*, pg. 7959
MM GRAPHIA BETEILIGUNGS- UND VERWALTUNGS GMBH—See Mayr-Melnhof Karton AG; *Int'l*, pg. 4746
MM GRAPHIA BIELEFELD GMBH—See Mayr-Melnhof Karton AG; *Int'l*, pg. 4746
MM GRAPHIA DORTMUND GMBH—See Mayr-Melnhof Karton AG; *Int'l*, pg. 4746
MM GRAPHIA INNOVAPRINT GMBH & CO KG—See Mayr-Melnhof Karton AG; *Int'l*, pg. 4746
MM GRAPHIA TRIER GMBH—See Mayr-Melnhof Karton AG; *Int'l*, pg. 4746
MM GROUP INDUSTRIAL & INTERNATIONAL TRADE; *Int'l*, pg. 5004
MMG—See Omnicom Group Inc.; *U.S. Public*, pg. 1588
MMGY GLOBAL LLC—See EagleTree Capital, LP; *U.S. Private*, pg. 1311
MMGY GLOBAL - NEW YORK—See EagleTree Capital, LP; *U.S. Private*, pg. 1311
MMGY GLOBAL - ORLANDO—See EagleTree Capital, LP; *U.S. Private*, pg. 1311
MMHE-EPIC MARINE & SERVICES SDN BHD—See Malaysia Marine and Heavy Engineering Holdings Berhad; *Int'l*, pg. 4662
MMH HOLDINGS INC.—See Konecranes Plc; *Int'l*, pg. 4252
MMI AGENCY, LLC—See Stagwell, Inc.; *U.S. Public*, pg. 1927
MMI ASIA (HONG KONG) LTD.—See Messe Munchen GmbH; *Int'l*, pg. 4841
MMI ASIA PTE. LTD.—See Messe Munchen GmbH; *Int'l*, pg. 4841
M & M IBERICA SL—See Spirax-Sarco Engineering plc; *Int'l*, pg. 7137
MMI BUSINESS SERVICES FZE—See Endress+Hauser (International) Holding AG; *Int'l*, pg. 2408
MMI CO., LTD.—See Nippon Steel Corporation; *Int'l*, pg. 5337
MMI DINING SYSTEMS—See MMI Hotel Group Inc.; *U.S. Private*, pg. 2755
MMI EURASIA FUARGILIK LTD. STI.—See Messe Munchen GmbH; *Int'l*, pg. 4841
MMI HOLDINGS LIMITED—See KKR & Co. Inc.; *U.S. Public*, pg. 1259
MMI HOTEL GROUP INC.; *U.S. Private*, pg. 2754
MMI INDIA PVT LTD—See Messe Munchen GmbH; *Int'l*, pg. 4841
MMI MARKETING MANAGEMENT INSTITUT GMBH—See Porsche Automobil Holding SE; *Int'l*, pg. 5929
MM INNOVAPRINT VERWALTUNGS GMBH—See Mayr-Melnhof Karton AG; *Int'l*, pg. 4746
MM INTERNATIONAL CO., LTD.—See Maruhan Corporation; *Int'l*, pg. 4712
M&M INTERNATIONAL S.R.L.—See Rotork Plc; *Int'l*, pg. 6405
M&M INTERNATIONAL TRADING; *U.S. Private*, pg. 2524
MMI PRODUCTS, INC.—See CRH plc; *Int'l*, pg. 1845
MMIP SERVICES SDN. BHD.—See MNRB Holdings Berhad; *Int'l*, pg. 5006
MMI PUBLIC RELATIONS; *U.S. Private*, pg. 2755
MMI PUBLIC RELATIONS—See MMI Public Relations; *U.S. Private*, pg. 2755
MMI SERVICES, INC.; *U.S. Private*, pg. 2755
MMI SERVICES LLC—See Mining Machinery Inc.; *U.S. Private*, pg. 2742
MMI (SHANGHAI) CO. LTD.—See Messe Munchen GmbH; *Int'l*, pg. 4841
MMI SOUTH AFRICA (PTY) LTD.—See Messe Munchen GmbH; *Int'l*, pg. 4841
M. MISTI CIGAR CO.; *U.S. Private*, pg. 2527

MMIX BISCOM INC.; *U.S. Private*, pg. 2755
MMJ, S.A. DE C.V.—See Medtronic plc; *Int'l*, pg. 4787
MM KARTON BULGARIA EOOD—See Mayr-Melnhof Karton AG; *Int'l*, pg. 4746
MM KARTON PRAHA S.R.O.—See Mayr-Melnhof Karton AG; *Int'l*, pg. 4746
MM KARTONVERTRIEB GMBH—See Mayr-Melnhof Karton AG; *Int'l*, pg. 4746
MMK ATAKAS METALURJI SANAYI VE LIMAN ISLETMECILGI A.S.—See OJSC Magnitogorsk Iron & Steel Works; *Int'l*, pg. 5540
MMK MACHINERY (THAILAND) CO., LTD.—See Mitsui & Co.; *Int'l*, pg. 4973
MMK METALURJI SANAYI TICARET VE LIMAN ISLETMECILIGI ANONIM SIRKETI—See Fraport AG; *Int'l*, pg. 2764
MMK STEEL TRADE AG—See OJSC Magnitogorsk Iron & Steel Works; *Int'l*, pg. 5540
MMK TOLL ROAD. PVT. LTD.—See IRB Infrastructure Developers Limited; *Int'l*, pg. 3805
MMK TRADING AG—See OJSC Magnitogorsk Iron & Steel Works; *Int'l*, pg. 5540
MML BAY STATE LIFE INSURANCE COMPANY—See Massachusetts Mutual Life Insurance Company; *U.S. Private*, pg. 2605
MML CAPITAL FRANCE SARL—See MML Capital Partners LLP; *Int'l*, pg. 5005
MML CAPITAL PARTNERS LLC—See MML Capital Partners LLP; *Int'l*, pg. 5005
MML CAPITAL PARTNERS LLP; *Int'l*, pg. 5005
MML DISTRIBUTORS, LLC—See Massachusetts Mutual Life Insurance Company; *U.S. Private*, pg. 2605
M&M LIGHTING LP; *U.S. Private*, pg. 2524
MML INVESTORS SERVICES, INC.—See Massachusetts Mutual Life Insurance Company; *U.S. Private*, pg. 2605
MMLJ, INC.; *U.S. Private*, pg. 2755
MML MARKETING PTE. LTD.—See Hap Seng Consolidated Berhad; *Int'l*, pg. 3268
MML (SHANGHAI) TRADING CO., LTD.—See Hap Seng Consolidated Berhad; *Int'l*, pg. 3268
MM MAIN-MORTEL GMBH & CO.KG—See Heidelberg Materials AG; *Int'l*, pg. 3318
MM MAIN-MORTEL VERWALTUNGSGESELLSCHAFT MBH—See Heidelberg Materials AG; *Int'l*, pg. 3318
M & M MANUFACTURING, INC.—See Rift Valley Equity Partners, LLC; *U.S. Private*, pg. 3435
M&M MANUFACTURING, LLC - DALLAS PLANT—See Berkshire Hathaway Inc.; *U.S. Public*, pg. 312
M&M MANUFACTURING, LLC - FORT WORTH (ADOLPH STREET) PLANT—See Berkshire Hathaway Inc.; *U.S. Public*, pg. 312
M&M MANUFACTURING, LLC - HOUSTON PLANT—See Berkshire Hathaway Inc.; *U.S. Public*, pg. 312
M&M MANUFACTURING, LLC—See Berkshire Hathaway Inc.; *U.S. Public*, pg. 312
M&M MEAT SHOPS LTD.—See Searchlight Capital Partners, L.P.; *U.S. Private*, pg. 3588
MMM HEALTHCARE, LLC—See Elevance Health, Inc.; *U.S. Public*, pg. 730
M & M MILLING, INC.; *U.S. Private*, pg. 2523
MMM MULTI HEALTH, LLC—See Elevance Health, Inc.; *U.S. Public*, pg. 730
M&M MORTGAGE SERVICES, INC.—See American Securities LLC; *U.S. Private*, pg. 250
MMM SALES, INC.; *U.S. Private*, pg. 2755
MMM STUDIO LIMITED—See Live Nation Entertainment, Inc.; *U.S. Public*, pg. 1330
MMO BEHAVIORAL HEALTH SYSTEMS LLC—See Acadia Healthcare Company, Inc.; *U.S. Public*, pg. 29
MMODAL GLOBAL SERVICES PVT. LTD.—See Solventum Corporation; *U.S. Public*, pg. 1902
MMODAL INC.—See Solventum Corporation; *U.S. Public*, pg. 1902
MM OMEGA PROJEKTENTWICKLUNGS GMBH—See UniCredit S.p.A.; *Int'l*, pg. 8037
MMO TECH CO., LTD.—See Advanced Info Service Plc; *Int'l*, pg. 160
MM PACKAGING BEHRENS GMBH—See Mayr-Melnhof Karton AG; *Int'l*, pg. 4746
MM PACKAGING CAESAR GMBH & CO KG—See Mayr-Melnhof Karton AG; *Int'l*, pg. 4746
MM PACKAGING CAESAR VERWALTUNGS GMBH—See Mayr-Melnhof Karton AG; *Int'l*, pg. 4746
MM PACKAGING COLOMBIA S.A.S.—See Mayr-Melnhof Karton AG; *Int'l*, pg. 4746
MM PACKAGING FRANCE S.A.S.—See Mayr-Melnhof Karton AG; *Int'l*, pg. 4746
MM PACKAGING POLSKA SP. Z O.O.—See Mayr-Melnhof Karton AG; *Int'l*, pg. 4746
MM PACKAGING SCHILLING GMBH—See Mayr-Melnhof Karton AG; *Int'l*, pg. 4746
MM PACKAGING UKRAINE LLC—See Mayr-Melnhof Karton AG; *Int'l*, pg. 4746
MM PACKAGING VIDON LIMITED LIABILITY COMPANY—See Mayr-Melnhof Karton AG; *Int'l*, pg. 4746
MM PAKISTAN (PRIVATE) LIMITED—See Mott MacDonald Group Ltd.; *Int'l*, pg. 5055

MMP EVENT GMBH—See ProSiebenSat.1 Media SE; *Int'l*, pg. 6000
MMP EVENT GMBH—See ProSiebenSat.1 Media SE; *Int'l*, pg. 6000
MMP INDUSTRIES LTD.; *U.S. Private*, pg. 5006
MMP NEUPACK POLSKA SP.Z.O.O.—See Mayr-Melnhof Karton AG; *Int'l*, pg. 4746
MM POLYGRAFOFORMLENIE PACKAGING LLC—See Mayr-Melnhof Karton AG; *Int'l*, pg. 4746
MMP PACKETIS S.A.S.—See Mayr-Melnhof Karton AG; *Int'l*, pg. 4746
MMP PREMIUM POLSKA SP. Z O.O.—See Mayr-Melnhof Karton AG; *Int'l*, pg. 4746
MMP PREMIUM PRINTING CENTER GMBH—See Mayr-Melnhof Karton AG; *Int'l*, pg. 4746
MMP PREMIUM S.A.S.—See Mayr-Melnhof Karton AG; *Int'l*, pg. 4746
M&M PUMP & SUPPLY CO. INC.; *U.S. Private*, pg. 2524
MMP VPERED JSC—See Russian Technologies State Corporation; *Int'l*, pg. 6431
MMR CANADA, LIMITED—See MMR Group Inc.; *U.S. Private*, pg. 2755
MMR CARIBBEAN, LIMITED—See MMR Group Inc.; *U.S. Private*, pg. 2755
MMR COLOMBIA, S.A.S.—See MMR Group Inc.; *U.S. Private*, pg. 2755
MMR CONSTRUCTORS INC. - CORPUS CHRISTI—See MMR Group Inc.; *U.S. Private*, pg. 2755
MMR CONSTRUCTORS INC.—See MMR Group Inc.; *U.S. Private*, pg. 2755
M&M RENTAL CENTER, INC.—See Dubin Clark & Company, Inc.; *U.S. Private*, pg. 1283
M&M RESTAURANT SUPPLY—See Tyson Foods, Inc.; *U.S. Public*, pg. 2210
MMRGLOBAL, INC.; *U.S. Private*, pg. 2755
MMR GROUP INC.; *U.S. Private*, pg. 2755
MMR OFFSHORE SERVICES, INC.—See MMR Group Inc.; *U.S. Private*, pg. 2755
MMR PROCOM, LLC—See MMR Group Inc.; *U.S. Private*, pg. 2755
MMR TECHNICAL SERVICES, INC.—See MMR Group Inc.; *U.S. Private*, pg. 2755
MM RUBBER COMPANY LIMITED; *Int'l*, pg. 5004
MMR VENEZUELA, S.A.—See MMR Group Inc.; *U.S. Private*, pg. 2755
M&M SALES INCORPORATED; *U.S. Private*, pg. 2525
MMS CO., LTD.—See Meiji Shipping Co., Ltd.; *Int'l*, pg. 4801
MMS COMMUNICATIONS (FINLAND) OY—See Publicis Groupe S.A.; *Int'l*, pg. 6102
MMS DEUTSCHLAND GMBH—See Investor AB; *Int'l*, pg. 3786
M&M SERVICE CO. INC.; *U.S. Private*, pg. 2525
MMSL PTE. LTD.—See Marubeni Corporation; *Int'l*, pg. 4705
MMS MARITIME (INDIA) PRIVATE LTD.—See Meiji Shipping Co., Ltd.; *Int'l*, pg. 4801
MMS MODULAR MOLDING SYSTEMS GMBH—See Shanghai Baolong Automotive Corporation; *Int'l*, pg. 6762
MMS ONLINE NEDERLAND B.V.—See Metro AG; *Int'l*, pg. 4859
MMSPHIL MARITIME SERVICES INC.—See Meiji Shipping Co., Ltd.; *Int'l*, pg. 4801
MMS TRADING INC.; *U.S. Private*, pg. 2755
M&M SUPPLY CO.; *U.S. Private*, pg. 2525
MMS VENTURES BERHAD; *Int'l*, pg. 5006
MM SYSTEMS CORPORATION; *U.S. Private*, pg. 2754
MMTC LIMITED; *Int'l*, pg. 5006
MMTC TRANSNATIONAL PTE. LTD.—See MMTC Limited; *Int'l*, pg. 5006
MMTEC, INC.; *Int'l*, pg. 5006
MM TELEPERFORMANCE HOLDINGS LTD—See Teleperformance SE; *Int'l*, pg. 7540
MMTH ENGINE CO., LTD.—See Mitsubishi Motors Corporation; *Int'l*, pg. 4966
MMT SALES, LLC—See Apollo Global Management, Inc.; *U.S. Public*, pg. 164
MMU CNERGY SDN BHD—See Telekom Malaysia Berhad; *Int'l*, pg. 7537
MMU CREATIVISTA SDN BHD—See Telekom Malaysia Berhad; *Int'l*, pg. 7537
M&M VALUE LIMITED—See Kitwave Group Plc; *Int'l*, pg. 4196
MMV BANK GMBH—See Landesbank Baden-Wurttemberg; *Int'l*, pg. 4405
M & M VISIONS OY—See BHG Group AB; *Int'l*, pg. 1015
MMV LEASING GMBH—See Landesbank Baden-Wurttemberg; *Int'l*, pg. 4405
M.M. WARBURG BANK (SCHWEIZ) AG—See M.M. Warburg & Co. KGaA; *Int'l*, pg. 4616
M.M. WARBURG & CO. ASSEKURANZMAKLER GMBH—See M.M. Warburg & Co. KGaA; *Int'l*, pg. 4616
M.M. WARBURG & CO. FONDS-VERTRIEB—See M.M. Warburg & Co. KGaA; *Int'l*, pg. 4616
M.M. WARBURG & CO HYPOTHEKENBANK AG—See M.M. Warburg & Co. KGaA; *Int'l*, pg. 4616
M.M. WARBURG & CO. KGAA; *Int'l*, pg. 4616

COMPANY NAME INDEX

M.M. WARBURG & CO LUXEMBOURG S.A.—See M.M. Warburg & Co. KGaA; *Int'l*, pg. 4616
M.M. WARBURG & CO. SCHIFFAHRTSTREUHAND GMBH—See M.M. Warburg & Co. KGaA; *Int'l*, pg. 4616
M.M. WARBURG-LUXINVEST S.A.—See M.M. Warburg & Co. KGaA; *Int'l*, pg. 4616
MMW FABRICATION, LTD.; *U.S. Private*, pg. 2755
MMX MINERACAO E METALICOS S.A.—See EBX Group Ltd.; *Int'l*, pg. 2287
MMY CONSULTING, INC.—See Global Commerce & Information, Inc.; *U.S. Private*, pg. 1712
MN8 ENERGY, INC.; *U.S. Public*, pg. 1453
MNB BANCSHARES, INC.; *U.S. Private*, pg. 2755
MNB HOLDINGS CORPORATION; *U.S. Public*, pg. 1453
MNC MEDIA INVESTMENT LTD; *Int'l*, pg. 5006
MNC SA—See Vivendi SE; *Int'l*, pg. 8278
MNC WIRELESS BERHAD; *Int'l*, pg. 5006
M N C WIRELESS BHD; *Int'l*, pg. 4610
M & N CONSTRUCTION LTD; *Int'l*, pg. 4610
MND EASTERN EUROPE, S.R.O—See Montagne et Neige Developpement SA; *Int'l*, pg. 5035
MND IBERIA, S.A.—See Montagne et Neige Developpement SA; *Int'l*, pg. 5035
MND SVERIGE AB—See Montagne et Neige Developpement SA; *Int'l*, pg. 5035
MNDUSTRIES, INC.; *U.S. Private*, pg. 2755
MNED CO., LTD.—See The Japan Steel Works, Ltd.; *Int'l*, pg. 7659
MNEMONIC—See King James Group Company; *Int'l*, pg. 4169
MNET MOBILE PTY. LTD.—See The Interpublic Group of Companies, Inc.; *U.S. Public*, pg. 2103
M-NET TELEKOMMUNIKATIONS GMBH—See Stadtwerke Munchen GmbH; *Int'l*, pg. 7162
M & N FOODS LLC; *U.S. Private*, pg. 2523
MN-FUND PJSC; *Int'l*, pg. 5006
MN HOLDINGS BERHAD; *Int'l*, pg. 5006
MNH SUSTAINABLE CABIN SERVICES PTY SYDNEY - AUSTRALASIA—See Harwood Capital LLP; *Int'l*, pg. 3282
MNI S.A.; *Int'l*, pg. 5006
MNI TARGETED MEDIA INC—See Meredith Corporation; *U.S. Public*, pg. 1423
MNI TARGETED MEDIA INC.—See Warner Bros. Discovery, Inc.; *U.S. Public*, pg. 2327
MNJ TECHNOLOGIES DIRECT, INC.; *U.S. Private*, pg. 2755
MNO-BMADSEN—See Pokagon Band of Potawatomi Indians; *U.S. Private*, pg. 3223
MNP AEROSPACE, LLC—See MNP Corporation; *U.S. Private*, pg. 2756
MNP CORPORATION - MNP PLANT II—See MNP Corporation; *U.S. Private*, pg. 2756
MNP CORPORATION - MNP PLANT I—See MNP Corporation; *U.S. Private*, pg. 2756
MNP CORPORATION; *U.S. Private*, pg. 2755
MNPL ALUMINIUM CENTRE SDN. BHD.—See New Wave Holdings Ltd.; *Int'l*, pg. 5231
M & N PLASTICS, INC.—See Gibraltar Industries, Inc.; *U.S. Public*, pg. 936
MNPL METALS CO., LTD.—See New Wave Holdings Ltd.; *Int'l*, pg. 5231
MNPM SOLUTIONS LTD—See ManpowerGroup Inc.; *U.S. Public*, pg. 1358
MNP PETROLEUM CORPORATION; *Int'l*, pg. 5006
MNP STEEL SERVICES & WAREHOUSING DIVISION—See MNP Corporation; *U.S. Private*, pg. 2756
MNP STEEL & WIRE DIVISION—See MNP Corporation; *U.S. Private*, pg. 2756
MNP STEEL & WIRE/UTICA WASHER DIVISION—See MNP Corporation; *U.S. Private*, pg. 2756
MNRB HOLDINGS BERHAD; *Int'l*, pg. 5006
MNRB RETAKAFUL BERHAD—See MNRB Holdings Berhad; *Int'l*, pg. 5006
MNR GROUP SA—See Mubadala Investment Company PJSC; *Int'l*, pg. 5074
MNS1 EXPRESS, INC.; *U.S. Private*, pg. 2756
MNTECH CO, LTD.; *Int'l*, pg. 5006
MN TECHNOLOGIES SAS; *Int'l*, pg. 5006
MNT HEALTHCARE SERVICES AND TRADE INC.—See Bozlu Holding; *Int'l*, pg. 1125
MOAB MINERALS LIMITED; *Int'l*, pg. 5007
MOAB OIL, INC.—See TP ICAP Finance PLC; *Int'l*, pg. 7882
MOAB REGIONAL HOSPITAL; *U.S. Private*, pg. 2756
MOA BREWING COMPANY LIMITED; *Int'l*, pg. 5006
MOADATA CO., LTD.; *Int'l*, pg. 5007
M.O. AIR INTERNATIONAL (TAIWAN) CO.,LTD.—See Mitsui O.S.K. Lines, Ltd.; *Int'l*, pg. 4990
M.O.AIR LOGISTICS, INC.—See Mitsui O.S.K. Lines, Ltd.; *Int'l*, pg. 4989
MOAI TECHNOLOGIES INC.; *U.S. Private*, pg. 2756
MO ALTERNATE INVESTMENT PRIVATE LIMITED—See Motilal Oswal Financial Services Ltd.; *Int'l*, pg. 5053
MO ALTERNATIVE IFSC LIMITED—See Motilal Financial Services Ltd.; *Int'l*, pg. 5053
MOANA NURSERY INC.; *U.S. Private*, pg. 2756

MOARA CIBIN S.A.; *Int'l*, pg. 5007
MOARK PRODUCTIONS INC.; *U.S. Private*, pg. 2756
MOATABLE, INC.; *Int'l*, pg. 5007
MOATECH CO., LTD. - INCHEON FACTORY—See Moatech Co., Ltd.; *Int'l*, pg. 5007
MOATECH CO., LTD.; *Int'l*, pg. 5007
MOATECH HONG KONG LIMITED—See Moatech Co., Ltd.; *Int'l*, pg. 5007
MOATECH PHILIPPINES INC.—See Moatech Co., Ltd.; *Int'l*, pg. 5007
MOBA B.V.—See FPS Food Processing Systems B.V.; *Int'l*, pg. 5007
MOBA CORPORATION—See MOBA Mobile Automation AG; *Int'l*, pg. 5007
MOBA (DALIAN) MOBILE AUTOMATION CO., LTD.—See MOBA Mobile Automation AG; *Int'l*, pg. 5007
MOBA ELECTRONIC S.R.L.—See MOBA Mobile Automation AG; *Int'l*, pg. 5007
MOBA FRANCE—See MOBA Mobile Automation AG; *Int'l*, pg. 5007
MOBA-ISE MOBILE AUTOMATION SL—See MOBA Mobile Automation AG; *Int'l*, pg. 5007
MOBA MOBILE AUTOMATION AG; *Int'l*, pg. 5007
MOBA MOBILE AUTOMATION (I) PVT. LTD.—See MOBA Mobile Automation AG; *Int'l*, pg. 5007
MOBA MOBILE AUTOMATION LTD.—See MOBA Mobile Automation AG; *Int'l*, pg. 5007
MOBAOKU CO., LTD.—See DeNA Co., Ltd.; *Int'l*, pg. 2026
MOBASE CO., LTD.; *Int'l*, pg. 5007
MOBASE ELECTRONICS CO., LTD.—See Mobase Co., Ltd.; *Int'l*, pg. 5007
MOBBY CO., LTD.—See Arata Corporation; *Int'l*, pg. 536
MOBCAST HOLDINGS, INC.; *Int'l*, pg. 5007
MOBEL INCORPORATED; *U.S. Private*, pg. 2756
MOBELVERTRIEB FORTE GMBH—See Fabryki Mebli Forte S.A.; *Int'l*, pg. 2600
MOBELWERKSTATTEN JOSEF RITTER GMBH.—See Nobia AB; *Int'l*, pg. 5395
MOBERG PHARMA AB; *Int'l*, pg. 5007
MOBERG PHARMA NORTH AMERICA LLC—See RoundTable Healthcare Management, Inc.; *U.S. Private*, pg. 3489
MOBERG PHARMA NORTH AMERICA LLC—See Signet Healthcare Partners, LLC; *U.S. Private*, pg. 3850
MOBERLY HBP MEDICAL GROUP, LLC—See Community Health Systems, Inc.; *U.S. Public*, pg. 555
MOBERLY MEDICAL CLINICS, INC.—See Community Health Systems, Inc.; *U.S. Public*, pg. 555
MOBERLY MOTOR; *U.S. Private*, pg. 2756
MOBESTREAM MEDIA, INC.—See inMarket Media LLC; *U.S. Private*, pg. 2079
MOBEST SA; *Int'l*, pg. 5007
MOBETIZE CORP.; *Int'l*, pg. 5008
MO' BETTER MARKETING, LLC—See New West, LLC; *U.S. Private*, pg. 2908
MOBEUS EQUITY PARTNERS LLP; *Int'l*, pg. 5008
MOBEUS INCOME & GROWTH VCT PLC; *Int'l*, pg. 5008
MOBEX COMMUNICATIONS INC.; *U.S. Private*, pg. 2756
MOBI724 GLOBAL SOLUTIONS INC.; *Int'l*, pg. 5008
MOBIAPPS SAS—See Neurones S.A.; *Int'l*, pg. 5219
MOBIASBANCA - OTP GROUP S.A.—See OTP Bank Plc; *Int'l*, pg. 5657
MOBIASBANCA S.A.—See OTP Bank Plc; *Int'l*, pg. 5657
MOBI BANKA A.D.—See PPF Group N.V.; *Int'l*, pg. 5950
MOBICA LIMITED SP. Z O.O.—See Cognizant Technology Solutions Corporation; *U.S. Public*, pg. 525
MOBICA LTD.—See Cognizant Technology Solutions Corporation; *U.S. Public*, pg. 524
MOBICA US INC.—See Cognizant Technology Solutions Corporation; *U.S. Public*, pg. 525
MOBICO GROUP PLC; *Int'l*, pg. 5008
MOBICOM CORPORATION—See KDDI Corporation; *Int'l*, pg. 4112
MOBICON (BVI) LIMITED—See Mobicon Group Limited; *Int'l*, pg. 5010
MOBICON ELECTRONIC TRADING (SHENZHEN) LIMITED—See Mobicon Group Limited; *Int'l*, pg. 5010
MOBICON GROUP LIMITED; *Int'l*, pg. 5009
MOBICON HOLDINGS LIMITED—See Mobicon Group Limited; *Int'l*, pg. 5010
MOBICON-MANTECH HOLDINGS LIMITED—See Mobicon Group Limited; *Int'l*, pg. 5010
MOBICON-REMOTE ELECTRONIC PTE LTD.—See Mobicon Group Limited; *Int'l*, pg. 5010
MOBICON-REMOTE ELECTRONIC SDN. BHD.—See Mobicon Group Limited; *Int'l*, pg. 5010
MOBICON (TAIWAN) LIMITED—See Mobicon Group Limited; *Int'l*, pg. 5010
MOBI CORP.—See Geotab, Inc.; *Int'l*, pg. 2941
MOBIDAYS, INC.; *Int'l*, pg. 5010
MOBI DEVELOPMENT CO., LTD.; *Int'l*, pg. 5010
MOBIDIAG UK LTD.—See Hologic, Inc.; *U.S. Public*, pg. 1045
MOBIENTS INC.; *U.S. Private*, pg. 2756
MOBIFUSION, INC.; *U.S. Private*, pg. 2756
MOBIHEAT GMBH—See Mainova AG; *Int'l*, pg. 4651
MOBIHEAT OSTERREICH GMBH—See MVV Energie AG; *Int'l*, pg. 5109

MOBILE FOREST PRODUCTS INC.

MOBIHEAT SCHWEIZ GMBH—See MVV Energie AG; *Int'l*, pg. 5109
MOBIIS CO., LTD.; *Int'l*, pg. 5010
MOBILA SA; *Int'l*, pg. 5010
MOBIL BAUSTOFFE GMBH—See STRABAG SE; *Int'l*, pg. 7231
MOBILCOM COMMUNICATIONSTECHNIK GMBH—See freenet AG; *Int'l*, pg. 2770
MOBILCOM-DEBITEL GMBH—See freenet AG; *Int'l*, pg. 2770
MOBILE ACCOUNT SOLUTIONS LIMITED; *Int'l*, pg. 5010
MOBILEACTIVE LIMITED - MOBILE EMBRACE DIVISION—See Impelus Limited; *Int'l*, pg. 3632
MOBILE AIRPORT AUTHORITY; *U.S. Private*, pg. 2756
MOBILE AIR TRANSPORT, INC.; *U.S. Private*, pg. 2756
MOBILE APPLIANCE INC.; *Int'l*, pg. 5010
MOBILE AREA WATER & SEWER SYSTEM; *U.S. Private*, pg. 2756
MOBILE ASPHALT CO., LLC - ATMORE PLANT—See Mobile Asphalt Co., LLC; *U.S. Private*, pg. 2757
MOBILE ASPHALT CO., LLC - BAY MINETTE PLANT—See Mobile Asphalt Co., LLC; *U.S. Private*, pg. 2757
MOBILE ASPHALT CO., LLC - FOLEY PLANT—See Mobile Asphalt Co., LLC; *U.S. Private*, pg. 2757
MOBILE ASPHALT CO., LLC - SARALAND PLANT—See Mobile Asphalt Co., LLC; *U.S. Private*, pg. 2757
MOBILE ASPHALT CO., LLC; *U.S. Private*, pg. 2757
MOBILE ASPHALT CO., LLC - SUMMERDALE PLANT—See Mobile Asphalt Co., LLC; *U.S. Private*, pg. 2757
MOBILE ASPHALT CO., LLC - WHATLEY PLANT—See Mobile Asphalt Co., LLC; *U.S. Private*, pg. 2757
MOBILEATION, INC.; *U.S. Private*, pg. 2757
MOBILEAXEPT NORTH AMERICA, INC.—See i3 Verticals, Inc.; *U.S. Public*, pg. 1081
MOBILE & BIRMINGHAM RAILROAD CO.—See Norfolk Southern Corporation; *U.S. Public*, pg. 1536
MOBILEBITS HOLDINGS CORPORATION; *U.S. Private*, pg. 2757
MOBILEBOOK.JP, INC.—See Dai Nippon Printing Co., Ltd.; *Int'l*, pg. 1916
MOBILE CARDIAC IMAGING, LLC; *U.S. Private*, pg. 2757
MOBILECAUSE, INC.—See Insight Venture Management, LLC; *U.S. Private*, pg. 2088
MOBILE CENTER(BEIJING) TECHNOLOGY CO., LTD.—See Wutong Holding Group Co., Ltd.; *Int'l*, pg. 8514
MOBILE CLIMATE CONTROL CORP.—See VBG Group AB; *Int'l*, pg. 8138
MOBILE CLIMATE CONTROL GMBH—See VBG Group AB; *Int'l*, pg. 8138
MOBILE CLIMATE CONTROL GROUP HOLDING AB—See VBG Group AB; *Int'l*, pg. 8138
MOBILE CLIMATE CONTROL INC.—See VBG Group AB; *Int'l*, pg. 8138
MOBILE CLIMATE CONTROL YORK CORPORATION—See VBG Group AB; *Int'l*, pg. 8138
MOBILECOMM PROFESSIONALS, INC.—See UST Global Inc.; *U.S. Private*, pg. 4324
MOBILE COMMUNICATIONS AMERICA, INC.—See Sentinel Capital Partners, L.L.C.; *U.S. Private*, pg. 3609
MOBILE COMMUNICATIONS CO., LTD.—See Bain Capital, LP; *U.S. Private*, pg. 434
MOBILE COMPUTING CORPORATION; *Int'l*, pg. 5010
MOBILE CONTROL SYSTEMS SA—See Addtech AB; *Int'l*, pg. 134
MOBILE CREATE CO., LTD.—See Future Innovation Group, Inc.; *Int'l*, pg. 2856
MOBILE CREATE USA, INC.—See Future Innovation Group, Inc.; *Int'l*, pg. 2856
MOBILEDATAFORCE, INC.; *U.S. Private*, pg. 2757
MOBILE DATA TECHNOLOGIES LTD.—See Patterson-UTI Energy, Inc.; *U.S. Public*, pg. 1654
MOBILE DEFENSE, INC.—See Assurant, Inc.; *U.S. Public*, pg. 215
MOBILE.DE GMBH—See eBay Inc.; *U.S. Public*, pg. 709
MOBILEDEMAND, LC; *U.S. Private*, pg. 2758
MOBILE DIGITAL COMMUNICATIONS LTD.; *Int'l*, pg. 5010
MOBILE DOCTORS GROUP LIMITED—See Watchstone Group plc; *Int'l*, pg. 8356
MOBILE DOCTORS LIMITED—See Watchstone Group plc; *Int'l*, pg. 8356
MOBILE DOCTORS SOLUTIONS LIMITED—See Watchstone Group plc; *Int'l*, pg. 8356
MOBILE DREDGING & PUMPING CO.—See Carylon Corporation; *U.S. Private*, pg. 777
MOBILE EDGE, LLC; *U.S. Private*, pg. 2757
MOBILE EIGHT APPAREL CORP—See Mobile Eight Holding Ltd.; *U.S. Private*, pg. 2757
MOBILE EIGHT HOLDING LTD.; *U.S. Private*, pg. 2757
MOBILE FACTORY INC.; *Int'l*, pg. 5010
MOBILE FLEET SERVICE INC.; *U.S. Private*, pg. 2757
MOBILE FOREST PRODUCTS INC.; *U.S. Private*, pg. 2757
MOBILE FUSION PTE. LTD.—See mTouche Technology Berhad; *Int'l*, pg. 5071

1805

MOBILE GAS SERVICE CORPORATION—See Sempra; *U.S. Public*, pg. 1863
MOBILE GLOBAL EXPORTS INC.; *U.S. Private*, pg. 2757
MOBILE-HEALTH NETWORK SOLUTIONS; *Int'l*, pg. 5011
MOBILE HEARTBEAT, LLC—See HCA Healthcare, Inc.; *U.S. Public*, pg. 1003
MOBILEHELP, LLC—See Water Street Healthcare Partners, LLC; *U.S. Private*, pg. 4452
MOBILE INDUSTRIAL ROBOTS A/S—See Teradyne, Inc.; *U.S. Public*, pg. 2018
MOBILE INDUSTRIAL ROBOTS GMBH—See Teradyne, Inc.; *U.S. Public*, pg. 2018
MOBILE INDUSTRIAL ROBOTS, INC.—See Teradyne, Inc.; *U.S. Public*, pg. 2018
MOBILE INDUSTRIAL ROBOTS PTE. LTD.—See Teradyne, Inc.; *U.S. Public*, pg. 2018
MOBILE INFRASTRUCTURE CORPORATION; *U.S. Public*, pg. 1453
MOBILE INFRASTRUCTURE CORPORATION—See Mobile Infrastructure Corporation; *U.S. Public*, pg. 1453
MOBILE INNOVATION CO. LTD—See Loxley Public Company Limited; *Int'l*, pg. 4567
MOBILE INSTRUMENT SERVICE & REPAIR, INC.—See Thomas H. Lee Partners, L.P.; *U.S. Private*, pg. 4156
MOBILE INTEGRATED TECHNOLOGIES, INC.—See Zebra Technologies Corporation; *U.S. Public*, pg. 2401
MOBILE INTERACTIVE GROUP BLGM N.V.—See Velti plc; *U.S. Public*, pg. 8150
MOBILE.INTERNATIONAL GMBH—See eBay Inc.; *U.S. Public*, pg. 709
MOBILE INTERNET (CHINA) HOLDINGS LIMITED; *Int'l*, pg. 5010
MOBILEIRON AUSTRALIA—See MobileIron, Inc.; *U.S. Private*, pg. 2758
MOBILEIRON CENTRAL & EASTERN EUROPE—See MobileIron, Inc.; *U.S. Private*, pg. 2758
MOBILEIRON EMEA—See MobileIron, Inc.; *U.S. Private*, pg. 2758
MOBILEIRON FRANCE—See MobileIron, Inc.; *U.S. Private*, pg. 2758
MOBILEIRON HONG KONG—See MobileIron, Inc.; *U.S. Private*, pg. 2758
MOBILEIRON, INC.; *U.S. Private*, pg. 2758
MOBILEIRON JAPAN—See MobileIron, Inc.; *U.S. Private*, pg. 2758
MOBILEIRON SINGAPORE—See MobileIron, Inc.; *U.S. Private*, pg. 2758
MOBILEIRON UK & IRELAND—See MobileIron, Inc.; *U.S. Private*, pg. 2758
MOBILE LADS CORP.; *U.S. Public*, pg. 1454
MOBIL ELECTRIC GMBH—See Nexans S.A.; *Int'l*, pg. 5241
MOBILE LINK INC.—See Striders Corporation; *Int'l*, pg. 7240
MOBILE LUMBER & MILLWORK INC.; *U.S. Private*, pg. 2757
MOBILE MARK, INC.; *U.S. Private*, pg. 2757
MOBILE MATCHMAKING, INC.; *U.S. Public*, pg. 1454
MOBILE MEALS; *U.S. Private*, pg. 2757
MOBILEMECH GMBH—See Delticom AG; *Int'l*, pg. 2021
MOBILE MEDIANET INC.—See Denso Corporation; *Int'l*, pg. 2032
MOBILE MINI CANADA ULC—See WillScot Mobile Mini Holdings Corp.; *U.S. Public*, pg. 2372
MOBILE MINI, INC.—See WillScot Mobile Mini Holdings Corp.; *U.S. Public*, pg. 2372
MOBILE MINI, LLC—See WillScot Mobile Mini Holdings Corp.; *U.S. Public*, pg. 2372
MOBILE MINI UK HOLDINGS LIMITED—See WillScot Mobile Mini Holdings Corp.; *U.S. Public*, pg. 2372
MOBILE MINI UK LTD.—See WillScot Mobile Mini Holdings Corp.; *U.S. Public*, pg. 2372
MOBILE MODULAR MANAGEMENT CORPORATION—See McGrath RentCorp; *U.S. Public*, pg. 1407
MOBILE MONEY INC.—See Continental Currency Services Inc.; *U.S. Private*, pg. 1028
MOBILE-ONE AUTO SOUND INC.; *U.S. Private*, pg. 2757
MOBILE ONE COURIER CARGO & LOGISTICS; *U.S. Private*, pg. 2757
MOBILEONE LLC; *U.S. Private*, pg. 2757
MOBILE PAINT CARRIBBEAN—See Mobile Paint Manufacturing Company of Delaware Inc.; *U.S. Private*, pg. 2757
MOBILE PAINT MANUFACTURING COMPANY OF DELAWARE INC.; *U.S. Private*, pg. 2757
MOBILE PAINT MANUFACTURING COMPANY OF PUERTO RICO INC.—See Mobile Paint Manufacturing Company of Delaware Inc.; *U.S. Private*, pg. 2757
MOBILEPAY DENMARK A/S—See Danske Bank A/S; *Int'l*, pg. 1969
MOBILEPAY FINLAND OY—See Danske Bank A/S; *Int'l*, pg. 1969
MOBILE POSSE, INC.—See Digital Turbine, Inc.; *U.S. Public*, pg. 664
MOBILEPRO AG—See Midwich Group Plc; *Int'l*, pg. 4887
MOBILE RADIO COMMUNICATIONS INC.; *U.S. Private*, pg. 2757

MOBILE-SC, LTD.—See UnitedHealth Group Incorporated; *U.S. Public*, pg. 2242
MOBILE SEMICONDUCTOR CORP.—See Nordic Semiconductor ASA; *Int'l*, pg. 5423
MOBILE SERVICE INTERNATIONAL CO. LTD.—See Digilife Technologies Limited; *Int'l*, pg. 2119
MOBILE SHIPBUILDING & REPAIR INC.—See Parker Towing Company, Inc.; *U.S. Private*, pg. 3097
MOBILESMITH, INC.; *U.S. Public*, pg. 1454
MOBILE SPINE & REHABILITATION, LIMITED PARTNERSHIP—See U.S. Physical Therapy, Inc.; *U.S. Public*, pg. 2215
MOBILE STEAM BOILER RENTAL CORP.—See Miller Proctor Nickolas Inc.; *U.S. Private*, pg. 2735
MOBILE STORAGE (UK) LTD.—See WillScot Mobile Mini Holdings Corp.; *U.S. Public*, pg. 2372
THE MOBILESTORE LTD.—See Essar Global Limited; *Int'l*, pg. 2508
MOBILESTORM, INC.; *U.S. Public*, pg. 2758
MOBILE STREAMS DE ARGENTINA S.R.L—See Mobile Streams Plc; *Int'l*, pg. 5010
MOBILE STREAMS INC—See Mobile Streams Plc; *Int'l*, pg. 5010
MOBILE STREAMS PLC; *Int'l*, pg. 5010
MOBILE STRUCTURES INC.; *U.S. Private*, pg. 2757
MOBILE SYSTEMS WIRELESS LLC; *U.S. Private*, pg. 2757
MOBILE TECHNIC SDN. BHD.—See Watta Holding Berhad; *Int'l*, pg. 8358
MOBILE-TECHNOLOGIES CO., LTD.; *Int'l*, pg. 5011
MOBILE TECHNOLOGIES INTERNATIONAL LLC—See ComfortDelGro Corporation Limited; *Int'l*, pg. 1712
MOBILE TECHNOLOGIES INTERNATIONAL PTY. LTD.—See ComfortDelGro Corporation Limited; *Int'l*, pg. 1712
MOBILE TELECOMMUNICATIONS COMPANY K.S.C.; *Int'l*, pg. 5010
MOBILE TELECOMMUNICATIONS COMPANY SAUDI ARABIA—See Mobile Telecommunications Company K.S.C.; *Int'l*, pg. 5010
MOBILE TELESYSTEMS B.V.—See MOBILE TELESYSTEMS PUBLIC JOINT STOCK COMPANY; *Int'l*, pg. 5011
MOBILE TELESYSTEMS PUBLIC JOINT STOCK COMPANY; *Int'l*, pg. 5010
MOBILETEL INC.—See RTC Holdings, L.L.C.; *U.S. Private*, pg. 3498
MOBILE TORNADO PLC—See InTechnology Plc; *Int'l*, pg. 3729
MOBILETOUCH AG—See mobilezone holding ag; *Int'l*, pg. 5011
MOBILETOUCH AUSTRIA GMBH—See mobilezone holding ag; *Int'l*, pg. 5011
MOBILE TOWER CRANES (MTC) B.V.—See Arcomet & Co.; *Int'l*, pg. 550
MOBILETRAC LLC—See OPENLANE, Inc.; *U.S. Public*, pg. 1607
MOBILETRON COMECIO DE AUTOPECAS E FERRAMENTAS LTDA—See Mobiletron Electronics Co., Ltd.; *Int'l*, pg. 5011
MOBILETRON ELECTRONICS CO., LTD.; *Int'l*, pg. 5011
MOBILETRON ELECTRONICS (NINGBO) CO., LTD.—See Mobiletron Electronics Co., Ltd.; *Int'l*, pg. 5011
MOBILETRON U.K. LTD.—See Mobiletron Electronics Co., Ltd.; *Int'l*, pg. 5011
MOBILE TV GROUP; *U.S. Private*, pg. 2757
MOBILEUM, INC.—See H.I.G. Capital, LLC; *U.S. Private*, pg. 1833
MOBILE VENTURES GMBH—See United Internet AG; *Int'l*, pg. 8069
MOBILEWAVE GROUP PLC; *Int'l*, pg. 5011
MOBILEWEBADZ LTD.; *Int'l*, pg. 5011
MOBILE WORLD INVESTMENT CORPORATION; *Int'l*, pg. 5011
MOBILEX—See X-Ray Industries Inc.; *U.S. Private*, pg. 4579
MOBILEYE GLOBAL INC.—See Intel Corporation; *U.S. Public*, pg. 1139
MOBILEYE INC.—See Intel Corporation; *U.S. Public*, pg. 1139
MOBILEYE JAPAN LTD.—See Intel Corporation; *U.S. Public*, pg. 1139
MOBILEYE N.V.—See Intel Corporation; *U.S. Public*, pg. 1139
MOBILEYE VISION TECHNOLOGIES LTD.—See Intel Corporation; *U.S. Public*, pg. 1139
MOBILEZONE AG—See mobilezone holding ag; *Int'l*, pg. 5011
MOBILEZONE BUSINESS AG—See mobilezone holding ag; *Int'l*, pg. 5011
MOBILEZONE HOLDING AG; *Int'l*, pg. 5011
MOBILIARIA MONESA S.A.; *Int'l*, pg. 5011
MOBILICOM LTD.; *Int'l*, pg. 5011
MOBILINK S.A.—See Motorola Solutions, Inc.; *U.S. Public*, pg. 1478
MOBILISE GROUP PTY LTD—See PeopleIn Limited; *Int'l*, pg. 5794
MOBILITAS SA; *Int'l*, pg. 5011

MOBILITIE, LLC—See BAI Communications Pty Ltd; *Int'l*, pg. 801
MOBILITY AUSTRALIA PTY LTD.—See Madison Dearborn Partners, LLC; *U.S. Private*, pg. 2540
MOBILITY CONCEPT GMBH—See HgCapital Trust plc; *Int'l*, pg. 3377
MOBILITY, INC.—See Chatham Asset Management, LLC; *U.S. Private*, pg. 863
MOBILITYLAND CORPORATION—See Honda Motor Co., Ltd.; *Int'l*, pg. 3463
MOBILITY MEDIA GMBH—See Robert Bosch GmbH; *Int'l*, pg. 6361
MOBILITY MIXX B.V.—See Mitsubishi HC Capital Inc.; *Int'l*, pg. 4952
MOBILITYONE LIMITED; *Int'l*, pg. 5011
MOBILITY SERVICES INTERNATIONAL LLC; *U.S. Private*, pg. 2758
MOBILITY SOLUTIONS AG—See Die Schweizerische Post AG; *Int'l*, pg. 2113
MOBILITY SOLUTIONS MANAGEMENT AG—See Die Schweizerische Post AG; *Int'l*, pg. 2113
MOBILITY WAY INC.—See VINCI S.A.; *Int'l*, pg. 8224
MOBIL LASER TEC GMBH—See Porsche Automobil Holding SE; *Int'l*, pg. 5931
MOBIL OIL A.G.—See Exxon Mobil Corporation; *U.S. Public*, pg. 814
MOBIL OIL AUSTRALIA PTY LTD—See Exxon Mobil Corporation; *U.S. Public*, pg. 817
MOBIL OIL CORPORATION—See Exxon Mobil Corporation; *U.S. Public*, pg. 817
MOBIL OIL CORPORATION—See Exxon Mobil Corporation; *U.S. Public*, pg. 817
MOBIL OIL DEL PERU S A R L—See Exxon Mobil Corporation; *U.S. Public*, pg. 817
MOBIL OIL NEW ZEALAND LIMITED—See Exxon Mobil Corporation; *U.S. Public*, pg. 817
MOBIL OIL NEW ZEALAND LTD.—See Exxon Mobil Corporation; *U.S. Public*, pg. 817
MOBIL OIL TURK AS—See Exxon Mobil Corporation; *U.S. Public*, pg. 817
MOBIL REFINING AUSTRALIA PTY LTD—See Exxon Mobil Corporation; *U.S. Public*, pg. 817
MOBILUM TECHNOLOGIES INC.; *Int'l*, pg. 5011
MOBIMEO GMBH—See Deutsche Bahn AG; *Int'l*, pg. 2052
MOBIMO FM SERVICE AG—See Mobimo Holding AG; *Int'l*, pg. 5012
MOBIMO HOLDING AG; *Int'l*, pg. 5012
MOBIMO MANAGEMENT AG—See Mobimo Holding AG; *Int'l*, pg. 5012
MOBIO TECHNOLOGIES INC.; *Int'l*, pg. 5012
MOBIQUITY, INC.—See EQT AB; *Int'l*, pg. 2470
MOBIQUITY NETWORKS, INC.—See Mobiquity Technologies, Inc.; *U.S. Public*, pg. 1454
MOBIQUITY TECHNOLOGIES, INC.; *U.S. Public*, pg. 1454
MOBIRIX CORPORATION; *Int'l*, pg. 5012
MOBIS ALABAMA, LLC—See Hyundai MOBIS Co., Ltd.; *Int'l*, pg. 3558
MOBIS AUTOMOTIVE CZECH S.R.O.—See Hyundai MOBIS Co., Ltd.; *Int'l*, pg. 3558
MOBIS GEORGIA LLC—See Hyundai MOBIS Co., Ltd.; *Int'l*, pg. 3558
MOBIS INDIA, LTD.—See Hyundai MOBIS Co., Ltd.; *Int'l*, pg. 3558
MOBIS NORTH AMERICA, LLC—See Hyundai MOBIS Co., Ltd.; *Int'l*, pg. 3558
MOBISOFT OY—See DDS Wireless International Inc.; *Int'l*, pg. 1994
MOBIS PARTS AMERICA, LLC—See Hyundai MOBIS Co., Ltd.; *Int'l*, pg. 3558
MOBIS PARTS AUSTRALIA PTY. LTD.—See Hyundai MOBIS Co., Ltd.; *Int'l*, pg. 3558
MOBIS PARTS CANADA CORPORATION—See Hyundai MOBIS Co., Ltd.; *Int'l*, pg. 3558
MOBIS PARTS EUROPE B.V.—See Hyundai MOBIS Co., Ltd.; *Int'l*, pg. 3558
MOBIS PARTS MIAMI, LLC—See Hyundai MOBIS Co., Ltd.; *Int'l*, pg. 3558
MOBIS PARTS MIDDLE EAST FZE—See Hyundai MOBIS Co., Ltd.; *Int'l*, pg. 3558
MOBIS SLOVAKIA S.R.O.—See Hyundai MOBIS Co., Ltd.; *Int'l*, pg. 3558
MOBISTAR ENTERPRISE SERVICES SA—See Orange S.A.; *Int'l*, pg. 5609
MOBITEC AB—See Audax Group, Limited Partnership; *U.S. Private*, pg. 389
MOBITEC BRASIL LTDA—See Audax Group, Limited Partnership; *U.S. Private*, pg. 389
MOBITEC GMBH—See Audax Group, Limited Partnership; *U.S. Private*, pg. 389
MOBITEL, D.D.—See Telekom Slovenije, d.d.; *Int'l*, pg. 7538
MOBITEL (PRIVATE) LIMITED—See Sri Lanka Telecom PLC; *Int'l*, pg. 7150
MOBI (THAI) CO., LTD.—See BEC World Public Company Limited; *Int'l*, pg. 936
MOBITV, INC.; *U.S. Private*, pg. 2758
MOBIUM—See Stagwell, Inc.; *U.S. Public*, pg. 1926

COMPANY NAME INDEX

MOBIUS365 DATA SERVICES PRIVATE LIMITED—See Mobius Knowledge Services Pvt. Ltd.; *Int'l*, pg. 5012
MOBIUS365 KNOWLEDGE SERVICES INCORPORATED—See Mobius Knowledge Services Pvt. Ltd.; *Int'l*, pg. 5012
MOBIUS ECOCAPITAL PLC; *Int'l*, pg. 5012
MOBIUS IMAGING, LLC—See Stryker Corporation; *U.S. Public*, pg. 1956
MOBIUS INVESTMENT TRUST PLC; *Int'l*, pg. 5012
MOBIUS KNOWLEDGE SERVICES PVT. LTD.; *Int'l*, pg. 5012
MOBIUS MANAGEMENT SYSTEMS, AUSTRALIA—See Allen Systems Group, Inc.; *U.S. Private*, pg. 180
MOBIUS MANAGEMENT SYSTEMS BENELUX B.V.—See Allen Systems Group, Inc.; *U.S. Private*, pg. 180
MOBIUS MEDICAL SYSTEMS, LP—See Siemens Aktiengesellschaft; *Int'l*, pg. 6894
MOBIUS PARTNERS ENTERPRISE SOLUTIONS; *U.S. Private*, pg. 2758
MOBIUS VENTURE CAPITAL, INC.; *U.S. Private*, pg. 2758
MOBIV ACQUISITION CORP.—See SRIVARU Holding Limited; *Int'l*, pg. 7152
MOBIVENTURES, INC.; *Int'l*, pg. 5012
MOBIVIA GROUPE SA; *Int'l*, pg. 5012
MOBIVITY HOLDINGS CORP.; *U.S. Public*, pg. 1454
MOBI WIRELESS MANAGEMENT, LLC—See Marlin Equity Partners, LLC; *U.S. Private*, pg. 2583
MOBIX LABS, INC.—See Mobix Labs, Inc.; *U.S. Public*, pg. 1454
MOBIX LABS, INC.; *U.S. Public*, pg. 1454
MOBIX STEVENS—See Ackermans & van Haaren NV; *Int'l*, pg. 105
MOBLEY CONTRACTORS INC.; *U.S. Private*, pg. 2758
MOBLEY HOMES OF FLORIDA INC.; *U.S. Private*, pg. 2758
MOBLICO SOLUTIONS, LLC—See SS&C Technologies Holdings, Inc.; *U.S. Public*, pg. 1923
MOBLY COMERCIO VAREJISTA LTDA—See XXXLutz KG; *Int'l*, pg. 8542
MOB MEDIA; *U.S. Private*, pg. 2756
MOBO CO., LTD.—See GAON Cable Co., Ltd.; *Int'l*, pg. 2882
MOBOMO; *U.S. Private*, pg. 2758
MOBOTEC EUROPE AB—See Ecolab Inc.; *U.S. Public*, pg. 715
MOBOTIX AG—See Konica Minolta, Inc.; *Int'l*, pg. 4260
MOBOTIX CORP.—See Konica Minolta, Inc.; *Int'l*, pg. 4260
MOBOTREX, INC.—See Warren Equity Partners, LLC; *U.S. Private*, pg. 4443
MOBPARTNER S.A.S.—See Kingsoft Corporation Limited; *Int'l*, pg. 4176
MOBREY AB—See Emerson Electric Co.; *U.S. Public*, pg. 748
MOBREY LIMITED—See Emerson Electric Co.; *U.S. Public*, pg. 750
MOBREY MEASUREMENT LTD.—See Emerson Electric Co.; *U.S. Public*, pg. 748
MO-BRUK S.A.; *Int'l*, pg. 5006
MOBVISTA, INC.; *Int'l*, pg. 5012
MOC ACQUISITION CORPORATION—See EssilorLuxottica SA; *Int'l*, pg. 2514
MOCANA CORPORATION—See Clearlake Capital Group, L.P.; *U.S. Private*, pg. 934
MOCANA CORPORATION—See Crosspoint Capital Partners LP; *U.S. Private*, pg. 1107
MOCANA CORPORATION—See TA Associates, Inc.; *U.S. Private*, pg. 3915
MOCANA SOLUTIONS PRIVATE LIMITED—See Clearlake Capital Group, L.P.; *U.S. Private*, pg. 934
MOCANA SOLUTIONS PRIVATE LIMITED—See Crosspoint Capital Partners LP; *U.S. Private*, pg. 1107
MOCANA SOLUTIONS PRIVATE LIMITED—See TA Associates, Inc.; *U.S. Private*, pg. 3915
MOCAP FRANCE—See MOCAP Inc.; *U.S. Private*, pg. 2758
MOCAP INC.; *U.S. Private*, pg. 2758
MOCAP LIMITED—See MOCAP Inc.; *U.S. Private*, pg. 2758
MOCAP SRL—See MOCAP Inc.; *U.S. Private*, pg. 2758
MO CASHEW LTD—See Mohammed Enterprises Tanzania Limited; *Int'l*, pg. 5018
MOCCA DIALYSIS, LLC—See DaVita Inc.; *U.S. Public*, pg. 641
MOCHE INVERSIONES S.A.; *Int'l*, pg. 5012
MOCHEM—See Momar, Inc.; *U.S. Private*, pg. 2768
MOCHIDA INTERNATIONAL CO., LTD.—See Mochida Pharmaceutical Co., Ltd.; *Int'l*, pg. 5012
MOCHIDA PHARMACEUTICAL CO., LTD.; *Int'l*, pg. 5012
MOCHIDA PHARMACEUTICAL PLANT CO., LTD.—See Mochida Pharmaceutical Co., Ltd.; *Int'l*, pg. 5012
MOCHIDA SIEMENS MEDICAL SYSTEMS CO. LTD.—See Siemens Aktiengesellschaft; *Int'l*, pg. 6887
MOCHILA, INC.; *U.S. Private*, pg. 2759
MOC HOA BINH MANUFACTURING & DECORATING JSC—See Hoa Binh Construction Group JSC; *Int'l*, pg. 3435
MOCKFJARDS FONSTERENTREPRENAD AB—See VKR Holding A/S; *Int'l*, pg. 8281

MOCKLER BEVERAGE CO. LP; *U.S. Private*, pg. 2759
MOCK PLUMBING & MECHANICAL, INC.; *U.S. Private*, pg. 2759
MOCOBE PROPERTIES (PTY) LIMITED—See The Bidvest Group Limited; *Int'l*, pg. 7625
MOCOM S.R.L.—See Cefla S.C.; *Int'l*, pg. 1390
MOCON EUROPE A/S—See AMETEK, Inc.; *U.S. Public*, pg. 120
MOCON, INC.—See AMETEK, Inc.; *U.S. Public*, pg. 120
MOCON ITALIA S.R.L.—See AMETEK, Inc.; *U.S. Public*, pg. 120
MOCOS JAPAN CO., LTD.—See TOKYO KEIKI INC.; *Int'l*, pg. 7792
MOC PORTFOLIO DELAWARE, INC.—See ConocoPhillips; *U.S. Public*, pg. 569
MOC PRODUCTS COMPANY, INC.; *U.S. Private*, pg. 2758
MOCSA REAL ESTATE BV—See Ascom Holding AG; *Int'l*, pg. 603
MOD21 GMBH—See Erbud S.A.; *Int'l*, pg. 2489
MODA BAGNO - N. VARVERIS S.A.; *Int'l*, pg. 5012
MODAGRAFICS INC.; *U.S. Private*, pg. 2759
MODA INC.; *Int'l*, pg. 5013
MODA-INNOCHIPS CO., LTD.; *Int'l*, pg. 5013
MODAL ADMINISTRADORA DE RECURSOS S.A.—See XP Inc.; *Int'l*, pg. 8537
MODAL DTVM—See XP Inc.; *Int'l*, pg. 8537
MODAL EHSAN SDN. BHD.—See MTD Capital Bhd.; *Int'l*, pg. 5070
MODALIS THERAPEUTICS CORPORATION; *Int'l*, pg. 5013
MODALITY SOLUTIONS, LLC—See Renovus Capital Partners; *U.S. Private*, pg. 3399
THE MODAL SHOP INC.—See Amphenol Corporation; *U.S. Public*, pg. 131
MODALTON LIMITED—See Hang Lung Group Limited; *Int'l*, pg. 3245
MODAMEDIA COMMUNICATIONS, INC.—See Dovetail Solutions Inc.; *U.S. Private*, pg. 1268
MODAR S.P.A.—See Dexelance S.p.A.; *Int'l*, pg. 2092
MODASUITE INC.—See Unified Commerce Group; *U.S. Private*, pg. 4282
MODAXO INC.—See Constellation Software Inc.; *Int'l*, pg. 1775
MODBE, INC.; *U.S. Private*, pg. 2759
MODCHEM LTD. AGENCIES—See Bischof + Klein GmbH & Co. KG; *Int'l*, pg. 1048
MODCO CREATIVE INC.; *U.S. Private*, pg. 2759
MODCOMP, INC.—See CSP Inc.; *U.S. Public*, pg. 601
MODCOMP, LTD.—See CSP Inc.; *U.S. Public*, pg. 601
MODEA CORP; *U.S. Private*, pg. 2759
MODEC, INC.—See Mitsui E&S Holdings Co., Ltd.; *Int'l*, pg. 4985
MODEC INTERNATIONAL, INC.—See Mitsui E&S Holdings Co., Ltd.; *Int'l*, pg. 4985
MODEC INTERNATIONAL LLC—See Mitsui E&S Holdings Co., Ltd.; *Int'l*, pg. 4985
MODEC MANAGEMENT SERVICES PTE LTD.—See Mitsui E&S Holdings Co., Ltd.; *Int'l*, pg. 4985
MODEC MANAGEMENT SERVICES PTE LTD.—See Mitsui E&S Holdings Co., Ltd.; *Int'l*, pg. 4985
MODEC MANAGEMENT SERVICES PTE LTD.—See Mitsui E&S Holdings Co., Ltd.; *Int'l*, pg. 4985
MODEC OFFSHORE PRODUCTION SYSTEMS (SINGAPORE) PTE LTD.—See Mitsui E&S Holdings Co., Ltd.; *Int'l*, pg. 4985
MODEC SERVICOS DE PETROLEO DO BRASIL LTDA—See Mitsui E&S Holdings Co., Ltd.; *Int'l*, pg. 4985
MODE FREIGHT SERVICES, LLC—See Hub Group, Inc.; *U.S. Public*, pg. 1065
MODE GLOBAL, LLC; *U.S. Private*, pg. 2759
MODE...INFORMATION GMBH; *Int'l*, pg. 5013
MODEL 2 MACHINING, INC.—See Generation Growth Capital, Inc.; *U.S. Private*, pg. 1668
MODEL DAIRY—See Dean Foods Company; *U.S. Private*, pg. 1183
THE MODEL GROUP INC.; *U.S. Private*, pg. 4080
MODELLA WOOLLENS LIMITED; *Int'l*, pg. 5013
MODELLBAU SCHONHEIDE GMBH—See ALFA, S.A.B. de C.V.; *Int'l*, pg. 313
MODELL'S SPORTING GOODS INC.—See Henry Modell & Company, Inc.; *U.S. Private*, pg. 1919
MODELL TECHNIK GMBH & CO. FORMENBAU KG—See Gesco AG; *Int'l*, pg. 2946
MODELLTEKNIK I ESKILSTUNA AB—See XANO Industri AB; *Int'l*, pg. 8519
MODEL N, INC.; *U.S. Public*, pg. 1454
MODEL N INDIA SOFTWARE PRIVATE LIMITED—See Model N, Inc.; *U.S. Public*, pg. 1454
MODEL N UK LIMITED—See Model N, Inc.; *U.S. Public*, pg. 1454
MODELO CONTINENTE, SGPA, SA—See Efanor Investimentos, SGPS, SA; *Int'l*, pg. 2318
MODEL RESTAURANTS COMPANY PLC; *Int'l*, pg. 5013
MODELS & TOOLS INC.; *U.S. Private*, pg. 2759
MODENA TERMINAL S.R.L.—See BPER BANCA S.p.A; *Int'l*, pg. 1132

MODERN ELECTRIC CO.

MODENA TRADING PTY LTD—See Autosports Group Limited; *Int'l*, pg. 732
MODENFIX ITALIA SRL—See Compagnie de Saint-Gobain SA; *Int'l*, pg. 1724
MODENFLEX HYDRAULICS S.R.L.—See Interpump Group S.p.A.; *Int'l*, pg. 3756
MODERA WEALTH MANAGEMENT, LLC; *U.S. Private*, pg. 2759
MODERNA ALIMENTOS, S.A.—See Seaboard Corporation; *U.S. Public*, pg. 1850
MODERN ACCESS SERVICES SINGAPORE PTE. LTD.—See AusGroup Limited; *Int'l*, pg. 716
MODERNA FORSAKRINGAR LIV AB—See Chesnara Plc; *Int'l*, pg. 1472
MODERNA FORSAKRINGAR SAK AB—See Tryg A/S; *Int'l*, pg. 7946
MODERNA FRANCE—See Moderna, Inc.; *U.S. Public*, pg. 1454
MODERNA GERMANY GMBH—See Moderna, Inc.; *U.S. Public*, pg. 1454
MODERNA HOMES PTE. LTD.—See BBR Holdings (S) Ltd.; *Int'l*, pg. 921
MODERNA, INC.; *U.S. Public*, pg. 1454
MODERNA ITALY S.R.L.—See Moderna, Inc.; *U.S. Public*, pg. 1454
MODERN ALPINE SDN. BHD.—See Hengan International Group Co. Ltd.; *Int'l*, pg. 3346
MODERN AMERICAN RECYCLING SERVICES, INC.; *U.S. Private*, pg. 2759
MODERN ANIMAL & AGRICULTURAL PRODUCTION; *Int'l*, pg. 5013
MODERN ART MUSEUM OF FORT WORTH; *U.S. Private*, pg. 2759
MODERN ASIA ENVIRONMENTAL HOLDINGS PTE. LTD.—See Dowa Holdings Co., Ltd.; *Int'l*, pg. 2184
MODERN AUTOMOBILE COMPANY LIMITED—See Baguio Green Group Limited; *Int'l*, pg. 799
MODERN AUTOMOTIVE PERFORMANCE; *U.S. Private*, pg. 2759
MODERN AVENUE GROUP CO., LTD.; *Int'l*, pg. 5013
MODERN BANK; *U.S. Private*, pg. 2759
MODERNBAU GMBH—See Bilfinger SE; *Int'l*, pg. 1024
MODERN BIOMEDICAL SERVICES, INC.—See Cressey & Company, LP; *U.S. Private*, pg. 1095
MODERN BIOMEDICAL SERVICES, INC.—See Health Enterprise Partners LLC; *U.S. Private*, pg. 1893
MODERN BIOSCIENCES PLC—See IP Group plc; *Int'l*, pg. 3795
MODERN BRIDE GROUP—See IAC Inc.; *U.S. Public*, pg. 1081
MODERN BUILDERS, INC.; *U.S. Private*, pg. 2759
MODERN BUILDERS SUPPLY, INC.—See SiteOne Landscape Supply, Inc.; *U.S. Public*, pg. 1889
MODERN BUSINESS ASSOCIATES, INC.; *U.S. Private*, pg. 2759
MODERN BUSINESS MACHINES, INC.—See Xerox Holdings Corporation; *U.S. Public*, pg. 2389
MODERN CHEMICAL INDUSTRIES CO.; *Int'l*, pg. 5013
MODERN CHEMICALS & SERVICES COMPANY LTD.—See Societe Anonyme d'Explosifs et de Produits Chimiques; *Int'l*, pg. 7035
MODERN CHINESE MEDICINE GROUP COMPANY LIMITED; *Int'l*, pg. 5013
MODERN CLASSIC MOTORS INC.—See Group 1 Automotive, Inc.; *U.S. Public*, pg. 972
MODERN CLIMATE; *U.S. Private*, pg. 2760
MODERN COIN WHOLESALE INC.; *U.S. Private*, pg. 2760
MODERN CONCRETE, INC.; *U.S. Private*, pg. 2760
MODERN CONSTRUCTION INC.; *U.S. Private*, pg. 2760
MODERN CONSTRUCTION MATERIALS INDUSTRY CO.; *Int'l*, pg. 5013
MODERN CORPORATION; *U.S. Private*, pg. 2760
MODERN COTTON YARN SPINNERS LTD—See Bengal & Assam Company Ltd.; *Int'l*, pg. 973
MODERN CUSTOM FABRICATION, INC.—See Modern Welding Company, Inc.; *U.S. Private*, pg. 2762
MODERN DAIRIES LTD.; *Int'l*, pg. 5013
MODERN DAR AL SHIFA PHARMACY LLC—See Aster DM Healthcare Ltd.; *Int'l*, pg. 654
MODERN DENIM LTD.; *Int'l*, pg. 5013
MODERN DENTAL GROUP LIMITED; *Int'l*, pg. 5013
MODERN DEVELOPMENT COMPANY; *U.S. Private*, pg. 2760
MODERN DISPERSIONS, INC.; *U.S. Private*, pg. 2760
MODERN DISPERSIONS SOUTH, INC.—See Modern Dispersions, Inc.; *U.S. Private*, pg. 2760
MODERN DISTRIBUTORS INC.; *U.S. Private*, pg. 2760
MODERN DOOR & EQUIPMENT SALES INC.; *U.S. Private*, pg. 2760
MODERN DROP FORGE CO.; *U.S. Private*, pg. 2760
MODERNE COMMUNICATIONS INC.; *U.S. Private*, pg. 2763
MODERN EKONOMI SVERIGE AB—See TowerBrook Capital Partners, L.P.; *U.S. Private*, pg. 4195
MODERN EKONOMI SVERIGE HOLDING AB; *Int'l*, pg. 5013
MODERN ELECTRIC CO.; *U.S. Private*, pg. 2760

MODERN ELECTRIC CO. CORPORATE AFFILIATIONS

MODERN ELECTRONICS COMPANY LTD.—See Al Faisaliah Group; *Int'l*, pg. 277
MODERN ELECTRONICS ESTABLISHMENT (MEE)—See Al Faisaliah Group; *Int'l*, pg. 277
MODERN ENGINEERING AND PROJECTS LIMITED; *Int'l*, pg. 5013
MODERN ENTERPRISE SOLUTIONS INC.; *U.S. Private*, pg. 2760
MODERN ENTERTAINMENT LTD—See Modern Times Group MTG AB; *Int'l*, pg. 5015
MODERN EQUIPMENT COMPANY, LLC—See Dunes Point Capital, LLC; *U.S. Private*, pg. 1288
MODERN EQUIPMENT SALES & RENTAL CO. - KING OF PRUSSIA—See Modern Group Ltd.; *U.S. Private*, pg. 2760
MODERN EQUIPMENT SALES & RENTAL CO.—See Modern Group Ltd.; *U.S. Private*, pg. 2760
MODERN EQUIPMENT SALES & RENTAL CO. - WILMINGTON—See Modern Group Ltd.; *U.S. Private*, pg. 2760
MODERN EVERYDAY, INC.—See Live Ventures Incorporated; *U.S. Public*, pg. 1332
MODERN EXPLORATION INC.; *U.S. Private*, pg. 2760
MODERN FABRICATING INC.—See Modern Ice Equipment & Supply Co.; *U.S. Private*, pg. 2761
MODERN FARM EQUIPMENT CORP.; *U.S. Private*, pg. 2760
MODERNFOLD, INC.—See dormakaba Holding AG; *Int'l*, pg. 2179
MODERNFOLD OF NEVADA, LLC—See dormakaba Holding AG; *Int'l*, pg. 2179
MODERNFOLD/STYLES INC.; *U.S. Private*, pg. 2763
MODERN FOODS LLC; *U.S. Private*, pg. 2760
MODERN FORGE/TENNESSEE—See Modern Drop Forge Co.; *U.S. Private*, pg. 2760
MODERNFORM INTEGRATION SERVICES COMPANY LIMITED—See MFEC Public Company Limited; *Int'l*, pg. 4870
MODERNFORM PUBLIC COMPANY LIMITED - PRODUCTION 1 PLANT—See MODERNFORM PUBLIC COMPANY LIMITED; *Int'l*, pg. 5015
MODERNFORM PUBLIC COMPANY LIMITED - PRODUCTION 2A PLANT—See MODERNFORM PUBLIC COMPANY LIMITED; *Int'l*, pg. 5015
MODERNFORM PUBLIC COMPANY LIMITED - PRODUCTION 2B PLANT—See MODERNFORM PUBLIC COMPANY LIMITED; *Int'l*, pg. 5015
MODERNFORM PUBLIC COMPANY LIMITED; *Int'l*, pg. 5015
MODERN GAS SALES INC; *U.S. Private*, pg. 2760
MODERN GROUP, LTD.; *U.S. Private*, pg. 2761
MODERN GROUP LTD.; *U.S. Private*, pg. 2760
MODERN HANDLING EQUIPMENT COMPANY—See Modern Group Ltd.; *U.S. Private*, pg. 2760
MODERN HANDLING EQUIPMENT OF N.J., INC.—See Modern Group Ltd.; *U.S. Private*, pg. 2761
MODERN HEALTHCARE TECHNOLOGY HOLDINGS LIMITED; *Int'l*, pg. 5013
MODERN HOLDINGS INCORPORATED; *U.S. Private*, pg. 2761
MODERN ICE EQUIPMENT & SUPPLY CO.; *U.S. Private*, pg. 2761
MODERN INDIA LTD; *Int'l*, pg. 5013
MODERN INDIA PROPERTY DEVELOPERS LTD.—See Modern India Ltd; *Int'l*, pg. 5013
MODERN INDUSTRIES COMPANY—See The Procter & Gamble Company; *U.S. Public*, pg. 2120
MODERN INDUSTRIES INC., HEAT TREAT DIVISION—See Modern Industries Inc.; *U.S. Private*, pg. 2761
MODERN INDUSTRIES INC. - KERSEY PLANT—See Modern Industries Inc.; *U.S. Private*, pg. 2761
MODERN INDUSTRIES, INC.; *U.S. Private*, pg. 2761
MODERN INDUSTRIES, INC.; *U.S. Private*, pg. 2761
MODERN INSULATORS LTD.; *Int'l*, pg. 5013
MODERN INSURANCE MARKETING, INC.—See Integrity Marketing Group LLC; *U.S. Private*, pg. 2103
MODERNISTA!; *U.S. Private*, pg. 2763
MODERNISTA!—See Modernista!; *U.S. Private*, pg. 2763
MODERNISTIC INC.; *U.S. Private*, pg. 2763
MODERNIZE, INC.—See QuinStreet, Inc.; *U.S. Public*, pg. 1757
MODERNIZING MEDICINE, INC.; *U.S. Private*, pg. 2763
MODERN LAND (CHINA) CO., LTD.; *Int'l*, pg. 5013
MODERN LANDFILL INC.—See Modern Corporation; *U.S. Private*, pg. 2760
MODERN LANGUAGE ASSOCIATION; *U.S. Private*, pg. 2761
MODERN LITHO-KANSAS CITY—See Modern Litho-Print Co.; *U.S. Private*, pg. 2761
MODERN LITHO-PRINT CO.; *U.S. Private*, pg. 2761
MODERN LITHO - ST LOUIS—See Modern Litho-Print Co.; *U.S. Private*, pg. 2761
MODERN LIVING INVESTMENTS HOLDINGS LIMITED—See Asia Allied Infrastructure Holdings Limited; *Int'l*, pg. 610
MODERN LUXURY MEDIA, LLC—See Clarity Partners, L.P.; *U.S. Private*, pg. 912

MODERN MACHINERY COMPANY—See Capital Machine Technologies, Inc.; *U.S. Private*, pg. 741
MODERN MACHINERY CO.—See Washington Corporations; *U.S. Private*, pg. 4446
MODERN MACHINERY INC—See Wajax Corporation; *Int'l*, pg. 8331
MODERN MALLEABLES LIMITED; *Int'l*, pg. 5014
MODERN MARKETING PARTNERS; *U.S. Private*, pg. 2761
MODERN MARKET MASTER INC.; *U.S. Private*, pg. 2761
MODERN MASS MEDIA INC.; *U.S. Private*, pg. 2761
MODERN MASTERS INC.—See RPM International Inc.; *U.S. Public*, pg. 1817
MODERN MEDIA ACQUISITION CORP.; *U.S. Public*, pg. 1454
MODERN MEDIA SYSTEMS—See Al Faisaliah Group; *Int'l*, pg. 277
MODERN MEDICAL GROUP PTY LTD—See Adamantem Capital Management Pty Limited; *Int'l*, pg. 124
MODERN MEDICAL GROUP PTY LTD—See Liverpool Partners Pty Ltd; *Int'l*, pg. 4530
MODERN MESSAGE, INC.—See Thoma Bravo, L.P.; *U.S. Private*, pg. 4153
MODERN MOBILITY AIDS, INC.; *Int'l*, pg. 5014
MODERN MUSHROOM FARMS, INC.; *U.S. Private*, pg. 2761
MODERN MUSHROOM SALES—See Modern Mushroom Farms, Inc.; *U.S. Private*, pg. 2761
MODERN NISSAN OF CONCORD, INC.; *U.S. Private*, pg. 2761
MODERN OFFICE METHODS INC.; *U.S. Private*, pg. 2761
MODERN OIL COMPANY INC.; *U.S. Private*, pg. 2762
MODERN PACKAGING, INC.—See Leonard Green & Partners, L.P.; *U.S. Private*, pg. 2428
MODERN PAINTS INDUSTRIES CO.; *Int'l*, pg. 5014
MODERN PARKING INC.; *U.S. Private*, pg. 2762
MODERN PHARMACEUTICAL COMPANY LLC; *Int'l*, pg. 5014
MODERN PLASTICS INC.—See Blackfriars Corp.; *U.S. Private*, pg. 575
MODERN POLY INDUSTRIES LTD.—See BSM Group Limited; *Int'l*, pg. 1202
MODERN POULTRY FARMS CO. SAOC—See Oman Flour Mills Co SAOG; *Int'l*, pg. 5559
MODERN POURED WALLS INC.; *U.S. Private*, pg. 2762
MODERN PRECAST CONCRETE; *U.S. Private*, pg. 2762
MODERN PRODUCTS COMPANY - JEDDAH—See The Procter & Gamble Company; *U.S. Public*, pg. 2120
MODERN PRODUCTS, INC.; *U.S. Private*, pg. 2762
MODERN PROTECTION & INVESTIGATIONS LTD.—See Sicagen India Ltd; *Int'l*, pg. 6877
MODERN PUBLISHING, INC.—See Kappa Publishing Group, Inc.; *U.S. Private*, pg. 2262
MODERN ROBOTICS INC.—See Boxlight Corporation; *U.S. Public*, pg. 377
MODERN ROUND ENTERTAINMENT CORPORATION—See Trutankless Inc.; *U.S. Public*, pg. 2202
MODERN SEWING CO.; *Int'l*, pg. 5014
MODERN SHARES & STOCK BROKERS LTD.; *Int'l*, pg. 5014
MODERN SOFTWARE TECHNOLOGIES LTD.—See Malam Systems Ltd.; *Int'l*, pg. 4659
MODERN STANDARD CO., LTD.—See GAtechnologies Co., Ltd.; *Int'l*, pg. 2889
MODERN STEELS LIMITED; *Int'l*, pg. 5014
MODERN SUPPLY CO., INC.—See Modern Welding Company, Inc.; *U.S. Private*, pg. 2762
MODERN SUPPLY CO., INC.—See Modern Welding Company, Inc.; *U.S. Private*, pg. 2762
MODERN SUPPLY CO., INC.—See Modern Welding Company, Inc.; *U.S. Private*, pg. 2762
MODERN SUPPLY CO., INC.—See Modern Welding Company, Inc.; *U.S. Private*, pg. 2762
MODERN SUPPLY CO., INC.—See Modern Welding Company, Inc.; *U.S. Private*, pg. 2762
MODERN SUPPLY CO., INC.—See Modern Welding Company, Inc.; *U.S. Private*, pg. 2762
MODERN SUPPLY COMPANY INC.; *U.S. Private*, pg. 2762
MODERN SURVEY, INC.—See Alight, Inc.; *U.S. Public*, pg. 76
MODERN SYNTEX (INDIA) LTD.; *Int'l*, pg. 5014
MODERN TECHNOLOGY SOLUTIONS, INC.; *U.S. Private*, pg. 2762
MODERN TERMINALS LIMITED—See Wheelock & Company Limited; *Int'l*, pg. 8397
MODERN TESTING SERVICES (DONGGUAN) CO., LTD.—See Eurofins Scientific S.E.; *Int'l*, pg. 2551
MODERN TESTING SERVICES (HONG KONG) CO., LTD.—See Eurofins Scientific S.E.; *Int'l*, pg. 2551
MODERN TESTING SERVICES (INDIA) PRIVATE LIMITED—See Eurofins Scientific S.E.; *Int'l*, pg. 2551
MODERN TESTING SERVICES LANKA PRIVATE LIMITED—See Eurofins Scientific S.E.; *Int'l*, pg. 2551
MODERN TESTING SERVICES (VIETNAM) CO., LTD.—See Eurofins Scientific S.E.; *Int'l*, pg. 2551
MODERN THREADS (INDIA) LTD.; *Int'l*, pg. 5014
MODERN TIMES GROUP MTG AB; *Int'l*, pg. 5014

MODERN TIMES GROUP—See Modern Times Group MTG AB; *Int'l*, pg. 5015
MODERN TOYOTA OF BOONE INC.; *U.S. Private*, pg. 2762
MODERN TOYOTA; *U.S. Private*, pg. 2762
MODERN TRACK MACHINERY, LTD.—See Geismar S.A.; *Int'l*, pg. 2912
MODERN TRACK MACHINERY—See Geismar S.A.; *Int'l*, pg. 2912
MODERN TRADE MANAGEMENT CO., LTD.—See Thai Beverage Public Company Limited; *Int'l*, pg. 7591
MODERN TRADING & SERVICES SARL—See BERICAP GmbH & Co. KG; *Int'l*, pg. 981
MODERN TRANSPORTATION SERVICES INC.; *U.S. Private*, pg. 2762
MODERN VIDEOFILM, INC.—See Point.360; *U.S. Public*, pg. 1700
MODERN WATER INC.—See Deepverge PLC; *Int'l*, pg. 2003
MODERN WATER MONITORING LIMITED—See Deepverge PLC; *Int'l*, pg. 2003
MODERN WATER PLC—See Deepverge PLC; *Int'l*, pg. 2003
MODERN WATER TECHNOLOGY (SHANGHAI) CO., LTD.—See Deepverge PLC; *Int'l*, pg. 2003
MODERN WEALTH MANAGEMENT, LLC—See Crestview Partners, L.P.; *U.S. Private*, pg. 1098
MODERN WELDING COMPANY, INC.; *U.S. Private*, pg. 2762
MODERN WELDING COMPANY, INC.—See Modern Welding Company, Inc.; *U.S. Private*, pg. 2763
MODERN WELDING COMPANY OF CALIFORNIA, INC.—See Modern Welding Company, Inc.; *U.S. Private*, pg. 2762
MODERN WELDING COMPANY OF FLORIDA, INC.—See Modern Welding Company, Inc.; *U.S. Private*, pg. 2762
MODERN WELDING COMPANY OF GEORGIA, INC.—See Modern Welding Company, Inc.; *U.S. Private*, pg. 2762
MODERN WELDING COMPANY OF KENTUCKY, INC.—See Modern Welding Company, Inc.; *U.S. Private*, pg. 2762
MODERN WELDING COMPANY OF KENTUCKY, INC.—See Modern Welding Company, Inc.; *U.S. Private*, pg. 2762
MODERN WELDING COMPANY OF OHIO, INC.—See Modern Welding Company, Inc.; *U.S. Private*, pg. 2762
MODERN WELDING COMPANY OF OWENSBORO, INC.—See Modern Welding Company, Inc.; *U.S. Private*, pg. 2762
MODERN WELDING COMPANY OF TEXAS, INC.—See Modern Welding Company, Inc.; *U.S. Private*, pg. 2763
MODERN WELDING COMPANY OF TEXAS, INC.—See Modern Welding Company, Inc.; *U.S. Private*, pg. 2763
MODERN WOMAN, INC.—See Mahwah Bergen Retail Group, Inc.; *U.S. Private*, pg. 2550
MODERN WOODCRAFTS LLC; *U.S. Private*, pg. 2763
MODERN WOODMEN OF AMERICA; *U.S. Private*, pg. 2763
MODEST INFRASTRUCTURE PVT. LTD.—See Goa Carbon Ltd.; *Int'l*, pg. 3018
THE MODESTO BEE—See Chatham Asset Management, LLC; *U.S. Private*, pg. 867
MODESTO IRRIGATION DISTRICT INC.; *U.S. Private*, pg. 2763
MODESTO MOTOR CARS INC.; *U.S. Private*, pg. 2763
MODESTO ON-CALL SERVICES, L.L.C.—See Tenet Healthcare Corporation; *U.S. Public*, pg. 2003
MODESTO RADIOLOGY IMAGING, INC.—See Tenet Healthcare Corporation; *U.S. Public*, pg. 2003
MODESTO STEEL CO INC.; *U.S. Private*, pg. 2763
MODETOUR INTERNATIONAL INC.—See MODETOUR Network Inc.; *Int'l*, pg. 5016
MODETOUR NETWORK INC.; *Int'l*, pg. 5015
MODE TOUR REAL ESTATE INVESTMENT TRUST INC.—See MODETOUR Network Inc.; *Int'l*, pg. 5015
MODEX INTERNATIONAL SECURITIES LTD.; *Int'l*, pg. 5016
MODFIN SYSTEMS PTY LTD—See HgCapital Trust plc; *Int'l*, pg. 3377
MODI AIRCRETE PRIVATE LIMITED—See Digilife Technologies Limited; *Int'l*, pg. 2119
MODIFIED CONCRETE SUPPLIERS INC.—See Hughes Group, Inc.; *U.S. Private*, pg. 2003
MODIGENT LLC; *U.S. Private*, pg. 2763
MODI INDONESIA 2020 PTE. LTD.—See Digilife Technologies Limited; *Int'l*, pg. 2119
MODIIN ENERGY LIMITED PARTNERSHIP; *Int'l*, pg. 5016
MODI NATURALS LIMITED; *Int'l*, pg. 5016
MODINE AUTOMOBILTECHNIK GMBH—See Modine Manufacturing Company; *U.S. Public*, pg. 1455
MODINE CIS ITALY SRL—See Modine Manufacturing Company; *U.S. Public*, pg. 1455
MODINEER COMPANY INC.; *U.S. Private*, pg. 2763
MODINE EUROPE GMBH—See Modine Manufacturing Company; *U.S. Public*, pg. 1455
MODINE HOLDING GMBH—See Modine Manufacturing Company; *U.S. Public*, pg. 1455

COMPANY NAME INDEX

MODINE HUNGARIA KFT.—See Modine Manufacturing Company; *U.S. Public*, pg. 1455
MODINE, INC.—See Modine Manufacturing Company; *U.S. Public*, pg. 1455
MODINE JACKSONVILLE INC.—See Modine Manufacturing Company; *U.S. Public*, pg. 1455
MODINE KOREA, LLC—See KB Synthetics Co., Ltd.; *Int'l*, pg. 4104
MODINE MANUFACTURING COMPANY; *U.S. Public*, pg. 1454
MODINE NEUENKIRCHEN GMBH—See Modine Manufacturing Company; *U.S. Public*, pg. 1455
MODINE PLIEZHAUSEN GMBH—See Modine Manufacturing Company; *U.S. Public*, pg. 1455
MODINE PONTEVICO S.R.L.—See Modine Manufacturing Company; *U.S. Public*, pg. 1455
MODINE SODERKOPING AB—See Modine Manufacturing Company; *U.S. Public*, pg. 1455
MODINE TRANSFERENCIA DE CALOR, S.A. DE C.V.—See Modine Manufacturing Company; *U.S. Public*, pg. 1455
MODINE UDEN B.V.—See Modine Manufacturing Company; *U.S. Public*, pg. 1455
MODIOTEK CO., LTD.—See Macronix International Co., Ltd.; *Int'l*, pg. 4632
MODIPON LIMITED; *Int'l*, pg. 5016
MODI RUBBER LIMITED; *Int'l*, pg. 5016
MODIS AMSTERDAM—See Adecco Group AG; *Int'l*, pg. 140
MODIS BULGARIA EOOD—See Adecco Group AG; *Int'l*, pg. 141
MODIS CANADA INC.—See Adecco Group AG; *Int'l*, pg. 140
MODIS GMBH—See Adecco Group AG; *Int'l*, pg. 141
MODIS, INC.-NATIONAL ENTERPRISE PRACTICE—See Adecco Group AG; *Int'l*, pg. 140
MODIS, INC.—See Adecco Group AG; *Int'l*, pg. 140
MODIS INTERNATIONAL-BRUSSELS—See Adecco Group AG; *Int'l*, pg. 140
MODIS INTERNATIONAL CO.—See Adecco Group AG; *Int'l*, pg. 140
MODIS INTERNATIONAL LIMITED—See Adecco Group AG; *Int'l*, pg. 140
MODIS LONDON—See Adecco Group AG; *Int'l*, pg. 140
MODI'S NAVNIRMAAN LIMITED; *Int'l*, pg. 5016
MODISON METALS LTD.; *Int'l*, pg. 5016
MODIS POLSKA SP.Z.O.O—See Adecco Group AG; *Int'l*, pg. 140
MODIS—See Adecco Group AG; *Int'l*, pg. 136
MODIS THERAPEUTICS, INC.—See UCB S.A.; *Int'l*, pg. 8012
MODIUM KONFEKSIYON SANAYI VE TICARET ANONIM SIRKETI—See Li & Fung Limited; *Int'l*, pg. 4480
MODIVCARE, INC.; *U.S. Public*, pg. 1455
MODIV INDUSTRIAL, INC.; *U.S. Public*, pg. 1455
MOD.LIVING PTE. LTD.—See TT International Limited; *Int'l*, pg. 7960
MOD MEDIA LLC; *U.S. Private*, pg. 2759
MODO MERCHANTS—See Metsaliitto Osuuskunta; *Int'l*, pg. 4864
MODO PAPER SA—See Metsaliitto Osuuskunta; *Int'l*, pg. 4864
MODOP, LLC; *U.S. Private*, pg. 2763
MODO VAN GELDER—See Metsaliitto Osuuskunta; *Int'l*, pg. 4864
MOD-PAC CORP.; *U.S. Private*, pg. 2759
MODRA PYRAMIDA STAVEBNI SPORITELNA AS—See Societe Generale S.A.; *Int'l*, pg. 7040
MOD RESOURCES LIMITED—See Sandfire Resources Limited; *Int'l*, pg. 6525
MODRICA MPI A.D.; *Int'l*, pg. 5016
MODS GRAPHIC STUDIO AB—See Nordic Morning Plc; *Int'l*, pg. 5422
MOD SUPER FAST PIZZA, LLC; *U.S. Private*, pg. 2759
MODSYS INTERNATIONAL LTD.—See Advanced Business Software & Solutions Ltd.; *Int'l*, pg. 157
MODUFORM, INC.; *U.S. Private*, pg. 2763
MODULAIRE GROUP—See Brookfield Corporation; *Int'l*, pg. 1176
MODULAR AUTOMATION IRELAND LTD.—See Ares Management Corporation; *U.S. Public*, pg. 190
MODULAR DOCUMENT SOLUTIONS, LLC—See Sycamore Partners Management, LP; *U.S. Private*, pg. 3896
MODULAR LIGHTING INSTRUMENTS NV—See Signify N.V.; *Int'l*, pg. 6912
MODULAR LIGHTING NEDERLAND B.V.—See Signify N.V.; *Int'l*, pg. 6912
MODULAR LIGHTING PARIS—See Signify N.V.; *Int'l*, pg. 6912
MODULAR MANUFACTURING HOLDINGS; *U.S. Private*, pg. 2763
MODULAR MEDICAL, INC.; *U.S. Public*, pg. 1456
MODULAR MINING SYSTEM AFRICA, PTY. LTD.—See Komatsu Ltd.; *Int'l*, pg. 4238
MODULAR MINING SYSTEMS CANADA, LTD.—See Komatsu Ltd.; *Int'l*, pg. 4238
MODULAR MINING SYSTEMS CHINA—See Komatsu Ltd.; *Int'l*, pg. 4238

MODULAR MINING SYSTEMS DO BRASIL LTDA—See Komatsu Ltd.; *Int'l*, pg. 4239
MODULAR MINING SYSTEMS EURASIA—See Komatsu Ltd.; *Int'l*, pg. 4238
MODULAR MINING SYSTEMS, INC.—See Komatsu Ltd.; *Int'l*, pg. 4238
MODULAR MINING SYSTEMS, INC. Y CIA LTDA—See Komatsu Ltd.; *Int'l*, pg. 4239
MODULAR MINING SYSTEMS INDIA PVT. LTD.—See Komatsu Ltd.; *Int'l*, pg. 4239
MODULAR MINING SYSTEMS PTY. LTD.—See Komatsu Ltd.; *Int'l*, pg. 4239
MODULAR MINING SYSTEMS SCRL—See Komatsu Ltd.; *Int'l*, pg. 4239
MODULAR SOFTWARE EXPERTISE CO., LTD.—See Thonburi Healthcare Group PCL; *Int'l*, pg. 7716
MODULAR TECHNOLOGIES INC.; *U.S. Private*, pg. 2763
MODULAR TECHNOLOGY LLC—See Frontenac Company LLC; *U.S. Private*, pg. 1614
MODULAR THERMAL TECHNOLOGIES, LLC; *U.S. Private*, pg. 2763
MODULAR TRAINING PTY LTD.—See Aquirian Limited; *Int'l*, pg. 528
MODULAR WOOD SYSTEMS INC.—See Panel Processing, Inc.; *U.S. Private*, pg. 3086
MODULAT INC.; *Int'l*, pg. 5016
MODULEMD LLC; *U.S. Private*, pg. 2764
MODULEO GMBH—See Mohawk Industries, Inc.; *U.S. Public*, pg. 1458
MODULEX CONSTRUCTION TECHNOLOGIES LIMITED—See Red Ribbon Asset Management PLC; *Int'l*, pg. 6245
MODULEX MODULAR BUILDINGS PLC—See Red Ribbon Asset Management PLC; *Int'l*, pg. 6245
MODULI ELETTRONICI E COMPONENTI S.P.A.—See Arlitech Electronic Corp.; *Int'l*, pg. 573
MODULIGHT CORPORATION; *Int'l*, pg. 5016
MODULINE INDUSTRIES (CANADA) LTD.—See Champion Homes, Inc.; *U.S. Public*, pg. 477
MODUL MARBLE & GRANITE—See Architectural Surfaces Group, LLC; *U.S. Private*, pg. 311
MODUL PLASTIC OY—See Indutrade AB; *Int'l*, pg. 3680
MODUL SYSTEME ENGINEERING GMBH—See ANDRITZ AG; *Int'l*, pg. 456
MODULYSS NV—See Balta Group NV; *Int'l*, pg. 812
MODUS CONSULT AG—See Bechtle AG; *Int'l*, pg. 938
MODUS CONSULT GMBH—See Bechtle AG; *Int'l*, pg. 938
MODUS CREATE, LLC; *U.S. Private*, pg. 2764
MODUS EDISCOVERY, INC.—See JLL Partners, LLC; *U.S. Private*, pg. 2213
MODUS GAMES LLC—See Maximum Entertainment AB; *Int'l*, pg. 4737
MODUSLINK AUSTRALIA PTY LIMITED—See Steel Connect, Inc.; *U.S. Public*, pg. 1941
MODUSLINK B.V.—See Steel Connect, Inc.; *U.S. Public*, pg. 1941
MODUSLINK CORP.—See Steel Connect, Inc.; *U.S. Public*, pg. 1941
MODUSLINK DE MEXICO, S.R.L. DE C.V.—See Steel Connect, Inc.; *U.S. Public*, pg. 1941
MODUSLINK INTERNATIONAL B.V. APELDOORN SOLUTION CENTER—See Steel Connect, Inc.; *U.S. Public*, pg. 1941
MODUSLINK INTERNATIONAL B.V.—See Steel Connect, Inc.; *U.S. Public*, pg. 1941
MODUSLINK INTERNATIONAL—See Steel Connect, Inc.; *U.S. Public*, pg. 1941
MODUSLINK KILDARE—See Steel Connect, Inc.; *U.S. Public*, pg. 1941
MODUSLINK PTS, INC.—See Steel Connect, Inc.; *U.S. Public*, pg. 1941
MODUSLINK RECOVERY LLC—See Steel Connect, Inc.; *U.S. Public*, pg. 1941
MODUSLINK SECURITIES CORPORATION—See Steel Connect, Inc.; *U.S. Public*, pg. 1941
MODUSLINK SERVICES EUROPE—See Steel Connect, Inc.; *U.S. Public*, pg. 1941
MODUSLINK (SHANGHAI) CO. LTD.—See Steel Connect, Inc.; *U.S. Public*, pg. 1941
MODUSLINK SOLUTIONS SERVICE PTE. LTD.—See Steel Connect, Inc.; *U.S. Public*, pg. 1942
MODUS MEDICAL DEVICES INC.—See Ion Beam Applications, S.A.; *Int'l*, pg. 3793
MODUS OPERANDI PARTNERS, LLC; *U.S. Private*, pg. 2764
MODUS SELECTIVE INVESTMENT MANAGEMENT & ADVICE LTD.—See FIBI Holdings Ltd.; *Int'l*, pg. 2652
MODUS THERAPEUTICS AB; *Int'l*, pg. 5016
MODWOOD TECHNOLOGIES PTY LTD—See Wesfarmers Limited; *Int'l*, pg. 8381
MODYF S.R.L.—See Wurth Verwaltungsgesellschaft mbH; *Int'l*, pg. 8513
MODY INDUSTRIES (F.C) PRIVATE LIMITED—See WPIL Limited; *Int'l*, pg. 8462
MOEBEL.DE EINRICHTEN & WOHNEN AG—See ProSiebenSat.1 Media SE; *Int'l*, pg. 6001
MOECO SOUTHWEST VIETNAM PETROLEUM CO., LTD.—See Mitsui & Co., Ltd.; *Int'l*, pg. 4979
MOEHL MILLWORK INC.; *U.S. Private*, pg. 2764

MOELVEN INDUSTRIER ASA

MOEHN ART CHEVROLET CO.; *U.S. Private*, pg. 2764
MOEHS IBERICA, S.L.—See PMC Capital Partners, LLC; *U.S. Private*, pg. 3217
MOEHWALD GMBH—See Robert Bosch GmbH; *Int'l*, pg. 6361
MOEL AB—See Rexel, S.A.; *Int'l*, pg. 6316
MOELIS ASSET MANAGEMENT LP; *U.S. Private*, pg. 2764
MOELIS AUSTRALIA ASSET MANAGEMENT LTD—See Moelis & Company; *U.S. Public*, pg. 1456
MOELIS CAPITAL PARTNERS LLC—See Moelis Asset Management LP; *U.S. Private*, pg. 2764
MOELIS & COMPANY ASIA LIMITED—See Moelis & Company; *U.S. Public*, pg. 1456
MOELIS & COMPANY CONSULTING (BEIJING) COMPANY LIMITED—See Moelis & Company; *U.S. Public*, pg. 1456
MOELIS & COMPANY EUROPE LIMITED—See Moelis & Company; *U.S. Public*, pg. 1456
MOELIS & COMPANY FRANCE SAS—See Moelis & Company; *U.S. Public*, pg. 1456
MOELIS & COMPANY GERMANY GMBH—See Moelis & Company; *U.S. Public*, pg. 1456
MOELIS & COMPANY INDIA PRIVATE LIMITED—See Moelis & Company; *U.S. Public*, pg. 1456
MOELIS & COMPANY LLC—See Moelis Asset Management LP; *U.S. Private*, pg. 2764
MOELIS & COMPANY NETHERLANDS BV—See Moelis & Company; *U.S. Public*, pg. 1456
MOELIS & COMPANY; *U.S. Public*, pg. 1456
MOELIS & COMPANY UK LLP—See Moelis & Company; *U.S. Public*, pg. 1456
MOELIS & COMPANY UK LLP—See Moelis & Company; *U.S. Public*, pg. 1456
MOELIS & COMPANY UK LLP—See Moelis & Company; *U.S. Public*, pg. 1456
MOELIS & COMPANY UK LLP—See Moelis & Company; *U.S. Public*, pg. 1456
MOELIS & COMPANY UK LLP—See Moelis Asset Management LP; *U.S. Private*, pg. 2764
MOELIS UK LLP—See Moelis & Company; *U.S. Public*, pg. 1456
MOELLER & DEVICON A/S—See Robert Bosch GmbH; *Int'l*, pg. 6361
MOELLER ELECTRIC NV/SA—See Eaton Corporation plc; *Int'l*, pg. 2281
MOELLERING INDUSTRIES CO. INC.; *U.S. Private*, pg. 2764
MOELLER MANUFACTURING & SUPPLY, INC.—See Tinicum Enterprises, Inc.; *U.S. Private*, pg. 4174
MOELLER MARINE PRODUCTS, INC.—See Dometic Group AB; *Int'l*, pg. 2160
MOELLER MFG. COMPANY, LLC.—See AE Industrial Partners, LP; *U.S. Private*, pg. 112
MOELVEN ARE AS—See Moelven Industrier ASA; *Int'l*, pg. 5016
MOELVEN ARJANG SAG AB—See Moelven Industrier ASA; *Int'l*, pg. 5017
MOELVEN ARJANGS SAG AB—See Moelven Industrier ASA; *Int'l*, pg. 5016
MOELVEN BIOENERGI AS—See Moelven Industrier ASA; *Int'l*, pg. 5016
MOELVEN BYGGMODUL AB—See Moelven Industrier ASA; *Int'l*, pg. 5016
MOELVEN BYGGMODUL AB—See Moelven Industrier ASA; *Int'l*, pg. 5016
MOELVEN COMPONENT AB—See Moelven Industrier ASA; *Int'l*, pg. 5016
MOELVEN DALATRA AB—See Moelven Industrier ASA; *Int'l*, pg. 5016
MOELVEN DANMARK A/S—See Moelven Industrier ASA; *Int'l*, pg. 5016
MOELVEN DEUTSCHLAND GMBH—See Moelven Industrier ASA; *Int'l*, pg. 5016
MOELVEN EDANESAGEN AB—See Moelven Industrier ASA; *Int'l*, pg. 5016
MOELVEN EIDSVOLL AS—See Moelven Industrier ASA; *Int'l*, pg. 5016
MOELVEN EIDSVOLL VAERK AS—See Moelven Industrier ASA; *Int'l*, pg. 5017
MOELVEN INDUSTRIER ASA; *Int'l*, pg. 5016
MOELVEN LANGMOEN AS—See Moelven Industrier ASA; *Int'l*, pg. 5016
MOELVEN LIMTRE AS—See Moelven Industrier ASA; *Int'l*, pg. 5016
MOELVEN LIST AB—See Moelven Industrier ASA; *Int'l*, pg. 5016
MOELVEN LOTEN AS—See Moelven Industrier ASA; *Int'l*, pg. 5017
MOELVEN MJOSBRUKET AS—See Moelven Industrier ASA; *Int'l*, pg. 5017
MOELVEN MODUS AS—See Moelven Industrier ASA; *Int'l*, pg. 5016
MOELVEN NOTNAS AB—See Moelven Industrier ASA; *Int'l*, pg. 5017
MOELVEN NOTNAS RANSBY AB—See Moelven Industrier ASA; *Int'l*, pg. 5017
MOELVEN NOTNAS WOOD AB—See Moelven Industrier ASA; *Int'l*, pg. 5017

MOELVEN INDUSTRIER ASA

MOELVEN NUMEDAL AS—See Moelven Industrier ASA; *Int'l*, pg. 5017
MOELVEN OSTERDALSBRUKET AS—See Moelven Industrier ASA; *Int'l*, pg. 5017
MOELVEN PELLETS AS—See Moelven Industrier ASA; *Int'l*, pg. 5017
MOELVEN RANSBYSAGEN AB—See Moelven Industrier ASA; *Int'l*, pg. 5017
MOELVEN SKOG AB—See Moelven Industrier ASA; *Int'l*, pg. 5017
MOELVEN SOKNABRUKET AS—See Moelven Industrier ASA; *Int'l*, pg. 5017
MOELVEN TELEMARKSBRUKET AS—See Moelven Industrier ASA; *Int'l*, pg. 5017
MOELVEN TIMBER AS—See Moelven Industrier ASA; *Int'l*, pg. 5017
MOELVEN TOREBODA AB—See Moelven Industrier ASA; *Int'l*, pg. 5017
MOELVEN TREINTERIOR AS—See Moelven Industrier ASA; *Int'l*, pg. 5017
MOELVEN TRYSIL AS—See Moelven Industrier ASA; *Int'l*, pg. 5017
MOELVEN VALASEN AB—See Moelven Industrier ASA; *Int'l*, pg. 5017
MOELVEN VALASEN WOOD AB—See Moelven Industrier ASA; *Int'l*, pg. 5017
MOELVEN VALER AS—See Moelven Industrier ASA; *Int'l*, pg. 5017
MOELVEN VAN SEVEREN AS—See Moelven Industrier ASA; *Int'l*, pg. 5017
MOELVEN VARMLANDS TRA AB—See Moelven Industrier ASA; *Int'l*, pg. 5017
MOELVEN VIRKE AS—See Moelven Industrier ASA; *Int'l*, pg. 5017
MOELVEN WOOD AB—See Moelven Industrier ASA; *Int'l*, pg. 5017
MOELVEN WOOD AS—See Moelven Industrier ASA; *Int'l*, pg. 5017
MOEN CHINA, LIMITED—See Fortune Brands Innovations, Inc.; *U.S. Public*, pg. 873
M.O. ENGINEERING CO., LTD.—See Mitsui O.S.K. Lines, Ltd.; *Int'l*, pg. 4989
MOEN GUANGZHOU FAUCET CO., LTD.—See Fortune Brands Innovations, Inc.; *U.S. Public*, pg. 873
MOEN INCORPORATED—See Fortune Brands Innovations, Inc.; *U.S. Public*, pg. 873
MOEN INC.—See Fortune Brands Innovations, Inc.; *U.S. Public*, pg. 873
MOENNICH GMBH—See Suddeutsche Zuckerruben-Verwertungs-Genossenschaft eG; *Int'l*, pg. 7252
MOEN (SHANGHAI) KITCHEN & BATH PRODUCTS CO., LTD.—See Fortune Brands Innovations, Inc.; *U.S. Public*, pg. 873
MOE'S SOUTHWEST GRILL, LLC—See Roark Capital Group Inc.; *U.S. Private*, pg. 3454
MOET HENNESSY ARGENTINA—See LVMH Moet Hennessy Louis Vuitton SE; *Int'l*, pg. 4599
MOET HENNESSY AUSTRALIA LTD—See LVMH Moet Hennessy Louis Vuitton SE; *Int'l*, pg. 4599
MOET HENNESSY CZECH REPUBLIC SRO—See LVMH Moet Hennessy Louis Vuitton SE; *Int'l*, pg. 4599
MOET HENNESSY DANMARK A/S—See LVMH Moet Hennessy Louis Vuitton SE; *Int'l*, pg. 4599
MOET HENNESSY DE MEXICO, SA DE C.V.—See LVMH Moet Hennessy Louis Vuitton SE; *Int'l*, pg. 4600
MOET HENNESSY DEUTSCHLAND GMBH—See LVMH Moet Hennessy Louis Vuitton SE; *Int'l*, pg. 4599
MOET HENNESSY DIAGEO HONG KONG LTD.—See LVMH Moet Hennessy Louis Vuitton SE; *Int'l*, pg. 4599
MOET-HENNESSY DIAGEO SAS—See LVMH Moet Hennessy Louis Vuitton SE; *Int'l*, pg. 4599
MOET HENNESSY DIAGEO SHANGHAI LTD.—See LVMH Moet Hennessy Louis Vuitton SE; *Int'l*, pg. 4599
MOET HENNESSY DO BRASIL VINHOS E DESTILADOS LTDA—See LVMH Moet Hennessy Louis Vuitton SE; *Int'l*, pg. 4599
MOET HENNESSY ESPANA SA—See LVMH Moet Hennessy Louis Vuitton SE; *Int'l*, pg. 4600
MOET HENNESSY INVESTISSEMENTS—See LVMH Moet Hennessy Louis Vuitton SE; *Int'l*, pg. 4599
MOET-HENNESSY ITALIA SPA—See LVMH Moet Hennessy Louis Vuitton SE; *Int'l*, pg. 4600
MOET HENNESSY LATIN AMERICA & CARIBBEAN—See LVMH Moet Hennessy Louis Vuitton SE; *Int'l*, pg. 4599
MOET-HENNESSY NEDERLAND B.V.—See LVMH Moet Hennessy Louis Vuitton SE; *Int'l*, pg. 4600
MOET HENNESSY NORGE AS—See LVMH Moet Hennessy Louis Vuitton SE; *Int'l*, pg. 4599
MOET HENNESSY OSTERREICH GMBH—See LVMH Moet Hennessy Louis Vuitton SE; *Int'l*, pg. 4600
MOET HENNESSY POLSKA SP Z.O.O.—See LVMH Moet Hennessy Louis Vuitton SE; *Int'l*, pg. 4600
MOET-HENNESSY SNC—See LVMH Moet Hennessy Louis Vuitton SE; *Int'l*, pg. 4599
MOET HENNESSY—See LVMH Moet Hennessy Louis Vuitton SE; *Int'l*, pg. 4604
MOET-HENNESSY (SUISSE) S.A.—See LVMH Moet Hennessy Louis Vuitton SE; *Int'l*, pg. 4600

MOET HENNESSY SUOMI OY—See LVMH Moet Hennessy Louis Vuitton SE; *Int'l*, pg. 4600
MOET HENNESSY SVERIGE AB—See LVMH Moet Hennessy Louis Vuitton SE; *Int'l*, pg. 4600
MOET HENNESSY TAIWAN—See LVMH Moet Hennessy Louis Vuitton SE; *Int'l*, pg. 4600
MOET HENNESSY UK LTD—See LVMH Moet Hennessy Louis Vuitton SE; *Int'l*, pg. 4600
MOET HENNESSY USA—See LVMH Moet Hennessy Louis Vuitton SE; *Int'l*, pg. 4599
MOEWS SEED CO., INC.; *U.S. Private*, pg. 2764
MOFAG MOSLI FLEISCHWAREN AG—See Orior AG; *Int'l*, pg. 5633
MOFFAT LTD—See Ali Holding S.r.l; *Int'l*, pg. 321
MOFFAT PTY LTD—See Ali Holding S.r.l; *Int'l*, pg. 321
MOFFETT ENGINEERING LTD—See Cargotec Corporation; *Int'l*, pg. 1329
MOFFETT TURF EQUIPMENT, INC.; *U.S. Private*, pg. 2765
MOFFITT DODGE CHRYSLER LTD.; *Int'l*, pg. 5017
MOFFITTS INCORPORATED; *U.S. Private*, pg. 2765
MOFFITT VOLKSWAGON -MAZDA; *U.S. Private*, pg. 2765
MOF TECHNOLOGIES LIMITED; *Int'l*, pg. 5017
MOGALE ALLOYS (PTY) LTD—See Afarak Group SE; *Int'l*, pg. 185
MOGALE GOLD (PTY) LTD—See Labyrinth Resources Limited; *Int'l*, pg. 4391
MOGAMI DENKI CORPORATION—See EQT AB; *Int'l*, pg. 2470
MOGAMI DONGGUAN ELECTRONICS CO., LTD.—See EQT AB; *Int'l*, pg. 2470
MOGAMI HONGKONG CO., LTD.—See EQT AB; *Int'l*, pg. 2470
MOGAN ENERJI YATIRIM HOLDING A.S.—See Parsan Makina Parcalari Sanayii AS; *Int'l*, pg. 5747
MOGAN TARIM A.S.—See Parsan Makina Parcalari Sanayii AS; *Int'l*, pg. 5747
MOGAR MUSIC S.P.A.—See ZOOM Corporation; *Int'l*, pg. 8689
MOGAS INDUSTRIES, INC.—See Flowserve Corporation; *U.S. Public*, pg. 856
MOGAS INDUSTRIES, LTD—See Flowserve Corporation; *U.S. Public*, pg. 857
MOGAS INDUSTRIES PTY LTD—See Flowserve Corporation; *U.S. Public*, pg. 857
MOGAS PIPELINE, LLC—See Spire, Inc; *U.S. Public*, pg. 1918
MOGAZ PETROL GAZLARI AS—See Koc Holding A.S.; *Int'l*, pg. 4223
MOGEMA 3.0—See Aalberts N.V.; *Int'l*, pg. 35
MOGEMA B.V.—See Aalberts N.V.; *Int'l*, pg. 35
MOGEMA VESSEM BV—See Aalberts N.V.; *Int'l*, pg. 35
MOGEN DAVID WINE CORP.—See The Wine Group, Inc.; *U.S. Private*, pg. 4137
MOG HOLDINGS LIMITED; *Int'l*, pg. 5017
MOGI PHARMACEUTICAL CO., LTD.—See MatsukiyoCocokara & Co.; *Int'l*, pg. 4730
MOGO FINANCE TECHNOLOGY, INC.—See Difference Capital Financial Inc.; *Int'l*, pg. 2118
MOGO, INC.; *Int'l*, pg. 5017
MOGO MARKETING & MEDIA, INC.—See Atairos Group, Inc.; *U.S. Private*, pg. 364
MOGS (PTY) LTD—See Royal Bafokeng Holdings (Pty) Limited; *Int'l*, pg. 6409
MOGU INC.; *Int'l*, pg. 5017
MOGUL AB—See Addnode Group AB; *Int'l*, pg. 130
MOGUL ENERGY INTERNATIONAL, INC.; *U.S. Public*, pg. 1456
MOGUL GAMES GROUP LTD; *Int'l*, pg. 5017
MOGULTECH INT'L LTD—See Shenzhen Huaqiang Industry Co., Ltd; *Int'l*, pg. 6812
MO HA GE MOMMSEN HANDELSGESELLSCHAFT MBH—See Bunzl plc; *Int'l*, pg. 1219
MOHAMED A. ALHAMRANI & CO INTERTRADE CO (LTD)—See Alhamrani Group; *Int'l*, pg. 319
MOHAMED ALI ABUDAWOOD FOR INDUSTRY AND PARTNERS FOR INDUSTRY COMPANY LTD.—See The Clorox Company; *U.S. Public*, pg. 2062
MOHAMED N. AL-HAJERY & SONS LTD.; *Int'l*, pg. 5017
MOHAMMAD FAROOQ TEXTILE MILLS LIMITED; *Int'l*, pg. 5017
MOHAMMAD SAAD ALDREES & SONS COMPANY LIMITED—See Aldrees Petroleum & Transport Services Company; *Int'l*, pg. 305
MOHAMMED ABDULMOHSIN AL-KHARAFI & SONS COMPANY W.L.L.—See Mohammed Abdulmohsin Al-Kharafi & Sons WLL; *Int'l*, pg. 5018
MOHAMMED ABDULMOHSIN AL-KHARAFI & SONS CO. W.L.L.—See Mohammed Abdulmohsin Al-Kharafi & Sons WLL; *Int'l*, pg. 5018
MOHAMMED ABDULMOHSIN AL-KHARAFI & SONS.—See Mohammed Abdulmohsin Al-Kharafi & Sons WLL; *Int'l*, pg. 5018
MOHAMMED ABDULMOHSIN AL-KHARAFI & SONS WLL; *Int'l*, pg. 5018
MOHAMMED ENTERPRISES TANZANIA LIMITED; *Int'l*, pg. 5018

MOHAMMED JALAL CATERING W.L.L.—See Mohammed Jalal & Sons WLL; *Int'l*, pg. 5018
MOHAMMED JALAL & SONS WLL - IDEAL HOME DIVISION—See Mohammed Jalal & Sons WLL; *Int'l*, pg. 5018
MOHAMMED JALAL & SONS WLL - MOHAMMED JALAL ENGINEERING & TECHNOLOGY DIVISION—See Mohammed Jalal & Sons WLL; *Int'l*, pg. 5018
MOHAMMED JALAL & SONS WLL; *Int'l*, pg. 5018
MOHAN MEAKIN LTD.; *Int'l*, pg. 5018
MOHAR INCORPORATED; *U.S. Private*, pg. 2765
MOHARRAM PRESS COMPANY—See Chemical Industries Holding Company; *Int'l*, pg. 1462
MOHAVE BLOCK INC.—See Paragon Building Products Inc.; *U.S. Private*, pg. 3090
MOHAVE CELLULAR LTD. PARTNER; *U.S. Private*, pg. 2765
MOHAVE ELECTRIC COOP INC.; *U.S. Private*, pg. 2765
MOHAVE HEALTHCARE, INC.—See The Ensign Group, Inc.; *U.S. Public*, pg. 2071
MOHAWK/COLUMBIA FLOORING—See Mohawk Industries, Inc.; *U.S. Public*, pg. 1458
MOHAWK ENERGY LTD.; *U.S. Private*, pg. 2765
MOHAWK FACTORING, INC.—See Mohawk Industries, Inc.; *U.S. Public*, pg. 1458
MOHAWK FIELD SERVICES INC—See Energy Process Technology Inc.; *U.S. Private*, pg. 1395
MOHAWK FINE PAPERS, INC.—See Fedrigoni SpA; *Int'l*, pg. 2631
MOHAWK FINISHING PRODUCTS, INC.—See RPM International Inc.; *U.S. Public*, pg. 1817
MOHAWK FLUSH DOORS, INC.—See Owens Corning; *U.S. Public*, pg. 1627
MOHAWK FORD SALES; *Int'l*, pg. 5018
MOHAWK HOME—See Mohawk Industries, Inc.; *U.S. Public*, pg. 1458
MOHAWK INDUSTRIES, INC. - DALTON—See Mohawk Industries, Inc.; *U.S. Public*, pg. 1458
MOHAWK INDUSTRIES, INC.; *U.S. Public*, pg. 1457
MOHAWK INTERNATIONAL SERVICES BVBA—See Mohawk Industries, Inc.; *U.S. Public*, pg. 1458
MOHAWK LABORATORIES DIVISION—See NCH Corporation; *U.S. Private*, pg. 2875
MOHAWK LABOR SERVICES, LLC—See Mitsubishi Heavy Industries, Ltd.; *Int'l*, pg. 4960
MOHAWK LTD.; *U.S. Private*, pg. 2765
MOHAWK MARKETING CORPORATION—See Konica Minolta, Inc.; *Int'l*, pg. 4259
MOHAWK NORTHEAST, INC.; *U.S. Private*, pg. 2765
MOHAWK SPRING—See American Securities LLC; *U.S. Private*, pg. 250
MOHAWK SURGERY CENTER, LLC—See UnitedHealth Group Incorporated; *U.S. Public*, pg. 2242
MOHAWK UNILIN INTERNATIONAL BV—See Mohawk Industries, Inc.; *U.S. Public*, pg. 1458
MOHAWK VALLEY DIALYSIS CENTER, INC.—See Nautic Partners, LLC; *U.S. Private*, pg. 2870
MOHEDA CHARK AB—See Atria Plc; *Int'l*, pg. 694
MOHEGAN COMMERCIAL VENTURES-PA, LLC—See Mohegan Tribal Gaming Authority; *U.S. Private*, pg. 2765
MOHEGAN LAKE MOTORS; *U.S. Private*, pg. 2765
MOHEGAN TRIBAL GAMING AUTHORITY; *U.S. Private*, pg. 2765
MOHENZ CO., LTD.; *Int'l*, pg. 5018
MOHG HOTEL (PARIS) SARL—See Jardine Matheson Holdings Limited; *Int'l*, pg. 3910
MOHIB EXPORTS LIMITED; *Int'l*, pg. 5018
MOHICAN MILLS, INC.—See Fab Industries Corp.; *U.S. Private*, pg. 1458
MOHINDRA FASTENERS LIMITED HARYANA PLANT—See Mohindra Fasteners Limited; *Int'l*, pg. 5018
MOHINDRA FASTENERS LIMITED; *Int'l*, pg. 5018
MOHINI HEALTH & HYGIENE LTD.; *Int'l*, pg. 5018
MOHITE INDUSTRIES LIMITED; *Int'l*, pg. 5019
MOHIT INDUSTRIES LTD.; *Int'l*, pg. 5019
MOHIT PAPER MILLS LIMITED; *Int'l*, pg. 5019
MOHLER MATERIAL HANDLING, INC.; *U.S. Private*, pg. 2765
MOH NIPPON PLC; *Int'l*, pg. 5017
MOHO RESOURCES LTD.; *Int'l*, pg. 5019
MOHOTA INDUSTRIES LTD; *Int'l*, pg. 5019
MOHR CONSTRUCTION CO. INC.; *U.S. Private*, pg. 2765
MOHR DAVIDOW VENTURES; *U.S. Private*, pg. 2765
MOHR GMBH; *Int'l*, pg. 5019
MOHR OIL COMPANY; *U.S. Private*, pg. 2765
MOHSIN HAIDER DARWISH LLC; *Int'l*, pg. 5019
MOI CORPORATION; *Int'l*, pg. 5019
MOI FOODS MALAYSIA SDN BHD—See Mewah International Inc.; *Int'l*, pg. 4868
MOI INTERNATIONAL (AUSTRALIA) PTY LTD—See Mewah International Inc.; *Int'l*, pg. 4868
MOI INTERNATIONAL (SINGAPORE) PTE. LTD.—See Mewah International Inc.; *Int'l*, pg. 4868
MOIL LIMITED; *Int'l*, pg. 5019
MOINHO PACIFICO LTDA.—See Bunge Limited; *U.S. Public*, pg. 412
M&O INSULATION COMPANY; *U.S. Private*, pg. 2525

COMPANY NAME INDEX

M. & O. INSULATION COMPANY; *U.S. Private*, pg. 2526
MO I RANA—See DNV GL Group AS; *Int'l*, pg. 2151
MOI ROR AS—See Instalco AB; *Int'l*, pg. 3722
MOISELLE INTERNATIONAL HOLDINGS LIMITED; *Int'l*, pg. 5019
  MOISELLE SINGAPORE PTE. LTD.—See Moiselle International Holdings Limited; *Int'l*, pg. 5019
MOISHE HOUSE; *U.S. Private*, pg. 2765
MOISSANITEOUTLET.COM, LLC—See Charles & Colvard Ltd; *U.S. Public*, pg. 479
MOI TECH HONG KONG LTD.—See Mitsuboshi Belting Ltd.; *Int'l*, pg. 4972
MOJACK DISTRIBUTORS; *U.S. Private*, pg. 2765
MOJANG AB—See Microsoft Corporation; *U.S. Public*, pg. 1440
MOJAVE AUTO GROUP; *U.S. Private*, pg. 2765
MOJAVE BRANDS INC; *Int'l*, pg. 5019
MOJAVE FOODS CORPORATION—See McCormick & Company, Incorporated; *U.S. Public*, pg. 1404
MOJAVE MOTORS LTD.; *U.S. Private*, pg. 2765
MOJAVE PIPELINE COMPANY, L.L.C.—See Kinder Morgan, Inc.; *U.S. Public*, pg. 1232
MOJAVE PIPELINE OPERATING COMPANY—See Kinder Morgan, Inc.; *U.S. Public*, pg. 1233
MOJIVA INC.; *U.S. Private*, pg. 2766
MOJIVA UK LTD.—See Mojiva Inc.; *U.S. Private*, pg. 2766
MOJO BRANDS MEDIA, LLC; *U.S. Private*, pg. 2766
MOJO CONCERTS B.V.—See Live Nation Entertainment, Inc.; *U.S. Public*, pg. 1330
MOJO CONCERTS BV—See Live Nation Entertainment, Inc.; *U.S. Public*, pg. 1330
MOJO DIGITAL ASSETS INC.; *U.S. Public*, pg. 1458
MOJO MARITIME FRANCE SAS—See James Fisher & Sons Public Limited Company; *Int'l*, pg. 3876
MOJO MARITIME LIMITED—See James Fisher & Sons Public Limited Company; *Int'l*, pg. 3876
MOJOTECH, LLC; *U.S. Private*, pg. 2766
MOJOTECH—See MojoTech, LLC; *U.S. Private*, pg. 2766
MOJOTECH—See MojoTech, LLC; *U.S. Private*, pg. 2766
MOJO WORKS B.V.—See Live Nation Entertainment, Inc.; *U.S. Public*, pg. 1330
MOJ S.A.; *Int'l*, pg. 5019
MOKABI S.A.—See Rougier S.A.; *Int'l*, pg. 6407
MOKA CORPORATION; *U.S. Private*, pg. 2766
MOKON—See Windjammer Capital Investors, LLC; *U.S. Private*, pg. 4538
MOKPO DAEBUL PIER OPERATION CO., LTD.—See Sebang Co., Ltd.; *Int'l*, pg. 6669
MOKSH ORNAMENTS LTD.; *Int'l*, pg. 5019
MOLA ADMINISTRATION GMBH—See Apex Fund Services Holdings Ltd.; *Int'l*, pg. 510
MOLAB AS—See SINTEF; *Int'l*, pg. 6957
MOL ACCOUNTING CO., LTD.—See Mitsui O.S.K. Lines, Ltd.; *Int'l*, pg. 4989
MOL ADJUSTMENT , LTD.—See Mitsui O.S.K. Lines, Ltd.; *Int'l*, pg. 4989
MOL (AMERICA) INC.—See Mitsui O.S.K. Lines, Ltd.; *Int'l*, pg. 4989
MOLAN STEEL COMPANY; *Int'l*, pg. 5021
MOL AUSTRIA GMBH.—See MOL Magyar Olaj- es Gazipari Nyrt.; *Int'l*, pg. 5020
MOL AUSTRIA HANDELS GMBH—See MOL Magyar Olaj- es Gazipari Nyrt.; *Int'l*, pg. 5020
MOL AUTO CARRIER EXPRESS SOUTH AFRICA (PTY.) LTD.—See Mitsui O.S.K. Lines, Ltd.; *Int'l*, pg. 4989
MOLAY TRAVEL SARL—See TUI AG; *Int'l*, pg. 7965
MOLBAKS LLC; *U.S. Private*, pg. 2766
MOL (BRASIL) LTDA.—See Mitsui O.S.K. Lines, Ltd.; *Int'l*, pg. 4989
MOL BUSINESS SUPPORT, LTD.—See Mitsui O.S.K. Lines, Ltd.; *Int'l*, pg. 4989
MOL CAMPUS KFT.—See MOL Magyar Olaj- es Gazipari Nyrt.; *Int'l*, pg. 5020
MOL CESKA REPUBLIKA S.R.O.—See MOL Magyar Olaj- es Gazipari Nyrt.; *Int'l*, pg. 5020
MOL-CEZ EUROPEAN POWER HUNGARY KFT.—See MOL Magyar Olaj- es Gazipari Nyrt.; *Int'l*, pg. 5020
MOL CHEMICAL TANKERS PTE. LTD.—See Mitsui O.S.K. Lines, Ltd.; *Int'l*, pg. 4989
MOL (CHINA) CO., LTD.—See Mitsui O.S.K. Lines, Ltd.; *Int'l*, pg. 4989
MOLCHIP TECHNOLOGY(SHANGHAI) CO., LTD.—See Shanghai Fullhan Microelectonics Co.,Ltd.; *Int'l*, pg. 6768
MOL CONSOLIDATION SERVICE LIMITED—See Mitsui O.S.K. Lines, Ltd.; *Int'l*, pg. 4990
MOL CONSOLIDATION SERVICE LIMITED—See Mitsui O.S.K. Lines, Ltd.; *Int'l*, pg. 4990
MOL CONTAINER CENTER (THAILAND) CO., LTD.—See Mitsui O.S.K. Lines, Ltd.; *Int'l*, pg. 4990
MOLDAMATIC INC.; *U.S. Private*, pg. 2766
MOLDAVIAN AIRLINES—See Carpatair SA; *Int'l*, pg. 1342
MOLD BASE INDUSTRIES INC.; *U.S. Private*, pg. 2766
MOLD CRAFT, INC.—See BlackBern Partners LLC; *U.S. Private*, pg. 573
MOLD CRAFT, INC.—See Lee Equity Partners LLC; *U.S. Private*, pg. 2413
MOLDEADOS ARGENTINOS SA—See Thornico A/S; *Int'l*, pg. 7719

MOLDED DEVICES, INC.—See TruArc Partners, L.P.; *U.S. Private*, pg. 4245
MOLDED DIMENSIONS INC.; *U.S. Private*, pg. 2766
MOLDED FIBER GLASS COMPANIES - MFG ALABAMA FACTORY—See Molded Fiber Glass Companies; *U.S. Private*, pg. 2766
MOLDED FIBER GLASS COMPANIES - MFG CONSTRUCTION PRODUCTS FACTORY—See Molded Fiber Glass Companies; *U.S. Private*, pg. 2766
MOLDED FIBER GLASS COMPANIES - MFG SOUTH DAKOTA FACTORY—See Molded Fiber Glass Companies; *U.S. Private*, pg. 2766
MOLDED FIBER GLASS COMPANIES - MFG SOUTHEAST FACTORY—See Molded Fiber Glass Companies; *U.S. Private*, pg. 2766
MOLDED FIBER GLASS COMPANIES; *U.S. Private*, pg. 2766
MOLDED FIBER GLASS COMPOSITE SYSTEMS CO.—See Molded Fiber Glass Companies; *U.S. Private*, pg. 2766
MOLDED FIBER GLASS NORTH CAROLINA—See Molded Fiber Glass Companies; *U.S. Private*, pg. 2766
MOLDED FIBER GLASS NORTHWEST—See Molded Fiber Glass Companies; *U.S. Private*, pg. 2766
MOLDED FIBER GLASS TEXAS—See Molded Fiber Glass Companies; *U.S. Private*, pg. 2766
MOLDED FIBER GLASS TRAY CO.—See Molded Fiber Glass Companies; *U.S. Private*, pg. 2766
MOLDED FIBER GLASS UNION CITY—See Molded Fiber Glass Companies; *U.S. Private*, pg. 2766
MOLDED FIBER GLASS WATER TREATMENT PRODUCTS—See Molded Fiber Glass Companies; *U.S. Private*, pg. 2766
MOLDED FIBER GLASS WEST—See Molded Fiber Glass Companies; *U.S. Private*, pg. 2766
MOLDED RUBBER & PLASTIC CORPORATION; *U.S. Private*, pg. 2766
MOLDES CERAMICOS S.A.—See Sacmi Imola S.C.A.R.L.; *Int'l*, pg. 6464
MOLDFLOW B.V.—See Autodesk, Inc.; *U.S. Public*, pg. 229
MOLDINDCONBANK S.A.—See Doverie United Holding AD; *Int'l*, pg. 2182
MOLDING BOX INC.; *U.S. Private*, pg. 2767
MOLDING CORPORATION OF AMERICA—See Performance Engineered Products Inc.; *U.S. Private*, pg. 3149
MOLDMAKERS DIE CAST TOOLING DIVISION INC.—See MGS Manufacturing Group, Inc.; *U.S. Private*, pg. 2695
MOLDMAKERS INCORPORATED—See MGS Manufacturing Group, Inc.; *U.S. Private*, pg. 2695
MOLDMAKERS MANAGEMENT INC.—See MGS Manufacturing Group, Inc.; *U.S. Private*, pg. 2695
MOLD-MASTERS (2007) LIMITED—See Hillenbrand, Inc.; *U.S. Public*, pg. 1037
MOLD-MASTERS EUROPA GMBH—See Hillenbrand, Inc.; *U.S. Public*, pg. 1037
MOLD-MASTERS HANDELSGESELLSCHAFT M.B.H.—See Hillenbrand, Inc.; *U.S. Public*, pg. 1037
MOLD MASTERS INTL. LLC; *U.S. Private*, pg. 2766
MOLD-MASTERS KABUSHIKI KAISHA—See Hillenbrand, Inc.; *U.S. Public*, pg. 1037
MOLD-MASTERS (KUNSHAN) CO. LTD.—See Hillenbrand, Inc.; *U.S. Public*, pg. 1037
MOLD-MASTERS (U.K.) LTD.—See Hillenbrand, Inc.; *U.S. Public*, pg. 1037
MOL DOHLE WORLDWIDE LOGISTICS GMBH—See Mitsui O.S.K. Lines, Ltd.; *Int'l*, pg. 4990
MOLDPRO, INC.—See Regimen Equity Partners Inc.; *Int'l*, pg. 6253
MOLD-RITE PLASTICS LLC—See Irving Place Capital Management, L.P.; *U.S. Private*, pg. 2142
MOL DRYBULK LTD.—See Mitsui O.S.K. Lines, Ltd.; *Int'l*, pg. 4990
MOLD-TECH (DONGGUAN) CO. LTD.—See Standex International; *U.S. Public*, pg. 1930
MOLD-TECH PORTUGAL LDA.—See Standex International; *U.S. Public*, pg. 1930
MOLD-TECH S.A.R.L.—See Standex International; *U.S. Public*, pg. 1930
MOLD-TECH SINGAPORE PTE. LTD.—See Standex International; *U.S. Public*, pg. 1930
MOLD-TECH (SUZHOU) CO. LTD.—See Standex International; *U.S. Public*, pg. 1930
MOLDTECS GMBH—See Mutares SE & Co. KGaA; *Int'l*, pg. 5105
MOLDTECS S. A. S.—See Mutares SE & Co. KGaA; *Int'l*, pg. 5105
MOLD-TEK PACKAGING LIMITED; *Int'l*, pg. 5021
MOLD-TEK TECHNOLOGIES LIMITED; *Int'l*, pg. 5021
MOLECARE VETERINARY SERVICES LTD.—See Mole Valley Farmers Ltd; *Int'l*, pg. 5021
MOLECOR (SEA) SDN. BHD.—See FITTERS Diversified Berhad; *Int'l*, pg. 2695
MOLECULAR BIOLOGY RESOURCES; *U.S. Private*, pg. 2767
MOLECULAR DATA INC.; *Int'l*, pg. 5021

MOLECULAR DEVICES CORPORATION-DOWNINGTOWN—See Danaher Corporation; *U.S. Public*, pg. 628
MOLECULAR DEVICES GMBH—See Danaher Corporation; *U.S. Public*, pg. 628
MOLECULAR DEVICES LLC—See Danaher Corporation; *U.S. Public*, pg. 628
MOLECULAR DEVICES LTD.—See Danaher Corporation; *U.S. Public*, pg. 628
MOLECULAR DIAGNOSTICS KOREA INC. (MDXK)—See Mycronic AB; *Int'l*, pg. 5112
MOLECULAR DIMENSIONS INC.—See StoneCalibre, LLC; *U.S. Private*, pg. 3827
MOLECULAR DIMENSIONS LTD.—See StoneCalibre, LLC; *U.S. Private*, pg. 3827
MOLECULAR ENERGIES PLC; *Int'l*, pg. 5021
MOLECULAR IMAGING INDUSTRY AND TRADING CO. INC.—See Bozlu Holding; *Int'l*, pg. 1125
MOLECULAR IMPRINTS, INC.—See Canon Inc.; *Int'l*, pg. 1297
MOLECULAR PARTNERS AG; *Int'l*, pg. 5022
MOLECULAR PROBES, INC.—See Thermo Fisher Scientific Inc.; *U.S. Public*, pg. 2149
MOLECULAR PRODUCTS GROUP LIMITED—See Madison Industries Holdings LLC; *U.S. Private*, pg. 2543
MOLECULAR RESPONSE LLC—See Advent International Corporation; *U.S. Private*, pg. 98
MOLECULAR TEMPLATES INC.; *U.S. Public*, pg. 1458
MOLECULIN BIOTECH, INC.; *U.S. Public*, pg. 1458
MOLECU WIRE CORPORATION; *U.S. Private*, pg. 2767
MOLEKULE GROUP, INC.; *U.S. Public*, pg. 1458
MOLENAAR, LLC—See Fey Industries, Inc.; *U.S. Private*, pg. 1500
MOLENWIJCK B.V.; *Int'l*, pg. 5022
MOLE-RICHARDSON CO.; *U.S. Private*, pg. 2767
MOLESKINE AMERICA INC.—See s.a. D'Ieteren n.v.; *Int'l*, pg. 6448
MOLESKINE GERMANY GMBH—See s.a. D'Ieteren n.v.; *Int'l*, pg. 6448
MOLESKINE SPA—See s.a. D'Ieteren n.v.; *Int'l*, pg. 6448
MOL (EUROPE) LTD.—See Mitsui O.S.K. Lines, Ltd.; *Int'l*, pg. 4989
MOLE VALLEY FARMERS LTD - FEED SUPPLEMENTS PLANT—See Mole Valley Farmers Ltd; *Int'l*, pg. 5021
MOLE VALLEY FARMERS LTD - LIFTON FEED MILL—See Mole Valley Farmers Ltd; *Int'l*, pg. 5021
MOLE VALLEY FARMERS LTD - PORTE MARSH MILL—See Mole Valley Farmers Ltd; *Int'l*, pg. 5021
MOLE VALLEY FARMERS LTD; *Int'l*, pg. 5021
MOLE VALLEY FARMERS LTD WITHERIDGE ENGINEERING DIVISION—See Mole Valley Farmers Ltd; *Int'l*, pg. 5021
MOLEX AUTOMOTIVE—See Koch Industries, Inc.; *U.S. Private*, pg. 2334
MOLEX BRAZIL LTDA.—See Koch Industries, Inc.; *U.S. Private*, pg. 2334
MOLEX B.V. - ESPANA—See Koch Industries, Inc.; *U.S. Private*, pg. 2334
MOLEX B.V.—See Koch Industries, Inc.; *U.S. Private*, pg. 2334
MOLEX CANADA LIMITED—See Koch Industries, Inc.; *U.S. Private*, pg. 2335
MOLEX CONNECTIVITY GMBH - LEINFELDEN-ECHTERDINGEN—See Koch Industries, Inc.; *U.S. Private*, pg. 2334
MOLEX CONNECTIVITY GMBH—See Koch Industries, Inc.; *U.S. Private*, pg. 2334
MOLEX DE MEXICO S.A. DE C.V.—See Koch Industries, Inc.; *U.S. Private*, pg. 2335
MOLEX ELECTRONICS LTD.—See Koch Industries, Inc.; *U.S. Private*, pg. 2334
MOLEX ELECTRONICS LTD.—See Koch Industries, Inc.; *U.S. Private*, pg. 2334
MOLEX ELEKTRONIK GMBH—See Koch Industries, Inc.; *U.S. Private*, pg. 2334
MOLEX EUROPEAN HOLDINGS BV—See Koch Industries, Inc.; *U.S. Private*, pg. 2334
MOLEX FIBER OPTICS—See Koch Industries, Inc.; *U.S. Private*, pg. 2335
MOLEX FRANCE—See Koch Industries, Inc.; *U.S. Private*, pg. 2334
MOLEX HOLDING GMBH—See Koch Industries, Inc.; *U.S. Private*, pg. 2334
MOLEX HONG KONG/CHINA LTD.—See Koch Industries, Inc.; *U.S. Private*, pg. 2334
MOLEX, INC. - TAMPA BAY OPERATIONS—See Koch Industries, Inc.; *U.S. Private*, pg. 2335
MOLEX (INDIA) LTD.—See Koch Industries, Inc.; *U.S. Private*, pg. 2334
MOLEX INTERCONNECT (BEIJING) CO., LTD.—See Koch Industries, Inc.; *U.S. Private*, pg. 2334
MOLEX INTERCONNECT GMBH—See Koch Industries, Inc.; *U.S. Private*, pg. 2334
MOLEX INTERCONNECT (SHANGHAI) CO., LTD.—See Koch Industries, Inc.; *U.S. Private*, pg. 2334
MOLEX INTERNATIONAL, INC.—See Koch Industries, Inc.; *U.S. Private*, pg. 2334
MOLEX IRELAND LTD.—See Koch Industries, Inc.; *U.S. Private*, pg. 2334

MOLE VALLEY FARMERS LTD

CORPORATE AFFILIATIONS

MOLEX JAPAN CO., LTD.—See Koch Industries, Inc.; *U.S. Private*, pg. 2334
MOLEX KNUTSEN DANMARK A/S—See Koch Industries, Inc.; *U.S. Private*, pg. 2334
MOLEX KNUTSEN NORGE AS—See Koch Industries, Inc.; *U.S. Private*, pg. 2334
MOLEX KOREA CO., LTD.—See Koch Industries, Inc.; *U.S. Private*, pg. 2334
MOLEX LLC—See Koch Industries, Inc.; *U.S. Private*, pg. 2333
MOLEX (MALAYSIA) SDN. BHD.—See Koch Industries, Inc.; *U.S. Private*, pg. 2334
MOLEX POLSKA SP. Z O.O.—See Koch Industries, Inc.; *U.S. Private*, pg. 2334
MOLEX PREMISE NETWORKS, INC.—See Koch Industries, Inc.; *U.S. Private*, pg. 2335
MOLEX S.A. DE C.V.—See Koch Industries, Inc.; *U.S. Private*, pg. 2335
MOLEX SERVICES GMBH—See Koch Industries, Inc.; *U.S. Private*, pg. 2334
MOLEX SINGAPORE PTE. LTD.—See Koch Industries, Inc.; *U.S. Private*, pg. 2334
MOLEX SWEDEN—See Koch Industries, Inc.; *U.S. Private*, pg. 2334
MOLEX TAIWAN LTD.—See Koch Industries, Inc.; *U.S. Private*, pg. 2334
MOLEX (THAILAND) LTD.—See Koch Industries, Inc.; *U.S. Private*, pg. 2334
MOLEX TURKEY—See Koch Industries, Inc.; *U.S. Private*, pg. 2335
MOLEX ZETRONIC S.R.L. UNICO SOCIO—See Koch Industries, Inc.; *U.S. Private*, pg. 2334
MOL FERRY CO., LTD.—See Mitsui O.S.K. Lines, Ltd.; *Int'l*, pg. 4990
MOL-GAZ TRADING LTD.—See MOL Magyar Olaj- es Gazipari Nyrt.; *Int'l*, pg. 5020
MOL GBS SLOVENSKO S.R.O—See MOL Magyar Olaj- es Gazipari Nyrt.; *Int'l*, pg. 5020
MOL GERMANY GMBH—See MOL Magyar Olaj- es Gazipari Nyrt.; *Int'l*, pg. 5020
MOL GLOBAL, INC.; *Int'l*, pg. 5019
MOLHOLM FORSIKRING A/S—See Gjensidige Forsikring ASA; *Int'l*, pg. 2982
MOLIBDENOS Y METALES S.A.; *Int'l*, pg. 5022
MOLI GROUP LIMITED—See Celestial Asia Securities Holdings Limited; *Int'l*, pg. 1392
MOL-IMAGE MOLECULAR IMAGING CO.—See Eczacibasi Holding A.S.; *Int'l*, pg. 2301
MOLINA BIANCHI; OGILVY & MATHER—See WPP plc; *Int'l*, pg. 8484
MOLINA CENTER LLC—See Molina Healthcare, Inc.; *U.S. Public*, pg. 1458
MOL & INA D.O.O.—See MOL Magyar Olaj- es Gazipari Nyrt.; *Int'l*, pg. 5020
MOLINA HEALTHCARE, INC.; *U.S. Public*, pg. 1458
MOLINA HEALTHCARE OF CALIFORNIA—See Molina Healthcare, Inc.; *U.S. Public*, pg. 1458
MOLINA HEALTHCARE OF FLORIDA, INC.—See Molina Healthcare, Inc.; *U.S. Public*, pg. 1459
MOLINA HEALTHCARE OF KENTUCKY, INC.—See Molina Healthcare, Inc.; *U.S. Public*, pg. 1459
MOLINA HEALTHCARE OF MICHIGAN, INC.—See Molina Healthcare, Inc.; *U.S. Public*, pg. 1459
MOLINA HEALTHCARE OF MISSISSIPPI, INC.—See Molina Healthcare, Inc.; *U.S. Public*, pg. 1459
MOLINA HEALTHCARE OF NEVADA, INC.—See Molina Healthcare, Inc.; *U.S. Public*, pg. 1459
MOLINA HEALTHCARE OF NEW MEXICO, INC.—See Molina Healthcare, Inc.; *U.S. Public*, pg. 1459
MOLINA HEALTHCARE OF NEW YORK, INC.—See Molina Healthcare, Inc.; *U.S. Public*, pg. 1459
MOLINA HEALTHCARE OF OHIO, INC.—See Molina Healthcare, Inc.; *U.S. Public*, pg. 1459
MOLINA HEALTHCARE OF PUERTO RICO, INC.—See Molina Healthcare, Inc.; *U.S. Public*, pg. 1459
MOLINA HEALTHCARE OF SOUTH CAROLINA, LLC—See Molina Healthcare, Inc.; *U.S. Public*, pg. 1459
MOLINA HEALTHCARE OF TEXAS, INC.—See Molina Healthcare, Inc.; *U.S. Public*, pg. 1459
MOLINA HEALTHCARE OF TEXAS INSURANCE COMPANY—See Molina Healthcare, Inc.; *U.S. Public*, pg. 1459
MOLINA HEALTHCARE OF UTAH, INC.—See Molina Healthcare, Inc.; *U.S. Public*, pg. 1459
MOLINA HEALTHCARE OF VIRGINIA, INC.—See Molina Healthcare, Inc.; *U.S. Public*, pg. 1459
MOLINA HEALTHCARE OF WASHINGTON, INC.—See Molina Healthcare, Inc.; *U.S. Public*, pg. 1459
MOLINA HEALTHCARE OF WISCONSIN, INC.—See Molina Healthcare, Inc.; *U.S. Public*, pg. 1459
MOLINA SP. Z O.O.—See PKO Bank Polski SA; *Int'l*, pg. 5887
MOLINE ACCESSORIES CORPORATION—See KONE Oyj; *Int'l*, pg. 4249
MOLINE DISPATCH PUBLISHING CO. LLC—See Lee Enterprises, Incorporated; *U.S. Public*, pg. 1300
MOLINEL SA; *Int'l*, pg. 5022

MOL INFORMATION TECHNOLOGY ASIA LIMITED—See Mitsui O.S.K. Lines, Ltd.; *Int'l*, pg. 4990
MOL INFORMATION TECHNOLOGY INDIA PRIVATE LIMITED—See Mitsui O.S.K. Lines, Ltd.; *Int'l*, pg. 4990
MOLINOS AZTECA, S.A. DE C.V.—See Gruma, S.A.B. de C.V.; *Int'l*, pg. 3114
MOLINOS DE HONDURAS S.A.—See ED&F Man Holdings Limited; *Int'l*, pg. 2303
MOLINOS DEL SUDESTE, S.A. DE C.V.—See Grupo La Moderna, S.A.B. de C.V.; *Int'l*, pg. 3131
MOLINOS INTERNATIONAL S.A.—See Molinos Rio de la Plata S.A.; *Int'l*, pg. 5022
MOLINOS MODERNOS, S.A.—See General Mills, Inc.; *U.S. Public*, pg. 922
MOLINOS NACIONALES, C.A.—See Gruma, S.A.B. de C.V.; *Int'l*, pg. 3114
MOLINOS RIO DE LA PLATA S.A.; *Int'l*, pg. 5022
MOLINOS SANTA MARTA S.A.S.—See Grupo Nutresa S.A.; *Int'l*, pg. 3133
MOLINOS USA CORP.—See Molinos Rio de la Plata S.A.; *Int'l*, pg. 5022
MOLINS SRO—See Coesia S.p.A.; *Int'l*, pg. 1690
MOLINS TOBACCO MACHINERY LTD.—See Coesia S.p.A.; *Int'l*, pg. 1690
MOL IT & DIGITAL GBS SLOVENSKO, S.R.O.—See MOL Magyar Olaj- es Gazipari Nyrt.; *Int'l*, pg. 5020
MOLITEC STEEL CO., LTD.; *Int'l*, pg. 5022
MOLITEC STEEL MEXICO, S.A. DE C.V.—See Molitec Steel Co., Ltd.; *Int'l*, pg. 5022
MOLITEC STEEL (VIETNAM) CO., LTD.—See Molitec Steel Co., Ltd.; *Int'l*, pg. 5022
MOLKARI VERMIETUNGSGESELLSCHAFT MBH & CO. OBJEKT FALKENSEE KG—See Pelikan International Corporation Berhad; *Int'l*, pg. 5782
MOLKEREI ALOIS MULLER GMBH & CO. KG—See Unternehmensgruppe Theo Muller S.e.c.s.; *Int'l*, pg. 8085
MOLKEREI BIEDERMANN AG—See Emmi AG; *Int'l*, pg. 2385
MOLKEREI NIESKY GMBH—See DMK Deutsches Milchkontor GmbH; *Int'l*, pg. 2146
MOLKEREI WEIHENSTEPHAN GMBH & CO. KG—See Unternehmensgruppe Theo Muller S.e.c.s.; *Int'l*, pg. 8085
MOL KOSAN CO., LTD—See Mitsui O.S.K. Lines, Ltd.; *Int'l*, pg. 4989
MOLLENBERG-BETZ INC.; *U.S. Private*, pg. 2767
MOLL ENGINEERING GMBH—See Ensinger GmbH; *Int'l*, pg. 2448
MOLLENHOUR GROSS LLC; *U.S. Private*, pg. 2767
MOLLER BALTIKUM AS—See MollerGruppen AS; *Int'l*, pg. 5022
MOLLER BILFINANS AS—See MollerGruppen AS; *Int'l*, pg. 5022
MOLLER BILL AS—See MollerGruppen AS; *Int'l*, pg. 5022
MOLLERGRUPPEN AS; *Int'l*, pg. 5022
MOLLER INTERNATIONAL, INC.; *U.S. Private*, pg. 2767
MOLLER MEDICAL GMBH—See CENTROTEC SE; *Int'l*, pg. 1414
MOLLER-WEDEL GMBH & CO. KG—See Metall Zug AG; *Int'l*, pg. 4847
MOLLER-WEDEL OPTICAL GMBH—See Metall Zug AG; *Int'l*, pg. 4847
MOLLETOFTA I KLIPPAN AB—See Peab AB; *Int'l*, pg. 5772
MOLLE TOYOTA INCORPORATED; *U.S. Private*, pg. 2767
MOLLE VOLKSWAGON AUDI; *U.S. Private*, pg. 2767
MOL LINER, LTD.—See Mitsui O.S.K. Lines, Ltd.; *Int'l*, pg. 4990
MOL LNG TRANSPORT CO., LTD.—See Mitsui O.S.K. Lines, Ltd.; *Int'l*, pg. 4990
MOL LOGISTICS (CAMBODIA) CO., LTD.—See Mitsui O.S.K. Lines, Ltd.; *Int'l*, pg. 4990
MOL LOGISTICS (CZECH) S.R.O.—See Mitsui O.S.K. Lines, Ltd.; *Int'l*, pg. 4990
MOL LOGISTICS (DEUTSCHLAND) GMBH—See Mitsui O.S.K. Lines, Ltd.; *Int'l*, pg. 4990
MOL LOGISTICS (H.K.) LTD.—See Mitsui O.S.K. Lines, Ltd.; *Int'l*, pg. 4990
MOL LOGISTICS (INDIA) PVT. LTD.—See Mitsui O.S.K. Lines, Ltd.; *Int'l*, pg. 4990
MOL LOGISTICS (JAPAN) CO., LTD.—See Mitsui O.S.K. Lines, Ltd.; *Int'l*, pg. 4990
MOL LOGISTICS (KYUSHU) CO., LTD.—See Mitsui O.S.K. Lines, Ltd.; *Int'l*, pg. 4990
MOL LOGISTICS LANKA (PRIVATE) LTD.—See Mitsui O.S.K. Lines, Ltd.; *Int'l*, pg. 4990
MOL LOGISTICS (MALAYSIA) SDN. BHD.—See Mitsui O.S.K. Lines, Ltd.; *Int'l*, pg. 4990
MOL LOGISTICS (MYANMAR) CO., LTD.—See Mitsui O.S.K. Lines, Ltd.; *Int'l*, pg. 4990
MOL LOGISTICS (NETHERLANDS) B.V.—See Mitsui O.S.K. Lines, Ltd.; *Int'l*, pg. 4990
MOL LOGISTICS (PHILIPPINES) INC.—See Mitsui O.S.K. Lines, Ltd.; *Int'l*, pg. 4990
MOL LOGISTICS (SHIZUOKA), INC.—See Mitsui O.S.K. Lines, Ltd.; *Int'l*, pg. 4990
MOL LOGISTICS (SINGAPORE) PTE. LTD.—See Mitsui O.S.K. Lines, Ltd.; *Int'l*, pg. 4990

MOL LOGISTICS (TAIWAN) CO., LTD.—See Mitsui O.S.K. Lines, Ltd.; *Int'l*, pg. 4990
MOL LOGISTICS (THAILAND) CO., LTD.—See Mitsui O.S.K. Lines, Ltd.; *Int'l*, pg. 4990
MOL LOGISTICS (UK) LTD.—See Mitsui O.S.K. Lines, Ltd.; *Int'l*, pg. 4990
MOL LOGISTICS (USA) INC.—See Mitsui O.S.K. Lines, Ltd.; *Int'l*, pg. 4990
MOL LOGISTICS (VIETNAM) INC.—See Mitsui O.S.K. Lines, Ltd.; *Int'l*, pg. 4990
MOL LOGISTICS (WBLZ) CO., LTD.—See Mitsui O.S.K. Lines, Ltd.; *Int'l*, pg. 4990
MOL-LUB KFT.—See MOL Magyar Olaj- es Gazipari Nyrt.; *Int'l*, pg. 5020
MOLLY MAID, INC.; *U.S. Private*, pg. 2767
MOLMAC ENGINEERING LTD.—See MPAC Group PLC; *Int'l*, pg. 5060
MOL MAGYAR OLAJ- ES GAZIPARI NYRT.; *Int'l*, pg. 5019
MOL MARINE CONSULTING, LTD.—See Mitsui O.S.K. Lines, Ltd.; *Int'l*, pg. 4990
MOL MARINE & ENGINEERING CO., LTD.—See Mitsui O.S.K. Lines, Ltd.; *Int'l*, pg. 4990
MOL MARITIME (INDIA) PVT. LTD.—See Mitsui O.S.K. Lines, Ltd.; *Int'l*, pg. 4990
MOL NAIKOU, LTD.—See Mitsui O.S.K. Lines, Ltd.; *Int'l*, pg. 4990
MOL NETHERLANDS BULKSHIP B.V.—See Mitsui O.S.K. Lines, Ltd.; *Int'l*, pg. 4990
MOLNLYCKE HEALTH CARE AB—See Investor AB; *Int'l*, pg. 3786
MOLNLYCKE HEALTH CARE AG—See Investor AB; *Int'l*, pg. 3786
MOLNLYCKE HEALTH CARE APS—See Investor AB; *Int'l*, pg. 3786
MOLNLYCKE HEALTH CARE ASIA-PACIFIC PTE LTD—See Investor AB; *Int'l*, pg. 3786
MOLNLYCKE HEALTH CARE AS—See Investor AB; *Int'l*, pg. 3786
MOLNLYCKE HEALTH CARE B.V.—See Investor AB; *Int'l*, pg. 3786
MOLNLYCKE HEALTH CARE GMBH—See Investor AB; *Int'l*, pg. 3786
MOLNLYCKE HEALTH CARE GMBH—See Investor AB; *Int'l*, pg. 3786
MOLNLYCKE HEALTH CARE INC.—See Investor AB; *Int'l*, pg. 3786
MOLNLYCKE HEALTH CARE INDIA PVT LTD—See Investor AB; *Int'l*, pg. 3786
MOLNLYCKE HEALTH CARE KFT—See Investor AB; *Int'l*, pg. 3786
MOLNLYCKE HEALTH CARE KOREA CO., LTD—See Investor AB; *Int'l*, pg. 3786
MOLNLYCKE HEALTH CARE LTD - IRLAM FACTORY—See Investor AB; *Int'l*, pg. 3787
MOLNLYCKE HEALTH CARE LTD - OLDHAM FACTORY—See Investor AB; *Int'l*, pg. 3787
MOLNLYCKE HEALTH CARE LTD.—See Investor AB; *Int'l*, pg. 3786
MOLNLYCKE HEALTH CARE NV/SA—See Investor AB; *Int'l*, pg. 3787
MOLNLYCKE HEALTH CARE OU—See Investor AB; *Int'l*, pg. 3787
MOLNLYCKE HEALTH CARE OY—See Investor AB; *Int'l*, pg. 3787
MOLNLYCKE HEALTH CARE PTY. LTD.—See Investor AB; *Int'l*, pg. 3787
MOLNLYCKE HEALTH CARE SAS—See Investor AB; *Int'l*, pg. 3787
MOLNLYCKE HEALTH CARE SDN. BHD.—See Investor AB; *Int'l*, pg. 3787
MOLNLYCKE HEALTH CARE S.L.—See Investor AB; *Int'l*, pg. 3787
MOLNLYCKE HEALTH CARE—See Investor AB; *Int'l*, pg. 3786
MOLNLYCKE HEALTH CARE—See Investor AB; *Int'l*, pg. 3786
MOLNLYCKE HEALTH CARE—See Investor AB; *Int'l*, pg. 3786
MOLNLYCKE HEALTH CARE S.R.L.—See Investor AB; *Int'l*, pg. 3787
MOLNLYCKE HEALTH CARE US, LLC—See Investor AB; *Int'l*, pg. 3787
MOL NORDIC TANKERS A/S—See Mitsui O.S.K. Lines, Ltd.; *Int'l*, pg. 4990
MOL NORGE AS—See MOL Magyar Olaj- es Gazipari Nyrt.; *Int'l*, pg. 5020
MOLOGEN AG; *Int'l*, pg. 5022
MOLOGIC LIMITED—See Abbott Laboratories; *U.S. Public*, pg. 19
MOLOKAI PROPERTIES LIMITED—See Hong Leong Investment Holdings Pte. Ltd.; *Int'l*, pg. 3468
MOLOK (VALAIS) S.A.—See Klockner & Co. SE; *Int'l*, pg. 4202
MOLON MOTOR & COIL CORPORATION; *U.S. Private*, pg. 2767
MOLO OIL COMPANY INC.; *U.S. Private*, pg. 2767
MOLOPO ENERGY LIMITED; *Int'l*, pg. 5022
MOLPUS COMPANY; *U.S. Private*, pg. 2767

COMPANY NAME INDEX

MOL RACING KFT.—See MOL Magyar Olaj- es Gazipari Nyrt.; *Int'l*, pg. 5020
MOL ROMANIA PETROCHEMICALS—See MOL Magyar Olaj- es Gazipari Nyrt.; *Int'l*, pg. 5020
MOL ROMANIA PETROLEUM PRODUCTS SRL—See MOL Magyar Olaj- es Gazipari Nyrt.; *Int'l*, pg. 5020
MOL ROMANIA PP S.R.L.—See MOL Magyar Olaj- es Gazipari Nyrt.; *Int'l*, pg. 5020
MOL-RUSS OOO.—See MOL Magyar Olaj- es Gazipari Nyrt.; *Int'l*, pg. 5020
MOLSA SAN SALVADOR—See General Mills, Inc.; *U.S. Public*, pg. 922
MOLSBERRY MARKETS INC.; *U.S. Private*, pg. 2767
MOL SERBIA D.O.O.—See MOL Magyar Olaj- es Gazipari Nyrt.; *Int'l*, pg. 5020
MOL SERBIA (INTERMOL) D.O.O.—See MOL Magyar Olaj- es Gazipari Nyrt.; *Int'l*, pg. 5020
MOL SHIP MANAGEMENT CO., LTD.—See Mitsui O.S.K. Lines, Ltd.; *Int'l*, pg. 4991
MOL SHIP TECH INC.—See Mitsui O.S.K. Lines, Ltd.; *Int'l*, pg. 4991
MOLSLINJEN A/S—See Polaris Management A/S; *Int'l*, pg. 5908
MOL SLOVENIA D.O.O.—See MOL Magyar Olaj- es Gazipari Nyrt.; *Int'l*, pg. 5020
MOL SLOVENIJA D.O.O.—See MOL Magyar Olaj- es Gazipari Nyrt.; *Int'l*, pg. 5020
MOL SLOVENSKO SPOL. S.R.O.—See MOL Magyar Olaj- es Gazipari Nyrt.; *Int'l*, pg. 5020
MOLSON BREWERY - BRITISH COLUMBIA—See Molson Coors Beverage Company; *U.S. Public*, pg. 1459
MOLSON BREWERY - ONTARIO—See Molson Coors Beverage Company; *U.S. Public*, pg. 1459
MOLSON CANADA 2005—See Molson Coors Beverage Company; *U.S. Public*, pg. 1459
MOLSON COORS BEVERAGE COMPANY; *U.S. Public*, pg. 1459
MOLSON COORS BREWING COMPANY (UK) LTD.—See Molson Coors Beverage Company; *U.S. Public*, pg. 1459
MOLSON COORS CANADA INC.—See Molson Coors Beverage Company; *U.S. Public*, pg. 1459
MOLSON COORS CANADA—See Molson Coors Beverage Company; *U.S. Public*, pg. 1459
MOLSON COORS CENTRAL EUROPE S.R.O.—See Molson Coors Beverage Company; *U.S. Public*, pg. 1459
MOLSON COORS NETHERLANDS BV—See Molson Coors Beverage Company; *U.S. Public*, pg. 1459
MOLSON COORS (UK) HOLDINGS LLP—See Molson Coors Beverage Company; *U.S. Public*, pg. 1459
MOLSON INC.—See Molson Coors Beverage Company; *U.S. Public*, pg. 1459
MOL SOUTH AFICA (PROPRIETARY) LIMITED—See Mitsui O.S.K. Lines, Ltd.; *Int'l*, pg. 4991
MOLSTANDA VERMIETUNGSGESELLSCHAFT MBH—See Infineon Technologies AG; *Int'l*, pg. 3687
MOL TANKSHIP MANAGEMENT PTE. LTD.—See Mitsui O.S.K. Lines, Ltd.; *Int'l*, pg. 4991
MOL TECHNO-TRADE, LTD.—See Mitsui O.S.K. Lines, Ltd.; *Int'l*, pg. 4991
MOLTEN METALS CORPORATION; *Int'l*, pg. 5022
MOLTEN VENTURES GROWTH SP GP LLP—See Molten Ventures VCT plc; *Int'l*, pg. 5023
MOLTEN VENTURES PLC; *Int'l*, pg. 5022
MOLTEN VENTURES VCT PLC; *Int'l*, pg. 5023
MOLTEX BABY-HYGIENE GMBH—See Ontex Group N.V.; *Int'l*, pg. 5591
MOLTON BROWN LIMITED—See Kao Corporation; *Int'l*, pg. 4075
MOLTRADE-MINERALIMPEX—See MOL Magyar Olaj- es Gazipari Nyrt.; *Int'l*, pg. 5020
MOL-TRANS KFT.—See MOL Magyar Olaj- es Gazipari Nyrt.; *Int'l*, pg. 5020
MOLTRANS—See MOL Magyar Olaj- es Gazipari Nyrt.; *Int'l*, pg. 5020
MOLUB-ALLOY AB—See Aspo Oyj; *Int'l*, pg. 631
MOL UKRAINE LLC—See MOL Magyar Olaj- es Gazipari Nyrt.; *Int'l*, pg. 5020
MOLYCORP CHEMICALS & OXIDES (EUROPE) LTD.—See Brookfield Corporation; *Int'l*, pg. 1181
MOLYE CHEVROLET OLDSMOBILE SALES; *U.S. Private*, pg. 2767
MOLYMET BELGIUM—See Molibdenos y Metales S.A.; *Int'l*, pg. 5022
MOLYMET CORPORATION—See Molibdenos y Metales S.A.; *Int'l*, pg. 5022
MOLYMET GERMANY GMBH—See Molibdenos y Metales S.A.; *Int'l*, pg. 5022
MOLYMET GERMANY GMBH—See Molibdenos y Metales S.A.; *Int'l*, pg. 5022
MOLYMET SERVICES LTD.—See Molibdenos y Metales S.A.; *Int'l*, pg. 5022
MOLYMEX S.A. DE C.V.—See Molibdenos y Metales S.A.; *Int'l*, pg. 5022
MOLZEN-CORBIN & ASSOCIATES, P.A.; *U.S. Private*, pg. 2767
MOLZEN-CORBIN & ASSOCIATES, P.A.—See Molzen-Corbin & Associates, P.A.; *U.S. Private*, pg. 2767
MOM365, INC.; *U.S. Private*, pg. 2767

MOMA FOODS LIMITED—See A.G. Barr plc; *Int'l*, pg. 24
MOMAR AUSTRALIA PTY LTD.—See Momar, Inc.; *U.S. Private*, pg. 2768
MOMAR, INC. - SAFETYMAN DIVISION—See Momar, Inc.; *U.S. Private*, pg. 2768
MOMAR, INC.; *U.S. Private*, pg. 2767
MOMARKET—See Momar, Inc.; *U.S. Private*, pg. 2768
MOMART LIMITED—See FIH group plc; *Int'l*, pg. 2661
MOM BRANDS COMPANY, LLC—See Post Holdings, Inc.; *U.S. Public*, pg. 1703
MOM BRANDS SSALES, LLC—See Post Holdings, Inc.; *U.S. Public*, pg. 1703
MOM CENTRAL CONSULTING; *U.S. Private*, pg. 2767
THE MOM CORPS, INC.; *U.S. Private*, pg. 4080
MOMENCE MEADOWS REALTY, LLC—See Strawberry Fields REIT, Inc.; *U.S. Public*, pg. 1954
MOMENCE PALLET CORPORATION; *U.S. Private*, pg. 2768
MOMENI INC.; *U.S. Private*, pg. 2768
MOMENTA PHARMACEUTICALS, INC.—See Johnson & Johnson; *U.S. Public*, pg. 1197
MOMENT DESIGN—See Verizon Communications Inc.; *U.S. Public*, pg. 2285
MOMENTFEED, INC.—See uberall GmbH; *Int'l*, pg. 8002
MOMENT GROUP AB; *Int'l*, pg. 5023
MOMENTIVE GLOBAL INC.—See Symphony Technology Group, LLC; *U.S. Private*, pg. 3901
MOMENTIVE PERFORMANCE MATERIALS INC.—See KCC Corporation; *Int'l*, pg. 4109
MOMENTIVE PERFORMANCE MATERIALS INC.—See SJL Partners LLC; *Int'l*, pg. 6969
MOMENTIVE PERFORMANCE MATERIALS INC.—See Wonik Corporation; *Int'l*, pg. 8448
MOMENTOUS HOLDINGS CORP.; *Int'l*, pg. 5023
MOMENTOUS INSURANCE BROKERAGE, INC.—See Marsh & McLennan Companies, Inc.; *U.S. Public*, pg. 1381
MOMENTUM AFRICA INVESTMENTS LIMITED—See Momentum Group Limited; *Int'l*, pg. 5024
MOMENTUM AUTO GROUP; *U.S. Private*, pg. 2768
MOMENTUM, A VOLT INFORMATION SCIENCES COMPANY, INC.—See American CyberSystems, Inc.; *U.S. Private*, pg. 230
MOMENTUM CONSULTING CORPORATION—See CGI Inc.; *Int'l*, pg. 1434
MOMENTUM CREATIONS PTE LTD—See Nobel Design Holdings Pte Ltd; *Int'l*, pg. 5394
MOMENTUM DIGITAL SOLUTIONS INC.—See Macquarie Group Limited; *Int'l*, pg. 4628
MOMENTUM ECM, LLC; *U.S. Private*, pg. 2768
MOMENTUM ENGINEERED SYSTEMS, INC.—See Flexaseal Engineered Seals and Systems, LLC; *U.S. Private*, pg. 1543
MOMENTUM FINANCIAL HOLDINGS LIMITED; *Int'l*, pg. 5023
MOMENTUM GROUP AB—See Nordstjernan AB; *Int'l*, pg. 5425
MOMENTUM GROUP LIMITED; *Int'l*, pg. 5023
MOMENTUM, INC.; *U.S. Private*, pg. 2768
MOMENTUM INDUSTRIAL AB—See Nordstjernan AB; *Int'l*, pg. 5425
MOMENTUM LIFE BOTSWANA LTD.—See Momentum Group Limited; *Int'l*, pg. 5024
MOMENTUM MANUFACTURING GROUP, LLC—See OEP Capital Advisors, L.P.; *U.S. Private*, pg. 2999
MOMENTUM MEDICAL SCHEME ADMINISTRATORS (PTY) LTD.—See Momentum Group Limited; *Int'l*, pg. 5024
MOMENTUM METROPOLITAN LIFE LTD.—See Momentum Group Limited; *Int'l*, pg. 5024
MOMENTUM, OGILVY & MATHER—See WPP plc; *Int'l*, pg. 8484
MOMENTUM PHYSICAL & SPORTS REHABILITATION, LIMITED PARTNERSHIP—See U.S. Physical Therapy, Inc.; *U.S. Public*, pg. 2215
MOMENTUM RESOURCES, INC.—See Aquiline Capital Partners LLC; *U.S. Private*, pg. 304
MOMENTUM SOLUTIONZ, LLC—See BGSF, Inc.; *U.S. Public*, pg. 330
MOMENTUM—See The Interpublic Group of Companies, Inc.; *U.S. Public*, pg. 2102
MOMENTUM—See The Interpublic Group of Companies, Inc.; *U.S. Public*, pg. 2102
MOMENTUM—See The Interpublic Group of Companies, Inc.; *U.S. Public*, pg. 2102
MOMENTUM—See The Interpublic Group of Companies, Inc.; *U.S. Public*, pg. 2102
MOMENTUM—See The Interpublic Group of Companies, Inc.; *U.S. Public*, pg. 2102
MOMENTUM—See The Interpublic Group of Companies, Inc.; *U.S. Public*, pg. 2102
MOMENTUM SPECIALIZED STAFFING—See AtWork-Group LLC; *U.S. Private*, pg. 384
MOMENTUM TELECOM, INC.—See Court Square Capital Partners, L.P.; *U.S. Private*, pg. 1069
MOMENTUM TEXTILES INC.; *U.S. Private*, pg. 2768
MOMENTUM VOLKSWAGEN OF JERSEY VILLAGE; *U.S. Private*, pg. 2768

MOMENTUM WEALTH INTERNATIONAL LTD.—See Momentum Group Limited; *Int'l*, pg. 5024
MOMENTUM WORLDWIDE LLC—See The Interpublic Group of Companies, Inc.; *U.S. Public*, pg. 2102
MOMENTUS INC.; *U.S. Public*, pg. 1460
MOMIJI BANK, LTD.—See Yamaguchi Financial Group Inc.; *Int'l*, pg. 8548
MOMIJI JISHO CO., LTD.—See Yamaguchi Financial Group Inc.; *Int'l*, pg. 8548
MOMIMO MANUFACTURING CO., LTD.—See MITSUBA Corporation; *Int'l*, pg. 4929
MOMINA KREPOST PLC; *Int'l*, pg. 5024
MOM LE PRELET SA—See The Swatch Group Ltd.; *Int'l*, pg. 7691
MOMO AUTOMOTIVE ACCESSORIES—See MOMO S.r.l.; *Int'l*, pg. 5024
MOMO.COM INC.; *Int'l*, pg. 5024
MOMONDO A/S—See Booking Holdings, Inc.; *U.S. Public*, pg. 368
MOMONDO GROUP LIMITED—See Booking Holdings, Inc.; *U.S. Public*, pg. 368
MOMONT SA DE MARTINVAL—See KWS SAAT SE & Co. KGaA; *Int'l*, pg. 4353
MOMO S.R.L.; *Int'l*, pg. 5024
MOMPER AUTO-CHEMIE GMBH—See Wurth Verwaltungsgesellschaft mbH; *Int'l*, pg. 8506
MOMS OUTDOOR MEDIA SOLUTIONS PVT. LTD.—See Madison Communications; *Int'l*, pg. 4634
MOMS PHARMACY, INC.—See AIDS Healthcare Foundation; *U.S. Private*, pg. 131
MOM'S TOUCH & CO.; *Int'l*, pg. 5023
MOM'S TOUCH TAIWAN CO., LTD.—See Mom's Touch & Co.; *Int'l*, pg. 5023
MOM'S TOUCH VIETNAM LIMITED LIABILITY COMPANY—See Mom's Touch & Co.; *Int'l*, pg. 5023
MONACHIA AG—See Bayerische Stadte- und Wohnungsbau GmbH & Co. KG; *Int'l*, pg. 913
MONACO CORPORATION LTD.—See Shriro Pacific Ltd.; *Int'l*, pg. 6866
MONACOFIERE SRL—See Messe Munchen GmbH; *Int'l*, pg. 4841
MONACO HICKEY PTY LTD—See Wilson Bayly Holmes-Ovcon Limited; *Int'l*, pg. 8422
MONACO NORTH URBAN RENEWAL L.L.C.—See Veris Residential, Inc.; *U.S. Public*, pg. 2281
MONACO RV, LLC—See Porsche Automobil Holding SE; *Int'l*, pg. 5930
MONACO TELECOM SAM—See Bahrain Telecommunications Company BSC; *Int'l*, pg. 801
MONADELPHOUS ENGINEERING ASSOCIATES PTY. LTD.—See Monadelphous Group Limited; *Int'l*, pg. 5024
MONADELPHOUS GROUP LIMITED; *Int'l*, pg. 5024
MONADNOCK LIFETIME PRODUCTS, INC.—See BAE Systems plc; *Int'l*, pg. 796
MONADNOCK PAPER MILLS, INC.; *U.S. Private*, pg. 2768
MONADNOCK—See LISI S.A.; *Int'l*, pg. 4524
MONA ELECTRIC GROUP INC.; *U.S. Private*, pg. 2768
MONAGHAN BELGIUM B.V.B.A—See Monaghan Middlebrook Mushrooms Unlimited Company; *Int'l*, pg. 5024
MONAGHAN CHAMPIGNONS B.V.—See Monaghan Middlebrook Mushrooms Unlimited Company; *Int'l*, pg. 5024
MONAGHAN MIDDLEBROOK MUSHROOMS UNLIMITED COMPANY; *Int'l*, pg. 5024
MONAGHAN MUSHROOMS IRELAND UNLIMITED COMPANY—See Monaghan Middlebrook Mushrooms Unlimited Company; *Int'l*, pg. 5024
MONAGHAN MUSHROOMS LIMITED—See Monaghan Middlebrook Mushrooms Unlimited Company; *Int'l*, pg. 5024
MONAGHAN MUSHROOMS LTD.—See Monaghan Middlebrook Mushrooms Unlimited Company; *Int'l*, pg. 5024
MONAGHAN PILZE GMBH—See Monaghan Middlebrook Mushrooms Unlimited Company; *Int'l*, pg. 5024
MONAGHAN, TILGHMAN & HOYLE, INC.—See Aon plc; *Int'l*, pg. 496
THE MONAHAN COMPANY; *U.S. Private*, pg. 4080
MONAHAN PRODUCTS, LLC—See The Seidler Company, LLC; *U.S. Private*, pg. 4116
MONALISA CO., LTD.; *Int'l*, pg. 5024
MONALISA GROUP; *Int'l*, pg. 5024
MONA LISA PRODUCTION—See De Agostini S.p.A.; *Int'l*, pg. 1995
MONAMI CO., LTD.; *Int'l*, pg. 5024
MONA NATURPRODUKTE GMBH—See The Hain Celestial Group, Inc.; *U.S. Public*, pg. 2087
MONARCA MINERALS INC.; *Int'l*, pg. 5025
MONARCH ANTENNA, INC.—See Aptiv PLC; *Int'l*, pg. 524
MONARCH ART PLASTICS LLC; *U.S. Private*, pg. 2768
MONARCH BEVERAGE CO. INC.; *U.S. Private*, pg. 2768
THE MONARCH BEVERAGE COMPANY, INC.; *U.S. Private*, pg. 4080
MONARCH BLACK HAWK, INC.—See Monarch Casino & Resort, Inc.; *U.S. Public*, pg. 1460
MONARCH CASINO & RESORT, INC.; *U.S. Public*, pg. 1460

MONARCH CEMENT COMPANY — CORPORATE AFFILIATIONS

Company Index

MONARCH CEMENT COMPANY; *U.S. Public*, pg. 1460
MONARCH CERAMIC TILES—See Mohawk Industries, Inc.; *U.S. Public*, pg. 1457
MONARCH COLOR CORPORATION; *U.S. Private*, pg. 2768
MONARCH CONSTRUCTION COMPANY; *U.S. Private*, pg. 2768
MONARCH CONSTRUCTION CORP.; *U.S. Private*, pg. 2769
MONARCH ELECTRIC COMPANY INC.—See Blackfriars Corp.; *U.S. Private*, pg. 574
MONARCH HOLDINGS PLC; *Int'l*, pg. 5025
THE MONARCH HOTEL & CONFERENCE CENTER; *U.S. Private*, pg. 4080
MONARCH INDUSTRIES, INC.—See Avery Dennison Corporation; *U.S. Public*, pg. 244
MONARCH INDUSTRIES LIMITED—See Bank of Montreal; *Int'l*, pg. 847
MONARCH INDUSTRIES LIMITED—See Business Development Bank of Canada; *Int'l*, pg. 1229
MONARCH INDUSTRIES LIMITED—See Export Development Canada; *Int'l*, pg. 2590
MONARCH INDUSTRIES LIMITED—See TriWest Capital Management Corp.; *Int'l*, pg. 7937
MONARCH KNITTING MACHINERY CORP.; *U.S. Private*, pg. 2769
MONARCH KNITTING MACHINERY (UK) LTD.—See Monarch Knitting Machinery Corp.; *U.S. Private*, pg. 2769
MONARCH LANDSCAPE HOLDINGS LLC—See Audax Group, Limited Partnership; *U.S. Private*, pg. 389
MONARCH LEASING INC.; *U.S. Private*, pg. 2769
MONARCH LIFE INSURANCE CO.; *U.S. Public*, pg. 2769
MONARCH LITHO INC.; *U.S. Private*, pg. 2769
MONARCH, LLC; *U.S. Private*, pg. 2769
MONARCH MANAGEMENT CORPORATION—See Players Health Cover USA Inc.; *U.S. Private*, pg. 3212
MONARCH MANAGEMENT SERVICES, INC.—See UnitedHealth Group Incorporated; *U.S. Public*, pg. 2242
MONARCH MANUFACTURING CORP.—See Monarch Knitting Machinery Corp.; *U.S. Private*, pg. 2769
MONARCH MATERIALS GROUP INC.; *U.S. Private*, pg. 2769
MONARCH MEDIA, INC.; *U.S. Private*, pg. 2769
MONARCH MESSENGER SERVICES LTD.—See Mullen Group Ltd.; *Int'l*, pg. 5080
MONARCH NC; *U.S. Private*, pg. 2769
MONARCH-NEDERLAND B.V.—See Max Weishaupt GmbH; *Int'l*, pg. 4735
MONARCH NETWORTH CAPITAL LTD.; *Int'l*, pg. 5025
MONARCH NUTRACEUTICALS, INC.—See HGGC, LLC; *U.S. Private*, pg. 1930
THE MONARCH PARTNERSHIP LIMITED; *Int'l*, pg. 7668
MONARCH PIPELINE LLC—See The Williams Companies, Inc.; *U.S. Public*, pg. 2142
MONARCH POOL SYSTEMS EUROPE S.A.S.—See Amotiv Limited; *Int'l*, pg. 431
MONARCH RECOVERY MANAGEMENT INC.; *U.S. Private*, pg. 2769
MONARCH SEPARATORS INC.—See Water Standard Management; *U.S. Private*, pg. 4451
MONARCH SERVICES, INC.; *U.S. Public*, pg. 1460
MONARCH SITE SERVICES; *U.S. Private*, pg. 2769
MONARCH SOLAR LLC—See MVV Energie AG; *Int'l*, pg. 5109
MONARCH STEEL ALABAMA INC.—See American Consolidated Industries; *U.S. Private*, pg. 228
MONARCH STEEL COMPANY—See American Consolidated Industries; *U.S. Private*, pg. 228
MONARCH TRANSPORT (1975) LTD.—See Landtran Systems Inc.; *Int'l*, pg. 4408
MONARCH WELDING & ENGINEERING; *U.S. Private*, pg. 2769
MONARCH WINDOWS & DOORS INC—See Woodgrain, Inc.; *U.S. Private*, pg. 4558
MONARFLEX S.R.O.—See GAF Materials Corporation; *U.S. Private*, pg. 1634
MONARIMPORT S.P.A.—See Clarins S.A.; *Int'l*, pg. 1649
MONARK EXERCISE AB—See Grimaldi Industri AB; *Int'l*, pg. 3086
MONARQUES GOLD CORPORATION; *Int'l*, pg. 5025
MON-ASAR JOINT STOCK COMPANY; *Int'l*, pg. 5024
MONAS FEED OY AB—See E-P:n Minkinrehu Oy; *Int'l*, pg. 2249
MONASH ABSOLUTE INVESTMENT COMPANY LIMITED; *Int'l*, pg. 5025
MONASH COAL HOLDINGS PTY LTD—See Yankuang Group Co., Limited; *Int'l*, pg. 8562
MONASH HOTEL (BMG) PTY LTD—See Woolworths Group Limited; *Int'l*, pg. 8451
MONASH IVF GROUP LIMITED; *Int'l*, pg. 5025
MONASH ULTRASOUND PTY. LTD.—See Monash IVF Group Limited; *Int'l*, pg. 5025
MONASTIRIOU TECHNICAL DEVELOPMENT S.A.—See Gek Terna Societe Anonyme Holdings Real Estate Constructions; *Int'l*, pg. 2913
MONBAT AD; *Int'l*, pg. 5025
MONCEAU ASSURANCES MUTUELLES ASSOCIEES; *Int'l*, pg. 5025

MON CHERI BRIDALS INC.; *U.S. Private*, pg. 2768
MON CHONG LOONG TRADING CORP.; *U.S. Private*, pg. 2768
MONCIGALE S.A.S.—See Marie Brizard Wine & Spirits S.A.; *Int'l*, pg. 4693
MONCLER BRASIL COMERCIO DE MODA E ACESSORIOS LTDA.—See Moncler S.p.A.; *Int'l*, pg. 5025
MONCLER DENMARK APS—See Moncler S.p.A.; *Int'l*, pg. 5025
MONCLER HOLLAND B.V.—See Moncler S.p.A.; *Int'l*, pg. 5025
MONCLER HUNGARY KFT—See Moncler S.p.A.; *Int'l*, pg. 5025
MONCLER NORWAY AS—See Moncler S.p.A.; *Int'l*, pg. 5025
MONCLER PRAGUE S.R.O.—See Moncler S.p.A.; *Int'l*, pg. 5025
MONCLER S.P.A.; *Int'l*, pg. 5025
MONCLER UKRAINE LLC—See Moncler S.p.A.; *Int'l*, pg. 5025
MONCLICK S.R.L.—See Rhone Group, LLC; *U.S. Private*, pg. 3424
MONCOA MEDICAL RESEARCH INC.; *Int'l*, pg. 5025
MONCOBRA, S.A.—See ACS, Actividades de Construccion y Servicios, S.A.; *Int'l*, pg. 115
MON COURTIER ENERGIE GROUPE S.A.S.; *Int'l*, pg. 5024
MON COURTIER ENERGIE SAS; *Int'l*, pg. 5024
MONCRIEF DIALYSIS CENTER/TOTAL RENAL CARE LIMITED PARTNERSHIP—See DaVita Inc.; *U.S. Public*, pg. 641
MONDADORI AUTO—See ReWorld Media SA; *Int'l*, pg. 6315
MONDADORI ELECTA S.P.A.—See Fininvest S.p.A.; *Int'l*, pg. 2675
MONDADORI FRANCE S.A.S.—See ReWorld Media SA; *Int'l*, pg. 6315
MONDADORI FRANCHISING S.P.A.—See Fininvest S.p.A.; *Int'l*, pg. 2675
MONDADORI NATURE—See ReWorld Media SA; *Int'l*, pg. 6315
MONDADORI SCIENZA S.P.A.—See Fininvest S.p.A.; *Int'l*, pg. 2675
MONDADORI STAR—See ReWorld Media SA; *Int'l*, pg. 6315
MONDAIS HOLDINGS B.V.—See Crane NXT, Co.; *U.S. Public*, pg. 591
MONDAY.COM LTD.; *Int'l*, pg. 5025
MONDEE HOLDINGS, INC.; *U.S. Public*, pg. 1460
MONDEE INC.—See Mondee Holdings, Inc.; *U.S. Public*, pg. 1460
MONDELANGE INDUSTRIES SAS—See VINCI S.A.; *Int'l*, pg. 8224
MONDELEZ ARGENTINA S.A.—See Mondelez International, Inc.; *U.S. Public*, pg. 1461
MONDELEZ AUSTRALIA (FOODS) LTD.—See Mondelez International, Inc.; *U.S. Public*, pg. 1461
MONDELEZ AUSTRALIA HOLDINGS PTY. LTD.—See Mondelez International, Inc.; *U.S. Public*, pg. 1462
MONDELEZ AUSTRALIA PTY. LTD. - FISHERMANS BEND—See Mondelez International, Inc.; *U.S. Public*, pg. 1462
MONDELEZ AUSTRALIA PTY. LTD.—See Mondelez International, Inc.; *U.S. Public*, pg. 1462
MONDELEZ BAHRAIN W.L.L.—See Mondelez International, Inc.; *U.S. Public*, pg. 1462
MONDELEZ BELGIUM BISCUITS PRODUCTION NV—See Mondelez International, Inc.; *U.S. Public*, pg. 1462
MONDELEZ BELGIUM BVBA—See Mondelez International, Inc.; *U.S. Public*, pg. 1462
MONDELEZ BELGIUM MANUFACTURING SERVICES BVBA—See Mondelez International, Inc.; *U.S. Public*, pg. 1462
MONDELEZ BELGIUM PRODUCTION BVBA—See Mondelez International, Inc.; *U.S. Public*, pg. 1463
MONDELEZ BRASIL LTDA.—See Mondelez International, Inc.; *U.S. Public*, pg. 1462
MONDELEZ BULGARIA AD—See Mondelez International, Inc.; *U.S. Public*, pg. 1463
MONDELEZ CANADA, INC.-MONTREAL—See Mondelez International, Inc.; *U.S. Public*, pg. 1462
MONDELEZ CANADA, INC.-SCARBOROUGH—See Mondelez International, Inc.; *U.S. Public*, pg. 1462
MONDELEZ CANADA, INC.—See Mondelez International, Inc.; *U.S. Public*, pg. 1462
MONDELEZ CHILE S.A.—See Mondelez International, Inc.; *U.S. Public*, pg. 1462
MONDELEZ CHINA CO., LTD.—See Mondelez International, Inc.; *U.S. Public*, pg. 1462
MONDELEZ CZECH REPUBLIC S.R.O.—See Mondelez International, Inc.; *U.S. Public*, pg. 1463
MONDELEZ CZECH REPUBLIC S.R.O.—See Mondelez International, Inc.; *U.S. Public*, pg. 1463
MONDELEZ DANMARK APS—See Mondelez International, Inc.; *U.S. Public*, pg. 1463
MONDELEZ DEUTSCHLAND BISCUITS PRODUCTION GMBH—See Mondelez International, Inc.; *U.S. Public*, pg. 1462

MONDELEZ DEUTSCHLAND PROFESSIONAL GMBH—See Mondelez International, Inc.; *U.S. Public*, pg. 1463
MONDELEZ D.O.O. BEOGRAD—See Mondelez International, Inc.; *U.S. Public*, pg. 1464
MONDELEZ ESPANA BISCUITS HOLDINGS Y CAMPANIA S.C.—See Mondelez International, Inc.; *U.S. Public*, pg. 1463
MONDELEZ ESPANA CONFECTIONERY PRODUCTION, SLU—See Mondelez International, Inc.; *U.S. Public*, pg. 1462
MONDELEZ ESPANA GALLETAS PRODUCTION, S.L.U.—See Mondelez International, Inc.; *U.S. Public*, pg. 1463
MONDELEZ ESPANA POSTRES PRODUCTION, S.A.U.—See Mondelez International, Inc.; *U.S. Public*, pg. 1463
MONDELEZ ESPANA SERVICES, S.L.U.—See Mondelez International, Inc.; *U.S. Public*, pg. 1463
MONDELEZ EUROPEAN BUSINESS SERVICES CENTRE S.R.O.—See Mondelez International, Inc.; *U.S. Public*, pg. 1463
MONDELEZ EUROPE GMBH—See Mondelez International, Inc.; *U.S. Public*, pg. 1462
MONDELEZ FINLAND OY—See Mondelez International, Inc.; *U.S. Public*, pg. 1463
MONDELEZ FRANCE BISCUITS PRODUCTION SAS—See Mondelez International, Inc.; *U.S. Public*, pg. 1463
MONDELEZ FRANCE SAS—See Mondelez International, Inc.; *U.S. Public*, pg. 1463
MONDELEZ HELLAS S.A.—See Mondelez International, Inc.; *U.S. Public*, pg. 1463
MONDELEZ HUNGARIA KFT—See Mondelez International, Inc.; *U.S. Public*, pg. 1463
MONDELEZ INDIA FOODS PRIVATE LIMITED—See Mondelez International, Inc.; *U.S. Public*, pg. 1462
MONDELEZ INTERNATIONAL FINANCE AG—See Mondelez International, Inc.; *U.S. Public*, pg. 1463
MONDELEZ INTERNATIONAL, INC.; *U.S. Public*, pg. 1460
MONDELEZ INTERNATIONAL MANAGEMENT CENTER-EAST HANOVER—See Mondelez International, Inc.; *U.S. Public*, pg. 1464
MONDELEZ INTERNATIONAL RUS—See Mondelez International, Inc.; *U.S. Public*, pg. 1463
MONDELEZ INTERNATIONAL (THAILAND) CO., LTD—See Mondelez International, Inc.; *U.S. Public*, pg. 1464
MONDELEZ IRELAND LIMITED—See Mondelez International, Inc.; *U.S. Public*, pg. 1463
MONDELEZ IRELAND PRODUCTION LIMITED—See Mondelez International, Inc.; *U.S. Public*, pg. 1464
MONDELEZ ITALIA S.R.L.—See Mondelez International, Inc.; *U.S. Public*, pg. 1463
MONDELEZ JAPAN LTD—See Mondelez International, Inc.; *U.S. Public*, pg. 1464
MONDELEZ JIANGMEN FOOD CO., LTD.—See Mondelez International, Inc.; *U.S. Public*, pg. 1462
MONDELEZ KINH DO VIETNAM JSC—See Mondelez International, Inc.; *U.S. Public*, pg. 1464
MONDELEZ MALAYSIA SALES SDN. BHD.—See Mondelez International, Inc.; *U.S. Public*, pg. 1462
MONDELEZ MALAYSIA SDN BHD.—See Mondelez International, Inc.; *U.S. Public*, pg. 1462
MONDELEZ NAMUR PRODUCTION SPRL—See Mondelez International, Inc.; *U.S. Public*, pg. 1463
MONDELEZ NEDERLAND B.V.—See Mondelez International, Inc.; *U.S. Public*, pg. 1464
MONDELEZ NEDERLAND SERVICES B.V.—See Mondelez International, Inc.; *U.S. Public*, pg. 1463
MONDELEZ NEW ZEALAND—See Mondelez International, Inc.; *U.S. Public*, pg. 1463
MONDELEZ NORGE AS—See Mondelez International, Inc.; *U.S. Public*, pg. 1463
MONDELEZ OESTERREICH PRODUCTION GMBH—See Mondelez International, Inc.; *U.S. Public*, pg. 1464
MONDELEZ OSTERREICH GMBH—See Mondelez International, Inc.; *U.S. Public*, pg. 1463
MONDELEZ PAKISTAN LIMITED—See Mondelez International, Inc.; *U.S. Public*, pg. 1464
MONDELEZ PHILIPPINES, INC.—See Mondelez International, Inc.; *U.S. Public*, pg. 1462
MONDELEZ POLSKA PRODUCTION SP. Z.O.O.—See Mondelez International, Inc.; *U.S. Public*, pg. 1464
MONDELEZ POLSKA S.A.—See Mondelez International, Inc.; *U.S. Public*, pg. 1463
MONDELEZ PORTUGAL IBERIA PRODUCTION, S.A.—See Mondelez International, Inc.; *U.S. Public*, pg. 1463
MONDELEZ PORTUGAL, UNIPESSOAL, LDA.—See Mondelez International, Inc.; *U.S. Public*, pg. 1463
MONDELEZ PUERTO RICO LLC—See Mondelez International, Inc.; *U.S. Public*, pg. 1464
MONDELEZ SCHWEIZ GMBH—See Mondelez International, Inc.; *U.S. Public*, pg. 1463
MONDELEZ SCHWEIZ PRODUCTION GMBH—See Mondelez International, Inc.; *U.S. Public*, pg. 1463

COMPANY NAME INDEX

MONDELEZ SHANGHAI FOOD CO., LTD.—See Mondelez International, Inc.; *U.S. Public*, pg. 1462
MONDELEZ SINGAPORE PTE. LTD.—See Mondelez International, Inc.; *U.S. Public*, pg. 1462
MONDELEZ SLOVAKIA S.R.O.—See Mondelez International, Inc.; *U.S. Public*, pg. 1462
MONDELEZ SOUTH AFRICA (PTY) LTD.—See Mondelez International, Inc.; *U.S. Public*, pg. 1464
MONDELEZ STRASBOURG PRODUCTION S.N.C.—See Mondelez International, Inc.; *U.S. Public*, pg. 1463
MONDELEZ SUZHOU FOOD CO., LTD.—See Mondelez International, Inc.; *U.S. Public*, pg. 1462
MONDELEZ SVERIGE AB—See Mondelez International, Inc.; *U.S. Public*, pg. 1463
MONDELEZ TAIWAN LIMITED—See Mondelez International, Inc.; *U.S. Public*, pg. 1462
MONDELEZ (THAILAND) CO., LTD.—See Mondelez International, Inc.; *U.S. Public*, pg. 1461
MONDELEZ TURKEY GIDA URETIM A.S.—See Mondelez International, Inc.; *U.S. Public*, pg. 1464
MONDELEZ UK CONFECTIONERY PRODUCTION LIMITED—See Mondelez International, Inc.; *U.S. Public*, pg. 1461
MONDELEZ UK LIMITED—See Mondelez International, Inc.; *U.S. Public*, pg. 1463
MONDELEZ URUGUAY S.A.—See Mondelez International, Inc.; *U.S. Public*, pg. 1462
MONDELEZ WORLD TRAVEL RETAIL GMBH—See Mondelez International, Inc.; *U.S. Public*, pg. 1462
MONDE NISSIN CORPORATION; *Int'l*, pg. 5025
MONDERA.COM; *U.S. Private*, pg. 2769
MONDE SANS FRONTIERES; *Int'l*, pg. 5025
MON DESERT-ALMA SUGAR MILLING COMPANY LIMITED—See ENL Limited; *Int'l*, pg. 2441
MONDI ABERDEEN LIMITED—See Mondi plc; *Int'l*, pg. 5026
MONDI AG—See Mondi plc; *Int'l*, pg. 5026
MONDI AKROSIL, LLC—See Mondi plc; *Int'l*, pg. 5026
MONDIAL ASSISTANCE AGENT DE ASIGURARE SRL—See Allianz SE; *Int'l*, pg. 354
MONDIAL ASSISTANCE ASIA PACIFIC LTD.—See Allianz SE; *Int'l*, pg. 354
MONDIAL ASSISTANCE/AUTO ASSIST CO., LTD.—See Allianz SE; *Int'l*, pg. 354
MONDIAL ASSISTANCE BELGIUM—See Allianz SE; *Int'l*, pg. 354
MONDIAL ASSISTANCE BRAZIL—See Allianz SE; *Int'l*, pg. 354
MONDIAL ASSISTANCE FRANCE—See Allianz SE; *Int'l*, pg. 354
MONDIAL ASSISTANCE GMBH—See Allianz SE; *Int'l*, pg. 354
MONDIAL ASSISTANCE GREECE—See Allianz SE; *Int'l*, pg. 354
MONDIAL ASSISTANCE GROUP—See Allianz SE; *Int'l*, pg. 342
MONDIAL ASSISTANCE IRELAND LIMITED—See Allianz SE; *Int'l*, pg. 354
MONDIAL ASSISTANCE OOO—See Allianz SE; *Int'l*, pg. 354
MONDIAL ASSISTANCE PORTUGAL—See Allianz SE; *Int'l*, pg. 342
MONDIAL ASSISTANCE REUNION S.A.—See Allianz SE; *Int'l*, pg. 354
MONDIAL ASSISTANCE SARL—See Allianz SE; *Int'l*, pg. 354
MONDIAL ASSISTANCE SIGORTA ARACILIK HIZMETLERI LIMITED SIRKETI, LS—See Allianz SE; *Int'l*, pg. 354
MONDIAL ASSISTANCE SINGAPORE—See Allianz SE; *Int'l*, pg. 342
MONDIAL ASSISTANCE SP. Z O.O.—See Allianz SE; *Int'l*, pg. 354
MONDIAL ASSISTANCE S.R.O—See Allianz SE; *Int'l*, pg. 354
MONDIAL ASSISTANCE TURKEY—See Allianz SE; *Int'l*, pg. 354
MONDIAL INTERNATIONAL CORPORATION; *U.S. Private*, pg. 2769
MONDIAL SERVICE- BELGIUM S.A.—See Allianz SE; *Int'l*, pg. 354
MONDIAL SERVICE ITALIA S.R.L—See Allianz SE; *Int'l*, pg. 354
MONDIAL SERVICES (INDIA) PVT. LTD.—See Allianz SE; *Int'l*, pg. 354
MONDIAL SERVICIOS S.A. DE C.V.—See Allianz SE; *Int'l*, pg. 354
MONDIAL VENTURES, INC.; *U.S. Private*, pg. 2769
MONDI ASCANIA GMBH—See Mondi plc; *Int'l*, pg. 5026
MONDI BAD RAPPENAU GMBH—See Mondi plc; *Int'l*, pg. 5026
MONDI BAGS HUNGARIA KFT.—See Mondi plc; *Int'l*, pg. 5026
MONDI BAGS IBERICA S.L.—See Mondi plc; *Int'l*, pg. 5026
MONDI BAGS MIELEC SP. Z O.O.—See Mondi plc; *Int'l*, pg. 5026
MONDI BAGS STETI A.S.—See Mondi plc; *Int'l*, pg. 5026
MONDI BAGS SWIECIE SP. Z O.O.—See Mondi plc; *Int'l*, pg. 5026
MONDI BAGS USA, LLC—See Mondi plc; *Int'l*, pg. 5026
MONDI BANGKOK COMPANY, LIMITED—See Mondi plc; *Int'l*, pg. 5026
MONDI BEKESCSABA KFT.—See Mondi plc; *Int'l*, pg. 5026
MONDI BUCHAREST S.R.L.—See Mondi plc; *Int'l*, pg. 5026
MONDI BUPAK S.R.O.—See Mondi plc; *Int'l*, pg. 5026
MONDI CARTAGENA SAS—See Mondi plc; *Int'l*, pg. 5026
MONDI COATING STETI A.S.—See Mondi plc; *Int'l*, pg. 5026
MONDI COATING (THAILAND) CO. LTD.—See Mondi plc; *Int'l*, pg. 5026
MONDI COATING ZELTWEG GMBH—See Mondi plc; *Int'l*, pg. 5026
MONDI CONSUMER BAGS & FILMS BENELUX B.V.—See Mondi plc; *Int'l*, pg. 5026
MONDI CONSUMER PACKAGING INTERNATIONAL AG—See Mondi plc; *Int'l*, pg. 5026
MONDI CORRUGATED SWIECIE SP. Z O.O—See Mondi plc; *Int'l*, pg. 5026
MONDICS INSURANCE GROUP INC; *U.S. Private*, pg. 2769
MONDI DEESIDE—See Mondi plc; *Int'l*, pg. 5026
MONDI DOROHUSK SP. Z O.O.—See Mondi plc; *Int'l*, pg. 5026
MONDI ESCHENBACH GMBH—See Mondi plc; *Int'l*, pg. 5026
MONDI GLOSSOP LTD.—See Mondi plc; *Int'l*, pg. 5026
MONDI GOURNAY SARL—See Mondi plc; *Int'l*, pg. 5026
MONDI GRADISAC S.R.L.—See Mondi plc; *Int'l*, pg. 5026
MONDI GRONAU GMBH—See Mondi plc; *Int'l*, pg. 5026
MONDI HALLE GMBH—See Mondi plc; *Int'l*, pg. 5026
MONDI HAMMELBURG GMBH—See Mondi plc; *Int'l*, pg. 5026
MONDI HEERLEN B.V.—See Mondi plc; *Int'l*, pg. 5026
MONDI INNCOAT GMBH—See Mondi plc; *Int'l*, pg. 5026
MONDI ISTANBUL AMBALAJ LIMITED STI—See Mondi plc; *Int'l*, pg. 5026
MONDI ITALIA S.R.L.—See Mondi plc; *Int'l*, pg. 5026
MONDI JACKSON LLC—See Mondi plc; *Int'l*, pg. 5026
MONDI JULICH GMBH—See Mondi plc; *Int'l*, pg. 5026
MONDI KALE NOBEL AMBALAJ SANAYI VE TICARET A.S.—See Mondi plc; *Int'l*, pg. 5026
MONDI KORNEUBURG GMBH—See Mondi plc; *Int'l*, pg. 5026
MONDI KUALA LUMPUR SDN. BHD.—See Mondi plc; *Int'l*, pg. 5026
MONDI LAMEX D.O.O.—See Lamex Foods UK Limited; *Int'l*, pg. 4401
MONDI LEBANON SAL—See Mondi plc; *Int'l*, pg. 5026
MONDI LOHJA OY—See Mondi plc; *Int'l*, pg. 5026
MONDI MAASTRICHT N.V.—See Mondi plc; *Int'l*, pg. 5026
MONDI MEXICO S. DE R.L. DE C.V.—See Mondi plc; *Int'l*, pg. 5026
MONDI MINNEAPOLIS, INC.—See Mondi plc; *Int'l*, pg. 5026
MONDI MOSS AS—See Mondi plc; *Int'l*, pg. 5026
MONDI NEUSIEDLER GMBH—See Mondi plc; *Int'l*, pg. 5026
MONDI OREBRO AB—See Mondi plc; *Int'l*, pg. 5026
MONDI PACKAGING AKROSIL, LLC—See Mondi plc; *Int'l*, pg. 5026
MONDI PACKAGING AKROSIL, LLC—See Mondi plc; *Int'l*, pg. 5027
MONDI PACKAGING BAGS UKRAINE LLC—See Mondi plc; *Int'l*, pg. 5027
MONDI PACKAGING LIMITED—See Mondi plc; *Int'l*, pg. 5027
MONDI PACKAGING LTD.—See Mondi plc; *Int'l*, pg. 5027
MONDI PACKAGING PAPER SALES ASIA PTE. LTD.—See Mondi plc; *Int'l*, pg. 5027
MONDI PACKAGING SERVICES GMBH—See Mondi plc; *Int'l*, pg. 5027
MONDI PADOVA S.R.L.—See Mondi plc; *Int'l*, pg. 5027
MONDI PAPER SALES DEUTSCHLAND GMBH—See Mondi plc; *Int'l*, pg. 5027
MONDI PAPER SALES FRANCE SARL—See Mondi plc; *Int'l*, pg. 5027
MONDI PAPER SALES GMBH—See Mondi plc; *Int'l*, pg. 5027
MONDI PAPER SALES NETHERLANDS B.V.—See Mondi plc; *Int'l*, pg. 5027
MONDI PLC; *Int'l*, pg. 5025
MONDI POPERINGE N.V.—See Mondi plc; *Int'l*, pg. 5027
MONDI POWERFLUTE OY—See Mondi plc; *Int'l*, pg. 5027
MONDI POZNAN SP. Z O.O.—See Mondi plc; *Int'l*, pg. 5027
MONDI ROMEOVILLE LLC—See Mondi plc; *Int'l*, pg. 5027
MONDI SABAC D.O.O.—See Mondi plc; *Int'l*, pg. 5027
MONDI SCP, A.S.—See Mondi plc; *Int'l*, pg. 5027
MONDI SOLEC SP. Z O.O.—See Mondi plc; *Int'l*, pg. 5027
MONDI SOUTH AFRICA LTD.—See Mondi plc; *Int'l*, pg. 5027
MONDI SOUTH AFRICA (PTY) LIMITED—See Mondi plc; *Int'l*, pg. 5027

MONETIVA, INC.

MONDI STAMBOLIJSKI E.A.D—See Mondi plc; *Int'l*, pg. 5027
MONDI STETI A.S.—See Mondi plc; *Int'l*, pg. 5027
MONDI STYRIA GMBH—See Mondi plc; *Int'l*, pg. 5027
MONDI SWIECIE S.A.—See Mondi plc; *Int'l*, pg. 5027
MONDI SZADA KFT.—See Mondi plc; *Int'l*, pg. 5027
MONDI SZCZECIN SP. Z O.O.—See Mondi plc; *Int'l*, pg. 5027
MONDI TEKKOTE LLC—See Mondi plc; *Int'l*, pg. 5027
MONDI THESSALONIKI A.E.—See Mondi plc; *Int'l*, pg. 5027
MONDI TIRE KUTSAN KAGIT VE AMBALAJ SANAYI A.S.—See Mondi plc; *Int'l*, pg. 5027
MONDI TIRE KUTSAN KAGIT VE AMBALAJ SANAYII AS—See Mondi plc; *Int'l*, pg. 5027
MONDI TOKYO KK—See Mondi plc; *Int'l*, pg. 5027
MONDI TOLENTINO S.R.L.—See Mondi plc; *Int'l*, pg. 5027
MONDI TREBSEN GMBH—See Mondi plc; *Int'l*, pg. 5027
MONDI TSP COMPANY LIMITED—See Mondi plc; *Int'l*, pg. 5027
MONDIV—See Lassonde Industries, Inc.; *Int'l*, pg. 4421
MONDI WARSZAWA SP. Z O.O.—See Mondi plc; *Int'l*, pg. 5027
MONDI WELLPAPPE ANSBACH GMBH—See Mondi plc; *Int'l*, pg. 5027
MONDI WIERZBICA SP. Z O.O.—See Mondi plc; *Int'l*, pg. 5027
MONDI ZIMELE PROPRIETARY LIMITED—See Mondi plc; *Int'l*, pg. 5027
MONDO ENTERTAINMENT GMBH—See Mondo TV S.p.A.; *Int'l*, pg. 5028
MONDOFARMA S.R.L.—See CompuGroup Medical SE & Co. KGaA; *Int'l*, pg. 1756
MONDOFFICE S.R.L.—See The RAJA Group; *Int'l*, pg. 7678
MONDO FOODS COMPANY LTD.; *Int'l*, pg. 5027
MONDO HOME ENTERTAINMENT S.P.A.—See Mondo TV S.p.A.; *Int'l*, pg. 5028
MONDOLIBRI S.P.A.—See Bertelsmann SE & Co. KGaA; *Int'l*, pg. 992
MONDOLIBRI S.P.A.—See Fininvest S.p.A.; *Int'l*, pg. 2675
MONDO MEDIA CORPORATION; *U.S. Private*, pg. 2769
MONDO MINERALS B.V.—See Elementis plc; *Int'l*, pg. 2359
MONDO PUBLISHING, INC.—See CIP Capital Fund, L.P.; *U.S. Private*, pg. 899
MONDO—See Odyssey Investment Partners, LLC; *U.S. Private*, pg. 2994
MONDO SYSTEMS INC.—See UbiVelox Co., Ltd.; *Int'l*, pg. 8004
MONDO TEES, LLC—See Funko Inc.; *U.S. Public*, pg. 893
MONDO TV FRANCE SA—See Mondo TV S.p.A.; *Int'l*, pg. 5028
MONDO TV IBEROAMERICA SA—See Mondo TV S.p.A.; *Int'l*, pg. 5028
MONDO TV SPAIN S.L.—See Mondo TV S.p.A.; *Int'l*, pg. 5028
MONDO TV S.P.A.; *Int'l*, pg. 5027
MONDO TV SUISSE SPA—See Mondo TV S.p.A.; *Int'l*, pg. 5028
MONDRAGON ASSEMBLY, S.COOP.—See Mondragón Corporation; *Int'l*, pg. 5031
MONDRAGON CORPORATION; *Int'l*, pg. 5028
MONDRIAN LOS ANGELES—See SBEEG Holdings, LLC; *U.S. Private*, pg. 3559
MONDSEE LIMITED—See Hysan Development Company Limited; *Int'l*, pg. 3554
MONDURA LIEGENSCHAFTEN AG; *Int'l*, pg. 5031
MONECAM; *Int'l*, pg. 5031
MONEDA ASSET MANAGEMENT S.A.; *Int'l*, pg. 5031
MONEDA LATAM CORPORATE BOND FUND—See The Bank of Nova Scotia; *Int'l*, pg. 7617
MONEDA RENTA VARIABLE CHILE FONDO DO INVERSION; *Int'l*, pg. 5031
MONEGROS DEPURA, S.A.—See ACS, Actividades de Construccion y Servicios, S.A.; *Int'l*, pg. 115
MONELEC, S.L.—See ACS, Actividades de Construccion y Servicios, S.A.; *Int'l*, pg. 115
MONEMAP INVESTMENT ADVISORS PRIVATE LIMITED—See Niyogin Fintech Limited; *Int'l*, pg. 5390
MONENCO CONSULTANCY SERVICES COMPANY—See MAPNA Group; *Int'l*, pg. 4687
MONERIS SOLUTIONS CORPORATION—See Bank of Montreal; *Int'l*, pg. 847
MONERIS SOLUTIONS CORPORATION—See Royal Bank of Canada; *Int'l*, pg. 6409
MONESSEN HOLDING COMPANY—See HNI Corporation; *U.S. Public*, pg. 1043
MONETA AUTO, S.R.O.—See MONETA Money Bank a.s.; *Int'l*, pg. 5032
MONETA GROUP, LLC.; *U.S. Private*, pg. 2769
MONETA LEASING, S.R.O.—See MONETA Money Bank a.s.; *Int'l*, pg. 5032
MONETA MONEY BANK A.S.; *Int'l*, pg. 5032
MONETARY AUTHORITY OF MACAU; *Int'l*, pg. 5032
MONETARY AUTHORITY OF SINGAPORE; *Int'l*, pg. 5032
MONETATE, INC.—See Centre Lane Partners, LLC; *U.S. Private*, pg. 827
MONETIVA, INC.; *U.S. Private*, pg. 2769

MONETRA TECHNOLOGIES, LLC—See i3 Verticals, Inc.; *U.S. Public*, pg. 1081
MONETTE SPORTS INC.; *Int'l*, pg. 5032
MONEXA SERVCIES, INC., *Int'l*, pg. 5032
MONEX ASSETS MANAGEMENT INC.—See Monex, S.A.P.I. de C.V.; *Int'l*, pg. 5032
MONEX BOOM SECURITIES (H.K.) LIMITED—See Monex Group, Inc.; *Int'l*, pg. 5032
MONEX BUSINESS INCUBATION, INC.—See Monex Group, Inc.; *Int'l*, pg. 5032
MONEX CANADA, INC.—See Monex, S.A.P.I. de C.V.; *Int'l*, pg. 5032
MONEX CAPITAL PARTNERS, INC.—See Monex Group, Inc.; *Int'l*, pg. 5032
MONEX DEPOSIT COMPANY; *U.S. Private*, pg. 2770
MONEX EUROPE LIMITED—See Monex, S.A.P.I. de C.V.; *Int'l*, pg. 5032
MONEX FX, INC.—See Monex Group, Inc.; *Int'l*, pg. 5032
MONEX GROUP, INC.; *Int'l*, pg. 5032
MONEX HAMBRECHT—See Monex Group, Inc.; *Int'l*, pg. 5032
MONEX, INC.—See Monex Group, Inc.; *Int'l*, pg. 5032
MONEX, S.A.P.I. DE C.V.; *Int'l*, pg. 5032
MONEX SECURITIES AUSTRALIA PTY LTD—See Monex Group, Inc.; *Int'l*, pg. 5032
MONEX SECURITIES, INC.—See Monex, S.A.P.I. de C.V.; *Int'l*, pg. 5032
MONEX UNIVERSITY, INC.—See Monex Group, Inc.; *Int'l*, pg. 5032
MONEY3 BALLARAT PTY LTD—See Solvar Limited; *Int'l*, pg. 7077
MONEY3 DANDENONG PTY LTD.—See Solvar Limited; *Int'l*, pg. 7077
MONEY3 RESERVOIR PTY LTD.—See Solvar Limited; *Int'l*, pg. 7077
MONEY3 WODONGA PTY LTD.—See Solvar Limited; *Int'l*, pg. 7077
MONEYAM LIMITED—See AJ Bell Plc.; *Int'l*, pg. 255
MONEY ATUOMOTIVE CENTER INC.; *U.S. Private*, pg. 2770
MONEYBARN LIMITED—See Vanquis Banking Group plc; *Int'l*, pg. 8130
MONEYBOXX FINANCE LIMITED; *Int'l*, pg. 5033
MONEY CLIP MAGAZINE; *U.S. Private*, pg. 2770
MONEYCORP US INC.—See TTT moneycorp Limited; *Int'l*, pg. 7961
MONEY DEBT & CREDIT GROUP LTD.; *Int'l*, pg. 5032
MONEY FORWARD, INC.; *Int'l*, pg. 5032
MONEYGRAM FOUNDATION, INC.—See Madison Dearborn Partners, LLC; *U.S. Private*, pg. 2541
MONEYGRAM INTERNATIONAL HOLDINGS LTD.—See Madison Dearborn Partners, LLC; *U.S. Private*, pg. 2541
MONEYGRAM INTERNATIONAL, INC.—See Madison Dearborn Partners, LLC; *U.S. Private*, pg. 2541
MONEYGRAM INTERNATIONAL LTD.—See Madison Dearborn Partners, LLC; *U.S. Private*, pg. 2541
MONEYGRAM OVERSEAS (PTY) LIMITED SOUTH AFRICA—See Madison Dearborn Partners, LLC; *U.S. Private*, pg. 2541
MONEYGRAM PAYMENT SYSTEMS BELGIUM N.V.—See Madison Dearborn Partners, LLC; *U.S. Private*, pg. 2541
MONEYGRAM PAYMENT SYSTEMS, INC.—See Madison Dearborn Partners, LLC; *U.S. Private*, pg. 2541
MONEYGRAM PAYMENT SYSTEMS ITALY, S.R.L.—See Madison Dearborn Partners, LLC; *U.S. Private*, pg. 2541
MONEYGRAM PAYMENT SYSTEMS SPAIN, S.A.—See Madison Dearborn Partners, LLC; *U.S. Private*, pg. 2541
MONEYGRAM PAYMENT SYSTEMS WORLDWIDE, INC.—See Madison Dearborn Partners, LLC; *U.S. Private*, pg. 2541
MONEYLINE FINANCIAL SERVICES (PTY) LTD—See Lesaka Technologies, Inc.; *Int'l*, pg. 4469
MONEYLION, INC.; *U.S. Public*, pg. 1464
MONEY MAILER, LLC—See Local Marketing Solutions Group, Inc.; *U.S. Private*, pg. 2477
MONEY MANAGEMENT INTERNATIONAL; *U.S. Private*, pg. 2770
MONEY MANAGEMENT PTY. LTD.—See Yellow Brick Road Holdings Ltd.; *Int'l*, pg. 8576
MONEY MART CANADA INC.—See Lone Star Global Acquisitions, LLC; *U.S. Private*, pg. 2487
MONEY MASTERS LEASING & FINANCE LIMITED; *Int'l*, pg. 5033
MONEY MATTERS (NORTH EAST) LIMITED—See Kingswood Holdings Ltd.; *Int'l*, pg. 4180
MONEYMAX FINANCIAL SERVICES LTD.; *Int'l*, pg. 5033
MONEYMAX LEASING PTE. LTD.—See MoneyMax Financial Services Ltd.; *Int'l*, pg. 5033
MONEY MEDIA INC—See Pearson plc; *Int'l*, pg. 5777
MONEYME LIMITED; *Int'l*, pg. 5033
MONEY.NET, INC.; *U.S. Private*, pg. 2770
MONEYNET S.P.A.—See IVS Group S.A.; *Int'l*, pg. 3848
MONEYONMOBILE, INC.; *U.S. Public*, pg. 1464
MONEYOU B.V.—See ABN AMRO Group N.V.; *Int'l*, pg. 65
MONEY PARTNERS GROUP CO., LTD.; *Int'l*, pg. 5033

MONEY PARTNERS SOLUTIONS CO., LTD.—See Money Partners Group Co., Ltd.; *Int'l*, pg. 5033
MONEY PLACE ASSETS PTY. LTD.—See Liberty Financial Group Limited; *Int'l*, pg. 4484
MONEY SAVER COUPON BOOK INC.; *U.S. Private*, pg. 2770
MONEY SERVICES INC.—See Aegon N.V.; *Int'l*, pg. 174
MONEYSHOW.COM, LLC; *U.S. Private*, pg. 2770
MONEY SQUARE HOLDINGS, INC.; *Int'l*, pg. 5033
MONEY SQUARE JAPAN, INC.—See Money Square Holdings, Inc.; *Int'l*, pg. 5033
MONEY STORE LP; *U.S. Private*, pg. 2770
MONEYSUPERMARKET.COM GROUP PLC; *Int'l*, pg. 5033
MONEYSUPERMARKET.COM LIMITED—See Moneysupermarket.com Group PLC; *Int'l*, pg. 5033
MONEYSWAP PLC; *Int'l*, pg. 5033
MONEYSWORTH & BEST INC; *Int'l*, pg. 5033
MONEYSWORTH & BEST SHOE CARE, INC.—See Moneysworth & Best Inc; *Int'l*, pg. 5033
MONEY TAP CO., LTD.—See SBI Holdings, Inc.; *Int'l*, pg. 6604
MONEYTREE, INC.; *U.S. Private*, pg. 2770
THE MONEY TREE INC.; *U.S. Private*, pg. 4080
MONEYWEB HOLDINGS LIMITED; *Int'l*, pg. 5033
MONEYWISE GLOBAL PTY. LTD.—See Flight Centre Travel Group Limited; *Int'l*, pg. 2706
MONEY WISE PAYROLL SOLUTIONS—See Blue Ridge Bankshares, Inc.; *U.S. Public*, pg. 365
MONEYWISE WEALTH MANAGEMENT; *U.S. Private*, pg. 2770
MONFAIR MODEN VERTRIEBS GMBH—See Aderans Co., Ltd.; *Int'l*, pg. 143
MONFER CEREALI SRL—See Vivescia; *Int'l*, pg. 8279
MONFER FRANCE S.A.—See Vivescia; *Int'l*, pg. 8279
MONGEO JOINT STOCK COMPANY; *Int'l*, pg. 5033
MONGKOLSAMAI CO., LTD.—See Thai Beverage Public Company Limited; *Int'l*, pg. 7591
MONGODB, INC.; *U.S. Public*, pg. 1464
MONGODB LIMITED—See MongoDB, Inc.; *U.S. Public*, pg. 1464
MONGOL CONTENT LLC—See T Scientific Co., Ltd; *Int'l*, pg. 7394
MONGOLIA ENERGY CORPORATION LIMITED; *Int'l*, pg. 5034
MONGOLIA GAO FENG CASHMERE CO., LTD.—See Suez Asia Holdings Pte. Ltd.; *Int'l*, pg. 7253
MONGOLIA GROWTH GROUP LTD.; *Int'l*, pg. 5034
MONGOLIA HOLDINGS, INC.; *U.S. Private*, pg. 2770
MONGOLIA OPERATING CO. LLC—See Kinderhook Industries, LLC; *U.S. Private*, pg. 2307
MONGOLIAN RESOURCE CORPORATION LIMITED; *Int'l*, pg. 5034
MONGOLIAN STAR MELCHERS CO., LTD.—See Jebsen & Jessen (SEA) Pte Ltd; *Int'l*, pg. 3926
MONGOLIAN STOCK EXCHANGE; *Int'l*, pg. 5034
MONGOL MAKH EXPO; *Int'l*, pg. 5033
MONGOL SECURITIES JOINT STOCK COMPANY; *Int'l*, pg. 5033
MONGOL SHILTGEEN JOINT STOCK COMPANY; *Int'l*, pg. 5033
MONGOL SHIR JOINT STOCK COMPANY; *Int'l*, pg. 5033
MONGOOSE MINING LTD.; *Int'l*, pg. 5034
MONGOOSE PROMOTIONS LTD.—See The Mission Group Public Limited Company; *Int'l*, pg. 7667
MONGOOSE SPORTS & ENTERTAINMENT—See The Mission Group Public Limited Company; *Int'l*, pg. 7667
MONICA ELECTRONICS LTD.; *Int'l*, pg. 5034
MONICO ALLOYS, INC.; *U.S. Private*, pg. 2770
MONICO INC.; *U.S. Private*, pg. 2770
MONIER A/S—See PAI Partners S.A.S.; *Int'l*, pg. 5701
MONIER AS—See PAI Partners S.A.S.; *Int'l*, pg. 5701
MONIER B.V.—See PAI Partners S.A.S.; *Int'l*, pg. 5701
MONIER GMBH—See PAI Partners S.A.S.; *Int'l*, pg. 5700
MONIER GROUP GMBH—See PAI Partners S.A.S.; *Int'l*, pg. 5700
MONIER LTD.—See PAI Partners S.A.S.; *Int'l*, pg. 5701
MONIER ROOF PRODUCTS BELGIUM N.V.—See PAI Partners S.A.S.; *Int'l*, pg. 5701
MONIER SAS—See PAI Partners S.A.S.; *Int'l*, pg. 5701
MONIER SDN BHD—See PAI Partners S.A.S.; *Int'l*, pg. 5701
MONIER S.P.A.—See PAI Partners S.A.S.; *Int'l*, pg. 5701
MONIER TECHNICAL CENTRE LTD.—See PAI Partners S.A.S.; *Int'l*, pg. 5701
MONIKER ONLINE SERVICES, LLC—See Oversee.net; *U.S. Private*, pg. 3053
MONIN ASIA KL SDN BHD—See Groupe Monin SAS; *Int'l*, pg. 3109
MONIND LTD.—See Apollo Global Management, Inc.; *U.S. Public*, pg. 152
MONIND LTD.—See JSW Steel Ltd.; *Int'l*, pg. 4015
MONIN, INC.—See Groupe Monin SAS; *Int'l*, pg. 3109
MONINJBAR JOINT STOCK COMPANY; *Int'l*, pg. 5034
MONIN SAS; *Int'l*, pg. 5034
MONIN SHANGHAI—See Groupe Monin SAS; *Int'l*, pg. 3109
MONITIN GROUP; *Int'l*, pg. 5034

MONITISE LIMITED—See Fiserv, Inc.; *U.S. Public*, pg. 851
MONITORAPP CO., LTD.; *Int'l*, pg. 5034
MONITOR CLIPPER PARTNERS GMBH—See Monitor Clipper Partners, LLC; *U.S. Private*, pg. 2770
MONITOR CLIPPER PARTNERS, LLC; *U.S. Private*, pg. 2770
MONITOR CLIPPER PARTNERS (UK), LLC—See Monitor Clipper Partners, LLC; *U.S. Private*, pg. 2770
MONITOR CONTROLS INC—See Halma plc; *Int'l*, pg. 3231
MONITOR DYNAMICS LLC—See Evergreen Fire Alarms, LLC; *U.S. Private*, pg. 1439
MONITOR ENERGY LIMITED—See The Garfield Weston Foundation; *Int'l*, pg. 7648
MONITORING SOLUTIONS, INC.; *U.S. Private*, pg. 2771
MONITOR LIABILITY MANAGERS, INC.—See W.R. Berkley Corporation; *U.S. Public*, pg. 2318
MONITOR LIFE INSURANCE COMPANY OF NEW YORK—See Commercial Travelers Mutual Insurance Company; *U.S. Private*, pg. 985
MONITOR PRODUCTS INC.; *U.S. Private*, pg. 2771
MONITOR PUBLICATIONS LIMITED—See Nation Media Group Limited; *Int'l*, pg. 5149
THE MONITOR—See AIM Media Texas, LLC; *U.S. Private*, pg. 132
MONITRONICS INTERNATIONAL, INC.—See Ascent Capital Group, Inc.; *U.S. Private*, pg. 348
MONIX CO., LTD.—See Siam Commercial Bank Public Company Limited; *Int'l*, pg. 6875
MONJASA NAMIBIA PROPRIETARY LIMITED—See The Bidvest Group Limited; *Int'l*, pg. 7625
MONKBARNS CARE HOME ARBROATH—See Balhousie Holdings Limited; *Int'l*, pg. 808
MONK DEVELOPMENT, INC.; *U.S. Private*, pg. 2771
MONKEDIA LLC; *U.S. Private*, pg. 2771
MONKEY KINGDOM LIMITED—See Comcast Corporation; *U.S. Public*, pg. 539
THE MONKEYS PTY. LTD.—See Accenture plc; *Int'l*, pg. 88
MONKI—See H&M Hennes & Mauritz AB; *Int'l*, pg. 3192
MONK OFFICE SUPPLY LTD.; *Int'l*, pg. 5034
MONKS' BREAD; *U.S. Private*, pg. 2771
MONKS & CRANE INDUSTRIAL GROUP LIMITED—See GIL Investments Ltd.; *Int'l*, pg. 2973
MONKSMEAD PARTNERSHIP LLP; *Int'l*, pg. 5034
MONLANGROUP—See Prab, Inc.; *U.S. Private*, pg. 3241
MONMOUTH CUSTOM BUILDERS; *U.S. Private*, pg. 2771
MONMOUTH MEDICAL CENTER—See Barnabas Health, Inc.; *U.S. Private*, pg. 476
MONMOUTH-OCEAN HOSPITAL SERVICE CORPORATION; *U.S. Private*, pg. 2771
MONMOUTH PETROLEUM CO. INC.; *U.S. Private*, pg. 2771
MONMOUTH REAL ESTATE INVESTMENT CORPORATION—See The RMR Group Inc.; *U.S. Public*, pg. 2126
MONMOUTHSHIRE BUILDING SOCIETY; *Int'l*, pg. 5034
MONNALISA S.P.A.; *Int'l*, pg. 5034
MONNARI TRADE S.A.; *Int'l*, pg. 5034
MONNET INDUSTRIES LTD.—See Apollo Global Management, Inc.; *U.S. Public*, pg. 153
MONNET INDUSTRIES LTD.—See JSW Steel Ltd.; *Int'l*, pg. 4015
MONNEX INDUSTRIES INC.—See Monnex International Inc.; *U.S. Private*, pg. 2771
MONNEX INTERNATIONAL INC.; *U.S. Private*, pg. 2771
MONNIER SARL SAS—See VINCI S.A.; *Int'l*, pg. 8224
MONNO CERAMIC INDUSTRIES LTD.; *Int'l*, pg. 5034
MONNO DESIGN LTD.—See Monno Ceramic Industries Ltd.; *Int'l*, pg. 5034
MONNOOS JOINT STOCK COMPANY; *Int'l*, pg. 5034
MONNOYEUR SAS; *Int'l*, pg. 5034
MONO ADVERTISING LLC—See Stagwell, Inc.; *U.S. Public*, pg. 1927
MONOCACY HEALTH PARTNERS; *U.S. Private*, pg. 2771
MONOCACY SURGERY CENTER, LLC—See Tenet Healthcare Corporation; *U.S. Public*, pg. 2004
MONO CERAMICS INC.—See S K Bajoria Group; *Int'l*, pg. 6443
MONOCON INTERNATIONAL REFRACTORIES LIMITED—See S K Bajoria Group; *Int'l*, pg. 6443
MONODRAUGHT LIMITED—See VKR Holding A/S; *Int'l*, pg. 8281
MONO EQUIPMENT LTD.—See Ali Holding S.r.l.; *Int'l*, pg. 322
MONOFUL INC.—See Trancom Co., Ltd.; *Int'l*, pg. 7891
THE MONOGATARI CORPORATION; *Int'l*, pg. 7668
MONOGRAM APPETIZERS, LLC—See Monogram Food Solutions, LLC; *U.S. Private*, pg. 2771
MONOGRAM BIOSCIENCES, INC.—See Laboratory Corporation of America Holdings; *U.S. Public*, pg. 1287
MONOGRAM COMFORT FOODS, LLC—See Monogram Food Solutions, LLC; *U.S. Private*, pg. 2771
MONOGRAM FOOD SOLUTIONS, LLC; *U.S. Private*, pg. 2771

COMPANY NAME INDEX

MONOGRAM MEAT SNACKS, LLC—See Monogram Food Solutions, LLC; *U.S. Private*, pg. 2771
MONOLITH CORPORATION—See Constellation Software Inc.; *Int'l*, pg. 1772
MONOLITHIC POWER SPAIN, S.L.—See Monolithic Power Systems, Inc.; *U.S. Public*, pg. 1464
MONOLITHIC POWER SYSTEMS, INC.; *U.S. Public*, pg. 1464
MONOLITH SOFTWARE INC.—See Nintendo Co., Ltd.; *Int'l*, pg. 5308
MONO MACHINES LLC.; *U.S. Private*, pg. 2771
MONOMATIC ITALIA S.R.L.—See NSC Groupe SA; *Int'l*, pg. 5476
MONOMATIC—See NSC Groupe SA; *Int'l*, pg. 5476
MONOMOY CAPITAL PARTNERS LLC; *U.S. Private*, pg. 2771
MONONA BANKSHARES, INC.; *U.S. Private*, pg. 2772
MONONA STATE BANK—See Monona Bankshares, Inc.; *U.S. Private*, pg. 2772
MONO NEXT PUBLIC COMPANY LIMITED; *Int'l*, pg. 5034
MONONGAHELA POWER COMPANY—See FirstEnergy Corp.; *U.S. Public*, pg. 849
MONOPAR THERAPEUTICS INC.; *U.S. Public*, pg. 1465
MONO PHARMACARE LIMITED; *Int'l*, pg. 5035
MONOPOLY, JSC; *Int'l*, pg. 5035
MONOPRICE, INC.—See YFC-BonEagle Electric Co., Ltd.; *Int'l*, pg. 8578
MONOPRIX S.A.—See Finatis SA; *Int'l*, pg. 2670
MONO PUMPS (AUSTRALIA) PROPRIETARY LIMITED—See NOV, Inc.; *U.S. Public*, pg. 1545
MONO PUMPS LIMITED—See NOV, Inc.; *U.S. Public*, pg. 1545
MONO PUMPS (MANUFACTURING) LIMITED—See NOV, Inc.; *U.S. Public*, pg. 1545
MONO PUMPS NEW ZEALAND COMPANY—See NOV, Inc.; *U.S. Public*, pg. 1545
MONORY ET FILS SA; *Int'l*, pg. 5035
MONOSEM, INC.—See Deere & Company; *U.S. Public*, pg. 647
MONOSOL AF, LTD.—See Kuraray Co., Ltd.; *Int'l*, pg. 4336
MONOSOL, LLC—See Kuraray Co., Ltd.; *Int'l*, pg. 4336
MONO; *U.S. Private*, pg. 2771
MONO-SYSTEMS, INC.; *U.S. Private*, pg. 2771
MONOTARO CO., LTD.—See W.W. Grainger, Inc.; *U.S. Public*, pg. 2320
MONOTECH OF MISSISSIPPI INC.—See The Herrick Corporation; *U.S. Private*, pg. 4052
MONOTEC REFRATARIOS LTDA—See S K Bajoria Group; *Int'l*, pg. 6443
MONOTONA TYRES LTD.—See Ruia Group; *Int'l*, pg. 6426
MONOTUBE PILE CORPORATION—See Ferguson plc; *Int'l*, pg. 2637
MONOTYPE GMBH—See HGGC, LLC; *U.S. Private*, pg. 1930
MONOTYPE HONG KONG LIMITED—See HGGC, LLC; *U.S. Private*, pg. 1930
MONOTYPE IMAGING HOLDINGS, INC.—See HGGC, LLC; *U.S. Private*, pg. 1930
MONOTYPE IMAGING, INC.—See HGGC, LLC; *U.S. Private*, pg. 1930
MONOTYPE ITC INC.—See HGGC, LLC; *U.S. Private*, pg. 1930
MONOTYPE KK—See HGGC, LLC; *U.S. Private*, pg. 1930
MONOTYPE LIMITED—See HGGC, LLC; *U.S. Private*, pg. 1930
MONOTYPE SOLUTIONS INDIA PRIVATE LIMITED—See HGGC, LLC; *U.S. Private*, pg. 1930
MONPI COFFEE EXPORTS LTD.—See Ecom Agroindustrial Corporation Ltd.; *Int'l*, pg. 2296
MONRIF NET S.R.L.—See Monrif S.p.A.; *Int'l*, pg. 5035
MONRIF S.P.A.; *Int'l*, pg. 5035
MONROE AUSTRALIA PTY. LIMITED—See Apollo Global Management, Inc.; *U.S. Public*, pg. 162
MONROE CABLEVISION INC.—See Block Communications, Inc.; *U.S. Private*, pg. 582
MONROE CAPITAL CORPORATION; *U.S. Public*, pg. 1465
MONROE CAPITAL INCOME PLUS CORPORATION; *U.S. Private*, pg. 2772
MONROE CAPITAL LLC; *U.S. Private*, pg. 2772
MONROE CLINIC; *U.S. Private*, pg. 2773
MONROE CONSULTING GROUP—See Empresaria Group Plc; *Int'l*, pg. 2389
MONROE CONSULTING GROUP VIETNAM LIMITED LIABILITY COMPANY—See Empresaria Group Plc; *Int'l*, pg. 2389
MONROE COUNTY BAR ASSOCIATION; *U.S. Private*, pg. 2773
MONROE COUNTY WATER AUTHORITY; *U.S. Private*, pg. 2773
MONROE ENERGY, LLC—See Delta Air Lines, Inc.; *U.S. Public*, pg. 652
MONROE ENGINEERING, LLC—See AEA Investors LP; *U.S. Private*, pg. 114
MONROE EQUIPMENT, INC.; *U.S. Private*, pg. 2773
MONROE GAS STORAGE COMPANY LLC; *U.S. Private*, pg. 2773

MONROE-GORMAN TITLE AGENCY, LLC—See Stewart Information Services Corporation; *U.S. Public*, pg. 1947
MONROE GROUP INC.; *U.S. Private*, pg. 2773
MONROE GUARANTY COMPANIES INC.—See FCCI Mutual Insurance Holding Company; *U.S. Private*, pg. 1485
MONROE HARDWARE COMPANY; *U.S. Private*, pg. 2773
MONROE HEALTHCARE, INC.—See The Ensign Group, Inc.; *U.S. Public*, pg. 2071
MONROE HMA, INC.—See Quorum Health Corporation; *U.S. Private*, pg. 3330
MONROE, LLC—See Huizenga Manufacturing Group, Inc.; *U.S. Private*, pg. 2004
MONROE MACHINED PRODUCTS, INC.; *U.S. Private*, pg. 2773
MONROE MEXICO S.A. DE C.V.—See Apollo Global Management, Inc.; *U.S. Public*, pg. 163
MONROE MOLD, LLC—See Talon LLC; *U.S. Private*, pg. 3927
MONROE MOTOR PRODUCTS CORP.—See Genuine Parts Company; *U.S. Public*, pg. 933
MONROE PACKAGING BVBA—See Apollo Global Management, Inc.; *U.S. Public*, pg. 162
MONROE PIPELINE LLC—See Antero Resources Corporation; *U.S. Public*, pg. 140
MONROE PIPING & SHEET METAL LLC; *U.S. Private*, pg. 2773
MONROE PUBLISHING COMPANY LLC—See Adams Publishing Group, LLC; *U.S. Private*, pg. 74
MONROE READY MIX—See Martin Marietta Materials, Inc.; *U.S. Public*, pg. 1389
MONROE RECRUITMENT CONSULTING GROUP CO LIMITED—See Empresaria Group Plc; *Int'l*, pg. 2389
MONROE RECRUITMENT CONSULTING GROUP COMPANY LIMITED—See Empresaria Group Plc; *Int'l*, pg. 2389
MONROE SCHOOL TRANSPORTATION INC.—See Mitsui & Co., Ltd.; *Int'l*, pg. 4979
MONROE SCHOOL TRANSPORTATION INC.—See Penske Automotive Group, Inc.; *U.S. Public*, pg. 1665
MONROE SCHOOL TRANSPORTATION INC.—See Penske Corporation; *U.S. Private*, pg. 3139
MONROE STAFFING SERVICES, LLC—See Staffing 360 Solutions, Inc.; *U.S. Public*, pg. 1925
MONROE STREET PARTNERS LLC; *U.S. Private*, pg. 2773
MONROE SYSTEMS FOR BUSINESS—See Carolina Wholesale Office Machine Company, Inc.; *U.S. Private*, pg. 769
MONROE TRACTOR & IMPLEMENT CO., INC.; *U.S. Private*, pg. 2774
MONROE TRANSPORTATION SERVICES; *U.S. Private*, pg. 2774
MONROE TRUCK EQUIPMENT, INC.; *U.S. Private*, pg. 2774
MONROEVILLE CHRYSLER JEEP; *U.S. Private*, pg. 2774
MONROEVILLE DODGE; *U.S. Private*, pg. 2774
MONROE WHEELCHAIR, INC.—See AEA Investors LP; *U.S. Private*, pg. 116
MONRO, INC.; *U.S. Public*, pg. 1465
MONRO SERVICE CORPORATION—See Monro, Inc.; *U.S. Public*, pg. 1465
MONROVIA GROWERS COMPANY; *U.S. Private*, pg. 2774
MONROVIA GROWERS-OREGON—See Monrovia Growers Company; *U.S. Private*, pg. 2774
MONRYO TRANSPORT CORPORATION—See Mitsubishi Logistics Corporation; *Int'l*, pg. 4963
MONSANTO AGRICOLTURA ITALIA S.P.A.—See Bayer Aktiengesellschaft; *Int'l*, pg. 908
MONSANTO AGRICULTURE FRANCE SAS—See Bayer Aktiengesellschaft; *Int'l*, pg. 908
MONSANTO ARGENTINA SRL—See Bayer Aktiengesellschaft; *Int'l*, pg. 908
MONSANTO AUSTRALIA LTD.—See Bayer Aktiengesellschaft; *Int'l*, pg. 908
MONSANTO CANADA, INC.—See Bayer Aktiengesellschaft; *Int'l*, pg. 908
MONSANTO CANADA, INC. - TILLSONBURG CORN & SOYBEAN MANUFACTURING/DISTRIBUTION—See Bayer Aktiengesellschaft; *Int'l*, pg. 908
MONSANTO CHILE S.A.—See Bayer Aktiengesellschaft; *Int'l*, pg. 908
MONSANTO CO. - ANKENY—See Bayer Aktiengesellschaft; *Int'l*, pg. 908
MONSANTO CO. - ASHTON—See Bayer Aktiengesellschaft; *Int'l*, pg. 908
MONSANTO CO. - BEAMAN—See Bayer Aktiengesellschaft; *Int'l*, pg. 908
MONSANTO CO. - BLOOMINGTON—See Bayer Aktiengesellschaft; *Int'l*, pg. 908
MONSANTO CO. - DAVIS—See Bayer Aktiengesellschaft; *Int'l*, pg. 908
MONSANTO CO. - DAYTON—See Bayer Aktiengesellschaft; *Int'l*, pg. 908
MONSANTO CO. - FARMER CITY—See Bayer Aktiengesellschaft; *Int'l*, pg. 908
MONSANTO CO. - GLYNDON—See Bayer Aktiengesellschaft; *Int'l*, pg. 908

MONROVIA GROWERS COMPANY

MONSANTO CO. - GRINNELL—See Bayer Aktiengesellschaft; *Int'l*, pg. 908
MONSANTO CO. - ILLIOPOLIS—See Bayer Aktiengesellschaft; *Int'l*, pg. 908
MONSANTO CO. - JANESVILLE—See Bayer Aktiengesellschaft; *Int'l*, pg. 908
MONSANTO CO. - KAHAHEO—See Bayer Aktiengesellschaft; *Int'l*, pg. 908
MONSANTO CO. - KEARNEY—See Bayer Aktiengesellschaft; *Int'l*, pg. 908
MONSANTO CO. - LINCOLN—See Bayer Aktiengesellschaft; *Int'l*, pg. 908
MONSANTO CO. - LOXLEY AGRONOMY CENTER—See Bayer Aktiengesellschaft; *Int'l*, pg. 908
MONSANTO CO. - MARSHALL—See Bayer Aktiengesellschaft; *Int'l*, pg. 908
MONSANTO CO. - MATTHEWS—See Bayer Aktiengesellschaft; *Int'l*, pg. 908
MONSANTO CO. - MAUI—See Bayer Aktiengesellschaft; *Int'l*, pg. 908
MONSANTO COMERCIAL, S DE RL DE CV—See Bayer Aktiengesellschaft; *Int'l*, pg. 909
MONSANTO COMMERCIAL, S.A. DE C.V.—See Bayer Aktiengesellschaft; *Int'l*, pg. 908
MONSANTO CO. - MONMOUTH AGRONOMY CENTER—See Bayer Aktiengesellschaft; *Int'l*, pg. 908
MONSANTO COMPANY—See Bayer Aktiengesellschaft; *Int'l*, pg. 908
MONSANTO CO. - MUSCATINE PLANT—See Bayer Aktiengesellschaft; *Int'l*, pg. 908
MONSANTO CO. - MYSTIC—See Bayer Aktiengesellschaft; *Int'l*, pg. 909
MONSANTO CO. - OLIVIA—See Bayer Aktiengesellschaft; *Int'l*, pg. 909
MONSANTO CO. - PARKERSBURG FOUNDATION—See Bayer Aktiengesellschaft; *Int'l*, pg. 909
MONSANTO CO. - REDWOOD FALLS-SOYBEAN RESEARCH—See Bayer Aktiengesellschaft; *Int'l*, pg. 909
MONSANTO CO. - REMINGTON—See Bayer Aktiengesellschaft; *Int'l*, pg. 909
MONSANTO CO. - SODA SPRINGS PLANT—See Bayer Aktiengesellschaft; *Int'l*, pg. 909
MONSANTO CO. - STONINGTON—See Bayer Aktiengesellschaft; *Int'l*, pg. 909
MONSANTO CO. - STROMSBURG—See Bayer Aktiengesellschaft; *Int'l*, pg. 909
MONSANTO CO. - STUTTGART—See Bayer Aktiengesellschaft; *Int'l*, pg. 909
MONSANTO CO. - WASHINGTON DC—See Bayer Aktiengesellschaft; *Int'l*, pg. 909
MONSANTO CO. - WATERMAN SEED TECHNOLOGY CENTER—See Bayer Aktiengesellschaft; *Int'l*, pg. 909
MONSANTO CO. - WEST FARGO—See Bayer Aktiengesellschaft; *Int'l*, pg. 909
MONSANTO CO. - WILLIAMSBURG—See Bayer Aktiengesellschaft; *Int'l*, pg. 909
MONSANTO DEUTSCHLAND GMBH—See Bayer Aktiengesellschaft; *Int'l*, pg. 909
MONSANTO DO BRASIL LTDA—See Bayer Aktiengesellschaft; *Int'l*, pg. 909
MONSANTO EUROPE S.A./N.V. (BELGIUM)—See Bayer Aktiengesellschaft; *Int'l*, pg. 909
MONSANTO FAR EAST LTD.—See Bayer Aktiengesellschaft; *Int'l*, pg. 909
MONSANTO GIDA VE TARIM TICARET LIMITED SIRKETI—See Bayer Aktiengesellschaft; *Int'l*, pg. 909
MONSANTO HELLAS, E.P.E.—See Bayer Aktiengesellschaft; *Int'l*, pg. 909
MONSANTO HOLDINGS PRIVATE LTD.—See Bayer Aktiengesellschaft; *Int'l*, pg. 909
MONSANTO HOLLAND BV—See Bayer Aktiengesellschaft; *Int'l*, pg. 909
MONSANTO HUNGARIA KFT.—See Bayer Aktiengesellschaft; *Int'l*, pg. 909
MONSANTO INTERNATIONAL S.A.R.L—See Bayer Aktiengesellschaft; *Int'l*, pg. 909
MONSANTO JAPAN LTD.—See Bayer Aktiengesellschaft; *Int'l*, pg. 909
MONSANTO KOREA LTD.—See Bayer Aktiengesellschaft; *Int'l*, pg. 909
MONSANTO (MALAYSIA) SDN BHD—See Bayer Aktiengesellschaft; *Int'l*, pg. 908
MONSANTO NL BV—See Bayer Aktiengesellschaft; *Int'l*, pg. 909
MONSANTO PAKISTAN (PRIVATE) LIMITED—See Bayer Aktiengesellschaft; *Int'l*, pg. 909
MONSANTO POLSKA SP. Z O.O.—See Bayer Aktiengesellschaft; *Int'l*, pg. 909
MONSANTO ROMANIA SRL—See Bayer Aktiengesellschaft; *Int'l*, pg. 909
MONSANTO SAS—See Bayer Aktiengesellschaft; *Int'l*, pg. 909
MONSANTO SINGAPORE COMPANY (PTE.) LTD.—See Bayer Aktiengesellschaft; *Int'l*, pg. 909
MONSANTO THAILAND LTD.—See Bayer Aktiengesellschaft; *Int'l*, pg. 909
MONSANTO UK LTD.—See Bayer Aktiengesellschaft; *Int'l*, pg. 909

MONSANTO UKRAINE LLC—See Bayer Aktiengesellschaft; *Int'l*, pg. 909
MONS BANK A/S; *Int'l*, pg. 5035
MONSEN ENGINEERING COMPANY; *U.S. Private*, pg. 2774
MONSET LTD.; *Int'l*, pg. 5035
MONSIEUR HENRI WINE COMPANY—See Sazerac Company, Inc.; *U.S. Private*, pg. 3559
MONSIEUR (M) SDN. BHD.—See Yoong Onn Corporation Berhad; *Int'l*, pg. 8598
MONSIEUR TOUTON SELECTION LTD.—See Touton Holdings Ltd; *U.S. Private*, pg. 4193
MONSMA MARKETING CORPORATION; *U.S. Private*, pg. 2774
MONSON COMPANIES INC.—See EQT AB; *Int'l*, pg. 2469
MONSOON ACCESSORIZE INTERNATIONAL LIMITED—See Monsoon Plc; *Int'l*, pg. 5035
MONSOON ACCESSORIZE IRELAND HOLDINGS LIMITED—See Monsoon Plc; *Int'l*, pg. 5035
MONSOON ACCESSORIZE IRELAND LIMITED—See Monsoon Plc; *Int'l*, pg. 5035
MONSOON ACCESSORIZE LIMITED—See Monsoon Plc; *Int'l*, pg. 5035
MONSOON COMPANY—See Capital One Financial Corporation; *U.S. Public*, pg. 431
MONSOON PLC; *Int'l*, pg. 5035
MON SPACE NET, INC.; *Int'l*, pg. 5024
MON SPACE NET INC.; *U.S. Private*, pg. 2768
MONSTARLAB HOLDINGS, INC.; *Int'l*, pg. 5035
MONSTAR LAB, INC.; *Int'l*, pg. 5035
MONSTER ARTS, INC.; *U.S. Public*, pg. 1465
MONSTERAS HAMN AB—See Sodra Skogsagarna; *Int'l*, pg. 7049
MONSTER BELGIUM NV—See Ontario Teachers' Pension Plan; *Int'l*, pg. 5588
MONSTER BEVERAGE CORPORATION; *U.S. Public*, pg. 1465
MONSTER COPPER CORPORATION—See Mega Uranium Ltd.; *Int'l*, pg. 4793
MONSTER DIGITAL, INC.; *U.S. Public*, pg. 1465
MONSTER ENERGY AUSTRIA GMBH—See Monster Beverage Corporation; *U.S. Public*, pg. 1465
MONSTER ENERGY COMPANY—See Monster Beverage Corporation; *U.S. Public*, pg. 1465
MONSTER ENERGY US LLC—See Monster Beverage Corporation; *U.S. Public*, pg. 1465
MONSTER EXECUTIVE SERVICES LIMITED—See Ontario Teachers' Pension Plan; *Int'l*, pg. 5588
MONSTER GOVERNMENT SOLUTIONS, LLC—See Ontario Teachers' Pension Plan; *Int'l*, pg. 5588
MONSTER, INC.—See Monster Products, Inc.; *U.S. Private*, pg. 2774
MONSTER, LLC—See Monster Products, Inc.; *U.S. Private*, pg. 2774
MONSTER MEDIA, LLC; *U.S. Private*, pg. 2774
MONSTERMOB GROUP PLC—See LaNetro Zed S.A.; *Int'l*, pg. 4408
MONSTER OY—See Alma Media Corporation; *Int'l*, pg. 362
MONSTER PRODUCTS, INC.; *U.S. Private*, pg. 2774
MONSTER SCOOTER PARTS; *U.S. Private*, pg. 2774
MONSTER TRANSMISSION & PERFORMANCE; *U.S. Private*, pg. 2774
MONSTER ULTRA INC—See AOI TYO Holdings Inc.; *Int'l*, pg. 488
MONSTER WORLDWIDE AUSTRIA GMBH—See Ontario Teachers' Pension Plan; *Int'l*, pg. 5588
MONSTER WORLDWIDE DEUTSCHLAND GMBH—See Ontario Teachers' Pension Plan; *Int'l*, pg. 5588
MONSTER WORLDWIDE, INC.—See Ontario Teachers' Pension Plan; *Int'l*, pg. 5588
MONTABERT S.A.S—See Komatsu Ltd.; *Int'l*, pg. 4239
MONTA BREDA B.V.—See Deutsche Post AG; *Int'l*, pg. 2082
MONTACHUSETT OPPORTUNITY COUNCIL, INC.; *U.S. Private*, pg. 2774
MONTA DEN BOSCH B.V.—See Deutsche Post AG; *Int'l*, pg. 2082
MONTA ENSCHEDE B.V.—See Deutsche Post AG; *Int'l*, pg. 2082
MONTAGE PARTNERS, INC.; *U.S. Private*, pg. 2774
MONTAGE RESOURCES CORP.—See Expand Energy Corporation; *U.S. Public*, pg. 808
MONTAGE SERVICES, INC.—See EQT AB; *Int'l*, pg. 2472
MONTAGE TECHNOLOGY GROUP LIMITED—See Shanghai Pudong Science & Technology Investment Co., Ltd.; *Int'l*, pg. 6777
MONTAGNE ET NEIGE DEVELOPPEMENT SA; *Int'l*, pg. 5035
MONTA GORINCHEM EDISONWEG B.V.—See Deutsche Post AG; *Int'l*, pg. 2082
MONTA GORINCHEM PAPLAND B.V.—See Deutsche Post AG; *Int'l*, pg. 2082
MONTA GORINCHEM WEIDE B.V.—See Deutsche Post AG; *Int'l*, pg. 2082
MONTAGUE INTERNATIONAL HOLDING LTD.; *U.S. Public*, pg. 1465
MONTAGUE SOLAR, LLC—See Iberdrola, S.A.; *Int'l*, pg. 3573

MONTAGU PRIVATE EQUITY LLP; *Int'l*, pg. 5036
MONTAGU PRIVATE EQUITY SAS—See Montagu Private Equity LLP; *Int'l*, pg. 5036
MONTAIGNE FASHION GROUP S.A.; *Int'l*, pg. 5036
MONTAIGNE KK—See LVMH Moet Hennessy Louis Vuitton SE; *Int'l*, pg. 4596
MONTAIR PROCESS TECHNOLOGY B.V.—See Manders Industries B.V.; *Int'l*, pg. 4668
MONTAJES ELECTRICOS ARRANZ, S.L.—See Elecnor, S.A.; *Int'l*, pg. 2347
MONTA KREFELD GMBH—See Deutsche Post AG; *Int'l*, pg. 2082
MONTALBANO INC.; *U.S. Private*, pg. 2774
MONTALBANO LUMBER COMPANY INC.; *U.S. Private*, pg. 2774
MONTA LELYSTAD B.V.—See Deutsche Post AG; *Int'l*, pg. 2082
MONTALIS INVESTMENT BV—See Societe Generale S.A.; *Int'l*, pg. 7040
MONTALVO SPIRITS, INC.; *U.S. Private*, pg. 2774
MONTA MOLENAARSGRAAF B.V.—See Deutsche Post AG; *Int'l*, pg. 2082
MONTANA ALIMENTARI GMBH—See Cremonini S.p.A.; *Int'l*, pg. 1838
MONTANA ALIMENTARI S.P.A.—See Cremonini S.p.A.; *Int'l*, pg. 1838
MONTANA ALIMENTARI S.P.A.—See JBS S.A.; *Int'l*, pg. 3919
MONTANA AVIATION RESEARCH COMPANY—See The Boeing Company; *U.S. Public*, pg. 2041
MONTANA BAUSYSTEME AG—See Tata Sons Limited; *Int'l*, pg. 7472
MONTANA CAPITAL PARTNERS AG—See Prudential Financial, Inc.; *U.S. Public*, pg. 1731
MONTANA COFFEE TRADERS INC.; *U.S. Private*, pg. 2775
MONTANA-DAKOTA UTILITIES CO.—See MDU Resources Group, Inc.; *U.S. Public*, pg. 1411
MONTANA ECONOMIC REVITALIZATION & DEVELOPMENT INSTITUTE INC.; *U.S. Private*, pg. 2775
MONTANA ENTERPRISES, INC.—See Delta Air Lines, Inc.; *U.S. Public*, pg. 652
MONTANA EXPLORATION CORP.; *Int'l*, pg. 5036
MONTANA INSTRUMENTS CORPORATION—See Atlas Copco AB; *Int'l*, pg. 683
MONTANA INTERACTIVE, LLC—See Tyler Technologies, Inc.; *U.S. Public*, pg. 2208
MONTANA LIMESTONE COMPANY—See Basin Electric Power Cooperative; *U.S. Private*, pg. 485
MONTANA LOGOS, L.L.C.—See Lamar Advertising Company; *U.S. Public*, pg. 1291
MONTANA METAL PRODUCTS LLC; *U.S. Private*, pg. 2775
MONTANA MILLS BREAD CO.—See Great Harvest Franchising, Inc.; *U.S. Private*, pg. 1763
MONTANA RAIL LINK, INC. - LIVINGSTON—See Washington Corporations; *U.S. Public*, pg. 4446
MONTANA RAIL LINK, INC.—See Washington Corporations; *U.S. Public*, pg. 4446
MONTANA REFINING COMPANY INC.—See Calumet, Inc.; *U.S. Public*, pg. 425
MONTANA RESOURCES—See Washington Corporations; *U.S. Private*, pg. 4446
MONTANARO EUROPEAN SMALLER COMPANIES TRUST PLC; *Int'l*, pg. 5036
MONTANARO UK SMALLER COMPANIES INVESTMENT TRUST PLC; *Int'l*, pg. 5036
MONTANA SILVERSMITHS, INC.—See Thompson Street Capital Manager LLC; *U.S. Private*, pg. 4161
THE MONTANA STANDARD—See Lee Enterprises, Incorporated; *U.S. Public*, pg. 1300
MONTANA TECH COMPONENTS AG—See Global Equity Partners Beteiligungs-Management AG; *Int'l*, pg. 2996
MONTANA TECHNOLOGIES CORPORATION; *U.S. Public*, pg. 1465
MONTANA TITLE AND ESCROW COMPANY—See First American Financial Corporation; *U.S. Public*, pg. 838
MONTAN GMBH ASSEKURANZ-MAKLER—See ThyssenKrupp AG; *Int'l*, pg. 7725
MONTA NIEUWVEEN B.V.—See Deutsche Post AG; *Int'l*, pg. 2082
MONTANO CIGARETTE CANDY & TOBACCO COMPANY INC.; *U.S. Private*, pg. 2775
MONTANO MOTORS, INC.; *U.S. Private*, pg. 2775
MONTANORE MINERALS CORP.—See Hecla Mining Company; *U.S. Public*, pg. 1019
MONTANSTAHL AG; *Int'l*, pg. 5036
MONTANWERKE BRIXLEGG AG—See Umcor AG; *Int'l*, pg. 8022
MONTANYA DISTILLERS, LLC—See Constellation Brands, Inc.; *U.S. Public*, pg. 571
MONTA OOSTERHOUT B.V.—See Deutsche Post AG; *Int'l*, pg. 2082
MONTA OUD GASTEL B.V.—See Deutsche Post AG; *Int'l*, pg. 2082
MONTAPLAN GMBH—See ManpowerGroup Inc.; *U.S. Public*, pg. 1361
MONTA PLATFORM B.V.—See Deutsche Post AG; *Int'l*, pg. 2082

MONTA SERVICES B.V.—See Deutsche Post AG; *Int'l*, pg. 2082
MONTA TWI B.V.—See Deutsche Post AG; *Int'l*, pg. 2082
MONTAUK DIALYSIS, LLC—See DaVita Inc.; *U.S. Public*, pg. 641
MONTAUK ENERGY CAPITAL LLC—See Hosken Consolidated Investments Limited; *Int'l*, pg. 3485
MONTAUK HOLDINGS LIMITED; *U.S. Public*, pg. 1465
MONTAUK METALS INC.; *Int'l*, pg. 5036
MONTAUK RENEWABLES, INC.; *U.S. Public*, pg. 1465
MONTAUK RUG & CARPET CORP.; *U.S. Private*, pg. 2775
MONTAVISTA SOFTWARE JAPAN, INC.—See MontaVista Software LLC; *U.S. Private*, pg. 2775
MONTAVISTA SOFTWARE KOREA LLC—See MontaVista Software LLC; *U.S. Private*, pg. 2775
MONTAVISTA SOFTWARE LLC; *U.S. Private*, pg. 2775
MONTAVO, INC.; *U.S. Private*, pg. 2775
MONTA WASPIK B.V.—See Deutsche Post AG; *Int'l*, pg. 2082
MONTAZA A.D.; *Int'l*, pg. 5036
MONTBLANC DEUTSCHLAND GMBH—See Compagnie Financiere Richemont S.A.; *Int'l*, pg. 1741
MONT BLANC FRANCE SAS—See Accent Equity Partners AB; *Int'l*, pg. 81
MONT BLANC GOURMET; *U.S. Private*, pg. 2774
MONT BLANC INDUSTRI AB—See Accent Equity Partners AB; *Int'l*, pg. 81
MONT BLANC INDUSTRI UK LTD—See Accent Equity Partners AB; *Int'l*, pg. 81
MONTBLANC INTERNATIONAL BV—See Compagnie Financiere Richemont S.A.; *Int'l*, pg. 1741
MONTBLANC ITALIA SRL—See Compagnie Financiere Richemont S.A.; *Int'l*, pg. 1741
MONT BLANC, S.A.S.—See Unibel SA; *Int'l*, pg. 8031
MONTBLANC-SIMPLO GMBH—See Compagnie Financiere Richemont S.A.; *Int'l*, pg. 1741
MONTBLANC SUISSE SA—See Compagnie Financiere Richemont S.A.; *Int'l*, pg. 1741
MONTBLEAU & ASSOCIATES INC; *U.S. Private*, pg. 2775
THE MONTCALM LONDON—See Japan Airlines Co., Ltd.; *Int'l*, pg. 3882
MONTCALM WINE IMPORTERS LTD.—See Assicurazioni Generali S.p.A.; *Int'l*, pg. 647
MONTCHEVRE-BETIN, INC.—See Saputo Inc.; *Int'l*, pg. 6575
MONTCLAIR GOLF CLUB; *U.S. Private*, pg. 2775
MONTCLAIR HOTEL INVESTORS, INC.; *U.S. Private*, pg. 2775
MONTCLAIR ROAD IMAGING, LLC—See US Radiology Specialists, Inc.; *U.S. Private*, pg. 4319
MONTCLAIR STATE UNIVERSITY; *U.S. Private*, pg. 2775
MONTEA NV; *Int'l*, pg. 5036
MONTEBALITO S.A.; *Int'l*, pg. 5036
MONTEBELLO BRANDS INC.; *U.S. Private*, pg. 2775
MONTEBELLO CONTAINER CORPORATION—See Goldberg Lindsay & Co., LLC; *U.S. Private*, pg. 1729
THE MONTEBELLO ON ACADEMY—See AlerisLife Inc.; *U.S. Private*, pg. 162
MONTEBELLO PACKAGING—See The Jim Pattison Group; *Int'l*, pg. 7660
MONTEBELLO SRL—See Azgard Nine Limited; *Int'l*, pg. 778
MONTEBELLO WELLNESS CENTER—See The Ensign Group, Inc.; *U.S. Public*, pg. 2071
MONTE BUSSAN K.K.—See Suntory Holdings Limited; *Int'l*, pg. 7326
MONTE CARLO CEILING FAN COMPANY—See AEA Investors LP; *U.S. Private*, pg. 114
MONTE CARLO FASHIONS LTD.; *Int'l*, pg. 5036
MONTE CARLO YACHT SPA—See Beneteau S.A; *Int'l*, pg. 972
MONTECASTILLO SPORT CATERING, S.L.—See Barcelo Corporacion Empresarial S.A.; *Int'l*, pg. 859
MONTE CELLO BV—See Vedanta Resources Ltd; *Int'l*, pg. 8146
MONTECITO BANCORP; *U.S. Private*, pg. 2775
MONTECITO BANK & TRUST—See Montecito Bancorp; *U.S. Private*, pg. 2775
MONTECITO RETIREMENT ASSOCIATION; *U.S. Private*, pg. 2775
MONTECON S.A.—See Ultramar Ltda.; *Int'l*, pg. 8018
MONTEFIBRE HISPANIA S.A.—See Orlandi S.p.A.; *Int'l*, pg. 5639
MONTEFIBRE S.P.A.—See Orlandi S.p.A.; *Int'l*, pg. 5639
MONTEFIORE INVESTMENT SAS; *Int'l*, pg. 5036
MONTEFIORE MEDICAL CENTER; *U.S. Private*, pg. 2776
MONTE-GENEROSO-BAHN AG—See The Federation of Migros Cooperatives; *Int'l*, pg. 7643
MONTEGO BAY ICE COMPANY LIMITED; *Int'l*, pg. 5037
MONTEGO RESOURCES INC.; *Int'l*, pg. 5037
MONTEIRO ARANHA S.A.; *Int'l*, pg. 5037
MONTE KLINIKUM DIAGNOSTICO POR IMAGEM LTDA.—See UnitedHealth Group Incorporated; *U.S. Public*, pg. 2242
MONTEL DISTRIBUTION SA—See Carrefour SA; *Int'l*, pg. 1345
MONTELLO RESOURCES LTD.; *Int'l*, pg. 5037

COMPANY NAME INDEX

MONTENEGRIN TELEKOM A.D.; *Int'l*, pg. 5037
MONTE PASCHI FIDUCIARIA S.P.A.—See Banca Monte dei Paschi di Siena S.p.A.; *Int'l*, pg. 815
MONTEPIO VALOR - SOCIEDADE GESTORA DE FUNDOS DE INVESTIMENTO, S.A.—See Caixa Economica Montepio Geral; *Int'l*, pg. 1259
MONTE RESOURCES INC.; *U.S. Private*, pg. 2775
MONTEREY BAY AQUARIUM FOUNDATION; *U.S. Private*, pg. 2776
MONTEREY BAY BEVERAGE, INC.; *U.S. Private*, pg. 2776
MONTEREY BENEFITS LLC—See S.C. Johnson & Son, Inc.; *U.S. Private*, pg. 3516
MONTEREY CHEMICAL COMPANY INC.—See Brandt Consolidated, Inc.; *U.S. Private*, pg. 638
MONTEREY COUNTY BANK—See PCB Financial, Inc; *U.S. Private*, pg. 3119
MONTEREY FISH COMPANY INC.; *U.S. Private*, pg. 2776
MONTEREY GOURMET FOODS, INC.—See Pulmuone Co., Ltd.; *Int'l*, pg. 6116
MONTEREY INC.; *U.S. Private*, pg. 2776
MONTEREY INNOVATION ACQUISITION CORP.; *U.S. Public*, pg. 1466
MONTEREY MECHANICAL COMPANY; *U.S. Private*, pg. 2776
MONTEREY MINERALS, INC.; *Int'l*, pg. 5037
MONTEREY MUSHROOMS, INC.; *U.S. Private*, pg. 2776
MONTEREY NEWSPAPERS, LLC—See Alden Global Capital LLC; *U.S. Private*, pg. 156
MONTEREY PENINSULA COUNTRY CLUB; *U.S. Private*, pg. 2776
MONTEREY PLAZA HOTEL; *U.S. Private*, pg. 2776
MONTEREY REGIONAL WATER POLLUTION CONTROL; *U.S. Private*, pg. 2776
MONTEREY-SALINAS TRANSIT; *U.S. Private*, pg. 2776
MONTERO MINING AND EXPLORATION LTD.; *Int'l*, pg. 5037
MONTE ROSA THERAPEUTICS, INC.; *U.S. Public*, pg. 1466
MONTERREY PROVISION COMPANY, INC.—See KeHE Distributors, LLC; *U.S. Private*, pg. 2273
MONTERRO INVESTMENT AB; *Int'l*, pg. 5037
MONTESA HONDA SPAIN—See Honda Motor Co., Ltd.; *Int'l*, pg. 3463
MONTES ARCHIMEDES ACQUISITION CORP.; *U.S. Public*, pg. 1466
MONTE SHELTON JAGUAR; *U.S. Private*, pg. 2775
MONTESI MOTORS, INC.; *U.S. Private*, pg. 2776
MONTESQUIEU; *U.S. Private*, pg. 2776
MONTESSORI ACADEMY GROUP HOLDINGS PTY LTD.—See Dalian Thermal Power Co., Ltd.; *Int'l*, pg. 1952
MONTE TITOLI S.P.A.—See London Stock Exchange Group plc; *Int'l*, pg. 4547
MONTE VISTA CO-OP ASSOCIATION, INC.; *U.S. Private*, pg. 2775
MONTE VISTA DISPOSAL, INC.—See Burrtec Waste Industries, Inc.; *U.S. Private*, pg. 692
MONTEVUE LANE SOLAR LLC—See Ameresco, Inc.; *U.S. Public*, pg. 95
MONTEZUMA MUTUAL TELEPHONE COMPANY—See Windstream Holdings, Inc.; *U.S. Public*, pg. 2373
MONTFORT CAPITAL CORPORATION; *Int'l*, pg. 5037
MONTFORT GROUP; *Int'l*, pg. 5037
MONTGERON DIS SAS; *Int'l*, pg. 5037
THE MONTGOMERY ADVERTISER—See Gannett Co., Inc.; *U.S. Public*, pg. 900
MONTGOMERY BANCORPORATION INC.; *U.S. Private*, pg. 2776
MONTGOMERY BANK—See Montgomery Bancorporation Inc.; *U.S. Private*, pg. 2776
MONTGOMERY BAPTIST OUTREACH SERVICES CORPORATION; *U.S. Private*, pg. 2776
MONTGOMERY CANCER CENTER, LLC—See HCA Healthcare, Inc.; *U.S. Public*, pg. 1003
MONTGOMERY CHEVROLET; *U.S. Private*, pg. 2776
MONTGOMERY COALITION FOR ADULT ENGLISH LITERACY; *U.S. Private*, pg. 2776
MONTGOMERY COCA COLA BOTTLING CO.—See The Coca-Cola Company; *U.S. Public*, pg. 2065
MONTGOMERY COMMUNITY MAGNETIC IMAGING CENTER LIMITED PARTNERSHIP—See RadNet, Inc.; *U.S. Public*, pg. 1761
MONTGOMERY COUNTY EMERGENCY SERVICE, INC.; *U.S. Private*, pg. 2776
MONTGOMERY ENTERPRISES LIMITED—See Tai Sang Land Development Ltd; *Int'l*, pg. 7408
MONTGOMERY EXHIBITIONS LTD.—See Angus Montgomery Ltd.; *Int'l*, pg. 463
MONTGOMERY EYE SURGERY CENTER, LLC—See KKR & Co. Inc.; *U.S. Public*, pg. 1246
MONTGOMERY GENERAL HOSPITAL, INC.; *U.S. Private*, pg. 2777
MONTGOMERY HOSPICE, INC.; *U.S. Private*, pg. 2777
MONTGOMERY MACHINE CO., INC.—See Oil States International, Inc.; *U.S. Public*, pg. 1565
MONTGOMERY MANUFACTURING CO.; *U.S. Private*, pg. 2777

MONTGOMERY MARTIN CONTRACTORS, LLC; *U.S. Private*, pg. 2777
MONTGOMERY MARTIN CONTRACTORS, LLC; *U.S. Private*, pg. 2777
MONTGOMERY MEDIA INTERNATIONAL, LLC—See mThink LLC; *U.S. Private*, pg. 2809
MONTGOMERY OFFICE EQUIPMENT CO.—See Pitney Bowes Inc.; *U.S. Public*, pg. 1694
MONTGOMERY PLACE RETIREMENT COMMUNITY; *U.S. Private*, pg. 2777
MONTGOMERY PROFESSIONAL SERVICES CORP.—See Global Upside, Inc.; *U.S. Private*, pg. 1718
MONTGOMERY REGIONAL HOSPITAL, INC.—See HCA Healthcare, Inc.; *U.S. Public*, pg. 1003
MONTGOMERY SURGERY ASSOCIATES, LLC—See HCA Healthcare, Inc.; *U.S. Public*, pg. 1003
MONTGOMERY SURGERY CENTER—See UnitedHealth Group Incorporated; *U.S. Public*, pg. 2251
MONTGOMERY TOMLINSON LTD; *Int'l*, pg. 5037
MONTGOMERY TRUSS AND PANEL; *U.S. Private*, pg. 2777
MONTGOMERY WATER WORKS & SANITARY SEWER BOARD; *U.S. Private*, pg. 2777
THE MONTICELLO COMPANIES, INC.; *U.S. Private*, pg. 4080
MONTICELLO DRUG CO.—See The Monticello Companies, Inc.; *U.S. Private*, pg. 4080
MONTICELLO MANAGEMENT CO.; *U.S. Private*, pg. 2777
MONTICELLO MANOR, LTD.—See Apartment Investment and Management Company; *U.S. Public*, pg. 144
MONTICELLO SOFTWARE, INC.—See Platinum Equity, LLC; *U.S. Private*, pg. 3202
MONTICELLO SPRING CORPORATION; *U.S. Private*, pg. 2777
MONTICIANO PARTICIPACOES S.A.; *Int'l*, pg. 5037
MONTI FOODS (PTY) LTD.—See Archer-Daniels-Midland Company; *U.S. Public*, pg. 185
MONTI INCORPORATED; *U.S. Private*, pg. 2777
MONTING D.D./PLC; *Int'l*, pg. 5037
MONTINVEST A.D.; *Int'l*, pg. 5037
MONTIVO KFT—See Fortum Oyj; *Int'l*, pg. 2741
MONTLAWN MEMORIAL PARK, INC.—See Axar Capital Management L.P.; *U.S. Private*, pg. 411
MONTLUCON VIANDES SAS; *Int'l*, pg. 5037
MONTMELIAN ENROBES SAS—See VINCI S.A.; *Int'l*, pg. 8224
MONTNETS CLOUD TECHNOLOGY GROUP CO., LTD.; *Int'l*, pg. 5037
MONTOSCO INC.—See Cosco Capital, Inc.; *Int'l*, pg. 1809
MONTPELLIER EVENTS; *Int'l*, pg. 5037
MONTREAL EXCHANGE INC.—See TMX Group Limited; *Int'l*, pg. 7767
MONTREAL GAZETTE—See Chatham Asset Management, LLC; *U.S. Private*, pg. 861
MONTREAL PIPE LINE LIMITED—See Exxon Mobil Corporation; *U.S. Public*, pg. 816
MONTREAL PIPE LINE LIMITED—See Suncor Energy Inc.; *Int'l*, pg. 7310
MONTREAL PIPE LINE LIMITED—See Exxon Mobil Corporation; *U.S. Public*, pg. 816
MONTREAL PIPE LINE LIMITED—See Suncor Energy Inc.; *Int'l*, pg. 7310
MONTREAL PORT AUTHORITY; *Int'l*, pg. 5037
MONTREIGN OPERATING COMPANY, LLC—See Empire Resorts, Inc.; *U.S. Private*, pg. 1385
MONTRES BREGUET S.A.—See The Swatch Group Ltd.; *Int'l*, pg. 7692
MONTRES CORUM S.A.R.L.—See Citychamp Watch & Jewellery Group Limited; *Int'l*, pg. 1629
MONTRES JAQUET DROZ SA—See The Swatch Group Ltd.; *Int'l*, pg. 7692
MONTRESOR & CO. S.R.L.—See Biesse S.p.A.; *Int'l*, pg. 1020
MONTREUX GOLF CLUB LIMITED; *U.S. Private*, pg. 2777
MONTREUX PUBLICATIONS S.A.—See Vivendi SE; *Int'l*, pg. 8275
MONTRIVE CORPORATION—See Sumitomo Corporation; *Int'l*, pg. 7269
MONTRONIC AB—See Inission AB; *Int'l*, pg. 3704
MONTROSE ENVIRONMENTAL CORP.; *U.S. Private*, pg. 2777
MONTROSE ENVIRONMENTAL GROUP, INC.; *U.S. Public*, pg. 1466
MONTROSE FORD LINCOLN; *U.S. Private*, pg. 2777
MONTROSE MEMORIAL HOSPITAL; *U.S. Private*, pg. 2777
MONT ROYAL RESOURCES LIMITED; *Int'l*, pg. 5035
MONTROY SIGN & GRAPHIC PRODUCTS—See JDW Management Co.; *U.S. Private*, pg. 2196
MONTRUSCO BOLTON INC.; *Int'l*, pg. 5037
MONTRUSCO BOLTON INVESTMENTS INC.—See Montrusco Bolton Inc.; *Int'l*, pg. 5037
MONTRUSCO BOLTON INVESTMENTS—See Montrusco Bolton Inc.; *Int'l*, pg. 5037
MONTRUSCO BOLTON INVESTMENTS—See Montrusco Bolton Inc.; *Int'l*, pg. 5037

MOODY BIBLE INSTITUTE

MONT SAINTE-MARGUERITE WIND FARM L.P.—See Canada Pension Plan Investment Board; *Int'l*, pg. 1281
MONT SAINT-SAUVEUR INTERNATIONAL, INC.; *Int'l*, pg. 5035
MONTSERRAT DH PTY LTD—See Healius Limited; *Int'l*, pg. 3303
MONTSERRAT HEALTHCARE PTY. LTD.—See QIC Limited; *Int'l*, pg. 6141
MONTSERRAT UTILITIES LIMITED; *Int'l*, pg. 5037
MONT TREMBLANT RESORTS & COMPANY, LIMITED PARTNERSHIP—See KSL Capital Partners, LLC; *U.S. Private*, pg. 2354
MONTUPET S.A.—See Linamar Corporation; *Int'l*, pg. 4502
MONTVALE PET/CT, LLC—See Akumin, Inc.; *U.S. Public*, pg. 70
MONTY MEX CORP.; *U.S. Private*, pg. 2777
MONUMENTAL LIFE INSURANCE COMPANY—See Aegon N.V.; *Int'l*, pg. 174
MONUMENTAL LIFE—See Aegon N.V.; *Int'l*, pg. 174
MONUMENTAL MINERALS CORPORATION; *Int'l*, pg. 5038
MONUMENTAL RESIDENCE SICAFI SA; *Int'l*, pg. 5038
MONUMENTAL SUPPLY CO. INC.; *U.S. Private*, pg. 2777
MONUMENT ASSURANCE LUXEMBOURG S.A.—See Enstar Group Limited; *Int'l*, pg. 2449
MONUMENT & CATHEDRAL HOLDINGS, LLC; *U.S. Private*, pg. 2777
MONUMENT CHEMICAL BVBA—See Heritage Group; *U.S. Private*, pg. 1923
MONUMENT CHEMICALS, INC.—See Heritage Group; *U.S. Private*, pg. 1923
MONUMENT CIRCLE ACQUISITION CORP.; *U.S. Public*, pg. 1466
MONUMENT HEALTH, LLC—See UnitedHealth Group Incorporated; *U.S. Public*, pg. 2242
MONUMENT INSURANCE (NZ) LIMITED—See Wesfarmers Limited; *Int'l*, pg. 8382
MONUMENT MINING LIMITED; *Int'l*, pg. 5037
MONUMENT OIL COMPANY; *U.S. Private*, pg. 2777
MONUMENT PRODUCTION, INC.—See Occidental Petroleum Corporation; *U.S. Public*, pg. 1561
MONUMENT RE LIMITED—See Enstar Group Limited; *Int'l*, pg. 2449
MONUMETRIC, LLC; *U.S. Private*, pg. 2778
MON VALLEY PETROLEUM INC.; *U.S. Private*, pg. 2768
MONVO HONDA BA AMAZONIA LTDA.—See Honda Motor Co., Ltd.; *Int'l*, pg. 3463
MON VOISIN PRODUCTIONS SAS—See Mediawan SA; *Int'l*, pg. 4774
MONY LIFE INSURANCE COMPANY OF THE AMERICAS, LTD.—See Equitable Holdings, Inc.; *U.S. Public*, pg. 790
MON YOUGH COMMUNITY SERVICES, INC.; *U.S. Private*, pg. 2768
MONZITE CORPORATION—See Omni-Lite Industries Canada Inc.; *U.S. Public*, pg. 1572
MOOCHIE & CO.—See Pet Stuff Illinois, LLC; *U.S. Private*, pg. 3156
MOOD MEDIA AB—See Vector Capital Management, L.P.; *U.S. Private*, pg. 4351
MOOD MEDIA A/S—See Vector Capital Management, L.P.; *U.S. Private*, pg. 4351
MOOD MEDIA AS—See Vector Capital Management, L.P.; *U.S. Private*, pg. 4351
MOOD MEDIA AUSTRALIA PTY LTD—See Vector Capital Management, L.P.; *U.S. Private*, pg. 4351
MOOD MEDIA BELGIUM NV—See Vector Capital Management, L.P.; *U.S. Private*, pg. 4351
MOOD MEDIA CORPORATION—See Vector Capital Management, L.P.; *U.S. Private*, pg. 4351
MOOD MEDIA FINLAND OY—See Vector Capital Management, L.P.; *U.S. Private*, pg. 4351
MOOD MEDIA GMBH—See Vector Capital Management, L.P.; *U.S. Private*, pg. 4351
MOOD MEDIA GMBH—See Vector Capital Management, L.P.; *U.S. Private*, pg. 4351
MOOD MEDIA GROUP CZ, S.R.O.—See Vector Capital Management, L.P.; *U.S. Private*, pg. 4351
MOOD MEDIA HUNGARY KFT—See Vector Capital Management, L.P.; *U.S. Private*, pg. 4351
MOOD MEDIA IRELAND LIMITED—See Vector Capital Management, L.P.; *U.S. Private*, pg. 4351
MOOD MEDIA JAPAN CO., LTD.—See Vector Capital Management, L.P.; *U.S. Private*, pg. 4351
MOOD MEDIA LIMITED—See Vector Capital Management, L.P.; *U.S. Private*, pg. 4351
MOOD MEDIA NETHERLANDS B.V.—See Vector Capital Management, L.P.; *U.S. Private*, pg. 4351
MOOD MEDIA POLSKA SP. Z O.O.—See Vector Capital Management, L.P.; *U.S. Private*, pg. 4351
MOOD MEDIA S.A.—See Vector Capital Management, L.P.; *U.S. Private*, pg. 4351
MOOD MEDIA S.A.—See Vector Capital Management, L.P.; *U.S. Private*, pg. 4351
MOOD MEDIA SAS—See Vector Capital Management, L.P.; *U.S. Private*, pg. 4351
MOODY BANCSHARES, INC.; *U.S. Private*, pg. 2778
MOODY BIBLE INSTITUTE; *U.S. Private*, pg. 2778

MOODY BIBLE INSTITUTE

CORPORATE AFFILIATIONS

MOODY DUNBAR FOODS CORPORATION—See Moody Dunbar Inc.; *U.S. Private*, pg. 2778
MOODY DUNBAR INC.; *U.S. Private*, pg. 2778
THE MOODY ENDOWMENT; *U.S. Private*, pg. 4080
MOODY ENERGY TECHNICAL SERVICE CO., LTD.—See Intertek Group plc; *Int'l*, pg. 3764
MOODY NATIONAL BANK—See Moody Bancshares, Inc.; *U.S. Private*, pg. 2778
MOODY NATIONAL REIT II, INC.; *U.S. Private*, pg. 2778
MOODY NATIONAL REIT I, INC.; *U.S. Private*, pg. 2778
MOODY.NOLAN, INC; *U.S. Private*, pg. 2778
MOODY-PRICE INC.; *U.S. Private*, pg. 2778
MOODY PUBLISHERS—See Moody Bible Institute; *U.S. Private*, pg. 2778
MOODY'S AMERICA LATINA LTDA.—See Moody's Corporation; *U.S. Public*, pg. 1468
MOODY'S ANALYTICS AUSTRALIA PTY. LTD.—See Moody's Corporation; *U.S. Public*, pg. 1468
MOODY'S ANALYTICS CZECH REPUBLIC S.R.O.—See Moody's Corporation; *U.S. Public*, pg. 1468
MOODY'S ANALYTICS DEUTSCHLAND GMBH—See Moody's Corporation; *U.S. Public*, pg. 1468
MOODY'S ANALYTICS (DIFC) LIMITED—See Moody's Corporation; *U.S. Public*, pg. 1468
MOODY'S ANALYTICS GLOBAL EDUCATION (CANADA) INC.—See Moody's Corporation; *U.S. Public*, pg. 1468
MOODY'S ANALYTICS, INC.—See Moody's Corporation; *U.S. Public*, pg. 1468
MOODY'S ANALYTICS JAPAN KK—See Moody's Corporation; *U.S. Public*, pg. 1468
MOODYS ANALYTICS KNOWLEDGE SERVICES (INDIA) PVT. LTD.—See Equistone Partners Europe Limited; *Int'l*, pg. 2486
MOODYS ANALYTICS KNOWLEDGE SERVICES LANKA (PRIVATE) LIMITED—See Equistone Partners Europe Limited; *Int'l*, pg. 2486
MOODY'S ANALYTICS SAS—See Moody's Corporation; *U.S. Public*, pg. 1468
MOODY'S ANALYTICS SINGAPORE PTE LTD.—See Moody's Corporation; *U.S. Public*, pg. 1468
MOODY'S ASIA PACIFIC LTD.—See Moody's Corporation; *U.S. Public*, pg. 1468
MOODY'S CANADA, INC.—See Moody's Corporation; *U.S. Public*, pg. 1468
MOODY'S CORPORATION; *U.S. Public*, pg. 1466
MOODY'S DEUTSCHLAND GMBH—See Moody's Corporation; *U.S. Public*, pg. 1468
MOODY'S EASTERN EUROPE LLC—See Moody's Corporation; *U.S. Public*, pg. 1468
MOODY'S EQUIPMENT; *Int'l*, pg. 5038
MOODY'S FRANCE S.A.S.—See Moody's Corporation; *U.S. Public*, pg. 1468
MOODYS FRANCE SAS—See Moody's Corporation; *U.S. Public*, pg. 1469
MOODY'S INTERFAX RATING AGENCY LTD.—See Moody's Corporation; *U.S. Public*, pg. 1468
MOODY'S INVESTMENT CO. INDIA PVT. LTD.—See Moody's Corporation; *U.S. Public*, pg. 1468
MOODY'S INVESTORS SERVICE CYPRUS LTD.—See Moody's Corporation; *U.S. Public*, pg. 1468
MOODY'S INVESTORS SERVICE ESPANA, S.A.—See Moody's Corporation; *U.S. Public*, pg. 1468
MOODY'S INVESTORS SERVICE, INC.—See Moody's Corporation; *U.S. Public*, pg. 1468
MOODY'S INVESTORS SERVICE INDIA PRIVATE LIMITED—See Moody's Corporation; *U.S. Public*, pg. 1468
MOODY'S INVESTORS SERVICE (KOREA) INC.—See Moody's Corporation; *U.S. Public*, pg. 1468
MOODY'S INVESTORS SERVICE LTD.—See Moody's Corporation; *U.S. Public*, pg. 1468
MOODY'S INVESTORS SERVICE MIDDLE EAST LIMITED—See Moody's Corporation; *U.S. Public*, pg. 1468
MOODY'S INVESTORS SERVICE PTY LIMITED—See Moody's Corporation; *U.S. Public*, pg. 1468
MOODY'S INVESTORS SERVICE PTY. LTD.—See Moody's Corporation; *U.S. Public*, pg. 1468
MOODY'S INVESTORS SERVICE (SOUTH AFRICA) PTY. LTD.—See Moody's Corporation; *U.S. Public*, pg. 1468
MOODY'S JAPAN KK—See Moody's Corporation; *U.S. Public*, pg. 1469
MOODY'S JEWELRY INC.; *U.S. Private*, pg. 2778
MOODY'S LATIN AMERICA AGENTE DE CALIFICACION DE RIESGO SA—See Moody's Corporation; *U.S. Public*, pg. 1469
MOODY'S MARKET INC.; *U.S. Private*, pg. 2778
MOODY'S SINGAPORE PTE. LTD.—See Moody's Corporation; *U.S. Public*, pg. 1468
MOODY TECHNOLOGY HOLDINGS LIMITED; *Int'l*, pg. 5038
MOOERS MOTOR CAR COMPANY INC.; *U.S. Private*, pg. 2778
MOOG AG—See Moog Inc.; *U.S. Public*, pg. 1469
MOOG AIRCRAFT GROUP—See Moog Inc.; *U.S. Public*, pg. 1469
MOOG AIRCRAFT GROUP - TORRANCE—See Moog Inc.; *U.S. Public*, pg. 1469

MOOG AUSTRALIA PTY. LTD.—See Moog Inc.; *U.S. Public*, pg. 1470
MOOG BRNO S.R.O.—See Moog Inc.; *U.S. Public*, pg. 1470
MOOG B.V.—See Moog Inc.; *U.S. Public*, pg. 1470
MOOG COMPONENTS GROUP—See Moog Inc.; *U.S. Public*, pg. 1470
MOOG CONTROLS CORP.-PHILIPPINES—See Moog Inc.; *U.S. Public*, pg. 1470
MOOG CONTROLS HONG KONG LTD.—See Moog Inc.; *U.S. Public*, pg. 1470
MOOG CONTROLS (INDIA) PRIVATE LTD.—See Moog Inc.; *U.S. Public*, pg. 1470
MOOG CONTROLS LTD.—See Moog Inc.; *U.S. Public*, pg. 1470
MOOG CONTROL SYSTEMS (SHANGHAI) CO., LTD.—See Moog Inc.; *U.S. Public*, pg. 1470
MOOG CSA ENGINEERING—See Moog Inc.; *U.S. Public*, pg. 1470
MOOG DE ARGENTINA SRL—See Moog Inc.; *U.S. Public*, pg. 1470
MOOG DO BRASIL CONTROLES LTDA.—See Moog Inc.; *U.S. Public*, pg. 1470
MOOG DUBLIN LTD.—See Moog Inc.; *U.S. Public*, pg. 1470
MOOG EM SOLUTIONS (INDIA) PRIVATE LIMITED—See Moog Inc.; *U.S. Public*, pg. 1470
MOOG FERNAU LIMITED—See Moog Inc.; *U.S. Public*, pg. 1470
MOOG GMBH—See Moog Inc.; *U.S. Public*, pg. 1470
MOOG INC.; *U.S. Public*, pg. 1469
MOOG IRELAND LTD.—See Moog Inc.; *U.S. Public*, pg. 1470
MOOG ITALIANA SRL—See Moog Inc.; *U.S. Public*, pg. 1470
MOOG JAPAN LTD.—See Moog Inc.; *U.S. Public*, pg. 1470
MOOG KOREA LTD.—See Moog Inc.; *U.S. Public*, pg. 1470
MOOG LOUISVILLE WAREHOUSE INC.; *U.S. Private*, pg. 2778
MOOG LUXEMBOURG—See Moog Inc.; *U.S. Public*, pg. 1471
MOOG MEDICAL DEVICES GROUP—See Moog Inc.; *U.S. Public*, pg. 1470
MOOG MEDICAL DEVICES GROUP—See Moog Inc.; *U.S. Public*, pg. 1470
MOOG MOTION CONTROLS PVT. LTD.—See Moog Inc.; *U.S. Public*, pg. 1470
MOOG MUSIC INC.—See inMusic, LLC; *U.S. Private*, pg. 2080
MOOG NORDEN A.B.—See Moog Inc.; *U.S. Public*, pg. 1471
MOOG READING LIMITED—See Moog Inc.; *U.S. Public*, pg. 1470
MOOG READING LIMITED—See Moog Inc.; *U.S. Public*, pg. 1470
MOOG REKOFA GMBH—See Moog Inc.; *U.S. Public*, pg. 1470
MOOG S.A.R.L.—See Moog Inc.; *U.S. Public*, pg. 1470
MOOG SINGAPORE PTE LTD.—See Moog Inc.; *U.S. Public*, pg. 1470
MOOG SPACE & DEFENSE GROUP—See Moog Inc.; *U.S. Public*, pg. 1470
MOOG WOLVERHAMPTON LIMITED—See Moog Inc.; *U.S. Public*, pg. 1470
MOOLARBEN COAL OPERATIONS PTY LTD—See Yankuang Group Co., Limited; *Int'l*, pg. 8562
MOOLA SYSTEMS LIMITED—See Marsh & McLennan Companies, Inc.; *U.S. Public*, pg. 1386
MOOLEC SCIENCE SA; *Int'l*, pg. 5038
MOOLMAN MINING BOTSWANA (PTY) LIMITED—See Aveng Limited; *Int'l*, pg. 738
MOOMOO INC.—See Futu Holdings Limited; *Int'l*, pg. 2852
MOONBAE STEEL CO., LTD.; *Int'l*, pg. 5038
MOONBAT CO., LTD.; *Int'l*, pg. 5038
MOONBEAM CAPITAL INVESTMENTS, LLC; *U.S. Private*, pg. 2779
MOONBLINK COMMUNICATIONS; *U.S. Private*, pg. 2779
MOONBOUND MINING LTD.; *Int'l*, pg. 5038
MOON DISTRIBUTORS, INC.; *U.S. Private*, pg. 2778
MOONDOG ENTERTAINMENT AB—See Live Nation Entertainment, Inc.; *U.S. Public*, pg. 1330
MOON ENVIRONMENT TECHNOLOGY CO., LTD.; *Int'l*, pg. 5038
MOONEY AEROSPACE GROUP, LTD.; *U.S. Private*, pg. 2779
MOONEY AIRPLANE COMPANY, INC.—See Mooney Aerospace Group, Ltd.; *U.S. Private*, pg. 2779
MOONEY SERVIZI S.P.A.—See Enel S.p.A.; *Int'l*, pg. 2414
MOONEY S.P.A.—See Enel S.p.A.; *Int'l*, pg. 2414
MOONGIPA CAPITAL FINANCE LIMITED; *Int'l*, pg. 5038
MOONG PATTANA INTERNATIONAL PUBLIC COMPANY LIMITED; *Int'l*, pg. 5038
MOON LAKE ELECTRIC ASSOCIATION INC.; *U.S. Private*, pg. 2778
MOONLAKE IMMUNOTHERAPEUTICS; *U.S. Public*, pg. 1471

MOONLIGHT BASIN LLC—See Lehman Brothers Holdings Inc. Plan Trust; *U.S. Private*, pg. 2419
MOONLIGHT BPO; *U.S. Private*, pg. 2779
MOONLIGHTING PTY LIMITED—See Bain Capital, LP; *U.S. Private*, pg. 439
MOONLIGHTING PTY LIMITED—See Investec Limited; *Int'l*, pg. 3777
MOONLIGHT PACKING CORPORATION; *U.S. Private*, pg. 2779
MOON MANAGEMENT, INC.; *U.S. Private*, pg. 2778
MOONPIG GROUP PLC; *Int'l*, pg. 5038
MOON RIVER MOLY LTD.; *Int'l*, pg. 5038
MOONS' INDUSTRIES (AMERICA), INC.—See Shanghai Moons' Electric Co., Ltd.; *Int'l*, pg. 6775
MOONS' INDUSTRIES EUROPE HEAD QUARTER S.R.L.—See Shanghai Moons' Electric Co., Ltd.; *Int'l*, pg. 6775
MOONS' INDUSTRIES (EUROPE) S.R.L.—See Shanghai Moons' Electric Co., Ltd.; *Int'l*, pg. 6775
MOONS' INDUSTRIES JAPAN CO., LTD.—See Shanghai Moons' Electric Co., Ltd.; *Int'l*, pg. 6775
MOONS' INDUSTRIES (SOUTH-EAST ASIA) PTE. LTD.—See Shanghai Moons' Electric Co., Ltd.; *Int'l*, pg. 6775
MOON VALLEY NURSERY, INC.; *U.S. Private*, pg. 2779
MOONWORKS, INC.; *U.S. Private*, pg. 2779
MOO & OINK INC.; *U.S. Private*, pg. 2778
MOO PRINT LIMITED; *Int'l*, pg. 5038
MOORABBIN AIRPORT CORPORATION PTY LTD—See Goodman Limited; *Int'l*, pg. 3041
MOORADIANS INC.; *U.S. Private*, pg. 2779
MOORBROOK TEXTILES LIMITED—See Lindengruppen AB; *Int'l*, pg. 4510
MOOREAST ASIA PTE. LTD.—See Mooreast Holdings Ltd.; *Int'l*, pg. 5039
MOOREAST EUROPE B.V.—See Mooreast Holdings Ltd.; *Int'l*, pg. 5039
MOOREAST HOLDINGS LTD.; *Int'l*, pg. 5038
MOORE BROTHERS ASPHALT INC.; *U.S. Private*, pg. 2779
MOORE BROTHERS CONSTRUCTION CO.; *U.S. Private*, pg. 2779
MOORE BROTHERS PAVING INC.—See Moore Brothers Asphalt Inc.; *U.S. Private*, pg. 2779
MOORE, BUCKLE (FLEXIBLE PACKAGING) LTD.—See Security Research Group plc; *Int'l*, pg. 6677
MOORE BUSINESS SERVICE INC.; *U.S. Private*, pg. 2779
MOORE CADILLAC HUMMER OF DULLES, LLC; *U.S. Private*, pg. 2779
MOORE CANADA CORPORATION—See DATA Communications Management Corp.; *Int'l*, pg. 1976
MOORE CHRYSLER, INC.; *U.S. Private*, pg. 2779
MOORE COMMUNICATIONS GROUP; *U.S. Private*, pg. 2779
MOORE COMMUNICATIONS SYSTEMS, INC.—See CloudScale365, Inc.; *U.S. Private*, pg. 947
MOORE COMPANY; *U.S. Private*, pg. 2779
MOORE DM GROUP, LLC; *U.S. Private*, pg. 2780
MOORE, EPSTEIN, MOORE; *U.S. Private*, pg. 2780
MOORE FANS LLC; *U.S. Private*, pg. 2780
MOORE FANS LTD—See Moore Fans LLC; *U.S. Private*, pg. 2780
MOOREFIELD CONSTRUCTION INC.; *U.S. Private*, pg. 2780
MOORE FREIGHT SERVICE—See Daseke, Inc.; *U.S. Private*, pg. 1161
MOORE FUND ADMINISTRATION (IOM) LIMITED—See AnaCap Financial Partners LLP; *Int'l*, pg. 445
MOORE FUND ADMINISTRATION (JERSEY) LIMITED—See AnaCap Financial Partners LLP; *Int'l*, pg. 445
MOORE GRAHAM SALES, INC.; *U.S. Private*, pg. 2780
MOORE HOLDINGS INC.; *U.S. Private*, pg. 2780
MOORE IMS BV—See Chatham Asset Management, LLC; *U.S. Private*, pg. 863
MOORE INDUSTRIES-EUROPE INC.—See Moore Industries International Inc.; *U.S. Private*, pg. 2780
MOORE INDUSTRIES INTERNATIONAL INC.; *U.S. Private*, pg. 2780
MOORELAND PARTNERS LLC—See Stifel Financial Corp.; *U.S. Public*, pg. 1950
MOORE LANDSCAPES, LLC—See SECOM Co., Ltd.; *Int'l*, pg. 6670
MOORE L.P. GAS—See UGI Corporation; *U.S. Public*, pg. 2222
MOORE NANOTECHNOLOGY SYSTEMS LLC—See PMT Group Inc; *U.S. Private*, pg. 3219
MOORE OIL CO., INC. - MONTGOMERY—See Moore Oil Co., Inc.; *U.S. Private*, pg. 2780
MOORE OIL CO., INC.; *U.S. Private*, pg. 2780
MOORE OIL INC.; *U.S. Private*, pg. 2780
MOORE PARAGON (CARIBBEAN) LTD.—See Chatham Asset Management, LLC; *U.S. Private*, pg. 864
MOOREPAY LIMITED—See Bain Capital, LP; *U.S. Private*, pg. 442
MOORE PRODUCTS CO. B.V.—See Siemens Aktiengesellschaft; *Int'l*, pg. 6895

MOORE RESOURCE SYSTEMS (ONTARIO) LIMITED—See Enghouse Systems Limited; *Int'l*, pg. 2427
MOORE RESPONSE MARKETING B.V.—See Chatham Asset Management, LLC; *U.S. Private*, pg. 864
MOORE RESTORATION, INC.—See FirstService Corporation; *Int'l*, pg. 2691
MOORE & SCARRY ADVERTISING, INC.; *U.S. Private*, pg. 2779
MOORES CLOTHING FOR MEN—See Tailored Brands, Inc.; *U.S. Public*, pg. 1979
MOORES CLOTHING FOR MEN—See Tailored Brands, Inc.; *U.S. Public*, pg. 1979
MOORE'S ELECTRICAL & MECHANICAL CONSTRUCTION, INC.; *U.S. Private*, pg. 2780
MOORES FURNITURE GROUP LTD.—See Masco Corporation; *U.S. Public*, pg. 1391
MOORE SPECIAL TOOL AG—See PMT Group Inc; *U.S. Private*, pg. 3219
MOORE'S RETREAD & TIRE CO.; *U.S. Private*, pg. 2780
MOORES TIRE SALES INC.; *U.S. Private*, pg. 2780
MOORESTOWN FINANCE, INC.—See Sbar's, Inc.; *U.S. Private*, pg. 3559
MOORESTOWN MALL LLC—See Pennsylvania Real Estate Investment Trust; *U.S. Public*, pg. 1663
MOORESTOWN VISITING NURSE ASSOCIATION; *U.S. Private*, pg. 2780
MOORE SUPPLY CO. INC.; *U.S. Private*, pg. 2780
MOORESVILLE HOSPITAL MANAGEMENT ASSOCIATES, INC.—See Community Health Systems, Inc.; *U.S. Public*, pg. 555
MOORE TOOL COMPANY, INC.—See PMT Group Inc; *U.S. Private*, pg. 3219
MOORETOWN RANCHERIA; *U.S. Private*, pg. 2781
MOORE TRANSPORT; *U.S. Private*, pg. 2780
MOORE & VAN ALLEN PLLC; *U.S. Private*, pg. 2779
MOORFEED CORPORATION—See Executive Management Services Inc.; *U.S. Private*, pg. 1447
MOORFIELD NANOTECHNOLOGY LIMITED—See Judges Scientific plc; *Int'l*, pg. 4021
MOORFIELD PARK MANAGEMENT COMPANY LIMITED—See Persimmon plc; *Int'l*, pg. 5816
MOORGATE LOAN SERVICING LIMITED—See Paragon Banking Group PLC; *Int'l*, pg. 5735
MOORIM CAPITAL CO., LTD.—See Moorim SP Co., Ltd.; *Int'l*, pg. 5039
MOORIM CHEMTECH CO., LTD.—See Moorim SP Co., Ltd.; *Int'l*, pg. 5039
MOORIM LOGITECH CO., LTD.—See Moorim SP Co., Ltd.; *Int'l*, pg. 5039
MOORIM PAPER CO., LTD.; *Int'l*, pg. 5039
MOORIM POWERTECH CO., LTD.—See Moorim SP Co., Ltd.; *Int'l*, pg. 5039
MOORIM P&P CO., LTD.; *Int'l*, pg. 5039
MOORIM SP CO., LTD.; *Int'l*, pg. 5039
THE MOORINGS, INC.; *U.S. Private*, pg. 4080
THE MOORINGS LIMITED—See TUI AG; *Int'l*, pg. 7968
MOORINGS MEXICO SA DE CV—See TUI AG; *Int'l*, pg. 7965
MOORINGS PARK INSTITUTE INC.; *U.S. Private*, pg. 2781
MOORINGS YACHTING SAS—See TUI AG; *Int'l*, pg. 7965
MOOROOLBARK & DISTRICT FINANCIAL SERVICES LIMITED—See Bendigo & Adelaide Bank Ltd.; *Int'l*, pg. 971
MOORS & CABOT INC.; *U.S. Private*, pg. 2781
MOORVALE COAL PTY LTD—See Peabody Energy Corporation; *U.S. Public*, pg. 1659
MOOSE BOATS, INC.—See Lind Marine, Inc.; *U.S. Private*, pg. 2459
MOOSE CHARITIES, INC.; *U.S. Private*, pg. 2781
MOOSEHEAD BREWERIES LIMITED; *Int'l*, pg. 5039
MOOSEJAW MOUNTAINEERING & BACKCOUNTRY TRAVEL, INC.—See Parallel Investment Partners LLC; *U.S. Private*, pg. 3092
MOOSE JAW REFINERY PARTNERSHIP—See Gibson Energy Inc.; *Int'l*, pg. 2963
MOOSE LAKE IMPLEMENT & SPORT—See Northland Lawn Sport & Equipment; *U.S. Private*, pg. 2955
MOOSYLVANIA MARKETING; *U.S. Private*, pg. 2781
MOOTER MEDIA LIMITED; *Int'l*, pg. 5039
M OOTOYA (THAILAND) CO., LTD.—See OOTOYA Holdings Co., Ltd.; *Int'l*, pg. 5595
MOOVE AND OINK INC.; *U.S. Private*, pg. 2781
MOOVE MEDIA AUSTRALIA PTY. LTD.—See ComfortDelGro Corporation Limited; *Int'l*, pg. 1713
MOOVE MEDIA PTE. LTD.—See ComfortDelGro Corporation Limited; *Int'l*, pg. 1713
MOOVIT GMBH—See Avemio AG; *Int'l*, pg. 738
MOOVIT SOFTWARE PRODUCTS GMBH—See Avemio AG; *Int'l*, pg. 738
MOOVLY MEDIA INC.; *Int'l*, pg. 5039
MOOYAH FRANCHISING, LLC—See Balmoral Funds LLC; *U.S. Private*, pg. 461
MOOYAH FRANCHISING, LLC—See Gala Capital Partners, LLC; *U.S. Private*, pg. 1635
M&O PACIFIC LIMITED—See John Wood Group PLC; *Int'l*, pg. 3983

M&O PARTNERS A/S—See Daeyang Electric Co., Ltd.; *Int'l*, pg. 1911
M&O PARTNERS LTDA—See Daeyang Electric Co., Ltd.; *Int'l*, pg. 1911
MOPE INVESTMENT ADVISORS PRIVATE LIMITED—See Motilal Oswal Financial Services Ltd.; *Int'l*, pg. 5053
MOPHIE INC.—See Evercel, Inc.; *U.S. Private*, pg. 1437
MOPOLI - PALMBOOMEN CULTUUR MAATSCHAPPIJ NV; *Int'l*, pg. 5039
MOPUB, INC.—See AppLovin Corp.; *U.S. Public*, pg. 173
MOQDIGITAL PTY LTD—See Brennan IT Pty. Limited; *Int'l*, pg. 1145
MOQ LTD.—See Brennan IT Pty. Limited; *Int'l*, pg. 1145
MORA ASSEGURANCES, SAU—See MoraBanc Group; *Int'l*, pg. 5039
MORABAHA MARINA FINANCING COMPANY; *Int'l*, pg. 5039
MORABANC GROUP; *Int'l*, pg. 5039
MORA BANC, SAU—See MoraBanc Group; *Int'l*, pg. 5039
MORADABAD BAREILY EXPRESSWAY LIMITED—See Infrastructure Leasing & Financial Services Limited; *Int'l*, pg. 3698
MORAE GLOBAL CORP.; *U.S. Private*, pg. 2781
MORA ENGINEERING CONTRACTORS, INC.; *U.S. Private*, pg. 2781
MORAFCO INDUSTRIES LIMITED; *Int'l*, pg. 5039
MORA GESTIO D'ACTIUS, SAU—See MoraBanc Group; *Int'l*, pg. 5039
MORA GMBH—See Ostnor AB; *Int'l*, pg. 5655
MORAINE DIALYSIS, LLC—See DaVita Inc.; *U.S. Public*, pg. 641
MORAL CARAIBES SARL—See CVC Capital Partners SICAV-FIS S.A.; *Int'l*, pg. 1882
MORALES GROUP INC.; *U.S. Private*, pg. 2781
MORALLY WHOLESALE, INC.; *U.S. Private*, pg. 2781
MORA MORAVIA S R.O.—See Hisense Co., Ltd.; *Int'l*, pg. 3407
MORAN AUTOMOTIVE GROUP, INC.—See General Motors Company; *U.S. Public*, pg. 926
MORAN CHEVROLET INC.; *U.S. Private*, pg. 2781
THE MORAN COMPANY, LLC—See Health Management Associates, Inc.; *U.S. Private*, pg. 1894
THE MORANDE AUTOMOTIVE GROUP; *U.S. Private*, pg. 4080
MORANDO S.R.L.—See Groupe Legris Industries; *Int'l*, pg. 3107
MORAN (EA) PUBLISHERS LTD—See Verlagsgruppe Georg von Holtzbrinck GmbH; *Int'l*, pg. 8171
MORAN EDWARDS ASSET MANAGEMENT GROUP; *U.S. Private*, pg. 2781
MORAN ENVIRONMENTAL RECOVERY, LLC—See Moran Towing Corporation; *U.S. Private*, pg. 2781
MORAN FOODS, LLC—See ONEX Corporation; *Int'l*, pg. 5578
MORAN PRINTING INC.; *U.S. Private*, pg. 2781
MORAN PUBLISHERS UGANDA LTD—See Verlagsgruppe Georg von Holtzbrinck GmbH; *Int'l*, pg. 8171
MORAN SHIPYARD CORPORATION—See Moran Towing Corporation; *U.S. Private*, pg. 2781
MORAN TOWING AND TRANSPORTATION, LLC—See Moran Towing Corporation; *U.S. Private*, pg. 2781
MORAN TOWING CORPORATION; *U.S. Private*, pg. 2781
MORAN TOWING OF CHARLESTON—See Moran Towing Corporation; *U.S. Private*, pg. 2781
MORAN TOWING OF FLORIDA—See Moran Towing Corporation; *U.S. Private*, pg. 2781
MORAN TOWING OF MARYLAND—See Moran Towing Corporation; *U.S. Private*, pg. 2781
MORAN TOWING OF MIAMI—See Moran Towing Corporation; *U.S. Private*, pg. 2781
MORAN TOWING OF NEW HAMPSHIRE—See Moran Towing Corporation; *U.S. Private*, pg. 2781
MORAN TOWING OF PENNSYLVANIA—See Moran Towing Corporation; *U.S. Private*, pg. 2782
MORAN TOWING OF SAVANNAH—See Moran Towing Corporation; *U.S. Private*, pg. 2782
MORAN TOWING OF TEXAS INC.—See Moran Towing Corporation; *U.S. Private*, pg. 2782
MORAN TOWING OF VIRGINIA INC.—See Moran Towing Corporation; *U.S. Private*, pg. 2782
MORAN TRANSPORTATION CORP.; *U.S. Private*, pg. 2782
MORARIT PANIFICATIE SA; *Int'l*, pg. 5039
MORARJEE INTERNATIONAL SRL—See Ashok Piramal Group; *Int'l*, pg. 608
MORARJEE TEXTILES LTD—See Ashok Piramal Group; *Int'l*, pg. 608
MORARKA FINANCE LIMITED; *Int'l*, pg. 5039
MORA-SAN MIGUEL ELECTRIC COOPERATIVE, INC.; *U.S. Private*, pg. 2781
MOR ASSOCIATES, LP—See Raymond James Financial, Inc.; *U.S. Public*, pg. 1764
MORAVA A.D.; *Int'l*, pg. 5039
MORAVA A.D.; *Int'l*, pg. 5039
MORAVACEM D.O.O.—See CRH plc; *Int'l*, pg. 1845
MORA VALLEY WIRELESS, LP—See ATN International, Inc.; *U.S. Public*, pg. 225
MORAVAMERMER A.D.; *Int'l*, pg. 5039

MORAVIAN HOME INCORPORATED; *U.S. Private*, pg. 2782
MORAVIAN MANORS, INC.; *U.S. Private*, pg. 2782
MORAVIAN VILLAGE OF BETHLEHEM; *U.S. Private*, pg. 2782
MORAVSKA BASTEI MOBA S.R.O.—See Bastei Lubbe AG; *Int'l*, pg. 888
MORA WEALTH MANAGEMENT AG—See MoraBanc Group; *Int'l*, pg. 5039
MORA WEALTH MANAGEMENT LLC—See MoraBanc Group; *Int'l*, pg. 5039
MORA WEALTH MANAGEMENT, SA—See MoraBanc Group; *Int'l*, pg. 5039
MORBARK LLC—See Alamo Group Inc.; *U.S. Public*, pg. 71
MORBELLI, RUSSO & PARTNERS ADVERTISING, INC.; *U.S. Private*, pg. 2782
MORCOM INTERNATIONAL, INC.; *U.S. Private*, pg. 2782
MORCON CONSTRUCTION INC.; *U.S. Private*, pg. 2782
MORCON, INC.; *U.S. Private*, pg. 2782
MORDECHAI AVIV TAASIOT BENIYAH (1973) LTD.; *Int'l*, pg. 5039
MORDOVSKAYA ENERGOSBYT COMP; *Int'l*, pg. 5040
MORE ALLIANCE NORDIC AB; *Int'l*, pg. 5040
MOREAS S.A.—See ELLAKTOR S.A.; *Int'l*, pg. 2365
MORE BOLIGKREDITT AS—See Sparebanken More; *Int'l*, pg. 7125
MORECO, INC.—See Modern Group Ltd.; *U.S. Private*, pg. 2761
MORE CONCEPT LIMITED—See China Automobile New Retail (Holdings) Limited; *Int'l*, pg. 1484
MOREDA RIVIERE TREFILERIAS, SA—See Celsa Group; *Int'l*, pg. 1395
MOREDIRECT, INC.—See PC Connection, Inc.; *U.S. Public*, pg. 1658
MORE DRIVING LIMITED—See The Logistics Partnership LLP; *Int'l*, pg. 7664
MORE EIENDOMSMEGLING AS—See Sparebanken More; *Int'l*, pg. 7125
MORE ELECTRONICS APS—See C C P Contact Probes Co., Ltd.; *Int'l*, pg. 1237
MOREFAR MARKETING, INC.—See American International Group, Inc.; *U.S. Public*, pg. 107
MOREFIELD COMMUNICATIONS INC.; *U.S. Private*, pg. 2782
MOREFILED GROUP N.V.; *Int'l*, pg. 5040
MOREHART CHEVROLET CO; *U.S. Private*, pg. 2782
MOREHEAD CAPITAL MANAGEMENT LLC—See Investors Management Corporation; *U.S. Private*, pg. 2132
MOREHOUSE-COWLES—See IDEX Corp; *U.S. Public*, pg. 1091
MOREHOUSE-HUBER, INC.—See Blue Sea Capital Management LLC; *U.S. Private*, pg. 592
MOREIN MOTOR COMPANY INC.; *U.S. Private*, pg. 2782
MORE INVESTMENT HOUSE LTD.; *Int'l*, pg. 5040
MORE I.T. RESOURCES LTD.—See Dell Technologies Inc.; *U.S. Public*, pg. 651
MORELAND ALTOBELLI ASSOCIATES, INC.—See GI Manager L.P.; *U.S. Private*, pg. 1691
MORELAND HOTEL (BMG) PTY LTD—See Woolworths Group Limited; *Int'l*, pg. 8451
MORELANDS INC.; *U.S. Private*, pg. 2782
MORELCO S.A.S.—See Aenza S.A.A.; *Int'l*, pg. 176
MORELLA CORPORATION LIMITED; *Int'l*, pg. 5040
MORELLI GROUP LIMITED; *Int'l*, pg. 5040
MORELO REISEMOBILE GMBH—See H.T.P. Investments BV; *Int'l*, pg. 3196
MORE MAGIC SOLUTIONS, INC.—See Advent International Corporation; *U.S. Private*, pg. 102
MORENO, PEELEN, PINTO & CLARK (MPC); *U.S. Private*, pg. 2782
MORENO TRENCHING, LTD.; *U.S. Private*, pg. 2782
MOREPEN LABORATORIES LIMITED; *Int'l*, pg. 5040
MORE RETURN PUBLIC COMPANY LIMITED; *Int'l*, pg. 5040
MORESCO CORPORATION; *Int'l*, pg. 5040
MORESCO DISTRIBUTING CO.—See Bain Capital, LP; *U.S. Private*, pg. 441
MORESCO HANANO DIE-CASTING COATING (SHANGHAI) CO., LTD.—See MORESCO Corporation; *Int'l*, pg. 5040
MORESCO HM&LUB INDIA PRIVATE LIMITED—See MORESCO Corporation; *Int'l*, pg. 5040
MORESCO SERVICE CO., LTD.—See MORESCO Corporation; *Int'l*, pg. 5040
MORESCO TECHNO CO., LTD.—See MORESCO Corporation; *Int'l*, pg. 5040
MORESCO (THAILAND) CO., LTD.—See MORESCO Corporation; *Int'l*, pg. 5040
MORESCO USA INC.—See MORESCO Corporation; *Int'l*, pg. 5040
MORESECURE LTD.—See Whittan Storage Systems Ltd.; *Int'l*, pg. 8400
MORE SPACE PLACE, INC.—See Closet & Storage Concepts; *U.S. Private*, pg. 946
MORE SRL—See Danieli & C. Officine Meccaniche S.p.A.; *Int'l*, pg. 1963
MORET CONSTRUCTION; *U.S. Private*, pg. 2782

MORET CONSTRUCTION | CORPORATE AFFILIATIONS

MORE THAN GOURMET, INC.—See Ajinomoto Company, Inc.; *Int'l*, pg. 256
MORET INDUSTRIES GROUP, SAS; *Int'l*, pg. 5040
MORETON RESOURCES LIMITED; *Int'l*, pg. 5040
MORETRENCH AMERICAN CORPORATION—See Keller Group plc; *Int'l*, pg. 4121
MORETTE COMPANY, INC.; *U.S. Private*, pg. 2782
MOREVISIBILITY.COM, INC.; *U.S. Private*, pg. 2782
THE MOREY CORPORATION; *U.S. Private*, pg. 4080
MOREY DEVELOPMENT CO. INC.—See Morey's Piers Incorporated; *U.S. Private*, pg. 2782
MOREY EVANS; *U.S. Private*, pg. 2782
MOREY'S PIERS INCORPORATED; *U.S. Private*, pg. 2782
MOREY'S SEAFOOD INTERNATIONAL LLC; *U.S. Private*, pg. 2782
MORF3D INC.—See Nikon Corporation; *Int'l*, pg. 5292
MOR FURNITURE FOR LESS; *U.S. Private*, pg. 2781
MORGAL MACHINE TOOL COMPANY, INC.; *U.S. Private*, pg. 2783
MORGAN ADHESIVES COMPANY, LLC—See LINTEC Corporation; *Int'l*, pg. 4516
MORGAN ADVANCED CERAMICS, INC.—See Morgan Advanced Materials plc; *Int'l*, pg. 5042
MORGAN ADVANCED CERAMICS LTD.—See Morgan Advanced Materials plc; *Int'l*, pg. 5042
MORGAN ADVANCED CERAMICS—See Morgan Advanced Materials plc; *Int'l*, pg. 5042
MORGAN ADVANCED CERAMICS—See Morgan Advanced Materials plc; *Int'l*, pg. 5042
MORGAN ADVANCED MATERIALS AND TECHNOLOGY CANADA—See Morgan Advanced Materials plc; *Int'l*, pg. 5041
MORGAN ADVANCED MATERIALS AND TECHNOLOGY—See Morgan Advanced Materials plc; *Int'l*, pg. 5041
MORGAN ADVANCED MATERIALS PLC; *Int'l*, pg. 5041
MORGAN ADVANCED MATERIALS - TECHNICAL CERAMICS—See Morgan Advanced Materials plc; *Int'l*, pg. 5042
MORGAN AM&T ITALIA SRL—See Morgan Advanced Materials plc; *Int'l*, pg. 5041
MORGAN AM&T (SHANGHAI) CO., LTD.—See Morgan Advanced Materials plc; *Int'l*, pg. 5042
MORGAN AM&T—See Morgan Advanced Materials plc; *Int'l*, pg. 5041
MORGAN AM&T SOUTH AFRICA PTY. LTD.—See Morgan Advanced Materials plc; *Int'l*, pg. 5041
MORGANA SYSTEMS LTD.—See Grimaldi Industri AB; *Int'l*, pg. 3085
MORGAN AUSTRIA GMBH—See Morgan Advanced Materials plc; *Int'l*, pg. 5042
MORGAN AUTO GROUP, LLC; *U.S. Private*, pg. 2783
MORGAN AUTO PARTS INC.; *U.S. Private*, pg. 2783
MORGAN & BANKS INVESTMENTS PTY. LTD.; *Int'l*, pg. 5040
MORGAN BORSZCZ CONSULTING; *U.S. Private*, pg. 2783
MORGAN & BROTHER MANHATTAN STORAGE INC.; *U.S. Private*, pg. 2783
MORGAN BUILDING & SPA MANUFACTURING CORPORATION—See GHM Corp.; *U.S. Private*, pg. 1690
MORGAN BUILDINGS & SPAS, INC.—See GHM Corp.; *U.S. Private*, pg. 1690
MORGAN BUILDING TRANSPORT CORP.—See GHM Corp.; *U.S. Private*, pg. 1691
MORGAN CARBON CZECH S.R.O—See Morgan Advanced Materials plc; *Int'l*, pg. 5042
MORGAN CARBON FRANCE S.A.—See Morgan Advanced Materials plc; *Int'l*, pg. 5042
MORGAN CARBON ITALIA S.R.L.—See Morgan Advanced Materials plc; *Int'l*, pg. 5042
MORGAN CERAMICS ASIA PTE. LTD.—See Morgan Advanced Materials plc; *Int'l*, pg. 5043
MORGAN CERAMICS MIDDLE EAST FZE—See Morgan Advanced Materials plc; *Int'l*, pg. 5043
MORGAN CERAMICS—See Morgan Advanced Materials plc; *Int'l*, pg. 5042
MORGAN & COMPANY; *U.S. Private*, pg. 2783
MORGAN CONCRETE COMPANY INC; *U.S. Private*, pg. 2783
MORGAN CORPORATION—See J.B. Poindexter & Co., Inc.; *U.S. Private*, pg. 2158
MORGAN CORP.; *U.S. Private*, pg. 2783
MORGAN COUNTY CITIZEN—See Times Journal Inc.; *U.S. Private*, pg. 4172
MORGAN COUNTY RURAL ELECTRIC ASSOCIATION; *U.S. Private*, pg. 2783
MORGAN DISTRIBUTING COMPANY INC.; *U.S. Private*, pg. 2783
MORGAN DISTRIBUTION; *U.S. Private*, pg. 2783
MORGAN ELECTRICAL CARBON DEUTSCHLAND GMBH—See Morgan Advanced Materials plc; *Int'l*, pg. 5043
MORGAN EST RAIL LIMITED—See Morgan Sindall Group Plc; *Int'l*, pg. 5045
MORGAN FINANCE LTD.—See First Steamship Co., Ltd.; *Int'l*, pg. 2688

MORGAN FIRE & SAFETY INC—See Littlejohn & Co., LLC; *U.S. Private*, pg. 2472
MORGAN FOODS, INC.; *U.S. Private*, pg. 2783
MORGANFRANKLIN CORPORATION; *U.S. Private*, pg. 2784
MORGAN GMC-BUICK; *U.S. Private*, pg. 2783
MORGAN GROUP HOLDING CO.; *U.S. Public*, pg. 1471
MORGAN/HARBOUR CONSTRUCTION, LLC.; *U.S. Private*, pg. 2784
MORGAN HILL TIMES—See Metro Publishing, Inc.; *U.S. Private*, pg. 2686
MORGAN HOLDING NETHERLANDS BV—See Morgan Advanced Materials plc; *Int'l*, pg. 5041
MORGAN INDUSTRIAL CARBON—See Morgan Advanced Materials plc; *Int'l*, pg. 5041
MORGAN INDUSTRIAL INC.; *U.S. Private*, pg. 2783
MORGAN INSURANCE SERVICES LIMITED—See Arthur J. Gallagher & Co.; *U.S. Public*, pg. 203
MORGANITE AUSTRALIA PTY LIMITED—See Morgan Advanced Materials plc; *Int'l*, pg. 5043
MORGANITE BRAZIL LTDA—See Morgan Advanced Materials plc; *Int'l*, pg. 5043
MORGANITE CANADA CORP.—See Morgan Advanced Materials plc; *Int'l*, pg. 5043
MORGANITE CARBON KABUSHIKI KAISHA—See Morgan Advanced Materials plc; *Int'l*, pg. 5043
MORGANITE CARBON SINGAPORE PTE. LIMITED—See Morgan Advanced Materials plc; *Int'l*, pg. 5042
MORGANITE CRUCIBLE INC.—See Morgan Advanced Materials plc; *Int'l*, pg. 5043
MORGANITE CRUCIBLE INDIA LTD.—See Morgan Advanced Materials plc; *Int'l*, pg. 5043
MORGANITE ELECTRICAL CARBON LIMITED—See Morgan Advanced Materials plc; *Int'l*, pg. 5042
MORGANITE ESPANOLA S.A.—See Morgan Advanced Materials plc; *Int'l*, pg. 5041
MORGANITE HONG KONG COMPANY LIMITED—See Morgan Advanced Materials plc; *Int'l*, pg. 5042
MORGANITE INDUSTRIES INC—See Morgan Advanced Materials plc; *Int'l*, pg. 5043
MORGANITE INSULATING PRODUCTS PTY. LIMITED—See Morgan Advanced Materials plc; *Int'l*, pg. 5042
MORGANITE LUXEMBOURG S.A.—See Morgan Advanced Materials plc; *Int'l*, pg. 5042
MORGANITE NATIONAL CARBON AG—See Morgan Advanced Materials plc; *Int'l*, pg. 5042
MORGANITE TAIWAN LIMITED—See Morgan Advanced Materials plc; *Int'l*, pg. 5042
MORGAN JEWELERS OF SALT LAKE CITY; *U.S. Private*, pg. 2783
MORGAN JOSEPH TRIARTISAN GROUP INC.; *U.S. Private*, pg. 2784
MORGAN JOSEPH TRIARTISAN LLC—See Morgan Joseph TriArtisan Group Inc.; *U.S. Private*, pg. 2784
MORGAN KAILONG (JINGMEN) THERMAL CERAMICS CO. LTD.—See Morgan Advanced Materials plc; *Int'l*, pg. 5043
MORGAN KARBON GRAFIT SANAYI A.S.—See Morgan Advanced Materials plc; *Int'l*, pg. 5041
MORGAN KOREA COMPANY LIMITED—See Morgan Advanced Materials plc; *Int'l*, pg. 5043
MORGAN LAW RECRUITMENT CONSULTANCY LTD; *Int'l*, pg. 5044
MORGAN, LEWIS & BOCKIUS LLP; *U.S. Private*, pg. 2784
MORGAN LINEN SERVICE INC.; *U.S. Private*, pg. 2784
MORGAN LLOYD ADMINISTRATION LTD—See Clifton Asset Management Plc; *Int'l*, pg. 1659
MORGAN LOVELL LONDON LIMITED—See Morgan Sindall Group Plc; *Int'l*, pg. 5045
MORGAN LOVELL PLC—See Morgan Sindall Group Plc; *Int'l*, pg. 5045
MORGAN MANAGEMENT CORPORATION—See GHM Corp.; *U.S. Private*, pg. 1691
MORGAN MARKETING & PUBLIC RELATIONS LLC; *U.S. Private*, pg. 2784
MORGAN MATERIALS HUNGARY LIMITED—See Morgan Advanced Materials plc; *Int'l*, pg. 5041
MORGAN-MCCLURE CHEVY BUICK CADILLAC, INC.; *U.S. Private*, pg. 2784
MORGAN MCKINLEY GROUP LIMITED—See Premier Recruitment (International) Unlimited Company; *Int'l*, pg. 5961
MORGAN MEIGHEN & ASSOCIATES LIMITED; *Int'l*, pg. 5044
MORGAN & MILO, LLC—See Zutano Global Inc.; *U.S. Private*, pg. 4610
MORGAN MOLTEN METAL PRODUCTS LTD.—See Morgan Advanced Materials plc; *Int'l*, pg. 5043
MORGAN MOLTEN METAL SYSTEMS—See Morgan Advanced Materials plc; *Int'l*, pg. 5043
MORGAN MOLTEN METAL SYSTEMS (SUZHOU) CO. LTD.—See Morgan Advanced Materials plc; *Int'l*, pg. 5043
MORGAN & MYERS, INC.—See Gibbs & Soell, Inc.; *U.S. Private*, pg. 1695
MORGAN & MYERS, INC.—See Gibbs & Soell, Inc.; *U.S. Private*, pg. 1695

MORGAN NATIONAL AB—See Morgan Advanced Materials plc; *Int'l*, pg. 5043
MORGAN OIL COMPANY INCORPORATED; *U.S. Private*, pg. 2784
MORGAN OIL COMPANY, INC.; *U.S. Private*, pg. 2784
MORGAN OLSON CORPORATION—See J.B. Poindexter & Co., Inc.; *U.S. Private*, pg. 2158
MORGAN PARK SUMMER MUSIC FESTIVAL ASSOCIATION INC.; *U.S. Private*, pg. 2784
MORGAN PHILIPS GROUP; *Int'l*, pg. 5044
MORGAN PHILIPS HUDSON ESPANA SLU—See Morgan Philips Group; *Int'l*, pg. 5044
MORGAN PHILIPS HUDSON SP. Z O.O.—See Morgan Philips Group; *Int'l*, pg. 5044
MORGAN PHILIPS LUXEMBOURG S.A.—See Morgan Philips Group; *Int'l*, pg. 5044
MORGAN PHILIPS SA—See Morgan Philips Group; *Int'l*, pg. 5044
MORGAN PHILIPS UK LIMITED. - EDINBURGH—See Morgan Philips Group; *Int'l*, pg. 5044
MORGAN PHILIPS UK LIMITED—See Morgan Philips Group; *Int'l*, pg. 5044
MORGAN PROPERTIES, LLC—See Raymond James Financial, Inc.; *U.S. Public*, pg. 1764
MORGAN PROPERTIES TRUST; *U.S. Private*, pg. 2784
MORGAN & SAMPSON USA; *U.S. Private*, pg. 2783
MORGAN SAMUELS COMPANY; *U.S. Private*, pg. 2784
MORGAN S.A.; *Int'l*, pg. 5044
MORGAN SCHAFFER LTD.—See ESCO Technologies, Inc.; *U.S. Public*, pg. 794
MORGAN'S FOODS, INC.—See Apex Restaurant Management, Inc.; *U.S. Private*, pg. 293
MORGANS HOTEL GROUP CO. LLC—See SBEEG Holdings, LLC; *U.S. Private*, pg. 3559
MORGAN SINDALL GROUP PLC; *Int'l*, pg. 5044
MORGAN SINDALL INVESTMENTS LIMITED—See Morgan Sindall Group Plc; *Int'l*, pg. 5045
MORGAN SINDALL PLC - CONSTRUCTION & INFRASTRUCTURE—See Morgan Sindall Group Plc; *Int'l*, pg. 5045
MORGAN SINDALL PROFESSIONAL SERVICES AG—See Morgan Sindall Group Plc; *Int'l*, pg. 5045
MORGAN SOLAR INC.—See Enbridge Inc.; *Int'l*, pg. 2397
MORGAN SOUTHERN, INC.—See Universal Logistics Holdings, Inc.; *U.S. Public*, pg. 2261
MORGAN STANLEY AB—See Morgan Stanley; *U.S. Public*, pg. 1473
MORGAN STANLEY AIP GP LP—See Morgan Stanley; *U.S. Public*, pg. 1472
MORGAN STANLEY ASIA LTD.—See Morgan Stanley; *U.S. Public*, pg. 1473
MORGAN STANLEY ASIA (SINGAPORE) SECURITIES PTE LTD.—See Morgan Stanley; *U.S. Public*, pg. 1472
MORGAN STANLEY ASIA (TAIWAN) LTD.—See Morgan Stanley; *U.S. Public*, pg. 1472
MORGAN STANLEY AUSTRALIA LIMITED—See Morgan Stanley; *U.S. Public*, pg. 1472
MORGAN STANLEY BANK AG—See Morgan Stanley; *U.S. Public*, pg. 1473
MORGAN STANLEY BANK ASIA LIMITED—See Morgan Stanley; *U.S. Public*, pg. 1472
MORGAN STANLEY BANK INTERNATIONAL LIMITED—See Morgan Stanley; *U.S. Public*, pg. 1472
MORGAN STANLEY B.V.—See Morgan Stanley; *U.S. Public*, pg. 1472
MORGAN STANLEY CANADA LTD.—See Morgan Stanley; *U.S. Public*, pg. 1473
MORGAN STANLEY CAPITAL MANAGEMENT, LLC—See Morgan Stanley; *U.S. Public*, pg. 1472
MORGAN STANLEY CAPITAL PARTNERS—See Morgan Stanley; *U.S. Public*, pg. 1474
MORGAN STANLEY (CHINA) PRIVATE EQUITY INVESTMENT MANAGEMENT CO., LTD.—See Morgan Stanley; *U.S. Public*, pg. 1472
MORGAN STANLEY & CO. COMMODITIES—See Morgan Stanley; *U.S. Public*, pg. 1472
MORGAN STANLEY & CO. INTERNATIONAL PLC—See Morgan Stanley; *U.S. Public*, pg. 1472
MORGAN STANLEY & CO. LLC - BROOKLYN—See Morgan Stanley; *U.S. Public*, pg. 1472
MORGAN STANLEY & CO. LLC—See Morgan Stanley; *U.S. Public*, pg. 1472
MORGAN STANLEY & CO. LLC—See Morgan Stanley; *U.S. Public*, pg. 1472
MORGAN STANLEY CORPORATE TRADER—See Morgan Stanley; *U.S. Public*, pg. 1472
MORGAN STANLEY CORRETORA DE TITULOS E VALORES MOBILIARIOS S.A.—See Morgan Stanley; *U.S. Public*, pg. 1473
MORGAN STANLEY DEAN WITTER (THAILAND) LTD.—See Morgan Stanley; *U.S. Public*, pg. 1473
MORGAN STANLEY DOMESTIC CAPITAL, INC.—See Morgan Stanley; *U.S. Public*, pg. 1472
MORGAN STANLEY DURANGO LLC—See Morgan Stanley; *U.S. Public*, pg. 1472
MORGAN STANLEY ELZ GMBH—See Morgan Stanley; *U.S. Public*, pg. 1472
MORGAN STANLEY (FRANCE) SAS—See Morgan Stanley; *U.S. Public*, pg. 1472

COMPANY NAME INDEX

MORGAN STANLEY FUND SERVICES (IRELAND) LIMITED—See Morgan Stanley; *U.S. Public*, pg. 1472
MORGAN STANLEY GATEWAY SECURITIES JSC—See JB Financial Group Co., Ltd.; *Int'l*, pg. 3917
MORGAN STANLEY HONG KONG LIMITED—See Morgan Stanley; *U.S. Public*, pg. 1472
MORGAN STANLEY INDIA COMPANY PRIVATE LIMITED—See Morgan Stanley; *U.S. Public*, pg. 1472
MORGAN STANLEY INFRASTRUCTURE, INC.—See Morgan Stanley; *U.S. Public*, pg. 1472
MORGAN STANLEY INTERNATIONAL HOLDINGS INC.—See Morgan Stanley; *U.S. Public*, pg. 1473
MORGAN STANLEY INTERNATIONAL LTD.—See Morgan Stanley; *U.S. Public*, pg. 1473
MORGAN STANLEY INVESTMENT MANAGEMENT (AUSTRALIA) PTY LIMITED—See Morgan Stanley; *U.S. Public*, pg. 1473
MORGAN STANLEY INVESTMENT MANAGEMENT, INC. - PHILADELPHIA—See Morgan Stanley; *U.S. Public*, pg. 1474
MORGAN STANLEY INVESTMENT MANAGEMENT, INC. - SAN FRANCISCO—See Morgan Stanley; *U.S. Public*, pg. 1475
MORGAN STANLEY INVESTMENT MANAGEMENT, INC.—See Morgan Stanley; *U.S. Public*, pg. 1474
MORGAN STANLEY INVESTMENT MANAGEMENT (JAPAN) CO., LTD.—See Morgan Stanley; *U.S. Public*, pg. 1473
MORGAN STANLEY INVESTMENT MANAGEMENT LIMITED—See Morgan Stanley; *U.S. Public*, pg. 1474
MORGAN STANLEY (ISRAEL) LTD.—See Morgan Stanley; *U.S. Public*, pg. 1472
MORGAN STANLEY JAPAN GROUP CO., LTD.—See Morgan Stanley; *U.S. Public*, pg. 1475
MORGAN STANLEY JAPAN HOLDINGS CO., LTD.—See Morgan Stanley; *U.S. Public*, pg. 1475
MORGAN STANLEY LATIN AMERICA INCORPORATED—See Morgan Stanley; *U.S. Public*, pg. 1474
MORGAN STANLEY MENKUL DEGERLER A.S.—See Morgan Stanley; *U.S. Public*, pg. 1475
MORGAN STANLEY MUFG SECURITIES CO., LTD.—See Morgan Stanley; *U.S. Public*, pg. 1475
MORGAN STANLEY PRIVATE EQUITY ASIA INC.—See Morgan Stanley; *U.S. Public*, pg. 1475
MORGAN STANLEY PROPERTIES CORSO VENEZIA S.R.L.—See Morgan Stanley; *U.S. Public*, pg. 1475
MORGAN STANLEY PROPERTIES FRANCE SAS—See Morgan Stanley; *U.S. Public*, pg. 1475
MORGAN STANLEY PROPERTIES, INC.—See Morgan Stanley; *U.S. Public*, pg. 1475
MORGAN STANLEY REAL ESTATE—See Morgan Stanley; *U.S. Public*, pg. 1475
MORGAN STANLEY REALTY INC.—See Morgan Stanley; *U.S. Public*, pg. 1475
MORGAN STANLEY SAUDI ARABIA—See Morgan Stanley; *U.S. Public*, pg. 1475
MORGAN STANLEY SERVICES CANADA CORP.—See Morgan Stanley; *U.S. Public*, pg. 1475
MORGAN STANLEY SERVICES PTY LIMITED—See Morgan Stanley; *U.S. Public*, pg. 1475
MORGAN STANLEY SINGAPORE PTE. LTD.—See Morgan Stanley; *U.S. Public*, pg. 1475
MORGAN STANLEY SMITH BARNEY LLC—See Citigroup Inc.; *U.S. Public*, pg. 503
MORGAN STANLEY SMITH BARNEY LLC—See Morgan Stanley; *U.S. Public*, pg. 1475
MORGAN STANLEY SOLUTIONS INDIA PRIVATE LIMITED—See Morgan Stanley; *U.S. Public*, pg. 1475
MORGAN STANLEY; *U.S. Public*, pg. 1471
MORGAN STANLEY SOUTH AFRICA (PTY) LTD.—See Morgan Stanley; *U.S. Public*, pg. 1473
MORGAN STANLEY, S.V.,S.A.U—See Morgan Stanley; *U.S. Public*, pg. 1473
MORGAN STANLEY SWISS HOLDINGS GMBH—See Morgan Stanley; *U.S. Public*, pg. 1473
MORGAN STANLEY (SWITZERLAND) AG—See Morgan Stanley; *U.S. Public*, pg. 1472
MORGAN STANLEY TAIWAN LIMITED—See Morgan Stanley; *U.S. Public*, pg. 1475
MORGAN STANLEY (THAILAND) LIMITED—See Morgan Stanley; *U.S. Public*, pg. 1472
MORGAN STANLEY TRADING BETEILIGUNGS-GMBH—See Morgan Stanley; *U.S. Public*, pg. 1475
MORGAN STANLEY UK LIMITED—See Morgan Stanley; *U.S. Public*, pg. 1475
MORGAN STANLEY WEALTH MANAGEMENT AUSTRALIA PTY LTD.—See Morgan Stanley; *U.S. Public*, pg. 1473
MORGAN STANLEY WEALTH MANAGEMENT AUSTRALIA PTY LTD—See Morgan Stanley; *U.S. Public*, pg. 1473
MORGAN STREET BREWERY & TAVERN INC.; *U.S. Private*, pg. 2784
MORGAN TECHNICAL CERAMICS-AUBURN—See Morgan Advanced Materials plc; *Int'l*, pg. 5042
MORGAN TECHNICAL CERAMICS AUSTRALIA PTY.LTD.—See Morgan Advanced Materials plc; *Int'l*, pg. 5043
MORGAN TECHNICAL CERAMICS CERTECH—See Morgan Advanced Materials plc; *Int'l*, pg. 5042
MORGAN TECHNICAL CERAMICS CERTECH—See Morgan Advanced Materials plc; *Int'l*, pg. 5042
MORGAN TECHNICAL CERAMICS CERTECH—See Morgan Advanced Materials plc; *Int'l*, pg. 5042
MORGAN TECHNICAL CERAMICS CERTECH—See Morgan Advanced Materials plc; *Int'l*, pg. 5042
MORGAN TECHNICAL CERAMICS LIMITED—See Morgan Advanced Materials plc; *Int'l*, pg. 5042
MORGAN TECHNICAL CERAMICS LIMITED—See Morgan Advanced Materials plc; *Int'l*, pg. 5042
MORGAN TECHNICAL CERAMICS-MELBOURNE—See Morgan Advanced Materials plc; *Int'l*, pg. 5042
MORGAN TECHNICAL CERAMICS S.A. DE C.V.—See Morgan Advanced Materials plc; *Int'l*, pg. 5043
MORGAN TECHNICAL CERAMICS (SUZHOU) CO. LTD.—See Morgan Advanced Materials plc; *Int'l*, pg. 5043
MORGAN THERMAL CERAMICS DEUTSCHLAND GMBH—See Morgan Advanced Materials plc; *Int'l*, pg. 5043
MORGAN THERMAL CERAMICS INC.—See Morgan Advanced Materials plc; *Int'l*, pg. 5042
MORGAN THERMAL CERAMICS INTERNATIONAL TRADING (SHANGHAI) CO. LTD.—See Morgan Advanced Materials plc; *Int'l*, pg. 5043
MORGAN THERMAL CERAMICS SHANGHAI LTD—See Morgan Advanced Materials plc; *Int'l*, pg. 5043
MORGAN THERMAL CERAMICS SUKHOY LOG LLC—See Morgan Advanced Materials plc; *Int'l*, pg. 5043
MORGAN THERMIC S.A.—See Morgan Advanced Materials plc; *Int'l*, pg. 5043
MORGAN & THORNBURG, INC.; *U.S. Private*, pg. 2783
MORGANTI FLORIDA INC.—See Morganti Group/SKH Holdings Inc.; *U.S. Private*, pg. 2785
THE MORGANTI GROUP, INC.—See Morganti Group/SKH Holdings Inc.; *U.S. Private*, pg. 2785
MORGANTI GROUP/SKH HOLDINGS INC.; *U.S. Private*, pg. 2785
MORGANTI TEXAS INC.—See Morganti Group/SKH Holdings Inc.; *U.S. Private*, pg. 2785
MORGANTOWN HOSPICE, LLC.—See Amedisys, Inc.; *U.S. Public*, pg. 94
MORGANTOWN MALL ASSOCIATES, LP—See Washington Prime Group Inc.; *U.S. Private*, pg. 4449
MORGAN TRUCK BODY, LLC—See J.B. Poindexter & Co., Inc.; *U.S. Private*, pg. 2158
MORGAN VENTURES LIMITED; *Int'l*, pg. 5045
MORGAN VINCI—See Morgan Sindall Group Plc; *Int'l*, pg. 5045
MORGAN WHITE GROUP, INC.; *U.S. Private*, pg. 2784
MORGAN-WIGHTMAN SUPPLY COMPANY; *U.S. Private*, pg. 2784
MORGARDSHAMMAR AB—See Danieli & C. Officine Meccaniche S.p.A.; *Int'l*, pg. 1963
MORGEN & MORGEN GMBH—See JDC Group AG; *Int'l*, pg. 3925
MORGENS WATERFALL VINTIADIS & CO. INC.; *U.S. Private*, pg. 2785
MORGENTHALER MANAGEMENT CORPORATION; *U.S. Private*, pg. 2785
MORGRO, INC.; *U.S. Private*, pg. 2785
MORGUARD CORPORATION; *Int'l*, pg. 5045
MORGUARD INVESTMENTS LIMITED—See Morguard Corporation; *Int'l*, pg. 5045
MORGUARD NORTH AMERICAN RESIDENTIAL REAL ESTATE INVESTMENT TRUST—See Morguard Corporation; *Int'l*, pg. 5045
MORGUARD REAL ESTATE INVESTMENT TRUST—See Morguard Corporation; *Int'l*, pg. 5045
MORGUARD RESIDENTIAL INC.—See Morguard Corporation; *Int'l*, pg. 5045
MORIA JAPAN COMPANY LTD.—See Nexon Co., Ltd.; *Int'l*, pg. 5245
MORIEN RESOURCES CORP.; *Int'l*, pg. 5045
MORI-GUMI CO., LTD.; *Int'l*, pg. 5045
MORI HAMADA & MATSUMOTO; *Int'l*, pg. 5045
MORIHA SHIGYO CO., LTD.—See Oji Holdings Corporation; *Int'l*, pg. 5537
MORI HILLS REIT INVESTMENT CORPORATION; *Int'l*, pg. 5045
MORII APPRAISAL & INVESTMENT CONSULTING INC.—See Jones Lang LaSalle Incorporated; *U.S. Public*, pg. 1205
MORI KAMIHANBAI, CO., LTD.—See Oji Holdings Corporation; *Int'l*, pg. 5537
MORI KAMIHANBAI CO., LTD. - TOKYO SHIKI PLANT—See Oji Holdings Corporation; *Int'l*, pg. 5537
MORI LTD—See Ipsos S.A.; *Int'l*, pg. 3802
MORI LUGGAGE AND GIFTS INC.; *U.S. Private*, pg. 2785
MORIMATSU INTERNATIONAL HOLDINGS COMPANY LIMITED; *Int'l*, pg. 5045
MORIMITSU INDUSTRIES COMPANY—See Nitta Corporation; *Int'l*, pg. 5382
MORIMOTO CO., LTD.; *Int'l*, pg. 5046

MORIROKU HOLDINGS COMPANY, LTD.

MORIMURA BROS.,(ASIA) CO., LTD.—See Morimura Bros., Inc.; *Int'l*, pg. 5046
MORIMURA BROS. (EUROPE) B.V.—See Morimura Bros., Inc.; *Int'l*, pg. 5046
MORIMURA BROS. (H.K.) LTD.—See Morimura Bros., Inc.; *Int'l*, pg. 5046
MORIMURA BROS., INC.; *Int'l*, pg. 5046
MORIMURA BROS. (SHANGHAI) CO., LTD.—See Morimura Bros., Inc.; *Int'l*, pg. 5046
MORIMURA BROS., (SINGAPORE) PTE. LTD.—See Morimura Bros., Inc.; *Int'l*, pg. 5046
MORIMURA BROS. (S.Z.) LTD.—See Morimura Bros., Inc.; *Int'l*, pg. 5046
MORIMURA BROS.(TAIWAN),INC.—See Morimura Bros., Inc.; *Int'l*, pg. 5046
MORIMURA BROS. (USA) INC.—See Morimura Bros., Inc.; *Int'l*, pg. 5046
MORIMURA BROTHERS TRADING INDIA PRIVATE LTD.—See Morimura Bros., Inc.; *Int'l*, pg. 5046
MORIMURA CHEMICALS LTD.—See Morimura Bros., Inc.; *Int'l*, pg. 5046
MORIMURA SOFC TECHNOLOGY CO., LTD.—See Niterra Co., Ltd.; *Int'l*, pg. 5380
MORIN ACTUATOR—See Emerson Electric Co.; *U.S. Public*, pg. 751
MORINAGA AMERICA INC.—See Morinaga & Co., Ltd.; *Int'l*, pg. 5046
MORINAGA ANGEL DESSERT CO., LTD.—See Morinaga & Co., Ltd.; *Int'l*, pg. 5046
MORINAGA ASIA PACIFIC CO., LTD.—See Morinaga & Co., Ltd.; *Int'l*, pg. 5046
MORINAGA BUSINESS PARTNER CO., LTD.—See Morinaga & Co., Ltd.; *Int'l*, pg. 5046
MORINAGA & CO., LTD.; *Int'l*, pg. 5046
MORINAGA INSTITUTE OF BIOLOGICAL SCIENCE, INC.—See Morinaga & Co., Ltd.; *Int'l*, pg. 5046
MORINAGA MARKET DEVELOPMENT CO., LTD.—See Morinaga & Co., Ltd.; *Int'l*, pg. 5046
MORINAGA MILK INDUSTRY CO., LTD.; *Int'l*, pg. 5046
MORINAGA MILK INDUSTRY (SHANGHAI) CO., LTD.—See Morinaga Milk Industry Co., Ltd.; *Int'l*, pg. 5046
MORINAGA NUTRITIONAL FOODS (ASIA PACIFIC) PTE. LTD.—See Morinaga Milk Industry Co., Ltd.; *Int'l*, pg. 5046
MORINAGA NUTRITIONAL FOODS DEUTSCHLAND GMBH—See Morinaga Milk Industry Co., Ltd.; *Int'l*, pg. 5046
MORINAGA NUTRITIONAL FOODS, INC.—See Morinaga Milk Industry Co., Ltd.; *Int'l*, pg. 5046
MORINAGA SHOJI CO., LTD.—See Morinaga & Co., Ltd.; *Int'l*, pg. 5046
MORINAGA TAKATAKI COUNTRY CO., LTD.—See Morinaga & Co., Ltd.; *Int'l*, pg. 5046
MORIN BRICK CO.; *U.S. Private*, pg. 2785
MORIN CORPORATION—See Kingspan Group PLC; *Int'l*, pg. 4178
MORINDA HOLDINGS INC.—See NewAge, Inc.; *U.S. Public*, pg. 1513
MORINDA INC.—See NewAge, Inc.; *U.S. Public*, pg. 1513
MORINGA ACQUISITION CORP.; *U.S. Public*, pg. 1476
MORINI SPA—See Avis Budget Group, Inc.; *U.S. Public*, pg. 249
MORIO DENKI CO., LTD. - RYUGASAKI PLANT—See Morio Denki Co., Ltd.; *Int'l*, pg. 5046
MORIO DENKI CO., LTD.; *Int'l*, pg. 5046
MORIOKA DELICA CO., LTD—See Yamazaki Baking Co., Ltd.; *Int'l*, pg. 8556
MORIOKA SEIKO INSTRUMENTS INC.—See Seiko Group Corporation; *Int'l*, pg. 6688
MORION, INC.; *Int'l*, pg. 5046
MORIO USA CORPORATION—See Morio Denki Co., Ltd.; *Int'l*, pg. 5046
MORI PLANT CO., LTD.—See Kyokuto Kaihatsu Kogyo Co. Ltd.; *Int'l*, pg. 4363
MORIRIN CO., LTD.; *Int'l*, pg. 5047
MORIROKU AGRI CO., LTD.—See Moriroku Holdings Company, Ltd.; *Int'l*, pg. 5047
MORIROKU AMERICA, INC.—See Moriroku Holdings Company, Ltd.; *Int'l*, pg. 5047
MORIROKU AUSTRIA GMBH—See Moriroku Holdings Company, Ltd.; *Int'l*, pg. 5047
MORIROKU CHEMICALS COMPANY, LTD.—See Moriroku Holdings Company, Ltd.; *Int'l*, pg. 5047
MORIROKU CHEMICALS INDIA PVT. LTD.—See Moriroku Holdings Company, Ltd.; *Int'l*, pg. 5047
MORIROKU CHEMICALS KOREA CO., LTD.—See Moriroku Holdings Company, Ltd.; *Int'l*, pg. 5047
MORIROKU COMPANY (HK) LTD.—See Moriroku Holdings Company, Ltd.; *Int'l*, pg. 5047
MORIROKU (GUANGZHOU) TRADING CO., LTD.—See Moriroku Holdings Company, Ltd.; *Int'l*, pg. 5047
MORIROKU HOLDINGS COMPANY, LTD.; *Int'l*, pg. 5047
MORIROKU PHILIPPINES, INC.—See Moriroku Holdings Company, Ltd.; *Int'l*, pg. 5047
MORIROKU PRECISION CO., LTD.—See Moriroku Holdings Company, Ltd.; *Int'l*, pg. 5047
MORIROKU (SHANGHAI) CO., LTD.—See Moriroku Holdings Company, Ltd.; *Int'l*, pg. 5047

MORIROKU HOLDINGS COMPANY, LTD. CORPORATE AFFILIATIONS

MORIROKU (SINGAPORE) PTE., LTD.—See Moriroku Holdings Company, Ltd.; *Int'l*, pg. 5047
MORIROKU TECHNOLOGY COMPANY, LTD. - KANTO PLANT—See Moriroku Holdings Company, Ltd.; *Int'l*, pg. 5047
MORIROKU TECHNOLOGY COMPANY, LTD.—See Moriroku Holdings Company, Ltd.; *Int'l*, pg. 5047
MORIROKU TECHNOLOGY COMPANY, LTD. - SUZUKA PLANT—See Moriroku Holdings Company, Ltd.; *Int'l*, pg. 5047
MORIROKU TECHNOLOGY DE MEXICO S.A. DE C.V.—See Moriroku Holdings Company, Ltd.; *Int'l*, pg. 5047
MORIROKU TECHNOLOGY INDIA PVT. LTD.—See Moriroku Holdings Company, Ltd.; *Int'l*, pg. 5047
MORIROKU TECHNOLOGY NORTH AMERICA INC.—See Moriroku Holdings Company, Ltd.; *Int'l*, pg. 5047
MORIROKU TECHNOLOGY (THAILAND) CO., LTD.—See Moriroku Holdings Company, Ltd.; *Int'l*, pg. 5047
MORIROKU (THAILAND) CO., LTD.—See Moriroku Holdings Company, Ltd.; *Int'l*, pg. 5047
MORIROKU (TIANJIN) CO., LTD.—See Moriroku Holdings Company, Ltd.; *Int'l*, pg. 5047
MORI SEIKI BRASIL LTDA.—See DMG MORI Co., Ltd.; *Int'l*, pg. 2145
MORI SEIKI ESPANA S.A.—See DMG MORI Co., Ltd.; *Int'l*, pg. 2145
MORI SEIKI HONG KONG LTD.—See DMG MORI Co., Ltd.; *Int'l*, pg. 2145
MORI SEIKI ISRAEL LTD.—See DMG MORI Co., Ltd.; *Int'l*, pg. 2145
MORI SEIKI (SHANGHAI) CO., LTD.—See DMG MORI Co., Ltd.; *Int'l*, pg. 2145
MORI SEIKI TECHNO GMBH—See DMG MORI Co., Ltd.; *Int'l*, pg. 2145
MORI SEIKI TECHNO LTD.—See DMG MORI Co., Ltd.; *Int'l*, pg. 2145
MORI SEIKI TRADING LTD.—See DMG MORI Co., Ltd.; *Int'l*, pg. 2145
MORISEM (SABAH) SDN BHD—See IOI Corporation Berhad; *Int'l*, pg. 3792
MORI SHIGYO CO., LTD. - KANSAI PLANT—See Oji Holdings Corporation; *Int'l*, pg. 5537
MORI SHIGYO CO., LTD. - KANTO PLANT—See Oji Holdings Corporation; *Int'l*, pg. 5537
MORI SHIGYO CO., LTD.—See Oji Holdings Corporation; *Int'l*, pg. 5536
MORI SHIGYO CO., LTD. - TOKYO PLANT—See Oji Holdings Corporation; *Int'l*, pg. 5537
MORI SHIGYO CO., LTD. - WRAPPING PAPER PLANT—See Oji Holdings Corporation; *Int'l*, pg. 5537
MORI SHIGYO CO., LTD. - YOKKAICHI PLANT—See Oji Holdings Corporation; *Int'l*, pg. 5537
MORISHITA JINTAN CO., LTD. - SHIGA PLANT—See Morishita Jintan Co., Ltd.; *Int'l*, pg. 5048
MORISHITA JINTAN CO., LTD.; *Int'l*, pg. 5048
MORISON INDUSTRIES PLC; *Int'l*, pg. 5048
MORISON LIMITED—See Hemas Holdings PLC; *Int'l*, pg. 3341
MORITA BOHSAI TECH CORPORATION—See Morita Holdings Corporation; *Int'l*, pg. 5048
MORITA CO., LTD.—See JFLA Holdings Inc.; *Int'l*, pg. 3939
MORITA CORPORATION - SANDA FACTORY—See Morita Holdings Corporation; *Int'l*, pg. 5048
MORITA ECONOS CORPORATION—See Morita Holdings Corporation; *Int'l*, pg. 5048
MORITA ENGINEERING CORPORATION—See Morita Holdings Corporation; *Int'l*, pg. 5048
MORITA ENVIRONMENTAL TECH CORPORATION—See Morita Holdings Corporation; *Int'l*, pg. 5048
MORITA HOLDINGS CORPORATION; *Int'l*, pg. 5048
MORITA MIYATA CORPORATION—See Morita Holdings Corporation; *Int'l*, pg. 5048
MORITANI AMERICA INC.—See IMV CORPORATION; *Int'l*, pg. 3638
MORITANI DAIKIN CO, LTD.—See Daikin Industries, Ltd.; *Int'l*, pg. 1936
MORITANI S.A.—See Aiphone Co., Ltd.; *Int'l*, pg. 235
MORITA SOGO SERVICE CORPORATION—See Morita Holdings Corporation; *Int'l*, pg. 5048
MORITA TECHNOS CORPORATION—See Morita Holdings Corporation; *Int'l*, pg. 5048
MORITA TOYO CORPORATION—See Morita Holdings Corporation; *Int'l*, pg. 5048
MORITEX ASIA PACIFIC PTE., LTD.—See Cognex Corporation; *U.S. Public*, pg. 523
MORITEX CORPORATION—See Cognex Corporation; *U.S. Public*, pg. 523
MORITEX NORTH AMERICA, INC.—See Cognex Corporation; *U.S. Public*, pg. 523
MORITEX TECHNOLOGIES (SHENZHEN) CO., LTD.—See Cognex Corporation; *U.S. Public*, pg. 523
MORITO APPAREL CO., LTD.—See Morito Co., Ltd.; *Int'l*, pg. 5048
MORITO CO., LTD.; *Int'l*, pg. 5048
MORITO (EUROPE) B.V.—See Morito Co., Ltd.; *Int'l*, pg. 5048

MORITO INDUSTRIAL CO., (H.K.) LTD.—See Morito Co., Ltd.; *Int'l*, pg. 5048
MORITO (SHENZHEN) CO., LTD.—See Morito Co., Ltd.; *Int'l*, pg. 5048
MORI TRUST HOTEL REIT, INC.; *Int'l*, pg. 5045
MORI TRUST SOGO REIT, INC.; *Int'l*, pg. 5045
MORITZ KIA F.T. WORTH; *U.S. Private*, pg. 2785
MORIXE HERMANOS S.A.C.I.; *Int'l*, pg. 5048
MORIYA CORPORATION. CO., LTD.; *Int'l*, pg. 5048
MORIYAMA CO., LTD.—See Qol Holdings Co., Ltd.; *Int'l*, pg. 6147
MORIYAMA HOSO CO., LTD.—See Senko Group Holdings Co., Ltd.; *Int'l*, pg. 6710
MORIYA TRANSPORTATION ENGINEERING & MANUFACTURING CO., LTD.; *Int'l*, pg. 5048
MORI YOUGYOJOU CO., LTD.—See Yoshimura Food Holdings K.K.; *Int'l*, pg. 8600
MORIZOU CO., LTD.—See Grandes Inc.; *Int'l*, pg. 3057
MORLANDS (GLASTONBURY) LIMITED—See G. R. (Holdings) plc; *Int'l*, pg. 2864
MORLEY BANCSHARES CORPORATION; *U.S. Private*, pg. 2785
MORLEY BUILDERS; *U.S. Private*, pg. 2785
MORLEY CANDY MAKERS, LLC—See Palladium Equity Partners, LLC; *U.S. Private*, pg. 3077
MORLEY CONSTRUCTION CO., INC.—See Morley Builders; *U.S. Private*, pg. 2785
MORLEY FINANCIAL SERVICES—See Principal Financial Group, Inc.; *U.S. Public*, pg. 1720
MORLEYS FUNERALS PTY LTD—See Propel Funeral Partners Limited; *Int'l*, pg. 5997
MORLUNDA SLIPSERVICE AB—See Investment AB Latour; *Int'l*, pg. 3782
MORMAC MARINE GROUP, INC.; *U.S. Private*, pg. 2785
MORMIL CORP.—See Radius Recycling, Inc.; *U.S. Public*, pg. 1760
MORNEAU SHEPELL LTD.—See LifeWorks; *Int'l*, pg. 4495
THE MORNING CALL, INC.—See Tribune Publishing Company; *U.S. Private*, pg. 4228
MORNING GLORY HEALTHCARE, INC.—See The Ensign Group, Inc.; *U.S. Public*, pg. 4086
MORNING JOURNAL—See The Nutting Company; *U.S. Private*, pg. 4086
MORNING LAVENDER LLC; *U.S. Private*, pg. 2785
MORNING NEWS—See Lee Enterprises, Incorporated; *U.S. Public*, pg. 1298
MORNING SENTINEL—See MaineToday Media, Inc.; *U.S. Private*, pg. 2553
MORNINGSIDE MINISTRIES; *U.S. Private*, pg. 2785
MORNINGSIDE OF ANDERSON, L.P.—See AlerisLife Inc.; *U.S. Private*, pg. 161
MORNINGSIDE OF BELMONT, LLC—See AlerisLife Inc.; *U.S. Private*, pg. 161
MORNINGSIDE OF BOWLING GREEN, LLC—See AlerisLife Inc.; *U.S. Private*, pg. 161
MORNINGSIDE OF CAMDEN, LLC—See AlerisLife Inc.; *U.S. Private*, pg. 161
MORNINGSIDE OF CLEVELAND, LLC—See AlerisLife Inc.; *U.S. Private*, pg. 161
MORNINGSIDE OF COLUMBUS, L.P.—See AlerisLife Inc.; *U.S. Private*, pg. 161
MORNINGSIDE OF CONYERS, LLC—See AlerisLife Inc.; *U.S. Private*, pg. 161
MORNINGSIDE OF COOKEVILLE, LLC—See AlerisLife Inc.; *U.S. Private*, pg. 161
MORNINGSIDE OF CULLMAN, LLC—See AlerisLife Inc.; *U.S. Private*, pg. 161
MORNINGSIDE OF DECATUR, L.P.—See AlerisLife Inc.; *U.S. Private*, pg. 161
MORNINGSIDE OF EVANS, LIMITED PARTNERSHIP—See AlerisLife Inc.; *U.S. Private*, pg. 161
MORNINGSIDE OF FRANKLIN, LLC—See AlerisLife Inc.; *U.S. Private*, pg. 161
MORNINGSIDE OF GAINESVILLE, LLC—See AlerisLife Inc.; *U.S. Private*, pg. 162
MORNINGSIDE OF GALLATIN, LLC—See AlerisLife Inc.; *U.S. Private*, pg. 162
MORNINGSIDE OF GASTONIA, LLC—See AlerisLife Inc.; *U.S. Private*, pg. 162
MORNINGSIDE OF GREENWOOD, L.P.—See AlerisLife Inc.; *U.S. Private*, pg. 162
MORNINGSIDE OF HARTSVILLE, LLC—See AlerisLife Inc.; *U.S. Private*, pg. 162
MORNINGSIDE OF HOPKINSVILLE, LIMITED PARTNERSHIP—See AlerisLife Inc.; *U.S. Private*, pg. 162
MORNINGSIDE OF JACKSON, LLC—See AlerisLife Inc.; *U.S. Private*, pg. 162
MORNINGSIDE OF LEXINGTON, LLC—See AlerisLife Inc.; *U.S. Private*, pg. 162
MORNINGSIDE OF ORANGEBURG, LLC—See AlerisLife Inc.; *U.S. Private*, pg. 162
MORNINGSIDE OF PADUCAH, LLC—See AlerisLife Inc.; *U.S. Private*, pg. 162
MORNINGSIDE OF PARIS, LLC—See AlerisLife Inc.; *U.S. Private*, pg. 162
MORNINGSIDE OF RALEIGH, LLC—See AlerisLife Inc.; *U.S. Private*, pg. 162

MORNINGSIDE OF SKIPWITH-RICHMOND, LLC—See AlerisLife Inc.; *U.S. Private*, pg. 162
MORNINGSIDE OF SOUTH CAROLINA, L.P.—See AlerisLife Inc.; *U.S. Private*, pg. 162
MORNINGSIDE OF SUMTER—See AlerisLife Inc.; *U.S. Private*, pg. 162
MORNINGSIDE OF WILLIAMSBURG, LLC—See AlerisLife Inc.; *U.S. Private*, pg. 162
MORNINGSTAR ASSET MANAGEMENT CO.—See SBI Holdings, Inc.; *Int'l*, pg. 6605
MORNINGSTAR ASSOCIATES KOREA CO., LTD.—See Morningstar, Inc.; *U.S. Public*, pg. 1476
MORNING STAR AUTOMOTIVE, INC.—See Kaixin Auto Holdings; *Int'l*, pg. 4053
MORNINGSTAR CANADA GROUP, INC.—See Morningstar, Inc.; *U.S. Public*, pg. 1476
MORNINGSTAR DANMARK A/S—See Morningstar, Inc.; *U.S. Public*, pg. 1476
MORNINGSTAR DEUTSCHLAND GMBH—See Morningstar, Inc.; *U.S. Public*, pg. 1476
MORNINGSTAR EUROPE, B.V.—See Morningstar, Inc.; *U.S. Public*, pg. 1476
MORNINGSTAR FRANCE FUND INFORMATION SARL—See Morningstar, Inc.; *U.S. Public*, pg. 1476
MORNINGSTAR GROUP AUSTRALIA PTY LIMITED—See Morningstar, Inc.; *U.S. Public*, pg. 1476
MORNINGSTAR, INC.; *U.S. Public*, pg. 1476
MORNINGSTAR INVESTMENT MANAGEMENT AUSTRALIA LIMITED—See Morningstar, Inc.; *U.S. Public*, pg. 1476
MORNINGSTAR INVESTMENT MANAGEMENT EUROPE LIMITED—See Morningstar, Inc.; *U.S. Public*, pg. 1476
MORNINGSTAR INVESTMENT MANAGEMENT SOUTH AFRICA (PTY) LIMITED—See Morningstar, Inc.; *U.S. Public*, pg. 1476
MORNINGSTAR ITALY, S.R.L.—See Morningstar, Inc.; *U.S. Public*, pg. 1476
MORNINGSTAR OPERATING LLC—See TXO Partners, L.P.; *U.S. Public*, pg. 2208
MORNING STAR PACKING CO. LP; *U.S. Private*, pg. 2785
MORNINGSTAR RESEARCH LIMITED—See Morningstar, Inc.; *U.S. Public*, pg. 1476
MORNINGSTAR RESEARCH THAILAND LIMITED—See Morningstar, Inc.; *U.S. Public*, pg. 1476
MORNINGSTAR SWEDEN AB—See Morningstar, Inc.; *U.S. Public*, pg. 1476
MORNINGSTAR SWITZERLAND GMBH—See Morningstar, Inc.; *U.S. Public*, pg. 1476
THE MORNING SUN—See Gannett Co., Inc.; *U.S. Public*, pg. 904
MORN SUN FEED MILL CO., LTD.; *Int'l*, pg. 5048
MOROCH PARTNERS; *U.S. Private*, pg. 2785
MOROCH—See Moroch Partners; *U.S. Private*, pg. 2786
MOROCH—See Moroch Partners; *U.S. Private*, pg. 2786
MOROCH—See Moroch Partners; *U.S. Private*, pg. 2786
MOROCH—See Moroch Partners; *U.S. Private*, pg. 2786
MOROCH—See Moroch Partners; *U.S. Private*, pg. 2786
MOROCH—See Moroch Partners; *U.S. Private*, pg. 2786
MOROCH—See Moroch Partners; *U.S. Private*, pg. 2786
MOROCH—See Moroch Partners; *U.S. Private*, pg. 2786
MOROCH—See Moroch Partners; *U.S. Private*, pg. 2786
MOROCH—See Moroch Partners; *U.S. Private*, pg. 2786
MOROCH—See Moroch Partners; *U.S. Private*, pg. 2786
MOROCH—See Moroch Partners; *U.S. Private*, pg. 2786
MOROCH—See Moroch Partners; *U.S. Private*, pg. 2786
MOROCH—See Moroch Partners; *U.S. Private*, pg. 2786
MOROCH—See Moroch Partners; *U.S. Private*, pg. 2786
MOROCH—See Moroch Partners; *U.S. Private*, pg. 2786
MOROCH—See Moroch Partners; *U.S. Private*, pg. 2786
MOROCH—See Moroch Partners; *U.S. Private*, pg. 2786
MORO CORP.; *U.S. Public*, pg. 1477
MORONEY & GILL, INC.; *U.S. Private*, pg. 2786
MORONG BRUNSWICK—See WSMC Inc.; *U.S. Private*, pg. 4574
MOROSO PERFORMANCE PRODUCTS, INC.; *U.S. Private*, pg. 2786
MOROZOFF LIMITED; *Int'l*, pg. 5049
MORPHEUS AIOLOS, S.L.—See Indra Sistemas, S.A.; *Int'l*, pg. 3661
MORPHIC HOLDING, INC.—See Eli Lilly & Company; *U.S. Public*, pg. 734
MORPHO INC.; *Int'l*, pg. 5049
MORPHOSYS AG—See Novartis AG; *Int'l*, pg. 5457
MORPHOSYS US INC.—See Novartis AG; *Int'l*, pg. 5457
MORPHOTEK, INC.—See Eisai Co., Ltd.; *Int'l*, pg. 2335
MORPHY RICHARDS LTD.—See The Glen Dimplex Group; *Int'l*, pg. 7650
MORPHY RICHARDS (N.I.) LTD.—See The Glen Dimplex Group; *Int'l*, pg. 7650
MORRELL INCORPORATED; *U.S. Private*, pg. 2786
MORRELLS WOODFINISHES LIMITED—See RPM International Inc.; *U.S. Public*, pg. 1817
MORREY SALES LTD; *Int'l*, pg. 5049
MORRICE TRANSPORTATION; *Int'l*, pg. 5049
MORRIE'S BUFFALO FORD—See Morrie's Imports, Inc.; *U.S. Private*, pg. 2786
MORRIE'S CADILLAC—See Morrie's Imports, Inc.; *U.S. Private*, pg. 2786

COMPANY NAME INDEX

MORRIE'S IMPORTS, INC.; *U.S. Private*, pg. 2786
MORRIHAN INTERNATIONAL CORP.—See WT Microelectronics Co., Ltd.; *Int'l*, pg. 8498
THE MORRILL & JANES BANK & TRUST COMPANY—See Heartland Financial USA, Inc.; *U.S. Public*, pg. 1018
MORRILL MOTORS, INC.1946—See Regal Rexnord Corporation; *U.S. Public*, pg. 1773
MORRILL MOTORS (JIAXING) CO., LTD.—See Regal Rexnord Corporation; *U.S. Public*, pg. 1773
MORRIS ARCHITECTS, INC.—See Huitt-Zollars, Inc.; *U.S. Private*, pg. 2004
MORRIS BANK—See Morris State Bancshares, Inc.; *U.S. Public*, pg. 1477
MORRIS-BATES FUNERAL HOME, INC.—See Service Corporation International; *U.S. Public*, pg. 1870
MORRIS BEAN & COMPANY; *U.S. Private*, pg. 2786
MORRIS BLACK & SONS INC.; *U.S. Private*, pg. 2786
MORRIS BUSINESS MEDIA, LLC—See Shivers Trading & Operating Company; *U.S. Private*, pg. 3638
MORRIS CAPITAL MANAGEMENT, LLC; *U.S. Private*, pg. 2786
MORRIS CERULLO WORLD EVANGELISM; *U.S. Private*, pg. 2786
MORRIS CERULLO WORLD EVANGELISM—See Morris Cerullo World Evangelism; *U.S. Private*, pg. 2787
MORRIS CERULLO WORLD EVANGELISM—See Morris Cerullo World Evangelism; *U.S. Private*, pg. 2787
MORRIS COMMUNICATIONS COMPANY, LLC—See Shivers Trading & Operating Company; *U.S. Private*, pg. 3638
MORRIS COMMUNICATIONS, INC.; *U.S. Private*, pg. 2787
MORRIS CORPORATION; *U.S. Private*, pg. 2787
MORRIS COUNTY LIBRARY; *U.S. Private*, pg. 2787
MORRIS COUNTY MUNICIPAL UTILITIES AUTHORITY; *U.S. Private*, pg. 2787
MORRIS COUPLING COMPANY; *U.S. Private*, pg. 2787
MORRIS & DICKSON CO., LLC - RETAIL AND HOSPITAL DIVISION—See Morris & Dickson Co., LLC; *U.S. Private*, pg. 2786
MORRIS & DICKSON CO., LLC; *U.S. Private*, pg. 2786
MORRIS DIGITAL WORKS, LLC—See Shivers Trading & Operating Company; *U.S. Private*, pg. 3638
MORRISETTE PAPER COMPANY INC.; *U.S. Private*, pg 2788
MORRIS FLAMINGO-STEPHAN, INC.—See The Stephan Company; *U.S. Public*, pg. 2132
MORRIS FURNITURE CO. INC.; *U.S. Private*, pg. 2787
MORRIS GROUP, INC. - MORRIS GREAT LAKES DIVISION—See Morris Group, Inc.; *U.S. Private*, pg. 2787
MORRIS GROUP, INC. - MORRIS SOUTH DIVISION—See Morris Group, Inc.; *U.S. Private*, pg. 2787
MORRIS GROUP, INC. - MORRIS TURBINE GROUP DIVISION—See Morris Group, Inc.; *U.S. Private*, pg. 2787
MORRIS GROUP, INC.; *U.S. Private*, pg. 2787
MORRIS GROUP, INC. - VELOCITY PRODUCTS DIVISION—See Morris Group, Inc.; *U.S. Private*, pg. 2787
MORRIS HARDWICK SCHNEIDER & LANDCASTLE TITLE; *U.S. Private*, pg. 2787
MORRIS HEIGHTS HEALTH CENTER, INC.; *U.S. Private*, pg. 2787
MORRIS HOME HOLDINGS LIMITED; *Int'l*, pg. 5049
MORRIS INDUSTRIES INC.; *U.S. Private*, pg. 2788
MORRIS INTERNATIONAL, INC.; *U.S. Private*, pg. 2788
MORRIS LEVIN AND SON; *U.S. Private*, pg. 2788
MORRIS, MANNING & MARTIN LLP; *U.S. Private*, pg. 2788
MORRIS MATERIAL HANDLING INC.—See Konecranes Plc; *Int'l*, pg. 4252
MORRIS MIDWEST, LLC—See Morris Group, Inc.; *U.S. Private*, pg. 2787
MORRIS MIDWEST, LLC—See Morris Group, Inc.; *U.S. Private*, pg. 2787
MORRIS MOORE CHEVROLET-BUICK, INC.; *U.S. Private*, pg. 2788
MORRIS MULTIMEDIA, INC.; *U.S. Private*, pg. 2788
MORRIS MURDOCK, LLC; *U.S. Private*, pg. 2788
MORRIS NETWORK, INC.—See Morris Multimedia, Inc.; *U.S. Private*, pg. 2788
MORRIS NEWSPAPER CORPORATION—See Morris Multimedia, Inc.; *U.S. Private*, pg. 2788
MORRIS OIL CO. INC.; *U.S. Private*, pg. 2788
MORRIS OIL OF MISSISSIPPI; *U.S. Private*, pg. 2788
THE MORRISON AGENCY; *U.S. Private*, pg. 4080
MORRISON BERKSHIRE INC.; *U.S. Private*, pg. 2789
MORRISON BOWMORE DISTILLERS, LTD.—See Suntory Holdings Limited; *Int'l*, pg. 7326
MORRISON BROTHERS COMPANY; *U.S. Private*, pg. 2789
MORRISON, BROWN, ARGIZ & FARRA, LLC—See BDO USA, LLP; *U.S. Private*, pg. 501
MORRISON CHEVROLET INC.; *U.S. Private*, pg. 2789
MORRISON COMMUNICATIONS, INC.; *U.S. Private*, pg. 2789

MORRISON CONSTRUCTION COMPANY; *U.S. Private*, pg. 2789
MORRISON CONSTRUCTION SCOTLAND—See Galliford Try Holdings plc; *Int'l*, pg. 2874
MORRISON DATA SERVICES LIMITED—See PAI Partners S.A.S.; *Int'l*, pg. 5701
MORRISON DISTRIBUTION & MARKETING; *U.S. Private*, pg. 2789
MORRISON ENTERPRISES; *U.S. Private*, pg. 2789
MORRISON EXPRESS CORPORATION USA; *U.S. Private*, pg. 2789
MORRISON FACILITIES SERVICES LIMITED—See Mears Group PLC; *Int'l*, pg. 4763
MORRISON & FOERSTER LLP; *U.S. Private*, pg. 2788
MORRISON GEOTECHNIC PTY LTD—See HRL Holdings Limited; *Int'l*, pg. 3501
MORRISON & HEAD LP—See Ryan, LLC; *U.S. Private*, pg. 3511
MORRISON HERSHFIELD CORP.—See Morrison Hershfield Group, Inc.; *Int'l*, pg. 5049
MORRISON HERSHFIELD GROUP, INC.; *Int'l*, pg. 5049
MORRISON INDUSTRIAL EQUIPMENT COMPANY; *U.S. Private*, pg. 2789
MORRISON INDUSTRIAL EQUIPMENT COMPANY—See Morrison Industrial Equipment Company; *U.S. Private*, pg. 2789
MORRISON MANAGEMENT SPECIALISTS, INC.—See Compass Group PLC; *Int'l*, pg. 1751
MORRISON PRODUCTS INC.; *U.S. Private*, pg. 2789
MORRISON & SYLVESTER INC.; *U.S. Private*, pg. 2789
MORRISON TERREBONNE LUMBER CENTER—See Tyndale Advisors, LLC; *U.S. Private*, pg. 4268
MORRISON TEXTILE MACHINERY CO. - MORRISON CONTRACT MANUFACTURING DIVISION—See Morrison Textile Machinery Co.; *U.S. Private*, pg. 2790
MORRISON TEXTILE MACHINERY CO.; *U.S. Private*, pg. 2789
MORRISON UTILITY CONNECTIONS—See PAI Partners S.A.S.; *Int'l*, pg. 5701
MORRISON UTILITY SERVICES GROUP LIMITED—See PAI Partners S.A.S.; *Int'l*, pg. 5701
MORRISON UTILITY SERVICES LIMITED—See PAI Partners S.A.S.; *Int'l*, pg. 5701
MORRISONVILLE FARMERS COOP CO; *U.S. Private*, pg. 2790
MORRISON (WM) SUPERMARKETS PLC; *Int'l*, pg. 5049
MORRIS PONTIAC GMC INC.; *U.S. Private*, pg. 2788
MORRIS PRINTING GROUP, INC.; *U.S. Private*, pg. 2788
MORRIS PUBLISHING GROUP, LLC—See Shivers Trading & Operating Company; *U.S. Private*, pg. 3638
MORRISSEY & COMPANY; *U.S. Private*, pg. 2790
THE MORRISSEY GROUP LLC; *U.S. Private*, pg. 4080
MORRIS-SHEA BRIDGE COMPANY, INC.; *U.S. Private*, pg. 2788
MORRIS SHEET METAL CORP.; *U.S. Private*, pg. 2788
MORRIS SOUTH, LLC-HUNTSVILLE—See Morris Group, Inc.; *U.S. Private*, pg. 2787
MORRIS SOUTH, LLC—See Morris Group, Inc.; *U.S. Private*, pg. 2787
MORRIS (S.P.) HOLDINGS LIMITED—See Commerzbank AG; *Int'l*, pg. 1719
MORRIS STATE BANCSHARES, INC.; *U.S. Public*, pg. 1477
MORRIS TILE DISTRIBUTORS INC.; *U.S. Private*, pg. 2788
MORRISTOWN DRIVERS SERVICE INC.; *U.S. Private*, pg. 2790
MORRISTOWN UTILITY COMMISSION; *U.S. Private*, pg. 2790
MORRIS VISITOR PUBLICATION—See Shivers Trading & Operating Company; *U.S. Private*, pg. 3638
MORRITT PROPERTIES CAYMAN LTD; *Int'l*, pg. 5049
MORRO DIALYSIS, LLC—See DaVita Inc.; *U.S. Public*, pg. 641
MORRO VERMELHO TAXI AEREO LTDA.—See Icon Aviation SA; *Int'l*, pg. 3583
MORROW BANK ASA; *Int'l*, pg. 5049
MORROW CONSTRUCTION COMPANY; *U.S. Private*, pg. 2790
MORROW CONTROL & SUPPLY CO; *U.S. Private*, pg. 2790
MORROW COUNTY GRAIN GROWERS; *U.S. Private*, pg. 2790
MORROW EQUIPMENT CO. LLC; *U.S. Private*, pg. 2790
MORROW FAMILY MEDICINE, LLC; *U.S. Private*, pg. 2790
MORROW-MEADOWS CORPORATION - ALTERNATIVE ENERGY DIVISION—See Morrow-Meadows Corporation; *U.S. Private*, pg. 2790
MORROW-MEADOWS CORPORATION - CHERRY CITY ELECTRIC DIVISION—See Morrow-Meadows Corporation; *U.S. Private*, pg. 2790
MORROW-MEADOWS CORPORATION; *U.S. Private*, pg. 2790
MORROW-MEADOWS CORP—See Morrow-Meadows Corporation; *U.S. Private*, pg. 2790
MORROW MOTOR SALES INC.; *U.S. Private*, pg. 2790
MORROW MOTORS INC.; *U.S. Private*, pg. 2790
MORROW PONTIAC BUICK; *Int'l*, pg. 5049

MORTGAGE INVESTORS CORPORATION

MORROW SODALI INTERNATIONAL LLC—See TPG Capital, L.P.; *U.S. Public*, pg. 2176
MORSCO, INC.—See Reece Limited; *Int'l*, pg. 6249
MORSE CHEVROLET INC.; *U.S. Private*, pg. 2790
MORSE DISTRIBUTION INC.; *U.S. Private*, pg. 2790
MORSE ELECTRIC INCORPORATED; *U.S. Private*, pg. 2790
MORSE INDUSTRIES INC.; *U.S. Private*, pg. 2790
MORSEKODE; *U.S. Private*, pg. 2791
MORSE OPERATIONS INC.; *U.S. Private*, pg. 2790
MORSE PROPERTIES, INC.; *U.S. Private*, pg. 2790
MORSE RUBBER, LLC—See FLSmidth & Co. A/S; *Int'l*, pg. 2711
MORSERV, INC.—See JPMorgan Chase & Co.; *U.S. Public*, pg. 1210
MORSES CLUB PLC; *Int'l*, pg. 5049
MORSE TEC EUROPE S.R.L.—See Enstar Group Limited; *Int'l*, pg. 2448
MORSE WATCHMANS INC.; *U.S. Private*, pg. 2791
MORSON GROUP LTD.; *Int'l*, pg. 5049
MORSON HUMAN RESOURCES LIMITED—See Morson Group Ltd.; *Int'l*, pg. 5049
MOR-SON LEASING INC.—See Morrison Industrial Equipment Company; *U.S. Private*, pg. 2789
MORSON PROJECTS LIMITED—See Morson Group Ltd.; *Int'l*, pg. 5049
MORSSMITT ASIA, LTD.—See Westinghouse Air Brake Technologies Corporation; *U.S. Public*, pg. 2358
MORS SMITT ASIA, LTD.—See Westinghouse Air Brake Technologies Corporation; *U.S. Public*, pg. 2358
MORS SMITT BV—See Westinghouse Air Brake Technologies Corporation; *U.S. Public*, pg. 2358
MORS SMITT FRANCE S.A.S.—See Westinghouse Air Brake Technologies Corporation; *U.S. Public*, pg. 2358
MORS SMITT TECHNOLOGIES, INC.—See Westinghouse Air Brake Technologies Corporation; *U.S. Public*, pg. 2358
MORS SMITT UK LTD.—See Westinghouse Air Brake Technologies Corporation; *U.S. Public*, pg. 2358
MORTAGEHUB INC—See K.K. Birla Group; *Int'l*, pg. 4044
MORTAR ADVERTISING; *U.S. Private*, pg. 2791
MORTARA INSTRUMENT, INC.—See Baxter International Inc.; *U.S. Public*, pg. 283
MORT DISTRIBUTING INC.—See Parkland Corporation; *Int'l*, pg. 5744
MORTECH, INC.—See Zillow Group, Inc.; *U.S. Public*, pg. 2405
MORTEN ENTERPRISES INC.; *U.S. Private*, pg. 2791
MORTENSEN WOODWORK INC.; *U.S. Private*, pg. 2791
MORTENSON DEVELOPMENT, INC.—See M.A. Mortenson Company; *U.S. Private*, pg. 2527
MORTEO NORD—See Marcegaglia S.p.A.; *Int'l*, pg. 4689
MORTERM LIMITED; *Int'l*, pg. 5049
MORTEROS DE GALICIA S.L.—See Camargo Correa S.A.; *Int'l*, pg. 1268
MORTERO SPA—See Sika AG; *Int'l*, pg. 6915
MORTEX CORPORATION; *U.S. Private*, pg. 2791
MORTGAGE ACCESS CORP.—See Weichert Co.; *U.S. Private*, pg. 4470
MORTGAGE ADVICE BUREAU (HOLDINGS) LTD; *Int'l*, pg. 5049
MORTGAGE ASSETS MANAGEMENT LLC—See Waterfall Asset Management LLC; *U.S. Private*, pg. 4452
MORTGAGEBOT LLC—See Spectrum Equity Investors, L.P.; *U.S. Private*, pg. 3752
MORTGAGE BUILDER SOFTWARE, INC.—See Constellation Software Inc.; *Int'l*, pg. 1774
MORTGAGE BUREAU LIMITED—See The Skipton Building Society; *Int'l*, pg. 7686
THE MORTGAGE BUSINESS PLC—See Lloyds Banking Group plc; *Int'l*, pg. 4538
MORTGAGE CADENCE LLC—See Accenture plc; *Int'l*, pg. 86
MORTGAGE CAPITAL ASSOCIATES, INC.; *U.S. Private*, pg. 2791
MORTGAGE CHOICE LIMITED—See News Corporation; *U.S. Public*, pg. 1521
MORTGAGE CONNECT, LP; *U.S. Private*, pg. 2791
MORTGAGE CONTRACTING SERVICES LLC—See American Securities LLC; *U.S. Private*, pg. 250
THE MORTGAGE CORPORATION OF JAPAN, LTD—See Sekisui House, Ltd.; *Int'l*, pg. 6698
MORTGAGEFLEX SYSTEMS INC.; *U.S. Private*, pg. 2791
THE MORTGAGE GENIE LIMITED—See The Property Franchise Group PLC; *Int'l*, pg. 7677
MORTGAGE GUARANTEE & TITLE COMPANY—See First American Financial Corporation; *U.S. Public*, pg. 837
MORTGAGE GUARANTY INSURANCE CORPORATION—See MGIC Investment Corporation; *U.S. Public*, pg. 1434
MORTGAGE INTELLIGENCE HOLDINGS LIMITED—See The Skipton Building Society; *Int'l*, pg. 7686
MORTGAGE INTELLIGENCE INC.; *Int'l*, pg. 5049
MORTGAGE INVESTMENT CORPORATION; *U.S. Private*, pg. 2791
MORTGAGE INVESTORS CORPORATION; *U.S. Private*, pg. 2791

MORTGAGE INVESTORS GROUP, INC.

CORPORATE AFFILIATIONS

MORTGAGE INVESTORS GROUP, INC.; *U.S. Private*, pg. 2791
MORTGAGE LENDER SERVICES, INC.—See Total Lender Solutions, Inc.; *U.S. Private*, pg. 4191
MORTGAGE LENDERS OF AMERICA, LLC; *U.S. Private*, pg. 2791
MORTGAGE OIL CORP.; *U.S. Public*, pg. 1477
MORTGAGE OUTLET INC.; *U.S. Private*, pg. 2791
THE MORTGAGE PARTNERSHIP OF AMERICA, L.L.C.—See Altisource Portfolio Solutions S.A.; *Int'l*, pg. 393
MORTGAGE RETURNS, LLC—See Intercontinental Exchange, Inc.; *U.S. Public*, pg. 1142
MORTGAGE SERVICE JAPAN LIMITED; *Int'l*, pg. 5049
MORTGAGE SERVICE NETWORK, INC.—See Movement Mortgage, LLC; *U.S. Private*, pg. 2802
MORTGAGES FIRST LTD.—See LSL Property Services plc; *Int'l*, pg. 4570
MORTGAGES PLC—See Bank of America Corporation; *U.S. Public*, pg. 272
MORTGAGE SUCCESS SOURCE, LLC; *U.S. Private*, pg. 2791
MORTGAGE TRUST LIMITED—See Paragon Banking Group PLC; *Int'l*, pg. 5735
MORTGAGE WAREHOUSE, LLC; *U.S. Private*, pg. 2791
THE MORTGAGE WORKS (UK) PLC—See Sun Life Financial Inc.; *Int'l*, pg. 7306
MORTGAGE WORLD BANKERS, INC.—See PDL Community Bancorp; *U.S. Public*, pg. 1658
MORTIMER CLARKE SOLICITORS LIMITED—See Encore Capital Group, Inc.; *U.S. Public*, pg. 760
MORTIMER COLLISION, LLC.—See AutoNation, Inc.; *U.S. Public*, pg. 236
MORTIMER & SON LUMBER CO. INC.; *U.S. Private*, pg. 2791
MORTLAKE LTD—See John Keells Holdings PLC; *Int'l*, pg. 3978
THE MORTON ARBORETUM; *U.S. Private*, pg. 4080
MORTON AUTO AUCTION INC.; *U.S. Private*, pg. 2791
MORTON BAHAMAS LTD.—See K+S Aktiengesellschaft; *Int'l*, pg. 4041
MORTON BUILDINGS INC.; *U.S. Private*, pg. 2791
MORTON CAPITAL MANAGEMENT—See U.S. Bancorp; *U.S. Public*, pg. 2212
MORTON COMMUNITY BANK—See Hometown Community Bancorp, Inc.; *U.S. Public*, pg. 1975
MORTON COMPREHENSIVE HEALTH SERVICES, INC.; *U.S. Private*, pg. 2792
MORTON CONSULTING LLC; *U.S. Private*, pg. 2792
MORTON FOODS LIMITED—See Palash Securities Ltd.; *Int'l*, pg. 5706
MORTON FRASER MACROBERTS LLP; *Int'l*, pg. 5049
MORTON GROVE PHARMACEUTICALS, INC.—See Wockhardt Limited; *Int'l*, pg. 8441
MORTON INDUSTRIES LLC; *U.S. Private*, pg. 2792
MORTON INTERNATIONAL CO., LTD.—See K+S Aktiengesellschaft; *Int'l*, pg. 4041
MORTON INTERNATIONAL, INC.—See K+S Aktiengesellschaft; *Int'l*, pg. 4040
MORTON NEWSPAPERS LTD—See JPIMedia Holdings Limited; *Int'l*, pg. 4006
MORTON PHOTONICS, INC.—See Coldquanta, Inc.; *U.S. Private*, pg. 966
MORTON PLANT HOSPITAL—See BayCare Health System Inc.; *U.S. Private*, pg. 495
MORTON PLANT MEASE HEALTH CARE—See BayCare Health System Inc.; *U.S. Private*, pg. 495
MORTON PLANT NORTH BAY HOSPITAL—See BayCare Health System Inc.; *U.S. Private*, pg. 495
MORTON PUBLISHING COMPANY, LLC—See Tophatmonocle Corp.; *Int'l*, pg. 7816
MORTON SALT INC - CINCINNATI PLANT—See K+S Aktiengesellschaft; *Int'l*, pg. 4041
MORTON SALT INC - DETROIT PLANT—See K+S Aktiengesellschaft; *Int'l*, pg. 4041
MORTON SALT INC - ELSTON PLANT—See K+S Aktiengesellschaft; *Int'l*, pg. 4041
MORTON SALT INC - GLENDALE PLANT—See K+S Aktiengesellschaft; *Int'l*, pg. 4041
MORTON SALT INC - GRAND SALINE PLANT—See K+S Aktiengesellschaft; *Int'l*, pg. 4041
MORTON SALT INC - GRANTSVILLE PLANT—See K+S Aktiengesellschaft; *Int'l*, pg. 4041
MORTON SALT INC - HUTCHINSON PLANT—See K+S Aktiengesellschaft; *Int'l*, pg. 4041
MORTON SALT INC - LONG BEACH PLANT—See K+S Aktiengesellschaft; *Int'l*, pg. 4041
MORTON SALT INC - MANISTEE PLANT—See K+S Aktiengesellschaft; *Int'l*, pg. 4041
MORTON SALT INC - NEWARK PLANT—See K+S Aktiengesellschaft; *Int'l*, pg. 4041
MORTON SALT INC - NEW IBERIA PLANT—See K+S Aktiengesellschaft; *Int'l*, pg. 4041
MORTON SALT INC - PAINESVILLE PLANT—See K+S Aktiengesellschaft; *Int'l*, pg. 4041
MORTON SALT INC - PERTH AMBOY PLANT—See K+S Aktiengesellschaft; *Int'l*, pg. 4041
MORTON SALT INC - PORT CANAVERAL PLANT—See K+S Aktiengesellschaft; *Int'l*, pg. 4041

MORTON SALT INC - RITTMAN PLANT—See K+S Aktiengesellschaft; *Int'l*, pg. 4041
MORTON SALT INC - SILVER SPRINGS PLANT—See K+S Aktiengesellschaft; *Int'l*, pg. 4041
MORTON SALT INC.—See K+S Aktiengesellschaft; *Int'l*, pg. 4041
MORTON SALT INC - ST. PAUL PLANT—See K+S Aktiengesellschaft; *Int'l*, pg. 4041
MORTONS ASSOCIATES, INC.—See Sunshine Ace Hardware Inc.; *U.S. Private*, pg. 3871
MORTON SECURITIES LTD.—See Da Yu Financial Holdings Ltd.; *Int'l*, pg. 1902
MORTON'S OF CHICAGO, INC.—See Morton's Restaurant Group, Inc.; *U.S. Private*, pg. 2792
MORTON'S RESTAURANT GROUP, INC.; *U.S. Private*, pg. 2792
MORTONS TRAVEL LIMITED—See Mobico Group PLC; *Int'l*, pg. 5008
MORTON TRUCKING, INC.; *U.S. Private*, pg. 2792
MORTRANS, INC.—See Meyers Transport Inc.; *Int'l*, pg. 4870
MORVEST GROUP LIMITED; *Int'l*, pg. 5050
MORYA COMUNICACAO E PROPAGANDA LTDA—See Omnicom Group Inc.; *U.S. Public*, pg. 1585
MORY INDUSTRIES INC.; *Int'l*, pg. 5050
MOSAICA EDUCATION; *U.S. Private*, pg. 2792
THE MOSAICA GROUP LLC; *U.S. Private*, pg. 4081
MOSAIC ATM, INC.; *U.S. Private*, pg. 2792
MOSAIC BRANDS LTD—See Alceon Group Pty Ltd.; *Int'l*, pg. 300
MOSAIC CANADA ULC—See The Mosaic Company; *U.S. Public*, pg. 2116
MOSAIC CAPITAL CORPORATION—See Fairfax Financial Holdings Limited; *Int'l*, pg. 2607
MOSAIC CAPITAL PARTNERS; *U.S. Private*, pg. 2792
THE MOSAIC COMPANY—See The Mosaic Company; *U.S. Public*, pg. 2116
THE MOSAIC COMPANY—See The Mosaic Company; *U.S. Public*, pg. 2116
THE MOSAIC COMPANY; *U.S. Public*, pg. 2116
THE MOSAIC COMPANY; *U.S. Public*, pg. 4081
MOSAIC CROP NUTRITION, LLC—See The Mosaic Company; *U.S. Public*, pg. 2116
MOSAIC ESTERHAZY HOLDINGS ULC—See The Mosaic Company; *U.S. Public*, pg. 2116
MOSAIC FERTILIZANTES P&K LTDA—See The Mosaic Company; *U.S. Public*, pg. 2116
MOSAIC FERTILIZANTES P&K S.A.—See The Mosaic Company; *U.S. Public*, pg. 2116
MOSAIC FERTILIZER, LLC—See The Mosaic Company; *U.S. Public*, pg. 2116
MOSAIC GLOBAL HOLDINGS INC.—See The Mosaic Company; *U.S. Public*, pg. 2116
MOSAIC IMMUNOENGINEERING, INC.; *U.S. Public*, pg. 1477
MOSAIC INSURANCE ALLIANCE, LLC—See Inszone Insurance Services, LLC; *U.S. Public*, pg. 2096
MOSAIC INTERACTIVE; *U.S. Private*, pg. 2792
MOSAIC LIFE CARE; *U.S. Private*, pg. 2792
MOSAIC MEDIA INVESTMENT PARTNERS LLC; *U.S. Private*, pg. 2792
MOSAIC MEDIA VENTURES PVT. LTD.—See HT Media Limited; *Int'l*, pg. 3508
MOSAICO+ SRL—See Mapei SpA; *Int'l*, pg. 4683
MOSAIC POTASH CARLSBAD INC—See The Mosaic Company; *U.S. Public*, pg. 2116
MOSAIC POTASH COLONSAY ULC—See The Mosaic Company; *U.S. Public*, pg. 2116
MOSAIC POTASH ESTERHAZY LIMITED PARTNERSHIP—See The Mosaic Company; *U.S. Public*, pg. 2116
MOSAIC; *U.S. Private*, pg. 2792
MOSAIC—See Caregiver, Inc.; *U.S. Private*, pg. 753
MOSAIC TECHNOLOGIES GROUP, LLC; *U.S. Private*, pg. 2792
MOSA INDUSTRIAL CORP.; *Int'l*, pg. 5050
MOSBACHER ENERGY COMPANY; *U.S. Private*, pg. 2792
MOSCA AG; *Int'l*, pg. 5050
MOSCA ASIA PTE LTD.—See Mosca AG; *Int'l*, pg. 5050
MOSCA ASIA (THAILAND) LTD.—See Mosca AG; *Int'l*, pg. 5050
MOSCA AUSTRALIA (PTY) LTD.—See Mosca AG; *Int'l*, pg. 5050
MOSCA DIRECT FINLAND OY—See Mosca AG; *Int'l*, pg. 5050
MOSCA DIRECT LTD.—See Mosca AG; *Int'l*, pg. 5050
MOSCA DIRECT POLAND SP. Z O.O.—See Mosca AG; *Int'l*, pg. 5050
MOSCA DIRECT SHANGHAI CO., LTD.—See Mosca AG; *Int'l*, pg. 5050
MOSCA DIRECT SPAIN S.L.—See Mosca AG; *Int'l*, pg. 5050
MOSCA MALAYSIA SDN. BHD.—See Mosca AG; *Int'l*, pg. 5050
MOSCHINO FRANCE S.A.R.L.—See Aeffe SpA; *Int'l*, pg. 173
MOSCHINO KOREA LTD.—See Aeffe SpA; *Int'l*, pg. 173
MOSCHINO RETAIL GMBH—See Aeffe SpA; *Int'l*, pg. 173

MOSCHINO S.P.A.—See Aeffe SpA; *Int'l*, pg. 173
MOSCHIP INSTITUTE OF SILICON SYSTEMS PRIVATE LIMITED—See Moschip Technologies Limited; *Int'l*, pg. 5050
MOSCHIP TECHNOLOGIES LIMITED; *Int'l*, pg. 5050
MOSCKER INSURANCE AGENCY, INC.—See GTCR LLC; *U.S. Private*, pg. 1803
MOSCOT OPTICAL CORP.; *U.S. Private*, pg. 2792
MOSCOVSKIY OBLASTNOI BANK PAO; *Int'l*, pg. 5050
MOSCOW BANCSHARES, INC.; *U.S. Private*, pg. 2792
MOSCOW CITY TELEPHONE NETWORK JSC—See MOBILE TELESYSTEMS PUBLIC JOINT STOCK COMPANY; *Int'l*, pg. 5010
MOSCOW COKE AND GAS PLANT OAO—See Mechel PAO; *Int'l*, pg. 4766
MOSCOW EXCHANGE INTERNATIONAL LTD.—See OJSC Moscow Exchange MICEX-RTS; *Int'l*, pg. 5540
MOSCOW INDUSTRIAL BANK PO JSCB—See Central Bank of the Russian Federation; *Int'l*, pg. 1405
MOSCOW INTEGRATED POWER COMPANY JSC; *Int'l*, pg. 5050
MOSCOW MACHINE BUILDING PLANT VPERED JSC; *Int'l*, pg. 5050
MOSCOW MILLS LUMBER COMPANY; *U.S. Private*, pg. 2792
MOSCOW PULLMAN DAILY NEWS—See TPC Holdings, Inc.; *U.S. Private*, pg. 4200
THE MOSCOW TIMES—See Novamedia Group; *Int'l*, pg. 5455
MOSDORFER CCL SYSTEMS LIMITED—See Knill Holding GmbH; *Int'l*, pg. 4208
MOSDORFER GMBH—See Knill Holding GmbH; *Int'l*, pg. 4208
MOSDORFER INDIA PRIVATE LIMITED—See Knill Holding GmbH; *Int'l*, pg. 4208
MOSDORFER NA INC.—See Knill Holding GmbH; *Int'l*, pg. 4208
MOSDORFER (THAILAND) CO. LTD.—See Knill Holding GmbH; *Int'l*, pg. 4208
MOSEBACH MANUFACTURING COMPANY, INC.—See Telema S.p.A; *Int'l*, pg. 7538
MOSELEY ARCHITECTS, P.C.; *U.S. Private*, pg. 2793
MOSELEY ASSOCIATES, INC.; *U.S. Private*, pg. 2793
MOSEL VITELIC INC.; *Int'l*, pg. 5050
MOSENKA LLC—See Enka Insaat ve Sanayi A.S.; *Int'l*, pg. 2440
MOSENKA OAO—See Enka Insaat ve Sanayi A.S.; *Int'l*, pg. 2440
MOSER BAER ENERGY LIMITED—See Moser Baer India Limited; *Int'l*, pg. 5050
MOSER BAER ENTERTAINMENT LIMITED—See Moser Baer India Limited; *Int'l*, pg. 5051
MOSER BAER INDIA LIMITED - BOM M& ES—See Moser Baer India Limited; *Int'l*, pg. 5051
MOSER BAER INDIA LIMITED - HOME ENTERTAINMENT DIVISION—See Moser Baer India Limited; *Int'l*, pg. 5051
MOSER BAER INDIA LIMITED; *Int'l*, pg. 5050
MOSER BAER PHOTO VOLTAIC LTD.—See Moser Baer India Limited; *Int'l*, pg. 5051
MOSER BAER SEZ DEVELOPER LIMITED—See Moser Baer India Limited; *Int'l*, pg. 5051
MOSER BAER SOLAR LIMITED—See Moser Baer India Limited; *Int'l*, pg. 5051
MOSER BAER SOLAR LIMITED—See Moser Baer India Limited; *Int'l*, pg. 5051
MOSER BAER TECHNOLOGIES INC.—See Moser Baer India Limited; *Int'l*, pg. 5051
MOSER CORPORATION; *U.S. Private*, pg. 2793
MOSER & PARTNER INGENIEURBURO GMBH—See CEZ, a.s.; *Int'l*, pg. 1428
MOSES ANSHELL, INC.; *U.S. Private*, pg. 2793
MOSES LAKE INDUSTRIES, INC.—See Tama Chemicals Co., Ltd.; *Int'l*, pg. 7448
MOSEY MANUFACTURING COMPANY INCORPORATED; *U.S. Private*, pg. 2793
MOSFLY INTERNATIONAL SDN. BHD.—See IMASPRO Corporation Berhad; *Int'l*, pg. 3620
MOS FOOD SERVICES, INC.; *Int'l*, pg. 5050
MOSHI MOSHI HOTLINE DALIAN, INC.—See Neusoft Corporation; *Int'l*, pg. 5220
MOSHI MOSHI RETAIL CORPORATION PUBLIC COMPANY LIMITED; *Int'l*, pg. 5051
MOS HOUSE GROUP LIMITED; *Int'l*, pg. 5050
MOSIER & COMPANY, INC.; *U.S. Private*, pg. 2793
MOSIER FLUID POWER OF INDIANA; *U.S. Private*, pg. 2793
MOSKOWITZ BROS INC.—See Cohen Brothers, Inc.; *U.S. Public*, pg. 962
MOSKVA KRASNYE HOLMY LLC—See Enka Insaat ve Sanayi A.S.; *Int'l*, pg. 2440
MOSLEY HOLDINGS LIMITED PARTNERSHIP; *U.S. Private*, pg. 2793
MOSMAN OIL AND GAS LIMITED; *Int'l*, pg. 5051
MOSMAN OPERATING, LLC—See Mosman Oil and Gas Limited; *Int'l*, pg. 5051
MOSO ELECTRONICS CORP.—See Shenzhen Moso Power Supply Technology Co., Ltd.; *Int'l*, pg. 6818
MOSPEC SEMICONDUCTOR CORP.; *Int'l*, pg. 5051

COMPANY NAME INDEX

MOSPEC SEMICONDUCTOR (SHENZHEN) CO., LTD.—See Mospec Semiconductor Corp.; *Int'l*, pg. 5051
MOS PLASTICS INC.—See Kennerley-Spratling Inc.; *U.S. Private*, pg. 2286
MOSQUITO FLEET, LLC—See FRS GmbH & Co. KG; *Int'l*, pg. 2797
MOSQUITONIX FRANCHISE SYSTEMS, LTD.; *U.S. Private*, pg. 2793
MOSQUITO SQUAD FRANCHISING CORPORATION; *U.S. Private*, pg. 2793
MOSSACK FONSECA & CO.; *Int'l*, pg. 5051
MOSS ADAMS CAPITAL LLC—See Meridian Capital, LLC; *U.S. Private*, pg. 2672
MOSS ADAMS LLP - BELLINGHAM—See Moss Adams LLP; *U.S. Private*, pg. 2794
MOSS ADAMS LLP - EUGENE—See Moss Adams LLP; *U.S. Private*, pg. 2794
MOSS ADAMS LLP - EVERETT—See Moss Adams LLP; *U.S. Private*, pg. 2794
MOSS ADAMS LLP - FRESNO—See Moss Adams LLP; *U.S. Private*, pg. 2794
MOSS ADAMS LLP - ISSAQUAH—See Moss Adams LLP; *U.S. Private*, pg. 2794
MOSS ADAMS LLP - LOS ANGELES—See Moss Adams LLP; *U.S. Private*, pg. 2794
MOSS ADAMS LLP - ORANGE COUNTY—See Moss Adams LLP; *U.S. Private*, pg. 2794
MOSS ADAMS LLP - PORTLAND—See Moss Adams LLP; *U.S. Private*, pg. 2794
MOSS ADAMS LLP - SACRAMENTO—See Moss Adams LLP; *U.S. Private*, pg. 2794
MOSS ADAMS LLP - SAN FRANCISCO—See Moss Adams LLP; *U.S. Private*, pg. 2794
MOSS ADAMS LLP - SANTA ROSA—See Moss Adams LLP; *U.S. Private*, pg. 2794
MOSS ADAMS LLP; *U.S. Private*, pg. 2793
MOSS ADAMS LLP - SPOKANE—See Moss Adams LLP; *U.S. Private*, pg. 2794
MOSS ADAMS LLP - TACOMA—See Moss Adams LLP; *U.S. Private*, pg. 2794
MOSS ADAMS LLP - YAKIMA—See Moss Adams LLP; *U.S. Private*, pg. 2794
MOSS ADAMS WEALTH ADVISORS LLC—See Moss Adams LLP; *U.S. Private*, pg. 2794
MOSS & ASSOCIATES, LLC; *U.S. Private*, pg. 2793
MOSSBERG CORPORATION; *U.S. Private*, pg. 2794
MOSSBERG INDUSTRIES - HUBBARD DIVISION—See Mossberg Industries, Inc.; *U.S. Private*, pg. 2794
MOSSBERG INDUSTRIES, INC.; *U.S. Private*, pg. 2794
MOSS BLUFF HUB, LLC—See Enbridge Inc.; *Int'l*, pg. 2397
MOSS BROS. CHRYSLER JEEP DODGE RAM; *U.S. Private*, pg. 2794
MOSS BROS GROUP PLC; *Int'l*, pg. 5051
MOSS BROS. TOYOTA, INC.; *U.S. Private*, pg. 2794
MOSS CONTAINER TERMINAL AS—See DFDS A/S; *Int'l*, pg. 2095
MOSSER CONSTRUCTION INC.; *U.S. Private*, pg. 2794
MOSSER LEE CO.—See Deli, Inc.; *U.S. Private*, pg. 1196
MOSS GENOMICS INC.; *Int'l*, pg. 5051
MOSSIMO HOLDINGS LLC—See Iconix Acquisition LLC; *U.S. Private*, pg. 2033
MOSS INC.—See EagleTree Capital, LP; *U.S. Private*, pg. 1312
MOSS LUMBER CO. INC.; *U.S. Private*, pg. 2794
MOSS MARITIME A/S—See Eni S.p.A.; *Int'l*, pg. 2438
MOSS MOTORS; *U.S. Private*, pg. 2794
MOSSO KEWPIE POLAND SP. Z O.O.—See Kewpie Corporation; *Int'l*, pg. 4144
MOSSOP WESTERN LEATHERS (PTY) LTD—See Bolton Footwear (Pty) Ltd.; *Int'l*, pg. 1103
MOSSO'S MEDICAL SUPPLY COMPANY; *U.S. Private*, pg. 2795
MOSS PIECES PLASTIQUES S.A.R.L.—See Essentra plc; *Int'l*, pg. 2511
MOSS PLASTIC PRODUCTS TRADING (NINGBO) CO., LTD.—See OpenGate Capital Management, LLC; *U.S. Private*, pg. 3030
MOSS SUPPLY COMPANY; *U.S. Private*, pg. 2794
MOSS TELECOMMUNICATIONS SERVICES; *U.S. Private*, pg. 2794
MOS STORE COMPANY, INC.—See MOS Food Services, Inc.; *Int'l*, pg. 5050
MOSS WARNER INC.; *U.S. Private*, pg. 2794
MOSSY NISSAN INC.; *U.S. Private*, pg. 2795
MOSSY TOYOTA INC.; *U.S. Private*, pg. 2795
MOST BRAND DEVELOPMENT + ADVERTISING; *U.S. Private*, pg. 2795
MOST-BUD SP. Z O.O.—See MSX Resources SA; *Int'l*, pg. 5069
MOSTCHOICE.COM; *U.S. Private*, pg. 2795
MOST CROWN INDUSTRIES LTD.—See Citizen Watch Co., Ltd.; *Int'l*, pg. 1625
MOSTEN MEDIA B.V.—See PopReach Corporation; *Int'l*, pg. 5921
MOSTERFARM AS—See Caiano AS; *Int'l*, pg. 1252
MOST INSURANCE AGENCY—See Stone Point Capital LLC; *U.S. Private*, pg. 3819

MOSTOBUD, PJSC; *Int'l*, pg. 5051
MOSTOLLER LANDFILL, LLC—See Waste Management, Inc.; *U.S. Public*, pg. 2331
MOSTOSTAL CHOJNICE S.A.—See Zamet Industry S.A.; *Int'l*, pg. 8623
MOSTOSTAL-EXPORT DEVELOPMENT S.A—See MSX Resources SA; *Int'l*, pg. 5069
MOSTOSTAL KRAKOW S.A.—See Ferrovial S.A.; *Int'l*, pg. 2644
MOSTOSTAL PLOCK S.A.; *Int'l*, pg. 5051
MOSTOSTAL SIEDLCE SP. Z O.O. SP.K.—See Polimex-Mostostal S.A.; *Int'l*, pg. 5909
MOSTOSTAL WROCLAW S.A.; *Int'l*, pg. 5051
MOSTOSTAL ZABRZE S.A.; *Int'l*, pg. 5051
MOSTOSTROY-11 AO; *Int'l*, pg. 5051
MOSTOTREST PAO; *Int'l*, pg. 5051
MOSTPROJEKT A.D.; *Int'l*, pg. 5051
MOSTRA, SA—See ICF International, Inc.; *U.S. Public*, pg. 1086
MOSTYLE CORPORATION; *Int'l*, pg. 5051
MOSUL BANK FOR DEVELOPMENT & INVESTMENT; *Int'l*, pg. 5051
MOSYS INC.—See Peraso Inc.; *U.S. Public*, pg. 1673
MOSYS INTERNATIONAL, INC.—See Peraso Inc.; *U.S. Public*, pg. 1673
MOTA-ENGIL ANGOLA, S.A.—See Mota-Engil SGPS, S.A.; *Int'l*, pg. 5052
MOTA-ENGIL CENTRAL EUROPE CESKA REPUBLIKA, AS—See Mota-Engil SGPS, S.A.; *Int'l*, pg. 5052
MOTA-ENGIL CENTRAL EUROPE, S.A.—See Mota-Engil SGPS, S.A.; *Int'l*, pg. 5052
MOTA-ENGIL CHILE S.A.—See Mota-Engil SGPS, S.A.; *Int'l*, pg. 5052
MOTA-ENGIL COLOMBIA, S.A.S—See Mota-Engil SGPS, S.A.; *Int'l*, pg. 5052
MOTA-ENGIL INDUSTRIA E INOVACAO, SGPS, S.A.—See Mota-Engil SGPS, S.A.; *Int'l*, pg. 5052
MOTA-ENGIL IRELAND CONSTRUCTION LIMITED—See Mota-Engil SGPS, S.A.; *Int'l*, pg. 5052
MOTA-ENGIL LATAM COLOMBIA S.A.S.—See Mota-Engil SGPS, S.A.; *Int'l*, pg. 5052
MOTA-ENGIL MINERALS & MINING (MALAWI) LIMITED—See Mota-Engil SGPS, S.A.; *Int'l*, pg. 5052
MOTA-ENGIL MINERALS & MINING (ZIMBABWE) (PRIVATE) LIMITED—See Mota-Engil SGPS, S.A.; *Int'l*, pg. 5052
MOTA-ENGIL PERU, S.A.—See Mota-Engil SGPS, S.A.; *Int'l*, pg. 5052
MOTA-ENGIL RAILWAY ENGINEERING, S.A.—See Mota-Engil SGPS, S.A.; *Int'l*, pg. 5052
MOTA-ENGIL SGPS, S.A.; *Int'l*, pg. 5051
MOTA-ENGIL S.TOME E PRINCIPE, LDA.—See Mota-Engil SGPS, S.A.; *Int'l*, pg. 5052
MOTA GROUP, INC.; *U.S. Private*, pg. 2795
MOTA INTERNACIONAL - COMERCIO E CONSULTADORIA ECONOMICA, LDA.—See Mota-Engil SGPS, S.A.; *Int'l*, pg. 5052
MOTALA HISSAR A.B.—See KONE Oyj; *Int'l*, pg. 4250
MOTAN, INC.; *U.S. Private*, pg. 2795
MOTAWI TILEWORKS, INC.; *U.S. Private*, pg. 2795
MOTCO, INC.; *U.S. Private*, pg. 2795
M.O.TEC CORPORATION—See Mitsubishi Corporation; *Int'l*, pg. 4940
M.O.TEC CORPORATION—See Sojitz Corporation; *Int'l*, pg. 7062
MOTEC GMBH—See AMETEK, Inc.; *U.S. Public*, pg. 121
MOTECH INDUSTRIES INC.; *Int'l*, pg. 5052
MOTEK-TEAM INDUSTRIES, INC.—See TEAM Industries, Inc.; *U.S. Private*, pg. 3949
MOTEL 6 OPERATING L.P.—See Blackstone Inc.; *U.S. Public*, pg. 353
MOTEL DESA SDN BHD—See Inch Kenneth Kajang Rubber Public Limited Company; *Int'l*, pg. 3646
MOTELES ANDALUCES, S.A.—See Melia Hotels International, S.A.; *Int'l*, pg. 4809
MOTE MARINE LABORATORY, INC.; *U.S. Private*, pg. 2795
MOTEN ASSOCIATES—See Brown & Brown, Inc.; *U.S. Public*, pg. 401
MOTENG INTERNATIONAL INCORPORATED; *U.S. Private*, pg. 2795
MOTEN TATE, INC. (MTI); *U.S. Private*, pg. 2795
MOTER SAS—See VINCI S.A.; *Int'l*, pg. 8224
MOTER TECHNOLOGIES, INC.—See MS&AD Insurance Group Holdings, Inc.; *Int'l*, pg. 5066
MOTESPLATSEN I NORDEN AB—See Schibsted ASA; *Int'l*, pg. 6617
MOTEURS LEROY-SOMER S.A.—See Nidec Corporation; *Int'l*, pg. 5277
MOTEX INC.—See KYOCERA Corporation; *Int'l*, pg. 4360
MOTHER ANGELINE MCCRORY MANOR; *U.S. Private*, pg. 2795
MOTHERCARE PLC; *Int'l*, pg. 5052
MOTHERCARE UK LIMITED—See Mothercare plc; *Int'l*, pg. 5052
MOTHER EARTH NEWS—See The Nutting Company, Inc.; *U.S. Private*, pg. 4086
MOTHERHOOD PTE LTD—See Eastern Holdings Ltd.; *Int'l*, pg. 2272

MOTHER LODE HOLDING COMPANY—See First American Financial Corporation; *U.S. Public*, pg. 838
MOTHER LTD.; *Int'l*, pg. 5052
MOTHERNATURE.COM, INC.; *U.S. Private*, pg. 2795
MOTHER NEW YORK—See Mother Ltd.; *Int'l*, pg. 5052
MOTHER'S COOKIE COMPANY, L.L.C.—See Ferrero International S.A.; *Int'l*, pg. 2641
MOTHERS NUTRITIONAL CENTER; *U.S. Private*, pg. 2795
MOTHERSON ADVANCED TOOLING SOLUTIONS LIMITED—See Samvardhana Motherson International Limited; *Int'l*, pg. 6516
MOTHERSON AIR TRAVEL AGENCIES LIMITED—See Samvardhana Motherson International Limited; *Int'l*, pg. 6516
MOTHERSON ELASTOMERS PTY, LIMITED—See Samvardhana Motherson International Limited; *Int'l*, pg. 6516
MOTHERSON INNOVATIONS DEUTSCHLAND GMBH—See Samvardhana Motherson International Limited; *Int'l*, pg. 6516
MOTHERSON INNOVATIONS LIGHTS GMBH & CO. KG—See Samvardhana Motherson International Limited; *Int'l*, pg. 6516
MOTHERSON INVENZEN XLAB PRIVATE LIMITED—See Samvardhana Motherson International Limited; *Int'l*, pg. 6516
MOTHERSON MACHINERY AND AUTOMATIONS LIMITED—See Samvardhana Motherson International Limited; *Int'l*, pg. 6516
MOTHERSON MOLDS AND DIE CASTING LIMITED—See Samvardhana Motherson International Limited; *Int'l*, pg. 6516
MOTHERSON PKC HARNESS SYSTEMS FZ-LLC—See Samvardhana Motherson International Limited; *Int'l*, pg. 6516
MOTHERSON SINTERMETAL PRODUCTS S.A.—See Samvardhana Motherson International Limited; *Int'l*, pg. 6516
MOTHERSON TECHNOLOGY SERVICES GMBH—See Samvardhana Motherson International Limited; *Int'l*, pg. 6517
MOTHERSON TECHNOLOGY SERVICES KABUSHIKI GAISHA—See Samvardhana Motherson International Limited; *Int'l*, pg. 6517
MOTHERSON TECHNOLOGY SERVICES LIMITED—See Samvardhana Motherson International Limited; *Int'l*, pg. 6517
MOTHERSON TECHNOLOGY SERVICES SG PTE. LIMITED—See Samvardhana Motherson International Limited; *Int'l*, pg. 6517
MOTHERSON TECHNOLOGY SERVICES UNITED KINGDOM LIMITED—See Samvardhana Motherson International Limited; *Int'l*, pg. 6517
MOTHERSON TECHNOLOGY SERVICES USA LIMITED—See Samvardhana Motherson International Limited; *Int'l*, pg. 6517
MOTHERSON TECHNO TOOLS LIMITED—See Samvardhana Motherson International Limited; *Int'l*, pg. 6516
MOTHERS WORK CANADA, INC.—See Destination Maternity Corporation; *U.S. Public*, pg. 656
MOTHERWELL BRIDGE INDUSTRIES LIMITED—See Hilti Ventures Ltd; *Int'l*, pg. 3391
MOTIC (XIAMEN) ELECTRIC GROUP CO., LTD.; *Int'l*, pg. 5052
MOTIF BIO PLC; *U.S. Private*, pg. 2795
MOTIF TECHNOLOGY CO., LTD.; *Int'l*, pg. 5052
MOTIFWORKS, INC.; *U.S. Private*, pg. 2795
MOTILAL OSWAL COMMODITIES BROKER PVT. LTD.—See Motilal Oswal Financial Services Ltd.; *Int'l*, pg. 5053
MOTILAL OSWAL FINANCIAL SERVICES LTD.; *Int'l*, pg. 5052
MOTILAL OSWAL HOME FINANCE LIMITED—See Motilal Oswal Financial Services Ltd.; *Int'l*, pg. 5053
MOTILAL OSWAL INVESTMENT ADVISORS PVT. LTD.—See Motilal Oswal Financial Services Ltd.; *Int'l*, pg. 5053
MOTILAL OSWAL PRIVATE EQUITY ADVISORS PVT. LTD.—See Motilal Oswal Financial Services Ltd.; *Int'l*, pg. 5053
MOTILAL OSWAL SECURITIES LIMITED—See Motilal Oswal Financial Services Ltd.; *Int'l*, pg. 5053
MOTILAL OSWAL WEALTH MANAGEMENT LIMITED—See Motilal Oswal Financial Services Ltd.; *Int'l*, pg. 5053
M.O.T. INTERMODAL SHIPPING INC.—See C.H. Robinson Worldwide, Inc.; *U.S. Public*, pg. 415
M.O.T. INTERMODAL SHIPPING USA INC.—See C.H. Robinson Worldwide, Inc.; *U.S. Public*, pg. 415
MOTIO LIMITED; *Int'l*, pg. 5053
MOTION ANALYSIS CORPORATION; *U.S. Private*, pg. 2795
MOTION ASIA PACIFIC PTY LTD—See Genuine Parts Company; *U.S. Public*, pg. 933
MOTION CONCEPTS, L.P.—See Invacare Corporation; *U.S. Private*, pg. 2131
MOTION CONTROL ENGINEERING—See Nidec Corporation; *Int'l*, pg. 5275

MOTION ANALYSIS CORPORATION

CORPORATE AFFILIATIONS

MOTION & CONTROL ENTERPRISES LLC—See Frontenac Company LLC; *U.S. Private*, pg. 1614
MOTION CONTROL, INC.—See Patient Square Capital, L.P.; *U.S. Private*, pg. 3107
MOTION CONTROL INDUSTRIES, INC.—See Carlisle Companies Incorporated; *U.S. Public*, pg. 437
MOTION DISPLAY SCANDINAVIA AB; *Int'l*, pg. 5053
MOTIONDSP, INC.—See Elliott Management Corporation; *U.S. Private*, pg. 1368
MOTIONDSP, INC.—See Veritas Capital Fund Management, LLC; *U.S. Private*, pg. 4362
MOTION ENGINEERING INCORPORATED—See Regal Rexnord Corporation; *U.S. Public*, pg. 1772
MOTION EQUITY PARTNERS LLP—See Motion Equity Partners S.A.S.; *Int'l*, pg. 5053
MOTION EQUITY PARTNERS S.A.S.; *Int'l*, pg. 5053
MOTION & FLOW CONTROL PRODUCTS, INC.—See Colville Capital LLC; *U.S. Private*, pg. 979
MOTION INDUSTRIES (CANADA) INC.—See Genuine Parts Company; *U.S. Public*, pg. 933
MOTION INDUSTRIES (CANADA) INC.—See Genuine Parts Company; *U.S. Public*, pg. 933
MOTION INDUSTRIES, INC.—See Genuine Parts Company; *U.S. Public*, pg. 933
MOTION MICRO INC.—See Taiwan Line Tek Electronic Co., Ltd.; *Int'l*, pg. 7422
MOTION PICTURE ASSOCIATION OF AMERICA, INC.; *U.S. Private*, pg. 2795
MOTION PICTURE INDUSTRY PENSION & HEALTH PLANS; *U.S. Private*, pg. 2795
MOTIONPOINT CORP.; *U.S. Private*, pg. 2796
MOTIONPORTRAIT, INC.—See Axell Corporation; *Int'l*, pg. 767
MOTION PT GROUP, INC.—See Confluent Health, LLC; *U.S. Private*, pg. 1013
MOTION RECRUITMENT PARTNERS, LLC—See Littlejohn & Co., LLC; *U.S. Private*, pg. 2471
MOTIONSOFT, INC.—See GI Manager L.P.; *U.S. Private*, pg. 1692
MOTION.TM VERTRIEBS GMBH—See freenet AG; *Int'l*, pg. 2770
MOTION WATER SPORTS INC.; *U.S. Private*, pg. 2796
MOTIONWERK GMBH—See RWE AG; *Int'l*, pg. 6434
MOTIONWORKS GMBH—See Bavaria Film GmbH; *Int'l*, pg. 899
MOTIS BRANDS, INC.—See Prospect Hill Growth Partners, L.P.; *U.S. Private*, pg. 3288
MOTISONS JEWELLERS LIMITED; *Int'l*, pg. 5053
MOTIVACTION LLC—See Augeo Affinity Marketing, Inc.; *U.S. Private*, pg. 392
MOTIVA ENTERPRISES LLC—See Saudi Arabian Oil Company; *Int'l*, pg. 6590
MOTIVA ENTERPRISES LLC—See Shell plc; *Int'l*, pg. 6796
MOTIVATING THE MASSES, INC.; *U.S. Public*, pg. 1477
MOTIVATIONAL SYSTEMS INC.; *U.S. Private*, pg. 2796
MOTIVATION DESIGN LLC; *U.S. Private*, pg. 2796
MOTIVATORS INC.; *U.S. Private*, pg. 2796
MOTIVCOM LTD—See Sodexo S.A.; *Int'l*, pg. 7045
MOTIVE DRILLING TECHNOLOGIES, INC.—See Helmerich & Payne, Inc.; *U.S. Public*, pg. 1024
MOTIVE EQUIPMENT, INC.—See Westinghouse Air Brake Technologies Corporation; *U.S. Public*, pg. 2358
MOTIVE INTERACTIVE INC.; *U.S. Private*, pg. 2796
MOTIVE OFFSHORE GROUP LTD—See H2 Equity Partners B.V.; *U.S. Private*, pg. 3199
MOTIVE PARTNERS GP, LLC; *U.S. Private*, pg. 2796
MOTIVE PARTS COMPANY FMP; *U.S. Private*, pg. 2796
MOTIVEPOWER, INC.—See Westinghouse Air Brake Technologies Corporation; *U.S. Public*, pg. 2358
MOTIVE—See Project: Worldwide, Inc.; *U.S. Private*, pg. 3281
MOTIV, INC.; *U.S. Private*, pg. 2796
MOTIVITY LABS, INC.—See Magellanic Cloud Limited; *Int'l*, pg. 4637
MOTIVITY SOLUTIONS LLC—See Intercontinental Exchange, Inc.; *U.S. Public*, pg. 1141
MOTIVUS—See AN Global I.T. S.A.P.I. de C.V.; *U.S. Private*, pg. 271
THE MOTLEY FOOL, INC.; *U.S. Private*, pg. 4081
MOTOBIZNES ONLINE SDN. BHD.—See Silverlake Axis Ltd.; *Int'l*, pg. 6926
MOTOCAB SARL; *Int'l*, pg. 5053
MOTOCAR SERVICE COMPANY (MSC)—See KKR & Co. Inc.; *U.S. Public*, pg. 1255
MOTOCAR SERVICE COMPANY (MSC)—See The Goldman Sachs Group, Inc.; *U.S. Public*, pg. 2079
MOTOCROSS TOYOTA; *U.S. Private*, pg. 2796
MOTODYNAMICS LTD.—See Motodynamics S.A.; *Int'l*, pg. 5053
MOTODYNAMICS S.A.; *Int'l*, pg. 5053
MOTODYNAMICS SRL—See Motodynamics S.A.; *Int'l*, pg. 5053
MOTOFIT LIMITED—See Advanex Inc.; *Int'l*, pg. 163
MOTOGEN CO.; *Int'l*, pg. 5053
MOTO, INC.; *U.S. Private*, pg. 2796
MOTO ITALIA SRL—See Pierer Konzerngesellschaft mbH; *Int'l*, pg. 5863

MOTOMACHI PARKING ACCESS CO., LTD.—See Nippon Telegraph & Telephone Corporation; *Int'l*, pg. 5343
MOTOMAN ROBOTEC D.O.O.—See Yaskawa Electric Corporation; *Int'l*, pg. 8569
MOTOMAN ROBOTEC GMBH—See Yaskawa Electric Corporation; *Int'l*, pg. 8569
MOTOMAN ROBOTICS EUROPE AB—See Yaskawa Electric Corporation; *Int'l*, pg. 8569
MOTOMAN ROBOTICS FINLAND OY—See Yaskawa Electric Corporation; *Int'l*, pg. 8569
MOTOMCO; *U.S. Private*, pg. 2796
MOTOMOVA INC.; *U.S. Public*, pg. 1477
MOTONIC CORPORATION - DAEGU FACTORY—See MOTONIC CORPORATION; *Int'l*, pg. 5053
MOTONIC CORPORATION; *Int'l*, pg. 5053
MOTONIC INDIA AUTOMOTIVE PRIVATE LIMITED—See MOTONIC CORPORATION; *Int'l*, pg. 5053
MOTO PALIC S.R.O.—See Scott Sports SA; *Int'l*, pg. 6652
MOTO-PFOHE EOOD—See Sumitomo Corporation; *Int'l*, pg. 7269
MOTORAIN CO., LTD.; *Int'l*, pg. 5054
MOTOR APPLIANCE CORPORATION; *U.S. Private*, pg. 2796
MOTORBOATING—See Bonnier AB; *Int'l*, pg. 1108
MOTORBODIES LUTON LIMITED—See General Motors Company; *U.S. Public*, pg. 928
MOTORCADE INDUSTRIES LTD.; *Int'l*, pg. 5054
MOTOR CAR AUTO CARRIERS, INC.; *U.S. Private*, pg. 2796
MOTORCARE SERVICES LIMITED—See The Innovation Group Ltd.; *Int'l*, pg. 7656
MOTORCAR PARTS OF AMERICA, INC.; *U.S. Public*, pg. 1477
MOTORCARS ACQUISITION IV, LLC—See Penske Automotive Group, Inc.; *U.S. Public*, pg. 1665
MOTORCARS ACQUISITION, LLC—See Penske Automotive Group, Inc.; *U.S. Public*, pg. 1665
MOTORCARS INTERNATIONAL INC.; *U.S. Private*, pg. 2797
MOTOR CENTER AUSTRIA GMBH—See DEUTZ AG; *Int'l*, pg. 2086
MOTOR CITY ACQUISITION CORP.; *U.S. Public*, pg. 1477
MOTOR CITY ELECTRIC CO., INC.; *U.S. Private*, pg. 2796
MOTOR CITY ELECTRIC TECHNOLOGY—See Motor City Electric Co., Inc.; *U.S. Private*, pg. 2796
MOTOR CITY ELECTRIC UTILITIES CO., INC.—See Motor City Electric Co., Inc.; *U.S. Private*, pg. 2796
MOTOR CITY FASTENER, LLC—See Kian Capital Partners, LLC; *U.S. Private*, pg. 2302
MOTOR CITY FASTENER, LLC—See Oakland Standard Co., LLC; *U.S. Private*, pg. 2985
MOTOR CITY INDUSTRIAL LLC—See Kian Capital Partners, LLC; *U.S. Private*, pg. 2302
MOTOR CITY INDUSTRIAL LLC—See Oakland Standard Co., LLC; *U.S. Private*, pg. 2985
MOTOR CITY POWERSPORTS, LLC; *U.S. Private*, pg. 2797
MOTOR CITY STAMPING, INC.; *U.S. Private*, pg. 2797
MOTORCLEAN LTD.—See Mobeus Equity Partners LLP; *Int'l*, pg. 5008
MOTOR COACH INDUSTRIES INTERNATIONAL, INC.—See NFI Group Inc.; *Int'l*, pg. 5252
MOTOR COMPONENTS, LLC—See BAM Enterprises, Inc.; *U.S. Private*, pg. 463
MOTOR CONTROLS, INC.; *U.S. Private*, pg. 2797
MOTORCYCLE HOLDINGS LIMITED; *Int'l*, pg. 5054
MOTORCYCLE RIDING SCHOOL PTY LTD—See Motorcycle Holdings Limited; *Int'l*, pg. 5054
MOTORCYCLE SAFETY FOUNDATION, INC.; *U.S. Private*, pg. 2797
MOTORDATA RESEARCH CONSORTIUM SDN. BHD—See HeiTech Padu Berhad; *Int'l*, pg. 3326
MOTOREDUCTORES U.S., S.A. DE C.V.—See Emerson Electric Co.; *U.S. Public*, pg. 750
MOTOREN JACOBS GMBH—See KSB SE & Co. KGaA; *Int'l*, pg. 4313
MOTOREN STEFFENS GMBH—See Caterpillar, Inc.; *U.S. Public*, pg. 453
MOTOR & EQUIPMENT MANUFACTURERS ASSOCIATION; *U.S. Private*, pg. 2796
MOTORES & EQUIPOS S.A.; *Int'l*, pg. 5054
MOTORES JOHN DEERE S.A. DE C.V.—See Deere & Company; *U.S. Public*, pg. 647
MOTORES REYNOSA, S.A. DE C.V.—See Nidec Corporation; *Int'l*, pg. 5277
MOTORES U.S. DE MEXICO, S.A. DE C.V.—See Nidec Corporation; *Int'l*, pg. 5277
MOTOR EV, LLC—See The AES Corporation; *U.S. Public*, pg. 2032
MOTOREX AG LANGENTHAL—See FUCHS SE; *Int'l*, pg. 2804
MOTORFLUG BADEN-BADEN GMBH—See Airbus SE; *Int'l*, pg. 244
MOTOR FUEL GROUP LTD.—See Clayton, Dubilier & Rice, LLC; *U.S. Public*, pg. 926
MOTOR FUEL LIMITED—See Clayton, Dubilier & Rice, LLC; *U.S. Private*, pg. 926

THE MOTOR & GENERAL FINANCE LIMITED; *Int'l*, pg. 7668
MOTORIA BIL AB—See Bilia AB; *Int'l*, pg. 1029
MOTOR IMAGE (CAMBODIA) LTD.—See Tan Chong International Limited; *Int'l*, pg. 7452
MOTOR IMAGE CHINA LIMITED—See Tan Chong International Limited; *Int'l*, pg. 7452
MOTOR IMAGE ENTERPRISES PTE LTD—See Tan Chong International Limited; *Int'l*, pg. 7453
MOTOR IMAGE (HK) LIMITED—See Tan Chong International Limited; *Int'l*, pg. 7452
MOTOR IMAGE KOWLOON LIMITED—See Tan Chong International Limited; *Int'l*, pg. 7452
MOTOR IMAGE MALAYSIA SDN BHD—See Tan Chong International Limited; *Int'l*, pg. 7453
MOTOR IMAGE PILIPINAS, INC.—See Tan Chong International Limited; *Int'l*, pg. 7453
MOTOR IMAGE SUBARU (THAILAND) CO. LTD.—See Tan Chong International Limited; *Int'l*, pg. 7453
MOTOR IMAGE VIETNAM CO., LTD.—See Tan Chong International Limited; *Int'l*, pg. 7452
MOTORI MARINI LAMBORGHINI S.P.A.—See Porsche Automobil Holding SE; *Int'l*, pg. 5926
MOTOR INFORMATION SYSTEMS—See The Hearst Corporation; *U.S. Private*, pg. 928
MOTORI SOMMERSI RIAVVOLGIBILI S.R.L.—See Franklin Electric Co., Inc.; *U.S. Public*, pg. 878
MOTORISTS LIFE INSURANCE COMPANY—See Motorists Mutual Insurance Co.; *U.S. Private*, pg. 2797
MOTORISTS MUTUAL INSURANCE CO.; *U.S. Private*, pg. 2797
MOTORIT AB—See Bilia AB; *Int'l*, pg. 1029
MOTORK ITALIA S.R.L.—See Motork Plc; *Int'l*, pg. 5054
MOTORK PLC; *Int'l*, pg. 5054
THE MOTORLEASE CORPORATION; *U.S. Private*, pg. 4081
MOTOR MAGAZINE—See The Hearst Corporation; *U.S. Private*, pg. 4045
MOTOR MART AUTO SALES; *U.S. Private*, pg. 2797
MOTOR NORGE AS—See MEKO AB; *Int'l*, pg. 4807
MOTOR OIL (HELLAS) CORINTH REFINERIES S. A.; *Int'l*, pg. 5053
MOTOR OILS INC.—See Abercrombie Oil Company Incorporated; *U.S. Private*, pg. 38
MOTOROLA AB—See Motorola Solutions, Inc.; *U.S. Public*, pg. 1478
MOTOROLA ARABIA, INC.—See Motorola Solutions, Inc.; *U.S. Public*, pg. 1478
MOTOROLA ASIA LIMITED—See Motorola Solutions, Inc.; *U.S. Public*, pg. 1478
MOTOROLA AUSTRALIA PTY. LTD.—See Motorola Solutions, Inc.; *U.S. Public*, pg. 1478
MOTOROLA B.V.—See Motorola Solutions, Inc.; *U.S. Public*, pg. 1478
MOTOROLA CHILE S.A.—See Motorola Solutions, Inc.; *U.S. Public*, pg. 1478
MOTOROLA (CHINA) ELECTRONICS LTD.—See Motorola Solutions, Inc.; *U.S. Public*, pg. 1478
MOTOROLA COMERCIAL, S.A. DE C.V.—See Lenovo Group Limited; *Int'l*, pg. 4453
MOTOROLA DE COSTA RICA S.A.—See Motorola Solutions, Inc.; *U.S. Public*, pg. 1479
MOTOROLA DE MEXICO, S.A.—See Motorola Solutions, Inc.; *U.S. Public*, pg. 1479
MOTOROLA ELECTRONIC GMBH—See Motorola Solutions, Inc.; *U.S. Public*, pg. 1478
MOTOROLA ELECTRONICS SDN. BHD.—See Motorola Solutions, Inc.; *U.S. Public*, pg. 1478
MOTOROLA FINANCE EMEA LIMITED—See Motorola Solutions, Inc.; *U.S. Public*, pg. 1478
MOTOROLA GMBH—See Motorola Solutions, Inc.; *U.S. Public*, pg. 1478
MOTOROLA GMBH—See Motorola Solutions, Inc.; *U.S. Public*, pg. 1478
MOTOROLA INDUSTRIAL LTDA.—See Lenovo Group Limited; *Int'l*, pg. 4453
MOTOROLA ISRAEL LIMITED—See Motorola Solutions, Inc.; *U.S. Public*, pg. 1478
MOTOROLA LIMITED—See Motorola Solutions, Inc.; *U.S. Public*, pg. 1478
MOTOROLA MOBILITY CANADA LTD.—See Lenovo Group Limited; *Int'l*, pg. 4453
MOTOROLA MOBILITY ESPANA, S.L.—See Lenovo Group Limited; *Int'l*, pg. 4453
MOTOROLA MOBILITY GERMANY GMBH—See Lenovo Group Limited; *Int'l*, pg. 4453
MOTOROLA MOBILITY HOLDINGS, INC.—See Lenovo Group Limited; *Int'l*, pg. 4453
MOTOROLA MOBILITY ITALIA S.R.L.—See Lenovo Group Limited; *Int'l*, pg. 4453
MOTOROLA MOBILITY LLC—See Lenovo Group Limited; *Int'l*, pg. 4453
MOTOROLA MOBILITY UK LTD.—See Lenovo Group Limited; *Int'l*, pg. 4453
MOTOROLA NEW ZEALAND LIMITED—See Motorola Solutions, Inc.; *U.S. Public*, pg. 1478
MOTOROLA RECEIVABLES CORPORATION—See Motorola Solutions, Inc.; *U.S. Public*, pg. 1478

COMPANY NAME INDEX

MOTOROLA S.A.S.—See Motorola Solutions, Inc.; *U.S. Public*, pg. 1478
MOTOROLA SOLUTIONS ARGENTINA, S.A.—See Motorola Solutions, Inc.; *U.S. Public*, pg. 1478
MOTOROLA SOLUTIONS AUSTRALIA PTE. LTD.—See Motorola Solutions, Inc.; *U.S. Public*, pg. 1478
MOTOROLA SOLUTIONS CANADA INC.—See Motorola Solutions, Inc.; *U.S. Public*, pg. 1478
MOTOROLA SOLUTIONS (CHINA) CO. LTD.—See Motorola Solutions, Inc.; *U.S. Public*, pg. 1478
MOTOROLA SOLUTIONS CZ S.R.O.—See Motorola Solutions, Inc.; *U.S. Public*, pg. 1478
MOTOROLA SOLUTIONS ESPANA S.A.—See Motorola Solutions, Inc.; *U.S. Public*, pg. 1478
MOTOROLA SOLUTIONS FRANCE SAS—See Motorola Solutions, Inc.; *U.S. Public*, pg. 1478
MOTOROLA SOLUTIONS GERMANY GMBH—See Motorola Solutions, Inc.; *U.S. Public*, pg. 1478
MOTOROLA SOLUTIONS, INC.; *U.S. Public*, pg. 1477
MOTOROLA SOLUTIONS INDIA PVT. LTD.—See Motorola Solutions, Inc.; *U.S. Public*, pg. 1478
MOTOROLA SOLUTIONS ISRAEL LIMITED—See Motorola Solutions, Inc.; *U.S. Public*, pg. 1478
MOTOROLA SOLUTIONS ITALIA S.P.A.—See Motorola Solutions, Inc.; *U.S. Public*, pg. 1478
MOTOROLA SOLUTIONS MALAYSIA SDN. BHD.—See Motorola Solutions, Inc.; *U.S. Public*, pg. 1478
MOTOROLA SOLUTIONS SINGAPORE PTE LTD—See Motorola Solutions, Inc.; *U.S. Public*, pg. 1478
MOTOROLA SOLUTIONS SYSTEMS POLSKA SP. Z O.O.—See Motorola Solutions, Inc.; *U.S. Public*, pg. 1478
MOTOROLA SOLUTIONS VENTURE CAPITAL—See Motorola Solutions, Inc.; *U.S. Public*, pg. 1478
MOTOROLA TECHNOLOGY SDN. BHD.—See Motorola Solutions, Inc.; *U.S. Public*, pg. 1478
MOTOROLA TRADING CENTER PTE. LTD.—See Motorola Solutions, Inc.; *U.S. Public*, pg. 1478
MOTOROLA VENEZUELA—See Motorola Solutions, Inc.; *U.S. Public*, pg. 1479
MOTORPOINT GROUP PLC; *Int'l*, pg. 5054
MOTOR POWER FINLAND OY—See Tym Corporation; *Int'l*, pg. 7995
MOTOR PRESSE STUTTGART GMBH & CO. KG; *Int'l*, pg. 5054
MOTOR PRODUCTS CORPORATION—See Allient Inc.; *U.S. Public*, pg. 80
MOTOR PROPANE SERVICE, INC.—See Ferrellgas Partners, L.P.; *U.S. Public*, pg. 829
MOTOR RACING NETWORK, INC.—See National Association for Stock Car Auto Racing, Inc.; *U.S. Private*, pg. 2846
MOTOR REPRIS AUTOMOCIO S.L.—See General Motors Company; *U.S. Public*, pg. 927
MOTORS & ARMATURES, INC.; *U.S. Private*, pg. 2797
MOTORS AUCTION GROUP, INC.—See Copart, Inc.; *U.S. Public*, pg. 575
MOTORSAZAN COMPANY; *Int'l*, pg. 5054
MOTORS & DRIVES LLC—See Troy Industrial Solutions LLC; *U.S. Private*, pg. 4243
MOTOR SICH MIDDLE EAST SAIF—See Motor Sich PJSC; *Int'l*, pg. 5054
MOTOR SICH PJSC; *Int'l*, pg. 5054
MOTORS INSURANCE COMPANY LIMITED—See Stone Point Capital LLC; *U.S. Private*, pg. 3821
MOTOR; *U.S. Private*, pg. 2796
MOTORSPORT.COM, INC.—See Enerfund, LLC; *U.S. Private*, pg. 1393
MOTORSPORT GAMES INC.—See GMF Capital LLC; *U.S. Private*, pg. 1721
MOTORSPORT MARKETING, INC.—See Peterson Manufacturing Company Inc.; *U.S. Private*, pg. 3160
MOTORSPORT NETWORK, LLC—See GMF Capital LLC; *U.S. Private*, pg. 1721
MOTORSPORTS ACCEPTANCE CORPORATION—See National Association for Stock Car Auto Racing, Inc.; *U.S. Private*, pg. 2846
MOTOR TALAVERA SA—See Stellantis N.V.; *Int'l*, pg. 7202
MOTORTECH AMERICAS LLC—See Generac Holdings Inc.; *U.S. Public*, pg. 912
MOTORTECH GMBH—See Generac Holdings Inc.; *U.S. Public*, pg. 912
MOTORTECH POLSKA SP. Z.O.O.—See Generac Holdings Inc.; *U.S. Public*, pg. 912
MOTORTECH SHANGHAI CO., LTD.—See Generac Holdings Inc.; *U.S. Public*, pg. 912
MOTOR TREND GROUP, LLC—See Warner Bros. Discovery, Inc.; *U.S. Public*, pg. 2327
MOTOR TREND—See TEN: The Enthusiast Network, Inc.; *U.S. Private*, pg. 3964
MOTORTRONICS, INC.—See Standard Motor Products, Inc.; *U.S. Public*, pg. 1929
MOTOR TRUCK EQUIPMENT COMPANY; *U.S. Private*, pg. 2797
MOTOR TRUCKS INC.; *U.S. Private*, pg. 2797
MOTORVAC TECHNOLOGIES, INC., *Int'l*, pg. 5054
MOTOR VEHICLE ACCIDENT INDEMNIFICATION CORPORATION; *U.S. Private*, pg. 2797

MOTOR VILLAGE AUSTRIA GMBH—See Stellantis N.V.; *Int'l*, pg. 7198
MOTOR WERKS PARTNERS LP; *U.S. Private*, pg. 2797
MOTORWORLD AUTOMOTIVE GROUP—See Atlantic Automotive Corp.; *U.S. Private*, pg. 371
MOTORXCHANGE S.A.R.L.—See LKQ Corporation; *U.S. Public*, pg. 1335
MOTOSIKAL DAN ENJIN NASIONAL SDN. BHD.—See DRB-HICOM Berhad; *Int'l*, pg. 2202
MOTO S.P.A.—See Cremonini S.p.A.; *Int'l*, pg. 1838
MOTOSPORT, LLC—See Qurate Retail, Inc.; *U.S. Public*, pg. 1758
M.O. TOURIST CO., LTD.—See Mitsui O.S.K. Lines, Ltd.; *Int'l*, pg. 4989
MOTOVARIO CORPORATION—See Teco Electric & Machinery Co., Ltd.; *Int'l*, pg. 7518
MOTOVARIO GEAR SOLUTION PRIVATE LTD.—See Teco Electric & Machinery Co., Ltd.; *Int'l*, pg. 7518
MOTOVARIO INTERNATIONAL TRADING CO. LTD.—See Teco Electric & Machinery Co., Ltd.; *Int'l*, pg. 7518
MOTOVARIO S.P.A.—See Teco Electric & Machinery Co., Ltd.; *Int'l*, pg. 7518
MOTOWN GOSPEL—See Universal Music Group N.V.; *Int'l*, pg. 8079
MOTOYAMA ENG WORKS, LTD.—See Kurimoto Ltd; *Int'l*, pg. 4339
MOTRAC HANDLING & CLEANING N.V.-S.A.—See KKR & Co. Inc.; *U.S. Public*, pg. 1255
MOTRAC HANDLING & CLEANING N.V.-S.A.—See The Goldman Sachs Group, Inc.; *U.S. Public*, pg. 2079
MOTREX CO., LTD.; *Int'l*, pg. 5054
MOTRICITY, INC.—See Voltari Corporation; *U.S. Private*, pg. 4411
MOTRON A/S—See NIBE Industrier AB; *Int'l*, pg. 5261
MOTRUX INC.; *Int'l*, pg. 5054
MOTSENG INVESTMENT HOLDINGS (PTY) LTD.; *Int'l*, pg. 5054
MOTSENG WOMEN INVESTMENTS (PTY) LTD.—See Motseng Investment Holdings (Pty) Ltd.; *Int'l*, pg. 5054
MOTTA-INTERNACIONAL, S.A.; *Int'l*, pg. 5056
MOTT & CHACE SOTHEBY'S INTERNATIONAL REALTY; *U.S. Private*, pg. 2797
MOTT CHILDREN'S HEALTH CENTER; *U.S. Private*, pg. 2797
MOTT CORP.—See IDEX Corp; *U.S. Public*, pg. 1091
MOTTECH WATER SOLUTIONS LTD.—See MTI Wireless Edge Ltd.; *Int'l*, pg. 5070
MOTT MACDONALD AFRICA LIMITED—See Mott MacDonald Group Ltd.; *Int'l*, pg. 5055
MOTT MACDONALD AND CO., LLC—See Mott MacDonald Group Ltd.; *Int'l*, pg. 5056
MOTT MACDONALD AUSTRALIA PTY LIMITED—See Mott MacDonald Group Ltd.; *Int'l*, pg. 5055
MOTT MACDONALD (BEIJING) LIMITED—See Mott MacDonald Group Ltd.; *Int'l*, pg. 5055
MOTT MACDONALD BENTLEY LTD.—See Mott MacDonald Group Ltd.; *Int'l*, pg. 5055
MOTT MACDONALD (BULGARIA) EOOD—See Mott MacDonald Group Ltd.; *Int'l*, pg. 5055
MOTT MACDONALD CANADA LTD—See Mott MacDonald Group Ltd.; *Int'l*, pg. 5055
MOTT MACDONALD ENVIRONMENTAL CONSULTANTS LTD.—See Mott MacDonald Group Ltd.; *Int'l*, pg. 5055
MOTT MACDONALD FRANCE SAS—See Mott MacDonald Group Ltd.; *Int'l*, pg. 5055
MOTT MACDONALD GROUP LTD.; *Int'l*, pg. 5054
MOTT MACDONALD HONG KONG LTD.—See Mott MacDonald Group Ltd.; *Int'l*, pg. 5055
MOTT MACDONALD HUNGARIA KFT—See Mott MacDonald Group Ltd.; *Int'l*, pg. 5055
MOTT MACDONALD INC—See Mott MacDonald Group Ltd.; *Int'l*, pg. 5055
MOTT MACDONALD INTERNATIONAL LIMITED—See Mott MacDonald Group Ltd.; *Int'l*, pg. 5055
MOTT MACDONALD IRELAND LIMITED—See Mott MacDonald Group Ltd.; *Int'l*, pg. 5055
MOTT MACDONALD JAPAN K.K.—See Mott MacDonald Group Ltd.; *Int'l*, pg. 5055
MOTT MACDONALD KAZAKHSTAN LLP—See Mott MacDonald Group Ltd.; *Int'l*, pg. 5055
MOTT MACDONALD LIMITED—See Mott MacDonald Group Ltd.; *Int'l*, pg. 5055
MOTT MACDONALD LIMITED—See Mott MacDonald Group Ltd.; *Int'l*, pg. 5055
MOTT MACDONALD LLC—See Mott MacDonald Group Ltd.; *Int'l*, pg. 5055
MOTT MACDONALD (MALAYSIA) SDN. BHD—See Mott MacDonald Group Ltd.; *Int'l*, pg. 5055
MOTT MACDONALD MONGOLIA LLC—See Mott MacDonald Group Ltd.; *Int'l*, pg. 5055
MOTT MACDONALD NEW ZEALAND LIMITED—See Mott MacDonald Group Ltd.; *Int'l*, pg. 5055
MOTT MACDONALD NOMINEES LTD.—See Mott MacDonald Group Ltd.; *Int'l*, pg. 5055
MOTT MACDONALD NORGE AS—See Mott MacDonald Group Ltd.; *Int'l*, pg. 5055
MOTT MACDONALD PETTIT LIMITED—See Mott MacDonald Group Ltd.; *Int'l*, pg. 5055

MOUNTAIN ALLIANCE AG

MOTT MACDONALD (PHILIPPINES) INC—See Mott MacDonald Group Ltd.; *Int'l*, pg. 5055
MOTT MACDONALD POLAND SP Z.O.O.—See Mott MacDonald Group Ltd.; *Int'l*, pg. 5055
MOTT MACDONALD PRAHA, SPOL SRO—See Mott MacDonald Group Ltd.; *Int'l*, pg. 5056
MOTT MACDONALD PRIVATE LIMITED—See Mott MacDonald Group Ltd.; *Int'l*, pg. 5055
MOTT MACDONALD ROMANIA SRL—See Mott MacDonald Group Ltd.; *Int'l*, pg. 5055
MOTT MACDONALD SA LTD.—See Mott MacDonald Group Ltd.; *Int'l*, pg. 5055
MOTT MACDONALD S D.O.O.—See Mott MacDonald Group Ltd.; *Int'l*, pg. 5055
MOTT MACDONALD SINGAPORE PTE LTD.—See Mott MacDonald Group Ltd.; *Int'l*, pg. 5055
MOTT MACDONALD SOUTH AFRICA (PTY) LTD.—See Mott MacDonald Group Ltd.; *Int'l*, pg. 5055
MOTT MACDONALD (TAIWAN) LIMITED—See Mott MacDonald Group Ltd.; *Int'l*, pg. 5055
MOTT MACDONALD T ENGINEERING CONSULTANTS LIMITED—See Mott MacDonald Group Ltd.; *Int'l*, pg. 5056
MOTT MACDONALD (THAILAND) LIMITED—See Mott MacDonald Group Ltd.; *Int'l*, pg. 5055
MOTT MACDONALD UGANDA LIMITED—See Mott MacDonald Group Ltd.; *Int'l*, pg. 5056
MOTT MANUFACTURING LTD.; *Int'l*, pg. 5056
MOTTO FRANCHISING, LLC—See RE/MAX Holdings, Inc.; *U.S. Public*, pg. 1768
MOTT'S HOLDINGS, INC.; *U.S. Private*, pg. 2797
MOTTS SUPERMARKETS—See Mott's Holdings, Inc.; *U.S. Private*, pg. 2797
MOTUKEA INTERNATIONAL TERMINAL LIMITED—See International Container Terminal Services, Inc.; *Int'l*, pg. 3746
MOTUL DEUTSCHLAND GMBH—See Motul S.A.; *Int'l*, pg. 5056
MOTUL IBERICA SA—See Motul S.A.; *Int'l*, pg. 5056
MOTUL ITALIA SRL—See Motul S.A.; *Int'l*, pg. 5056
MOTUL S.A.; *Int'l*, pg. 5056
MOTUL U.S.A. INC.—See Motul S.A.; *Int'l*, pg. 5056
MOTUM AB—See Mitsubishi Electric Corporation; *Int'l*, pg. 4946
MOTUS GI HOLDINGS, INC.; *U.S. Public*, pg. 1479
MOTUS GROUP (UK) PROPRIETARY LIMITED—See Motus Holdings Limited; *Int'l*, pg. 5056
MOTUS HOLDINGS LIMITED; *Int'l*, pg. 5056
MOTUS, LLC—See Thoma Bravo, L.P.; *U.S. Private*, pg. 4150
THE MOTWANE MANUFACTURING COMPANY PVT. LTD—See NAGPUR POWER & INDUSTRIES LIMITED; *Int'l*, pg. 5129
MOUAT COMPANY INC.; *U.S. Private*, pg. 2797
MOUAWAD INTERNATIONAL GOLD JEWELLERY COMPANY—See Mondera.com; *U.S. Private*, pg. 2769
MOUCHEL EWAN LIMITED—See Kier Group plc; *Int'l*, pg. 4159
MOUCHEL LIMITED—See Kier Group plc; *Int'l*, pg. 4159
MOUKA LIMITED—See Abraaj Capital Limited; *Int'l*, pg. 67
MOULAGES INDUSTRIELS DU HAUT BUGEY; *Int'l*, pg. 5056
MOULAGES PLASTIQUES INDUSTRIELS DE L'ESSONNE SARL—See HEICO Corporation; *U.S. Public*, pg. 1020
MOULDAGRAPH CORPORATION; *U.S. Private*, pg. 2797
MOULINS SOUFFLET PANTIN S.A.—See Etablissements J. Soufflet; *Int'l*, pg. 2519
MOULINVEST SA; *Int'l*, pg. 5056
MOULTON INSURANCE AGENCY, INC.—See Peter C. Foy & Associates Insurance Services, Inc.; *U.S. Private*, pg. 3158
MOULTON LOGISTICS MANAGEMENT—See Rotunda Capital Partners LLC; *U.S. Private*, pg. 3488
MOULTON-NIGUEL WATER DISTRICT; *U.S. Private*, pg. 2797
MOULTRIE DIE CAST—See Joseph L. Ertl, Inc.; *U.S. Private*, pg. 2237
MOULURE ALEXANDRIA MOULDING INC.—See Specialty Building Products, LLC; *U.S. Private*, pg. 3749
MOUND TECHNOLOGIES, INC.—See Heartland, Inc.; *U.S. Private*, pg. 1901
MOUNTADAM VINEYARDS PTY LIMITED—See LVMH Moet Hennessy Louis Vuitton SE; *Int'l*, pg. 4604
MOUNTAIN ACQUISITION COMPANY, LLC; *U.S. Private*, pg. 2798
MOUNTAIN AGENCY INC.; *U.S. Private*, pg. 2798
MOUNTAIN AIR CARGO INC.—See Air T, Inc.; *U.S. Public*, pg. 67
MOUNTAIN AIR COMPRESSOR INC.—See Hitachi, Ltd.; *Int'l*, pg. 3417
MOUNTAIN AIR MECHANICAL CONTRACTORS, INC.—See DLVA, Inc.; *U.S. Private*, pg. 1248
MOUNTAIN AIR SYSTEMS, INC.—See Investcorp Holdings B.S.C.; *U.S. Private*, pg. 3775
MOUNTAIN ALLIANCE AG; *Int'l*, pg. 5057
MOUNTAIN AREA COUNCIL—See Dairy Farmers of America, Inc.; *U.S. Private*, pg. 1146

MOUNTAIN AREA HEALTH EDUCATION CENTER — CORPORATE AFFILIATIONS

MOUNTAIN AREA HEALTH EDUCATION CENTER; *U.S. Private*, pg. 2798
MOUNTAIN AVIATION, INC.—See Wheels Up Experience Inc.; *U.S. Public*, pg. 2366
MOUNTAIN BROADCASTING, LLC—See Northwest Broadcasting, Inc.; *U.S. Private*, pg. 2959
MOUNTAIN CAPITAL MANAGEMENT AG; *Int'l*, pg. 5057
MOUNTAIN CAPITAL PARTNERS, LP; *U.S. Private*, pg. 2799
MOUNTAIN CEMENT COMPANY—See Eagle Materials Inc.; *U.S. Public*, pg. 702
MOUNTAIN CHINA RESORTS (HOLDING) LIMITED; *Int'l*, pg. 5057
MOUNTAIN COMMERCE BANCORP, INC.; *U.S. Public*, pg. 1479
MOUNTAIN COMMERCE BANK—See Mountain Commerce Bancorp, Inc.; *U.S. Public*, pg. 1479
MOUNTAIN COMPANY INC.; *U.S. Private*, pg. 2799
THE MOUNTAIN CORPORATION—See Gladstone Management Corporation; *U.S. Private*, pg. 1705
MOUNTAIN COUNTRY, LLC—See CHS INC.; *U.S. Public*, pg. 492
MOUNTAIN CREEK RESORT, INC.—See Crystal Springs Resort; *U.S. Private*, pg. 1115
MOUNTAIN CREST BREWING CO.; *Int'l*, pg. 5057
MOUNTAIN DEVELOPMENT CORP.; *U.S. Private*, pg. 2799
MOUNTAIN DIVISION - CVH, LLC—See HCA Healthcare, Inc.; *U.S. Public*, pg. 1003
MOUNTAINEER CAPITAL, LP—See Alpha Natural Resources, Inc.; *U.S. Private*, pg. 199
MOUNTAINEER CONTRACTORS INC.; *U.S. Private*, pg. 2801
MOUNTAINEER FABRICATORS INC.; *U.S. Private*, pg. 2801
MOUNTAINEER GAS COMPANY—See UGI Corporation; *U.S. Public*, pg. 2222
MOUNTAINEER HOMECARE, LLC—See UnitedHealth Group Incorporated; *U.S. Public*, pg. 2246
MOUNTAINEER PARK, INC.—See Century Casinos, Inc.; *U.S. Public*, pg. 474
MOUNTAIN ELECTRIC COOPERATIVE INC.; *U.S. Private*, pg. 2799
MOUNTAIN EMPIRE OIL COMPANY INC.; *U.S. Private*, pg. 2799
MOUNTAIN EMPIRE SURGERY CENTER, L.P.—See Tenet Healthcare Corporation; *U.S. Public*, pg. 2011
MOUNTAIN ENTERPRISES, INC.—See CRH plc; *Int'l*, pg. 1847
MOUNTAIN ENVIRONMENTAL SERVICES, INC.—See Palladium Equity Partners, LLC; *U.S. Private*, pg. 3078
MOUNTAIN EQUIPMENT CO-OPERATIVE; *Int'l*, pg. 5057
MOUNTAIN FINANCIAL, INC.—See Nobility Homes, Inc.; *U.S. Public*, pg. 1531
MOUNTAIN GAS RESOURCES, LLC—See Western Midstream Partners, LP; *U.S. Public*, pg. 2356
MOUNTAINGATE CAPITAL MANAGEMENT, L.P.; *U.S. Private*, pg. 2801
MOUNTAIN GLACIER LLC—See Primo Water Corporation; *U.S. Public*, pg. 1718
MOUNTAIN HARDWEAR, INC.—See Columbia Sportswear Company; *U.S. Public*, pg. 535
MOUNTAIN HIGH KNITWEAR LTD.—See CCP Fund III Management LLC; *U.S. Public*, pg. 801
MOUNTAIN HIGH LLC—See General Mills, Inc.; *U.S. Public*, pg. 922
MOUNTAIN HIGH PRODUCTS, LLC; *U.S. Private*, pg. 2799
MOUNTAIN HIGH TREE SERVICE, INC.—See Apax Partners LLP; *Int'l*, pg. 506
MOUNTAIN HOUSE—See OFD Foods, LLC; *U.S. Private*, pg. 3000
MOUNTAIN LAKE HOTEL—See Gal-Tex Hotel Corporation; *U.S. Private*, pg. 1635
MOUNTAINLAND SUPPLY COMPANY; *U.S. Private*, pg. 2801
MOUNTAIN LIFE INSURANCE COMPANY—See Forcht Group of Kentucky, Inc.; *U.S. Private*, pg. 1564
MOUNTAIN LUMBER COMPANY, INC.—See The Building Center, Inc.; *U.S. Private*, pg. 4002
MOUNTAIN MANAGERS, INC.—See Hammersmith Data Management, Inc.; *U.S. Private*, pg. 1849
MOUNTAIN MAN NUT & FRUIT CO.; *U.S. Private*, pg. 2799
MOUNTAIN MAN RESORTS INC.—See Moore Holdings Inc.; *U.S. Private*, pg. 2780
MOUNTAIN MECHANICAL CONTRACTORS INC.; *U.S. Private*, pg. 2799
MOUNTAIN MINING & SUPPLY COMPANY INC.—See Appalachian Tire Products Inc.; *U.S. Private*, pg. 295
MOUNTAINONE BANK—See Mountain One Financial Partners; *U.S. Private*, pg. 2799
MOUNTAIN ONE FINANCIAL PARTNERS; *U.S. Private*, pg. 2799
MOUNTAIN PACIFIC BANCORP, INC.; *U.S. Public*, pg. 1479
MOUNTAIN PACIFIC MACHINERY; *U.S. Private*, pg. 2799
MOUNTAIN PARK HEALTH CENTER; *U.S. Private*, pg. 2799

MOUNTAIN PARTNERS AG—See Mountain Capital Management AG; *Int'l*, pg. 5057
MOUNTAIN PRAIRIE, LLC—See Hormel Foods Corporation; *U.S. Public*, pg. 1054
MOUNTAIN PRESS PTY LTD—See Nine Entertainment Co. Holdings Limited; *Int'l*, pg. 5299
MOUNTAIN PRODUCTIONS, INC.; *U.S. Private*, pg. 2799
MOUNTAIN PROVINCE DIAMONDS INC; *Int'l*, pg. 5057
MOUNTAIN PURE BEVERAGE COMPANY; *U.S. Private*, pg. 2799
MOUNTAIN RANGE RESTAURANT LLC; *U.S. Private*, pg. 2799
MOUNTAIN RUG MILLS, INC.—See CAP Carpet, Inc.; *U.S. Private*, pg. 737
MOUNTAIN RURAL TELEPHONE COOPERATIVE CORPORATION, INC.; *U.S. Private*, pg. 2799
MOUNTAIN SECURE SYSTEMS (MSS)—See Phillips Service Industries, Inc. (PSI); *U.S. Private*, pg. 3171
MOUNTAINSIDE COAL COMPANY INC.—See White Energy Company Limited; *Int'l*, pg. 8398
MOUNTAINS PLUS OUTDOOR GEAR; *U.S. Private*, pg. 2801
MOUNTAIN SPORTS USA LLC—See Frasers Group plc; *Int'l*, pg. 2765
MOUNTAINSTAR BEHAVIORAL HEALTH, LLC—See HCA Healthcare, Inc.; *U.S. Public*, pg. 1003
MOUNTAINSTAR CARDIOLOGY ST. MARKS, LLC—See HCA Healthcare, Inc.; *U.S. Public*, pg. 1003
MOUNTAINSTAR CARDIOVASCULAR SERVICES, LLC—See HCA Healthcare, Inc.; *U.S. Public*, pg. 1003
MOUNTAINSTAR CARE PARTNERS ACO, LLC—See HCA Healthcare, Inc.; *U.S. Public*, pg. 1003
MOUNTAINSTAR CARE PARTNERS, LLC—See HCA Healthcare, Inc.; *U.S. Public*, pg. 1003
MOUNTAINSTAR GOLD INC.; *Int'l*, pg. 5057
MOUNTAINSTAR INTENSIVIST SERVICES, LLC—See HCA Healthcare, Inc.; *U.S. Public*, pg. 1003
MOUNTAINSTAR MEDICAL GROUP - CACHE VALLEY, LLC—See HCA Healthcare, Inc.; *U.S. Public*, pg. 1003
MOUNTAINSTAR MEDICAL GROUP NEUROSURGERY - ST. MARKS, LLC—See HCA Healthcare, Inc.; *U.S. Public*, pg. 1003
MOUNTAINSTAR MEDICAL GROUP TIMPANOGOS SPECIALTY CARE, LLC—See HCA Healthcare, Inc.; *U.S. Public*, pg. 1003
MOUNTAINSTAR OGDEN PEDIATRICS, LLC—See HCA Healthcare, Inc.; *U.S. Public*, pg. 1003
MOUNTAINSTAR SPECIALTY SERVICES, LLC—See HCA Healthcare, Inc.; *U.S. Public*, pg. 1003
MOUNTAINSTAR URGENT CARE, LLC—See HCA Healthcare, Inc.; *U.S. Public*, pg. 1003
MOUNTAIN STATE AUTO AUCTION INC.; *U.S. Private*, pg. 2799
MOUNTAIN STATE CARBON, LLC—See Cleveland-Cliffs, Inc.; *U.S. Public*, pg. 514
MOUNTAIN STATES EMPLOYERS COUNCIL, INC.; *U.S. Private*, pg. 2800
MOUNTAIN STATES HEALTH ALLIANCE; *U.S. Private*, pg. 2800
MOUNTAIN STATES INSURANCE COMPANY—See Donegal Group Inc.; *U.S. Public*, pg. 676
MOUNTAIN STATES PIPE & SUPPLY COMPANY; *U.S. Private*, pg. 2800
MOUNTAIN STATES STEEL, INC.—See INNOVATE Corp.; *U.S. Public*, pg. 1125
MOUNTAIN SUPPLY CO; *U.S. Private*, pg. 2800
MOUNTAIN TELECOMMUNICATIONS SALES INC.; *U.S. Private*, pg. 2800
THE MOUNTAIN TIMES—See Adams Publishing Group, LLC; *U.S. Private*, pg. 75
MOUNTAIN TOWER, LTD.—See LS telcom AG; *Int'l*, pg. 4570
MOUNTAIN-VALLEY BANCSHARES, INC.; *U.S. Private*, pg. 2800
MOUNTAIN VALLEY BANK, N.A.—See Mountain-Valley Bancshares, Inc.; *U.S. Private*, pg. 2801
MOUNTAIN VALLEY COMMUNITY BANK—See Piedmont Bancorp, Inc.; *U.S. Private*, pg. 3177
MOUNTAIN VALLEY EXPRESS CO; *U.S. Private*, pg. 2800
MOUNTAIN VALLEY MD HOLDINGS, INC.; *Int'l*, pg. 5057
MOUNTAIN VALLEY PRODUCE, LLC; *U.S. Private*, pg. 2800
MOUNTAIN VALLEY SPRING COMPANY, LLC—See Primo Water Corporation; *U.S. Public*, pg. 1718
MOUNTAIN VIEW CO-OP; *U.S. Private*, pg. 2800
MOUNTAIN VIEW COUNTRY CLUB, INC.—See Toll Brothers, Inc.; *U.S. Public*, pg. 2162
MOUNTAIN VIEW ELECTRIC ASSOCIATION; *U.S. Private*, pg. 2800
MOUNTAINVIEW ENERGY LTD.; *U.S. Public*, pg. 1479
MOUNTAIN VIEW EQUIPMENT CO. INC.; *U.S. Private*, pg. 2800
MOUNTAIN VIEW FORD LINCOLN; *U.S. Private*, pg. 2800
MOUNTAIN VIEW HOSPITAL, INC—See HCA Healthcare, Inc.; *U.S. Public*, pg. 1003
MOUNTAIN VIEW HOSPITAL, LLC—See Bain Capital, LP; *U.S. Private*, pg. 445

MOUNTAINVIEW HOSPITAL (PAYSON UT)—See HCA Healthcare, Inc.; *U.S. Public*, pg. 1003
MOUNTAIN VIEW HOSPITAL—See HCA Healthcare, Inc.; *U.S. Public*, pg. 1003
MOUNTAINVIEW HOSPITAL—See HCA Healthcare, Inc.; *U.S. Public*, pg. 1003
MOUNTAIN VIEW MARKETING INC.; *U.S. Private*, pg. 2800
MOUNTAIN VIEW MEDICAL GROUP—See DaVita Inc.; *U.S. Public*, pg. 641
MOUNTAIN VIEW NURSING, LLC—See Regional Health Properties, Inc.; *U.S. Public*, pg. 1776
MOUNTAIN VIEW PHYSICIAN PRACTICE, INC.—See Rennova Health, Inc.; *U.S. Public*, pg. 1783
MOUNTAINVIEW REGIONAL HOME HEALTH—See Community Health Systems, Inc.; *U.S. Public*, pg. 555
MOUNTAIN VIEW RENDERING COMPANY; *U.S. Private*, pg. 2800
MOUNTAIN VIEW TIRE & SERVICE CO; *U.S. Private*, pg. 2800
MOUNTAIN VIEW TITLE & ESCROW CO.—See Old Republic International Corporation; *U.S. Public*, pg. 1569
MOUNTAIN VISTA SENIOR LIVING, INC.—See The Ensign Group, Inc.; *U.S. Public*, pg. 2070
MOUNTAIN WAREHOUSE LTD.; *Int'l*, pg. 5057
MOUNTAIN WATER SYSTEMS, INC.—See New England Services Company; *U.S. Public*, pg. 1511
MOUNTAIN WEST AVIATION, LLC; *U.S. Private*, pg. 2800
MOUNTAIN WEST BANK—See Glacier Bancorp, Inc.; *U.S. Public*, pg. 939
MOUNTAIN WEST DISTRIBUTORS; *U.S. Private*, pg. 2800
MOUNTAIN WEST ENDOSCOPY CENTER—See HCA Healthcare, Inc.; *U.S. Public*, pg. 991
MOUNTAIN WEST FARM BUREAU MUTUAL INSURANCE COMPANY INC.; *U.S. Private*, pg. 2800
MOUNTAIN WEST, LLC; *U.S. Private*, pg. 2800
MOUNTAIN WEST LOGISTICS, LLC—See Vulcan Materials Company; *U.S. Public*, pg. 2313
MOUNTAINWEST OVERTHRUST PIPELINE, LLC—See The Williams Companies, Inc.; *U.S. Public*, pg. 2142
MOUNTAINWEST PIPELINE, LLC—See The Williams Companies, Inc.; *U.S. Public*, pg. 2142
MOUNTAIN WEST SURGERY CENTER, LLC—See HCA Healthcare, Inc.; *U.S. Public*, pg. 1003
MOUNTAIN WEST TELECOM INC.; *U.S. Private*, pg. 2800
MOUNTAIRE CORPORATION; *U.S. Private*, pg. 2801
MOUNT AIRY GAZETTE—See Nash Holdings LLC; *U.S. Private*, pg. 2835
MOUNT AIRY IMAGING CENTER, LLC—See RadNet, Inc.; *U.S. Public*, pg. 1761
MOUNT AUBURN CEMETERY; *U.S. Private*, pg. 2797
MOUNT BACHELOR EDUCATIONAL CENTER, INC.—See Acadia Healthcare Company, Inc.; *U.S. Public*, pg. 29
MOUNT BACHELOR VILLAGE DRIVE—See Brooks Resources Corporation; *U.S. Private*, pg. 664
MOUNT BURGESS MINING N.L.; *Int'l*, pg. 5056
MOUNT CARMEL PUBLIC UTILITY CO.; *U.S. Public*, pg. 1479
MOUNTCASTLE PTY LTD—See Hancock & Gore Ltd.; *Int'l*, pg. 3242
MOUNTCASTLE VEIN CENTERS INTERNATIONAL, INC.; *U.S. Private*, pg. 2801
MOUNT CLEMENS KIA; *U.S. Private*, pg. 2801
MOUNT COOK AIRLINE LIMITED—See Air New Zealand Limited; *Int'l*, pg. 239
MOUNT CRANMORE SKI RESORT, INC.—See Booth Creek Management Corporation; *U.S. Private*, pg. 616
MOUNTCREST LTD—See Dragon Ukrainian Properties & Development Plc; *Int'l*, pg. 2199
MOUNT DAKOTA ENERGY CORP.; *Int'l*, pg. 5056
MOUNT DESERT ISLAND BIOLOGICAL LABORATORY; *U.S. Private*, pg. 2798
MOUNT DORA ACE HARDWARE, INC.—See Ace Hardware Corporation; *U.S. Private*, pg. 56
MOUNT DORA FARMS DE HONDURAS SRL—See Seaboard Corporation; *U.S. Public*, pg. 1850
MOUNT DORA FARMS, INC.—See Seaboard Corporation; *U.S. Public*, pg. 1850
MOUNT DORA OPHTHALMOLOGY ASC, LLC—See KKR & Co. Inc.; *U.S. Public*, pg. 1246
MOUNTED MEMORIES, INC.—See Kynetic LLC; *U.S. Private*, pg. 2360
MOUNT ELIZABETH MEDICAL HOLDINGS LTD—See Khazanah Nasional Berhad; *Int'l*, pg. 4152
MOUNTFIELD BUILDING GROUP LTD—See U.K. Spac Plc; *Int'l*, pg. 7998
MOUNT FRANKLIN FOODS, LLC; *U.S. Private*, pg. 2798
MOUNT GIBSON IRON LIMITED; *Int'l*, pg. 5056
MOUNT GIBSON MINING LIMITED—See Mount Gibson Iron Limited; *Int'l*, pg. 5056
MOUNT HAMILL ELEVATOR; *U.S. Private*, pg. 2798
MOUNT HOOD MEADOWS OREGON LTD. PARTNERSHIP; *U.S. Private*, pg. 2798
MOUNT HOUSING & INFRASTRUCTURE LTD.; *Int'l*, pg. 5056
MOUNTING SYSTEMS GMBH—See Kawa Capital Management, Inc.; *U.S. Private*, pg. 2266

COMPANY NAME INDEX

MOUNT ISA MINES LIMITED—See Glencore plc; *Int'l*, pg. 2991
MOUNTJOY CHILTON MEDLEY LLP; *U.S. Private,* pg. 2801
MOUNT KELLETT CAPITAL MANAGEMENT LP; *U.S. Private,* pg. 2798
MOUNT KISCO TRANSFER STATION, INC.—See EQT AB; *Int'l,* pg. 2474
MOUNT LOGAN CAPITAL INC.; *Int'l,* pg. 5056
MOUNT LOGAN RESOURCES LTD.—See Inventus Mining Corp.; *Int'l,* pg. 3774
MOUNT NITTANY HEALTH SYSTEM; *U.S. Private,* pg. 2798
MOUNT NITTANY MEDICAL CENTER; *U.S. Private,* pg. 2798
MOUNT OLIVE LIVESTOCK MARKET; *U.S. Private,* pg. 2798
MOUNT OLIVET ROLLING ACRES; *U.S. Private,* pg. 2798
MOUNTPAC AB—See Beijer Alma AB; *Int'l,* pg. 943
MOUNT PLEASANT CAPITAL CORP.; *U.S. Private,* pg. 2798
MOUNT PLEASANT OUTPATIENT SURGERY CENTER, LLC—See Tenet Healthcare Corporation; *U.S. Public,* pg. 2004
MOUNT PLEASANT WATERWORKS; *U.S. Private,* pg. 2798
MOUNT POLLEY MINING CORPORATION—See Imperial Metals Corporation; *Int'l,* pg. 3635
MOUNTRAIL-WILLIAMS ELECTRIC COOPERATIVE; *U.S. Private,* pg. 2801
MOUNT RAINIER ACQUISITION CORP.; *U.S. Public,* pg. 1479
MOUNT RIDLEY MINES LTD; *Int'l,* pg. 5057
MOUNT ROBERTS TRAMWAY, LTD.—See Gold Belt Incorporated; *U.S. Private,* pg. 1727
MOUNT ROMMEL MINING LIMITED; *Int'l,* pg. 5057
MOUNT ROYAL PRINTING & COMMUNICATIONS, INC.; *U.S. Private,* pg. 2798
MOUNT SAINT JOSEPH; *U.S. Private,* pg. 2798
MOUNT SHIVALIK INDUSTRIES LIMITED; *Int'l,* pg. 5057
MOUNT SINAI MEDICAL CENTER; *U.S. Private,* pg. 2798
MOUNT SNOW, LTD.—See Vail Resorts, Inc.; *U.S. Public,* pg. 2271
MOUNT STEPHEN PROPERTIES INC.—See Canadian Pacific Kansas City Limited; *Int'l,* pg. 1285
MOUNT ST. MARY'S HOSPITAL OF NIAGARA FALLS; *U.S. Private,* pg. 2798
MOUNT THORLEY COAL LOADING PTY LTD.—See Peabody Energy Corporation; *U.S. Public,* pg. 1659
THE MOUNT VERNON COMPANY , INC.; *U.S. Private,* pg. 4081
MOUNT VERNON FIRE INSURANCE COMPANY—See Berkshire Hathaway Inc.; *U.S. Public,* pg. 319
THE MOUNT VERNON LADIES' ASSOCIATION OF THE UNION; *U.S. Private,* pg. 4081
MOUNT VERNON MEMORIAL PARK & MORTUARY—See Service Corporation International; *U.S. Public,* pg. 1870
MOUNT VERNON MILLS, INC., RIEGEL CONSUMER PRODUCTS DIV.—See R.B. Pamplin Corporation; *U.S. Private,* pg. 3334
MOUNT VERNON MILLS, INC., RIEGEL TEXTILE DIV. (ALTO)—See R.B. Pamplin Corporation; *U.S. Private,* pg. 3334
MOUNT VERNON MILLS, INC., RIEGEL TEXTILE DIV.—See R.B. Pamplin Corporation; *U.S. Private,* pg. 3334
MOUNT VERNON MILLS, INC.—See R.B. Pamplin Corporation; *U.S. Private,* pg. 3334
MOUNT VERNON MILLS, INC.—See R.B. Pamplin Corporation; *U.S. Private,* pg. 3334
MOUNT VERNON NEIGHBORHOOD HEALTH CENTER; *U.S. Private,* pg. 2798
MOUNT VERNON NEON—See Everbrite, LLC; *U.S. Private,* pg. 1437
MOUNT VERNON PRINTING COMPANY—See Chatham Asset Management, LLC; *U.S. Private,* pg. 863
MOUNTVIEW ESTATES PLC; *Int'l,* pg. 5057
MOUNTVILLE MILLS CANADA—See Mountville Mills Inc.; *U.S. Private,* pg. 2801
MOUNTVILLE MILLS CHINA CO.—See Mountville Mills Inc.; *U.S. Private,* pg. 2801
MOUNTVILLE MILLS EUROPE BVBA—See Mountville Mills Inc.; *U.S. Private,* pg. 2801
MOUNTVILLE MILLS INC.; *U.S. Private,* pg. 2801
MOUNTVILLE RUBBER COMPANY, LLC—See Mountville Mills Inc.; *U.S. Private,* pg. 2801
MOUNT WHEELER POWER INC; *U.S. Private,* pg. 2798
MOUNTZ, INC—See Snap-on Incorporated; *U.S. Public,* pg. 1897
MOUNTZ TORQUE LIMITED—See Snap-on Incorporated; *U.S. Public,* pg. 1897
MOURA SOLAR FARM SPV PTY LTD.—See Metlen Energy & Metals S.A.; *Int'l,* pg. 4855
MOURNING GLORY FUNERAL SERVICES INC.—See Service Corporation International; *U.S. Public,* pg. 1870
MOURY CONSTRUCT SA; *Int'l,* pg. 5058
MOUSAM VENTURES LLC; *U.S. Private,* pg. 2801
MOUSE COMPUTER CO., LTD.—See MCJ Co., Ltd.; *Int'l,* pg. 4759
MOUSER CUSTOM CABINETRY LLC—See Pfingsten Partners, LLC; *U.S. Private,* pg. 3164
MOUSER CUSTOM CABINETRY LLC—See Promus Holdings, LLC; *U.S. Private,* pg. 3284
MOUSER ELECTRONICS INC.—See Berkshire Hathaway Inc.; *U.S. Public,* pg. 316
MOUSER ELECTRONICS PTE. LTD.—See Berkshire Hathaway Inc.; *U.S. Public,* pg. 316
MOUSTIK GMBH—See Yoc AG; *Int'l,* pg. 8591
MOUSTIK SPRL—See Yoc AG; *Int'l,* pg. 8591
MOUVEMENT DES CAISSES DESJARDINS; *Int'l,* pg. 5058
MOUVENT AG—See Bobst Group S.A.; *Int'l,* pg. 1096
MOUVEX SASU—See Dover Corporation; *U.S. Public,* pg. 682
MOVABLE, INC.; *U.S. Private,* pg. 2801
MOVACO, S.A.—See Grifols, S.A.; *Int'l,* pg. 3084
MOVADIS SA—See Adecco Group AG; *Int'l,* pg. 137
MOVAD, LLC—See Strata Graphics, Inc.; *U.S. Private,* pg. 3833
MOVADO GROUP DEUTSCHLAND G.M.B.H.—See Movado Group, Inc.; *U.S. Public,* pg. 1479
MOVADO GROUP, INC.; *U.S. Public,* pg. 1479
MOVADO GROUP OF CANADA, INC.—See Movado Group, Inc.; *U.S. Public,* pg. 1480
MOVADO RETAIL GROUP, INC.—See Movado Group, Inc.; *U.S. Public,* pg. 1480
MOVADO WATCH COMPANY, S.A.—See Movado Group, Inc.; *U.S. Public,* pg. 1479
MOVANO INC.; *U.S. Public,* pg. 1480
MOVANT AB—See AcadeMedia AB; *Int'l,* pg. 77
MOVE ABOUT GROUP AB; *Int'l,* pg. 5058
MOVEA SAS—See TDK Corporation; *Int'l,* pg. 7489
MOVEBYBIKE EUROPE AB; *Int'l,* pg. 5058
MOVEDYNAMICS—See EAC Invest AS; *Int'l,* pg. 2262
MOVE, INC.—See Base Intelligence, Inc; *U.S. Private,* pg. 484
MOVE, INC.—See News Corporation; *U.S. Public,* pg. 1519
MOVEIX INC—See SeriesOne, LLC; *U.S. Private,* pg. 3613
MOVELIA TECNOLOGIAS, S.L.—See Mobico Group PLC; *Int'l,* pg. 5008
MOVELLA HOLDINGS INC.; *U.S. Public,* pg. 1480
MOVE LOGISTICS GROUP LIMITED; *Int'l,* pg. 5058
MOVEMENT INDUSTRIES CORP.; *U.S. Public,* pg. 1480
MOVEMENT MORTGAGE, LLC; *U.S. Private,* pg. 2802
MOVENPICK FOODS SWITZERLAND LTD.—See Movenpick Holding AG; *Int'l,* pg. 5058
MOVENPICK GASTRONOMIE SCHWEIZ AG—See Movenpick Holding AG; *Int'l,* pg. 5058
MOVENPICK HOLDING AG; *Int'l,* pg. 5058
MOVENPICK HOTELS & RESORTS AG—See Accor S.A.; *Int'l,* pg. 92
MOVENPICK HOTELS & RESORTS MANAGEMENT AG—See Accor S.A.; *Int'l,* pg. 92
MOVEO SOFTWARE GMBH—See PSI Software SE; *Int'l,* pg. 6017
MOVE-PRO USA INC.—See HI-Boy Group Inc.; *U.S. Private,* pg. 1931
MOVERA GMBH—See Thor Industries, Inc.; *U.S. Public,* pg. 2157
MOVERO, INC. - COLUMBUS—See Movero, Inc.; *U.S. Private,* pg. 2802
MOVERO, INC.; *U.S. Private,* pg. 2802
MOVE SOLUTIONS LTD.; *U.S. Private,* pg. 2801
MOVESTIC KAPITALFORVALTNING AB—See Chesnara Plc; *Int'l,* pg. 1472
MOVETEC OY—See Addtech AB; *Int'l,* pg. 134
MOVET OY—See IDEXX Laboratories, Inc.; *U.S. Public,* pg. 1093
MOVETRO S.R.L.—See Biesse S.p.A.; *Int'l,* pg. 1020
MOVE WITH US PLC; *Int'l,* pg. 5058
MOVEX, INC.; *U.S. Private,* pg. 2802
MOVIANTO BELGIUM NV—See Owens & Minor, Inc.; *U.S. Public,* pg. 1626
MOVIANTO CESKA REPUBLIKA SRO—See Owens & Minor, Inc.; *U.S. Public,* pg. 1626
MOVIANTO DEUTSCHLAND GMBH—See Walden Group; *Int'l,* pg. 8333
MOVIANTO ESPANA SL—See Owens & Minor, Inc.; *U.S. Public,* pg. 1626
MOVIANTO FRANCE SAS—See Owens & Minor, Inc.; *U.S. Public,* pg. 1626
MOVIANTO NORDIC APS—See Owens & Minor, Inc.; *U.S. Public,* pg. 1626
MOVIANTO SCHWEIZ GMBH—See Owens & Minor, Inc.; *U.S. Public,* pg. 1626
MOVIANTO SLOVENSKO SRO—See Owens & Minor, Inc.; *U.S. Public,* pg. 1626
MOVIANTO TRANSPORT SOLUTIONS LTD.—See Owens & Minor, Inc.; *U.S. Public,* pg. 1626
MOVIANTO UK LTD.—See Owens & Minor, Inc.; *U.S. Public,* pg. 1626
MOVIATEC GMBH—See EnBW Energie Baden-Wurttemberg AG; *Int'l,* pg. 2400
MOVIDA PARTICIPACOES S.A.—See JSL S.A.; *Int'l,* pg. 4013
MOVIE BRANDS INC.; *U.S. Private,* pg. 2802
THE MOVIE CHANNEL—See National Amusements, Inc.; *U.S. Private,* pg. 2843
MOVIE FACTS INC.; *U.S. Private,* pg. 2802
MOVIE GAMES SA; *Int'l,* pg. 5058
MOVIEMAX ITALIA S.R.L.—See Mondo TV S.p.A.; *Int'l,* pg. 5028
MOVI ERECORD CINE S.A.U.—See Atresmedia Corporacion de Medios de Comunicacion, S.A.; *Int'l,* pg. 693
THE MOVIE STUDIO, INC.; *U.S. Public,* pg. 2116
MOVIES UNLIMITED INC.; *U.S. Private,* pg. 2802
MOVIE TAVERN, INC.—See The Marcus Corporation; *U.S. Public,* pg. 2112
MOVIETICKETS.COM, LLC—See Comcast Corporation; *U.S. Public,* pg. 540
MOVIETICKETS.CO.UK, LTD.—See Comcast Corporation; *U.S. Public,* pg. 540
MOVIE TRADING COMPANY—See Live Ventures Incorporated; *U.S. Public,* pg. 1332
MOVIL@CCESS, S.A. DE C.V.—See Grupo Salinas, S.A. de C.V.; *Int'l,* pg. 3135
MOVILNET—See Compania Anonima Nacional Telefonos de Venezuela; *Int'l,* pg. 1748
MOVING CO., LTD.—See Marui Group Co., Ltd.; *Int'l,* pg. 4713
MOVING.COM, INC.—See News Corporation; *U.S. Public,* pg. 1519
MOVING CONTENT SOLUTIONS PTE LTD.—See Hakuhodo DY Holdings Incorporated; *Int'l,* pg. 3222
MOVING IMAGE TECHNOLOGIES, INC.; *U.S. Public,* pg. 1480
THE MOVING PICTURE COMPANY LTD.—See Vantiva SA; *Int'l,* pg. 8131
MOVINGPLACE, LLC—See Porch Group, Inc.; *U.S. Public,* pg. 1702
MOVING SOLUTIONS, INC.—See ArcBest Corporation; *U.S. Public,* pg. 180
MOVINN A/S; *Int'l,* pg. 5058
MOVIR N.V.—See NN Group N.V.; *Int'l,* pg. 5393
MOVISTA INC.; *U.S. Private,* pg. 2802
MOVIUS INTERACTIVE CORPORATION—See Movius Interactive Corporation; *U.S. Private,* pg. 2802
MOVIUS INTERACTIVE CORPORATION; *U.S. Private,* pg. 2802
MOVOMATIC SA—See Marposs S.p.A.; *Int'l,* pg. 4699
MOVOMECH AB—See Amplex AB; *Int'l,* pg. 434
MOVOMECH PRONOMIC GMBH—See Amplex AB; *Int'l,* pg. 434
MOVORA LLC—See Vimian Group AB; *Int'l,* pg. 8208
MOVOTO LLC; *U.S. Private,* pg. 2802
MOWAG GMBH—See General Dynamics Corporation; *U.S. Public,* pg. 914
MOWAT CONSTRUCTION COMPANY; *U.S. Private,* pg. 2802
MOWI ASA; *Int'l,* pg. 5058
MOWI BELGIUM NV—See Mowi ASA; *Int'l,* pg. 5059
MOWI BRETAGNE S.A.S.—See Mowi ASA; *Int'l,* pg. 5059
MOWI CANADA WEST INC.—See Mowi ASA; *Int'l,* pg. 5059
MOWI CHILE S.A.—See Mowi ASA; *Int'l,* pg. 5059
MOWI CUISERY SAS—See Mowi ASA; *Int'l,* pg. 5059
MOWI DUCKTRAP LLC—See Mowi ASA; *Int'l,* pg. 5059
MOWI DUNKERQUE SAS—See Mowi ASA; *Int'l,* pg. 5059
MOWI FRANCE SAS—See Mowi ASA; *Int'l,* pg. 5059
MOWI FRANCE SAS—See Mowi ASA; *Int'l,* pg. 5059
MOWI IRELAND LTD.—See Mowi ASA; *Int'l,* pg. 5059
MOWI ITALIA S.R.L.—See Mowi ASA; *Int'l,* pg. 5059
MOWI JAPAN CO., LTD.—See Mowi ASA; *Int'l,* pg. 5059
MOWI JAPAN K.K.—See Mowi ASA; *Int'l,* pg. 5059
MOWI LABRUS AS—See Mowi ASA; *Int'l,* pg. 5059
MOWI LEMMER BV—See Mowi ASA; *Int'l,* pg. 5059
MOWI SCOTLAND LIMITED—See Mowi ASA; *Int'l,* pg. 5059
MOWI SCOTLAND LTD.—See Mowi ASA; *Int'l,* pg. 5059
MOWI SINGAPORE PTE LTD—See Mowi ASA; *Int'l,* pg. 5058
MOWI SINGAPORE PTE. LTD.—See Mowi ASA; *Int'l,* pg. 5059
MOWI—See Mowi ASA; *Int'l,* pg. 5059
MOWI STERK B.V.—See Mowi ASA; *Int'l,* pg. 5059
MOWI TURKEY SU URUNLERI TICARET A.S.—See Mowi ASA; *Int'l,* pg. 5059
MOWI TURKIYE SU URUNLERI TICARET A.S.—See Mowi ASA; *Int'l,* pg. 5059
MOWI USA HOLDING LLC—See Mowi ASA; *Int'l,* pg. 5059
MOWI USA LLC—See Mowi ASA; *Int'l,* pg. 5059
MOWI VIETNAM COMPANY LTD.—See Mowi ASA; *Int'l,* pg. 5059
MOWLA PTY. LTD—See AMP Limited; *Int'l,* pg. 433
MOW LIMITED—See Top Standard Corporation; *Int'l,* pg. 7813
MOWL USA LLC—See Mowi ASA; *Int'l,* pg. 5060
MOW POWER, INC.—See Teamshares Inc.; *U.S. Private,* pg. 3951
MOWREY ELEVATOR CO., INC.; *U.S. Private,* pg. 2802
MOX BANK LIMITED—See Standard Chartered PLC; *Int'l,* pg. 7167

MOWREY ELEVATOR CO., INC.   CORPORATE AFFILIATIONS

MOXIAN (HONG KONG) LIMITED—See Abits Group Inc.; *Int'l*, pg. 62
MOXIE INTERACTIVE INC.—See Publicis Groupe S.A.; *Int'l*, pg. 6114
MOXIE INTERACTIVE—See Publicis Groupe S.A.; *Int'l*, pg. 6114
MOXIE INTERACTIVE—See Publicis Groupe S.A.; *Int'l*, pg. 6114
MOXIE MEDIA MN, LLC—See Daggett Ventures, LLC; *U.S. Private*, pg. 1144
MOXIE SOFTWARE GERMANY—See NICE Ltd.; *Int'l*, pg. 5265
MOXIE SOFTWARE, INC.—See NICE Ltd.; *Int'l*, pg. 5265
MOXIE SOFTWARE UK—See NICE Ltd.; *Int'l*, pg. 5265
MOXIE SOZO; *U.S. Private*, pg. 2802
MOXIWORKS, LLC—See Vector Capital Management, L.P.; *U.S. Private*, pg. 4351
MOXTEK, INC.—See Nippon Kayaku Co., Ltd.; *Int'l*, pg. 5321
MOXX B.V.—See Diebold Nixdorf, Inc.; *U.S. Public*, pg. 661
MOYA HOLDINGS ASIA LIMITED; *Int'l*, pg. 5060
MOYER & SON INC.; *U.S. Private*, pg. 2802
MOYER VINEYARDS INC; *U.S. Private*, pg. 2802
MOYGASHEL FURNISHINGS—See John Hogg & Co. Ltd.; *Int'l*, pg. 3978
MOY-ISOVER LTD.—See Compagnie de Saint-Gobain SA; *Int'l*, pg. 1725
MOYLAN ENGINEERING LIMITED—See CTI Engineering Co., Ltd.; *Int'l*, pg. 1871
MOYLE PETROLEUM COMPANY INC.; *U.S. Private*, pg. 2802
MOYNES FORD SALES LTD.; *Int'l*, pg. 5060
MOYNESS CARE HOME DUNDEE—See Balhousie Holdings Limited; *Int'l*, pg. 808
MOYNO, INC.—See NOV, Inc.; *U.S. Public*, pg. 1545
MOYO GROUP, INC.—See Kalio, Inc.; *U.S. Private*, pg. 2257
MOY PARK LIMITED—See JBS S.A.; *Int'l*, pg. 3919
MOZAIK KNJIGA ZAGREB—See Mladinska knjiga Zalozba, d.d.; *Int'l*, pg. 5003
MOZAMBIQUE LEAF TOBACCO, LIMITADA—See Universal Corporation; *U.S. Public*, pg. 2254
MOZ DESIGNS, INC.—See Armstrong World Industries, Inc.; *U.S. Public*, pg. 194
MOZEL DEVELOPMENT CORP.; *U.S. Private*, pg. 2802
MOZILLA CORPORATION—See Mozilla Foundation; *U.S. Private*, pg. 2803
MOZILLA FOUNDATION; *U.S. Private*, pg. 2802
MP2 ENERGY LLC—See Shell plc; *Int'l*, pg. 6800
MP3 S.R.L.—See Lindab International AB; *Int'l*, pg. 4504
MPAC GROUP PLC; *Int'l*, pg. 5060
MPAC LANGEN PTE. LTD.—See MPAC Group PLC; *Int'l*, pg. 5060
MPACT LIMITED; *Int'l*, pg. 5060
MPACT STRATEGIC CONSULTING LLC; *U.S. Private*, pg. 2803
MP.AGRO CO., LTD.—See Medipal Holdings Corporation; *Int'l*, pg. 4779
M.P. AGRO INDUSTRIES LIMITED; *Int'l*, pg. 4616
M-PAK, INC.; *U.S. Private*, pg. 2526
MPA SYSTEMS, LLC—See Black Diamond Group Limited; *Int'l*, pg. 1059
M-PATHY GMBH—See Verint Systems Inc.; *U.S. Public*, pg. 2281
MPAY, INC.; *U.S. Private*, pg. 2803
MPAY SA; *Int'l*, pg. 5060
MP BALANCE ENGINEERING—See AMETEK, Inc.; *U.S. Public*, pg. 118
THE MPB GROUP, LLC—See Waste Management, Inc.; *U.S. Public*, pg. 2332
MP BIOMEDICALS, LLC—See CECEP Environmental Protection Co., Ltd.; *Int'l*, pg. 1372
MPB TECHNOLOGIES, INC.; *Int'l*, pg. 5060
MPC CASH-WAY LUMBER CO., INC.; *U.S. Private*, pg. 2803
MPC CASH-WAY LUMBER CO. WILLIAMSTON, INC.—See MPC Cash-Way Lumber Co., Inc.; *U.S. Private*, pg. 2803
MPC CONTAINER SHIPS ASA; *Int'l*, pg. 5060
MPC ENERGY SOLUTIONS N.V.; *Int'l*, pg. 5060
MPC INC.—See CECO Environmental Corp.; *U.S. Public*, pg. 464
MPC MUNCHMEYER PETERSEN CAPITAL AG—See MPC Munchmeyer Petersen & Co. GmbH; *Int'l*, pg. 5061
MPC MUNCHMEYER PETERSEN & CO. GMBH; *Int'l*, pg. 5060
MPC MUNCHMEYER PETERSEN REAL ESTATE SERVICES B.V.—See MPC Munchmeyer Petersen & Co. GmbH; *Int'l*, pg. 5061
M.P. COLINET S.P.R.L.U.—See Park-Ohio Holdings Corp.; *U.S. Public*, pg. 1639
MPC PLUS INC; *Int'l*, pg. 5061
MPC PORT JOIN STOCK COMPANY—See The Van Cargoes & Foreign Trade Logistics Joint Stock Company; *Int'l*, pg. 7698

MPC REAL VALUE FUND VERWALTUNGSGESELLSCHAFT MBH—See MPC Munchmeyer Petersen & Co. GmbH; *Int'l*, pg. 5061
MPC RENDITE-FONDS LEBEN PLUS MANAGEMENT GMBH—See MPC Munchmeyer Petersen & Co. GmbH; *Int'l*, pg. 5061
MPC (SHANGHAI) DIGITAL TECHNOLOGY CO., LTD.—See Vantiva SA; *Int'l*, pg. 8130
MPC SP.Z.O.O.—See Bharti Enterprises Limited; *Int'l*, pg. 1012
MPDC GABON CO. LTD.—See Mitsubishi Corporation; *Int'l*, pg. 4939
MPD CHEMICALS LLC—See Entegris, Inc.; *U.S. Public*, pg. 777
MPD COMPONENTS—See MPD, Inc.; *U.S. Private*, pg. 2803
M & P DEVELOPMENT COMPANY—See Apartment Investment and Management Company; *U.S. Public*, pg. 144
MPD, INC.; *U.S. Private*, pg. 2803
MP DISPLAYS, LLC; *U.S. Private*, pg. 2803
MPDL LTD.—See Apollo Global Management, Inc.; *U.S. Public*, pg. 152
MPDL LTD.—See JSW Steel Ltd.; *Int'l*, pg. 4015
MPDV ASIA PTE. LTD.—See MPDV Mikrolab GmbH; *Int'l*, pg. 5061
MPDV MIKROLAB GMBH; *Int'l*, pg. 5061
MPDV S.A.R.L.—See MPDV Mikrolab GmbH; *Int'l*, pg. 5061
MPDV SCHWEIZ AG—See MPDV Mikrolab GmbH; *Int'l*, pg. 5061
MPDV SOFTWARE AND TECHNOLOGY SERVICES (SHANGHAI) CO., LTD.—See MPDV Mikrolab GmbH; *Int'l*, pg. 5061
MPDV USA INC.—See MPDV Mikrolab GmbH; *Int'l*, pg. 5061
MPEARLROCK LP—See MidOcean Partners, LLP; *U.S. Private*, pg. 2717
MPEARLROCK LP—See The Kroger Co.; *U.S. Public*, pg. 2108
MPEG LA LLC; *U.S. Private*, pg. 2804
MP&E, LLC—See TE Connectivity Ltd.; *Int'l*, pg. 7496
MP ENVIRONMENTAL SERVICES; *U.S. Private*, pg. 2803
MPE PARTNERS, LLC; *U.S. Private*, pg. 2803
MP EQUIPMENT, LLC—See The Middleby Corporation; *U.S. Public*, pg. 2114
M.P. EVANS GROUP PLC; *Int'l*, pg. 4616
MPF SYSTEMS LIMITED—See Royal Nirman Pvt Ltd.; *Int'l*, pg. 6413
MP GAYRIMENKUL YONETIM HIZMETLERI ANONIM SIRKETI—See Metro AG; *Int'l*, pg. 4859
MPG CROP SERVICES, LLC.—See Maine Potato Growers, Inc.; *U.S. Private*, pg. 2552
MPG LOGISTICS, INC.; *U.S. Private*, pg. 2804
MP GROUP INC.; *Int'l*, pg. 5060
MPG TRUCK & TRACTOR, INC.—See Maine Potato Growers, Inc.; *U.S. Private*, pg. 2552
MP HANKANG CO., LTD.; *Int'l*, pg. 5060
MPHASE TECHNOLOGIES, INC.; *U.S. Public*, pg. 1480
MPHASIS CONSULTING LIMITED—See Blackstone Inc.; *U.S. Public*, pg. 356
MPHASIS LIMITED—See Blackstone Inc.; *U.S. Public*, pg. 356
MPHB CAPITAL BERHAD; *Int'l*, pg. 5061
MPH CONSULTING SERVICES DMCC; *Int'l*, pg. 5061
MPH HEALTH CARE AG; *Int'l*, pg. 5061
MPH HOTELS, INC.; *U.S. Private*, pg. 2804
MPH INDUSTRIES, INC.—See MPD, Inc.; *U.S. Private*, pg. 2803
MP HUSKY CORPORATION—See Gower Corporation; *U.S. Private*, pg. 1747
MPI AMERICA, INC.—See MPI Corporation; *Int'l*, pg. 5062
MPI CORPORATION; *Int'l*, pg. 5062
MPI GENERALI INSURANS BERHAD—See Assicurazioni Generali S.p.A.; *Int'l*, pg. 647
MPI HOLDINGS, INC.; *U.S. Private*, pg. 2804
MPI HOLDINGS LTD; *Int'l*, pg. 5062
MPI, INC.—See Leggett & Platt, Incorporated; *U.S. Public*, pg. 1303
MPI INTERNATIONAL, INC.—See MW Universal Inc.; *U.S. Private*, pg. 2822
MPIL CORPORATION LIMITED; *Int'l*, pg. 5062
MPI MLIN D.D.; *Int'l*, pg. 5062
MPI NICKEL PTY. LTD.—See PJSC MMC Norilsk Nickel; *Int'l*, pg. 5882
MP INTERNATIONAL (ASIA PACIFIC) LTD.—See Pico Far East Holdings Limited; *Int'l*, pg. 5861
MP INTERNATIONAL (HONG KONG) LTD.—See Mitsubishi Chemical Group Corporation; *Int'l*, pg. 4931
M&P INTERNATIONAL MESS-UND RECHNERTECHNIK GMBH—See INDUS Holding AG; *Int'l*, pg. 3663
MP INTERNATIONAL PTE. LTD.—See Pico Far East Holdings Limited; *Int'l*, pg. 5861
MP INTERNATIONAL (SHANGHAI) PTE. LTD.—See Pico Far East Holdings Limited; *Int'l*, pg. 5861
MPIRICAL LIMITED—See Hexatronic Group AB; *Int'l*, pg. 3371
MP JUAREZ LLC—See Mitsubishi Paper Mills Limited; *Int'l*, pg. 4967

MPK EQUITY PARTNERS; *U.S. Private*, pg. 2804
THE M&P LAB, INC.—See Lucideon; *Int'l*, pg. 4573
MP-LOGISTICS CORPORATION—See Mitsubishi Chemical Group Corporation; *Int'l*, pg. 4935
MPL PLASTICS LTD.; *Int'l*, pg. 5062
MPLT HEALTHCARE, LLC; *U.S. Private*, pg. 2804
M PLUS CORPORATION—See Sony Group Corporation; *Int'l*, pg. 7102
MPLUS CORP.; *Int'l*, pg. 5062
MPLUS TECHNOLOGY CO., LTD.—See Cipherlab Co., Ltd.; *Int'l*, pg. 1616
MPLX LP—See Marathon Petroleum Corporation; *U.S. Public*, pg. 1364
MP MATERIALS CORP.—See SoftBank Group Corp.; *Int'l*, pg. 7053
MPM CAPITAL LLC; *U.S. Private*, pg. 2804
MPM CAPITAL - SAN FRANCISCO—See MPM Capital LLC; *U.S. Private*, pg. 2804
MPM-DURRANS REFRACOAT PVT LTD—See James Durrans & Sons Limited; *Int'l*, pg. 3875
MPM HOLDINGS INC.—See KCC Corporation; *Int'l*, pg. 4109
MPM HOLDINGS INC.—See SJL Partners LLC; *Int'l*, pg. 6969
MPM HOLDINGS INC.—See Wonik Corporation; *Int'l*, pg. 8448
MP MINERAL LTD.—See Access Industries, Inc.; *U.S. Private*, pg. 51
M.P.M. INTERNATIONAL OIL COMPANY B.V.—See LKQ Corporation; *U.S. Public*, pg. 1335
MPM PROPERTIES LLC—See Abu Dhabi Islamic Bank PJSC; *Int'l*, pg. 72
MPM S.R.L.—See Koch Industries, Inc.; *U.S. Private*, pg. 2335
MPM TECHNOLOGIES, INC.; *U.S. Public*, pg. 1480
MPO GROUP; *Int'l*, pg. 5062
MPORIUM GROUP PLC; *Int'l*, pg. 5062
MPO-RUMYANTSEV JSC—See Moscow Machine Building Plant Vpered JSC; *Int'l*, pg. 5050
MPOWER ELECTRONICS, INC.—See Jade Bird Fire Co., Ltd.; *Int'l*, pg. 3868
MPOWER GROUP LIMITED; *Int'l*, pg. 5062
MPOWER GROUP PTY. LIMITED—See Mpower Group Limited; *Int'l*, pg. 5062
MPOWER, INC.; *U.S. Private*, pg. 2804
MPOWER PRODUCTS PTY. LTD.—See Mpower Group Limited; *Int'l*, pg. 5062
MPOWER PROJECTS PTY. LTD.—See Mpower Group Limited; *Int'l*, pg. 5062
M-POWER SOLUTIONS PTY LTD—See DXC Technology Company; *U.S. Public*, pg. 696
MPP BETEILIGUNGSGESELLSCHAFT MBH—See Deutsche Bank Aktiengesellschaft; *Int'l*, pg. 2061
MPP GLOBAL SOLUTIONS LIMITED—See Aptitude Software Group Plc; *Int'l*, pg. 523
MP PUMPS, INC.—See KKR & Co. Inc.; *U.S. Public*, pg. 1239
MPR PLASTICS INC.—See Thunderbird LLC; *U.S. Private*, pg. 4166
MPR SERVICES, INC.—See ORG CHEM Group, LLC; *U.S. Private*, pg. 3041
MPS BUILDERS & MERCHANTS LTD.; *Int'l*, pg. 5062
MPS CAPITAL SERVICES BANCA PER LE IMPRESE S.P.A.—See Banca Monte dei Paschi di Siena S.p.A.; *Int'l*, pg. 815
MPS-CT LLC—See Mitsubishi Heavy Industries, Ltd.; *Int'l*, pg. 4955
MPS DEVELOPMENT INC—See Trimble, Inc.; *U.S. Public*, pg. 2190
MPS ENTERPRISES, INC.—See Winsupply, Inc.; *U.S. Private*, pg. 4545
MP SERVICES SP. Z O.O.—See ManpowerGroup Inc.; *U.S. Public*, pg. 1358
MPS EUROPA AG—See MPS Limited; *Int'l*, pg. 5063
MPS EUROPE SARL—See Monolithic Power Systems, Inc.; *U.S. Public*, pg. 1464
MPS FRANCE, S.A.R.L.—See Equistone Partners Europe Limited; *Int'l*, pg. 2486
MPS GERMANY GMBH—See Equistone Partners Europe Limited; *Int'l*, pg. 2486
MPS HOLLAND, INC.—See WestRock Company; *U.S. Public*, pg. 2362
MPS INFOTECNICS LIMITED; *Int'l*, pg. 5062
MPS INTERACTIVE SYSTEMS LIMITED—See MPS Limited; *Int'l*, pg. 5063
MPS INTERNATIONAL KOREA CO., LTD.—See Monolithic Power Systems, Inc.; *U.S. Public*, pg. 1464
MPS INTERNATIONAL (SHANGHAI) LTD.—See Monolithic Power Systems, Inc.; *U.S. Public*, pg. 1464
MPS INTERNATIONAL (TAIWAN) LTD.—See Monolithic Power Systems, Inc.; *U.S. Public*, pg. 1464
MPS JAPAN K.K.—See Monolithic Power Systems, Inc.; *U.S. Public*, pg. 1464
MPS LIMITED; *Int'l*, pg. 5062
MPS MEAT PROCESSING SYSTEMS B.V.—See Equistone Partners Europe Limited; *Int'l*, pg. 2486
MPS MEDIZINISCHE PERSONAL- UND SERVICEGESELLSCHAFT MBH KETTWIG—See Asklepios Kliniken GmbH & Co. KGaA; *Int'l*, pg. 623

COMPANY NAME INDEX

MPS NORTH AMERICA, INC.—See Equistone Partners Europe Limited; *Int'l*, pg. 2486
MPS RED MEAT SLAUGHTERING CO., LTD.—See Equistone Partners Europe Limited; *Int'l*, pg. 2486
MPS SOUTH PLAINFIELD, LLC—See WestRock Company; *U.S. Public*, pg. 2362
MPS SPAIN, S.A.U.—See Equistone Partners Europe Limited; *Int'l*, pg. 2486
MPS TECH SWITZERLAND SARL—See Monolithic Power Systems, Inc.; *U.S. Public*, pg. 1465
MP STORAGE & BLENDING—See Banner Chemicals Limited; *Int'l*, pg. 851
MP SYSTEMS, INC.—See Morris Group, Inc.; *U.S. Private*, pg. 2787
MPT OF ALLEN FCER, LLC—See Medical Properties Trust, Inc.; *U.S. Public*, pg. 1412
MPT OF DALLAS, LLC—See Medical Properties Trust, Inc.; *U.S. Public*, pg. 1412
MPT OF ST. LUKE'S LEAWOOD, LLC—See Medical Properties Trust, Inc.; *U.S. Public*, pg. 1412
MPT OF ST. LUKE'S OLATHE, LLC—See Medical Properties Trust, Inc.; *U.S. Public*, pg. 1412
MPT OF ST. LUKE'S PARALLEL PARKWAY, LLC—See Medical Properties Trust, Inc.; *U.S. Public*, pg. 1412
MPT OF ST. LUKE'S ROELAND PARK, LLC—See Medical Properties Trust, Inc.; *U.S. Public*, pg. 1412
MPT OF ST. LUKE'S SHAWNEE, LLC—See Medical Properties Trust, Inc.; *U.S. Public*, pg. 1412
MPT OF ST VINCENT AVON, LLC—See Medical Properties Trust, Inc.; *U.S. Public*, pg. 1412
MPT OF ST VINCENT BROWNSBURG, LLC—See Medical Properties Trust, Inc.; *U.S. Public*, pg. 1412
MPT OF ST VINCENT CASTLETON, LLC—See Medical Properties Trust, Inc.; *U.S. Public*, pg. 1412
MPT OF ST VINCENT INDIANAPOLIS SOUTH, LLC—See Medical Properties Trust, Inc.; *U.S. Public*, pg. 1412
MPT OF ST VINCENT NOBLESVILLE SOUTH, LLC—See Medical Properties Trust, Inc.; *U.S. Public*, pg. 1412
MPT OF ST VINCENT PLAINFIELD, LLC—See Medical Properties Trust, Inc.; *U.S. Public*, pg. 1412
MPT OPERATING PARTNERSHIP, L.P.—See Medical Properties Trust, Inc.; *U.S. Public*, pg. 1412
MPT SOLUTION CO., LTD.; *Int'l*, pg. 5063
MP VENTURES, INC.; *U.S. Private*, pg. 2803
MPV - MATERIALPRUFUNGS UND VERTRIEBS GMBH—See VINCI S.A.; *Int'l*, pg. 8224
MPW CONTAINER MANAGEMENT CORP.—See MPW Industrial Services Group, Inc.; *U.S. Private*, pg. 2804
MPW INDUSTRIAL CLEANING CORP.—See MPW Industrial Services Group, Inc.; *U.S. Private*, pg. 2804
MPW INDUSTRIAL SERVICES GROUP, INC.; *U.S. Private*, pg. 2804
MPW INDUSTRIAL SERVICES GROUP—See MPW Industrial Services Group, Inc.; *U.S. Private*, pg. 2804
MPW INDUSTRIAL SERVICES GROUP—See MPW Industrial Services Group, Inc.; *U.S. Private*, pg. 2804
MPW INDUSTRIAL SERVICES, LTD.—See MPW Industrial Services Group, Inc.; *U.S. Private*, pg. 2804
MPW INDUSTRIAL SERVICES OF INDIANA, LLC—See MPW Industrial Services Group, Inc.; *U.S. Private*, pg. 2804
MPW INDUSTRIAL WATER SERVICES, INC.—See MPW Industrial Services Group, Inc.; *U.S. Private*, pg. 2804
MPW MOVENPICK WEIN AG—See Movenpick Holding AG; *Int'l*, pg. 5058
MPX BIOCEUTICAL CORPORATION—See iAnthus Capital Holdings, Inc.; *U.S. Public*, pg. 1083
MPX INC.—See Windstream Holdings, Inc.; *U.S. Public*, pg. 2373
MPX INTERNATIONAL CORPORATION; *Int'l*, pg. 5063
MP ZHONGMAO INTERNATIONAL (SHANGHAI) PTE. LTD.—See Pico Far East Holdings Limited; *Int'l*, pg. 5861
MQ&C ADVERTISING & MARKETING; *U.S. Private*, pg. 2804
MQ HOLDING AB; *Int'l*, pg. 5063
MQI BRNO, SPOL. S R.O.—See WPP plc; *Int'l*, pg. 8465
MQ MANAGEMENT GMBH & CO.KG—See Jagenberg AG; *Int'l*, pg. 3870
MQ MEDICAL TECHNOLOGIES CORPORATION; *U.S. Private*, pg. 2804
M&Q PACKAGING CORPORATION—See M&Q Plastic Products, Inc.; *U.S. Private*, pg. 2525
M&Q PLASTIC PRODUCTS, INC.; *U.S. Private*, pg. 2525
MQ PORTFOLIO MANAGEMENT LIMITED—See Macquarie Group Limited; *Int'l*, pg. 4625
MQ RETAIL AB; *Int'l*, pg. 5063
MQSOFTWARE GMBH MIDDLEWARE SOLUTIONS—See KKR & Co. Inc.; *U.S. Public*, pg. 1241
MQ TECHNOLOGY BERHAD; *Int'l*, pg. 5063
MR2 GROUP, INC.; *U.S. Private*, pg. 2805
MRA GMBH—See AGRAVIS Raiffeisen AG; *Int'l*, pg. 215
MRAIL, INC.—See Manila Electric Company; *Int'l*, pg. 4671
MRA INTERNATIONAL, INC.; *U.S. Private*, pg. 2805
MR. ALAN'S MEN'S BOOTERY INC.—See Deichmann SE; *Int'l*, pg. 2005
MR. AMAZING LOANS CORPORATION; *U.S. Private*, pg. 2804

MR. AMOTO LAWN & TREE SERVICE, LLC—See Apax Partners LLP; *Int'l*, pg. 506
MR APPLE NEW ZEALAND LIMITED—See Scales Corporation Limited; *Int'l*, pg. 6611
MR. APPLIANCE LLC—See Harvest Partners L.P.; *U.S. Private*, pg. 1877
MRA SEARCH, INC.—See Cross Country Healthcare, Inc.; *U.S. Public*, pg. 595
MRA SYSTEMS INC.—See Temasek Holdings (Private) Limited; *Int'l*, pg. 7552
MRA-THE MANAGEMENT ASSOCIATION, INC.; *U.S. Private*, pg. 2805
MRB ACQUISITION CORP.—See Linde plc; *Int'l*, pg. 4505
MR BETEILIGUNGEN 14. GMBH—See Munchener Ruckversicherungs AG; *Int'l*, pg. 5089
MR BETEILIGUNGEN USD AG & CO. KG—See Munchener Ruckversicherungs AG; *Int'l*, pg. 5089
MRBL LIMITED—See Kier Group plc; *Int'l*, pg. 4159
MR. BLUE; *Int'l*, pg. 5063
MR BOGDANKA SP. Z O.O.—See Lubelski Wegiel BOGDANKA Spolka Akcyjna; *Int'l*, pg. 4572
MR. BOX LTD—See WillScot Mobile Mini Holdings Corp.; *U.S. Public*, pg. 2372
MR BRICOLAGE SA; *Int'l*, pg. 5063
MRC AGROTECH LIMITED; *Int'l*, pg. 5063
MRC ALLIED INC.; *Int'l*, pg. 5063
MRCB LAND SDN. BHD.—See Malaysian Resources Corporation Berhad; *Int'l*, pg. 4662
MRC CANADA ULC—See MRC Global Inc.; *U.S. Public*, pg. 1481
MRCE DISPOLOK GMBH—See Mitsui & Co., Ltd.; *Int'l*, pg. 4974
MRC ENERGY PIPING AS—See MRC Global Inc.; *U.S. Public*, pg. 1480
MR CENTRUM MELNICK, S.R.O.—See Centene Corporation; *U.S. Public*, pg. 469
MRC FLANGEFITT LIMITED—See MRC Global Inc.; *U.S. Public*, pg. 1480
MRC GLOBAL AUSTRALIA PTY LTD—See MRC Global Inc.; *U.S. Public*, pg. 1481
MRC GLOBAL (BELGIUM) NV—See MRC Global Inc.; *U.S. Public*, pg. 1480
MRC GLOBAL (CANADA) ULC—See MRC Global Inc.; *U.S. Public*, pg. 1480
MRC GLOBAL (FINLAND) OY—See MRC Global Inc.; *U.S. Public*, pg. 1480
MRC GLOBAL (FRANCE) SAS—See MRC Global Inc.; *U.S. Public*, pg. 1481
MRC GLOBAL (GERMANY) GMBH—See MRC Global Inc.; *U.S. Public*, pg. 1480
MRC GLOBAL INC.; *U.S. Public*, pg. 1480
MRC GLOBAL (ITALY) SRL—See MRC Global Inc.; *U.S. Public*, pg. 1481
MRC GLOBAL (KOREA) LIMITED—See MRC Global Inc.; *U.S. Public*, pg. 1481
MRC GLOBAL (NETHERLANDS) B.V.—See MRC Global Inc.; *U.S. Public*, pg. 1481
MRC GLOBAL (NEW ZEALAND) LIMITED—See MRC Global Inc.; *U.S. Public*, pg. 1481
MRC GLOBAL (SINGAPORE) PTE. LTD.—See MRC Global Inc.; *U.S. Public*, pg. 1481
MRC GLOBAL (SWEDEN) AB—See MRC Global Inc.; *U.S. Public*, pg. 1481
MRC GLOBAL (THAILAND) COMPANY LIMITED—See MRC Global Inc.; *U.S. Public*, pg. 1481
MRC GLOBAL (US) INC.—See MRC Global Inc.; *U.S. Public*, pg. 1481
MRC GOLF, INC.—See Mitsubishi Chemical Group Corporation; *Int'l*, pg. 4933
MRC HOLDINGS, INC.—See Citigroup Inc.; *U.S. Public*, pg. 504
MRC HOLDINGS, LTD.—See Mitsubishi Chemical Group Corporation; *Int'l*, pg. 4931
MRC HONG KONG CO., LTD.—See Mitsubishi Chemical Group Corporation; *Int'l*, pg. 4931
MR. CHRISTMAS INC.; *U.S. Private*, pg. 2804
MR. CHRISTMAS LIMITED—See Mr. Christmas Inc.; *U.S. Private*, pg. 2805
MRC MANAGEMENT COMPANY—See MRC Global Inc.; *U.S. Public*, pg. 1481
MRC MANUFACTURING, INC.—See Lanzo Construction Company Inc.; *U.S. Private*, pg. 2391
MRC MARSH RISK CONSULTING GMBH—See Marsh & McLennan Companies, Inc.; *U.S. Public*, pg. 1377
MRC MEDICAL COMMUNICATIONS; *U.S. Private*, pg. 2805
MRC MSD ENGINEERING PTE. LTD.—See MRC Global Inc.; *U.S. Public*, pg. 1481
MR. COOPER GROUP INC.; *U.S. Public*, pg. 1480
MRC POLYMERS, INC.; *U.S. Private*, pg. 2805
MRC RENSUI ASIA PTE LTD—See Mitsubishi Chemical Group Corporation; *Int'l*, pg. 4933
MRC SMART TECHNOLOGY SOLUTIONS, INC.—See Xerox Holdings Corporation; *U.S. Public*, pg. 2388
MRC SOLBERG & ANDERSEN AS—See MRC Global Inc.; *U.S. Public*, pg. 1481
MRC SYSTEMS FZE—See ADDvise Group AB; *Int'l*, pg. 136

MRC TEAMTRADE AS—See MRC Global Inc.; *U.S. Public*, pg. 1481
MRC TRANSMARK B.V.—See MRC Global Inc.; *U.S. Public*, pg. 1481
MRC TRANSMARK GROUP B.V.—See MRC Global Inc.; *U.S. Public*, pg. 1481
MRC TRANSMARK HOLDINGS UK LTD.—See MRC Global Inc.; *U.S. Public*, pg. 1481
MRC TRANSMARK ITALY SRL—See MRC Global Inc.; *U.S. Public*, pg. 1481
MRC TRANSMARK KAZAKHSTAN LLP—See MRC Global Inc.; *U.S. Public*, pg. 1481
MRC TRANSMARK LIMITED—See MRC Global Inc.; *U.S. Public*, pg. 1481
MRC TRANSMARK NV—See MRC Global Inc.; *U.S. Public*, pg. 1481
MRC TRANSMARK—See MRC Global Inc.; *U.S. Public*, pg. 1481
MRC VALVE AUTOMATION CENTER—See MRC Global Inc.; *U.S. Public*, pg. 1481
M.R. DANIELSON ADVERTISING LLC; *U.S. Private*, pg. 2529
MRD (CENTRAL) SDN. BHD.—See Mr D.I.Y. Group (M) Berhad; *Int'l*, pg. 5063
MR/DD BOARD, INC.; *U.S. Private*, pg. 2805
MR&D INSTITUTE S.R.L.—See Gewiss S.p.A.; *Int'l*, pg. 2955
MR D.I.Y. GROUP (M) BERHAD; *Int'l*, pg. 5063
MR. DOLLAR SDN. BHD.—See Mr D.I.Y. Group (M) Berhad; *Int'l*, pg. 5063
M-REAL CORPORATION, BOARD DIVISION—See Metsaliitto Osuuskunta; *Int'l*, pg. 4864
M-REAL CORPORATION CORPORATE ADMINISTRATION—See Metsaliitto Osuuskunta; *Int'l*, pg. 4864
M-REAL CORPORATION PACKAGING GROUP—See Metsaliitto Osuuskunta; *Int'l*, pg. 4864
M-REAL FINLAND—See Metsaliitto Osuuskunta; *Int'l*, pg. 4864
M-REAL FRANCE SAS—See Metsaliitto Osuuskunta; *Int'l*, pg. 4864
M-REAL S.A.—See Metsaliitto Osuuskunta; *Int'l*, pg. 4864
MRE CONSULTING, INC.; *U.S. Private*, pg. 2805
MRE-III-PROYECTO CINCO, SOCIMI, S.A.; *Int'l*, pg. 5063
MREIT INC.; *Int'l*, pg. 5063
MR. ELECTRIC LLC—See Harvest Partners L.P.; *U.S. Private*, pg. 1877
M&R ENVIRONMENTAL LTD.—See BC Partners LLP; *Int'l*, pg. 924
MR ERWERBS GMBH & CO KG—See Wienerberger AG; *Int'l*, pg. 8405
M-RESOURCES GROUP LIMITED; *Int'l*, pg. 4614
MRESULT CORP.; *U.S. Private*, pg. 2805
MRF CORP LTD.—See MRF Limited; *Int'l*, pg. 5064
MRF LANKA (P) LTD.—See MRF Limited; *Int'l*, pg. 5064
MR FLEET S.R.L.—See Sesa S.p.A.; *Int'l*, pg. 6728
MRF LIMITED; *Int'l*, pg. 5064
MR. FORMAL INC.; *U.S. Private*, pg. 2805
MR. GASKET COMPANY; *U.S. Private*, pg. 2805
MR. GASKET INC.—See Mr. Gasket Company; *U.S. Private*, pg. 2805
MR. GASKET MALLORY PRODUCTS DIVISION—See Mr. Gasket Company; *U.S. Private*, pg. 2805
MR. GATTI'S, L.P.—See Sovrano LLC; *U.S. Private*, pg. 3743
MRG ATX HOLDINGS, LLC—See Hyatt Hotels Corporation; *U.S. Public*, pg. 1078
MRG CRW HOLDINGS, LLC—See Hyatt Hotels Corporation; *U.S. Public*, pg. 1078
MRG ENTERTAINMENT, INC.—See L.F.P., Inc.; *U.S. Private*, pg. 2365
MRG LOS ANGELES, LLC—See W.H. Smith PLC; *Int'l*, pg. 8322
MRG MASSNAHMETRAGER MUNCHEN-RIEM GMBH—See BayernLB Holding AG; *Int'l*, pg. 914
MRG METALS LIMITED; *Int'l*, pg. 5064
MRG SACRAMENTO, LLC—See W.H. Smith PLC; *Int'l*, pg. 8322
M.R.G. SYSTEMS LIMITED—See Panther Securities PLC; *Int'l*, pg. 5731
MR. HANDYMAN INTERNATIONAL, LLC—See Harvest Partners L.P.; *U.S. Private*, pg. 1877
M&R HOLDINGS INC.; *U.S. Private*, pg. 2525
MRI BOTSWANA LIMITED; *Int'l*, pg. 5064
MRI CO., LTD.—See Marui Group Co., Ltd.; *Int'l*, pg. 4713
MRI FLEXIBLE PACKAGING COMPANY—See First Atlantic Capital Ltd.; *U.S. Private*, pg. 1513
MRIGLOBAL; *U.S. Private*, pg. 2805
MRI & IMAGING OF GEORGIA—See Novant Health, Inc.; *U.S. Private*, pg. 2967
MRI RESEARCH ASSOCIATES, INC.—See Mitsubishi Research Institute, Inc.; *Int'l*, pg. 4968
MRI SOFTWARE LIMITED—See GI Manager L.P.; *U.S. Private*, pg. 1693
MRI SOFTWARE, LLC—See GI Manager L.P.; *U.S. Private*, pg. 1693
MRI TRADING AG—See PSA Corporation Pte Ltd.; *Int'l*, pg. 6014

MRIGLOBAL — CORPORATE AFFILIATIONS

MRK CORPORATION—See Nichia Steel Works Co., Ltd.; *Int'l*, pg. 5266
MRK HOLDINGS INC.; *Int'l*, pg. 5064
MRK INDUSTRIES, INC.—See Armstrong World Industries, Inc.; *U.S. Public*, pg. 194
MRL MANNESMANNROHREN LOGISTIC GMBH—See HPI AG; *Int'l*, pg. 3500
MR. MAGIC CAR WASH INC.—See Incline MGMT Corp.; *U.S. Private*, pg. 2053
MR MAX HOLDINGS LTD.; *Int'l*, pg. 5063
MRM BRAZIL—See The Interpublic Group of Companies, Inc.; *U.S. Public*, pg. 2098
MRM CHINA—See The Interpublic Group of Companies, Inc.; *U.S. Public*, pg. 2098
MRM CONSTRUCTION SERVICES, INC.; *U.S. Private*, pg. 2805
MRM GILLESPIE—See The Interpublic Group of Companies, Inc.; *U.S. Public*, pg. 2098
MRM LONDON—See The Interpublic Group of Companies, Inc.; *U.S. Public*, pg. 2098
MRM MANCHESTER—See The Interpublic Group of Companies, Inc.; *U.S. Public*, pg. 2098
MRM/MCCANN CHINA—See The Interpublic Group of Companies, Inc.; *U.S. Public*, pg. 2098
MRM/MCCANN—See The Interpublic Group of Companies, Inc.; *U.S. Public*, pg. 2098
MRM MEXICO—See The Interpublic Group of Companies, Inc.; *U.S. Public*, pg. 2098
MRM MINING AB / EPS SWEDEN AB—See Instalco AB; *Int'l*, pg. 3722
MRM MINING SERVICES PTY LTD.—See Runge ICT Group Pty Limited; *Int'l*, pg. 6427
MRM MUNICH—See The Interpublic Group of Companies, Inc.; *U.S. Public*, pg. 2098
MRM PARIS—See The Interpublic Group of Companies, Inc.; *U.S. Public*, pg. 2098
MRM PARTNERS DIALOGO—See The Interpublic Group of Companies, Inc.; *U.S. Public*, pg. 2098
MRM PHILIPPINES—See The Interpublic Group of Companies, Inc.; *U.S. Public*, pg. 2098
MRM PROPERTY & LIABILITY TRUST; *U.S. Private*, pg. 2805
MRM; *Int'l*, pg. 5064
MRM SPAIN—See The Interpublic Group of Companies, Inc.; *U.S. Public*, pg. 2098
MRM THAILAND—See The Interpublic Group of Companies, Inc.; *U.S. Public*, pg. 2098
MRM TURKEY—See The Interpublic Group of Companies, Inc.; *U.S. Public*, pg. 2098
MRM WORLDWIDE BRAZIL—See The Interpublic Group of Companies, Inc.; *U.S. Public*, pg. 2098
MRM WORLDWIDE HONG KONG—See The Interpublic Group of Companies, Inc.; *U.S. Public*, pg. 2098
MRM WORLDWIDE INDIA—See The Interpublic Group of Companies, Inc.; *U.S. Public*, pg. 2098
MRM WORLDWIDE NEW YORK—See The Interpublic Group of Companies, Inc.; *U.S. Public*, pg. 2098
MRM WORLDWIDE PARAGUAY—See The Interpublic Group of Companies, Inc.; *U.S. Public*, pg. 2098
MRM WORLDWIDE SINGAPORE—See The Interpublic Group of Companies, Inc.; *U.S. Public*, pg. 2098
MRM WORLDWIDE—See The Interpublic Group of Companies, Inc.; *U.S. Public*, pg. 2098
MRM WORLDWIDE—See The Interpublic Group of Companies, Inc.; *U.S. Public*, pg. 2098
MRM WORLDWIDE—See The Interpublic Group of Companies, Inc.; *U.S. Public*, pg. 2098
MRM WORLDWIDE—See The Interpublic Group of Companies, Inc.; *U.S. Public*, pg. 2098
MRM WORLDWIDE—See The Interpublic Group of Companies, Inc.; *U.S. Public*, pg. 2098
MRM WORLDWIDE—See The Interpublic Group of Companies, Inc.; *U.S. Public*, pg. 2098
MRM WORLDWIDE—See The Interpublic Group of Companies, Inc.; *U.S. Public*, pg. 2098
MRM WORLDWIDE—See The Interpublic Group of Companies, Inc.; *U.S. Public*, pg. 2098
MRM WORLDWIDE SPAIN—See The Interpublic Group of Companies, Inc.; *U.S. Public*, pg. 2098
MRO CORPORATION—See PCP Enterprise, L.P.; *U.S. Private*, pg. 3121
M ROGERS DESIGN, INC.; *U.S. Private*, pg. 2523
MRO HOLDINGS LP; *U.S. Private*, pg. 2805
MRO JAPAN CO., LTD.—See JAMCO Corporation; *Int'l*, pg. 3874
MRO KOREA CO., LTD.—See SK Networks Co., Ltd.; *Int'l*, pg. 6974
MR. ONION CORP.; *Int'l*, pg. 5063
M.R. ORGANISATION LIMITED; *Int'l*, pg. 4617
MRO-TEK REALTY LIMITED; *Int'l*, pg. 5064
MRO-TEK TECHNOLOGIES PRIVATE LIMITED—See MRO-TEK Realty Limited; *Int'l*, pg. 5064
MRP AGRO LIMITED; *Int'l*, pg. 5064
MR. PAPERBACK; *U.S. Private*, pg. 2805
MR PARKVIEW HOLDING CORPORATION—See Munchener Ruckversicherungs AG; *Int'l*, pg. 5089
MR. PAYROLL CORPORATION—See FirstCash Holdings, Inc.; *U.S. Public*, pg. 849
MRP CONSULT GMBH; *Int'l*, pg. 5064
MRP INVESTMENTS LTD.; *Int'l*, pg. 5064

MRPI PIPES SDN. BHD.—See YLI Holdings Berhad; *Int'l*, pg. 8590
MR POPRAD S.R.O.—See Centene Corporation; *U.S. Public*, pg. 469
MR PRICE GROUP LIMITED; *Int'l*, pg. 5063
M&R PRINTING EQUIPMENT INC.—See M&R Holdings Inc.; *U.S. Private*, pg. 2525
MRP S.A.—See TPG Capital, L.P.; *U.S. Public*, pg. 2174
MR RENT-INVESTMENT GMBH—See Munchener Ruckversicherungs AG; *Int'l*, pg. 5089
MR. ROOF HOLDING COMPANY LLC.; *U.S. Private*, pg. 2805
MR. ROOTER LLC—See Harvest Partners L.P.; *U.S. Private*, pg. 1877
M&R SALES & SERVICE INC.—See M&R Holdings Inc.; *U.S. Private*, pg. 2525
M&R SALES & SERVICE INC.—See M&R Holdings Inc.; *U.S. Private*, pg. 2525
MRS BAIRD'S BAKERIES BUSINESS TRUST; *U.S. Private*, pg. 2806
MRS. BAIRD'S BAKERIES, INC.—See Grupo Bimbo, S.A.B. de C.V.; *Int'l*, pg. 3122
MRS. BEASLEYS LLC—See KA Industries Inc.; *U.S. Private*, pg. 2253
MRS. BECTOR'S FOOD SPECIALITIES LTD.; *Int'l*, pg. 5064
MRS BIOUL S.A.—See Apollo Global Management, Inc.; *U.S. Public*, pg. 147
MRS. CLARK'S FOODS L.C.; *U.S. Private*, pg. 2806
MRS. CUBBISON'S KITCHEN, LLC—See The Pritzker Group - Chicago, LLC; *U.S. Private*, pg. 4099
MR. SERVICE CO., LTD.—See Yoshinoya Holdings Co., Ltd.; *Int'l*, pg. 8600
MRS. FIELDS FAMOUS BRANDS, LLC—See Capricorn Holdings, Inc.; *U.S. Public*, pg. 745
MRS. FIELDS GIFTS, INC.—See Capricorn Holdings, Inc.; *U.S. Private*, pg. 745
MRS. FIELDS' ORIGINAL COOKIES, INC.—See Capricorn Holdings, Inc.; *U.S. Private*, pg. 745
MRS. GERRY'S KITCHEN, INC.; *U.S. Private*, pg. 2806
MRS. GOOCH'S NATURAL FOOD MARKETS, INC.—See Amazon.com, Inc.; *U.S. Public*, pg. 91
MRS. GREEN'S NATURAL MARKETS—See The Catalyst Capital Group Inc.; *Int'l*, pg. 7631
MR. SHOWER DOOR INC.; *U.S. Private*, pg. 2805
MRSI AUTOMATION (SHENZHEN) CO., LTD.—See Mycronic AB; *Int'l*, pg. 5112
MRSI SYSTEMS, LLC—See Mycronic AB; *Int'l*, pg. 5112
MRS LOGISTICA S.A.; *Int'l*, pg. 5064
MRS MAC'S PTY. LTD.; *Int'l*, pg. 5064
MRS. NELSON'S BOOK FAIR COMPANY—See Scholastic Corporation; *U.S. Public*, pg. 1847
MRS OIL NIGERIA PLC; *Int'l*, pg. 5064
MR SOLAR GMBH & CO. KG—See Munchener Ruckversicherungs AG; *Int'l*, pg. 5089
MR. SPECIAL SUPERMARKETS INC.; *U.S. Private*, pg. 2805
MR SUNSTROM GMBH; *Int'l*, pg. 5063
M.R. TANNER DEVELOPMENT & CONSTRUCTION; *U.S. Private*, pg. 2529
MRT-ENGINES B.V.—See LKQ Corporation; *U.S. Public*, pg. 1335
MRT INC.; *Int'l*, pg. 5064
MR. TIRE, INC.—See Monro, Inc.; *U.S. Public*, pg. 1465
MRT MANUFACTURING, INC.—See Utility One Source L.P.; *U.S. Private*, pg. 4326
M.R.T. POLSKA SP. Z O.O.—See LKQ Corporation; *U.S. Public*, pg. 1335
M. RUBIN & SONS INC.; *U.S. Private*, pg. 2527
MRUGESH TRADING LIMITED; *Int'l*, pg. 5064
MRV COMMUNICATIONS AMERICAS, INC.—See ADTRAN Holdings, Inc.; *U.S. Public*, pg. 44
MRV COMMUNICATIONS, INC. - LITTLETON—See ADTRAN Holdings, Inc.; *U.S. Public*, pg. 44
MRV ENGENHARIA E PARTICIPACOES S.A.; *Int'l*, pg. 5064
MR. WHEELS, INC.—See AutoNation, Inc.; *U.S. Public*, pg. 236
MR. WHEELS SOLUTIONS, LLC—See AutoNation, Inc.; *U.S. Public*, pg. 236
MR. YOUTH—See Publicis Groupe S.A.; *Int'l*, pg. 6103
MRY US LLC—See Publicis Groupe S.A.; *Int'l*, pg. 6102
MR ZILINA S.R.O.—See Centene Corporation; *U.S. Public*, pg. 469
MSA ADVERTISING & PUBLIC RELATIONS; *U.S. Private*, pg. 2806
MSA AFRICA (PTY.) LTD.—See MSA Safety Incorporated; *U.S. Public*, pg. 1481
MSA AIRCRAFT PRODUCTS, INC.—See Aero Shade Technologies, Inc.; *U.S. Private*, pg. 118
M.SAAS LANKA (PRIVATE) LIMITED—See Multi-Chem Limited; *Int'l*, pg. 5082
MSA A.S.—See PAO TMK; *Int'l*, pg. 5732
MSA-AUER VERTRIEBS GMBH—See MSA Safety Incorporated; *U.S. Public*, pg. 1482
MSA AUSTRALIA PTY. LIMITED—See MSA Safety Incorporated; *U.S. Public*, pg. 1481
MSA BELGIUM NV—See MSA Safety Incorporated; *U.S. Public*, pg. 1482

MSAB INCORPORATED—See Micro Systemation AB; *Int'l*, pg. 4878
MSAB JAPAN K.K.—See Micro Systemation AB; *Int'l*, pg. 4878
MSA (BRITAIN) LIMITED—See MSA Safety Incorporated; *U.S. Public*, pg. 1481
MSA CANADA—See MSA Safety Incorporated; *U.S. Public*, pg. 1481
MSA CO., LTD.—See Meidensha Corporation; *Int'l*, pg. 4798
MSA DE CHILE, EQUIPOS DE SEGURIDAD LTDA.—See MSA Safety Incorporated; *U.S. Public*, pg. 1482
MSA DEL PERU S.A.C.—See MSA Safety Incorporated; *U.S. Public*, pg. 1482
MSA DE MEXICO, S.A. DE C.V.—See MSA Safety Incorporated; *U.S. Public*, pg. 1482
MS&AD INSURANCE GROUP HOLDINGS, INC.; *Int'l*, pg. 5065
MS&AD INTERRISK RESEARCH INSTITUTE & CONSULTING, INC.—See MS&AD Insurance Group Holdings, Inc.; *Int'l*, pg. 5066
MSA DO BRASIL EQUIPAMENTOS E INSTRUMENTOS DE SEGURANCA LTDA.—See MSA Safety Incorporated; *U.S. Public*, pg. 1482
MSA EGYPT LLC—See MSA Safety Incorporated; *U.S. Public*, pg. 1481
MSA EUROPE HOLDINGS GMBH—See MSA Safety Incorporated; *U.S. Public*, pg. 1481
M.S.A. FORD SALES LTD.; *Int'l*, pg. 4617
M'S AGENCY CO., LTD.—See MTG Co., Ltd.; *Int'l*, pg. 5070
MSA HONG KONG LTD.—See MSA Safety Incorporated; *U.S. Public*, pg. 1482
MSA INDIA LIMITED—See MSA Safety Incorporated; *U.S. Public*, pg. 1482
MSA INTERNATIONAL, INC.—See MSA Safety Incorporated; *U.S. Public*, pg. 1482
MSA ITALIANA S.P.A.—See MSA Safety Incorporated; *U.S. Public*, pg. 1482
MSA ITALIA S.R.L.—See MSA Safety Incorporated; *U.S. Public*, pg. 1482
MSA JAPAN LTD.—See MSA Safety Incorporated; *U.S. Public*, pg. 1482
M & S ALLOYS LTD.—See CRONIMET Holding GmbH; *Int'l*, pg. 1855
M/S. AMARAVATI INTERNATIONAL—See BASF SE; *Int'l*, pg. 884
MSA MIDDLE EAST FZE—See MSA Safety Incorporated; *U.S. Public*, pg. 1482
MS AMLIN AG—See MS&AD Insurance Group Holdings, Inc.; *Int'l*, pg. 5066
MS AMLIN CORPORATE SERVICES LIMITED—See MS&AD Insurance Group Holdings, Inc.; *Int'l*, pg. 5066
MS AMLIN INSURANCE SE—See MS&AD Insurance Group Holdings, Inc.; *Int'l*, pg. 5066
MS AMLIN PLC—See MS&AD Insurance Group Holdings, Inc.; *Int'l*, pg. 5066
MSA NEDERLAND, B.V.—See MSA Safety Incorporated; *U.S. Public*, pg. 1482
MSA NORDIC AB—See MSA Safety Incorporated; *U.S. Public*, pg. 1482
MSA OSTERREICH GMBH—See MSA Safety Incorporated; *U.S. Public*, pg. 1482
MSA PRODUKTION DEUTSCHLAND GMBH—See MSA Safety Incorporated; *U.S. Public*, pg. 1482
MSA PROFESSIONAL SERVICES, INC.; *U.S. Private*, pg. 2806
MSA SAFETY HUNGARY LTD.—See MSA Safety Incorporated; *U.S. Public*, pg. 1482
MSA SAFETY INCORPORATED; *U.S. Public*, pg. 1481
MSA SAFETY MALAYSIA SDN BHD—See MSA Safety Incorporated; *U.S. Public*, pg. 1482
MSA SAFETY POLAND SP.Z.O.O.—See MSA Safety Incorporated; *U.S. Public*, pg. 1482
MSA SAFETY ROMANIA S.R.L.—See MSA Safety Incorporated; *U.S. Public*, pg. 1482
MSA SAFETY SERVICES GMBH—See MSA Safety Incorporated; *U.S. Public*, pg. 1482
MSA SCHWEIZ GMBH—See MSA Safety Incorporated; *U.S. Public*, pg. 1482
MSA S.E. ASIA PTE. LTD.—See MSA Safety Incorporated; *U.S. Public*, pg. 1482
MSA SORDIN AB—See MSA Safety Incorporated; *U.S. Public*, pg. 1482
MSA SOURCING BV—See Cambria Africa Plc; *Int'l*, pg. 1269
MSA SPAIN, S.L.—See MSA Safety Incorporated; *U.S. Public*, pg. 1482
MSA SUZHOU SAFETY EQUIPMENT R&D CO., LTD.—See MSA Safety Incorporated; *U.S. Public*, pg. 1482
M S A SYSTEMS, INC.—See Odyssey Investment Partners, LLC; *U.S. Private*, pg. 2994
MSAT CABLE JSC—See Holding Varna AD-Varna; *Int'l*, pg. 3450
MSA TECHNOLOGIES AND ENTERPRISE SERVICES GMBH—See MSA Safety Incorporated; *U.S. Public*, pg. 1482

COMPANY NAME INDEX

MSA TECHNOLOGIES AND ENTERPRISE SERVICES SAS—See MSA Safety Incorporated; *U.S. Public*, pg. 1482
MSA THAILAND LIMITED—See MSA Safety Incorporated; *U.S. Public*, pg. 1482
MSA: THE THINK AGENCY; *U.S. Private*, pg. 2806
MS AUTOTECH COMPANY LIMITED; *Int'l*, pg. 5065
MS AVON, L.P.—See Welltower Inc.; *U.S. Public*, pg. 2348
M&S BARGAIN HUNTER INC.; *U.S. Private*, pg. 2525
MSB DESIGN INC.—See Sogeclair; *Int'l*, pg. 7058
M'S BEVERAGE CO., LTD.—See Maeil Holdings Co., Ltd.; *Int'l*, pg. 4636
MSB FINANCIAL CORP.—See Kearny Financial Corp.; *U.S. Public*, pg. 1217
MSB GROUP, INC.—See Advanced Electronic Services, Inc.; *U.S. Private*, pg. 89
MSB MUTUAL HOLDING COMPANY; *U.S. Private*, pg. 2806
MSB PERFUME HOLDING DIFFUSION GMBH—See BI-Invest Advisors S.A.; *Int'l*, pg. 1017
MSB PERFUME HOLDINGS LTD.—See BI-Invest Advisors S.A.; *Int'l*, pg. 1017
MSB REAL ESTATE CORP.—See M&T Bank Corporation; *U.S. Public*, pg. 1351
MS BRICO—See Compagnie de Saint-Gobain SA; *Int'l*, pg. 1724
MS BUBBLES INC.; *U.S. Private*, pg. 2806
MSC AGENCY A.G.—See Mediterranean Shipping Company, S.A.; *Int'l*, pg. 4781
MSC AGENCY PAKISTAN (PVT) LTD—See Mediterranean Shipping Company, S.A.; *Int'l*, pg. 4781
MSC ANESTHESIA, INC.—See KKR & Co. Inc.; *U.S. Public*, pg. 1246
MSC (ANGOLA) - NAVEGACAO LOGISTICA E SERVICOS MARITIMOS LDA—See Mediterranean Shipping Company, S.A.; *Int'l*, pg. 4781
MS CARVER LUMBER CO.; *U.S. Private*, pg. 2806
M-S CASH DRAWER CORPORATION; *U.S. Private*, pg. 2526
MSC BAHAMAS LTD.—See Mediterranean Shipping Company, S.A.; *Int'l*, pg. 4781
MSC BELGIUM N.V.—See Mediterranean Shipping Company, S.A.; *Int'l*, pg. 4781
MSC CANADA INC.—See Mediterranean Shipping Company, S.A.; *Int'l*, pg. 4781
MSC CO., LTD.; *Int'l*, pg. 5067
MSC CREWING SERVICES LLC—See Mediterranean Shipping Company, S.A.; *Int'l*, pg. 4781
MSC CREWING SERVICES PVT LTD—See Mediterranean Shipping Company, S.A.; *Int'l*, pg. 4781
MSC CROATIA D.O.O.—See Mediterranean Shipping Company, S.A.; *Int'l*, pg. 4781
MSC CRUCEROS, S.A.U.—See Mediterranean Shipping Company, S.A.; *Int'l*, pg. 4781
MSC CRUISES SCANDINAVIA AB—See Mediterranean Shipping Company, S.A.; *Int'l*, pg. 4781
MSC CRUISES (USA) INC.—See Mediterranean Shipping Company, S.A.; *Int'l*, pg. 4781
MSC CRUZEIROS DO BRASIL LTDA.—See Mediterranean Shipping Company, S.A.; *Int'l*, pg. 4781
MSC DE NICARAGUA, S.A. DE C.V.—See Mediterranean Shipping Company, S.A.; *Int'l*, pg. 4781
MSC DENMARK A/S—See Mediterranean Shipping Company, S.A.; *Int'l*, pg. 4781
MSC DISTRIBUTING INC.; *U.S. Private*, pg. 2806
MSC DOMINICANA S.R.L—See Mediterranean Shipping Company, S.A.; *Int'l*, pg. 4781
MSC EESTI AS—See Mediterranean Shipping Company, S.A.; *Int'l*, pg. 4782
MSC FINLAND OY—See Mediterranean Shipping Company, S.A.; *Int'l*, pg. 4782
MSC FRANCE S.A.—See Mediterranean Shipping Company, S.A.; *Int'l*, pg. 4782
MSC GEMI ACENTELIGI AS.—See Mediterranean Shipping Company, S.A.; *Int'l*, pg. 4782
MSC GERMANY GMBH—See Mediterranean Shipping Company, S.A.; *Int'l*, pg. 4782
MSC GREECE S.A.—See Mediterranean Shipping Company, S.A.; *Int'l*, pg. 4782
MSCI BARRA SA—See MSCI Inc.; *U.S. Public*, pg. 1483
MSCI BARRA (SUISSE) SARL—See MSCI Inc.; *U.S. Public*, pg. 1483
MSCI CANADA INC.—See MSCI Inc.; *U.S. Public*, pg. 1483
M SCIENCE LLC—See Jefferies Financial Group Inc.; *U.S. Public*, pg. 1189
MSCI INC.; *U.S. Public*, pg. 1483
MSC INCOME FUND, INC.; *U.S. Public*, pg. 1482
MSC INDUSTRIAL DIRECT CO., INC.; *U.S. Public*, pg. 1483
MSC INVESTOREN GMBH—See Avnet, Inc.; *U.S. Public*, pg. 253
MSC IRELAND LTD.—See Mediterranean Shipping Company, S.A.; *Int'l*, pg. 4781
MSCI S. DE R.L. DE C.V.—See MSCI Inc.; *U.S. Public*, pg. 1483
MSCI SERVICES PRIVATE LIMITED—See MSCI Inc.; *U.S. Public*, pg. 1483

MSC (ISRAEL) LTD.—See Mediterranean Shipping Company, S.A.; *Int'l*, pg. 4781
MSC KOPER D.O.O.—See Mediterranean Shipping Company, S.A.; *Int'l*, pg. 4782
MSC KOREA LTD.—See Mediterranean Shipping Company, S.A.; *Int'l*, pg. 4782
MSC KREUZFAHRTEN AG—See Mediterranean Shipping Company, S.A.; *Int'l*, pg. 4782
MSC KREUZFAHRTEN GMBH—See Mediterranean Shipping Company, S.A.; *Int'l*, pg. 4782
MSC KRSTARENJA DOO—See Mediterranean Shipping Company, S.A.; *Int'l*, pg. 4782
MSC LANKA (PRIVATE) LIMITED—See Mediterranean Shipping Company, S.A.; *Int'l*, pg. 4782
MSC LATVIA SIA—See Mediterranean Shipping Company, S.A.; *Int'l*, pg. 4782
MSC LOGISTICS (PTY) LTD—See Mediterranean Shipping Company, S.A.; *Int'l*, pg. 4782
MSC MAGYARORSZAG KFT—See Mediterranean Shipping Company, S.A.; *Int'l*, pg. 4782
MSC MALAWI LIMITED—See Mediterranean Shipping Company, S.A.; *Int'l*, pg. 4782
MSC MALI S.A.—See Mediterranean Shipping Company, S.A.; *Int'l*, pg. 4782
MSC (MALTA) LIMITED—See Avnet, Inc.; *U.S. Public*, pg. 253
MSC (MAURITIUS) LTD—See Mediterranean Shipping Company, S.A.; *Int'l*, pg. 4781
MSC MEDITERRANEAN SHIPPING COMPANY GHANA LTD.—See Mediterranean Shipping Company, S.A.; *Int'l*, pg. 4782
MSC MEDITERRANEAN SHIPPING COMPANY (JAPAN) K.K.—See Mediterranean Shipping Company, S.A.; *Int'l*, pg. 4782
MSC MEDITERRANEAN SHIPPING CO. (PANAMA) S.A.—See Mediterranean Shipping Company, S.A.; *Int'l*, pg. 4782
MSC MEDITERRANEAN SHIPPING DO BRASIL LTDA.—See Mediterranean Shipping Company, S.A.; *Int'l*, pg. 4782
MSC MONERIS SERVICES CORP.—See Bank of Montreal; *Int'l*, pg. 847
MSC MONERIS SERVICES CORP.—See Royal Bank of Canada; *Int'l*, pg. 6409
MSC MORTGAGE—See Wells Fargo & Company; *U.S. Public*, pg. 2344
MSC NIGERIA LTD—See Mediterranean Shipping Company, S.A.; *Int'l*, pg. 4782
MSC NORWAY AS.—See Mediterranean Shipping Company, S.A.; *Int'l*, pg. 4782
MSCO INC.; *U.S. Private*, pg. 2806
M'S COMMUNICATE CO., LTD—See Dai Nippon Printing Co., Ltd.; *Int'l*, pg. 1915
MS CONCEPT LIMITED; *Int'l*, pg. 5065
MS & CONSULTING CO., LTD.; *Int'l*, pg. 5064
MS&CONSULTING (THAILAND) CO., LTD.—See MS & Consulting Co., Ltd.; *Int'l*, pg. 5065
MSCP III, LLC—See Morgan Stanley; *U.S. Public*, pg. 1472
MSC POLAND SP. Z.O.O.—See Mediterranean Shipping Company, S.A.; *Int'l*, pg. 4782
MSC (PTY) LTD.—See Mediterranean Shipping Company, S.A.; *Int'l*, pg. 4781
MSCRIPTS, LLC—See Cardinal Health, Inc.; *U.S. Public*, pg. 434
MSC ROMANIA SRL.—See Mediterranean Shipping Company, S.A.; *Int'l*, pg. 4782
MSC SENEGAL S.A.—See Mediterranean Shipping Company, S.A.; *Int'l*, pg. 4782
MSC SHIP MANAGEMENT (CYPRUS) LTD—See Mediterranean Shipping Company, S.A.; *Int'l*, pg. 4782
MSC.SOFTWARE AB—See Hexagon AB; *Int'l*, pg. 3369
MSC.SOFTWARE BENELUX B.V.—See Hexagon AB; *Int'l*, pg. 3369
MSC.SOFTWARE CORP. - ANN ARBOR—See Hexagon AB; *Int'l*, pg. 3369
MSC SOFTWARE CORPORATION—See Hexagon AB; *Int'l*, pg. 3369
MSC SOFTWARE GMBH—See Hexagon AB; *Int'l*, pg. 3369
MSC.SOFTWARE JAPAN LTD. - OSAKA OFFICE—See Hexagon AB; *Int'l*, pg. 3369
MSC.SOFTWARE JAPAN LTD.—See Hexagon AB; *Int'l*, pg. 3369
MSC.SOFTWARE LTD. - BEIJING OFFICE—See Hexagon AB; *Int'l*, pg. 3369
MSC.SOFTWARE LTD. - CHENGDU OFFICE—See Hexagon AB; *Int'l*, pg. 3369
MSC.SOFTWARE LTD.—See Hexagon AB; *Int'l*, pg. 3369
MSC.SOFTWARE SARL - SAINT-FONS—See Hexagon AB; *Int'l*, pg. 3369
MSC.SOFTWARE SARL—See Hexagon AB; *Int'l*, pg. 3369
MSC.SOFTWARE SIMULATING REALITY S.A.—See Hexagon AB; *Int'l*, pg. 3369
MSC.SOFTWARE S.R.L.—See Hexagon AB; *Int'l*, pg. 3369
MSC.SOFTWARE S.R.L.—See Hexagon AB; *Int'l*, pg. 3369

MSD INVESTMENT CORP.

MSC.SOFTWARE S.R.O.—See Hexagon AB; *Int'l*, pg. 3369
MSC SOUTH EAST ASIA (SINGAPORE) PTE LTD.—See Mediterranean Shipping Company, S.A.; *Int'l*, pg. 4782
MSC STE MAURITANIENNE DE PECHE ET DE NAVIGATION—See Mediterranean Shipping Company, S.A.; *Int'l*, pg. 4782
MSC SUDAN LTD.—See Mediterranean Shipping Company, S.A.; *Int'l*, pg. 4782
MSC SWEDEN AB—See Mediterranean Shipping Company, S.A.; *Int'l*, pg. 4782
MSC SYRIA LTD.—See Mediterranean Shipping Company, S.A.; *Int'l*, pg. 4782
MSC (TANZANIA) LTD.—See Mediterranean Shipping Company, S.A.; *Int'l*, pg. 4781
MSC TECHNOLOGIES GMBH—See Avnet, Inc.; *U.S. Public*, pg. 253
MSC TECHNOLOGIES SYSTEMS GMBH—See Avnet, Inc.; *U.S. Public*, pg. 253
MSC TOGO, S.A.—See Mediterranean Shipping Company, S.A.; *Int'l*, pg. 4782
MSC TRADING (SHANGHAI) CO., LTD.—See Mitsui-Soko Holdings Co., Ltd.; *Int'l*, pg. 4992
MSC TUNISIE S.A.R.L.—See Mediterranean Shipping Company, S.A.; *Int'l*, pg. 4782
M S C - VERTRIEBS - SK S. R. O.—See Avnet, Inc.; *U.S. Public*, pg. 253
MSC VIETNAM COMPANY LIMITED—See Mediterranean Shipping Company, S.A.; *Int'l*, pg. 4782
MSC VILNIUS UAB.—See Mediterranean Shipping Company, S.A.; *Int'l*, pg. 4782
MSCW CO., LTD.—See AKS Corporation Public Company Limited; *Int'l*, pg. 264
MSC YEMEN LTD.—See Mediterranean Shipping Company, S.A.; *Int'l*, pg. 4782
MSD ACQUISITION CORP.; *U.S. Private*, pg. 2806
MSD ANIMAL HEALTH A/S—See Merck & Co., Inc.; *U.S. Public*, pg. 1417
MSD ANIMAL HEALTH BVBA—See Merck & Co., Inc.; *U.S. Public*, pg. 1417
MSD ANIMAL HEALTH BVBA—See Merck & Co., Inc.; *U.S. Public*, pg. 1417
MSD ANIMAL HEALTH DANUBE BIOTECH GMBH—See Merck & Co., Inc.; *U.S. Public*, pg. 1417
MSD ANIMAL HEALTH FZ-LLC—See Merck & Co., Inc.; *U.S. Public*, pg. 1417
MSD ANIMAL HEALTH GMBH—See Merck & Co., Inc.; *U.S. Public*, pg. 1417
MSD ANIMAL HEALTH INNOVATION AS—See Merck & Co., Inc.; *U.S. Public*, pg. 1417
MSD ANIMAL HEALTH K.K.—See Merck & Co., Inc.; *U.S. Public*, pg. 1417
MSD ANIMAL HEALTH KOREA LTD.—See Merck & Co., Inc.; *U.S. Public*, pg. 1417
MSD ANIMAL HEALTH, LDA.—See Merck & Co., Inc.; *U.S. Public*, pg. 1418
MSD ANIMAL HEALTH LIMITED—See Merck & Co., Inc.; *U.S. Public*, pg. 1418
MSD ANIMAL HEALTH NORGE AS—See Merck & Co., Inc.; *U.S. Public*, pg. 1418
MSD ANIMAL HEALTH (PHILS.), INC.—See Merck & Co., Inc.; *U.S. Public*, pg. 1417
MSD ANIMAL HEALTH (SHANGHAI) TRADING CO., LTD.—See Merck & Co., Inc.; *U.S. Public*, pg. 1417
MSD ANIMAL HEALTH S.R.L.—See Merck & Co., Inc.; *U.S. Public*, pg. 1418
MSD ANIMAL HEALTH VIETNAM CO. LTD.—See Merck & Co., Inc.; *U.S. Public*, pg. 1418
MSD ARGENTINA SRL—See Merck & Co., Inc.; *U.S. Public*, pg. 1418
MSD AUSTRALIA - MANUFACTURING DIVISION—See Merck & Co., Inc.; *U.S. Public*, pg. 1418
MSD AUSTRALIA—See Merck & Co., Inc.; *U.S. Public*, pg. 1418
MSD BELGIUM BVBA/SPRL—See Merck & Co., Inc.; *U.S. Public*, pg. 1418
MSD BRAZIL—See Merck & Co., Inc.; *U.S. Public*, pg. 1420
MSD BV HAARLEM—See Merck & Co., Inc.; *U.S. Public*, pg. 1418
MSD CAPITAL, L.P.; *U.S. Private*, pg. 2806
MSD CHIBROPHARM GMBH—See Merck & Co., Inc.; *U.S. Public*, pg. 1418
MSD DANMARK APS—See Merck & Co., Inc.; *U.S. Public*, pg. 1418
MS DEUTSCHLAND BETEILIGUNGSGESELLSCHAFT MBH—See Callista Private Equity GmbH & Co. KG; *Int'l*, pg. 1265
MSD FINLAND OY—See Merck & Co., Inc.; *U.S. Public*, pg. 1418
MSD FRANCE S.A.S.—See Merck & Co., Inc.; *U.S. Public*, pg. 1418
MSD GREECE—See Merck & Co., Inc.; *U.S. Public*, pg. 1418
MSD HUMAN HEALTH HOLDING B.V.—See Merck & Co., Inc.; *U.S. Public*, pg. 1418
MSD INTERNATIONAL HOLDINGS GMBH—See Merck & Co., Inc.; *U.S. Public*, pg. 1418
MSD INVESTMENT CORP.; *U.S. Private*, pg. 2807

1835

MSD INVESTMENT CORP. — CORPORATE AFFILIATIONS

MS DIRECTIONAL, LLC—See Patterson-UTI Energy, Inc.; *U.S. Public*, pg. 1654
MS DISTRIBUTORS OF TOLEDO; *U.S. Private*, pg. 2806
MSD (ITALIA) S.R.L.—See Merck & Co., Inc.; *U.S. Public*, pg. 1417
MSD ITALIA S.R.L.—See Merck & Co., Inc.; *U.S. Public*, pg. 1418
MSD IT GLOBAL INNOVATION CENTER S.R.O.—See Merck & Co., Inc.; *U.S. Public*, pg. 1418
MSD K.K.—See Merck & Co., Inc.; *U.S. Public*, pg. 1418
MSD KOREA LTD.—See Merck & Co., Inc.; *U.S. Public*, pg. 1418
MSD (L-SP) UNTERSTUTZUNGSKASSE GMBH—See Merck & Co., Inc.; *U.S. Public*, pg. 1418
MSD MAGYARORSZAG KERESKEDELMI ES SZOLGALTATO KORLATOLT FELELOSSEGU TARSASAG—See Merck & Co., Inc.; *U.S. Public*, pg. 1418
MSD MERCK SHARP & DOHME AG—See Merck & Co., Inc.; *U.S. Public*, pg. 1418
MSD MEXICO—See Merck & Co., Inc.; *U.S. Public*, pg. 1420
MSD (NORGE) A/S—See Merck & Co., Inc.; *U.S. Public*, pg. 1417
MSD OSS—See Merck & Co., Inc.; *U.S. Public*, pg. 1420
MSD PANAMA—See Merck & Co., Inc.; *U.S. Public*, pg. 1418
MSD PARTNERS, L.P.—See MSD Capital, L.P.; *U.S. Private*, pg. 2806
MSD PHARMACEUTICALS LLC—See Merck & Co., Inc.; *U.S. Public*, pg. 1418
MSD PHARMACEUTICALS PRIVATE LIMITED—See Merck & Co., Inc.; *U.S. Public*, pg. 1418
MSD PHARMACEUTICALS—See Merck & Co., Inc.; *U.S. Public*, pg. 1418
MSD PHARMA HUNGARY KORLATOLT FELELOSSEGU TARSASAG—See Merck & Co., Inc.; *U.S. Public*, pg. 1418
MSD PHARMA (SINGAPORE) PTE. LTD.—See Merck & Co., Inc.; *U.S. Public*, pg. 1418
MSD PHILIPPINES—See Merck & Co., Inc.; *U.S. Public*, pg. 1418
MSD POLSKA DYSTRYBUCJA SP. Z.O.O.—See Merck & Co., Inc.; *U.S. Public*, pg. 1418
MSD POLSKA SP. Z.O.O.—See Merck & Co., Inc.; *U.S. Public*, pg. 1418
MSD (PTY) LTD—See Merck & Co., Inc.; *U.S. Public*, pg. 1417
MSD SECURE SERVICE INC.—See Pole To Win Holdings, Inc.; *Int'l*, pg. 5908
MSD SHARP & DOHME GESELLSCHAFT MIT BESCHRANKTER HAFTUNG—See Merck & Co., Inc.; *U.S. Public*, pg. 1418
MSD SHARP & DOHME GMBH—See Merck & Co., Inc.; *U.S. Public*, pg. 1418
MSDSONLINE, INC.—See CVC Capital Partners SICAV-FIS S.A.; *Int'l*, pg. 1885
MSD-SP LTD.—See Merck & Co., Inc.; *U.S. Public*, pg. 1418
MSD SWORDS—See Merck & Co., Inc.; *U.S. Public*, pg. 1418
MSD (THAILAND) LTD.—See Merck & Co., Inc.; *U.S. Public*, pg. 1417
MSD UKRAINE LIMITED LIABILITY COMPANY—See Merck & Co., Inc.; *U.S. Public*, pg. 1418
MSD VACCINS—See Merck & Co., Inc.; *U.S. Public*, pg. 1418
MSD VERWALTUNGS GMBH—See Merck & Co., Inc.; *U.S. Public*, pg. 1418
M SEALS AB—See Diploma PLC; *Int'l*, pg. 2129
M SEALS A/S—See Diploma PLC; *Int'l*, pg. 2129
M SEALS UK LIMITED—See Diploma PLC; *Int'l*, pg. 2129
MSE AUGSBURG GMBH—See Advent International Corporation; *U.S. Private*, pg. 97
MSE AUGSBURG GMBH—See Centerbridge Partners, L.P.; *U.S. Private*, pg. 813
MSE CHINA (BEIJING) CO., LTD.—See Mitsui-Soko Holdings Co., Ltd.; *Int'l*, pg. 4992
MSE CHINA (GUANGZHOU) CO., LTD.—See Mitsui-Soko Holdings Co., Ltd.; *Int'l*, pg. 4993
MS E-COMMERCE GMBH—See Metro AG; *Int'l*, pg. 4859
M-SECURITY TECHNOLOGY INDOCHINA PTE. LTD.—See Multi-Chem Limited; *Int'l*, pg. 5082
M-SECURITY TECHNOLOGY SDN. BHD.—See Multi-Chem Limited; *Int'l*, pg. 5082
M-SECURITY TECH PHILIPPINES INC.—See Multi-Chem Limited; *Int'l*, pg. 5082
MSE DO BRASIL LOGISTICA LTDA.—See Mitsui-Soko Holdings Co., Ltd.; *Int'l*, pg. 4992
MSE EUROPE TASIMACILIK, ORGANIZASYON LOJISTIK LIMITED SIRKETI—See Mitsui-Soko Holdings Co., Ltd.; *Int'l*, pg. 4992
MSE EXPRESS AMERICA, INC.—See Mitsui-Soko Holdings Co., Ltd.; *Int'l*, pg. 4993
MSE EXPRESS MEXICO, S.A. DE C.V.—See Mitsui-Soko Holdings Co., Ltd.; *Int'l*, pg. 4992
MSE EXPRESS (THAILAND) CO., LTD.—See Mitsui-Soko Holdings Co., Ltd.; *Int'l*, pg. 4993
MSE FORWARDERS INDIA PVT. LTD.—See Mitsui-Soko Holdings Co., Ltd.; *Int'l*, pg. 4993

MSE GROUP, LLC—See Montrose Environmental Group, Inc.; *U.S. Public*, pg. 1466
MSE IMMOBILIENSOFTWARE GMBH—See Advent International Corporation; *U.S. Private*, pg. 97
MSE IMMOBILIENSOFTWARE GMBH—See Centerbridge Partners, L.P.; *U.S. Private*, pg. 813
M+S ELEKTRONIK AG; *Int'l*, pg. 4612
MS ELEVATORS SDN. BHD.—See Japan Industrial Partners, Inc.; *Int'l*, pg. 3894
MSEM, A.S.; *Int'l*, pg. 5067
MSE MOBILE SCHLAMMENTWASSERUNGS GMBH—See EnBW Energie Baden-Wurttemberg AG; *Int'l*, pg. 2399
M&S ENGINEERING, LLC; *U.S. Private*, pg. 2525
M-SENKO LOGISTICS CO., LTD.—See Senko Group Holdings Co., Ltd.; *Int'l*, pg. 6710
MSE—See Veolia Environnement S.A.; *Int'l*, pg. 8161
MSE TECHNOLOGY APPLICATIONS INC.—See Montana Economic Revitalization & Development Institute Inc.; *U.S. Private*, pg. 2775
M.SETEK CO., LTD.—See AUO Corporation; *Int'l*, pg. 706
MS EUROPE B.V.—See World Kinect Corporation; *U.S. Public*, pg. 2380
MS EXPRESS SOUTH AFRICA (PTY) LTD.—See Mitsui-Soko Holdings Co., Ltd.; *Int'l*, pg. 4993
M&S FAB INC.; *U.S. Private*, pg. 2525
MS FIRST CAPITAL INSURANCE LIMITED—See MS&AD Insurance Group Holdings, Inc.; *Int'l*, pg. 5066
M&S FOOD SERVICE LTD.—See Gordon Food Service Inc.; *U.S. Private*, pg. 1743
MSF SUGAR LIMITED—See Mitr Phol Sugar Corporation Limited; *Int'l*, pg. 4927
M.S.G. ASSOCIATES INC.; *U.S. Private*, pg. 2529
MSG DAVID GMBH—See msg group GmbH; *Int'l*, pg. 5067
MSG DISTRIBUTORS, INC.; *U.S. Private*, pg. 2807
MSGGILLARDON AG—See msg group GmbH; *Int'l*, pg. 5068
MSG GLOBAL DIGITAL SOUTH EAST EUROPE D.O.O.—See msg group GmbH; *Int'l*, pg. 5067
MSG GLOBAL SOLUTIONS AG—See msg group GmbH; *Int'l*, pg. 5067
MSG GLOBAL SOLUTIONS ASIA PRIVATE LIMITED—See msg group GmbH; *Int'l*, pg. 5067
MSG GLOBAL SOLUTIONS BENELUX B.V.—See msg group GmbH; *Int'l*, pg. 5067
MSG GLOBAL SOLUTIONS BULGARIA LTD.—See msg group GmbH; *Int'l*, pg. 5067
MSG GLOBAL SOLUTIONS CANADA INC.—See msg group GmbH; *Int'l*, pg. 5067
MSG GLOBAL SOLUTIONS DEUTSCHLAND GMBH—See msg group GmbH; *Int'l*, pg. 5067
MSG GLOBAL SOLUTIONS DO BRASIL LTDA.—See msg group GmbH; *Int'l*, pg. 5067
MSG GLOBAL SOLUTIONS IBERIA S.L.U.—See msg group GmbH; *Int'l*, pg. 5067
MSG GLOBAL SOLUTIONS INC.—See msg group GmbH; *Int'l*, pg. 5068
MSG GLOBAL SOLUTIONS INDIA PRIVATE LIMITED—See msg group GmbH; *Int'l*, pg. 5067
MSG GLOBAL SOLUTIONS ITALIA S.R.L.—See msg group GmbH; *Int'l*, pg. 5067
MSG GLOBAL SOLUTIONS KOREA LTD.—See msg group GmbH; *Int'l*, pg. 5067
MSG GLOBAL SOLUTIONS PHILIPPINES INC.—See msg group GmbH; *Int'l*, pg. 5067
MSG GLOBAL SOLUTIONS SOUTH EAST EUROPE D.O.O.—See msg group GmbH; *Int'l*, pg. 5067
MSG GROUP GMBH; *Int'l*, pg. 5067
MSG INDUSTRY ADVISORS AG—See msg group GmbH; *Int'l*, pg. 5068
MSG LIFE AG—See msg group GmbH; *Int'l*, pg. 5068
MSG LIFE AUSTRIA GES.M.B.H.—See msg group GmbH; *Int'l*, pg. 5068
MSG LIFE BENELUX B.V.—See msg group GmbH; *Int'l*, pg. 5068
MSG LIFE CENTRAL EUROPE GMBH—See msg group GmbH; *Int'l*, pg. 5068
MSG LIFE CONSULTING GMBH—See msg group GmbH; *Int'l*, pg. 5068
MSG LIFE CZECHIA SPOL. S.R.O.—See msg group GmbH; *Int'l*, pg. 5068
MSG LIFE DEUTSCHLAND GMBH—See msg group GmbH; *Int'l*, pg. 5068
MSG LIFE IBERIA, UNIPESSOAL LDA.—See msg group GmbH; *Int'l*, pg. 5068
MSG LIFE IBERIA UNIPESSOAL LDA—See msg group GmbH; *Int'l*, pg. 5068
MSG LIFE METRIS GMBH—See msg group GmbH; *Int'l*, pg. 5068
MSG LIFE ODATEAM D.O.O.—See msg group GmbH; *Int'l*, pg. 5068
MSG LIFE POLAND SP. Z.O.O.—See msg group GmbH; *Int'l*, pg. 5068
MSG LIFE SLOVAKIA S.R.O.—See msg group GmbH; *Int'l*, pg. 5068
MSG LIFE SWITZERLAND AG—See msg group GmbH; *Int'l*, pg. 5068

MSG NETCONOMY INC.—See msg group GmbH; *Int'l*, pg. 5068
MSG NETWORKS INC.—See Sphere Entertainment Co.; *U.S. Public*, pg. 1918
MSG NEXINSURE AG—See msg group GmbH; *Int'l*, pg. 5068
MSGN HOLDINGS, L.P.—See Sphere Entertainment Co.; *U.S. Public*, pg. 1918
MS GOVERN—See Constellation Software Inc.; *Int'l*, pg. 1774
MSG PLAUT DEUTSCHLAND GMBH—See msg group GmbH; *Int'l*, pg. 5068
MS GROUP HOLDINGS LTD.; *Int'l*, pg. 5065
MSG SERVICES AG—See msg group GmbH; *Int'l*, pg. 5068
MSG SPORTS & ENTERTAINMENT, LLC—See Madison Square Garden Sports Corp.; *U.S. Public*, pg. 1353
MSG SYSTEMS AG—See msg group GmbH; *Int'l*, pg. 5068
MSG SYSTEMS AG—See msg group GmbH; *Int'l*, pg. 5068
MSG SYSTEMS ROMANIA S.R.L.—See msg group GmbH; *Int'l*, pg. 5068
MSG SYSTEMS (SHANGHAI) CO., LTD.—See msg group GmbH; *Int'l*, pg. 5068
MSG TREORBIS GMBH—See msg group GmbH; *Int'l*, pg. 5068
M/S GULF DYNAMIC SWITCHGEAR CO. LTD—See Dubai Investments PJSC; *Int'l*, pg. 2219
MSG VENTURES, LLC—See Sphere Entertainment Co.; *U.S. Public*, pg. 1918
MSHALE COMMODITIES LIMITED (SUGAR)—See ED&F Man Holdings Limited; *Int'l*, pg. 2303
MS HAMMONIA BAVARIA SCHIFFAHRTS GMBH & CO. KG—See HCI Hammonia Shipping AG; *Int'l*, pg. 3297
MS HAMMONIA MASSILIA SCHIFFAHRTS GMBH & CO. KG—See HCI Hammonia Shipping AG; *Int'l*, pg. 3297
MS HAMMONIA ROMA SCHIFFAHRTS GMBH & CO. KG—See HCI Hammonia Shipping AG; *Int'l*, pg. 3297
MS HAMMONIA TEUTONICA SCHIFFAHRTS GMBH & CO. KG—See HCI Hammonia Shipping AG; *Int'l*, pg. 3297
MSHARIE LLC—See Dubai Investments PJSC; *Int'l*, pg. 2219
MSHC, INC.—See Leonard Green & Partners, L.P.; *U.S. Private*, pg. 2426
MSHIFT, INC.—See MTI Ltd.; *Int'l*, pg. 5070
MS HIYOSHI KOUZAI CO., LTD.—See Hanwa Co., Ltd.; *Int'l*, pg. 3263
MS HOLDINGS LIMITED; *Int'l*, pg. 5065
M+S HYDRAULIC AD-KAZANLAK; *Int'l*, pg. 4613
M+S HYDRAULIC POWER TRANSMISSION GMBH—See M+S Hydraulic AD-Kazanlak; *Int'l*, pg. 4613
MSI BUILDING SUPPLIES INC.; *U.S. Private*, pg. 2807
MSI/CANTERBURY CORP.—See Canterbury Consulting Group, Inc.; *U.S. Private*, pg. 735
MSI CAPITAL PARTNERS LLC; *U.S. Private*, pg. 2807
MSI COMPUTER (AUSTRALIA) PTY. LTD.—See Micro-Star International Co., Ltd.; *Int'l*, pg. 4878
MSI COMPUTER CORP.; *U.S. Private*, pg. 2807
MSI COMPUTER EUROPE B.V.—See Micro-Star International Co., Ltd.; *Int'l*, pg. 4878
MSI COMPUTER JAPAN CO., LTD.—See Micro-Star International Co., Ltd.; *Int'l*, pg. 4878
MSI COMPUTER SARL—See Micro-Star International Co., Ltd.; *Int'l*, pg. 4878
MSI COMPUTER (UK) LIMITED—See Micro-Star International Co., Ltd.; *Int'l*, pg. 4878
MSI CREDIT SOLUTIONS; *U.S. Private*, pg. 2807
MSI-DEFENCE SYSTEMS INC.—See MS International plc; *Int'l*, pg. 5065
MSI-DEFENCE SYSTEMS LTD.—See MS International plc; *Int'l*, pg. 5065
M. SIDERIS & SON LTD.—See REHAU Verwaltungszentrale AG; *Int'l*, pg. 6255
MSI-ECS PHILS., INC.—See VSTECS Holdings Limited; *Int'l*, pg. 8314
MSI ELECTRONICS (KUNGSHAN) CO., LTD.—See Micro-Star International Co., Ltd.; *Int'l*, pg. 4878
MSI- EL MOTALA STROMS INSTALLATIONS AB—See Instalco AB; *Int'l*, pg. 3722
MSI ENGINEERING SOFTWARE LTD.—See Hexagon AB; *Int'l*, pg. 3369
MSI EXPRESS, INC.—See HCI Equity Management, L.P.; *U.S. Private*, pg. 1889
MSI-FORKS GARFOS INDUSTRIAIS LTDA.—See MS International plc; *Int'l*, pg. 5065
MSI-FORKS INC.—See MS International plc; *Int'l*, pg. 5065
MSI-FORKS LTD.—See MS International plc; *Int'l*, pg. 5065
MSI GENERAL CORPORATION; *U.S. Private*, pg. 2807
MSIG HOLDINGS (U.S.A.), INC.—See MS&AD Insurance Group Holdings, Inc.; *Int'l*, pg. 5066
MSIGHTS INC.; *U.S. Private*, pg. 2807
MSIG INSURANCE EUROPE AG—See MS&AD Insurance Group Holdings, Inc.; *Int'l*, pg. 5066
MSIG INSURANCE (HONG KONG) LIMITED—See MS&AD Insurance Group Holdings, Inc.; *Int'l*, pg. 5066

COMPANY NAME INDEX

MSIG INSURANCE (MALAYSIA) BHD.—See MS&AD Insurance Group Holdings, Inc.; *Int'l*, pg. 5066
MSIG INSURANCE SERVICES, INC.—See MS&AD Insurance Group Holdings, Inc.; *Int'l*, pg. 5066
MSIG INSURANCE (SINGAPORE) PTE. LTD.—See MS&AD Insurance Group Holdings, Inc.; *Int'l*, pg. 5066
MSIG INSURANCE (THAILAND) PUBLIC COMPANY LIMITED—See MS&AD Insurance Group Holdings, Inc.; *Int'l*, pg. 5066
MSIG INSURANCE (VIETNAM) COMPANY LIMITED—See MS&AD Insurance Group Holdings, Inc.; *Int'l*, pg. 5066
MSIG MINGTAI INSURANCE CO., LTD.—See MS&AD Insurance Group Holdings, Inc.; *Int'l*, pg. 5066
MSIG SERVICE AND ADJUSTING (THAILAND) COMPANY LIMITED—See MS&AD Insurance Group Holdings, Inc.; *Int'l*, pg. 5066
MSI GUARANTEEDWEATHER, LLC—See MS&AD Insurance Group Holdings, Inc.; *Int'l*, pg. 5066
M.S.I. INTERNATIONAL EAST, INC.—See Next 15 Group plc; *Int'l*, pg. 5246
MSI INTERNATIONAL (THAILAND) LTD.—See IMC Pan Asia Alliance Pte. Ltd.; *Int'l*, pg. 3621
MSI ITALY S.R.L.—See Micro-Star International Co., Ltd.; *Int'l*, pg. 4878
MSI-JARN AB—See Instalco AB; *Int'l*, pg. 3722
MSI KOREA CO., LTD.—See Micro-Star International Co., Ltd.; *Int'l*, pg. 4878
MSI MEDSERV INTERNATIONAL DEUTSCHLAND GMBH—See Permira Advisers LLP; *Int'l*, pg. 5808
M. SIMON ZOOK CO. INC.; *U.S. Private*, pg. 2527
MS INDUSTRIE AG; *Int'l*, pg. 5065
MS INDUSTRIE VERWALTUNGS GMBH—See MS Industrie AG; *Int'l*, pg. 5065
MS INTERNATIONAL CORP.—See Fuji Corporation; *Int'l*, pg. 2810
MS INTERNATIONAL INC.; *U.S. Private*, pg. 2806
MS INTERNATIONAL PLC; *Int'l*, pg. 5065
MSI-PRO COMPANY—See Jewett-Cameron Trading Company Ltd.; *U.S. Public*, pg. 1190
MSI-QUALITY FORGINGS LTD.—See MS International plc; *Int'l*, pg. 5065
MSI-ROR AB—See Instalco AB; *Int'l*, pg. 3722
MSI SHIP MANAGEMENT PTE. LTD.—See IMC Pan Asia Alliance Pte. Ltd.; *Int'l*, pg. 3621
MSI SHIP MANAGEMENT (QINGDAO) CO. LTD.—See IMC Pan Asia Alliance Pte. Ltd.; *Int'l*, pg. 3621
MSI-SIGN GROUP BV—See MS International plc; *Int'l*, pg. 5065
MSI SSL; *U.S. Private*, pg. 2807
MSI SUPPLY, INC.—See Winsupply, Inc.; *U.S. Private*, pg. 4545
MSI TECHNOLOGY, L.L.C.—See Mitsubishi Chemical Group Corporation; *Int'l*, pg. 4934
MSI TRANSDUCERS CORP.—See Amphenol Corporation; *U.S. Public*, pg. 130
MS IT-SYSTEME GMBH—See PAO Severstal; *Int'l*, pg. 5731
M.S. JACOBS & ASSOCIATES; *U.S. Private*, pg. 2529
M.S. JACOVIDES & CO. LTD.; *Int'l*, pg. 4617
MSK FARM MACHINERY CORPORATION—See Mitsubishi Corporation; *Int'l*, pg. 4940
MSK MARITIME SPEDITION-KONTOR GMBH; *Int'l*, pg. 5068
MS LAND & BUILDINGS LLC—See MS Industrie AG; *Int'l*, pg. 5065
M. SLAVIN & SONS LTD.; *U.S. Private*, pg. 2527
MSL CHINA—See Publicis Groupe S.A.; *Int'l*, pg. 6102
MSL DIGITAL—See Publicis Groupe S.A.; *Int'l*, pg. 6103
MSL DUBAI—See Publicis Groupe S.A.; *Int'l*, pg. 6103
MSL ENTERPRISES, INC.—See Enterprise Onsite Services Co.; *U.S. Private*, pg. 1404
MSL FRANCE—See Publicis Groupe S.A.; *Int'l*, pg. 6103
MSLGROUP - ATLANTA—See Publicis Groupe S.A.; *Int'l*, pg. 6103
MSLGROUP GERMANY GMBH—See Publicis Groupe S.A.; *Int'l*, pg. 6103
MSL GROUP LONDON LTD.—See Publicis Groupe S.A.; *Int'l*, pg. 6102
MSLGROUP—See Publicis Groupe S.A.; *Int'l*, pg. 6102
MSL ITALIA—See Publicis Groupe S.A.; *Int'l*, pg. 6103
MSL JAPAN—See Publicis Groupe S.A.; *Int'l*, pg. 6103
MS LOGISTICS CO., LTD.—See Mitsui-Soko Holdings Co., Ltd.; *Int'l*, pg. 4992
MSL PROPERTY MANAGEMENT; *U.S. Private*, pg. 2807
MSL SHANGHAI—See Publicis Groupe S.A.; *Int'l*, pg. 6103
MSL SOLUTIONS LIMITED—See FirstRand Limited; *Int'l*, pg. 2690
MS&L—See Publicis Groupe S.A.; *Int'l*, pg. 6103
MS&L—See Publicis Groupe S.A.; *Int'l*, pg. 6103
MS&L—See Publicis Groupe S.A.; *Int'l*, pg. 6103
MSL&L SOUTH AFRICA—See Publicis Groupe S.A.; *Int'l*, pg. 6103
MS&L SWEDEN—See Publicis Groupe S.A.; *Int'l*, pg. 6103
MSL VERTEDA LIMITED—See FirstRand Limited; *Int'l*, pg. 2690
MS&L WORLDWIDE—See Publicis Groupe S.A.; *Int'l*, pg. 6103

MS. MAGAZINE—See Liberty Media for Women, LLC; *U.S. Private*, pg. 2445
MSM CEBU, INC.—See Mitsubishi Steel Mfg. Co., Ltd.; *Int'l*, pg. 4968
MSM CONTRACTS LTD.; *Int'l*, pg. 5068
MSM CORPORATION INTERNATIONAL LTD.; *Int'l*, pg. 5068
MSMC RESIDENTIAL REALTY LLC; *U.S. Private*, pg. 2808
MSM EQUIPMENT MANUFACTURER SDN. BHD.—See MSM International Limited; *Int'l*, pg. 5069
MSM INTERNATIONAL LIMITED; *Int'l*, pg. 5068
MS MISHAWAKA, L.P.—See Welltower Inc.; *U.S. Public*, pg. 2348
MSM KITCHEN SDN. BHD.—See MSM International Limited; *Int'l*, pg. 5069
MSM LOGISTICS SDN. BHD.—See FGV Holdings Bhd; *Int'l*, pg. 2649
MSM MALAYSIA HOLDINGS BERHAD—See FGV Holdings Bhd; *Int'l*, pg. 2649
MSM MANUFACTURING DE MEXICO, S.A. DE C.V.—See Littlejohn & Co., LLC; *U.S. Private*, pg. 2471
M-SMM ELECTRONICS SDN. BHD.—See Sumitomo Metal Mining Co., Ltd.; *Int'l*, pg. 7291
MSM METAL INDUSTRIES SDN. BHD.—See MSM International Limited; *Int'l*, pg. 5069
MSM NINGBO CO., LTD.—See Mitsubishi Steel Mfg. Co., Ltd.; *Int'l*, pg. 4968
MSM NINGBO SPRING CO., LTD.—See Mitsubishi Steel Mfg. Co., Ltd.; *Int'l*, pg. 4968
MS MODE NEDERLAND B.V.—See B. Riley Financial, Inc.; *U.S. Public*, pg. 261
M.S. MOTORS (1998) LTD.—See The Colonial Motor Company Limited; *Int'l*, pg. 7634
MS MOTOR SERVICE AFTERMARKET IBERICA S.L.—See Rheinmetall AG; *Int'l*, pg. 6322
MS MOTORSERVICE AFTERMARKET IBERICA S.L.—See Rheinmetall AG; *Int'l*, pg. 6322
MS MOTOR SERVICE ASIA PACIFIC CO., LTD.—See Rheinmetall AG; *Int'l*, pg. 6322
MS MOTOR SERVICE DEUTSCHLAND GMBH—See Rheinmetall AG; *Int'l*, pg. 6322
MS MOTORSERVICE DEUTSCHLAND GMBH—See Rheinmetall AG; *Int'l*, pg. 6322
MS MOTORSERVICE FRANCE SAS—See Rheinmetall AG; *Int'l*, pg. 6322
MS MOTOR SERVICE FRANCE S.A.S.—See Rheinmetall AG; *Int'l*, pg. 6322
MS MOTOR SERVICE INTERNATIONAL GMBH—See Rheinmetall AG; *Int'l*, pg. 6322
MS MOTOR SERVICE ISTANBUL DIS TICARET VE PAZARLAMA A.S.—See Rheinmetall AG; *Int'l*, pg. 6322
MS MOTORSERVICE TRADING (ASIA) PTE. LTD.—See Rheinmetall AG; *Int'l*, pg. 6322
MSM PERLIS SDN. BHD.—See FGV Holdings Bhd; *Int'l*, pg. 2650
MSM PRAI BERHAD—See FGV Holdings Bhd; *Int'l*, pg. 2650
MSM PROTEIN TECHNOLOGIES, INC.; *U.S. Private*, pg. 2807
MSM SPRING INDIA PVT. LTD.—See Mitsubishi Steel Mfg. Co., Ltd.; *Int'l*, pg. 4968
MSM (THAILAND) CO., LTD.—See Mitsubishi Steel Mfg. Co., Ltd.; *Int'l*, pg. 4968
MSM TRADING INTERNATIONAL DMCC—See FGV Holdings Bhd; *Int'l*, pg. 2650
MSNBC CABLE LLC—See Comcast Corporation; *U.S. Public*, pg. 539
M/S NILA SPACES LIMITED; *Int'l*, pg. 4617
MS NONWOVENS INC.—See The Shinih Enterprise Co., Ltd.; *Int'l*, pg. 6845
MS NORTH STAR LOGISTICS CO., LTD.—See Mitsui-Soko Holdings Co., Ltd.; *Int'l*, pg. 4992
MSNW GROUP, LLC; *U.S. Private*, pg. 2808
MSOFT THAILAND CO., LTD.; *Int'l*, pg. 5069
MSOL-TW LTD.—See Management Solutions Co., Ltd.; *Int'l*, pg. 4666
M-SOLUTIONS TECHNOLOGY (THAILAND) CO., LTD.—See Multi-Chem Limited; *Int'l*, pg. 5082
M-SOLV LIMITED—See CN Innovations Holdings Limited; *Int'l*, pg. 1673
MSO MISCHANLAGEN GMBH—See PORR AG; *Int'l*, pg. 5923
MSO NASH INC.—See Nash Health Care Systems Inc.; *U.S. Private*, pg. 2835
MSO OF PUERTO RICO, LLC—See Elevance Health, Inc.; *U.S. Public*, pg. 730
MSOUTH EQUITY PARTNERS, LLC; *U.S. Private*, pg. 2808
MSPACE; *U.S. Private*, pg. 2808
MSP CAPITAL MANAGEMENT, L.L.C.; *U.S. Private*, pg. 2808
MSP CORPORATION—See TSI Incorporated; *U.S. Private*, pg. 4253
MSPECTRUM, INC.—See Manila Electric Company; *Int'l*, pg. 4671
MSP EQUIPMENT RENTALS, INC.—See Ashtead Group Plc; *Int'l*, pg. 609

M.S.T. STEEL CORPORATION

MSP INDUSTRIES CORPORATION—See American Axle & Manufacturing Holdings, Inc.; *U.S. Public*, pg. 96
M&S PIPE SYSTEMS CO., LTD.—See Sekisui Chemical Co., Ltd.; *Int'l*, pg. 6694
MSP KALA NAFT CO.—See National Iranian Oil Company; *Int'l*, pg. 5160
MS PLASTIC WELDERS LLC—See MS Industrie AG; *Int'l*, pg. 5065
M SPLIT CORP.—See Quadravest Capital Management Inc.; *Int'l*, pg. 6150
MSP MEDIEN-SERVICE UND PROMOTION GMBH—See Bertelsmann SE & Co. KGaA; *Int'l*, pg. 993
MSP METALL SERVICE PEDACK GMBH—See CRONIMET Holding GmbH; *Int'l*, pg. 1855
MSP MUNZSPIELPARTNER GMBH & CO. KG—See Gauselmann AG; *Int'l*, pg. 2891
MS PORTUGAL—See Microsoft Corporation; *U.S. Public*, pg. 1439
MSPOT, INC.—See Samsung Group; *Int'l*, pg. 6513
MS POWERTRAIN TECHNOLOGIE GMBH—See MS Industrie AG; *Int'l*, pg. 5065
MSP PROPERTY LIMITED—See S&P Syndicate Public Company Limited; *Int'l*, pg. 6445
MSP RECOVERY, INC.; *U.S. Public*, pg. 1484
MS PRINTING SOLUTIONS S.R.L.—See Dover Corporation; *U.S. Public*, pg. 681
MSP STEEL & POWER LIMITED; *Int'l*, pg. 5069
MSQ PARTNERS GROUP LTD.—See OEP Capital Advisors, L.P.; *U.S. Private*, pg. 2999
M SQUARED CONSULTING, INC.—See SolomonEdwardsGroup, LLC; *U.S. Private*, pg. 3710
MS "BUTES" SCHIFFAHRTS GMBH & CO. KG—See K+S Aktiengesellschaft; *Int'l*, pg. 4041
MSREF REAL ESTATE ADVISOR, INC.—See Morgan Stanley; *U.S. Public*, pg. 1472
M.S. RESISTANCES (MICROELETTRICA SCIENTIFICA) S.A.S.—See Knorr-Bremse AG; *Int'l*, pg. 4211
THE MSR GROUP; *U.S. Private*, pg. 4081
MSR INDIA LIMITED; *Int'l*, pg. 5069
MSR PUBLIC POWER AGENCY; *U.S. Private*, pg. 2808
MSSC AHLE GMBH—See Mitsubishi Steel Mfg. Co., Ltd.; *Int'l*, pg. 4968
MSSC CANADA INC.—See Mitsubishi Steel Mfg. Co., Ltd.; *Int'l*, pg. 4968
MSSC COMPANY—See Leonardo S.p.A.; *Int'l*, pg. 4459
MSSC INC.—See Mitsubishi Steel Mfg. Co., Ltd.; *Int'l*, pg. 4968
MSSC US INC.—See Mitsubishi Steel Mfg. Co., Ltd.; *Int'l*, pg. 4968
MSS INTERIORS LIMITED—See Kazera Global plc; *Int'l*, pg. 4103
MSSL MIDEAST FZE—See Samvardhana Motherson International Limited; *Int'l*, pg. 6516
MSSL - MONCLOVA—See Samvardhana Motherson International Limited; *Int'l*, pg. 6516
MSSL - PORTLAND—See Samvardhana Motherson International Limited; *Int'l*, pg. 6516
MSSL - SALTILLO—See Samvardhana Motherson International Limited; *Int'l*, pg. 6516
MSSL WIRING SYSTEM INC.—See Samvardhana Motherson International Limited; *Int'l*, pg. 6516
M SS NG P ECES; *U.S. Private*, pg. 2523
MS SOLAR INVESTMENTS LLC—See Morgan Stanley; *U.S. Public*, pg. 1472
MSS PROJECTS LIMITED—See Kazera Global plc; *Int'l*, pg. 4103
MSS TECHNOLOGIES INC.; *U.S. Private*, pg. 2808
MS SUPPLY CHAIN SOLUTIONS (THAILAND) LTD.—See Mitsui-Soko Holdings Co., Ltd.; *Int'l*, pg. 4993
MSTAR SEMICONDUCTOR, INC.—See MediaTek Inc.; *Int'l*, pg. 4773
MST & ASSOCIATES INC.—See Southern Pan Services Company; *U.S. Private*, pg. 3734
MSTC LTD.; *Int'l*, pg. 5069
MST CONSTRUCTORS INC.; *U.S. Private*, pg. 2808
M&S TECHNOLOGIES, INC.—See Windjammer Capital Investors, LLC; *U.S. Private*, pg. 4538
MS TECHNOLOGY, INC.; *U.S. Private*, pg. 2806
MST GOLF GROUP BERHAD; *Int'l*, pg. 5069
MST INSURANCE SERVICE CO., LTD.—See Meiji Yasuda Life Insurance Company; *Int'l*, pg. 4802
M-STORES PROPRIETARY LIMITED—See Bayport Management Limited; *Int'l*, pg. 915
M STRATEGIES, INC.; *U.S. Private*, pg. 2523
MSTS ASIA SDN. BHD.—See Lundbeckfonden; *Int'l*, pg. 4583
MSTS ASIA (SINGAPORE) PTE LTD—See Lundbeckfonden; *Int'l*, pg. 4583
MST SOLUTIONS, LLC—See Mastek Ltd.; *Int'l*, pg. 4724
M.S.T. STEEL CORPORATION; *U.S. Private*, pg. 2529
MSU MANAGEMENT - SERVICE - UND UNTERNEHMENSBERATUNG GMBH—See DZ BANK AG Deutsche Zentral-Genossenschaftsbank; *Int'l*, pg. 2244
M/S VENTURA ALLIED SERVICES PRIVATE LIMITED—See Ventura Guaranty Limited; *Int'l*, pg. 8151
M/S. VENTURA SECURITIES LIMITED—See Ventura Guaranty Limited; *Int'l*, pg. 8151

1837

M.S. WALKER, INC. - MSW NEW HAMPSHIRE FACILITY—See M.S. Walker, Inc.; *U.S. Private*, pg. 2529
M.S. WALKER, INC. - MSW RHODE ISLAND FACILITY—See M.S. Walker, Inc.; *U.S. Private*, pg. 2529
M.S. WALKER, INC.; *U.S. Private*, pg. 2529
M. SWAROVSKI GMBH—See SWARCO AG; *Int'l*, pg. 7360
MSW-CHEMIE GMBH—See K+S Aktiengesellschaft; *Int'l*, pg. 4041
MS & WOOD D.D. SARAJEVO—See Unipromet d.d.; *Int'l*, pg. 8057
MSW (UK) LTD.; *Int'l*, pg. 5069
MSX INTERNATIONAL, INC.—See Bain Capital, LP; *U.S. Private*, pg. 441
MSX RESOURCES SA; *Int'l*, pg. 5069
MTAB LLC—See Poplar Capital Partners LLC; *U.S. Private*, pg. 3228
MTA BUS COMPANY—See Metropolitan Transportation Authority; *U.S. Private*, pg. 2689
MTA DISTRIBUTORS, LLC—See Thompson Distribution, LLC; *U.S. Private*, pg. 4159
MT AEROSPACE AG—See OHB SE; *Int'l*, pg. 5532
MTAG GROUP BERHAD; *Int'l*, pg. 5069
MTA GMBH MEDIZIN-TECHNISCHER ANLAGENBAU—See Linde plc; *Int'l*, pg. 4508
M TAIRHAIZ RAKTAIROZAISI EIS SZOLGAILTATOI KORLAITOLT FELELOSSEIGU TAIRSASAIG—See CHS INC.; *U.S. Public*, pg. 492
M TAMPA CORP.—See Mobley Homes of Florida Inc.; *U.S. Private*, pg. 2758
MTANKCO SUPPLY, LLC—See TerraVest Industries, Inc.; *Int'l*, pg. 7568
MT AQUAPOLYMER, INC. - MOBARA PLANT—See Toagosei Co. Ltd.; *Int'l*, pg. 7770
MT AQUAPOLYMER, INC. - SAKAIDE PLANT—See Toagosei Co. Ltd.; *Int'l*, pg. 7770
MT AQUAPOLYMER, INC—See Toagosei Co. Ltd.; *Int'l*, pg. 7770
MT AQUAPOLYMER, INC.—See Toagosei Co. Ltd.; *Int'l*, pg. 7770
MTAR TECHNOLOGIES LIMITED; *Int'l*, pg. 5069
MT ATLANTIC INC.—See Hojgaard Holding A/S; *Int'l*, pg. 3442
MT. BAKER PETCT, LLC—See Akumin, Inc.; *U.S. Public*, pg. 70
MT. BAKER PRODUCTS, INC.—See Swaner Hardwood Company, Inc.; *U.S. Private*, pg. 3890
M&T BANK CORPORATION; *U.S. Public*, pg. 1350
MT BARKER CHICKEN—See Milne AgriGroup Pty., Ltd.; *Int'l*, pg. 4897
MTB CAPITAL LIMITED—See Mutual Trust Bank PLC; *Int'l*, pg. 5107
MTBE MALAYSIA SDN. BHD.—See Petroliam Nasional Berhad; *Int'l*, pg. 5829
MTB EXCHANGE (UK) LIMITED—See Mutual Trust Bank PLC; *Int'l*, pg. 5107
MTB METALS CORP.; *Int'l*, pg. 5069
MTB SECURITIES LIMITED—See Mutual Trust Bank PLC; *Int'l*, pg. 5107
MT BUSINESS TECHNOLOGIES, INC.—See Xerox Holdings Corporation; *U.S. Public*, pg. 2389
MT. CARMEL REGISTER COMPANY—See Brehm Communications Inc.; *U.S. Private*, pg. 644
MTC CO., LTD. - NAGAOKA FACTORY—See Takatori Corporation; *Int'l*, pg. 7436
MTC CO., LTD.—See Takatori Corporation; *Int'l*, pg. 7436
MTC DIRECT; *U.S. Private*, pg. 2808
MTC DISTRIBUTING; *U.S. Private*, pg. 2808
MTC ELECTROCERAMICS LIMITED—See Morgan Advanced Materials plc; *Int'l*, pg. 5042
MTC ENGINEERING, LLC; *U.S. Private*, pg. 2808
MTC INC.; *U.S. Private*, pg. 2809
MTCI-NORTHEAST—See Management Training & Consulting Inc.; *U.S. Private*, pg. 2561
MTCI-SOUTH CENTRAL—See Management Training & Consulting Inc.; *U.S. Private*, pg. 2561
MTC KENWORTH INC.; *U.S. Private*, pg. 2809
MTC MICRO TECH COMPONENTS GMBH—See discoverIE Group plc; *Int'l*, pg. 2133
MT COMMUNITY STAFF CO., LTD.—See Mitsubishi Estate Co., Ltd.; *Int'l*, pg. 4946
M&T CREDIT CORPORATION—See M&T Bank Corporation; *U.S. Public*, pg. 1350
MTC SUSPENSION INC.—See Genuine Parts Company; *U.S. Public*, pg. 932
MTC TRANSFORMERS, INC.; *U.S. Private*, pg. 2809
MTD ACPI ENGINEERING BERHAD—See MTD Capital Bhd.; *Int'l*, pg. 5070
MTD AIRCAP—See Stanley Black & Decker, Inc.; *U.S. Public*, pg. 1933
M.T.D. ASSOCIATES, L.L.C.—See Aon plc; *Int'l*, pg. 496
MTD AUSTRIA HANDELSGESELLSCHAFT M.B.H.—See Stanley Black & Decker, Inc.; *U.S. Public*, pg. 1933
MTD CAPITAL BHD.; *Int'l*, pg. 5070
MTD CONSTRUCTION SDN. BHD.—See MTD Capital Bhd.; *Int'l*, pg. 5070

M.T.D. FRANCE SAS—See Stanley Black & Decker, Inc.; *U.S. Public*, pg. 1933
MTD HUNGARIA KFT.—See Stanley Black & Decker, Inc.; *U.S. Public*, pg. 1933
MTD MICRO MOLDING; *U.S. Private*, pg. 2809
M.T. DONAHOE & ASSOCIATES, LLC—See AmWINS Group, Inc.; *U.S. Private*, pg. 269
MTD PRODUCTS BENELUX B.V.—See Stanley Black & Decker, Inc.; *U.S. Public*, pg. 1933
MTD PRODUCTS DENMARK APS—See Stanley Black & Decker, Inc.; *U.S. Public*, pg. 1933
MTD PRODUCTS, INC.—See Stanley Black & Decker, Inc.; *U.S. Public*, pg. 1933
MTD PRODUCTS INDIA PRIVATE INDIA LIMITED—See Stanley Black & Decker, Inc.; *U.S. Public*, pg. 1933
MTD PRODUCTS LIMITED—See Stanley Black & Decker, Inc.; *U.S. Public*, pg. 1933
MT DRUITT AUTOBODY REPAIRS PTY LTD—See AMA Group Limited; *Int'l*, pg. 403
MTD SCHWEIZ AG—See Stanley Black & Decker, Inc.; *U.S. Public*, pg. 1933
MTD SOUTHWEST INC.—See Stanley Black & Decker, Inc.; *U.S. Public*, pg. 1933
MTD TECHNOLOGIES INC.; *U.S. Private*, pg. 2809
M-TEC CZ S.R.O.—See Zoomlion Heavy Industry Science & Technology Co., Ltd.; *Int'l*, pg. 8690
MTECH ACQUISITION CORP.—See Gryphon Digital Mining, Inc.; *U.S. Public*, pg. 973
M.TECH CO., LTD.—See Oriental Land Co., Ltd.; *Int'l*, pg. 5625
MTECH COMMUNICATIONS PLC; *Int'l*, pg. 5070
M-TECH INDUSTRIAL (PTY) LTD—See Royal Bafokeng Holdings (Pty) Limited; *Int'l*, pg. 6409
M.TECH PRODUCTS AUST PTY LIMITED—See Multi-Chem Limited; *Int'l*, pg. 5082
M.TECH PRODUCTS (HK) PTE LIMITED—See Multi-Chem Limited; *Int'l*, pg. 5082
M.TECH PRODUCTS JAPAN KABUSHIKI KAISHA—See Multi-Chem Limited; *Int'l*, pg. 5082
M.TECH PRODUCTS KOREA LIMITED LIABILITY COMPANY—See Multi-Chem Limited; *Int'l*, pg. 5082
M.TECH PRODUCTS NEW ZEALAND LIMITED—See Multi-Chem Limited; *Int'l*, pg. 5082
M.TECH PRODUCTS PHILIPPINES, INC.—See Multi-Chem Limited; *Int'l*, pg. 5082
M.TECH PRODUCTS PTE LTD—See Multi-Chem Limited; *Int'l*, pg. 5082
M.TECH PRODUCTS TW PTE. LTD.—See Multi-Chem Limited; *Int'l*, pg. 5082
M.TECH (SHANGHAI) CO., LTD.—See Multi-Chem Limited; *Int'l*, pg. 5082
M.TECH SOLUTIONS (INDIA) PRIVATE LIMITED—See Multi-Chem Limited; *Int'l*, pg. 5082
MTECH SYSTEMS AMERICA LATINA LTDA.—See Munters Group AB; *Int'l*, pg. 5094
M-TECH SYSTEMS USA, LLC—See Munters AB; *Int'l*, pg. 5093
M-TEC MATHIS TECHNIK GMBH—See Zoomlion Heavy Industry Science & Technology Co., Ltd.; *Int'l*, pg. 8690
MTE CORPORATION—See Steel Partners Holdings L.P.; *U.S. Public*, pg. 1943
MT EDUCARE LIMITED; *Int'l*, pg. 5069
MTEKVISION AMERICA, INC.—See MtekVision Co., Ltd; *Int'l*, pg. 5070
MTEKVISION CO., LTD; *Int'l*, pg. 5070
MTELLIGENCE CORPORATION—See Emerson Electric Co.; *U.S. Public*, pg. 742
MTEM LIMITED—See PGS ASA; *Int'l*, pg. 5838
MT ETHYLENE CARBONATE CO., LTD.—See Toagosei Co. Ltd.; *Int'l*, pg. 7770
MT EVELYN & DISTRICTS FINANCIAL SERVICES LIMITED; *Int'l*, pg. 5069
MTF SOLUTIONS LTD.—See Swisscom AG; *Int'l*, pg. 7374
MTG ACCOUNTING AB—See Modern Times Group MTG AB; *Int'l*, pg. 5014
MTG A/S DANMARK—See Modern Times Group MTG AB; *Int'l*, pg. 5014
MT GAS JOINT STOCK COMPANY; *Int'l*, pg. 5069
MTG AS NORGE—See Modern Times Group MTG AB; *Int'l*, pg. 5014
MTG BROADCAST CENTRE STOCKHOLM AB—See Modern Times Group MTG AB; *Int'l*, pg. 5014
MTG BROADCASTING AB—See Modern Times Group MTG AB; *Int'l*, pg. 5014
MTG BROADCASTING HOLDING AB—See Modern Times Group MTG AB; *Int'l*, pg. 5014
MTG CO., LTD.; *Int'l*, pg. 5070
MTG DISPOSAL, LLC—See Waste Connections, Inc.; *Int'l*, pg. 8352
MT GENEX CORPORATION; *Int'l*, pg. 5069
MTG FINANCING PARTNERS HB—See Modern Times Group MTG AB; *Int'l*, pg. 5014
MTG FORMAVITA CO., LTD.—See MTG Co., Ltd.; *Int'l*, pg. 5070
MTG HOLDING AB—See Modern Times Group MTG AB; *Int'l*, pg. 5014
MTGLQ INVESTORS, L.P.—See The Goldman Sachs Group, Inc.; *U.S. Public*, pg. 2082

MTG MEDICAL CO., LTD.—See MTG Co., Ltd.; *Int'l*, pg. 5070
MTG METRO GRATIS KST; *Int'l*, pg. 5070
MTG MODERN SERVICES AB—See Modern Times Group MTG AB; *Int'l*, pg. 5014
MTG MODERN STUDIOS HOLDING AB—See Modern Times Group MTG AB; *Int'l*, pg. 5014
MTG ONLINE AB—See Modern Times Group MTG AB; *Int'l*, pg. 5015
MTG PACIFIC PTE. LTD.—See MTG Co., Ltd.; *Int'l*, pg. 5070
MTG PROFESSIONAL CO., LTD.—See MTG Co., Ltd.; *Int'l*, pg. 5070
MTG PUBLISHING AB—See Modern Times Group MTG AB; *Int'l*, pg. 5015
MTG RADIO AB—See Modern Times Group MTG AB; *Int'l*, pg. 5015
MTG RADIO SALES AB—See Modern Times Group MTG AB; *Int'l*, pg. 5015
MT. GRAHAM REGIONAL MEDICAL CENTER; *U.S. Private*, pg. 2808
MTG (SHANGHAI) TRADING CO., LTD.—See MTG Co., Ltd.; *Int'l*, pg. 5070
MTG (SHENZHEN) TRADING CO., LTD.—See MTG Co., Ltd.; *Int'l*, pg. 5070
MTG TAIWAN CO., LTD.—See MTG Co., Ltd.; *Int'l*, pg. 5070
MTG TV ONLINE AB—See Modern Times Group MTG AB; *Int'l*, pg. 5015
MT. HAMILTON, LLC—See Bendito Resources Inc.; *U.S. Private*, pg. 524
MT. HAWLEY INSURANCE COMPANY—See RLI Corp.; *U.S. Public*, pg. 1801
MTHAYIZA FARMING (PTY) LTD—See CROOKES BROTHERS LIMITED; *Int'l*, pg. 1855
MTHINK LLC; *U.S. Private*, pg. 2809
M THIRTY COMMUNICATIONS INC.—See DGTL Holdings Inc.; *Int'l*, pg. 2097
MT HOJGAARD A/S—See Hojgaard Holding A/S; *Int'l*, pg. 3442
MT HOJGAARD FOROYAR P/F—See Hojgaard Holding A/S; *Int'l*, pg. 3442
MT HOJGAARD GRONLAND A.P.S.—See Hojgaard Holding A/S; *Int'l*, pg. 3442
MTHOMBO IT SERVICES (PTY) LIMITED—See EOH HOLDINGS LIMITED; *Int'l*, pg. 2457
MTH RETAIL GROUP HOLDING GMBH—See Management Trust Holding AG; *Int'l*, pg. 4666
MT-IDEAS S.A.; *Int'l*, pg. 5069
MTI DISTRIBUTING COMPANY INC.—See The Toro Company; *U.S. Public*, pg. 2135
MTI ELECTRONICS INC.—See Insight Equity Holdings LLC; *U.S. Private*, pg. 2086
MTI ENTERPRISES INC.; *U.S. Private*, pg. 2809
MTI FRANCE S.A.S.—See Ricoh Company, Ltd.; *Int'l*, pg. 6334
MTI HOME VIDEO; *U.S. Private*, pg. 2809
MTI INSTRUMENTS INC.—See Branford Castle, Inc.; *U.S. Private*, pg. 639
MTI LTD.; *Int'l*, pg. 5070
MTI MICROFUEL CELLS INC.—See Soluna Holdings, Inc.; *U.S. Public*, pg. 1901
MT INDUSTRIAL SUPPLIES & SERVICES CO., LTD.—See Endress+Hauser (International) Holding AG; *Int'l*, pg. 2408
M&T INSURANCE AGENCY, INC.—See M&T Bank Corporation; *U.S. Public*, pg. 1350
MTI PHARMA SOLUTIONS, INC.—See Catalent, Inc.; *U.S. Public*, pg. 448
MTI POLYFAB INC.—See 3M Company; *U.S. Public*, pg. 5
M.T.I.—See Figeac-Aero SA; *Int'l*, pg. 2660
M.T.I SUMMIT SPB LTD.—See MTI Wireless Edge Ltd.; *Int'l*, pg. 5070
MTI SYSTEMS INC.; *U.S. Private*, pg. 2809
MTI TECHNOLOGY GMBH—See Ricoh Company, Ltd.; *Int'l*, pg. 6334
MTI TECHNOLOGY LIMITED—See Ricoh Company, Ltd.; *Int'l*, pg. 6334
MTI WIRELESS EDGE LTD.; *Int'l*, pg. 5070
MTJV (THAILAND) CO., LTD.—See Marubeni Corporation; *Int'l*, pg. 4705
M.T.K. AUTO WEST LTD.—See Auto West Group; *Int'l*, pg. 725
MTK WIRELESS LIMITED (UK)—See MediaTek Inc.; *Int'l*, pg. 4773
M. T. LANEY COMPANY, INC.; *U.S. Private*, pg. 2527
MTL INSTRUMENTS BV—See Eaton Corporation plc; *Int'l*, pg. 2278
MTL INSTRUMENTS GMBH—See Eaton Corporation plc; *Int'l*, pg. 2278
THE MTL INSTRUMENTS GROUP LTD.—See Eaton Corporation plc; *Int'l*, pg. 2278
MTL INSTRUMENTS PTY. LIMITED—See Eaton Corporation plc; *Int'l*, pg. 2278
MTL INSTRUMENTS PVT. LIMITED—See Eaton Corporation plc; *Int'l*, pg. 2278
MTL INSTRUMENTS SARL—See Eaton Corporation plc; *Int'l*, pg. 2278
MTL INSURANCE COMPANY; *U.S. Private*, pg. 2809

COMPANY NAME INDEX

MTL ITALIA SRL—See Eaton Corporation plc; *Int'l*, pg. 2282
MTL LEASING, LLC—See MetLife, Inc.; *U.S. Public*, pg. 1430
MTLLINK MULTIMODAL SOLUTIONS INC.—See Blue Wolf Capital Partners LLC; *U.S. Private*, pg. 595
MT. LOGAN MANAGEMENT, LTD.—See Everest Group, Ltd.; *Int'l*, pg. 2564
MT. LOGAN RE, LTD.—See Everest Group, Ltd.; *Int'l*, pg. 2564
MTL PHILIPPINES—See Metals Exploration PLC; *Int'l*, pg. 4849
M.T.L. PRINT LTD.; *Int'l*, pg. 4617
MTL US CORP.—See Mullen Group Ltd.; *Int'l*, pg. 5080
MT MALCOLM MINES NL; *Int'l*, pg. 5069
MT. MCKINLEY MANAGERS, LLC—See Everest Group, Ltd.; *Int'l*, pg. 2564
MTM CRITICAL METALS LIMITED; *Int'l*, pg. 5070
MT MECATRONICA SPA—See OHB SE; *Int'l*, pg. 5532
MTM ENGINEERING PTE. LTD.—See Beng Kuang Marine Limited; *Int'l*, pg. 973
M&T MORTGAGE CORP.—See M&T Bank Corporation; *U.S. Public*, pg. 1350
MTM RECOGNITION CORPORATION; *U.S. Private*, pg. 2809
MTM TECHNOLOGIES INC.—See MTM Technologies, Inc.; *U.S. Private*, pg. 2809
MTM TECHNOLOGIES, INC.; *U.S. Private*, pg. 2809
MTM-TV2 BEFEKTETESI KFT.—See ProSiebenSat.1 Media SE; *Int'l*, pg. 6000
MTN AFGHANISTAN LIMITED—See MTN Group Limited; *Int'l*, pg. 5071
MTN BUSINESS SOLUTIONS BOTSWANA PROPRIETARY LIMITED—See MTN Group Limited; *Int'l*, pg. 5071
MTN BUSINESS SOLUTIONS NAMIBIA PROPRIETARY LIMITED—See MTN Group Limited; *Int'l*, pg. 5071
MTN BUSINESS SOLUTIONS PROPRIETARY LIMITED—See MTN Group Limited; *Int'l*, pg. 5071
MTN CAPITAL PARTNERS LLC; *U.S. Private*, pg. 2809
MTN GROUP LIMITED; *Int'l*, pg. 5070
MTNL-STPI IT SERVICES LIMITED—See Mahanagar Telephone Nigam Limited; *Int'l*, pg. 4644
MTN NETWORK SOLUTIONS—See MTN Group Limited; *Int'l*, pg. 5071
MTN NIGERIA COMMUNICATIONS LTD.—See MTN Group Limited; *Int'l*, pg. 5071
MTN RWANDACELL LIMITED—See MTN Group Limited; *Int'l*, pg. 5071
MTN SOUTH AFRICA (PTY) LTD.—See MTN Group Limited; *Int'l*, pg. 5071
MTN UGANDA LTD.—See MTN Group Limited; *Int'l*, pg. 5071
MTN (ZAMBIA) LIMITED—See MTN Group Limited; *Int'l*, pg. 5071
MT. OGDEN SURGICAL CENTER—See HCA Healthcare, Inc.; *U.S. Public*, pg. 1003
MT. OGDEN UTAH SURGICAL CENTER, LLC—See HCA Healthcare, Inc.; *U.S. Public*, pg. 1003
MTONE WIRELESS CORPORATION; *U.S. Private*, pg. 2809
MTONE WIRELESS TELECOMMUNICATIONS (SHANGHAI) CO., LTD.—See Mtone Wireless Corporation; *U.S. Private*, pg. 2809
MT OPTICS INC.—See Mitsubishi Gas Chemical Company, Inc.; *Int'l*, pg. 4949
MTORRES DISENOS INDUSTRIALES SAU; *Int'l*, pg. 5071
MTOUCHE (CAMBODIA) CO., LTD.—See mTouche Technology Berhad; *Int'l*, pg. 5071
MTOUCHE (HK) LIMITED—See mTouche Technology Berhad; *Int'l*, pg. 5071
MTOUCHE PTE. LTD.—See mTouche Technology Berhad; *Int'l*, pg. 5071
MTOUCHE TECHNOLOGY BERHAD; *Int'l*, pg. 5071
MTOUCHE (THAILAND) COMPANY LIMITED—See mTouche Technology Berhad; *Int'l*, pg. 5071
MTOUCHE (VIETNAM) CO. LTD.—See mTouche Technology Berhad; *Int'l*, pg. 5071
MTOUCH SRL—See IQVIA Holdings Inc.; *U.S. Public*, pg. 1169
MT OWEN PTY LIMITED—See Glencore plc; *Int'l*, pg. 2991
MT PACKAGING INC.; *U.S. Private*, pg. 2808
M&T PARTNERS—See Pacific Realty Associates, LP; *U.S. Private*, pg. 3070
MTPCS, LLC; *U.S. Private*, pg. 2809
MT. PLEASANT NEWS—See Inland Industries, Inc.; *U.S. Private*, pg. 2078
MT. PLEASANT SURGERY CENTER, L.P.—See UnitedHealth Group Incorporated; *U.S. Public*, pg. 2242
MTP MEDICAL TECHNOLOGIES GMBH—See Schneider Schreibgerate GmbH; *Int'l*, pg. 6636
MTP MESSTECHNIK PRODUKTIONS GMBH—See METRAWATT International GmbH; *Int'l*, pg. 4856
MTQ CORPORATION LIMITED; *Int'l*, pg. 5071
MTQ ENGINEERING PTE LTD—See MTQ Corporation Limited; *Int'l*, pg. 5071

MTQ ENGINE SYSTEMS (AUST) PTY LTD—See Bapcor Limited; *Int'l*, pg. 857
MTQ EQUIPMENT RENTAL PTE. LTD.—See MTQ Corporation Limited; *Int'l*, pg. 5071
MTQ FABRICATION PTE. LTD.—See MTQ Corporation Limited; *Int'l*, pg. 5071
MTQ HOLDINGS PTY LTD—See MTQ Corporation Limited; *Int'l*, pg. 5071
MTQ OILFIELD SERVICES W.L.L.—See MTQ Corporation Limited; *Int'l*, pg. 5071
MTR ACADEMY (HK) COMPANY LIMITED—See MTR Corporation Limited; *Int'l*, pg. 5072
MTR CORPORATION (CROSSRAIL) LIMITED—See MTR Corporation Limited; *Int'l*, pg. 5072
MTR CORPORATION LIMITED; *Int'l*, pg. 5072
M&T REALTY CAPITAL CORPORATION—See M&T Bank Corporation; *U.S. Public*, pg. 1350
MTREC LIMITED—See Open Up Group Inc; *Int'l*, pg. 5598
MTR EXPRESS (SWEDEN) AB—See MTR Corporation Limited; *Int'l*, pg. 5072
MTR FLEET SERVICES, LLC—See American Securities LLC; *U.S. Private*, pg. 248
MTR FOODS PVT. LIMITED—See Orkla ASA; *Int'l*, pg. 5638
MTR GROUP LIMITED—See DCC plc; *Int'l*, pg. 1991
MTR MARTCO, LLC—See Triosim Corporation; *U.S. Private*, pg. 4236
MT R&O LLC.—See Meyer Tool Inc.; *U.S. Private*, pg. 2693
M-TRON INDUSTRIES, INC.; *U.S. Public*, pg. 1351
M-TRON INDUSTRIES, LTD.—See M-tron Industries, Inc.; *U.S. Public*, pg. 1351
MTS3 INC.; *U.S. Private*, pg. 2810
MTS ASIA LTD.—See SharpLink Gaming, Inc.; *U.S. Public*, pg. 1873
MTS BANKA A.D.—See Telekom Srbija AD; *Int'l*, pg. 7538
MTSC SOLUTION SDN BHD—See ViTrox Corporation Berhad; *Int'l*, pg. 8262
MT SEALING TECHNOLOGY INC—See Burckhardt Compression Holding AG; *Int'l*, pg. 1221
M&T SECURITIES, INC.—See M&T Bank Corporation; *U.S. Public*, pg. 1351
MTS ENVIRONMENTAL GMBH—See Babcock & Wilcox Enterprises, Inc.; *U.S. Public*, pg. 263
MT SERVICE 2016 CO., LTD.—See Thanachart Capital PCL; *Int'l*, pg. 7607
MT SERVICE JAPAN EAST CO., LTD.—See Screen Holdings Co., Ltd.; *Int'l*, pg. 6655
MT SERVICE JAPAN WEST CO., LTD.—See Screen Holdings Co., Ltd.; *Int'l*, pg. 6655
MT SERVICES LTD—See Mauritius Telecom Ltd.; *Int'l*, pg. 4732
MTS EUROPE HOLDINGS LLC—See Illinois Tool Works Inc.; *U.S. Public*, pg. 1109
MT. SHASTA MALL—See Brookfield Corporation; *Int'l*, pg. 1185
MT. SHASTA TITLE & ESCROW COMPANY—See First American Financial Corporation; *U.S. Public*, pg. 838
MTS HEALTH PARTNERS, L.P.; *U.S. Private*, pg. 2809
MTS HOLDINGS FRANCE, SARL—See Amphenol Corporation; *U.S. Public*, pg. 131
MTSI, NORTHEAST DIVISION, INC.—See Microwave Transmission Systems, Inc.; *U.S. Private*, pg. 2704
MTS (JAPAN) LTD.—See Amphenol Corporation; *U.S. Public*, pg. 131
MTS KOREA, INC.—See Amphenol Corporation; *U.S. Public*, pg. 131
MTS MARKETS INTERNATIONAL, INC.—See Viel & Compagnie SA; *Int'l*, pg. 8192
MT SPORTS LLC—See Peak Global Holdings, LLC; *U.S. Private*, pg. 3123
MTS QUANTA, LLC—See Quanta Services, Inc.; *U.S. Public*, pg. 1752
MTS SENSORS TECHNOLOGY K.K.—See Amphenol Corporation; *U.S. Public*, pg. 131
MTS SENSOR TECHNOLOGIE GMBH AND CO. KG—See Amphenol Corporation; *U.S. Public*, pg. 131
MTS SENSOR TECHNOLOGIE UND VERWALTUNGS-GMBH—See Amphenol Corporation; *U.S. Public*, pg. 131
MTS SENSOR TECHNOLOGY CORP—See Amphenol Corporation; *U.S. Public*, pg. 131
MTS S.P.A.—See London Stock Exchange Group plc; *Int'l*, pg. 4547
MTS S.P.A. - UK CORPORATE OFFICE—See London Stock Exchange Group plc; *Int'l*, pg. 4547
MTS SYSTEMS (CHINA) LTD.—See Amphenol Corporation; *U.S. Public*, pg. 131
MTS SYSTEMS CORPORATION—See Amphenol Corporation; *U.S. Public*, pg. 130
MTS SYSTEMS GMBH—See Amphenol Corporation; *U.S. Public*, pg. 131
MTS SYSTEMS (HONG KONG) INC.—See Amphenol Corporation; *U.S. Public*, pg. 131
MTS SYSTEMS LTD.—See Amphenol Corporation; *U.S. Public*, pg. 131
MTS SYSTEMS NORDEN AB—See Amphenol Corporation; *U.S. Public*, pg. 131

MTS SYSTEMS SA—See Amphenol Corporation; *U.S. Public*, pg. 131
MTS SYSTEMS SRL—See Amphenol Corporation; *U.S. Public*, pg. 131
MT STAHL HANDELSGESELLSCHAFT GMBH—See Financiere SNOP Dunois SA; *Int'l*, pg. 2669
MTS TESTING SYSTEMS (CANADA) LTD.—See Amphenol Corporation; *U.S. Public*, pg. 131
MTS TRAVEL - COLORADO SPRINGS—See Menno Travel Service, Inc.; *U.S. Private*, pg. 2666
MT SUPPLY, INC.—See TruArc Partners, L.P.; *U.S. Private*, pg. 4245
MT TECHNOLOGIES GMBH—See Callista Private Equity GmbH & Co. KG; *Int'l*, pg. 1265
MT TEXAS LLC.—See Meyer Tool Inc.; *U.S. Private*, pg. 2693
MT TEXTURE DISPLAY INDONESIA—See Panasonic Holdings Corporation; *Int'l*, pg. 5717
MTT GROUP HOLDINGS LIMITED; *Int'l*, pg. 5072
MT. TOM GENERATING COMPANY LLC—See ENGIE SA; *Int'l*, pg. 2433
MTT-PRO S.R.L.—See Ardian SAS; *Int'l*, pg. 555
MTU AERO ENGINES AG; *Int'l*, pg. 5072
MTU AERO ENGINES FINANCE B.V.—See MTU Aero Engines AG; *Int'l*, pg. 5072
MTU AERO ENGINES GMBH—See MTU Aero Engines AG; *Int'l*, pg. 5072
MTU AERO ENGINES NORTH AMERICA INC.-DESIGN & ENGINEERING—See MTU Aero Engines AG; *Int'l*, pg. 5072
MTU AERO ENGINES POLSKA SP. Z.O.O.—See MTU Aero Engines AG; *Int'l*, pg. 5072
MTU AERO ENGINES SHANGHAI LTD.—See MTU Aero Engines AG; *Int'l*, pg. 5072
MTU AFRICA (PROPRIETARY) LIMITED—See Rolls-Royce Holdings plc; *Int'l*, pg. 6391
MTU AMERICA INC.—See Rolls-Royce Holdings plc; *Int'l*, pg. 6393
MTU ASIA PTE. LTD.—See Rolls-Royce Holdings plc; *Int'l*, pg. 6393
MTU BENELUX B.V.—See Rolls-Royce Holdings plc; *Int'l*, pg. 6393
MTU CHINA CO. LTD.—See Rolls-Royce Holdings plc; *Int'l*, pg. 6393
MTU DD BENELUX B.V.—See Rolls-Royce Holdings plc; *Int'l*, pg. 6393
MTU DETROIT DIESEL ISRAEL LTD.—See Rolls-Royce Holdings plc; *Int'l*, pg. 6393
MTU DETROIT DIESEL UK LTD—See Rolls-Royce Holdings plc; *Int'l*, pg. 6393
MTU DO BRASIL LTDA.—See Rolls-Royce Holdings plc; *Int'l*, pg. 6393
MTU ENGINEERING (SUZHOU) CO. LTD.—See Rolls-Royce Holdings plc; *Int'l*, pg. 6393
MTU FRANCE SAS—See Rolls-Royce Holdings plc; *Int'l*, pg. 6393
MTU FRIEDRICHSHAFEN GMBH—See Rolls-Royce Holdings plc; *Int'l*, pg. 6393
MTU HONG KONG LIMITED—See Rolls-Royce Holdings plc; *Int'l*, pg. 6391
MTU IBERICA PROPULSION Y ENERGIA S.L.—See Rolls-Royce Holdings plc; *Int'l*, pg. 6394
MTU INDIA PVT. LTD.—See Rolls-Royce Holdings plc; *Int'l*, pg. 6393
MTU ITALIA S.R.L.—See Rolls-Royce Holdings plc; *Int'l*, pg. 6394
MTU JAPAN CO. LIMITED—See Rolls-Royce Holdings plc; *Int'l*, pg. 6391
MTU KOREA LIMITED—See Rolls-Royce Holdings plc; *Int'l*, pg. 6391
MTU MAINTENANCE BERLIN-BRANDENBURG GMBH—See MTU Aero Engines AG; *Int'l*, pg. 5072
MTU MAINTENANCE CANADA LTD.—See MTU Aero Engines AG; *Int'l*, pg. 5072
MTU MAINTENANCE DALLAS INC.—See MTU Aero Engines AG; *Int'l*, pg. 5072
MTU MAINTENANCE DO BRASIL LTDA.—See MTU Aero Engines AG; *Int'l*, pg. 5072
MTU MAINTENANCE HANNOVER GMBH—See MTU Aero Engines AG; *Int'l*, pg. 5072
MTU MAINTENANCE IGTSERVICE DO BRASIL LTD.—See MTU Aero Engines AG; *Int'l*, pg. 5072
MTU MAINTENANCE LEASE SERVICES B.V.—See MTU Aero Engines AG; *Int'l*, pg. 5072
MTU MAINTENANCE SERBIA D.O.O—See MTU Aero Engines AG; *Int'l*, pg. 5072
MTU MAINTENANCE SERVICE CENTER AYUTTHAYA LTD.—See MTU Aero Engines AG; *Int'l*, pg. 5072
MTU MAINTENANCE SERVICE CENTRE AUSTRALIA PTY. LTD.—See MTU Aero Engines AG; *Int'l*, pg. 5072
MTU MAINTENANCE SERVICE CENTRE AYUTTHAYA LTD.—See MTU Aero Engines AG; *Int'l*, pg. 5072
MTU MARUBENI CO. LTD.—See Rolls-Royce Holdings plc; *Int'l*, pg. 6393
MTU MOJE TOWARZYSTWO UBEZPIECZENIOWE S. A.—See Munchener Ruckversicherungs AG; *Int'l*, pg. 5089
MTU MOTOR TURBIN SANAYI VE TICARET A.S.—See Rolls-Royce Holdings plc; *Int'l*, pg. 6394

MTU AERO ENGINES AG
CORPORATE AFFILIATIONS

MTUNZINI FOREST LODGE—See Gooderson Leisure Corporation; *Int'l*, pg. 3040
MTU ONSITE ENERGY GMBH—See Rolls-Royce Holdings plc; *Int'l*, pg. 6394
MTU ONSITE ENERGY—See Rolls-Royce Holdings plc; *Int'l*, pg. 6393
MTU POLSKA SP. Z O.O.—See Rolls-Royce Holdings plc; *Int'l*, pg. 6391
MTU REMAN TECHNOLOGIES GMBH—See Rolls-Royce Holdings plc; *Int'l*, pg. 6394
MTU SOUTH AFRICA PTY. LTD.—See Rolls-Royce Holdings plc; *Int'l*, pg. 6394
MTU TURBOMECA ROLLS-ROYCE GMBH—See MTU Aero Engines AG; *Int'l*, pg. 5072
MTU TURBOMECA ROLLS-ROYCE GMBH—See Safran SA; *Int'l*, pg. 6476
MTU UK LTD.—See Rolls-Royce Holdings plc; *Int'l*, pg. 6394
MTU VIETNAM CO. LTD.—See Rolls-Royce Holdings plc; *Int'l*, pg. 6393
MTV CHANNEL ESPANA S.L.U.—See National Amusements, Inc.; *U.S. Private*, pg. 2841
MT VENTURES INC.—See Jackpot Digital Inc.; *Int'l*, pg. 3864
MTV HONG KONG LIMITED—See National Amusements, Inc.; *U.S. Private*, pg. 2841
MTV NETWORKS AFRICA (PTY) LIMITED—See National Amusements, Inc.; *U.S. Private*, pg. 2841
MTV NETWORKS AUSTRALIA PTY LTD—See National Amusements, Inc.; *U.S. Private*, pg. 2841
MTV NETWORKS BELGIUM BVBA—See National Amusements, Inc.; *U.S. Private*, pg. 2841
MTV NETWORKS B.V.—See National Amusements, Inc.; *U.S. Private*, pg. 2841
MTV NETWORKS COMPANY—See National Amusements, Inc.; *U.S. Private*, pg. 2841
MTV NETWORKS GERMANY GMBH—See National Amusements, Inc.; *U.S. Private*, pg. 2841
MTV NETWORKS JAPAN K.K.—See National Amusements, Inc.; *U.S. Private*, pg. 2841
MTV NETWORKS LATIN AMERICA INC.—See National Amusements, Inc.; *U.S. Private*, pg. 2841
MTV NETWORKS LTDA—See National Amusements, Inc.; *U.S. Private*, pg. 2841
MTV NETWORKS ON CAMPUS INC.—See National Amusements, Inc.; *U.S. Private*, pg. 2841
MTV NETWORKS POLSKA B.V.—See National Amusements, Inc.; *U.S. Private*, pg. 2841
MTV NETWORKS SCHWEIZ AG—See National Amusements, Inc.; *U.S. Private*, pg. 2842
MTVN VIDEO HITS INC.—See National Amusements, Inc.; *U.S. Private*, pg. 2842
MTV OWNERSHIP (PORTUGAL), LDA—See National Amusements, Inc.; *U.S. Private*, pg. 2842
MTV OY—See Bonnier AB; *Int'l*, pg. 1109
MTV PUBBLICITA S.R.L.—See National Amusements, Inc.; *U.S. Private*, pg. 2842
MTV SISALLOT OY—See Bonnier AB; *Int'l*, pg. 1109
MT. WASHINGTON ASSURANCE CORPORATION—See The Plymouth Rock Co.; *U.S. Private*, pg. 4097
MT WATERWORKS, LLC—See Dakota Supply Group Inc.; *U.S. Private*, pg. 1147
MTWO AG—See Schneider Electric SE; *Int'l*, pg. 6625
MTX WEALTH MANAGEMENT, LLC—See Keystone Group, L.P.; *U.S. Private*, pg. 2297
MTY FOOD GROUP INC.; *Int'l*, pg. 5072
MTZ POLYFILMS LIMITED; *Int'l*, pg. 5073
MUA INSURANCE ACCEPTANCES (PTY.) LTD.—See Talanx AG; *Int'l*, pg. 7445
MUA INSURANCE (KENYA) LIMITED—See MUA Ltd.; *Int'l*, pg. 5073
MUA INSURANCE (RWANDA) LIMITED—See MUA Ltd.; *Int'l*, pg. 5073
MUA INSURANCE (UGANDA) LIMITED—See MUA Ltd.; *Int'l*, pg. 5073
MUA LTD.; *Int'l*, pg. 5073
MUAMALAT INVEST SDN. BHD.—See DRB-HICOM Berhad; *Int'l*, pg. 2202
MUANALYSIS INC.—See Grafoid, Inc.; *Int'l*, pg. 3050
MUANG MAI GUTHRIE PUBLIC COMPANY LIMITED - PHUKET PLANT—See Muang Mai Guthrie Public Company Limited; *Int'l*, pg. 5073
MUANG MAI GUTHRIE PUBLIC COMPANY LIMITED; *Int'l*, pg. 5073
MUANG MAI GUTHRIE PUBLIC COMPANY LIMITED - SURATTHANI PLANT—See Muang Mai Guthrie Public Company Limited; *Int'l*, pg. 5073
MUANG MAI GUTHRIE PUBLIC COMPANY LIMITED - THUNGSONG PLANT—See Muang Mai Guthrie Public Company Limited; *Int'l*, pg. 5073
MUANGTHAI CAPITAL PUBLIC COMPANY LIMITED; *Int'l*, pg. 5073
MUANG THAI INSURANCE PUBLIC COMPANY LIMITED; *Int'l*, pg. 5073
MUANG THAI LIFE ASSURANCE CO., LTD.—See Ageas SA/NV; *Int'l*, pg. 205
MUANGTHONG CERAMIC CO., LTD.—See Dynasty Ceramic Public Company Limited; *Int'l*, pg. 2242

MUANG THONG SEIKO LTD.—See Seiko Group Corporation; *Int'l*, pg. 6688
MUAR BAN LEE GROUP BERHAD; *Int'l*, pg. 5073
MUBADALA INVESTMENT COMPANY PJSC; *Int'l*, pg. 5074
MUBADALA PETROLEUM LLC—See Mubadala Investment Company PJSC; *Int'l*, pg. 5076
MUBADALA PETROLEUM (SE ASIA) LIMITED—See Mubadala Investment Company PJSC; *Int'l*, pg. 5076
MUBARAK TEXTILE MILLS LIMITED; *Int'l*, pg. 5076
MUBARRAD HOLDING COMPANY (K.S.C)—See A'ayan Leasing and Investment Company KSCC; *Int'l*, pg. 19
MUBASHER FINANCIAL SERVICES BSC—See National Technology Group; *Int'l*, pg. 5164
MUBELL FINANCE, LLC—See Shore Bancshares, Inc.; *U.S. Public*, pg. 1875
MUBELO ELECTRICAL PROPRIETARY LIMITED—See The Bidvest Group Limited; *Int'l*, pg. 7625
MU BUSINESS ENGINEERING, LTD.—See Mitsubishi UFJ Financial Group, Inc.; *Int'l*, pg. 4969
MUCA WELLNESS SDN. BHD.—See MY E.G. Services Berhad; *Int'l*, pg. 5111
MUCELL EXTRUSION LLC—See Zotefoams plc; *Int'l*, pg. 8690
MUCH ASPHALT (PROPRIETARY) LIMITED—See AECI Limited; *Int'l*, pg. 171
MUCHNIK, ALURRALDE, JASPER & ASSOC./MS&L—See Publicis Groupe S.A.; *Int'l*, pg. 6103
MUCHO MOVIES, INC.—See Lions Gate Entertainment Corp.; *Int'l*, pg. 4521
MUCOS EMULSIONSGESELLSCHAFT MBH—See Nestle S.A.; *Int'l*, pg. 5206
MUCOS PHARMA CZ, S.R.O.—See Nestle S.A.; *Int'l*, pg. 5203
MUCOS PHARMA GMBH & CO. KG—See Nestle S.A.; *Int'l*, pg. 5203
MUCOS PHARMA VERWALTUNGS GMBH—See Nestle S.A.; *Int'l*, pg. 5206
MUDA HOLDINGS BERHAD; *Int'l*, pg. 5076
MUDAJAYA CORPORATION BERHAD—See Mudajaya Group Berhad; *Int'l*, pg. 5077
MUDAJAYA GROUP BERHAD; *Int'l*, pg. 5077
MUDAJAYA LAND SDN BHD—See Mudajaya Group Berhad; *Int'l*, pg. 5077
MUDANJIANG HENGFENG PAPER CO., LTD.; *Int'l*, pg. 5077
MUDANJIANG OTC WELDING MACHINES CO., LTD.—See Daihen Corporation; *Int'l*, pg. 1926
MUDA PACKAGING INDUSTRIES (QINGYUAN) LTD.—See Muda Holdings Berhad; *Int'l*, pg. 5076
MUDA PACKAGING INDUSTRIES SDN. BHD.—See Muda Holdings Berhad; *Int'l*, pg. 5076
MUDA PAPER CONVERTING SDN. BHD.—See Muda Holdings Berhad; *Int'l*, pg. 5077
MUDA PAPER MILLS SDN. BHD.—See Muda Holdings Berhad; *Int'l*, pg. 5077
MUDA PASIFIK SDN. BHD.—See Muda Holdings Berhad; *Int'l*, pg. 5077
MUD BAY DRILLING LTD.—See VINCI S.A.; *Int'l*, pg. 8224
MUDD ADVERTISING; *U.S. Private*, pg. 2810
MUDD ADVERTISING—See Mudd Advertising; *U.S. Private*, pg. 2810
MUDD-LYMAN SALES & SERVICES CORPORATION; *U.S. Private*, pg. 2810
MU-DEL ELECTRONICS, INC.—See Ironwave Technologies LLC; *U.S. Private*, pg. 2140
MUD HOUSE WINE—See The Carlyle Group Inc.; *U.S. Public*, pg. 2044
MUDIT FINLEASE LIMITED; *Int'l*, pg. 5077
MUDIX JOINT STOCK COMPANY; *Int'l*, pg. 5077
MUDLOGGING SYSTEMS, INC.—See ALS Limited; *Int'l*, pg. 379
MUDMAN PUBLIC COMPANY LIMITED—See Subsrithai Public Company Limited; *Int'l*, pg. 7249
MUD PIE LLC; *U.S. Private*, pg. 2810
MUDRA COMMUNICATIONS PVT. LTD.—See Omnicom Group Inc.; *U.S. Public*, pg. 1582
MUDRA FINANCIAL SERVICES LIMITED; *Int'l*, pg. 5077
MUDRICK CAPITAL ACQUISITION CORPORATION II; *U.S. Public*, pg. 1484
MUDRICK CAPITAL MANAGEMENT L.P.; *U.S. Private*, pg. 2810
MUDUNURU LIMITED; *Int'l*, pg. 5077
MUEBLES FINO BUENO S.A.—See Good Companies; *U.S. Private*, pg. 1737
MUEGGE GMBH—See Harald Quandt Holding GmbH; *Int'l*, pg. 3270
MUEHLBAUER HOLDING AG; *Int'l*, pg. 5077
MUEHLHAN AG; *Int'l*, pg. 5077
MUEHLHAN A/S—See Muehlhan AG; *Int'l*, pg. 5077
MUEHLHAN BULGARIA LTD.—See Muehlhan AG; *Int'l*, pg. 5077
MUEHLHAN B.V.—See Muehlhan AG; *Int'l*, pg. 5077
MUEHLHAN CANADA INC.—See Muehlhan AG; *Int'l*, pg. 5077
MUEHLHAN CYPRUS LIMITED—See Muehlhan AG; *Int'l*, pg. 5077
MUEHLHAN DEHAN QATAR W.L.L.—See Muehlhan AG; *Int'l*, pg. 5077

MUEHLHAN DEUTSCHLAND GMBH—See Muehlhan AG; *Int'l*, pg. 5077
MUEHLHAN ELLAS S.A.—See Muehlhan AG; *Int'l*, pg. 5077
MUEHLHAN HELLAS S.A.—See Muehlhan AG; *Int'l*, pg. 5077
MUEHLHAN INDUSTRIAL SERVICES LTD.—See Muehlhan AG; *Int'l*, pg. 5077
MUEHLHAN MORFLOT OOO—See Muehlhan AG; *Int'l*, pg. 5077
MUEHLHAN POLSKA SP. Z O.O.—See Muehlhan AG; *Int'l*, pg. 5077
MUEHLHAN S.A.R.L.—See Muehlhan AG; *Int'l*, pg. 5077
MUEHLHAN WIND SERVICE A/S—See Muehlhan AG; *Int'l*, pg. 5077
MUEHL PRODUCT & SERVICE AG; *Int'l*, pg. 5077
MUEHLSTEIN HOLDING CORPORATION—See Ravago Holding S.A.; *Int'l*, pg. 6222
MUEHLSTEIN INTERNATIONAL LTD.—See Ravago Holding S.A.; *Int'l*, pg. 6222
MUELINK & GROL B.V.—See Egeria Capital Management B.V.; *Int'l*, pg. 2323
MUELLER BRASS CO.—See Mueller Industries, Inc.; *U.S. Public*, pg. 1484
MUELLER BRASS FORGING COMPANY, INC.—See Mueller Industries, Inc.; *U.S. Public*, pg. 1484
MUELLER CANADA HOLDINGS CORP.—See Mueller Water Products, Inc.; *U.S. Public*, pg. 1485
MUELLER CANADA LTD. - ECHOLOGICS DIVISION—See Mueller Water Products, Inc.; *U.S. Public*, pg. 1485
MUELLER CANADA LTD.—See Mueller Water Products, Inc.; *U.S. Public*, pg. 1485
MUELLER CO. LTD.—See Mueller Water Products, Inc.; *U.S. Public*, pg. 1486
MUELLER COMERCIAL DE MEXICO S. DE R.L. DE C.V.—See Mueller Industries, Inc.; *U.S. Public*, pg. 1485
MUELLER CONCRETE CONSTRUCTION COMPANY—See Primoris Services Corporation; *U.S. Public*, pg. 1719
MUELLER COPPER FITTINGS COMPANY, INC.—See Mueller Industries, Inc.; *U.S. Public*, pg. 1485
MUELLER COPPER TUBE COMPANY, INC.—See Mueller Industries, Inc.; *U.S. Public*, pg. 1484
MUELLER COPPER TUBE PRODUCTS, INC.—See Mueller Industries, Inc.; *U.S. Public*, pg. 1485
MUELLER CORPORATION; *U.S. Private*, pg. 2810
MUELLER DENMARK APS—See Mueller Water Products, Inc.; *U.S. Public*, pg. 1486
MUELLER DIE CUT SOLUTIONS, INC.—See Sur-Seal, Inc.; *U.S. Private*, pg. 3883
MUELLER ELECTRIC COMPANY; *U.S. Private*, pg. 2810
MUELLER EUROPE INVESTMENT COMPANY LTD.—See Mueller Industries, Inc.; *U.S. Public*, pg. 1485
MUELLER EUROPE LTD.—See Mueller Industries, Inc.; *U.S. Public*, pg. 1485
MUELLER FIELD OPERATIONS, INC.; *U.S. Private*, pg. 2810
MUELLER FITTINGS COMPANY—See Mueller Industries, Inc.; *U.S. Public*, pg. 1484
MUELLER FORMED TUBE COMPANY, INC.—See Mueller Industries, Inc.; *U.S. Public*, pg. 1484
MUELLER GRAPHIC SUPPLY INC.; *U.S. Private*, pg. 2810
MUELLER IMPACTS COMPANY, INC.—See Mueller Industries, Inc.; *U.S. Public*, pg. 1484
MUELLER INC.; *U.S. Private*, pg. 2810
MUELLER INDUSTRIES, INC.; *U.S. Public*, pg. 1484
MUELLER INTERNATIONAL, LLC—See Mueller Water Products, Inc.; *U.S. Public*, pg. 1486
MUELLER JAPAN—See Mueller Sports Medicine, Inc.; *U.S. Private*, pg. 2810
MUELLER LICHTENVOORDE B.V.—See Paul Mueller Company; *U.S. Public*, pg. 1655
MUELLER METALS INC.; *U.S. Private*, pg. 2810
MUELLER MIDDLE EAST B.S.C.—See Mueller Industries, Inc.; *U.S. Public*, pg. 1485
MUELLER MIDDLE EAST (FZE)—See Mueller Water Products, Inc.; *U.S. Public*, pg. 1485
MUELLER PACKAGING, LLC—See Mueller Industries, Inc.; *U.S. Public*, pg. 1484
MUELLER PLASTICS CORPORATION, INC.—See Mueller Industries, Inc.; *U.S. Public*, pg. 1484
MUELLER PLASTICS CORPORATION, INC.—See Mueller Industries, Inc.; *U.S. Public*, pg. 1484
MUELLER PLASTICS CORPORATION, INC.—See Mueller Industries, Inc.; *U.S. Public*, pg. 1484
MUELLER PROPERTY HOLDINGS, LLC—See Mueller Water Products, Inc.; *U.S. Public*, pg. 1486
MUELLER REFRIGERATION LLC—See Mueller Industries, Inc.; *U.S. Public*, pg. 1484
MUELLER REFRIGERATION PRODUCTS COMPANY, INC.—See Mueller Industries, Inc.; *U.S. Public*, pg. 1484
MUELLER ROOFING DISTRIBUTORS INC.; *U.S. Private*, pg. 2810
MUELLER SALES CORP.—See Central States Industrial Supply, Inc.; *U.S. Private*, pg. 825

COMPANY NAME INDEX

MUELLER SERVICE CO., LLC—See Mueller Water Products, Inc.; *U.S. Public*, pg. 1486
MUELLER SERVICES, INC.; *U.S. Private*, pg. 2810
MUELLER SOUTHEAST, INC.—See Mueller Industries, Inc.; *U.S. Public*, pg. 1484
MUELLER SPORTS MEDICINE, INC.; *U.S. Private*, pg. 2810
MUELLER STEAM SPECIALTY—See Watts Water Technologies, Inc.; *U.S. Public*, pg. 2337
MUELLER STREAMLINE COPPER AND BRASS LTD.—See Mueller Industries, Inc.; *U.S. Public*, pg. 1485
MUELLER STREAMLINE CO.—See Mueller Industries, Inc.; *U.S. Public*, pg. 1484
MUELLER SV, LTD.—See Mueller Water Products, Inc.; *U.S. Public*, pg. 1485
MUELLER SYSTEMS, LLC—See Mueller Water Products, Inc.; *U.S. Public*, pg. 1486
MUELLER TRANSPORTATION, INC.—See Paul Mueller Company; *U.S. Public*, pg. 1655
MUELLER WATER PRODUCTS, INC.; *U.S. Public*, pg. 1485
MUELLES DE PENCO S.A.; *Int'l*, pg. 5077
MUELLES Y BALLESTAS HISPANI-ALEMANAS S.A.—See NHK Spring Co., Ltd.; *Int'l*, pg. 5257
MUELLES Y BALLESTAS HISPANI-ALEMANAS S.A.—See The Boler Company; *U.S. Private*, pg. 3996
MUE MATERIALS TAIWAIN CO., LTD.—See Mitsubishi Materials Corporation; *Int'l*, pg. 4965
MUE MATERIALS TAIWAN CO., LTD.—See Mitsubishi Materials Corporation; *Int'l*, pg. 4964
MUENCHENER TIERPARK HELLABRUNN AG; *Int'l*, pg. 5078
MUENCH-KREUZER CANDLE COMPANY; *U.S. Private*, pg. 2810
MUENSTER MILLING COMPANY, LLC—See Kainos Capital, LLC; *U.S. Private*, pg. 2255
MUFFLER MAN SUPPLY CO; *U.S. Private*, pg. 2811
MUFFLER AMERICAS HOLDINGS CORPORATION—See Mitsubishi UFJ Financial Group, Inc.; *Int'l*, pg. 4970
MUFG BANK (CHINA), LTD.—See Mitsubishi UFJ Financial Group, Inc.; *Int'l*, pg. 4969
MUFG BANK (EUROPE) N.V.—See Mitsubishi UFJ Financial Group, Inc.; *Int'l*, pg. 4970
MUFG BANK LTD.—See Mitsubishi UFJ Financial Group, Inc.; *Int'l*, pg. 4969
MUFG BANK, LTD.—See Mitsubishi UFJ Financial Group, Inc.; *Int'l*, pg. 4970
MUFG BANK MEXICO, S.A.—See Mitsubishi UFJ Financial Group, Inc.; *Int'l*, pg. 4970
MUFG BANK TURKEY ANONIM SIRKETI—See Mitsubishi UFJ Financial Group, Inc.; *Int'l*, pg. 4970
MUFG CAPITAL ANALYTICS, LLC—See Mitsubishi UFJ Financial Group, Inc.; *Int'l*, pg. 4972
MUFG INVESTOR SERVICES FINTECH LIMITED—See Mitsubishi UFJ Financial Group, Inc.; *Int'l*, pg. 4970
MUFG INVESTOR SERVICES (US), LLC—See Mitsubishi UFJ Financial Group, Inc.; *Int'l*, pg. 4972
MUFG LUX MANAGEMENT COMPANY S.A.—See Mitsubishi UFJ Financial Group, Inc.; *Int'l*, pg. 4970
MUFG PARTICIPATION (THAILAND) CO., LTD.—See Mitsubishi UFJ Financial Group, Inc.; *Int'l*, pg. 4970
MUFG SECURITIES AMERICAS INC.—See Mitsubishi UFJ Financial Group, Inc.; *Int'l*, pg. 4971
MUFG SECURITIES ASIA LIMITED—See Mitsubishi UFJ Financial Group, Inc.; *Int'l*, pg. 4970
MUFG SECURITIES (CANADA), LTD.—See Mitsubishi UFJ Financial Group, Inc.; *Int'l*, pg. 4970
MUFG UNION BANK, N.A.—See U.S. Bancorp; *U.S. Public*, pg. 2212
MUFIN GMBH.—See MAGIX AG; *Int'l*, pg. 4638
MUFIN GREEN FINANCE LIMITED; *Int'l*, pg. 5078
MUF - PRO S.R.O.—See Dominique Dutscher SAS; *Int'l*, pg. 2161
MUGELLO CIRCUIT S.P.A.—See Stellantis N.V.; *Int'l*, pg. 7200
MUGEN ESTATE CO., LTD.; *Int'l*, pg. 5078
MUGEN FUNDING CO., LTD.—See Mugen Estate Co., Ltd.; *Int'l*, pg. 5078
MUGEN INVESTMENT ADVISORS CO., LTD.—See Mugen Estate Co., Ltd.; *Int'l*, pg. 5078
MUGG & BEAN FRANCHISING (PTY) LTD.—See Famous Brands Limited; *Int'l*, pg. 2612
MUGHAL IRON & STEEL INDUSTRIES LTD.; *Int'l*, pg. 5078
MUGINOHO CO., LTD.—See Mitsubishi Corporation; *Int'l*, pg. 4940
MUGIPANKOUBOU CO., LTD.—See Kobe Bussan Co., Ltd.; *Int'l*, pg. 4217
MUGSTYLE CO., LTD.—See PAL GROUP Holdings Co., Ltd.; *Int'l*, pg. 5705
MUHAK CO., LTD.; *Int'l*, pg. 5078
MU HANDS-ON CAPITAL CO., LTD.—See Mitsubishi UFJ Financial Group, Inc.; *Int'l*, pg. 4971
MUHAN INVESTMENT CO., LTD.; *Int'l*, pg. 5078
MUHIBBAH AIRLINE SUPPORT INDUSTRIES SDN. BHD.—See Muhibbah Engineering (M) Bhd.; *Int'l*, pg. 5078

MUHIBBAH CONSTRUCTION PTY. LTD.—See Muhibbah Engineering (M) Bhd.; *Int'l*, pg. 5078
MUHIBBAH ENGINEERING (CAMBODIA) CO. LTD.—See Muhibbah Engineering (M) Bhd.; *Int'l*, pg. 5078
MUHIBBAH ENGINEERING CO (QATAR)—See Muhibbah Engineering (M) Bhd.; *Int'l*, pg. 5079
MUHIBBAH ENGINEERING (M) BHD.; *Int'l*, pg. 5078
MUHIBBAH ENGINEERING MIDDLE EAST LLC—See Muhibbah Engineering (M) Bhd.; *Int'l*, pg. 5079
MUHIBBAH ENGINEERING (PHILIPPINES) CORPORATION—See Muhibbah Engineering (M) Bhd.; *Int'l*, pg. 5079
MUHIBBAH ENGINEERING (SINGAPORE) PTE. LTD.—See Muhibbah Engineering (M) Bhd.; *Int'l*, pg. 5079
MUHIBBAH MARINE ENGINEERING (DEUTSCHLAND) GMBH—See Muhibbah Engineering (M) Bhd.; *Int'l*, pg. 5079
MUHIBBAH MARINE ENGINEERING SDN. BHD.—See Muhibbah Engineering (M) Bhd.; *Int'l*, pg. 5079
MUHIBBAH OFFSHORE SERVICES LTD.—See Muhibbah Engineering (M) Bhd.; *Int'l*, pg. 5079
MUHIBBAH PERMAI SDN BHD—See Sunway Berhad; *Int'l*, pg. 7329
MUHIBBAH PETROCHEMICAL ENGINEERING SDN. BHD..—See Muhibbah Engineering (M) Bhd.; *Int'l*, pg. 5079
MUHIBBAH REEFERS SDN. BHD.—See Muhibbah Engineering (M) Bhd.; *Int'l*, pg. 5079
MUHIBBAH STEEL INDUSTRIES SDN. BHD.—See Muhibbah Engineering (M) Bhd.; *Int'l*, pg. 5079
MUHLEHOF GEWURZE AG—See International Flavors & Fragrances Inc.; *U.S. Public*, pg. 1154
MUHLENBERG COMMUNITY HOSPITAL; *U.S. Private*, pg. 2811
MUHLENBERG GREENE ARCHITECTS LTD.; *U.S. Private*, pg. 2811
MUHLENBRUCH STINNES GMBH & CO. KG—See Marquard & Bahls AG; *Int'l*, pg. 4699
MUHLENDORFER KREIDEFABRIK MARGIT HOFFMAN-OSTENHOF KG—See Omya (Schweiz) AG; *Int'l*, pg. 5570
MUHLENHOFF + PARTNER GMBH—See Randstad N.V.; *Int'l*, pg. 6202
MUHR UND BENDER KG—See Brd. Klee A/S; *Int'l*, pg. 1143
MU INVESTMENTS CO., LTD.—See Mitsubishi UFJ Financial Group, Inc.; *Int'l*, pg. 4969
MUI PROPERTIES BERHAD—See Malayan United Industries Berhad; *Int'l*, pg. 4661
MUIR/DIABLO OCCUPATIONAL MEDICINE—See Community Health Systems, Inc.; *U.S. Public*, pg. 555
MUIR ENTERPRISES INC; *U.S. Private*, pg. 2811
MUIRHEAD AEROSPACE—See AMETEK, Inc.; *U.S. Public*, pg. 117
MUJI CANADA LIMITED—See Ryohin Keikaku Co., Ltd.; *Int'l*, pg. 6441
MUJI DEUTSCHLAND GMBH—See Ryohin Keikaku Co., Ltd.; *Int'l*, pg. 6441
MUJI EUROPE HOLDINGS LIMITED—See Ryohin Keikaku Co., Ltd.; *Int'l*, pg. 6441
MUJI FINLAND OY—See Ryohin Keikaku Co., Ltd.; *Int'l*, pg. 6441
MUJI (HONG KONG) CO., LTD.—See Ryohin Keikaku Co., Ltd.; *Int'l*, pg. 6441
MUJI HOUSE CO., LTD.—See Ryohin Keikaku Co., Ltd.; *Int'l*, pg. 6441
MUJI KOREA CO., LTD.—See Ryohin Keikaku Co., Ltd.; *Int'l*, pg. 6441
MUJI PORTUGAL, LDA.—See Ryohin Keikaku Co., Ltd.; *Int'l*, pg. 6441
MUJI RETAIL (AUSTRALIA) PTY. LTD.—See Ryohin Keikaku Co., Ltd.; *Int'l*, pg. 6441
MUJI (SINGAPORE) PRIVATE LTD.—See Ryohin Keikaku Co., Ltd.; *Int'l*, pg. 6441
MUJI SPAIN, S.L.—See Ryohin Keikaku Co., Ltd.; *Int'l*, pg. 6441
MUJI SWITZERLAND AG—See Ryohin Keikaku Co., Ltd.; *Int'l*, pg. 6441
MUJI U.S.A. LTD.—See Mitsubishi Corporation; *Int'l*, pg. 4942
MUKAFAT PORTFOY YONETIMI A.S.—See Aktif Yatirim Bankasi A.S.; *Int'l*, pg. 267
MUKA METAL TICARET VE SANAYI ANONIM SIRKETI—See Stryker Corporation; *U.S. Public*, pg. 1956
MUKAND ENGINEERS LTD—See Bajaj Auto Ltd.; *Int'l*, pg. 804
MUKAND LTD.—See Bajaj Auto Ltd.; *Int'l*, pg. 804
MUKESH BABU FINANCIAL SERVICES LTD; *Int'l*, pg. 5079
MUKESH BABU SECURITIES LIMITED—See Mukesh Babu Financial Services Ltd; *Int'l*, pg. 5079
MUKESH STEELS LIMITED; *Int'l*, pg. 5079
MUKHTAR TEXTILE MILLS LIMITED; *Int'l*, pg. 5079
MUKLUK TELEPHONE COMPANY INC—See Telalaska Inc.; *U.S. Private*, pg. 3959
MUKOGAWA KASEI CORPORATION—See Tigers Polymer Corporation; *Int'l*, pg. 7746

MULLER DIE LILA LOGISTIK AG

MUKTA ARTS LTD; *Int'l*, pg. 5079
MUKTINATH BIKAS BANK LIMITED; *Int'l*, pg. 5079
MUKTINATH CAPITAL LIMITED—See Muktinath Bikas Bank Limited; *Int'l*, pg. 5079
MUKUNDAN HOLDINGS LTD—See The Braj Binani Group; *Int'l*, pg. 7627
MULANN SA; *Int'l*, pg. 5079
MULAUT ABATTOIR SDN. BHD—See Royal Brunei Airlines Sdn. Bhd.; *Int'l*, pg. 6411
MULBERRY COMPANY (SALES) LIMITED—See Mulberry Group plc; *Int'l*, pg. 5079
MULBERRY COMPANY (SWITZERLAND) GMBH—See Mulberry Group plc; *Int'l*, pg. 5079
MULBERRY FARM, LLC—See Dominion Energy, Inc.; *U.S. Public*, pg. 674
MULBERRY GRANGE (CASTLEFORD) MANAGEMENT COMPANY LIMITED—See Persimmon plc; *Int'l*, pg. 5816
MULBERRY GROUP PLC; *Int'l*, pg. 5079
MULBERRY JAPAN CO., LTD.—See Onward Holdings Co., Ltd.; *Int'l*, pg. 5592
MULBERRY LEARNING CENTRE AT TANJONG PAGAR PTE LTD—See NetDragon Websoft Holdings Limited; *Int'l*, pg. 5213
MULBERRY METAL PRODUCTS, INC.; *U.S. Private*, pg. 2811
MULBERRY MOTOR PARTS INC.; *U.S. Private*, pg. 2811
MULBERRYS, LLC; *U.S. Private*, pg. 2811
MUL BUSINESS COMPANY LIMITED—See Mitsubishi HC Capital Inc.; *Int'l*, pg. 4951
MULDER HEALTH CARE FACILITY, INC.; *U.S. Private*, pg. 2811
MULDER LIFTSERVICE B.V.—See ThyssenKrupp AG; *Int'l*, pg. 7725
MULDOON MARINE SERVICES, INC.—See GenNx360 Capital Partners, L.P.; *U.S. Private*, pg. 1672
MUL ECO-BUSINESS CO., LTD.—See Mitsubishi HC Capital Inc.; *Int'l*, pg. 4951
MULE-HIDE PRODUCTS CO., INC.—See Hendricks Holding Company, Inc.; *U.S. Private*, pg. 1915
MUL ENERGY INVESTMENT COMPANY LIMITED—See Mitsubishi HC Capital Inc.; *Int'l*, pg. 4952
MULESOFT ARGENTINA—See Salesforce, Inc.; *U.S. Public*, pg. 1837
MULESOFT AUSTRALIA—See Salesforce, Inc.; *U.S. Public*, pg. 1837
MULESOFT INC.—See Salesforce, Inc.; *U.S. Public*, pg. 1837
MULFORD PLASTICS (M) SDN BHD—See PT Impack Pratama Industri Tbk; *Int'l*, pg. 6044
MULGEE DIALYSIS, LLC—See DaVita Inc.; *U.S. Public*, pg. 641
THE MULGRAVE CENTRAL MILL CO., LTD.—See Mitr Phol Sugar Corporation Limited; *Int'l*, pg. 4927
MULHEARN REALTORS INC.; *U.S. Private*, pg. 2811
MULHEIM PIPECOATINGS GMBH—See Salzgitter AG; *Int'l*, pg. 6497
MULHERIN LUMBER CO; *U.S. Private*, pg. 2811
MULHERN BELTING, INC.; *U.S. Private*, pg. 2811
MULIANG VIAGOO TECHNOLOGY, INC.; *Int'l*, pg. 5079
MUL INSURANCE COMPANY LIMITED—See Mitsubishi HC Capital Inc.; *Int'l*, pg. 4952
MULLANE MOTORS; *U.S. Private*, pg. 2811
MULLANEY CORPORATION; *U.S. Private*, pg. 2811
MULLEN ADVERTISING & PUBLIC RELATIONS, INC.; *U.S. Private*, pg. 2811
MULLEN AUTOMOTIVE, INC.; *U.S. Public*, pg. 1486
MULLEN COMMUNICATIONS, INC.—See The Interpublic Group of Companies, Inc.; *U.S. Public*, pg. 2103
MULLEN GROUP LTD.; *Int'l*, pg. 5079
MULLENLOWE ACCRA—See The Interpublic Group of Companies, Inc.; *U.S. Public*, pg. 2092
MULLEN LOWE BRASIL—See The Interpublic Group of Companies, Inc.; *U.S. Public*, pg. 2092
MULLENLOWE GROUP; *Int'l*, pg. 5080
MULLEN LOWE LINTAS GROUP—See The Interpublic Group of Companies, Inc.; *U.S. Public*, pg. 2092
MULLEN MOTORS INC.; *U.S. Private*, pg. 2811
MULLEN OILFIELD SERVICES L.P.—See Mullen Group Ltd.; *Int'l*, pg. 5080
MULLEN—See The Interpublic Group of Companies, Inc.; *U.S. Public*, pg. 2103
MULLEN—See The Interpublic Group of Companies, Inc.; *U.S. Public*, pg. 2103
MULLEN—See The Interpublic Group of Companies, Inc.; *U.S. Public*, pg. 2103
MULLEN TESTERS—See Standex International; *U.S. Public*, pg. 1930
MULLEN TRUCKING L.P.—See Mullen Group Ltd.; *Int'l*, pg. 5080
MULLER BRESSLER BROWN; *U.S. Private*, pg. 2811
MULLER CONSTRUCTION SUPPLY; *U.S. Private*, pg. 2811
MULLER DAIRY (UK) LIMITED—See Unternehmensgruppe Theo Muller S.e.c.s.; *Int'l*, pg. 8085
MULLER DIE LILA LOGISTIK AG; *Int'l*, pg. 5080
MULLER - DIE LILA LOGISTIK BOBLINGEN GMBH—See Muller Die Lila Logistik AG; *Int'l*, pg. 5080

1841

MULLER DIE LILA LOGISTIK AG

MULLER - DIE LILA LOGISTIK CESKA K.S.—See Muller Die Lila Logistik AG; *Int'l*, pg. 5081
MULLER - DIE LILA LOGISTIK FULFILLMENT SOLUTIONS GMBH & CO. KG—See Muller Die Lila Logistik AG; *Int'l*, pg. 5081
MULLER - DIE LILA LOGISTIK MARBACH GMBH & CO. KG—See Muller Die Lila Logistik AG; *Int'l*, pg. 5081
MULLER - DIE LILA LOGISTIK MITTLERER NECKAR GMBH—See Muller Die Lila Logistik AG; *Int'l*, pg. 5081
MULLER - DIE LILA LOGISTIK NORD GMBH & CO. KG—See Muller Die Lila Logistik AG; *Int'l*, pg. 5081
MULLER - DIE LILA LOGISTIK OST GMBH & CO. KG—See Muller Die Lila Logistik AG; *Int'l*, pg. 5081
MULLER - DIE LILA LOGISTIK POLSKA SP. Z O.O.—See Muller Die Lila Logistik AG; *Int'l*, pg. 5081
MULLER - DIE LILA LOGISTIK ROUTE GMBH—See Muller Die Lila Logistik AG; *Int'l*, pg. 5081
MULLER - DIE LILA LOGISTIK SUD GMBH & CO. KG—See Muller Die Lila Logistik AG; *Int'l*, pg. 5081
MULLER - DIE LILA LOGISTIK SUDOST GMBH & CO. KG—See Muller Die Lila Logistik AG; *Int'l*, pg. 5081
MULLER - DIE LILA LOGISTIK SUDWEST GMBH & CO. KG—See Muller Die Lila Logistik AG; *Int'l*, pg. 5081
MULLER - DIE LILA LOGISTIK ZWENKAU GMBH—See Muller Die Lila Logistik AG; *Int'l*, pg. 5081
MULLER-ELEKTRONIK GMBH & CO. KG—See Trimble, Inc.; *U.S. Public*, pg. 2190
MULLER HRM ENGINEERING AB—See ATON GmbH; *Int'l*, pg. 689
MULLER INC.; *U.S. Private*, pg. 2811
MULLER INTERNATIONAL LTD—See Unternehmensgruppe Theo Muller S.e.c.s.; *Int'l*, pg. 8085
MULLER + KREMPEL AG—See Vetropack Holding AG; *Int'l*, pg. 8181
MULLER KUNSTSTOFFE GMBH—See HEXPOL AB; *Int'l*, pg. 3372
MULLER & PHIPPS (INDIA) LIMITED; *Int'l*, pg. 5080
MULLER-PINEHURST DAIRY INC.—See Prairie Farms Dairy, Inc.; *U.S. Private*, pg. 3242
MULLER'S MUHLE GMBH—See Raiffeisen-Holding Niederosterreich-Wien reg. Gen.m.b.H.; *Int'l*, pg. 6185
MULLER-STEINAG ELEMENT AG—See MULLER-STEINAG Group; *Int'l*, pg. 5081
MULLER-STEINAG GROUP; *Int'l*, pg. 5081
MULLER WISEMAN DAIRIES LIMITED—See Unternehmensgruppe Theo Muller S.e.c.s.; *Int'l*, pg. 8085
MULLICAN BA LUMBER & MANUFACTURING CO. INC.—See Baillie Lumber Co., Inc.; *U.S. Private*, pg. 426
MULLIGAN CONSTRUCTORS INC.; *U.S. Private*, pg. 2811
MULLIGAN LTD.; *U.S. Private*, pg. 2811
MULLIGAN'S BEACH HOUSE BAR & GRILL—See J.P.B. Enterprises, Inc.; *U.S. Private*, pg. 2170
MULLIGAN SECURITY CORP.—See Southfield Capital Advisors, LLC; *U.S. Private*, pg. 3736
MULLIGAN'S PTE LTD—See LifeBrandz Ltd.; *Int'l*, pg. 4494
MULLIGAN TECHNOLOGIES, INC.; *U.S. Private*, pg. 2811
MULLIN/ASHLEY ASSOCIATES, INC.; *U.S. Private*, pg. 2811
MULLINAX EAST, LLC—See AutoNation, Inc.; *U.S. Public*, pg. 236
MULLINAX FORD NORTH CANTON, INC.—See AutoNation, Inc.; *U.S. Public*, pg. 236
MULLINAX FORD SOUTH, INC.—See AutoNation, Inc.; *U.S. Public*, pg. 236
MULLINAX LINCOLN-MERCURY, INC.—See AutoNation, Inc.; *U.S. Public*, pg. 236
MULL INDUSTRIES INC.; *U.S. Private*, pg. 2811
MULLINIX PACKAGES INC.—See Sabert Corporation; *U.S. Private*, pg. 3520
MULLINS & ASSOCIATES INC.; *U.S. Private*, pg. 2811
MULLINS BUILDING PRODUCTS, INC.—See Platinum Equity, LLC; *U.S. Private*, pg. 3209
MULLINS FOOD PRODUCTS INC.; *U.S. Private*, pg. 2812
MULLION CO., LTD.; *Int'l*, pg. 5081
MULLVERWERTUNG BORSIGSTRASSE GMBH; *Int'l*, pg. 5081
MULOX DE MEXICO C. V.—See Greif Inc.; *U.S. Public*, pg. 967
MULPHA AUSTRALIA LIMITED—See Mulpha International Bhd.; *Int'l*, pg. 5081
MULPHA CAPITAL PARTNERS SDN BHD—See Mulpha International Bhd.; *Int'l*, pg. 5081
MULPHA HOTEL INVESTMENTS (AUSTRALIA) PTY LIMITED—See Mulpha International Bhd.; *Int'l*, pg. 5081
MULPHA HOTELS AUSTRALIA PTY LTD—See Mulpha International Bhd.; *Int'l*, pg. 5081
MULPHA INTERNATIONAL BHD.; *Int'l*, pg. 5081
MULPHA INVESTMENTS PTY LIMITED—See Mulpha International Bhd.; *Int'l*, pg. 5081
MULPHA PRIVATE WEALTH PTY. LIMITED—See Mulpha International Bhd.; *Int'l*, pg. 5081
MULPHA SANCTUARY COVE HARBOUR ONE PTY. LIMITED—See Mulpha International Bhd.; *Int'l*, pg. 5081

MULPHA TRANSPORT HOUSE PTY LIMITED—See Mulpha International Bhd.; *Int'l*, pg. 5081
MUL PRINCIPAL INVESTMENTS COMPANY LIMITED—See Mitsubishi HC Capital Inc.; *Int'l*, pg. 4952
MUL PROPERTY CO., LTD.—See Mitsubishi HC Capital Inc.; *Int'l*, pg. 4952
MUL RAILCARS, INC.—See Mitsubishi HC Capital Inc.; *Int'l*, pg. 4952
MUL REALTY ADVISERS COMPANY LIMITED—See Mitsubishi HC Capital Inc.; *Int'l*, pg. 4952
MUL REALTY INVESTMENT COMPANY LIMITED—See Mitsubishi HC Capital Inc.; *Int'l*, pg. 4952
MULSANNE GROUP HOLDING LIMITED; *Int'l*, pg. 5081
MULTAN FABRICS (PVT.) LIMITED—See Mahmood Group of Companies LLC; *Int'l*, pg. 4649
MULTANOVA AG; *Int'l*, pg. 5081
MULTEC ENTERPRISE SDN. BHD.—See Woodlandor Holdings Berhad; *Int'l*, pg. 8450
MULTEK BRAZIL LTDA—See Flex Ltd.; *Int'l*, pg. 2704
MULTEK CORPORATION—See Suzhou Dongshan Precision Manufacturing Co., Ltd.; *Int'l*, pg. 7349
MULTEK DISPLAY (HONG KONG) LIMITED—See Flex Ltd.; *Int'l*, pg. 2704
MULTEK FLEXIBLE CIRCUITS, INC.—See Flex Ltd.; *Int'l*, pg. 2703
MULTEK HONG KONG LIMITED—See Flex Ltd.; *Int'l*, pg. 2704
MULTELINK SERVICES PTY LIMITED—See Aware Super Pty Ltd; *Int'l*, pg. 752
MULTELINK SERVICES PTY LIMITED—See Macquarie Group Limited; *Int'l*, pg. 4629
MULTI24 SA; *Int'l*, pg. 5083
MULTI-AD, INC; *U.S. Private*, pg. 2812
MULTI-AD RECAS—See Multi-Ad, Inc.; *U.S. Private*, pg. 2812
MULTI-AERO, INC.—See Surf Air Mobility Inc.; *U.S. Public*, pg. 1967
MULTIAIR BELUX NV—See Atlas Copco AB; *Int'l*, pg. 683
MULTIAIR ITALIA S.R.L.—See Atlas Copco AB; *Int'l*, pg. 679
MULTI ASSET GLOBAL INVESTMENTS CO., LTD.—See Mirae Asset Financial Group; *Int'l*, pg. 4916
MULTIBAND CORPORATION—See Goodman Networks, Inc.; *U.S. Private*, pg. 1739
MULTIBAND NC INC.—See Goodman Networks, Inc.; *U.S. Private*, pg. 1739
MULTIBANK, INC.; *Int'l*, pg. 5083
MULTI-BANK SERVICES LTD.; *U.S. Private*, pg. 2812
MULTIBASE INDIA LIMITED—See Dow Inc.; *U.S. Public*, pg. 684
MULTIBASE S.A.—See DuPont de Nemours, Inc.; *U.S. Public*, pg. 694
MULTIBAX PCL; *Int'l*, pg. 5083
MULTIBIND BIOTECH GMBH—See Illinois Tool Works Inc.; *U.S. Public*, pg. 1109
MULTIBOND, INC.—See CFS Group, Inc.; *Int'l*, pg. 1430
MULTIBOND, INC.—See CFS Group, Inc.; *Int'l*, pg. 1430
MULTICAMPUS CORPORATION; *Int'l*, pg. 5083
MULTICANAL S.A.—See Grupo Clarin S.A.; *Int'l*, pg. 3125
MULTI CAPITAL GROUP I, LLC; *U.S. Private*, pg. 2812
MULTICARD AG—See Adon Production AG; *Int'l*, pg. 152
MULTICARD AUSTRALIA PTY LTD—See Identiv, Inc.; *U.S. Public*, pg. 1089
MULTICARD GMBH—See Mountain Capital Management AG; *Int'l*, pg. 5057
MULTICARD LTD.—See PannErgy Nyrt.; *Int'l*, pg. 5728
MULTICARD NETHERLANDS B.V.—See Mountain Capital Management AG; *Int'l*, pg. 5057
MULTICARE HEALTH SYSTEM; *U.S. Private*, pg. 2812
MULTICARE PHARMACEUTICALS PHILIPPINES, INC.—See Lupin Limited; *Int'l*, pg. 4586
MULTICARE - SEGUROS DE SAUDE, S.A.—See Fosun International Limited; *Int'l*, pg. 2752
MULTICARTA LTD—See PJSC VTB Bank; *Int'l*, pg. 5886
MULTICENTER S.R.L.—See Einhell Germany AG; *Int'l*, pg. 2334
MULTI CHANNEL SYSTEMS MCS GMBH—See Harvard Bioscience, Inc.; *U.S. Public*, pg. 987
MULTI-CHEM ELECTRONICS (KUNSHAN) CO., LTD.—See Multi-Chem Limited; *Int'l*, pg. 5082
MULTI-CHEM GROUP, LLC—See Halliburton Company; *U.S. Public*, pg. 980
MULTI-CHEM (HUAIAN) CO., LTD.—See Multi-Chem Limited; *Int'l*, pg. 5082
MULTI-CHEM LIMITED; *Int'l*, pg. 5082
MULTI-CHEM PCB (KUNSHAN) CO., LTD.—See Multi-Chem Limited; *Int'l*, pg. 5082
MULTI CHEVROLET INC.; *U.S. Private*, pg. 2812
MULTICHOICE ANGOLA LIMITADA—See MultiChoice Group Limited; *Int'l*, pg. 5083
MULTICHOICE GROUP LIMITED; *Int'l*, pg. 5083
MULTICHOICE KENYA LIMITED—See MultiChoice Group Limited; *Int'l*, pg. 5083
MULTICHOICE NIGERIA LIMITED—See MultiChoice Group Limited; *Int'l*, pg. 5083
MULTICHOICE SOUTH AFRICA HOLDINGS (PROPRIETARY) LIMITED—See MultiChoice Group Limited; *Int'l*, pg. 5083

CORPORATE AFFILIATIONS

MULTICHOICE ZAMBIA LIMITED—See MultiChoice Group Limited; *Int'l*, pg. 5083
MULTI-CLEAN, INC.—See L. Possehl & Co. mbH; *Int'l*, pg. 4383
MULTICLEAN, INC.—See L. Possehl & Co. mbH; *Int'l*, pg. 4383
MULTI-CODE ELECTRONICS INDUSTRIES (M) BERHAD—See MCE Holdings Berhad; *Int'l*, pg. 4758
MULTI-CODE TECHNOLOGIES (M) SDN. BHD.—See MCE Holdings Berhad; *Int'l*, pg. 4758
MULTI-COLOR (BAROSSA) PTY. LTD.—See Platinum Equity, LLC; *U.S. Private*, pg. 3206
MULTI-COLOR CLYDEBANK SCOTLAND LIMITED—See Platinum Equity, LLC; *U.S. Private*, pg. 3206
MULTI-COLOR CORPORATION—See Platinum Equity, LLC; *U.S. Private*, pg. 3206
MULTI-COLOR CORPORATION - WATERTOWN PLANT—See Platinum Equity, LLC; *U.S. Private*, pg. 3206
MULTI-COLOR DAVENTRY ENGLAND LTD.—See Platinum Equity, LLC; *U.S. Private*, pg. 3206
MULTI-COLOR (GRIFFITH) PTY. LTD.—See Platinum Equity, LLC; *U.S. Private*, pg. 3206
MULTI-COLOR HARO SPAIN, S.L.—See Platinum Equity, LLC; *U.S. Private*, pg. 3206
MULTI-COLOR ITALIA S.P.A.—See Platinum Equity, LLC; *U.S. Private*, pg. 3206
MULTI-COLOR LABEL CANADA CORPORATION—See Platinum Equity, LLC; *U.S. Private*, pg. 3206
MULTI-COLOR (QLD) PTY LTD—See Platinum Equity, LLC; *U.S. Private*, pg. 3206
MULTI-COLOR SUISSE S.A.—See Platinum Equity, LLC; *U.S. Private*, pg. 3206
MULTI COMMODITY EXCHANGE CLEARING CORPORATION LIMITED—See Multi Commodity Exchange of India Ltd.; *Int'l*, pg. 5081
MULTI COMMODITY EXCHANGE OF INDIA LTD.; *Int'l*, pg. 5081
MULTICONSULT ASA; *Int'l*, pg. 5083
MULTICONSULT ASIA PTE. LTD.—See Multiconsult ASA; *Int'l*, pg. 5083
MULTICONSULT POLSKA SP. Z O.O.—See Multiconsult ASA; *Int'l*, pg. 5083
MULTICONSULT UK LTD.—See Multiconsult ASA; *Int'l*, pg. 5083
MULTICORE SOLDERS LTD.—See Henkel AG & Co. KGaA; *Int'l*, pg. 3351
MULTICORP INTERNATIONAL, INC.; *U.S. Public*, pg. 1486
MULTICULTURAL COMMUNITY SERVICES OF THE PIONEER VALLEY, INC.; *U.S. Private*, pg. 2812
MULTICULTURAL HOME CARE, INC.—See ModivCare, Inc.; *U.S. Public*, pg. 1455
MULTI-CURRENCY FX CORP.—See First Metro Investment Corporation; *Int'l*, pg. 2685
MULTIDENT GMBH—See Fagron NV; *Int'l*, pg. 2603
MULTI DESIGNS COMPANY LIMITED—See Pico (Thailand) Public Company Limited; *Int'l*, pg. 5860
MULTIDIMENSIONALES S.A.—See Genstar Capital, LLC; *U.S. Private*, pg. 1679
MULTI DISCOVERY SDN. BHD.—See Ingress Corporation Berhad; *Int'l*, pg. 3703
MULTIEXPORT FOODS S.A.; *Int'l*, pg. 5083
MULTIEXPO SPOL SRO—See KPP Group Holdings Co., Ltd.; *Int'l*, pg. 4298
MULTIFAG AS; *Int'l*, pg. 5083
MULTIFAMILY TECHNOLOGY SOLUTIONS, INC.—See Thoma Bravo, L.P.; *U.S. Private*, pg. 4153
MULTIFIELD GEOPHYSICS AS—See CGG; *Int'l*, pg. 1432
MULTIFIELD INTERNATIONAL HOLDINGS LTD; *Int'l*, pg. 5083
MULTIFILM PACKAGING CORP.—See Transcontinental Inc.; *Int'l*, pg. 7897
MULTI-FINELINE ELECTRONIX, INC.—See Suzhou Dongshan Precision Manufacturing Co., Ltd.; *Int'l*, pg. 7349
MULTI FITTINGS CORPORATION—See Aliaxis S.A./N.V.; *Int'l*, pg. 325
MULTI-FIX BVBA—See Avery Dennison Corporation; *U.S. Public*, pg. 244
MULTI FLOW INDUSTRIES, LLC—See Falconhead Capital, LLC; *U.S. Private*, pg. 1467
MULTIFOOD INTERNATIONAL LTD.—See Meiji Holdings Co., Ltd.; *Int'l*, pg. 4801
MULTIGESTION IBERIA 2014, S.L.—See D. E. Shaw & Co., L.P.; *U.S. Private*, pg. 1140
MULTIGIOCO SRL—See Elys Game Technology, Corp.; *Int'l*, pg. 2371
MULTIGRAINS, INC.; *U.S. Private*, pg. 2813
MULTI-HEALTH SYSTEMS, INC.; *U.S. Private*, pg. 2812
MULTIHEIGHT SCAFFOLDING PTE. LTD.—See Nordic Group Limited; *Int'l*, pg. 5422
MULTIHURT. SP. Z O.O.—See Marie Brizard Wine & Spirits S.A.; *Int'l*, pg. 4693
MULTI IMAGE GROUP INC.; *U.S. Private*, pg. 2812
MULTI INDOCITRA TBK; *Int'l*, pg. 5083
MULTIJOINT SA—See Descours & Cabaud SA; *Int'l*, pg. 2044
MULTIKLIENT INVEST A.S.—See PGS ASA; *Int'l*, pg. 5838

COMPANY NAME INDEX

MULTILATERAL INVESTMENT GUARANTEE AGENCY—See The World Bank Group; *U.S. Private*, pg. 4139
MULTILIFT WELLTEC LLC—See Forum Energy Technologies, Inc.; *U.S. Public*, pg. 874
MULTILINE A/S—See Bunzl plc; *Int'l*, pg. 1219
MULTILINE TECHNOLOGY, INC., PRINTED CIRCUIT BOARD DIVISION—See Multiline Technology Inc.; *U.S. Private*, pg. 2813
MULTILINE TECHNOLOGY, INC., PRINTING PRODUCTS DIVISION—See Multiline Technology Inc.; *U.S. Private*, pg. 2813
MULTILINE TECHNOLOGY INC.; *U.S. Private*, pg. 2813
MULTI-LINK TERMINALS LTD OY—See Delo Group; *Int'l*, pg. 2014
MULTIMAP AUSTRALASIA—See Microsoft Corporation; *U.S. Public*, pg. 1440
MULTIMAQ - PISTOLAS E EQUIPAMENTOS PARA PINTURA LTDA—See Graco, Inc.; *U.S. Public*, pg. 954
MULTI MARKET SERVICES FRANCE HOLDINGS SAS—See Publicis Groupe S.A.; *Int'l*, pg. 6103
MULTI MAXIMUM SENDIRIAN BERHAD—See Ta Ann Holdings Berhad; *Int'l*, pg. 7398
MULTI MECHANICAL, INC.—See Gemspring Capital Management, LLC; *U.S. Private*, pg. 1658
MULTI MEDIA CHANNELS, LLC; *U.S. Private*, pg. 2812
MULTIMEDIA COLLEGE SDN. BHD.—See Telekom Malaysia Berhad; *Int'l*, pg. 7537
MULTI MEDIA CONNECT (AUST) PTY LTD—See TKH Group N.V.; *Int'l*, pg. 7764
MULTIMEDIA DEVICES LIMITED—See Alco Holdings Limited; *Int'l*, pg. 301
MULTI-MEDIA DISTRIBUTION CORP.; *U.S. Private*, pg. 2812
MULTIMEDIA GAMES HOLDING COMPANY, INC.—See Everi Holdings Inc.; *U.S. Public*, pg. 801
MULTIMEDIA GAMES, INC.—See Everi Holdings Inc.; *U.S. Public*, pg. 801
MULTIMEDIA HOLDINGS CORPORATION—See TEGNA Inc.; *U.S. Public*, pg. 1990
MULTI-MEDIA JAMAICA LIMITED—See Radio Jamaica Limited; *Int'l*, pg. 6176
MULTIMEDIA KSDK, INC.—See TEGNA Inc.; *U.S. Public*, pg. 1990
MULTIMEDIA PLUS, INC.; *U.S. Private*, pg. 2813
MULTIMEDIA POLSKA S.A.—See Vectra S.A.; *Int'l*, pg. 8145
MULTIMEDIA PROSPECT SDN BHD—See ManagePay Systems Berhad; *Int'l*, pg. 4667
MULTIMEDIA, S.A.—See Promotora de Informaciones S.A.; *Int'l*, pg. 5995
MULTI MEDIA SERVICES CORP.; *U.S. Private*, pg. 2812
MULTI-MEDIA SYSTEMS—See The Interpublic Group of Companies, Inc.; *U.S. Public*, pg. 2101
MULTIMEDIA TELECOM, S.A. DE C.V.—See Grupo Televisa, S.A.B.; *Int'l*, pg. 3136
MULTIMEDIA UNIVERSITY—See Telekom Malaysia Berhad; *Int'l*, pg. 7537
MULTIMERCADOS ZONALES S.A.—See Grupo Romero; *Int'l*, pg. 3134
MULTI-METAL DEVELOPMENT LTD.; *Int'l*, pg. 5082
MULTI-METALS; *U.S. Private*, pg. 2812
MULTIMETAVERSE HOLDINGS LIMITED; *Int'l*, pg. 5083
MULTIMETRIX GMBH—See R-Biopharm AG; *Int'l*, pg. 6169
MULTIMICRO CLOUD SA; *Int'l*, pg. 5084
MULTIMODAL ENGINEERING CORPORATION—See Kawasaki Kisen Kaisha, Ltd.; *Int'l*, pg. 4100
MULTIMODAL TECHNOLOGIES, LLC—See Solventum Corporation; *U.S. Public*, pg. 1902
MULTINA, INC.; *Int'l*, pg. 5084
MULTINATIONAL MARITIME INC.—See Meiji Shipping Co., Ltd.; *Int'l*, pg. 4802
MULTINER S.A.—See Bolognesi Empreendimentos Ltda.; *Int'l*, pg. 1103
MULTI-NET MARKETING, INC.; *U.S. Private*, pg. 2812
MULTINET PAKISTAN (PRIVATE) LIMITED—See Axiata Group Berhad; *Int'l*, pg. 768
MULTI PACKAGING SOLUTIONS, INC. - ALLEGAN; *U.S. Private*, pg. 2812
MULTI PACKAGING SOLUTIONS, INC.—See WestRock Company; *U.S. Public*, pg. 2362
MULTI PACKAGING SOLUTIONS INTERNATIONAL LIMITED—See WestRock Company; *U.S. Public*, pg. 2362
MULTI PACKAGING SOLUTIONS LIMITED—See WestRock Company; *U.S. Public*, pg. 2362
MULTI PACKAGING SOLUTIONS SERVICES GMBH—See WestRock Company; *U.S. Public*, pg. 2362
MULTI-PACK - ATLANTA—See Cameron Holdings Corporation; *U.S. Private*, pg. 729
MULTI-PACK - CHICAGO—See Wind Point Advisors LLC; *U.S. Private*, pg. 4536
MULTI-PACK - MILWAUKEE—See Cameron Holdings Corporation; *U.S. Private*, pg. 729
MULTI-PACK SOLUTIONS LLC—See Cameron Holdings Corporation; *U.S. Private*, pg. 728
MULTIPANEL UK LTD.; *Int'l*, pg. 5084

MULTIPET GMBH—See Veolia Environnement S.A.; *Int'l*, pg. 8153
MULTIPHONE—See FAYAT SAS; *Int'l*, pg. 2626
MULTIPLAN CORP.; *U.S. Public*, pg. 1486
MULTIPLAN EMPREENDIMENTOS IMOBILIARIOS S.A.; *Int'l*, pg. 5084
MULTIPLAN, INC.—See MultiPlan Corp.; *U.S. Public*, pg. 1486
MULTIPLAN INC.—See MultiPlan Corp.; *U.S. Public*, pg. 1486
MULTI-PLASTICS EUROPE LTD.—See Multi-Plastics, Inc.; *U.S. Private*, pg. 2812
MULTI-PLASTICS EXTRUSIONS, INC.—See Multi-Plastics, Inc.; *U.S. Private*, pg. 2812
MULTI-PLASTICS, INC.—See Multi-Plastics, Inc.; *U.S. Private*, pg. 2812
MULTI-PLASTICS, INC.—See Multi-Plastics, Inc.; *U.S. Private*, pg. 2812
MULTI-PLASTICS, INC.; *U.S. Private*, pg. 2812
MULTI-PLASTICS, INC.—See Multi-Plastics, Inc.; *U.S. Private*, pg. 2812
MULTI-PLASTICS, INC.—See Multi-Plastics, Inc.; *U.S. Private*, pg. 2812
MULTI-PLASTICS, INC.—See Multi-Plastics, Inc.; *U.S. Private*, pg. 2812
MULTIPLE CONCRETE ACCESSORIES; *U.S. Private*, pg. 2813
MULTIPLE ORGANICS, INC.; *U.S. Private*, pg. 2813
MULTIPLE REWARD SDN BHD—See Focus Point Holdings Berhad; *Int'l*, pg. 2720
MULTIPLEX COMPANY INC.; *U.S. Private*, pg. 2813
MULTIPLEX CONTROL & ENGINEERING SERVICES PTE. LTD.—See UNIMECH Group Berhad; *Int'l*, pg. 8049
MULTIPLEX INTERNATIONAL SALES CORP.—See Multiplex Company Inc.; *U.S. Private*, pg. 2813
MULTIPLEX SITES TRUST; *Int'l*, pg. 5084
MULTIPLICA INSIDE S.L.; *Int'l*, pg. 5084
MULTI PLUS DM INC.; *Int'l*, pg. 5082
MULTIPLUS HOLDINGS LTD; *Int'l*, pg. 5084
MULTIPLUS S.A.—See LATAM Airlines Group S.A.; *Int'l*, pg. 4422
MULTIPLY GROUP PJSC—See International Holding Company PJSC; *Int'l*, pg. 3750
MULTIPONT PROGRAM ZRT.—See MOL Magyar Olaj- es Gazipari Nyrt.; *Int'l*, pg. 5021
MULTIPORT GMBH—See Veolia Environnement S.A.; *Int'l*, pg. 8153
MULTIPROJEKT AUTOMATYKA SP. Z O.O.; *Int'l*, pg. 5084
MULTI-PURPOSE INSURANS BHD.—See MPHB Capital Berhad; *Int'l*, pg. 5062
MULTIPURPOSE TRADING & AGENCIES LTD.; *Int'l*, pg. 5084
MULTIQ INTERNATIONAL AB; *Int'l*, pg. 5084
MULTIQUIP, INC.—See ITOCHU Corporation; *Int'l*, pg. 3838
MULTI-REALTY DEVELOPMENT CORPORATION—See SM Investments Corporation; *Int'l*, pg. 6998
MULTIREGIONAL TRANSITTELECOM OJSC—See MOBILE TELESYSTEMS PUBLIC JOINT STOCK COMPANY; *Int'l*, pg. 5011
MULTI RISK CONSULTANTS (THAILAND) LTD.—See Mitsubishi Chemical Group Corporation; *Int'l*, pg. 4933
MULTISEAL INC.; *U.S. Private*, pg. 2813
MULTI SERVICE AERO B.V.—See World Kinect Corporation; *U.S. Public*, pg. 2380
MULTI SERVICE CENTER; *U.S. Private*, pg. 2812
MULTI SERVICE PTY LIMITED—See World Kinect Corporation; *U.S. Public*, pg. 2381
MULTI SERVICES DECOUPE S.A.—See Simpson Manufacturing Company, Inc.; *U.S. Public*, pg. 1882
MULTI-SERVICE SUPPLY—See The Buncher Company; *U.S. Private*, pg. 4002
MULTISERV LOGISTICS LIMITED—See Enviri Corporation; *U.S. Public*, pg. 781
MULTI-SHOT, LLC—See Patterson-UTI Energy, Inc.; *U.S. Public*, pg. 1654
MULTISISTEMA PJSC; *Int'l*, pg. 5084
MULTI SOFT II, INC.—See Japan Tobacco Inc.; *Int'l*, pg. 3907
MULTISOFT LIMITED—See MTT Group Holdings Limited; *Int'l*, pg. 5072
MULTISOL GROUP LIMITED—See BRENNTAG SE; *Int'l*, pg. 1149
MULTISOL LIMITED—See BRENNTAG SE; *Int'l*, pg. 1149
MULTISOL RAAMBEKLEDING B.V.—See 3G Capital Partners L.P.; *U.S. Private*, pg. 13
MULTISORB TECHNOLOGIES, INC.—See Summer Street Capital Partners LLC; *U.S. Private*, pg. 3853
MULTISPARES LIMITED—See Supply Network Limited; *Int'l*, pg. 7340
MULTISPARES N.Z. LIMITED—See Supply Network Limited; *Int'l*, pg. 7340
MULTI SPORTS HOLDINGS LTD.; *Int'l*, pg. 5082
MULTI SQUARE COATING (THAILAND) CO., LTD.—See Sersol Berhad; *Int'l*, pg. 6724

MULVIHILL CAPITAL MANAGEMENT INC.

MULTI SQUARE SDN. BHD.—See Sersol Berhad; *Int'l*, pg. 6724
MULTISTACK INTERNATIONAL LIMITED; *Int'l*, pg. 5084
MULTISTACK, LLC; *U.S. Private*, pg. 2813
MULTISTATE ASSOCIATES INC.—See Public Policy Holding Company; *U.S. Public*, pg. 1735
MULTI SURFACE SOLUTIONS ASA; *Int'l*, pg. 5082
MULTISYS TECHNOLOGIES CORPORATION—See PLDT Inc.; *Int'l*, pg. 5896
MULTI-SYSTEMS INC.—See Constellation Software Inc.; *Int'l*, pg. 1773
MULTISYSTEMS RESTAURANTS INC.; *U.S. Private*, pg. 2813
MULTI TEC CO., LTD.—See Bain Capital, LP; *U.S. Private*, pg. 434
MULTITECH SITE SERVICES LTD.—See Sdiptech AB; *Int'l*, pg. 6659
MULTI-TECH SYSTEMS INC.—See Northlane Capital Partners, LLC; *U.S. Private*, pg. 2956
MULTITECH SYSTEMS PTE LTD—See Venture Corporation Limited; *Int'l*, pg. 8151
MULTITEC; *Int'l*, pg. 5084
MULTITEST ELECTRONIC SYSTEMS, INC.—See Cohu, Inc.; *U.S. Public*, pg. 530
MULTITEST ELECTRONIC SYSTEMS (PENANG) SDN. BHD.—See Cohu, Inc.; *U.S. Public*, pg. 530
MULTITEST ELECTRONIC SYSTEMS (PHILIPPINES) CORPORATION—See Cohu, Inc.; *U.S. Public*, pg. 530
MULTITEST ELEKTRONISCHE SYSTEME GMBH—See Cohu, Inc.; *U.S. Public*, pg. 530
MULTITEST GMBH—See Cohu, Inc.; *U.S. Public*, pg. 530
MULTITHEMATIQUES—See Vivendi SE; *Int'l*, pg. 8266
MULTI-TILE LTD—See Topps Tiles Plc; *Int'l*, pg. 7820
MULTITONE ELECTRONICS PLC—See Champion Technology Holdings Ltd; *Int'l*, pg. 1440
MULTITON ELEKTRONIK GMBH—See Champion Technology Holdings Ltd; *Int'l*, pg. 1440
MULTITRODE PTY LTD—See Xylem Inc.; *U.S. Public*, pg. 2394
MULTITUDE SE; *Int'l*, pg. 5084
MULTI-USAGE CEMENT PRODUCTS SDN. BHD.—See Multi-Usage Holdings Berhad; *Int'l*, pg. 5082
MULTI-USAGE HOLDINGS BERHAD; *Int'l*, pg. 5082
MULTI-USAGE TRADING SDN. BHD.—See Multi-Usage Holdings Berhad; *Int'l*, pg. 5083
MULTIVANS INC.—See J.B. Poindexter & Co., Inc.; *U.S. Private*, pg. 2158
MULTIVEND SERVICES LTD.—See Nayax Ltd.; *Int'l*, pg. 5178
MULTIVERSE MINING & EXPLORATION PLC; *Int'l*, pg. 5084
MULTIVIEW INC.—See Stagwell, Inc.; *U.S. Public*, pg. 1928
MULTIVISION S.A.—See Empresas Publicas de Medellin ESP; *Int'l*, pg. 2392
MULTIVISON INC.; *U.S. Private*, pg. 2813
MULTIVITA D.O.O.—See ATLANTIC GRUPA d.d.; *Int'l*, pg. 675
MULTI-WALL PACKAGING CORP.—See Illinois Tool Works Inc.; *U.S. Public*, pg. 1109
MULTI-WALL PACKAGING—See Illinois Tool Works Inc.; *U.S. Public*, pg. 1109
MULTIWAVE GEOPHYSICAL COMPANY AS—See CGG; *Int'l*, pg. 1431
MULTIWAVE SENSORS INC.—See Hubbell Incorporated; *U.S. Public*, pg. 1067
MULTI WAYS HOLDINGS LIMITED; *Int'l*, pg. 5082
MULTIWIN DE MEXICO S.A. DE C.V.—See Eson Precision Ind. Co., Ltd.; *Int'l*, pg. 2504
MULTIX PTY. LTD.—See International Consolidated Business Group Pty Ltd.; *Int'l*, pg. 3746
MUL-T-LOCK CZECH, S.R.O.—See ASSA ABLOY AB; *Int'l*, pg. 640
MUL-T-LOCK LTD.—See ASSA ABLOY AB; *Int'l*, pg. 640
MUL-T-LOCK MACHINERY LTD.—See ASSA ABLOY AB; *Int'l*, pg. 640
MUL-T-LOCK MACHINERY LTD.—See ASSA ABLOY AB; *Int'l*, pg. 640
MUL-T-LOCK TECHNOLOGIES ITALY SRL—See ASSA ABLOY AB; *Int'l*, pg. 640
MUL-T-LOCK USA, INC.—See ASSA ABLOY AB; *Int'l*, pg. 640
MULTNOMAH ATHLETIC CLUB; *U.S. Private*, pg. 2813
MULTOS INTERNATIONAL PTE LTD—See Thales S.A.; *Int'l*, pg. 7600
MULTOS INTERNATIONAL PTY LTD—See Thales S.A.; *Int'l*, pg. 7600
MULTRI PRECISION, LLC; *U.S. Private*, pg. 2813
MUL UTILITY INNOVATION COMPANY LIMITED—See Mitsubishi HC Capital Inc.; *Int'l*, pg. 4952
MULVANE COOPERATIVE UNION INC.; *U.S. Private*, pg. 2813
MULVIHILL CAPITAL MANAGEMENT INC.; *Int'l*, pg. 5085
MULVIHILL PREMIUM CANADIAN BANK—See Mulvihill Capital Management Inc.; *Int'l*, pg. 5085
MULVIHILL PREMIUM CANADIAN—See Mulvihill Capital Management Inc.; *Int'l*, pg. 5085
MULVIHILL PREMIUM YIELD FUND—See Mulvihill Capital Management Inc.; *Int'l*, pg. 5085

MULVIHILL CAPITAL MANAGEMENT INC. — CORPORATE AFFILIATIONS

MULZER CRUSHED STONE INC.—See CRH plc; *Int'l*, pg. 1845
MUMBAI METRO ONE PRIVATE LIMITED—See Reliance - ADA Group Limited; *Int'l*, pg. 6263
MUMIAS SUGAR COMPANY LIMITED; *Int'l*, pg. 5085
MUMMES INC.; *U.S. Private*, pg. 2813
MUMMIES OF THE WORLD TOURING COMPANY INC.—See American Exhibitions, Inc.; *U.S. Private*, pg. 232
MUNA FEDERAL CREDIT UNION; *U.S. Private*, pg. 2813
MUNAFO INC.; *U.S. Private*, pg. 2813
MUNAITAS LLP—See KazTransOil JSC; *Int'l*, pg. 4103
MUNA NOOR MANUFACTURING AND TRADING CO. L.L.C—See Boubyan Petrochemical Co. KSC; *Int'l*, pg. 1119
MUN (AUSTRALIA) PTY LIMITED—See Hartalega Holdings Berhad; *Int'l*, pg. 3279
MUNAWLA CARGO CO. LTD.; *Int'l*, pg. 5085
MUNCHENER BAUGESELLSCHAFT MBH—See ADLER Group SA; *Int'l*, pg. 150
MUNCHENER DE ARGENTINA SERVICIOS TECNICOS S.R.L.—See Muncherner Ruckversicherungs AG; *Int'l*, pg. 5090
MUNCHENER DE VENEZUELA C.A.—See Muncherner Ruckversicherungs AG; *Int'l*, pg. 5090
MUNCHENER HYPOTHEKENBANK EG; *Int'l*, pg. 5085
MUNCHENER RUCKVERSICHERUNGS AG; *Int'l*, pg. 5085
MUNCHENER UND MAGDEBURGER AGRARVERSICHERUNG AKTIENGESELLSCHAFT—See Allianz SE; *Int'l*, pg. 354
MUNCHKIN, INC.; *U.S. Private*, pg. 2813
MUNCHNER MORTEL GMBH & CO. KG—See BERGER Holding GmbH; *Int'l*, pg. 979
MUNCHNER VERKEHRSGESELLSCHAFT MBH—See Stadtwerke Munchen GmbH; *Int'l*, pg. 7162
MUNCHOLM A/S—See Lindab International AB; *Int'l*, pg. 4504
MUNCH'S SUPPLY LLC—See Ridgemont Partners Management LLC; *U.S. Private*, pg. 3433
MUNCIE AVIATION CO.; *U.S. Private*, pg. 2813
MUNCIE MALL, LLC—See Washington Prime Group Inc.; *U.S. Private*, pg. 4448
MUNCIE POWER PRODUCTS, INC—See Interpump Group S.p.A.; *Int'l*, pg. 3756
MUNCIE TREATMENT CENTER, LLC—See Acadia Healthcare Company, Inc.; *U.S. Public*, pg. 29
MUNCY BANK FINANCIAL, INC.—See Muncy Columbia Financial Corporation; *U.S. Public*, pg. 1487
MUNCY COLUMBIA FINANCIAL CORPORATION; *U.S. Public*, pg. 1486
MUNDAY MAZDA—See Group 1 Automotive, Inc.; *U.S. Public*, pg. 972
MUNDAYS LLP—See Knights Group Holdings PLC; *Int'l*, pg. 4208
MUNDER CAPITAL MANAGEMENT INC.—See Crestview Partners, L.P.; *U.S. Private*, pg. 1098
MUNDIAL S.A. - PRODUTOS DE CONSUMO; *Int'l*, pg. 5093
MUNDIAL S.A.; *Int'l*, pg. 5093
MUNDIFEIRAS, LDA.—See Messe Munchen GmbH; *Int'l*, pg. 4842
MUNDINTERACTIVOS S.A.U.—See RCS MediaGroup S.p.A.; *Int'l*, pg. 6229
MUNDIPAGG TECNOLOGIA EM PAGAMENTO S.A.—See StoneCo Ltd.; *Int'l*, pg. 7222
MUNDIPHARMA INTERNATIONAL LTD.—See Purdue Pharma LP; *U.S. Private*, pg. 3305
MUNDI RISO S.R.L.—See Ebro Foods S.A.; *Int'l*, pg. 2287
MUNDIRIZ, S.A.—See Ebro Foods S.A.; *Int'l*, pg. 2287
MUNDO DULCE S.A. DE C.V.—See Arcor Sociedad Anonima, Industrial y Comercial; *Int'l*, pg. 550
MUNDO DULCE S.A. DE C.V.—See Grupo Bimbo, S.A.B. de C.V.; *Int'l*, pg. 3123
MUNDORO CAPITAL INC.; *Int'l*, pg. 5093
MUNDORO EXPLORATIE COOPERATIE U.A.—See Mundoro Capital Inc.; *Int'l*, pg. 5093
MUNDRA SOLAR TECHNOPARK PRIVATE LIMITED—See Adani Enterprises Limited; *Int'l*, pg. 125
MUNDUS GROUP, INC.; *U.S. Public*, pg. 1487
THE MUNDY COMPANIES; *U.S. Private*, pg. 4081
MUNDY CONTRACT MAINTENANCE—See The Mundy Companies; *U.S. Private*, pg. 4081
MUNDY INDUSTRIAL CONTRACTORS—See The Mundy Companies; *U.S. Private*, pg. 4081
MUNDYS S.P.A.—See Edizione S.r.l.; *Int'l*, pg. 2312
MUNGANA PTY LTD—See Kagara Ltd.; *Int'l*, pg. 4049
MUNGER TOLLES & OLSON LLP; *U.S. Private*, pg. 2813
MUN GLOBAL SDN. BHD.—See Hartalega Holdings Berhad; *Int'l*, pg. 3279
THE MUNGO COMPANY, INC.—See Berkshire Hathaway Inc.; *U.S. Public*, pg. 304
MUNGO HOMES OF GEORGIA LLC—See Berkshire Hathaway Inc.; *U.S. Public*, pg. 304
MUNGO HOMES OF NORTH CAROLINA, INC.—See Berkshire Hathaway Inc.; *U.S. Public*, pg. 304
MUNGO HOMES—See Berkshire Hathaway Inc.; *U.S. Public*, pg. 304

MUNGOS SICHER & SAUBER GMBH & CO KG—See OBB-Holding AG; *Int'l*, pg. 5509
MUN HEALTH PRODUCT (INDIA) PVT LTD—See Hartalega Holdings Berhad; *Int'l*, pg. 3279
MUNICH AIRPORT MARRIOTT HOTELMANAGEMENT GMBH—See Marriott International, Inc.; *U.S. Public*, pg. 1371
MUNICH-AMERICAN GLOBAL SERVICES (MUNICH) GMBH—See Munchener Ruckversicherungs AG; *Int'l*, pg. 5091
MUNICH AMERICAN REASSURANCE CO.—See Muncherner Ruckversicherungs AG; *Int'l*, pg. 5090
MUNICH-CANADA MANAGEMENT CORP. LTD.—See Muncherner Ruckversicherungs AG; *Int'l*, pg. 5091
MUNICH HEALTH HOLDING AG—See Munchener Ruckversicherungs AG; *Int'l*, pg. 5090
MUNICH HEALTH NORTH AMERICA, INC. - REINSURANCE DIVISION—See Muncherner Ruckversicherungs AG; *Int'l*, pg. 5090
MUNICH HEALTH NORTH AMERICA, INC.—See Muncherner Ruckversicherungs AG; *Int'l*, pg. 5090
MUNICH LIFE MANAGEMENT CORPORATION LTD.—See Muncherner Ruckversicherungs AG; *Int'l*, pg. 5090
MUNICH MANAGEMENT PTE. LTD.—See Muncherner Ruckversicherungs AG; *Int'l*, pg. 5090
MUNICH MAURITIUS REINSURANCE CO. LTD.—See Muncherner Ruckversicherungs AG; *Int'l*, pg. 5091
MUNICH OPCO GMBH—See Hyatt Hotels Corporation; *U.S. Public*, pg. 1078
MUNICH RE AMERICA BROKER MARKET—See Muncherner Ruckversicherungs AG; *Int'l*, pg. 5090
MUNICH RE AMERICA BROKERS, INC.—See Muncherner Ruckversicherungs AG; *Int'l*, pg. 5090
MUNICH RE AMERICA CORPORATION—See Muncherner Ruckversicherungs AG; *Int'l*, pg. 5090
MUNICH RE AMERICA DIRECT FACULTATIVE—See Muncherner Ruckversicherungs AG; *Int'l*, pg. 5090
MUNICH RE AMERICA DIRECT TREATY—See Muncherner Ruckversicherungs AG; *Int'l*, pg. 5090
MUNICH RE AMERICA HEALTHCARE—See Muncherner Ruckversicherungs AG; *Int'l*, pg. 5090
MUNICH RE AMERICA SPECIALTY MARKETS—See Muncherner Ruckversicherungs AG; *Int'l*, pg. 5090
MUNICH RE CAPITAL LIMITED—See Munchener Ruckversicherungs AG; *Int'l*, pg. 5090
MUNICH RE CAPITAL MARKETS NEW YORK, INC.—See Muncherner Ruckversicherungs AG; *Int'l*, pg. 5090
MUNICH RE DO BRASIL RESSEGURADORA S.A.—See Muncherner Ruckversicherungs AG; *Int'l*, pg. 5091
MUNICH RE HOLDING COMPANY (UK) LTD.—See Muncherner Ruckversicherungs AG; *Int'l*, pg. 5091
MUNICH RE INDIA SERVICES PRIVATE LIMITED—See Muncherner Ruckversicherungs AG; *Int'l*, pg. 5091
MUNICH REINSURANCE AMERICA, INC—See Muncherner Ruckversicherungs AG; *Int'l*, pg. 5090
MUNICH REINSURANCE COMPANY OF AFRICA LTD—See Munchener Ruckversicherungs AG; *Int'l*, pg. 5091
MUNICH REINSURANCE COMPANY OF CANADA—See Muncherner Ruckversicherungs AG; *Int'l*, pg. 5091
MUNICH RE JAPAN SERVICES K.K.—See Muncherner Ruckversicherungs AG; *Int'l*, pg. 5091
MUNICHRE NEW ZEALAND SERVICE LIMITED—See Muncherner Ruckversicherungs AG; *Int'l*, pg. 5091
MUNICH RE OFICINA DE REPRESENTACION EN COLOMBIA—See Muncherner Ruckversicherungs AG; *Int'l*, pg. 5091
MUNICH RE OF MALTA HOLDING LIMITED—See Muncherner Ruckversicherungs AG; *Int'l*, pg. 5091
MUNICH RE OF MALTA P.L.C.—See Munchener Ruckversicherungs AG; *Int'l*, pg. 5091
MUNICH RE STOP LOSS, INC.—See Munchener Ruckversicherungs AG; *Int'l*, pg. 5090
MUNICH RE UK SERVICES LIMITED—See Munchener Ruckversicherungs AG; *Int'l*, pg. 5091
MUNICH RE UNDERWRITING AGENTS (DIFC) LIMITED—See Muncherner Ruckversicherungs AG; *Int'l*, pg. 5091
MUNICH RE UNDERWRITING LIMITED—See Muncherner Ruckversicherungs AG; *Int'l*, pg. 5091
MUNICIBID.COM LLC; *U.S. Private*, pg. 2813
MUNICIPAL ASSURANCE CORP.—See Assured Guaranty Ltd.; *Int'l*, pg. 650
MUNICIPAL AUTHORITY OF WESTMORELAND COUNTY; *U.S. Private*, pg. 2813
MUNICIPAL BANK LTD.—See Dexia SA; *Int'l*, pg. 2092
MUNICIPAL BANK PLC; *Int'l*, pg. 5093
MUNICIPAL DESIGN GROUP, LLC—See Tetra Tech, Inc.; *U.S. Public*, pg. 2023
MUNICIPAL ELECTRIC AUTHORITY OF GEORGIA; *U.S. Private*, pg. 2814
MUNICIPAL EMERGENCY SERVICES, INC.—See Platte River Ventures, LLC; *U.S. Private*, pg. 3211
MUNICIPAL ENTERPRISES LIMITED; *Int'l*, pg. 5093
MUNICIPAL IMPROVEMENT CORPORATION OF LOS ANGELES; *U.S. Private*, pg. 2814
MUNICIPAL SUPPLY INC.; *U.S. Private*, pg. 2814

MUNICIPAL TAX EQUITY CONSULTANTS INC.—See Voxtur Analytics Corp.; *Int'l*, pg. 8311
MUNICIPAL TRUST & SAVINGS BANK; *U.S. Private*, pg. 2814
MUNICIPAY, LLC—See Stella Point Capital, LP; *U.S. Private*, pg. 3799
MUNICIPIA S.P.A.—See Apax Partners LLP; *Int'l*, pg. 504
MUNIC S.A.; *Int'l*, pg. 5093
MUNIE GREENCARE—See Munie Outdoor Services, Inc.; *U.S. Private*, pg. 2814
MUNIE OUTDOOR SERVICES, INC.; *U.S. Private*, pg. 2814
MUNI FUNDING COMPANY OF AMERICA, LLC—See Tiptree Inc.; *U.S. Public*, pg. 2159
MUNISERVICES, LLC—See Guggenheim Partners, LLC; *U.S. Private*, pg. 1812
MUNIVAC SDN. BHD—See Venture Corporation Limited; *Int'l*, pg. 8151
MUNJAL AUTO INDUSTRIES LIMITED—See Hero Corp.; *Int'l*, pg. 3364
MUNJAL SHOWA LIMITED—See Hero Corp.; *Int'l*, pg. 3364
MUNJAL SHOWA LIMITED—See Hitachi Astemo, Ltd.; *Int'l*, pg. 3409
MUNKEBO CLEMCO A/S—See Clemco Industries Corp.; *U.S. Private*, pg. 939
MUNNELL & SHERRILL INC.; *U.S. Private*, pg. 2814
MUNN RABOT LLC; *U.S. Private*, pg. 2814
MUNNSVILLE INVESTCO, LLC—See E.ON SE; *Int'l*, pg. 2258
MUNN WORKS LLC—See Applied UV, Inc.; *U.S. Public*, pg. 173
MUNOTH CAPITAL MARKET LTD.; *Int'l*, pg. 5093
MUNOTH COMMUNICATION LIMITED; *Int'l*, pg. 5093
MUNOTH FINANCIAL SERVICES LIMITED; *Int'l*, pg. 5093
MUNRO COMPANIES, INC.; *U.S. Private*, pg. 2814
MUNRO & COMPANY, INC.; *U.S. Private*, pg. 2814
MUNROE CREATIVE PARTNERS; *U.S. Private*, pg. 2814
MUNROE CREATIVE PARTNERS—See Munroe Creative Partners; *U.S. Private*, pg. 2814
MUNROE, INC.—See Woodings Industrial Corporation; *U.S. Private*, pg. 4558
MUNROE REGIONAL HOMECARE, LLC—See UnitedHealth Group Incorporated; *U.S. Public*, pg. 2246
MUNSHAAT REAL ESTATE PROJECTS COMPANY KSCC; *Int'l*, pg. 5093
MUN SIONG ENGINEERING LIMITED; *Int'l*, pg. 5085
MUNSON HILL TOWERS, L.L.C.—See Elme Communities; *U.S. Public*, pg. 735
MUNSON LAKES NUTRITION LLC; *U.S. Private*, pg. 2814
MUNSTER CATTLE BREEDING GROUP LIMITED—See Dairygold Co-Operative Society Ltd; *Int'l*, pg. 1940
MUNSTERLANDISCHE BANK THIE & CO. KG—See Allianz SE; *Int'l*, pg. 354
MUNSTER SIMMS ENGINEERING LIMITED—See Brunswick Corporation; *U.S. Public*, pg. 408
MUNSTER SPECIALTY SURGERY CENTER, LLC—See Tenet Healthcare Corporation; *U.S. Public*, pg. 2004
MUNTENIA MEDICAL COMPETENCES S.A.; *Int'l*, pg. 5093
MUNTERS AB; *Int'l*, pg. 5093
MUNTERS AG—See Munters AB; *Int'l*, pg. 5094
MUNTERS AIR TREATMENT EQUIPMENT CO. LTD.—See Munters AB; *Int'l*, pg. 5093
MUNTERS A/S—See Munters AB; *Int'l*, pg. 5094
MUNTERS BELGIUM S.A.—See Munters Group AB; *Int'l*, pg. 5094
MUNTERS BRAZIL INDUSTRIA COMERICO LTDA—See Munters AB; *Int'l*, pg. 5093
MUNTERS BV—See Munters AB; *Int'l*, pg. 5094
MUNTERS CANADA INC.—See Munters Group AB; *Int'l*, pg. 5094
MUNTERS CORPORATION—See Munters AB; *Int'l*, pg. 5093
MUNTERS CZECH S.R.O.—See Munters Group AB; *Int'l*, pg. 5094
MUNTERS DE MEXICO S.A. DE C.V.—See Munters AB; *Int'l*, pg. 5094
MUNTERS DES CHAMPS—See Munters AB; *Int'l*, pg. 5094
MUNTERS EUROPE AB—See Munters AB; *Int'l*, pg. 5094
MUNTERS FINLAND OY—See Munters AB; *Int'l*, pg. 5094
MUNTERS-FORM ENDUSTRI SISTEMLERI SANAYIVE TICARET AS—See Munters Group AB; *Int'l*, pg. 5095
MUNTERS FRANCE S.A.S.—See Munters AB; *Int'l*, pg. 5094
MUNTERS GMBH—See Munters AB; *Int'l*, pg. 5094
MUNTERS GMBH—See Munters AB; *Int'l*, pg. 5094
MUNTERS GMBH—See Munters AB; *Int'l*, pg. 5094
MUNTERS GROUP AB; *Int'l*, pg. 5094
MUNTERS (HK) PTE. LTD.—See Munters AB; *Int'l*, pg. 5093
MUNTERS, INC.—See Munters AB; *Int'l*, pg. 5094
MUNTERS INDIA HUMIDITY CONTROL PVT LTD—See Munters AB; *Int'l*, pg. 5094
MUNTERS ISRAEL LTD.—See Munters Group AB; *Int'l*, pg. 5094
MUNTERS ITALY S.P.A.—See Munters AB; *Int'l*, pg. 5094

COMPANY NAME INDEX

MUNTERS KERULAI AIR TREATMENT EQUIPMENT (GUANGDONG) CO LTD—See Munters AB; *Int'l*, pg. 5094
MUNTERS KK—See Munters AB; *Int'l*, pg. 5094
MUNTERS KOREA CO., LTD.—See Munters Group AB; *Int'l*, pg. 5094
MUNTERS LTD.—See Munters AB; *Int'l*, pg. 5094
MUNTERS MOISTURE CONTROL SERVICES—See Munters AB; *Int'l*, pg. 5094
MUNTERS NEDERLAND B.V.—See Munters AB; *Int'l*, pg. 5094
MUNTERS NETHERLANDS B.V.—See Munters Group AB; *Int'l*, pg. 5094
MUNTERS NV—See Munters AB; *Int'l*, pg. 5094
MUNTERS OY—See Munters AB; *Int'l*, pg. 5094
MUNTERS PTE. LTD.—See Munters AB; *Int'l*, pg. 5094
MUNTERS (PTY) LTD.—See Munters AB; *Int'l*, pg. 5093
MUNTERS PTY LTD.—See Munters AB; *Int'l*, pg. 5094
MUNTERS REVENTA GMBH—See Munters Group AB; *Int'l*, pg. 5094
MUNTERS SERVICES SA—See Munters AB; *Int'l*, pg. 5094
MUNTERS SPAIN SA—See Munters AB; *Int'l*, pg. 5094
MUNTERS SP. Z O.O.—See Munters AB; *Int'l*, pg. 5094
MUNTERS (THAILAND) CO. LTD.—See Munters AB; *Int'l*, pg. 5093
MUNTERS TROCKNUNGSSERVICE GES M.B.H—See Munters AB; *Int'l*, pg. 5094
MUNTERS (VIETNAM) CO., LTD.—See Munters Group AB; *Int'l*, pg. 5094
MUNZE OSTERREICH AKTIENGESELLSCHAFT—See Oesterreichische Nationalbank; *Int'l*, pg. 5529
MUNZING AUSTRALIA PTY. LTD.—See MUNZING Chemie GmbH; *Int'l*, pg. 5095
MUNZING CHEMIE GMBH; *Int'l*, pg. 5095
MUNZING CHEMIE IBERIA S.A.—See MUNZING Chemie GmbH; *Int'l*, pg. 5095
MUNZING CORPORATION—See MUNZING Chemie GmbH; *Int'l*, pg. 5095
MUNZING EMULSIONS CHEMIE GMBH—See MUNZING Chemie GmbH; *Int'l*, pg. 5095
MUNZING INTERNATIONAL S.A.R.L.—See MUNZING Chemie GmbH; *Int'l*, pg. 5095
MUNZING MALAYSIA SDN. BHD.—See MUNZING Chemie GmbH; *Int'l*, pg. 5095
MUNZING MICRO TECHNOLOGIES GMBH—See MUNZING Chemie GmbH; *Int'l*, pg. 5095
MUNZING MUMBAI PVT. LTD.—See MUNZING Chemie GmbH; *Int'l*, pg. 5095
MUNZING SHANGHAI CO. LTD.—See MUNZING Chemie GmbH; *Int'l*, pg. 5095
M-UP HOLDINGS, INC.; *Int'l*, pg. 4614
MURAD SKIN RESEARCH LABS INC.; *U.S. Private*, pg. 2814
MURA EUROPEAN FASHION DESIGN, PROIZVODNJA OBLACIL D.D.; *Int'l*, pg. 5095
MURAKAMI AMPAS (THAILAND) CO., LTD.—See Murakami Corporation; *Int'l*, pg. 5095
MURAKAMI BUSINESS SERVICE CORPORATION—See Murakami Corporation; *Int'l*, pg. 5095
MURAKAMI CORPORATION - OIGAWA PLANT—See Murakami Corporation; *Int'l*, pg. 5095
MURAKAMI CORPORATION; *Int'l*, pg. 5095
MURAKAMI CORPORATION (THAILAND) LTD.—See Murakami Corporation; *Int'l*, pg. 5095
MURAKAMI CORPORATION - TSUIJI PLANT—See Murakami Corporation; *Int'l*, pg. 5095
MURAKAMI EAST JAPAN CORPORATION—See Murakami Corporation; *Int'l*, pg. 5095
MURAKAMI ENVIRONMENT TECHNOLOGY CO., LTD.—See Hitachi Zosen Corporation; *Int'l*, pg. 3411
MURAKAMI EXPRESS CORPORATION—See Murakami Corporation; *Int'l*, pg. 5095
MURAKAMI GERMANY GMBH—See Murakami Corporation; *Int'l*, pg. 5095
MURAKAMI KASEI CORPORATION—See Murakami Corporation; *Int'l*, pg. 5095
MURAKAMI KYUSHU CORPORATION—See Murakami Corporation; *Int'l*, pg. 5095
MURAKAMI MANUFACTURING INDIA PRIVATE LIMITED—See Murakami Corporation; *Int'l*, pg. 5095
MURAKAMI MANUFACTURING MEXICO, S.A. DE C.V.—See Murakami Corporation; *Int'l*, pg. 5095
MURAKAMI MANUFACTURING (THAILAND) CO., LTD.—See Murakami Corporation; *Int'l*, pg. 5095
MURAKAMI MANUFACTURING USA INC.—See Murakami Corporation; *Int'l*, pg. 5095
MURAKAMI MOLD ENGINEERING (THAILAND) CO., LTD.—See Murakami Corporation; *Int'l*, pg. 5095
MURAKAMI SAIKYU (THAILAND) CO., LTD.—See Murakami Corporation; *Int'l*, pg. 5095
MURAKI CORPORATION; *Int'l*, pg. 5095
MURAL ONCOLOGY PLC; *Int'l*, pg. 5095
MURAMOTA ASIA PTE., LTD.—See Muramoto Electron (Thailand) PCL; *Int'l*, pg. 5096
MURAMOTA AUDIO-VISUAL PHILIPPINES, INC.—See Muramoto Electron (Thailand) PCL; *Int'l*, pg. 5096
MURAMOTA INDUSTRY COMPANY LIMITED—See Muramoto Electron (Thailand) PCL; *Int'l*, pg. 5096

MURAMOTO ELECTRON (THAILAND) PCL; *Int'l*, pg. 5095
MURAMOTO MANUFACTURING DE MEXICO, S. DE R.L.—See Muramoto Electron (Thailand) PCL; *Int'l*, pg. 5096
MURAMOTO MANUFACTURING EUROPE S.R.O.—See Muramoto Electron (Thailand) PCL; *Int'l*, pg. 5096
MURAMOTO USA INC.—See Muramoto Electron (Thailand) PCL; *Int'l*, pg. 5096
MURANOWSKA SP. Z O.O.—See Accor S.A.; *Int'l*, pg. 92
MURARI HOLDINGS LTD.—See The Braj Binani Group; *Int'l*, pg. 7627
MURASAKI TECHNOLOGY SDN. BHD.—See EA Holdings Berhad; *Int'l*, pg. 2261
MURASPEC DECORATIVE SOLUTIONS LIMITED—See a2e Venture Catalysts Limited; *Int'l*, pg. 30
MURATA ACTIVE PARTNER CO., LTD.—See Murata Manufacturing Co., Ltd.; *Int'l*, pg. 5097
MURATA COMPANY LIMITED—See Murata Manufacturing Co., Ltd.; *Int'l*, pg. 5097
MURATA DO BRASIL COMERCIO E REPRESENTACAO DE MAQUINAS LTDA.—See Murata Machinery, Ltd.; *Int'l*, pg. 5096
MURATA EIKO CO., LTD.—See Murata Manufacturing Co., Ltd.; *Int'l*, pg. 5097
MURATA ELECTRONICS CO., LTD.—See Murata Manufacturing Co., Ltd.; *Int'l*, pg. 5097
MURATA ELECTRONICS EUROPE B.V.—See Murata Manufacturing Co., Ltd.; *Int'l*, pg. 5097
MURATA ELECTRONICS EUROPE B.V.—See Murata Manufacturing Co., Ltd.; *Int'l*, pg. 5097
MURATA ELECTRONICS EUROPE B.V.—See Murata Manufacturing Co., Ltd.; *Int'l*, pg. 5097
MURATA ELECTRONICS EUROPE B.V.—See Murata Manufacturing Co., Ltd.; *Int'l*, pg. 5097
MURATA ELECTRONICS EUROPE B.V.—See Murata Manufacturing Co., Ltd.; *Int'l*, pg. 5097
MURATA ELECTRONICS EUROPE B.V.—See Murata Manufacturing Co., Ltd.; *Int'l*, pg. 5097
MURATA ELECTRONICS EUROPE B.V.—See Murata Manufacturing Co., Ltd.; *Int'l*, pg. 5097
MURATA ELECTRONICS (INDIA) PRIVATE LIMITED—See Murata Manufacturing Co., Ltd.; *Int'l*, pg. 5097
MURATA ELECTRONICS (MALAYSIA) SDN. BHD.—See Murata Manufacturing Co., Ltd.; *Int'l*, pg. 5097
MURATA ELECTRONICS (NETHERLANDS) B.V.—See Murata Manufacturing Co., Ltd.; *Int'l*, pg. 5097
MURATA ELECTRONICS NORTH AMERICA, INC.—See Murata Manufacturing Co., Ltd.; *Int'l*, pg. 5097
MURATA ELECTRONICS OY—See Murata Manufacturing Co., Ltd.; *Int'l*, pg. 5097
MURATA ELECTRONICS PHILIPPINES INC.—See Murata Manufacturing Co., Ltd.; *Int'l*, pg. 5097
MURATA ELECTRONICS SINGAPORE (PTE.) LTD.—See Murata Manufacturing Co., Ltd.; *Int'l*, pg. 5097
MURATA ELECTRONICS (THAILAND), LTD.—See Murata Manufacturing Co., Ltd.; *Int'l*, pg. 5097
MURATA ELECTRONICS TRADING MEXICO, S. A. DE C.V.—See Murata Manufacturing Co., Ltd.; *Int'l*, pg. 5098
MURATA ELECTRONICS TRADING (SHANGHAI) CO., LTD.—See Murata Manufacturing Co., Ltd.; *Int'l*, pg. 5097
MURATA ELECTRONICS TRADING (SHENZHEN) CO., LTD.—See Murata Manufacturing Co., Ltd.; *Int'l*, pg. 5098
MURATA ELECTRONICS TRADING (TIANJIN) CO., LTD.—See Murata Manufacturing Co., Ltd.; *Int'l*, pg. 5098
MURATA ELECTRONICS (UK) LIMITED—See Murata Manufacturing Co., Ltd.; *Int'l*, pg. 5097
MURATA ELECTRONICS (VIETNAM) CO., LTD.—See Murata Manufacturing Co., Ltd.; *Int'l*, pg. 5097
MURATA ELECTRONIQUE SAS—See Murata Manufacturing Co., Ltd.; *Int'l*, pg. 5098
MURATA ELETTRONICA S.P.A.—See Murata Manufacturing Co., Ltd.; *Int'l*, pg. 5098
MURATA ENERGY DEVICE WUXI CO., LTD.—See Murata Manufacturing Co., Ltd.; *Int'l*, pg. 5098
MURATA INTEGRATED PASSIVE SOLUTIONS SAS—See Murata Manufacturing Co., Ltd.; *Int'l*, pg. 5098
MURATA LAND & BUILDING CO., LTD.—See Murata Manufacturing Co., Ltd.; *Int'l*, pg. 5098
MURATA MACHINERY EUROPE GMBH—See Murata Machinery, Ltd.; *Int'l*, pg. 5096
MURATA MACHINERY (H.K.), LTD.—See Murata Machinery, Ltd.; *Int'l*, pg. 5096
MURATA MACHINERY INDIA PRIVATE LTD.—See Murata Machinery, Ltd.; *Int'l*, pg. 5096
MURATA MACHINERY, LTD. - INUYAMA PLANT—See Murata Machinery, Ltd.; *Int'l*, pg. 5096
MURATA MACHINERY, LTD. - ISE FACTORY—See Murata Machinery, Ltd.; *Int'l*, pg. 5096
MURATA MACHINERY, LTD. - KAGA FACTORY—See Murata Machinery, Ltd.; *Int'l*, pg. 5096
MURATA MACHINERY, LTD.; *Int'l*, pg. 5096
MURATA MACHINERY MEXICO S.DE R.L.DE C.V.—See Murata Machinery, Ltd.; *Int'l*, pg. 5096

MURDOCK WEBBING COMPANY INCORPORATED

MURATA MACHINERY (SHANGHAI) CO., LTD.—See Murata Machinery, Ltd.; *Int'l*, pg. 5096
MURATA MACHINERY SINGAPORE PTE. LTD.—See Murata Machinery, Ltd.; *Int'l*, pg. 5096
MURATA MACHINERY TAIWAN, LTD.—See Murata Machinery, Ltd.; *Int'l*, pg. 5096
MURATA MACHINERY USA, INC.—See Murata Machinery, Ltd.; *Int'l*, pg. 5096
MURATA MANUFACTURING CO., LTD.; *Int'l*, pg. 5096
MURATA MANUFACTURING COMPANY, LTD. - OYAMA PLANT—See Murata Manufacturing Co., Ltd.; *Int'l*, pg. 5098
MURATA MANUFACTURING COMPANY, LTD. - YASU DIVISION—See Murata Manufacturing Co., Ltd.; *Int'l*, pg. 5098
MURATA MANUFACTURING COMPANY, LTD. - YOKAICHI PLANT—See Murata Manufacturing Co., Ltd.; *Int'l*, pg. 5098
MURATA PARTS SALES, LTD.—See Murata Machinery, Ltd.; *Int'l*, pg. 5096
MURATA POWER SOLUTIONS (CELAB) LIMITED—See Murata Manufacturing Co., Ltd.; *Int'l*, pg. 5098
MURATA POWER SOLUTIONS CO., LTD.—See Murata Manufacturing Co., Ltd.; *Int'l*, pg. 5098
MURATA POWER SOLUTIONS (GUANGZHOU) LIMITED—See Murata Manufacturing Co., Ltd.; *Int'l*, pg. 5098
MURATA POWER SOLUTIONS INC.—See Murata Manufacturing Co., Ltd.; *Int'l*, pg. 5098
MURATA POWER SOLUTIONS (MILTON KEYNES) LIMITED—See Murata Manufacturing Co., Ltd.; *Int'l*, pg. 5098
MURATA POWER SOLUTIONS (SHANGHAI) CO., LIMITED—See Murata Manufacturing Co., Ltd.; *Int'l*, pg. 5098
MURATA SHIZUKI FC SOLUTIONS CO., LTD.—See Murata Manufacturing Co., Ltd.; *Int'l*, pg. 5098
MURATA SOFTWARE CO., LTD.—See Murata Manufacturing Co., Ltd.; *Int'l*, pg. 5098
MURATA (THAILAND) CO., LTD.—See Murata Machinery, Ltd.; *Int'l*, pg. 5096
MURATA TOOLS, LTD.—See Murata Machinery, Ltd.; *Int'l*, pg. 5096
MURATA VIOS, INC.—See Murata Manufacturing Co., Ltd.; *Int'l*, pg. 5098
MURATA WORLD COMERCIAL LTDA.—See Murata Manufacturing Co., Ltd.; *Int'l*, pg. 5098
MURATEC AMERICA, INC.—See Murata Machinery, Ltd.; *Int'l*, pg. 5096
MURATEC AUTOMATION CO., LTD.—See Murata Machinery, Ltd.; *Int'l*, pg. 5096
MURATEC AUTOMATION EUROPE SARL—See Murata Machinery, Ltd.; *Int'l*, pg. 5096
MURATEC (BEIJING) CO.,LTD.—See Murata Machinery, Ltd.; *Int'l*, pg. 5096
MURATEC INFORMATION SYSTEMS, LTD.—See Murata Machinery, Ltd.; *Int'l*, pg. 5096
MURATEC-KDS CORPORATION—See Murata Machinery, Ltd.; *Int'l*, pg. 5096
MURATEC MECHATRONICS CO., LTD.—See Murata Machinery, Ltd.; *Int'l*, pg. 5096
MURCHISON HOLDINGS LIMITED; *Int'l*, pg. 5099
MURCHISON MINERALS LTD.; *Int'l*, pg. 5099
MURCHISON PROPERTIES INC.—See J.D. Murchison Interests Inc.; *U.S. Private*, pg. 2161
MURCIANA DE TRAFICO, S.A.—See ACS, Actividades de Construccion y Servicios, S.A.; *Int'l*, pg. 115
MURCO PETROLEUM LTD.—See Murphy Oil Corporation; *U.S. Public*, pg. 1487
MURDOCH GROUP INC.; *Int'l*, pg. 5099
MURDOCK AMBULATORY SURGICAL CENTER, LLC—See Tenet Healthcare Corporation; *U.S. Public*, pg. 2005
MURDOCK COMPANIES INC.; *U.S. Private*, pg. 2814
MURDOCK HOLDINGS, LLC; *U.S. Private*, pg. 2814
MURDOCK-SUPER SECUR—See Acorn Engineering Company, Inc.; *U.S. Private*, pg. 63
MURDOCK WEBBING COMPANY INCORPORATED; *U.S. Private*, pg. 2815
MURE S.A.—See ThyssenKrupp AG; *Int'l*, pg. 7732
MUREX ADVANCED TECHNOLOGIES LTD.—See Murex S.A.S; *Int'l*, pg. 5099
MUREX AMERICA LATINA—See Murex S.A.S; *Int'l*, pg. 5099
MUREX ANDINO PACIFICO—See Murex S.A.S; *Int'l*, pg. 5099
MUREX AUSTRALIA PTY LTD—See Murex S.A.S; *Int'l*, pg. 5099
MUREX BIOTECH SOUTH AFRICA—See Abbott Laboratories; *U.S. Public*, pg. 20
MUREX CANADA SOFTWARE LIMITED—See Murex S.A.S; *Int'l*, pg. 5099
MUREX DIAGNOSTICOS S.A.—See Abbott Laboratories; *U.S. Public*, pg. 20
MUREX FINANCIAL SOFTWARE—See Murex S.A.S; *Int'l*, pg. 5099
MUREX GULF LLC—See Murex S.A.S; *Int'l*, pg. 5099
MUREX HONG KONG LIMITED—See Murex S.A.S; *Int'l*, pg. 5099

MUREX INTERNATIONAL LUXEMBOURG SA—See Murex S.A.S; *Int'l*, pg. 5099
MUREX KOREA LTD.—See Murex S.A.S; *Int'l*, pg. 5099
MUREX NORTH AMERICA, INC.—See Murex S.A.S; *Int'l*, pg. 5099
MUREX PROPERTIES, LLC; *U.S. Private*, pg. 2815
MUREX S.A.S; *Int'l*, pg. 5099
MUREX SOFTWARE—See Murex S.A.S; *Int'l*, pg. 5099
MUREX SOUTHEAST ASIA PTE LTD—See Murex S.A.S; *Int'l*, pg. 5099
MUREX SYSTEMS SAL—See Murex S.A.S; *Int'l*, pg. 5099
MUREX TOKYO—See Murex S.A.S; *Int'l*, pg. 5099
MUREX (UK) LIMITED—See Murex S.A.S; *Int'l*, pg. 5099
MURFIN DRILLING COMPANY INC.; *U.S. Private*, pg. 2815
MURFREESBORO BUSINESS MACHINES, INC.—See Bow-Boeck Enterprises LLC; *U.S. Private*, pg. 625
MURFREESBORO PURE MILK COMPANY; *U.S. Private*, pg. 2815
MURGITROYD & COMPANY LIMITED—See Murgitroyd Group Limited; *Int'l*, pg. 5099
MURGITROYD GROUP LIMITED; *Int'l*, pg. 5099
MURIEL SIEBERT & CO., INC.—See Siebert Financial Corp.; *U.S. Public*, pg. 1876
MURITZ MILCH GMBH—See DMK Deutsches Milchkontor GmbH; *Int'l*, pg. 2146
MURKETTS OF CAMBRIDGE LIMITED—See EMG Holdings Ltd; *Int'l*, pg. 2380
MURMANSKAYA TEC AO; *Int'l*, pg. 5099
MURNANE BUILDING CONTRACTORS INC; *U.S. Private*, pg. 2815
MURNANE PACKAGING CORPORATION; *U.S. Private*, pg. 2815
MURNANE PAPER COMPANY; *U.S. Private*, pg. 2815
MURO CORPORATION; *Int'l*, pg. 5099
MUROMACHI CHEMICALS, INC.; *Int'l*, pg. 5099
MURO NORTH AMERICA INC.—See MURO CORPORATION; *Int'l*, pg. 5099
MURORAN ENVIRONMENTAL PLANT SERVICE, LTD.—See The Japan Steel Works, Ltd.; *Int'l*, pg. 7659
MUROTECH OHIO CORPORATION—See MURO CORPORATION; *Int'l*, pg. 5099
MURO TECH VIETNAM CORPORATION—See MURO CORPORATION; *Int'l*, pg. 5099
MURO TECH XIAOGAN HUBEI CO., LTD.—See MURO CORPORATION; *Int'l*, pg. 5099
MURPHCO OF FLORIDA INC.; *U.S. Private*, pg. 2815
MURPHEY TAYLOR AND ELLIS INC.; *U.S. Private*, pg. 2815
MURPHREE PAVING LLC—See Harbor Beach Capital, LLC; *U.S. Private*, pg. 1858
MURPHREE VENTURE PARTNERS; *U.S. Private*, pg. 2815
MURPHY BED CO., INC.; *U.S. Private*, pg. 2815
MURPHY BROTHERS INC.; *U.S. Private*, pg. 2815
MURPHY-BROWN LLC - ROSE HILL—See WH Group Limited; *Int'l*, pg. 8395
MURPHY-BROWN LLC—See WH Group Limited; *Int'l*, pg. 8395
MURPHY-BROWN OF MISSOURI LLC—See WH Group Limited; *Int'l*, pg. 8395
MURPHY BUILDING CORPORATION—See Murphy Oil Corporation; *U.S. Public*, pg. 1487
MURPHY BUSINESS & FINANCIAL CORPORATION; *U.S. Private*, pg. 2815
MURPHY CAPITAL MANAGEMENT, INC.—See Peapack-Gladstone Financial Corporation; *U.S. Public*, pg. 1659
MURPHY COMPANY MECHANICAL CONTRACTORS & ENGINEERING INC.—See Murphy Company Mechanical Contractors & Engineers Inc.; *U.S. Private*, pg. 2815
MURPHY COMPANY MECHANICAL CONTRACTORS & ENGINEERS INC.; *U.S. Private*, pg. 2815
MURPHY COMPANY; *U.S. Private*, pg. 2815
MURPHY DOOR, INC.; *U.S. Private*, pg. 2815
MURPHY & DURIEU; *U.S. Private*, pg. 2815
MURPHY EXPLORATION & PRODUCTION COMPANY—See Murphy Oil Corporation; *U.S. Public*, pg. 1487
MURPHY FORD SALES LTD.; *Int'l*, pg. 5099
MURPHY-GOODE WINERY—See Jackson Family Wines, Inc.; *U.S. Private*, pg. 2176
MURPHY-HOFFMAN COMPANY; *U.S. Private*, pg. 2816
MURPHY & NOLAN INC.; *U.S. Private*, pg. 2815
MURPHY O'BRIEN, INC.; *U.S. Private*, pg. 2815
MURPHY OIL CO., LTD.—See Murphy Oil Corporation; *U.S. Public*, pg. 1487
MURPHY OIL CORPORATION; *U.S. Public*, pg. 1487
MURPHY OIL TRADING COMPANY (EASTERN)—See Murphy USA Inc.; *U.S. Public*, pg. 1487
MURPHY OIL USA, INC.—See Murphy USA Inc.; *U.S. Public*, pg. 1487
MURPHY PETROLEUM LTD.—See Murphy Oil Corporation; *U.S. Public*, pg. 1487
MURPHY PIPELINE CONTRACTORS, LLC—See J.F. Lehman & Company, Inc.; *U.S. Private*, pg. 2163
MURPHY PLYWOOD—See Murphy Company; *U.S. Private*, pg. 2815

MURPHY SARAWAK OIL CO., LTD.—See PTT Public Company Limited; *Int'l*, pg. 6092
MURPHY'S WASTE OIL SERVICE, INC.—See Clean Harbors, Inc.; *U.S. Public*, pg. 510
MURPHY TRACTOR & EQUIPMENT CO., INC.; *U.S. Private*, pg. 2816
MURPHY TRANSPORTATION INC.; *U.S. Private*, pg. 2816
MURPHY USA INC.; *U.S. Public*, pg. 1487
MURPHY WAREHOUSE COMPANY; *U.S. Private*, pg. 2816
MURRAY A. GOLDENBERG TEXTILES; *U.S. Private*, pg. 2816
MURRAY BISCUIT COMPANY, L.L.C.—See Ferrero International S.A.; *Int'l*, pg. 2641
MURRAY CATERING COMPANY LIMITED—See Four Seas Mercantile Holdings Limited; *Int'l*, pg. 2755
MURRAY COD AUSTRALIA LTD; *Int'l*, pg. 5100
MURRAY COMPANY; *U.S. Private*, pg. 2816
MURRAY COMPANY; *U.S. Private*, pg. 2816
MURRAY DARLING FISHERIES PTY LTD—See Murray Cod Australia Ltd; *Int'l*, pg. 5100
MURRAY ENERGY CORPORATION—See American Consolidated Natural Resources, Inc.; *U.S. Private*, pg. 228
MURRAY FABRICS, INC.; *U.S. Private*, pg. 2816
MURRAY FEISS IMPORT CORP; *U.S. Private*, pg. 2816
MURRAY GM FORT ST JOHN; *Int'l*, pg. 5100
MURRAY GUARD, INC.; *U.S. Private*, pg. 2816
MURRAY HALBERG RETIREMENT VILLAGE LIMITED—See Ryman Healthcare Limited; *Int'l*, pg. 6439
MURRAY HOUSE INVESTMENTS LIMITED—See Barclays PLC; *Int'l*, pg. 862
MURRAY, JONSON, WHITE & ASSOCIATES, LTD., P.C.—See Yount, Hyde & Barbour PC; *U.S. Private*, pg. 4594
MURRAY RESOURCES, LTD.; *U.S. Private*, pg. 2816
MURRAY RIVER ORGANICS GROUP LIMITED; *Int'l*, pg. 5100
MURRAY & ROBERTS (BOTSWANA) LIMITED; *Int'l*, pg. 5100
MURRAY & ROBERTS BUILDING PRODUCTS (PROPRIETARY) LIMITED—See Murray & Roberts Holdings Ltd.; *Int'l*, pg. 5100
MURRAY & ROBERTS CEMENTATION (PROPRIETARY) LIMITED—See Murray & Roberts Holdings Ltd.; *Int'l*, pg. 5100
MURRAY & ROBERTS CONCESSIONS (PROPRIETARY) LIMITED—See Murray & Roberts Holdings Ltd.; *Int'l*, pg. 5100
MURRAY & ROBERTS CONSTRUCTION (PROPRIETARY) LIMITED—See Murray & Roberts Holdings Ltd.; *Int'l*, pg. 5100
MURRAY & ROBERTS HOLDINGS LTD.; *Int'l*, pg. 5100
MURRAY & ROBERTS LIMITED—See Murray & Roberts Holdings Ltd.; *Int'l*, pg. 5100
MURRAY & ROBERTS LIMITED—See Murray & Roberts Holdings Ltd.; *Int'l*, pg. 5100
MURRAY & ROBERTS LIMITED—See Murray & Roberts Holdings Ltd.; *Int'l*, pg. 5100
MURRAY & ROBERTS LIMITED—See Murray & Roberts Holdings Ltd.; *Int'l*, pg. 5100
MURRAY & ROBERTS MARINE (PROPRIETARY) LIMITED—See Murray & Roberts Holdings Ltd.; *Int'l*, pg. 5100
MURRAY & ROBERTS (NAMIBIA) LIMITED; *Int'l*, pg. 5100
MURRAY & ROBERTS PROJECTS (PROPRIETARY) LIMITED—See Murray & Roberts Holdings Ltd.; *Int'l*, pg. 5100
MURRAY & ROBERTS PROPERTIES SERVICES (PROPRIETARY) LIMITED—See Murray & Roberts Holdings Ltd.; *Int'l*, pg. 5100
MURRAYS CHEESE LLC—See The Kroger Co.; *U.S. Public*, pg. 2108
MURRAYS FORD INC.; *U.S. Private*, pg. 2816
MURRAY'S LIC LLC—See The Kroger Co.; *U.S. Public*, pg. 2108
MURRAY WISE ASSOCIATES LLC—See Farmland Partners Inc.; *U.S. Public*, pg. 823
MURREE BREWERY COMPANY LIMITED; *Int'l*, pg. 5100
MURREE GLASS LTD.—See Murree Brewery Company Limited; *Int'l*, pg. 5100
MURREY'S DISPOSAL COMPANY, INC.—See Waste Connections, Inc.; *Int'l*, pg. 8353
MURRIN MURRIN INVESTMENTS PTY LTD—See Glencore plc; *Int'l*, pg. 2991
MURRIN MURRIN OPERATIONS PTY LTD—See Glencore plc; *Int'l*, pg. 2991
MURRY'S, INC.; *U.S. Private*, pg. 2816
MURSIX CORPORATION; *U.S. Private*, pg. 2816
MURTECH CONSULTING; *U.S. Private*, pg. 2817
MURTHY LAW FIRM; *U.S. Private*, pg. 2817
MURTRON HAULING LTD.—See Petrowest Corp.; *Int'l*, pg. 5833
MURUDESHWAR CERAMICS LIMITED; *Int'l*, pg. 5101
THE MURUGAPPA GROUP, LTD.; *Int'l*, pg. 7668
MURUGAPPA MORGAN THERMAL CERAMICS LTD.—See Morgan Advanced Materials plc; *Int'l*, pg. 5043

MUSASHI ABC CO., LTD.—See MUSASHI CO., LTD.; *Int'l*, pg. 5101
MUSASHI ASIA CO.,LTD.—See Musashi Seimitsu Industry Co., Ltd.; *Int'l*, pg. 5101
MUSASHI AUTO PARTS CANADA INC.—See Musashi Seimitsu Industry Co., Ltd.; *Int'l*, pg. 5101
MUSASHI AUTO PARTS CO., LTD.—See Musashi Seimitsu Industry Co., Ltd.; *Int'l*, pg. 5101
MUSASHI AUTO PARTS INDIA PVT. LTD.—See Musashi Seimitsu Industry Co., Ltd.; *Int'l*, pg. 5101
MUSASHI AUTO PARTS MEXICO, S.A. DE C.V.—See Musashi Seimitsu Industry Co., Ltd.; *Int'l*, pg. 5101
MUSASHI AUTO PARTS MICHIGAN INC.—See Musashi Seimitsu Industry Co., Ltd.; *Int'l*, pg. 5101
MUSASHI AUTO PARTS (NANTONG) CO., LTD.—See Musashi Seimitsu Industry Co., Ltd.; *Int'l*, pg. 5101
MUSASHI AUTO PARTS (TIANJIN) CO., LTD.—See Musashi Seimitsu Industry Co., Ltd.; *Int'l*, pg. 5101
MUSASHI AUTO PARTS UK LTD.—See Musashi Seimitsu Industry Co., Ltd.; *Int'l*, pg. 5101
MUSASHI AUTO PARTS VIETNAM CO.,LTD.—See Musashi Seimitsu Industry Co., Ltd.; *Int'l*, pg. 5101
MUSASHI AUTO PARTS (ZHONGSHAN)CO., LTD.—See Musashi Seimitsu Industry Co., Ltd.; *Int'l*, pg. 5101
MUSASHI BAD SOBERNHEIM GMBH & CO. KG—See Musashi Seimitsu Industry Co., Ltd.; *Int'l*, pg. 5101
MUSASHI CASTING CO., LTD.—See Musashi Seimitsu Industry Co., Ltd.; *Int'l*, pg. 5101
MUSASHI CO., LTD.; *Int'l*, pg. 5101
MUSASHI DA AMAZONIA LTDA.—See Musashi Seimitsu Industry Co., Ltd.; *Int'l*, pg. 5102
MUSASHI DO BRASIL LTDA.—See Musashi Seimitsu Industry Co., Ltd.; *Int'l*, pg. 5102
MUSASHI ENERGY SOLUTIONS CO., LTD.—See Musashi Seimitsu Industry Co., Ltd.; *Int'l*, pg. 5101
MUSASHI ENGINEERING CO., LTD.—See MUSASHI CO., LTD.; *Int'l*, pg. 5101
MUSASHI EUROPE GMBH—See Musashi Seimitsu Industry Co., Ltd.; *Int'l*, pg. 5101
MUSASHI HANN. MUENDEN HOLDING GMBH—See Musashi Seimitsu Industry Co., Ltd.; *Int'l*, pg. 5101
MUSASHI HUNGARY FUZESABONY KFT.—See Musashi Seimitsu Industry Co., Ltd.; *Int'l*, pg. 5101
MUSASHI HUNGARY MANUFACTURING, LTD.—See Musashi Seimitsu Industry Co., Ltd.; *Int'l*, pg. 5101
MUSASHI IMAGE JOHO CO., LTD.—See MUSASHI CO., LTD.; *Int'l*, pg. 5101
MUSASHI INDIA PVT. LTD.—See Musashi Seimitsu Industry Co., Ltd.; *Int'l*, pg. 5101
MUSASHI I TECHNO CO., LTD.—See MUSASHI CO., LTD.; *Int'l*, pg. 5101
MUSASHI KOGYO CO., LTD.; *Int'l*, pg. 5101
MUSASHI KOUSAN CO., LTD.—See MUSASHI CO., LTD.; *Int'l*, pg. 5101
MUSASHI LEINEFELDE MACHINING GMBH & CO. KG—See Musashi Seimitsu Industry Co., Ltd.; *Int'l*, pg. 5101
THE MUSASHINO BANK, LTD.; *Int'l*, pg. 7669
THE MUSASHINO CARD CO., LTD.—See The Musashino Bank, Ltd.; *Int'l*, pg. 7669
MUSASHINO ELECTRIC CO., LTD.—See Nisshinbo Holdings Inc.; *Int'l*, pg. 5373
MUSASHINO FINE GLASS CO., LTD.—See Inabata & Co. Ltd.; *Int'l*, pg. 3644
MUSASHINO KOGYO CO., LTD.; *Int'l*, pg. 5102
MUSASHI NO MORI COUNTRY CLUB CO., LTD.—See ANA Holdings Inc.; *Int'l*, pg. 444
MUSASHI NORTH AMERICA INC.—See Musashi Seimitsu Industry Co., Ltd.; *Int'l*, pg. 5101
MUSASHI SEIMITSU CO., LTD.—See Honda Motor Co., Ltd.; *Int'l*, pg. 3463
MUSASHI SEIMITSU INDUSTRY CO., LTD. - AKEMI PLANT 1—See Musashi Seimitsu Industry Co., Ltd.; *Int'l*, pg. 5101
MUSASHI SEIMITSU INDUSTRY CO., LTD. - AKEMI PLANT 2—See Musashi Seimitsu Industry Co., Ltd.; *Int'l*, pg. 5101
MUSASHI SEIMITSU INDUSTRY CO., LTD. - HORAI PLANT—See Musashi Seimitsu Industry Co., Ltd.; *Int'l*, pg. 5101
MUSASHI SEIMITSU INDUSTRY CO., LTD.; *Int'l*, pg. 5101
MUSASHI SEIMITSU INDUSTRY CO., LTD. - SUZUKA PLANT—See Musashi Seimitsu Industry Co., Ltd.; *Int'l*, pg. 5101
MUSASHI SEIMITSU INVESTMENT (ZHONGSHAN) CO., LTD.—See Musashi Seimitsu Industry Co., Ltd.; *Int'l*, pg. 5101
MUSASHI SPAIN VILLALBA S.L.—See Musashi Seimitsu Industry Co., Ltd.; *Int'l*, pg. 5102
MUSATINII SA; *Int'l*, pg. 5102
MUSCAT CITY DESALINATION CO SAOG; *Int'l*, pg. 5102
MUSCAT ELECTRONICS COMPANY L.L.C. - AC DIVISION—See Muscat Electronics Company L.L.C.; *Int'l*, pg. 5102
MUSCAT ELECTRONICS COMPANY L.L.C. - OFFICE AUTOMATION DIVISION—See Muscat Electronics Company L.L.C.; *Int'l*, pg. 5102

COMPANY NAME INDEX

MUSCAT ELECTRONICS COMPANY L.L.C.; *Int'l*, pg. 5102
MUSCAT FINANCE CO. LTD. SAOG—See Omar Zawawi Establishment LLC; *Int'l*, pg. 5561
MUSCAT GASES COMPANY S.A.O.G; *Int'l*, pg. 5102
MUSCATINE JOURNAL—See Lee Enterprises, Incorporated; *U.S. Public*, pg. 1300
MUSCATINE POWER & WATER; *U.S. Private*, pg. 2817
MUSCAT INSURANCE COMPANY SAOG; *Int'l*, pg. 5102
MUSCATO GROUP, INC.—See Digital Payments PLC; *Int'l*, pg. 2123
MUSCAT OVERSEAS AGRICULTURE CO. LLC.—See Muscat Overseas Co., L.L.C.; *Int'l*, pg. 5102
MUSCAT OVERSEAS CO., L.L.C.; *Int'l*, pg. 5102
MUSCAT OVERSEAS ENGINEERING CO. LLC—See Muscat Overseas Co., L.L.C.; *Int'l*, pg. 5102
MUSCAT OVERSEAS INDUSTRIAL & MARINE EQUIPMENT TRADING CO. LLC—See Muscat Overseas Co., L.L.C.; *Int'l*, pg. 5102
MUSCAT OVERSEAS OILFIELD SUPPLIES CO. LLC—See Muscat Overseas Co., L.L.C.; *Int'l*, pg. 5102
MUSCAT SECURITY HOUSE LLC—See Bank Muscat SAOG; *Int'l*, pg. 839
MUSCAT THREAD MILLS SAOG; *Int'l*, pg. 5102
MUSCLE MAKER FRANCHISING LLC—See American Restaurant Holdings, Inc.; *U.S. Private*, pg. 246
MUSCLEPHARM CORPORATION—See FitLife Brands, Inc.; *U.S. Public*, pg. 852
MUSCO CORPORATION; *U.S. Private*, pg. 2817
MUSCO FAMILY OLIVE COMPANY; *U.S. Private*, pg. 2817
MUSCULAR MOVING MEN, LLC; *U.S. Private*, pg. 2817
MUSCULOSKELETAL TRANSPLANT FOUNDATION; *U.S. Private*, pg. 2817
MUSE COMMUNICATIONS, INC.—See Quantasy, LLC; *U.S. Private*, pg. 3322
MUSE CORPORATION COMPANY LIMITED—See CMO Public Company Limited; *Int'l*, pg. 1671
MUSE DEVELOPMENTS LTD.—See Morgan Sindall Group Plc; *Int'l*, pg. 5045
MUSEE GREVIN SA—See Compagnie des Alpes S.A.; *Int'l*, pg. 1738
MUSEGLOBAL, INC.; *U.S. Private*, pg. 2817
MUSEMENT S.P.A.—See TUI AG; *Int'l*, pg. 7965
MUSE PLACES LIMITED—See Morgan Sindall Group Plc; *Int'l*, pg. 5045
MUSEUM HACK, LLC; *U.S. Private*, pg. 2817
MUSEUM OF AMERICAN FINANCE; *U.S. Private*, pg. 2817
THE MUSEUM OF CONTEMPORARY ART, LOS ANGELES; *U.S. Private*, pg. 4081
MUSEUM OF FINE ARTS OF ST. PETERSBURG FLORIDA INC.; *U.S. Private*, pg. 2817
MUSEUM OF FLIGHT FOUNDATION; *U.S. Private*, pg. 2817
MUSEUM OF HISTORY & INDUSTRY; *U.S. Private*, pg. 2817
THE MUSEUM OF MODERN ART; *U.S. Private*, pg. 4081
MUSEUM OF NEW MEXICO FOUNDATION; *U.S. Private*, pg. 2817
MUSEUM OF PHOTOGRAPHIC ARTS—See The San Diego Museum of Art; *U.S. Private*, pg. 4113
MUSEUM OF SCIENCE AND INDUSTRY; *U.S. Private*, pg. 2817
MUSEUM OF SCIENCE & HISTORY OF JACKSONVILLE, INC.; *U.S. Private*, pg. 2817
MUSEUM QUALITY DISCOUNT FRAMING; *U.S. Private*, pg. 2817
MUSEUM QUARTER, B.V.—See Minor International PCL; *Int'l*, pg. 4911
MUSGRAVE BUDGENS LONDIS—See Musgrave Group plc; *Int'l*, pg. 5102
MUSGRAVE ESPANA, S.A.U.—See Musgrave Group plc; *Int'l*, pg. 5102
MUSGRAVE GROUP PLC; *Int'l*, pg. 5102
MUSGRAVE MINERALS LIMITED; *Int'l*, pg. 5102
MUSGRAVE OPERATING PARTNERS IRELAND LIMITED—See Musgrave Group plc; *Int'l*, pg. 5102
MUSGROVE CONSTRUCTION, INC.—See Asplundh Tree Expert Co.; *U.S. Private*, pg. 353
MUSGROVE MILLS, INC.; *U.S. Private*, pg. 2817
MUSHKO ELECTRONICS (PVT) LIMITED—See Hewlett Packard Enterprise Company; *U.S. Public*, pg. 1031
MUSHRIF TRADING & CONTRACTING COMPANY K.S.C.P.—See Al-Wazzan Holding Group; *Int'l*, pg. 289
THE MUSHROOM COMPANY—See South Mill Mushrooms Sales, Inc.; *U.S. Private*, pg. 3723
MUSICA APARTE S.A.U.—See Atresmedia Corporacion de Medios de Comunicacion, S.A.; *Int'l*, pg. 693
THE MUSIC ACQUISITION CORPORATION; *U.S. Public*, pg. 2116
MUSICAL ARTS ASSOCIATION; *U.S. Private*, pg. 2818
MUSICAL HERITAGE SOCIETY INC.; *U.S. Private*, pg. 2818
MUSIC & ARTS CENTER INC.—See Bain Capital, LP; *U.S. Private*, pg. 440
MUSIC BROADCAST LIMITED—See Jagran Prakashan Limited; *Int'l*, pg. 3870
MUSIC CENTER, INC.; *U.S. Private*, pg. 2817

MUSIC CHOICE—See Charter Communications, Inc.; *U.S. Public*, pg. 483
MUSIC CHOICE—See Comcast Corporation; *U.S. Public*, pg. 537
MUSIC CHOICE—See Cox Enterprises, Inc.; *U.S. Private*, pg. 1078
MUSIC CHOICE—See Microsoft Corporation; *U.S. Public*, pg. 1441
MUSIC CHOICE—See Sony Group Corporation; *Int'l*, pg. 7103
MUSIC DEALERS, LLC—See BrandSpins, LLC; *U.S. Private*, pg. 638
MUSICIAN'S FRIEND, INC.—See Bain Capital, LP; *U.S. Private*, pg. 440
MUSICMAGPIE PLC; *Int'l*, pg. 5102
MUSIC MARKETING SP. Z.O.O.—See Live Nation Entertainment, Inc.; *U.S. Public*, pg. 1330
MUSICNET—See Baker Capital Partners, LLC; *U.S. Private*, pg. 455
MUSICNOTES, INC.; *U.S. Private*, pg. 2818
MUSICORP—See TPG Capital, L.P.; *U.S. Public*, pg. 2173
MUSIC REPORTS, INC.—See MidOcean Partners, LLP; *U.S. Private*, pg. 2717
MUSIC SALES CORPORATION; *U.S. Private*, pg. 2817
MUSIC SALES LIMITED—See Music Sales Corporation; *U.S. Private*, pg. 2818
MUSIC SALES PTY. LIMITED—See Music Sales Corporation; *U.S. Private*, pg. 2818
MUSIC SALES WEST—See Music Sales Corporation; *U.S. Private*, pg. 2818
MUSIC SEMICONDUCTORS PHILIPPINES, INC—See Greenergy Holdings Inc.; *Int'l*, pg. 3074
MUSICTODAY II, LLC; *U.S. Private*, pg. 2818
MUSICWAY CORPORATION LTD.—See Thai Beverage Public Company Limited; *Int'l*, pg. 7590
MUSIC WORLD RETAIL LIMITED—See CESC Limited; *Int'l*, pg. 1424
MU SIGMA BUSINESS SOLUTIONS PVT LTD.—See Mu Sigma, Inc.; *Int'l*, pg. 5073
MU SIGMA, INC.; *Int'l*, pg. 5073
MU SIGMA LIMITED—See Mu Sigma, Inc.; *Int'l*, pg. 5073
MUSIKHAUS THOMANN E.K.; *Int'l*, pg. 5103
MUSIQUEPLUS INC.—See Remstar Corporation; *Int'l*, pg. 6271
MUSKA ELECTRIC COMPANY; *U.S. Private*, pg. 2818
MUSKEGON CASTINGS CORP; *U.S. Private*, pg. 2818
MUSKET CORPORATION—See Love's Travel Stops & Country Stores, Inc.; *U.S. Private*, pg. 2501
MUSKINGUM VALLEY HEALTH CENTERS; *U.S. Private*, pg. 2818
MUSK METALS CORP.; *Int'l*, pg. 5103
MUSKOGEE DIALYSIS, LLC—See DaVita Inc.; *U.S. Public*, pg. 641
MUSKOKA DELIVERY SERVICES INC.; *Int'l*, pg. 5103
MUSKOVARVET AB—See Saab AB; *Int'l*, pg. 6459
MUSSALON VOIMA OY—See Pohjolan Voima Oy; *Int'l*, pg. 5904
MUSS DEVELOPMENT CO; *U.S. Private*, pg. 2818
MUSSELMAN BROTHERS INC.; *U.S. Private*, pg. 2818
MUSSELMAN & HALL CONTRACTORS LLC.; *U.S. Private*, pg. 2818
MUSSELMAN LUMBER INC.—See Bain Capital, LP; *U.S. Private*, pg. 451
MUSSELMAN'S DODGE INC.; *U.S. Private*, pg. 2818
MUSSER-DAVIS LAND COMPANY; *U.S. Private*, pg. 2818
MUSSER FORESTS, INC.; *U.S. Private*, pg. 2818
MUSSER MOTORS INC.; *U.S. Private*, pg. 2818
MUSSERS, INC.; *U.S. Private*, pg. 2818
MUSSER—See Paulson & Co. Inc.; *U.S. Private*, pg. 3114
MUSSON BROS., INC. - BROOKFIELD OFFICE—See Musson Bros., Inc.; *U.S. Private*, pg. 2819
MUSSON BROS., INC.; *U.S. Private*, pg. 2818
MUSSON-PATOUT AUTOMOTIVE GROUP INC.; *U.S. Private*, pg. 2819
MUSTACHE, LLC—See Daniel J. Edelman Holdings, Inc.; *U.S. Private*, pg. 1154
MUSTAFA NEVZAT ILAC SANAYII ANONIM SIRKETI—See Amgen Inc.; *U.S. Public*, pg. 123
MUSTAFA SULTAN ELECTRONICS CO. LLC-LIGHTING BUSINESS UNIT—See Mustafa Sultan Enterprises LLC; *Int'l*, pg. 5103
MUSTAFA SULTAN ELECTRONICS CO. LLC—See Mustafa Sultan Enterprises LLC; *Int'l*, pg. 5103
MUSTAFA SULTAN ENTERPRISES LLC; *Int'l*, pg. 5103
MUSTAFA SULTAN ENTERPRISES MILITARY DIVISION—See Mustafa Sultan Enterprises LLC; *Int'l*, pg. 5103
MUSTAFA SULTAN EXCHANGE CO. LLC—See Mustafa Sultan Enterprises LLC; *Int'l*, pg. 5103
MUSTAFA SULTAN OFFICE TECHNOLOGY CO. LLC—See Mustafa Sultan Enterprises LLC; *Int'l*, pg. 5103
MUSTAFA SULTAN REFRIGERATION & AIR CONDITIONING SERVICES CO. LLC.—See Mustafa Sultan Enterprises LLC; *Int'l*, pg. 5103
MUSTAFA SULTAN SCIENCE & INDUSTRY CO. LLC—See Mustafa Sultan Enterprises LLC; *Int'l*, pg. 5103

MUTO COMMUNICATIONS, LLC

MUSTAFA SULTAN SECURITY & COMMUNICATION SYSTEMS CO. LLC—See Mustafa Sultan Enterprises LLC; *Int'l*, pg. 5103
MUSTAFA SULTAN TELECOMMUNICATIONS CO. LLC—See Mustafa Sultan Enterprises LLC; *Int'l*, pg. 5103
MUSTANG AL-HEJAILAN DAR PI—See Al-Hejailan Group; *Int'l*, pg. 286
MUSTANG ALLIANCES, INC.; *U.S. Private*, pg. 2819
MUSTANG BIO, INC.; *U.S. Public*, pg. 1487
MUSTANG DYNAMOMETER, CHINA—See Mustang Dynamometer; *U.S. Private*, pg. 2819
MUSTANG DYNAMOMETER, LOS ANGELES—See Mustang Dynamometer; *U.S. Private*, pg. 2819
MUSTANG DYNAMOMETER; *U.S. Private*, pg. 2819
MUSTANG ENERGY PLC; *Int'l*, pg. 5103
MUSTANG FUEL CORPORATION; *U.S. Private*, pg. 2819
MUSTANG GAS PRODUCTS LLC; *U.S. Private*, pg. 2819
MUSTANG GAS PRODUCTS—See Mustang Gas Products LLC; *U.S. Private*, pg. 2819
THE MUSTANG GROUP, LLC; *U.S. Private*, pg. 4081
MUSTANG HEAVY HAUL LLC—See Latshaw Drilling and Exploration Company; *U.S. Private*, pg. 2397
MUSTANG MANUFACTURING COMPANY, INC.—See Manitou BF S.A.; *Int'l*, pg. 4672
MUSTANG MOTORCYCLE PRODUCTS, LLC—See LDR Growth Partners; *U.S. Private*, pg. 2404
MUSTANG POWER SYSTEMS—See Mustang Tractor & Equipment Company; *U.S. Private*, pg. 2819
MUSTANG PROPERTY CORPORATION—See BASF SE; *Int'l*, pg. 876
MUSTANG RENTAL SERVICES INC.—See Mustang Tractor & Equipment Company; *U.S. Private*, pg. 2819
MUSTANG SURVIVAL CORP.—See Wing Inflatables, Inc.; *U.S. Private*, pg. 4541
MUSTANG SURVIVAL, INC.—See Wing Inflatables, Inc.; *U.S. Private*, pg. 4541
MUSTANG SURVIVAL MFG, INC.—See Wing Inflatables, Inc.; *U.S. Private*, pg. 4541
MUSTANG TRACTOR & EQUIPMENT COMPANY; *U.S. Private*, pg. 2819
MUSTANG VACUUM SYSTEMS INC.—See Mustang Dynamometer; *U.S. Private*, pg. 2819
MUSTA PORSSI LTD—See Kesko Corporation; *Int'l*, pg. 4142
MUSTARD SEED HEALTH FOOD MARKET; *U.S. Private*, pg. 2819
MUST CAPITAL INC.; *Int'l*, pg. 5103
MUST EHSAN DEVELOPMENT SDN BHD—See Lembaga Kemajuan Tanah Persekutuan; *Int'l*, pg. 4448
MUSTEK, INC.—See Mustek Systems, Inc.; *Int'l*, pg. 5103
MUSTEK LIMITED; *Int'l*, pg. 5103
MUSTEK PACIFIC, INC.—See Mustek Systems, Inc.; *Int'l*, pg. 5103
MUSTEK SYSTEMS, INC.; *Int'l*, pg. 5103
MUSTEQ HYDRO SDN. BHD.—See Eden Inc. Berhad; *Int'l*, pg. 2306
MUSTERA PROPERTY GROUP LIMITED; *Int'l*, pg. 5103
MUSTGROW BIOLOGICS CORP.; *Int'l*, pg. 5103
MUSTIKA RATU TBK; *Int'l*, pg. 5103
MUSTO LIMITED—See Canadian Tire Corporation Limited; *Int'l*, pg. 1286
MUSWELLBROOK COAL COMPANY LIMITED—See Idemitsu Kosan Co., Ltd.; *Int'l*, pg. 3590
MUTANDIS SCA; *Int'l*, pg. 5104
MUTANT ASSURANCES SARL—See CVC Capital Partners SICAV-FIS S.A.; *Int'l*, pg. 1882
MUTARES AUSTRIA GMBH—See Mutares SE & Co. KGaA; *Int'l*, pg. 5105
MUTARES BENELUX B. V—See Mutares SE & Co. KGaA; *Int'l*, pg. 5105
MUTARES FRANCE S.A.S.—See Mutares SE & Co. KGaA; *Int'l*, pg. 5105
MUTARES IBERIA S. L. U.—See Mutares SE & Co. KGaA; *Int'l*, pg. 5105
MUTARES ITALY S.R.L.—See Mutares SE & Co. KGaA; *Int'l*, pg. 5105
MUTARES NORDICS OY—See Mutares SE & Co. KGaA; *Int'l*, pg. 5105
MUTARES SE & CO. KGAA; *Int'l*, pg. 5104
MUTESIX, LLC—See Dentsu Group Inc.; *Int'l*, pg. 2037
MU-TEST S.A.S.—See AEM Holdings Ltd.; *Int'l*, pg. 175
M-U-T GMBH—See Nynomic AG; *Int'l*, pg. 5501
MUTHIG INDUSTRIES, INC.—See LFM Capital LLC; *U.S. Private*, pg. 2441
MUTHOOT CAPITAL SERVICES LTD.; *Int'l*, pg. 5106
MUTHOOT FINANCE LIMITED; *Int'l*, pg. 5106
MUTHOOT MICROFIN LIMITED; *Int'l*, pg. 5106
MUTIARA HOTELS & RESORTS SDN. BHD.—See Tradewinds Corporation Berhad; *Int'l*, pg. 7888
MUTIARA RINI SDN BHD—See Lembaga Tabung Angkatan Tentera; *Int'l*, pg. 4448
MUTIARA-TCB HOTEL MANAGEMENT SDN. BHD.—See Tradewinds Corporation Berhad; *Int'l*, pg. 7888
MUTO COMMUNICATIONS, LLC; *U.S. Private*, pg. 2819
MUTOH AMERICA INC.—See Mutoh Holdings Co., Ltd.; *Int'l*, pg. 5106
MUTOH BELGIUM NV—See Mutoh Holdings Co., Ltd.; *Int'l*, pg. 5106

MUTO COMMUNICATIONS, LLC — CORPORATE AFFILIATIONS

MUTOH DEUTSCHLAND GMBH—See Mutoh Holdings Co., Ltd.; *Int'l*, pg. 5106
MUTOH HOLDINGS CO., LTD.; *Int'l*, pg. 5106
MUTOH ITEX CO., LTD.—See Mutoh Holdings Co., Ltd.; *Int'l*, pg. 5106
MUTOH NORTH EUROPE S.A.—See Mutoh Holdings Co., Ltd.; *Int'l*, pg. 5106
MUTO SEIKO CO.; *Int'l*, pg. 5106
MUTOW CREDIT CO., LTD—See Scroll Corporation; *Int'l*, pg. 6656
MUTSCHLER HOLDING AG; *Int'l*, pg. 5106
MUTTER MEDIA AB—See LOV Group Invest SAS; *Int'l*, pg. 4565
MUTTER VENTURES, S.A.; *Int'l*, pg. 5106
MUTTO OPTRONICS CORPORATION; *Int'l*, pg. 5106
MUT-TSCHAMBER MISCH- UND TRENNTECHNIK GMBH; *Int'l*, pg. 5103
MUTUAIDE ASSISTANCE—See Groupama SA; *Int'l*, pg. 3091
MUTUAL ACE HARDWARE—See Ace Hardware Corporation; *U.S. Private*, pg. 56
MUTUAL BANCORP; *U.S. Private*, pg. 2819
MUTUAL BENEFICIAL ASSOCIATION, INC.; *U.S. Private*, pg. 2819
MUTUAL BENEFIT ASSOCIATION HAWAII; *U.S. Private*, pg. 2819
MUTUAL BENEFIT INSURANCE COMPANY; *U.S. Private*, pg. 2819
MUTUAL BENEFITS ASSURANCE PLC; *Int'l*, pg. 5106
MUTUAL BENEFITS MICROFINANCE BANK LIMITED—See Mutual Benefits Assurance Plc; *Int'l*, pg. 5106
MUTUAL BOILER RE—See Factory Mutual Insurance Company; *U.S. Private*, pg. 1461
MUTUAL CAPITAL GROUP, INC.; *U.S. Private*, pg. 2819
MUTUAL CAPITAL HOLDINGS, INC.—See Mutual Capital Group, Inc.; *U.S. Private*, pg. 2819
MUTUAL CENTRAL ALARM SERVICE INC.—See Kastle Systems International LLC; *U.S. Private*, pg. 2264
MUTUAL CONSTRUCTION COMPANY TRANSVAAL (PTY) LIMITED—See eXtract Group Limited; *Int'l*, pg. 2592
MUTUAL CONSTRUCTION; *Int'l*, pg. 5106
MUTUAL CORPORATION - KANTO FACTORY—See Mutual Corporation; *Int'l*, pg. 5106
MUTUAL CORPORATION; *Int'l*, pg. 5106
MUTUAL FEDERAL, A DIVISION OF FIRST BANK RICHMOND—See First Mutual of Richmond, Inc.; *U.S. Private*, pg. 1521
MUTUAL FEDERAL BANK; *U.S. Public*, pg. 1487
MUTUAL & FEDERAL INSURANCE COMPANY LIMITED—See OM Residual UK Limited; *Int'l*, pg. 5559
MUTUAL FEDERAL INVESTMENT COMPANY—See Northwest Bancshares, Inc.; *U.S. Public*, pg. 1541
MUTUALFIRST FINANCIAL, INC.—See Northwest Bancshares, Inc.; *U.S. Public*, pg. 1541
MUTUAL FUND RDIF—See VEB.RF; *Int'l*, pg. 8143
MUTUAL HEALTH SERVICES—See Medical Mutual of Ohio; *U.S. Private*, pg. 2655
MUTUAL INDUSTRIES NORTH INC.; *U.S. Private*, pg. 2820
MUTUAL LIQUID GAS & EQUIPMENT CO., INC.; *U.S. Private*, pg. 2820
MUTUAL MATERIALS COMPANY; *U.S. Private*, pg. 2820
MUTUAL MED, INC.—See Truist Financial Corporation; *U.S. Public*, pg. 2199
MUTUAL OF AMERICA CAPITAL MANAGEMENT CORPORATION—See Mutual of America Life Insurance Company; *U.S. Private*, pg. 2820
MUTUAL OF AMERICA LIFE INSURANCE COMPANY; *U.S. Private*, pg. 2820
MUTUAL OF ENUMCLAW INSURANCE CO. INC.; *U.S. Private*, pg. 2820
MUTUAL OF OMAHA INSURANCE COMPANY; *U.S. Private*, pg. 2820
MUTUAL OF OMAHA INVESTOR SERVICES, INC.—See Mutual of Omaha Insurance Company; *U.S. Private*, pg. 2820
MUTUAL OIL CO. INC.—See Truman Arnold Companies; *U.S. Private*, pg. 4250
MUTUALONE BANK; *U.S. Private*, pg. 2820
MUTUAL-PAK TECHNOLOGY CO., LTD.—See Taiwan Semiconductor Manufacturing Company Ltd.; *Int'l*, pg. 7423
MUTUAL REINSURANCE BUREAU; *U.S. Private*, pg. 2820
MUTUAL SAVINGS BANK—See Oconee Federal Financial Corp.; *U.S. Public*, pg. 1563
MUTUAL SAVINGS CREDIT UNION INC.; *U.S. Private*, pg. 2820
MUTUAL SAVINGS FIRE INSURANCE CO. INC.—See Kemper Corporation; *U.S. Public*, pg. 1220
MUTUAL SAVINGS LIFE INSURANCE CO. INC.—See Kemper Corporation; *U.S. Public*, pg. 1220
MUTUAL SAVINGS LIFE INSURANCES COMPANY—See Kemper Corporation; *U.S. Public*, pg. 1220
MUTUAL SECURITY CREDIT UNION, INC.; *U.S. Private*, pg. 2820

MUTUAL SHAREHOLDER SERVICES, LLC (MSS); *U.S. Private*, pg. 2820
MUTUAL-TEK INDUSTRIES CO., LTD.; *Int'l*, pg. 5107
MUTUAL TELECOM SERVICES INC.—See Black Box Limited; *Int'l*, pg. 1058
MUTUAL (THAILAND) CO., LTD.—See Mutual Corporation; *Int'l*, pg. 5106
MUTUAL TRADING CO., INC.—See Takara Holdings, Inc.; *Int'l*, pg. 7433
MUTUAL TRANSPORTATION SERVICES INC.; *Int'l*, pg. 5107
MUTUAL TRUST BANK PLC; *Int'l*, pg. 5107
MUTUAL TRUST PTY LTD.; *Int'l*, pg. 5107
MUTUAL WELDING CO., LTD.; *U.S. Private*, pg. 2820
MUTUAL WHEEL COMPANY INC.; *U.S. Private*, pg. 2820
MUTUAL WHOLESALE LIQUOR INC.; *U.S. Private*, pg. 2820
MUTUA MADRILENA AUTOMOVILISTA, SOCIEDAD DE SEGUROS A PRIMA FIJA; *Int'l*, pg. 5106
MUTUELLE DES FONCTIONNAIRES DU QUEBEC, CORPORATION DE GESTION; *Int'l*, pg. 5107
MUTUELLE SAINT-CHRISTOPHE—See AXA S.A.; *Int'l*, pg. 759
MUTZ MOTORS L.P.; *U.S. Private*, pg. 2820
MUUTO A/S—See MillerKnoll, Inc.; *U.S. Public*, pg. 1447
MUV-ALL TRAILER COMPANY; *U.S. Private*, pg. 2820
MUV, INC.; *U.S. Private*, pg. 2820
MUV MARKETPLACE SDN BHD—See Warisan TC Holdings Berhad; *Int'l*, pg. 8345
MUVONI TECHNOLOGY GROUP LIMITED; *Int'l*, pg. 5107
MUXTEC GMBH—See Mutares SE & Co. KGaA; *Int'l*, pg. 5105
MU YAN TECHNOLOGY GROUP CO., LIMITED; *Int'l*, pg. 5073
MUYLE ELECTRO-MACHINERY SA—See Emerson Electric Co.; *U.S. Public*, pg. 750
MUYS NV—See Macintosh Retail Group NV; *Int'l*, pg. 4622
MUYUAN FOOD CO., LTD.; *Int'l*, pg. 5107
MUZAK HOLDINGS LLC—See Vector Capital Management, L.P.; *U.S. Private*, pg. 4351
MUZAK LLC—See Vector Capital Management, L.P.; *U.S. Private*, pg. 4351
MUZALI ARTS LIMITED; *Int'l*, pg. 5107
MUZA S.A.; *Int'l*, pg. 5107
MUZHU MINING LTD.; *Int'l*, pg. 5107
MUZI MOTORS INC.; *U.S. Private*, pg. 2820
MUZINICH BDC, INC.; *U.S. Private*, pg. 2821
MUZINICH & CO., INC.; *U.S. Private*, pg. 2821
MV AGUSTA S.P.A.; *Int'l*, pg. 5107
MV AUGUSTAANLAGE GMBH & CO. KG—See UNIQA Insurance Group AG; *Int'l*, pg. 8057
MVB BANK, INC.—See MVB Financial Corp.; *U.S. Public*, pg. 1487
MVB FINANCIAL CORP.; *U.S. Public*, pg. 1487
MVC ACQUISITION CORP.; *U.S. Private*, pg. 2821
MVC CAPITAL, INC.—See Barings BDC, Inc.; *U.S. Public*, pg. 276
MVC CO., LTD.—See Medipal Holdings Corporation; *Int'l*, pg. 4779
MVC FINANCIAL SERVICES, INC.—See Barings BDC, Inc.; *U.S. Public*, pg. 276
MVC HOLDINGS LLC; *U.S. Private*, pg. 2821
MVCI ASIA PACIFIC PTE. LTD.—See Marriott Vacations Worldwide Corporation; *U.S. Public*, pg. 1374
MVCI HOLIDAYS, S.L.—See Marriott Vacations Worldwide Corporation; *U.S. Public*, pg. 1374
MVC MOBILE VIDEOCOMMUNICATION GMBH; *Int'l*, pg. 5107
MV COTSPIN LTD.; *Int'l*, pg. 5107
MV CREDIT LIMITED—See Groupe BPCE; *Int'l*, pg. 3098
MVD COMMUNICATIONS, LLC.; *U.S. Private*, pg. 2821
MVD EXPRESS; *U.S. Private*, pg. 2821
MVD MEDIEN-VERTRIEB DRESDEN GMBH—See Bertelsmann SE & Co. KGaA; *Int'l*, pg. 993
MVE BIOLOGICAL SOLUTIONS US, LLC—See Cryoport, Inc.; *U.S. Public*, pg. 600
MVEC EXHIBITION AND EVENT SERVICES SDN. BHD.—See IGB Berhad; *Int'l*, pg. 3601
MV EESTI OU—See MG Baltic UAB; *Int'l*, pg. 4871
MVELA PHANDA CONSTRUCTION (PTY) LIMITED—See Basil Read Holdings Limited; *Int'l*, pg. 887
MVELASERVE LIMITED—See The Bidvest Group Limited; *Int'l*, pg. 7625
M-VENTURE INVESTMENT, INC.; *Int'l*, pg. 4614
M-VENTURE INVESTMENT MANAGEMENT (SHANGHAI) CO., LTD.—See M-Venture Investment, Inc.; *Int'l*, pg. 4614
MV EQUIPMENT LLC; *U.S. Private*, pg. 2821
MV EQUIPMENT—See MV Equipment LLC; *U.S. Private*, pg. 2821
M VERTICA SDN. BHD.—See Mah Sing Group Berhad; *Int'l*, pg. 4643
M VEST WATER AS; *Int'l*, pg. 4610
MVF US LLC—See Marketing V F Limited; *Int'l*, pg. 4697
MVG DINH VU CO., LTD.—See Mitsui O.S.K. Lines, Ltd.; *Int'l*, pg. 4991
MV GENETIX GMBH—See Eurofins Scientific S.E.; *Int'l*, pg. 2551

MVG METALLVERKAUFSGESELLSCHAFT MBH & CO. KG—See GEA Group Aktiengesellschaft; *Int'l*, pg. 2903
MV GROUP UAB—See MG Baltic UAB; *Int'l*, pg. 4871
MVH PROFESSIONAL SERVICES, LLC—See HCA Healthcare, Inc.; *U.S. Public*, pg. 1001
MVISE AG; *Int'l*, pg. 5107
MVISIA DESENV. INOVADORES S.A.—See WEG S.A.; *Int'l*, pg. 8367
M VISION PCL; *Int'l*, pg. 4610
MV LATVIA SIA—See MG Baltic UAB; *Int'l*, pg. 4871
MVL GROUP, INC.; *U.S. Private*, pg. 2821
MVL LIMITED; *Int'l*, pg. 5107
MV MARKETING INC.; *U.S. Private*, pg. 2821
MVM BSZK ZRT.—See MVM Magyar Villamos Muvek Zrt.; *Int'l*, pg. 5107
MVM ERBE ZRT.—See MVM Magyar Villamos Muvek Zrt.; *Int'l*, pg. 5107
MVM ESZAK-BUDAI FUTOEROMU KFT.—See MVM Magyar Villamos Muvek Zrt.; *Int'l*, pg. 5107
MVM GTER ZRT.—See MVM Magyar Villamos Muvek Zrt.; *Int'l*, pg. 5107
MVM HUNGAROWIND KFT.—See MVM Magyar Villamos Muvek Zrt.; *Int'l*, pg. 5107
MVMI INFORMATIKA ZRT.—See MVM Magyar Villamos Muvek Zrt.; *Int'l*, pg. 5108
MVMI INFORMATION TECHNOLOGIES SERVICE CENTRE LTD.—See MVM Magyar Villamos Muvek Zrt.; *Int'l*, pg. 5108
MVM, INC.; *U.S. Private*, pg. 2821
MVM KONTO ZRT.—See MVM Magyar Villamos Muvek Zrt.; *Int'l*, pg. 5107
MVM MAGYAR VILLAMOS MUVEK ZRT.; *Int'l*, pg. 5107
MVM MIFU KFT.—See MVM Magyar Villamos Muvek Zrt.; *Int'l*, pg. 5107
MVM NET TAVKOZLESI SZOLGALTATO ZRT.—See MVM Magyar Villamos Muvek Zrt.; *Int'l*, pg. 5107
MVM OVIT ZRT.—See MVM Magyar Villamos Muvek Zrt.; *Int'l*, pg. 5108
MVM PAKSI ATOMEROMU ZRT.—See MVM Magyar Villamos Muvek Zrt.; *Int'l*, pg. 5108
MVM PAKS II. ZRT.—See MVM Magyar Villamos Muvek Zrt.; *Int'l*, pg. 5108
MVM PARTNER ZRT.—See MVM Magyar Villamos Muvek Zrt.; *Int'l*, pg. 5108
MVM VILLKESZ KFT.—See MVM Magyar Villamos Muvek Zrt.; *Int'l*, pg. 5108
MVNP; *U.S. Private*, pg. 2821
MV OIL TRUST; *U.S. Public*, pg. 1487
MV ONCOLOGY, LLC—See Bain Capital, LP; *U.S. Private*, pg. 445
MVO USA INC.—See Georgsmarienhutte Holding GmbH; *Int'l*, pg. 2940
MVP CAPITAL CO. LTD.; *Int'l*, pg. 5108
MVP DISTRIBUTION PARTNERS—See Wells Fargo & Company; *U.S. Public*, pg. 2344
MVP FINANCIAL, LLC—See Olie, Inc.; *Int'l*, pg. 5553
MVP GROUP INTERNATIONAL, INC.; *U.S. Private*, pg. 2821
MVP HEALTH CARE, INC.—See MVP Health Care Inc.; *U.S. Private*, pg. 2821
MVP HEALTH CARE INC.—See MVP Health Care Inc.; *U.S. Private*, pg. 2822
MVP HEALTH CARE INC.; *U.S. Private*, pg. 2821
MVP HEALTH CARE INC.—See MVP Health Care Inc.; *U.S. Private*, pg. 2822
MVP HEALTH CARE INC.—See MVP Health Care Inc.; *U.S. Private*, pg. 2822
MVP HOLDINGS, INC.; *U.S. Public*, pg. 1487
MVP MANUFACTURING—See Magnum Venus Products; *U.S. Private*, pg. 2549
MVP NISSAN OF EXTON; *U.S. Private*, pg. 2822
MV POLAND S.P.Z.O.O.—See MG Baltic UAB; *Int'l*, pg. 4871
MV PORTFOLIOS, INC.; *U.S. Private*, pg. 2821
M&V PROVISIONS CO. INC.; *U.S. Private*, pg. 2525
MVP (SEARCH AND SELECTION) LIMITED—See The Logistics Partnership LLP; *Int'l*, pg. 7664
MVR MULLVERWERTUNG RUGENBERGER DAMM GMBH & CO. KG—See Stadtreinigung Hamburg A.O.R.; *Int'l*, pg. 7161
MVR PRODUCTS PTE. LIMITED—See Motorcar Parts of America, Inc.; *U.S. Public*, pg. 1477
M.V. SPORTS (HONG KONG) LIMITED—See Tandem Group PLC; *Int'l*, pg. 7456
MV SPORTS & LEISURE LIMITED—See Tandem Group PLC; *Int'l*, pg. 7456
MVT CANADIAN BUS, INC.—See MV Transportation Inc.; *U.S. Private*, pg. 2821
MVTRAC, LLC; *U.S. Public*, pg. 2822
MV TRANSPORTATION INC.; *U.S. Private*, pg. 2821
MVV BIOPOWER GMBH.—See MVV Energie AG; *Int'l*, pg. 5108
MVV DECON GMBH—See MVV Energie AG; *Int'l*, pg. 5109
MVV ENAMIC GMBH—See MVV Energie AG; *Int'l*, pg. 5108
MVV ENAMIC REGIOPLAN GMBH—See MVV Energie AG; *Int'l*, pg. 5108
MVV ENERGIE AG; *Int'l*, pg. 5108

COMPANY NAME INDEX

MVV ENERGIEDIENSTLEISTUNGEN GMBH IK KORBACH—See MVV Energie AG; *Int'l*, pg. 5108
MVV ENERGIEDIENSTLEISTUNGEN GMBH—See MVV Energie AG; *Int'l*, pg. 5108
MVV ENSERVIS A.S.—See Groupe BPCE; *Int'l*, pg. 3094
MVV ENVIRONMENT DEVONPORT LIMITED—See MVV Energie AG; *Int'l*, pg. 5108
MVV ENVIRONMENT RIDHAM LIMITED—See MVV Energie AG; *Int'l*, pg. 5108
MVV IMMOSOLUTIONS GMBH—See MVV Energie AG; *Int'l*, pg. 5108
MVV INDUSTRIEPARK GERSTHOFEN GMBH—See MVV Energie AG; *Int'l*, pg. 5108
MVV INSURANCE SERVICES GMBH—See MVV Energie AG; *Int'l*, pg. 5108
MVV NETZE GMBH—See MVV Energie AG; *Int'l*, pg. 5108
MVV TRADING GMBH—See MVV Energie AG; *Int'l*, pg. 5108
MVV UMWELT GMBH—See MVV Energie AG; *Int'l*, pg. 5108
MVV UMWELT RESSOURCEN GMBH—See MVV Energie AG; *Int'l*, pg. 5109
MVV WINDENERGIE GMBH—See MVV Energie AG; *Int'l*, pg. 5109
MV WERFTEN ROSTOCK GMBH—See Genting Hong Kong Limited; *Int'l*, pg. 2929
MV WERFTEN STRALSUND GMBH—See Genting Hong Kong Limited; *Int'l*, pg. 2929
MV WERFTEN WISMAR GMBH—See OEP Capital Advisors, L.P.; *U.S. Private*, pg. 3000
MV WERFTEN WISMAR GMBH—See ThyssenKrupp AG; *Int'l*, pg. 7733
MVW INTERNATIONAL FINANCE COMPANY LLC—See Marriott Vacations Worldwide Corporation; *U.S. Public*, pg. 1374
MVZ ASKLEPIOS KLINIK SELIGENSTADT GMBH—See Asklepios Kliniken GmbH & Co. KGaA; *Int'l*, pg. 623
MVZ AUGENARZTLICHES DIAGNOSTIK- UND THERAPIEZENTRUM DUSSELDORF GMBH—See Asklepios Kliniken GmbH & Co. KGaA; *Int'l*, pg. 624
MVZ BAD NEUSTADT/ SAALE GMBH—See Asklepios Kliniken GmbH & Co. KGaA; *Int'l*, pg. 624
MVZ CAMPUS GIFHORN GMBH—See Fresenius SE & Co. KGaA; *Int'l*, pg. 2780
MVZ DAVITA ALZEY GMBH—See DaVita Inc.; *U.S. Public*, pg. 640
MVZ DAVITA AMBULANTES KARDIOLOGISCHES ZENTRUM PEINE GMBH—See DaVita Inc.; *U.S. Public*, pg. 640
MVZ DAVITA BAD AIBLING GMBH—See DaVita Inc.; *U.S. Public*, pg. 640
MVZ DAVITA CARDIO CENTRUM DUSSELDORF GMBH—See DaVita Inc.; *U.S. Public*, pg. 640
MVZ DAVITA DILLENBURG GMBH—See DaVita Inc.; *U.S. Public*, pg. 640
MVZ DAVITA DINKELSBUHL GMBH—See DaVita Inc.; *U.S. Public*, pg. 640
MVZ DAVITA EMDEN GMBH—See DaVita Inc.; *U.S. Public*, pg. 640
MVZ DAVITA GEILENKIRCHEN GMBH—See DaVita Inc.; *U.S. Public*, pg. 640
MVZ DAVITA GERA GMBH—See DaVita Inc.; *U.S. Public*, pg. 640
MVZ DAVITA NEUSS GMBH—See DaVita Inc.; *U.S. Public*, pg. 640
MVZ DAVITA NIERENZENTRUM BERLIN-BRITZ GMBH—See DaVita Inc.; *U.S. Public*, pg. 640
MVZ DAVITA RHEIN-AHR GMBH—See DaVita Inc.; *U.S. Public*, pg. 640
MVZ DAVITA RHEIN RUHR GMBH—See DaVita Inc.; *U.S. Public*, pg. 640
MVZ DAVITA SALZGITTER-SEESEN GMBH—See DaVita Inc.; *U.S. Public*, pg. 640
MVZ DAVITA VIERSEN GMBH—See DaVita Inc.; *U.S. Public*, pg. 640
MVZ DRESDEN BETRIEBS GMBH—See DaVita Inc.; *U.S. Public*, pg. 640
MVZ FUR HISTOLOGIE, ZYTOLOGIE UND MOLEKULARE DIAGNOSTIK TRIER GMBH—See Sonic Healthcare Limited; *Int'l*, pg. 7097
MVZ FUR MOLEKULARDIAGNOSTIK GMBH—See Starnberger Kliniken GmbH; *Int'l*, pg. 7178
MVZ GELSENKIRCHEN-BUER GMBH—See Fresenius Medical Care AG; *Int'l*, pg. 2776
MVZ HANSE HISTOLOGIKUM GMBH—See Asklepios Kliniken GmbH & Co. KGaA; *Int'l*, pg. 623
MVZ LABOR BOCHUM MLB GMBH—See Sonic Healthcare Limited; *Int'l*, pg. 7097
MVZ MANAGEMENT GMBH ATTENDORN—See Fresenius SE & Co. KGaA; *Int'l*, pg. 2779
MVZ MANAGEMENT GMBH BADEN-WURTTEMBERG—See Fresenius SE & Co. KGaA; *Int'l*, pg. 2779
MVZ MANAGEMENT GMBH SUD—See Fresenius SE & Co. KGaA; *Int'l*, pg. 2779
MVZ MEDICLIN BONN GMBH—See Asklepios Kliniken GmbH & Co. KGaA; *Int'l*, pg. 623
MVZ MEDIZINISCHES LABOR CELLE GMBH—See Sonic Healthcare Limited; *Int'l*, pg. 7097

MVZ PATHOLOGIE BERLIN BERGER FIETZE LINKE NADJARI GMBH—See Sonic Healthcare Limited; *Int'l*, pg. 7097
MVZ SOBERNHEIM GMBH—See Asklepios Kliniken GmbH & Co. KGaA; *Int'l*, pg. 623
MVZ UNIVERSITATSKLINIKUM MARBURG GMBH—See Asklepios Kliniken GmbH & Co. KGaA; *Int'l*, pg. 624
MWAGIA, INC.—See Modern Woodmen of America; *U.S. Private*, pg. 2763
MWA INTELLIGENCE, INC.—See Konica Minolta, Inc.; *Int'l*, pg. 4258
MWALIMU COOPERATIVE SAVINGS & CREDIT SOCIETY LIMITED; *Int'l*, pg. 5110
M+W ASIA LIMITED—See M+W Group GmbH; *Int'l*, pg. 4613
MWAVE INDUSTRIES, LLC—See Alaris Holdings Limited; *Int'l*, pg. 291
MWB BUSINESS EXCHANGE LIMITED—See IWG Plc; *Int'l*, pg. 3850
MWB FAIRTRADE WERTPAPIERHANDELSBANK AG; *Int'l*, pg. 5110
MWB MARINE SERVICES GMBH—See Zeppelin GmbH; *Int'l*, pg. 8637
MWBRANDS SAS—See Thai Union Group Public Company Limited; *Int'l*, pg. 7596
MW BRANDS SEYCHELLES LIMITED—See Thai Union Group Public Company Limited; *Int'l*, pg. 7596
M+W BRASIL PROJETOS TECNICOS LTDA.—See M+W Group GmbH; *Int'l*, pg. 4613
M.W. BUILDERS INC.—See MMC Corp.; *U.S. Private*, pg. 2754
MWB WERTPAPIERHANDELSBANK AG—See mwb fairtrade Wertpapierhandelsbank AG; *Int'l*, pg. 5110
M+W CENTRAL EUROPE SP. Z O.O.—See M+W Group GmbH; *Int'l*, pg. 4613
MW COMPONENTS—See MW Industries, Inc.; *U.S. Private*, pg. 2822
M+W DENTAL GMBH—See Carl Bennet AB; *Int'l*, pg. 1332
MWE ADVANCED STRUCTURE SDN BHD—See MWE Holdings Berhad; *Int'l*, pg. 5110
MWE GOLF & COUNTRY CLUB BERHAD—See MWE Holdings Berhad; *Int'l*, pg. 5110
MWE HOLDINGS BERHAD; *Int'l*, pg. 5110
MW EMERALD LTD.—See Meltwater N.V.; *Int'l*, pg. 4814
MWE PROPERTIES SDN BHD—See MWE Holdings Berhad; *Int'l*, pg. 5110
M+W FACILITY ENGINEERING GMBH—See M+W Group GmbH; *Int'l*, pg. 4613
M+W FRANCE S.A.R.L.—See M+W Group GmbH; *Int'l*, pg. 4613
MWG BIOTECH AG—See Eurofins Scientific S.E.; *Int'l*, pg. 2551
MWG BIOTECH INC.—See Eurofins Scientific S.E.; *Int'l*, pg. 2549
MWG BIOTECH PVT LTD.—See Eurofins Scientific S.E.; *Int'l*, pg. 2551
M+W GROUP GMBH; *Int'l*, pg. 4613
MWH ARABTECH-JARDANEH—See Stantec Inc.; *Int'l*, pg. 7171
MWH EUROPE LIMITED—See Stantec Inc.; *Int'l*, pg. 7171
MWH FARRER LIMITED—See Stantec Inc.; *Int'l*, pg. 7171
MWH GLOBAL, INC.—See Stantec Inc.; *Int'l*, pg. 7171
MWH GMBH.—See Yotrio Group Co., Ltd.; *Int'l*, pg. 8601
MW HIGH TECH PROJECTS INDIA PVT. LTD.—See M+W Group GmbH; *Int'l*, pg. 4614
M+W HIGH TECH PROJECTS ISRAEL LTD.—See M+W Group GmbH; *Int'l*, pg. 4613
M+W HIGH TECH PROJECTS LLC—See M+W Group GmbH; *Int'l*, pg. 4613
M+W HIGH TECH PROJECTS (MALAYSIA) SDN. BHD.—See M+W Group GmbH; *Int'l*, pg. 4613
M+W HIGH TECH PROJECTS MEXICO, S. DE R.L. DE C.V.—See M+W Group GmbH; *Int'l*, pg. 4613
M+W HIGH TECH PROJECTS PHILIPPINES INC.—See M+W Group GmbH; *Int'l*, pg. 4613
M+W HIGH TECH PROJECTS TAIWAN CO., LTD—See M+W Group GmbH; *Int'l*, pg. 4613
M & W HOT OIL INC; *U.S. Private*, pg. 2523
MWH PRESERVATION LTD. PARTNER; *U.S. Private*, pg. 2822
MWH TREATMENT LIMITED—See Stantec Inc.; *Int'l*, pg. 7171
MWI CORPORATION; *U.S. Private*, pg. 2822
MWI, INC.—See KBR, Inc.; *U.S. Private*, pg. 2268
M WINDS CO., LTD.—See Meidensha Corporation; *Int'l*, pg. 4797
MW INDUSTRIES, INC.—See American Securities LLC; *U.S. Private*, pg. 249
MW INDUSTRIES, INC.; *U.S. Private*, pg. 2822
M WINKWORTH PLC; *Int'l*, pg. 4610
MW INSTRUMENTS B.V.—See Indutrade AB; *Int'l*, pg. 3680
M-WISE INC.; *Int'l*, pg. 4614
M+W ITALY S.R.L.—See M+W Group GmbH; *Int'l*, pg. 4613
MWI VETERINARY SUPPLY, CO.—See Cencora, Inc.; *U.S. Public*, pg. 467
MW MANUFACTURERS INC.—See Clayton, Dubilier & Rice, LLC; *U.S. Private*, pg. 921

MW MARKETING GROUP; *U.S. Private*, pg. 2822
MWM AUSTRIA GMBH—See Caterpillar, Inc.; *U.S. Public*, pg. 452
MWM (BEIJING) CO., LTD.—See Caterpillar, Inc.; *U.S. Public*, pg. 452
MWM BENELUX B.V.—See Caterpillar, Inc.; *U.S. Public*, pg. 452
MWM DEXTER INC.; *U.S. Private*, pg. 2822
MWM ENERGY AUSTRALIA PTY LTD—See Caterpillar, Inc.; *U.S. Public*, pg. 452
MWM FRANCE S.A.S.—See Caterpillar, Inc.; *U.S. Public*, pg. 452
MWM GMBH—See Caterpillar, Inc.; *U.S. Public*, pg. 452
M+W MIDDLE EAST LTD.—See M+W Group GmbH; *Int'l*, pg. 4613
MWM INTERNATIONAL INDUSTRIA DE MOTORES DA AMERICA DO SUL LTDA.—See FreightCar America, Inc.; *U.S. Public*, pg. 885
MWM INVESTMENT CONSULTING, LLC—See Keystone Group, L.P.; *U.S. Private*, pg. 2297
MWM LATIN AMERICA SOLUCOES ENERGETICAS LTDA.—See Caterpillar, Inc.; *U.S. Public*, pg. 453
MWMPC CORP.—See Cappadonna Electrical Management Corporation; *U.S. Private*, pg. 745
MWM REAL ESTATE GMBH—See Caterpillar, Inc.; *U.S. Public*, pg. 453
MWO; *Int'l*, pg. 5110
M+W POWER SOLUTIONS GMBH—See M+W Group GmbH; *Int'l*, pg. 4613
M+W PROCESS ENGINEERING D.O.O.—See M+W Group GmbH; *Int'l*, pg. 4613
M+W PRODUCTS (SHANGHAI) CO. LTD.—See M+W Group GmbH; *Int'l*, pg. 4613
M W RECYCLING, LLC—See Icahn Enterprises L.P.; *U.S. Public*, pg. 1084
MWS ALUGUSS GMBH - KLAGENFURT PLANT—See MWS Industrieholding GmbH; *Int'l*, pg. 5110
MWS ALUGUSS GMBH—See MWS Industrieholding GmbH; *Int'l*, pg. 5110
M+W SAUDI ARABIA LTD.—See M+W Group GmbH; *Int'l*, pg. 4613
MWS CASTING S.R.O.—See MWS Industrieholding GmbH; *Int'l*, pg. 5110
MWS ENTERPRISES INC.; *U.S. Private*, pg. 2822
MWS FRIEDRICHSHAFEN GMBH—See MWS Industrieholding GmbH; *Int'l*, pg. 5110
MWS GARCHING GMBH—See MWS Industrieholding GmbH; *Int'l*, pg. 5110
M+W SHANGHAI CO., LTD.—See M+W Group GmbH; *Int'l*, pg. 4613
MWS HIGHTEC GMBH—See MWS Industrieholding GmbH; *Int'l*, pg. 5110
MWS INDUSTRIEHOLDING GMBH; *Int'l*, pg. 5110
M.W. SMITH EQUIPMENT, INC.—See DXP Enterprises, Inc.; *U.S. Public*, pg. 697
MWS VENTILSERVICE AB—See Indutrade AB; *Int'l*, pg. 3680
M+W (THAILAND) LTD.—See M+W Group GmbH; *Int'l*, pg. 4613
M.W. TRADE S.A.—See Getin Holding S.A.; *Int'l*, pg. 2947
MWUK HOLDING COMPANY LIMITED; *Int'l*, pg. 5110
MWUK LIMITED—See MWUK Holding Company Limited; *Int'l*, pg. 5110
MW UNIVERSAL INC.; *U.S. Private*, pg. 2822
M+W U.S., INC.—See M+W Group GmbH; *Int'l*, pg. 4613
M+W VIETNAM CO., LTD.—See M+W Group GmbH; *Int'l*, pg. 4614
MWW GROUP LLC; *U.S. Private*, pg. 2822
MWW GROUP—See MWW Group LLC; *U.S. Private*, pg. 2822
MWW GROUP—See MWW Group LLC; *U.S. Private*, pg. 2822
THE MWW GROUP—See MWW Group LLC; *U.S. Private*, pg. 2822
THE MWW GROUP—See MWW Group LLC; *U.S. Private*, pg. 2822
THE MWW GROUP—See MWW Group LLC; *U.S. Private*, pg. 2822
THE MWW GROUP—See MWW Group LLC; *U.S. Private*, pg. 2822
THE MWW GROUP—See MWW Group LLC; *U.S. Private*, pg. 2822
MX1 GMBH—See SES S.A.; *Int'l*, pg. 6727
MXC CAPITAL LIMITED; *Int'l*, pg. 5110
MX CORPORATION; *U.S. Private*, pg. 2822
MX GOLD CORP.; *Int'l*, pg. 5110
THE MX GROUP; *U.S. Private*, pg. 4081
MXLAB AG—See SRG SSR Idee Suisse; *Int'l*, pg. 7149
MXL INDUSTRIES, INC.—See The Pritzker Group - Chicago, LLC; *U.S. Private*, pg. 4099
MX MOBILING CO., LTD.—See Marubeni Corporation; *Int'l*, pg. 4705
MXOTECH, INC.—See Southfield Capital Advisors, LLC; *U.S. Private*, pg. 3736
MXP PARTNERS LLP; *Int'l*, pg. 5110
MXSECURE, INC.; *U.S. Private*, pg. 2823
MXTRAN INC.—See Macronix International Co., Ltd.; *Int'l*, pg. 5110
MY1STOP LLC; *U.S. Private*, pg. 2823

MY AGENCY — CORPORATE AFFILIATIONS

MY AGENCY; *Int'l*, pg. 5110
MY ALARM CENTER LLC; *U.S. Private*, pg. 2823
MYALERT MEXICO SERVICIOS S.A. DE CV—See Nippon Telegraph & Telephone Corporation; *Int'l*, pg. 5349
MYANMAR AIRWAYS INTERNATIONAL; *Int'l*, pg. 5111
MYANMAR ARYSTA LIFESCIENCE CO LTD—See UPL Limited; *Int'l*, pg. 8089
MYANMAR BEHN MEYER CO., LTD.—See Behn Meyer (D) Holding AG & Co.; *Int'l*, pg. 941
MYANMAR BREWERY LIMITED—See Kirin Holdings Company, Limited; *Int'l*, pg. 4189
MYANMAR CENTURY STEEL STURCTURE LIMITED—See Century Iron & Steel Industrial Co., Ltd.; *Int'l*, pg. 1418
MYANMAR C.P LIVESTOCK CO., LTD—See Charoen Pokphand Group Co., Ltd.; *Int'l*, pg. 1453
MYANMAR DAEWOO LTD.—See POSCO Holdings Inc.; *Int'l*, pg. 5938
MYANMAR DHL LIMITED—See Deutsche Post AG; *Int'l*, pg. 2078
MYANMAR FAW INTL.—See China FAW Group Corporation; *Int'l*, pg. 1502
MYANMAR GOLD COIN INTERNATIONAL CO., LTD.—See Gold Coin Holdings Sdn Bhd; *Int'l*, pg. 3024
MYANMAR HYOSUNG CO., LTD.—See Hyosung Corporation; *Int'l*, pg. 3552
MYANMAR INDO BEST CO., LTD.—See Berli Jucker Public Co. Ltd.; *Int'l*, pg. 985
MYANMAR INVESTMENTS INTERNATIONAL LIMITED; *Int'l*, pg. 5111
MYANMAR JARDINE SCHINDLER LTD.—See Jardine Matheson Holdings Limited; *Int'l*, pg. 3909
MYANMAR JARDINE SCHINDLER LTD,—See Schindler Holding AG; *Int'l*, pg. 6620
MYANMAR KOEI INTERNATIONAL LTD.—See Nippon Koei Co., Ltd.; *Int'l*, pg. 5321
MYANMAR NEW HOPE FARMS CO., LTD—See New Hope Group Co., Ltd.; *Int'l*, pg. 5224
MYANMAR PARA LIGHT LED & LIGHTING ACCESSORY COMPANY LTD.—See Para Light Electronics Co., Ltd.; *Int'l*, pg. 5734
MYANMAR POSCO STEEL CO., LTD.—See POSCO Holdings Inc.; *Int'l*, pg. 5936
MYANMAR SECURITIES EXCHANGE CENTRE CO., LTD.—See Daiwa Securities Group Inc.; *Int'l*, pg. 1949
MYANMAR SEGYE INTERNATIONAL LTD.—See SG Corporation; *Int'l*, pg. 6740
MYANMAR STARTS CORPORATE SERVICES CO., LTD.—See Starts Corporation, Inc.; *Int'l*, pg. 7179
MYANMAR SUPPLY CHAIN & MARKETING SERVICES CO., LTD.—See Thai Beverage Public Company Limited; *Int'l*, pg. 7591
MYANMAR SUZUKI MOTOR CO., LTD.—See Suzuki Motor Corporation; *Int'l*, pg. 7354
MYANMAR TAH HSIN INDUSTRIAL CO., LTD.—See Tah Hsin Industrial Corporation; *Int'l*, pg. 7407
MYANMAR TASAKI CO., LTD.—See MBK Partners Ltd.; *Int'l*, pg. 4754
MYANMAR TOYOTA TSUSHO CO. LTD—See Toyota Tsusho Corporation; *Int'l*, pg. 7878
MYANMAR TRACTORS LIMITED.—See TIL Limited; *Int'l*, pg. 7748
MYANMAR YUNGSHIN PHARM. LTD.—See YungShin Global Holding Corporation; *Int'l*, pg. 8614
M.Y ASSOCIATES CO., LTD.—See Y.H.O Co., Ltd.; *Int'l*, pg. 8543
MY AUTOGROUP; *U.S. Private*, pg. 2823
MYBENEFIT SP. Z O.O.—See Benefit Systems SA; *Int'l*, pg. 972
MY BENETECH INC.—See NexgenRx Inc.; *Int'l*, pg. 5243
MY BEST FRIEND'S HAIR, LLC—See Sally Beauty Holdings, Inc.; *U.S. Public*, pg. 1839
MYBEST GROUP SPA; *Int'l*, pg. 5111
MYBET HOLDING SE; *Int'l*, pg. 5111
MYBI CO., LTD.—See Lotte Co., Ltd.; *Int'l*, pg. 4560
MY BOOT STORE, INC.—See Northern Imports, Inc.; *U.S. Private*, pg. 2953
MY.BOOX—See Vivendi SE; *Int'l*, pg. 8274
MYBUCKS BANKING CORPORATION LTD.—See MyBucks S.A.; *Int'l*, pg. 5111
MYBUCKS BANK MOZAMBIQUE S.A.—See MyBucks S.A.; *Int'l*, pg. 5111
MYBUCKS S.A.; *Int'l*, pg. 5111
MY BUS (ITALY) S.R.L.—See JTB Corp.; *Int'l*, pg. 4016
MYCARE UNICHARM.CO., LTD.—See Unicharm Corporation; *Int'l*, pg. 8032
MYCELX TECHNOLOGIES CORPORATION; *U.S. Public*, pg. 1487
MYCHARITY, LTD.—See Blackbaud, Inc.; *U.S. Public*, pg. 341
MY CHAU PRINTING & PACKAGING HOLDINGS COMPANY; *Int'l*, pg. 5111
MY CHEVROLET—See MY Autogroup; *U.S. Private*, pg. 2823
MYCIO WEALTH PARTNERS, LLC—See Affiliated Managers Group, Inc.; *U.S. Public*, pg. 55
MY CITY BUILDERS, INC.; *U.S. Public*, pg. 1487
MYCLIKS INC.; *U.S. Private*, pg. 2823

MYCOM CHEMICAL PROCESS CORP. DE VENEZUELA S.A.—See Mayekawa Mfg. Co. Ltd.; *Int'l*, pg. 4744
MYCO MEDICAL; *U.S. Private*, pg. 2823
MYCOM GROUP LTD.—See Inflexion Private Equity Partners LLP; *Int'l*, pg. 3689
MYCOM KOREA CO., LTD.—See Mayekawa Mfg. Co. Ltd.; *Int'l*, pg. 4744
MYCOM NORTH AMERICA INC. - ORLANDO—See Inflexion Private Equity Partners LLP; *Int'l*, pg. 3689
MYCOM NORTH AMERICA, INC.—See Mayekawa Mfg. Co. Ltd.; *Int'l*, pg. 4744
MYCOM NORTH AMERICA INC.—See Inflexion Private Equity Partners LLP; *Int'l*, pg. 3689
MYCOM PERU S.A.C.—See Mayekawa Mfg. Co. Ltd.; *Int'l*, pg. 4744
MYCOMPUTERCAREER INC.; *U.S. Private*, pg. 2823
MY COMPUTER WORKS, INC; *U.S. Private*, pg. 2823
MYCOM SOFTWARE—See Inflexion Private Equity Partners LLP; *Int'l*, pg. 3689
MYCOM VENEZUELA SALES & SERVICE, C.A.—See Mayekawa Mfg. Co. Ltd.; *Int'l*, pg. 4744
MYCONE DENTAL SUPPLY CO. INC.; *U.S. Private*, pg. 2824
MYCON GENERAL CONTRACTORS INC.; *U.S. Private*, pg. 2823
MYCONIC CAPITAL CORP.; *Int'l*, pg. 5111
MYCORRHIZAL APPLICATIONS, LLC—See Sumitomo Chemical Company, Limited; *Int'l*, pg. 7264
MYCOTOPIA THERAPIES INC.—See Ehave, Inc.; *U.S. Public*, pg. 721
MYCO TRAILERS, LLC—See Propst Properties, LLC; *U.S. Private*, pg. 3286
MY COURIER DEPOT INC.—See PUDO Inc.; *Int'l*, pg. 6115
MYCOVIA PHARMACEUTICALS, INC.—See NovaQuest Capital Management, LLC; *U.S. Private*, pg. 2967
MYCROFT BUSINESS COMPUTERS INC.; *Int'l*, pg. 5112
MYCROFT INC.; *U.S. Private*, pg. 2824
MYCRONIC AB; *Int'l*, pg. 5112
MYCRONIC BV—See Mycronic AB; *Int'l*, pg. 5112
MYCRONIC CO., LTD.—See Mycronic AB; *Int'l*, pg. 5112
MYCRONIC FUKUOKA CO., LTD.—See Mycronic AB; *Int'l*, pg. 5112
MYCRONIC GMBH—See Mycronic AB; *Int'l*, pg. 5112
MYCRONIC INC.—See Mycronic AB; *Int'l*, pg. 5112
MYCRONIC LTD.—See Mycronic AB; *Int'l*, pg. 5112
MYCRONIC PTE. LTD.—See Mycronic AB; *Int'l*, pg. 5112
MYCRONIC S.A.S.—See Mycronic AB; *Int'l*, pg. 5112
MYCRONIC (SHANGHAI) CO., LTD.—See Mycronic AB; *Int'l*, pg. 5112
MYCRONIC TECHNOLOGIES CORP.—See Mycronic AB; *Int'l*, pg. 5112
MYCRON STEEL BERHAD—See Melewar Industrial Group Berhad; *Int'l*, pg. 4808
MYCRON STEEL CRC SDN BHD—See Melewar Industrial Group Berhad; *Int'l*, pg. 4808
MYCSP LIMITED—See Siris Capital Group, LLC; *U.S. Private*, pg. 3673
MYDAS REAL ESTATE INVESTMENTS LTD.; *Int'l*, pg. 5112
MYDATA AUTOMATION AB—See Mycronic AB; *Int'l*, pg. 5112
MYDATA AUTOMATION, INC.—See Mycronic AB; *Int'l*, pg. 5112
MY DATA INTELLIGENCE INC.—See Dentsu Group Inc.; *Int'l*, pg. 2039
MYDATT SERVICES, INC.—See SMS Holdings Corporation; *U.S. Private*, pg. 3699
MYDAYS EVENT GMBH—See ProSiebenSat.1 Media SE; *Int'l*, pg. 6001
MYDAYS GMBH—See ProSiebenSat.1 Media SE; *Int'l*, pg. 6001
MYDECINE INNOVATIONS GROUP INC.; *Int'l*, pg. 5112
MYDENT INTERNATIONAL, INC.—See The Jordan Company, L.P.; *U.S. Private*, pg. 4063
MY-D HAN-D MFG. INC.; *U.S. Private*, pg. 2823
MYDIGITALOFFICE.COM, LLC—See myDigitalOffice Holdings Inc.; *U.S. Private*, pg. 2824
MYDIGITALOFFICE HOLDINGS INC.; *U.S. Private*, pg. 2824
MYDRIN FINDLEY SRL—See Arkema S.A.; *Int'l*, pg. 570
MYDX, INC.; *U.S. Public*, pg. 2824
MYE CANADA OPERATIONS INC.—See Myers Industries, Inc.; *U.S. Public*, pg. 1488
MYECHECK, INC.; *U.S. Private*, pg. 2824
MYEDGE LLC; *U.S. Private*, pg. 2824
MY E.G. CAPITAL SDN. BHD.—See MY E.G. Services Berhad; *Int'l*, pg. 5111
MY E.G. SERVICES BERHAD; *Int'l*, pg. 5111
MYELIN HEALTH COMMUNICATIONS, INC.; *U.S. Private*, pg. 2824
MY ENT SPECIALIST PTE. LTD.—See Alliance Healthcare Group Limited; *Int'l*, pg. 340
MYEONGSHIN FERTILIZER CO., LTD.—See MSC Co., Ltd.; *Int'l*, pg. 5067
MYERCONNEX; *U.S. Private*, pg. 2824
THE MYER EMPORIUM PTY LTD—See Myer Pty Ltd; *Int'l*, pg. 5112
MYER PTY LTD; *Int'l*, pg. 5112

MYER PTY LTD—See Myer Pty Ltd; *Int'l*, pg. 5112
MYERS CONTAINER, LLC; *U.S. Private*, pg. 2824
MYERS-COX CO; *U.S. Private*, pg. 2824
MYERS DE EL SALVADOR S.A. DE C.V.—See Myers Industries, Inc.; *U.S. Public*, pg. 1488
MYERS DE PANAMA S.A.—See Myers Industries, Inc.; *U.S. Public*, pg. 1488
MYERS DIESEL & EQUIPMENT; *U.S. Private*, pg. 2824
MYERS FAMILY LP; *U.S. Private*, pg. 2824
MYERS GROVE INVESTMENTS LIMITED—See Barclays PLC; *Int'l*, pg. 862
MYERS-HOLUM, INC.; *U.S. Private*, pg. 2824
MYERS INDUSTRIES, INC.; *U.S. Public*, pg. 1488
MYERS PARK COUNTRY CLUB; *U.S. Private*, pg. 2824
MYERS POWER PRODUCTS, INC.; *U.S. Private*, pg. 2824
MYERS POWER PRODUCTS, INC.—See Myers Power Products, Inc.; *U.S. Private*, pg. 2824
MYERS POWER PRODUCTS—See Myers Power Products, Inc.; *U.S. Private*, pg. 2824
MYERS & SONS CONSTRUCTION, LLC—See Sterling Infrastructure, Inc.; *U.S. Public*, pg. 1946
MYERS & SONS CONSTRUCTION, L.P.—See Sterling Infrastructure, Inc.; *U.S. Public*, pg. 1946
MYERS-STEVENS & CO. INC.; *U.S. Private*, pg. 2824
MYERSTIRESUPPLY.COM, INC.—See Myers Industries, Inc.; *U.S. Public*, pg. 1488
MYERS TIRE SUPPLY INTERNATIONAL, INC.—See Myers Industries, Inc.; *U.S. Public*, pg. 1488
MYERS TIRE SUPPLY—See Myers Industries, Inc.; *U.S. Public*, pg. 1488
MY EYE MEDIA, LLC—See Eurofins Scientific S.E.; *Int'l*, pg. 2549
MY EYE STORE—See Compulink Business Systems, Inc.; *U.S. Private*, pg. 1004
MY FAMILY CLINIC (ANGSANA BREEZE@YISHUN) PTE. LTD.—See Alliance Healthcare Group Limited; *Int'l*, pg. 340
MY FAMILY CLINIC (CCK) PTE. LTD.—See Alliance Healthcare Group Limited; *Int'l*, pg. 340
MY FAMILY CLINIC (CLEMENTI 325) PTE. LTD.—See Alliance Healthcare Group Limited; *Int'l*, pg. 340
MY FAMILY CLINIC (CLEMENTI) PTE. LTD.—See Alliance Healthcare Group Limited; *Int'l*, pg. 340
MY FAMILY CLINIC (HOUGANG CENTRAL) PTE. LTD.—See Alliance Healthcare Group Limited; *Int'l*, pg. 340
MY FAMILY CLINIC (PN) PTE. LTD.—See Alliance Healthcare Group Limited; *Int'l*, pg. 340
MY FAMILY CLINIC (PUNGGOL CENTRAL) PTE. LTD.—See Alliance Healthcare Group Limited; *Int'l*, pg. 340
MY FAMILY CLINIC (RV) PTE. LTD.—See Alliance Healthcare Group Limited; *Int'l*, pg. 340
MY FAMILY CLINIC (SEGAR) PTE. LTD.—See Alliance Healthcare Group Limited; *Int'l*, pg. 340
MY FAMILY CLINIC (SJ) PTE. LTD.—See Alliance Healthcare Group Limited; *Int'l*, pg. 340
MY FAMILY CLINIC (ST GEORGE) PTE. LTD.—See Alliance Healthcare Group Limited; *Int'l*, pg. 340
MY FAMILY CLINIC (TH) PTE. LTD.—See Alliance Healthcare Group Limited; *Int'l*, pg. 340
MY FAMILY CLINIC (TPY) PTE. LTD.—See Alliance Healthcare Group Limited; *Int'l*, pg. 340
MY FAMILY CLINIC (WD) PTE. LTD.—See Alliance Healthcare Group Limited; *Int'l*, pg. 340
MY FAMILY CLINIC (WOODLANDS GLEN) PTE. LTD.—See Alliance Healthcare Group Limited; *Int'l*, pg. 340
MY FAMILY CLUB LIMITED—See D.C. Thomson & Co. Ltd.; *Int'l*, pg. 1900
MY FAVORITE NEIGHBOR, LLC—See Constellation Brands, Inc.; *U.S. Public*, pg. 571
MY FAVORITE THINGS, INC.—See Nu Skin Enterprises, Inc.; *U.S. Public*, pg. 1551
MY FAVORITE THINGS, LLC—See Forcht Group of Kentucky, Inc.; *U.S. Private*, pg. 1564
MYFC HOLDING AB; *Int'l*, pg. 5112
MYFIN EAD—See First Investment Bank AD; *Int'l*, pg. 2685
MYFLORIST.NET, LLC—See 1-800-FLOWERS.COM, Inc.; *U.S. Public*, pg. 1
MYFONTS, INC.—See HGGC, LLC; *U.S. Private*, pg. 1930
MY FOOD BAG GROUP LIMITED; *Int'l*, pg. 5111
MY FOODIE BOX LIMITED; *Int'l*, pg. 5111
MY FORWARDER INTERNATIONAL SDN. BHD.—Worldgate Global Logistics Ltd; *Int'l*, pg. 8458
MY FREIGHTWORLD TECHNOLOGIES, INC.; *U.S. Public*, pg. 1487
MYGO GAMES HOLDING CO.; *U.S. Private*, pg. 2825
MYGRANT GLASS COMPANY INC.; *U.S. Private*, pg. 2825
MYGREENBUILDINGS, LLC; *U.S. Private*, pg. 2825
M.Y GROUP LIMITED; *Int'l*, pg. 4617
MY G SAS—See Devoteam SA; *Int'l*, pg. 2090
MYHAMMER HOLDING AG; *Int'l*, pg. 5112
M Y H COMERCIAL E INDUSTRIAL LIMITADA—See Air Products & Chemicals, Inc.; *U.S. Public*, pg. 66

COMPANY NAME INDEX

MY HD MEDIA FZ LLC—See Sandmartin International Holdings Limited; *Int'l*, pg. 6526
MYHEALTHCHECKED PLC; *Int'l*, pg. 5112
MY HEALTH DIRECT, INC.—See Experian plc; *Int'l*, pg. 2588
MY HEALTH SERVICES (THAILAND) CO., LTD.—See Allianz Ayudhya Capital Public Company Limited; *Int'l*, pg. 341
MYHERITAGE LTD; *Int'l*, pg. 5112
MYHOME, A WILLISTON FINANCIAL GROUP COMPANY, LLC—See Williston Financial Group, LLC; *U.S. Private*, pg. 4528
MY HOME LINER CO., LTD.—See Hoosiers Holdings; *Int'l*, pg. 3472
MYHOME LLC; *U.S. Private*, pg. 2825
MYHOME REAL ESTATE DEVELOPMENT GROUP CO., LTD.; *Int'l*, pg. 5112
MYHOTELSHOP GMBH—See RateGain Travel Technologies Limited; *Int'l*, pg. 6213
MYHOUSE CO., LTD.—See Apaman Co., Ltd.; *Int'l*, pg. 500
MY HUMBLE HOUSE HOSPITALITY MANAGEMENT CONSULTING CO., LTD.; *Int'l*, pg. 5111
MY HUMBLE HOUSE IN BEIJING (RESTAURANT) COMPANY LTD—See Tung Lok Restaurants (2000) Ltd; *Int'l*, pg. 7971
MY INSURANCE CLAIM LIMITED—See Shine Justice Ltd.; *Int'l*, pg. 6842
MY JOB MATCHER, INC.; *U.S. Private*, pg. 2823
MYK CORPORATION—See NOK Corporation; *Int'l*, pg. 5402
MYKLEBUST VERFT AS; *Int'l*, pg. 5113
MYKONOS TANKER LLC—See Saltchuk Resources Inc.; *U.S. Private*, pg. 3534
MYKRIS ASIA SDN BHD—See UOB-Kay Hian Holdings Limited; *Int'l*, pg. 8086
MYLAN AB—See Viatris Inc.; *U.S. Public*, pg. 2294
MYLAN APS—See Viatris Inc.; *U.S. Public*, pg. 2294
MYLAN BERTEK PHARMACEUTICALS, INC.—See Viatris Inc.; *U.S. Public*, pg. 2294
MYLAN BVBA—See Viatris Inc.; *U.S. Public*, pg. 2294
MYLAN B.V.—See Viatris Inc.; *U.S. Public*, pg. 2293
MYLAN DURA GMBH—See Viatris Inc.; *U.S. Public*, pg. 2294
MYLAN EMEA S.A.S.—See Viatris Inc.; *U.S. Public*, pg. 2294
MYLAN EPD KFT.—See Viatris Inc.; *U.S. Public*, pg. 2294
MYLAN GENERICS FRANCE HOLDING S.A.S.—See Viatris Inc.; *U.S. Public*, pg. 2294
MYLAN GROUP B.V.—See Viatris Inc.; *U.S. Public*, pg. 2294
MYLAN HEALTHCARE NORGE AS—See Viatris Inc.; *U.S. Public*, pg. 2293
MYLAN HEALTHCARE S.P. Z O.O.—See Viatris Inc.; *U.S. Public*, pg. 2293
MYLAN HEALTH PTY. LTD.—See Viatris Inc.; *U.S. Public*, pg. 2293
MYLAN HOSPITAL AS—See Viatris Inc.; *U.S. Public*, pg. 2294
MYLAN II B.V.—See Viatris Inc.; *U.S. Public*, pg. 2293
MYLAN, INC.—See Viatris Inc.; *U.S. Public*, pg. 2293
MYLAN INSTITUTIONAL INC.—See Viatris Inc.; *U.S. Public*, pg. 2294
MYLAN INSTITUTIONAL LLC—See Viatris Inc.; *U.S. Public*, pg. 2294
MYLAN IRE HEALTHCARE LIMITED—See Viatris Inc.; *U.S. Public*, pg. 2293
MYLAN LABORATORIES INC.—See Viatris Inc.; *U.S. Public*, pg. 2294
MYLAN LABORATORIES LIMITED—See Viatris Inc.; *U.S. Public*, pg. 2294
MYLAN LABORATORIES SAS—See Viatris Inc.; *U.S. Public*, pg. 2294
MYLAN MEDICAL SAS—See Viatris Inc.; *U.S. Public*, pg. 2294
MYLAN NETHERLANDS B.V.—See Viatris Inc.; *U.S. Public*, pg. 2294
MYLAN NEW ZEALAND LTD—See Viatris Inc.; *U.S. Public*, pg. 2294
MYLAN PHARMACEUTICALS INC.—See Viatris Inc.; *U.S. Public*, pg. 2294
MYLAN PHARMACEUTICALS PRIVATE LIMITED—See Viatris Inc.; *U.S. Public*, pg. 2294
MYLAN PHARMACEUTICALS SP. Z O.O.—See Viatris Inc.; *U.S. Public*, pg. 2294
MYLAN PHARMACEUTICALS ULC—See Viatris Inc.; *U.S. Public*, pg. 2294
MYLAN PHARMA GROUP LTD—See Viatris Inc.; *U.S. Public*, pg. 2294
MYLAN PHARMA UK LIMITED—See Viatris Inc.; *U.S. Public*, pg. 2294
MYLAN SEIYAKU LTD.—See Viatris Inc.; *U.S. Public*, pg. 2294
MYLAN SPECIALTY L.P.—See Viatris Inc.; *U.S. Public*, pg. 2294
MYLAN SPECIALTY LP—See Viatris Inc.; *U.S. Public*, pg. 2294
MYLAN SWITZERLAND GMBH—See Viatris Inc.; *U.S. Public*, pg. 2294
MYLAN TECHNOLOGIES, INCORPORATED—See Viatris Inc.; *U.S. Public*, pg. 2294
MYLAN TEORANTA—See Viatris Inc.; *U.S. Public*, pg. 2294
MYLAPS ASIA PACIFIC LTY LTD—See HAL Trust N.V.; *Int'l*, pg. 3224
MYLER CHURCH BUILDING SYSTEMS, INC.—See The Myler Company Inc.; *U.S. Private*, pg. 4081
THE MYLER COMPANY INC.; *U.S. Private*, pg. 4081
MYLES F. KELLY INC.; *U.S. Private*, pg. 2825
MYLIFE.COM, INC.; *U.S. Private*, pg. 2825
MY LIFE COVERED LLC—See Reinsurance Group of America, Inc.; *U.S. Public*, pg. 1778
MYLIFE LEBENSVERSICHERUNG AG; *Int'l*, pg. 5113
MY LITTLE PARIS SAS—See Television Francaise 1 S.A.; *Int'l*, pg. 7543
MYLOANCARE VENTURES PRIVATE LIMITED—See PB Fintech Limited; *Int'l*, pg. 5764
MYLOC MANAGED IT AG—See WIIT SpA; *Int'l*, pg. 8408
MYMARKET.COM (PTY) LIMITED—See The Bidvest Group Limited; *Int'l*, pg. 7625
MYMBN BERHAD; *Int'l*, pg. 5113
MYM COMMUNITY CO., LTD.—See Biken Techno Corporation Ltd.; *Int'l*, pg. 1023
MYMETICS B.V.—See Mymetics Corporation; *Int'l*, pg. 5113
MYMETICS CORPORATION; *Int'l*, pg. 5113
MY MICHELLE—See Sun Capital Partners, Inc.; *U.S. Private*, pg. 3859
MYMIC LLC; *U.S. Private*, pg. 2825
MYM NUTRACEUTICALS INC.—See IM Cannabis Corp.; *Int'l*, pg. 3617
MY MONEY BANK S.A.—See Cerberus Capital Management, L.P.; *U.S. Private*, pg. 839
MY MONEY SECURITIES LIMITED; *Int'l*, pg. 5111
MYNARIC AG; *Int'l*, pg. 5113
MY NATURAL MARKET; *U.S. Private*, pg. 2823
MYND.AI, INC.—See NetDragon Websoft Holdings Limited; *Int'l*, pg. 5213
MYND PROPERTY MANAGEMENT, INC.; *U.S. Private*, pg. 2825
MYNDTEC INC.; *Int'l*, pg. 5113
MYNEIGE S.A.S. - SAINTE-LUCE-SUR-LOIRE—See TechnoAlpin S.p.A.; *Int'l*, pg. 7509
MYNEIGE S.R.L.—See TechnoAlpin S p A; *Int'l*, pg. 7509
MYNESIGHT PTY LTD—See Metarock Group Limited; *Int'l*, pg. 4851
MY NET FONE AUSTRALIA PTY LIMITED—See Aussie Broadband Ltd.; *Int'l*, pg. 716
MYNET INC.; *Int'l*, pg. 5113
MYNETWORKTV, INC.—See Fox Corporation; *U.S. Public*, pg. 876
MYNEWSDESK AB—See Fred. Olsen & Co.; *Int'l*, pg. 2768
MYNEWSDESK APS—See Fred. Olsen & Co.; *Int'l*, pg. 2768
MYNEWSDESK AS—See Fred. Olsen & Co.; *Int'l*, pg. 2768
MYNEWSDESK GMBH—See Fred. Olsen & Co.; *Int'l*, pg. 2768
MYNEWSDESK- GOTHENBURG—See Fred. Olsen & Co.; *Int'l*, pg. 2768
MYNEWSDESK LTD.—See Fred. Olsen & Co.; *Int'l*, pg. 2768
MYNEWSDESK- MALMO—See Fred. Olsen & Co.; *Int'l*, pg. 2768
MYNEWSDESK OY—See Fred. Olsen & Co.; *Int'l*, pg. 2768
MYNEWSDESK- UMEA—See Fred. Olsen & Co.; *Int'l*, pg. 2768
MYNEWS HOLDINGS BERHAD; *Int'l*, pg. 5113
MYNEXUS, INC.—See Elevance Health, Inc.; *U.S. Public*, pg. 731
MY NISSAN - KIA; *U.S. Private*, pg. 2823
MYNK1906 INDUSTRIES INDIA LIMITED; *Int'l*, pg. 5113
MYNTRA DESIGNS PRIVATE LIMITED—See Walmart Inc.; *U.S. Public*, pg. 2325
MYOB ASIA SDN BHD—See Bain Capital, LP; *U.S. Private*, pg. 442
MYOB AUSTRALIA PTY LTD—See Bain Capital, LP; *U.S. Private*, pg. 442
MYOB GROUP LIMITED—See KKR & Co. Inc.; *U.S. Public*, pg. 1259
MYOB HONG KONG LIMITED—See Bain Capital, LP; *U.S. Private*, pg. 442
MYOB LIMITED—See Bain Capital, LP; *U.S. Private*, pg. 441
MYOB SINGAPORE PTE LIMITED—See Bain Capital, LP; *U.S. Private*, pg. 442
MYOFFICE, INC.; *U.S. Private*, pg. 2825
MYOFFICEPRODUCTS LLC—See MyOfficeProducts LLC; *U.S. Private*, pg. 2825
MYOFFICEPRODUCTS LLC; *U.S. Private*, pg. 2825
MYOGEM HEALTH COMPANY S.L.—See 1nKemia IUCT Group, S.A.; *Int'l*, pg. 3
MYOJODENKI CO., LTD.—See The Furukawa Electric Co., Ltd.; *Int'l*, pg. 7646
MYOJO FOODS CO., LTD—See Nissin Foods Holdings Co., Ltd.; *Int'l*, pg. 5376
MYOJO U.S.A., INC.—See Nissin Foods Holdings Co., Ltd.; *Int'l*, pg. 5376
MYOJYO CEMENT CO., LTD.—See Taiheiyo Cement Corporation; *Int'l*, pg. 7411
MYOKARDIA, INC.—See Bristol-Myers Squibb Company; *U.S. Public*, pg. 387
MYOMO, INC.; *U.S. Public*, pg. 1488
MYONE SERVICES AG—See Maus Freres S.A.; *Int'l*, pg. 4732
MYONEX, LLC; *U.S. Private*, pg. 2825
MYONIC GMBH—See Minebea Mitsumi Inc.; *Int'l*, pg. 4904
MYONIC HOLDING GMBH—See Minebea Mitsumi Inc.; *Int'l*, pg. 4904
MYONIC LTD.—See Minebea Mitsumi Inc.; *Int'l*, pg. 4904
MYONIC S.R.O.—See Minebea Mitsumi Inc.; *Int'l*, pg. 4904
MYOPTIQUE GROUP LTD.—See EssilorLuxottica SA; *Int'l*, pg. 2515
MYOTCSTORE.COM; *U.S. Private*, pg. 2825
MYOTEK INDUSTRIES INC.—See New Water Capital, L.P.; *U.S. Private*, pg. 2908
MYOTOKU CONVUM CHINA CO., LTD.—See Convum Ltd.; *Int'l*, pg. 1788
MYOTOKU LTD. - IWATE PLANT—See Convum Ltd.; *Int'l*, pg. 1788
MYOTOKU TECHNOLOGIES INC.—See Convum Ltd.; *Int'l*, pg. 1788
MYOUNG SHIN INDUSTRY CO., LTD.; *Int'l*, pg. 5113
MYOVANT SCIENCES LTD.—See Sumitomo Chemical Company, Limited; *Int'l*, pg. 7267
MY OWN MEALS, INC.; *U.S. Private*, pg. 2823
MY PET CHICKEN LLC; *U.S. Private*, pg. 2823
MYPHOTOALBUM, INC.; *U.S. Public*, pg. 1488
MYPHOTOBOOK GMBH—See Carl Bennet AB; *Int'l*, pg. 1332
MYPLANET INTERNATIONAL A/S—See TUI AG; *Int'l*, pg. 7965
MYPLANET SWEDEN AB—See TUI AG; *Int'l*, pg. 7965
MYP LTD.; *Int'l*, pg. 5113
MY PLUMBER INC.; *U.S. Private*, pg. 2823
MYPRINT CORP.—See Triton Pacific Capital Partners LLC; *U.S. Private*, pg. 4239
THE MYR CORPORATION—See EqualizeRCM; *U.S. Private*, pg. 1415
MY RECEPTIONIST, INC.; *U.S. Private*, pg. 2823
MYRESJOHUS AB—See OBOS BBL; *Int'l*, pg. 5512
MYRESJOKOK AB—See Nobia AB; *Int'l*, pg. 5395
MYREX INDUSTRIES; *U.S. Private*, pg. 2825
MYREXIS, INC.; *U.S. Public*, pg. 1489
MYR GROUP CONSTRUCTION CANADA, LTD.—See MYR Group Inc.; *U.S. Public*, pg. 1489
MYR GROUP INC.; *U.S. Public*, pg. 1488
MYRIAD360, LLC; *U.S. Private*, pg. 2826
MYRIAD DEVELOPMENT, INC.; *U.S. Private*, pg. 2825
MYRIAD FRANCE SAS—See Myriad Group AG; *Int'l*, pg. 5113
MYRIAD GENETIC LABORATORIES, INC.—See Myriad Genetics, Inc.; *U.S. Public*, pg. 1489
MYRIAD GENETICS, INC.; *U.S. Public*, pg. 1489
MYRIAD GENETICS LTD—See Myriad Genetics, Inc.; *U.S. Public*, pg. 1489
MYRIAD GROUP AG; *Int'l*, pg. 5113
MYRIAD GROUP KOREA CO., LTD.—See Myriad Group AG; *Int'l*, pg. 5113
MYRIAD INTERACTIVE MEDIA, INC.; *Int'l*, pg. 5113
MYRIAD MOBILE, INC.; *U.S. Private*, pg. 2825
MYRIAD RBM, INC.—See Myriad Genetics, Inc.; *U.S. Public*, pg. 1489
MYRIAD RESTAURANT GROUP; *U.S. Private*, pg. 2825
MYRIAD SUPPLY COMPANY, LLC; *U.S. Private*, pg. 2825
MYRIAD TECHNOLOGY AG—See Myriad Group AG; *Int'l*, pg. 5113
MYRIAD TRAVEL MARKETING—See EagleTree Capital, LP; *U.S. Private*, pg. 1311
MYRIAD TRAVEL MARKETING—See EagleTree Capital, LP; *U.S. Private*, pg. 1311
MYRIAD URANIUM CORP.; *Int'l*, pg. 5113
MYRIANT CORPORATION—See PTT Global Chemical Public Company Limited; *Int'l*, pg. 6091
MYRICK CONSTRUCTION INC.; *U.S. Private*, pg. 2826
MYRICK GUROSKY & ASSOCIATES; *U.S. Private*, pg. 2826
MYRICOM, INC.—See CSP Inc.; *U.S. Public*, pg. 601
MYRON BOWLING AUCTIONEERS INC.; *U.S. Private*, pg. 2826
MYRON EVENSON'S CARDS & GIFTS; *U.S. Private*, pg. 2826
MYRON F. STEVES & COMPANY; *U.S. Private*, pg. 2826
MYRON F. STEVES & COMPANY—See Myron F. Steves & Company; *U.S. Private*, pg. 2826
MYRON MANUFACTURING CORPORATION; *U.S. Private*, pg. 2826
MYRRA POWER SP ZOO—See discoverIE Group plc; *Int'l*, pg. 2133
MYRRA SAS—See discoverIE Group plc; *Int'l*, pg. 2133
MYRTLE BEACH COMMUNICATIONS, INC.—See Sentinel Capital Partners, L.L.C.; *U.S. Private*, pg. 3609

MYRON MANUFACTURING CORPORATION

CORPORATE AFFILIATIONS

MYRTLE BEACH PELICANS BASEBALL CLUB—See Greenberg Sports Group Inc.; *U.S. Private*, pg. 1775
MYRTLE BEACH REHABILITATION HOSPITAL, LLC—See Encompass Health Corporation; *U.S. Public*, pg. 758
MYRTLE CONSULTING GROUP LLC—See Accenture plc; *Int'l*, pg. 87
MYRTLE DIALYSIS, LLC—See DaVita Inc.; *U.S. Public*, pg. 641
MYRTLE HILLIARD DAVIS COMPREHENSIVE HEALTH CENTERS, INC.; *U.S. Private*, pg. 2826
MYR TRANSMISSION SERVICES CANADA, LTD.—See MYR Group Inc.; *U.S. Public*, pg. 1489
MYR TRANSMISSION SERVICES, INC.—See MYR Group Inc.; *U.S. Public*, pg. 1489
MYSAFETY GROUP AB; *Int'l*, pg. 5114
MYSALE GROUP PLC—See Frasers Group plc; *Int'l*, pg. 2765
MY SECRET KITCHEN LTD.—See JRjr33, Inc.; *U.S. Private*, pg. 2240
MYS GROUP CO., LTD.; *Int'l*, pg. 5113
MYSIGN AG—See Allgeier SE; *Int'l*, pg. 337
MY SIGNATURE LIVING, LLC; *U.S. Private*, pg. 2823
MY SIZE, INC.; *Int'l*, pg. 5111
MY SOLID TECHNOLOGIES & DEVICES CORP—See Solid Group, Inc.; *Int'l*, pg. 7072
MYSON CENTURY, INC.; *Int'l*, pg. 5114
MYSORE PAPER MILLS LIMITED; *Int'l*, pg. 5114
MYSORE PETRO CHEMICALS LIMITED; *Int'l*, pg. 5114
MYSPACE, LLC—See Specific Media Inc.; *U.S. Private*, pg. 3751
MY SPORTS DREAMS; *U.S. Private*, pg. 2823
MYSPRAY THERAPEUTICS INC.—See SOUL BIOTECHNOLOGY CORPORATION; *U.S. Private*, pg. 3716
MYSQL AB—See Oracle Corporation; *U.S. Public*, pg. 1611
MY SQUARES DEVELOPMENT SDN. BHD.—See Minho (M) Berhad; *Int'l*, pg. 4910
MYS TAIWAN CO., LIMITED—See MYS Group Co., Ltd.; *Int'l*, pg. 5114
MYSTAR COMPUTER B.V.—See Micro-Star International Co., Ltd.; *Int'l*, pg. 4878
MYSTAR ENGINEERING CORPORATION; *Int'l*, pg. 5114
MYSTATE BANK LIMITED—See MyState Limited; *Int'l*, pg. 5114
MYSTATE FINANCIAL—See MyState Limited; *Int'l*, pg. 5114
MYSTATE LIMITED; *Int'l*, pg. 5114
MYSTERY CREEK RESOURCES, INC.—See New Age Metals Inc.; *Int'l*, pg. 5221
MYSTERY GUILD—See Bertelsmann SE & Co. KGaA; *Int'l*, pg. 992
MYSTIC COLOR LAB, INC.—See District Photo Inc.; *U.S. Private*, pg. 1239
MYSTIC DUNES RESORT & GOLF CLUB—See Apollo Global Management, Inc.; *U.S. Public*, pg. 150
MYSTIC DUNES RESORT & GOLF CLUB—See Reverence Capital Partners LLC; *U.S. Private*, pg. 3415
MYSTIC SCENIC STUDIOS INC.; *U.S. Private*, pg. 2826
MYSTIC SEAPORT; *U.S. Private*, pg. 2826
MYSTIC STAMP COMPANY; *U.S. Private*, pg. 2826
MYSTIC VALLEY ELDER SERVICES, INC.; *U.S. Private*, pg. 2826
MYSTIC VALLEY WHEEL WORKS INCORPORATED; *U.S. Private*, pg. 2826
MYSTIQUE BLUE HOLBOX—See Sunwing Travel Group, Inc.; *Int'l*, pg. 7332
MYSTIQUE MECHANICAL LTD.; *Int'l*, pg. 5114
MYSTIQUE ROYAL ST. LUCIA—See Sunwing Travel Group, Inc.; *Int'l*, pg. 7332
MY.STOCKFUND SECURITIES, INC.—See Remark Holdings, Inc.; *U.S. Public*, pg. 1782
MYSTRENGTH, INC.—See Teladoc Health, Inc.; *U.S. Public*, pg. 1992
MY STYLE CO., LTD.—See Yamano Holdings Corporation; *Int'l*, pg. 8553
MY SUPPLY CHAIN GROUP, LLC—See Nippon Telegraph & Telephone Corporation; *Int'l*, pg. 5343
MYSUPPLYCHAINGROUP (MSCG); *U.S. Private*, pg. 2826
MY SUPPORT CO., LTD.—See Pan Pacific International Holdings Corporation; *Int'l*, pg. 5715
MYTABLE SRL—See TripAdvisor, Inc.; *U.S. Public*, pg. 2195
MYTECH GROUP BHD; *Int'l*, pg. 5114
MYTECHNIC MRO TECHNIC SERVIS A.S.—See Hainan Traffic Administration Holding Co., Ltd.; *Int'l*, pg. 3216
MYTEK NETWORK SOLUTIONS; *U.S. Private*, pg. 2826
MYTEX POLYMERS US CORPORATION—See Mitsubishi Chemical Group Corporation; *Int'l*, pg. 4932
MY THEATER D.D. INC.—See Dentsu Group Inc.; *Int'l*, pg. 2999
MYTHICS INC.—See OEP Capital Advisors, L.P.; *U.S. Private*, pg. 2999
MYTHOS BREWERY S.A.—See Carlsberg A/S; *Int'l*, pg. 1340
MYTHOS FILM PRODUKTIONS-GMBH & CO. KG—See Highlight Communications AG; *Int'l*, pg. 3388
MYTICKETIN.COM; *U.S. Private*, pg. 2826

MYTIC MYTICKET AG—See DEAG Deutsche Entertainment AG; *Int'l*, pg. 1998
MYT NETHERLANDS PARENT B.V.; *Int'l*, pg. 5114
MYTOYS.DE GMBH—See Otto GmbH & Co. KG; *Int'l*, pg. 5663
MYTRADE, INC.—See The Charles Schwab Corporation; *U.S. Public*, pg. 2058
MYTRAX INC.—See MTI Ltd.; *Int'l*, pg. 5070
MYUNGJIN HOLDINGS CORP.; *Int'l*, pg. 5114
MYUNGMOON PHARMACEUTICAL CO., LTD. - HWA-SUNG FACTORY—See Myungmoon pharmaceutical Co., Ltd.; *Int'l*, pg. 5115
MYUNGMOON PHARMACEUTICAL CO., LTD.; *Int'l*, pg. 5114
MYUNGSHIN INDUSTRIAL CO.—See MS Autotech Company Limited; *Int'l*, pg. 5065
MYUNMOON PHARM CO., LTD.; *Int'l*, pg. 5115
MYU PLANNING AND OPERATIONS, INC.—See Suntory Holdings Limited; *Int'l*, pg. 7326
MY VEGETABLE CORPORATION—See Sojitz Corporation; *Int'l*, pg. 7062
MYVEST CORPORATION—See Teachers Insurance Association - College Retirement Fund; *U.S. Private*, pg. 3945
MYVIDEO BROADBAND S.R.L.—See ProSiebenSat.1 Media SE; *Int'l*, pg. 6000
MY-VILLAGES, INC.; *U.S. Private*, pg. 2823
MYWEBGROCER INC.—See Mi9 Retail, Inc.; *U.S. Private*, pg. 2696
MYWEDDING.COM LLC; *U.S. Private*, pg. 2826
MY XUAN BRICK TILE POTTERY & CONSTRUCTION; *Int'l*, pg. 5111
MYYRMANNI KOY—See Citycon Oyj; *Int'l*, pg. 1629
MZANSIGO SOUTH AFRICA PROPRIETARY LIMITED—See Super Group Limited; *Int'l*, pg. 7334
MZ ASIA-PACIFIC LTD.—See Grupo MZ; *Int'l*, pg. 3133
M.Z. BERGER & CO., INC.; *U.S. Private*, pg. 2529
MZB TECHNOLOGIES, LLC—See South Dakota Wheat Growers Association; *U.S. Private*, pg. 3722
MZ CONSULT NY LLC—See Grupo MZ; *Int'l*, pg. 3133
MZ CONSULT PARTICIPACOES S.A.—See Grupo MZ; *Int'l*, pg. 3133
MZD ADVERTISING; *U.S. Private*, pg. 2826
MZILIOS LLC—See Grupo MZ; *Int'l*, pg. 3133
MZINGA, INC.; *U.S. Private*, pg. 2826
MZINGA—See Mzinga, Inc.; *U.S. Private*, pg. 2826
MZI RESOURCES LTD.; *Int'l*, pg. 5115
MZ TAIWAN—See Grupo MZ; *Int'l*, pg. 3133
MZT HEPOS POLSKA SP. ZO.O—See Westinghouse Air Brake Technologies Corporation; *U.S. Public*, pg. 2358
MZT PUMPI A.D.; *Int'l*, pg. 5115
MZV DIREKT GMBH & CO.KG—See Westdeutsche Allgemeine verlagsgesellschaft; *Int'l*, pg. 8387
MZV GMBH & CO. KG—See Westdeutsche Allgemeine verlagsgesellschaft; *Int'l*, pg. 8387

N

N1 EHF.—See Festi hf; *Int'l*, pg. 2646
N1 HOLDINGS LIMITED; *Int'l*, pg. 5117
N+1 MERCAPITAL SL—See N Mas Uno IBG SA; *Int'l*, pg. 5117
N1 TECHNOLOGIES, INC.; *Int'l*, pg. 5117
N200 HOLDING B.V.—See Viad Corp.; *U.S. Public*, pg. 2291
N200 LIMITED—See Viad Corp.; *U.S. Public*, pg. 2291
N24 MEDIA GMBH—See Axel Springer SE; *Int'l*, pg. 766
N2 ACQUISITION HOLDINGS CORP.; *U.S. Private*, pg. 2828
N2GRATE GOVERNMENT TECHNOLOGY SOLUTIONS, LLC—See Source Capital, LLC; *U.S. Private*, pg. 3718
N2 IMAGING SYSTEMS, LLC—See RTX Corporation; *U.S. Public*, pg. 1821
N2N ADVANCED LEARNING SDN. BHD.—See N2N Connect Berhad; *Int'l*, pg. 5117
N2N-AFE (HONG KONG) LIMITED—See N2N Connect Berhad; *Int'l*, pg. 5117
N2N CONNECT BERHAD; *Int'l*, pg. 5117
N2N CONNECT PTE. LTD.—See N2N Connect Berhad; *Int'l*, pg. 5117
N2N TECHNOLOGIES LIMITED; *Int'l*, pg. 5117
N2OFF INC.; *Int'l*, pg. 5117
N2PLAY CO., LTD.—See CJ Corporation; *Int'l*, pg. 1634
N2 SOLUTIONS LLC; *U.S. Private*, pg. 2829
N2Y LLC—See Rothschild & Co SCA; *Int'l*, pg. 6403
N3K INFORMATIK GMBH—See DZ BANK AG Deutsche Zentral-Genossenschaftsbank; *Int'l*, pg. 2245
N6 CONCESSION LTD.—See Sacyr, S.A.; *Int'l*, pg. 6466
NAAMAN GROUP NV LTD.; *Int'l*, pg. 5117
NAAMLOZE VENNOOTSCHAP LINDE GAS BENELUX—See Linde plc; *Int'l*, pg. 4508
NAANDAN AGRO-PRO LTD—See Jain Irrigation Systems Limited; *Int'l*, pg. 3872
NAANDAN JAIN AUSTRALIA PTY LTD—See Jain Irrigation Systems Limited; *Int'l*, pg. 3872
NAANDANJAIN FRANCE SAS—See Jain Irrigation Systems Limited; *Int'l*, pg. 3872
NAANDAN JAIN IBERICA S.C.—See Jain Irrigation Systems Limited; *Int'l*, pg. 3872

NAANDAN JAIN IRRIGATION CS LTD—See Jain Irrigation Systems Limited; *Int'l*, pg. 3872
NAANDAN JAIN MEXICO, S.A. DE C.V.—See Jain Irrigation Systems Limited; *Int'l*, pg. 3872
NAANDAN JAIN PERU S.A.C.—See Jain Irrigation Systems Limited; *Int'l*, pg. 3872
NAANDAN JAIN SRL—See Jain Irrigation Systems Limited; *Int'l*, pg. 3872
NAAPBOOKS LIMITED; *Int'l*, pg. 5117
NAAPURIN MAALAISKANA OY—See Scandi Standard AB; *Int'l*, pg. 6612
NAAS TECHNOLOGY INC.; *Int'l*, pg. 5118
NABA ALSAHA MEDICAL SERVICES CO.; *Int'l*, pg. 5118
NABALTEC AG; *Int'l*, pg. 5118
NABARI KINTETSU GAS CO., LTD.—See Osaka Gas Co., Ltd.; *Int'l*, pg. 5645
NABARRO LLP—See CMS Cameron McKenna Nabarro Olswang LLP; *Int'l*, pg. 1672
NABATI FOODS GLOBAL INC.; *Int'l*, pg. 5118
NABC, INC.—See NewAge, Inc.; *U.S. Public*, pg. 1513
NABCO AUTO DOOR (BEIJING) CO., LTD.—See Nabtesco Corporation; *Int'l*, pg. 5119
NABCO CANADA INC.—See Nabtesco Corporation; *Int'l*, pg. 5119
NABCO DOOR LTD.—See Nabtesco Corporation; *Int'l*, pg. 5119
NABCO ELECTRIC; *U.S. Private*, pg. 2829
NABCO ENGINEERING LTD.—See Nabtesco Corporation; *Int'l*, pg. 5119
NABCO ENTRANCES, INC.—See Nabtesco Corporation; *Int'l*, pg. 5119
NABCO HOUSING INC.; *Int'l*, pg. 5118
NABCO, INC.; *U.S. Private*, pg. 2829
NAB CONSTRUCTION CORP.; *U.S. Private*, pg. 2829
NAB CORPORATION.—See Konoike Transport Co., Ltd.; *Int'l*, pg. 4275
NABCO SYSTEM CO., LTD.—See Nabtesco Corporation; *Int'l*, pg. 5119
NABCO SYSTEMS CO., LTD.—See Nabtesco Corporation; *Int'l*, pg. 5119
NABCO TOTO LTD.—See Nabtesco Corporation; *Int'l*, pg. 5119
NABEEL LIMITED—See Quetta Group of Companies LLC; *Int'l*, pg. 6161
NABEEL'S CAFE & MARKET; *U.S. Private*, pg. 2829
NABER CHRYSLER DODGE JEEP RAM; *U.S. Private*, pg. 2829
NABERTHERM GMBH; *Int'l*, pg. 5118
NABERTHERM IBERICA, SL—See Nabertherm GmbH; *Int'l*, pg. 5118
NABERTHERM INC.—See Nabertherm GmbH; *Int'l*, pg. 5118
NABERTHERM ITALIA—See Nabertherm GmbH; *Int'l*, pg. 5118
NABERTHERM SARL—See Nabertherm GmbH; *Int'l*, pg. 5118
NABERTHERM (SHANGHAI) INDUSTRIAL FURNACES LTD.—See Nabertherm GmbH; *Int'l*, pg. 5118
NABERTHERM SWITZERLAND AG—See Nabertherm GmbH; *Int'l*, pg. 5118
NABHA POWER LIMITED—See Larsen & Toubro Limited; *Int'l*, pg. 4419
NABHOLZ CONSTRUCTION CORP. - OZARK DIVISION—See Nabholz Construction Corp.; *U.S. Private*, pg. 2829
NABHOLZ CONSTRUCTION CORP.; *U.S. Private*, pg. 2829
NABHOLZ CONSTRUCTION CORP. - TULSA DIVISION—See Nabholz Construction Corp.; *U.S. Private*, pg. 2829
NABIACE CO., LTD.—See Japan Pulp and Paper Company Limited; *Int'l*, pg. 3904
NABI GYARTO ES KERESKEDELMI KFT.; *Int'l*, pg. 5118
NABIL BANK LTD.; *Int'l*, pg. 5118
NABIL INVESTMENT BANKING LTD.—See NABIL Bank Ltd.; *Int'l*, pg. 5118
NAB INVESTMENTS LIMITED—See National Australia Bank Limited; *Int'l*, pg. 5151
NABLE COMMUNICATIONS, INC.; *Int'l*, pg. 5118
N-ABLE, INC.; *U.S. Public*, pg. 1489
N-ABLE SERVICES LIMITED—See Frenkel Topping Group plc; *Int'l*, pg. 2773
NABLUS SURGICAL CENTER; *Int'l*, pg. 5118
NABMIC B.V.—See Nabtesco Corporation; *Int'l*, pg. 5119
NABO CAPITAL LIMITED—See Centum Investment Company Limited; *Int'l*, pg. 1416
NABORS ALASKA DRILLING, INC.—See Nabors Industries Ltd.; *Int'l*, pg. 5118
NABORS DRILLING INTERNATIONAL LIMITED—See Nabors Industries Ltd.; *Int'l*, pg. 5118
NABORS DRILLING TECHNOLOGIES USA, INC.—See Nabors Industries Ltd.; *Int'l*, pg. 5118
NABORS ENERGY TRANSITION CORP.; *U.S. Public*, pg. 1489
NABORS GLOBAL HOLDINGS LTD.—See Nabors Industries Ltd.; *Int'l*, pg. 5118
NABORS INDUSTRIES INC.—See Nabors Industries Ltd.; *Int'l*, pg. 5118
NABORS INDUSTRIES LTD.; *Int'l*, pg. 5118

COMPANY NAME INDEX

NABORS INTERNATIONAL ARGENTINA S.R.L.—See Nabors Industries Ltd.; *Int'l*, pg. 5118
NABORS INTERNATIONAL FINANCE INC.—See Nabors Industries Ltd.; *Int'l*, pg. 5118
NABORS OFFSHORE—See Nabors Industries Ltd.; *Int'l*, pg. 5118
NABORS OFFSHORE—See Nabors Industries Ltd.; *Int'l*, pg. 5118
NABORS WELL SERVICES CO—See Nabors Industries Ltd.; *Int'l*, pg. 5119
NABORS WELL SERVICES—See Nabors Industries Ltd.; *Int'l*, pg. 5118
NABRIVA THERAPEUTICS GMBH—See Nabriva Therapeutics PLC; *Int'l*, pg. 5119
NABRIVA THERAPEUTICS IRELAND DESIGNATED ACTIVITY COMPANY—See Nabriva Therapeutics PLC; *Int'l*, pg. 5119
NABRIVA THERAPEUTICS PLC; *Int'l*, pg. 5119
NABRO ABLE LLC; *U.S. Private*, pg. 2829
NABROS INC; *U.S. Private*, pg. 2829
NABSYS, INC.—See Hitachi, Ltd.; *Int'l*, pg. 3418
NABTEC CO., LTD.—See Nabtesco Corporation; *Int'l*, pg. 5119
NABTESCO AEROSPACE EUROPE GMBH—See Nabtesco Corporation; *Int'l*, pg. 5120
NABTESCO AEROSPACE, INC.—See Nabtesco Corporation; *Int'l*, pg. 5120
NABTESCO AEROSPACE SINGAPORE PTE. LTD.—See Nabtesco Corporation; *Int'l*, pg. 5120
NABTESCO AUTOMOTIVE CORPORATION—See Nabtesco Corporation; *Int'l*, pg. 5120
NABTESCO AUTOMOTIVE CORPORATION - YAMAGATA PLANT—See Nabtesco Corporation; *Int'l*, pg. 5120
NABTESCO AUTOMOTIVE PRODUCTS (THAILAND) CO., LTD.—See Nabtesco Corporation; *Int'l*, pg. 5120
NABTESCO (CHINA) PRECISION EQUIPMENT CO., LTD.—See Nabtesco Corporation; *Int'l*, pg. 5120
NABTESCO CORPORATION - GIFU PLANT—See Nabtesco Corporation; *Int'l*, pg. 5120
NABTESCO CORPORATION - IWAKUNI PLANT—See Nabtesco Corporation; *Int'l*, pg. 5120
NABTESCO CORPORATION - KOBE PLANT—See Nabtesco Corporation; *Int'l*, pg. 5120
NABTESCO CORPORATION - KONAN PLANT—See Nabtesco Corporation; *Int'l*, pg. 5120
NABTESCO CORPORATION - SEISHIN PLANT—See Nabtesco Corporation; *Int'l*, pg. 5120
NABTESCO CORPORATION; *Int'l*, pg. 5119
NABTESCO CORPORATION - TARUI PLANT—See Nabtesco Corporation; *Int'l*, pg. 5120
NABTESCO CORPORATION - TSU PLANT—See Nabtesco Corporation; *Int'l*, pg. 5120
NABTESCO EUROPE GMBH—See Nabtesco Corporation; *Int'l*, pg. 5120
NABTESCO GILGEN HONG KONG LIMITED.—See Nabtesco Corporation; *Int'l*, pg. 5120
NABTESCO INDIA PRIVATE LIMITED—See Nabtesco Corporation; *Int'l*, pg. 5120
NABTESCO ITG GMBH—See Nabtesco Corporation; *Int'l*, pg. 5120
NABTESCO LINK CORPORATION—See Nabtesco Corporation; *Int'l*, pg. 5120
NABTESCO MARINE CONTROL SYSTEMS (SHANGHAI) CO., LTD.—See Nabtesco Corporation; *Int'l*, pg. 5120
NABTESCO MARINE EUROPE B.V.—See Nabtesco Corporation; *Int'l*, pg. 5120
NABTESCO MARINE MACHINERY (SHANGHAI) CO., LTD.—See Nabtesco Corporation; *Int'l*, pg. 5120
NABTESCO MARINE SERVICE CO., LTD.—See Nabtesco Corporation; *Int'l*, pg. 5120
NABTESCO MARINE SERVICE SINGAPORE PTE LTD.—See Nabtesco Corporation; *Int'l*, pg. 5120
NABTESCO MARINE SHIKOKU CO., LTD.—See Nabtesco Corporation; *Int'l*, pg. 5120
NABTESCO MARINETEC CO., LTD.—See Nabtesco Corporation; *Int'l*, pg. 5120
NABTESCO MOTION CONTROL, INC.—See Nabtesco Corporation; *Int'l*, pg. 5120
NABTESCO OCLAP S.R.L.—See Nabtesco Corporation; *Int'l*, pg. 5120
NABTESCO POWER CONTROL EUROPE B.V.—See Nabtesco Corporation; *Int'l*, pg. 5120
NABTESCO POWER CONTROL (THAILAND) CO., LTD.—See Nabtesco Corporation; *Int'l*, pg. 5120
NABTESCO PRECISION EUROPE GMBH—See Nabtesco Corporation; *Int'l*, pg. 5120
NABTESCO RAILROAD PRODUCTS (BEIJING) CO., LTD.—See Nabtesco Corporation; *Int'l*, pg. 5120
NABTESCO SERVICE CO., LTD—See Nabtesco Corporation; *Int'l*, pg. 5120
NABTESCO SERVICE SOUTHEAST ASIA CO., LTD.—See Nabtesco Corporation; *Int'l*, pg. 5120
NABTESCO TECHNOLOGY VENTURES AG—See Nabtesco Corporation; *Int'l*, pg. 5120
NACALAI TESQUE, INC. - KYOTO FACTORY—See Nacalai Tesque, Inc.; *Int'l*, pg. 5121
NACALAI TESQUE, INC.; *Int'l*, pg. 5121
NACALAI USA, INC.—See Nacalai Tesque, Inc.; *Int'l*, pg. 5121

NACA LOGISTICS (USA), INC.; *U.S. Private*, pg. 2829
NACAMAR GMBH—See UPLINK Digital GmbH; *Int'l*, pg. 8090
NACAP AUSTRALIA PTY LTD.—See Quanta Services, Inc.; *U.S. Public*, pg. 1752
NACAP PTY LTD.—See Quanta Services, Inc.; *U.S. Public*, pg. 1752
NACARATO TRUCKS, INC.—See SF Holding Corp.; *U.S. Private*, pg. 3621
NACAR COMERCIAL IMPORTADORA E EXPORTADORA LTDA.—See Shoei Co., Ltd.; *Int'l*, pg. 6857
NACCO INDUSTRIES, INC.; *U.S. Public*, pg. 1489
NAC CO., LTD.—See Nippon Kayaku Co., Ltd.; *Int'l*, pg. 5320
NAC CO., LTD.; *Int'l*, pg. 5121
NACCO MATERIALS HANDLING FRANCE S.A.R.L.—See Hyster-Yale Materials Handling, Inc.; *U.S. Public*, pg. 1080
NACCO MATERIALS HANDLING GROUP BRASIL LTDA.—See Hyster-Yale Materials Handling, Inc.; *U.S. Public*, pg. 1080
NACCO MATERIALS HANDLING GROUP, LTD.—See Hyster-Yale Materials Handling, Inc.; *U.S. Public*, pg. 1080
NACCO MATERIALS HANDLING GROUP PTY. LTD.—See Hyster-Yale Materials Handling, Inc.; *U.S. Public*, pg. 1080
NACCO MATERIALS HANDLING LTD. - CRAIGAVON PLANT—See Hyster-Yale Materials Handling, Inc.; *U.S. Public*, pg. 1080
NAC CONSTRUCTORS LTD.; *Int'l*, pg. 5121
NACE INTERNATIONAL; *U.S. Private*, pg. 2829
NACEL OPEN DOOR, INC.; *U.S. Private*, pg. 2830
NAC GROUP INC; *U.S. Private*, pg. 2829
THE NACHER CORPORATION—See Mistras Group, Inc.; *U.S. Public*, pg. 1451
NACHI AMERICA INC. - MIAMI BRANCH-LATIN AMERICA DIVISION—See Nachi-Fujikoshi Corp.; *Int'l*, pg. 5122
NACHI AMERICA INC.—See Nachi-Fujikoshi Corp.; *Int'l*, pg. 5122
NACHI (AUSTRALIA) PTY. LTD.—See Nachi-Fujikoshi Corp.; *Int'l*, pg. 5122
NACHI BEARING MANUFACTURING CO., LTD.—See Nachi-Fujikoshi Corp.; *Int'l*, pg. 5121
NACHI BRASIL LTDA.—See Nachi-Fujikoshi Corp.; *Int'l*, pg. 5121
NACHI CANADA INC.—See Nachi-Fujikoshi Corp.; *Int'l*, pg. 5122
NACHI C.H. DONGGUAN CORP.—See Nachi-Fujikoshi Corp.; *Int'l*, pg. 5122
NACHI C.Y. CORP.—See Nachi-Fujikoshi Corp.; *Int'l*, pg. 5122
NACHI CZECH S.R.O.—See Nachi-Fujikoshi Corp.; *Int'l*, pg. 5121
NACHI EUROPE GMBH—See Nachi-Fujikoshi Corp.; *Int'l*, pg. 5122
NACHI FORGING TECHNOLOGY (THAILAND) CO., LTD.—See Nachi-Fujikoshi Corp.; *Int'l*, pg. 5122
NACHI-FUJIKOSHI (CHINA) CO., LTD.—See Nachi-Fujikoshi Corp.; *Int'l*, pg. 5122
NACHI-FUJIKOSHI CORP. - HIGASHI-TOYAMA PLANT—See Nachi-Fujikoshi Corp.; *Int'l*, pg. 5122
NACHI-FUJIKOSHI CORP. - MIZUHASHI PLANT—See Nachi-Fujikoshi Corp.; *Int'l*, pg. 5122
NACHI-FUJIKOSHI CORP. - NAGARESUGI PLANT—See Nachi-Fujikoshi Corp.; *Int'l*, pg. 5122
NACHI-FUJIKOSHI CORP. - NAMERIKAWA PLANT—See Nachi-Fujikoshi Corp.; *Int'l*, pg. 5122
NACHI-FUJIKOSHI CORP.; *Int'l*, pg. 5121
NACHI HOKURIKU CO., LTD.—See Nachi-Fujikoshi Corp.; *Int'l*, pg. 5121
NACHI HYDRAULICS CO., LTD.—See Nachi-Fujikoshi Corp.; *Int'l*, pg. 5121
NACHI INDUSTRIES PTE. LTD.—See Nachi-Fujikoshi Corp.; *Int'l*, pg. 5121
NACHI (JIANGSU) INDUSTRIES CO., LTD.—See Nachi-Fujikoshi Corp.; *Int'l*, pg. 5122
NACHI KANSAI CO., LTD.—See Nachi-Fujikoshi Corp.; *Int'l*, pg. 5122
NACHI KANTO CO., LTD.—See Nachi-Fujikoshi Corp.; *Int'l*, pg. 5122
NACHI KOUZAI CO., LTD.—See Nachi-Fujikoshi Corp.; *Int'l*, pg. 5121
NACHI KYUSHU CO., LTD.—See Nachi-Fujikoshi Corp.; *Int'l*, pg. 5121
NACHI LOGISTICS CO., LTD.—See Nachi-Fujikoshi Corp.; *Int'l*, pg. 5121
NACHI MACHINERY ENGINEERING CO., LTD.—See Nachi-Fujikoshi Corp.; *Int'l*, pg. 5121
NACHI MACHINING TECHNOLOGY CO.; *U.S. Private*, pg. 2830
NACHI MEXICANA, S.A. DE C.V.—See Nachi-Fujikoshi Corp.; *Int'l*, pg. 5122
NACHI NIHONKAI BEARING CO., LTD.—See Nachi-Fujikoshi Corp.; *Int'l*, pg. 5121
NACHI PILIPINAS INDUSTRIES, INC.—See Nachi-Fujikoshi Corp.; *Int'l*, pg. 5122
NACHI PRECISION TOOL INDIA PRIVATE LTD.—See Nachi-Fujikoshi Corp.; *Int'l*, pg. 5122

NACKARD BOTTLING COMPANY

NACHI ROBOT ENGINEERING CO., LTD.—See Nachi-Fujikoshi Corp.; *Int'l*, pg. 5122
NACHI ROBOTIC SYSTEMS INC.—See Nachi-Fujikoshi Corp.; *Int'l*, pg. 5122
NACHI SANYO CO., LTD.—See Nachi-Fujikoshi Corp.; *Int'l*, pg. 5122
NACHI SEIKO CO., LTD.—See Nachi-Fujikoshi Corp.; *Int'l*, pg. 5122
NACHI (SHANGHAI) CO., LTD.—See Nachi-Fujikoshi Corp.; *Int'l*, pg. 5122
NACHI (SHANGHAI) PRECISION TOOLS CO., LTD.—See Nachi-Fujikoshi Corp.; *Int'l*, pg. 5121
NACHI SINGAPORE PTE. LTD.—See Nachi-Fujikoshi Corp.; *Int'l*, pg. 5122
NACHI TAIWAN CO., LTD.—See Nachi-Fujikoshi Corp.; *Int'l*, pg. 5122
NACHI TATEYAMA BEARING CO., LTD.—See Nachi-Fujikoshi Corp.; *Int'l*, pg. 5122
NACHI TECHNOLOGY INC.—See Nachi-Fujikoshi Corp.; *Int'l*, pg. 5122
NACHI TECHNOLOGY INDIA PRIVATE LIMITED—See Nachi-Fujikoshi Corp.; *Int'l*, pg. 5122
NACHI TECHNOLOGY MEXICO S.A. DE C.V.—See Nachi-Fujikoshi Corp.; *Int'l*, pg. 5122
NACHI TECHNOLOGY (THAILAND) CO., LTD.—See Nachi-Fujikoshi Corp.; *Int'l*, pg. 5122
NACHI THERMOTECH CO., LTD.—See Nachi-Fujikoshi Corp.; *Int'l*, pg. 5122
NACHI TOHOKU SEIKO CO., LTD.—See Nachi-Fujikoshi Corp.; *Int'l*, pg. 5122
NACHI TOKAI CO., LTD.—See Nachi-Fujikoshi Corp.; *Int'l*, pg. 5122
NACHI-TOKIWA CORP.—See Nachi-Fujikoshi Corp.; *Int'l*, pg. 5122
NACHI TOOL AMERICA INC.—See Nachi-Fujikoshi Corp.; *Int'l*, pg. 5122
NACHI TOOL ENGINEERING CO., LTD.—See Nachi-Fujikoshi Corp.; *Int'l*, pg. 5122
NACHI TOOL GENESIS CO., LTD.—See Nachi-Fujikoshi Corp.; *Int'l*, pg. 5122
NACHI TOOL TECHNOLOGY CO., LTD.—See Nachi-Fujikoshi Corp.; *Int'l*, pg. 5122
NACHI TOYAMA BEARING CO., LTD.—See Nachi-Fujikoshi Corp.; *Int'l*, pg. 5122
NACHI VIETNAM CO., LTD.—See Nachi-Fujikoshi Corp.; *Int'l*, pg. 5122
NACHI YATSUO BEARING CO., LTD.—See Nachi-Fujikoshi Corp.; *Int'l*, pg. 5122
NACHMO KNITEX LTD.; *Int'l*, pg. 5123
NACHON ENTERPRISES INC.; *U.S. Private*, pg. 2830
NACHSENDEAUFTRAG DE ONLINE GMBH—See Stroer SE & Co. KGaA; *Int'l*, pg. 7242
NACHURS ALPINE SOLUTIONS, LLC—See Wilbur-Ellis Company; *U.S. Private*, pg. 4517
NAC, INC.; *U.S. Private*, pg. 2829
NAC INTERNATIONAL INC.—See Hitachi Zosen Corporation; *Int'l*, pg. 3411
NACIONAL A.D.; *Int'l*, pg. 5123
NACIONAL DE ACERO—See Grupo Acerero del Norte S.A. de C.V.; *Int'l*, pg. 3118
NACIONAL FINANCIERA F.N.C.; *Int'l*, pg. 5123
NACION BURSATIL S.A—See Banco de la Nacion Argentina; *Int'l*, pg. 820
NACION REASEGUROS S.A—See Banco de la Nacion Argentina; *Int'l*, pg. 820
NACION SERVICIOS S.A—See Banco de la Nacion Argentina; *Int'l*, pg. 820
NACITY PROPERTY SERVICE GROUP CO., LTD.; *Int'l*, pg. 5123
NACKARD BOTTLING COMPANY; *U.S. Private*, pg. 2830
NACL INDUSTRIES LTD—See Nagarjuna Fertilizers & Chemicals Ltd.; *Int'l*, pg. 5126
NACL MEDICAL, INC.—See Medley, Inc.; *Int'l*, pg. 4784
NACO CORP.—See Equity LifeStyle Properties, Inc.; *U.S. Public*, pg. 790
NACODE CORPORATION—See Taiheiyo Cement Corporation; *Int'l*, pg. 7411
NACO, NETHERLANDS AIRPORT CONSULTANTS B.V.—See Koninklijke HaskoningDHV Groep B.V.; *Int'l*, pg. 4266
NACON S.P.A.—See Natuzzi S.p.A.; *Int'l*, pg. 5170
NACORA AGENCIES AG—See Kuehne + Nagel International AG; *Int'l*, pg. 4325
NACORA BROKINS INTERNATIONAL AE—See Kuehne + Nagel International AG; *Int'l*, pg. 4325
NACORA CORREDURIA DE SEGUROS S.A.—See Kuehne + Nagel International AG; *Int'l*, pg. 4325
NACORA COURTAGE D'ASSURANCES SAS—See Kuehne + Nagel International AG; *Int'l*, pg. 4325
NACORA INSURANCE BROKERS GMBH—See Kuehne + Nagel International AG; *Int'l*, pg. 4325
NACORA INSURANCE BROKERS INC.—See Kuehne + Nagel International AG; *Int'l*, pg. 4325
NACORA INSURANCE BROKERS LIMITED—See Kuehne + Nagel International AG; *Int'l*, pg. 4325
NACORA INSURANCE BROKERS LTD.—See Kuehne + Nagel International AG; *Int'l*, pg. 4325
NACORA INSURANCE BROKERS LTD.—See Kuehne + Nagel International AG; *Int'l*, pg. 4325

NACORA INSURANCE BROKERS (PROPRIETARY) LIMITED—See Kuehne + Nagel International AG; *Int'l*, pg. 4325
NACORA INTERNATIONAL INSURANCE BROKERS AB—See Kuehne + Nagel International AG; *Int'l*, pg. 4325
NACORA LTDA AGENCIA DE SEGUROS—See Kuehne + Nagel International AG; *Int'l*, pg. 4325
NACORA (LUXEMBOURG) S.A.R.L.—See Kuehne + Nagel International AG; *Int'l*, pg. 4325
NACORA SIGORTA BROKERLIGI A.S.—See Kuehne + Nagel International AG; *Int'l*, pg. 4325
NACORA SRL—See Kuehne + Nagel International AG; *Int'l*, pg. 4325
NACORA VERSICHERUNGSMAKLER GMBH—See Kuehne + Nagel International AG; *Int'l*, pg. 4325
NACO TRADING AS—See Thai Union Group Public Company Limited; *Int'l*, pg. 7596
NACO TULSH; *Int'l*, pg. 5123
NACT EUROPE LTD.—See Kinderhook Industries, LLC; *U.S. Private*, pg. 2307
NACTIS BENELUX—See Nactis SAS; *Int'l*, pg. 5123
NACTIS SAS; *Int'l*, pg. 5123
NACT TELECOMMUNICATIONS, INC.—See Kinderhook Industries, LLC; *U.S. Private*, pg. 2307
NACX NAKAMURA CO. LTD.—See Marubeni Corporation; *Int'l*, pg. 4709
NADACE AGROFERT HOLDING—See Agrofert Holding, a.s.; *Int'l*, pg. 219
NADAMAN CO., LTD.—See ONODERA GROUP Co., Ltd.; *Int'l*, pg. 5583
NADA PROPERTIES CO., LTD.—See Petroliam Nasional Berhad; *Int'l*, pg. 5830
NADATHUR ESTATES PVT LTD.; *Int'l*, pg. 5123
NADATHUR FAREAST PTE LTD.—See Nadathur Estates Pvt Ltd.; *Int'l*, pg. 5123
NADAYU PROPERTIES BERHAD; *Int'l*, pg. 5123
NADEAU CORP.; *U.S. Private*, pg. 2830
NADEEM TEXTILE MILLS LTD.; *Int'l*, pg. 5123
N.A. DEGERSTROM INC.; *U.S. Private*, pg. 2827
NADEL ARCHITECTS, INC.; *U.S. Private*, pg. 2830
NADEL & GUSSMAN LLC; *U.S. Private*, pg. 2830
NADELLA GMBH—See The Timken Company; *U.S. Public*, pg. 2133
NADELLA INC.—See The Timken Company; *U.S. Public*, pg. 2133
NADELLA S.P.A.—See The Timken Company; *U.S. Public*, pg. 2133
NADEL PHELAN, INC.; *U.S. Private*, pg. 2830
NADEP LAGHUBITTA BITTIYA SANSTHA LTD.; *Int'l*, pg. 5123
NADER HOLDING GMBH & CO. KG; *Int'l*, pg. 5123
NADER'S PEST RAIDERS, INC.—See Arrow Exterminators Inc.; *U.S. Private*, pg. 335
NADER WHOLESALE GROCERS INC.; *U.S. Private*, pg. 2830
NADEX CO., LTD.; *Int'l*, pg. 5123
NADEX ENGINEERING CO., LTD.—See NADEX CO., LTD.; *Int'l*, pg. 5124
NADEX, INC.—See IG Group Holdings plc; *Int'l*, pg. 3601
NADEX MACHINERY (SHANGHAI) CO., LTD.—See NADEX CO., LTD.; *Int'l*, pg. 5124
NADEX MEXICANA, S.A. DE C.V.—See NADEX CO., LTD.; *Int'l*, pg. 5123
NADEX OF AMERICA CORPORATION—See NADEX CO., LTD.; *Int'l*, pg. 5124
NADEX PRODUCTS CO., LTD.—See NADEX CO., LTD.; *Int'l*, pg. 5124
NADEX (THAILAND) CO., LTD.—See NADEX CO., LTD.; *Int'l*, pg. 5123
NADEX USA CO., LTD.—See NADEX CO., LTD.; *Int'l*, pg. 5124
NADHI INFORMATION TECHNOLOGIES PRIVATE LIMITED—See Bentley Systems, Inc.; *U.S. Public*, pg. 297
NADIA INC.; *U.S. Private*, pg. 2830
NADI AIRTECHNICS PRIVATE LIMITED—See Twin City Fan Companies, Ltd.; *U.S. Private*, pg. 4265
NADI AIRTECHNICS PRIVATE LIMITED - UNIT 4—See Twin City Fan Companies, Ltd.; *U.S. Private*, pg. 4265
NADIA SIGNALISATION; *Int'l*, pg. 5124
NADIA S.P.A.—See BPER BANCA S.p.A; *Int'l*, pg. 1132
NADI JELITA SDN. BHD.—See Tropicana Corporation Berhad; *Int'l*, pg. 7939
NADLER LARIMER E MARTINELLI S.R.L.; *Int'l*, pg. 5124
NADLER MODULAR STRUCTURES; *U.S. Private*, pg. 2830
NADRO S.A. DE C.V.; *Int'l*, pg. 5124
NADUDVARI LTD.—See OTP Bank Plc; *Int'l*, pg. 5657
NADY SYSTEMS, INC.; *U.S. Private*, pg. 2830
NAECO LLC; *U.S. Private*, pg. 2830
NAEEM FINANCIAL INVESTMENTS S.A.E.—See Naeem Holding; *Int'l*, pg. 5124
NAEEM HOLDING; *Int'l*, pg. 5124
N&A ENTERPRISES INC.; *U.S. Private*, pg. 2826
NAERODYNAMICS, INC.; *U.S. Private*, pg. 1490
NAES CORPORATION—See ITOCHU Corporation; *Int'l*, pg. 3838

NAES POWER CONTRACTORS—See ITOCHU Corporation; *Int'l*, pg. 3838
NAF AB—See ANDRITZ AG; *Int'l*, pg. 452
NAFAIS HOLDING COMPANY K.S.C.; *Int'l*, pg. 5124
NAFA POLSKA SP.Z O.O.—See North American Fur Producers Marketing Inc; *Int'l*, pg. 5439
NAFAS JENTERA SDN BHD—See Mitsubishi Heavy Industries, Ltd.; *Int'l*, pg. 4960
NAFA USA, INC.—See North American Fur Producers Marketing Inc; *Int'l*, pg. 5439
NAFCO CO., LTD.; *Int'l*, pg. 5124
NAFCO SUZHOU PRECISION LIMITED CORPORATION—See National Aerospace Fasteners Corporation; *Int'l*, pg. 5150
NAFFICS CORPORATION—See Noda Corporation; *Int'l*, pg. 5398
NAFOODS GROUP JOINT STOCK COMPANY; *Int'l*, pg. 5124
NAFPAKTOS TEXTILE INDUSTRY S.A.; *Int'l*, pg. 5124
NAFSA; *U.S. Private*, pg. 2830
NAFTA AD; *Int'l*, pg. 5124
NAFTEX ENERGY CORPORATION—See Norse Energy Corp. ASA; *Int'l*, pg. 5432
NAFTEX HOLDINGS LTD.—See Norse Energy Corp. ASA; *Int'l*, pg. 5432
NAFTIRAN INTERTRADE COMPANY SARL—See National Iranian Oil Company; *Int'l*, pg. 5160
NAFTNA INDUSTRIJA SRBIJE A.D. NOVI SAD—See PJSC Gazprom; *Int'l*, pg. 5879
NAFTOREMONT-NAFTOBUDOWA SP. Z O.O.—See Polimex-Mostostal S.A.; *Int'l*, pg. 5909
NAFUKO CO., LTD.—See Nagase & Co., Ltd.; *Int'l*, pg. 5127
NAGACORP LTD.; *Int'l*, pg. 5124
NAGA DDB SDN. BHD.—See Omnicom Group Inc.; *U.S. Public*, pg. 1582
NAGA DHUNSERI GROUP LIMITED; *Int'l*, pg. 5124
NAGAE-INSHOH DO CO., LTD.—See Mitsubishi Pencil Co., Ltd.; *Int'l*, pg. 4967
THE NAGA GROUP AG; *Int'l*, pg. 7669
NAGAHAMA CANON INC.—See Canon Inc.; *Int'l*, pg. 1298
NAGAHORI CORPORATION - MOBARA PLANT—See NAGAHORI CORPORATION; *Int'l*, pg. 5125
NAGAHORI CORPORATION; *Int'l*, pg. 5124
NAGAILEBEN CO., LTD.; *Int'l*, pg. 5125
NAGA ISTIMEWA SDN. BHD.—See Brem Holding Berhad; *Int'l*, pg. 1144
NAGAIZUMI HIGH TRUST CO., LTD.—See Takuma Co., Ltd.; *Int'l*, pg. 7442
NAGAKAWA GROUP JOINT STOCK COMPANY; *Int'l*, pg. 5125
NAGAMBIE RESOURCES LIMITED; *Int'l*, pg. 5125
NAGANO AD BUREAU INC.—See Dentsu Group Inc.; *Int'l*, pg. 2039
NAGANO AICHI ELECTRIC CO., LTD.—See Aichi Electric Co., Ltd.; *Int'l*, pg. 229
THE NAGANO BANK LTD.; *Int'l*, pg. 7669
NAGANO CAN CORPORATION—See JFE Holdings, Inc.; *Int'l*, pg. 3937
NAGANO CO., LTD.—See Nagano Keiki Co., Ltd.; *Int'l*, pg. 5125
NAGANO COMMUNICATIONS SALES CO., LTD.—See Nisshinbo Holdings Inc.; *Int'l*, pg. 5373
NAGANO ELECTRONICS INDUSTRIAL CO., LTD—See Shin-Etsu Chemical Co. Ltd.; *Int'l*, pg. 6838
NAGANO FUKUDA (TIANJIN) INSTRUMENTS CO., LTD.—See Nagano Keiki Co., Ltd.; *Int'l*, pg. 5125
NAGANO JAPAN RADIO CO., LTD.—See Nisshinbo Holdings Inc.; *Int'l*, pg. 5373
NAGANO JAPAN RADIO ENGINEERING CO., LTD.—See Nisshinbo Holdings Inc.; *Int'l*, pg. 5373
NAGANO JAPAN RADIO (HK) CO., LTD.—See Nisshinbo Holdings Inc.; *Int'l*, pg. 5373
NAGANO JAPAN RADIO SERVICE CO., LTD.—See Nisshinbo Holdings Inc.; *Int'l*, pg. 5373
NAGANO JECO CO., LTD.—See Denso Corporation; *Int'l*, pg. 2032
NAGANO KEIKI CO., LTD.; *Int'l*, pg. 5125
NAGANO KEIKI CO., LTD. - THE ELECTRONIC INSTRUMENT PLANT—See Nagano Keiki Co., Ltd.; *Int'l*, pg. 5125
NAGANO KEIKI CO., LTD. - THE MEASUREMENT INSTRUMENT PLANT—See Nagano Keiki Co., Ltd.; *Int'l*, pg. 5125
NAGANO KEISO CO., LTD.—See Nagano Keiki Co., Ltd.; *Int'l*, pg. 5125
NAGANOKEN PATROL CO.—See Central Security Patrols Co., Ltd.; *Int'l*, pg. 1410
NAGANO MITSUBA CORPORATION—See MITSUBA Corporation; *Int'l*, pg. 4929
NAGANO MORI SHIGYO CO., LTD. - KAWANAKAJIMA PLANT—See Oji Holdings Corporation; *Int'l*, pg. 5537
NAGANO MORI SHIGYO CO., LTD.—See Oji Holdings Corporation; *Int'l*, pg. 5537
NAGANO MORITA LLP—See Prager Metis CPAs, LLC; *U.S. Private*, pg. 3241
NAGANO NISSAN AUTO CO., LTD.—See VT Holdings Co., Ltd.; *Int'l*, pg. 8315

NAGANO OKI ELECTRIC CO., LTD.—See Oki Electric Industry Co., Ltd.; *Int'l*, pg. 5548
NAGANO OLYMPUS CO., LTD.—See Olympus Corporation; *Int'l*, pg. 5556
NAGANO SARAYA SYOKAI INC.—See Mitani Sangyo Co., Ltd.; *Int'l*, pg. 4925
NAGANO TOKYU DEPARTMENT STORE CO.—See Tokyu Corporation; *Int'l*, pg. 7797
NAGAOKA (BEIJING) TRADING CO., LTD.—See Nagaoka International Corporation; *Int'l*, pg. 5125
NAGAOKA EQUIPMENT (DALIAN) CO., LTD.—See Nagaoka International Corporation; *Int'l*, pg. 5125
NAGAOKA EQUIPMENT (DALIAN) CO., LTD.—See Nagaoka International Corporation; *Int'l*, pg. 5125
NAGAOKA INTERNATIONAL CORPORATION - KAIZUKA FACTORY—See Nagaoka International Corporation; *Int'l*, pg. 5125
NAGAOKA INTERNATIONAL CORPORATION; *Int'l*, pg. 5125
NAGAOKA VIETNAM CO., LTD.—See Nagaoka International Corporation; *Int'l*, pg. 5125
NAGAO KOGYO CO., LTD.—See Toyota Industries Corporation; *Int'l*, pg. 7866
NAGARJUNA AGRITECH LIMITED; *Int'l*, pg. 5125
NAGARJUNA FERTILIZERS & CHEMICALS LTD. - KAKINADA PLANT—See Nagarjuna Fertilizers & Chemicals Ltd.; *Int'l*, pg. 5126
NAGARJUNA FERTILIZERS & CHEMICALS LTD.; *Int'l*, pg. 5126
NAGARJUNA OIL CORPORATION LIMITED—See Nagarjuna Fertilizers & Chemicals Ltd.; *Int'l*, pg. 5126
NAGARRO ALLGEIER ES DENMARK A/S—See Nagarro SE; *Int'l*, pg. 5126
NAGARRO ALLGEIER ES FRANCE SAS—See Nagarro SE; *Int'l*, pg. 5126
NAGARRO ALLGEIER ES GMBH—See Nagarro SE; *Int'l*, pg. 5126
NAGARRO AS—See Allgeier SE; *Int'l*, pg. 337
NAGARRO ES DENMARK A/S—See Nagarro SE; *Int'l*, pg. 5126
NAGARRO ES GMBH—See Nagarro SE; *Int'l*, pg. 5126
NAGARRO GMBH—See Allgeier SE; *Int'l*, pg. 337
NAGARRO GMBH—See Nagarro SE; *Int'l*, pg. 5126
NAGARRO INC.—See Allgeier SE; *Int'l*, pg. 337
NAGARRO IQUEST TECHNOLOGIES SRL—See Nagarro SE; *Int'l*, pg. 5126
NAGARRO K.K.—See Allgeier SE; *Int'l*, pg. 337
NAGARRO PTY. LTD.—See Allgeier SE; *Int'l*, pg. 337
NAGARRO SDN. BHD.—See Allgeier SE; *Int'l*, pg. 337
NAGARRO SE; *Int'l*, pg. 5126
NAGARRO SOFTWARE AB—See Allgeier SE; *Int'l*, pg. 337
NAGARRO SOFTWARE A/S—See Allgeier SE; *Int'l*, pg. 337
NAGARRO SOFTWARE GMBH—See Allgeier SE; *Int'l*, pg. 337
NAGARRO SOFTWARE PVT. LTD.—See Allgeier SE; *Int'l*, pg. 337
NAGARRO SOFTWARE S.A. DE C.V.—See Nagarro SE; *Int'l*, pg. 5126
NAGARRO SOFTWARE S.A.—See Allgeier SE; *Int'l*, pg. 337
NAGARRO SOFTWARE SAS—See Allgeier SE; *Int'l*, pg. 337
NAGARRO SOFTWARE SRL—See Allgeier SE; *Int'l*, pg. 337
NAGASAKI CANON INC.—See Canon Inc.; *Int'l*, pg. 1298
NAGASAKI-CHUHATSU CO., LTD.—See Chuo Spring Co., Ltd.; *Int'l*, pg. 1599
NAGASAKI DIAMOND STAFF KK—See Pasona Group Inc.; *Int'l*, pg. 5753
NAGASAKI ECONOMIC RESEARCH INSTITUTE LTD—See Fukuoka Financial Group, Inc.; *Int'l*, pg. 2840
NAGASAKI GUARANTEE SERVICE CO., LTD.—See Fukuoka Financial Group, Inc.; *Int'l*, pg. 2840
NAGASAKI HOSHO SERVICE CO., LTD.—See Fukuoka Financial Group, Inc.; *Int'l*, pg. 2840
NAGASAKI-NIPPON HAM CO., LTD.—See NH Foods Ltd.; *Int'l*, pg. 5256
NAGASAKI NISHI ECO-CREATION CO., LTD.—See Mitsubishi Heavy Industries, Ltd.; *Int'l*, pg. 4960
NAGASAKI RESEARCH INSTITUTE LIMITED—See Fukuoka Financial Group, Inc.; *Int'l*, pg. 2840
NAGASAKI SHIPYARD CO., LTD.—See Nissui Corporation; *Int'l*, pg. 5378
NAGASAKI VISION CORP.—See Nippon Television Holdings Inc.; *Int'l*, pg. 5356
NAGASAKIYA CO., LTD.—See Pan Pacific International Holdings Corporation; *Int'l*, pg. 5715
NAGASARI BITUMEN PRODUCTS SDN. BHD.—See Engtex Group Berhad; *Int'l*, pg. 2436
NAGASAWASHOUJI CO., LTD.—See Kanematsu Corporation; *Int'l*, pg. 4069
NAGASE ABRASIVE MATERIALS CO., LTD.—See Nagase & Co., Ltd.; *Int'l*, pg. 5127
NAGASE AMERICA CORPORATION—See Nagase & Co., Ltd.; *Int'l*, pg. 5127

COMPANY NAME INDEX

NAGASE BEAUTY CARE CO., LTD.—See Nagase & Co., Ltd.; *Int'l*, pg. 5127
NAGASE BROTHERS INC.; *Int'l*, pg. 5128
NAGASE BUSINESS EXPERT CO., LTD.—See Nagase & Co., Ltd.; *Int'l*, pg. 5127
NAGASE BUSINESS MANAGEMENT AND PLANNING (SHANGHAI) CO., LTD.—See Nagase & Co., Ltd.; *Int'l*, pg. 5127
NAGASE CALIFORNIA CORPORATION—See Nagase & Co., Ltd.; *Int'l*, pg. 5127
NAGASE C&G TECHNOLOGY (SHANGHAI) CO., LTD.—See Nagase & Co., Ltd.; *Int'l*, pg. 5127
NAGASE CHEMICAL CO., LTD.—See Nagase & Co., Ltd.; *Int'l*, pg. 5127
NAGASE CHEMSPEC CO., LTD.—See Nagase & Co., Ltd.; *Int'l*, pg. 5127
NAGASE CHEMTEX AMERICA CORP.—See Nagase & Co., Ltd.; *Int'l*, pg. 5127
NAGASE CHEMTEX CORPORATION—See Nagase & Co., Ltd.; *Int'l*, pg. 5127
NAGASE CHEMTEX (WUXI) CORPORATION—See Nagase & Co., Ltd.; *Int'l*, pg. 5127
NAGASE (CHINA) CO., LTD.—See Nagase & Co., Ltd.; *Int'l*, pg. 5127
NAGASE CMS TECHNOLOGY (SHANGHAI) CO., LTD.—See Nagase & Co., Ltd.; *Int'l*, pg. 5127
NAGASE & CO., LTD.; *Int'l*, pg. 5126
NAGASE DO BRASIL COMERCIO DE PRODUTOS QUIMICOS LTDA.—See Nagase & Co., Ltd.; *Int'l*, pg. 5128
NAGASE ELECTRONICS TECHNOLOGY (XIAMEN) CO., LTD.—See Nagase & Co., Ltd.; *Int'l*, pg. 5127
NAGASE ELEX CO., LTD.—See Nagase & Co., Ltd.; *Int'l*, pg. 5127
NAGASE ENGINEERING SERVICE KOREA CO.,LTD—See Nagase & Co., Ltd.; *Int'l*, pg. 5127
NAGASE ENTERPRISE MEXICO S.A.DE C.V.—See Nagase & Co., Ltd.; *Int'l*, pg. 5127
NAGASE (EUROPA) GMBH—See Nagase & Co., Ltd.; *Int'l*, pg. 5127
NAGASE FILTER CO., LTD—See Nagase & Co., Ltd.; *Int'l*, pg. 5127
NAGASE GENERAL SERVICE CO., LTD—See Nagase & Co., Ltd.; *Int'l*, pg. 5127
NAGASE HOLDINGS AMERICA CORPORATION—See Nagase & Co., Ltd.; *Int'l*, pg. 5127
NAGASE (HONG KONG) LTD.—See Nagase & Co., Ltd.; *Int'l*, pg. 5127
NAGASE INDIA PRIVATE LTD.—See Nagase & Co., Ltd.; *Int'l*, pg. 5127
NAGASE INFORMATION DEVELOPMENT, LTD—See Nagase & Co., Ltd.; *Int'l*, pg. 5127
NAGASE KOREA CORPORATION—See Nagase & Co., Ltd.; *Int'l*, pg. 5127
NAGASE-LANDAUER, LTD.—See Fortive Corporation; *U.S. Public*, pg. 871
NAGASE-LANDAUER, LTD.—See Nagase & Co., Ltd.; *Int'l*, pg. 5128
NAGASE LOGISTICS CO., LTD.—See Nagase & Co., Ltd.; *Int'l*, pg. 5127
NAGASE LOGISTICS SUPPORT CO., LTD.—See Nagase & Co., Ltd.; *Int'l*, pg. 5127
NAGASE (MALAYSIA) SDN BHD—See Nagase & Co., Ltd.; *Int'l*, pg. 5127
NAGASE MEDICALS CO., LTD.—See Nagase & Co., Ltd.; *Int'l*, pg. 5127
NAGASE-OG COLORS & CHEMICALS CO., LTD.—See Nagase & Co., Ltd.; *Int'l*, pg. 5126
NAGASE PHILIPPINES CORPORATION—See Nagase & Co., Ltd.; *Int'l*, pg. 5127
NAGASE PHILIPPINES INTERNATIONAL SERVICES CORP.—See Nagase & Co., Ltd.; *Int'l*, pg. 5127
NAGASE PLASTICS CO., LTD.—See Nagase & Co., Ltd.; *Int'l*, pg. 5127
NAGASE SANBIO CO., LTD.—See Nagase & Co., Ltd.; *Int'l*, pg. 5127
NAGASE SINGAPORE (PTE) LTD.—See Nagase & Co., Ltd.; *Int'l*, pg. 5127
NAGASE SPECIALTY MATERIALS NA LLC—See Nagase & Co., Ltd.; *Int'l*, pg. 5128
NAGASE (TAIWAN) CO., LTD.—See Nagase & Co., Ltd.; *Int'l*, pg. 5127
NAGASE TECHNO-ENGINEERING CO., LTD—See Nagase & Co., Ltd.; *Int'l*, pg. 5128
NAGASE TECHNO SERVICE CO., LTD.—See Nagase & Co., Ltd.; *Int'l*, pg. 5128
NAGASE (THAILAND) CO., LTD.—See Nagase & Co., Ltd.; *Int'l*, pg. 5127
NAGASE TRADE MANAGEMENT CO., LTD.—See Nagase & Co., Ltd.; *Int'l*, pg. 5128
NAGASE VIETNAM CO., LTD.—See Nagase & Co., Ltd.; *Int'l*, pg. 5127
NAGASE WAHLEE PLASTICS CORPORATION—See Nagase & Co., Ltd.; *Int'l*, pg. 5128
NAGASHIMA SHOKUHIN CO., LTD.—See Kaneka Corporation; *Int'l*, pg. 4067
NAGATA LINES CO.,LTD.—See Mitsubishi Logistics Corporation; *Int'l*, pg. 4963

NAGATANIEN FOODS CO., LTD.—See Mitsubishi Corporation; *Int'l*, pg. 4940
NAGATANIEN HOLDINGS CO., LTD.—See Mitsubishi Corporation; *Int'l*, pg. 4940
NAGATOMO CO., LTD.—See YW Co., Ltd.; *Int'l*, pg. 8618
NAGAWA CO., LTD.; *Int'l*, pg. 5128
NAGAWORLD LIMITED—See Nagacorp Ltd.; *Int'l*, pg. 5124
NAGEL AIRFREIGHT FRANCE SAS—See STEF SA; *Int'l*, pg. 7190
NAGELBUSH MECHANICAL, INC.—See Tutor Perini Corporation; *U.S. Public*, pg. 2206
NAGEL CHASE INC.—See Payson Casters, Inc.; *U.S. Private*, pg. 3117
NAGELE HOCH- UND TIEFBAU GMBH—See PORR AG; *Int'l*, pg. 5923
NAGELE TIEFBAU GMBH—See PORR AG; *Int'l*, pg. 5923
NAGEL FARM SERVICE INC.; *U.S. Private*, pg. 2830
NAGE LOKALVERMIETUNGSGESELLSCHAFT M.B.H.—See UniCredit S.p.A.; *Int'l*, pg. 8037
NAGINA COTTON MILLS LIMITED—See Nagina Group; *Int'l*, pg. 5129
NAGINA GROUP; *Int'l*, pg. 5128
NAGLE LUMBER CO.—See Alexander Lumber Co., Inc.; *U.S. Private*, pg. 163
NAGLE PAVING COMPANY; *U.S. Private*, pg. 2830
NAGLER GROUP; *U.S. Private*, pg. 2830
NAGOYA CITY ENERGY CO., LTD.—See Chubu Electric Power Co., Inc.; *Int'l*, pg. 1593
NAGOYA DAIICHI TRAFFIC CO., LTD.—See Daiichi Koutsu Sangyo Co., Ltd.; *Int'l*, pg. 1928
NAGOYA DIA BUIL-TECH CO.,LTD.—See Mitsubishi Logistics Corporation; *Int'l*, pg. 4963
NAGOYA ELECTRIC WORKS CO., LTD.; *Int'l*, pg. 5129
NAGOYAKA CARELINK CO., LTD.—See Solasto Corporation; *Int'l*, pg. 7070
NAGOYA KANKO HOTEL CO., LTD.—See Kowa Co., Ltd.; *Int'l*, pg. 4294
NAGOYA LEASE CO., LTD.—See The Bank of Nagoya, Ltd.; *Int'l*, pg. 7616
NAGOYA LUMBER CO., LTD.; *Int'l*, pg. 5129
NAGOYA MITSUKOSHI, LTD.—See Isetan Mitsukoshi Holdings Ltd.; *Int'l*, pg. 3815
NAGOYA NICHIREI SERVICE INC.—See Nichirei Corporation; *Int'l*, pg. 5270
NAGOYA NIPPON STEEL TRADING COIL CENTER CO.,LTD—See Nippon Steel Corporation; *Int'l*, pg. 5337
NAGOYA PLANT—See Mitsubishi Motors Corporation; *Int'l*, pg. 4966
NAGOYA RAILROAD CO., LTD.; *Int'l*, pg. 5129
NAGOYA RYOJU ESTATE CO., LTD.—See Mitsubishi Heavy Industries, Ltd.; *Int'l*, pg. 4961
NAGOYA SEIREN CO., LTD.—See Seiren Co., Ltd.; *Int'l*, pg. 6691
NAGOYA STATION AREA DEVELOPMENT CORPORATION—See Central Japan Railway Company; *Int'l*, pg. 1408
NAGOYA STOCK EXCHANGE, INC.; *Int'l*, pg. 5129
NAGOYA SUBARU INC.—See SUBARU CO., LTD.; *Int'l*, pg. 7246
NAGPUR POWER & INDUSTRIES LIMITED; *Int'l*, pg. 5129
NAGRACARD SA—See Kudelski S.A.; *Int'l*, pg. 4323
NAGRA FRANCE SARL—See Kudelski S.A.; *Int'l*, pg. 4323
NAGRA KUDELSKI (GB) LTD.—See Kudelski S.A.; *Int'l*, pg. 4323
NAGRA MEDIA AUSTRALIA PTY. LTD.—See Kudelski S.A.; *Int'l*, pg. 4323
NAGRA MEDIA GERMANY GMBH—See Kudelski S.A.; *Int'l*, pg. 4323
NAGRA MEDIA JAPAN—See Kudelski S.A.; *Int'l*, pg. 4323
NAGRA MEDIA KOREA LLC—See Kudelski S.A.; *Int'l*, pg. 4323
NAGRA MEDIA PRIVATE LIMITED—See Kudelski S.A.; *Int'l*, pg. 4323
NAGRA MEDIA (TAIWAN) CO., LTD.—See Kudelski S.A.; *Int'l*, pg. 4323
NAGRA MEDIA UK LTD—See Kudelski S.A.; *Int'l*, pg. 4323
NAGRASTAR, LLC—See EchoStar Corporation; *U.S. Public*, pg. 711
NAGRASTAR, LLC—See Kudelski S.A.; *Int'l*, pg. 4323
NAGRA TRADING SA—See Kudelski S.A.; *Int'l*, pg. 4323
NAGRA TRAVEL SARL—See Kudelski S.A.; *Int'l*, pg. 4323
NAGRA USA, INC.—See Kudelski S.A.; *Int'l*, pg. 4323
NAGRAVISION ASIA PTE. LTD.—See Kudelski S.A.; *Int'l*, pg. 4323
NAGRAVISION AS—See Kudelski S.A.; *Int'l*, pg. 4323
NAGRAVISION IBERICA S.L.—See Kudelski S.A.; *Int'l*, pg. 4323
NAGRAVISION INDIA PVT. LTD.—See Kudelski S.A.; *Int'l*, pg. 4323
NAGRAVISION ITALIA SRL—See Kudelski S.A.; *Int'l*, pg. 4323
NAGRAVISION LTDA—See Kudelski S.A.; *Int'l*, pg. 4323
NAGRAVISION SA—See Kudelski S.A.; *Int'l*, pg. 4323
NAGRAVISION STB SOLUTIONS INC.—See Kudelski S.A.; *Int'l*, pg. 4323

NAGREEKA CAPITAL & INFRASTRUCTURE LTD.; *Int'l*, pg. 5129
NAGREEKA EXPORTS LIMITED; *Int'l*, pg. 5129
NAHA INTERNATIONAL CONTAINER TERMINAL, INC.—See International Container Terminal Services, Inc.; *Int'l*, pg. 3746
NAHANNI CONSTRUCTION LTD.; *Int'l*, pg. 5129
NAHAR CAPITAL AND FINANCIAL SERVICES LIMITED; *Int'l*, pg. 5129
NAHAR INDUSTRIAL ENTERPRISES LIMITED; *Int'l*, pg. 5129
NAHAR POLY FILMS LIMITED; *Int'l*, pg. 5129
NAHAR SPINNING MILLS LIMITED; *Int'l*, pg. 5129
NAHDI MEDICAL COMPANY; *Int'l*, pg. 5129
NAHEE ALUMINUM COMPOSITE PANEL LTD.—See Nahee Group; *Int'l*, pg. 5130
NAHEE GEO-TEXTILE INDUSTRIES LIMITED—See Nahee Group; *Int'l*, pg. 5130
NAHEE GROUP; *Int'l*, pg. 5129
NAHEE SS PIPES INDUSTRIES LTD.—See Nahee Group; *Int'l*, pg. 5130
NAH FINANCIAL SERVICES, INC.—See Hoganas AB; *Int'l*, pg. 3441
NAHL GROUP PLC; *Int'l*, pg. 5130
NA HOKU, INC.; *U.S. Private*, pg. 2829
NAHRIN AG; *Int'l*, pg. 5130
NAHUELSAT S.A.—See Airbus SE; *Int'l*, pg. 247
NAHUELSAT S.A.—See SES S.A.; *Int'l*, pg. 6727
NAHWARME DUSSELDORF GMBH—See EnBW Energie Baden-Wurttemberg AG; *Int'l*, pg. 2399
NAIAD DYNAMICS HOLLAND, BV—See Naiad Maritime Group, Inc.; *U.S. Private*, pg. 2831
NAIAD DYNAMICS UK, LTD.—See Naiad Maritime Group, Inc.; *U.S. Private*, pg. 2831
NAIAD DYNAMICS US, INC.—See Naiad Maritime Group, Inc.; *U.S. Private*, pg. 2831
NAIAD MARITIME GROUP, INC.; *U.S. Private*, pg. 2831
NAI CRANES, LLC—See Dearborn Crane & Engineering Co.; *U.S. Private*, pg. 1185
NAICS ASSOCIATION, LLC; *U.S. Private*, pg. 2831
NAI EUROPE—See Natural Alternatives International, Inc.; *U.S. Public*, pg. 1499
NAI EXCEL—See Island Capital Group LLC; *U.S. Private*, pg. 2144
NAIGAI BUSAN LOGISTICS CENTER CO., LTD.—See Naigai Trans Line Ltd.; *Int'l*, pg. 5130
NAIGAI CO., LTD. - RONDEX DIVISION—See Naigai Co., Ltd.; *Int'l*, pg. 5130
NAIGAI CO., LTD.; *Int'l*, pg. 5130
NAIGAI-EUNSAN LOGISTICS CO., LTD.—See Naigai Trans Line Ltd.; *Int'l*, pg. 5130
NAIGAI FORWARDING CO., LTD.—See Mitsubishi Logistics Corporation; *Int'l*, pg. 4963
NAIGAIKIZAI TRADING SHANGHAI CO., LTD.—See Naigai TEC Corporation; *Int'l*, pg. 5130
NAIGAI SHIRTS CO., LTD.—See Nisshinbo Holdings Inc.; *Int'l*, pg. 5373
NAIGAI STEEL CORPORATION—See JFE Holdings, Inc.; *Int'l*, pg. 3937
NAIGAI TEC CORPORATION; *Int'l*, pg. 5130
NAIGAI TECHNOS CORPORATION—See Obayashi Corporation; *Int'l*, pg. 5508
NAIGAI TRANS LINE LTD.; *Int'l*, pg. 5130
NAIGAI TRAVEL SERVICE CO., LTD.—See ITOCHU Corporation; *Int'l*, pg. 3841
NAI GLOBAL, INC.—See Island Capital Group LLC; *U.S. Private*, pg. 2144
NAI HUNNEMAN—See Island Capital Group LLC; *U.S. Private*, pg. 2144
NAIKAI TUG BOAT SERVICE CO., LTD—See Nippon Yusen Kabushiki Kaisha; *Int'l*, pg. 5359
NAIKAI ZOSEN CORPORATION; *Int'l*, pg. 5130
NAIL COMMUNICATIONS; *U.S. Private*, pg. 2831
NAIL MEDIA GROUP; *U.S. Private*, pg. 2831
NAILOR INDUSTRIES; *U.S. Private*, pg. 2831
NAIMAN GMBH—See G-III Apparel Group, Ltd.; *U.S. Public*, pg. 894
NAIM HOLDINGS BERHAD; *Int'l*, pg. 5131
NAI MID-MICHIGAN; *U.S. Private*, pg. 2830
NAIMOR, INC.; *U.S. Private*, pg. 2831
NA INDUSTRIES, INC.—See Nippon Shokubai Co., Ltd.; *Int'l*, pg. 5332
THE NAINITAL BANK LTD.—See Bank of Baroda; *Int'l*, pg. 840
NAIN TECH CO., LTD.; *Int'l*, pg. 5131
NAIPU MINING MACHINE MEXICO CO., LTD.—See Naipu Mining Machinery Co., Ltd.; *Int'l*, pg. 5131
NAIPU MINING MACHINERY CHILE CO., LTD.—See Naipu Mining Machinery Co., Ltd.; *Int'l*, pg. 5131
NAIPU MINING MACHINERY CO., LTD.; *Int'l*, pg. 5131
NAIPU MINING MACHINERY MONGOLIA CO., LTD.—See Naipu Mining Machinery Co., Ltd.; *Int'l*, pg. 5131
NAIPU MINING PERU LIMITED LIABILITY COMPANY—See Naipu Mining Machinery Co., Ltd.; *Int'l*, pg. 5131
NAIRN FLOORS BENELUX B.V.—See Forbo Holding Ltd.; *Int'l*, pg. 2730
NAIROBI STOCK EXCHANGE LIMITED; *Int'l*, pg. 5131

NAIROBI STOCK EXCHANGE LIMITED

CORPORATE AFFILIATIONS

NAIS, INC—See Inszone Insurance Services, LLC; *U.S. Private*, pg. 2096
NAISMITH ENGINEERING & MANUFACTURING CO PTY LTD.—See Miki Pulley Co., Ltd.; *Int'l*, pg. 4891
NAI SOUTHWEST FLORIDA, INC.; *U.S. Private*, pg. 2830
NAI TALCOR; *U.S. Private*, pg. 2830
N-AITEC S.R.L.—See InfraVia Capital Partners SAS; *Int'l*, pg. 3699
NAITO & CO. LTD.—See Okaya & Co., Ltd.; *Int'l*, pg. 5546
NAITO VIETNAM CO., LTD.—See Okaya & Co., Ltd.; *Int'l*, pg. 5546
NAJAFI COMPANIES, LLC; *U.S. Private*, pg. 2831
THE NAJAFI COMPANIES; *U.S. Private*, pg. 4081
NAJARDVARVET AB—See Linnea Yacht Group; *Int'l*, pg. 4515
NAJARIAN FURNITURE COMPANY; *U.S. Private*, pg. 2831
NAJDA MAGHREB SPA—See Sonatrach International Holding Corporation; *Int'l*, pg. 7089
NAJEDO PTY. LTD.—See Petsec Energy Ltd.; *Int'l*, pg. 5834
NAJRAN CEMENT COMPANY; *Int'l*, pg. 5131
NAKABAYASHI CO., LTD.; *Int'l*, pg. 5131
NAKABOHTEC CORROSION PROTECTING CO., LTD.; *Int'l*, pg. 5131
NAKADAYA CORP.—See Rever Holdings Corporation; *Int'l*, pg. 6313
NAKAGAWA ENGINEERING CONSULTING (SHANGHAI) CO., LTD.—See Hisaka Works, Ltd.; *Int'l*, pg. 3406
NAKAGAWA KINZOKU CO., LTD.—See Yuasa Trading Co., Ltd.; *Int'l*, pg. 8609
NAKAGAWA OIL CO., LTD—See Idemitsu Kosan Co., Ltd.; *Int'l*, pg. 3592
NAKAHATA INC.—See Dentsu Group Inc.; *Int'l*, pg. 2039
NAKAHATSU CO., LTD.—See CROSS PLUS INC.; *Int'l*, pg. 1856
NAKAJIMAKOKI COPORATION—See TORQ Inc.; *Int'l*, pg. 7829
NAKAJIMA MEDICAL SUPPLY CO., LTD.—See Ship Healthcare Holdings, Inc.; *Int'l*, pg. 6852
NAKAJO JAMCO CORPORATION—See JAMCO Corporation; *Int'l*, pg. 3874
NAKAKIN LEASE CO., LTD.—See Sugiko Group Holdings Co., Ltd.; *Int'l*, pg. 7254
NAKAKITA SEISAKUSHO CO., LTD.; *Int'l*, pg. 5131
NAKAKITASORACHI ENVIRONMENT TECHNOLOGY CO., LTD.—See Hitachi Zosen Corporation; *Int'l*, pg. 3411
NAKAKITA YAKUHIN CO., LTD.; *Int'l*, pg. 5131
NAKAMICHI, INC.—See Relo Group, Inc.; *Int'l*, pg. 6265
NAKAMICHI LEASING CO., LTD.; *Int'l*, pg. 5132
NAKAMOTO PACKS CO., LTD.; *Int'l*, pg. 5132
NAKAMOTO PACKS USA,INC—See Nakamoto Packs Co., Ltd.; *Int'l*, pg. 5132
NAKAMURA CHOUKOU CO., LTD. - IZUMI FACTORY—See Nakamura Choukou Co., Ltd.; *Int'l*, pg. 5132
NAKAMURA CHOUKOU CO., LTD.; *Int'l*, pg. 5132
NAKAMURA KOZAI CO., LTD.—See Okaya & Co., Ltd.; *Int'l*, pg. 5546
NAKAMURA SHAJI CO., LTD.—See Takamatsu Construction Group Co., Ltd.; *Int'l*, pg. 7430
NAKAMURAYA CO., LTD.; *Int'l*, pg. 5132
NAKANIHON KOGYO CO., LTD.; *Int'l*, pg. 5132
NAKANISHI INC.; *Int'l*, pg. 5132
NAKANISHI MFG. CO., LTD.; *Int'l*, pg. 5132
NAKANO CONSTRUCTION SDN. BHD.—See Nakano Corporation; *Int'l*, pg. 5132
NAKANO CONSULTING SHANGHAI CO., LTD.—See Nakano Corporation; *Int'l*, pg. 5132
NAKANO CORPORATION; *Int'l*, pg. 5132
NAKANO DEVELOPMENT CO., LTD.—See Nakano Corporation; *Int'l*, pg. 5132
NAKANO INTERNATIONAL CORPORATION—See Nakano Corporation; *Int'l*, pg. 5132
NAKANO METAL PRESS (SINGAPORE) PTE. LTD.—See Shimano, Inc.; *Int'l*, pg. 6833
NAKANO REFRIGERATORS CO., LTD.; *Int'l*, pg. 5133
NAKANO SINGAPORE (PTE.) LTD.—See Nakano Corporation; *Int'l*, pg. 5132
NAKANO VIETNAM CO., LTD.—See Nakano Corporation; *Int'l*, pg. 5132
NAKAN TECHNO CO., LTD.—See Helios Techno Holding Co., Ltd.; *Int'l*, pg. 3330
NAKASHIMA UCHIDA CORPORATION—See Uchida Yoko Co., Ltd.; *Int'l*, pg. 8012
NAKASHO MACHINE CO., LTD.—See TORQ Inc.; *Int'l*, pg. 7829
NAKA'S, INC.; *U.S. Private*, pg. 2831
NAKAS MUSIC CYPRUS LTD—See PHILIPPOS NAKAS S.A.; *Int'l*, pg. 5846
NAKATA ENGINEERING CO., LTD.—See Sumitomo Rubber Industries, Ltd.; *Int'l*, pg. 7299
NAKATAKE CO., LTD.; *Int'l*, pg. 5133
NAKATANI SUISAN CO., LTD—See Nissui Corporation; *Int'l*, pg. 5378
NAKAU CO., LTD.—See Zensho Holdings Co., Ltd.; *Int'l*, pg. 8634
NAKAYAMAFUKU CO., LTD.; *Int'l*, pg. 5133

NAKAYAMA KENZAI LTD.—See Toto Ltd.; *Int'l*, pg. 7845
NAKAYAMA STEEL PRODUCTS CO., LTD.—See Kyoei Steel Ltd.; *Int'l*, pg. 4362
NAKAYAMA STEEL WORKS LTD.; *Int'l*, pg. 5133
NAKAYO, INC.; *Int'l*, pg. 5133
NAKAZAWA UJIKE PHARMACEUTICAL CO., LTD.—See Medipal Holdings Corporation; *Int'l*, pg. 4779
NAK DO BRASIL INDUSTRIA E COMERCIO DE COMPONENTES DE VEDACAO LTDA.—See NAK Sealing Technologies Corporation; *Int'l*, pg. 5131
NAKED BRAND GROUP INC.—See Cenntro Electric Group Limited; *Int'l*, pg. 1401
NAKED COMMUNICATIONS AUSTRALIA PTY LIMITED—See Enero Group Limited; *Int'l*, pg. 2424
NAKED COMMUNICATIONS LTD.—See Enero Group Limited; *Int'l*, pg. 2424
NAKED COMMUNICATIONS NORDIC—See Enero Group Limited; *Int'l*, pg. 2424
NAKED JUICE COMPANY, INC.—See PAI Partners S.A.S.; *Int'l*, pg. 5702
NAKED JUICE CO. OF GLENDORA, INC.—See PAI Partners S.A.S.; *Int'l*, pg. 5702
NAKED NZ LIMITED—See Enero Group Limited; *Int'l*, pg. 2424
NAKED PAPERS BRANDS, INC.—See Telco Cuba, Inc.; *U.S. Public*, pg. 1992
NAKED RESTAURANTS, INC.; *U.S. Private*, pg. 2831
NAKED WINES AUSTRALIA PTY LIMITED—See Naked Wines Plc; *Int'l*, pg. 5133
NAKEDWINES.COM, INC.—See Naked Wines Plc; *Int'l*, pg. 5133
NAKED WINES INTERNATIONAL LIMITED—See Naked Wines Plc; *Int'l*, pg. 5133
NAKED WINES PLC; *Int'l*, pg. 5133
NAKHEEL PVT JSC—See Dubai World Corporation; *Int'l*, pg. 2222
NAKHODKA TELECOM—See PJSC Megafon; *Int'l*, pg. 5882
NAK INTERNATIONAL LTD.—See NAK Sealing Technologies Corporation; *Int'l*, pg. 5131
NAKLADATELSTVI DR. JOSEF RAABE, S.R.O.—See Ernst Klett AG; *Int'l*, pg. 2495
NAKODA GROUP OF INDUSTRIES LTD.; *Int'l*, pg. 5133
NAKODA LIMITED; *Int'l*, pg. 5133
NAKOMA GROUP ENTERPRISE SOLUTIONS—See Nakoma Group; *U.S. Private*, pg. 2831
NAKOMA GROUP; *U.S. Private*, pg. 2831
NAKOMA GROUP—See Nakoma Group; *U.S. Private*, pg. 2831
NAKOR INC.—See DAEDUCK Co., Ltd.; *Int'l*, pg. 1906
NAKORNSAWAN WATER SUPPLY COMPANY LIMITED—See Eastern Water Resources Development & Management Public Company Limited; *Int'l*, pg. 2274
NAK SEALING PRODUCTS (THAILAND) CO., LTD.—See NAK Sealing Technologies Corporation; *Int'l*, pg. 5131
NAK SEALING TECHNOLOGIES CORPORATION; *Int'l*, pg. 5131
NAK SEALING TECHNOLOGIES (INDIA) PVT. LTD.—See NAK Sealing Technologies Corporation; *Int'l*, pg. 5131
NAKSH PRECIOUS METALS LTD.; *Int'l*, pg. 5133
NAKUFREIGHT LIMITED—See Kuehne + Nagel International AG; *Int'l*, pg. 4325
NAKUURUQ SOLUTIONS, LLC—See Nana Regional Corporation, Inc.; *U.S. Private*, pg. 2832
NALANDA POWER COMPANY LIMITED—See CESC Limited; *Int'l*, pg. 1424
NALCO AB—See Ecolab Inc.; *U.S. Public*, pg. 715
NALCO AFRICA (PTY.) LTD.—See Ecolab Inc.; *U.S. Public*, pg. 715
NALCO ANADOLU KIMYA SANAYI VE TICARET LIMITED SIRKETI—See Ecolab Inc.; *U.S. Public*, pg. 715
NALCO ARGENTINA S.R.L.—See Ecolab Inc.; *U.S. Public*, pg. 715
NALCO AUSTRALIA PTY. LTD.—See Ecolab Inc.; *U.S. Public*, pg. 715
NALCO AZERBAIJAN LLC—See Ecolab Inc.; *U.S. Public*, pg. 715
NALCO BELGIUM BVBA—See Ecolab Inc.; *U.S. Public*, pg. 715
NALCO CAL WATER, LLC—See Ecolab Inc.; *U.S. Public*, pg. 715
NALCO CANADA COMPANY—See Ecolab Inc.; *U.S. Public*, pg. 715
NALCO CHEMICALS INDIA LIMITED—See Ecolab Inc.; *U.S. Public*, pg. 715
NALCO (CHINA) ENVIRONMENTAL SOLUTION CO. LTD.—See Ecolab Inc.; *U.S. Public*, pg. 715
NALCO COMPANY LLC—See Ecolab Inc.; *U.S. Public*, pg. 715
NALCO COMPANY OOO—See Ecolab Inc.; *U.S. Public*, pg. 715
NALCO COMPANY - SUGAR LAND—See Ecolab Inc.; *U.S. Public*, pg. 715
NALCO CROSSBOW WATER LLC—See Ecolab Inc.; *U.S. Public*, pg. 715
NALCO CZECHIA S.R.O.—See Ecolab Inc.; *U.S. Public*, pg. 715
NALCO DANMARK APS—See Ecolab Inc.; *U.S. Public*, pg. 715

NALCO DE COLOMBIA LTDA—See Ecolab Inc.; *U.S. Public*, pg. 715
NALCO DELAWARE COMPANY—See Ecolab Inc.; *U.S. Public*, pg. 715
NALCO DE MEXICO, S. DE R. L. DE C.V.—See Ecolab Inc.; *U.S. Public*, pg. 715
NALCO DEUTSCHLAND GMBH—See Ecolab Inc.; *U.S. Public*, pg. 715
NALCO DEUTSCHLAND MANUFACTURING GMBH UND CO. KG—See Ecolab Inc.; *U.S. Public*, pg. 715
NALCO DISTRIBUTING, INC.; *U.S. Private*, pg. 2831
NALCO DUTCH HOLDINGS B.V.—See Ecolab Inc.; *U.S. Public*, pg. 715
NALCO EGYPT, LTD.—See Ecolab Inc.; *U.S. Public*, pg. 715
NALCO ENERGY SERVICES LIMITED—See Ecolab Inc.; *U.S. Public*, pg. 715
NALCO ENERGY SERVICES, L.P.—See Ecolab Inc.; *U.S. Public*, pg. 715
NALCO ENERGY SERVICES MIDDLE EAST HOLDINGS, INC.—See Ecolab Inc.; *U.S. Public*, pg. 715
NALCO ENVIRONMENTAL SOLUTIONS LLC—See Ecolab Inc.; *U.S. Public*, pg. 715
NALCO ESPANOLA MANUFACTURING, S.L.U.—See Ecolab Inc.; *U.S. Public*, pg. 715
NALCO ESPANOLA, S.L.—See Ecolab Inc.; *U.S. Public*, pg. 715
NALCO EUROPE BV—See Ecolab Inc.; *U.S. Public*, pg. 715
NALCO FAB-TECH LLC—See Modern Group, Ltd.; *U.S. Private*, pg. 2761
NALCO FINLAND OY—See Ecolab Inc.; *U.S. Public*, pg. 715
NALCO FRANCE—See Ecolab Inc.; *U.S. Public*, pg. 715
NALCO HELLAS S.A.—See Ecolab Inc.; *U.S. Public*, pg. 715
NALCO HOLDING COMPANY—See Ecolab Inc.; *U.S. Public*, pg. 715
NALCO HOLDINGS G.M.B.H.—See Ecolab Inc.; *U.S. Public*, pg. 715
NALCO INDUSTRIAL SERVICES CHILE LIMITADA—See Ecolab Inc.; *U.S. Public*, pg. 716
NALCO INDUSTRIAL SERVICES MALAYSIA SDN. BHD—See Ecolab Inc.; *U.S. Public*, pg. 716
NALCO INDUSTRIAL SERVICES (NANJING) CO., LTD.—See Ecolab Inc.; *U.S. Public*, pg. 715
NALCO INDUSTRIAL SERVICES (SUZHOU) CO., LTD.—See Ecolab Inc.; *U.S. Public*, pg. 716
NALCO INDUSTRIAL SERVICES (THAILAND) CO. LTD.—See Ecolab Inc.; *U.S. Public*, pg. 716
NALCO INTERNATIONAL HOLDINGS B.V.—See Ecolab Inc.; *U.S. Public*, pg. 716
NALCO ISRAEL INDUSTRIAL SERVICES LTD.—See Ecolab Inc.; *U.S. Public*, pg. 716
NALCO ITALIANA MANUFACTURING S.R.L.—See Ecolab Inc.; *U.S. Public*, pg. 716
NALCO ITALIANA SRL—See Ecolab Inc.; *U.S. Public*, pg. 716
NALCO JAPAN G.K.—See Ecolab Inc.; *U.S. Public*, pg. 716
NALCO KOREA LIMITED—See Ecolab Inc.; *U.S. Public*, pg. 716
NALCO KORIYAMA CO., LTD.—See UACJ Corporation; *Int'l*, pg. 7999
NALCO LATIN AMERICAN OPERATIONS—See Ecolab Inc.; *U.S. Public*, pg. 716
NALCO LIBYA—See Ecolab Inc.; *U.S. Public*, pg. 716
NALCO LIMITED—See Ecolab Inc.; *U.S. Public*, pg. 716
NALCO NETHERLANDS BV—See Ecolab Inc.; *U.S. Public*, pg. 716
NALCO NORGE AS—See Ecolab Inc.; *U.S. Public*, pg. 716
NALCO OSTERREICH GES M.B.H.—See Ecolab Inc.; *U.S. Public*, pg. 716
NALCO PAKISTAN (PRIVATE) LIMITED—See Ecolab Inc.; *U.S. Public*, pg. 716
NALCO PHILIPPINES INC.—See Ecolab Inc.; *U.S. Public*, pg. 716
NALCO POLSKA SP. Z O. O.—See Ecolab Inc.; *U.S. Public*, pg. 716
NALCO PORTUGUESA (QUIMICA INDUSTRIAL) LTD.—See Ecolab Inc.; *U.S. Public*, pg. 716
NALCO SAUDI CO. LTD.—See Ecolab Inc.; *U.S. Public*, pg. 716
NALCO SCHWEIZ GMBH—See Ecolab Inc.; *U.S. Public*, pg. 716
NALCO TAIWAN CO., LTD.—See Ecolab Inc.; *U.S. Public*, pg. 716
NALCO VENEZUELA S. C. A.—See Ecolab Inc.; *U.S. Public*, pg. 716
NALCO WATER INDIA LIMITED—See Ecolab Inc.; *U.S. Public*, pg. 716
NAL DO BRASIL INDUSTRIA E COMERCIO DE COMPONENTES DE ILUMINACAO LTDA.—See Koito Manufacturing Co., Ltd.; *Int'l*, pg. 4230
NAL ENERGY CORP.—See Waterous Energy Fund; *Int'l*, pg. 8358
NALEWAY FOODS LTD.—See Beaumont Select Corporations Inc.; *Int'l*, pg. 934

COMPANY NAME INDEX

NALGE NUNC INTERNATIONAL CORPORATION—See Thermo Fisher Scientific Inc.; *U.S. Public*, pg. 2149
NALGE NUNC INTERNATIONAL CORPORATION—See Thermo Fisher Scientific Inc.; *U.S. Public*, pg. 2149
NALIN LEASE FINANCE LIMITED; *Int'l*, pg. 5133
NALKA INVEST AB—See Interogo Holding AG; *Int'l*, pg. 3754
NALLEY AUTOMOTIVE GROUP—See Asbury Automotive Group, Inc.; *U.S. Public*, pg. 209
NALLEY COLLISION CENTER - ROSWELL BODY SHOP—See Asbury Automotive Group, Inc.; *U.S. Public*, pg. 210
NALLY & GIBSON GEORGETOWN, LLC—See Summit Materials, Inc.; *U.S. Public*, pg. 1960
NAL MAROC LTD.—See Eusu Holdings Co., Ltd.; *Int'l*, pg. 2559
NALPROPION PHARMACEUTICALS, INC.—See JPMorgan Chase & Co.; *U.S. Public*, pg. 1207
NALPROPION PHARMACEUTICALS, INC.—See Pernix Therapeutics Holdings, Inc.; *U.S. Private*, pg. 3152
NALPROPION PHARMACEUTICALS, INC.—See Whitebox Advisors, LLC; *U.S. Private*, pg. 4511
NAL RESEARCH CORP.—See Blue Sky Network, LLC; *U.S. Private*, pg. 593
NALU MEDICAL, INC.; *U.S. Public*, pg. 1490
NALURI CORPORATION BERHAD—See Atlan Holdings Berhad; *Int'l*, pg. 674
NALURI PROPERTIES SDN. BHD.—See Atlan Holdings Berhad; *Int'l*, pg. 674
NALWA SONS INVESTMENTS LIMITED; *Int'l*, pg. 5133
NAMA A.D.; *Int'l*, pg. 5134
NAMA CHEMICALS COMPANY; *Int'l*, pg. 5134
NAMA D.D.; *Int'l*, pg. 5134
NAMA EUROPE LLC—See NAMA Chemicals Company; *Int'l*, pg. 5134
NAMA GERMANY GMBH—See NAMA Chemicals Company; *Int'l*, pg. 5134
NAMAKWA DIAMOND HOLDINGS (PTY) LTD.—See Namakwa Diamonds Limited; *Int'l*, pg. 5135
NAMAKWA DIAMONDS LIMITED; *Int'l*, pg. 5135
N.A. MANS SONS INC.; *U.S. Private*, pg. 2827
NAMASCOR B.V.—See Tata Sons Limited; *Int'l*, pg. 7472
NAMASTE BITTIYA SANSTHA LIMITED; *Int'l*, pg. 5135
NAMASTEMD INC.—See Lifeist Wellness Inc.; *Int'l*, pg. 4404
NAMASTE SOLAR ELECTRIC, INC.; *U.S. Private*, pg. 2831
NAMASTE WORLD ACQUISITION CORPORATION; *U.S. Public*, pg. 1490
NAMBA PRESS WORKS CO., LTD.; *Int'l*, pg. 5135
NAMBE LLC—See Portmeirion Group Plc; *Int'l*, pg. 5934
NAMBE MILLS INC.; *U.S. Private*, pg. 2831
NAM CHEONG LIMITED; *Int'l*, pg. 5133
NAMCHOW FOOD GROUP SHANGHAI CO., LTD.; *Int'l*, pg. 5135
NAMCHOW HOLDINGS CO., LTD.; *Int'l*, pg. 5135
NAMCHOW (THAILAND) LTD.—See Namchow Holdings Co., Ltd.; *Int'l*, pg. 5135
NAMCO CONTROLS CORPORATION—See Danaher Corporation; *U.S. Public*, pg. 628
NAMCO ENTERPRISES ASIA LTD.—See BANDAI NAMCO Holdings Inc.; *Int'l*, pg. 829
NAMCO ENTERTAINMENT INC.—See BANDAI NAMCO Holdings Inc.; *Int'l*, pg. 829
NAMCO LTD.—See BANDAI NAMCO Holdings Inc.; *Int'l*, pg. 829
NAMCO OPERATIONS EUROPE LTD.—See BANDAI NAMCO Holdings Inc.; *Int'l*, pg. 829
NAMCO OPERATIONS SPAIN S.L.—See BANDAI NAMCO Holdings Inc.; *Int'l*, pg. 829
NAM DINH EXPORT FOODSTUFF AND AGRICULTURAL PRODUCTS PROCESSING JSC; *Int'l*, pg. 5133
NAM DINH VU PORT JOINT STOCK COMPANY—See Gemadept Corporation; *Int'l*, pg. 2915
NAME BRANDS INC.; *U.S. Private*, pg. 2831
NAMEJET, LLC—See Siris Capital Group, LLC; *U.S. Private*, pg. 3675
NAMELY, INC.; *U.S. Private*, pg. 2832
NAMEMEDIA, INC.; *U.S. Private*, pg. 2832
NAMESCO LTD—See HgCapital Trust plc; *Int'l*, pg. 3377
NAMESILO TECHNOLOGIES CORP.; *Int'l*, pg. 5135
NAMESON HOLDINGS LIMITED; *Int'l*, pg. 5135
NAM FATT CORPORATION BERHAD; *Int'l*, pg. 5133
NAM FATT FABRICATORS SDN. BHD.—See Nam Fatt Corporation Berhad; *Int'l*, pg. 5133
NAMHAE CHEMICAL CORP.; *Int'l*, pg. 5135
NAM HAI DINH VU PORT J.S.C.—See Gemadept Corporation; *Int'l*, pg. 2915
NAM HAI ICD JOINT STOCK COMPANY—See Gemadept Corporation; *Int'l*, pg. 2915
NAM HENG OIL MILL CO. SDN. BHD.; *Int'l*, pg. 5134
NAM HING CIRCUIT BOARD COMPANY LIMITED—See China Environmental Energy Investment Limited; *Int'l*, pg. 1500
NAM HING INDUSTRIAL LAMINATE LIMITED—See China Environmental Energy Investment Limited; *Int'l*, pg. 1500
NAM HONG PROPERTIES PTE. LTD.—See Blackgold Natural Resources Ltd.; *Int'l*, pg. 1061
NAM HUA RUBBER CO., LTD.—See Sri Trang Agro-Industry Public Company Limited; *Int'l*, pg. 7150
NAM HWA CONSTRUCTION CO., LTD.; *Int'l*, pg. 5134
NAMHWA INDUSTRIAL CO., LTD.; *Int'l*, pg. 5135
NAMI-AEW EUROPE—See Groupe BPCE; *Int'l*, pg. 3096
NAMIBIA ASSET MANAGEMENT LIMITED; *Int'l*, pg. 5135
NAMIBIA BREWERIES LIMITED; *Int'l*, pg. 5135
NAMIBIA BUREAU DE CHANGE (PTY) LIMITED—See The Bidvest Group Limited; *Int'l*, pg. 7625
NAMIBIA CRITICAL METALS INC.; *Int'l*, pg. 5135
NAMIBIAN SEA PRODUCTS LIMITED—See The Bidvest Group Limited; *Int'l*, pg. 7625
NAMIBIAN STOCK EXCHANGE ASSOCIATION; *Int'l*, pg. 5135
NAMIBIA RARE EARTHS (PTY) LTD.—See Namibia Critical Metals Inc.; *Int'l*, pg. 5135
NAMI CORP.; *Int'l*, pg. 5135
NAMICOS CORPORATION—See Ono Pharmaceutical Co., Ltd.; *Int'l*, pg. 5582
NAMIFY LLC; *U.S. Private*, pg. 2832
NAMING'OMBA TEA ESTATES LIMITED—See Gillanders Arbuthnot & Co., Ltd.; *Int'l*, pg. 2976
NAMITAKIKO CO., LTD.—See Carlit Co., Ltd.; *Int'l*, pg. 1338
NAMJAI THAIBEV (SOCIAL ENTERPRISE) CO., LTD.—See Thai Beverage Public Company Limited; *Int'l*, pg. 7591
NAMJESTAJ D.D.; *Int'l*, pg. 5135
NAM KIJJAKARN CO., LTD.—See Thai Beverage Public Company Limited; *Int'l*, pg. 7591
NAM KIM STEEL JOINT STOCK COMPANY; *Int'l*, pg. 5134
NAMKWANG ENGINEERING & CONSTRUCTION; *Int'l*, pg. 5135
NAM LEE PRESSED METAL INDUSTRIES LIMITED; *Int'l*, pg. 5134
NAM LIONG GLOBAL CORPORATION; *Int'l*, pg. 5134
NAMLIONG SKYCOSMOS, INC.; *Int'l*, pg. 5136
NAM LONG INVESTMENT CORPORATION; *Int'l*, pg. 5134
NAMMO ARTILLERY CENTER OY—See Patria Oyj; *Int'l*, pg. 5757
NAMMO AS—See Patria Oyj; *Int'l*, pg. 5757
NAMMO AUSTRALIA PTY LTD.—See Patria Oyj; *Int'l*, pg. 5757
NAMMO BAKELITTFABRIKKEN AS—See Patria Oyj; *Int'l*, pg. 5757
NAMMO CHELTENHAM LTD.—See Patria Oyj; *Int'l*, pg. 5757
NAMMO DEMIL DIVISION AB—See Patria Oyj; *Int'l*, pg. 5758
NAMMO GERMANY GMBH—See Patria Oyj; *Int'l*, pg. 5757
NAMMO INC.—See Patria Oyj; *Int'l*, pg. 5757
NAMMO IRELAND LIMITED—See Patria Oyj; *Int'l*, pg. 5757
NAMMO LAPUA OY—See Patria Oyj; *Int'l*, pg. 5757
NAMMO LIAB AB—See Patria Oyj; *Int'l*, pg. 5758
NAMMO NAD AS—See Patria Oyj; *Int'l*, pg. 5757
NAMMO WORKS OY—See Patria Oyj; *Int'l*, pg. 5758
NAMMO PERRY INC.—See Patria Oyj; *Int'l*, pg. 5757
NAMMO POCAL INC.—See Patria Oyj; *Int'l*, pg. 5757
NAMMO RAUFOSS AS—See Patria Oyj; *Int'l*, pg. 5758
NAMMO SCHONEBECK GMBH—See Patria Oyj; *Int'l*, pg. 5758
NAMMO SWEDEN AB—See Patria Oyj; *Int'l*, pg. 5758
NAMMO SWEDEN AB—See Patria Oyj; *Int'l*, pg. 5758
NAMMO TALLEY, INC.—See Patria Oyj; *Int'l*, pg. 5758
NAMMO (U.K.) LIMITED—See Moog Inc.; *U.S. Public*, pg. 1470
NAMMO VIHTAVUORI OY—See Patria Oyj; *Int'l*, pg. 5758
NAMMO WESTCOTT LTD.—See Patria Oyj; *Int'l*, pg. 5758
NAM MUANG CO., LTD.—See Thai Beverage Public Company Limited; *Int'l*, pg. 7591
NAM MU HYDROELECTRICITY JSC—See SONG DA 9 JOINT STOCK COMPANY; *Int'l*, pg. 7095
NAM MU HYDROPOWER JSC—See SONG DA 9 JOINT STOCK COMPANY; *Int'l*, pg. 7095
NAMOI COTTON LIMITED—See Louis Dreyfus Company B.V.; *Int'l*, pg. 4562
NAMOI MINING PTY LTD.—See Whitehaven Coal Limited; *Int'l*, pg. 8400
NAMPAK BEVCAN NIGERIA LTD.—See Nampak Ltd.; *Int'l*, pg. 5136
NAMPAK CORRUGATED (SWAZILAND) LTD—See Nampak Ltd.; *Int'l*, pg. 5136
NAMPAK DIVFOOD BOTSWANA (PTY) LTD—See Nampak Ltd.; *Int'l*, pg. 5136
NAMPAK HEALTHCARE DARMSTADT GMBH—See Nampak Ltd.; *Int'l*, pg. 5136
NAMPAK INTERNATIONAL LTD—See Nampak Ltd.; *Int'l*, pg. 5136
NAMPAK KENYA LTD.—See Nampak Ltd.; *Int'l*, pg. 5136
NAMPAK LIQUID BOTSWANA (PTY.) LTD.—See Nampak Ltd.; *Int'l*, pg. 5136
NAMPAK LTD.; *Int'l*, pg. 5136
NAMPAK METAL PACKAGING LTD.—See Nampak Ltd.; *Int'l*, pg. 5136
NAMPAK NIGERIA LTD.—See Nampak Ltd.; *Int'l*, pg. 5136
NAMPAK PLASTICS EUROPE LTD.—See Greybull Capital LLP; *Int'l*, pg. 3082
NAMPAK PRODUCTS LTD.—See Nampak Ltd.; *Int'l*, pg. 5136
NAMPAK TANZANIA LTD.—See Nampak Ltd.; *Int'l*, pg. 5136
NAMPAK WIEGAND GLASS (PTY) LTD.—See Nampak Ltd.; *Int'l*, pg. 5136
NAMPAK ZAMBIA LTD.—See Nampak Ltd.; *Int'l*, pg. 5136
NAM PALANG CO., LTD.—See Thai Beverage Public Company Limited; *Int'l*, pg. 7591
NAMPA VALLEY HELICOPTERS INC.—See PHI, Inc.; *U.S. Private*, pg. 3168
NAM PEI HONG SUM YUNG DRUGS COMPANY LIMITED—See China Healthwise Holdings Limited; *Int'l*, pg. 1507
NAM PHAT LOGISTICS CO., LTD.—See Hai Minh Corporation; *Int'l*, pg. 3209
NAM PHAT LTD—See Hai Minh Corporation; *Int'l*, pg. 3209
NAMRA FINANCE LIMITED—See Arman Financial Services Ltd.; *Int'l*, pg. 574
NAM.R SA; *Int'l*, pg. 5134
NAMSAE INTERNATIONAL TRADING CO., LTD—See Miki Pulley Co., Ltd.; *Int'l*, pg. 4891
NAMSCO INC.—See Charles River Laboratories International, Inc.; *U.S. Public*, pg. 480
NAMSENBYGG AS—See Norske Skog ASA; *Int'l*, pg. 5437
NAM SENG INSURANCE PUBLIC COMPANY LIMITED; *Int'l*, pg. 5136
NAMSUN ALUMINUM CO., LTD.; *Int'l*, pg. 5136
NAMSUNG CORP.; *Int'l*, pg. 5136
NAMSYS INC.; *Int'l*, pg. 5136
NAM TAI ELECTRONIC & ELECTRICAL PRODUCTS LIMITED—See Nam Tai Property Inc.; *Int'l*, pg. 5134
NAM TAI ELECTRONIC (SHENZHEN) CO., LTD.—See Nam Tai Property Inc.; *Int'l*, pg. 5134
NAM TAI INVESTMENT LIMITED—See Nam Tai Property Inc.; *Int'l*, pg. 5134
NAM TAI INVESTMENTS CONSULTANT (MACAO COMMERCIAL OFFSHORE) COMPANY LIMITED—See Nam Tai Property Inc.; *Int'l*, pg. 5134
NAM TAI PROPERTY INC.; *Int'l*, pg. 5134
NAMTEK CORP; *U.S. Private*, pg. 2832
NAM THEUN 2 POWER COMPANY LIMITED; *Int'l*, pg. 5134
NAM THURAKIJ CO., LTD.—See Thai Beverage Public Company Limited; *Int'l*, pg. 7591
NAMTRA BUSINESS SOLUTIONS, INC.; *U.S. Private*, pg. 2832
NAMUGA CO.,LTD; *Int'l*, pg. 5136
NAMU INTELLIGENCE CO., LTD.—See Namutech Co., Ltd.; *Int'l*, pg. 5137
NAMU LIFE PLUS COMPANY LIMITED—See Do Day Dream PCL; *Int'l*, pg. 2152
NAMUNUKULA PLANTATIONS LTD—See Richard Pieris & Co. Ltd.; *Int'l*, pg. 6330
NAMURA ENGINEERING CO., LTD.—See Namura Shipbuilding Co., Ltd.; *Int'l*, pg. 5136
NAMURA INFORMATION SYSTEMS CO., LTD.—See Namura Shipbuilding Co., Ltd.; *Int'l*, pg. 5136
NAMURA MARINE CO., LTD.—See Namura Shipbuilding Co., Ltd.; *Int'l*, pg. 5136
NAMURA MINERAL RESOURCES (PTY.) LTD.—See Xemplar Energy Corp.; *Int'l*, pg. 8521
NAMURA SHIPBUILDING CO., LTD.; *Int'l*, pg. 5136
NAMUTECH CO., LTD.; *Int'l*, pg. 5136
NAM VIET CORPORATION; *Int'l*, pg. 5134
NAM VIET JOINT STOCK COMPANY; *Int'l*, pg. 5134
NAMYANG DAIRY PRODUCTS CO., LTD. - CHEONAN FACTORY—See Namyang Dairy Products Co., Ltd.; *Int'l*, pg. 5137
NAMYANG DAIRY PRODUCTS CO., LTD. - CHEONAN NEW FACTORY—See Namyang Dairy Products Co., Ltd.; *Int'l*, pg. 5137
NAMYANG DAIRY PRODUCTS CO., LTD. - CHEONAN PLANT 1—See Namyang Dairy Products Co., Ltd.; *Int'l*, pg. 5137
NAMYANG DAIRY PRODUCTS CO., LTD. - CHEONAN PLANT 2—See Namyang Dairy Products Co., Ltd.; *Int'l*, pg. 5137
NAMYANG DAIRY PRODUCTS CO., LTD. - GONGJU FACTORY—See Namyang Dairy Products Co., Ltd.; *Int'l*, pg. 5137
NAMYANG DAIRY PRODUCTS CO., LTD. - GYEONGJU FACTORY—See Namyang Dairy Products Co., Ltd.; *Int'l*, pg. 5137
NAMYANG DAIRY PRODUCTS CO., LTD. - GYEONGJU PLANT—See Namyang Dairy Products Co., Ltd.; *Int'l*, pg. 5137
NAMYANG DAIRY PRODUCTS CO., LTD. - HONAM FACTORY—See Namyang Dairy Products Co., Ltd.; *Int'l*, pg. 5137
NAMYANG DAIRY PRODUCTS CO., LTD. - NAJU PLANT—See Namyang Dairy Products Co., Ltd.; *Int'l*, pg. 5137
NAMYANG DAIRY PRODUCTS CO., LTD. - SEJONG PLANT—See Namyang Dairy Products Co., Ltd.; *Int'l*, pg. 5137
NAMYANG DAIRY PRODUCTS CO., LTD.; *Int'l*, pg. 5137

NAMYANG DAIRY PRODUCTS CO., LTD.   CORPORATE AFFILIATIONS

NAM YANG METALS CO., LTD.—See Hitachi, Ltd.; *Int'l*, pg. 3423
NAMYONG TERMINAL PUBLIC COMPANY LIMITED; *Int'l*, pg. 5137
NAMYUE HOLDINGS LIMITED—See GDH Limited; *Int'l*, pg. 2896
NAMYUNG LIGHTING CO., LTD.—See Taekyung Industrial Co., Ltd.; *Int'l*, pg. 7405
NANA DEVELOPMENT CORPORATION—See Nana Regional Corporation, Inc.; *U.S. Private*, pg. 2832
NANAIMO CHRYSLER LTD.; *Int'l*, pg. 5138
NANAIMO DAILY NEWS—See Glacier Media Inc.; *Int'l*, pg. 2987
NANALYSIS CORP.—See Nanalysis Scientific Corp.; *Int'l*, pg. 5138
NANALYSIS GMBH—See Nanalysis Scientific Corp.; *Int'l*, pg. 5138
NANALYSIS SCIENTIFIC CORP.; *Int'l*, pg. 5138
NANAMICA INC.—See Goldwin, Inc.; *Int'l*, pg. 3035
NANAO AGENCY CORPORATION—See EIZO Corporation; *Int'l*, pg. 2337
NANA REGIONAL CORPORATION, INC.; *U.S. Private*, pg. 2832
NANASAI CO., LTD.—See Wacoal Holdings Corp.; *Int'l*, pg. 8326
NANAVAC INVESTMENTS (PVT) LTD—See Choppies Enterprises Ltd.; *Int'l*, pg. 1582
NANAVATI VENTURES LIMITED; *Int'l*, pg. 5138
NANBU PLASTICS CO., LTD.—See Nisshinbo Holdings Inc.; *Int'l*, pg. 5374
NANCAL TECHNOLOGY CO., LTD.; *Int'l*, pg. 5138
NANCHANG CREATIVE SENSOR TECHNOLOGY CO., LTD.—See Creative Sensor Inc.; *Int'l*, pg. 1833
NANCHANG DALI FOODS CO., LTD.—See Dali Foods Group Co. Ltd.; *Int'l*, pg. 1951
NANCHANG KAMA CO., LTD.—See China Hi-Tech Group Corporation; *Int'l*, pg. 1508
NANCHANG KINDLY MEDICAL DEVICES CO., LTD.—See Shanghai Kindly Enterprise Development Group Co., Ltd; *Int'l*, pg. 6773
NANCHANG TONGXINGDA INTELLIGENT DISPLAY CO., LTD.—See Shenzhen TXD Technology Co Ltd; *Int'l*, pg. 6823
NANCHANG TONGXINGDA PRECISION OPTOELECTRONICS CO., LTD.—See Shenzhen TXD Technology Co Ltd; *Int'l*, pg. 6823
NANCHANG WEIFU LIDA AUTOMOBILE COMPONENTS CO., LTD.—See Wuxi Weifu High-technology Co., Ltd.; *Int'l*, pg. 8516
NANCHANG YALI CONCRETE PRODUCE LTD.—See Asia Cement Corporation; *Int'l*, pg. 611
NANCHONG THREE CIRCLE ELECTRONIC CO. LTD.—See Chaozhou Three-Circle Group Co., Ltd.; *Int'l*, pg. 1447
NANCHONG THREE-CIRCLE ELECTRONICS CO., LTD.—See Chaozhou Three-Circle Group Co., Ltd.; *Int'l*, pg. 1447
NANCY K. BROWN (NKB) AESTHETICS, INC.; *Int'l*, pg. 5138
NANCY LOPEZ GOLF—See Tournament Sports Marketing Inc.; *Int'l*, pg. 7848
NANCY MARSHALL COMMUNICATIONS; *U.S. Private*, pg. 2833
NANCY MYERS BEAUTY SHOP; *U.S. Private*, pg. 2833
NANCY PHANEUF COMMERCIAL REALTY & DEVELOPMENT; *U.S. Private*, pg. 2833
NANCY SERVICES AUTOMOBILES NASA; *Int'l*, pg. 5138
NANCY'S NOTIONS—See Tacony Corporation; *U.S. Private*, pg. 3921
NANDAN DENIM LIMITED—See Chiripal Industries Ltd.; *Int'l*, pg. 1573
NANDANI CREATION LTD.; *Int'l*, pg. 5138
NANDEE INTER-TRADE CO., LTD.—See Daikin Industries, Ltd.; *Int'l*, pg. 1936
NANDI INFRASTRUCTURE CORRIDOR ENTERPRISES LTD.—See BF Utilities Ltd.; *Int'l*, pg. 1006
NANDORF INC.; *U.S. Private*, pg. 2833
NANDO'S GROUP HOLDINGS, LTD.; *Int'l*, pg. 5138
NANETTE LEPORE; *U.S. Private*, pg. 2833
NANEXA AB; *Int'l*, pg. 5138
NANFANG BLACK SESAME GROUP CO., LTD.; *Int'l*, pg. 5138
NANFANG COMMUNICATION HOLDINGS LIMITED; *Int'l*, pg. 5139
NANFANG WATER CO., LTD.—See SIIC Environment Holdings Ltd.; *Int'l*, pg. 6913
NANFANG ZHONGJIN ENVIRONMENT CO., LTD.; *Int'l*, pg. 5139
NANFENG VENTILATOR CO., LTD.-A; *Int'l*, pg. 5139
NANG KUANG PHARMACEUTICAL CO., LTD.; *Int'l*, pg. 5139
NANGOKU RS LIQUOR LTD.—See Mitsubishi Corporation; *Int'l*, pg. 4942
NANGONG ZHONGYU GAS CO., LTD.—See Zhongyu Energy Holdings Limited; *Int'l*, pg. 8676
NANGTONG NS ADVANTECH CO., LTD.—See Nippon Seiki Co., Ltd.; *Int'l*, pg. 5330
NAN HAI CORPORATION LIMITED; *Int'l*, pg. 5137

NANHAI HAIXIN PLUSH CO., LTD.—See Shanghai Haixin Group Co., Ltd.; *Int'l*, pg. 6769
NANHAI JO YEH ELECTRONICS CO., LTD.—See BizLink Holding Inc.; *Int'l*, pg. 1053
NANHAI NEUSOFT INSTITUTE OF INFORMATION—See Neusoft Corporation; *Int'l*, pg. 5220
NANHUA BIO-MEDICINE CO., LTD.; *Int'l*, pg. 5139
NANHUA FINANCIAL UK CO. LIMITED—See Nanhua Futures Co., Ltd.; *Int'l*, pg. 5139
NANHUA FUTURES CO., LTD.; *Int'l*, pg. 5139
NANHUA INSTRUMENTS CO., LTD.; *Int'l*, pg. 5139
NAN HWA CEMENT CORP.—See Asia Cement Corporation; *Int'l*, pg. 611
NANIGANS, INC.; *U.S. Private*, pg. 2833
NAN, INC.; *U.S. Private*, pg. 2832
NANITAS INC.; *U.S. Private*, pg. 2833
NANIWA EXTERIOR, INC.—See LIXIL Group Corporation; *Int'l*, pg. 4535
NANIWA RUBBER CO., LTD.—See Nitta Corporation; *Int'l*, pg. 5382
NANJI E-COMMERCE CO., LTD.; *Int'l*, pg. 5139
NANJING ACCELAS PHARMACEUTICAL CO., LTD.—See Jiangsu Aidea Pharmaceutical Co., Ltd.; *Int'l*, pg. 3943
NANJING AIMECHATEC LTD.—See Aimechatec Ltd.; *Int'l*, pg. 233
NANJING AOLIAN AE & EA CO., LTD.; *Int'l*, pg. 5139
NANJING AUCHAN HYPERMARKETS CO., LTD.—See Alibaba Group Holding Limited; *Int'l*, pg. 326
NANJING AUTO ITALIA CAR TRADING CO., LTD.—See Auto Italia Holdings Limited; *Int'l*, pg. 725
NANJING AUTOMOBILE GROUP CORPORATION—See Shanghai Automotive Industry Corporation; *Int'l*, pg. 6762
NANJING BAOCHUN CHEMICAL INDUSTRY CO., LTD.—See Hongbaoli Group Co., Ltd; *Int'l*, pg. 3469
NANJING BAOSE CO., LTD.; *Int'l*, pg. 5139
NANJING BESTWAY INTELLIGENT CONTROL TECHNOLOGY CO., LTD.; *Int'l*, pg. 5139
NANJING BOAN BIOTECHNOLOGY CO., LTD.—See Shandong Boan Biotechnology Co., Ltd.; *Int'l*, pg. 6752
NANJING BUSINESS AND TOURISM CORP., LTD.; *Int'l*, pg. 5139
NANJING CANATAL DATA-CENTRE ENVIRONMENTAL TECH CO., LTD.; *Int'l*, pg. 5139
NANJING CBAK NEW ENERGY TECHNOLOGY CO., LTD.—See CBAK Energy Technology, Inc.; *Int'l*, pg. 1364
NANJING CENTRAL EMPORIUM (GROUP) STOCKS CO., LTD.; *Int'l*, pg. 5139
NANJING CHEMICAL FIBRE CO., LTD.; *Int'l*, pg. 5140
NANJING CHENGUANG MORITA ENVIRONMENT PROTECTION SCIENCE & TECHNOLOGY CO., LTD.—See Morita Holdings Corporation; *Int'l*, pg. 5048
NANJING CHERVON AUTO PRECISION TECHNOLOGY CO., LTD.; *Int'l*, pg. 5140
NANJING CHIA-CHAN PRECIOUS ELECTRONICS CO., LTD.—See Chia Chang Co., Ltd.; *Int'l*, pg. 1475
NANJING CHIXIA DEVELOPMENT CO., LTD.; *Int'l*, pg. 5140
NANJING CITY INTELLIGENT TRANSPORTATION CO., LTD.—See Nanjing Sample Technology Company Limited; *Int'l*, pg. 5141
NANJING CML GRANDLINK LOGISTICS CO., LTD.—See China Master Logistics Co., Ltd.; *Int'l*, pg. 1517
NANJING CO., LTD.—See SK Engineering & Construction Co., Ltd.; *Int'l*, pg. 6970
NANJING COMFORTDELGRO DAJIAN TAXI CO.—See ComforDelGro Corporation Limited; *Int'l*, pg. 1713
NANJING COMFORTDELGRO XIXIA DRIVER TRAINING CO., LTD.—See ComfortDelGro Corporation Limited; *Int'l*, pg. 1713
NANJING CORPORATION OF SHINHEUNG GLOBAL CO., LTD.—See Shinsung Delta Tech Co., Ltd.; *Int'l*, pg. 6849
NANJING CORPORATION OF SHINSUNG DELTA TECH CO., LTD.—See Shinsung Delta Tech Co., Ltd.; *Int'l*, pg. 6849
NANJING CRYOMAX AUTO PARTS CO., LTD.—See Cryomax Cooling System Corp.; *Int'l*, pg. 1860
NANJING DAJI REAL ESTATE DEVELOPMENT CO., LTD.—See Yanlord Land Group Limited; *Int'l*, pg. 8562
NANJING DALUGE HIGH-TECH CO., LTD.—See Beijing Zhong Ke San Huan High-tech Co., Ltd.; *Int'l*, pg. 961
NANJING DEVELP ADVANCED MANUFACTURING CO., LTD.; *Int'l*, pg. 5140
NANJING DIGITAL CHINA LIMITED—See Digital China Holdings Limited; *Int'l*, pg. 2121
NANJING DONGMU POWDER METALLURGY CO., LTD.—See NBTM New Materials Group Co., Ltd.; *Int'l*, pg. 5179
NANJING DOULE REFRIGERATION EQUIPMENT CO., LTD.—See WELLE Environmental Group Co., Ltd.; *Int'l*, pg. 8374
NANJING DRAGON CROWN LIQUID CHEMICAL TERMINAL COMPANY LIMITED—See Dragon Crown Group Holdings Limited; *Int'l*, pg. 2199
NANJING DRAGON TREASURE BOAT DEVELOPMENT CO., LTD.—See ASTI Holdings Limited; *Int'l*, pg. 655

NANJING EASTERN LASER CO., LTD.—See Coherent Corp.; *U.S. Public*, pg. 527
NANJING EASTERN TECHNOLOGIES COMPANY, LTD.—See Coherent Corp.; *U.S. Public*, pg. 527
NANJING ENGGE LANBO MICRO-ELECTRONICS CO., LTD.—See Suntech Power Holdings Co., Ltd.; *Int'l*, pg. 7325
NANJING ESTUN AUTOMATION CO., LTD.; *Int'l*, pg. 5140
NANJING FENGDONG HEAT TREATMENT ENGINEERING CO., LTD.—See JC Finance & Tax Interconnect Holding Ltd.; *Int'l*, pg. 3919
NANJING GAOKE COMPANY LIMITED; *Int'l*, pg. 5140
NANJING GRANDLAND BOSEN INDUSTRIAL CO., LTD.—See Shenzhen Grandland Group Co., Ltd.; *Int'l*, pg. 6811
NANJING GUO ZHONG MAGNETIC MATERIAL CO., LTD.—See CEC International Holdings Limited; *Int'l*, pg. 1372
NANJING HANRUI COBALT CO LTD; *Int'l*, pg. 5140
NANJING HBL INTERNATIONAL CO., LTD.—See Hongbaoli Group Co., Ltd; *Int'l*, pg. 3469
NANJING HEALVITY BIOTECH CO., LTD.—See Zhejiang Orient Gene Biotech Co., Ltd.; *Int'l*, pg. 8661
NAN JING H&H GARMENT CO., LTD.—See Younghyun Trading co.,Ltd; *Int'l*, pg. 8603
NANJING HICIN PHARMACEUTICAL CO.,LTD; *Int'l*, pg. 5140
NANJING HITACHI TECHNO. CO., LTD.—See Hitachi, Ltd.; *Int'l*, pg. 3423
NANJING HONGGUANG AUTOLIV LTD.—See Autoliv, Inc.; *Int'l*, pg. 730
NANJING HUAMAI TECHNOLOGY CO., LTD.; *Int'l*, pg. 5140
NANJING HUASHI ELECTRONIC SCIENTIFIC COMPANY LIMITED—See China Automation Group Limited; *Int'l*, pg. 1483
NANJING INFORM STORAGE EQUIPMENT (GROUO) CO., LTD.; *Int'l*, pg. 5140
NANJING IRON & STEEL CO., LTD.—See CITIC Group Corporation; *Int'l*, pg. 1621
NANJING JINGQIAO ZHONGYU GAS CO., LTD.—See Zhongyu Energy Holdings Limited; *Int'l*, pg. 8676
NANJING JING XING PAPER THE LIMITED COMPANY—See Zhejiang Jingxing Paper Joint Stock Co., Ltd.; *Int'l*, pg. 8658
NANJING JIN MEI GALLIUM CO., LTD—See AXT, Inc.; *U.S. Public*, pg. 256
NANJING JULONG SCIENCE & TECHNOLOGY CO., LTD.; *Int'l*, pg. 5140
NANJING KANGNI MECHANICAL & ELECTRICAL CO., LTD.; *Int'l*, pg. 5140
NANJING KING-FRIEND BIOCHEMICAL PHARMACEUTICAL CO., LTD.; *Int'l*, pg. 5140
THE NANJING LINCOLN ELECTRIC CO., LTD.—See Lincoln Electric Holdings, Inc.; *U.S. Public*, pg. 1318
NANJING MINDRAY BIO-MEDICAL ELECTRONICS CO., LTD.—See Mindray Medical International Ltd.; *Int'l*, pg. 4901
NANJING MPI PUBLIC TRANSPORT ADVERTISING CO., LTD.—See JCDecaux S.A.; *Int'l*, pg. 3921
NANJING NANGANG IRON & STEEL UNITED CO., LTD.; *Int'l*, pg. 5140
NANJING NBTM POWDER METALLURGY CO., LTD.—See NBTM New Materials Group Co., Ltd.; *Int'l*, pg. 5179
NANJING NIKON JIANGNAN OPTICAL INSTRUMENT CO., LTD.—See Nikon Corporation; *Int'l*, pg. 5292
NANJING NOVOGENE BIO TECHNOLOGY CO.,—See Novogene Co., Ltd.; *Int'l*, pg. 5465
NANJING OLQ HOME FURNISHING CO., LTD.; *Int'l*, pg. 5140
NANJING PACIFIC MILLENNIUM PACKAGING & PAPER INDUSTRIES CO., LTD.—See Pacific Millennium Packaging Group Corporation; *Int'l*, pg. 5691
NANJING PANDA ELECTRONICS CO., LTD.; *Int'l*, pg. 5141
NANJING PAN-PACIFIC ANIMAL BY- PRODUCTS CO., LTD.—See Pan-Pacific Co., Ltd.; *Int'l*, pg. 5716
NANJING PHARMACEUTICAL COMPANY LIMITED; *Int'l*, pg. 5141
NANJING PORT CO., LTD.; *Int'l*, pg. 5141
NANJING POSTEL WONG ZHI TELECOMMUNICATIONS CO., LTD.—See Japan Industrial Partners, Inc.; *Int'l*, pg. 3890
NANJING PUBLIC UTILITIES DEVELOPMENT CO., LTD.; *Int'l*, pg. 5141
NANJING PUTIAN TELECOMMUNICATIONS CO., LTD.; *Int'l*, pg. 5141
NANJING PUTIAN TELEGE INTELLIGENT BUILDING LTD.—See Chengdu SIWI Science and Technology Company Limited; *Int'l*, pg. 1469
NANJING QUANXIN CABLE TECHNOLOGY CO., LTD.; *Int'l*, pg. 5141
NANJING RAILWAY NEW TECHNOLOGY CO., LTD.; *Int'l*, pg. 5141
NANJING REAL PHARMACEUTICAL CO LTD.—See Nanjing Business and Tourism Corp., Ltd.; *Int'l*, pg. 5139
NANJING RED SUN CO., LTD.; *Int'l*, pg. 5141

COMPANY NAME INDEX

NANJING RENEWABLE ENERGY CO., LTD.—See China Sunergy Co., Ltd.; *Int'l*, pg. 1556
NANJING RESEARCH INSTITUTE OF SURVEYING MAPPING & GEOTECHNICAL INVESTIGATION CO., LTD.; *Int'l*, pg. 5141
NANJING SAES HUADONG GETTERS CO., LTD.—See SAES Getters S.p.A.; *Int'l*, pg. 6467
NANJING SAMPLE TECHNOLOGY COMPANY LIMITED; *Int'l*, pg. 5141
NANJING SANAI INDUSTRIAL AUTOMATION CO., LTD.—See Saimo Technology Co., Ltd.; *Int'l*, pg. 6484
NANJING SANCHAO ADVANCED MATERIALS CO., LTD.; *Int'l*, pg. 5141
NANJING SCIYON WISDOM TECHNOLOGY GROUP CO., LTD.; *Int'l*, pg. 5141
NANJING SECURITIES CO., LTD.; *Int'l*, pg. 5141
NANJING SHAGANG MATERIALS TRADE CO., LTD.—See Jiangsu Shagang Group Ltd.; *Int'l*, pg. 3954
NANJING SHENGHANG SHIPPING CO., LTD.; *Int'l*, pg. 5141
NANJING SHENGNUE HEAT PIPE CO., LTD.—See Sunpower Group Ltd.; *Int'l*, pg. 7320
NANJING SILVERSTONE COMPUTER SYSTEM CO., LTD.—See Beijing Shiji Information Technology Co., Ltd.; *Int'l*, pg. 956
NANJING SIME DARBY MOTORS SALES & SERVICES CO. LTD.—See Sime Darby Berhad; *Int'l*, pg. 6928
NANJING SINOLIFE UNITED COMPANY LIMITED; *Int'l*, pg. 5141
NANJING SUNLORD ELECTRONICS CORPORATION LTD.; *Int'l*, pg. 5141
NANJING TALIANG NUMERIC CONTROL TECH. CO., LTD.—See Ta Liang Technology Co., Ltd.; *Int'l*, pg. 7400
NANJING TANKER CORPORATION; *Int'l*, pg. 5142
NANJING TINGJIN FOOD CO., LTD.—See Tingyi (Cayman Islands) Holding Corp.; *Int'l*, pg. 7754
NANJING TONGREN HOSPITAL CO., LTD.—See China Medical & HealthCare Group Limited; *Int'l*, pg. 1518
NANJING TOTO CO., LTD.—See Toto Ltd.; *Int'l*, pg. 7846
NANJING TOUA HARDWARE & TOOLS CO., LTD.; *Int'l*, pg. 5142
NANJING TP THERMAL ENGINEERING CO., LTD.—See TPH Ltd.; *Int'l*, pg. 7884
NANJING USA, INC.—See Roo Hsing Co., Ltd.; *Int'l*, pg. 6397
NANJING VISHEE MEDICAL TECHNOLOGY CO., LTD.; *Int'l*, pg. 5142
NANJING WALSIN METAL CO., LTD.—See Walsin Lihwa Corporation; *Int'l*, pg. 8335
NANJING WANT WANT FOODS LTD—See Want Want China Holdings Ltd.; *Int'l*, pg. 8342
NANJING WEIFU JINNING CO., LTD.—See Wuxi Weifu High-technology Co., Ltd.; *Int'l*, pg. 8516
NANJING WELL PHARMACEUTICAL GROUP CO., LTD.; *Int'l*, pg. 5142
NANJING WONDUX ENVIRONMENTAL PROTECTION TECHNOLOGY CORP., LTD.; *Int'l*, pg. 5142
NANJING XINJIEKOU DEPARTMENT STORE CO., LTD.—See Sanpower Group Co., Ltd.; *Int'l*, pg. 6554
NANJING XINLIAN ELECTRONICS CO., LTD.; *Int'l*, pg. 5142
NANJING XINSU THERMOELECTRICITY CO., LTD.—See CGN Power Co., Ltd.; *Int'l*, pg. 1435
NANJING YANGZI EASTMAN CHEMICAL LTD.—See Eastman Chemical Company; *U.S. Public*, pg. 705
NANJING YANGZI PETROCHEMICAL DESIGN & ENGINEERING CO., LTD.—See China International Marine Containers (Group) Co., Ltd.; *Int'l*, pg. 1512
NANJING YUEBOO POWER SYSTEM CO., LTD.; *Int'l*, pg. 5142
NANJING YURUN FOOD CO., LTD.—See China Yurun Food Group Limited; *Int'l*, pg. 1566
NANJING ZHONGCHAO NEW MATERIALS CORPORATION—See Jiangsu Zhongchao Holding Co., Ltd.; *Int'l*, pg. 3957
NANJINH NTN CORP.—See NTN Corporation; *Int'l*, pg. 5483
NAN JUEN INTERNATIONAL CO., LTD.; *Int'l*, pg. 5137
NANKAI CHEMICAL CO., LTD.; *Int'l*, pg. 5142
NANKAIDENSETSU CO., LTD.—See NITTO KOGYO CORPORATION; *Int'l*, pg. 5387
NANKAI ELECTRIC RAILWAY CO., LTD.; *Int'l*, pg. 5142
NANKAI PLYWOOD CO., LTD.; *Int'l*, pg. 5142
NANKAI SERVICE CORPORATION—See Nichia Steel Works Co., Ltd.; *Int'l*, pg. 5267
NANKAI TATSUMURA CONSTRUCTION CO., LTD.—See Nankai Electric Railway Co., Ltd.; *Int'l*, pg. 5142
NANKAI TSUUN CO., LTD.—See Senko Group Holdings Co., Ltd.; *Int'l*, pg. 6710
NANKANG RUBBER TIRE CORPORATION LTD.; *Int'l*, pg. 5142
NANKO PAPER CENTER CO., LTD.—See Japan Pulp and Paper Company Limited; *Int'l*, pg. 3904
NANKO UNYU CO., LTD.—See Nippon Paper Industries Co., Ltd.; *Int'l*, pg. 5327
NANKYO JAPAN CO., LTD.—See Namchow Holdings Co., Ltd.; *Int'l*, pg. 5135

NANKYU BUTSURYU SUPPORT CO., LTD.—See Mercedes-Benz Group AG; *Int'l*, pg. 4828
NANKYU GEO TECHNICS CORPORATION—See OYO Corporation; *Int'l*, pg. 5678
NANLIEN INTERNATIONAL CORP.—See Uni-President Enterprises Corporation; *Int'l*, pg. 8028
NAN LIU ENTERPRISES CO., LTD.; *Int'l*, pg. 5137
NAN NAN RESOURCES ENTERPRISE LIMITED; *Int'l*, pg. 5137
NANNI INDUSTRIES; *Int'l*, pg. 5142
NANNING BALING TECHNOLOGY CO., LTD.; *Int'l*, pg. 5142
NANNING BRILLIANT PARKSON COMMERCIAL CO LTD—See Parkson Holdings Berhad; *Int'l*, pg. 5744
NANNING BULK COMMODITIES EXCHANGE CORPORATION LIMITED—See Forlink Software Corporation, Inc.; *Int'l*, pg. 2733
NANNING COMFORT TRANSPORTATION CO., LTD.—See ComfortDelGro Corporation Limited; *Int'l*, pg. 1713
NANNING DEPARTMENT STORE CO., LTD.; *Int'l*, pg. 5142
NANNING HARIMA CHEMICALS CO., LTD.—See Harima Chemicals Group, Inc.; *Int'l*, pg. 3276
NANNING QIAOHONG NEW MATERIALS CO., LTD.—See Guangxi Rural Investment Sugar Industry Group Co., Ltd; *Int'l*, pg. 3163
NANNING XIANGDA CAMEL FEED CO., LTD.—See Tangrenshen Group Co., Ltd.; *Int'l*, pg. 7458
NANNI TRADING SRL—See Nanni Industries; *Int'l*, pg. 5142
NANNO CONSTRUCTION CO., LTD.—See Fantasista Co., Ltd.; *Int'l*, pg. 2614
THE NANNY TAX COMPANY; *U.S. Private*, pg. 4081
NANOAL LLC—See Unity Aluminum, Inc.; *U.S. Private*, pg. 4302
NANO AUTOMOTIVE SL—See Nano Co., Ltd.; *Int'l*, pg. 5142
NANOAVIONICS US LLC—See Kongsberg Gruppen ASA; *Int'l*, pg. 4256
NANOBASE, INC.—See Openbase, Inc.; *Int'l*, pg. 5599
NANOBIOSYS INC.; *Int'l*, pg. 5143
NANOBIOTIX CORP.—See Nanobiotix; *Int'l*, pg. 5143
NANOBIOTIX; *Int'l*, pg. 5143
NANOBIT TECH. CO., LTD.—See Ways Technical Corp.; *Int'l*, pg. 8360
NANOBRICK CO., LTD.; *Int'l*, pg. 5143
NANOCHEM SOLUTIONS INC.—See Flexible Solutions International, Inc.; *Int'l*, pg. 2704
NANOCHEMTECH INC. - ANSUNG 2 FACTORY—See NanoChemTech Inc.; *Int'l*, pg. 5143
NANOCHEMTECH INC.; *Int'l*, pg. 5143
NANOCMS CO., LTD.; *Int'l*, pg. 5143
NANOCO GROUP PLC; *Int'l*, pg. 5143
NANO CO., LTD.; *Int'l*, pg. 5142
NANOCOMP TECHNOLOGIES, INC.—See Huntsman Corporation; *U.S. Public*, pg. 1075
NANO CONTROL CO., LTD.—See THK CO., LTD.; *Int'l*, pg. 7712
NANOCYL SA—See The Aditya Birla Group; *Int'l*, pg. 7610
NANO DIMENSION LTD; *Int'l*, pg. 5142
NANODROP TECHNOLOGIES LLC—See Thermo Fisher Scientific Inc.; *U.S. Public*, pg. 2149
NANOENTEK BIO-TECHNOLOGY(BEIJING) LTD.—See NanoEnTek Inc.; *Int'l*, pg. 5143
NANOENTEK INC.; *Int'l*, pg. 5143
NANOENTEK USA INC.—See NanoEnTek Inc.; *Int'l*, pg. 5143
NANOFILM TECHNOLOGIES INTERNATIONAL LIMITED; *Int'l*, pg. 5143
NANOFILM TECHNOLOGIES JAPAN LIMITED—See NanoFilm Technologies International Limited; *Int'l*, pg. 5143
NANOFIL TECHNOLOGIES PVT. LTD.—See Flexituff Ventures International Limited; *Int'l*, pg. 2705
NANOFLEX POWER CORPORATION; *U.S. Public*, pg. 1490
NANOFORM FINLAND OYJ; *Int'l*, pg. 5143
NANOGAN LIMITED—See IQE plc; *Int'l*, pg. 3803
NANOGATE ELECTRONIC SYSTEMS GMBH—See Nanogate SE; *Int'l*, pg. 5143
NANOGATE HET ENGINEERING GMBH—See Nanogate SE; *Int'l*, pg. 5143
NANOGATE HET ENGINEERING INDIA PVT LTD.—See Nanogate SE; *Int'l*, pg. 5143
NANOGATE KIERSPE GMBH—See Nanogate SE; *Int'l*, pg. 5144
NANOGATE MANAGEMENT SERVICES GMBH—See Nanogate SE; *Int'l*, pg. 5144
NANOGATE MEDICAL SYSTEMS GMBH—See Nanogate SE; *Int'l*, pg. 5144
NANOGATE NETHERLANDS BV—See Nanogate SE; *Int'l*, pg. 5144
NANOGATE NEUNKIRCHEN GMBH—See Nanogate SE; *Int'l*, pg. 5144
NANOGATE NRW GMBH—See Nanogate SE; *Int'l*, pg. 5144

NANOGATE PD SYSTEMS GMBH—See Nanogate SE; *Int'l*, pg. 5144
NANOGATE SCHWABISCH GMUND GMBH—See Nanogate SE; *Int'l*, pg. 5144
NANOGATE SE; *Int'l*, pg. 5143
NANOGATE SLOVAKIA S.R.O.—See Nanogate SE; *Int'l*, pg. 5144
NANOGATE TEXTILE & CARE SYSTEMS GMBH—See Nanogate SE; *Int'l*, pg. 5144
NANOGROUP SA; *Int'l*, pg. 5144
NANOHELIX CO., LTD.; *Int'l*, pg. 5144
NANO LABS LTD.; *Int'l*, pg. 5143
NANOLAB TECHNOLOGIES, INC.; *U.S. Private*, pg. 2833
NANOLEK LLC—See Otisifarm ao; *Int'l*, pg. 5657
NANOLINK APS—See PNC Process Systems Co Ltd; *Int'l*, pg. 5900
NANOLLOSE LIMITED; *Int'l*, pg. 5144
NANOLOGICA AB; *Int'l*, pg. 5144
NANOLOGIX, INC.; *U.S. Public*, pg. 1490
NANO MAGIC INC.; *U.S. Public*, pg. 1490
NANOMECHANICS INC.—See KLA Corporation; *U.S. Public*, pg. 1268
NANO MEDIA INC.; *Int'l*, pg. 5143
NANOMETRICS CHINA COMPANY LTD.—See Onto Innovation Inc.; *U.S. Public*, pg. 1605
NANOMETRICS INC. - OIL & GAS DIVISION—See Nanometrics Inc.; *Int'l*, pg. 5144
NANOMETRICS INC.; *Int'l*, pg. 5144
NANOMETRICS U.K. LTD.—See Onto Innovation Inc.; *U.S. Public*, pg. 1605
NANOMI B.V.—See Lupin Limited; *Int'l*, pg. 4586
NANOMIX CORPORATION; *U.S. Public*, pg. 1490
NANOMIX, INC.—See NANOMIX CORPORATION; *U.S. Public*, pg. 1490
NANO MOBILE HEALTHCARE, INC.; *U.S. Public*, pg. 1490
NANOMOTION LTD.—See Johnson Electric Holdings Limited; *Int'l*, pg. 3990
NANOMR, INC.—See Genting Berhad; *Int'l*, pg. 2928
NANOOMTECH CO., LTD.; *Int'l*, pg. 5144
NANO ONE MATERIALS CORP.; *Int'l*, pg. 5143
NANOPAC (M) SDN BHD; *Int'l*, pg. 5144
NANO PARTICLE TECHNOLOGY CENTER—See Hosokawa Micron Corporation; *Int'l*, pg. 3486
NANOPHARM INC.—See AptarGroup, Inc.; *U.S. Public*, pg. 174
NANOPHASE TECHNOLOGIES CORPORATION; *U.S. Public*, pg. 1490
NANO PRECISION CORPORATION—See Coretronic Corporation; *Int'l*, pg. 1800
NANO PRECISION (SUZHOU) CO., LTD.—See Coretronic Corporation; *Int'l*, pg. 1800
NANOREPRO AG; *Int'l*, pg. 5144
NANOSAVE TECHNOLOGIES, INC.; *U.S. Private*, pg. 2833
NANOSCRIBE GMBH—See BICO Group AB; *Int'l*, pg. 1019
NANOSONICS EUROPE GMBH—See Nanosonics Limited; *Int'l*, pg. 5144
NANOSONICS EUROPE LIMITED—See Nanosonics Limited; *Int'l*, pg. 5144
NANOSONICS JAPAN KK—See Nanosonics Limited; *Int'l*, pg. 5144
NANOSONICS LIMITED; *Int'l*, pg. 5144
NANOSONICS UK LIMITED—See Nanosonics Limited; *Int'l*, pg. 5144
NANOSPACE AB—See GomSpace Group AB; *Int'l*, pg. 3037
NANOSPHERE HEALTH SCIENCES INC.; *Int'l*, pg. 5144
NANOSTRING TECHNOLOGIES, INC.—See Bruker Corporation; *U.S. Public*, pg. 407
NANOSYNTH GROUP PLC; *Int'l*, pg. 5144
NANOSYS, INC.—See SHOEI CHEMICAL INC.; *Int'l*, pg. 6857
NANOTECH ENTERTAINMENT, INC.; *U.S. Public*, pg. 1490
NANOTECH GAMING, INC.; *U.S. Public*, pg. 1490
NANOTECHNOLOGY CENTRE OF COMPOSITES LLC—See Aksa Akrilik Kimya Sanayii A.S.; *Int'l*, pg. 264
NANOTECHNOLOGY MANUFACTURING PTE. LTD.—See Fu Yu Corporation Limited; *Int'l*, pg. 2801
NANO TECHNO RESEARCH CORPORATION—See Sodick Co., Ltd.; *Int'l*, pg. 7048
NANOTECH SECURITY CORPORATION - OPTICAL THIN FILM DIVISION—See Meta Materials Inc.; *Int'l*, pg. 4844
NANOTECH SECURITY CORP.—See Meta Materials Inc.; *Int'l*, pg. 4844
NANOTECH SYSTEMS INC.; *Int'l*, pg. 5144
NANOTEC INTERNATIONAL GMBH—See Hanmi Semiconductor Co., Ltd.; *Int'l*, pg. 3256
NANOTEQ (PTY) LIMITED—See Reunert Limited; *Int'l*, pg. 6312
NANOTHERAPEUTICS, INC.; *U.S. Private*, pg. 2833
NANOTOX, INC.; *U.S. Private*, pg. 2833
NANOTRONIX CO., LTD.; *Int'l*, pg. 5144
NANOTRON TECHNOLOGIES GMBH—See XTI Aerospace, Inc.; *U.S. Public*, pg. 2393

NANOTRONIX CO., LTD.
CORPORATE AFFILIATIONS

NANO-TUNA ENGINEERING CO., LTD.—See Zhejiang Tuna Environmental Science & Technology Co., Ltd.; *Int'l*, pg. 8664

NANO UNIVERSE CO., LTD.—See TSI Holdings Co., Ltd.; *Int'l*, pg. 7950

NANOVATION MICROTECH, INC.; *Int'l*, pg. 5144

NANOVEU LTD.; *Int'l*, pg. 5144

NANOVEU PTE LTD—See Nanoveu Ltd.; *Int'l*, pg. 5145

NANOVIBRONIX, INC.; *U.S. Public*, pg. 1490

NANOVIRICIDES, INC.; *U.S. Public*, pg. 1490

NANOX CORPORATION—See Nippon Sheet Glass Co., Ltd.; *Int'l*, pg. 5331

NANO-X IMAGING LTD.; *Int'l*, pg. 5143

NANOX PHILIPPINES INC.—See Japan Display Inc.; *Int'l*, pg. 3887

NANOXPLORE INC.; *Int'l*, pg. 5145

NANO YUFEIDA CO., LTD.—See Nano Co., Ltd.; *Int'l*, pg. 5142

NAN PAO ELECTRONIC MATERIAL COMPANY—See Nan Pao Resins Chemical Co., Ltd.; *Int'l*, pg. 5138

NAN PAO RESINS CHEMICAL CO., LTD.; *Int'l*, pg. 5138

NAN PAO RESINS CHEMICAL PHILS., INC—See Nan Pao Resins Chemical Co., Ltd.; *Int'l*, pg. 5138

NAN PAO RESINS (CHINA) CO., LTD—See Nan Pao Resins Chemical Co., Ltd.; *Int'l*, pg. 5138

NAN PAO RESINS (DONG-GUAN) CO., LTD—See Nan Pao Resins Chemical Co., Ltd.; *Int'l*, pg. 5138

NAN PAO RESINS (FO SHAN) CO., LTD—See Nan Pao Resins Chemical Co., Ltd.; *Int'l*, pg. 5138

NAN PAO RESINS INDIA PVT LTD.—See Nan Pao Resins Chemical Co., Ltd.; *Int'l*, pg. 5138

NAN PAO RESINS (VIETNAM) CO., LTD—See Nan Pao Resins Chemical Co., Ltd.; *Int'l*, pg. 5138

NANPU FINE WINE & SPIRITS INTERNATIONAL COMPANY LIMITED—See Tenwow International Holdings Limited; *Int'l*, pg. 7562

NANSAI SHIKI CO., LTD.—See Tomoku Co., Ltd.; *Int'l*, pg. 7801

NANSEI CERAMIC CO., LTD.—See Niterra Co., Ltd.; *Int'l*, pg. 5380

NANSEN INC.—See CapMan PLC; *Int'l*, pg. 1315

NANSEN INSTRUMENTOS DE PRECISAO LTDA.—See Ningbo Sanxing Medical Electric Co., Ltd.; *Int'l*, pg. 5305

NAN SHAN GENERAL INSURANCE CO., LTD.—See Ruentex Group; *Int'l*, pg. 6425

NAN SHAN LIFE INSURANCE COMPANY, LTD.—See Ruentex Group; *Int'l*, pg. 6425

NANSHA SAKATA INK CORP.—See Sakata INX Corporation; *Int'l*, pg. 6487

NANSHIN TAKAMORI KAIHATSU CO., LTD.—See Yahagi Construction Co., Ltd.; *Int'l*, pg. 8546

NANSIN CO., LTD. - CHIBA NEW TOWN PLANT—See NANSIN CO., LTD.; *Int'l*, pg. 5145

NANSIN CO., LTD.; *Int'l*, pg. 5145

NANSO TRANSPORTATION CO., LTD.; *Int'l*, pg. 5145

NANTAHALA OUTDOOR CENTER; *U.S. Private*, pg. 2833

NANTAISE DES EAUX SERVICES SAS—See Veolia Environnement S.A.; *Int'l*, pg. 8155

NANT CAPITAL, LLC; *U.S. Private*, pg. 2833

NANTCELL, INC.—See NantWorks, LLC; *U.S. Private*, pg. 2833

NANT DE DRANCE SA—See Alpiq Holding AG; *Int'l*, pg. 373

NANTERO, INC.; *U.S. Private*, pg. 2833

NANTEX INDUSTRY CO., LTD.; *Int'l*, pg. 5145

NANTHEALTH, INC.—See NantWorks, LLC; *U.S. Private*, pg. 2834

NANTO BANK BUSINESS DIVISION—See The Nanto Bank, Ltd.; *Int'l*, pg. 7669

THE NANTO BANK, LTD.; *Int'l*, pg. 7669

NANTO BANK SECURITIES & INTERNATIONAL DIVISION (NARA)—See The Nanto Bank, Ltd.; *Int'l*, pg. 7669

NANTO BANK SECURITIES & INTERNATIONAL DIVISION (TOKYO)—See The Nanto Bank, Ltd.; *Int'l*, pg. 7669

NANTO BUSINESS SERVICE CO., LTD.—See The Nanto Bank, Ltd.; *Int'l*, pg. 7669

NANTO CARD SERVICES CO., LTD.—See The Nanto Bank, Ltd.; *Int'l*, pg. 7669

NANTO COMPUTER SERVICE CO., LTD.—See The Nanto Bank, Ltd.; *Int'l*, pg. 7669

NANTO CREDIT GUARANTEE CO., LTD.—See The Nanto Bank, Ltd.; *Int'l*, pg. 7669

NANTO DC CARD CO., LTD.—See The Nanto Bank, Ltd.; *Int'l*, pg. 7669

NANTO LEASE CO., LTD.—See The Nanto Bank, Ltd.; *Int'l*, pg. 7669

NANTONG ACETIC ACID CHEMICAL CO., LTD.; *Int'l*, pg. 5145

NANTONG ARAKAWA CHEMICAL INDUSTRIES, LTD.—See Arakawa Chemical Industries, Ltd.; *Int'l*, pg. 535

NANTONG BAOSTEEL STEEL & IRON CO., LTD.—See China Baowu Steel Group Corp., Ltd.; *Int'l*, pg. 1486

NANTONG BAOZEN AUTOMOBILE SALES AND SERVICES CO., LTD.—See China Yongda Automobiles Services Holdings Limited; *Int'l*, pg. 1564

NANTONG CAPCHEM HIGH PURE CHEMICAL CO., LTD.—See Shenzhen Capchem Technology Co., Ltd.; *Int'l*, pg. 6805

NANTONG CENTURY TEXHONG TEXTILE CO., LTD.—See Texhong Textile Group Limited; *Int'l*, pg. 7583

NANTONG CHAODA EQUIPMENT CO., LTD.; *Int'l*, pg. 5145

NANTONG CIMC SPECIAL TRANSPORTATION EQUIPMENT MANUFACTURE CO., LTD.—See China International Marine Containers (Group) Co., Ltd.; *Int'l*, pg. 1512

NANTONG CIMC TANK EQUIPMENT CO., LTD.—See China International Marine Containers (Group) Co., Ltd.; *Int'l*, pg. 1512

NANTONG COSCO KHI SHIP ENGINEERING CO., LTD.—See Kawasaki Heavy Industries, Ltd.; *Int'l*, pg. 4098

NANTONG DAS CHEMICAL CO., LTD.—See Corteva, Inc.; *U.S. Public*, pg. 580

NANTONG DIC COLOR CO., LTD.—See DIC Corporation; *Int'l*, pg. 2109

NANTONG DOCHARM AMPHENOL AUTOMOTIVE ELECTRONICS, LTD.—See Amphenol Corporation; *U.S. Public*, pg. 131

NANTONG GUOSHENG INTELLIGENCE TECHNOLOGY GROUP CO., LTD.; *Int'l*, pg. 5145

NANTONG GUOSHENG MACHINE COMPONENTS CO., LTD.—See Nantong Guosheng Intelligence Technology Group Co., Ltd.; *Int'l*, pg. 5145

NANTONG GUOSHENG PRECISION MACHINERY CO., LTD.—See Nantong Guosheng Intelligence Technology Group Co., Ltd.; *Int'l*, pg. 5145

NANTONG HAIXING ELECTRONICS CO., LTD.; *Int'l*, pg. 5145

NANTONG HAIXUM DRAKA ELEVATOR PRODUCTS CO., LTD.—See Prysmian S.p.A.; *Int'l*, pg. 6012

NANTONG HAIXUN DRAKA ELEVATOR PRODUCTS CO., LTD.—See Prysmian S.p.A.; *Int'l*, pg. 6012

NANTONG HEMEIJIA OBSTETRICS & GYNECOLOGY HOSPITAL CO. LTD.—See Harbin Electric Corporation; *Int'l*, pg. 3270

NANTONG HENGCHENG PAPER INDUSTRY CO., LTD.—See PSC Corporation Ltd.; *Int'l*, pg. 6015

NANTONG HILONG STEEL PIPE CO., LTD.—See Hilong Holding Limited; *Int'l*, pg. 3393

NANTONG JIANGHAI CAPACITOR CO., LTD.; *Int'l*, pg. 5145

NANTONG JIANGSHAN AGROCHEMICAL & CHEMICAL CO., LTD.; *Int'l*, pg. 5145

NANTONG JIANGTIAN CHEMICAL CO., LTD.; *Int'l*, pg. 5146

NANTONG KINEDYNE LIMITED—See Kinedyne Corporation; *U.S. Private*, pg. 2307

NANTONG NS ADVANTECH CO., LTD.—See Nippon Seiki Co., Ltd.; *Int'l*, pg. 5330

NANTONG RAINBOW HEAVY MACHINERIES CO., LTD.—See Jiangsu Rainbow Heavy Industries Co., Ltd.; *Int'l*, pg. 3952

NANTONG RAINBOW MARINE TECHNOLOGY CO., LTD.—See Jiangsu Rainbow Heavy Industries Co., Ltd.; *Int'l*, pg. 3952

NANTONG RAINBOW OFFSHORE & ENGINEERING EQUIPMENTS CO., LTD.—See Jiangsu Rainbow Heavy Industries Co., Ltd.; *Int'l*, pg. 3952

NANTONG RICH HOSPITAL CO., LTD.—See Rici Healthcare Holdings Limited; *Int'l*, pg. 6332

NANTONG ROAD AND BRIDGE ENGINEERING CO., LTD.—See Shanghai Dasheng Agriculture Finance Technology Co., Ltd.; *Int'l*, pg. 6764

NANTONG RUNHOPE ENVIRONMENT TECHNOLOGY CO., LTD.—See Jiangsu Rainbow Heavy Industries Co., Ltd.; *Int'l*, pg. 3952

NANTONG SHENGYI PRECISION MACHINERY CO., LTD.—See Chung-Hsin Electric & Machinery Manufacturing Corp.; *Int'l*, pg. 1597

NANTONG SHIBAKE RUBBER PRODUCT CO., LTD.—See GIIB HOLDINGS BERHAD; *Int'l*, pg. 2972

NANTONG SINAVICO INTERNATIONAL LOGISTICS CO., LTD.—See Mitsui-Soko Holdings Co., Ltd.; *Int'l*, pg. 4993

NANTONG SLD NEW ENERGY TECHNOLOGY CO., LTD.—See Nantong Guosheng Intelligence Technology Group Co., Ltd.; *Int'l*, pg. 5145

NANTONG S.LEADING INTELLIGENCE TECHNOLOGY CO., LTD.—See Nantong Guosheng Intelligence Technology Group Co., Ltd.; *Int'l*, pg. 5145

NANTONG SLW.MT EQUIPMENT TECHNOLOGY CO., LTD.—See Nantong Guosheng Intelligence Technology Group Co., Ltd.; *Int'l*, pg. 5145

NANTONG TANK CONTAINER CO., LTD.—See Square Technology Group Co. Ltd.; *Int'l*, pg. 7147

NANTONG TAT SENG PACKAGING CO., LTD.—See PSC Corporation Ltd.; *Int'l*, pg. 6015

NANTONG TEIJIN CO LTD—See Teijin Limited; *Int'l*, pg. 7522

NANTONG XINGCHEN SYNTHETIC MATERIAL CO., LTD.—See Bluestar Adisseo Company Limited; *Int'l*, pg. 1074

NANTONG XINGQIU GRAPHITE CO., LTD.; *Int'l*, pg. 5146

NANTONG YONGSHENG FIBER NEW MATERIALS CO., LTD—See Yongsheng Advanced Materials Company Limited; *Int'l*, pg. 8597

NANTONG YONGSHENG HUVIS FIBER ADVANCED MATERIALS CO., LTD.—See Yongsheng Advanced Materials Company Limited; *Int'l*, pg. 8597

NANTON NICKEL CORP.; *Int'l*, pg. 5145

NANTO STAFF SERVICE CO., LTD.—See The Nanto Bank, Ltd.; *Int'l*, pg. 7669

NAN TSAN CO., LTD.; *Int'l*, pg. 5138

NANTUCKET COTTAGE HOSPITAL FOUNDATION—See Partners HealthCare System, Inc.; *U.S. Private*, pg. 3102

NANTUCKET COTTAGE HOSPITAL—See Partners HealthCare System, Inc.; *U.S. Private*, pg. 3102

NANTUCKET DREAMLAND FOUNDATION; *U.S. Private*, pg. 2833

NANTUCKET ELECTRIC COMPANY—See National Grid plc; *Int'l*, pg. 5158

NANTUCKET HARVEST CO., INC.; *U.S. Private*, pg. 2833

NANTWORKS, LLC; *U.S. Private*, pg. 2833

NANTZE SPRINGS INC.; *U.S. Private*, pg. 2834

NANXING MACHINERY CO., LTD.; *Int'l*, pg. 5146

NANYA NEW MATERIAL TECHNOLOGY CO., LTD.; *Int'l*, pg. 5146

NANYANG BROTHERS TOBACCO CO LTD—See Shanghai Industrial Holdings Limited; *Int'l*, pg. 6771

NANYANG CIJAN AUTO SHOCK ABSORBER CO., LTD.—See China First Capital Group Limited; *Int'l*, pg. 1503

NANYANG COMMERCIAL BANK LIMITED—See China Cinda Asset Management Co., Ltd.; *Int'l*, pg. 1488

NANYANG DTECH CO., LTD.—See Guangdong Dtech Technology Co., Ltd.; *Int'l*, pg. 3154

NAN YANG DYEING & FINISHING CO., LTD.; *Int'l*, pg. 5138

NANYANG HOLDINGS LIMITED; *Int'l*, pg. 5146

NANYANG PRESS HOLDINGS BERHAD—See Media Chinese International Limited; *Int'l*, pg. 4770

NANYANG SIANG PAU SDN BHD—See Media Chinese International Limited; *Int'l*, pg. 4770

NANYANG TOPSEC TECHNOLOGIES GROUP INC.; *Int'l*, pg. 5146

NAN YA PLASTICS CORPORATION—See Formosa Plastics Corporation; *Int'l*, pg. 2736

NAN YA PRINTED CIRCUIT BOARD CORPORATION—See Formosa Plastics Corporation; *Int'l*, pg. 2736

NANYA TECHNOLOGY CORPORATION; *Int'l*, pg. 5146

NANYA TECHNOLOGY CORPORATION, U.S.A.—See Nanya Technology Corporation; *Int'l*, pg. 5146

NANYA TECHNOLOGY EUROPE GMBH—See Nanya Technology Corporation; *Int'l*, pg. 5146

NANYA TECHNOLOGY (HK) CO., LTD.—See Nanya Technology Corporation; *Int'l*, pg. 5146

NANYA TECHNOLOGY JAPAN—See Nanya Technology Corporation; *Int'l*, pg. 5146

NANYA TECHNOLOGY (SH) CO., LTD.—See Nanya Technology Corporation; *Int'l*, pg. 5146

NANYO CORPORATION; *Int'l*, pg. 5146

NANYO HEAVY VEHICLES CO., LTD.—See NANYO Corporation; *Int'l*, pg. 5146

NANYO INTERNATIONAL TRADING (SHANGHAI) CO., LTD.—See NANYO Corporation; *Int'l*, pg. 5146

NANYO RENTEC CO., LTD.—See NANYO Corporation; *Int'l*, pg. 5146

NAOC HOLDINGS; *U.S. Private*, pg. 2834

NAOE BUSSAN CO., LTD.—See Okabe Co., Ltd.; *Int'l*, pg. 5544

NAOETSU ELECTRONICS CO., LTD.—See Shin-Etsu Chemical Co. Ltd.; *Int'l*, pg. 6838

NAOETSU PRECISION CO., LTD.—See Shin-Etsu Chemical Co. Ltd.; *Int'l*, pg. 6838

NAOETSU SANGYO LIMITED—See Shin-Etsu Chemical Co. Ltd.; *Int'l*, pg. 6838

NAO, INC.; *U.S. Private*, pg. 2834

NA ORION INTERNATIONAL CONSULTING GROUP, INC.; *U.S. Private*, pg. 2829

NAOS EMERGING OPPORTUNITIES COMPANY LIMITED; *Int'l*, pg. 5146

NAOS EX-50 OPPORTUNITIES COMPANY LIMITED; *Int'l*, pg. 5146

NAOSHIMA BENESSE—See EQT AB; *Int'l*, pg. 2467

NAOSHIMA CULTURAL VILLAGE CO., LTD.—See EQT AB; *Int'l*, pg. 2467

NAOS SMALL CAP OPPORTUNITIES COMPANY LIMITED—See Contango Group Pty. Ltd.; *Int'l*, pg. 1779

NAO TEXAS—See NAO, Inc.; *U.S. Private*, pg. 2834

NAPA AUTOMOTIVE PARTS DISTRIBUTION CENTER—See Genuine Parts Company; *U.S. Public*, pg. 932

NAPA AUTO PARTS GENUINE PARTS COMPANY—See Genuine Parts Company; *U.S. Public*, pg. 932

NAPA AUTO PARTS—See Genuine Parts Company; *U.S. Public*, pg. 932

NAPA CHRYSLER JEEP DODGE RAM VOLVO KIA—See Hanlees Hilltop Toyota; *U.S. Private*, pg. 1854
NAPAC, INC.—See WJ Partners, LLC; *U.S. Private*, pg. 4551
NAP ACOUSTICS FAR EAST LIMITED—See Embelton Limited; *Int'l*, pg. 2375
NAPATECH A/S; *Int'l*, pg. 5146
NAPATECH INC.—See Napatech A/S; *Int'l*, pg. 5146
NAPA VALLEY PETROLEUM INC.; *U.S. Private*, pg. 2834
NAPA VALLEY PUBLISHING CO.—See Lee Enterprises, Incorporated; *U.S. Public*, pg. 1300
NAPA VALLEY WEALTH MANAGEMENT—See TA Associates, Inc.; *U.S. Private*, pg. 3919
NAPA VALLEY WINE TRAIN, INC.—See Noble House Hotels & Resorts, Ltd.; *U.S. Private*, pg. 2932
NAPA WINE CO. LLC—See Golden Triangle Ventures, Inc.; *U.S. Public*, pg. 951
NAPC DEFENSE, INC.; *U.S. Public*, pg. 1491
NAPC LTD.—See VINCI S.A.; *Int'l*, pg. 8220
NAPCO DR, S.A.—See Napco Security Technologies, Inc.; *U.S. Public*, pg. 1491
NAPCO, INC.; *U.S. Private*, pg. 2834
NAPCO, INC.—See Thermo Fisher Scientific Inc.; *U.S. Public*, pg. 2149
NAPCO INTERNATIONAL, INC.—See Jata LLC; *U.S. Private*, pg. 2191
NAP CO., LTD.—See Naigai Co., Ltd.; *Int'l*, pg. 5130
NAPCO SECURITY TECHNOLOGIES, INC.; *U.S. Public*, pg. 1491
NAPCO STEEL INC.; *U.S. Private*, pg. 2834
NAP DE LAS AMERICAS-MADRID, S.A.—See Verizon Communications Inc.; *U.S. Public*, pg. 2285
NAPER HOLDING A/S; *Int'l*, pg. 5147
NAPEROL INVESTMENTS LIMITED—See The Wadia Group; *Int'l*, pg. 7698
NAPERVILLE IMPORTS, INC.—See AutoNation, Inc.; *U.S. Public*, pg. 236
NAPERVILLE PARK DISTRICT; *U.S. Private*, pg. 2834
NAPESCO INDIA LLP—See Kuwait Projects Company (Holding) K.S.C.P.; *Int'l*, pg. 4346
NAP GLADU - MARIEVILLE—See Audax Group, Limited Partnership; *U.S. Private*, pg. 389
NAP GLADU—See Audax Group, Limited Partnership; *U.S. Private*, pg. 389
NAP GLADU - TORONTO—See Audax Group, Limited Partnership; *U.S. Private*, pg. 389
NAPHTHA ISRAEL PETROLEUM CORPORATION LTD.—See Equital Ltd.; *Int'l*, pg. 2487
NAPIER TURBOCHARGERS AUSTRALIA PTY LTD.—See Westinghouse Air Brake Technologies Corporation; *U.S. Public*, pg. 2358
NAPIER TURBOCHARGERS LIMITED—See Westinghouse Air Brake Technologies Corporation; *U.S. Public*, pg. 2358
NAPIER VENTURES INC.; *Int'l*, pg. 5147
NAPIERVILLE REFINERIES INC.—See Recochem Inc.; *Int'l*, pg. 6238
NAPLES BEACH HOTEL & GOLF CLUB; *U.S. Private*, pg. 2834
NAPLES CHILDREN & EDUCATION FOUNDATION; *U.S. Private*, pg. 2834
NAPLES DAILY NEWS, LLC—See Gannett Co., Inc.; *U.S. Public*, pg. 898
NAPLES DODGE INC.; *U.S. Private*, pg. 2834
NAPLES GRANDE RESORT AND CLUB—See Blackstone Inc.; *U.S. Public*, pg. 352
NAPLES HARLEY-DAVIDSON—See Scott Fischer Enterprises LLC; *U.S. Private*, pg. 3577
NAPLES HMA, INC.—See Community Health Systems, Inc.; *U.S. Public*, pg. 555
NAPLES ILLUSTRATED—See Hour Media Group, LLC; *U.S. Private*, pg. 1991
NAPLES LUMBER & SUPPLY INC.; *U.S. Private*, pg. 2834
NAPLES NISSAN; *U.S. Private*, pg. 2834
NAPLES REALTY SERVICES INC.; *U.S. Private*, pg. 2834
NAPLES REDEVELOPMENT INC.; *U.S. Private*, pg. 2834
NAPLES SHUTTER, INC.; *U.S. Private*, pg. 2834
NAPLES SOAP COMPANY, INC.—See The GNS Group, Inc.; *U.S. Public*, pg. 2075
THE NAPLES TRUST COMPANY—See The Sanibel Captiva Trust Company; *U.S. Private*, pg. 4114
NAPLES WOMENS CENTER—See HealthLynked Corp.; *U.S. Public*, pg. 1016
NAPLETON AUTO WERKS; *U.S. Private*, pg. 2834
NAPLETON BUICK GMC; *U.S. Private*, pg. 2834
NAPLETON NISSAN; *U.S. Private*, pg. 2834
NAPLETON RIVER OAKS CHRYSLER JEEP DODGE; *U.S. Private*, pg. 2834
NAPLETON SCHAUMBURG MOTORS, INC.—See North American Automotive Services, Inc.; *U.S. Private*, pg. 2940
NAPLOY CORP.; *Int'l*, pg. 5147
NAP OF THE AMERICAS/WEST INC.—See Verizon Communications Inc.; *U.S. Public*, pg. 2285
NAPOLEON FRANCO & CO.—See Ipsos S.A.; *Int'l*, pg. 3800
NAPOLI FOODS, INC.; *U.S. Private*, pg. 2835

NAPOLI MANAGEMENT GROUP—See Blue Equity, LLC; *U.S. Private*, pg. 2835
NAPOMAR S.A.—See SIF Banat-Crisana S.A.; *Int'l*, pg. 6905
NAPO PHARMACEUTICALS, INC.—See Jaguar Health, Inc.; *U.S. Public*, pg. 1186
NAPOTEX S.A.—See SIF Banat-Crisana S.A.; *Int'l*, pg. 6905
NAPPEN & ASSOCIATES; *U.S. Private*, pg. 2835
NAPP-GRECCO COMPANY; *U.S. Private*, pg. 2835
NAPP PHARMACEUTICALS LTD.—See Purdue Pharma LP; *U.S. Private*, pg. 3305
NAPREDAK A.D.; *Int'l*, pg. 5147
NAPREDAK A.D.; *Int'l*, pg. 5147
NAPREDAK A.D.; *Int'l*, pg. 5147
NAPREDAK A.D.; *Int'l*, pg. 5147
NAPREDAK A.D.; *Int'l*, pg. 5147
NAPREDAK A.D.; *Int'l*, pg. 5147
NAPREDAK A.D.; *Int'l*, pg. 5147
NAPROTEK, INC.—See Edgewater Capital Partners, L.P.; *U.S. Private*, pg. 1335
NAPS NORWAY A/S—See Fortum Oyj; *Int'l*, pg. 2742
NAPS SYSTEMS OY—See Fortum Oyj; *Int'l*, pg. 2742
NAPSTER GROUP PLC; *Int'l*, pg. 5147
NAP-STOLLER THAILAND—See Corteva, Inc.; *U.S. Public*, pg. 584
NAPS UNITED KINGDOM—See Fortum Oyj; *Int'l*, pg. 2742
NAPW, INC.—See Professional Diversity Network, Inc.; *U.S. Public*, pg. 1724
NARACAMICIE CO., LTD.—See Sumitomo Corporation; *Int'l*, pg. 7269
NARA CELLAR CO., LTD.; *Int'l*, pg. 5147
NARADA ASIA PACIFIC PTE. LTD.—See Zhejiang Narada Power Source Co., Ltd.; *Int'l*, pg. 8660
NARADA EUROPE (UK) LIMITED—See Zhejiang Narada Power Source Co., Ltd.; *Int'l*, pg. 8660
NARAE ENERGY SERVICE CO., LTD.—See SK Inc.; *Int'l*, pg. 6972
NARAE NANOTECH CORPORATION; *Int'l*, pg. 5147
NARAENANOTECH (GUANGZHOU) CO., LTD.—See Narae Nanotech Corporation; *Int'l*, pg. 5147
NARAGANSETT BAY INSURANCE COMPANY—See Heritage Insurance Holdings, Inc.; *U.S. Public*, pg. 1028
NARA GARDEN CREATE CO. LTD—See Takasho Co.,Ltd.; *Int'l*, pg. 7436
NARA HOTEL CO., LTD.—See West Japan Railway Company; *Int'l*, pg. 8385
NARAINGARH SUGAR MILLS LTD.; *Int'l*, pg. 5147
NARA ISEKI SALES CO., LTD.—See Iseki & Co., Ltd.; *Int'l*, pg. 3814
NARA KUNSHAN STAMPING DIE CO., LTD.—See NARA Mold & Die Co., Ltd.; *Int'l*, pg. 5147
NARA M&D CO., LTD—See NARA Mold & Die Co., Ltd.; *Int'l*, pg. 5147
NARA M&D CO., LTD - SUNGSAN FACTORY—See NARA Mold & Die Co., Ltd.; *Int'l*, pg. 5147
NARA MOLD & DIE CO., LTD; *Int'l*, pg. 5147
NARA M TECH CO., LTD - OKSAN FACTORY—See NARA Mold & Die Co., Ltd.; *Int'l*, pg. 5147
NARA M TECH CO., LTD.—See NARA Mold & Die Co., Ltd.; *Int'l*, pg. 5147
NARA PLA TECH CO., LTD—See NARA Mold & Die Co., Ltd.; *Int'l*, pg. 5147
NARASAKI SANGYO CO., LTD.; *Int'l*, pg. 5147
NARASAKI SEISAKUSYO CO., LTD.—See Yokogawa Bridge Holdings Corp.; *Int'l*, pg. 8591
NARASAKI STAX CO., LTD.—See Narasaki Sangyo Co., Ltd.; *Int'l*, pg. 5147
NARASAKI TRADE (SHANGHAI) CO., LTD.—See Narasaki Sangyo Co., Ltd.; *Int'l*, pg. 5147
NARA SENKO LOGISTICS CO., LTD.—See Senko Group Holdings Co., Ltd.; *Int'l*, pg. 6710
NARASOFT CO., LTD.; *Int'l*, pg. 5147
NARA TRAINING AND ASSESSING PTY. LTD.—See Skill Hire WA; *Int'l*, pg. 6986
NARAYANA HRUDAYALAYA LTD.; *Int'l*, pg. 5147
NARBADA GEMS & JEWELLERY LTD.; *Int'l*, pg. 5147
NARBONI HOLDINGS, SARL—See Taylor Corporation; *U.S. Private*, pg. 3939
THE NARBOROUGH PLANTATIONS, PLC—See Riverview Rubber Estates Berhad; *Int'l*, pg. 6353
NARCO FREEDOM, INC.; *U.S. Private*, pg. 2835
NARDA SAFETY TEST SOLUTIONS GMBH—See L3Harris Technologies, Inc.; *U.S. Public*, pg. 1284
NARDA SAFETY TEST SOLUTIONS S.R.L.—See L3Harris Technologies, Inc.; *U.S. Public*, pg. 1284
NARDELLO & CO. LLC; *U.S. Private*, pg. 2835
NARDI ARMOAS LTDA.—See International Flavors & Fragrances Inc.; *U.S. Public*, pg. 1154
NARDI AROMAS LTDA.—See International Flavors & Fragrances Inc.; *U.S. Public*, pg. 1154
NARDOBEL SAS—See Otsuka Holdings Co., Ltd.; *Int'l*, pg. 5658
NARENDRA PROPERTIES LIMITED; *Int'l*, pg. 5148
NARF INDUSTRIES PLC; *Int'l*, pg. 5148
N. ARGYROPOULOS & SIA E.E.—See Doppelmayr Group; *Int'l*, pg. 2175

NARI HAMICO MINERALS JOINT STOCK COMPANY; *Int'l*, pg. 5148
NARITA DRY ICE CO., LTD.—See Temasek Holdings (Private) Limited; *Int'l*, pg. 7550
NARITA GATEWAY HOTEL CO., LTD.—See Striders Corporation; *Int'l*, pg. 7240
NARITA GIKEN CO., LTD.—See ROHM Co., Ltd.; *Int'l*, pg. 6385
NARITA LOGISTIC TERMINAL CO., LTD.—See Japan Airlines Co., Ltd.; *Int'l*, pg. 3885
NARITA NIKKO HOTEL CO., LTD.—See Japan Airlines Co., Ltd.; *Int'l*, pg. 3882
NARI TECHNOLOGY CO., LTD.—See State Grid Corporation of China; *Int'l*, pg. 7183
NARMADA AGROBASE LTD.; *Int'l*, pg. 5148
NARMADA CEMENT COMPANY LIMITED—See The Aditya Birla Group; *Int'l*, pg. 7611
NARMADA GELATINES LIMITED; *Int'l*, pg. 5148
NARMADA MACPLAST DRIP IRRIGATION SYSTEMS LTD.; *Int'l*, pg. 5148
NARMAPLAN OY—See Sweco AB; *Int'l*, pg. 7363
NARMOD SP. Z O.O.—See Cantoni Motor S.A.; *Int'l*, pg. 1299
N. ARMSTRONG ADVERTISING; *U.S. Private*, pg. 2827
NARNIA (HONG KONG) GROUP COMPANY LIMITED; *Int'l*, pg. 5148
NARODNA BANKA SLOVENSKA; *Int'l*, pg. 5148
NARODOWY BANK POLSKI; *Int'l*, pg. 5148
NARPLAST LLC—See Dohler GmbH; *Int'l*, pg. 2156
NARRABRI COAL OPERATIONS PTY LTD—See Whitehaven Coal Limited; *Int'l*, pg. 8400
NARRAGANSETT BREWING CO; *U.S. Private*, pg. 2835
NARRAGANSETT FINANCIAL CORP.; *U.S. Private*, pg. 2835
NARRAGANSETT IMAGING—See Global Imaging Holdings Realty, LLC; *U.S. Private*, pg. 1714
NARRAGANSETT IMPROVEMENT CO; *U.S. Private*, pg. 2835
NARRAGANSETT TIMES—See R.I.S.N. Operations Inc.; *U.S. Private*, pg. 3336
THE NARRATIVE GROUP LLC—See Bluefocus Intelligent Communications Group Co., Ltd.; *Int'l*, pg. 1071
NARROW FABRIC AMERICA CORPORATION; *U.S. Private*, pg. 2835
NARROW FABRIC INDUSTRIES CORP.—See Cheynet S.A.S; *Int'l*, pg. 1474
NARRYER METALS LIMITED; *Int'l*, pg. 5148
NAR TRAINING, LLC—See Henry Schein, Inc.; *U.S. Public*, pg. 1027
NARUCO CORPORATION—See Toyota Boshoku Corporation; *Int'l*, pg. 7864
NARUMI CORPORATION—See Ishizuka Glass Co., Ltd.; *Int'l*, pg. 3818
NARUMI SHANGHAI COMPANY LTD.—See Ishizuka Glass Co., Ltd.; *Int'l*, pg. 3818
NARUMI SINGAPORE PTE. LTD.—See Ishizuka Glass Co., Ltd.; *Int'l*, pg. 3818
NARUMIYA INTERNATIONAL CO., LTD.—See World Co., Ltd.; *Int'l*, pg. 8457
NARUTO CRUISE SERVICE CO., LTD—See Otsuka Holdings Co., Ltd.; *Int'l*, pg. 5658
NARUTO SALT MFG. CO., LTD.—See Otsuka Holdings Co., Ltd.; *Int'l*, pg. 5658
NARVA ELEKTRIJAAMAD AS—See Eesti Energia AS; *Int'l*, pg. 2317
NARVA POLSKA SP. Z.O.O.—See A.A.G. STUCCHI s.r.l.; *Int'l*, pg. 23
NARVA SOOJUSVORK AS—See Eesti Energia AS; *Int'l*, pg. 2318
NARVESEN BALTIJA SIA—See Reitangruppen AS; *Int'l*, pg. 6258
NASA BANKA AD BIJELJINA; *Int'l*, pg. 5148
NAS AIRPORT SERVICES LIMITED; *Int'l*, pg. 5148
NA SALES COMPANY INC.; *U.S. Private*, pg. 2829
NASA MULTIPLEX LLC—See Brookfield Corporation; *Int'l*, pg. 1185
NASA SLOGA A.D.; *Int'l*, pg. 5148
NASB FINANCIAL, INC.; *U.S. Public*, pg. 1491
NASB NIROO COMPANY—See MAPNA Group; *Int'l*, pg. 4687
NASCANS PTE. LTD.—See NetDragon Websoft Holdings Limited; *Int'l*, pg. 5213
NASCENT BIOTECH INC.; *U.S. Public*, pg. 1491
NASCENTBIOTECHNOLOGY MANUFACTURING, INC.—See Newava Technology, Inc.; *U.S. Private*, pg. 2913
NASCO AIRCRAFT BRAKE INC.—See Parker Hannifin Corporation; *U.S. Public*, pg. 1642
NASCO INTERNATIONAL, INC.—See Geneve Holdings Corp.; *U.S. Public*, pg. 1671
N.A.S CO., LTD.—See Kameda Seika Co., Ltd.; *Int'l*, pg. 4061
N.A.S. CO., LTD.—See Kameda Seika Co., Ltd.; *Int'l*, pg. 4061
NASCO MODESTO—See Geneve Holdings Corp.; *U.S. Private*, pg. 1671
NASCON ALLIED INDUSTRIES PLC; *Int'l*, pg. 5148
NAS CREATE CO., LTD.—See Nippon Yakin Kogyo Co., Ltd.; *Int'l*, pg. 5357
NASDAQ AB—See Nasdaq, Inc.; *U.S. Public*, pg. 1492

NASDAQ AUSTRALIA HOLDINGS PTY. LTD.—See Nasdaq, Inc.; *U.S. Public*, pg. 1491
NASDAQ COPENHAGEN A/S—See Nasdaq, Inc.; *U.S. Public*, pg. 1492
NASDAQ CSD ICELAND HF—See Nasdaq, Inc.; *U.S. Public*, pg. 1492
NASDAQ DUBAI LTD.—See Investment Corporation of Dubai; *Int'l*, pg. 3785
NASDAQ HELSINKI LTD—See Nasdaq, Inc.; *U.S. Public*, pg. 1492
NASDAQ ICELAND HF—See Nasdaq, Inc.; *U.S. Public*, pg. 1492
NASDAQ, INC.; *U.S. Public*, pg. 1491
NASDAQ OMX CLEARING AB—See Nasdaq, Inc.; *U.S. Public*, pg. 1492
NASDAQ OMX COPENHAGEN A/S—See Nasdaq, Inc.; *U.S. Public*, pg. 1492
NASDAQ OMX EUROPE LIMITED—See Nasdaq, Inc.; *U.S. Public*, pg. 1492
NASDAQ OMX HELSINKI OY—See Nasdaq, Inc.; *U.S. Public*, pg. 1492
NASDAQ OMX ICELAND HF.—See Nasdaq, Inc.; *U.S. Public*, pg. 1492
NASDAQ OMX NORDIC OY—See Nasdaq, Inc.; *U.S. Public*, pg. 1492
NASDAQ OMX PHLX, INC.—See Nasdaq, Inc.; *U.S. Public*, pg. 1492
NASDAQ OMX (SOUTH EAST ASIA & PACIFIC) PTE. LTD.—See Nasdaq, Inc.; *U.S. Public*, pg. 1492
NASDAQ OMX STOCKHOLM AB—See Nasdaq, Inc.; *U.S. Public*, pg. 1492
NASDAQ OMX TALLINN AS—See Nasdaq, Inc.; *U.S. Public*, pg. 1492
NASDAQ OPTIONS SERVICES, LLC—See Nasdaq, Inc.; *U.S. Public*, pg. 1492
NASDAQ OSLO ASA—See Nasdaq, Inc.; *U.S. Public*, pg. 1492
THE NASDAQ PRIVATE MARKET, LLC—See Nasdaq, Inc.; *U.S. Public*, pg. 1492
NASDAQ RIGA, AS—See Nasdaq, Inc.; *U.S. Public*, pg. 1492
THE NASDAQ STOCK MARKET LLC—See Nasdaq, Inc.; *U.S. Public*, pg. 1492
NASEEJ FABRIC MANUFACTURING L.L.C.—See Dubai Islamic Bank PSJ; *Int'l*, pg. 2220
NASEKI SEIMITSUKAKO CO., LTD.—See Sekisui Chemical Co., Ltd.; *Int'l*, pg. 6694
NAS ENGINEERING CO., LTD.—See Nippon Yakin Kogyo Co., Ltd.; *Int'l*, pg. 5357
NASH CHEVROLET CO., INC.; *U.S. Private*, pg. 2835
NASH DOM BULGARIA HOLDING AD SOFIA; *Int'l*, pg. 5148
NA SHENG LEATHER (HUAI'AN) CO., LTD.—See WW Holding Inc; *Int'l*, pg. 8516
NASH HEALTH CARE SYSTEMS INC.; *U.S. Private*, pg. 2835
NASH HOLDINGS LLC; *U.S. Private*, pg. 2835
NASH JOHNSON & SONS FARMS INC.; *U.S. Private*, pg. 2836
NASHOBA PUBLISHING—See Alden Global Capital LLC; *U.S. Private*, pg. 157
NASHOBA VALLEY SPIRITS, LTD.; *U.S. Private*, pg. 2836
NASH OIL COMPANY INC.; *U.S. Private*, pg. 2836
NASH PRODUCE, LLC.; *U.S. Private*, pg. 2836
NASHUA CORPORATION—See Cenveo, Inc.; *U.S. Private*, pg. 835
NASHUA HOMES OF IDAHO INC.; *U.S. Private*, pg. 2836
NASHUA LTD—See Reunert Limited; *Int'l*, pg. 6312
NASHUA MERRIMACK COATED PAPER PRODUCTS PLANT—See Cenveo, Inc.; *U.S. Private*, pg. 835
NASHUA MOBILE (PTY) LTD—See Reunert Limited; *Int'l*, pg. 6312
NASHUA TELEGRAPH—See Independent Publications, Inc.; *U.S. Private*, pg. 2061
NASHVILLE AUTO AUCTION—See Cox Enterprises, Inc.; *U.S. Private*, pg. 1077
NASHVILLE CAPITAL CORP.—See Renasant Corporation; *U.S. Public*, pg. 1783
NASHVILLE CARES; *U.S. Private*, pg. 2836
NASHVILLE DENTAL INC.; *U.S. Private*, pg. 2836
NASHVILLE ELECTRIC SERVICE; *U.S. Private*, pg. 2836
NASHVILLE GASTROINTESTINAL SPECIALISTS, LLC—See KKR & Co. Inc.; *U.S. Public*, pg. 1250
NASHVILLE MACHINE COMPANY, INC.; *U.S. Private*, pg. 2836
NASHVILLE PETERBILT INC.—See Rush Enterprises, Inc.; *U.S. Private*, pg. 1826
NASHVILLE PREDATORS, LLC; *U.S. Private*, pg. 2836
NASHVILLE READY MIX INC.; *U.S. Private*, pg. 2836
NASHVILLE RECORDS, INC.; *U.S. Public*, pg. 1492
NASHVILLE RUBBER & GASKET COMPANY, INC.; *U.S. Private*, pg. 2836
NASHVILLE SPEEDWAY, USA, INC.—See Sonic Financial Corporation; *U.S. Private*, pg. 3713
NASHVILLE SPORTING GOODS, LLC—See Genesco Inc.; *U.S. Public*, pg. 930
NASHVILLE STATIONERY CO. INC.; *U.S. Private*, pg. 2836

NASHVILLE STEEL CORP.; *U.S. Private*, pg. 2836
NASHVILLE SYMPHONY ASSOCIATION; *U.S. Private*, pg. 2836
THE NASHVILLE TN OPHTHALMOLOGY ASC, LLC—See KKR & Co. Inc.; *U.S. Public*, pg. 1248
NASHVILLE TRANSMISSION PARTS—See Jordan Industries, Inc.; *U.S. Private*, pg. 2235
NASHVILLE WIRE PRODUCTS, INC. - MATERIAL HANDLING - BORDEAUX FACILITY—See Nashville Wire Products, Inc.; *U.S. Private*, pg. 2837
NASHVILLE WIRE PRODUCTS, INC. - MATERIAL HANDLING - FRANKFORT FACILITY—See Nashville Wire Products, Inc.; *U.S. Private*, pg. 2837
NASHVILLE WIRE PRODUCTS, INC. - NASHVILLE DISPLAY - DOVER FACILITY—See Nashville Wire Products, Inc.; *U.S. Private*, pg. 2837
NASHVILLE WIRE PRODUCTS, INC. - NASHVILLE DISPLAY - LEBANON FACILITY—See Nashville Wire Products, Inc.; *U.S. Private*, pg. 2837
NASHVILLE WIRE PRODUCTS, INC. - OEM PARTS - AUBURN FACILITY—See Nashville Wire Products, Inc.; *U.S. Private*, pg. 2837
NASHVILLE WIRE PRODUCTS, INC. - OEM PARTS - JUAREZ FACILITY—See Nashville Wire Products, Inc.; *U.S. Private*, pg. 2837
NASHVILLE WIRE PRODUCTS, INC. - OEM PARTS - WHITE BLUFF FACILITY—See Nashville Wire Products, Inc.; *U.S. Private*, pg. 2837
NASHVILLE WIRE PRODUCTS, INC.; *U.S. Private*, pg. 2836
NASHVILLE ZOO AT GRASSMERE; *U.S. Private*, pg. 2837
NASICECEMENT D.D.—See Nexe Grupa d.d.; *Int'l*, pg. 5243
NASICKI AUTOCENTAR D.O.O.—See Nexe Grupa d.d.; *Int'l*, pg. 5243
NASINSA SECURITIES—See Nacional Financiera F.N.C.; *Int'l*, pg. 5123
NAS INSURANCE SERVICES LLC—See Tokio Marine Holdings, Inc.; *Int'l*, pg. 7784
NASIRMACHINE ENGINEERING CO.; *Int'l*, pg. 5148
N. A. SITARAS LTD.—See Svenska Cellulosa Aktiebolaget SCA; *Int'l*, pg. 7357
NASLON FUJI FILTER (CHANGSHU) CO., LTD.—See Daido Steel Co., Ltd.; *Int'l*, pg. 1923
NASLON KOREA CO., LTD.—See Daido Steel Co., Ltd.; *Int'l*, pg. 1923
NASLUCK CO., LTD.—See Token Corporation; *Int'l*, pg. 7781
NASMARK SDN. BHD.—See Kato Sangyo Co., Ltd.; *Int'l*, pg. 4090
NASMEDIA CO., LTD.—See KT Corporation; *Int'l*, pg. 4315
NASMEDIA THAILAND CO., LTD.—See KT Corporation; *Int'l*, pg. 4315
NASON CONSTRUCTION, INC.; *U.S. Private*, pg. 2837
NASON CONTRACTING GROUP LTD.—See Bird Construction Inc.; *Int'l*, pg. 1046
NASON HOSPITAL—See Apollo Global Management, Inc.; *U.S. Public*, pg. 158
NASON PHYSICIAN PRACTICES, LLC—See Apollo Global Management, Inc.; *U.S. Public*, pg. 158
NASON, YEAGER, GERSON, HARRIS & FUMERO P.A.; *U.S. Private*, pg. 2837
NASOSENERGOMASH SUMY JSC—See HMS Hydraulic Machines & Systems Group plc; *Int'l*, pg. 3432
NASOYA FOOD USA LLC—See Pulmuone Co., Ltd.; *Int'l*, pg. 6116
NASPAC MARKETING PTE. LTD.—See Kato Sangyo Co., Ltd.; *Int'l*, pg. 4090
NASPERS LIMITED; *Int'l*, pg. 5148
NAS RECRUITMENT COMMUNICATIONS, LLC—See Sony Group Corporation; *Int'l*, pg. 7102
NAS RECRUITMENT COMMUNICATIONS—See Sony Group Corporation; *Int'l*, pg. 7102
NAS RECRUITMENT COMMUNICATIONS—See Sony Group Corporation; *Int'l*, pg. 7102
NAS RECRUITMENT COMMUNICATIONS—See Sony Group Corporation; *Int'l*, pg. 7102
NAS RECRUITMENT COMMUNICATIONS—See Sony Group Corporation; *Int'l*, pg. 7102
NAS RECRUITMENT COMMUNICATIONS—See Sony Group Corporation; *Int'l*, pg. 7102
NAS RECRUITMENT COMMUNICATIONS—See Sony Group Corporation; *Int'l*, pg. 7102
NAS RECRUITMENT COMMUNICATIONS—See Sony Group Corporation; *Int'l*, pg. 7102
NAS RECRUITMENT COMMUNICATIONS—See Sony Group Corporation; *Int'l*, pg. 7102
NAS RECRUITMENT COMMUNICATIONS—See Sony Group Corporation; *Int'l*, pg. 7102
NAS RECRUITMENT COMMUNICATIONS—See Sony Group Corporation; *Int'l*, pg. 7102
THE NASSAL COMPANY—See PCL Employees Holdings Ltd.; *Int'l*, pg. 5769
NASSA LLC—See Lennar Corporation; *U.S. Public*, pg. 1306

NASSAU CANDY DISTRIBUTORS INC.; *U.S. Private*, pg. 2837
NASSAU CROSSING ENDOSCOPY CENTER, LLC—See Tenet Healthcare Corporation; *U.S. Public*, pg. 2004
NASSAU CRUISE PORT LTD.—See Global Yatirim Holding A.S.; *Int'l*, pg. 3003
NASSAU ENERGY CORP.—See ENGIE SA; *Int'l*, pg. 2429
NASSAU FARMERS ELEVATOR CO.; *U.S. Private*, pg. 2837
NASSAU FINANCIAL GROUP, LP—See Golden Gate Capital Management II, LLC; *U.S. Private*, pg. 1731
NASSAU HOLDING CORP.; *U.S. Private*, pg. 2837
NASSAU INCASSO SERVICES DEN HAAG B.V.—See Munchener Ruckversicherungs AG; *Int'l*, pg. 5091
NASSAUISCHE SPARKASSE; *Int'l*, pg. 5149
NASSAU LENS CO., INC.; *U.S. Private*, pg. 2837
NASSAU PARADISE ISLAND PROMOTION BOARD; *U.S. Private*, pg. 2837
NASSAU POOLS CONSTRUCTION, INC.; *U.S. Private*, pg. 2837
NASSAU REGIONAL OFF-TRACK BETTING; *U.S. Private*, pg. 2837
NASSAU REINSURANCE GROUP HOLDINGS L.P.—See Golden Gate Capital Management II, LLC; *U.S. Private*, pg. 1731
NASSAU SUFFOLK LUMBER & SUPPLY CORPORATION; *U.S. Private*, pg. 2837
NASSAU TERMINALS LLC—See Worldwide Terminals Fernandina, LLC; *U.S. Private*, pg. 4570
NASSAU TOOL WORKS, INC.—See Air Industries Group; *U.S. Public*, pg. 64
NASSCO HOLDINGS INCORPORATED—See General Dynamics Corporation; *U.S. Public*, pg. 915
NASSCO, INC.; *U.S. Private*, pg. 2837
NASS COMMERICAL—See Abdulla Ahmed Nass Group WLL; *Int'l*, pg. 58
NASSCO-NORFOLK—See General Dynamics Corporation; *U.S. Public*, pg. 915
NASS CORPORATION BSC (C) - NASS FOODS DIVISION—See Abdulla Ahmed Nass Group WLL; *Int'l*, pg. 58
NASS CORPORATION B.S.C.—See Abdulla Ahmed Nass Group WLL; *Int'l*, pg. 58
NASS ELECTRICAL—See Abdulla Ahmed Nass Group WLL; *Int'l*, pg. 58
NASSER COMPANY INC.; *U.S. Private*, pg. 2837
NASSIMI CORPORATION; *U.S. Private*, pg. 2837
NASSJO TEKNIKPROJEKTERING AB—See Instalco AB; *Int'l*, pg. 3722
NASS MECHANICAL—See Abdulla Ahmed Nass Group WLL; *Int'l*, pg. 58
NASS SCAFFORM—See Abdulla Ahmed Nass Group WLL; *Int'l*, pg. 58
NAS STAINLESS STEEL STRIP MANUFACTURING CO., LTD.—See Nippon Yakin Kogyo Co., Ltd.; *Int'l*, pg. 5357
NAS STAN A.D.; *Int'l*, pg. 5148
NASSTAR SERVICES LIMITED—See Mayfair Equity Partners LLP; *Int'l*, pg. 4745
NASS VALLEY GATEWAY LTD.; *Int'l*, pg. 5149
NAS TOA CO., LTD.—See Nippon Yakin Kogyo Co., Ltd.; *Int'l*, pg. 5357
NAS TOA (THAILAND) CO., LTD.—See Nippon Yakin Kogyo Co., Ltd.; *Int'l*, pg. 5357
NASTOP PLUS—See Pristop d.o.o.; *Int'l*, pg. 5983
NASTOS CONSTRUCTION INC.; *U.S. Private*, pg. 2837
NAS TRADING CO., LTD.—See Nippon Yakin Kogyo Co., Ltd.; *Int'l*, pg. 5357
NASTYGOAT CORPORATION; *U.S. Private*, pg. 2837
NASU DAIWA, INC.—See Globeride, Inc.; *Int'l*, pg. 3007
NASU DENKI-TEKKO CO., LTD.; *Int'l*, pg. 5149
NASU NIKON CO., LTD.—See EssilorLuxottica SA; *Int'l*, pg. 2512
NASU NIKON CO., LTD.—See Nikon Corporation; *Int'l*, pg. 5294
NASU SEIKI MFG. CO., LTD.—See Hitachi Astemo, Ltd.; *Int'l*, pg. 3409
NATADOLA BAY RESORT LIMITED—See Fiji National Provident Fund; *Int'l*, pg. 2661
NATA IMMOBILIEN-LEASING GESELLSCHAFT M.B.H.—See UniCredit S.p.A.; *Int'l*, pg. 8035
NATAL PORTLAND CEMENT COMPANY (PTY) LTD.—See Camargo Correa S.A.; *Int'l*, pg. 1268
NATAM MANAGEMENT COMPANY S.A.—See Banca Finnat Euramerica S.p.A.; *Int'l*, pg. 815
NATARE CORPORATION; *U.S. Private*, pg. 2838
NATASA MINING LTD; *Int'l*, pg. 5149
NATBANK, N.A.—See National Bank of Canada; *Int'l*, pg. 5152
NATCAN TRUST COMPANY—See National Bank of Canada; *Int'l*, pg. 5152
NAT CHARTERING AS—See Nordic American Tankers Limited; *Int'l*, pg. 5419
NATCHEZ COCA-COLA BOTTLING CO.—See The Coca-Cola Company; *U.S. Public*, pg. 2065
NATCHEZ HOSPITAL COMPANY, LLC—See Community Health Systems, Inc.; *U.S. Public*, pg. 555
NATCHEZ TRACE ELECTRIC POWER ASSOCIATION; *U.S. Private*, pg. 2838

COMPANY NAME INDEX

NATCO AL RAZI COMPANY—See Hayel Saeed Anam Group of Companies; *Int'l*, pg. 3290
NATCO ECONOMICALS LTD.; *Int'l*, pg. 5149
NATCOFARMA DO BRASIL LTDA.—See Natco Pharma Ltd; *Int'l*, pg. 5149
NATCOM BANCSHARES, INC.; *U.S. Private*, pg. 2838
NATCOM MARKETING; *U.S. Private*, pg. 2838
NATCON—See The Kuwait Company for Process Plant Construction & Contracting K.S.C.; *Int'l*, pg. 7663
NATCO PHARMA ASIA PTE. LTD.—See Natco Pharma Ltd; *Int'l*, pg. 5149
NATCO PHARMA (CANADA) INC.—See Natco Pharma Ltd; *Int'l*, pg. 5149
NATCO PHARMA INC.—See Natco Pharma Ltd; *Int'l*, pg. 5149
NATCO PHARMA LIMITED - CHEMICAL-R & D DIVISION—See Natco Pharma Ltd; *Int'l*, pg. 5149
NATCO PHARMA LIMITED - PHARMA DIVISION-PARENTERALS—See Natco Pharma Ltd; *Int'l*, pg. 5149
NATCO PHARMA LIMITED - PHARMA DIVISION—See Natco Pharma Ltd; *Int'l*, pg. 5149
NATCO PHARMA LTD; *Int'l*, pg. 5149
NATCO PRODUCTS CORPORATION; *U.S. Private*, pg. 2838
NATCORE TECHNOLOGY INC.; *U.S. Public*, pg. 1492
NATECH PLASTICS, INC—See Stratec SE; *Int'l*, pg. 7235
NATEC—See Compagnie de Saint-Gobain SA; *Int'l*, pg. 1724
NATEC USA LLC—See Hochland SE; *Int'l*, pg. 3437
NATEECHAI CO., LTD.—See Thai Beverage Public Company Limited; *Int'l*, pg. 7591
NATEL ENGINEERING CO., INC. - AGAVE PLANT—See Natel Engineering Company, Inc.; *U.S. Private*, pg. 2838
NATEL ENGINEERING COMPANY, INC.; *U.S. Private*, pg. 2838
NATENCO WINDPARK 1 MANAGEMENT GMBH—See Electricite de France S.A.; *Int'l*, pg. 2350
NATERA, INC.; *U.S. Public*, pg. 1492
NATERA INTERNATIONAL, INC.—See Natera, Inc.; *U.S. Public*, pg. 1493
NATERRA INTERNATIONAL INC.; *U.S. Private*, pg. 2838
NATERRA LAND; *U.S. Private*, pg. 2838
NATERRA LAND—See Naterra Land; *U.S. Private*, pg. 2838
NATERRA LAND TENNESSEE LLC—See Naterra Land; *U.S. Private*, pg. 2838
NATE'S FOOD CO.; *U.S. Public*, pg. 1492
NATE WADE SUBARU; *U.S. Private*, pg. 2838
NATEXPORT—See National Bank of Canada; *Int'l*, pg. 5152
NATFOOD IBERICA S.L.—See Bioera S.p.A.; *Int'l*, pg. 1037
NATFOOD PORTUGAL LDA—See Bioera S.p.A.; *Int'l*, pg. 1037
NATFOOD S.R.L.—See Bioera S.p.A.; *Int'l*, pg. 1037
NATFORM PTY LTD—See Acrow Limited; *Int'l*, pg. 109
NATFORM (QLD) PTY LTD—See Acrow Limited; *Int'l*, pg. 109
NATFRESH BEVERAGES CORP.; *U.S. Private*, pg. 2838
NAT GAMES CO., LTD.—See Nexon Co., Ltd.; *Int'l*, pg. 5245
NATGRAPH LTD.—See Indutrade AB; *Int'l*, pg. 3680
NATHALIN SHIPPING PTE. LTD.—See Prima Marine PCL; *Int'l*, pg. 5975
THE NATHAN ADELSON HOSPICE; *U.S. Private*, pg. 4081
NATHAN ASSOCIATES INC.; *U.S. Private*, pg. 2838
NATHAN & LEWIS SECURITIES INC; *U.S. Private*, pg. 2838
NATHAN LITTAUER HOSPITAL & NURSING HOME; *U.S. Private*, pg. 2838
NATHAN PROJECTS BVBA—See NIBE Industrier AB; *Int'l*, pg. 5261
NATHAN'S FAMOUS INC.; *U.S. Public*, pg. 1493
NATHAN'S FAMOUS OF YONKERS, INC.—See Nathan's Famous Inc.; *U.S. Public*, pg. 1493
NATHAN SPORTS—See Wells Fargo & Company; *U.S. Public*, pg. 2344
NATHAN SYSTEMS B.V.—See NIBE Industrier AB; *Int'l*, pg. 5261
NATHANTABOR.COM; *U.S. Private*, pg. 2839
NATHAN WEINER & ASSOCIATES INC.—See Sterling Supply Co. Inc.; *U.S. Private*, pg. 3807
NATH BIO-GENES (INDIA) LIMITED; *Int'l*, pg. 5149
NATH COMPANIES INCORPORATED; *U.S. Private*, pg. 2838
NATH FLORIDA FRANCHISE GROUP—See Nath Companies Incorporated; *U.S. Private*, pg. 2838
NATH INDUSTRIES LIMITED; *Int'l*, pg. 5149
NATH MANAGEMENT INC—See Nath Companies Incorporated; *U.S. Private*, pg. 2838
NATH MINNESOTA FRANCHISE GROUP—See Nath Companies Incorporated; *U.S. Private*, pg. 2838
NATH PULP & PAPER MILLS LIMITED—See Nath Industries Limited; *Int'l*, pg. 5149
NATICK BULLETIN & TAB—See Gannett Co., Inc.; *U.S. Public*, pg. 902

NATIO ASSURANCE, SA—See BNP Paribas SA; *Int'l*, pg. 1092
NATIOBAIL 2 S.A.—See BNP Paribas SA; *Int'l*, pg. 1092
NATIOCREDIBAIL SA—See BNP Paribas SA; *Int'l*, pg. 1092
NATIOCREDIMURS SNC—See BNP Paribas SA; *Int'l*, pg. 1092
NATIONAL ACADEMY OF SCIENCES; *U.S. Private*, pg. 2839
NATIONAL ACCESS CANNABIS CORP.; *Int'l*, pg. 5150
NATIONAL ACCIDENT HELPLINE LIMITED; *Int'l*, pg. 5150
NATIONAL ACTION FINANCIAL SERVICES, INC.—See ONEX Corporation; *Int'l*, pg. 5578
NATIONAL ADHESIVES CO. LTD.—See Henkel AG & Co. KGaA; *Int'l*, pg. 3349
NATIONAL ADVANTAGE INSURANCE SERVICES, INC.—See R.E. Chaix & Associates Insurance Brokers, Inc.; *U.S. Private*, pg. 3335
NATIONAL AEROSPACE FASTENERS CORPORATION; *Int'l*, pg. 5150
NATIONAL AGENTS ALLIANCE—See Integrity Marketing Group LLC; *U.S. Private*, pg. 2103
NATIONAL AGRICULTURAL DEVELOPMENT COMPANY; *Int'l*, pg. 5150
NATIONAL AGRICULTURAL HOLDINGS LIMITED; *Int'l*, pg. 5150
NATIONAL AGRICULTURE MARKETING CO.; *Int'l*, pg. 5150
NATIONAL AIR CARGO INC.; *U.S. Private*, pg. 2839
NATIONAL AIRCRAFT FINANCE COMPANY—See Lake Michigan Credit Union; *U.S. Private*, pg. 2375
NATIONAL AIR FILTER SERVICE CO OF NEW JERSEY—See Daikin Industries, Ltd.; *Int'l*, pg. 1936
NATIONAL AIRWAYS CORPORATION—See Dubai World Corporation; *Int'l*, pg. 2221
NATIONAL ALARM & PROTECTION; *U.S. Private*, pg. 2839
NATIONAL ALLIANCE ON MENTAL ILLNESS; *U.S. Private*, pg. 2839
NATIONAL ALUMINIUM COMPANY LIMITED; *Int'l*, pg. 5150
NATIONAL ALUMINIUM LIMITED—See Capral Limited; *Int'l*, pg. 1315
NATIONAL ALUMINIUM PRODUCTS COMPANY SAOG; *Int'l*, pg. 5150
NATIONAL ALUMINUM INDUSTRIAL COMPANY; *Int'l*, pg. 5150
NATIONAL ALUMINUM & PROFILE CO.; *Int'l*, pg. 5150
NATIONAL ALUMINUM & PROFILES COMPANY PLC—See Arab Palestinian Investment Company; *Int'l*, pg. 531
NATIONAL AMERICAN INSURANCE COMPANY OF CALIFORNIA—See EQT AB; *Int'l*, pg. 2474
NATIONAL AMERICAN INSURANCE COMPANY; *U.S. Private*, pg. 2839
NATIONAL AMERICAN UNIVERSITY HOLDINGS, INC.; *U.S. Public*, pg. 1493
NATIONAL AMUSEMENTS, INC.; *U.S. Private*, pg. 2839
NATIONAL ANALYSIS CENTER, INC.—See Underwriters Laboratories Inc.; *U.S. Private*, pg. 4280
NATIONAL APARTMENT ASSOCIATION; *U.S. Private*, pg. 2844
NATIONAL AQUARIUM IN BALTIMORE INC.; *U.S. Private*, pg. 2845
NATIONAL ART EXCHANGE, INC.; *U.S. Public*, pg. 1493
NATIONAL ARTS CENTRE CORPORATION; *Int'l*, pg. 5150
NATIONAL ARTS COUNCIL; *Int'l*, pg. 5150
NATIONAL ARTS ENTERTAINMENT & CULTURE GROUP LIMITED; *Int'l*, pg. 5150
NATIONAL ARTS TRAVEL LIMITED—See National Arts Entertainment & Culture Group Limited; *Int'l*, pg. 5150
NATIONAL ASPHALT (PTY) LTD.—See Raubex Group Limited; *Int'l*, pg. 6221
NATIONAL ASSET MANAGEMENT, INC.—See B. Riley Financial, Inc.; *U.S. Public*, pg. 261
NATIONAL ASSET RECONSTRUCTION COMPANY LIMITED; *Int'l*, pg. 5150
NATIONAL ASSET RECOVERY SERVICES; *U.S. Private*, pg. 2845
NATIONAL ASSOCIATES, INC.—See Farmers National Banc Corp.; *U.S. Public*, pg. 822
NATIONAL ASSOCIATION FOR COLLEGE ADMISSION COUNSELING; *U.S. Private*, pg. 2845
THE NATIONAL ASSOCIATION FOR FEMALE EXECUTIVES—See Bonnier AB; *Int'l*, pg. 1109
THE NATIONAL ASSOCIATION FOR GUN RIGHTS, INC.; *U.S. Private*, pg. 4081
THE NATIONAL ASSOCIATION FOR HISPANIC ELDERLY; *U.S. Private*, pg. 4082
NATIONAL ASSOCIATION FOR STOCK CAR AUTO RACING, INC.; *U.S. Private*, pg. 2845
NATIONAL ASSOCIATION FOR THE SELF-EMPLOYED, INC.; *U.S. Private*, pg. 2846
NATIONAL ASSOCIATION OF BOILER AND PRESSURE VESSEL OWNERS AND OPERATORS, INC.—See TUV SUD AG; *Int'l*, pg. 7984

NATIONAL BANK OF EGYPT

NATIONAL ASSOCIATION OF CHARTER SCHOOL AUTHORIZERS; *U.S. Private*, pg. 2846
NATIONAL ASSOCIATION OF CHRONIC DISEASE DIRECTORS; *U.S. Private*, pg. 2846
NATIONAL ASSOCIATION OF COLLEGE AND UNIVERSITY BUSINESS OFFICERS; *U.S. Private*, pg. 2846
NATIONAL ASSOCIATION OF COLLEGE STORES, INC.; *U.S. Private*, pg. 2846
NATIONAL ASSOCIATION OF COMMUNITY HEALTH CENTERS; *U.S. Private*, pg. 2846
NATIONAL ASSOCIATION OF COUNTY AND CITY HEALTH OFFICIALS; *U.S. Private*, pg. 2846
NATIONAL ASSOCIATION OF FEDERAL CREDIT UNIONS; *U.S. Private*, pg. 2846
NATIONAL ASSOCIATION OF HOME BUILDERS; *U.S. Private*, pg. 2847
NATIONAL ASSOCIATION OF INDEPENDENT FEE APPRAISERS, INC.—See American Society of Appraisers; *U.S. Private*, pg. 254
NATIONAL ASSOCIATION OF INDEPENDENT SCHOOLS, INC.; *U.S. Private*, pg. 2847
NATIONAL ASSOCIATION OF INSURANCE AND FINANCIAL ADVISORS; *U.S. Private*, pg. 2847
NATIONAL ASSOCIATION OF PROFESSIONAL BASEBALL LEAGUES, INC.; *U.S. Private*, pg. 2847
NATIONAL ASSOCIATION OF REALTORS; *U.S. Private*, pg. 2847
NATIONAL ASSOCIATION OF SECONDARY SCHOOL PRINCIPALS; *U.S. Private*, pg. 2847
NATIONAL AUDUBON SOCIETY, INC.; *U.S. Private*, pg. 2847
NATIONAL AUSTRALIA BANK LIMITED; *Int'l*, pg. 5151
NATIONAL AUSTRALIA BANK-LONDON—See National Australia Bank Limited; *Int'l*, pg. 5151
NATIONAL AUSTRALIA FINANCE (ASIA) LIMITED—See National Australia Bank Limited; *Int'l*, pg. 5151
NATIONAL AUSTRALIA FINANCIAL MANAGEMENT LTD.—See National Australia Bank Limited; *Int'l*, pg. 5151
NATIONAL AUSTRALIA TRUSTEES LTD.—See National Australia Bank Limited; *Int'l*, pg. 5151
NATIONAL AUTO CARE CORPORATION—See Lovell Minnick Partners LLC; *U.S. Private*, pg. 2503
NATIONAL AUTOMOBILE CLUB, INC.; *U.S. Private*, pg. 2847
NATIONAL AUTOMOTIVE INSURANCE COMPANY—See The Allstate Corporation; *U.S. Public*, pg. 2034
NATIONAL AUTOMOTIVE PARTS ASSOCIATION, LLC—See Genuine Parts Company; *U.S. Public*, pg. 932
NATIONAL AUTO PARTS WAREHOUSE, LLC; *U.S. Private*, pg. 2847
NATIONAL AUTO RESEARCH—See The Hearst Corporation; *U.S. Private*, pg. 4045
NATIONAL AVIATION ACADEMY; *U.S. Private*, pg. 2847
NATIONAL AVIATION SERVICES COMPANY W.L.L.—See Agility; *Int'l*, pg. 210
NATIONAL BAND & TAG CO.; *U.S. Private*, pg. 2847
NATIONAL BANK ACQUISITION HOLDING INC—See National Bank of Canada; *Int'l*, pg. 5152
NATIONAL BANK AG; *Int'l*, pg. 5151
NATIONAL BANKCARD SYSTEMS, INC.; *U.S. Private*, pg. 2848
NATIONAL BANK FINANCIAL & CO. INC.—See National Bank of Canada; *Int'l*, pg. 5152
NATIONAL BANK FINANCIAL & CO. INC. - TORONTO OFFICE—See National Bank of Canada; *Int'l*, pg. 5152
NATIONAL BANK FOR FOREIGN ECONOMIC ACTIVITY OF THE REPUBLIC OF UZBEKISTAN; *Int'l*, pg. 5151
NATIONAL BANK HOLDINGS CORPORATION; *U.S. Public*, pg. 1493
NATIONAL BANK INSURANCE FIRM INC.—See National Bank of Canada; *Int'l*, pg. 5152
NATIONAL BANK INVESTMENTS INC.—See National Bank of Canada; *Int'l*, pg. 5152
NATIONAL BANK LIFE INSURANCE COMPANY—See National Bank of Canada; *Int'l*, pg. 5152
NATIONAL BANK LIMITED; *Int'l*, pg. 5151
NATIONAL BANK OF ANGUILLA LTD; *Int'l*, pg. 5152
NATIONAL BANK OF ARIZONA—See Zions Bancorporation, National Association; *U.S. Public*, pg. 2408
NATIONAL BANK OF AZERBAIJAN; *Int'l*, pg. 5152
NATIONAL BANK OF BAHRAIN; *Int'l*, pg. 5152
THE NATIONAL BANK OF BLACKSBURG—See National Bankshares, Inc.; *U.S. Public*, pg. 1493
NATIONAL BANK OF CAMBODIA; *Int'l*, pg. 5152
NATIONAL BANK OF CANADA FINANCIAL INC.—See National Bank of Canada; *Int'l*, pg. 5152
NATIONAL BANK OF CANADA; *Int'l*, pg. 5152
NATIONAL BANK OF COMMERCE LIMITED—See Absa Group Limited; *Int'l*, pg. 69
NATIONAL BANK OF COMMERCE—See NATCOM Bancshares, Inc.; *U.S. Private*, pg. 2838
NATIONAL BANK OF COXSACKIE; *U.S. Public*, pg. 1493
NATIONAL BANK OF DUBAI PJSC—See Emirates NBD PJSC; *Int'l*, pg. 2382
NATIONAL BANK OF EGYPT; *Int'l*, pg. 5152
NATIONAL BANK OF EGYPT (UK) LIMITED.—See National Bank of Egypt; *Int'l*, pg. 5152

1863

NATIONAL BANK OF ETHIOPIA

CORPORATE AFFILIATIONS

NATIONAL BANK OF ETHIOPIA; *Int'l*, pg. 5152
NATIONAL BANK OF FUJAIRAH; *Int'l*, pg. 5152
NATIONAL BANK OF GEORGIA; *Int'l*, pg. 5152
NATIONAL BANK OF GREECE S.A.; *Int'l*, pg. 5152
THE NATIONAL BANK OF INDIANAPOLIS CORPORATION; *U.S. Private*, pg. 4082
THE NATIONAL BANK OF INDIANAPOLIS—See The National Bank of Indianapolis Corporation; *U.S. Private*, pg. 4082
THE NATIONAL BANK OF KAZAKHSTAN; *Int'l*, pg. 7669
NATIONAL BANK OF KENYA LIMITED—See KCB Group PLC; *Int'l*, pg. 4108
NATIONAL BANK OF KUWAIT-EGYPT; *Int'l*, pg. 5154
NATIONAL BANK OF KUWAIT FRANCE SA—See National Bank of Kuwait S.A.K.; *Int'l*, pg. 5154
NATIONAL BANK OF KUWAIT (LEBANON) S.A.L.—See National Bank of Kuwait S.A.K.; *Int'l*, pg. 5153
NATIONAL BANK OF KUWAIT S.A.K.; *Int'l*, pg. 5153
NATIONAL BANK OF KUWAIT—See National Bank of Kuwait S.A.K.; *Int'l*, pg. 5153
NATIONAL BANK OF KYRGYZ REPUBLIC; *Int'l*, pg. 5154
NATIONAL BANK OF MALAWI; *Int'l*, pg. 5154
NATIONAL BANK OF MIDDLEBURY—See Middlebury National Corp.; *U.S. Public*, pg. 1445
NATIONAL BANK OF NEW YORK CITY—See NEWTEKONE, INC.; *U.S. Public*, pg. 1521
THE NATIONAL BANK OF NEW ZEALAND LTD.—See Australia & New Zealand Banking Group Limited; *Int'l*, pg. 720
NATIONAL BANK OF OMAN SAOG; *Int'l*, pg. 5154
NATIONAL BANK OF PAKISTAN—See State Bank of Pakistan; *Int'l*, pg. 7182
THE NATIONAL BANK OF RAS AL-KHAIMAH PSC; *Int'l*, pg. 7670
NATIONAL BANK OF ROMANIA; *Int'l*, pg. 5154
NATIONAL BANK OF SALLISAW—See First Bank Corp.; *U.S. Private*, pg. 1514
NATIONAL BANK OF SERBIA; *Int'l*, pg. 5154
NATIONAL BANK OF SUDAN—See Bank Audi sal; *Int'l*, pg. 837
NATIONAL BANK OF TAJIKISTAN; *Int'l*, pg. 5154
NATIONAL BANK OF THE REPUBLIC OF BELARUS; *Int'l*, pg. 5154
NATIONAL BANK OF THE REPUBLIC OF MACEDONIA; *Int'l*, pg. 5154
NATIONAL BANK OF UKRAINE; *Int'l*, pg. 5154
NATIONAL BANK OF UMM AL QAIWAIN; *Int'l*, pg. 5154
NATIONAL BANK REALTY INC.—See National Bank of Canada; *Int'l*, pg. 5152
NATIONAL BANKSHARES FINANCIAL SERVICES, INC.—See National Bankshares, Inc.; *U.S. Public*, pg. 1493
NATIONAL BANKSHARES, INC.; *U.S. Public*, pg. 1493
THE NATIONAL BANK; *Int'l*, pg. 7669
NATIONAL BANK TRUST COMPANY (ST. KITTS-NEVIS-ANGUILLA) LTD.—See St. Kitts-Nevis-Anguilla National Bank Limited; *Int'l*, pg. 7159
NATIONAL BANK TRUST CO. OF SYCAMORE; *U.S. Private*, pg. 2848
NATIONAL BANK TRUST PJSC; *Int'l*, pg. 5154
NATIONAL BANK TRUST—See National Bank of Canada; *Int'l*, pg. 5152
NATIONAL BANNER COMPANY, INC.; *U.S. Private*, pg. 2848
NATIONAL BASKETBALL ASSOCIATION; *U.S. Private*, pg. 2848
NATIONAL BASKETBALL PLAYERS ASSOCIATION; *U.S. Private*, pg. 2848
NATIONAL BATTERIES COMPANY LTD—See National Industrialization Company; *Int'l*, pg. 5158
NATIONAL BEARINGS CO.—See Compagnie Generale des Etablissements Michelin SCA; *Int'l*, pg. 1745
NATIONAL BEDDING CO.—See Ares Management Corporation; *U.S. Public*, pg. 190
NATIONAL BEDDING CO.—See Ontario Teachers' Pension Plan; *Int'l*, pg. 5590
NATIONAL BEEF - DODGE CITY—See Marfrig Global Foods S.A.; *Int'l*, pg. 4692
NATIONAL BEEF LEATHERS, LLC—See Marfrig Global Foods S.A.; *Int'l*, pg. 4692
NATIONAL BEEF - LIBERAL—See Marfrig Global Foods S.A.; *Int'l*, pg. 4692
NATIONAL BEEF PACKING COMPANY, LLC—See Marfrig Global Foods S.A.; *Int'l*, pg. 4692
NATIONAL BEER WHOLESALERS ASSOCIATION; *U.S. Private*, pg. 2848
NATIONAL BENEFIT LIFE INSURANCE COMPANY—See Primerica, Inc.; *U.S. Public*, pg. 1717
NATIONAL BEVERAGE CORP.; *U.S. Public*, pg. 1493
NATIONAL BISCUIT INDUSTRIES LTD SAOG; *Int'l*, pg. 5154
NATIONAL BISCUITS & CONFECTIONERY COMPANY LTD.—See Hayel Saeed Anam Group of Companies; *Int'l*, pg. 3291
NATIONAL BLUES MUSEUM; *U.S. Private*, pg. 2848
NATIONAL BOARD FOR CERTIFICATION IN OCCUPATIONAL THERAPY, INC.; *U.S. Private*, pg. 2848

NATIONAL BOARD FOR PROFESSIONAL TEACHING STANDARDS; *U.S. Private*, pg. 2849
NATIONAL BOARD OF MEDICAL EXAMINERS; *U.S. Private*, pg. 2849
NATIONAL BOARD OF OSTEOPATHIC MEDICAL EXAMINERS, INC.; *U.S. Private*, pg. 2849
NATIONAL BOILER SERVICE INC.; *U.S. Private*, pg. 2849
NATIONAL BONDS CORPORATION PJSC—See Investment Corporation of Dubai; *Int'l*, pg. 3785
NATIONAL BOOK COMPANY INC.—See W.W. Norton & Company, Inc.; *U.S. Private*, pg. 4423
NATIONAL BOOK NETWORK, INC.—See The Rowman & Littlefield Publishing Group, Inc.; *U.S. Private*, pg. 4112
NATIONAL BRANDS, INC.; *U.S. Private*, pg. 2849
NATIONAL BRANDS LIMITED—See AVI Limited; *Int'l*, pg. 740
NATIONAL BRANDS LIMITED—See AVI Limited; *Int'l*, pg. 740
NATIONAL BRANDS LIMITED—See AVI Limited; *Int'l*, pg. 740
NATIONAL BRANDS LIMITED—See AVI Limited; *Int'l*, pg. 740
NATIONAL BREAST CANCER FOUNDATION, INC.; *U.S. Private*, pg. 2849
NATIONAL BRICK COMPANY LIMITED—See Heidelberg Materials AG; *Int'l*, pg. 3318
NATIONAL BROKERAGE SERVICES, INC.; *U.S. Private*, pg. 2849
NATIONAL BUILDING MAINTENANCE, INC.; *U.S. Private*, pg. 2849
NATIONAL BUILDING & ROOFING SUPPLIES, INC.—See Leonard Green & Partners, L.P.; *U.S. Private*, pg. 2429
NATIONAL BUILDING SOCIETY OF CAYMAN—See Jamaica National Building Society; *Int'l*, pg. 3874
NATIONAL BULK EQUIPMENT, INC.; *U.S. Private*, pg. 2849
NATIONAL BULK HANDLING CORPORATION—See 63 moons technologies limited; *Int'l*, pg. 14
NATIONAL BUSINESS AVIATION ASSOCIATION, INC.; *U.S. Private*, pg. 2849
NATIONAL BUSINESS FURNITURE INC.—See Franz Haniel & Cie. GmbH; *Int'l*, pg. 2763
NATIONAL BUSINESS FURNITURE INC—See Franz Haniel & Cie. GmbH; *Int'l*, pg. 2763
NATIONAL BUSINESS INITIATIVE; *Int'l*, pg. 5154
NATIONAL BUSINESS INSTITUTE; *U.S. Private*, pg. 2849
NATIONAL BUSINESS SUPPLY INC.; *U.S. Private*, pg. 2849
NATIONAL BUSINESS SYSTEMS, INC.—See Aquiline Capital Partners LLC; *U.S. Private*, pg. 305
NATIONAL BUS SALES & LEASING, INC.—See Creative Bus Sales Inc.; *U.S. Private*, pg. 1088
NATIONAL CABLE & WIRE MFG. CO.; *U.S. Private*, pg. 5154
NATIONAL CAMERA EXCHANGE INC.; *U.S. Private*, pg. 2849
NATIONAL CAN AUSTRALIA PTY. LTD.—See National Can Industries Limited; *Int'l*, pg. 5154
THE NATIONAL CANCER COALITION, INC.; *U.S. Private*, pg. 4082
NATIONAL CAN INDUSTRIES LIMITED; *Int'l*, pg. 5154
NATIONAL CANS & PACKING INDUSTRY LLC—See Al Batinah Development & Investment Holding Co. SAOG; *Int'l*, pg. 276
NATIONAL CAPITAL ADMINISTRATIVE SERVICES INC.—See CareFirst, Inc.; *U.S. Private*, pg. 753
NATIONAL CAPITAL BANK OF WASHINGTON; *U.S. Private*, pg. 2849
NATIONAL CAPITAL INDUSTRIES; *U.S. Private*, pg. 2849
NATIONAL CAPITOL CONTRACTING; *U.S. Private*, pg. 2850
NATIONAL CAPTIONING INSTITUTE; *U.S. Private*, pg. 2850
NATIONAL CARIBBEAN INSURANCE COMPANY—See St. Kitts-Nevis-Anguilla National Bank Limited; *Int'l*, pg. 7159
NATIONAL CAR RENTAL OF PHOENIX; *U.S. Private*, pg. 2850
NATIONAL CAR RENTALS OF CORPUS CHRISTI, INC.—See Enterprise Holdings, Inc.; *U.S. Private*, pg. 1403
NATIONAL CAR RENTAL—See Enterprise Holdings, Inc.; *U.S. Private*, pg. 1404
NATIONAL CARRIERS, INC.—See Marfrig Global Foods S.A.; *Int'l*, pg. 4692
THE NATIONAL CARTON INDUSTRY COMPANY—See Arab Supply & Trading Co.; *Int'l*, pg. 532
NATIONAL CARWASH SOLUTIONS, INC.—See Berkshire Partners LLC; *U.S. Private*, pg. 535
NATIONAL CASEIN CO. INC.; *U.S. Private*, pg. 2850
NATIONAL CATASTROPHE ADJUSTERS LLC—See Aquiline Capital Partners LLC; *U.S. Private*, pg. 305
NATIONAL CAUCUS & CENTER ON BLACK AGING, INC.; *U.S. Private*, pg. 2850
NATIONAL CEMENT COMPANY OF ALABAMA—See Vicat S.A.; *Int'l*, pg. 8186
NATIONAL CEMENT COMPANY OF CALIFORNIA—See Vicat S.A.; *Int'l*, pg. 8186
NATIONAL CEMENT COMPANY P.S.C; *Int'l*, pg. 5154

NATIONAL CEMENT COMPANY—See Chemical Industries Holding Company; *Int'l*, pg. 1462
NATIONAL CEMENT CO.—See Vicat S.A.; *Int'l*, pg. 8186
NATIONAL CEMENT HOLDINGS LIMITED—See Devki Group of Companies; *Int'l*, pg. 2089
NATIONAL CENTER FOR MANUFACTURING SCIENCES INC.; *U.S. Private*, pg. 2850
NATIONAL CENTER FOR MISSING & EXPLOITED CHILDREN; *U.S. Private*, pg. 2850
NATIONAL CENTER FOR SAFETY INITIATIVES, LLC—See Comcast Corporation; *U.S. Public*, pg. 541
NATIONAL CENTER FOR STATE COURTS; *U.S. Private*, pg. 2850
NATIONAL CENTRAL COOLING COMPANY PJSC; *Int'l*, pg. 5154
NATIONAL CERAMIC INDUSTRIES PTY LTD—See Ceramic Industries Limited; *Int'l*, pg. 1421
NATIONAL CHARITY SERVICES; *U.S. Private*, pg. 2850
NATIONAL CHEMICAL CARRIERS LTD. CO.—See National Shipping Company of Saudi Arabia; *Int'l*, pg. 5163
NATIONAL CHEMICAL CARRIERS LTD. CO.—See Saudi Basic Industries Corporation; *Int'l*, pg. 6590
NATIONAL CHEMICAL COMPANY; *Int'l*, pg. 5155
NATIONAL CHEMICAL FERTILIZER CO.—See Saudi Basic Industries Corporation; *Int'l*, pg. 6590
NATIONAL CHEMICAL & PLASTIC INDUSTRIES COMPANY; *Int'l*, pg. 5155
NATIONAL CHEMSEARCH OF CANADA LTD.—See NCH Corporation; *U.S. Private*, pg. 4268
NATIONAL CHICK LIMITED—See Astral Foods Limited; *Int'l*, pg. 658
NATIONAL CHICKS SWAZILAND (PTY) LIMITED—See Astral Foods Limited; *Int'l*, pg. 658
NATIONAL CHILDREN'S CENTER, INC.; *U.S. Private*, pg. 2850
NATIONAL CHLORINE INDUSTRIES CO. LTD.; *Int'l*, pg. 5155
NATIONAL CHRISTIAN CHARITABLE FOUNDATION, INC.; *U.S. Private*, pg. 2850
NATIONAL CHURCH RESIDENCES; *U.S. Private*, pg. 2850
NATIONAL CIGAR CORPORATION; *U.S. Private*, pg. 2850
NATIONAL CINEMEDIA, INC.; *U.S. Public*, pg. 1494
NATIONAL CINEMEDIA, LLC—See National CineMedia, Inc.; *U.S. Public*, pg. 1494
NATIONAL CITIZEN COMMERCIAL JOINT STOCK BANK; *Int'l*, pg. 5155
NATIONAL CITY MORTGAGE CO.—See The PNC Financial Services Group, Inc.; *U.S. Public*, pg. 2119
NATIONAL CITY VOLKSWAGEN; *U.S. Private*, pg. 2850
NATIONAL CLEANING COMPANY K.S.C.C.; *Int'l*, pg. 5155
NATIONAL CLEANING PRODUCTS LTD.—See The Clorox Company; *U.S. Public*, pg. 2063
NATIONAL CLOSING SOLUTIONS, INC.—See First American Financial Corporation; *U.S. Public*, pg. 838
NATIONAL CLOSING SOLUTIONS, INC. - TEXAS DIVISION—See First American Financial Corporation; *U.S. Public*, pg. 838
NATIONAL CLOSING SOLUTIONS, INC. - UTAH DIVISION—See First American Financial Corporation; *U.S. Public*, pg. 838
NATIONAL COAL SUPPLY CORPORATION LTD.—See The Israel Electric Corporation Ltd.; *Int'l*, pg. 7657
NATIONAL COATING & LINING CO.—See Brand Industrial Services, Inc.; *U.S. Private*, pg. 636
NATIONAL COATINGS & SUPPLIES, INC.; *U.S. Private*, pg. 2850
NATIONAL COLLEGIATE ATHLETIC ASSOCIATION; *U.S. Private*, pg. 2850
NATIONAL COLLEGIATE SCOUTING ASSOCIATION; *U.S. Private*, pg. 2850
NATIONAL COMMERCE BANK SERVICES, INC.—See Lincoln Property Company; *U.S. Private*, pg. 2458
NATIONAL COMMERCIAL BANK JAMAICA LIMITED—See Portland Investment Counsel Inc.; *Int'l*, pg. 5934
NATIONAL COMMERCIAL BANK LTD.—See British American Investment Co. (Mtius) Ltd.; *Int'l*, pg. 1165
NATIONAL COMMITTEE FOR QUALITY ASSURANCE; *U.S. Private*, pg. 2851
NATIONAL COMMODITY EXCHANGE, INC.—See Custom Protein Corporation; *U.S. Private*, pg. 1129
NATIONAL COMMUNICATIONS GROUP, INC.—See Dugal Visual Solutions, Inc.; *U.S. Private*, pg. 1285
NATIONAL COMMUNICATIONS SERVICES, INC.—See Affinitech, Inc.; *U.S. Private*, pg. 122
NATIONAL COMMUNITY REINVESTMENT COALITION, INC.; *U.S. Private*, pg. 2851
NATIONAL COMPANY FOOD CONTRACT CORPORATION; *Int'l*, pg. 5155
NATIONAL COMPANY FOR GLASS INDUSTRIES; *Int'l*, pg. 5155
NATIONAL COMPANY FOR MANGEMENT & SERVICES LTD—See Sodexo S.A.; *Int'l*, pg. 7045

COMPANY NAME INDEX

NATIONAL COMPANY FOR SPONGE AND PLASTIC INDUSTRY LTD.—See Hayel Saeed Anam Group of Companies; *Int'l*, pg. 3291
NATIONAL COMPANY FOR TOURISIM INVESTMENT; *Int'l*, pg. 5155
NATIONAL COMPANY KAZAKHSTAN ENGINEERING JSC; *Int'l*, pg. 5155
NATIONAL COMPREHENSIVE CANCER NETWORK; *U.S. Private*, pg. 2851
NATIONAL COMPUTER SERVICES; *U.S. Private*, pg. 2851
NATIONAL COMPUTER SERVICES—See Al-Babtain Group; *Int'l*, pg. 284
NATIONAL COMPUTER SYSTEM CO. LTD.—See Haji Husein Alireza & Co. Ltd.; *Int'l*, pg. 3219
NATIONAL COMPUTER SYSTEMS JAPAN CO LTD—See Pearson plc; *Int'l*, pg. 5776
NATIONAL CONCRETE ACCESSORIES LTD—See Nova Capital Management Limited; *Int'l*, pg. 5450
NATIONAL CONCRETE PRODUCTS COMPANY; *U.S. Private*, pg. 2851
NATIONAL CONEY ISLAND INC.; *U.S. Private*, pg. 2851
NATIONAL CONGRESS OF PARENTS AND TEACHERS; *U.S. Private*, pg. 2851
NATIONAL CONSOLIDATION SERVICES, LLC—See Menasha Corporation; *U.S. Private*, pg. 2665
NATIONAL CONSORTIUM OF BREAST CENTERS INC.; *U.S. Private*, pg. 2851
NATIONAL CONSTRUCTION ENTERPRISES INC.; *U.S. Private*, pg. 2851
NATIONAL CONSTRUCTORS INC.; *U.S. Private*, pg. 2851
NATIONAL CONSUMER HOLDING COMPANY; *Int'l*, pg. 5155
NATIONAL CONSUMER LAW CENTER, INC.; *U.S. Private*, pg. 2851
NATIONAL CONVEYORS COMPANY, INC.—See Nederman Holding AB; *Int'l*, pg. 5189
NATIONAL COOPERATIVE BUSINESS ASSOCIATION CLUSA INTERNATIONAL; *U.S. Private*, pg. 2851
NATIONAL COPPER & SMELTING COMPANY INC.—See National Tube Holding Company Inc.; *U.S. Private*, pg. 2864
NATIONAL CORPORATE HOUSING; *U.S. Private*, pg. 2851
NATIONAL CORPORATION FOR TOURISM AND HOTELS; *Int'l*, pg. 5155
NATIONAL CORSET SUPPLY HOUSE; *U.S. Private*, pg. 2852
THE NATIONAL CORVETTE MUSEUM; *U.S. Private*, pg. 4082
NATIONAL COUNCIL FOR AIR AND STREAM IMPROVEMENT, INC.; *U.S. Private*, pg. 2852
NATIONAL COUNCIL FOR BEHAVIORAL HEALTH; *U.S. Private*, pg. 2852
NATIONAL COUNCIL OF JUVENILE & FAMILY COURT JUDGES; *U.S. Private*, pg. 2852
NATIONAL COUNCIL OF STATE BOARDS OF NURSING; *U.S. Private*, pg. 2852
NATIONAL COUNCIL OF TEACHERS OF MATHEMATICS; *U.S. Private*, pg. 2852
NATIONAL COUNCIL YMCA OF THE USA; *U.S. Private*, pg. 2852
NATIONAL COURT APPOINTED SPECIAL ADVOCATE ASSOCIATION; *U.S. Private*, pg. 2852
NATIONAL CREDIT AND COMMERCE BANK PLC; *Int'l*, pg. 5155
NATIONAL CREDIT INSURANCE (BROKERS) NZ LIMITED—See QBE Insurance Group Limited; *Int'l*, pg. 6136
NATIONAL CREDIT INSURANCE (BROKERS) PTY LIMITED—See QBE Insurance Group Limited; *Int'l*, pg. 6136
NATIONAL CREDIT MANAGEMENT LIMITED—See Credit Corp Group Limited; *Int'l*, pg. 1835
NATIONAL CREMATION SERVICE, INC.—See Service Corporation International; *U.S. Public*, pg. 1870
NATIONAL CROP INSURANCE SERVICES INC.; *U.S. Private*, pg. 2852
NATIONAL CUSTOMER ENGINEERING, INC.; *U.S. Private*, pg. 2852
NATIONAL CUSTOM PACKING INC.—See The VPS Companies Inc.; *U.S. Private*, pg. 4132
NATIONAL CUTTING HORSE ASSOCIATION; *U.S. Private*, pg. 2852
NATIONAL DAIRY AND FOOD COMPANY LTD.—See Hayel Saeed Anam Group of Companies; *Int'l*, pg. 3291
THE NATIONAL DEAF ACADEMY, LLC—See Universal Health Services, Inc.; *U.S. Public*, pg. 2260
NATIONAL DECISION SUPPORT COMPANY, LLC—See UnitedHealth Group Incorporated; *U.S. Public*, pg. 2248
NATIONAL DEFENSE CORP.—See National Presto Industries, Inc; *U.S. Public*, pg. 1497
NATIONAL DEFENSE INDUSTRIAL ASSOCIATION; *U.S. Private*, pg. 2852
NATIONAL DELI, LLC—See River Associates Investments, LLC; *U.S. Private*, pg. 3443
NATIONAL DELIVERY SYSTEMS; *U.S. Private*, pg. 2852
NATIONAL DENTEX CORPORATION—See Cerberus Capital Management, L.P.; *U.S. Private*, pg. 839
NATIONAL DESIGN & TRADE NETWORK; *U.S. Private*, pg. 2852
THE NATIONAL DETERGENT COMPANY SAOG; *Int'l*, pg. 7670
NATIONAL DEVELOPMENT BANK PLC; *Int'l*, pg. 5155
NATIONAL DEVELOPMENT & RESEARCH INSTITUTES, INC.; *U.S. Private*, pg. 2852
NATIONAL DEVELOPMENT; *U.S. Private*, pg. 2852
NATIONAL DIAGNOSTIC IMAGING CENTERS, INC.—See Tenet Healthcare Corporation; *U.S. Public*, pg. 2004
NATIONAL DIRECT FINANCE (AUSTRALIA) PTY LIMITED—See Consolidated Operations Group Limited; *Int'l*, pg. 1771
NATIONAL DISTRIBUTING COMPANY, INC.—See Republic National Distributing Company; *U.S. Private*, pg. 3402
NATIONAL DISTRIBUTION CENTERS; *U.S. Private*, pg. 2852
NATIONAL DISTRIBUTION—See Public Investment Corporation; *U.S. Private*, pg. 3299
NATIONAL DISTRIBUTORS INC.; *U.S. Private*, pg. 2852
NATIONAL DIVERSIFIED SALES INC.; *U.S. Private*, pg. 2852
NATIONAL DME, L.C.; *U.S. Private*, pg. 2852
NATIONAL DOOR SYSTEMS, LLC—See National Construction Enterprises Inc.; *U.S. Private*, pg. 2851
NATIONAL DRILLING CO.; *Int'l*, pg. 5156
NATIONAL ECONOMIC RESEARCH ASSOCIATES, INC.—See Marsh & McLennan Companies, Inc.; *U.S. Public*, pg. 1387
NATIONAL ECONOMIC RESEARCH ASSOCIATES KK—See Marsh & McLennan Companies, Inc; *U.S. Public*, pg. 1387
NATIONAL EDUCATION LOAN NETWORK, INC.—See Nelnet, Inc.; *U.S. Public*, pg. 1504
NATIONAL ELDERCARE REFERRAL SYSTEMS, LLC—See Genworth Financial, Inc.; *U.S. Public*, pg. 934
NATIONAL ELECTRICAL CARBON B.V.—See Morgan Advanood Matorials plc; *Int'l*, pg. 5043
NATIONAL ELECTRICAL CARBON CORPORATION—See Morgan Advanced Materials plc; *Int'l*, pg. 5041
NATIONAL ELECTRICAL CARBON PRODUCTS INC—See Morgan Advanced Materials plc; *Int'l*, pg. 5041
NATIONAL ELECTRICAL MANUFACTURERS ASSOCIATION - MEDICAL IMAGING AND TECHNOLOGY ALLIANCE DIVISION—See National Electrical Manufacturers Association; *U.S. Private*, pg. 2853
NATIONAL ELECTRICAL MANUFACTURERS ASSOCIATION; *U.S. Private*, pg. 2853
NATIONAL ELECTRIC COIL; *U.S. Private*, pg. 2853
NATIONAL ELECTRIC SUPPLY CO., INC.—See Crescent Electric Supply Company; *U.S. Private*, pg. 1093
NATIONAL ELECTRIC VEHICLE SWEDEN AB; *Int'l*, pg. 5156
NATIONAL ELECTRONIC ALLOYS; *U.S. Private*, pg. 2853
NATIONAL ELECTRONIC ATTACHMENT, INC.—See Accel Partners L.P.; *U.S. Private*, pg. 48
NATIONAL ELECTRONIC ATTACHMENT, INC.—See KKR & Co. Inc.; *U.S. Public*, pg. 1238
NATIONAL ELECTRONICS (CONSOLIDATED) LIMITED—See National Electronics Holdings Limited; *Int'l*, pg. 5156
NATIONAL ELECTRONICS HOLDINGS LIMITED; *Int'l*, pg. 5156
NATIONAL ELECTRONICS & WATCH COMPANY LTD.—See National Electronics Holdings Limited; *Int'l*, pg. 5156
NATIONAL ELECTROSTATICS CORPORATION; *U.S. Private*, pg. 2853
NATIONAL EMPLOYEE ASSISTANCE SERVICES INC.—See ProHealth Care, Inc.; *U.S. Private*, pg. 3280
NATIONAL ENCLOSURE COMPANY—See National Construction Enterprises Inc.; *U.S. Private*, pg. 2851
NATIONALE-NEDERLANDEN BANK N.V.—See NN Group N.V.; *Int'l*, pg. 5394
NATIONALE-NEDERLANDEN GENERALES, COMPANIA DE SEGUROS Y REASEGUROS S.A.—See NN Group N.V.; *Int'l*, pg. 5394
NATIONALE-NEDERLANDEN OTWARTY FUNDUSZ EMERYTALNY; *Int'l*, pg. 5164
NATIONALE-NEDERLANDEN POWSZECHNE TOWARZYSTWO EMERYTALNE S.A.—See NN Group N.V.; *Int'l*, pg. 5394
NATIONALE-NEDERLANDEN SCHADEVERZEKERING MAATSCHAPPIJ N.V.—See NN Group N.V.; *Int'l*, pg. 5394
NATIONALE-NEDERLANDEN SERVICES N.V.—See NN Group N.V.; *Int'l*, pg. 5394
NATIONALE-NEDERLANDEN VIDA, COMPANIA DE SEGUROS Y REASEGUROS S.A.—See NN Group N.V.; *Int'l*, pg. 5394

NATIONAL FINANCE CO. S.A.O.G

NATIONAL ENERGY CORPORATION OF TRINIDAD AND TOBAGO LIMITED—See National Gas Company of Trinidad & Tobago Limited; *Int'l*, pg. 5157
NATIONAL ENERGY EQUIPMENT, INC.; *Int'l*, pg. 5156
NATIONAL ENERGY HOLDING COMPANY INC.—See Raleigh Mine & Industrial Supply, Inc.; *U.S. Private*, pg. 3350
NATIONAL ENERGY & LIGHT, LLC; *U.S. Private*, pg. 2853
NATIONAL ENERGY SERVICES, INC.; *U.S. Private*, pg. 2853
NATIONAL ENERGY SERVICES REUNITED CORP.; *U.S. Public*, pg. 1494
NATIONAL ENGINEERING INDUSTRIES LTD—See CK Birla Group; *Int'l*, pg. 1636
NATIONAL ENGINEERING PRODUCTS COMPANY, INC.—See Sanmar Holdings Ltd.; *Int'l*, pg. 6546
NATIONAL ENGINEERING PTY LTD; *Int'l*, pg. 5156
NATIONAL ENGINEERING & TECHNICAL COMPANY LIMITED—See Nigerian National Petroleum Corporation; *Int'l*, pg. 5282
THE NATIONAL ENQUIRER—See Chatham Asset Management, LLC; *U.S. Private*, pg. 860
NATIONAL ENROLLMENT SERVICES, INC.—See Aon plc; *Int'l*, pg. 497
NATIONAL ENTERPRISES LIMITED; *Int'l*, pg. 5156
NATIONAL ENTERTAINMENT COLLECTIBLES ASSOCIATION, INC; *U.S. Private*, pg. 2853
NATIONAL ENTERTAINMENT NETWORK, INC.; *U.S. Private*, pg. 2853
NATIONAL ENVIRONMENTAL TRAINERS INC.—See Frontenac Company LLC; *U.S. Private*, pg. 1614
NATIONAL ENZYME COMPANY; *U.S. Private*, pg. 2853
NATIONAL EQUICOM, INC.—See RES PUBLICA Consulting Group Inc.; *Int'l*, pg. 6295
NATIONAL EQUIPMENT CORP.; *U.S. Private*, pg. 2853
NATIONAL EQUITIES LIMITED—See National Australia Bank Limited; *Int'l*, pg. 5151
NATIONAL EQUITY TITLE AGENCY; *U.S. Private*, pg. 2853
NATIONALE WAARBORG B.V.—See Stone Point Capital LLC; *U.S. Private*, pg. 3821
NATIONAL EWP, INC.; *U.S. Private*, pg. 2853
NATIONAL EXAMINATION CENTER INC.—See Pasona Group Inc.; *Int'l*, pg. 5753
NATIONAL EXCELSIOR COMPANY—See Carrier Global Corporation; *U.S. Public*, pg. 444
NATIONAL EXCELSIOR COMPANY—See Watsco, Inc.; *U.S. Public*, pg. 2336
NATIONAL EXCHANGE BANK & TRUST—See NEB Corporation; *U.S. Private*, pg. 2878
NATIONAL EXPERT WITNESS NETWORK; *U.S. Private*, pg. 2853
NATIONAL EXPRESS CORPORATION—See Mobico Group PLC.; *Int'l*, pg. 5009
NATIONAL EXPRESS LIMITED—See Mobico Group PLC.; *Int'l*, pg. 5009
NATIONAL EXPRESS LLC—See Mobico Group PLC.; *Int'l*, pg. 5009
NATIONAL EXPRESS MANCHESTER METROLINK LIMITED—See Mobico Group PLC.; *Int'l*, pg. 5009
NATIONAL EXPRESS WEST MIDLANDS—See Mobico Group PLC.; *Int'l*, pg. 5009
NATIONAL FACTORY FOR GLASS BOTTLES—See National Company for Glass Industries; *Int'l*, pg. 5155
NATIONAL FAMILY CARE LIFE INSURANCE; *U.S. Private*, pg. 2853
NATIONAL FARMERS UNION LIFE INSURANCE COMPANY—See Financial Holding Corp.; *U.S. Private*, pg. 1507
NATIONAL FARMERS UNION PROPERTY & CASUALTY COMPANY—See The Allstate Corporation; *U.S. Public*, pg. 2034
NATIONAL FEDERATION OF AGRICULTURAL CO-OPERATIVE ASSOCIATIONS; *Int'l*, pg. 5156
NATIONAL FEDERATION OF INDEPENDENT BUSINESS; *U.S. Private*, pg. 2853
NATIONAL FEDERATION OF THE BLIND; *U.S. Private*, pg. 2853
NATIONAL FERTILIZER CORPORATION OF PAKISTAN (PRIVATE) LIMITED—See Agritech Limited; *Int'l*, pg. 218
NATIONAL FERTILIZERS LTD; *Int'l*, pg. 5156
NATIONAL FFA FOUNDATION; *U.S. Private*, pg. 2853
NATIONAL FIBER, INC.; *U.S. Private*, pg. 2853
NATIONAL FIBER SUPPLY LLC; *U.S. Private*, pg. 2853
NATIONAL FIBRES LIMITED; *Int'l*, pg. 5156
NATIONAL FILM BOARD OF CANADA; *Int'l*, pg. 5156
NATIONAL FILM BOARD OF CANADA—See National Film Board of Canada; *Int'l*, pg. 5156
NATIONAL FILTER MEDIA—See Perma-Pipe International Holdings, Inc.; *U.S. Public*, pg. 1676
NATIONAL FINANCE CO. S.A.O.G; *Int'l*, pg. 5156
NATIONAL FINANCIAL INSURANCE AGENCY INC.—See iA Financial Corporation Inc.; *Int'l*, pg. 3567
NATIONAL FINANCIAL SERVICES LLC—See FMR LLC; *U.S. Private*, pg. 1555
NATIONAL FIRE HOLDINGS PTY. LIMITED—See Evergreen Capital L.P.; *U.S. Private*, pg. 1438

NATIONAL FINANCE CO. S.A.O.G

CORPORATE AFFILIATIONS

NATIONAL FIRE & MARINE INSURANCE COMPANY—See Berkshire Hathaway Inc.; *U.S. Public*, pg. 302

NATIONAL FIRE PROTECTION ASSOCIATION; *U.S. Private*, pg. 2853

NATIONAL FIRE PROTECTION INC.; *U.S. Private*, pg. 2854

NATIONAL FIRE & SAFETY, INC.—See Highview Capital, LLC; *U.S. Private*, pg. 1942

NATIONAL FIRE SOLUTIONS (QLD) PTY LTD—See Evergreen Capital L.P.; *U.S. Private*, pg. 1439

NATIONAL FIRE SOLUTIONS (WA) PTY LTD—See Evergreen Capital L.P.; *U.S. Private*, pg. 1439

NATIONAL FISHERIES INSTITUTE INC.; *U.S. Private*, pg. 2854

NATIONAL FITTINGS LIMITED; *Int'l*, pg. 5156

NATIONAL FLAVORS, LLC—See The Riverside Company; *U.S. Private*, pg. 4109

NATIONAL FLEET & LEASE—See Stellantis N.V.; *Int'l*, pg. 7199

NATIONAL FLEET MANAGEMENT, INC.; *U.S. Private*, pg. 2854

NATIONAL FLEET SOLUTIONS LIMITED—See Pinewood Technologies Group PLC; *Int'l*, pg. 5869

NATIONAL FLIGHT SERVICES INC—See NFS Holdings Inc.; *U.S. Private*, pg. 2923

NATIONAL FLOOD SERVICES, INC.—See Aon plc; *Int'l*, pg. 489

NATIONAL FLORAL SUPPLY OF MARYLAND; *U.S. Private*, pg. 2854

NATIONAL FLOUR MILLS - LEBANON WLL—See Al Ghurair Investment LLC; *Int'l*, pg. 278

NATIONAL FLOUR MILLS LIMITED; *Int'l*, pg. 5157

NATIONAL FOOD COMPANY—See Qatar Industrial Manufacturing Company (S.A.Q.); *Int'l*, pg. 6133

NATIONAL FOOD GROUP; *U.S. Private*, pg. 2854

NATIONAL FOOD INDUSTRIES COMPANY LIMITED—See Adeptio LLC; *Int'l*, pg. 143

NATIONAL FOOD INGREDIENTS LIMITED—See Kerry Group plc; *Int'l*, pg. 4139

THE NATIONAL FOOD LAB, INC.—See Eurofins Scientific S.E.; *Int'l*, pg. 2552

NATIONAL FOODS DMCC—See NATIONAL FOODS LIMITED; *Int'l*, pg. 5157

NATIONAL FOODS HOLDINGS LTD.; *Int'l*, pg. 5157

NATIONAL FOODS LIMITED; *Int'l*, pg. 5157

NATIONAL FOOD STORES, INC.; *U.S. Private*, pg. 2854

NATIONAL FOOTBALL LEAGUE PLAYERS ASSOCIATION; *U.S. Private*, pg. 2854

NATIONAL FOOTBALL LEAGUE PLAYERS INCORPORATED—See National Football League Players Association; *U.S. Private*, pg. 2854

NATIONAL FOOTBALL LEAGUE; *U.S. Private*, pg. 2854

NATIONAL FOOTBALL MUSEUM, INC.; *U.S. Private*, pg. 2854

NATIONAL FORENSIC SCIENCE TECHNOLOGY CENTER, INC.; *U.S. Private*, pg. 2854

NATIONAL FOREST FOUNDATION; *U.S. Private*, pg. 2854

NATIONAL FOUNDATION FOR CANCER RESEARCH; *U.S. Private*, pg. 2854

NATIONAL FOUNDATION FOR CREDIT COUNSELING; *U.S. Private*, pg. 2854

NATIONAL FOUNDATION LIFE INSURANCE COMPANY—See UnitedHealth Group Incorporated; *U.S. Public*, pg. 2242

NATIONAL FROZEN FOODS CORPORATION - ALBANY—See National Frozen Foods Corporation; *U.S. Private*, pg. 2855

NATIONAL FROZEN FOODS CORPORATION - CHEHALIS—See National Frozen Foods Corporation; *U.S. Private*, pg. 2855

NATIONAL FROZEN FOODS CORPORATION - MOSES LAKE—See National Frozen Foods Corporation; *U.S. Private*, pg. 2855

NATIONAL FROZEN FOODS CORPORATION - QUINCY DIVISION—See National Frozen Foods Corporation; *U.S. Private*, pg. 2855

NATIONAL FROZEN FOODS CORPORATION; *U.S. Private*, pg. 2854

NATIONAL FRUIT PRODUCT COMPANY, INC. - BRAND RETAIL DIVISION—See National Fruit Product Company, Inc.; *U.S. Private*, pg. 2855

NATIONAL FRUIT PRODUCT COMPANY, INC. - FOOD SERVICES DIVISION—See National Fruit Product Company, Inc.; *U.S. Private*, pg. 2855

NATIONAL FRUIT PRODUCT COMPANY, INC. - PRIVATE LABEL RETAIL DIVISION—See National Fruit Product Company, Inc.; *U.S. Private*, pg. 2855

NATIONAL FRUIT PRODUCT COMPANY, INC.; *U.S. Private*, pg. 2855

NATIONAL FUEL GAS COMPANY; *U.S. Public*, pg. 1494

NATIONAL FUEL GAS DISTRIBUTION CORPORATION—See National Fuel Gas Company; *U.S. Public*, pg. 1494

NATIONAL FUEL GAS SUPPLY CORPORATION—See National Fuel Gas Company; *U.S. Public*, pg. 1494

NATIONAL FUEL OIL INC.; *U.S. Private*, pg. 2855

NATIONAL FUEL RESOURCES, INC.—See National Fuel Gas Company; *U.S. Public*, pg. 1494

NATIONAL FULLERTON ASSET MANAGEMENT LIMITED—See State Bank of Pakistan; *Int'l*, pg. 7182

NATIONAL FUNDING INC.; *U.S. Private*, pg. 2855

NATIONAL GALVANIZING LP—See Heidtman Steel Products, Inc.; *U.S. Private*, pg. 1904

NATIONAL GARDEN WHOLESALE; *U.S. Private*, pg. 2855

NATIONAL GAS COMPANY OF TRINIDAD & TOBAGO LIMITED; *Int'l*, pg. 5157

NATIONAL GAS COMPANY SOAG; *Int'l*, pg. 5157

NATIONAL GAS & INDUSTRIALIZATION CO.; *Int'l*, pg. 5157

NATIONAL GAS & OIL COMPANY—See The Energy Cooperative, Inc.; *U.S. Private*, pg. 4026

NATIONAL GAS & OIL COOPERATIVE—See The Energy Cooperative, Inc.; *U.S. Private*, pg. 4026

NATIONAL GAS SHIPPING COMPANY LTD. (NGSCO)—See Abu Dhabi National Oil Company; *Int'l*, pg. 73

NATIONAL GENERAL HOLDINGS CORP.—See The Allstate Corporation; *U.S. Public*, pg. 2033

NATIONAL GENERAL INDUSTRIES LIMITED; *Int'l*, pg. 5157

NATIONAL GENERAL INSURANCE COMPANY—See The Allstate Corporation; *U.S. Public*, pg. 2034

NATIONAL GENERAL INSURANCE CO. (P.S.C.); *Int'l*, pg. 5157

NATIONAL GENERAL MANAGEMENT CORP.—See The Allstate Corporation; *U.S. Public*, pg. 2034

NATIONAL GENERAL MOTOR CLUB, INC.—See The Allstate Corporation; *U.S. Public*, pg. 2034

NATIONAL-GENERAL SUPPLY, INC.; *U.S. Private*, pg. 2865

NATIONAL GENETICS INSTITUTE—See Laboratory Corporation of America Holdings; *U.S. Public*, pg. 1287

NATIONAL GEOGRAPHIC BOOKS GROUP—See National Geographic Society; *U.S. Private*, pg. 2855

NATIONAL GEOGRAPHIC CHANNEL ADVENTURE MEDYA HIZMETLERI A.S.—See The Walt Disney Company; *U.S. Public*, pg. 2141

NATIONAL GEOGRAPHIC CHANNEL DENMARK APS—See The Walt Disney Company; *U.S. Public*, pg. 2141

NATIONAL GEOGRAPHIC MAGAZINE GROUP—See National Geographic Society; *U.S. Private*, pg. 2855

NATIONAL GEOGRAPHIC PARTNERS, LLC—See The Walt Disney Company; *U.S. Public*, pg. 2140

NATIONAL GEOGRAPHIC SOCIETY; *U.S. Private*, pg. 2855

NATIONAL GIFT CARD CORPORATION—See LSCG Management, Inc.; *U.S. Private*, pg. 2508

NATIONAL GOLF CLUB, INC.—See Pinehurst, LLC; *U.S. Private*, pg. 3183

NATIONAL GOVERNMENT SERVICES, INC.—See Elevance Health, Inc.; *U.S. Public*, pg. 730

THE NATIONAL GRAND BANK OF MARBLEHEAD—See Grand Bank Corporation; *U.S. Public*, pg. 956

NATIONAL GRAPE CO-OP ASSOCIATION, INC.; *U.S. Private*, pg. 2855

NATIONAL GRAPHITE CORP.; *U.S. Public*, pg. 1494

NATIONAL GREENHOUSE COMPANY—See Gibraltar Industries, Inc.; *U.S. Public*, pg. 936

NATIONAL GRID CORPORATION OF THE PHILIPPINES—See State Grid Corporation of China; *Int'l*, pg. 7183

NATIONAL GRID ELECTRICITY SYSTEM OPERATOR LIMITED—See National Grid plc; *Int'l*, pg. 5157

NATIONAL GRID ELECTRICITY TRANSMISSION PLC—See National Grid plc; *Int'l*, pg. 5157

NATIONAL GRID GAS PLC—See National Grid plc; *Int'l*, pg. 5157

NATIONAL GRID GRAIN LNG LIMITED—See National Grid plc; *Int'l*, pg. 5157

NATIONAL GRID HOLDINGS LIMITED—See National Grid plc; *Int'l*, pg. 5157

NATIONAL GRID METERING LIMITED—See National Grid plc; *Int'l*, pg. 5157

NATIONAL GRID PLC; *Int'l*, pg. 5157

NATIONAL GRID PROPERTY LIMITED—See National Grid plc; *Int'l*, pg. 5157

NATIONAL GRID RENEWABLES, LLC—See National Grid plc; *Int'l*, pg. 5157

NATIONAL GRID USA—See National Grid plc; *Int'l*, pg. 5157

NATIONAL GROUP OF COMPANIES LLC; *Int'l*, pg. 5158

THE NATIONAL GUARD ASSOCIATION OF THE UNITED STATES; *U.S. Private*, pg. 4082

NATIONAL GUARDIAN LIFE INSURANCE COMPANY; *U.S. Private*, pg. 2855

NATIONAL GULF PETROLEUM SERVICES WLL—See National Energy Services Reunited Corp.; *U.S. Public*, pg. 1494

NATIONAL GYPSUM COMPANY; *Int'l*, pg. 5158

NATIONAL GYPSUM SERVICES COMPANY—See Spangler Companies, Inc.; *U.S. Private*, pg. 3745

NATIONAL HANOVER PRESS LTD; *U.S. Private*, pg. 2855

NATIONAL HARMONY MEMORIAL PARK, INC.—See Service Corporation International; *U.S. Public*, pg. 1871

NATIONAL HEALTHCARE CENTER OF FORT OGLETHORPE, L.P.—See National HealthCare Corporation; *U.S. Public*, pg. 1496

NATIONAL HEALTHCARE CORPORATION—See National HealthCare Corporation; *U.S. Public*, pg. 1496

NATIONAL HEALTHCARE CORPORATION—See National HealthCare Corporation; *U.S. Public*, pg. 1496

NATIONAL HEALTHCARE CORPORATION; *U.S. Public*, pg. 1495

NATIONAL HEALTHCARE DISTRIBUTION, INC.; *U.S. Private*, pg. 2856

NATIONAL HEALTHCARE LOGISTICS, INC.; *U.S. Public*, pg. 1497

NATIONAL HEALTHCARE OF LEESVILLE, INC.—See Community Health Systems, Inc.; *U.S. Public*, pg. 555

NATIONAL HEALTHCARE OF MT. VERNON, INC.—See Quorum Health Corporation; *U.S. Private*, pg. 3330

NATIONAL HEALTHCARE OF NEWPORT, INC.—See Unity Health - White County Medical Center; *U.S. Private*, pg. 4303

NATIONAL HEALTHCARE PROPERTIES, INC.; *U.S. Public*, pg. 1497

NATIONAL HEALTHCARE RESEARCH & EDUCATION FINANCE CORPORATION; *U.S. Private*, pg. 2856

NATIONAL HEALTHCARE RESOURCES, INC—See Greenbriar Equity Group, L.P.; *U.S. Private*, pg. 1776

NATIONAL HEALTHCARE RESOURCES, INC—See Revolent Capital Solutions; *U.S. Private*, pg. 3416

NATIONAL HEALTHCARE REVIEW INC.; *U.S. Private*, pg. 2856

NATIONAL HEALTH CORPORATION; *U.S. Private*, pg. 2855

NATIONAL HEALTH FINANCE DM, LLC—See LawFinance Ltd.; *Int'l*, pg. 4425

NATIONAL HEALTH INFUSION—See Option Care Health, Inc.; *U.S. Public*, pg. 1610

NATIONAL HEALTH INSURANCE CO—See National Health Corporation; *U.S. Private*, pg. 2856

NATIONAL HEALTH INVESTORS, INC.; *U.S. Public*, pg. 1494

NATIONAL HEALTH PARTNERS, INC.; *U.S. Private*, pg. 2856

NATIONAL HEATERS INDUSTRIES CO. LLC—See Omar Zawawi Establishment LLC; *Int'l*, pg. 5561

NATIONAL HEATING & AIR CONDITIONING COMPANY—See Heartland Home Services, Inc.; *U.S. Private*, pg. 1900

NATIONAL HEAT & POWER CORP; *U.S. Private*, pg. 2856

NATIONAL HERITAGE ACADEMIES, INC.; *U.S. Private*, pg. 2856

NATIONAL HERITAGE FOUNDATION, INC.; *U.S. Private*, pg. 2856

NATIONAL HIGH POWER TEST LABORATORY PRIVATE LIMITED—See NHPC Ltd.; *Int'l*, pg. 5259

NATIONAL HIGHWAYS AUTHORITY OF INDIA; *Int'l*, pg. 5158

NATIONAL HIGHWAYS LOGISTIC MANAGEMENT LIMITED—See National Highways Authority of India; *Int'l*, pg. 5158

NATIONAL HIRE GROUP LIMITED—See Seven Group Holdings Limited; *Int'l*, pg. 6733

NATIONAL HIRE TRADING PTY LIMITED—See Seven Group Holdings Limited; *Int'l*, pg. 6733

NATIONAL HME, INC.—See New Mountain Capital, LLC; *U.S. Private*, pg. 2903

NATIONAL HOCKEY LEAGUE; *U.S. Private*, pg. 2856

NATIONAL HOLDING INVESTMENT CO.—See National Presto Industries, Inc; *U.S. Public*, pg. 1497

NATIONAL HOLDING KAZAGRO JSC; *Int'l*, pg. 5158

NATIONAL HOLDINGS CORPORATION—See B. Riley Financial, Inc.; *U.S. Public*, pg. 261

NATIONAL HOME COMMUNITIES LLC; *U.S. Private*, pg. 2856

NATIONAL HOME HEALTH CARE CORP.—See Blue Wolf Capital Partners LLC; *U.S. Private*, pg. 595

NATIONAL HOSE & ACCESSORY, INC.—See AEA Investors LP; *U.S. Private*, pg. 115

NATIONAL HOTELS COMPANY B.S.C.; *Int'l*, pg. 5158

NATIONAL HOUSEHOLD FURNITURE INDUSTRY CO.; *Int'l*, pg. 5158

NATIONAL HOUSING BANK—See Reserve Bank of India; *Int'l*, pg. 6295

NATIONAL HOUSING FINANCE PLC; *Int'l*, pg. 5158

NATIONAL HVAC SERVICE LTD.; *U.S. Private*, pg. 2856

NATIONAL IMAGING ASSOCIATES INC.—See Centene Corporation; *U.S. Public*, pg. 470

NATIONAL IMAGING OF CARTERVILLE, LLC—See Quorum Health Corporation; *U.S. Private*, pg. 3330

NATIONAL IMAGING OF MOUNT VERNON, LLC—See Quorum Health Corporation; *U.S. Private*, pg. 3330

NATIONAL IMPRINT CORPORATION—See Ennis, Inc.; *U.S. Public*, pg. 769

NATIONAL INDEMNITY COMPANY OF MID-AMERICA—See Berkshire Hathaway Inc.; *U.S. Public*, pg. 302

COMPANY NAME INDEX

NATIONAL INDEMNITY COMPANY OF THE SOUTH—See Berkshire Hathaway Inc.; *U.S. Public*, pg. 302
NATIONAL INDEMNITY COMPANY—See Berkshire Hathaway Inc.; *U.S. Public*, pg. 302
NATIONAL INDUSTRIAL FUEL EFFICIENCY LIMITED—See Grovepoint Capital LLP; *Int'l*, pg. 3112
NATIONAL INDUSTRIAL FUEL EFFICIENCY LIMITED—See Rubicon Partners Limited; *Int'l*, pg. 6422
NATIONAL INDUSTRIALIZATION COMPANY; *Int'l*, pg. 5158
NATIONAL INDUSTRIALIZATION & ENERGY SERVICES COMPANY CO. LTD.—See National Industrialization Company; *Int'l*, pg. 5158
NATIONAL INDUSTRIALIZATION PETROCHEMICAL MARKETING COMPANY—See National Industrialization Company; *Int'l*, pg. 5158
NATIONAL INDUSTRIAL LUMBER CO (NILCO); *U.S. Private*, pg. 2856
NATIONAL INDUSTRIAL MAINTENANCE, INC.—See Carylon Corporation; *U.S. Private*, pg. 777
NATIONAL INDUSTRIES COMPANY K.S.C.—See National Industries Group Holding S.A.K.; *Int'l*, pg. 5159
NATIONAL INDUSTRIES GROUP HOLDING S.A.K.; *Int'l*, pg. 5159
NATIONAL INFORMATION SOLUTIONS COOPERATIVE (NISC); *U.S. Private*, pg. 2856
NATIONAL INSPECTION AND TECHNICAL TESTING CO. LTD.—See National Industrialization Company; *Int'l*, pg. 5158
NATIONAL INSPECTION & CONSULTANTS, LLC—See Edgewater Services, LLC; *U.S. Private*, pg. 1335
NATIONAL INSPECTION & CONSULTANTS, LLC—See JZ Capital Partners Limited; *Int'l*, pg. 4037
NATIONAL INSTITUTE FOR HEALTH & CLINICAL EXCELLENCE; *Int'l*, pg. 5159
THE NATIONAL INSTITUTE FOR HOMETOWN SECURITY; *U.S. Private*, pg. 4082
NATIONAL INSTITUTE OF AEROSPACE; *U.S. Private*, pg. 2856
NATIONAL INSTRUMENTS AM LLC—See National Instruments Corporation; *U.S. Private*, pg. 2857
NATIONAL INSTRUMENTS ASIA MINOR OLOUM CI HAZLARI TICARET LIMITED SIRKETI—See National Instruments Corporation; *U.S. Private*, pg. 2857
NATIONAL INSTRUMENTS AUSTRALIA CORPORATION—See National Instruments Corporation; *U.S. Private*, pg. 2857
NATIONAL INSTRUMENTS BELGIUM N.V.—See National Instruments Corporation; *U.S. Private*, pg. 2857
NATIONAL INSTRUMENTS BRAZIL LTDA.—See National Instruments Corporation; *U.S. Private*, pg. 2857
NATIONAL INSTRUMENTS CHILE SPA.—See National Instruments Corporation; *U.S. Private*, pg. 2857
NATIONAL INSTRUMENTS CHINA CORPORATION—See National Instruments Corporation; *U.S. Private*, pg. 2857
NATIONAL INSTRUMENTS COLOMBIA SAS—See National Instruments Corporation; *U.S. Private*, pg. 2857
NATIONAL INSTRUMENTS CORPORATION DENMARK—See National Instruments Corporation; *U.S. Private*, pg. 2857
NATIONAL INSTRUMENTS CORPORATION FRANCE—See National Instruments Corporation; *U.S. Private*, pg. 2857
NATIONAL INSTRUMENTS CORPORATION GERMANY—See National Instruments Corporation; *U.S. Private*, pg. 2857
NATIONAL INSTRUMENTS CORPORATION ITALY—See National Instruments Corporation; *U.S. Private*, pg. 2857
NATIONAL INSTRUMENTS CORPORATION JAPAN—See National Instruments Corporation; *U.S. Private*, pg. 2857
NATIONAL INSTRUMENTS CORPORATION SINGAPORE—See National Instruments Corporation; *U.S. Private*, pg. 2857
NATIONAL INSTRUMENTS CORPORATION; *U.S. Private*, pg. 2856
NATIONAL INSTRUMENTS CORPORATION SPAIN—See National Instruments Corporation; *U.S. Private*, pg. 2857
NATIONAL INSTRUMENTS CORPORATION (UK) LIMITED—See National Instruments Corporation; *U.S. Private*, pg. 2857
NATIONAL INSTRUMENTS DENMARK APS—See National Instruments Corporation; *U.S. Private*, pg. 2857
NATIONAL INSTRUMENTS DRESDEN GMBH—See National Instruments Corporation; *U.S. Private*, pg. 2857
NATIONAL INSTRUMENTS EGYPT LLC—See National Instruments Corporation; *U.S. Private*, pg. 2857
NATIONAL INSTRUMENTS FRANCE SAS—See National Instruments Corporation; *U.S. Private*, pg. 2857
NATIONAL INSTRUMENTS GERMANY GMBH—See National Instruments Corporation; *U.S. Private*, pg. 2857
NATIONAL INSTRUMENTS HUNGARY KFT.—See National Instruments Corporation; *U.S. Private*, pg. 2857
NATIONAL INSTRUMENTS INSTRUMENTACIJA, AVTOMATIZACIJA IN UPRAVLJANJE PROCESOV D.O.O.—See National Instruments Corporation; *U.S. Private*, pg. 2857
NATIONAL INSTRUMENTS ITALY S.R.L.—See National Instruments Corporation; *U.S. Private*, pg. 2857
NATIONAL INSTRUMENTS JAPAN KK—See National Instruments Corporation; *U.S. Private*, pg. 2857
NATIONAL INSTRUMENTS LEBANON SARL—See National Instruments Corporation; *U.S. Private*, pg. 2857
NATIONAL INSTRUMENTS POLAND SP. Z.O.O.—See National Instruments Corporation; *U.S. Private*, pg. 2857
NATIONAL INSTRUMENTS PORTUGAL UNIPESSOAL LDA.—See National Instruments Corporation; *U.S. Private*, pg. 2857
NATIONAL INSTRUMENTS RUS LLC—See National Instruments Corporation; *U.S. Private*, pg. 2857
NATIONAL INSTRUMENTS SAUDI ARABIA, LLC—See National Instruments Corporation; *U.S. Private*, pg. 2857
NATIONAL INSTRUMENTS SINGAPORE (PTE) LTD.—See National Instruments Corporation; *U.S. Private*, pg. 2857
NATIONAL INSTRUMENTS SPAIN, S.L.—See National Instruments Corporation; *U.S. Private*, pg. 2857
NATIONAL INSTRUMENTS SWITZERLAND CORPORATION—See National Instruments Corporation; *U.S. Private*, pg. 2857
NATIONAL INSTRUMENTS TAIWAN CORPORATION—See National Instruments Corporation; *U.S. Private*, pg. 2857
NATIONAL INSTRUMENTS (THAILAND) CO., LTD.—See National Instruments Corporation; *U.S. Private*, pg. 2857
NATIONAL INSULATED BLOCKS INDUSTRIES—See Dubai Investments PJSC; *Int'l*, pg. 2857
NATIONAL INSULATION, CO.—See Shook & Fletcher Insulation Co., Inc.; *U.S. Private*, pg. 3639
NATIONAL INSURANCE AGENCY—See Assurant, Inc.; *U.S. Public*, pg. 215
NATIONAL INSURANCE AND GUARANTEE CORPORATION LIMITED—See Direct Line Insurance Group plc; *Int'l*, pg. 2130
NATIONAL INSURANCE BROKERAGE, LLC—See Aon plc; *Int'l*, pg. 497
NATIONAL INSURANCE COMPANY BERHAD; *Int'l*, pg. 5159
NATIONAL INSURANCE COMPANY (P.S.C); *Int'l*, pg. 5159
NATIONAL INSURANCE COMPANY; *U.S. Private*, pg. 2858
NATIONAL INSURANCE COMPANY; *Int'l*, pg. 5159
NATIONAL INSURANCE CORPORATION—See Industrial & General Insurance Plc; *Int'l*, pg. 3671
NATIONAL INSURANCE SERVICES, INC.; *U.S. Private*, pg. 2858
NATIONAL INSURANCE SOLUTIONS INC.—See Seeman Holtz Property & Casualty, LLC; *U.S. Private*, pg. 3598
NATIONAL INTEGRITY LIFE INSURANCE COMPANY—See Western & Southern Financial Group, Inc.; *U.S. Private*, pg. 4490
NATIONAL INTERNATIONAL HOLDING COMPANY K.S.C.P.; *Int'l*, pg. 5159
NATIONAL INTERSTATE CORPORATION—See American Financial Group, Inc.; *U.S. Public*, pg. 103
NATIONAL INTERSTATE INSURANCE AGENCY, INC.—See American Financial Group, Inc.; *U.S. Public*, pg. 103
NATIONAL INTERSTATE INSURANCE COMPANY OF HAWAII, INC.—See American Financial Group, Inc.; *U.S. Public*, pg. 103
NATIONAL INVESTMENTS COMPANY K.S.C.C.; *Int'l*, pg. 5159
NATIONAL INVESTMENT SERVICES, INC.; *U.S. Private*, pg. 2858
NATIONAL INVESTMENTS FUND LIMITED; *Int'l*, pg. 5160
NATIONAL INVESTMENT TRUST LIMITED; *Int'l*, pg. 5159
NATIONAL INVESTORS TITLE INSURANCE COMPANY—See Investors Title Company; *U.S. Public*, pg. 1165
NATIONAL INVESTORS TITLE INSURANCE COMPANY—See Investors Title Company; *U.S. Public*, pg. 1165
NATIONAL IRANIAN COPPER INDUSTRIES COMPANY; *Int'l*, pg. 5160
NATIONAL IRANIAN DRILLING COMPANY—See National Iranian Oil Company; *Int'l*, pg. 5160
NATIONAL IRANIAN LEAD & ZINC COMPANY; *Int'l*, pg. 5160
NATIONAL IRANIAN OIL COMPANY; *Int'l*, pg. 5160
NATIONAL IRANIAN SOUTH OIL COMPANY—See National Iranian Oil Company; *Int'l*, pg. 5160
NATIONAL IRISH BANK LIMITED—See Danske Bank A/S; *Int'l*, pg. 1969
NATIONAL JETS, INC.—See Carolina Aircraft Corp.; *U.S. Private*, pg. 767

NATIONAL MEDICAL SERVICES, INC.

NATIONAL JOINT-STOCK COMPANY NAFTOGAZ OF UKRAINE; *Int'l*, pg. 5160
NATIONAL JOURNAL GROUP; *U.S. Private*, pg. 2858
NATIONAL JUVENILE DEFENDER CENTER; *U.S. Private*, pg. 2858
NATIONAL LADDER & SCAFFOLD COMPANY, INC.; *U.S. Private*, pg. 2858
NATIONAL LAGHUBITTA BITTIYA SANSTHA LIMITED; *Int'l*, pg. 5160
NATIONAL LAND REALTY, LLC; *U.S. Private*, pg. 2858
NATIONAL LAW ENFORCEMENT OFFICERS MEMORIAL FUND; *U.S. Private*, pg. 2858
NATIONAL LEAD SMELTING CO. LTD—See National Industrialization Company; *Int'l*, pg. 5158
NATIONAL LEAGUE FOR NURSING; *U.S. Private*, pg. 2858
NATIONAL LEASING GROUP INC.—See Canadian Western Bank; *Int'l*, pg. 1287
NATIONAL LIABILITY AND FIRE INSURANCE COMPANY—See Berkshire Hathaway Inc.; *U.S. Public*, pg. 303
NATIONAL LIABILITY & FIRE INSURANCE COMPANY—See Berkshire Hathaway Inc.; *U.S. Public*, pg. 313
NATIONAL LIFE & GENERAL INSURANCE COMPANY SAOC—See Oman International Development & Investment Company SAOG; *Int'l*, pg. 5560
NATIONAL LIFE INSURANCE COMPANY LIMITED; *Int'l*, pg. 5161
NATIONAL LIFE INSURANCE COMPANY; *U.S. Private*, pg. 2858
THE NATIONAL LIGHTING COMPANY LTD.; *Int'l*, pg. 7670
NATIONALLINK, INC.; *U.S. Private*, pg. 2865
NATIONAL LLOYDS CORPORATION—See Align Financial Group, LLC; *U.S. Private*, pg. 168
NATIONAL LLOYDS INSURANCE CORPORATION—See ReAlign Capital Strategies; *U.S. Private*, pg. 3368
NATIONALL RESPONSE CORPORATION OF PUERTO RICO—See AIP, LLC; *U.S. Private*, pg. 136
NATIONAL LUMBER COMPANY—See Builders FirstSource, Inc.; *U.S. Public*, pg. 410
NATIONAL LUMBER CO.; *U.S. Private*, pg. 2859
NATIONAL MACHINE COMPANY; *U.S. Private*, pg. 2859
NATIONAL MACHINERY LLC—See Alpha Capital Partners, Ltd.; *U.S. Private*, pg. 197
NATIONAL MADISON GROUP, INC.—See Aon plc; *Int'l*, pg. 497
THE NATIONAL MAGAZINE COMPANY LTD.—See The Hearst Corporation; *U.S. Private*, pg. 4046
NATIONAL MAGNETICS GROUP, INC.; *U.S. Private*, pg. 2859
NATIONAL MAINTENANCE SERVICES, LLC—See National Construction Enterprises Inc.; *U.S. Private*, pg. 2851
NATIONAL MANAGING HOLDING BAITEREK JSC; *Int'l*, pg. 5161
NATIONAL MARINE DREDGING COMPANY PJSC; *Int'l*, pg. 5161
NATIONAL MARINE & INFRASTRUCTURE INDIA PRIVATE LIMITED—See National Marine Dredging Company PJSC; *Int'l*, pg. 5161
NATIONAL MARINE INSURANCE AGENCY LIMITED—See Suncorp Group Limited; *Int'l*, pg. 7311
NATIONAL MARINE SALES INC.—See AMCON Distributing Company; *U.S. Public*, pg. 92
NATIONAL MARKER COMPANY—See The Riverside Company; *U.S. Private*, pg. 4109
NATIONAL MARKETING SOLUTIONS (NMS); *U.S. Private*, pg. 2859
NATIONAL MARKETING & TRADING CO LLC—See Aurelius Equity Opportunities SE & Co. KGaA; *Int'l*, pg. 710
NATIONAL MARROW DONOR PROGRAM, INC.; *U.S. Private*, pg. 2859
NATIONAL MATERIAL LIMITED PARTNERSHIP—See Tang Industries Inc.; *U.S. Private*, pg. 3930
NATIONAL MECHANICAL SERVICES, LLC; *U.S. Private*, pg. 2859
NATIONAL MEDIA GROUP; *Int'l*, pg. 5161
NATIONAL MEDICAL BILLING SERVICES LLC—See Aquiline Capital Partners LLC; *U.S. Private*, pg. 304
NATIONAL MEDICAL CARE COMPANY; *Int'l*, pg. 5161
NATIONAL MEDICAL CARE OF SPAIN, S.A.—See Fresenius Medical Care AG; *Int'l*, pg. 2776
NATIONAL MEDICAL SERVICES, INC.; *U.S. Private*, pg. 2859
NATIONAL MEDTRANS, LLC—See ModivCare, Inc.; *U.S. Public*, pg. 1455
NATIONAL MEDTRANS NETWORK INC.—See UnitedHealth Group Incorporated; *U.S. Public*, pg. 2242
NATIONAL MENTOR HEALTHCARE, LLC—See Centerbridge Partners, L.P.; *U.S. Private*, pg. 814
NATIONAL MENTOR HOLDINGS, INC—See Centerbridge Partners, L.P.; *U.S. Private*, pg. 814
NATIONAL MENTOR HOLDINGS, LLC—See Centerbridge Partners, L.P.; *U.S. Private*, pg. 814
NATIONAL MERIT INSURANCE CO.—See Kemper Corporation; *U.S. Public*, pg. 1221

1867

NATIONAL MERIT SCHOLARSHIP CORP.

NATIONAL MERIT SCHOLARSHIP CORP.; *U.S. Private,* pg. 2859
NATIONAL METALLIC INDUSTRIES & BICYCLES CO.; *Int'l,* pg. 5161
NATIONAL METAL MANUFACTURING & CASTING COMPANY LTD—See National Industrialization Company; *Int'l,* pg. 5158
NATIONAL METER AND AUTOMATION, INC.—See Badger Meter, Inc.; *U.S. Public,* pg. 263
NATIONAL MICRO RENTAL; *U.S. Private,* pg. 2859
NATIONAL MILK PRODUCERS FEDERATION; *U.S. Private,* pg. 2859
NATIONAL MILK RECORDS PLC—See The Garfield Weston Foundation; *Int'l,* pg. 7647
NATIONAL MILL INDUSTRY, INC.; *U.S. Private,* pg. 2859
NATIONAL MINERAL WATER COMPANY SAOG; *Int'l,* pg. 5161
NATIONAL MINING COMPANY TAU-KEN SAMRUK JSC; *Int'l,* pg. 5161
NATIONAL MOLDING CORPORATION; *U.S. Private,* pg. 2859
NATIONAL MORTGAGE & FINANCE CO. LTD.; *U.S. Private,* pg. 2859
NATIONAL MORTGAGE MARKET CORPORATION PTY LTD—See Bendigo & Adelaide Bank Ltd.; *Int'l,* pg. 971
NATIONAL MOTOR COMPANY W.L.L.—See Bahrain Commercial Facilities Company BSC; *Int'l,* pg. 800
NATIONAL MUSIC PUBLISHERS' ASSOCIATION; *U.S. Private,* pg. 2859
NATIONAL MUTUAL BENEFIT; *U.S. Private,* pg. 2859
NATIONAL MUTUAL FUND LTD—See The Mauritius Union Assurance Company Limited; *Int'l,* pg. 7666
NATIONAL MUTUAL FUNDS MANAGEMENT LTD.—See AMP Limited; *Int'l,* pg. 432
NATIONAL MUTUAL LIFE ASSOCIATION OF AUSTRALIA LTD.—See AMP Limited; *Int'l,* pg. 432
NATIONAL NAIL CORP.; *U.S. Private,* pg. 2859
NATIONAL NET VENTURES—See National Technology Group; *Int'l,* pg. 5164
NATIONAL NETWORK DIGITAL SCHOOLS; *U.S. Private,* pg. 2859
NATIONAL NEWS BUREAU AGENCY; *U.S. Private,* pg. 2859
NATIONAL NONWOVENS; *U.S. Private,* pg. 2860
NATIONAL NOODLE INC.; *U.S. Private,* pg. 2860
NATIONAL OAK DISTRIBUTORS INC.; *U.S. Private,* pg. 2860
NATIONAL OFFICE FURNITURE, INC. - FORDSVILLE—See HNI Corporation; *U.S. Public,* pg. 1043
NATIONAL OFFICE FURNITURE, INC. - JASPER, 11TH AVE—See HNI Corporation; *U.S. Public,* pg. 1043
NATIONAL OFFICE FURNITURE, INC. - SANTA CLAUS—See HNI Corporation; *U.S. Public,* pg. 1043
NATIONAL OFFICE FURNITURE, INC.—See HNI Corporation; *U.S. Public,* pg. 1043
NATIONAL OILFIELD SUPPLY CO. LLC—See Omar Zawawi Establishment LLC; *Int'l,* pg. 5561
NATIONAL OIL SHALE COMPANY PLC; *Int'l,* pg. 5161
NATIONAL OILWELL CANADA ULC—See NOV, Inc.; *U.S. Public,* pg. 1545
NATIONAL OILWELL DE MEXICO S.A. DE C.V.—See NOV, Inc.; *U.S. Public,* pg. 1546
NATIONAL OILWELL NORWAY MANUFACTURING AS—See NOV, Inc.; *U.S. Public,* pg. 1546
NATIONAL OILWELL POLAND S.P.Z.O.O.—See NOV, Inc.; *U.S. Public,* pg. 1546
NATIONAL-OILWELL PTE. LTD.—See NOV, Inc.; *U.S. Public,* pg. 1546
NATIONAL OILWELL SERVICES DE MEXICO, S.A. DE C.V.—See NOV, Inc.; *U.S. Public,* pg. 1546
NATIONAL OILWELL VARCO ALMANSOORI SERVICES—See NOV, Inc.; *U.S. Public,* pg. 1546
NATIONAL OILWELL VARCO DENMARK I/S—See NOV, Inc.; *U.S. Public,* pg. 1546
NATIONAL OILWELL VARCO-ESTEVAN SERVICE CENTER—See NOV, Inc.; *U.S. Public,* pg. 1546
NATIONAL OILWELL VARCO KOREA CO., LTD.—See NOV, Inc.; *U.S. Public,* pg. 1546
NATIONAL OILWELL VARCO, L.P.—See NOV, Inc.; *U.S. Public,* pg. 1546
NATIONAL OILWELL VARCO, L.P.—See NOV, Inc.; *U.S. Public,* pg. 1546
NATIONAL OILWELL VARCO MSW S.A.—See NOV, Inc.; *U.S. Public,* pg. 1546
NATIONAL OILWELL VARCO NORWAY AS—See NOV, Inc.; *U.S. Public,* pg. 1546
NATIONAL OILWELL VARCO PTE. LTD.—See NOV, Inc.; *U.S. Public,* pg. 1546
NATIONAL OILWELL VARCO-P&T SERVICIOS PETROLEROS—See NOV, Inc.; *U.S. Public,* pg. 1546
NATIONAL OILWELL VARCO RIG EQUIPMENT TRADING (SHANGHAI) CO., LTD.—See NOV, Inc.; *U.S. Public,* pg. 1546
NATIONAL OILWELL VARCO - SERVICE CENTER—See NOV, Inc.; *U.S. Public,* pg. 1546
NATIONAL OILWELL VARCO—See NOV, Inc.; *U.S. Public,* pg. 1546

NATIONAL OILWELL VARCO—See NOV, Inc.; *U.S. Public,* pg. 1546
NATIONAL OILWELL VARCO—See NOV, Inc.; *U.S. Public,* pg. 1546
NATIONAL OILWELL VARCO—See NOV, Inc.; *U.S. Public,* pg. 1546
NATIONAL OILWELL VARCO UK LIMITED—See NOV, Inc.; *U.S. Public,* pg. 1546
NATIONAL OLDER WORKER CAREER CENTER; *U.S. Private,* pg. 2860
NATIONAL OPERATION AND INDUSTRIAL SERVICES CO.LTD—See National Industrialization Company; *Int'l,* pg. 5158
NATIONAL OPINION RESEARCH CENTER COLORADO; *U.S. Private,* pg. 2860
NATIONAL OPTRONICS INC.; *U.S. Private,* pg. 2860
NATIONAL OUTDOOR SPORTS ADVERTISING, INC.—See Market Development Group, Inc.; *U.S. Private,* pg. 2579
NATIONAL OXYGEN LTD; *Int'l,* pg. 5161
NATIONAL PACKAGING SERVICES CORPORATION; *U.S. Private,* pg. 2860
NATIONAL PACKAGING SERVICES; *U.S. Private,* pg. 2860
NATIONAL PACKAGING SPECIALISTS, INC.; *U.S. Private,* pg. 2860
NATIONAL PAIN CENTERS, INC.—See Wellness Center USA, Inc.; *U.S. Public,* pg. 2342
NATIONAL PAINT INDUSTRIES, INC.—See Huron Capital Partners LLC; *U.S. Private,* pg. 2012
NATIONAL PAINTS FACTORIES CO. LTD.; *Int'l,* pg. 5161
NATIONAL PAINTS - JORDAN—See National Paints Factories Co. Ltd.; *Int'l,* pg. 5161
NATIONAL PAINTS - KAZAKHSTAN—See National Paints Factories Co. Ltd.; *Int'l,* pg. 5161
NATIONAL PAINTS - KYRGYZSTAN—See National Paints Factories Co. Ltd.; *Int'l,* pg. 5161
NATIONAL PAINTS - QATAR—See National Paints Factories Co. Ltd.; *Int'l,* pg. 5162
NATIONAL PAINTS - RUSSIA—See National Paints Factories Co. Ltd.; *Int'l,* pg. 5162
NATIONAL PAINTS - SUDAN—See National Paints Factories Co. Ltd.; *Int'l,* pg. 5162
NATIONAL PAPER INDUSTRIES COMPANY—See Qatar Industrial Manufacturing Company (S.A.Q.); *Int'l,* pg. 6133
NATIONAL PARTNERS IN HEALTHCARE, LLC—See Assured Guaranty Ltd.; *Int'l,* pg. 650
NATIONAL PARTNERS PFCO, LLC—See Steel Partners Holdings L.P.; *U.S. Public,* pg. 1943
NATIONAL PARTS DEPOT; *U.S. Private,* pg. 2860
NATIONAL PARTS SUPPLY COMPANY INC.; *U.S. Private,* pg. 2860
NATIONAL P&A SECURITIES—See National Bank of Greece S.A.; *Int'l,* pg. 5153
NATIONAL PATIENT ACCOUNT SERVICES, INC.—See HCA Healthcare, Inc.; *U.S. Public,* pg. 1004
NATIONAL PATIENT SERVICES CORPORATION; *U.S. Private,* pg. 2860
NATIONAL PATIENT TRANSPORT PTY. LTD.—See ComfortDelGro Corporation Limited; *Int'l,* pg. 1713
NATIONAL PAWN—See Envela Corporation; *U.S. Public,* pg. 780
NATIONAL PAYMENT CARD ASSOCIATION—See TA Associates, Inc.; *U.S. Private,* pg. 3917
NATIONAL PAYROLL SYSTEMS PTY. LTD.—See Allegis Group, Inc.; *U.S. Private,* pg. 177
NATIONAL PAYROLL SYSTEMS PTY. LTD.—See Morgan & Banks Investments Pty. Ltd.; *Int'l,* pg. 5040
NATIONAL PEENING, INC.—See Sintokogio Ltd.; *Int'l,* pg. 6958
NATIONAL PEN CO., LLC—See Cimpress plc; *Int'l,* pg. 1609
NATIONAL PEN PROMOTIONAL PRODUCTS LIMITED—See Cimpress plc; *Int'l,* pg. 1609
NATIONAL PENSION SERVICE OF KOREA; *Int'l,* pg. 5162
NATIONAL PERSONNEL ASSOCIATES COOPERATIVE, INC.; *U.S. Private,* pg. 2860
NATIONAL PEST CONTROL LLC—See Rentokil Initial plc; *Int'l,* pg. 6287
NATIONAL PETROCHEMICAL COMPANY—See SAUDI INDUSTRIAL INVESTMENT GROUP; *Int'l,* pg. 6593
NATIONAL PETROCHEMICAL INDUSTRIALIZATION COMPANY LTD.—See National Industrialization Company; *Int'l,* pg. 5158
NATIONAL PETROLEUM CONSTRUCTION CO. (SAUDI) LTD.—See Alpha Dhabi Holding PJSC; *Int'l,* pg. 367
NATIONAL PETROLEUM CORPORATION; *Int'l,* pg. 5162
NATIONAL PETROLEUM INC.; *U.S. Private,* pg. 2860
NATIONAL PETROLEUM INVESTMENT & MANAGEMENT SERVICES—See Nigerian National Petroleum Corporation; *U.S. Private,* pg. 5282
NATIONAL PETROLEUM REFINERS OF SOUTH AFRICA (PTY) LTD.—See Sasol Limited; *Int'l,* pg. 6583
NATIONAL PETROLEUM SERVICES COMPANY K.S.C.G.—See Kuwait Projects Company (Holding) K.S.C.P.; *Int'l,* pg. 4347

NATIONAL PETROLEUM SERVICES JSC—See National Energy Services Reunited Corp.; *U.S. Public,* pg. 1494
NATIONAL PHARMACEUTICAL ASSOCIATION LIMITED; *Int'l,* pg. 5162
NATIONAL PIPE HANGER CO. CORP; *U.S. Private,* pg. 2860
NATIONAL PLANT SERVICES INC.—See Carylon Corporation; *U.S. Public,* pg. 777
NATIONAL PLASTIC CO.—See Saudi Basic Industries Corporation; *Int'l,* pg. 6590
NATIONAL PLASTIC INDUSTRIES LIMITED - PATNA UNIT—See NATIONAL PLASTIC INDUSTRIES LIMITED; *Int'l,* pg. 5162
NATIONAL PLASTIC INDUSTRIES LIMITED - SILVASSA UNIT—See NATIONAL PLASTIC INDUSTRIES LIMITED; *Int'l,* pg. 5162
NATIONAL PLASTIC INDUSTRIES LIMITED; *Int'l,* pg. 5162
NATIONAL PLASTICS COLOR INC.; *U.S. Private,* pg. 2860
NATIONAL PLASTICS COMPANY—See Chemical Industries Holding Company; *Int'l,* pg. 1462
NATIONAL PLASTICS, INC.—See Cameron Holdings Corporation; *U.S. Private,* pg. 729
NATIONAL PLASTIC TECHNOLOGIES LTD.; *Int'l,* pg. 5162
NATIONAL PLYWOOD INDUSTRIES LIMITED; *Int'l,* pg. 5162
NATIONAL POLYMER INDUSTRIES LTD.; *Int'l,* pg. 5162
NATIONAL POOL CONSTRUCTION; *U.S. Private,* pg. 2860
NATIONAL PORK BOARD; *U.S. Private,* pg. 2860
NATIONAL PORTFOLIO SECURITIES PLC.; *Int'l,* pg. 5162
NATIONAL PORTS AUTHORITY OF SOUTH AFRICA—See Transnet Ltd.; *Int'l,* pg. 7902
NATIONAL POSITIONS; *U.S. Private,* pg. 2860
NATIONAL POST, INC.—See Chatham Asset Management, LLC; *U.S. Private,* pg. 861
NATIONAL POULTRY P.L.C.; *Int'l,* pg. 5162
NATIONAL POWER CORPORATION—See Valley Ridge Investment Partners; *U.S. Private,* pg. 4385
NATIONAL POWERLINE LLC—See Southwest Gas Holdings, Inc.; *U.S. Public,* pg. 1913
NATIONAL POWER RODDING CORPORATION—See Carylon Corporation; *U.S. Public,* pg. 777
NATIONAL PRECISION—See EACO Corporation; *U.S. Public,* pg. 701
NATIONAL PREMIUM, INC.; *U.S. Private,* pg. 2861
NATIONAL PRESORT, LP—See Warburg Pincus LLC; *U.S. Private,* pg. 4438
NATIONAL PRESTO INDUSTRIES, INC; *U.S. Public,* pg. 1497
NATIONAL PRETZEL COMPANY—See Conagra Brands, Inc.; *U.S. Public,* pg. 564
NATIONAL PRINT GROUP-DIGITAL & SCREEN—See Wingate Partners, LLP; *U.S. Private,* pg. 4541
NATIONAL PRINT GROUP, INC.—See Wingate Partners, LLP; *U.S. Private,* pg. 4541
NATIONAL PROCESS EQUIPMENT, INC.—See DXP Enterprises, Inc.; *U.S. Public,* pg. 697
NATIONAL PROCESSING COMPANY—See GTCR LLC; *U.S. Private,* pg. 1806
NATIONAL PROCESSORS LTD.—See GraceKennedy Limited; *Int'l,* pg. 3049
NATIONAL PRODUCT SALES INC.; *U.S. Private,* pg. 2861
NATIONAL PRODUCT SERVICES; *U.S. Private,* pg. 2861
NATIONAL PRODUCTS MARKETING COMPANY—See Hayel Saeed Anam Group of Companies; *Int'l,* pg. 3291
NATIONAL PROFESSIONAL SERVICES, INC.—See Environmental Service Professionals, Inc.; *U.S. Public,* pg. 781
NATIONAL PROJECTS AND CONSTRUCTION LLC—See Alpha Dhabi Holding PJSC; *Int'l,* pg. 367
NATIONAL PROPERTIES HOLDINGS LIMITED—See National Electronics Holdings Limited; *Int'l,* pg. 5156
NATIONAL PROPERTY ANALYSTS; *U.S. Private,* pg. 2861
NATIONAL PROPERTY FUND OF THE SLOVAK REPUBLIC; *Int'l,* pg. 5162
NATIONAL PUBLIC RELATIONS INC.—See RES PUBLICA Consulting Group Inc.; *Int'l,* pg. 6295
NATIONAL PUBLIC RELATIONS—See RES PUBLICA Consulting Group Inc.; *Int'l,* pg. 6295
NATIONAL PUBLIC RELATIONS—See RES PUBLICA Consulting Group Inc.; *Int'l,* pg. 6295
NATIONAL PUBLIC RELATIONS—See RES PUBLICA Consulting Group Inc.; *Int'l,* pg. 6295
NATIONAL PUBLIC RELATIONS—See RES PUBLICA Consulting Group Inc.; *Int'l,* pg. 6295
NATIONAL PUBLIC RELATIONS—See RES PUBLICA Consulting Group Inc.; *Int'l,* pg. 6295
NATIONAL PUBLIC RELATIONS—See RES PUBLICA Consulting Group Inc.; *Int'l,* pg. 6295
NATIONAL PUBLIC RELATIONS—See RES PUBLICA Consulting Group Inc.; *Int'l,* pg. 6295

COMPANY NAME INDEX

NATIONAL PUBLIC RELATIONS—See RES PUBLICA Consulting Group Inc.; *Int'l*, pg. 6295
NATIONAL PUBLIC RELATIONS—See RES PUBLICA Consulting Group Inc.; *Int'l*, pg. 6295
NATIONAL PUBLISHING COMPANY—See Atlas Holdings, LLC; *U.S. Private*, pg. 377
NATIONAL PUMP COMPANY - LUBBOCK—See The Gorman-Rupp Company; *U.S. Public*, pg. 2085
NATIONAL PUMP COMPANY—See The Gorman-Rupp Company; *U.S. Public*, pg. 2085
NATIONAL PUMP COMPANY—See The Gorman-Rupp Company; *U.S. Public*, pg. 2085
NATIONAL PUMP & ENERGY LTD.—See Atlas Copco AB; *Int'l*, pg. 683
NATIONAL PURCHASING CORP; *U.S. Private*, pg. 2861
NATIONAL QUALITY FORUM; *U.S. Private*, pg. 2861
NATIONAL QUALITY REVIEW, LLC—See Terminus Capital Partners, LLC; *U.S. Private*, pg. 3970
NATIONAL RAILROAD PASSENGER CORPORATION; *U.S. Private*, pg. 2861
NATIONAL RAILWAY EQUIPMENT COMPANY; *U.S. Private*, pg. 2861
NATIONAL RAILWAY HISTORICAL SOCIETY.; *U.S. Private*, pg. 2861
NATIONAL RAILWAY SUPPLY INC.; *U.S. Private*, pg. 2861
NATIONAL READY MIXED INC.—See Vicat S.A.; *Int'l*, pg. 8186
NATIONAL REAL ESTATE COMPANY K.S.C.; *Int'l*, pg. 5162
NATIONAL REAL ESTATE DEVELOPMENT AND INVESTMENTS COMPANY SAOG; *Int'l*, pg. 5163
NATIONAL REAL ESTATE INFORMATION SERVICES INC.; *U.S. Private*, pg. 2861
NATIONAL REALTY & DEVELOPMENT CORP.; *U.S. Private*, pg. 2861
NATIONAL RECOGNITION PRODUCTS, INC.—See Taylor Corporation; *U.S. Private*, pg. 3938
NATIONAL RECOVERY AGENCY; *U.S. Private*, pg. 2861
NATIONAL REFINERY LIMITED—See Attock Refinery Ltd; *Int'l*, pg. 697
NATIONAL REGISTERED AGENTS, INC.—See Wolters Kluwer n.v.; *Int'l*, pg. 8445
NATIONAL REGULATORY SERVICES—See Compliance Science, Inc.; *U.S. Private*, pg. 1001
NATIONAL REINSURANCE CORPORATION OF THE PHILIPPINES; *Int'l*, pg. 5163
NATIONAL RELIGIOUS BROADCASTERS; *U.S. Private*, pg. 2861
NATIONAL REPROGRAPHICS INC.; *U.S. Private*, pg. 2862
NATIONAL RESEARCH CORPORATION CANADA—See National Research Corporation; *U.S. Public*, pg. 1497
NATIONAL RESEARCH CORPORATION; *U.S. Public*, pg. 1497
NATIONAL RESERVE BANK JSC; *Int'l*, pg. 5163
NATIONAL RESERVE BANK OF TONGA; *Int'l*, pg. 5163
NATIONAL RESPONSE CORPORATION (ANGOLA) LDA—See Republic Services, Inc.; *U.S. Public*, pg. 1788
NATIONAL RESPONSE CORPORATION (NRC) ENVIRONMENTAL SERVICES UAE L LC—See Republic Services, Inc.; *U.S. Public*, pg. 1788
NATIONAL RESPONSE CORPORATION—See Republic Services, Inc.; *U.S. Public*, pg. 1788
NATIONAL RESTAURANT ASSOCIATION; *U.S. Private*, pg. 2862
NATIONAL RESTAURANT DEVELOPMENT, INC.; *U.S. Private*, pg. 2862
NATIONAL RESTAURANT MANAGEMENT, INC.—See The Riese Organization; *U.S. Private*, pg. 4107
NATIONAL RESTAURANT SUPPLY COMPANY; *U.S. Private*, pg. 2862
NATIONAL RESTORATION SYSTEMS; *U.S. Private*, pg. 2862
NATIONAL RETAIL CORPORATION; *U.S. Private*, pg. 2862
NATIONAL RETAIL SYSTEMS, INC.; *U.S. Private*, pg. 2862
NATIONAL RETAIL TRANSPORTATION—See National Retail Systems, Inc.; *U.S. Private*, pg. 2862
NATIONAL RETIREMENT SERVICES, INC.—See Aquiline Capital Partners LLC; *U.S. Private*, pg. 304
NATIONAL RETIREMENT SERVICES, INC.—See Genstar Capital, LLC; *U.S. Private*, pg. 1675
NATIONAL REVIEW, INC.; *U.S. Private*, pg. 2862
NATIONAL RIGHT TO WORK COMMITTEE; *U.S. Private*, pg. 2862
NATIONAL RIVET & MANUFACTURING CO.; *U.S. Private*, pg. 2862
NATIONAL ROAD UTILITY SUPPLY, INC.—See The C.I. Thornburg Co., Inc.; *U.S. Private*, pg. 4003
NATIONAL ROOFING CO. INC.; *U.S. Private*, pg. 2862
NATIONAL RUBBER TECHNOLOGIES—See Kinderhook Industries, LLC; *U.S. Private*, pg. 2307
NATIONAL RURAL ELECTRIC COOPERATIVE ASSOCIATION—See Touchstone Energy Cooperative, Inc.; *U.S. Private*, pg. 4192
NATIONAL RURAL TELECOMMUNICATIONS COOPERATIVE; *U.S. Private*, pg. 2862
NATIONAL RURAL UTILITIES COOPERATIVE FINANCE CORPORATION; *U.S. Public*, pg. 1497
NATIONAL SAFE PLACE; *U.S. Private*, pg. 2862
NATIONAL SAFETY APPAREL, INC.—See Blue Point Capital Partners, LLC; *U.S. Private*, pg. 590
NATIONAL SAFETY ASSOCIATES; *U.S. Private*, pg. 2862
NATIONAL SAFETY COMMISSION (NSC); *U.S. Private*, pg. 2862
NATIONAL SAFETY COUNCIL; *U.S. Private*, pg. 2862
NATIONAL SALON RESOURCES—See Mikara Corporation; *U.S. Private*, pg. 2724
NATIONAL SAVINGS BANK; *Int'l*, pg. 5163
NATIONAL SCHOOL BOARDS ASSOCIATION; *U.S. Private*, pg. 2862
NATIONAL SCIENCE TEACHERS ASSOCIATION; *U.S. Private*, pg. 2863
NATIONAL SCIENTIFIC COMPANY LTD.—See Dabbagh Group Holding Company Ltd.; *Int'l*, pg. 1902
NATIONAL SCOUTING REPORT INC.; *U.S. Private*, pg. 2863
NATIONAL SEATING & MOBILITY, INC. - DUNBAR—See Court Square Capital Partners, L.P.; *U.S. Private*, pg. 1069
NATIONAL SEATING & MOBILITY, INC.—See Court Square Capital Partners, L.P.; *U.S. Private*, pg. 1069
NATIONAL SECURITIES CLEARING CORPORATION—See The Depository Trust & Clearing Corporation; *U.S. Private*, pg. 4020
NATIONAL SECURITIES CORPORATION—See B. Riley Financial, Inc.; *U.S. Public*, pg. 261
NATIONAL SECURITIES DEPOSITORY LTD.—See National Stock Exchange of India Limited; *Int'l*, pg. 5163
NATIONAL SECURITIES & INVESTMENTS INC.—See National Mortgage & Finance Co. Ltd.; *U.S. Private*, pg. 2859
NATIONAL SECURITY FIRE AND CASUALTY COMPANY—See The National Security Group, Inc.; *U.S. Public*, pg. 2116
THE NATIONAL SECURITY GROUP, INC.; *U.S. Public*, pg. 2116
NATIONAL SECURITY INSURANCE COMPANY—See The National Security Group, Inc.; *U.S. Public*, pg. 2116
NATIONAL SECURITY SYSTEMS INC.; *U.S. Private*, pg. 2863
NATIONAL SEMICONDUCTOR CORPORATION—See Texas Instruments Incorporated; *U.S. Public*, pg. 2025
NATIONAL SEMICONDUCTOR INTERNATIONAL B.V.—See Texas Instruments Incorporated; *U.S. Public*, pg. 2026
NATIONAL SEMICONDUCTOR (MAINE), INC.—See Texas Instruments Incorporated; *U.S. Public*, pg. 2025
NATIONAL SEMICONDUCTOR (PTE) LIMITED—See Texas Instruments Incorporated; *U.S. Public*, pg. 2025
NATIONAL SEMICONDUTORES DA AMERICA DO SUL LTDA.—See Texas Instruments Incorporated; *U.S. Public*, pg. 2026
NATIONAL SEMICONDUTORES DO BRASIL LTDA.—See Texas Instruments Incorporated; *U.S. Public*, pg. 2026
NATIONAL SEPTEMBER 11 MEMORIAL & MUSEUM; *U.S. Private*, pg. 2863
NATIONAL SERVICES GROUP INC.; *U.S. Private*, pg. 2863
NATIONAL SHIPPING COMPANY OF SAUDI ARABIA (AMERICA) INC—See National Shipping Company of Saudi Arabia; *Int'l*, pg. 5163
NATIONAL SHIPPING COMPANY OF SAUDI ARABIA; *Int'l*, pg. 5163
NATIONAL SHIPPING GULF AGENCY COMPANY (ABU DHABI) LTD. L.L.C.—See Gulf Agency Company Ltd.; *Int'l*, pg. 3179
NATIONAL SHOOTING COMPANY K.S.C.C.; *Int'l*, pg. 5163
NATIONAL SHOWER SPARES LIMITED—See Travis Perkins plc; *Int'l*, pg. 7908
NATIONAL SIGNAL, INC.—See Hill & Smith PLC; *Int'l*, pg. 3392
NATIONAL SILICATES PARTNERSHIP—See Ecovyst Inc.; *U.S. Public*, pg. 717
NATIONAL SILICON INDUSTRY GROUP CO., LTD.; *Int'l*, pg. 5163
THE NATIONAL SILK & RAYON MILLS LTD.; *Int'l*, pg. 7670
NATIONAL SLEEP THERAPY; *U.S. Private*, pg. 2863
NATIONAL SLOVAK SOCIETY; *U.S. Private*, pg. 2863
NATIONAL SMOKELESS TOBACCO COMPANY LTD.—See Altria Group, Inc.; *U.S. Public*, pg. 89
NATIONAL SOCIETY DAUGHTERS OF THE AMERICAN REVOLUTION; *U.S. Private*, pg. 2863
NATIONAL SOCIETY OF BLACK ENGINEERS; *U.S. Private*, pg. 2863
NATIONAL SPECIALTY ALLOYS, INC.—See Reliance Steel & Aluminum Co.; *U.S. Public*, pg. 1781
NATIONAL SPECIALTY ALLOYS; *U.S. Private*, pg. 2863
NATIONAL SPECIALTY CLINICS, LLC—See Acadia Healthcare Company, Inc.; *U.S. Public*, pg. 29
NATIONAL SPECIALTY PRODUCTS—See Morgan Advanced Materials plc; *Int'l*, pg. 5041
NATIONAL SPINE & PAIN CENTERS, LLC—See Avista Capital Partners, L.P.; *U.S. Private*, pg. 408
NATIONAL SPINNING COMPANY, INC - ALAMANCE DYE PLANT—See National Spinning Company, Inc.; *U.S. Private*, pg. 2863
NATIONAL SPINNING COMPANY, INC - BEULAVILLE SPINNING PLANT—See National Spinning Company, Inc.; *U.S. Private*, pg. 2863
NATIONAL SPINNING COMPANY, INC.; *U.S. Private*, pg. 2863
NATIONAL SPINNING COMPANY LTD. CO.—See Al Abdullatif Industrial Investment Company; *Int'l*, pg. 275
NATIONAL SPINNING CO.—See National Spinning Company, Inc.; *U.S. Private*, pg. 2863
NATIONAL SPOT EXCHANGE LIMITED—See 63 moons technologies limited; *Int'l*, pg. 14
NATIONAL STANDARD BANK JSC; *Int'l*, pg. 5163
NATIONAL-STANDARD CO.—See The Heico Companies, L.L.C.; *U.S. Private*, pg. 4050
NATIONAL STANDARD (INDIA) LIMITED; *Int'l*, pg. 5163
NATIONAL STANDARD—See The Heico Companies, L.L.C.; *U.S. Private*, pg. 4050
NATIONAL STARCH & CHEMICAL (HOLDINGS) LTD.—See Ingredion Incorporated; *U.S. Public*, pg. 1124
NATIONAL STARCH & CHEMICAL-LINCOLNSHIRE—See Ingredion Incorporated; *U.S. Public*, pg. 1124
NATIONAL STARCH & CHEMICAL LTD.-NAM DINH—See Ingredion Incorporated; *U.S. Public*, pg. 1124
NATIONAL STARCH & CHEMICAL PTY LTD.—See Ingredion Incorporated; *U.S. Public*, pg. 1124
NATIONAL STARCH & CHEMICAL—See Ingredion Incorporated; *U.S. Public*, pg. 1124
NATIONAL STARCH & CHEMICAL (THAILAND) LTD.—See Ingredion Incorporated; *U.S. Public*, pg. 1124
NATIONAL STARCH & CHEMICAL (THAILAND) LTD.—See Ingredion Incorporated; *U.S. Public*, pg. 1124
NATIONAL STARCH COMPANY—See Ingredion Incorporated; *U.S. Public*, pg. 1124
NATIONAL STARCH PERSONAL CARE—See Akzo Nobel N.V.; *Int'l*, pg. 274
NATIONAL STARCH SERVICIOS, S.A. DE C.V.—See Ingredion Incorporated; *U.S. Public*, pg. 1124
NATIONAL STARCH SPECIALTIES (SHANGHAI) LTD.—See Ingredion Incorporated; *U.S. Public*, pg. 1124
NATIONAL STAR LIMITED—See Heidelberg Materials AG; *Int'l*, pg. 3318
NATIONAL STEEL AND AGRO INDUSTRIES LIMITED; *Int'l*, pg. 5163
NATIONAL STEEL COMPANY LIMITED—See Al-Tuwairqi Group; *Int'l*, pg. 289
NATIONAL STEEL COMPRESSING—See M. Lipsitz & Co., Ltd.; *U.S. Private*, pg. 2527
NATIONAL STEEL FABRICATION LTD.—See Orascom Construction PLC; *Int'l*, pg. 5613
NATIONAL STEEL INDUSTRY COMPANY P.L.C.; *Int'l*, pg. 5163
NATIONAL STEEL RULE CO. INC.; *U.S. Private*, pg. 2863
NATIONAL STOCK EXCHANGE OF AUSTRALIA LIMITED—See NSX Limited; *Int'l*, pg. 5481
NATIONAL STOCK EXCHANGE OF INDIA LIMITED; *Int'l*, pg. 5163
NATIONAL STOCK YARDS CO.; *U.S. Public*, pg. 1497
NATIONAL STORAGE AFFILIATES TRUST; *U.S. Public*, pg. 1497
NATIONAL STORAGE REIT; *Int'l*, pg. 5164
NATIONAL STORES, INC.; *U.S. Private*, pg. 2863
NATIONAL STRATEGIES PUBLIC RELATIONS, LLC; *U.S. Private*, pg. 2863
NATIONAL STUDENT CLEARINGHOUSE; *U.S. Private*, pg. 2863
NATIONAL SURETY CORPORATION—See Allianz SE; *Int'l*, pg. 354
NATIONAL SURGERY CENTER HOLDINGS, INC.—See Tenet Healthcare Corporation; *U.S. Public*, pg. 2005
NATIONAL SURGICAL HOSPITALS, INC.—See Bain Capital, LP; *U.S. Private*, pg. 445
NATIONAL SURGICAL PTY LTD—See EBOS Group Limited; *Int'l*, pg. 2285
NATIONAL SYSTEMS CONSULTING L.P.; *U.S. Private*, pg. 2863
NATIONAL TAKAFUL COMPANY (WATANIA) PJSC—See Dar Al Takaful House PJSC; *Int'l*, pg. 1971
NATIONAL TANK SERVICES—See Trimac Transportation Ltd.; *Int'l*, pg. 7923
NATIONAL TANNERIES OF PAKISTAN LIMITED—See Quetta Group of Companies LLC; *Int'l*, pg. 6161
NATIONAL TAX AGENCY; *Int'l*, pg. 5164
NATIONAL TAXNET—See Fidelity National Financial, Inc.; *U.S. Public*, pg. 831
NATIONAL TAX SEARCH, LLC—See Insight Venture Management, LLC; *U.S. Private*, pg. 2089
NATIONAL TAX SEARCH, LLC—See Stone Point Capital LLC; *U.S. Private*, pg. 3823

NATIONAL TAX AGENCY / CORPORATE AFFILIATIONS

NATIONAL TEACHERS ASSOCIATES LIFE INSURANCE COMPANY—See Horace Mann Educators Corporation; *U.S. Public*, pg. 1053
NATIONAL TEA COMPANY LIMITED; *Int'l*, pg. 5164
NATIONAL TECHNICAL SYSTEMS, INC. - ACTON—See Aurora Capital Group, LLC; *U.S. Private*, pg. 393
NATIONAL TECHNICAL SYSTEMS, INC. - DETROIT—See Aurora Capital Group, LLC; *U.S. Private*, pg. 393
NATIONAL TECHNICAL SYSTEMS, INC. - FULLERTON—See Aurora Capital Group, LLC; *U.S. Private*, pg. 393
NATIONAL TECHNICAL SYSTEMS, INC. - LOS ANGELES—See Aurora Capital Group, LLC; *U.S. Private*, pg. 393
NATIONAL TECHNICAL SYSTEMS, INC. - SANTA CLARITA—See Aurora Capital Group, LLC; *U.S. Private*, pg. 393
NATIONAL TECHNICAL SYSTEMS, INC.—See Aurora Capital Group, LLC; *U.S. Private*, pg. 393
NATIONAL TECHNICAL SYSTEMS, INC - WICHITA—See Aurora Capital Group, LLC; *U.S. Private*, pg. 393
NATIONAL TECHNOLOGY GROUP; *Int'l*, pg. 5164
NATIONAL TELECONSULTANTS INC.—See Deloitte LLP; *U.S. Private*, pg. 1198
NATIONAL TELECONSULTANTS INC.—See Deloitte Touche Tohmatsu Limited; *Int'l*, pg. 2015
NATIONAL TELEPHONE OF ALABAMA, INC.—See Telephone Electronics Corporation; *U.S. Private*, pg. 3961
NATIONAL TELEPHONE SERVICES CO. LLC—See Al Yousef Group; *Int'l*, pg. 283
NATIONAL TEXTILES, LLC—See Hanesbrands Inc.; *U.S. Public*, pg. 983
THE NATIONAL THEATRE CORPORATION; *U.S. Private*, pg. 4082
NATIONAL THEATRE PRODUCTIONS LIMITED—See Royal National Theatre; *Int'l*, pg. 6413
NATIONAL THOROUGHBRED RACING ASSOCIATION; *U.S. Private*, pg. 2864
NATIONAL TICKET COMPANY; *U.S. Private*, pg. 2864
NATIONAL TITANIUM DIOXIDE COMPANY LTD.—See Tronox Holdings plc; *U.S. Public*, pg. 2197
NATIONAL TOBACCO COMPANY LP—See North Atlantic Trading Company, Inc.; *U.S. Private*, pg. 2942
NATIONAL TOOL HARDENING INC.—See YG-1 Co., Ltd; *Int'l*, pg. 8579
NATIONAL TOOL & MANUFACTURING COMPANY; *U.S. Private*, pg. 2864
NATIONAL TRADE SUPPLY, LLC; *U.S. Private*, pg. 2864
NATIONAL TRADING CO.—See Hayel Saeed Anam Group of Companies; *Int'l*, pg. 3291
NATIONAL TRADING INC.—See Tohokushinsha Film Corporation; *Int'l*, pg. 7777
NATIONAL TRADING & SERVICES CO. LTD.—See Bank of Khartoum; *Int'l*, pg. 845
NATIONAL TRAIL DIALYSIS, LLC—See DaVita Inc.; *U.S. Public*, pg. 641
NATIONAL TRAINING INSTITUTE LLC—See Babcock International Group PLC; *Int'l*, pg. 793
NATIONAL TRANSFER SERVICES, LLC—See Stewart Information Services Corporation; *U.S. Public*, pg. 1947
NATIONAL TRANSFER & STORAGE, INC.—See Chipman Corporation; *U.S. Private*, pg. 886
NATIONAL TRANSPORTATION & LOGISTICS, INC.; *U.S. Private*, pg. 2864
NATIONAL TRANSPORT SERVICES CO.—See Wakefern Food Corporation; *U.S. Private*, pg. 4427
NATIONAL TRAVELERS INC.; *U.S. Private*, pg. 2864
NATIONAL TRENCH SAFETY, LLC—See Brookfield Corporation; *Int'l*, pg. 1184
NATIONAL TRUCK LEASING SYSTEM—See AmeriQuest Business Services; *U.S. Private*, pg. 260
NATIONAL TRUCK PARTS, INC.—See Illinois Tool Works Inc.; *U.S. Public*, pg. 1109
NATIONAL TRUCK PARTS OF THE MIDWEST, INC.—See Illinois Tool Works Inc.; *U.S. Public*, pg. 1109
NATIONAL TRUCK PROTECTION CO, INC.—See Kinderhook Industries, LLC; *U.S. Private*, pg. 2307
NATIONAL TRUCK REPAIR—See American Securities LLC; *U.S. Private*, pg. 248
NATIONAL TRUCK UNDERWRITING MANAGERS, INC.—See AmWINS Group, Inc.; *U.S. Private*, pg. 269
NATIONAL TRUST FOR HISTORIC PRESERVATION; *U.S. Private*, pg. 2864
NATIONAL TUBE HOLDING COMPANY INC.; *U.S. Private*, pg. 2864
NATIONAL TUBES LIMITED; *Int'l*, pg. 5164
NATIONAL TURF SERVICE-CLINTON M. QUINN, INC.—See Senske Lawn & Tree Care, Inc.; *U.S. Private*, pg. 3608
NATIONAL TYRE SERVICES LTD.—See Halfords Group plc; *Int'l*, pg. 3229
NATIONAL TYRE & WHEEL LIMITED; *Int'l*, pg. 5164
NATIONAL ULTRASOUND, INC.—See Avista Capital Partners, L.P.; *U.S. Private*, pg. 408
NATIONAL UNDERGROUND GROUP, INC.—See ORIX Corporation; *Int'l*, pg. 5636
THE NATIONAL UNDERGROUND RAILROAD FREEDOM CENTER; *U.S. Private*, pg. 4082

THE NATIONAL UNDERWRITER COMPANY—See Summit Business Media, LLC; *U.S. Private*, pg. 3853
NATIONAL UNDERWRITING AGENCIES PTY. LTD.—See Assurant, Inc.; *U.S. Public*, pg. 215
NATIONAL UNION FIRE INSURANCE COMPANY OF PITTSBURGH, PA.—See American International Group, Inc.; *U.S. Public*, pg. 107
NATIONAL UNITED RESOURCES HOLDINGS LTD; *Int'l*, pg. 5164
NATIONAL URBAN LEAGUE; *U.S. Private*, pg. 2864
NATIONAL URGENT CARE HOLDINGS, INC.—See Tenet Healthcare Corporation; *U.S. Public*, pg. 2005
NATIONAL UTILITY SERVICE (CANADA) LTD.—See National Utility Service, Inc.; *U.S. Private*, pg. 2864
NATIONAL UTILITY SERVICE, INC.; *U.S. Private*, pg. 2864
NATIONAL UTILITY SERVICE, S.A.—See National Utility Service, Inc.; *U.S. Private*, pg. 2864
NATIONAL UTILITY SERVICE, S.A.—See National Utility Service, Inc.; *U.S. Private*, pg. 2864
NATIONAL UTILITY SERVICE, S.A.—See National Utility Service, Inc.; *U.S. Private*, pg. 2864
NATIONAL VAN LINES, INC.; *U.S. Private*, pg. 2864
NATIONAL VENDOR, INC.; *U.S. Private*, pg. 2864
NATIONAL VETERINARY ASSOCIATES, INC.—See JAB Holding Company S.a.r.l.; *Int'l*, pg. 3862
NATIONAL VETERINARY CARE LTD; *Int'l*, pg. 5164
NATIONAL VETERINARY SERVICES LIMITED—See Patterson Companies, Inc.; *U.S. Public*, pg. 1654
NATIONAL VETERINARY SERVICES LIMITED—See Patterson Companies, Inc.; *U.S. Public*, pg. 1654
NATIONAL VISION HOLDINGS, INC.; *U.S. Public*, pg. 1498
NATIONAL VISION, INC.—See KKR & Co. Inc.; *U.S. Public*, pg. 1261
NATIONAL VISION - ST. CLOUD OPTICAL LABOARTORY—See KKR & Co. Inc.; *U.S. Public*, pg. 1261
NATIONAL VITAMIN CO. INC.; *U.S. Private*, pg. 2864
NATIONAL WASTE MANAGEMENT HOLDINGS, INC.; *U.S. Public*, pg. 1498
NATIONAL WASTE PARTNERS, LLC—See Bestige Holdings LLC; *U.S. Private*, pg. 544
NATIONAL WATER MAIN CLEANING CO.—See Carylon Corporation; *U.S. Private*, pg. 777
NATIONAL WEALTH MANAGEMENT HOLDINGS LIMITED—See National Australia Bank Limited; *Int'l*, pg. 5151
NATIONAL WESTERN LIFE GROUP, INC.—See Prosperity Group Holdings, LP; *U.S. Private*, pg. 3289
NATIONAL WESTERN LIFE INSURANCE COMPANY—See Prosperity Group Holdings, LP; *U.S. Private*, pg. 3289
NATIONAL WESTMINSTER BANK PLC—See NatWest Group plc; *Int'l*, pg. 5170
NATIONAL WESTMINSTER HOME LOANS LIMITED—See NatWest Group plc; *Int'l*, pg. 5170
NATIONAL WESTMINSTER LIFE ASSURANCE LIMITED—See NatWest Group plc; *Int'l*, pg. 5171
NATIONAL WHEEL-O-VATOR CO. INC.—See Advent International Corporation; *U.S. Private*, pg. 106
NATIONAL WHEEL-O-VATOR CO. INC.—See Cinven Limited; *Int'l*, pg. 1615
NATIONAL WHEEL-O-VATOR CO. INC.—See RAG-Stiftung; *Int'l*, pg. 6180
NATIONAL WHOLESALE COMPANY INC.; *U.S. Private*, pg. 2864
NATIONAL WHOLESALE LIQUIDATORS INC.; *U.S. Private*, pg. 2865
NATIONAL WILDLIFE FEDERATION; *U.S. Private*, pg. 2865
NATIONAL WILD TURKEY FEDERATION; *U.S. Private*, pg. 2865
NATIONAL WINE & SPIRITS, INC.; *U.S. Private*, pg. 2865
NATIONAL WOOD PRODUCTS, INC.; *U.S. Private*, pg. 2865
NATIONAL WORLD PLC; *Int'l*, pg. 5164
NATIONAL WORLDWIDE INDUSTRIAL ADVANCEMENT COMPANY LTD—See National Industrialization Company; *Int'l*, pg. 5159
NATIONAL YOUTH ADVOCATE PROGRAM; *U.S. Private*, pg. 2865
NATIONAWIDE SCREENING SERVICES, INC.; *U.S. Private*, pg. 2865
NATION FUNDING GROUP INC.—See US Buildings LLC; *U.S. Private*, pg. 4318
NATIONGATE HOLDINGS BERHAD; *Int'l*, pg. 5164
NATION GOLD CORP.; *Int'l*, pg. 5149
NATION GROUP (THAILAND) PUBLIC COMPANY LIMITED; *Int'l*, pg. 5149
NATION LANKA FINANCE PLC; *Int'l*, pg. 5149
NATION MARKETING & PUBLISHING LIMITED—See Nation Media Group Limited; *Int'l*, pg. 5149
NATION MEDIA GROUP LIMITED - BROADCASTING DIVISION—See Nation Media Group Limited; *Int'l*, pg. 5150
NATION MEDIA GROUP LIMITED - NATION CARRIERS DIVISION—See Nation Media Group Limited; *Int'l*, pg. 5150

NATION MEDIA GROUP LIMITED - NEWSPAPER DIVISION—See Nation Media Group Limited; *Int'l*, pg. 5150
NATION MEDIA GROUP LIMITED; *Int'l*, pg. 5149
NATION PIZZA AND FOODS; *U.S. Private*, pg. 2839
NATION REALTY INC.—See Cosco Capital, Inc.; *Int'l*, pg. 1809
NATION'S BEST HOLDINGS, LLC; *U.S. Private*, pg. 2839
NATIONSBUILDERS INSURANCE SERVICES, INC.—See Align Financial Group, LLC; *U.S. Private*, pg. 168
NATIONS INSURANCE BROKERS LIMITED—See Nations Trust Bank PLC; *Int'l*, pg. 5165
NATIONS RELIABLE LENDING, LLC; *U.S. Private*, pg. 2865
NATIONS ROOF EAST—See AEA Investors LP; *U.S. Private*, pg. 115
NATIONS ROOF LLC—See AEA Investors LP; *U.S. Private*, pg. 115
NATIONSTAR MORTGAGE HOLDINGS INC.—See Mr. Cooper Group Inc.; *U.S. Public*, pg. 1480
NATIONSTAR MORTGAGE LLC—See Mr. Cooper Group Inc.; *U.S. Public*, pg. 1480
NATIONS TRUST BANK PLC; *Int'l*, pg. 5164
NATIONWIDE ACCEPTANCE CORPORATION—See Nationwide Group; *U.S. Private*, pg. 2866
NATIONWIDE ACCIDENT REPAIR SERVICES LTD.—See The Carlyle Group Inc.; *U.S. Public*, pg. 2050
NATIONWIDE APPRAISAL NETWORK (NAN); *U.S. Private*, pg. 2865
NATIONWIDE ARCHIVE SYSTEMS—See Nucor Corporation; *U.S. Public*, pg. 1553
NATIONWIDE ARGOSY SOLUTIONS, LLC; *U.S. Private*, pg. 2865
NATIONWIDE BUILDING SOCIETY; *Int'l*, pg. 5165
NATIONWIDE COURT SERVICES, INC.; *U.S. Private*, pg. 2865
NATIONWIDE COURT SERVICES, INC.—See Nationwide Court Services, Inc.; *U.S. Private*, pg. 2865
NATIONWIDE CREDIT, INC.; *U.S. Private*, pg. 2865
NATIONWIDE DISTRIBUTION SERVICES LTD.—See Ferrovial S.A.; *Int'l*, pg. 2645
NATIONWIDE ENERGY PARTNERS, LTD.—See LMS Capital plc; *Int'l*, pg. 4538
NATIONWIDE EXPRESS COURIER SERVICES BERHAD; *Int'l*, pg. 5165
NATIONWIDE EXPRESS HOLDINGS BHD; *Int'l*, pg. 5165
NATIONWIDE EXPRESS INC.—See Jones Capital, LLC; *U.S. Private*, pg. 2232
NATIONWIDE FLEET INSTALLATIONS LTD.; *Int'l*, pg. 5165
NATIONWIDE FOODS INC.; *U.S. Private*, pg. 2865
NATIONWIDE GROUP; *U.S. Private*, pg. 2866
NATIONWIDE GUTTER, LLC—See Installed Building Products, Inc.; *U.S. Public*, pg. 1133
NATIONWIDE HOMES, INC.—See Cavco Industries, Inc.; *U.S. Public*, pg. 455
NATIONWIDE INDUSTRIES, INC.—See Harbour Group Industries, Inc.; *U.S. Private*, pg. 1860
NATIONWIDE LIFE—See Nationwide Building Society; *Int'l*, pg. 5165
NATIONWIDE LIFT TRUCKS INC.; *U.S. Private*, pg. 2866
NATIONWIDE LOGISTICS INC—See Van Plycon Lines Inc.; *U.S. Private*, pg. 4340
NATIONWIDE MAGAZINE & BOOK DISTRIBUTORS; *U.S. Private*, pg. 2866
NATIONWIDE MORTGAGE BANKERS, INC.; *U.S. Private*, pg. 2866
NATIONWIDE MOTOR SALES CORP; *U.S. Private*, pg. 2866
NATIONWIDE NETWORK SERVICES LTD—See The Carlyle Group Inc.; *U.S. Public*, pg. 2050
NATIONWIDE NEWSPAPERS ADVERTISING, LLC; *U.S. Private*, pg. 2866
NATIONWIDE NEWS PTY. LIMITED—See News Corporation; *U.S. Public*, pg. 1520
NATIONWIDE NTERTAINMENT SERVICES, INC.—See GLOBAL AXCESS CORP.; *U.S. Private*, pg. 1712
NATIONWIDE OIL PTY LTD—See Cleanaway Waste Management Limited; *Int'l*, pg. 1655
NATIONWIDE PAYMENT SOLUTIONS, LLC; *U.S. Private*, pg. 2866
NATIONWIDE PLASTICS, INC.—See Curbell, Inc.; *U.S. Private*, pg. 1124
NATIONWIDE PLATFORMS—See Loxam SAS; *Int'l*, pg. 4566
NATIONWIDE PLATFORMS—See Loxam SAS; *Int'l*, pg. 4566
NATIONWIDE SECURITY & BUILDING SERVICES; *U.S. Private*, pg. 2866
NATIONWIDE SECURITY SOLUTIONS INC.; *U.S. Private*, pg. 2866
NATIONWIDE SOUTHEAST INC.; *U.S. Private*, pg. 2866
NATIONWIDE STUDIOS, INC.; *U.S. Private*, pg. 2866
NATIONWIDE TARPS INC.; *U.S. Private*, pg. 2866
NATIONWIDE TITLE CLEARING, LLC—See Coyius Holdings, Inc.; *U.S. Private*, pg. 1073
NATIONWIDE TRUCK BROKERS INC.; *U.S. Private*, pg. 2866

NATIONWIDE TRUST LTD.—See Nationwide Building Society; *Int'l*, pg. 5165
NATIONZ TECHNOLOGIES INC.; *Int'l*, pg. 5165
NATIO PTY LTD—See Sa Sa International Holdings Limited; *Int'l*, pg. 6459
NATIVE AMERICAN ENERGY GROUP, INC.; *U.S. Private*, pg. 2866
NATIVE AMERICAN HEALTH CENTER; *U.S. Private*, pg. 2866
NATIVE AMERICAN HERITAGE ASSOCIATION; *U.S. Private*, pg. 2866
NATIVE ENVIRONMENTAL, LLC; *U.S. Private*, pg. 2866
NATIVE LAND DESIGN, LLC; *U.S. Private*, pg. 2866
NATIVE MINERAL RESOURCES HOLDINGS LIMITED; *Int'l*, pg. 5165
NATIVE NATION B.V.—See Liberty Global plc; *Int'l*, pg. 4485
NATIVE PATHS LLC; *U.S. Private*, pg. 2866
NATIXIS ALGERIE SP.A.—See Groupe BPCE; *Int'l*, pg. 3096
NATIXIS ASSET MANAGEMENT ADVISORS, L.P.—See Groupe BPCE; *Int'l*, pg. 3096
NATIXIS ASSET MANAGEMENT S.A.—See Groupe BPCE; *Int'l*, pg. 3096
NATIXIS ASSURANCES S.A.—See Groupe BPCE; *Int'l*, pg. 3096
NATIXIS AUSTRALIA PTY LTD.—See Groupe BPCE; *Int'l*, pg. 3098
NATIXIS BANK JSC; *Int'l*, pg. 5165
NATIXIS BLEICHROEDER INC.—See Groupe BPCE; *Int'l*, pg. 3094
NATIXIS - BOGOTA—See Groupe BPCE; *Int'l*, pg. 3094
NATIXIS - BUENOS AIRES—See Groupe BPCE; *Int'l*, pg. 3094
NATIXIS CAPITAL MARKETS INC.—See Groupe BPCE; *Int'l*, pg. 3094
NATIXIS - CORPORATE & INVESTMENT BANKING—See Groupe BPCE; *Int'l*, pg. 3094
NATIXIS DISTRIBUTION, LP—See Groupe BPCE; *Int'l*, pg. 3098
NATIXIS DISTRIBUTORS, L.P.—See Groupe BPCE; *Int'l*, pg. 3096
NATIXIS DUBAI LIMITED—See Groupe BPCE; *Int'l*, pg. 3098
NATIXIS FACTOR S.A.—See Groupe BPCE; *Int'l*, pg. 3096
NATIXIS FINANCE—See Groupe BPCE; *Int'l*, pg. 3094
NATIXIS GLOBAL ASSET MANAGEMENT CANADA CORP.—See Groupe BPCE; *Int'l*, pg. 3096
NATIXIS GLOBAL ASSET MANAGEMENT (FRANCE)—See Groupe BPCE; *Int'l*, pg. 3096
NATIXIS GLOBAL ASSET MANAGEMENT, L.P.—See Groupe BPCE; *Int'l*, pg. 3096
NATIXIS GLOBAL ASSET MANAGEMENT S.A.—See Groupe BPCE; *Int'l*, pg. 3096
NATIXIS GLOBAL ASSOCIATES INTERNATIONAL—See Groupe BPCE; *Int'l*, pg. 3096
NATIXIS GLOBAL ASSOCIATES, LLC—See Groupe BPCE; *Int'l*, pg. 3096
NATIXIS - HANOI—See Groupe BPCE; *Int'l*, pg. 3094
NATIXIS - HO CHI MINH—See Groupe BPCE; *Int'l*, pg. 3094
NATIXIS - HONG KONG—See Groupe BPCE; *Int'l*, pg. 3094
NATIXIS IM MEXICO, S. DE R.L. DE C.V.—See Groupe BPCE; *Int'l*, pg. 3098
NATIXIS INTEREPARGNE S.A.—See Groupe BPCE; *Int'l*, pg. 3097
NATIXIS INVESTISSEMENT PARTNERS—See Groupe BPCE; *Int'l*, pg. 3095
NATIXIS INVESTMENT MANAGERS AUSTRALIA PTY LIMITED—See Groupe BPCE; *Int'l*, pg. 3098
NATIXIS INVESTMENT MANAGERS HONG KONG LIMITED—See Groupe BPCE; *Int'l*, pg. 3098
NATIXIS INVESTMENT MANAGERS INTERNATIONAL SA—See Groupe BPCE; *Int'l*, pg. 3098
NATIXIS INVESTMENT MANAGERS KOREA LIMITED—See Groupe BPCE; *Int'l*, pg. 3098
NATIXIS INVESTMENT MANAGERS, LP—See Groupe BPCE; *Int'l*, pg. 3098
NATIXIS INVESTMENT MANAGERS MIDDLE EAST LLC—See Groupe BPCE; *Int'l*, pg. 3098
NATIXIS INVESTMENT MANAGERS, NEDERLANDS S.A—See Groupe BPCE; *Int'l*, pg. 3098
NATIXIS INVESTMENT MANAGERS, NORDICS FILIAL AB—See Groupe BPCE; *Int'l*, pg. 3098
NATIXIS INVESTMENT MANAGERS S.A—See Groupe BPCE; *Int'l*, pg. 3098
NATIXIS INVESTMENT MANAGERS SA—See Groupe BPCE; *Int'l*, pg. 3098
NATIXIS INVESTMENT MANAGERS S.A,ZWEIGNIERDERLAASUNG DEUTSCHLAND—See Groupe BPCE; *Int'l*, pg. 3098
NATIXIS INVESTMENT MANAGERS SECURITIES INVESTMENT CONSULTING CO., LTD.—See Groupe BPCE; *Int'l*, pg. 3098
NATIXIS INVESTMENT MANAGERS, SUCURSAL EN ESPANA SL—See Groupe BPCE; *Int'l*, pg. 3098
NATIXIS INVESTMENT MANAGERS SWITZERLAND SARL—See Groupe BPCE; *Int'l*, pg. 3098
NATIXIS INVESTMENT MANAGERS UK LTD.—See Groupe BPCE; *Int'l*, pg. 3098
NATIXIS INVESTMENT MANAGERS URUGUAY S.A.—See Groupe BPCE; *Int'l*, pg. 3098
NATIXIS JAPAN SECURITIES CO., LTD.—See Groupe BPCE; *Int'l*, pg. 3098
NATIXIS - KUALA LUMPUR—See Groupe BPCE; *Int'l*, pg. 3094
NATIXIS - LABUAN—See Groupe BPCE; *Int'l*, pg. 3094
NATIXIS LEASE—See Groupe BPCE; *Int'l*, pg. 3094
NATIXIS LIFE SA—See Groupe BPCE; *Int'l*, pg. 3098
NATIXIS - LONDON—See Groupe BPCE; *Int'l*, pg. 3094
NATIXIS LUXEMBOURG S.A.—See Groupe BPCE; *Int'l*, pg. 3097
NATIXIS MILAN S.A—See Groupe BPCE; *Int'l*, pg. 3098
NATIXIS NORTH AMERICA INC.—See Groupe BPCE; *Int'l*, pg. 3094
NATIXIS PARTNERS—See Groupe BPCE; *Int'l*, pg. 3097
NATIXIS PAYMENT SOLUTIONS SA—See Groupe BPCE; *Int'l*, pg. 3098
NATIXIS PFANDBRIEFBANK AG—See Groupe BPCE; *Int'l*, pg. 3098
NATIXIS PRIVATE EQUITY INTERNATIONAL—See Groupe BPCE; *Int'l*, pg. 3095
NATIXIS - PRIVATE EQUITY & PRIVATE BANKING—See Groupe BPCE; *Int'l*, pg. 3095
NATIXIS PRIVATE EQUITY—See Groupe BPCE; *Int'l*, pg. 3095
NATIXIS REAL ESTATE CAPITAL INC.—See Groupe BPCE; *Int'l*, pg. 3095
NATIXIS - RECEIVABLES MANAGEMENT—See Groupe BPCE; *Int'l*, pg. 3096
NATIXIS, S.A.—See Groupe BPCE; *Int'l*, pg. 3094
NATIXIS SECURITIES AMERICAS LLC—See Groupe BPCE; *Int'l*, pg. 3098
NATIXIS SECURITIES NORTH AMERICA INC.—See Groupe BPCE; *Int'l*, pg. 3095
NATIXIS - SINGAPORE—See Groupe BPCE; *Int'l*, pg. 3094
NATIXIS TAIWAN LIMITED—See Groupe BPCE; *Int'l*, pg. 3098
NATIXIS WEALTH MANAGEMENT LUXEMBOURG SA—See Groupe BPCE; *Int'l*, pg. 3098
NATIXIS WEALTH MANAGEMENT SA—See Groupe BPCE; *Int'l*, pg. 3098
NATIXIS ZWEIGNIEDERLASSUNG DEUTSCHLAND SE—See Groupe BPCE; *Int'l*, pg. 3099
NAT LANDAU HYMAN JEWELS LTD.—See Landau Direct; *U.S. Private*, pg. 2384
NATLOYAL (M) SDN BHD—See Malayan United Industries Berhad; *Int'l*, pg. 4661
NATOCO CO.,LTD.; *Int'l*, pg. 5165
NATOCO PAINT CHEMICAL INDUSTRY (QINGDAO) CO., LTD.—See Natoco Co.,Ltd.; *Int'l*, pg. 5165
NATOLI ENGINEERING CO. INC.; *U.S. Private*, pg. 2866
NATOM A.D.; *Int'l*, pg. 5165
NATOMAS DIALYSIS, LLC—See DaVita Inc.; *U.S. Public*, pg. 641
NATOM LOGISTIC SP. Z O.O.—See Troax Group AB; *Int'l*, pg. 7937
NATORI CO., LTD.; *Int'l*, pg. 5165
NATPAK (PVT) LIMITED—See Innscor Africa Ltd.; *Int'l*, pg. 3713
NATRA ALLCRUMP—See Investindustrial Advisors Ltd.; *Int'l*, pg. 3779
NATRACACAO—See Investindustrial Advisors Ltd.; *Int'l*, pg. 3779
NATRAJACALI—See Investindustrial Advisors Ltd.; *Int'l*, pg. 3779
NATRAJ PROTEINS LIMITED; *Int'l*, pg. 5165
NATRAN LLC; *U.S. Private*, pg. 2866
NATRA SAINT ETIENNE SAS—See Investindustrial Advisors Ltd.; *Int'l*, pg. 3779
NATRA S.A.—See Investindustrial Advisors Ltd.; *Int'l*, pg. 3779
NATRA US—See Investindustrial Advisors Ltd.; *Int'l*, pg. 3779
NATRAZAHOR—See Investindustrial Advisors Ltd.; *Int'l*, pg. 3779
NATREL COMMUNICATIONS; *U.S. Private*, pg. 2866
NATREON INC.—See Kerry Group plc; *Int'l*, pg. 4139
NATRE VINDUER AS—See VKR Holding A/S; *Int'l*, pg. 8281
NATROL GLOBAL FZ-LLC—See Plethico Pharmaceuticals Ltd.; *Int'l*, pg. 5897
NATROL, LLC—See Aurobindo Pharma Ltd.; *Int'l*, pg. 712
NATRONIX SEMICONDUCTOR TECHNOLOGY LTD.; *Int'l*, pg. 5165
NATRON RESOURCES, INC.—See Willcrest Partners; *U.S. Private*, pg. 4521
NATRO TECH S.R.L.—See Mondi plc; *Int'l*, pg. 5027
NATS EN-ROUTE LIMITED—See NATS Holdings Limited; *Int'l*, pg. 5166
NATSEVEN TV SDN BHD—See Media Prima Berhad; *Int'l*, pg. 4771
NAT SHERMAN INC.; *U.S. Private*, pg. 2837
NATS HOLDINGS LIMITED; *Int'l*, pg. 5165
NATSOURCE LLC; *U.S. Private*, pg. 2867
NATS SERVICES (ASIA PACIFIC) PTE. LIMITED—See NATS Holdings Limited; *Int'l*, pg. 5166
NATS SERVICES (HONG KONG) LIMITED—See NATS Holdings Limited; *Int'l*, pg. 5166
NATS SERVICES LIMITED—See NATS Holdings Limited; *Int'l*, pg. 5166
NATS SERVICES LLC—See NATS Holdings Limited; *Int'l*, pg. 5166
NATSTEEL AUSTRALIA PTY. LTD.—See Tata Sons Limited; *Int'l*, pg. 7472
NATSTEEL (XIAMEN) LTD.—See Tata Sons Limited; *Int'l*, pg. 7472
NATS (USA) INC—See NATS Holdings Limited; *Int'l*, pg. 5165
NATTOPHARMA ASA—See Compagnie des Levures Lesaffre SA; *Int'l*, pg. 1739
NATTOPHARMA USA, INC.—See Compagnie des Levures Lesaffre SA; *Int'l*, pg. 1739
NATTYSWANKY HOLDINGS CO., LTD.; *Int'l*, pg. 5166
NATUDIS NEDERLAND B.V.—See Udea B.V.; *Int'l*, pg. 8014
NATUMI AG—See The Hain Celestial Group, Inc.; *U.S. Public*, pg. 2087
NATUNA VENTURES PTE. LTD.—See PGS ASA; *Int'l*, pg. 5838
NATUNOLA AGRITECH INC.; *Int'l*, pg. 5166
NATURA & CO HOLDING S.A.; *Int'l*, pg. 5166
NATURA COSMETICOS SA—See Natura & Co Holding S.A.; *Int'l*, pg. 5166
NATURA COSMETICOS S.A.—See Natura & Co Holding S.A.; *Int'l*, pg. 5167
NATURA DISTRIBUIDORA DE MEXICO, S.A. DE C.V.—See Natura & Co Holding S.A.; *Int'l*, pg. 5167
NATURA EUROPA S.A.S.—See Natura & Co Holding S.A.; *Int'l*, pg. 5167
NATURALAC NUTRITION LIMITED—See Hansells Masterton Ltd.; *Int'l*, pg. 3260
NATURAL ADCAMPAIGN LIMITED—See Optibiotix Health PLC; *Int'l*, pg. 5602
NATURAL ALTERNATIVES INTERNATIONAL EUROPE S.A.—See Natural Alternatives International, Inc.; *U.S. Public*, pg. 1499
NATURAL ALTERNATIVES INTERNATIONAL, INC.; *U.S. Public*, pg. 1498
NATURAL AMERICAN FOODS, INC.—See Peak Rock Capital LLC; *U.S. Private*, pg. 3124
NATURAL AVENUE SDN. BHD.—See Berjaya Assets Berhad; *Int'l*, pg. 981
NATURAL AVENUE SDN. BHD.—See Berjaya Assets Berhad; *Int'l*, pg. 981
NATURAL AVENUE SDN. BHD.—See Berjaya Assets Berhad; *Int'l*, pg. 981
NATURAL AVENUE SDN. BHD.—See Berjaya Assets Berhad; *Int'l*, pg. 982
THE NATURAL BABY CATALOG—See Kids Stuff, Inc.; *U.S. Private*, pg. 2303
THE NATURAL BABY COMPANY, LLC; *U.S. Private*, pg. 4082
NATURAL BALANCE PET FOODS, INC.—See The J.M. Smucker Company; *U.S. Public*, pg. 2107
NATURAL BEAUTY BIO TECHNOLOGY LTD; *Int'l*, pg. 5167
NATURAL BIOCON INDIA LIMITED; *Int'l*, pg. 5167
NATURAL CAPITALISM SOLUTIONS; *U.S. Private*, pg. 2867
NATURAL CAPSULES LIMITED; *Int'l*, pg. 5167
NATURAL CHEMISTRY, INC.; *U.S. Private*, pg. 2867
NATURAL CO., LTD.—See Bain Capital, LP; *U.S. Private*, pg. 434
THE NATURAL CONFECTIONERY CO. PTY LTD—See Mondelez International, Inc.; *U.S. Public*, pg. 1462
NATURAL COOL AIRCONDITIONING & ENGINEERING PTE LTD—See Natural Cool Holdings Limited; *Int'l*, pg. 5167
NATURAL COOL HOLDINGS LIMITED; *Int'l*, pg. 5167
NATURAL COOL INVESTMENTS PTE. LTD.—See Natural Cool Holdings Limited; *Int'l*, pg. 5168
NATURAL COTTON EXCHANGE CO., LTD.—See Toyota Tsusho Corporation; *Int'l*, pg. 7877
NATURAL DECORATIONS, INC.; *U.S. Private*, pg. 2867
NATURAL DESIGNS LANDSCAPING INC.; *U.S. Private*, pg. 2867
NATURAL DESTINY INC.; *Int'l*, pg. 5168
NATURALENDO TECH CO., LTD. - ICHEON FACTORY—See Naturalendo Tech Co., Ltd.; *Int'l*, pg. 5168
NATURALENDO TECH CO., LTD.; *Int'l*, pg. 5168
NATURAL ENERGY DEVELOPMENT CO., LTD.—See Electricity Generating Public Co., Ltd.; *Int'l*, pg. 2352
NATURAL ENERGY JAPAN CORPORATION—See Hitachi Zosen Corporation; *Int'l*, pg. 3411
NATURAL ENERGY, S.A.—See Naturgy Energy Group, S.A.; *Int'l*, pg. 5169
NATURAL FLAVORS, INC.—See Firmenich International SA; *Int'l*, pg. 2680
NATURAL FOOD HOLDINGS, INC.—See Perdue Farms Incorporated; *U.S. Private*, pg. 3147
NATURAL FOOD INTERNATIONAL HOLDING LIMITED; *Int'l*, pg. 5168

NATURAL FOOD INTERNATIONAL HOLDING LIMITED   CORPORATE AFFILIATIONS

NATURAL FOOD SRL—See Orkla ASA; *Int'l*, pg. 5638
NATURAL FOOD WORKS, LLC—See Campbell Soup Company; *U.S. Public*, pg. 427
NATURAL F&P CORP.; *Int'l*, pg. 5168
NATURAL GAS PIPELINE COMPANY OF AMERICA LLC—See Brookfield Infrastructure Partners L.P.; *Int'l*, pg. 1193
NATURAL GAS PIPELINE COMPANY OF AMERICA LLC—See Kinder Morgan, Inc.; *U.S. Public*, pg. 1234
NATURAL GAS PROCESSING COMPANY; *U.S. Private*, pg. 2867
NATURAL GAS SERVICES GROUP, INC.; *U.S. Public*, pg. 1499
NATURAL GAS TECHNOLOGY CENTRE—See Caisse de Depot et Placement du Quebec; *Int'l*, pg. 1256
NATURAL GROCERS BY VITAMIN COTTAGE, INC.; *U.S. Public*, pg. 1499
NATURAL HEALTH MAGAZINE—See Meredith Corporation; *U.S. Public*, pg. 1423
NATURAL HEALTH TRENDS CORP.; *Int'l*, pg. 5168
NATURAL HERBS & SPICES PTY LTD—See Libstar Holdings Ltd.; *Int'l*, pg. 4487
NATURALIFE ECO VITE LABS; *U.S. Private*, pg. 2867
NATURAL LANDS TRUST, INC.; *U.S. Private*, pg. 2867
NATURAL LIVING, INC.—See Option Care Health, Inc.; *U.S. Public*, pg. 1610
NATURALLY FRESH, INC.—See TreeHouse Foods, Inc.; *U.S. Public*, pg. 2187
NATURALLY SPLENDID ENTERPRISES LTD.; *Int'l*, pg. 5168
NATURALLY YOU—See Southeastern Medequip, Inc.; *U.S. Private*, pg. 3728
THE NATURAL MARKETING INSTITUTE INC—See Research America, Inc.; *U.S. Private*, pg. 3403
NATURALMOTION LIMITED—See Zynga Inc.; *U.S. Private*, pg. 4611
NATURAL OLEOCHEMICALS SDN. BHD.—See Wilmar International Limited; *Int'l*, pg. 8421
NATURAL ORDER ACQUISITION CORP.; *U.S. Public*, pg. 1499
NATURAL ORGANIC FOOD GROUP PEI INC.; *Int'l*, pg. 5168
NATURAL ORGANICS, INC.; *U.S. Private*, pg. 2867
NATURAL OVENS BAKERY INC.—See Alpha Baking Company; *U.S. Private*, pg. 196
NATURALPOINT, INC.—See Leyard Optoelectronic Co., Ltd.; *Int'l*, pg. 4472
NATURAL POINT S.R.L—See Recordati S.p.A.; *Int'l*, pg. 6239
NATURAL PRODUCTS, INC.—See Kent Corporation; *U.S. Private*, pg. 2287
NATURAL RESOURCE GOVERNANCE INSTITUTE; *U.S. Private*, pg. 2867
NATURAL RESOURCE HOLDINGS, INC.; *Int'l*, pg. 5168
NATURAL RESOURCE HOLDINGS, LTD.; *Int'l*, pg. 5168
NATURAL RESOURCE PARTNERS L.P.; *U.S. Public*, pg. 1499
NATURAL RESOURCES CONSULTING, INC.; *U.S. Private*, pg. 2867
NATURAL RESOURCES CORPORATION; *Int'l*, pg. 5168
NATURAL RESOURCE TECHNOLOGY, INC.—See The O'Brien & Gere Companies; *U.S. Private*, pg. 4087
NATURAL RETAIL GROUP, INC.—See United Natural Foods, Inc.; *U.S. Public*, pg. 2231
NATURAL RETREATS US LLC; *U.S. Private*, pg. 2867
NATURALS BASEBALL, INC.—See Rich Holdings, Inc.; *U.S. Private*, pg. 3426
NATURAL SEASONING COMPANY; *U.S. Private*, pg. 2867
NATURALSHRIMP, INC.; *U.S. Public*, pg. 1499
NATURAL SPRINGS WATER GROUP, LLC—See The H.T. Hackney Company; *U.S. Private*, pg. 4041
NATURAL SPROUT COMPANY, LLC; *U.S. Private*, pg. 2867
NATURAL STONE CONCEPTS LLC; *U.S. Private*, pg. 2867
NATURAL SUPPLEMENT ASSOCIATION INC.; *U.S. Private*, pg. 2867
NATURAL SYSTEMS INTERNATIONAL, LLC—See Biohabitats, Inc.; *U.S. Private*, pg. 562
NATURAL WAY, INC.; *U.S. Private*, pg. 2867
NATURAL WELLNESS CORPORATION LTD.—See Essel Corporate Resources Pvt. Ltd.; *Int'l*, pg. 2509
NATURAL WELLNESS USA, INC.—See Essel Corporate Resources Pvt. Ltd.; *Int'l*, pg. 2509
NATURAL WORLD S.R.L.—See BRENNTAG SE; *Int'l*, pg. 1149
NATURA MEDIA INC.—See PAPERCOREA CO., LTD.; *Int'l*, pg. 5733
NATURAMED PHARMA AB—See Volati AB; *Int'l*, pg. 8300
NATURAMED PHARMA AS—See Vision Healthcare N.V.; *Int'l*, pg. 8252
NATUR COMPAGNIE GMBH—See Coop-Gruppe Genossenschaft; *Int'l*, pg. 1790
NATURE AMERICA, INC.—See Verlagsgruppe Georg von Holtzbrinck GmbH; *Int'l*, pg. 8171
NATURE BIO FOODS LIMITED—See LT Foods Ltd; *Int'l*, pg. 4571
NATUREBRIDGE; *U.S. Private*, pg. 2867

NATURECELL CO., LTD; *Int'l*, pg. 5169
NATURECELL CO., LTD.- YEONGYANG FACTORY—See Naturecell Co., Ltd; *Int'l*, pg. 5169
THE NATURE CONSERVANCY; *U.S. Private*, pg. 4082
NATURE ENERGY BIOGAS A/S—See Davidson Kempner Capital Management LP; *U.S. Private*, pg. 1172
NATURE ENERGY CONSTRUCTION A/S—See Davidson Kempner Capital Management LP; *U.S. Private*, pg. 1172
NATURE ENERGY TECHNOLOGY HOLDINGS LIMITED; *Int'l*, pg. 5168
NATURE & ENVIRONMENT CO., LTD.; *Int'l*, pg. 5168
NATURE FLOORING INDUSTRIES INC.—See Nature Home Holding Limited; *Int'l*, pg. 5168
NATURE GROUP PLC; *Int'l*, pg. 5168
THE NATURE HOLDINGS CO., LTD.; *Int'l*, pg. 7670
NATURE HOME (CHINA) CO., LTD.—See Nature Home Holding Limited; *Int'l*, pg. 5168
NATURE HOME HOLDING LIMITED; *Int'l*, pg. 5168
NATURELGAZ SANAYI VE TICARET A.S.—See Global Yatirim Holding A.S.; *Int'l*, pg. 3003
NATURE & LOGIS SA; *Int'l*, pg. 5168
NATUREL YENILENEBILIR ENERJI TICARET AS; *Int'l*, pg. 5169
NATURE MADE NUTRITIONAL PRODUCTS INC.—See Otsuka Holdings Co., Ltd.; *Int'l*, pg. 5660
NATURENER ENERGY CANADA INC.—See Morgan Stanley; *U.S. Public*, pg. 1475
NATURENER RIM ROCK WIND ENERGY, LLC—See Morgan Stanley; *U.S. Public*, pg. 1475
NATURENER USA, LLC—See Morgan Stanley; *U.S. Public*, pg. 1475
NATURE ODYSSEY (PVT) LTD.—See John Keells Holdings PLC; *Int'l*, pg. 3979
NATUREPLEX LLC; *U.S. Private*, pg. 2867
NATURE PURE LLC; *U.S. Private*, pg. 2867
NATURERIPE FARMS LLC; *U.S. Private*, pg. 2867
NATURES BASKET LTD.—See CESC Limited; *Int'l*, pg. 1424
NATURE'S BEST, INC.—See KeHE Distributors, LLC; *U.S. Private*, pg. 2273
NATURE'S DISCOUNT, INC.; *Int'l*, pg. 5169
NATURESEAL, INC.—See RPM International Inc.; *U.S. Public*, pg. 1817
NATURE'S FOOTPRINT, INC.; *U.S. Private*, pg. 2867
NATURES INNOVATION, INC.; *U.S. Private*, pg. 2867
NATURE'S MIRACLE HOLDING INC.; *U.S. Public*, pg. 1499
NATURE'S NEEDS LLC—See Arakelian Enterprises, Inc.; *U.S. Private*, pg. 307
NATURE'S ONE, LLC—See Bobbie Baby, Inc.; *U.S. Private*, pg. 606
NATURES ORGANICS PTY. LTD.; *Int'l*, pg. 5169
NATURE SOY LLC—See Keystone Capital, Inc.; *U.S. Private*, pg. 2295
NATURE'S PATH FOODS INC.; *Int'l*, pg. 5169
NATURE'S PRODUCTS, INC.—See The Clorox Company; *U.S. Public*, pg. 2062
NATURE'S SELECTION FOODS—See AAB Holdings Pty Limited; *Int'l*, pg. 30
NATURE'S SUNSHINE PRODUCTS DE MEXICO S.A. DE C.V.—See Nature's Sunshine Products, Inc.; *U.S. Public*, pg. 1499
NATURE'S SUNSHINE PRODUCTS DE VENEZUELA, C.A.—See Nature's Sunshine Products, Inc.; *U.S. Public*, pg. 1499
NATURE'S SUNSHINE PRODUCTS, INC.; *U.S. Public*, pg. 1499
NATURE'S SUNSHINE PRODUCTS, INC. - UK BRANCH—See Nature's Sunshine Products, Inc.; *U.S. Public*, pg. 1499
NATURE'S SUNSHINE PRODUCTS OF CANADA, LTD.—See Nature's Sunshine Products, Inc.; *U.S. Public*, pg. 1499
NATURESTAR BIO-TEC INC.; *U.S. Private*, pg. 2868
NATURE'S VALUE, INC.; *U.S. Private*, pg. 2867
NATURE'S WAY HOLDING CO.—See Dr. Willmar Schwabe GmbH & Co. KG; *Int'l*, pg. 2195
NATURE'S WAY PRODUCTS, INC.—See Dr. Willmar Schwabe GmbH & Co. KG; *Int'l*, pg. 2195
NATUREWISE BIOTECH & MEDICALS CORP.; *Int'l*, pg. 5169
NATURE WOOD GROUP LIMITED; *Int'l*, pg. 5168
NATUREWORKS LLC—See Cargill, Inc.; *U.S. Private*, pg. 759
NATUREWORKS LLC—See PTT Global Chemical Public Company Limited; *Int'l*, pg. 6091
NATUREX AUSTRALIA PTY LTD—See Givaudan S.A.; *Int'l*, pg. 2981
NATUREX GMBH—See Givaudan S.A.; *Int'l*, pg. 2981
NATUREX HOLDINGS SINGAPORE PTE. LTD.—See Givaudan S.A.; *Int'l*, pg. 2981
NATUREX INC.—See Givaudan S.A.; *Int'l*, pg. 2981
NATUREX INDIA PRIVATE LIMITED—See Givaudan S.A.; *Int'l*, pg. 2981
NATUREX K.K.—See Givaudan S.A.; *Int'l*, pg. 2981
NATUREX LTD.—See Givaudan S.A.; *Int'l*, pg. 2981
NATUREX S.A.—See Givaudan S.A.; *Int'l*, pg. 2981
NATUREX S.P.A—See Givaudan S.A.; *Int'l*, pg. 2981

NATUREX UK LTD.—See Givaudan S.A.; *Int'l*, pg. 2981
NATURGAS ENERGIA COMERCIALIZADORAS ULTIMO RECURSO, S.A.—See EDP - Energias de Portugal, S.A.; *Int'l*, pg. 2314
NATURGAS ENERGIA GRUPO, S.A.—See EDP - Energias de Portugal, S.A.; *Int'l*, pg. 2314
NATURGAS ENERGIA SERVICIOS COMUNES, S.A.—See Enagas, S.A.; *Int'l*, pg. 2396
NATURGAS ENERGIA TRANSPORTE, S.A.U.—See Enagas, S.A.; *Int'l*, pg. 2396
NATURGY BAN, S.A.—See Naturgy Energy Group, S.A.; *Int'l*, pg. 5169
NATURGY ENERGY GROUP, S.A.; *Int'l*, pg. 5169
NATURGY LTD.—See Naturgy Energy Group, S.A.; *Int'l*, pg. 5169
NATURHOUSE HEALTH, S.A.; *Int'l*, pg. 5169
NATUR INTERNATIONAL CORP.; *Int'l*, pg. 5166
NATURIN VISCOFAN GMBH—See Viscofan SA; *Int'l*, pg. 8250
NATURIPE BERRY GROWERS INC.; *U.S. Private*, pg. 2868
NATURITE AGRO PRODUCTS LTD.; *Int'l*, pg. 5169
NATURKOMPANIET AB—See Fenix Outdoor International AG; *Int'l*, pg. 2634
NATURLICHENERGIE EMH GMBH—See EnBW Energie Baden-Wurttemberg AG; *Int'l*, pg. 2399
NATURLICHENERGIE SWISS NES GMBH—See EnBW Energie Baden-Wurttemberg AG; *Int'l*, pg. 2399
NATURLI FOODS A/S—See Orkla ASA; *Int'l*, pg. 5638
NATURO INDIABULL LIMITED; *Int'l*, pg. 5170
NATURPRODUKT KFT—See Dr. Theiss Naturwaren GmbH; *Int'l*, pg. 2195
NATURPUR ENERGIE AG—See HEAG Sudhessische Energie AG; *Int'l*, pg. 3302
NATURSTEIN VETTER GMBH—See Laing O'Rourke Plc; *Int'l*, pg. 4396
NATURUM CO., LTD.—See Scroll Corporation; *Int'l*, pg. 6656
NATURWAREN ITALIA S.R.L.—See Dr. Theiss Naturwaren GmbH; *Int'l*, pg. 2195
NATURWATT GMBH—See EWE Aktiengesellschaft; *Int'l*, pg. 2575
NATURWOOD HOME FURNISHINGS, INC.; *U.S. Private*, pg. 2868
NATUS EUROPE GMBH—See ArchiMed SAS; *Int'l*, pg. 548
NATUS MANUFACTURING IRELAND, LTD.—See ArchiMed SAS; *Int'l*, pg. 548
NATUS MEDICAL DENMARK APS—See ArchiMed SAS; *Int'l*, pg. 548
NATUS MEDICAL INCORPORATED—See ArchiMed SAS; *Int'l*, pg. 548
NATUS MEDICAL INC.—See ArchiMed SAS; *Int'l*, pg. 549
NATUS NEUROLOGY INC. - GRASS PRODUCTS—See ArchiMed SAS; *Int'l*, pg. 549
NATUS NEUROLOGY INCORPORATED—See ArchiMed SAS; *Int'l*, pg. 549
NATUVION GMBH—See Nippon Telegraph & Telephone Corporation; *Int'l*, pg. 5354
NATUZZI AMERICAS, INC.—See Natuzzi S.p.A.; *Int'l*, pg. 5170
NATUZZI BENELUX S.A.—See Natuzzi S.p.A.; *Int'l*, pg. 5170
NATUZZI GERMANY GMBH—See Natuzzi S.p.A.; *Int'l*, pg. 5170
NATUZZI IBERICA S.A.—See Natuzzi S.p.A.; *Int'l*, pg. 5170
NATUZZI JAPAN K.K.—See Natuzzi S.p.A.; *Int'l*, pg. 5170
NATUZZI RUSSIA OOO—See Natuzzi S.p.A.; *Int'l*, pg. 5170
NATUZZI SERVICES LIMITED—See Natuzzi S.p.A.; *Int'l*, pg. 5170
NATUZZI S.P.A.; *Int'l*, pg. 5170
NATUZZI SWITZERLAND AG—See Natuzzi S.p.A.; *Int'l*, pg. 5170
NATUZZI TRADE SERVICE S.R.L.—See Natuzzi S.p.A.; *Int'l*, pg. 5170
NATUZZI TRADING SHANGHAI LTD—See Natuzzi S.p.A.; *Int'l*, pg. 5170
NATVAR TEKNI-PLEX, INC.—See Genstar Capital, LLC; *U.S. Private*, pg. 1679
NATWEST GROUP PLC; *Int'l*, pg. 5170
NATWEST INSURANCE SERVICES—See NatWest Group plc; *Int'l*, pg. 5170
NATWEST MORTGAGE SERVICES—See NatWest Group plc; *Int'l*, pg. 5170
NATWEST NEW YORK—See NatWest Group plc; *Int'l*, pg. 5170
NATWEST PERSONAL BANKING—See NatWest Group plc; *Int'l*, pg. 5170
NATWEST PRIVATE BANKING—See NatWest Group plc; *Int'l*, pg. 5170
NATWEST STOCKBROKERS LIMITED—See The Toronto-Dominion Bank; *Int'l*, pg. 7695
NAU CA CROP INS—See NAU Holding Company; *U.S. Private*, pg. 2868
NAU COUNTRY INSURANCE COMPANY—See NAU Holding Company; *U.S. Private*, pg. 2868

COMPANY NAME INDEX

NAUGHTONE MANUFACTURING LTD.—See MillerKnoll, Inc.; *U.S. Public*, pg. 1447
NAUGHTON ENERGY CORPORATION; *U.S. Private*, pg. 2868
NAUGHTON'S PLUMBING SALES CO., INC.; *U.S. Private*, pg. 2868
NAUGHTY VEGAN LIMITED—See Volvere plc; *Int'l*, pg. 8304
NAU HOLDING COMPANY; *U.S. Private*, pg. 2868
NAU IB CAPITAL CO., LTD.—See Soulbrain Holdings Co., Ltd.; *Int'l*, pg. 7114
NAU INSURANCE COMPANY—See NAU Holding Company; *U.S. Private*, pg. 2868
NAUKA-SVYAZ OAO; *Int'l*, pg. 5172
NAUKRI INTERNET SERVICES PRIVATE LIMITED—See Info Edge India Ltd; *Int'l*, pg. 3689
NAULTS ENTERPRISES INC.; *U.S. Private*, pg. 2868
NAUMANN GROUP REAL ESTATE INC.; *U.S. Private*, pg. 2868
NAUMANN/HOBBS MATERIAL HANDLING, INC.—See HCI Equity Management, L.P.; *U.S. Public*, pg. 1889
NAUMES INC.; *U.S. Private*, pg. 2868
NAURA AKRION INC.—See NAURA Technology Group Co., Ltd.; *Int'l*, pg. 5172
NAURA TECHNOLOGY GROUP CO., LTD.; *Int'l*, pg. 5172
NAUTALIA VIAJES, S.L.—See Gowaii Vacation Holding S.L.; *Int'l*, pg. 3044
NAUTALIA VIAJES, S.L.—See Springwater Capital LLC; *Int'l*, pg. 7144
NAUTICA APPAREL, INC.—See Leonard Green & Partners, L.P.; *U.S. Private*, pg. 2426
NAUTICA ENTERPRISES, INC.—See Leonard Green & Partners, L.P.; *U.S. Private*, pg. 2426
NAUTICAL, LUIS ARBULU, S.L.U.—See Grupo Arbulu S.L.; *Int'l*, pg. 3120
NAUTICAL MARINE INC.; *U.S. Private*, pg. 2872
NAUTICA RETAIL USA, INC.—See Leonard Green & Partners, L.P.; *U.S. Private*, pg. 2426
NAUTICAWT LIMITED; *Int'l*, pg. 5172
NAUTIC PARTNERS, LLC; *U.S. Private*, pg. 2868
NAUTIC STAR, LLC—See MasterCraft Boat Holdings, Inc.; *U.S. Public*, pg. 1395
NAUTIC TARRAGONA, S.A.—See Industry Super Holdings Pty. Ltd.; *Int'l*, pg. 3676
NAUTICUS ROBOTICS HOLDINGS, INC.—See Nauticus Robotics, Inc.; *U.S. Public*, pg. 1500
NAUTICUS ROBOTICS, INC.; *U.S. Public*, pg. 1500
NAUTILUS BIOTECHNOLOGY, INC.; *U.S. Public*, pg. 1500
NAUTILUS COMMERCIAL FITNESS—See Core Health & Fitness LLC; *U.S. Public*, pg. 1048
NAUTILUS ENVIRONMENTAL, LLC.; *U.S. Private*, pg. 2872
NAUTILUS HEALTHCARE, INC.—See The Ensign Group, Inc.; *U.S. Public*, pg. 2071
NAUTILUS HEALTH & FITNESS GROUP—See Johnson Health Tech. Co., Ltd.; *Int'l*, pg. 3991
NAUTILUS HYOSUNG AMERICA, INC.—See Hyosung Corporation; *Int'l*, pg. 3551
NAUTILUS HYOSUNG, LTD.—See Hyosung Corporation; *Int'l*, pg. 3552
NAUTILUS INSURANCE COMPANY—See W.R. Berkley Corporation; *U.S. Public*, pg. 2318
NAUTILUS INSURANCE GROUP, LLC—See W.R. Berkley Corporation; *U.S. Public*, pg. 2318
NAUTILUS INVESTIGATIONS, INC.—See The Carlyle Group Inc.; *U.S. Public*, pg. 2053
NAUTILUS MARINE SERVICES PLC—See HKN, Inc.; *U.S. Public*, pg. 1042
NAUTILUS PLUS INC; *Int'l*, pg. 5172
NAUTILUS SOLAR ENERGY, LLC—See Power Corporation of Canada; *Int'l*, pg. 5943
NAUTISK FORLAG AS—See EQT AB; *Int'l*, pg. 2478
N AUTO SOFIA EAD—See Eurohold Bulgaria AD; *Int'l*, pg. 2553
NAUTRONIX BRASIL LTDA.—See Riverstone Holdings LLC; *U.S. Private*, pg. 3447
NAUTRONIX LTD—See Riverstone Holdings LLC; *U.S. Private*, pg. 3447
NAUVATA ENGINEERING PVT. LTD; *Int'l*, pg. 5172
NAVA BANKA D.D.; *Int'l*, pg. 5173
NAVA BHARAT ENERGY INDIA LIMITED—See Nava Limited; *Int'l*, pg. 5173
NAVA BHARAT (SINGAPORE) PTE LIMITED—See Nava Limited; *Int'l*, pg. 5173
NAVAJO AGRICULTURAL PRODUCTS INDUSTRY INC.; *U.S. Private*, pg. 2872
NAVAJO EXPRESS INC.—See Navajo Shippers Inc.; *U.S. Private*, pg. 2872
NAVAJO HOLDINGS, INC.—See HF Sinclair Corporation; *U.S. Public*, pg. 1034
NAVAJO PIPELINE CO., L.P.—See HF Sinclair Corporation; *U.S. Public*, pg. 1034
NAVAJO PIPELINE GP, LLC—See HF Sinclair Corporation; *U.S. Public*, pg. 1034
NAVAJO PIPELINE LP, LLC—See HF Sinclair Corporation; *U.S. Public*, pg. 1034
NAVAJO REFINING LP, L.L.C.—See HF Sinclair Corporation; *U.S. Public*, pg. 1034

NAVAJO SHIPPERS INC.; *U.S. Private*, pg. 2872
NAVAJO SOUTH, INC.—See HF Sinclair Corporation; *U.S. Public*, pg. 1034
NAVAJO TRACTOR SALES INC.; *U.S. Private*, pg. 2872
NAVAJO TRIBAL UTILITY AUTHORITY; *U.S. Private*, pg. 2872
THE NAVAKIJ INSURANCE CO., LTD.—See Allianz SE; *Int'l*, pg. 356
NAVAL CONTINUING CARE RETIREMENT FOUNDATION, INC.; *U.S. Private*, pg. 2872
NAVAL ELECTRONICS AB—See Advent International Corporation; *U.S. Private*, pg. 100
NAVAL ENERGIES SAS—See Naval Group SA; *Int'l*, pg. 5173
NAVAL GROUP AUSTRALIA PTY LTD—See Naval Group SA; *Int'l*, pg. 5173
NAVAL GROUP INDIA PTE LTD—See Naval Group SA; *Int'l*, pg. 5173
NAVAL GROUP SA; *Int'l*, pg. 5173
NAVA LIMITED; *Int'l*, pg. 5173
NAVALO FINANCIAL SERVICES GROUP LIMITED; *Int'l*, pg. 5173
NAVALRIA - DOCAS, CONSTRUCOES E REPARACOES NAVAIS, S.A.—See Martifer SGPS S.A.; *Int'l*, pg. 4703
NAVAMEDIC AB—See Navamedic ASA; *Int'l*, pg. 5173
NAVAMEDIC ASA; *Int'l*, pg. 5173
NAVAM LANKA LTD.—See Gravita India Limited; *Int'l*, pg. 3062
NAVANA BATTERY LTD.—See Navana Group of Companies; *Int'l*, pg. 5173
NAVANA CNG LIMITED—See Navana Group of Companies; *Int'l*, pg. 5173
NAVANA CONSTRUCTION LTD.—See Navana Group of Companies; *Int'l*, pg. 5173
NAVANA ELECTRONICS LTD.—See Navana Group of Companies; *Int'l*, pg. 5173
NAVANA FURNITURE LTD.—See Navana Group of Companies; *Int'l*, pg. 5173
NAVANA GROUP OF COMPANIES; *Int'l*, pg. 5173
NAVANA INTERLINKS LTD.—See Navana Group of Companies; *Int'l*, pg. 5173
NAVA NAKORN PUBLIC COMPANY LIMITED; *Int'l*, pg. 5173
NAVANA LIMITED—See Navana Group of Companies; *Int'l*, pg. 5173
NAVANA LOGISTICS LIMITED—See Navana Group of Companies; *Int'l*, pg. 5173
NAVANA PAINTS LTD.—See Navana Group of Companies; *Int'l*, pg. 5173
NAVANA REAL ESTATE LTD.—See Navana Group of Companies; *Int'l*, pg. 5173
NAVANA TAXI CAB CO. LTD.—See Navana Group of Companies; *Int'l*, pg. 5174
NAVANTIA, S.A.—See Sociedad Estatal de Participaciones Industriales; *Int'l*, pg. 7032
NAVANTIS INC.—See CIVC Partners LLC; *U.S. Private*, pg. 907
NAVARRA DE COMPONENTES ELECTRONICOS SA (NACESA)—See Parker Hannifin Corporation; *U.S. Public*, pg. 1643
NAVARRA TERRASSEMENTS SPECIAUX SAS—See VINCI S.A.; *Int'l*, pg. 8224
NAVARRA TS—See VINCI S.A.; *Int'l*, pg. 8236
NAVARRE CHEVROLET INC.; *U.S. Private*, pg. 2872
NAVARRE DISTRIBUTION SERVICES, INC.—See WYNIT, Inc.; *U.S. Private*, pg. 4576
NAVARRE FAMILY CARE, LLC—See HCA Healthcare, Inc.; *U.S. Public*, pg. 1004
NAVARRE MINERALS LIMITED; *Int'l*, pg. 5174
NAVARRO COUNTY ELECTRIC COOPERATIVE, INC.; *U.S. Private*, pg. 2872
NAVARRO DIALYSIS, LLC—See DaVita Inc.; *U.S. Public*, pg. 641
NAVARRO DISCOUNT PHARMACIES, LLC—See CVS Health Corporation; *U.S. Public*, pg. 616
NAVARRO HOSPITAL, L.P.—See Community Health Systems, Inc.; *U.S. Public*, pg. 552
NAVARRO REGIONAL, LLC—See Community Health Systems, Inc.; *U.S. Public*, pg. 552
NAVARRO RESEARCH & ENGINEERING, INC.; *U.S. Private*, pg. 2872
NAVASOTA VALLEY ELECTRIC COOPERATIVE; *U.S. Private*, pg. 2872
NAVATEK, LTD.—See Pacific Marine & Supply Co. Ltd. Inc.; *U.S. Private*, pg. 3068
NAVBHARAT ARCHIVE XPRESS PRIVATE LIMITED—See Iron Mountain Incorporated; *U.S. Public*, pg. 1174
NAVBLUE—See Airbus SE; *Int'l*, pg. 247
NAVBLUE UK—See Airbus SE; *Int'l*, pg. 247
NAV CANADA; *Int'l*, pg. 5173
NAVCOM DEFENSE ELECTRONICS, INC.—See TransDigm Group Incorporated; *U.S. Public*, pg. 2182
NAVCOM INDUSTRIES LIMITED; *Int'l*, pg. 5174
NAVCOM TECHNOLOGY INC—See Deere & Company; *U.S. Public*, pg. 647
NAVD CO., LTD.—See Sun Frontier Fudousan Co. Ltd.; *Int'l*, pg. 7303
NAVE A VELA LTDA.—See Dragoneer Investment Group, LLC; *U.S. Private*, pg. 1272

NAVE A VELA LTDA.—See General Atlantic Service Company, L.P.; *U.S. Private*, pg. 1662
NAVE COMMUNICATIONS COMPANY—See ADDvantage Technologies Group, Inc.; *U.S. Public*, pg. 40
NAVEGAR LP—See A. Soriano Corporation; *Int'l*, pg. 22
NAVEGATE LOGISTICS, LTD.—See Radiant Logistics, Inc.; *U.S. Public*, pg. 1759
NAVEGATE SUPPLY CHAIN (SHANGHAI) CO., LTD.—See Radiant Logistics, Inc.; *U.S. Public*, pg. 1759
NAVEN HEALTH, INC.—See Option Care Health, Inc.; *U.S. Public*, pg. 1610
NAVER BUSINESS PLATFORM CORP.—See NAVER Corporation; *Int'l*, pg. 5174
NAVER CHINA CORP.—See NAVER Corporation; *Int'l*, pg. 5174
NAVER CORPORATION; *Int'l*, pg. 5174
NAVER I&S CORPORATION—See NAVER Corporation; *Int'l*, pg. 5174
NAVER LABS CORP.—See NAVER Corporation; *Int'l*, pg. 5174
NAVERUS, INC.—See General Electric Company; *U.S. Public*, pg. 919
NAVEX GLOBAL, INC.—See BC Partners LLP; *Int'l*, pg. 925
NAVEXIM SA; *Int'l*, pg. 5174
NAVEX, INC.—See Vista Equity Partners, LLC; *U.S. Private*, pg. 4400
NAVHOUSE CORPORATION—See Reliance Aerotech Inc.; *U.S. Private*, pg. 3394
NAVICLE PTY. LTD.—See Crayon Group Holding ASA; *Int'l*, pg. 1829
NAVICO AUSTRALIA PTY LIMITED—See Brunswick Corporation; *U.S. Public*, pg. 408
NAVICO HOLDING AS—See Brunswick Corporation; *U.S. Public*, pg. 408
NAVICO, INC.—See Brunswick Corporation; *U.S. Public*, pg. 408
NAVI CO., LTD.—See Crestec Inc.; *Int'l*, pg. 1841
NAVICRE OY—See Nordhealth AS; *Int'l*, pg. 5419
NAVICURE, INC.—See Canada Pension Plan Investment Board; *Int'l*, pg. 1282
NAVICURE, INC.—See EQT AB; *Int'l*, pg. 2481
NAVICUS; *U.S. Private*, pg. 2872
NAVIDEA BIOPHARMACEUTICALS, INC.; *U.S. Public*, pg. 2069
NAVIDUL COGENERACION, S.A.—See Iberdrola, S.A.; *Int'l*, pg. 3573
NAVIEN AMERICA., INC—See KyungDong Navien Co., Ltd.; *Int'l*, pg. 4367
NAVIEN LTD.—See KyungDong Navien Co., Ltd.; *Int'l*, pg. 4367
NAVIEN RUS LLC—See KyungDong Navien Co., Ltd.; *Int'l*, pg. 4367
NAVIENT CORPORATION; *U.S. Public*, pg. 1500
NAVIENT CREDIT FUNDING, LLC—See Navient Corporation; *U.S. Public*, pg. 1500
NAVIENT SOLUTIONS, INC.—See Navient Corporation; *U.S. Public*, pg. 1500
NAVIERA DEL MERCOSUR S.A.—See Grupo Boluda; *Int'l*, pg. 3123
NAVIERA DEL PACIFICO, S.A. DE C.V.—See Grupo TMM, S.A.B.; *Int'l*, pg. 3137
NAVIERA TRANS GAS, A.I.E.—See Banco Santander, S.A.; *Int'l*, pg. 826
NAVIERA ULTRANAV LIMITADA—See Ultramar Ltda.; *Int'l*, pg. 8018
NAVIG8 EUROPE LTD.—See Navig8 Limited; *Int'l*, pg. 5174
NAVIG8 LIMITED; *Int'l*, pg. 5174
NAVIGA BUSINESS SERVICES, LLC; *U.S. Private*, pg. 2872
NAVIGA INC.—See Vista Equity Partners, LLC; *U.S. Private*, pg. 4398
NAVIGANCE GMBH—See Clariant AG; *Int'l*, pg. 1648
NAVIGANT BPM (INDIA) PRIVATE LIMITED—See Bain Capital, LP; *U.S. Private*, pg. 432
NAVIGANT CAPITAL ADVISORS, LLC—See Bain Capital, LP; *U.S. Private*, pg. 432
NAVIGANT CONSULTING (APAC) PTE. LTD.—See Bain Capital, LP; *U.S. Private*, pg. 432
NAVIGANT CONSULTING ASIA LIMITED—See Bain Capital, LP; *U.S. Private*, pg. 432
NAVIGANT CONSULTING (EUROPE) LIMITED—See Bain Capital, LP; *U.S. Private*, pg. 432
NAVIGANT CONSULTING LTD.—See Bain Capital, LP; *U.S. Private*, pg. 432
NAVIGANT CONSULTING (PI) LLC—See Bain Capital, LP; *U.S. Private*, pg. 432
NAVIGANT CORPORATE ADVISORS LIMITED; *Int'l*, pg. 5174
NAVIGANT CREDIT UNION; *U.S. Private*, pg. 2873
NAVIGANT ECONOMICS, LLC - NEW YORK—See Bain Capital, LP; *U.S. Private*, pg. 432
NAVIGANT ECONOMICS, LLC—See Bain Capital, LP; *U.S. Private*, pg. 432
NAVIGANT EUROPE LIMITED—See Bain Capital, LP; *U.S. Private*, pg. 432

NAVIGANT CREDIT UNION
CORPORATE AFFILIATIONS

NAVIGANT GERMANY GMBH—See Bain Capital, LP; *U.S. Private*, pg. 432

NAVIGARE STAUEREI UND SPEDITIONS GMBH—See Stadtwerke Koln GmbH; *Int'l*, pg. 7161

NAVIGATE AFFORDABLE HOUSING PARTNERS, INC.; *U.S. Private*, pg. 2873

NAVIGATE BIOPHARMA SERVICES, INC.—See Novartis AG; *Int'l*, pg. 5457

NAVIGATE CORPORATION; *U.S. Private*, pg. 2873

NAVIGATION CAPITAL PARTNERS, INC.; *U.S. Private*, pg. 2873

NAVIGATION SOLUTIONS LLC—See Hertz Global Holdings, Inc.; *U.S. Public*, pg. 1029

NAVIGATOR ACQUISITION CORP.; *U.S. Public*, pg. 1500

NAVIGATOR AUSTRALIA LIMITED—See National Australia Bank Limited; *Int'l*, pg. 5151

THE NAVIGATOR COMPANY, S.A.—See SODIM, SGPS, SA; *Int'l*, pg. 7049

NAVIGATOR CREDIT UNION; *U.S. Private*, pg. 2873

NAVIGATOR EQUITY SOLUTIONS SE; *Int'l*, pg. 5174

NAVIGATOR GLOBAL INVESTMENTS LIMITED; *Int'l*, pg. 5174

NAVIGATOR HOLDINGS LTD.; *Int'l*, pg. 5174

NAVIGATOR INVESTMENT SERVICES LIMITED—See Aviva plc; *Int'l*, pg. 746

NAVIGATOR MANAGEMENT PARTNERS LLC—See Avaap Inc.; *U.S. Private*, pg. 403

NAVIGATOR PAPER UK LIMITED—See SODIM, SGPS, SA; *Int'l*, pg. 7049

NAVIGATORS (ASIA) LTD.—See The Hartford Financial Services Group, Inc.; *U.S. Public*, pg. 2088

NAVIGATORS CALIFORNIA INSURANCE SERVICES, INC.—See The Hartford Financial Services Group, Inc.; *U.S. Public*, pg. 2088

THE NAVIGATORS GROUP, INC.—See The Hartford Financial Services Group, Inc.; *U.S. Public*, pg. 2088

NAVIGATORS HOLDINGS UK LTD.—See The Hartford Financial Services Group, Inc.; *U.S. Public*, pg. 2088

NAVIGATORS INSURANCE COMPANY—See The Hartford Financial Services Group, Inc.; *U.S. Public*, pg. 2088

NAVIGATORS MANAGEMENT COMPANY, INC.—See The Hartford Financial Services Group, Inc.; *U.S. Public*, pg. 2088

NAVIGATORS MANAGEMENT UK LTD.—See The Hartford Financial Services Group, Inc.; *U.S. Public*, pg. 2088

NAVIGATORS UNDERWRITING AGENCY LTD.—See The Hartford Financial Services Group, Inc.; *U.S. Public*, pg. 2088

NAVIGAZIONE MONTANARI S.P.A.; *Int'l*, pg. 5174

NAVIGERA AB—See Willis Towers Watson Public Limited Company; *Int'l*, pg. 8414

NAVIGO INVEST AB; *Int'l*, pg. 5175

NAVIGOS GROUP JOINT STOCK COMPANY—See en-japan Inc.; *Int'l*, pg. 2395

NAVIGOS SEARCH—See en-japan Inc.; *Int'l*, pg. 2395

NAVIGY INC.—See GuideWell Mutual Holding Corporation; *U.S. Private*, pg. 1814

NAVIHEALTH, INC.—See Cardinal Health, Inc.; *U.S. Public*, pg. 434

NAVILAND CARGO—See SNCF; *Int'l*, pg. 7026

NAVILLE DIALYSIS, LLC—See DaVita Inc.; *U.S. Public*, pg. 641

NAVILLE S.A. - NAVILLE DETAIL UNIT—See Vivendi SE; *Int'l*, pg. 8276

NAVILLE S.A. - NAVILLE LIVRE UNIT—See Vivendi SE; *Int'l*, pg. 8276

NAVILLE S.A. - NAVILLE PRESSE UNIT—See Vivendi SE; *Int'l*, pg. 8276

NAVILLE S.A. - NAVILLE SERVICE UNIT—See Vivendi SE; *Int'l*, pg. 8276

NAVILLE S.A.—See Vivendi SE; *Int'l*, pg. 8276

NAVILYST MEDICAL, INC. - NEW YORK—See AngioDynamics, Inc.; *U.S. Public*, pg. 137

NAVILYST MEDICAL, INC.—See AngioDynamics, Inc.; *U.S. Public*, pg. 137

NAVIMENTUM INFORMATION SYSTEM LIMITED—See Digital China Holdings Limited; *Int'l*, pg. 2121

NAVIMO ESPANA—See Navimo International; *Int'l*, pg. 5175

NAVIMO HOLLAND BV—See Navimo International; *Int'l*, pg. 5175

NAVIMO INTERNATIONAL; *Int'l*, pg. 5175

NAVIMO NORDIC AB—See Navimo International; *Int'l*, pg. 5175

NAVIMO UK LTD.—See Navimo International; *Int'l*, pg. 5175

NAVIMRO CO., LTD.—See W.W. Grainger, Inc.; *U.S. Public*, pg. 2320

NAVINET, INC.—See NantWorks, LLC; *U.S. Private*, pg. 2834

NAVIN FLUORINE INTERNATIONAL LTD; *Int'l*, pg. 5175

NAVINFO CO., LTD.; *Int'l*, pg. 5175

NAVIN, HAFFTY & ASSOCIATES LLC—See Providence St. Joseph Health; *U.S. Private*, pg. 3294

NAVINT PARTNERS, LLC—See Boathouse Capital Management, LLC; *U.S. Private*, pg. 603

NAVION CAPITAL, INC.; *Int'l*, pg. 5175

NAVIONICS INC.—See Garmin Ltd.; *Int'l*, pg. 2885

NAVIONICS SRL—See Garmin Ltd.; *Int'l*, pg. 2885

NAVIOS MARITIME ACQUISITION CORPORATION—See Navios Maritime Partners L.P.; *Int'l*, pg. 5175

NAVIOS MARITIME CONTAINERS L.P.; *Int'l*, pg. 5175

NAVIOS MARITIME HOLDINGS INC.; *Int'l*, pg. 5175

NAVIOS MARITIME MIDSTREAM PARTNERS LP—See Navios Maritime Partners L.P.; *Int'l*, pg. 5175

NAVIOS MARITIME PARTNERS L.P.; *Int'l*, pg. 5175

NAVIOS SOUTH AMERICAN LOGISTICS INC.—See Navios Maritime Holdings Inc.; *Int'l*, pg. 5175

NAVIOS TANKERS MANAGEMENT INC.—See Navios Maritime Partners L.P.; *Int'l*, pg. 5175

NAVIPLUS CO., LTD.—See Digital Garage, Inc.; *Int'l*, pg. 2122

NAVIPOR - OPERADORA PORTUARIA GERAL, LDA.—See Sapec S.A.; *Int'l*, pg. 6571

NAVIS CAPITAL AUSTRALIA PTY. LTD.—See Navis Capital Partners Limited; *Int'l*, pg. 5176

NAVIS CAPITAL HOLDING LTD.—See Navis Capital Partners Limited; *Int'l*, pg. 5176

NAVIS CAPITAL (INDIA) PRIVATE LIMITED—See Navis Capital Partners Limited; *Int'l*, pg. 5176

NAVIS CAPITAL PARTNERS (HONG KONG) LIMITED—See Navis Capital Partners Limited; *Int'l*, pg. 5176

NAVIS CAPITAL PARTNERS LIMITED; *Int'l*, pg. 5175

NAVIS CAPITAL PARTNERS (SINGAPORE) PTE. LTD.—See Navis Capital Partners Limited; *Int'l*, pg. 5176

NAVIS HOLDING LLC—See Cargotec Corporation; *Int'l*, pg. 1329

NAVIS INDIA TECHNOLOGIES PRIVATE LIMITED—See Cargotec Corporation; *Int'l*, pg. 1329

NAVISITE EUROPE LIMITED—See Accenture plc; *Int'l*, pg. 87

NAVISITE INDIA PRIVATE LIMITED—See Accenture plc; *Int'l*, pg. 87

NAVISITE LLC—See Accenture plc; *Int'l*, pg. 87

NAVIS MANAGEMENT SDN. BHD.—See Navis Capital Partners Limited; *Int'l*, pg. 5176

NAVIS; *U.S. Private*, pg. 2873

NAVISTAR CANADA, INC.—See FreightCar America, Inc.; *U.S. Public*, pg. 885

NAVISTAR DEFENSE, LLC—See FreightCar America, Inc.; *U.S. Public*, pg. 885

NAVISTAR, INC.—See FreightCar America, Inc.; *U.S. Public*, pg. 885

NAVISTAR INTERNATIONAL CORPORATION—See Porsche Automobil Holding SE; *Int'l*, pg. 5930

NAVISTAR MEXICO, S. DE R.L. DE C.V.—See Porsche Automobil Holding SE; *Int'l*, pg. 5930

NAVISYS, INC.—See Accenture plc; *Int'l*, pg. 86

NAVITAIRE INTERNATIONAL INC.—See Amadeus IT Group, S.A.; *Int'l*, pg. 406

NAVITAIRE LLC—See Amadeus IT Group, S.A.; *Int'l*, pg. 406

NAVITAR COATING LABS, INC.—See AMETEK, Inc.; *U.S. Public*, pg. 121

NAVITAR, INC.—See AMETEK, Inc.; *U.S. Public*, pg. 121

NAVITAR INDUSTRIES, LLC—See AMETEK, Inc.; *U.S. Public*, pg. 121

NAVITAS BUSINESS CONSULTING INC; *U.S. Private*, pg. 2873

NAVITAS COLLEGE OF PUBLIC SAFETY PTY LTD.—See Navitas Limited; *Int'l*, pg. 5176

NAVITAS CREDIT CORP.—See United Community Banks, Inc.; *U.S. Public*, pg. 2230

NAVITAS DATA SCIENCES INC.—See TAKE Solutions Limited; *Int'l*, pg. 7436

NAVITAS EDUCATION CENTRE PTE LTD.—See Navitas Limited; *Int'l*, pg. 5176

NAVITAS INMOLDING SOLUTIONS CO., LTD.—See SiriusVision Co., Ltd.; *Int'l*, pg. 6962

NAVITAS LIMITED; *Int'l*, pg. 5176

NAVITAS LLP—See TAKE Solutions Limited; *Int'l*, pg. 7436

NAVITAS PETROLEUM LIMITED PARTNERSHIP; *U.S. Public*, pg. 1500

NAVITAS SEMICONDUCTOR CORPORATION; *U.S. Public*, pg. 1500

NAVITAS (SHANGHAI) CO., LTD.—See SiriusVision Co., Ltd.; *Int'l*, pg. 6962

NAVITAS (SUZHOU) CO., LTD.—See SiriusVision Co., Ltd.; *Int'l*, pg. 6962

NAVITAS SYSTEMS, LLC—See East Penn Manufacturing Co., Inc.; *U.S. Private*, pg. 1317

NAVITAS UK HOLDINGS LIMITED—See Navitas Limited; *Int'l*, pg. 5176

NAVITAS WORKFORCE SOLUTIONS PTY LTD.—See Navitas Limited; *Int'l*, pg. 5177

NAVITASYS TECHNOLOGY LIMITED—See TDK Corporation; *Int'l*, pg. 7487

NAVITEK OY—See BHG Group AB; *Int'l*, pg. 1015

NAVITOR EAST—See Taylor Corporation; *U.S. Private*, pg. 3938

NAVITRANS S.R.L.—See Carnival Corporation; *U.S. Public*, pg. 438

NAVITUS ENERGY PLC; *Int'l*, pg. 5177

NAVITUS HEALTH SOLUTIONS, LLC—See SSM Health Care Corporation; *U.S. Private*, pg. 3769

NAVIX DISTRIBUTION (PTY) LTD—See Stellar Capital Partners Limited; *Int'l*, pg. 7204

NAVKAR CORPORATION LTD.—See JSW Steel Ltd.; *Int'l*, pg. 4015

NAVKAR URBANSTRUCTURE LIMITED; *Int'l*, pg. 5177

NAVKETAN MERCHANTS LIMITED; *Int'l*, pg. 5177

NAVLETS GARDEN CENTERS INC.; *U.S. Private*, pg. 2873

NAVL LLC—See Madison Dearborn Partners, LLC; *U.S. Private*, pg. 2542

NAVMAN WIRELESS AUSTRALIA PTY.LTD.—See Vontier Corporation; *U.S. Public*, pg. 2309

NAVNEET EDUCATION LTD; *Int'l*, pg. 5177

NAVODAY ENTERPRISES LTD.; *Int'l*, pg. 5177

NAVOPACHE ELECTRIC COOPERATIVE INC.; *U.S. Private*, pg. 2873

NAVOS FARM TECHNIC S.R.O.—See Agrofert Holding, a.s.; *Int'l*, pg. 219

NAVOS MENTAL HEALTH SOLUTIONS; *U.S. Private*, pg. 2873

NAVROM BAC S.R.L.—See Compania de Navigatie Fluviala Romana NAVROM S.A. Galati; *Int'l*, pg. 1749

NAVROM CENTRU DE AFACERI S.R.L.—See Compania de Navigatie Fluviala Romana NAVROM S.A. Galati; *Int'l*, pg. 1749

NAVROM DELTA S.A.—See Compania de Navigatie Fluviala Romana NAVROM S.A. Galati; *Int'l*, pg. 1749

NAVROM SHIPYARD S.R.L.—See Compania de Navigatie Fluviala Romana NAVROM S.A. Galati; *Int'l*, pg. 1749

NAVTEAM A/S—See Grupo Arbulu S.L.; *Int'l*, pg. 3120

NAVTECH RADAR LIMITED—See Halma plc; *Int'l*, pg. 3232

NAVTRAK LIMITED—See Vodafone Group Plc; *Int'l*, pg. 8284

NAVTRONICS BVBA—See CNH Industrial N.V.; *Int'l*, pg. 1676

NAVVIS HEALTHCARE, LLC; *U.S. Private*, pg. 2873

NAVY ARMY COMMUNITY CREDIT UNION; *U.S. Private*, pg. 2873

NAVYA SA; *Int'l*, pg. 5177

NAVY FEDERAL CREDIT UNION; *U.S. Private*, pg. 2873

NAVY-MARINE CORPS RELIEF SOCIETY; *U.S. Private*, pg. 2874

NAVY MUTUAL AID ASSOCIATION; *U.S. Private*, pg. 2873

NAVY SEAL FOUNDATION, INC.; *U.S. Private*, pg. 2873

NAWA INTERTECH CO., LTD.—See The Siam Cement Public Company Limited; *Int'l*, pg. 7683

THE NAWALOHA INDUSTRY CO., LTD.—See The Siam Cement Public Company Limited; *Int'l*, pg. 7682

NAWALOKA HOSPITALS PLC; *Int'l*, pg. 5177

NAWAPLASTIC (CAMBODIA) CO., LTD.—See The Siam Cement Public Company Limited; *Int'l*, pg. 7683

NAWAPLASTIC INDUSTRIES (SARABURI) CO., LTD.—See The Siam Cement Public Company Limited; *Int'l*, pg. 7683

NAWARAT PATANAKARN PUBLIC COMPANY LIMITED; *Int'l*, pg. 5177

NAWI BROTHERS GROUP LTD.; *Int'l*, pg. 5177

NAXICAP PARTNERS SA—See Groupe BPCE; *Int'l*, pg. 3095

NAXOR FINLAND OY—See Wulff-Group Plc; *Int'l*, pg. 8502

NAXOS DENMARK APS.—See HNH International Ltd.; *Int'l*, pg. 3434

NAXOS DEUTSCHLAND GMBH—See HNH International Ltd.; *Int'l*, pg. 3434

NAXOS DEUTSCHLAND MUSIK UND VIDEO VERTRIEBS GMBH—See HNH International Ltd.; *Int'l*, pg. 3434

NAXOS DIGITAL SERVICES LIMITED—See HNH International Ltd.; *Int'l*, pg. 3434

NAXOS GLOBAL DISTRIBUTION LIMITED—See HNH International Ltd.; *Int'l*, pg. 3434

NAXOS JAPAN INC—See HNH International Ltd.; *Int'l*, pg. 3434

NAXOS KOREA—See HNH International Ltd.; *Int'l*, pg. 3434

NAXOS NORWAY AS—See HNH International Ltd.; *Int'l*, pg. 3434

NAXOS OF AMERICA INC.—See HNH International Ltd.; *Int'l*, pg. 3434

NAXOS OF CANADA LTD.—See HNH International Ltd.; *Int'l*, pg. 3434

NAXOS RIGHTS INTERNATIONAL LIMITED—See HNH International Ltd.; *Int'l*, pg. 3434

NAXOS SHIPPING (PTE.) LTD.—See Minerva Bunkering; *Int'l*, pg. 4908

NAXOS SWEDEN AB—See HNH International Ltd.; *Int'l*, pg. 3434

NAXPAR PHARMA PRIVATE LIMITED—See Parnax Lab Ltd.; *Int'l*, pg. 5745

NAXS AB; *Int'l*, pg. 5177

NAYAMODE, INC.; *U.S. Private*, pg. 2874

NAYA P.A.I.TECHNOLOGIES LTD.—See EPAM Systems, Inc.; *U.S. Public*, pg. 783

COMPANY NAME INDEX

NAYAPAY (PRIVATE) LIMITED—See COLGATE-PALMOLIVE (PAKISTAN) LTD; *Int'l*, pg. 1698
NAYARA ENERGY LIMITED—See OJSC Rosneftegaz; *Int'l*, pg. 5541
NAYARA ENERGY LIMITED—See United Capital Partners Advisory LLC; *Int'l*, pg. 8065
NAYA VENTURES LLC; *U.S. Private*, pg. 2874
NAYA WATERS INC.—See Champlain Financial Corporation; *Int'l*, pg. 1440
NAYAX AUSTRALIA PTY. LTD.—See Nayax Ltd.; *Int'l*, pg. 5178
NAYAX CHINA LTD.—See Nayax Ltd.; *Int'l*, pg. 5178
NAYAX GMBH—See Nayax Ltd.; *Int'l*, pg. 5178
NAYAX KK—See Nayax Ltd.; *Int'l*, pg. 5178
NAYAX LTD.; *Int'l*, pg. 5177
NAYAX NZ LTD.—See Nayax Ltd.; *Int'l*, pg. 5178
NAYAX UK LTD.—See Nayax Ltd.; *Int'l*, pg. 5178
NAYLER PETROSEALS LTD—See Tailwind Capital Group, LLC; *U.S. Private*, pg. 3924
NAYLOR & BREEN BUILDERS, INC.; *U.S. Private*, pg. 2874
NAYLOR COMMERCIAL INTERIORS, INC.; *U.S. Private*, pg. 2874
NAYLOR CONCRETE PRODUCTS LTD—See Naylor Industries plc.; *Int'l*, pg. 5178
NAYLOR DRAINAGE LTD—See Naylor Industries plc.; *Int'l*, pg. 5178
NAYLOR INDUSTRIES PLC; *Int'l*, pg. 5178
NAYLOR, LLC—See The RLJ Companies, LLC; *U.S. Private*, pg. 4111
NAYLOR PIPE COMPANY; *U.S. Private*, pg. 2874
NAYLOR PUBLICATIONS INCORPORATED—See Clarity Partners, L.P.; *U.S. Private*, pg. 912
NAYLOR PUBLICATIONS INCORPORATED—See Zelnick-Media Corp.; *U.S. Private*, pg. 4600
NAYLOR SPECIALIST PLASTICS LTD—See Naylor Industries plc.; *Int'l*, pg. 5178
NAYSAA SECURITIES LIMITED; *Int'l*, pg. 5178
NAYTEMPORIKI PUBLISHING S.A.; *Int'l*, pg. 5178
NAZA AUTOMOTIVE MANUFACTURING SDN. BHD.—See Stellantis N.V.; *Int'l*, pg. 7202
NAZA CORPORATION HOLDINGS SDN BHD; *Int'l*, pg. 5178
NAZARA TECHNOLOGIES LIMITED; *Int'l*, pg. 5178
NAZARENE PUBLISHING HOUSE; *U.S. Private*, pg. 2874
NAZARETH LIVING CENTER; *U.S. Private*, pg. 2874
NAZARETH PALLET CO., INC.—See Audax Group, Limited Partnership; *U.S. Private*, pg. 386
NAZARETH VOLUNTEER AMBULANCE CORPS; *U.S. Private*, pg. 2874
NAZAR NORDIC AB—See TUI AG; *Int'l*, pg. 7965
NAZCA SAATCHI & SAATCHI—See Publicis Groupe S.A.; *Int'l*, pg. 6107
NAZCA SAATCHI & SAATCHI—See Publicis Groupe S.A.; *Int'l*, pg. 6107
NAZCA SAATCHI & SAATCHI—See Publicis Groupe S.A.; *Int'l*, pg. 6108
NAZDAR COMPANY - NAZDAR CONSULTING SERVICES DIVISION—See Thrall Enterprises, Inc.; *U.S. Private*, pg. 4163
NAZDAR COMPANY - NAZDAR SOURCEONE DIVISION—See Thrall Enterprises, Inc.; *U.S. Private*, pg. 4163
NAZ-DAR COMPANY—See Thrall Enterprises, Inc.; *U.S. Private*, pg. 4163
NAZDAR LTD.—See Thrall Enterprises, Inc.; *U.S. Private*, pg. 4163
NAZIR COTTON MILLS LIMITED; *Int'l*, pg. 5178
NAZTEC INTERNATIONAL GROUP, LLC; *U.S. Private*, pg. 2874
NBA CHINA—See National Basketball Association; *U.S. Private*, pg. 2848
NBAD AMERICAS N.V.—See First Abu Dhabi Bank P.J.S.C.; *Int'l*, pg. 2681
NBA DIGITAL—See National Basketball Association; *U.S. Private*, pg. 2848
NBAD PRIVATE BANK (SUISSE) SA—See First Abu Dhabi Bank P.J.S.C.; *Int'l*, pg. 2681
NBAD SECURITIES LLC—See First Abu Dhabi Bank P.J.S.C.; *Int'l*, pg. 2681
NB ALTERNATIVES ADVISERS LLC—See Neuberger Berman Group LLC; *U.S. Private*, pg. 2890
NBA (PRIVATE BANKING AND TRUST) LIMITED—See National Bank of Anguilla Ltd; *Int'l*, pg. 5152
NBA PROPERTIES, INC.—See National Basketball Association; *U.S. Private*, pg. 2848
NBA PROPERTIES LIMITED—See National Australia Bank Limited; *Int'l*, pg. 5151
NBA QUANTUM PLC; *Int'l*, pg. 5179
NB BANCORP, INC.; *U.S. Public*, pg. 1500
NBBJ GROUP; *U.S. Private*, pg. 2874
NBBJ—See NBBJ Group; *U.S. Private*, pg. 2874
NBB NETZ GESELLSCHAFT BERLIN-BRANDENBURG MBH—See ENGIE SA; *Int'l*, pg. 2429
NBB NETZ GESELLSCHAFT BERLIN-BRANDENBURG MBH—See E.ON SE; *Int'l*, pg. 2257
NBB NETZ GESELLSCHAFT BERLIN-BRANDENBURG MBH—See Vattenfall AB; *Int'l*, pg. 8137

NBC APPAREL, INC.—See The TJX Companies, Inc.; *U.S. Public*, pg. 2134
NBCC (INDIA) LIMITED; *Int'l*, pg. 5179
NBC CORP. OF OKLAHOMA; *U.S. Private*, pg. 2874
NBC ENVIRONMENT LIMITED—See Rollins, Inc.; *U.S. Public*, pg. 1809
NB CHINA CO., LTD.—See Nippon Bearing Co., Ltd.; *Int'l*, pg. 5310
NBC MESHTEC AMERICAS INC.—See Nisshin Seifun Group, Inc.; *Int'l*, pg. 5372
NBC MESHTEC THAILAND CO., LTD.—See Nisshin Seifun Group, Inc.; *Int'l*, pg. 5372
NBC METALMESH INC.—See Nisshin Seifun Group, Inc.; *Int'l*, pg. 5372
NBC NEWS BUREAUS LLC—See Comcast Corporation; *U.S. Public*, pg. 539
NBC NEWS DIGITAL LLC—See Comcast Corporation; *U.S. Public*, pg. 539
NBC NEWS WORLDWIDE LLC—See Comcast Corporation; *U.S. Public*, pg. 539
NB COATINGS, INC.—See Nippon Paint Holdings Co., Ltd.; *Int'l*, pg. 5326
NBC OKLAHOMA—See NBC Corp. of Oklahoma; *U.S. Private*, pg. 2874
NBC OLYMPICS LLC—See Comcast Corporation; *U.S. Public*, pg. 539
N.B.COMMERCIAL ENTERPRISES LTD.—See Sayaji Industries Limited; *Int'l*, pg. 6603
NB CORPORATION OF AMERICA—See Nippon Bearing Co., Ltd.; *Int'l*, pg. 5310
NBC PALM SPRINGS—See Entravision Communications Corporation; *U.S. Public*, pg. 779
NBC (SHANGHAI) MESH CO., LTD.—See Nisshin Seifun Group, Inc.; *Int'l*, pg. 5372
NBC SPORTS BAY AREA—See Comcast Corporation; *U.S. Public*, pg. 539
NBC SPORTS NETWORK, L.P.—See Comcast Corporation; *U.S. Public*, pg. 539
NBC SPORTS VENTURES LLC—See Comcast Corporation; *U.S. Public*, pg. 539
NBC STATIONS MANAGEMENT II LLC—See Comcast Corporation; *U.S. Public*, pg. 539
NBC-SYS SAS—See GIAT Industries S.A.; *Int'l*, pg. 2962
NBC TELEVISION AFFILIATES ASSOCIATION; *U.S. Private*, pg. 2874
NBC TRUCK EQUIPMENT INC.; *U.S. Private*, pg. 2874
NBC UNIVERSAL DIGITAL SOLUTIONS LLC—See Comcast Corporation; *U.S. Public*, pg. 540
NBCUNIVERSAL ENTERTAINMENT JAPAN LLC—See Comcast Corporation; *U.S. Public*, pg. 539
NBCUNIVERSAL INTERNATIONAL LIMITED—See Comcast Corporation; *U.S. Public*, pg. 540
NBCUNIVERSAL, LLC—See Comcast Corporation; *U.S. Public*, pg. 540
NBCUNIVERSAL MEDIA, LLC—See Comcast Corporation; *U.S. Public*, pg. 539
NBD-BANK JSC; *Int'l*, pg. 5179
NB DISTRESSED DEBT INVESTMENT FUND LIMITED; *Int'l*, pg. 5178
NBE BANCSHARES, INC.; *U.S. Private*, pg. 2874
NB EUROPE B.V.—See Nippon Bearing Co., Ltd.; *Int'l*, pg. 5310
N.B. FAIRCLOUGH & SONS INC.; *U.S. Private*, pg. 2827
NBF OFFICE MANAGEMENT CO., LTD.—See Mitsui Fudosan Co., Ltd.; *Int'l*, pg. 4988
NB FOOTWEAR LIMITED; *Int'l*, pg. 5179
NBG ASSET MANAGEMENT LUXEMBURG S.A.—See National Bank of Greece S.A.; *Int'l*, pg. 5153
NBG ASSET MANAGEMENT MUTUAL FUNDS S.A.—See National Bank of Greece S.A.; *Int'l*, pg. 5153
NBG BANK MALTA LTD—See National Bank of Greece S.A.; *Int'l*, pg. 5153
NBG FINANCE PLC—See National Bank of Greece S.A.; *Int'l*, pg. 5153
NBG INSURANCE BROKERS S.A.—See National Bank of Greece S.A.; *Int'l*, pg. 5153
NBG INTERNATIONAL LIMITED—See National Bank of Greece S.A.; *Int'l*, pg. 5153
NBGI PRIVATE EQUITY LIMITED—See National Bank of Greece S.A.; *Int'l*, pg. 5153
NBGI PRIVATE EQUITY LIMITED - TURKEY—See National Bank of Greece S.A.; *Int'l*, pg. 5153
NBGI PRIVATE EQUITY S.A.S—See National Bank of Greece S.A.; *Int'l*, pg. 5153
NBG LEASING IFN S.A.—See National Bank of Greece S.A.; *Int'l*, pg. 5153
NB GLOBAL CORPORATE INCOME TRUST; *Int'l*, pg. 5179
NB GLOBAL MONTHLY INCOME FUND LIMITED; *Int'l*, pg. 5179
NBG (MALTA) HOLDINGS LTD—See National Bank of Greece S.A.; *Int'l*, pg. 5153
N.B. GOODWYN & SONS INC.; *U.S. Private*, pg. 2827
NBG PANGAEA REAL ESTATE INVESTMENT COMPANY—See Invel Real Estate Advisors LLP; *Int'l*, pg. 3772
NBG PROPERTY SERVICES S.A.—See National Bank of Greece S.A.; *Int'l*, pg. 5153

NBG SECURITIES S.A.—See National Bank of Greece S.A.; *Int'l*, pg. 5153
N B HANDY & CO INC.—See Industrial Opportunity Partners, LLC; *U.S. Private*, pg. 2067
N.B. HANDY COMPANY; *U.S. Private*, pg. 2827
NBH BANK—See National Bank Holdings Corporation; *U.S. Public*, pg. 1493
NBH CAPITAL CO., LTD.; *Int'l*, pg. 5179
NBHX TRIM MANAGEMENT SERVICES GMBH—See Ningbo Huaxiang Electronic Co., Ltd.; *Int'l*, pg. 5302
NBHX TRIM USA CORPORATION—See Ningbo Huaxiang Electronic Co., Ltd.; *Int'l*, pg. 5302
NBI, INC.; *U.S. Private*, pg. 2875
N.B.I. INDUSTRIAL FINANCE COMPANY LIMITED; *Int'l*, pg. 5115
NB-IMMOBILIEN GMBH—See National Bank AG; *Int'l*, pg. 5151
NBIM S.A R.L.—See Norges Bank; *Int'l*, pg. 5427
NBK BANQUE PRIVEE (SUISSE) S.A.—See National Bank of Kuwait S.A.K.; *Int'l*, pg. 5153
NBK (INTERNATIONAL) PLC—See National Bank of Kuwait S.A.K.; *Int'l*, pg. 5153
NBK INVESTMENT MANAGEMENT LIMITED—See National Bank of Kuwait S.A.K.; *Int'l*, pg. 5153
NBK (LEBANON) S.A.L.—See National Bank of Kuwait S.A.K.; *Int'l*, pg. 5153
NBL CAPITAL & EQUITY MANAGEMENT LTD.—See National Bank Limited; *Int'l*, pg. 5151
N.B. LIEBMAN & CO. INC.; *U.S. Private*, pg. 2827
NBL INTERNATIONAL FINANCE B.V.—See Chevron Corporation; *U.S. Public*, pg. 487
NBL MONEY TRANSFER (MALDIVES) PVT. LTD.—See National Bank Limited; *Int'l*, pg. 5151
NBL MONEY TRANSFER PAYMENT FOUNDATION S.A.—See National Bank Limited; *Int'l*, pg. 5151
NBL MONEY TRANSFER PTE LTD.—See National Bank Limited; *Int'l*, pg. 5151
NBL MONEY TRANSFER SDN BHD—See National Bank Limited; *Int'l*, pg. 5151
NBL TEXAS, LLC—See Chevron Corporation; *U.S. Public*, pg. 487
N.B.M. CORPORATION; *U.S. Private*, pg. 2827
NBN CO. LIMITED; *Int'l*, pg. 5179
NBN ELEKTRONIK S.R.O.—See Yokogawa Electric Corporation; *Int'l*, pg. 8592
NBO SYSTEMS, INC.; *U.S. Private*, pg. 2875
NBP CAPITAL LIMITED—See State Bank of Pakistan; *Int'l*, pg. 7182
NB PRIVATE EQUITY PARTNERS LIMITED; *Int'l*, pg. 5179
NB RENAISSANCE PARTNERS—See Neuberger Berman Group LLC; *U.S. Private*, pg. 2890
N BROWN GROUP PLC; *Int'l*, pg. 5115
NBS BANK LIMTED—See NICO Holdings Plc; *Int'l*, pg. 5272
NBS BANK PLC—See NICO Holdings Plc; *Int'l*, pg. 5272
NBS-BAY CITY—See National Business Supply Inc.; *U.S. Private*, pg. 2849
NBS BIOLOGICALS LIMITED—See BBI Life Sciences Corporation; *Int'l*, pg. 920
NBS CAPITAL, INC.; *Int'l*, pg. 5179
NBS CO., LTD.—See Senshu Electric Co., Ltd.; *Int'l*, pg. 6713
NBS INTERNATIONAL LIMITED—See Mahindra & Mahindra Limited; *Int'l*, pg. 4646
NBS-TOLEDO—See National Business Supply Inc.; *U.S. Private*, pg. 2849
NBT BANCORP INC.; *U.S. Public*, pg. 1500
NBT BANK, N.A.—See NBT Bancorp Inc.; *U.S. Public*, pg. 1500
NBT BANK, N.A.—See NBT Bancorp Inc.; *U.S. Public*, pg. 1500
NBT BANK, N.A.—See NBT Bancorp Inc.; *U.S. Public*, pg. 1500
NBT BANK, N.A.—See NBT Bancorp Inc.; *U.S. Public*, pg. 1500
NBT (BRUNEI) SDN. BHD.—See Inchcape plc; *Int'l*, pg. 3647
NBT CAPITAL CORP.—See NBT Bancorp Inc.; *U.S. Public*, pg. 1500
NBT CAPITAL CORP.—See NBT Bancorp Inc.; *U.S. Public*, pg. 1501
NBT FINANCIAL SERVICES, INC.—See NBT Bancorp Inc.; *U.S. Public*, pg. 1501
NBT INC.; *Int'l*, pg. 5179
NBTM NEW MATERIALS GROUP CO., LTD.; *Int'l*, pg. 5179
NBTM (TIANJIN) POWDER METALLURGY CO., LTD.—See NBTM New Materials Group Co., Ltd.; *Int'l*, pg. 5179
NBTY ACQUISITION, LLC—See KKR & Co. Inc.; *U.S. Public*, pg. 1264
NB VENTURES, INC.; *U.S. Private*, pg. 2874
NB-VERSICHERUNGS-SERVICE GMBH—See National Bank AG; *Int'l*, pg. 5151
N.B. WEST CONTRACTING COMPANY; *U.S. Private*, pg. 2827
NC2 MEDIA, LLC; *U.S. Private*, pg. 2875

NC2 MEDIA, LLC

Company Index

NC4 PUBLIC SECTOR, LLC—See Thoma Bravo, L.P.; *U.S. Private*, pg. 4147
NCAB GROUP AB; *Int'l*, pg. 5180
NCAB GROUP BENELUX B.V.—See NCAB Group AB; *Int'l*, pg. 5180
NCAB GROUP DENMARK A/S—See NCAB Group AB; *Int'l*, pg. 5180
NCAB GROUP FRANCE S.A.S.—See NCAB Group AB; *Int'l*, pg. 5180
NCAB GROUP GERMANY GMBH—See NCAB Group AB; *Int'l*, pg. 5180
NCAB GROUP IBERIA S.A.U.—See NCAB Group AB; *Int'l*, pg. 5180
NCAB GROUP ITALY S.R.L.—See NCAB Group AB; *Int'l*, pg. 5180
NCAB GROUP NORWAY AS—See NCAB Group AB; *Int'l*, pg. 5180
NCAB GROUP POLSKA SP. Z.O.O—See NCAB Group AB; *Int'l*, pg. 5180
NCAB GROUP SHENZHEN ELECTRONICS CO LTD.—See NCAB Group AB; *Int'l*, pg. 5180
NCAB GROUP SOUTH EAST ASIA SDN BHD—See NCAB Group AB; *Int'l*, pg. 5180
NCAB GROUP SWEDEN AB—See NCAB Group AB; *Int'l*, pg. 5180
NCAB GROUP UK LTD.—See NCAB Group AB; *Int'l*, pg. 5180
NCAB GROUP USA, INC.—See NCAB Group AB; *Int'l*, pg. 5180
NCAB MACEDONIA A.D.—See NCAB Group AB; *Int'l*, pg. 5180
NC ADVISORY AS—See Nordic Capital AB; *Int'l*, pg. 5420
NC ADVISORY GMBH—See Nordic Capital AB; *Int'l*, pg. 5420
NC ADVISORY OY—See Nordic Capital AB; *Int'l*, pg. 5420
NC ADVISORY (UK) LLP—See Nordic Capital AB; *Int'l*, pg. 5420
NC AGRO HAKODATE CORPORATION—See Nissan Chemical Corporation; *Int'l*, pg. 5366
NCA JAPAN CO., LTD.—See Nippon Yusen Kabushiki Kaisha; *Int'l*, pg. 5359
NCALABS CO., LTD.—See H.I.G. Capital, LLC; *U.S. Private*, pg. 1831
NCALA, LLC; *U.S. Private*, pg. 2875
NCA PARTNERS, INC.; *U.S. Private*, pg. 2875
NC BANK UGANDA LIMITED—See NIC Group PLC; *Int'l*, pg. 5263
NCB CAPITAL MARKETS LTD.—See Portland Investment Counsel Inc.; *Int'l*, pg. 5934
NCB (CAYMAN) LIMITED—See Portland Investment Counsel Inc.; *Int'l*, pg. 5934
NCB CORPORATE FINANCE LIMITED—See Investec Limited; *Int'l*, pg. 3778
NCB GROUP LTD.—See Investec Limited; *Int'l*, pg. 3778
NCB INSURANCE COMPANY LIMITED—See Portland Investment Counsel Inc.; *Int'l*, pg. 5934
NCB JAMAICA (NOMINEES) LTD.—See Portland Investment Counsel Inc.; *Int'l*, pg. 5934
NCB RESEARCH & CONSULTING CO., LTD.—See The Nishi-Nippon City Bank, Ltd.; *Int'l*, pg. 7670
N.C. BROWN (STORAGE EQUIPMENT) LTD.—See Whittan Storage Systems Ltd.; *Int'l*, pg. 8400
NCB STOCKBROKERS LIMITED—See Investec Limited; *Int'l*, pg. 3778
NCB TURNAROUND CO., LTD.—See The Nishi-Nippon City Bank, Ltd.; *Int'l*, pg. 7670
NCB VENTURES LIMITED—See Investec Limited; *Int'l*, pg. 3778
NCC AB—See Nordstjernan AB; *Int'l*, pg. 5425
NCC AUTOMATED SYSTEMS, INC.—See ATS Corporation; *Int'l*, pg. 695
NCC BLUEWATER PRODUCTS LIMITED; *Int'l*, pg. 5180
NCCB SECURITIES & FINANCIAL SERVICES LIMITED—See National Credit and Commerce Bank PLC; *Int'l*, pg. 5155
NCC BUILDING—See Nordstjernan AB; *Int'l*, pg. 5425
NCC BUSINESS SERVICES INC.—See Platinum Equity, LLC; *U.S. Private*, pg. 3209
NCC CONSTRUCTION—See Nordstjernan AB; *Int'l*, pg. 5425
NCC DENMARK A/S—See Nordstjernan AB; *Int'l*, pg. 5425
NCC DEUTSCHE GMBH—See Nordstjernan AB; *Int'l*, pg. 5425
NCC EDUCATION (BEIJING) CONSULTING CO., LTD.—See Informatics Education Ltd; *Int'l*, pg. 3694
NCC EDUCATION LIMITED—See Informatics Education Ltd; *Int'l*, pg. 3694
NCC EDUCATION (M) SDN BHD—See Informatics Education Ltd; *Int'l*, pg. 3694
NCC EUROPE GMBH—See Toyo Seikan Group Holdings, Ltd.; *Int'l*, pg. 7856
NCC FORSAKRINGS AB—See Nordstjernan AB; *Int'l*, pg. 5425
NCC GROUP ESCROW EUROPE (SWITZERLAND) AG—See NCC Group Plc; *Int'l*, pg. 5180
NCC GROUP GMBH—See NCC Group Plc; *Int'l*, pg. 5180
NCC GROUP INC.—See NCC Group Plc; *Int'l*, pg. 5180
NCC GROUP JAPAN KK—See NCC Group Plc; *Int'l*, pg. 5181
NCC GROUP PLC; *Int'l*, pg. 5180
NCC GROUP SECURITY SERVICES ESPANA SLU—See NCC Group Plc; *Int'l*, pg. 5181
NCC GROUP SOFTWARE RESILIENCE (EUROPE) BV—See NCC Group Plc; *Int'l*, pg. 5181
NCC HERCULES—See Nordstjernan AB; *Int'l*, pg. 5425
NCCI HOLDINGS INC.; *U.S. Private*, pg. 2875
NCC IMMOBILIEN GMBH—See Nordstjernan AB; *Int'l*, pg. 5425
NCC INFRASTRUCTURE HOLDINGS LIMITED—See NCC Limited; *Int'l*, pg. 5181
NCC LIMITED; *Int'l*, pg. 5181
NCCN FOUNDATION—See National Comprehensive Cancer Network; *U.S. Private*, pg. 2851
NCC NORWAY AS—See Nordstjernan AB; *Int'l*, pg. 5425
NC& CO., LTD.; *Int'l*, pg. 5180
NCC RAKENNUS OY—See Nordstjernan AB; *Int'l*, pg. 5425
NCC SYSTEMS INC.—See Frontier Communications Parent, Inc.; *U.S. Public*, pg. 887
NCC TELECOM A/S—See Nordstjernan AB; *Int'l*, pg. 5425
NCC TREASURY AB—See Nordstjernan AB; *Int'l*, pg. 5425
NCC URBAN INFRASTRUCTURE LIMITED—See NCC Limited; *Int'l*, pg. 5181
NCDH GROUP AG; *Int'l*, pg. 5181
NC DYNAMICS INC.—See Harlow Aerostructures, LLC; *U.S. Private*, pg. 1865
NC ELITE VOLLEYBALL CLUB; *U.S. Private*, pg. 2875
NCELL PRIVATE LIMITED—See Axiata Group Berhad; *Int'l*, pg. 768
N.C. FARM BUREAU MUTUAL INSURANCE CO. INC.; *U.S. Private*, pg. 2827
NCG-ERC, LLC—See Stone Canyon Industries, LLC; *U.S. Private*, pg. 3817
NCH AG—See NCH Corporation; *U.S. Private*, pg. 2875
NCH BELGIUM INC—See NCH Corporation; *U.S. Private*, pg. 2875
NCH CHILE S.A.—See NCH Corporation; *U.S. Private*, pg. 2875
NCH COLOMBIA, S.A.—See NCH Corporation; *U.S. Private*, pg. 2875
NCH CORPORATION KOREA—See NCH Corporation; *U.S. Private*, pg. 2875
NCH CORPORATION PUERTO RICO—See NCH Corporation; *U.S. Private*, pg. 2875
NCH CORPORATION; *U.S. Private*, pg. 2875
NCH CROATIA D.O.O.—See NCH Corporation; *U.S. Private*, pg. 2875
NCH CZECHOSLOVAKIA SPOL S.R.O.—See NCH Corporation; *U.S. Private*, pg. 2875
NCH D.O.O. LJUBLJANA—See NCH Corporation; *U.S. Private*, pg. 2875
NCH ECUADOR S.A.—See NCH Corporation; *U.S. Private*, pg. 2875
NCH ESPANOLA S.A.—See NCH Corporation; *U.S. Private*, pg. 2875
NCH GMBH—See NCH Corporation; *U.S. Private*, pg. 2875
NCH HEALTHCARE SYSTEM, INC.; *U.S. Private*, pg. 2876
NCH - HUNGARY KFT.—See NCH Corporation; *U.S. Private*, pg. 2875
NCH IRELAND LTD.—See NCH Corporation; *U.S. Private*, pg. 2875
NCH ITALIA SRL—See NCH Corporation; *U.S. Private*, pg. 2876
NCH KOREA LTD—See NCH Corporation; *U.S. Private*, pg. 2876
NCH MANAGEMENT SYSTEMS, INC.—See Evolent Health, Inc.; *U.S. Public*, pg. 804
NCH MANAGEMENT SYSTMES, INC.—See Evolent Health, Inc.; *U.S. Public*, pg. 804
NCH MARKETING SERVICES, INC.—See MacAndrews & Forbes Incorporated; *U.S. Private*, pg. 2532
NCH NORGE AS—See NCH Corporation; *U.S. Private*, pg. 2876
NC HOLDINGS CO., LTD.; *Int'l*, pg. 5180
NC HOLDINGS—See Rapala VMC Oyj; *Int'l*, pg. 6209
N.C. HOUSING PCL; *Int'l*, pg. 5116
NCH PERU, S.A.—See NCH Corporation; *U.S. Private*, pg. 2876
NCH ROMANIA PRODUSE DE INTRETINERE SRL—See NCH Corporation; *U.S. Private*, pg. 2876
NCH SLOVAKIA S. R. O.—See NCH Corporation; *U.S. Private*, pg. 2876
NCH (UK) LTD.—See NCH Corporation; *U.S. Private*, pg. 2875
NCI CONSULTING INC.—See Publicis Groupe S.A.; *Int'l*, pg. 6106
NCI ELECTRONICS CO., LTD.—See NIPPON CARBIDE INDUSTRIES CO., INC.; *Int'l*, pg. 5311
NCI HOLDINGS PTY. LTD.—See National Can Industries Limited; *U.S. Public*, pg. 5154
NCI HOLDING (THAILAND) CO., LTD.—See NIPPON CARBIDE INDUSTRIES CO., INC.; *Int'l*, pg. 5311
NCI, INC.—See H.I.G. Capital, LLC; *U.S. Private*, pg. 1831
NCINO APAC PTY LTD—See nCino, Inc.; *U.S. Public*, pg. 1501

CORPORATE AFFILIATIONS

NCINO CANADA, INC.—See nCino, Inc.; *U.S. Public*, pg. 1501
NCINO GLOBAL, LTD.—See nCino, Inc.; *U.S. Public*, pg. 1501
NCINO, INC.; *U.S. Public*, pg. 1501
NCINO K.K.—See nCino, Inc.; *U.S. Public*, pg. 1501
NCINO OPCO, INC.—See nCino, Inc.; *U.S. Public*, pg. 1501
NC INTERACTIVE, INC.—See NCsoft Corporation; *Int'l*, pg. 5181
N CITRON, INC.; *Int'l*, pg. 5115
NCI VIETNAM CO., LTD.—See NIPPON CARBIDE INDUSTRIES CO., INC.; *Int'l*, pg. 5311
NC JAPAN K.K.—See NCsoft Corporation; *Int'l*, pg. 5182
NCJ MEDIA LIMITED—See Reach PLC; *Int'l*, pg. 6231
NC KAIHARA CONCRETE CO., LTD.—See Nippon Concrete Industries Co., Ltd.; *Int'l*, pg. 5313
NC KAZAKHSTAN TEMIR ZHOLY JSC; *Int'l*, pg. 5180
NCK CAPITAL LLC; *U.S. Private*, pg. 2876
NCK CO., LTD.—See Nissan Chemical Corporation; *Int'l*, pg. 5366
NCL ALLTEK AND SECCOLOR LTD.—See NCL Industries Limited; *Int'l*, pg. 5181
NCL (BAHAMAS) LTD.—See Norwegian Cruise Line Holdings Ltd.; *U.S. Public*, pg. 1543
NCL COMMUNICATIONS K.K.—See TECHMATRIX CORPORATION; *Int'l*, pg. 7505
NCL COMMUNICATIONS—See Consolidated Press, Inc.; *U.S. Private*, pg. 1021
NCL CORPORATION LTD.—See Norwegian Cruise Line Holdings Ltd.; *U.S. Public*, pg. 1543
NCL GRAPHIC SPECIALTIES, INC.; *U.S. Private*, pg. 2876
NCL HOMES LTD—See NCL Industries Limited; *Int'l*, pg. 5181
NCL INDUSTRIES LIMITED - BOARDS DIVISION—See NCL Industries Limited; *Int'l*, pg. 5181
NCL INDUSTRIES LIMITED - CEMENT DIVISION—See NCL Industries Limited; *Int'l*, pg. 5181
NCL INDUSTRIES LIMITED; *Int'l*, pg. 5181
NCL INTER LOGISTICS (S) PTE. LTD.—See NCL International Logistics Public Company Limited; *Int'l*, pg. 5181
NCL INTERNATIONAL LOGISTICS PUBLIC COMPANY LIMITED; *Int'l*, pg. 5181
NCL INTERNATIONAL LOGISTICS USA INC.—See NCL International Logistics Public Company Limited; *Int'l*, pg. 5181
NCL RESEARCH & FINANCIAL SERVICES LIMITED; *Int'l*, pg. 5181
NCM ASSOCIATES, INC.; *U.S. Private*, pg. 2876
NC MAX WORLD CO., LTD.—See Fantasista Co., Ltd.; *Int'l*, pg. 2614
NC MEPRO S.A.—See Nicolas Correa S.A.; *Int'l*, pg. 5273
NCM FATHOM—See National CineMedia, Inc.; *U.S. Public*, pg. 1494
NCM FINANCIAL, INC.; *U.S. Private*, pg. 2876
NCMIC GROUP INC.; *U.S. Private*, pg. 2876
NCMIC INSURANCE CO.—See NCMIC Group Inc.; *U.S. Private*, pg. 2876
NCM ODOR CONTROL, INC.—See Palo Duro Capital, LLC; *U.S. Private*, pg. 3082
NC NETWORK FACTORY, CO., LTD.—See Di-Nikko Engineering Co., Ltd.; *Int'l*, pg. 2101
NC NETWORK, INC.—See Di-Nikko Engineering Co., Ltd.; *Int'l*, pg. 2101
NCO CJSC NATIONAL SETTLEMENT DEPOSITORY—See OJSC Moscow Exchange MICEX-RTS; *Int'l*, pg. 5540
N-COMPASS DEVELOPMENT LLC—See SK Engineering & Construction Co., Ltd.; *Int'l*, pg. 6970
NCOMPUTING, INC.—See ZeroDesktop, Inc.; *U.S. Private*, pg. 4602
NCONDEZI ENERGY LIMITED; *Int'l*, pg. 5181
NCONDEZI SERVICES UK LTD—See Ncondezi Energy Limited; *Int'l*, pg. 5181
NCONTACT SURGICAL INC.—See AtriCure, Inc.; *U.S. Public*, pg. 629
NCP COATINGS INC.; *U.S. Private*, pg. 2876
NC PRECON CO., LTD.—See Nippon Concrete Industries Co., Ltd.; *Int'l*, pg. 5313
N.C. PRODUCTS—See CRH plc; *Int'l*, pg. 1846
NCP SOLUTIONS, LLC—See Aquiline Capital Partners LLC; *U.S. Private*, pg. 305
NCP YEAST (PTY) LIMITED—See The Bidvest Group Limited; *Int'l*, pg. 7625
NCR A/O—See NCR Voyix Corporation.; *U.S. Public*, pg. 1502
NCR ATLEOS CORPORATION; *U.S. Public*, pg. 1501
NCR AUSTRALIA PTY. LIMITED—See NCR Voyix Corporation.; *U.S. Public*, pg. 1502
NCR (BAHRAIN) W.L.L.—See NCR Voyix Corporation.; *U.S. Public*, pg. 1502
NCR BELGIUM & CO. SNC—See NCR Voyix Corporation.; *U.S. Public*, pg. 1502
NCR BILISIM SISTEMLERI LS—See NCR Voyix Corporation.; *U.S. Public*, pg. 1502
NCR BRASIL LTDA.—See NCR Voyix Corporation.; *U.S. Public*, pg. 1502

COMPANY NAME INDEX

NCR CANADA LTD.—See NCR Voyix Corporation.; *U.S. Public*, pg. 1503
NCR CHILE INDUSTRIAL Y COMERCIAL LIMITADA—See NCR Voyix Corporation.; *U.S. Public*, pg. 1503
NCR COLOMBIA LTDA—See NCR Voyix Corporation.; *U.S. Public*, pg. 1503
NCR COMMERCE JAPAN LTD.—See NCR Voyix Corporation.; *U.S. Public*, pg. 1503
NCR CORPORATION (PHILIPPINES)—See NCR Voyix Corporation.; *U.S. Public*, pg. 1503
NCR CORP. - UAE BRANCH—See NCR Voyix Corporation.; *U.S. Public*, pg. 1502
NCR (CYPRUS) LIMITED—See NCR Voyix Corporation.; *U.S. Public*, pg. 1502
NCR CZESKA REPUBLIKA SPOL. S.R.O.—See NCR Voyix Corporation.; *U.S. Public*, pg. 1503
NCR DANMARK A/S—See NCR Voyix Corporation.; *U.S. Public*, pg. 1503
NCR DE CHILE, S.A.—See NCR Voyix Corporation.; *U.S. Public*, pg. 1503
NCR DEL PERU S.A.—See NCR Voyix Corporation.; *U.S. Public*, pg. 1503
NCR DOMINICANA C. POR A.—See NCR Voyix Corporation.; *U.S. Public*, pg. 1503
NCR ESPANA, S.A.—See NCR Voyix Corporation.; *U.S. Public*, pg. 1503
NCR FINANCIAL SOLUTIONS GROUP LTD.—See NCR Voyix Corporation.; *U.S. Public*, pg. 1503
NCR FINLAND OY—See NCR Voyix Corporation.; *U.S. Public*, pg. 1503
NCR GHANA LIMITED—See NCR Voyix Corporation.; *U.S. Public*, pg. 1503
NCR GLOBAL SOLUTIONS LIMITED—See NCR Voyix Corporation.; *U.S. Public*, pg. 1503
NCR GOVERNMENT SYSTEMS LLC—See NCR Voyix Corporation.; *U.S. Public*, pg. 1503
NCR (HONG KONG) LIMITED—See NCR Voyix Corporation.; *U.S. Public*, pg. 1502
NCR INTERNATIONAL OF PUERTO RICO—See NCR Voyix Corporation.; *U.S. Public*, pg. 1503
NCR (IRI) LTD.—See NCR Voyix Corporation.; *U.S. Public*, pg. 1502
NCR ITALIA S.R.L.—See NCR Voyix Corporation.; *U.S. Public*, pg. 1503
NCR JAPAN, LTD.—See NCR Voyix Corporation.; *U.S. Public*, pg. 1503
NCR KENYA LTD.—See NCR Voyix Corporation.; *U.S. Public*, pg. 1503
NCR MAGYARORSZAG KFT.—See NCR Voyix Corporation.; *U.S. Public*, pg. 1503
NCR (MALAYSIA) SDN. BHD.—See NCR Voyix Corporation.; *U.S. Public*, pg. 1502
NCR (MIDDLE EAST) LIMITED—See NCR Voyix Corporation.; *U.S. Public*, pg. 1502
NCR NEDERLAND N.V.—See NCR Voyix Corporation.; *U.S. Public*, pg. 1503
NCR (NIGERIA) PLC—See NCR Voyix Corporation.; *U.S. Public*, pg. 1502
NCR (NORTH AFRICA) LIMITED—See NCR Voyix Corporation.; *U.S. Public*, pg. 1502
NCR (NZ) CORPORATION—See NCR Voyix Corporation.; *U.S. Public*, pg. 1502
NCR OSTERREICH GES.M.B.H.—See NCR Voyix Corporation.; *U.S. Public*, pg. 1503
NCR POLSKA SP.Z.O.O.—See NCR Voyix Corporation.; *U.S. Public*, pg. 1503
NCR SINGAPORE PTE LTD.—See NCR Voyix Corporation.; *U.S. Public*, pg. 1503
NCR SOLUTIONS DE MEXICO S. DE R.L. DE C.V.—See NCR Voyix Corporation.; *U.S. Public*, pg. 1503
NCR SYSTEMS TAIWAN LIMITED—See NCR Voyix Corporation.; *U.S. Public*, pg. 1503
NCR TAIWAN SOFTWARE LTD—See NCR Voyix Corporation.; *U.S. Public*, pg. 1503
NCR (THAILAND) LIMITED—See NCR Voyix Corporation.; *U.S. Public*, pg. 1502
NCR UK GROUP LIMITED—See NCR Voyix Corporation.; *U.S. Public*, pg. 1503
NCR VOYIX CORPORATION.; *U.S. Public*, pg. 1501
NCS&A CO., LTD.; *Int'l*, pg. 5181
NCS&A SHANGHAI CO. LTD.—See NCS&A Co., Ltd.; *Int'l*, pg. 5181
NCSB ENGINEERING SDN. BHD.—See Naim Holdings Berhad; *Int'l*, pg. 5131
NCS COLD STORES (S) PTE LTD—See QAF Limited; *Int'l*, pg. 6132
NCS COMMUNICATIONS ENGINEERING PTE. LTD.—See Temasek Holdings (Private) Limited; *Int'l*, pg. 7553
NCSG CRANE & HEAVY HAUL CORPORATION—See TriWest Capital Management Corp.; *Int'l*, pg. 7937
NCSG CRANE & HEAVY HAUL SERVICES, INC.—See TriWest Capital Management Corp.; *Int'l*, pg. 7937
NCSG CRANE & HEAVY HAUL SERVICES LTD.—See TriWest Capital Management Corp.; *Int'l*, pg. 7937
NCS HEALTHCARE OF MONTANA, INC.—See CVS Health Corporation; *U.S. Public*, pg. 616
NCSI (CHENGDU) CO., LTD—See Temasek Holdings (Private) Limited; *Int'l*, pg. 7553
NCSI (HK) LIMITED—See Temasek Holdings (Private) Limited; *Int'l*, pg. 7553
NCSI (MALAYSIA) SDN. BHD.—See Temasek Holdings (Private) Limited; *Int'l*, pg. 7553
NCS INDUSTRIES, INC.—See Leveling 8, Inc.; *U.S. Private*, pg. 2434
NCS INFORMATION TECHNOLOGY (SUZHOU) CO., LTD.—See Temasek Holdings (Private) Limited; *Int'l*, pg. 7553
NC (SINGAPORE) PTE. LTD.—See Natural Cool Holdings Limited; *Int'l*, pg. 5167
NCS INTERNATIONAL PTY. LTD.—See The British Standards Institution; *Int'l*, pg. 7629
NCSI (PHILIPPINES) INC.—See Globe Telecom, Inc.; *Int'l*, pg. 3006
NCSI (SHANGHAI) CO. LTD.—See Temasek Holdings (Private) Limited; *Int'l*, pg. 7553
NCS MULTISTAGE HOLDINGS, INC.; *U.S. Public*, pg. 1503
NCS MULTISTAGE INC.—See NCS Multistage Holdings, Inc.; *U.S. Public*, pg. 1503
NCSOFT CHINA CO., LTD.—See NCsoft Corporation; *Int'l*, pg. 5182
NCSOFT CORPORATION; *Int'l*, pg. 5181
NCSOFT EUROPE LTD.—See NCsoft Corporation; *Int'l*, pg. 5182
NCS PEARSON, INC.—See Pearson plc; *Int'l*, pg. 5777
NCS PEARSON (INDIA) PRIVATE LTD—See Pearson plc; *Int'l*, pg. 5776
NCS PEARSON PTY LTD—See Pearson plc; *Int'l*, pg. 5776
NCS PTE. LTD - BEDOK—See Temasek Holdings (Private) Limited; *Int'l*, pg. 7553
NCS PTE. LTD.—See Temasek Holdings (Private) Limited; *Int'l*, pg. 7553
N.C.S. PYROTECHNIE ET TECHNOLOGIES SAS—See Autoliv, Inc.; *Int'l*, pg. 730
NCS SUBSEA INC.—See OYO Corporation; *Int'l*, pg. 5678
NC STOLT CHUKYO TRANSPORTATION SERVICES CO. LTD.—See Stolt-Nielsen Limited; *Int'l*, pg. 7221
NC TAIWAN CO., LTD.—See NCsoft Corporation; *Int'l*, pg. 5182
NCT ALLIANCE BERHAD; *Int'l*, pg. 5182
NCT FINLAND—See NCT International B.V.; *Int'l*, pg. 5182
NCT GERMANY—See NCT International B.V.; *Int'l*, pg. 5182
NCT HOLLAND B.V.—See NCT International B.V.; *Int'l*, pg. 5182
NCT INDIA—See NCT International B.V.; *Int'l*, pg. 5182
NCT INTERNATIONAL B.V.; *Int'l*, pg. 5182
NCT ITALY—See NCT International B.V.; *Int'l*, pg. 5182
NCT LEATHER LIMITED—See Scottish Leather Group Ltd.; *Int'l*, pg. 6653
NCT MIDDLE EAST—See Fortum Oyj; *Int'l*, pg. 2742
NCT POLAND—See NCT International B.V.; *Int'l*, pg. 5182
NC TRANSACTION, INC.—See News Corporation; *U.S. Public*, pg. 1519
NCT SPAIN—See NCT International B.V.; *Int'l*, pg. 5182
NCT TURKEY—See NCT International B.V.; *Int'l*, pg. 5182
NCT VENTURES LLC; *U.S. Private*, pg. 2876
NCW GROUP INC.—See Financial Gravity Companies, Inc.; *U.S. Public*, pg. 834
NDA COMMODITY BROKERS PVT. LTD.—See NDA Securities Limited; *Int'l*, pg. 5182
ND ADHESIVES & SEALANTS DIVISION—See H.B. Fuller Company; *U.S. Public*, pg. 978
NDA DISTRIBUTORS, LLC.—See Elbi S.P.A.; *Int'l*, pg. 2344
NDA SECURITIES LIMITED; *Int'l*, pg. 5182
NDATALYZE CORP.; *Int'l*, pg. 5182
NDB CAPITAL HOLDINGS LIMITED—See National Development Bank PLC; *Int'l*, pg. 5155
NDB CAPITAL LIMITED—See National Development Bank PLC; *Int'l*, pg. 5155
NDB GIDA SANAYI VE TICARET ANONIM SIRKETI—See Nestle S.A.; *Int'l*, pg. 5203
NDB SECURITIES (PVT) LIMITED—See National Development Bank PLC; *Int'l*, pg. 5155
NDB WEALTH MANAGEMENT LIMITED—See National Development Bank PLC; *Int'l*, pg. 5155
NDB ZEPHYR PARTNERS LANKA (PVT) LIMITED—See National Development Bank PLC; *Int'l*, pg. 5156
NDC AUSTRALIA PTY LTD; *Int'l*, pg. 5182
NDC CO., LTD.—See Daido Metal Corporation; *Int'l*, pg. 1922
NDC CONSTRUCTION COMPANY; *U.S. Private*, pg. 2876
NDC INFRARED ENGINEERING INC.—See Spectris Plc; *Int'l*, pg. 7131
NDC LLC—See Ecolab Inc.; *U.S. Public*, pg. 715
ND COMPOUND BLENDING DIVISION/MICHIGAN—See H.B. Fuller Company; *U.S. Public*, pg. 978
ND COMPOUND BLENDING DIVISION/TEXAS—See H.B. Fuller Company; *U.S. Public*, pg. 978
NDC SALES CO., LTD.—See Daido Metal Corporation; *Int'l*, pg. 1922
NDC TECHNOLOGIES, INC.—See Nordson Corporation; *U.S. Public*, pg. 1533
NDC TECHNOLOGIES LIMITED—See Nordson Corporation; *U.S. Public*, pg. 1533
NDC TECHNOLOGIES SRL—See Nordson Corporation; *U.S. Public*, pg. 1533
NDCUBE CO., LTD.—See Nintendo Co., Ltd.; *Int'l*, pg. 5308
ND ELECTRONICS (KUNSHAN) CO., LTD.—See H.B. Fuller Company; *U.S. Public*, pg. 978
N-DESIGN GESELLSCHAFT FUR SYSTEMATISCHE GESTALTUNGEN MBH—See CompuGroup Medical SE & Co. KGaA; *Int'l*, pg. 1757
NDF AZTECA MILLING EUROPE SRL—See Gruma, S.A.B. de C.V.; *Int'l*, pg. 3114
NDF ENTERPRISES LTD.; *Int'l*, pg. 5182
ND FLUOROPOLYMER COATINGS DIVISION—See H.B. Fuller Company; *U.S. Public*, pg. 978
NDFOS CO.,LTD.; *Int'l*, pg. 5182
ND GRAPHIC PRODUCT LIMITED; *Int'l*, pg. 5182
NDH ADVISORS LLC—See Unity Partners LP; *U.S. Public*, pg. 2253
NDIAS, LTD.—See Nomura Research Institute, Ltd.; *Int'l*, pg. 5413
NDIC. CO., LTD.—See Shimizu Corporation; *Int'l*, pg. 6835
NDI CONSTRUCTION; *U.S. Private*, pg. 2876
NDI EUROPE GMBH—See Roper Technologies, Inc.; *U.S. Public*, pg. 1812
ND INDUSTRIES A.S.—See H.B. Fuller Company; *U.S. Public*, pg. 978
ND INDUSTRIES INC. - EASTERN FASTENER PROCESSING DIVISION—See H.B. Fuller Company; *U.S. Public*, pg. 978
ND INDUSTRIES INC. - MIDWESTERN FASTENER PROCESSING DIVISION—See H.B. Fuller Company; *U.S. Public*, pg. 978
ND INDUSTRIES INC.—See H.B. Fuller Company; *U.S. Public*, pg. 978
ND INDUSTRIES INC. - SOUTHEASTERN FASTENER PROCESSING DIVISION—See H.B. Fuller Company; *U.S. Public*, pg. 978
ND INDUSTRIES INC. - SOUTHWESTERN FASTENER PROCESSING DIVISION—See H.B. Fuller Company; *U.S. Public*, pg. 978
ND INDUSTRIES INC. - WESTERN FASTENER PROCESSING DIVISION—See H.B. Fuller Company; *U.S. Public*, pg. 978
ND INDUSTRIES—See H.B. Fuller Company; *U.S. Public*, pg. 978
NDI RECOGNITION SYSTEMS; *U.S. Private*, pg. 2876
NDIVISION, INC.; *U.S. Public*, pg. 1504
NDK AMERICA, INC.—See NIHON DEMPA KOGYO Co Ltd; *Int'l*, pg. 5283
NDK CRYSTAL ASIA PTE. LTD.—See NIHON DEMPA KOGYO Co Ltd; *Int'l*, pg. 5283
NDK ELECTRONICS (HK) LIMITED—See NIHON DEMPA KOGYO Co Ltd; *Int'l*, pg. 5283
NDK-ELECTRONICS SHANGHAI CO., LTD—See NIHON DEMPA KOGYO Co Ltd; *Int'l*, pg. 5283
NDK EUROPE LTD.—See NIHON DEMPA KOGYO Co Ltd; *Int'l*, pg. 5283
NDK ITALY SRL—See NIHON DEMPA KOGYO Co Ltd; *Int'l*, pg. 5283
ND KOREA CO., LTD.—See NIHON DENKEI CO., LTD.; *Int'l*, pg. 5284
NDL CONSTRUCTION LTD.; *Int'l*, pg. 5182
ND LEASING SYSTEM CO., LTD.—See Shimizu Corporation; *Int'l*, pg. 6835
ND MANUFACTURING ENGINEERING GROUP—See H.B. Fuller Company; *U.S. Public*, pg. 978
NDM CASMYN LTD—See New Dawn Mining Corp.; *Int'l*, pg. 5222
N.D. METAL INDUSTRIES LTD.; *Int'l*, pg. 5116
NDOLA LIME COMPANY LIMITED—See ZCCM Investments Holdings Plc.; *Int'l*, pg. 8627
NDOVU RESOURCES LIMITED—See Aminex PLC; *Int'l*, pg. 428
ND PAPER INC.—See Nine Dragons Paper Holdings Limited; *Int'l*, pg. 5297
NDP, LLC; *U.S. Private*, pg. 2876
NDR AUTO COMPONENTS LIMITED—See Sharda Motor Industries Limited; *Int'l*, pg. 6789
N.D. RUBBER PUBLIC COMPANY LIMITED; *Int'l*, pg. 5116
ND SATCOM DEFENCE GMBH—See Airbus SE; *Int'l*, pg. 245
ND SATCOM GMBH—See Airbus SE; *Int'l*, pg. 245
ND SATCOM, INC.—See Airbus SE; *Int'l*, pg. 245
ND SATCOM PRODUCTS GMBH—See Airbus SE; *Int'l*, pg. 245
ND SATCOM SATELLITE COMMUNICATION SYSTEMS (BEIJING) CO. LTD.—See Airbus SE; *Int'l*, pg. 245
NDS CO., LTD.—See COMSYS Holdings Corporation; *Int'l*, pg. 1761
NDS HOLDINGS B.V—See Cisco Systems, Inc.; *U.S. Public*, pg. 499
NDS INFORMATION SYSTEM CO., LTD—See COMSYS Holdings Corporation; *Int'l*, pg. 1761
NDS LEASE CO., LTD.—See COMSYS Holdings Corporation; *Int'l*, pg. 1761
NDSM LIMITED—See Eurofins Scientific S.E.; *Int'l*, pg. 2551
ND SOFTWARE CO., LTD.; *Int'l*, pg. 5182

ND SOFTWARE CO., LTD.

CORPORATE AFFILIATIONS

NDS SOLUTION CO., LTD.—See COMSYS Holdings Corporation; *Int'l*, pg. 1762
NDS SURGICAL IMAGING BV—See Novanta Inc.; *U.S. Public*, pg. 1548
NDS SURGICAL IMAGING, LLC—See Novanta Inc.; *U.S. Public*, pg. 1548
NDS SWEDEN—See Cisco Systems, Inc.; *U.S. Public*, pg. 499
NDS.TS CO., LTD.—See COMSYS Holdings Corporation; *Int'l*, pg. 1762
NDT CORPORATION LTD.—See Mitsubishi Corporation; *Int'l*, pg. 4942
NDT DO BRASIL LTD.—See Mistras Group, Inc.; *U.S. Public*, pg. 1451
NDT SYSTEMS, INC.; *U.S. Private*, pg. 2876
NDT (THAILAND) CO., LTD.—See Mitsubishi Corporation; *Int'l*, pg. 4942
NDTV CONVERGENCE LIMITED—See New Delhi Television Limited; *Int'l*, pg. 5222
NDTV LIFESTYLE LIMITED—See New Delhi Television Limited; *Int'l*, pg. 5222
NDTV NETWORKS BV—See New Delhi Television Limited; *Int'l*, pg. 5222
NDV (THAILAND) CO., LTD.—See Seika Corporation; *Int'l*, pg. 6685
NDX ALBENSI—See Cerberus Capital Management, L.P.; *U.S. Private*, pg. 839
NDX ENERGIJA UAB—See NDX UAB; *Int'l*, pg. 5182
NDX UAB; *Int'l*, pg. 5182
NEACE VENTURES; *U.S. Private*, pg. 2877
NEAD ELECTRIC INC—See Nead Organization Inc.; *U.S. Private*, pg. 2877
NEAD ORGANIZATION INC.; *U.S. Private*, pg. 2877
NEA INTERNATIONAL BV—See INDUS Holding AG; *Int'l*, pg. 3663
NEAL COMMUNITIES INC.—See Estuary Investment Corp.; *U.S. Private*, pg. 1429
NEALES WASTE MANAGEMENT LTD.—See Cementir Holding N.V.; *Int'l*, pg. 1397
NEAL H. KNAPP, LLC; *U.S. Private*, pg. 2877
NEANY INC.; *U.S. Private*, pg. 2877
NEA ODOS SA—See Gek Terna Societe Anonyme Holdings Real Estate Constructions; *Int'l*, pg. 2913
NEA OPTICAL LLC—See EssilorLuxottica SA; *Int'l*, pg. 2513
NEAPCO COMPONENTS, LLC—See Neapco Holdings, LLC; *U.S. Private*, pg. 2877
NEAPCO DRIVELINES, LLC—See Neapco Holdings, LLC; *U.S. Private*, pg. 2877
NEAPCO DRIVELINES (SHANGHAI) CO., LTD.—See Neapco Holdings, LLC; *U.S. Private*, pg. 2877
NEAPCO EUROPE GMBH—See Neapco Holdings, LLC; *U.S. Private*, pg. 2877
NEAPCO EUROPE SP. Z O.O.—See Neapco Holdings, LLC; *U.S. Private*, pg. 2877
NEAPCO HOLDINGS, LLC; *U.S. Private*, pg. 2877
NEAPOLITAN WAY SHOPPING CENTER, LLC—See Blackstone Inc.; *U.S. Public*, pg. 351
NEARBUY INDIA PRIVATE LIMITED—See One97 Communications Limited; *Int'l*, pg. 5575
NEARCTIC NICKEL MINES, INC.; *Int'l*, pg. 5182
NEAR EARTH AUTONOMY, INC.; *U.S. Private*, pg. 2877
NEARFIELD SYSTEMS, INC.—See AMETEK, Inc.; *U.S. Public*, pg. 121
NEAR INTELLIGENCE, INC.—See Blue Torch Capital, LP; *U.S. Private*, pg. 594
NEARMAP AUSTRALIA PTY LTD—See NBTM New Materials Group Co., Ltd.; *Int'l*, pg. 5179
NEARMAP LTD.—See Thoma Bravo, L.P.; *U.S. Private*, pg. 4150
NEARMAP PTY. LTD.—See Thoma Bravo, L.P.; *U.S. Private*, pg. 4150
NEAR NORTH NATIONAL TITLE, LLC; *U.S. Private*, pg. 2877
NEARON ENTERPRISES - PROPERTY MANAGEMENT DIVISION—See Nearon Enterprises; *U.S. Private*, pg. 2877
NEARON ENTERPRISES; *U.S. Private*, pg. 2877
NEARSHORE TECHNOLOGY COMPANY, LLC; *U.S. Private*, pg. 2877
NEARU SERVICES; *U.S. Private*, pg. 2877
NEASE CORPORATION—See International Chemical Investors S.E.; *Int'l*, pg. 3745
NEASE LAGANA EDEN & CULLEY, INC.—See Winged Keel Group, LLC; *U.S. Private*, pg. 4541
NEATA ALUMINIUM (MALAYSIA) SDN. BHD.—See Vinvest Capital Holdings Berhad; *Int'l*, pg. 8242
THE NEAT COMPANY; *U.S. Private*, pg. 4082
NEATE ROLLER LIMITED; *Int'l*, pg. 5183
NEATHAWK DUBUQUE & PACKETT; *U.S. Private*, pg. 2878
NEATHAWK DUBUQUE & PACKETT—See Neathawk Dubuque & Packett; *U.S. Private*, pg. 2878
NEATHAWK DUBUQUE & PACKETT—See Neathawk Dubuque & Packett; *U.S. Private*, pg. 2878
NEAT IDEAS LTD—See Sycamore Partners Management, LP; *U.S. Private*, pg. 3897
NEAT MANAGEMENT GROUP—See Integrity Marketing Group LLC; *U.S. Private*, pg. 2103

NEAT N' TRIM UNIFORMS PTY LTD—See Wesfarmers Limited; *Int'l*, pg. 8381
THE NEAT NURSERY CO.—See Nordic Group of Companies, Ltd.; *U.S. Private*, pg. 2936
NEATON AUTO MEXICANA, S.A. DE C.V.—See Nihon Plast Co., Ltd.; *Int'l*, pg. 5287
NEATON AUTO PRODUCTS MFG, INC.—See Nihon Plast Co., Ltd.; *Int'l*, pg. 5287
NEATON ROME INC.—See Nihon Plast Co., Ltd.; *Int'l*, pg. 5287
NEATO ROBOTICS, INC.—See Vorwerk & Co. KG; *Int'l*, pg. 8307
NEBAG AG; *Int'l*, pg. 5183
NEBCO INC.; *U.S. Private*, pg. 2878
NEB CORPORATION; *U.S. Private*, pg. 2878
NEBO AGENCY LLC; *U.S. Private*, pg. 2878
NEBOKO LIVE—See Omnicom Group Inc.; *U.S. Public*, pg. 1596
NEBRASKA ALUMINUM CASTINGS, INC.; *U.S. Private*, pg. 2878
NEBRASKA BANKSHARES, INC.; *U.S. Private*, pg. 2878
NEBRASKA BOOK COMPANY, INC.—See Concise Capital Management LP; *U.S. Private*, pg. 1009
NEBRASKA BOOK HOLDINGS, INC.—See Concise Capital Management LP; *U.S. Private*, pg. 1009
NEBRASKA DEPARTMENT OF CORRECTIONAL SERVICES; *U.S. Private*, pg. 2878
NEBRASKA ELECTRIC GENERATION & TRANSMISSION COOPERATIVE, INC.; *U.S. Private*, pg. 2878
NEBRASKA FAMILIES COLLABORATIVE; *U.S. Private*, pg. 2878
NEBRASKA FURNITURE MART, INC.—See Berkshire Hathaway Inc.; *U.S. Public*, pg. 313
NEBRASKA HARVEST CENTER INC.—See Claas KGaA mbH; *Int'l*, pg. 1640
NEBRASKA INTERACTIVE, LLC—See Tyler Technologies, Inc.; *U.S. Public*, pg. 2208
NEBRASKA INVESTMENT FINANCE AUTHORITY INC.; *U.S. Private*, pg. 2878
NEBRASKA-IOWA SUPPLY COMPANY; *U.S. Private*, pg. 2879
NEBRASKA, KANSAS & COLORADO RAILWAY, LLC—See The Broe Companies, Inc.; *U.S. Private*, pg. 4001
NEBRASKALAND; *U.S. Private*, pg. 2879
NEBRASKALAND TIRE COMPANY; *U.S. Private*, pg. 2879
NEBRASKA LASER EYE ASSOCIATES—See Vance Thompson Vision Clinic Prof LLC; *U.S. Private*, pg. 4342
NEBRASKA LOGOS, INC.—See Lamar Advertising Company; *U.S. Public*, pg. 1291
NEBRASKA MACHINERY COMPANY INC.; *U.S. Private*, pg. 2878
NEBRASKA METHODIST HEALTH SYSTEM INC.; *U.S. Private*, pg. 2878
NEBRASKA ORTHOTIC & PROSTHETIC SERVICES, INC.—See Patient Square Capital, L.P.; *U.S. Private*, pg. 3107
NEBRASKA PLASTICS, INC.; *U.S. Private*, pg. 2878
NEBRASKA PUBLIC POWER DISTRICT; *U.S. Private*, pg. 2879
NEBRASKA SOYBEAN BOARD; *U.S. Private*, pg. 2879
NEBRASKA TITLE COMPANY; *U.S. Private*, pg. 2879
NEBRASKA TOTAL CARE, INC.—See Centene Corporation; *U.S. Public*, pg. 470
NEBRASKA TRANSPORT CO. INC.; *U.S. Private*, pg. 2879
NEBRASKA TRUCK CENTER, INC.; *U.S. Private*, pg. 2879
NEBS BUSINESS PRODUCTS LIMITED—See Deluxe Corporation; *U.S. Public*, pg. 652
NEBS PAYROLL SERVICE LIMITED—See Deluxe Corporation; *U.S. Public*, pg. 652
NEBTA FOR GEOLOGY & MINING LTD.—See ASEC Company for Mining; *Int'l*, pg. 605
NEBULA CARAVEL ACQUISITION CORP.; *U.S. Public*, pg. 1504
NEBULA, INC.; *U.S. Private*, pg. 2879
NEBU RESOURCES INC.; *Int'l*, pg. 5183
NEC ACCESS TECHNICA, LTD.—See NEC Corporation; *Int'l*, pg. 5183
NEC ADVANCED SOFTWARE TECHNOLOGY (BEIJING) CO., LTD.—See NEC Corporation; *Int'l*, pg. 5183
NEC AFRICA (PTY) LTD.—See NEC Corporation; *Int'l*, pg. 5183
NEC AFRICA (PTY) LTD.—See NEC Corporation; *Int'l*, pg. 5183
NEC AMERICA—See NEC Corporation; *Int'l*, pg. 5184
NEC ARGENTINA S.A.—See NEC Corporation; *Int'l*, pg. 5183
NEC ASIA PACIFIC PTE. LTD.—See NEC Corporation; *Int'l*, pg. 5183
NEC ASIA PTE LTD.—See NEC Corporation; *Int'l*, pg. 5183
NEC AUSTRALIA PTY. LTD.—See NEC Corporation; *Int'l*, pg. 5183
NEC CANADA, INC.—See NEC Corporation; *Int'l*, pg. 5184

NEC CAPITAL SOLUTIONS HONG KONG LIMITED—See NEC Capital Solutions Limited; *Int'l*, pg. 5183
NEC CAPITAL SOLUTIONS LIMITED; *Int'l*, pg. 5183
NEC CAPITAL SOLUTIONS MALAYSIA SDN. BHD.—See NEC Capital Solutions Limited; *Int'l*, pg. 5183
NEC CAPITAL SOLUTIONS SINGAPORE PTE. LIMITED—See NEC Capital Solutions Limited; *Int'l*, pg. 5183
NEC CAPITAL (UK) PLC—See NEC Corporation; *Int'l*, pg. 5184
NEC CHILE S.A.—See NEC Corporation; *Int'l*, pg. 5184
NEC (CHINA) CO., LTD.—See NEC Corporation; *Int'l*, pg. 5183
NECCHI S.P.A.—See CF Italia srl; *Int'l*, pg. 1429
NEC COMPUTERS NETHERLAND B.V.—See NEC Corporation; *Int'l*, pg. 5184
NEC COMPUTERTECHNO, LTD.—See NEC Corporation; *Int'l*, pg. 5184
NEC CORPORATION ABIKO PLANT—See NEC Corporation; *Int'l*, pg. 5184
NEC CORPORATION FUCHU PLANT—See NEC Corporation; *Int'l*, pg. 5184
NEC CORPORATION INDIA PRIVATE LIMITED—See NEC Corporation; *Int'l*, pg. 5184
NEC CORPORATION MITA PLANT—See NEC Corporation; *Int'l*, pg. 5184
NEC CORPORATION OF AMERICA, INC.—See NEC Corporation; *Int'l*, pg. 5184
NEC CORPORATION OF AMERICA—See NEC Corporation; *Int'l*, pg. 5184
NEC CORPORATION SAGAMIHARA PLANT—See NEC Corporation; *Int'l*, pg. 5184
NEC CORPORATION; *Int'l*, pg. 5183
NEC CORPORATION—See NEC Corporation; *Int'l*, pg. 5184
NEC CORPORATION (THAILAND) LTD.—See NEC Corporation; *Int'l*, pg. 5184
NEC CORPORATION YOKOHAMA PLANT—See NEC Corporation; *Int'l*, pg. 5184
NECCO; *U.S. Private*, pg. 2879
NECC TELECOM, INC.; *U.S. Private*, pg. 2879
NEC DE COLOMBIA S.A.—See NEC Corporation; *Int'l*, pg. 5186
NEC DE MEXICO, S.A. DE C.V.—See NEC Corporation; *Int'l*, pg. 5186
NEC DEUTSCHLAND GMBH—See NEC Corporation; *Int'l*, pg. 5184
NEC DEUTSCHLAND GMBH—See NEC Corporation; *Int'l*, pg. 5184
NEC DE VENEZUELA, C.A.—See NEC Corporation; *Int'l*, pg. 5186
NEC DISPLAY SOLUTIONS POLAND—See NEC Corporation; *Int'l*, pg. 5184
NEC DISPLAY SOLUTIONS—See NEC Corporation; *Int'l*, pg. 5185
NEC EASTERN EUROPE KFT.—See NEC Corporation; *Int'l*, pg. 5184
NEC EASTERN EUROPE LTD.—See NEC Corporation; *Int'l*, pg. 5184
NECEC TRANSMISSION, LLC—See Iberdrola, S.A.; *Int'l*, pg. 3573
NEC ENERGY DEVICES (WUJIANG) CO., LTD.—See NEC Corporation; *Int'l*, pg. 5184
NEC ENERGY SOLUTIONS, INC.—See LG Chem Ltd.; *Int'l*, pg. 4474
NEC ENGINEERING, LTD.—See NEC Corporation; *Int'l*, pg. 5184
NEC ENTERPRISE COMMUNICATION TECHNOLOGIES, INC.—See NEC Corporation; *Int'l*, pg. 5184
THE NECESSITY RETAIL REIT, INC.—See AR Global Investments, LLC; *U.S. Private*, pg. 306
NEC EUROPE LTD. - NEC LABORATORIES EUROPE DIVISION—See NEC Corporation; *Int'l*, pg. 5184
NEC EUROPE & UK LTD.—See NEC Corporation; *Int'l*, pg. 5184
NEC FACILITIES, LTD.—See Marubeni Corporation; *Int'l*, pg. 4706
NEC FIELDING INFORMATION TECHNOLOGY SERVICES (BEIJING) CO., LTD.—See NEC Corporation; *Int'l*, pg. 5184
NEC FIELDING, LTD.—See NEC Corporation; *Int'l*, pg. 5185
NEC FINANCIAL SERVICES, LLC—See NEC Corporation; *Int'l*, pg. 5184
NEC FRANCE S.A.S.—See NEC Corporation; *Int'l*, pg. 5185
NECHAKO REAL ESTATE LTD; *Int'l*, pg. 5187
N.E. CHEMCAT CORPORATION—See BASF SE; *Int'l*, pg. 875
N.E. CHEMCAT CORPORATION—See Sumitomo Metal Mining Co., Ltd.; *Int'l*, pg. 7291
NECHES RIVER TREATMENT CORP.—See Exxon Mobil Corporation; *U.S. Public*, pg. 817
NEC HONG KONG LTD.—See NEC Corporation; *Int'l*, pg. 5185
NEC IBERICA S.L.—See NEC Corporation; *Int'l*, pg. 5185
NEC INFORMATION SYSTEMS (SHANGHAI), LTD.—See NEC Corporation; *Int'l*, pg. 5185

COMPANY NAME INDEX

NEC INTERNATIONAL LOGISTICS (SHANGHAI) LTD.—See NEC Corporation; *Int'l*, pg. 5185
NEC ITALIA S.P.A.—See NEC Corporation; *Int'l*, pg. 5185
NEC IT SERVICES AUSTRALIA PTY. LTD.—See NEC Corporation; *Int'l*, pg. 5183
NEC IT SOLUTIONS AUSTRALIA PTY LTD—See NEC Corporation; *Int'l*, pg. 5183
NECKARCOM TELEKOMMUNIKATION GMBH—See EnBW Energie Baden-Wurttemberg AG; *Int'l*, pg. 2399
NECKERMANN UTAZAS SZOLGALTATO KFT.—See Raiffeisen Touristik Group GmbH; *Int'l*, pg. 6185
NECKS ELECTRIC AB—See Addtech AB; *Int'l*, pg. 134
NEC LABORATORIES AMERICA, INC.—See NEC Corporation; *Int'l*, pg. 5184
NEC LABORATORIES EUROPE GMBH—See NEC Corporation; *Int'l*, pg. 5185
NEC LATIN AMERICA S.A.—See NEC Corporation; *Int'l*, pg. 5185
NEC LOGISTICS HONG KONG LIMITED—See NEC Corporation; *Int'l*, pg. 5185
NEC LOGISTICS HONG KONG LIMITED—See Nippon Express Holdings, Inc.; *Int'l*, pg. 5315
NEC LOGISTICS, LTD.—See NEC Corporation; *Int'l*, pg. 5185
NEC LOGISTICS, LTD.—See Nippon Express Holdings, Inc.; *Int'l*, pg. 5315
NEC LOGISTICS (SHENZHEN) LTD.—See NEC Corporation; *Int'l*, pg. 5185
NEC LOGISTICS (SHENZHEN) LTD.—See Nippon Express Holdings, Inc.; *Int'l*, pg. 5315
NEC LOGISTICS SINGAPORE PTE. LTD.—See NEC Corporation; *Int'l*, pg. 5185
NEC LOGISTICS SINGAPORE PTE. LTD.—See Nippon Express Holdings, Inc.; *Int'l*, pg. 5315
NEC LOGISTICS TAIWAN LTD.—See NEC Corporation; *Int'l*, pg. 5185
NEC LOGISTICS TAIWAN LTD.—See Nippon Express Holdings, Inc.; *Int'l*, pg. 5315
NEC LOGISTICS (THAILAND) CO., LTD—See NEC Corporation; *Int'l*, pg. 5185
NEC LOGISTICS (THAILAND) CO., LTD—See Nippon Express Holdings, Inc.; *Int'l*, pg. 5315
NEC MALAYSIA SDN. BHD.—See NEC Corporation; *Int'l*, pg. 5185
NEC-MITSUBISHI ELECTRONICS—See Mitsubishi Electric Corporation; *Int'l*, pg. 4944
NEC NEDERLAND B.V.—See NEC Corporation; *Int'l*, pg. 5185
NEC NETWORK AND SENSOR SYSTEMS, LTD.—See NEC Corporation; *Int'l*, pg. 5185
NEC NETWORKS & SYSTEM INTEGRATION CORPORATION—See NEC Corporation; *Int'l*, pg. 5185
NEC NETWORKS & SYSTEM INTEGRATION SERVICES LTD.—See NEC Corporation; *Int'l*, pg. 5185
NEC NEVA COMMUNICATIONS SYSTEMS JSC—See NEC Corporation; *Int'l*, pg. 5185
NEC NEVA COMMUNICATIONS SYSTEMS JSC—See NEC Corporation; *Int'l*, pg. 5185
NEC NEW ZEALAND LIMITED—See NEC Corporation; *Int'l*, pg. 5185
NEC NEXSOLUTIONS, LTD.—See NEC Corporation; *Int'l*, pg. 5185
NECO INSURANCE LIMITED; *Int'l*, pg. 5187
NECOLICO LLC—See Chubu Electric Power Co., Inc.; *Int'l*, pg. 1593
NEC ONCOIMMUNITY AS—See NEC Corporation; *Int'l*, pg. 5185
NECON CONTROLS GEN. TRAD. & CONT. W.L.L.—See The Kuwait Company for Process Plant Construction & Contracting K.S.C.; *Int'l*, pg. 7663
NEC PHILIPPINES, INC.—See NEC Corporation; *Int'l*, pg. 5185
NEC PLATFORMS, LTD.—See NEC Corporation; *Int'l*, pg. 5185
NEC PLATFORM TECHNOLOGIES HONG KONG LIMITED—See NEC Corporation; *Int'l*, pg. 5185
NEC PLATFORM TECHNOLOGIES (SUZHOU) CO., LTD.—See NEC Corporation; *Int'l*, pg. 5185
NEC PORTUGAL TELECOMUNICACOES E SISTEMAS, S.A.—See NEC Corporation; *Int'l*, pg. 5185
NEC PORTUGAL-TELECOMUNICACOES E SISTEMAS SA—See NEC Corporation; *Int'l*, pg. 5185
NEC SAITAMA, LTD.—See Marubeni Corporation; *Int'l*, pg. 4706
NECSA, NUEVOS ESPACIOS COMERCIALES, S.A.—See Inmobiliaria Colonial SOCIMI SA; *Int'l*, pg. 3706
NEC SAUDI ARABIA LTD.—See NEC Corporation; *Int'l*, pg. 5186
NEC SCANDINAVIA AB—See NEC Corporation; *Int'l*, pg. 5186
NEC SCANDINAVIA AB—See NEC Corporation; *Int'l*, pg. 5186
NEC SCHOTT COMPONENTS CORPORATION—See Carl-Zeiss-Stiftung; *Int'l*, pg. 1336
NECSEL INTELLECTUAL PROPERTY, INC.—See Ushio, Inc.; *Int'l*, pg. 8097
NEC SOFT (JINAN) CO., LTD.—See NEC Corporation; *Int'l*, pg. 5186
NEC SOFT, LTD.—See NEC Corporation; *Int'l*, pg. 5186

NEC SOLUTION INNOVATORS, LTD.—See NEC Corporation; *Int'l*, pg. 5186
NEC SOLUTIONS (CHINA) CO., LTD.—See NEC Corporation; *Int'l*, pg. 5186
NEC SOLUTIONS INC.—See NEC Corporation; *Int'l*, pg. 5184
NEC SPACE TECHNOLOGIES, LTD.—See Japan Industrial Partners, Inc.; *Int'l*, pg. 3890
NEC SPACE TECHNOLOGIES, LTD.—See NEC Corporation; *Int'l*, pg. 5186
NEC SPHERE COMMUNICATIONS INC.—See NEC Corporation; *Int'l*, pg. 5184
NEC SYSTEM TECHNOLOGIES (HANGZHOU), LTD.—See NEC Corporation; *Int'l*, pg. 5186
NEC TAIWAN LTD.—See NEC Corporation; *Int'l*, pg. 5186
NECTAR 360 LIMITED—See Aimia Inc.; *Int'l*, pg. 233
NECTAR 360 LIMITED—See J Sainsbury plc; *Int'l*, pg. 3852
NECTAR IMPORTS LIMITED—See Asahi Group Holdings Ltd.; *Int'l*, pg. 594
NECTAR LABORATORIES PRIVATE LIMITED—See TGV Sraac Limited; *Int'l*, pg. 7588
NECTAR LIFESCIENCES LIMITED; *Int'l*, pg. 5187
NEC TECHNOLOGIES (THAILAND) CO., LTD.—See NEC Corporation; *Int'l*, pg. 5186
NEC TECHNOLOGIES (UK) LTD.—See NEC Corporation; *Int'l*, pg. 5186
NEC TELECOMMUNICATIONS AND INFORMATION TECHNOLOGY LTD.—See NEC Corporation; *Int'l*, pg. 5186
NEC TELECOMMUNICATIONS & INFORMATION TECHNOLOGY LTD.—See NEC Corporation; *Int'l*, pg. 5186
NEC TELECOMMUNICATIONS & INFORMATION TECHNOLOGY LTD.—See NEC Corporation; *Int'l*, pg. 5186
NEC TELECOMMUNICATIONS & INFORMATION TECHNOLOGY LTD.—See NEC Corporation; *Int'l*, pg. 5186
NEC TELECOM SOFTWARE PHILIPPINES, INC.—See NEC Corporation; *Int'l*, pg. 5186
NEC TOKIN AMERICA, INC.—See NEC Corporation; *Int'l*, pg. 5184
NEC TOKIN CORPORATION—See Yageo Corporation; *Int'l*, pg. 8545
NEC TOKIN ELECTRONICS (PHILIPPINES), INC.; *Int'l*, pg. 5187
NEC TOKIN ELECTRONICS (THAILAND) CO., LTD—See NEC Corporation; *Int'l*, pg. 5186
NEC TOKIN ELECTRONICS (XIAMEN) CORPORATION—See NEC Corporation; *Int'l*, pg. 5186
NEC TOKIN EUROPE GMBH—See NEC Corporation; *Int'l*, pg. 5186
NEC TOKIN KOREA, CO., LTD.—See NEC Corporation; *Int'l*, pg. 5186
NEC TOKIN SINGAPORE PTE. LTD.—See NEC Corporation; *Int'l*, pg. 5186
NEC TOKIN TAIWAN CO.,LTD.—See NEC Corporation; *Int'l*, pg. 5186
NEC TOPPAN CIRCUIT SOLUTIONS PHILIPPINES, INC.—See TOPPAN Holdings Inc.; *Int'l*, pg. 7817
NEC TOPPAN CIRCUIT SOLUTIONS USA INC.—See TOPPAN Holdings Inc.; *Int'l*, pg. 7817
NEC (UK) LTD.—See NEC Corporation; *Int'l*, pg. 5183
NEC UKRAINE, LLC—See NEC Corporation; *Int'l*, pg. 5186
NEC UNIFIED SOLUTIONS HELLAS S.A.—See NEC Corporation; *Int'l*, pg. 5186
NEC VIETNAM CO., LTD.—See NEC Corporation; *Int'l*, pg. 5186
NEC VIEWTECHNOLOGY TRADING (SHENZHEN), LTD.—See NEC Corporation; *Int'l*, pg. 5186
NEC WEST AFRICA LIMITED—See NEC Corporation; *Int'l*, pg. 5186
NEC XON HOLDINGS (PROPRIETARY) LIMITED—See NEC Corporation; *Int'l*, pg. 5186
NEC XON SYSTEMS NAMIBIA (PROPRIETARY) LIMITED—See NEC Corporation; *Int'l*, pg. 5186
NEC YAMANASHI LTD.—See NEC Corporation; *Int'l*, pg. 5186
NED AIR B.V.—See CENTROTEC SE; *Int'l*, pg. 1414
NEDALPAC B.V.—See Dole plc; *Int'l*, pg. 2158
NEDAL—See 3G Capital Partners L.P.; *U.S. Private*, pg. 13
NEDAMCO NORTH AMERICA CORPORATION—See Elcat Inc.; *U.S. Private*, pg. 1350
NEDAP ASIA LTD—See Nedap N.V.; *Int'l*, pg. 5187
NEDAP BELGIE N.V.—See Nedap N.V.; *Int'l*, pg. 5187
NEDAP BELGIUM NV—See Nedap N.V.; *Int'l*, pg. 5187
NEDAP BEVEILIGINGSTECHNIEK B.V.—See Nedap N.V.; *Int'l*, pg. 5187
NEDAP CHINA LTD—See Nedap N.V.; *Int'l*, pg. 5187
NEDAP DEUTSCHLAND GMBH—See Nedap N.V.; *Int'l*, pg. 5187
NEDAP FRANCE S.A.—See Nedap N.V.; *Int'l*, pg. 5187
NEDAP FZE—See Nedap N.V.; *Int'l*, pg. 5187
NEDAP GMBH—See Nedap N.V.; *Int'l*, pg. 5187
NEDAP GREAT BRITAIN LTD.—See Nedap N.V.; *Int'l*, pg. 5187
NEDAP IBERIA S.A.—See Nedap N.V.; *Int'l*, pg. 5187
NEDAP INC.—See Nedap N.V.; *Int'l*, pg. 5187
NEDAP N.V.; *Int'l*, pg. 5187

NEDERMAN HOLDING AB

NEDAP POLSKA SP. Z O.O.—See Nedap N.V.; *Int'l*, pg. 5187
NEDASCO B.V.—See Aegon N.V.; *Int'l*, pg. 175
NEDBANK GROUP INSURANCE COMPANY LTD.—See Nedbank Group Limited; *Int'l*, pg. 5187
NEDBANK GROUP LIMITED; *Int'l*, pg. 5187
NEDBANK (LESOTHO) LIMITED—See Nedbank Group Limited; *Int'l*, pg. 5187
NEDBANK LIMITED—See Nedbank Group Limited; *Int'l*, pg. 5187
NEDBANK (MALAWI) LIMITED—See Nedbank Group Limited; *Int'l*, pg. 5187
NEDBANK MOCAMBIQUE S.A.—See Nedbank Group Limited; *Int'l*, pg. 5187
NEDBANK NAMIBIA LIMITED—See Nedbank Group Limited; *Int'l*, pg. 5187
NEDBANK PRIVATE WEALTH LIMITED—See Nedbank Group Limited; *Int'l*, pg. 5187
NEDBANK (SWAZILAND) LIMITED—See Nedbank Group Limited; *Int'l*, pg. 5187
NED BARD & SON CO.; *U.S. Private*, pg. 2879
NEDCO ELECTRICAL SUPPLY, INC.; *U.S. Private*, pg. 2879
NEDCO ELECTRONICS INCORPORATED; *U.S. Private*, pg. 2879
NEDCOFFEE BV—See Amtrada Holding B.V.; *Int'l*, pg. 442
NEDCON BOHEMIA S.R.O.—See voestalpine AG; *Int'l*, pg. 8294
NEDCON B.V.—See voestalpine AG; *Int'l*, pg. 8289
NEDCON FRANCE SASU—See voestalpine AG; *Int'l*, pg. 8294
NEDCON GROEP N.V.—See voestalpine AG; *Int'l*, pg. 8294
NEDCON LAGERTECHNIK GMBH—See voestalpine AG; *Int'l*, pg. 8294
NEDCON MAGAZIJNINRICHTING B.V.—See voestalpine AG; *Int'l*, pg. 8294
NEDCON USA INC.—See voestalpine AG; *Int'l*, pg. 8294
NEDCOR INVESTMENTS LIMITED—See Nedbank Group Limited; *Int'l*, pg. 5187
NED CORP.; *U.S. Private*, pg. 2879
NEDCOR TRADE SERVICES LIMITED—See Nedbank Group Limited; *Int'l*, pg. 5188
NED DAVIS RESEARCH INC.—See Astorg Partners S.A.S.; *Int'l*, pg. 656
NED DAVIS RESEARCH INC.—See Epiris Managers LLP; *Int'l*, pg. 2461
NEDELCO INC.; *U.S. Private*, pg. 2879
NEDELJNE NOVINE A.D.; *Int'l*, pg. 5188
NEDELKO B.V.—See Nimbus B.V.; *Int'l*, pg. 5296
NEDELKO N.V.-S.A.—See Nimbus B.V.; *Int'l*, pg. 5296
NEDELKO S.R.O.—See Nimbus B.V.; *Int'l*, pg. 5296
NED ENERGY LTD.—See Time Technoplast Limited; *Int'l*, pg. 7751
NEDERBURG WINES (PROPRIETARY) LIMITED—See L'Arche Green N.V.; *Int'l*, pg. 4376
NEDERLANDSE AARDOLIE MAATSCHAPPIJ B.V.—See Shell plc; *Int'l*, pg. 6797
NEDERLANDSE FINANCIERINGS-MAATSCHAPPIJ VOOR ONTWIKKELINGSLANDEN N.V.; *Int'l*, pg. 5188
NEDERLANDSE GLUCOSE INDUSTRIE BV—See Tate & Lyle PLC; *Int'l*, pg. 7474
NEDERLANDSE HARDMETAAL FABRIEKEN B.V.—See Kennametal Inc.; *U.S. Public*, pg. 1222
NEDERLANDSE OBESITAS KLINIEK B.V.—See Medtronic plc; *Int'l*, pg. 4790
NEDERLANDSE OBESITAS KLINIEK WEST B.V.—See Medtronic plc; *Int'l*, pg. 4790
NEDERLANDSE RADIATEUREN FABRIEK BV—See Banco Products (I) Ltd.; *Int'l*, pg. 824
NEDERLANDSE WATERSCHAPSBANK N.V.; *Int'l*, pg. 5188
NEDERMAN A/S—See Nederman Holding AB; *Int'l*, pg. 5189
NEDERMAN CANADA LTD.—See Nederman Holding AB; *Int'l*, pg. 5189
NEDERMAN & CO S.R.L.—See Nederman Holding AB; *Int'l*, pg. 5188
NEDERMAN CR S.R.O.—See Nederman Holding AB; *Int'l*, pg. 5189
NEDERMAN DANMARK A/S—See Nederman Holding AB; *Int'l*, pg. 5189
NEDERMAN DANMARK AS—See Nederman Holding AB; *Int'l*, pg. 5189
NEDERMAN DANMARK—See Nederman Holding AB; *Int'l*, pg. 5189
NEDERMAN DO BRASIL COMERCIO DE PRODUTOS DE EXAUSTAO LTDA.—See Nederman Holding AB; *Int'l*, pg. 5190
NEDERMAN DO BRASIL—See Nederman Holding AB; *Int'l*, pg. 5190
NEDERMAN FILTRATION GMBH—See Nederman Holding AB; *Int'l*, pg. 5189
NEDERMAN GMBH—See Nederman Holding AB; *Int'l*, pg. 5189
NEDERMAN GMBH—See Nederman Holding AB; *Int'l*, pg. 5189
NEDERMAN HOLDING AB; *Int'l*, pg. 5188

NEDERMAN HOLDING AB

CORPORATE AFFILIATIONS

NEDERMAN HOLDING AB; *Int'l,* pg. 5190
NEDERMAN IBERICA S.A.—See Nederman Holding AB; *Int'l,* pg. 5189
NEDERMAN INC.—See Nederman Holding AB; *Int'l,* pg. 5189
NEDERMAN INDIA PRIVATE LIMITED—See Nederman Holding AB; *Int'l,* pg. 5189
NEDERMAN INTERNATIONAL TRADING SHANGHAI CO. LTD—See Nederman Holding AB; *Int'l,* pg. 5188
NEDERMAN LTD.—See Nederman Holding AB; *Int'l,* pg. 5189
NEDERMAN MAGYARORSZAG KFT—See Nederman Holding AB; *Int'l,* pg. 5189
NEDERMAN MAKINE SANAYI VE TICARET LIMITED SIRKETI—See Nederman Holding AB; *Int'l,* pg. 5189
NEDERMAN MAKINE SANAYI VE TICARET LIMITED—See Nederman Holding AB; *Int'l,* pg. 5189
NEDERMAN MIKROPUL GMBH—See Nederman Holding AB; *Int'l,* pg. 5189
NEDERMAN MIKROPUL POLAND SP. Z O.O.—See Nederman Holding AB; *Int'l,* pg. 5189
NEDERMAN MIKROPUL PTY LTD—See Nederman Holding AB; *Int'l,* pg. 5189
NEDERMAN NEDERLAND B.V.—See Nederman Holding AB; *Int'l,* pg. 5189
NEDERMAN NORCLEAN B.V.—See Nederman Holding AB; *Int'l,* pg. 5189
NEDERMAN NORDIC AB—See Nederman Holding AB; *Int'l,* pg. 5189
NEDERMAN N.V.—See Nederman Holding AB; *Int'l,* pg. 5189
NEDERMAN OOO—See Nederman Holding AB; *Int'l,* pg. 5189
NEDERMAN POLSKA SP ZO.O.—See Nederman Holding AB; *Int'l,* pg. 5188
NEDERMAN S.A.S.—See Nederman Holding AB; *Int'l,* pg. 5188
NEDERMAN S. DE R.L. DE C.V.—See Nederman Holding AB; *Int'l,* pg. 5190
NEDERMAN SEA CO., LTD.—See Nederman Holding AB; *Int'l,* pg. 5190
NEDERMAN SVENSKA FORSALJNINGS AB—See Nederman Holding AB; *Int'l,* pg. 5190
NED ESPANA DISTRIBUCION GAS, S.A.U.—See Covalis Capital LP; *Int'l,* pg. 1820
NED ESPANA DISTRIBUCION GAS, S.A.U.—See JPMorgan Chase & Co.; *U.S. Public,* pg. 1209
NED ESPANA DISTRIBUCION GAS, S.A.U.—See Swiss Life Holding; *Int'l,* pg. 7369
NEDGEX GMBH—See Erich Netzsch GmbH & Co. Holding KG; *Int'l,* pg. 2492
NEDGIA, S.A.—See Naturgy Energy Group, S.A.; *Int'l,* pg. 5169
NEDGRAPHICS BVBA—See Constellation Software Inc.; *Int'l,* pg. 1773
NEDGRAPHICS B.V.—See Cadac Group Holding B.V.; *Int'l,* pg. 1247
NEDGRAPHICS, INC.—See Constellation Software Inc.; *Int'l,* pg. 1773
NEDGRAPHICS OF TENNESSEE, INC.—See Constellation Software Inc.; *Int'l,* pg. 1773
NEDGRAPHICS SAS—See Constellation Software Inc.; *Int'l,* pg. 1773
NEDGRAPHICS SRL—See Constellation Software Inc.; *Int'l,* pg. 1773
NEDGROUP COLLECTIVE INVESTMENTS LIMITED—See Nedbank Group Limited; *Int'l,* pg. 5188
NEDGROUP INSURANCE COMPANY LIMITED—See Nedbank Group Limited; *Int'l,* pg. 5188
NEDGROUP LIFE ASSURANCE COMPANY LTD—See Nedbank Group Limited; *Int'l,* pg. 5188
NEDGROUP TRUST LIMITED—See Nedbank Group Limited; *Int'l,* pg. 5188
NEDGROUP WEALTH MANAGEMENT LIMITED—See Nedbank Group Limited; *Int'l,* pg. 5188
NEDIC AGRAR A.D.; *Int'l,* pg. 5189
NEDIN PTY. LTD.—See AFGRI Limited; *Int'l,* pg. 188
NED LIQUIDATING INC.—See Graybar Electric Company, Inc.; *U.S. Private,* pg. 1760
NEDRAILWAYS LTD.—See NV Nederlandse Spoorwegen; *Int'l,* pg. 5497
NE DRILLING SERVICOS DO BRASIL LTDA.—See Noble Corporation plc; *Int'l,* pg. 5396
NEDSENSE ENTERPRISES B.V.—See Value8 N.V.; *Int'l,* pg. 8124
NEDSENSE ENTERPRISES N.V.—See Value8 N.V.; *Int'l,* pg. 8124
NEDSENSE LOFT B.V.—See LOFT Inc.; *U.S. Private,* pg. 2480
NEDSENSE NEDGRAPHICS B.V.—See Constellation Software Inc.; *Int'l,* pg. 1773
NED STEVENS GUTTER CLEANING & GENERAL CONTRACTING, INC.—See AVALT, LLC; *U.S. Private,* pg. 403
NEDTRAIN EMATECH BV—See NV Nederlandse Spoorwegen; *Int'l,* pg. 5497
NEDVIZHIMOST OF THE SOUTH ENERGY ENGINEERING CENTER OPEN JOINT-STOCK COMPANY—See JSC ROSSETI; *Int'l,* pg. 4010

NEDVIZHIMOST OF THE VOLGA REGION ENERGY ENGINEERING CENTER OPEN JOINT-STOCK COMPANY—See JSC ROSSETI; *Int'l,* pg. 4010
NEEB CORPORATION; *U.S. Private,* pg. 2879
NEEDHAM & COMPANY INC.; *U.S. Private,* pg. 2879
NEEDHAM COOPERATIVE BANK INC.; *U.S. Private,* pg. 2880
NEEDHAM ELECTRIC SUPPLY - FITCHBURG—See WESCO International, Inc.; *U.S. Public,* pg. 2352
NEEDHAM ELECTRIC SUPPLY, LLC—See WESCO International, Inc.; *U.S. Public,* pg. 2351
NEEDHAM TIMES—See Gannett Co., Inc.; *U.S. Public,* pg. 902
NEEDLE, INC.—See The Stage Fund, LLC; *U.S. Private,* pg. 4120
NEEDLEMAN DROSSMAN & PARTNERS; *U.S. Private,* pg. 2880
NEEDLERS LIMITED—See RS Group plc; *Int'l,* pg. 6417
NEEDSPACE LIMITED—See Wates Group Limited; *Int'l,* pg. 8358
NEEDSPLUS INC.—See Amana Inc.; *Int'l,* pg. 409
NEEDS WELL, INC.; *Int'l,* pg. 5190
NEE INTERNATIONAL, LLC—See New Era Electronics, Co., Ltd.; *Int'l,* pg. 5223
NEEKO-SUAVE, INC.; *U.S. Private,* pg. 2880
NEELAMALAI AGRO INDUSTRIES LTD.; *Int'l,* pg. 5190
NEELKANTH ROCKMINERALS LIMITED; *Int'l,* pg. 5190
NEELTRAN, INC.—See American Superconductor Corporation; *U.S. Public,* pg. 110
NEELY COBLE COMPANY, INC.—See Velocity Vehicle Group; *U.S. Private,* pg. 4355
NEENAH COLDENHOVE BV—See Mativ Holdings, Inc.; *U.S. Public,* pg. 1396
NEENAH ENTERPRISES, INC.—See Charlotte Pipe & Foundry Company; *U.S. Private,* pg. 857
NEENAH FOUNDRY COMPANY—See Charlotte Pipe & Foundry Company; *U.S. Private,* pg. 857
NEENAH GESSNER GMBH—See Mativ Holdings, Inc.; *U.S. Public,* pg. 1396
NEENAH, INC.—See Mativ Holdings, Inc.; *U.S. Public,* pg. 1396
NEENAH PAPER MICHIGAN, INC.—See Mativ Holdings, Inc.; *U.S. Public,* pg. 1396
NEENAH TECHNICAL MATERIALS, INC.—See Mativ Holdings, Inc.; *U.S. Public,* pg. 1396
NEENAN COMPANY; *U.S. Private,* pg. 2880
NEENAN COMPANY; *U.S. Private,* pg. 2880
NEERAJ PAPER MARKETING LIMITED; *Int'l,* pg. 5190
NEESE, INC.—See 1847 Holdings LLC; *U.S. Public,* pg. 2
NEESSEN CHEVROLET INC.; *U.S. Private,* pg. 2880
NEESVIG'S, INC.—See Investcorp Holdings B.S.C.; *Int'l,* pg. 3776
NEFAB AB; *Int'l,* pg. 5190
NEFAB BIJL B.V.—See Nefab AB; *Int'l,* pg. 5190
NEFAB CHINA MARKETING DEPARTMENT—See Nefab AB; *Int'l,* pg. 5190
NEFAB DANMARK A/S—See Nefab AB; *Int'l,* pg. 5190
NEFAB EMBALAGENS LTDA—See Nefab AB; *Int'l,* pg. 5190
NEFAB INC.—See Nefab AB; *Int'l,* pg. 5190
NEFAB INDIA PRIVATE LTD.—See Nefab AB; *Int'l,* pg. 5190
NEFAB LOGISTICS AB—See Nefab AB; *Int'l,* pg. 5190
NEFAB (MALAYSIA) SDN BHD—See Nefab AB; *Int'l,* pg. 5190
NEFAB MEXICO SA DE CV—See Nefab AB; *Int'l,* pg. 5190
NEFAB PACKAGING BELGIUM N.V.—See Nefab AB; *Int'l,* pg. 5191
NEFAB PACKAGING CZECH REPUBLIC S.R.O.—See Nefab AB; *Int'l,* pg. 5191
NEFAB PACKAGING ENGINEERING (DONGGUAN) CO., LTD.—See Nefab AB; *Int'l,* pg. 5191
NEFAB PACKAGING ENGINEERING (SHENZHEN) CO. LTD.—See Nefab AB; *Int'l,* pg. 5191
NEFAB PACKAGING ENGINEERING (WUXI) CO. LTD—See Nefab AB; *Int'l,* pg. 5191
NEFAB PACKAGING FRANCE S.A.S.—See Nefab AB; *Int'l,* pg. 5191
NEFAB PACKAGING GERMANY GMBH—See Nefab AB; *Int'l,* pg. 5191
NEFAB PACKAGING HUNGARY KFT.—See Nefab AB; *Int'l,* pg. 5191
NEFAB PACKAGING, INC.-COLLIERVILLE—See Nefab AB; *Int'l,* pg. 5191
NEFAB PACKAGING INC.—See Nefab AB; *Int'l,* pg. 5191
NEFAB PACKAGING INC.—See Nefab AB; *Int'l,* pg. 5191
NEFAB PACKAGING NETHERLANDS B.V.—See Nefab AB; *Int'l,* pg. 5191
NEFAB PACKAGING NORWAY A/S—See Nefab AB; *Int'l,* pg. 5191
NEFAB PACKAGING OU—See Nefab AB; *Int'l,* pg. 5191
NEFAB PACKAGING POLAND SP. Z O.O.—See Nefab AB; *Int'l,* pg. 5191
NEFAB PACKAGING ROMANIA S.R.L.—See Nefab AB; *Int'l,* pg. 5191
NEFAB PACKAGING SLOVAKIA S.R.O.—See Nefab AB; *Int'l,* pg. 5191
NEFAB PACKAGING—See Nefab AB; *Int'l,* pg. 5191

NEFAB PACKAGING—See Nefab AB; *Int'l,* pg. 5191
NEFAB PACKAGING SWEDEN AB—See Nefab AB; *Int'l,* pg. 5191
NEFAB PACKAGING UK LIMITED—See Nefab AB; *Int'l,* pg. 5191
NEFAB PLYWOOD PONTEVEDRA, S.L.—See Nefab AB; *Int'l,* pg. 5191
NEFAB RA-PRODUTOS DE EMBALAGEM LDA—See Nefab AB; *Int'l,* pg. 5191
NEFAB S.A.—See Nefab AB; *Int'l,* pg. 5191
NEFAB, S.A.U.—See Nefab AB; *Int'l,* pg. 5191
NEFAB SINGAPORE PTE LTD—See Nefab AB; *Int'l,* pg. 5191
NEFAB SPECIALEMBALLAGE AB—See Nefab AB; *Int'l,* pg. 5191
NEFAB SRL—See Nefab AB; *Int'l,* pg. 5191
NEFAB TEKNIK AB—See Nefab AB; *Int'l,* pg. 5191
NEFAB TURKEY AMBALAJ SAN. VE TIC. LTD. STI—See Nefab AB; *Int'l,* pg. 5190
NEFAB VERPACKUNGSTECHNIK GMBH—See Nefab AB; *Int'l,* pg. 5191
NEFCO CORP.; *U.S. Private,* pg. 2880
NEFF + ASSOCIATES, INC.; *U.S. Private,* pg. 2880
NEFF CO.; *U.S. Private,* pg. 2880
NEFF DIALYSIS, LLC—See DaVita Inc.; *U.S. Public,* pg. 641
NEFF ENGINEERING COMPANY, INC.; *U.S. Private,* pg. 2880
NEFF KITCHENS, INC.; *Int'l,* pg. 5191
NEFF, LLC—See Platinum Equity, LLC; *U.S. Private,* pg. 3205
NEFF MOTIVATION INC.; *U.S. Private,* pg. 2880
NEFF PACKAGING SOLUTIONS INC.; *U.S. Private,* pg. 2880
NEFF-PERKINS COMPANY INC.; *U.S. Private,* pg. 2880
NEFFS BANCORP, INC.; *U.S. Public,* pg. 1504
THE NEFFS NATIONAL BANK—See Neffs Bancorp, Inc.; *U.S. Public,* pg. 1504
NEFF-UK—See Robert Bosch GmbH; *Int'l,* pg. 6358
N.E. FINCH CO.; *U.S. Private,* pg. 2827
NEFINSA S.A.; *Int'l,* pg. 5191
NEF POWER (TAIZHOU) CO., LTD.—See Central Development Holdings Ltd.; *Int'l,* pg. 1406
NEFRODIAL D.O.O.—See Fresenius Medical Care AG; *Int'l,* pg. 2775
NEFTEPROMBANK CJSC; *Int'l,* pg. 5192
NEGAFILE SYSTEMS—See The Graham Group, Inc.; *U.S. Private,* pg. 4037
NEGAMI CHEMICAL INDUSTRIAL CO., LTD. - FUKUI FACTORY—See KOMATSU MATERE Co.,Ltd.; *Int'l,* pg. 4239
NEGAMI CHEMICAL INDUSTRIAL CO., LTD.—See KOMATSU MATERE Co.,Ltd.; *Int'l,* pg. 4239
NEGARA PROPERTIES BUILDERS SDN. BHD.—See Sime Darby Berhad; *Int'l,* pg. 6930
NEGARA PROPERTIES (M) BERHAD—See Sime Darby Berhad; *Int'l,* pg. 6930
NEGELE MESSTECHNIK GMBH—See Danaher Corporation; *U.S. Public,* pg. 628
NEGIBOZU AGRICULTURAL PRODUCERS' COOPERATIVE CORPORATION—See Daiei Kankyo Co., Ltd.; *Int'l,* pg. 1924
NEGIN TABAS COAL COMPANY; *Int'l,* pg. 5192
NEGOCIANTS INTERNATIONAL P/L—See S. Smith & Son Pty. Ltd.; *Int'l,* pg. 6447
NEGOCIANTS USA INC.—See The Winebow Group, LLC; *U.S. Private,* pg. 4137
NEGOCIOS DIGITALES COLOMBIA S.A.S.—See Bancolombia S.A.; *Int'l,* pg. 828
NEGOCIOS Y TELEFONIA NEDETEL SA—See Enel S.p.A.; *Int'l,* pg. 2414
NEGOTIUM INTERNATIONAL TRADE LIMITED; *Int'l,* pg. 5192
NEGRI BOSSI BRASIL LTDA—See Sacmi Imola S.C.A.R.L.; *Int'l,* pg. 6464
NEGRI BOSSI FRANCE S.A.S.—See Sacmi Imola S.C.A.R.L.; *Int'l,* pg. 6464
NEGRI BOSSI S.P.A.—See Sacmi Imola S.C.A.R.L.; *Int'l,* pg. 6464
NEGRI BOSSI USA INC—See Sacmi Imola S.C.A.R.L.; *Int'l,* pg. 6464
NEGRI ELECTRONICS; *U.S. Private,* pg. 2880
NEGRI SEMBILAN OIL PALMS BERHAD; *Int'l,* pg. 5192
NEGROS NAVIGATION CO., INC.—See SM Investments Corporation; *Int'l,* pg. 6998
NEGWER MATERIALS INCORPORATED; *U.S. Private,* pg. 2880
NEHA INTERNATIONAL LIMITED; *Int'l,* pg. 5192
NEHEMIAH CORPORATION OF AMERICA; *U.S. Private,* pg. 2880
NEHEMIAH HOUSING DEVELOPMENT FUND; *U.S. Private,* pg. 2880
NEHER ELECTRIC SUPPLY INC.; *U.S. Private,* pg. 2880
NEHMEN-KODNER; *U.S. Private,* pg. 2880
NEHOC INC.; *U.S. Private,* pg. 2880
NEHTRUH-EBA CONSULTING LTD.—See Tetra Tech, Inc.; *U.S. Public,* pg. 2023
NEIDHARDT GRUNDBAU GMBH—See Per Aarsleff Holding A/S; *Int'l,* pg. 5796

COMPANY NAME INDEX

NEIDIGER TUCKER BRUNER INC.; *U.S. Private*, pg. 2880
NEIGHBORCARE HEALTH; *U.S. Private*, pg. 2881
NEIGHBORCARE OF INDIANA, LLC—See CVS Health Corporation; *U.S. Public*, pg. 616
NEIGHBORCARE OF VIRGINIA, LLC—See CVS Health Corporation; *U.S. Public*, pg. 616
NEIGHBORHOOD ASSISTANCE CORPORATION OF AMERICA; *U.S. Private*, pg. 2881
NEIGHBORHOOD CREDIT UNION; *U.S. Private*, pg. 2881
NEIGHBORHOOD HEALTH CENTER CORPORATION; *U.S. Private*, pg. 2881
NEIGHBORHOOD HEALTH CLINICS; *U.S. Private*, pg. 2881
NEIGHBORHOOD HEALTH PLAN INC.; *U.S. Private*, pg. 2881
NEIGHBORHOOD HEALTH PLAN OF RHODE ISLAND, INC.; *U.S. Private*, pg. 2881
NEIGHBORHOOD HOUSING SERVICES OF CHICAGO INC.; *U.S. Private*, pg. 2881
NEIGHBORHOOD HOUSING SERVICES OF SOUTH FLORIDA; *U.S. Private*, pg. 2881
NEIGHBORHOOD LEGAL SERVICES OF LOS ANGELES COUNTY; *U.S. Private*, pg. 2881
NEIGHBORHOOD LOANS; *U.S. Private*, pg. 2881
NEIGHBORHOOD NATIONAL BANK—See Peoples Bankshares, Inc.; *U.S. Private*, pg. 3141
NEIGHBORHOOD NETWORKS PUBLISHING; *U.S. Private*, pg. 2881
NEIGHBORHOOD RESTAURANTS INC.; *U.S. Private*, pg. 2881
NEIGHBORHOOD VISITING NURSE ASSOCIATION; *U.S. Private*, pg. 2881
NEIGHBORIMPACT; *U.S. Private*, pg. 2881
NEIGHBOR, INC.—See Zealot Networks, Inc.; *U.S. Private*, pg. 4599
NEIGHBOR INSURANCE SERVICES; *U.S. Private*, pg. 2881
NEIGHBORLY CARE NETWORK; *U.S. Private*, pg. 2881
NEIGHBORLY, INC.—See Harvest Partners L.P.; *U.S. Private*, pg. 1876
NEIGHBORS CONSTRUCTION CO. INC.; *U.S. Private*, pg. 2881
NEIGHBORS IN NEED OF SERVICES, INC.; *U.S. Private*, pg. 2881
NEIGHBOR'S INSURANCE ADVISORS, INC.—See Seeman Holtz Property & Casualty, LLC; *U.S. Private*, pg. 3598
NEIGHBOURHOOD CABLE LIMITED—See TVG Capital Partners Limited; *Int'l*, pg. 7988
NEIGHBOURLY PHARMACY INC.—See Persistence Capital Partners LP; *Int'l*, pg. 5818
NEIL ENTERPRISES INC—See Neil International Inc.; *U.S. Private*, pg. 2882
NEIL HUFFMAN NISSAN INC.; *U.S. Private*, pg. 2882
NEIL HUFFMAN VOLKSWAGEN MAZDA SUBURU—See Neil Huffman Nissan Inc.; *U.S. Private*, pg. 2882
NEIL INDUSTRIES LIMITED; *Int'l*, pg. 5192
NEIL INTERNATIONAL INC.; *U.S. Private*, pg. 2882
NEIL KELLY CO. INC.; *U.S. Private*, pg. 2882
NEILL AIRCRAFT COMPANY; *U.S. Private*, pg. 2882
NEILL CORPORATION; *U.S. Private*, pg. 2882
NEILL-LAVIELLE SUPPLY CO.; *U.S. Private*, pg. 2882
NEILL SUPPLY CO., INC—See Core & Main, Inc.; *U.S. Public*, pg. 576
NEIL PRYDE LTD.—See Shriro Pacific Ltd.; *Int'l*, pg. 6866
NEILSON ACTIVE HOLIDAYS LIMITED—See Risk Capital Partners Ltd.; *Int'l*, pg. 6350
NEILSON DAIRY LIMITED—See Saputo Inc.; *Int'l*, pg. 6575
NEIMAN MARCUS GROUP, INC.—See Ares Management Corporation; *U.S. Public*, pg. 190
NEIMAN MARCUS GROUP, INC.—See Canada Pension Plan Investment Board; *Int'l*, pg. 1281
NEIMAN MARCUS GROUP LTD LLC—See Ares Management Corporation; *U.S. Public*, pg. 190
NEIMAN MARCUS GROUP LTD LLC—See Canada Pension Plan Investment Board; *Int'l*, pg. 1281
NEIMAN MARCUS STORES—See Ares Management Corporation; *U.S. Public*, pg. 190
NEIMAN MARCUS STORES—See Canada Pension Plan Investment Board; *Int'l*, pg. 1281
NEIMCKE GMBH & CO. KG—See Stahlgruber Otto Gruber GmbH & Co. KG; *Int'l*, pg. 7164
NEIMENGGU FUFENG BIOTECHNOLOGIES CO., LTD.—See Fufeng Group Limited; *Int'l*, pg. 2805
NEIMETH INTERNATIONAL PHARMACEUTICALS PLC; *Int'l*, pg. 5192
THE NE INC.—See UOMO Media Inc.; *Int'l*, pg. 8086
NEINOR HOMES SA; *Int'l*, pg. 5192
NEISEN BANCSHARES, INC.; *U.S. Private*, pg. 2882
NEISEWANDER ENTERPRISES INC; *U.S. Private*, pg. 2882
NEJ, INC.; *U.S. Private*, pg. 2882
NEKADSATU JAYA SDN BHD—See IJM Corporation Berhad; *Int'l*, pg. 3609
NEK CO., LTD.—See Eagle Industry Co., Ltd.; *Int'l*, pg. 2265
NEKHEESGUI EDLEL JOINT STOCK COMPANY; *Int'l*, pg. 5192
NE KID PARIS—See Enero Group Limited; *Int'l*, pg. 2424
NEK INSURANCE INC.—See Arthur J. Gallagher & Co.; *U.S. Public*, pg. 206
NEKISON ENGINEERING & CONTRACTORS LTD.; *Int'l*, pg. 5192
NEKKAR ASA; *Int'l*, pg. 5192
NEKOOSA COATED PRODUCTS LLC—See Sentinel Capital Partners, L.L.C.; *U.S. Private*, pg. 3609
NEK SERVICES, INC.—See Elliott Management Corporation; *U.S. Private*, pg. 1368
NEK SERVICES, INC.—See Veritas Capital Fund Management, LLC; *U.S. Private*, pg. 4362
NEKSVISION CO., LTD.—See Honda Motor Co., Ltd.; *Int'l*, pg. 3463
NEKTAN PLC; *Int'l*, pg. 5193
NEKTAR THERAPEUTICS (INDIA) PVT. LTD.—See Nektar Therapeutics; *U.S. Public*, pg. 1504
NEKTAR THERAPEUTICS; *U.S. Public*, pg. 1504
NEL AMERICA, INC.—See Nippon Telegraph & Telephone Corporation; *Int'l*, pg. 5352
NEL ASA; *Int'l*, pg. 5193
NELCAST LIMITED; *Int'l*, pg. 5193
NELCAST USA INC—See Nelcast Limited; *Int'l*, pg. 5193
NELCO LIMITED; *Int'l*, pg. 5193
NELCO PRODUCTS, INC.—See AGC Inc.; *Int'l*, pg. 204
NELCO PRODUCTS INC.; *U.S. Private*, pg. 2882
NELCO PRODUCTS PTE. LTD.—See AGC Inc.; *Int'l*, pg. 204
NELES OYJ—See Valmet Oyj; *Int'l*, pg. 8118
NEL FREQUENCY CONTROLS, INC.—See Genstar Capital, LLC; *U.S. Private*, pg. 1673
NEL GROUP, INC.; *U.S. Private*, pg. 2882
NEL HYDROGEN A/S—See Nel ASA; *Int'l*, pg. 5193
NEL HYDROGEN ELECTROLYSER AS—See Nel ASA; *Int'l*, pg. 5193
NELIPAK B.V.—See Kohlberg & Company, LLC; *U.S. Private*, pg. 2338
NELIPAK CORPORATION, INC.—See Kohlberg & Company, LLC; *U.S. Private*, pg. 2338
NELITO SYSTEMS PRIVATE LIMITED—See DTS Corporation; *Int'l*, pg. 2217
NELITO SYTEMS LIMITED—See DTS Corporation; *Int'l*, pg. 2217
NELLCOR PURITAN BENNETT LLC—See Medtronic plc; *Int'l*, pg. 4787
NELLCOR PURITAN BENNETT MEXICO, S.A. DE C.V.—See Medtronic plc; *Int'l*, pg. 4787
NELLIE MAE CORPORATION—See SLM Corporation; *U.S. Public*, pg. 1894
NELLIE MELBA RETIREMENT VILLAGE PTY. LTD.—See Ryman Healthcare Ltd.; *Int'l*, pg. 6439
NELLIS MANAGEMENT CORPORATION; *U.S. Private*, pg. 2882
NELLIX, INC.—See Endologix, Inc.; *U.S. Private*, pg. 1392
NELLSON NUTRACEUTICAL, LLC—See Kohlberg & Company, LLC; *U.S. Private*, pg. 2338
NELLSON-SALT LAKE CITY POWDER DIVISION—See Kohlberg & Company, LLC; *U.S. Private*, pg. 2338
NELLY GROUP AB; *Int'l*, pg. 5193
NELLYMOSER, INC.; *U.S. Private*, pg. 2882
NELNET BUSINESS SOLUTIONS, INC.—See Nelnet, Inc.; *U.S. Public*, pg. 1504
NELNET DIVERSIFIED SOLUTIONS, LLC—See Nelnet, Inc.; *U.S. Public*, pg. 1504
NELNET FINANCE CORP.—See Nelnet, Inc.; *U.S. Public*, pg. 1504
NELNET, INC.; *U.S. Public*, pg. 1504
NELNET TECHNOLOGY SERVICES LLC—See Nelnet, Inc.; *U.S. Public*, pg. 1504
NELNET TRANSACTION SERVICES, LLC—See Nelnet, Inc.; *U.S. Public*, pg. 1504
NELSA S.R.L.—See MOL Magyar Olaj- es Gazipari Nyrt.; *Int'l*, pg. 5021
NELSEN STEEL & WIRE CO.; *U.S. Private*, pg. 2882
NELS GUNDERSON CHEVROLET, INC.; *U.S. Private*, pg. 2882
NELSON ADVERTISING SOLUTIONS; *U.S. Private*, pg. 2883
NELSON AIR DEVICE CORP; *U.S. Private*, pg. 2883
NELSON BOSTOCK GROUP LIMITED—See Accenture plc; *Int'l*, pg. 87
NELSON BROS. OILFIELD SERVICES (1997) LTD.; *Int'l*, pg. 5193
NELSON BROTHERS INC.; *U.S. Private*, pg. 2883
NELSON CAPITAL MANAGEMENT, LLC—See Wells Fargo & Company; *U.S. Public*, pg. 2344
NELSON CHEESE FACTORY INC.; *U.S. Private*, pg. 2883
NELSON DIAGNOSTIC LABORATORY—See BGH Capital Pty Ltd; *Int'l*, pg. 1008
NELSON DIAGNOSTIC LABORATORY—See Ontario Teachers' Pension Plan; *Int'l*, pg. 5586
NELSON DISTRIBUTING INC.; *U.S. Private*, pg. 2883
NELSON EDUCATION LTD.—See Apax Partners LLP; *Int'l*, pg. 503
NELSON EDUCATION LTD.—See Apollo Global Management, Inc.; *U.S. Public*, pg. 168
NELSON EDUCATION LTD.—See KKR & Co. Inc.; *U.S. Public*, pg. 1256
NELSON EDUCATION LTD.—See Searchlight Capital Partners, L.P.; *U.S. Private*, pg. 3587
NELSON ELECTRIC CO.; *U.S. Private*, pg. 2883
NELSON ELECTRIC SUPPLY CO. INC.; *U.S. Private*, pg. 2883
NELSON ENVIRONMENTAL INC.—See Nelson River Construction Inc.; *Int'l*, pg. 5193
NELSON FORD-LINCOLN-MERCURY, INC.; *U.S. Private*, pg. 2883
NELSON FORD MAZDA; *U.S. Private*, pg. 2883
NELSON & GILMORE; *U.S. Private*, pg. 2882
NELSON GLOBAL PRODUCTS, INC. - ARCADIA MANUFACTURING FACILITY—See Wind Point Advisors LLC; *U.S. Private*, pg. 4534
NELSON GLOBAL PRODUCTS, INC. - BLACK RIVER FALLS MANUFACTURING FACILITY—See Wind Point Advisors LLC; *U.S. Private*, pg. 4534
NELSON GLOBAL PRODUCTS, INC. - FORT WAYNE MANUFACTURING FACILITY—See Wind Point Advisors LLC; *U.S. Private*, pg. 4534
NELSON GLOBAL PRODUCTS, INC.—See Wind Point Advisors LLC; *U.S. Private*, pg. 4534
NELSON GLOBAL PRODUCTS, INC. - VIROQUA MANUFACTURING FACILITY—See Wind Point Advisors LLC; *U.S. Private*, pg. 4534
NELSON HALL CHEVROLET, INC.; *U.S. Private*, pg. 2883
NELSON HOMES, INC.; *U.S. Private*, pg. 2883
NELSON HYDRAULICS LIMITED—See Flowtech Fluidpower plc; *Int'l*, pg. 2709
NELSON IRRIGATION CORPORATION; *U.S. Private*, pg. 2883
NELSON-JAMESON INC.; *U.S. Private*, pg. 2884
NELSON LABORATORIES FAIRFIELD, INC.—See Sotera Health Company; *U.S. Public*, pg. 1909
NELSON LABORATORIES, LLC—See Sotera Health Company; *U.S. Public*, pg. 1909
NELSON LABS NV—See Sotera Health Company; *U.S. Public*, pg. 1909
NELSON LEASING INC.; *U.S. Private*, pg. 2883
NELSON LUMBER COMPANY LTD; *Int'l*, pg. 5193
THE NELSON MAIL—See Nine Entertainment Co. Holdings Limited; *Int'l*, pg. 5298
NELSON MILL & AGRI-CENTER; *U.S. Private*, pg. 2883
NELSON-MILLER, INC.; *U.S. Private*, pg. 2884
NELSON MULLINS RILEY & SCARBOROUGH LLP; *U.S. Private*, pg. 2883
NELSON NISSAN; *U.S. Private*, pg. 2883
NELSON PACKAGING SUPPLIES LIMITED—See Bunzl plc; *Int'l*, pg. 1219
NELSON PIPING COMPANY; *U.S. Private*, pg. 2883
NELSON RIVER CONSTRUCTION INC.; *Int'l*, pg. 5193
NELSON & SCHMIDT, INC.; *U.S. Private*, pg. 2883
NELSON'S GREEN BRIER DISTILLERY, LLC—See Constellation Brands, Inc.; *U.S. Public*, pg. 571
NELSONS LABELS (MANCHESTER) LIMITED—See Jourdan plc; *Int'l*, pg. 4003
NELSON & SMALL INC.; *U.S. Private*, pg. 2883
NELSONS OIL & GAS INCORPORATED; *U.S. Private*, pg. 2884
NELSON'S RV'S, INC.—See Camping World Holdings, Inc.; *U.S. Public*, pg. 428
NELSONS SOLICITORS LIMITED—See Blixt Group Limited; *Int'l*, pg. 1064
NELSON STEEL CONSULTING & TECHNOLOGY GROUP—See Samuel, Son & Co., Limited; *Int'l*, pg. 6515
NELSON STEEL—See Samuel, Son & Co., Limited; *Int'l*, pg. 6515
NELSON STUD WELDING, INC.—See Dubai Holding LLC; *Int'l*, pg. 2218
NELSON TREE SERVICE INC.; *U.S. Private*, pg. 2883
NELSON TRUCK EQUIPMENT CO. INC.; *U.S. Private*, pg. 2883
NELSON WESTERBERG ATLAS—See Nelson Westerberg, Inc.; *U.S. Private*, pg. 2884
NELSON WESTERBERG ATLAS—See Nelson Westerberg, Inc.; *U.S. Private*, pg. 2884
NELSON WESTERBERG/ATLAS VAN LINES—See Nelson Westerberg, Inc.; *U.S. Private*, pg. 2884
NELSON WESTERBERG, INC.; *U.S. Private*, pg. 2883
NELSON WESTERBERG INTERNATIONAL INC.—See Nelson Westerberg, Inc.; *U.S. Private*, pg. 2884
NELSON WESTERBERG OF ILLINOIS—See Nelson Westerberg, Inc.; *U.S. Private*, pg. 2884
NELSON WHITE SYSTEMS, INC.; *U.S. Private*, pg. 2884
NELSON-YOUNG LUMBER CO.; *U.S. Private*, pg. 2884
NELVANA LIMITED—See Corus Entertainment Inc.; *Int'l*, pg. 1808
NEMAHA COUNTY COOPERATIVE ASSOCIATION; *U.S. Private*, pg. 2884
NEMAK ARGENTINA, S.R.L.—See ALFA, S.A.B. de C.V.; *Int'l*, pg. 313
NEMAK CZECH REPUBLIC, S.R.O.—See ALFA, S.A.B. de C.V.; *Int'l*, pg. 313
NEMAK DILLINGEN GMBH—See ALFA, S.A.B. de C.V.; *Int'l*, pg. 313

NEMAK EUROPE GMBH—See ALFA, S.A.B. de C.V.; *Int'l*, pg. 313
NEMAK GYOR KFT—See ALFA, S.A.B. de C.V.; *Int'l*, pg. 313
NEMAK LINZ GMBH—See ALFA, S.A.B. de C.V.; *Int'l*, pg. 313
NEMAK POLAND SP. Z.O.O.—See ALFA, S.A.B. de C.V.; *Int'l*, pg. 313
NEMAK, S.A. DE C.V.—See ALFA, S.A.B. de C.V.; *Int'l*, pg. 313
NEMAK, S.A.—See ALFA, S.A.B. de C.V.; *Int'l*, pg. 313
NEMAK SLOVAKIA, S.R.O.—See ALFA, S.A.B. de C.V.; *Int'l*, pg. 313
NEMAK WERNIGERODE GMBH—See ALFA, S.A.B. de C.V.; *Int'l*, pg. 313
NEMAK WISCONSIN-TAYLOR FACILITY—See ALFA, S.A.B. de C.V.; *Int'l*, pg. 313
NEMA PROPERTIES, LLC—See AMEN Properties, Inc.; *U.S. Public*, pg. 94
NEMARIS, INC.—See Globus Medical, Inc.; *U.S. Public*, pg. 947
NEMASKA LITHIUM INC.; *Int'l*, pg. 5193
NEM ASSET MANAGEMENT LTD.—See NEM Insurance Plc; *Int'l*, pg. 5193
NEMATIQ PTY. LTD.—See Clean TeQ Water Limited; *Int'l*, pg. 1654
NEMATRON CORPORATION—See Comark, LLC; *U.S. Private*, pg. 980
NEMAURA MEDICAL INC.; *U.S. Public*, pg. 1505
NEMCO BROKERAGE, INC.—See Aon plc; *Int'l*, pg. 497
NEMCO, INC.; *U.S. Private*, pg. 2884
NEMCO METALS INTERNATIONAL LTD.—See Wieland-Werke AG; *Int'l*, pg. 8403
NE MEDIA GROUP, INC.; *U.S. Private*, pg. 2876
NEMEF B.V.—See ASSA ABLOY AB; *Int'l*, pg. 640
NEMER CHRYSLER PLYMOUTH DODGE; *U.S. Private*, pg. 2884
NEMER FIEGER; *U.S. Private*, pg. 2884
NEMETALI A.D.; *Int'l*, pg. 5193
NEMETALI OGRAZDEN AD; *Int'l*, pg. 5193
NEMET MOTORS; *U.S. Private*, pg. 2884
NEMETSCHEK BAUSOFTWARE GMBH—See Nemetschek SE; *Int'l*, pg. 5195
NEMETSCHEK CREM SOLUTIONS GMBH & CO. KG—See Nemetschek SE; *Int'l*, pg. 5195
NEMETSCHEK CREM VERWALTUNGS GMBH—See Nemetschek SE; *Int'l*, pg. 5195
NEMETSCHEK DEUTSCHLAND GMBH—See Nemetschek SE; *Int'l*, pg. 5195
NEMETSCHEK ENGINEERING GMBH—See Nemetschek SE; *Int'l*, pg. 5195
NEMETSCHEK ESPANA S.A—See Nemetschek SE; *Int'l*, pg. 5194
NEMETSCHEK FIDES & PARTNER AG—See Nemetschek SE; *Int'l*, pg. 5195
NEMETSCHEK FRANCE SARL—See Nemetschek SE; *Int'l*, pg. 5195
NEMETSCHEK SCIA B.V.—See Nemetschek SE; *Int'l*, pg. 5195
NEMETSCHEK SE; *Int'l*, pg. 5193
NEMETSCHEK SLOVENSKO S.R.O—See Nemetschek SE; *Int'l*, pg. 5194
NEMETSCHEK S.R.O—See Nemetschek SE; *Int'l*, pg. 5195
NEMETSCHEK VECTORWORKS INC—See Nemetschek SE; *Int'l*, pg. 5194
NEM HEALTH LIMITED—See NEM Insurance Plc; *Int'l*, pg. 5193
NEMIC LAMBDA LTD.—See TDK Corporation; *Int'l*, pg. 7489
NEMICON CORPORATION—See Broadcom Inc.; *U.S. Public*, pg. 390
NEM INSURANCE IRELAND LIMITED—See Allianz SE; *Int'l*, pg. 354
NEM INSURANCE PLC; *Int'l*, pg. 5193
NEMIROFF HOLDING; *Int'l*, pg. 5195
NEMITH MOTOR CORP.; *U.S. Private*, pg. 2884
NEMO (AKS) LIMITED—See Xerox Holdings Corporation; *U.S. Public*, pg. 2388
NEMOCNICE SV. ZDISLAVY, A.S.—See Fresenius SE & Co. KGaA; *Int'l*, pg. 2780
NEMOCNICE TANVALD, S.R.O.—See Fresenius SE & Co. KGaA; *Int'l*, pg. 2781
NEMOCOMMERCE CO., LTD.—See Korea Information Engineering Services Co., Ltd.; *Int'l*, pg. 4285
NEMO MOTORS CORP.; *U.S. Private*, pg. 2884
NEMONT TELEPHONE CO-OPERATIVE; *U.S. Private*, pg. 2884
NEMO; *U.S. Private*, pg. 2884
NEMO S.R.L.; *Int'l*, pg. 5195
NEMOS S.R.L.—See Tas Tecnologia Avanzata Dei Sistemi Spa; *Int'l*, pg. 7464
NEMO TILE CO., LLC—See Saw Mill Capital LLC; *U.S. Private*, pg. 3557
THE NEMOURS FOUNDATION; *U.S. Private*, pg. 4082
NEMPARTNERS—See Groupe BPCE; *Int'l*, pg. 3096
NEMSCHOFF CHAIRS, INC.—See MillerKnoll, Inc.; *U.S. Public*, pg. 1447

NEMSCHOFF, INC.—See MillerKnoll, Inc.; *U.S. Public*, pg. 1447
NEM (WEST INDIES) INSURANCE LTD—See Guardian Holdings Limited; *Int'l*, pg. 3171
NEMZETI TANKONYVKIADO ZRT—See DPG Media Group NV; *Int'l*, pg. 2188
NE NEUNGYULE, INC.; *Int'l*, pg. 5182
NENE WHITEWATER CENTRE LTD.—See AssetCo plc; *Int'l*, pg. 643
NENPLAS LIMITED—See Surteco Group SE; *Int'l*, pg. 7345
NENTEC GMBH—See PSI Software SE; *Int'l*, pg. 6017
NEO ADVERTISING GMBH—See Stroer SE & Co. KGaA; *Int'l*, pg. 7242
NEO ALA CO. LTD.—See NMC Health PLC; *Int'l*, pg. 5392
NEOASISTENCIA MANOTERAS S.L.—See Allianz SE; *Int'l*, pg. 354
NEOAXIS CO., LTD.—See TIS Inc.; *Int'l*, pg. 7757
NEOCARE B.V.—See Bain Capital, LP; *U.S. Private*, pg. 443
NEOCARE B.V.—See Cinven Limited; *Int'l*, pg. 1613
NEO CARE L.L.C.—See NMC Health PLC; *Int'l*, pg. 5392
NEOCARTA VENTURES, INC. - BOSTON—See Neocarta Ventures, Inc.; *U.S. Private*, pg. 2884
NEOCARTA VENTURES, INC.; *U.S. Private*, pg. 2884
NEOCHEM PHARMACEUTICAL LABORATORIES LIMITED—See Jacobson Pharma Corporation Limited; *Int'l*, pg. 3866
NEOCHIM AD; *Int'l*, pg. 5196
NEOCITY GROUP; *Int'l*, pg. 5196
NEOCLES CORPORATE S.A.S.—See Orange S.A.; *Int'l*, pg. 5609
NEOCLYDE SAS—See I Squared Capital Advisors (US) LLC; *U.S. Private*, pg. 2025
NEOCOM MULTIMEDIA SA; *Int'l*, pg. 5196
NEOCOM SOLUTIONS, INC.—See Dycom Industries, Inc.; *U.S. Public*, pg. 698
NEO-CONCEPT INTERNATIONAL GROUP HOLDINGS LIMITED; *Int'l*, pg. 5196
NEOCONIX, INC.—See Unimicron Technology Corporation; *Int'l*, pg. 8050
NEOCON—See Exco Technologies Limited; *Int'l*, pg. 2580
NEOCORE TECHNOLOGY CO., LTD; *Int'l*, pg. 5196
NEO CORPORATION—See NRG Energy, Inc.; *U.S. Public*, pg. 1550
NEO CREMAR CO., LTD.; *Int'l*, pg. 5195
NEO CYON INC.—See Gravity Co., Ltd.; *Int'l*, pg. 3062
NEODECORTECH S.P.A.; *Int'l*, pg. 5196
NEOENERGIA S.A.—See Iberdrola, S.A.; *Int'l*, pg. 3573
NEO ENERGY METALS PLC; *Int'l*, pg. 5195
NEOEN SA; *Int'l*, pg. 5196
NEOFACTURE FURNITURE GMBH—See Prevent DEV GmbH; *Int'l*, pg. 5967
NEOFECT CO., LTD.; *Int'l*, pg. 5197
NEOFILM AS—See Egmont Fonden; *Int'l*, pg. 2326
NEO FINANCE AB; *Int'l*, pg. 5195
THE NEO FIRST LIFE INSURANCE COMPANY, LIMITED—See Dai-ichi Life Holdings, Inc.; *Int'l*, pg. 1918
NEOFORCE GROUP INC.—See Soleno Therapeutics, Inc.; *U.S. Public*, pg. 1900
NEOGAMA BBH—See Publicis Groupe S.A.; *Int'l*, pg. 6104
NEOGAMES S.A.; *Int'l*, pg. 5197
NEOGARD AG—See Outside Living Industries France SARL; *Int'l*, pg. 5669
NEOGARD CONSTRUCTION COATINGS—See Hempel A/S; *Int'l*, pg. 3341
NEOGEM INDIA LIMITED; *Int'l*, pg. 5197
NEOGEN ARGENTINA S.A.—See Neogen Corporation; *U.S. Public*, pg. 1505
NEOGEN AUSTRALASIA PTY LIMITED—See Neogen Corporation; *U.S. Public*, pg. 1505
NEOGEN BIO-SCIENTIFIC TECHNOLOGY (SHANGHAI) CO., LTD.—See Neogen Corporation; *U.S. Public*, pg. 1505
NEOGEN CANADA—See Neogen Corporation; *U.S. Public*, pg. 1505
NEOGEN CHEMICALS LTD.; *Int'l*, pg. 5197
NEOGEN CHILE SPA—See Neogen Corporation; *U.S. Public*, pg. 1505
NEOGEN CORPORATION; *U.S. Public*, pg. 1505
NEOGEN DO BRASIL PRODUTOS PARA LABRATORIOS LTDA.—See Neogen Corporation; *U.S. Public*, pg. 1505
NEOGEN EUROPE LIMITED—See Neogen Corporation; *U.S. Public*, pg. 1505
NEOGEN FOOD & ANIMAL SECURITY (INDIA) PVT. LTD.—See Neogen Corporation; *U.S. Public*, pg. 1505
NEOGEN GUATEMALA S.A.—See Neogen Corporation; *U.S. Public*, pg. 1505
NEOGENIX LABORATOIRE SDN. BHD.—See Hong Seng Consolidated Berhad; *Int'l*, pg. 3469
NEOGEN LATINOAMERICA S.A.P.I. DE C.V.—See Neogen Corporation; *U.S. Public*, pg. 1505
NEOGENOMICS, INC.; *U.S. Public*, pg. 1505
NEOGEN URUGUAY—See Neogen Corporation; *U.S. Public*, pg. 1505
NEOGLORY PROSPERITY INC.; *Int'l*, pg. 5197
NEOGOV; *U.S. Private*, pg. 2884

NEOGRID INFORMATICA LTDA.—See M. Abuhab Participacoes S.A.; *Int'l*, pg. 4615
NEO GROUP LIMITED; *Int'l*, pg. 5195
NEO HUNGARY KFT.—See The Heico Companies, L.L.C.; *U.S. Private*, pg. 4050
NEOIMMUNETECH, INC.; *Int'l*, pg. 5197
NEO INDUSTRIES, INC.—See The Heico Companies, L.L.C.; *U.S. Private*, pg. 4050
NEO INFRACON LTD.; *Int'l*, pg. 5196
NEOJAPAN INC.; *Int'l*, pg. 5197
NEOLANE, INC.—See Adobe Inc.; *U.S. Public*, pg. 43
NEOLANE NORDIC—See Adobe Inc.; *U.S. Public*, pg. 43
NEOLANE S.A.—See Adobe Inc.; *U.S. Public*, pg. 42
NEOLARA CORP.; *Int'l*, pg. 5197
NEOL BIOSOLUTIONS SA—See Neuron Biopharma SA; *Int'l*, pg. 5219
NEOLEUKIN THERAPEUTICS, INC.; *U.S. Public*, pg. 1506
NEOLIFE SA; *Int'l*, pg. 5197
NEOLINE CREDIT CO., LTD.—See J Trust Co., Ltd.; *Int'l*, pg. 3852
NEO LITHIUM CORP.—See Zijin Mining Group Company Limited; *Int'l*, pg. 8683
NEOLOGY, INC.—See Avery Dennison Corporation; *U.S. Public*, pg. 245
NEOMAGIC CORPORATION; *U.S. Public*, pg. 1506
NEOMAGIC ISRAEL LTD.—See NeoMagic Corporation; *U.S. Public*, pg. 1506
NEOMAGIC SEMICONDUCTOR INDIA PRIVATE LIMITED—See NeoMagic Corporation; *U.S. Public*, pg. 1506
NEO MARKETING CO., LTD.; *Int'l*, pg. 5196
NEOMAT AG—See ThyssenKrupp AG; *Int'l*, pg. 7725
NEOMAX ENGINEERING CO., LTD.—See Hitachi, Ltd.; *Int'l*, pg. 3423
NEOMAX KINKI CO., LTD.—See Hitachi, Ltd.; *Int'l*, pg. 3423
NEOMAX KYUSHUU CO., LTD.—See Hitachi, Ltd.; *Int'l*, pg. 3423
NEOMEDIA EUROPE AG—See NeoMedia Technologies, Inc.; *U.S. Public*, pg. 1506
NEOMEDIA TECHNOLOGIES, INC.; *U.S. Public*, pg. 1506
NEOMEDIC S.A.—See Medicover AB; *Int'l*, pg. 4776
NEOMEDICS, INC.—See Orthofix Medical Inc.; *U.S. Public*, pg. 1619
NEOMED, INC.—See Avanos Medical, Inc.; *U.S. Public*, pg. 241
NEOMEND, INC.—See Becton, Dickinson & Company; *U.S. Public*, pg. 291
NEOMETALS LTD; *Int'l*, pg. 5197
NEOM MARITIME (SINGAPORE) PTE. LTD.—See Meiji Shipping Co., Ltd.; *Int'l*, pg. 4802
NEO MONITORS AS—See Nederman Holding AB; *Int'l*, pg. 5189
NEOM SAS—See VINCI S.A.; *Int'l*, pg. 8235
NEON BLOOM, INC.; *U.S. Public*, pg. 1506
NEON CAPITAL LIMITED—See American Financial Group, Inc.; *U.S. Public*, pg. 103
NEO-NEON HOLDINGS LIMITED—See Tsinghua Tongfang Co., Ltd.; *Int'l*, pg. 7951
NEON EQUITY AG; *Int'l*, pg. 5197
NEONET AB—See Hay Tor Capital LLP; *Int'l*, pg. 3289
NEONLIGHT KFT—See APG/SGA SA; *Int'l*, pg. 513
NEONODE AMERICAS INC.—See Neonode, Inc.; *Int'l*, pg. 5197
NEONODE, INC.—See Neonode, Inc.; *Int'l*, pg. 5197
NEONODE, INC.; *Int'l*, pg. 5197
NEONODE JAPAN INC.—See Neonode, Inc.; *Int'l*, pg. 5197
NEONODE KOREA LTD.—See Neonode, Inc.; *Int'l*, pg. 5197
NEONODE TAIWAN LTD.—See Neonode, Inc.; *Int'l*, pg. 5197
NEONODE TECHNOLOGIES AB—See Neonode, Inc.; *Int'l*, pg. 5197
NEON ONE LLC; *U.S. Private*, pg. 2885
NEONOVA NETWORK SERVICES INC.—See National Rural Telecommunications Cooperative; *U.S. Private*, pg. 2862
NEON PLAY LTD.—See Vivendi SE; *Int'l*, pg. 8278
NEONTECH CO., LTD.; *Int'l*, pg. 5197
NEON TECHNOLOGY INC.—See Neonode, Inc.; *Int'l*, pg. 5197
NEONWORX COMMUNICATIONS (THAILAND) CO., LTD.—See Communication and System Solution Public Company Limited; *Int'l*, pg. 1720
NEO@OGILVY—See WPP plc; *Int'l*, pg. 8484
NEO@OGILVY—See WPP plc; *Int'l*, pg. 8484
NEO OIL PTY LTD—See Havilah Resources Limited; *Int'l*, pg. 3287
NEOOTO CO.,LTD.; *Int'l*, pg. 5197
NEOPAL LLC; *U.S. Private*, pg. 2885
NEOPAN 22 BAHMAN COMPANY; *Int'l*, pg. 5197
NEO PERFORMANCE MATERIALS INC.—See Brookfield Corporation; *Int'l*, pg. 1181
NEOPHARMA LLC—See NMC Health PLC; *Int'l*, pg. 5392
NEOPHARM CO., LTD.; *Int'l*, pg. 5198
NEOPHARM LABS INC.; *Int'l*, pg. 5198

COMPANY NAME INDEX

NEOPHOTONICS (CHINA) CO., LTD.—See Lumentum Holdings Inc.; *U.S. Public*, pg. 1348
NEOPHOTONICS CORPORATION—See Lumentum Holdings Inc.; *U.S. Public*, pg. 1348
NEOPLAN BUS GMBH—See Porsche Automobil Holding SE; *Int'l*, pg. 5930
NEOPLANTA A.D.; *Int'l*, pg. 5198
NEOPLE INC.—See Nexon Co., Ltd.; *Int'l*, pg. 5245
NEO PLUS ASIA CO., LTD.—See Sodick Co., Ltd.; *Int'l*, pg. 7048
NEOPLUX CO., LTD.—See Shinhan Financial Group Co., Ltd.; *Int'l*, pg. 6843
NEOPOST AG—See Quadient SA; *Int'l*, pg. 6148
NEOPOST AUSTRALIA PTY LTD—See Quadient SA; *Int'l*, pg. 6148
NEOPOST BVBA—See Quadient SA; *Int'l*, pg. 6148
NEOPOST BV—See Quadient SA; *Int'l*, pg. 6148
NEOPOST CANADA LIMITED—See Quadient SA; *Int'l*, pg. 6148
NEOPOST DANMARK A/S—See Quadient SA; *Int'l*, pg. 6148
NEOPOST FINLAND OY—See Quadient SA; *Int'l*, pg. 6148
NEOPOST GMBH & CO—See Quadient SA; *Int'l*, pg. 6148
NEOPOST GMBH & CO—See Quadient SA; *Int'l*, pg. 6148
NEOPOST INC.—See Quadient SA; *Int'l*, pg. 6148
NEOPOST INDUSTRIE AG—See Quadient SA; *Int'l*, pg. 6148
NEOPOST IRELAND LTD.—See Quadient SA; *Int'l*, pg. 6148
NEOPOST ITALIA S.R.L.—See Quadient SA; *Int'l*, pg. 6148
NEOPOST JAPAN INC.—See Quadient SA; *Int'l*, pg. 6148
NEOPOST LIMITED—See Quadient SA; *Int'l*, pg. 6148
NEOPOST LUXEMBOURG—See Quadient SA; *Int'l*, pg. 6149
NEOPOST NORGE AS—See Quadient SA; *Int'l*, pg. 6149
NEOPOST SVERIGE AB—See Quadient SA; *Int'l*, pg. 6149
NEOPREX LIMITED—See Hayleys PLC; *Int'l*, pg. 3291
NEOPROJEKT A.D.; *Int'l*, pg. 5198
NEO PROPERTY SERVICES ZRT.—See AKKO Invest Nyrt.; *Int'l*, pg. 263
NEOPT CORPORATION—See NOK Corporation; *Int'l*, pg. 5402
NEOPTIX CANADA LP—See Fortive Corporation; *U.S. Public*, pg. 871
NEOPUR GMBH—See Uzin Utz AG; *Int'l*, pg. 8103
NEORION HOLDINGS S.A.; *Int'l*, pg. 5198
NEORIS N.V.—See CEMEX, S.A.B. de C.V.; *Int'l*, pg. 1400
NEOS CORPORATION; *Int'l*, pg. 5198
NEOSEM INC.—See Neosem Inc.; *Int'l*, pg. 5198
NEOSEM INC.; *Int'l*, pg. 5198
NEOSEM TECHNOLOGY, INC.—See Neosem Inc.; *Int'l*, pg. 5198
NEOSFER GMBH—See Commerzbank AG; *Int'l*, pg. 1719
NEOS GORDONPLY—See Richelieu Hardware Ltd.; *Int'l*, pg. 6331
NEOSID AUSTRALIA PTY. LIMITED—See TT Electronics plc; *Int'l*, pg. 7959
NEOS LLC—See Clayton, Dubilier & Rice, LLC; *U.S. Private*, pg. 927
NEO SLOVAKIA, S.R.O.—See The Heico Companies, L.L.C.; *U.S. Private*, pg. 4050
NEOSPEECH, INC.—See Hoya Corporation; *Int'l*, pg. 3497
NEOSPERIENCE SPA; *Int'l*, pg. 5198
NEOSPINE PUYALLUP SPINE CENTER, LLC—See Bain Capital, LP; *U.S. Private*, pg. 445
NEOS PRODUCTS—See Richelieu Hardware Ltd.; *Int'l*, pg. 6331
NEOS RESOURCES PLC; *Int'l*, pg. 5198
NEOSS AB—See Neoss Limited; *Int'l*, pg. 5198
NEOSS AUSTRALIA PTY. LTD—See Neoss Limited; *Int'l*, pg. 5198
NEOSS GMBH—See Neoss Limited; *Int'l*, pg. 5198
NEOSS INC.—See Neoss Limited; *Int'l*, pg. 5198
NEOSS ITALIA S.R.L.—See Neoss Limited; *Int'l*, pg. 5198
NEOSS LIMITED; *Int'l*, pg. 5198
NEOSTAR AD; *Int'l*, pg. 5198
NEOS THERAPEUTICS, INC.—See Aytu BioPharma, Inc.; *U.S. Public*, pg. 257
NEOSTRATA COMPANY INC—See Kenvue Inc.; *U.S. Public*, pg. 1224
NEOSTREET INC.—See Akebono Brake Industry Co., Ltd.; *Int'l*, pg. 262
NEOS VIETNAM INTERNATIONAL CO., LTD.—See Neos Corporation; *Int'l*, pg. 5198
NEOSYSTEMS CORP.; *U.S. Private*, pg. 2885
NEOSYSTEMS INC.—See AppDirect Inc.; *U.S. Private*, pg. 296
NEO TECHNICAL SYSTEM CO., LTD.; *Int'l*, pg. 5196
NEO TECHNOLOGY ACQUISITION CORP.; *U.S. Public*, pg. 1505
NEO TECH PACKAGING (SHANGHAI) CO., LTD—See Crown Holdings, Inc.; *U.S. Public*, pg. 599
NEOTEK CORPORATION INC.; *U.S. Private*, pg. 2885
NEOTEL 2000 S.L.U.—See Gamma Communications PLC; *Int'l*, pg. 2878
NEO TELEMEDIA LIMITED; *Int'l*, pg. 5196
NEOTISS, INC.—See Vallourec SA; *Int'l*, pg. 8118

NEOTRACT, INC.—See Teleflex Incorporated; *U.S. Public*, pg. 1995
NEOTROPE; *U.S. Private*, pg. 2885
NEOTRUST CO., LTD.—See NIPPON KANZAI Holdings Co.,Ltd.; *Int'l*, pg. 5319
NEOVA AB—See Vapo Oy; *Int'l*, pg. 8132
NEOVACS S.A.; *Int'l*, pg. 5198
NEOVA INSURANCE CORPORATION—See International Financial Advisors K.S.C.C.; *Int'l*, pg. 3748
NEOVASC INC.—See Johnson & Johnson; *U.S. Public*, pg. 1200
NEOVASC MEDICAL INC.—See Johnson & Johnson; *U.S. Public*, pg. 1200
NEOVEST, INC.—See JPMorgan Chase & Co.; *U.S. Public*, pg. 1210
NEOVIA LOGISTICS GERMANY GMBH—See Rhone Group, LLC; *U.S. Private*, pg. 3424
NEOVIA LOGISTICS GERMANY GMBH—See The Goldman Sachs Group, Inc.; *U.S. Public*, pg. 2080
NEOVIA LOGISTICS SERVICES INTERNATIONAL NV—See Rhone Group, LLC; *U.S. Private*, pg. 3424
NEOVIA LOGISTICS SERVICES INTERNATIONAL NV—See The Goldman Sachs Group, Inc.; *U.S. Public*, pg. 2080
NEOVIA LOGISTICS SERVICES, LLC—See Rhone Group, LLC; *U.S. Private*, pg. 3424
NEOVIA LOGISTICS SERVICES, LLC—See The Goldman Sachs Group, Inc.; *U.S. Public*, pg. 2080
NEOVIA LOGISTICS SERVICES SPAIN S.A.—See Rhone Group, LLC; *U.S. Private*, pg. 3424
NEOVIA LOGISTICS SERVICES SPAIN S.A.—See The Goldman Sachs Group, Inc.; *U.S. Public*, pg. 2080
NEOVIA LOGISTICS SERVICES (U.K.) LTD.—See Rhone Group, LLC; *U.S. Private*, pg. 3424
NEOVIA LOGISTICS SERVICES (U.K.) LTD.—See The Goldman Sachs Group, Inc.; *U.S. Public*, pg. 2080
NEOVIA SAS—See Archer-Daniels-Midland Company; *U.S. Public*, pg. 185
NEOVOLTA, INC.; *U.S. Public*, pg. 1506
NEOWIZ HOLDINGS CORPORATION; *Int'l*, pg. 5198
NEOWIZ—See NEOWIZ Holdings Corporation; *Int'l*, pg. 5198
NE PACIFIC SHOPPING CENTERS CORP.—See Cosco Capital, Inc.; *Int'l*, pg. 1809
NEPAL BANGLADESH BANK LTD; *Int'l*, pg. 5199
NEPAL BANK LIMITED; *Int'l*, pg. 5199
NEPAL COMMUNITY DEVELOPMENT BANK LIMITED; *Int'l*, pg. 5199
NEPAL CREDIT & COMMERCE BANK LTD.; *Int'l*, pg. 5199
NEPAL DOORSANCHAR CO., LTD.; *Int'l*, pg. 5199
NEPAL FILM DEVELOPMENT COMPANY LIMITED; *Int'l*, pg. 5199
NEPAL FINANCE LIMITED; *Int'l*, pg. 5199
NEPAL HOUSING & MERCHANT FINANCE LTD.—See Citizens Bank International Limited; *Int'l*, pg. 1625
NEPAL HYDRO & ELECTRIC LIMITED—See Butwal Power Company Limited; *Int'l*, pg. 1229
NEPAL INSURANCE COMPANY LIMITED; *Int'l*, pg. 5199
NEPAL INVESTMENT BANK LIMITED—See Nepal Investment Mega Bank Limited; *Int'l*, pg. 5199
NEPAL INVESTMENT MEGA BANK LIMITED; *Int'l*, pg. 5199
NEPAL LIFE INSURANCE COMPANY LIMITED; *Int'l*, pg. 5199
NEPAL RASTRA BANK; *Int'l*, pg. 5199
NEPAL ROPEWAY SYSTEMS (P) LTD—See Doppelmayr Group; *Int'l*, pg. 2175
NEPAL SBI BANK LIMITED; *Int'l*, pg. 5199
NEPAL SEVA LAGHUBITTA BITTIYA SANSTHA LTD.; *Int'l*, pg. 5199
NEPAL SHARE MARKETS & FINANCE LIMITED; *Int'l*, pg. 5199
NEPAL STOCK EXCHANGE LTD.; *Int'l*, pg. 5199
NEPAL WATER & ENERGY DEVELOPMENT COMPANY PRIVATE LIMITED—See Korea Electric Power Corporation; *Int'l*, pg. 4284
NE PARKING LTD.—See Smart Parking Ltd.; *Int'l*, pg. 7000
NEP BROADCASTING, LLC—See The Carlyle Group Inc.; *U.S. Public*, pg. 2049
NEPC INDIA LTD.; *Int'l*, pg. 5199
NEP ELECTRONICS INC.; *U.S. Private*, pg. 2885
NEPES ADVANCED MATERIALS CORPORATION.—See Nepes Corporation Limited; *Int'l*, pg. 5199
NEPES ARK CORPORATION; *Int'l*, pg. 5199
NEPES CORPORATION LIMITED; *Int'l*, pg. 5199
NEPES ENC—See Nepes Corporation Limited; *Int'l*, pg. 5200
NEPES JAPAN—See Nepes Corporation Limited; *Int'l*, pg. 5200
NEPES LED—See Nepes Corporation Limited; *Int'l*, pg. 5200
NEP GROUP, INC.—See The Carlyle Group Inc.; *U.S. Public*, pg. 2049
NEPHILA CAPITAL LTD.—See Markel Group Inc.; *U.S. Public*, pg. 1369
NEPHILA SYNDICATE MANAGEMENT LTD.—See Markel Group Inc.; *U.S. Public*, pg. 1369

NEPHI RUBBER PRODUCTS; *U.S. Private*, pg. 2885
NEPHOS (HEFEI) CO., LTD.—See MediaTek Inc.; *Int'l*, pg. 4773
NEPHOS INC.—See MediaTek Inc.; *Int'l*, pg. 4773
NEPHOS PTE. LTD.—See MediaTek Inc.; *Int'l*, pg. 4774
NEPHOS (TAIWAN) INC.—See MediaTek Inc.; *Int'l*, pg. 4773
NEPHROCARE AHRENSBURG GMBH—See Fresenius Medical Care AG; *Int'l*, pg. 2776
NEPHROCARE BERLIN-WEISSENSEE GMBH—See Fresenius Medical Care AG; *Int'l*, pg. 2776
NEPHROCARE BETZDORF GMBH—See Fresenius Medical Care AG; *Int'l*, pg. 2776
NEPHROCARE BIELEFELD GMBH—See Fresenius Medical Care AG; *Int'l*, pg. 2776
NEPHROCARE BUCHHOLZ GMBH—See Fresenius Medical Care AG; *Int'l*, pg. 2776
NEPHROCARE DAUN GMBH—See Fresenius Medical Care AG; *Int'l*, pg. 2776
NEPHROCARE DEUTSCHLAND GMBH—See Fresenius Medical Care AG; *Int'l*, pg. 2776
NEPHROCARE DOBELN GMBH—See Fresenius Medical Care AG; *Int'l*, pg. 2776
NEPHROCARE DORTMUND GMBH—See Fresenius Medical Care AG; *Int'l*, pg. 2776
NEPHROCARE FRIEDBERG GMBH—See Fresenius Medical Care AG; *Int'l*, pg. 2776
NEPHROCARE GREVENBROICH GMBH—See Fresenius Medical Care AG; *Int'l*, pg. 2776
NEPHROCARE HAGEN GMBH—See Fresenius Medical Care AG; *Int'l*, pg. 2776
NEPHROCARE HAMBURG-ALTONA GMBH—See Fresenius Medical Care AG; *Int'l*, pg. 2776
NEPHROCARE HAMBURG-BARMBEK GMBH—See Fresenius Medical Care AG; *Int'l*, pg. 2776
NEPHROCARE HAMBURG-SUDERELBE GMBH—See Fresenius Medical Care AG; *Int'l*, pg. 2776
NEPHROCARE INGOLSTADT GMBH—See Fresenius Medical Care AG; *Int'l*, pg. 2776
NEPHROCARE KAUFERING GMBH—See Fresenius Medical Care AG; *Int'l*, pg. 2776
NEPHROCARE KREFELD GMBH—See Fresenius Medical Care AG; *Int'l*, pg. 2776
NEPHROCARE LAHR GMBH—See Fresenius Medical Care AG; *Int'l*, pg. 2776
NEPHROCARE LEVERKUSEN GMBH—See Fresenius Medical Care AG; *Int'l*, pg. 2776
NEPHROCARE LUDWIGSHAFEN GMBH—See Fresenius Medical Care AG; *Int'l*, pg. 2776
NEPHROCARE METTMANN GMBH—See Fresenius Medical Care AG; *Int'l*, pg. 2776
NEPHROCARE MUHLHAUSEN GMBH—See Fresenius Medical Care AG; *Int'l*, pg. 2776
NEPHROCARE MUNCHEN-OST GMBH—See Fresenius Medical Care AG; *Int'l*, pg. 2776
NEPHROCARE MUNSTER GMBH—See Fresenius Medical Care AG; *Int'l*, pg. 2776
NEPHROCARE MVZ AALEN GMBH—See Fresenius Medical Care AG; *Int'l*, pg. 2776
NEPHROCARE OBERHAUSEN GMBH—See Fresenius Medical Care AG; *Int'l*, pg. 2776
NEPHROCARE PAPENBURG GMBH—See Fresenius Medical Care AG; *Int'l*, pg. 2776
NEPHROCARE PIRMASENS GMBH—See Fresenius Medical Care AG; *Int'l*, pg. 2776
NEPHROCARE PORTUGAL S.A.—See Fresenius Medical Care AG; *Int'l*, pg. 2776
NEPHROCARE PUTTLINGEN GMBH—See Fresenius Medical Care AG; *Int'l*, pg. 2776
NEPHROCARE RECKLINGHAUSEN GMBH—See Fresenius Medical Care AG; *Int'l*, pg. 2776
NEPHROCARE ROSTOCK GMBH—See Fresenius Medical Care AG; *Int'l*, pg. 2776
NEPHROCARE SALZGITTER GMBH—See Fresenius Medical Care AG; *Int'l*, pg. 2776
NEPHROCARE SCHROBENHAUSEN GMBH—See Fresenius Medical Care AG; *Int'l*, pg. 2776
NEPHROCARE SCHWANDORF-REGENSTAUF GMBH—See Fresenius Medical Care AG; *Int'l*, pg. 2776
NEPHROCARE (THAILAND) CO., LTD.—See Fresenius Medical Care AG; *Int'l*, pg. 2776
NEPHROCARE WETZLAR GMBH—See Fresenius Medical Care AG; *Int'l*, pg. 2776
NEPHROCARE WITTEN GMBH—See Fresenius Medical Care AG; *Int'l*, pg. 2776
NEPHROLOGISCH-INTERNISTISCHE VERSORGUNG INGOLSTADT GMBH—See Fresenius Medical Care AG; *Int'l*, pg. 2776
NEPHROLOGY CENTER OF DETROIT, LLC—See Nautic Partners, LLC; *U.S. Private*, pg. 2870
NEPHROLOGY FOUNDATION OF BROOKLYN; *U.S. Private*, pg. 2885
NEPHROLOGY MEDICAL ASSOCIATES OF GEORGIA, LLC—See DaVita Inc.; *U.S. Public*, pg. 641
NEPHRON PHARMACEUTICALS CORPORATION; *U.S. Private*, pg. 2885
NEPHROS, INC.; *U.S. Public*, pg. 1506

NEPHROS, INC. CORPORATE AFFILIATIONS

NEPI CROATIA MANAGEMENT D.O.O.—See NEPI Rockcastle N.V.; *Int'l*, pg. 5200
NEPI CZECH MANAGEMENT S.R.O.—See NEPI Rockcastle N.V.; *Int'l*, pg. 5200
NEPI INVESTMENT MANAGEMENT SRL—See NEPI Rockcastle N.V.; *Int'l*, pg. 5200
NEPIOM LTD.—See NEPI Rockcastle N.V.; *Int'l*, pg. 5200
NEPI REAL ESTATE DEVELOPMENT D.O.O.—See NEPI Rockcastle N.V.; *Int'l*, pg. 5200
NEPI ROCKCASTLE HUNGARY KFT.—See NEPI Rockcastle N.V.; *Int'l*, pg. 5200
NEPI ROCKCASTLE LITHUANIA UAB—See NEPI Rockcastle N.V.; *Int'l*, pg. 5200
NEPI ROCKCASTLE N.V.; *Int'l*, pg. 5200
NEPI SLOVAKIA MANAGEMENT S.R.O.—See NEPI Rockcastle N.V.; *Int'l*, pg. 5200
NEP LOGISTICS, INC—See Nippon Express Holdings, Inc.; *Int'l*, pg. 5315
NEPLUS CO., LTD.—See Yumeshin Holdings Co., Ltd.; *Int'l*, pg. 8613
NEP NEW ZEALAND HOLDINGS LTD.—See The Carlyle Group Inc.; *U.S. Public*, pg. 2050
NEP NORWAY SAS; *Int'l*, pg. 5198
NEPON INC.; *Int'l*, pg. 5200
NEPRA FOODS INC.; *U.S. Public*, pg. 1506
NEP REALTY & INDUSTRY PUBLIC COMPANY LIMITED; *Int'l*, pg. 5199
NEPRO CREATE CO., LTD.—See NJ Holdings Inc.; *Int'l*, pg. 5390
NEPSIS INC.; *U.S. Private*, pg. 2885
NEPTCO INCORPORATED—See KKR & Co. Inc.; *U.S. Public*, pg. 1243
NEPTUNE-BENSON, INC.—See Xylem Inc.; *U.S. Public*, pg. 2394
NEPTUNE COMPANY; *Int'l*, pg. 5200
NEPTUNE DEVELOPERS LIMITED; *Int'l*, pg. 5200
NEPTUNE DIGITAL ASSETS CORP.; *Int'l*, pg. 5200
NEPTUNE ENERGY GROUP LIMITED—See Eni S.p.A.; *Int'l*, pg. 2438
NEPTUNE ENERGY NORGE AS—See Eni S.p.A.; *Int'l*, pg. 2438
NEPTUNE E&P NORGE—See Eni S.p.A.; *Int'l*, pg. 2438
NEPTUNE EXPORTS LTD.; *Int'l*, pg. 5200
NEPTUNE FOODS—See Red Chamber Co.; *U.S. Private*, pg. 3373
NEPTUNE HOLDING LIMITED—See CCT Fortis Holdings Limited; *Int'l*, pg. 1370
NEPTUNE LNG LLC—See ENGIE SA; *Int'l*, pg. 2428
NEPTUNE MARINE PACIFIC PTE LTD—See MTQ Corporation Limited; *Int'l*, pg. 5071
NEPTUNE MARINE SERVICES INTERNATIONAL PTY LTD—See MTQ Corporation Limited; *Int'l*, pg. 5071
NEPTUNE MARINE SERVICES LIMITED—See MTQ Corporation Limited; *Int'l*, pg. 5071
NEPTUNE MARKETING TECHNOLOGIES; *U.S. Private*, pg. 2885
NEPTUNE MOUNTAINEERING, INC.—See The Ute Mountaineer, Ltd.; *U.S. Private*, pg. 4130
NEPTUNE OFFSHORE SERVICES LTD—See MTQ Corporation Limited; *Int'l*, pg. 5071
NEPTUNE ORIENT LINES LIMITED—See CMA CGM S.A.; *Int'l*, pg. 1668
NEPTUNE PACIFIC AGENCY AUSTRALIA PTY. LIMITED—See The Wonderful Company LLC; *U.S. Private*, pg. 4138
NEPTUNE PETROLEUM (UGANDA) LIMITED—See Tower Resources plc; *Int'l*, pg. 7850
NEPTUNE PLANT HIRE (PTY) LIMITED—See enX Group Limited; *Int'l*, pg. 2456
NEPTUNE RESEARCH, LLC—See Wind Point Advisors LLC; *U.S. Private*, pg. 4534
NEPTUNE SOCIETY INC.; *U.S. Private*, pg. 2885
NEPTUNE TECHNOLOGY GROUP (CANADA) LIMITED—See Roper Technologies, Inc.; *U.S. Public*, pg. 1812
NEPTUNE TECHNOLOGY GROUP INC.—See Roper Technologies, Inc.; *U.S. Public*, pg. 1812
NEPTUNE WELLNESS SOLUTIONS, INC.; *Int'l*, pg. 5200
NEPTUN-OLIMP SA; *Int'l*, pg. 5200
NEPTUN WERFT GMBH & CO. KG—See MEYER WERFT GmbH; *Int'l*, pg. 4870
NEPW LOGISTICS, INC.—See Hyde Park Holdings LLC; *U.S. Private*, pg. 2017
NERA AUSTRALIA PTY LIMITED—See Marsh & McLennan Companies, Inc.; *U.S. Public*, pg. 1387
NERA ECONOMIC CONSULTING—See Marsh & McLennan Companies, Inc.; *U.S. Public*, pg. 1387
NERA INFOCOM (M) SDN BHD—See Ennoconn Corporation; *Int'l*, pg. 2443
NERA (MALAYSIA) SDN. BHD.—See Ennoconn Corporation; *Int'l*, pg. 2443
NERA PHILIPPINES, INC.—See Ennoconn Corporation; *Int'l*, pg. 2443
NERA S.R.L.—See Marsh & McLennan Companies, Inc.; *U.S. Public*, pg. 1387
NERA TELECOMMUNICATIONS (INDIA) PVT LTD—See Ennoconn Corporation; *Int'l*, pg. 2443
NERA TELECOMMUNICATIONS LTD. (INDONESIA)—See Ennoconn Corporation; *Int'l*, pg. 2443

NERA TELECOMMUNICATIONS LTD.—See Ennoconn Corporation; *Int'l*, pg. 2443
NERA TELECOMMUNICATIONS LTD.—See Ennoconn Corporation; *Int'l*, pg. 2443
NERA TELECOMMUNICATIONS (TAIWAN) CO. LTD—See Ennoconn Corporation; *Int'l*, pg. 2443
NERA (THAILAND) LTD—See Ennoconn Corporation; *Int'l*, pg. 2443
NERA UK LIMITED—See Marsh & McLennan Companies, Inc.; *U.S. Public*, pg. 1387
NERBE PLUS GMBH & CO. KG—See Tarsons Products Limited; *Int'l*, pg. 7464
NERCON ENGINEERING & MANUFACTURING INC.; *U.S. Private*, pg. 2885
NER CONSTRUCTION MANAGEMENT, INC.; *U.S. Private*, pg. 2885
NER DATA PRODUCTS, INC.—See NER Holdings Inc.; *U.S. Private*, pg. 2885
THE NERDERY; *U.S. Private*, pg. 4082
NERDS ON CALL; *U.S. Private*, pg. 2885
NERDS ON SITE, INC.; *Int'l*, pg. 5201
NERDWALLET; *U.S. Public*, pg. 1506
NERDY INC.; *U.S. Public*, pg. 1506
NERESON AUTOMOTIVE INC.; *U.S. Private*, pg. 2885
NERETVA A.D.; *Int'l*, pg. 5201
NEREUS OY—See Georg Fischer AG; *Int'l*, pg. 2937
NER HOLDINGS INC.; *U.S. Private*, pg. 2885
NER HOLDINGS INC. - TORONTO FACILITY—See NER Holdings Inc.; *U.S. Private*, pg. 2885
NERIM SASU—See Bouygues S.A.; *Int'l*, pg. 1122
NERI S.P.A.—See Bunzl plc; *Int'l*, pg. 1219
NERO AG; *Int'l*, pg. 5201
NERO DEVELOPMENT & SERVICES GMBH—See Nero AG; *Int'l*, pg. 5201
NERO K.K.—See Nero AG; *Int'l*, pg. 5201
NERSTRANDA AS—See BNP Paribas SA; *Int'l*, pg. 1092
NERTUS MANTENIMIENTO FERROVIARIO Y SERVICIOS S.A.—See Siemens Aktiengesellschaft; *Int'l*, pg. 6887
NERUDE LAGHUBITTA BITTIYA SANSTHA; *Int'l*, pg. 5201
NERUDIA LIMITED—See Imperial Brands PLC; *Int'l*, pg. 3634
NERVACERO, S.A.—See Celsa Group; *Int'l*, pg. 1395
NERVE.COM, INC.—See This Life, Inc.; *U.S. Private*, pg. 4145
NERVE SOLUTIONS GROUP PTY. LTD.—See Shine Justice Ltd.; *Int'l*, pg. 6842
NERVGEN PHARMA CORP.; *Int'l*, pg. 5201
NERVGRID NETHERLANDS—See Droege Group AG; *Int'l*, pg. 2205
NESBITT CONTRACTING CO INC—See Nesbitt Investment Company; *U.S. Private*, pg. 2886
NESBITT INVESTMENT COMPANY; *U.S. Private*, pg. 2885
NESCALIN, S.A. DE C.V.—See Nestle S.A.; *Int'l*, pg. 5203
NESCHEN AG—See Blue Cap AG; *Int'l*, pg. 1067
NESCO AMERICAN HARVEST INC.—See The Metal Ware Corp.; *U.S. Private*, pg. 4078
NESCO, INC.; *U.S. Private*, pg. 2886
NESCO LIMITED - KARAMSAD PLANT—See Nesco Limited; *Int'l*, pg. 5201
NESCO LIMITED; *Int'l*, pg. 5201
NESCO LIMITED - VISHNOLI PLANT—See Nesco Limited; *Int'l*, pg. 5201
NESCO LLC—See Custom Truck One Source, Inc.; *U.S. Public*, pg. 612
NES ECOLOGICAL SERVICES—See Robert E. Lee & Associates, Inc.; *U.S. Private*, pg. 3457
NES FINANCIAL; *U.S. Private*, pg. 2885
NES FIRCROFT LIMITED—See AEA Investors LP; *U.S. Private*, pg. 114
NES GLOBAL TALENT LIMITED—See AEA Investors LP; *U.S. Private*, pg. 115
NESHER ISRAEL CEMENT ENTERPRISES LTD.—See Access Industries, Inc.; *U.S. Private*, pg. 51
NESHER PHARMACEUTICALS (USA) LLC—See Zydus Lifesciences Limited; *Int'l*, pg. 8701
NESHKIN CONSTRUCTION COMPANY INCORPORATED; *U.S. Private*, pg. 2886
NES HOLDINGS, INC.; *U.S. Private*, pg. 2885
NESIC PHILIPPINES INC.—See NEC Corporation; *Int'l*, pg. 5185
NESKA SCHIFFAHRTS- UND SPEDITIONSKONTOR GMBH—See Stadtwerke Koln GmbH; *Int'l*, pg. 7161
NESMA AIRLINES—See NESMA Holding Co. Ltd.; *Int'l*, pg. 5201
NESMA BATTERJEE—See NESMA Holding Co. Ltd.; *Int'l*, pg. 5201
NESMA ELECTRIC—See NESMA Holding Co. Ltd.; *Int'l*, pg. 5201
NESMA EMBROIDERY—See NESMA Holding Co. Ltd.; *Int'l*, pg. 5201
NESMA HOLDING CO. LTD.; *Int'l*, pg. 5201
NESMA MEDICAL SUPPLIES CO.—See NESMA Holding Co. Ltd.; *Int'l*, pg. 5201
NESMA & PARTNERS CONTRACTING LTD.—See Costain Group PLC; *Int'l*, pg. 1815

NESMA & PARTNERS CONTRACTING LTD.—See NESMA Holding Co. Ltd.; *Int'l*, pg. 5201
NES MERCHANDISING INC—See Nintendo Co., Ltd.; *Int'l*, pg. 5308
NES MILJOPARK AS—See AF Gruppen ASA; *Int'l*, pg. 184
NESMITH CHEVROLET BUICK PONTIAC GMC; *U.S. Private*, pg. 2886
NESPAK IMBALLAGGI SPA—See Groupe Guillin SA; *Int'l*, pg. 3104
NES PETROL D.O.O; *Int'l*, pg. 5201
NESPRESSO BELGIQUE S.A.—See Nestle S.A.; *Int'l*, pg. 5203
NESPRESSO HELLAS S.A.—See Nestle S.A.; *Int'l*, pg. 5203
NESPRESSO ISRAEL LTD—See Nestle S.A.; *Int'l*, pg. 5203
NESPRESSO ITALIANA S.P.A.—See Nestle S.A.; *Int'l*, pg. 5203
NESPRESSO NEDERLAND B.V.—See Nestle S.A.; *Int'l*, pg. 5203
NESPRESSO OSTERREICH GMBH & CO. OHG—See Nestle S.A.; *Int'l*, pg. 5207
NESPRESSO UK LTD—See Nestle S.A.; *Int'l*, pg. 5203
NESPRESSO USA INC.—See Nestle S.A.; *Int'l*, pg. 5207
NESS CANADA INC—See KKR & Co. Inc.; *U.S. Public*, pg. 1261
NESSCAP KOREA CO., LTD—See Tesla, Inc.; *U.S. Public*, pg. 2021
NESS CZECH S.R.O. - BRNO—See KKR & Co. Inc.; *U.S. Public*, pg. 1261
NESS CZECH S.R.O. - OSTRAVA—See KKR & Co. Inc.; *U.S. Public*, pg. 1261
NESS CZECH S.R.O.—See KKR & Co. Inc.; *U.S. Public*, pg. 1261
NESS GLOBAL SERVICES LTD.—See KKR & Co. Inc.; *U.S. Public*, pg. 1261
NESS HUNGARY LTD.—See KKR & Co. Inc.; *U.S. Public*, pg. 1261
NESS KDC S.R.O.—See KKR & Co. Inc.; *U.S. Public*, pg. 1261
NESSKIP HF.—See Caiano AS; *Int'l*, pg. 1252
NESS PLUS TRADING SDN. BHD.—See Darco Water Technologies Limited; *Int'l*, pg. 1972
NESSPRO ITALY S.P.A. - MILAN—See Advantech Technologies Ltd.; *Int'l*, pg. 165
NESSPRO ITALY S.P.A. - ROME—See Advantech Technologies Ltd.; *Int'l*, pg. 165
NESSPRO PORTUGAL—See Advantech Technologies Ltd.; *Int'l*, pg. 165
NESSPRO SPAIN S.A.—See Advantech Technologies Ltd.; *Int'l*, pg. 165
NESS ROMANIA—See KKR & Co. Inc.; *U.S. Public*, pg. 1261
NESS S.A.—See KKR & Co. Inc.; *U.S. Public*, pg. 1261
NESS SLOVENSKO A.S.—See KKR & Co. Inc.; *U.S. Public*, pg. 1261
NESS TECHNOLOGIES, INC.—See KKR & Co. Inc.; *U.S. Public*, pg. 1261
NESS TECHNOLOGIES, INC. - TECHNOLOGY INNOVATION CENTER—See KKR & Co. Inc.; *U.S. Public*, pg. 1262
NESS TECHNOLOGIES (INDIA) PVT. LTD. - HYDERABAD—See KKR & Co. Inc.; *U.S. Public*, pg. 1262
NESS TECHNOLOGIES (INDIA) PVT. LTD.—See KKR & Co. Inc.; *U.S. Public*, pg. 1261
NESS TECHNOLOGIES ISRAEL LTD—See Hilan Ltd.; *Int'l*, pg. 3390
NESSTRA COMMERCIAL LTDA—See Nesstra Services (UK) Ltd; *Int'l*, pg. 5201
NESSTRA GHANA LTD—See Nesstra Services (UK) Ltd; *Int'l*, pg. 5201
NESSTRA SERVICES SOUTH AFRICA (PTY) LIMITED—See Nesstra Services (UK) Ltd; *Int'l*, pg. 5201
NESSTRA SERVICES (UK) LTD; *Int'l*, pg. 5201
NESS USA, INC.—See KKR & Co. Inc.; *U.S. Public*, pg. 1262
NESSUS HOTELES PERU SA; *Int'l*, pg. 5201
NESTAWAY—See Aurora Capital Group, LLC; *U.S. Private*, pg. 394
NESTAWAY TECHNOLOGIES PRIVATE LIMITED—See Aurum PropTech Ltd.; *Int'l*, pg. 715
NESTBUILDER.COM CORP.; *U.S. Public*, pg. 1506
NESTE AIR—See Neste Oyj; *Int'l*, pg. 5201
NESTE ASIA PACIFIC PTE. LTD.—See Neste Oyj; *Int'l*, pg. 5201
NESTE CANADA INC.—See Neste Oyj; *Int'l*, pg. 5201
NESTE CRUDE OIL, INC.—See Neste Oyj; *Int'l*, pg. 5202
NESTEC YORK LTD—See Nestle S.A.; *Int'l*, pg. 5203
NESTE EESTI AS—See Neste Oyj; *Int'l*, pg. 5202
NESTE JACOBS OY—See Neste Oyj; *Int'l*, pg. 5202
NESTEK KOREA CO., LTD.—See AEM Holdings Ltd.; *Int'l*, pg. 175
NESTE LPG AB—See Neste Oyj; *Int'l*, pg. 5202
NESTE MARKKINOINTI OY—See Neste Oyj; *Int'l*, pg. 5202
NESTE OIL NETHERLANDS B.V.—See Neste Oyj; *Int'l*, pg. 5202

COMPANY NAME INDEX

NESTE OIL N.V.—See Neste Oyj; *Int'l*, pg. 5202
NESTE OIL SINGAPORE PTE. LTD—See Neste Oyj; *Int'l*, pg. 5202
NESTE OIL (SUISSE) S.A.—See Neste Oyj; *Int'l*, pg. 5202
NESTE OIL US INC—See Neste Oyj; *Int'l*, pg. 5202
NESTE OYJ; *Int'l*, pg. 5201
NESTE PETROLEUM, INC.—See Neste Oyj; *Int'l*, pg. 5202
NESTE PETROLEUM (PRODUCTS), INC.—See Neste Oyj; *Int'l*, pg. 5202
NESTER CONSULTING LLC—See Welsh, Carson, Anderson & Stowe; *U.S. Private*, pg. 4480
NESTE RENEWABLE FUELS OY—See Neste Oyj; *Int'l*, pg. 5202
NESTE (SHANGHAI) TRADING COMPANY LIMITED—See Neste Oyj; *Int'l*, pg. 5202
NESTE ST. PETERSBURG OOO—See Neste Oyj; *Int'l*, pg. 5202
NESTE (SUISSE) S.A.—See Neste Oyj; *Int'l*, pg. 5201
NESTE US, INC.—See Neste Oyj; *Int'l*, pg. 5202
NEST FEATHERINGS INC.; *U.S. Private*, pg. 2886
NEST FRAGRANCES, LLC—See Eurazeo SE; *Int'l*, pg. 2529
NEST INTERNATIONAL; *U.S. Private*, pg. 2886
NEST LABS, INC.—See Alphabet Inc.; *U.S. Public*, pg. 84
NESTLE ADRIATIC B&H D.O.O.—See Nestle S.A.; *Int'l*, pg. 5204
NESTLE ADRIATIC FOODS D.O.O.—See Nestle S.A.; *Int'l*, pg. 5204
NESTLE ADRIATIK MAKEDONIJA D.O.O.E.L.—See Nestle S.A.; *Int'l*, pg. 5204
NESTLE ALGERIE SPA—See Nestle S.A.; *Int'l*, pg. 5204
NESTLE ANGOLA LDA—See Nestle S.A.; *Int'l*, pg. 5204
NESTLE ARGENTINA S.A.—See Nestle S.A.; *Int'l*, pg. 5204
NESTLE ASEAN (MALAYSIA) SDN. BHD.—See Nestle S.A.; *Int'l*, pg. 5204
NESTLE AUSTRALIA LTD.—See Nestle S.A.; *Int'l*, pg. 5204
NESTLE BALTICS, UAB—See Nestle S.A.; *Int'l*, pg. 5204
NESTLE BANGLADESH LTD.—See Nestle S.A.; *Int'l*, pg. 5204
NESTLE BELGILUX S.A.—See Nestle S.A.; *Int'l*, pg. 5209
NESTLE BELGILUX S.A.—See Nestle S.A.; *Int'l*, pg. 5204
NESTLE BOLIVIA S.R.L.—See Nestle S.A.; *Int'l*, pg. 5204
NESTLE BRASIL LTDA.—See Nestle S.A.; *Int'l*, pg. 5204
NESTLE BULGARIA A.D.—See Nestle S.A.; *Int'l*, pg. 5204
NESTLE BUSINESS SERVICES AOA, INC.—See Nestle S.A.; *Int'l*, pg. 5204
NESTLE CAMEROUN—See Nestle S.A.; *Int'l*, pg. 5204
NESTLE CANADA INC. - BRAMPTON—See Nestle S.A.; *Int'l*, pg. 5204
NESTLE CANADA INC. - CALGARY—See Nestle S.A.; *Int'l*, pg. 5204
NESTLE CANADA INC. - DORVAL—See Nestle S.A.; *Int'l*, pg. 5204
NESTLE CANADA INC. - EDMONTON—See Nestle S.A.; *Int'l*, pg. 5204
NESTLE CANADA INC. - LONDON—See Nestle S.A.; *Int'l*, pg. 5204
NESTLE CANADA INC. - MONTREAL—See Nestle S.A.; *Int'l*, pg. 5204
NESTLE CANADA INC.—See Nestle S.A.; *Int'l*, pg. 5204
NESTLE CANADA INC. - TORONTO—See Nestle S.A.; *Int'l*, pg. 5204
NESTLE CANADA INC. - TRENTON—See Nestle S.A.; *Int'l*, pg. 5204
NESTLE CAPITAL CANADA LTD—See Nestle S.A.; *Int'l*, pg. 5204
NESTLE CAPITAL CORPORATION—See Nestle S.A.; *Int'l*, pg. 5204
NESTLE CARIBBEAN, INC.—See Nestle S.A.; *Int'l*, pg. 5204
NESTLE CATERING SERVICES N.V.—See Nestle S.A.; *Int'l*, pg. 5204
NESTLE CESKI S.R.O.—See Nestle S.A.; *Int'l*, pg. 5204
NESTLE CHILE S.A.—See Nestle S.A.; *Int'l*, pg. 5204
NESTLE CHINA LTD—See Nestle S.A.; *Int'l*, pg. 5204
NESTLE CLINICAL NUTRITION S.A.—See Nestle S.A.; *Int'l*, pg. 5205
NESTLE CLINICAL NUTRITION—See Nestle S.A.; *Int'l*, pg. 5208
NESTLE COFFEE SPECIALTIES FRANCE S.A.—See Nestle S.A.; *Int'l*, pg. 5205
NESTLE COLD STORAGE (MALAYSIA) SDN. BHD.—See Nestle S.A.; *Int'l*, pg. 5206
NESTLE CONFECTIONARIES LTD—See Nestle S.A.; *Int'l*, pg. 5206
NESTLE CONFECTIONERY LTD.—See Nestle S.A.; *Int'l*, pg. 5204
NESTLE COTE D'IVOIRE—See Nestle S.A.; *Int'l*, pg. 5204
NESTLE DAIRY FARM QINGDAO LTD.—See Nestle S.A.; *Int'l*, pg. 5204
NESTLE DAIRY FARM TIANJIN LTD.—See Nestle S.A.; *Int'l*, pg. 5204
NESTLE DANMARK A/S—See Nestle S.A.; *Int'l*, pg. 5205
NESTLE DE COLOMBIA S.A.—See Nestle S.A.; *Int'l*, pg. 5210

NESTLE DEL URUGUAY S.A.—See Nestle S.A.; *Int'l*, pg. 5205
NESTLE DEUTSCHLAND AG—See Nestle S.A.; *Int'l*, pg. 5205
NESTLE DOMINICANA, S.A.—See Nestle S.A.; *Int'l*, pg. 5205
NESTLE DONGGUAN LIMITED—See Nestle S.A.; *Int'l*, pg. 5205
NESTLE DREYER'S ICE CREAM COMPANY—See Nestle S.A.; *Int'l*, pg. 5208
NESTLE ECUADOR S.A.—See Nestle S.A.; *Int'l*, pg. 5205
NESTLE EGYPT S.A.E.—See Nestle S.A.; *Int'l*, pg. 5205
NESTLE EL SALVADOR S.A.—See Nestle S.A.; *Int'l*, pg. 5205
NESTLE ENTERPRISES S.A.—See Nestle S.A.; *Int'l*, pg. 5205
NESTLE ESPANA S.A.—See Nestle S.A.; *Int'l*, pg. 5205
NESTLE (FIJI) LTD.—See Nestle S.A.; *Int'l*, pg. 5203
NESTLE FINANCE FRANCE S.A.—See Nestle S.A.; *Int'l*, pg. 5205
NESTLE FINANCE INTERNATIONAL LTD—See Nestle S.A.; *Int'l*, pg. 5205
NESTLE FINANCE S.A.—See Nestle S.A.; *Int'l*, pg. 5205
NESTLE-FINDUS OY—See Nestle S.A.; *Int'l*, pg. 5210
NESTLE FOOD LLC—See Nestle S.A.; *Int'l*, pg. 5205
NESTLE FOODSERVICES CANADA—See Nestle S.A.; *Int'l*, pg. 5204
NESTLE FOODSERVICES—See Nestle S.A.; *Int'l*, pg. 5208
NESTLE FOODS KENYA LTD.—See Nestle S.A.; *Int'l*, pg. 5205
NESTLE FOODS (MALAYSIA) SDN. BHD.—See Nestle S.A.; *Int'l*, pg. 5203
NESTLE FOOD S.R.O.—See Nestle S.A.; *Int'l*, pg. 5205
NESTLE FOODS (THAILAND) LTD.—See Nestle S.A.; *Int'l*, pg. 5204
NESTLE FOREIGN TRADE—See Nestle S.A.; *Int'l*, pg. 5208
NESTLE FRANCE SAS—See Nestle S.A.; *Int'l*, pg. 5205
NESTLE GABON—See Nestle S.A.; *Int'l*, pg. 5205
NESTLE GHANA LTD.—See Nestle S.A.; *Int'l*, pg. 5205
NESTLE GLOBE INC.—See Nestle S.A.; *Int'l*, pg. 5205
NESTLE GUATEMALA S.A.—See Nestle S.A.; *Int'l*, pg. 5205
NESTLE GUINEE—See Nestle S.A.; *Int'l*, pg. 5205
NESTLE HEALTHCARE NUTRITION, INC.—See Nestle S.A.; *Int'l*, pg. 5206
NESTLE HEALTHCARE NUTRITION, S.A.—See Nestle S.A.; *Int'l*, pg. 5206
NESTLE HEALTHCARE NUTRITION—See Nestle S.A.; *Int'l*, pg. 5206
NESTLE HEALTH SCIENCE S.A.—See Nestle S.A.; *Int'l*, pg. 5205
NESTLE HELLAS S.A.—See Nestle S.A.; *Int'l*, pg. 5206
NESTLE HELLAS S.A.—See Nestle S.A.; *Int'l*, pg. 5206
NESTLE HOLDINGS, INC.—See Nestle S.A.; *Int'l*, pg. 5208
NESTLE HOLDINGS (U.K.) PLC—See Nestle S.A.; *Int'l*, pg. 5206
NESTLE HOMECARE S.A.S.—See Nestle S.A.; *Int'l*, pg. 5206
NESTLE HONDURENA S.A.—See Nestle S.A.; *Int'l*, pg. 5206
NESTLE HONG KONG LIMITED—See Nestle S.A.; *Int'l*, pg. 5206
NESTLE HONG KONG LTD.—See Nestle S.A.; *Int'l*, pg. 5206
NESTLE HULUNBEIR LIMITED—See Nestle S.A.; *Int'l*, pg. 5205
NESTLE HUNGARIA KFT.—See Nestle S.A.; *Int'l*, pg. 5206
NESTLE INDIA LTD.—See Nestle S.A.; *Int'l*, pg. 5206
NESTLE INTERNATIONAL TRAVEL RETAIL S.A.—See Nestle S.A.; *Int'l*, pg. 5206
NESTLE IRAN (PRIVATE JOINT STOCK COMPANY)—See Nestle S.A.; *Int'l*, pg. 5206
NESTLE (IRELAND) LTD.—See Nestle S.A.; *Int'l*, pg. 5206
NESTLE ITALIANA S.P.A.—See Nestle S.A.; *Int'l*, pg. 5206
NESTLE JAPAN LTD.—See Nestle S.A.; *Int'l*, pg. 5206
NESTLE-JMP JAMAICA LTD.—See Nestle S.A.; *Int'l*, pg. 5210
NESTLE JORDAN TRADING CO., LTD.—See Nestle S.A.; *Int'l*, pg. 5206
NESTLE KENYA LTD.—See Nestle S.A.; *Int'l*, pg. 5206
NESTLE KOREA LTD.—See Nestle S.A.; *Int'l*, pg. 5206
NESTLE KUBAN LLC—See Nestle S.A.; *Int'l*, pg. 5206
NESTLE KUWAIT GENERAL TRADING CO., W.L.L.—See Nestle S.A.; *Int'l*, pg. 5207
NESTLE LANKA LTD.—See Nestle S.A.; *Int'l*, pg. 5207
NESTLE (LRELAND) LTD.—See Nestle S.A.; *Int'l*, pg. 5204
NESTLE MAGHREB S.A.—See Nestle S.A.; *Int'l*, pg. 5207
NESTLE (MALAYSIA) BHD.—See Nestle S.A.; *Int'l*, pg. 5203
NESTLE MALI S.A.U.—See Nestle S.A.; *Int'l*, pg. 5207
NESTLE MALTA LTD—See Nestle S.A.; *Int'l*, pg. 5207
NESTLE MANUFACTURING (MALAYSIA) SDN. BHD. - SHAH ALAM COMPLEX FACTORY—See Groupe Lactalis SA; *Int'l*, pg. 3106

NEST INTERNATIONAL

NESTLE MANUFACTURING (MALAYSIA) SDN. BHD.—See Groupe Lactalis SA; *Int'l*, pg. 3106
NESTLE MARCAS PERU, S.A.C.—See Nestle S.A.; *Int'l*, pg. 5207
NESTLE MAROC S.A.—See Nestle S.A.; *Int'l*, pg. 5207
NESTLE MEXICO S.A. DE C.V.—See Nestle S.A.; *Int'l*, pg. 5207
NESTLE MIDDLE EAST FZE—See Nestle S.A.; *Int'l*, pg. 5207
NESTLE MILKPAK LTD—See Nestle S.A.; *Int'l*, pg. 5207
NESTLE MOCAMBIQUE LDA—See Nestle S.A.; *Int'l*, pg. 5207
NESTLE NEDERLAND B.V.—See Nestle S.A.; *Int'l*, pg. 5207
NESTLE NESPRESSO BEIJING LIMITED—See Nestle S.A.; *Int'l*, pg. 5207
NESTLE NESPRESSO S.A.—See Nestle S.A.; *Int'l*, pg. 5207
NESTLE NEW ZEALAND LIMITED - MANUKAU FACTORY—See Nestle S.A.; *Int'l*, pg. 5207
NESTLE NEW ZEALAND LTD.—See Nestle S.A.; *Int'l*, pg. 5207
NESTLE NIGERIA PLC—See Nestle S.A.; *Int'l*, pg. 5207
NESTLE NORDESTE ALIMENTOS E BEBIDAS LTDA—See Nestle S.A.; *Int'l*, pg. 5207
NESTLE NOUVELLE-CALEDONIA S.A.S.—See Nestle S.A.; *Int'l*, pg. 5207
NESTLE NUTRITION GMBH—See Nestle S.A.; *Int'l*, pg. 5205
NESTLE NUTRITION—See Nestle S.A.; *Int'l*, pg. 5209
NESTLE OSTERREICH GMBH—See Nestle S.A.; *Int'l*, pg. 5207
NESTLE PAKISTAN LIMITED—See Nestle S.A.; *Int'l*, pg. 5207
NESTLE PANAMA S.A.—See Nestle S.A.; *Int'l*, pg. 5207
NESTLE PARAGUAY S.A.—See Nestle S.A.; *Int'l*, pg. 5207
NESTLE PERU S.A.—See Nestle S.A.; *Int'l*, pg. 5207
NESTLE PHILIPPINES, INC.—See Nestle S.A.; *Int'l*, pg. 5207
NESTLE PIZZA DIVISION-MEDFORD—See Nestle S.A.; *Int'l*, pg. 5209
NESTLE PIZZA DIVISION—See Nestle S.A.; *Int'l*, pg. 5209
NESTLE PIZZA DIVISION-TOMBSTONE PIZZA—See Nestle S.A.; *Int'l*, pg. 5209
NESTLE (PNG) LTD.—See Nestle S.A.; *Int'l*, pg. 5203
NESTLE POLSKA S.A.—See Nestle S.A.; *Int'l*, pg. 5207
NESTLE POLYNESIE S.A.S.—See Nestle S.A.; *Int'l*, pg. 5207
NESTLE PORTUGAL S.A.—See Nestle S.A.; *Int'l*, pg. 5205
NESTLE PREPARED FOODS CO. - HANDHELD FOODS GROUP—See Nestle S.A.; *Int'l*, pg. 5209
NESTLE PREPARED FOODS COMPANY—See Nestle S.A.; *Int'l*, pg. 5209
NESTLE PRODUCTS (MAURITIUS) LTD.—See Nestle S.A.; *Int'l*, pg. 5207
NESTLE PRODUCTS SDN. BHD.—See Nestle S.A.; *Int'l*, pg. 5203
NESTLE PRODUCT TECHNOLOGY CENTRE LEBENSMITTELFORSCHUNG GMBH—See Nestle S.A.; *Int'l*, pg. 5207
NESTLE PROFESSIONAL FOOD A/S—See Nestle S.A.; *Int'l*, pg. 5207
NESTLE PURINA PETCARE CANADA—See Nestle S.A.; *Int'l*, pg. 5209
NESTLE PURINA PETCARE COMPANY—See Nestle S.A.; *Int'l*, pg. 5209
NESTLE PURINA PETCARE CO. - NEBRASKA—See Nestle S.A.; *Int'l*, pg. 5209
NESTLE PURINA PETCARE CO. - OHIO—See Nestle S.A.; *Int'l*, pg. 5209
NESTLE PURINA PETCARE CO. - WISCONSIN—See Nestle S.A.; *Int'l*, pg. 5209
NESTLE PURINA PETCARE DE COLOMBIA S.A.—See Nestle S.A.; *Int'l*, pg. 5207
NESTLE PURINA PETCARE DEUTSCHLAND GMBH—See Nestle S.A.; *Int'l*, pg. 5207
NESTLE PURINA PETCARE ESPANA S.A.—See Nestle S.A.; *Int'l*, pg. 5207
NESTLE PURINA PETCARE FRANCE S.A.S.—See Nestle S.A.; *Int'l*, pg. 5207
NESTLE PURINA PETCARE GLOBAL RESOURCES, INC.—See Nestle S.A.; *Int'l*, pg. 5209
NESTLE PURINA PETCARE HUNGARY KFT.—See Nestle S.A.; *Int'l*, pg. 5207
NESTLE PURINA PETCARE ITALIANA S.P.A.—See Nestle S.A.; *Int'l*, pg. 5207
NESTLE PURINA PETCARE KOREA—See Nestle S.A.; *Int'l*, pg. 5209
NESTLE PURINA PETFOODS—See Nestle S.A.; *Int'l*, pg. 5209
NESTLE PURINA PRODUCT TECHNOLOGY CENTER—See Nestle S.A.; *Int'l*, pg. 5209
NESTLE QINGDAO LTD.—See Nestle S.A.; *Int'l*, pg. 5204
NESTLE R&D CENTER (PTE) LTD—See Nestle S.A.; *Int'l*, pg. 5207
NESTLE R&D CENTER—See Nestle S.A.; *Int'l*, pg. 5209

NEST INTERNATIONAL

NESTLE ROMANIA S.R.L.—See Nestle S.A.; *Int'l*, pg. 5207
NESTLE ROSSIYA LLC—See Nestle S.A.; *Int'l*, pg. 5207
NESTLE S.A.; *Int'l*, pg. 5202
NESTLE SCHOLLER GMBH & CO. KG—See Nestle S.A.; *Int'l*, pg. 5205
NESTLE SCHOLLER PRODUKTIONS GMBH—See Nestle S.A.; *Int'l*, pg. 5207
NESTLE SENEGAL—See Nestle S.A.; *Int'l*, pg. 5207
NESTLE SERVICIOS CORPORATIVOS, S.A. DE C.V.—See Nestle S.A.; *Int'l*, pg. 5208
NESTLE SERVICIOS INDUSTRIALES, S.A. DE C.V.—See Nestle S.A.; *Int'l*, pg. 5208
NESTLE SHANGHAI LIMITED—See Nestle S.A.; *Int'l*, pg. 5208
NESTLE SINGAPORE PTE. LTD.—See Nestle S.A.; *Int'l*, pg. 5208
NESTLE SKIN HEALTH INDIA PRIVATE LTD.—See Nestle S.A.; *Int'l*, pg. 5208
NESTLE SLOVAKIA LTD.—See Nestle S.A.; *Int'l*, pg. 5208
NESTLE (SOUTH AFRICA) (PTY) LTD - ESTCOURT FACTORY—See Nestle S.A.; *Int'l*, pg. 5203
NESTLE (SOUTH AFRICA) (PTY) LTD - MOSSEL BAY FACTORY—See Nestle S.A.; *Int'l*, pg. 5203
NESTLE (SOUTH AFRICA) (PTY) LTD - NDABENI FACTORY—See Nestle S.A.; *Int'l*, pg. 5203
NESTLE (SOUTH AFRICA) (PTY.) LTD.—See Nestle S.A.; *Int'l*, pg. 5203
NESTLES PURINA PETCARE—See Nestle S.A.; *Int'l*, pg. 5209
NESTLE SUISSE S.A.—See Nestle S.A.; *Int'l*, pg. 5208
NESTLE SUL ALIMENTOS E BEBIDAS LTDA—See Nestle S.A.; *Int'l*, pg. 5208
NESTLE SVERIGE AB—See Nestle S.A.; *Int'l*, pg. 5208
NESTLE SYRIA S.A.—See Nestle S.A.; *Int'l*, pg. 5208
NESTLE TAIWAN LIMITED—See Nestle S.A.; *Int'l*, pg. 5208
NESTLE TC ASIA PACIFIC PTE LTD—See Nestle S.A.; *Int'l*, pg. 5208
NESTLE (THAILAND) LTD.—See Nestle S.A.; *Int'l*, pg. 5203
NESTLE TIANJIN LTD.—See Nestle S.A.; *Int'l*, pg. 5204
NESTLE TOGO S.A.U—See Nestle S.A.; *Int'l*, pg. 5208
NESTLE TRADING PRIVATE LIMITED COMPANY—See Nestle S.A.; *Int'l*, pg. 5208
NESTLE TRANSPORTATION CO.—See Nestle S.A.; *Int'l*, pg. 5209
NESTLE TRANSPORTATION CO.—See Nestle S.A.; *Int'l*, pg. 5209
NESTLE TREASURY CENTRE-MIDDLE EAST & AFRICA LTD—See Nestle S.A.; *Int'l*, pg. 5208
NESTLE TRINIDAD AND TOBAGO LTD.—See Nestle S.A.; *Int'l*, pg. 5208
NESTLE TUNISIA S.A.—See Nestle S.A.; *Int'l*, pg. 5208
NESTLE TURKIYE A.S.—See Nestle S.A.; *Int'l*, pg. 5208
NESTLE TURKIYE GIDA SANAYI A.S.—See Nestle S.A.; *Int'l*, pg. 5208
NESTLE UK LTD - DALSTON FACTORY—See Nestle S.A.; *Int'l*, pg. 5206
NESTLE UK LTD - FAWDON FACTORY—See Nestle S.A.; *Int'l*, pg. 5206
NESTLE UK LTD - GIRVAN FACTORY—See Nestle S.A.; *Int'l*, pg. 5206
NESTLE UK LTD - HALIFAX FACTORY—See Nestle S.A.; *Int'l*, pg. 5206
NESTLE UK LTD - HAYES FACTORY—See Nestle S.A.; *Int'l*, pg. 5206
NESTLE UK LTD.—See Nestle S.A.; *Int'l*, pg. 5206
NESTLE UK LTD - YORK FACTORY—See Nestle S.A.; *Int'l*, pg. 5206
NESTLE UNTERNEHMUNGEN DEUTSCHLAND GMBH—See Nestle S.A.; *Int'l*, pg. 5210
NESTLE USA, INC. - BLOOMINGTON—See Nestle S.A.; *Int'l*, pg. 5209
NESTLE USA, INC. - CHARLOTTE—See Nestle S.A.; *Int'l*, pg. 5209
NESTLE USA, INC. - DEKALB—See Nestle S.A.; *Int'l*, pg. 5209
NESTLE USA, INC. - DENVER—See Nestle S.A.; *Int'l*, pg. 5209
NESTLE USA, INC. - DUBLIN—See Nestle S.A.; *Int'l*, pg. 5209
NESTLE USA, INC. - EAU CLAIRE—See Nestle S.A.; *Int'l*, pg. 5209
NESTLE USA, INC. - EDEN PRAIRIE—See Nestle S.A.; *Int'l*, pg. 5209
NESTLE USA, INC. - EDISON—See Nestle S.A.; *Int'l*, pg. 5209
NESTLE USA, INC. - HONOLULU—See Nestle S.A.; *Int'l*, pg. 5209
NESTLE USA, INC. - ITASCA—See Nestle S.A.; *Int'l*, pg. 5209
NESTLE USA, INC. - JACKSONVILLE—See Nestle S.A.; *Int'l*, pg. 5209
NESTLE USA, INC. - MCDONOUGH—See Nestle S.A.; *Int'l*, pg. 5209
NESTLE USA, INC. - MIRA LOMA—See Nestle S.A.; *Int'l*, pg. 5210

CORPORATE AFFILIATIONS

NESTLE USA, INC. - NEW MILFORD—See Nestle S.A.; *Int'l*, pg. 5210
NESTLE USA, INC. - PHOENIX—See Nestle S.A.; *Int'l*, pg. 5210
NESTLE USA, INC. - QUINCY—See Nestle S.A.; *Int'l*, pg. 5210
NESTLE USA, INC. - SAN RAMON—See Nestle S.A.; *Int'l*, pg. 5210
NESTLE USA, INC. - SOLON—See Nestle S.A.; *Int'l*, pg. 5210
NESTLE USA, INC.—See Nestle S.A.; *Int'l*, pg. 5208
NESTLE VENEZUELA S.A.—See Nestle S.A.; *Int'l*, pg. 5210
NESTLE VERSORGUNGSKASSE GMBH—See Nestle S.A.; *Int'l*, pg. 5210
NESTLE VIETNAM LTD.—See Nestle S.A.; *Int'l*, pg. 5210
NESTLE WAGNER GMBH—See Nestle S.A.; *Int'l*, pg. 5210
NESTLE WATER CANADA LTD.—See Metropoulos & Co.; *U.S. Private*, pg. 2690
NESTLE WATER CANADA LTD.—See One Rock Capital Partners, LLC; *U.S. Private*, pg. 3021
NESTLE WATERCOOLERS SERVICE LLC—See Nestle S.A.; *Int'l*, pg. 5210
NESTLE WATERS BENELUX S.A.—See Nestle S.A.; *Int'l*, pg. 5210
NESTLE WATERS BRASIL - BEBIDAS E ALIMENTOS LTDA—See Nestle S.A.; *Int'l*, pg. 5210
NESTLE WATERS CANADA INC.—See Metropoulos & Co.; *U.S. Private*, pg. 2690
NESTLE WATERS CANADA INC.—See One Rock Capital Partners, LLC; *U.S. Private*, pg. 3021
NESTLE WATERS CANADA INC.—See Metropoulos & Co.; *U.S. Private*, pg. 2690
NESTLE WATERS CANADA INC.—See One Rock Capital Partners, LLC; *U.S. Private*, pg. 3021
NESTLE WATERS DIRECT DEUTSCHLAND GMBH—See Nestle S.A.; *Int'l*, pg. 5210
NESTLE WATERS DIRECT PORTUGAL, COMERCIO E DISTRIBUICAO DE PRODUTOS ALIMENTARES, S.A.—See Nestle S.A.; *Int'l*, pg. 5210
NESTLE WATERS EGYPT S.A.E.—See Nestle S.A.; *Int'l*, pg. 5210
NESTLE WATERS ESPANA, S.A.—See Nestle S.A.; *Int'l*, pg. 5210
NESTLE WATERS GB LTD.—See Nestle S.A.; *Int'l*, pg. 5210
NESTLE WATERS GIDA VE MESRUBAT SANAYI TICARET A.S.—See Nestle S.A.; *Int'l*, pg. 5210
NESTLE WATERS MIDDLE EAST INVESTMENTS FZCO—See Nestle S.A.; *Int'l*, pg. 5210
NESTLE WATERS NORTH AMERICA HOLDINGS, INC.—See Metropoulos & Co.; *U.S. Private*, pg. 2690
NESTLE WATERS NORTH AMERICA HOLDINGS, INC.—See One Rock Capital Partners, LLC; *U.S. Private*, pg. 3021
NESTLE WATERS NORTH AMERICA INC. - BREA—See Metropoulos & Co.; *U.S. Private*, pg. 2690
NESTLE WATERS NORTH AMERICA INC. - BREA—See One Rock Capital Partners, LLC; *U.S. Private*, pg. 3021
NESTLE WATERS NORTH AMERICA INC. - BREINIGSVILLE—See Metropoulos & Co.; *U.S. Private*, pg. 2690
NESTLE WATERS NORTH AMERICA INC. - BREINIGSVILLE—See One Rock Capital Partners, LLC; *U.S. Private*, pg. 3021
NESTLE WATERS NORTH AMERICA INC. - COPPELL—See Metropoulos & Co.; *U.S. Private*, pg. 2690
NESTLE WATERS NORTH AMERICA INC. - COPPELL—See One Rock Capital Partners, LLC; *U.S. Private*, pg. 3021
NESTLE WATERS NORTH AMERICA INC. - DRACUT—See Metropoulos & Co.; *U.S. Private*, pg. 2690
NESTLE WATERS NORTH AMERICA INC. - DRACUT—See One Rock Capital Partners, LLC; *U.S. Private*, pg. 3021
NESTLE WATERS NORTH AMERICA INC. - FORT LAUDERDALE—See Metropoulos & Co.; *U.S. Private*, pg. 2690
NESTLE WATERS NORTH AMERICA INC. - FORT LAUDERDALE—See One Rock Capital Partners, LLC; *U.S. Private*, pg. 3021
NESTLE WATERS NORTH AMERICA INC. - GREENWICH—See Metropoulos & Co.; *U.S. Private*, pg. 2690
NESTLE WATERS NORTH AMERICA INC. - GREENWICH—See One Rock Capital Partners, LLC; *U.S. Private*, pg. 3021
NESTLE WATERS NORTH AMERICA INC. - JACKSONVILLE—See Metropoulos & Co.; *U.S. Private*, pg. 2690
NESTLE WATERS NORTH AMERICA INC. - JACKSONVILLE—See One Rock Capital Partners, LLC; *U.S. Private*, pg. 3021

NESTLE WATERS NORTH AMERICA INC. - LANHAM—See Metropoulos & Co.; *U.S. Private*, pg. 2690
NESTLE WATERS NORTH AMERICA INC. - LANHAM—See One Rock Capital Partners, LLC; *U.S. Private*, pg. 3021
NESTLE WATERS NORTH AMERICA INC. - NORTHBROOK—See Metropoulos & Co.; *U.S. Private*, pg. 2690
NESTLE WATERS NORTH AMERICA INC. - NORTHBROOK—See One Rock Capital Partners, LLC; *U.S. Private*, pg. 3021
NESTLE WATERS NORTH AMERICA INC. - RAYNHAM—See Metropoulos & Co.; *U.S. Private*, pg. 2690
NESTLE WATERS NORTH AMERICA INC. - RAYNHAM—See One Rock Capital Partners, LLC; *U.S. Private*, pg. 3021
NESTLE WATERS NORTH AMERICA INC. - ROCHESTER—See Metropoulos & Co.; *U.S. Private*, pg. 2690
NESTLE WATERS NORTH AMERICA INC. - ROCHESTER—See One Rock Capital Partners, LLC; *U.S. Private*, pg. 3021
NESTLE WATERS NORTH AMERICA INC. - THOUSAND PALMS—See Metropoulos & Co.; *U.S. Private*, pg. 2690
NESTLE WATERS NORTH AMERICA INC. - THOUSAND PALMS—See One Rock Capital Partners, LLC; *U.S. Private*, pg. 3021
NESTLE WATERS NORTH AMERICA INC. - WOODRIDGE—See Metropoulos & Co.; *U.S. Private*, pg. 2690
NESTLE WATERS NORTH AMERICA INC. - WOODRIDGE—See One Rock Capital Partners, LLC; *U.S. Private*, pg. 3021
NESTLE WATERS NORTH AMERICA INC. - ZEPHYRHILLS—See Metropoulos & Co.; *U.S. Private*, pg. 2690
NESTLE WATERS NORTH AMERICA INC. - ZEPHYRHILLS—See One Rock Capital Partners, LLC; *U.S. Private*, pg. 3021
NESTLE WATERS POLSKA S.A.—See Nestle S.A.; *Int'l*, pg. 5210
NESTLE WATERS S.A.S.—See Nestle S.A.; *Int'l*, pg. 5210
NESTLE WATERS (SUISSE) S.A.—See Nestle S.A.; *Int'l*, pg. 5210
NESTLE WATERS (UK) HOLDINGS LTD.—See Nestle S.A.; *Int'l*, pg. 5210
NESTLE WCO GMBH CONOW—See Nestle S.A.; *Int'l*, pg. 5210
NESTLE ZAMBIA TRADING LIMITED—See Nestle S.A.; *Int'l*, pg. 5210
NESTLE ZHUKOVSKY ICE CREAM LLC—See Nestle S.A.; *Int'l*, pg. 5205
NESTLE ZIMBABWE (PVT) LTD.—See Nestle S.A.; *Int'l*, pg. 5210
NESTOR CABLES LTD.—See Clearfield, Inc.; *U.S. Public*, pg. 512
NESTOR CO., LTD—See Hoshizaki Corporation; *Int'l*, pg. 3484
NESTOR-FONDS-VERTRIEBS-GMBH—See M.M. Warburg & Co. KGaA; *Int'l*, pg. 4616
NESTOR HOTEL OBJEKT LUDWIGSBURG GMBH—See Aurelius Equity Opportunities SE & Co. KGaA; *Int'l*, pg. 710
NESTOR HOTEL OBJEKT NECKARSULM GMBH—See Aurelius Equity Opportunities SE & Co. KGaA; *Int'l*, pg. 710
NESTOR PARTNERS; *U.S. Private*, pg. 2886
NESTOR PRIMECARE SERVICES LTD.—See Charterhouse Capital Partners LLP; *Int'l*, pg. 1454
NESTOR PRIMECARE SERVICES LTD.—See CVC Capital Partners SICAV-FIS S.A.; *Int'l*, pg. 1882
NESTOR PRIMECARE SERVICES LTD.—See Permira Advisers LLP; *Int'l*, pg. 5803
NESTOR SALES LLC—See Sycamore Partners Management, LP; *U.S. Private*, pg. 3896
NESTRADE SA—See Nestle S.A.; *Int'l*, pg. 5210
NESTRONICS LTD.; *Int'l*, pg. 5211
NESTRO PETROL A.D. BANJA LUKA; *Int'l*, pg. 5211
NEST SEEKERS LLC; *U.S. Private*, pg. 2886
NESTUCCA RIDGE STORAGE; *U.S. Private*, pg. 2886
NESTWORTH FINANCIAL STRATEGISTS PTY. LTD.—See Azimut Holding SpA; *Int'l*, pg. 779
NET100 LTD.—See Aterian Investment Management, L.P.; *U.S. Private*, pg. 366
NET1 APPLIED TECHNOLOGIES AUSTRIA GMBH—See Lesaka Technologies, Inc.; *Int'l*, pg. 4469
NET1 APPLIED TECHNOLOGIES SOUTH AFRICA (PTY) LTD—See Lesaka Technologies, Inc.; *Int'l*, pg. 4469
NET1 APPLIED TECHNOLOGIES SOUTH AFRICA (PTY) LTD—See Lesaka Technologies, Inc.; *Int'l*, pg. 4469
NET1 FIHRST HOLDINGS (PTY) LTD—See Lesaka Technologies, Inc.; *Int'l*, pg. 4469
NET1 MOBILE SOLUTIONS (PTY) LTD.—See Lesaka Technologies, Inc.; *Int'l*, pg. 4469
NET 1 UNIVERSAL TECHNOLOGIES (AUSTRIA) GMBH—See Lesaka Technologies, Inc.; *Int'l*, pg. 4469

COMPANY NAME INDEX

NET1 UNIVERSAL TECHNOLOGIES INDIA PVT. LTD.—See Lesaka Technologies, Inc.; *Int'l*, pg. 4469
NET263 LTD.; *Int'l*, pg. 5212
NET2EZ INC.; *U.S. Private*, pg. 2886
NET2PHONE CABLE TELEPHONY, LLC—See IDT Corporation; *U.S. Public*, pg. 1094
NET2PHONE, INC.—See IDT Corporation; *U.S. Public*, pg. 1094
NET 2 TECHNOLOGY GROUP INC.; *U.S. Private*, pg. 2886
NET4GAS, S.R.O.—See Allianz SE; *Int'l*, pg. 344
NET4GAS, S.R.O.—See Ontario Municipal Employees Retirement System; *Int'l*, pg. 5584
NET4 INDIA LIMITED; *Int'l*, pg. 5212
NET 5—See Talpa Holding B.V.; *Int'l*, pg. 7448
NETAC TECHNOLOGY CO., LTD.; *Int'l*, pg. 5212
NET ACTIVITY, INC.—See Custom Computer Specialists, LLC; *U.S. Public*, pg. 1128
NET ADVANTAGE—See National Technology Group; *Int'l*, pg. 5164
NETAFIM IRRIGATION INC.; *U.S. Private*, pg. 2887
NET-A-GO TECHNOLOGY COMPANY LIMITED; *Int'l*, pg. 5212
NETANEL GROUP LTD.; *Int'l*, pg. 5212
THE NET-A-PORTER GROUP LTD.—See Compagnie Financiere Richemont S.A.; *Int'l*, pg. 1741
NETAPP ASIA PACIFIC HOLDINGS B.V.—See NetApp, Inc.; *U.S. Public*, pg. 1507
NETAPP AUSTRALIA PTY. LTD.—See NetApp, Inc.; *U.S. Public*, pg. 1507
NETAPP BELGIUM BVBA—See NetApp, Inc.; *U.S. Public*, pg. 1507
NETAPP BRASIL SGAD LTDA—See NetApp, Inc.; *U.S. Public*, pg. 1507
NETAPP B.V.—See NetApp, Inc.; *U.S. Public*, pg. 1507
NETAPP CHILE LIMITADA—See NetApp, Inc.; *U.S. Public*, pg. 1507
NETAPP (CHINA) LTD.—See NetApp, Inc.; *U.S. Public*, pg. 1507
NETAPP DENMARK APS—See NetApp, Inc.; *U.S. Public*, pg. 1507
NETAPP FRANCE SAS—See NetApp, Inc.; *U.S. Public*, pg. 1507
NETAPP G.K.—See NetApp, Inc.; *U.S. Public*, pg. 1507
NETAPP (HONG KONG) LIMITED—See NetApp, Inc.; *U.S. Public*, pg. 1507
NETAPP, INC.; *U.S. Public*, pg. 1507
NETAPP INDIA PRIVATE LTD.—See NetApp, Inc.; *U.S. Public*, pg. 1507
NETAPP ISRAEL SALES LTD.—See NetApp, Inc.; *U.S. Public*, pg. 1507
NETAPP JAPAN K.K.—See NetApp, Inc.; *U.S. Public*, pg. 1507
NETAPP MEXICO—See NetApp, Inc.; *U.S. Public*, pg. 1507
NETAPP RTP—See NetApp, Inc.; *U.S. Public*, pg. 1507
NETAPP (SHANGHAI) COMMERCIAL CO., LTD.—See NetApp, Inc.; *U.S. Public*, pg. 1507
NETAPP SINGAPORE PTE. LTD.—See NetApp, Inc.; *U.S. Public*, pg. 1507
NETAPP SOUTH AFRICA (PTY) LIMITED—See NetApp, Inc.; *U.S. Public*, pg. 1507
NETAPP SWEDEN AB—See NetApp, Inc.; *U.S. Public*, pg. 1507
NETAPP TEKNOLOJI LIMITED SIRKETI—See NetApp, Inc.; *U.S. Public*, pg. 1507
NETAPP (THAILAND) LIMITED—See NetApp, Inc.; *U.S. Public*, pg. 1507
NETAPP UK LTD.—See NetApp, Inc.; *U.S. Public*, pg. 1507
NETAS BILISIM TEKNOLOJILERI A.S.—See Netas Telekomunikasyon Anonim Sirketi; *Int'l*, pg. 5212
NETAS TELEKOMUNIKASYON ANONIM SIRKETI; *Int'l*, pg. 5212
NET ATLANTIC, INC.; *U.S. Private*, pg. 2886
NET AVENUE TECHNOLOGIES LIMITED; *Int'l*, pg. 5211
NETBASE SOLUTIONS, INC.; *U.S. Private*, pg. 2887
NETBAY PUBLIC COMPANY LIMITED; *Int'l*, pg. 5212
NETBIL I SKANDINAVIEN AB—See Bilia AB; *Int'l*, pg. 1029
NETBISCUITS GMBH; *Int'l*, pg. 5212
NETBISCUITS, INC.—See Netbiscuits GmbH; *Int'l*, pg. 5213
NETBISCUITS PTE LTD—See Netbiscuits GmbH; *Int'l*, pg. 5213
N ET B KNAUF ET CIE S.C.S.—See Gebr. Knauf KG; *Int'l*, pg. 2908
NETBOOSTER AGENCY ITALY SRL—See Ardian SAS; *Int'l*, pg. 554
NETBOOSTER GMBH—See Ardian SAS; *Int'l*, pg. 554
NETBOOSTER HOLDING A/S—See Ardian SAS; *Int'l*, pg. 554
NETBOOSTER MENA MIDDLE EAST & NORTH AFRICA FZ-LLC—See Ardian SAS; *Int'l*, pg. 554
NETBOOSTER SPAIN SL—See Ardian SAS; *Int'l*, pg. 555
NETBOOSTER SWEDEN AB—See Ardian SAS; *Int'l*, pg. 555
NETBOOSTER UK LIMITED—See Ardian SAS; *Int'l*, pg. 555

NETBOOST MEDIA LIMITED—See The Rank Group Plc; *Int'l*, pg. 7678
NETBRANDS CORP.; *U.S. Public*, pg. 1507
NETBRIEFINGS, INC.; *U.S. Private*, pg. 2887
NET BRILL, S.L.—See ACS, Actividades de Construccion y Servicios, S.A.; *Int'l*, pg. 115
NETCALLIDUS LIMITED—See dotdigital Group PLC; *Int'l*, pg. 2180
NETCALL PLC; *Int'l*, pg. 5213
NETCALL TECHNOLOGY LIMITED—See Netcall plc; *Int'l*, pg. 5213
NETCAPITAL INC.; *U.S. Public*, pg. 1507
NETCARE 911 PTY LTD—See Netcare Limited; *Int'l*, pg. 5213
NETCARE ACCESS; *U.S. Private*, pg. 2887
NETCARE HOSPITALS PROPRIETARY LIMITED—See Netcare Limited; *Int'l*, pg. 5213
NET CARE, INC.—See Internet Initiative Japan Inc.; *Int'l*, pg. 3753
NETCARE INTERNATIONAL UK LIMITED—See Netcare Limited; *Int'l*, pg. 5213
NETCARE LIMITED; *Int'l*, pg. 5213
NETCENTRIC AG—See Cognizant Technology Solutions Corporation; *U.S. Public*, pg. 525
NETCENTRIC BENELUX BV—See Cognizant Technology Solutions Corporation; *U.S. Public*, pg. 525
NETCENTRIC DEUTSCHLAND GMBH—See Cognizant Technology Solutions Corporation; *U.S. Public*, pg. 525
NETCENTRIC EASTERN EUROPE S.R.L.—See Cognizant Technology Solutions Corporation; *U.S. Public*, pg. 525
NETCENTRIC IBERICA SLU—See Cognizant Technology Solutions Corporation; *U.S. Public*, pg. 525
NETCENTRICS CORP.—See Edgewater Services, LLC; *U.S. Private*, pg. 1335
NETCENTRIC TECHNOLOGY INC.—See Vistronix, Inc.; *U.S. Private*, pg. 4403
NETCENTS TECHNOLOGY, INC.; *Int'l*, pg. 5213
NET CHART JAPAN INC.—See Internet Initiative Japan Inc.; *Int'l*, pg. 3753
NETCITADEL, INC.—See Thoma Bravo, L.P.; *U.S. Private*, pg. 4151
NETCLIME-BULGARIA EOOD—See Deluxe Corporation; *U.S. Public*, pg. 653
NETCLOUD (HONG KONG) TECHNOLOGY LIMITED—See Forgame Holdings Limited; *Int'l*, pg. 2733
NETCOM3 INC.; *U.S. Private*, pg. 2887
NETCOM BW GMBH—See EnBW Energie Baden-Wurttemberg AG; *Int'l*, pg. 2399
NETCOM BW GMBH—See EnBW Energie Baden-Wurttemberg AG; *Int'l*, pg. 2399
NETCOM, INC.—See Cedar Creek Partners LLC; *U.S. Private*, pg. 804
NETCOM LEARNING; *U.S. Private*, pg. 2887
NETCOM LIMITED—See Logicom Public Ltd; *Int'l*, pg. 4542
NETCOMM WIRELESS LIMITED—See Casa Systems, Inc.; *U.S. Public*, pg. 778
NETCOMM WIRELESS LIMITED—See Casa Systems, Inc.; *U.S. Public*, pg. 778
NETCOMM WIRELESS—See Casa Systems, Inc.; *U.S. Private*, pg. 778
NETCOMPANY GROUP AS; *Int'l*, pg. 5213
NETCOM INSURANCE CORP.—See Marsh & McLennan Companies, Inc.; *U.S. Public*, pg. 1386
NETCOM TECHNOLOGIES, INC.; *U.S. Private*, pg. 2887
NETCRACKER TECHNOLOGY CORPORATION—See NEC Corporation; *Int'l*, pg. 5184
NETCRACKER TECHNOLOGY DO BRASIL LTDA—See NEC Corporation; *Int'l*, pg. 5184
NETCRACKER TECHNOLOGY EMEA LIMITED—See NEC Corporation; *Int'l*, pg. 5184
NETCRACKER TECHNOLOGY SOLUTIONS INC.—See NEC Corporation; *Int'l*, pg. 5184
NETCRACKER TECHNOLOGY SOLUTIONS SINGAPORE PTE. LTD.—See NEC Corporation; *Int'l*, pg. 5184
NET D CONSULTING, INC.—See Gawk, Incorporated; *U.S. Private*, pg. 1652
NET DETERGENT JSC—See Masan Consumer Corp.; *Int'l*, pg. 4719
NETDIMENSIONS (HOLDINGS) LIMITED—See Learning Technologies Group plc; *Int'l*, pg. 4435
NETDIMENSIONS, INC.—See Learning Technologies Group plc; *Int'l*, pg. 4435
NETDIMENSIONS (UK) LIMITED—See Learning Technologies Group plc; *Int'l*, pg. 4435
NET DIRECT MERCHANTS; *U.S. Private*, pg. 2886
NETDIRECTOR; *U.S. Private*, pg. 2887
NETDRAGON WEBSOFT HOLDINGS LIMITED; *Int'l*, pg. 5213
NETDRAGON WEBSOFT (HONG KONG) LIMITED—See NetDragon Websoft Holdings Limited; *Int'l*, pg. 5213
NETEASE, INC.; *Int'l*, pg. 5214
NETEASE INFORMATION TECHNOLOGY (BEIJING) CO., LTD.—See NetEase, Inc.; *Int'l*, pg. 5214
NE TECHNO CO., LTD.—See DN HOLDINGS CO.,LTD; *Int'l*, pg. 2147
NETEDI LTD.—See Cegedim S.A.; *Int'l*, pg. 1390

NETEL AB—See IK Investment Partners Limited; *Int'l*, pg. 3609
NETEL AS—See IK Investment Partners Limited; *Int'l*, pg. 3609
NET ELEMENT SERVICES, LLC—See Mullen Automotive, Inc.; *U.S. Public*, pg. 1486
NETEL TECHNOLOGY (HOLDINGS) LIMITED; *Int'l*, pg. 5214
NET ENFORCERS, INC.—See General Catalyst Partners; *U.S. Private*, pg. 1664
NET ENFORCERS, INC.—See iSubscribed Inc.; *U.S. Private*, pg. 2147
NET ENFORCERS, INC.—See WndrCo Holdings, LLC; *U.S. Private*, pg. 4552
NETENT AB; *Int'l*, pg. 5214
NET ENTERTAINMENT MALTA LTD.—See NetEnt AB; *Int'l*, pg. 5214
NET ESOLUTIONS CORPORATION—See Nippon Telegraph & Telephone Corporation; *Int'l*, pg. 5348
NETE; *U.S. Private*, pg. 2887
NETEVEN S.A.—See Lectra SA; *Int'l*, pg. 4438
NETEX KNOWLEDGE FACTORY SA; *Int'l*, pg. 5214
NETEZZA CORPORATION LTD.—See International Business Machines Corporation; *U.S. Public*, pg. 1149
NETEZZA CORPORATION—See International Business Machines Corporation; *U.S. Public*, pg. 1149
NETFABB GMBH—See Autodesk, Inc.; *U.S. Public*, pg. 229
NETFACILITIES, INC.—See GI Manager L.P.; *U.S. Private*, pg. 1693
NETFIN ACQUISITION CORP.; *U.S. Public*, pg. 1507
NETFLIX, INC.; *U.S. Public*, pg. 1508
NETFLIX PTE. LTD.—See Netflix, Inc.; *U.S. Public*, pg. 1508
NETFONDS AG; *Int'l*, pg. 5214
NETFORTIS, INC.; *U.S. Private*, pg. 2887
NETFORTUNE (SHANGHAI) ALUMINIUM WORKS CO. LTD.—See China State Construction International Holdings Limited; *Int'l*, pg. 1554
NETFRONT INFORMATION TECHNOLOGY LTD.—See Liberty Global plc; *Int'l*, pg. 4485
NET FUND ADMINISTRATION SP. Z.O.O.—See KBC Group NV; *Int'l*, pg. 4106
NETFUSION, INC.—See Tonka Bay Equity Partners LLC; *U.S. Private*, pg. 4185
NET FUTURE CO., LTD.—See Sumitomo Mitsui Financial Group, Inc.; *Int'l*, pg. 7294
NETGAIN INFORMATION SYSTEMS CO. LLC—See Aunalytics, Inc.; *U.S. Public*, pg. 393
NETGAIN TECHNOLOGIES INC.—See Alpine Investors; *U.S. Private*, pg. 201
NETGAIN TECHNOLOGY INC.; *U.S. Private*, pg. 2887
NETGEAR AUSTRALIA PTY. LTD.—See NETGEAR, Inc.; *U.S. Public*, pg. 1508
NETGEAR (BEIJING) NETWORK TECHNOLOGY CO., LTD.—See NETGEAR, Inc.; *U.S. Public*, pg. 1508
NETGEAR DENMARK APS—See NETGEAR, Inc.; *U.S. Public*, pg. 1508
NETGEAR DEUTSCHLAND GMBH—See NETGEAR, Inc.; *U.S. Public*, pg. 1508
NETGEAR DO BRASIL PRODUTOS ELECTRONICOS LTDA.—See NETGEAR, Inc.; *U.S. Public*, pg. 1508
NETGEAR FILIAL SWEDEN—See NETGEAR, Inc.; *U.S. Public*, pg. 1508
NETGEAR FRANCE SAS—See NETGEAR, Inc.; *U.S. Public*, pg. 1508
NETGEAR HONG KONG LIMITED—See NETGEAR, Inc.; *U.S. Public*, pg. 1508
NETGEAR, INC.; *U.S. Public*, pg. 1508
NETGEAR INTERNATIONAL, INC. - ITALY—See NETGEAR, Inc.; *U.S. Public*, pg. 1508
NETGEAR INTERNATIONAL, INC. - KOREA—See NETGEAR, Inc.; *U.S. Public*, pg. 1508
NETGEAR INTERNATIONAL, INC. - MIDDLE EAST—See NETGEAR, Inc.; *U.S. Public*, pg. 1508
NETGEAR INTERNATIONAL, INC. - RUSSIA—See NETGEAR, Inc.; *U.S. Public*, pg. 1508
NETGEAR INTERNATIONAL, INC. - SPAIN—See NETGEAR, Inc.; *U.S. Public*, pg. 1508
NETGEAR JAPAN GK—See NETGEAR, Inc.; *U.S. Public*, pg. 1508
NETGEAR NETHERLANDS B.V.—See NETGEAR, Inc.; *U.S. Public*, pg. 1508
NETGEAR POLAND SP. Z O.O.—See NETGEAR, Inc.; *U.S. Public*, pg. 1508
NETGEAR RESEARCH INDIA PVT. LTD.—See NETGEAR, Inc.; *U.S. Public*, pg. 1508
NETGEAR RUSSIA LLC—See NETGEAR, Inc.; *U.S. Public*, pg. 1508
NETGEAR TECHNOLOGIES INDIA PTE. LTD.—See NETGEAR, Inc.; *U.S. Public*, pg. 1508
NETGEAR UK LIMITED—See NETGEAR, Inc.; *U.S. Public*, pg. 1508
NETGEM SA; *Int'l*, pg. 5214
NETGEM TV LTD.—See Netgem SA; *Int'l*, pg. 5214
NETGENII TECHNOLOGY LIMITED—See NOIZ Group Limited; *Int'l*, pg. 5401
NETHAWK S.A.R.L—See EXFO Inc.; *Int'l*, pg. 2584

NETHAWK SOLUTIONS PVT. LTD.—See EXFO Inc.; *Int'l*, pg. 2584
NET HEALTH SYSTEMS, INC.—See Level Equity Management, LLC; *U.S. Private*, pg. 2434
NET HEALTH SYSTEMS, INC.—See Silversmith Management, L.P.; *U.S. Private*, pg. 3664
NET HEALTH SYSTEMS, INC.—See The Carlyle Group Inc.; *U.S. Public*, pg. 2050
NETHERLANDS AIRCRAFT COMPANY—See Panta Holdings B.V.; *Int'l*, pg. 5730
NETHERLANDS REFINING COMPANY B.V.—See BP plc; *Int'l*, pg. 1129
NETHERLOCKS SAFETY SYSTEMS—See Halma plc; *Int'l*, pg. 3233
NET HOLDING A.S.; *Int'l*, pg. 5211
NETH & SON INC.; *U.S. Private*, pg. 2887
NETH & SONS INC.; *U.S. Private*, pg. 2887
NETIA SA—See Cyfrowy Polsat S.A.; *Int'l*, pg. 1895
NETIJAM TECHNOLOGIES SL—See Prosegur Cash SA; *Int'l*, pg. 5999
NETIMPACT HOLDINGS, INC.; *U.S. Public*, pg. 1508
THE NET IMPACT—See Unified Development, Inc.; *U.S. Private*, pg. 4282
NETINFO, INC.; *Int'l*, pg. 5214
NET INSIGHT AB; *Int'l*, pg. 5211
NET INSIGHT, INC.—See Net Insight AB; *Int'l*, pg. 5212
NET INSIGHT PTE. LTD.—See Net Insight AB; *Int'l*, pg. 5212
NET-INSPECT; *U.S. Private*, pg. 2886
NET INSURANCE S.P.A.; *Int'l*, pg. 5212
NETINTELLIGENCE LIMITED—See iomart Group plc; *Int'l*, pg. 3793
NETIQ - AUSTRALIA—See Micro Focus International plc; *Int'l*, pg. 4876
NETIQ IRELAND LIMITED—See Micro Focus International plc; *Int'l*, pg. 4876
NETIQ - JAPAN—See Micro Focus International plc; *Int'l*, pg. 4876
NETIQ NEDERLANDS—See Micro Focus International plc; *Int'l*, pg. 4876
NETIQ—See Micro Focus International plc; *Int'l*, pg. 4876
NETIX S.R.L.—See Delticom AG; *Int'l*, pg. 2021
NET JAPAN CO. LTD.—See TKH Group N.V.; *Int'l*, pg. 7764
NETJETS INC.—See Berkshire Hathaway Inc.; *U.S. Public*, pg. 313
NET JINZAI BANK, INC.—See Will Group, Inc.; *Int'l*, pg. 8412
NETJOBS GROUP AB—See Trottholmen AB; *Int'l*, pg. 7939
NETJOY HOLDINGS LIMITED; *Int'l*, pg. 5214
NET LEASE OFFICE PROPERTIES; *U.S. Public*, pg. 1506
NETLEIH GMBH & CO.KG—See Telepool GmbH; *Int'l*, pg. 7541
NETLIBRARY, INC.—See Online Computer Library Center, Inc.; *U.S. Private*, pg. 3027
NETLINK BV—See VINCI S.A.; *Int'l*, pg. 8224
NETLINK COMPUTER INC.; *Int'l*, pg. 5214
NETLINK NBN TRUST; *Int'l*, pg. 5214
NETLINK SOLUTIONS (INDIA) LIMITED; *Int'l*, pg. 5214
NETLINK; *U.S. Private*, pg. 2887
NETLINKZ LIMITED; *Int'l*, pg. 5214
NET-LINX AG; *Int'l*, pg. 5212
NETLIST ELECTRONICS (SUZHOU) CO., LTD—See Netlist, Inc.; *U.S. Public*, pg. 1509
NETLIST, INC.; *U.S. Public*, pg. 1508
NET LOGISTICS PTY LTD.—See Dreamscape Networks Limited; *Int'l*, pg. 2203
NETMAGIC II SARL—See ManpowerGroup Inc.; *U.S. Public*, pg. 1361
NETMAP ANALYTICS—See Verisk Analytics, Inc.; *U.S. Public*, pg. 2283
NETMARBLE CORP.; *Int'l*, pg. 5214
NETMARBLE (THAILAND) CO., LTD.—See Netmarble Corp.; *Int'l*, pg. 5215
NETMARK.COM; *U.S. Private*, pg. 2887
NET MARKETING CO., LTD.—See Macbee Planet, Inc.; *Int'l*, pg. 4620
NET MATRIX SOLUTIONS; *U.S. Private*, pg. 2886
NETMEDIA S.A.; *Int'l*, pg. 5215
NET MEDICAL XPRESS SOLUTIONS, INC.; *U.S. Public*, pg. 1506
NETMED, INC.; *U.S. Public*, pg. 1509
NETMERCURY, INC. - AUSTIN—See Wynnchurch Capital, L.P.; *U.S. Private*, pg. 4577
NETMERCURY, INC. - FREMONT—See Wynnchurch Capital, L.P.; *U.S. Private*, pg. 4577
NETMERCURY, INC.—See Wynnchurch Capital, L.P.; *U.S. Private*, pg. 4577
NETMILE, INC.—See Transcosmos Inc.; *Int'l*, pg. 7898
NET MONTENEGRO D.O.O.—See Net Holding A.S.; *Int'l*, pg. 5211
NETMORE GROUP AB; *Int'l*, pg. 5215
NETMOTION SOFTWARE CANADA, INC.—See Crosspoint Capital Partners LP; *U.S. Private*, pg. 1107
NETMOTION SOFTWARE, INC.—See Crosspoint Capital Partners LP; *U.S. Private*, pg. 1107
NETMOTION WIRELESS GMBH—See Crosspoint Capital Partners LP; *U.S. Private*, pg. 1107

NETMOTION WIRELESS, LTD.—See Crosspoint Capital Partners LP; *U.S. Private*, pg. 1107
NETMOVE CORPORATION—See SBI Holdings, Inc.; *Int'l*, pg. 6606
NETMOVE CORPORATION—See Sumitomo Mitsui Trust Holdings, Inc.; *Int'l*, pg. 7296
NETMRO INC.—See Platinum Equity, LLC; *U.S. Private*, pg. 3210
NETNAMES A/S—See HgCapital Trust plc; *Int'l*, pg. 3377
NETNAMES AS—See HgCapital Trust plc; *Int'l*, pg. 3377
NETNAMES HOLDINGS LIMITED—See HgCapital Trust plc; *Int'l*, pg. 3377
NETNAMES INC.—See HgCapital Trust plc; *Int'l*, pg. 3377
NET NANNY SOFTWARE INTERNATIONAL INC.—See SafeTonet Limited; *Int'l*, pg. 6470
NET NEW ENERGY TECHNOLOGIES AG; *Int'l*, pg. 5212
N. E. TOJITSU, LTD.—See Topy Industries, Ltd.; *Int'l*, pg. 7822
NETO MALINDA TRADING LTD.; *Int'l*, pg. 5215
NETO M.E HOLDINGS LTD.; *Int'l*, pg. 5215
NET ONE ASIA PTE. LTD.; *Int'l*, pg. 5212
NET ONE CONNECT G.K.—See Sumitomo Corporation; *Int'l*, pg. 7270
NETONE NETWORK SOLUTION CO. LTD—See Loxley Public Company Limited; *Int'l*, pg. 4567
NET ONE NEXT CO., LTD.—See Sumitomo Corporation; *Int'l*, pg. 7270
NET ONE PARTNERS CO., LTD.—See Sumitomo Corporation; *Int'l*, pg. 7270
NET ONE SYSTEMS CO LTD - CHUGOKU—See Sumitomo Corporation; *Int'l*, pg. 7270
NET ONE SYSTEMS CO LTD—See Sumitomo Corporation; *Int'l*, pg. 7270
NETOP SOLUTIONS A/S; *Int'l*, pg. 5215
NET OPTICS, INC.—See Keysight Technologies, Inc.; *U.S. Public*, pg. 1227
NETPACE, INC.; *U.S. Private*, pg. 2887
NET PACIFIC FINANCIAL HOLDINGS LIMITED; *Int'l*, pg. 5212
NETPARK21 CO., LTD.—See SYS Holdings Co., Ltd.; *Int'l*, pg. 7388
NETPAY INTERNATIONAL, INC.; *Int'l*, pg. 5215
NET PIX SHORTS DIGITAL MEDIA LIMITED; *Int'l*, pg. 5212
NETPLAN CO., LTD.—See OTSUKA CORPORATION; *Int'l*, pg. 5658
NETPLUS MARKETING, INC.; *U.S. Private*, pg. 2887
NETPOSA TECHNOLOGIES LIMITED; *Int'l*, pg. 5215
NET POSITIVE BUSINESS ANALYTICS PRIVATE LIMITED—See Equifax Inc.; *U.S. Public*, pg. 787
NET POWER INC.; *U.S. Public*, pg. 1506
NETPRESS GMBH—See Adelis Equity Partners AB; *Int'l*, pg. 142
NETPR, INC.; *U.S. Private*, pg. 2887
NETPROFILE FINLAND OY; *Int'l*, pg. 5215
NET PROTECTIONS HOLDINGS, INC.; *Int'l*, pg. 5212
NETPRPRO, INC.; *U.S. Private*, pg. 2887
NETPUBLICATOR APPS AB—See Addnode Group AB; *Int'l*, pg. 130
NETQUOTE, INC.—See Red Ventures, LLC; *U.S. Private*, pg. 3376
NETRAMARK HOLDINGS INC.; *Int'l*, pg. 5215
NETRANGE MMH GMBH—See Access Co., Ltd.; *Int'l*, pg. 88
NETRANOM COMMUNICATIONS, INC.—See Alpine Investors; *U.S. Private*, pg. 201
NETRATE SYSTEMS, INC.—See Roper Technologies, Inc.; *U.S. Public*, pg. 1814
NETRATINGS FRANCE SAS—See Brookfield Corporation; *Int'l*, pg. 1179
NETRATINGS FRANCE SAS—See Elliott Management Corporation; *U.S. Private*, pg. 1371
NETRATINGS, LLC—See Brookfield Corporation; *Int'l*, pg. 1179
NETRATINGS, LLC—See Elliott Management Corporation; *U.S. Private*, pg. 1371
NETRAUTA FINLAND OY—See BHG Group AB; *Int'l*, pg. 1015
NETRD BILGI TEKNOLOJILERI VE TELEKOMUNIKASYON A.S.—See Netas Telekomunikasyon Anonim Sirketi; *Int'l*, pg. 5212
NET RECRUIT UK LIMITED—See Reach PLC; *Int'l*, pg. 6231
NETRED AB—See Storskogen Group AB; *Int'l*, pg. 7228
NETREO, INC.; *U.S. Private*, pg. 2887
NET REPLY S.R.L.—See Reply S.p.A.; *Int'l*, pg. 6291
NETRICOM INC.; *Int'l*, pg. 5215
NETRION GMBH—See MVV Energie AG; *Int'l*, pg. 5109
NETRIPPLES SOFTWARE LIMITED; *Int'l*, pg. 5215
NETRISK.HU—See TA Associates, Inc.; *U.S. Private*, pg. 3916
NETRIVER INCORPORATED—See Lincoln Property Company; *U.S. Private*, pg. 2458
NETRIX LLC; *U.S. Private*, pg. 2887
NETROADSHOW, INC.; *U.S. Private*, pg. 2888
NETRONIX INTEGRATION, INC.—See Wind Point Advisors LLC; *U.S. Private*, pg. 4535
NETRONOME, INC.; *U.S. Private*, pg. 2888

NETRUCK CO., LTD.—See SK Innovation Co., Ltd.; *Int'l*, pg. 6973
NET SAFETY MONITORING INC.—See Emerson Electric Co.; *U.S. Public*, pg. 750
NETS A/S—See Advent International Corporation; *U.S. Private*, pg. 105
NETS A/S—See Bain Capital, LP; *U.S. Private*, pg. 442
NETS A/S—See GIC Pte. Ltd.; *Int'l*, pg. 2965
NETS A/S—See Hellman & Friedman LLC; *U.S. Private*, pg. 1910
NET-SAT MEDIA SP ZOO—See Liberty Global plc; *Int'l*, pg. 4485
NETSAVE CO LTD—See Kandenko Co., Ltd.; *Int'l*, pg. 4065
NET SAVINGS LINK, INC.; *U.S. Private*, pg. 2886
NETSCALIBUR LTD.—See Claranet Limited; *Int'l*, pg. 1642
NETSCIENTIFIC PLC; *Int'l*, pg. 5215
NETSCOPE SOLUTIONS S.A.—See Yokogawa Electric Corporation; *Int'l*, pg. 8592
NETSCOUT BERLIN GMBH & CO. KG—See NetScout Systems, Inc.; *U.S. Public*, pg. 1509
NETSCOUT SYSTEMS CANADA, INC.—See NetScout Systems, Inc.; *U.S. Public*, pg. 1509
NETSCOUT SYSTEMS (HK) LIMITED—See NetScout Systems, Inc.; *U.S. Public*, pg. 1509
NETSCOUT SYSTEMS, INC.; *U.S. Public*, pg. 1509
NETSCOUT SYSTEMS INDIA PTE LTD—See NetScout Systems, Inc.; *U.S. Public*, pg. 1509
NETSCOUT SYSTEMS JAPAN K.K.—See NetScout Systems, Inc.; *U.S. Public*, pg. 1509
NETSCOUT SYSTEMS MEXICO, S.A. DE C.V.—See NetScout Systems, Inc.; *U.S. Public*, pg. 1509
NETSCOUT SYSTEMS SINGAPORE PTE LTD.—See NetScout Systems, Inc.; *U.S. Public*, pg. 1509
NETSCOUT SYSTEMS TEXAS, LLC—See NetScout Systems, Inc.; *U.S. Public*, pg. 1509
NETSCOUT SYSTEMS (UK) LIMITED—See NetScout Systems, Inc.; *U.S. Public*, pg. 1509
NETS DENMARK A/S—See Advent International Corporation; *U.S. Private*, pg. 105
NETS DENMARK A/S—See Bain Capital, LP; *U.S. Private*, pg. 442
NETS DENMARK A/S—See GIC Pte. Ltd.; *Int'l*, pg. 2965
NETS DENMARK A/S—See Hellman & Friedman LLC; *U.S. Private*, pg. 1910
NETSENSE BUSINES SOLUTIONS PTE. LTD.—See Censof Holdings Berhad; *Int'l*, pg. 1402
NETSERTIVE, INC.; *U.S. Private*, pg. 2888
NET SERVICE SRL—See Leonardo S.p.A.; *Int'l*, pg. 4460
NET SERVICOS DE COMUNICACAO S.A.—See America Movil, S.A.B. de C.V.; *Int'l*, pg. 422
NETSHAPE TECHNOLOGIES, INC.—See Guggenheim Partners, LLC; *U.S. Private*, pg. 1812
NETSHELTER, INC.; *U.S. Private*, pg. 2888
NETSHOES (CAYMAN) LIMITED—See Magazine Luiza S.A.; *Int'l*, pg. 4637
NETSIP PTY LTD—See Over the Wire Holdings Limited; *Int'l*, pg. 5671
NETSKOPE, INC.; *U.S. Private*, pg. 2888
NETSMART TECHNOLOGIES, INC. - MISSOURI—See GI Manager L.P.; *U.S. Private*, pg. 1693
NETSMART TECHNOLOGIES, INC. - MISSOURI—See TA Associates, Inc.; *U.S. Private*, pg. 3916
NETSMART TECHNOLOGIES, INC.—See GI Manager L.P.; *U.S. Private*, pg. 1693
NETSMART TECHNOLOGIES, INC.—See TA Associates, Inc.; *U.S. Private*, pg. 3916
NETS NORWAY AS—See Advent International Corporation; *U.S. Private*, pg. 105
NETS NORWAY AS—See Bain Capital, LP; *U.S. Private*, pg. 442
NETS NORWAY AS—See GIC Pte. Ltd.; *Int'l*, pg. 2965
NETS NORWAY AS—See Hellman & Friedman LLC; *U.S. Private*, pg. 1910
NETSOFT HOLDINGS, LLC; *U.S. Private*, pg. 2888
NETSOL-ABRAXAS AUSTRALIA PTY LTD.—See NetSol Technologies, Inc.; *U.S. Public*, pg. 1509
NETSOL CONNECT (PRIVATE), LTD.—See NetSol Technologies, Inc.; *U.S. Public*, pg. 1509
NETSOL OMNI (PRIVATE) LTD.—See NetSol Technologies, Inc.; *U.S. Public*, pg. 1509
NETSOL TECHNOLOGIES AUSTRALIA PTY LIMITED—See NetSol Technologies, Inc.; *U.S. Public*, pg. 1509
NETSOL TECHNOLOGIES EUROPE LTD.—See NetSol Technologies, Inc.; *U.S. Public*, pg. 1509
NETSOL TECHNOLOGIES, INC.; *U.S. Public*, pg. 1509
NETSOL TECHNOLOGIES LTD. (CHINA)—See NetSol Technologies, Inc.; *U.S. Public*, pg. 1509
NETSOL TECHNOLOGIES LTD.—See NetSol Technologies, Inc.; *U.S. Public*, pg. 1509
NETSOL TECHNOLOGIES LTD.—See NetSol Technologies, Inc.; *U.S. Public*, pg. 1509
NETSOL TECHNOLOGIES THAILAND LIMITED—See NetSol Technologies, Inc.; *U.S. Public*, pg. 1509
NETSOURCE TECHNOLOGY INC.; *U.S. Private*, pg. 2888
NETSPEND CORPORATION—See Rev Worldwide, Inc.; *U.S. Private*, pg. 3412

COMPANY NAME INDEX

NETSPEND CORPORATION—See Searchlight Capital Partners, L.P.; *U.S. Private*, pg. 3590
NETSPEND HOLDINGS, INC.—See Global Payments Inc.; *U.S. Public*, pg. 944
NETS SWEDEN AB—See Advent International Corporation; *U.S. Private*, pg. 105
NETS SWEDEN AB—See Bain Capital, LP; *U.S. Private*, pg. 442
NETS SWEDEN AB—See GIC Pte. Ltd.; *Int'l*, pg. 2965
NETS SWEDEN AB—See Hellman & Friedman LLC; *U.S. Private*, pg. 1910
NETSTAR-1, INC.; *U.S. Private*, pg. 2888
NETSTAR AUSTRALIA PTY LTD—See Altron Limited.; *Int'l*, pg. 399
NETSTARLOGICALIS MALAYSIA SDN BHD—See Datatec Limited; *Int'l*, pg. 1980
NETSTAR PROPRIETARY LIMITED—See Altron Limited.; *Int'l*, pg. 399
NETSTARS CO., LTD.; *Int'l*, pg. 5215
NET STAR TELECOMMUNICATIONS, INC.—See Astra Capital Management LLC; *U.S. Private*, pg. 361
NETSTEPS; *U.S. Private*, pg. 2888
NETSTRATEGIES; *U.S. Private*, pg. 2888
NETSTREIT CORP.; *U.S. Public*, pg. 1509
NETSUITE AUSTRALIA PTY. LTD.—See Oracle Corporation; *U.S. Public*, pg. 1611
NETSUITE CANADA INC.—See Oracle Corporation; *U.S. Public*, pg. 1611
NETSUITE INC.—See Oracle Corporation; *U.S. Public*, pg. 1611
NETSUITE PHILIPPINES INC.—See Oracle Corporation; *U.S. Public*, pg. 1611
NETSURION, LLC—See Providence Equity Partners L.L.C.; *U.S. Private*, pg. 3293
NETSURIT INC.—See Netsurit (Pty) Ltd; *Int'l*, pg. 5215
NETSURIT (PTY) LTD; *Int'l*, pg. 5215
NETSURVEY BOLINDER AB; *Int'l*, pg. 5215
NETSWEEPER INC.; *Int'l*, pg. 5215
NETSWEEPER INDIA—See Netsweeper Inc.; *Int'l*, pg. 5215
NETSWEEPER LIMITED—See Netsweeper Inc.; *Int'l*, pg. 5215
NETSWEEPER MEA—See Netsweeper Inc.; *Int'l*, pg. 5216
NETSWORK INC.; *U.S. Private*, pg. 2888
NET SYSTEMS; *U.S. Private*, pg. 2886
NETTBIL AS—See Schibsted ASA; *Int'l*, pg. 6617
NET-TECH PRODUCTS LIMITED—See Suga International Holdings Limited; *Int'l*, pg. 7253
NETTER GMBH; *Int'l*, pg. 5216
NETTERVIBRATION ESPANA S.L.—See Netter GmbH; *Int'l*, pg. 5216
NETTERVIBRATION POLSKA SP. Z O.O.—See Netter GmbH; *Int'l*, pg. 5216
NETTIME SOLUTIONS LLC—See Paychex, Inc.; *U.S. Public*, pg. 1655
NETTINGSDORFER PAPIERFABRIK AG & CO KG - ABERCARN PLANT—See Smurfit Kappa Group plc; *Int'l*, pg. 7018
NETTINGSDORFER PAPIERFABRIK AG & CO KG - AGRIPACK PLANT—See Smurfit Kappa Group plc; *Int'l*, pg. 7018
NETTINGSDORFER PAPIERFABRIK AG & CO KG - ALCALA PLANT—See Smurfit Kappa Group plc; *Int'l*, pg. 7018
NETTINGSDORFER PAPIERFABRIK AG & CO KG - ALICANTE PLANT—See Smurfit Kappa Group plc; *Int'l*, pg. 7018
NETTINGSDORFER PAPIERFABRIK AG & CO KG - ANIA PAPER—See Smurfit Kappa Group plc; *Int'l*, pg. 7018
NETTINGSDORFER PAPIERFABRIK AG & CO KG - ASTI PLANT—See Smurfit Kappa Group plc; *Int'l*, pg. 7018
NETTINGSDORFER PAPIERFABRIK AG & CO KG - BADEN KARTON PLANT—See Smurfit Kappa Group plc; *Int'l*, pg. 7018
NETTINGSDORFER PAPIERFABRIK AG & CO KG - BAG-IN-BOX ITALY PLANT—See Smurfit Kappa Group plc; *Int'l*, pg. 7018
NETTINGSDORFER PAPIERFABRIK AG & CO KG - BAG IN BOX PLANT—See Smurfit Kappa Group plc; *Int'l*, pg. 7018
NETTINGSDORFER PAPIERFABRIK AG & CO KG - BENELUX PLANT—See Smurfit Kappa Group plc; *Int'l*, pg. 7017
NETTINGSDORFER PAPIERFABRIK AG & CO KG - BERNAL PLANT—See Smurfit Kappa Group plc; *Int'l*, pg. 7018
NETTINGSDORFER PAPIERFABRIK AG & CO KG - BIRMINGHAM RECYCLING DEPOT PLANT—See Smurfit Kappa Group plc; *Int'l*, pg. 7018
NETTINGSDORFER PAPIERFABRIK AG & CO KG - BIZET PLANT—See Smurfit Kappa Group plc; *Int'l*, pg. 7018
NETTINGSDORFER PAPIERFABRIK AG & CO KG - BRANNOGARD PLANT—See Smurfit Kappa Group plc; *Int'l*, pg. 7018
NETTINGSDORFER PAPIERFABRIK AG & CO KG - BURGOS I AND BURGOS II PLANT—See Smurfit Kappa Group plc; *Int'l*, pg. 7019
NETTINGSDORFER PAPIERFABRIK AG & CO KG - CARTOMILLS ARLON PLANT—See Smurfit Kappa Group plc; *Int'l*, pg. 7019
NETTINGSDORFER PAPIERFABRIK AG & CO KG - CARTOMILLS GHLIN PLANT—See Smurfit Kappa Group plc; *Int'l*, pg. 7019
NETTINGSDORFER PAPIERFABRIK AG & CO KG - CARTOMILLS GROOT-BIJGAARDEN PLANT—See Smurfit Kappa Group plc; *Int'l*, pg. 7019
NETTINGSDORFER PAPIERFABRIK AG & CO KG - CARTON FRANCE PLANT—See Smurfit Kappa Group plc; *Int'l*, pg. 7019
NETTINGSDORFER PAPIERFABRIK AG & CO KG - CARTONNAGES DE LORRAINE PLANT—See Smurfit Kappa Group plc; *Int'l*, pg. 7019
NETTINGSDORFER PAPIERFABRIK AG & CO KG - CARTONNERIE D'AQUITAINE PLANT—See Smurfit Kappa Group plc; *Int'l*, pg. 7019
NETTINGSDORFER PAPIERFABRIK AG & CO KG - CARTONNERIE DE BIGNY PLANT—See Smurfit Kappa Group plc; *Int'l*, pg. 7019
NETTINGSDORFER PAPIERFABRIK AG & CO KG - CARTONNERIE DE DIJON PLANT—See Smurfit Kappa Group plc; *Int'l*, pg. 7019
NETTINGSDORFER PAPIERFABRIK AG & CO KG - CARTONNERIE DE GALLARGUES PLANT—See Smurfit Kappa Group plc; *Int'l*, pg. 7019
NETTINGSDORFER PAPIERFABRIK AG & CO KG - CARTONNERIE DE MORTAGNE PLANT—See Smurfit Kappa Group plc; *Int'l*, pg. 7019
NETTINGSDORFER PAPIERFABRIK AG & CO KG - CARTONNERIE DE ROUBAIX PLANT—See Smurfit Kappa Group plc; *Int'l*, pg. 7019
NETTINGSDORFER PAPIERFABRIK AG & CO KG - CARTONNERIE D—See Smurfit Kappa Group plc; *Int'l*, pg. 7019
NETTINGSDORFER PAPIERFABRIK AG & CO KG - CARTONNERIE D—See Smurfit Kappa Group plc; *Int'l*, pg. 7019
NETTINGSDORFER PAPIERFABRIK AG & CO KG - CARTONNERIE NOUVELLE DE CHAMPAGNE PLANT—See Smurfit Kappa Group plc; *Int'l*, pg. 7019
NETTINGSDORFER PAPIERFABRIK AG & CO KG - CELLULOSE DU PIN PLANT—See Smurfit Kappa Group plc; *Int'l*, pg. 7019
NETTINGSDORFER PAPIERFABRIK AG & CO KG - CENTRAL FORESTAL PLANT—See Smurfit Kappa Group plc; *Int'l*, pg. 7019
NETTINGSDORFER PAPIERFABRIK AG & CO KG - CIUDAD JUAREZ CORRUGATED PLANT—See Smurfit Kappa Group plc; *Int'l*, pg. 7019
NETTINGSDORFER PAPIERFABRIK AG & CO KG - CORDOBA PLANT—See Smurfit Kappa Group plc; *Int'l*, pg. 7019
NETTINGSDORFER PAPIERFABRIK AG & CO KG - CORRPRINT PLANT—See Smurfit Kappa Group plc; *Int'l*, pg. 7019
NETTINGSDORFER PAPIERFABRIK AG & CO KG - CORRUGATED EQUIPMENT PLANT—See Smurfit Kappa Group plc; *Int'l*, pg. 7019
NETTINGSDORFER PAPIERFABRIK AG & CO KG - CULIACAN CORRUGATED PLANT—See Smurfit Kappa Group plc; *Int'l*, pg. 7019
NETTINGSDORFER PAPIERFABRIK AG & CO KG - CUSINATI DI ROSA PLANT—See Smurfit Kappa Group plc; *Int'l*, pg. 7019
NETTINGSDORFER PAPIERFABRIK AG & CO KG - DEVELOPMENT CENTRE PLANT—See Smurfit Kappa Group plc; *Int'l*, pg. 7017
NETTINGSDORFER PAPIERFABRIK AG & CO KG - DISPLAY PLANT—See Smurfit Kappa Group plc; *Int'l*, pg. 7019
NETTINGSDORFER PAPIERFABRIK AG & CO KG - DISS PLANT—See Smurfit Kappa Group plc; *Int'l*, pg. 7019
NETTINGSDORFER PAPIERFABRIK AG & CO KG - DISTRIBUTION PLANT—See Smurfit Kappa Group plc; *Int'l*, pg. 7019
NETTINGSDORFER PAPIERFABRIK AG & CO KG - DORE EMBALLAGE PLANT—See Smurfit Kappa Group plc; *Int'l*, pg. 7019
NETTINGSDORFER PAPIERFABRIK AG & CO KG - DUBLIN PLANT—See Smurfit Kappa Group plc; *Int'l*, pg. 7019
NETTINGSDORFER PAPIERFABRIK AG & CO KG - EINDHOVEN RECYCLING DEPOT PLANT—See Smurfit Kappa Group plc; *Int'l*, pg. 7017
NETTINGSDORFER PAPIERFABRIK AG & CO KG - ESLOV PLANT—See Smurfit Kappa Group plc; *Int'l*, pg. 7019
NETTINGSDORFER PAPIERFABRIK AG & CO KG - ESPAC PLANT—See Smurfit Kappa Group plc; *Int'l*, pg. 7019
NETTINGSDORFER PAPIERFABRIK AG & CO KG - ESPANA Y PORTUGAL PLANT—See Smurfit Kappa Group plc; *Int'l*, pg. 7019
NETTINGSDORFER PAPIERFABRIK AG & CO KG - EUROPEAN PAPER SOURCING BV PLANT—See Smurfit Kappa Group plc; *Int'l*, pg. 7017
NETTINGSDORFER PAPIERFABRIK AG & CO KG - FIBERS PLANT—See Smurfit Kappa Group plc; *Int'l*, pg. 7019
NETTINGSDORFER PAPIERFABRIK AG & CO KG - FLEXOLINE PLANT—See Smurfit Kappa Group plc; *Int'l*, pg. 7019
NETTINGSDORFER PAPIERFABRIK AG & CO KG - FORLI PLANT—See Smurfit Kappa Group plc; *Int'l*, pg. 7019
NETTINGSDORFER PAPIERFABRIK AG & CO KG - FRANCE SAS PLANT—See Smurfit Kappa Group plc; *Int'l*, pg. 7019
NETTINGSDORFER PAPIERFABRIK AG & CO KG - FUSTELPACK PLANT—See Smurfit Kappa Group plc; *Int'l*, pg. 7019
NETTINGSDORFER PAPIERFABRIK AG & CO KG - GALSGOW RECYCLING DEPOT PLANT—See Smurfit Kappa Group plc; *Int'l*, pg. 7019
NETTINGSDORFER PAPIERFABRIK AG & CO KG - GOSPORT PLANT—See Smurfit Kappa Group plc; *Int'l*, pg. 7019
NETTINGSDORFER PAPIERFABRIK AG & CO KG - GRANTORTO PLANT—See Smurfit Kappa Group plc; *Int'l*, pg. 7019
NETTINGSDORFER PAPIERFABRIK AG & CO KG - GUANAJUATO CORRUGATED PLANT—See Smurfit Kappa Group plc; *Int'l*, pg. 7019
NETTINGSDORFER PAPIERFABRIK AG & CO KG - HAMBURG RECYCLING DEPOT PLANT—See Smurfit Kappa Group plc; *Int'l*, pg. 7019
NETTINGSDORFER PAPIERFABRIK AG & CO KG - HERZBERGER PAPIERFABRIK - BOARD MILL PLANT—See Smurfit Kappa Group plc; *Int'l*, pg. 7019
NETTINGSDORFER PAPIERFABRIK AG & CO KG - HERZBERGER PAPIERFABRIK - CONVERTING PLANT—See Smurfit Kappa Group plc; *Int'l*, pg. 7019
NETTINGSDORFER PAPIERFABRIK AG & CO KG - HERZBERGER PAPIERFABRIK - MACHINE SYSTEMS PLANT—See Smurfit Kappa Group plc; *Int'l*, pg. 7020
NETTINGSDORFER PAPIERFABRIK AG & CO KG - HERZBERGER WELLPAPPE PLANT—See Smurfit Kappa Group plc; *Int'l*, pg. 7020
NETTINGSDORFER PAPIERFABRIK AG & CO KG - HOYA KARTON PLANT—See Smurfit Kappa Group plc; *Int'l*, pg. 7020
NETTINGSDORFER PAPIERFABRIK AG & CO KG - HUELVA PLANT—See Smurfit Kappa Group plc; *Int'l*, pg. 7020
NETTINGSDORFER PAPIERFABRIK AG & CO KG - INTERWELL PLANT—See Smurfit Kappa Group plc; *Int'l*, pg. 7020
NETTINGSDORFER PAPIERFABRIK AG & CO KG - KAWELL PLANT—See Smurfit Kappa Group plc; *Int'l*, pg. 7020
NETTINGSDORFER PAPIERFABRIK AG & CO KG - KOLDING PLANT—See Smurfit Kappa Group plc; *Int'l*, pg. 7020
NETTINGSDORFER PAPIERFABRIK AG & CO KG - KRAFTLINER PITEA PLANT—See Smurfit Kappa Group plc; *Int'l*, pg. 7020
NETTINGSDORFER PAPIERFABRIK AG & CO KG - LA FRANCAISE PLANT—See Smurfit Kappa Group plc; *Int'l*, pg. 7020
NETTINGSDORFER PAPIERFABRIK AG & CO KG - LIQUIWELL PLANT—See Smurfit Kappa Group plc; *Int'l*, pg. 7020
NETTINGSDORFER PAPIERFABRIK AG & CO KG - LOKFAST PLANT—See Smurfit Kappa Group plc; *Int'l*, pg. 7020
NETTINGSDORFER PAPIERFABRIK AG & CO KG - LOS REYES MILL PLANT—See Smurfit Kappa Group plc; *Int'l*, pg. 7020
NETTINGSDORFER PAPIERFABRIK AG & CO KG - LUNATA PLANT—See Smurfit Kappa Group plc; *Int'l*, pg. 7020
NETTINGSDORFER PAPIERFABRIK AG & CO KG - LURGAN PLANT—See Smurfit Kappa Group plc; *Int'l*, pg. 7020
NETTINGSDORFER PAPIERFABRIK AG & CO KG - MAINE EMBALLAGES PLANT—See Smurfit Kappa Group plc; *Int'l*, pg. 7020
NETTINGSDORFER PAPIERFABRIK AG & CO KG - MANTOVA PLANT—See Smurfit Kappa Group plc; *Int'l*, pg. 7020
NETTINGSDORFER PAPIERFABRIK AG & CO KG - MASSA LOMBARDS PLANT—See Smurfit Kappa Group plc; *Int'l*, pg. 7020
NETTINGSDORFER PAPIERFABRIK AG & CO KG - MENGIBAR PAPER PLANT—See Smurfit Kappa Group plc; *Int'l*, pg. 7020
NETTINGSDORFER PAPIERFABRIK AG & CO KG - MEXICO HEADQUARTERS PLANT—See Smurfit Kappa Group plc; *Int'l*, pg. 7020
NETTINGSDORFER PAPIERFABRIK AG & CO KG - MNL GOLFKARTON DE ZEEUW PLANT—See Smurfit Kappa Group plc; *Int'l*, pg. 7017
NETTINGSDORFER PAPIERFABRIK AG & CO KG - MNL GOLFKARTON SOEST PLANT—See Smurfit Kappa Group plc; *Int'l*, pg. 7020

NETTINGSDORFER PAPIERFABRIK AG & CO KG - MONTERREY CORRUGATED GUADALUPE PLANT—See Smurfit Kappa Group plc; *Int'l*, pg. 7020
NETTINGSDORFER PAPIERFABRIK AG & CO KG - MORAVA PAPER PLANT—See Smurfit Kappa Group plc; *Int'l*, pg. 7020
NETTINGSDORFER PAPIERFABRIK AG & CO KG - NERVION PLANT—See Smurfit Kappa Group plc; *Int'l*, pg. 7020
NETTINGSDORFER PAPIERFABRIK AG & CO KG - NETTINGSDORFER PLANT—See Smurfit Kappa Group plc; *Int'l*, pg. 7020
NETTINGSDORFER PAPIERFABRIK AG & CO KG - NETTINGSDORFER SERVICE CENTER PLANT—See Smurfit Kappa Group plc; *Int'l*, pg. 7020
NETTINGSDORFER PAPIERFABRIK AG & CO KG - NORDWELL PLANT—See Smurfit Kappa Group plc; *Int'l*, pg. 7020
NETTINGSDORFER PAPIERFABRIK AG & CO KG - NORTHAMPTON PLANT—See Smurfit Kappa Group plc; *Int'l*, pg. 7020
NETTINGSDORFER PAPIERFABRIK AG & CO KG - ONWELL PLANT—See Smurfit Kappa Group plc; *Int'l*, pg. 7020
NETTINGSDORFER PAPIERFABRIK AG & CO KG - ORKO-PAK PLANT—See Smurfit Kappa Group plc; *Int'l*, pg. 7017
NETTINGSDORFER PAPIERFABRIK AG & CO KG - ORSENIGO CANS PLANT—See Smurfit Kappa Group plc; *Int'l*, pg. 7020
NETTINGSDORFER PAPIERFABRIK AG & CO KG - ORSENIGO PLANT—See Smurfit Kappa Group plc; *Int'l*, pg. 7020
NETTINGSDORFER PAPIERFABRIK AG & CO KG - PACKAGING SOLUTIONS CZECH PLANT—See Smurfit Kappa Group plc; *Int'l*, pg. 7020
NETTINGSDORFER PAPIERFABRIK AG & CO KG - PACKAGING SOLUTIONS DUBLIN PLANT—See Smurfit Kappa Group plc; *Int'l*, pg. 7020
NETTINGSDORFER PAPIERFABRIK AG & CO KG - PACKAGING SOLUTIONS WATERFORD PLANT—See Smurfit Kappa Group plc; *Int'l*, pg. 7020
NETTINGSDORFER PAPIERFABRIK AG & CO KG - PAPER PRODUCTION TECHNOLOGY PLANT—See Smurfit Kappa Group plc; *Int'l*, pg. 7017
NETTINGSDORFER PAPIERFABRIK AG & CO KG - PAPER SALES BENELUX PLANT—See Smurfit Kappa Group plc; *Int'l*, pg. 7017
NETTINGSDORFER PAPIERFABRIK AG & CO KG - PAPER SALES GERMANY PLANT—See Smurfit Kappa Group plc; *Int'l*, pg. 7020
NETTINGSDORFER PAPIERFABRIK AG & CO KG - PAPER SALES ITALY PLANT—See Smurfit Kappa Group plc; *Int'l*, pg. 7020
NETTINGSDORFER PAPIERFABRIK AG & CO KG - PAPER SALES UK & IRELAND PLANT—See Smurfit Kappa Group plc; *Int'l*, pg. 7020
NETTINGSDORFER PAPIERFABRIK AG & CO KG - PARNALLAND PLANT—See Smurfit Kappa Group plc; *Int'l*, pg. 7020
NETTINGSDORFER PAPIERFABRIK AG & CO KG - PASTRENGO PLANT—See Smurfit Kappa Group plc; *Int'l*, pg. 7020
NETTINGSDORFER PAPIERFABRIK AG & CO KG - PEGEWELL PLANT—See Smurfit Kappa Group plc; *Int'l*, pg. 7020
NETTINGSDORFER PAPIERFABRIK AG & CO KG - PLV FRANCE EMBALLAGES PLANT—See Smurfit Kappa Group plc; *Int'l*, pg. 7020
NETTINGSDORFER PAPIERFABRIK AG & CO KG - PLV LYON PLANT—See Smurfit Kappa Group plc; *Int'l*, pg. 7020
NETTINGSDORFER PAPIERFABRIK AG & CO KG - POITOU CARTONS PLANT—See Smurfit Kappa Group plc; *Int'l*, pg. 7021
NETTINGSDORFER PAPIERFABRIK AG & CO KG - PRINT VISION CHELMSFORD—See Smurfit Kappa Group plc; *Int'l*, pg. 7021
NETTINGSDORFER PAPIERFABRIK AG & CO KG - PRINT VISION PLANT—See Smurfit Kappa Group plc; *Int'l*, pg. 7021
NETTINGSDORFER PAPIERFABRIK AG & CO KG - PRINT VISION TANNOCHSIDE PLANT—See Smurfit Kappa Group plc; *Int'l*, pg. 7021
NETTINGSDORFER PAPIERFABRIK AG & CO KG - QUART PLANT—See Smurfit Kappa Group plc; *Int'l*, pg. 7021
NETTINGSDORFER PAPIERFABRIK AG & CO KG - RAPIDCORR EINDHOVEN PLANT—See Smurfit Kappa Group plc; *Int'l*, pg. 7017
NETTINGSDORFER PAPIERFABRIK AG & CO KG - RAPIDCORR EUSKIRCHEN PLANT—See Smurfit Kappa Group plc; *Int'l*, pg. 7021
NETTINGSDORFER PAPIERFABRIK AG & CO KG - RECYCLING GERMANY & CENTRAL FIBRE MANAGEMENT PLANT—See Smurfit Kappa Group plc; *Int'l*, pg. 7021
NETTINGSDORFER PAPIERFABRIK AG & CO KG - RECYCLING NETHERLANDS & CENTRAL FIBRE MANAGEMENT PLANT—See Smurfit Kappa Group plc; *Int'l*, pg. 7017
NETTINGSDORFER PAPIERFABRIK AG & CO KG - RHEINWELLE PLANT—See Smurfit Kappa Group plc; *Int'l*, pg. 7021
NETTINGSDORFER PAPIERFABRIK AG & CO KG - ROERMOND PAPIER PLANT—See Smurfit Kappa Group plc; *Int'l*, pg. 7017
NETTINGSDORFER PAPIERFABRIK AG & CO KG - ROL PIN - MOURENX PLANT—See Smurfit Kappa Group plc; *Int'l*, pg. 7021
NETTINGSDORFER PAPIERFABRIK AG & CO KG - ROVIGO PLANT—See Smurfit Kappa Group plc; *Int'l*, pg. 7021
NETTINGSDORFER PAPIERFABRIK AG & CO KG - SAN FELIPE MILL PLANT—See Smurfit Kappa Group plc; *Int'l*, pg. 7021
NETTINGSDORFER PAPIERFABRIK AG & CO KG - SANTIAGO PLANT—See Smurfit Kappa Group plc; *Int'l*, pg. 7021
NETTINGSDORFER PAPIERFABRIK AG & CO KG - SEVIAC PLANT—See Smurfit Kappa Group plc; *Int'l*, pg. 7021
NETTINGSDORFER PAPIERFABRIK AG & CO KG - SHEETFEEDING WINDRUSH PLANT—See Smurfit Kappa Group plc; *Int'l*, pg. 7021
NETTINGSDORFER PAPIERFABRIK AG & CO KG - SIEMCO PLANT—See Smurfit Kappa Group plc; *Int'l*, pg. 7021
NETTINGSDORFER PAPIERFABRIK AG & CO KG - SMURFIT KAPPA PACKAGING SOLUTIONS PLANT—See Smurfit Kappa Group plc; *Int'l*, pg. 7021
NETTINGSDORFER PAPIERFABRIK AG & CO KG - SMURFIT KAPPA TREASURY PLANT—See Smurfit Kappa Group plc; *Int'l*, pg. 7021
NETTINGSDORFER PAPIERFABRIK AG & CO KG - SNODLAND RECYCLING DEPOT PLANT—See Smurfit Kappa Group plc; *Int'l*, pg. 7021
NETTINGSDORFER PAPIERFABRIK AG & CO KG—See Smurfit Kappa Group plc; *Int'l*, pg. 7018
NETTINGSDORFER PAPIERFABRIK AG & CO KG - SP. Z O.O. ODDZIAL W DREZDENKU PLANT—See Smurfit Kappa Group plc; *Int'l*, pg. 7021
NETTINGSDORFER PAPIERFABRIK AG & CO KG - SP. Z O.O. ODDZIAL W KONINIE PLANT—See Smurfit Kappa Group plc; *Int'l*, pg. 7021
NETTINGSDORFER PAPIERFABRIK AG & CO KG - SP. Z O.O. ODDZIAL W WARSZAWIE PLANT—See Smurfit Kappa Group plc; *Int'l*, pg. 7021
NETTINGSDORFER PAPIERFABRIK AG & CO KG - SSK PLANT—See Smurfit Kappa Group plc; *Int'l*, pg. 7021
NETTINGSDORFER PAPIERFABRIK AG & CO KG - STALYBRIDGE PLANT—See Smurfit Kappa Group plc; *Int'l*, pg. 7021
NETTINGSDORFER PAPIERFABRIK AG & CO KG - SUSEGANA PLANT—See Smurfit Kappa Group plc; *Int'l*, pg. 7021
NETTINGSDORFER PAPIERFABRIK AG & CO KG - TEZZE / CARMIGNANO PLANT—See Smurfit Kappa Group plc; *Int'l*, pg. 7021
NETTINGSDORFER PAPIERFABRIK AG & CO KG - TOTANA PLANT—See Smurfit Kappa Group plc; *Int'l*, pg. 7021
NETTINGSDORFER PAPIERFABRIK AG & CO KG - TROBOX KARTONNAGES PLANT—See Smurfit Kappa Group plc; *Int'l*, pg. 7017
NETTINGSDORFER PAPIERFABRIK AG & CO KG - TROBOX VERPAKKING PLANT—See Smurfit Kappa Group plc; *Int'l*, pg. 7017
NETTINGSDORFER PAPIERFABRIK AG & CO KG - TURNHOUT PLANT—See Smurfit Kappa Group plc; *Int'l*, pg. 7021
NETTINGSDORFER PAPIERFABRIK AG & CO KG - TWINCORR PLANT—See Smurfit Kappa Group plc; *Int'l*, pg. 7017
NETTINGSDORFER PAPIERFABRIK AG & CO KG - VAN DAM GOLFKARTON PLANT—See Smurfit Kappa Group plc; *Int'l*, pg. 7017
NETTINGSDORFER PAPIERFABRIK AG & CO KG - VAN MIERLO PLANT—See Smurfit Kappa Group plc; *Int'l*, pg. 7021
NETTINGSDORFER PAPIERFABRIK AG & CO KG - VARDE PLANT—See Smurfit Kappa Group plc; *Int'l*, pg. 7021
NETTINGSDORFER PAPIERFABRIK AG & CO KG - VERCELLI PLANT—See Smurfit Kappa Group plc; *Int'l*, pg. 7021
NETTINGSDORFER PAPIERFABRIK AG & CO KG - VIGNATE PLANT—See Smurfit Kappa Group plc; *Int'l*, pg. 7021
NETTINGSDORFER PAPIERFABRIK AG & CO KG - VIGO PLANT—See Smurfit Kappa Group plc; *Int'l*, pg. 7021
NETTINGSDORFER PAPIERFABRIK AG & CO KG - VITOP MOULDING PLANT—See Smurfit Kappa Group plc; *Int'l*, pg. 7021
NETTINGSDORFER PAPIERFABRIK AG & CO KG - WAREN RECYCLING DEPOT PLANT—See Smurfit Kappa Group plc; *Int'l*, pg. 7021
NETTINGSDORFER PAPIERFABRIK AG & CO KG - WELLIT WELLPAPPENWERK PLANT—See Smurfit Kappa Group plc; *Int'l*, pg. 7021
NETTINGSDORFER PAPIERFABRIK AG & CO KG - WELLKART PLANT—See Smurfit Kappa Group plc; *Int'l*, pg. 7021
NETTINGSDORFER PAPIERFABRIK AG & CO KG - WELLPACK PLANT—See Smurfit Kappa Group plc; *Int'l*, pg. 7021
NETTINGSDORFER PAPIERFABRIK AG & CO KG - WELLPAPPE BRUHL PLANT—See Smurfit Kappa Group plc; *Int'l*, pg. 7021
NETTINGSDORFER PAPIERFABRIK AG & CO KG - WELLPAPPE HANAU PLANT—See Smurfit Kappa Group plc; *Int'l*, pg. 7021
NETTINGSDORFER PAPIERFABRIK AG & CO KG - WELLPAPPENWERK DELITZSCH PLANT—See Smurfit Kappa Group plc; *Int'l*, pg. 7022
NETTINGSDORFER PAPIERFABRIK AG & CO KG - WELLPAPPENWERK DUSSELDORF PLANT—See Smurfit Kappa Group plc; *Int'l*, pg. 7022
NETTINGSDORFER PAPIERFABRIK AG & CO KG - WELLPAPPENWERK GERMERSHEIM PLANT—See Smurfit Kappa Group plc; *Int'l*, pg. 7022
NETTINGSDORFER PAPIERFABRIK AG & CO KG - WELLPAPPENWERK JULICH PLANT—See Smurfit Kappa Group plc; *Int'l*, pg. 7022
NETTINGSDORFER PAPIERFABRIK AG & CO KG - WELLPAPPENWERK LUBBECKE PLANT—See Smurfit Kappa Group plc; *Int'l*, pg. 7022
NETTINGSDORFER PAPIERFABRIK AG & CO KG - WELLPAPPENWERK NEUBURG PLANT—See Smurfit Kappa Group plc; *Int'l*, pg. 7022
NETTINGSDORFER PAPIERFABRIK AG & CO KG - WELLPAPPENWERK PLATTLING PLANT—See Smurfit Kappa Group plc; *Int'l*, pg. 7022
NETTINGSDORFER PAPIERFABRIK AG & CO KG - WELLPAPPENWERK WAREN PLANT—See Smurfit Kappa Group plc; *Int'l*, pg. 7022
NETTINGSDORFER PAPIERFABRIK AG & CO KG - WELLPAPPE ST.LEON PLANT—See Smurfit Kappa Group plc; *Int'l*, pg. 7021
NETTINGSDORFER PAPIERFABRIK AG & CO KG - WELLTILLVERKAREN PLANT—See Smurfit Kappa Group plc; *Int'l*, pg. 7022
NETTINGSDORFER PAPIERFABRIK AG & CO KG - ZEDEK PLANT—See Smurfit Kappa Group plc; *Int'l*, pg. 7018
NETTINGSDORFER PAPIERFABRIK AG & CO KG - ZEDEK PLANT—See Smurfit Kappa Group plc; *Int'l*, pg. 7022
NETTINGSDORFER PAPIERFABRIK AG & CO KG - ZIMROVICE PLANT—See Smurfit Kappa Group plc; *Int'l*, pg. 7022
NETTINGSDORFER PAPIERFABRIK AG & CO KG - ZULPICH PAPIER PLANT—See Smurfit Kappa Group plc; *Int'l*, pg. 7022
NETTINGSDORFER PAPIERFABRIK AG & CO KG - ZWIESEL PLANT—See Smurfit Kappa Group plc; *Int'l*, pg. 7022
NETTLINX, INC.—See Nettlinx Limited; *Int'l*, pg. 5216
NETTLINX LIMITED; *Int'l*, pg. 5216
NETTLINX REALITY PVT LIMITED—See Nettlinx Limited; *Int'l*, pg. 5216
NETTOLINE A/S—See TCM Group A/S; *Int'l*, pg. 7484
NETTO MARKEN-DISCOUNT AG & CO. KG—See EDEKA Zentrale AG & Co. KG; *Int'l*, pg. 2305
NET TRANSCRIPTS, INC.—See VIQ Solutions Inc.; *Int'l*, pg. 8245
NETT SOLUTIONS INC.; *U.S. Private*, pg. 2888
NETTUNO S.R.L.—See KONE Oyj; *Int'l*, pg. 4250
NET TURISTIK YAYINLAR SANAYI VE TIC. A.S.—See Net Holding A.S.; *Int'l*, pg. 5211
NETUM GROUP PLC; *Int'l*, pg. 5216
NETUNO INTERNATIONAL S.A.—See Nissui Corporation; *Int'l*, pg. 5378
NETUNO USA INC.; *U.S. Private*, pg. 2888
NETUREN AMERICA CORPORATION—See Neturen Co., Ltd.; *Int'l*, pg. 5216
NETUREN CO. LTD. - AKO PLANT—See Neturen Co., Ltd.; *Int'l*, pg. 5216
NETUREN CO. LTD. - AMAGASAKI PLANT—See Neturen Co., Ltd.; *Int'l*, pg. 5216
NETUREN CO. LTD. - HIRATSUKA PLANT—See Neturen Co., Ltd.; *Int'l*, pg. 5216
NETUREN CO. LTD. - HIRATSUKA PLANT—See Neturen Co., Ltd.; *Int'l*, pg. 5216
NETUREN CO. LTD. - INDUCTION HEATING DIVISION—See Neturen Co., Ltd.; *Int'l*, pg. 5216
NETUREN CO. LTD. - IWAKI PLANT—See Neturen Co., Ltd.; *Int'l*, pg. 5216
NETUREN CO. LTD. - KANI PLANT—See Neturen Co., Ltd.; *Int'l*, pg. 5216
NETUREN CO. LTD. - KARIYA PLANT—See Neturen Co., Ltd.; *Int'l*, pg. 5216

COMPANY NAME INDEX

NETUREN CO. LTD. - KOBE PLANT—See Neturen Co., Ltd.; *Int'l*, pg. 5216
NETUREN CO. LTD. - NAGOYA PLANT—See Neturen Co., Ltd.; *Int'l*, pg. 5216
NETUREN CO. LTD. - SAMUKAWA PLANT—See Neturen Co., Ltd.; *Int'l*, pg. 5216
NETUREN CO., LTD.; *Int'l*, pg. 5216
NETUREN CO. LTD. - SPECIALTY STEEL & WIRE PRODUCTS DIVISION—See Neturen Co., Ltd.; *Int'l*, pg. 5216
NETUREN HEAT TREAT CO. LTD.—See Neturen Co., Ltd.; *Int'l*, pg. 5216
NETUREN HIRAKATA CO., LTD.—See Neturen Co., Ltd.; *Int'l*, pg. 5216
NETUREN HYMEC CO., LTD.—See Neturen Co., Ltd.; *Int'l*, pg. 5216
NETUREN KAKOGAWA CO., LTD.—See Neturen Co., Ltd.; *Int'l*, pg. 5216
NETUREN KOMATSU CO., LTD.—See Neturen Co., Ltd.; *Int'l*, pg. 5216
NETUREN MEINAN CO., LTD.—See Neturen Co., Ltd.; *Int'l*, pg. 5216
NETUREN RYUGASAKI CO., LTD.—See Neturen Co., Ltd.; *Int'l*, pg. 5216
NETUREN TAKUTO CO., LTD.—See Neturen Co., Ltd.; *Int'l*, pg. 5216
NETUREN USA, INC.—See Neturen Co., Ltd.; *Int'l*, pg. 5217
NETVALUE CO., LTD.—See MIT Holdings Co., Ltd.; *Int'l*, pg. 4923
NETVERSANT SOLUTIONS LLC—See Patriarch Partners, LLC; *U.S. Private*, pg. 3109
NETVISION RESOURCES, INC.; *U.S. Private*, pg. 2888
NETVISTA VENTURES LTD.; *Int'l*, pg. 5217
NETWEALTH GROUP LIMITED; *Int'l*, pg. 5217
NETWEALTH INVESTMENT LIMITED—See Netwealth Group Limited; *Int'l*, pg. 5217
NETWEAVE SOCIAL NETWORKING LLC; *U.S. Private*, pg. 2888
NETWEB TECHNOLOGIES INDIA LIMITED; *Int'l*, pg. 5217
NETWEEK S.P.A.; *Int'l*, pg. 5217
NETWHEELS OY—See Sanoma Oyj; *Int'l*, pg. 6553
NETWOLVES, LLC—See Vaso Corporation; *U.S. Public*, pg. 2276
NETWORK 18 MEDIA & INVESTMENTS LIMITED—See Reliance - ADA Group Limited; *Int'l*, pg. 6262
NETWORK-1 TECHNOLOGIES, INC.; *U.S. Public*, pg. 1509
NETWORK21 CO., LTD.—See Digital Hearts Holdings Co., Ltd.; *Int'l*, pg. 2122
NETWORK9, LLC; *U.S. Private*, pg. 2889
NETWORK ADJUSTERS INC.; *U.S. Private*, pg. 2888
NETWORK ADVANTAGE—See DD & SF Investments, Inc.; *U.S. Private*, pg. 1180
NETWORK AFFILIATES INC.; *U.S. Private*, pg. 2888
NETWORK ALLIANCE, INC.—See Southfield Capital Advisors, LLC; *U.S. Private*, pg. 3736
NETWORK AND SIMULATION TECHNOLOGIES INCORPORATED—See Saalex Corp.; *U.S. Private*, pg. 3520
NETWORK APPLIANCE BV THE NETHERLANDS—See NetApp, Inc.; *U.S. Public*, pg. 1507
NETWORK APPLIANCE INDIA—See NetApp, Inc.; *U.S. Public*, pg. 1507
NETWORK APPLIANCE SAUDI ARABIA LTD—See NetApp, Inc.; *U.S. Public*, pg. 1507
NET#WORK BBDO—See Omnicom Group Inc.; *U.S. Public*, pg. 1576
NETWORK BILLING SYSTEMS, LLC—See Fusion Connect, Inc.; *U.S. Private*, pg. 1625
NETWORK BUSINESS PRODUCTS—See Methode Electronics, Inc.; *U.S. Public*, pg. 1429
NETWORK CABLING SERVICES, INC.; *U.S. Private*, pg. 2888
NETWORK CAPITAL FUNDING CORP.; *U.S. Private*, pg. 2889
NETWORK CHICAGO—See Window to the World Communications, Inc.; *U.S. Private*, pg. 4538
NETWORK CN INC.; *Int'l*, pg. 5217
NETWORK CO. A.D.; *Int'l*, pg. 5217
NETWORK COMMERCIAL SERVICE, INC.; *U.S. Private*, pg. 2889
NETWORK COMPUTING ARCHITECTS, INC.—See IS-SQUARED Inc.; *U.S. Private*, pg. 2147
NETWORK COMPUTING TECHNOLOGY & SERVICES SARL—See ManpowerGroup Inc.; *U.S. Public*, pg. 1362
THE NETWORK CONNECTIONS SDN. BHD.—See Telekom Malaysia Berhad; *Int'l*, pg. 7537
NETWORK CONSULTING SERVICES, INC.; *U.S. Private*, pg. 2889
NET WORK CORPORATION—See Nikon Corporation; *Int'l*, pg. 5292
NETWORK COURIER SERVICES INC.; *U.S. Private*, pg. 2889
NETWORK DATA, INC.—See EQT AB; *Int'l*, pg. 2477
NETWORK DATA SYSTEMS INC.; *U.S. Private*, pg. 2889

NETWORKD CORP.—See Signal Peak Venture Partners, LLC; *U.S. Private*, pg. 3649
NETWORK DESIGN & INTEGRATION, INC.—See Novacoast, Inc.; *U.S. Private*, pg. 2966
NETWORK DIGITAL DISTRIBUTION SERVICES FZ-LLC—See National Amusements, Inc.; *U.S. Private*, pg. 2844
NETWORK DIGITAL DISTRIBUTION SERVICES FZ-LLC—See Reliance - ADA Group Limited; *Int'l*, pg. 6263
NETWORK DYNAMICS INC.—See Global Convergence, Inc.; *U.S. Private*, pg. 1713
NETWORKED INSIGHTS, INC.—See American Family Mutual Insurance Company; *U.S. Private*, pg. 233
NETWORK ENGINEERING SERVICES—See Amphenol Corporation; *U.S. Public*, pg. 132
NETWORK ENHANCED TELECOM LLP; *U.S. Private*, pg. 2889
NETWORK ENTERTAINMENT INC.—See Network Media Group Inc.; *Int'l*, pg. 5217
NETWORK EQUIPMENT TECHNOLOGIES, INC.—See Ribbon Communications Inc.; *U.S. Public*, pg. 1797
NETWORKERS FUNDING, LLC; *U.S. Private*, pg. 2889
NETWORKERS INTERNATIONAL (CHINA) CO. LTD—See Gattaca plc; *Int'l*, pg. 2890
NETWORKERS INTERNATIONAL LIMITED—See Gattaca plc; *Int'l*, pg. 2890
NETWORKERS INTERNATIONAL LLC—See Gattaca plc; *Int'l*, pg. 2890
NETWORKERS INTERNATIONAL (MALAYSIA) SDN BHD—See Gattaca plc; *Int'l*, pg. 2890
NETWORKERS TELECOMMUNICATIONS INC—See Gattaca plc; *Int'l*, pg. 2890
NETWORKERS TELECOMMUNICATIONS PTY LTD—See Gattaca plc; *Int'l*, pg. 2890
NETWORK FOODS INDUSTRIES SDN BHD—See Malayan United Industries Berhad; *Int'l*, pg. 4661
NETWORK FOR ELECTRONIC TRANSFERS (SINGAPORE) PTE LTD.; *Int'l*, pg. 5217
NETWORK FOR GOOD, INC.; *U.S. Private*, pg. 2889
NETWORK FOR MEDICAL COMMUNICATION & RESEARCH, LLC—See Cencora, Inc.; *U.S. Public*, pg. 467
NETWORK FOR TEACHING ENTREPRENEURSHIP; *U.S. Private*, pg. 2889
NETWORK GLOBAL LOGISTICS, LLC—See United Parcel Service, Inc.; *U.S. Public*, pg. 2233
NETWORK GROUP HOLDINGS PLC—See Lloyds Banking Group plc; *Int'l*, pg. 4537
NETWORK HARDWARE RESALE, LLC; *U.S. Private*, pg. 2889
NETWORK HEALTH PLAN—See Affinity Health System; *U.S. Private*, pg. 123
NETWORK HOLDINGS INC.—See Align Financial Group, LLC; *U.S. Private*, pg. 168
NETWORK HOLDINGS INC.—See Excellere Capital Management LLC; *U.S. Private*, pg. 1446
NETWORK IMAGING SOLUTIONS INC.; *U.S. Private*, pg. 2889
NET@WORK, INC.; *U.S. Private*, pg. 2886
NETWORK INFRASTRUCTURE TECHNOLOGIES, INC.—See Asseco Poland S.A.; *Int'l*, pg. 642
NETWORKING TECHNOLOGIES & SUPPORT, INC.; *U.S. Private*, pg. 2889
NETWORK INNOVATION AB; *Int'l*, pg. 5217
NETWORK INNOVATIONS INC.; *Int'l*, pg. 5217
NETWORK INSTRUMENTS, LLC—See Viavi Solutions Inc.; *U.S. Public*, pg. 2295
NETWORK INSURANCE GROUP PTY LTD—See Steadfast Group Limited; *Int'l*, pg. 7187
NETWORK INTERNATIONAL HOLDINGS PLC—See Brookfield Corporation; *Int'l*, pg. 1189
NETWORK INTERNATIONAL INC.—See Liquidity Services, Inc.; *U.S. Public*, pg. 1321
NETWORK INTERNATIONAL LLC—See Emirates NBD PJSC; *Int'l*, pg. 2382
NETWORK INTERNATIONAL PAYMENT SERVICES PROPRIETARY LIMITED—See Brookfield Corporation; *Int'l*, pg. 1189
NETWORK INTERNATIONAL PAYMENTS SERVICES NIGERIA LIMITED—See Brookfield Corporation; *Int'l*, pg. 1189
NETWORK INTERNATIONAL SERVICES LIMITED—See Brookfield Corporation; *Int'l*, pg. 1189
NETWORK LOGISTICS UK LTD—See CitySprint (UK) Limited; *Int'l*, pg. 1630
NETWORK LTD.; *Int'l*, pg. 5217
NETWORK MAPPING INC.—See Trimble, Inc.; *U.S. Public*, pg. 2190
NETWORK MAPPING LIMITED—See Trimble, Inc.; *U.S. Public*, pg. 2190
NETWORK MEDIA GROUP INC.; *Int'l*, pg. 5217
NETWORK MEDIA PARTNERS, LLC—See MCI Group Holding SA; *Int'l*, pg. 4758
NETWORK MEDICAL, LLC—See StateServ Medical, LLC; *U.S. Private*, pg. 3793
NETWORK MEDICAL MANAGEMENT, INC.—See Astrana Health Inc.; *U.S. Public*, pg. 217

NET ZERO RENEWABLE ENERGY INC.

NETWORK MEDICS, INC.—See Tonka Bay Equity Partners LLC; *U.S. Private*, pg. 4185
NETWORK MERCHANTS, LLC—See Francisco Partners Management, LP; *U.S. Private*, pg. 1590
NETWORK NURSING AGENCY PTY LTD—See PeopleIn Limited; *Int'l*, pg. 5794
NETWORKOMNI; *U.S. Private*, pg. 2889
NETWORK ONE SOLUTIONS INC.—See UPSTACK, Inc.; *U.S. Private*, pg. 4313
NETWORK OUTSOURCE, INC.; *U.S. Private*, pg. 2889
NETWORK PACKAGING GROUP LLC—See Beecken Petty O'Keefe & Company, LLC; *U.S. Private*, pg. 514
NETWORK PEOPLE, INC.—See Frontenac Company LLC; *U.S. Private*, pg. 1614
NETWORK PEOPLE SERVICES TECHNOLOGIES LIMITED; *Int'l*, pg. 5217
NETWORK POLYMERS INC.—See LyondellBasell Industries N.V.; *Int'l*, pg. 4607
THE NETWORK PRO, INC.—See IT Solutions Consulting LLC; *U.S. Private*, pg. 2148
NETWORK RAIL CERTIFICATION BODY LIMITED—See Network Rail Limited; *Int'l*, pg. 5218
NETWORK RAIL CONSULTING LIMITED—See Network Rail Limited; *Int'l*, pg. 5218
NETWORK RAIL (HIGH SPEED) LIMITED—See Network Rail Limited; *Int'l*, pg. 5217
NETWORK RAIL INFRASTRUCTURE FINANCE PLC—See Network Rail Limited; *Int'l*, pg. 5218
NETWORK RAIL INFRASTRUCTURE LTD—See Network Rail Limited; *Int'l*, pg. 5218
NETWORK RAIL LIMITED; *Int'l*, pg. 5217
NETWORK RELATED SERVICES SA—See Orange S.A.; *Int'l*, pg. 5609
NETWORKS CENTRE B.V.—See Alcadon Group AB; *Int'l*, pg. 300
NETWORKS CENTRE LTD.—See Alcadon Group AB; *Int'l*, pg. 300
NETWORKS CENTRE (SCOTLAND) LIMITED—See Alcadon Group AB; *Int'l*, pg. 300
NETWORK SERVICES COMPANY; *U.S. Private*, pg. 2889
NETWORK SERVICES GROUP, LLC—See Windstream Holdings, Inc.; *U.S. Public*, pg. 2373
NETWORK SOLUTIONS PROVIDER (NSP); *U.S. Private*, pg. 2889
NETWORKS UNLIMITED, INC.; *U.S. Private*, pg. 2889
NETWORK SUPPORT COMPANY, LLC—See The Riverside Company; *U.S. Private*, pg. 4109
NETWORK SYSTEMS INTERNATIONAL, INC.; *U.S. Private*, pg. 2889
NETWORK TECHNOLOGY PLC; *Int'l*, pg. 5218
NETWORK TEN (ADELAIDE) PTY LIMITED—See National Amusements, Inc.; *U.S. Private*, pg. 2844
NETWORK TEN (BRISBANE) PTY LIMITED—See National Amusements, Inc.; *U.S. Private*, pg. 2844
NETWORK TEN (MELBOURNE) PTY LIMITED—See National Amusements, Inc.; *U.S. Private*, pg. 2844
NETWORK TEN (PERTH) PTY LIMITED—See National Amusements, Inc.; *U.S. Private*, pg. 2844
NETWORK TEN PTY. LIMITED—See National Amusements, Inc.; *U.S. Private*, pg. 2844
NETWORK VALUE COMPONENTS LTD.—See Nippon Steel Corporation; *Int'l*, pg. 5335
NETWORK WORLD, INC.—See China Oceanwide Holdings Group Co., Ltd.; *Int'l*, pg. 1538
NETWORK WORLD, INC.—See IDG Capital; *Int'l*, pg. 3594
NETWORLD ALLIANCE, LLC; *U.S. Private*, pg. 2889
NETWORLD CORPORATION—See OTSUKA CORPORATION; *Int'l*, pg. 5658
NETWORTH SOFFTECH LTD.—See Monarch Networth Capital Ltd.; *Int'l*, pg. 5025
NETWORTH SYSTEMS CO. W.L.L—See Taleb Group; *Int'l*, pg. 7446
NETWORTH WEALTH SOLUTIONS LTD—See Monarch Networth Capital Ltd.; *Int'l*, pg. 5025
NETWOVEN INC.; *U.S. Private*, pg. 2889
NETWRIX CORPORATION—See TA Associates, Inc.; *U.S. Private*, pg. 3916
NETXCOM (PTY) LTD—See Stellar Capital Partners Limited; *Int'l*, pg. 7204
NETX HOLDINGS BERHAD; *Int'l*, pg. 5218
NET XPERTS LLC; *U.S. Private*, pg. 2886
NETXPOSURE, INC.; *U.S. Private*, pg. 2890
NETXUSA, INC.—See Hainan Traffic Administration Holding Co., Ltd.; *Int'l*, pg. 3215
NETYEAR GROUP CORPORATION; *Int'l*, pg. 5218
NETZE BW GMBH—See EnBW Energie Baden-Wurttemberg AG; *Int'l*, pg. 2399
NETZE BW WASSER GMBH—See EnBW Energie Baden-Wurttemberg AG; *Int'l*, pg. 2399
NETZE-GESELLSCHAFT SUDWEST MBH—See EnBW Energie Baden-Wurttemberg AG; *Int'l*, pg. 2399
NET ZERO INFRASTRUCTURE PLC; *Int'l*, pg. 5212
NET ZERO RENEWABLE ENERGY INC.; *Int'l*, pg. 5212
NET ZERO TEESSIDE POWER LIMITED—See BP plc; *Int'l*, pg. 1131
NETZGESELLSCHAFT DUSSELDORF MBH—See EnBW Energie Baden-Wurttemberg AG; *Int'l*, pg. 2399

NETZGESELLSCHAFT ELZ-NECKAR GMBH & CO. KG—See EnBW Energie Baden-Wurttemberg AG; *Int'l*, pg. 2399
NETZGESELLSCHAFT HERRENWALD VERWALTUNG GMBH—See E.ON SE; *Int'l*, pg. 2258
NETZGESELLSCHAFT KOTHEN MBH—See MVV Energie AG; *Int'l*, pg. 5109
NETZGESELLSCHAFT OSTWURTTEMBERG DONAURIES GMBH—See EnBW Energie Baden-Wurttemberg AG; *Int'l*, pg. 2399
NETZGESELLSCHAFT STEINHEIM GMBH & CO. KG—See EnBW Energie Baden-Wurttemberg AG; *Int'l*, pg. 2399
NETZGESELLSCHAFT STEINHEIM VERWALTUNGSGESELLSCHAFT MBH.—See EnBW Energie Baden-Wurttemberg AG; *Int'l*, pg. 2399
NETZ GROUP LTD.; *Int'l*, pg. 5218
NETZIKON GMBH—See Zech Group SE; *Int'l*, pg. 8628
NETZ NIEDEROSTERREICH GMBH—See EVN AG; *Int'l*, pg. 2571
NETZSCH ARGENTINA S. A.—See Erich Netzsch GmbH & Co. Holding KG; *Int'l*, pg. 2491
NETZSCH ASIA PACIFIC PTE LTD.—See Erich Netzsch GmbH & Co. Holding KG; *Int'l*, pg. 2491
NETZSCH AUSTRALIA PTY LTD—See Erich Netzsch GmbH & Co. Holding KG; *Int'l*, pg. 2491
NETZSCH CANADA, INC.—See Erich Netzsch GmbH & Co. Holding KG; *Int'l*, pg. 2491
NETZSCH CESKA REPUBLIKA S.R.O.—See Erich Netzsch GmbH & Co. Holding KG; *Int'l*, pg. 2493
NETZSCH-CONDUX MAHLTECHNIK GMBH—See Erich Netzsch GmbH & Co. Holding KG; *Int'l*, pg. 2492
NETZSCH DO BRASIL LTDA.—See Erich Netzsch GmbH & Co. Holding KG; *Int'l*, pg. 2492
NETZSCH ESPANA S.A.—See Erich Netzsch GmbH & Co. Holding KG; *Int'l*, pg. 2491
NETZSCH-FEINMAHLTECHNIK GMBH—See Erich Netzsch GmbH & Co. Holding KG; *Int'l*, pg. 2492
NETZSCH FRERES S.A.R.L.—See Erich Netzsch GmbH & Co. Holding KG; *Int'l*, pg. 2492
NETZSCH GERATEBAU GMBH—See Erich Netzsch GmbH & Co. Holding KG; *Int'l*, pg. 2492
NETZSCH INDUSTRIA E COMERCIO DE EQUIPAMENTOS DE MOAGEM LTDA.—See Erich Netzsch GmbH & Co. Holding KG; *Int'l*, pg. 2492
NETZSCH INSTRUMENTS NORTH AMERICA, LLC—See Erich Netzsch GmbH & Co. Holding KG; *Int'l*, pg. 2493
NETZSCH INSTRUMENTS SP.Z.O.O.—See Erich Netzsch GmbH & Co. Holding KG; *Int'l*, pg. 2492
NETZSCH JAPAN K.K.—See Erich Netzsch GmbH & Co. Holding KG; *Int'l*, pg. 2492
NETZSCH KOREA CO. LTD.—See Erich Netzsch GmbH & Co. Holding KG; *Int'l*, pg. 2492
NETZSCH LANZHOU PUMPS CO. LTD.—See Erich Netzsch GmbH & Co. Holding KG; *Int'l*, pg. 2492
NETZSCH LOHNMAHLTECHNIK GMBH—See Erich Netzsch GmbH & Co. Holding KG; *Int'l*, pg. 2492
NETZSCH MAKINE SANAYI VE TICARET LTD. STI.—See Erich Netzsch GmbH & Co. Holding KG; *Int'l*, pg. 2492
NETZSCH MALAYSIA SDN.BHD—See Erich Netzsch GmbH & Co. Holding KG; *Int'l*, pg. 2492
NETZSCH MASTERMIX LTD.—See Erich Netzsch GmbH & Co. Holding KG; *Int'l*, pg. 2492
NETZSCH MEXICO S.A. DE C.V.—See Erich Netzsch GmbH & Co. Holding KG; *Int'l*, pg. 2492
NETZSCH MILANTECNICA S.R.L.—See Erich Netzsch GmbH & Co. Holding KG; *Int'l*, pg. 2492
NETZSCH-OILFIELD PRODUCTS GMBH—See Erich Netzsch GmbH & Co. Holding KG; *Int'l*, pg. 2492
NETZSCH PERU SOCIEDAD ANONIMA CERRADO—See Erich Netzsch GmbH & Co. Holding KG; *Int'l*, pg. 2492
NETZSCH POMPEN NEDERLAND B.V.—See Erich Netzsch GmbH & Co. Holding KG; *Int'l*, pg. 2492
NETZSCH POMPE & SISTEMI ITALIA SRL—See Erich Netzsch GmbH & Co. Holding KG; *Int'l*, pg. 2492
NETZSCH PREMIER TECHNOLOGIES, LLC.—See Erich Netzsch GmbH & Co. Holding KG; *Int'l*, pg. 2492
NETZSCH PUMPEN & SYSTEME GMBH—See Erich Netzsch GmbH & Co. Holding KG; *Int'l*, pg. 2492
NETZSCH PUMPS BELLUX BVBA—See Erich Netzsch GmbH & Co. Holding KG; *Int'l*, pg. 2492
NETZSCH PUMPS NORTH AMERICA, LLC—See Erich Netzsch GmbH & Co. Holding KG; *Int'l*, pg. 2492
NETZSCH PUMPS RUS OOO—See Erich Netzsch GmbH & Co. Holding KG; *Int'l*, pg. 2492
NETZSCH PUMPS & SYSTEMS LTD.—See Erich Netzsch GmbH & Co. Holding KG; *Int'l*, pg. 2492
NETZSCH SCIENTIFIC INSTRUMENTS TRADING (SHANGHAI) LTD.—See Erich Netzsch GmbH & Co. Holding KG; *Int'l*, pg. 2492
NETZSCH SERVICE NORDESTE LTDA.—See Erich Netzsch GmbH & Co. Holding KG; *Int'l*, pg. 2492
NETZSCH (SHANGHAI) MACHINERY AND INSTRUMENTS CO. LTD.—See Erich Netzsch GmbH & Co. Holding KG; *Int'l*, pg. 2491
NETZSCH SOUTHERN AFRICA (PTY) LTD.—See Erich Netzsch GmbH & Co. Holding KG; *Int'l*, pg. 2493
NETZSCH TAURUS INSTRUMENTS GMBH—See Erich Netzsch GmbH & Co. Holding KG; *Int'l*, pg. 2493

NETZSCH TECHNOLOGIES INDIA PVT. LTD. - SALCETTE FACTORY—See Erich Netzsch GmbH & Co. Holding KG; *Int'l*, pg. 2492
NETZSCH TECHNOLOGIES, INDIA PVT. LTD.—See Erich Netzsch GmbH & Co. Holding KG; *Int'l*, pg. 2492
NETZSCH THAILAND LTD.—See Erich Netzsch GmbH & Co. Holding KG; *Int'l*, pg. 2492
NETZSCH TROCKENMAHLTECHNIK GMBH—See Erich Netzsch GmbH & Co. Holding KG; *Int'l*, pg. 2493
NETZSCH TULA ZAO—See Erich Netzsch GmbH & Co. Holding KG; *Int'l*, pg. 2492
NETZSCH USA HOLDINGS, INC.—See Erich Netzsch GmbH & Co. Holding KG; *Int'l*, pg. 2492
NETZSCH VAKUMIX GMBH—See Erich Netzsch GmbH & Co. Holding KG; *Int'l*, pg. 2492
NETZSCH VIETNAM LIMITED—See Erich Netzsch GmbH & Co. Holding KG; *Int'l*, pg. 2493
NETZSCH WERBE- UND SERVICE- GMBH—See Erich Netzsch GmbH & Co. Holding KG; *Int'l*, pg. 2492
NETZ TOYOTA CENTRO GIFU CO., LTD.—See Seino Holdings Co., Ltd.; *Int'l*, pg. 6690
NETZ TOYOTA FUKUI CO., LTD.—See Mitani Corporation; *Int'l*, pg. 4924
NETZ TOYOTA GIFU CO., LTD.—See Seino Holdings Co., Ltd.; *Int'l*, pg. 6690
NETZ- UND STRECKENENTWICKLUNG GMBH—See OBB-Holding AG; *Int'l*, pg. 5509
NETZ-UND WINDSERVICE (NWS) GMBH—See E.ON SE; *Int'l*, pg. 2256
NETZ UNITED STATES (H.Y) LTD.—See Netz Group Ltd.; *Int'l*, pg. 5218
NETZ VELTHEIM GMBH—See E.ON SE; *Int'l*, pg. 2258
NEU AUTOMATION SAS—See Groupe SFPI SA; *Int'l*, pg. 3111
NEUBASE THERAPEUTICS, INC.; *U.S. Public*, pg. 1509
NEUBERGER BERMAN ENERGY INFRASTRUCTURE AND INCOME FUND INC.—See Neuberger Berman Group LLC; *U.S. Private*, pg. 2890
NEUBERGER BERMAN GROUP LLC; *U.S. Private*, pg. 2890
NEUBERGER BERMAN LLC—See Neuberger Berman Group LLC; *U.S. Private*, pg. 2890
NEUBERGER GEBAUDEAUTOMATION GMBH—See Max Weishaupt GmbH; *Int'l*, pg. 4735
NEUCA-MED SP. Z O.O.—See NEUCA S.A.; *Int'l*, pg. 5218
NEUCA S.A.; *Int'l*, pg. 5218
NEUDESIC, LLC—See International Business Machines Corporation; *U.S. Public*, pg. 1149
NEUE AARGAUER BANK—See UBS Group AG; *Int'l*, pg. 8007
NEUE ALNO GMBH—See RiverRock European Capital Partners LLP; *Int'l*, pg. 6353
NEUE HALBERG-GUSS GMBH—See Prevent DEV GmbH; *Int'l*, pg. 5967
NEUEHEALTH, INC.; *U.S. Public*, pg. 1510
NEUE LEBEN HOLDING AG—See Talanx AG; *Int'l*, pg. 7445
NEUE LEBEN UNFALLVERSICHERUNG AG—See Talanx AG; *Int'l*, pg. 7445
NEUE PRESSEGESELLSCHAFT MBH & CO. KG; *Int'l*, pg. 5218
NEUFELD PETROLEUM & PROPANE LTD.—See Parkland Corporation; *Int'l*, pg. 5743
NEUFFER FENSTER & TUREN GMBH—See Investment AB Latour; *Int'l*, pg. 3784
NEUFLIZE VIE S.A.—See ABN AMRO Group N.V.; *Int'l*, pg. 63
NEUFTECH PHILIPPINES INC.—See Komax Holding AG; *Int'l*, pg. 4241
NEUGELB STUDIOS GMBH—See Commerzbank AG; *Int'l*, pg. 1719
NEUGER COMMUNICATIONS GROUP, INC.; *U.S. Private*, pg. 2890
NEUHAUS & COMPANY INC.; *U.S. Private*, pg. 2890
NEUHAUS NV—See Compagnie du Bois Sauvage SA; *Int'l*, pg. 1740
NEUHEIM LUX GROUP HOLDING V S.A.R.L.—See Sun Capital Partners, Inc.; *U.S. Private*, pg. 3862
NEU INTERNATIONAL RAILWAYS S.A.S.—See Groupe SFPI SA; *Int'l*, pg. 3111
NEUKIRCHEN IMMOBILIEN VERWALTUNGS GMBH—See KAJO NEUKIRCHEN Management und Beteiligungs GmbH; *Int'l*, pg. 4056
NEUKOM INSTALLATIONEN AG—See BKW AG; *Int'l*, pg. 1055
NEULAND LABORATORIES K.K.—See Neuland Laboratories Ltd; *Int'l*, pg. 5218
NEULAND LABORATORIES LTD; *Int'l*, pg. 5218
NEULAND WOHNUNGSGESELLSCHAFT MBH—See Porsche Automobil Holding SE; *Int'l*, pg. 5929
NEULIFT SERVICE MOLISE S.R.L.—See KONE Oyj; *Int'l*, pg. 4250
NEULIFT SERVICE TRIVENETO S.R.L.—See KONE Oyj; *Int'l*, pg. 4250
NEUMAN ALUMINIUM FLIESSPRESSWERK GMBH—See CAG Holding GmbH; *Int'l*, pg. 1250
NEUMAN ALUMINIUM IMPACT EXTRUSION INC.—See CAG Holding GmbH; *Int'l*, pg. 1250

NEUMAN ALUMINIUM SERVICES S.R.O.—See CAG Holding GmbH; *Int'l*, pg. 1250
NEUMANN BROTHERS INC.; *U.S. Private*, pg. 2890
NEUMANN CO., LTD.—See SOLXYZ Co., Ltd.; *Int'l*, pg. 7083
NEUMANN ENTERPRISES, INC.; *U.S. Private*, pg. 2890
NEUMANN FAMILY SERVICES; *U.S. Private*, pg. 2890
NEUMANN PRESS—See Saint Benedict Press; *U.S. Private*, pg. 3529
NEUMANN SYSTEMS GROUP, INC.; *U.S. Private*, pg. 2890
NEUMANN (USA)—See Sennheiser Electronic GmbH & Co. KG; *Int'l*, pg. 6712
NEUMAN (XINHUI) ALLOY MATERIAL CO LTD.—See CAG Holding GmbH; *Int'l*, pg. 1250
NEUMARKTER LAMMSBRAEU GEBR. EHRNSPERGER E.K.; *Int'l*, pg. 5218
NEUMATIC CZ S.R.O—See LEONI AG; *Int'l*, pg. 4464
NEUMATICOS GOODYEAR S.R.L.—See The Goodyear Tire & Rubber Company; *U.S. Public*, pg. 2082
NEUMAYER TEKFOR AUTOMOTIVE BRASIL LTDA.—See Amtek Auto Limited; *Int'l*, pg. 441
NEUMAYER TEKFOR SCHMOLLN GMBH—See Amtek Auto Limited; *Int'l*, pg. 441
NEUMIN PRODUCTION COMPANY—See Formosa Plastics Corporation; *Int'l*, pg. 2736
NEUMODX INC.—See QIAGEN N.V.; *Int'l*, pg. 6139
NEUMORA THERAPEUTICS, INC.; *U.S. Public*, pg. 1510
NEUPACK GESELLSCHAFT M.B.H.—See Mayr-Melnhof Karton AG; *Int'l*, pg. 4747
NEUPACK POLSKA SP.Z.O.O—See Mayr-Melnhof Karton AG; *Int'l*, pg. 4747
NEUPATH HEALTH, INC.; *Int'l*, pg. 5218
NEURAL GROUP INC.; *Int'l*, pg. 5218
NEURAL GROUP (THAILAND) CO., LTD.—See Neural Group Inc.; *Int'l*, pg. 5219
NEURAL MARKETING INC.—See Neural Group Inc.; *Int'l*, pg. 5219
NEURAL TECHNOLOGY LIMITED—See Thoma Bravo, L.P.; *U.S. Private*, pg. 4149
NEURAVI LIMITED—See Johnson & Johnson; *U.S. Public*, pg. 1200
NEURAXIS, INC.; *U.S. Public*, pg. 1510
NEURAXON INC.—See Knight Therapeutics Inc.; *Int'l*, pg. 4207
NEURELEC S.A.S.—See Demant A/S; *Int'l*, pg. 2024
NEUREN PHARMACEUTICALS (AUSTRALIA) PTY LTD.—See Neuren Pharmaceuticals Limited; *Int'l*, pg. 5219
NEUREN PHARMACEUTICALS INC.—See Neuren Pharmaceuticals Limited; *Int'l*, pg. 5219
NEUREN PHARMACEUTICALS LIMITED; *Int'l*, pg. 5219
NEURILINK LLC—See AVI Systems, Inc.; *U.S. Private*, pg. 406
NEURIO TECHNOLOGY ULC—See Generac Holdings Inc.; *U.S. Public*, pg. 912
NEURIZER LTD; *Int'l*, pg. 5219
NEUROBO PHARMACEUTICALS, INC.; *U.S. Public*, pg. 1510
NEUROCRINE BIOSCIENCES INC.; *U.S. Public*, pg. 1510
NEURODERM LTD.—See Mitsubishi Chemical Group Corporation; *Int'l*, pg. 4935
NEURODIMENSION, INC.; *U.S. Private*, pg. 2890
NEUROFIT SAS—See Bionomics Limited; *Int'l*, pg. 1040
NEUROFOCUS, INC.—See Brookfield Corporation; *Int'l*, pg. 1179
NEUROFOCUS, INC.—See Elliott Management Corporation; *U.S. Private*, pg. 1371
NEUROGENESIS, INC.; *U.S. Public*, pg. 1510
THE NEUROHEALTH SCIENCES CENTER, LLC—See HCA Healthcare, Inc.; *U.S. Public*, pg. 1012
NEURO-ID, INC.—See Experian plc; *Int'l*, pg. 2588
NEURO INSTITUTE OF AUSTIN, L.P.—See Universal Health Services, Inc.; *U.S. Public*, pg. 2258
NEUROLOGICA CORP.—See Samsung Group; *Int'l*, pg. 6512
NEUROLOGICAL SPECIALISTS OF MCKINNEY, PLLC—See HCA Healthcare, Inc.; *U.S. Public*, pg. 1004
NEUROLOGISCHE KLINIK GMBH—See Asklepios Kliniken GmbH & Co. KGaA; *Int'l*, pg. 624
NEUROLOGISCHES THERAPIEZENTRUM GMUNDNERBERG GMBH—See Fresenius SE & Co. KGaA; *Int'l*, pg. 2780
NEUROLOGISCHES THERAPIEZENTRUM KAPFENBERG GMBH—See Fresenius SE & Co. KGaA; *Int'l*, pg. 2780
NEUROMAMA, LTD.; *Int'l*, pg. 5219
NEUROMEKA CO., LTD.; *Int'l*, pg. 5219
NEUROMETRIX, INC.; *U.S. Public*, pg. 1510
NEURON BIOPHARMA SA; *Int'l*, pg. 5219
NEURONES IT ASIA PTE. LTD.—See Neurones S.A.; *Int'l*, pg. 5219
NEURONES IT SAS—See Neurones S.A.; *Int'l*, pg. 5219
NEURONES S.A.; *Int'l*, pg. 5219
NEURONETICS, INC.; *U.S. Public*, pg. 1510
NEURONEXUS TECHNOLOGIES, INC.—See NEL Group, Inc.; *U.S. Private*, pg. 2882

COMPANY NAME INDEX

NEUROONE MEDICAL TECHNOLOGIES CORPORATION; *U.S. Public*, pg. 1510
NEUROPATHIX, INC.; *U.S. Public*, pg. 1510
NEURORESTORATIVE—See Centerbridge Partners, L.P.; *U.S. Private*, pg. 814
NEUROSCIENCE ASSOCIATES OF KANSAS CITY, LLC—See HCA Healthcare, Inc.; *U.S. Public*, pg. 1004
NEUROSCIENTIFIC BIOPHARMACEUTICALS LIMITED; *Int'l*, pg. 5219
NEUROS CO., LTD.; *Int'l*, pg. 5219
NEUROSEARCH SWEDEN AB—See Nordic Transport Group Holding A/S; *Int'l*, pg. 5423
NEUROSENSE THERAPEUTICS LTD.; *Int'l*, pg. 5219
NEUROSIGMA, INC.; *U.S. Private*, pg. 2890
NEUROSKELETAL IMAGING, LLC—See Community Health Systems, Inc.; *U.S. Public*, pg. 555
NEUROSOFT ROMANIA SOFTWARE AND SERVICES SRL—See Neurosoft S.A.; *Int'l*, pg. 5220
NEUROSOFT S.A.; *Int'l*, pg. 5220
NEUROSOLUTIONS LIMITED—See OncoSil Medical Limited; *Int'l*, pg. 5574
NEUROSTAR SOLUTIONS, INC.—See Microsoft Corporation; *U.S. Public*, pg. 1442
NEUROS TURBO MACHINERY CORPORATION INC.—See Neuros Co., Ltd.; *Int'l*, pg. 5219
NEUROSURGERY ATLANTA, LLC—See HCA Healthcare, Inc.; *U.S. Public*, pg. 1004
NEUROSURGERY OF KINGWOOD, PLLC—See HCA Healthcare, Inc.; *U.S. Public*, pg. 1004
NEUROSURGICAL ASSOCIATES OF NORTH TEXAS, PLLC—See HCA Healthcare, Inc.; *U.S. Public*, pg. 1004
NEUROSURGICAL SPECIALISTS OF EL PASO, PLLC—See HCA Healthcare, Inc.; *U.S. Public*, pg. 1004
NEUROSURGICAL SPECIALISTS OF NORTH TEXAS, PLLC—See HCA Healthcare, Inc.; *U.S. Public*, pg. 1004
NEUROTECH INTERNATIONAL LIMITED; *Int'l*, pg. 5220
NEURO TEXAS, PLLC—See HCA Healthcare, Inc.; *U.S. Public*, pg. 1004
NEUROTRONICS INC.—See Nihon Kohden Corporation; *Int'l*, pg. 5285
NEUROWAVE MONITORING INC.—See Calder Development Associates, Inc.; *U.S. Private*, pg. 710
NEU'S BUILDING CENTER, INC.; *U.S. Private*, pg. 2890
NEUSOFT AMERICA INC.—See Neusoft Corporation; *Int'l*, pg. 5220
NEUSOFT CHC MEDICAL SERVICE CO., LTD.—See CHC Healthcare Group; *Int'l*, pg. 1458
NEUSOFT CLOUD TECHNOLOGY CO., LTD.—See Neusoft Corporation; *Int'l*, pg. 5220
NEUSOFT CORPORATION; *Int'l*, pg. 5220
NEUSOFT EDUCATION TECHNOLOGY COMPANY LIMITED; *Int'l*, pg. 5220
NEUSOFT JAPAN CO., LTD.—See Neusoft Corporation; *Int'l*, pg. 5220
NEUSOFT MEDICAL SYSTEMS CO., LTD—See Neusoft Corporation; *Int'l*, pg. 5220
NEUSOFT TECHNOLOGY SOLUTIONS GMBH—See Neusoft Corporation; *Int'l*, pg. 5220
NEU SPECIALTY ENGINEERED MATERIALS, LLC—See Avient Corporation; *U.S. Public*, pg. 247
NEUSTAR COSTA RICA LIMITADA—See TransUnion; *U.S. Public*, pg. 2184
NEUSTAR DATA INFOTECH (INDIA) PRIVATE LIMITED—See TransUnion; *U.S. Public*, pg. 2184
NEUSTAR, INC.—See TransUnion; *U.S. Public*, pg. 2184
NEUSTAR INFORMATION SERVICES, INC.—See TransUnion; *U.S. Public*, pg. 2184
NEUSTAR TECHNOLOGIES LIMITED—See TransUnion; *U.S. Public*, pg. 2184
NEUSTRATEGY, INC.—See Gryphon Investors, LLC; *U.S. Private*, pg. 1798
NEUTECH PACKAGING SYSTEMS, LLC; *U.S. Private*, pg. 2890
NEUTEX AG—See Bystronic AG; *Int'l*, pg. 1236
NEUTEX HOME DECO GMBH—See Hoftex Group AG; *Int'l*, pg. 3440
NEUTRA CORP.; *U.S. Public*, pg. 1510
NEUTRAHEALTH PLC—See Elder Pharmaceuticals Ltd.; *Int'l*, pg. 2346
NEUTRAL GLASS & ALLIED INDUSTRIES PRIVATE LTD.—See Gerresheimer AG; *Int'l*, pg. 2944
NEUTRAL HOLDINGS LTD—See Kape Technologies plc; *Int'l*, pg. 4076
NEUTRAL POSTURE, INC.; *U.S. Private*, pg. 2891
NEUTRIK AG; *Int'l*, pg. 5220
NEUTRIK FRANCE SARL—See Neutrik AG; *Int'l*, pg. 5220
NEUTRIK HONG KONG LTD.—See Neutrik AG; *Int'l*, pg. 5220
NEUTRIK INDIA PVT. LTD.—See Neutrik AG; *Int'l*, pg. 5220
NEUTRIK LIMITED—See Neutrik AG; *Int'l*, pg. 5220
NEUTRIK UK LTD.—See Neutrik AG; *Int'l*, pg. 5220
NEUTRIK USA INC.—See Neutrik AG; *Int'l*, pg. 5220
NEUTRIK VERTRIEB GMBH—See Neutrik AG; *Int'l*, pg. 5220
NEUTRISCI INTERNATIONAL INC.; *Int'l*, pg. 5220

NEUTROGENA CORPORATION—See Johnson & Johnson; *U.S. Public*, pg. 1200
NEUTRONA NETWORKS INTERNATIONAL LLC—See Transtelco Holding, Inc.; *U.S. Private*, pg. 4211
NEUTRONICS INC.—See FFL Partners, LLC; *U.S. Private*, pg. 1500
NEUTRON INTERACTIVE; *U.S. Private*, pg. 2891
NEUVE A CO., LTD.—See J. Front Retailing Co., Ltd.; *Int'l*, pg. 3855
NEUVIBOX SAS—See Sonoco Products Company; *U.S. Public*, pg. 1904
NEUVIE—See MichaelKate Interiors and Gallery; *U.S. Private*, pg. 2699
NEUVILLE CHRYSLER-DODGE-JEEP LLC.; *U.S. Private*, pg. 2891
NEUWAVE MEDICAL, INC.—See Johnson & Johnson; *U.S. Public*, pg. 1196
NEUWEG FERTIGUNG GMBH—See NSK Ltd.; *Int'l*, pg. 5479
NEVADA BEVERAGE CO.; *U.S. Private*, pg. 2891
NEVADA CANYON GOLD CORP.; *U.S. Public*, pg. 1510
NEVADA CEMENT COMPANY—See Eagle Materials Inc.; *U.S. Public*, pg. 702
NEVADA CHEMICALS SA DE CV—See Sapec S.A.; *Int'l*, pg. 6571
NEVADA CLASSICS, INC.; *U.S. Private*, pg. 2891
NEVADA CLASSIC THOROUGHBREDS, INC.; *U.S. Private*, pg. 2891
NEVADA CONSTRUCTION SERVICES—See Partner Engineering & Science, Inc; *U.S. Private*, pg. 3101
NEVADA COPPER CORP.; *Int'l*, pg. 5220
NEVADA COPPER, INC.—See Nevada Copper Corp.; *Int'l*, pg. 5220
NEVADA CORPORATE HEADQUARTERS, INC.; *U.S. Private*, pg. 2891
NEVADA EXPLORATION INC.; *Int'l*, pg. 5220
NEVADA GENERAL INSURANCE COMPANY; *U.S. Private*, pg. 2891
NEVADA GENERAL INSURANCE CO—See Nevada General Insurance Company; *U.S. Private*, pg. 2891
NEVADA GOLD BVR, L.L.C.—See Maverick Gold LLC; *U.S. Private*, pg. 2616
NEVADA GOLD & CASINOS, INC.—See Maverick Gold LLC; *U.S. Private*, pg. 2616
NEVADA GOLD MINES LLC—See Barrick Gold Corporation; *Int'l*, pg. 869
NEVADA IRRIGATION DISTRICT; *U.S. Private*, pg. 2891
NEVADA LITHIUM RESOURCES INC.; *Int'l*, pg. 5221
NEVADA LOGOS, INC.—See Lamar Advertising Company; *U.S. Public*, pg. 1291
NEVADA MORAY INC—See Western Magnesium Corporation; *Int'l*, pg. 8388
NEVADA PACIFIC DENTAL—See UnitedHealth Group Incorporated; *U.S. Public*, pg. 2242
NEVADA PACIFIC INSURANCE SERVICES—See Topa Equities Ltd, Inc.; *U.S. Private*, pg. 4187
NEVADA PALACE, LLC—See Boyd Gaming Corporation; *U.S. Public*, pg. 378
NEVADA PF LLC; *U.S. Private*, pg. 2891
NEVADA POWER COMPANY—See Berkshire Hathaway Inc.; *U.S. Public*, pg. 300
NEVADA PREFERRED HEALTHCARE PROVIDERS, LLC—See Universal Health Services, Inc.; *U.S. Public*, pg. 2258
NEVADA PROPERTY 1 LLC—See Deutsche Bank Aktiengesellschaft; *Int'l*, pg. 2061
NEVADA READY MIX CORP.—See Mitsubishi Materials Corporation; *Int'l*, pg. 4965
NEVADA REALTY ASSOCIATES, LLC—See Wynn Resorts Limited; *U.S. Public*, pg. 2384
NEVADA SOLAR SOLUTIONS, LLC—See MDU Resources Group, Inc.; *U.S. Public*, pg. 1411
NEVADA SPEEDWAY, LLC—See Sonic Financial Corporation; *U.S. Private*, pg. 3713
NEVADA STATE BANK—See Zions Bancorporation, National Association; *U.S. Public*, pg. 2408
NEVADA STATE CORPORATE NETWORK, INC.; *U.S. Private*, pg. 2891
NEVADA SUNRISE METALS CORPORATION; *Int'l*, pg. 5221
NEVADA TRIO INC.; *U.S. Private*, pg. 2891
NEVADA WEST BUSINESS INSURANCE SERVICES—See GTCR LLC; *U.S. Private*, pg. 1803
NEVADA ZINC CORPORATION; *Int'l*, pg. 5221
NEVADO RESOURCES CORPORATION; *Int'l*, pg. 5221
NEVA ONE LLC; *U.S. Private*, pg. 2891
NEVA RIDGE TECHNOLOGIES, INC.—See General Atomics; *U.S. Private*, pg. 1663
NEVARIS BAUSOFTWARE GMBH—See Nemetschek SE; *Int'l*, pg. 5195
NEVARIS BAUSOFTWARE GMBH—See Nemetschek SE; *Int'l*, pg. 5195
NEVARIS BIM SOFTWARE GMBH—See Nemetschek SE; *Int'l*, pg. 5195
NEVCO, INC.—See Neville Chemical Company; *U.S. Private*, pg. 2891
NEVE FLEETWOOD—See The Bidvest Group Limited; *Int'l*, pg. 7622
NEVELING.NET GMBH—See Reply S.p.A.; *Int'l*, pg. 6291

NEVENA A.D.; *Int'l*, pg. 5221
NEVEON HOLDING GMBH—See Greiner Holding AG; *Int'l*, pg. 3079
NEVERBLUE MEDIA INCORPORATED—See Vertrue Inc.; *U.S. Private*, pg. 4370
NEVERBOUNCE, LLC—See ZoomInfo Technologies Inc.; *U.S. Public*, pg. 2411
NEVERFAIL BOTTLED WATER CO PTY LIMITED—See COCA-COLA EUROPACIFIC PARTNERS PLC; *Int'l*, pg. 1684
NEVERFAIL GROUP LTD.—See Artisan Infrastructure Inc.; *U.S. Private*, pg. 343
NEVERFAIL, INC.—See Schurz Communications, Inc.; *U.S. Private*, pg. 3571
NEVERFAIL SPRINGWATER CO (QLD) PTY LIMITED—See COCA-COLA EUROPACIFIC PARTNERS PLC; *Int'l*, pg. 1684
NEVERFAIL SPRINGWATER LIMITED—See COCA-COLA EUROPACIFIC PARTNERS PLC; *Int'l*, pg. 1684
NEVERG CO., LTD.—See Okins Electronics Co., Ltd.; *Int'l*, pg. 5550
NEVERSOFT ENTERTAINMENT, INC—See Microsoft Corporation; *U.S. Public*, pg. 1439
NEVE YERUSHALAYIM INC.; *U.S. Private*, pg. 2891
NEVILL DOCUMENT SOLUTIONS, LLC—See KYOCERA Corporation; *Int'l*, pg. 4357
NEVILLE CENTER AT FRESH POND; *U.S. Private*, pg. 2891
NEVILLE CHEMICAL COMPANY; *U.S. Private*, pg. 2891
NEVINAR COSMETICS LTD.—See Clarins S.A.; *Int'l*, pg. 1649
NEVINS-ADAMS-LEWBEL-SCHELL PROPERTIES INC; *U.S. Private*, pg. 2891
NEVINS FAMILY OF SERVICES; *U.S. Private*, pg. 2891
NEVO ENERGY, INC.; *U.S. Private*, pg. 2891
NEVOTEK MIDDLE EAST FZ LIMITED LIABILITY COMPANY—See Turkiye Is Bankasi A.S.; *Int'l*, pg. 7976
NEVRO CORP.; *U.S. Public*, pg. 1511
NEVSUN RESOURCES LTD.—See Zijin Mining Group Company Limited; *Int'l*, pg. 8683
NEVTAH CAPITAL MANAGEMENT CORP.; *U.S. Public*, pg. 1511
NEW10 B.V.—See ABN AMRO Group N.V.; *Int'l*, pg. 65
NEW 24, INC—See Pinnacle Exhibits, Inc.; *U.S. Private*, pg. 3185
THE NEW 42ND STREET, INC; *U.S. Private*, pg. 4082
NEW ADVENTURE TRAVEL LIMITED—See ComfortDelGro Corporation Limited; *Int'l*, pg. 1713
NEW AGC LLC—See Drive Shack Inc.; *U.S. Public*, pg. 688
NEW AGE COMPUTER SOLUTIONS; *U.S. Private*, pg. 2892
NEW AGE ELECTRONICS, INC.—See TD Synnex Corp; *U.S. Public*, pg. 1984
NEW AGE EXPLORATION LIMITED; *Int'l*, pg. 5221
NEWAGE, INC.; *U.S. Public*, pg. 1513
NEWAGE INDUSTRIES, INC. - ADVANTAPURE DIVISION—See NewAge Industries, Inc.; *U.S. Private*, pg. 2913
NEWAGE INDUSTRIES, INC.; *U.S. Private*, pg. 2913
NEW AGE INVESTMENTS INC.; *U.S. Private*, pg. 2892
NEW AGE MEDIA ROMANIA SRL—See Cineworld Group plc; *Int'l*, pg. 1610
NEW AGE MEDIA VENTURES LLC; *U.S. Private*, pg. 2892
NEW AGE METALS INC.; *Int'l*, pg. 5221
NEWAGESYS, INC.; *U.S. Private*, pg. 2913
NEW AGE TECHNOLOGIES, INC.—See Insight Equity Holdings LLC; *U.S. Private*, pg. 2086
NEWAGE TESTING INSTRUMENTS, INC.—See AMETEK, Inc.; *U.S. Public*, pg. 117
NEWAG SA; *Int'l*, pg. 5232
NEW ALBANY MOTOR CO. INC.; *U.S. Private*, pg. 2892
NEW ALBANY OUTPATIENT SURGERY, LLC—See Bain Capital, LP; *U.S. Private*, pg. 447
NEW ALBERTSON'S, INC.—See Cerberus Capital Management, L.P.; *U.S. Private*, pg. 836
NEWALL ELECTRONICS INC.—See Sensata Technologies Holding plc; *U.S. Public*, pg. 1866
NEWALL MEASUREMENT SYSTEMS LTD.—See Sensata Technologies Holding plc; *U.S. Public*, pg. 1866
NEWALL UK LTD—See Mondragon Corporation; *Int'l*, pg. 5028
NEW AMERICA ENERGY CORP.; *U.S. Public*, pg. 1511
NEW AMERICA HIGH INCOME FUND, INC.; *U.S. Public*, pg. 1511
NEW AMSTERDAM INVEST N.V.; *Int'l*, pg. 5221
NEW ANGLE MEDIA LLC; *U.S. Private*, pg. 2892
NEW ARCHERY PRODUCTS, INC.—See Bruckmann, Rosser, Sherrill & Co., LLC; *U.S. Private*, pg. 671
NEWARK BETH ISRAEL MEDICAL CENTER—See Barnabas Health, Inc.; *U.S. Private*, pg. 476
NEWARK COMMUNITY HEALTH CENTERS, INC.; *U.S. Private*, pg. 2913
NEWARK CORPORATION—See Avnet, Inc.; *U.S. Public*, pg. 254
THE NEWARK ENDOSCOPY ASC, LLC—See KKR & Co. Inc.; *U.S. Public*, pg. 1248

NEWARK COMMUNITY HEALTH CENTERS, INC.   CORPORATE AFFILIATIONS

NEWARK HERITAGE PARTNERS I, LLC—See AlerisLife Inc.; *U.S. Private*, pg. 162
NEWARK LEGAL & COMMUNICATIONS CENTER URBAN RENEWAL CORPORATION—See Port Authority of New York & New Jersey; *U.S. Private*, pg. 3229
NEWARK MORNING LEDGER COMPANY—See Advance Publications, Inc.; *U.S. Private*, pg. 86
NEWARK TOBACCO & CANDY CO. INC.; *U.S. Private*, pg. 2913
NEWARK TOYOTA WORLD; *U.S. Private*, pg. 2913
NEWARK VETS4PETS LIMITED—See Pets at Home Group Plc; *Int'l*, pg. 5834
NEWARK WIRE CLOTH CO.; *U.S. Private*, pg. 2913
NEW ART HOLDINGS CO., LTD.; *Int'l*, pg. 5221
NEW ASIA CONSTRUCTION & DEVELOPMENT CORP.; *Int'l*, pg. 5221
NEW ASIA HOLDINGS, INC.; *Int'l*, pg. 5221
NEW ASIA INDUSTRIES CO., LTD.—See The Siam Cement Public Company Limited; *Int'l*, pg. 7683
NEWATER TECHNOLOGY, INC.; *Int'l*, pg. 5232
NEWAVA TECHNOLOGY, INC.; *U.S. Private*, pg. 2913
NEWAVE CONTRACTING PTY. LTD.—See SRG Global Limited; *Int'l*, pg. 7148
NEWAVE ENERGY AG—See ABB Ltd.; *Int'l*, pg. 54
NEWAVE ENERGY HOLDING SA—See ABB Ltd.; *Int'l*, pg. 54
NEWAVE ENERGY (JIANGMEN) LTD.—See ABB Ltd.; *Int'l*, pg. 54
NEWAVE ESPANA S.A.—See ABB Ltd.; *Int'l*, pg. 55
NEWAVE FINLAND OY—See ABB Ltd.; *Int'l*, pg. 55
NEWAVE ITALIA SRL—See ABB Ltd.; *Int'l*, pg. 55
NEW AVENUES TO INDEPENDENCE, INC.; *U.S. Private*, pg. 2892
NEWAVE OSTERREICH GMBH—See ABB Ltd.; *Int'l*, pg. 55
NEWAVE S.A.—See ABB Ltd.; *Int'l*, pg. 55
NEWAVE SOUTH AMERICA ELETTROELETTRONICA LTDA—See ABB Ltd.; *Int'l*, pg. 55
NEWAVE UPS SYSTEMS BV—See ABB Ltd.; *Int'l*, pg. 55
NEWAVE USV SYSTEME GMBH—See ABB Ltd.; *Int'l*, pg. 55
NEW AXIA HOLDINGS INC.—See Aurora Capital Group, LLC; *U.S. Private*, pg. 394
NEWAX, INC.; *U.S. Private*, pg. 2913
NEWAY FLOW CONTROL DMCC—See Neway Valve (Suzhou) Co., Ltd.; *Int'l*, pg. 5232
NEWAY GROUP HOLDINGS LIMITED - SHENZHEN FACTORY—See Neway Group Holdings Limited; *Int'l*, pg. 5232
NEWAY GROUP HOLDINGS LIMITED; *Int'l*, pg. 5232
NEWAY PACKAGING CORP.; *U.S. Private*, pg. 2913
NEWAYS ADVANCED APPLICATIONS B.V.—See Neways Electronics International NV; *Int'l*, pg. 5232
NEWAYS CABLE & WIRE SOLUTIONS B.V.—See Neways Electronics International NV; *Int'l*, pg. 5232
NEWAYS ELECTRONICS ECHT B.V.—See Neways Electronics International NV; *Int'l*, pg. 5232
NEWAYS ELECTRONICS INTERNATIONAL NV; *Int'l*, pg. 5232
NEWAYS ELECTRONICS PRODUCTION GMBH—See Neways Electronics International NV; *Int'l*, pg. 5233
NEWAYS ELECTRONICS US INC.—See Neways Electronics International NV; *Int'l*, pg. 5233
NEWAYS INC.; *U.S. Private*, pg. 2913
NEWAYS INDUSTRIAL SYSTEMS B.V.—See Neways Electronics International NV; *Int'l*, pg. 5233
NEWAYS LEEUWARDEN B.V.—See Neways Electronics International NV; *Int'l*, pg. 5233
NEWAYS MICRO ELECTRONICS B.V.—See Neways Electronics International NV; *Int'l*, pg. 5233
NEWAYS MICRO ELECTRONICS CHINA CO, LTD.—See Neways Electronics International NV; *Int'l*, pg. 5233
NEWAYS NEUNKIRCHEN GMBH—See Neways Electronics International NV; *Int'l*, pg. 5233
NEWAYS SLOVAKIA A.S.—See Neways Electronics International NV; *Int'l*, pg. 5233
NEWAYS TECHNOLOGIES B.V.—See Neways Electronics International NV; *Int'l*, pg. 5233
NEWAYS TECHNOLOGIES GMBH—See Neways Electronics International NV; *Int'l*, pg. 5233
NEWAYS VERTRIEBS-GMBH—See Neways Electronics International NV; *Int'l*, pg. 5233
NEWAY VALVE EUROPE B.V.—See Neway Valve (Suzhou) Co., Ltd.; *Int'l*, pg. 5232
NEWAY VALVE (EUROPE) S.R.L.—See Neway Valve (Suzhou) Co., Ltd.; *Int'l*, pg. 5232
NEWAY VALVE INTERNATIONAL INC—See Neway Valve (Suzhou) Co., Ltd.; *Int'l*, pg. 5232
NEWAY VALVE (SINGAPORE) PTE LTD—See Neway Valve (Suzhou) Co., Ltd.; *Int'l*, pg. 5232
NEWAY VALVE (SUZHOU) CO., LTD.; *Int'l*, pg. 5232
NEWAY VALVE WEST AFRICA FZE—See Neway Valve (Suzhou) Co., Ltd.; *Int'l*, pg. 5232
NEWAY VALVULAS DO BRASIL LTDA.—See Neway Valve (Suzhou) Co., Ltd.; *Int'l*, pg. 5232
NEW BALANCE ATHLETIC SHOE, INC.; *U.S. Private*, pg. 2892
NEW BALANCE CANADA, INC.—See New Balance Athletic Shoe, Inc.; *U.S. Private*, pg. 2892

NEW BANGPOO MANUFACTURING CO., LTD.—See JFE Holdings, Inc.; *Int'l*, pg. 3937
NEW BARON LEVEQUE INTERNATIONAL AFRIQUE—See George Forrest International S.A.; *Int'l*, pg. 2938
NEWBASIS—See Echo Rock Ventures Inc.; *U.S. Private*, pg. 1327
NEWBATH; *U.S. Private*, pg. 2913
NEW BAY DIALYSIS, LLC—See DaVita Inc.; *U.S. Public*, pg. 641
NEWBAY MEDIA, LLC—See Future plc; *Int'l*, pg. 2857
NEW BEDFORD PANORAMEX CORPORATION; *U.S. Private*, pg. 2892
NEW BEGINNINGS TREATMENT CENTER INC.—See Corecivic, Inc.; *U.S. Public*, pg. 577
NEW BELGIUM BREWING COMPANY, INC.—See Kirin Holdings Company, Limited; *Int'l*, pg. 4189
NEW BERLIN PLASTICS, INC.; *U.S. Private*, pg. 2892
NEWBERRY BP EXPRESS MARKET—See Autore Oil & Propane Company; *U.S. Private*, pg. 401
THE NEWBERRY GROUP, INC.; *U.S. Private*, pg. 4083
THE NEWBERRY; *U.S. Private*, pg. 4083
NEWBERRY SPECIALTY BAKERS, INC.; *U.S. Public*, pg. 1513
NEW BEST WIRE INDUSTRIAL CO., LTD.; *Int'l*, pg. 5221
NEW BEST WIRE VIETNAM INDUSTRIAL COMPANY LIMITED—See New Best Wire Industrial Co., Ltd.; *Int'l*, pg. 5221
NEWBEVCO, INC.—See National Beverage Corp.; *U.S. Public*, pg. 1494
NEWBOLD CORPORATION - ADDRESSOGRAPH DIVISION—See Fort Point Capital, LLC; *U.S. Private*, pg. 1574
NEWBOLD LLC—See Fort Point Capital, LLC; *U.S. Private*, pg. 1574
NEWBORN TOWN, INC.; *Int'l*, pg. 5233
NEW BOSTON FUND, INC.; *U.S. Private*, pg. 2892
NEW BOSTON GARDEN CORP.—See Delaware North Companies, Inc.; *U.S. Private*, pg. 1194
NEW BOSTON MANAGEMENT SERVICES INC.—See New Boston Fund, Inc.; *U.S. Private*, pg. 2892
NEWBRANDANALYTICS INC.—See Sprinklr, Inc.; *U.S. Public*, pg. 1920
NEW BRAUNFELS UTILITIES; *U.S. Private*, pg. 2892
NEWBRIDGE EDUCATIONAL PUBLISHING—See The Rowman & Littlefield Publishing Group, Inc.; *U.S. Private*, pg. 4112
NEWBRIDGE FINANCIAL, INC.; *U.S. Private*, pg. 2913
NEWBRIDGE GLOBAL VENTURES, INC.; *U.S. Public*, pg. 1513
NEWBRIDGE SERVICES INC.; *U.S. Private*, pg. 2914
NEW BRIGHTON BUSINESS CENTER, LLC—See Laboratory Corporation of America Holdings; *U.S. Public*, pg. 1287
NEW BRIGHTON FORD, INC.; *U.S. Private*, pg. 2892
NEW BRITAIN BASEBALL CLUB, INC.—See Pohlad Companies; *U.S. Private*, pg. 3221
NEW BRITAIN MEDICAL SUPPLIES, INC.—See DENTSPLY SIRONA Inc.; *U.S. Public*, pg. 655
NEW BRITAIN PALM OIL LIMITED—See Sime Darby Berhad; *Int'l*, pg. 6929
NEWBROOK SOLUTIONS, INC.—See Edgesource Corporation; *U.S. Private*, pg. 1334
NEW BRUNSWICK DEVELOPMENT CORPORATION; *U.S. Private*, pg. 2892
NEW BRUNSWICK EMS—See Medavie Blue Cross; *Int'l*, pg. 4768
NEW BRUNSWICK PLATING INC.; *U.S. Private*, pg. 2892
NEW BRUNSWICK POWER CORPORATION; *Int'l*, pg. 5221
NEW BRUNSWICK SCIENTIFIC B.V.—See Eppendorf AG; *Int'l*, pg. 2464
NEW BRUNSWICK SCIENTIFIC CO., INC.—See Eppendorf AG; *Int'l*, pg. 2464
NEW BRUNSWICK SCIENTIFIC CO., INC.—See Eppendorf AG; *Int'l*, pg. 2464
NEW BRUNSWICK SCIENTIFIC GMBH—See Eppendorf AG; *Int'l*, pg. 2464
NEW BRUNSWICK SCIENTIFIC (UK) LTD.—See Eppendorf AG; *Int'l*, pg. 2464
NEW BUBBLEROOM SWEDEN AB; *Int'l*, pg. 5221
NEWBUCKS OPERATIONS PTY., LTD.—See FirstRand Limited; *Int'l*, pg. 2690
NEW BUFFALO CORPORATION; *U.S. Private*, pg. 2892
NEWBURGH AUTO AUCTION—See Cox Enterprises, Inc.; *U.S. Private*, pg. 1077
NEWBURGH & SOUTH SHORE RAILROAD COMPANY—See The Broe Companies, Inc.; *U.S. Private*, pg. 4001
NEWBURY BUILDERS, LLC; *U.S. Private*, pg. 2914
NEWBURY BUILDING SOCIETY; *Int'l*, pg. 5233
NEWBURY COMICS INC.; *U.S. Private*, pg. 2914
NEWBURY FRANKLIN INDUSTRIALS LLC—See Ironwood Capital Management LLC; *U.S. Private*, pg. 2140
NEWBURY PARTNERS LLC—See Bridge Investment Group Holdings Inc.; *U.S. Public*, pg. 381
NEWBURY PHARMACEUTICALS AB; *Int'l*, pg. 5233
NEWBURYPORT FIVE CENTS SAVINGS BANK; *U.S. Private*, pg. 2914

NEWBURY RACECOURSE PLC; *Int'l*, pg. 5233
NEWBURY STREET ACQUISITION CORP; *U.S. Public*, pg. 1513
NEW BUSCH CO., INC.—See CECO Environmental Corp.; *U.S. Public*, pg. 463
NEWBY BUICK-OLDSMBILE-PONTIAC-GMC; *U.S. Private*, pg. 2914
NEW CALIFORNIA LIFE HOLDINGS, INC.—See Financiere Pinault SCA; *Int'l*, pg. 2668
NEWCAPEC ELECTRONICS CO., LTD.; *Int'l*, pg. 5233
NEWCAPEC MALAYSIA SDN. BHD.—See Newcapec Electronics Co., Ltd.; *Int'l*, pg. 5233
NEWCAP HOLDING A/S; *Int'l*, pg. 5233
NEW CAPITAL PARTNERS; *U.S. Private*, pg. 2892
NEWCAP RADIO—See Stingray Group Inc.; *Int'l*, pg. 7216
NEW CARBON CO, LLC—See Arbor Private Investment Company, LLC; *U.S. Private*, pg. 309
NEW CAROLIN GOLD CORP.—See Talisker Resources Ltd.; *Int'l*, pg. 7447
NEW CARS INC.; *U.S. Private*, pg. 2893
NEWCASTLE ADVISORS LLC—See Newcastle Limited; *U.S. Private*, pg. 2914
NEWCASTLE BUILDING SOCIETY; *Int'l*, pg. 5233
NEW CASTLE CHEVROLET, INC.—See General Motors Company; *U.S. Public*, pg. 926
NEWCASTLE CHRONICLE & JOURNAL LTD—See Reach PLC; *Int'l*, pg. 6231
NEWCASTLE COMMERCIAL VEHICLES PTY LTD—See Eagers Automotive Limited; *Int'l*, pg. 2263
NEWCASTLE CONSTRUCTION, INC.; *U.S. Private*, pg. 2914
NEWCASTLE CONSTRUCTION MANAGEMENT, LLC—See AvalonBay Communities, Inc.; *U.S. Public*, pg. 240
NEW CASTLE CORP.—See MGM Resorts International; *U.S. Public*, pg. 1435
NEWCASTLE ENERGY CORP.; *Int'l*, pg. 5233
NEWCASTLE FINANCIAL SERVICES LIMITED—See Newcastle Building Society; *Int'l*, pg. 5233
NEW CASTLE HOTELS, LLC; *U.S. Private*, pg. 2893
NEWCASTLE LIMITED; *U.S. Private*, pg. 2914
NEWCASTLE MORTGAGE CORPORATION LIMITED—See Newcastle Building Society; *Int'l*, pg. 5233
NEW CASTLE MORTGAGE, LLC—See Newcastle Building Society; *Int'l*, pg. 5233
NEWCASTLE NEWSPAPERS PTY. LIMITED—See Rural Press Pty Limited; *Int'l*, pg. 6429
THE NEWCASTLE NUFFIELD HOSPITAL—See Nuffield Health; *Int'l*, pg. 5487
NEWCASTLE PARTNERS LLC; *U.S. Private*, pg. 2914
NEWCASTLE PARTNERS LP; *U.S. Private*, pg. 2914
NEWCASTLE PIPE LINE COMPANY PTY LTD—See Ampol Limited; *Int'l*, pg. 436
NEW CASTLE ROLLS, INC.—See Nordson Corporation; *U.S. Public*, pg. 1533
NEWCASTLE STRATEGIC SOLUTIONS LIMITED—See Newcastle Building Society; *Int'l*, pg. 5233
NEWCASTLE TAXIS LTD—See ComfortDelGro Corporation Limited; *Int'l*, pg. 1712
NEW CASTLE TELEPHONE COMPANY—See Telephone & Data Systems, Inc.; *U.S. Public*, pg. 1998
NEW CAST—See Publicis Groupe S.A.; *Int'l*, pg. 6113
NEW CATERING S.R.L.—See Cremonini S.p.A.; *Int'l*, pg. 1838
NEW CELL, INC.—See Northeast Communications of Wisconsin Incorporated; *U.S. Private*, pg. 2949
NEW CENTAUR, LLC—See Caesars Entertainment, Inc.; *U.S. Public*, pg. 420
NEW CENTRAL AIR SERVICE CO., LTD.—See Kawada Technologies Inc.; *Int'l*, pg. 4093
NEW CENTRUY RESOURCES; *Int'l*, pg. 5221
NEW CENTURY DECAL (SHENZHEN) LIMITED—See China COSCO Shipping Corporation Limited; *Int'l*, pg. 1495
NEW CENTURY FARM SERVICE INC.; *U.S. Private*, pg. 2893
NEW CENTURY GROUP HONG KONG LIMITED; *Int'l*, pg. 5221
NEW CENTURY HEALTHCARE HOLDING CO. LIMITED; *Int'l*, pg. 5221
NEW CENTURY PRODUCTIONS, INC.—See The Carlyle Group Inc.; *U.S. Public*, pg. 2050
NEW CENTURY SHIPBUILDING CORPORATION; *Int'l*, pg. 5221
NEW CENTURY SOFTWARE, INC.—See Mistras Group, Inc.; *U.S. Public*, pg. 1451
NEW CENTURY TRANSPORTATION LLC—See Energy Transfer LP; *U.S. Public*, pg. 764
NEW CHAPEL ELECTRONICS LIMITED—See TT Electronics plc; *Int'l*, pg. 7959
NEW CHAPTER, INC.—See The Procter & Gamble Company; *U.S. Public*, pg. 2121
NEW CHARLOTTE CORPORATION; *U.S. Private*, pg. 2893
NEW CHARTER TECHNOLOGIES, LLC—See Oval Partners; *U.S. Private*, pg. 3052
NEW CHENNAI TOWNSHIP PRIVATE LIMITED—See Marg Ltd; *Int'l*, pg. 4692

COMPANY NAME INDEX

THE NEW CHILDRENS MUSEUM; *U.S. Private,* pg. 4083
NEW CHINA FUND MANAGEMENT CO., LTD.—See HengTai Securities CO., LTD; *Int'l,* pg. 3347
NEW CHINA HOMES LTD.—See Far East Consortium International Limited; *Int'l,* pg. 2615
NEW CHINA LIFE INSURANCE CO., LTD.; *Int'l,* pg. 5222
NEW CINGULAR WIRELESS SERVICES, INC.—See AT&T Inc.; *U.S. Public,* pg. 220
NEWCITY (BANGKOK) PUBLIC COMPANY LIMITED; *Int'l,* pg. 5234
NEW CITY DEVELOPMENT GROUP LIMITED; *Int'l,* pg. 5222
NEW CITY MOVING LLC; *U.S. Private,* pg. 2893
NEW CLICKS SOUTH AFRICA (PROPRIETARY) LIMITED—See Clicks Group Limited; *Int'l,* pg. 1658
NEWCOAST FINANCIAL SERVICES, INC.—See MarineMax, Inc.; *U.S. Public,* pg. 1367
NEW COBURG LIMITED—See Tudeley Holdings Limited; *Int'l,* pg. 7963
NEWCO (H.K.) LIMITED—See Honghua Group Ltd; *Int'l,* pg. 3471
NEWCO INC.; *U.S. Private,* pg. 2914
NEW COLD STORAGE COMPANY LIMITED—See Ireland Blyth Limited; *Int'l,* pg. 3807
NEWCOMB ANDERSON MCCORMICK, INC.—See Willdan Group, Inc.; *U.S. Public,* pg. 2371
NEWCOMB SPRING CORP.; *U.S. Private,* pg. 2914
NEWCO METALS INC.; *U.S. Private,* pg. 2914
NEW-COM INC.; *U.S. Private,* pg. 2913
NEWCOM INTERNATIONAL, INC.—See SpeedCast International Limited; *Int'l,* pg. 7133
NEW COMMERCE SPLIT CORP.; *Int'l,* pg. 5222
NEW CONCEPT ENERGY, INC.; *U.S. Public,* pg. 1511
NEW CONCEPT MINING CHILE SPA—See Epiroc AB; *Int'l,* pg. 2463
NEW CONCEPT MINING PERU S.A.C.—See Epiroc AB; *Int'l,* pg. 2463
NEW CONCEPT MINING (PTY) LTD.—See Epiroc AB; *Int'l,* pg. 2463
NEW CONCEPTS FOUNDATION LIMITED—See New Concepts Holdings Limited; *Int'l,* pg. 5222
NEW CONCEPTS HOLDINGS LIMITED; *Int'l,* pg. 5222
NEW CONSTRUCTOR'S NETWORK CO., LTD.; *Int'l,* pg. 5222
NEW CONTEXT SERVICES, INC.; *U.S. Private,* pg. 2000
NEW COOPERATIVE, INC.; *U.S. Private,* pg. 2893
NEWCO PHARMA GMBH—See Medios AG; *Int'l,* pg. 4778
NEWCORE GOLD LTD.; *Int'l,* pg. 5234
NEWCOR, INC.—See Cie Automotive S.A.; *Int'l,* pg. 1604
NEW COSMOS BIE B.V.—See New Cosmos Electric Co., Ltd.; *Int'l,* pg. 5222
NEW COSMOS ELECTRIC CO., LTD.; *Int'l,* pg. 5222
NEW COSMOS ELECTRIC KOREA CO., LTD.—See New Cosmos Electric Co., Ltd.; *Int'l,* pg. 5222
NEW COSMOS ELECTRIC (SHANGHAI) CO., LTD.—See New Cosmos Electric Co., Ltd.; *Int'l,* pg. 5222
NEW COSMOS USA, INC.—See New Cosmos Electric Co., Ltd.; *Int'l,* pg. 5222
NEW COUNTRY LEXUS OF WESTPORT; *U.S. Private,* pg. 2893
NEW COUNTRY MEDICAL SUPPLIES COMPANY LLC; *Int'l,* pg. 5222
NEW COUNTRY MOTOR CAR GROUP INC.; *U.S. Private,* pg. 2893
NEWCOURT ACQUISITION CORP.; *U.S. Public,* pg. 1513
THE NEWCOURTLAND LIFE PROGRAM; *U.S. Private,* pg. 4083
NEWCO VALVES, LLC—See Schlumberger Limited; *U.S. Public,* pg. 1844
NEWCO VALVES LP; *U.S. Private,* pg. 2914
THE NEW COVENT GARDEN SOUP COMPANY LIMITED—See The Hain Celestial Group, Inc.; *U.S. Public,* pg. 2086
NEW CRAFT TOOL & DIE—See MNP Corporation; *U.S. Private,* pg. 2756
NEW CREATION ADVERTISING AGENCY LIMITED—See Bexcellent Group Holdings Limited; *Int'l,* pg. 1005
NEW CREATURE; *U.S. Private,* pg. 2893
NEW CREDIT AMERICA, LLC; *U.S. Private,* pg. 2893
NEWCREST EXPLORATION HOLDINGS PTY LTD—See Newmont Corporation; *U.S. Public,* pg. 1517
NEWCREST FINANCE PTY LTD—See Newmont Corporation; *U.S. Public,* pg. 1517
NEWCREST INSURANCE PTE LTD—See Newmont Corporation; *U.S. Public,* pg. 1517
NEWCREST INTERNATIONAL PTY LTD—See Newmont Corporation; *U.S. Public,* pg. 1517
NEWCREST MINING LIMITED—See Newmont Corporation; *U.S. Public,* pg. 1517
NEWCREST OPERATIONS LIMITED—See Newmont Corporation; *U.S. Public,* pg. 1517
NEWCREST SERVICES PTY LTD—See Newmont Corporation; *U.S. Public,* pg. 1517
N.E.W. CUSTOMER SERVICES COMPANIES, INC.; *U.S. Private,* pg. 2827
NEWCYTECH BUSINESS SOLUTIONS LTD.—See Logicom Public Ltd; *Int'l,* pg. 4542
NEWCYTECH DISTRIBUTION LTD.—See Logicom Public Ltd; *Int'l,* pg. 4542

NEW DAWN ENERGY LIMITED; *Int'l,* pg. 5222
NEW DAWN MINING CORP.; *Int'l,* pg. 5222
NEW DAWN TECHNOLOGIES, INC.—See Daily Journal Corporation; *U.S. Public,* pg. 620
NEWDAY COMMUNICATIONS INC.; *U.S. Private,* pg. 2914
NEW DAY DIAGNOSTICS LLC; *U.S. Private,* pg. 2893
NEW DAY MARKETING, LTD.; *U.S. Private,* pg. 2893
NEW DEAL MERCANTILE INC.; *U.S. Private,* pg. 2893
NEWDEAL SAS—See Integra LifeSciences Holdings Corporation; *U.S. Public,* pg. 1136
NEW DELHI TELEVISION LIMITED; *Int'l,* pg. 5222
THE NEWDELL COMPANY—See SHV Holdings N.V.; *Int'l,* pg. 6871
NEW DELTA INDUSTRIAL CO., LTD.—See Yanmar Co., Ltd.; *Int'l,* pg. 8563
NEW DESSERTS; *U.S. Private,* pg. 2893
NEW DESTINY MINING CORP.; *Int'l,* pg. 5222
NEW DIMENSION METALS CORP.—See Gray America Corp.; *U.S. Private,* pg. 1759
NEW DIMENSIONS INC.; *U.S. Private,* pg. 2893
NEW DIMENSIONS RESEARCH CORP.—See Westminster Capital Inc.; *U.S. Public,* pg. 4499
NEW DIRECTIONS BEHAVIORAL HEALTH LLC—See GuideWell Mutual Holding Corporation; *U.S. Private,* pg. 1814
NEW DIRECTIONS COUNSELING SERVICES, LLC—See NorthEast Health Services, LLC; *U.S. Private,* pg. 2950
NEW DIRECTIONS GMBH—See freenet AG; *Int'l,* pg. 2771
NEW DIRECTIONS (ST. LEONARDS ON SEA) LIMITED—See Acadia Healthcare Company, Inc.; *U.S. Public,* pg. 29
NEW DIXIE OIL CORPORATION; *U.S. Private,* pg. 2893
NEW DOMINION PACKAGING COMPANY INC.; *U.S. Private,* pg. 2893
NEW DRUG RESEARCH CENTER, INC.—See Trans Genic Inc.; *Int'l,* pg. 7894
NEW EARTH LIFE SCIENCES, INC.; *U.S. Private,* pg. 2893
NEW EAST NEW MATERIALS CO., LTD.; *Int'l,* pg. 5222
NEWEDGE CANADA, INC.—See Societe Generale S.A.; *Int'l,* pg. 7040
NEWEDGE GROUP SA—See Societe Generale S.A.; *Int'l,* pg. 7040
NEWEDGE USA, LLC—See Societe Generale S.A.; *Int'l,* pg. 7040
NEW EDITIONS CONSULTING, INC.; *U.S. Private,* pg. 2893
NEW EEZY-GRO INC.—See The Andersons Incorporated; *U.S. Public,* pg. 2034
NEWEGG COMMERCE, INC.; *Int'l,* pg. 5234
NEWEGG INC.—See Newegg Commerce, Inc.; *Int'l,* pg. 5234
NEWELL AUSTRALIA PTY. LIMITED—See Newell Brands Inc.; *U.S. Public,* pg. 1514
NEWELL BRANDS DE COLOMBIA S.A.S.—See Newell Brands Inc.; *U.S. Public,* pg. 1514
NEWELL BRANDS DE PERU, S.A.C.—See Newell Brands Inc.; *U.S. Public,* pg. 1514
NEWELL BRANDS INC.; *U.S. Public,* pg. 1513
NEWELL BRIDGE & RAILWAY COMPANY—See The Homer Laughlin China Company; *U.S. Private,* pg. 4054
THE NEWELL COMPANY—See The Homer Laughlin China Company; *U.S. Private,* pg. 4054
NEWELL EUROPE SARL—See Newell Brands Inc.; *U.S. Public,* pg. 1514
NEWELL FUEL SERVICE INC.; *U.S. Private,* pg. 2914
NEWELL MACHINERY COMPANY INC.; *U.S. Private,* pg. 2914
NEWELL OPERATING COMPANY—See Newell Brands Inc.; *U.S. Public,* pg. 1514
NEWELL PAPER CO. OF GULFPORT—See Jackson Paper Company; *U.S. Private,* pg. 2178
NEWELL PAPER CO. OF HATTIESBURG—See Jackson Paper Company; *U.S. Private,* pg. 2178
NEWELL PAPER CO. OF MERIDIAN—See Jackson Paper Company; *U.S. Private,* pg. 2178
NEWELL PUERTO RICO, LTD.—See 3G Capital Partners L.P.; *U.S. Private,* pg. 13
NEWELL RECYCLING OF ATLANTA, LLC—See Newell Recycling Southeast, LLC; *U.S. Private,* pg. 2914
NEWELL RECYCLING SOUTHEAST, LLC; *U.S. Private,* pg. 2914
NEWELL RUBBERMAID ARGENTINA S.A.—See Newell Brands Inc.; *U.S. Public,* pg. 1514
NEWELL RUBBERMAID ASIA PACIFIC LIMITED—See Newell Brands Inc.; *U.S. Public,* pg. 1514
NEWELL RUBBERMAID COMMERCIAL PRODUCTS—See Newell Brands Inc.; *U.S. Public,* pg. 1514
NEWELL RUBBERMAID DE MEXICO S. DE R.L. DE C.V.—See Newell Brands Inc.; *U.S. Public,* pg. 1514
NEWELL RUBBERMAID DISTRIBUTION LLC—See Newell Brands Inc.; *U.S. Public,* pg. 1514
NEWELL RUBBERMAID GERMAN HOLDING GMBH—See Newell Brands Inc.; *U.S. Public,* pg. 1514

NEW ENGLAND LIFE FLIGHT, INC.

NEWELL RUBBERMAID INC.—See Newell Brands Inc.; *U.S. Public,* pg. 1514
NEWELL RUBBERMAID JAPAN LTD.—See Newell Brands Inc.; *U.S. Public,* pg. 1514
NEWELL RUBBERMAID MIDDLE EAST FZE—See Newell Brands Inc.; *U.S. Public,* pg. 1514
NEWELL RUBBERMAID (THAILAND) CO., LTD.—See Newell Brands Inc.; *U.S. Public,* pg. 1514
NEWELL RUBBERMAID UK SERVICES LIMITED—See Newell Brands Inc.; *U.S. Public,* pg. 1514
NEW EMPIRE CONTRACTORS LTD; *Int'l,* pg. 5223
NEW ENERGY DISTRIBUTING, INC.—See Olympia Chimney Supply Holdings, LLC; *U.S. Private,* pg. 3012
NEW ENERGY EQUIPMENT CO., LTD.—See Taiyuan Heavy Industry Co., Ltd.; *Int'l,* pg. 7427
NEW ENERGY EQUITY LLC—See ALLETE, Inc.; *U.S. Public,* pg. 79
NEW ENERGY EXCHANGE LTD.; *Int'l,* pg. 5223
NEW ENERGY METALS CORP.; *Int'l,* pg. 5223
NEW ENERGY MINERALS LTD; *Int'l,* pg. 5223
NEW ENERGY ONE ACQUISITION CORPORATION PLC; *Int'l,* pg. 5223
NEW ENERGY RISK, INC.—See AXA S.A.; *Int'l,* pg. 760
NEW ENERGY SYSTEMS GROUP; *U.S. Private,* pg. 2893
NEW ENG KONG CONTAINER LOGISTIC SERVICES (M) SDN BHD—See Eng Kong Holdings Pte Ltd.; *Int'l,* pg. 2426
NEW ENGLAND ACCEPTANCE CORPORATION—See Citizens Financial Group, Inc.; *U.S. Public,* pg. 506
NEW ENGLAND ADVERTISING CORPORATION—See Hilton Grand Vacations Inc.; *U.S. Public,* pg. 1040
NEW ENGLAND AIR SYSTEMS INC.; *U.S. Private,* pg. 2893
NEW ENGLAND ANESTHESIA ASSOCIATES, LLC—See WELL Health Technologies Corp.; *Int'l,* pg. 8372
NEW ENGLAND AQUARIUM; *U.S. Private,* pg. 2894
NEW ENGLAND BONSAI GARDENS—See Bonsai Outlet; *U.S. Private,* pg. 615
NEW ENGLAND CABLE NEWS—See Comcast Corporation; *U.S. Public,* pg. 540
NEW ENGLAND CAPITAL PARTNERS, INC.; *U.S. Private,* pg. 2894
NEW ENGLAND CATHETER CORP.—See MJM Holdings Inc.; *U.S. Private,* pg. 2753
NEW ENGLAND CENTRAL RAILROAD, INC.—See Brookfield Infrastructure Partners L.P.; *Int'l,* pg. 1192
NEW ENGLAND CENTRAL RAILROAD, INC.—See GIC Pte. Ltd.; *Int'l,* pg. 2966
NEW ENGLAND COMMERCIAL PROPERTIES LLC—See NORTHEAST COMMUNITY BANCORP, INC.; *U.S. Public,* pg. 1537
NEW ENGLAND COMMUNICATIONS SYSTEMS CORP.—See Kavveri Telecom Products Ltd; *Int'l,* pg. 4093
NEW ENGLAND CONFECTIONERY COMPANY INC.—See Ares Management Corporation; *U.S. Public,* pg. 190
NEW ENGLAND CONSERVATION SERVICES LLC—See PosiGen LLC; *U.S. Private,* pg. 3233
NEW ENGLAND CONTROLS, INC.—See Enerpac Tool Group Corp.; *U.S. Public,* pg. 766
NEW ENGLAND COUNTRY PIES, INC.; *U.S. Private,* pg. 2894
NEW ENGLAND DEVELOPMENT CORPORATION; *U.S. Private,* pg. 2894
NEW ENGLAND ENVIROSTRATEGIES, INC.—See Terracon Consultants, Inc.; *U.S. Private,* pg. 3971
NEW ENGLAND FARM WORKERS COUNCIL INC.; *U.S. Private,* pg. 2894
NEW ENGLAND FOUNDATION CO. INC.; *U.S. Private,* pg. 2894
NEW ENGLAND GYPSUM SUPPLY, INC.—See GMS Inc.; *U.S. Public,* pg. 948
NEW ENGLAND HOME CARE, INC.—See Blue Wolf Capital Partners LLC; *U.S. Private,* pg. 595
NEW ENGLAND HOME MEDICAL EQUIPMENT LLC—See AdaptHealth Corp.; *U.S. Public,* pg. 39
NEW ENGLAND HOME THERAPIES INC.—See Option Care Health, Inc.; *U.S. Public,* pg. 1610
NEW ENGLAND INDUSTRIAL TRUCK, INC.—See Mitsubishi Heavy Industries, Ltd.; *Int'l,* pg. 4959
THE NEW ENGLAND INSTITUTE OF ART, LLC—See Dream Center Foundation, a California Nonprofit Corp.; *U.S. Private,* pg. 1275
NEW ENGLAND INVESTMENT & RETIREMENT GROUP, INC.; *U.S. Private,* pg. 2894
THE NEW ENGLAND JOURNAL OF MEDICINE—See Massachusetts Medical Society; *U.S. Private,* pg. 2604
NEW ENGLAND LAMINATES CO., INC.—See AGC Inc.; *Int'l,* pg. 204
NEW ENGLAND LAW BOSTON; *U.S. Private,* pg. 2894
NEW ENGLAND LEAD BURNING CO.; *U.S. Private,* pg. 2894
NEW ENGLAND LIFE CARE INC.; *U.S. Private,* pg. 2894
NEW ENGLAND LIFE FLIGHT, INC.; *U.S. Private,* pg. 2894
NEW ENGLAND LIFE INSURANCE CO.—See MetLife, Inc.; *U.S. Public,* pg. 1431

NEW ENGLAND LOW VISION & BLINDNESS CORPORATE AFFILIATIONS

NEW ENGLAND LOW VISION & BLINDNESS; *U.S. Private*, pg. 2894
NEW ENGLAND MACHINERY, INC.—See Granite Equity Partners LLC; *U.S. Private*, pg. 1755
NEW ENGLAND MECHANICAL SERVICES, INC.—See EMCOR Group, Inc.; *U.S. Public*, pg. 738
NEW ENGLAND MEDICAL TRANSCRIPTION; *U.S. Private*, pg. 2894
NEW ENGLAND MEDICAL TRANSPORTATION, INC.—See The Ensign Group, Inc.; *U.S. Public*, pg. 2071
NEW ENGLAND MOBILE BOOK FAIR; *U.S. Private*, pg. 2894
NEW ENGLAND MOTOR FREIGHT, INC.; *U.S. Private*, pg. 2894
NEW ENGLAND MUTUAL TRADING INC.—See Takara Holdings, Inc.; *Int'l*, pg. 7433
NEW ENGLAND OFFICE SUPPLY INC.; *U.S. Private*, pg. 2894
NEW ENGLAND ORGAN BANK; *U.S. Private*, pg. 2894
NEW ENGLAND PATRIOTS FOOTBALL CLUB, INC.—See The Kraft Group LLC; *U.S. Private*, pg. 4066
NEW ENGLAND PENSION PLAN SYSTEMS, LLC—See Hellman & Friedman LLC; *U.S. Private*, pg. 1908
NEW ENGLAND PLASTICS CORP; *U.S. Private*, pg. 2894
NEW ENGLAND POTTERY, LLC—See Central Garden & Pet Company; *U.S. Public*, pg. 473
NEW ENGLAND POWER COMPANY—See National Grid plc; *Int'l*, pg. 5158
NEW ENGLAND PRESS SERVICE; *U.S. Private*, pg. 2894
NEW ENGLAND REALTY ASSOCIATES LIMITED PARTNERSHIP; *U.S. Public*, pg. 1511
NEW ENGLAND REHABILITATION SERVICES OF CENTRAL MASSACHUSETTS, INC.—See Encompass Health Corporation; *U.S. Public*, pg. 758
NEW ENGLAND RESEARCH INSTITUTES, INC.—See Elevance Health, Inc.; *U.S. Public*, pg. 730
NEW ENGLAND RISK SPECIALISTS—See American International Group, Inc.; *U.S. Public*, pg. 107
NEW ENGLAND SERVICES COMPANY; *U.S. Public*, pg. 1511
NEW ENGLAND SILICA INC—See SiteOne Landscape Supply, Inc.; *U.S. Public*, pg. 1889
NEW ENGLAND SPORTS ENTERPRISES, LLC—See Fenway Sports Group Holdings, LLC; *U.S. Private*, pg. 1496
NEW ENGLAND SYSTEMS INC.—See Micro Strategies Inc.; *U.S. Private*, pg. 2702
NEW ENGLAND SYSTEMS, INC.; *U.S. Private*, pg. 2894
NEW ENGLAND TEA & COFFEE COMPANY, LLC—See Reily Foods Company; *U.S. Private*, pg. 3391
NEW ENGLAND TECHNOLOGY GROUP, INC.; *U.S. Private*, pg. 2894
NEW ENGLAND TISSUE ISSUE, PLLC—See Sonic Healthcare Limited; *Int'l*, pg. 7098
NEW ENGLAND TRADING GLOBAL, INC.; *U.S. Private*, pg. 2894
NEW ENGLAND TRUCK SALES & SERVICES INC.; *U.S. Private*, pg. 2895
NEW ENGLAND UTILITY CONSTRUCTORS, INC.—See Southwest Gas Holdings, Inc.; *U.S. Public*, pg. 1913
NEW ENGLAND WASTE SERVICES OF VERMONT, INC.—See Casella Waste Systems, Inc.; *U.S. Public*, pg. 446
NEW ENGLAND WATER UTILITY SERVICES, INC.—See SJW Group; *U.S. Public*, pg. 1891
NEW ENGLAND WIRE TECHNOLOGIES—See MJM Holdings Inc.; *U.S. Private*, pg. 2753
NEW ENGLAND WOODEN WARE CORP.; *U.S. Private*, pg. 2895
NEW ENGLAND WOOD PELLET, LLC—See Rentech, Inc.; *U.S. Private*, pg. 3400
NEWEN STUDIOS—See Television Francaise 1 S.A.; *Int'l*, pg. 7543
NEW ENTERPRISE ASSOCIATES, LLC; *U.S. Private*, pg. 2895
NEW ENTERPRISE STONE & LIME CO., INC.; *U.S. Private*, pg. 2895
NEW ENTERTAINMENT RESEARCH AND DESIGN LIMITED—See ProSiebenSat.1 Media SE; *Int'l*, pg. 6001
NEW EQUITY VENTURE INT. AB; *Int'l*, pg. 5223
NEW ERA ASIA PACIFIC LIMITED—See ACON Investments, LLC; *U.S. Private*, pg. 62
NEW ERA BUILDERS; *U.S. Private*, pg. 2895
NEW ERA CAP COMPANY LTD.—See ACON Investments, LLC; *U.S. Private*, pg. 62
NEW ERA CAP LLC—See ACON Investments, LLC; *U.S. Private*, pg. 62
NEW ERA CAP S.R.L.—See ACON Investments, LLC; *U.S. Private*, pg. 62
NEW-ERA CO., LTD.—See Nagano Keiki Co., Ltd.; *Int'l*, pg. 5125
NEW ERA ELECTRONICS CO., LTD.; *Int'l*, pg. 5223
NEW ERA FARMS, LLC—See Live Nation Entertainment, Inc.; *U.S. Public*, pg. 1330
NEW ERA FINANCIAL ADVISORS, INC.—See TA Associates, Inc.; *U.S. Private*, pg. 3919

NEW ERA INDIA CONSULTANCY PVT. LTD.—See en-japan Inc.; *Int'l*, pg. 2395
NEW-ERA INTERNATIONAL CO., LTD.—See Nagano Keiki Co., Ltd.; *Int'l*, pg. 5125
NEW ERA LIFE INSURANCE COMPANY OF THE MIDWEST; *U.S. Private*, pg. 2895
NEW ERA PORTFOLIO; *U.S. Private*, pg. 2896
NEW ERA SALES CO., LTD.—See AAPICO Hitech plc; *Int'l*, pg. 37
NEW ERA TECHNOLOGY, INC.; *U.S. Private*, pg. 2896
NEW ERA TECHNOLOGY, INC.; *U.S. Private*, pg. 2896
NEWEVER TRADE WINGS LIMITED; *Int'l*, pg. 5234
NEW EVOLUTION VENTURES, LLC; *U.S. Private*, pg. 2896
NEWEY & EYRE INDUSTRIAL SOLUTIONS—See Rexel, S.A.; *Int'l*, pg. 6317
NEWEY & EYRE—See Rexel, S.A.; *Int'l*, pg. 6317
NEW FAR EAST CABLE CO., LTD.—See Far East Smarter Energy Co., Ltd.; *Int'l*, pg. 2617
NEW FARM HOSPITALS PTY LIMITED—See Ramsay Health Care Limited; *Int'l*, pg. 6200
NEW FASHION—See Ringier Holding AG; *Int'l*, pg. 6344
NEWFIELD BANCORP INC.; *U.S. Private*, pg. 2914
NEWFIELD CONSTRUCTION, INC.; *U.S. Private*, pg. 2914
NEWFIELD CONSTRUCTION INC.—See Emerson Developments (Holdings) Limited; *Int'l*, pg. 2380
NEWFIELD INFORMATION TECHNOLOGY LIMITED—See Xerox Holdings Corporation; *U.S. Public*, pg. 2388
NEWFIELD INFORMATION TECHNOLOGY LLC—See Xerox Holdings Corporation; *U.S. Public*, pg. 2388
NEWFIELD NATIONAL BANK—See Newfield Bancorp Inc.; *U.S. Private*, pg. 2914
NEWFIELD RESOURCES LIMITED; *Int'l*, pg. 5234
NEWFLEET ASSET MANAGEMENT LLC—See Virtus Investment Partners, Inc.; *U.S. Public*, pg. 2301
NEWFLEX TECHNOLOGY CO., LTD.; *Int'l*, pg. 5234
NEW FLIGHT CHARTERS; *U.S. Private*, pg. 2896
NEW FLUID SOLUTIONS INC.—See OMNOVA Solutions Inc.; *U.S. Private*, pg. 3017
NEW FLYER INDUSTRIES CANADA ULC—See NFI Group Inc.; *Int'l*, pg. 5252
NEW FLYER OF AMERICA INC. - CROOKSTON FACILITY—See NFI Group Inc.; *Int'l*, pg. 5252
NEW FLYER OF AMERICA INC.—See NFI Group Inc.; *Int'l*, pg. 5252
NEW FOCUS AUTO TECH HOLDINGS LIMITED; *Int'l*, pg. 5223
NEWFOCUS FINANCIAL GROUP LLC—See EP Wealth Advisors, LLC; *U.S. Private*, pg. 1411
NEW FOCUS LIGHTING & POWER TECHNOLOGY (SHANGHAI) CO., LTD.—See New Focus Auto Tech Holdings Limited; *Int'l*, pg. 5223
NEW FOCUS RICHAHAUS CO. LTD.—See New Focus Auto Tech Holdings Limited; *Int'l*, pg. 5223
NEW FOCUS—See MKS Instruments, Inc.; *U.S. Public*, pg. 1453
NEWFOLD DIGITAL INC.—See Clearlake Capital Group, L.P.; *U.S. Private*, pg. 934
NEWFOLD DIGITAL INC.—See Siris Capital Group, LLC; *U.S. Private*, pg. 3673
NEW FOOD CLASSICS; *Int'l*, pg. 5223
NEW FOREST POST LIMITED—See Gannett Co., Inc.; *U.S. Public*, pg. 898
NEW FORESTS INC.—See New Forests Pty. Limited; *Int'l*, pg. 5223
NEW FORESTS PTY. LIMITED; *Int'l*, pg. 5223
NEWFORMA, INC.—See Ethos Capital, LLC; *U.S. Private*, pg. 1432
NEW FORTRESS ENERGY INC.; *U.S. Public*, pg. 1511
NEWFOUND AREA NURSING ASSOCIATION—See Lakes Region Visiting Nurse Association; *U.S. Private*, pg. 2376
NEW FOUND GOLD CORP.; *Int'l*, pg. 5223
NEWFOUNDLAND CAPITAL CORPORATION LIMITED—See Stingray Group Inc.; *Int'l*, pg. 7215
NEWFOUNDLAND DISCOVERY CORP.; *Int'l*, pg. 5234
NEWFOUNDLAND HARD-ROK INC.—See Incitec Pivot Limited; *Int'l*, pg. 3648
NEWFOUNDLAND POWER INC.—See Fortis Inc.; *Int'l*, pg. 2740
NEWFOUNDLAND TRANSSHIPMENT LIMITED—See Macquarie Group Limited; *Int'l*, pg. 4630
THE NEW FRENCH BAKERY, INC.—See Starbucks Corporation; *U.S. Public*, pg. 1939
NEW FRONTIER ENERGY, INC.; *U.S. Public*, pg. 1511
NEW FRONTIER EQUIPMENT SALES & RENTAL CORP.—See Tym Corporation; *Int'l*, pg. 7995
NEW FRONTIER HEALTH CORPORATION; *Int'l*, pg. 5223
NEW FRONTIER INDUSTRIES INC.—See U.S. Bronze Foundry & Machine, Inc.; *U.S. Private*, pg. 4270
NEW FRONTIER MEDIA, INC.—See L.F.P., Inc.; *U.S. Private*, pg. 2365
NEW FRONTIER PARTNERS CO LTD—See AIFUL Corporation; *Int'l*, pg. 232
NEW FRONTIER PROPERTIES LIMITED; *Int'l*, pg. 5223
NEW FRONTIERS HOLDINGS—See Northern Holdings Inc.; *U.S. Private*, pg. 2953

NEW FRONTIERS NATURAL FOODS V—See Northern Holdings Inc.; *U.S. Private*, pg. 2953
NEW FRONTIERS TOURS PROPRIETARY LIMITED—See The Bidvest Group Limited; *Int'l*, pg. 7625
NEW FRONTIER VENTURES INC.; *Int'l*, pg. 5223
NEWFRONT INSURANCE, INC.; *U.S. Private*, pg. 2914
NEW FUJI CO., LTD.—See Koito Manufacturing Co., Ltd.; *Int'l*, pg. 4230
NEWFUNDS PROPRIETARY LIMITED—See Barclays PLC; *Int'l*, pg. 862
NEW GALAXY ENTERTAINMENT COMPANY LIMITED—See Galaxy Entertainment Group Limited; *Int'l*, pg. 2871
NEWGARD DEVELOPMENT GROUP INC.; *U.S. Private*, pg. 2915
NEW GARDEN LANDSCAPING & NURSERY INC.; *U.S. Private*, pg. 2896
NEWGATE COMMUNICATIONS LLP—See SEC Newgate S.p.A.; *Int'l*, pg. 6670
NEWGATE PRIVATE EQUITY LIMITED—See Newgate Private Equity LLP; *Int'l*, pg. 5234
NEWGATE PRIVATE EQUITY LLP; *Int'l*, pg. 5234
NEWGATE THREADNEEDLE LIMITED—See SEC Newgate S.p.A.; *Int'l*, pg. 6670
NEW GENERATION COMPUTING—See American Software, Inc.; *U.S. Public*, pg. 109
NEW GENERATION CONSUMER GROUP, INC.; *U.S. Public*, pg. 1511
NEWGEN RESULTS CORPORATION—See Publicis Groupe S.A.; *Int'l*, pg. 6098
NEWGEN SOFTWARE INC.—See Newgen Software Technologies Limited; *Int'l*, pg. 5235
NEWGEN SOFTWARE TECHNOLOGIES CANADA LIMITED—See Newgen Software Technologies Limited; *Int'l*, pg. 5235
NEWGEN SOFTWARE TECHNOLOGIES LIMITED; *Int'l*, pg. 5235
NEWGEN SOFTWARE TECHNOLOGIES PTE LTD.—See Newgen Software Technologies Limited; *Int'l*, pg. 5235
NEWGISTICS, INC.—See Pitney Bowes Inc.; *U.S. Public*, pg. 1694
NEWGLAB PHARMA CO.,LTD; *Int'l*, pg. 5235
NEW GLARUS BREWING COMPANY; *U.S. Private*, pg. 2896
NEW GLASS S.A.—See Yioula Glassworks S.A.; *Int'l*, pg. 8585
NEW GLAZING INDUSTRIES, LTD.—See Clayton, Dubilier & Rice, LLC; *U.S. Private*, pg. 921
NEW GLOBAL ACREAGE RESOURCES LTD.; *Int'l*, pg. 5223
NEW GLOBAL MINING LTD; *Int'l*, pg. 5223
NEW GOLD DISCOVERIES, INC.; *U.S. Private*, pg. 2896
NEW GOLDEN SEA SHIPPING PTE., LTD.—See China COSCO Shipping Corporation Limited; *Int'l*, pg. 1494
NEW GOLD INC.; *Int'l*, pg. 5223
NEW GRAND HOTEL AB—See FAM AB; *Int'l*, pg. 2611
NEWGROUND CONSULTING—See NewGround Resources; *U.S. Private*, pg. 2915
NEWGROUND RESOURCES; *U.S. Private*, pg. 2915
NEWGROUND RESOURCES—See NewGround Resources; *U.S. Private*, pg. 2915
NEWGROWTH CORP.—See The Bank of Nova Scotia; *Int'l*, pg. 7617
NEW GROWTH PLUS B.V.—See Electricity Generating Public Co., Ltd.; *Int'l*, pg. 2352
NEW GUARDS GROUP HOLDING S.P.A—See Coupang, Inc.; *Int'l*, pg. 1819
NEW GUARDS GROUP HOLDING S.P.A—See Greenoaks Capital Partners LLC; *U.S. Private*, pg. 1779
NEW GUINEA GOLD CORPORATION; *Int'l*, pg. 5223
NEW GULF COAST SURGERY CENTER, LLC—See Community Health Systems, Inc.; *U.S. Public*, pg. 555
NEW GUOMAI DIGITAL CULTURE CO., LTD.; *Int'l*, pg. 5224
NEW H3C TECHNOLOGIES CO., LTD.—See Tsinghua Holdings Co., Ltd.; *Int'l*, pg. 7951
NEWHALL LABORATORIES, INC.—See Brynwood Partners Management LLC; *U.S. Private*, pg. 674
THE NEWHALL LAND & FARMING COMPANY, INC.—See Lennar Corporation; *U.S. Public*, pg. 1307
NEW HAMPSHIRE BALL BEARINGS HIGH TECH DIV—See Minebea Mitsumi Inc.; *Int'l*, pg. 4904
NEW HAMPSHIRE BALL BEARINGS, INC. - CHATSWORTH PLANT—See Minebea Mitsumi Inc.; *Int'l*, pg. 4904
NEW HAMPSHIRE BALL BEARINGS, INC. - LACONIA PLANT—See Minebea Mitsumi Inc.; *Int'l*, pg. 4904
NEW HAMPSHIRE BALL BEARINGS, INC. - PETERBOROUGH PLANT—See Minebea Mitsumi Inc.; *Int'l*, pg. 4904
NEW HAMPSHIRE BALL BEARINGS, INC.—See Minebea Mitsumi Inc.; *Int'l*, pg. 4904
NEW HAMPSHIRE ELECTRIC COOPERATIVE INC.; *U.S. Private*, pg. 2896
NEW HAMPSHIRE GAS CORPORATION—See Iberdrola, S.A.; *Int'l*, pg. 3570
NEW HAMPSHIRE HOUSING FINANCE AUTHORITY; *U.S. Private*, pg. 2896

NEW HAMPSHIRE INDUSTRIES INC.; *U.S. Private,* pg. 2896

NEW HAMPSHIRE MOTOR SPEEDWAY, INC.—See Sonic Financial Corporation; *U.S. Private,* pg. 3713

NEW HAMPSHIRE NORTHCOAST CORP.—See Boston Sand & Gravel Company; *U.S. Public,* pg. 373

NEW HAMPSHIRE PLASTICS INC.; *U.S. Private,* pg. 2896

NEW HANOVER COUNTY ABC BOARD; *U.S. Private,* pg. 2896

NEW HARBOR CAPITAL MANAGEMENT LLC; *U.S. Private,* pg. 2896

NEW HARQUAHALA GENERATING CO, LLC—See Beal Financial Corporation; *U.S. Private,* pg. 505

NEW HARRAH'S NORTH KANSAS CITY LLC—See VICI Properties Inc.; *U.S. Public,* pg. 2296

NEW HARVEST WIND PROJECT, LLC—See Iberdrola, S.A; *Int'l,* pg. 3571

NEW HAVEN CENTER—See Formation Capital, LLC; *U.S. Private,* pg. 1571

NEW HAVEN CITY PARKING AUTHORITY; *U.S. Private,* pg. 2896

NEWHAVEN FUNERALS (NORTH QUEENSLAND) PTY LTD—See Propel Funeral Partners Limited; *Int'l,* pg. 5997

NEW HAVEN HOTEL LLC—See Noble Investment Group, LLC; *U.S. Private,* pg. 2933

NEW HAVEN RADIOLOGY ASSOCIATES, P.C.—See Midstate Radiology Associates LLC; *U.S. Private,* pg. 2718

NEW HAVEN REGISTER, INC.—See Alden Global Capital LLC; *U.S. Private,* pg. 157

NEW HEIGHTS LTD.; *Int'l,* pg. 5224

NEWHERE, INC.; *U.S. Private,* pg. 2915

NEW HERITAGE CAPITAL LLC; *U.S. Private,* pg. 2896

NEW HIGH GLASS INC—See Industrie Zignago Santa Margherita SpA; *Int'l,* pg. 3674

NEW HILL MANAGEMENT, LLC; *U.S. Private,* pg. 2897

NEWHOLD ENTERPRISES LLC; *U.S. Private,* pg. 2915

NEW HOLLAND CONSTRUCTION—See CNH Industrial N.V.; *Int'l,* pg. 1674

NEW HOLLAND FIAT (INDIA) PRIVATE LIMITED—See CNH Industrial N.V.; *Int'l,* pg. 1676

NEW HOLLAND FIAT (INDIA) PVT. LTD. - PARTS DIVISION—See CNH Industrial N.V.; *Int'l,* pg. 1676

NEW HOLLAND FIAT (INDIA) PVT. LTD. - TRACTOR DIVISION—See CNH Industrial N.V.; *Int'l,* pg. 1676

NEW HOLLAND MOTOR COMPANY, INC.; *U.S. Private,* pg. 2897

NEW HOLLAND SA (PTY) LTD.—See Invicta Holdings Limited; *Int'l,* pg. 3788

NEW HOLLAND WINE COMPANY PTY. LTD.; *Int'l,* pg. 5224

THE NEW HOME COMPANY INC.—See Apollo Global Management, Inc.; *U.S. Public,* pg. 164

THE NEW HOME COMPANY NORTHERN CALIFORNIA LLC—See Apollo Global Management, Inc.; *U.S. Public,* pg. 164

NEW HOME TECHNOLOGIES, LLC—See Builder Homesite, Inc.; *U.S. Private,* pg. 681

NEW HONG KONG TUNNEL COMPANY LIMITED—See CITIC Group Corporation; *Int'l,* pg. 1621

NEW HONOR SOCIETY, INC.—See The Interpublic Group of Companies, Inc.; *U.S. Public,* pg. 2103

NEW HOONG FATT AUTO SUPPLIES SDN. BHD.—See New Hoong Fatt Holdings Berhad; *Int'l,* pg. 5224

NEW HOONG FATT HOLDINGS BERHAD; *Int'l,* pg. 5224

NEW HOPE AGROTECH BANGLADESH LTD—See New Hope Group Co., Ltd.; *Int'l,* pg. 5224

NEW HOPE BULACAN AGRICULTURE INC.—See New Hope Group Co., Ltd.; *Int'l,* pg. 5224

NEW HOPE CENTRAL LUZON AGRICULTURE INC.—See New Hope Group Co., Ltd.; *Int'l,* pg. 5224

NEW HOPE COMMUNITY, INC.; *U.S. Private,* pg. 2897

NEW HOPE CORPORATION LIMITED; *Int'l,* pg. 5224

NEW HOPE COUNSELING—See Crystal Cathedral Ministries Inc.; *U.S. Private,* pg. 1115

NEW HOPE DAIRY CO., LTD.; *Int'l,* pg. 5224

NEW HOPE DONG THAP AQUAFEED PRODUUCTION CO., LTD.—See New Hope Group Co., Ltd.; *Int'l,* pg. 5224

NEW HOPE EGYPT CO. LTD—See New Hope Group Co., Ltd.; *Int'l,* pg. 5224

NEW HOPE FARMS BANGLADESH CO., LTD—See New Hope Group Co., Ltd.; *Int'l,* pg. 5224

NEW HOPE FEED MILL BANGLADESH LTD.—See New Hope Group Co., Ltd.; *Int'l,* pg. 5224

NEW HOPE GROUP CO., LTD.; *Int'l,* pg. 5224

NEW HOPE HANOI CO., LTD.—See New Hope Group Co.; *Int'l,* pg. 5224

NEW HOPE HOCHIMINH CITY CO., LTD.—See New Hope Group Co., Ltd.; *Int'l,* pg. 5224

NEWHOPE IMAGING CENTER, INC.—See Tenet Healthcare Corporation; *U.S. Public,* pg. 2006

NEW HOPE LANKA LTD—See New Hope Group Co., Ltd.; *Int'l,* pg. 5224

NEW HOPE LIUHE CO., LTD.—See New Hope Group Co., Ltd.; *Int'l,* pg. 5224

NEW HOPE MARINE INC.—See Family Federation for World Peace & Unification; *U.S. Private,* pg. 1469

NEW HOPE PAMPANGA AGRICULTURE INC.—See New Hope Group Co., Ltd.; *Int'l,* pg. 5224

NEW HOPE RANCH LLC—See Discovery Behavioral Health, Inc; *U.S. Private,* pg. 1237

NEW HOPE SOUTH AFRICA (PTY) LTD—See New Hope Group Co., Ltd.; *Int'l,* pg. 5224

NEW HOPE SOUTH INC.—See Florida Crystals Corporation; *U.S. Private,* pg. 1548

NEW HOPE TARLAC AGRICULTURE INC.—See New Hope Group Co., Ltd.; *Int'l,* pg. 5224

NEW HOPE TURKEY YEM HAYVANCILIK GIDA ITHALAT IHRACAT SANAYI VE TICARET LIMITED SIRKETI—See New Hope Group Co., Ltd.; *Int'l,* pg. 5224

NEW HORIZON AIRCRAFT LTD.; *Int'l,* pg. 5225

NEW HORIZON BANK, N.A.—See CSBH LLC; *U.S. Private,* pg. 1116

NEW HORIZON CAPITAL CO. LTD.; *Int'l,* pg. 5225

NEW HORIZON CAPITAL; *Int'l,* pg. 5225

NEW HORIZON COMMUNICATIONS GROUP; *U.S. Private,* pg. 2897

NEW HORIZON COUNSELING CENTER, INC.; *U.S. Private,* pg. 2897

NEW HORIZON EQUITY GROUP, INC.; *U.S. Private,* pg. 2897

NEW HORIZON FARM LLP—See Hord Livestock Company, Inc.; *U.S. Private,* pg. 1980

NEW HORIZON FARM SERVICE—See New Horizon F S Inc.; *U.S. Private,* pg. 2897

NEW HORIZON F S INC.; *U.S. Private,* pg. 2897

NEW HORIZON GROUP LTD.; *Int'l,* pg. 5225

NEW HORIZON HEALTH LIMITED; *Int'l,* pg. 5225

NEW HORIZON KIDS QUEST, INC.; *U.S. Private,* pg. 2897

NEW HORIZONS ASSET MANAGEMENT GROUP, LLC—See Rhinebeck Bank; *U.S. Private,* pg. 3421

NEW HORIZONS BAKING COMPANY; *U.S. Private,* pg. 2897

NEW HORIZONS COMPUTER LEARNING CENTER OF CLEVELAND, LLC—See Camden Partners Holdings, LLC; *U.S. Private,* pg. 728

NEW HORIZONS COMPUTER LEARNING CENTER OF METROPOLITAN NEW YORK, INC.—See Camden Partners Holdings, LLC; *U.S. Private,* pg. 728

NEW HORIZONS COMPUTER LEARNING CENTER OF SOUTHERN CALIFORNIA—See Camden Partners Holdings, LLC; *U.S. Private,* pg. 728

NEW HORIZONS COMPUTER LEARNING CENTERS, INC.—See Camden Partners Holdings, LLC; *U.S. Private,* pg. 728

NEW HORIZONS CREDIT UNION; *U.S. Private,* pg. 2897

NEW HORIZON SECURITY SERVICES, INC.—See Allied Universal Manager LLC; *U.S. Private,* pg. 190

NEW HORIZONS FOR NEW HAMPSHIRE—See FIT/NHNH, INC.; *U.S. Private,* pg. 1535

NEW HORIZONS HEALTH SYSTEMS, INC.; *U.S. Private,* pg. 2897

NEW HORIZONS IN CHILD DEVELOPMENT—See Measured Progress Inc.; *U.S. Private,* pg. 2648

NEW HORIZONS INCORPORATED; *U.S. Private,* pg. 2897

NEW HORIZONS INSURANCE MARKETING INC.—See Integrity Marketing Group LLC; *U.S. Private,* pg. 2103

NEW HORIZONS OF THE TREASURE COAST AND OKEECHOBEE; *U.S. Private,* pg. 2897

NEW HORIZONS PICTURE CORP.; *U.S. Private,* pg. 2897

NEW HORIZONS PT, LIMITED PARTNERSHIP—See U.S. Physical Therapy, Inc.; *U.S. Public,* pg. 2215

NEW HORIZONS REHABILITATION SERVICES, INC.; *U.S. Private,* pg. 2897

NEW HORIZONS SURGERY CENTER, LLC—See Tenet Healthcare Corporation; *U.S. Public,* pg. 2011

NEW HORIZON SUPPLY COOPERATIVE; *U.S. Private,* pg. 2897

NEW HORIZONS WORLDWIDE, INC.—See Camden Partners Holdings, LLC; *U.S. Private,* pg. 728

NEW HORSESHOE HAMMOND LLC—See VICI Properties Inc.; *U.S. Public,* pg. 2296

NEWHOUSE NEWS SERVICE—See Advance Publications, Inc.; *U.S. Private,* pg. 86

NEW HUADU SUPERCENTER CO., LTD.; *Int'l,* pg. 5225

NEW HUO ASSET MANAGEMENT (HONG KONG) LIMITED—See Sinohope Technology Holdings Limited; *Int'l,* pg. 6952

NEWHYDROGEN, INC.; *U.S. Public,* pg. 1515

NEW IMAGE GROUP LIMITED; *Int'l,* pg. 5225

NEW IMAGE HEALTH SCIENCES (PTY) LIMITED—See New Image Group Limited; *Int'l,* pg. 5225

NEW IMAGE INTERNATIONAL LIMITED—See New Image Group Limited; *Int'l,* pg. 5225

NEW IMAGE INTERNATIONAL SINGAPORE (PTE) LIMITED—See New Image Group Limited; *Int'l,* pg. 5225

NEW IMAGE TOWING & RECOVERY, LLC—See Marietta Wrecker Service LLC; *U.S. Private,* pg. 2574

NEW & IMPROVED MEDIA; *U.S. Private,* pg. 2892

NEWIND GROUP INC—See Enel S.p.A.; *Int'l,* pg. 2413

THE NEW INDIA ASSURANCE COMPANY LIMITED; *Int'l,* pg. 7670

THE NEW INDIA ASSURANCE COMPANY (SIERRA LEONE) LIMITED—See The New India Assurance Company Limited; *Int'l,* pg. 7670

THE NEW INDIA ASSURANCE CO. (SIERRA LEONE) LIMITED—See The New India Assurance Company Limited; *Int'l,* pg. 7670

THE NEW INDIA ASSURANCE CO. (TRINIDAD & TOBAGO) LIMITED—See The New India Assurance Company Limited; *Int'l,* pg. 7670

NEW INDIA CONSTRUCTION CO. LIMITED—See Unitech Limited; *Int'l,* pg. 8064

NEW-INDY CONTAINERBOARD LLC—See Schwarz Partners, LP; *U.S. Private,* pg. 3572

NEW-INDY CONTAINERBOARD LLC—See The Kraft Group LLC; *U.S. Private,* pg. 4066

NEW INFINITY HOLDINGS LTD.; *Int'l,* pg. 5225

NEWINGTON HEALTH & WELLNESS CENTER—See Healthtrax Inc.; *U.S. Private,* pg. 1898

NEWINS INSURANCE AGENCY HOLDINGS, LLC—See Kemper Corporation; *U.S. Public,* pg. 1221

NEW INSPIRATION BROADCASTING CO. INC.—See Salem Media Group, Inc.; *U.S. Public,* pg. 1836

NEW INTELLIGENCE CO., LTD.—See Okins Electronics Co., Ltd.; *Int'l,* pg. 5550

NEW IRELAND ASSURANCE COMPANY PLC—See Bank of Ireland Group plc; *Int'l,* pg. 844

NEW ISLAND PRINTING COMPANY LIMITED—See China Huajun Group Limited; *Int'l,* pg. 1509

NEW ISLAND PRINTING (LIAONING) COMPANY LIMITED—See China Huajun Group Limited; *Int'l,* pg. 1509

NEW ISLAND PRINTING (US) INC.—See China Huajun Group Limited; *Int'l,* pg. 1509

NEW ISRAEL FUND; *U.S. Private,* pg. 2897

NEWJAISA TECHNOLOGIES PVT LTD.; *Int'l,* pg. 5235

NEW JAPAN CHEMICAL CO., LTD. - KAWASAKI PLANT—See New Japan Chemical Co., Ltd.; *Int'l,* pg. 5225

NEW JAPAN CHEMICAL CO., LTD. - KYOTO PLANT—See New Japan Chemical Co., Ltd.; *Int'l,* pg. 5225

NEW JAPAN CHEMICAL CO., LTD. - SAKAI PLANT—See New Japan Chemical Co., Ltd.; *Int'l,* pg. 5225

NEW JAPAN CHEMICAL CO., LTD.; *Int'l,* pg. 5225

NEW JAPAN CHEMICAL CO., LTD. - TOKUSHIMA PLANT—See New Japan Chemical Co., Ltd.; *Int'l,* pg. 5225

NEW JAPAN MACHINERY CO. LTD.—See Denyo Co., Ltd.; *Int'l,* pg. 2040

NEW JAPAN RADIO CO., LTD.—See Nisshinbo Holdings Inc.; *Int'l,* pg. 5373

NEW JCM GROUP CO., LTD; *Int'l,* pg. 5225

NEWJEC INC.—See The Kansai Electric Power Co., Inc.; *Int'l,* pg. 7662

NEW JERSEY 101.5—See Brookfield Corporation; *Int'l,* pg. 1183

NEW JERSEY ADDICTION TREATMENT CENTER, LLC—See AAC Holdings, Inc.; *U.S. Private,* pg. 30

NEW JERSEY-AMERICAN WATER COMPANY, INC.—See American Water Works Company, Inc.; *U.S. Public,* pg. 112

NEW JERSEY AMERICAN WATER—See American Water Works Company, Inc.; *U.S. Public,* pg. 112

NEW JERSEY BUSINESS FORMS MANUFACTURING CORPORATION; *U.S. Private,* pg. 2898

NEW JERSEY DEVILS LLC—See Devils Holdings, LLC; *U.S. Private,* pg. 1218

NEW JERSEY HERALD INC.—See Gray Television, Inc.; *U.S. Public,* pg. 961

NEW JERSEY IMAGING NETWORK, LLC—See RadNet, Inc.; *U.S. Public,* pg. 1761

NEW JERSEY LIFE & HEALTH INSURANCE GUARANTY ASSOCIATION; *U.S. Private,* pg. 2897

NEW JERSEY MANUFACTURERS INSURANCE COMPANY; *U.S. Private,* pg. 2898

NEW JERSEY METER CO.—See Elaine, Inc.; *U.S. Private,* pg. 1349

NEW JERSEY MONTHLY; *U.S. Private,* pg. 2898

NEW JERSEY NATURAL GAS COMPANY—See New Jersey Resources Corporation; *U.S. Public,* pg. 1512

NEW JERSEY NATURAL RESOURCES COMPANY—See New Jersey Resources Corporation; *U.S. Public,* pg. 1512

NEW JERSEY PERFORMING ARTS CENTER; *U.S. Private,* pg. 2898

NEW JERSEY RESOURCES CORPORATION; *U.S. Public,* pg. 1511

NEW JERSEY SPORTS & EXPOSITION AUTHORITY; *U.S. Private,* pg. 2898

NEW JERSEY TRANSIT BUS OPERATIONS—See NJ Transit Corporation; *U.S. Private,* pg. 2930

NEW JERSEY TRANSIT RAIL OPERATIONS—See NJ Transit Corporation; *U.S. Private,* pg. 2930

NEW JERSEY TURNPIKE AUTHORITY INC.; *U.S. Private,* pg. 2898

THE NEW JERSEY WIRE STITCHING MACHINE CO.—See Precision Automation Co., Inc.; *U.S. Private,* pg. 3244

NEW JIGU TRADING CORP.; *U.S. Private,* pg. 2898

NEW JOULES ENGINEERING NORTH AMERICA INC.—See ARGENT INDUSTRIAL LIMITED; *Int'l*, pg. 561
NEW JOURNEY HEALTH TECHNOLOGY GROUP CO., LTD.; *Int'l*, pg. 5226
NEW J'S CO., LTD.—See Japan Oil Transportation Co., Ltd.; *Int'l*, pg. 3899
NEW KEAN TAT AUTO PARTS SDN. BHD.—See New Hoong Fatt Holdings Berhad; *Int'l*, pg. 5224
NEW KING INC.; *U.S. Private*, pg. 2898
NEW KINPO GROUP; *Int'l*, pg. 5226
NEWKIRK, DENNIS & BUCKLES, INC.; *U.S. Private*, pg. 2915
NEWKIRK ELECTRIC ASSOCIATES; *U.S. Private*, pg. 2915
NEW KLEINFONTEIN GOLDMINE (PROPRIETARY) LIMITED—See Baiyin Nonferrous Metal (Group) Co., Ltd.; *Int'l*, pg. 803
NEW KLEINFONTEIN GOLDMINE (PROPRIETARY) LIMITED—See Long March Capital Ltd.; *Int'l*, pg. 4549
NEW KLEINFONTEIN MINING COMPANY LIMITED—See Baiyin Nonferrous Metal (Group) Co., Ltd.; *Int'l*, pg. 803
NEW KLEINFONTEIN MINING COMPANY LIMITED—See Long March Capital Ltd.; *Int'l*, pg. 4549
THE NEW KNOXVILLE TELEPHONE COMPANY—See Schurz Communications, Inc.; *U.S. Private*, pg. 3571
NEW KONDO TRADING COMPANY LIMITED—See Four Seas Mercantile Holdings Limited; *Int'l*, pg. 2755
NEW KRUNG THAI SUGAR FACTORY CO., LTD.—See Khon Kaen Sugar Industry Public Company Limited; *Int'l*, pg. 4155
NEWK'S FRANCHISE COMPANY; *U.S. Private*, pg. 2915
NEW LACHAUSSEE S.A.—See George Forrest International S.A.; *Int'l*, pg. 2938
NEWLAKE CAPITAL PARTNERS, INC.; *U.S. Public*, pg. 1515
NEWLAND DIGITAL TECHNOLOGY CO., LTD.; *Int'l*, pg. 5235
NEW LAND TITLE AGENCY, L.L.C.—See Hovnanian Enterprises, Inc.; *U.S. Public*, pg. 1060
NEWLAND VIETNAM JAPAN JOINT STOCK COMPANY—See Sojitz Corporation; *Int'l*, pg. 7062
NEWLANE COSMETICS COMPANY LIMITED—See McBride plc; *Int'l*, pg. 4756
NEW LANTAO BUS COMPANY (1973) LIMITED—See KWOON CHUNG BUS HOLDINGS LIMITED; *Int'l*, pg. 4155
NEWLAT FOOD S.P.A.; *Int'l*, pg. 5235
NEWLAT GMBH—See Newlat Food S.p.A.; *Int'l*, pg. 5235
NEWLAT - SANSEPOLCRO—See TMT Finance SA; *Int'l*, pg. 7767
NEWLAT SPA—See TMT Finance SA; *Int'l*, pg. 7767
NEWLAW LEGAL LIMITED—See ZIGUP plc; *Int'l*, pg. 8682
THE NEW LEADER; *U.S. Private*, pg. 4083
NEWLEAD HOLDINGS LTD.; *Int'l*, pg. 5235
NEWLEADS, INC.; *U.S. Private*, pg. 2915
NEW LEAF ACADEMY, INC.—See Acadia Healthcare Company, Inc.; *U.S. Public*, pg. 29
NEW LEAF COMMUNITY MARKETS INC.; *U.S. Private*, pg. 2898
NEW LEAF ENERGY, INC.—See Energy Capital Partners Management, LP; *U.S. Private*, pg. 1394
NEW LEAF PAPER, LLC; *U.S. Private*, pg. 2898
NEW LEAF REAL ESTATE, LLC—See New Leaf Ventures, Inc.; *Int'l*, pg. 5226
NEW LEAF SERVICES LLC—See New Leaf Ventures, Inc.; *Int'l*, pg. 5226
NEW LEAF VENTURES, INC.; *Int'l*, pg. 5226
NEW LEGEND, INC.; *U.S. Private*, pg. 2898
NEW LESHI INFORMATION & TECHNOLOGY CORP.; *Int'l*, pg. 5226
NEWL & EUROPE BV—See Newland Digital Technology Co., Ltd.; *Int'l*, pg. 5235
NEW LEYTE EDIBLE OIL MFG. CORP.—See Fuji Oil Holdings Inc.; *Int'l*, pg. 2815
NEWLIFE BIKES, INC.; *U.S. Private*, pg. 2915
NEW LIFE CHEMICAL & EQUIPMENT, INC.—See Makai Capital Partners LLC; *U.S. Private*, pg. 2556
NEW LIFE HIKING SPA, INC.; *U.S. Private*, pg. 2898
NEW LIFE MOTORS, S.A DE C.V.—See Prolab Technologies Inc.; *Int'l*, pg. 5991
NEW LIFE SOLUTION, INC.; *U.S. Private*, pg. 2898
NEW LIGHT APPARELS LIMITED; *Int'l*, pg. 5226
NEW LIMECO, LLC.; *U.S. Private*, pg. 2898
NEW LINE CINEMA CORPORATION—See Warner Bros. Discovery, Inc.; *U.S. Public*, pg. 2327
NEW LINE CINEMA—See Warner Bros. Discovery, Inc.; *U.S. Public*, pg. 2327
NEW LINE DISTRIBUTION, INC.—See Warner Bros. Discovery, Inc.; *U.S. Public*, pg. 2327
NEW LINE HOME ENTERTAINMENT, INC.—See Warner Bros. Discovery, Inc.; *U.S. Public*, pg. 2327
NEW LINE INTERNATIONAL RELEASING, INC.—See Warner Bros. Discovery, Inc.; *U.S. Public*, pg. 2327
NEW LINE PRODUCTIONS, INC.—See Warner Bros. Discovery, Inc.; *U.S. Public*, pg. 2327
NEWLINE UNDERWRITING MANAGEMENT LTD.—See Fairfax Financial Holdings Limited; *Int'l*, pg. 2607

NEWLINK TECHNOLOGY, INC.; *Int'l*, pg. 5235
NEWLOG SAS—See Schneider Electric SE; *Int'l*, pg. 6628
NEW LONDON COMMUNICATIONS, LLC; *U.S. Private*, pg. 2898
NEW LONDON COUNTY MUTUAL INSURANCE COMPANY, INC.; *U.S. Private*, pg. 2898
NEW LONDON FARMERS COOPERATIVE; *U.S. Private*, pg. 2898
NEWLOOK CAPITAL INC.; *Int'l*, pg. 5235
NEW LOOK GROUP LIMITED—See Brait S.E.; *Int'l*, pg. 1137
NEW LOOK RETAIL GROUP LIMITED—See Brait S.E.; *Int'l*, pg. 1137
NEW LOOK VISION GROUP, INC.—See Caisse de Depot et Placement du Quebec; *Int'l*, pg. 1254
NEW LOOK VISION GROUP, INC.—See FFL Partners, LLC; *U.S. Private*, pg. 1500
NEWLOX GOLD VENTURES CORP.; *Int'l*, pg. 5235
NEWL & PAYMENT TECHNOLOGY LIMITED—See Newland Digital Technology Co., Ltd.; *Int'l*, pg. 5235
NEWLY WEDS FOODS ASIA PACIFIC—See Newly Weds Foods, Inc.; *U.S. Private*, pg. 2915
NEWLY WEDS FOODS, INC.—See Newly Weds Foods, Inc.; *U.S. Private*, pg. 2915
NEWLY WEDS FOODS, INC.; *U.S. Private*, pg. 2915
NEWLY WEDS FOODS, INC.—See Newly Weds Foods, Inc.; *U.S. Private*, pg. 2915
NEWLY WEDS FOODS, INC.—See Newly Weds Foods, Inc.; *U.S. Private*, pg. 2915
NEWLY WEDS FOODS, INC.—See Newly Weds Foods, Inc.; *U.S. Private*, pg. 2915
NEWLY WEDS FOODS, LTD.—See Newly Weds Foods, Inc.; *U.S. Private*, pg. 2915
NEW MAC ELECTRIC COOPERATIVE; *U.S. Private*, pg. 2898
NEWMAC MFG. INC.—See United States Stove Company; *U.S. Private*, pg. 4300
NEWMAN ASSOCIATES, INC—See NEFCO Corp.; *U.S. Private*, pg. 2880
NEWMAN CRANE & ASSOCIATES INSURANCE, INC.—See ABRY Partners, LLC; *U.S. Private*, pg. 43
NEWMAN DISPLAYS LTD—See Reach4Entertainment Enterprises PLC; *Int'l*, pg. 6232
NEWMAN FINANCIAL SERVICES, LLC—See Thrivent Financial for Lutherans Foundation; *U.S. Private*, pg. 4165
NEWMAN & GOH PROPERTY CONSULTANTS PTE. LTD.—See Advancer Global Limited; *Int'l*, pg. 163
NEWMAN/HAAS RACING, LLC; *U.S. Private*, pg. 2916
NEWMAN & KENG PAVING COMPANY; *U.S. Private*, pg. 2915
NEWMAN LAWN CARE INC.—See Crux Capital Ltd; *U.S. Private*, pg. 1114
NEWMAN LUMBER CO., INC.; *U.S. Private*, pg. 2915
NEWMAN REGENCY GROUP, INC.—See H.J.G. Capital, LLC; *U.S. Private*, pg. 1834
NEWMAN S.A.; *Int'l*, pg. 5235
NEWMAN'S OWN, INC.; *U.S. Private*, pg. 2916
NEWMAN & SPURR CONSULTANCY LTD.—See QinetiQ Group plc; *Int'l*, pg. 6141
NEWMANS VALVE LLC—See Schlumberger Limited; *U.S. Public*, pg. 1844
NEWMAN & ULLMAN, INC.; *U.S. Private*, pg. 2915
NEWMAR CORPORATION—See Winnebago Industries, Inc.; *U.S. Public*, pg. 2374
NEWMARK ADVERTISING, INC.; *U.S. Private*, pg. 2916
NEWMARK ASSOCIATES, INC.; *U.S. Private*, pg. 2916
NEWMARK BH2 LLP—See Newmark Group, Inc.; *U.S. Public*, pg. 1516
NEWMARK & COMPANY REAL ESTATE, INC.—See BGC Group, Inc.; *U.S. Public*, pg. 329
NEWMARK CONSTRUCTION SERVICES, LLC—See BGC Group, Inc.; *U.S. Public*, pg. 329
NEWMARK CORNISH & CAREY—See BGC Group, Inc.; *U.S. Public*, pg. 329
NEWMARKET CO-OPERATIVE CREAMERIES LIMITED—See Kerry Group plc; *Int'l*, pg. 4139
NEWMARKET CO-OP SUPERVALU LIMITED—See Kerry Group plc; *Int'l*, pg. 4139
NEWMARKET CORPORATION; *U.S. Public*, pg. 1516
NEWMARKET INFORMATION (PUBLICATIONS) LIMITED—See Byggfakta Group Nordic HoldCo AB; *Int'l*, pg. 1235
NEWMARKET INTERNATIONAL, INC. - MTECH DIVISION—See Amadeus IT Group, S.A.; *Int'l*, pg. 406
NEWMARKET INTERNATIONAL, INC.—See Amadeus IT Group, S.A.; *Int'l*, pg. 406
NEWMARKET INTERNATIONAL LTD.—See Amadeus IT Group, S.A.; *Int'l*, pg. 406
NEWMARKET INTERNATIONAL SOFTWARE PTE. LTD.—See Amadeus IT Group, S.A.; *Int'l*, pg. 406
NEWMARKET INTERNATIONAL SOFTWARE (SHANGHAI) CO., LTD.—See Amadeus IT Group, S.A.; *Int'l*, pg. 406
NEW MARKET LAND COMPANY—See Alpha Natural Resources, Inc.; *U.S. Private*, pg. 199
NEW MARKET POULTRY, LLC—See Tip Top Poultry, Inc.; *U.S. Private*, pg. 4175
NEW MARKETS ADVISORY LIMITED; *Int'l*, pg. 5226

NEW MARKETS MEDIA & INTELLIGENCE LTD.—See APQ Global Limited; *Int'l*, pg. 522
NEWMARK GROUP, INC.; *U.S. Public*, pg. 1515
NEWMARK GRUBB KNIGHT FRANK - ATLANTA—See BGC Group, Inc.; *U.S. Public*, pg. 329
NEWMARK GRUBB KNIGHT FRANK - CHICAGO—See BGC Group, Inc.; *U.S. Public*, pg. 329
NEWMARK GRUBB KNIGHT FRANK - DETROIT—See BGC Group, Inc.; *U.S. Public*, pg. 329
NEWMARK GRUBB PHOENIX REALTY GROUP, INC.—See BGC Group, Inc.; *U.S. Public*, pg. 329
NEWMARK KNIGHT FRANK CANADA LIMITED—See Newmark Group, Inc.; *U.S. Public*, pg. 1515
NEWMARK KNIGHT FRANK VALUATION & ADVISORY, LLC—See Newmark Group, Inc.; *U.S. Public*, pg. 1515
NEWMARK MEDICAL COMPONENTS INC.—See The Platt Brothers & Company, Inc.; *U.S. Private*, pg. 4096
NEWMARK OF LONG ISLAND LLC—See BGC Group, Inc.; *U.S. Public*, pg. 329
NEWMARK OF WASHINGTON D.C. LLC—See BGC Group, Inc.; *U.S. Public*, pg. 329
NEWMARK REAL ESTATE OF DALLAS, LLC—See BGC Group, Inc.; *U.S. Public*, pg. 329
NEWMARK REAL ESTATE OF HOUSTON, LLC—See BGC Group, Inc.; *U.S. Public*, pg. 329
NEWMARK REAL ESTATE OF NEW JERSEY, LLC—See BGC Group, Inc.; *U.S. Public*, pg. 329
NEWMARK REAL ESTATE PANAMA, S.A.—See Newmark Group, Inc.; *U.S. Public*, pg. 1516
NEWMARK REIT MANAGEMENT LIMITED; *Int'l*, pg. 5235
NEWMARK SECURITY PLC; *Int'l*, pg. 5235
NEWMARK TECHNOLOGY LIMITED—See Newmark Security Plc; *Int'l*, pg. 5235
NEW MARTINSVILLE CENTER—See Formation Capital, LLC; *U.S. Private*, pg. 1571
NEW MATERIAL HONG KONG LIMITED—See Texchem Resources Bhd; *Int'l*, pg. 7583
NEW MATERIAL (MALAYSIA) SDN. BHD.—See Texchem Resources Bhd; *Int'l*, pg. 7583
NEW MATHER METALS INC.—See NHK Spring Co., Ltd.; *Int'l*, pg. 5258
NEW MAURITIUS HOTELS LIMITED; *Int'l*, pg. 5226
NEW MAVERICK DESK INC.—See H.S. Morgan Limited Partnership; *U.S. Private*, pg. 1836
NEWMAX TECHNOLOGY CO., LTD.; *Int'l*, pg. 5235
NEW MCI HOLDINGS, INC.—See NFI Group Inc.; *Int'l*, pg. 5252
NEWMEDIAROCKSTARS, INC.—See Zealot Networks, Inc.; *U.S. Private*, pg. 4599
NEW MEDIA STRATEGIES—See Meredith Corporation; *U.S. Public*, pg. 1423
NEW MEDICAL CENTRE LLC—See NMC Health PLC; *Int'l*, pg. 5392
NEW MEDICAL CENTRE SPECIALTY HOSPITAL LLC—See NMC Health PLC; *Int'l*, pg. 5392
NEW METAL ENGINEERING, LLC—See IHI Corporation; *Int'l*, pg. 3606
NEW MEXICO AMERICAN WATER—See EPCOR Utilities, Inc.; *Int'l*, pg. 2459
NEW MEXICO BANK & TRUST—See Heartland Financial USA, Inc.; *U.S. Public*, pg. 1018
NEW MEXICO EDUCATIONAL ASSISTANCE FOUNDATION; *U.S. Private*, pg. 2898
NEW MEXICO FOOD DISTRIBUTORS, INC.—See Tattooed Chef, Inc.; *U.S. Public*, pg. 1983
NEW MEXICO GAS COMPANY, INC.—See Emera, Inc.; *Int'l*, pg. 2377
NEW MEXICO LOGOS, INC.—See Lamar Advertising Company; *U.S. Public*, pg. 1291
NEW MEXICO MUTUAL CASUALTY COMPANY; *U.S. Private*, pg. 2898
NEW MEXICO ORTHOPAEDIC SURGERY CENTER, L.P.—See Tenet Healthcare Corporation; *U.S. Public*, pg. 2011
NEW MEXICO SPACEPORT AUTHORITY; *U.S. Private*, pg. 2898
NEW MEXICO WATER SERVICE COMPANY—See California Water Service Group; *U.S. Public*, pg. 424
NEW MILFORD FARMS—See Hendricks Holding Company, Inc.; *U.S. Private*, pg. 1915
NEW MILFORD LANDFILL, L.L.C.—See Waste Management, Inc.; *U.S. Public*, pg. 2331
NEW MILLENNIUM ACADEMY LLC—See NRG Energy, Inc.; *U.S. Public*, pg. 1550
NEW MILLENNIUM BANK; *U.S. Public*, pg. 1512
NEW MILLENNIUM BUILDING SYSTEMS, LLC—See Steel Dynamics, Inc.; *U.S. Public*, pg. 1942
NEW MILLENNIUM BUILDING SYSTEMS—See Steel Dynamics, Inc.; *U.S. Public*, pg. 1942
NEW MIND (HONG KONG) LIMITED—See China Healthwise Holdings Limited; *Int'l*, pg. 1507
NEW MOMENTUM CORP.; *Int'l*, pg. 5226
NEW MOMS, INC.—See Parenthesis, Inc.; *U.S. Private*, pg. 3094
NEWMONT AUSTRALIA PTY LIMITED—See Newmont Corporation; *U.S. Public*, pg. 1517
NEWMONT AUSTRALIA SUPERANNUATION PLAN PTY LTD—See Newmont Corporation; *U.S. Public*, pg. 1517
NEWMONT CORPORATION; *U.S. Public*, pg. 1516

COMPANY NAME INDEX

NEWMONT GOLD COMPANY—See Newmont Corporation; *U.S. Public*, pg. 1517
NEWMONT MINING CORPORATION OF CANADA LIMITED—See Newmont Corporation; *U.S. Public*, pg. 1517
NEWMONT NORTH AMERICA EXPLORATION LIMITED—See Newmont Corporation; *U.S. Public*, pg. 1517
NEWMONT NUSA TENGGARA HOLDINGS B.V.—See Newmont Corporation; *U.S. Public*, pg. 1517
NEW MORGAN LANDFILL COMPANY, INC.—See Republic Services, Inc.; *U.S. Public*, pg. 1786
THE NEW MOTION DEUTSCHLAND GMBH—See Shell plc; *Int'l*, pg. 6800
NEW MOTION LIMITED—See Bucher Industries AG; *Int'l*, pg. 1208
NEW MOTORS INC.; *U.S. Private*, pg. 2899
NEW MOUNTAIN CAPITAL, LLC; *U.S. Private*, pg. 2899
NEW MOUNTAIN FINANCE CORPORATION—See New Mountain Capital, LLC; *U.S. Public*, pg. 2903
NEW MUARA CONTAINER TERMINAL SERVICES SDN. BHD.—See International Container Terminal Services, Inc.; *Int'l*, pg. 3746
NEW NAUTICAL COATINGS, INC.—See Akzo Nobel N.V.; *Int'l*, pg. 274
NEWNEEDS CO., LTD.—See Japan System Techniques Co., Ltd.; *Int'l*, pg. 3905
NEWNET COMMUNICATION TECHNOLOGIES, LLC—See Skyview Capital, LLC; *U.S. Private*, pg. 3686
NEW NIPPON BRASS CO., LTD.—See Dowa Holdings Co., Ltd.; *Int'l*, pg. 2183
NEW NORDIC HEALTHBRANDS AB; *Int'l*, pg. 5226
NEWNORTH PRINT LTD; *Int'l*, pg. 5236
NEWNOTE FINANCIAL CORP.; *Int'l*, pg. 5236
NEW OCEAN CAPITAL MANAGEMENT LIMITED—See AXA S.A.; *Int'l*, pg. 760
NEWOCEAN ENERGY HOLDINGS LIMITED; *Int'l*, pg. 5236
NEW OMNI BANK, N.A.; *U.S. Private*, pg. 2904
NEWONDER SPECIAL ELECTRIC CO., LTD.; *Int'l*, pg. 5236
NEW OPTICS LTD.—See Wooree E&L Co., Ltd.; *Int'l*, pg. 8453
NEW ORIENTAL EDUCATION & TECHNOLOGY GROUP INC.; *Int'l*, pg. 5226
NEW ORIENTAL ENERGY & CHEMICAL CORP; *Int'l*, pg. 5226
NEWORIGIN GOLD CORP.—See Harfang Exploration Inc.; *Int'l*, pg. 3274
NEWORLD ELECTRONICS LTD.—See Chroma ATE Inc.; *Int'l*, pg. 1588
NEW ORLEANS FISH HOUSE & SEAFOOD, INC.—See Investcorp Holdings B.S.C.; *Int'l*, pg. 3776
NEW ORLEANS HEARST-ARGYLE TELEVISION, INC.—See The Hearst Corporation; *U.S. Private*, pg. 4048
NEW ORLEANS JAZZ AND HERITAGE FOUNDATION; *U.S. Private*, pg. 2904
NEW ORLEANS METROPOLITAN CONVENTION & VISITORS BUREAU; *U.S. Private*, pg. 2904
NEW ORLEANS MUSEUM OF ART; *U.S. Private*, pg. 2904
NEW ORLEANS PELICANS NBA, LLC; *U.S. Private*, pg. 2904
NEW ORLEANS PIZZA CANADA INC—See Chairman's Brands Corporation; *Int'l*, pg. 1437
NEW ORLEANS PUBLISHING GROUP, L.L.C.—See The Dolan Company; *U.S. Private*, pg. 4022
NEW ORLEANS REGIONAL PHYSICIAN HOSPITAL ORGANIZATION, LLC—See UnitedHealth Group Incorporated; *U.S. Public*, pg. 2242
NEW ORLEANS SAINTS L.P.; *U.S. Private*, pg. 2904
NEW ORLEANS SHIP YARD—See Archer-Daniels-Midland Company; *U.S. Public*, pg. 185
NEW OXFORD ALUMINUM LLC—See Koninklijke Philips N.V.; *Int'l*, pg. 4268
NEW PACIFIC INDUSTRY CO., LTD.—See Cheng Shin Rubber (Xiamen) Ind., Ltd.; *Int'l*, pg. 1466
NEW PACIFIC INDUSTRY CO., LTD.—See Toyo Tire Corporation; *Int'l*, pg. 7859
NEW PACIFIC METALS CORP.; *Int'l*, pg. 5226
NEW PALACE INTERNATIONAL CO., LTD.; *Int'l*, pg. 5226
NEW PAPER LLC—See PA Acquisition Corp.; *U.S. Private*, pg. 3062
NEWPARK AUSTRALIA PTY LTD.—See Newpark Resources, Inc.; *U.S. Public*, pg. 1517
NEWPARK CANADA, INC.—See Newpark Resources, Inc.; *U.S. Public*, pg. 1517
NEWPARK CHILE LIMITADA—See Newpark Resources, Inc.; *U.S. Public*, pg. 1517
NEWPARK DRILLING FLUIDS ASIA PACIFIC LLC—See Newpark Resources, Inc.; *U.S. Public*, pg. 1517
NEWPARK DRILLING FLUIDS (AUSTRALIA) LIMITED—See Newpark Resources, Inc.; *U.S. Public*, pg. 1517

NEWPARK DRILLING FLUIDS DO BRASIL TRATAMENTO DE FLUIDOS LTDA.—See Newpark Resources, Inc.; *U.S. Public*, pg. 1517
NEWPARK DRILLING FLUIDS GERMANY GMBH—See Newpark Resources, Inc.; *U.S. Public*, pg. 1517
NEWPARK DRILLING FLUIDS INDIA PRIVATE LIMITED—See Newpark Resources, Inc.; *U.S. Public*, pg. 1517
NEWPARK DRILLING FLUIDS LLC—See SCF Partners Ltd.; *U.S. Private*, pg. 3562
NEWPARK MALL, LP—See Brookfield Corporation; *Int'l*, pg. 1185
NEWPARK MATS & INTEGRATED SERVICES LLC—See Newpark Resources, Inc.; *U.S. Public*, pg. 1518
NEWPARK RESOURCES, INC.; *U.S. Public*, pg. 1517
NEWPATH RESOURCES INC; *Int'l*, pg. 5236
NEWPEAK METALS LIMITED; *Int'l*, pg. 5236
NEW PENDULUM CORPORATION; *U.S. Private*, pg. 2905
NEW PENN MOTOR EXPRESS, INC.—See Yellow Corporation; *U.S. Public*, pg. 2398
NEW PEOPLES BANKSHARES, INC.; *U.S. Public*, pg. 1512
NEW PEOPLES BANK—See New Peoples Bankshares, Inc.; *U.S. Public*, pg. 1512
NEW PETCETERA RETAIL LIMITED; *Int'l*, pg. 5227
NEW PHARMACY COMPANY LIMITED—See NMC Health PLC; *Int'l*, pg. 5392
NEW PIG CORPORATION—See New Pendulum Corporation; *U.S. Private*, pg. 2905
NEW PLACER DOME GOLD CORP.—See CopAur Minerals Inc.; *Int'l*, pg. 1793
N.E.W. PLASTICS CORP.; *U.S. Private*, pg. 2828
NEW PLUS KNITTING PUBLIC COMPANY LIMITED; *Int'l*, pg. 5227
NEWPOINT FINANCIAL CORP.; *U.S. Public*, pg. 1518
NEWPOINT FRANCHISOR, LLC—See Lion Equity Partners, LLC; *U.S. Private*, pg. 2463
NEWPOINT MEDIA GROUP, LLC—See Lion Equity Partners, LLC; *U.S. Private*, pg. 2463
NEWPOINT SP. Z.O.O.—See New Wave Group AB; *Int'l*, pg. 5230
NEW POINT STONE CO.; *U.S. Private*, pg. 2905
NEWPORT ADHESIVES & COMPOSITES, INC.—See Mitsubishi Chemical Group Corporation; *Int'l*, pg. 4933
NEWPORT APPAREL CORPORATION; *U.S. Private*, pg. 2916
NEW PORT AUTO CENTER, INC.; *U.S. Private*, pg. 2905
NEWPORT AUTO CENTER INC.; *U.S. Private*, pg. 2916
NEWPORT BEACH CARS, LLC—See AutoNation, Inc.; *U.S. Public*, pg. 236
THE NEWPORT BEACH COUNTRY CLUB—See Eagle Four Equities LLC; *U.S. Private*, pg. 1309
THE NEWPORT BEACH COUNTRY CLUB—See Pacific Hospitality Group, Inc.; *U.S. Private*, pg. 3067
NEWPORT CAPITAL GROUP PTY LTD.; *Int'l*, pg. 5236
NEWPORT CONSTRUCTION (PTY) LIMITED—See Basil Read Holdings Limited; *Int'l*, pg. 887
NEWPORT CORPORATION—See MKS Instruments, Inc.; *U.S. Public*, pg. 1453
NEWPORT CORP. - SPECTRA-PHYSICS DIVISION—See MKS Instruments, Inc.; *U.S. Public*, pg. 1453
NEWPORT CREAMERY LLC—See The Jan Companies; *U.S. Private*, pg. 4058
NEWPORT DIVERSIFIED INC.; *U.S. Private*, pg. 2916
NEWPORT ELECTRONICS B.V.—See Arcline Investment Management LP; *U.S. Private*, pg. 314
NEWPORT ELECTRONICS, INC.—See Arcline Investment Management LP; *U.S. Private*, pg. 314
NEWPORT EXPLORATION LIMITED; *Int'l*, pg. 5236
NEWPORT FAB LLC—See Tower Semiconductor Ltd.; *Int'l*, pg. 7850
NEWPORT FBO TWO LLC—See Macquarie Group Limited; *Int'l*, pg. 4627
NEWPORT FEDERAL BANK—See United Tennessee Bankshares, Inc.; *U.S. Public*, pg. 2237
NEWPORT GLOBAL ADVISORS, L.P.; *U.S. Private*, pg. 2916
NEWPORT GOLD, INC.; *Int'l*, pg. 5236
THE NEWPORT GROUP, INC.—See Aquiline Capital Partners LLC; *U.S. Private*, pg. 304
THE NEWPORT GROUP, INC.—See Genstar Capital, LLC; *U.S. Private*, pg. 1675
NEWPORT HARBOR CORPORATION—See Deutsche Bank Aktiengesellschaft; *Int'l*, pg. 2061
NEWPORT HEALTH NETWORK, INC.—See Sonova Holding AG; *Int'l*, pg. 7100
NEWPORT INTERNATIONAL OF TIERRA VERDE, INC.; *U.S. Private*, pg. 2916
NEWPORT LABORATORIES, INC.—See C.H. Boehringer Sohn AG & Co. KG; *Int'l*, pg. 1243
NEWPORT MEAT NORTHERN CALIFORNIA, INC.—See Sysco Corporation; *U.S. Public*, pg. 1974
NEWPORT MEAT OF NEVADA, INC.—See Sysco Corporation; *U.S. Public*, pg. 1974
NEWPORT MEAT PACIFIC NORTHWEST, INC.—See Sysco Corporation; *U.S. Public*, pg. 1974
NEWPORT MEAT SOUTHERN CALIFORNIA, INC.—See Sysco Corporation; *U.S. Public*, pg. 1974

NEWPORT MEDICAL INSTRUMENTS, INC.—See Medtronic plc; *Int'l*, pg. 4787
NEWPORT NEWS GENERAL AND NON SECTARIAN HOSPITAL ASSOCIATION INC.; *U.S. Private*, pg. 2916
NEWPORT NEWS INDUSTRIAL CORPORATION—See Huntington Ingalls Industries, Inc.; *U.S. Public*, pg. 1072
NEWPORT NEWS NUCLEAR BWXT-LOS ALAMOS, LLC—See Huntington Ingalls Industries, Inc.; *U.S. Public*, pg. 1072
NEWPORT NEWS NUCLEAR, INC.—See Huntington Ingalls Industries, Inc.; *U.S. Public*, pg. 1072
NEWPORT NEWS SHIPBUILDING AND DRY DOCK COMPANY—See Huntington Ingalls Industries, Inc.; *U.S. Public*, pg. 1072
NEWPORT NEWS TIMES—See News Media Corporation; *U.S. Private*, pg. 2916
NEWPORT OPTO-ELECTRONICS TECHNOLOGIES (SINGAPORE) PTE. LTD.—See MKS Instruments, Inc.; *U.S. Public*, pg. 1453
NEWPORT PARTNERS, LLC; *U.S. Private*, pg. 2916
NEW PORT RICHEY-H, LLC—See Lithia Motors, Inc.; *U.S. Public*, pg. 1325
NEW PORT RICHEY SURGERY CENTER AT TRINITY—See HCA Healthcare, Inc.; *U.S. Public*, pg. 1004
NEW PORT RICHEY-V, LLC—See Lithia Motors, Inc.; *U.S. Public*, pg. 1325
NEWPORT SALES INC.; *U.S. Private*, pg. 2916
NEWPORT SAND & GRAVEL CO. INC.; *U.S. Private*, pg. 2916
NEWPORT SOLAR, LLC—See CMS Energy Corporation; *U.S. Public*, pg. 518
NEWPORT SPECTRA-PHYSICS GMBH—See MKS Instruments, Inc.; *U.S. Public*, pg. 1453
NEWPORT SPECTRA-PHYSICS LTD.—See MKS Instruments, Inc.; *U.S. Public*, pg. 1453
NEWPORT-ST. PAUL COLD STORAGE CO.—See Americold Realty Trust, Inc.; *U.S. Public*, pg. 113
NEWPORT TELEVISION LLC—See Providence Equity Partners L.L.C.; *U.S. Private*, pg. 3293
NEWPORT TIMBER LLC—See Interstate Resources, Inc.; *U.S. Private*, pg. 2125
NEWPORT UTILITIES BOARD INC.; *U.S. Private*, pg. 2916
NEW POWER PLASMA CO LTD - JEON-JU FACTORY—See New Power Plasma Co Ltd; *Int'l*, pg. 5227
NEW POWER PLASMA CO LTD; *Int'l*, pg. 5227
NEW PRESTITEMPO S.P.A.—See Deutsche Bank Aktiengesellschaft; *Int'l*, pg. 2061
NEW PRICE RETAIL PTY LTD—See Wesfarmers Limited; *Int'l*, pg. 8380
NEW PRIDE CORPORATION; *U.S. Public*, pg. 1512
NEW PRIMEBAKE LTD—See Bakkavor Group plc; *Int'l*, pg. 806
NEW PROCESS GEAR INC.—See Magna International Inc.; *Int'l*, pg. 4640
NEW PROCESS STEEL LP; *U.S. Private*, pg. 2905
NEW PRODUCT INTEGRATION SOLUTIONS, INC.—See Amphenol Corporation; *U.S. Public*, pg. 131
NEW PROIMAGE AMERICA INC.—See Agfa-Gevaert N.V.; *Int'l*, pg. 209
NEW PROIMAGE LTD.—See Agfa-Gevaert N.V.; *Int'l*, pg. 209
NEWPRO, INC.; *U.S. Private*, pg. 2916
NEW PROVENANCE EVERLASTING HOLDINGS LIMITED; *Int'l*, pg. 5227
NEWQUAY CORNWALL INTERNATIONAL AIRPORT LIMITED—See Sutton Harbour Group PLC; *Int'l*, pg. 7347
NEWQUEST CAPITAL ADVISORS (HK) LTD.; *Int'l*, pg. 5236
NEWQUEST, LLC—See The Cigna Group; *U.S. Public*, pg. 2061
NEWRACE LTD.; *Int'l*, pg. 5236
NEWRANGE GOLD CORPORATION; *Int'l*, pg. 5236
NEW RAY MEDICINE INTERNATIONAL HOLDINGS LIMITED; *Int'l*, pg. 5227
NEW REAL PROPERTY CORPORATION—See JINUSHI Co., Ltd.; *Int'l*, pg. 3970
NEW REGENCY PRODUCTIONS INC.; *U.S. Private*, pg. 2905
NEWREGEN, INC.; *U.S. Public*, pg. 1518
NEW RE GMBH—See RWE AG; *Int'l*, pg. 6434
NEW REINSURANCE COMPANY LTD.—See Munchener Ruckversicherungs AG; *Int'l*, pg. 5091
NEW RELIC, INC.—See Francisco Partners Management, LP; *U.S. Private*, pg. 1590
NEW RELIC, INC.—See TPG Capital, L.P.; *U.S. Public*, pg. 2175
THE NEW REPUBLIC INC.; *U.S. Private*, pg. 4083
NEW RESOURCE BANK; *U.S. Public*, pg. 1512
NEW RESOURCES COMPANIES; *U.S. Private*, pg. 2905
NEW RESOURCES CONSULTING, LLC; *U.S. Private*, pg. 2905
NEW RESOURCES CONSULTING—See New Resources Companies; *U.S. Private*, pg. 2905

1899

NEW RESOURCES CONSULTING, LLC   CORPORATE AFFILIATIONS

NEWREST ALGERIE HOLDING SPA—See Newrest Group International S.A.S.; *Int'l*, pg. 5236
NEWREST ALL LTD—See Newrest Group International S.A.S.; *Int'l*, pg. 5236
NEWREST ANGOLA SA—See Newrest Group International S.A.S.; *Int'l*, pg. 5236
NEWREST ANTILLES SAS—See Newrest Group International S.A.S.; *Int'l*, pg. 5236
NEWREST ASL NIGERIA PLC; *Int'l*, pg. 5236
NEWREST BOLIVIA SOPORTE SRL—See Newrest Group International S.A.S.; *Int'l*, pg. 5236
NEWREST CAMEROUN SA—See Newrest Group International S.A.S.; *Int'l*, pg. 5236
NEWREST CANONICA CATERING SA—See Newrest Group International S.A.S.; *Int'l*, pg. 5236
NEWREST CATERING LTD.—See Newrest Group International S.A.S.; *Int'l*, pg. 5237
NEWREST CATERING POLYNESIE SA—See Newrest Group International S.A.S.; *Int'l*, pg. 5237
NEWREST CATERING SA—See Newrest Group International S.A.S.; *Int'l*, pg. 5237
NEWREST CHILE SOPORTE LDA—See Newrest Group International S.A.S.; *Int'l*, pg. 5237
NEWREST CONGO—See Newrest Group International S.A.S.; *Int'l*, pg. 5237
NEWREST DUBROVNIK, D.O.O.—See Newrest Group International S.A.S.; *Int'l*, pg. 5237
NEWREST GABON SAURL—See Newrest Group International S.A.S.; *Int'l*, pg. 5237
NEWREST GHANA—See Newrest Group International S.A.S.; *Int'l*, pg. 5237
NEWREST GROUP HOLDING, S.L.—See Newrest Group International S.A.S.; *Int'l*, pg. 5237
NEWREST GROUP INTERNATIONAL S.A.S.; *Int'l*, pg. 5236
NEWREST GULF LLC—See Newrest Group International S.A.S.; *Int'l*, pg. 5237
NEWREST HELLAS SA—See Newrest Group International S.A.S.; *Int'l*, pg. 5237
NEWREST HOLDING CANADA INC.—See Newrest Group International S.A.S.; *Int'l*, pg. 5237
NEWREST INFLIGHT SERVICES BV—See Newrest Group International S.A.S.; *Int'l*, pg. 5237
NEWREST LIBERIA LIMITED—See Newrest Group International S.A.S.; *Int'l*, pg. 5237
NEWREST MADAGASCAR SARL—See Newrest Group International S.A.S.; *Int'l*, pg. 5237
NEWREST MAROC SERVICES SA—See Newrest Group International S.A.S.; *Int'l*, pg. 5237
NEWREST MOZAMBIQUE—See Newrest Group International S.A.S.; *Int'l*, pg. 5237
NEWREST PERU SAC—See Newrest Group International S.A.S.; *Int'l*, pg. 5237
NEWREST SERVAIR BELGIUM BVBA—See Newrest Group International S.A.S.; *Int'l*, pg. 5237
NEWREST SERVAIR, S.L.—See Newrest Group International S.A.S.; *Int'l*, pg. 5237
NEWREST SUPPLY OILFIELDS SERVICES INC.—See Newrest Group International S.A.S.; *Int'l*, pg. 5237
NEWREST UGANDA INFLIGHT SERVICES LTD.—See Newrest Group International S.A.S.; *Int'l*, pg. 5237
NEWREST WAGONS-LITS AUSTRIA GMBH—See Newrest Group International S.A.S.; *Int'l*, pg. 5237
NEWREST WAGONS-LITS S.A.S.—See Accor S.A.; *Int'l*, pg. 92
NEWREST WAGONS-LITS S.A.S.—See Newrest Group International S.A.S.; *Int'l*, pg. 5237
NEWREST ZAMBIA LIMITED—See Newrest Group International S.A.S.; *Int'l*, pg. 5237
NEW RETAIL CO., LTD.; *Int'l*, pg. 5227
NEWREZ LLC—See Rithm Capital Corp.; *U.S. Public*, pg. 1800
NEWREZ LLC—See Rithm Capital Corp.; *U.S. Public*, pg. 1800
NEW RITE AID, LLC; *U.S. Private*, pg. 2905
NEW RIVER COMMUNICATIONS, INC.; *U.S. Private*, pg. 2906
THE NEW RIVER COMPANY LIMITED—See Derwent London plc; *Int'l*, pg. 2043
NEW RIVER ELECTRICAL CORPORATION; *U.S. Private*, pg. 2906
NEW RIVER ENERGY CORPORATION—See Alpha Natural Resources, Inc.; *U.S. Private*, pg. 198
NEW RIVER INDUSTRIES INC.; *U.S. Private*, pg. 2906
NEW RIVER INFORMATION TECHNOLOGY & SERVICES CO.—See Yu Tak International Holdings Limited; *Int'l*, pg. 8607
NEWRIVER REIT PLC; *Int'l*, pg. 5237
NEWRIVER RETAIL LTD; *Int'l*, pg. 5237
NEWRIVER RETAIL (UK) LIMITED—See NewRiver Retail Ltd; *Int'l*, pg. 5237
NEW RIVER VALLEY BENEFITS CONSORTIUM; *U.S. Private*, pg. 2906
NEW-ROAD AGENCIES LTD.—See HORIBA Ltd; *Int'l*, pg. 3477
NEWROADS CHRYSLER DODGE JEEP RAM; *Int'l*, pg. 5237
NEW ROCHELLE TOYOTA; *U.S. Private*, pg. 2906
NEWRON PHARMACEUTICALS SPA; *Int'l*, pg. 5237

NEWRON PHARMACEUTICALS U.S. INC.—See Newron Pharmaceuticals SpA; *Int'l*, pg. 5237
NEWRON SPORT; *U.S. Public*, pg. 1518
NEWRON SWEDEN AB—See Newron Pharmaceuticals SpA; *Int'l*, pg. 5237
NEWRY CORP; *U.S. Private*, pg. 2916
NEWS 12 NEW JERSEY, INC.—See Altice USA, Inc.; *U.S. Public*, pg. 87
NEWS2U HOLDINGS, INC.; *Int'l*, pg. 5238
NEW SABINA INDUSTRIES, INC.—See Nippon Seiki Co., Ltd.; *Int'l*, pg. 5330
THE NEWS & ADVANCE—See Lee Enterprises, Incorporated; *U.S. Public*, pg. 1299
NEW SAGAYA; *U.S. Private*, pg. 2906
NEWS AMERICA MARKETING FSI L.L.C.—See Charlesbank Capital Partners, LLC; *U.S. Private*, pg. 854
NEWS AMERICA MARKETING IN-STORE SERVICES, L.L.C.—See Charlesbank Capital Partners, LLC; *U.S. Private*, pg. 854
NEWS AMERICA MARKETING INTERACTIVE L.L.C.—See Charlesbank Capital Partners, LLC; *U.S. Private*, pg. 854
NEWS AMERICA MARKETING PROPERTIES L.L.C.—See Charlesbank Capital Partners, LLC; *U.S. Private*, pg. 854
THE NEWS AND OBSERVER PUBLISHING COMPANY—See Chatham Asset Management, LLC; *U.S. Private*, pg. 867
NEW SANKO INC.—See Sapporo Holdings Limited; *Int'l*, pg. 6573
NEW SANKO LIMITED—See Sapporo Holdings Limited; *Int'l*, pg. 6573
NEW SANKYO TOOL CO., LTD.—See YG-1 Co., Ltd; *Int'l*, pg. 8579
NEWSAN S.A.—See Panasonic Holdings Corporation; *Int'l*, pg. 5723
NEW SARASWATI HOUSE (INDIA) PRIVATE LIMITED—See S Chand & Company Limited; *Int'l*, pg. 6442
NEWSBANK, INC.; *U.S. Private*, pg. 2917
NEWSCHANNEL 5 NETWORK—See The E.W. Scripps Company; *U.S. Public*, pg. 2068
NEWS CHIEF—See Gannett Co., Inc.; *U.S. Public*, pg. 905
NEW SCHOOL PROPERTIES, INC.; *U.S. Private*, pg. 2906
NEWS COMMUNICATIONS, INC.; *U.S. Private*, pg. 2916
NEWSCON INC.—See Envipro Holdings Inc.; *Int'l*, pg. 2454
NEWSCOPE CAPITAL CORPORATION; *Int'l*, pg. 5238
NEWS CORP AUSTRALIA PTY. LIMITED—See News Corporation; *U.S. Public*, pg. 1519
NEWS CORP INVESTMENTS UK & IRELAND—See News Corporation; *U.S. Public*, pg. 1520
NEWS CORPORATION; *U.S. Public*, pg. 1518
NEWS CORP UK & IRELAND LIMITED—See News Corporation; *U.S. Public*, pg. 1520
NEWSCO USA INC.—See Marquard & Bahls AG; *Int'l*, pg. 4700
NEWSCRED, INC.—See Insight Venture Management, LLC; *U.S. Private*, pg. 2090
NEWSCYCLE SOLUTIONS AB—See Vista Equity Partners, LLC; *U.S. Private*, pg. 4399
NEWSCYCLE SOLUTIONS AMERICAS, LLC—See Vista Equity Partners, LLC; *U.S. Private*, pg. 4399
NEWSCYCLE SOLUTIONS A/S—See Vista Equity Partners, LLC; *U.S. Private*, pg. 4399
NEWSCYCLE SOLUTIONS AS—See Vista Equity Partners, LLC; *U.S. Private*, pg. 4399
NEWSCYCLE SOLUTIONS—See Vista Equity Partners, LLC; *U.S. Private*, pg. 4399
NEWSDAY LLC—See Altice USA, Inc.; *U.S. Public*, pg. 87
NEW SEABURY BEACH CLUB LLC—See Icahn Enterprises L.P.; *U.S. Public*, pg. 1084
NEW SEABURY GOLF CLUB LLC—See Icahn Enterprises L.P.; *U.S. Public*, pg. 1084
NEW SEABURY PROPERTIES, LLC—See Icahn Enterprises L.P.; *U.S. Public*, pg. 1084
NEW SEASONS MARKET, LLC—See Good Food Holdings LLC; *U.S. Private*, pg. 1738
NEW SEA UNION TECHNOLOGY GROUP CO., LTD.; *Int'l*, pg. 5227
NEW SECURITIES EXCHANGE; *Int'l*, pg. 5227
NEW SENIOR INVESTMENT GROUP INC.—See Ventas, Inc.; *U.S. Public*, pg. 2278
NEW SENSE RESEARCH LTD.—See Brookfield Corporation; *Int'l*, pg. 1180
NEW SENSE RESEARCH LTD.—See Elliott Management Corporation; *Int'l*, pg. 1372
NEW SENSOR CORPORATION; *U.S. Private*, pg. 2906
NEWS-ENTERPRISE CORPORATION—See Irish Times; *U.S. Private*, pg. 2139
THE NEWS-ENTERPRISE—See Irish Times; *U.S. Private*, pg. 2138
THE NEWS EXAMINER—See Gannett Co., Inc.; *U.S. Public*, pg. 900
NEWSFORCE INTERN HOLDING COMPANY—See Orange S.A.; *Int'l*, pg. 5609

NEWSGATOR TECHNOLOGIES, INC.; *U.S. Private*, pg. 2917
NEWSGATOR TECHNOLOGIES—See NewsGator Technologies, Inc.; *U.S. Private*, pg. 2917
NEWSGATOR TECHNOLOGIES—See NewsGator Technologies, Inc.; *U.S. Private*, pg. 2917
NEWSGATOR TECHNOLOGIES—See NewsGator Technologies, Inc.; *U.S. Private*, pg. 2917
NEWSGATOR TECHNOLOGIES—See NewsGator Technologies, Inc.; *U.S. Private*, pg. 2917
NEWSGATOR TECHNOLOGIES—See NewsGator Technologies, Inc.; *U.S. Private*, pg. 2917
NEWS GAZETTE INC.; *U.S. Private*, pg. 2916
NEWS GROUP INTERNATIONAL HOLDING; *Int'l*, pg. 5237
NEWSHAM CHOICE GENETICS—See Groupe Grimaud La Corbiere SA; *Int'l*, pg. 3103
THE NEWS-HERALD (LAKE COUNTY)—See Alden Global Capital LLC; *U.S. Private*, pg. 159
THE NEWS-HERALD—See Alden Global Capital LLC; *U.S. Private*, pg. 159
NEWS HERALD—See Gannett Co., Inc.; *U.S. Public*, pg. 906
NEWSHIP LTD; *Int'l*, pg. 5238
NEWSHIP PROPERTY—See Newship Ltd; *Int'l*, pg. 5238
NEW SIA GREECE S.A.—See Cassa Depositi e Prestiti S.p.A.; *Int'l*, pg. 1355
NEW SIGNATURE CANADA INC.—See Cognizant Technology Solutions Corporation; *U.S. Public*, pg. 525
NEW SIGNATURE UK LIMITED—See Cognizant Technology Solutions Corporation; *U.S. Public*, pg. 525
NEW SIGNATURE US, INC.—See Cognizant Technology Solutions Corporation; *U.S. Public*, pg. 525
NEW SILKROAD CULTURALTAINMENT LIMITED—See Macrolink Culturaltainment Development Co., Ltd.; *Int'l*, pg. 4632
NEW SILK ROUTE ADVISORS (DUBAI) LIMITED—See New Silk Route Advisors Pvt. Ltd.; *Int'l*, pg. 5227
NEW SILK ROUTE ADVISORS PVT. LTD. - BENGALURU—See New Silk Route Advisors Pvt. Ltd.; *Int'l*, pg. 5227
NEW SILK ROUTE ADVISORS PVT. LTD.; *Int'l*, pg. 5227
NEW SILK ROUTE PARTNERS LLC—See New Silk Route Advisors Pvt. Ltd.; *Int'l*, pg. 5227
NEW SILKROUTES GROUP (EUROPE) LIMITED—See New Silkroutes Group Limited; *Int'l*, pg. 5227
NEW SILKROUTES GROUP LIMITED; *Int'l*, pg. 5227
NEW SINO GASES COMPANY LIMITED—See Linde plc; *Int'l*, pg. 4508
NEWS INTERNATIONAL NEWSPAPERS LIMITED—See News Corporation; *U.S. Public*, pg. 1521
NEWS INVEST SA; *Int'l*, pg. 5238
NEWS-JOURNAL CORPORATION; *U.S. Private*, pg. 2917
THE NEWS JOURNAL—See Gannett Co., Inc.; *U.S. Public*, pg. 900
NEW SKIES SATELLITES AUSTRALIA PTY LTD—See SES S.A.; *Int'l*, pg. 6727
NEW SKIES SATELLITES, INC.—See SES S.A.; *Int'l*, pg. 6727
NEWS LEADER, INC.—See Gannett Co., Inc.; *U.S. Public*, pg. 904
NEWS-LEADER—See Community Newspapers Inc.; *U.S. Private*, pg. 996
THE NEWS LEADER—See Gannett Co., Inc.; *U.S. Public*, pg. 900
NEW SLEEPER GOLD, LLC—See Paramount Gold Nevada Corp.; *U.S. Public*, pg. 1637
NEWS LIMITED—See News Corporation; *U.S. Public*, pg. 1519
NEWSLINE GROUP AB—See Ratos AB; *Int'l*, pg. 6217
NEWSLINK GROUP, LLC.; *U.S. Private*, pg. 2917
NEWSLINK PTY LTD—See Vivendi SE; *Int'l*, pg. 8276
NEWS MARKETING CANADA—See News Corporation; *U.S. Public*, pg. 1521
NEWSMAX MEDIA, INC.; *U.S. Private*, pg. 2917
NEWS MEDIA CORPORATION—See News Media Corporation; *U.S. Private*, pg. 2917
NEWS MEDIA CORPORATION; *U.S. Private*, pg. 2916
THE NEWS-MESSENGER—See Gannett Co., Inc.; *U.S. Public*, pg. 900
NEWS NETWORK CORPORATION PUBLIC COMPANY LIMITED; *Int'l*, pg. 5238
THE NEWS & OBSERVER—See Chatham Asset Management, LLC; *U.S. Private*, pg. 867
NEWS OF WORCESTER LLC—See Casella Waste Systems, Inc.; *U.S. Public*, pg. 446
NEWSOM SEED INC.—See SiteOne Landscape Supply, Inc.; *U.S. Public*, pg. 1889
NEW SOURCE ENERGY CORPORATION; *U.S. Private*, pg. 2906
NEW SOURCES ENERGY N.V.; *Int'l*, pg. 5227
NEW SOUTH BANCSHARES INC.; *U.S. Private*, pg. 2906
NEW SOUTH EQUIPMENT MATS; *U.S. Private*, pg. 2906
NEW SOUTH FEDERAL SAVINGS BANK—See New South Bancshares Inc.; *U.S. Private*, pg. 2906
NEW SOUTH FORD, INC.; *U.S. Private*, pg. 2906
NEW SOUTH RESTORATIONS INC.; *U.S. Private*, pg. 2906
NEW SOUTH SUPPLY LLC; *U.S. Private*, pg. 2906
NEW SOUTH WALES RUGBY LEAGUE LTD; *Int'l*, pg. 5228

COMPANY NAME INDEX

NEW SOUTH WALES SUGAR MILLING CO-OPERATIVE LIMITED - BROADWATER MILL—See New South Wales Sugar Milling Co-Operative Limited; *Int'l*, pg. 5228

NEW SOUTH WALES SUGAR MILLING CO-OPERATIVE LIMITED - CONDONG MILL—See New South Wales Sugar Milling Co-Operative Limited; *Int'l*, pg. 5228

NEW SOUTH WALES SUGAR MILLING CO-OPERATIVE LIMITED; *Int'l*, pg. 5228

NEW SOUTH WALES TREASURY CORPORATION; *Int'l*, pg. 5228

NEW SOUTHWEST BAKING COMPANY; *U.S. Private*, pg. 2906

NEWSOUTH WINDOW SOLUTIONS, LLC—See Koch Industries, Inc.; *U.S. Private*, pg. 2332

NEWSOUTH WINDOW SOLUTIONS OF BONITA SPRINGS, LLC—See Koch Industries, Inc.; *U.S. Private*, pg. 2332

NEWSOUTH WINDOW SOLUTIONS OF CHARLESTON, LLC—See Koch Industries, Inc.; *U.S. Private*, pg. 2332

NEWSOUTH WINDOW SOLUTIONS OF FT. LAUDERDALE, LLC—See Koch Industries, Inc.; *U.S. Private*, pg. 2332

NEWSOUTH WINDOW SOLUTIONS OF JACKSONVILLE, LLC—See Koch Industries, Inc.; *U.S. Private*, pg. 2332

NEWSOUTH WINDOW SOLUTIONS OF ORLANDO, LLC—See Koch Industries, Inc.; *U.S. Private*, pg. 2332

NEWSOUTH WINDOW SOLUTIONS OF PENSACOLA, LLC—See Koch Industries, Inc.; *U.S. Private*, pg. 2332

NEWSOUTH WINDOW SOLUTIONS OF WEST PALM BEACH, LLC—See Koch Industries, Inc.; *U.S. Private*, pg. 2333

NEW SPACE MARGATE LTD.—See The Skipton Building Society; *Int'l*, pg. 7687

NEWSPAPER ASSOCIATION OF AMERICA; *U.S. Private*, pg. 2917

NEWSPAPER SERVICES OF AMERICA, INC.—See The Interpublic Group of Companies, Inc.; *U.S. Public*, pg. 2096

NEW SPARKLE ROLL INTERNATIONAL GROUP LIMITED; *Int'l*, pg. 5228

NEWSPHONE HELLAS S.A.; *Int'l*, pg. 5238

NEW SPIRIT ELECTRONIC TECHNOLOGY DEVELOPMENT (SHENZHEN) CO., LTD.—See Karin Technology Holdings Limited; *Int'l*, pg. 4081

NEW SPIRIT TECHNOLOGY LIMITED—See Karin Technology Holdings Limited; *Int'l*, pg. 4081

NEWSPREAD LIMITED—See Mediahuis Partners NV; *Int'l*, pg. 4772

NEWSPREAD LIMITED—See VP Exploitatie N.V.; *Int'l*, pg. 8311

NEWS-PRESS DIGITAL—See News-Press & Gazette Company; *U.S. Private*, pg. 2917

NEWS-PRESS & GAZETTE COMPANY; *U.S. Private*, pg. 2917

THE NEWS-PRESS—See Gannett Co., Inc.; *U.S. Public*, pg. 900

NEWSPRING CAPITAL LLC; *U.S. Private*, pg. 2917

NEWSQUEST (HERALD & TIMES) LIMITED—See Gannett Co., Inc.; *U.S. Public*, pg. 899

NEWSQUEST MEDIA GROUP LTD.—See Gannett Co., Inc.; *U.S. Public*, pg. 899

NEWSQUEST (NORTH EAST) LIMITED—See Gannett Co., Inc.; *U.S. Public*, pg. 898

NEWSQUEST PLC—See TEGNA Inc.; *U.S. Public*, pg. 1990

NEWSQUEST SPECIALIST MEDIA LIMITED—See Gannett Co., Inc.; *U.S. Public*, pg. 898

NEWS & RECORD—See Irish Times; *U.S. Private*, pg. 2139

THE NEWS-SENTINEL—See The Nutting Company, Inc.; *U.S. Private*, pg. 4086

THE NEWS—See Evening Post Publishing Co.; *U.S. Private*, pg. 1436

THE NEWS-STAR—See Gannett Co., Inc.; *U.S. Public*, pg. 900

THE NEWS SUN—See Chicago Public Media, Inc.; *U.S. Private*, pg. 879

NEW STANDARD CORPORATION - ROCKY MOUNT PLANT—See New Standard Corporation; *U.S. Private*, pg. 2906

NEW STANDARD CORPORATION; *U.S. Private*, pg. 2906

NEW STANDARD ENERGY LIMITED; *Int'l*, pg. 5228

NEWSTAR CAPITAL; *Int'l*, pg. 2138

NEW STAR INVESTMENT TRUST PLC; *Int'l*, pg. 5228

NEW STAR METALS, INC.—See Insight Equity Holdings LLC; *U.S. Private*, pg. 2086

NEW STAR REALTY & INVESTMENT—See Berkshire Hathaway Inc.; *U.S. Public*, pg. 307

NEW STATE CAPITAL PARTNERS LLC; *U.S. Private*, pg. 2906

NEW STATES CONTRACTING—See Irex Corporation; *U.S. Private*, pg. 2138

NEWSTEAD INSURANCE BROKERS LIMITED—See Brown & Brown, Inc.; *U.S. Public*, pg. 401

NEWS TECHNOLOGY.INC.—See Vector Inc.; *Int'l*, pg. 8144

NEW STEEL INC.—See American Agencies Co. Inc.; *U.S. Private*, pg. 222

NEWS-TIMES PUBLISHING COMPANY INC.—See Wehco Media, Inc.; *U.S. Private*, pg. 4469

THE NEWS-TIMES—See The Hearst Corporation; *U.S. Private*, pg. 4048

NEWSTONE CAPITAL PARTNERS, LLC; *U.S. Private*, pg. 2918

NEWSTONE TECHNOLOGY (SHENZHEN) COMPANY LIMITED—See Serial System Ltd.; *Int'l*, pg. 6722

THE NEW STRAITS TIMES PRESS (MALAYSIA) BERHAD—See Media Prima Berhad; *Int'l*, pg. 4771

NEW STRATUS ENERGY, INC.; *Int'l*, pg. 5228

NEWSTREAM ENTERPRISES, LLC.—See SRC Holdings Corporation; *U.S. Private*, pg. 3767

NEWS TRIBUNE CO.; *U.S. Private*, pg. 2917

NEWS TRIBUNE—See Chatham Asset Management, LLC; *U.S. Private*, pg. 866

THE NEWS TRIBUNE—See Chatham Asset Management, LLC; *U.S. Private*, pg. 866

NEWSTRIKE BRANDS LTD—See Tilray Brands, Inc.; *Int'l*, pg. 7748

NEWSTYLE—See Omnicom Group Inc.; *U.S. Public*, pg. 1585

NEWS UK & IRELAND LIMITED—See News Corporation; *U.S. Public*, pg. 1521

NEWS (UK) LIMITED—See The Walt Disney Company; *U.S. Public*, pg. 2141

NEW SUNCADIA, LLC—See Commune Hotels & Resorts, LLC; *U.S. Private*, pg. 987

NEW SUNF PU ELECTRIC WIRE & CABLE (SHENZHEN) CO., LTD.—See SUNF PU TECHNOLOGY CO., Ltd.; *Int'l*, pg. 7313

NEW SUNWARD HOLDING B.V.—See CEMEX, S.A.B. de C.V.; *Int'l*, pg. 1399

NEW SUNWARD HOLDING FINANCIAL VENTURES B.V.—See CEMEX, S.A.B. de C.V.; *Int'l*, pg. 1399

NEWSURE INSURANCE BROKERS PTY LTD—See Steadfast Group Limited; *Int'l*, pg. 7187

THE NEWS VIRGINIAN—See Lee Enterprises, Incorporated; *U.S. Public*, pg. 1299

NEWSWAYS DISTRIBUTORS; *U.S. Private*, pg. 2918

NEWSWEEK LLC—See IBT Media Inc.; *U.S. Private*, pg. 2029

NEWSWEST CORP.; *Int'l*, pg. 5238

NEWS WEST PUBLISHING COMPANY INC.—See Brehm Communicationo Ino.; *U.S. Private*, pg. 644

NEWS WORLD COMMUNICATIONS, INC.—See Family Federation for World Peace & Unification; *U.S. Private*, pg. 1469

NEW SYSTEM S.R.L.—See KLA Corporation; *U.S. Public*, pg. 1268

NEW TAC KASEI CO., LTD.—See Oji Holdings Corporation; *Int'l*, pg. 5537

NEW TALENT MEDIA COMPANY LIMITED—See Creative China Holdings Limited; *Int'l*, pg. 1832

NEW TALISMAN GOLD MINES LIMITED; *Int'l*, pg. 5228

NEW TAMPA SURGERY CENTER, LLC—See Bain Capital, LP; *U.S. Private*, pg. 445

NEW TANATEX S.P.A.—See Transfar Group Co., Ltd.; *Int'l*, pg. 7899

NEW TANGRAM, LLC - NEWPORT BEACH—See New Tangram, LLC; *U.S. Private*, pg. 2907

NEW TANGRAM, LLC; *U.S. Private*, pg. 2907

NEW TEACHER CENTER; *U.S. Private*, pg. 2907

NEW TEAM LLC—See Stagwell, Inc.; *U.S. Public*, pg. 1927

NEWTECH CO., LTD.—See Yamabiko Corporation; *Int'l*, pg. 8547

NEW TECH CO., LTD.—See Kyowa Electronic Instruments Co., Ltd.; *Int'l*, pg. 4366

NEW TECH COMPUTER SYSTEMS INC.—See Morris & Dickson Co., LLC; *U.S. Private*, pg. 2786

NEW TECH GLOBAL VENTURES, LLC; *U.S. Private*, pg. 2907

NEW-TECH INFRASTRUCTURE PVT. LTD.—See NEO INFRACON LTD.; *Int'l*, pg. 5196

NEW TECH MACHINERY CORP.—See Mazzella Lifting Technologies; *U.S. Private*, pg. 2623

NEW TECHNOLOGY BOTTLING COMPANY K.S.C.C.—See The Securities House K.S.C.C.; *Int'l*, pg. 7681

NEW TECHNOLOGY INVESTMENTS, INC.—See RMS Omega Technologies Group, Inc.; *U.S. Private*, pg. 3452

NEWTECH PULP INC.—See Glatfelter Corporation; *U.S. Public*, pg. 939

NEWTECH SCIENTIFIC TECHNOLOGY CORP.—See CHIALIN Precision Industrial Co., Ltd.; *Int'l*, pg. 1475

NEWTECH SYSTEMS, INC.—See GTCR LLC; *U.S. Private*, pg. 1802

NEW-TEC OST VERTRIEBSGESELLSCHAFT FUR AGRARTECHNIK MBH—See AGRAVIS Raiffeisen AG; *Int'l*, pg. 215

NEWTEC UMWELTTECHNIK GMBH; *Int'l*, pg. 5238

NEWTEC WATER SYSTEMS NV—See Newtec Umwelttechnik GmbH; *Int'l*, pg. 5238

NEW-TEC WEST VERTRIEBSGESELLSCHAFT FUR AGRARTECHNIK MBH—See AGRAVIS Raiffeisen AG; *Int'l*, pg. 215

NEWTEKONE, INC.; *U.S. Public*, pg. 1521

NEWTEK SMALL BUSINESS FINANCE, INC.—See NEWTEKONE, INC.; *U.S. Public*, pg. 1521

NEWTEL CORPORATION COMPANY LIMITED—See Digilife Technologies Limited; *Int'l*, pg. 2119

THE NEW TELEPHONE COMPANY, INC—See Fortran Corporation; *U.S. Public*, pg. 872

NEWTEL PARTICIPACOES S.A.; *Int'l*, pg. 5238

NEWTERRA GMBH—See Newterra Ltd.; *Int'l*, pg. 5238

NEWTERRA GROUP LTD. - AIR INSTRUMENTS DIVISION—See Newterra Ltd.; *Int'l*, pg. 5238

NEWTERRA LTD.; *Int'l*, pg. 5238

NEWTERRA S.P.A.—See Newterra Ltd.; *Int'l*, pg. 5239

NEWTEX INDUSTRIES INC.; *U.S. Private*, pg. 2918

NEW THERMOSERV, LTD.; *U.S. Private*, pg. 2907

NEW TIMES BPB, LLC—See Village Voice Media Holdings, LLC; *U.S. Private*, pg. 4384

NEW TIMES ENERGY CORPORATION LIMITED; *Int'l*, pg. 5228

NEW TIMES SHIPBUILDING CO., LTD.—See New Century Shipbuilding Corporation; *Int'l*, pg. 5222

NEW TOKYO SERVICE CO., LTD.—See Japan Airlines Co., Ltd.; *Int'l*, pg. 3885

NEWTON 21 EUROPE SA; *Int'l*, pg. 5239

NEWTON 21 ROMA—See Newton 21 Europe SA; *Int'l*, pg. 5239

NEWTON CAPITAL MANAGEMENT LIMITED—See The Bank of New York Mellon Corporation; *U.S. Public*, pg. 2037

NEWTON CAPITAL PARTNERS, L.P.—See Juniper Investment Company, LLC; *U.S. Private*, pg. 2244

NEWTON CONSULTING, LLC; *U.S. Private*, pg. 2918

NEWTON COUNTY ENTERPRISES INC.—See Community Media Group; *U.S. Private*, pg. 995

NEWTON-DAVIS INC.; *U.S. Private*, pg. 2918

NEWTON EUROPE LTD; *Int'l*, pg. 5239

NEWTON FACILITIES COMPUTER LEASING LIMITED—See Newcastle Building Society; *Int'l*, pg. 5233

NEWTON FACILITIES COMPUTER PURCHASING LTD—See Newcastle Building Society; *Int'l*, pg. 5233

NEWTON FALLOWELL LIMITED—See The Property Franchise Group PLC; *Int'l*, pg. 7676

NEWTON FOOD EQUIPMENT CO. LTD.—See Ali Holding S.r.l; *Int'l*, pg. 323

NEWTON HEALTHCARE CORPORATION; *U.S. Private*, pg. 2918

NEWTON INSTRUMENT COMPANY; *U.S. Private*, pg. 2918

THE NEWTON KANSAN—See Gannett Co., Inc.; *U.S. Public*, pg. 904

NEWTON KOMPETENSUTVECKLING AB—See Storskogen Group AB; *Int'l*, pg. 7228

NEWTON MEDIA ASSOCIATES, INC.; *U.S. Private*, pg. 2918

NEWTON NISSAN OF GALLATIN, INC.; *U.S. Private*, pg. 2918

NEWTON NORDIC AB; *Int'l*, pg. 5239

NEWTON OFFICINE MECCANICHE SRL—See Camozzi Group; *Int'l*, pg. 1274

NEWTON OIL COMPANY, INC.; *U.S. Private*, pg. 2918

NEWTON RESEARCH & DEVELOPMENT CENTRE SDN. BHD.—See Thong Guan Industries Berhad; *Int'l*, pg. 7717

NEWTON RESOURCES LTD; *Int'l*, pg. 5239

NEWTON TAB—See Gannett Co., Inc.; *U.S. Public*, pg. 902

NEWTON VINEYARDS—See LVMH Moet Hennessy Louis Vuitton SE; *Int'l*, pg. 4599

NEWTON WALL COMPANY; *U.S. Private*, pg. 2918

NEWTON-WELLESLEY CHILDREN'S CORNER INC.—See Partners HealthCare System, Inc.; *U.S. Private*, pg. 3101

NEWTON-WELLESLEY HEALTHCARE SYSTEM—See Partners HealthCare System, Inc.; *U.S. Private*, pg. 3101

NEWTON-WELLESLEY HOSPITAL CHARITABLE FOUNDATION INC.—See Partners HealthCare System, Inc.; *U.S. Private*, pg. 3101

NEWTON-WELLESLEY HOSPITAL—See Partners HealthCare System, Inc.; *U.S. Private*, pg. 3101

NEWTOPIA, INC.; *Int'l*, pg. 5239

NEW TOP WIN CORPORATION SDN. BHD.—See Hengan International Group Co. Ltd.; *Int'l*, pg. 3346

NEWTOUCH SOFTWARE (KUNSHAN)CO., LTD.—See Shanghai Newtouch Software Co., Ltd.; *Int'l*, pg. 6776

NEW TOWERS LLC—See American Tower Corporation; *U.S. Public*, pg. 111

NEWTOWER TRUST COMPANY—See Sun Life Financial Inc.; *Int'l*, pg. 7305

NEWTOWNARDS VETS4PETS LIMITED—See Pets at Home Group Plc; *Int'l*, pg. 5834

NEWTOWN INSURANCE SERVICE, LLC—See Manzi Insurance; *U.S. Private*, pg. 2567

NEWTOWN SAVINGS BANK; *U.S. Private*, pg. 2918

NEW TOYO ALUMINIUM PAPER PRODUCT CO (PTE) LTD—See New Toyo International Holdings Ltd.; *Int'l*, pg. 5228

NEW TOYO INTERNATIONAL CO (PTE) LTD—See New Toyo International Holdings Ltd.; *Int'l*, pg. 5228

NEW TOYO INTERNATIONAL HOLDINGS LTD. CORPORATE AFFILIATIONS

NEW TOYO INTERNATIONAL HOLDINGS LTD.; *Int'l*, pg. 5228
NEW TOYO (VIETNAM) ALUMINIUM PAPER PACKAGING CO., LTD.—See New Toyo International Holdings Ltd.; *Int'l*, pg. 5228
NEW TRANSPORT APPLICATIONS, S.A. DE C.V.—See Deutsche Post AG; *Int'l*, pg. 2082
NEWTRAX HOLDINGS INC.—See Sandvik AB; *Int'l*, pg. 6530
NEWTRAX PTY. LTD.—See Sandvik AB; *Int'l*, pg. 6530
NEWTREE AMERICA, INC.—See NEWTREE SA; *Int'l*, pg. 5239
NEWTREE CO., LTD.; *Int'l*, pg. 5239
NEWTREE SARL—See NEWTREE SA; *Int'l*, pg. 5239
NEWTREE SA; *Int'l*, pg. 5239
NEW TREND INTERNATIONAL LOGIS-TECH COLTD; *Int'l*, pg. 5228
NEW TREND TECHNOLOGY INC.—See Macronix International Co., Ltd.; *Int'l*, pg. 4632
NEW TRIPOLI BANCORP, INC.; *U.S. Public*, pg. 1512
NEW TRIPOLI BANK—See New Tripoli Bancorp, Inc.; *U.S. Public*, pg. 1512
NEW TROIS ELECTRONICS (SHENZHEN) LTD.; *Int'l*, pg. 5228
THE NEWTRON GROUP INC.; *U.S. Private*, pg. 4083
NEW TRONICS CO., LTD.—See Disco Corporation; *Int'l*, pg. 2132
NEWTRON INC.—See The Newtron Group Inc.; *U.S. Private*, pg. 4084
NEWTRON MECHANICAL, L.L.C.—See The Newtron Group Inc.; *U.S. Private*, pg. 4084
NEW UNIVERSE ENVIRONMENTAL GROUP LIMITED; *Int'l*, pg. 5228
NEW URBAN FORESTRY, LLC—See Warren Equity Partners, LLC; *U.S. Private*, pg. 4443
NEW URBAN WEST INC.; *U.S. Private*, pg. 2907
NEW VALLEY LLC—See Japan Tobacco Inc.; *Int'l*, pg. 3907
NEW VALUE CAPITAL LLC; *U.S. Private*, pg. 2907
NEWVANTAGE PARTNERS, LLC—See Wavestone SA; *Int'l*, pg. 8360
NEW VENTURE FUND; *U.S. Private*, pg. 2907
NEW VENTURE PARTNERS LLC; *U.S. Private*, pg. 2907
NEW VENTURES GROUP LLC—See Jabil Inc.; *U.S. Public*, pg. 1181
NEW VENTURETEC LTD.; *Int'l*, pg. 5229
NEW VIDEO CHANNEL LLC—See British Broadcasting Corporation; *Int'l*, pg. 1169
NEW VISION CHINA LIGHTING W.L.L—See NVC International Holdings Limited; *Int'l*, pg. 5498
NEW VISION CO-OP; *U.S. Private*, pg. 2907
NEW VISION DISPLAY, INC.; *U.S. Private*, pg. 2907
NEW VISION PRINTING & PUBLISHING COMPANY LIMITED; *Int'l*, pg. 5229
NEW VISIONS FOR PUBLIC SCHOOLS; *U.S. Private*, pg. 2907
NEW VISION USA, INC.; *U.S. Private*, pg. 2907
NEW VISTA ACQUISITION CORP.; *U.S. Public*, pg. 1512
NEWVOICEMEDIA GERMANY GMBH—See Telefonaktiebolaget LM Ericsson; *Int'l*, pg. 7534
NEWVOICEMEDIA PTY. LTD.—See Telefonaktiebolaget LM Ericsson; *Int'l*, pg. 7534
NEWVOICEMEDIA SP. Z O.O.—See Telefonaktiebolaget LM Ericsson; *Int'l*, pg. 7534
NEW WASHINGTON STATE BANK INC.; *U.S. Private*, pg. 2907
NEW WATER CAPITAL, L.P.; *U.S. Private*, pg. 2907
NEW WATER STREET CORP.; *U.S. Private*, pg. 2908
NEW WAVE ATM INSTALLATIONS LIMITED—See NCR Voyix Corporation.; *U.S. Public*, pg. 1501
NEW WAVE AUSTRIA GMBH—See New Wave Group AB; *Int'l*, pg. 5229
NEW WAVE DANMARK A/S—See New Wave Group AB; *Int'l*, pg. 5229
NEW WAVE ESPORTS CORP.; *Int'l*, pg. 5229
NEW WAVE FOOTWEAR AB—See New Wave Group AB; *Int'l*, pg. 5229
NEW WAVE FRANCE SAS—See New Wave Group AB; *Int'l*, pg. 5229
NEW WAVE GMBH—See New Wave Group AB; *Int'l*, pg. 5229
NEW WAVE GROUP AB; *Int'l*, pg. 5229
NEW WAVE GROUP BANGLADESH—See New Wave Group AB; *Int'l*, pg. 5229
NEW WAVE GROUP CHINA—See New Wave Group AB; *Int'l*, pg. 5230
NEW WAVE GROUP FACTORY SHOP AB—See New Wave Group AB; *Int'l*, pg. 5230
NEW WAVE GROUP INCENTIVES AB—See New Wave Group AB; *Int'l*, pg. 5230
NEW WAVE GROUP INDIA PVT LTD.—See New Wave Group AB; *Int'l*, pg. 5230
NEW WAVE GROUP INTERNATIONAL TRADING LTD.—See New Wave Group AB; *Int'l*, pg. 5230
NEW WAVE GROUP SA—See New Wave Group AB; *Int'l*, pg. 5230
NEW WAVE GROUP VIETNAM—See New Wave Group AB; *Int'l*, pg. 5230
NEW WAVE HOLDINGS LTD.; *Int'l*, pg. 5231
NEW WAVE ICELAND EHF.—See New Wave Group AB; *Int'l*, pg. 5230
NEW WAVE INDUSTRIES, LTD.—See New Mountain Capital, LLC; *U.S. Private*, pg. 2904
NEW WAVE INNOVATIONS, LLC—See MarineMax, Inc.; *U.S. Public*, pg. 1367
NEW WAVE ITALIA S.R.L.—See New Wave Group AB; *Int'l*, pg. 5230
NEW WAVE LEATHERS PTY LTD—See NH Foods Ltd.; *Int'l*, pg. 5256
NEW WAVE MODE AB—See New Wave Group AB; *Int'l*, pg. 5230
NEW WAVE NORWAY A/S—See New Wave Group AB; *Int'l*, pg. 5230
NEW WAVE PROFILE PROFESSIONALS AB—See New Wave Group AB; *Int'l*, pg. 5230
THE NEW WAVE RESEARCH LTD.—See Brookfield Corporation; *Int'l*, pg. 1180
THE NEW WAVE RESEARCH LTD.—See Elliott Management Corporation; *U.S. Private*, pg. 1372
NEW WAVE SPORTS AB—See New Wave Group AB; *Int'l*, pg. 5230
NEW WAVE SPORTSWEAR AS—See New Wave Group AB; *Int'l*, pg. 5230
NEW WAVE SPORTSWEAR B.V.—See New Wave Group AB; *Int'l*, pg. 5230
NEW WAVE SPORTSWEAR LTD.—See New Wave Group AB; *Int'l*, pg. 5230
NEW WAVE SPORTSWEAR S.A.—See New Wave Group AB; *Int'l*, pg. 5230
NEW WAVE TRADING SHANGHAI LTD—See New Wave Group AB; *Int'l*, pg. 5230
NEW WAVE TRAVEL—See Vision Travel Solutions; *Int'l*, pg. 8253
NEW WAVE YACHTS, DEALERSHIP—See New Wave Yachts; *U.S. Private*, pg. 2908
NEW WAVE YACHTS; *U.S. Private*, pg. 2908
NEW WAY AIR BEARINGS; *U.S. Private*, pg. 2908
NEW WAY MOTOR & DIESEL ENGINEERING (PTY) LTD—See enX Group Limited; *Int'l*, pg. 2456
NEW WAY POWER (PTY) LIMITED—See enX Group Limited; *Int'l*, pg. 2456
NEW WEST DISTRIBUTING, INC.; *U.S. Private*, pg. 2908
NEW WEST ENERGY SERVICES INC.; *Int'l*, pg. 5231
NEW WESTERN ENERGY CORPORATION; *U.S. Private*, pg. 2908
NEW WESTERN GROUP LIMITED; *Int'l*, pg. 5231
NEW WEST, LLC; *U.S. Private*, pg. 2908
NEW WEST NEWSPAPERS INC.; *U.S. Private*, pg. 2908
NEW WEST PHYSICIANS, INC.—See UnitedHealth Group Incorporated; *U.S. Public*, pg. 2242
NEW WEST PIPELINES LTD.—See Vertex Resource Group Ltd.; *Int'l*, pg. 8174
THE NEW WEST PORT CORPORATION LIMITED—See VKR Holding A/S; *Int'l*, pg. 8281
NEW WEST REALTY DEVELOPMENT CORP.; *U.S. Private*, pg. 2908
NEW WINCUP HOLDINGS, INC.—See ATAR Capital, LLC; *U.S. Private*, pg. 364
NEW WINDSOR VOLUNTEER AMBULANCE CORPS INC.; *U.S. Private*, pg. 2908
NEW WORK SE—See Hubert Burda Media Holding Kommanditgesellschaft; *Int'l*, pg. 3520
NEW WORLD CAR NISSAN, INC.; *U.S. Private*, pg. 2908
NEW WORLD CHINA LAND INVESTMENTS COMPANY LIMITED—See Chow Tai Fook Enterprises Limited; *Int'l*, pg. 1585
NEW WORLD CHINA LAND LIMITED—See Chow Tai Fook Enterprises Limited; *Int'l*, pg. 1585
NEW WORLD COMMUNICATIONS OF ATLANTA, INC.—See Fox Corporation; *U.S. Public*, pg. 876
NEW WORLD COMMUNICATIONS OF DETROIT, INC.—See Fox Corporation; *U.S. Public*, pg. 876
NEW WORLD COMMUNICATIONS OF TAMPA, INC.—See Fox Corporation; *U.S. Public*, pg. 876
NEW WORLD DEPARTMENT STORE CHINA LIMITED—See Chow Tai Fook Enterprises Limited; *Int'l*, pg. 1585
NEW WORLD DEVELOPMENT COMPANY LIMITED—See Chow Tai Fook Enterprises Limited; *Int'l*, pg. 1584
NEW WORLD GOLD CORP.; *U.S. Public*, pg. 1512
NEW WORLD HEALTH BRANDS, INC.—See SPARTA COMMERCIAL SERVICES, INC.; *U.S. Public*, pg. 1914
NEW WORLD HOTEL MANAGEMENT LIMITED—See Chow Tai Fook Enterprises Limited; *Int'l*, pg. 1585
NEW WORLD HOTELS (HOLDINGS) LIMITED—See Chow Tai Fook Enterprises Limited; *Int'l*, pg. 1585
NEW WORLD IMPORTS INC.; *U.S. Private*, pg. 2908
NEW WORLD INTERNATIONAL INC.—See United Commerce Centers Inc.; *U.S. Private*, pg. 4289
NEW WORLD PASTA COMPANY—See Ebro Foods S.A.; *Int'l*, pg. 2287
NEW WORLD PASTA COMPANY—See Ebro Foods S.A.; *Int'l*, pg. 2287
NEW WORLD PRODUCTION CO., LTD.—See BEC World Public Company Limited; *Int'l*, pg. 936
NEW WORLD RESOURCE BOLIVIA S.A.—See New World Resource Corp.; *Int'l*, pg. 5231
NEW WORLD RESOURCE CORP.; *Int'l*, pg. 5231
NEW WORLD RESOURCES LIMITED; *Int'l*, pg. 5231
NEW WORLD SOLUTIONS INC.; *Int'l*, pg. 5231
NEW WORLD TECHNOLOGIES, INC.; *U.S. Private*, pg. 2908
NEW WORLD VIDEO—See The Walt Disney Company; *U.S. Public*, pg. 2141
NEW WORLD VIDEO—See The Walt Disney Company; *U.S. Public*, pg. 2140
NEW WORQ, LLC; *U.S. Private*, pg. 2908
NEW YORK AIR BRAKE LLC—See Knorr-Bremse AG; *Int'l*, pg. 4212
NEW YORK AMERICAN WATER COMPANY, INC.—See Algonquin Power & Utilities Corp.; *Int'l*, pg. 319
NEW YORK ATHLETIC CLUB; *U.S. Private*, pg. 2908
NEW YORK BAKERY COMPANY LIMITED—See Grupo Bimbo, S.A.B. de C.V.; *Int'l*, pg. 3123
NEW YORK BITUMINOUS PRODUCTS CORP.; *U.S. Private*, pg. 2908
NEW YORK BLOOD CENTER, INC.; *U.S. Private*, pg. 2908
THE NEW YORK BLOWER COMPANY, INC.; *U.S. Private*, pg. 4083
THE NEW YORK BOTANICAL GARDEN; *U.S. Private*, pg. 4083
NEW YORK CALLIBRATION LAB—See Ontario Municipal Employees Retirement System; *Int'l*, pg. 5585
NEW YORK CAROLINA EXPRESS; *U.S. Private*, pg. 2908
NEW YORK CENTER FOR CHILD DEVELOPMENT; *U.S. Private*, pg. 2908
NEW YORK CENTRAL ART SUPPLY, INC.; *U.S. Private*, pg. 2908
NEW YORK CENTRAL MUTUAL FIRE INSURANCE COMPANY INC.; *U.S. Private*, pg. 2908
NEW YORK CITY BALLET; *U.S. Private*, pg. 2909
NEW YORK CITY CRIMINAL JUSTICE AGENCY, INC.; *U.S. Private*, pg. 2909
NEW YORK CITY HOUSING DEVELOPMENT CORPORATION; *U.S. Private*, pg. 2909
NEW YORK CITY HOUSING DEVELOPMENT CORP—See New York City Housing Development Corporation; *U.S. Private*, pg. 2909
NEW YORK CITY OFF-TRACK BETTING CORPORATION; *U.S. Private*, pg. 2909
NEW YORK CITY OPERA INC.; *U.S. Private*, pg. 2909
NEW YORK CITY TRANSIT AUTHORITY—See Metropolitan Transportation Authority; *U.S. Private*, pg. 2689
NEW YORK CLEARING HOUSE ASSOCIATION LLC—See Bank Policy Institute; *U.S. Private*, pg. 467
NEW YORK COMMERCIAL BANK—See New York Community Bancorp, Inc.; *U.S. Public*, pg. 1513
NEW YORK COMMUNITY BANCORP, INC.; *U.S. Public*, pg. 1512
NEW YORK COMMUNITY BANK—See New York Community Bancorp, Inc.; *U.S. Public*, pg. 1513
NEW YORK COMMUNITY TRUST; *U.S. Private*, pg. 2909
NEW YORK & COMPANY, INC.—See Irving Place Capital Management, L.P.; *U.S. Private*, pg. 2142
NEW YORK COMPENSATION INSURANCE RATING BOARD; *U.S. Private*, pg. 2909
NEW YORK COUNTY HEALTH SERVICES REVIEW ORGANIZATION; *U.S. Private*, pg. 2909
NEW YORK CRUISE LINES INC.; *U.S. Private*, pg. 2909
NEW YORK DISASTER INTERFAITH SERVICES; *U.S. Private*, pg. 2909
NEW YORK EHEALTH COLLABORATIVE, INC.; *U.S. Private*, pg. 2909
NEW YORKER BOILER CO. INC.—See Burnham Holdings, Inc.; *U.S. Public*, pg. 412
NEWYORKER LTD.—See Daidoh Limited; *Int'l*, pg. 1924
THE NEW YORKER MAGAZINE, INC.—See Advance Publications, Inc.; *U.S. Private*, pg. 86
THE NEW YORKER MAGAZINE—See Advance Publications, Inc.; *U.S. Private*, pg. 86
NEW YORK FOOTBALL GIANTS, INC.; *U.S. Private*, pg. 2909
NEW YORK FRAGRANCE INC.; *U.S. Private*, pg. 2909
NEW YORK FRIES; *Int'l*, pg. 5231
NEW YORK FROZEN FOODS INC.—See Lancaster Colony Corporation; *U.S. Public*, pg. 1291
NEW YORK FUNERAL CHAPELS, LLC—See Service Corporation International; *U.S. Public*, pg. 1870
THE NEW YORK GENOME CENTER; *U.S. Private*, pg. 4083
NEW YORK HALL OF SCIENCE; *U.S. Private*, pg. 2909
NEW-YORK HAMBURGER GUMMI-WAAREN COMPAGNIE AG; *Int'l*, pg. 5232
NEW YORK HEALTH CARE, INC.; *U.S. Private*, pg. 2909
NEW YORK HEALTH CLUB INC.; *U.S. Private*, pg. 2909
NEW-YORK HISTORICAL SOCIETY; *U.S. Private*, pg. 2913
THE NEW YORK INSTITUTE FOR SPECIAL EDUCATION; *U.S. Private*, pg. 4083
NEW YORK INSTITUTE OF FINANCE—See Pearson plc; *Int'l*, pg. 5777
NEW YORK INSTITUTE OF TECHNOLOGY; *U.S. Private*, pg. 2910
NEW YORK ISLANDERS HOCKEY CLUB, L.P.; *U.S. Private*, pg. 2910

COMPANY NAME INDEX

NEW YORK JETS FOOTBALL CLUB, INC.; *U.S. Private*, pg. 2910
NEW YORK KIDS CLUB; *U.S. Private*, pg. 2910
NEW YORK KNICKS, LLC—See Madison Square Garden Sports Corp.; *U.S. Public*, pg. 1354
THE NEW YORK LAW PUBLISHING COMPANY—See Apax Partners LLP; *Int'l*, pg. 504
NEW YORK LEGAL ASSISTANCE GROUP; *U.S. Private*, pg. 2910
NEW YORK LIBERTY, LLC—See Madison Square Garden Sports Corp.; *U.S. Public*, pg. 1354
NEW YORK LIFE ANNUITY INC—See New York Life Insurance Company; *U.S. Private*, pg. 2910
NEW YORK LIFE FOUNDATION—See New York Life Insurance Company; *U.S. Private*, pg. 2910
NEW YORK LIFE & HEALTH INSURANCE COMPANY INC.—See New York Life Insurance Company; *U.S. Private*, pg. 2910
NEW YORK LIFE INC.—See New York Life Insurance Company; *U.S. Private*, pg. 2910
NEW YORK LIFE INSURANCE & ANNUITY CORPORATION—See New York Life Insurance Company; *U.S. Private*, pg. 2910
NEW YORK LIFE INSURANCE COMPANY—See New York Life Insurance Company; *U.S. Private*, pg. 2910
NEW YORK LIFE INSURANCE COMPANY; *U.S. Private*, pg. 2910
NEW YORK LIFE INSURANCE COMPANY—See New York Life Insurance Company; *U.S. Private*, pg. 2910
NEW YORK LIFE INSURANCE LTD.—See New York Life Insurance Company; *U.S. Private*, pg. 2910
NEW YORK LIFE INTERNATIONAL INC.—See New York Life Insurance Company; *U.S. Private*, pg. 2910
NEW YORK LIFE INTERNATIONAL INVESTMENT—See New York Life Insurance Company; *U.S. Private*, pg. 2910
NEW YORK LIFE INVESTMENT MANAGEMENT GUARANTEED PRODUCTS—See New York Life Insurance Company; *U.S. Private*, pg. 2911
NEW YORK LIFE INVESTMENT MANAGEMENT LLC—See New York Life Insurance Company; *U.S. Private*, pg. 2910
NEW YORK LIFE LONG TERM CARE INSURANCE—See New York Life Insurance Company; *U.S. Private*, pg. 2911
NEW YORK LIFE SECURITIES INC.—See New York Life Insurance Company; *U.S. Private*, pg. 2911
NEW YORK LIFE STRUCTURED ASSET MANAGEMENT COMPANY LTD.—See New York Life Insurance Company; *U.S. Private*, pg. 2911
NEW YORK LOOK AT FIFTH AVE INC.—See The New York Look Inc.; *U.S. Private*, pg. 4083
THE NEW YORK LOOK INC.; *U.S. Private*, pg. 4083
THE NEW YORK LOOK INC.—See The New York Look Inc.; *U.S. Private*, pg. 4083
NEW YORK MAGAZINE—See New York Media, LLC; *U.S. Private*, pg. 2911
NEW YORK MEDIA, LLC; *U.S. Private*, pg. 2911
NEW YORK MERCANTILE EXCHANGE, INC.—See CME Group, Inc.; *U.S. Public*, pg. 518
NEW YORK MORTGAGE TRUST, INC.; *U.S. Public*, pg. 1513
NEW YORK MUNICIPAL POWER AGENCY; *U.S. Private*, pg. 2911
NEW YORK MUTUAL TRADING, INC.—See Takara Holdings, Inc.; *Int'l*, pg. 7433
NEW YORK-NEW YORK HOTEL & CASINO, LLC—See MGM Resorts International; *U.S. Public*, pg. 1435
NEW YORK ORGAN DONOR NETWORK, INC.; *U.S. Private*, pg. 2911
THE NEW YORK PALM TOO—See Palm Restaurant Group; *U.S. Private*, pg. 3080
NEW YORK PAVING INC.; *U.S. Private*, pg. 2911
THE NEW YORK POST—See Charlesbank Partners, LLC; *U.S. Private*, pg. 855
NEW YORK POWER AUTHORITY, INC.; *U.S. Private*, pg. 2911
NEW YORK-PRESBYTERIAN HEALTHCARE SYSTEM, INC.; *U.S. Private*, pg. 2912
NEW YORK PRETZEL, LLC—See J&J Snack Foods Corporation; *U.S. Public*, pg. 1180
NEW YORK PRIVATE BANK & TRUST CORPORATION; *U.S. Private*, pg. 2911
THE NEW YORK PUBLIC LIBRARY; *U.S. Private*, pg. 4083
NEW YORK PUBLIC RADIO; *U.S. Private*, pg. 2911
NEW YORK RACING ASSOCIATION, INC.; *U.S. Private*, pg. 2912
NEW YORK RANGERS, LLC—See Madison Square Garden Sports Corp.; *U.S. Public*, pg. 1354
NEW YORK RAVIOLI & PASTA CO.; *U.S. Private*, pg. 2912
NEW YORK REPLACEMENT PARTS CORP.; *U.S. Private*, pg. 2912
NEW YORK SAND & STONE LLC—See Vulcan Materials Company; *U.S. Public*, pg. 2314
NEW YORK SHIPPING ASSOCIATION, INC.; *U.S. Private*, pg. 2912

NEW YORK SPACES, INC.—See MOD Media LLC; *U.S. Private*, pg. 2759
NEW YORK STATE BAR ASSOCIATION; *U.S. Private*, pg. 2912
NEW YORK STATE BRIDGE AUTHORITY; *U.S. Private*, pg. 2912
NEW YORK STATE CANAL CORPORATION—See New York State Thruway Authority; *U.S. Private*, pg. 2912
THE NEW YORK STATE CATHOLIC HEALTH PLAN, INC.—See Centene Corporation; *U.S. Public*, pg. 470
NEW YORK STATE CORRECTIONAL OFFICERS & POLICE BENEVOLENT ASSOCIATION, INC.; *U.S. Private*, pg. 2912
NEW YORK STATE ELECTRIC & GAS CORPORATION—See Iberdrola, S.A.; *Int'l*, pg. 3571
NEW YORK STATE ELECTRIC & GAS CORP.—See Iberdrola, S.A.; *Int'l*, pg. 3571
NEW YORK STATE ELECTRIC & GAS CORP.—See Iberdrola, S.A.; *Int'l*, pg. 3571
NEW YORK STATE ELECTRIC & GAS CORP.—See Iberdrola, S.A.; *Int'l*, pg. 3571
NEW YORK STATE ELECTRIC & GAS CORP.—See Iberdrola, S.A.; *Int'l*, pg. 3571
NEW YORK STATE ELECTRIC & GAS CORP.—See Iberdrola, S.A.; *Int'l*, pg. 3571
NEW YORK STATE ELECTRIC & GAS CORP.—See Iberdrola, S.A.; *Int'l*, pg. 3571
NEW YORK STATE ENERGY RESEARCH & DEVELOPMENT AUTHORITY; *U.S. Private*, pg. 2912
NEW YORK STATE NURSES ASSOCIATION; *U.S. Private*, pg. 2912
NEW YORK STATE THRUWAY AUTHORITY; *U.S. Private*, pg. 2912
NEW YORK STOCK EXCHANGE LLC—See Intercontinental Exchange, Inc.; *U.S. Public*, pg. 1143
THE NEW YORK SUSQUEHANNA & WESTERN RAILWAY CORP—See Delaware Otsego Corp.; *U.S. Private*, pg. 1195
NEW YORK TELECOM PARTNERS, LLC—See DigitalBridge Group, Inc.; *U.S. Public*, pg. 664
THE NEW YORK TIMES COMPANY; *U.S. Public*, pg. 2116
NEW YORK TIMES LIMITED—See The New York Times Company; *U.S. Public*, pg. 2117
THE NEW YORK TIMES NEWS SERVICE—See The New York Times Company; *U.S. Public*, pg. 2117
THE NEW YORK TIMES—See The New York Times Company; *U.S. Public*, pg. 2117
THE NEW YORK TIMES SYNDICATION SALES CORPORATION—See The New York Times Company; *U.S. Public*, pg. 2117
NEW YORK TIMES TELEVISION—See The New York Times Company; *U.S. Public*, pg. 2117
NEW YORK TRANSIT INC.; *U.S. Private*, pg. 2912
NEW YORK WIRE COMPANY—See Compagnie de Saint-Gobain SA; *Int'l*, pg. 1730
NEW YORK WIRE COMPANY—See Compagnie de Saint-Gobain SA; *Int'l*, pg. 1730
NEW YORK YANKEES PARTNERSHIP; *U.S. Private*, pg. 2912
NEW YORK YANKEES—See New York Yankees Partnership; *U.S. Private*, pg. 2912
NEWYOU, INC.; *U.S. Public*, pg. 1521
NEW YUNG WAH TRADING LLC; *U.S. Private*, pg. 2913
NEW ZEALAND AGRISEEDS LTD.—See Barenbrug Holding B.V.; *Int'l*, pg. 864
NEW ZEALAND ALUMINIUM SMELTERS LTD.—See Rio Tinto plc; *Int'l*, pg. 6346
NEW ZEALAND BUS FINANCE LIMITED—See Infratil Limited; *Int'l*, pg. 3698
NEW ZEALAND BUS LIMITED—See Next Capital Pty Limited; *Int'l*, pg. 5248
NEW ZEALAND CEILING & DRYWALL SUPPLIES LIMITED—See Fletcher Building Limited; *Int'l*, pg. 2700
NEW ZEALAND COURIERS LIMITED—See Freightways Group Limited; *Int'l*, pg. 2771
NEW ZEALAND ENERGY CORP.; *Int'l*, pg. 5231
THE NEW ZEALAND FILM COMMISSION; *Int'l*, pg. 7670
THE NEW ZEALAND GUARDIAN TRUST COMPANY LIMITED—See Bath Street Capital Limited; *Int'l*, pg. 889
NEW ZEALAND HOLDINGS (UK) LTD—See Alliance Group Limited; *Int'l*, pg. 339
THE NEW ZEALAND HOME LOAN COMPANY LIMITED—See New Zealand Post Limited; *Int'l*, pg. 5232
NEW ZEALAND INSURANCE COMPANY LTD.—See Insurance Australia Group Limited; *Int'l*, pg. 3725
NEW ZEALAND INTERNATIONAL FAR EAST PHILIPPINES LIMITED—See New Image Group Limited; *Int'l*, pg. 5225
NEW ZEALAND KING SALMON; *Int'l*, pg. 5231
NEW ZEALAND LABORATORY SERVICES LTD—See Eurofins Scientific S.E.; *Int'l*, pg. 2551
NEW ZEALAND LAMB COMPANY—See New Zealand Lamb Cooperative, Inc.; *U.S. Private*, pg. 2913
NEW ZEALAND LAMB COOPERATIVE, INC.; *U.S. Private*, pg. 2913

NEXAM CHEMICAL HOLDING AB

NEW ZEALAND LIGHT LEATHERS LTD—See Argent Group Europe Limited; *Int'l*, pg. 560
NEW ZEALAND MORTGAGE FINANCE LIMITED—See RTO Limited; *Int'l*, pg. 6420
NEW ZEALAND NEW IMAGE LIMITED—See New Image Group Limited; *Int'l*, pg. 5225
NEW ZEALAND OIL & GAS LIMITED; *Int'l*, pg. 5231
NEW ZEALAND POST HOLDINGS LIMITED—See New Zealand Post Limited; *Int'l*, pg. 5232
NEW ZEALAND POST LIMITED; *Int'l*, pg. 5232
NEW ZEALAND RADIOLOGY GROUP LIMITED—See Sonic Healthcare Limited; *Int'l*, pg. 7098
NEW ZEALAND RURAL LAND COMPANY LIMITED; *Int'l*, pg. 5232
NEW ZEALAND STEEL (AUST) PTY LTD.—See BlueScope Steel Limited; *Int'l*, pg. 1074
NEW ZEALAND STEEL DEVELOPMENT LTD.—See BlueScope Steel Limited; *Int'l*, pg. 1074
NEW ZEALAND STEEL HOLDINGS LTD.—See BlueScope Steel Limited; *Int'l*, pg. 1074
NEW ZEALAND STEEL LIMITED—See BlueScope Steel Limited; *Int'l*, pg. 1074
NEW ZEALAND TRANSLATIONS CENTRE LIMITED—See Straker Limited; *Int'l*, pg. 7235
NEW ZEALAND WINE CELLARS LIMITED—See Woolworths Group Limited; *Int'l*, pg. 8452
NEW ZEALAND WOOL SERVICES INTERNATIONAL LIMITED—See Lempriere Pty. Ltd.; *Int'l*, pg. 4450
NEW ZEALAND WOOL SERVICES INTERNATIONAL LTD. (CHINA) LIMITED—See Lempriere Pty. Ltd.; *Int'l*, pg. 4450
THE NEW ZIPPER COMPANY LTD.—See YKK Corporation; *Int'l*, pg. 8588
NEW ZONE FASHION LIMITED—See Ruentex Group; *Int'l*, pg. 6426
NEWZOOM, INC.—See Swyft, Inc.; *U.S. Private*, pg. 3895
NEX ABIDE TRADE REPOSITORY AB—See CME Group, Inc.; *U.S. Public*, pg. 516
NEXACOR REALTY MANAGEMENT INC.—See Atkins-Realis Group Inc.; *Int'l*, pg. 671
NEXAGE TECHNOLOGIES USA, INC.—See Securekloud Technologies Ltd.; *Int'l*, pg. 6674
NEXAIOT CO., LTD.—See NEXCOM International Co., Ltd.; *Int'l*, pg. 5242
NEXAIR, LLC—See Linde plc; *Int'l*, pg. 4508
NEXAIR—See Linde plc; *Int'l*, pg. 4509
NEXALA LTD—See Trimble, Inc.; *U.S. Public*, pg. 2190
NEXALIN TECHNOLOGY, INC.; *U.S. Public*, pg. 1521
NEXAM CHEMICAL HOLDING AB; *Int'l*, pg. 5239
NEXAMP, INC.—See Mitsubishi Corporation; *Int'l*, pg. 4942
NEXAM S.A.S.—See OSG Corporation Co., Ltd.; *Int'l*, pg. 5649
NEXAM ST ANDREWS LTD.—See Nexam Chemical Holding AB; *Int'l*, pg. 5239
NEXANS ANGOLA, LDA—See Nexans S.A.; *Int'l*, pg. 5240
NEXANS AUSTRALIA HOLDING PTY LIMITED—See Nexans S.A.; *Int'l*, pg. 5240
NEXANS AUTOELECTRIC GMBH—See Nexans S.A.; *Int'l*, pg. 5241
NEXANS AUTOELECTRIC GMBH—See Nexans S.A.; *Int'l*, pg. 5241
NEXANS BENELUX S.A.—See Nexans S.A.; *Int'l*, pg. 5240
NEXANS BRASIL SA—See Nexans S.A.; *Int'l*, pg. 5240
NEXANS CANADA INC.—See Nexans S.A.; *Int'l*, pg. 5240
NEXANS CHILE S.A.—See Nexans S.A.; *Int'l*, pg. 5240
NEXANS CHINA WIRE & CABLES CO. LTD - WAIGAOQIAO PLANT—See Nexans S.A.; *Int'l*, pg. 5240
NEXANS (CHINA) WIRES & CABLES CO., LTD.—See Nexans S.A.; *Int'l*, pg. 5240
NEXANS COLOMBIA S.A.—See Nexans S.A.; *Int'l*, pg. 5240
NEXANS COMMUNICATIONS (SHANGHAI) CABLE CO. LTD—See Nexans S.A.; *Int'l*, pg. 5241
NEXANS COPPER FRANCE SAS—See Nexans S.A.; *Int'l*, pg. 5241
NEXANS DEUTSCHLAND GMBH & CO. KG—See Nexans S.A.; *Int'l*, pg. 5241
NEXANS DEUTSCHLAND INDUSTRIES GMBH & CO. KG—See Nexans S.A.; *Int'l*, pg. 5241
NEXANS ENERGY USA INC.—See Nexans S.A.; *Int'l*, pg. 5242
NEXANS FRANCE—See Nexans S.A.; *Int'l*, pg. 5241
NEXANS HARNESSES SA—See Nexans S.A.; *Int'l*, pg. 5240
NEXANS HELLAS INDUSTRIAL SA—See Nexans S.A.; *Int'l*, pg. 5241
NEXANS HIGH VOLTAGE USA INC.—See Nexans S.A.; *Int'l*, pg. 5240
NEXANS IBERIA, S.L.—See Nexans S.A.; *Int'l*, pg. 5241
NEXANS IKO SWEDEN AB—See Nexans S.A.; *Int'l*, pg. 5241
NEXANS ILETISIM ENDUSTRI VE TICARET AS—See Nexans S.A.; *Int'l*, pg. 5241
NEXANS INDELQUI S.A.—See Nexans S.A.; *Int'l*, pg. 5241
NEXANS INDUSTRY SOLUTIONS A/S—See Nexans S.A.; *Int'l*, pg. 5240

NEXAM CHEMICAL HOLDING AB
CORPORATE AFFILIATIONS

NEXANS INTERFACE SA—See Nexans S.A.; *Int'l*, pg. 5241
NEXANS IRELAND LTD—See Nexans S.A.; *Int'l*, pg. 5241
NEXANS ITALIA SPA—See Nexans S.A.; *Int'l*, pg. 5241
NEXANS JYDSK DENMARK A/S—See Nexans S.A.; *Int'l*, pg. 5241
NEXANS KABELMETAL GHANA LTD.—See Nexans S.A.; *Int'l*, pg. 5240
NEXANS KAZAKHSTAN—See Nexans S.A.; *Int'l*, pg. 5241
NEXANS KOREA LTD—See Nexans S.A.; *Int'l*, pg. 5241
NEXANS LOGISTICS LTD.—See Nexans S.A.; *Int'l*, pg. 5242
NEXANS MAROC SA—See Nexans S.A.; *Int'l*, pg. 5241
NEXANS (NANNING) COMMUNICATIONS CO., LTD.—See Nexans S.A.; *Int'l*, pg. 5240
NEXANS NEDERLAND BV—See Nexans S.A.; *Int'l*, pg. 5240
NEXANS NETWORK SOLUTIONS NV - EUROMOLD DIVISION—See Nexans S.A.; *Int'l*, pg. 5240
NEXANS NETWORK SOLUTIONS NV—See Nexans S.A.; *Int'l*, pg. 5240
NEXANS NORWAY A/S—See Nexans S.A.; *Int'l*, pg. 5242
NEXANS PARTICIPATIONS—See Nexans S.A.; *Int'l*, pg. 5240
NEXANS POWER ACCESSOIRES FRANCE SAS—See Nexans S.A.; *Int'l*, pg. 5242
NEXANS POWER ACCESSORIES FRANCE SAS—See Nexans S.A.; *Int'l*, pg. 5242
NEXANS POWER ACCESSORIES GERMANY GMBH—See Nexans S.A.; *Int'l*, pg. 5241
NEXANS POWER ACCESSORIES POLAND SP. Z.O.O.—See Nexans S.A.; *Int'l*, pg. 5242
NEXANS POWER ACCESSORIES UK LTD—See Nexans S.A.; *Int'l*, pg. 5242
NEXANS POWER NETWORKS NIGERIA LTD—See Nexans S.A.; *Int'l*, pg. 5242
NEXANS POWERS ACCESSORIES GERMANY GMBH—See Nexans S.A.; *Int'l*, pg. 5241
NEXANS RE SA—See Nexans S.A.; *Int'l*, pg. 5240
NEXANS ROMANIA SRL—See Nexans S.A.; *Int'l*, pg. 5242
NEXANS RUSSIA—See Impex Electro LLC; *Int'l*, pg. 3635
NEXANS RUSSIA - UGLICH FACTORY—See Impex Electro LLC; *Int'l*, pg. 3635
NEXANS S.A.; *Int'l*, pg. 5239
NEXANS SCHWEIZ AG (BREITENBACH)—See Nexans S.A.; *Int'l*, pg. 5242
NEXANS SCHWEIZ AG—See Nexans S.A.; *Int'l*, pg. 5242
NEXANS (SHANGHAI) ELECTRICAL MATERIALS CO., LTD.—See Nexans S.A.; *Int'l*, pg. 5240
NEXANS SINGAPORE PTE. LTD.—See Nexans S.A.; *Int'l*, pg. 5242
NEXANS SUISSE S.A.—See Nexans S.A.; *Int'l*, pg. 5242
NEXANS SUPERCONDUCTORS GMBH—See Nexans S.A.; *Int'l*, pg. 5241
NEXANS (SUZHOU) CABLES SOLUTIONS CO. LTD.—See Nexans S.A.; *Int'l*, pg. 5240
NEXANS TURKIYE ILETISIM ENDUSTRI VE TICARET AS - DENIZLI FACTORY—See Nexans S.A.; *Int'l*, pg. 5241
NEXANS TURKIYE ILETISIM ENDUSTRI VE TICARET AS - TUZLA FACTORY—See Nexans S.A.; *Int'l*, pg. 5241
NEXANS UK LTD—See Nexans S.A.; *Int'l*, pg. 5242
NEXANS USA INC—See Nexans S.A.; *Int'l*, pg. 5242
NEXANS WIRES ITALIA SPA—See Nexans S.A.; *Int'l*, pg. 5241
NEXANS WIRES—See Nexans S.A.; *Int'l*, pg. 5242
NEXANS (YANGGU) NEW RIHUI CABLES CO. LTD.—See Nexans S.A.; *Int'l*, pg. 5240
NEXANT, INC.—See BV Investment Partners, LLC; *U.S. Private*, pg. 699
NEXANTIS CORPORATION—See Dai Nippon Printing Co., Ltd.; *Int'l*, pg. 1916
NEXA RECURSOS MINERIAS S.A.—See Votorantim S.A.; *Int'l*, pg. 8310
NEXA RESOURCES PERU S.A.A.—See Votorantim S.A.; *Int'l*, pg. 8310
NEXA RESOURCES S.A.; *Int'l*, pg. 5239
NEXA TECHNOLOGIES, INC.—See Mouvement des caisses Desjardins; *Int'l*, pg. 5058
NEXAWEB EUROPE—See TOBESOFT Co., Ltd.; *Int'l*, pg. 7771
NEXAWEB JAPAN, INC.—See TOBESOFT Co., Ltd.; *Int'l*, pg. 7771
NEXBANK CAPITAL, INC.; *U.S. Private*, pg. 2918
NEXBANK, SSB—See NexBank Capital, Inc.; *U.S. Private*, pg. 2919
NEXBIS LIMITED; *Int'l*, pg. 5242
NEXCELOM BIOSCIENCE LLC—See Revvity, Inc.; *U.S. Public*, pg. 1794
NEXCESS.NET LLC; *U.S. Private*, pg. 2919
NEXCOBOT CO., LTD.—See NEXCOM International Co., Ltd.; *Int'l*, pg. 5242
NEXCOM CHINA CO., LTD.—See NEXCOM International Co., Ltd.; *Int'l*, pg. 5242
NEXCOM EUROPE LTD.—See NEXCOM International Co., Ltd.; *Int'l*, pg. 5242
NEXCOM GROUP; *U.S. Private*, pg. 2919
NEXCOM INTERNATIONAL CO., LTD.; *Int'l*, pg. 5242

NEXCOM SHANGHAI CO., LTD.—See NEXCOM International Co., Ltd.; *Int'l*, pg. 5242
NEXCOM SURVEILLANCE TECHNOLOGY CORP.—See NEXCOM International Co., Ltd.; *Int'l*, pg. 5242
NEXCORE HEALTHCARE CAPITAL CORP.; *U.S. Public*, pg. 1522
NEXCO RESOURCES, INC.; *Int'l*, pg. 5242
NEXCYCLE PLASTICS INC.; *Int'l*, pg. 5242
NEXE BETON D.O.O. NASICE—See Nexe Grupa d.d.; *Int'l*, pg. 5243
NEXE BLOCKCHAIN, INC.; *U.S. Public*, pg. 2919
NEXEC HOLDING GMBH; *Int'l*, pg. 5243
NEXE D.O.O. SARAJEVO—See Nexe Grupa d.d.; *Int'l*, pg. 5243
NEXE GRUPA D.D.; *Int'l*, pg. 5242
NEXE INNOVATIONS INC.; *Int'l*, pg. 5243
NEXE KAMEN D.O.O.—See Nexe Grupa d.d.; *Int'l*, pg. 5243
NEXEL INDUSTRIES, INC.—See Global Industrial Company; *U.S. Public*, pg. 942
NEXELIS—See Ampersand Management LLC; *U.S. Private*, pg. 265
NEXEN CORPORATION - GIMHAE PLANT—See Nexen Corporation; *Int'l*, pg. 5243
NEXEN CORPORATION - SIHWA PLANT—See Nexen Corporation; *Int'l*, pg. 5243
NEXEN CORPORATION; *Int'l*, pg. 5243
NEXEN GROUP INC.; *U.S. Private*, pg. 2919
NEXEN S.P.A.—See Apax Partners LLP; *Int'l*, pg. 504
NEXEN TIRE CORP.—See Nexen Corporation; *Int'l*, pg. 5243
NEXEO PLASCHEM (SHANGHAI) CO., LTD.—See Apollo Global Management, Inc.; *U.S. Public*, pg. 165
NEXEO PLASTICS, LLC—See One Rock Capital Partners, LLC; *U.S. Private*, pg. 3022
NEXEO SOLUTIONS GERMANY GMBH—See Apollo Global Management, Inc.; *U.S. Public*, pg. 165
NEXEO SOLUTIONS HOLDINGS, LLC—See Apollo Global Management, Inc.; *U.S. Public*, pg. 165
NEXEO SOLUTIONS, INC.—See Apollo Global Management, Inc.; *U.S. Public*, pg. 165
NEXEO SOLUTIONS ITALY SRL—See Apollo Global Management, Inc.; *U.S. Public*, pg. 165
NEXEO SOLUTIONS, LLC—See One Rock Capital Partners, LLC; *U.S. Private*, pg. 3022
NEXEO SOLUTIONS MEXICO S. DE R.L. DE C.V.—See Apollo Global Management, Inc.; *U.S. Public*, pg. 165
NEXEO SOLUTIONS PLASTICS UK LIMITED—See Apollo Global Management, Inc.; *U.S. Public*, pg. 165
NEXEO SOLUTIONS POLAND SP. Z O.O.—See Apollo Global Management, Inc.; *U.S. Public*, pg. 165
NEXEO SOLUTIONS RUS LLC—See Apollo Global Management, Inc.; *U.S. Public*, pg. 165
NEXEO SOLUTIONS SPAIN SLU—See Apollo Global Management, Inc.; *U.S. Public*, pg. 165
NEXEO SOLUTIONS SWEDEN AB—See Apollo Global Management, Inc.; *U.S. Public*, pg. 165
NEXERA ENERGY, INC.; *Int'l*, pg. 5243
NEXERA, LLC—See Premier, Inc.; *U.S. Public*, pg. 1715
NEX EXCHANGE LIMITED—See CME Group, Inc.; *U.S. Public*, pg. 516
NEXEYA CANADA INC.—See HENSOLDT AG; *Int'l*, pg. 3356
NEXEYA FRANCE SAS—See HENSOLDT AG; *Int'l*, pg. 3355
NEXEYA SAS—See HENSOLDT AG; *Int'l*, pg. 3355
NEXEYA USA INC.—See HENSOLDT AG; *Int'l*, pg. 3356
NEXG CO., LTD.—See Hansol Group; *Int'l*, pg. 3261
NEXGEL, INC.; *U.S. Public*, pg. 1522
NEXGEN BUILDING SUPPLY—See NexGen Building Supply; *U.S. Private*, pg. 2919
NEXGEN BUILDING SUPPLY; *U.S. Private*, pg. 2919
NEXGEN ENERGY LTD.; *Int'l*, pg. 5243
NEXGENIX, INC.; *U.S. Private*, pg. 2919
NEXGEN MEDIA WORLDWIDE, INC.; *U.S. Private*, pg. 2919
NEXGEN METALS, INC.; *U.S. Private*, pg. 2919
NEXGEN MINING, INC.; *U.S. Public*, pg. 1522
NEXGENRX, INC.; *Int'l*, pg. 5243
NEXGEN RXMARKETING LLC—See Insignia Capital Group, L.P.; *U.S. Private*, pg. 2091
NEX GLOBAL ENGINEERING PTE. LTD.—See Nippon Express Holdings, Inc.; *Int'l*, pg. 5315
NEX GLOBAL LOGISTICS DE MEXICO, S.A. DE C.V.—See Nippon Express Holdings, Inc.; *Int'l*, pg. 5315
NEX GLOBAL LOGISTICS KOREA CO., LTD.—See Nippon Express Holdings, Inc.; *Int'l*, pg. 5315
NEXGOLD MINING CORP.; *Int'l*, pg. 5243
NEXGRAM BIOMEDIC SDN. BHD.—See Nexgram Holdings Berhad; *Int'l*, pg. 5244
NEXGRAM HOLDINGS BERHAD; *Int'l*, pg. 5243
NEX GROUP LIMITED—See CME Group, Inc.; *U.S. Public*, pg. 516
NEX HEALTHCARE PTE. LTD.—See Medinex Limited; *Int'l*, pg. 4778
NEXIA HEALTH TECHNOLOGIES INC.; *Int'l*, pg. 5244
NEXICORE SERVICES, LLC - CALL CENTER—See Avnet, Inc.; *U.S. Public*, pg. 253

NEXICORE SERVICES, LLC—See Avnet, Inc.; *U.S. Public*, pg. 253
NEXIDIA INC.—See NICE Ltd.; *Int'l*, pg. 5265
NEXI DIGITAL POLSKA SP. Z O.O.—See Reply S.p.A.; *Int'l*, pg. 6291
NEXIEN BIOPHARMA INC.—See Intiva Inc.; *U.S. Private*, pg. 2129
NEXION GROUP LTD.; *Int'l*, pg. 5244
NEXION HEALTH, INC.; *U.S. Private*, pg. 2919
NEXION NETWORKS PTY. LTD.—See Nexion Group Ltd.; *Int'l*, pg. 5244
NEXION—See Travel Leaders Group, LLC; *U.S. Private*, pg. 4213
NEXION TECHNOLOGIES LIMITED; *Int'l*, pg. 5244
NEXI PAYMENTS S.P.A.—See Nexi SpA; *Int'l*, pg. 5244
NEXIS FIBERS A.S.; *Int'l*, pg. 5244
NEXIS FIBERS SIA; *Int'l*, pg. 5244
NEXI SPA; *Int'l*, pg. 5244
NEXITY BELGIUM SA—See Nexity SA; *Int'l*, pg. 5244
NEXITY GLOBAL SA—See Graviton Capital S.A.; *Int'l*, pg. 3062
NEXITY HOLDINC ITALIA SARL—See Nexity SA; *Int'l*, pg. 5244
NEXITY POLSKA SP.Z.O.O—See Nexity SA; *Int'l*, pg. 5244
NEXITY PORTUGAL SARL—See Nexity SA; *Int'l*, pg. 5244
NEXITY SA; *Int'l*, pg. 5244
NEXITY STUDEA SA—See Nexity SA; *Int'l*, pg. 5244
NEXIUM PORTUGAL - CONSULTARIO E SOFTWARE LDA.—See Brookfield Corporation; *Int'l*, pg. 1178
NEXIUM PORTUGAL - CONSULTARIO E SOFTWARE LDA.—See Elliott Management Corporation; *U.S. Private*, pg. 1371
NEXIUM SOFTWARE FACTORY, S.L.—See Brookfield Corporation; *Int'l*, pg. 1179
NEXIUM SOFTWARE FACTORY, S.L.—See Elliott Management Corporation; *U.S. Private*, pg. 1371
NEXIUS SOLUTIONS INC.; *U.S. Private*, pg. 2919
NEXJEN SYSTEMS—See Averna Technologies Inc.; *Int'l*, pg. 739
NEXJ HEALTH INC.—See NexJ Systems, Inc.; *Int'l*, pg. 5244
NEXJ SYSTEMS, INC.; *Int'l*, pg. 5244
NEXKEMIA PETROCHEMICALS INC.—See Integreon Global; *U.S. Private*, pg. 2102
NEXLAN AS—See Lagercrantz Group AB; *Int'l*, pg. 4394
NEXLIVING COMMUNITIES INC.; *Int'l*, pg. 5244
NEXLOGIC TECHNOLOGIES INC.; *U.S. Private*, pg. 2919
NEX LOGISTICS EUROPE GMBH—See Nippon Express Holdings, Inc.; *Int'l*, pg. 5315
NEXLUBE TAMPA LLC; *U.S. Private*, pg. 2919
NEXMART GMBH & CO. KG—See Dr. Helmut Rothenberger Holding GmbH; *Int'l*, pg. 2192
NEX METALS EXPLORATIONS LTD; *Int'l*, pg. 5239
NEXMO ASIA PACIFIC LIMITED—See Telefonaktiebolaget LM Ericsson; *Int'l*, pg. 7534
NEXOLON CO., LTD.; *Int'l*, pg. 5245
NEXON AMERICA INC.—See Nexon Co., Ltd.; *Int'l*, pg. 5245
NEXON CO., LTD.; *Int'l*, pg. 5245
NEXON EUROPE S.A.R.L.—See Nexon Co., Ltd.; *Int'l*, pg. 5245
NEXON GAMES CO., LTD.; *Int'l*, pg. 5245
NEXON GT CO., LTD.; *Int'l*, pg. 5245
NEXONIA, INC.; *Int'l*, pg. 5245
NEXON KOREA CORPORATION—See Nexon Co., Ltd.; *Int'l*, pg. 5245
NEXON-M INC.—See Nexon Co., Ltd.; *Int'l*, pg. 5245
NEXON NETWORKS CORPORATION—See Nexon Co., Ltd.; *Int'l*, pg. 5245
NEXONTIS CONSULTING GMBH—See msg group GmbH; *Int'l*, pg. 5067
NEXOPTIC ASIA LTD.—See NexOptic Technology Corp.; *Int'l*, pg. 5245
NEXOPTIC TECHNOLOGY CORP.; *Int'l*, pg. 5245
NEXO S.A.—See Yamaha Corporation; *Int'l*, pg. 8549
NEX PERFORMANCE FILMS—See Mason Wells, Inc.; *U.S. Private*, pg. 2602
NEXPHASE CAPITAL, LP—See Moelis Asset Management LP; *U.S. Private*, pg. 2764
NEXPLANAR CORPORATION—See Entegris, Inc.; *U.S. Public*, pg. 776
NEXPOINT ADVISORS, L.P.—See Highland Capital Management, L.P.; *U.S. Private*, pg. 1938
NEXPOINT CAPITAL, INC.—See Highland Capital Management, L.P.; *U.S. Private*, pg. 1938
NEXPOINT DIVERSIFIED REAL ESTATE TRUST; *U.S. Public*, pg. 1522
NEXPOINT HOSPITALITY TRUST, INC.—See Highland Capital Management, L.P.; *U.S. Private*, pg. 1938
NEXPOINT MULTIFAMILY CAPITAL TRUST, INC.—See Highland Capital Management, L.P.; *U.S. Private*, pg. 1938
NEX POINT PUBLIC COMPANY LIMITED; *Int'l*, pg. 5239
NEXPOINT REAL ESTATE FINANCE, INC.; *U.S. Public*, pg. 1522
NEXPOINT RESIDENTIAL TRUST, INC.—See Highland Capital Management, L.P.; *U.S. Private*, pg. 1938
NEXPONOR SICAFI SA; *Int'l*, pg. 5245

COMPANY NAME INDEX

NEXPRISE, INC.; *U.S. Private*, pg. 2919
NEXR CO., LTD.—See KT Corporation; *Int'l*, pg. 4315
NEXSAN CORPORATION; *U.S. Private*, pg. 2919
NEXSAN TECHNOLOGIES CANADA INC—See Nexsan Corporation; *U.S. Private*, pg. 2919
NEXSAN TECHNOLOGIES INCORPORATED—See Nexsan Corporation; *U.S. Private*, pg. 2919
NEXSAN TECHNOLOGIES LIMITED—See Nexsan Corporation; *U.S. Private*, pg. 2919
NEXSCIENT, INC.; *U.S. Public*, pg. 1522
NEX SERVICES LIMITED—See CME Group, Inc.; *U.S. Public*, pg. 518
NEX SERVICES PTE. LTD.—See CME Group, Inc.; *U.S. Public*, pg. 518
NEXSTAR BROADCASTING, INC.—See Nexstar Media Group, Inc.; *U.S. Public*, pg. 1522
NEXSTAR CAPITAL, LLC—See InterDigital, Inc.; *U.S. Public*, pg. 1144
NEXSTAR FINANCE HOLDINGS, INC.—See Nexstar Media Group, Inc.; *U.S. Public*, pg. 1524
NEXSTAR MEDIA GROUP, INC.; *U.S. Public*, pg. 1522
NEXSTGO COMPANY LIMITED—See Alco Holdings Limited; *Int'l*, pg. 301
NEXSTIM GERMANY GMBH—See Nexstim Plc; *Int'l*, pg. 5245
NEXSTIM, INC.—See Nexstim Plc; *Int'l*, pg. 5245
NEXSTIM PLC; *Int'l*, pg. 5245
NEXSYS CORP.—See SYSTEX Corporation; *Int'l*, pg. 7393
NEXSYS TECHNOLOGIES LLC—See Rocket Companies, Inc.; *U.S. Public*, pg. 1804
NEXT10, INC.; *U.S. Public*, pg. 1525
NEXT 15 GROUP PLC; *Int'l*, pg. 5245
NEXTAFF, LLC—See Malone Workforce Solutions; *U.S. Private*, pg. 2558
NEXTAGE CO., LTD.; *Int'l*, pg. 5248
NEXTAGE THERAPEUTICS LTD.; *Int'l*, pg. 5248
NEXTAG, INC.—See Regent, L.P.; *U.S. Private*, pg. 3388
NEXTALARM AG; *Int'l*, pg. 5248
NEXTA LTD.—See CHL S.p.A.; *Int'l*, pg. 1576
NEXTANCE, INC.—See ESW Capital, LLC; *U.S. Private*, pg. 1430
NEXTA SRL—See Stellantis N.V.; *Int'l*, pg. 7200
NEXT BATTER'S CIRCLE INC.—See Allied Architects, Inc.; *Int'l*, pg. 356
NEXTBILLION TECHNOLOGY PRIVATE LIMITED; *Int'l*, pg. 5248
NEXT BIOMETRICS CHINA LTD.—See NEXT Biometrics Group ASA; *Int'l*, pg. 5247
NEXT BIOMETRICS GROUP ASA; *Int'l*, pg. 5247
NEXT BIOMETRICS INC.—See NEXT Biometrics Group ASA; *Int'l*, pg. 5247
NEXT BIOMETRICS S.R.O.—See NEXT Biometrics Group ASA; *Int'l*, pg. 5247
NEXT BIOMETRICS TAIWAN LTD.—See NEXT Biometrics Group ASA; *Int'l*, pg. 5247
NEXTBIO—See Illumina, Inc.; *U.S. Public*, pg. 1112
NEXTBRIDGE INFRASTRUCTURE LP—See Enbridge Inc.; *Int'l*, pg. 2397
NEXT CAN INNOVATION CO., LTD.—See Toyo Seikan Group Holdings, Ltd.; *Int'l*, pg. 7856
NEXT CAPITAL COMPANY LIMITED—See Mitsui & Co., Ltd.; *Int'l*, pg. 4979
NEXT CAPITAL LIMITED; *Int'l*, pg. 5247
NEXT CAPITAL PTY LIMITED; *Int'l*, pg. 5247
NEXTCARE CLAIMS MANAGEMENT LLC—See Allianz SE; *Int'l*, pg. 354
NEXTCARE EGYPT LLC—See Allianz SE; *Int'l*, pg. 354
NEXTCARE HOLDINGS, INC.; *U.S. Private*, pg. 2920
NEXTCARE HOLDING WLL—See Allianz SE; *Int'l*, pg. 354
NEXTCARE, INC.—See NextCare Holdings, Inc.; *U.S. Private*, pg. 2920
NEXTCARE LEBANON SAL—See Allianz SE; *Int'l*, pg. 354
NEXTCARE UAE, AGHS LLC—See Allianz SE; *Int'l*, pg. 354
NEXT CENTURY CORPORATION; *U.S. Private*, pg. 2919
NEXT CENTURY TECHNOLOGIES, INC.; *U.S. Private*, pg. 2919
NEXTCHEM S.P.A.—See Maire Tecnimont S.p.A.; *Int'l*, pg. 4652
NEXT-CHEMX CORPORATION; *U.S. Public*, pg. 1525
NEXTCOM GROUP; *Int'l*, pg. 5248
NEXTCURE, INC.; *U.S. Public*, pg. 1526
NEXTDATA S.R.L.—See Vivendi SE; *Int'l*, pg. 8275
NEXT DAY BLINDS CORPORATION; *U.S. Private*, pg. 2919
NEXT DAY FLYERS; *U.S. Private*, pg. 2919
NEXTDC LIMITED; *Int'l*, pg. 5248
NEXTDECADE CORPORATION; *U.S. Public*, pg. 1526
NEXTDENT B.V.—See 3D Systems Corporation; *U.S. Public*, pg. 4
NEXT DIGITAL, INC.—See Meyers Norris Penny LLP; *Int'l*, pg. 4870
NEXT DIGITAL LIMITED; *Int'l*, pg. 5248
NEXTDOCS CORPORATION; *U.S. Private*, pg. 2920
NEXTDOOR HOLDINGS, INC.; *U.S. Public*, pg. 1526
NEXT DYNAMICS INC.; *U.S. Public*, pg. 1525
NEXTEBANK S.A.—See MBH Bank Nyrt.; *Int'l*, pg. 4752
NEXTECH3D.AI CORPORATION; *Int'l*, pg. 5248

NEXTECH CO., LTD.—See Takamiya Co., Ltd.; *Int'l*, pg. 7430
NEXTECH SOLUTIONS, INC.; *U.S. Public*, pg. 1526
NEXT EDGE CAPITAL CORP.; *Int'l*, pg. 5248
NEXTEDIA SA; *Int'l*, pg. 5249
NEXTEER AUTOMOTIVE GROUP LTD.—See Aviation Industry Corporation of China; *Int'l*, pg. 742
NEXTEK, INC.—See Kontron AG; *Int'l*, pg. 4277
NEXTEL COMMUNICATIONS ARGENTINA S.R.L.—See Cablevision Holding S.A.; *Int'l*, pg. 1246
NEXT ELECTRIC, LLC—See IES Holdings, Inc.; *U.S. Public*, pg. 1094
NEXTEL ITALIA SRL; *Int'l*, pg. 5249
NEXTEL TELECOMUNICACIONES S.A.; *Int'l*, pg. 5249
NEXTEL TELECOMUNICACOES LTDA.—See America Movil, S.A.B. de C.V.; *Int'l*, pg. 421
NEXT ENERGY CO., LTD.—See INPEX CORPORATION; *Int'l*, pg. 3717
NEXTENERGY SOLAR FUND LIMITED; *Int'l*, pg. 5249
NEXTENSA NV—See Ackermans & van Haaren NV; *Int'l*, pg. 106
NEXT ENTERTAINMENT WORLD CO., LTD.; *Int'l*, pg. 5248
NEXTEP TV WORKSHOP CO., LTD.—See Fuji Media Holdings, Inc.; *Int'l*, pg. 2814
NEXTERA COMMUNICATIONS LLC—See Trive Capital Inc.; *U.S. Public*, pg. 4239
NEXTERA ENERGY CAPITAL HOLDINGS, INC.—See NextEra Energy, Inc.; *U.S. Public*, pg. 1526
NEXTERA ENERGY, INC.; *U.S. Public*, pg. 1526
NEXTERA ENERGY PARTNERS, LP—See NextEra Energy, Inc.; *U.S. Public*, pg. 1526
NEXTERA ENERGY RESOURCES, LLC—See NextEra Energy, Inc.; *U.S. Public*, pg. 1526
NEXTERA MEDIA, LLC; *U.S. Private*, pg. 2920
NEXTER DIGITAL CO., LTD.—See The Siam Cement Public Company Limited; *Int'l*, pg. 7683
NEXTER ELECTRONICS S.A.—See GIAT Industries S.A.; *Int'l*, pg. 2962
NEXTER MECHANICS S.A.—See GIAT Industries S.A.; *Int'l*, pg. 2962
NEXTER MUNITIONS S.A.—See GIAT Industries S.A.; *Int'l*, pg. 2962
NEXTERNAL SOLUTIONS INC.—See Accellos, Inc.; *U.S. Private*, pg. 50
NEXTER ROBOTICS—See GIAT Industries S.A.; *Int'l*, pg. 2962
NEXTER SYSTEMS S.A.—See GIAT Industries S.A.; *Int'l*, pg. 2962
NEXTER TRAINING—See GIAT Industries S.A.; *Int'l*, pg. 2962
NEXTEYE CO., LTD.; *Int'l*, pg. 5249
NEXTFERM TECHNOLOGIES; *Int'l*, pg. 5249
NEXTFERM TECHNOLOGIES USA INC.—See Nextferm Technologies; *Int'l*, pg. 5249
NEXT FIFTEEN COMMUNICATIONS HONG KONG LIMITED—See Next 15 Group plc; *Int'l*, pg. 5246
NEXT FILM SP. Z O.O.—See Agora S.A.; *Int'l*, pg. 212
NEXT FINANCIAL GROUP, INC.—See Lee Equity Partners LLC; *U.S. Private*, pg. 2412
NEXT FINANCIAL LIMITED—See Pinnacle Investment Management Group Limited; *Int'l*, pg. 5870
NEXT FUEL, INC.; *U.S. Private*, pg. 2919
NEXT GALAXY CORP.; *U.S. Private*, pg. 2919
NEXT GAMES; *Int'l*, pg. 5248
NEXT GEAR SOLUTIONS, LLC—See Insight Venture Management, LLC; *U.S. Private*, pg. 2089
NEXT GEAR SOLUTIONS, LLC—See Stone Point Capital LLC; *U.S. Private*, pg. 3823
NEXTGEN BIOMED LTD.; *Int'l*, pg. 5249
NEXTGEN BUSINESS SOLUTIONS, INC.—See NextGen, Inc.; *Int'l*, pg. 5249
NEXTGEN CONSULTING INC.; *U.S. Private*, pg. 2921
NEXT GENERATION BEHAVIORAL HEALTH, LLC—See Acadia Healthcare Company, Inc.; *U.S. Public*, pg. 29
NEXT GENERATION ENROLLMENT, INC.—See Vista Equity Partners, LLC; *U.S. Public*, pg. 4399
NEXT GENERATION FILMS, INC.; *U.S. Private*, pg. 2919
NEXT GENERATION FUNDRAISING, INC.; *U.S. Private*, pg. 2919
NEXT GENERATION, INC.—See Kova Fertilizer Inc.; *U.S. Private*, pg. 2345
NEXT GENERATION LOTTERIES GMBH—See Pollard Banknote Limited; *Int'l*, pg. 5910
NEXT GENERATION VENDING, LLC—See H.I.G. Capital, LLC; *U.S. Private*, pg. 1831
NEXT GENERATION WIRELESS INC.; *U.S. Private*, pg. 2920
NEXTGENESIS HOLDINGS CORP.; *Int'l*, pg. 5249
NEXTGEN FOOD ROBOTICS CORP.; *Int'l*, pg. 5249
NEXTGEN GLOBAL RESOURCES, LLC—See Kelly Services, Inc.; *U.S. Public*, pg. 1220
NEXTGEN HEALTHCARE, INC.—See Thoma Bravo, L.P.; *U.S. Private*, pg. 4150
NEXTGEN HEALTHCARE INDIA PVT. LTD.—See Thoma Bravo, L.P.; *U.S. Private*, pg. 4150
NEXTGEN HEALTHCARE INFORMATION SYSTEMS, LLC - ATLANTA—See Thoma Bravo, L.P.; *U.S. Private*, pg. 4150

NEXTGEN HEALTHCARE INFORMATION SYSTEMS, LLC—See Thoma Bravo, L.P.; *U.S. Private*, pg. 4150
NEXTGENID, INC.—See Zeva Inc.; *U.S. Private*, pg. 4603
NEXTGEN, INC.; *Int'l*, pg. 5249
NEXTGEN INFORMATION SERVICES, INC.; *U.S. Private*, pg. 2921
NEXTGEN REPORTING LLC; *U.S. Private*, pg. 2921
NEXTGEN SECURITY, LLC—See Dunes Point Capital, LLC; *U.S. Private*, pg. 1288
NEXTGENTEL AS—See Kistefos AS; *Int'l*, pg. 4193
NEXTGENTEL HOLDING ASA—See Kistefos AS; *Int'l*, pg. 4192
NEXT GEN WATER CORP. LTD.; *Int'l*, pg. 5248
NEXTGLASS TECHNOLOGIES CORPORATION; *U.S. Private*, pg. 2921
NEXT GLOBAL TECHNOLOGY SDN. BHD.—See Green Packet Berhad; *Int'l*, pg. 3072
NEXT GRAPHITE, INC.; *U.S. Public*, pg. 1525
NEXT GREEN°CAR LTD.—See Good Energy Group PLC; *Int'l*, pg. 3038
NEXTGREEN GLOBAL BERHAD; *Int'l*, pg. 5249
NEXT GREEN WAVE HOLDINGS, INC.—See Planet 13 Holdings, Inc.; *U.S. Public*, pg. 1697
NEXTHEALTH MILAN—See WPP plc; *Int'l*, pg. 8492
NEXTIA LIFE INSURANCE CO., LTD.—See AXA S.A.; *Int'l*, pg. 757
NEXTIDEA SAS—See Vivendi SE; *Int'l*, pg. 8275
NEXT ID GMBH—See freenet AG; *Int'l*, pg. 2770
NEXTIER BANK, N.A.—See NexTier, Inc.; *U.S. Private*, pg. 2921
NEXTIER, INC.; *U.S. Private*, pg. 2921
NEXTIER OILFIELD SOLUTIONS INC.—See Patterson-UTI Energy, Inc.; *U.S. Public*, pg. 1654
NEXTIER SOLUTIONS CORPORATION—See Billerud AB; *Int'l*, pg. 1030
NEXTIMAGE MEDICAL, INC.—See Chrysalis Ventures; *U.S. Private*, pg. 893
NEXTIN INC.; *Int'l*, pg. 5249
NEXTINPUT, INC.—See Qorvo, Inc.; *U.S. Public*, pg. 1743
NEXT INSURANCE, INC.; *U.S. Private*, pg. 2920
NEXTIRAONE—See Black Box Limited; *Int'l*, pg. 1058
NEXTIT RESEARCH INSTITUTE, INC.—See Toho Holdings Co., Ltd.; *Int'l*, pg. 7776
NEXTLEAF SOLUTIONS; *Int'l*, pg. 5249
NEXT LEVEL BURGER COMPANY, INC.; *U.S. Private*, pg. 2920
NEXT LEVEL CHURCH, INC.; *U.S. Private*, pg. 2920
NEXT LEVEL HOSPITALITY SERVICES, LLC—See Aramark; *U.S. Public*, pg. 178
NEXTLEVEL INTERNET, INC.—See Digerati Technologies, Inc.; *U.S. Public*, pg. 661
NEXTLOT, INC; *U.S. Private*, pg. 2921
NEXT MANAGEMENT, LLC; *U.S. Private*, pg. 2920
NEXT MARKETING; *U.S. Private*, pg. 2920
NEXTMART, INC.; *U.S. Public*, pg. 1526
NEXTMEDIA GROUP, INC.—See Strategic Value Partners, LLC; *U.S. Private*, pg. 3836
NEXTMEDIA GROUP, INC.—See TPG Capital, L.P.; *U.S. Public*, pg. 2168
NEXT MEDIAWORKS LTD.; *Int'l*, pg. 5248
NEXT MEDICAL STAFFING LLC—See Health Carousel, LLC; *U.S. Private*, pg. 1893
NEXTMUNE AB; *Int'l*, pg. 5249
NEXTMUNE B.V.—See Vimian Group AB; *Int'l*, pg. 8208
NEXTMUNE ITALY S.R.L.—See Vimian Group AB; *Int'l*, pg. 8208
NEXTMUNE SCANDINAVIA AB—See Vimian Group AB; *Int'l*, pg. 8208
NEXTMUNE S.L.—See Vimian Group AB; *Int'l*, pg. 8208
NEXTMUNE US LLC—See Vimian Group AB; *Int'l*, pg. 8208
NEXTNAV INC.; *U.S. Public*, pg. 1526
NEXTNET AS—See Hafslund ASA; *Int'l*, pg. 3206
NEXTONE, INC.; *Int'l*, pg. 5249
NEXTONE SYSTEMS INC—See NexTone, Inc.; *Int'l*, pg. 5249
NEXTONLINE LIMITED—See Compass Group PLC; *Int'l*, pg. 1752
NEXTOP CO., LTD.—See TRADERS HOLDINGS CO., LTD.; *Int'l*, pg. 7888
NEXTOPIA SOFTWARE CORPORATION—See Scaleworks, Inc.; *U.S. Private*, pg. 3561
NEXTOP SOFTWARE (DALIAN) CO., LTD.—See TRADERS HOLDINGS CO., LTD.; *Int'l*, pg. 7888
NEXT PAGE, INC.; *U.S. Private*, pg. 2920
NEXTPHARMA TECHNOLOGIES HOLDING LTD.—See Sun Capital Partners, Inc.; *U.S. Private*, pg. 3862
NEXTPHASE MEDICAL DEVICES LLC—See Kidd & Company LLC; *U.S. Private*, pg. 2302
NEXTPLAT CORP.; *U.S. Public*, pg. 1526
NEXTPLAY TECHNOLOGIES, INC.; *U.S. Public*, pg. 1527
NEXT PLC; *Int'l*, pg. 5248
NEXTPOINT ACQUISITION CORP.; *U.S. Public*, pg. 1527
NEXT POINT BEARING GROUP, LLC; *U.S. Private*, pg. 2920
NEXT POLYMERS LIMITED—See Celanese Corporation; *U.S. Public*, pg. 465
NEXTPREMIUM SAS—See Vivendi SE; *Int'l*, pg. 8275

NEXT POINT BEARING GROUP, LLC — CORPORATE AFFILIATIONS

NEXTRACKER AUSTRALIA PTY. LTD.—See Flex Ltd.; *Int'l*, pg. 2704
NEXTRACKER INC.; *U.S. Public*, pg. 1527
NEXTRACKER MEXICO, S. DE R.L. DE C.V.—See Flex Ltd.; *Int'l*, pg. 2704
NEXTRACTION ENERGY CORP.; *Int'l*, pg. 5249
NEXTRADIOTV; *Int'l*, pg. 5249
NEXTRAN CORPORATION; *U.S. Private*, pg. 2921
NEX TRANSPORT, INC.—See Nippon Express Holdings, Inc.; *Int'l*, pg. 5317
NEXTRAQ LLC—See Compagnie Generale des Etablissements Michelin SCA; *Int'l*, pg. 1745
NEX TREASURY—See CME Group, Inc.; *U.S. Public*, pg. 517
NEXT RETAIL LIMITED—See NEXT plc; *Int'l*, pg. 5248
NEXTRIALS, INC.—See ICON plc; *Int'l*, pg. 3585
NEXTRIDGE, INC.—See Charge Enterprises, Inc.; *U.S. Public*, pg. 479
NEXTRIO, LLC; *U.S. Private*, pg. 2921
NEXTROM OY—See Knill Holding GmbH; *Int'l*, pg. 4208
NEXTROM USA INC.—See Knill Holding GmbH; *Int'l*, pg. 4208
NEXTRON CORPORATION—See Powell Industries, Inc.; *U.S. Public*, pg. 1705
NEXTRONICS ENGINEERING CORP.; *Int'l*, pg. 5249
NEXTRUSION GMBH—See Serafin Unternehmensgruppe GmbH; *Int'l*, pg. 6720
NEXTSCAN INC.—See Digital Check Corp.; *U.S. Private*, pg. 1230
NEXTSOURCE INC.—See Asseco Poland S.A.; *Int'l*, pg. 642
NEXTSOURCE MATERIALS INC.; *Int'l*, pg. 5249
NEXT SOURCING SERVICES LIMITED—See NEXT plc; *Int'l*, pg. 5248
NEXTSTAGE AM; *Int'l*, pg. 5250
NEXT STAR COMMUNICATIONS, INC.; *U.S. Private*, pg. 2920
NEXT STEP DOMESTIC VIOLENCE PROJECT; *U.S. Private*, pg. 2920
NEXT STEP EDUCATION GROUP, INC.; *U.S. Private*, pg. 2920
NEXT STEP LEARNING INC.; *U.S. Private*, pg. 2920
NEXT STEP LIVING, INC.; *U.S. Private*, pg. 2920
NEXT STEP ORTHOPAEDICS, INC.—See Patient Square Capital, L.P.; *U.S. Private*, pg. 3107
NEXT STEP SOLUTION S.R.L.—See Sesa S.p.A.; *Int'l*, pg. 6728
NEXTTCARE PTY LTD—See Adamantem Capital Management Pty Limited; *Int'l*, pg. 124
NEXTTCARE PTY LTD—See Liverpool Partners Pty Ltd; *Int'l*, pg. 4530
NEXT TECHNOLOGY HOLDING INC.; *Int'l*, pg. 5248
NEXT TELECOMMUNICATIONS SDN. BHD.—See Green Packet Berhad; *Int'l*, pg. 3072
NEXT TELECOM PTY. LTD.—See Comms Group Ltd; *Int'l*, pg. 1720
NEXT TIER CONCEPTS, INC.; *U.S. Private*, pg. 2920
NEXT TOWER S.A.S.—See Carmila SA; *Int'l*, pg. 1342
NEXTTRIP HOLDINGS, INC.; *U.S. Private*, pg. 2921
NEXTTRIP, INC.—See NextTrip Holdings, Inc.; *U.S. Private*, pg. 2921
NEXTURE CORPORATION; *Int'l*, pg. 5250
NEXTURNBIOSCIENCE CO., LTD.; *Int'l*, pg. 5250
NEXT VISION CO., LTD.—See Tsuzuki Denki Co., Ltd.; *Int'l*, pg. 7958
NEXTWARE LTD.; *Int'l*, pg. 5250
NEXT WAVE MULTIMEDIA PRIVATE LIMITED—See Nazara Technologies Limited; *Int'l*, pg. 5178
NEXT WORLD CAPITAL LLC—See Next World Capital Partners LLC; *U.S. Private*, pg. 2920
NEXT WORLD CAPITAL PARTNERS LLC; *U.S. Private*, pg. 2920
NEXTWORLD, LLC; *U.S. Private*, pg. 2921
NEXTWORTH SOLUTIONS, INC.; *U.S. Private*, pg. 2921
NEXTY ELECTRONICS CORPORATION—See Tomen Devices Corporation; *Int'l*, pg. 7800
NEXUM INC.; *U.S. Private*, pg. 2922
NEXUS AG (PTY) LTD—See Element Solutions Inc.; *U.S. Public*, pg. 728
NEXUS AG; *Int'l*, pg. 5250
NEXUS ANALYTICS SDN BHD—See HORIBA Ltd; *Int'l*, pg. 3477
NEXUS/ASTRAIA GMBH—See NEXUS AG; *Int'l*, pg. 5250
NEXUS AUSTRALASIA PTY LTD—See EBOS Group Limited; *Int'l*, pg. 2285
NEXUS BANK CO., LTD.—See J Trust Co., Ltd.; *Int'l*, pg. 3852
NEXUS BAY RESORT KARAMBUNAI SDN. BHD.—See Nagacorp Ltd.; *Int'l*, pg. 5124
NEXUS BIOSYSTEMS NIHON K.K.—See Azenta, Inc.; *U.S. Public*, pg. 258
NEXUS BONDS LIMITED; *Int'l*, pg. 5251
NEXUS CAPITAL MANAGEMENT LP; *U.S. Private*, pg. 2922
NEXUS CARD CO., LTD.—See PT Bank JTrust Indonesia Tbk.; *Int'l*, pg. 6026
NEXUS/CHILI GMBH—See NEXUS AG; *Int'l*, pg. 5250
NEXUS / CLOUD IT GMBH—See NEXUS AG; *Int'l*, pg. 5250

NEXUS CMF, L.L.C.—See Crocker Ventures LLC; *U.S. Private*, pg. 1102
NEXUS CORPORATE FINANCE LLP—See Primary Health Properties Plc; *Int'l*, pg. 5975
NEXUS CORPORATION—See Gibraltar Industries, Inc.; *U.S. Public*, pg. 936
NEXUS DAY HOSPITALS HOLDINGS PTY LTD—See QIC Limited; *Int'l*, pg. 6141
NEXUS DAY HOSPITALS PTY LTD—See QIC Limited; *Int'l*, pg. 6141
NEXUS DIGITALE DOKUMENTATIONSSYSTEME PROJEKTENTWICKLUNGSGES.MBH—See NEXUS AG; *Int'l*, pg. 5250
NEXUS/DIGITAL PATHOLOGY GMBH—See NEXUS AG; *Int'l*, pg. 5250
NEXUS DIRECT; *U.S. Private*, pg. 2922
NEXUS/DIS GMBH—See NEXUS AG; *Int'l*, pg. 5250
NEXUS DISTRIBUTION CORPORATION; *U.S. Private*, pg. 2922
NEXUS DX, INC.—See Samsung Group; *Int'l*, pg. 6512
NEXUS ELECTRICAL (JIAXING) LTD—See Nexus Industries Ltd.; *Int'l*, pg. 5251
NEXUS / E&L GMBH—See NEXUS AG; *Int'l*, pg. 5250
NEXUS ENERGY SERVICES, INC.; *U.S. Public*, pg. 1527
NEXUS ENGINEERING—See Gryphon Investors, LLC; *U.S. Private*, pg. 1798
NEXUS ENTERPRISE SOLUTIONS, INC.; *U.S. Public*, pg. 1527
NEXUS FRANCE S.A.S—See NEXUS AG; *Int'l*, pg. 5250
NEXUS GOLD CORP.; *Int'l*, pg. 5251
NEXUS GROUP HOLDINGS LTD.—See Primary Health Properties Plc; *Int'l*, pg. 5975
THE NEXUS GROUP, INC.—See EverWatch Capital; *U.S. Private*, pg. 1441
NEXUS/H LTD.—See Hakuhodo DY Holdings Incorporated; *Int'l*, pg. 3222
NEXUS INDUSTRIAL REIT; *Int'l*, pg. 5251
NEXUS INDUSTRIES GMBH—See Nexus Industries Ltd.; *Int'l*, pg. 5251
NEXUS INDUSTRIES LTD.; *Int'l*, pg. 5251
NEXUS INFRASTRUCTURE PLC; *Int'l*, pg. 5251
NEXUS/IPS GMBH—See NEXUS AG; *Int'l*, pg. 5250
NEXUS IS—See Nippon Telegraph & Telephone Corporation; *Int'l*, pg. 5342
NEXUS JADE SDN BHD—See Majuperak Holdings Berhad; *Int'l*, pg. 4655
NEXUS LOGISTICS (INTERNATIONAL) LIMITED—See Heng Tai Consumables Group Limited; *Int'l*, pg. 3345
NEXUS/MARABU GMBH—See NEXUS AG; *Int'l*, pg. 5250
NEXUS MID EAST ELECTRICAL LLC—See Nexus Industries Ltd.; *Int'l*, pg. 5251
NEXUS MINERALS LIMITED; *Int'l*, pg. 5251
NEXUS NEDERLAND B.V.—See NEXUS AG; *Int'l*, pg. 5250
NEXUS NETWORKS (PVT) LIMITED—See John Keells Holdings PLC; *Int'l*, pg. 3979
NEXUS / PASCHMANN GMBH—See NEXUS AG; *Int'l*, pg. 5250
NEXUS PHARMACEUTICALS, INC.; *U.S. Private*, pg. 2922
NEXUS PHP MANAGEMENT LIMITED—See Primary Health Properties Plc; *Int'l*, pg. 5975
NEXUS PLASTICS, INC.; *U.S. Private*, pg. 2922
NEXUS POLSKA SP. Z O.O.—See NEXUS AG; *Int'l*, pg. 5250
NEXUS RESORT KARAMBUNAI SDN. BHD.—See Nagacorp Ltd.; *Int'l*, pg. 5124
NEXUS SCHWEIZ GMBH—See NEXUS AG; *Int'l*, pg. 5250
NEXUS SDN. BHD.—See Lum Chang Holdings Limited; *Int'l*, pg. 4577
NEXUS SEALAND TRADING PTE. LTD.—See Beng Kuang Marine Limited; *Int'l*, pg. 973
NEXUS SISINF SL—See NEXUS AG; *Int'l*, pg. 5250
NEXUS; *U.S. Private*, pg. 2922
NEXUS SURGICAL AND MEDICARE LIMITED; *Int'l*, pg. 5251
NEXUS SWISSLAB GMBH—See NEXUS AG; *Int'l*, pg. 5250
NEXUS/SWITSPOT GMBH—See NEXUS AG; *Int'l*, pg. 5250
NEXUS SYSTEMS, INC.—See Thoma Bravo, L.P.; *U.S. Private*, pg. 4146
NEXUS TECHNOLOGIES PTY LTD—See Resideo Technologies, Inc.; *U.S. Public*, pg. 1790
NEXUSTEK, INC.—See ABRY Partners, LLC; *U.S. Private*, pg. 42
NEXUSTOURS CORP.—See Sunwing Travel Group, Inc.; *Int'l*, pg. 7332
NEXUS URANIUM CORP.; *Int'l*, pg. 5251
NEXUS VALVE, INC.—See Aalberts N.V.; *Int'l*, pg. 35
NEXUS VEHICLE MANAGEMENT LIMITED—See Equistone Partners Europe Limited; *Int'l*, pg. 2486
NEXVORTEX INC.—See Thompson Street Capital Manager, LLC; *U.S. Private*, pg. 4160
NEXV SYNERGY SDN. BHD.—See Careplus Group Berhad; *Int'l*, pg. 1325
NEXVUE INFORMATION SYSTEMS, INC.—See Net@Work, Inc.; *U.S. Private*, pg. 2886

NEXWISE INTELLIGENCE CHINA LIMITED; *Int'l*, pg. 5251
NEXXAR GROUP INC.; *U.S. Private*, pg. 2922
NEXXCHANGE AG; *Int'l*, pg. 5251
NEXXEN INTERNATIONAL LTD.; *Int'l*, pg. 5251
NEXXO S.A.—See Echeverria Izquierdo S.A.; *Int'l*, pg. 2289
NEXXTEP TECHNOLOGY SERVICES, INC.—See Spire Capital Partners, LLC; *U.S. Private*, pg. 3757
NEXXTWORKS, INC.; *U.S. Private*, pg. 2922
NEXXUS LIGHTING-POOL & SPA—See Revolution Lighting Technologies, Inc.; *U.S. Public*, pg. 1793
NEXXUS VENTURES; *U.S. Private*, pg. 2922
NEXYZ.BB CORPORATION—See Nexyz.Group Corporation; *Int'l*, pg. 5252
NEXYZ.GROUP CORPORATION; *Int'l*, pg. 5251
NEXYZ.TRADE, INC.—See Nexyz.Group Corporation; *Int'l*, pg. 5252
NEXYZ.VP, INC.—See Nexyz.Group Corporation; *Int'l*, pg. 5252
NEYA SYSTEMS, LLC—See Applied Research Associates, Inc.; *U.S. Private*, pg. 299
NEYCER INDIA LTD.; *Int'l*, pg. 5252
NEYER HOLDINGS—See Al Neyer, LLC; *U.S. Private*, pg. 147
NEYER MANAGEMENT; *U.S. Private*, pg. 2922
NEY OIL COMPANY; *U.S. Private*, pg. 2922
NEYRPERSE COMPANY—See MAPNA Group; *Int'l*, pg. 4687
NEZHEGOL-AGRO—See Gruppa Kompaniy Rusagro OOO; *Int'l*, pg. 3140
NEZIVOTNO OSIGURANJE BASLER A.D.O.—See UNIQA Insurance Group AG; *Int'l*, pg. 8059
NF AGENCY CO., LTD.—See Nakano Corporation; *Int'l*, pg. 5132
NFB PRIVATE WEALTH MANAGEMENT (PTY) LTD—See NVest Financial Holdings Limited; *Int'l*, pg. 5498
NFC CORPORATION; *Int'l*, pg. 5252
NFC HOLDINGS, INC.—See Hikari Tsushin, Inc.; *Int'l*, pg. 3390
NFCO INC.; *U.S. Private*, pg. 2922
NF CORPORATION; *Int'l*, pg. 5252
NFC PUBLIC COMPANY LIMITED—See SC Group Thai; *Int'l*, pg. 6609
NFD HOLDING D.D.; *Int'l*, pg. 5252
NFF, INC.; *U.S. Private*, pg. 2922
NF FLEET AB—See ALD Automotive; *Int'l*, pg. 303
NF FLEET AS—See ALD Automotive; *Int'l*, pg. 303
NF FLEET A/S—See ALD Automotive; *Int'l*, pg. 303
NF FLEET OY—See ALD Automotive; *Int'l*, pg. 303
NFFS INC.; *U.S. Private*, pg. 2922
NFG DISTRIBUTION CORP NYD VEBA FOR COLLECTIVELY BARGAINED EES; *U.S. Private*, pg. 2922
NFG ITALIA S.R.L.—See Organto Foods Inc.; *Int'l*, pg. 5619
NFG MIDSTREAM COVINGTON, LLC—See National Fuel Gas Company; *U.S. Public*, pg. 1494
NFG NEW FRUIT GROUP GMBH—See Organto Foods Inc.; *Int'l*, pg. 5619
NFI CANADA—See NFI Industries, Inc.; *U.S. Private*, pg. 2923
N FIELD CO., LTD.—See Unison Capital, Inc.; *Int'l*, pg. 8061
NFI GROUP INC.; *Int'l*, pg. 5252
NFI INDUSTRIES, INC.; *U.S. Private*, pg. 2922
NFI LOGISTICS—See NFI Industries, Inc.; *U.S. Private*, pg. 2923
NFINANSE INC.—See AccountNow, Inc.; *U.S. Private*, pg. 54
NFINITI INC.; *U.S. Public*, pg. 1527
NFINITY ATHLETIC CORPORATION; *U.S. Private*, pg. 2923
NFI WAREHOUSING & DISTRIBUTION DIVISION - ARLINGTON FACILITY—See NFI Industries, Inc.; *U.S. Private*, pg. 2923
NFI WAREHOUSING & DISTRIBUTION DIVISION - BENSENVILLE FACILITY—See NFI Industries, Inc.; *U.S. Private*, pg. 2923
NFI WAREHOUSING & DISTRIBUTION DIVISION - BRAMPTON FACILITY—See NFI Industries, Inc.; *U.S. Private*, pg. 2923
NFI WAREHOUSING & DISTRIBUTION DIVISION - CHAMPLAIN FACILITY—See NFI Industries, Inc.; *U.S. Private*, pg. 2923
NFI WAREHOUSING & DISTRIBUTION DIVISION - CHINO FACILITY—See NFI Industries, Inc.; *U.S. Private*, pg. 2923
NFI WAREHOUSING & DISTRIBUTION DIVISION - DAYTON FACILITY—See NFI Industries, Inc.; *U.S. Private*, pg. 2923
NFI WAREHOUSING & DISTRIBUTION DIVISION - HEBRON FACILITY—See NFI Industries, Inc.; *U.S. Private*, pg. 2923
NFI WAREHOUSING & DISTRIBUTION DIVISION - LOGAN TOWNSHIP FACILITY—See NFI Industries, Inc.; *U.S. Private*, pg. 2923
NFI WAREHOUSING & DISTRIBUTION DIVISION - ONTARIO FACILITY—See NFI Industries, Inc.; *U.S. Private*, pg. 2923

COMPANY NAME INDEX

NFI WAREHOUSING & DISTRIBUTION DIVISION - ORLANDO FACILITY—See NFI Industries, Inc.; *U.S. Private*, pg. 2923

NFI WAREHOUSING & DISTRIBUTION DIVISION - PENNSAUKEN FACILITY—See NFI Industries, Inc.; *U.S. Private*, pg. 2923

NFI WAREHOUSING & DISTRIBUTION—See NFI Industries, Inc.; *U.S. Private*, pg. 2923

NFJ INVESTMENT GROUP LP—See Allianz SE; *Int'l*, pg. 346

NFK HOLDINGS CO., LTD.; *Int'l*, pg. 5252

N.F.LABORATORIES INC.—See Nippon Telegraph & Telephone Corporation; *Int'l*, pg. 5343

NFL BIOSCIENCES SA; *Int'l*, pg. 5252

NF-LEASING GMBH—See NordFinanz Bank AG; *Int'l*, pg. 5419

NFL FILMS, INC.—See National Football League; *U.S. Private*, pg. 2854

NFL HOLDINGS LTD.; *Int'l*, pg. 5252

NFL HOME CENTER—See Tyndale Advisors, LLC; *U.S. Private*, pg. 4268

NFL MANAGEMENT COUNCIL—See National Football League; *U.S. Private*, pg. 2854

NFL VENTURES, INC.—See National Football League; *U.S. Private*, pg. 2854

NFM (DALIAN) MACHINERY CO., LTD.—See NFM/Welding Engineers, Inc.; *U.S. Private*, pg. 2923

NFM GROUP INC.; *U.S. Private*, pg. 2923

NFM IDDON LTD.—See NFM/Welding Engineers, Inc.; *U.S. Private*, pg. 2923

NFM OF KANSAS INC—See Berkshire Hathaway Inc.; *U.S. Public*, pg. 302

NFM/WELDING ENGINEERS, INC.; *U.S. Private*, pg. 2923

NF OBJEKTE BERLIN GMBH—See UniCredit S.p.A.; *Int'l*, pg. 8038

NF OBJEKT FFM GMBH—See UniCredit S.p.A.; *Int'l*, pg. 8038

NF OBJEKT MUNCHEN GMBH—See UniCredit S.p.A.; *Int'l*, pg. 8038

NFO DRIVES AB; *Int'l*, pg. 5252

NFON AG; *Int'l*, pg. 5252

NFON FRANCE S.A.S—See NFON AG; *Int'l*, pg. 5253

NFON GMBH—See NFON AG; *Int'l*, pg. 5253

NFON IBERIA SL—See NFON AG; *Int'l*, pg. 5253

NFON POLSKA SP.Z.O.O.—See NFON AG; *Int'l*, pg. 5253

NFON UK LTD.—See NFON AG; *Int'l*, pg. 5253

NFP-AIS INSURANCE SERVICES, INC.—See Aon plc; *Int'l*, pg. 497

NFP BENEFIT PLANNING SERVICES, INC.—See Aon plc; *Int'l*, pg. 496

NFP BROKERAGE INSURANCE SERVICES, INC.—See Aon plc; *Int'l*, pg. 496

NFP CLIPPINGER FINANCIAL GROUP, LLC—See Aon plc; *Int'l*, pg. 496

NFP CORPORATE SERVICES (NY), LLC.—See Aon plc; *Int'l*, pg. 496

NFP CORPORATE SERVICES—See Aon plc; *Int'l*, pg. 496

NFP CORP.—See Aon plc; *Int'l*, pg. 495

NFP FDR FINANCIAL GROUP, INC.—See Aon plc; *Int'l*, pg. 496

NFP MID-ATLANTIC SG, LLC—See Aon plc; *Int'l*, pg. 497

NFP MITCHELL & MORONESO INSURANCE SERVICES, INC.—See Aon plc; *Int'l*, pg. 497

NFP MOSSE & MOSSE ASSOCIATES, INC.—See Aon plc; *Int'l*, pg. 497

NFP-NATIONAL ACCOUNT SERVICES, INC.—See Aon plc; *Int'l*, pg. 497

NFP NATIONAL MADISON GROUP, INC.—See Aon plc; *Int'l*, pg. 497

NFP PROPERTY & CASUALTY SERVICES, INC.—See Aon plc; *Int'l*, pg. 497

NFP STRUCTURED SETTLEMENTS, INC.—See Aon plc; *Int'l*, pg. 497

NFP THE BENEFITS SOLUTION GROUP, INC.—See Aon plc; *Int'l*, pg. 497

NFP THE HARTFIELD COMPANY, INC.—See Aon plc; *Int'l*, pg. 497

NFQ ADVERTISING GROUP; *Int'l*, pg. 5253

NF REALTY CO., LTD.—See Nakano Corporation; *Int'l*, pg. 5132

NFS ASSET MANAGEMENT CO., LTD.—See Thanachart Capital PCL; *Int'l*, pg. 7607

NF SERVICE KK—See Oi Electric Co., Ltd.; *Int'l*, pg. 5533

N.F. SHELDON INC.; *U.S. Private*, pg. 2828

NFS HOLDINGS INC.; *U.S. Private*, pg. 2923

N.F. SMITH & ASSOCIATES, LP; *U.S. Private*, pg. 2828

NFT DISTRIBUTION OPERATIONS LIMITED—See EmergeVest Limited; *Int'l*, pg. 2378

NF TECHNO COMMERCE CO., LTD.—See NF Corporation; *Int'l*, pg. 5252

N&F TECHNO SERVICE CO., LTD.—See Noritsu Koki Co., Ltd.; *Int'l*, pg. 5429

NF TORMATIC GMBH—See Sanwa Holdings Corporation; *Int'l*, pg. 6560

NFUSION GROUP, LLC; *U.S. Private*, pg. 2923

NFUZION CONSULTING, INC.—See NNG Software Developing & Commercial LLC; *Int'l*, pg. 5394

NG4T GMBH—See Viavi Solutions Inc.; *U.S. Public*, pg. 2295

NG ADVANTAGE LLC—See Clean Energy Fuels Corp.; *U.S. Public*, pg. 508

NGAGE SPECIALIST RECRUITMENT LIMITED; *Int'l*, pg. 5253

NGA HOLDCO, LLC; *U.S. Private*, pg. 2923

NGA HR SP. Z O.O.—See Alight, Inc.; *U.S. Public*, pg. 76

NGA HUMAN RESOURCES SWEDEN AB—See Alight, Inc.; *U.S. Public*, pg. 76

NGAI HING ENGINEERING PLASTIC (HONG KONG) LIMITED—See Ngai Hing Hong Co Ltd; *Int'l*, pg. 5253

NGAI HING ENGINEERING PLASTIC (HONG KONG) LTD.—See Ngai Hing Hong Co Ltd; *Int'l*, pg. 5253

NGAI HING HONG CO LTD; *Int'l*, pg. 5253

NGAI HING HONG PLASTIC MATERIALS (HONG KONG) LTD.—See Ngai Hing Hong Co Ltd; *Int'l*, pg. 5253

NGAI HING PLASTCHEM CO., LTD.—See Ngai Hing Hong Co Ltd; *Int'l*, pg. 5253

NGAI LIK ELECTRONICS ENTERPRISES LIMITED—See Yuan Heng Gas Holdings Limited; *Int'l*, pg. 8607

NGAIO MARSH RETIREMENT VILLAGE LIMITED—See Ryman Healthcare Ltd.; *Int'l*, pg. 6439

NGAI SHUN CONSTRUCTION & DRILLING COMPANY LIMITED—See Boill Healthcare Holdings Limited; *Int'l*, pg. 1101

NGAI SING HOLDINGS LIMITED—See Yuan Heng Gas Holdings Limited; *Int'l*, pg. 8607

NGAI STAR XANH TRANSPORTATION COMPANY LIMITED; *Int'l*, pg. 5253

NGA, LLC—See Newmark Group, Inc.; *U.S. Public*, pg. 1516

NGAM CANADA LP—See Groupe BPCE; *Int'l*, pg. 3096

N.G. BAILEY & CO. LTD.; *Int'l*, pg. 5116

NG BAILEY LIMITED—See N.G. Bailey & Co. Ltd.; *Int'l*, pg. 5116

N.G. BAILEY MANUFACTURING LTD.—See N.G. Bailey & Co. Ltd.; *Int'l*, pg. 5116

NG BAILEY—See N.G. Bailey & Co. Ltd.; *Int'l*, pg. 5116

NG BAILEY—See N.G. Bailey & Co. Ltd.; *Int'l*, pg. 5116

NGC CONSOLIDATED HOLDING SDN. BHD.—See NATIONAL GAS Company SOAG; *Int'l*, pg. 5157

NGC CORPORATION—See Sojitz Corporation; *Int'l*, pg. 7063

NGC ENERGY FZE—See NATIONAL GAS Company SOAG; *Int'l*, pg. 5157

NGC ENERGY INDIA PRIVATE LIMITED—See NATIONAL GAS Company SOAG; *Int'l*, pg. 5157

NGC ENERGY SAUDI LLC—See NATIONAL GAS Company SOAG; *Int'l*, pg. 5157

NGC ENERGY SDN. BHD.—See NATIONAL GAS Company SOAG; *Int'l*, pg. 5157

N.G.C. MEDICAL SRL—See Medtronic plc; *Int'l*, pg. 4790

NGC NACHFOLGEKAPITAL GMBH—See MEDIQON Group AG; *Int'l*, pg. 4780

NGC NETWORK ASIA, LLC - SINGAPORE—See The Walt Disney Company; *U.S. Public*, pg. 2141

NGC NETWORK ASIA, LLC—See The Walt Disney Company; *U.S. Public*, pg. 2141

NGC NETWORK ASIA, LLC - TAIWAN—See The Walt Disney Company; *U.S. Public*, pg. 2141

NGC NETWORK (INDIA) PRIVATE LIMITED—See The Walt Disney Company; *U.S. Public*, pg. 2141

NGC NETWORK INTERNATIONAL, LLC—See The Walt Disney Company; *U.S. Public*, pg. 2140

NGC NETWORK US, LLC—See The Walt Disney Company; *U.S. Public*, pg. 2141

NGC TRINIDAD & TOBAGO LNG LIMITED—See National Enterprises Limited; *Int'l*, pg. 5156

NGE CAPITAL LIMITED; *Int'l*, pg. 5253

NGECK SENG CHIANG METAL CO., LTD—See Lohakit Metal Public Company Limited; *Int'l*, pg. 4543

NGEE ANN DEVELOPMENT PTE. LTD.—See Ngee Ann Kongsi; *Int'l*, pg. 5253

NGEE ANN KONGSI; *Int'l*, pg. 5253

NGEE ANN TRADITIONAL CHINESE MEDICINE CENTRE LTD—See Ngee Ann Kongsi; *Int'l*, pg. 5253

NGENEBIO CO., LTD.; *Int'l*, pg. 5253

NG ENERGY INTERNATIONAL CORP.; *Int'l*, pg. 5253

NGENIC AB; *Int'l*, pg. 5253

NGEN TECHNOLOGIES HOLDINGS CORP.; *U.S. Public*, pg. 1527

NGENX CORPORATION—See Windstream Holdings, Inc.; *U.S. Public*, pg. 2373

NGE OUD B.V.—See Novomatic AG; *Int'l*, pg. 5467

NGERN TID LOR PUBLIC COMPANY LIMITED; *Int'l*, pg. 5253

NGF CANADA LIMITED—See Nippon Sheet Glass Co. Ltd.; *Int'l*, pg. 5330

NGF EUROPE LIMITED—See Nippon Sheet Glass Co. Ltd.; *Int'l*, pg. 5330

NG&G FACILITY SERVICES INTERNATIONAL; *U.S. Private*, pg. 2923

NGG FINANCE PLC—See National Grid plc; *Int'l*, pg. 5157

N.G. GILBERT CORPORATION—See The Townsend Corporation; *U.S. Private*, pg. 4127

NGH AGRAR GMBH & CO. AGRARGESELLSCHAFT HOHENSEEFELD KG—See KTG Agrar SE; *Int'l*, pg. 4316

NGH JAPAN CO., LTD.—See Mitsui E&S Holdings Co., Ltd.; *Int'l*, pg. 4986

NGHT, LLC—See National Geographic Society; *U.S. Private*, pg. 2855

NGI CONTEXT—See News Group International Holding; *Int'l*, pg. 5238

NGI NATIONAL CONSTRUCTORS, L.L.C.—See The Newtron Group Inc.; *U.S. Private*, pg. 4084

N G INDUSTRIES LTD.; *Int'l*, pg. 5115

N. GINSBURG & SON INCORPORATED; *U.S. Private*, pg. 2827

NGI TECHNICAL SERVICES, L.L.C.—See The Newtron Group Inc.; *U.S. Private*, pg. 4084

NGIU KEE (BINTULU) SDN. BHD.—See Ngiu Kee Corporation (M) Berhad; *Int'l*, pg. 5253

NGIU KEE CORPORATION (M) BERHAD; *Int'l*, pg. 5253

NGIU KEE (LAWAS) SDN. BHD.—See Ngiu Kee Corporation (M) Berhad; *Int'l*, pg. 5253

NGIU KEE (SIBU) SDN. BHD.—See Ngiu Kee Corporation (M) Berhad; *Int'l*, pg. 5253

NGIU KEE (WISMA SABERKAS) SDN. BHD.—See Ngiu Kee Corporation (M) Berhad; *Int'l*, pg. 5254

NGK ADREC CO LTD—See NGK Insulators, Ltd.; *Int'l*, pg. 5254

NGK AUTOMOTIVE CERAMICS KOREA CO LTD—See NGK Insulators, Ltd.; *Int'l*, pg. 5254

NGK AUTOMOTIVE CERAMICS MEXICO, S DE R.L. DE C.V.—See NGK Insulators, Ltd.; *Int'l*, pg. 5254

NGK AUTOMOTIVE CERAMICS USA INC—See NGK Insulators, Ltd.; *Int'l*, pg. 5254

NGK BERYLCO FRANCE—See NGK Insulators, Ltd.; *Int'l*, pg. 5254

NGK BERYLCO U.K. LTD.—See NGK Insulators, Ltd.; *Int'l*, pg. 5254

NGK BUILDING SERVICE, LTD.—See NGK Insulators, Ltd.; *Int'l*, pg. 5254

NGK CERAMIC DEVICE CO., LTD.—See NGK Insulators, Ltd.; *Int'l*, pg. 5254

NGK CERAMICS EUROPE S.A—See NGK Insulators, Ltd.; *Int'l*, pg. 5254

NGK CERAMICS MEXICO, S.DE R.L.DE C.V.—See NGK Insulators, Ltd.; *Int'l*, pg. 5254

NGK CERAMICS POLSKA SP Z O.O—See NGK Insulators, Ltd.; *Int'l*, pg. 5254

NGK CERAMICS SOUTH AFRICA (PTY) LTD—See NGK Insulators, Ltd.; *Int'l*, pg. 5254

NGK CERAMICS SUZHOU CO., LTD.—See NGK Insulators, Ltd.; *Int'l*, pg. 5254

NGK CERAMICS (THAILAND) CO., LTD.—See NGK Insulators, Ltd.; *Int'l*, pg. 5254

NGK CERAMICS USA INC—See NGK Insulators, Ltd.; *Int'l*, pg. 5254

NGK CHEM-TECH, LTD.—See NGK Insulators, Ltd.; *Int'l*, pg. 5254

NGK DEUTSCHE BERYLCO GMBH—See NGK Insulators, Ltd.; *Int'l*, pg. 5254

NGK ELECTONICS DEVICES (M) SDN. BHD.—See NGK Insulators, Ltd.; *Int'l*, pg. 5254

NGK ELECTRONICS DEVICES, INC.—See NGK Insulators, Ltd.; *Int'l*, pg. 5254

NGK ELECTRONICS USA, INC.—See NGK Insulators, Ltd.; *Int'l*, pg. 5254

NGK EUROPE GMBH—See NGK Insulators, Ltd.; *Int'l*, pg. 5254

NGK FILTEC LTD—See NGK Insulators, Ltd.; *Int'l*, pg. 5254

NGK FINE MOLDS LTD—See NGK Insulators, Ltd.; *Int'l*, pg. 5254

NGK GLOBETRONICS TECHNOLOGY SDN. BHD.—See NGK Insulators, Ltd.; *Int'l*, pg. 5254

NGK INSULATORS (CHINA) INVESTMENT CO., LTD.—See NGK Insulators, Ltd.; *Int'l*, pg. 5254

NGK INSULATORS, LTD - HIGH PERFORMANCE CERAMICS DIVISION—See NGK Insulators, Ltd.; *Int'l*, pg. 5255

NGK INSULATORS, LTD. - ISHIKAWA PLANT—See NGK Insulators, Ltd.; *Int'l*, pg. 5255

NGK INSULATORS, LTD.; *Int'l*, pg. 5254

NGK INSULATORS OF CANADA LTD—See NGK Insulators, Ltd.; *Int'l*, pg. 5254

NGK INSULATORS SHANGHAI CO LTD—See NGK Insulators, Ltd.; *Int'l*, pg. 5254

NGK INSULATORS SUZHOU CO., LTD.—See NGK Insulators, Ltd.; *Int'l*, pg. 5254

NGK KILNTECH CORPORATION—See NGK Insulators, Ltd.; *Int'l*, pg. 5255

NGK LIFE CO LTD—See NGK Insulators, Ltd.; *Int'l*, pg. 5255

NGK LOCKE INC—See NGK Insulators, Ltd.; *Int'l*, pg. 5255

NGK LOCKE POLYMER INSULATORS INC—See NGK Insulators, Ltd.; *Int'l*, pg. 5255

NGK LOGISTICS LTD—See NGK Insulators, Ltd.; *Int'l*, pg. 5255

NGK METALS CORPORATION—See NGK Insulators, Ltd.; *Int'l*, pg. 5255

NGK METEX CORPORATION—See NGK Insulators, Ltd.; *Int'l*, pg. 5255

NGK METTEX CORPORATION—See NGK Insulators, Ltd.; *Int'l*, pg. 5255

NGK INSULATORS, LTD. CORPORATE AFFILIATIONS

Company Index

NGK NORTH AMERICA, INC.—See NGK Insulators, Ltd.; *Int'l*, pg. 5255
NGK OKHOTSK LTD—See NGK Insulators, Ltd.; *Int'l*, pg. 5255
NGK OPTOCERAMICS CO LTD—See NGK Insulators, Ltd.; *Int'l*, pg. 5255
NGK PRINTER CERAMICS CO LTD—See NGK Insulators, Ltd.; *Int'l*, pg. 5255
NGK SPARK PLUG (AUSTRALIA) PTY LTD.—See Niterra Co., Ltd.; *Int'l*, pg. 5380
NGK SPARK PLUG CO., LTD. - KAGOSHIMA-MIYANOJO FACTORY—See Niterra Co., Ltd.; *Int'l*, pg. 5380
NGK SPARK PLUG CO., LTD. - KOMAKI FACTORY—See Niterra Co., Ltd.; *Int'l*, pg. 5380
NGK SPARK PLUG EUROPE GMBH—See Niterra Co., Ltd.; *Int'l*, pg. 5380
NGK SPARK PLUG MIDDLE EAST FZE—See Niterra Co., Ltd.; *Int'l*, pg. 5380
NGK SPARK PLUGS (ASIA) CO., LTD.—See Niterra Co., Ltd.; *Int'l*, pg. 5380
NGK SPARK PLUGS CANADA LIMITED—See Niterra Co., Ltd.; *Int'l*, pg. 5380
NGK SPARK PLUGS (FRANCE) S.A.S.—See Niterra Co., Ltd.; *Int'l*, pg. 5380
NGK SPARK PLUG (SHANGHAI) CO., LTD.—See Niterra Co., Ltd.; *Int'l*, pg. 5380
NGK SPARK PLUG (SHANGHAI) TRADING CO., LTD.—See Niterra Co., Ltd.; *Int'l*, pg. 5380
NGK SPARK PLUGS (INDIA) PVT. LTD.—See Niterra Co., Ltd.; *Int'l*, pg. 5380
NGK SPARK PLUGS MALAYSIA BER HAD—See Niterra Co., Ltd.; *Int'l*, pg. 5380
NGK SPARK PLUGS (PHILIPPINES), INC.—See Niterra Co., Ltd.; *Int'l*, pg. 5380
NGK SPARK PLUGS SA (PTY) LTD.—See Niterra Co., Ltd.; *Int'l*, pg. 5380
NGK SPARK PLUGS (THAILAND) CO., LTD.—See Niterra Co., Ltd.; *Int'l*, pg. 5380
NGK SPARK PLUGS (U.K.) LTD.—See Niterra Co., Ltd.; *Int'l*, pg. 5380
NGK SPARK PLUGS (U.S.A.), INC.—See Niterra Co., Ltd.; *Int'l*, pg. 5380
NGK SPARK PLUGS (U.S.A.), INC. - WEST VIRGINIA FACTORY—See Niterra Co., Ltd.; *Int'l*, pg. 5380
NGK SPARK PLUGS (VIETNAM) CO., LTD.—See Niterra Co., Ltd.; *Int'l*, pg. 5380
NGK SPORTS DEVELOPMENT CO., LTD / MORONOKI TENNIS CLUB—See NGK Insulators, Ltd.; *Int'l*, pg. 5255
NGK STANGER PTY. LTD.—See NGK Insulators, Ltd.; *Int'l*, pg. 5255
NGK TECHNICA, LTD.—See NGK Insulators, Ltd.; *Int'l*, pg. 5255
NGK TECHNIOCERA SUZHOU CO., LTD.—See NGK Insulators, Ltd.; *Int'l*, pg. 5255
NGK TECHNOCERA SUZHOU CO., LTD.—See NGK Insulators, Ltd.; *Int'l*, pg. 5255
NGK TECHNOLOGIES INDIA PVT. LTD.—See NGK Insulators, Ltd.; *Int'l*, pg. 5255
NGK YU-SERVICE CO LTD—See NGK Insulators, Ltd.; *Int'l*, pg. 5255
NGL AMERICAN LIFE—See National Guardian Life Insurance Company; *U.S. Private*, pg. 2855
N. GLANTZ & SON; *U.S. Private*, pg. 2827
NGL CRUDE LOGISTICS, LLC—See NGL Energy Partners LP; *U.S. Public*, pg. 1527
NGL CRUDE TERMINALS, LLC—See NGL Energy Partners LP; *U.S. Public*, pg. 1527
NGL CRUDE TRANSPORTATION, LLC—See NGL Energy Partners LP; *U.S. Public*, pg. 1527
NGL ENERGY PARTNERS LP; *U.S. Public*, pg. 1527
NGL FINE-CHEM LTD.; *Int'l*, pg. 5255
NGL HOLDINGS INC.—See National Guardian Life Insurance Company; *U.S. Private*, pg. 2855
NGL INVESTMENT SERVICES INC.—See National Guardian Life Insurance Company; *U.S. Private*, pg. 2855
NGL MILAN INVESTMENTS, LLC—See NGL Energy Partners LP; *U.S. Public*, pg. 1527
NGL SOLIDS SOLUTIONS, LLC—See NGL Energy Partners LP; *U.S. Public*, pg. 1527
NGL SUPPLY CO. LTD.; *Int'l*, pg. 5255
NGL SUPPLY TERMINALS COMPANY—See NGL Supply Co. Ltd.; *Int'l*, pg. 5255
NGM BIOPHARMACEUTICALS, INC.; *U.S. Public*, pg. 1527
NG MICROSYSTEMS INDIA PVT. LTD.—See Trident Microsystems, Inc.; *U.S. Private*, pg. 4230
NGM INSURANCE COMPANY—See American Family Mutual Insurance Company; *U.S. Private*, pg. 233
NGMOCO INC.—See DeNA Co., Ltd.; *Int'l*, pg. 2026
NGNIRA GOLD SARL—See Thor Explorations Limited; *Int'l*, pg. 7717
NGO CHEW HONG EDIBLE OIL PTE LTD—See Mewah International Inc.; *Int'l*, pg. 4869
NGO CHEW HONG INDUSTRIES PTE LTD—See Mewah International Inc.; *Int'l*, pg. 4869
NGO CHEW HONG OILS & FATS (M) SDN BHD—See Mewah International Inc.; *Int'l*, pg. 4869
NGOC HUNG FOOTWEAR CO., LTD.—See Fulgent Sun International (Holding) Co., Ltd.; *Int'l*, pg. 2842
NGO DEVELOPMENT CORPORATION—See The Energy Cooperative, Inc.; *U.S. Private*, pg. 4026
NGO HAN JOINT STOCK COMPANY; *Int'l*, pg. 5255
NGONG PING 360 LIMITED—See MTR Corporation Limited; *Int'l*, pg. 5072
NGO PROPANE COOPERATIVE—See The Energy Cooperative, Inc.; *U.S. Private*, pg. 4026
NGO QUYEN PROCESSING EXPORT JOINT STOCK COMPANY; *Int'l*, pg. 5255
NGO TRANSMISSION, INC.—See The Energy Cooperative, Inc.; *U.S. Private*, pg. 4026
NGP BLUE MOUNTAIN I LLC—See Alternative Earth Resources Inc.; *Int'l*, pg. 391
NGP ENERGY CAPITAL MANAGEMENT, LLC; *U.S. Private*, pg. 2923
NGP MELBOURNE PTY. LTD.; *Int'l*, pg. 5255
NGP REALTY SUB GP, LLC—See Drive Shack Inc.; *U.S. Public*, pg. 688
NGP REALTY SUB, L.P.—See Drive Shack Inc.; *U.S. Public*, pg. 688
NGP S.P.A.—See Orlandi S.p.A.; *Int'l*, pg. 5639
NGP VAN, INC.; *U.S. Private*, pg. 2924
NGS ADVANCED FIBERS CO., LTD.—See Nippon Carbon Co., Ltd.; *Int'l*, pg. 5311
NGSC LIMITED; *Int'l*, pg. 5256
NGS GROUP AB; *Int'l*, pg. 5255
NGSOFT CORPORATION—See Sky Israel Private Equity Fund; *Int'l*, pg. 6992
NG SOLUTIONS INC.—See Nutritional Growth Solutions Ltd.; *Int'l*, pg. 5494
NGS SECURE—See NCC Group Plc; *Int'l*, pg. 5181
NGS SECURE—See NCC Group Plc; *Int'l*, pg. 5181
NGT NETWORKS PTE. LTD.—See Green Packet Berhad; *Int'l*, pg. 3072
NGT NEUE GEBAUDETECHNIK GMBH—See E.ON SE; *Int'l*, pg. 2255
NGX LIMITED; *Int'l*, pg. 5256
NH3 SERVICE COMPANY; *U.S. Private*, pg. 2924
NHA BE REAL ESTATE JSC—See Keppel Corporation Limited; *Int'l*, pg. 4132
NHA BE WATER SUPPLY JOINT STOCK COMPANY; *Int'l*, pg. 5257
N. HARRIS COMPUTER CORPORATION—See Constellation Software Inc.; *Int'l*, pg. 1773
NH ATARDECER CARIBENO, S.L.—See Minor International PCL; *Int'l*, pg. 4911
NHA TRANG VACCINES & BIOLOGICAL PRODUCTS JOINT-STOCK COMPANY—See Ben Tre Pharmaceutical JSC; *Int'l*, pg. 969
NHAT VIET GROUP CO., LTD.—See Ringier Holding AG; *Int'l*, pg. 6343
NHAVA SHEVA INTERNATIONAL CONTAINER TERMINAL PRIVATE LIMITED—See Dubai World Corporation; *Int'l*, pg. 2221
NH BALAGO—See Minor International PCL; *Int'l*, pg. 4912
NH BARCELONA STADIUM HOTEL—See Minor International PCL; *Int'l*, pg. 4912
NH BELGIUM CVBA—See Minor International PCL; *Int'l*, pg. 4912
NH BERLIN CITY OST—See Minor International PCL; *Int'l*, pg. 4912
NH BERLIN CITY WEST—See Minor International PCL; *Int'l*, pg. 4912
N.H. BRAGG & SONS; *U.S. Private*, pg. 2828
NH CARIBBEAN MANAGEMENT, B.V.—See Minor International PCL; *Int'l*, pg. 4912
NHC COMMUNICATIONS, INC.; *Int'l*, pg. 5257
NHC COMMUNICATIONS USA, INC.—See NHC Communications, Inc.; *Int'l*, pg. 5257
NH CENTRAL EUROPE, GMBH & CO. KG—See Minor International PCL; *Int'l*, pg. 4912
NHC EUROPE S.A.—See NHC Communications, Inc.; *Int'l*, pg. 5257
NHC FARRAGUT MEMORY CARE, LLC—See National HealthCare Corporation; *U.S. Public*, pg. 1495
NHC FOODS LIMITED; *Int'l*, pg. 5257
NHC GROUP PTY. LTD.—See Amplifon S.p.A.; *Int'l*, pg. 435
NHC HEALTHCARE/ANDERSON, LLC—See National HealthCare Corporation; *U.S. Public*, pg. 1495
NHC HEALTHCARE/ANNISTON, LLC—See National HealthCare Corporation; *U.S. Public*, pg. 1495
NHC HEALTHCARE/ATHENS, LLC—See National HealthCare Corporation; *U.S. Public*, pg. 1495
NHC HEALTHCARE/BLUFFTON, LLC—See National HealthCare Corporation; *U.S. Public*, pg. 1495
NHC HEALTHCARE-CHARLESTON, LLC—See National HealthCare Corporation; *U.S. Public*, pg. 1495
NHC HEALTHCARE/CHATTANOOGA, LLC—See National HealthCare Corporation; *U.S. Public*, pg. 1495
NHC HEALTHCARE/CLINTON, LLC—See National HealthCare Corporation; *U.S. Public*, pg. 1495
NHC HEALTHCARE/COLUMBIA, LLC—See National HealthCare Corporation; *U.S. Public*, pg. 1495
NHC HEALTHCARE/COOL SPRINGS, LLC—See National HealthCare Corporation; *U.S. Public*, pg. 1495
NHC HEALTHCARE/DESLOGE, LLC—See National HealthCare Corporation; *U.S. Public*, pg. 1495
NHC HEALTHCARE/DICKSON, LLC—See National HealthCare Corporation; *U.S. Public*, pg. 1495
NHC HEALTHCARE/FARRAGUT, LLC—See National HealthCare Corporation; *U.S. Public*, pg. 1495
NHC HEALTHCARE/FRANKLIN, LLC—See National HealthCare Corporation; *U.S. Public*, pg. 1495
NHC HEALTHCARE/GARDEN CITY, LLC—See National HealthCare Corporation; *U.S. Public*, pg. 1495
NHC HEALTHCARE/GLASGOW, LLC—See National HealthCare Corporation; *U.S. Public*, pg. 1495
NHC HEALTHCARE/GREENVILLE, LLC—See National HealthCare Corporation; *U.S. Public*, pg. 1495
NHC HEALTHCARE/GREENWOOD, LLC—See National HealthCare Corporation; *U.S. Public*, pg. 1495
NHC HEALTHCARE/HEARTLAND, LLC—See National HealthCare Corporation; *U.S. Public*, pg. 1495
NHC HEALTHCARE/HENDERSONVILLE, LLC—See National HealthCare Corporation; *U.S. Public*, pg. 1495
NHC HEALTHCARE/HOLSTON HILLS, LLC—See National HealthCare Corporation; *U.S. Public*, pg. 1495
NHC HEALTHCARE/JOHNSON CITY, LLC—See National HealthCare Corporation; *U.S. Public*, pg. 1495
NHC HEALTHCARE/JOPLIN, LLC—See National HealthCare Corporation; *U.S. Public*, pg. 1495
NHC HEALTHCARE/KENNETT, LLC—See National HealthCare Corporation; *U.S. Public*, pg. 1496
NHC HEALTHCARE/KINGSPORT, LLC—See National HealthCare Corporation; *U.S. Public*, pg. 1496
NHC HEALTHCARE/KNOXVILLE, LLC—See National HealthCare Corporation; *U.S. Public*, pg. 1496
NHC HEALTHCARE/LAURENS, LLC—See National HealthCare Corporation; *U.S. Public*, pg. 1496
NHC HEALTHCARE/LEXINGTON, LLC—See National HealthCare Corporation; *U.S. Public*, pg. 1496
NHC HEALTHCARE-MACON, LLC—See National HealthCare Corporation; *U.S. Public*, pg. 1495
NHC HEALTHCARE/MADISONVILLE, LLC—See National HealthCare Corporation; *U.S. Public*, pg. 1496
NHC HEALTHCARE/MARYLAND HEIGHTS, LLC—See National HealthCare Corporation; *U.S. Public*, pg. 1496
NHC HEALTHCARE/MAULDIN, LLC—See National HealthCare Corporation; *U.S. Public*, pg. 1496
NHC HEALTHCARE/MCMINNVILLE, LLC—See National HealthCare Corporation; *U.S. Public*, pg. 1496
NHC HEALTHCARE/MILAN, LLC—See National HealthCare Corporation; *U.S. Public*, pg. 1496
NHC HEALTHCARE/MOULTON, LLC—See National HealthCare Corporation; *U.S. Public*, pg. 1496
NHC HEALTHCARE/NORTH AUGUSTA, LLC—See National HealthCare Corporation; *U.S. Public*, pg. 1496
NHC HEALTHCARE/OAKWOOD, LLC—See National HealthCare Corporation; *U.S. Public*, pg. 1496
NHC HEALTHCARE-OSAGE BEACH, LLC—See National HealthCare Corporation; *U.S. Public*, pg. 1495
NHC HEALTHCARE/PENSACOLA, INC.—See National HealthCare Corporation; *U.S. Public*, pg. 1496
NHC HEALTHCARE/PULASKI, LLC—See National HealthCare Corporation; *U.S. Public*, pg. 1496
NHC HEALTHCARE/ROSSVILLE, LLC—See National HealthCare Corporation; *U.S. Public*, pg. 1496
NHC HEALTHCARE/SCOTT, LLC—See National HealthCare Corporation; *U.S. Public*, pg. 1496
NHC HEALTHCARE/SMITHVILLE, LLC—See National HealthCare Corporation; *U.S. Public*, pg. 1496
NHC HEALTHCARE/SOMERVILLE, LLC—See National HealthCare Corporation; *U.S. Public*, pg. 1496
NHC HEALTHCARE/SPARTA, LLC—See National HealthCare Corporation; *U.S. Public*, pg. 1496
NHC HEALTHCARE/SPRINGFIELD, LLC—See National HealthCare Corporation; *U.S. Public*, pg. 1496
NHC HEALTHCARE-SPRINGFIELD MISSOURI, LLC—See National HealthCare Corporation; *U.S. Public*, pg. 1495
NHC HEALTHCARE/ST. CHARLES, LLC—See National HealthCare Corporation; *U.S. Public*, pg. 1496
NHC HEALTHCARE-SUMNER, LLC—See National HealthCare Corporation; *U.S. Public*, pg. 1495
NHC HEALTHCARE/TOWN & COUNTRY—See National HealthCare Corporation; *U.S. Public*, pg. 1496
NHC HEALTHCARE/TULLAHOMA, LLC—See National HealthCare Corporation; *U.S. Public*, pg. 1496
NHC HOMECARE MISSOURI, LLC—See National HealthCare Corporation; *U.S. Public*, pg. 1496
NHC HOMECARE-SOUTH CAROLINA, LLC—See National HealthCare Corporation; *U.S. Public*, pg. 1496
NHC HOMECARE - SOUTH CAROLINA, LLC—See National HealthCare Corporation; *U.S. Public*, pg. 1496
NH CIGARS, LLC—See MGM Resorts International; *U.S. Public*, pg. 1435
NHCI OF HILLSBORO, INC.—See Community Health Systems, Inc.; *U.S. Public*, pg. 555
NH CITY & TOWER—See Minor International PCL; *Int'l*, pg. 4912
NH CLINICAL SERVICES, PLLC—See Nobilis Health Corp.; *U.S. Private*, pg. 2932
NHC-MAURY REGIONAL TRANSITIONAL CARE CENTER, LLC—See National HealthCare Corporation; *U.S. Public*, pg. 1496

COMPANY NAME INDEX

NH.CO NUTRITION S.A.S.—See Chiesi Farmaceutici SpA; *Int'l*, pg. 1478
NHC/OP, L.P.—See National HealthCare Corporation; *U.S. Public*, pg. 1496
NHC/OP, L.P.—See National HealthCare Corporation; *U.S. Public*, pg. 1496
NHC/OP, L.P.—See National HealthCare Corporation; *U.S. Public*, pg. 1496
NHC/OP, L.P.—See National HealthCare Corporation; *U.S. Public*, pg. 1496
NHC/OP, L.P.—See National HealthCare Corporation; *U.S. Public*, pg. 1496
NHC/OP, L.P.—See National HealthCare Corporation; *U.S. Public*, pg. 1496
NHC PLACE/ANNISTON, LLC—See National HealthCare Corporation; *U.S. Public*, pg. 1496
NHC PLACE AT THE TRACE, LLC—See National HealthCare Corporation; *U.S. Public*, pg. 1496
NHC PLACE/LAKE ST. CHARLES, LLC—See National HealthCare Corporation; *U.S. Public*, pg. 1496
NHC PLACE MERRITT ISLAND, LLC—See National HealthCare Corporation; *U.S. Public*, pg. 1496
NH DANUBE CITY—See Minor International PCL; *Int'l*, pg. 4912
NHDC LIMITED—See NHPC Ltd.; *Int'l*, pg. 5259
NH ENTERPRISES (2008) PTE. LTD.—See Blackgold Natural Resources Ltd.; *Int'l*, pg. 1061
NHF NETZGESELLSCHAFT HEILBRONN-FRANKEN MBH—See EnBW Energie Baden-Wurttemberg AG; *Int'l*, pg. 2399
NH FOODS AUSTRALIA PTY. LTD.—See NH Foods Ltd.; *Int'l*, pg. 5256
NH FOODS CHILE Y COMPANIA LIMITADA—See NH Foods Ltd.; *Int'l*, pg. 5256
NH FOODS LTD.; *Int'l*, pg. 5256
NH FOODS TAIWAN LTD.—See NH Foods Ltd.; *Int'l*, pg. 5256
NH FOODS U.K. LTD.—See NH Foods Ltd.; *Int'l*, pg. 5256
NH FUENLABRADA—See Minor International PCL; *Int'l*, pg. 4912
NH HAMBURG MITTE—See Minor International PCL; *Int'l*, pg. 4912
NHH COLTEC LTD.—See Ngai Hing Hong Co Ltd; *Int'l*, pg. 5253
NHH INTERNATIONAL TRADING LIMITED—See Ngai Hing Hong Co Ltd; *Int'l*, pg. 5253
NH HOTEL CIUTAT DE REUS, S.A.—See Minor International PCL; *Int'l*, pg. 4912
NH HOTEL DE VILLE—See Minor International PCL; *Int'l*, pg. 4912
NH HOTELES AUSTRIA, GMBH—See Minor International PCL; *Int'l*, pg. 4912
NH HOTELES DEUTSCHLAND, GMBH—See Minor International PCL; *Int'l*, pg. 4912
NH HOTELES ESPANA, S.L.—See Minor International PCL; *Int'l*, pg. 4912
NH HOTELES SWITZERLAND GMBH—See Minor International PCL; *Int'l*, pg. 4912
NH HOTEL GROUP, SA—See Minor International PCL; *Int'l*, pg. 4911
NH HOTELS USA, INC.—See Minor International PCL; *Int'l*, pg. 4912
NH HUNGARY HOTEL MANAGEMENT, LTD.—See Minor International PCL; *Int'l*, pg. 4912
NHIC, CORP.—See Veritas Capital Fund Management, LLC; *U.S. Private*, pg. 4364
NHI HIEP BRICK - TILE JOINT STOCK COMPANY; *Int'l*, pg. 5257
NH INVESTMENT & SECURITIES CO., LTD.—See NongHyup Financial Group, Inc.; *Int'l*, pg. 5414
NHI OMAN; *Int'l*, pg. 5257
NH ITALIA S.R.L.—See Intesa Sanpaolo S.p.A.; *Int'l*, pg. 3766
NH ITALIA S.R.L.—See Minor International PCL; *Int'l*, pg. 4912
NH ITALY MANAGEMENT, S.R.L.—See Minor International PCL; *Int'l*, pg. 4912
NHK ART, INC.—See Nippon Hoso Kyokai; *Int'l*, pg. 5318
NHK-ASSOCIATED SPRING SUSPENSION COMPONENTS INC.—See NHK Spring Co., Ltd.; *Int'l*, pg. 5258
NHK-ASSOCIATED SPRING SUSPENSION COMPONENTS INC.—See OEP Capital Advisors, L.P.; *U.S. Private*, pg. 2998
NHK BUSINESS SERVICES INC.—See Nippon Hoso Kyokai; *Int'l*, pg. 5318
NHK COSMOMEDIA AMERICA, INC.—See Nippon Hoso Kyokai; *Int'l*, pg. 5319
NHK COSMOMEDIA (EUROPE) LIMITED—See Nippon Hoso Kyokai; *Int'l*, pg. 5319
NHK CULTURE CENTER, INC.—See Nippon Hoso Kyokai; *Int'l*, pg. 5319
NHK EDUCATIONAL CORPORATION—See Nippon Hoso Kyokai; *Int'l*, pg. 5319
NHK ENGINEERING SYSTEM, INC.—See Nippon Hoso Kyokai; *Int'l*, pg. 5319
NHK KENSINGTON—See Minor International PCL; *Int'l*, pg. 4912
NHK ENTERPRISES, INC.—See Nippon Hoso Kyokai; *Int'l*, pg. 5319
NHK FASTENER DO BRASIL INDUSTRIA E COMERCIO LTDA.—See NHK Spring Co., Ltd.; *Int'l*, pg. 5257
NHK FLEX CO., LTD.—See NHK Spring Co., Ltd.; *Int'l*, pg. 5257
NHK GLOBAL MEDIA SERVICES, INC.—See Nippon Hoso Kyokai; *Int'l*, pg. 5319
NHK INTEGRATED TECHNOLOGY INC.—See Nippon Hoso Kyokai; *Int'l*, pg. 5319
NHK INTERNATIONAL CORP.—See NHK Spring Co., Ltd.; *Int'l*, pg. 5257
NHK INTERNATIONAL, INC.—See Nippon Hoso Kyokai; *Int'l*, pg. 5319
NHK MANUFACTURING (MALAYSIA) SDN. BHD—See NHK Spring Co., Ltd.; *Int'l*, pg. 5257
NHK MEC CORPORATION—See NHK Spring Co., Ltd.; *Int'l*, pg. 5257
NHK MEDIA TECHNOLOGY, INC.—See Nippon Hoso Kyokai; *Int'l*, pg. 5319
NHK MORSE CO., LTD.—See NHK Spring Co., Ltd.; *Int'l*, pg. 5258
NHK OF AMERICA SUSPENSION COMPONENTS INC.—See NHK Spring Co., Ltd.; *Int'l*, pg. 5258
NHK PARKING SYSTEMS CO., LTD—See NHK Spring Co., Ltd.; *Int'l*, pg. 5258
NHK PRECISION CO., LTD.—See NHK Spring Co., Ltd.; *Int'l*, pg. 5258
NHK PRECISION (THAILAND) CO., LTD.—See NHK Spring Co., Ltd.; *Int'l*, pg. 5258
NHK PROMOTIONS INC.—See Nippon Hoso Kyokai; *Int'l*, pg. 5319
NHK PUBLISHING, INC.—See Nippon Hoso Kyokai; *Int'l*, pg. 5319
NHK SALES CO., LTD.—See NHK Spring Co., Ltd.; *Int'l*, pg. 5258
NHK SEATING OF AMERICA, INC.—See Lear Corporation; *U.S. Public*, pg. 1297
NHK SEATING OF AMERICA, INC.—See NHK Spring Co., Ltd.; *Int'l*, pg. 5258
NHK SEATING OF AMERICA INC.—See NHK Spring Co., Ltd.; *Int'l*, pg. 5258
NHK SERVICE CENTER, INC.—See Nippon Hoso Kyokai; *Int'l*, pg. 5319
NHK SPRING CO., LTD.; *Int'l*, pg. 5257
NHK SPRING INDIA LTD.—See NHK Spring Co., Ltd.; *Int'l*, pg. 5258
NHK SPRING PHILIPPINES, INC.—See NHK Spring Co., Ltd.; *Int'l*, pg. 5258
NHK SPRING PRECISION (GUANGZHOU) CO., LTD.—See NHK Spring Co., Ltd.; *Int'l*, pg. 5258
NHK SPRING PRECISION OF AMERICA INC.—See NHK Spring Co., Ltd.; *Int'l*, pg. 5258
NHK SPRING PRODUCTION COMPANY—See NHK Spring Co., Ltd.; *Int'l*, pg. 5258
NHK SPRING R&D CENTER, INC.—See NHK Spring Co., Ltd.; *Int'l*, pg. 5258
NHK SPRING (THAILAND) CO., LTD.—See NHK Spring Co., Ltd.; *Int'l*, pg. 5258
NHK TRANSPORT CO., LTD.—See NHK Spring Co., Ltd.; *Int'l*, pg. 5258
NHK-UNI SPRING (GUANGZHOU) CO., LTD.—See NHK Spring Co., Ltd.; *Int'l*, pg. 5258
NHK WORLD RADIO JAPAN—See Nippon Hoso Kyokai; *Int'l*, pg. 5319
NHK WORLD TV—See Nippon Hoso Kyokai; *Int'l*, pg. 5319
NH LAS PALMAS, S.A.—See Minor International PCL; *Int'l*, pg. 4912
NH LEARNING SOLUTIONS CORPORATION—See Camden Partners Holdings, LLC; *U.S. Private*, pg. 728
NHL NETZGESELLSCHAFT HEILBRONER LAND GMBH & CO. KG—See EnBW Energie Baden-Wurttemberg AG; *Int'l*, pg. 2399
NH LOGRONO, S.A.—See Minor International PCL; *Int'l*, pg. 4912
NH LUXEMBOURG—See Minor International PCL; *Int'l*, pg. 4912
NH MALAGA—See Minor International PCL; *Int'l*, pg. 4912
NHM BRUGES NV—See Group de Cloedt SA; *Int'l*, pg. 3088
NHM NIEUWPOORT NV—See Group de Cloedt SA; *Int'l*, pg. 3088
NHN BIGFOOT CORP.—See NHN Corp.; *Int'l*, pg. 5258
NHN BUGS CORPORATION—See NEOWIZ Holdings Corporation; *Int'l*, pg. 5198
NHN CHINA CORPORATION—See NAVER Corporation; *Int'l*, pg. 5174
NHN CORP.; *Int'l*, pg. 5258
NHN KCP CORP.; *Int'l*, pg. 5258
NHN TICKETLINK CORPORATION—See NHN Corp.; *Int'l*, pg. 5258
NHONG SHIM KELLOGG CO. LTD.—See Kellanova; *U.S. Public*, pg. 1218
NHON TRACH INVESTMENT JOINT STOCK COMPANY—See Tin Nghia Corp.; *Int'l*, pg. 7752
NHOW MILANO—See Minor International PCL; *Int'l*, pg. 4912
NHPC LTD.; *Int'l*, pg. 5258
NHP ELECTRICAL ENGINEERING PRODUCTS (NZ) LTD.—See TERASAKI ELECTRIC CO.,LTD; *Int'l*, pg. 7564
NHP PRODUCTION IMPORT - EXPORT JSC; *Int'l*, pg. 5258
NH PRIME REIT CO., LTD.; *Int'l*, pg. 5257
NH RALLYE PORTUGAL LDA.—See Minor International PCL; *Int'l*, pg. 4912
NHR, LLC; *U.S. Private*, pg. 2924
NH SANTA FE—See Minor International PCL; *Int'l*, pg. 4912
NH SANTO STEFANO—See Minor International PCL; *Int'l*, pg. 4912
NH SANTS BARCELONA—See Minor International PCL; *Int'l*, pg. 4912
N.H. SCHEPPERS DISTRIBUTING CO; *U.S. Private*, pg. 2828
NH-SENKO LOGISTICS CO., LTD.—See Senko Group Holdings Co., Ltd.; *Int'l*, pg. 6710
NHS HUMAN SERVICES, INC.; *U.S. Private*, pg. 2924
NH SL SPECIAL PURPOSE ACQUISITION CO., LTD.; *Int'l*, pg. 5257
NHS MANAGEMENT, LLC.; *U.S. Private*, pg. 2924
NH SPECIAL PURPOSE ACQUISITION 7 CO., LTD.; *Int'l*, pg. 5257
NHS SHARED BUSINESS SERVICES LIMITED—See Sopra Steria Group S.A.; *Int'l*, pg. 7110
NHST MEDIA GROUP AS—See Fred. Olsen & Co.; *Int'l*, pg. 2768
N.H. STONE INC.; *U.S. Private*, pg. 2828
NHTC GLOBAL SINGAPORE PTE. LTD.—See Natural Health Trends Corp.; *Int'l*, pg. 5168
NH TECHNOLOGY GMBH—See C C P Contact Probes Co., Ltd.; *Int'l*, pg. 1237
NHT GLOBAL HONG KONG LIMITED—See Natural Health Trends Corp.; *Int'l*, pg. 5168
NHT GLOBAL INC.—See Natural Health Trends Corp.; *Int'l*, pg. 5168
NH THE NETHERLANDS, B.V.—See Minor International PCL; *Int'l*, pg. 4912
NH TIMISOARA—See Minor International PCL; *Int'l*, pg. 4912
NHTK LTD.—See Natural Health Trends Corp.; *Int'l*, pg. 5168
NH TORTONA, SRL.—See Minor International PCL; *Int'l*, pg. 4912
NHU EUROPE GMBH—See Zhejiang NHU Company Ltd.; *Int'l*, pg. 8661
NHULUNBUY CORPORATION LIMITED—See Rio Tinto plc; *Int'l*, pg. 6346
NHUMO, S.A.P.I. DE C.V.—See Cabot Corporation; *U.S. Public*, pg. 417
NHV ACCELERATOR TECHNOLOGIES SHANGHAI CO., LTD.—See Sumitomo Electric Industries, Ltd.; *Int'l*, pg. 7278
NHV AMERICA INC.—See Sumitomo Electric Industries, Ltd.; *Int'l*, pg. 7278
NH WAALWIJK—See Minor International PCL; *Int'l*, pg. 4912
N.H. YATES & CO., INC.; *U.S. Private*, pg. 2828
NIACC-AVITECH TECHNOLOGIES INC.—See HEICO Corporation; *U.S. Public*, pg. 1020
NIACET B.V.—See Kerry Group plc; *Int'l*, pg. 4139
NIACET CORPORATION—See Kerry Group plc; *Int'l*, pg. 4139
NIAFLEX CORPORATION—See Inteplast Group, Ltd.; *U.S. Private*, pg. 2106
NIAGARA BLOWER COMPANY—See Alfa Laval AB; *Int'l*, pg. 309
NIAGARA CONSERVATION CORPORATION; *U.S. Private*, pg. 2924
NIAGARA CUTTER, INC.; *U.S. Private*, pg. 2924
NIAGARA FALLS MEMORIAL MEDICAL CENTER; *U.S. Private*, pg. 2924
NIAGARA FRONTIER TRANSIT & METRO SYSTEM—See Niagara Frontier Transportation Authority; *U.S. Private*, pg. 2924
NIAGARA FRONTIER TRANSPORTATION AUTHORITY; *U.S. Private*, pg. 2924
NIAGARA LASALLE CORPORATION - BUFFALO PLANT—See Optima Specialty Steel, Inc.; *U.S. Private*, pg. 3034
NIAGARA LASALLE CORPORATION—See Optima Specialty Steel, Inc.; *U.S. Private*, pg. 3034
NIAGARA LASALLE CORPORATION - WARREN PLANT—See Optima Specialty Steel, Inc.; *U.S. Private*, pg. 3034
NIAGARA-LOCKPORT ENTERPRISES INC.—See Supermarket Management Inc.; *U.S. Private*, pg. 3881
NIAGARA MOTORS LTD; *Int'l*, pg. 5259
NIAGARASTEEL—See Canerector Inc.; *Int'l*, pg. 1290
NIAGARA STRUCTURAL STEEL—See Canerector Inc.; *Int'l*, pg. 1290
NIAGARA THERAPY; *Int'l*, pg. 5259
NIAGARA TRANSFORMER CORP.; *U.S. Private*, pg. 2924

NIAGARA VENTURES CORPORATION

NIAGARA VENTURES CORPORATION; *Int'l*, pg. 5259
NIANDC NETSYSTEM INC.—See International Business Machines Corporation; *U.S. Public*, pg. 1147
NIANDC NETSYSTEM INC.—See Nippon Telegraph & Telephone Corporation; *Int'l*, pg. 5354
NIANDC PARTNERS INC.—See Nippon Telegraph & Telephone Corporation; *Int'l*, pg. 5343
NIANDC SOFT INC.—See International Business Machines Corporation; *U.S. Public*, pg. 1147
NIANDC SOFT INC.—See Nippon Telegraph & Telephone Corporation; *Int'l*, pg. 5354
NIANTIC, INC.; *U.S. Private*, pg. 2924
NIANTIC SEAL INC.—See INSCO, Inc.; *U.S. Private*, pg. 2085
NIASA MEXICO, S. A. DE C. V.—See Grupo Lamosa S.A. de C.V.; *Int'l*, pg. 3132
NIBANKOHBOH PRODUCTIONS CORP.—See Tohokushinsha Film Corporation; *Int'l*, pg. 7777
NIBBI BROTHERS; *U.S. Private*, pg. 2924
NIBC BANK N.V. - BRUSSELLS OFFICE—See Blackstone Inc.; *U.S. Public*, pg. 356
NIBC BANK N.V. - LONDON OFFICE—See Blackstone Inc.; *U.S. Public*, pg. 356
NIBC BANK N.V.—See Blackstone Inc.; *U.S. Public*, pg. 356
NIBC HOLDING N.V.—See Blackstone Inc.; *U.S. Public*, pg. 356
NIBC MARKETS N.V.—See Blackstone Inc.; *U.S. Public*, pg. 356
NIBCO INC. - LEBANON PLANT—See NIBCO Inc.; *U.S. Private*, pg. 2924
NIBCO INC.; *U.S. Private*, pg. 2924
NIBCO SP. Z O.O.—See NIBCO Inc.; *U.S. Private*, pg. 2924
NIBE AB—See NIBE Industrier AB; *Int'l*, pg. 5261
NIBE AIRSITE AB—See NIBE Industrier AB; *Int'l*, pg. 5261
NIBE-BIAWAR SP. Z.O.O.—See NIBE Industrier AB; *Int'l*, pg. 5262
NIBEC CO., LTD.; *Int'l*, pg. 5263
NIBE ELEMENT—See NIBE Industrier AB; *Int'l*, pg. 5261
NIBE ENERGIETECHNIEK B.V.—See NIBE Industrier AB; *Int'l*, pg. 5261
NIBE ENERGY SYSTEMS FRANCE SAS—See NIBE Industrier AB; *Int'l*, pg. 5261
NIBE ENERGY SYSTEMS LIMITED—See NIBE Industrier AB; *Int'l*, pg. 5261
NIBE ENERGY SYSTEMS OY—See NIBE Industrier AB; *Int'l*, pg. 5261
NIBE FOYERS FRANCE S.A.S.—See NIBE Industrier AB; *Int'l*, pg. 5261
NIBE INDUSTRIER AB - NIBE WIND COMPONENTS DIVISION—See NIBE Industrier AB; *Int'l*, pg. 5261
NIBE INDUSTRIER AB; *Int'l*, pg. 5259
NIBE STOVES—See NIBE Industrier AB; *Int'l*, pg. 5261
NIBE SYSTEMTECHNIK GMBH—See NIBE Industrier AB; *Int'l*, pg. 5261
NIBE WARMETECHNIK AG—See NIBE Industrier AB; *Int'l*, pg. 5261
NIBL ACE CAPITAL LTD.—See Nepal Investment Mega Bank Limited; *Int'l*, pg. 5199
NIBLOCK (BUILDERS) LTD.; *Int'l*, pg. 5263
NIBLOCK DEVELOPMENT CORP.; *U.S. Private*, pg. 2924
NIBLOCK EXCAVATING INC.; *U.S. Private*, pg. 2924
NIBONG TEBAL ENTERPRISE SENDIRIAN BERHAD—See NTPM Holdings Berhad; *Int'l*, pg. 5484
NIBONG TEBAL PAPER MILL SDN. BHD.—See NTPM Holdings Berhad; *Int'l*, pg. 5484
NIBONG TEBAL TECHNOLOGY SDN. BHD.—See NTPM Holdings Berhad; *Int'l*, pg. 5484
NIBSA SA; *Int'l*, pg. 5263
NIC 15 KIRKWOOD CORNERS LEASING LLC—See Ventas, Inc.; *U.S. Public*, pg. 2278
NIC 15 PINES OF NEW MARKET LEASING LLC—See Ventas, Inc.; *U.S. Public*, pg. 2278
NIC 20 GRAND VIEW LEASING LLC—See Ventas, Inc.; *U.S. Public*, pg. 2278
NICARAGUA SUGAR ESTATES LIMITED; *Int'l*, pg. 5263
NIC ASIA BANK LIMITED; *Int'l*, pg. 5263
NIC AUTOTEC, INC.; *Int'l*, pg. 5263
NIC AUTOTEC (THAILAND) CO., LTD.—See NIC Autotec, Inc.; *Int'l*, pg. 5263
NICCA CHEMICAL (CHINA) CO., LTD.—See Nicca Chemical Co., Ltd.; *Int'l*, pg. 5263
NICCA CHEMICAL CO., LTD. - KANTO FACTORY—See Nicca Chemical Co., Ltd.; *Int'l*, pg. 5264
NICCA CHEMICAL CO., LTD. - KASHIMA FACTORY—See Nicca Chemical Co., Ltd.; *Int'l*, pg. 5264
NICCA CHEMICAL CO., LTD - SABAE FACTORY—See Nicca Chemical Co., Ltd.; *Int'l*, pg. 5264
NICCA CHEMICAL CO., LTD.; *Int'l*, pg. 5263
NICCA CHEMICAL RESEARCH & DEVELOPMENT CENTER (SHANGHAI) CO., LTD.—See Nicca Chemical Co., Ltd.; *Int'l*, pg. 5264
NICCA KOREA CO., LTD. - DAEGU FACTORY—See Nicca Chemical Co., Ltd.; *Int'l*, pg. 5264
NICCA KOREA CO., LTD.—See Nicca Chemical Co., Ltd.; *Int'l*, pg. 5264
NICCA U.S.A., INC.—See Nicca Chemical Co., Ltd.; *Int'l*, pg. 5264

NICCA VIETNAM CO., LTD.—See Nicca Chemical Co., Ltd.; *Int'l*, pg. 5264
NICCO CORPORATION LTD. - BARIPADA WORKS—See Nicco Corporation Ltd.; *Int'l*, pg. 5264
NICCO CORPORATION LTD.; *Int'l*, pg. 5264
N. I. C CO., LTD.—See Inabata & Co. Ltd.; *Int'l*, pg. 3644
NIC COMPONENTS ASIA PTE LTD.—See Arrow Electronics, Inc.; *U.S. Public*, pg. 199
NIC COMPONENTS CORP.—See Arrow Electronics, Inc.; *U.S. Public*, pg. 199
NICCO PARKS & RESORTS LIMITED; *Int'l*, pg. 5264
NICCO UCO ALLIANCE CREDIT LIMITED; *Int'l*, pg. 5264
NICDC LOGISTICS DATA SERVICES LIMITED—See NEC Corporation; *Int'l*, pg. 5186
NICE ACTIMIZE, INC.—See NICE Ltd.; *Int'l*, pg. 5265
N*ICE AIRCRAFT SERVICE & SUPPORTS GMBH—See Fraport AG; *Int'l*, pg. 2764
NICE APAC LTD.—See NICE Ltd.; *Int'l*, pg. 5265
NICE-BAG INTERNATIONAL INDUSTRIES CO., LTD.—See WW Holding Inc; *Int'l*, pg. 8516
NICE BALL BEARINGS INC.—See RBC Bearings Incorporated; *U.S. Public*, pg. 1766
NICE-BUSINESS CONSULTING OY—See Fujitsu Limited; *Int'l*, pg. 2837
NICE-BUSINESS CONSULTING OY—See Nokia Corporation; *Int'l*, pg. 5404
NICE-BUSINESS SOLUTIONS - BRIGHTON—See Fujitsu Limited; *Int'l*, pg. 2837
NICE-BUSINESS SOLUTIONS - BRIGHTON—See Nokia Corporation; *Int'l*, pg. 5404
NICE-BUSINESS SOLUTIONS FINLAND OY—See Fujitsu Limited; *Int'l*, pg. 2837
NICE-BUSINESS SOLUTIONS FINLAND OY—See Nokia Corporation; *Int'l*, pg. 5404
NICE CASH MANAGEMENT & SECURITY CO., LTD.—See NICE Holdings Co., Ltd.; *Int'l*, pg. 5265
NICE CLAUP CO., LTD.—See PAL GROUP Holdings Co., Ltd.; *Int'l*, pg. 5705
NICE COMBINET CO., LTD.—See NICE Holdings Co., Ltd.; *Int'l*, pg. 5265
NICE CORPORATION; *Int'l*, pg. 5264
NICE CTI SYSTEMS UK LTD.—See NICE Ltd.; *Int'l*, pg. 5265
NICE-DATA INC.—See NICE Holdings Co., Ltd.; *Int'l*, pg. 5265
NICE D&B CO., LTD.; *Int'l*, pg. 5264
NICE DYEING FACTORY (MACAO COMMERCIAL OFFSHORE) LIMITED—See Texwinca Holdings Limited; *Int'l*, pg. 7584
NICE GROUP S.P.A.; *Int'l*, pg. 5264
NICE HOLDINGS CO., LTD.; *Int'l*, pg. 5264
NICE INFORMATION SERVICE CO., LTD.; *Int'l*, pg. 5265
NICE INFORMATION & TELECOMMUNICATION, INC.; *Int'l*, pg. 5265
NICE INTERACTIVE SOLUTIONS INDIA PVT LTD.—See NICE Ltd.; *Int'l*, pg. 5265
NICE INTERNATIONAL AMERICA CORPORATION—See Nice Corporation; *Int'l*, pg. 5264
NICE INTERNATIONAL CANADA CORPORATION—See Nice Corporation; *Int'l*, pg. 5264
NICE INVEST NORDIC AB—See Intrum AB; *Int'l*, pg. 3771
NICE INVESTORS SERVICE CO. LTD.—See NICE Holdings Co., Ltd.; *Int'l*, pg. 5265
NICE JAPAN LTD.—See NICE Ltd.; *Int'l*, pg. 5265
NICE LTD.; *Int'l*, pg. 5265
NICE PAK INTERNATIONAL LTD.—See Nice-Pak Products, Inc.; *U.S. Private*, pg. 2925
NICE-PAK PRODUCTS, INC.; *U.S. Private*, pg. 2925
NICE PAYMENTS CO., LTD.—See NICE Information & Telecommunication, Inc.; *Int'l*, pg. 5265
NICE PRICING & INFORMATION INC.—See NICE Holdings Co., Ltd.; *Int'l*, pg. 5265
NICERA AMERICA CORP.—See Nippon Ceramic Co., Ltd.; *Int'l*, pg. 5312
NICERA EUROPEAN WORKS LTD.—See Nippon Ceramic Co., Ltd.; *Int'l*, pg. 5312
NICERA HONG KONG LTD.—See Nihon Kohden Corporation; *Int'l*, pg. 5285
NICERA PHILIPPINES INC.—See Nippon Ceramic Co., Ltd.; *Int'l*, pg. 5312
NICE RIKA BIOTECHNOLOGIES SDN. BHD.—See New Japan Chemical Co., Ltd.; *Int'l*, pg. 5225
NICE SHOES, LLC; *U.S. Private*, pg. 2925
NICE SKYLINE SDN BHD—See IOI Corporation Berhad; *Int'l*, pg. 3792
NICE S.P.A.—See NIce Group S.p.A.; *Int'l*, pg. 5264
NICE SWITZERLAND AG—See NICE Ltd.; *Int'l*, pg. 5265
NICE SYSTEMS AUSTRALIA PTY LTD.—See NICE Ltd.; *Int'l*, pg. 5265
NICE SYSTEMS GMBH—See NICE Ltd.; *Int'l*, pg. 5265
NICE SYSTEMS INC.—See NICE Ltd.; *Int'l*, pg. 5265
NICE SYSTEMS (SINGAPORE) PTE. LTD.—See NICE Ltd.; *Int'l*, pg. 5265
NICE TOTAL CASH MANAGEMENT CO., LTD.; *Int'l*, pg. 5265
NICEVILLE FAMILY PRACTICE, LLC—See HCA Healthcare, Inc.; *U.S. Public*, pg. 1004
NIC FREIGHT CO., LTD.—See Dynic Corporation; *Int'l*, pg. 2243

NIC GLOBAL MANUFACTURING SOLUTIONS, INC.; *U.S. Private*, pg. 2925
NIC GROUP PLC; *Int'l*, pg. 5263
NICHE CAPITAL EMAS HOLDINGS BERHAD; *Int'l*, pg. 5266
NICHE GENERICS LIMITED—See Ipca Laboratories Ltd.; *Int'l*, pg. 3796
NICHEL LEGHE SPA—See CRONIMET Holding GmbH; *Int'l*, pg. 1855
NICHE LOGISTICS PTY. LTD.—See Singapore Post Limited; *Int'l*, pg. 6942
NI CHEMICAL CORPORATION—See Sojitz Corporation; *Int'l*, pg. 7062
NICHENETMARKETING PLC; *Int'l*, pg. 5266
NICHE PRODUCTIONS, LLC—See Lions Gate Entertainment Corp.; *Int'l*, pg. 4521
NICHE RETAIL, LLC; *U.S. Private*, pg. 2925
NICHE-TECH GROUP LTD. - SHANTOU FACTORY—See Niche-Tech Semiconductor Materials Limited; *Int'l*, pg. 5266
NICHE-TECH SEMICONDUCTOR MATERIALS LIMITED; *Int'l*, pg. 5266
NICHIA AMERICA CORPORATION—See Nichia Corporation; *Int'l*, pg. 5266
NICHIA CHEMICAL EUROPE GMBH—See Nichia Corporation; *Int'l*, pg. 5266
NICHIA CHEMICAL HONG KONG., LTD.—See Nichia Corporation; *Int'l*, pg. 5266
NICHIA CHEMICAL (INDIA) PVT. LTD.—See Nichia Corporation; *Int'l*, pg. 5266
NICHIA CHEMICAL PTE LTD—See Nichia Corporation; *Int'l*, pg. 5266
NICHIA CHEMICAL (THAILAND) CO., LTD.—See Nichia Corporation; *Int'l*, pg. 5266
NICHIA CORPORATION - A-PLANT—See Nichia Corporation; *Int'l*, pg. 5266
NICHIA CORPORATION - K-PLANT—See Nichia Corporation; *Int'l*, pg. 5266
NICHIA CORPORATION - N-PLANT—See Nichia Corporation; *Int'l*, pg. 5266
NICHIA CORPORATION; *Int'l*, pg. 5266
NICHIA CORPORATION - TN-PLANT—See Nichia Corporation; *Int'l*, pg. 5266
NICHIA CORPORATION - TS-PLANT—See Nichia Corporation; *Int'l*, pg. 5266
NICHIA CORPORATION - V-PLANT—See Nichia Corporation; *Int'l*, pg. 5266
NICHIA EUROPE B.V.—See Nichia Corporation; *Int'l*, pg. 5266
NICHIA KOREA CORPORATION—See Nichia Corporation; *Int'l*, pg. 5266
NICHIALLOY CO., LTD.—See Aisan Industry Co., Ltd.; *Int'l*, pg. 251
NICHIA PHARMACEUTICAL INDUSTRIES LTD.—See Shionogi & Co., Ltd.; *Int'l*, pg. 6851
NICHIA RUS LLC—See Nichia Corporation; *Int'l*, pg. 5266
NICHIAS AUTOPARTS EUROPE A.S.—See Nichias Corporation; *Int'l*, pg. 5267
NICHIAS AUTOPARTS EUROPE GMBH—See Nichias Corporation; *Int'l*, pg. 5267
NICHIAS CORPORATION; *Int'l*, pg. 5267
NICHIAS CZECH, S.R.O.—See Nichias Corporation; *Int'l*, pg. 5267
NICHIAS FGS SDN. BHD.—See Nichias Corporation; *Int'l*, pg. 5267
NICHIA SHANGHAI CORPORATION—See Nichia Corporation; *Int'l*, pg. 5266
NICHIAS INDUSTRIAL PRODUCTS PVT. LTD.—See Nichias Corporation; *Int'l*, pg. 5267
NICHIAS SEALTECH CORPORATION—See Nichias Corporation; *Int'l*, pg. 5267
NICHIAS (SHANGHAI) AUTOPARTS TRADING CO., LTD.—See Nichias Corporation; *Int'l*, pg. 5267
NICHIAS (SHANGHAI) TRADING CO., LTD.—See Nichias Corporation; *Int'l*, pg. 5267
NICHIAS SINGAPORE PTE. LTD.—See Nichias Corporation; *Int'l*, pg. 5267
NICHIAS SOUTHEAST ASIA SDN. BHD.—See Nichias Corporation; *Int'l*, pg. 5267
NICHIA STEEL WORKS CO., LTD.; *Int'l*, pg. 5266
NICHIAS (THAILAND) CO., LTD.—See Nichias Corporation; *Int'l*, pg. 5267
NICHIAS VIETNAM CO., LTD.—See Nichias Corporation; *Int'l*, pg. 5267
NICHIA TAIWAN CORPORATION—See Nichia Corporation; *Int'l*, pg. 5266
NICHIBAN CO., LTD.; *Int'l*, pg. 5267
NICHIBAN PRINT CORPORATION—See Nichiban Co., Ltd.; *Int'l*, pg. 5267
NICHICON (AMERICA) CORP.—See NICHICON CORPORATION; *Int'l*, pg. 5267
NICHICON (AUSTRIA) GMBH—See NICHICON CORPORATION; *Int'l*, pg. 5267
NICHICON CORPORATION - NAGANO FACTORY—See NICHICON CORPORATION; *Int'l*, pg. 5268
NICHICON CORPORATION - OHMACHI FACTORY—See NICHICON CORPORATION; *Int'l*, pg. 5268

COMPANY NAME INDEX

NICHICON CORPORATION - POWER SUPPLY DIVISION—See NICHICON CORPORATION; *Int'l*, pg. 5268
NICHICON CORPORATION; *Int'l*, pg. 5267
NICHICON CORPORATION - TOMITA FACTORY—See NICHICON CORPORATION; *Int'l*, pg. 5268
NICHICON ELECTRONICS (SUQIAN) CO., LTD.—See NICHICON CORPORATION; *Int'l*, pg. 5268
NICHICON ELECTRONICS (TIANJIN) CO., LTD.—See NICHICON CORPORATION; *Int'l*, pg. 5268
NICHICON ELECTRONICS TRADING (SHANGHAI) CO., LTD.—See NICHICON CORPORATION; *Int'l*, pg. 5268
NICHICON ELECTRONICS TRADING (SHENZHEN) CO., LTD.—See NICHICON CORPORATION; *Int'l*, pg. 5268
NICHICON ELECTRONICS (WUXI) CO. LTD.—See NICHICON CORPORATION; *Int'l*, pg. 5268
NICHICON EUROPE B.V.—See Nippon Concept Corporation; *Int'l*, pg. 5313
NICHICON (FUKUI) CORPORATION—See NICHICON CORPORATION; *Int'l*, pg. 5267
NICHICON HI-TECH FOIL CORPORATION—See NICHICON CORPORATION; *Int'l*, pg. 5268
NICHICON (HONG KONG) LTD.—See NICHICON CORPORATION; *Int'l*, pg. 5267
NICHICON (IWATE) CORPORATION—See NICHICON CORPORATION; *Int'l*, pg. 5268
NICHICON (KAMEOKA) CORPORATION—See NICHICON CORPORATION; *Int'l*, pg. 5268
NICHICON (KUSATSU) CORPORATION—See NICHICON CORPORATION; *Int'l*, pg. 5268
NICHICON (MALAYSIA) SDN. BHD.—See NICHICON CORPORATION; *Int'l*, pg. 5268
NICHICON (OHNO) CORPORATION—See NICHICON CORPORATION; *Int'l*, pg. 5268
NICHICON (SINGAPORE) PTE. LTD.—See NICHICON CORPORATION; *Int'l*, pg. 5268
NICHICON (TAIWAN) CO., LTD.—See NICHICON CORPORATION; *Int'l*, pg. 5268
NICHICON TANTALUM CORPORATION—See NICHICON CORPORATION; *Int'l*, pg. 5268
NICHICON (THAILAND) CO., LTD.—See NICHICON CORPORATION; *Int'l*, pg. 5268
NICHICON UK LIMITED—See Nippon Concept Corporation; *Int'l*, pg. 5313
NICHICON (WAKASA) CORPORATION—See NICHICON CORPORATION; *Int'l*, pg. 5268
NICHIDAI CORPORATION; *Int'l*, pg. 5268
NICHIDAI CORPORATION - UJITAWARA FACTORY—See NICHIDAI CORPORATION; *Int'l*, pg. 5268
NICHIDAI (THAILAND) LTD.—See Mitsubishi Heavy Industries, Ltd.; *Int'l*, pg. 4960
NICHIDAI U.S.A. CORPORATION—See NICHIDAI CORPORATION; *Int'l*, pg. 5268
NICHIDAN CO., LTD.—See Rengo Co., Ltd.; *Int'l*, pg. 6280
NICHIDENBO CORPORATION; *Int'l*, pg. 5268
NICHIDENBO (SHENZHEN) TRADING CO., LTD.—See Nichidenbo Corporation; *Int'l*, pg. 5268
NICHIDEN CORPORATION; *Int'l*, pg. 5268
NICHIDENKOGYO CO., LTD.—See The Chugoku Electric Power Co., Inc.; *Int'l*, pg. 7632
NICHIDEN (SHANGHAI) CO., LTD.—See NICHIDEN Corporation; *Int'l*, pg. 5268
NICHIDEN (THAILAND) CO., LTD.—See NICHIDEN Corporation; *Int'l*, pg. 5268
NICHIDEN TRADING (THAILAND) CO., LTD.—See NICHIDEN Corporation; *Int'l*, pg. 5268
NICHIDEN USA CORPORATION—See NICHIDEN Corporation; *Int'l*, pg. 5268
NICHIDEN VIETNAM CO., LTD.—See NICHIDEN Corporation; *Int'l*, pg. 5268
NICHIEI ELECTRONICS CORP.—See Nippon Chemi-Con Corporation; *Int'l*, pg. 5312
NICHIEI KOUN CO., LTD.—See Senko Group Holdings Co., Ltd.; *Int'l*, pg. 6710
NICHIEI PRINTING CO., LTD.—See Takeda iP Holdings Co.,Ltd.; *Int'l*, pg. 7437
NICHIEI SANGYO CO., LTD.—See Sumitomo Chemical Company, Limited; *Int'l*, pg. 7267
NICHIEI SHIKOU CO., LTD.—See Tomoku Co., Ltd.; *Int'l*, pg. 7801
NICHIEI-TOKAI CO., LTD.—See TOHOKU CHEMICAL CO., LTD.; *Int'l*, pg. 7777
NICHIE-KOSAN CO., LTD.—See Kowa Co., Ltd.; *Int'l*, pg. 4294
NICHIFU AMERICA, INC.—See Nichifu Company Ltd.; *Int'l*, pg. 5269
NICHIFU COMPANY LTD.; *Int'l*, pg. 5269
NICHIFU EUROPE B.V.—See Nichifu Company Ltd.; *Int'l*, pg. 5269
NICHIFUKU CO., LTD.—See Nippon Sheet Glass Co. Ltd.; *Int'l*, pg. 5331
NICHIFU SINGAPORE PTE LTD.—See Nichifu Company Ltd.; *Int'l*, pg. 5269
NICHIGAS BUTSURYUKEISANCENTER CO., LTD.—See Nippon Gas Co., Ltd.; *Int'l*, pg. 5318
NICHIHA CORPORATION; *Int'l*, pg. 5269
NICHIHA MATEX CO., LTD.—See Nichiha Corporation; *Int'l*, pg. 5269

NICHIHA USA, INC.—See Nichiha Corporation; *Int'l*, pg. 5269
NICHII CARENET CO., LTD.—See Bain Capital, LP; *U.S. Private*, pg. 442
NICHII CAREPALACE CAMPANY—See Bain Capital, LP; *U.S. Private*, pg. 442
NICHIIGAKKAN CO., LTD.—See Bain Capital, LP; *U.S. Private*, pg. 442
NICHII GREEN FARM COMPANY—See Bain Capital, LP; *U.S. Private*, pg. 442
NICHI-IKO GIFU PLANT CO., LTD.—See Nichi-Iko Pharmaceutical Co., Ltd.; *Int'l*, pg. 5266
NICHI-IKO PHARMACEUTICAL CO., LTD. - AICHI PLANT—See Nichi-Iko Pharmaceutical Co., Ltd.; *Int'l*, pg. 5266
NICHI-IKO PHARMACEUTICAL CO., LTD. - SAITAMA PLANT—See Nichi-Iko Pharmaceutical Co., Ltd.; *Int'l*, pg. 5266
NICHI-IKO PHARMACEUTICAL CO., LTD.; *Int'l*, pg. 5266
NICHI-IKO PHARMACEUTICAL CO., LTD. - TOYAMA PLANT 1—See Nichi-Iko Pharmaceutical Co., Ltd.; *Int'l*, pg. 5266
NICHI-IKO PHARMACEUTICAL CO., LTD. - TOYAMA PLANT 2—See Nichi-Iko Pharmaceutical Co., Ltd.; *Int'l*, pg. 5266
NICHI-IKO PHARMACEUTICAL CO., LTD. - YAMAGATA PLANT—See Nichi-Iko Pharmaceutical Co., Ltd.; *Int'l*, pg. 5266
NICHI-IKO (THAILAND) CO., LTD.—See Nichi-Iko Pharmaceutical Co., Ltd.; *Int'l*, pg. 5266
NICHIJO CORPORATION—See Kawasaki Heavy Industries, Ltd.; *Int'l*, pg. 4098
NICHIJO MANUFACTURING CO., LTD.—See Kawasaki Heavy Industries, Ltd.; *Int'l*, pg. 4098
NICHIKURE CO., LTD.—See Nihonwasou Holdings, Inc.; *Int'l*, pg. 5288
NICHIMO BIOTICS CO., LTD.—See NICHIMO CO. LTD.; *Int'l*, pg. 5269
NICHIMO CO. LTD.; *Int'l*, pg. 5269
NICHIMO FOODS CO., LTD.—See NICHIMO CO. LTD.; *Int'l*, pg. 5269
NICHIMOKU SANGYOU LTD.—See Hitachi, Ltd.; *Int'l*, pg. 3423
NICHIMO LOGISTICS CO., LTD.—See NICHIMO CO. LTD.; *Int'l*, pg. 5269
NICHIMO MARICULTURE CO., LTD.—See NICHIMO CO. LTD.; *Int'l*, pg. 5269
NICHINAN CO., LTD.—See Hakuten Corporation; *Int'l*, pg. 3222
NICHINAN NOK CORPORATION—See NOK Corporation; *Int'l*, pg. 5402
NICHING INDUSTRIAL CORP.; *Int'l*, pg. 5269
NICHINO AMERICA INC.—See Adeka Corporation; *Int'l*, pg. 142
NICHINO CHEMICAL INDIA PVT. LTD.—See Adeka Corporation; *Int'l*, pg. 142
NICHINO EUROPE CO., LTD.—See Adeka Corporation; *Int'l*, pg. 142
NICHINOH SEIKEN CO., LTD.—See Yamazaki Baking Co. Ltd.; *Int'l*, pg. 8556
NICHINO INDIA PVT. LTD.—See Adeka Corporation; *Int'l*, pg. 142
NICHINO RYOKKA CO., LTD.—See Adeka Corporation; *Int'l*, pg. 142
NICHINO SERVICE CO., LTD.—See Adeka Corporation; *Int'l*, pg. 142
NICHION, INC—See TBS Holdings, Inc.; *Int'l*, pg. 7481
NICHIPAC CO., LTD.—See Sojitz Corporation; *Int'l*, pg. 7062
NICHIRAKU MACHINERY CO., LTD.—See MEGMILK SNOW BRAND Co., Ltd.; *Int'l*, pg. 4796
NICHIREI AUSTRALIA PTY. LTD.—See Nichirei Corporation; *Int'l*, pg. 5269
NICHIREI AUSTRALIA PTY—See Nichirei Corporation; *Int'l*, pg. 5269
NICHIREI CORPORATION SHANGHAI LTD.—See Nichirei Corporation; *Int'l*, pg. 5269
NICHIREI CORPORATION; *Int'l*, pg. 5269
NICHIREI DO BRASIL AGRICOLA LTDA.—See Nichirei Corporation; *Int'l*, pg. 5270
NICHIREI FOODS INC. - FUNABASHI FACTORY—See Nichirei Corporation; *Int'l*, pg. 5269
NICHIREI FOODS INC. - SHIROISHI FACTORY—See Nichirei Corporation; *Int'l*, pg. 5269
NICHIREI FOODS INC.—See Nichirei Corporation; *Int'l*, pg. 5269
NICHIREI FOODS U.S.A., INC.—See Nichirei Corporation; *Int'l*, pg. 5269
NICHIREI FRESH HONG KONG, LTD.—See Nichirei Corporation; *Int'l*, pg. 5269
NICHIREI FRESH INC.—See Nichirei Corporation; *Int'l*, pg. 5269
NICHIREI FRESH VIETNAM CO., LTD.—See Nichirei Corporation; *Int'l*, pg. 5269
NICHIREI HOLDING HOLLAND B.V.—See Nichirei Corporation; *Int'l*, pg. 5270
NICHIREI LOGISTICS CHUSHIKOKU INC.—See Nichirei Corporation; *Int'l*, pg. 5270

NICHIREI LOGISTICS ENGINEERING INC.—See Nichirei Corporation; *Int'l*, pg. 5270
NICHIREI LOGISTICS GROUP INC.—See Nichirei Corporation; *Int'l*, pg. 5270
NICHIREI LOGISTICS HOKKAIDO INC.—See Nichirei Corporation; *Int'l*, pg. 5270
NICHIREI LOGISTICS KANTO INC.—See Nichirei Corporation; *Int'l*, pg. 5270
NICHIREI LOGISTICS TOHOKU INC.—See Nichirei Corporation; *Int'l*, pg. 5270
NICHIREI LOGISTICS TOKAI INC.—See Nichirei Corporation; *Int'l*, pg. 5270
NICHIREI PROSERVE INC.—See Nichirei Corporation; *Int'l*, pg. 5270
NICHIREI SEAFOODS, INC.—See Nichirei Corporation; *Int'l*, pg. 5270
NICHIREI U.S.A., INC.—See Nichirei Corporation; *Int'l*, pg. 5270
NICHIREI U.S.A., INC.—See Nichirei Corporation; *Int'l*, pg. 5270
NICHIREKI CO., LTD.; *Int'l*, pg. 5270
NICHIRIN AUTOPARTS INDIA PVT., LTD.—See Nichirin Co., Ltd.; *Int'l*, pg. 5271
NICHIRIN CO., LTD. - HIMEJI FACTORY—See Nichirin Co., Ltd.; *Int'l*, pg. 5271
NICHIRIN CO., LTD.; *Int'l*, pg. 5271
NICHIRIN COUPLER TEC MEXICO S.A. DE C.V.—See Nichirin Co., Ltd.; *Int'l*, pg. 5271
NICHIRIN-FLEX U.S.A., INC.—See Nichirin Co., Ltd.; *Int'l*, pg. 5271
NICHIRIN HAKUSAN CO., LTD.—See Nichirin Co., Ltd.; *Int'l*, pg. 5271
NICHIRIN IMPERIAL AUTOPARTS INDIA PVT. LTD.—See Nichirin Co., Ltd.; *Int'l*, pg. 5271
NICHIRIN KIKO CO., LTD.—See Nichirin Co., Ltd.; *Int'l*, pg. 5271
NICHIRIN RUBBER INDUSTRIAL (SHANGHAI) CO., LTD.—See Nichirin Co., Ltd.; *Int'l*, pg. 5271
NICHIRIN SERVICE CO., LTD.—See Nichirin Co., Ltd.; *Int'l*, pg. 5271
NICHIRIN SPAIN S.L.U.—See Nichirin Co., Ltd., *Int'l*, pg. 5271
NICHIRIN TENNESSEE INC.—See Nichirin Co., Ltd.; *Int'l*, pg. 5271
NICHIRIN (THAILAND) CO., LTD.—See Nichirin Co., Ltd.; *Int'l*, pg. 5271
NICHIRIN U.K. LTD—See Nichirin Co., Ltd.; *Int'l*, pg. 5271
NICHIRIN VIETNAM CO., LTD.—See Nichirin Co., Ltd.; *Int'l*, pg. 5271
NICHIRO CHIKUSAN CO., LTD.—See Maruha Nichiro Corporation; *Int'l*, pg. 4711
NICHIRO FUR CO., LTD.—See Maruha Nichiro Corporation; *Int'l*, pg. 4711
NICHIRO SEAFOODS CORPORATION—See Maruha Nichiro Corporation; *Int'l*, pg. 4711
NICHIRO SUNPACK CO., LTD.—See Air Water Inc.; *Int'l*, pg. 240
NICHIRO TOKACHI SHOKUHIN CO., LTD.—See Maruha Nichiro Corporation; *Int'l*, pg. 4711
NICHIRYO BAKING CO., LTD.; *Int'l*, pg. 5271
NICHIRYOKU CO., LTD.; *Int'l*, pg. 5271
NICHIUN CORPORATION—See Konoike Transport Co., Ltd.; *Int'l*, pg. 4275
NICHIURA TRADING (SHANGHAI) CO., LTD.—See Azearth Corporation; *Int'l*, pg. 778
NICHIWA CO., LTD.—See NEC Corporation; *Int'l*, pg. 5185
NICHIWA KIKI CO., LTD.—See Niterra Co., Ltd.; *Int'l*, pg. 5381
NICHIWA SANGYO CO., LTD.; *Int'l*, pg. 5271
NICHIWA SERVICE CO., LTD.—See Hitachi, Ltd.; *Int'l*, pg. 3423
NICHIWA SOUGOU SETSUBI CO., LTD.—See Hitachi, Ltd.; *Int'l*, pg. 3423
NICHIYO CO., LTD.—See Warabeya Nichiyo Holdings Co., Ltd.; *Int'l*, pg. 8344
NICHIYO ENGINEERING CORPORATION—See ENEOS Holdings, Inc.; *Int'l*, pg. 2417
NICHIYU ASIALIFT PHILIPPINES, INC.—See Mitsubishi Heavy Industries, Ltd.; *Int'l*, pg. 4959
NICHIYU ASIA PTE. LTD.—See Mitsubishi Heavy Industries, Ltd.; *Int'l*, pg. 4959
NICHIYU ASIA (THAILAND) CO., LTD.—See Mitsubishi Heavy Industries, Ltd.; *Int'l*, pg. 4959
NICHIYU FORKLIFT EUROPE SAS—See Mitsubishi Heavy Industries, Ltd.; *Int'l*, pg. 4959
NICHIYU FORKLIFT (SHANGHAI) CO., LTD.—See Mitsubishi Heavy Industries, Ltd.; *Int'l*, pg. 4959
NICHIYU FORKLIFT (SHENZHEN) CO., LTD.—See Mitsubishi Heavy Industries, Ltd.; *Int'l*, pg. 4959
NICHIYU FORKLIFTS INDIA PVT. LTD—See Mitsubishi Heavy Industries, Ltd.; *Int'l*, pg. 4959
NICHIYU GIKEN KOGYO CO., LTD.—See NOF Corporation; *Int'l*, pg. 5400
NICHIYU HONG KONG CO., LTD.—See Mitsubishi Heavy Industries, Ltd.; *Int'l*, pg. 4959
NICHIYU KOGYO CO., LTD.—See NOF Corporation; *Int'l*, pg. 5400
NICHIYU LOGISTICS CO., LTD.—See NOF Corporation; *Int'l*, pg. 5400

NICHIWA SANGYO CO., LTD.

CORPORATE AFFILIATIONS

NICHIYU SINGAPORE PTE. LTD.—See Mitsubishi Heavy Industries, Ltd.; *Int'l*, pg. 4959
NICHIYU TECHNO CO., LTD.—See NOF Corporation; *Int'l*, pg. 5400
NICHIYU TRADING CO., LTD.—See NOF Corporation; *Int'l*, pg. 5400
NICHIZO HOKKAIDO SERVICE CORP.—See Hitachi Zosen Corporation; *Int'l*, pg. 3411
NICHIZO KYUSHU SERVICE CORPORATION—See Hitachi Zosen Corporation; *Int'l*, pg. 3411
NICHIZO TECH INC.—See Hitachi Zosen Corporation; *Int'l*, pg. 3411
NICHOLAS ANDREWS LIMITED—See ManpowerGroup Inc.; *U.S. Public*, pg. 1359
NICHOLAS CONSOLIDATED INC.; *U.S. Private*, pg. 2925
NICHOLAS CONSULTING GROUP, INC.—See Independence Capital Partners, LLC; *U.S. Private*, pg. 2057
NICHOLAS CONTURA, LLC—See Alpha Metallurgical Resources, Inc.; *U.S. Public*, pg. 82
NICHOLAS DATA SERVICES, INC.—See Nicholas Financial, Inc.; *U.S. Public*, pg. 1528
NICHOLAS EARTH PRINTING—See Mittera Group, Inc.; *U.S. Private*, pg. 2752
NICHOLAS ENERGY COMPANY—See Alpha Natural Resources, Inc.; *U.S. Private*, pg. 199
NICHOLAS FINANCIAL, INC.; *U.S. Public*, pg. 1527
NICHOLAS & HARRIS LTD.—See DBAY Advisors Limited; *Int'l*, pg. 1987
NICHOLAS HOMES INC.; *U.S. Private*, pg. 2925
NICHOLAS MARKETS INC.; *U.S. Private*, pg. 2925
NIC HOLDING CORPORATION; *U.S. Private*, pg. 2925
NIC HOLDINGS (UK) PLC—See National Industries Group Holding S.A.K.; *Int'l*, pg. 5159
NICHOLS AGRISERVICE, LLC.; *U.S. Private*, pg. 2925
NICHOLS BROSCH WURTE WOLFE & ASSOCIATES, INC.; *U.S. Private*, pg. 2925
NICHOLS BROTHERS BOAT BUILDERS; *U.S. Private*, pg. 2925
NICHOLS CONSTRUCTION, LLC—See Dycom Industries, Inc.; *U.S. Public*, pg. 698
NICHOLS DISPENSE—See Nichols Plc; *Int'l*, pg. 5271
NICHOLS FORD, LTD.—See AutoNation, Inc.; *U.S. Public*, pg. 236
NICHOLS MOTORCYCLE SUPPLY INC.; *U.S. Private*, pg. 2925
NICHOLSON & CATES LIMITED; *Int'l*, pg. 5271
NICHOLSON CONSTRUCTION COMPANY—See VINCI S.A.; *Int'l*, pg. 8234
NICHOLSON & HALL CORPORATION; *U.S. Private*, pg. 2925
NICHOLSON INDUSTRIES INC.; *U.S. Private*, pg. 2925
NICHOLSON MANUFACTURING LTD.—See Kadant Inc.; *U.S. Public*, pg. 1212
NICHOLSON MEXICANA, S.A. DE C.V.—See Bain Capital, LP; *U.S. Private*, pg. 430
NICHOLSON STEAM TRAP—See Emerson Electric Co.; *U.S. Public*, pg. 752
NICHOLS PAPER & SUPPLY CO. INC.—See Bain Capital, LP; *U.S. Private*, pg. 441
NICHOLS PLC; *Int'l*, pg. 5271
NICHOLS PORTLAND, LLC—See Altus Capital Partners, Inc.; *U.S. Private*, pg. 211
NICHOLS & STONE CO.—See L. & J.G. Stickley Inc.; *U.S. Private*, pg. 2364
NICHOLS TEAM, INC.; *U.S. Private*, pg. 2925
NIC INC.—See Tyler Technologies, Inc.; *U.S. Public*, pg. 2208
NICIRA, INC.—See Broadcom Inc.; *U.S. Public*, pg. 390
NICK ALEXANDER IMPORTS, INC—See Car Pros Automotive Group, Inc.; *U.S. Private*, pg. 747
NICK AT NITE'S TV LAND RETROMERCIALS INC.—See National Amusements, Inc.; *U.S. Private*, pg. 2842
NICK BARBIERI TRUCKING, LLC—See AIP, LLC; *U.S. Private*, pg. 136
NICK CHEVROLET & PONTIAC; *U.S. Private*, pg. 2925
NICK CORSELLO CHEVROLET INC.; *U.S. Private*, pg. 2925
NICKEL 28 CAPITAL CORP.—See Pala Investments Limited; *Int'l*, pg. 5705
NICKEL ASIA CORPORATION; *Int'l*, pg. 5271
NICKEL CARS OF ABILENE, INC.; *U.S. Private*, pg. 2925
NICKEL CREEK PLATINUM CORP.; *Int'l*, pg. 5271
NICKEL INDUSTRIES LIMITED; *Int'l*, pg. 5271
NICKEL KLIMA KFT.—See VINCI S.A.; *Int'l*, pg. 8238
NICKEL KRAFTWERK SERVICE GMBH—See VINCI S.A.; *Int'l*, pg. 8224
NICKELL MOULDING COMPANY INC.—See Patrick Industries, Inc.; *U.S. Public*, pg. 1653
NICKEL & LYONS, LTD.—See The Sumitomo Warehouse Co. Ltd.; *Int'l*, pg. 7690
NICKEL NIK, WHEEL DEALS & DRIVELINE—See Digital Air Strike Inc.; *U.S. Private*, pg. 1230
NICKEL NORTH EXPLORATION CORP.; *Int'l*, pg. 5272
NICKELODEON AUSTRALIA—See National Amusements, Inc.; *U.S. Private*, pg. 2842
NICKELODEON DIRECT INC.—See National Amusements, Inc.; *U.S. Private*, pg. 2842

NICKELODEON GLOBAL NETWORK VENTURES INC.—See National Amusements, Inc.; *U.S. Private*, pg. 2842
NICKELODEON INDIA PVT. LTD.—See National Amusements, Inc.; *U.S. Private*, pg. 2842
NICKELODEON INTERNATIONAL LIMITED—See National Amusements, Inc.; *U.S. Private*, pg. 2842
THE NICKEL OF MEDFORD, INC.—See Gannett Co., Inc.; *U.S. Public*, pg. 904
NICKEL RESOURCES INTERNATIONAL HOLDINGS COMPANY LIMITED; *Int'l*, pg. 5272
NICKELS & DIMES INC.; *U.S. Private*, pg. 2926
NICKELSEARCH LIMITED; *Int'l*, pg. 5272
NICKELS PERFORMANCE WAREHOUSE—See Blue Point Capital Partners, LLC; *U.S. Private*, pg. 591
NICKELX LIMITED; *Int'l*, pg. 5272
NICKERSON BUSINESS SYSTEMS, INC.; *U.S. Private*, pg. 2926
NICKERSON LUMBER COMPANY; *U.S. Private*, pg. 2926
NICKERSON STREET ASSOCIATES, LLC—See Banner Corporation; *U.S. Public*, pg. 275
NICKERSON ZWAAN B.V.—See Groupe Limagrain Holding SA; *Int'l*, pg. 3108
NICKERSON ZWAAN GMBH—See Groupe Limagrain Holding SA; *Int'l*, pg. 3108
NICKERSON ZWAAN LTD.—See Groupe Limagrain Holding SA; *Int'l*, pg. 3108
NICKLAS SUPPLY INC.; *U.S. Private*, pg. 2926
NICKLAUS COMPANIES, LLC; *U.S. Private*, pg. 2926
NICKLAUS DESIGN, LLC—See Nicklaus Companies, LLC; *U.S. Private*, pg. 2926
NICKLAUS GOLF EQUIPMENT COMPANY, L.C.—See Nicklaus Companies, LLC; *U.S. Private*, pg. 2926
NICKLAUS OF FLORIDA, INC.; *U.S. Private*, pg. 2926
NICKLES BAKERY, INC.—See Alfred Nickles Bakery, Inc.; *U.S. Private*, pg. 165
NICK MAYER LINCOLN-MERCURY, INC.; *U.S. Private*, pg. 2925
NICK NICHOLAS FORD, INC.; *U.S. Private*, pg. 2925
NICK SCALI LIMITED; *Int'l*, pg. 5271
NICK & STEF'S STEAKHOUSE—See Delaware North Companies, Inc.; *U.S. Private*, pg. 1195
NICK STRIMBU INC.; *U.S. Private*, pg. 2925
NICKY FOODS CO., LTD.—See Nissin Foods Holdings Co., Ltd.; *Int'l*, pg. 5376
NIC NADEJDA AD; *Int'l*, pg. 5263
NIC NEDERLAND B.V.—See Orkla ASA; *Int'l*, pg. 5638
NICO ASSET MANAGERS LIMITED—See NICO Holdings Plc; *Int'l*, pg. 5272
NICO CAPITAL LIMITED—See NICO Holdings Plc; *Int'l*, pg. 5272
NICOCCINO HOLDING AB; *Int'l*, pg. 5272
NICO FOUR SEAS (SHANTOU) COMPANY LIMITED—See Four Seas Mercantile Holdings Limited; *Int'l*, pg. 2755
NICO GENERAL INSURANCE COMPANY LIMITED—See NICO Holdings Plc; *Int'l*, pg. 5272
NICO HOLDINGS PLC; *Int'l*, pg. 5272
NICO INSURANCE SERVICES, INC.—See Marsh & McLennan Companies, Inc.; *U.S. Public*, pg. 1381
NICO INSURANCE (ZAMBIA) LIMITED—See NICO Holdings Plc; *Int'l*, pg. 5272
NICOLAI MEDIZINTECHNIK GMBH—See Werfen Life Group, S.A.U.; *Int'l*, pg. 8379
NICOLA MINING INC.; *Int'l*, pg. 5272
NICOLAS BERGGRUEN HOLDINGS GMBH—See Berggruen Holdings, Inc.; *U.S. Private*, pg. 531
NICOLAS CORREA CALDERERIA S.L.—See Nicolas Correa S.A.; *Int'l*, pg. 5273
NICOLAS CORREA CHINA—See Nicolas Correa S.A.; *Int'l*, pg. 5273
NICOLAS CORREA DEUTSCHLAND GMBH—See Nicolas Correa S.A.; *Int'l*, pg. 5273
NICOLAS CORREA ELECTRONICA S.A.—See Nicolas Correa S.A.; *Int'l*, pg. 5273
NICOLAS CORREA INDIA LTD.—See Nicolas Correa S.A.; *Int'l*, pg. 5273
NICOLAS CORREA MACHINE TOOLS (KUNMING) COMPANY LTD.—See Nicolas Correa S.A.; *Int'l*, pg. 5273
NICOLAS CORREA PORTUGAL LTD.—See Nicolas Correa S.A.; *Int'l*, pg. 5273
NICOLAS CORREA S.A. - BURGOS PLANT—See Nicolas Correa S.A.; *Int'l*, pg. 5273
NICOLAS CORREA S.A. - ITZIAR PLANT—See Nicolas Correa S.A.; *Int'l*, pg. 5273
NICOLAS CORREA S.A. (PLANTA BURGOS)—See Nicolas Correa S.A.; *Int'l*, pg. 5273
NICOLAS CORREA S.A.; *Int'l*, pg. 5273
NICOLAS ENTRETIEN SAS—See Bunzl plc; *Int'l*, pg. 1219
NICOLAS MIGUET & ASSOCIES SA; *Int'l*, pg. 5273
NICOLAS VILLALBA WHOLESALERS; *U.S. Private*, pg. 2926
NICOLAY GMBH; *Int'l*, pg. 5273
NICOLAY ROMANIA S.R.L.—See Nicolay GmbH; *Int'l*, pg. 5273
NICOLAZZO & ASSOCIATES INC.; *U.S. Private*, pg. 2926
NICOLE RACING JAPAN, LLC—See Penske Automotive Group, Inc.; *U.S. Public*, pg. 1665

NICOLET ADVISORY SERVICES, LLC—See Nicolet Bankshares, Inc.; *U.S. Public*, pg. 1528
NICOLET BANKSHARES, INC.; *U.S. Public*, pg. 1528
NICOLET CAPITAL PARTNERS, LLC; *U.S. Private*, pg. 2926
NICOLET NATIONAL BANK—See Nicolet Bankshares, Inc.; *U.S. Public*, pg. 1528
NICOLET PLASTICS, INC.; *U.S. Private*, pg. 2926
NICOLIA READY-MIX INC.; *U.S. Private*, pg. 2926
NICO LIFE INSURANCE COMPANY LIMITED—See NICO Holdings Plc; *Int'l*, pg. 5272
NICOLL BELGIUM S.A.—See Aliaxis S.A./N.V.; *Int'l*, pg. 325
NICOLL E.P.E.—See Aliaxis S.A./N.V.; *Int'l*, pg. 325
NICOLL CATTLE COMPANY, INC.; *U.S. Private*, pg. 2926
NICOLL ETERPLAST S.A.—See Aliaxis S.A./N.V.; *Int'l*, pg. 325
NICOLL INDUSTRIA PLASTICA LTDA—See Aliaxis S.A./N.V.; *Int'l*, pg. 325
NICOLL PERU S.A.—See Aliaxis S.A./N.V.; *Int'l*, pg. 325
NICOLL POLSKA SP. Z O.O.—See Aliaxis S.A./N.V.; *Int'l*, pg. 325
NICOLL S.A.—See Aliaxis S.A./N.V.; *Int'l*, pg. 325
NICOLL S.A.—See Aliaxis S.A./N.V.; *Int'l*, pg. 325
NICOLL SPA—See Aliaxis S.A./N.V.; *Int'l*, pg. 325
NICOLL S.R.L.—See Aliaxis S.A./N.V.; *Int'l*, pg. 325
NICOLL URUGUAY S.A.—See Aliaxis S.A./N.V.; *Int'l*, pg. 325
NICOMAC CLEAN ROOMS FAR EAST LLP—See Taikisha Ltd.; *Int'l*, pg. 7413
NICOMAC TAIKISHA CLEAN ROOMS PRIVATE LIMITED—See Taikisha Ltd.; *Int'l*, pg. 7413
NICOMATIC LP—See NICOMATIC SA; *Int'l*, pg. 5273
NICOMATIC SA; *Int'l*, pg. 5273
NICON GROUP OF COMPANIES PLC; *Int'l*, pg. 5273
NICON INSURANCE PLC—See Nicon Group of Companies Plc; *Int'l*, pg. 5273
NICONOVUM AB—See British American Tobacco plc; *Int'l*, pg. 1168
NICON PROPERTIES LTD—See Nicon Group of Companies Plc; *Int'l*, pg. 5273
NICO PENSION SERVICES LIMITED—See NICO Holdings Plc; *Int'l*, pg. 5272
NICO PRECISION CO., INC.—See IHI Corporation; *Int'l*, pg. 3606
NICOR ENERCHANGE, LLC—See The Southern Company; *U.S. Public*, pg. 2131
NICO RESOURCES LIMITED; *Int'l*, pg. 5272
NICOR GAS COMPANY—See The Southern Company; *U.S. Public*, pg. 2131
NICO STEEL CENTRE (THAILAND) CO., LTD.—See NICO STEEL HOLDINGS LIMITED; *Int'l*, pg. 5272
NICO STEEL HOLDINGS LIMITED; *Int'l*, pg. 5272
NICO STEEL SOLUTIONS (S) PTE LTD—See NICO STEEL HOLDINGS LIMITED; *Int'l*, pg. 5272
NICOTEC CO., LTD.—See Amada Holdings Co., Ltd.; *Int'l*, pg. 404
NICO TECHNOLOGIES LIMITED—See NICO Holdings Plc; *Int'l*, pg. 5272
NICO TECHNOS CO., LTD.—See Hitachi, Ltd.; *Int'l*, pg. 3423
NICOTRA GEBHARDT AB—See Regal Rexnord Corporation; *U.S. Public*, pg. 1773
NICOTRA GEBHARDT GMBH—See Regal Rexnord Corporation; *U.S. Public*, pg. 1773
NICOTRA GEBHARDT LTD.—See Regal Rexnord Corporation; *U.S. Public*, pg. 1773
NICOTRA GEBHARDT NV—See Regal Rexnord Corporation; *U.S. Public*, pg. 1773
NICOTRA GEBHARDT PTE LTD—See Regal Rexnord Corporation; *U.S. Public*, pg. 1773
NICOTRA GEBHARDT PVT. LTD.—See Regal Rexnord Corporation; *U.S. Public*, pg. 1773
NICOTRA GEBHARDT S.A.—See Regal Rexnord Corporation; *U.S. Public*, pg. 1773
NICOTRA GEBHARDT S.P.A—See Regal Rexnord Corporation; *U.S. Public*, pg. 1773
NICOX OPHTHALMICS, INC.—See Nicox S.A.; *Int'l*, pg. 5273
NICOX RESEARCH INSTITUTE—See Nicox S.A.; *Int'l*, pg. 5273
NICOX S.A.; *Int'l*, pg. 5273
NICOZDIAMOND INSURANCE LIMITED; *Int'l*, pg. 5273
NIC SERVICES, LLC—See Tyler Technologies, Inc.; *U.S. Public*, pg. 2208
NIC SOLUTIONS, LLC—See Tyler Technologies, Inc.; *U.S. Public*, pg. 2208
NICSTECH CO., LTD.; *Int'l*, pg. 5274
NIC TECHNOLOGIES, LLC—See Tyler Technologies, Inc.; *U.S. Public*, pg. 2208
NICTUS LIMITED; *Int'l*, pg. 5274
NIDACON LIFE SCIENCE (SHANGHAI) CO., LTD.—See Shenzhen Changhong Technology Co., Ltd.; *Int'l*, pg. 6806
NIDAN LABORATORIES & HEALTHCARE LIMITED; *Int'l*, pg. 5274
NIDAPLAST-HONEYCOMBS S.A.S.—See Etex SA/NV; *Int'l*, pg. 2522

COMPANY NAME INDEX

NIDAR AS—See Orkla ASA; *Int'l*, pg. 5638
NIDAROS SPAREBANK; *Int'l*, pg. 5274
NIDEC ACIM GERMANY GMBH—See Nidec Corporation; *Int'l*, pg. 5275
NIDEC AMERICA CORPORATION—See Nidec Corporation; *Int'l*, pg. 5275
NIDEC AMERICA CORP. - TORRINGTON—See Nidec Corporation; *Int'l*, pg. 5275
NIDEC ASI GMBH—See Nidec Corporation; *Int'l*, pg. 5274
NIDEC ASI LLC—See Nidec Corporation; *Int'l*, pg. 5274
NIDEC ASI RO SRL—See Nidec Corporation; *Int'l*, pg. 5275
NIDEC ASI S.P.A.—See Nidec Corporation; *Int'l*, pg. 5274
NIDEC ASI VEI—See Nidec Corporation; *Int'l*, pg. 5275
NIDEC AUTOMOBILE MOTOR (ZHEJIANG) CORPORATION—See Nidec Corporation; *Int'l*, pg. 5275
NIDEC (BEIJING) CO., LTD.—See Nidec Corporation; *Int'l*, pg. 5275
NIDEC BMS PTE. LTD.—See Nidec Corporation; *Int'l*, pg. 5275
NIDEC BMS (SUZHOU) CO., LTD.—See Nidec Corporation; *Int'l*, pg. 5275
NIDEC CHAUN CHOUNG TECHNOLOGY AMERICA INC.—See Nidec Chaun-Choung Technology Corporation; *Int'l*, pg. 5274
NIDEC CHAUN-CHOUNG TECHNOLOGY CORPORATION; *Int'l*, pg. 5274
NIDEC COMPONENT TECHNOLOGY BANGPA-IN CO., LTD.—See Nidec Corporation; *Int'l*, pg. 5275
NIDEC COMPONENT TECHNOLOGY CO., LTD.—See Nidec Corporation; *Int'l*, pg. 5275
NIDEC CONTROL TECHNIQUES LTD.—See Nidec Corporation; *Int'l*, pg. 5275
NIDEC COPAL CORP. - KORIYAMA (DIES) TECHNICAL CENTER—See Nidec Corporation; *Int'l*, pg. 5276
NIDEC COPAL CORPORATION—See Nidec Corporation; *Int'l*, pg. 5276
NIDEC COPAL ELECTRONICS CORPORATION—See Nidec Corporation; *Int'l*, pg. 5276
NIDEC COPAL ELECTRONICS GMBH—See Nidec Corporation; *Int'l*, pg. 5276
NIDEC COPAL ELECTRONICS, INC.—See Nidec Corporation; *Int'l*, pg. 5276
NIDEC COPAL ELECTRONICS (KOREA) CO., LTD.—See Nidec Corporation; *Int'l*, pg. 5276
NIDEC COPAL ELECTRONICS (SHANGHAI) CO., LTD.—See Nidec Corporation; *Int'l*, pg. 5276
NIDEC COPAL ELECTRONICS SINGAPORE PTE. LTD.—See Nidec Corporation; *Int'l*, pg. 5276
NIDEC COPAL ELECTRONICS (TAIWAN) CO., LTD.—See Nidec Corporation; *Int'l*, pg. 5276
NIDEC COPAL ELECTRONICS (ZHEJIANG) CO., LTD.—See Nidec Corporation; *Int'l*, pg. 5276
NIDEC COPAL GMBH—See Nidec Corporation; *Int'l*, pg. 5276
NIDEC COPAL (HONG KONG) CO., LTD.—See Nidec Corporation; *Int'l*, pg. 5276
NIDEC COPAL PHILIPPINES CORPORATION—See Nidec Corporation; *Int'l*, pg. 5276
NIDEC COPAL PRECISION PARTS CORPORATION—See Nidec Corporation; *Int'l*, pg. 5276
NIDEC COPAL PRECISION (VIETNAM) CORPORATION—See Nidec Corporation; *Int'l*, pg. 5276
NIDEC COPAL (THAILAND) CO., LTD.—See Nidec Corporation; *Int'l*, pg. 5276
NIDEC COPAL (VIETNAM) CO., LTD.—See Nidec Corporation; *Int'l*, pg. 5276
NIDEC COPAL (ZHEJIANG) CO., LTD.—See Nidec Corporation; *Int'l*, pg. 5276
NIDEC CORPORATION; *Int'l*, pg. 5274
NIDEC (DALIAN) LIMITED—See Nidec Corporation; *Int'l*, pg. 5274
NIDEC (DONGGUAN) LIMITED—See Nidec Corporation; *Int'l*, pg. 5274
NIDEC ELECTRONICS GMBH—See Nidec Corporation; *Int'l*, pg. 5276
NIDEC ELECTRONICS (THAILAND) CO., LTD. - RANGSIT FACTORY—See Nidec Corporation; *Int'l*, pg. 5276
NIDEC ELECTRONICS (THAILAND) CO., LTD. - ROJANA FACTORY—See Nidec Corporation; *Int'l*, pg. 5276
NIDEC ELECTRONICS (THAILAND) CO., LTD.—See Nidec Corporation; *Int'l*, pg. 5276
NIDEC EUROPE B.V.—See Nidec Corporation; *Int'l*, pg. 5276
NIDEC GLOBAL APPLIANCE ITALY S.R.L.—See Nidec Corporation; *Int'l*, pg. 5276
NIDEC GLOBAL SERVICE CORPORATION—See Nidec Corporation; *Int'l*, pg. 5274
NIDEC (H.K.) CO., LTD.—See Nidec Corporation; *Int'l*, pg. 5274
NIDEC INDIA PRIVATE LIMITED—See Nidec Corporation; *Int'l*, pg. 5275
NIDEC INDUSTRIAL AUTOMATION BELGIUM NV—See Nidec Corporation; *Int'l*, pg. 5275
NIDEC INDUSTRIAL AUTOMATION IBERIA S.A.—See Nidec Corporation; *Int'l*, pg. 5275
NIDEC INDUSTRIAL AUTOMATION INDIA PVT. LTD. - BANGALORE—See Nidec Corporation; *Int'l*, pg. 5275
NIDEC INDUSTRIAL AUTOMATION ITALY SPA—See Nidec Corporation; *Int'l*, pg. 5275
NIDEC INDUSTRIAL AUTOMATION SINGAPORE PTE LIMITED—See Nidec Corporation; *Int'l*, pg. 5275
NIDEC INDUSTRIAL AUTOMATION SOUTHERN AFRICA (PTY) LIMITED—See Nidec Corporation; *Int'l*, pg. 5275
NIDEC INDUSTRIAL AUTOMATION UK LIMITED—See Nidec Corporation; *Int'l*, pg. 5275
NIDEC INDUSTRIAL AUTOMATION USA LLC—See Nidec Corporation; *Int'l*, pg. 5277
NIDEC INDUSTRIAL AUTOMATION USA LLC—See Emerson Electric Co.; *U.S. Public*, pg. 750
NIDEC KOREA CORPORATION—See Nidec Corporation; *Int'l*, pg. 5276
NIDEC-KYORI CORPORATION—See Nidec Corporation; *Int'l*, pg. 5279
NIDEC-KYORI MACHINERY (ZHEJIANG) CORPORATION—See Nidec Corporation; *Int'l*, pg. 5279
NIDEC-KYORI (SHANGHAI) MACHINERY CORPORATION—See Nidec Corporation; *Int'l*, pg. 5279
NIDEC LAMINACIONES DE ACERO, S.A. DE C.V.—See Nidec Corporation; *Int'l*, pg. 5276
NIDEC LEROY-SOMER HOLDING SA—See Nidec Corporation; *Int'l*, pg. 5276
NIDEC LOGISTICS CORPORATION—See Nidec Corporation; *Int'l*, pg. 5277
NIDEC LOGISTICS (H.K.) CO., LIMITED—See Nidec Corporation; *Int'l*, pg. 5277
NIDEC MACHINERY CORPORATION—See Nidec Corporation; *Int'l*, pg. 5277
NIDEC MACHINERY (SHANGHAI) CO., LTD.—See Nidec Corporation; *Int'l*, pg. 5277
NIDEC MACHINERY (THAILAND) CO., LTD.—See Nidec Corporation; *Int'l*, pg. 5277
NIDEC MACHINERY (ZHEJIANG) CORPORATION—See Nidec Corporation; *Int'l*, pg. 5277
NIDEC MANAGEMENT SHANGHAI CORPORATION—See Nidec Corporation; *Int'l*, pg. 5277
NIDEC MINSTER CORPORATION—See Nidec Corporation; *Int'l*, pg. 5280
NIDEC MOBILITY CORPORATION—See Nidec Corporation; *Int'l*, pg. 5277
NIDEC MOTOR CANADA CORPORATION—See Nidec Corporation; *Int'l*, pg. 5277
NIDEC MOTOR COLOMBIA SAS—See Nidec Corporation; *Int'l*, pg. 5277
NIDEC MOTOR CORP. - HURST MOTORS—See Nidec Corporation; *Int'l*, pg. 5277
NIDEC MOTOR CORPORATION—See Nidec Corporation; *Int'l*, pg. 5277
NIDEC MOTOR HOLDINGS CORPORATION—See Nidec Corporation; *Int'l*, pg. 5277
NIDEC MOTOR (QINGDAO) CORPORATION—See Nidec Corporation; *Int'l*, pg. 5277
NIDEC MOTORS & ACTUATORS (GERMANY) GMBH—See Nidec Corporation; *Int'l*, pg. 5277
NIDEC MOTORS & ACTUATORS MEXICO S. DE R.L. DE C.V.—See Nidec Corporation; *Int'l*, pg. 5277
NIDEC MOTORS & ACTUATORS (POLAND), SP. Z O.O.—See Nidec Corporation; *Int'l*, pg. 5277
NIDEC MOTORS & ACTUATORS S.A.S.—See Nidec Corporation; *Int'l*, pg. 5277
NIDEC MOTORS & ACTUATORS (SPAIN) S.A.—See Nidec Corporation; *Int'l*, pg. 5277
NIDEC MOTORS & ACTUATORS (USA), INC.—See Nidec Corporation; *Int'l*, pg. 5277
NIDEC NETHERLANDS B.V.—See Nidec Corporation; *Int'l*, pg. 5275
NIDEC NISSIN CORPORATION—See Nidec Corporation; *Int'l*, pg. 5278
NIDEC NISSIN (DONGGUAN) CORPORATION—See Nidec Corporation; *Int'l*, pg. 5278
NIDEC NISSIN (HK) CO., LTD.—See Nidec Corporation; *Int'l*, pg. 5278
NIDEC NISSIN TOHOKU CORPORATION—See Nidec Corporation; *Int'l*, pg. 5278
NIDEC NISSIN VIETNAM CORPORATION—See Nidec Corporation; *Int'l*, pg. 5278
NIDEC PHILIPPINES CORPORATION—See Nidec Corporation; *Int'l*, pg. 5278
NIDEC PIGEON CORPORATION—See Nidec Corporation; *Int'l*, pg. 5278
NIDEC POWER MOTOR (SHANGHAI) INTERNATIONAL TRADING CO., LTD.—See Nidec Corporation; *Int'l*, pg. 5278
NIDEC PRECISION PHILIPPINES CORPORATION—See Nidec Corporation; *Int'l*, pg. 5278
NIDEC PRECISION (THAILAND) CO., LTD. - ROJANA FACTORY—See Nidec Corporation; *Int'l*, pg. 5278
NIDEC PRECISION (THAILAND) CO., LTD.—See Nidec Corporation; *Int'l*, pg. 5278
NIDEC-READ CORPORATION—See Nidec Corporation; *Int'l*, pg. 5279
NIDEC SANKYO AMERICA CORPORATION—See Nidec Corporation; *Int'l*, pg. 5278

NIDEC CORPORATION

NIDEC SANKYO CMI CORPORATION—See Nidec Corporation; *Int'l*, pg. 5278
NIDEC SANKYO CORPORATION - INA FACILITY—See Nidec Corporation; *Int'l*, pg. 5274
NIDEC SANKYO CORPORATION - KOMAGANE FACILITY—See Nidec Corporation; *Int'l*, pg. 5278
NIDEC SANKYO CORPORATION—See Nidec Corporation; *Int'l*, pg. 5278
NIDEC SANKYO (DALIAN) CORPORATION—See Nidec Corporation; *Int'l*, pg. 5278
NIDEC SANKYO DO BRASIL LTDA.—See Nidec Corporation; *Int'l*, pg. 5278
NIDEC SANKYO ELECTRONICS (SHAOGUAN) CO., LTD.—See Nidec Corporation; *Int'l*, pg. 5278
NIDEC SANKYO ELECTRONICS (SHENZHEN) CORPORATION—See Nidec Corporation; *Int'l*, pg. 5278
NIDEC SANKYO EUROPE GMBH—See Nidec Corporation; *Int'l*, pg. 5278
NIDEC SANKYO (H.K.) CO., LIMITED—See Nidec Corporation; *Int'l*, pg. 5278
NIDEC SANKYO KOREA CORPORATION—See Nidec Corporation; *Int'l*, pg. 5278
NIDEC SANKYO SHOJI CORPORATION—See Nidec Corporation; *Int'l*, pg. 5278
NIDEC SANKYO SINGAPORE PTE. LTD.—See Nidec Corporation; *Int'l*, pg. 5278
NIDEC SANKYO TAIWAN CORPORATION—See Nidec Corporation; *Int'l*, pg. 5278
NIDEC SANKYO (THAILAND) CO., LTD.—See Nidec Corporation; *Int'l*, pg. 5278
NIDEC SANKYO VIETNAM CORPORATION—See Nidec Corporation; *Int'l*, pg. 5278
NIDEC SANKYO (ZHEJIANG) CORPORATION—See Nidec Corporation; *Int'l*, pg. 5278
NIDEC SCHWEIZ AG—See Nidec Corporation; *Int'l*, pg. 5277
NIDEC SEIMITSU CORPORATION—See Nidec Corporation; *Int'l*, pg. 5278
NIDEC SEIMITSU MOTOR TECHNOLOGY (DONGGUAN) CO., LTD.—See Nidec Corporation; *Int'l*, pg. 5278
NIDEC SEIMITSU SINGAPORE PTE. LTD.—See Nidec Corporation; *Int'l*, pg. 5278
NIDEC SERVO CORPORATION - KIRYU TECHNICAL CENTER PLANT—See Nidec Corporation; *Int'l*, pg. 5279
NIDEC SERVO CORPORATION—See Nidec Corporation; *Int'l*, pg. 5278
NIDEC SERVO EUROPE B.V.—See Nidec Corporation; *Int'l*, pg. 5278
NIDEC SERVO (HONG KONG) CO., LIMITED—See Nidec Corporation; *Int'l*, pg. 5278
NIDEC SERVO HOTAKA CORPORATION—See Nidec Corporation; *Int'l*, pg. 5279
NIDEC SERVO (SHANGHAI) CO., LTD—See Nidec Corporation; *Int'l*, pg. 5279
NIDEC SERVO VIETNAM CORPORATION—See Nidec Corporation; *Int'l*, pg. 5279
NIDEC (SHANGHAI) INTERNATIONAL TRADING CO., LTD.—See Nidec Corporation; *Int'l*, pg. 5274
NIDEC (SHAOGUAN) LIMITED—See Nidec Corporation; *Int'l*, pg. 5274
NIDEC (SHENZHEN) CO., LTD.—See Nidec Corporation; *Int'l*, pg. 5274
NIDEC SHIBAURA ELECTRONICS (THAILAND) CO., LTD.—See Nidec Corporation; *Int'l*, pg. 5279
NIDEC SHIBAURA (H.K.) LIMITED—See Nidec Corporation; *Int'l*, pg. 5279
NIDEC SHIBAURA (ZHEJIANG) CORPORATION—See Nidec Corporation; *Int'l*, pg. 5279
NIDEC-SHIMPO AMERICA CORPORATION—See Nidec Corporation; *Int'l*, pg. 5279
NIDEC-SHIMPO CORPORATION—See Nidec Corporation; *Int'l*, pg. 5279
NIDEC-SHIMPO INDIA SALES AND TRADING PRIVATE LIMITED—See Nidec Corporation; *Int'l*, pg. 5279
NIDEC-SHIMPO KOREA CORPORATION—See Nidec Corporation; *Int'l*, pg. 5279
NIDEC-SHIMPO (SHANGHAI) INT'L TRADING CO., LTD.—See Nidec Corporation; *Int'l*, pg. 5279
NIDEC-SHIMPO (TAIWAN) CORPORATION—See Nidec Corporation; *Int'l*, pg. 5279
NIDEC-SHIMPO (ZHEJIANG) CORPORATION—See Nidec Corporation; *Int'l*, pg. 5280
NIDEC SINGAPORE PTE. LTD.—See Nidec Corporation; *Int'l*, pg. 5279
NIDEC SOLE MOTOR CORPORATION S.R.L.—See Nidec Corporation; *Int'l*, pg. 5279
NIDEC SOLE MOTOR HUNGARY K.F.T.—See Nidec Corporation; *Int'l*, pg. 5279
NIDEC SR DRIVES LTD.—See Nidec Corporation; *Int'l*, pg. 5279
NIDEC SUBIC PHILIPPINES CORPORATION—See Nidec Corporation; *Int'l*, pg. 5278
NIDEC TAIWAN CORPORATION—See Nidec Corporation; *Int'l*, pg. 5279
NIDEC TECHNO MOTOR HOLDINGS CORPORATION—See Nidec Corporation; *Int'l*, pg. 5279

Company Index
NIDEC CORPORATION
CORPORATE AFFILIATIONS

NIDEC (THAILAND) CO LTD—See Nidec Corporation; *Int'l*, pg. 5275
NIDEC TOSOK AKIBA (VIETNAM) CO., LTD.—See Nidec Corporation; *Int'l*, pg. 5279
NIDEC TOSOK CORPORATION—See Nidec Corporation; *Int'l*, pg. 5279
NIDEC TOSOK CORPORATION - YAMANASHI FACTORY—See Nidec Corporation; *Int'l*, pg. 5279
NIDEC TOSOK (SHANGHAI) CO., LTD.—See Nidec Corporation; *Int'l*, pg. 5279
NIDEC TOSOK (VIETNAM) CO., LTD.—See Nidec Corporation; *Int'l*, pg. 5279
NIDEC TOSOK (ZHEJIANG) CORPORATION—See Nidec Corporation; *Int'l*, pg. 5279
NIDEC TOTAL SERVICE CORPORATION—See Nidec Corporation; *Int'l*, pg. 5279
NIDEC VAMCO CORPORATION—See Nidec Corporation; *Int'l*, pg. 5275
NIDEC VIETNAM CORPORATION—See Nidec Corporation; *Int'l*, pg. 5279
NIDEC (ZHEJIANG) CORPORATION—See Nidec Corporation; *Int'l*, pg. 5274
NIDEK SA; *Int'l*, pg. 5280
NIDHI GRANITES LIMITED; *Int'l*, pg. 5280
NID-IS CO, LTD.—See Nippon Information Development Co., Ltd.; *Int'l*, pg. 5319
NIDOCO AB; *Int'l*, pg. 5280
NIDO PETROLEUM LIMITED—See Bangchak Corporation Public Company Limited; *Int'l*, pg. 832
NID SA—See Advent International Corporation; *U.S. Private*, pg. 102
NIECO CORPORATION—See The Middleby Corporation; *U.S. Public*, pg. 2115
NIECO EQUIPMENT CORPORATION; *U.S. Private*, pg. 2926
NIEDERAUER INC.; *U.S. Private*, pg. 2926
NIEDEROSTERREICHISCHE FACILITY MANAGEMENT GMBH—See Fresenius SE & Co. KGaA; *Int'l*, pg. 2780
NIEDERRHEINISCHE GAS- UND WASSERWERKE GMBH—See Gelsenwasser AG; *Int'l*, pg. 2914
NIEDNER INC.—See Blue Wolf Capital Partners LLC; *U.S. Private*, pg. 595
NIEF PLASTIC SAS—See Sintex Industries, Ltd.; *Int'l*, pg. 6957
NIEHAUS COMPANIES INC.; *U.S. Private*, pg. 2926
THE NIELLO COMPANY; *U.S. Private*, pg. 4084
NIELLO VOLVO OF SACRAMENTO; *U.S. Private*, pg. 2927
NIELSEN ADMOSPHERE, A.S—See Brookfield Corporation; *Int'l*, pg. 1177
NIELSEN ADMOSPHERE, A.S—See Elliott Management Corporation; *U.S. Private*, pg. 1370
NIELSEN ADMOSPHERE BULGARIA JSC.—See Brookfield Corporation; *Int'l*, pg. 1179
NIELSEN ADMOSPHERE BULGARIA JSC.—See Elliott Management Corporation; *U.S. Private*, pg. 1371
NIELSEN ADMOSPHERE SLOVAKIA, S.R.O.—See Brookfield Corporation; *Int'l*, pg. 1179
NIELSEN ADMOSPHERE SLOVAKIA, S.R.O.—See Elliott Management Corporation; *U.S. Private*, pg. 1371
NIELSEN ARASTIRMA HIZMETLERI LIMITED SIRKET—See Brookfield Corporation; *Int'l*, pg. 1177
NIELSEN ARASTIRMA HIZMETLERI LIMITED SIRKET—See Elliott Management Corporation; *U.S. Private*, pg. 1370
NIELSEN AUDIENCE MEASUREMENT (CYPRUS) LTD.—See Brookfield Corporation; *Int'l*, pg. 1179
NIELSEN AUDIENCE MEASUREMENT (CYPRUS) LTD.—See Elliott Management Corporation; *U.S. Private*, pg. 1371
NIELSEN AUDIENCE MEASUREMENT DOO BEOGRAD—See Brookfield Corporation; *Int'l*, pg. 1179
NIELSEN AUDIENCE MEASUREMENT DOO BEOGRAD—See Elliott Management Corporation; *U.S. Private*, pg. 1371
NIELSEN AUDIO, INC.—See Brookfield Corporation; *Int'l*, pg. 1179
NIELSEN AUDIO, INC.—See Elliott Management Corporation; *U.S. Private*, pg. 1371
NIELSEN & BAINBRIDGE, LLC - NIELSEN MANUFACTURING—See Sycamore Partners Management, LP; *U.S. Private*, pg. 3896
NIELSEN & BAINBRIDGE, LLC—See Sycamore Partners Management, LP; *U.S. Private*, pg. 3896
NIELSEN BROTHERS, INC.; *U.S. Private*, pg. 2927
NIELSEN CO., LTD.—See Transcosmos Inc.; *Int'l*, pg. 7898
THE NIELSEN COMPANY - ADVISORY SERVICES—See Brookfield Corporation; *Int'l*, pg. 1180
THE NIELSEN COMPANY - ADVISORY SERVICES—See Elliott Management Corporation; *U.S. Private*, pg. 1373
THE NIELSEN COMPANY (AUSTRALIA) PTY. LTD.—See Brookfield Corporation; *Int'l*, pg. 1178
THE NIELSEN COMPANY (AUSTRALIA) PTY. LTD.—See Elliott Management Corporation; *U.S. Private*, pg. 1370
THE NIELSEN COMPANY (BANGLADESH) LTD.—See Brookfield Corporation; *Int'l*, pg. 1180
THE NIELSEN COMPANY (BANGLADESH) LTD.—See Elliott Management Corporation; *U.S. Private*, pg. 1372
THE NIELSEN COMPANY (BELGIUM) SPRL—See Brookfield Corporation; *Int'l*, pg. 1180
THE NIELSEN COMPANY (BELGIUM) SPRL—See Elliott Management Corporation; *U.S. Private*, pg. 1372
THE NIELSEN COMPANY B.V.—See Brookfield Corporation; *Int'l*, pg. 1176
THE NIELSEN COMPANY B.V.—See Elliott Management Corporation; *U.S. Private*, pg. 1369
THE NIELSEN COMPANY (DENMARK) APS—See Brookfield Corporation; *Int'l*, pg. 1177
THE NIELSEN COMPANY (DENMARK) APS—See Elliott Management Corporation; *U.S. Private*, pg. 1370
THE NIELSEN COMPANY (GERMANY) GMBH—See Brookfield Corporation; *Int'l*, pg. 1180
THE NIELSEN COMPANY (GERMANY) GMBH—See Elliott Management Corporation; *U.S. Private*, pg. 1372
THE NIELSEN COMPANY (GREECE) S.A.—See Brookfield Corporation; *Int'l*, pg. 1180
THE NIELSEN COMPANY (GREECE) S.A.—See Elliott Management Corporation; *U.S. Private*, pg. 1372
THE NIELSEN COMPANY (ITALY) S.R.L.—See Brookfield Corporation; *Int'l*, pg. 1178
THE NIELSEN COMPANY (ITALY) S.R.L.—See Elliott Management Corporation; *U.S. Private*, pg. 1370
THE NIELSEN COMPANY JAPAN—See Brookfield Corporation; *Int'l*, pg. 1180
THE NIELSEN COMPANY JAPAN—See Elliott Management Corporation; *U.S. Private*, pg. 1373
THE NIELSEN COMPANY LANKA (PRIVATE) LIMITED—See Brookfield Corporation; *Int'l*, pg. 1180
THE NIELSEN COMPANY LANKA (PRIVATE) LIMITED—See Elliott Management Corporation; *U.S. Private*, pg. 1373
THE NIELSEN COMPANY (MALAYSIA) SDN. BHD.—See Brookfield Corporation; *Int'l*, pg. 1180
THE NIELSEN COMPANY (MALAYSIA) SDN. BHD.—See Elliott Management Corporation; *U.S. Private*, pg. 1372
THE NIELSEN COMPANY MEDYA YAYINCILIK VE TANITIM HIZMETLERI ANONIM SIRKETII—See Brookfield Corporation; *Int'l*, pg. 1180
THE NIELSEN COMPANY MEDYA YAYINCILIK VE TANITIM HIZMETLERI ANONIM SIRKETII—See Elliott Management Corporation; *U.S. Private*, pg. 1373
THE NIELSEN COMPANY NEPAL PVT LTD.—See Brookfield Corporation; *Int'l*, pg. 1179
THE NIELSEN COMPANY NEPAL PVT LTD.—See Elliott Management Corporation; *U.S. Private*, pg. 1371
THE NIELSEN COMPANY (PHILIPPINES), INC.—See Brookfield Corporation; *Int'l*, pg. 1180
THE NIELSEN COMPANY (PHILIPPINES), INC.—See Elliott Management Corporation; *U.S. Private*, pg. 1372
THE NIELSEN COMPANY (SHANGHAI) LTD.—See Brookfield Corporation; *Int'l*, pg. 1180
THE NIELSEN COMPANY (SHANGHAI) LTD.—See Elliott Management Corporation; *U.S. Private*, pg. 1373
THE NIELSEN COMPANY TAIWAN LTD.—See Brookfield Corporation; *Int'l*, pg. 1178
THE NIELSEN COMPANY TAIWAN LTD.—See Elliott Management Corporation; *U.S. Private*, pg. 1370
THE NIELSEN COMPANY (THAILAND) LIMITED—See Brookfield Corporation; *Int'l*, pg. 1180
THE NIELSEN COMPANY (THAILAND) LIMITED—See Elliott Management Corporation; *U.S. Private*, pg. 1373
THE NIELSEN COMPANY (US), LLC—See Brookfield Corporation; *Int'l*, pg. 1176
THE NIELSEN COMPANY (US), LLC—See Elliott Management Corporation; *U.S. Private*, pg. 1369
NIELSEN CONSULTANCY LLC—See Brookfield Corporation; *Int'l*, pg. 1179
NIELSEN CONSULTANCY LLC—See Elliott Management Corporation; *U.S. Private*, pg. 1371
NIELSEN CONSUMER INSIGHTS, INC—See Brookfield Corporation; *Int'l*, pg. 1179
NIELSEN CONSUMER INSIGHTS, INC—See Elliott Management Corporation; *U.S. Private*, pg. 1371
NIELSEN CONSUMER LLC—See Advent International Corporation; *U.S. Private*, pg. 105
NIELSEN DESIGN GMBH—See Sycamore Partners Management, LP; *U.S. Private*, pg. 3896
NIELSEN EGYPT LLC—See Brookfield Corporation; *Int'l*, pg. 1179
NIELSEN EGYPT LLC—See Elliott Management Corporation; *U.S. Private*, pg. 1371
NIELSEN ENTERTAINMENT, LLC—See Brookfield Corporation; *Int'l*, pg. 1179
NIELSEN ENTERTAINMENT, LLC—See Elliott Management Corporation; *U.S. Private*, pg. 1371
NIELSEN FOR CONSULTANCIES LIMITED LIABILITY COMPANY—See Brookfield Corporation; *Int'l*, pg. 1180
NIELSEN FOR CONSULTANCIES LIMITED LIABILITY COMPANY—See Elliott Management Corporation; *U.S. Private*, pg. 1372
NIELSEN FOR MARKET RESEARCH LLC—See Brookfield Corporation; *Int'l*, pg. 1180
NIELSEN FOR MARKET RESEARCH LLC—See Elliott Management Corporation; *U.S. Private*, pg. 1372
NIELSEN HARDWARE CORPORATION—See Enerpac Tool Group Corp.; *U.S. Public*, pg. 766
NIELSEN HOLDINGS PLC—See Brookfield Corporation; *Int'l*, pg. 1176
NIELSEN HOLDINGS PLC—See Elliott Management Corporation; *U.S. Private*, pg. 1369
NIELSEN IBOPE DOMINICANA, S.R.L.—See Brookfield Corporation; *Int'l*, pg. 1179
NIELSEN IBOPE DOMINICANA, S.R.L.—See Elliott Management Corporation; *U.S. Private*, pg. 1371
NIELSEN (INDIA) PRIVATE LIMITED—See Brookfield Corporation; *Int'l*, pg. 1179
NIELSEN (INDIA) PRIVATE LIMITED—See Elliott Management Corporation; *U.S. Private*, pg. 1371
NIELSEN INNOVATE FUND, LP—See Brookfield Corporation; *Int'l*, pg. 1179
NIELSEN INNOVATE FUND, LP—See Elliott Management Corporation; *U.S. Private*, pg. 1371
NIELSEN INNOVATE LTD.—See Brookfield Corporation; *Int'l*, pg. 1179
NIELSEN INNOVATE LTD.—See Elliott Management Corporation; *U.S. Private*, pg. 1371
NIELSEN KELLERMAN INC.; *U.S. Private*, pg. 2927
NIELSEN KOREA LTD.—See Brookfield Corporation; *Int'l*, pg. 1179
NIELSEN KOREA LTD.—See Elliott Management Corporation; *U.S. Private*, pg. 1371
NIELSEN KOZONSEGMERES KFT.—See Brookfield Corporation; *Int'l*, pg. 1179
NIELSEN KOZONSEGMERES KFT.—See Elliott Management Corporation; *U.S. Private*, pg. 1371
NIELSEN MEDIA RESEARCH AS—See Brookfield Corporation; *Int'l*, pg. 1179
NIELSEN MEDIA RESEARCH AS—See Elliott Management Corporation; *U.S. Private*, pg. 1371
NIELSEN MEDIA RESEARCH, INC.—See Brookfield Corporation; *Int'l*, pg. 1179
NIELSEN MEDIA RESEARCH, INC.—See Elliott Management Corporation; *U.S. Private*, pg. 1371
NIELSEN MMRD (MYANMAR) CO., LTD—See Brookfield Corporation; *Int'l*, pg. 1179
NIELSEN MMRD (MYANMAR) CO., LTD—See Elliott Management Corporation; *U.S. Private*, pg. 1371
NIELSEN MUSIC CONTROL NEDERLAND B.V.—See Brookfield Corporation; *Int'l*, pg. 1179
NIELSEN MUSIC CONTROL NEDERLAND B.V.—See Elliott Management Corporation; *U.S. Private*, pg. 1372
NIELSEN NATIONAL RESEARCH GROUP, INC.—See Stagwell, Inc.; *U.S. Public*, pg. 1928
THE NIELSEN NEPAL PVT. LTD.—See Brookfield Corporation; *Int'l*, pg. 1178
THE NIELSEN NEPAL PVT. LTD.—See Elliott Management Corporation; *U.S. Private*, pg. 1370
THE NIELSEN NORMAN GROUP; *U.S. Private*, pg. 4084
NIELSEN+PARTNER PTE. LTD.—See Larsen & Toubro Limited; *Int'l*, pg. 4419
NIELSEN+PARTNER UNTERNEHMENSBERATER AG—See Larsen & Toubro Limited; *Int'l*, pg. 4419
NIELSEN+PARTNER UNTERNEHMENSBERATER GMBH—See Larsen & Toubro Limited; *Int'l*, pg. 4419
NIELSEN SCARBOROUGH—See Brookfield Corporation; *Int'l*, pg. 1179
NIELSEN SCARBOROUGH—See Elliott Management Corporation; *U.S. Private*, pg. 1372
NIELSEN SERVICES GERMANY GMBH—See Brookfield Corporation; *Int'l*, pg. 1180
NIELSEN SERVICES GERMANY GMBH—See Elliott Management Corporation; *U.S. Private*, pg. 1372
NIELSEN SERVICES ITALY S.R.L.—See Brookfield Corporation; *Int'l*, pg. 1178
NIELSEN SERVICES ITALY S.R.L.—See Elliott Management Corporation; *U.S. Private*, pg. 1370
NIELSEN SERVICES POLAND SP. Z.O.O.—See Brookfield Corporation; *Int'l*, pg. 1179
NIELSEN SERVICES POLAND SP. Z.O.O.—See Elliott Management Corporation; *U.S. Private*, pg. 1372
NIELSEN SERVICES SPAIN, S.L.—See Brookfield Corporation; *Int'l*, pg. 1179
NIELSEN SERVICES SPAIN, S.L.—See Elliott Management Corporation; *U.S. Private*, pg. 1372
NIELSEN SERVICES SWEDEN AB—See Brookfield Corporation; *Int'l*, pg. 1177
NIELSEN SERVICES SWEDEN AB—See Elliott Management Corporation; *U.S. Private*, pg. 1370
NIELSEN SOUNDSCAN—See Brookfield Corporation; *Int'l*, pg. 1179
NIELSEN SOUNDSCAN—See Elliott Management Corporation; *U.S. Private*, pg. 1371
NIELSEN SPORTS AMERICA, LLC.—See Brookfield Corporation; *Int'l*, pg. 1179
NIELSEN SPORTS AMERICA, LLC.—See Elliott Management Corporation; *U.S. Private*, pg. 1372
NIELSEN SPORTS ASIA PTE. LTD.—See Brookfield Corporation; *Int'l*, pg. 1179
NIELSEN SPORTS ASIA PTE. LTD.—See Elliott Management Corporation; *U.S. Private*, pg. 1372
NIELSEN SPORTS BELGIUM SA—See Brookfield Corporation; *Int'l*, pg. 1179
NIELSEN SPORTS BELGIUM SA—See Elliott Management Corporation; *U.S. Private*, pg. 1372

COMPANY NAME INDEX

NIELSEN SPORTS DEUTSCHLAND GMBH—See Brookfield Corporation; *Int'l*, pg. 1179
NIELSEN SPORTS DEUTSCHLAND GMBH—See Elliott Management Corporation; *U.S. Private*, pg. 1372
NIELSEN SPORTS ESPANA S.L.U.—See Brookfield Corporation; *Int'l*, pg. 1179
NIELSEN SPORTS ESPANA S.L.U.—See Elliott Management Corporation; *U.S. Private*, pg. 1372
NIELSEN SPORTS FRANCE SARL—See Brookfield Corporation; *Int'l*, pg. 1179
NIELSEN SPORTS FRANCE SARL—See Elliott Management Corporation; *U.S. Private*, pg. 1372
NIELSEN SPORTS INDIA PRIVATE LIMITED—See Brookfield Corporation; *Int'l*, pg. 1179
NIELSEN SPORTS INDIA PRIVATE LIMITED—See Elliott Management Corporation; *U.S. Private*, pg. 1372
NIELSEN SPORTS ITALIA SRL.—See Brookfield Corporation; *Int'l*, pg. 1179
NIELSEN SPORTS ITALIA SRL.—See Elliott Management Corporation; *U.S. Private*, pg. 1372
NIELSEN SPORTS JAPAN K.K.—See Brookfield Corporation; *Int'l*, pg. 1179
NIELSEN SPORTS JAPAN K.K.—See Elliott Management Corporation; *U.S. Private*, pg. 1372
NIELSEN SPORTS KOREA LLC—See Brookfield Corporation; *Int'l*, pg. 1179
NIELSEN SPORTS KOREA LLC—See Elliott Management Corporation; *U.S. Private*, pg. 1372
NIELSEN SPORTS NEDERLAND B.V.—See Brookfield Corporation; *Int'l*, pg. 1180
NIELSEN SPORTS NEDERLAND B.V.—See Elliott Management Corporation; *U.S. Private*, pg. 1372
NIELSEN SPORTS PTY. LTD.—See Brookfield Corporation; *Int'l*, pg. 1180
NIELSEN SPORTS PTY. LTD.—See Elliott Management Corporation; *U.S. Private*, pg. 1372
NIELSEN SPORTS UK & IRELAND LIMITED—See Brookfield Corporation; *Int'l*, pg. 1180
NIELSEN SPORTS UK & IRELAND LIMITED—See Elliott Management Corporation; *U.S. Private*, pg. 1372
NIELSEN TELE MEDICAL GMBH—See Brookfield Corporation; *Int'l*, pg. 1180
NIELSEN TELE MEDICAL GMBH—See Elliott Management Corporation; *U.S. Private*, pg. 1372
NIELSEN TELEVISION AUDIENCE MEASUREMENT PTY. LTD.—See Brookfield Corporation; *Int'l*, pg. 1180
NIELSEN TELEVISION AUDIENCE MEASUREMENT PTY. LTD.—See Elliott Management Corporation; *U.S. Private*, pg. 1372
NIELSEN TUNISIA SARL—See Brookfield Corporation; *Int'l*, pg. 1180
NIELSEN TUNISIA SARL—See Elliott Management Corporation; *U.S. Private*, pg. 1372
NIELSEN TV AUDIENCE MEASUREMENT S.A.—See Brookfield Corporation; *Int'l*, pg. 1180
NIELSEN TV AUDIENCE MEASUREMENT S.A.—See Elliott Management Corporation; *U.S. Private*, pg. 1372
NIELSEN TV AUDIENCE MEASUREMENT S.R.L.—See Brookfield Corporation; *Int'l*, pg. 1180
NIELSEN TV AUDIENCE MEASUREMENT S.R.L.—See Elliott Management Corporation; *U.S. Private*, pg. 1372
NIELS FUGAL SONS COMPANY, LLC—See Dycom Industries, Inc.; *U.S. Public*, pg. 698
NIELSON & COMPANY INCORPORATED; *U.S. Private*, pg. 2927
NIELSON CONSTRUCTION; *U.S. Private*, pg. 2927
NIEMANN FOODS INC.; *U.S. Private*, pg. 2927
NIEMEYER BROTHERS PLUMBING, INC.—See Ontario Municipal Employees Retirement System; *Int'l*, pg. 5584
THE NIEMEYER CORPORATION; *U.S. Private*, pg. 4084
NIEN HSING INTERNATIONAL LESOTHO PTY LTD.—See Nien Hsing Textile Co., Ltd.; *Int'l*, pg. 5280
NIEN HSING INTERNATIONAL VICTORIA S.A.DE C.V—See Nien Hsing Textile Co., Ltd.; *Int'l*, pg. 5280
NIEN HSING NINH BINH GARMENT CO., LTD—See Nien Hsing Textile Co., Ltd.; *Int'l*, pg. 5280
NIEN HSING TEXTILE CO., LTD.; *Int'l*, pg. 5280
NIENKAMPER FURNITURE & ACCESSORIES INC.—See ICF Group; *U.S. Private*, pg. 2031
NIEN MADE ENTERPRISE CO., LTD.; *Int'l*, pg. 5280
NIERENGARTEN & HIPPERT LTD.—See Blethen, Gage & Krause, PLLP; *U.S. Private*, pg. 581
NIES/ARTCRAFT COMPANIES, INC.—See Chatham Asset Management, LLC; *U.S. Private*, pg. 863
NIES/ARTCRAFT, INC.—See Chatham Asset Management, LLC; *U.S. Private*, pg. 864
NIESMANN+ BISCHOFF GMBH—See Thor Industries, Inc.; *U.S. Public*, pg. 2157
NIESSING (AUSTRALIA) PTY. LTD.—See Aspial Corporation Limited; *Int'l*, pg. 630
NIESSING (HONG KONG) LIMITED—See Aspial Corporation Limited; *Int'l*, pg. 630
NIESSING MANUFAKTUR GMBH & CO. KG—See Aspial Corporation Limited; *Int'l*, pg. 630
NIETZ ELECTRIC, INC.—See The Egan Companies; *U.S. Private*, pg. 4025

NIEUWE HOLLANDSE LLOYD VERZEKERINGSGROEP NV—See Munchener Ruckversicherungs AG; *Int'l*, pg. 5087
NIEUWENHUIS BETONRENOVATIE B.V.; *Int'l*, pg. 5280
NIFAST CORPORATION—See Sojitz Corporation; *Int'l*, pg. 7064
NIFCO AMERICA CORPORATION - KENTUCKY MANUFACTURING FACILITY—See Nifco Inc.; *Int'l*, pg. 5281
NIFCO AMERICA CORPORATION—See Nifco Inc.; *Int'l*, pg. 5281
NIFCO AMERICA CORPORATION - TENNESSEE MANUFACTURING FACILITY—See Nifco Inc.; *Int'l*, pg. 5281
NIFCO BUSINESS SERVICE INC.—See Nifco Inc.; *Int'l*, pg. 5281
NIFCO CENTRAL MEXICO S.DE R.L.DE C.V.—See Nifco Inc.; *Int'l*, pg. 5281
NIFCO (CHONGQING) LIMITED LIABILITY COMPANY—See Nifco Inc.; *Int'l*, pg. 5281
NIFCO DEUTSCHLAND GMBH—See Nifco Inc.; *Int'l*, pg. 5281
NIFCO ENTERPRISE MANAGEMENT (SHANGHAI) CO., LTD.—See Nifco Inc.; *Int'l*, pg. 5281
NIFCO (HK) LIMITED—See Nifco Inc.; *Int'l*, pg. 5281
NIFCO (HUBEI) CO., LTD.—See Nifco Inc.; *Int'l*, pg. 5281
NIFCO INC.; *Int'l*, pg. 5281
NIFCO INDIA PRIVATE LTD.—See Nifco Inc.; *Int'l*, pg. 5281
NIFCO (JIANGSU) CO., LTD.—See Nifco Inc.; *Int'l*, pg. 5281
NIFCO KITAKANTO INC.—See Nifco Inc.; *Int'l*, pg. 5281
NIFCO KOREA INC. - CHEONAN PLANT—See Nifco Inc.; *Int'l*, pg. 5281
NIFCO KOREA INC.—See Nifco Inc.; *Int'l*, pg. 5281
NIFCO KOREA INC.- ULSAN PLANT—See Nifco Inc.; *Int'l*, pg. 5281
NIFCO KOREA PLAND SP. Z O.O.—See Nifco Inc.; *Int'l*, pg. 5281
NIFCO KOREA USA INC.—See Nifco Inc.; *Int'l*, pg. 5281
NIFCO KTS GMBH & CO. KG—See Nifco Inc.; *Int'l*, pg. 5281
NIFCO KTW AMERICA CORPORATION—See Nifco Inc.; *Int'l*, pg. 5281
NIFCO KUMAMOTO INC.—See Nifco Inc.; *Int'l*, pg. 5281
NIFCO MANUFACTURING (MALAYSIA) SDN. BHD.—See Nifco Inc.; *Int'l*, pg. 5281
NIFCO POLAND SP. Z O.O.—See Nifco Inc.; *Int'l*, pg. 5281
NIFCO PRODUCTS ESPANA, S. L. U.—See Nifco Inc.; *Int'l*, pg. 5281
NIFCO (SINGAPORE) PTE. LTD.—See Nifco Inc.; *Int'l*, pg. 5281
NIFCO SOUTH INDIA MANUFACTURING PRIVATE LTD.—See Nifco Inc.; *Int'l*, pg. 5281
NIFCO TAIWAN CORPORATION - CHUNGLI FACTORY—See Nifco Inc.; *Int'l*, pg. 5281
NIFCO TAIWAN CORPORATION—See Nifco Inc.; *Int'l*, pg. 5281
NIFCO (THAILAND) CO., LTD.—See Nifco Inc.; *Int'l*, pg. 5281
NIFCO (TIANJIN) CO., LTD.—See Nifco Inc.; *Int'l*, pg. 5281
NIFCO U.K. LTD.—See Nifco Inc.; *Int'l*, pg. 5281
NIFCO VIETNAM LTD.—See Nifco Inc.; *Int'l*, pg. 5281
NIFCO YAMAGATA INC.—See Nifco Inc.; *Int'l*, pg. 5281
NIFCO YANCHENG CO., LTD.—See Nifco Inc.; *Int'l*, pg. 5281
NIF GROUP, INC.—See The Carlyle Group Inc.; *U.S. Public*, pg. 2047
NIFTY CORPORATION—See Fujitsu Limited; *Int'l*, pg. 2837
NIFTYLIFT INC.—See Niftylift Limited; *Int'l*, pg. 5282
NIFTYLIFT LIMITED; *Int'l*, pg. 5282
NIFTYLIFT SA—See Niftylift Limited; *Int'l*, pg. 5282
NIFTY PTY LTD—See Niftylift Limited; *Int'l*, pg. 5282
NIGACHEM NIGERIA LIMITED—See Solar Industries India Limited; *Int'l*, pg. 7069
NIGATA SHIPBUILDING & REPAIR, INC.—See Mitsui E&S Holdings Co., Ltd.; *Int'l*, pg. 4986
NIGBAS NIGDE BETON SANAYI VE TICARET A.S.; *Int'l*, pg. 5282
NIGER-AFRIQUE S.A.—See General Atlantic Service Company, L.P.; *U.S. Private*, pg. 1661
NIGERIA EAGLE FLOUR MILLS LIMITED—See Flour Mills of Nigeria Plc.; *Int'l*, pg. 2709
NIGERIA ENAMELWARE CO. PLC; *Int'l*, pg. 5282
NIGERIAN AGIP OIL CO. LTD.—See Oando PLC; *Int'l*, pg. 5505
NIGERIAN AVIATION HANDLING COMPANY PLC; *Int'l*, pg. 5282
NIGERIAN BOTTLING COMPANY LTD.—See Coca-Cola HBC AG; *Int'l*, pg. 1686
NIGERIAN BREWERIES PLC—See L'Arche Green N.V.; *Int'l*, pg. 4377
NIGERIAN EAGLE FLOUR MILLS LIMITED—See Flour Mills of Nigeria Plc.; *Int'l*, pg. 2709
THE NIGERIAN GAS COMPANY LIMITED—See Nigerian National Petroleum Corporation; *Int'l*, pg. 5282
NIGERIAN-GERMAN CHEMICALS PLC; *Int'l*, pg. 5282

NI HOLDINGS, INC.

NIGERIAN MOTOR INDUSTRIES LTD.—See Toyota Tsusho Corporation; *Int'l*, pg. 7876
NIGERIAN NATIONAL PETROLEUM CORPORATION; *Int'l*, pg. 5282
NIGERIAN PETROLEUM DEVELOPMENT COMPANY LTD.—See Nigerian National Petroleum Corporation; *Int'l*, pg. 5282
NIGERIAN SEWING MACHINE MANUFACTURING PLC; *Int'l*, pg. 5282
THE NIGERIAN STOCK EXCHANGE; *Int'l*, pg. 7670
NIGERIAN WESTMINSTER DREDGING & MARINE LTD.—See HAL Trust N.V.; *Int'l*, pg. 3226
NIGERIAN WIRE AND CABLE CO., LTD.—See Sumitomo Electric Industries, Ltd.; *Int'l*, pg. 7284
NIGER INSURANCE PLC.; *Int'l*, pg. 5282
NIGER TERMINAL SA—See Financiere de L'Odet; *Int'l*, pg. 2667
NIG GASES SDN BHD—See Mitsubishi Chemical Group Corporation; *Int'l*, pg. 4936
NIG GASES SDN BHD—See Mitsubishi Chemical Group Corporation; *Int'l*, pg. 4936
NIGHTCAP PLC; *Int'l*, pg. 5282
NIGHTDRAGON ACQUISITION CORP.; *U.S. Public*, pg. 1528
NIGHTFOOD HOLDINGS, INC.; *U.S. Public*, pg. 1528
NIGHTFOOD, INC.—See NightFood Holdings, Inc.; *U.S. Public*, pg. 1528
NIGHTHAWK ENERGY PLC; *Int'l*, pg. 5282
NIGHTHAWK GOLD CORP.—See STLLR Gold Inc.; *Int'l*, pg. 7216
NIGHTHAWK RADIOLOGY, INC.—See MEDNAX, Inc.; *U.S. Public*, pg. 1413
NIGHTINGALE ARCHITECTS LIMITED—See ARCADIS N.V.; *Int'l*, pg. 542
NIGHTINGALE-CONANT CORPORATION; *U.S. Private*, pg. 2927
NIGHTINGALE-CONANT RECORDING & TAPE DUPLICATING DIVISION—See Nightingale-Conant Corporation; *U.S. Private*, pg. 2927
NIGHTINGALE HEALTH OYJ; *Int'l*, pg. 5282
NIGHTINGALE INTELLIGENT SYSTEMS INC.; *U.S. Public*, pg. 1528
NIGHTINGALE LEGAL SERVICES LTD.—See Munchener Ruckversicherungs AG; *Int'l*, pg. 5091
NIGHT OPTICS USA, INC.—See Vista Outdoor Inc.; *U.S. Public*, pg. 2305
NIGHTSEA LLC—See Physical Sciences Inc.; *U.S. Private*, pg. 3175
NIGHTSTAR THERAPEUTICS PLC—See Biogen Inc.; *U.S. Public*, pg. 337
NIGHT VISION ENTERTAINMENT; *U.S. Private*, pg. 2927
NIGICO CO., LTD.—See Nissui Corporation; *Int'l*, pg. 5378
NIG INDUSTRIAL GASES SDN BHD—See Mitsubishi Chemical Group Corporation; *Int'l*, pg. 4936
NIGK CORPORATION—See NOF Corporation; *Int'l*, pg. 5400
NIGOLICE TRADING PRIVATE LIMITED—See Tantia Constructions Ltd.; *Int'l*, pg. 7460
NIGU CHEMIE GMBH—See BLUO SICAV-SIF; *Int'l*, pg. 1075
NIHAKI SYSTEMS, INC.; *U.S. Private*, pg. 2927
NIHAN PIGMENT SDN. BHD.—See Omni-Plus System Limited; *Int'l*, pg. 5563
NIHAO MINERAL RESOURCES INTERNATIONAL, INC.; *Int'l*, pg. 5283
NIHAR INFO GLOBAL LTD.; *Int'l*, pg. 5283
NIHEI CO., LTD.—See Sumitomo Forestry Co., Ltd.; *Int'l*, pg. 7285
NIHILENT ANALYTICS LTD—See Nihilent Technologies Ltd.; *Int'l*, pg. 5283
NIHILENT AUSTRALIA PTY. LIMITED—See Nippon Telegraph & Telephone Corporation; *Int'l*, pg. 5354
NIHILENT LIMITED—See Nippon Telegraph & Telephone Corporation; *Int'l*, pg. 5354
NIHILENT TECHNOLOGIES LTD.; *Int'l*, pg. 5283
NIHLEN ELMONTAGE AB—See Instalco AB; *Int'l*, pg. 3722
NIH NORDINVEST HAMBURG GMBH; *Int'l*, pg. 5283
NI HOLDINGS, INC.; *U.S. Public*, pg. 1527
NIHON AIRPAX CO., LTD.—See Sensata Technologies Holding plc; *U.S. Public*, pg. 1866
NIHON APOCH CO., LTD.—See Alfresa Holdings Corporation; *Int'l*, pg. 317
NIHON ARIBA, K.K.—See SAP SE; *Int'l*, pg. 6567
NIHON AXIS CO., LTD.—See Open Up Group Inc; *Int'l*, pg. 5599
NIHON BALZERS CO. LTD.—See OC Oerlikon Corporation AG; *Int'l*, pg. 5512
NIHON B.F. & CO., LTD.—See Inabata & Co. Ltd.; *Int'l*, pg. 3644
NIHON BISOH CO., LTD.—See Mitani Corporation; *Int'l*, pg. 4924
NIHON BUILDING CO. LTD.—See Japan Securities Finance Co., Ltd.; *Int'l*, pg. 3905
NIHON BUSINESS SOFT CO., LTD.—See FUJISOFT INCORPORATED; *Int'l*, pg. 2830
NIHON BUTSURYU SHINBUN CO., LTD.—See Yamazen Corporation; *Int'l*, pg. 8558

NI HOLDINGS, INC.

NIHON CABOT MICROELECTRONICS K.K.—See Entegris, Inc.; *U.S. Public*, pg. 776
NIHON CANPACK CO. LTD.; *Int'l*, pg. 5283
NIHON CANPACK VIETNAM CO LTD.—See Nihon Canpack Co. Ltd.; *Int'l*, pg. 5283
NIHON CEVA K.K.—See CEVA, Inc.; *U.S. Public*, pg. 476
NIHON CHEMICAL COAT CO., LTD.—See Asahi Intecc Co., Ltd.; *Int'l*, pg. 594
NIHON CHOUZAI CO., LTD.; *Int'l*, pg. 5283
NIHON COCHLEAR CO LIMITED—See Cochlear Limited; *Int'l*, pg. 1687
NIHON COOLER CO., LTD.—See UACJ Corporation; *Int'l*, pg. 7999
NIHON CORNET TECHNOLOGY K.K.—See Cornet Technology Inc.; *U.S. Private*, pg. 1053
NIHON DATA MATERIAL CO., LTD.—See Nihon Handa Co., Ltd.; *Int'l*, pg. 5284
NIHON DECOLUXE CO., LTD.; *Int'l*, pg. 5283
NIHON DEMPA KOGYO CO., LTD. - SAYAMA PLANT—See NIHON DEMPA KOGYO Co Ltd; *Int'l*, pg. 5283
NIHON DEMPA KOGYO CO LTD; *Int'l*, pg. 5283
NIHON DENGI CO., LTD.; *Int'l*, pg. 5283
NIHON DENKEI CO., LTD.—See NIHON DENKEI CO., LTD.; *Int'l*, pg. 5284
NIHON DENKEI CO., LTD.; *Int'l*, pg. 5283
NIHON DENKEI (HONG KONG) LIMITED—See NIHON DENKEI CO., LTD.; *Int'l*, pg. 5284
NIHON DENKEI INDIA PRIVATE LIMITED—See NIHON DENKEI CO., LTD.; *Int'l*, pg. 5284
NIHON DENKEI (MALAYSIA) SDN BHD—See NIHON DENKEI CO., LTD.; *Int'l*, pg. 5284
NIHON DENKEI (THAILAND) CO., LTD.—See NIHON DENKEI CO., LTD.; *Int'l*, pg. 5284
NIHON DENKEI VIETNAM CO., LTD.—See NIHON DENKEI CO., LTD.; *Int'l*, pg. 5284
NIHON DENNETSU CO., LTD.—See Air Water Inc.; *Int'l*, pg. 240
NIHON ECOAGRO CO., LTD—See Sumitomo Chemical Company, Limited; *Int'l*, pg. 7264
NIHON ECOTECH CO., LTD.—See Adeka Corporation; *Int'l*, pg. 142
NIHON ELECTRIC WIRE & CABLE CO., LTD. - HYOGO FACTORY—See JMACS Japan Co., Ltd.; *Int'l*, pg. 3974
NIHON ENTEGRIS K.K.—See Entegris, Inc.; *U.S. Public*, pg. 777
NIHON ENTERPRISE CO., LTD.; *Int'l*, pg. 5284
NIHON FALCOM CORPORATION; *Int'l*, pg. 5284
NIHON FIRMENICH K.K. - OSAKA BRANCH—See Firmenich International SA; *Int'l*, pg. 2681
NIHON FIRMENICH K.K.—See Firmenich International SA; *Int'l*, pg. 2681
NIHON FLUSH CO., LTD.; *Int'l*, pg. 5284
NIHON FORM SERVICE CO., LTD.; *Int'l*, pg. 5284
NIHON FUREKI SANGYO CO., LTD.—See Noritake Co., Limited; *Int'l*, pg. 5428
NIHONGAS KOJI, INC.—See Nippon Gas Co., Ltd.; *Int'l*, pg. 5318
NIHON GENERIC CO., LTD.—See Nihon Chouzai Co., Ltd.; *Int'l*, pg. 5283
NIHON HANDA CO., LTD. - FUNABASHI PLANT—See Nihon Handa Co., Ltd.; *Int'l*, pg. 5284
NIHON HANDA CO., LTD.; *Int'l*, pg. 5284
NIHON HANDA (HK) LIMITED—See Nihon Handa Co., Ltd.; *Int'l*, pg. 5284
NIHON HANDA MANUFACTURING (MALAYSIA) SDN. BHD.—See Nihon Handa Co., Ltd.; *Int'l*, pg. 5284
NIHON HANDA (SHANGHAI) CO., LTD.—See Nihon Handa Co., Ltd.; *Int'l*, pg. 5284
NIHON HARD METAL CO., LTD.—See OSG Corporation; *Int'l*, pg. 5649
NIHON HARTMANN K.K.—See Thornico A/S; *Int'l*, pg. 7719
NIHON HIRYO CO., LTD.—See Nissan Chemical Corporation; *Int'l*, pg. 5366
NIHON HONSHOU CO., LTD.—See PT Bank JTrust Indonesia Tbk.; *Int'l*, pg. 6026
NIHON HOSO YOKI CO., LTD.—See Oji Holdings Corporation; *Int'l*, pg. 5537
NIHON HOUSE HOLDINGS CO., LTD.; *Int'l*, pg. 5284
NIHON HOUSING CO. LTD.; *Int'l*, pg. 5284
NIHON ISK COMPANY, LIMITED; *Int'l*, pg. 5284
NIHON JUNYAKU CO., LTD.—See Toagosei Co. Ltd.; *Int'l*, pg. 7770
NIHON JYOHO CREATE CO., LTD.; *Int'l*, pg. 5284
NIHON JYUTAKU RYUTU CO., LTD.—See Daiwa House Industry Co., Ltd.; *Int'l*, pg. 1947
NIHON KAGAKU SANGYO CO., LTD. - AOYAGI PLANT—See Nihon Kagaku Sangyo Co., Ltd.; *Int'l*, pg. 5285
NIHON KAGAKU SANGYO CO., LTD. - FUKUSHIMA NO.1 PLANT—See Nihon Kagaku Sangyo Co., Ltd.; *Int'l*, pg. 5285
NIHON KAGAKU SANGYO CO., LTD. - FUKUSHIMA NO.2 PLANT—See Nihon Kagaku Sangyo Co., Ltd.; *Int'l*, pg. 5285

NIHON KAGAKU SANGYO CO., LTD. - OTONE PLANT—See Nihon Kagaku Sangyo Co., Ltd.; *Int'l*, pg. 5285
NIHON KAGAKU SANGYO CO., LTD. - SAITAMA PLANT—See Nihon Kagaku Sangyo Co., Ltd.; *Int'l*, pg. 5285
NIHON KAGAKU SANGYO CO., LTD.; *Int'l*, pg. 5284
NIHONKAI CONCRETE INDUSTRIES CO.—See Hokuriku Electric Power Co.; *Int'l*, pg. 3445
NIHON KAIHATSU KOSAN CO., LTD.—See Takasago Thermal Engineering Co., Ltd.; *Int'l*, pg. 7434
NIHONKAI LNG CO., LTD.—See Tohoku Electric Power Co., Inc.; *Int'l*, pg. 7777
NIHON KAISER CO., LTD.—See Kurimoto Ltd; *Int'l*, pg. 4339
NIHON KANZUME, CO., LTD.—See Meiji Holdings Co., Ltd.; *Int'l*, pg. 4801
NIHON KEIZAI ADVERTISING CO., LTD.; *Int'l*, pg. 5285
NIHON KEIZAI SHIMBUN EUROPE LTD.—See Nikkei Inc.; *Int'l*, pg. 5289
NIHON KENKI LEASE CO., LTD.—See Caterpillar, Inc.; *U.S. Public*, pg. 453
NIHON KENSETSU KOGYO CO., LTD.—See Mitsubishi Heavy Industries, Ltd.; *Int'l*, pg. 4960
NIHON KENSHI CO., LTD.—See Mipox Corporation; *Int'l*, pg. 4915
NIHON KIKAI KOGYO CO., LTD.—See Katakura Industries Co., Ltd.; *Int'l*, pg. 4089
NIHON KNOWLEDGE CO., LTD.; *Int'l*, pg. 5285
NIHON KOGYO CO., LTD.; *Int'l*, pg. 5285
NIHON KOHDEN AMERICA, INC.—See Nihon Kohden Corporation; *Int'l*, pg. 5285
NIHON KOHDEN CHUBU CORPORATION—See Nihon Kohden Corporation; *Int'l*, pg. 5285
NIHON KOHDEN CHUSHIKOKU CORPORATION—See Nihon Kohden Corporation; *Int'l*, pg. 5285
NIHON KOHDEN CORPORATION - INTERNATIONAL DIVISION—See Nihon Kohden Corporation; *Int'l*, pg. 5285
NIHON KOHDEN CORPORATION; *Int'l*, pg. 5285
NIHON KOHDEN DEUTSCHLAND GMBH—See Nihon Kohden Corporation; *Int'l*, pg. 5285
NIHON KOHDEN DIGITAL HEALTH SOLUTIONS, LLC—See Nihon Kohden Corporation; *Int'l*, pg. 5285
NIHON KOHDEN DO BRASIL LTDA.—See Nihon Kohden Corporation; *Int'l*, pg. 5285
NIHON KOHDEN EUROPE GMBH—See Nihon Kohden Corporation; *Int'l*, pg. 5285
NIHON KOHDEN FIRENZE S.R.L.—See Nihon Kohden Corporation; *Int'l*, pg. 5285
NIHON KOHDEN FRANCE S.A.R.L.—See Nihon Kohden Corporation; *Int'l*, pg. 5285
NIHON KOHDEN HIGASHI KANTO CORPORATION—See Nihon Kohden Corporation; *Int'l*, pg. 5285
NIHON KOHDEN IBERICA S.L.—See Nihon Kohden Corporation; *Int'l*, pg. 5285
NIHON KOHDEN INDIA PVT. LTD.—See Nihon Kohden Corporation; *Int'l*, pg. 5285
NIHON KOHDEN INNOVATION CENTER, INC.—See Nihon Kohden Corporation; *Int'l*, pg. 5285
NIHON KOHDEN ITALIA S.R.L.—See Nihon Kohden Corporation; *Int'l*, pg. 5285
NIHON KOHDEN KOREA, INC.—See Nihon Kohden Corporation; *Int'l*, pg. 5285
NIHON KOHDEN LATIN AMERICA S.A.S—See Nihon Kohden Corporation; *Int'l*, pg. 5285
NIHON KOHDEN MALAYSIA SDN. BHD.—See Nihon Kohden Corporation; *Int'l*, pg. 5285
NIHON KOHDEN MEXICO S.A. DE C.V.—See Nihon Kohden Corporation; *Int'l*, pg. 5285
NIHON KOHDEN MIDDLE EAST FZE—See Nihon Kohden Corporation; *Int'l*, pg. 5285
NIHON KOHDEN MINAMI KANTO CORPORATION—See Nihon Kohden Corporation; *Int'l*, pg. 5285
NIHON KOHDEN ORANGEMED, INC.—See Nihon Kohden Corporation; *Int'l*, pg. 5285
NIHON KOHDEN SINGAPORE PTE LTD—See Nihon Kohden Corporation; *Int'l*, pg. 5285
NIHON KOHDEN (THAILAND) CO., LTD.—See Nihon Kohden Corporation; *Int'l*, pg. 5285
NIHON KOHDEN TOHOKU CO., LTD.—See Nihon Kohden Corporation; *Int'l*, pg. 5286
NIHON KOHDEN TOKYO CORPORATION—See Nihon Kohden Corporation; *Int'l*, pg. 5286
NIHON KOHDEN TOMIOKA CORPORATION—See Nihon Kohden Corporation; *Int'l*, pg. 5286
NIHON KOHDEN TRADING (SHANGHAI) CO., LTD.—See Nihon Kohden Corporation; *Int'l*, pg. 5286
NIHON KOHDEN UK LTD.—See Nihon Kohden Corporation; *Int'l*, pg. 5286
NIHON KOLMAR CO., LTD.; *Int'l*, pg. 5286
NIHON L'OREAL KK—See L'Oreal S.A.; *Int'l*, pg. 4381
NIHON M&A CENTER HOLDINGS INC.; *Int'l*, pg. 5286
NIHON MAGNESIO S.A DE C.V—See Nihon Plast Co., Ltd.; *Int'l*, pg. 5287
NIHON MATAI CO., LTD.—See Rengo Co., Ltd.; *Int'l*, pg. 6280

CORPORATE AFFILIATIONS

NIHONMATSU NOK CORPORATION—See NOK Corporation; *Int'l*, pg. 5402
NIHON MECCS CO., LTD.—See Nippon Telegraph & Telephone Corporation; *Int'l*, pg. 5354
NIHON MEDI-PHYSICS CO., LTD.—See Sumitomo Chemical Company, Limited; *Int'l*, pg. 7264
NIHON MERCURY COMPUTER SYSTEMS K.K.—See Mercury Systems, Inc.; *U.S. Public*, pg. 1422
NIHON MICHELIN TIRE CO., LTD.—See Compagnie Generale des Etablissements Michelin SCA; *Int'l*, pg. 1743
NIHON MILLIPORE K.K.—See Merck KGaA; *Int'l*, pg. 4831
NIHONMUSEN GLASS CO., LTD.—See Nisshinbo Holdings Inc.; *Int'l*, pg. 5373
NIHON NETWORK SERVICE CO., LTD.—See Ship Healthcare Holdings, Inc.; *Int'l*, pg. 6852
NIHON NETWORK SUPPORT CO., LTD.—See The Kansai Electric Power Co., Inc.; *Int'l*, pg. 7662
NIHON NEWTOUCH SOFTWARE CO., LTD.—See Shanghai Newtouch Software Co., Ltd.; *Int'l*, pg. 6776
NIHON NOHYAKU CO., LTD.—See Adeka Corporation; *Int'l*, pg. 142
NIHON PACKAGING MATERIAL CO., LTD.—See DIC Corporation; *Int'l*, pg. 2109
NIHON PALL LTD.—See Danaher Corporation; *U.S. Public*, pg. 629
NIHON PALL MANUFACTURING LIMITED—See Danaher Corporation; *U.S. Public*, pg. 628
NIHON PARKERIZING CO., LTD.; *Int'l*, pg. 5286
NIHON PARKERIZING (INDIA) PVT. LTD.—See Nihon Parkerizing Co., Ltd.; *Int'l*, pg. 5286
NIHON PARKERIZING MALAYSIA SDN. BHD.—See Nihon Parkerizing Co., Ltd.; *Int'l*, pg. 5286
NIHON PARKING CORPORATION—See Tokyo Tatemono Co. Ltd.; *Int'l*, pg. 7796
NIHON PHARMACEUTICAL CO., LTD.—See Takeda Pharmaceutical Company Limited; *Int'l*, pg. 7437
NIHON PHARMACEUTICAL INDUSTRY CO., LTD.—See Nippon Chemiphar Co., Ltd.; *Int'l*, pg. 5313
NIHON PIPE SYSTEM CO., LTD.—See Nippon Steel Corporation; *Int'l*, pg. 5336
NIHON PLAST CO., LTD.; *Int'l*, pg. 5287
NIHON PLAST MEXICANA S.A DE C.V—See Nihon Plast Co., Ltd.; *Int'l*, pg. 5287
NIHON PLAST THAILAND CO., LTD.—See Nihon Plast Co., Ltd.; *Int'l*, pg. 5287
NIHON PLAST (WUHAN) CO., LTD.—See Nihon Plast Co., Ltd.; *Int'l*, pg. 5287
NIHON PLAST (ZHONGSHAN) CO., LTD.—See Nihon Plast Co., Ltd.; *Int'l*, pg. 5287
NIHON PREVENTIVE MEDICAL LABORATORY CO., LTD.—See AFC-HD AMS Life Science Co., Ltd.; *Int'l*, pg. 185
NIHON RADIALL K.K.—See Radiall S.A.; *Int'l*, pg. 6174
NIHON RESIN CO., LTD.—See Shin-Etsu Chemical Co. Ltd.; *Int'l*, pg. 6839
NIHON RIKA SEISHI CO., LTD.—See Tomoegawa Co., Ltd.; *Int'l*, pg. 7801
NIHON RINSHO, INC.—See H.U. Group Holdings, Inc.; *Int'l*, pg. 3197
NIHON SECURITIES JOURNAL INC.—See Japan Investment Adviser Co., Ltd.; *Int'l*, pg. 3898
NIHON SEIKAN K.K.; *Int'l*, pg. 5287
NIHON SEIKO CO. LTD.—See Sojitz Corporation; *Int'l*, pg. 7062
THE NIHON SEIMA CO., LTD.; *Int'l*, pg. 7670
NIHON SEIMITSU CO., LTD.; *Int'l*, pg. 5287
NIHON SENKO CO., LTD.—See Godo Steel, Ltd.; *Int'l*, pg. 3020
NIHON SENSITECH CORPORATION—See Carrier Global Corporation; *U.S. Public*, pg. 443
NIHON SETSUBI KOGYO CO., LTD.—See Takasago Thermal Engineering Co., Ltd.; *Int'l*, pg. 7434
NIHON SHOKUHIN KAKO CO., LTD.; *Int'l*, pg. 5287
NIHON SHOKUZAI CO., LTD.—See Fujiya Co., Ltd.; *Int'l*, pg. 2838
NIHON SINGAPORE POLYOLEFIN CO., LTD—See Sumitomo Chemical Company, Limited; *Int'l*, pg. 7264
NIHON SPINDLE COOLING TOWERS SDN. BHD.—See Sumitomo Heavy Industries, Ltd.; *Int'l*, pg. 7287
NIHON SPINDLE MANUFACTURING CO., LTD.—See Sumitomo Heavy Industries, Ltd.; *Int'l*, pg. 7287
NIHON SPINDLE MFG. CO., LTD.—See Sumitomo Heavy Industries, Ltd.; *Int'l*, pg. 7287
NIHON STERY, INC.—See H.U. Group Holdings, Inc.; *Int'l*, pg. 3197
NIHON SYNOPSYS G.K.—See Synopsys, Inc.; *U.S. Public*, pg. 1970
NIHON SYNOPSYS GK—See Synopsys, Inc.; *U.S. Public*, pg. 1971
NIHON SYSTEM SHUNO, INC.—See T&D Holdings, Inc.; *Int'l*, pg. 7395
NIHON TENNEN GAS CO., LTD.—See K&O Energy Group Inc.; *Int'l*, pg. 4038
NIHON TETRA PAK K.K.—See Tetra Laval International S.A.; *Int'l*, pg. 7577
NIHON TIMKEN K.K.—See The Timken Company; *U.S. Public*, pg. 2133
NIHON TOKUSHU TORYO CO., LTD.; *Int'l*, pg. 5287
NIHON TRIM CO., LTD.; *Int'l*, pg. 5287

COMPANY NAME INDEX

NIHON TUG-BOAT CO., LTD.—See Mitsui O.S.K. Lines, Ltd.; *Int'l*, pg. 4991
NIHONWASOU HOLDINGS, INC.; *Int'l*, pg. 5288
NIHON WENDIES, LTD.—See Zensho Holdings Co., Ltd.; *Int'l*, pg. 8634
NIHON YAMAMURA GLASS CO., LTD. - AMAGASAKI PLANT—See Nihon Yamamura Glass Co., Ltd.; *Int'l*, pg. 5288
NIHON YAMAMURA GLASS CO., LTD. - HARIMA PLANT—See Nihon Yamamura Glass Co., Ltd.; *Int'l*, pg. 5288
NIHON YAMAMURA GLASS CO., LTD. - KANSAI PLANT—See Nihon Yamamura Glass Co., Ltd.; *Int'l*, pg. 5288
NIHON YAMAMURA GLASS CO., LTD. - KAWAJIMA PLANT—See Nihon Yamamura Glass Co., Ltd.; *Int'l*, pg. 5288
NIHON YAMAMURA GLASS CO., LTD. - NARUOHAMA PLANT—See Nihon Yamamura Glass Co., Ltd.; *Int'l*, pg. 5288
NIHON YAMAMURA GLASS CO., LTD. - OSAKA PLANT—See Nihon Yamamura Glass Co., Ltd.; *Int'l*, pg. 5288
NIHON YAMAMURA GLASS CO., LTD. - SAITAMA PLANT—See Nihon Yamamura Glass Co., Ltd.; *Int'l*, pg. 5288
NIHON YAMAMURA GLASS CO., LTD.; *Int'l*, pg. 5288
NIHON YAMAMURA GLASS CO., LTD. - UTSUNOMIYA PLANT—See Nihon Yamamura Glass Co., Ltd.; *Int'l*, pg. 5288
NIHON YOSHOKKI CO.,LTD.—See Sato shoji Corporation; *Int'l*, pg. 6586
NIHO (SINGAPORE) PTE LTD—See HG Metal Manufacturing Limited; *Int'l*, pg. 3375
NI HSIN CORPORATION SDN. BHD.—See Ni Hsin Group Berhad; *Int'l*, pg. 5259
NI HSIN ECOLOGISTICS SDN. BHD.—See Ni Hsin Group Berhad; *Int'l*, pg. 5259
NI HSIN GROUP BERHAD; *Int'l*, pg. 5259
NI HUNGARY KFT.—See National Instruments Corporation; *U.S. Private*, pg. 2857
NIIB GROUP LIMITED—See Bank of Ireland Group plc; *Int'l*, pg. 844
NIIGATA BANDAIJIMA BUILDING CO., LTD.—See Kajima Corporation; *Int'l*, pg. 4055
NIIGATA FRESH DELICA CO., LTD.—See Maruha Nichiro Corporation; *Int'l*, pg. 4711
NIIGATA HAKUHODO INC.—See Hakuhodo DY Holdings Incorporated; *Int'l*, pg. 3222
NIIGATA HITACHI CO., LTD.—See Hitachi, Ltd.; *Int'l*, pg. 3423
NIIGATA ISETAN MITSUKOSHI LTD.—See Isetan Mitsukoshi Holdings Ltd.; *Int'l*, pg. 3815
NIIGATA JAMCO CORPORATION—See JAMCO Corporation; *Int'l*, pg. 3874
NIIGATA JOINT OIL STOCKPILING CO., LTD—See Idemitsu Kosan Co., Ltd.; *Int'l*, pg. 3592
NIIGATA KOTSU CO., LTD.; *Int'l*, pg. 5288
NIIGATA MACHINE TECHNO CO., LTD.—See Fair Friend Group; *Int'l*, pg. 2604
NIIGATA MAZDA CO., LTD.—See Nippon Seiki Co., Ltd.; *Int'l*, pg. 5330
NIIGATA MIRAI CO., LTD.—See Takamatsu Construction Group Co., Ltd.; *Int'l*, pg. 7430
NIIGATA MOLDING CO., LTD.—See Maezawa Kasei Industries Co., Ltd.; *Int'l*, pg. 4636
NIIGATA MORISHIGYO CO., LTD.—See Oji Holdings Corporation; *Int'l*, pg. 5537
NIIGATA OKAMOTO GLASS CO., LTD.—See Okamoto Glass Co., Ltd; *Int'l*, pg. 5544
NIIGATA PCC CO., LTD.—See Taiheiyo Cement Corporation; *Int'l*, pg. 7412
NIIGATA POWER SYSTEMS CO., LTD.—See IHI Corporation; *Int'l*, pg. 3606
NIIGATA POWER SYSTEMS (EUROPE) B.V.—See IHI Corporation; *Int'l*, pg. 3606
NIIGATA POWER SYSTEMS PHILIPPINES, INC.—See IHI Corporation; *Int'l*, pg. 3606
NIIGATA POWER SYSTEMS (SINGAPORE) PTE. LTD.—See IHI Corporation; *Int'l*, pg. 3606
NIIGATA POWER SYTEMS (SHANGHAI) CO., LTD.—See IHI Corporation; *Int'l*, pg. 3606
NIIGATA SANYO ELECTRONIC CO., LTD.—See Panasonic Holdings Corporation; *Int'l*, pg. 5723
NIIGATA SHOWA K.K.—See Resonac Holdings Corporation; *Int'l*, pg. 6298
NIIGATA STEEL CORPORATION—See JFE Holdings, Inc.; *Int'l*, pg. 3937
NIIGATA SUBARU INC.—See SUBARU CO., LTD.; *Int'l*, pg. 7246
NIIGATA TAIYO YUDEN CO., LTD.—See Taiyo Yuden Company Ltd.; *Int'l*, pg. 7427
NIIGATA TRSNSYS CO., LTD.—See IHI Corporation; *Int'l*, pg. 3606
NIIGATA WACOAL SEWING CORP.—See Wacoal Holdings Corp.; *Int'l*, pg. 8326
NIIGATA YOSHINO GYPSUM CO., LTD.—See Central Glass Co., Ltd.; *Int'l*, pg. 1407

NIIGATA YUSO CO., LTD—See Kameda Seika Co., Ltd.; *Int'l*, pg. 4061
NIIHAMA COAL CENTER CO., LTD.—See Sumitomo Chemical Company, Limited; *Int'l*, pg. 7264
NIIHAMA ELECTRONICS CO., LTD.—See Sumitomo Metal Mining Co., Ltd.; *Int'l*, pg. 7291
NII HOLDINGS, INC.; *U.S. Private*, pg. 2927
NIIIO FINANCE GROUP AG; *Int'l*, pg. 5288
NIIKAWA SANKYO CO., LTD.—See NIPPON CARBIDE INDUSTRIES CO., INC.; *Int'l*, pg. 5311
NI INFORMATION SYSTEM CO., LTD.—See International Business Machines Corporation; *U.S. Public*, pg. 1147
NIIT AIRLINE TECHNOLOGIES GMBH—See Coforge Ltd.; *Int'l*, pg. 1693
NIITAKA CO., LTD.; *Int'l*, pg. 5289
NIIT C&G LIMITED—See Car & General (Kenya) Limited; *Int'l*, pg. 1319
NIIT CHINA (SHANGHAI) LIMITED—See NIIT Limited; *Int'l*, pg. 5289
NIIT INSTITUTE OF FINANCE BANKING & INSURANCE TRAINING LIMITED—See NIIT Limited; *Int'l*, pg. 5289
NIIT LEARNING LIMITED—See Car & General (Kenya) Limited; *Int'l*, pg. 1319
NIIT LEARNING SOLUTIONS (CANADA) LIMITED—See NIIT Limited; *Int'l*, pg. 5289
NIIT LIMITED; *Int'l*, pg. 5288
NIIT LIMITED—See NIIT Limited; *Int'l*, pg. 5289
NIIT MALAYSIA SDN BHD.—See Coforge Ltd.; *Int'l*, pg. 1693
NIIT SMART SERVE LTD—See Coforge Ltd.; *Int'l*, pg. 1693
NIIT TECHNOLOGIES AG—See Coforge Ltd.; *Int'l*, pg. 1693
NIIT TECHNOLOGIES FZ LLC—See Coforge Ltd.; *Int'l*, pg. 1693
NIIT TECHNOLOGIES GMBH—See Coforge Ltd.; *Int'l*, pg. 1693
NIIT TECHNOLOGIES GMBH—See Coforge Ltd.; *Int'l*, pg. 1693
NIIT TECHNOLOGIES INC.—See Coforge Ltd.; *Int'l*, pg. 1693
NIIT TECHNOLOGIES LIMITED—See Coforge Ltd.; *Int'l*, pg. 1693
NIIT TECHNOLOGIES PTE LTD—See Coforge Ltd.; *Int'l*, pg. 1693
NIIT TECHNOLOGIES PTY LIMITED—See Coforge Ltd.; *Int'l*, pg. 1693
NIIT (USA) INC.—See NIIT Limited; *Int'l*, pg. 5289
NIIYAMA KAMOTSU CO., LTD.—See Rengo Co., Ltd.; *Int'l*, pg. 6280
NIJECT SERVICES COMPANY—See Ingersoll Rand Inc.; *U.S. Public*, pg. 1122
NIJECT SERVICES COMPANY—See Linde plc; *Int'l*, pg. 4509
NIJGH INTERPARTNERS B.V.; *Int'l*, pg. 5289
NIJIGENNOMORI INC.—See Pasona Group Inc.; *Int'l*, pg. 5753
NIKA BIOTECHNOLOGY, INC.—See Nika Pharmaceuticals, Inc.; *U.S. Public*, pg. 1528
NIKAHO GAS CORPORATION—See TOKAI Holdings Corporation; *Int'l*, pg. 7779
NIKAIA, INC.; *U.S. Private*, pg. 2927
NIKA PHARMACEUTICALS, INC.; *U.S. Public*, pg. 1528
NIKA SUGAR—See Gruppa Kompaniy Rusagro OOO; *Int'l*, pg. 3140
NIKA TECHNOLOGIES, INC.; *U.S. Private*, pg. 2927
NIKE 360 HOLDING B.V.—See NIKE, Inc.; *U.S. Public*, pg. 1529
NIKE ARGENTINA S.R.L.—See NIKE, Inc.; *U.S. Public*, pg. 1529
NIKE AUSTRALIA PTY. LTD.—See NIKE, Inc.; *U.S. Public*, pg. 1529
NIKE CANADA LTD.—See NIKE, Inc.; *U.S. Public*, pg. 1529
NIKE COMMUNICATIONS, INC.; *U.S. Private*, pg. 2927
NIKE DE CHILE LTDA.—See NIKE, Inc.; *U.S. Public*, pg. 1529
NIKE DE MEXICO S DE R.L. DE C.V.—See NIKE, Inc.; *U.S. Public*, pg. 1529
NIKE DENMARK APS—See NIKE, Inc.; *U.S. Public*, pg. 1529
NIKE DEUTSCHLAND GMBH—See NIKE, Inc.; *U.S. Public*, pg. 1529
NIKE DO BRASIL COMERCIO E PARTICIPACOES LTDA.—See NIKE, Inc.; *U.S. Public*, pg. 1529
NIKE EUROPEAN OPERATIONS NETHERLANDS B.V.—See NIKE, Inc.; *U.S. Public*, pg. 1529
NIKE FINLAND OY—See NIKE, Inc.; *U.S. Public*, pg. 1529
NIKE FRANCE S.A.R.L.—See NIKE, Inc.; *U.S. Public*, pg. 1529
NIKE GESELLSCHAFT M.B.H.—See NIKE, Inc.; *U.S. Public*, pg. 1529
NIKE GROUP HOLDING B.V.—See NIKE, Inc.; *U.S. Public*, pg. 1529
NIKE HONG KONG LIMITED—See NIKE, Inc.; *U.S. Public*, pg. 1529
NIKE IHM, INC.—See NIKE, Inc.; *U.S. Public*, pg. 1529
NIKE, INC.; *U.S. Public*, pg. 1528

NIKKEI INC.

NIKE INDIA PRIVATE LIMITED—See NIKE, Inc.; *U.S. Public*, pg. 1529
NIKE ISRAEL LTD.—See NIKE, Inc.; *U.S. Public*, pg. 1529
NIKE ITALY S.R.L.—See NIKE, Inc.; *U.S. Public*, pg. 1529
NIKE JAPAN CORP.—See NIKE, Inc.; *U.S. Public*, pg. 1529
NIKE POLAND SP.ZO.O—See NIKE, Inc.; *U.S. Public*, pg. 1529
NIKE RETAIL ISRAEL LTD.—See NIKE, Inc.; *U.S. Public*, pg. 1529
NIKE RETAIL SERVICES INC.—See NIKE, Inc.; *U.S. Public*, pg. 1529
NIKE SPORTS KOREA CO., LTD.—See NIKE, Inc.; *U.S. Public*, pg. 1529
NIKE SWEDEN AB—See NIKE, Inc.; *U.S. Public*, pg. 1529
NIKE (SWITZERLAND) GMBH—See NIKE, Inc.; *U.S. Public*, pg. 1528
NIKE (THAILAND) LIMITED—See NIKE, Inc.; *U.S. Public*, pg. 1528
NIKE (U.K.) LIMITED—See NIKE, Inc.; *U.S. Public*, pg. 1529
NIKHIL ADHESIVES LTD.; *Int'l*, pg. 5289
NIKIFOROVSKY ELEVATOR—See Gruppa Kompaniy Rusagro OOO; *Int'l*, pg. 3140
NIKIFOROVSKY SUGAR—See Gruppa Kompaniy Rusagro OOO; *Int'l*, pg. 3140
NIKITA EHF—See ANTA Sports Products Limited; *Int'l*, pg. 480
NIKITA ENGINE S.R.O.—See Zip Co Limited; *Int'l*, pg. 8685
NIKKA COATING CO., LTD.—See NOF Corporation; *Int'l*, pg. 5400
NIKKA CO., LTD.—See Bell-Park Co., Ltd.; *Int'l*, pg. 966
NIKKA-EN CO., LTD.—See Nippon Carbon Co., Ltd.; *Int'l*, pg. 5311
NIKKA FINE TECHNO CO., LTD.—See Nippon Kayaku Co., Ltd.; *Int'l*, pg. 5320
NIKKA MAINTENANCE CO., LTD.—See Yamada Holdings Co., Ltd.; *Int'l*, pg. 8548
NIKKAN CO., LTD.—See Nippon Light Metal Holdings Company, Ltd.; *Int'l*, pg. 5323
NIKKAN KOGYO SHIMBUN, LTD.; *Int'l*, pg. 5289
NIKKAN SPORTS NEWSPAPER—See The Asahi Shimbun Company; *Int'l*, pg. 7614
NIKKARIT AB—See Mellby Gard Holding AB; *Int'l*, pg. 4811
NIKKATO CORPORATION; *Int'l*, pg. 5289
NIKKATSU CORPORATION; *Int'l*, pg. 5289
THE NIKKA WHISKY DISTILLING CO., LTD.—See Asahi Group Holdings Ltd.; *Int'l*, pg. 594
NIKKEI ADVERTISING CO.; *Int'l*, pg. 5289
NIKKEI ADVERTISING CO.—See Nikkei Advertising Co.; *Int'l*, pg. 5289
NIKKEI ADVERTISING CO.—See Nikkei Advertising Co.; *Int'l*, pg. 5289
NIKKEI AMERICA, INC.—See Nikkei Inc.; *Int'l*, pg. 5289
NIKKEI BP AD. PARTNERS, INC.—See Nikkei Inc.; *Int'l*, pg. 5289
NIKKEI BUSINESS PUBLICATIONS ASIA LTD—See Nikkei Inc.; *Int'l*, pg. 5289
NIKKEI BUSINESS PUBLICATIONS EUROPE LTD.—See Nikkei Inc.; *Int'l*, pg. 5289
NIKKEI BUSINESS PUBLICATIONS, INC.—See Nikkei Inc.; *Int'l*, pg. 5289
NIKKEI CHINA (HONG KONG) LTD.—See Nikkei Inc.; *Int'l*, pg. 5289
NIKKEI CNBC JAPAN INC.—See TV TOKYO Holdings Corporation; *Int'l*, pg. 7987
NIKKEI CULTURE, INC.—See Nikkei Inc.; *Int'l*, pg. 5289
NIKKEI ENGINEERING CO., LTD.—See Nippon Light Metal Holdings Company, Ltd.; *Int'l*, pg. 5323
NIKKEI EUROPE LTD.—See Nikkei Inc.; *Int'l*, pg. 5289
NIKKEI EXTRUSIONS CO., LTD.—See Nippon Light Metal Holdings Company, Ltd.; *Int'l*, pg. 5323
NIKKEI GROUP ASIA PTE. LTD.—See Nikkei Inc.; *Int'l*, pg. 5289
NIKKEI HEAT EXCHANGER CO., LTD—See Modine Manufacturing Company; *U.S. Public*, pg. 1455
NIKKEI HEAT EXCHANGER CO., LTD.—See Nippon Light Metal Holdings Company, Ltd.; *Int'l*, pg. 5323
NIKKEI HOKKAIDO CO., LTD.—See Nippon Light Metal Holdings Company, Ltd.; *Int'l*, pg. 5323
NIKKEI HUMAN RESOURCES, INC.—See Nikkei Inc.; *Int'l*, pg. 5289
NIKKEI IBARAKI NEWSPAPER PRINTING CENTER, INC.—See Nikkei Inc.; *Int'l*, pg. 5289
NIKKEI INAZAWA CO., LTD.—See Nippon Light Metal Holdings Company, Ltd.; *Int'l*, pg. 5323
NIKKEI INC.; *Int'l*, pg. 5289
NIKKEI INFORMATION SYSTEM CO., LTD—See Nippon Light Metal Holdings Company, Ltd.; *Int'l*, pg. 5323
NIKKEI INTERNATIONAL LTD.—See Nikkei Inc.; *Int'l*, pg. 5289
NIKKEI KAMBARA CO., LTD.—See Nippon Light Metal Holdings Company, Ltd.; *Int'l*, pg. 5323
NIKKEIKIN ALUMINIUM CORE TECHNOLOGY CO., LTD.—See Nippon Light Metal Holdings Company, Ltd.; *Int'l*, pg. 5324

NIKKEI INC.   CORPORATE AFFILIATIONS

NIKKEIKIN KAKOH KAIHATSU HOLDINGS COMPANY, LTD.—See Nippon Light Metal Holdings Company, Ltd.; *Int'l*, pg. 5323
NIKKEI LOGISTICS CO., LTD.—See Nippon Light Metal Holdings Company, Ltd.; *Int'l*, pg. 5323
NIKKEI MATSUO CO., LTD.—See Nippon Light Metal Holdings Company, Ltd.; *Int'l*, pg. 5324
NIKKEI MC ALUMINIUM CO., LTD.—See Nippon Light Metal Holdings Company, Ltd.; *Int'l*, pg. 5323
NIKKEI MC ALUMINUM (KUNSHAN) CO., LTD.—See Nippon Light Metal Holdings Company, Ltd.; *Int'l*, pg. 5323
NIKKEI MC ALUMINUM (THAILAND) CO., LTD.—See Nippon Light Metal Holdings Company, Ltd.; *Int'l*, pg. 5324
NIKKEI MEDIA MARKETING, INC.—See Nikkei Inc.; *Int'l*, pg. 5290
NIKKEI METAL CO., LTD.—See Nippon Light Metal Holdings Company, Ltd.; *Int'l*, pg. 5324
NIKKEI-MUTLU DERGI GRUBU A.S.—See Nikkei Inc.; *Int'l*, pg. 5289
NIKKEI NEW BUSINESS CO., LTD.—See Nippon Light Metal Holdings Company, Ltd.; *Int'l*, pg. 5323
NIKKEI NEWSPAPER PRINTING, INC.—See Nikkei Inc.; *Int'l*, pg. 5290
NIKKEI NIIGATA CO., LTD.—See Nippon Light Metal Holdings Company, Ltd.; *Int'l*, pg. 5323
NIKKEI PANEL SYSTEM CO., LTD.—See Nippon Light Metal Holdings Company, Ltd.; *Int'l*, pg. 5324
NIKKEI PANEL SYSTEM VIETNAM COMPANY LIMITED—See Nippon Light Metal Holdings Company, Ltd.; *Int'l*, pg. 5323
NIKKEI PARTNERS CO., LTD.—See Nippon Light Metal Holdings Company, Ltd.; *Int'l*, pg. 5323
NIKKEI PR ADVERTISING CO., LTD.—See Nikkei Inc.; *Int'l*, pg. 5290
NIKKEI RADIO BROADCASTING CORPORATION—See Nikkei Inc.; *Int'l*, pg. 5290
NIKKEI RESEARCH, INC.—See Nikkei Inc.; *Int'l*, pg. 5290
NIKKEI SANGYO CO., LTD.—See Nippon Light Metal Holdings Company, Ltd.; *Int'l*, pg. 5324
NIKKEI SCIENCE, INC.—See Nikkei Inc.; *Int'l*, pg. 5290
NIKKEISHA, INC.—See Nikkei Inc.; *Int'l*, pg. 5290
NIKKEI (SHANGHAI) BODY PARTS CO., LTD.—See Nippon Light Metal Holdings Company, Ltd.; *Int'l*, pg. 5323
NIKKEI (SHANGHAI) INTERNATIONAL TRADING CO., LTD.—See Nippon Light Metal Holdings Company, Ltd.; *Int'l*, pg. 5323
NIKKEI SIAM ALUMINIUM LIMITED—See Nippon Light Metal Holdings Company, Ltd.; *Int'l*, pg. 5324
NIKKEI SINGAPORE ALUMINIUM PTE LTD.—See Nippon Light Metal Holdings Company, Ltd.; *Int'l*, pg. 5324
NIKKEI (SUZHOU) PRECISION PARTS CO., LTD.—See Nippon Light Metal Holdings Company, Ltd.; *Int'l*, pg. 5323
NIKKEI TAIWAN SYSTEM ENGINEERING CO., LTD.—See Nippon Light Metal Holdings Company, Ltd.; *Int'l*, pg. 5324
NIKKEI TECHNOLOGY CENTER CO., LTD.—See Nippon Light Metal Holdings Company, Ltd.; *Int'l*, pg. 5323
NIKKEI VISUAL IMAGES, INC.—See Nikkei Inc.; *Int'l*, pg. 5290
NIKKEI WEST NEWSPAPER PRINTING, INC.—See Nikkei Inc.; *Int'l*, pg. 5289
NIKKEL & ASSOCIATES INC.; *U.S. Private*, pg. 2927
NIKKEL TRADING 392 PROPRIETARY LIMITED; *Int'l*, pg. 5290
NIKKEN CORPORATION CO., LTD.—See Mitsubishi Corporation; *Int'l*, pg. 4942
NIKKEN IGAKU, INC.—See BML, Inc.; *Int'l*, pg. 1076
NIKKEN KOGAKU CO., LTD.; *Int'l*, pg. 5290
NIKKEN REAL ESTATE CO., LTD.—See Mitsubishi Corporation; *Int'l*, pg. 4942
NIKKEN SANGYO CO., LTD.—See Mitsubishi Corporation; *Int'l*, pg. 4942
NIKKEY COMPANY LIMITED—See Hibiya Engineering Ltd; *Int'l*, pg. 3383
NIKKI AMERICA FUEL SYSTEMS, LLC—See NIKKI CO. LTD.; *Int'l*, pg. 5290
NIKKI AMERICA, INC.—See NIKKI CO. LTD.; *Int'l*, pg. 5290
NIKKI BUSINESS SERVICES CO., LTD.—See JGC Holdings Corporation; *Int'l*, pg. 3940
NIKKI CO. LTD.; *Int'l*, pg. 5290
NIKKI CONSTRUCTION CO., LTD.—See JGC Holdings Corporation; *Int'l*, pg. 3940
NIKKI DENSO INTERNATIONAL KOREA CO., LTD.—See CKD Corporation; *Int'l*, pg. 1639
NIKKI GLOBAL FINANCE LIMITED; *Int'l*, pg. 5290
NIKKI INDIA FUEL SYSTEMS PRIVATE LIMITED—See NIKKI CO. LTD.; *Int'l*, pg. 5290
NIKKI KOREA CO., LTD.—See NIKKI CO. LTD.; *Int'l*, pg. 5290
NIKKIN CO., LTD.—See UACJ Corporation; *Int'l*, pg. 7999
NIKKISO AMERICA, INC.—See Nikkiso Co., Ltd.; *Int'l*, pg. 5291
NIKKISO CO., LTD. - HIGASHIMURAYAMA PLANT—See Nikkiso Co., Ltd.; *Int'l*, pg. 5291
NIKKISO CO., LTD. - KANAZAWA PLANT—See Nikkiso Co., Ltd.; *Int'l*, pg. 5291

NIKKISO CO., LTD. - SHIZUOKA PLANT—See Nikkiso Co., Ltd.; *Int'l*, pg. 5291
NIKKISO CO., LTD.; *Int'l*, pg. 5290
NIKKISO CRITICAL CARE MEDICAL SUPPLIES (SHANGHAI) CO., LTD.—See Nikkiso Co., Ltd.; *Int'l*, pg. 5291
NIKKISO CRYO, INC.—See Nikkiso Co., Ltd.; *Int'l*, pg. 5291
NIKKISO EIKO CO., LTD.—See Nikkiso Co., Ltd.; *Int'l*, pg. 5291
NIKKISO EUROPE GMBH—See Nikkiso Co., Ltd.; *Int'l*, pg. 5291
NIKKISO GIKEN CO., LTD.—See Nikkiso Co., Ltd.; *Int'l*, pg. 5291
NIKKI SOLTECH SERVICE CO., LTD.—See NIKKI CO. LTD.; *Int'l*, pg. 5290
NIKKISO MEDICAL (THAILAND) CO., LTD.—See Nikkiso Co., Ltd.; *Int'l*, pg. 5291
NIKKISO M.E.S. CO., LTD.—See Nikkiso Co., Ltd.; *Int'l*, pg. 5291
NIKKISO MIYAZAKI CO., LTD.—See Nikkiso Co., Ltd.; *Int'l*, pg. 5291
NIKKISO PUMPS KOREA LTD.—See Nikkiso Co., Ltd.; *Int'l*, pg. 5291
NIKKISO (SHANGHAI) CONSULTING CO., LTD.—See Nikkiso Co., Ltd.; *Int'l*, pg. 5291
NIKKISO-THERM CO., LTD.—See Nikkiso Co., Ltd.; *Int'l*, pg. 5291
NIKKISO VIETNAM, INC.—See Nikkiso Co., Ltd.; *Int'l*, pg. 5291
NIKKISO VIETNAM MFG CO., LTD.—See Nikkiso Co., Ltd.; *Int'l*, pg. 5291
NIKKI TECHNO CO., LTD.—See NIKKI CO. LTD.; *Int'l*, pg. 5290
NIKKI THAILAND CO., LTD.—See NIKKI CO. LTD.; *Int'l*, pg. 5290
NIKKO ASSET MANAGEMENT AMERICAS, INC.—See Sumitomo Mitsui Trust Holdings, Inc.; *Int'l*, pg. 7296
NIKKO ASSET MANAGEMENT ASIA LIMITED—See Sumitomo Mitsui Trust Holdings, Inc.; *Int'l*, pg. 7296
NIKKO ASSET MANAGEMENT CO., LTD.—See Sumitomo Mitsui Trust Holdings, Inc.; *Int'l*, pg. 7296
NIKKO ASSET MANAGEMENT EUROPE LTD.—See Sumitomo Mitsui Trust Holdings, Inc.; *Int'l*, pg. 7296
NIKKO CO., LTD.; *Int'l*, pg. 5291
NIKKO CO., LTD.—See Takano Co., Ltd.; *Int'l*, pg. 7431
NIKKO DENKI SEISAKUSHO CO., LTD.—See Oki Electric Industry Co., Ltd.; *Int'l*, pg. 5548
NIKKO FUJI ELECTRONICS DONGGUAN CO., LTD.—See ENEOS Holdings, Inc.; *Int'l*, pg. 2416
NIKKO FUJI PRECISION (WUXI) CO., LTD.—See ENEOS Holdings, Inc.; *Int'l*, pg. 2416
NIKKO HANSEN & CO., LTD.—See AS ONE Corporation; *Int'l*, pg. 591
NIKKOH FOOD CORP. - NENOJI PLANT—See Itoham Yonekyu Holdings Inc.; *Int'l*, pg. 3843
NIKKOH FOOD CORP.—See Itoham Yonekyu Holdings Inc.; *Int'l*, pg. 3843
NIKKO HOTELS INTERNATIONAL-USA—See Japan Airlines Co., Ltd.; *Int'l*, pg. 3885
NIKKO INSPECTION SERVICE CO., LTD.—See The Japan Steel Works, Ltd.; *Int'l*, pg. 7659
NIKKO KINZOKU CO., LTD.—See Hanwa Co., Ltd.; *Int'l*, pg. 3263
NIKKO KOSAN CO., LTD.—See The Japan Steel Works, Ltd.; *Int'l*, pg. 7659
NIKKO KOUKI CO., LTD.—See The Japan Steel Works, Ltd.; *Int'l*, pg. 7659
NIKKO LOGISTICS CORP.—See Japan Aviation Electronics Industry, Ltd.; *Int'l*, pg. 3887
NIKKO MATERIALS CO., LTD.—See Eternal Materials Co., Ltd.; *Int'l*, pg. 2521
NIKKO MECHANICS CO., LTD.—See Eternal Materials Co., Ltd.; *Int'l*, pg. 2521
NIKKO METALS HONG KONG LTD.—See ENEOS Holdings, Inc.; *Int'l*, pg. 2416
NIKKO METALS SHANGHAI CO., LTD.—See ENEOS Holdings, Inc.; *Int'l*, pg. 2416
NIKKO METALS TAIWAN CO., LTD. - KUANYIN WORKS—See ENEOS Holdings, Inc.; *Int'l*, pg. 2416
NIKKO METALS TAIWAN CO., LTD.—See ENEOS Holdings, Inc.; *Int'l*, pg. 2416
NIKKO METALS TRADING & SERVICES (SHANGHAI) CO., LTD.—See ENEOS Holdings, Inc.; *Int'l*, pg. 2416
NIKKON HOLDINGS CO., LTD.; *Int'l*, pg. 5291
NIKKO NILKHOSOL CO., LTD.—See Nikko Co., Ltd.; *Int'l*, pg. 5291
NIKKON LIGHTING & ELECTRICAL PTE. LTD.—See Success Transformer Corporation Berhad; *Int'l*, pg. 7250
NIKKO PRINT CORPORATION—See The Pack Corporation; *Int'l*, pg. 7672
NIKKO SEKKEI CO., LTD.—See The Japan Steel Works, Ltd.; *Int'l*, pg. 7659
NIKKO SYSTEMS SOLUTIONS, LTD.—See Sumitomo Mitsui Financial Group, Inc.; *Int'l*, pg. 7294
NIKKO SYSTEMS SOLUTIONS—See Sumitomo Mitsui Financial Group, Inc.; *Int'l*, pg. 7294
NIKKO TECHNO CO., LTD.—See The Japan Steel Works, Ltd.; *Int'l*, pg. 7659
NIKKO TEXTILES LTD.—See Unitika Ltd.; *Int'l*, pg. 8075

NIKKO TOKKI CO., LTD.—See The Japan Steel Works, Ltd.; *Int'l*, pg. 7659
NIKKO TRAVEL CO., LTD.; *Int'l*, pg. 5291
NIKKO TRUCK CO., LTD.—See The Japan Steel Works, Ltd.; *Int'l*, pg. 7659
NIKKOU MURORAN SERVICE CO., LTD.—See The Japan Steel Works, Ltd.; *Int'l*, pg. 7659
NIKKO UNYU CO., LTD.—See The Japan Steel Works, Ltd.; *Int'l*, pg. 7659
NIKKO-YPK SHOJI CO., LTD.—See The Japan Steel Works, Ltd.; *Int'l*, pg. 7659
NIKKYO FOODS CO., LTD.—See Nippon Steel Corporation; *Int'l*, pg. 5337
NIK. M. KOURAKOS & CO., LTD.—See Aiphone Co., Ltd.; *Int'l*, pg. 235
NIKODAN CONVEYOR SYSTEMS A/S—See Lagercrantz Group AB; *Int'l*, pg. 4394
NIKODAN PROCESS EQUIPMENT A/S—See Lagercrantz Group AB; *Int'l*, pg. 4394
NIKO GROUP N.V.; *Int'l*, pg. 5291
NIKOLA CORP.; *U.S. Public*, pg. 1529
NIKOLA TESLA ELEKTRONSKA INDUSTRIJA A.D.; *Int'l*, pg. 5292
NIKOLE S.A.—See Industria de Diseno Textil, S.A.; *Int'l*, pg. 3666
NIKON AMERICAS INC.—See Nikon Corporation; *Int'l*, pg. 5292
NIKON AUSTRALIA PTY. LTD.—See Nikon Corporation; *Int'l*, pg. 5292
NIKON BUSINESS SERVICE CO., LTD.—See Nikon Corporation; *Int'l*, pg. 5292
NIKON CANADA, INC.—See Nikon Corporation; *Int'l*, pg. 5292
NIKON CELL INNOVATION CO., LTD.—See Nikon Corporation; *Int'l*, pg. 5292
NIKON CORPORATION - GLASS DIVISION—See Nikon Corporation; *Int'l*, pg. 5292
NIKON CORPORATION; *Int'l*, pg. 5292
NIKON DO BRASIL LTDA.—See Nikon Corporation; *Int'l*, pg. 5294
NIKON ENGINEERING CO., LTD.—See Nikon Corporation; *Int'l*, pg. 5292
NIKON-ESSILOR CO., LTD.—See EssilorLuxottica SA; *Int'l*, pg. 2512
NIKON-ESSILOR CO., LTD.—See Nikon Corporation; *Int'l*, pg. 5294
NIKON EUROPE B.V.—See Nikon Corporation; *Int'l*, pg. 5292
NIKON FRANCE S.A.—See Nikon Corporation; *Int'l*, pg. 5292
NIKON GMBH—See Nikon Corporation; *Int'l*, pg. 5292
NIKON HOLDINGS EUROPE B.V.—See Nikon Corporation; *Int'l*, pg. 5292
NIKON HOLDINGS HONG KONG LIMITED—See Nikon Corporation; *Int'l*, pg. 5293
NIKON HONG KONG LTD.—See Nikon Corporation; *Int'l*, pg. 5293
NIKON IMAGING (CHINA) CO., LTD.—See Nikon Corporation; *Int'l*, pg. 5293
NIKON IMAGING (CHINA) SALES CO., LTD.—See Nikon Corporation; *Int'l*, pg. 5293
NIKON IMAGING JAPAN INC.—See Nikon Corporation; *Int'l*, pg. 5293
NIKON IMAGING KOREA CO., LTD.—See Nikon Corporation; *Int'l*, pg. 5293
NIKON INC.—See Nikon Corporation; *Int'l*, pg. 5293
NIKON INDIA PRIVATE LIMITED—See Nikon Corporation; *Int'l*, pg. 5293
NIKON INSTECH CO., LTD.—See Nikon Corporation; *Int'l*, pg. 5293
NIKON INSTRUMENT INC.—See Nikon Corporation; *Int'l*, pg. 5292
NIKON INSTRUMENTS EUROPE B.V.—See Nikon Corporation; *Int'l*, pg. 5292
NIKON INSTRUMENTS KOREA CO., LTD.—See Nikon Corporation; *Int'l*, pg. 5293
NIKON INSTRUMENTS (SHANGHAI) CO., LTD.—See Nikon Corporation; *Int'l*, pg. 5293
NIKON INSTRUMENTS S.P.A.—See Nikon Corporation; *Int'l*, pg. 5292
NIKON INTERNATIONAL TRADING (SHENZHEN) CO., LTD.—See Nikon Corporation; *Int'l*, pg. 5293
NIKON KFT.—See Nikon Corporation; *Int'l*, pg. 5293
NIKON LAO CO., LTD.—See Nikon Corporation; *Int'l*, pg. 5293
NIKON LENSWEAR EXPERIENCE CENTER CO., LTD.—See Nikon Corporation; *Int'l*, pg. 5293
NIKON LIFE CO., LTD.—See Nikon Corporation; *Int'l*, pg. 5293
NIKON LOGISTICS CORPORATION—See Nikon Corporation; *Int'l*, pg. 5293
NIKON (MALAYSIA) SDN BHD—See Nikon Corporation; *Int'l*, pg. 5292
NIKON METROLOGY CANADA INC.—See Nikon Corporation; *Int'l*, pg. 5293
NIKON METROLOGY GMBH—See Nikon Corporation; *Int'l*, pg. 5293
NIKON METROLOGY, INC.—See Nikon Corporation; *Int'l*, pg. 5293

COMPANY NAME INDEX

NIKON METROLOGY N.V.—See Nikon Corporation; *Int'l*, pg. 5293
NIKON METROLOGY SARL—See Nikon Corporation; *Int'l*, pg. 5293
NIKON METROLOGY UK LTD.—See Nikon Corporation; *Int'l*, pg. 5293
NIKON MEXICO, S.A. DE C.V.—See Nikon Corporation; *Int'l*, pg. 5293
NIKON MIDDLE EAST FZE—See Nikon Corporation; *Int'l*, pg. 5293
NIKON NISSO PRIME CORPORATION—See Nikon Corporation; *Int'l*, pg. 5293
NIKON NORDIC AB—See Nikon Corporation; *Int'l*, pg. 5293
NIKON OPTICAL CANADA, INC.—See Nikon Corporation; *Int'l*, pg. 5293
NIKON OPTICAL SHOP CO., LTD.—See Nikon Corporation; *Int'l*, pg. 5293
NIKON OPTICAL U.K. LTD.—See Nikon Corporation; *Int'l*, pg. 5293
NIKON OPTICAL USA INC.—See Nikon Corporation; *Int'l*, pg. 5293
NIKON PHOTO PRODUCTS, INC.—See Nikon Corporation; *Int'l*, pg. 5293
NIKON POLSKA SP. Z O.O.—See Nikon Corporation; *Int'l*, pg. 5293
NIKON PRECISION EUROPE GMBH—See Nikon Corporation; *Int'l*, pg. 5293
NIKON PRECISION INC.—See Nikon Corporation; *Int'l*, pg. 5292
NIKON PRECISION KOREA LTD.—See Nikon Corporation; *Int'l*, pg. 5293
NIKON PRECISION SHANGHAI CO., LTD.—See Nikon Corporation; *Int'l*, pg. 5293
NIKON PRECISION SINGAPORE PTE LTD—See Nikon Corporation; *Int'l*, pg. 5294
NIKON PRECISION TAIWAN LTD.—See Nikon Corporation; *Int'l*, pg. 5294
NIKON PRODUCT SUPPORT CORPORATION—See Nikon Corporation; *Int'l*, pg. 5294
NIKON RESEARCH CORPORATION OF AMERICA—See Nikon Corporation; *Int'l*, pg. 5292
NIKON (RUSSIA) LLC—See Nikon Corporation; *Int'l*, pg. 5292
NIKON SALES (THAILAND) CO., LTD.—See Nikon Corporation; *Int'l*, pg. 5294
NIKON SINGAPORE PTE. LTD.—See Nikon Corporation; *Int'l*, pg. 5294
NIKON SOLUTIONS CO., LTD.—See Nikon Corporation; *Int'l*, pg. 5294
NIKON S.R.O.—See Nikon Corporation; *Int'l*, pg. 5294
NIKON STAFF SERVICE CORPORATION—See Nikon Corporation; *Int'l*, pg. 5293
NIKON SYSTEMS, INC.—See Nikon Corporation; *Int'l*, pg. 5294
NIKON TEC CORPORATION—See Nikon Corporation; *Int'l*, pg. 5294
NIKON (THAILAND) CO., LTD.—See Nikon Corporation; *Int'l*, pg. 5294
NIKON-TRIMBLE CO., LTD.—See Nikon Corporation; *Int'l*, pg. 5294
NIKON-TRIMBLE CO., LTD.—See Trimble, Inc.; *U.S. Public*, pg. 2190
NIKON TSUBASA, INC.—See Nikon Corporation; *Int'l*, pg. 5294
NIKON U.K. LTD.—See Nikon Corporation; *Int'l*, pg. 5294
NIKON VISION CO., LTD.—See Nikon Corporation; *Int'l*, pg. 5294
NIKON X-TEK SYSTEMS LTD.—See Nikon Corporation; *Int'l*, pg. 5294
NIKO RESOURCES LIMITED; *Int'l*, pg. 5292
NIKOSAX A/S—See Edenred S.A.; *Int'l*, pg. 2308
NIKOS CO., LTD.—See Nippon Kayaku Co., Ltd.; *Int'l*, pg. 5320
NIKO SEMICONDUCTOR CO., LTD.; *Int'l*, pg. 5292
NIKOTIANA BT HOLDING AD; *Int'l*, pg. 5294
NIKSOFT SYSTEMS CORPORATION; *U.S. Private*, pg. 2927
NIK SOFTWARE GMBH—See Alphabet Inc.; *U.S. Public*, pg. 83
NIK SOFTWARE, INC.—See Alphabet Inc.; *U.S. Public*, pg. 83
NIKS PROFESSIONAL LTD.; *Int'l*, pg. 5294
NIKS TECHNOLOGY LTD.; *Int'l*, pg. 5294
NIKUNOTAIKO CO., LTD.—See Kobe Bussan Co., Ltd.; *Int'l*, pg. 4217
NILACHAL REFRACTORIES LIMITED; *Int'l*, pg. 5294
NILAI CIPTA SDN BHD—See IJM Corporation Berhad; *Int'l*, pg. 3609
NILAI LANDSCAPE SDN. BHD.—See Nilai Resources Group Sdn Berhad; *Int'l*, pg. 5295
NILA INFRASTRUCTURES LIMITED; *Int'l*, pg. 5294
NILAI RESOURCES GROUP SDN BERHAD; *Int'l*, pg. 5295
NILAM HEALTHCARE EDUCATION CENTRE SDN. BHD.—See Oriental Holdings Berhad; *Int'l*, pg. 5624
NILAM RESOURCES, INC.; *Int'l*, pg. 5295
NILAX CO., LTD.—See Bain Capital, LP; *U.S. Private*, pg. 444

NILE BREWERIES LTD.—See Anheuser-Busch InBev SA/NV; *Int'l*, pg. 466
NILE CITY INVESTMENTS; *Int'l*, pg. 5295
NILEG COMMERCIAL ASSET GMBH & CO. KG—See Vonovia SE; *Int'l*, pg. 8305
NILEG NORDDEUTSCHE IMMOBILIENGESELLSCHAFT MBH—See Vonovia SE; *Int'l*, pg. 8305
NILE LTD.; *Int'l*, pg. 5295
NILE MATCH COMPANY—See Chemical Industries Holding Company; *Int'l*, pg. 1462
NILESAT THE EGYPTIAN SATELLITE COMPANY; *Int'l*, pg. 5295
NILES FENCE & SECURITY PRODUCTS, LLC—See NMC Metals Inc.; *U.S. Private*, pg. 2931
NILES IRON & METAL CO. INC.; *U.S. Private*, pg. 2927
NILES SALES & SERVICE, INC.—See Warren Henry Automobiles Inc.; *U.S. Private*, pg. 4444
NILEX INC.—See Fulcrum Capital Partners Inc.; *Int'l*, pg. 2841
NILFISK-ADVANCE, INC.—See Nilfisk Holding A/S; *Int'l*, pg. 5295
NILFISK-ALTO DANMARK A/S—See Nilfisk Holding A/S; *Int'l*, pg. 5295
NILFISK A/S—See Nilfisk Holding A/S; *Int'l*, pg. 5295
NILFISK HOLDING A/S; *Int'l*, pg. 5295
NILFISK LTD.—See Nilfisk Holding A/S; *Int'l*, pg. 5295
NILGIRIS MECHANISED BAKERY PRIVATE LIMITED—See Future Corporate Resources Limited; *Int'l*, pg. 2853
NILKAMAL CRATES & BINS PVT. LTD.—See Nilkamal Ltd; *Int'l*, pg. 5295
NILKAMAL ESWARAN PLASTICS PVT. LTD.—See Nilkamal Ltd; *Int'l*, pg. 5295
NILKAMAL LTD; *Int'l*, pg. 5295
NILKANTH ENGINEERING LIMITED; *Int'l*, pg. 5295
NILODOR, INC.; *U.S. Private*, pg. 2927
NILORN AB—See Duroc AB; *Int'l*, pg. 2229
NILORN BELGIUM NV—See Duroc AB; *Int'l*, pg. 2229
NILORN DENMARK A/S—See Duroc AB; *Int'l*, pg. 2229
NILORN DENMARK - FORSALJNING—See Duroc AB; *Int'l*, pg. 2229
NILORN EAST ASIA LTD.—See Duroc AB; *Int'l*, pg. 2229
NILORN ETIKET SA. VE TIC. LTD. STI.—See Duroc AB; *Int'l*, pg. 2229
NILORN GERMANY GMBH—See Duroc AB; *Int'l*, pg. 2229
NILORNGRUPPEN AB—See Duroc AB; *Int'l*, pg. 2229
NILORN PORTUGAL LDA.—See Duroc AB; *Int'l*, pg. 2229
NILORN UK LTD.—See Duroc AB; *Int'l*, pg. 2229
NILOS GMBH & CO. KG—See Fukuda Corporation; *Int'l*, pg. 2839
NILOU TILE COMPANY; *Int'l*, pg. 5295
NILOX—See Esprinet S.p.A.; *Int'l*, pg. 2506
NILOY INC.; *U.S. Private*, pg. 2927
NILSEN ELECTRIC (WA) PTY LIMITED—See Oliver J. Nilsen (Australia) Limited; *Int'l*, pg. 5554
NILSEN FEED & GRAIN COMPANY; *U.S. Private*, pg. 2927
NILSEN NETWORKS PTY.LTD.—See Oliver J. Nilsen (Australia) Limited; *Int'l*, pg. 5554
NILSEN (NSW) PTY. LTD.—See Oliver J. Nilsen (Australia) Limited; *Int'l*, pg. 5553
NILSEN (NT) PTY. LTD.—See Oliver J. Nilsen (Australia) Limited; *Int'l*, pg. 5553
NILSEN (QLD) PTY. LTD.—See Oliver J. Nilsen (Australia) Limited; *Int'l*, pg. 5553
NILSEN (SA) PTY. LTD.—See Oliver J. Nilsen (Australia) Limited; *Int'l*, pg. 5553
NILSEN (VIC) PTY. LTD.—See Oliver J. Nilsen (Australia) Limited; *Int'l*, pg. 5553
NILSEN (WA) PTY. LTD.—See Oliver J. Nilsen (Australia) Limited; *Int'l*, pg. 5553
NILS HANSSON LOGISTICS AB—See Nordstjernan AB; *Int'l*, pg. 5425
NILSON AND COMPANY INC.; *U.S. Private*, pg. 2927
NILSON VAN & STORAGE INC.; *U.S. Private*, pg. 2927
NILSSON ARCHITECTS LIMITED—See SHUAA Capital psc; *Int'l*, pg. 6868
NILSSON BROS., INC.; *Int'l*, pg. 5295
NILSSON SPECIAL VEHICLES AB; *Int'l*, pg. 5295
NIMAB ENTREPRENAD AB—See STRABAG SE; *Int'l*, pg. 7231
NIMAG (PTY) LTD; *Int'l*, pg. 5295
NIMAN RANCH, INC.—See Perdue Farms Incorporated; *U.S. Private*, pg. 3147
NIMANS LTD; *Int'l*, pg. 5295
NIMATOPAAL AB—See Orkla ASA; *Int'l*, pg. 5638
NIMAX THEATRES LIMITED; *Int'l*, pg. 5295
NIMBELINK CORP.—See Airgain, Inc.; *U.S. Public*, pg. 68
NIMBIT, INC.—See PreSonus Audio Electronics, Inc.; *U.S. Private*, pg. 3255
NIMBLE HOLDINGS COMPANY LIMITED; *Int'l*, pg. 5295
NIMBLE STORAGE, INC.—See Hewlett Packard Enterprise Company; *U.S. Public*, pg. 1032
NIMBO INC.—See Equinix, Inc.; *U.S. Public*, pg. 788
NIMBUS BOATS AB—See R12 Kapital Fund I AB; *Int'l*, pg. 6171
NIMBUS B.V.; *Int'l*, pg. 5296
NIMBUS FOODS INDUSTRIES LTD.; *Int'l*, pg. 5297

NINER BIKES

NIMBUS FOODS LTD—See Meadow Foods Limited; *Int'l*, pg. 4763
NIMBUS GROUP AB; *Int'l*, pg. 5297
NIMBUS INDUSTRIES LIMITED; *Int'l*, pg. 5297
NIMBUSNOW, LLC; *U.S. Private*, pg. 2927
NIMBUS PROJECTS LTD.; *Int'l*, pg. 5297
NIMBUS SUPPORT B.V.; *Int'l*, pg. 5297
NIMBUS WATER SYSTEMS—See Axel Johnson Gruppen AB; *Int'l*, pg. 765
N.I.M. CO., LTD.—See Thai Central Chemical Public Company Limited; *Int'l*, pg. 7592
NIMES AUTO SPORTS; *Int'l*, pg. 5297
NIMES VI SAS; *Int'l*, pg. 5297
NIMET SRL—See Palfinger AG; *Int'l*, pg. 5707
NI MIDSTAR LLC—See The Nisshin OilliO Group, Ltd.; *Int'l*, pg. 7671
NIMIR INDUSTRIAL CHEMICALS LTD.; *Int'l*, pg. 5297
NIMIR RESINS LIMITED; *Int'l*, pg. 5297
NIMITZ PARTNERS, INC. BEST WESTERN PLAZA HOTEL; *U.S. Private*, pg. 2927
NIMLOK COMPANY; *U.S. Private*, pg. 2928
NIMNICHT CHEVROLET COMPANY; *U.S. Private*, pg. 2928
NIMONIK, INC.; *Int'l*, pg. 5297
NIMPON TRADE AND SERVICES B.V.—See Nimbus B.V.; *Int'l*, pg. 5296
NIMPON TRADE AND SERVICES B.V.—See Pon Holdings B.V.; *Int'l*, pg. 5918
NIMY RESOURCES LIMITED; *Int'l*, pg. 5297
NINA BIOTHERAPEUTICS, INC—See Atara Biotherapeutics, Inc.; *U.S. Public*, pg. 220
NINA FOOTWEAR CORP.; *U.S. Private*, pg. 2928
NINA INDUSTRIES LIMITED; *Int'l*, pg. 5297
NINA MIA, INC.; *U.S. Private*, pg. 2928
NINA PERCEPT PRIVATE LIMITED—See Pidilite Industries Limited; *Int'l*, pg. 5862
NINA PLASTICS, INC.; *U.S. Private*, pg. 2928
NINE ALLIANCE SCIENCE & TECHNOLOGY GROUP.; *Int'l*, pg. 5297
NINEBOT INC.—See Ninebot Limited; *Int'l*, pg. 5300
NINEBOT LIMITED; *Int'l*, pg. 5300
NINEBOT POLSKA SP. Z O.O.—See Ninebot Limited; *Int'l*, pg. 5300
NINE DRAGONS PAPER HOLDINGS LIMITED; *Int'l*, pg. 5297
NINE DRAGONS PAPER INDUSTRIES (CHONGQING) CO., LTD.—See Nine Dragons Paper Holdings Limited; *Int'l*, pg. 5297
NINE DRAGONS PAPER INDUSTRIES CO., LTD.—See Nine Dragons Paper Holdings Limited; *Int'l*, pg. 5298
NINE DRAGONS PAPER INDUSTRIES (HEBEI) CO., LTD.—See Nine Dragons Paper Holdings Limited; *Int'l*, pg. 5297
NINE DRAGONS PAPER INDUSTRIES (LESHAN) CO., LTD.—See Nine Dragons Paper Holdings Limited; *Int'l*, pg. 5297
NINE DRAGONS PAPER INDUSTRIES (QUANZHOU) CO., LTD.—See Nine Dragons Paper Holdings Limited; *Int'l*, pg. 5298
NINE DRAGONS PAPER INDUSTRIES (SHENYANG) CO. LTD.—See Nine Dragons Paper Holdings Limited; *Int'l*, pg. 5298
NINE DRAGONS PAPER INDUSTRIES (TAICANG) CO., LTD.—See Nine Dragons Paper Holdings Limited; *Int'l*, pg. 5298
NINE DRAGONS PAPER INDUSTRIES (TIANJIN) CO., LTD.—See Nine Dragons Paper Holdings Limited; *Int'l*, pg. 5298
NINE ENERGY CANADA INC.—See Nine Energy Service, Inc.; *U.S. Public*, pg. 1529
NINE ENERGY SERVICE, INC.; *U.S. Public*, pg. 1529
NINE ENTERTAINMENT CO. HOLDINGS LIMITED; *Int'l*, pg. 5298
NINE ENTERTAINMENT CO. PTY. LTD.—See Nine Entertainment Co. Holdings Limited; *Int'l*, pg. 5299
NINE MILE METALS LTD.; *Int'l*, pg. 5300
NINEMSN PTY. LTD.—See Microsoft Corporation; *U.S. Public*, pg. 1441
NINEMSN PTY. LTD.—See Nine Entertainment Co. Holdings Limited; *Int'l*, pg. 5300
NINE NETWORK AUSTRALIA PTY. LTD.—See Nine Entertainment Co. Holdings Limited; *Int'l*, pg. 5299
NINE PALMS 1, LP—See Amedisys, Inc.; *U.S. Public*, pg. 94
NINE PALMS 2, LLP—See Amedisys, Inc.; *U.S. Public*, pg. 94
NINE POINT MEDICAL—See Corning Incorporated; *U.S. Public*, pg. 579
NINEPOINT PARTNERS LP; *Int'l*, pg. 5300
NINE RADIO PTY LIMITED—See Nine Entertainment Co. Holdings Limited; *Int'l*, pg. 5299
NINE RADIO SYNDICATION PTY LIMITED—See Nine Entertainment Co. Holdings Limited; *Int'l*, pg. 5300
NINE RADIO SYNDICATION PTY LTD—See Nine Entertainment Co. Holdings Limited; *Int'l*, pg. 5299
NINER BIKES; *U.S. Private*, pg. 2928
NINE RIVERS CAPITAL PARTNERS LIMITED—See M-Resources Group Limited; *Int'l*, pg. 4614

NINER BIKES / CORPORATE AFFILIATIONS

Company Index

NINESTAR CORPORATION—See Zhuhai Seine Technology Co., Ltd.; *Int'l*, pg. 8678
NINESTAR IMAGE TECH LIMITED—See Zhuhai Seine Technology Co., Ltd.; *Int'l*, pg. 8678
NINESTAR TECHNOLOGY CO., LTD.—See Zhuhai Seine Technology Co., Ltd.; *Int'l*, pg. 8678
NINETOWNS HOLDINGS LIMITED; *Int'l*, pg. 5300
NINETOWNS INTERNET TECHNOLOGY GROUP COMPANY LIMITED—See Ninetowns Holdings Limited; *Int'l*, pg. 5300
NINETY FIVE 5 LLC—See Franklin Covey Company; *U.S. Public*, pg. 878
NINETY NINE PER CENT DEVELOPMENT S.A.—See T&M Phaedra Public Company Ltd.; *Int'l*, pg. 7395
NINETY NINE PTY. LTD.—See Hipages Group Holdings Limited; *Int'l*, pg. 3402
NINETY ONE PLC; *Int'l*, pg. 5300
NINETY PARK PROPERTY LLC—See Vornado Realty Trust; *U.S. Public*, pg. 2310
NINEVEH FOOD INDUSTRIES; *Int'l*, pg. 5300
NINE WEST GROUP, INC.—See Premier Brands Group Holdings LLC; *U.S. Private*, pg. 3249
NINE WEST JEANSWEAR GROUP, INC.—See Premier Brands Group Holdings LLC; *U.S. Private*, pg. 3249
NINFA'S HOLDINGS, L.P.; *U.S. Private*, pg. 2928
NINGBO AIRTAC AUTOMATIC INDUSTRIAL CO., LTD.—See Airtac International Group; *Int'l*, pg. 249
NINGBO ALPS ELECTRONICS CO., LTD.—See Alps Alpine Co., Ltd.; *Int'l*, pg. 376
NINGBO ANJI MICROELECTRONICS TECHNOLOGY CO., LTD.—See Anji Microelectronics Technology Shanghai Co., Ltd.; *Int'l*, pg. 472
NINGBO ARTTEC CO. LTD.—See Tecnolama S.A.; *Int'l*, pg. 7516
NINGBO AUCHAN HYPERMARKETS CO., LTD.—See Alibaba Group Holding Limited; *Int'l*, pg. 326
NINGBO BAOSI ENERGY EQUIPMENT CO., LTD.; *Int'l*, pg. 5300
NINGBO BAOXIN STAINLESS STEEL CO., LTD.—See China Baowu Steel Group Corp.; *Int'l*, pg. 1486
NINGBO BEILUN PORT EXPRESSWAY CO., LTD.—See Ping An Insurance (Group) Company of China, Ltd.; *Int'l*, pg. 5869
NINGBO BIRD CO., LTD.; *Int'l*, pg. 5300
NINGBO BOHUI CHEMICAL TECHNOLOGY CO., LTD.; *Int'l*, pg. 5300
NINGBO CHAIN CHON METAL TECHNOLOGY CO., LTD.—See Chain Chon Industrial Co., Ltd.; *Int'l*, pg. 1437
NINGBO CHANGHONG OPTOELECTRONICS LTD.—See Wah Hong Industrial Corp.; *Int'l*, pg. 8328
NINGBO CHANGHONG POLYMER SCIENTIFIC & TECHNICAL, INC.; *Int'l*, pg. 5300
NINGBO CHARGEURS YAK TEXTILE TRADING CO. LTD—See Chargeurs SA; *Int'l*, pg. 1450
NING BO CHIA CHANG ELECTROINC HARDWARE CO., LTD.—See Chia Chang Co., Ltd.; *Int'l*, pg. 1475
NINGBO CHIA CHANG ELECTRONICS HARDWARE CO., LTD.—See Chia Chang Co., Ltd.; *Int'l*, pg. 1475
NINGBO CIMC CONTAINER SERVICE CO., LTD.—See China International Marine Containers (Group) Co., Ltd.; *Int'l*, pg. 1512
NINGBO CIMC LOGISTICS EQUIPMENT CO., LTD.—See China International Marine Containers (Group) Co., Ltd.; *Int'l*, pg. 1512
NINGBO CIXING CO., LTD.; *Int'l*, pg. 5301
NINGBO CML GRANDCORP LOGISTICS CO., LTD.—See China Master Logistics Co., Ltd.; *Int'l*, pg. 1517
NINGBO COLOR MASTER BATCH CO., LTD.; *Int'l*, pg. 5301
NINGBO COMBI BABY GOODS CO., LTD—See Combi Corporation; *Int'l*, pg. 1708
NINGBO CONSTRUCTION CO., LTD.; *Int'l*, pg. 5301
NINGBO CULTURE SQUARE POLY GRAND THEATRE MANAGEMENT CO., LTD.—See Poly Culture Group Corporation Limited; *Int'l*, pg. 5914
NINGBO DA-AN CHEMICAL INDUSTRIES CO., LTD.—See Daicel Corporation; *Int'l*, pg. 1919
NINGBO DALING SEAFOOD PROCESSING CO., LTD.—See Mitsubishi Corporation; *Int'l*, pg. 4942
NINGBO DAVID MEDICAL DEVICE CO., LTD.; *Int'l*, pg. 5301
NINGBO DAXIE DEVELOPMENT ZONE—See CITIC Group Corporation; *Int'l*, pg. 1621
NINGBO DAXIE DEVELOPMENT ZONE WANHUA INDUSTRY PARK THERMAL POWER CO., LTD.—See Wanhua Chemical Group Co., Ltd.; *Int'l*, pg. 8341
NINGBO DAXIE WANHUA PORT CO., LTD.—See Wanhua Chemical Group Co., Ltd.; *Int'l*, pg. 8341
NINGBO DAYE GARDEN MACHINERY CO., LTD.; *Int'l*, pg. 5301
NINGBO DEVELOPMENT CO., LTD.; *Int'l*, pg. 5301
NINGBO DEYE DAILY ELECTRICAL APPLIANCE TECHNOLOGY CO., LTD.—See Ningbo Deye Technology Co., Ltd.; *Int'l*, pg. 5301
NINGBO DEYE TECHNOLOGY CO., LTD.; *Int'l*, pg. 5301
NINGBO DIOCHANGE MEDICAL TECHNOLOGY CO., LTD.—See Jenscare Scientific Co., Ltd.; *Int'l*, pg. 3929

NINGBO DONGMU NEW MATERIALS GROUP CO., LTD.—See NBTM New Materials Group Co., Ltd.; *Int'l*, pg. 5179
NINGBO DONLY CO., LTD.; *Int'l*, pg. 5301
NINGBO DOOYA MECHANIC & ELECTRONIC TECHNOLOGY CO. LTD.—See Somfy SA; *Int'l*, pg. 7085
NINGBO E&J BRUSHES CO LTD.—See Freudenberg SE; *Int'l*, pg. 2790
NINGBO ENERGY GROUP CO., LTD.; *Int'l*, pg. 5301
NINGBO EPZ TS TRIMONT AUTOMOTIVE INTERIOR INC.—See TS Tech Co Ltd.; *Int'l*, pg. 7948
NINGBO EST TECHNOLOGY CO., LTD.—See Shenzhen Inovance Technology Co., Ltd.; *Int'l*, pg. 6813
NINGBO FANGZHENG AUTOMOBILE MOULD CO., LTD.; *Int'l*, pg. 5301
NINGBO FUBANG JINGYE GROUP CO., LTD.; *Int'l*, pg. 5301
NINGBO FUDA COMPANY LIMITED; *Int'l*, pg. 5301
NINGBO FUERDA SMARTECH CO., LTD. - MELVINDALE BRANCH—See Beijing WKW Automotive Parts Co., Ltd.; *Int'l*, pg. 960
NINGBO FUERDA SMARTECH CO., LTD.—See Beijing WKW Automotive Parts Co., Ltd.; *Int'l*, pg. 960
NINGBO GAOFA AUTOMOTIVE CONTROL SYSTEM CO., LTD.; *Int'l*, pg. 5301
NINGBO GIGA-BYTE TECHNOLOGY CO., LTD.—See Giga-Byte Technology Co., Ltd.; *Int'l*, pg. 2971
NINGBO GP ENERGY CO., LTD.—See Gold Peak Technology Group Limited; *Int'l*, pg. 3025
NINGBO GQY VIDEO & TELECOM JOINT-STOCK CO., LTD.; *Int'l*, pg. 5301
NINGBO GUANGXIN IMPORT & EXPORT CO., LTD.—See Jiangsu Boqian New Materials Co., Ltd.; *Int'l*, pg. 3944
NINGBO GUANGXIN NANO MATERIALS CO., LTD.—See Jiangsu Boqian New Materials Co., Ltd.; *Int'l*, pg. 3944
NINGBO GUOHONG AUTOMOTIVE CO., LTD.—See Minth Group Limited; *Int'l*, pg. 4914
NINGBO HAITIAN HUAYUAN MACHINERY CO., LTD.—See Haitian International Holdings Ltd.; *Int'l*, pg. 3217
NINGBO HAITIAN PRECISION MACHINERY CO.,LTD.; *Int'l*, pg. 5301
NINGBO HELI TECHNOLOGY CO., LTD.; *Int'l*, pg. 5302
NINGBO HENGHE PRECISION INDUSTRY CO., LTD.; *Int'l*, pg. 5301
NINGBO HENGSHUAI CO., LTD.; *Int'l*, pg. 5302
NINGBO HOMELINK ECO-ITECH CO., LTD.; *Int'l*, pg. 5302
NINGBO HUAKUN MEDICAL EQUIPMENT CO., LTD—See Yunda Holding Co., Ltd.; *Int'l*, pg. 8613
NINGBO HUAXIANG ELECTRONIC CO., LTD.; *Int'l*, pg. 5302
NINGBO HUAYANG ALUMINIUM-TECH CO., LTD.—See China Steel Corporation; *Int'l*, pg. 1556
NINGBO IRON & STEEL CO., LTD.—See China Baowu Steel Group Corp.; *Int'l*, pg. 1486
NINGBO JIANAN ELECTRONICS CO., LTD.; *Int'l*, pg. 5302
NINGBO JIEKELONG PRECISION MANUFACTURING CO., LTD.—See Ningbo Jintian Copper (Group) Co., Ltd.; *Int'l*, pg. 5303
NINGBO JIFENG AUTO PARTS CO., LTD.; *Int'l*, pg. 5302
NINGBO JINTIAN COPPER (GROUP) CO., LTD.; *Int'l*, pg. 5302
NINGBO JINTIAN COPPER STRIP COMPANY LTD.—See Ningbo Jintian Copper (Group) Co., Ltd.; *Int'l*, pg. 5303
NINGBO JINTIAN COPPER TUBE CO., LTD.—See Ningbo Jintian Copper (Group) Co., Ltd.; *Int'l*, pg. 5303
NINGBO JINTIAN ELECTRIC MATERIAL CO., LTD.—See Ningbo Jintian Copper (Group) Co., Ltd.; *Int'l*, pg. 5303
NINGBO JINTIAN IMPORT & EXPORT CO., LTD.—See Ningbo Jintian Copper (Group) Co., Ltd.; *Int'l*, pg. 5303
NINGBO JINTIAN NEW MATERIAL CO., LTD.—See Ningbo Jintian Copper (Group) Co., Ltd.; *Int'l*, pg. 5303
NINGBO JOY INTELLIGENT LOGISTICS TECHNOLOGY CO., LTD.; *Int'l*, pg. 5303
NINGBO JOYSON ELECTRONIC CORP.; *Int'l*, pg. 5303
NINGBO JUHUA CHEMICAL SCIENCE & TECHNOLOGY CO., LTD.—See Zhejiang Juhua Co., Ltd.; *Int'l*, pg. 8658
NINGBO KAIMIKE LOGISTICS CO., LTD.—See Yongtaiyun Chemical Logistics Co., Ltd.; *Int'l*, pg. 8598
NINGBO KANGQIANG ELECTRONICS CO., LTD.; *Int'l*, pg. 5304
NINGBO KBE ELEETRICAL TECHNOLOGY CO., LTD.; *Int'l*, pg. 5304
NINGBO KETIAN MAGNET CO., LTD.—See Ningbo Jintian Copper (Group) Co., Ltd.; *Int'l*, pg. 5303
NINGBO KIBING PHOTOVOLTAIC TECHNOLOGY CO., LTD.—See Zhuzhou Kibing Group Co., Ltd.; *Int'l*, pg. 8680
NINGBO KIN LONG KEXING PRECISION MANUFACTURING CO., LTD.—See Guangdong Kinlong Hardware Prdcts Co., Ltd.; *Int'l*, pg. 3157
NINGBO KONIT INDUSTRIAL INC. LTD.—See Beijing Zhong Ke San Huan High-tech Co., Ltd.; *Int'l*, pg. 961
NINGBO LEHUI INTERNATIONAL ENGINEERING EQUIPMENT CO., LTD.; *Int'l*, pg. 5304

NINGBO LIGONG ONLINE MONITORING TECHNOLOGY CO., LTD.; *Int'l*, pg. 5304
NINGBO L.K. TECHNOLOGY CO., LTD.—See L.K. Technology Holdings Limited; *Int'l*, pg. 4386
NINGBO LONGYUAN SHENGHONG ECOLOGICAL CONSTRUCTION ENGINEERING CO.—See Long Yuan Construction Group Co., Ltd; *Int'l*, pg. 4549
NINGBO LULIN MACHINERY CASTING CO., LTD.—See Yeong Guan Energy Technology Group Co., Ltd.; *Int'l*, pg. 8577
NINGBO LULIN MACHINE TOOL FOUNDRY CO., LTD.—See Yeong Guan Energy Technology Group Co., Ltd.; *Int'l*, pg. 8577
NINGBO MARINE CO., LTD.; *Int'l*, pg. 5304
NINGBO MENOVO PHARMACEUTICAL CO., LTD.; *Int'l*, pg. 5304
NINGBO MENOVO TIANKANG PHARMACEUTICAL CO., LTD.—See Ningbo Menovo Pharmaceutical Co., Ltd.; *Int'l*, pg. 5304
NINGBO MILE MOULD MANUFACTURING CO., LTD.—See Ningbo Huaxiang Electronic Co., Ltd.; *Int'l*, pg. 5302
NINGBO NEUTRIK TRADING CO., LTD.—See Neutrik AG; *Int'l*, pg. 5220
NINGBO NINGXIANG LIQUID CHEMICALS TERMINAL CO., LTD.—See Dragon Crown Group Holdings Limited; *Int'l*, pg. 2199
NINGBO NUOBAI PHARMACEUTICAL CO., LTD.—See VIVA Biotech Holdings; *Int'l*, pg. 8264
NINGBO OCEAN FAMILY FOOD CO., LTD.—See Mitsubishi Corporation; *Int'l*, pg. 4942
NINGBO ORIENT WIRES & CABLES CO., LTD.; *Int'l*, pg. 5304
NINGBO PACIFIC CONTAINER CO., LTD.—See China COSCO Shipping Corporation Limited; *Int'l*, pg. 1493
NINGBO PACIFIC E-CONTROL SYSTEM LTD.—See Jiangsu Pacific Precision Forging; *Int'l*, pg. 3951
NINGBO PEACEBIRD FASHION CO., LTD; *Int'l*, pg. 5305
NINGBO PHARMACEUTICAL CO., LTD.—See Shanghai Pharmaceuticals Holding Co., Ltd.; *Int'l*, pg. 6776
NINGBO POWERWAY ALLOY MATERIALS CO., LTD.; *Int'l*, pg. 5305
NINGBO POWERWAY ALLOY PLATE& STRIP CO.,LTD—See Ningbo Powerway Alloy Materials Co., Ltd.; *Int'l*, pg. 5305
NINGBO POWERWAY INVESTMENT COMPANY—See Ningbo Powerway Alloy Materials Co., Ltd.; *Int'l*, pg. 5305
NINGBO POWERWAY MATERIALISE CO., LTD.—See Ningbo Powerway Alloy Materials Co., Ltd.; *Int'l*, pg. 5305
NINGBO POWERWAY NEW ENERGY CO., LTD—See Ningbo Powerway Alloy Materials Co., Ltd.; *Int'l*, pg. 5305
NINGBO PRECA CONSTRUCTION TECHNOLOGY CO., LTD.—See Ningbo Construction Co., Ltd.; *Int'l*, pg. 5301
NINGBO QIYI PRECISION METALS CO., LTD.—See Yuen Chang Stainless Steel Co., Ltd.; *Int'l*, pg. 8610
NINGBO RONBAY NEW ENERGY TECHNOLOGY CO., LTD.; *Int'l*, pg. 5305
NINGBO RONBAY TECHNOLOGY MATERIALS CO., LTD.—See Ningbo Ronbay New Energy Technology Co., Ltd.; *Int'l*, pg. 5305
NINGBO RUIYUAN BIOTECHNOLOGY CO., LTD.; *Int'l*, pg. 5305
NINGBO RUNHE HIGH-TECH MATERIALS CO., LTD.; *Int'l*, pg. 5305
NINGBO SANHE STEEL PIPE CO., LTD.—See Chu Kong Petroleum and Natural Gas Steel Pipe Holdings Limited; *Int'l*, pg. 1589
NINGBO SANXING MEDICAL ELECTRIC CO., LTD. - KAREO FACTORY—See Ningbo Sanxing Medical Electric Co.,Ltd.,; *Int'l*, pg. 5305
NINGBO SANXING MEDICAL ELECTRIC CO.,LTD.,; *Int'l*, pg. 5305
NINGBO SANXING SMART ELECTRIC CO.,LTD.—See Ningbo Sanxing Medical Electric Co.,Ltd.,; *Int'l*, pg. 5305
NINGBO SANYO SPECIAL STEEL PRODUCTS CO., LTD.—See Nippon Steel Corporation; *Int'l*, pg. 5340
NINGBO SCHLEMMER AUTOMOTIVE PARTS CO., LTD.—See Ningbo Huaxiang Electronic Co., Ltd.; *Int'l*, pg. 5302
NINGBO SENSCURE BIOTECHNOLOGY CO., LTD.—See Cryofocus Medtech (Shanghai) Co., Ltd.; *Int'l*, pg. 1859
NINGBO SHANSHAN CO., LTD.; *Int'l*, pg. 5305
NINGBO SHANSHAN NEW MATERIAL TECHNOLOGY CO., LTD.—See Ningbo Shanshan Co., Ltd.; *Int'l*, pg. 5305
NINGBO SHENGLONG AUTOMOTIVE POWERTRAIN SYSTEM CO., LTD.; *Int'l*, pg. 5305
NINGBO SHIMADZU VACUUM TECHNOLOGY DEVELOPMENT CO., LTD.—See Shimadzu Corporation; *Int'l*, pg. 6832
NINGBO SHINING GOLD CEREAL OIL PORT CO., LTD—See Golden Agri-Resources Ltd.; *Int'l*, pg. 3028

COMPANY NAME INDEX

NINGBO SHUANGLIN AUTO PARTS CO., LTD. - NINGBO PLANT—See Ningbo Shuanglin Auto Parts Co., Ltd.; *Int'l*, pg. 5305
NINGBO SHUANGLIN AUTO PARTS CO., LTD.; *Int'l*, pg. 5305
NINGBO SINYUAN CARBON MATERIAL CO., LTD.—See Ningbo SINYUAN Industrial Material Co., Ltd.; *Int'l*, pg. 5306
NINGBO SINYUAN INDUSTRIAL MATERIAL CO., LTD.; *Int'l*, pg. 5306
NINGBO SINYUAN ZM TECHNOLOGY CO., LTD.; *Int'l*, pg. 5306
NINGBO SK PERFORMANCE RUBBER CO., LTD.—See SK Innovation Co., Ltd.; *Int'l*, pg. 6973
NINGBO SOLARTRON TECHNOLOGY CO., LTD.; *Int'l*, pg. 5306
NINGBO SUCCESS GUSHI INTERNATIONAL TRADING CO. LTD.—See Success Transformer Corporation Berhad; *Int'l*, pg. 7250
NINGBO SUMIJU MACHINERY, LTD—See Sumitomo Heavy Industries, Ltd.; *Int'l*, pg. 7287
NINGBO SUNLIGHT ELECTRICAL APPLIANCE CO., LTD.; *Int'l*, pg. 5306
NINGBO SUNNY AUTOMOTIVE OPTECH CO., LTD.—See Sunny Optical Technology (Group) Company Limited; *Int'l*, pg. 7318
NINGBO SUNNY ELECTRONIC CO. LTD.; *Int'l*, pg. 5306
NINGBO SUNNY INSTRUMENTS CO., LTD.—See Sunny Optical Technology (Group) Company Limited; *Int'l*, pg. 7319
NINGBO SUNRISE ELC TECHNOLOGY CO., LTD.; *Int'l*, pg. 5306
NINGBO TECHMATION CO., LTD.; *Int'l*, pg. 5306
NINGBO TIANLONG ELECTRONICS CO., LTD.; *Int'l*, pg. 5306
NINGBO TIANYI MEDICAL DEVICES CO., LTD.; *Int'l*, pg. 5306
NINGBO TIP RUBBER TECHNOLOGY CO., LTD.; *Int'l*, pg. 5306
NINGBO TODAY FOOD CO., LTD.—See Mitsubishi Corporation; *Int'l*, pg. 4942
NINGBO TO NGYON PLASTIC MACHINERY MANUFACTURING CO., LTD.—See The Japan Steel Works, Ltd.; *Int'l*, pg. 7659
NINGBO TOSHIBA HUATONG SWITCHGEAR CO., LTD.—See Japan Industrial Partners, Inc.; *Int'l*, pg. 3890
NINGBO TOYOTA BOSHOKU AUTOMOTIVE PARTS CO., LTD.—See Toyota Boshoku Corporation; *Int'l*, pg. 7864
NINGBO TUOPU GROUP CO., LTD.; *Int'l*, pg. 5306
NINGBO UNIOR FORGING, CO. LTD.—See Unior Kovaska industrija d.d.; *Int'l*, pg. 8055
NINGBO UNITED GROUP CO., LTD.; *Int'l*, pg. 5306
NINGBO UNITED GROUP IMPORT & EXPORT CO., LTD.—See Ningbo United Group Co., Ltd.; *Int'l*, pg. 5306
NINGBO VEKEN BATTERY CO., LTD.—See Veken Technology Co., Ltd.; *Int'l*, pg. 8148
NINGBO VEKEN NEW ENERGY SCIENCE & TECHNOLOGY CO., LTD.—See Veken Technology Co., Ltd.; *Int'l*, pg. 8148
NINGBO WATER METER CO., LTD.; *Int'l*, pg. 5306
NINGBO WEIFU TIANLI SUPERCHARGING TECHNIQUE CO., LTD.—See Wuxi Weifu High-technology Co., Ltd.; *Int'l*, pg. 8516
NINGBO WT BEARING CO., LTD.; *Int'l*, pg. 5307
NINGBO XIANFENG NEW MATERIAL CO. LTD; *Int'l*, pg. 5307
NINGBO XINGPU FIVE STAR APPLIANCE CO., LTD—See Best Buy Co., Inc.; *U.S. Public*, pg. 326
NINGBO XUSHENG AUTO TECHNOLOGY CO., LTD.; *Int'l*, pg. 5307
NINGBO YEM CHIO CO., LTD.—See Yem Chio Co., Ltd.; *Int'l*, pg. 8577
NINGBO YEONG SHANG CASTING IRON CO., LTD.—See Yeong Guan Energy Technology Group Co., Ltd.; *Int'l*, pg. 8577
NINGBO YEONGXIANG CASTING CO., LTD.—See Yeong Guan Energy Technology Group Co., Ltd.; *Int'l*, pg. 8577
NINGBO YONGHEXING MACHINERY INDUSTRY CO., LTD.—See Yeong Guan Energy Technology Group Co., Ltd.; *Int'l*, pg. 8577
NINGBO YONGXIN OPTICS CO., LTD.; *Int'l*, pg. 5307
NINGBO YOUNGOR DRESSES CO., LTD—See Youngor Group Co. Ltd.; *Int'l*, pg. 8603
NINGBO YOUNGOR KNITTING D&F CO. LTD.—See Youngor Group Co. Ltd.; *Int'l*, pg. 8603
NINGBO YOUNGOR PANTS CO., LTD—See Youngor Group Co. Ltd.; *Int'l*, pg. 8603
NINGBO YOUNGOR SHIRTS CO LTD—See Youngor Group Co. Ltd.; *Int'l*, pg. 8603
NINGBO YOUNGOR SUNRISE TEXTILE DYEING & FINISHING CO., LTD.—See Youngor Group Co. Ltd.; *Int'l*, pg. 8603
NINGBO YOUNGOR YINGCHENG UNIFORM CO., LTD.—See Youngor Group Co. Ltd.; *Int'l*, pg. 8604
NINGBO YOUNG TOP GARMENTS CO., LTD—See Fountain Set (Holdings) Limited; *Int'l*, pg. 2754

NINGBO YUNSHENG BONDED MAGNET CO., LTD.—See Ningbo Yunsheng Co., Ltd.; *Int'l*, pg. 5307
NINGBO YUNSHENG CO., LTD. - SERVO CONTROL DIVISION—See Ningbo Yunsheng Co., Ltd.; *Int'l*, pg. 5307
NINGBO YUNSHENG CO., LTD.; *Int'l*, pg. 5307
NINGBO YUNSHENG MAGNET DEVICES TECHNOLOGY CO., LTD.—See Ningbo Yunsheng Co., Ltd.; *Int'l*, pg. 5307
NINGBO YUTIAN RENEWABLE RESOURCES CO., LTD.—See Yeong Guan Energy Technology Group Co., Ltd.; *Int'l*, pg. 8577
NINGBO ZHAFIR PLASTICS MACHINERY CO., LTD.—See Haitian International Holdings Ltd.; *Int'l*, pg. 3217
NINGBO ZHENYU SCIENCE & TECHNOLOGY CO., LTD.; *Int'l*, pg. 5307
NINGBO ZHONGBAI CO., LTD.; *Int'l*, pg. 5307
NINGBO ZHONGDA LEADER INTELLIGENT TRANSMISSION CO., LTD.; *Int'l*, pg. 5307
NINGBO ZHONGJIN PETROCHEMICAL CO., LTD.; *Int'l*, pg. 5307
NINGBO ZHOUSHAN PORT CO., LTD.; *Int'l*, pg. 5307
NINGDE AMPEREX TECHNOLOGY LIMITED—See TDK Corporation; *Int'l*, pg. 7487
NINGDE ITG ZHONGBANG MOTOR SALES & SERVICE CO., LTD.—See Xiamen ITG Group Corp., Ltd.; *Int'l*, pg. 8524
NINGGUO KAIYUAN ELECTRICAL POWER WEAR RESISTANT MATERIALS CO., LTD.—See Ruitai Materials Technology Co., Ltd.; *Int'l*, pg. 6427
NINGGUO LONCH ELECTRIC CO., LTD.; *Int'l*, pg. 5307
NINGHAI JINHAI GRAND NEW CENTURY HOTEL CO., LTD.—See Zhejiang New Century Hotel Management Co., Ltd.; *Int'l*, pg. 8660
NING, INC.—See Glam Media, Inc.; *U.S. Private*, pg. 1706
NINGJIN ZHONGYU GAS CO., LTD.—See Zhongyu Energy Holdings Limited; *Int'l*, pg. 8676
NINGXIA BAOFENG ENERGY GROUP CO., LTD.—See China Baofeng (International) Ltd.; *Int'l*, pg. 1485
NINGXIA BUILDING MATERIALS GROUP CO., LTD.—See China National Materials; *Int'l*, pg. 1532
NINGXIA DUOWEITAIRUI PHARMACEUTICAL CO., LTD.; *Int'l*, pg. 5307
NINGXIA ELECTRIC POWER COMPANY—See State Grid Corporation of China; *Int'l*, pg. 7183
NINGXIA JIAZE RENEWABLES CORPORATION LIMITED; *Int'l*, pg. 5307
NINGXIA LITTLE GIANT MACHINE TOOL CO., LTD.—See Yamazaki Mazak Corporation; *Int'l*, pg. 8557
NINGXIA NIIT EDUCATION TECHNOLOGY COMPANY LIMTED—See NIIT Limited; *Int'l*, pg. 5289
NINGXIA ORIENT TANTALUM INDUSTRY CO., LTD.—See China Nonferrous Metal Mining (Group) Co., Ltd.; *Int'l*, pg. 1535
NINGXIA QINGLONG PIPES INDUSTRY CO., LTD.; *Int'l*, pg. 5307
NINGXIA TIANYUAN MANGANESE INDUSTRY GROUP CO., LTD.; *Int'l*, pg. 5307
NINGXIA WESTERN VENTURE INDUSTRIAL CO., LTD.; *Int'l*, pg. 5307
NINGXIA WINDEY CO., LTD.—See Zhejiang Windey Co., Ltd.; *Int'l*, pg. 8666
NINGXIA XIAOMING AGRICULTURE & ANIMAL HUSBANDRY CO., LTD.; *Int'l*, pg. 5307
NING XIA YIN XING ENERGY CO., LTD.; *Int'l*, pg. 5300
NINGXIA YOUNGLIGHT CHEMICALS CO., LTD.; *Int'l*, pg. 5308
NINGXIA ZHONGKE BIOTECHNOLOGY CO., LTD.; *Int'l*, pg. 5308
NINGXIA ZHONGSHENG CABLE TECHNOLOGY CO., LTD.—See Jiangsu Zhongli Group Co., Ltd.; *Int'l*, pg. 3957
NINGXIA ZHONGYIN CASHMERE CO., LTD.; *Int'l*, pg. 5308
NINH BINH PHOSPHATE FERTILIZER JOINT STOCK COMPANY—See Masan Consumer Corp.; *Int'l*, pg. 4719
NINH BINH THERMAL POWER JOINT-STOCK COMPANY; *Int'l*, pg. 5308
NINH VAN BAY TRAVEL REAL ESTATE JOINT STOCK COMPANY; *Int'l*, pg. 5308
NINIAN SOLUTIONS LTD.—See HgCapital Trust plc; *Int'l*, pg. 3377
NI NIKKEI SHENZHEN CO., LTD.—See Nippon Light Metal Holdings Company, Ltd.; *Int'l*, pg. 5323
NINJA JUMP INC.; *U.S. Private*, pg. 2928
NIN MIE CORP.—See NTN Corporation; *Int'l*, pg. 5481
NINNESCAH RURAL ELECTRIC COOPERATIVE ASSOCIATION, INC.; *U.S. Private*, pg. 2928
NINO AS—See Orkla ASA; *Int'l*, pg. 5638
NINOHE TOKEI KOGYO CO., LTD.—See Seiko Group Corporation; *Int'l*, pg. 6688
NINTAMED HANDELS GMBH—See DexCom Inc; *U.S. Public*, pg. 657
NINTEC SYSTEMS LIMITED; *Int'l*, pg. 5308
NINTENDO AUSTRALIA PTY., LTD.—See Nintendo Co., Ltd.; *Int'l*, pg. 5308

NINTENDO BENELUX B.V.—See Nintendo Co., Ltd.; *Int'l*, pg. 5308
NINTENDO CO., LTD.; *Int'l*, pg. 5308
NINTENDO FRANCE S.A.R.L.—See Nintendo Co., Ltd.; *Int'l*, pg. 5308
NINTENDO IBERICA—See Nintendo Co., Ltd.; *Int'l*, pg. 5308
NINTENDO NETHERLANDS B.V.—See Nintendo Co., Ltd.; *Int'l*, pg. 5308
NINTENDO OF AMERICA, INC.—See Nintendo Co., Ltd.; *Int'l*, pg. 5308
NINTENDO OF CANADA LTD.—See Nintendo Co., Ltd.; *Int'l*, pg. 5308
NINTENDO OF EUROPE GMBH—See Nintendo Co., Ltd.; *Int'l*, pg. 5308
NINTENDO PHUTEN CO.,LTD.—See Nintendo Co., Ltd.; *Int'l*, pg. 5308
NINTENDO SOFTWARE TECHNOLOGY CORPORATION—See Nintendo Co., Ltd.; *Int'l*, pg. 5308
NINTEX GLOBAL LTD.—See TPG Capital, L.P.; *U.S. Public*, pg. 2175
NINTHDECIMAL, INC.—See inMarket Media LLC; *U.S. Private*, pg. 2079
NINTH DISTRICT OPPORTUNITY, INC.; *U.S. Private*, pg. 2928
NIOA NOMINEES PTY. LIMITED; *Int'l*, pg. 5308
NIOBAY METALS INC.; *Int'l*, pg. 5309
NIOBEC INC.—See Magris Resources Inc.; *Int'l*, pg. 4642
NIOCORP DEVELOPMENTS LTD.; *U.S. Public*, pg. 1529
NIO INC.; *Int'l*, pg. 5308
NION, CO.—See Bruker Corporation; *U.S. Public*, pg. 407
NIONEX GMBH—See Bertelsmann SE & Co. KGaA; *Int'l*, pg. 995
NIO STRATEGIC METALS INC.; *Int'l*, pg. 5308
NIOX GROUP PLC; *Int'l*, pg. 5309
NIOX INC.—See Niox Group PLC; *Int'l*, pg. 5309
NIPCO PLC; *Int'l*, pg. 5309
NIP GROUP, INC.; *U.S. Private*, pg. 2928
NIPHIX KK—See ICON plc; *Int'l*, pg. 3584
NIP KOMPANIJA NOVOSTI A.D.; *Int'l*, pg. 5309
NIPO BV—See Bain Capital, LP; *U.S. Private*, pg. 447
NIPPAN RENTAL CO., LTD.; *Int'l*, pg. 5309
NIPPATSU SERVICE CO., LTD.—See NHK Spring Co., Ltd.; *Int'l*, pg. 5258
NIPPECRAFT LIMITED; *Int'l*, pg. 5309
NIPPE HOME PRODUCTS CO., LTD.—See Nippon Paint Holdings Co., Ltd.; *Int'l*, pg. 5325
NIPPEI TOYAMA (THAILAND) CO., LTD.—See Komatsu Ltd.; *Int'l*, pg. 4239
NIPPE TRADING CO., LTD—See Nippon Paint Holdings Co., Ltd.; *Int'l*, pg. 5325
NIPPI CORPORATION—See Kawasaki Heavy Industries, Ltd.; *Int'l*, pg. 4098
NIPPI. INC. - FUJI FACTORY—See Nippi. Inc.; *Int'l*, pg. 5309
NIPPI. INC.; *Int'l*, pg. 5309
NIPPI KOSAN CO., LTD.—See Kawasaki Heavy Industries, Ltd.; *Int'l*, pg. 4098
NIPPI (SHANGHAI) INC.—See Nippi. Inc.; *Int'l*, pg. 5309
NIPPI SKILL CORPORATION—See Kawasaki Heavy Industries, Ltd.; *Int'l*, pg. 4098
NIPPLA INC.—See The Japan Steel Works, Ltd.; *Int'l*, pg. 7659
NIPPN CALIFORNIA INC.—See NIPPN Corporation; *Int'l*, pg. 5309
NIPPN CORPORATION; *Int'l*, pg. 5309
NIPPN DONUT KANSAI CO., LTD.—See NIPPN Corporation; *Int'l*, pg. 5309
NIPPN FOODS CORPORATION (THAILAND) LTD.—See NIPPN Corporation; *Int'l*, pg. 5310
NIPPN (SHANGHAI) TRADING CO., LTD.—See NIPPN Corporation; *Int'l*, pg. 5309
NIPPN (THAILAND) CO., LTD.—See NIPPN Corporation; *Int'l*, pg. 5309
NIPPO CORPORATION—See ENEOS Holdings, Inc.; *Int'l*, pg. 2418
NIPPO DENKO CO., LTD.—See Dai Nippon Toryo Co., Ltd.; *Int'l*, pg. 1916
NIPPOH CHEMICALS CO., LTD. - CHIMACHI FACTORY—See Nippon Shokubai Co., Ltd.; *Int'l*, pg. 5333
NIPPOH CHEMICALS CO., LTD.—See Nippon Shokubai Co., Ltd.; *Int'l*, pg. 5333
NIPPO (HONG KONG) LTD.—See NIPPO LTD; *Int'l*, pg. 5310
NIPPO KOGYO CO., LTD.—See NOF Corporation; *Int'l*, pg. 5400
NIPPO LTD; *Int'l*, pg. 5310
NIPPO MECHATRONICS (M) SDN. BHD.—See NIPPO LTD; *Int'l*, pg. 5310
NIPPO MECHATRONICS (THAILAND) CO., LTD.—See NIPPO LTD; *Int'l*, pg. 5310
NIPPO MECHATRONICS (VIETNAM) CO., LTD.—See NIPPO LTD; *Int'l*, pg. 5310
NIPPO METALTECH CO., LTD.—See NIPPO LTD; *Int'l*, pg. 5310
NIPPO METAL TECH PHILS., INC.—See NIPPO LTD; *Int'l*, pg. 5310

NIPPO LTD

Company Index

NIPPON ACCESS, INC.—See ITOCHU Corporation; *Int'l*, pg. 3841
NIPPON ACCOMMODATIONS FUND, INC.; *Int'l*, pg. 5310
NIPPON AIR CONDITIONING SERVICES CO., LTD.; *Int'l*, pg. 5310
NIPPON AIR CONDITIONING TOKAI CO., LTD.—See Nippon Air conditioning Services Co., Ltd.; *Int'l*, pg. 5310
NIPPON AIRPORT RADIO SERVICE CO., LTD.—See Nippon Telegraph & Telephone Corporation; *Int'l*, pg. 5354
NIPPON A&L, INC.—See Mitsui Chemicals, Inc.; *Int'l*, pg. 4983
NIPPON A&L, INC.—See Sumitomo Chemical Company, Limited; *Int'l*, pg. 7264
NIPPON ALKYL PHENOL CO., LTD.—See Mitsui Chemicals, Inc.; *Int'l*, pg. 4983
NIPPON ALUMINUM ALKYLS, LTD.—See Albemarle Corporation; *U.S. Public*, pg. 73
NIPPON ALUMINUM ALKYLS, LTD.—See Mitsui Chemicals, Inc.; *Int'l*, pg. 4983
NIPPON AMAZON ALUMINIUM CO., LTD.—See Mitsui & Co., Ltd.; *Int'l*, pg. 4979
NIPPON ANTENNA CO., LTD.; *Int'l*, pg. 5310
NIPPON AQUA CO., LTD.; *Int'l*, pg. 5310
NIPPON ATHLETIC SERVICE CO., LTD.—See Daiwa House Industry Co., Ltd.; *Int'l*, pg. 1947
NIPPON AUTO-PHOTO KABUSHIKI KAISHA—See ME Group International plc; *Int'l*, pg. 4762
NIPPON AUTO-PHOTO KK—See ME Group International plc; *Int'l*, pg. 4762
NIPPON AVIONICS CO., LTD.—See Japan Industrial Partners, Inc.; *Int'l*, pg. 3889
NIPPON BALL VALVE CO., LTD.—See Nittetsu Mining Co., Ltd.; *Int'l*, pg. 5383
NIPPON BAUER Y.K.—See BAUER Aktiengesellschaft; *Int'l*, pg. 893
NIPPON BEARING CO., LTD.; *Int'l*, pg. 5310
NIPPON BECTON DICKINSON COMPANY, LTD.—See Becton, Dickinson & Company; *U.S. Public*, pg. 292
NIPPON BEET SUGAR MANUFACTURING CO., LTD.; *Int'l*, pg. 5310
NIPPON BOEHRINGER INGELHEIM CO. LTD.—See C.H. Boehringer Sohn AG & Co. KG; *Int'l*, pg. 1243
NIPPON BRADY K.K.—See Brady Corporation; *U.S. Public*, pg. 379
NIPPON BROADCASTING PROJECT INC.—See Fuji Media Holdings, Inc.; *Int'l*, pg. 2814
NIPPON BS BROADCASTING CORPORATION—See Bic Camera Inc.; *Int'l*, pg. 1018
NIPPON BUILCON CORPORATION—See Totech Corporation; *Int'l*, pg. 7845
NIPPON BUILDING FUND, INC.; *Int'l*, pg. 5311
NIPPON BUILDING FUND MANAGEMENT LTD.—See Mitsui Fudosan Co., Ltd.; *Int'l*, pg. 4988
NIPPON BUSCH K.K.—See Dr. Ing. K. Busch GmbH; *Int'l*, pg. 2193
NIPPON CABLE CO. LTD.—See Doppelmayr Group; *Int'l*, pg. 2175
NIPPON CARBIDE INDIA PVT. LTD.—See NIPPON CARBIDE INDUSTRIES CO., INC.; *Int'l*, pg. 5311
NIPPON CARBIDE INDUSTRIA DO BRASIL LTDA.—See NIPPON CARBIDE INDUSTRIES CO., INC.; *Int'l*, pg. 5311
NIPPON CARBIDE INDUSTRIES CO., INC. - HAYATSUKI FACTORY—See NIPPON CARBIDE INDUSTRIES CO., INC.; *Int'l*, pg. 5311
NIPPON CARBIDE INDUSTRIES CO., INC.; *Int'l*, pg. 5311
NIPPON CARBIDE INDUSTRIES ESPANA S.A.U.—See NIPPON CARBIDE INDUSTRIES CO., INC.; *Int'l*, pg. 5311
NIPPON CARBIDE INDUSTRIES (EUROPE) GMBH—See NIPPON CARBIDE INDUSTRIES CO., INC.; *Int'l*, pg. 5311
NIPPON CARBIDE INDUSTRIES FRANCE S.A.S.—See NIPPON CARBIDE INDUSTRIES CO., INC.; *Int'l*, pg. 5311
NIPPON CARBIDE INDUSTRIES (HANGZHOU) CO., LTD.—See NIPPON CARBIDE INDUSTRIES CO., INC.; *Int'l*, pg. 5311
NIPPON CARBIDE INDUSTRIES (NETHERLANDS) B.V.—See NIPPON CARBIDE INDUSTRIES CO., INC.; *Int'l*, pg. 5311
NIPPON CARBIDE INDUSTRIES (SOUTH CAROLINA) INC.—See NIPPON CARBIDE INDUSTRIES CO., INC.; *Int'l*, pg. 5311
NIPPON CARBIDE INDUSTRIES (THAILAND) CO., INC.—See NIPPON CARBIDE INDUSTRIES CO., INC.; *Int'l*, pg. 5311
NIPPON CARBIDE INDUSTRIES (USA), INC.—See NIPPON CARBIDE INDUSTRIES CO., INC.; *Int'l*, pg. 5311
NIPPON CARBON CO., LTD. - SHIGA PLANT—See Nippon Carbon Co., Ltd.; *Int'l*, pg. 5311
NIPPON CARBON CO., LTD. - SHIRAKAWA PLANT—See Nippon Carbon Co., Ltd.; *Int'l*, pg. 5311
NIPPON CARBON CO., LTD.; *Int'l*, pg. 5311
NIPPON CARBON CO., LTD. - TOYAMA PLANT—See Nippon Carbon Co., Ltd.; *Int'l*, pg. 5312
NIPPON CARBON CO., LTD. - YAMANASHI PLANT—See Nippon Carbon Co., Ltd.; *Int'l*, pg. 5312
NIPPON CARBON ENGINEERING CO., LTD.—See Nippon Carbon Co., Ltd.; *Int'l*, pg. 5312
NIPPON CARBON MERSEN CO., LTD.—See Nippon Carbon Co., Ltd.; *Int'l*, pg. 5312
NIPPON CARBON OF AMERICA, LLC—See Nippon Carbon Co., Ltd.; *Int'l*, pg. 5312
NIPPON CARBON SHANGHAI CO., LTD.—See Nippon Carbon Co., Ltd.; *Int'l*, pg. 5312
NIPPON CARD CO., LTD.—See Tomoegawa Co., Ltd.; *Int'l*, pg. 7801
NIPPON CARE COMMUNICATIONS CO., LTD.—See Mitsubishi Research Institute, Inc.; *Int'l*, pg. 4968
NIPPON CARE SUPPLY CO., LTD.; *Int'l*, pg. 5312
NIPPON CARGO AIRLINES CO., LTD.—See Nippon Yusen Kabushiki Kaisha; *Int'l*, pg. 5359
NIPPON CAR SOLUTIONS CO., LTD.—See Nippon Telegraph & Telephone Corporation; *Int'l*, pg. 5354
NIPPON CAR SOLUTIONS CO., LTD.—See Tokyo Century Corporation; *Int'l*, pg. 7789
NIPPON CERAMIC CO., LTD. - NAN-EI FACTORY—See Nippon Ceramic Co., Ltd.; *Int'l*, pg. 5312
NIPPON CERAMIC CO., LTD.; *Int'l*, pg. 5312
NIPPON CHEMICAL INDUSTRIAL CO LTD; *Int'l*, pg. 5313
NIPPON CHEMICALS CO., LTD.—See Nippon Shokubai Co., Ltd.; *Int'l*, pg. 5333
NIPPON CHEMI-CON CORPORATION - NIIGATA PLANT—See Nippon Chemi-Con Corporation; *Int'l*, pg. 5312
NIPPON CHEMI-CON CORPORATION; *Int'l*, pg. 5312
NIPPON CHEMI-CON CORPORATION - TAKAHAGI PLANT—See Nippon Chemi-Con Corporation; *Int'l*, pg. 5312
NIPPON CHEMIPHAR CO., LTD.; *Int'l*, pg. 5313
NIPPON CHILLED LOGISTICS, INC.—See NH Foods Ltd.; *Int'l*, pg. 5256
NIPPON CHUNKY CO., LTD.—See Marubeni Corporation; *Int'l*, pg. 4709
NIPPON CHUTETSUKAN K.K.—See JFE Holdings, Inc.; *Int'l*, pg. 3939
NIPPON CHUZO K.K.—See JFE Holdings, Inc.; *Int'l*, pg. 3939
NIPPON CIVIC CONSULTING ENGINEERS CO., LTD.—See Nippon Koei Co., Ltd.; *Int'l*, pg. 5321
NIPPON CLEARING SERVICES CO., LTD.—See Nomura Holdings, Inc.; *Int'l*, pg. 5412
NIPPON CLOSURES CO., LTD.—See Toyo Seikan Group Holdings, Ltd.; *Int'l*, pg. 7856
NIPPON COKE & ENGINEERING CO., LTD.; *Int'l*, pg. 5313
NIPPON COLUMBIA CO., LTD.—See Faith, Inc.; *Int'l*, pg. 2609
NIPPON COMPUTER ARTS, INC.—See NTT Advertising, Inc.; *Int'l*, pg. 5485
NIPPON COMPUTER DYNAMICS CO., LTD.; *Int'l*, pg. 5313
NIPPON COMSYS CORPORATION—See COMSYS Holdings Corporation; *Int'l*, pg. 1762
NIPPON CONCEPT AMERICA, LLC—See Nippon Concept Corporation; *Int'l*, pg. 5313
NIPPON CONCEPT CORPORATION; *Int'l*, pg. 5313
NIPPON CONCEPT MALAYSIA SDN. BHD.—See Nippon Concept Corporation; *Int'l*, pg. 5313
NIPPON CONCEPT SINGAPORE PTE. LTD.—See Nippon Concept Corporation; *Int'l*, pg. 5313
NIPPON CONCRETE INDUSTRIES CO., LTD.; *Int'l*, pg. 5313
NIPPON CONLUX CO. LTD.—See Crane NXT, Co.; *U.S. Public*, pg. 591
NIPPON CONTAINER TERMINALS CO., LTD.—See Nippon Yusen Kabushiki Kaisha; *Int'l*, pg. 5359
NIPPON CONTAINER YUSO CO., LTD.—See Nippon Yusen Kabushiki Kaisha; *Int'l*, pg. 5359
NIPPON CONVEYOR CO., LTD. - HIMEJI PLANT—See NC Holdings Co., Ltd.; *Int'l*, pg. 5180
NIPPON CONVEYOR CO., LTD.—See NC Holdings Co., Ltd.; *Int'l*, pg. 5180
NIPPON COOKERY CO., LTD.—See Nissui Corporation; *Int'l*, pg. 5378
NIPPON CROWN CO., LTD.—See DAIICHIKOUSHO CO., LTD.; *Int'l*, pg. 1930
NIPPON CRUCIBLE CO., LTD.; *Int'l*, pg. 5313
NIPPON CUTTING & WELDING EQUIPMENT CO., LTD.—See Mitsubishi Chemical Group Corporation; *Int'l*, pg. 4937
NIPPON C&Z CO., LTD.—See NOF Corporation; *Int'l*, pg. 5400
NIPPON DAILY HEALTH CO., LTD.—See NIPPN Corporation; *Int'l*, pg. 5310
NIPPON DAISHOWA PAPERBOARD CO., LTD. - AKITA MILL—See Nippon Paper Industries Co., Ltd.; *Int'l*, pg. 5327
NIPPON DAISHOWA PAPERBOARD CO., LTD. - ASHIKAGA MILL—See Nippon Paper Industries Co., Ltd.; *Int'l*, pg. 5327
NIPPON DAISHOWA PAPERBOARD CO., LTD. - OTAKE MILL—See Nippon Paper Industries Co., Ltd.; *Int'l*, pg. 5327
NIPPON DAISHOWA PAPERBOARD CO., LTD. - SOKA MILL—See Nippon Paper Industries Co., Ltd.; *Int'l*, pg. 5327
NIPPON DAISHOWA PAPERBOARD CO., LTD.—See Nippon Paper Industries Co., Ltd.; *Int'l*, pg. 5327
NIPPON DAISHOWA PAPERBOARD CO., LTD. - YOSHINAGA MILL—See Nippon Paper Industries Co., Ltd.; *Int'l*, pg. 5327
NIPPON DAIYA VALVE CO., LTD.—See Seika Corporation; *Int'l*, pg. 6685
NIPPON DEL MONTE CORPORATION—See Kikkoman Corporation; *Int'l*, pg. 4161
NIPPON DENKO CO., LTD.; *Int'l*, pg. 5313
NIPPON DENSETSU KOGYO CO., LTD.; *Int'l*, pg. 5314
NIPPON DENTSU CO., LTD.—See EXEO Group Inc.; *Int'l*, pg. 2583
NIPPON DEVELOPMENT KOSAN CO., LTD.—See Takasago Thermal Engineering Co., Ltd.; *Int'l*, pg. 7434
NIPPON DIC CO., LTD.—See Nippon Thompson Co., Ltd.; *Int'l*, pg. 5357
NIPPON DIESEL SERVICE GMBH—See Daeyang Electric Co., Ltd.; *Int'l*, pg. 1911
NIPPON DONALDSON LTD.—See Donaldson Company, Inc.; *U.S. Public*, pg. 676
NIPPON DRY-CHEMICAL CO., LTD.; *Int'l*, pg. 5314
NIPPON DRY FOODS CO., LTD.—See NH Foods Ltd.; *Int'l*, pg. 5256
NIPPON DYNEEMA CO., LTD.—See Koninklijke DSM N.V.; *Int'l*, pg. 4262
NIPPON EIRICH CO., LTD.—See Maschinenfabrik Gustav Eirich GmbH & Co KG; *Int'l*, pg. 4720
NIPPON ELECTRIC GLASS AMERICA, INC.—See Nippon Electric Glass Co., Ltd.; *Int'l*, pg. 5314
NIPPON ELECTRIC GLASS CO., LTD. - FUJISAWA PLANT—See Nippon Electric Glass Co., Ltd.; *Int'l*, pg. 5314
NIPPON ELECTRIC GLASS CO., LTD - NOTOGAWA PLANT—See Nippon Electric Glass Co., Ltd.; *Int'l*, pg. 5314
NIPPON ELECTRIC GLASS CO., LTD - OTSU PLANT—See Nippon Electric Glass Co., Ltd.; *Int'l*, pg. 5314
NIPPON ELECTRIC GLASS CO., LTD - SHIGA-TAKATSUKI PLANT—See Nippon Electric Glass Co., Ltd.; *Int'l*, pg. 5314
NIPPON ELECTRIC GLASS CO., LTD.; *Int'l*, pg. 5314
NIPPON ELECTRIC GLASS CO., LTD.—See Nippon Electric Glass Co., Ltd.; *Int'l*, pg. 5314
NIPPON ELECTRIC GLASS CO., LTD - WAKASA-KAMINAKA PLANT—See Nippon Electric Glass Co., Ltd.; *Int'l*, pg. 5314
NIPPON ELECTRIC GLASS EUROPE GMBH—See Nippon Electric Glass Co., Ltd.; *Int'l*, pg. 5314
NIPPON ELECTRIC GLASS (FUZHOU) CO., LTD.—See Nippon Electric Glass Co., Ltd.; *Int'l*, pg. 5314
NIPPON ELECTRIC GLASS (KOREA) CO., LTD.—See Nippon Electric Glass Co., Ltd.; *Int'l*, pg. 5314
NIPPON ELECTRIC GLASS (MALAYSIA) SDN. BHD.—See Nippon Electric Glass Co., Ltd.; *Int'l*, pg. 5314
NIPPON ELECTRIC GLASS TAIWAN CO., LTD.—See Nippon Electric Glass Co., Ltd.; *Int'l*, pg. 5314
NIPPON ELECTRODE CO., LTD.—See Nippon Light Metal Holdings Company, Ltd.; *Int'l*, pg. 5324
NIPPON ELEKTRISOLA LTD.—See Elektrisola Dr. Gerd Schildbach GmbH & Co. KG; *Int'l*, pg. 2356
NIPPON ENGINEERING CONSULTANTS CO., LTD.—See DN HOLDINGS CO.,LTD; *Int'l*, pg. 2147
NIPPON ENGINEERING-VIETNAM CO., LTD.—See DN HOLDINGS CO.,LTD; *Int'l*, pg. 2147
NIPPON ENVIRONMENT AMENITY CO., LTD.—See Hibino Corporation; *Int'l*, pg. 3383
NIPPON EPOXY RESIN MANUFACTURING CO., LTD.—See Mitsui Chemicals, Inc.; *Int'l*, pg. 4983
NIPPON ERICSSON K.K.—See Telefonaktiebolaget LM Ericsson; *Int'l*, pg. 7534
NIPPON ESTER CO., LTD.—See Unitika Ltd.; *Int'l*, pg. 8074
NIPPON EVENT PLANNING CO., LTD.—See Sun Messe Co., Ltd.; *Int'l*, pg. 7306
NIPPONEX HOLDINGS LLC—See Bayer Aktiengesellschaft; *Int'l*, pg. 902
NIPPONEX INC.—See Bayer Aktiengesellschaft; *Int'l*, pg. 902
NIPPON EXPRESS (AUSTRALIA) PTY. LTD.—See Nippon Express Holdings, Inc.; *Int'l*, pg. 5315
NIPPON EXPRESS AUTOMOTIVE LOGISTICS (CHINA) CO., LTD.—See Nippon Express Holdings, Inc.; *Int'l*, pg. 5316
NIPPON EXPRESS BANGLADESH LTD.—See Nippon Express Holdings, Inc.; *Int'l*, pg. 5316
NIPPON EXPRESS (BELGIUM) N.V./S.A.—See Nippon Express Holdings, Inc.; *Int'l*, pg. 5315
NIPPON EXPRESS (CAMBODIA) CO., LTD.—See Nippon Express Holdings, Inc.; *Int'l*, pg. 5316
NIPPON EXPRESS CANADA, LTD.—See Nippon Express Holdings, Inc.; *Int'l*, pg. 5316
NIPPON EXPRESS CAPITAL CO., LTD.—See Nippon Express Holdings, Inc.; *Int'l*, pg. 5316

COMPANY NAME INDEX

NIPPON EXPRESS CARGO SERVICE (SHENZHEN) CO.,LTD.—See Nippon Express Holdings, Inc.; *Int'l*, pg. 5316
NIPPON EXPRESS (CHINA) CO., LTD.—See Nippon Express Holdings, Inc.; *Int'l*, pg. 5315
NIPPON EXPRESS CO., LTD.—See Nippon Express Holdings, Inc.; *Int'l*, pg. 5314
NIPPON EXPRESS DE ESPANA, S.A.—See Nippon Express Holdings, Inc.; *Int'l*, pg. 5317
NIPPON EXPRESS DE MEXICO, S.A. DE C.V.—See Nippon Express Holdings, Inc.; *Int'l*, pg. 5317
NIPPON EXPRESS (DEUTSCHLAND) GMBH—See Nippon Express Holdings, Inc.; *Int'l*, pg. 5315
NIPPON EXPRESS (DEUTSCHLAND) GMBH—See Nippon Express Holdings, Inc.; *Int'l*, pg. 5315
NIPPON EXPRESS (DEUTSCHLAND) GMBH—See Nippon Express Holdings, Inc.; *Int'l*, pg. 5315
NIPPON EXPRESS (DEUTSCHLAND) GMBH—See Nippon Express Holdings, Inc.; *Int'l*, pg. 5315
NIPPON EXPRESS (DEUTSCHLAND) GMBH—See Nippon Express Holdings, Inc.; *Int'l*, pg. 5315
NIPPON EXPRESS DO BRASIL—See Nippon Express Holdings, Inc.; *Int'l*, pg. 5317
NIPPON EXPRESS ENGINEERING (THAILAND) CO., LTD.—See Nippon Express Holdings, Inc.; *Int'l*, pg. 5316
NIPPON EXPRESS ENGINEERING (VIETNAM) CO., LTD.—See Nippon Express Holdings, Inc.; *Int'l*, pg. 5316
NIPPON EXPRESS EURO CARGO B.V.—See Nippon Express Holdings, Inc.; *Int'l*, pg. 5316
NIPPON EXPRESS EUROPE GMBH—See Nippon Express Holdings, Inc.; *Int'l*, pg. 5316
NIPPON EXPRESS EUROPE GMBH—See Nippon Express Holdings, Inc.; *Int'l*, pg. 5316
NIPPON EXPRESS FRANCE S.A.S.—See Nippon Express Holdings, Inc.; *Int'l*, pg. 5316
NIPPON EXPRESS FRANCE, S.A.S.—See Nippon Express Holdings, Inc.; *Int'l*, pg. 5316
NIPPON EXPRESS GLOBAL SCM (SHANGHAI) CO. LTD.—See Nippon Express Holdings, Inc.; *Int'l*, pg. 5316
NIPPON EXPRESS HAWAII, INC.—See Nippon Express Holdings, Inc.; *Int'l*, pg. 5317
NIPPON EXPRESS (H.K.) CO., LTD.—See Nippon Express Holdings, Inc.; *Int'l*, pg. 5315
NIPPON EXPRESS HOLDINGS, INC.; *Int'l*, pg. 5314
NIPPON EXPRESS (INDIA) PRIVATE LIMITED—See Nippon Express Holdings, Inc.; *Int'l*, pg. 5316
NIPPON EXPRESS (IRELAND) LTD.—See Nippon Express Holdings, Inc.; *Int'l*, pg. 5316
NIPPON EXPRESS (ISTANBUL) GLOBAL LOGISTICS A.S.—See Nippon Express Holdings, Inc.; *Int'l*, pg. 5316
NIPPON EXPRESS (ITALIA) S.R.L.—See Nippon Express Holdings, Inc.; *Int'l*, pg. 5316
NIPPON EXPRESS (JIAXING) CO., LTD.—See Nippon Express Holdings, Inc.; *Int'l*, pg. 5315
NIPPON EXPRESS KOREA CO., LTD.—See Nippon Express Holdings, Inc.; *Int'l*, pg. 5317
NIPPON EXPRESS (MALAYSIA) SDN. BHD.—See Nippon Express Holdings, Inc.; *Int'l*, pg. 5316
NIPPON EXPRESS (MIDDLE EAST) LLC—See Nippon Express Holdings, Inc.; *Int'l*, pg. 5316
NIPPON EXPRESS (MYANMAR) CO., LTD.—See Nippon Express Holdings, Inc.; *Int'l*, pg. 5316
NIPPON EXPRESS NEC LOGISTICS (SHANGHAI) LTD.—See NEC Corporation; *Int'l*, pg. 5185
NIPPON EXPRESS NEC LOGISTICS (SHANGHAI) LTD.—See Nippon Express Holdings, Inc.; *Int'l*, pg. 5315
NIPPON EXPRESS (NEDERLAND) B.V.—See Nippon Express Holdings, Inc.; *Int'l*, pg. 5316
NIPPON EXPRESS (NEW ZEALAND) LTD.—See Nippon Express Holdings, Inc.; *Int'l*, pg. 5316
NIPPON EXPRESS (PHILIPPINES) CORPORATION—See Nippon Express Holdings, Inc.; *Int'l*, pg. 5316
NIPPON EXPRESS PORTUGAL SA—See Nippon Express Holdings, Inc.; *Int'l*, pg. 5315
NIPPON EXPRESS (RUSSIA) LIMITED LIABILITY COMPANY—See Nippon Express Holdings, Inc.; *Int'l*, pg. 5315
NIPPON EXPRESS (SCHWEIZ) AG—See Nippon Express Holdings, Inc.; *Int'l*, pg. 5315
NIPPON EXPRESS (SHANGHAI) CO., LTD.—See Nippon Express Holdings, Inc.; *Int'l*, pg. 5315
NIPPON EXPRESS (SHENZHEN) CO., LTD.—See Nippon Express Holdings, Inc.; *Int'l*, pg. 5315
NIPPON EXPRESS (SINGAPORE) PTE. LTD.—See Nippon Express Holdings, Inc.; *Int'l*, pg. 5316
NIPPON EXPRESS (SOUTH ASIA & OCEANIA) PTE. LTD.—See Nippon Express Holdings, Inc.; *Int'l*, pg. 5316
NIPPON EXPRESS (SOUTH ASIA & OCEANIA) PTE. LTD.—See Nippon Express Holdings, Inc.; *Int'l*, pg. 5316
NIPPON EXPRESS (SOUTH CHINA) CO., LTD.—See Nippon Express Holdings, Inc.; *Int'l*, pg. 5315
NIPPON EXPRESS (SUZHOU) CO., LTD.—See Nippon Express Holdings, Inc.; *Int'l*, pg. 5316
NIPPON EXPRESS (TAIWAN) CO., LTD.—See Nippon Express Holdings, Inc.; *Int'l*, pg. 5316
NIPPON EXPRESS (THAILAND) CO., LTD.—See Nippon Express Holdings, Inc.; *Int'l*, pg. 5316
NIPPON EXPRESS TOURS (NEDERLAND) B.V.—See Nippon Express Holdings, Inc.; *Int'l*, pg. 5316
NIPPON EXPRESS TRAVEL (H.K.) CO., LTD.—See Nippon Express Holdings, Inc.; *Int'l*, pg. 5315
NIPPON EXPRESS TRAVEL U.S.A., INC.—See Nippon Express Holdings, Inc.; *Int'l*, pg. 5317
NIPPON EXPRESS (U.K.), LTD.—See Nippon Express Holdings, Inc.; *Int'l*, pg. 5316
NIPPON EXPRESS U.S.A., INC.—See Nippon Express Holdings, Inc.; *Int'l*, pg. 5317
NIPPON EXPRESS USA, INC.—See Nippon Express Holdings, Inc.; *Int'l*, pg. 5317
NIPPON EXPRESS (VIETNAM) CO., LTD.—See Nippon Express Holdings, Inc.; *Int'l*, pg. 5316
NIPPON EXPRESS (XIAMEN) CO., LTD.—See Nippon Express Holdings, Inc.; *Int'l*, pg. 5316
NIPPON EXPRESS (XIAN) CO., LTD.—See Nippon Express Holdings, Inc.; *Int'l*, pg. 5316
NIPPON EXPRESS (ZHUHAI) CO., LTD.—See Nippon Express Holdings, Inc.; *Int'l*, pg. 5315
NIPPON FELT CO., LTD. - SAITAMA MILL—See Nippon Felt Co., Ltd.; *Int'l*, pg. 5317
NIPPON FELT CO., LTD.; *Int'l*, pg. 5317
NIPPON FELT CO., LTD. - TOCHIGI MILL—See Nippon Felt Co., Ltd.; *Int'l*, pg. 5317
NIPPON FIELD ENGINEERING CO., LTD.—See Oi Electric Co., Ltd.; *Int'l*, pg. 5533
NIPPON FILCON CO., LTD. - SHIZUOKA PLANT—See Nippon Filcon Co., Ltd.; *Int'l*, pg. 5318
NIPPON FILCON CO., LTD.; *Int'l*, pg. 5317
NIPPON FILLER METALS, LTD.—See Harima Chemicals Group; *Int'l*, pg. 3276
NIPPON FINE CHEMICAL CO., LTD. - KAKOGAWA-HIGASHI PLANT—See Nippon Fine Chemical Co., Ltd.; *Int'l*, pg. 5318
NIPPON FINE CHEMICAL CO., LTD. - KAKOGAWA-NISHI PLANT—See Nippon Fine Chemical Co., Ltd.; *Int'l*, pg. 5318
NIPPON FINE CHEMICAL CO., LTD. - KOBE PLANT—See Nippon Fine Chemical Co., Ltd.; *Int'l*, pg. 5318
NIPPON FINE CHEMICAL CO., LTD.; *Int'l*, pg. 5318
NIPPON FINE CHEMICAL CO., LTD. - TAKASAGO PLANT—See Nippon Fine Chemical Co., Ltd.; *Int'l*, pg. 5318
NIPPON FINE CO., LTD.—See Kurita Water Industries Ltd.; *Int'l*, pg. 4341
NIPPON FISHER CO., LTD.—See Emerson Electric Co.; *U.S. Public*, pg. 748
NIPPON FLODA CO., LTD.—See Takasago Thermal Engineering Co., Ltd.; *Int'l*, pg. 7434
NIPPON FLOUR MILLS (SHANGHAI) CO.—See NIPPN Corporation; *Int'l*, pg. 5310
NIPPON FLOUR MILLS (THAILAND) CO., —See NIPPN Corporation; *Int'l*, pg. 5310
NIPPON FOIL MFG. CO., LTD. - NOGI PLANT—See UACJ Corporation; *Int'l*, pg. 7999
NIPPON FOIL MFG. CO., LTD. - SHIGA PLANT—See UACJ Corporation; *Int'l*, pg. 7999
NIPPON FOOD PACKER, INC.—See NH Foods Ltd.; *Int'l*, pg. 5256
NIPPON FOOD PACKER SHIKOKU, INC.—See Nissin Foods Holdings Co., Ltd.; *Int'l*, pg. 5376
NIPPON FOOD SUPPLIES COMPANY PTY. LTD.—See Takara Holdings Inc.; *Int'l*, pg. 7432
NIPPON FREEZE DRYING CO., LTD.—See Asahi Group Holdings Ltd.; *Int'l*, pg. 594
NIPPON FRUEHAUF CO., LTD. - ATSUGI PLANT—See Nippon Light Metal Holdings Company, Ltd.; *Int'l*, pg. 5324
NIPPON FRUEHAUF CO., LTD.—See Nippon Light Metal Holdings Company, Ltd.; *Int'l*, pg. 5324
NIPPON GAS CO., LTD.; *Int'l*, pg. 5318
NIPPON GAS CO., LTD. - TANASHI PLANT—See Nippon Gas Co., Ltd.; *Int'l*, pg. 5318
NIPPON GASES BELGIUM N.V.-SCHOTEN—See Mitsubishi Chemical Group Corporation; *Int'l*, pg. 4936
NIPPON GASES BELGIUM N.V.—See Mitsubishi Chemical Group Corporation; *Int'l*, pg. 4936
NIPPON GASES EURO-HOLDING, S.L.U.—See Mitsubishi Chemical Group Corporation; *Int'l*, pg. 4937
NIPPON GASES NORGE AS—See Mitsubishi Chemical Group Corporation; *Int'l*, pg. 4936
NIPPON GASES OFFSHORE TANKS LIMITED—See Mitsubishi Chemical Group Corporation; *Int'l*, pg. 4936
NIPPON GASES SVERIGE AB—See Mitsubishi Chemical Group Corporation; *Int'l*, pg. 4936
NIPPON GASES UK LIMITED—See Mitsubishi Chemical Group Corporation; *Int'l*, pg. 4937
NIPPON GASKET CO., LTD.—See Taiho Kogyo Co., Ltd; *Int'l*, pg. 7412
NIPPON GASSES DANMARK A/S—See Mitsubishi Chemical Group Corporation; *Int'l*, pg. 4937
NIPPON GASSES DEUTSCHLAND GMBH—See Mitsubishi Chemical Group Corporation; *Int'l*, pg. 4937
NIPPON GASSES ESPANA S.L.—See Mitsubishi Chemical Group Corporation; *Int'l*, pg. 4937
NIPPON GASSES EURO-HOLDING, S. L.—See Mitsubishi Chemical Group Corporation; *Int'l*, pg. 4936
NIPPON GASSES NETHERLANDS B.V.—See Mitsubishi Chemical Group Corporation; *Int'l*, pg. 4937
NIPPON GAS UNYUSEIBI CO., LTD.—See Nippon Gas Co., Ltd.; *Int'l*, pg. 5318
NIPPON GEAR CO., LTD.; *Int'l*, pg. 5318
NIPPON GLOBAL TANKER CO., LTD.—See ENEOS Holdings, Inc.; *Int'l*, pg. 2417
NIPPON GOHSEI EUROPE GMBH—See Mitsubishi Chemical Group Corporation; *Int'l*, pg. 4934
NIPPON GOHSEI (UK) LIMITED—See Mitsubishi Chemical Group Corporation; *Int'l*, pg. 4934
NIPPON GOHSEI (U.S.A.) CO., LTD.—See Mitsubishi Chemical Group Corporation; *Int'l*, pg. 4934
NIPPON GOODYEAR LTD—See The Goodyear Tire & Rubber Company; *U.S. Public*, pg. 2084
NIPPON GOURMET TRADING COMPANY LIMITED—See Future Bright Holdings Limited; *Int'l*, pg. 2852
NIPPON GPS DATA SERVICE CORPORATION—See Hitachi Zosen Corporation; *Int'l*, pg. 3412
NIPPON GREASE CO., LTD.—See Idemitsu Kosan Co., Ltd.; *Int'l*, pg. 3592
NIPPON HAM BUSINESS EXPERT CORPORATION—See NH Foods Ltd.; *Int'l*, pg. 5256
NIPPON HAM CUSTOMER COMMUNICATION CO., LTD.—See NH Foods Ltd.; *Int'l*, pg. 5256
NIPPON HAM HOKKAIDO FACTORY CO., LTD.—See NH Foods Ltd.; *Int'l*, pg. 5256
NIPPON HAM LIFE SERVICE CO., LTD.—See NH Foods Ltd.; *Int'l*, pg. 5256
NIPPON HEALTHCARE INVESTMENT CORPORATION; *Int'l*, pg. 5318
NIPPON HELIUM INC.—See Air Water Inc.; *Int'l*, pg. 240
NIPPON HIGH VOLTAGE CABLE CORPORATION—See Nexans S.A.; *Int'l*, pg. 5242
NIPPON HOSO KYOKAI; *Int'l*, pg. 5318
NIPPON HOTEL CO. LTD.—See East Japan Railway Company; *Int'l*, pg. 2270
NIPPON HUME CORPORATION; *Int'l*, pg. 5319
NIPPON ICHI SOFTWARE, INC.; *Int'l*, pg. 5319
NIPPON IDT G.K.—See Renesas Electronics Corporation; *Int'l*, pg. 6276
NIPPON INDUSTRIES, INC.; *U.S. Private*, pg. 2928
NIPPON INFORMATION & COMMUNICATION CORPORATION—See International Business Machines Corporation; *U.S. Public*, pg. 1147
NIPPON INFORMATION & COMMUNICATION CORPORATION—See Nippon Telegraph & Telephone Corporation; *Int'l*, pg. 5354
NIPPON INFORMATION DEVELOPMENT CO., LTD.; *Int'l*, pg. 5319
NIPPON INSURANCE SERVICE CO., LTD.—See Nippon Life Insurance Company; *Int'l*, pg. 5322
NIPPON INSURE CO., LTD.; *Int'l*, pg. 5319
NIPPON I.T.F INC.—See Sumitomo Electric Industries, Ltd.; *Int'l*, pg. 7278
NIPPON JORDAN FERTILIZERS COMPANY LIMITED—See Jordan Phosphate Mines Company Ltd.; *Int'l*, pg. 3999
NIPPON KANZAI CO., LTD.—See NIPPON KANZAI Holdings Co.,Ltd.; *Int'l*, pg. 5319
NIPPON KANZAI ENVIRONMENT SERVICE CO., LTD.—See NIPPON KANZAI Holdings Co.,Ltd.; *Int'l*, pg. 5319
NIPPON KANZAI HOLDINGS CO.,LTD.; *Int'l*, pg. 5319
NIPPON KANZAI HOUSING MANAGEMENT CO., LTD.—See NIPPON KANZAI Holdings Co.,Ltd.; *Int'l*, pg. 5319
NIPPON KATAN CO., LTD.—See Sumitomo Corporation; *Int'l*, pg. 7269
NIPPON KAYAKU AMERICA, INC.—See Nippon Kayaku Co., Ltd.; *Int'l*, pg. 5320
NIPPON KAYAKU CO., LTD. - AGROCHEMICALS DIVISION—See Nippon Kayaku Co., Ltd.; *Int'l*, pg. 5320
NIPPON KAYAKU CO., LTD. - ASA PLANT—See Nippon Kayaku Co., Ltd.; *Int'l*, pg. 5320
NIPPON KAYAKU CO., LTD. - CORPORATE PLANNING DIVISION—See Nippon Kayaku Co., Ltd.; *Int'l*, pg. 5320
NIPPON KAYAKU CO., LTD. - EXPLOSIVES RESEARCH LABORATORIES—See Nippon Kayaku Co., Ltd.; *Int'l*, pg. 5320
NIPPON KAYAKU CO., LTD. - FUKUYAMA PLANT—See Nippon Kayaku Co., Ltd.; *Int'l*, pg. 5320
NIPPON KAYAKU CO., LTD. - FUNCTIONAL MATERIALS DIVISION—See Nippon Kayaku Co., Ltd.; *Int'l*, pg. 5320

NIPPON KAYAKU CO., LTD. - HIMEJI PLANT—See Nippon Kayaku Co., Ltd.; *Int'l*, pg. 5320
NIPPON KAYAKU CO., LTD. - KASHIMA PLANT—See Nippon Kayaku Co., Ltd.; *Int'l*, pg. 5320
NIPPON KAYAKU CO., LTD.; *Int'l*, pg. 5320
NIPPON KAYAKU CO., LTD. - TAKASAKI PLANT—See Nippon Kayaku Co., Ltd.; *Int'l*, pg. 5320
NIPPON KAYAKU CO., LTD. - TOKYO PLANT—See Nissui Corporation; *Int'l*, pg. 5378
NIPPON KAYAKU CZ, S.R.O.—See Nippon Kayaku Co., Ltd.; *Int'l*, pg. 5320
NIPPON KAYAKU FOOD TECHNO CO., LTD.—See Nippon Kayaku Co., Ltd.; *Int'l*, pg. 5320
NIPPON KAYAKU FUKUYAMA CO., LTD.—See Nippon Kayaku Co., Ltd.; *Int'l*, pg. 5320
NIPPON KAYAKU KOREA CO., LTD.—See Nippon Kayaku Co., Ltd.; *Int'l*, pg. 5320
NIPPON KAYAKU (THAILAND) CO., LTD.—See Nippon Kayaku Co., Ltd.; *Int'l*, pg. 5320
NIPPON KAYAKU TOKYO CO., LTD.—See Nippon Kayaku Co., Ltd.; *Int'l*, pg. 5320
NIPPON KEICAL LIMITED—See Meisei Industrial Co., Ltd.; *Int'l*, pg. 4804
NIPPON KETJEN CO., LTD.—See Albemarle Corporation; *U.S. Public*, pg. 73
NIPPON KETJEN CO., LTD.—See Sumitomo Metal Mining Co., Ltd.; *Int'l*, pg. 7291
NIPPON KINZOKU CO., LTD. - FUKUSHIMA PLANT—See Nippon kinzoku co., Ltd.; *Int'l*, pg. 5321
NIPPON KINZOKU CO., LTD. - GIFU PLANT—See Nippon kinzoku co., Ltd.; *Int'l*, pg. 5321
NIPPON KINZOKU CO., LTD. - ITABASHI PLANT—See Nippon kinzoku co., Ltd.; *Int'l*, pg. 5321
NIPPON KINZOKU CO., LTD.; *Int'l*, pg. 5321
NIPPON KINZOKU (THAILAND) CO., LTD.—See Nippon kinzoku co., Ltd.; *Int'l*, pg. 5321
NIPPONKOA INSURANCE COMPANY (CHINA) LIMITED—See Sompo Holdings, Inc.; *Int'l*, pg. 7087
NIPPON KODOSHI CORPORATION - AKI PLANT—See NIPPON KODOSHI CORPORATION; *Int'l*, pg. 5321
NIPPON KODOSHI CORPORATION - NANKOKU PLANT—See NIPPON KODOSHI CORPORATION; *Int'l*, pg. 5321
NIPPON KODOSHI CORPORATION; *Int'l*, pg. 5321
NIPPON KODOSHI CORPORATION - YONAGO PLANT—See NIPPON KODOSHI CORPORATION; *Int'l*, pg. 5321
NIPPON KODOSHI KOGYO (MALAYSIA) SDN. BHD.—See NIPPON KODOSHI CORPORATION; *Int'l*, pg. 5321
NIPPON KOEI CO., LTD.; *Int'l*, pg. 5321
NIPPON KOEI LAC, INC.—See Nippon Koei Co., Ltd.; *Int'l*, pg. 5321
NIPPON KOEI LATIN AMERICA-CARIBBEAN CO., LTD.—See Nippon Koei Co., Ltd.; *Int'l*, pg. 5321
NIPPON KOEI URBAN SPACE CO., LTD.—See Nippon Koei Co., Ltd.; *Int'l*, pg. 5321
NIPPON KOEI VIETNAM INTERNATIONAL CO., LTD.—See Nippon Koei Co., Ltd.; *Int'l*, pg. 5321
NIPPON KOHBUNSHI CO. LTD.—See Nisshinbo Holdings Inc.; *Int'l*, pg. 5373
NIPPON KOKI CO., LTD.—See NOF Corporation; *Int'l*, pg. 5400
NIPPON KORNMEYER CARBON GROUP GMBH—See Nippon Carbon Co., Ltd.; *Int'l*, pg. 5312
NIPPON KOSHUHA STEEL CO., LTD.—See Kobe Steel, Ltd.; *Int'l*, pg. 4220
NIPPON KREIS CO., LTD.—See Maruyama Mfg. Co., Inc.; *Int'l*, pg. 4715
NIPPON LIFE AMERICAS, INC.—See Nippon Life Insurance Company; *Int'l*, pg. 5322
NIPPON LIFE BENEFITS—See Nippon Life Insurance Company; *Int'l*, pg. 5322
NIPPON LIFE BENEFITS—See Nippon Life Insurance Company; *Int'l*, pg. 5322
NIPPON LIFE (DEUTSCHLAND) GMBH—See Nippon Life Insurance Company; *Int'l*, pg. 5322
NIPPON LIFE GLOBAL INVESTORS AMERICAS, INC.—See Nippon Life Insurance Company; *Int'l*, pg. 5322
NIPPON LIFE GLOBAL INVESTORS EUROPE PLC—See Nippon Life Insurance Company; *Int'l*, pg. 5322
NIPPON LIFE INDIA ASSET MANAGEMENT LIMITED—See Nippon Life Insurance Company; *Int'l*, pg. 5322
NIPPON LIFE INDIA ASSET MANAGEMENT (SINGAPORE) PTE. LTD.—See Nippon Life Insurance Company; *Int'l*, pg. 5322
NIPPON LIFE INSURANCE COMPANY - LONDON REPRESENTATIVE OFFICE—See Nippon Life Insurance Company; *Int'l*, pg. 5322
NIPPON LIFE INSURANCE COMPANY; *Int'l*, pg. 5322
NIPPON LIFE INSURANCE CO. - TOKYO OFFICE—See Nippon Life Insurance Company; *Int'l*, pg. 5322
NIPPON LIFE REALTY MANAGEMENT INC.—See Nippon Life Insurance Company; *Int'l*, pg. 5322
NIPPON LIFE SCHRODERS ASSET MANAGEMENT EUROPE LIMITED—See Nippon Life Insurance Company; *Int'l*, pg. 5322

NIPPON LIGHT METAL COMPANY, LTD.—See Nippon Light Metal Holdings Company, Ltd.; *Int'l*, pg. 5323
NIPPON LIGHT METAL GEORGIA, INC.—See Nippon Light Metal Holdings Company, Ltd.; *Int'l*, pg. 5324
NIPPON LIGHT METAL HOLDINGS COMPANY, LTD.; *Int'l*, pg. 5323
NIPPON LIGHT METAL NORTH AMERICA, INC.—See Nippon Light Metal Holdings Company, Ltd.; *Int'l*, pg. 5324
NIPPON LINIAX CO., LTD.—See NICHICON CORPORATION; *Int'l*, pg. 5268
NIPPON LIQUOR LTD.—See Kirin Holdings Company, Limited; *Int'l*, pg. 4187
NIPPON LOGISTECH CORPORATION; *Int'l*, pg. 5324
NIPPON LOGISTECH SUPPORT CORPORATION—See NIPPON LOGISTECH CORPORATION; *Int'l*, pg. 5324
NIPPON LOGISTICS CENTER, INC—See NH Foods Ltd.; *Int'l*, pg. 5256
NIPPON LUNA, INC.—See NH Foods Ltd.; *Int'l*, pg. 5256
NIPPON MACDERMID CO., LTD.—See Element Solutions Inc.; *U.S. Public*, pg. 728
NIPPON MARINE CO., LTD.—See ENEOS Holdings, Inc.; *Int'l*, pg. 2416
NIPPON MARINE ENTERPRISES, LTD.—See Nissui Corporation; *Int'l*, pg. 5378
NIPPON MAYER LTD.—See KARL MAYER Textilmaschinenfabrik GmbH; *Int'l*, pg. 4082
NIPPON MEDICAL CARE PTE LTD—See Khazanah Nasional Berhad; *Int'l*, pg. 4152
NIPPON MEKTRON, LTD. - FUJISAWA PLANT—See NOK Corporation; *Int'l*, pg. 5402
NIPPON MEKTRON, LTD. - KASHIMA PLANT—See NOK Corporation; *Int'l*, pg. 5402
NIPPON MEKTRON, LTD. - MINAMI IBARAKI PLANT—See NOK Corporation; *Int'l*, pg. 5402
NIPPON MEKTRON, LTD. - OKUHARA PLANT—See NOK Corporation; *Int'l*, pg. 5402
NIPPON MEKTRON, LTD.—See NOK Corporation; *Int'l*, pg. 5402
NIPPON MICROTHERM CO. LTD.—See Etex SA/NV; *Int'l*, pg. 2522
NIPPON MIK CORP.—See Arlitech Electronic Corp.; *Int'l*, pg. 573
NIPPON MINING & METALS (SUZHOU) CO., LTD.—See ENEOS Holdings, Inc.; *Int'l*, pg. 2416
NIPPON MIRAI CAPITAL CO., LTD.; *Int'l*, pg. 5324
NIPPON MOLYMER CO., LTD.; *Int'l*, pg. 5324
NIPPON MUKI CO., LTD.—See Daikin Industries, Ltd.; *Int'l*, pg. 1936
NIPPON NO-DIG TECHNOLOGY CO., LTD.—See HIROSE HOLDINGS & CO.,LTD.; *Int'l*, pg. 3405
NIPPON NOISE CONTROL LTD.—See Taikisha Ltd.; *Int'l*, pg. 7413
NIPPON NOZZLE CO., LTD.—See Nakamura Choukou Co., Ltd.; *Int'l*, pg. 5132
NIPPON NYUKAZAI CO., LTD.—See Nippon Shokubai Co., Ltd.; *Int'l*, pg. 5333
NIPPON OFFICE SYSTEMS LTD.—See Kanematsu Corporation; *Int'l*, pg. 4068
NIPPON OIL-DHABI—See ENEOS Holdings, Inc.; *Int'l*, pg. 2417
NIPPON OIL FINANCE (NETHERLANDS) B.V.—See ENEOS Holdings, Inc.; *Int'l*, pg. 2417
NIPPON OIL LUBRICANTS (AMERICA) LLC—See ENEOS Holdings, Inc.; *Int'l*, pg. 2417
NIPPON OIL (U.K.) PLC—See ENEOS Holdings, Inc.; *Int'l*, pg. 2417
NIPPON OTIS ELEVATOR COMPANY—See Otis Worldwide Corporation; *U.S. Public*, pg. 1623
NIPPON OUTSOURCE INCORPORATION—See RISKMONSTER.COM; *Int'l*, pg. 6350
NIPPON PAINT AUTOMOTIVE AMERICAS, INC.—See Nippon Paint Holdings Co., Ltd.; *Int'l*, pg. 5326
NIPPON PAINT AUTOMOTIVE COATINGS CO., LTD.—See Nippon Paint Holdings Co., Ltd.; *Int'l*, pg. 5326
NIPPON PAINT (BANGLADESH) PRIVATE LIMITED—See Nippon Paint Holdings Co., Ltd.; *Int'l*, pg. 5325
NIPPON PAINT (CHENGDU) CO., LTD.—See Nippon Paint Holdings Co., Ltd.; *Int'l*, pg. 5325
NIPPON PAINT (CHINA) CO., LTD.—See Nippon Paint Holdings Co., Ltd.; *Int'l*, pg. 5325
NIPPON PAINT (CHONGQING) CHEMICALS CO., LTD.—See Nippon Paint Holdings Co., Ltd.; *Int'l*, pg. 5325
NIPPON PAINT COATINGS (TAIWAN) CO., LTD.—See Nippon Paint Holdings Co., Ltd.; *Int'l*, pg. 5326
NIPPON PAINT COMPANY LTD. - TOKYO OFFICE—See Nippon Paint Holdings Co., Ltd.; *Int'l*, pg. 5326
NIPPON PAINT CORPORATE SOLUTIONS CO., LTD.—See Nippon Paint Holdings Co., Ltd.; *Int'l*, pg. 5326
NIPPON PAINT (EUROPE) LTD.—See Nippon Paint Holdings Co., Ltd.; *Int'l*, pg. 5325
NIPPON PAINT (GUANGDONG) CO., LTD.—See Nippon Paint Holdings Co., Ltd.; *Int'l*, pg. 5325
NIPPON PAINT (H.K.) CO., LTD.—See Nippon Paint Holdings Co., Ltd.; *Int'l*, pg. 5325
NIPPON PAINT HOLDINGS CO., LTD.; *Int'l*, pg. 5325

NIPPON PAINT (INDIA) PRIVATE LIMITED—See Nippon Paint Holdings Co., Ltd.; *Int'l*, pg. 5325
NIPPON PAINT LANKA (PRIVATE) LIMITED—See Nippon Paint Holdings Co., Ltd.; *Int'l*, pg. 5326
NIPPON PAINT (MALAYSIA) SDN. BHD.—See Nippon Paint Holdings Co., Ltd.; *Int'l*, pg. 5325
NIPPON PAINT MARINE COATINGS CO., LTD—See Nippon Paint Holdings Co., Ltd.; *Int'l*, pg. 5326
NIPPON PAINT MARINE (HONG KONG) CO., LTD.—See Nippon Paint Holdings Co., Ltd.; *Int'l*, pg. 5326
NIPPON PAINT MARINE (KOREA) CO., LTD.—See Nippon Paint Holdings Co., Ltd.; *Int'l*, pg. 5326
NIPPON PAINT MARINE (MALAYSIA) SDN. BHD.—See Nippon Paint Holdings Co., Ltd.; *Int'l*, pg. 5326
NIPPON PAINT MARINE (SINGAPORE) PTE. LTD.—See Nippon Paint Holdings Co., Ltd.; *Int'l*, pg. 5326
NIPPON PAINT MARINE (TAIWAN) CO., LTD.—See Nippon Paint Holdings Co., Ltd.; *Int'l*, pg. 5326
NIPPON PAINT (MYANMAR) SERVICE CO., LTD.—See Nippon Paint Holdings Co., Ltd.; *Int'l*, pg. 5325
NIPPON PAINT (PAKISTAN) PRIVATE LIMITED—See Nippon Paint Holdings Co., Ltd.; *Int'l*, pg. 5325
NIPPON PAINT (PHILIPPINES) INC.—See Nippon Paint Holdings Co., Ltd.; *Int'l*, pg. 5325
NIPPON PAINT (SINGAPORE) CO., PTE. LTD.—See Nippon Paint Holdings Co., Ltd.; *Int'l*, pg. 5326
NIPPON PAINT SURF CHEMICALS CO., LTD.—See Nippon Paint Holdings Co., Ltd.; *Int'l*, pg. 5326
NIPPON PAINT (THAILAND) CO., LTD. - BANGPAKONG FACTORY—See Nippon Paint Holdings Co., Ltd.; *Int'l*, pg. 5326
NIPPON PAINT (THAILAND) CO., LTD.—See Nippon Paint Holdings Co., Ltd.; *Int'l*, pg. 5326
NIPPON PAINT TURKEY BOYA SANAYI VE TICARET ANONIM SIRKETI—See Nippon Paint Holdings Co., Ltd.; *Int'l*, pg. 5326
NIPPON PAINT (USA) INC.—See Nippon Paint Holdings Co., Ltd.; *Int'l*, pg. 5326
NIPPON PAINT (VIETNAM) CO., LTD.—See Nippon Paint Holdings Co., Ltd.; *Int'l*, pg. 5326
NIPPON PAINT VIETNAM (HANOI) CO., LTD.—See Nippon Paint Holdings Co., Ltd.; *Int'l*, pg. 5326
NIPPON PALLET POOL CO., LTD.; *Int'l*, pg. 5326
NIPPON PAPER CHEMICALS CO., LTD.—See Nippon Paper Industries Co., Ltd.; *Int'l*, pg. 5327
NIPPON PAPER CHEMICALS SUPPORT CO., LTD.—See Nippon Paper Industries Co., Ltd.; *Int'l*, pg. 5327
NIPPON PAPER CRECIA CO., LTD. - IWAKUNI MILL—See Nippon Paper Industries Co., Ltd.; *Int'l*, pg. 5327
NIPPON PAPER CRECIA CO., LTD. - KAISEI MILL—See Nippon Paper Industries Co., Ltd.; *Int'l*, pg. 5327
NIPPON PAPER CRECIA CO., LTD. - KYOTO MILL—See Nippon Paper Industries Co., Ltd.; *Int'l*, pg. 5327
NIPPON PAPER CRECIA CO., LTD.—See Nippon Paper Industries Co., Ltd.; *Int'l*, pg. 5327
NIPPON PAPER CRECIA CO., LTD. - TOKYO MILL—See Nippon Paper Industries Co., Ltd.; *Int'l*, pg. 5327
NIPPON PAPER DEVELOPMENT CO., LTD.—See Nippon Paper Industries Co., Ltd.; *Int'l*, pg. 5327
NIPPON PAPER INDUSTRIES CO., LTD. - FUJI MILL—See Nippon Paper Industries Co., Ltd.; *Int'l*, pg. 5327
NIPPON PAPER INDUSTRIES CO., LTD. - HOKKAIDO MILL—See Nippon Paper Industries Co., Ltd.; *Int'l*, pg. 5327
NIPPON PAPER INDUSTRIES CO., LTD. - ISHINOMAKI MILL—See Nippon Paper Industries Co., Ltd.; *Int'l*, pg. 5327
NIPPON PAPER INDUSTRIES CO., LTD. - IWAKUNI MILL—See Nippon Paper Industries Co., Ltd.; *Int'l*, pg. 5327
NIPPON PAPER INDUSTRIES CO., LTD. - IWANUMA MILL—See Nippon Paper Industries Co., Ltd.; *Int'l*, pg. 5327
NIPPON PAPER INDUSTRIES CO., LTD. - KUSHIRO MILL—See Nippon Paper Industries Co., Ltd.; *Int'l*, pg. 5327
NIPPON PAPER INDUSTRIES CO., LTD. - NAKOSO MILL—See Nippon Paper Industries Co., Ltd.; *Int'l*, pg. 5327
NIPPON PAPER INDUSTRIES CO., LTD.; *Int'l*, pg. 5326
NIPPON PAPER INDUSTRIES CO., LTD. - YATSUSHIRO MILL—See Nippon Paper Industries Co., Ltd.; *Int'l*, pg. 5327
NIPPON PAPER INDUSTRIES TRADING (SHANGHAI) CO., LTD.—See Nippon Paper Industries Co., Ltd.; *Int'l*, pg. 5327
NIPPON PAPER INDUSTRIES USA CO., LTD.—See Nippon Paper Industries Co., Ltd.; *Int'l*, pg. 5327
NIPPON PAPER LOGISTICS CO., LTD.—See Nippon Paper Industries Co., Ltd.; *Int'l*, pg. 5327
NIPPON PAPER LUMBER CO., LTD.—See Nippon Paper Industries Co., Ltd.; *Int'l*, pg. 5327
NIPPON PAPER-PAK CO., LTD.—See Nippon Paper Industries Co., Ltd.; *Int'l*, pg. 5328
NIPPON PAPER PAPYLIA CO., LTD. - HARADA MILL—See Nippon Paper Industries Co., Ltd.; *Int'l*, pg. 5327

COMPANY NAME INDEX

NIPPON PAPER PAPYLIA CO., LTD. - KOCHI MILL—See Nippon Paper Industries Co., Ltd.; *Int'l*, pg. 5328
NIPPON PAPER PAPYLIA CO., LTD.—See Nippon Paper Industries Co., Ltd.; *Int'l*, pg. 5327
NIPPON PAPER PAPYLIA CO., LTD. - SUITA MILL—See Nippon Paper Industries Co., Ltd.; *Int'l*, pg. 5328
NIPPON PAPER VIET HOA MY JSC—See Nippon Paper Industries Co., Ltd.; *Int'l*, pg. 5328
NIPPON PARISON CO., LTD.—See Ishizuka Glass Co., Ltd.; *Int'l*, pg. 3818
NIPPON PARKING DEVELOPMENT CO., LTD.; *Int'l*, pg. 5328
NIPPON PARKING DEVELOPMENT SAPPORO CO., LTD.—See Nippon Parking Development Co., Ltd.; *Int'l*, pg. 5328
NIPPON PARTS CO., LTD.—See Nippon Sheet Glass Co. Ltd.; *Int'l*, pg. 5331
NIPPON PETROLEUM REFINING CO., LTD.—See ENEOS Holdings, Inc.; *Int'l*, pg. 2417
NIPPON PGM AMERICA INC.—See Dowa Holdings Co., Ltd.; *Int'l*, pg. 2184
NIPPON PGM AMERICA INC.—See Dowa Holdings Co., Ltd.; *Int'l*, pg. 2184
NIPPON PGM AMERICA INC.—See Tanaka Holdings Co., Ltd.; *Int'l*, pg. 7455
NIPPON PGM CO., LTD.—See Dowa Holdings Co., Ltd.; *Int'l*, pg. 2184
NIPPON PGM CO., LTD.—See Dowa Holdings Co., Ltd.; *Int'l*, pg. 2184
NIPPON PGM CO., LTD.—See Tanaka Holdings Co., Ltd.; *Int'l*, pg. 7455
NIPPON PGM EUROPE S.R.O.—See Dowa Holdings Co., Ltd.; *Int'l*, pg. 2184
NIPPON PHOSPHORIC ACID CO., LTD.—See Nissan Chemical Corporation; *Int'l*, pg. 5366
NIPPON PHYSICAL ACOUSTICS LTD.—See Mistras Group, Inc.; *U.S. Public*, pg. 1451
NIPPON PIGMENT CO., LTD.—See NPK Co., Ltd.; *Int'l*, pg. 5472
NIPPON PIGMENT (M) SDN. BHD.—See NPK Co., Ltd.; *Int'l*, pg. 5472
NIPPON PIGMENT (S) PTE. LTD.—See NPK Co., Ltd.; *Int'l*, pg. 5472
NIPPON PILLAR CORPORATION OF AMERICA CO., LTD.—See Nippon Pillar Packing Co., Ltd.; *Int'l*, pg. 5328
NIPPON PILLAR MIDDLE EAST FZE—See Nippon Pillar Packing Co., Ltd.; *Int'l*, pg. 5328
NIPPON PILLAR PACKING CO., LTD. - KYUSHU FACTORY—See Nippon Pillar Packing Co., Ltd.; *Int'l*, pg. 5328
NIPPON PILLAR PACKING CO., LTD. - SANDA FACTORY—See Nippon Pillar Packing Co., Ltd.; *Int'l*, pg. 5328
NIPPON PILLAR PACKING CO., LTD.; *Int'l*, pg. 5328
NIPPON PLANT SEEDER CO., LTD.—See Ozu Corporation; *Int'l*, pg. 5679
NIPPON PLASTIC INDUSTRY CO., LTD—See Kubota Corporation; *Int'l*, pg. 4322
NIPPON PMAC CO., LTD.—See Takasago Thermal Engineering Co., Ltd.; *Int'l*, pg. 7434
NIPPON PNEUMATIC MFG. CO., LTD. - NABARI PLANT—See Nippon Pneumatic Mfg. Co., Ltd.; *Int'l*, pg. 5329
NIPPON PNEUMATIC MFG. CO., LTD.; *Int'l*, pg. 5329
NIPPON POLAROID KABUSHIKI KAISHA—See Gordon Brothers Group, LLC; *U.S. Private*, pg. 1742
NIPPON POLAROID KABUSHIKI KAISHA—See Hilco Trading, LLC; *U.S. Private*, pg. 1943
NIPPON POLYESTER CO., LTD.—See Nippon Shokubai Co., Ltd.; *Int'l*, pg. 5333
NIPPON POLYMER INDUSTRIES, CO., LTD.—See Nippon Shokubai Co., Ltd.; *Int'l*, pg. 5333
NIPPON POLYTECH CORP.—See Resonac Holdings Corporation; *Int'l*, pg. 6298
NIPPON POLYURETHANE INDUSTRY CO., LTD.—See Tosoh Corporation; *Int'l*, pg. 7832
NIPPON POLYURETHANE (RUIAN) CO., LTD.—See Tosoh Corporation; *Int'l*, pg. 7832
NIPPON POP RIVETS & FASTENERS LTD.—See Stanley Black & Decker, Inc.; *U.S. Public*, pg. 1934
NIPPON PREMIUM BAKERY INC.—See Sojitz Corporation; *Int'l*, pg. 7062
NIPPON PRIMEX INC.; *Int'l*, pg. 5329
NIPPON PRINTER ENGINEERING, INC.—See Nippon Primex Inc.; *Int'l*, pg. 5329
NIPPON PROLOGIS REIT, INC.; *Int'l*, pg. 5329
NIPPON PURE FOOD, INC.—See NH Foods Ltd.; *Int'l*, pg. 5256
NIPPON PURETEC CO., LTD.—See Nippon Chemical Industrial Co Ltd; *Int'l*, pg. 5313
NIPPON PUSNES CO., LTD.—See Hitachi Zosen Corporation; *Int'l*, pg. 3412
NIPPON QUAKER CHEMICAL, LTD.—See Quaker Chemical Corporation; *U.S. Public*, pg. 1746
NIPPON RAD INC; *Int'l*, pg. 5329
NIPPON REINZ CO., LTD.—See Nichias Corporation; *Int'l*, pg. 5267

NIPPON REIT INVESTMENT CORPORATION; *Int'l*, pg. 5329
NIPPON RENSUI CO.—See Mitsubishi Chemical Group Corporation; *Int'l*, pg. 4933
NIPPON RENSUI CO. - SPECIALTY PLANT & MATERIALS DIVISION—See Mitsubishi Chemical Group Corporation; *Int'l*, pg. 4933
NIPPON RENSUI CO. - WATER TREATMENT DIVISION—See Mitsubishi Chemical Group Corporation; *Int'l*, pg. 4933
NIPPON RENSUI ENGINEERING CO., LTD.—See Mitsubishi Chemical Group Corporation; *Int'l*, pg. 4933
NIPPON RENT-A-CAR SERVICE, INC.—See Tokyo Century Corporation; *Int'l*, pg. 7789
NIPPON RESIBON CORPORATION—See Noritake Co., Limited; *Int'l*, pg. 5428
NIPPON RESTAURANT SYSTEM, INC.—See Doutor-Nichires Holdings Co., Ltd.; *Int'l*, pg. 2182
NIPPON RETARDER SYSTEM CO., LTD.—See Exedy Corporation; *Int'l*, pg. 2581
NIPPON RICH CO., LTD.—See NIPPN Corporation; *Int'l*, pg. 5310
NIPPON RIETEC CO., LTD.; *Int'l*, pg. 5329
THE NIPPON ROAD CO., LTD.—See Shimizu Corporation; *Int'l*, pg. 6836
NIPPON ROAD (M) SDN. BHD.—See Shimizu Corporation; *Int'l*, pg. 6836
NIPPON ROBALLO CO. LTD.—See ThyssenKrupp AG; *Int'l*, pg. 7731
NIPPON ROCKWOOL CORPORATION—See Nichias Corporation; *Int'l*, pg. 5267
NIPPON SANGYO SUISHIN KIKO LTD; *Int'l*, pg. 5329
NIPPON SANSO HOLDINGS CORPORATION—See Mitsubishi Chemical Group Corporation; *Int'l*, pg. 4935
NIPPON SEAGATE INC.—See Seagate Technology Holdings PLC; *Int'l*, pg. 6663
NIPPON SECURITIES TECHNOLOGY CO., LTD.—See Mizuho Financial Group, Inc.; *Int'l*, pg. 4998
NIPPON SEIKI CO., LTD.; *Int'l*, pg. 5329
NIPPON SEIKI CONSUMER PRODUCTS (THAILAND) CO., LTD.—See Nippon Seiki Co., Ltd.; *Int'l*, pg. 5330
NIPPON SEIKI DE MEXICO S.A. DE C.V.—See Nippon Seiki Co., Ltd.; *Int'l*, pg. 5330
NIPPON SEIKI DO BRASIL LTDA.—See Nippon Seiki Co., Ltd.; *Int'l*, pg. 5330
NIPPON SEIKI (EUROPE) B.V.—See Nippon Seiki Co., Ltd.; *Int'l*, pg. 5330
NIPPON SEIKI SHOKAI CO., LTD.—See Okuma Corporation; *Int'l*, pg. 5550
NIPPON SEIRO CO., LTD.; *Int'l*, pg. 5330
NIPPON SEIRO (THAILAND) CO., LTD.—See Nippon Seiro Co., Ltd.; *Int'l*, pg. 5330
NIPPON SEISEN CO., LTD. - HIRAKATA FACTORY—See Daido Steel Co., Ltd.; *Int'l*, pg. 1923
NIPPON SEISEN CO., LTD. - NAGOYA FACTORY—See Daido Steel Co., Ltd.; *Int'l*, pg. 1923
NIPPON SEISEN CO., LTD. - OSAKA FACTORY—See Daido Steel Co., Ltd.; *Int'l*, pg. 1923
NIPPON SEISEN CO., LTD.—See Daido Steel Co., Ltd.; *Int'l*, pg. 1923
NIPPON SEITAI CORPORATION—See Nippon Paper Industries Co., Ltd.; *Int'l*, pg. 5328
NIPPON SELAS CO., LTD.—See Lionheart Ventures; *U.S. Private*, pg. 2464
NIPPON SHAFT CO., LTD.—See NHK Spring Co., Ltd.; *Int'l*, pg. 5258
NIPPON SHARYO, LTD.; *Int'l*, pg. 5330
NIPPON SHARYO MANUFACTURING, LLC—See Nippon Sharyo, Ltd.; *Int'l*, pg. 5330
NIPPON SHEET GLASS CO. LTD.; *Int'l*, pg. 5330
NIPPON SHIKIZAI INC; *Int'l*, pg. 5332
NIPPON SHINDO CO., LTD.; *Int'l*, pg. 5332
NIPPON SHINYAKU CO., LTD. - CHITOSE SYNTHESIS PLANT & CHITOSE FUNCTIONAL FOOD PLANT—See Nippon Shinyaku Co., Ltd.; *Int'l*, pg. 5332
NIPPON SHINYAKU CO., LTD. - ODAWARA CENTRAL FACTORY—See Nippon Shinyaku Co., Ltd.; *Int'l*, pg. 5332
NIPPON SHINYAKU CO., LTD.; *Int'l*, pg. 5332
NIPPON SHIPPING CO., LTD.—See Nippon Express Holdings, Inc.; *Int'l*, pg. 5317
NIPPON SHOKUBAI AMERICA INDUSTRIES, INC.—See Nippon Shokubai Co., Ltd.; *Int'l*, pg. 5333
NIPPON SHOKUBAI (ASIA) PTE. LTD.—See Nippon Shokubai Co., Ltd.; *Int'l*, pg. 5333
NIPPON SHOKUBAI CO., LTD.; *Int'l*, pg. 5332
NIPPON SHOKUBAI EUROPE N.V.—See Nippon Shokubai Co., Ltd.; *Int'l*, pg. 5333
NIPPON SHOKUBAI KOREA CO., LTD.—See Nippon Shokubai Co., Ltd.; *Int'l*, pg. 5333
NIPPON SHOKUBAI TRADING CO., LTD.—See Nippon Shokubai Co., Ltd.; *Int'l*, pg. 5333
NIPPON SHOKUHIN MEXICANA S.A. DE C.V.—See NH Foods Ltd.; *Int'l*, pg. 5256
NIPPON SIGNAL CO., LTD. - KUKI PLANT—See Nippon Signal Co., Ltd.; *Int'l*, pg. 5333
NIPPON SIGNAL CO., LTD.; *Int'l*, pg. 5333
NIPPON SIGNAL CO., LTD. - UTSUNOMIYA PLANT—See Nippon Signal Co., Ltd.; *Int'l*, pg. 5333

NIPPON SIGNAL INDIA PVT., LTD.—See Nippon Signal Co., Ltd.; *Int'l*, pg. 5333
NIPPON SKI RESORT DEVELOPMENT CO., LTD.; *Int'l*, pg. 5334
NIPPON SLIDE CO., LTD.—See THK CO., LTD.; *Int'l*, pg. 7712
NIPPON SODA CO., LTD.; *Int'l*, pg. 5334
NIPPON SODA CO., LTD. - TAKAOKA PLANT—See Nippon Soda Co., Ltd.; *Int'l*, pg. 5334
NIPPON SODA TRADING (SHANGHAI) CO., LTD.—See Nippon Soda Co., Ltd.; *Int'l*, pg. 5334
NIPPON SOKEN, INC.—See Denso Corporation; *Int'l*, pg. 2032
NIPPON SOKEN, INC.—See Toyota Motor Corporation; *Int'l*, pg. 7872
NIPPON SOLVAY K.K.—See Solvay S.A.; *Int'l*, pg. 7078
NIPPON STEEL AUSTRALIA PTY. LIMITED—See Nippon Steel Corporation; *Int'l*, pg. 5335
NIPPON STEEL BAR & CH WIRE (CHINA) CO., LTD.—See Nippon Steel Corporation; *Int'l*, pg. 5338
NIPPON STEEL BLAST FURNACE SLAG CEMENT CO., LTD.—See Nippon Steel Corporation; *Int'l*, pg. 5335
NIPPON STEEL CARBON CO., LTD.—See Nippon Steel Corporation; *Int'l*, pg. 5335
NIPPON STEEL CHEMICAL & MATERIAL CO., LTD.—See Nippon Steel Corporation; *Int'l*, pg. 5335
NIPPON STEEL CHEMICAL & MATERIAL KOREA CO., LTD.—See Nippon Steel Corporation; *Int'l*, pg. 5335
NIPPON STEEL CHEMICAL & MATERIAL TRADINGS HONG KONG CO., LTD.—See Nippon Steel Corporation; *Int'l*, pg. 5335
NIPPON STEEL COATED SHEET CORPORATION—See Nippon Steel Corporation; *Int'l*, pg. 5335
NIPPON STEEL CORPORATION - EUROPEAN REPRESENTATIVE OFFICE—See Nippon Steel Corporation; *Int'l*, pg. 5335
NIPPON STEEL CORPORATION - HIROHATA WORKS—See Nippon Steel Corporation; *Int'l*, pg. 5335
NIPPON STEEL CORPORATION - KAMAISHI WORKS—See Nippon Steel Corporation; *Int'l*, pg. 5335
NIPPON STEEL CORPORATION - KIMITSU WORKS—See Nippon Steel Corporation; *Int'l*, pg. 5335
NIPPON STEEL CORPORATION - MURORAN WORKS—See Nippon Steel Corporation; *Int'l*, pg. 5335
NIPPON STEEL CORPORATION - NAGOYA WORKS—See Nippon Steel Corporation; *Int'l*, pg. 5335
NIPPON STEEL CORPORATION - SAKAI WORKS—See Nippon Steel Corporation; *Int'l*, pg. 5335
NIPPON STEEL CORPORATION; *Int'l*, pg. 5334
NIPPON STEEL CORPORATION - TOKYO WORKS—See Nippon Steel Corporation; *Int'l*, pg. 5335
NIPPON STEEL CORPORATION - YAWATA WORKS—See Nippon Steel Corporation; *Int'l*, pg. 5335
NIPPON STEEL DRUM CO., LTD. - CHIBA PLANT—See Nippon Steel Corporation; *Int'l*, pg. 5335
NIPPON STEEL DRUM CO., LTD. - NAGOYA PLANT—See Nippon Steel Corporation; *Int'l*, pg. 5335
NIPPON STEEL DRUM CO., LTD. - OSAKA PLANT—See Nippon Steel Corporation; *Int'l*, pg. 5335
NIPPON STEEL DRUM CO., LTD. - SAGAMIHARA PLANT—See Nippon Steel Corporation; *Int'l*, pg. 5335
NIPPON STEEL DRUM CO., LTD.—See Nippon Steel Corporation; *Int'l*, pg. 5335
NIPPON STEEL DRUM TECHNO CO., LTD.—See Nippon Steel Corporation; *Int'l*, pg. 5335
NIPPON STEEL ENGINEERING CO., LTD.—See Nippon Steel Corporation; *Int'l*, pg. 5335
NIPPON STEEL INDIA PVT. LTD.—See Nippon Steel Corporation; *Int'l*, pg. 5336
NIPPON STEEL KOWA REAL ESTATE CO., LTD.—See Mizuho Leasing Company, Limited; *Int'l*, pg. 4999
NIPPON STEEL LOGISTICS CO., LTD.—See Nippon Steel Corporation; *Int'l*, pg. 5336
NIPPON STEEL METAL PRODUCTS CO., LTD.—See Nippon Steel Corporation; *Int'l*, pg. 5336
NIPPON STEEL NISSHIN CO., LTD.—See Nippon Steel Corporation; *Int'l*, pg. 5336
NIPPON STEEL NORTH AMERICA, INC. - CHICAGO—See Nippon Steel Corporation; *Int'l*, pg. 5336
NIPPON STEEL NORTH AMERICA, INC. - HOUSTON—See Nippon Steel Corporation; *Int'l*, pg. 5336
NIPPON STEEL NORTH AMERICA., INC.—See Nippon Steel Corporation; *Int'l*, pg. 5336
NIPPON STEEL PIPE AMERICA, INC.—See Sumitomo Corporation; *Int'l*, pg. 7269
NIPPON STEEL PIPE CO., LTD.—See Nippon Steel Corporation; *Int'l*, pg. 5336
NIPPON STEEL SG WIRE CO., LTD.—See Nippon Steel Corporation; *Int'l*, pg. 5336
NIPPON STEEL SOUTHEAST ASIA PTE. LTD.—See Nippon Steel Corporation; *Int'l*, pg. 5336
NIPPON STEEL SPIRAL PIPE VIETNAM CO., LTD.—See Nippon Steel Corporation; *Int'l*, pg. 5336
NIPPON STEEL STAINLESS STEEL CORPORATION - HIKARI WORKS—See Nippon Steel Corporation; *Int'l*, pg. 5336

NIPPON STEEL CORPORATION

NIPPON STEEL STAINLESS STEEL CORPORATION - KASHIMA WORKS—See Nippon Steel Corporation; *Int'l*, pg. 5336
NIPPON STEEL STAINLESS STEEL CORPORATION—See Nippon Steel Corporation; pg. 5336
NIPPON STEEL STAINLESS STEEL CORPORATION - YAWATA WORKS—See Nippon Steel Corporation; *Int'l*, pg. 5336
NIPPON STEEL & SUMIKIN BUSSAN AMERICAS, INC.—See Nippon Steel Corporation; *Int'l*, pg. 5338
NIPPON STEEL & SUMIKIN BUSSAN CORPORATION - TOKYO (OTEMACHI) HEAD OFFICE—See Nippon Steel Corporation; *Int'l*, pg. 5338
NIPPON STEEL & SUMIKIN BUSSAN (M) SDN. BHD.—See Nippon Steel Corporation; *Int'l*, pg. 5337
NIPPON STEEL & SUMIKIN CRANKSHAFT LLC—See Nippon Steel Corporation; *Int'l*, pg. 5335
NIPPON STEEL & SUMIKIN PLANT ENGINEERING (SHANGHAI) CO., LTD—See Nippon Steel Corporation; *Int'l*, pg. 5335
NIPPON STEEL & SUMITOMO METAL CONSULTING (BEIJING) CO., LTD.—See Nippon Steel Corporation; *Int'l*, pg. 5335
NIPPON STEEL & SUMITOMO METAL EMPREENDIMENTOS SIDERURGIA LTDA.—See Nippon Steel Corporation; *Int'l*, pg. 5335
NIPPON STEEL TEXENG CO., LTD.—See Nippon Steel Corporation; *Int'l*, pg. 5336
NIPPON STEEL (THAILAND) CO., LTD.—See Nippon Steel Corporation; *Int'l*, pg. 5335
NIPPON STEEL TRADING AMERICA, INC.—See Nippon Steel Corporation; *Int'l*, pg. 5338
NIPPON STEEL TRADING AMERICAS, INC.—See Nippon Steel Corporation; *Int'l*, pg. 5338
NIPPON STEEL TRADING (CHINA) CO., LTD.—See Nippon Steel Corporation; *Int'l*, pg. 5338
NIPPON STEEL TRADING CORPORATION—See Nippon Steel Corporation; *Int'l*, pg. 5336
NIPPON STEEL TRADING (DONGGUAN) ECONOMY CONSULTANT CO.,LTD.—See Nippon Steel Corporation; *Int'l*, pg. 5338
NIPPON STEEL TRADING (EUROPE) S. A. S.—See Nippon Steel Corporation; *Int'l*, pg. 5338
NIPPON STEEL TRADING (EUROPE) S. A. S.—See Nippon Steel Corporation; *Int'l*, pg. 5338
NIPPON STEEL TRADING (HK) CO., LTD.—See Nippon Steel Corporation; *Int'l*, pg. 5338
NIPPON STEEL TRADING (HK) CO., LTD.—See Nippon Steel Corporation; *Int'l*, pg. 5338
NIPPON STEEL TRADING INDIA PVT. LTD.—See Nippon Steel Corporation; *Int'l*, pg. 5338
NIPPON STEEL TRADING KOREA CO., LTD.—See Nippon Steel Corporation; *Int'l*, pg. 5338
NIPPON STEEL TRADING (MALAYSIA) SDN.BHD.—See Nippon Steel Corporation; *Int'l*, pg. 5338
NIPPON STEEL TRADING METALS CO., LTD.—See Nippon Steel Corporation; *Int'l*, pg. 5338
NIPPON STEEL TRADING MEXICO S.A.DE C.V.—See Nippon Steel Corporation; *Int'l*, pg. 5338
NIPPON STEEL TRADING (SHANGHAI) CO.,LTD.—See Nippon Steel Corporation; *Int'l*, pg. 5338
NIPPON STEEL TRADING (SINGAPORE) PTE. LTD.—See Nippon Steel Corporation; *Int'l*, pg. 5338
NIPPON STEEL TRADING (TAIWAN) CO., LTD.—See Nippon Steel Corporation; *Int'l*, pg. 5338
NIPPON STEEL TRADING (THAILAND) CO., LTD.—See Nippon Steel Corporation; *Int'l*, pg. 5338
NIPPON STEEL TRADING (VIETNAM) CO., LTD.—See Nippon Steel Corporation; *Int'l*, pg. 5338
NIPPON SUISAN AMERICA LATINA S.A.—See Nissui Corporation; *Int'l*, pg. 5378
NIPPON SUISAN (EUROPE) B.V.—See Nissui Corporation; *Int'l*, pg. 5378
NIPPON SUISAN KAISHA, LTD - ANJO PLANT—See Nissui Corporation; *Int'l*, pg. 5378
NIPPON SUISAN KAISHA, LTD - HACHIOJI GENERAL PLANT—See Nissui Corporation; *Int'l*, pg. 5378
NIPPON SUISAN KAISHA, LTD - HIMEJI GENERAL PLANT—See Nissui Corporation; *Int'l*, pg. 5378
NIPPON SUISAN KAISHA, LTD - IMARI FISH FEED AND OIL PLANT—See Nissui Corporation; *Int'l*, pg. 5378
NIPPON SUISAN KAISHA, LTD - KASHIMA PLANT—See Nissui Corporation; *Int'l*, pg. 5378
NIPPON SUISAN KAISHA, LTD - TOBATA PLANT—See Nissui Corporation; *Int'l*, pg. 5378
NIPPON SUISAN KAISHA, LTD - TSUKUBA PLANT—See Nissui Corporation; *Int'l*, pg. 5378
NIPPON SUISAN (SINGAPORE) PTE. LTD.—See Nissui Corporation; *Int'l*, pg. 5378
NIPPON SUISAN (U.S.A.), INC.—See Nissui Corporation; *Int'l*, pg. 5378
NIPPON SUPPLEMENT INC.—See Coca-Cola Bottlers Japan Holdings Inc.; *Int'l*, pg. 1684
NIPPON SWAGELOK FST INC.—See Swagelok Company; *U.S. Private*, pg. 3889
THE NIPPON SYNTHETIC CHEMICAL INDUSTRY CO., LTD. - KUMAMOTO PLANT—See Mitsubishi Chemical Group Corporation; *Int'l*, pg. 4934

THE NIPPON SYNTHETIC CHEMICAL INDUSTRY CO., LTD. - MIZUSHIMA PLANT—See Mitsubishi Chemical Group Corporation; *Int'l*, pg. 4934
THE NIPPON SYNTHETIC CHEMICAL INDUSTRY CO., LTD. - OGAKI PLANT—See Mitsubishi Chemical Group Corporation; *Int'l*, pg. 4934
THE NIPPON SYNTHETIC CHEMICAL INDUSTRY CO., LTD.—See Mitsubishi Chemical Group Corporation; *Int'l*, pg. 4934
NIPPON SYSTEM INDUSTRIES CORPORATION—See Kyokuto Boeki Kaisha, Ltd.; *Int'l*, pg. 4362
NIPPON SYSTEMWARE CO., LTD. - PRODUCT SOLUTION DIVISION—See NSW Inc.; *Int'l*, pg. 5481
NIPPON TECHNICAL SERVICE CO., LTD.—See Oi Electric Co., Ltd.; *Int'l*, pg. 5533
NIPPON TECHNO-CARBON CO., LTD.—See Nippon Carbon Co., Ltd.; *Int'l*, pg. 5312
NIPPON TECHNO LAB, INC.; *Int'l*, pg. 5340
NIPPON TELEGRAPH & TELEPHONE CORPORATION; *Int'l*, pg. 5340
NIPPON TELEGRAPH & TELEPHONE EAST CORPORATION—See Nippon Telegraph & Telephone Corporation; *Int'l*, pg. 5354
NIPPON TELEGRAPH & TELEPHONE WEST CORPORATION—See Nippon Telegraph & Telephone Corporation; *Int'l*, pg. 5354
NIPPON TELEMATIQUE INC.—See Nippon Telegraph & Telephone Corporation; *Int'l*, pg. 5354
NIPPON TELEVISION ART CORP.—See Nippon Television Holdings Inc.; *Int'l*, pg. 5356
NIPPON TELEVISION HOLDINGS INC.; *Int'l*, pg. 5356
NIPPON TELEVISION MUSIC CORPORATION—See Nippon Television Holdings Inc.; *Int'l*, pg. 5356
NIPPON TELEVISION NETWORK EUROPE B.V.—See Nippon Television Holdings Inc.; *Int'l*, pg. 5356
NIPPON TELEVISION WORK 24 CORPORATION—See Nippon Television Holdings Inc.; *Int'l*, pg. 5356
NIPPON TENSAR LTD.—See Mitsui Chemicals, Inc.; *Int'l*, pg. 4983
NIPPON THERMO CO., LTD.—See Sumitomo Chemical Company, Limited; *Int'l*, pg. 7264
NIPPON THERMOENER CO., LTD.—See Takuma Co., Ltd.; *Int'l*, pg. 7442
NIPPON THOMPSON CO., LTD.; *Int'l*, pg. 5356
NIPPON THOMPSON EUROPE B.V.—See Nippon Thompson Co., Ltd.; *Int'l*, pg. 5357
NIPPON THOMPSON SALES CO., LTD.—See Nippon Thompson Co., Ltd.; *Int'l*, pg. 5357
NIPPON TOKAN PACKAGE CO., LTD.—See Toyo Seikan Group Holdings, Ltd.; *Int'l*, pg. 7856
NIPPON TOKUSHU GOUKIN MFG CO., LTD.—See Tokyo Rope Manufacturing Co., Ltd.; *Int'l*, pg. 7794
NIPPON TOYOCOM CO., LTD.—See MIRAIT ONE Corporation; *Int'l*, pg. 4917
NIPPON TRAVEL AGENCY CO., LTD.—See West Japan Railway Company; *Int'l*, pg. 8385
NIPPON TREX CO., LTD.—See Kyokuto Kaihatsu Kogyo Co. Ltd.; *Int'l*, pg. 4363
NIPPON TSUSHINSHI CO., LTD.—See Nakabayashi Co., Ltd.; *Int'l*, pg. 5131
NIPPON TUNGSTEN CO., LTD.; *Int'l*, pg. 5357
NIPPON TUNGSTEN (SHANGHAI) COMMERCE CO.,LTD—See Nippon Tungsten Co., Ltd.; *Int'l*, pg. 5357
NIPPON TUNGSTEN USA, INC.—See Nippon Tungsten Co., Ltd.; *Int'l*, pg. 5357
NIPPON TURNING CO., LTD.—See Nitto Seimo Co., Ltd.; *Int'l*, pg. 5388
NIPPON UNISYS, LIMITED—See Mitsui & Co., Ltd.; *Int'l*, pg. 4979
NIPPON VENDER NET CO., LTD.—See Shindengen Electric Manufacturing Co., Ltd.; *Int'l*, pg. 6842
NIPPON VIEW HOTEL CO., LTD.—See Hulic Co., Ltd.; *Int'l*, pg. 3528
NIPPON WELLCOME KK—See GSK plc; *Int'l*, pg. 3149
NIPPON WHITE FARM CO., LTD.—See NH Foods Ltd.; *Int'l*, pg. 5256
NIPPON WIPER BLADE CO., LTD.—See Denso Corporation; *Int'l*, pg. 2032
NIPPON YAKIN AMERICA, INC.—See Nippon Yakin Kogyo Co., Ltd.; *Int'l*, pg. 5357
NIPPON YAKIN ASIA PTE. LTD.—See Nippon Yakin Kogyo Co., Ltd.; *Int'l*, pg. 5357
NIPPON YAKIN EUROPE LIMITED—See Nippon Yakin Kogyo Co., Ltd.; *Int'l*, pg. 5357
NIPPON YAKIN KOGYO CO., LTD.; *Int'l*, pg. 5357
NIPPON YAKIN SHANGHAI CO., LTD.—See Nippon Yakin Kogyo Co., Ltd.; *Int'l*, pg. 5357
NIPPON YUSEN KABUSHIKI KAISHA; *Int'l*, pg. 5357
NIPPO PRECISION INDUSTRY (SHENZHEN) CO.—See NIPPO LTD.; *Int'l*, pg. 5310
NIPPO (SHANGHAI) LTD.—See NIPPO LTD.; *Int'l*, pg. 5310
NIPPO SHOKUHIN KOGYO CO., LTD.—See Nissui Corporation; *Int'l*, pg. 5378
NIPRESS TBK; *Int'l*, pg. 5361
NIPRO ASIA PTE. LTD.—See Nipro Corporation; *Int'l*, pg. 5361

NIPRO CORPORATION - OHDATE FACTORY—See Nipro Corporation; *Int'l*, pg. 5361
NIPRO CORPORATION - OHTSU FACTORY—See Nipro Corporation; *Int'l*, pg. 5361
NIPRO CORPORATION; *Int'l*, pg. 5361
NIPRO DIAGNOSTICS (UK) LIMITED—See Nipro Corporation; *Int'l*, pg. 5361
NIPRO EUROPE GROUP COMPANIES N.V.—See Nipro Corporation; *Int'l*, pg. 5361
NIPRO EUROPE N.V.—See Nipro Corporation; *Int'l*, pg. 5361
NIPRO INDIA CORPORATION PVT. LTD.—See Nipro Corporation; *Int'l*, pg. 5361
NIPRO JMI PHARMA LTD.—See Nipro Corporation; *Int'l*, pg. 5361
NIPRO MEDICA DE MEXICO, S.A. DE C.V.—See Nipro Corporation; *Int'l*, pg. 5361
NIPRO MEDICAL CORPORATION—See HORIBA Ltd; *Int'l*, pg. 3477
NIPRO MEDICAL CORPORATION—See HORIBA Ltd; *Int'l*, pg. 3477
NIPRO MEDICAL CORPORATION—See Nipro Corporation; *Int'l*, pg. 5361
NIPRO MEDICAL (INDIA) PVT. LTD.—See Nipro Corporation; *Int'l*, pg. 5361
NIPRO MEDICAL INDUSTRIES, LTD.—See Nipro Corporation; *Int'l*, pg. 5361
NIPRO MEDICAL LTDA—See Nipro Corporation; *Int'l*, pg. 5361
NIPRO MEDICAL PANAMA S.A.—See Nipro Corporation; *Int'l*, pg. 5361
NIPRO PATCH CO., LTD—See Nipro Corporation; *Int'l*, pg. 5362
NIPRO PHARMA CORPORATION - ISE PLANT—See Nipro Corporation; *Int'l*, pg. 5362
NIPRO PHARMA CORPORATION - ODATE PLANT—See Nipro Corporation; *Int'l*, pg. 5362
NIPRO PHARMA CORPORATION - SHIKI PLANT—See Nipro Corporation; *Int'l*, pg. 5362
NIPRO PHARMA CORPORATION - SHIROKITA PLANT—See Nipro Corporation; *Int'l*, pg. 5362
NIPRO PHARMA CORPORATION—See Nipro Corporation; *Int'l*, pg. 5362
NIPRO PHARMA HIDA FACTORY CORPORATION—See Nipro Corporation; *Int'l*, pg. 5362
NIPRO PHARMA VIETNAM CO., LTD.—See Nipro Corporation; *Int'l*, pg. 5362
NIPRO SALES (THAILAND) CO., LTD.—See Nipro Corporation; *Int'l*, pg. 5362
NIPRO (SHANGHAI) CO., LTD.—See Nipro Corporation; *Int'l*, pg. 5361
NIPRO (THAILAND) CORPORATION LTD.—See Nipro Corporation; *Int'l*, pg. 5361
NIPRO TRADING (SHANGHAI) CO., LTD.—See Nipro Corporation; *Int'l*, pg. 5362
NIPSEA CHEMICAL KOREA CO., LTD.—See Nippon Paint Holdings Co., Ltd.; *Int'l*, pg. 5326
NIPSEA TECHNOLOGIES PTE. LTD.—See Nippon Paint Holdings Co., Ltd.; *Int'l*, pg. 5326
NIPSON SAS; *Int'l*, pg. 5362
NIP'S SYSTEM CENTER CO., LTD.—See AJIS Co., Ltd.; *Int'l*, pg. 258
NIP ZRENJANIN A.D.; *Int'l*, pg. 5309
NIRA DYNAMICS AB; *Int'l*, pg. 5362
NI RAILWAYS—See Northern Ireland Transport Holding Company; *Int'l*, pg. 5444
NIRAJ CEMENT STRUCTURALS LIMITED; *Int'l*, pg. 5362
NIRAJ CONSULTING GROUP LIMITED—See Niraj Cement Structurals Limited; *Int'l*, pg. 5362
NIRAJ ISPAT INDUSTRIES LIMITED; *Int'l*, pg. 5362
NIRAKU GC HOLDINGS, INC.; *Int'l*, pg. 5362
NIRAM, INC.; *U.S. Private*, pg. 2928
NIRAS GRUPPEN A/S; *Int'l*, pg. 5362
NIRAV COMMERCIALS LIMITED; *Int'l*, pg. 5362
NIRBHAY COLOURS INDIA LIMITED; *Int'l*, pg. 5362
NIRDHAN UTTHAN LAGHUBITTA BITTIYA SANSTHA LIMITED; *Int'l*, pg. 5362
NIRECO AUTOMATIC CONTROLLER (SHANGHAI) CO., LTD—See NIRECO CORPORATION; *Int'l*, pg. 5362
NIRECO CORPORATION; *Int'l*, pg. 5362
NIRECO DELTA CO., LTD.—See NIRECO CORPORATION; *Int'l*, pg. 5362
NIRECO TAIWAN CORPORATION—See NIRECO CORPORATION; *Int'l*, pg. 5362
NIREUS S.A.—See AMERRA Capital Management LLC; *Int'l*, pg. 424
NIREUS S.A.—See Mubadala Investment Company PJSC; *Int'l*, pg. 5076
NIRLON LTD - FABRIC DIVISION—See Nirlon Ltd; *Int'l*, pg. 5362
NIRLON LTD - REAL ESTATE DIVISION—See Nirlon Ltd; *Int'l*, pg. 5362
NIRLON LTD; *Int'l*, pg. 5362
NIRMA LIMITED; *Int'l*, pg. 5363
NIRMITEE ROBOTICS AC MAINTENANCE LLC—See Nirmitee Robotics India Limited; *Int'l*, pg. 5363
NIRMITEE ROBOTICS INDIA LIMITED; *Int'l*, pg. 5363
NIR-OR ISRAEL LTD.—See Imco Industries Ltd.; *Int'l*, pg. 3623

COMPANY NAME INDEX

NIROUMOHAREKE MACHINE TOOLS; *Int'l*, pg. 5363
NIROU TRANS CO.; *Int'l*, pg. 5363
NIRVANA ASIA LTD.; *Int'l*, pg. 5363
NIRVANA DEVELOPMENT PUBLIC COMPANY LIMITED; *Int'l*, pg. 5363
NIRVANAHEALTH, LLC—See Centene Corporation; *U.S. Public*, pg. 471
NIRVANA, INC.; *U.S. Private*, pg. 2928
NIRVANA LIFE SCIENCES INC.; *Int'l*, pg. 5363
NIRVANA MEMORIAL GARDEN PTE. LTD.—See Nirvana Asia Ltd.; *Int'l*, pg. 5363
NIRVANA MEMORIAL PARK CO., LTD.—See Nirvana Asia Ltd.; *Int'l*, pg. 5363
NIRVANA MEMORIAL PARK (JOHOR) SDN. BHD.—See NV Multi Asia Sdn. Bhd.; *Int'l*, pg. 5497
NIRVANA MEMORIAL PARK SDN. BHD.—See NV Multi Asia Sdn. Bhd.; *Int'l*, pg. 5497
NIRVANA MEMORIAL PARK (SHAH ALAM) SDN. BHD.—See NV Multi Asia Sdn. Bhd.; *Int'l*, pg. 5497
NIRVANA MEMORIAL PARK (SIBU) SDN. BHD.—See NV Multi Asia Sdn. Bhd.; *Int'l*, pg. 5497
NIRVANA U CO., LTD.—See Singha Estate PCL; *Int'l*, pg. 6944
NIRVANIX, INC.; *U.S. Private*, pg. 2928
NISA INVESTMENT ADVISORS LLC; *U.S. Private*, pg. 2928
NISAUTO HOLDING A.D.; *Int'l*, pg. 5363
NISBET OIL COMPANY; *U.S. Private*, pg. 2928
NISBETS PLC; *Int'l*, pg. 5363
NISCA CORPORATION—See Canon Inc.; *Int'l*, pg. 1295
NISCAYAH AB—See Stanley Black & Decker, Inc.; *U.S. Public*, pg. 1935
NISCAYAH HOLDING SPAIN, S.L.—See Stanley Black & Decker, Inc.; *U.S. Public*, pg. 1933
NISCAYAH, INC.—See Stanley Black & Decker, Inc.; *U.S. Public*, pg. 1935
NISCAYAH TEKNIK AB—See Stanley Black & Decker, Inc.; *U.S. Public*, pg. 1933
NISC HANBAI CO., LTD.—See Nippon Steel Corporation; *Int'l*, pg. 5337
NISCHER PROPERTIES AB; *Int'l*, pg. 5363
NISCOM INC.—See Randstad N.V.; *Int'l*, pg. 6202
NISCO NIPPON YAKIN KOGYO NANJING CO., LTD.—See Nippon Yakin Kogyo Co., Ltd.; *Int'l*, pg. 5357
NISEKO TOKYU RESORT CO., LTD.—See Tokyu Fudosan Holdings Corporation; *Int'l*, pg. 7798
NIS-EKSPRES A.D.; *Int'l*, pg. 5363
N.I.S. FINANCIAL SERVICES, INC.—See Prosperity Group Holdings, LP; *U.S. Private*, pg. 3289
NISGA'A DATA SYSTEMS, LLC—See Gold Belt Incorporated; *U.S. Private*, pg. 1727
NISHAT CHUNIAN LIMITED; *Int'l*, pg. 5363
NISHAT CHUNIAN POWER LIMITED—See Nishat Chunian Limited; *Int'l*, pg. 5363
NISHAT DAIRY (PVT) LIMITED—See Pakgen Power Ltd.; *Int'l*, pg. 5703
NISHA TECHNOLOGIES INC.; *Int'l*, pg. 5363
NISHAT HOSPITALITY (PRIVATE) LIMITED—See Pakgen Power Ltd.; *Int'l*, pg. 5703
NISHAT INTERNATIONAL FZE—See Nishat Mills Ltd.; *Int'l*, pg. 5363
NISHAT LINEN (PRIVATE) LIMITED—See Nishat Mills Ltd.; *Int'l*, pg. 5363
NISHAT MILLS LTD.; *Int'l*, pg. 5363
NISHAT POWER LIMITED—See Nishat Mills Ltd.; *Int'l*, pg. 5363
NISHI ATHLETIC GOODS CO., LTD.—See ASICS Corporation; *Int'l*, pg. 621
NISHIDA TECHNO SERVICE CO., INC.—See Kyushu Electric Power Co., Inc.; *Int'l*, pg. 4368
NISHIFU MEAT CO., LTD.—See Okaya & Co., Ltd.; *Int'l*, pg. 5546
NISHIGEN COMPANY—See DAIKOKUTENBUSSAN CO., LTD.; *Int'l*, pg. 1937
NISHIGI KOGYO, CO., INC.—See Kyushu Electric Power Co., Inc.; *Int'l*, pg. 4368
NISHIHARA ENGINEERING CO., LTD.—See Kinden Corporation; *Int'l*, pg. 4166
NISHIHARIMA UBE CO., LTD—See UBE Corporation; *Int'l*, pg. 8001
NISHIHATSU CO., LTD.—See Denyo Co., Ltd.; *Int'l*, pg. 2040
NISHI-IKEBUKURO HEAT SUPPLY CO., LTD—See Tobu Railway Co., Ltd.; *Int'l*, pg. 7771
NISHIKANTO SENKO LOGI CO., LTD.—See Senko Group Holdings Co., Ltd.; *Int'l*, pg. 6710
NISHIKAWA BIG OCEAN CO., LTD—See Nishikawa Rubber Co., Ltd.; *Int'l*, pg. 5364
NISHIKAWA BUSSAN CO., LTD.—See Nishikawa Rubber Co., Ltd.; *Int'l*, pg. 5364
NISHIKAWA COOPER LLC—See Cooper-Standard Holdings, Inc.; *U.S. Public*, pg. 574
NISHIKAWA COOPER LLC—See Nishikawa Rubber Co., Ltd.; *Int'l*, pg. 5364
NISHIKAWA DESIGN TECHNO CO., LTD.—See Nishikawa Rubber Co., Ltd.; *Int'l*, pg. 5364
NISHIKAWA KEISOKU CO., LTD.; *Int'l*, pg. 5364

NISHIKAWA LIVING CO., LTD.—See Nishikawa Rubber Co., Ltd.; *Int'l*, pg. 5364
NISHIKAWA OF AMERICA INC.—See Nishikawa Rubber Co., Ltd.; *Int'l*, pg. 5364
NISHIKAWA RUBBER CO., LTD. - ASA PLANT—See Nishikawa Rubber Co., Ltd.; *Int'l*, pg. 5364
NISHIKAWA RUBBER CO., LTD. - MIHARA PLANT—See Nishikawa Rubber Co., Ltd.; *Int'l*, pg. 5364
NISHIKAWA RUBBER CO., LTD. - SHIRAKI PLANT—See Nishikawa Rubber Co., Ltd.; *Int'l*, pg. 5364
NISHIKAWA RUBBER CO., LTD.; *Int'l*, pg. 5364
NISHIKAWA RUBBER CO., LTD. - YOSHIDA PLANT—See Nishikawa Rubber Co., Ltd.; *Int'l*, pg. 5364
NISHIKAWA TACHAPLALERT RUBBER CO., LTD.—See Nishikawa Rubber Co., Ltd.; *Int'l*, pg. 5364
NISHIKEN CO., LTD.—See Kanamoto Co., Ltd.; *Int'l*, pg. 4064
NISHIKI ELECTRONICS CO., LTD.—See Alps Alpine Co., Ltd.; *Int'l*, pg. 376
NISHI-KOBE WORKS—See Kawasaki Heavy Industries, Ltd.; *Int'l*, pg. 4098
NISHI-KYUSHU CREDIT GUARANTEE CO., LTD.—See Fukuoka Financial Group, Inc.; *Int'l*, pg. 2840
NISHIMATSU CONSTRUCTION CO., LTD.; *Int'l*, pg. 5365
NISHIMATSU-JISHO CO., LTD.—See Nishimatsu Construction Co., Ltd.; *Int'l*, pg. 5365
NISHIMATSU VIETNAM CO., LTD.—See Nishimatsu Construction Co., Ltd.; *Int'l*, pg. 5365
NISHIMATSUYA CHAIN CO., LTD.; *Int'l*, pg. 5365
NISHIMINATO DRIVING SCHOOL CO., LTD.—See Nippon Kayaku Co., Ltd.; *Int'l*, pg. 5320
NISHIMOTO CO., LTD.; *Int'l*, pg. 5365
NISHIMOTO TRADING CO., LTD.—See Nishimoto Co., Ltd.; *Int'l*, pg. 5365
NISHIMOTO TRADING CO., LTD.—See Nishimoto Co., Ltd.; *Int'l*, pg. 5365
NISHIMOTO TRADING FOODSTUFF SHANGHAI CO., LTD—See Nishimoto Co., Ltd.; *Int'l*, pg. 5365
NISHIMU ELECTRONICS INDUSTRIES, CO., LTD.—See Kyushu Electric Power Co., Inc.; *Int'l*, pg. 4368
NISHINA INDUSTRIAL CO., LTD.—See Toyota Industries Corporation; *Int'l*, pg. 7866
NISHIINA INDUSTRIAL CO., LTD. - SUZAKA FACTORY—See Toyota Industries Corporation; *Int'l*, pg. 7866
NISHINIHONDENKO CORPORATION—See MIRAIT ONE Corporation; *Int'l*, pg. 4917
NISHI NIHON EIZO CORPORATION—See Nippon Television Holdings Inc.; *Int'l*, pg. 5356
NISHINIHON GENERATOR MFG. CO., LTD.—See Denyo Co., Ltd.; *Int'l*, pg. 2040
NISHINIHON-JKO CO., LTD.—See Mitsubishi Heavy Industries, Ltd.; *Int'l*, pg. 4960
NISHINIHON KAIUN KAISHA, LTD.—See Nippon Yusen Kabushiki Kaisha; *Int'l*, pg. 5359
NISHINIHON MODULAR WINDOW CO., LTD.—See Nippon Sheet Glass Co., Ltd.; *Int'l*, pg. 5331
NISHINIHON NAGASE CO., LTD.—See Nagase & Co., Ltd.; *Int'l*, pg. 5128
NISHI NIHON NICHIMO CO., LTD.—See NICHIMO CO. LTD.; *Int'l*, pg. 5269
NISHINIHON OFFICEMATION CO., LTD.—See Uchida Yoko Co., Ltd.; *Int'l*, pg. 8012
NISHINIHON PRINTING CO., LTD.—See The Pack Corporation; *Int'l*, pg. 7672
NISHINIHON RYOJU ESTATE FUKUOKA CO., LTD.—See Mitsubishi Heavy Industries, Ltd.; *Int'l*, pg. 4961
NISHI NIPPON AIRLINES CO., LTD.—See Kyushu Electric Power Co., Inc.; *Int'l*, pg. 4368
NISHI-NIPPON CITY BANK CAPITAL MARKETS—See The Nishi-Nippon City Bank, Ltd.; *Int'l*, pg. 7670
NISHI-NIPPON CITY BANK HONG KONG—See The Nishi-Nippon City Bank, Ltd.; *Int'l*, pg. 7670
THE NISHI-NIPPON CITY BANK, LTD. - INTERNATIONAL BUSINESS DIVISION—See The Nishi-Nippon City Bank, Ltd.; *Int'l*, pg. 7670
THE NISHI-NIPPON CITY BANK, LTD.; *Int'l*, pg. 7670
THE NISHI-NIPPON CITY BANK, LTD. - TREASURY & PORTFOLIO INVESTMENT DIVISION—See The Nishi-Nippon City Bank, Ltd.; *Int'l*, pg. 7670
NISHI-NIPPON CITY BANK SECURITIES & INTL DIV—See The Nishi-Nippon City Bank, Ltd.; *Int'l*, pg. 7670
NISHI-NIPPON CITY BANK SHANGHAI—See The Nishi-Nippon City Bank, Ltd.; *Int'l*, pg. 7670
NISHI-NIPPON CITY TOKAI TOKYO SECURITIES CO., LTD.—See Tokai Tokyo Financial Holdings, Inc.; *Int'l*, pg. 7781
NISHI NIPPON ELECTRIC WIRE & CABLE CO., LTD.—See Mitsui & Co., Ltd.; *Int'l*, pg. 4979
NISHINIPPON ENVIRONMENTAL ENERGY CO., INC.—See Kyushu Electric Power Co., Inc.; *Int'l*, pg. 4368
NISHI-NIPPON FINANCIAL HOLDINGS, INC.; *Int'l*, pg. 5364
NISHINIPPON KOGYO KAISHA, LTD.—See Nippon Steel Corporation; *Int'l*, pg. 5338

NISHINIPPON PLANT ENGINEERING AND CONSTRUCTION CO., LTD.—See Kyushu Electric Power Co., Inc.; *Int'l*, pg. 4368
NISHI-NIPPON RAILROAD CO., LTD.; *Int'l*, pg. 5364
NISHI-NIPPON STEEL CENTER CO., LTD.—See Onoken Co., Ltd.; *Int'l*, pg. 5583
NISHINO MEDICAL INSTRUMENTS CO., LTD.—See Ship Healthcare Holdings, Inc.; *Int'l*, pg. 6852
NISHINOMIYA MERCHANDISING CENTER—See Bain Capital, LP; *U.S. Private*, pg. 444
NISHIO HOLDINGS CO., LTD.; *Int'l*, pg. 5365
NISHIO RENT ALL HOKKAIDO CO., LTD.—See Nishio Holdings Co., Ltd.; *Int'l*, pg. 5365
NISHIO RENT ALL (M) SDN. BHD.—See Nishio Holdings Co., Ltd.; *Int'l*, pg. 5365
NISHIO RENT ALL SHANGHAI CO., LTD.—See Nishio Holdings Co., Ltd.; *Int'l*, pg. 5365
NISHIO RENT ALL SINGAPORE PTE LTD—See Nishio Holdings Co., Ltd.; *Int'l*, pg. 5365
NISHIO RENT ALL (THAILAND) CO., LTD.—See Nishio Holdings Co., Ltd.; *Int'l*, pg. 5365
NISHIO RENT ALL VIETNAM CO., LTD.—See Nishio Holdings Co., Ltd.; *Int'l*, pg. 5365
NISHIO T&M COMPANY LIMITED—See Nishio Holdings Co., Ltd.; *Int'l*, pg. 5365
NISHIO T&M (HONG KONG) CO., LTD—See Nishio Holdings Co., Ltd.; *Int'l*, pg. 5365
NISHIO WORK SUPPORT CO., LTD.—See Nishio Holdings Co., Ltd.; *Int'l*, pg. 5365
NISHISHIBA ELECTRIC CO., LTD.—See Japan Industrial Partners, Inc.; *Int'l*, pg. 3890
NISHI SHIKOKU MAZDA CO., LTD.—See Mazda Motor Corporation; *Int'l*, pg. 4749
NISHITELE INFORMATION & SCIENCE CO., LTD.—See Computer Engineering & Consulting Ltd.; *Int'l*, pg. 1759
NISHITETSU-PLAZA CORPORATION—See Nishi-Nippon Railroad Co., Ltd.; *Int'l*, pg. 5364
NISHITETSU TRAVEL CO., LTD.—See Nishi-Nippon Railroad Co., Ltd.; *Int'l*, pg. 5364
NISHI TOHOKU HINO MOTOR LTD.—See Toyota Motor Corporation; *Int'l*, pg. 7871
NISHI TOKYO CHEMIX CORPORATION—See AICA Kogyo Company, Limited; *Int'l*, pg. 229
NISHIWAKI ROYAL HOTEL CO., LTD.—See Daiwa House Industry Co., Ltd.; *Int'l*, pg. 1947
NISHOKU PLASTIC MOLD (SHENZHEN) CO., LTD.—See Nishoku Technology Inc.; *Int'l*, pg. 5366
NISHOKU TECHNOLOGY INC.; *Int'l*, pg. 5366
NISHOKU TECHNOLOGY VIETNAM CO., LTD.—See Nishoku Technology Inc.; *Int'l*, pg. 5366
NISHSHIBA ELECTRIC CO., LTD.—See Japan Industrial Partners, Inc.; *Int'l*, pg. 3890
NISHTHA FINANCE & INVESTMENT (INDIA) LTD.; *Int'l*, pg. 5366
NISKA MLEKARA A.D.; *Int'l*, pg. 5366
NISKOGRADNJA A.D.; *Int'l*, pg. 5366
NISKOGRADNJA A.D.; *Int'l*, pg. 5366
NISKOGRADNJA A.D.; *Int'l*, pg. 5366
NI SOLUTIONS (PROPRIETARY) LIMITED—See National Instruments Corporation; *U.S. Private*, pg. 2857
NISOURCE ENERGY TECHNOLOGIES, INC.—See NiSource Inc.; *U.S. Public*, pg. 1530
NISOURCE INC.; *U.S. Public*, pg. 1530
NI SOUTHEAST ASIA SDN. BHD.—See National Instruments Corporation; *U.S. Private*, pg. 2857
NISSAL COMPANY; *Int'l*, pg. 5366
NISSAN AGRO TECH INDIA PVT.LTD.—See Nissan Chemical Corporation; *Int'l*, pg. 5366
NISSAN ARC LTD.—See Nissan Motor Co., Ltd.; *Int'l*, pg. 5367
NISSAN ARGENTINA S.A.—See Nissan Motor Co., Ltd.; *Int'l*, pg. 5367
NISSAN ASIA PACIFIC PTE. LTD.—See Nissan Motor Co., Ltd.; *Int'l*, pg. 5367
NISSAN AUTOMOTIVE TECHNOLOGY CO., LTD.—See Nissan Motor Co., Ltd.; *Int'l*, pg. 5368
NISSAN BHARAT RASAYAN PVT.LTD.—See Nissan Chemical Corporation; *Int'l*, pg. 5366
NISSAN BONDESEN-HARDY INC.; *U.S. Private*, pg. 2928
NISSAN BUSINESS SERVICE CO., LTD.—See Nissan Motor Co., Ltd.; *Int'l*, pg. 5368
NISSAN BUTSURYU CO., LTD.—See Nissan Chemical Corporation; *Int'l*, pg. 5366
NISSAN CANADA INC.—See Nissan Motor Co., Ltd.; *Int'l*, pg. 5368
NISSAN CAR RENTAL SOLUTIONS CO., LTD—See Nissan Motor Co., Ltd.; *Int'l*, pg. 5368
NISSAN CASTING AUSTRALIA PTY. LTD.—See Nissan Motor Co., Ltd.; *Int'l*, pg. 5368
NISSAN CENTER EUROPE GMBH—See Nissan Motor Co., Ltd.; *Int'l*, pg. 5368
NISSAN CHEMICAL AGRO KOREA LTD.—See Nissan Chemical Corporation; *Int'l*, pg. 5366
NISSAN CHEMICAL AMERICA CORPORATION—See Nissan Chemical Corporation; *Int'l*, pg. 5366
NISSAN CHEMICAL AMERICA CORPORATION—See Nissan Chemical Corporation; *Int'l*, pg. 5366
NISSAN CHEMICAL CORPORATION; *Int'l*, pg. 5366

NISSAN CHEMICAL CORPORATION

NISSAN CHEMICAL EUROPE S.A.R.L—See Nissan Chemical Corporation; *Int'l*, pg. 5366
NISSAN CHEMICAL HOUSTON CORPORATION—See Nissan Chemical Corporation; *Int'l*, pg. 5366
NISSAN CHEMICAL INDUSTRIES LIMITED - GOI WORKS—See Nissan Chemical Corporation; *Int'l*, pg. 5366
NISSAN CHEMICAL INDUSTRIES LIMITED - NAGOYA PLANT—See Nissan Chemical Corporation; *Int'l*, pg. 5366
NISSAN CHEMICAL INDUSTRIES LIMITED - ONODA PLANT—See Nissan Chemical Corporation; *Int'l*, pg. 5367
NISSAN CHEMICAL INDUSTRIES LIMITED - SAITAMA PLANT—See Nissan Chemical Corporation; *Int'l*, pg. 5367
NISSAN CHEMICAL INDUSTRIES LIMITED - SODEGAURA PLANT—See Nissan Chemical Corporation; *Int'l*, pg. 5367
NISSAN CHEMICAL INDUSTRIES LIMITED - TOYAMA PLANT—See Nissan Chemical Corporation; *Int'l*, pg. 5367
NISSAN CHEMICAL KOREA CO., LTD.—See Nissan Chemical Corporation; *Int'l*, pg. 5367
NISSAN CHEMICAL MATERIALS RESEARCH (SUZHOU) CO., LTD.—See Nissan Chemical Corporation; *Int'l*, pg. 5367
NISSAN CHEMICAL PRODUCT(SHANGHAI) CO., LTD.—See Nissan Chemical Corporation; *Int'l*, pg. 5367
NISSAN CHEMICAL TAIWAN CO., LTD.—See Nissan Chemical Corporation; *Int'l*, pg. 5367
NISSAN CREATIVE SERVICES CO., LTD.—See Nissan Motor Co., Ltd.; *Int'l*, pg. 5368
NISSAN DESIGN AMERICA—See Nissan Motor Co., Ltd.; *Int'l*, pg. 5369
NISSAN DIESEL (THAILAND) CO., LTD.—See Tan Chong International Limited; *Int'l*, pg. 7453
NISSAN DIGITAL INDIA LLP—See Nissan Motor Co., Ltd.; *Int'l*, pg. 5368
NISSAN ENGINEERING, LTD.—See Nissan Chemical Corporation; *Int'l*, pg. 5367
NISSAN FINANCIACION, S.A.—See Nissan Motor Co., Ltd.; *Int'l*, pg. 5368
NISSAN FINANCIAL SERVICES AUSTRALIA PTY. LTD.—See Nissan Motor Co., Ltd.; *Int'l*, pg. 5368
NISSAN FINANCIAL SERVICES CO., LTD.—See Nissan Motor Co., Ltd.; *Int'l*, pg. 5368
NISSAN GREEN & LANDSCAPE CO., LTD.—See Nissan Chemical Corporation; *Int'l*, pg. 5367
NISSAN GROUP FINANCE CO., LTD.—See Nissan Motor Co., Ltd.; *Int'l*, pg. 5368
NISSAN HUMAN INFORMATION SERVICE CO., LTD.—See Nissan Motor Co., Ltd.; *Int'l*, pg. 5368
NISSAN IBERIA, S.A.—See Nissan Motor Co., Ltd.; *Int'l*, pg. 5368
NISSAN INTERNATIONAL SA—See Nissan Motor Co., Ltd.; *Int'l*, pg. 5368
NISSAN ITALIA S.P.A.—See Nissan Motor Co., Ltd.; *Int'l*, pg. 5368
NISSAN KENZAI CO., LTD.—See Nissan Chemical Corporation; *Int'l*, pg. 5367
NISSAN KIA WORLD; *U.S. Private*, pg. 2928
NISSAN KOHKI CO., LTD.—See Nissan Motor Co., Ltd.; *Int'l*, pg. 5368
NISSAN LEASING CO., LTD.—See Mizuho Leasing Company, Limited; *Int'l*, pg. 4999
NISSAN LEASING (THAILAND) CO., LTD.—See Nissan Motor Co., Ltd.; *Int'l*, pg. 5368
NISSAN LYNNES CITY INC.; *U.S. Private*, pg. 2928
NISSAN MANUFACTURING RUSSIA LLC—See Nissan Motor Co., Ltd.; *Int'l*, pg. 5368
NISSAN MARINE & POWER PRODUCTS—See Tohatsu America Corporation; *U.S. Private*, pg. 4181
NISSAN MEDICAL INDUSTRIES LTD.; *Int'l*, pg. 5367
NISSAN MEXICANA, S.A. DE C.V.—See Nissan Motor Co., Ltd.; *Int'l*, pg. 5368
NISSAN MIDDLE EAST F.Z.E.—See Nissan Motor Co., Ltd.; *Int'l*, pg. 5368
NISSAN MOTOR ACCEPTANCE CORPORATION—See Nissan Motor Co., Ltd.; *Int'l*, pg. 5369
NISSAN MOTOR CAR CARRIER CO., LTD.—See Mitsui O.S.K. Lines, Ltd.; *Int'l*, pg. 4991
NISSAN MOTOR (CHINA) LTD.—See Nissan Motor Co., Ltd.; *Int'l*, pg. 5368
NISSAN MOTOR CO. (AUSTRALIA) PTY. LTD.—See Nissan Motor Co., Ltd.; *Int'l*, pg. 5368
NISSAN MOTOR CO., LTD. - IWAKI PLANT—See Nissan Motor Co., Ltd.; *Int'l*, pg. 5368
NISSAN MOTOR CO., LTD. - KYUSHU PLANT—See Nissan Motor Co., Ltd.; *Int'l*, pg. 5368
NISSAN MOTOR CO., LTD. - OPPAMA PLANT—See Nissan Motor Co., Ltd.; *Int'l*, pg. 5368
NISSAN MOTOR CO., LTD.; *Int'l*, pg. 5367
NISSAN MOTOR CO., LTD. - TOCHIGI PLANT—See Nissan Motor Co., Ltd.; *Int'l*, pg. 5368
NISSAN MOTOR CO., LTD. - YOKOHAMA PLANT—See Nissan Motor Co., Ltd.; *Int'l*, pg. 5368

NISSAN MOTOR CORPORATION HAWAII, LTD.—See Nissan Motor Co., Ltd.; *Int'l*, pg. 5368
NISSAN MOTOR ESPANA S.A.—See Nissan Motor Co., Ltd.; *Int'l*, pg. 5368
NISSAN MOTOR (GB) LTD.—See Nissan Motor Co., Ltd.; *Int'l*, pg. 5368
NISSAN MOTOR IBERICA, S.A.—See Nissan Motor Co., Ltd.; *Int'l*, pg. 5368
NISSAN MOTOR INDIA PRIVATE LIMITED—See Nissan Motor Co., Ltd.; *Int'l*, pg. 5368
NISSAN MOTOR KYUSHU CO., LTD.—See Nissan Motor Co., Ltd.; *Int'l*, pg. 5368
NISSAN MOTOR LIGHT TRUCK CO., LTD.—See Nissan Motor Co., Ltd.; *Int'l*, pg. 5368
NISSAN MOTOR MANUFACTURING (UK) LTD.—See Nissan Motor Co., Ltd.; *Int'l*, pg. 5368
NISSAN MOTOR NETHERLAND B.V.—See Nissan Motor Co., Ltd.; *Int'l*, pg. 5368
NISSAN MOTOR PART CENTER B.V.—See Nissan Motor Co., Ltd.; *Int'l*, pg. 5368
NISSAN MOTOR PHILIPPINES, INC.—See Nissan Motor Co., Ltd.; *Int'l*, pg. 5368
NISSAN MOTOR RUS LTD.—See Nissan Motor Co., Ltd.; *Int'l*, pg. 5369
NISSAN MOTOR (SCHWEIZ) AG—See Nissan Motor Co., Ltd.; *Int'l*, pg. 5368
NISSAN MOTORSPORTS & CUSTOMIZING CO., LTD.—See Nissan Motor Co., Ltd.; *Int'l*, pg. 5369
NISSAN MOTORSPORTS INTERNATIONAL CO., LTD.—See Nissan Motor Co., Ltd.; *Int'l*, pg. 5369
NISSAN MOTOR THAILAND CO., LTD.—See Nissan Motor Co., Ltd.; *Int'l*, pg. 5369
NISSAN NETWORK HOLDINGS CO., LTD.—See Nissan Motor Co., Ltd.; *Int'l*, pg. 5369
NISSAN NEW ZEALAND LTD.—See Nissan Motor Co., Ltd.; *Int'l*, pg. 5369
NISSAN NORDIC EUROPE OY—See Nissan Motor Co., Ltd.; *Int'l*, pg. 5369
NISSAN NORTH AMERICA, INC. - CANTON—See Nissan Motor Co., Ltd.; *Int'l*, pg. 5369
NISSAN NORTH AMERICA, INC. DECHERD—See Nissan Motor Co., Ltd.; *Int'l*, pg. 5369
NISSAN NORTH AMERICA, INC.—See Nissan Motor Co., Ltd.; *Int'l*, pg. 5369
NISSAN OF BAKERSFIELD; *U.S. Private*, pg. 2928
NISSAN OF BERGENFIELD INC.; *U.S. Private*, pg. 2928
NISSAN OF BOURNE; *U.S. Private*, pg. 2929
NISSAN OF BRANDON, INC.—See AutoNation, Inc.; *U.S. Public*, pg. 236
NISSAN OF COOL SPRINGS LLC; *U.S. Private*, pg. 2929
NISSAN OF HAWTHORNE; *U.S. Private*, pg. 2929
NISSAN OF HUNTINGTON; *U.S. Private*, pg. 2929
NISSAN OF MANHATTAN; *U.S. Private*, pg. 2929
NISSAN OF MELBOURNE; *U.S. Private*, pg. 2929
NISSAN OF NORWICH; *U.S. Private*, pg. 2929
NISSAN OF RENO; *U.S. Private*, pg. 2929
NISSAN OF ROANOKE RAPIDS; *U.S. Private*, pg. 2929
NISSAN OTOMOTIV A.S.—See Nissan Motor Co., Ltd.; *Int'l*, pg. 5369
NISSAN PHILIPPINES, INC.—See Nissan Motor Co., Ltd.; *Int'l*, pg. 5369
NISSAN PLAZASOL CO., LTD.—See Nissan Motor Co., Ltd.; *Int'l*, pg. 5368
NISSAN PRINCE TOKYO MOTOR SALES CO., LTD—See Nissan Motor Co., Ltd.; *Int'l*, pg. 5369
NISSAN PS FIELD CRAFT CO., LTD.—See Nissan Tokyo Sales Holdings Co., Ltd.; *Int'l*, pg. 5370
NISSAN SATIO NARA CO., LTD.—See VT Holdings Co., Ltd.; *Int'l*, pg. 8315
NISSAN-SATIO-SAITAMA CO., LTD.—See VT Holdings Co., Ltd.; *Int'l*, pg. 8315
NISSAN SAUDI ARABIA CO., LTD.—See Nissan Motor Co., Ltd.; *Int'l*, pg. 5369
NISSAN SECURITIES GROUP CO., LTD.; *Int'l*, pg. 5370
NISSAN SHATAI CO., LTD.—See Nissan Motor Co., Ltd.; *Int'l*, pg. 5369
NISSAN SHATAI KYUSHU CO., LTD.—See Nissan Motor Co., Ltd.; *Int'l*, pg. 5369
NISSAN SOUTH AFRICA PTY. LTD.—See Nissan Motor Co., Ltd.; *Int'l*, pg. 5369
NISSAN SOUTH; *U.S. Private*, pg. 2929
NISSAN TECHNICAL CENTER N.A.—See Nissan Motor Co., Ltd.; *Int'l*, pg. 5369
NISSAN TECHNICAL CENTER NORTH AMERICA, INC.—See Nissan Motor Co., Ltd.; *Int'l*, pg. 5369
NISSAN TECHNICAL CENTRE EUROPE, LTD.—See Nissan Motor Co., Ltd.; *Int'l*, pg. 5369
NISSAN TECHNO CO., LTD.—See Nissan Motor Co., Ltd.; *Int'l*, pg. 5369
NISSAN TOKYO SALES CO., LTD.—See Nissan Tokyo Sales Holdings Co., Ltd.; *Int'l*, pg. 5370
NISSAN TOKYO SALES HOLDINGS CO., LTD.; *Int'l*, pg. 5370
NISSAN TRADING CO., LTD.—See Nissan Motor Co., Ltd.; *Int'l*, pg. 5369
NISSAN TRADING CORP., U.S.A.—See Nissan Motor Co., Ltd.; *Int'l*, pg. 5369
NISSAN TRADING EUROPE LTD.—See Nissan Motor Co., Ltd.; *Int'l*, pg. 5369

CORPORATE AFFILIATIONS

NISSAN TRI STAR CONSTRUCTION, INC.—See TOKAI Holdings Corporation; *Int'l*, pg. 7779
NISSAN VIETNAM CO. LTD.—See Tan Chong Motor Holdings Berhad; *Int'l*, pg. 7453
NISSAN WEST EUROPE SAS—See Nissan Motor Co., Ltd.; *Int'l*, pg. 5369
NISSAY ASSET MANAGEMENT CORPORATION—See Nippon Life Insurance Company; *Int'l*, pg. 5322
NISSAY BUSINESS SERVICE CO., LTD.—See Nippon Life Insurance Company; *Int'l*, pg. 5322
NISSAY CREDIT GUARANTEE CO., LTD.—See Nippon Life Insurance Company; *Int'l*, pg. 5322
NISSAY CULTURE FOUNDATION—See Nippon Life Insurance Company; *Int'l*, pg. 5322
NISSAY-GREATWALL LIFE INSURANCE CO., LTD.—See China Great Wall Asset Management Corporation; *Int'l*, pg. 1505
NISSAY-GREATWALL LIFE INSURANCE CO., LTD.—See Nippon Life Insurance Company; *Int'l*, pg. 5323
NISSAY GREEN FOUNDATION—See Nippon Life Insurance Company; *Int'l*, pg. 5322
NISSAY INVESTMENT CO., LTD.—See Nippon Life Insurance Company; *Int'l*, pg. 5322
NISSAY SCHRODERS ASSET MANAGEMENT ASIA LIMITED—See Nippon Life Insurance Company; *Int'l*, pg. 5322
NISSAY SCHRODERS ASSET MANAGEMENT EUROPE LIMITED—See Nippon Life Insurance Company; *Int'l*, pg. 5322
NISSCO RESTAURANT DEALER GROUP, INC.; *U.S. Private*, pg. 2929
NISSEI ADVANTECH MEXICO S.A. DE C.V.—See Nippon Seiki Co., Ltd.; *Int'l*, pg. 5330
NISSEI AMERICA, INC.—See Nissei Plastic Industrial Co., Ltd.; *Int'l*, pg. 5370
NISSEI ASB AFRICA LIMITED—See NISSEI ASB MACHINE CO., LTD.; *Int'l*, pg. 5370
NISSEI ASB CENTRO AMERICA, S.A. DE C.V.—See NISSEI ASB MACHINE CO., LTD.; *Int'l*, pg. 5370
NISSEI ASB CO.—See NISSEI ASB MACHINE CO., LTD.; *Int'l*, pg. 5370
NISSEI ASB FZEFZE—See NISSEI ASB MACHINE CO., LTD.; *Int'l*, pg. 5370
NISSEI ASB GMBH—See NISSEI ASB MACHINE CO., LTD.; *Int'l*, pg. 5370
NISSEI ASB LTD.—See NISSEI ASB MACHINE CO., LTD.; *Int'l*, pg. 5370
NISSEI ASB MACHINE CO., LTD.; *Int'l*, pg. 5370
NISSEI ASB MEDITERRANEA, S.L.U.—See NISSEI ASB MACHINE CO., LTD.; *Int'l*, pg. 5370
NISSEI ASB PTE LTD.—See NISSEI ASB MACHINE CO., LTD.; *Int'l*, pg. 5370
NISSEI ASB SOUTH AFRICA (PTY) LTD.—See NISSEI ASB MACHINE CO., LTD.; *Int'l*, pg. 5370
NISSEI ASB SUDAMERICA LTDA.—See NISSEI ASB MACHINE CO., LTD.; *Int'l*, pg. 5370
NISSEI BILIS CO., LTD.—See Nippon Fine Chemical Co., Ltd.; *Int'l*, pg. 5318
NISSEI BIRU KANRI K.K.—See NSK Ltd.; *Int'l*, pg. 5480
NISSEI BLDG. MANAGEMENT LTD.—See NSK Ltd.; *Int'l*, pg. 5478
NISSEI BUILD ASIA PTE. LTD.—See Nissei Build Kogyo Co., Ltd.; *Int'l*, pg. 5370
NISSEI BUILD KOGYO CO., LTD.; *Int'l*, pg. 5370
NISSEI CORPORATION—See Nissan Chemical Corporation; *Int'l*, pg. 5367
NISSEI DISPLAY SALES & DEVELOPMENT CO., LTD.—See Nippon Seiki Co., Ltd.; *Int'l*, pg. 5330
NISSEI GEAR MOTOR MFG. (CHANGZHOU) CO., LTD.—See Brother Industries, Ltd.; *Int'l*, pg. 1198
NISSEI INDUSTRIES CO., LTD.—See Koito Manufacturing Co., Ltd.; *Int'l*, pg. 4230
NISSEI KOSAN CO., LTD.—See Nippon Fine Chemical Co., Ltd.; *Int'l*, pg. 5318
NISSEI KYUSYOKU CO., LTD.—See Nippon Seiki Co., Ltd.; *Int'l*, pg. 5330
NISSEI (MALAYSIA) SDN. BHD.—See Nissei Plastic Industrial Co., Ltd.; *Int'l*, pg. 5370
NISSEI PLAS-TECH CORPORATION—See Nippon Fine Chemical Co., Ltd.; *Int'l*, pg. 5318
NISSEI PLASTIC (HONG KONG) LTD.—See Nissei Plastic Industrial Co., Ltd.; *Int'l*, pg. 5370
NISSEI PLASTIC INDUSTRIAL CO., LTD.; *Int'l*, pg. 5370
NISSEI PLASTIC MACHINERY (TAICANG) CO., LTD.—See Nissei Plastic Industrial Co., Ltd.; *Int'l*, pg. 5370
NISSEI PLASTIC (SHANGHAI) CO., LTD.—See Nissei Plastic Industrial Co., Ltd.; *Int'l*, pg. 5370
NISSEI PLASTIC SINGAPORE PTE LTD.—See Nissei Plastic Industrial Co., Ltd.; *Int'l*, pg. 5370
NISSEI PLASTIC (THAILAND) CO., LTD.—See Nissei Plastic Industrial Co., Ltd.; *Int'l*, pg. 5371
NISSEI PLASTIC (VIETNAM) CO., LTD.—See Nissei Plastic Industrial Co., Ltd.; *Int'l*, pg. 5370
NISSEI SEIKO CO., LTD.—See Daido Steel Co., Ltd.; *Int'l*, pg. 1923
NISSEI SERVICE CO., LTD.—See Nippon Seiki Co., Ltd.; *Int'l*, pg. 5330

COMPANY NAME INDEX

NISSEI TECHNOLOGY CORPORATION—See Nagase & Co., Ltd.; *Int'l*, pg. 5128
NISSEI TRADING (SHANGHAI) CO., LTD.—See Brother Industries, Ltd.; *Int'l*, pg. 1198
NISSEN CHEMITEC AMERICA—See Nissen Chemitec Corporation; *Int'l*, pg. 5371
NISSEN CHEMITEC CORPORATION; *Int'l*, pg. 5371
NISSEN FRANCE—See Standard Motor Products, Inc.; *U.S. Public*, pg. 1929
NISSEN HOLDINGS CO., LTD.—See Seven & i Holdings Co., Ltd.; *Int'l*, pg. 6731
NISSEN, INC.; *Int'l*, pg. 5371
NISSENS A/S—See Standard Motor Products, Inc.; *U.S. Public*, pg. 1929
NISSENS BENELUX S.A.—See Standard Motor Products, Inc.; *U.S. Public*, pg. 1929
NISSENS DEUTSCHLAND GMBH—See Standard Motor Products, Inc.; *U.S. Public*, pg. 1929
NISSENS FINLAND OY—See Standard Motor Products, Inc.; *U.S. Public*, pg. 1929
NISSENS HUNGARIA KFT.—See Standard Motor Products, Inc.; *U.S. Public*, pg. 1929
NISSENS ITALIA SRL—See Standard Motor Products, Inc.; *U.S. Public*, pg. 1929
NISSENS NORTH AMERICA, INC.—See Standard Motor Products, Inc.; *U.S. Public*, pg. 1929
NISSENS OSTERREICH G.M.B.H.—See Standard Motor Products, Inc.; *U.S. Public*, pg. 1929
NISSENS SCHWEIZ AG—See Standard Motor Products, Inc.; *U.S. Public*, pg. 1929
NISSENS (SHANGHAI) AUTO PARTS TRADING CO., LTD.—See Standard Motor Products, Inc.; *U.S. Public*, pg. 1929
NISSENS SLOVAKIA S.R.O.—See Standard Motor Products, Inc.; *U.S. Public*, pg. 1929
NISSENS SVERIGE AB—See Standard Motor Products, Inc.; *U.S. Public*, pg. 1929
NISSENS (UK) LTD.—See Standard Motor Products, Inc.; *U.S. Public*, pg. 1929
NISSENS UKRAINE LTD.—See Standard Motor Products, Inc.; *U.S. Public*, pg. 1929
NISSETSU CO., LTD.—See NIPPON CARBIDE INDUSTRIES CO., INC.; *Int'l*, pg. 5311
NISSEY CAMBODIA CO., LTD—See Nihon Seimitsu Co., Ltd.; *Int'l*, pg. 5287
NISSEY VIETNAM CO., LTD.—See Nihon Seimitsu Co., Ltd.; *Int'l*, pg. 5287
NISSHA BACK STICKERS INTERNATIONAL B.V.—See Nissha Co., Ltd.; *Int'l*, pg. 5371
NISSHA BUSINESS SERVICE, INC.—See Nissha Co., Ltd.; *Int'l*, pg. 5371
NISSHA BUTSURYU CO., LTD.—See Toyota Motor Corporation; *Int'l*, pg. 7871
NISSHA CO., LTD.; *Int'l*, pg. 5371
NISSHA EUROPE GMBH—See Nissha Co., Ltd.; *Int'l*, pg. 5371
NISSHA F8, INC.—See Nissha Co., Ltd.; *Int'l*, pg. 5371
NISSHA FIS, INC.—See Nissha Co., Ltd.; *Int'l*, pg. 5371
NISSHA GSI TECHNOLOGIES, INC.—See Nissha Co., Ltd.; *Int'l*, pg. 5371
NISSHA INDUSTRIAL AND ELECTRONICS TRADING (SHANGHAI) CO., LTD.—See Nissha Co., Ltd.; *Int'l*, pg. 5371
NISSHA INDUSTRIAL & TRADING MALAYSIA SDN. BHD.—See Nissha Co., Ltd.; *Int'l*, pg. 5371
NISSHA INDUSTRIAL & TRADING (SHENZHEN) CO., LTD.—See Nissha Co., Ltd.; *Int'l*, pg. 5371
NISSHA INTERACTIVE CORPORATION—See Nissha Co., Ltd.; *Int'l*, pg. 5371
NISSHA KOREA HIGH PRECISION PLASTICS INC.—See Nissha Co., Ltd.; *Int'l*, pg. 5371
NISSHA KOREA INC.—See Nissha Co., Ltd.; *Int'l*, pg. 5371
NISSHA (KUNSHAN) PRECISION IMD MOLD CO., LTD.—See Nissha Co., Ltd.; *Int'l*, pg. 5371
NISSHA MEDICAL TECHNOLOGIES GMBH & CO. KG—See Nissha Co., Ltd.; *Int'l*, pg. 5371
NISSHA MEDICAL TECHNOLOGIES SAS—See Nissha Co., Ltd.; *Int'l*, pg. 5371
NISSHA METALLIZING SOLUTIONS GMBH—See Nissha Co., Ltd.; *Int'l*, pg. 5371
NISSHA METALLIZING SOLUTIONS LTD.—See Nissha Co., Ltd.; *Int'l*, pg. 5371
NISSHA METALLIZING SOLUTIONS N.V.—See Nissha Co., Ltd.; *Int'l*, pg. 5371
NISSHA METALLIZING SOLUTIONS PRODUTOS METALIZADOS LTDA.—See Nissha Co., Ltd.; *Int'l*, pg. 5371
NISSHA METALLIZING SOLUTIONS S.R.L.—See Nissha Co., Ltd.; *Int'l*, pg. 5371
NISSHA PMX TECHNOLOGIES, S.A. DE C.V.—See Nissha Co., Ltd.; *Int'l*, pg. 5371
NISSHA PRECISION TECHNOLOGIES MALAYSIA SDN. BHD.—See Nissha Co., Ltd.; *Int'l*, pg. 5372
NISSHA PRINTING CO. LTD. - OSAKA DIVISION—See Nissha Co., Ltd.; *Int'l*, pg. 5371
NISSHA PRINTING CO. LTD. - TOKYO DIVISION—See Nissha Co., Ltd.; *Int'l*, pg. 5371
NISSHA PRINTING COMMUNICATIONS, INC.—See Nissha Co., Ltd.; *Int'l*, pg. 5372

NISSHA SB POLAND SP.ZO.O.—See Nissha Co., Ltd.; *Int'l*, pg. 5372
NISSHA SCHUSTER KUNSTSTOFFTECHNIK GMBH—See Nissha Co., Ltd.; *Int'l*, pg. 5372
NISSHA SIMICS, INC.—See Nissha Co., Ltd.; *Int'l*, pg. 5372
NISSHA USA INC.—See Nissha Co., Ltd.; *Int'l*, pg. 5372
NISSHA VIETNAM CO., LTD.—See Nissha Co., Ltd.; *Int'l*, pg. 5372
NISSHINBO ALPS TECH CO., LTD.—See Nisshinbo Holdings Inc.; *Int'l*, pg. 5373
NISSHINBO AUTOMOTIVE MANUFACTURING INC.—See Nisshinbo Holdings Inc.; *Int'l*, pg. 5373
NISSHINBO BRAKE INC.—See Nisshinbo Holdings Inc.; *Int'l*, pg. 5373
NISSHINBO BRAKE SALES CO. LTD.—See Nisshinbo Holdings Inc.; *Int'l*, pg. 5374
NISSHINBO CHEMICAL INC. - ASAHI PLANT—See Nisshinbo Holdings Inc.; *Int'l*, pg. 5374
NISSHINBO CHEMICAL INC. - CHIBA PLANT—See Nisshinbo Holdings Inc.; *Int'l*, pg. 5374
NISSHINBO CHEMICAL INC.—See Nisshinbo Holdings Inc.; *Int'l*, pg. 5374
NISSHINBO CHEMICAL INC. - TOKUSHIMA PLANT—See Nisshinbo Holdings Inc.; *Int'l*, pg. 5374
NISSHINBO DO BRASIL INDUSTRIA TEXTIL LTDA.—See Nisshinbo Holdings Inc.; *Int'l*, pg. 5374
NISSHINBO EUROPE B.V.—See Nisshinbo Holdings Inc.; *Int'l*, pg. 5374
NISSHINBO HOLDINGS INC.; *Int'l*, pg. 5372
NISSHINBO MECHATRONICS INC. - HAMAKITA PLANT—See Nisshinbo Holdings Inc.; *Int'l*, pg. 5374
NISSHINBO MECHATRONICS INC. - MIAI MACHINERY PLANT—See Nisshinbo Holdings Inc.; *Int'l*, pg. 5374
NISSHINBO MECHATRONICS INC.—See Nisshinbo Holdings Inc.; *Int'l*, pg. 5374
NISSHINBO MECHATRONICS (SHANGHAI) CO., LTD.—See Nisshinbo Holdings Inc.; *Int'l*, pg. 5374
NISSHINBO MECHATRONICS (THAILAND) LTD.—See Nisshinbo Holdings Inc.; *Int'l*, pg. 5374
NISSHINBO MICRO DEVICES AMERICAS INC.—See Nisshinbo Holdings Inc.; *Int'l*, pg. 5374
NISSHINBO MICRO DEVICES AT CO., LTD.—See Nisshinbo Holdings Inc.; *Int'l*, pg. 5374
NISSHINBO MICRO DEVICES EUROPE GMBH—See Nisshinbo Holdings Inc.; *Int'l*, pg. 5374
NISSHINBO MICRO DEVICES FUKUOKA CO., LTD.—See Nisshinbo Holdings Inc.; *Int'l*, pg. 5374
NISSHINBO MICRO DEVICES INC.—See Nisshinbo Holdings Inc.; *Int'l*, pg. 5374
NISSHINBO MICRO DEVICES (SHANGHAI) CO., LTD.—See Nisshinbo Holdings Inc.; *Int'l*, pg. 5374
NISSHINBO MICRO DEVICES SINGAPORE PTE. LTD.—See Nisshinbo Holdings Inc.; *Int'l*, pg. 5374
NISSHINBO MICRO DEVICES (THAILAND) CO., LTD.—See Nisshinbo Holdings Inc.; *Int'l*, pg. 5374
NISSHINBO MOBIX CO. LTD.—See Nisshinbo Holdings Inc.; *Int'l*, pg. 5374
NISSHINBO PHOTOVOLTAIC KOREA CORPORATION—See Nisshinbo Holdings Inc.; *Int'l*, pg. 5374
NISSHINBO POSTAL CHEMICAL CO. LTD.—See Nisshinbo Holdings Inc.; *Int'l*, pg. 5374
NISSHINBO PRECISION INSTRUMENT & MACHINERY HIROSHIMA CORPORATION—See Nisshinbo Holdings Inc.; *Int'l*, pg. 5374
NISSHINBO (SHANGHAI) CO., LTD.—See Nisshinbo Holdings Inc.; *Int'l*, pg. 5373
NISSHINBO SOMBOON AUTOMOTIVE CO. LTD.—See Nisshinbo Holdings Inc.; *Int'l*, pg. 5374
NISSHINBO TEXTILE INC.—See Nisshinbo Holdings Inc.; *Int'l*, pg. 5374
NISSHINBO YARN DYED CO. LTD.—See Nisshinbo Holdings Inc.; *Int'l*, pg. 5375
NISSHINBO-YAWEI PRECISION INSTRUMENTS & MACHINERY (JIANGSU) CO., LTD.—See Nisshinbo Holdings Inc.; *Int'l*, pg. 5374
NISSHIN CAREER SERVICE CO., LTD.—See Nippon Signal Co., Ltd.; *Int'l*, pg. 5333
NISSHIN COLORING CO., LTD.—See Mitsubishi Gas Chemical Company, Inc.; *Int'l*, pg. 4950
NISSHIN ELECTRIC CONSTRUCTION CO., LTD.—See Nippon Signal Co., Ltd.; *Int'l*, pg. 5333
NISSHIN ELECTRONICS SERVICE CO., LTD.—See Nippon Signal Co., Ltd.; *Int'l*, pg. 5333
NISSHIN ENVIRONMENTAL PLANNING INC.—See Nisshinbo Holdings Inc.; *Int'l*, pg. 5373
NISSHIN FIRE INSURANCE SERVICE COMPANY, LIMITED—See Tokio Marine Holdings, Inc.; *Int'l*, pg. 7782
NISSHIN FIRE & MARINE INSURANCE CO., LTD.—See Tokio Marine Holdings, Inc.; *Int'l*, pg. 7782
NISSHIN FLOUR MILLING CO., LTD.—See Nisshin Seifun Group, Inc.; *Int'l*, pg. 5372
NISSHIN FOODS INC.—See Nisshin Seifun Group, Inc.; *Int'l*, pg. 5372
NISSHIN GLOBAL LOGISTICS (SHANGHAI) CO., LTD.; *Int'l*, pg. 5372

NISSHIN GROUP HOLDINGS COMPANY, LIMITED; *Int'l*, pg. 5372
NISSHIN INFORMATION SYSTEM DEVELOPMENT COMPANY, LIMITED—See Tokio Marine Holdings, Inc.; *Int'l*, pg. 7782
NISSHIN INTERNATIONAL TRADING CO., LTD.; *Int'l*, pg. 5372
NISSHIN IT FIELD SERVICE CO., LTD.—See Nippon Signal Co., Ltd.; *Int'l*, pg. 5333
NISSHIN KASAI SOGO SERVICE COMPANY, LIMITED—See Tokio Marine Holdings, Inc.; *Int'l*, pg. 7782
NISSHIN KOHGYO CORPORATION—See GSI Creos Corporation; *Int'l*, pg. 3145
NISSHIN KOKAN CO., LTD.—See Nippon Steel Corporation; *Int'l*, pg. 5336
NISSHIN METAL-WORKING CO., LTD.—See Nippon Steel Corporation; *Int'l*, pg. 5336
NISSHIN (MYANMAR) CO., LTD.; *Int'l*, pg. 5372
THE NISSHIN OILLIO GROUP, LTD.; *Int'l*, pg. 7670
NISSHIN OKABE NIKOH CO., LTD.—See Nippon Signal Co., Ltd.; *Int'l*, pg. 5333
NISSHIN SANSO CO., LTD.—See Nippon Steel Corporation; *Int'l*, pg. 5336
NISSHIN SEIFUN GROUP, INC.; *Int'l*, pg. 5372
NISSHIN SEIKA CO., LTD.—See Kameda Seika Co., Ltd.; *Int'l*, pg. 4061
NISSHIN SHOJI CO., LTD.—See The Nisshin OilliO Group, Ltd.; *Int'l*, pg. 7671
NISSHIN SHOKAI CO., LTD.—See The Nisshin OilliO Group, Ltd.; *Int'l*, pg. 7671
NISSHIN SOFTWARE ENGINEERING CO., LTD.—See Nippon Signal Co., Ltd.; *Int'l*, pg. 5333
NISSHIN-STC FLOUR MILLING CO., LTD.—See Nisshin Seifun Group, Inc.; *Int'l*, pg. 5372
NISSHIN TECHNO ENGINEERING CO., LTD.—See Nippon Signal Co., Ltd.; *Int'l*, pg. 5333
NISSHIN TECHNO SERVICE CO., LTD.—See Nippon Signal Co., Ltd.; *Int'l*, pg. 5333
NISSHIN TOA INC.—See Nisshinbo Holdings Inc.; *Int'l*, pg. 5373
NISSHINTOA IWAO INC.—See Nisshinbo Holdings Inc.; *Int'l*, pg. 5375
NISSHIN TOKKI CO., LTD.—See Nippon Signal Co., Ltd.; *Int'l*, pg. 5333
NISSHIN TRANSPORTATION CO., LTD.—See AIT Corporation; *Int'l*, pg. 254
NISSHIN TRANSPORTATION (QINGDAO) CO., LTD.—See KKR & Co. Inc.; *U.S. Public*, pg. 1259
NISSHIN TRANSPORTATION (SHANGHAI) CO., LTD.—See KKR & Co. Inc.; *U.S. Public*, pg. 1259
NISSHIN UNYU CO., LTD.—See Mitsubishi Gas Chemical Company, Inc.; *Int'l*, pg. 4950
NISSHIN UNYU (SHANGHAI) CO., LTD.—See KKR & Co. Inc.; *U.S. Public*, pg. 1259
NISSHO CO., LTD.—See Nippon Sheet Glass Co. Ltd.; *Int'l*, pg. 5331
NISSHO CORPORATION - KYUSHU PLANT—See Nitto Denko Corporation; *Int'l*, pg. 5385
NISSHO CORPORATION - NAGOYA PLANT—See Nitto Denko Corporation; *Int'l*, pg. 5385
NISSHO CORPORATION - OSAKA PLANT—See Nitto Denko Corporation; *Int'l*, pg. 5385
NISSHO CORPORATION - SHIGA PLANT—See Nitto Denko Corporation; *Int'l*, pg. 5385
NISSHO CORPORATION - TOHOKU PLANT—See Nitto Denko Corporation; *Int'l*, pg. 5385
NISSHO (DALIAN F.T.Z.) INTERNATIONAL TRADING CO., LTD.—See Nitto Denko Corporation; *Int'l*, pg. 5385
NISSHO ELECTRONICS (ASIA) CO., LTD.—See Sojitz Corporation; *Int'l*, pg. 7063
NISSHO ELECTRONICS CORPORATION—See Sojitz Corporation; *Int'l*, pg. 7062
NISSHO (HONG KONG) LTD.—See Nitto Denko Corporation; *Int'l*, pg. 5384
NISSHO HUNGARY PRECISION KFT.—See Nitto Denko Corporation; *Int'l*, pg. 5384
NISSHO IWAI CEMENT CORPORATION—See Sojitz Corporation; *Int'l*, pg. 7063
NISSHO IWAI PAPER & PULP CORPORATION—See Sojitz Corporation; *Int'l*, pg. 7063
NISSHO KAKO CO., LTD.—See Nippon Sheet Glass Co. Ltd.; *Int'l*, pg. 5331
NISSHO KOSAN CO., LTD.—See Nippon Sheet Glass Co. Ltd.; *Int'l*, pg. 5331
NISSHOKU BUTSURYU CORPORATION—See Nippon Shokubai Co., Ltd.; *Int'l*, pg. 5333
NISSHOKU CHEMICAL INDUSTRY (ZHANGJIAGANG) CO., LTD.—See Nippon Shokubai Co., Ltd.; *Int'l*, pg. 5333
NISSHOKU ENGINEERING SERVICE CO., LTD.—See Nippon Shokubai Co., Ltd.; *Int'l*, pg. 5333
NISSHOKU TECHNO FINE CHEMICAL CO., LTD.—See Nippon Shokubai Co., Ltd.; *Int'l*, pg. 5333
NISSHO TRADING (SHANGHAI) CO., LTD.—See Nippon Shokubai Co., Ltd.; *Int'l*, pg. 5333
NISSHO LINEN—See Aramark; *U.S. Public*, pg. 178
NISSHO LINEN SUPPLY CO., LTD.—See Yamashita Corporation; *Int'l*, pg. 8553

NISSHIN SEIFUN GROUP, INC.   CORPORATE AFFILIATIONS

NISSHO PETROLEUM GAS CORPORATION—See Osaka Gas Co., Ltd.; *Int'l*, pg. 5645
NISSHO PRECISION (DONGGUAN) CO., LTD.—See Nitto Denko Corporation; *Int'l*, pg. 5385
NISSHO PRECISION (MALAYSIA) SDN. BHD.—See Nitto Denko Corporation; *Int'l*, pg. 5384
NISSHO PRECISION PHILIPPINES INCORPORATED—See Nitto Denko Corporation; *Int'l*, pg. 5385
NISSHO PRECISION (SUZHOU) CO., LTD.—See Nitto Denko Corporation; *Int'l*, pg. 5385
NISSHO PRECISION (THAILAND) CO., LTD.—See Nitto Denko Corporation; *Int'l*, pg. 5385
NISSHO PRECISION VIETNAM CO., LTD.—See Nitto Denko Corporation; *Int'l*, pg. 5385
NISSHO PRECISION (WUXI) CO., LTD.—See Nitto Denko Corporation; *Int'l*, pg. 5385
NISSHO PROPANE SEKIYU CORP.—See Sojitz Corporation; *Int'l*, pg. 7063
NISSHO SANGYO CO. LTD.; *Int'l*, pg. 5375
NISSHO SANGYO (SHANGHAI) CO., LTD.—See Nitto Denko Corporation; *Int'l*, pg. 5385
NISSHO SEIKI CO., LTD.—See Nihon Yamamura Glass Co., Ltd.; *Int'l*, pg. 5288
NISSHO SHIPPING CO., LTD.—See ENEOS Holdings, Inc.; *Int'l*, pg. 2417
NISSHO (SINGAPORE) PTE. LTD.—See Nitto Denko Corporation; *Int'l*, pg. 5385
NISSHO (TAIWAN) CORPORATION—See Nitto Denko Corporation; *Int'l*, pg. 5384
NISSHO VECS CO., LTD.—See Relo Group, Inc.; *Int'l*, pg. 6265
NISSIN ABC LOGISTICS PRIVATE LIMITED—See Nissin Corporation; *Int'l*, pg. 5375
NISSIN ADVANCED COATING INDO CO., PRIVATE LTD.—See Sumitomo Electric Industries, Ltd.; *Int'l*, pg. 7279
NISSIN ADVANCED COATING (SHENYANG) CO., LTD.—See Sumitomo Electric Industries, Ltd.; *Int'l*, pg. 7279
NISSIN ADVANCED COATING (TIANJIN) CO.,LTD—See ITOCHU Corporation; *Int'l*, pg. 3840
NISSIN-AJINOMOTO ALIMENTOS LTDA.—See Ajinomoto Company, Inc.; *Int'l*, pg. 257
NISSIN-AJINOMOTO ALIMENTOS LTDA.—See Nissin Foods Holdings Co., Ltd.; *Int'l*, pg. 5377
NISSIN ALLIS ELECTRIC CO., LTD.—See Sumitomo Electric Industries, Ltd.; *Int'l*, pg. 7279
NISSIN ALLIS ION EQUIPMENT (SHANGHAI) CO., LTD.—See Sumitomo Electric Industries, Ltd.; *Int'l*, pg. 7279
NISSIN ALLIS UNION ION EQUIPMENT CO. LTD—See Sumitomo Electric Industries, Ltd.; *Int'l*, pg. 7279
NISSIN BELGIUM N.V.—See Nissin Corporation; *Int'l*, pg. 5375
NISSIN BRAKE DE MEXICO,S.A. DE C.V.—See Honda Motor Co., Ltd.; *Int'l*, pg. 3463
NISSIN BRAKE DO BRASIL LTDA—See Honda Motor Co., Ltd.; *Int'l*, pg. 3463
NISSIN BRAKE EUROPE, S.L.U—See Honda Motor Co., Ltd.; *Int'l*, pg. 3463
NISSIN BRAKE GEORGIA INC.—See Honda Motor Co., Ltd.; *Int'l*, pg. 3463
NISSIN BRAKE INDIA PVT. LTD.—See Honda Motor Co., Ltd.; *Int'l*, pg. 3463
NISSIN BRAKE OHIO, INC.—See Honda Motor Co., Ltd.; *Int'l*, pg. 3463
NISSIN BRAKE PHILIPPINES CORPORATION—See Honda Motor Co., Ltd.; *Int'l*, pg. 3463
NISSIN BRAKE REALTY PHILIPPINES CORPORATION—See Honda Motor Co., Ltd.; *Int'l*, pg. 3463
NISSIN BRAKE (THAILAND) CO., LTD.—See Honda Motor Co., Ltd.; *Int'l*, pg. 3463
NISSIN BRAKE VIETNAM CO., LTD.—See Honda Motor Co., Ltd.; *Int'l*, pg. 3463
NISSIN BUSINESS SUPPORT CO., LTD—See Nissin Foods Holdings Co., Ltd.; *Int'l*, pg. 5376
NISSIN BUSINESS SUPPORT PLUS CO., LTD.—See Nissin Foods Holdings Co., Ltd.; *Int'l*, pg. 5376
NISSIN (CHANGSHU) INTERNATIONAL LOGISTICS CO., LTD.—See Nissin Corporation; *Int'l*, pg. 5375
NISSIN CHEMICAL CO., LTD.—See New Japan Chemical Co., Ltd.; *Int'l*, pg. 5225
NISSIN CHEMICAL INDUSTRY CO., LTD,—See Shin-Etsu Chemical Co. Ltd.; *Int'l*, pg. 6839
NISSIN CHILLED FOODS CO., LTD.—See Nissin Foods Holdings Co., Ltd.; *Int'l*, pg. 5376
NISSIN CISCO CO., LTD.—See Nissin Foods Holdings Co., Ltd.; *Int'l*, pg. 5376
NISSIN CORPORATION; *Int'l*, pg. 5375
NISSIN DENKI SHOUJI CO., LTD.—See Sumitomo Electric Industries, Ltd.; *Int'l*, pg. 7279
NISSIN DIAMOND CO., LTD.—See OSG Corporation; *Int'l*, pg. 5649
NISSIN ELECTRIC CO., LTD.—See Sumitomo Electric Industries, Ltd.; *Int'l*, pg. 7278
NISSIN ELECTRIC MYANMAR CO., LTD.—See Sumitomo Electric Industries, Ltd.; *Int'l*, pg. 7279

NISSIN ELECTRIC (THAILAND) CO., LTD—See Sumitomo Electric Industries, Ltd.; *Int'l*, pg. 7279
NISSIN ELECTRIC VIETNAM CO., LTD.—See Sumitomo Electric Industries, Ltd.; *Int'l*, pg. 7279
NISSIN ELECTRIC WUXI CO. LTD—See Sumitomo Electric Industries, Ltd.; *Int'l*, pg. 7279
NISSIN ENTERPRISE CORPORATION—See Nissin Foods Holdings Co., Ltd.; *Int'l*, pg. 5376
NISSIN FOOD PRODUCTS CO., LTD—See Nissin Foods Holdings Co., Ltd.;*Int'l*, pg. 5376
NISSIN FOODS (ASIA) PTE. LTD.—See Nissin Foods Holdings Co., Ltd.; *Int'l*, pg. 5376
NISSIN FOODS CO. LTD.—See Nissin Foods Holdings Co., Ltd.; *Int'l*, pg. 5376
NISSIN FOODS GMBH—See Nissin Foods Holdings Co., Ltd.; *Int'l*, pg. 5377
NISSIN FOODS (HK) MANAGEMENT CO., LTD.—See Nissin Foods Holdings Co., Ltd.; *Int'l*, pg. 5377
NISSIN FOODS HOLDINGS CO., LTD.; *Int'l*, pg. 5376
NISSIN FOODS INDIA LTD.—See Nissin Foods Holdings Co., Ltd.; *Int'l*, pg. 5377
NISSIN FOODS KFT.—See Nissin Foods Holdings Co., Ltd.; *Int'l*, pg. 5377
NISSIN FOODS SINGAPORE PTE. LTD.—See Mitsubishi Corporation; *Int'l*, pg. 4942
NISSIN FOODS (THAILAND) CO., LTD.—See Nissin Foods Holdings Co., Ltd.; *Int'l*, pg. 5376
NISSIN FOODS (U.S.A.) INC.—See Nissin Foods Holdings Co., Ltd.; *Int'l*, pg. 5377
NISSIN FOODS VIETNAM CO., LTD.—See Nissin Foods Holdings Co., Ltd.; *Int'l*, pg. 5377
NISSIN FRANCE S.A.S.—See Nissin Corporation; *Int'l*, pg. 5375
NISSIN FROZEN FOODS CO., LTD—See Nissin Foods Holdings Co., Ltd.; *Int'l*, pg. 5376
NISSIN INTERNATIONAL LOGISTICS (M) SDN. BHD.—See Nissin Corporation; *Int'l*, pg. 5375
NISSIN INTERNATIONAL TRANSPORT USA, INC.—See Nissin Corporation; *Int'l*, pg. 5375
NISSIN ION EQUIPMENT CO., LTD.—See Sumitomo Electric Industries, Ltd.; *Int'l*, pg. 7279
NISSIN ION EQUIPMENT USA, INC.—See Sumitomo Electric Industries, Ltd.; *Int'l*, pg. 7279
NISSIN ION HIGHTECH (YANGZHOU) CO., LTD—See Sumitomo Electric Industries, Ltd.; *Int'l*, pg. 7279
NISSIN ION KOREA CO., LTD.—See Sumitomo Electric Industries, Ltd.; *Int'l*, pg. 7279
NISSIN KOGYO CO., LTD. - NAOETSU PLANT—See Honda Motor Co., Ltd.; *Int'l*, pg. 3463
NISSIN KOGYO CO., LTD.—See Honda Motor Co., Ltd.; *Int'l*, pg. 3463
NISSIN KOGYO CO., LTD. - TOBU PLANT—See Honda Motor Co., Ltd.; *Int'l*, pg. 3463
NISSIN KOIKEYA FOODS (CHINA & HK) CO., LTD.—See Nissin Foods Holdings Co., Ltd.; *Int'l*, pg. 5377
NISSIN KOKI CO., LTD.—See Fair Friend Group; *Int'l*, pg. 2604
NISSIN LOGISTICS POLAND SP. Z O.O.—See Nissin Corporation; *Int'l*, pg. 5375
NISSIN LOGISTICS SHENZHEN CO., LTD.—See Nissin Corporation; *Int'l*, pg. 5375
NISSIN LOGISTICS (VN) CO., LTD.—See Nissin Corporation; *Int'l*, pg. 5375
NISSIN MIDDLE EAST FZE—See Nissin Corporation; *Int'l*, pg. 5375
NISSIN MIDDLE EAST L.L.C.—See Nissin Corporation; *Int'l*, pg. 5375
NISSIN NETCOM CO., LTD.—See Nissin Foods Holdings Co., Ltd.; *Int'l*, pg. 5377
NISSIN PLASTICS CO., LTD.—See Nissin Foods Holdings Co., Ltd.; *Int'l*, pg. 5377
NISSIN PRECISION METAL MANUFACTURING LIMITED—See Highway Holdings Limited; *Int'l*, pg. 3389
NISSIN PULSE ELECTRONICS CO., LTD.—See Sumitomo Electric Industries, Ltd.; *Int'l*, pg. 7279
NISSIN R&D ASIA CO., LTD—See Honda Motor Co., Ltd.; *Int'l*, pg. 3463
NISSIN R&D EUROPE, S.L.U—See Honda Motor Co., Ltd.; *Int'l*, pg. 3463
NISSIN SEIGYO CO., LTD.—See ULVAC, Inc.; *Int'l*, pg. 8020
NISSIN (SHANGHAI) LOGISTICS CO., LTD.—See Nissin Corporation; *Int'l*, pg. 5375
NISSIN SHOJI CO., LTD.; *Int'l*, pg. 5377
NISSIN-SINOTRANS INTERNATIONAL LOGISTICS CO., LTD.—See Nissin Corporation; *Int'l*, pg. 5376
NISSIN SYSTEMS CO., LTD.—See Sumitomo Electric Industries, Ltd.; *Int'l*, pg. 7279
NISSIN TANSPORTATION & WAREHOUSING (H.K.) LTD.—See Nissin Corporation; *Int'l*, pg. 5375
NISSIN TRANSPORTATION & WAREHOUSING (H.K.) LTD.—See Nissin Corporation; *Int'l*, pg. 5376
NISSIN TRANSPORT (CANADA) INC.—See Nissin Corporation; *Int'l*, pg. 5376
NISSIN TRANSPORT (CANADA) INC.—See Nissin Corporation; *Int'l*, pg. 5376
NISSIN TRANSPORTES ESPANA S.A.—See Nissin Corporation; *Int'l*, pg. 5376

NISSIN TRANSPORT GES.MBH—See Nissin Corporation; *Int'l*, pg. 5375
NISSIN TRANSPORT GMBH—See Nissin Corporation; *Int'l*, pg. 5375
NISSIN TRANSPORT PHILIPPINES CORP.—See Nissin Corporation; *Int'l*, pg. 5376
NISSIN TRANSPORT SINGAPORE PTE. LTD.—See Nissin Corporation; *Int'l*, pg. 5376
NISSIN TRANSPORT (S) PTE. LTD.—See Nissin Corporation; *Int'l*, pg. 5375
NISSIN UK LTD.—See Nissin Corporation; *Int'l*, pg. 5376
NISSIN-UNIVERSAL ROBINA CORPORATION—See JG Summit Holdings, Inc.; *Int'l*, pg. 3939
NISSIN-UNIVERSAL ROBINA CORPORATION—See Nissin Foods Holdings Co., Ltd.; *Int'l*, pg. 5377
NISSIN YORK CO., LTD.—See Nissin Foods Holdings Co., Ltd.; *Int'l*, pg. 5377
NISSO AMERICA INC.—See Nippon Soda Co., Ltd.; *Int'l*, pg. 5334
NISSO BASF AGRO CO., LTD.—See BASF SE; *Int'l*, pg. 878
NISSO BASF AGRO CO., LTD.—See Mitsui & Co., Ltd.; *Int'l*, pg. 4979
NISSO BASF AGRO CO., LTD.—See Nippon Soda Co., Ltd.; *Int'l*, pg. 5334
NISSO BRAIN CO., LTD.—See Nisso Corporation; *Int'l*, pg. 5377
NISSO BRASILEIRA REPRESENTA CAO LTDA.—See Nippon Soda Co., Ltd.; *Int'l*, pg. 5334
NISSO CHEMICAL ANALYSIS SERVICE CO., LTD.—See Nippon Soda Co., Ltd.; *Int'l*, pg. 5334
NISSO CHEMICAL EUROPE GMBH—See Nippon Soda Co., Ltd.; *Int'l*, pg. 5334
NISSO CONSTRUCTION CO., LTD.—See Nippon Soda Co., Ltd.; *Int'l*, pg. 5334
NISSO CORPORATION; *Int'l*, pg. 5377
NISSO ENGINEERING CO., LTD.—See Nippon Soda Co., Ltd.; *Int'l*, pg. 5334
NISSO FINE CHEMICALS CO., LTD.—See Nippon Soda Co., Ltd.; *Int'l*, pg. 5334
NISSO GREEN CO., LTD.—See Nippon Soda Co., Ltd.; *Int'l*, pg. 5334
NISSO HOLDINGS CO LTD.—See Nisso Corporation; *Int'l*, pg. 5377
NISSOKEN ARCHITECTS/ENGINEERS INC.—See CTI Engineering Co., Ltd.; *Int'l*, pg. 1871
NISSO KOREA CO., LTD.—See Nippon Soda Co., Ltd.; *Int'l*, pg. 5334
NISSO METALLOCHEMICAL CO., LTD.—See Nippon Soda Co., Ltd.; *Int'l*, pg. 5334
NISSO NIFTY CO., LTD.—See Nisso Corporation; *Int'l*, pg. 5377
NISSO PRONITY CO., LTD.; *Int'l*, pg. 5377
NISSO PURE CO., LTD.—See Nisso Corporation; *Int'l*, pg. 5377
NISSO SHOJI CO., LTD.—See Nippon Soda Co., Ltd.; *Int'l*, pg. 5334
NISSOU CO., LTD.; *Int'l*, pg. 5377
NISSUI CORPORATION; *Int'l*, pg. 5377
NISSUI FOOD SYSTEM CO., LTD.—See Nissui Corporation; *Int'l*, pg. 5378
NISSUI LOGISTICS CORPORATION—See Nissui Corporation; *Int'l*, pg. 5378
NISSUI MARINE INDUSTRIES CO., LTD—See Nissui Corporation; *Int'l*, pg. 5378
NISSUI PHARMACEUTICAL CO. LTD.; *Int'l*, pg. 5379
NISSUI PHARMACEUTICAL CO., LTD. - TSUKUBA PLANT—See Nissui Pharmaceutical Co. Ltd.; *Int'l*, pg. 5379
NISSUI (THAILAND) CO., LTD.—See Nissui Corporation; *Int'l*, pg. 5378
NISSWA MARINE, LLC—See MarineMax, Inc.; *U.S. Public*, pg. 1367
NISTEC DESIGN LTD.—See Nistec Ltd.; *Int'l*, pg. 5379
NISTEC GOLAN LTD.—See Nistec Ltd.; *Int'l*, pg. 5379
NISTEC LTD.; *Int'l*, pg. 5379
NISTEC MERKAZ LTD.—See Nistec Ltd.; *Int'l*, pg. 5379
NISTEC ZAFON LTD.—See Nistec Ltd.; *Int'l*, pg. 5379
N.I STEEL CO., LTD. - BU-SAN DIVISION—See N.I STEEL Co., Ltd.; *Int'l*, pg. 5116
N.I STEEL CO., LTD. - DAE-GU DIVISION—See N.I STEEL Co., Ltd.; *Int'l*, pg. 5116
N.I STEEL CO., LTD. - DANG-JIN DIVISION—See N.I STEEL Co., Ltd.; *Int'l*, pg. 5116
N.I STEEL CO., LTD. - KWANG-YANG DIVISION—See N.I STEEL Co., Ltd.; *Int'l*, pg. 5116
N.I STEEL CO., LTD. - PO-HANG DIVISION—See N.I STEEL Co., Ltd.; *Int'l*, pg. 5116
N.I STEEL CO., LTD.; *Int'l*, pg. 5116
NISTEC PRECISION INC.—See Nitto Denko Corporation; *Int'l*, pg. 5387
NISTERHAMMER MASCHINENBAU GMBH & CO. KG—See INDUS Holding AG; *Int'l*, pg. 3663
NISTRANS INTERNACIONAL DE MEXICO, S. DE R.L. DE C.V.—See Nissin Corporation; *Int'l*, pg. 5376
NISTRANS (M) SDN. BHD.—See Nissin Corporation; *Int'l*, pg. 5376
NISUN INTERNATIONAL ENTERPRISE DEVELOPMENT GROUP CO., LTD.; *Int'l*, pg. 5379

COMPANY NAME INDEX

NI TAIWAN CORPORATION—See National Instruments Corporation; *U.S. Private*, pg. 2857
NITCHITSU CO., LTD.; *Int'l*, pg. 5379
NITCO HOLDING CORPORATION; *U.S. Private*, pg. 2929
NITCO LTD - ALIBAUG PLANT—See Nitco Ltd.; *Int'l*, pg. 5379
NITCO LTD - NITCO MARBLE PLANT—See Nitco Ltd.; *Int'l*, pg. 5379
NITCO LTD.; *Int'l*, pg. 5379
NITEC INDUSTRIES, INC.—See Nissha Co., Ltd.; *Int'l*, pg. 5372
NITEC PRECISION & TECHNOLOGIES, INC.—See Nissha Co., Ltd.; *Int'l*, pg. 5372
N.I. TEIJIN AIRBAG FABRIC (NANTONG) CO., LTD.,—See Teijin Limited; *Int'l*, pg. 7522
N.I. TEIJIN SHOJI (SHANGAI) CO., LTD—See Teijin Limited; *Int'l*, pg. 7522
N.I. TEIJIN SHOJI (USA) INC—See Teijin Limited; *Int'l*, pg. 7522
NITEK, INC.—See Seoul Semiconductor Co., Ltd.; *Int'l*, pg. 6717
NITEK, INC.—See Seoul Semiconductor Co., Ltd.; *Int'l*, pg. 6717
NITEL, INC.; *U.S. Private*, pg. 2929
NITEO PRODUCTS, LLC—See Highlander Partners, LP.; *U.S. Private*, pg. 1939
NITERRA CO., LTD.; *Int'l*, pg. 5379
NITETRAIN COACH CO INC.—See Encore Luxury Coach Leasing LLC; *U.S. Private*, pg. 1391
NITIN ALLOYS GLOBAL LIMITED - SILVASSA WORKS—See Nitin Castings Limited; *Int'l*, pg. 5381
NITIN CASTINGS LIMITED; *Int'l*, pg. 5381
NITIN CYLINDERS LIMITED—See Nitin Fire Protection Industries Ltd; *Int'l*, pg. 5381
NITIN FIRE PROTECTION INDUSTRIES LTD; *Int'l*, pg. 5381
NITIN LIFESCIENCES LTD.—See TA Associates, Inc.; *U.S. Private*, pg. 3918
NITIN SPINNERS LIMITED; *Int'l*, pg. 5381
NITIN VENTURES FZE—See Nitin Fire Protection Industries Ltd; *Int'l*, pg. 5381
NITIRAJ ENGINEERS LTD.; *Int'l*, pg. 5381
NITIRIN METALS CO., LTD.—See Nippon Steel Corporation; *Int'l*, pg. 5336
NITIVY COMPANY LIMITED—See Katakura Industries Co., Ltd.; *Int'l*, pg. 4089
NITODAN A/S—See Nilfisk Holding A/S; *Int'l*, pg. 5295
NITOL INSURANCE COMPANY LIMITED; *Int'l*, pg. 5381
NITOMS INC.—See Nitto Denko Corporation; *Int'l*, pg. 5385
NITORI CHINA CO., LTD.—See Nitori Holdings Co., Ltd.; *Int'l*, pg. 5381
NITORI CO., LTD.—See Nitori Holdings Co., Ltd.; *Int'l*, pg. 5381
NITORI FURNITURE VIETNAM CO., LTD—See Nitori Holdings Co., Ltd.; *Int'l*, pg. 5381
NITORI HOLDINGS CO., LTD.; *Int'l*, pg. 5381
NITORI USA, INC.—See Nitori Holdings Co., Ltd.; *Int'l*, pg. 5381
NITRAM, LLC; *U.S. Private*, pg. 2929
NITRAM METAL FABRICATORS INC.; *U.S. Private*, pg. 2929
NITRATOS DE CHILE SA; *Int'l*, pg. 5381
NITREX METAL INC.—See Novacap Management Inc.; *Int'l*, pg. 5454
NITRIANSKA TEPLARENSKA SPOLOCNOST, A.S.—See Arca Capital Slovakia, A.S.; *Int'l*, pg. 539
NITRIDE SOLUTIONS INC.; *U.S. Private*, pg. 2929
NITRITEX LIMITED—See Ansell Limited; *Int'l*, pg. 478
NITRITEX (M) SDN. BHD.—See Ansell Limited; *Int'l*, pg. 478
NITROAMONIA DE MEXICO S.A DE C.V.—See Orica Limited; *Int'l*, pg. 5619
NITRO CHEMICAL INDUSTRY LTD.; *Int'l*, pg. 5381
NITROCHEMIE AG—See Rheinmetall AG; *Int'l*, pg. 6323
NITROCHEMIE ASCHAU GMBH—See Rheinmetall AG; *Int'l*, pg. 6323
NITROCHEMIE WIMMIS AG—See Rheinmetall AG; *Int'l*, pg. 6323
NITROCISION, LLC—See IHI Corporation; *Int'l*, pg. 3604
NITRO CONSTRUCTION SERVICES, INC.—See Energy Services of America Corporation; *U.S. Public*, pg. 762
NITRO CONSULT AB—See Orica Limited; *Int'l*, pg. 5620
NITRO CONSULT AS—See Orica Limited; *Int'l*, pg. 5619
NITROERG S.A—See KGHM Polska Miedz S.A.; *Int'l*, pg. 4149
NITROGENMUVEK RT.—See MOL Magyar Olaj- es Gazipari Nyrt.; *Int'l*, pg. 5021
NITROGEN - SAN FRANCISCO—See Clayton, Dubilier & Rice, LLC; *U.S. Private*, pg. 925
NITROGEN—See Clayton, Dubilier & Rice, LLC; *U.S. Private*, pg. 925
NITROKEMINE GUINEE SA—See Societe Anonyme d'Explosifs et de Produits Chimiques; *Int'l*, pg. 7035
NITRO LIFT TECHNOLOGIES, LLC—See H.I.G. Capital, LLC; *U.S. Private*, pg. 1834
NITROMAK DNX KIMYA SANAYII A.S.—See Incitec Pivot Limited; *Int'l*, pg. 3648
NITRO MOBILE SOLUTIONS LLC; *U.S. Private*, pg. 2929

NITRO QUIMICA S.A.—See Votorantim S.A.; *Int'l*, pg. 8310
NITRO RIGGING, LLC.; *U.S. Private*, pg. 2929
NITRO SOFTWARE, INC.; *U.S. Private*, pg. 2929
NITRUVID SAS—See Bodycote plc; *Int'l*, pg. 1098
NIT SERVICE CORP.—See NAVER Corporation; *Int'l*, pg. 5174
NITSUKO ELECTRONICS CORPORATION—See Walsin Technology Corporation; *Int'l*, pg. 8335
NITTA AIR SOLUTIONS COMPANY—See Nitta Corporation; *Int'l*, pg. 5382
NITTA ASOCIO COMPANY—See Nitta Corporation; *Int'l*, pg. 5382
NITTA BIOLAB INC.—See Nitta Gelatin Inc.; *Int'l*, pg. 5382
NITTA CHEMICAL INDUSTRIAL PRODUCTS CO., LTD.—See Nitta Corporation; *Int'l*, pg. 5382
NITTA CORPORATION INDIA PVT LTD—See Nitta Corporation; *Int'l*, pg. 5382
NITTA CORPORATION - KOCHI PLANT—See Nitta Corporation; *Int'l*, pg. 5382
NITTA CORPORATION - NABARI PLANT—See Nitta Corporation; *Int'l*, pg. 5382
NITTA CORPORATION - NARA PLANT—See Nitta Corporation; *Int'l*, pg. 5382
NITTA CORPORATION OF AMERICA—See Nitta Corporation; *Int'l*, pg. 5382
NITTA CORPORATION OF CHANGZHOU—See Nitta Corporation; *Int'l*, pg. 5382
NITTA CORPORATION OF HOLLAND B.V.—See Nitta Corporation; *Int'l*, pg. 5382
NITTA CORPORATION OF SINGAPORE PTE. LTD.—See Nitta Corporation; *Int'l*, pg. 5382
NITTA CORPORATION; *Int'l*, pg. 5382
NITTA CORPORATION (THAILAND) LIMITED—See Nitta Corporation; *Int'l*, pg. 5382
NITTA DO BRAZIL—See Nitta Corporation; *Int'l*, pg. 5382
NITTA DUPONT INCORPORATED—See DuPont de Nemours, Inc.; *U.S. Public*, pg. 694
NITTA DUPONT INCORPORATED—See Nitta Corporation; *Int'l*, pg. 5382
NITTA GELATIN CANADA INC.—See Nitta Gelatin Inc.; *Int'l*, pg. 5382
NITTA GELATIN INC. - NARA PLANT—See Nitta Gelatin Inc.; *Int'l*, pg. 5382
NITTA GELATIN INC. - OSAKA PLANT—See Nitta Gelatin Inc.; *Int'l*, pg. 5383
NITTA GELATIN INC.; *Int'l*, pg. 5382
NITTA GELATIN INDIA LIMITED; *Int'l*, pg. 5383
NITTA GELATIN NA INC.—See Nitta Gelatin Inc.; *Int'l*, pg. 5383
NITTA GELATIN USA INC.—See Nitta Gelatin Inc.; *Int'l*, pg. 5383
NITTA INDUSTRIES EUROPE GMBH—See Nitta Corporation; *Int'l*, pg. 5382
NITTA MECHATRONICS (CHANGZHOU) CO., LTD.—See Nitta Corporation; *Int'l*, pg. 5382
NITTA MOORE COMPANY—See Nitta Corporation; *Int'l*, pg. 5382
NITTA MOORE (GUANGZHOU) TUBE CO., LTD.—See Nitta Corporation; *Int'l*, pg. 5382
NITTA MOORE MEXICO S. DE R.L. DE C.V.—See Nitta Corporation; *Int'l*, pg. 5382
NITTA MOORE TECHNOLOGY (CHANGZHOU) CO., LTD.—See Nitta Corporation; *Int'l*, pg. 5382
NITTAN ASEAN CO., LTD.—See SECOM Co., Ltd.; *Int'l*, pg. 6671
NITTAN CAPITAL GROUP CO., LTD.—See Central Tanshi Co., Ltd.; *Int'l*, pg. 1410
NITTAN CO., LTD.—See SECOM Co., Ltd.; *Int'l*, pg. 6671
NITTAN CORPORATION; *Int'l*, pg. 5383
NITTAN DENKO CO., LTD.—See SECOM Co., Ltd.; *Int'l*, pg. 6671
NITTAN EUROPE LIMITED—See SECOM Co., Ltd.; *Int'l*, pg. 6671
NITTAN EURO TECH SP. Z O.O.—See NITTAN Corporation; *Int'l*, pg. 5383
NITTAN GLOBAL TECH CO., LTD.—See NITTAN Corporation; *Int'l*, pg. 5383
NITTAN INDIA TECH PVT. LTD.—See NITTAN Corporation; *Int'l*, pg. 5383
NITTAN KOREA CO., LTD.—See NITTAN Corporation; *Int'l*, pg. 5383
NITTAN (THAILAND) CO., LTD.—See NITTAN Corporation; *Int'l*, pg. 5383
NITTAN VIETNAM CO., LTD.—See NITTAN Corporation; *Int'l*, pg. 5383
NITTANY BUILDING SPECIALITES, INC., FLOORING DIVISION—See Nittany Building Specialties, Inc.; *U.S. Private*, pg. 2929
NITTANY BUILDING SPECIALTIES, INC., GLASS DIVISION—See Nittany Building Specialties, Inc.; *U.S. Private*, pg. 2929
NITTANY BUILDING SPECIALTIES, INC.; *U.S. Private*, pg. 2929
NITTANY OIL COMPANY INC.; *U.S. Private*, pg. 2929
NITTANY PRINTING & PUBLISHING CO.—See Chatham Asset Management, LLC; *U.S. Private*, pg. 866
NITTA RANCH CORPORATION—See Nitta Corporation; *Int'l*, pg. 5382

NITTA (SHANGHAI) MANAGEMENT CO., LTD—See Nitta Corporation; *Int'l*, pg. 5382
NITTA TECHNO COMPANY—See Nitta Corporation; *Int'l*, pg. 5382
NITTA TECHNO SOLUTIONS COMPANY—See Nitta Corporation; *Int'l*, pg. 5382
NITTELESEVEN CO., LTD—See Nippon Television Holdings Inc.; *Int'l*, pg. 5356
NITTEN PHARMACEUTICAL CO., LTD.—See Rohto Pharmaceutical Co. Ltd.; *Int'l*, pg. 6387
NITTERHOUSE CONCRETE PRODUCTS INC.; *U.S. Private*, pg. 2930
NITTETSU CEMENT CO., LTD—See Nippon Steel Corporation; *Int'l*, pg. 5339
NITTETSU HITACHI SYSTEMS ENGINEERING, INC.—See Nippon Steel Corporation; *Int'l*, pg. 5335
NITTETSUKOU DONAN KOHATSU CO., LTD.—See Nittetsu Mining Co., Ltd.; *Int'l*, pg. 5383
NITTETSUKOUKENZAI CO., LTD—See Nittetsu Mining Co., Ltd.; *Int'l*, pg. 5383
NITTETSUKOU (SHANGHAI) CO., LTD.—See Nittetsu Mining Co., Ltd.; *Int'l*, pg. 5383
NITTETSU MINING CO., LTD.; *Int'l*, pg. 5383
NITTETSU MINING CONSULTANTS CO., LTD.—See Nittetsu Mining Co., Ltd.; *Int'l*, pg. 5383
NITTETSU TOKAI STEEL WIRE CO., LTD.—See Nippon Steel Corporation; *Int'l*, pg. 5339
NITTO AIRCRAFT MAINTENANCE CO., LTD.—See Japan Airlines Co., Ltd.; *Int'l*, pg. 3885
NITTO ANALYTICAL TECHNO-CENTER CO., LTD.—See Nitto Denko Corporation; *Int'l*, pg. 5385
NITTO AUTOMOTIVE, INC.—See Nitto Denko Corporation; *Int'l*, pg. 5387
NITTO AVECIA PHARMA SERVICES INC.—See Nitto Denko Corporation; *Int'l*, pg. 5387
NITTO BELGIUM N.V.—See Nitto Denko Corporation; *Int'l*, pg. 5385
NITTO BENTO BANTCILIK SAN. VE TIC. A. S.—See Nitto Denko Corporation; *Int'l*, pg. 5385
NITTOBEST CORPORATION; *Int'l*, pg. 5388
NITTO BEVERAGE CO., LTD.—See NITTO BOSEKI CO., LTD.; *Int'l*, pg. 5384
NITTO BIOPHARMA, INC.—See Nitto Denko Corporation; *Int'l*, pg. 5387
NITTOBO ACOUSTIC ENGINEERING CO., LTD.—See NITTO BOSEKI CO., LTD.; *Int'l*, pg. 5384
NITTOBO AMERICA INC.—See NITTO BOSEKI CO., LTD.; *Int'l*, pg. 5384
NITTOBO (CHINA) CO., LTD.—See NITTO BOSEKI CO., LTD.; *Int'l*, pg. 5384
NITTOBO ECOLOGY CO., LTD.—See NITTO BOSEKI CO., LTD.; *Int'l*, pg. 5384
NITTOBO INTERLINING CO., LTD.—See NITTO BOSEKI CO., LTD.; *Int'l*, pg. 5384
NITTOBO MACAU GLASS WEAVING CO., LTD.—See NITTO BOSEKI CO., LTD.; *Int'l*, pg. 5384
NITTOBO MEDICAL CO., LTD.—See NITTO BOSEKI CO., LTD.; *Int'l*, pg. 5384
NITTO BOSEKI CO., LTD. - BUILDING MATERIALS DIVISION—See NITTO BOSEKI CO., LTD.; *Int'l*, pg. 5384
NITTO BOSEKI CO., LTD. - CHIBA FACTORY—See NITTO BOSEKI CO., LTD.; *Int'l*, pg. 5384
NITTO BOSEKI CO., LTD. - FUKUSHIMA NO.1 FACTORY—See NITTO BOSEKI CO., LTD.; *Int'l*, pg. 5384
NITTO BOSEKI CO., LTD. - FUKUSHIMA NO.2 FACTORY—See NITTO BOSEKI CO., LTD.; *Int'l*, pg. 5384
NITTO BOSEKI CO., LTD. - NEW BUSINESS OPERATION & PROMOTION DIVISION—See NITTO BOSEKI CO., LTD.; *Int'l*, pg. 5384
NITTO BOSEKI CO., LTD.; *Int'l*, pg. 5384
NITTO BOSEKI CO., LTD. - SPECIALTY CHEMICALS DIVISION—See NITTO BOSEKI CO., LTD.; *Int'l*, pg. 5384
NITTO BOSEKI CO., LTD. - TEXTILES DIVISION—See NITTO BOSEKI CO., LTD.; *Int'l*, pg. 5384
NITTOBO TECHNO CO., LTD.—See NITTO BOSEKI CO., LTD.; *Int'l*, pg. 5384
NITTO BUSINESS EXPERT CORPORATION—See Nitto Denko Corporation; *Int'l*, pg. 5385
NITTO BUSINESS SUPPORT CORPORATION—See Nitto Denko Corporation; *Int'l*, pg. 5385
NITTOC CONSTRUCTION CO., LTD.—See Aso Co., Ltd.; *Int'l*, pg. 628
NITTO CHEMICAL CO., LTD.—See Dai Nippon Toryo Co., Ltd.; *Int'l*, pg. 1916
NITTO (CHINA) NEW MATERIALS CO., LTD.—See Nitto Denko Corporation; *Int'l*, pg. 5385
NITTO CO., LTD.—See Meiji Holdings Co., Ltd.; *Int'l*, pg. 4801
NITTO DENKO AMERICA LATINA LTDA.—See Nitto Denko Corporation; *Int'l*, pg. 5385
NITTO DENKO ASIA TECHNICAL CENTRE PTE. LTD.—See Nitto Denko Corporation; *Int'l*, pg. 5385
NITTO DENKO (AUSTRALIA) PTY. LTD.—See Nitto Denko Corporation; *Int'l*, pg. 5385

NITTO BOSEKI CO., LTD.

NITTO DENKO AUTOMOTIVE DE MEXICO S. DE R.L. DE C.V.—See Nitto Denko Corporation; *Int'l*, pg. 5386
NITTO DENKO AUTOMOTIVE DE MEXICO SERVICIOS S. DE R.L. DE C.V.—See Nitto Denko Corporation; *Int'l*, pg. 5386
NITTO DENKO AVECIA INC.—See Nitto Denko Corporation; *Int'l*, pg. 5387
NITTO DENKO (CHINA) INVESTMENT CO., LTD.—See Nitto Denko Corporation; *Int'l*, pg. 5386
NITTO DENKO CORPORATION - IBARAKI PLANT—See Nitto Denko Corporation; *Int'l*, pg. 5386
NITTO DENKO CORPORATION - KAMEYAMA PLANT—See Nitto Denko Corporation; *Int'l*, pg. 5386
NITTO DENKO CORPORATION - KANTO PLANT—See Nitto Denko Corporation; *Int'l*, pg. 5386
NITTO DENKO CORPORATION - ONOMICHI PLANT—See Nitto Denko Corporation; *Int'l*, pg. 5386
NITTO DENKO CORPORATION - SHIGA PLANT—See Nitto Denko Corporation; *Int'l*, pg. 5386
NITTO DENKO CORPORATION; *Int'l*, pg. 5384
NITTO DENKO CORPORATION - TOHOKU PLANT—See Nitto Denko Corporation; *Int'l*, pg. 5386
NITTO DENKO CORPORATION - TOYOHASHI PLANT—See Nitto Denko Corporation; *Int'l*, pg. 5386
NITTO DENKO CS SYSTEM CORPORATION—See Nitto Denko Corporation; *Int'l*, pg. 5386
NITTO DENKO CZECH S.R.O.—See Nitto Denko Corporation; *Int'l*, pg. 5385
NITTO DENKO DE MEXICO S.DE R.L. DE C.V.—See Nitto Denko Corporation; *Int'l*, pg. 5386
NITTO DENKO ELECTRONICS (MALAYSIA) SDN. BHD.—See Nitto Denko Corporation; *Int'l*, pg. 5386
NITTO DENKO FINE CIRCUIT TECHNOLOGY(SHENZHEN) CO., LTD.—See Nitto Denko Corporation; *Int'l*, pg. 5385
NITTO DENKO (FOSHAN) CO., LTD.—See Nitto Denko Corporation; *Int'l*, pg. 5385
NITTO DENKO HIMAWARI CORPORATION—See Nitto Denko Corporation; *Int'l*, pg. 5385
NITTO DENKO (HK) CO. LTD.—See Nitto Denko Corporation; *Int'l*, pg. 5386
NITTO DENKO INDIA PRIVATE LIMITED—See Nitto Denko Corporation; *Int'l*, pg. 5385
NITTO DENKO LTD.—See Nitto Denko Corporation; *Int'l*, pg. 5386
NITTO DENKO MATERIALS (MALAYSIA) SDN. BHD.—See Nitto Denko Corporation; *Int'l*, pg. 5386
NITTO DENKO MATERIALS (SHENZHEN) CO., LTD.—See Nitto Denko Corporation; *Int'l*, pg. 5385
NITTO DENKO MATERIAL (THAILAND) CO., LTD.—See Nitto Denko Corporation; *Int'l*, pg. 5386
NITTO DENKO MEDICAL MFG. CO., LTD.—See Nitto Denko Corporation; *Int'l*, pg. 5386
NITTO DENKO NITOMS KOREA CO., LTD.—See Nitto Denko Corporation; *Int'l*, pg. 5385
NITTO DENKO (PHILIPPINES) CORP.—See Nitto Denko Corporation; *Int'l*, pg. 5386
NITTO DENKO (SHANGHAI) ELECTRO-ENERGY CO., LTD.—See Nitto Denko Corporation; *Int'l*, pg. 5385
NITTO DENKO (SHANGHAI) PHARMACEUTICAL CONSULTING CO., LTD.—See Nitto Denko Corporation; *Int'l*, pg. 5385
NITTO DENKO (SHANGHAI PU DONG NEW AREA) CO., LTD.—See Nitto Denko Corporation; *Int'l*, pg. 5386
NITTO DENKO (SHANGHAI SONGJIANG) CO., LTD.—See Nitto Denko Corporation; *Int'l*, pg. 5386
NITTO DENKO (SINGAPORE) PTE. LTD.—See Nitto Denko Corporation; *Int'l*, pg. 5386
NITTO DENKO (TAIWAN) CORPORATION—See Nitto Denko Corporation; *Int'l*, pg. 5386
NITTO DENKO (TAIWAN) CORP.—See Nitto Denko Corporation; *Int'l*, pg. 5386
NITTO DENKO TAPE MATERIALS (VIETNAM) CO., LTD.—See Nitto Denko Corporation; *Int'l*, pg. 5385
NITTO DENKO TECHNICAL CORPORATION—See Nitto Denko Corporation; *Int'l*, pg. 5387
NITTO DENKO (TIANJIN) CO., LTD.—See Nitto Denko Corporation; *Int'l*, pg. 5386
NITTO DENKO (TIANJIN) INTERNATIONAL TRADE CO., LTD.—See Nitto Denko Corporation; *Int'l*, pg. 5385
NITTO DENKO TURKEY TAPE MATERIALS INDUSTRY AND TRADE LIMITED—See Nitto Denko Corporation; *Int'l*, pg. 5386
NITTO DENKO UK LTD.—See Nitto Denko Corporation; *Int'l*, pg. 5386
NITTO DENKO VIETNAM CO., LTD.—See Nitto Denko Corporation; *Int'l*, pg. 5386
NITTO DENKO (XIAMEN) CO., LTD.—See Nitto Denko Corporation; *Int'l*, pg. 5386
NITTO DEUTSCHLAND GMBH—See Nitto Denko Corporation; *Int'l*, pg. 5386
NITTO ELECTRONICS KYUSYU CORPORATION—See Nitto Denko Corporation; *Int'l*, pg. 5385
NITTO EMEA N.V.—See Nitto Denko Corporation; *Int'l*, pg. 5386
NITTO ENGINEERING CO., LTD.—See Dai Nippon Toryo Co., Ltd.; *Int'l*, pg. 1916
NITTO EUROPE N.V.—See Nitto Denko Corporation; *Int'l*, pg. 5386

NITTO FC CO., LTD.—See Integral Corporation; *Int'l*, pg. 3730
NITTO FRANCE S.A.R.L.—See Nitto Denko Corporation; *Int'l*, pg. 5386
NITTO FUDOHSAN CO., LTD.—See Dai Nippon Toryo Co., Ltd.; *Int'l*, pg. 1916
NITTO-FUJI FLOUR MILLING CO., LTD.—See Mitsubishi Corporation; *Int'l*, pg. 4942
NITTO-FUJI INTERNATIONAL VIETNAM CO., LTD.—See Mitsubishi Corporation; *Int'l*, pg. 4942
NITTO HIMAWARI KAMEYAMA CORPORATION—See Nitto Denko Corporation; *Int'l*, pg. 5386
NITTO HIMAWARI ONOMICHI CORPORATION—See Nitto Denko Corporation; *Int'l*, pg. 5386
NITTOH INDUSTRY (H.K.) CO., LTD.—See NOK Corporation; *Int'l*, pg. 5402
NITTO, INC. - NOVI PLANT—See Nitto Denko Corporation; *Int'l*, pg. 5387
NITTO, INC.—See Nitto Denko Corporation; *Int'l*, pg. 5387
NITTO INNOVATIONS, INC.—See Nitto Denko Corporation; *Int'l*, pg. 5387
NITTO ITALIA S.R.L.—See Nitto Denko Corporation; *Int'l*, pg. 5386
NITTO JAPAN CO., LTD.—See Toyo Tire Corporation; *Int'l*, pg. 7859
NITTO KAKO CO., LTD.; *Int'l*, pg. 5387
NITTO KASEI KOGYO K.K.—See New Japan Chemical Co., Ltd.; *Int'l*, pg. 5225
NITTO KOGYO BM (THAILAND) CO., LTD.—See NITTO KOGYO CORPORATION; *Int'l*, pg. 5387
NITTO KOGYO (CHINA) CORPORATION—See NITTO KOGYO CORPORATION; *Int'l*, pg. 5387
NITTO KOGYO CORPORATION; *Int'l*, pg. 5387
NITTO KOHKI AUSTRALIA MFG PTY LTD—See NITTO KOHKI Co., Ltd.; *Int'l*, pg. 5388
NITTO KOHKI AUSTRALIA PTY LTD—See NITTO KOHKI Co., Ltd.; *Int'l*, pg. 5388
NITTO KOHKI CO., LTD.; *Int'l*, pg. 5387
NITTO KOHKI COUPLING (THAILAND) CO., LTD.—See NITTO KOHKI Co., Ltd.; *Int'l*, pg. 5388
NITTO KOHKI DEUTSCHLAND GMBH—See NITTO KOHKI Co., Ltd.; *Int'l*, pg. 5388
NITTO KOHKI EUROPE CO., LTD.—See NITTO KOHKI Co., Ltd.; *Int'l*, pg. 5388
NITTO KOHKI INDUSTRY (THAILAND) CO., LTD.—See NITTO KOHKI Co., Ltd.; *Int'l*, pg. 5388
NITTO KOHKI (SHANGHAI) CO., LTD.—See NITTO KOHKI Co., Ltd.; *Int'l*, pg. 5388
NITTO KOHKI (THAILAND) CO., LTD.—See NITTO KOHKI Co., Ltd.; *Int'l*, pg. 5388
NITTO KOHKI USA, INC. - CUPLA DIVISION—See NITTO KOHKI Co., Ltd.; *Int'l*, pg. 5388
NITTO KOHKI USA, INC.—See NITTO KOHKI Co., Ltd.; *Int'l*, pg. 5388
NITTOKU ALPHA SERVICE CO., LTD.—See Niterra Co., Ltd.; *Int'l*, pg. 5381
NITTOKU AMERICA INC.—See Nittoku Co., Ltd.; *Int'l*, pg. 5389
NITTOKU CO., LTD.; *Int'l*, pg. 5389
NITTOKU CO., LTD.—See Nittoku Co., Ltd.; *Int'l*, pg. 5389
NITTOKU ENGINEERING CO., LTD. - IINO FACTORY—See Nittoku Co., Ltd.; *Int'l*, pg. 5389
NITTOKU ENGINEERING CO., LTD. - NAGASAKI FACTORY—See Nittoku Co., Ltd.; *Int'l*, pg. 5389
NITTOKU ENGINEERING CO., LTD.—See Nittoku Co., Ltd.; *Int'l*, pg. 5389
NITTOKU ENGINEERING CO., LTD.—See Nittoku Co., Ltd.; *Int'l*, pg. 5389
NITTOKU EUROPE GMBH—See Nittoku Co., Ltd.; *Int'l*, pg. 5389
NITTOKU HONG KONG LTD.—See Nittoku Co., Ltd.; *Int'l*, pg. 5389
NITTOKU KOIDE CO., LTD.—See Nittoku Co., Ltd.; *Int'l*, pg. 5389
NITTOKU KOSEI CO., LTD.—See Nittoku Co., Ltd.; *Int'l*, pg. 5389
NITTOKU PRECISION(M) SDN. BHD.—See Nittoku Co., Ltd.; *Int'l*, pg. 5389
NITTOKU SEISAKUSHO CO., LTD.—See Niterra Co., Ltd.; *Int'l*, pg. 5381
NITTOKU SINGAPORE PTE. LTD.—See Nittoku Co., Ltd.; *Int'l*, pg. 5381
NITTOKU SMILE CO., LTD.—See Niterra Co., Ltd.; *Int'l*, pg. 5381
NITTOKU (THAILAND) CO., LTD.—See Nittoku Co., Ltd.; *Int'l*, pg. 5389
NITTOKU UNYU CO., LTD.—See Niterra Co., Ltd.; *Int'l*, pg. 5381
NITTO LIFETEC CORPORATION—See Nitto Denko Corporation; *Int'l*, pg. 5385
NITTO L MATERIALS CORPORATION—See Nitto Denko Corporation; *Int'l*, pg. 5386
NITTO LOGI-COM CORPORATION—See Nitto Denko Corporation; *Int'l*, pg. 5386
NITTO MATERIAL TECHNOLOGY (CHENGDU) CO., LTD.—See Nitto Denko Corporation; *Int'l*, pg. 5387
NITTO MATEX (SHENZEN) CO., LTD.—See Nitto Denko Corporation; *Int'l*, pg. 5387

CORPORATE AFFILIATIONS

NITTO MATEX (THAILAND) CO., LTD.—See Nitto Denko Corporation; *Int'l*, pg. 5385
NITTO MEDICAL CORPORATION—See Nitto Denko Corporation; *Int'l*, pg. 5385
NITTO NET CO., LTD. - DOUTO FACTORY—See Nitto Seimo Co., Ltd.; *Int'l*, pg. 5388
NITTO NET CO., LTD. - HAKODATE FACTORY—See Nitto Seimo Co., Ltd.; *Int'l*, pg. 5388
NITTO NET CO., LTD.—See Nitto Seimo Co., Ltd.; *Int'l*, pg. 5388
NITTO OTOMOTIV SAN. VE TIC. LTD. STI.—See Nitto Denko Corporation; *Int'l*, pg. 5387
NITTO POLSKA SP. Z O.O.—See Nitto Denko Corporation; *Int'l*, pg. 5386
NITTO PRECISION SCREW INDUSTRIAL (ZHEJIANG) CO., LTD.—See Nitto Seiko Co., Ltd.; *Int'l*, pg. 5388
NITTO (QINGDAO)TECHNOLOGY RESEARCH INSTITUTE, CO., LTD.—See Nitto Denko Corporation; *Int'l*, pg. 5385
NITTO RUS LLC—See Nitto Denko Corporation; *Int'l*, pg. 5387
NITTO SANWA TORYO CO., LTD.—See Dai Nippon Toryo Co., Ltd.; *Int'l*, pg. 1916
NITTO SCANDINAVIA AB—See Nitto Denko Corporation; *Int'l*, pg. 5386
NITTO SEIKI CO., LTD.—See Nitto Denko Corporation; *Int'l*, pg. 5385
NITTO SEIKO AMERICA CORPORATION—See Nitto Seiko Co., Ltd.; *Int'l*, pg. 5388
NITTOSEIKO ANALYTECH CO., LTD.—See Nitto Seiko Co., Ltd.; *Int'l*, pg. 5388
NITTO SEIKO CO., LTD. - CONTROL SYSTEM DIVISION—See Nitto Seiko Co., Ltd.; *Int'l*, pg. 5388
NITTO SEIKO CO., LTD. - SHIROYAMA PLANT—See Nitto Seiko Co., Ltd.; *Int'l*, pg. 5388
NITTO SEIKO CO., LTD.; *Int'l*, pg. 5388
NITTO SEIKO CO., LTD. - YATA PLANT—See Nitto Seiko Co., Ltd.; *Int'l*, pg. 5388
NITTO SEIKO (THAILAND) CO., LTD.—See Nitto Seiko Co., Ltd.; *Int'l*, pg. 5388
NITTO SEIMO CO., LTD. - FUKUYAMA FACTORY—See Nitto Seimo Co., Ltd.; *Int'l*, pg. 5388
NITTO SEIMO CO., LTD.; *Int'l*, pg. 5388
NITTO SERVICE CO., LTD.—See Dai Nippon Toryo Co., Ltd.; *Int'l*, pg. 1916
NITTOSHA CO., LTD.—See Sumitomo Metal Mining Co., Ltd.; *Int'l*, pg. 7291
NITTO SHIKI KOGYO CO., LTD.—See Rengo Co., Ltd.; *Int'l*, pg. 6280
NITTO SHINKO CORPORATION—See Nitto Denko Corporation; *Int'l*, pg. 5385
NITTO SHINKO (SUZHOU) CO., LTD.—See Nitto Denko Corporation; *Int'l*, pg. 5387
NITTO SWITZERLAND AG—See Nitto Denko Corporation; *Int'l*, pg. 5387
NITTO TIRE CANADA INC.—See Toyo Tire Corporation; *Int'l*, pg. 7859
NITTO TIRE U.S.A INC—See Toyo Tire Corporation; *Int'l*, pg. 7859
NITTO TOTAL LOGISTICS LTD.—See Kawasaki Kisen Kaisha, Ltd.; *Int'l*, pg. 4100
NITTO TUGBOAT CO., LTD.—See Kawasaki Kisen Kaisha, Ltd.; *Int'l*, pg. 4100
NITTO U.K. LIMITED—See Nitto Denko Corporation; *Int'l*, pg. 5386
NITTO VIETNAM CO., LTD.—See Nitto Denko Corporation; *Int'l*, pg. 5387
NITTSU DRIVING SCHOOL CO., LTD.—See Nippon Express Holdings, Inc.; *Int'l*, pg. 5317
NITTSU LOGISTICS (INDIA) PRIVATE LIMITED—See Nippon Express Holdings, Inc.; *Int'l*, pg. 5317
NITTSU LOGISTICS MYANMAR CO., LTD.—See Nippon Express Holdings, Inc.; *Int'l*, pg. 5317
NITTSU LOGISTICS (THAILAND) CO., LTD.—See Nippon Express Holdings, Inc.; *Int'l*, pg. 5317
NITTSU REAL ESTATE CO., LTD.—See Nippon Express Holdings, Inc.; *Int'l*, pg. 5317
NITTSU RESEARCH INSTITUTE AND CONSULTING,LNC.—See Nippon Express Holdings, Inc.; *Int'l*, pg. 5317
NITTSU SAPPORO UNYU CO., LTD.—See Nippon Express Holdings, Inc.; *Int'l*, pg. 5317
NITTSU SHOJI CO., LTD.—See Nippon Express Holdings, Inc.; *Int'l*, pg. 5317
NITTSU SINOTRANS LOGISTIC DALIAN LTD.—See Nippon Express Holdings, Inc.; *Int'l*, pg. 5315
NITTSU TRANSPORT SERVICE (M) SDN. BHD.—See Nippon Express Holdings, Inc.; *Int'l*, pg. 5316
NITYO INFOTECH CORPORATION; *U.S. Private*, pg. 2930
NITYO INFOTECH INC.—See Nityo Infotech Corporation; *U.S. Private*, pg. 2930
NITYO INFOTECH LIMITED—See Nityo Infotech Corporation; *U.S. Private*, pg. 2930
NITYO INFOTECH SERVICES PTE LTD.—See Nityo Infotech Corporation; *U.S. Private*, pg. 2930
NITYO INFOTECH SERVICES PVT. LTD.—See Nityo Infotech Corporation; *U.S. Private*, pg. 2930

COMPANY NAME INDEX

NITYO INFOTECH SERVICES SDN BHD—See Nityo Infotech Corporation; *U.S. Private*, pg. 2930
NITYO INFOTECH (THAILAND) LTD—See Nityo Infotech Corporation; *U.S. Private*, pg. 2930
NIUIF, OJSC—See PJSC PhosAgro; *Int'l*, pg. 5883
NIUMINCO GROUP LIMITED; *Int'l*, pg. 5389
NIUMINCO PTY LTD—See Niuminco Group Limited; *Int'l*, pg. 5389
NIUM PTE. LTD.; *Int'l*, pg. 5389
NIUTECH ENVIRONMENT TECHNOLOGY CORPORATION; *Int'l*, pg. 5389
NIU TECHNOLOGIES; *Int'l*, pg. 5389
NIVA AD NOVI SAD; *Int'l*, pg. 5389
NIVAKA FASHIONS LIMITED; *Int'l*, pg. 5389
NIVAROX-FAR S.A.—See The Swatch Group Ltd.; *Int'l*, pg. 7692
NIVEA BEIERSDORF TURKEY KOZMETIK SANAYI VE TICARET A.S.—See maxingvest ag; *Int'l*, pg. 4740
NIVEA INDIA PVT. LTD.—See maxingvest ag; *Int'l*, pg. 4740
NIVEA-KAO CO. LTD.—See Kao Corporation; *Int'l*, pg. 4075
NIVEA-KAO CO. LTD.—See maxingvest ag; *Int'l*, pg. 4740
NIVEA POLSKA S.A.—See maxingvest ag; *Int'l*, pg. 4740
NIVEA (SHANGHAI) COMPANY LIMITED—See maxingvest ag; *Int'l*, pg. 4740
NIVEA (TAIWAN) LTD.—See maxingvest ag; *Int'l*, pg. 4740
NIVEL HOLDINGS, LLC—See Morgan Stanley; *U.S. Public*, pg. 1474
NIVEL PARTS & MANUFACTURING COMPANY, LLC—See Morgan Stanley; *U.S. Public*, pg. 1474
NIVEN FAMILY WINE ESTATES; *U.S. Private*, pg. 2930
NIVEUS INVESTMENTS LIMITED; *Int'l*, pg. 5389
NIVIKA FASTIGHETER AB; *Int'l*, pg. 5389
NIVIS LLC; *U.S. Private*, pg. 2930
NIVI TRADING LIMITED; *Int'l*, pg. 5389
NIVS INTELLIMEDIA TECHNOLOGY GROUP, INC.; *Int'l*, pg. 5389
NIVUS AG—See NIVUS GmbH; *Int'l*, pg. 5389
NIVUS AUSTRIA—See NIVUS GmbH; *Int'l*, pg. 5389
NIVUS FRANCE—See NIVUS GmbH; *Int'l*, pg. 5389
NIVUS GMBH; *Int'l*, pg. 5389
NIVUS KOREA CO. LTD.—See NIVUS GmbH; *Int'l*, pg. 5389
NIVUS MIDDLE EAST—See NIVUS GmbH; *Int'l*, pg. 5389
NIVUS SP. Z O.O.—See NIVUS GmbH; *Int'l*, pg. 5390
NIVUS U.K. LTD.—See NIVUS GmbH; *Int'l*, pg. 5390
NIV VERONA S.P.A.—See Sacmi Imola S.C.A.R.L.; *Int'l*, pg. 6464
NIWAS SPINNING MILLS LIMITED; *Int'l*, pg. 5390
NIWA SUSHI PTE. LTD.—See Neo Group Limited; *Int'l*, pg. 5196
NI WELDING CORPORATION—See Kobe Steel, Ltd.; *Int'l*, pg. 4221
NI WELDING SUPPLY, L.L.C.; *U.S. Private*, pg. 2924
NIXIL PTY. LTD.—See Axxiome AG; *Int'l*, pg. 773
NIX, INC.; *U.S. Private*, pg. 5390
NIX OF AMERICA—See NIX, Inc.; *Int'l*, pg. 5390
NIXON CLEANING COMPANY LIMITED—See Sun Hung Kai Properties Limited; *Int'l*, pg. 7304
NIXON & COMPANY—See TorQuest Partners Inc.; *Int'l*, pg. 7830
NIXON-EGLI EQUIPMENT CO.; *U.S. Private*, pg. 2930
NIXON ENERGY SOLUTIONS—See Geneva Corporation; *U.S. Private*, pg. 1670
NIXON EUROPE S.A.R.L.—See Trilantic Capital Management L.P.; *U.S. Private*, pg. 4231
NIXON, INC.—See Trilantic Capital Management L.P.; *U.S. Private*, pg. 4231
NIXON PEABODY LLP; *U.S. Private*, pg. 2930
NIXON POWER SERVICES COMPANY—See Geneva Corporation; *U.S. Private*, pg. 1670
NIXON STATE BANK; *U.S. Private*, pg. 2930
NIXON UNIFORM SERVICE INC.; *U.S. Private*, pg. 2930
NIXSOL INC.; *U.S. Private*, pg. 2930
NIXU CORPORATION—See DNV GL Group AS; *Int'l*, pg. 2151
NIYOGIN FINTECH LIMITED; *Int'l*, pg. 5390
NIZEROLLES S.A.—See Groupe Bruxelles Lambert SA; *Int'l*, pg. 3100
NIZET ENTREPRISE SA—See Ackermans & van Haaren NV; *Int'l*, pg. 105
NIZHEX SCANDINAVIA LTD OY—See PSC TAIF; *Int'l*, pg. 6016
NIZHNEKAMSKNEFTEKHIM OAO—See PSC TAIF; *Int'l*, pg. 6016
NIZHNEKAMSKSHINA PJSC; *Int'l*, pg. 5390
NIZHNEVARTOVSKBURNEFT, CJSC—See Weatherford International plc; *U.S. Public*, pg. 2339
NIZHNEVARTOVSKREMSERVIS CJSC—See HMS Hydraulic Machines & Systems Group plc; *Int'l*, pg. 3432
NJBIZ—See Journal Publications, Inc.; *U.S. Private*, pg. 2238
NJC EUROPE LTD.—See New Japan Chemical Co., Ltd.; *Int'l*, pg. 5225
NJC KOREA CO., LTD.—See New Japan Chemical Co., Ltd.; *Int'l*, pg. 5225
N.J. CONSTRUCTION PTY LTD—See Quanta Services, Inc.; *U.S. Public*, pg. 1752

NJ CORPORATION—See Kuwayama Corporation; *Int'l*, pg. 4348
NJD SPECIALTY RETAIL, INC.; *U.S. Private*, pg. 2930
NJEVITY, INC.; *U.S. Private*, pg. 2930
N.J. FROMENT & CO. LIMITED—See Emerson Electric Co.; *U.S. Public*, pg. 750
NJ HOLDINGS INC.; *Int'l*, pg. 5390
NJK CORPORATION—See Nippon Telegraph & Telephone Corporation; *Int'l*, pg. 5346
NJK STAFF SERVICE CO., LTD.—See NIPPON KANZAI Holdings Co.,Ltd.; *Int'l*, pg. 5319
NJ LENDERS CORP.; *U.S. Private*, pg. 2930
N.J. MALIN & ASSOCIATES, LP; *U.S. Private*, pg. 2828
NJ MANUFACTURING INDUSTRIES SDN. BHD.—See New Hoong Fatt Holdings Berhad; *Int'l*, pg. 5224
NJM BANK FSB—See New Jersey Manufacturers Insurance Company; *U.S. Private*, pg. 2898
NJM-CLI PACKAGING SYSTEMS INTERNATIONAL; *U.S. Private*, pg. 2931
NJM PACKAGING—See Leonard Green & Partners, L.P.; *U.S. Private*, pg. 2428
NJM PACKAGING—See Leonard Green & Partners, L.P.; *U.S. Private*, pg. 2428
N. JONAS & COMPANY, INC.; *U.S. Private*, pg. 2827
NJOY ELECTRONIC CIGARETTE; *U.S. Private*, pg. 2931
NJR CAPITAL SERVICES CORPORATION—See New Jersey Resources Corporation; *U.S. Public*, pg. 1511
NJR CLEAN ENERGY VENTURES—See New Jersey Resources Corporation; *U.S. Public*, pg. 1512
NJR ENERGY CORP—See New Jersey Resources Corporation; *U.S. Public*, pg. 1512
NJR ENERGY HOLDINGS CORPORATION—See New Jersey Resources Corporation; *U.S. Public*, pg. 1512
NJR ENERGY SERVICES COMPANY—See New Jersey Resources Corporation; *U.S. Public*, pg. 1512
NJR FUKUOKA CO. LTD.—See Nisshinbo Holdings Inc.; *Int'l*, pg. 5373
NJR HOME SERVICES COMPANY—See New Jersey Resources Corporation; *U.S. Public*, pg. 1512
NJR RETAIL HOLDINGS CORPORATION—See New Jersey Resources Corporation; *U.S. Public*, pg. 1512
NJR SERVICE CORPORATION—See New Jersey Resources Corporation; *U.S. Public*, pg. 1512
NJR SHANGHAI CO., LTD.—See Nisshinbo Holdings Inc.; *Int'l*, pg. 5373
NJR (SINGAPORE) PTE LTD.—See Nisshinbo Holdings Inc.; *Int'l*, pg. 5373
NJR TRADING CO. LTD.—See Nisshinbo Holdings Inc.; *Int'l*, pg. 5373
NJS CO., LTD.; *Int'l*, pg. 5390
NJS CONSULTANTS CO., LTD.—See NJS Co., Ltd.; *Int'l*, pg. 5390
NJS E&M CO., LTD.—See NJS Co., Ltd.; *Int'l*, pg. 5390
NJS ENGINEERS INDIA PVT. LTD.—See NJS Co., Ltd.; *Int'l*, pg. 5390
NJ SHARING NETWORK; *U.S. Private*, pg. 2930
NJ TRANSIT CORPORATION; *U.S. Private*, pg. 2930
NJ TRANSIT MERCER, INC.—See NJ Transit Corporation; *U.S. Private*, pg. 2930
NK AGRI CO., LTD.—See Noritsu Koki Co., Ltd.; *Int'l*, pg. 5429
NKARTA, INC.; *U.S. Public*, pg. 1530
NK ASPHALT PARTNERS—See HF Sinclair Corporation; *U.S. Public*, pg. 1034
NK BANK JSC; *Int'l*, pg. 5390
NKB INC.; *Int'l*, pg. 5390
NKC BOCA RATON, LLC—See Fresenius Medical Care AG; *Int'l*, pg. 2776
NK CO., LTD.; *Int'l*, pg. 5390
NK-EAST OY—See Rettig Group Ltd.; *Int'l*, pg. 6310
NK ENGINEERING CO., LTD.—See Endress+Hauser (International) Holding AG; *Int'l*, pg. 2408
NKFE INSURANCE AGENCY COMPANY LIMITED—See Assicurazioni Generali S.p.A.; *Int'l*, pg. 647
NKGEN BIOTECH, INC.—See NKMAX Co., Ltd.; *Int'l*, pg. 5390
NK GLOBAL CO., LTD.—See Shoko Co., Ltd.; *Int'l*, pg. 6858
NKHP AO; *Int'l*, pg. 5390
N.K. HURST CO., INC.; *U.S. Private*, pg. 2828
NKI GROUP B.V.—See SBM Offshore N.V.; *Int'l*, pg. 6607
N.K.INDUSTRIES LTD.; *Int'l*, pg. 5116
N.K. INDUSTRIES LTD.; *Int'l*, pg. 5116
NKK CO., LTD.—See SNT Corporation; *Int'l*, pg. 7029
NKK IMPORT & EXPORT TRADING PTE. LTD.—See Neo Group Limited; *Int'l*, pg. 5196
NKK-STEEL ENGINEERING, INC.—See JFE Holdings, Inc.; *Int'l*, pg. 3935
NKK SWITCHES CHINA CO., LTD.—See NKK Switches Co., Ltd.; *Int'l*, pg. 5390
NKK SWITCHES CO., LTD.; *Int'l*, pg. 5390
NKK SWITCHES HONG KONG CO., LTD.—See NKK Switches Co., Ltd.; *Int'l*, pg. 5390
NKK SWITCHES—See NKK Switches Co., Ltd.; *Int'l*, pg. 5390
NKMAX AMERICA, INC.—See NKMAX Co., Ltd.; *Int'l*, pg. 5391
NKMAX CO., LTD.; *Int'l*, pg. 5390

NK MECHATRONICS CO., LTD.—See NIPPO LTD; *Int'l*, pg. 5310
NK MEDICO CO., LTD.—See Noritsu Koki Co., Ltd.; *Int'l*, pg. 5429
NKMIP CELLARS INC.—See Ontario Teachers' Pension Plan; *Int'l*, pg. 5587
N KOLAY ODEME KURULU U A.S.—See Aktif Yatirim Bankasi A.S.; *Int'l*, pg. 267
NK POWER SOLA CO., LTD.—See Gunkul Engineering Co., Ltd.; *Int'l*, pg. 3183
NKP POWER SOLAR CO., LTD.—See Gunkul Engineering Co., Ltd.; *Int'l*, pg. 3184
NKR CONTINENTAL PTE. LTD.—See Yoshimura Food Holdings K.K.; *Int'l*, pg. 8600
NK RELATIONS CO., LTD.—See Noritsu Koki Co., Ltd.; *Int'l*, pg. 5429
NKS BANGKOK CO., LTD.—See Nihon Kohden Corporation; *Int'l*, pg. 5285
NKS CO., LTD.—See Nippon Light Metal Holdings Company, Ltd.; *Int'l*, pg. 5323
N.K.S. DISTRIBUTORS, INC.; *U.S. Private*, pg. 2828
N.K. SHACOLAS (HOLDINGS) LTD.; *Int'l*, pg. 5116
NKS HOLDING CO., LTD.—See Konoike Transport Co., Ltd.; *Int'l*, pg. 4275
N&K SPEDITION SPAIN S.L.—See DFDS A/S; *Int'l*, pg. 2095
NKT AS—See NKT A/S; *Int'l*, pg. 5391
NKT A/S; *Int'l*, pg. 5391
NKT CABLE ITALIA S.R.L.—See NKT A/S; *Int'l*, pg. 5391
NKT CABLES AB—See NKT A/S; *Int'l*, pg. 5391
NKT CABLES A/S—See NKT A/S; *Int'l*, pg. 5391
NKT CABLES AS—See NKT A/S; *Int'l*, pg. 5391
NKT CABLES GROUP GMBH—See NKT A/S; *Int'l*, pg. 5391
NKT CABLES LTD., CHANGZHOU—See NKT A/S; *Int'l*, pg. 5391
NKT CABLES LTD.—See NKT A/S; *Int'l*, pg. 5391
NKT CABLES S.A.—See NKT A/S; *Int'l*, pg. 5391
NKT CABLES SPAIN S.L.—See NKT A/S; *Int'l*, pg. 5391
NKT CABLES S.R.O.—See NKT A/S; *Int'l*, pg. 5391
NKT DRIVING SCHOOL LIMITED—See The Cross-Harbour (Holdings) Limited; *Int'l*, pg. 7636
NKTECH CO., LTD.—See NK Co., Ltd.; *Int'l*, pg. 5390
NKTELCO, INC.—See Schurz Communications, Inc.; *U.S. Private*, pg. 3571
NKT GMBH & CO. KG—See NKT A/S; *Int'l*, pg. 5391
NKT GMBH—See NKT A/S; *Int'l*, pg. 5391
NKT HV CABLES AB—See NKT A/S; *Int'l*, pg. 5391
NKT (IBERICA) S.L.—See NKT A/S; *Int'l*, pg. 5391
NKT OPERATIONS INDIA PRIVATE LIMITED—See NKT A/S; *Int'l*, pg. 5391
NKT PHOTONICS A/S—See Hamamatsu Photonics K.K.; *Int'l*, pg. 3235
NKT PHOTONICS GMBH—See NKT A/S; *Int'l*, pg. 5391
NKT PHOTONICS INC.—See NKT A/S; *Int'l*, pg. 5391
NKT PHOTONICS LTD.—See NKT A/S; *Int'l*, pg. 5391
NKT PHOTONICS SWITZERLAND GMBH—See NKT A/S; *Int'l*, pg. 5391
NKT PHOTONICS (ZHENZHEN) CO., LTD.—See NKT A/S; *Int'l*, pg. 5391
NKT PTY LTD—See NKT A/S; *Int'l*, pg. 5391
NK TRANS INC.—See Nichirei Corporation; *Int'l*, pg. 5270
NKT ROAD AND TOLL PVT. LTD.—See IRB Infrastructure Developers Ltd.; *Int'l*, pg. 3805
NKT (U.K.) LTD.—See NKT A/S; *Int'l*, pg. 5391
NKUS LAB INC.—See Nihon Kohden Corporation; *Int'l*, pg. 5285
NK WORKS CO., LTD.: - DOMESTIC SALES DIVISION—See Noritsu Koki Co., Ltd.; *Int'l*, pg. 5429
NK WORKS CO., LTD.—See Noritsu Koki Co., Ltd.; *Int'l*, pg. 5429
NLASCO NATIONAL LLOYDS, INC.—See Align Financial Group, LLC; *U.S. Private*, pg. 168
NLAYER COMMUNICATIONS, INC.—See GTT Communications, Inc.; *U.S. Private*, pg. 1808
NLB BANKA A.D., BANJA LUKA—See Nova Ljubljanska banka d.d.; *Int'l*, pg. 5451
NLB BANKA A.D., BELGRADE—See Nova Ljubljanska banka d.d.; *Int'l*, pg. 5451
NLB BANKA A.D., PODGORICA—See Nova Ljubljanska banka d.d.; *Int'l*, pg. 5451
NLB BANKA A.D., SKOPJE—See Nova Ljubljanska banka d.d.; *Int'l*, pg. 5451
NLB BANKA D.D., SARAJEVO—See Nova Ljubljanska banka d.d.; *Int'l*, pg. 5451
NLB BANKA SH.A., PRISHTINA—See Nova Ljubljanska banka d.d.; *Int'l*, pg. 5451
NLB CORPORATION INC.—See Interpump Group S.p.A.; *Int'l*, pg. 3756
NLB CORP.—See Interpump Group S.p.A.; *Int'l*, pg. 3756
NLB KOMERCIJALNA BANKA AD—See Nova Ljubljanska banka d.d.; *Int'l*, pg. 5451
NLB NOV PENZISKI FOND A.D.—See Nova Ljubljanska banka d.d.; *Int'l*, pg. 5451
NLB POLAND CORP. SP. Z.O.O.—See Interpump Group S.p.A.; *Int'l*, pg. 3756
NL BRANDBEVEILIGING B.V.—See London Security PLC; *Int'l*, pg. 4547

NLB SRBIJA D.O.O., BELGRADE—See Nova Ljubljanska banka d.d.; *Int'l*, pg. 5451
NLC INDIA LIMITED; *Int'l*, pg. 5391
NL COLD CHAIN NETWORK (M) SDN. BHD.—See Nichirei Corporation; *Int'l*, pg. 5269
NLC PROCESS & WATER SERVICES SARL—See Ecolab Inc.; *U.S. Public*, pg. 715
NLC TAMILNADU POWER LIMITED—See NLC India Limited; *Int'l*, pg. 5391
NL ENTERPRISES LLC—See Mid America Pet Food LLC.; *U.S. Private*, pg. 2705
NL ENVIRONMENTAL MANAGEMENT SERVICES, INC.—See Contran Corporation; *U.S. Private*, pg. 1033
NLETS, INC.; *U.S. Private*, pg. 2931
N. LEVENTERIS S.A. - HIGH CARBON STEEL WIRE UNIT—See N. LEVENTERIS S.A.; *Int'l*, pg. 5115
N. LEVENTERIS S.A.; *Int'l*, pg. 5115
NL FILM—See LOV Group Invest SAS; *Int'l*, pg. 4564
NLIGHT, INC.; *U.S. Public*, pg. 1530
NLI INSURANCE AGENCY INC. - CENTRAL REGION OFFICE—See Nippon Life Insurance Company; *Int'l*, pg. 5322
NLI INSURANCE AGENCY INC.—See Nippon Life Insurance Company; *Int'l*, pg. 5322
NL INDUSTRIES, INC.—See Contran Corporation; *U.S. Private*, pg. 1033
N-LINK CORPORATION; *U.S. Private*, pg. 2827
NLINKS CO., LTD.; *Int'l*, pg. 5391
NLI PROPERTIES WEST, INC.—See Nippon Life Insurance Company; *Int'l*, pg. 5322
NLI RESEARCH INSTITUTE—See Nippon Life Insurance Company; *Int'l*, pg. 5322
NLI SECURITIES LTD.—See National Life Insurance Company Limited; *Int'l*, pg. 5161
NLM ECAL CO., LTD.—See Nippon Light Metal Holdings Company, Ltd.; *Int'l*, pg. 5323
NL METALS SDN BHD—See Nam Lee Pressed Metal Industries Limited; *Int'l*, pg. 5134
NLM INC.; *U.S. Private*, pg. 2931
NLMK CLABECQ S.A.—See Novolipetski Metallurgicheski Komb OAO; *Int'l*, pg. 5466
NLMK ENGINEERING JSC—See Novolipetski Metallurgicheski Komb OAO; *Int'l*, pg. 5466
NLMK INDIANA LLC—See Novolipetski Metallurgicheski Komb OAO; *Int'l*, pg. 5466
NLMK LA LOUVIERE S.A.—See Novolipetski Metallurgicheski Komb OAO; *Int'l*, pg. 5466
NLMK PENNSYLVANIA LLC—See Novolipetski Metallurgicheski Komb OAO; *Int'l*, pg. 5466
NLMK - URAL SERVICE OOO—See Novolipetski Metallurgicheski Komb OAO; *Int'l*, pg. 5466
NLMK VERONA SPA—See Novolipetski Metallurgicheski Komb OAO; *Int'l*, pg. 5466
NLOGIC; *U.S. Private*, pg. 2931
NLP LOGIX, LLC; *U.S. Private*, pg. 2931
NLR, INC.; *U.S. Private*, pg. 2931
NL (SHANGHAI) CO., LTD.—See Lite-On Technology Corporation; *Int'l*, pg. 4525
NL(SHANGHAI)CO., LTD.—See Lite-On Technology Corporation; *Int'l*, pg. 4525
NLS PHARMACEUTICS LTD.; *Int'l*, pg. 5391
NLSSEI MEXICO, S.A. DE C.V.—See Nissei Plastic Industrial Co., Ltd.; *Int'l*, pg. 5371
NLSUPERVISION COMPANY ANGOLA, LTDA.—See FLSmidth & Co. A/S; *Int'l*, pg. 2711
NL SUPERVISION COMPANY A/S—See FLSmidth & Co. A/S; *Int'l*, pg. 2712
NL SUPERVISION COMPANY TUNISIA SARL—See FLSmidth & Co. A/S; *Int'l*, pg. 2711
NLT TITLE, LLC—See Guaranteed Rate, Inc.; *U.S. Private*, pg. 1809
NLYTE SOFTWARE AMERICAS LIMITED; *U.S. Private*, pg. 2931
NLYTE SOFTWARE LIMITED—See Carrier Global Corporation; *U.S. Public*, pg. 440
N MAS UNO IBG SA; *Int'l*, pg. 5115
NMB BANK LIMITED; *Int'l*, pg. 5391
NMB BANK LIMITED—See NMBZ Holdings Limited; *Int'l*, pg. 5391
NMB BANK PLC; *Int'l*, pg. 5391
NMB CAPITAL LIMITED—See NMB Bank Limited; *Int'l*, pg. 5391
NMB CO., LTD.—See BASF SE; *Int'l*, pg. 874
NMB CORPORATION—See Minebea Mitsumi Inc.; *Int'l*, pg. 4904
NMB ITALIA S.R.L.—See Minebea Mitsumi Inc.; *Int'l*, pg. 4904
NMB KOREA CO., LTD.—See Minebea Mitsumi Inc.; *Int'l*, pg. 4904
NMB-MINEBEA DE MEXICO, S. DE R.L. DE C.V.—See Minebea Mitsumi Inc.; *Int'l*, pg. 4905
NMB-MINEBEA DO BRASIL IMPORTACAO E COMERCIO DE COMPONENTES DE PRECISAO LTDA.—See Minebea Mitsumi Inc.; *Int'l*, pg. 4905
NMB-MINEBEA-GMBH—See Minebea Mitsumi Inc.; *Int'l*, pg. 4905
NMB-MINEBEA INDIA PRIVATE LTD.—See Minebea Mitsumi Inc.; *Int'l*, pg. 4904

NMB MINEBEA S.A.R.L.—See Minebea Mitsumi Inc.; *Int'l*, pg. 4904
NMB-MINEBEA THAI LTD.—See Minebea Mitsumi Inc.; *Int'l*, pg. 4904
NMB-MINEBEA UK LTD.—See Minebea Mitsumi Inc.; *Int'l*, pg. 4905
NMB PRECISION INC.—See Minebea Mitsumi Inc.; *Int'l*, pg. 4904
NMB SALES CO., LTD.—See Minebea Mitsumi Inc.; *Int'l*, pg. 4904
NMB SINGAPORE LTD.—See Minebea Mitsumi Inc.; *Int'l*, pg. 4904
NMB SINGAPORE LTD.—See Minebea Mitsumi Inc.; *Int'l*, pg. 4904
NMB TECHNOLOGIES CORPORATION - ASTRO DIVISION—See Minebea Mitsumi Inc.; *Int'l*, pg. 4904
NMB TECHNOLOGIES CORPORATION - HITECH DIVISION—See Minebea Mitsumi Inc.; *Int'l*, pg. 4904
NMB TECHNOLOGIES CORPORATION - MYONIC USA DIVISION—See Minebea Mitsumi Inc.; *Int'l*, pg. 4904
NMB TECHNOLOGIES CORPORATION—See Minebea Mitsumi Inc.; *Int'l*, pg. 4904
NMB TECHNOLOGIES CORPORATION—See Minebea Mitsumi Inc.; *Int'l*, pg. 4904
NMB THAI LIMITED—See Minebea Mitsumi Inc.; *Int'l*, pg. 4904
NMB (USA) INC.—See Minebea Mitsumi Inc.; *Int'l*, pg. 4904
NMBZ HOLDINGS LIMITED; *Int'l*, pg. 5391
NMC CAT—See Nebraska Machinery Company Inc.; *U.S. Private*, pg. 2878
NMC DAY SURGERY CENTRE LLC—See NMC Health PLC; *Int'l*, pg. 5392
NMC DUBAI INVESTMENT PARK LLC—See NMC Health PLC; *Int'l*, pg. 5392
NMC HEALTHCARE LLC—See NMC Health PLC; *Int'l*, pg. 5392
NMC HEALTH PLC; *Int'l*, pg. 5392
NMC HEARING CARE CENTRE—See NMC Health PLC; *Int'l*, pg. 5392
NMC HOLDING CO LLC—See NMC Health PLC; *Int'l*, pg. 5392
NMC HOSPITALS—See NMC Health PLC; *Int'l*, pg. 5392
NMC MATERIAL HANDLING INC.—See Nebraska Machinery Company Inc.; *U.S. Private*, pg. 2878
NMC METALS INC.; *U.S. Private*, pg. 2931
NMCN PLC; *Int'l*, pg. 5392
N&M COOL TODAY, INC.; *U.S. Private*, pg. 2827
NMC OPTICALS—See NMC Health PLC; *Int'l*, pg. 5392
NMC PHARMACIES—See NMC Health PLC; *Int'l*, pg. 5392
NMCR ANALYTICS—See Cencora, Inc.; *U.S. Public*, pg. 467
NMC SHANGHAI, LTD.—See National Molding Corporation; *U.S. Private*, pg. 2859
NMC SPECIAL MEDICAL SERVICES—See NMC Health PLC; *Int'l*, pg. 5392
NMC TECHNOLOGIES—See Nebraska Machinery Company Inc.; *U.S. Private*, pg. 2878
NMC TRADING L.L.C.—See NMC Health PLC; *Int'l*, pg. 5392
NMC/WOLLARD COMPANY; *U.S. Private*, pg. 2931
NMDC ENERGY—See Abu Dhabi National Oil Company; *Int'l*, pg. 73
NMDC LIMITED; *Int'l*, pg. 5393
N MEDIA PLATFORM CO., LTD.—See Nexon Co., Ltd.; *Int'l*, pg. 5245
NME REHABILITATION PROPERTIES, INC.—See Tenet Healthcare Corporation; *U.S. Public*, pg. 2004
N. MERFISH PLUMBING SUPPLY CO.; *U.S. Private*, pg. 2827
NM GROUP GLOBAL LLC—See Alpha Capital Partners, Ltd.; *U.S. Private*, pg. 197
NM GROUP NETWORK MAPPING CORP.—See Trimble, Inc.; *U.S. Public*, pg. 2190
NMG SAN DIEGO, LLC—See Body and Mind Inc.; *Int'l*, pg. 1097
NMHG AUSTRALIA HOLDING PTY LTD.—See Hyster-Yale Materials Handling, Inc.; *U.S. Public*, pg. 1080
NMHG DISTRIBUTION PTY. LIMITED—See Hyster-Yale Materials Handling, Inc.; *U.S. Public*, pg. 1080
NMHG MEXICO S.A. DE C.V.—See Hyster-Yale Materials Handling, Inc.; *U.S. Public*, pg. 1080
NMHG OREGON, LLC—See Hyster-Yale Materials Handling, Inc.; *U.S. Public*, pg. 1080
NMH TRADING & DISTRIBUTION (JAMAICA) LIMITED—See Massy Holdings Ltd.; *Int'l*, pg. 4723
NMI CORPORATION—See NEC Corporation; *Int'l*, pg. 5184
NMI DURBAN SOUTH MOTORS (PTY) LTD.—See Barloworld Ltd.; *Int'l*, pg. 866
NMI HEALTH, INC.; *U.S. Private*, pg. 2931
NMI HOLDINGS, INC.; *U.S. Public*, pg. 1530
NM INCITE, LLC—See Brookfield Corporation; *Int'l*, pg. 1178
NM INCITE, LLC—See Elliott Management Corporation; *U.S. Private*, pg. 1371
NMK MIDDLE EAST TRADING LLC—See Midwich Group Plc; *Int'l*, pg. 4887

NMKV CO., LTD.—See Nissan Motor Co., Ltd.; *Int'l*, pg. 5367
NM LIFE GROUP LIMITED—See Swiss Re Ltd.; *Int'l*, pg. 7371
NM MARKETING COMMUNICATIONS, INC.; *U.S. Private*, pg. 2931
NMP SYSTEMS GMBH—See Salzgitter AG; *Int'l*, pg. 6497
NMR CONSULTING; *U.S. Private*, pg. 2931
N M ROTHSCHILD & SONS (BRASIL) LIMITEDA—See Rothschild & Co SCA; *Int'l*, pg. 6403
NMS CAPITAL SERVICES, LLC; *U.S. Private*, pg. 2931
NMS ENGINEERING CO.,LTD.—See nms Holdings Corporation; *Int'l*, pg. 5393
NMS HOLDINGS CORPORATION; *Int'l*, pg. 5393
NMS - IMAGING; *U.S. Private*, pg. 2931
NMS INTERNATIONAL RESOURCES CO., LTD.—See nms Holdings Corporation; *Int'l*, pg. 5393
NMS LAO SOLE CO., LTD.—See nms Holdings Corporation; *Int'l*, pg. 5393
NMS RESOURCES GLOBAL LTD.; *Int'l*, pg. 5393
NMS—See Nana Regional Corporation, Inc.; *U.S. Private*, pg. 2832
NMS (THAILAND) CO., LTD.—See nms Holdings Corporation; *Int'l*, pg. 5393
NMS VIETNAM CO., LTD.—See nms Holdings Corporation; *Int'l*, pg. 5393
NMT LIMITED—See Minor International PCL; *Int'l*, pg. 4913
N&M TRANSFER CO., INC.; *U.S. Private*, pg. 2827
NMTRONICS INDIA PVT. LTD.—See Sojitz Corporation; *Int'l*, pg. 7062
NMU-3—See PSC TAIF; *Int'l*, pg. 6016
NMU GROUP LIMITED—See Munchener Ruckversicherungs AG; *Int'l*, pg. 5091
N.M.U. (HOLDINGS) LIMITED—See Munchener Ruckversicherungs AG; *Int'l*, pg. 5091
NN ACQUISITION, LLC—See Lincoln Educational Services Corporation; *U.S. Public*, pg. 1316
NN ASIGURARI DE VIATA S.A.—See NN Group N.V.; *Int'l*, pg. 5393
NN BIZTOSITO ZARTKORUEN MUKODO RT.—See NN Group N.V.; *Int'l*, pg. 5393
NNC FOOD INDUSTRIES MALAYSIA SDN. BHD.—See ST Group Food Industries Holdings Limited; *Int'l*, pg. 7158
NNE A/S; *Int'l*, pg. 5394
N&N FOODS COMPANY LTD.—See Maruha Nichiro Corporation; *Int'l*, pg. 4711
NNG FINANCIAL CORPORATION—See Northwest Natural Holding Company; *U.S. Public*, pg. 1542
NN GREEK LIFE INSURANCE COMPANY S.A.—See NN Group N.V.; *Int'l*, pg. 5393
NN GROUP N.V.; *Int'l*, pg. 5393
NNG SOFTWARE DEVELOPING & COMMERCIAL LLC; *Int'l*, pg. 5394
NN HAYAT VE EMEKLILIK A.S.—See NN Group N.V.; *Int'l*, pg. 5393
NN, INC.; *U.S. Public*, pg. 1530
NN INSURANCE BELGIUM N.V.—See NN Group N.V.; *Int'l*, pg. 5393
NN INVESTMENT PARTNERS BELGIUM N.V.—See The Goldman Sachs Group, Inc.; *U.S. Public*, pg. 2082
NN INVESTMENT PARTNERS (FRANCE) S.A.—See The Goldman Sachs Group, Inc.; *U.S. Public*, pg. 2082
NN INVESTMENT PARTNERS HOLDINGS N.V.—See The Goldman Sachs Group, Inc.; *U.S. Public*, pg. 2082
NN INVESTMENT PARTNERS SPAIN—See The Goldman Sachs Group, Inc.; *U.S. Public*, pg. 2082
NNIT A/S—See Novo Nordisk Fonden; *Int'l*, pg. 5463
NN LIFE INSURANCE COMPANY LIMITED—See NN Group N.V.; *Int'l*, pg. 5393
NN LIFE SCIENCES DESIGN & DEVELOPMENT, LLC—See NN, Inc.; *U.S. Public*, pg. 1531
NN LIFE SCIENCES - VANDALIA, LLC—See NN, Inc.; *U.S. Public*, pg. 1531
NN NETHERLANDS B.V.—See NN, Inc.; *U.S. Public*, pg. 1531
NNN REIT, INC.; *U.S. Public*, pg. 1531
NNPC RETAIL LTD.—See Nigerian National Petroleum Corporation; *Int'l*, pg. 5282
NN PENZIJNI SPOLECNOST, A.S.—See NN Group N.V.; *Int'l*, pg. 5393
NN POJISTOVNA A.S.—See NN Group N.V.; *Int'l*, pg. 5393
NNR + DACSHER GMBH—See Nishi-Nippon Railroad Co., Ltd.; *Int'l*, pg. 5364
NN RE (NETHERLANDS) N.V.—See NN Group N.V.; *Int'l*, pg. 5393
NNRF, INC.; *U.S. Private*, pg. 2932
NNR GLOBAL LOGISTICS (GUANGZHOU) CO., LIMITED—See Nishi-Nippon Railroad Co., Ltd.; *Int'l*, pg. 5364
NNR GLOBAL LOGISTICS (HK) LIMITED—See Nishi-Nippon Railroad Co., Ltd.; *Int'l*, pg. 5364
NNR GLOBAL LOGISTICS INDIA PRIVATE LIMITED—See Nishi-Nippon Railroad Co., Ltd.; *Int'l*, pg. 5364
NNR GLOBAL LOGISTICS (M) SDN. BHD.—See Nishi-Nippon Railroad Co., Ltd.; *Int'l*, pg. 5364

COMPANY NAME INDEX

NNR GLOBAL LOGISTICS NETHERLANDS B.V.—See Nishi-Nippon Railroad Co., Ltd.; *Int'l*, pg. 5364
NNR GLOBAL LOGISTICS (PHILIPPINES) CO., LTD.—See Nishi-Nippon Railroad Co., Ltd.; *Int'l*, pg. 5364
NNR GLOBAL LOGISTICS (SHANGHAI) CO., LTD.—See Nishi-Nippon Railroad Co., Ltd.; *Int'l*, pg. 5364
NNR GLOBAL LOGISTICS (S) PTE. LTD.—See Nishi-Nippon Railroad Co., Ltd.; *Int'l*, pg. 5364
NNR GLOBAL LOGISTICS TAIWAN INC.—See Nishi-Nippon Railroad Co., Ltd.; *Int'l*, pg. 5364
NNR GLOBAL LOGISTICS (THAILAND) CO., LTD.—See Nishi-Nippon Railroad Co., Ltd.; *Int'l*, pg. 5364
NN ZIVOTNA POISTOVNA A.S.—See NN Group N.V.; *Int'l*, pg. 5393
NO.1 CO., LTD.; *Int'l*, pg. 5394
NOAH EDUCATION HOLDINGS LTD.; *Int'l*, pg. 5394
NOAH HOLDINGS (HONG KONG) LIMITED—See Noah Holdings Limited; *Int'l*, pg. 5394
NOAH HOLDINGS LIMITED; *Int'l*, pg. 5394
NOAH TECHNOLOGIES CORPORATION; *U.S. Private*, pg. 2932
NOAH W. KREIDER & SON; *U.S. Private*, pg. 2932
NO/AIDS TASK FORCE; *U.S. Private*, pg. 2932
NOA NATUROEL ANKLAM AG—See KTG Agrar SE; *Int'l*, pg. 4316
NOA NOA APS—See Greystone Capital Partners A/S; *Int'l*, pg. 3082
NOARK ELECTRIC (EUROPE) S.R.O.—See Chint Group Corporation; *Int'l*, pg. 1571
NOARK ELECTRIC (ROMANIA) S.R.O.—See Chint Group Corporation; *Int'l*, pg. 1571
NOARK ELECTRIC (SHANGHAI) CO., LTD.—See Chint Group Corporation; *Int'l*, pg. 1571
NOARK ELECTRIC (USA) INC.—See Chint Group Corporation; *Int'l*, pg. 1571
NOARUS AUTO GROUP; *U.S. Private*, pg. 2932
NOA: S SNICKERI I TIBRO AB—See Storskogen Group AB; *Int'l*, pg. 7228
NOATUM LOGISTICS, LLC—See Noatum Maritime Holdings, S.L.U; *Int'l*, pg. 5394
NOATUM MARITIME HOLDINGS, S.L.U; *Int'l*, pg. 5394
NOBAO RENEWABLE ENERGY HOLDINGS LIMITED; *Int'l*, pg. 5394
NOBEL BIOCARE AB—See Danaher Corporation; *U.S. Public*, pg. 628
NOBEL BIOCARE ASIA-AFRICA HOLDING AG—See Danaher Corporation; *U.S. Public*, pg. 628
NOBEL BIOCARE COMMERCIAL (SHANGHAI) CO. LTD.—See Danaher Corporation; *U.S. Public*, pg. 629
NOBEL BIOCARE DANMARK A/S—See Danaher Corporation; *U.S. Public*, pg. 629
NOBEL BIOCARE DISTRIBUTION CENTER BV—See Danaher Corporation; *U.S. Public*, pg. 629
NOBEL BIOCARE HOLDING AG—See Danaher Corporation; *U.S. Public*, pg. 628
NOBEL BIOCARE HOLDING USA INC.—See Danaher Corporation; *U.S. Public*, pg. 629
NOBEL BIOCARE INDIA PVT. LTD.—See Danaher Corporation; *U.S. Public*, pg. 629
NOBEL BIOCARE MAGYARORSZAG KFT.—See Danaher Corporation; *U.S. Public*, pg. 629
NOBEL BIOCARE MANAGEMENT AG—See Danaher Corporation; *U.S. Public*, pg. 629
NOBEL BIOCARE MEXICO S.A. DE C.V.—See Danaher Corporation; *U.S. Public*, pg. 629
NOBEL BIOCARE NEDERLAND BV—See Danaher Corporation; *U.S. Public*, pg. 629
NOBEL BIOCARE NORWAY AS—See Danaher Corporation; *U.S. Public*, pg. 629
NOBEL BIOCARE PORTUGAL S.A.—See Danaher Corporation; *U.S. Public*, pg. 629
NOBEL BIOCARE PROCERA K.K.—See Danaher Corporation; *U.S. Public*, pg. 629
NOBEL BIOCARE PROCERA SERVICES INC.—See Danaher Corporation; *U.S. Public*, pg. 629
NOBEL BIOCARE RUSSIA LLC—See Danaher Corporation; *U.S. Public*, pg. 629
NOBEL BIOCARE SERVICES AG—See Danaher Corporation; *U.S. Public*, pg. 629
NOBEL BIOCARE SINGAPORE PTE LTD.—See Danaher Corporation; *U.S. Public*, pg. 629
NOBEL BIOCARE SOUTH AFRICA (PTY) LTD—See Danaher Corporation; *U.S. Public*, pg. 629
NOBEL BIOCARE SOUTH AFRICA—See Danaher Corporation; *U.S. Public*, pg. 629
NOBEL BIOCARE SUOMI OY—See Danaher Corporation; *U.S. Public*, pg. 629
NOBEL BIOCARE UAB—See Danaher Corporation; *U.S. Public*, pg. 629
NOBELCLAD EUROPE GMBH & CO., KG—See DMC Global Inc.; *U.S. Public*, pg. 671
NOBEL DESIGN HOLDINGS PTE LTD; *Int'l*, pg. 5394
NOBEL DESIGN HOUSE (M) SDN BHD—See Nobel Design Holdings Pte Ltd; *Int'l*, pg. 5394
NOBEL DESIGN SDN BHD—See Nobel Design Holdings Pte Ltd; *Int'l*, pg. 5394
NOBEL INDUSTRIES HOLDING B.V.—See Akzo Nobel N.V.; *Int'l*, pg. 274

NOBEL INDUSTRIES USA INC.—See Akzo Nobel N.V.; *Int'l*, pg. 274
NOBELIUM TECH CORP.; *Int'l*, pg. 5394
NOBEL LEARNING COMMUNITIES, INC.—See Investcorp Holdings B.S.C.; *Int'l*, pg. 3776
NOBEL LIMITED COMPANY; *U.S. Private*, pg. 2932
NOBEL NC COMPANY LIMITED—See Inabata & Co. Ltd.; *Int'l*, pg. 3644
NOBEL NC COMPANY LIMITED—See Nitro Chemical Industry Ltd.; *Int'l*, pg. 5381
NOBEL NC EUROPE LTD.—See Inabata & Co. Ltd.; *Int'l*, pg. 3644
NOBEL NC EUROPE LTD.—See Nitro Chemical Industry Ltd.; *Int'l*, pg. 5382
NOB HILL FOODS, INC.—See Raley's Inc.; *U.S. Private*, pg. 3350
NOBIA AB; *Int'l*, pg. 5394
NOBIAN CHEMICALS B.V.—See GIC Pte. Ltd.; *Int'l*, pg. 2967
NOBIAN CHEMICALS B.V.—See The Carlyle Group Inc.; *U.S. Public*, pg. 2050
NOBIAN INDUSTRIAL CHEMICALS B.V.—See GIC Pte. Ltd.; *Int'l*, pg. 2967
NOBIAN INDUSTRIAL CHEMICALS B.V.—See The Carlyle Group Inc.; *U.S. Public*, pg. 2050
NOBIA SVERIGE AB—See Nobia AB; *Int'l*, pg. 5395
NOBILES MEDIA BV—See Mediahuis Partners NV; *Int'l*, pg. 4772
NOBILES MEDIA BV—See VP Exploitatie N.V.; *Int'l*, pg. 8312
NOBILIS HEALTH CORP.; *U.S. Private*, pg. 2932
NOBILIS INC.; *U.S. Private*, pg. 2932
NOBILITY HOMES, INC.; *U.S. Public*, pg. 1531
NOBINA AB; *Int'l*, pg. 5396
NOBINA AS—See Nobina AB; *Int'l*, pg. 5396
NOBINA A/S—See Nobina AB; *Int'l*, pg. 5396
NOBINA FINLAND EAST OY—See Nobina AB; *Int'l*, pg. 5396
NOBINA FINLAND SOUTH OY—See Nobina AB; *Int'l*, pg. 5396
NOBINA FINLAND WEST OY—See Nobina AB; *Int'l*, pg. 5396
NOBINA OY—See Nobina AB; *Int'l*, pg. 5396
NOBINA SVERIGE AB—See Nobina AB; *Int'l*, pg. 5396
NOBINA TECHNOLOGY AB—See Nobina AB; *Int'l*, pg. 5396
NOBISKRUG GMBH; *Int'l*, pg. 5396
NOBLE ASSET (U.K.) LIMITED—See Noble Corporation plc; *Int'l*, pg. 5396
NOBLE BROADBAND LLC—See Guggenheim Partners, LLC; *U.S. Private*, pg. 1812
NOBLE BUSINESS INTERNATIONAL LTD.—See Mitsui-Soko Holdings Co., Ltd.; *Int'l*, pg. 4992
NOBLE CAPITAL MARKETS; *U.S. Private*, pg. 2932
NOBLE CARBON CREDITS LIMITED—See Noble Group Holdings Limited; *Int'l*, pg. 5397
NOBLE CHARTERING LIMITED—See Noble Group Holdings Limited; *Int'l*, pg. 5397
NOBLE CLEAN FUELS LIMITED—See Noble Group Holdings Limited; *Int'l*, pg. 5397
THE NOBLE COMPANY—See Federal Process Corporation; *U.S. Public*, pg. 1489
NOBLE COMPUTER SERVICES (PVT) LIMITED—See House of Habib; *Int'l*, pg. 3491
NOBLE CONSULTANTS, INC.—See GEC, Inc.; *U.S. Private*, pg. 1655
NOBLE CONTRACTING OFFSHORE DRILLING (M) SDN BHD—See Noble Corporation plc; *Int'l*, pg. 5396
NOBLE CORPORATION HOLDINGS LIMITED—See Noble Corporation plc; *Int'l*, pg. 5396
NOBLE CORPORATION PLC; *Int'l*, pg. 5396
NOBLE DEVELOPMENT PUBLIC COMPANY LIMITED; *Int'l*, pg. 5397
NOBLE DRILLING AMERICAS LLC—See Noble Corporation plc; *Int'l*, pg. 5396
NOBLE DRILLING CORPORATION—See Noble Corporation plc; *Int'l*, pg. 5396
NOBLE DRILLING (DENMARK) APS—See Noble Corporation plc; *Int'l*, pg. 5396
NOBLE DRILLING DOHA W.L.L.—See Noble Corporation plc; *Int'l*, pg. 5396
NOBLE DRILLING INTERNATIONAL GMBH—See Noble Corporation plc; *Int'l*, pg. 5396
NOBLE DRILLING (LAND SUPPORT) LIMITED—See Noble Corporation plc; *Int'l*, pg. 5396
NOBLE DRILLING (NEDERLAND) II B.V.—See Noble Corporation plc; *Int'l*, pg. 5396
NOBLE DRILLING (NIGERIA) LTD.—See Noble Corporation plc; *Int'l*, pg. 5396
NOBLE DRILLING (NORWAY) AS—See Noble Corporation plc; *Int'l*, pg. 5396
NOBLE DRILLING SERVICES INC.—See Noble Corporation plc; *Int'l*, pg. 5396
NOBLE DRILLING SINGAPORE PTE. LTD.—See Noble Corporation plc; *Int'l*, pg. 5396
NOBLE DRILLING (U.K.) LTD.—See Noble Corporation plc; *Int'l*, pg. 5396
NOBLE DRILLING (U.S.) INC.—See Noble Corporation plc; *Int'l*, pg. 5396

NOBLES COOPERATIVE ELECTRIC

NOBLE EDUCATION ACQUISITION CORP.; *U.S. Public*, pg. 1531
NOBLE ELECTRONICS (THAILAND) CO., LTD.—See Teikoku Tsushin Kogyo Co., Ltd.; *Int'l*, pg. 7524
NOBLE ENERGY - ARDMORE—See Chevron Corporation; *U.S. Public*, pg. 487
NOBLE ENERGY - DENVER—See Chevron Corporation; *U.S. Public*, pg. 487
NOBLE ENERGY, INC.—See Chevron Corporation; *U.S. Public*, pg. 487
NOBLE ENERGY MEXICO, S. DE R.L. DE C.V.—See Chevron Corporation; *U.S. Public*, pg. 487
NOBLE ENERGY NEW VENTURES, LLC—See Chevron Corporation; *U.S. Public*, pg. 487
NOBLE ENGINEERING GROUP HOLDINGS LIMITED; *Int'l*, pg. 5397
NOBLE ENVIRONMENTAL POWER LLC—See CCMP Capital Advisors, LP; *U.S. Private*, pg. 800
NOBLE EUROPE LIMITED—See Noble Group Holdings Limited; *Int'l*, pg. 5397
NOBLE EXPLOCHEM LIMITED; *Int'l*, pg. 5397
NOBLE FINANCE CORPORATION—See Gentry Finance Corporation; *U.S. Public*, pg. 1680
NOBLE FINANCE CORPORATION—See Gentry Finance Corporation; *U.S. Private*, pg. 1680
NOBLE FINANCIALS SA; *Int'l*, pg. 5397
NOBLE FOODS LTD.; *Int'l*, pg. 5397
NOBLE FORD; *U.S. Private*, pg. 2932
NOBLE FURANO GODO KAISHA—See Noble Development Public Company Limited; *Int'l*, pg. 5397
NOBLE GROUP HOLDINGS LIMITED; *Int'l*, pg. 5397
NOBLE HELIUM LIMITED; *Int'l*, pg. 5397
NOBLE HOLDING (U.S.) CORPORATION—See Noble Corporation plc; *Int'l*, pg. 5396
NOBLE HOUSE HOTELS & RESORTS, LTD.; *U.S. Private*, pg. 2932
NOBLE INTERNATIONAL LIMITED—See Noble Corporation plc; *Int'l*, pg. 5396
NOBLE INVESTMENT GROUP, LLC; *U.S. Private*, pg. 2932
NOBLE IRON INC.—See Uptake Technologies, LLC; *U.S. Private*, pg. 4313
NOBLE IRON TEXAS—See Uptake Technologies, LLC; *U.S. Private*, pg. 4313
NOBLE JEWELRY INVESTMENT LIMITED; *Int'l*, pg. 5397
NOBLE JEWELRY LIMITED—See Noble Jewelry Investment Limited; *Int'l*, pg. 5397
NOBLE LEASING III (SWITZERLAND) GMBH—See Noble Corporation plc; *Int'l*, pg. 5396
NOBLE LEASING II (SWITZERLAND) GMBH—See Noble Corporation plc; *Int'l*, pg. 5396
NOBLE LEASING (SWITZERLAND) GMBH—See Noble Corporation plc; *Int'l*, pg. 5396
NOBLELIFT CANADA INC.—See Noblelift Intelligent Equipment Co.,Ltd; *Int'l*, pg. 5398
NOBLELIFT EUROPE GMBH—See Noblelift Intelligent Equipment Co.,Ltd; *Int'l*, pg. 5398
NOBLELIFT INTELLIGENT EQUIPMENT CO.,LTD; *Int'l*, pg. 5398
NOBLELIFT RUS LLC—See Noblelift Intelligent Equipment Co.,Ltd; *Int'l*, pg. 5398
NOBLE LUMBER INC.; *U.S. Private*, pg. 2933
NOBLE MARINE (INSURANCE BROKERS) LIMITED—See Intact Financial Corporation; *Int'l*, pg. 3727
NOBLE MARINE (INSURANCE BROKERS) LIMITED—See Tryg A/S; *Int'l*, pg. 7946
NOBLE MARINE (UNDERWRITING AGENCIES) LIMITED—See Intact Financial Corporation; *Int'l*, pg. 3727
NOBLE MARINE (UNDERWRITING AGENCIES) LIMITED—See Tryg A/S; *Int'l*, pg. 7946
NOBLE MARKETING INC.; *U.S. Private*, pg. 2933
NOBLE M&B CO., LTD.; *Int'l*, pg. 5397
NOBLE METAL GROUP INCORPORATED; *Int'l*, pg. 5397
NOBLE METALS LIMITED; *Int'l*, pg. 5398
NOBLE MIDSTREAM PARTNERS LP—See Chevron Corporation; *U.S. Public*, pg. 487
NOBLE MINERAL EXPLORATION INC.; *Int'l*, pg. 5398
NOBLE NETHERLANDS BV—See Noble Group Holdings Limited; *Int'l*, pg. 5397
NOBLEOAK LIFE LIMITED; *Int'l*, pg. 5398
NOBLE OIL SERVICES, INC.; *U.S. Private*, pg. 2933
NOBLE PARAGUAY SOCIEDAD ANONIMA—See Noble Group Holdings Limited; *Int'l*, pg. 5397
NOBLE POLYMERS LIMITED; *Int'l*, pg. 5398
NOBLE POLYMERS LLC—See Cascade Engineering, Inc.; *U.S. Private*, pg. 779
NOBLE RESOURCES LIMITED—See Noble Group Holdings Limited; *Int'l*, pg. 5397
NOBLE RESOURCES PTE. LTD.—See Noble Group Holdings Limited; *Int'l*, pg. 5397
NOBLE RESOURCES S.A.—See Noble Group Holdings Limited; *Int'l*, pg. 5397
NOBLE RESTAURANT GROUP INC.; *U.S. Private*, pg. 2933
NOBLE ROMAN'S, INC.; *U.S. Public*, pg. 1531
NOBLES COOPERATIVE ELECTRIC; *U.S. Private*, pg. 2933

1935

NOBLES COOPERATIVE ELECTRIC / CORPORATE AFFILIATIONS

NOBLES COUNTY LANDFILL, INC.—See Waste Connections, Inc.; *Int'l*, pg. 8353
NOBLE SECURITIES S.A.—See Getin Noble Bank S.A.; *Int'l*, pg. 2947
NOBLE SERVICES INTERNATIONAL LIMITED—See Noble Corporation plc; *Int'l*, pg. 5397
NOBLE SERVICES (SWITZERLAND) LLC—See Noble Corporation plc; *Int'l*, pg. 5397
NOBLE SG PTE. LTD.—See Noble Development Public Company Limited; *Int'l*, pg. 5397
NOBLES MANUFACTURING, INC.—See The Graham Group, Inc.; *U.S. Private*, pg. 4037
NOBLES MEDICAL TECHNOLOGIES, INC.—See Medtronic plc; *Int'l*, pg. 4790
NOBLES WORLDWIDE, INC.—See Ducommun Incorporated; *U.S. Public*, pg. 690
NOBLE SYSTEMS AUSTRALIA PTY LIMITED—See Vector Capital Management, L.P.; *U.S. Private*, pg. 4350
NOBLE SYSTEMS CORPORATION—See Vector Capital Management, L.P.; *U.S. Private*, pg. 4350
NOBLE SYSTEMS FRANCE S.A.R.L.—See Vector Capital Management, L.P.; *U.S. Private*, pg. 4350
NOBLE SYSTEMS INDIA PVT. LTD.—See Vector Capital Management, L.P.; *U.S. Private*, pg. 4350
NOBLE SYSTEMS PHILIPPINES CORPORATION—See Vector Capital Management, L.P.; *U.S. Private*, pg. 4350
NOBLE SYSTEMS UK—See Vector Capital Management, L.P.; *U.S. Private*, pg. 4350
NOBLE TITLE & TRUST—See Stock Development, LLC; *U.S. Private*, pg. 3814
NOBLE TRADING (BANGKOK) CO., LTD.—See Teikoku Tsushin Kogyo Co., Ltd.; *Int'l*, pg. 7524
NOBLE TRADING (SHANGHAI) CO., LTD.—See Teikoku Tsushin Kogyo Co., Ltd.; *Int'l*, pg. 7524
NOBLE VENTURES CORP.; *U.S. Private*, pg. 2933
NOBLE VICI GROUP, INC.; *Int'l*, pg. 5398
NOBLE VICI PRIVATE LIMITED—See Noble Vici Group, Inc.; *Int'l*, pg. 5398
NOBLE VOICE LLC—See Professional Diversity Network, Inc.; *U.S. Public*, pg. 1724
NOBLE WATER TECHNOLOGIES, INC.—See Xylem Inc.; *U.S. Public*, pg. 2394
NOBLEZA PICCARDO SAIC Y F—See British American Tobacco plc; *Int'l*, pg. 1167
NOBLY A/S—See Virtus Holding ApS; *Int'l*, pg. 8249
NOBO AUTOMOTIVE SYSTEMS GERMANY GMBH—See Great Wall Motor Company Limited; *Int'l*, pg. 3066
NOBO HEATING UK LIMITED—See The Glen Dimplex Group; *Int'l*, pg. 7650
NOBOX MARKETING GROUP, INC.; *U.S. Private*, pg. 2933
NOBU ARMANI SRL—See Giorgio Armani S.p.A.; *Int'l*, pg. 2978
NOBU FIFTY SEVEN—See Myriad Restaurant Group; *U.S. Private*, pg. 2825
NOBUL AI CORP.; *Int'l*, pg. 5398
NOBU LONDON—See Myriad Restaurant Group; *U.S. Private*, pg. 2825
NOBU NEW YORK—See Myriad Restaurant Group; *U.S. Private*, pg. 2825
NOBU NEXT DOOR—See Myriad Restaurant Group; *U.S. Private*, pg. 2825
NOCA AS—See Guardian Capital Group Limited; *Int'l*, pg. 3170
NOCADIS; *Int'l*, pg. 5398
NOCA HOLDING AS—See Guardian Capital Group Limited; *Int'l*, pg. 3170
NOC ASIA LIMITED—See Sumitomo Chemical Company, Limited; *Int'l*, pg. 7264
NOCERA, INC.; *Int'l*, pg. 5398
NOCIBE FRANCE SAS—See CVC Capital Partners SICAV-FIS S.A.; *Int'l*, pg. 1883
NOCIL LIMITED—See Arvind Mafatlal Group; *Int'l*, pg. 587
NOCO ENERGY CORP.; *U.S. Private*, pg. 2933
NOCO-NOCO INC.; *Int'l*, pg. 5398
NOCOPI TECHNOLOGIES, INC.; *U.S. Public*, pg. 1531
NOC OUTSOURCING & CONSULTING INC—See Fuyo General Lease Co., Limited; *Int'l*, pg. 2859
NOCOWANIE.PL SP. Z O.O.—See Wirtualna Polska Holding S.A.; *Int'l*, pg. 8434
NOCTILUCA SA; *Int'l*, pg. 5398
NOCTURNA SLEEP CENTER, LLC—See Foundation Healthcare, Inc.; *U.S. Private*, pg. 1580
NOCTURNA SLEEP THERAPY, LP—See Foundation Healthcare, Inc.; *U.S. Private*, pg. 1580
NOCTURNE ACQUISITION CORPORATION; *U.S. Public*, pg. 1531
NODA BIO POWER JP CO., LTD.—See Japan Pulp and Paper Company Limited; *Int'l*, pg. 3904
NODA CORPORATION; *Int'l*, pg. 5398
NODA INTELLIGENT SYSTEM AB—See Investment AB Latour; *Int'l*, pg. 3782
NODAK ELECTRIC COOPERATIVE, INC.; *U.S. Private*, pg. 2933
NODAK INSURANCE COMPANY; *U.S. Private*, pg. 2933
NODAL CLEAR, LLC—See Deutsche Borse AG; *Int'l*, pg. 2064

NODAL EXCHANGE HOLDINGS, LLC—See Deutsche Borse AG; *Int'l*, pg. 2064
NODAL EXCHANGE, LLC—See Deutsche Borse AG; *Int'l*, pg. 2064
NODA PRECISION INC.—See OSG Corporation Co., Ltd.; *Int'l*, pg. 5649
NODA SENKO LOGI SERVICE CO., LTD.—See Senko Group Holdings Co., Ltd.; *Int'l*, pg. 6710
NODAWAY VALLEY BANK; *U.S. Private*, pg. 2933
NODECHAIN, INC.; *U.S. Public*, pg. 1531
NODEN PHARMA DAC; *Int'l*, pg. 5398
NODO DI PALERMO, S.P.A.—See Sacyr, S.A.; *Int'l*, pg. 6466
NODUS TECHNOLOGIES, INC.—See Global Payments Inc.; *U.S. Public*, pg. 943
NODWIN GAMING PRIVATE LIMITED—See Nazara Technologies Limited; *Int'l*, pg. 5178
NOECKER AGENCY LLC—See The Ayres Group, LLC; *U.S. Private*, pg. 3990
NOEL ARNOLD & ASSOCIATES PTY. LTD.—See WSP Global, Inc.; *Int'l*, pg. 8497
NOEL CANNING CORPORATION; *U.S. Private*, pg. 2933
NOEL FURNITURE LTD.; *U.S. Private*, pg. 2933
NOEL GIFTS INTERNATIONAL LTD.; *Int'l*, pg. 5398
NOEL GROUP, LLC; *U.S. Private*, pg. 2933
NOELL, AGNEW & MORSE—See KCoe Isom, LLP; *U.S. Private*, pg. 2270
NOEL LEEMING GROUP LIMITED—See The Warehouse Group Limited; *Int'l*, pg. 7699
NOELL REGGIANE FRANCE SARL; *Int'l*, pg. 5398
NOEMALIFE ARGENTINA SRL—See Ardian SAS; *Int'l*, pg. 555
NOEMALIFE CHILE—See Ardian SAS; *Int'l*, pg. 555
NOEMALIFE GMBH—See Ardian SAS; *Int'l*, pg. 555
NOEMALIFE MENA FZ-LLC—See Ardian SAS; *Int'l*, pg. 555
NOEMALIFE MEXICO DE RL DE CV—See Ardian SAS; *Int'l*, pg. 555
NOEMALIFE S.P.A.—See Ardian SAS; *Int'l*, pg. 555
NOEMALIFE UK LTD—See Ardian SAS; *Int'l*, pg. 555
NOEO, GMBH—See The Healing Company Inc.; *U.S. Public*, pg. 2088
NOESIS COMMUNICAZIONE—See Clayton, Dubilier & Rice, LLC; *U.S. Private*, pg. 925
NOESIS ENERGY, INC.—See SoftBank Group Corp.; *Int'l*, pg. 7053
NOESIS INDUSTRIES LIMITED; *Int'l*, pg. 5399
NOESIS SOLUTIONS NV—See FUJISOFT INCORPORATED; *Int'l*, pg. 2830
NOETIX CORPORATION—See TA Associates, Inc.; *U.S. Private*, pg. 3916
NOETRON SA—See NEWSPHONE HELLAS S.A.; *Int'l*, pg. 5234
NOEVIR AVIATION CO., LTD.—See Noevir Holdings Co., Ltd.; *Int'l*, pg. 5399
NOEVIR AVIATION, INC.—See Noevir Holdings Co., Ltd.; *Int'l*, pg. 5399
NOEVIR CANADA, INC.—See Noevir Holdings Co., Ltd.; *Int'l*, pg. 5399
NOEVIR CO., LTD.—See Noevir Holdings Co., Ltd.; *Int'l*, pg. 5399
NOEVIR HOLDING OF AMERICA, INC.—See Noevir Holdings Co., Ltd.; *Int'l*, pg. 5399
NOEVIR HOLDINGS CO., LTD.; *Int'l*, pg. 5399
NOEVIR TAIWAN, INC.—See Noevir Holdings Co., Ltd.; *Int'l*, pg. 5399
NOEVIR TOURIST CO., LTD.—See Noevir Holdings Co., Ltd.; *Int'l*, pg. 5399
NOEVIR U.S.A. INC.—See Noevir Holdings Co., Ltd.; *Int'l*, pg. 5399
NOF AMERICA CORPORATION—See NOF Corporation; *Int'l*, pg. 5399
NOFAR ENERGY LTD.; *Int'l*, pg. 5400
NOF CORPORATION - AICHI WORKS—See NOF Corporation; *Int'l*, pg. 5399
NOF CORPORATION - AMAGASAKI PLANT—See NOF Corporation; *Int'l*, pg. 5399
NOF CORPORATION - DISPLAY MATERIALS PLANT—See NOF Corporation; *Int'l*, pg. 5399
NOF CORPORATION - OITA PLANT—See NOF Corporation; *Int'l*, pg. 5399
NOF CORPORATION; *Int'l*, pg. 5399
NOF CORPORATION - TANEGASHIMA PLANT—See NOF Corporation; *Int'l*, pg. 5399
NOF EUROPE (BELGIUM) N.V.—See NOF Corporation; *Int'l*, pg. 5399
NOF EUROPE GMBH—See NOF Corporation; *Int'l*, pg. 5399
NOFIRE TECHNOLOGIES, INC.; *U.S. Public*, pg. 1532
NOF METAL COATINGS ASIA PACIFIC CO., LTD.—See NOF Corporation; *Int'l*, pg. 5399
NOF METAL COATINGS EUROPE N.V.—See NOF Corporation; *Int'l*, pg. 5399
NOF METAL COATINGS EUROPE S.A.—See NOF Corporation; *Int'l*, pg. 5399
NOF METAL COATINGS KOREA CO., LTD.—See NOF Corporation; *Int'l*, pg. 5399
NOF METAL COATINGS NORTH AMERICA INC.—See NOF Corporation; *Int'l*, pg. 5399

NOF METAL COATINGS SHANGHAI CO., LTD.—See NOF Corporation; *Int'l*, pg. 5399
NOF METAL COATINGS SOUTH AMERICA IND. E COM. LTDA.—See NOF Corporation; *Int'l*, pg. 5400
NOFRAYANE SA—See VINCI S.A.; *Int'l*, pg. 8224
NO FRILLS SUPERMARKETS INC.; *U.S. Private*, pg. 2932
NOF (SHANGHAI) CO., LTD.—See NOF Corporation; *Int'l*, pg. 5399
NOF (THAILAND) LTD.—See BASF SE; *Int'l*, pg. 884
NOFZIGER DOOR SALES, INC.; *U.S. Private*, pg. 2933
NOGALES RESOURCES CORP.; *Int'l*, pg. 5400
NOGA LUXE SL—See Kering S.A.; *Int'l*, pg. 4136
NOGAMA CONSTRUCTION CORP.; *U.S. Private*, pg. 2933
NOGE GESELLSCHAFT FUR MEDIZINPRODUKTE UND -DIENSTLEISTUNGEN MBH—See PAUL HARTMANN AG; *Int'l*, pg. 5761
NOGGERATH FRANCE EURL—See Bilfinger SE; *Int'l*, pg. 1028
NOGGINLABS, INC.; *U.S. Private*, pg. 2933
NOGIN, INC.; *U.S. Public*, pg. 1532
NOGOON TOLGOI UUL LLC—See Endress+Hauser (International) Holding AG; *Int'l*, pg. 2443
NO GRAVITY GAMES SA; *Int'l*, pg. 5394
NOHAB INDUSTRI AB—See Pomona-Gruppen AB; *Int'l*, pg. 5918
NOHELS GROUP INC.—See Vertex Resource Group Ltd.; *Int'l*, pg. 8174
NOHI SEINO TRANSPORTATION CO., LTD.—See Seino Holdings Co., Ltd.; *Int'l*, pg. 6690
NOHL BRANDSCHUTZ GMBH—See VINCI S.A.; *Int'l*, pg. 8238
NOHMI BAOLI (BEIJING) INTELLIGENT FIRE PROTECTION CO., LTD.—See Nohmi Bosai Ltd.; *Int'l*, pg. 5400
NOHMI BOSAI LTD.; *Int'l*, pg. 5400
NOHMI ENGINEERING CORPORATION—See Nohmi Bosai Ltd.; *Int'l*, pg. 5400
NOHMI SYSTEM CO., LTD.—See Nohmi Bosai Ltd.; *Int'l*, pg. 5400
NOHMI TECHNO ENGINEERING CO., LTD.—See Nohmi Bosai Ltd.; *Int'l*, pg. 5400
NOHO HEALTH INC.—See Bayer Aktiengesellschaft; *Int'l*, pg. 909
NOHO PARTNERS PLC; *Int'l*, pg. 5400
NOH & PARTNERS CO., LTD.; *Int'l*, pg. 5400
NOIDA MEDICARE CENTRE LTD.; *Int'l*, pg. 5400
NOIDA TOLL BRIDGE COMPANY LIMITED; *Int'l*, pg. 5400
NOISE CONTROL ENGINEERING, LLC—See Glosten, Inc.; *U.S. Private*, pg. 1720
NOISE FIBER—See Fujikura Ltd.; *Int'l*, pg. 2827
NOISELESS ACCOUSTICS OY—See Teledyne Technologies Incorporated; *U.S. Public*, pg. 1992
NOI-SIRIUS HF—See Orkla ASA; *Int'l*, pg. 5638
NOIZ GROUP LIMITED; *Int'l*, pg. 5401
NOJIMA (CAMBODIA) CO., LTD.—See Nojima Corporation; *Int'l*, pg. 5401
NOJIMA CORPORATION; *Int'l*, pg. 5401
NOJIMA STELLA SPORTS CLUB CO., LTD.—See Nojima Corporation; *Int'l*, pg. 5401
NOK9 AB; *Int'l*, pg. 5403
NOK AIRLINES PUBLIC COMPANY LIMITED; *Int'l*, pg. 5401
NOKAS AS—See Avarn Security Group Holding AS; *Int'l*, pg. 737
NOK ASIA CO. PTE LTD.—See NOK Corporation; *Int'l*, pg. 5402
NOKAS SVERIGE—See Avarn Security Group Holding AS; *Int'l*, pg. 737
NOKAS VARDEHANTERING AB—See Loomis AB; *Int'l*, pg. 4556
NOK CORPORATION; *Int'l*, pg. 5401
NOK ELASTOMERS PROCESSING CO., LTD.—See NOK Corporation; *Int'l*, pg. 5402
NOK-FREUDENBERG GROUP SALES (CHINA) CO., LTD.—See NOK Corporation; *Int'l*, pg. 5402
NOKIA ARABIA LIMITED—See Nokia Corporation; *Int'l*, pg. 5405
NOKIA ARGENTINA S.A.—See Nokia Corporation; *Int'l*, pg. 5405
NOKIA AUSTRIA GMBH—See Nokia Corporation; *Int'l*, pg. 5405
NOKIA BELL LABS - DUBLIN—See Nokia Corporation; *Int'l*, pg. 5406
NOKIA BELL LABS—See Nokia Corporation; *Int'l*, pg. 5406
NOKIA BELL NV—See Nokia Corporation; *Int'l*, pg. 5404
NOKIA BENELUX N.V./S.A.—See Nokia Corporation; *Int'l*, pg. 5405
NOKIA BYDGOSZCZ—See Nokia Corporation; *Int'l*, pg. 5404
NOKIA CANADA CORPORATION—See Nokia Corporation; *Int'l*, pg. 5405
NOKIA CANADA INC. - MARKHAM—See Nokia Corporation; *Int'l*, pg. 5404
NOKIA CANADA INC. - MONTREAL—See Nokia Corporation; *Int'l*, pg. 5404
NOKIA CANADA INC.—See Nokia Corporation; *Int'l*, pg. 5404

COMPANY NAME INDEX

NOKIA (CHINA) INVESTMENT CO., LTD.—See Nokia Corporation; *Int'l*, pg. 5405
NOKIA COLOMBIA S.A.—See Nokia Corporation; *Int'l*, pg. 5405
NOKIA COMMUNICATIONS TURKEY—See Nokia Corporation; *Int'l*, pg. 5405
NOKIA CORPORATION; *Int'l*, pg. 5403
NOKIA COSTA RICA S.A.—See Nokia Corporation; *Int'l*, pg. 5405
NOKIA CZECH REPUBLIC S.R.O.—See Nokia Corporation; *Int'l*, pg. 5405
NOKIA DANMARK A/S—See Nokia Corporation; *Int'l*, pg. 5405
NOKIA DENMARK A/S—See Nokia Corporation; *Int'l*, pg. 5404
NOKIA DE VENEZUELA, C.A.—See Nokia Corporation; *Int'l*, pg. 5406
NOKIA DO BRASIL LTDA.—See Nokia Corporation; *Int'l*, pg. 5406
NOKIA DO BRASIL TECNOLOGIA LTDA.—See Nokia Corporation; *Int'l*, pg. 5406
NOKIA EGYPT S.A.E.—See Nokia Corporation; *Int'l*, pg. 5405
NOKIA ENTERPRISES LTD—See Nokia Corporation; *Int'l*, pg. 5405
NOKIA FRANCE—See Nokia Corporation; *Int'l*, pg. 5405
NOKIA (H.K.) LIMITED—See Nokia Corporation; *Int'l*, pg. 5405
NOKIA HUNGARY LTD.—See Nokia Corporation; *Int'l*, pg. 5405
NOKIA INC.—See Nokia Corporation; *Int'l*, pg. 5405
NOKIA INC.—See Nokia Corporation; *Int'l*, pg. 5405
NOKIA INDIA PRIVATE LIMITED—See Nokia Corporation; *Int'l*, pg. 5405
NOKIA IRELAND LTD.—See Nokia Corporation; *Int'l*, pg. 5405
NOKIA ITALIA S.P.A.—See Nokia Corporation; *Int'l*, pg. 5405
NOKIA JAPAN CO. LTD.—See Nokia Corporation; *Int'l*, pg. 5405
NOKIA KOMAROM KFT.—See Nokia Corporation; *Int'l*, pg. 5405
NOKIA LATVIJA SIA—See Nokia Corporation; *Int'l*, pg. 5405
NOKIA (MALAYSIA) SDN. BHD.—See Nokia Corporation; *Int'l*, pg. 5405
NOKIA MEXICO S.A. DE C.V.—See Nokia Corporation; *Int'l*, pg. 5405
NOKIA MOBILE PHONES (KOREA) LTD.—See Microsoft Corporation; *U.S. Public*, pg. 1441
NOKIA MOBILE PHONES (SEA) PTE LTD.—See Microsoft Corporation; *U.S. Public*, pg. 1441
NOKIA MOBILE PHONES—See Microsoft Corporation; *U.S. Public*, pg. 1441
NOKIA MOBILE PHONES—See Microsoft Corporation; *U.S. Public*, pg. 1441
NOKIA MOBILE PHONES—See Microsoft Corporation; *U.S. Public*, pg. 1441
NOKIA MOBILE PHONES WIRELESS DATA—See Microsoft Corporation; *U.S. Public*, pg. 1441
NOKIAN DACK AB—See Nokian Renkaat Oyj; *Int'l*, pg. 5407
NOKIAN DEKK A/S—See Nokian Renkaat Oyj; *Int'l*, pg. 5407
NOKIAN NEDERLAND B.V.—See Nokia Corporation; *Int'l*, pg. 5405
NOKIA NETWORKS INC.-ATM SYSTEMS R&D—See Nokia Corporation; *Int'l*, pg. 5406
NOKIA NETWORKS INC.—See Nokia Corporation; *Int'l*, pg. 5406
NOKIA NORGE AS—See Nokia Corporation; *Int'l*, pg. 5405
NOKIAN PORTTI OY—See Nokian Renkaat Oyj; *Int'l*, pg. 5407
NOKIAN REIFEN AG—See Nokian Renkaat Oyj; *Int'l*, pg. 5407
NOKIAN REIFEN GMBH—See Nokian Renkaat Oyj; *Int'l*, pg. 5407
NOKIAN RENKAAT OYJ; *Int'l*, pg. 5407
NOKIAN SHINA LLC—See Nokian Renkaat Oyj; *Int'l*, pg. 5407
NOKIAN TYRES INC., USA—See Nokian Renkaat Oyj; *Int'l*, pg. 5407
NOKIAN TYRES—See Nokian Renkaat Oyj; *Int'l*, pg. 5407
NOKIAN TYRES S.R.O—See Nokian Renkaat Oyj; *Int'l*, pg. 5407
NOKIA OF AMERICA CORPORATION - RALEIGH—See Nokia Corporation; *Int'l*, pg. 5406
NOKIA OF AMERICA CORPORATION—See Nokia Corporation; *Int'l*, pg. 5406
NOKIA PHILIPPINES INC.—See Nokia Corporation; *Int'l*, pg. 5405
NOKIA PORTUGAL S.A.—See Nokia Corporation; *Int'l*, pg. 5405
NOKIA RESEARCH CENTER—See Nokia Corporation; *Int'l*, pg. 5405
NOKIA ROMANIA—See Nokia Corporation; *Int'l*, pg. 5405
NOKIA RUSSIA (ZAO)—See Nokia Corporation; *Int'l*, pg. 5405
NOKIA SERVICES LIMITED—See Nokia Corporation; *Int'l*, pg. 5404
NOKIA SHANGHAI BELL CO., LTD—See Nokia Corporation; *Int'l*, pg. 5404
NOKIA SLOVAKIA S.R.O.—See Nokia Corporation; *Int'l*, pg. 5405
NOKIA SOLUTIONS AND NETWORK ECUADOR S.A.—See Nokia Corporation; *Int'l*, pg. 5404
NOKIA SOLUTIONS AND NETWORKS BRANCH OPERATIONS OY - BRUNEI—See Nokia Corporation; *Int'l*, pg. 5404
NOKIA SOLUTIONS AND NETWORKS B.V.—See Nokia Corporation; *Int'l*, pg. 5404
NOKIA SOLUTIONS AND NETWORKS GMBH & CO. KG—See Nokia Corporation; *Int'l*, pg. 5403
NOKIA SOLUTIONS AND NETWORKS HELLAS S.A.—See Nokia Corporation; *Int'l*, pg. 5404
NOKIA SOLUTIONS AND NETWORKS OU—See Nokia Corporation; *Int'l*, pg. 5404
NOKIA SOLUTIONS AND NETWORKS SLOVAKIA, S. R. O.—See Nokia Corporation; *Int'l*, pg. 5404
NOKIA SOLUTIONS AND NETWORKS—See Nokia Corporation; *Int'l*, pg. 5406
NOKIA SOLUTIONS AND NETWORKS SP. Z O.O.—See Nokia Corporation; *Int'l*, pg. 5404
NOKIA SOLUTIONS AND NETWORKS TAIWAN CO., LTD.—See Nokia Corporation; *Int'l*, pg. 5404
NOKIA SOLUTIONS & NETWORKS ARGENTINA S.A.—See Nokia Corporation; *Int'l*, pg. 5405
NOKIA SOLUTIONS & NETWORKS BOLIVIA S.A.—See Nokia Corporation; *Int'l*, pg. 5405
NOKIA SOLUTIONS & NETWORKS COLOMBIA LTDA.—See Nokia Corporation; *Int'l*, pg. 5405
NOKIA SOLUTIONS & NETWORKS ECUADOR S.A.—See Nokia Corporation; *Int'l*, pg. 5405
NOKIA SOLUTIONS & NETWORKS (HANGZHOU) CO., LTD.—See Nokia Corporation; *Int'l*, pg. 5406
NOKIA SOLUTIONS & NETWORKS HELLAS AE—See Nokia Corporation; *Int'l*, pg. 5406
NOKIA SOLUTIONS & NETWORKS JAPAN G.K.—See Nokia Corporation; *Int'l*, pg. 5406
NOKIA SOLUTIONS & NETWORKS KFT.—See Nokia Corporation; *Int'l*, pg. 5406
NOKIA SOLUTIONS & NETWORKS MEA FZ-LLC—See Nokia Corporation; *Int'l*, pg. 5406
NOKIA SOLUTIONS & NETWORKS MOROCCO SARL—See Nokia Corporation; *Int'l*, pg. 5406
NOKIA SOLUTIONS & NETWORKS NORGE AS—See Nokia Corporation; *Int'l*, pg. 5406
NOKIA SOLUTIONS & NETWORKS OY—See Nokia Corporation; *Int'l*, pg. 5406
NOKIA SOLUTIONS & NETWORKS PHILIPPINES, INC.—See Nokia Corporation; *Int'l*, pg. 5406
NOKIA SOLUTIONS & NETWORKS POLAND SP.Z.O.O.—See Nokia Corporation; *Int'l*, pg. 5406
NOKIA SOLUTIONS & NETWORKS PTY LTD.—See Nokia Corporation; *Int'l*, pg. 5406
NOKIA SOLUTIONS & NETWORKS SCHWEIZ AG—See Nokia Corporation; *Int'l*, pg. 5406
NOKIA SOLUTIONS & NETWORKS SINGAPORE PTE. LTD.—See Nokia Corporation; *Int'l*, pg. 5406
NOKIA SOLUTIONS & NETWORKS TANZANIA LIMITED—See Nokia Corporation; *Int'l*, pg. 5406
NOKIA SOLUTIONS & NETWORKS TRAFFICOM KFT.—See Nokia Corporation; *Int'l*, pg. 5406
NOKIA SOLUTIONS & NETWORKS US LLC—See Nokia Corporation; *Int'l*, pg. 5406
NOKIA SPAIN S.A.U—See Nokia Corporation; *Int'l*, pg. 5406
NOKIA TAIWAN CO. LTD.—See Nokia Corporation; *Int'l*, pg. 5406
NOKIA TELECOMMUNICATIONS LTD.—See Nokia Corporation; *Int'l*, pg. 5406
NOKIA (THAILAND) LTD.—See Nokia Corporation; *Int'l*, pg. 5405
NOKIA TMC LTD.—See Nokia Corporation; *Int'l*, pg. 5406
NOKIA TREASURY ASIA LTD.—See Nokia Corporation; *Int'l*, pg. 5406
NOKIA UK LIMITED—See Nokia Corporation; *Int'l*, pg. 5404
NOKIA UK LIMITED—See Nokia Corporation; *Int'l*, pg. 5406
NOKIA URUGUAY S.A.—See Nokia Corporation; *Int'l*, pg. 5406
NOKIA (VIETNAM) LLC—See Nokia Corporation; *Int'l*, pg. 5405
NOKIA WEST & CENTRAL AFRICA SA—See Nokia Corporation; *Int'l*, pg. 5406
NOKK EHF.—See BEWi ASA; *Int'l*, pg. 1004
NOK-KLUBER CO., LTD.—See Freudenberg SE; *Int'l*, pg. 2786
NOK-KLUBER CO., LTD.—See NOK Corporation; *Int'l*, pg. 5402
NOKMETAL CO., LTD.—See NOK Corporation; *Int'l*, pg. 5402
NOK PRECISION COMPONENT SINGAPORE PTE LTD.—See NOK Corporation; *Int'l*, pg. 5402
NOK PRECISION COMPONENT (THAILAND) LTD.—See NOK Corporation; *Int'l*, pg. 5402
NOKSEL A.S.—See Cukurova Holding A.S.; *Int'l*, pg. 1876
NOKSEL A.S.—See Nokia Corporation; *Int'l*, pg. 5406
NOKSEL ESPANA S.A.—See Cukurova Holding A.S.; *Int'l*, pg. 1876
NOKSEL ESPANA S.A.—See Nokia Corporation; *Int'l*, pg. 5406
NOKWON COMMERCIALS & INDUSTRIES, INC.; *Int'l*, pg. 5407
NOK (WUXI) WATER TREATMENT TECHNOLOGY CO., LTD.—See NOK Corporation; *Int'l*, pg. 5402
NOLAN CAPITAL, INC.; *U.S. Private*, pg. 2934
NOLAND COMPANY—See Winsupply Inc.; *U.S. Private*, pg. 4544
NOLAND HEALTH SERVICES, INC.; *U.S. Private*, pg. 2934
NOLAND PROPERTIES, INC.—See Winsupply Inc.; *U.S. Private*, pg. 4544
NOLAND SALES CORP.; *U.S. Private*, pg. 2934
NOLAN ORIGINALS, LLC—See BioWorld Merchandising, Inc.; *U.S. Private*, pg. 563
NOLAN POWER GROUP, LLC—See High Road Capital Partners, LLC; *U.S. Private*, pg. 1936
NOLAN'S RV CENTER INC.; *U.S. Private*, pg. 2934
NOLAN TRANSPORTATION GROUP, INC.—See Gryphon Investors, LLC; *U.S. Private*, pg. 1799
NOLATO AB; *Int'l*, pg. 5407
NOLATO ALPHA AB—See Nolato AB; *Int'l*, pg. 5407
NOLATO AUTOMOTIVE COMPONENTS (BEIJING) CO. LTD.—See Nolato AB; *Int'l*, pg. 5407
NOLATO CERBO AB—See Nolato AB; *Int'l*, pg. 5407
NOLATO CONTOUR INC.—See Nolato AB; *Int'l*, pg. 5408
NOLATO EMC PRODUCTION CENTER SDN BHD—See Nolato AB; *Int'l*, pg. 5408
NOLATO GOTA AB—See Nolato AB; *Int'l*, pg. 5408
NOLATO HUNGARY KFT—See Nolato AB; *Int'l*, pg. 5408
NOLATO JABAR LLC—See Nolato AB; *Int'l*, pg. 5408
NOLATO LOVEPAC AB—See Nolato AB; *Int'l*, pg. 5408
NOLATO (MALAYSIA) SDN. BHD.—See Nolato AB; *Int'l*, pg. 5407
NOLATO MEDITECH—See Nolato AB; *Int'l*, pg. 5408
NOLATO MEDITOR AB—See Nolato AB; *Int'l*, pg. 5408
NOLATO MOBILE COMMUNICATION POLYMERS (BEIJING) CO. LTD.—See Nolato AB; *Int'l*, pg. 5408
NOLATO PLASTTEKNIK AB—See Nolato AB; *Int'l*, pg. 5408
NOLATO POLYMER AB—See Nolato AB; *Int'l*, pg. 5408
NOLATO POLYMER AB—See Nolato AB; *Int'l*, pg. 5408
NOLATO SILIKONTEKNIK AB—See Nolato AB; *Int'l*, pg. 5408
NOLATO STARGARD SP. Z O.O.—See Nolato AB; *Int'l*, pg. 5408
NOLATO STG AB—See Nolato AB; *Int'l*, pg. 5408
NOLATO SUNNE AB—See Nolato AB; *Int'l*, pg. 5408
NOLATO TEC AB—See Nolato AB; *Int'l*, pg. 5408
NOLATO TECHNOLOGY (DONGGUAN) CO., LTD.—See Nolato AB; *Int'l*, pg. 5408
NOLATO TOREKOV AB—See Nolato AB; *Int'l*, pg. 5408
NOLATO TREFF AG—See Nolato AB; *Int'l*, pg. 5408
NOLEK AB—See Indutrade AB; *Int'l*, pg. 3680
NOLEK A/S—See Indutrade AB; *Int'l*, pg. 3680
NOLEK (BEIJING) TECHNOLOGY CO., LTD.—See Indutrade AB; *Int'l*, pg. 3680
NOLEK CENTRAL EUROPE KFT.—See Indutrade AB; *Int'l*, pg. 3680
NOLEK, INC.—See Indutrade AB; *Int'l*, pg. 3680
NOLEK SDN. BHD.—See Indutrade AB; *Int'l*, pg. 3680
NOLET DISTILLERY BV—See Nolet Holding B.V.; *Int'l*, pg. 5408
NOLET HOLDING B.V.; *Int'l*, pg. 5408
NOLET SPIRITS USA INC.—See Nolet Holding B.V.; *Int'l*, pg. 5408
NOLIAC AS—See CTS Corporation; *U.S. Public*, pg. 603
NOLIA DIALYSIS, LLC—See DaVita Inc.; *U.S. Public*, pg. 641
NOLIN RURAL ELECTRIC COOPERATIVE CORPORATION; *U.S. Private*, pg. 2934
NOLIS-SPA—See Cevital S.p.A.; *Int'l*, pg. 1425
NOLIT A.D.; *Int'l*, pg. 5408
NOLL HUMAN RESOURCE SERVICE; *U.S. Private*, pg. 2934
NOLL/NORWESCO, LLC—See Gibraltar Industries, Inc.; *U.S. Public*, pg. 936
NOLL/NORWESCO LLC—See Gibraltar Industries, Inc.; *U.S. Public*, pg. 936
NOLL/NORWESCO LLC—See Gibraltar Industries, Inc.; *U.S. Public*, pg. 936
NOLOCK SOFTWARELOSUNGEN GMBH—See CTS Eventim AG & Co. KGAA; *Int'l*, pg. 1874
NOLO CLIMAT S.R.L.—See ANDREWS SYKES GROUP PLC; *Int'l*, pg. 452
NOLO INC.—See KKR & Co. Inc.; *U.S. Public*, pg. 1253
NOL-TEC EUROPE, S.R.L.—See Nol-Tec Systems Inc.; *U.S. Private*, pg. 2933
NOL-TEC SYSTEMS (ASIA) PTE. LTD.—See Nol-Tec Systems Inc.; *U.S. Private*, pg. 2933
NOL-TEC SYSTEMS INC.; *U.S. Private*, pg. 2933
NOLTE GMBH—See Fagron NV; *Int'l*, pg. 2603
NOLTEX LLC—See Mitsubishi Chemical Group Corporation; *Int'l*, pg. 4934

NOLUMA INTERNATIONAL, LLC—See The Chemours Company; *U.S. Public*, pg. 2059
NOMACO, INC.—See Noel Group, LLC; *U.S. Private*, pg. 2933
NOMACORC, LLC—See Global Leisure Partners LLP; *Int'l*, pg. 2998
NOMACORC, LLC—See Noel Group, LLC; *U.S. Private*, pg. 2933
NOMAD CAMPERVANS LTD.—See Tourism Holdings Limited; *Int'l*, pg. 7848
NOMAD COFFEE GROUP PTY. LTD.—See Minor International PCL; *Int'l*, pg. 4911
NOMAD DIGITAL BELGIUM S.A.—See Alstom S.A.; *Int'l*, pg. 383
NOMAD DIGITAL BV—See Alstom S.A.; *Int'l*, pg. 381
NOMAD DIGITAL FRANCE SARL—See Alstom S.A.; *Int'l*, pg. 383
NOMAD DIGITAL GMBH—See Alstom S.A.; *Int'l*, pg. 381
NOMAD DIGITAL INC.—See Alstom S.A.; *Int'l*, pg. 381
NOMAD DIGITAL ITALIA S.R.L.—See Alstom S.A.; *Int'l*, pg. 383
NOMAD DIGITAL LIMITED—See Alstom S.A.; *Int'l*, pg. 381
NOMAD DIGITAL PTY LIMITED—See Alstom S.A.; *Int'l*, pg. 381
NOMAD FOODS EUROPE HOLDINGS LIMITED—See Nomad Foods Limited; *Int'l*, pg. 5408
NOMAD FOODS EUROPE LIMITED—See Nomad Foods Limited; *Int'l*, pg. 5409
NOMAD FOODS LIMITED; *Int'l*, pg. 5408
NOMADIX, INC.—See Nippon Telegraph & Telephone Corporation; *Int'l*, pg. 5350
THE NOMAD RESIDENCES BANGSAR SDN. BHD.—See Plenitude Berhad; *Int'l*, pg. 5896
NOMAD ROYALTY COMPANY LTD.—See Sandstorm Gold Ltd.; *Int'l*, pg. 6527
NOMAD TECH, LDA.—See Alstom S.A.; *Int'l*, pg. 383
NO MAGIC INC.—See Dassault Systemes S.A.; *Int'l*, pg. 1975
NOM AG—See Raiffeisen-Holding Niederosterreich-Wien reg. Gen.m.b.H.; *Int'l*, pg. 6185
NOMECO A/S—See PHOENIX Pharmahandel GmbH & Co. KG; *Int'l*, pg. 5854
NOMENCA LTD.—See NMCN PLC; *Int'l*, pg. 5393
NOMINALIA INTERNET S.L.—See HgCapital Trust plc; *Int'l*, pg. 3377
NOMINA PLC—See Hampden Holdings Limited; *Int'l*, pg. 3239
NOMI S.A.—See i4ventures Sp. z o.o.; *Int'l*, pg. 3567
NOMIS D.O.O.—See Arburg GmbH & Co.; *Int'l*, pg. 539
NOMIS SOLUTIONS, INC.—See Symphony Technology Group, LLC; *U.S. Private*, pg. 3901
NOMO AB—See Axel Johnson Gruppen AB; *Int'l*, pg. 763
NOMO KULLAGER AB—See Axel Johnson Gruppen AB; *Int'l*, pg. 763
NOMU PAY—See Finch Capital Partners B.V.; *Int'l*, pg. 2672
NOMURA ADVISORY COMPANY S.A.—See Nomura Holdings, Inc.; *Int'l*, pg. 5410
NOMURA AGRI PLANNING & ADVISORY CO., LTD.—See Nomura Holdings, Inc.; *Int'l*, pg. 5410
NOMURA AMERICA MORTGAGE FINANCE, LLC—See Nomura Holdings, Inc.; *Int'l*, pg. 5411
NOMURA AMERICA SECURITIES, LLC—See Nomura Holdings, Inc.; *Int'l*, pg. 5411
NOMURA AMERICA SERVICES, LLC—See Nomura Holdings, Inc.; *Int'l*, pg. 5409
NOMURA ASIA HOLDING N.V.—See Nomura Holdings, Inc.; *Int'l*, pg. 5409
NOMURA ASIA LTD.—See Nomura Holdings, Inc.; *Int'l*, pg. 5410
NOMURA ASSET CAPITAL CORPORATION—See Nomura Holdings, Inc.; *Int'l*, pg. 5411
NOMURA ASSET MANAGEMENT AUSTRALIA PTY LIMITED—See Nomura Holdings, Inc.; *Int'l*, pg. 5409
NOMURA ASSET MANAGEMENT CO., LIMITED—See Nomura Holdings, Inc.; *Int'l*, pg. 5410
NOMURA ASSET MANAGEMENT CO., LTD.—See Nomura Holdings, Inc.; *Int'l*, pg. 5410
NOMURA ASSET MANAGEMENT DEUTSCHLAND KAG MBH—See Nomura Holdings, Inc.; *Int'l*, pg. 5410
NOMURA ASSET MANAGEMENT EUROPE KVG. MBH—See Nomura Holdings, Inc.; *Int'l*, pg. 5410
NOMURA ASSET MANAGEMENT (HONG KONG) LIMITED—See Nomura Holdings, Inc.; *Int'l*, pg. 5410
NOMURA ASSET MANAGEMENT MALAYSIA SDN. BHD.—See Nomura Holdings, Inc.; *Int'l*, pg. 5410
NOMURA ASSET MANAGEMENT (SINGAPORE) LIMITED—See Nomura Holdings, Inc.; *Int'l*, pg. 5410
NOMURA ASSET MANAGEMENT (U.K.) LIMITED—See Nomura Holdings, Inc.; *Int'l*, pg. 5410
NOMURA ASSET MANAGEMENT U.S.A. INC.—See Nomura Holdings, Inc.; *Int'l*, pg. 5410
NOMURA AUSTRALIA LIMITED—See Nomura Holdings, Inc.; *Int'l*, pg. 5409
NOMURA BABCOCK & BROWN CO., LTD.—See Nomura Holdings, Inc.; *Int'l*, pg. 5410
NOMURA BANK (DEUTSCHLAND) GMBH—See Nomura Holdings, Inc.; *Int'l*, pg. 5410
NOMURA BANK INTERNATIONAL PLC—See Nomura Holdings, Inc.; *Int'l*, pg. 5410
NOMURA BANK (LUXEMBOURG) S.A.—See Nomura Holdings, Inc.; *Int'l*, pg. 5410
NOMURA BANK (SWITZERLAND) LTD.—See Nomura Holdings, Inc.; *Int'l*, pg. 5410
NOMURA (BEIJING) CO., LTD.—See Nomura Co., Ltd.; *Int'l*, pg. 5409
NOMURA BUSINESS SERVICES CO., LTD.—See Nomura Holdings, Inc.; *Int'l*, pg. 5410
NOMURA CANADA INC.—See Nomura Holdings, Inc.; *Int'l*, pg. 5411
NOMURA CAPITAL (INDIA) PRIVATE LIMITED—See Nomura Holdings, Inc.; *Int'l*, pg. 5409
NOMURA CAPITAL INVESTMENT CO., LTD.—See Nomura Holdings, Inc.; *Int'l*, pg. 5410
NOMURA CAPITAL PARTNERS CO., LTD.—See Nomura Holdings, Inc.; *Int'l*, pg. 5410
NOMURA CHINA INVESTMENT CO., LTD.—See Nomura Holdings, Inc.; *Int'l*, pg. 5412
NOMURA CO., LTD.; *Int'l*, pg. 5409
NOMURA COMMODITIES SINGAPORE PTE. LTD.—See Nomura Holdings, Inc.; *Int'l*, pg. 5410
NOMURA CORPORATE ADVISORY CEE SP. Z O.O.—See Nomura Holdings, Inc.; *Int'l*, pg. 5410
NOMURA CORPORATE ADVISORY (CENTRAL EUROPE) LTD.—See Nomura Holdings, Inc.; *Int'l*, pg. 5410
NOMURA CORPORATE ADVISORY (SHANGHAI) LTD.—See Nomura Holdings, Inc.; *Int'l*, pg. 5409
NOMURA CORPORATE RESEARCH AND ASSET MANAGEMENT INC.—See Nomura Holdings, Inc.; *Int'l*, pg. 5411
NOMURA CREDIT AND CAPITAL INC.—See Nomura Holdings, Inc.; *Int'l*, pg. 5411
NOMURA DERIVATIVE PRODUCTS, INC.—See Nomura Holdings, Inc.; *Int'l*, pg. 5411
NOMURA DESIGN & ENGINEERING SINGAPORE PTE. LTD.—See Nomura Co., Ltd.; *Int'l*, pg. 5409
NOMURA DEVELOPMENT CO., LTD.—See Nomura Co., Ltd.; *Int'l*, pg. 5409
NOMURA DUO CO., LTD.—See Nomad Foods Limited; *Int'l*, pg. 5409
NOMURA EUROPE FINANCE N.V.—See Nomura Holdings, Inc.; *Int'l*, pg. 5411
NOMURA EUROPE HOLDINGS PLC—See Nomura Holdings, Inc.; *Int'l*, pg. 5410
NOMURA FACILITIES, INC.—See Nomura Holdings, Inc.; *Int'l*, pg. 5411
NOMURA FARM CO., LTD.—See Nomura Holdings, Inc.; *Int'l*, pg. 5409
NOMURA FINANCIAL ADVISORY AND SECURITIES (INDIA) PRIVATE LIMITED—See Nomura Holdings, Inc.; *Int'l*, pg. 5409
NOMURA FINANCIAL ADVISORY CO., LTD.—See Nomura Holdings, Inc.; *Int'l*, pg. 5409
NOMURA FINANCIAL INVESTMENT (KOREA) CO. LIMITED—See Nomura Holdings, Inc.; *Int'l*, pg. 5409
NOMURA FINANCIAL PRODUCTS EUROPE GMBH—See Nomura Holdings, Inc.; *Int'l*, pg. 5411
NOMURA FINANCIAL PRODUCTS & SERVICES, INC.—See Nomura Holdings, Inc.; *Int'l*, pg. 5411
NOMURA FIN SERVICES (INDIA) PRIVATE LIMITED—See Nomura Holdings, Inc.; *Int'l*, pg. 5409
NOMURA FIXED INCOME SECURITIES PRIVATE LIMITED—See Nomura Holdings, Inc.; *Int'l*, pg. 5409
NOMURA FUNDS RESEARCH & TECHNOLOGIES AMERICA, INC.—See Nomura Holdings, Inc.; *Int'l*, pg. 5411
NOMURA FUNDS RESEARCH & TECHNOLOGIES CO., LTD.—See Nomura Holdings, Inc.; *Int'l*, pg. 5411
NOMURA FUTURES (HONG LONG) LIMITED—See Nomura Holdings, Inc,; *Int'l*, pg. 5410
NOMURA GLOBAL FINANCIAL PRODUCTS, INC.—See Nomura Holdings, Inc.; *Int'l*, pg. 5411
NOMURA GLOBAL FUNDING PLC—See Nomura Holdings, Inc.; *Int'l*, pg. 5411
NOMURA GREENTECH CAPITAL ADVISORS, AG—See Nomura Holdings, Inc.; *Int'l*, pg. 5411
NOMURA HEALTHCARE CO., LTD.—See Nomura Holdings, Inc.; *Int'l*, pg. 5411
NOMURA HOLDING AMERICA INC.—See Nomura Holdings, Inc.; *Int'l*, pg. 5411
NOMURA HOLDINGS, INC.; *Int'l*, pg. 5409
NOMURA (HONG KONG) LTD—See Nomura Holdings, Inc.; *Int'l*, pg. 5409
NOMURA INFRASTRUCTURE INVESTMENT ADVISORS PRIVATE LIMITED—See Nomura Holdings, Inc.; *Int'l*, pg. 5411
NOMURA INSTITUTE OF CAPITAL MARKETS RESEARCH, LTD.—See Nomura Holdings, Inc.; *Int'l*, pg. 5411
NOMURA INTERNATIONAL (HONG KONG) LIMITED—See Nomura Holdings, Inc.; *Int'l*, pg. 5409
NOMURA INTERNATIONAL PLC—See Nomura Holdings, Inc.; *Int'l*, pg. 5410
NOMURA INTERNATIONAL TRUST COMPANY—See Nomura Holdings, Inc.; *Int'l*, pg. 5411
NOMURA INVESTMENT BANKING (MIDDLE EAST) B.S.C. (C)—See Nomura Holdings, Inc.; *Int'l*, pg. 5410
NOMURA INVESTMENT MANAGEMENT (SHANGHAI) CO., LTD.—See Nomura Holdings, Inc.; *Int'l*, pg. 5411
NOMURA INVESTMENTS (SINGAPORE) PTE. LIMITED—See Nomura Holdings, Inc.; *Int'l*, pg. 5411
NOMURA INVESTOR RELATIONS CO., LTD.—See Nomura Holdings, Inc.; *Int'l*, pg. 5411
NOMURA ISLAMIC ASSET MANAGEMENT SDN. BHD.—See Nomura Holdings, Inc.; *Int'l*, pg. 5411
NOMURA ITALIA S.I.M. P.A.—See Nomura Holdings, Inc.; *Int'l*, pg. 5410
NOMURA KAGAYAKI CO., LTD.—See Nomura Holdings, Inc.; *Int'l*, pg. 5411
NOMURA KOREA CO., LTD.—See Nomura Micro Science Co., Ltd.; *Int'l*, pg. 5412
NOMURA LAND AND BUILDING CO., LTD.—See Nomura Holdings, Inc.; *Int'l*, pg. 5411
NOMURA MALAYSIA SDN. BHD—See Nomura Holdings, Inc.; *Int'l*, pg. 5410
NOMURA MEZZANINE PARTNERS CO., LTD.—See Nomura Holdings, Inc.; *Int'l*, pg. 5411
NOMURA MICRO SCIENCE CO., LTD.; *Int'l*, pg. 5412
NOMURA MICRO SCIENCE U.S.A. LTD., CO.—See Nomura Micro Science Co., Ltd.; *Int'l*, pg. 5412
NOMURA NEDERLAND N.V.—See Nomura Holdings, Inc.; *Int'l*, pg. 5410
NOMURA PENSION SUPPORT & SERVICE CO., LTD.—See Nomura Holdings, Inc.; *Int'l*, pg. 5411
NOMURA PHILIPPINES, INC.—See Nomura Holdings, Inc.; *Int'l*, pg. 5411
NOMURA PRINCIPAL FINANCE CO., LTD.—See Nomura Holdings, Inc.; *Int'l*, pg. 5411
NOMURA PRIVATE EQUITY CAPITAL CO., LTD.—See Nomura Holdings, Inc.; *Int'l*, pg. 5412
NOMURA PRODUCTS CO., LTD.—See Nomad Foods Limited; *Int'l*, pg. 5409
NOMURA PROPERTIES, INC.—See Nomura Holdings, Inc.; *Int'l*, pg. 5412
NOMURA REAL ESTATE ASSET MANAGEMENT CO., LTD.—See Nomura Real Estate Holdings, Inc.; *Int'l*, pg. 5412
NOMURA REAL ESTATE DEVELOPMENT CO., LTD.—See Nomura Real Estate Holdings, Inc.; *Int'l*, pg. 5412
NOMURA REAL ESTATE HOLDINGS, INC.; *Int'l*, pg. 5412
NOMURA REAL ESTATE MASTER FUND, INC.; *Int'l*, pg. 5412
NOMURA REINSURANCE INTERMEDIARY INC.—See Nomura Holdings, Inc.; *Int'l*, pg. 5412
NOMURA RESEARCH & ADVISORY CO., LTD.—See Nomura Holdings, Inc.; *Int'l*, pg. 5412
NOMURA RESEARCH INSTITUTE AMERICA INC.—See Nomura Research Institute, Ltd.; *Int'l*, pg. 5413
NOMURA RESEARCH INSTITUTE ASIA PACIFIC PRIVATE LIMITED—See Nomura Research Institute, Ltd.; *Int'l*, pg. 5413
NOMURA RESEARCH INSTITUTE AUSTRALIA, PTY LTD—See Nomura Research Institute, Ltd.; *Int'l*, pg. 5413
NOMURA RESEARCH INSTITUTE CONSULTING & SOLUTIONS INDIA PRIVATE LIMITED—See Nomura Research Institute, Ltd.; *Int'l*, pg. 5413
NOMURA RESEARCH INSTITUTE (DAILAN), LTD.—See Nomura Research Institute, Ltd.; *Int'l*, pg. 5413
NOMURA RESEARCH INSTITUTE EUROPE LIMITED—See Nomura Research Institute, Ltd.; *Int'l*, pg. 5413
NOMURA RESEARCH INSTITUTE FINANCIAL TECHNOLOGIES INDIA PVT. LTD.—See Nomura Research Institute, Ltd.; *Int'l*, pg. 5413
NOMURA RESEARCH INSTITUTE HOLDINGS AMERICA, INC.—See Nomura Research Institute, Ltd.; *Int'l*, pg. 5413
NOMURA RESEARCH INSTITUTE HONG KONG LIMITED—See Nomura Research Institute, Ltd.; *Int'l*, pg. 5413
NOMURA RESEARCH INSTITUTE, LTD.; *Int'l*, pg. 5412
NOMURA RESEARCH INSTITUTE SEOUL CO., LTD.—See Nomura Research Institute, Ltd.; *Int'l*, pg. 5413
NOMURA RESEARCH INSTITUTE SHANGHAI LIMITED—See Nomura Research Institute, Ltd.; *Int'l*, pg. 5413
NOMURA RESEARCH INSTITUTE (SINGAPORE) PTE. LTD.—See Nomura Research Institute, Ltd.; *Int'l*, pg. 5413
NOMURA RESEARCH INSTITUTE TAIWAN CO., LTD.—See Nomura Research Institute, Ltd.; *Int'l*, pg. 5413
NOMURA SAUDI ARABIA—See Nomura Holdings, Inc.; *Int'l*, pg. 5411
NOMURA SECURITIES (BERMUDA) LTD.—See Nomura Holdings, Inc.; *Int'l*, pg. 5411
NOMURA SECURITIES CO., LTD.—See Nomura Holdings, Inc.; *Int'l*, pg. 5412
NOMURA SECURITIES HONG KONG LIMITED—See Nomura Holdings, Inc.; *Int'l*, pg. 5410
NOMURA SECURITIES INTERNATIONAL, INC. - BRAZIL—See Nomura Holdings, Inc.; *Int'l*, pg. 5411

COMPANY NAME INDEX

NOMURA SECURITIES INTERNATIONAL, INC.—See Nomura Holdings, Inc.; *Int'l*, pg. 5411
NOMURA SECURITIES INVESTMENT ADVISORY CO., LTD.—See Nomura Holdings, Inc.; *Int'l*, pg. 5409
NOMURA SECURITIES MALAYSIA SDN. BHD.—See Nomura Holdings, Inc.; *Int'l*, pg. 5412
NOMURA SECURITIES PHILIPPINES, INC.—See Nomura Holdings, Inc.; *Int'l*, pg. 5409
NOMURA SECURITIES SINGAPORE PTE. LTD.—See Nomura Holdings, Inc.; *Int'l*, pg. 5410
NOMURA SERVICES INDIA PRIVATE LIMITED—See Nomura Holdings, Inc.; *Int'l*, pg. 5410
NOMURA SINGAPORE LIMITED—See Nomura Holdings, Inc.; *Int'l*, pg. 5410
NOMURA STRUCTURED FINANCE SERVICES PRIVATE LIMITED—See Nomura Holdings, Inc.; *Int'l*, pg. 5410
NOMURA SWEDEN AB—See Nomura Holdings, Inc.; *Int'l*, pg. 5411
NOMURA SYSTEM CORPORATION CO., LTD.; *Int'l*, pg. 5414
NOMURA TECHNO CO., LTD.—See Nomad Foods Limited; *Int'l*, pg. 5409
NOMURA TEKKOSHO CO., LTD.—See NSK Ltd.; *Int'l*, pg. 5478
THE NOMURA TRUST & BANKING CO., LTD.—See Nomura Holdings, Inc.; *Int'l*, pg. 5412
NOMURA TRUST COMPANY (SINGAPORE) LTD—See Nomura Holdings, Inc.; *Int'l*, pg. 5410
NONAGASE CO., LTD.—See Kawakin Holdings Co., Ltd.; *Int'l*, pg. 4094
NO NAME STEAKS LLC—See J&B Group, Inc.; *U.S. Private*, pg. 2153
NONANTUM CAPITAL PARTNERS LLC; *U.S. Private*, pg. 2934
NONBOX; *U.S. Private*, pg. 2934
NONBOX—See Nonbox; *U.S. Private*, pg. 2934
NONBOX—See Nonbox; *U.S. Private*, pg. 2934
N-ONE RACING SDN BHD.—See HKS CO., LTD.; *Int'l*, pg. 3404
NONFEMET INTERNATIONAL (CHINA-CANADA-JAPAN) ALUMINIUM CO., LTD.—See Nippon Light Metal Holdings Company, Ltd.; *Int'l*, pg. 5324
NON FERRUM KRANJ D.O.O.—See Palladium Equity Partners, LLC; *U.S. Private*, pg. 3078
NONGFU SPRING CO., LTD.; *Int'l*, pg. 5414
NONGHYUP FINANCIAL GROUP, INC.; *Int'l*, pg. 5414
NONG'S HEALTHCARE 16 LIMITED—See PuraPharm Corporation Limited; *Int'l*, pg. 6121
NONGSHIM AMERICA, INC.—See Nongshim Co., Ltd.; *Int'l*, pg. 5414
NONGSHIM AUSTRALIA PTY. LTD.—See Nongshim Co., Ltd.; *Int'l*, pg. 5414
NONGSHIM CO., LTD - ANSEONG PLANT—See Nongshim Co., Ltd.; *Int'l*, pg. 5414
NONGSHIM CO., LTD - ANYANG PLANT—See Nongshim Co., Ltd.; *Int'l*, pg. 5414
NONGSHIM CO., LTD - ASAN PLANT—See Nongshim Co., Ltd.; *Int'l*, pg. 5414
NONGSHIM CO., LTD - BUSAN PLANT—See Nongshim Co., Ltd.; *Int'l*, pg. 5414
NONGSHIM CO., LTD - GUMI PLANT—See Nongshim Co., Ltd.; *Int'l*, pg. 5414
NONGSHIM CO., LTD - NOKSAN PLANT—See Nongshim Co., Ltd.; *Int'l*, pg. 5414
NONGSHIM CO., LTD.; *Int'l*, pg. 5414
NONGSHIM COMMUNICATIONS CO., LTD.—See Nongshim Co., Ltd.; *Int'l*, pg. 5414
NONGSHIM HOLDINGS CO., LTD.; *Int'l*, pg. 5414
NONGSHIM JAPAN, INC.—See Nongshim Co., Ltd.; *Int'l*, pg. 5414
NONGSHIM VIETNAM CO., LTD.—See Nongshim Co., Ltd.; *Int'l*, pg. 5414
NONG WOO BIO CO., LTD.; *Int'l*, pg. 5414
NON-INTRUSIVE INSPECTION TECHNOLOGY, INC. - CHARLOTTESVILLE FACILITY—See Chemring Group PLC; *Int'l*, pg. 1463
NON-INTRUSIVE INSPECTION TECHNOLOGY, INC.—See Chemring Group PLC; *Int'l*, pg. 1463
NONINVASIVE MEDICAL TECHNOLOGIES, INC.; *U.S. Private*, pg. 2934
NON-INVASIVE MONITORING SYSTEMS, INC.; *U.S. Public*, pg. 1532
NON-METALLIC COMPONENTS INC.; *U.S. Private*, pg. 2934
NON-METALLIC SOLUTIONS, INC.—See Repligen Corporation; *U.S. Public*, pg. 1784
NONNI'S FOODS LLC—See Vestar Capital Partners, LLC; *U.S. Private*, pg. 4372
NONNI'S FOODS LLC—See Wind Point Advisors LLC; *U.S. Private*, pg. 4534
NONN'S FLOORING INC.—See The Sterling Group, L.P.; *U.S. Private*, pg. 4122
NONPANIC SRL—See LOV Group Invest SAS; *Int'l*, pg. 4563
NONPAREIL CORPORATION; *U.S. Private*, pg. 2934
NONPROFITEASY, INC.; *U.S. Private*, pg. 2934
NONPROFIT VOTE; *U.S. Private*, pg. 2934
NONSCALE CORPORATION—See SEMBA Corporation; *Int'l*, pg. 6702

NON-STANDARD FINANCE PLC; *Int'l*, pg. 5414
NONSTOPDELIVERY, LLC—See Hub Group, Inc.; *U.S. Public*, pg. 1066
NONTHAVEJ HOSPITAL PCL; *Int'l*, pg. 5414
NON TRADING PS LIMITED—See Sky Network Television Limited; *Int'l*, pg. 6992
NOODLES BY LEONARDO INC.; *U.S. Private*, pg. 2934
NOODLES & COMPANY—See Catterton Management Company, LLC; *U.S. Private*, pg. 793
NOOKA INC.; *U.S. Private*, pg. 2934
NOOK DIGITAL, LLC—See Elliott Management Corporation; *U.S. Private*, pg. 1364
NOOK INDUSTRIES INC.; *U.S. Private*, pg. 2934
NOONA HEALTHCARE OY—See Siemens Aktiengesellschaft; *Int'l*, pg. 6894
NOONAN BROTHERS PETROLEUM PRODUCTS; *U.S. Private*, pg. 2935
NOONAN ENERGY CORPORATION; *U.S. Private*, pg. 2935
NOON FILMTECHNIK SPOL.S R.O.—See Bavaria Film GmbH; *Int'l*, pg. 899
NOON HOUR FOOD PRODUCTS, INC.; *U.S. Private*, pg. 2934
NOON IMPORT-EXPORT SALES, INC.; *U.S. Private*, pg. 2935
NOON SUGAR MILLS LIMITED; *Int'l*, pg. 5414
NOON TURF CARE; *U.S. Private*, pg. 2935
NOOR AL KHALEEJ LLC—See Al Hassan Engineering Company S.A.O.G.; *Int'l*, pg. 279
NOOR AL SHEFA CLINIC LLC—See Aster DM Healthcare Ltd.; *Int'l*, pg. 654
NOOR CAPITAL MARKETS FOR DIVERSIFIED INVESTMENTS—See SHUAA Capital psc; *Int'l*, pg. 6868
NOORDGASTRANSPORT B.V.—See ENGIE SA; *Int'l*, pg. 2434
NOORDKOEL B.V.—See China International Marine Containers (Group) Co., Ltd.; *Int'l*, pg. 1512
NOORD-NEDERLANDSE SCHROOTVERWERKING B.V.—See Benteler International AG; *Int'l*, pg. 977
NOOR FINANCIAL INVESTMENT CO. K.S.C.C—See National Industries Group Holding S.A.K.; *Int'l*, pg. 5159
NOOR, INC.; *U.S. Private*, pg. 2935
NOOR ISLAMIC BANK PJSC—See Dubai Islamic Bank PSJ; *Int'l*, pg. 2220
NOOR SILK MILLS LIMITED; *Int'l*, pg. 5414
NOOSA YOGHURT LLC—See Advent International Corporation; *U.S. Private*, pg. 105
NOOSH INC.; *U.S. Private*, pg. 2935
NOOTEBOOM BIDCO B.V.—See BENCIS Capital Partners B.V.; *Int'l*, pg. 970
NOOTER CONSTRUCTION CO.—See CIC Group, Inc.; *U.S. Private*, pg. 896
NOOTER CORPORATION—See CIC Group, Inc.; *U.S. Private*, pg. 896
NOOTER/ERIKSEN, INC.—See CIC Group, Inc.; *U.S. Private*, pg. 896
NOOTER/ERIKSEN SRL—See CIC Group, Inc.; *U.S. Private*, pg. 896
NOPAR FOR TRADING & INVESTMENT COMPANY LTD.; *Int'l*, pg. 5414
NOPETRO, LLC; *U.S. Private*, pg. 2935
NO PICTURES PLEASE PRODUCTIONS B.V.—See Bertelsmann SE & Co. KGaA; *Int'l*, pg. 993
NOP-NASS WLL—See Abdulla Ahmed Nass Group WLL; *Int'l*, pg. 58
NOPTEL OY—See Herstal, S.A.; *Int'l*, pg. 3365
NORAC COMPANY INC.; *U.S. Private*, pg. 2935
NORAFIN INDUSTRIES (GERMANY) GMBH—See DZ BANK AG Deutsche Zentral-Genossenschaftsbank; *Int'l*, pg. 2245
NORAG RESOURCES INC.; *Int'l*, pg. 5415
NORAIR ENGINEERING CORPORATION; *U.S. Private*, pg. 2935
NOR-AM AGRO LLC—See Bayer Aktiengesellschaft; *Int'l*, pg. 902
NORAMCO, INC.—See SK Capital Partners, LP; *U.S. Private*, pg. 3679
NORAM INTERNATIONAL PARTNERS LLC; *U.S. Private*, pg. 2935
NORAM LITHIUM CORP.; *Int'l*, pg. 5415
NORAMPAC INC. - DRUMMONDVILLE—See Cascades Inc.; *Int'l*, pg. 1350
NORAMPAC INC. - NEWFOUNDLAND—See Cascades Inc.; *Int'l*, pg. 1350
NORAMPAC INC.—See Cascades Inc.; *Int'l*, pg. 1350
NORAMPAC INC. - VAUDREUIL—See Cascades Inc.; *Int'l*, pg. 1350
NORAMPAC INDUSTRIES INC. - LANCASTER—See Cascades Inc.; *Int'l*, pg. 1350
NORAMPAC INDUSTRIES INC.—See Cascades Inc.; *Int'l*, pg. 1350
NORAMPAC NEW ENGLAND INC.—See Cascades Inc.; *Int'l*, pg. 1350
NORAMPAC NEW YORK CITY INC.—See Cascades Inc.; *Int'l*, pg. 1350
NORAMPAC SCHENECTADY INC.—See Cascades Inc.; *Int'l*, pg. 1350

NOR-CAL FOODS, INC.

NOR-AM SERVICE CORPORATION—See NASB Financial, Inc.; *U.S. Public*, pg. 1491
NORANCO INC. - DEER VALLEY DIVISION—See Berkshire Hathaway Inc.; *U.S. Public*, pg. 314
NORANCO INC.—See Berkshire Hathaway Inc.; *U.S. Public*, pg. 314
NORANDA INC.—See Glencore plc; *Int'l*, pg. 2991
NORAN TEL, INC.—See Westell Technologies, Inc.; *U.S. Public*, pg. 2354
NORA PHARMA INC.—See SUNSHINE BIOPHARMA, INC.; *Int'l*, pg. 7322
NORASIAN ENERGY LIMITED—See Otto Energy Limited; *Int'l*, pg. 5662
NORASIAN ENERGY PHILS. INC.—See Otto Energy Limited; *Int'l*, pg. 5662
NORA SYSTEMS GMBH—See Interface, Inc.; *U.S. Public*, pg. 1144
NORA SYSTEMS, INC.—See Interface, Inc.; *U.S. Public*, pg. 1144
NORATEL AS—See discoverIE Group plc; *Int'l*, pg. 2133
NORATEL DENMARK A/S—See discoverIE Group plc; *Int'l*, pg. 2133
NORATEL FINLAND OY—See discoverIE Group plc; *Int'l*, pg. 2133
NORATEL GERMANY AG—See discoverIE Group plc; *Int'l*, pg. 2133
NORATEL INDIA POWER COMPONENTS PVT LTD—See discoverIE Group plc; *Int'l*, pg. 2133
NORATEL INTERNATIONAL PVT LTD—See discoverIE Group plc; *Int'l*, pg. 2133
NORATEL NORTH AMERICA INC.—See discoverIE Group plc; *Int'l*, pg. 2133
NORATEL POWER ENGINEERING INC.—See discoverIE Group plc; *Int'l*, pg. 2133
NORATEL SP Z.O.O—See discoverIE Group plc; *Int'l*, pg. 2133
NORATEL SWEDEN AB—See discoverIE Group plc; *Int'l*, pg. 2133
NORATEL UK LTD.—See discoverIE Group plc; *Int'l*, pg. 2133
NORATIS AG; *Int'l*, pg. 5415
NORATIS WEST GMBH—See Noratis AG; *Int'l*, pg. 5415
NORAUTO HUNGARY KFT—See Mobivia Groupe SA; *Int'l*, pg. 5012
NORAUTO ITALIA SPA—See Mobivia Groupe SA; *Int'l*, pg. 5012
NORAUTO POLSKA SP. Z O.O.—See Mobivia Groupe SA; *Int'l*, pg. 5012
NORAUTO PORTUGAL - PECAS E ACESSORIOS, LDA—See Mobivia Groupe SA; *Int'l*, pg. 5012
NORAUTO SA—See Mobivia Groupe SA; *Int'l*, pg. 5012
NORAUTO SHERRY SL—See Mobivia Groupe SA; *Int'l*, pg. 5012
NORAUTRON GROUP AS; *Int'l*, pg. 5415
NORBA A/S—See Geesink Group B.V.; *Int'l*, pg. 2911
NORBAR TORQUE TOOLS (AUSTRALIA) PTY. LTD.—See Snap-on Incorporated; *U.S. Public*, pg. 1898
NORBAR TORQUE TOOLS, INC.—See Snap-on Incorporated; *U.S. Public*, pg. 1898
NORBAR TORQUE TOOLS INDIA PRIVATE LIMITED—See Snap-on Incorporated; *U.S. Public*, pg. 1898
NORBAR TORQUE TOOLS LIMITED—See Snap-on Incorporated; *U.S. Public*, pg. 1898
NORBAR TORQUE TOOLS (NZ) LIMITED—See Snap-on Incorporated; *U.S. Public*, pg. 1898
NORBAR TORQUE TOOLS PRIVATE LIMITED—See Snap-on Incorporated; *U.S. Public*, pg. 1898
NORBAR TORQUE TOOLS (SHANGHAI) LTD—See Snap-on Incorporated; *U.S. Public*, pg. 1898
NORBA SA—See Atrya SAS; *Int'l*, pg. 694
NORBECK COUNTRY CLUB, INC.—See Apollo Global Management, Inc.; *U.S. Public*, pg. 150
NORBEC S.A.S.—See Optimum Group Inc.; *Int'l*, pg. 5604
NORBELLA INC.; *U.S. Private*, pg. 2935
NORBEN TEA & EXPORTS LIMITED; *Int'l*, pg. 5415
NORBERT E. MITCHELL CO. INC.; *U.S. Private*, pg. 2935
NORBEST, INC.; *U.S. Private*, pg. 2935
NORBETONG A.S.—See Heidelberg Materials AG; *Int'l*, pg. 3315
NORBETONG PUMPING AS—See Heidelberg Materials AG; *Int'l*, pg. 3318
NORBIT ASA; *Int'l*, pg. 5415
NORBIT EMS AS—See Norbit ASA; *Int'l*, pg. 5415
NORBIT GMBH—See Norbit ASA; *Int'l*, pg. 5415
NORBIT KABELPARTNER AS—See Norbit ASA; *Int'l*, pg. 5415
NORBORD INC.—See West Fraser Timber Co., Ltd.; *Int'l*, pg. 8383
NORBORD INDUSTRIES, INC.—See West Fraser Timber Co., Ltd.; *Int'l*, pg. 8383
NORBORD JEFFERSON—See West Fraser Timber Co., Ltd.; *Int'l*, pg. 8384
NORBORD NACOGDOCHES—See West Fraser Timber Co., Ltd.; *Int'l*, pg. 8384
NORBY DISTRIBUTING CO.; *U.S. Private*, pg. 2935
NOR-CAL BEVERAGE CO., INC.; *U.S. Private*, pg. 2935
NOR-CAL FOODS, INC.; *U.S. Private*, pg. 2935

NOR-CAL FOODS, INC.

CORPORATE AFFILIATIONS

NORCAL GOLD, INC. - FAIR OAKS—See Norcal Gold, Inc.; *U.S. Private*, pg. 2935
NORCAL GOLD, INC. - LODI—See Norcal Gold, Inc.; *U.S. Private*, pg. 2935
NORCAL GOLD, INC. - SACRAMENTO—See Norcal Gold, Inc.; *U.S. Private*, pg. 2935
NORCAL GOLD, INC.; *U.S. Private*, pg. 2935
NORCAL KENWORTH - ANDERSON—See SSMB Pacific Holding Company, Inc.; *U.S. Private*, pg. 3769
NORCAL KENWORTH - SACRAMENTO—See SSMB Pacific Holding Company, Inc.; *U.S. Private*, pg. 3769
NORCAL KENWORTH - SAN LEANDRO—See SSMB Pacific Holding Company, Inc.; *U.S. Private*, pg. 3769
NOR-CAL MOVING SERVICES; *U.S. Private*, pg. 2935
NORCAL MUTUAL INSURANCE CO.—See ProAssurance Corporation; *U.S. Public*, pg. 1723
NOR-CAL PRODUCE, INC.—See United Natural Foods, Inc.; *U.S. Public*, pg. 2231
NOR-CAL PRODUCTS ASIA PACIFIC PTE. LTD.—See Dr. Ing. K. Busch GmbH; *Int'l*, pg. 2193
NOR-CAL PRODUCTS, INC.—See Dr. Ing. K. Busch GmbH; *Int'l*, pg. 2193
NOR-CAL PRODUCTS KOREA CO., LTD.—See Dr. Ing. K. Busch GmbH; *Int'l*, pg. 2193
NORCAL RENTAL GROUP LLC; *U.S. Private*, pg. 2935
NORCAL RESPIRATORY INC.—See Quipt Home Medical Corp.; *U.S. Public*, pg. 1757
NORCEM A.S.—See Heidelberg Materials AG; *Int'l*, pg. 3318
NORCES EQUIPAMIENTO CIENTIFICO SRL—See HORIBA Ltd; *Int'l*, pg. 3477
NORCHEM, INC.—See Grupo Villar Mir, S.A.U.; *Int'l*, pg. 3138
NORCHIM S.A.S.—See PMC Capital Partners, LLC; *U.S. Private*, pg. 3217
NORCOD AS; *Int'l*, pg. 5415
NORCO DELIVERY SERVICES; *U.S. Private*, pg. 2935
NORCO INC. - EPHRATA FILL GAS PLANT—See Norco, Inc.; *U.S. Private*, pg. 2936
NORCO INC. - LEWISTON FILL GAS PLANT—See Norco, Inc.; *U.S. Private*, pg. 2936
NORCO INC. - MOSES LAKE A.S.U. PLANT—See Norco, Inc.; *U.S. Private*, pg. 2936
NORCO INC. - NAMPA A.S.U. PLANT—See Norco, Inc.; *U.S. Private*, pg. 2936
NORCO, INC.; *U.S. Private*, pg. 2936
NORCO INDUSTRIES, INC.; *U.S. Private*, pg. 2936
NORCOLD—See The Dyson-Kissner-Moran Corporation; *U.S. Private*, pg. 4024
NORCOM INC.; *U.S. Private*, pg. 2936
NORCOM INFORMATION TECHNOLOGY GMBH & CO. KGAA; *Int'l*, pg. 5415
NORCOM SYSTEMS TECHNOLOGY GMBH—See NorCom Information Technology GmbH & Co. KGaA; *Int'l*, pg. 5415
NORCON INC.; *U.S. Private*, pg. 2936
NORCON INDUSTRIES INC.; *U.S. Private*, pg. 2936
NORCON PLC; *Int'l*, pg. 5415
NORCONTROL CHILE, S.A.—See I Squared Capital Advisors (US) LLC; *U.S. Private*, pg. 2023
NORCONTROL CHILE, S.A.—See TDR Capital LLP; *Int'l*, pg. 7492
NORCONTROL NICARAGUA, S.A.—See I Squared Capital Advisors (US) LLC; *U.S. Private*, pg. 2023
NORCONTROL NICARAGUA, S.A.—See TDR Capital LLP; *Int'l*, pg. 7492
NORCOR TECHNOLOGIES CORPORATION; *U.S. Private*, pg. 2936
NORCOSTCO, INC.; *U.S. Private*, pg. 2936
NOR-COTE INTERNATIONAL INC.; *U.S. Private*, pg. 2935
NORCRAFT CANADA CORPORATION—See MasterBrand, Inc.; *U.S. Public*, pg. 1394
NORCRAFT COMPANIES, INC.—See MasterBrand, Inc.; *U.S. Public*, pg. 1394
NORCRAFT COMPANIES, L.P.—See MasterBrand, Inc.; *U.S. Public*, pg. 1394
NORCRAFT HOLDINGS, L.P.—See MasterBrand, Inc.; *U.S. Public*, pg. 1394
NORCROS ADHESIVES LTD.—See Norcros plc; *Int'l*, pg. 5415
NORCROS PLC; *Int'l*, pg. 5415
NORCROS SA (PTY) LTD—See Norcros plc; *Int'l*, pg. 5415
NORCROSS COMPANY; *U.S. Private*, pg. 2936
NORCROSS CORPORATION—See Saint Clair Systems, Inc.; *U.S. Private*, pg. 3529
NORD AANDRIJVINGEN BELGIE NV—See Getriebebau NORD GmbH & Co. KG; *Int'l*, pg. 2953
NORD AANDRIJVINGEN NEDERLAND B.V.—See Getriebebau NORD GmbH & Co. KG; *Int'l*, pg. 2953
NORDALU GMBH—See ALCO Hellas S.A.; *Int'l*, pg. 301
NORDAM EUROPE LIMITED—See General Dynamics Corporation; *U.S. Public*, pg. 913
THE NORDAM GROUP, INC.—See General Dynamics Corporation; *U.S. Public*, pg. 913
THE NORDAM GROUP, INC.—See General Dynamics Corporation; *U.S. Public*, pg. 913

NORDAM SINGAPORE PTE LTD—See General Dynamics Corporation; *U.S. Public*, pg. 913
NORD ANGLIA EDUCATION, INC.—See Canada Pension Plan Investment Board; *Int'l*, pg. 1281
NORD ANGLIA EDUCATION, INC.—See EQT AB; *Int'l*, pg. 2470
NORD ANGLIA EDUCATION LIMITED—See Canada Pension Plan Investment Board; *Int'l*, pg. 1281
NORD ANGLIA EDUCATION LIMITED—See EQT AB; *Int'l*, pg. 2470
NORDANIA LEASING—See Danske Bank A/S; *Int'l*, pg. 1969
NORDA S.P.A.; *Int'l*, pg. 5416
NOR-DAT COMPUTER SERVICES, LTD.; *Int'l*, pg. 5414
NORD AUDIO ELECTRONIQUE SAS—See VINCI S.A.; *Int'l*, pg. 8224
NORDAUTOMATION AB—See Addtech AB; *Int'l*, pg. 134
NORDAUTOMATION OY—See Addtech AB; *Int'l*, pg. 134
NORDAX GROUP AB; *Int'l*, pg. 5416
NORDBLADS VVS-KONSTRUKTIONER AB—See AFRY AB; *Int'l*, pg. 194
NORDBODEN IMMOBILIEN- UND HANDELSGESELL-SCHAFT MBH—See Commerzbank AG; *Int'l*, pg. 1718
NORDBRAND NORDHAUSEN GMBH—See Rotkappchen-Mumm Sektkellereien GmbH; *Int'l*, pg. 6404
NORDBYEN SENTER AS—See BNP Paribas SA; *Int'l*, pg. 1092
NORDCAPITAL GMBH—See E.R. CAPITAL HOLDING GmbH & Cie. KG; *Int'l*, pg. 2260
NORDCARGO S.R.L.—See Deutsche Bahn AG; *Int'l*, pg. 2050
THE NORD CENTER; *U.S. Private*, pg. 4084
NORD (CHINA) POWER TRANSMISSION CO., LTD.—See Getriebebau NORD GmbH & Co. KG; *Int'l*, pg. 2953
NORD COFFRAGE S.A.—See Hiolle Industries S.A.; *Int'l*, pg. 3401
NORDCO, INC.—See Greenbriar Equity Group, L.P.; *U.S. Private*, pg. 1776
NORD COMAT SHPK.—See Ading AD; *Int'l*, pg. 149
NORDCOM S.P.A.—See FNM S.p.A.; *Int'l*, pg. 2718
NORD CONSTRUCTIONS NOUVELLES; *Int'l*, pg. 5415
NORD DATA A/S—See NorgesGruppen ASA; *Int'l*, pg. 5427
NORDDEICH TV PRODUKTIONSGESELLSCHAFT MBH—See Bertelsmann SE & Co. KGaA; *Int'l*, pg. 995
NORDDEUTSCHE FLUSSIGZUCKER GMBH & CO. KG—See Nordzucker AG; *Int'l*, pg. 5426
NORDDEUTSCHE GESELLSCHAFT ZUR ABLAGERUNG VON MINERALSTOFFEN MBH—See E.ON SE; *Int'l*, pg. 2258
NORDDEUTSCHE GRUNDSTUCKSAUKTIONEN AG—See Deutsche Grundstuecksauktionen AG; *Int'l*, pg. 2065
NORDDEUTSCHE KUNSTSTOFF UND ELEKTROGE-SELLSCHAFT STACKER MBH & CO. KG; *Int'l*, pg. 5416
NORDDEUTSCHE LANDESBANK GIROZENTRALE; *Int'l*, pg. 5416
NORDDEUTSCHER LLOYD GMBH—See Albert Ballin KG; *Int'l*, pg. 295
NORDDEUTSCHE SECURITIES PLC—See Norddeutsche Landesbank Girozentrale; *Int'l*, pg. 5417
NORDDEUTSCHE SEEKABELWERKE GMBH—See Prysmian S.p.A.; *Int'l*, pg. 6011
NORDDEUTSCHE STEINGUT AG; *Int'l*, pg. 5417
NORD-DIREKT GMBH—See E.ON SE; *Int'l*, pg. 2258
NORD DRIVESYSTEMS BRASIL LTDA.—See Getriebebau NORD GmbH & Co. KG; *Int'l*, pg. 2953
NORD DRIVESYSTEMS CO., LTD.—See Getriebebau NORD GmbH & Co. KG; *Int'l*, pg. 2953
NORD DRIVESYSTEMS GUC AKTARMA SISTEMLERI SAN. VE TIC. LTD. STI.—See Getriebebau NORD GmbH & Co. KG; *Int'l*, pg. 2953
NORD DRIVESYSTEMS PTP, LDA.—See Getriebebau NORD GmbH & Co. KG; *Int'l*, pg. 2953
NORD DRIVESYSTEMS PTY LTD—See Getriebebau NORD GmbH & Co. KG; *Int'l*, pg. 2953
NORD DRIVESYSTEMS PVT. LTD.—See Getriebebau NORD GmbH & Co. KG; *Int'l*, pg. 2953
NORD DRIVE SYSTEMS SA DE CV—See Getriebebau NORD GmbH & Co. KG; *Int'l*, pg. 2953
NORD DRIVSYSTEM AB—See Getriebebau NORD GmbH & Co. KG; *Int'l*, pg. 2953
NORDEA BANK ABP; *Int'l*, pg. 5417
NORDEA BANK DANMARK A/S—See Nordea Bank Abp; *Int'l*, pg. 5417
NORDEA BANK ESTONIA—See Nordea Bank Abp; *Int'l*, pg. 5418
NORDEA BANK FINLAND PLC - GERMANY REPRESENTATIVE OFFICE—See Nordea Bank Abp; *Int'l*, pg. 5417
NORDEA BANK FINLAND PLC—See Nordea Bank Abp; *Int'l*, pg. 5417
NORDEA BANK FINLAND PLC - UK REPRESENTATIVE OFFICE—See Nordea Bank Abp; *Int'l*, pg. 5417
NORDEA BANK FINLAND PLC - US REPRESENTATIVE OFFICE—See Nordea Bank Abp; *Int'l*, pg. 5417
NORDEA BANK JSC; *Int'l*, pg. 5418

NORDEA BANK MOSCOW—See Nordea Bank Abp; *Int'l*, pg. 5417
NORDEA BANK NORWAY ASA—See Nordea Bank Abp; *Int'l*, pg. 5417
NORDEA BANK SA—See Nordea Bank Abp; *Int'l*, pg. 5418
NORDEA BANK SA—See Nordea Bank Abp; *Int'l*, pg. 5418
NORDEA BANK SWEDEN AB—See Nordea Bank Abp; *Int'l*, pg. 5418
NORDEA CORPORATE FINANCE OY—See Nordea Bank Abp; *Int'l*, pg. 5417
NORDEA DANMARK, FILIAL AF NORDEA BANK APS—See Nordea Bank Abp; *Int'l*, pg. 5418
NORDEA EIENDOMSKREDITT AS—See Nordea Bank Abp; *Int'l*, pg. 5417
NORDEA EJENDOMSINVESTERING A/S—See Nordea Bank Abp; *Int'l*, pg. 5417
NORDEA FINANCE EQUIPMENT AS—See Nordea Bank Abp; *Int'l*, pg. 5418
NORDEA FINANCE FINLAND LTD.—See Nordea Bank Abp; *Int'l*, pg. 5417
NORDEA FINANS A/S—See Nordea Bank Abp; *Int'l*, pg. 5417
NORDEA FINANS DANMARK A/S—See Nordea Bank Abp; *Int'l*, pg. 5417
NORDEA FINANS NORGE AS—See Nordea Bank Abp; *Int'l*, pg. 5417
NORDEA FONDER AB—See Nordea Bank Abp; *Int'l*, pg. 5418
NORDEA INVESTMENT FUND COMPANY, FINLAND LTD—See Nordea Bank Abp; *Int'l*, pg. 5417
NORDEA INVESTMENT FUND MANAGEMENT A/S—See Nordea Bank Abp; *Int'l*, pg. 5417
NORDEA INVESTMENT FUNDS S.A.—See Nordea Bank Abp; *Int'l*, pg. 5418
NORDEA INVESTMENT MANAGEMENT AB—See Nordea Bank Abp; *Int'l*, pg. 5418
NORDEA INVESTMENT MANAGEMENT—See Nordea Bank Abp; *Int'l*, pg. 5417
NORDEA KREDIT REALKREDITAKTIESELSKAB—See Nordea Bank Abp; *Int'l*, pg. 5417
NORDEAKREDITT A/S—See Nordea Bank Abp; *Int'l*, pg. 5418
NORDEA LIFE ASSURANCE FINLAND LTD—See Nordea Bank Abp; *Int'l*, pg. 5418
NORDEA LIFE HOLDING FINLAND LTD—See Nordea Bank Abp; *Int'l*, pg. 5418
NORDEA LIV AS—See Nordea Bank Abp; *Int'l*, pg. 5418
NORDEA LIVFORSAKRING SVERIGE AB—See Nordea Bank Abp; *Int'l*, pg. 5418
NORDEA LIV HOLDING NORGE AS—See Nordea Bank Abp; *Int'l*, pg. 5417
NORDEA NORTH AMERICA INC.—See Nordea Bank Abp; *Int'l*, pg. 5418
NORDEA NORWAY A/S—See Nordea Bank Abp; *Int'l*, pg. 5417
NORDEA PENSION, LIVSFORSIKRINGSSELSKAB A/S—See Nordea Bank Abp; *Int'l*, pg. 5418
NORDEA PENSIONS ESTONIA AS—See Nordea Bank Abp; *Int'l*, pg. 5418
NORDEA PRIVATE BANKING—See Nordea Bank Abp; *Int'l*, pg. 5418
NORDEA SECURITIES—See Nordea Bank Abp; *Int'l*, pg. 5418
NORDEC ENVELOPE OY—See Mutares SE & Co. KGaA; *Int'l*, pg. 5105
NORDECON AS; *Int'l*, pg. 5418
NORDEC OY—See Mutares SE & Co. KGaA; *Int'l*, pg. 5105
NORDEC SP.Z. O.O.—See Mutares SE & Co. KGaA; *Int'l*, pg. 5105
NORDEC S. R. O.—See Mutares SE & Co. KGaA; *Int'l*, pg. 5105
NORDEKA MADEN A.S.—See Rettig Group Ltd.; *Int'l*, pg. 6310
NORDELTAÇO A/S—See DistIT AB; *Int'l*, pg. 2136
NORDEN CROWN METALS CORP.; *Int'l*, pg. 5418
NORDENFJELDSKE SPUNT OG PELESERVICE AS—See Peab AB; *Int'l*, pg. 5772
NORDEN GMBH—See Coesia S.p.A.; *Int'l*, pg. 1690
NORDENHAMER TRANSPORTBETON GMBH & CO. KG—See Buzzi SpA; *Int'l*, pg. 1230
NORDENHAMER ZINKHUTTE GMBH—See Glencore plc; *Int'l*, pg. 2991
NORDEN MACHINERY AB—See Coesia S.p.A.; *Int'l*, pg. 1690
NORDEN SHIPPING ABIDJAN SARLU—See Dampskibsselskabet NORDEN A/S; *Int'l*, pg. 1957
NORDEN SHIPPING MIDDLE EAST DMCC—See Dampskibsselskabet NORDEN A/S; *Int'l*, pg. 1957
NORDEN SHIPPING (SINGAPORE) PTE. LTD—See Dampskibsselskabet NORDEN A/S; *Int'l*, pg. 1957
NORDEN TANKERS & BULKERS DO BRAZIL LTDA—See Dampskibsselskabet NORDEN A/S; *Int'l*, pg. 1957
NORDEN TANKERS & BULKERS INDIA PVT. LTD—See Dampskibsselskabet NORDEN A/S; *Int'l*, pg. 1957
NORDEON GMBH—See Varova BV; *Int'l*, pg. 8133
NORDER SUPPLY, INC (NSI); *U.S. Private*, pg. 2936

COMPANY NAME INDEX

NORDEX (BEIJING) WIND POWER ENGINEERING & TECHNOLOGY CO. LTD.—See Nordex SE; *Int'l*, pg. 5418
NORDEX (CHILE) SPA—See Nordex SE; *Int'l*, pg. 5418
NORDEX CHINA—See Nordex SE; *Int'l*, pg. 5418
NORDEX ENERGY IRELAND LTD.—See Nordex SE; *Int'l*, pg. 5418
NORDEX ENERGY ROMANIA S.R.L.—See Nordex SE; *Int'l*, pg. 5418
NORDEX ENERGY SOUTH AFRICA RF (PTY.) LTD.—See Nordex SE; *Int'l*, pg. 5418
NORDEXENERGY URUGUAY S.A.—See Nordex SE; *Int'l*, pg. 5419
NORDEX ENERJI A.S.—See Nordex SE; *Int'l*, pg. 5418
NORDEX FINLAND OY—See Nordex SE; *Int'l*, pg. 5418
NORDEX FRANCE S.A.S.—See Nordex SE; *Int'l*, pg. 5418
NORDEX GERMANY GMBH—See Nordex SE; *Int'l*, pg. 5418
NORDEX ITALIA S.R.L.—See Nordex SE; *Int'l*, pg. 5418
NORDEX NETHERLANDS B.V.—See Nordex SE; *Int'l*, pg. 5418
NORDEX PAKISTAN (PRIVATE) LTD.—See Nordex SE; *Int'l*, pg. 5418
NORDEX POLSKA SP. Z O.O.—See Nordex SE; *Int'l*, pg. 5418
NORDEX SE; *Int'l*, pg. 5418
NORDEX SVERIGE AB—See Nordex SE; *Int'l*, pg. 5419
NORDEX UK LTD.—See Nordex SE; *Int'l*, pg. 5419
NORDEX USA, INC.—See Nordex SE; *Int'l*, pg. 5419
NORDFAB EUROPE AS—See Nederman Holding AB; *Int'l*, pg. 5190
NORDFAB LLC—See Nederman Holding AB; *Int'l*, pg. 5190
NORDFAB PTY. LTD.—See Nederman Holding AB; *Int'l*, pg. 5190
NORD FARM SP. Z O.O.—See Farmak JSC; *Int'l*, pg. 2619
NORDFINANZ BANK AG; *Int'l*, pg. 5419
NORD/FM NORDDEUTSCHE FACILITY MANAGEMENT GMBH—See Norddeutsche Landesbank Girozentrale; *Int'l*, pg. 5417
NORDFOLIEN GMBH—See Berry Global Group, Inc; *U.S. Public*, pg. 322
NORDFOLIEN POLSKA SP. Z O.O.—See Berry Global Group, Inc; *U.S. Public*, pg. 322
NORD-FOSEN PUKKVERK AS—See Heidelberg Materials AG; *Int'l*, pg. 3318
NORD FRANCE CONSTRUCTIONS COMPIEGNE—See FAYAT SAS; *Int'l*, pg. 2626
NORD FRANCE CONSTRUCTIONS—See FAYAT SAS; *Int'l*, pg. 2626
NORDFYNS BANK A/S; *Int'l*, pg. 5419
NORD GEAR CORPORATION—See Getriebebau NORD GmbH & Co. KG; *Int'l*, pg. 2953
NORD GEAR DANMARK A/S—See Getriebebau NORD GmbH & Co. KG; *Int'l*, pg. 2953
NORD GEAR LIMITED—See Getriebebau NORD GmbH & Co. KG; *Int'l*, pg. 2953
NORD GEAR LTD.—See Getriebebau NORD GmbH & Co. KG; *Int'l*, pg. 2953
NORD GEAR NORGE A/S—See Getriebebau NORD GmbH & Co. KG; *Int'l*, pg. 2953
NORD GEAR OY—See Getriebebau NORD GmbH & Co. KG; *Int'l*, pg. 2953
NORD GEAR PTE LTD—See Getriebebau NORD GmbH & Co. KG; *Int'l*, pg. 2953
NORDGLASS DANMARK A/S—See AGC Inc.; *Int'l*, pg. 202
NORDGLASS DISTRIBUCE S.R.O.—See AGC Inc.; *Int'l*, pg. 202
NORDGLASS DISTRIBUTION GMBH—See AGC Inc.; *Int'l*, pg. 202
NORDGLASS FRANCE SARL—See AGC Inc.; *Int'l*, pg. 202
NORDGLASS SP. Z O.O.—See AGC Inc.; *Int'l*, pg. 202
NORDGLASS SVERIGE AB—See AGC Inc.; *Int'l*, pg. 202
NORD GOLD SE; *Int'l*, pg. 5415
NORD HAJTASTECHNIKA KFT.—See Getriebebau NORD GmbH & Co. KG; *Int'l*, pg. 2953
NORDHEALTH AS; *Int'l*, pg. 5419
NORDHEALTH OY—See Nordhealth AS; *Int'l*, pg. 5419
NORD HELIKOPTER AS—See Flakk Holding AS; *Int'l*, pg. 2698
NORD HELIO SERVICE SAS—See Janoschka GmbH; *Int'l*, pg. 3880
NORD HOLDING UNTERNEHMENSBETEILIGUNGSGESELLSCHAFT MBH; *Int'l*, pg. 5416
NORDIALOG OSLO AS—See Teki Solutions AS; *Int'l*, pg. 7527
NORDIC ALARM AB—See Lagercrantz Group AB; *Int'l*, pg. 4394
NORDICA LIFE (BERMUDA) LTD.; *Int'l*, pg. 5424
NORDIC ALUMINIUM, INC.—See Lival Oy; *Int'l*, pg. 4529
NORDIC ALUMINIUM PLC—See Lival Oy; *Int'l*, pg. 4529
NORDIC AMERICAN TANKERS LIMITED; *Int'l*, pg. 5419
NORDIC AQUA PARTNERS A/S; *Int'l*, pg. 5419
NORDIC AVIATION CAPITAL INC.; *U.S. Private*, pg. 2936
NORDIC BATTERY AB—See Addtech AB; *Int'l*, pg. 134
NORDIC BATTERY AS—See Addtech AB; *Int'l*, pg. 134

NORDIC BULK CARRIERS A/S—See Pangaea Logistics Solutions Ltd.; *U.S. Public*, pg. 1635
NORDIC BULK CARRIERS SINGAPORE PTE. LTD.—See Pangaea Logistics Solutions Ltd.; *U.S. Public*, pg. 1635
NORDIC CAPITAL AB; *Int'l*, pg. 5419
NORDIC CAPITAL LIMITED—See Nordic Capital AB; *Int'l*, pg. 5420
NORDIC CAPITAL SARL—See Nordic Capital AB; *Int'l*, pg. 5420
NORDIC CARE AB—See Humana AB; *Int'l*, pg. 3530
NORDIC COLD STORAGE, LLC; *U.S. Private*, pg. 2936
NORDIC CONTRACTING COMPANY, INCORPORATED; *U.S. Private*, pg. 2936
NORDIC CORPORATE BANK ASA; *Int'l*, pg. 5421
NORDIC DEFENCE SUPPLY AS—See Rheinmetall AG; *Int'l*, pg. 6323
NORDIC DISTRIBUTION OY—See Patria Oyj; *Int'l*, pg. 5757
NORDIC ELEMENTS AB; *Int'l*, pg. 5421
NORDIC ENERGY LINK AS—See Eesti Energia AS; *Int'l*, pg. 2318
NORDIC ENERGY SERVICES, LLC; *U.S. Private*, pg. 2936
NORDIC ENGINEERED WOOD—See Les Chantiers De Chibougamau Ltee; *Int'l*, pg. 4467
NORDIC FIBREBOARD AS; *Int'l*, pg. 5422
NORDIC FIBREBOARD LTD OU—See Nordic Fibreboard AS; *Int'l*, pg. 5422
NORDIC FLANGES GROUP AB; *Int'l*, pg. 5422
NORDIC FLOW CONTROL PTE. LTD.—See Nordic Group Limited; *Int'l*, pg. 5422
NORDIC FLOW CONTROL (SUZHOU) CO., LTD.—See Nordic Group Limited; *Int'l*, pg. 5422
NORDIC FORSAKRING & RISKHANTERING AB—See Arthur J. Gallagher & Co.; *U.S. Public*, pg. 206
NORDIC FRUIT HOLDING AB—See Dole plc; *Int'l*, pg. 2158
NORDIC GAMES GMBH—See Nordic Games Holding AB; *Int'l*, pg. 5422
NORDIC GAMES HOLDING AB; *Int'l*, pg. 5422
NORDIC GROUP LIMITED; *Int'l*, pg. 5422
NORDIC GROUP OF COMPANIES, LTD.; *U.S. Private*, pg. 2936
NORDIC HALIBUT AS; *Int'l*, pg. 5422
NORDIC HEAT & VENT AB—See Litorina Capital Management AB; *Int'l*, pg. 4528
NORDIC INDUSTRIES INC.; *U.S. Private*, pg. 2937
NORDIC INFRASTRUCTURE GROUP AS—See Inin Group AS; *Int'l*, pg. 3703
NORDICINFU CARE A.B—See L'Air Liquide S.A.; *Int'l*, pg. 4375
THE NORDIC INSURANCE COMPANY OF CANADA—See Intact Financial Corporation; *Int'l*, pg. 3726
NORDIC INSURANCE SOFTWARE A/S—See Acturis Ltd.; *Int'l*, pg. 121
NORDIC INVESTMENT BANK; *Int'l*, pg. 5422
NORDIC IRON ORE AB; *Int'l*, pg. 5422
NORDIC LEVEL GROUP AB; *Int'l*, pg. 5422
NORDIC LIGHT AB—See ITAB Shop Concept AB; *Int'l*, pg. 3828
NORDIC LIGHT AMERICA INC.—See ITAB Shop Concept AB; *Int'l*, pg. 3828
NORDIC LIGHT GROUP (HK) CO., LTD.—See ITAB Shop Concept AB; *Int'l*, pg. 3828
NORDIC LIGHT SOUTH AMERICA SPA—See ITAB Shop Concept AB; *Int'l*, pg. 3828
NORDIC LIGHTS OY—See Methode Electronics, Inc.; *U.S. Public*, pg. 1429
NORDIC LIGHT (SUZHOU) CO., LTD.—See ITAB Shop Concept AB; *Int'l*, pg. 3828
NORDIC LUBRICANTS AB—See BP plc; *Int'l*, pg. 1131
NORDIC LUBRICANTS A/S—See BP plc; *Int'l*, pg. 1131
NORDIC MINING ASA; *Int'l*, pg. 5422
NORDIC MORNING AB—See Nordic Morning Plc; *Int'l*, pg. 5422
NORDIC MORNING PLC; *Int'l*, pg. 5422
NORDIC MORNING SWEDEN AB—See Nordic Morning Plc; *Int'l*, pg. 5422
NORDIC NANOVECTOR GMBH—See Thor Medical ASA; *Int'l*, pg. 7717
NORDIC NATURALS, INC.; *U.S. Private*, pg. 2937
NORDIC NEST AB—See BHG Group AB; *Int'l*, pg. 1015
NORDIC NICKEL LIMITED; *Int'l*, pg. 5423
NORDIC OIL & GAS LTD.; *Int'l*, pg. 5423
NORDIC PAPER AS—See Nordic Paper Holding AB; *Int'l*, pg. 5423
NORDIC PAPER BACKHAMMAR AB—See Nordic Paper Holding AB; *Int'l*, pg. 5423
NORDIC PAPER HOLDING AB; *Int'l*, pg. 5423
NORDIC PAPER QUEBEC INC.—See Nordic Paper Holding AB; *Int'l*, pg. 5423
NORDIC PAPER SEFFLE AB—See Nordic Paper Holding AB; *Int'l*, pg. 5423
NORDIC PCL CONSTRUCTION, INC.—See PCL Employees Holdings Ltd.; *Int'l*, pg. 5769
NORDIC PRODUCTS, INC.—See Monomoy Capital Partners LLC; *U.S. Private*, pg. 2772

NORDIC RETAIL A/S—See CCL Industries Inc.; *Int'l*, pg. 1368
NORDIC SEAFOOD A/S—See Nissui Corporation; *Int'l*, pg. 5378
NORDIC SEMICONDUCTOR ASA; *Int'l*, pg. 5423
NORDIC SEMICONDUCTOR GERMANY GMBH—See Nordic Semiconductor ASA; *Int'l*, pg. 5423
NORDIC SEMICONDUCTOR INC.—See Nordic Semiconductor ASA; *Int'l*, pg. 5423
NORDIC SEMICONDUCTOR JAPAN KK—See Nordic Semiconductor ASA; *Int'l*, pg. 5423
NORDIC SEMICONDUCTOR NORWAY AS—See Nordic Semiconductor ASA; *Int'l*, pg. 5423
NORDIC SEMICONDUCTOR POLAND S.P. Z O.O.—See Nordic Semiconductor ASA; *Int'l*, pg. 5423
NORDIC SERVICE PARTNERS HOLDING AB; *Int'l*, pg. 5423
NORDIC SHIPHOLDING A/S; *Int'l*, pg. 5423
NORDIC SUGAR A/S—See Nordzucker AG; *Int'l*, pg. 5426
NORDIC SUGAR SIA—See Nordzucker AG; *Int'l*, pg. 5426
NORDIC SUGAR—See Nordzucker AG; *Int'l*, pg. 5426
NORDIC TALENT PROFESSIONALS—See ManpowerGroup Inc.; *U.S. Public*, pg. 1360
NORDIC TANKERS (COLOMBIA) LTDA.—See Mitsui O.S.K. Lines, Ltd.; *Int'l*, pg. 4990
NORDIC TANKERS MARINE SIA—See Mitsui O.S.K. Lines, Ltd.; *Int'l*, pg. 4990
NORDIC TANKERS TRADING A/S—See Mitsui O.S.K. Lines, Ltd.; *Int'l*, pg. 4990
NORDIC TRANSPORT GROUP HOLDING A/S; *Int'l*, pg. 5423
NORDIC TUGS INC.; *U.S. Private*, pg. 2937
NORDIC UNMANNED ASA; *Int'l*, pg. 5423
NORDICUS PARTNERS CORPORATION—See Mitsubishi Chemical Group Corporation; *Int'l*, pg. 4932
NORDIC VISITOR HF; *Int'l*, pg. 5423
NORDIC WATER GMBH—See Sulzer Ltd.; *Int'l*, pg. 7256
NORDIC WATER PRODUCTS A/S—See Sulzer Ltd.; *Int'l*, pg. 7256
NORDIC WATER PRODUCTS (BEIJING) CO., LTD.—See Sulzer Ltd.; *Int'l*, pg. 7256
NORDIC WATERPROOFING AB—See Axcel Management A/S; *Int'l*, pg. 762
NORDIC WATERPROOFING AS—See Kingspan Group PLC; *Int'l*, pg. 4178
NORDIC WATERPROOFING HOLDING AB—See Kingspan Group PLC; *Int'l*, pg. 4178
NORDIC WATERPROOFING OY—See Kingspan Group PLC; *Int'l*, pg. 4178
NORDIC WATERPROOFING SP. Z O.O.—See Kingspan Group PLC; *Int'l*, pg. 4178
NORDIC WHEEL & AUTOSUPPLY AB—See Storskogen Group AB; *Int'l*, pg. 7228
NORDICWHEELS AB—See Nokian Renkaat Oyj; *Int'l*, pg. 5407
NORDIC WOOD INDUSTRIES A/S; *Int'l*, pg. 5423
NORDIC YARDS HOLDING GMBH; *Int'l*, pg. 5423
NORDIC YARDS STRALSUND GMBH—See Nordic Yards Holding GmbH; *Int'l*, pg. 5423
NORDIC YARDS WARNEMUNDE GMBH—See Nordic Yards Holding GmbH; *Int'l*, pg. 5423
NORDIC YARDS WISMAR GMBH—See Nordic Yards Holding GmbH; *Int'l*, pg. 5424
NORDION INC.—See Warburg Pincus LLC; *U.S. Private*, pg. 4439
NORDIQUE RESOURCES INC.; *Int'l*, pg. 5424
NORDIS DIRECT, INC.; *U.S. Private*, pg. 2937
NORDISKA FONSTER I ANGELHOLM AB—See BHG Group AB; *Int'l*, pg. 1014
NORDISKA INDUSTRI AB—See Investment AB Latour; *Int'l*, pg. 3783
NORDISKA KOMPANIET AB—See L. E. Lundbergforetagen AB; *Int'l*, pg. 4381
NORDISK ASIA PACIFIC LTD—See TransDigm Group Incorporated; *U.S. Public*, pg. 2183
NORDISKA UNIPOL AB—See Kulczyk Investments S.A.; *Int'l*, pg. 4328
NORDISK AVIATION PRODUCTS AS—See TransDigm Group Incorporated; *U.S. Public*, pg. 2183
NORDISK BERGTEKNIK AB; *Int'l*, pg. 5424
NORDISK ENERGIPARTNER A/S—See World Kinect Corporation; *U.S. Public*, pg. 2381
NORDISK FILM AB—See Egmont Fonden; *Int'l*, pg. 2326
NORDISK FILM A/S—See Egmont Fonden; *Int'l*, pg. 2326
NORDISK FILM AS—See Egmont Fonden; *Int'l*, pg. 2326
NORDISK FILM BIOGRAFER A/S—See Egmont Fonden; *Int'l*, pg. 2326
NORDISK FILM KINO AS—See Egmont Fonden; *Int'l*, pg. 2326
NORDISK FILM POST PRODUCTION A/S—See Egmont Fonden; *Int'l*, pg. 2326
NORDISK FILM POST PRODUCTION STOCKHOLM AB—See Egmont Fonden; *Int'l*, pg. 2326
NORDISK FILM PRODUCTION SVERIGE AB—See Egmont Fonden; *Int'l*, pg. 2326
NORDISK FILM SHORTCUT AB—See Egmont Fonden; *Int'l*, pg. 2326
NORDISK FILM SHORTCUT A/S—See Egmont Fonden; *Int'l*, pg. 2326

NORDISK BERGTEKNIK AB

NORDISK FILM SHORTCUT AS—See Egmont Fonden; *Int'l*, pg. 2326
NORDISK FILM TV AB—See LOV Group Invest SAS; *Int'l*, pg. 4563
NORDISK FILM TV A/S—See LOV Group Invest SAS; *Int'l*, pg. 4563
NORDISK FILM TV AS—See LOV Group Invest SAS; *Int'l*, pg. 4563
NORDISK KELLOGGS APS—See Kellanova; *U.S. Public*, pg. 1218
NORDISK PROFIL A/S—See Purso Group Oy; *Int'l*, pg. 6123
NORDISK RENTING AB—See NatWest Group plc; *Int'l*, pg. 5171
NORDISK RENTING OY—See NatWest Group plc; *Int'l*, pg. 5171
NORDISK SYSTEMS INC.—See Converge Technology Solutions Corp.; *Int'l*, pg. 1787
NORDISK WAVIN A/S—See Bharti Enterprises Limited; *Int'l*, pg. 1012
NORDITEK GROUP AB; *Int'l*, pg. 5424
NORDIX PHARMA VERTRIEB GMBH—See Nordmark Arzneimittel GmbH & Co. KG; *Int'l*, pg. 5424
NORDJYSKE BANK A/S—See Ringkjobing Landbobank A/S; *Int'l*, pg. 6344
NORDKALK AB—See SigmaRoc Plc; *Int'l*, pg. 6909
NORDKALK AB—See SigmaRoc Plc; *Int'l*, pg. 6909
NORDKALK AB—See SigmaRoc Plc; *Int'l*, pg. 6909
NORDKALK AS—See SigmaRoc Plc; *Int'l*, pg. 6909
NORDKALK AS—See SigmaRoc Plc; *Int'l*, pg. 6909
NORDKALK CORPORATION—See SigmaRoc Plc; *Int'l*, pg. 6909
NORDKALK GMBH—See Rettig Group Ltd.; *Int'l*, pg. 6310
NORDKALK SP. Z.O.O.—See SigmaRoc Plc; *Int'l*, pg. 6909
NORDKALK UKRAINE TOV—See Rettig Group Ltd.; *Int'l*, pg. 6310
NORD-KURS GMBH & CO. KG—See TUV NORD AG; *Int'l*, pg. 7980
NORD-KURS VERWALTUNGSGESELLSCHAFT MBH—See TUV NORD AG; *Int'l*, pg. 7980
NORDLAND HAVFISKE AS—See Austevoll Seafood ASA; *Int'l*, pg. 717
NORDLAND MUHLEN GMBH—See Raiffeisen-Holding Niederosterreich-Wien reg. Gen.m.b.H.; *Int'l*, pg. 6185
NORDLAND PAPIER GMBH—See UPM-Kymmene Corporation; *Int'l*, pg. 8090
NORD/LB ASSET MANAGEMENT HOLDING GMBH—See Norddeutsche Landesbank Girozentrale; *Int'l*, pg. 5417
NORD/LB COVERED FINANCE BANK S. A.—See Norddeutsche Landesbank Girozentrale; *Int'l*, pg. 5417
NORD/LB LUXEMBOURG S.A. COVERED BOND BANK—See Norddeutsche Landesbank Girozentrale; *Int'l*, pg. 5417
NORD/LB PROJECT HOLDING LTD.—See Norddeutsche Landesbank Girozentrale; *Int'l*, pg. 5417
NORDLICHT GMBH—See The Carlyle Group Inc.; *U.S. Public*, pg. 2052
NORDLIE INC.; *U.S. Private*, pg. 2937
NORD-LOCK AB—See Investment AB Latour; *Int'l*, pg. 3783
NORD-LOCK AG—See Investment AB Latour; *Int'l*, pg. 3784
NORD-LOCK APS—See Investment AB Latour; *Int'l*, pg. 3784
NORD-LOCK AS—See Investment AB Latour; *Int'l*, pg. 3784
NORD-LOCK BENELUX BV—See Investment AB Latour; *Int'l*, pg. 3783
NORD-LOCK CANADA, INC.—See Investment AB Latour; *Int'l*, pg. 3784
NORD-LOCK FRANCE S.A.R.L.—See Investment AB Latour; *Int'l*, pg. 3783
NORD-LOCK GMBH—See Investment AB Latour; *Int'l*, pg. 3783
NORD-LOCK HOLDING GMBH—See Investment AB Latour; *Int'l*, pg. 3783
NORD-LOCK IBERIA S.L.—See Investment AB Latour; *Int'l*, pg. 3784
NORD-LOCK INC.—See Investment AB Latour; *Int'l*, pg. 3783
NORD-LOCK INDIA PVT. LTD.—See Investment AB Latour; *Int'l*, pg. 3784
NORD-LOCK INTERNATIONAL AB—See Investment AB Latour; *Int'l*, pg. 3783
NORD-LOCK ITALY S.R.I.—See Investment AB Latour; *Int'l*, pg. 3784
NORD-LOCK JAPAN CO, LTD—See Investment AB Latour; *Int'l*, pg. 3783
NORD-LOCK KOREA CO., LTD.—See Investment AB Latour; *Int'l*, pg. 3784
NORD-LOCK LTD—See Investment AB Latour; *Int'l*, pg. 3783
NORD-LOCK OY—See Investment AB Latour; *Int'l*, pg. 3783
NORD-LOCK POLAND SP. Z.O.O.—See Investment AB Latour; *Int'l*, pg. 3783
NORD-LOCK PTE. LTD.—See Investment AB Latour; *Int'l*, pg. 3784

NORD-LOCK S.R.O.—See Investment AB Latour; *Int'l*, pg. 3783
NORD-LOCK SWITZERLAND GMBH—See Investment AB Latour; *Int'l*, pg. 3783
NORDMARK ARZNEIMITTEL GMBH & CO. KG; *Int'l*, pg. 5424
NORD MASON CO., LTD.; *Int'l*, pg. 5416
NORDMAX EQUIPMENT INC.—See Tym Corporation; *Int'l*, pg. 7995
NORDMEYER SMAG DRILLING TECHNOLOGIES GMBH—See Salzgitter AG; *Int'l*, pg. 6499
NORD-MOTORIDUTTORI S.R.L.—See Getriebebau NORD GmbH & Co. KG; *Int'l*, pg. 2953
NORD MOTORREDUCTORES S.A.—See Getriebebau NORD GmbH & Co. KG; *Int'l*, pg. 2953
NORD NAPEDY SP. Z O.O.—See Getriebebau NORD GmbH & Co. KG; *Int'l*, pg. 2953
NORDNET AB—See E. Ohman J:or AB; *Int'l*, pg. 2250
NORDNET—See Orange S.A.; *Int'l*, pg. 5609
NORDNETZ GMBH—See E.ON SE; *Int'l*, pg. 2258
NORD OFFSET DRUCK GMBH—See Johler Norddruck GmbH; *Int'l*, pg. 3977
NORDON INC; *U.S. Private*, pg. 2937
NORDON INDUSTRIAS METALURGICAS SA; *Int'l*, pg. 5424
NORDOTEL S.A.U.—See TUI AG; *Int'l*, pg. 7965
NORD PAPIER SA—See CVC Capital Partners SICAV-FIS S.A.; *Int'l*, pg. 1886
NORDPEIS AS—See NIBE Industrier AB; *Int'l*, pg. 5262
NORD PICARDIE MAINTENANCE SERVICE SAS—See VINCI S.A.; *Int'l*, pg. 8224
NORDPIPE COMPOSITE ENGINEERING OY—See Instalco AB; *Int'l*, pg. 3722
NORD POGONI D.O.O—See Getriebebau NORD GmbH & Co. KG; *Int'l*, pg. 2953
NORD-POHANECI TECHNIKA, S. R. O.—See Getriebebau NORD GmbH & Co. KG; *Int'l*, pg. 2953
NORD POHONY, S.R.O.—See Getriebebau NORD GmbH & Co. KG; *Int'l*, pg. 2953
NORD POOL FINLAND OY—See Euronext N.V.; *Int'l*, pg. 2554
NORD POOL HOLDING AS—See Euronext N.V.; *Int'l*, pg. 2554
NORD REDUCTEURS SARL—See Getriebebau NORD GmbH & Co. KG; *Int'l*, pg. 2953
NORDROHR GMBH—See L. Possehl & Co. mbH; *Int'l*, pg. 4384
NORD SA; *Int'l*, pg. 5416
NORDSEE COMERCIAL IMPORTADORA Y EXPORTADORA, LTDA.—See Nissui Corporation; *Int'l*, pg. 5378
NORDSEE HOLDING GMBH—See KHARIS CAPITAL GP; *Int'l*, pg. 4151
NORDSEE ONE GMBH—See Northland Power Inc.; *Int'l*, pg. 5446
NORDSEEWERKE EMDEN SHIPYARD GMBH—See Beaufort Capital GmbH; *Int'l*, pg. 934
NORDSEEWERKE EMDEN SHIPYARD—See ThyssenKrupp AG; *Int'l*, pg. 7725
NORD SERVICE PROJECTS GMBH—See L'Air Liquide S.A.; *Int'l*, pg. 4374
NORD SIMEX S.R.L.—See Grup Simex S.R.L.; *Int'l*, pg. 3115
NORDSJO BUTIKER AB—See Akzo Nobel N.V.; *Int'l*, pg. 274
NORDSKIFFER AB—See Volati AB; *Int'l*, pg. 8300
NORD-SOFT EDV-UNTERNEHMENSBERATUNG GMBH—See OVB Holding AG; *Int'l*, pg. 5670
NORDSON AB—See Nordson Corporation; *U.S. Public*, pg. 1533
NORDSON ADVANCED TECHNOLOGY (JAPAN) K.K.—See Nordson Corporation; *U.S. Public*, pg. 1533
NORDSON ADVANCED TECHNOLOGY (SINGAPORE) PTE. LTD.—See Nordson Corporation; *U.S. Public*, pg. 1533
NORDSON ANDINA LIMITADA—See Nordson Corporation; *U.S. Public*, pg. 1533
NORDSON ASIA PACIFIC, LTD.—See Nordson Corporation; *U.S. Public*, pg. 1533
NORDSON ASYMTEK, INC.—See Nordson Corporation; *U.S. Public*, pg. 1533
NORDSON ASYMTEK, INC.—See Nordson Corporation; *U.S. Public*, pg. 1533
NORDSON ASYMTEK K.K.—See Nordson Corporation; *U.S. Public*, pg. 1533
NORDSON AUSTRALIA PTY. LIMITED.—See Nordson Corporation; *U.S. Public*, pg. 1533
NORDSON AUSTRALIA PTY., LTD.—See Nordson Corporation; *U.S. Public*, pg. 1533
NORDSON BENELUX B.V.—See Nordson Corporation; *U.S. Public*, pg. 1533
NORDSON BKG LLC—See Nordson Corporation; *U.S. Public*, pg. 1533
NORDSON B.V.—See Nordson Corporation; *U.S. Public*, pg. 1533
NORDSON CANADA LTD.—See Nordson Corporation; *U.S. Public*, pg. 1533
NORDSON CHINA CO., LTD.—See Nordson Corporation; *U.S. Public*, pg. 1533

CORPORATE AFFILIATIONS

NORDSON CORP. - ADHESIVE DISPENSING SYSTEMS DIVISION—See Nordson Corporation; *U.S. Public*, pg. 1533
NORDSON CORP. - INDUSTRIAL COATING SYSTEMS DIVISION—See Nordson Corporation; *U.S. Public*, pg. 1533
NORDSON CORPORATION; *U.S. Public*, pg. 1532
NORDSON CORP. - UV CURING DIVISION—See Nordson Corporation; *U.S. Public*, pg. 1533
NORDSON CS, SPOL.S.R.O.—See Nordson Corporation; *U.S. Public*, pg. 1533
NORDSON DAGE, INC.—See Nordson Corporation; *U.S. Public*, pg. 1533
NORDSON DANMARK A/S—See Nordson Corporation; *U.S. Public*, pg. 1533
NORDSON DE MEXICO, S.A. DE C.V.—See Nordson Corporation; *U.S. Public*, pg. 1534
NORDSON DEUTSCHLAND GMBH—See Nordson Corporation; *U.S. Public*, pg. 1533
NORDSON DIMA B.V.—See Nordson Corporation; *U.S. Public*, pg. 1533
NORDSON DO BRASIL INDUSTRIA E COMERCIO LTDA.—See Nordson Corporation; *U.S. Public*, pg. 1534
NORDSON EFD LLC—See Nordson Corporation; *U.S. Public*, pg. 1533
NORDSON ENGINEERING GMBH—See Nordson Corporation; *U.S. Public*, pg. 1533
NORDSON EXTRUSION DIES INDUSTRIES, LLC.—See Nordson Corporation; *U.S. Public*, pg. 1534
NORDSON FINLAND OY—See Nordson Corporation; *U.S. Public*, pg. 1534
NORDSON FRANCE, S.A.—See Nordson Corporation; *U.S. Public*, pg. 1534
NORDSON GMBH (AUSTRIA)—See Nordson Corporation; *U.S. Public*, pg. 1534
NORDSON IBERICA S.A.—See Nordson Corporation; *U.S. Public*, pg. 1534
NORDSON INDIA PRIVATE LIMITED—See Nordson Corporation; *U.S. Public*, pg. 1534
NORDSON ITALIA S.P.A.—See Nordson Corporation; *U.S. Public*, pg. 1534
NORDSON K.K.—See Nordson Corporation; *U.S. Public*, pg. 1534
NORDSON KOREA—See Nordson Corporation; *U.S. Public*, pg. 1534
NORDSON (MALAYSIA) SDN. BHD.—See Nordson Corporation; *U.S. Public*, pg. 1533
NORDSON MARCH, INC—See Nordson Corporation; *U.S. Public*, pg. 1534
NORDSON MEDICAL (NH), INC.—See Nordson Corporation; *U.S. Public*, pg. 1534
NORDSON MEDICAL—See Nordson Corporation; *U.S. Public*, pg. 1534
NORDSON NORGE A/S—See Nordson Corporation; *U.S. Public*, pg. 1534
NORDSON OSTERREICH GMBH—See Nordson Corporation; *U.S. Public*, pg. 1534
NORDSON PACIFIC, INC.—See Nordson Corporation; *U.S. Public*, pg. 1534
NORDSON POLSKA SP.Z.O.O.—See Nordson Corporation; *U.S. Public*, pg. 1534
NORDSON PORTUGAL EQUIPAMENTO INDUSTRIAL, LTDA.—See Nordson Corporation; *U.S. Public*, pg. 1534
NORDSON PPS GMBH—See Nordson Corporation; *U.S. Public*, pg. 1534
NORDSON PPS (SHANGHAI) CO. LTD.—See Nordson Corporation; *U.S. Public*, pg. 1534
NORDSON RUSSIA LIMITED LIABILITY COMPANY—See Nordson Corporation; *U.S. Public*, pg. 1534
NORDSON SA (PTY) LTD.—See Nordson Corporation; *U.S. Public*, pg. 1534
NORDSON SCHWEIZ AG—See Nordson Corporation; *U.S. Public*, pg. 1533
NORDSON SEALANT EQUIPMENT, INC.—See Nordson Corporation; *U.S. Public*, pg. 1533
NORDSON S.E. ASIA (PTE.) LIMITED,—See Nordson Corporation; *U.S. Public*, pg. 1534
NORDSON S.E. ASIA (PTE.), LTD.—See Nordson Corporation; *U.S. Public*, pg. 1534
NORDSON SELECT GMBH—See Nordson Corporation; *U.S. Public*, pg. 1534
NORDSON (SHANGHAI) BUSINESS CONSULTING CO., LTD.—See Nordson Corporation; *U.S. Public*, pg. 1533
NORDSON SVERIGE AB—See Nordson Corporation; *U.S. Public*, pg. 1534
NORDSON TECHNOLOGY B.V.—See Nordson Corporation; *U.S. Public*, pg. 1534
NORDSON TEST AND INSPECTION AMERICAS, INC.—See Nordson Corporation; *U.S. Public*, pg. 1534
NORDSON (U.K.) LIMITED—See Nordson Corporation; *U.S. Public*, pg. 1533
NORDSON XALOY ASIA (THAILAND) LTD.—See Nordson Corporation; *U.S. Public*, pg. 1534
NORDSON XALOY EUROPE GMBH—See Nordson Corporation; *U.S. Public*, pg. 1534
NORDSON XALOY INCORPORATED—See Nordson Corporation; *U.S. Public*, pg. 1534

COMPANY NAME INDEX

NORDSON XALOY ITALIA S.R.L.—See Nordson Corporation; *U.S. Public*, pg. 1534
NORDSON XALOY K.K.—See Nordson Corporation; *U.S. Public*, pg. 1534
NORDSON YESTECH, INC.—See Nordson Corporation; *U.S. Public*, pg. 1534
NORDS PORTER NOVELLI—See Omnicom Group Inc.; *U.S. Public*, pg. 1591
NORDSTAHL GMBH—See L. Possehl & Co. mbH; *Int'l*, pg. 4384
NORDSTJERNAN AB; *Int'l*, pg. 5424
NORD STREAM AG—See PJSC Gazprom; *Int'l*, pg. 5879
NORDSTROM CREDIT, INC.—See Nordstrom, Inc.; *U.S. Public*, pg. 1535
NORDSTROM DIRECT—See Nordstrom, Inc.; *U.S. Public*, pg. 1535
NORDSTROM DISTRIBUTION #89—See Nordstrom, Inc.; *U.S. Public*, pg. 1535
NORDSTROM FSB—See Nordstrom, Inc.; *U.S. Public*, pg. 1535
NORDSTROM, INC.; *U.S. Public*, pg. 1535
NORDSVITEN AB—See ACADIA Pharmaceuticals Inc.; *U.S. Public*, pg. 31
NORDTELEKOM TELECOMMUNICATIONS SERVICE PROVIDER PLC; *Int'l*, pg. 5426
NORDURAL EHF—See Century Aluminum Company; *U.S. Public*, pg. 474
NORDURAL HF—See Century Aluminum Company; *U.S. Public*, pg. 474
NORDVACC LAKEMEDEL AB—See Intervacc AB; *Int'l*, pg. 3764
NORDVALLS ETIKETT AB—See L. Possehl & Co. mbH; *Int'l*, pg. 4384
NORDVERS GMBH—See MLP SE; *Int'l*, pg. 5004
NORDVLIES GMBH; *Int'l*, pg. 5426
NORDWEST HANDEL AG; *Int'l*, pg. 5426
NORD-WEST OELLEITUNG GMBH—See BP plc; *Int'l*, pg. 1131
NORDZUCKER AG CLAUEN FACTORY—See Nordzucker AG; *Int'l*, pg. 5427
NORDZUCKER AG KLEIN WANZLEBEN FACTORY—See Nordzucker AG; *Int'l*, pg. 5427
NORDZUCKER AG NORDSTEMMEN FACTORY—See Nordzucker AG; *Int'l*, pg. 5427
NORDZUCKER AG SCHLADEN FACTORY—See Nordzucker AG; *Int'l*, pg. 5427
NORDZUCKER AG; *Int'l*, pg. 5426
NORDZUCKER AG UELZEN FACTORY—See Nordzucker AG; *Int'l*, pg. 5427
NORDZUCKER BIOERDGAS VERWALTUNG-GMBH—See E.ON SE; *Int'l*, pg. 2258
NORDZUCKER IRELAND LIMITED—See Nordzucker AG; *Int'l*, pg. 5427
NORDZUCKER POLSKA S.A.—See Nordzucker AG; *Int'l*, pg. 5427
NOR'EASTERN TRAWL SYSTEMS INC.—See NICHIMO CO. LTD.; *Int'l*, pg. 5269
NOREEN HERON & ASSOCIATES; *U.S. Private*, pg. 2937
NORELCO CONSUMER PRODUCTS COMPANY—See Koninklijke Philips N.V.; *Int'l*, pg. 4269
NOREMA AS—See Nobia AB; *Int'l*, pg. 5395
NOREMAT SAS; *Int'l*, pg. 5427
NORENERGI A/S—See World Kinect Corporation; *U.S. Public*, pg. 2381
NORE NUTRITION AS—See Hofseth Biocare AS; *Int'l*, pg. 3440
NORESCO, LLC—See Carrier Global Corporation; *U.S. Public*, pg. 442
NORESCO, LLC—See Carrier Global Corporation; *U.S. Public*, pg. 442
NORESCO—See Carrier Global Corporation; *U.S. Public*, pg. 442
NORESCO—See Carrier Global Corporation; *U.S. Public*, pg. 442
NOREVA GMBH—See Goodwin PLC; *Int'l*, pg. 3042
NOREX AS—See Eaton Corporation plc; *Int'l*, pg. 2282
NORFALCO INC.—See Glencore plc; *Int'l*, pg. 2991
NORFALCO SALES INC.—See Glencore plc; *Int'l*, pg. 2991
NORFI ABSAUGTECHNIK GMBH; *Int'l*, pg. 5427
NORFIELD INDUSTRIES; *U.S. Private*, pg. 2937
NORFLEX, INC.—See Arsenal Capital Management LP; *U.S. Private*, pg. 339
NORFOLIER BALTIC OU—See Katalysator S.A.; *Int'l*, pg. 4089
NORFOLIER GREENTEC AS—See Katalysator S.A.; *Int'l*, pg. 4089
NORFOLIER NORGE A/S—See Katalysator S.A.; *Int'l*, pg. 4089
NORFOLK AND PORTSMOUTH BELT LINE RAILROAD COMPANY—See Norfolk Southern Corporation; *U.S. Public*, pg. 1536
NORFOLK DREDGING COMPANY; *U.S. Private*, pg. 2937
NORFOLK FOODS (PRIVATE) LIMITED—See Charoen Pokphand Foods Public Company Limited; *Int'l*, pg. 1453
NORFOLK IRON & METAL CO. INC.; *U.S. Private*, pg. 2937
NORFOLKLINE B.V.—See DFDS A/S; *Int'l*, pg. 2095

NORFOLK MARINE COMPANY—See OneWater Marine Inc.; *U.S. Public*, pg. 1604
NORFOLK METALS LIMITED; *Int'l*, pg. 5427
NORFOLK SOUTHERN CORPORATION; *U.S. Public*, pg. 1535
NORFOLK SOUTHERN INTERMODAL—See Norfolk Southern Corporation; *U.S. Public*, pg. 1535
NORFOLK SOUTHERN PROPERTIES, INC.—See Norfolk Southern Corporation; *U.S. Public*, pg. 1535
NORFOLK SOUTHERN RAILWAY COMPANY—See Norfolk Southern Corporation; *U.S. Public*, pg. 1535
NORFOLK TRUCK CENTER INCORPORATED; *U.S. Private*, pg. 2937
NORFOXX REFRIGERATION, LLC—See Saw Mill Capital LLC; *U.S. Private*, pg. 3557
NORFRA SHIPPING AS—See Odfjell SE; *Int'l*, pg. 5525
NORFRE FOOD INC.—See Cross Marketing Group Inc.; *Int'l*, pg. 1856
NORGAL—See UGI Corporation; *U.S. Public*, pg. 2222
NORGANI FINLAND HOLDING OY—See Eiendomsspar ASA; *Int'l*, pg. 2329
NORGANI HOTELS ASA—See Eiendomsspar ASA; *Int'l*, pg. 2329
NORGARD MIKKELSEN REKLAMEBUREAU A/S—See WPP plc; *Int'l*, pg. 8464
NORGE BUILDERS INC.; *U.S. Private*, pg. 2937
NORGES BANK INVESTMENT MANAGEMENT—See Norges Bank; *Int'l*, pg. 5427
NORGES BANK; *Int'l*, pg. 5427
NORGESENERGI AS—See Hafslund ASA; *Int'l*, pg. 3206
NORGESGRUPPEN ASA; *Int'l*, pg. 5427
NORGINE B.V.; *Int'l*, pg. 5427
NORGINE INTERNATIONAL LIMITED; *Int'l*, pg. 5427
NORGLEN CORPORATION; *U.S. Private*, pg. 2937
NORGREN AG—See IMI plc; *Int'l*, pg. 3626
NORGREN A/S—See IMI plc; *Int'l*, pg. 3626
NORGREN AS—See IMI plc; *Int'l*, pg. 3626
NORGREN AUTOMATION SOLUTIONS LLC—See IMI plc; *Int'l*, pg. 3626
NORGREN BV—See IMI plc; *Int'l*, pg. 3626
NORGREN EUROPEAN LOGISTICS COMPANY LTD—See IMI plc; *Int'l*, pg. 3626
NORGREN FINLAND OY—See IMI plc; *Int'l*, pg. 3626
NORGREN GESMBH—See IMI plc; *Int'l*, pg. 3626
NORGREN GMBH—See IMI plc; *Int'l*, pg. 3626
NORGREN, INC.—See IMI plc; *Int'l*, pg. 3626
NORGREN LIMITED—See IMI plc; *Int'l*, pg. 3626
NORGREN LTDA—See IMI plc; *Int'l*, pg. 3626
NORGREN LTD—See IMI plc; *Int'l*, pg. 3626
NORGREN LTD—See IMI plc; *Int'l*, pg. 3626
NORGREN MANUFACTURING CO LTD—See IMI plc; *Int'l*, pg. 3626
NORGREN MANUFACTURING DE MEXICO SA DE CV—See IMI plc; *Int'l*, pg. 3626
NORGREN MANUFACTURING (SUZHOU) CO., LTD.—See IMI plc; *Int'l*, pg. 3626
NORGREN NV—See IMI plc; *Int'l*, pg. 3626
NORGREN PTE LTD—See IMI plc; *Int'l*, pg. 3626
NORGREN PTY LTD—See IMI plc; *Int'l*, pg. 3626
NORGREN SAS—See IMI plc; *Int'l*, pg. 3626
NORGREN—See IMI plc; *Int'l*, pg. 3626
NORGREN SPA—See IMI plc; *Int'l*, pg. 3626
NORGREN SWEDEN AB—See IMI plc; *Int'l*, pg. 3626
NORGREN TAIWAN CO. LIMITED—See IMI plc; *Int'l*, pg. 3626
NORGUARD INSURANCE COMPANY—See Berkshire Hathaway Inc.; *U.S. Public*, pg. 302
NOR HOLZ VERKAUFSGESELLSCHAFT—See Norske Skog ASA; *Int'l*, pg. 5437
NORIAN ACCOUNTING AB—See TowerBrook Capital Partners, L.P.; *U.S. Private*, pg. 4195
NORIAN ACCOUNTING OY—See TowerBrook Capital Partners, L.P.; *U.S. Private*, pg. 4195
NORIAN ACCOUNTING SP. Z O.O.—See TowerBrook Capital Partners, L.P.; *U.S. Private*, pg. 4195
NORIAN ACCOUNTING UAB—See TowerBrook Capital Partners, L.P.; *U.S. Private*, pg. 4195
NORIAN REGNSKAP AS—See TowerBrook Capital Partners, L.P.; *U.S. Private*, pg. 4195
NORICAN GROUP APS—See Altor Equity Partners AB; *Int'l*, pg. 395
NORIDIAN HEALTHCARE SOLUTIONS, LLC—See Noridian Mutual Insurance Company; *U.S. Private*, pg. 2938
NORIDIAN MUTUAL INSURANCE COMPANY; *U.S. Private*, pg. 2937
NORILSK NICKEL ASIA LTD.—See PJSC MMC Norilsk Nickel; *Int'l*, pg. 5883
NORILSK NICKEL (CYPRUS) LIMITED—See PJSC MMC Norilsk Nickel; *Int'l*, pg. 5882
NORILSK NICKEL MARKETING (SHANGHAI) CO., LTD.—See PJSC MMC Norilsk Nickel; *Int'l*, pg. 5883
NORILSK NICKEL SOUTH AFRICA—See PJSC MMC Norilsk Nickel; *Int'l*, pg. 5883
NORILSK NICKEL USA—See PJSC MMC Norilsk Nickel; *Int'l*, pg. 5883
NORIMAX SDN. BHD.—See Eonmetall Group Berhad; *Int'l*, pg. 2458
NORINCHUKIN AUSTRALIA PTY LIMITED—See The Norinchukin Bank; *Int'l*, pg. 7671

NORITSU KOKI CO., LTD.

NORINCHUKIN BANK EUROPE N.V.—See The Norinchukin Bank; *Int'l*, pg. 7671
THE NORINCHUKIN BANK; *Int'l*, pg. 7671
NORINCHUKIN RESEARCH INSTITUTE CO., LTD.—See The Norinchukin Bank; *Int'l*, pg. 7671
THE NORINCHUKIN TRUST & BANKING CO., LTD.—See The Norinchukin Bank; *Int'l*, pg. 7671
NORINCHUKIN ZENKYOREN ASSET MANAGEMENT CO., LTD.—See The Norinchukin Bank; *Int'l*, pg. 7671
NORINCO-IMC LOGISTICS CO., LTD.—See NORINCO International Cooperation Ltd.; *Int'l*, pg. 5427
NORINCO INTERNATIONAL COOPERATION LTD.; *Int'l*, pg. 5427
NORINCO INTERNATIONAL REAL ESTATE CO., LTD.—See NORINCO International Cooperation Ltd.; *Int'l*, pg. 5427
NORINVEST HOLDING SA; *Int'l*, pg. 5427
NORISBANK GMBH—See Deutsche Bank Aktiengesellschaft; *Int'l*, pg. 2061
NORISH LIMITED—See Roebuck Food Group PLC; *Int'l*, pg. 6383
NORISK IT GROEP B.V.—See Dustin Group AB; *Int'l*, pg. 2235
NORITAKE ABRASIVES (SUZHOU) CO., LTD.—See Noritake Co., Limited; *Int'l*, pg. 5428
NORITAKE (AUSTRALIA) PTY LTD—See Noritake Co., Limited; *Int'l*, pg. 5428
NORITAKE COATED ABRASIVE CO., LIMITED - NOTO PLANT—See Noritake Co., Limited; *Int'l*, pg. 5428
NORITAKE COATED ABRASIVE CO., LIMITED—See Noritake Co., Limited; *Int'l*, pg. 5428
NORITAKE CO., INC.—See Noritake Co., Limited; *Int'l*, pg. 5428
NORITAKE CO., INC.—See Noritake Co., Limited; *Int'l*, pg. 5428
NORITAKE CO., LIMITED - IMARI FACTORY—See Noritake Co., Limited; *Int'l*, pg. 5428
NORITAKE CO., LIMITED - KAMORI FACTORY—See Noritake Co., Limited; *Int'l*, pg. 5428
NORITAKE CO., LIMITED - KOMAKI FACTORY—See Noritake Co., Limited; *Int'l*, pg. 5428
NORITAKE CO., LIMITED - KURUME FACTORY—See Noritake Co., Limited; *Int'l*, pg. 5428
NORITAKE CO., LIMITED - MATSUSAKA FACTORY—See Noritake Co., Limited; *Int'l*, pg. 5428
NORITAKE CO., LIMITED - MINATO FACTORY—See Noritake Co., Limited; *Int'l*, pg. 5428
NORITAKE CO., LIMITED; *Int'l*, pg. 5428
NORITAKE CO., LIMITED - YOSHIDA FACTORY—See Noritake Co., Limited; *Int'l*, pg. 5428
NORITAKE DENTAL SUPPLY CO., LIMITED—See Noritake Co., Limited; *Int'l*, pg. 5428
NORITAKE EUROPE GMBH—See Noritake Co., Limited; *Int'l*, pg. 5428
NORITAKE GARDEN CO., LTD—See Noritake Co., Limited; *Int'l*, pg. 5428
NORITAKE (GUAM), INC.—See Noritake Co., Limited; *Int'l*, pg. 5428
NORITAKE HONG KONG LTD. ELECTRONICS DIVISION—See Noritake Co., Limited; *Int'l*, pg. 5428
NORITAKE ITRON CORPORATION—See Noritake Co., Limited; *Int'l*, pg. 5428
NORITAKE LANKA PORCELAIN (PVT) LIMITED—See Noritake Co., Limited; *Int'l*, pg. 5428
NORITAKE LANKA PORCELAIN (PVT) LIMITED—See Noritake Co., Limited; *Int'l*, pg. 5428
NORITAKE RECYCLE CENTER CO., LIMITED—See Noritake Co., Limited; *Int'l*, pg. 5428
NORITAKE SA (THAILAND) CO., LTD.—See Noritake Co., Limited; *Int'l*, pg. 5428
NORITAKE SCG PLASTER CO., LTD .—See Noritake Co., Limited; *Int'l*, pg. 5428
NORITAKE SHANGHAI TRADING CO., LTD.—See Noritake Co., Limited; *Int'l*, pg. 5428
NORITAKE (SIAM) CO., LTD.—See Noritake Co., Limited; *Int'l*, pg. 5428
NORITAKE TAIPEI CO., LTD.—See Noritake Co., Limited; *Int'l*, pg. 5428
NORITAKE TCF CO., LTD.—See Noritake Co., Limited; *Int'l*, pg. 5428
NORIT REAL ESTATE B.V.—See Cabot Corporation; *U.S. Public*, pg. 417
NORITSU AMERICA CORPORATION—See Noritsu Koki Co., Ltd.; *Int'l*, pg. 5429
NORITSU CANADA LTD—See Noritsu Koki Co., Ltd.; *Int'l*, pg. 5429
NORITSU (DEUTSCHLAND) GMBH—See Noritsu Koki Co., Ltd.; *Int'l*, pg. 5429
NORITSU DO BRASIL LTDA.—See Noritsu Koki Co., Ltd.; *Int'l*, pg. 5429
NORITSU (FAR EAST) LTD—See Noritsu Koki Co., Ltd.; *Int'l*, pg. 5429
NORITSU INDIA PRIVATE LIMITED—See Noritsu Koki Co., Ltd.; *Int'l*, pg. 5429
NORITSU ITALIA S.R.L—See Noritsu Koki Co., Ltd.; *Int'l*, pg. 5429
NORITSU KOKI AUSTRALIA PTY.LTD—See Noritsu Koki Co., Ltd.; *Int'l*, pg. 5429
NORITSU KOKI CO., LTD.; *Int'l*, pg. 5429

NORITSU KOKI CO., LTD.

NORITSU KOKI (MALAYSIA) SDN. BHD—See Noritsu Koki Co., Ltd.; *Int'l*, pg. 5429
NORITSU MEXICO, S.A. DE C.V.—See Noritsu Koki Co., Ltd.; *Int'l*, pg. 5429
NORITSU PHILIPPINES INC—See Noritsu Koki Co., Ltd.; *Int'l*, pg. 5429
NORITSU (SHANGHAI) ELECTRONICS EQUIPMENT MANUFACTURING CO., LTD—See Noritsu Koki Co., Ltd.; *Int'l*, pg. 5429
NORITSU (SHANGHAI) PHOTOFINISHING EQUIPMENT MANUFACTURING CO., LTD.—See Noritsu Koki Co., Ltd.; *Int'l*, pg. 5429
NORITSU (SHANGHAI) P.M.E. CO., LTD.—See Noritsu Koki Co., Ltd.; *Int'l*, pg. 5429
NORITSU (SHANGHAI) PRECISION MACHINERY MANUFACTURING CO., LTD—See Noritsu Koki Co., Ltd.; *Int'l*, pg. 5429
NORITSU SINGAPORE PTE. LTD.—See Noritsu Koki Co., Ltd.; *Int'l*, pg. 5429
NORITSU TAIWAN CO., LTD—See Noritsu Koki Co., Ltd.; *Int'l*, pg. 5429
NORITSU (UK) LTD—See Noritsu Koki Co., Ltd.; *Int'l*, pg. 5429
NORIT (UK) HOLDING LIMITED—See Cabot Corporation; *U.S. Public*, pg. 417
NORITZ AMERICA CORPORATION—See Noritz Corporation; *Int'l*, pg. 5430
NORITZ (CHINA) CO., LTD.—See Noritz Corporation; *Int'l*, pg. 5429
NORITZ CORPORATION; *Int'l*, pg. 5429
NORITZ ELECTRONICS TECHNOLOGY CORPORATION—See Noritz Corporation; *Int'l*, pg. 5430
NORITZ (HK) ELECTRONICS TECHNOLOGY CO LTD—See Noritz Corporation; *Int'l*, pg. 5429
NORITZ HONG KONG CO., LTD.—See Noritz Corporation; *Int'l*, pg. 5430
NORITZ HONG KONG HOLDINGS CO., LTD.—See Noritz Corporation; *Int'l*, pg. 5430
NORITZ (SHANGHAI) HOME APPLIANCE CO., LTD.—See Noritz Corporation; *Int'l*, pg. 5429
NORKA LIGHTING SALES PTY. LTD.—See Norddeutsche Kunststoff und Elektrogesellschaft Stacker mbH & Co. KG; *Int'l*, pg. 5416
NORKING ALUMINIUM LTD.—See Foga System International AB; *Int'l*, pg. 2721
NORKOL CONVERTING CORPORATION; *U.S. Private*, pg. 2938
NORKOTE OF WASHINGTON, LLC—See Installed Building Products, Inc.; *U.S. Public*, pg. 1133
NORKRING AS—See Telenor ASA; *Int'l*, pg. 7539
NORKRING BELGIE N.V.—See Cordiant Digital Infrastructure Limited; *Int'l*, pg. 1796
NORKUS ENTERPRISES INC.; *U.S. Private*, pg. 2938
NORLAC GMBH—See DMK Deutsches Milchkontor GmbH; *Int'l*, pg. 2146
NORLAINE INC.; *U.S. Private*, pg. 2938
NOR-LAKE INC.—See Ten Oaks Group; *U.S. Private*, pg. 3964
NOR-LAN CHRYSLER INC.; *Int'l*, pg. 5414
NORLANDIA CARE GROUP AS—See The Adolfsen Group; *Int'l*, pg. 7612
NORLANKA BRANDS PRIVATE LIMITED—See PDS Limited; *Int'l*, pg. 5770
NOR LANKA COLOMBO MANUFACTURING LIMITED—See PDS Limited; *Int'l*, pg. 5770
NORLEASE, INC.—See Northern Trust Corporation; *U.S. Public*, pg. 1539
NORLEN, INC.—See Ryerson Holding Corporation; *U.S. Public*, pg. 1829
NORLIFT OF OREGON, INC.; *U.S. Private*, pg. 2938
NORLITE CORPORATION—See Grupo Tradebe Medioambiente S.L.; *Int'l*, pg. 3138
NOR LIVESTOCK FARM SDN. BHD.—See Rhone Ma Holdings Berhad; *Int'l*, pg. 6327
NOR-LOG GRUPPEN AS; *Int'l*, pg. 5414
NORLOP JWT—See WPP plc; *Int'l*, pg. 8481
NORLUX; *U.S. Private*, pg. 2938
NOR-MAALI OY—See Jotun A/S; *Int'l*, pg. 4003
NORMA A/S—See Autoliv, Inc.; *Int'l*, pg. 730
NORMA CHINA CO., LTD.—See NORMA Group SE; *Int'l*, pg. 5430
NORMAC INCORPORATED; *U.S. Private*, pg. 2938
NORMACO LTD.—See Axel Johnson Gruppen AB; *Int'l*, pg. 765
NORMACTION SA—See Bouygues S.A.; *Int'l*, pg. 1122
NORMA CZECH SRO—See NORMA Group SE; *Int'l*, pg. 5430
NORMA DISTRIBUTION CENTER GMBH—See NORMA Group SE; *Int'l*, pg. 5430
NORMA DISTRIBUTION FRANCE SAS—See NORMA Group SE; *Int'l*, pg. 5430
NORMA DO BRASIL SISTEMAS DE CONEXAO LTDA.—See NORMA Group SE; *Int'l*, pg. 5431
NORMA EJT (CHANGZHOU) CO., LTD.—See NORMA Group SE; *Int'l*, pg. 5430
NORMA EJT (WUXI) CO., LTD.—See NORMA Group SE; *Int'l*, pg. 5430

NORMA FRANCE SAS—See NORMA Group SE; *Int'l*, pg. 5430
NORMA GERMANY GMBH—See NORMA Group SE; *Int'l*, pg. 5430
NORMA GROUP ASIA PACIFIC HOLDING PTE. LTD.—See NORMA Group SE; *Int'l*, pg. 5430
NORMA GROUP CIS LLC—See NORMA Group SE; *Int'l*, pg. 5430
NORMA GROUP DISTRIBUTION POLSKA SP. Z.O.O.—See NORMA Group SE; *Int'l*, pg. 5430
NORMA GROUP HOLDING GMBH—See NORMA Group SE; *Int'l*, pg. 5430
NORMA GROUP MEXICO S DE RL DE C.V.—See NORMA Group SE; *Int'l*, pg. 5430
NORMA GROUP PRODUCTS INDIA PVT. LTD.—See NORMA Group SE; *Int'l*, pg. 5430
NORMA GROUP SE; *Int'l*, pg. 5430
NORMA GRUPA JUGOISTOCNA EVROPA D.O.O.—See NORMA Group SE; *Int'l*, pg. 5430
NORMA (INDIA) LIMITED—See NORMA Group SE; *Int'l*, pg. 5431
NORMA ITALIA SPA—See NORMA Group SE; *Int'l*, pg. 5430
NORMA JAPAN INC.—See NORMA Group SE; *Int'l*, pg. 5430
NORMA KOREA INC.—See NORMA Group SE; *Int'l*, pg. 5430
NORMALAB FRANCE SAS—See HORIBA Ltd; *Int'l*, pg. 3477
NORMA MICHIGAN, INC.—See NORMA Group SE; *Int'l*, pg. 5430
NORMAN ASA—See FSN Capital Partners AS; *Int'l*, pg. 2799
NORMAN BROADBENT INTERNATIONAL LTD.—See Norman Broadbent Plc; *Int'l*, pg. 5431
NORMAN BROADBENT OVERSEAS LTD—See Norman Broadbent Plc; *Int'l*, pg. 5431
NORMAN BROADBENT PLC; *Int'l*, pg. 5431
NORMAN & COMPANY, INC.; *U.S. Private*, pg. 2938
NORMANDEAU ASSOCIATES, INC.; *U.S. Private*, pg. 2938
NORMANDIE ENROBES SAS—See VINCI S.A.; *Int'l*, pg. 8224
NORMANDIE PORTUAIRE SERVICES SAS—See VINCI S.A.; *Int'l*, pg. 8224
NORMANDY CONSTRUCTION CO. INC.; *U.S. Private*, pg. 2938
THE NORMANDY GROUP S.A.; *Int'l*, pg. 7671
NORMANDY HOMES APPLES CROSSING, LLC—See Green Brick Partners, Inc.; *U.S. Public*, pg. 962
NORMANDY HOMES CYPRESS MEADOWS, LLC—See Green Brick Partners, Inc.; *U.S. Public*, pg. 962
NORMANDY HOMES EDGEWOOD, LLC—See Green Brick Partners, Inc.; *U.S. Public*, pg. 962
NORMANDY HOMES ESSEX PARK, LLC—See Green Brick Partners, Inc.; *U.S. Public*, pg. 962
NORMANDY HOMES FRISCO SPRINGS, LLC—See Green Brick Partners, Inc.; *U.S. Public*, pg. 962
NORMANDY HOMES LAKESIDE, LLC—See Green Brick Partners, Inc.; *U.S. Public*, pg. 962
NORMANDY HOMES LEGENDS AT TWIN CREEKS, LLC—See Green Brick Partners, Inc.; *U.S. Public*, pg. 962
NORMANDY HOMES LIBERTY HILLS, LLC—See Green Brick Partners, Inc.; *U.S. Public*, pg. 962
NORMANDY INDUSTRIES INC.; *U.S. Private*, pg. 2938
NORMANDY REAL ESTATE MANAGEMENT, LLC—See Allianz SE; *Int'l*, pg. 346
NORMANDY SHORES GOLF CLUB—See Professional Course Management, Inc.; *U.S. Private*, pg. 3275
NORMAN ELLISON CARPETS LIMITED—See Bremworth Limited; *Int'l*, pg. 1145
NORMAN ELLISON CARPETS PTY LIMITED—See Bremworth Limited; *Int'l*, pg. 1145
NORMAN EQUIPMENT COMPANY; *U.S. Private*, pg. 2938
NORMA NETHERLANDS BV—See NORMA Group SE; *Int'l*, pg. 5430
NORMAN HAY ENGINEERING LTD.—See Quaker Chemical Corporation; *U.S. Public*, pg. 1746
NORMAN JAPAN LIMITED—See Nien Made Enterprise Co., Ltd.; *Int'l*, pg. 5280
NORMAN LOVE CONFECTIONS; *U.S. Private*, pg. 2938
NORMAN NOBLE INCORPORATED; *U.S. Private*, pg. 2938
NORMAN PHYSICAL THERAPY, LIMITED PARTNERSHIP—See U.S. Physical Therapy, Inc.; *U.S. Public*, pg. 2215
NORMAN REGIONAL HEALTH SYSTEM; *U.S. Private*, pg. 2938
NORMAN'S NURSERY; *U.S. Private*, pg. 2938
NORMAN-SPENCER AGENCY, INC.; *U.S. Private*, pg. 2938
NORMAN SUPPLY COMPANY; *U.S. Private*, pg. 2938
NORMAN S. WRIGHT & CO.; *U.S. Private*, pg. 2938
NORMAN W. FRIES INC.; *U.S. Private*, pg. 2938
NORMAN WRIGHT MECHANICAL EQUIPMENT CORP.; *U.S. Private*, pg. 2938

CORPORATE AFFILIATIONS

NORMA PACIFIC ASIA PTE LTD.—See NORMA Group SE; *Int'l*, pg. 5430
NORMA PACIFIC PTY LTD.—See NORMA Group SE; *Int'l*, pg. 5430
NORMA PACIFIC (THAILAND) LTD.—See NORMA Group SE; *Int'l*, pg. 5430
NORMA PENNSYLVANIA, INC.—See NORMA Group SE; *Int'l*, pg. 5430
NORMA POLSKA SP. Z.O.O.—See NORMA Group SE; *Int'l*, pg. 5430
NORMA PRECISION AB—See RUAG Holding AG; *Int'l*, pg. 6421
NORMA PRODUCTS MALAYSIA SDN. BHD.—See NORMA Group SE; *Int'l*, pg. 5430
NOR-MAR INC.; *U.S. Private*, pg. 2935
NORMARK ADRIATIK D.O.O.—See Rapala VMC Oyj; *Int'l*, pg. 6209
NORMARK CHILE LTD.—See Rapala VMC Oyj; *Int'l*, pg. 6209
NORMARK CORPORATION—See Rapala VMC Oyj; *Int'l*, pg. 6209
NORMARK DENMARK A/S—See Rapala VMC Oyj; *Int'l*, pg. 6209
NORMARK EESTI OU—See Rapala VMC Oyj; *Int'l*, pg. 6209
NORMARK HUNGARY LTD.—See Rapala VMC Oyj; *Int'l*, pg. 6209
NORMARK INC.—See Rapala VMC Oyj; *Int'l*, pg. 6209
NORMARK INNOVATIONS, INC.—See Rapala VMC Oyj; *Int'l*, pg. 6209
NORMARK ITALIA S.R.L.—See Rapala VMC Oyj; *Int'l*, pg. 6209
NORMARK POLSKA SP.Z.O.O.—See Rapala VMC Oyj; *Int'l*, pg. 6209
NORMARK PORTUGAL SA—See Rapala VMC Oyj; *Int'l*, pg. 6209
NORMARK SCANDINAVIA AB—See Rapala VMC Oyj; *Int'l*, pg. 6209
NORMARK SPAIN SA—See Rapala VMC Oyj; *Int'l*, pg. 6209
NORMARK SUOMI OY—See Rapala VMC Oyj; *Int'l*, pg. 6209
NORMARK UAB—See Rapala VMC Oyj; *Int'l*, pg. 6209
NORMA SWEDEN AB—See NORMA Group SE; *Int'l*, pg. 5430
NORMATEC INDUSTRIES, LP.—See Hyperice, Inc.; *U.S. Private*, pg. 2019
NORMA TURKEY BAGLANTI YE BIRLESTIRME TEKNOLOJILER SANAYI VE TICARET LIMITED SIRKETI—See NORMA Group SE; *Int'l*, pg. 5430
NORMA UK LTD.—See NORMA Group SE; *Int'l*, pg. 5430
NORMBAU BESCHLAGE UND AUSSTATTUNGS GMBH—See Allegion Public Limited Company; *Int'l*, pg. 335
NORMBAU BESCHLAGE UND AUSSTATTUNGS GMBH—See Ingersoll Rand Inc.; *Int'l*, pg. 1122
NORMBAU FRANCE S.A.S.—See Ingersoll Rand Inc.; *U.S. Public*, pg. 1122
NORMEDIX, LLC—See SurModics, Inc.; *U.S. Public*, pg. 1967
NORMEK OY—See Mutares SE & Co. KGaA; *Int'l*, pg. 5104
NORMERICA INC—See Minerals Technologies, Inc.; *U.S. Public*, pg. 1449
NORMETIMPEX—See PJSC MMC Norilsk Nickel; *Int'l*, pg. 5882
NORMFEST GMBH - DRESS & SAFE—See Wurth Verwaltungsgesellschaft mbH; *Int'l*, pg. 8506
NORMFEST GMBH—See Wurth Verwaltungsgesellschaft mbH; *Int'l*, pg. 8506
NORMFEST POLSKA SP. Z O.O.—See Wurth Verwaltungsgesellschaft mbH; *Int'l*, pg. 8507
NORMFEST, S.R.O.—See Wurth Verwaltungsgesellschaft mbH; *Int'l*, pg. 8507
NORMISKA CORPORATION; *Int'l*, pg. 5431
NORMOND INFO SAS—See Danaher Corporation; *U.S. Public*, pg. 629
NORM PACIFIC AUTOMATION CORP.—See Nien Made Enterprise Co., Ltd.; *Int'l*, pg. 5280
NORM REEVES HONDA SUPERSTORE—See The Conant Auto Retail Group; *U.S. Private*, pg. 4013
NORMS RESTAURANTS; *U.S. Private*, pg. 2939
NORMSTAHL CRAWFORD TOR GMBH—See ASSA ABLOY AB; *Int'l*, pg. 635
NORMSTAHL GMBH—See ASSA ABLOY AB; *Int'l*, pg. 640
NORMSTAHL SCHWEIZ AG—See ASSA ABLOY AB; *Int'l*, pg. 635
NORM THOMPSON OUTFITTERS INC.—See Bluestem Brands, Inc.; *U.S. Private*, pg. 598
NORNEW ENERGY SUPPLY, INC.—See Norse Energy Corp. ASA; *Int'l*, pg. 5432
NORNEW, INC.—See Norse Energy Corp. ASA; *Int'l*, pg. 5432
NORO AB—See BHG Group AB; *Int'l*, pg. 1015
NOROFERT S.A.; *Int'l*, pg. 5431
NOROIL, S.A.—See Repsol, S.A.; *Int'l*, pg. 6292
NORONEX LTD; *Int'l*, pg. 5431
NORONT RESOURCES LTD.—See Tattarang Pty. Ltd.; *Int'l*, pg. 7475

COMPANY NAME INDEX

NOROO AUTOMOTIVE COATINGS CO., LTD.—See Nippon Paint Holdings Co., Ltd.; *Int'l*, pg. 5326
NOROO AUTOMOTIVE COATINGS CO., LTD.—See Noroo Holdings Co., Ltd.; *Int'l*, pg. 5431
NOROO BEE CHEMICAL CO., LTD—See Noroo Holdings Co., Ltd.; *Int'l*, pg. 5431
NOROO CHEMICALS CO., LTD.—See NOROO Paint & Coatings Co., Ltd.; *Int'l*, pg. 5431
NOROO COIL COATINGS CO., LTD.—See NOROO Paint & Coatings Co., Ltd.; *Int'l*, pg. 5431
NOROO HOLDINGS CO., LTD.; *Int'l*, pg. 5431
NOROO HOLDINGS(HONG KONG) CO., LTD.—See NOROO Paint & Coatings Co., Ltd.; *Int'l*, pg. 5431
NOROO KOSSAN PAINT SND. BHD.—See NOROO Paint & Coatings Co., Ltd.; *Int'l*, pg. 5431
NOROO LOGINET CO., LTD.—See NOROO Paint & Coatings Co., Ltd.; *Int'l*, pg. 5431
NOROO-NANPAO PAINT & COATINGS (VIETNAM) CO., LTD.—See NOROO Paint & Coatings Co., Ltd.; *Int'l*, pg. 5431
NOROO PAINT & COATINGS CO., LTD.; *Int'l*, pg. 5431
NOROO PAINT CO., LTD.—See Noroo Holdings Co., Ltd.; *Int'l*, pg. 5431
NOROO PAINT (SHANGHAI) CO., LTD.—See NOROO Paint & Coatings Co., Ltd.; *Int'l*, pg. 5431
NOROO R&C CO., LTD.—See NOROO Paint & Coatings Co., Ltd.; *Int'l*, pg. 5431
NOROO VINA CO., LTD.—See NOROO Paint & Coatings Co., Ltd.; *Int'l*, pg. 5431
NORPAC CONSTRUCTION, LLC—See UFP Industries, Inc.; *U.S. Public*, pg. 2219
NORPAC FOODS, INC. - BROOKS PLANT—See Norpac Foods, Inc.; *U.S. Private*, pg. 2939
NORPAC FOODS, INC. - PLANT 6—See Norpac Foods, Inc.; *U.S. Private*, pg. 2939
NORPAC FOODS, INC. - PLANT 7—See Norpac Foods, Inc.; *U.S. Private*, pg. 2939
NORPAC FOODS, INC.; *U.S. Private*, pg. 2939
NORPAC SA—See Bouygues S.A.; *Int'l*, pg. 1123
NORPAL S. DE R.L. DE C.V.—See UFP Industries, Inc.; *U.S. Public*, pg. 2219
NORPATAGONICA S.A.—See Sophia Capital S.A.; *Int'l*, pg. 7109
NORQUAY TECHNOLOGY, INC.—See Entegris, Inc.; *U.S. Public*, pg. 777
NORQUIST SALVAGE CORPORATION; *U.S. Private*, pg. 2939
NORRA METALS CORP.—See EMX Royalty Corporation; *Int'l*, pg. 2395
NORR ARCHITECTS & ENGINEERS (PVT.) LTD.—See The Ingenium Group Inc.; *Int'l*, pg. 7655
NORR ASIA LIMITED—See The Ingenium Group Inc.; *Int'l*, pg. 7655
NORRA SKEPPNINGS GRUPPEN AB—See Aspo Oyj; *Int'l*, pg. 631
NORRBODA CHARKUTERIFABRIK AB—See Atria Plc; *Int'l*, pg. 694
NORRBOTTENS BERGTEKNIK AB—See Nordisk Bergteknik AB; *Int'l*, pg. 5424
NORRENBERNS FOODS; *U.S. Private*, pg. 2939
NORR GROUP CONSULTANTS INTERNATIONAL LIMITED—See The Ingenium Group Inc.; *Int'l*, pg. 7655
NORRHYDRO GROUP OYJ; *Int'l*, pg. 5431
NORRICH WEST INC; *Int'l*, pg. 5431
NORR ILLINOIS INC.—See The Ingenium Group Inc.; *Int'l*, pg. 7655
NORRIS ACURA WEST; *U.S. Private*, pg. 2939
NORRIS AGGREGATE PAVING CO.; *U.S. Private*, pg. 2939
NORRIS AUTOMOTIVE GROUP; *U.S. Private*, pg. 2939
NORRIS BEGGS & SIMPSON NORTHWEST LIMITED PARTNERSHIP; *U.S. Private*, pg. 2939
NORRIS CYLINDER COMPANY—See TriMas Corporation; *U.S. Public*, pg. 2189
NORRIS ELECTRIC COOPERATIVE; *U.S. Private*, pg. 2939
NORRIS FORD SALES LTD; *Int'l*, pg. 5431
NORRIS FURNITURE INC.; *U.S. Private*, pg. 2939
NORRIS INDUSTRIES, INC.; *U.S. Public*, pg. 1536
NORRIS MEDICINES LTD.; *Int'l*, pg. 5431
NORRIS PRODUCTION SOLUTIONS COLOMBIA SAS—See Dover Corporation; *U.S. Public*, pg. 682
NORRIS PRODUCTION SOLUTIONS MIDDLE EAST LLC—See Dover Corporation; *U.S. Public*, pg. 682
NORRIS PUBLIC POWER DISTRICT; *U.S. Private*, pg. 2939
NORRIS RODS, INC.—See Dover Corporation; *U.S. Public*, pg. 682
NORRIS SALES ASSOCIATES INC.; *U.S. Private*, pg. 2939
NORRISTOWN BRICK INC.—See Trilantic Capital Management L.P.; *U.S. Private*, pg. 4231
NORRIS TRAINING SYSTEMS, INC.—See Surge Private Equity LLC; *U.S. Private*, pg. 3884
NORRKOPINGS HANDELSSTAL AB—See SSAB AB; *Int'l*, pg. 7153
NORRKOPINGS SAND AB—See Heidelberg Materials AG; *Int'l*, pg. 3315
NORRLAND GOLD CORP.; *Int'l*, pg. 5432

NORR LIMITED—See The Ingenium Group Inc.; *Int'l*, pg. 7655
NORR, LLC—See The Ingenium Group Inc.; *Int'l*, pg. 7655
NORRSKEN FINANCE SA—See BNP Paribas SA; *Int'l*, pg. 1092
NORRSTYR AB—See Bravida Holding AB; *Int'l*, pg. 1142
NORR SYSTEMS KOREA CO., LTD—See Technics Oil & Gas Limited; *Int'l*, pg. 7506
NORR SYSTEMS PTE. LTD.—See Technics Oil & Gas Limited; *Int'l*, pg. 7506
NORSAT INTERNATIONAL INC.—See Hytera Communications Corporation Limited; *Int'l*, pg. 3555
NORSEA AS—See Eidesvik Holding A/S; *Int'l*, pg. 2329
NORSEA AS—See Simon Mokster Shipping A/S; *Int'l*, pg. 6932
NORSEA AS—See Wilh. Wilhelmsen Holding ASA; *Int'l*, pg. 8410
NOR SEAFOOD AS—See Salmar ASA; *Int'l*, pg. 6494
NORSEA GROUP AS—See Eidesvik Holding A/S; *Int'l*, pg. 2329
NORSEA GROUP AS—See Simon Mokster Shipping A/S; *Int'l*, pg. 6932
NORSEA GROUP AS—See Wilh. Wilhelmsen Holding ASA; *Int'l*, pg. 8410
NORSE ATLANTIC AIRWAYS AS; *Int'l*, pg. 5432
NORSECHEM MARKETING SDN. BHD.—See Hexza Corporation Berhad; *Int'l*, pg. 3373
NORSECHEM RESINS SDN. BERHAD—See Hexza Corporation Berhad; *Int'l*, pg. 3373
NORSECRAFT TEC AS—See Indutrade AB; *Int'l*, pg. 3680
NORSE CROWN CO. (M) SDN. BHD.—See Ferd AS; *Int'l*, pg. 2636
NORSE CROWN CO. (M) SDN BHD—See Ferd AS; *Int'l*, pg. 2636
NORSE DAIRY SYSTEMS LLC—See George Weston Limited; *Int'l*, pg. 2939
NORSE ENERGY AS—See Norse Energy Corp. ASA; *Int'l*, pg. 5432
NORSE ENERGY CORP. ASA; *Int'l*, pg. 5432
NORSE ENERGY CORP USA—See Norse Energy Corp. ASA; *Int'l*, pg. 5432
NORSE ENERGY DO BRASIL LTDA.—See Norse Energy Corp. ASA; *Int'l*, pg. 5432
NORSE ENERGY HOLDINGS, INC.—See Norse Energy Corp. ASA; *Int'l*, pg. 5432
NORSE EXPLORATION, INC.—See Norse Energy Corp. ASA; *Int'l*, pg. 5432
NORSE GOLD CORP.; *Int'l*, pg. 5432
NORSELAND, INC.—See TINE SA; *Int'l*, pg. 7753
NORSELAND LTD.—See TINE SA; *Int'l*, pg. 7753
NORSEMAN INC.; *Int'l*, pg. 5432
NORSEMAN SILVER, INC.; *Int'l*, pg. 5432
NORSEMONT MINING INC.; *Int'l*, pg. 5432
NORSE PIPELINE, LLC—See Norse Energy Corp. ASA; *Int'l*, pg. 5432
NORSERVICE GMBH—See UPM-Kymmene Corporation; *Int'l*, pg. 8090
NORSHIELD SECURITY PRODUCTS LLC—See Spell Capital Partners, LLC; *U.S. Private*, pg. 3754
NORSILK SAS—See Mutares SE & Co. KGaA; *Int'l*, pg. 5105
NORSJOKOMPONENTER AB—See Ratos AB; *Int'l*, pg. 6220
NORSK ALCOA AS—See Alcoa Corporation; *U.S. Public*, pg. 74
NORSK ANALYSE AS—See Addtech AB; *Int'l*, pg. 134
NORSK ANALYSE A/S—See Addtech AB; *Int'l*, pg. 134
NORSK ANALYSE OY—See Addtech AB; *Int'l*, pg. 134
NORSK BUTIKKDRIFT AS—See Coop Norge SA; *Int'l*, pg. 1789
NORSKE BACKER AS—See NIBE Industrier AB; *Int'l*, pg. 5262
NORSKE GEOTECH AS—See Indutrade AB; *Int'l*, pg. 3680
NORSKE SKOG ADRIA D.O.O.—See Norske Skog ASA; *Int'l*, pg. 5437
NORSKE SKOG ASA; *Int'l*, pg. 5437
NORSKE SKOG BRUCK GMBH—See Norske Skog ASA; *Int'l*, pg. 5437
NORSKE SKOG (CYPRUS) LTD.—See Norske Skog ASA; *Int'l*, pg. 5432
NORSKE SKOG CZECH & SLOVAK REPUBLIC SPOL. S.R.O.—See Norske Skog ASA; *Int'l*, pg. 5437
NORSKE SKOG DEUTSCHLAND GMBH—See Norske Skog ASA; *Int'l*, pg. 5437
NORSKE SKOG EUROPE RECOVERED PAPER N.V.—See Norske Skog ASA; *Int'l*, pg. 5437
NORSKE SKOG FLOORING AS—See Norske Skog ASA; *Int'l*, pg. 5437
NORSKE SKOG FOLLUM AS—See Norske Skog ASA; *Int'l*, pg. 5437
NORSKE SKOG FRANCE SARL—See Norske Skog ASA; *Int'l*, pg. 5437
NORSKE SKOG GOLBEY SA—See Norske Skog ASA; *Int'l*, pg. 5437
NORSKE SKOG HOLDING AS—See Norske Skog ASA; *Int'l*, pg. 5437
NORSKE SKOG HOLDINGS (NO.1) LTD.—See Norske Skog ASA; *Int'l*, pg. 5437

NORSK SOLAR AS

NORSKE SKOG HOLLAND B.V.—See Norske Skog ASA; *Int'l*, pg. 5437
NORSKE SKOG HUNGARY KFT.—See Norske Skog ASA; *Int'l*, pg. 5437
NORSKE SKOGINDUSTRIER ASA - NORSKE SKOG BOYER UNIT—See Norske Skog ASA; *Int'l*, pg. 5438
NORSKE SKOG ITALIA SRL—See Norske Skog ASA; *Int'l*, pg. 5437
NORSKE SKOG JAMTLAND AB—See FriaSkog AB; *Int'l*, pg. 2791
NORSKE SKOG (JAPAN) LTD.—See Norske Skog ASA; *Int'l*, pg. 5437
NORSKE SKOG LOGISTICS N.V.—See Norske Skog ASA; *Int'l*, pg. 5437
NORSKE SKOG OSTERREICH GMBH—See Norske Skog ASA; *Int'l*, pg. 5437
NORSKE SKOG PAPIER RECYCLING GMBH—See Norske Skog ASA; *Int'l*, pg. 5437
NORSKE SKOG PISA LTDA.—See Papeles Bio Bio S.A.; *Int'l*, pg. 5733
NORSKE SKOG POLSKA SP. Z.O.O.—See Norske Skog ASA; *Int'l*, pg. 5437
NORSKE SKOG PRESSPAIER GMBH—See Norske Skog ASA; *Int'l*, pg. 5437
NORSKE SKOG SAUGBRUGS AS—See Norske Skog ASA; *Int'l*, pg. 5437
NORSKE SKOG (SCHWEIZ) AG—See Norske Skog ASA; *Int'l*, pg. 5437
NORSKE SKOG SKOGN AS—See Norske Skog ASA; *Int'l*, pg. 5438
NORSKE SKOG—See Norske Skog ASA; *Int'l*, pg. 5437
NORSKE SKOG TASMAN LTD.—See Norske Skog ASA; *Int'l*, pg. 5438
NORSKE SKOG (UK) LIMITED—See Norske Skog ASA; *Int'l*, pg. 5437
NORSKE SKOG US RECOVERED PAPER INC.—See Norske Skog ASA; *Int'l*, pg. 5438
NORSKE SKOG WALSUM GMBH—See Norske Skog ASA; *Int'l*, pg. 5438
NORSKE TREINDUSTRIER AS—See Norske Skog ASA; *Int'l*, pg. 5438
NORSK FILMDISTRIBUSJON AS—See Egmont Fonden; *Int'l*, pg. 2326
NORSK FJELLSPRENGNING AS—See Nordisk Bergteknik AB; *Int'l*, pg. 5424
NORSK HELSEINFORMATIKK AS—See Bonnier AB; *Int'l*, pg. 1108
NORSK HYDRO ASA - ARDAL PLANT—See Norsk Hydro ASA; *Int'l*, pg. 5435
NORSK HYDRO ASA - HOYANGER PLANT—See Norsk Hydro ASA; *Int'l*, pg. 5435
NORSK HYDRO ASA - HYDRO ALUMINIUM COMMERCE FACILITY—See Norsk Hydro ASA; *Int'l*, pg. 5435
NORSK HYDRO ASA - HYDRO ALUMINIUM HENDERSON FACILITY—See Norsk Hydro ASA; *Int'l*, pg. 5435
NORSK HYDRO ASA - KARMOY PLANT—See Norsk Hydro ASA; *Int'l*, pg. 5435
NORSK HYDRO ASA - NEUSS PLANT—See Norsk Hydro ASA; *Int'l*, pg. 5435
NORSK HYDRO ASA; *Int'l*, pg. 5432
NORSK HYDRO A/S BREVIK PACKAGING DEPT.—See Norsk Hydro ASA; *Int'l*, pg. 5435
NORSK HYDRO A/S-DEVELOPMENT & COMMERCIALIZATION—See Norsk Hydro ASA; *Int'l*, pg. 5435
NORSK HYDRO A.S. HUNGARY—See Norsk Hydro ASA; *Int'l*, pg. 5435
NORSK HYDRO DENMARK A.S.—See Norsk Hydro ASA; *Int'l*, pg. 5435
NORSK HYDRO DEUTSCHLAND GMBH & CO. KG—See Norsk Hydro ASA; *Int'l*, pg. 5435
NORSK HYDRO HOLLAND B.V.—See Norsk Hydro ASA; *Int'l*, pg. 5435
NORSK HYDRO PHILIPPINES INC.—See Norsk Hydro ASA; *Int'l*, pg. 5435
NORSK HYDRO PRODUKSJON AS—See Norsk Hydro ASA; *Int'l*, pg. 5435
NORSK HYDRO U.K. LTD.—See Norsk Hydro ASA; *Int'l*, pg. 5435
NORSK HYDRO ZIMBABWE PRIVATE LTD.—See Norsk Hydro ASA; *Int'l*, pg. 5435
NORSK JOHNSON'S WAX A/S—See S.C. Johnson & Son, Inc.; *U.S. Private*, pg. 3516
NORSK KJOPESENTERFORVALTNING AS—See BNP Paribas SA; *Int'l*, pg. 1092
NORSK MEDISINALDEPOT AS—See McKesson Corporation; *U.S. Public*, pg. 1408
NORSK OPPDRETTSERVICE AS—See Austevoll Seafood ASA; *Int'l*, pg. 717
NORSK OPPDRETTSSERVICE AS—See Austevoll Seafood ASA; *Int'l*, pg. 717
NORSK PENSJON AS—See Storebrand ASA; *Int'l*, pg. 7226
NORSK SJOMAT AS; *Int'l*, pg. 5437
NORSK SOLAR AS; *Int'l*, pg. 5437
NORSK STAAL TYNNPLATER AS—See SSAB AB; *Int'l*, pg. 7153
NORSK STAAL TYNNPLATER AS—See Tata Sons Limited; *Int'l*, pg. 7472

1945

NORSK SOLAR AS / CORPORATE AFFILIATIONS

NORSK STEIN AS—See Heidelberg Materials AG; *Int'l*, pg. 3318
NORSK TELEGRAMBYRA AS; *Int'l*, pg. 5437
NORSK TITANIUM AS—See Rose Park Advisors LLC; *U.S. Private*, pg. 3481
NORSK WAVIN A/S—See Bharti Enterprises Limited; *Int'l*, pg. 1012
NORSON ALIMENTOS S DE RL DE CV—See Agroindustrial del Noroeste S. de R.L. de C.V.; *Int'l*, pg. 219
NORSON ALIMENTOS S DE RL DE CV—See WH Group Limited; *Int'l*, pg. 8395
NORSOUTH CONSTRUCTS; *U.S. Private*, pg. 2939
NORS S.A.; *Int'l*, pg. 5432
NORSTAN, INC.—See Black Box Limited; *Int'l*, pg. 1058
NORSTAR HOLDINGS INC.; *Int'l*, pg. 5438
NORSTAR INC.; *U.S. Private*, pg. 2939
NORSTEDTS JURIDIK AB—See Wolters Kluwer n.v.; *Int'l*, pg. 8444
NORSTEEL LIMITED—See Canerector Inc.; *Int'l*, pg. 1290
NORSTEVE A/S—See Grimaldi Group SpA; *Int'l*, pg. 3085
NORSTEVE DRAMMEN A/S—See Grimaldi Group SpA; *Int'l*, pg. 3085
NORSTONE A.S.—See Heidelberg Materials AG; *Int'l*, pg. 3315
NORSTRA ENERGY INC.; *U.S. Private*, pg. 2939
NORSULFID A/S—See Outokumpu Oyj; *Int'l*, pg. 5668
NORSUN AS; *Int'l*, pg. 5438
NORSUN FOOD GROUP LLC—See Sentinel Capital Partners, L.L.C.; *U.S. Private*, pg. 3609
NORSYN CROP TECHNOLOGY CO., LTD.; *Int'l*, pg. 5438
NORTAL AS; *Int'l*, pg. 5438
NORTECH SYSTEMS -AUGUSTA—See Nortech Systems Incorporated; *U.S. Public*, pg. 1536
NORTECH SYSTEMS -BEMIDJI—See Nortech Systems Incorporated; *U.S. Public*, pg. 1536
NORTECH SYSTEMS INCORPORATED; *U.S. Public*, pg. 1536
NORTECH SYSTEMS -INTERCON 1—See Nortech Systems Incorporated; *U.S. Public*, pg. 1536
NORTECH SYSTEMS -MERRIFIELD—See Nortech Systems Incorporated; *U.S. Public*, pg. 1536
NORTEC HUMIDITY INC.—See Meier Capital AG; *Int'l*, pg. 4799
NORTEC HUMIDITY LTD.—See Meier Capital AG; *Int'l*, pg. 4799
NORTEC MINERALS CORP.; *Int'l*, pg. 5438
NORTEC QUIMICA S.A.; *Int'l*, pg. 5438
NORTE DIALYSIS, LLC—See DaVita Inc.; *U.S. Public*, pg. 641
NORTEGAS ENERGIA DISTRIBUCION, S.A.U.—See Covalis Capital LP; *Int'l*, pg. 1820
NORTEGAS ENERGIA DISTRIBUCION, S.A.U.—See JPMorgan Chase & Co.; *U.S. Public*, pg. 1209
NORTEGAS ENERGIA DISTRIBUCION, S.A.U.—See Swiss Life Holding; *Int'l*, pg. 7369
NORTEHISPANA, SA DE SEGUROS Y REASEGUROS—See Grupo Catalana Occidente, S.A.; *Int'l*, pg. 3124
NORTEK AIR SOLUTIONS, LLC—See Melrose Industries PLC; *Int'l*, pg. 4813
NORTEK GLOBAL HVAC BELGIUM NV—See Melrose Industries PLC; *Int'l*, pg. 4813
NORTEK GLOBAL HVAC FRANCE SAS—See Melrose Industries PLC; *Int'l*, pg. 4813
NORTEK GLOBAL HVAC, LLC—See Melrose Industries PLC; *Int'l*, pg. 4813
NORTEK GLOBAL HVAC (UK) LIMITED—See Melrose Industries PLC; *Int'l*, pg. 4813
NORTEK SECURITY & CONTROL LLC—See Melrose Industries PLC; *Int'l*, pg. 4813
NORTEL CHINA—See Nortel Networks Corporation; *Int'l*, pg. 5438
NORTEL INVERSORA S.A.—See Gregorio, Numo y Noel Werthein S.A.; *Int'l*, pg. 3078
NORTEL INVERSORA S.A.—See TIM S.p.A.; *Int'l*, pg. 7749
NORTEL NETWORKS AG—See Nortel Networks Corporation; *Int'l*, pg. 5438
NORTEL NETWORKS (AUSTRIA) GMBH—See Nortel Networks Corporation; *Int'l*, pg. 5438
NORTEL NETWORKS B.V.—See Nortel Networks Corporation; *Int'l*, pg. 5438
NORTEL NETWORKS CALA INC.—See Nortel Networks Corporation; *Int'l*, pg. 5438
NORTEL NETWORKS CHILE S.A.—See Nortel Networks Corporation; *Int'l*, pg. 5438
NORTEL NETWORKS CORPORATION-DIGITAL SWITCHING DIV.—See Nortel Networks Corporation; *Int'l*, pg. 5439
NORTEL NETWORKS CORPORATION; *Int'l*, pg. 5438
NORTEL NETWORKS DE ARGENTINA, S.A.—See Nortel Networks Corporation; *Int'l*, pg. 5439
NORTEL NETWORKS DE COLOMBIA S.A.—See Nortel Networks Corporation; *Int'l*, pg. 5439
NORTEL NETWORKS DE MEXICO, S.A. DE C.V.—See Nortel Networks Corporation; *Int'l*, pg. 5439
NORTEL NETWORKS DO BRASIL—See Nortel Networks Corporation; *Int'l*, pg. 5439

NORTEL NETWORKS ENGINEERING SERVICE KFT—See Nortel Networks Corporation; *Int'l*, pg. 5438
NORTEL NETWORKS HISPANIA, S.A.—See Nortel Networks Corporation; *Int'l*, pg. 5438
NORTEL NETWORKS INC.—See Nortel Networks Corporation; *Int'l*, pg. 5438
NORTEL NETWORKS (INDIA) PRIVATE LIMITED—See Nortel Networks Corporation; *Int'l*, pg. 5438
NORTEL NETWORKS JAPAN, INC.—See Nortel Networks Corporation; *Int'l*, pg. 5439
NORTEL NETWORKS LIMITED—See Nortel Networks Corporation; *Int'l*, pg. 5439
NORTEL NETWORKS MALAYSIA SDN. BHD.—See Nortel Networks Corporation; *Int'l*, pg. 5439
NORTEL NETWORKS MAURITIUS LTD.—See Nortel Networks Corporation; *Int'l*, pg. 5439
NORTEL NETWORKS NETAS TELEKOMUNIKASYON A.S.—See Nortel Networks Corporation; *Int'l*, pg. 5439
NORTEL NETWORKS N.V.—See Nortel Networks Corporation; *Int'l*, pg. 5439
NORTEL NETWORKS PERU S.A.C.—See Nortel Networks Corporation; *Int'l*, pg. 5439
NORTEL NETWORKS PLC—See Nortel Networks Corporation; *Int'l*, pg. 5439
NORTEL NETWORKS PORTUGAL, S.A.—See Nortel Networks Corporation; *Int'l*, pg. 5439
NORTEL NETWORKS S.A.—See Nortel Networks Corporation; *Int'l*, pg. 5439
NORTEL NETWORKS SLOVENSKO, S.R.O.—See Nortel Networks Corporation; *Int'l*, pg. 5439
NORTEL NETWORKS—See Nortel Networks Corporation; *Int'l*, pg. 5438
NORTEL NETWORKS—See Nortel Networks Corporation; *Int'l*, pg. 5439
NORTEL TECHNOLOGY EXCELLENCE CENTER PRIVATE LIMITED—See Nortel Networks Corporation; *Int'l*, pg. 5439
NORTEL UK LTD.—See Nortel Networks Corporation; *Int'l*, pg. 5439
NORTEL UK LTD.—See Nortel Networks Corporation; *Int'l*, pg. 5439
NORTEL VIETNAM LIMITED—See Nortel Networks Corporation; *Int'l*, pg. 5439
NORTEM BIOGROUP S.A.; *Int'l*, pg. 5439
NORTEX COMMUNICATIONS COMPANY; *U.S. Private*, pg. 2939
NORTEX MIDSTREAM PARTNERS, LLC—See The Williams Companies, Inc.; *U.S. Public*, pg. 2143
NOR-TEX PUBLISHING, INC.—See Chatham Asset Management, LLC; *U.S. Private*, pg. 866
NORTH 6TH AGENCY, INC.; *U.S. Private*, pg. 2939
NORTHACRE PLC—See SHUAA Capital psc; *Int'l*, pg. 6868
NORTH ADAMS TRANSCRIPT—See Alden Global Capital LLC; *U.S. Private*, pg. 157
NORTH AEGEAN RENEWABLES A.E.—See Metlen Energy & Metals S.A.; *Int'l*, pg. 4855
NORTH AFRICA HOLDING COMPANY K.S.C.—See Kuwait Projects Company (Holding) K.S.C.P.; *Int'l*, pg. 4346
NORTH ALABAMA FABRICATING CO.; *U.S. Private*, pg. 2939
NORTHAMBER PLC; *Int'l*, pg. 5441
NORTH AMERICA CEREAL CO.—See Kellanova; *U.S. Public*, pg. 1218
NORTH AMERICA CONSTRUCTION (1993) LTD.—See NAC Constructors Ltd.; *Int'l*, pg. 5121
NORTH AMERICA FIRE EQUIPMENT COMPANY; *U.S. Private*, pg. 2939
NORTH AMERICA FOOD & BEVERAGE INC.; *U.S. Private*, pg. 2939
NORTH AMERICA FRAC SAND, INC.; *U.S. Public*, pg. 1536
NORTH AMERICA FUEL SYSTEMS REMANUFACTURING LLC—See Mercedes-Benz Group AG; *Int'l*, pg. 4823
NORTH AMERICA MAZDA INFORMATION BUREAU—See Mazda Motor Corporation; *Int'l*, pg. 4749
NORTH AMERICAN ADVANTAGE INSURANCE SERVICES, LLC—See Doma Holdings, Inc.; *U.S. Public*, pg. 673
NORTH AMERICAN ASSEMBLIES, LLC—See TAG Holdings, LLC; *U.S. Private*, pg. 3922
NORTH AMERICAN AUTOMOTIVE SERVICES, INC.; *U.S. Private*, pg. 2940
NORTH AMERICAN BANCARD, LLC; *U.S. Private*, pg. 2940
NORTH AMERICAN BISON COOPERATIVE; *U.S. Private*, pg. 2940
NORTH AMERICAN BOLT & SCREW CO. INC.; *U.S. Private*, pg. 2940
NORTH AMERICAN BREAKER CO., LLC—See The PNC Financial Services Group, Inc.; *U.S. Public*, pg. 2120
NORTH AMERICAN BREWERIES, INC.—See Florida Ice and Farm Co. S.A.; *Int'l*, pg. 2707
NORTH AMERICAN BULK TRANSPORT INC.—See Tankstar USA, Inc.; *U.S. Private*, pg. 3931
NORTH AMERICAN CAISSON LTD.—See North American Construction Group Ltd.; *Int'l*, pg. 5439

NORTH AMERICAN CANNABIS HOLDINGS, INC.; *U.S. Public*, pg. 1536
NORTH AMERICAN CAPACITY INSURANCE COMPANY—See Swiss Re Ltd.; *Int'l*, pg. 7371
NORTH AMERICAN CASUALTY CO.—See Berkshire Hathaway Inc.; *U.S. Public*, pg. 313
THE NORTH AMERICAN COAL CORPORATION—See NACCO Industries, Inc.; *U.S. Public*, pg. 1490
NORTH AMERICAN COAL ROYALTY COMPANY—See NACCO Industries, Inc.; *U.S. Public*, pg. 1489
NORTH AMERICAN COATINGS, INC.; *U.S. Private*, pg. 2940
NORTH AMERICAN COMMUNICATIONS, INC. (NAC)—See North American Communications Inc.; *U.S. Private*, pg. 2940
NORTH AMERICAN COMMUNICATIONS INC.; *U.S. Private*, pg. 2940
NORTH AMERICAN COMPANY FOR LIFE & HEALTH INSURANCE—See Sammons Enterprises, Inc.; *U.S. Private*, pg. 3537
NORTH AMERICAN COMPANY; *U.S. Private*, pg. 2940
NORTH AMERICAN COMPOSITES—See Interplastic Corporation; *U.S. Private*, pg. 2123
NORTH AMERICAN CONSTRUCTION GROUP LTD.; *Int'l*, pg. 5439
NORTH AMERICAN CONTAINER CORPORATION - CALHOUN FACILITY—See UFP Industries, Inc.; *U.S. Public*, pg. 2219
NORTH AMERICAN CONTAINER CORPORATION - LAWRENCEBURG FACILITY—See UFP Industries, Inc.; *U.S. Public*, pg. 2219
NORTH AMERICAN CONTAINER CORPORATION - MARTIN FACILITY—See UFP Industries, Inc.; *U.S. Public*, pg. 2219
NORTH AMERICAN CONTAINER CORPORATION - MCINTYRE FACILITY—See UFP Industries, Inc.; *U.S. Public*, pg. 2219
NORTH AMERICAN CONTAINER CORPORATION - NEWNAN FACILITY—See UFP Industries, Inc.; *U.S. Public*, pg. 2219
NORTH AMERICAN CONTAINER CORPORATION - ORANGEBURG FACILITY—See UFP Industries, Inc.; *U.S. Public*, pg. 2219
NORTH AMERICAN CONTAINER CORPORATION - SHARON FACILITY—See UFP Industries, Inc.; *U.S. Public*, pg. 2219
NORTH AMERICAN CONTAINER CORPORATION—See UFP Industries, Inc.; *U.S. Public*, pg. 2219
NORTH AMERICAN CORP.; *U.S. Private*, pg. 2940
NORTH AMERICAN DEVELOPMENT GROUP; *U.S. Private*, pg. 2940
NORTHAMERICAN ENERGY GROUP CORP.; *U.S. Public*, pg. 1537
NORTH AMERICAN EQUIPMENT SALES (CANADA) LTD.—See ERS Industries Inc.; *U.S. Private*, pg. 1423
NORTH AMERICAN EQUIPMENT UPFITTERS, INC.; *U.S. Private*, pg. 2940
NORTH AMERICAN ESSENTIAL HOME SERVICES—See Gryphon Investors, LLC; *U.S. Private*, pg. 1799
NORTH AMERICAN EXPLORATION CORP.; *U.S. Public*, pg. 1536
NORTH AMERICAN FILTER CORPORATION; *U.S. Private*, pg. 2940
NORTH AMERICAN FINANCIAL 15 SPLIT CORPORATION—See Quadravest Capital Management Inc.; *Int'l*, pg. 6150
NORTH AMERICAN FIRE AND GENERAL INSURANCE COMPANY—See Edward B. Beharry & Co. Ltd.; *Int'l*, pg. 2316
NORTH AMERICAN FOOD DISTRIBUTING CO., INC.—See Sociedad Quimica y Minera de Chile S.A.; *Int'l*, pg. 7032
NORTH AMERICAN FOREST PRODUCTS, INC.—See Patrick Industries, Inc.; *U.S. Public*, pg. 1653
NORTH AMERICAN FUR PRODUCERS MARKETING INC; *Int'l*, pg. 5439
NORTH AMERICAN GALVANIZING & COATINGS, INC.—See AZZ, Inc.; *U.S. Public*, pg. 259
NORTH AMERICAN GOLD & MINERALS FUND; *U.S. Private*, pg. 2940
NORTH AMERICAN GRAIN INVESTMENTS, INC.—See Cargill, Inc.; *U.S. Private*, pg. 759
NORTH AMERICAN GREEN INC.—See Commercial Metals Company; *U.S. Public*, pg. 547
NORTH AMERICAN HERITAGE SERVICES, INC.—See PKDM Holdings, Inc.; *U.S. Private*, pg. 3193
NORTH AMERICAN HOGANAS HIGH ALLOYS LLC—See Hoganas AB; *Int'l*, pg. 3441
NORTH AMERICAN HOGANAS HOLDINGS, INC.—See Hoganas AB; *Int'l*, pg. 3441
NORTH AMERICAN HOGANAS, INC.—See Hoganas AB; *Int'l*, pg. 3441
NORTH AMERICAN HOGANAS-PYRON PLANT—See Hoganas AB; *Int'l*, pg. 3441
NORTH AMERICAN HYDRAULICS INC.; *U.S. Private*, pg. 2940
NORTH AMERICAN INCOME TRUST PLC; *Int'l*, pg. 5439
NORTH AMERICAN INDUSTRIAL SERVICES, INC.—See The Sterling Group, L.P.; *U.S. Private*, pg. 4123

COMPANY NAME INDEX — NORTH CAROLINA ELECTRIC MEMBERSHIP CORPORATION

NORTH AMERICAN INTERNATIONAL HOLDING CORPORATION—See Madison Dearborn Partners, LLC; *U.S. Private*, pg. 2542

NORTH AMERICAN LIGHTING, INC.—See Koito Manufacturing Co., Ltd.; *Int'l*, pg. 4230

NORTH AMERICAN LIGHTING MEXICO, S.A. DE C.V.—See Koito Manufacturing Co., Ltd.; *Int'l*, pg. 4230

NORTH AMERICAN MAINTENANCE LTD.—See North American Construction Group Ltd.; *Int'l*, pg. 5439

NORTH AMERICAN MARKETING CORPORATION; *U.S. Private*, pg. 2941

NORTH AMERICAN MEDICAL MANAGEMENT CALIFORNIA, INC.—See UnitedHealth Group Incorporated; *U.S. Public*, pg. 2242

NORTH AMERICAN MEDICAL MANAGEMENT - ILLINOIS, INC.—See UnitedHealth Group Incorporated; *U.S. Public*, pg. 2242

NORTH AMERICAN MEMBERSHIP GROUP, INC.—See Pilot Group, LLC; *U.S. Private*, pg. 3181

NORTH AMERICAN NATIONAL TITLE SOLUTIONS, LLC—See Lennar Corporation; *U.S. Public*, pg. 1307

NORTH AMERICAN NATURAL RESOURCES, LLC—See Kinder Morgan, Inc.; *U.S. Public*, pg. 1234

NORTH AMERICAN NEW CARS, INC.—See General Motors Company; *U.S. Public*, pg. 926

NORTH AMERICAN OIL & GAS CORP.; *U.S. Private*, pg. 2941

NORTH AMERICAN PACKAGING LLC; *U.S. Private*, pg. 2941

NORTH AMERICAN PARTNERS IN ANESTHESIA LLP; *U.S. Private*, pg. 2941

NORTH AMERICAN PIPE CORPORATION—See Westlake Corporation; *U.S. Public*, pg. 2360

NORTH AMERICAN PIPELINE INC.—See North American Construction Group Ltd.; *Int'l*, pg. 5439

NORTH AMERICAN POWER AND GAS, LLC—See Energy Capital Partners Management, LP; *U.S. Private*, pg. 1394

NORTH AMERICAN PROPERTIES INC.; *U.S. Private*, pg. 2941

NORTH AMERICAN PROVISIONER INC.—See North American Bison Cooperative; *U.S. Private*, pg. 2940

NORTH AMERICAN PUBLISHING CO.—See Specialty Graphic Imag; *U.S. Private*, pg. 3750

NORTH AMERICAN REAL ESTATE GROUP, LLC—See Lennar Corporation; *U.S. Public*, pg. 1307

NORTH AMERICAN RECYCLING AND CRUSHING, LLC—See Vulcan Materials Company; *U.S. Public*, pg. 2313

NORTH AMERICAN RESCUE, LLC—See Henry Schein, Inc.; *U.S. Public*, pg. 1027

NORTH AMERICAN ROAD INC.—See North American Construction Group Ltd.; *Int'l*, pg. 5439

NORTH AMERICAN ROOFING SYSTEMS, INC.; *U.S. Private*, pg. 2941

NORTH AMERICAN SAVINGS BANK, F.S.B.—See NASB Financial, Inc.; *U.S. Public*, pg. 1491

NORTH AMERICAN SCIENCE ASSOCIATES, INC.—See ArchiMed SAS; *Int'l*, pg. 549

NORTH AMERICAN SIGNS INC.; *U.S. Private*, pg. 2941

NORTH AMERICAN SITE DEVELOPERS, INC.—See Great Lakes Dredge & Dock Corporation; *U.S. Public*, pg. 962

NORTH AMERICAN SOLUTIONS INC.—See Big Lots, Inc.; *U.S. Public*, pg. 330

NORTH AMERICAN SPECIALTY GLASS LLC—See Stellex Capital Management LP; *U.S. Private*, pg. 3800

NORTH AMERICAN SPECIALTY INSURANCE COMPANY—See Swiss Re Ltd.; *Int'l*, pg. 7371

NORTH AMERICAN SPECIALTY LAMINATIONS, LLC—See Building Industry Partners LLC; *U.S. Private*, pg. 683

NORTH AMERICAN SPECIALTY PRODUCTS LLC—See Westlake Corporation; *U.S. Public*, pg. 2360

NORTH AMERICAN SPINE SOCIETY; *U.S. Private*, pg. 2941

NORTH AMERICAN STAINLESS, INC.—See Acerinox, S.A.; *Int'l*, pg. 101

NORTH AMERICAN STAINLESS MEXICO S.A. DE C.V.—See Acerinox, S.A.; *Int'l*, pg. 101

NORTH AMERICAN STEEL CANADA, INC.—See Acerinox, S.A.; *Int'l*, pg. 101

NORTH AMERICAN TEA & COFFEE INC.—See TreeHouse Foods, Inc.; *U.S. Public*, pg. 2187

NORTH AMERICAN TECHNOLOGIES GROUP, INC. (NAMC); *U.S. Private*, pg. 2941

NORTH AMERICAN TESTING COMPANY, INC.—See National Association for Stock Car Auto Racing, Inc.; *U.S. Private*, pg. 2846

NORTH AMERICAN TITLE COMPANY (AZ)—See Doma Holdings, Inc.; *U.S. Public*, pg. 673

NORTH AMERICAN TITLE COMPANY, INC.—See Doma Holdings, Inc.; *U.S. Public*, pg. 673

NORTH AMERICAN TITLE COMPANY (MD)—See Doma Holdings, Inc.; *U.S. Public*, pg. 673

NORTH AMERICAN TITLE COMPANY (MN)—See Doma Holdings, Inc.; *U.S. Public*, pg. 673

NORTH AMERICAN TITLE COMPANY (NV)—See Doma Holdings, Inc.; *U.S. Public*, pg. 673

NORTH AMERICAN TITLE COMPANY OF COLORADO—See Doma Holdings, Inc.; *U.S. Public*, pg. 673

NORTH AMERICAN TITLE COMPANY—See Doma Holdings, Inc.; *U.S. Public*, pg. 673

NORTH AMERICAN TITLE COMPANY (TX)—See Doma Holdings, Inc.; *U.S. Public*, pg. 673

NORTH AMERICAN TITLE GROUP, LLC—See Doma Holdings, Inc.; *U.S. Public*, pg. 673

NORTH AMERICAN TITLE INSURANCE COMPANY—See Doma Holdings, Inc.; *U.S. Public*, pg. 673

NORTH AMERICAN TOOL CORPORATION—See L Squared Capital Management LP; *U.S. Private*, pg. 2361

NORTH AMERICAN TRADING, LLC.; *U.S. Private*, pg. 2941

NORTH AMERICAN TRAILER LLC; *U.S. Private*, pg. 2941

NORTH AMERICAN TRANSMISSION & DISTRIBUTION GROUP—See Falfurrias Capital Partners, LP; *U.S. Private*, pg. 1467

NORTH AMERICAN TRANSPORT CONCEPTS; *U.S. Private*, pg. 2941

NORTH AMERICAN TRUCK & TRAILER, INC.; *U.S. Private*, pg. 2941

NORTH AMERICAN TUNGSTEN CORPORATION LTD.—See Alvarez & Marsal, Inc.; *U.S. Private*, pg. 213

NORTH AMERICAN VAN LINES, INC.—See Madison Dearborn Partners, LLC; *U.S. Private*, pg. 2542

NORTH AMERICAN VAN LINES—See Madison Dearborn Partners, LLC; *U.S. Private*, pg. 2542

NORTH AMERICAN VIDEO CORPORATION; *U.S. Private*, pg. 2941

NORTH AMERICAN VIDEO, INC.—See The Halifax Group LLC; *U.S. Private*, pg. 4042

NORTH AMERICAN VIDEO - NORTH EAST REGIONAL HEADQUARTERS—See The Halifax Group LLC; *U.S. Private*, pg. 4042

NORTH AMERICA PROCUREMENT COUNCIL, INC.—See Byggfakta Group Nordic HoldCo AB; *Int'l*, pg. 1235

NORTH AMERICA SEKISUI HOUSE, LLC—See Sekisui House, Ltd.; *Int'l*, pg. 6697

NORTH AMERICA SEOUL SEMICONDUCTOR INC.—See Seoul Semiconductor Co., Ltd.; *Int'l*, pg. 6717

NORTHAM PLATINUM LIMITED; *Int'l*, pg. 5441

NORTHAMPTON CHRONICLE & ECHO—See JPIMedia Holdings Limited; *Int'l*, pg. 4006

NORTHAMPTON CLINIC COMPANY, LLC—See Community Health Systems, Inc.; *U.S. Public*, pg. 555

NORTHAMPTON COMMUNITY COLLEGE; *U.S. Private*, pg. 2948

NORTHAMPTON GROUP INC.; *Int'l*, pg. 5441

NORTHAMPTON GROWERS PRODUCE SALES, INC.; *U.S. Private*, pg. 2948

NORTHAMPTON HOME CARE, LLC—See Community Health Systems, Inc.; *U.S. Public*, pg. 555

NORTHAMPTON INNS (OAKVILLE EAST) INC.—See Northampton Group Inc.; *Int'l*, pg. 5442

NORTHAMPTON INNS (OAKVILLE) INC.—See Northampton Group Inc.; *Int'l*, pg. 5442

NORTHAMPTON SHOPPING CENTRE LIMITED PARTNERSHIP—See Legal & General Group Plc; *Int'l*, pg. 4443

NORTHAMPTON TRANSPORT LIMITED—See FirstGroup plc; *Int'l*, pg. 2689

NORTH ANAHEIM SURGERY CENTER, LLC—See Tenet Healthcare Corporation; *U.S. Public*, pg. 2005

NORTH ANAHEIM SURGICENTER, LTD.—See Tenet Healthcare Corporation; *U.S. Public*, pg. 2014

NORTH ANDOVER CITIZEN—See Gannett Co., Inc.; *U.S. Public*, pg. 902

NORTH ANDRE JUICE (USA) INC.—See Yantai North Andre Juice Co., Ltd.; *Int'l*, pg. 8565

NORTHANN CORP.; *U.S. Public*, pg. 1537

NORTHANTS EVENING TELEGRAPH—See JPIMedia Holdings Limited; *Int'l*, pg. 4006

NORTH ARC CAPITAL PARTNERS; *Int'l*, pg. 5439

NORTH ARKANSAS ELECTRIC COOPERATIVE, INC.; *U.S. Private*, pg. 2942

NORTH ARKANSAS HOMECARE—See UnitedHealth Group Incorporated; *U.S. Public*, pg. 2246

NORTH ARROW MINERALS INC.; *Int'l*, pg. 5439

NORTH ASIA LTD CRM TECHNOLOGIES—See Teleperformance SE; *Int'l*, pg. 7540

NORTH ASIA STRATEGIC HOLDINGS LIMITED; *Int'l*, pg. 5439

NORTH ATLANTIC COMPONENTS, INC.; *U.S. Private*, pg. 2942

NORTH ATLANTIC CREW AS—See SeaDrill Limited; *Int'l*, pg. 6662

NORTH ATLANTIC DRILLING LTD.—See SeaDrill Limited; *Int'l*, pg. 6662

NORTH ATLANTIC DRILLING MANAGEMENT AS—See SeaDrill Limited; *Int'l*, pg. 6662

NORTH ATLANTIC ENERGY SERVICE CORPORATION—See Eversource Energy; *U.S. Public*, pg. 801

NORTH ATLANTIC INDUSTRIES INC.; *U.S. Private*, pg. 2942

NORTH ATLANTIC MANAGEMENT AS—See SeaDrill Limited; *Int'l*, pg. 6662

THE NORTH ATLANTIC MARINE GROUP; *U.S. Private*, pg. 4084

NORTH ATLANTIC NATURAL RESOURCES AB—See Lundin Mining Corporation; *Int'l*, pg. 4584

NORTH ATLANTIC POTASH INC.—See Public Joint Stock Company Acron; *Int'l*, pg. 6095

NORTH ATLANTIC REFINING LTD.—See Silverpeak Strategic Partners LP; *U.S. Private*, pg. 3663

NORTH ATLANTIC SMALLER COMPANIES INVESTMENT TRUST PLC; *Int'l*, pg. 5440

NORTH ATLANTIC STATES REGIONAL COUNCIL OF CARPENTERS; *U.S. Private*, pg. 2942

NORTH ATLANTIC SURGICAL SUITES, LLC—See Tenet Healthcare Corporation; *U.S. Public*, pg. 2005

NORTH ATLANTIC TRADING COMPANY, INC.; *U.S. Private*, pg. 2942

NORTH AURORA MEDICAL CENTER LLC—See Adeptus Health Inc.; *U.S. Private*, pg. 78

NORTH AUSTIN SURGERY CENTER—See HCA Healthcare, Inc.; *U.S. Public*, pg. 1004

NORTH AUSTRALIAN CATTLE COMPANY PTY. LTD.; *Int'l*, pg. 5440

NORTH BAJA PIPELINE, LLC—See TC Energy Corporation; *Int'l*, pg. 7482

NORTH BANK FOR FINANCE AND INVESTMENT; *Int'l*, pg. 5440

NORTH BATTLEFORD POWER L.P.—See Northland Power Inc.; *Int'l*, pg. 5446

NORTH BAY CADILLAC CO. INC.; *U.S. Private*, pg. 2942

NORTH BAY FORD LINCOLN MERCURY; *U.S. Private*, pg. 2942

NORTHBAY HEALTHCARE; *U.S. Private*, pg. 2948

NORTH BAY IMPORTS, INC.; *U.S. Private*, pg. 2942

NORTH BAY JOBS WITH JUSTICE; *U.S. Private*, pg. 2942

THE NORTH BAY NUGGET—See Chatham Asset Management, LLC; *U.S. Private*, pg. 861

NORTH BAY PRODUCE, INC.; *U.S. Private*, pg. 2942

NORTH BAY REGIONAL CENTER; *U.S. Private*, pg. 2942

NORTH BAY REHABILITATION SERVICES; *U.S. Private*, pg. 2942

NORTH BAY RESOURCES INC.; *U.S. Private*, pg. 2942

NORTHBAZE GROUP AB; *Int'l*, pg. 5442

NORTH BELT RESTAURANT, INC.—See Louisiana Fine Food Companies, Inc.; *U.S. Private*, pg. 2499

NORTH BERGEN MUNICIPAL UTILITY AUTHORITY; *U.S. Private*, pg. 2942

NORTH BRANCH CAPITAL, LLC; *U.S. Private*, pg. 2942

NORTH BRIDGE CHICAGO LLC—See The Macerich Company; *U.S. Public*, pg. 2110

NORTHBRIDGE COMMERCIAL INSURANCE CORPORATION—See Fairfax Financial Holdings Limited; *Int'l*, pg. 2607

NORTHBRIDGE FINANCIAL CORPORATION—See Fairfax Financial Holdings Limited; *Int'l*, pg. 2607

NORTHBRIDGE GENERAL INSURANCE CORPORATION—See Fairfax Financial Holdings Limited; *Int'l*, pg. 2607

NORTHBRIDGE INDEMNITY INSURANCE CORPORATION—See Fairfax Financial Holdings Limited; *Int'l*, pg. 2607

NORTHBRIDGE INDEMNITY INSURANCE CORPORATION—See Fairfax Financial Holdings Limited; *Int'l*, pg. 2607

NORTHBRIDGE INSURANCE AGENCY INC.—See Arthur J. Gallagher & Co.; *U.S. Public*, pg. 204

NORTH BRIDGE PROPERTY AS—See Samhallsbyggnadsbolaget I Norden AB; *Int'l*, pg. 6504

NORTH BRIDGE VENTURE MANAGEMENT COMPANY, INC.; *U.S. Private*, pg. 2942

NORTHBROOK BANK & TRUST COMPANY, N.A.—See Wintrust Financial Corporation; *U.S. Public*, pg. 2375

THE NORTHBROOK PALM—See Palm Restaurant Group; *U.S. Private*, pg. 3080

NORTHBROOK PUBLISHING—See Aurora Capital Group, LLC; *U.S. Private*, pg. 394

NORTHBROOK WYNYARD LIMITED—See Winton Land Limited; *Int'l*, pg. 8431

NORTH BROS. FORD; *U.S. Private*, pg. 2942

NORTH BUD FARMS, INC.; *Int'l*, pg. 5440

NORTHBURN INDUSTRIAL SERVICES LTD—See Turner & Co. (Glasgow) Limited; *Int'l*, pg. 7978

NORTH CAIRO MILLS & BAKERIES COMPANY; *Int'l*, pg. 5440

NORTH CAMBRIA FUEL CO.; *U.S. Private*, pg. 2942

NORTH CAMPUS SURGERY CENTER, LLC—See Tenet Healthcare Corporation; *U.S. Public*, pg. 2005

NORTH CANTON TRANSFER COMPANY—See Rhone Group, LLC; *U.S. Public*, pg. 3424

NORTH CANTON TRANSFER COMPANY—See The Goldman Sachs Group, Inc.; *U.S. Public*, pg. 2080

NORTH CAROLINA ELECTRIC MEMBERSHIP CORPORATION; *U.S. Private*, pg. 2943

NORTH CAROLINA ELECTRIC MEMBERSHIP CORPORATION — CORPORATE AFFILIATIONS

NORTH CAROLINA FOAM INDUSTRIES, INC. - DALTON FOAM DIVISION—See Barnhardt Manufacturing Company; *U.S. Private*, pg. 478

NORTH CAROLINA FOAM INDUSTRIES, INC.—See Barnhardt Manufacturing Company; *U.S. Private*, pg. 478

NORTH CAROLINA GRANITE CORP.; *U.S. Private*, pg. 2943

NORTH CAROLINA HMA REGIONAL SERVICE CENTER, LLC—See Community Health Systems, Inc.; *U.S. Public*, pg. 555

NORTH CAROLINA IN-HOME PARTNER-IV, LLC—See UnitedHealth Group Incorporated; *U.S. Public*, pg. 2246

NORTH CAROLINA IN-HOME PARTNER-V, LLC—See UnitedHealth Group Incorporated; *U.S. Public*, pg. 2246

NORTH CAROLINA JOINT UNDERWRITING ASSOCIATION; *U.S. Private*, pg. 2943

NORTH CAROLINA LUMBER COMPANY; *U.S. Private*, pg. 2943

NORTH CAROLINA MUTUAL LIFE INSURANCE COMPANY; *U.S. Private*, pg. 2943

NORTH CAROLINA MUTUAL WHOLESALE DRUG COMPANY; *U.S. Private*, pg. 2943

NORTH CAROLINA OPERA; *U.S. Private*, pg. 2943

THE NORTH CAROLINA PARTNERSHIP FOR CHILDREN, INC.; *U.S. Private*, pg. 4084

NORTH CAROLINA RATE BUREAU; *U.S. Private*, pg. 2943

NORTH CAROLINA RENEWABLE PROPERTIES, LLC—See Duke Energy Corporation; *U.S. Public*, pg. 691

NORTH CAROLINA RURAL ECONOMIC DEVELOPMENT CENTER, INC.; *U.S. Private*, pg. 2943

NORTH CAROLINA SPECIALTY HOSPITAL, LLC—See Bain Capital, LP; *U.S. Private*, pg. 445

NORTH CAROLINA SYMPHONY; *U.S. Private*, pg. 2943

NORTH CAROLINA TITLE CENTER, LLC—See First Horizon Corporation; *U.S. Public*, pg. 844

NORTH CAROLINA & VIRGINIA RAILROAD COMPANY, LLC—See Brookfield Infrastructure Partners L.P.; *Int'l*, pg. 1192

NORTH CAROLINA & VIRGINIA RAILROAD COMPANY, LLC—See GIC Pte. Ltd.; *Int'l*, pg. 2966

NORTH CASCADE BUILDING MATERIALS; *U.S. Private*, pg. 2943

NORTH CASCADES BANK—See Glacier Bancorp, Inc.; *U.S. Public*, pg. 939

NORTH CASPIAN PETROLEUM JSC; *Int'l*, pg. 5440

NORTH CASTLE PARTNERS, LLC; *U.S. Private*, pg. 2943

NORTH CENTER FOODSERVICE CORP.—See Performance Food Group Company; *U.S. Public*, pg. 1675

NORTH CENTRAL CO-OP INC.; *U.S. Private*, pg. 2943

NORTH CENTRAL DIGITAL SYSTEMS, INC.—See Wells Fargo & Company; *U.S. Public*, pg. 2344

NORTH CENTRAL EQUITY LLC; *U.S. Private*, pg. 2943

NORTH CENTRAL FARMERS ELEVATOR, INC.; *U.S. Private*, pg. 2943

NORTH CENTRAL GRAIN COOPERATIVE, INC.; *U.S. Private*, pg. 2943

NORTH CENTRAL INSTRUMENTS, INC.—See Thomas Scientific, LLC; *U.S. Private*, pg. 4157

NORTH CENTRAL KANSAS COOP; *U.S. Private*, pg. 2944

NORTH CENTRAL METHODIST ASC, L.P.—See HCA Healthcare, Inc.; *U.S. Public*, pg. 1004

NORTHCENTRAL MISSISSIPPI ELECTRIC POWER ASSOCIATION; *U.S. Private*, pg. 2948

NORTH CENTRAL MISSOURI ELECTRIC COOPERATIVE, INC.; *U.S. Private*, pg. 2944

NORTH CENTRAL SURGICAL CENTER, L.L.P.—See Tenet Healthcare Corporation; *U.S. Public*, pg. 2005

NORTHCENTRAL TELCOM INC.; *U.S. Private*, pg. 2949

NORTH CENTRAL TELEPHONE COOPERATIVE; *U.S. Private*, pg. 2944

NORTH CHARLESTON SEWER DISTRICT; *U.S. Private*, pg. 2944

NORTH CHINA GRID COMPANY LIMITED—See State Grid Corporation of China; *Int'l*, pg. 7183

NORTH CHINA INTERNATIONAL POWER ECONOMIC AND TRADE CORP.—See State Grid Corporation of China; *Int'l*, pg. 7183

NORTH CHINA PHARMACEUTICAL COMPANY LTD.; *Int'l*, pg. 5440

NORTH CITY (1981) PTY LTD—See Eagers Automotive Limited; *Int'l*, pg. 2263

NORTH CLIFF CONSULTANTS, INC.—See GHO Capital Partners LLP; *Int'l*, pg. 2959

NORTHCLIFFE MEDIA HOLDINGS LIMITED—See Daily Mail & General Trust plc; *Int'l*, pg. 1938

NORTHCLIFF RESOURCES LTD.—See Hunter Dickinson Inc.; *Int'l*, pg. 3536

NORTH COAST BEHAVIORAL RESEARCH GROUP—See Wyse; *U.S. Private*, pg. 4579

NORTHCOAST BUILDING PRODUCTS LTD.; *Int'l*, pg. 5442

NORTH COAST COMMERCIAL ROOFING SYSTEMS—See Beacon Roofing Supply, Inc.; *U.S. Public*, pg. 286

NORTH COAST CONTAINER CORP.—See Myers Container, LLC; *U.S. Private*, pg. 2824

NORTH COAST COOPERATIVE INC.; *U.S. Private*, pg. 2944

NORTH COAST ELECTRIC COMPANY—See Sonepar S.A.; *Int'l*, pg. 7093

NORTH COAST ENERGY, INC.—See EXCO Resources, Inc.; *U.S. Public*, pg. 805

NORTH COAST LIGHTING—See Sonepar S.A.; *Int'l*, pg. 7093

NORTH COAST MEDIA, LLC; *U.S. Private*, pg. 2944

NORTH COAST MEDICAL SUPPLY, INC.—See Court Square Capital Partners, L.P.; *U.S. Private*, pg. 1069

NORTH COAST MERCANTILE CO.; *U.S. Private*, pg. 2944

NORTH COAST OPPORTUNITIES, INC.; *U.S. Private*, pg. 2944

NORTH COAST S.A.; *Int'l*, pg. 5440

NORTH COAST TECHNICAL SALES, INC.—See Sole Source Capital LLC; *U.S. Private*, pg. 3708

NORTH COAST TECHNOLOGY INVESTORS, L.P.; *U.S. Private*, pg. 2944

NORTHCOAST WARRANTY SERVICES, INC.—See Stone Point Capital LLC; *U.S. Private*, pg. 3821

NORTHCODERS GROUP PLC; *Int'l*, pg. 5442

NORTHCODERS LIMITED—See Northcoders Group Plc; *Int'l*, pg. 5442

NORTH COLORADO SPRINGS DIALYSIS, LLC—See DaVita Inc.; *U.S. Public*, pg. 641

NORTH COPPER CO., LTD.; *Int'l*, pg. 5440

NORTHCORE RESOURCES INC.; *Int'l*, pg. 5442

NORTHCOTE OGILVY & MATHER—See WPP plc; *Int'l*, pg. 8488

NORTHCOTT HOSPITALITY INTERNATIONAL, LLC; *U.S. Private*, pg. 2949

NORTH COUNTRY BUSINESS PRODUCTS; *U.S. Private*, pg. 2944

NORTH COUNTRY HOSPITAL; *U.S. Private*, pg. 2944

NORTH COUNTRY INSURANCE CO.; *U.S. Private*, pg. 2944

NORTH COUNTRY MARKETING LTD.; *U.S. Private*, pg. 2944

NORTH COUNTRY WINDOWS & DOORS, LLC; *U.S. Private*, pg. 2944

NORTH COUNTY FORD INC.; *U.S. Private*, pg. 2944

NORTH COUNTY HEALTH PROJECT, LNC.; *U.S. Private*, pg. 2944

NORTH COUNTY INSURANCE—See Stone Point Capital LLC; *U.S. Private*, pg. 3819

NORTH COUNTY SURGICENTER—See HCA Healthcare, Inc.; *U.S. Public*, pg. 1004

NORTH COVE PARTNERS; *U.S. Private*, pg. 2944

NORTHCREST MEDICAL CENTER; *U.S. Private*, pg. 2949

NORTHCURRENT PARTNERS, LLC; *U.S. Private*, pg. 2949

NORTHCUTT CHEVROLET-BUICK CO.; *U.S. Private*, pg. 2949

NORTHCUTT INC.; *U.S. Private*, pg. 2949

NORTH CUTTING SYSTEMS, LLC—See Windway Capital Corp.; *U.S. Private*, pg. 4539

NORTH DAKOTA MILL & ELEVATOR ASSOCIATION; *U.S. Private*, pg. 2945

NORTH DAKOTA SURGERY CENTER, LLC—See Bain Capital, LP; *U.S. Private*, pg. 445

NORTHDALE OIL INC.; *U.S. Private*, pg. 2949

NORTH DALLAS BANK & TRUST CO.; *U.S. Public*, pg. 1536

NORTH DALLAS MOVING & STORAGE COMPANY CO., INC.; *U.S. Private*, pg. 2945

NORTH DALLAS TOLLWAY MEDICAL CENTER LLC—See Adeptus Health Inc.; *U.S. Private*, pg. 78

NORTH DAVIDSON GARBAGE SERVICE, INC.—See BC Partners LLP; *Int'l*, pg. 924

NORTH DENTON PIPELINE, L.L.C.—See Kinder Morgan, Inc.; *U.S. Public*, pg. 1234

NORTH DETAIL CO., LTD.—See Smartvalue Co., Ltd.; *Int'l*, pg. 7003

NORTH DEVELOPMENT AB—See Kindred Group plc; *Int'l*, pg. 4166

NORTH DOWNS DAIRY COMPANY LTD—See Ornua Cooperative Limited; *Int'l*, pg. 5642

NORTH DRILLING COMPANY; *Int'l*, pg. 5442

NORTHEAST AGENCIES INC.—See The Allstate Corporation; *U.S. Public*, pg. 2034

NORTHEAST AIR SOLUTIONS INC—See Daikin Industries, Ltd.; *Int'l*, pg. 1936

NORTHEAST AREA COUNCIL—See Dairy Farmers of America, Inc.; *U.S. Private*, pg. 1146

NORTHEAST ASSOCIATION MANAGEMENT, INC.—See The Carlyle Group Inc.; *U.S. Public*, pg. 2054

NORTHEAST BANK; *U.S. Public*, pg. 1537

NORTHEAST BATTERY & ALTERNATOR INC.—See Colville Capital LLC; *U.S. Private*, pg. 979

NORTHEAST BEHAVIORAL HEALTH CORPORATION; *U.S. Private*, pg. 2949

NORTHEAST BLUEPRINT & SUPPLY CO., INC.; *U.S. Private*, pg. 2949

NORTHEAST BUILDERS SUPPLY HOME CENTER LLC; *U.S. Private*, pg. 2949

NORTHEAST BUILDING PRODUCTS CORP.—See Clayton, Dubilier & Rice, LLC; *U.S. Private*, pg. 920

NORTHEAST CAPITAL & ADVISORY INC; *U.S. Private*, pg. 2949

NORTHEAST COMMUNICATIONS INC.; *U.S. Private*, pg. 2949

NORTHEAST COMMUNICATIONS OF WISCONSIN INCORPORATED; *U.S. Private*, pg. 2949

NORTHEAST COMMUNITY BANCORP, INC.; *U.S. Public*, pg. 1537

NORTHEAST COMMUNITY BANK—See NORTHEAST COMMUNITY BANCORP, INC.; *U.S. Public*, pg. 1537

NORTHEAST CONCEPTS INC.—See Metz Enterprises Inc.; *U.S. Private*, pg. 2691

NORTHEAST CONSTRUCTION SERVICES—See LeChase Construction Services, LLC; *U.S. Private*, pg. 2410

NORTHEAST CONTRACTORS INC.; *U.S. Private*, pg. 2949

NORTHEAST CONTROLS INC.; *U.S. Private*, pg. 2949

NORTHEAST COPIER SYSTEMS, LLC—See Xerox Holdings Corporation; *U.S. Public*, pg. 2388

NORTHEAST DATA DESTRUCTION & RECYCLING, LLC—See National Waste Management Holdings, Inc.; *U.S. Public*, pg. 1498

NORTHEAST DONUT SHOP MANAGEMENT; *U.S. Private*, pg. 2950

NORTHEAST DRINKS GROUP LLC; *U.S. Private*, pg. 2950

NORTHEAST ELECTRICAL, INC.—See Sonepar S.A.; *Int'l*, pg. 7093

NORTHEAST ELECTRIC DEVELOPMENT COMPANY LIMITED; *Int'l*, pg. 5442

NORTHEAST ENDOSCOPY CENTER, LLC—See KKR & Co. Inc.; *U.S. Public*, pg. 1250

NORTHEAST ENERGY ASSOCIATES, A LIMITED PARTNERSHIP—See NextEra Energy, Inc.; *U.S. Public*, pg. 1526

NORTHEASTERN APPRAISAL ASSOCIATES RESIDENTIAL, INC.—See Opteon Property Group Pty Ltd.; *Int'l*, pg. 5601

NORTH EASTERN CARRYING CORPORATION LIMITED; *Int'l*, pg. 5440

NORTHEASTERN ENVELOPE COMPANY; *U.S. Private*, pg. 2951

NORTHEASTERN NONWOVENS, INC.—See Metapoint Partners LP; *U.S. Private*, pg. 2682

NORTHEASTERN RURAL ELECTRIC MEMBERSHIP CORPORATION; *U.S. Private*, pg. 2951

NORTH EASTERN STATES, INC.—See Nippon Gas Co., Ltd.; *Int'l*, pg. 5318

NORTHEASTERN SUPPLY INC.; *U.S. Private*, pg. 2951

NORTHEAST FOODS, INC.; *U.S. Private*, pg. 2950

NORTHEAST GENERATION SERVICES COMPANY—See Eversource Energy; *U.S. Public*, pg. 801

NORTHEAST GEORGIA BANK—See First Security Bankshares Inc.; *U.S. Private*, pg. 1527

NORTHEAST GEORGIA HEALTH SYSTEM INC.; *U.S. Private*, pg. 2950

NORTHEAST GROCERY, INC.; *U.S. Private*, pg. 2950

NORTHEAST GROUP; *U.S. Private*, pg. 2950

NORTHEAST GUIDANCE CENTER; *U.S. Private*, pg. 2950

THE NORTHEAST HEALTH GROUP INC; *U.S. Private*, pg. 4084

NORTHEAST HEALTH SERVICES, LLC; *U.S. Private*, pg. 2950

NORTH EAST HEAT & LIGHT CO.; *U.S. Private*, pg. 2945

NORTH-EAST HNA INVESTMENT GROUP CO., LTD—See Hainan Traffic Administration Holding Co., Ltd.; *Int'l*, pg. 3215

NORTHEAST HOSPITAL CORPORATION; *U.S. Private*, pg. 2950

NORTHEAST HOTEL ASSOCIATES—See AVR Realty Company, LLC; *U.S. Private*, pg. 410

NORTHEAST HOT-FILL CO-OP, INC.; *U.S. Private*, pg. 2950

NORTHEAST ILLINOIS REGIONAL COMMUTER RAILROAD CORPORATION—See Regional Transportation Authority; *U.S. Private*, pg. 3389

NORTHEAST INDIANA BANCORP, INC.; *U.S. Public*, pg. 1537

NORTHEAST INDUSTRIES GROUP CO., LTD.—See China North Industries Group Corporation; *Int'l*, pg. 1536

NORTHEAST KANSAS COMMUNITY ACTION PROGRAM, INC.; *U.S. Private*, pg. 2950

NORTHEAST LOUISIANA POWER COOP; *U.S. Private*, pg. 2950

NORTHEAST MERCHANT SYSTEMS INC—See Ryvyl Inc.; *U.S. Public*, pg. 1830

NORTHEAST METHODIST HOSPITAL—See HCA Healthcare, Inc.; *U.S. Public*, pg. 1002

COMPANY NAME INDEX

NORTHEAST METHODIST HOSPITAL—See Methodist Healthcare Ministries of South Texas, Inc.; *U.S. Private*, pg. 2684

NORTHEAST METHODIST SURGICARE, LTD.—See HCA Healthcare, Inc.; *U.S. Public*, pg. 1004

NORTHEAST MICHIGAN COMMUNITY SERVICE AGENCY, INC.; *U.S. Private*, pg. 2950

NORTHEAST MISSISSIPPI COCA-COLA BOTTLING CO., INC.—See C.C. Clark, Inc.; *U.S. Private*, pg. 706

NORTH EAST MISSISSIPPI ELECTRIC POWER ASSOCIATION; *U.S. Private*, pg. 2945

NORTHEAST MONTANA HEALTH SERVICES; *U.S. Private*, pg. 2950

NORTHEAST NUCLEAR ENERGY COMPANY—See Eversource Energy; *U.S. Public*, pg. 801

NORTHEAST OFFICE SYSTEMS, LLC—See Xerox Holdings Corporation; *U.S. Public*, pg. 2388

NORTHEAST OHIO NATURAL GAS CORP.—See First Reserve Management, L.P.; *U.S. Private*, pg. 1525

NORTHEAST OHIO NEIGHBORHOOD HEALTH SERVICES, INC.; *U.S. Private*, pg. 2950

NORTHEAST OHIO REGIONAL SEWER DISTRICT - EASTERLY WASTEWATER TREATMENT PLANT—See Northeast Ohio Regional Sewer District; *U.S. Private*, pg. 2950

NORTHEAST OHIO REGIONAL SEWER DISTRICT; *U.S. Private*, pg. 2950

NORTHEAST OHIO REGIONAL SEWER DISTRICT - SOUTHERLY WASTEWATER TREATMENT PLANT—See Northeast Ohio Regional Sewer District; *U.S. Private*, pg. 2950

NORTHEAST OHIO REGIONAL SEWER DISTRICT - WESTERLY WASTEWATER TREATMENT PLANT—See Northeast Ohio Regional Sewer District; *U.S. Private*, pg. 2950

NORTHEAST OKLAHOMA ELECTRIC COOPERATIVE INC.; *U.S. Private*, pg. 2950

NORTHEAST OKLAHOMA PUBLIC FACILTIES AUTHORITY; *U.S. Private*, pg. 2951

NORTH EASTON SAVINGS BANK—See 1864 Bancorp, Inc; *U.S. Private*, pg. 3

NORTHEAST PARENT & CHILD SOCIETY, INC.; *U.S. Private*, pg. 2951

NORTHEAST PHARMACEUTICAL GROUP CO., LTD.; *Int'l*, pg. 5442

NORTHEAST PHILADELPHIA DIALYSIS CENTER, LLC—See Nautic Partners, LLC; *U.S. Private*, pg. 2870

NORTHEAST PHO, INC.—See HCA Healthcare, Inc.; *U.S. Public*, pg. 1004

NORTHEAST POWER SYSTEMS, INC.—See American Superconductor Corporation; *U.S. Public*, pg. 110

NORTHEAST PRESS LTD—See JPIMedia Holdings Limited; *Int'l*, pg. 4006

NORTHEAST REMSCO CONSTRUCTION, INC.; *U.S. Private*, pg. 2951

NORTHEAST RETIREMENT SERVICES, LLC—See Community Bank System, Inc.; *U.S. Public*, pg. 550

NORTH EAST RIG-OUT LIMITED—See V. F. Corporation; *U.S. Public*, pg. 2268

NORTHEAST RUBBER PUBLIC COMPANY LIMITED; *Int'l*, pg. 5442

NORTHEAST RURAL SERVICES INC.—See Northeast Oklahoma Electric Cooperative Inc.; *U.S. Private*, pg. 2950

NORTHEAST SALES DISTRIBUTING INC.; *U.S. Private*, pg. 2951

NORTHEAST SECURITIES CO., LTD.; *Int'l*, pg. 5442

NORTHEAST SECURITIES INC.; *U.S. Private*, pg. 2951

NORTHEAST SECURITY BANK—See Independence Bancshares, Inc.; *U.S. Private*, pg. 2055

NORTHEAST SENIOR HEALTH CORPORATION; *U.S. Private*, pg. 2951

NORTHEAST SOLITE CORPORATION; *U.S. Private*, pg. 2951

THE NORTHEAST TEXAS DATA CORP—See i3 Verticals, Inc.; *U.S. Public*, pg. 1081

NORTHEAST TEXAS FARMERS CO-OP; *U.S. Private*, pg. 2951

NORTHEAST TREATERS INC.; *U.S. Private*, pg. 2951

NORTHEAST UTILITIES SERVICE COMPANY—See Eversource Energy; *U.S. Public*, pg. 802

NORTHEAST VALLEY HEALTH CORPORATION; *U.S. Private*, pg. 2951

NORTHEAST WASHINGTON HOME HEALTH, INC.—See UnitedHealth Group Incorporated; *U.S. Public*, pg. 2246

NORTHEAST WHOLESALE TIRE CORP.—See I&E Tire Corp.; *U.S. Private*, pg. 2026

NORTHEAST WINDOW & DOOR ASSOCIATION; *U.S. Private*, pg. 2951

NORTHEDGE CAPITAL LLP; *Int'l*, pg. 5442

NORTH ELECTRIC SUPPLY, INC.; *U.S. Private*, pg. 2945

NORTH ELECTRO-OPTIC CO., LTD.; *Int'l*, pg. 5440

NORTH END MAZDA OF LUNENBURG—See Colonial Automotive Group, Inc.; *U.S. Private*, pg. 970

NORTH END SUBARU OF LUNENBURG—See Colonial Automotive Group, Inc.; *U.S. Private*, pg. 970

NORTHEND TRUCK EQUIPMENT, LLC—See Federal Signal Corporation; *U.S. Public*, pg. 826

NORTH ENERGY ASA; *Int'l*, pg. 5440

NORTHERN 2 VCT PLC—See Mercia Asset Management PLC; *Int'l*, pg. 4830

NORTHERN 3 VCT PLC—See Mercia Asset Management PLC; *Int'l*, pg. 4830

NORTHERN AG SERVICE INC.; *U.S. Private*, pg. 2951

NORTHERN AIR CARGO INC.; *U.S. Private*, pg. 2951

NORTHERN ALBERTA OIL LTD.—See Deep Well Oil & Gas, Inc.; *Int'l*, pg. 2002

NORTHERN ARIZONA BEHAVIORAL HEALTH AUTHORITY, INC.; *U.S. Private*, pg. 2951

NORTHERN ARIZONA HEALTHCARE CORPORATION; *U.S. Private*, pg. 2951

NORTHERN AUTOMOTIVE, INC.; *U.S. Private*, pg. 2952

NORTHERN AUTOMOTIVE SYSTEMS LIMITED—See Ningbo Huaxiang Electronic Co., Ltd.; *Int'l*, pg. 5302

NORTHERN BANK LIMITED—See Danske Bank A/S; *Int'l*, pg. 1969

NORTHERN BANK & TRUST COMPANY; *U.S. Private*, pg. 2952

NORTHERN BEAR PLC; *Int'l*, pg. 5442

NORTHERN BERKSHIRE EMS, INC.; *U.S. Private*, pg. 2952

NORTHERN BOILER & MECHANICAL CONTRACTORS; *U.S. Private*, pg. 2952

NORTHERN BRANDS INTERNATIONAL, INC.—See British American Tobacco plc; *Int'l*, pg. 1168

NORTHERN BUILDING PRODUCTS; *U.S. Private*, pg. 2952

NORTHERN BUSINESS MACHINES INC; *U.S. Private*, pg. 2952

NORTHERN BUSINESS PRODUCTS, INC.—See Innovative Office Solutions LLC; *U.S. Private*, pg. 2083

NORTHERN CALIFORNIA BANCORP, INC.—See PCB Financial, Inc; *U.S. Private*, pg. 3119

NORTHERN CALIFORNIA CONGREGATIONAL RETIREMENT HOMES, INC.; *U.S. Private*, pg. 2952

NORTHERN CALIFORNIA INSTITUTE FOR RESEARCH AND EDUCATION; *U.S. Private*, pg. 2952

NORTHERN CALIFORNIA NATIONAL BANK; *U.S. Public*, pg. 1537

NORTHERN CALIFORNIA POWER AGENCY; *U.S. Private*, pg. 2952

NORTHERN CAPITAL MANAGEMENT, LLC—See Clayton, Dubilier & Rice, LLC; *U.S. Private*, pg. 923

NORTHERN CAPITAL MANAGEMENT, LLC—See Stone Point Capital LLC; *U.S. Private*, pg. 3824

NORTHERN CATV SALES INC.; *U.S. Private*, pg. 2952

NORTHERN CEMENT COMPANY; *Int'l*, pg. 5443

NORTHERN CEMENT LTD—See CRH plc; *Int'l*, pg. 1842

NORTHERN CHILDRENS SERVICES; *U.S. Private*, pg. 2952

NORTHERN COALFIELDS LIMITED—See Coal India Limited; *Int'l*, pg. 1680

NORTHERN COCHISE COMMUNITY HOSPITAL, INC.; *U.S. Private*, pg. 2952

NORTHERN COLORADO TRAFFIC CONTROL, INC.—See Kohlberg & Company, LLC; *U.S. Private*, pg. 2337

NORTHERN COMMERCIALS (MIRFIELD) LTD—See Clipper Logistics Group Ltd.; *Int'l*, pg. 1660

NORTHERN CONTOURS HOLDING CORP.; *U.S. Private*, pg. 2952

NORTHERN CONTOURS INC.—See Northern Contours Holding Corp.; *U.S. Private*, pg. 2952

NORTHERN COPPER INDUSTRIAL CO., LTD.—See SK Networks Co., Ltd.; *Int'l*, pg. 6974

NORTHERN CROSS, LTD.—See Barancorp, Ltd.; *U.S. Private*, pg. 471

NORTHERN DATA AG; *Int'l*, pg. 5443

NORTHERN DIGITAL INC.—See Roper Technologies, Inc.; *U.S. Public*, pg. 1812

NORTHERN DRILLING LTD.; *Int'l*, pg. 5443

NORTHERN DRY-BULK, INC.—See Ontario Municipal Employees Retirement System; *Int'l*, pg. 5585

NORTHERN DYNASTY MINERALS LTD.; *Int'l*, pg. 5443

NORTHERN ELASTOMERIC, INC.—See Owens Corning; *U.S. Public*, pg. 1627

NORTHERN ELECTRICITY DEVELOPMENT & INVESTMENT JOINT-STOCK COMPANY NO 2—See Vietnam Construction Stock Corporation; *Int'l*, pg. 8198

NORTHERN ELECTRIC PLC—See Berkshire Hathaway Inc.; *U.S. Public*, pg. 313

NORTHERN EMPIRE PIZZA INCORPORATED; *U.S. Private*, pg. 2952

NORTHERN ENERGY CORPORATION LIMITED—See New Hope Corporation Limited; *Int'l*, pg. 5224

NORTHERN ENERGY INC.; *U.S. Private*, pg. 2952

NORTHERN ENGINE & SUPPLY CO.; *U.S. Private*, pg. 2952

NORTHERN ENGRAVING CORPORATION; *U.S. Private*, pg. 2952

NORTHERN ENTERTAINMENT PRODUCTIONS LLC—See Comcast Corporation; *U.S. Public*, pg. 541

THE NORTHERNER—See Glacier Media Inc.; *Int'l*, pg. 2987

NORTHERN FACTORY SALES INC.; *U.S. Private*, pg. 2952

NORTHERN FEED & BEAN OF LUCERN; *U.S. Private*, pg. 2953

NORTHERN FINANCIAL CORPORATION; *Int'l*, pg. 5443

NORTHERN FOODS LIMITED—See Boparan Holdings Limited; *Int'l*, pg. 1111

NORTHERN FOODS PLC-TECHNICAL SERVICES—See Boparan Holdings Limited; *Int'l*, pg. 1111

NORTHERN FREIGHT SERVICE, INC.—See Allen Lund Company, LLC; *U.S. Private*, pg. 179

NORTHERN FRONTIER CORP.; *Int'l*, pg. 5443

NORTHERN FRONTIER FACILITIES LP—See Northern Frontier Corp.; *Int'l*, pg. 5443

NORTHERN FRUIT COMPANY, INC.; *U.S. Private*, pg. 2953

NORTHERN GC, LLC—See WCS, Inc.; *U.S. Private*, pg. 4462

NORTHERN GENERAL INSURANCE CO. LTD.; *Int'l*, pg. 5443

NORTHERN GRAPHITE CORPORATION; *Int'l*, pg. 5443

NORTHERN GROWERS LLC; *U.S. Public*, pg. 1537

NORTHERN HARDWOODS—See H.I.G. Capital, LLC; *U.S. Private*, pg. 1832

NORTHERN HEAVY INDUSTRIES GROUP CO. LTD.; *Int'l*, pg. 5443

NORTHERN HIGHWAY OPERATION LLC—See VINCI S.A.; *Int'l*, pg. 8239

NORTHERN HOLDINGS INC.; *U.S. Private*, pg. 2953

NORTHERN ILLINOIS GAS COMPANY—See The Southern Company; *U.S. Public*, pg. 2131

NORTHERN ILLINOIS STEEL SUPPLY COMPANY—See Reliance Steel & Aluminum Co.; *U.S. Public*, pg. 1781

NORTHERN IMPORTS, INC.; *U.S. Private*, pg. 2953

NORTHERN INDIANA PAINT SUPPLY, INC.; *U.S. Private*, pg. 2953

NORTHERN INDIANA PUBLIC SERVICE COMPANY LLC—See NiSource Inc.; *U.S. Public*, pg. 1530

NORTHERN INDUSTRIAL INC.; *U.S. Private*, pg. 2953

NORTHERN INDUSTRIAL INSULATION CONTRACTORS, INC.—See Bird Construction Inc.; *Int'l*, pg. 1047

NORTHERN INSURANCE COMPANY OF NEW YORK—See Zurich Insurance Group Limited; *Int'l*, pg. 8699

NORTHERN IRELAND TRANSPORT HOLDING COMPANY; *Int'l*, pg. 5443

NORTHERN IRON AND BRASS FOUNDRY PTY. LTD.—See Fletcher Building Limited; *Int'l*, pg. 2699

NORTHERN IRON OF ST. PAUL, LLC; *U.S. Private*, pg. 2953

NORTHERN JUTE MANUFACTURING COMPANY LIMITED; *Int'l*, pg. 5444

NORTHERN KENTUCKY AREA DEVELOPMENT DISTRICT; *U.S. Private*, pg. 2953

NORTHERN KENTUCKY WATER DISTRICT; *U.S. Private*, pg. 2953

NORTHERN LABS, INC.—See Novacap Management Inc.; *Int'l*, pg. 5454

NORTHERN LAKES CONCRETE, INC.—See Pitlik & Wick, Inc.; *U.S. Private*, pg. 3190

NORTHERN LAKES COOPERATIVE; *U.S. Private*, pg. 2953

NORTHERN LAND HOLDINGS LTD—See Finasucre S.A.; *Int'l*, pg. 2670

NORTHERN LIGHTS ENTERPRISES, INC.—See Zippo Manufacturing Company, Inc.; *U.S. Private*, pg. 4606

NORTHERN LIGHTS INC.; *U.S. Private*, pg. 2953

NORTHERN LIGHT; *Int'l*, pg. 5444

NORTHERN LIGHT—See Chatham Asset Management, LLC; *U.S. Private*, pg. 861

NORTHERN LIGHTS RESOURCES CORP.; *Int'l*, pg. 5444

NORTHERN LION GOLD CORP.; *Int'l*, pg. 5444

NORTHERN MACHINING & REPAIR, INC.; *U.S. Private*, pg. 2953

NORTHERN MAINE MEDICAL CENTER; *U.S. Private*, pg. 2953

NORTHERN MANOR MULTICARE CENTER; *U.S. Private*, pg. 2953

NORTHERN MANUFACTURING CO, INC.; *U.S. Private*, pg. 2953

NORTHERN MARINE GROUP—See STENA AB; *Int'l*, pg. 7206

NORTHERN MARINE UNDERWRITERS LIMITED—See Munchener Ruckversicherungs AG; *Int'l*, pg. 5091

NORTHERN MICHIGAN SUBSTANCE ABUSE SERVICES INC.; *U.S. Private*, pg. 2953

NORTHERN MICHIGAN SURGICAL SUITES, LLC—See Tenet Healthcare Corporation; *U.S. Public*, pg. 2005

NORTHERN MICHIGAN TRACTOR & EQUIPMENT, LLC—See Tym Corporation; *U.S. Private*, pg. 7995

NORTHERN MICHIGAN VENEERS, INC.—See The Hoffmann Family of Companies; *U.S. Private*, pg. 4053

NORTHERN MICRO; *Int'l*, pg. 5444

NORTHERN MINERALS & EXPLORATION LTD.; *U.S. Public*, pg. 1537

NORTHERN MINERALS LIMITED; *Int'l*, pg. 5444

NORTHERN MINER—See Glacier Media Inc.; *Int'l*, pg. 2987

NORTHERN MISSOURI BANCSHARES, INC.; *U.S. Private*, pg. 2953

NORTHERN MISSOURI BANCSHARES, INC.

CORPORATE AFFILIATIONS

NORTHERN MONMOUTH REGIONAL SURGERY CENTER, L.L.C.—See Tenet Healthcare Corporation; *U.S. Public*, pg. 2011

NORTHERN MONTANA HEALTH CARE; *U.S. Private*, pg. 2953

NORTHERN MOTOR COMPANY; *U.S. Private*, pg. 2953

NORTHERN NATURAL GAS COMPANY—See Berkshire Hathaway Inc.; *U.S. Public*, pg. 301

NORTHERN NECK OIL COMPANY—See Quarles Petroleum Incorporated; *U.S. Private*, pg. 3324

NORTHERN NECK PHYSICAL THERAPY, LIMITED PARTNERSHIP—See U.S. Physical Therapy, Inc.; *U.S. Public*, pg. 2215

NORTHERN NEVADA CARDIOLOGY PC—See Universal Health Services, Inc.; *U.S. Public*, pg. 2258

NORTHERN NEVADA MEDICAL CENTER—See Universal Health Services, Inc.; *U.S. Public*, pg. 2260

NORTHERN NEVADA MEDICAL GROUP, LLC—See Universal Health Services, Inc.; *U.S. Public*, pg. 2258

NORTHERN NEW ENGLAND ENERGY CORPORATION—See Caisse de Depot et Placement du Quebec; *Int'l*, pg. 1256

THE NORTHERN NEWS—See Chatham Asset Management, LLC; *U.S. Private*, pg. 861

NORTHERN NEW YORK COMMUNITY FOUNDATION, INC.; *U.S. Private*, pg. 2953

NORTHERN NIGERIA FLOUR MILLS PLC—See Flour Mills of Nigeria Plc.; *Int'l*, pg. 2709

NORTHERN NURSERIES, INC.—See The Robert Baker Companies; *U.S. Private*, pg. 4111

THE NORTHERN NV ENDOSCOPY ASC, LLC—See KKR & Co. Inc.; *U.S. Public*, pg. 1248

NORTHERN OAKS HEALTHCARE, INC.—See The Ensign Group, Inc.; *U.S. Public*, pg. 2071

NORTHERN OAK WEALTH MANAGEMENT INC.—See Old National Bancorp; *U.S. Public*, pg. 1567

NORTHERN OFFSHORE LTD.; *U.S. Private*, pg. 2953

NORTHERN OHIO & WESTERN RAILWAY, LLC—See The Broe Companies, Inc.; *U.S. Private*, pg. 4001

NORTHERN OILFIELD SERVICES, INC.—See Saltchuk Resources Inc.; *U.S. Private*, pg. 3534

NORTHERN OIL & GAS, INC.; *U.S. Public*, pg. 1537

NORTHERN OPERATING SERVICES PRIVATE LIMITED—See Northern Trust Corporation; *U.S. Public*, pg. 1539

NORTHERN PACIFIC GROUP; *U.S. Private*, pg. 2954

NORTHERN PARKLIFE AB; *Int'l*, pg. 5444

NORTHERN PARKLIFE FRANCE SAS—See Northern Parklife AB; *Int'l*, pg. 5444

NORTHERN PARKLIFE, INC.—See Northern Parklife AB; *Int'l*, pg. 5444

NORTHERN PARKLIFE—See Northern Parklife AB; *Int'l*, pg. 5444

NORTHERN PARTNERS COOPERATIVE; *U.S. Private*, pg. 2954

NORTHERN PETROLEUM (GB) LIMITED—See Cabot Energy Plc; *Int'l*, pg. 1246

NORTHERN PIPELINE CONSTRUCTION CO.—See Southwest Gas Holdings, Inc.; *U.S. Public*, pg. 1913

NORTHERN PIPE PRODUCT INC.—See Otter Tail Corporation; *U.S. Public*, pg. 1624

NORTHERN PLAINS ELECTRIC COOPERATIVE; *U.S. Private*, pg. 2954

NORTHERN PLAINS STEEL CO.—See Owen Industries, Inc.; *U.S. Private*, pg. 3054

NORTHERN PLAINS TRUCKING, LLC—See Superior Energy Services, Inc.; *U.S. Public*, pg. 3877

NORTHERN PLANET LLC; *U.S. Private*, pg. 2954

NORTHERN POTASH CO.; *Int'l*, pg. 5444

NORTHERN POWERGRID LIMITED—See Berkshire Hathaway Inc.; *U.S. Public*, pg. 313

NORTHERN POWERGRID U.K. HOLDINGS—See Berkshire Hathaway Inc.; *U.S. Public*, pg. 313

NORTHERN POWERLINE CONSTRUCTORS, INC.—See Quanta Services, Inc.; *U.S. Public*, pg. 1752

NORTHERN POWER SYSTEMS CORP.; *U.S. Private*, pg. 2954

NORTHERN PRODUCTION COMPANY, LLC—See Nine Energy Service, Inc.; *U.S. Public*, pg. 1529

NORTHERN PROJECT & CONSTRUCTION DIVISION—See CPC Corporation; *Int'l*, pg. 1824

NORTHERN PROPERTY R.E.I.T. HOLDINGS INC.—See KingSett Capital; *Int'l*, pg. 4174

NORTHERN PROPERTY R.E.I.T. HOLDINGS INC.—See Starlight Investments Ltd.; *Int'l*, pg. 7177

NORTHERN PULP NOVA SCOTIA CORPORATION—See PT Sinar Mas Group; *Int'l*, pg. 6074

NORTHERN RAIL LIMITED—See Mobico Group PLC; *Int'l*, pg. 5009

NORTHERN RECRUITMENT GROUP PLC; *Int'l*, pg. 5444

NORTHERN REFLECTIONS LTD.—See York Management Services, Inc.; *U.S. Private*, pg. 4590

NORTHERN REFRIGERATED TRANSPORTATION INC.; *U.S. Private*, pg. 2954

NORTHERN REGION CEMENT COMPANY; *Int'l*, pg. 5444

NORTHERN RELIABILITY INC.—See KORE Power, Inc.; *U.S. Public*, pg. 2343

NORTHERN RESOURCES COOPERATIVE; *U.S. Private*, pg. 2954

NORTHERN RESOURCES NOVA SCOTIA CORPORATION—See PT Sinar Mas Group; *Int'l*, pg. 6074

NORTHERN ROCKIES SURGICENTER, INC.—See UnitedHealth Group Incorporated; *U.S. Public*, pg. 2242

NORTHERN RV PTY. LTD.—See Fleetwood Limited; *Int'l*, pg. 2699

NORTHERN SAFETY CO., INC.—See Wurth Verwaltungsgesellschaft mbH; *Int'l*, pg. 8511

NORTHERN SALES COMPANY OF ALASKA, INC.; *U.S. Private*, pg. 2954

NORTHERN SANITATION, INC.—See Casella Waste Systems, Inc.; *U.S. Public*, pg. 446

NORTHERN SECURITY INSURANCE CO. INC.—See Vermont Mutual Insurance Co., Inc.; *U.S. Private*, pg. 4367

NORTHERN & SHELL PLC—See Reach PLC; *Int'l*, pg. 6231

NORTHERN SHIELD RESOURCES INC.; *Int'l*, pg. 5444

NORTHERN SOFT DRINKS & MINERAL WATER CO.; *Int'l*, pg. 5444

NORTHERN SOUND & LIGHT, INC—See Alarmax Distributors Inc.; *U.S. Private*, pg. 150

NORTHERN SOUTHLAND TRANSPORT—See Trojan Holdings Ltd.; *Int'l*, pg. 7938

NORTHERN SPHERE MINING CORP.; *Int'l*, pg. 5444

NORTHERN SPIRITS LTD.; *Int'l*, pg. 5444

NORTHERN STAMPING INC.; *U.S. Private*, pg. 2954

NORTHERN STAR COOPERATIVE; *U.S. Private*, pg. 2954

NORTHERN STAR GENERATION SERVICES COMPANY LLC—See Ontario Teachers' Pension Plan; *Int'l*, pg. 5590

NORTHERN STAR GENERATION SERVICES COMPANY LLC—See UBS Group AG; *Int'l*, pg. 8008

NORTHERN STAR INDUSTRIES INC.; *U.S. Private*, pg. 2954

NORTHERN STAR MANAGEMENT, INC.—See Norman-Spencer Agency, Inc.; *U.S. Private*, pg. 2938

NORTHERN STAR RESOURCES LTD; *Int'l*, pg. 5444

NORTHERN STATES COMPLETIONS, INC.—See Nine Energy Service, Inc.; *U.S. Public*, pg. 1529

NORTHERN STATES METALS CORP.; *U.S. Private*, pg. 2954

NORTHERN STATES POWER COMPANY—See Xcel Energy Inc.; *U.S. Public*, pg. 2385

NORTHERN STATES POWER COMPANY—See Xcel Energy Inc.; *U.S. Public*, pg. 2385

NORTHERN STATES SUPPLY INC.—See Building Fasteners of Minnesota Inc.; *U.S. Private*, pg. 682

NORTHERN STEEL CASTINGS INC.; *U.S. Private*, pg. 2954

NORTHERN STEEL GROUP, INC.—See Aurora Capital Group, LLC; *U.S. Private*, pg. 394

NORTHERN STEEL TRANSPORT CO.; *U.S. Private*, pg. 2954

NORTHERN SUN MINING CORP.; *Int'l*, pg. 5444

NORTHERN SUPERIOR RESOURCES INC.; *Int'l*, pg. 5444

NORTHERN TECH CO., LTD.—See Sumitomo Forestry Co., Ltd.; *Int'l*, pg. 7285

NORTHERN TECHNICAL, L.L.C.—See Donaldson Company, Inc.; *U.S. Public*, pg. 676

NORTHERN TECHNOLOGIES GROUP INC.; *U.S. Private*, pg. 2954

NORTHERN TECHNOLOGIES INTERNATIONAL CORPORATION; *U.S. Public*, pg. 1537

NORTHERNTEL LIMITED PARTNERSHIP—See BCE Inc.; *Int'l*, pg. 926

NORTHERN TEXTILES & GARMENTS JOINT STOCK COMPANY; *Int'l*, pg. 5445

NORTHERN TIER BAKERY LLC—See Marathon Petroleum Corporation; *U.S. Public*, pg. 1363

NORTHERN TIER ENERGY GP LLC—See Marathon Petroleum Corporation; *U.S. Public*, pg. 1363

NORTHERN TIER ENERGY LLC—See Marathon Petroleum Corporation; *U.S. Public*, pg. 1363

NORTHERN TIER ENERGY LLC—See Marathon Petroleum Corporation; *U.S. Public*, pg. 1363

NORTHERN TIER OIL TRANSPORT LLC—See Marathon Petroleum Corporation; *U.S. Public*, pg. 1363

NORTHERN TIER RETAIL LLC—See Marathon Petroleum Corporation; *U.S. Public*, pg. 1363

NORTHERN TOOL & EQUIPMENT CO. LTD.—See Northern Tool & Equipment Company, Inc.; *U.S. Private*, pg. 2954

NORTHERN TOOL & EQUIPMENT COMPANY, INC.; *U.S. Private*, pg. 2954

NORTHERN TRANSMISSION SERVICES, LTD.—See MYR Group Inc.; *U.S. Public*, pg. 1489

NORTHERN TRUST CAYMAN INTERNATIONAL, LTD.—See Northern Trust Corporation; *U.S. Public*, pg. 1538

THE NORTHERN TRUST COMPANY CANADA—See Northern Trust Corporation; *U.S. Public*, pg. 1539

THE NORTHERN TRUST COMPANY OF CALIFORNIA—See Northern Trust Corporation; *U.S. Public*, pg. 1539

THE NORTHERN TRUST COMPANY OF DELAWARE—See Northern Trust Corporation; *U.S. Public*, pg. 1539

THE NORTHERN TRUST COMPANY OF NEW YORK—See Northern Trust Corporation; *U.S. Public*, pg. 1539

THE NORTHERN TRUST COMPANY OF SAUDI ARABIA—See Northern Trust Corporation; *U.S. Public*, pg. 1539

THE NORTHERN TRUST COMPANY—See Northern Trust Corporation; *U.S. Public*, pg. 1539

THE NORTHERN TRUST COMPANY—See Northern Trust Corporation; *U.S. Public*, pg. 1538

NORTHERN TRUST CORPORATION; *U.S. Public*, pg. 1538

NORTHERN TRUST CORPORATION - UNITED KINGDOM—See Northern Trust Corporation; *U.S. Public*, pg. 1538

NORTHERN TRUST FIDUCIARY SERVICES (GUERNSEY) LIMITED—See Northern Trust Corporation; *U.S. Public*, pg. 1538

NORTHERN TRUST FUND MANAGERS (IRELAND) LIMITED—See Northern Trust Corporation; *U.S. Public*, pg. 1539

NORTHERN TRUST GLOBAL FUND SERVICES CAYMAN LIMITED—See Northern Trust Corporation; *U.S. Public*, pg. 1539

NORTHERN TRUST GROUP LTD.; *Int'l*, pg. 5445

NORTHERN TRUST (GUERNSEY) LIMITED—See Northern Trust Corporation; *U.S. Public*, pg. 1538

THE NORTHERN TRUST INTERNATIONAL BANKING CORPORATION—See Northern Trust Corporation; *U.S. Public*, pg. 1539

NORTHERN TRUST INTERNATIONAL FUND ADMINISTRATION SERVICES (GUERNSEY) LIMITED—See Northern Trust Corporation; *U.S. Public*, pg. 1538

NORTHERN TRUST INTERNATIONAL FUND ADMINISTRATION SERVICES (IRELAND) LIMITED—See Northern Trust Corporation; *U.S. Public*, pg. 1538

NORTHERN TRUST LUXEMBOURG MANAGEMENT COMPANY S.A.—See Northern Trust Corporation; *U.S. Public*, pg. 1538

NORTHERN TRUST MANAGEMENT SERVICES (DEUTSCHLAND) GMBH—See Northern Trust Corporation; *U.S. Public*, pg. 1538

NORTHERN TRUST MANAGEMENT SERVICES LIMITED—See Northern Trust Corporation; *U.S. Public*, pg. 1539

NORTHERN TRUST SECURITIES LLP—See Northern Trust Corporation; *U.S. Public*, pg. 1539

NORTHERN TRUST SECURITIES SERVICES (IRELAND) LIMITED—See Northern Trust Corporation; *U.S. Public*, pg. 1538

NORTHERN TRUST SWITZERLAND AG—See Northern Trust Corporation; *U.S. Public*, pg. 1538

NORTHERN UNITED PUBLISHING & MEDIA (GROUP) COMPANY LIMITED; *Int'l*, pg. 5445

NORTHERN URANIUM CORP.; *Int'l*, pg. 5445

NORTHERN UTAH HEALTHCARE CORPORATION—See HCA Healthcare, Inc.; *U.S. Public*, pg. 1004

NORTHERN UTAH IMAGING, LLC—See HCA Healthcare, Inc.; *U.S. Public*, pg. 1004

NORTHERN VALET INC.—See Indigo Group S.A.S.; *Int'l*, pg. 3655

NORTHERN VENTURE TRUST PLC—See Mercia Asset Management PLC; *Int'l*, pg. 4830

NORTHERN VERTEX MINING CORP.; *Int'l*, pg. 5445

NORTHERN VIDEO SYSTEMS, INC.—See WESCO International, Inc.; *U.S. Public*, pg. 2351

NORTHERN VIRGINIA ELECTRIC COOPERATIVE INC.; *U.S. Private*, pg. 2954

NORTHERN VIRGINIA HOMES; *U.S. Private*, pg. 2955

NORTHERN VIRGINIA MEDIA SERVICES; *U.S. Private*, pg. 2955

NORTHERN WHITE SAND LLC—See Eagle Materials Inc.; *U.S. Public*, pg. 702

NORTHERN WHOLESALE SUPPLY, LLC—See Sun Capital Partners, Inc.; *U.S. Private*, pg. 3860

NORTHERN WIND INC.; *U.S. Private*, pg. 2955

NORTHERN YIELD SHIPPING LTD—See StealthGas Inc.; *Int'l*, pg. 7188

NORTH EUROPEAN OIL ROYALTY TRUST; *U.S. Public*, pg. 1536

THE NORTH FACE, INC.—See V. F. Corporation; *U.S. Public*, pg. 2269

NORTHFIELD BANCORP, INC.; *U.S. Public*, pg. 1539

NORTHFIELD BANK—See Northfield Bancorp, Inc.; *U.S. Public*, pg. 1539

NORTHFIELD BLOCK CO.—See CRH plc; *Int'l*, pg. 1845

NORTHFIELD BLOCK—See CRH plc; *Int'l*, pg. 1846

NORTHFIELD CAPITAL CORPORATION; *Int'l*, pg. 5445

NORTHFIELD GLASS GROUP INC.; *Int'l*, pg. 5445

NORTHFIELD METAL PRODUCTS LTD.—See Leggett & Platt, Incorporated; *U.S. Public*, pg. 1303

NORTHFIELD PARK ASSOCIATES LLC—See MGM Resorts International; *U.S. Public*, pg. 1435

NORTHFIELD PRECISION INSTRUMENT CORP.; *U.S. Public*, pg. 1539

NORTHFIELD SAVINGS BANK INC.; *U.S. Private*, pg. 2955

NORTHFIELD TELEPHONE COMPANY—See Telephone & Data Systems, Inc.; *U.S. Public*, pg. 1998

COMPANY NAME INDEX

NORTH FLORIDA ANESTHESIA CONSULTANTS, P.A.—See KKR & Co. Inc.; *U.S. Public*, pg. 1250
NORTH FLORIDA CANCER CENTER LAKE CITY, LLC—See HCA Healthcare, Inc.; *U.S. Public*, pg. 1004
NORTH FLORIDA ENDOSCOPY CENTER—See HCA Healthcare, Inc.; *U.S. Public*, pg. 1004
NORTH FLORIDA ENDOSCOPY CENTER—See HCA Healthcare, Inc.; *U.S. Public*, pg. 1004
NORTH FLORIDA MOTOR COMPANY; *U.S. Private*, pg. 2945
NORTH FLORIDA OUTPATIENT IMAGING CENTER, LTD.—See HCA Healthcare, Inc.; *U.S. Public*, pg. 1004
NORTH FLORIDA PERINATAL ASSOCIATES, INC.—See KKR & Co. Inc.; *U.S. Public*, pg. 1246
NORTH FLORIDA RADIATION ONCOLOGY, LLC—See HCA Healthcare, Inc.; *U.S. Public*, pg. 1004
NORTH FLORIDA REGIONAL MEDICAL CENTER, INC.—See HCA Healthcare, Inc.; *U.S. Public*, pg. 1004
NORTH FLORIDA REGIONAL OTOLARYNGOLOGY, LLC—See HCA Healthcare, Inc.; *U.S. Public*, pg. 1004
NORTH FLORIDA ROCK, LTD.—See Arcosa, Inc.; *U.S. Public*, pg. 186
NORTH FLORIDA SALES; *U.S. Private*, pg. 2945
NORTH FLORIDA SHIPYARDS INC. - MAYPORT FACILITY—See North Florida Shipyards Inc.; *U.S. Private*, pg. 2945
NORTH FLORIDA SHIPYARDS INC.; *U.S. Private*, pg. 2945
NORTH FLORIDA SURGICAL ASSOCIATES, LLC—See HCA Healthcare, Inc.; *U.S. Public*, pg. 1004
NORTH FLORIDA SURGICAL ASSOCIATES, LLC—See HCA Healthcare, Inc.; *U.S. Public*, pg. 1004
NORTHFORGE INNOVATIONS INC.—See Access Co., Ltd.; *Int'l*, pg. 88
NORTH GARLAND SURGERY CENTER, L.L.P.—See Tenet Healthcare Corporation; *U.S. Public*, pg. 2011
NORTHGATEARINSO ARGENTINA SA—See Alight, Inc.; *U.S. Public*, pg. 77
NORTHGATEARINSO AUSTRALIA PTY LTD—See Alight, Inc.; *U.S. Public*, pg. 77
NORTHGATEARINSO AUSTRIA GMBH—See Alight, Inc.; *U.S. Public*, pg. 77
NORTHGATEARINSO BELGIUM BV—See Alight, Inc.; *U.S. Public*, pg. 77
NORTHGATEARINSO BELGIUM PEOPLE SERVICES SA—See Alight, Inc.; *U.S. Public*, pg. 77
NORTHGATEARINSO BRAZIL INFORMATICA LTDA.—See Alight, Inc.; *U.S. Public*, pg. 77
NORTHGATEARINSO CANADA INC.—See Alight, Inc.; *U.S. Public*, pg. 77
NORTHGATEARINSO DEUTSCHLAND AG—See Alight, Inc.; *U.S. Public*, pg. 77
NORTHGATEARINSO FINLAND OY—See Alight, Inc.; *U.S. Public*, pg. 77
NORTHGATEARINSO FRANCE S.A.S.—See Alight, Inc.; *U.S. Public*, pg. 77
NORTHGATEARINSO ITALIA S.R.L.—See Alight, Inc.; *U.S. Public*, pg. 77
NORTHGATEARINSO LUXEMBOURG SA—See Alight, Inc.; *U.S. Public*, pg. 77
NORTHGATEARINSO MADRID SA—See Alight, Inc.; *U.S. Public*, pg. 77
NORTHGATEARINSO MALAYSIA SDN BHD—See Alight, Inc.; *U.S. Public*, pg. 77
NORTHGATEARINSO MILANO S.R.L.—See Alight, Inc.; *U.S. Public*, pg. 77
NORTHGATEARINSO PHILIPPINES INC.—See Alight, Inc.; *U.S. Public*, pg. 77
NORTHGATEARINSO SINGAPORE PTE LTD—See Alight, Inc.; *U.S. Public*, pg. 77
NORTHGATEARINSO SWITZERLAND LTD.—See Alight, Inc.; *U.S. Public*, pg. 77
NORTHGATEARINSO THAILAND (CO.) LTD—See Alight, Inc.; *U.S. Public*, pg. 77
NORTHGATE ELECTRIC CORP.; *U.S. Private*, pg. 2955
NORTH GATE EXECUTIVE SEARCH LIMITED—See Diales; *Int'l*, pg. 2104
NORTHGATE FORD LINCOLN MERCURY—See Kenwood Dealer Group, Inc.; *U.S. Private*, pg. 2289
NORTHGATE GONZALEZ INC.; *U.S. Private*, pg. 2955
NORTHGATE INFORMATION SOLUTIONS HOLDINGS LIMITED—See Alight, Inc.; *U.S. Public*, pg. 76
NORTHGATE INFORMATION SOLUTIONS LIMITED—See Alight, Inc.; *U.S. Public*, pg. 76
NORTHGATE MALL ASSOCIATES—See The Macerich Company; *U.S. Public*, pg. 2110
NORTHGATE (MALTA) LIMITED—See ZIGUP plc; *Int'l*, pg. 8682
NORTHGATE PETROLEUM COMPANY; *U.S. Private*, pg. 2955
NORTHGATE PUBLIC SERVICES LIMITED—See NEC Corporation; *Int'l*, pg. 5186
NORTHGATE READY MIX, LLC—See CRH plc; *Int'l*, pg. 1845
NORTHGATE VEHICLE HIRE (IRELAND) LIMITED—See ZIGUP plc; *Int'l*, pg. 8682
NORTHGATE VEHICLE HIRE LIMITED—See ZIGUP plc; *Int'l*, pg. 8682
NORTHGATE VEHICLE HIRE—See ZIGUP plc; *Int'l*, pg. 8682
NORTH GEORGIA BRICK COMPANY INC.; *U.S. Private*, pg. 2945
NORTH GEORGIA ELECTRIC MEMBERSHIP CORPORATION; *U.S. Private*, pg. 2945
NORTH GEORGIA NEWSPAPER GROUP—See The Retirement Systems of Alabama; *U.S. Private*, pg. 4105
NORTH GROVE CARE HOME PERTH—See Balhousie Holdings Limited; *Int'l*, pg. 808
NORTH HARBOR TUGS CORPORATION—See SM Investments Corporation; *Int'l*, pg. 6998
NORTH HAVEN PRIVATE EQUITY ASIA ANGEL CO. LTD.; *Int'l*, pg. 5440
NORTH HAVEN PRIVATE INCOME FUND LLC; *U.S. Private*, pg. 2945
NORTH HAVEN SURGERY CENTER, LLC—See Tenet Healthcare Corporation; *U.S. Public*, pg. 2011
THE NORTH HIGHLAND COMPANY; *U.S. Private*, pg. 4084
NORTH HILL NEEDHAM, INC.; *U.S. Private*, pg. 2945
NORTH HILLS SIGNAL PROCESSING CORP.—See TransDigm Group Incorporated; *U.S. Public*, pg. 2183
NORTH HILLS SURGICARE, L.P.—See HCA Healthcare, Inc.; *U.S. Public*, pg. 1004
NORTH HILL VETERINARY CLINIC PTY. LTD.—See Apiam Animal Health Limited; *Int'l*, pg. 515
NORTH HOUSTON POLE LINE, L.P.—See Quanta Services, Inc.; *U.S. Public*, pg. 1752
NORTH HUAJIN CHEMICAL INDUSTRIES CO., LTD.; *Int'l*, pg. 5440
NORTH IDAHO DAY SURGERY, LLC—See Bain Capital, LP; *U.S. Private*, pg. 445
NORTH IDAHO TITLE COMPANY—See First American Financial Corporation; *U.S. Public*, pg. 838
NORTHILL CAPITAL LLP; *Int'l*, pg. 5445
NORTHILL DISTRIBUTION US INC.—See Northill Capital LLP; *Int'l*, pg. 5445
NORTH INCH CARE HOME PERTH—See Balhousie Holdings Limited; *Int'l*, pg. 808
NORTH INDUSTRIES GROUP RED ARROW CO., LTD.; *Int'l*, pg. 5440
NORTH IOC HOLDINGS PTY LIMITED—See Rio Tinto plc; *Int'l*, pg. 6346
NORTH IOWA COOPERATIVE; *U.S. Private*, pg. 2945
NORTH ISLAND CREDIT UNION—See California Credit Union; *U.S. Public*, pg. 718
NORTHISLE COPPER AND GOLD INC.; *Int'l*, pg. 5445
NORTH JAPAN OIL CO., LTD.—See Japan Petroleum Exploration Co. Ltd.; *Int'l*, pg. 3900
NORTH JAPAN SECURITY SERVICE CO., LTD.—See Japan Petroleum Exploration Co. Ltd.; *Int'l*, pg. 3900
NORTH JERSEY GASTROENTEROLOGY & ENDOSCOPY CENTER, PA—See KKR & Co. Inc.; *U.S. Public*, pg. 1250
NORTH JERSEY MEDIA GROUP, INC.—See Gannett Co., Inc.; *U.S. Public*, pg. 899
NORTH KANSAS CITY BEVERAGE CO.; *U.S. Private*, pg. 2945
NORTH KARNATAKA EXPRESSWAY LIMITED—See Infrastructure Leasing & Financial Services Limited; *Int'l*, pg. 3698
NORTH KAZAKHSTAN ELECTRIC DISTRIBUTION COMPANY, JOINT-STOCK COMPANY—See SevKazEnergo JSC; *Int'l*, pg. 6736
NORTH-KAZAKHSTAN REGIONAL ELECTRIC DISTRIBUTION COMPANY JSC—See Central-Asian Power Energy JSC; *Int'l*, pg. 1410
NORTHKING INFORMATION TECHNOLOGY CO., LTD.; *Int'l*, pg. 5445
NORTHLAKE ENGINEERING, INC.—See Standex International; *U.S. Public*, pg. 1930
NORTHLAKE MALL, LLC—See Washington Prime Group Inc.; *U.S. Private*, pg. 4448
NORTHLAND ALUMINUM PRODUCTS INC. - NORDIC WARE DIVISION—See Northland Aluminum Products Inc.; *U.S. Private*, pg. 2955
NORTHLAND ALUMINUM PRODUCTS INC.; *U.S. Private*, pg. 2955
NORTHLAND ASSOCIATES, INC.; *U.S. Private*, pg. 2955
NORTHLAND BUILDINGS INC.; *U.S. Private*, pg. 2955
NORTHLAND CASUALTY COMPANY—See The Travelers Companies, Inc.; *U.S. Public*, pg. 2136
NORTHLAND CHRYSLER JEEP DODGE; *Int'l*, pg. 5445
NORTHLAND COLD STORAGE, INC.; *U.S. Private*, pg. 2955
NORTHLAND COMMUNICATIONS CORP.—See GTCR LLC; *U.S. Private*, pg. 1805
NORTHLAND CONSTRUCTORS OF DULUTH, INC.—See APi Group Corporation; *Int'l*, pg. 514
NORTHLAND CORPORATION; *U.S. Private*, pg. 2955
NORTHLANDER INDUSTRIES; *Int'l*, pg. 5446
NORTHLAND FARMS, LLC; *U.S. Private*, pg. 2955
NORTHLAND FORD SALES LTD.; *Int'l*, pg. 5445
NORTHLAND FOREST MANAGERS (1995) LIMITED—See Greenheart Group Limited; *Int'l*, pg. 3075
NORTHLAND FOREST PRODUCTS INC.; *U.S. Private*, pg. 2955
NORTHLAND GROUP—See Radius Global Solutions LLC; *U.S. Private*, pg. 3345
NORTHLAND HOLDINGS INC.; *U.S. Private*, pg. 2955
NORTHLAND INDUSTRIAL TRUCK CO. INC.—See Alta Equipment Group Inc.; *U.S. Public*, pg. 86
NORTHLAND INSURANCE COMPANY—See The Travelers Companies, Inc.; *U.S. Public*, pg. 2136
NORTHLAND INVESTMENT CORPORATION; *U.S. Private*, pg. 2955
NORTHLAND LAWN SPORT & EQUIPMENT; *U.S. Private*, pg. 2955
NORTHLAND LTACH, LLC—See Apollo Global Management, Inc.; *U.S. Public*, pg. 157
NORTHLAND PATHOLOGY LABORATORY LIMITED—See Brookfield Corporation; *Int'l*, pg. 1176
NORTHLAND POWER INC.; *Int'l*, pg. 5445
NORTHLAND POWER PREFERRED EQUITY INC.—See Northland Power Inc.; *Int'l*, pg. 5446
NORTHLAND PRODUCTS, LLC—See Lassonde Industries, Inc.; *Int'l*, pg. 4421
NORTHLAND PROPERTIES CORPORATION; *Int'l*, pg. 5446
NORTHLAND SERVICES, INC.—See Lynden Incorporated; *U.S. Private*, pg. 2521
NORTHLAND TELEPHONE SYSTEMS, LTD.; *U.S. Private*, pg. 2955
NORTHLAND TRUCKING INC.; *U.S. Private*, pg. 2955
NORTHLAND UTILITIES ENTERPRISES LTD.—See ATCO Ltd.; *Int'l*, pg. 667
NORTHLAND UTILITIES (NWT) LIMITED—See ATCO Ltd.; *Int'l*, pg. 667
NORTHLAND UTILITIES (YELLOWKNIFE) LIMITED—See ATCO Ltd.; *Int'l*, pg. 667
NORTHLANE CAPITAL PARTNERS, LLC; *U.S. Private*, pg. 2955
NORTHLAWN MEMORIAL GARDENS—See Axar Capital Management L.P.; *U.S. Private*, pg. 411
NORTHLEAF CAPITAL PARTNERS LTD.; *Int'l*, pg. 5446
NORTHLICH-COLUMBUS—See Northlich; *U.S. Private*, pg. 2956
NORTHLICH PUBLIC RELATIONS—See Northlich; *U.S. Private*, pg. 2956
NORTHLICH; *U.S. Private*, pg. 2956
NORTHLICH—See Northlich; *U.S. Private*, pg. 2956
NORTHLICH—See Northlich; *U.S. Private*, pg. 2956
NORTHLIGHT FINANCIAL LLC; *U.S. Private*, pg. 2956
NORTH LIGHT SPECIALTY INSURANCE COMPANY—See The Allstate Corporation; *U.S. Public*, pg. 2034
NORTHLINE FREIGHT PTY LTD; *Int'l*, pg. 5446
NORTH LINGYUN INDUSTRIAL GROUP CO., LTD.—See China North Industries Group Corporation; *Int'l*, pg. 1535
NORTHLINK FISCAL & CAPITAL SERVICES LIMITED; *Int'l*, pg. 5446
NORTH-LINK M1 LTD.—See Groupe Egis S.A.; *Int'l*, pg. 3102
NORTH LOS ANGELES COUNTY REGIONAL CENTER INC.; *U.S. Private*, pg. 2945
NORTH LOUISIANA ROOFING SUPPLY; *U.S. Private*, pg. 2945
NORTH MAIN KIDNEY CENTER, LLC—See Nautic Partners, LLC; *U.S. Private*, pg. 2870
NORTH MALAYA ENGINEERS OVERSEAS SDN. BHD.—See Oriental Holdings Berhad; *Int'l*, pg. 5624
NORTH MALAYA ENGINEERS TRADING COMPANY SDN. BHD.—See Oriental Holdings Berhad; *Int'l*, pg. 5624
NORTH MALAYA (XIAMEN) STEEL CO., LTD.—See Oriental Holdings Berhad; *Int'l*, pg. 5624
NORTH MAN SVERIGE AB—See BNP Paribas SA; *Int'l*, pg. 1092
NORTHMARK BANK—See Cambridge Bancorp; *U.S. Public*, pg. 426
NORTHMARQ CAPITAL, LLC—See Pohlad Companies; *U.S. Private*, pg. 3220
NORTHMARQ CAPITAL, LLC—See Pohlad Companies; *U.S. Private*, pg. 3220
NORTHMARQ CAPITAL, LLC—See Pohlad Companies; *U.S. Private*, pg. 3220
NORTHMARQ COMPANIES LLC—See Pohlad Companies; *U.S. Private*, pg. 3220
NORTH MEDIA A/S; *Int'l*, pg. 5440
NORTH MEDIA AVISER A/S—See North Media A/S; *Int'l*, pg. 5440
NORTH MEDIA ONLINE A/S—See North Media A/S; *Int'l*, pg. 5441
NORTH METRO COMMUNITY SERVICES, INC.; *U.S. Private*, pg. 2945
NORTH METRO MEDICAL CENTER; *U.S. Private*, pg. 2945
NORTH MIAMI BEACH SURGERY CENTER LIMITED PARTNERSHIP—See HCA Healthcare, Inc.; *U.S. Public*, pg. 1004
NORTH MIAMI BEACH SURGICAL CENTER, LLC—See HCA Healthcare, Inc.; *U.S. Public*, pg. 1004
NORTH MIDDLESEX SAVINGS BANK; *U.S. Private*, pg. 2946

NORTH MIDLAND BUILDING LTD.—See NMCN PLC; *Int'l*, pg. 5393
NORTH MILL CAPITAL LLC—See SLR Investment Corp.; *U.S. Public*, pg. 1895
NORTH MINING SHARES COMPANY LIMITED; *Int'l*, pg. 5441
NORTH MISSOURI TIRE, INC; *U.S. Private*, pg. 2946
NORTH MOUNTAIN MERGER CORP.; *U.S. Public*, pg. 1537
NORTH NAVIGATION CONTROL TECHNOLOGY CO., LTD.; *Int'l*, pg. 5441
NORTH NIGHT VISION TECHNOLOGY CO., LTD.—See China North Industries Group Corporation; *Int'l*, pg. 1536
NORTH NOTTS NEWSPAPERS LTD—See JPIMedia Holdings Limited; *Int'l*, pg. 4006
NORTH OCHRONA SP. Z O.O.—See Impel S.A.; *Int'l*, pg. 3632
NORTH OKALOOSA CLINIC CORP.—See Community Health Systems, Inc.; *U.S. Public*, 555
NORTH PACIFIC BANK, LTD.; *Int'l*, pg. 5441
NORTH PACIFIC CORPORATION; *U.S. Private*, pg. 2946
NORTH PACIFIC PAPER COMPANY, LLC—See One Rock Capital Partners, LLC; *U.S. Private*, pg. 3022
NORTH PACIFIC SEAFOODS, INC. - SITKA SOUND SEAFOODS FACILITY—See Marubeni Corporation; *Int'l*, pg. 4706
NORTH PACIFIC SEAFOODS, INC.—See Marubeni Corporation; *Int'l*, pg. 4706
NORTH PALM HYUNDAI, LLC.; *U.S. Private*, pg. 2946
NORTH PARK LINCOLN MERCURY INC.; *U.S. Private*, pg. 2946
NORTH PARK TRANSPORTATION CO. INC.; *U.S. Private*, pg. 2946
NORTH PEAK (NEVADA) LTD.—See North Peak Resources Ltd.; *Int'l*, pg. 5441
NORTH PEAK RESOURCES LTD.; *Int'l*, pg. 5441
NORTH PENN TECHNOLOGY, INC.—See PMC Capital Partners, LLC; *U.S. Private*, pg. 3217
NORTH PENN WATER AUTHORITY; *U.S. Private*, pg. 2946
NORTH PETRO VIETNAM FERTILIZER & CHEMICALS JOINT STOCK COMPANY—See Vietnam Oil and Gas Group; *Int'l*, pg. 8202
NORTH PLAINS MALL, LLC—See Brookfield Corporation; *Int'l*, pg. 1185
NORTH PLAINS SYSTEMS INC.; *Int'l*, pg. 5441
NORTHPOINT CHEVROLET, LLC—See AutoNation, Inc.; *U.S. Public*, pg. 236
NORTHPOINT COMMERCIAL FINANCE CANADA INC.—See Laurentian Bank of Canada; *Int'l*, pg. 4425
NORTHPOINT COMMERCIAL FINANCE LLC—See Laurentian Bank of Canada; *Int'l*, pg. 4425
NORTHPOINT COMMUNICATIONS GROUP, INC.; *U.S. Private*, pg. 2956
NORTH POINTE CASUALTY INSURANCE COMPANY—See QBE Insurance Group Limited; *Int'l*, pg. 6136
NORTH POINTE FINANCIAL SERVICES, INC.—See QBE Insurance Group Limited; *Int'l*, pg. 6136
NORTH POINTE INSURANCE COMPANY—See QBE Insurance Group Limited; *Int'l*, pg. 6136
NORTHPOINTE PERSONNEL—See Asset Staffing Incorporated; *U.S. Private*, pg. 354
NORTHPOINTE SURGICAL SUITES, LLC—See Tenet Healthcare Corporation; *U.S. Public*, pg. 2005
NORTHPOINT FORD, INC.—See AutoNation, Inc.; *U.S. Public*, pg. 236
NORTH POINT GEOGRAPHIC SOLUTIONS—See Avineon, Inc.; *U.S. Private*, pg. 407
NORTH POINT HOLDINGS LTD—See Gamma-Civic Ltd; *Int'l*, pg. 2878
NORTH POINT PRESS—See Verlagsgruppe Georg von Holtzbrinck GmbH; *Int'l*, pg. 8170
NORTHPOINT SOLUTIONS LLC.; *U.S. Private*, pg. 2957
NORTHPOINT TECHNICAL SERVICES ULC—See Wajax Corporation; *Int'l*, pg. 8331
NORTH POLE INVESTMENT COMPANY LIMITED—See Electricity Generating Public Co., Ltd.; *Int'l*, pg. 2352
NORTHPORT (MALAYSIA) BHD.—See MMC Corporation Berhad; *Int'l*, pg. 5005
NORTHPORT NETWORK SYSTEMS, INC.; *U.S. Private*, pg. 2957
NORTHPOWER LIMITED; *Int'l*, pg. 5446
NORTH PRAIRIE DEVELOPMENTS LTD.; *Int'l*, pg. 5441
NORTH RANCH COUNTRY CLUB; *U.S. Private*, pg. 2946
NORTH RICHLAND HILLS ENDOSCOPY CENTER, LLC—See KKR & Co. Inc.; *U.S. Public*, pg. 1246
NORTHRIDGE ACADEMY, LLC; *U.S. Private*, pg. 2957
NORTHRIDGE CORP.; *U.S. Private*, pg. 2957
NORTH RIDGE DEVELOPMENT CORPORATION; *Int'l*, pg. 5441
NORTHRIDGE FINANCE LTD.—See Bank of Ireland Group plc; *Int'l*, pg. 845
NORTHRIDGE HOSPITAL MEDICAL CENTER—See Catholic Health Initiatives; *U.S. Private*, pg. 789
NORTHRIDGE SURGERY CENTER, L.P.—See Tenet Healthcare Corporation; *U.S. Public*, pg. 2012

NORTHRIDING COLLEGE (PTY) LTD.—See Curro Holdings Ltd.; *Int'l*, pg. 1879
NORTHRIM BANCORP, INC.; *U.S. Public*, pg. 1539
NORTHRIM BANK—See Northrim BanCorp, Inc.; *U.S. Public*, pg. 1539
NORTH RIM PULP & PAPER INC.—See Heinzel Holding GmbH; *Int'l*, pg. 3325
NORTH RIVER CAPITAL LLC; *U.S. Private*, pg. 2946
THE NORTH RIVER INSURANCE COMPANY—See Fairfax Financial Holdings Limited; *Int'l*, pg. 2606
NORTHROP GRUMMAN AEROSPACE SYSTEMS-BETHPAGE—See Northrop Grumman Corporation; *U.S. Public*, pg. 1540
NORTHROP GRUMMAN AEROSPACE SYSTEMS-EL SEGUNDO—See Northrop Grumman Corporation; *U.S. Public*, pg. 1540
NORTHROP GRUMMAN AEROSPACE SYSTEMS-SAINT AUGUSTINE—See Northrop Grumman Corporation; *U.S. Public*, pg. 1540
NORTHROP GRUMMAN AEROSPACE SYSTEMS-SAN DIEGO—See Northrop Grumman Corporation; *U.S. Public*, pg. 1540
NORTHROP GRUMMAN AEROSPACE SYSTEMS—See Northrop Grumman Corporation; *U.S. Public*, pg. 1539
NORTHROP GRUMMAN - CORPORATE GOVERNMENT RELATIONS—See Northrop Grumman Corporation; *U.S. Public*, pg. 1539
NORTHROP GRUMMAN CORPORATION; *U.S. Public*, pg. 1539
NORTHROP GRUMMAN DEFENSIVE SYSTEMS—See Northrop Grumman Corporation; *U.S. Public*, pg. 1540
NORTHROP GRUMMAN ELECTRONIC SYSTEMS—See Northrop Grumman Corporation; *U.S. Public*, pg. 1540
NORTHROP GRUMMAN ELECTRONIC SYSTEMS—See Northrop Grumman Corporation; *U.S. Public*, pg. 1540
NORTHROP GRUMMAN ELECTRONIC SYSTEMS—See Northrop Grumman Corporation; *U.S. Public*, pg. 1540
NORTHROP GRUMMAN ELECTRONIC SYSTEMS—See Northrop Grumman Corporation; *U.S. Public*, pg. 1540
NORTHROP GRUMMAN ELECTRONIC SYSTEMS—See Northrop Grumman Corporation; *U.S. Public*, pg. 1540
NORTHROP GRUMMAN INFORMATION TECHNOLOGY, INC.—See Northrop Grumman Corporation; *U.S. Public*, pg. 1540
NORTHROP GRUMMAN INNOVATION SYSTEMS, INC.—See Northrop Grumman Corporation; *U.S. Public*, pg. 1540
NORTHROP GRUMMAN INTEGRATED DEFENCE SERVICES PTY. LTD.—See Northrop Grumman Corporation; *U.S. Public*, pg. 1541
NORTHROP GRUMMAN INTELLIGENCE, SURVEILLANCE & RECONNAISSANCE SYSTEMS—See Northrop Grumman Corporation; *U.S. Public*, pg. 1540
NORTHROP GRUMMAN INTERNATIONAL, INC.—See Northrop Grumman Corporation; *U.S. Public*, pg. 1541
NORTHROP GRUMMAN ITALIA S.P.A.—See Northrop Grumman Corporation; *U.S. Public*, pg. 1540
NORTHROP GRUMMAN LITEF GMBH—See Northrop Grumman Corporation; *U.S. Public*, pg. 1540
NORTHROP GRUMMAN MISSION SYSTEMS EUROPE LIMITED—See Northrop Grumman Corporation; *U.S. Public*, pg. 1541
NORTHROP GRUMMAN - NAVIGATION SYSTEMS—See Northrop Grumman Corporation; *U.S. Public*, pg. 1540
NORTHROP GRUMMAN NAVIGATION SYSTEMS—See Northrop Grumman Corporation; *U.S. Public*, pg. 1540
NORTHROP GRUMMAN-NORDEN SYSTEMS—See Northrop Grumman Corporation; *U.S. Public*, pg. 1540
NORTHROP GRUMMAN OHIO CORPORATION—See Northrop Grumman Corporation; *U.S. Public*, pg. 1541
NORTHROP GRUMMAN SPERRY MARINE GMBH & CO. KG—See Northrop Grumman Corporation; *U.S. Public*, pg. 1540
NORTHROP GRUMMAN SPERRY MARINE LIMITED—See Northrop Grumman Corporation; *U.S. Public*, pg. 1540
NORTHROP GRUMMAN SYNOPTICS—See Northrop Grumman Corporation; *U.S. Public*, pg. 1540
NORTHROP GRUMMAN TECHNICAL SERVICES, INC.—See Northrop Grumman Corporation; *U.S. Public*, pg. 1541
NORTHROP GRUMMAN TECHNICAL SERVICES-KANSAS CITY—See Northrop Grumman Corporation; *U.S. Public*, pg. 1541
NORTHROP GRUMMAN TECHNICAL SERVICES-NORFOLK—See Northrop Grumman Corporation; *U.S. Public*, pg. 1541
NORTHROP GRUMMAN UK LIMITED—See Northrop Grumman Corporation; *U.S. Public*, pg. 1541
NORTHROP GRUMMAN-XETRON—See Northrop Grumman Corporation; *U.S. Public*, pg. 1541
NORTHROP & JOHNSON MONACO S.A.M.—See MarineMax, Inc.; *U.S. Public*, pg. 1367
NORTHROP & JOHNSON YACHTS-SHIPS LLC—See MarineMax, Inc.; *U.S. Public*, pg. 1367
NORTH RYDE COMMUNITY FINANCE LIMITED—See Bendigo & Adelaide Bank Ltd.; *Int'l*, pg. 971
NORTH SAFETY PRODUCTS EUROPE B.V.—See Honeywell International Inc.; *U.S. Public*, pg. 1049
NORTH SAILS COLLECTION USA—See Windway Capital Corp.; *U.S. Private*, pg. 4539

NORTH SAILS DIRECT—See Windway Capital Corp.; *U.S. Private*, pg. 4539
NORTH SAILS GROUP, LLC—See Windway Capital Corp.; *U.S. Private*, pg. 4539
NORTH SAN DIEGO COUNTY TRANSIT; *U.S. Private*, pg. 2946
NORTH SCOTTSDALE INDEPENDENT—See Independent Newspapers, Inc.; *U.S. Private*, pg. 2060
NORTH SEA CABLES NORGE AS—See DNOW Inc.; *U.S. Public*, pg. 671
NORTH SEA PARTNERS LLC; *U.S. Private*, pg. 2946
NORTH SEATTLE COMMUNITY COLLEGE FOUNDATION; *U.S. Private*, pg. 2946
NORTH SEA VENTILATION LIMITED—See Dynac Sdn. Bhd.; *Int'l*, pg. 2239
NORTH SHORE BANCORP; *U.S. Private*, pg. 2946
NORTH SHORE BANK, A CO-OPERATIVE BANK—See Hometown Financial Group, Inc.; *U.S. Private*, pg. 1975
NORTH SHORE BANK, FSB; *U.S. Private*, pg. 2946
NORTH SHORE BANK OF COMMERCE—See North Shore Financial Corporation; *U.S. Private*, pg. 2946
NORTH SHORE COMMUNITY BANK & TRUST—See Wintrust Financial Corporation; *U.S. Public*, pg. 2376
NORTH SHORE COMMUNITY HEALTH CENTER, INC.; *U.S. Private*, pg. 2946
NORTH SHORE CORP.—See Continental Holdings Corp.; *Int'l*, pg. 1784
NORTHSHORE EXTENDED CARE HOSPITAL, LLC—See UnitedHealth Group Incorporated; *U.S. Public*, pg. 2246
NORTH SHORE FINANCIAL CORPORATION; *U.S. Private*, pg. 2946
NORTH SHORE GAS COMPANY—See WEC Energy Group, Inc.; *U.S. Public*, pg. 2342
NORTH SHORE INFINITI INC.; *U.S. Private*, pg. 2946
NORTHSHORE INTERNATIONAL INSURANCE SERVICES INC.—See HGGC, LLC; *U.S. Private*, pg. 1929
NORTH SHORE LIJ HEALTH SYSTEMS; *U.S. Private*, pg. 2946
NORTH SHORE MEDICAL CENTER INC.—See Partners HealthCare System, Inc.; *U.S. Private*, pg. 3102
NORTH SHORE MEDICAL CENTER, INC.—See Tenet Healthcare Corporation; *U.S. Public*, pg. 2005
NORTHSHORE MINING COMPANY—See Cleveland-Cliffs, Inc.; *U.S. Public*, pg. 514
NORTH SHORE MORTGAGE INCORPORATED; *U.S. Private*, pg. 2946
NORTH SHORE MOVERS, INC.; *U.S. Private*, pg. 2946
NORTH SHORE NEWS—See Glacier Media Inc.; *Int'l*, pg. 2987
NORTH SHORE OIL COMPANY INC.; *U.S. Private*, pg. 2947
NORTH SHORE PEDIATRIC THERAPY; *U.S. Private*, pg. 2947
NORTH SHORE PHYSICIANS GROUP INC.—See Partners HealthCare System, Inc.; *U.S. Private*, pg. 3102
NORTH SHORE PRIVATE HOSPITAL PTY LIMITED—See Ramsay Health Care Limited; *Int'l*, pg. 6200
NORTH SHORE PRODUCTIONS INC.—See National Amusements, Inc.; *U.S. Private*, pg. 2842
NORTH SHORE REALTY GROUP; *U.S. Private*, pg. 2947
NORTH SHORE REFRIGERATION CO. INC.; *U.S. Private*, pg. 2947
NORTH SHORE SAME DAY SURGERY, L.L.C.—See Tenet Healthcare Corporation; *U.S. Public*, pg. 2011
NORTH SHORE SANITARY DISTRICT; *U.S. Private*, pg. 2947
NORTH SHORE SPECIALIST DAY HOSPITAL PTY LTD—See Virtus Health Limited; *Int'l*, pg. 8249
NORTH SHORE SPORTS & PHYSICAL THERAPY, LIMITED PARTNERSHIP—See U.S. Physical Therapy, Inc.; *U.S. Public*, pg. 2215
NORTH SHORE SUNDAY—See Gannett Co., Inc.; *U.S. Public*, pg. 902
NORTH SHORE SUPPLY COMPANY INC.; *U.S. Private*, pg. 2947
NORTH SHORE SURGICAL SUITES, LLC—See Tenet Healthcare Corporation; *U.S. Public*, pg. 2005
NORTH SHORE TRANSIT, INC.—See Cook-Illinois Corp.; *U.S. Public*, pg. 1038
NORTH SHORE TRUST AND SAVINGS; *U.S. Private*, pg. 2947
NORTHSHORE UNIVERSITY HEALTHSYSTEM; *U.S. Private*, pg. 2957
NORTHSHORE UTILITY DISTRICT; *U.S. Private*, pg. 2957
NORTH SIDE BANK & TRUST CO.; *U.S. Private*, pg. 2947
NORTHSIDE CENTER FOR CHILD DEVELOPMENT; *U.S. Private*, pg. 2957
NORTHSIDE ENGINEERING SERVICES, INC.; *U.S. Private*, pg. 2957
NORTH SIDE FOODS CORP.—See WH Group Limited; *Int'l*, pg. 8395
NORTH SIDE FORD; *U.S. Private*, pg. 2947
NORTHSIDE GASTROENTEROLOGY ENDOSCOPY CENTER, LLC—See KKR & Co. Inc.; *U.S. Public*, pg. 1246
NORTHSIDE HOSPITAL AND HEART INSTITUTE—See HCA Healthcare, Inc.; *U.S. Public*, pg. 1004

COMPANY NAME INDEX

NORTHSIDE HOSPITAL; *U.S. Private,* pg. 2957
NORTH SIDE IMPORTS INC.; *U.S. Private,* pg. 2947
NORTHSIDE NISSAN (1986) PTY. LTD.—See Eagers Automotive Limited; *Int'l,* pg. 2264
NORTHSIDE OXYGEN & MEDICAL EQUIPMENT—See Genesis HealthCare System; *U.S. Private,* pg. 1669
NORTHSIDE RECRUITMENT SERVICES LIMITED—See Bain Capital, LP; *U.S. Private,* pg. 434
NORTHSIDE SERVICES, INC.; *U.S. Private,* pg. 2957
NORTHSIDE TRUCKS; *U.S. Private,* pg. 2957
NORTHSIGHT CAPITAL, INC.; *U.S. Public,* pg. 1541
NORTH SKY COMMUNICATIONS, INC.—See Dycom Industries, Inc.; *U.S. Public,* pg. 699
NORTH SNOHOMISH ENTERPRISES; *U.S. Private,* pg. 2947
NORTH; *U.S. Private,* pg. 2939
NORTHSOUTH PRODUCTIONS—See The Hearst Corporation; *U.S. Private,* pg. 4049
NORTH SOUTH SUPPLY INC.; *U.S. Private,* pg. 2947
NORTH SPRING BEHAVIORAL HEALTHCARE, INC.—See Universal Health Services, Inc.; *U.S. Public,* pg. 2258
NORTH SQUARE INVESTMENTS, LLC—See Estancia Capital Management, LLC; *U.S. Private,* pg. 1428
THE NORTH STAFFORDSHIRE NUFFIELD HOSPITAL—See Nuffield Health; *Int'l,* pg. 5487
NORTHSTAR ACCESS—See Windstream Holdings, Inc.; *U.S. Public,* pg. 2373
NORTHSTAR ADVISORS PTE. LTD.; *Int'l,* pg. 5446
NORTHSTAR AEROSPACE - CHICAGO—See Wynnchurch Capital, L.P.; *U.S. Private,* pg. 4577
NORTHSTAR AEROSPACE, INC.—See Wynnchurch Capital, L.P.; *U.S. Private,* pg. 4577
NORTHSTAR AEROSPACE - MILTON—See Wynnchurch Capital, L.P.; *U.S. Private,* pg. 4577
NORTHSTAR AEROSPACE - PHOENIX—See Wynnchurch Capital, L.P.; *U.S. Private,* pg. 4577
NORTHSTAR AEROSPACE - WINDSOR—See Wynnchurch Capital, L.P.; *U.S. Private,* pg. 4577
NORTH STAR AIR LTD.—See The North West Company Inc.; *Int'l,* pg. 7671
NORTHSTAR ANESTHESIA P.A.—See The Cranemere Group Limited; *Int'l,* pg. 7635
NORTH STAR AUTOMOTIVE GROUP; *U.S. Private,* pg. 2947
NORTHSTAR BATTERY CO. LLC—See Altor Equity Partners AB; *Int'l,* pg. 395
NORTHSTAR BATTERY DMCC—See EnerSys; *U.S. Public,* pg. 767
NORTH STAR BLUESCOPE STEEL LLC—See BlueScope Steel Limited; *Int'l,* pg. 1074
NORTHSTAR CAPITAL, LLC; *U.S. Private,* pg. 2957
NORTH STAR CHEVROLET, INC.—See North Star Automotive Group; *U.S. Private,* pg. 2947
NORTHSTAR CLEAN ENERGY—See CMS Energy Corporation; *U.S. Public,* pg. 518
NORTHSTAR COMPUTER FORMS, INC.—See Ennis, Inc.; *U.S. Public,* pg. 769
NORTH STAR CONSTRUCTION MANAGEMENT; *U.S. Private,* pg. 2947
NORTHSTAR CONTRACTING GROUP, INC.—See J.F. Lehman & Company, Inc.; *U.S. Private,* pg. 2164
NORTHSTAR CONTRACTING GROUP, INC.—See J.F. Lehman & Company, Inc.; *U.S. Private,* pg. 2164
NORTHSTAR CONTRACTING GROUP, INC.—See J.F. Lehman & Company, Inc.; *U.S. Private,* pg. 2164
NORTHSTAR CONTRACTING GROUP, INC.—See J.F. Lehman & Company, Inc.; *U.S. Private,* pg. 2164
NORTHSTAR CONTRACTING GROUP, INC.—See J.F. Lehman & Company, Inc.; *U.S. Private,* pg. 2164
NORTHSTAR CONTRACTING GROUP, INC.—See J.F. Lehman & Company, Inc.; *U.S. Private,* pg. 2164
NORTH STAR CONTRACTORS INC.; *U.S. Private,* pg. 2947
NORTHSTAR COOPERATIVE INC.; *U.S. Private,* pg. 2957
NORTHSTAR COUNSELORS INC.; *U.S. Private,* pg. 2957
NORTHSTAR DEMOLITION AND REMEDIATION, INC.—See J.F. Lehman & Company, Inc.; *U.S. Private,* pg. 2164
NORTHSTAR DEMOLITION AND REMEDIATION, INC.—See J.F. Lehman & Company, Inc.; *U.S. Private,* pg. 2164
NORTHSTAR DEMOLITION AND REMEDIATION, LP—See J.F. Lehman & Company, Inc.; *U.S. Private,* pg. 2164
NORTHSTAR DEMOLITION AND REMEDIATION, LP—See J.F. Lehman & Company, Inc.; *U.S. Private,* pg. 2164
NORTHSTAR DEMOLITION AND REMEDIATION, LP—See J.F. Lehman & Company, Inc.; *U.S. Private,* pg. 2164
NORTHSTAR DEMOLITION & REMEDIATION, INC.—See J.F. Lehman & Company, Inc.; *U.S. Private,* pg. 2164
NORTHSTAR DEMOLITION & REMEDIATION, LP—See J.F. Lehman & Company, Inc.; *U.S. Private,* pg. 2164
NORTH STAR DESTINATION STRATEGIES LLC; *U.S. Private,* pg. 2947
NORTH STAR DRILLING LLC.—See Major Drilling Group International Inc.; *Int'l,* pg. 4654

NORTHSTAR EDUCATION FINANCE, INC.; *U.S. Private,* pg. 2957
NORTHSTAR ELECTRONICS, INC.; *U.S. Public,* pg. 1541
NORTHSTAR ENERGY LIMITED; *Int'l,* pg. 5446
NORTHSTAR ENERGY SERVICES, INC.—See Quanta Services, Inc.; *U.S. Public,* pg. 1752
NORTHSTAR FINANCIAL SERVICES GROUP LLC—See TA Associates, Inc.; *U.S. Private,* pg. 3917
NORTHSTAR FIRE PROTECTION OF TEXAS, INC.; *U.S. Private,* pg. 2957
NORTH STAR FORD SALES; *Int'l,* pg. 5441
NORTHSTAR GENETICS LTD.—See Rob-See-Co; *U.S. Private,* pg. 3456
NORTHSTAR GOLD CORP.; *Int'l,* pg. 5446
NORTHSTAR GROUP HOLDINGS, LLC—See J.F. Lehman & Company, Inc.; *U.S. Private,* pg. 2163
NORTH STAR GROUP, LLC; *U.S. Private,* pg. 2947
NORTHSTAR GROUP SERVICES, INC.—See J.F. Lehman & Company, Inc.; *U.S. Private,* pg. 2164
NORTHSTAR HEALTHCARE INCOME, INC.—See DigitalBridge Group, Inc.; *U.S. Public,* pg. 665
NORTH STAR ICE EQUIPMENT CORPORATION; *U.S. Private,* pg. 2947
NORTH STAR IMAGING EUROPE SAS—See Illinois Tool Works Inc.; *U.S. Public,* pg. 1109
NORTH STAR IMAGING, INC.—See Illinois Tool Works Inc.; *U.S. Public,* pg. 1109
NORTHSTAR INDUSTRIES INC.; *U.S. Private,* pg. 2958
NORTHSTAR.IO, INC.; *U.S. Private,* pg. 2958
NORTHSTAR MACHINE & TOOL CO., INC.; *U.S. Private,* pg. 2958
NORTHSTAR MARINE ELECTRONICS—See Altor Equity Partners AB; *Int'l,* pg. 395
NORTH STAR MARKETING CORPORATION—See Assurant, Inc.; *U.S. Public,* pg. 215
NORTHSTAR MEMORIAL GROUP, LLC; *U.S. Private,* pg. 2958
NORTHSTAR MOVING CORP.; *U.S. Private,* pg. 2958
NORTH STAR MUTUAL INSURANCE CO.; *U.S. Private,* pg. 2947
NORTH STAR PETROLEUM—See Saltchuk Resources Inc.; *U.S. Private,* pg. 3534
NORTHSTAR POLAND SP. Z.O.O.—See NIBE Industrier AB; *Int'l,* pg. 5262
NORTH STAR PONTIAC, GMC, OLDSMOBILE, INC.—See North Star Automotive Group; *U.S. Private,* pg. 2947
NORTH STAR POWER LLC—See Brandt Holdings Company; *U.S. Private,* pg. 639
NORTH STAR PROCESSING, LLC—See Welcome Dairy Inc.; *U.S. Private,* pg. 4473
NORTH STAR PULP AND PAPER CO.—See Casella Waste Systems, Inc.; *U.S. Public,* pg. 446
NORTHSTAR REALTY EUROPE CORP.—See AXA S.A.; *Int'l,* pg. 757
NORTHSTAR RECYCLING GROUP; *U.S. Private,* pg. 2958
NORTHSTAR RESEARCH HOLDINGS CANADA INC.—See Stagwell, Inc.; *U.S. Public,* pg. 1927
NORTHSTAR RESEARCH HOLDINGS USA LP—See Stagwell, Inc.; *U.S. Public,* pg. 1927
NORTHSTAR RESEARCH PARTNERS INC.—See Stagwell, Inc.; *U.S. Public,* pg. 1927
NORTHSTAR RESEARCH PARTNERS (UK) LIMITED—See Stagwell, Inc.; *U.S. Public,* pg. 1927
NORTHSTAR RESEARCH PARTNERS (USA) LLC—See Stagwell, Inc.; *U.S. Public,* pg. 1927
NORTHSTAR RESTORATION SERVICES, LLC; *U.S. Private,* pg. 2958
NORTHSTAR RISK MANAGEMENT & INSURANCE SERVICES INC.; *U.S. Private,* pg. 2958
NORTHSTAR/RXR NEW YORK METRO REAL ESTATE, INC.; *U.S. Private,* pg. 2958
NORTHSTAR SCAFFOLD INC.—See Andover Capital Corporation; *Int'l,* pg. 451
NORTH STAR SEAFOOD, LLC—See Sysco Corporation; *U.S. Public,* pg. 1975
NORTHSTAR SHARPS FOUNDATION SPECIALISTS LTD.—See Quanta Services, Inc.; *U.S. Public,* pg. 1752
NORTHSTAR SOLUTIONS GROUP; *U.S. Private,* pg. 2958
NORTHSTAR STEEL & ALUMINUM; *U.S. Private,* pg. 2958
NORTH STAR SURFACES, LLC—See Christ's Household of Faith; *U.S. Private,* pg. 890
NORTH STAR TELECOM GMBH—See Salzgitter AG; *Int'l,* pg. 6497
NORTH STAR TERMINAL & STEVEDORE COMPANY, LLC; *U.S. Private,* pg. 2948
NORTH STAR TRANSPORTATION INC.—See Armellini Industries, Inc.; *U.S. Private,* pg. 330
NORTHSTAR TRAVEL MEDIA LLC—See EagleTree Capital, LP; *U.S. Private,* pg. 1312
NORTHSTAR VAN LINES—See UniGroup, Inc.; *U.S. Private,* pg. 4283
NORTH STATE ACCEPTANCE, LLC—See Fourshore Capital LLC; *U.S. Private,* pg. 1583
NORTH STATE BANCORP; *U.S. Private,* pg. 2948

NORTHVIEW ENTERPRISES

NORTH STATE COMMUNICATIONS, LLC—See EQT AB; *Int'l,* pg. 2480
NORTH STATE GROCERY INC.; *U.S. Private,* pg. 2948
NORTH STATES INDUSTRIES INC.; *U.S. Private,* pg. 2948
NORTH STATE STEEL INC.; *U.S. Private,* pg. 2948
NORTH STATE SUPPLY CO., INC.—See Cadent Energy Partners, LLC; *U.S. Private,* pg. 713
NORTH STATE TELECOMMUNICATIONS CORPORATION—See EQT AB; *Int'l,* pg. 2480
NORTHSTONE (NI) LIMITED—See CRH plc; *Int'l,* pg. 1845
NORTH SUBURBAN MEDICAL CENTER—See HCA Healthcare, Inc.; *U.S. Public,* pg. 1004
NORTHSYDE PROCESSING LIMITED—See Louisbourg Seafoods Ltd.; *Int'l,* pg. 4563
NORTH TAMPA CHRYSLER JEEP DODGE, INC.—See Stellantis N.V.; *Int'l,* pg. 7200
NORTHTEC LLC—See The Estee Lauder Companies Inc.; *U.S. Public,* pg. 2073
NORTH TERRACE PM LLC; *U.S. Private,* pg. 2948
NORTH TEXAS ENERGY, INC.; *U.S. Private,* pg. 2948
NORTH TEXAS FLEET SERVICES LLC—See Merx Truck & Trailer, Inc.; *U.S. Private,* pg. 2677
NORTH TEXAS FOOD BANK; *U.S. Private,* pg. 2948
NORTH TEXAS HEART SURGERY CENTER, PLLC—See HCA Healthcare, Inc.; *U.S. Public,* pg. 1004
NORTH TEXAS INTERNAL MEDICINE SPECIALISTS, PLLC—See HCA Healthcare, Inc.; *U.S. Public,* pg. 1004
NORTH TEXAS - MCA, LLC—See HCA Healthcare, Inc.; *U.S. Public,* pg. 1004
NORTH TEXAS MEDICAL CENTER, INC.—See HCA Healthcare, Inc.; *U.S. Public,* pg. 1004
NORTH TEXAS MUNICIPAL WATER DISTRICT; *U.S. Private,* pg. 2948
NORTH TEXAS PUBLIC BROADCASTING; *U.S. Private,* pg. 2948
NORTH TEXAS PULMONARY CRITICAL CARE, PLLC—See HCA Healthcare, Inc.; *U.S. Public,* pg. 1004
NORTH TEXAS STATE SOCCER ASSOCIATION, INC.; *U.S. Private,* pg. 2948
NORTH TEXAS STEEL COMPANY, INC.—See Laurus Capital Management, LLC; *U.S. Private,* pg. 2400
NORTH TEXAS STROKE CENTER, PLLC—See HCA Healthcare, Inc.; *U.S. Public,* pg. 1004
NORTH TEXAS WATERPROOFING & RESTORATION CO.—See Western Construction Group; *U.S. Private,* pg. 4492
NORTH THIN PLY TECHNOLOGY, SARL—See Windway Capital Corp.; *U.S. Private,* pg. 4539
NORTHTOWN AUTOMOTIVE CO., INC.; *U.S. Private,* pg. 2958
NORTH TOWNE GRILL & SEAFOOD; *U.S. Private,* pg. 2948
NORTH TOWN ESTATES PRIVATE LIMITED—See Arihant Foundations & Housing Limited; *Int'l,* pg. 564
NORTHTOWN FORD MERCURY; *U.S. Private,* pg. 2958
NORTHTOWN MOTOR HOMES, INC.—See Fun Town RV LP; *U.S. Private,* pg. 1622
NORTH TRANSFER CENTER, LLC—See HCA Healthcare, Inc.; *U.S. Public,* pg. 1004
NORTHUMBERLAND BANCORP; *U.S. Public,* pg. 1541
NORTHUMBERLAND CO-OPERATIVE LTD.; *Int'l,* pg. 5446
NORTHUMBERLAND & DURHAM PROPERTY TRUST LIMITED—See Grainger plc; *Int'l,* pg. 3052
THE NORTHUMBERLAND NATIONAL BANK—See Northumberland Bancorp; *U.S. Public,* pg. 1541
NORTHUMBRIAN ROADS LIMITED; *Int'l,* pg. 5446
NORTHUMBRIAN SERVICES LIMITED—See CK Hutchison Holdings Limited; *Int'l,* pg. 1637
NORTHUMBRIAN WATER GROUP PLC—See CK Hutchison Holdings Limited; *Int'l,* pg. 1637
NORTHUMBRIAN WATER LIMITED—See CK Hutchison Holdings Limited; *Int'l,* pg. 1637
NORTHUMBRIAN WATER PROJECTS LIMITED—See CK Hutchison Holdings Limited; *Int'l,* pg. 1637
NORTHUMBRIAN WATER SCIENTIFIC SERVICES (NWSS)—See CK Hutchison Holdings Limited; *Int'l,* pg. 1637
NORTH VALLEY ENDOSCOPY CENTER, LLC—See KKR & Co. Inc.; *U.S. Public,* pg. 1246
NORTH VALLEY HOSPITAL; *U.S. Private,* pg. 2948
NORTH VERNON INDUSTRY CORP.—See Toyota Industries Corporation; *Int'l,* pg. 7869
NORTHVIEW ACQUISITION CORPORATION; *U.S. Public,* pg. 1541
NORTHVIEW APARTMENT REAL ESTATE INVESTMENT TRUST—See KingSett Capital; *Int'l,* pg. 4174
NORTHVIEW APARTMENT REAL ESTATE INVESTMENT TRUST—See Starlight Investments Ltd.; *Int'l,* pg. 7177
NORTHVIEW BANK—See Finlayson Bancshares, Inc.; *U.S. Private,* pg. 1510
NORTHVIEW CANADIAN HIGH YIELD RESIDENTIAL FUND—See Starlight Investments Ltd.; *Int'l,* pg. 7177
NORTHVIEW ENTERPRISES; *U.S. Private,* pg. 2958

1953

NORTHVIEW ENTERPRISES

THE NORTHVIEW GROUP LIMITED—See Barclays PLC; *Int'l*, pg. 860

NORTHVILLE NATURAL GAS, LLC—See NIC Holding Corporation; *U.S. Private*, pg. 2925

THE NORTH WARD CENTER, INC.; *U.S. Private*, pg. 4084

NORTHWATER CAPITAL MANAGEMENT, INC.; *Int'l*, pg. 5446

NORTH WATERLOO FARMERS MUTUAL INSURANCE COMPANY; *Int'l*, pg. 5441

NORTHWAY BANK—See Northway Financial, Inc.; *U.S. Public*, pg. 1541

NORTHWAY FINANCIAL, INC.; *U.S. Public*, pg. 1541

NORTHWAY MOTORCAR CORPORATION—See Langan Automotive Group; *U.S. Private*, pg. 2388

NORTHWELL HEALTH, INC.; *U.S. Private*, pg. 2958

NORTHWEST ADMINISTRATORS INC.; *U.S. Private*, pg. 2958

NORTHWEST ADVISORS, INC.—See Northwest Bancshares, Inc.; *U.S. Public*, pg. 1542

NORTHWEST AGRICULTURAL PRODUCTS, INC.—See AEA Investors LP; *U.S. Private*, pg. 116

NORTHWEST ALABAMA GAS DISTRICT; *U.S. Private*, pg. 2958

NORTHWEST ALLIED PHYSICIANS, LLC—See Community Health Systems, Inc.; *U.S. Public*, pg. 555

NORTHWEST ALUMINUM SPECIALTIES, INC.; *U.S. Private*, pg. 2958

NORTHWEST AMBULATORY SURGERY CENTER, LLC—See Tenet Healthcare Corporation; *U.S. Public*, pg. 2012

NORTHWEST AMBULATORY SURGERY SERVICES, LLC—See Bain Capital, LP; *U.S. Private*, pg. 445

NORTHWEST ARKANSAS HOSPITALS, LLC—See Community Health Systems, Inc.; *U.S. Public*, pg. 555

NORTHWEST ARKANSAS NEWSPAPERS LLC—See Wehco Media, Inc.; *U.S. Private*, pg. 4470

NORTHWEST ARKANSAS PAPER CO., INC.; *U.S. Private*, pg. 2958

NORTHWEST ARKANSAS REHABILITATION ASSOCIATES—See Encompass Health Corporation; *U.S. Public*, pg. 758

NORTHWEST BANCORPORATION OF ILLINOIS, INC.; *U.S. Private*, pg. 2959

NORTHWEST BANCSHARES, INC.; *U.S. Public*, pg. 1541

NORTHWEST BANK OF ROCKFORD—See Foresight Financial Group Inc; *U.S. Public*, pg. 867

NORTHWEST BANK—See Northwest Bancshares, Inc.; *U.S. Public*, pg. 1542

NORTHWEST BANK—See Northwest Financial Corp.; *U.S. Private*, pg. 2960

NORTHWEST BANK—See Western Capital Corporation; *U.S. Private*, pg. 4491

NORTHWEST BANK & TRUST COMPANY; *U.S. Private*, pg. 2959

NORTHWEST BEDDING CO.; *U.S. Private*, pg. 2959

NORTHWEST BENTON COUNTY PHYSICIAN SERVICES, LLC—See Community Health Systems, Inc.; *U.S. Public*, pg. 555

NORTHWEST BEVERAGES INC.—See Johnson Brothers Liquor Company; *U.S. Private*, pg. 2227

NORTHWEST BIOTHERAPEUTICS, INC.; *U.S. Public*, pg. 1542

NORTHWEST BOATS INDUSTRIES, INC.—See Renaissance Marine Group, Inc.; *U.S. Private*, pg. 3397

NORTHWEST BROADCASTING, INC.; *U.S. Private*, pg. 2959

NORTHWEST BUILDING MATERIALS & SUPPLY CO.; *U.S. Private*, pg. 2959

NORTHWEST BUSINESS PRESS INC.—See Cowles Company; *U.S. Private*, pg. 1074

NORTHWEST CAPITAL GROUP, INC.—See Northwest Bancshares, Inc.; *U.S. Public*, pg. 1542

NORTHWEST CARPET INC.—See Tarkett S.A.; *Int'l*, pg. 7463

NORTHWEST CASCADE INC.; *U.S. Private*, pg. 2959

NORTHWEST CENTER; *U.S. Private*, pg. 2959

NORTHWEST CHINA GRID COMPANY LIMITED—See State Grid Corporation of China; *Int'l*, pg. 7183

NORTHWEST COMMERCIAL CREDIT CORP.—See Northwest Financial Corp.; *U.S. Private*, pg. 2960

NORTHWEST COMMUNITY ACTION PROGRAMS OF WYOMING INC.; *U.S. Private*, pg. 2959

NORTHWEST COMMUNITY BANK; *U.S. Private*, pg. 2959

NORTHWEST COMMUNITY CARE NETWORK; *U.S. Private*, pg. 2959

NORTHWEST COMMUNITY CREDIT UNION; *U.S. Private*, pg. 2959

NORTHWEST COMMUNITY HEALTHCARE CORPORATION—See NorthShore University HealthSystem; *U.S. Private*, pg. 2957

THE NORTH WEST COMPANY INC.; *Int'l*, pg. 7671

THE NORTHWEST COMPANY; *U.S. Private*, pg. 4084

NORTHWEST CONSUMER DISCOUNT COMPANY—See Northwest Bancshares, Inc.; *U.S. Public*, pg. 1542

NORTHWEST CONTAINER SERVICES INC.; *U.S. Private*, pg. 2959

NORTHWEST COPPER CORP.; *Int'l*, pg. 5446

NORTHWEST CRANE SERVICE, LLC; *U.S. Private*, pg. 2959

NORTHWEST DAIRY ASSOCIATION; *U.S. Private*, pg. 2959

NORTHWEST DEMOLITION & DISMANTLING, INC.—See Arctic Slope Regional Corporation; *U.S. Private*, pg. 316

NORTHWEST DENTISTS INSURANCE COMPANY INC.—See Health Services Group, Inc.; *U.S. Private*, pg. 1894

NORTHWEST DOOR INC.; *U.S. Private*, pg. 2959

NORTHWEST ELECTRICAL SUPPLY CO. INC.; *U.S. Private*, pg. 2959

NORTHWESTEL INC.—See BCE Inc.; *Int'l*, pg. 926

NORTHWEST ENERGY EFFICIENCY ALLIANCE; *U.S. Private*, pg. 2960

NORTHWEST ENERGY ENGINEERING CENTER OPEN JOINT-STOCK—See JSC ROSSETI; *Int'l*, pg. 4010

NORTHWEST ENTERPRISES INC.; *U.S. Private*, pg. 2960

NORTH WEST ENTERPRISES—See Caribou Corporation; *U.S. Private*, pg. 761

NORTHWEST EQUIPMENT SALES INC.; *U.S. Private*, pg. 2960

NORTHWESTERN BANCSHARES, INC.; *U.S. Private*, pg. 2962

NORTHWESTERN BANK, N.A.—See Northwestern Bancshares, Inc.; *U.S. Private*, pg. 2962

NORTHWESTERN BANK; *U.S. Public*, pg. 2962

NORTHWESTERN CORPORATION; *U.S. Public*, pg. 1542

NORTHWESTERN COUNSELING & SUPPORT SERVICES, INC.; *U.S. Private*, pg. 2962

NORTHWESTERN ELECTRIC COOPERATIVE, INC.; *U.S. Private*, pg. 2962

NORTHWESTERN ENGINEERING COMPANY; *U.S. Private*, pg. 2962

NORTHWESTERN ENTERPRISES LTD.; *Int'l*, pg. 5447

NORTHWESTERN FLAVORS, LLC—See Mars, Incorporated; *U.S. Private*, pg. 2590

NORTHWESTERN INDUSTRIES-ARIZONA, INC.—See GlassWerks LA Co.; *U.S. Private*, pg. 1707

NORTHWESTERN LONG TERM CARE INSURANCE COMPANY—See The Northwestern Mutual Life Insurance Company; *U.S. Private*, pg. 4085

NORTHWESTERN MEAT, INC.; *U.S. Private*, pg. 2962

NORTHWESTERN MEDICAL CENTER, INC.; *U.S. Private*, pg. 2962

NORTHWESTERN MEDICAL FACULTY FOUNDATION, INC.—See Northwestern Memorial HealthCare; *U.S. Private*, pg. 2963

NORTHWESTERN MEMORIAL FOUNDATION—See Northwestern Memorial HealthCare; *U.S. Private*, pg. 2963

NORTHWESTERN MEMORIAL HEALTHCARE; *U.S. Private*, pg. 2962

NORTHWESTERN MEMORIAL HOME HEALTH CARE—See Northwestern Memorial HealthCare; *U.S. Private*, pg. 2963

NORTHWESTERN MEMORIAL HOSPITAL—See Northwestern Memorial HealthCare; *U.S. Private*, pg. 2963

NORTHWESTERN MEMORIAL PHYSICIANS GROUP—See Northwestern Memorial HealthCare; *U.S. Private*, pg. 2963

NORTHWESTERN MUTUAL ATLANTIC BENEFIT GROUP—See The Northwestern Mutual Life Insurance Company; *U.S. Private*, pg. 4085

NORTHWESTERN MUTUAL INVESTMENT SERVICES, LLC—See The Northwestern Mutual Life Insurance Company; *U.S. Private*, pg. 4085

THE NORTHWESTERN MUTUAL LIFE INSURANCE COMPANY; *U.S. Private*, pg. 4084

NORTHWESTERN NETWORKS, INC.—See NorthWestern Corporation; *U.S. Public*, pg. 1543

NORTH-WESTERN PHOSPHOROUS COMPANY—See Public Joint Stock Company Acron; *Int'l*, pg. 6095

NORTHWESTERN REGION EMPLOYEE BENEFIT TRUST; *U.S. Private*, pg. 2963

NORTHWESTERN SELECTA, INC.—See Northwestern Meat, Inc.; *U.S. Private*, pg. 2962

NORTHWESTERN WISCONSIN ELECTRIC CO.; *U.S. Private*, pg. 2963

NORTHWEST EVALUATION ASSOCIATION—See Veritas Capital Fund Management, LLC; *U.S. Private*, pg. 4363

NORTHWEST EXTERMINATING CO., INC.—See EQT AB; *Int'l*, pg. 2468

NORTHWEST EXTERMINATING, LLC—See Rollins, Inc.; *U.S. Public*, pg. 1809

NORTHWEST FARM CREDIT SERVICES ACA; *U.S. Private*, pg. 2960

NORTHWEST FARM FOOD COOPERATIVE, INC.—See The Scoular Company; *U.S. Private*, pg. 4115

NORTHWEST FASTENER SALES INC—See AEA Investors LP; *U.S. Private*, pg. 114

NORTHWEST FIBER LLC; *U.S. Private*, pg. 2960

NORTHWEST FINANCIAL CORP.; *U.S. Private*, pg. 2960

NORTHWEST FINANCIAL GROUP, INC.—See AutoNation, Inc.; *U.S. Public*, pg. 236

NORTHWEST FINANCIAL SERVICES, INC.—See Northwest Bancshares, Inc.; *U.S. Public*, pg. 1542

CORPORATE AFFILIATIONS

NORTHWEST FIRESTOP; *U.S. Private*, pg. 2960

NORTHWEST FLORIDA COMMUNITY HOSPITAL; *U.S. Private*, pg. 2960

NORTHWEST FLORIDA DAILY NEWS—See Gannett Co., Inc.; *U.S. Public*, pg. 906

NORTHWEST FLORIDA MULTISPECIALTY PHYSICIANS, LLC—See HCA Healthcare, Inc.; *U.S. Public*, pg. 1004

NORTHWEST FLORIDA PRIMARY CARE, LLC—See HCA Healthcare, Inc.; *U.S. Public*, pg. 1004

NORTHWEST FRAMING; *U.S. Private*, pg. 2960

NORTHWEST FUEL INJECTION SERVICE, INC.; *U.S. Private*, pg. 2960

NORTHWEST FUEL INJECTION SERVICE OF INDIANA, L.L.C.—See Northwest Fuel Injection Service, Inc.; *U.S. Private*, pg. 2960

NORTHWEST FUEL INJECTION SERVICE OF MICHIGAN, LLC—See Northwest Fuel Injection Service, Inc.; *U.S. Private*, pg. 2960

NORTHWEST GEORGIA BANK—See NW Services Corporation; *U.S. Private*, pg. 2975

NORTHWEST GEORGIA ONCOLOGY SUPPLY; *U.S. Private*, pg. 2960

NORTHWEST GEORGIA ORTHOPAEDIC SURGERY CENTER, LLC—See Tenet Healthcare Corporation; *U.S. Public*, pg. 2012

NORTH WEST GOPRO—See Set Point Group Limited; *Int'l*, pg. 6730

NORTHWEST GRAIN GROWERS, INC.; *U.S. Private*, pg. 2960

NORTHWEST GRAIN—See CHS INC.; *U.S. Public*, pg. 492

THE NORTHWEST GROUP; *U.S. Private*, pg. 4084

NORTHWEST HANDLING SYSTEMS, INC.; *U.S. Private*, pg. 2960

NORTHWEST HARDWOODS, INC.—See Littlejohn & Co., LLC; *U.S. Private*, pg. 2471

NORTHWEST HEALTHCARE ALLIANCE, INC.—See UnitedHealth Group Incorporated; *U.S. Public*, pg. 2246

NORTHWEST HEALTH CAREERS, LLC; *U.S. Private*, pg. 2960

NORTHWEST HEALTHCARE PROPERTIES AUSTRALIA REIT—See NorthWest Value Partners Inc.; *Int'l*, pg. 5446

NORTHWEST HEALTHCARE PROPERTIES REAL ESTATE INVESTMENT TRUST—See NorthWest Value Partners Inc.; *Int'l*, pg. 5446

NORTHWEST HNA PROPERTY CO., LTD.—See Hainan Traffic Administration Holding Co., Ltd.; *Int'l*, pg. 3215

NORTHWEST HOSPITAL, LLC—See Community Health Systems, Inc.; *U.S. Public*, pg. 552

NORTHWEST HYDRO INC.—See Enel S.p.A.; *Int'l*, pg. 2414

NORTHWEST INC.; *U.S. Private*, pg. 2960

NORTHWEST INDIANA BANCORP; *U.S. Public*, pg. 1542

NORTHWEST INSULATION CO. INC.; *U.S. Private*, pg. 2960

NORTHWEST INSULATION, LLC—See Installed Building Products, Inc.; *U.S. Public*, pg. 1133

NORTHWEST INTERNATIONAL HEALTHCARE PROPERTIES REAL ESTATE INVESTMENT TRUST—See NorthWest Value Partners Inc.; *Int'l*, pg. 5447

NORTHWEST INVESTMENT GROUP LIMITED; *Int'l*, pg. 5446

NORTHWEST INVESTMENTS NZ LIMITED—See The Skipton Building Society; *Int'l*, pg. 7687

NORTHWEST IOWA POWER COOPERATIVE; *U.S. Private*, pg. 2960

NORTHWEST IOWA SYMPHONY ORCHESTRA; *U.S. Private*, pg. 2961

NORTHWEST JUSTICE PROJECT; *U.S. Private*, pg. 2961

NORTHWEST KIDNEY CENTERS; *U.S. Private*, pg. 2961

NORTHWEST LOGIC, INC.—See Rambus Inc.; *U.S. Public*, pg. 1762

NORTHWEST LOGISTICS INC.; *U.S. Private*, pg. 2961

NORTHWEST MACK PARTS & SERVICE CO.—See Celli Enterprises Inc.; *U.S. Private*, pg. 807

NORTHWEST MALL, INC.—See Levcor, Inc.; *U.S. Private*, pg. 2434

NORTHWEST MEDICAL CENTER, INC.—See Curae Health, Inc.; *U.S. Private*, pg. 1124

NORTHWEST METALCRAFT, INC.—See Metalcraft Industries, Inc.; *U.S. Public*, pg. 2680

NORTH WEST MINING & CIVIL PTY LTD—See E&A Limited; *Int'l*, pg. 2247

NORTHWEST MINING & GEOLOGY GROUP CO., LTD.; *Int'l*, pg. 5446

NORTHWEST NATURAL GAS COMPANY—See Northwest Natural Holding Company; *U.S. Public*, pg. 1542

NORTHWEST NATURAL HOLDING COMPANY; *U.S. Public*, pg. 1542

NORTHWEST NATURALS LLC—See Tree Top, Inc.; *U.S. Private*, pg. 4216

NORTHWEST NEW JERSEY COMMUNITY ACTION PROGRAM; *U.S. Private*, pg. 2961

NORTHWEST NEWS CO., INC.; *U.S. Private*, pg. 2961

NORTHWEST OFFICE TECHNOLOGIES INC.—See Pacific Office Automation, Inc.; *U.S. Private*, pg. 3069

NORTHWEST OIL COMPANY INC; *U.S. Private*, pg. 2961

COMPANY NAME INDEX

NORTHWEST OIL & GAS TRADING COMPANY, INC.; *U.S. Private,* pg. 2961
NORTHWEST PACKAGING INC.; *U.S. Private,* pg. 2961
NORTHWEST PACKING COMPANY INC.; *U.S. Private,* pg. 2961
NORTHWEST PAINTING, INC.—See UFP Industries, Inc.; *U.S. Public,* pg. 2219
NORTHWEST PERMANENTE P.C.—See Kaiser Permanente; *U.S. Private,* pg. 2256
NORTHWEST PET PRODUCTS INC.; *U.S. Private,* pg. 2961
NORTHWEST PHARMACY SERVICES—See Prescryptive Health, Inc.; *U.S. Private,* pg. 3254
NORTHWEST PHYSICIANS, LLC—See Community Health Systems, Inc.; *U.S. Public,* pg. 555
NORTHWEST PIONEER INC.—See Pioneer Packing Inc.; *U.S. Private,* pg. 3187
NORTHWEST PIPE COMPANY; *U.S. Public,* pg. 1542
NORTHWEST PIPE FITTINGS, INC.; *U.S. Private,* pg. 2961
NORTH-WEST PIPELINE COMPANY MUNAITAS JSC—See KazTransOil JSC; *Int'l,* pg. 4103
NORTHWEST PIPELINE CORPORATION—See The Williams Companies, Inc.; *U.S. Public,* pg. 2144
NORTHWEST PIPELINE CORPORATION—See The Williams Companies, Inc.; *U.S. Public,* pg. 2144
NORTHWEST PIPELINE CORPORATION—See The Williams Companies, Inc.; *U.S. Public,* pg. 2144
NORTHWEST PIPELINE CORPORATION—See The Williams Companies, Inc.; *U.S. Public,* pg. 2144
NORTHWEST PIPELINE CORPORATION—See The Williams Companies, Inc.; *U.S. Public,* pg. 2144
NORTHWEST PIPELINE CORPORATION—See The Williams Companies, Inc.; *U.S. Public,* pg. 2144
NORTHWEST PIPELINE LLC—See The Williams Companies, Inc.; *U.S. Public,* pg. 2143
NORTHWEST PLAN SERVICES, INC.; *U.S. Private,* pg. 2961
NORTHWEST POLYMERS LLC—See Clayton, Dubilier & Rice, LLC; *U.S. Private,* pg. 920
NORTHWEST POWER, INC.—See Vicor Corporation; *U.S. Public,* pg. 2296
NORTH WEST PROJECTS LIMITED—See VINCI S.A.; *Int'l,* pg. 8224
NORTHWEST PUMP & EQUIPMENT CO.—See H.I.G. Capital, LLC; *U.S. Private,* pg. 1833
NORTHWEST REGIONAL ASC, LLC—See Tenet Healthcare Corporation; *U.S. Public,* pg. 2012
NORTHWEST REGIONAL SURGERY CENTER, LLC—See Tenet Healthcare Corporation; *U.S. Public,* pg. 2005
NORTHWEST RESTAURANTS; *U.S. Private,* pg. 2961
NORTH WEST RURAL ELECTRIC COOPERATIVE; *U.S. Private,* pg. 2948
NORTHWEST SEAFOOD PROCESSORS, INC.—See Odyssey Enterprises, Inc.; *U.S. Private,* pg. 2993
NORTHWEST SENIOR & DISABILITY SERVICES; *U.S. Private,* pg. 2961
NORTHWEST STAFFING RESOURCES INC.; *U.S. Private,* pg. 2961
NORTHWEST STEEL ERECTION CO.—See Ridgetop Holding Co., Inc.; *U.S. Private,* pg. 3433
NORTHWEST STEEL & PIPE INC.; *U.S. Private,* pg. 2961
NORTHWEST STRATEGIES; *U.S. Private,* pg. 2961
NORTHWEST SUPPLY COMPANY INC.; *U.S. Private,* pg. 2961
NORTHWEST SURGERY CENTER, LLP—See Tenet Healthcare Corporation; *U.S. Public,* pg. 2012
NORTHWEST SURGERY CENTER, LTD—See Tenet Healthcare Corporation; *U.S. Public,* pg. 2005
NORTHWEST SURGICARE, LLC—See UnitedHealth Group Incorporated; *U.S. Public,* pg. 2243
NORTHWEST SURGICARE, LTD.—See UnitedHealth Group Incorporated; *U.S. Public,* pg. 2243
NORTHWEST TENNESSEE DISPOSAL CORPORATION—See Republic Services, Inc.; *U.S. Public,* pg. 1786
NORTHWEST TERRITORIAL MINT, LLC.; *U.S. Private,* pg. 2962
NORTHWEST TEXAS HEALTHCARE SYSTEM, INC.—See Universal Health Services, Inc.; *U.S. Public,* pg. 2258
NORTHWEST TEXAS PHYSICIAN GROUP—See Universal Health Services, Inc.; *U.S. Public,* pg. 2258
NORTHWEST TEXAS SURGICAL HOSPITAL, L.L.C.—See Universal Health Services, Inc.; *U.S. Public,* pg. 2258
NORTHWEST TEXAS WYATT CLINIC, PLLC—See Universal Health Services, Inc.; *U.S. Public,* pg. 2258
NORTHWEST TIRE & SERVICE INC.; *U.S. Private,* pg. 2962
NORTHWEST TOBACCO & CANDY CO.; *U.S. Private,* pg. 2962
NORTHWEST TOWER CRANES—See The Sowles Company; *U.S. Private,* pg. 4119
NORTHWEST TRAINING CENTER—See Delta Air Lines, Inc.; *U.S. Public,* pg. 652
NORTHWEST TUCSON DIALYSIS, LLC—See DaVita Inc.; *U.S. Public,* pg. 641
NORTHWEST VALUE PARTNERS INC.; *Int'l,* pg. 5446

NORTHWEST WATER HEATER INC.; *U.S. Private,* pg. 2962
NORTHWEST WEALTH ADVISORS LLC—See tru Independce LLC; *U.S. Private,* pg. 4244
NORTHWEST WEALTH MANAGEMENT, LLC—See Northwest Financial Corp.; *U.S. Private,* pg. 2960
NORTHWEST WEB CO.; *U.S. Private,* pg. 2962
NORTHWEST WHOLESALE INC.; *U.S. Private,* pg. 2962
NORTHWEST WIRE ROPE & SLING COMPANY—See ALP Industries, Inc.; *U.S. Private,* pg. 196
NORTHWEST WOOLEN MILLS—See Hyman Brickle & Son, Inc.; *U.S. Private,* pg. 2019
NORTHWICH VETS4PETS LIMITED—See Pets at Home Group Plc; *Int'l,* pg. 5834
NORTH WIND, INC.—See Cook Inlet Region, Inc.; *U.S. Private,* pg. 1038
NORTHWIND INVESTMENTS INC.; *U.S. Private,* pg. 2963
NORTH WIND SERVICES, LLC330420—See Cook Inlet Region, Inc.; *U.S. Private,* pg. 1038
NORTHWINDS MARKETING GROUP LLC—See American Express Company; *U.S. Public,* pg. 102
NORTHWIRE, INC.—See Lemo S.A.; *Int'l,* pg. 4450
NORTHWOOD AUTO PLAZA INC.; *U.S. Private,* pg. 2963
NORTHWOOD EQUITY ELEVATOR CO.; *U.S. Private,* pg. 2963
NORTHWOOD FOODS INC.; *U.S. Private,* pg. 2963
NORTHWOOD HEALTH SYSTEMS; *U.S. Private,* pg. 2963
NORTHWOOD HOMES INCORPORATED—See Northwood Investment Corporation; *U.S. Private,* pg. 2963
NORTHWOOD INVESTMENT CORPORATION; *U.S. Private,* pg. 2963
NORTHWOOD INVESTORS, LLC; *U.S. Private,* pg. 2963
NORTHWOOD MANUFACTURING, INC.—See Northwood Investment Corporation; *U.S. Private,* pg. 2963
NORTHWOOD PAPER SALES LTD.; *Int'l,* pg. 5447
NORTHWOOD REALTY SERVICES—See Everest Consulting Group LP; *U.S. Private,* pg. 1438
NORTH WOODS ADVERTISING; *U.S. Private,* pg. 2948
NORTHWOODS PHYSICAL THERAPY, LIMITED PARTNERSHIP—See U.S. Physical Therapy, Inc.; *U.S. Public,* pg. 2215
THE NORTHWOODS RIVER NEWS—See Lakeland Printing Co Inc; *U.S. Private,* pg. 2376
NORTHWOOD & WEPA LTD.—See WEPA Hygieneprodukte GmbH & Co. KG; *Int'l,* pg. 8378
NORTH YORKSHIRE MORTGAGES LIMITED—See The Skipton Building Society; *Int'l,* pg. 7687
NORTON ABRASIVE EXPORTS—See Compagnie de Saint-Gobain SA; *Int'l,* pg. 1730
THE NORTON COMPANY; *U.S. Private,* pg. 4085
NORTON COMPANY—See Compagnie de Saint-Gobain SA; *Int'l,* pg. 1730
NORTON CONSTRUCTION CO.; *U.S. Private,* pg. 2963
NORTON FOLGATE MARKETING LTD—See Argent Group Europe Limited; *Int'l,* pg. 560
NORTON GOLD FIELDS LIMITED—See Zijin Mining Group Company Limited; *Int'l,* pg. 8683
NORTON HALL MEADOW MANAGEMENT LIMITED—See Persimmon plc; *Int'l,* pg. 5816
NORTON HEALTHCARE, INC.; *U.S. Private,* pg. 2963
NORTON HMA, INC.—See Community Health Systems, Inc.; *U.S. Public,* pg. 555
NORTON INDUSTRIES; *U.S. Private,* pg. 2964
NORTON INSURANCE LIMITED—See Compagnie de Saint-Gobain SA; *Int'l,* pg. 1731
NORTON LILLY INTERNATIONAL INC.; *U.S. Private,* pg. 2964
NORTON MIRROR—See Gannett Co., Inc.; *U.S. Public,* pg. 902
NORTON MOTORCYCLE (UK) LTD.; *Int'l,* pg. 5447
NORTON PACKAGING INC.; *U.S. Private,* pg. 2964
NORTON PAMPUS GMBH—See Compagnie de Saint-Gobain SA; *Int'l,* pg. 1731
NORTON & PROFFITT DEVELOPMENTS LIMITED—See Blackstone Inc.; *U.S. Public,* pg. 358
NORTON ROSE FULBRIGHT AUSTRALIA—See Norton Rose Fulbright LLP; *Int'l,* pg. 5447
NORTON ROSE FULBRIGHT CANADA LLP—See Norton Rose Fulbright LLP; *Int'l,* pg. 5447
NORTON ROSE FULBRIGHT COLOMBIA S.A.S.—See Norton Rose Fulbright LLP; *Int'l,* pg. 5447
NORTON ROSE FULBRIGHT (GERMANY) LLP—See Norton Rose Fulbright LLP; *Int'l,* pg. 5447
NORTON ROSE FULBRIGHT GREECE—See Norton Rose Fulbright LLP; *Int'l,* pg. 5447
NORTON ROSE FULBRIGHT (KAZAKHSTAN) LIMITED—See Norton Rose Fulbright LLP; *Int'l,* pg. 5447
NORTON ROSE FULBRIGHT LLP; *Int'l,* pg. 5447
NORTON ROSE FULBRIGHT (MIDDLE EAST) LLP—See Norton Rose Fulbright LLP; *Int'l,* pg. 5447
NORTON ROSE FULBRIGHT MOROCCO, SARL—See Norton Rose Fulbright LLP; *Int'l,* pg. 5447
NORTON ROSE FULBRIGHT PIOTR STRAWA AND PARTNERS, LIMITED PARTNERSHIP—See Norton Rose Fulbright LLP; *Int'l,* pg. 5447
NORTON ROSE FULBRIGHT STUDIO LEGALE—See Norton Rose Fulbright LLP; *Int'l,* pg. 5447

NORTON ROSE FULBRIGHT TANZANIA—See Norton Rose Fulbright LLP; *Int'l,* pg. 5447
NORTON ROSE FULBRIGHT (THAILAND) LIMITED—See Norton Rose Fulbright LLP; *Int'l,* pg. 5447
NORTON ROSE FULBRIGHT US LLP—See Norton Rose Fulbright LLP; *Int'l,* pg. 5447
NORTON SOUND ECONOMIC DEVELOPMENT CORPORATION; *U.S. Private,* pg. 2964
NORTON SOUND SEAFOOD PRODUCTS—See Norton Sound Economic Development Corporation; *U.S. Private,* pg. 2964
NORTRAK-DAMY, CAMBIOS DE VIA, S.A.P.I. DE C.V.—See voestalpine AG; *Int'l,* pg. 8293
NORTRUX INC; *Int'l,* pg. 5447
NORVANCO INTERNATIONAL, INC.; *U.S. Private,* pg. 2964
NORVAX, INC.—See Centerbridge Partners, L.P.; *U.S. Private,* pg. 815
NORVELL SKIN SOLUTIONS, LLC—See Castle Harlan, Inc.; *U.S. Private,* pg. 785
NORVESTOR EQUITY AS; *Int'l,* pg. 5447
NORVIAL S.A.—See Aenza S.A.A.; *Int'l,* pg. 176
NORVIK HF; *Int'l,* pg. 5447
NORVILLE (20/20) LIMITED—See Inspecs Group Plc; *Int'l,* pg. 3719
NORVISTA CAPITAL CORP.; *Int'l,* pg. 5448
NORWALK AUTO AUCTION; *U.S. Private,* pg. 2964
NORWALK COMPRESSOR COMPANY, INC.; *U.S. Private,* pg. 2964
NORWALK COVE MARINA, INC.—See Rex Marine Center, Inc.; *U.S. Private,* pg. 3417
NORWALK CUSTOM ORDER FURNITURE; *U.S. Private,* pg. 2964
NORWALK POWDERED METALS, INC.; *U.S. Private,* pg. 2964
NORWALK READY-MIXED CONCRETE, INC.; *U.S. Private,* pg. 2964
NORWALL GROUP INC.; *Int'l,* pg. 5448
NORWAY BANCORP, INC.; *U.S. Private,* pg. 2964
NORWAY FOODS EUROPE NV—See Thai Union Group Public Company Limited; *Int'l,* pg. 7596
NORWAY HOUSE; *U.S. Private,* pg. 2964
NORWAY REGISTERS DEVELOPMENT AS—See INVL Technology AB; *Int'l,* pg. 3790
NORWAY ROYAL SALMON ASA—See Salmar ASA; *Int'l,* pg. 6494
NORWAY SAVINGS BANK—See Norway Bancorp, Inc.; *U.S. Private,* pg. 2964
NORWAY TELEPHONE CO. INC.—See Telephone & Data Systems, Inc.; *U.S. Public,* pg. 1998
NORWEGIAN AIR SHUTTLE ASA; *Int'l,* pg. 5448
NORWEGIAN AIR SHUTTLE SWEDEN AB—See Norwegian Air Shuttle ASA; *Int'l,* pg. 5448
NORWEGIAN BEVERAGE GROUP AS—See Viva Wine Group AB; *Int'l,* pg. 8264
NORWEGIAN BLOCK EXCHANGE AS; *Int'l,* pg. 5448
NORWEGIAN CAR CARRIERS AS—See Klaveness Marine Holding AS; *Int'l,* pg. 4200
NORWEGIAN CRUISE LINE HOLDINGS LTD.; *U.S. Public,* pg. 1543
NORWEGIAN FINANS HOLDING ASA—See Nordax Group AB; *Int'l,* pg. 5416
NORWEGIAN INSURANCE PARTNERS AS—See Howden Group Holdings Limited; *Int'l,* pg. 3493
NORWEGIAN PIPING AS—See HitecVision AS; *Int'l,* pg. 3426
NORWEGIAN PROPERTY ASA; *Int'l,* pg. 5448
NORWEGIAN PROPERTY HOLDING AS—See Norwegian Property ASA; *Int'l,* pg. 5448
NORWEGIAN SCHOOL OF TECHNOLOGY AS—See Lumi Gruppen AS; *Int'l,* pg. 4578
NORWELL ENGINEERING LIMITED—See Elemental Energies Holdings Limited; *Int'l,* pg. 2358
NORWELL MANUFACTURING CO., INC.; *U.S. Private,* pg. 2964
NORWELL MARINER—See Gannett Co., Inc.; *U.S. Public,* pg. 902
NORWESCO AB—See Lagercrantz Group AB; *Int'l,* pg. 4394
NORWESCO, INC. - HANFORD—See Olympus Partners; *U.S. Private,* pg. 3013
NORWESCO, INC.—See Olympus Partners; *U.S. Private,* pg. 3013
NORWEST CENTER, INC.—See Wells Fargo & Company; *U.S. Public,* pg. 2344
NORWEST ENERGY NL—See Mineral Resources Limited; *Int'l,* pg. 4906
NORWEST EQUITY PARTNERS IX, LP—See Wells Fargo & Company; *U.S. Public,* pg. 2344
NORWEST HOLST SOIL ENGINEERING LTD.—See VINCI S.A.; *Int'l,* pg. 8236
NORWEST INDUSTRIES LTD.—See Pearl Global Industries Limited; *Int'l,* pg. 5774
NORWEST MEZZANINE PARTNERS—See Wells Fargo & Company; *U.S. Public,* pg. 2344
NORWEST MINERALS LIMITED—See Australian Mines Limited; *Int'l,* pg. 722

1955

NORWELL MANUFACTURING CO., INC.

CORPORATE AFFILIATIONS

NORWEST VENTURE CAPITAL MANAGEMENT, INC.—See Wells Fargo & Company; *U.S. Public*, pg. 2344
NORWEST VENTURE PARTNERS; *U.S. Private*, pg. 2964
NORWICH AERO PRODUCTS, INC.—See TransDigm Group Incorporated; *U.S. Public*, pg. 2180
NORWICH AND PETERBOROUGH ESTATE AGENTS LTD—See Yorkshire Building Society; *Int'l*, pg. 8599
NORWICH AND PETERBOROUGH INSURANCE BROKERS LIMITED—See Yorkshire Building Society; *Int'l*, pg. 8599
NORWICH & PETERBOROUGH BUILDING SOCIETY—See Yorkshire Building Society; *Int'l*, pg. 8599
NORWIX INC.; *U.S. Public*, pg. 1543
NORWOOD AUTO PARTS—See Hahn Automotive Warehouse, Inc.; *U.S. Private*, pg. 1840
NORWOOD COMMERCIAL CONTRACTORS INC.; *U.S. Private*, pg. 2964
THE NORWOOD COMPANY INC.; *U.S. Private*, pg. 4085
NORWOOD CO-OPERATIVE BANK; *U.S. Private*, pg. 2964
NORWOOD FINANCIAL CORP.; *U.S. Public*, pg. 1543
NORWOOD FOUNDRY LTD.; *Int'l*, pg. 5448
NORWOOD MARKING SYSTEMS—See Illinois Tool Works Inc.; *U.S. Public*, pg. 1109
NORWOOD MEDICAL; *U.S. Private*, pg. 2964
NORWOOD PROMOTIONAL PRODUCTS EUROPE S.L.U—See Societe BIC S.A.; *Int'l*, pg. 7037
NORWOOD PROMOTIONAL PRODUCTS ITALIA S.P.A.—See Societe BIC S.A.; *Int'l*, pg. 7037
NORWOOD PROMOTIONAL PRODUCTS, LLC—See Societe BIC S.A.; *Int'l*, pg. 7036
NORWOOD SASH & DOOR MANUFACTURING CO.; *U.S. Private*, pg. 2964
NORWOOD SYSTEMS LIMITED; *Int'l*, pg. 5448
NORYARDS AS—See JSC Zaliv Shipyard; *Int'l*, pg. 4012
NORYARDS BMV AS—See JSC Zaliv Shipyard; *Int'l*, pg. 4012
NORYARDS FOSEN AS—See JSC Zaliv Shipyard; *Int'l*, pg. 4012
NORZINC LTD.—See RCF Management LLC; *U.S. Private*, pg. 3362
NO SABE FALLAR, S.A. DE C.V.—See Societe BIC S.A.; *Int'l*, pg. 7036
NOSA EMPLOYMENT AGENCY—See Sebata Holdings; *Int'l*, pg. 6669
NO-SAG PRODUCTS DIVISION—See Leggett & Platt, Incorporated; *U.S. Public*, pg. 1303
N'OSAIRIS TECHNOLOGIES SOLUTIONS SDN BHD—See SMRT Holdings Berhad; *Int'l*, pg. 7014
NOSAN CORPORATION—See Mitsubishi Corporation; *Int'l*, pg. 4942
NOSA PLUGS AB; *Int'l*, pg. 5448
NOSA—See Sebata Holdings; *Int'l*, pg. 6669
NOSCIRA S.A.—See Zeltia, S.A.; *Int'l*, pg. 8631
NOSCO, INC.—See Holden Industries, Inc.; *U.S. Private*, pg. 1962
NOSCO, INC.—See Holden Industries, Inc.; *U.S. Private*, pg. 1962
NOSCO, INC.—See Holden Industries, Inc.; *U.S. Private*, pg. 1962
NOS COMMUNICATIONS INC.; *U.S. Private*, pg. 2964
NOSE ELECTRIC RAILWAY CO., LTD.—See Hankyu Hanshin Holdings Inc.; *Int'l*, pg. 3256
NOS ENERGY COMPANY—See Monster Beverage Corporation; *U.S. Public*, pg. 1465
NOSHOK INC.; *U.S. Private*, pg. 2965
NO SIGNBOARD HOLDINGS LTD.; *Int'l*, pg. 5394
N.O. SIMMONS & ASSOCIATES INCORPORATED; *U.S. Private*, pg. 2828
NO SLEEP PRODUCTIONS LLC—See Stagwell, Inc.; *U.S. Public*, pg. 1927
NOS LTD.—See Startia Holdings, Inc.; *Int'l*, pg. 7179
NOSSA SENHORA DA GUIA EXPORTADORA DE CAFE LTDA.—See Segafredo Zanetti S.p.A.; *Int'l*, pg. 6682
NOS SGPS, S.A.; *Int'l*, pg. 5448
NOSTAG GMBH & CO. KG—See Prysmian S.p.A.; *Int'l*, pg. 6011
NOSTALGIA FAMILY BRANDS, INC.; *U.S. Private*, pg. 2965
NOSTALGIC IMAGES INC.; *U.S. Private*, pg. 2965
NOSTALGIC PROPERTIES SDN. BHD.—See Omesti Berhad; *Int'l*, pg. 5562
NOSTER DIALYSIS, LLC—See DaVita Inc.; *U.S. Public*, pg. 641
NOSTERS (PVT) LTD.—See BELIMO Holding AG; *Int'l*, pg. 965
NOSTRA CEMENT KFT.—See STRABAG SE; *Int'l*, pg. 7231
NOSTRA TERRA OIL AND GAS COMPANY PLC; *Int'l*, pg. 5448
NOSTROMO ENERGY LTD.; *Int'l*, pg. 5449
NOSTRUM OIL & GAS PLC; *Int'l*, pg. 5449
NOSTURIEXPERTIT OY-NOSTURILLOYDS—See Konecranes Plc; *Int'l*, pg. 4252
NOTABLE SOLUTIONS, INC.—See Microsoft Corporation; *U.S. Public*, pg. 1442

NOTAMI HOSPITALS OF FLORIDA, INC.—See HCA Healthcare, Inc.; *U.S. Public*, pg. 1004
NOTAMI, LLC—See HCA Healthcare, Inc.; *U.S. Public*, pg. 1005
NOTCENTER VIKEN AB—See Lantmannen ek for; *Int'l*, pg. 4414
NOTCH HOLDINGS PTY LTD—See Mitchell Services Limited; *Int'l*, pg. 4925
NOTCUTTS LTD.; *Int'l*, pg. 5449
NOTE AB; *Int'l*, pg. 5449
NOTEBOOKSBILLIGER.DE AG—See ElectronicPartner Handel SE; *Int'l*, pg. 2354
NOTE COMPONENTS AB—See Note AB; *Int'l*, pg. 5449
NOTEDOM LIMITED—See Manali Petrochemicals Ltd; *Int'l*, pg. 4667
NOTE HERRLJUNGA AB—See Note AB; *Int'l*, pg. 5449
NOTE HYVINKAA OY—See Note AB; *Int'l*, pg. 5449
NOTE INTERNATIONAL AB—See Note AB; *Int'l*, pg. 5449
NOTE LUND AB—See Note AB; *Int'l*, pg. 5449
NOTEMACHINE LIMITED—See The Brink's Company; *U.S. Public*, pg. 2043
NOTE NORGE AS—See Note AB; *Int'l*, pg. 5449
NOTE NORRTELJE AB—See Note AB; *Int'l*, pg. 5449
NOTE OSLO AS—See Note AB; *Int'l*, pg. 5449
NOTE PARNU OU—See Note AB; *Int'l*, pg. 5449
NOTE PRINTING AUSTRALIA LIMITED—See The Reserve Bank of Australia; *Int'l*, pg. 7678
NOTESHARK, LLC—See SAP SE; *Int'l*, pg. 6566
NOTE TAURAGE UAB—See Note AB; *Int'l*, pg. 5449
NOTE TORSBY AB—See Note AB; *Int'l*, pg. 5449
NOTE UK LTD.—See Note AB; *Int'l*, pg. 5449
NOTEVAULT, INC.—See Bentley Systems, Inc.; *U.S. Public*, pg. 297
NOTE WORLD—See Credit-Based Asset Servicing & Securitization LLC; *U.S. Private*, pg. 1092
NOTHERN CAPITAL INC.; *U.S. Private*, pg. 2965
NOTHING BUT NET, LLC—See PLJ Information Systems, Inc.; *U.S. Private*, pg. 3214
NOTHNAGLE REALTORS—See Hanna Holdings, Inc.; *U.S. Private*, pg. 1854
NOTICIAS LIBRES SURESTE DE TENNESSEE—See Wehco Media, Inc.; *U.S. Private*, pg. 4470
NOTIFIER (BENELUX) S.A.—See Honeywell International Inc.; *U.S. Public*, pg. 1050
NOTIFIER CO.—See Honeywell International Inc.; *U.S. Public*, pg. 1050
NOTIFIER DEUTSCHLAND GMBH—See Honeywell International Inc.; *U.S. Public*, pg. 1050
NOTIFIER ESPANA S.L.—See Honeywell International Inc.; *U.S. Public*, pg. 1050
NOTIFIER INERTIA FIRE SYSTEM—See Honeywell International Inc.; *U.S. Public*, pg. 1050
NOTIFIER ITALIA S.R.L.—See Honeywell International Inc.; *U.S. Public*, pg. 1050
NOTION CAPITAL LIMITED; *Int'l*, pg. 5449
NOTION ONE, LLC—See DVHP Inc.; *U.S. Private*, pg. 1295
NOTION VTEC BERHAD; *Int'l*, pg. 5449
NOTIS GLOBAL, INC.; *U.S. Public*, pg. 1543
NOTISUM AB—See Karnov Group AB; *Int'l*, pg. 4084
NOTOCO INDUSTRIES LLC; *U.S. Private*, pg. 2965
NOT ORDINARY MEDIA, LLC—See Pico Far East Holdings Limited; *Int'l*, pg. 5861
NOTORIOUS PICTURES SPA; *Int'l*, pg. 5449
NOTOX TECHNOLOGIES CORP.; *Int'l*, pg. 5449
NOTRAX - MATS FOR PROFESSIONAL USE—See Audax Group, Limited Partnership; *U.S. Private*, pg. 387
NOTRE DAME FEDERAL CREDIT UNION; *U.S. Private*, pg. 2965
NOTRE DAME HEALTH CARE CENTER, INC.; *U.S. Private*, pg. 2965
NOTRE DAME INTERMEDICA PARTICIPACOES S.A.—See Hapvida Participacoes e Investimentos S.A.; *Int'l*, pg. 3269
NOTREFAMILLE.COM; *Int'l*, pg. 5449
NOTT COMPANY; *U.S. Private*, pg. 2965
NOTTINGHAM ADVISORS, INC.—See Community Bank System, Inc.; *U.S. Public*, pg. 550
NOTTINGHAM BUILDING SOCIETY; *Int'l*, pg. 5449
NOTTINGHAM COATED STONE—See CEMEX, S.A.B. de C.V.; *Int'l*, pg. 1399
NOTTINGHAM COMPANY INC.—See Performance Process, Inc.; *U.S. Private*, pg. 3149
NOTTINGHAM RECYCLING LIMITED—See Macfarlane Group PLC; *Int'l*, pg. 4622
NOTTINGHAM REHAB LIMITED—See H2 Equity Partners B.V.; *Int'l*, pg. 3199
THE NOTTINGHAM WOODTHORPE HOSPITAL—See Ramsay Health Care Limited; *Int'l*, pg. 6200
NOTUS AVIATION, INC.—See The ODP Corporation; *U.S. Public*, pg. 2117
NOTZ PLASTICS AG—See ThyssenKrupp AG; *Int'l*, pg. 7725
NOUL CO., LTD.; *Int'l*, pg. 5449
NOUMI LIMITED; *Int'l*, pg. 5449
NOUR COMMUNICATION COMPANY—See Arab Supply & Trading Co.; *Int'l*, pg. 532
NOURIA ENERGY CORP.; *U.S. Private*, pg. 2965

NOURI PETROCHEMICAL CO.—See Persian Gulf Petrochemical Industry Commercial Company; *Int'l*, pg. 5815
NOURISON RUG CORP.; *U.S. Private*, pg. 2965
NOURITRANS EXIM PRIVATE LIMITED; *Int'l*, pg. 5450
NOURYON CHEMICALS ARGENTINA SAU—See GIC Pte. Ltd.; *Int'l*, pg. 2968
NOURYON CHEMICALS ARGENTINA SAU—See GIC Pte. Ltd.; *Int'l*, pg. 2968
NOURYON CHEMICALS ARGENTINA SAU—See The Carlyle Group Inc.; *U.S. Public*, pg. 2051
NOURYON CHEMICALS ARGENTINA SAU—See The Carlyle Group Inc.; *U.S. Public*, pg. 2051
NOURYON CHEMICALS ARGENTINA SAU—See GIC Pte. Ltd.; *Int'l*, pg. 2968
NOURYON CHEMICALS ARGENTINA SAU—See The Carlyle Group Inc.; *U.S. Public*, pg. 2051
NOURYON CHEMICALS GMBH—See GIC Pte. Ltd.; *Int'l*, pg. 2968
NOURYON CHEMICALS GMBH—See GIC Pte. Ltd.; *Int'l*, pg. 2968
NOURYON CHEMICALS GMBH—See The Carlyle Group Inc.; *U.S. Public*, pg. 2051
NOURYON CHEMICALS GMBH—See The Carlyle Group Inc.; *U.S. Public*, pg. 2051
NOURYON CHEMICALS HOLDING B.V.—See GIC Pte. Ltd.; *Int'l*, pg. 2967
NOURYON CHEMICALS HOLDING B.V.—See The Carlyle Group Inc.; *U.S. Public*, pg. 2050
NOURYON CHEMICALS INTERNATIONAL B.V.—See GIC Pte. Ltd.; *Int'l*, pg. 2967
NOURYON CHEMICALS INTERNATIONAL B.V.—See The Carlyle Group Inc.; *U.S. Public*, pg. 2050
NOURYON CHEMICALS LIMITED—See GIC Pte. Ltd.; *Int'l*, pg. 2968
NOURYON CHEMICALS LIMITED—See The Carlyle Group Inc.; *U.S. Public*, pg. 2051
NOURYON CHEMICALS MCA (TAIXING) CO. LTD—See GIC Pte. Ltd.; *Int'l*, pg. 2968
NOURYON CHEMICALS MCA (TAIXING) CO. LTD—See The Carlyle Group Inc.; *U.S. Public*, pg. 2051
NOURYON FUNCTIONAL CHEMICALS AB—See GIC Pte. Ltd.; *Int'l*, pg. 2968
NOURYON FUNCTIONAL CHEMICALS AB—See The Carlyle Group Inc.; *U.S. Public*, pg. 2051
NOURYON FUNCTIONAL CHEMICALS B.V.—See GIC Pte. Ltd.; *Int'l*, pg. 2968
NOURYON FUNCTIONAL CHEMICALS B.V.—See The Carlyle Group Inc.; *U.S. Public*, pg. 2051
NOURYON FUNCTIONAL CHEMICALS GMBH—See GIC Pte. Ltd.; *Int'l*, pg. 2968
NOURYON FUNCTIONAL CHEMICALS GMBH—See The Carlyle Group Inc.; *U.S. Public*, pg. 2051
NOURYON PULP AND PAPER CHEMICALS B.V.—See GIC Pte. Ltd.; *Int'l*, pg. 2968
NOURYON PULP AND PAPER CHEMICALS B.V.—See The Carlyle Group Inc.; *U.S. Public*, pg. 2051
NOURYON PULP AND PERFORMANCE CHEMICALS (TAIWAN) CO. LTD—See GIC Pte. Ltd.; *Int'l*, pg. 2968
NOURYON PULP AND PERFORMANCE CHEMICALS (TAIWAN) CO. LTD—See The Carlyle Group Inc.; *U.S. Public*, pg. 2051
NOUSBO CO., LTD.; *Int'l*, pg. 5450
NOUSOUKEN CORPORATION; *Int'l*, pg. 5450
NOUVEAU EYEWEAR, INC.—See SunTx Capital Partners, L.P.; *U.S. Private*, pg. 3874
NOUVEAU GLOBAL VENTURES LIMITED; *Int'l*, pg. 5450
NOUVEAU LIFE PHARMACEUTICALS, INC.; *U.S. Public*, pg. 1543
NOUVEAU MONDE GRAPHITE INC.; *Int'l*, pg. 5450
NOUVEAU SOLUTIONS LIMITED—See VINCI S.A.; *Int'l*, pg. 8224
NOUVELLE AUDITION SAS—See Amplifon S.p.A.; *Int'l*, pg. 435
NOUVELLE EVENTS HOLDINGS PTE. LTD.—See Sakae Holdings Ltd.; *Int'l*, pg. 6486
NOUVELLES FRONTIERES DISTRIBUTION S.A.—See TUI AG; *Int'l*, pg. 7965
NOUVELLES FRONTIERES SENEGAL S.R.L.—See TUI AG; *Int'l*, pg. 7965
NOUVELLES FRONTIERES; *Int'l*, pg. 5450
NOUVELLE SOCIETE MAGIDEUTZ S.A.—See DEUTZ AG; *Int'l*, pg. 2086
NOUVELLES SOLUTIONS INFORMATIQUES-N.S.I.—See Cegeka Groep NV; *Int'l*, pg. 1391
NOUVELLE VAGUE—See Omnicom Group Inc.; *U.S. Public*, pg. 1596
NOVAAGRO GROUP; *Int'l*, pg. 5453
NOVAAGRO UKRAINE, LLC—See NOVAAGRO group; *Int'l*, pg. 5453
NOVA AIRLINES AB—See REWE-Zentral-Aktiengesellschaft; *Int'l*, pg. 6314
NOVA AMERICAN GROUP, INC.—See The Hanover Insurance Group, Inc.; *U.S. Public*, pg. 2087
NOVA ANALITICA LTDA.; *Int'l*, pg. 5450
NOVA ARGENT CANADA INC.; *Int'l*, pg. 5450
NOVA ARGENT CANADA INC.—See Nova Capital Management Limited; *Int'l*, pg. 5450
NOVA BANKA A.D.; *Int'l*, pg. 5450

COMPANY NAME INDEX

NOVABASE NEOTALENT ESPANA S.A.U.—See Novabase SGPS, SA; *Int'l*, pg. 5453
NOVABASE SGPS, SA; *Int'l*, pg. 5453
NOVABASE SOLUTIONS MIDDLE EAST FZ-LLC—See Novabase SGPS, SA; *Int'l*, pg. 5453
NOVABAY PHARMACEUTICALS, INC.; *U.S. Public*, pg. 1547
NOVABEV GROUP; *Int'l*, pg. 5453
NOVA BIOMEDICAL CANADA, LTD.—See Nova Biomedical Corporation; *U.S. Private*, pg. 2965
NOVA BIOMEDICAL CORPORATION; *U.S. Private*, pg. 2965
NOVA BIOMEDICAL GMBH—See Nova Biomedical Corporation; *U.S. Private*, pg. 2965
NOVA BIOMEDICAL K.K.—See Nova Biomedical Corporation; *U.S. Private*, pg. 2965
NOVA BIOMEDICAL U.K.—See Nova Biomedical Corporation; *U.S. Private*, pg. 2965
NOVA BOCANA BARCELONA, S.A.—See Grupo Villar Mir, S.A.U.; *Int'l*, pg. 3139
NOVABONE PRODUCTS - INTERNATIONAL—See Halma plc; *Int'l*, pg. 3232
NOVABONE PRODUCTS, LLC—See Halma plc; *Int'l*, pg. 3232
NOVA BUILDERS INC; *Int'l*, pg. 5450
NOVA BUS CORPORATION—See AB Volvo; *Int'l*, pg. 42
NOVA BUS INCORPORATED—See AB Volvo; *Int'l*, pg. 43
NOVA CAPITAL MANAGEMENT LIMITED; *Int'l*, pg. 5450
NOVACAP LLC—See Dover Corporation; *U.S. Public*, pg. 682
NOVACAP MANAGEMENT INC.; *Int'l*, pg. 5453
NOVACARE OCCUPATIONAL HEALTH SERVICES, INC.—See Select Medical Holdings Corporation; *U.S. Public*, pg. 1858
NOVACARE OUTPATIENT REHABILITATION, INC.—See Select Medical Holdings Corporation; *U.S. Public*, pg. 1858
NOVACARE REHABILITATION OF OHIO, INC.—See Select Medical Holdings Corporation; *U.S. Public*, pg. 1858
NOVACARE REHABILITATION SERVICES, INC.—See Select Medical Holdings Corporation; *U.S. Public*, pg. 1858
NOVACARE REHABILITATION—See Select Medical Holdings Corporation; *U.S. Public*, pg. 1858
NOVACARE REHABILITATION—See Select Medical Holdings Corporation; *U.S. Public*, pg. 1859
NOVACCESS GLOBAL INC.; *U.S. Public*, pg. 1547
NOVACCESS GMBH—See Chargeurs SA; *Int'l*, pg. 1449
NOVACEL IBERICA S.P.A.—See Chargeurs SA; *Int'l*, pg. 1449
NOVACEL, INC.—See Chargeurs SA; *Int'l*, pg. 1449
NOVACEL ITALIA S.R.L—See Chargeurs SA; *Int'l*, pg. 1449
NOVACEL KOREA LTD.—See Chargeurs SA; *Int'l*, pg. 1450
NOVACEL SHANGHAI—See Chargeurs SA; *Int'l*, pg. 1449
NOVACEL—See Chargeurs SA; *Int'l*, pg. 1449
NOVACEL UK LTD—See Chargeurs SA; *Int'l*, pg. 1449
NOVA CENTURY SCIENTIFIC, INC.—See Trinity Biotech Plc; *Int'l*, pg. 7924
NOVACERO S.A.—See CAP S.A.; *Int'l*, pg. 1301
NOVACES, LLC; *U.S. Private*, pg. 2966
NOVA CHEMICALS CORPORATION - MOORE PLANT—See Mubadala Investment Company PJSC; *Int'l*, pg. 5075
NOVA CHEMICALS CORPORATION - SARNIA PLANT—See Mubadala Investment Company PJSC; *Int'l*, pg. 5075
NOVA CHEMICALS CORPORATION—See Mubadala Investment Company PJSC; *Int'l*, pg. 5074
NOVA CHEMICALS CORPORATION - ST. CLAIR RIVER PLANT—See Mubadala Investment Company PJSC; *Int'l*, pg. 5075
NOVA CHEMICALS, INC. - PERFORMANCE STYRENICS—See Mubadala Investment Company PJSC; *Int'l*, pg. 5075
NOVA CHEMICALS, INC.—See Mubadala Investment Company PJSC; *Int'l*, pg. 5075
NOVA CHEMICALS OLEFINS LLC—See Mubadala Investment Company PJSC; *Int'l*, pg. 5075
NOVA CHIMICA, S.R.L.—See Illinois Tool Works Inc.; *U.S. Public*, pg. 1109
NOVA CIMANGOLA S.A.R.L.—See Heidelberg Materials AG; *Int'l*, pg. 3315
NOVA CINEMAZ PRIVATE LIMITED—See UFO Moviez India Ltd; *Int'l*, pg. 8015
NOVACK AND MACEY LLP—See Armstrong Teasdale LLP; *U.S. Private*, pg. 332
NOVACOAST, INC.; *U.S. Private*, pg. 2966
NOVA COMET S.R.L.—See Aalberts N.V.; *Int'l*, pg. 35
NOVACOM SERVICES SA—See Collecte Localisation Satellites; *Int'l*, pg. 1699
NOVA CONSTRUCTORS LLC—See Quanta Services, Inc.; *U.S. Public*, pg. 1752
NOVA CONSTRUCTORS LTD—See Quanta Services, Inc.; *U.S. Public*, pg. 1752
NOVACON TECHNOLOGY GROUP LIMITED; *Int'l*, pg. 5454

NOVACYT SA; *Int'l*, pg. 5454
NOVADAL PRIVAT SAS—See Chequers SA; *Int'l*, pg. 1471
NOVADAN APS—See Illinois Tool Works Inc.; *U.S. Public*, pg. 1109
NOVA DARSENA ESPORTIVA DE BARA, S.A.—See Industry Super Holdings Pty. Ltd.; *Int'l*, pg. 3676
NOVA DEVELOPMENT CORP.—See Claranova SA; *Int'l*, pg. 1642
NOVA DS SMITH EMBALAGEM, S.A.—See DS Smith Plc; *Int'l*, pg. 2209
NOVAE AEROSPACE SERVICES SA; *Int'l*, pg. 5454
NOVAE CORPORATION—See Brightstar Capital Partners, L.P.; *U.S. Private*, pg. 653
NOVA ELECTRIC—See Technology Dynamics, Inc.; *U.S. Private*, pg. 3955
NOVA ENTERTAINMENT PTY. LTD.; *Int'l*, pg. 5450
NOVAETUS INC.—See SurveyVitals, Inc.; *U.S. Private*, pg. 3885
NOVA FINANCIAL HOLDINGS, INC.; *U.S. Private*, pg. 2965
NOVAFLEX SAS—See Bobst Group S.A.; *Int'l*, pg. 1096
NOVA FORGE CORP.—See Reserve Group Management Company; *U.S. Private*, pg. 3404
NOVA FURNITURE (DONGGUAN) CO., LTD.; *Int'l*, pg. 5450
NOVAGANT CORP.; *Int'l*, pg. 5454
NOVAGOLD PETRO-RESOURCES LIMITED; *Int'l*, pg. 5454
NOVAGOLD RESOURCES INC.; *U.S. Public*, pg. 1547
NOVAGOLD RESOURCES USA—See Novagold Resources Inc.; *U.S. Public*, pg. 1547
NOVAGOLD USA, INC.—See Novagold Resources Inc.; *U.S. Public*, pg. 1547
NOVAGO SP. Z O.O. - KOSINY PLANT—See China Everbright Group Limited; *Int'l*, pg. 1501
NOVAGO SP. Z O.O. - ROZANKI PLANT—See China Everbright Group Limited; *Int'l*, pg. 1501
NOVAGO SP. Z O.O.—See China Everbright Group Limited; *Int'l*, pg. 1501
NOVAGO SP. Z O.O. - ZLOTOW PLANT—See China Everbright Group Limited; *Int'l*, pg. 1501
NOVAGO SP. Z O.O. - ZNIN PLANT—See China Everbright Group Limited; *Int'l*, pg. 1501
NOVACNEE S.A. See Panariagroup Industrie Ceramiche S.p.A.; *Int'l*, pg. 5717
NOVA GROUP HOLDINGS LIMITED; *Int'l*, pg. 5450
NOVA GROUP, INC.—See Quanta Services, Inc.; *U.S. Public*, pg. 1752
THE NOVA GROUP; *U.S. Private*, pg. 4085
NOVAHEALTH PTE. LTD.—See Nova MSC Berhad; *Int'l*, pg. 5452
NOVA HOLDINGS CO., LTD.; *Int'l*, pg. 5450
NOVA HOME HEALTH CARE INC.—See Searchlight Capital Partners, L.P.; *U.S. Private*, pg. 3586
NOVA HOTEL RENOVATION & CONSTRUCTION LLC; *U.S. Private*, pg. 2965
NOVA HYDRAULICS INC.—See Frontenac Company LLC; *U.S. Private*, pg. 1614
NOVA IMMO SAS—See Groupe BPCE; *Int'l*, pg. 3099
NOVA INFRASTRUCTURE MANAGEMENT, LLC; *U.S. Private*, pg. 2965
NOVA INSURANCE CONSULTANTS LIMITED—See FSE Services Group Limited; *Int'l*, pg. 2798
NOVA INTEGRATED SYSTEMS LIMITED—See Tata Sons Limited; *Int'l*, pg. 7468
NOVA INTEGRATION SOLUTIONS, INC.—See Technology Dynamics, Inc.; *U.S. Private*, pg. 3955
NOVA IRON & STEEL LTD.; *Int'l*, pg. 5450
NOVAK BIDDLE VENTURE PARTNERS, LP; *U.S. Private*, pg. 2966
NOVAK FORNEY & ASSOCIATES, LLC; *U.S. Private*, pg. 2966
NOVAK GROUP LLC; *U.S. Private*, pg. 2966
NOVA KREDITNA BANKA MARIBOR, D.D.—See OTP Bank Plc; *Int'l*, pg. 5657
NOVA LABORATORIES SDN. BHD.—See Nova Wellness Group Bhd; *Int'l*, pg. 5453
NOVA LEAP HEALTH CORP.; *Int'l*, pg. 5450
NOVA LEATHERS (PVT.) LTD.—See Quetta Group of Companies LLC; *Int'l*, pg. 6161
NOVALED AG—See Samsung Group; *Int'l*, pg. 6511
NOVALIA S.A.S.—See Durr AG; *Int'l*, pg. 2233
NOVA LIBRA, INC.—See GrubMarket, Inc.; *U.S. Private*, pg. 1797
NOVA LIFESTYLE, INC.; *U.S. Public*, pg. 1547
NOVA LIGHTING LTD—See Hadco Limited; *Int'l*, pg. 3205
NOVA LJUBLJANSKA BANKA D.D.; *Int'l*, pg. 5451
NOVALPINA CAPITAL LLP; *Int'l*, pg. 5454
NOVAL S.A.—See Viohalco SA/NV; *Int'l*, pg. 8243
NOVA LTD.; *Int'l*, pg. 5451
NOVALUX AMERICA INC.—See Shinko Shoji Co., Ltd.; *Int'l*, pg. 6846
NOVALUX HONG KONG ELECTRONICS LIMITED—See Shinko Shoji Co., Ltd.; *Int'l*, pg. 6846
NOVALUX JAPAN CO., LTD.—See Shinko Shoji Co., Ltd.; *Int'l*, pg. 6846
NOVALUX MALAYSIA SDN. BHD.—See Shinko Shoji Co., Ltd.; *Int'l*, pg. 6846

NOVANT HEALTH, INC.

NOVALUX SHANGHAI ELECTRONICS LIMITED—See Shinko Shoji Co., Ltd.; *Int'l*, pg. 6846
NOVALUX TAIWAN ELECTRONICS LTD.—See Shinko Shoji Co., Ltd.; *Int'l*, pg. 6846
NOVALUX THAILAND CO., LTD.—See Shinko Shoji Co., Ltd.; *Int'l*, pg. 6846
NOVA MARKETING SERVICES LLC; *U.S. Private*, pg. 2966
NOVA MEASURING INSTRUMENTS B.V.—See Nova Ltd.; *Int'l*, pg. 5451
NOVA MEASURING INSTRUMENTS INC.—See Nova Ltd.; *Int'l*, pg. 5451
NOVA MEASURING INSTRUMENTS K.K.—See Nova Ltd.; *Int'l*, pg. 5451
NOVA MEASURING INSTRUMENTS TAIWAN—See Nova Ltd.; *Int'l*, pg. 5451
NOVAMED EYE SURGERY CENTER OF MARYVILLE, LLC—See Bain Capital, LP; *U.S. Private*, pg. 445
NOVAMED EYE SURGERY CENTER OF NEW ALBANY, L.L.C.—See Bain Capital, LP; *U.S. Private*, pg. 445
NOVAMED EYE SURGERY CENTER OF NORTH COUNTY, LLC—See Bain Capital, LP; *U.S. Private*, pg. 445
NOVAMED EYE SURGERY CENTER OF OVERLAND PARK, LLC—See Bain Capital, LP; *U.S. Private*, pg. 445
NOVAMEDIA GROUP; *Int'l*, pg. 5455
NOVAMEDI S.A.—See Abbott Laboratories; *U.S. Public*, pg. 20
NOVAMED, LLC—See Bain Capital, LP; *U.S. Private*, pg. 446
NOVAMED MANAGEMENT SERVICES, LLC—See Bain Capital, LP; *U.S. Private*, pg. 445
NOVAMED SURGERY CENTER OF BATON ROUGE, LLC—See Bain Capital, LP; *U.S. Private*, pg. 445
NOVAMED SURGERY CENTER OF CHATTANOOGA, LLC—See Bain Capital, LP; *U.S. Private*, pg. 446
NOVAMED SURGERY CENTER OF CHICAGO-NORTHSHORE, LLC—See Bain Capital, LP; *U.S. Private*, pg. 446
NOVAMED SURGERY CENTER OF CLEVELAND, LLC—See Bain Capital, LP; *U.S. Private*, pg. 446
NOVAMED SURGERY CENTER OF COLORADO SPRINGS, LLC—See Bain Capital, LP; *U.S. Private*, pg. 446
NOVAMED SURGERY CENTER OF DENVER, LLC—See Bain Capital, LP; *U.S. Private*, pg. 446
NOVAMED SURGERY CENTER OF JONESBORO, LLC—See Bain Capital, LP; *U.S. Private*, pg. 446
NOVAMED SURGERY CENTER OF MADISON, LIMITED PARTNERSHIP—See Bain Capital, LP; *U.S. Private*, pg. 446
NOVAMED SURGERY CENTER OF NASHUA, LLC—See Bain Capital, LP; *U.S. Private*, pg. 446
NOVAMED SURGERY CENTER OF OAK LAWN, LLC—See Bain Capital, LP; *U.S. Private*, pg. 446
NOVAMED SURGERY CENTER OF ORLANDO, LLC—See Bain Capital, LP; *U.S. Private*, pg. 446
NOVAMED SURGERY CENTER OF RIVER FOREST, LLC—See Bain Capital, LP; *U.S. Private*, pg. 446
NOVAMED SURGERY CENTER OF SAN ANTONIO, L.P.—See Bain Capital, LP; *U.S. Private*, pg. 446
NOVAMED SURGERY CENTER OF SANDUSKY, LLC—See Bain Capital, LP; *U.S. Private*, pg. 446
NOVAMED SURGERY CENTER OF ST. PETERS, LLC—See Bain Capital, LP; *U.S. Private*, pg. 446
NOVAMED SURGERY CENTER OF TYLER, L.P.—See Bain Capital, LP; *U.S. Private*, pg. 446
NOVAMED SURGERY CENTER OF WARRENSBURG, LLC—See Bain Capital, LP; *U.S. Private*, pg. 446
NOVAMED SURGERY CENTER OF WHITTIER, LLC—See Bain Capital, LP; *U.S. Private*, pg. 446
NOVA MENTIS BIOTECH CORP.—See Nova Mentis Life Science Corp.; *Int'l*, pg. 5451
NOVA MENTIS LIFE SCIENCE CORP.; *Int'l*, pg. 5451
NOVAMEX ENERGY, INC.; *U.S. Private*, pg. 2966
NOVAMEX, INC.; *U.S. Private*, pg. 2966
NOVAMEX SA; *Int'l*, pg. 5455
NOVA MICROWAVE, INC.—See Electro Technik Industries; *U.S. Private*, pg. 1354
NOVAMIND INC.; *Int'l*, pg. 5455
NOVA MINERALS LIMITED; *Int'l*, pg. 5451
NOVA MOSILANA A.S—See Marzotto S.p.A.; *Int'l*, pg. 4718
NOVA MSC BERHAD; *Int'l*, pg. 5452
NOVA NET LEASE REIT; *Int'l*, pg. 5452
NOVAN, INC.; *U.S. Public*, pg. 1547
NOVANTA EUROPE GMBH—See Novanta Inc.; *U.S. Public*, pg. 1548
NOVANTA HOLDINGS BV—See Novanta Inc.; *U.S. Public*, pg. 1548
NOVANTA INC.; *U.S. Public*, pg. 1547
NOVANTA ITALY SRL—See Novanta Inc.; *U.S. Public*, pg. 1548
NOVANTA JAPAN CORPORATION—See Novanta Inc.; *U.S. Public*, pg. 1548
NOVANTAS, INC.—See Informa plc; *Int'l*, pg. 3693
NOVANT HEALTH, INC.; *U.S. Private*, pg. 2966

1957

NOVANT HEALTH, INC.

NOVANT HEALTH REHABILITATION HOSPITAL OF WINSTON-SALEM, LLC—See Encompass Health Corporation; *U.S. Public*, pg. 758
NOVAOL AUSTRIA G.M.B.H.—See Bunge Limited; *U.S. Public*, pg. 412
NOVA PACIFIC METALS CORP.; *Int'l*, pg. 5452
NOVA PESCARA A.D.; *Int'l*, pg. 5452
NOVA PHARMACEUTICALS AUSTRALASIA PTY LTD—See Marksans Pharma Ltd; *Int'l*, pg. 4697
NOVA PRESSROOM PRODUCTS, LLC; *U.S. Private*, pg. 2966
NOVAPRO—See Cross Country Healthcare, Inc.; *U.S. Public*, pg. 595
NOVAQUEST CAPITAL MANAGEMENT, LLC; *U.S. Private*, pg. 2967
NOVA RADINOST A.D.; *Int'l*, pg. 5452
NOVAR CONTROLS CORPORATION—See Honeywell International Inc.; *U.S. Public*, pg. 1051
NOVA RECYD, S.A.U.—See Cie Automotive S.A.; *Int'l*, pg. 1605
NOVAR ED & S LIMITED—See Honeywell International Inc.; *U.S. Public*, pg. 1051
NOVARE NATIONAL SETTLEMENT SERVICE, LLC—See Starwood Property Trust, Inc.; *U.S. Public*, pg. 1940
NOVARESE INC.—See Polaris Capital Group Co., Ltd.; *Int'l*, pg. 5907
NOVARESE KOREA INC.—See Polaris Capital Group Co., Ltd.; *Int'l*, pg. 5907
NOVARES GROUP SA—See Equistone Partners Europe Limited; *Int'l*, pg. 2486
NOVA RE SIIQ S.P.A.—See Sorgente Group S.p.A.; *Int'l*, pg. 7112
NOVA RESOURCES B.V.; *Int'l*, pg. 5452
NOVARES US LLC - FELTON—See Equistone Partners Europe Limited; *Int'l*, pg. 2487
NOVARES US LLC—See Equistone Partners Europe Limited; *Int'l*, pg. 2487
NOVAREX CO., LTD.; *Int'l*, pg. 5455
NOVAR GMBH—See Honeywell International Inc.; *U.S. Public*, pg. 1051
NOVARIA HOLDINGS LLC—See KKR & Co. Inc.; *U.S. Public*, pg. 1262
NOVARISE RENEWABLE RESOURCES INTERNATIONAL LTD; *Int'l*, pg. 5455
NOVA ROYALTY CORP.—See Metalla Royalty & Streaming Ltd.; *Int'l*, pg. 4847
NOVARTIS AG; *Int'l*, pg. 5455
NOVARTIS ARGENTINA S.A.—See Novartis AG; *Int'l*, pg. 5457
NOVARTIS ASIA PACIFIC PHARMACEUTICALS PTE LTD.—See Novartis AG; *Int'l*, pg. 5457
NOVARTIS AUSTRALIA PTY LTD.—See Novartis AG; *Int'l*, pg. 5457
NOVARTIS AUSTRIA GMBH—See Novartis AG; *Int'l*, pg. 5457
NOVARTIS BALTICS SIA—See Novartis AG; *Int'l*, pg. 5457
NOVARTIS (BANGLADESH) LTD.—See Novartis AG; *Int'l*, pg. 5457
NOVARTIS BIOCIENCIAS S.A.—See Novartis AG; *Int'l*, pg. 5457
NOVARTIS BIOSCIENCES PERU S.A.—See Novartis AG; *Int'l*, pg. 5457
NOVARTIS CAPITAL CORPORATION—See Novartis AG; *Int'l*, pg. 5458
NOVARTIS CHILE S.A.—See Novartis AG; *Int'l*, pg. 5457
NOVARTIS CONSUMER HEALTH AUSTRALASIA PTY LTD.—See Novartis AG; *Int'l*, pg. 5457
NOVARTIS CONSUMER HEALTH GMBH—See Novartis AG; *Int'l*, pg. 5457
NOVARTIS CONSUMER HEALTH, INC.—See Novartis AG; *Int'l*, pg. 5458
NOVARTIS CONSUMER HEALTH, INC.—See Novartis AG; *Int'l*, pg. 5458
NOVARTIS CONSUMER HEALTH LLC—See Novartis AG; *Int'l*, pg. 5457
NOVARTIS CONSUMER HEALTH NEDERLAND B.V.—See Novartis AG; *Int'l*, pg. 5457
NOVARTIS CONSUMER HEALTH S.A.—See Novartis AG; *Int'l*, pg. 5457
NOVARTIS CONSUMER HEALTH, S.A.—See Novartis AG; *Int'l*, pg. 5458
NOVARTIS CONSUMER HEALTH SCHWEIZ AG—See Novartis AG; *Int'l*, pg. 5458
NOVARTIS CONSUMER HEALTH UK LIMITED—See Novartis AG; *Int'l*, pg. 5458
NOVARTIS CORPORATION (MALAYSIA) SDN. BHD.—See Novartis AG; *Int'l*, pg. 5458
NOVARTIS CORPORATION—See Novartis AG; *Int'l*, pg. 5458
NOVARTIS DE COLOMBIA S.A.—See Novartis AG; *Int'l*, pg. 5460
NOVARTIS DEUTSCHLAND GMBH—See Novartis AG; *Int'l*, pg. 5458
NOVARTIS ECUADOR S.A.—See Novartis AG; *Int'l*, pg. 5458
NOVARTIS FARMACEUTICA, S.A. (AC)—See Novartis AG; *Int'l*, pg. 5459
NOVARTIS FARMACEUTICA, S.A. DE C.V.—See Novartis AG; *Int'l*, pg. 5459

NOVARTIS FARMACEUTICA, S.A.—See Novartis AG; *Int'l*, pg. 5459
NOVARTIS FARMA - PRODUTOS FARMACEUTICOS S.A.—See Novartis AG; *Int'l*, pg. 5459
NOVARTIS FARMA SA—See Novartis AG; *Int'l*, pg. 5459
NOVARTIS FARMA S.P.A.—See Novartis AG; *Int'l*, pg. 5459
NOVARTIS FINANCE CORPORATION—See Novartis AG; *Int'l*, pg. 5458
NOVARTIS FINANCE S.A.—See Novartis AG; *Int'l*, pg. 5458
NOVARTIS FINLAND OY—See Novartis AG; *Int'l*, pg. 5458
NOVARTIS GENE THERAPIES, INC.—See Novartis AG; *Int'l*, pg. 5458
NOVARTIS GRIMSBY LTD.—See Novartis AG; *Int'l*, pg. 5460
NOVARTIS GROUPE FRANCE S.A.—See Novartis AG; *Int'l*, pg. 5458
NOVARTIS HEALTHCARE A/S—See Novartis AG; *Int'l*, pg. 5458
NOVARTIS HEALTHCARE PRIVATE LIMITED—See Novartis AG; *Int'l*, pg. 5458
NOVARTIS (HELLAS) S.A.C.I.—See Novartis AG; *Int'l*, pg. 5457
NOVARTIS HOLDING AG—See Novartis AG; *Int'l*, pg. 5458
NOVARTIS HOLDING JAPAN K.K.—See Novartis AG; *Int'l*, pg. 5458
NOVARTIS HORSHAM RESEARCH CENTRE—See Novartis AG; *Int'l*, pg. 5460
NOVARTIS HUNGARY HEALTHCARE LIMITED LIABILITY COMPANY—See Novartis AG; *Int'l*, pg. 5458
NOVARTIS INDIA LIMITED—See Novartis AG; *Int'l*, pg. 5458
NOVARTIS INSTITUTE FOR FUNCTIONAL GENOMICS, INC.—See Novartis AG; *Int'l*, pg. 5458
NOVARTIS INSTITUTES FOR BIOMEDICAL RESEARCH, INC.—See Novartis AG; *Int'l*, pg. 5458
NOVARTIS INSTITUTES FOR BIOMEDICAL RESEARCH, INC.—See Novartis AG; *Int'l*, pg. 5458
NOVARTIS INTERNATIONAL AG—See Novartis AG; *Int'l*, pg. 5458
NOVARTIS INTERNATIONAL PHARMACEUTICAL LTD.—See Novartis AG; *Int'l*, pg. 5459
NOVARTIS INVESTMENTS S.A.R.L.—See Novartis AG; *Int'l*, pg. 5459
NOVARTIS IRELAND LIMITED—See Novartis AG; *Int'l*, pg. 5459
NOVARTIS ISRAEL LTD.—See Novartis AG; *Int'l*, pg. 5459
NOVARTIS KOREA LTD.—See Novartis AG; *Int'l*, pg. 5459
NOVARTIS MIDDLE EAST FZE—See Novartis AG; *Int'l*, pg. 5459
NOVARTIS NETHERLANDS B.V.—See Novartis AG; *Int'l*, pg. 5459
NOVARTIS NEVA LLC—See Novartis AG; *Int'l*, pg. 5459
NOVARTIS NEW ZEALAND LTD.—See Novartis AG; *Int'l*, pg. 5459
NOVARTIS NORGE AS—See Novartis AG; *Int'l*, pg. 5459
NOVARTIS NUTRITION GMBH—See Nestle S.A.; *Int'l*, pg. 5211
NOVARTIS OPHTHALMICS AG—See Novartis AG; *Int'l*, pg. 5459
NOVARTIS PHARMA AG—See Novartis AG; *Int'l*, pg. 5459
NOVARTIS PHARMA B.V.—See Novartis AG; *Int'l*, pg. 5459
NOVARTIS PHARMACEUTICALS AUSTRALIA PTY LTD.—See Novartis AG; *Int'l*, pg. 5459
NOVARTIS PHARMACEUTICALS CANADA INC.—See Novartis AG; *Int'l*, pg. 5459
NOVARTIS PHARMACEUTICALS CORPORATION—See Novartis AG; *Int'l*, pg. 5458
NOVARTIS PHARMACEUTICALS CORP.—See Novartis AG; *Int'l*, pg. 5458
NOVARTIS PHARMACEUTICALS CORP.—See Novartis AG; *Int'l*, pg. 5458
NOVARTIS PHARMACEUTICALS (HK) LIMITED—See Novartis AG; *Int'l*, pg. 5459
NOVARTIS PHARMACEUTICALS—See Novartis AG; *Int'l*, pg. 5458
NOVARTIS PHARMACEUTICALS UK LIMITED—See Novartis AG; *Int'l*, pg. 5459
NOVARTIS PHARMA GMBH—See Novartis AG; *Int'l*, pg. 5459
NOVARTIS PHARMA GMBH—See Novartis AG; *Int'l*, pg. 5459
NOVARTIS PHARMA K.K.—See Novartis AG; *Int'l*, pg. 5459
NOVARTIS PHARMA LLC—See Novartis AG; *Int'l*, pg. 5459
NOVARTIS PHARMA (LOGISTICS), INC.—See Novartis AG; *Int'l*, pg. 5459
NOVARTIS PHARMA MAROC SA—See Novartis AG; *Int'l*, pg. 5459
NOVARTIS PHARMA N.V.—See Novartis AG; *Int'l*, pg. 5460
NOVARTIS PHARMA (PAKISTAN) LIMITED—See Novartis AG; *Int'l*, pg. 5459
NOVARTIS PHARMA PRODUKTIONS GMBH—See Novartis AG; *Int'l*, pg. 5459

CORPORATE AFFILIATIONS

NOVARTIS PHARMA S.A.S.—See Novartis AG; *Int'l*, pg. 5459
NOVARTIS PHARMA SCHWEIZ AG—See Novartis AG; *Int'l*, pg. 5459
NOVARTIS PHARMA SCHWEIZERHALLE AG—See Novartis AG; *Int'l*, pg. 5459
NOVARTIS PHARMA SERVICES AG—See Novartis AG; *Int'l*, pg. 5459
NOVARTIS PHARMA SERVICES ROMANIA S.R.L.—See Novartis AG; *Int'l*, pg. 5460
NOVARTIS PHARMA STEIN AG—See Novartis AG; *Int'l*, pg. 5459
NOVARTIS POLAND SP. Z O.O.—See Novartis AG; *Int'l*, pg. 5460
NOVARTIS PORTUGAL SGPS LDA—See Novartis AG; *Int'l*, pg. 5460
NOVARTIS RESEARCH FOUNDATION—See Novartis AG; *Int'l*, pg. 5460
NOVARTIS RINGASKIDDY LIMITED—See GHO Capital Partners LLP; *Int'l*, pg. 2959
NOVARTIS SAGLIK, GIDA VE TARIM URUNLERI SANAYI VE TICARET A.S.—See Novartis AG; *Int'l*, pg. 5460
NOVARTIS SANTE FAMILIALE S.A.S.—See Novartis AG; *Int'l*, pg. 5458
NOVARTIS SAUDI LTD.—See Novartis AG; *Int'l*, pg. 5460
NOVARTIS SECURITIES INVESTMENT LTD.—See Novartis AG; *Int'l*, pg. 5460
NOVARTIS SERVICES, INC.—See Novartis AG; *Int'l*, pg. 5460
NOVARTIS SINGAPORE PHARMACEUTICAL MANUFACTURING PTE. LTD.—See Novartis AG; *Int'l*, pg. 5460
NOVARTIS (SINGAPORE) PTE LTD.—See Novartis AG; *Int'l*, pg. 5457
NOVARTIS SLOVAKIA S.R.O.—See Novartis AG; *Int'l*, pg. 5460
NOVARTIS SOUTH AFRICA (PTY) LTD.—See Novartis AG; *Int'l*, pg. 5460
NOVARTIS S.R.O.—See Novartis AG; *Int'l*, pg. 5460
NOVARTIS SVERIGE AB—See Novartis AG; *Int'l*, pg. 5460
NOVARTIS SVERIGE PARTICIPATIONS AB—See Novartis AG; *Int'l*, pg. 5460
NOVARTIS (TAIWAN) CO., LTD.—See Novartis AG; *Int'l*, pg. 5457
NOVARTIS (THAILAND) LTD.—See Novartis AG; *Int'l*, pg. 5457
NOVARTIS TIERGESUNDHEIT GMBH—See Novartis AG; *Int'l*, pg. 5460
NOVARTIS UK LIMITED—See Novartis AG; *Int'l*, pg. 5460
NOVARTIS URUGUAY S.A.—See Novartis AG; *Int'l*, pg. 5460
NOVARTIS VACCINES AND DIAGNOSTICS, S.L.—See Novartis AG; *Int'l*, pg. 5458
NOVARTIS VACCINES & DIAGNOSTICS GMBH—See Novartis AG; *Int'l*, pg. 5458
NOVARTIS VACCINES & DIAGNOSTICS, INC.—See Novartis AG; *Int'l*, pg. 5458
NOVARTIS VACCINES & DIAGNOSTICS LIMITED—See Novartis AG; *Int'l*, pg. 5458
NOVARTIS VACCINES & DIAGNOSTICS S.A.S.—See Novartis AG; *Int'l*, pg. 5458
NOVARTIS VACCINES & DIAGNOSTICS S.R.L.—See Novartis AG; *Int'l*, pg. 5458
NOVART OY—See Nobia AB; *Int'l*, pg. 5395
NOVASAID AB—See Karolinska Development AB; *Int'l*, pg. 4084
NOVA SALON SYSTEMS; *U.S. Private*, pg. 2966
NOVASALUD S.A.—See Abbott Laboratories; *U.S. Public*, pg. 20
NOVA SAVINGS BANK—See NOVA Financial Holdings, Inc.; *U.S. Private*, pg. 2965
NOVA SCOTIA POWER INC.—See Emera, Inc.; *Int'l*, pg. 2377
NOVASEIS SP. Z O.O.—See San Leon Energy plc; *Int'l*, pg. 6521
NOVASENTIS, INC.—See General Motors Company; *U.S. Public*, pg. 926
NOV ASEP ELMAR (MIDDLE EAST) LIMITED—See NOV, Inc.; *U.S. Public*, pg. 1545
NOVA SIROVINA A.D.; *Int'l*, pg. 5452
NOVA SMART SOLUTIONS, INC.; *U.S. Private*, pg. 2966
NOVA SOLUTIONS INC.; *U.S. Private*, pg. 2966
NOVASOLUTIONS (PHILIPPINES), INC.—See Nova MSC Berhad; *Int'l*, pg. 5452
NOVASPECT INC.; *U.S. Private*, pg. 2967
NOVA SRBIJA A.D.; *Int'l*, pg. 5452
NOVASTAR DEVELOPMENT INC.; *U.S. Private*, pg. 2967
NOVA STAR INNOVATIONS, INC.; *U.S. Private*, pg. 2966
NOVA STEEL - BAIE D'URFE—See Nova Steel, Inc.; *Int'l*, pg. 5452
NOVA STEEL INC.; *Int'l*, pg. 5452
NOVA STEEL INC.—See Nova Steel Inc.; *Int'l*, pg. 5452
NOVASTEP INC.—See PAI Partners S.A.S.; *Int'l*, pg. 5699
NOVASTEP SAS—See Enovis Corporation; *U.S. Public*, pg. 773
NOVA STOKOVNA KUKA AD; *Int'l*, pg. 5452
NOVASYS HEALTH, INC.—See Centene Corporation; *U.S. Public*, pg. 470
NOVA SYSTEM CO., LTD.; *Int'l*, pg. 5452

COMPANY NAME INDEX

NOVASYTE, LLC—See IQVIA Holdings Inc.; *U.S. Public*, pg. 1170
NOVATAE RISK GROUP, LLC; *U.S. Private*, pg. 2967
NOVA TAIPA - URBANIZACOES, LIMITADA—See Shun Tak Holdings Limited; *Int'l*, pg. 6870
NOVATECH APS; *Int'l*, pg. 5461
NOVATECH ENGINEERING & CONSTRUCTION PTE., LTD.—See Acter Co., Ltd.; *Int'l*, pg. 117
NOVA-TECH ENGINEERING, LP—See Advanced Integration Technology, LP; *U.S. Private*, pg. 90
NOVA TECH ENTERPRISES, INC.; *U.S. Public*, pg. 1547
NOVATECH GROUP, INC—See Garaga Inc.; *Int'l*, pg. 2883
NOVATECH INC. - HATTIESBURG—See Perpetual Capital, LLC; *U.S. Private*, pg. 3153
NOVATECH, INC.—See Perpetual Capital, LLC; *U.S. Private*, pg. 3153
NOVATECH INDUSTRIES SA; *Int'l*, pg. 5461
NOVA-TECH INTERNATIONAL, INC.; *U.S. Private*, pg. 2966
NOVATECH, LLC - ORION UTILITY AUTOMATION DIVISION—See NovaTech, LLC; *U.S. Private*, pg. 2967
NOVATECH, LLC—See The Weir Group PLC; *Int'l*, pg. 7700
NOVATECH, LLC; *U.S. Private*, pg. 2967
NOVA TECHNOLOGY CORPORATION LIMITED; *Int'l*, pg. 5452
NOVA TECHNOLOGY CORP.—See Acter Co., Ltd.; *Int'l*, pg. 117
NOVATECH PATIO DOORS ONTARIO INC.—See Garaga Inc.; *Int'l*, pg. 2883
NOVATECH TECHNOLOGIES SA—See Novatech Industries SA; *Int'l*, pg. 5461
NOVATEC IMMUNDIAGNOSTICA GMBH—See Eurofins Scientific S.E.; *Int'l*, pg. 2551
NOVATEC INC.; *U.S. Private*, pg. 2967
NOVATEK JAPAN KABUSHIKI-KAISHA—See Novatek Microelectronics Corporation; *Int'l*, pg. 5461
NOVATEK MICROELECTRONICS CORPORATION; *Int'l*, pg. 5461
NOVATEK POLSKA SP. Z O.O.—See PAO Novatek; *Int'l*, pg. 5731
NOVATEK (SHANGHAI) CO., LTD.—See Novatek Microelectronics Corporation; *Int'l*, pg. 5461
NOVATEK (SHENZHEN) CO., LTD.—See Novatek Microelectronics Corporation; *Int'l*, pg. 5461
NOVATEK (SUZHOU) CO., LTD.—See Novatek Microelectronics Corporation; *Int'l*, pg. 5461
NOVA TELEVIZIA FIRST PRIVATE CHANNEL EAD—See Modern Times Group MTG AB; *Int'l*, pg. 5015
NOVATEL INC.—See Hexagon AB; *Int'l*, pg. 3368
NOVATEL WIRELESS SOLUTIONS, INC.—See Inseego Corp.; *U.S. Public*, pg. 1129
NOVATEL WIRELESS TECHNOLOGIES, LTD.—See Inseego Corp.; *U.S. Public*, pg. 1129
NOVATEOR RESEARCH LABORATORIES LTD.; *Int'l*, pg. 5461
NOVATEX GMBH; *Int'l*, pg. 5461
NOVATEX NORTH AMERICA INC.—See NOVATEX GmbH; *Int'l*, pg. 5461
NOVATIME TECHNOLOGY, INC.—See Hellman & Friedman LLC; *U.S. Private*, pg. 1910
NOVATION COMPANIES, INC.; *U.S. Public*, pg. 1548
NOVATION HOLDINGS, INC.; *U.S. Private*, pg. 2967
NOVATION INDUSTRIES; *U.S. Private*, pg. 2967
NOVATION SOLUTIONS LIMITED—See Jing King Tech Holdings Pte Ltd.; *Int'l*, pg. 3967
NOVATOR EHF—See Novator Partners LLP; *Int'l*, pg. 5461
NOVATOR (LUXEMBOURG) S.A.R.L.—See Novator Partners LLP; *Int'l*, pg. 5461
NOVATOR PARTNERS LLP; *Int'l*, pg. 5461
NOVA TRANSPORTADORA DO SUDESTE S.A.; *Int'l*, pg. 5453
NOVATRONICS, INC.—See Curtiss-Wright Corporation; *U.S. Public*, pg. 611
NOVATTI GROUP LIMITED; *Int'l*, pg. 5461
NOVA TUBE INDIANA, LLC—See Nova Steel Inc.; *Int'l*, pg. 5452
NOVATURAS AB; *Int'l*, pg. 5461
NOV AUSTRALIA PTY LTD—See NOV, Inc.; *U.S. Public*, pg. 1545
NOVA VAROS A.D.; *Int'l*, pg. 5453
NOVAVAX AB—See Novavax, Inc.; *U.S. Public*, pg. 1548
NOVAVAX CZ—See Novavax, Inc.; *U.S. Public*, pg. 1548
NOVAVAX, INC.; *U.S. Public*, pg. 1548
NOVAVENTA S.A.S.—See Grupo Nutresa S.A.; *Int'l*, pg. 3133
NOVA VENTURES GROUP CORP.; *U.S. Private*, pg. 2966
NOVA VERANDA 2010 SL—See Vivendi SE; *Int'l*, pg. 8278
NOVAVEST REAL ESTATE AG; *Int'l*, pg. 5461
NOVAVIS GROUP SA; *Int'l*, pg. 5461
NOVA VISION ACQUISITION CORP.; *Int'l*, pg. 5453
NOVAVISION, INC.—See Incline MGMT Corp.; *U.S. Private*, pg. 2054
NOVAVISION, INC.—See Vycor Medical, Inc.; *U.S. Public*, pg. 2315
NOVA WELLNESS GROUP BHD; *Int'l*, pg. 5453
NOVAXA AB—See Axel Johnson Gruppen AB; *Int'l*, pg. 765

NOV-BLM SAS—See NOV, Inc.; *U.S. Public*, pg. 1545
NOV BRANDT EUROPE FRANCE—See NOV, Inc.; *U.S. Public*, pg. 1545
NOV BRANDT OILFIELD SERVICES MIDDLE EAST LLC—See NOV, Inc.; *U.S. Public*, pg. 1545
NOV CANADA ULC—See NOV, Inc.; *U.S. Public*, pg. 1545
NOV DH DE MEXICO, S. DE R.L. DE C.V.—See NOV, Inc.; *U.S. Public*, pg. 1545
NOV DOWNHOLE AZERBAIJAN, LLC—See NOV, Inc.; *U.S. Public*, pg. 1545
NOV DOWNHOLE BOLIVIA S.R.L.—See NOV, Inc.; *U.S. Public*, pg. 1545
NOV DOWNHOLE DEL ECUADOR CIA. LTDA.—See NOV, Inc.; *U.S. Public*, pg. 1545
NOV DOWNHOLE EURASIA LIMITED—See NOV, Inc.; *U.S. Public*, pg. 1545
NOV DOWNHOLE GERMANY GMBH—See NOV, Inc.; *U.S. Public*, pg. 1545
NOV DOWNHOLE ITALIA S.R.L.—See NOV, Inc.; *U.S. Public*, pg. 1545
NOV DOWNHOLE PTY LTD—See NOV, Inc.; *U.S. Public*, pg. 1545
NOV DOWNHOLE—See NOV, Inc.; *U.S. Public*, pg. 1545
NOVEAL SASU—See L'Oreal S.A.; *Int'l*, pg. 4381
NOVEA SAS—See TCS SASU; *Int'l*, pg. 7485
NOVECO S.P.A.—See Michael Weinig AG; *Int'l*, pg. 4875
NOVEDA TECHNOLOGIES, INC.; *U.S. Private*, pg. 2967
NOVEKO INTERNATIONAL INC.; *Int'l*, pg. 5461
NOVELAIRE TECHNOLOGIES; *U.S. Private*, pg. 2968
NOVELAN GMBH—See NIBE Industrier AB; *Int'l*, pg. 5262
NOVEL APPAREL (BVI) LTD.; *Int'l*, pg. 5461
NOVELART MANUFACTURING COMPANY; *U.S. Private*, pg. 2968
NOVEL DENIM HOLDINGS LIMITED—See Novel Apparel (BVI) Ltd.; *Int'l*, pg. 5461
NOVEL ENVIRONMENTAL TECHNOLOGIES LTD.—See Emerson Electric Co.; *U.S. Public*, pg. 750
NOVELEX AG—See Heitkamp & Thumann KG; *Int'l*, pg. 3326
NOVEL INGREDIENT SERVICES, LLC—See One Rock Capital Partners, LLC; *U.S. Private*, pg. 3022
NOVEL IRON WORKS INC.; *U.S. Private*, pg. 2967
NOVELIS AG—See The Aditya Birla Group; *Int'l*, pg. 7611
NOVELIS CORPORATION—See The Aditya Birla Group; *Int'l*, pg. 7611
NOVELIS DO BRASIL LTDA.—See The Aditya Birla Group; *Int'l*, pg. 7612
NOVELIS INC.—See The Aditya Birla Group; *Int'l*, pg. 7611
NOVELIS INDUSTRIAL PRODUCTS GROUP—See The Aditya Birla Group; *Int'l*, pg. 7611
NOVELIS ITALIA SPA—See The Aditya Birla Group; *Int'l*, pg. 7611
NOVELIS KOREA LIMITED—See The Aditya Birla Group; *Int'l*, pg. 7611
NOVELIS LIGHT GAUGE PRODUCTS—See The Aditya Birla Group; *Int'l*, pg. 7611
NOVELIS MADEIRA, UNIPESSOAL, LIMITED—See The Aditya Birla Group; *Int'l*, pg. 7611
NOVELIS MEA LIMITED—See The Aditya Birla Group; *Int'l*, pg. 7612
NOVELIS SERVICES LIMITED—See The Aditya Birla Group; *Int'l*, pg. 7611
NOVELIS SHEET INGOT GMBH—See The Aditya Birla Group; *Int'l*, pg. 7612
NOVELIS SWITZERLAND SA—See The Aditya Birla Group; *Int'l*, pg. 7611
NOVEL LABORATORIES, INC.—See Lupin Limited; *Int'l*, pg. 4586
NOVELL CANADA—See Micro Focus International plc; *Int'l*, pg. 4877
NOVELL CHILE S.A.—See Micro Focus International plc; *Int'l*, pg. 4877
NOVELL DE ARGENTINA S.A.—See Micro Focus International plc; *Int'l*, pg. 4877
NOVELL DE PUERTO RICO, INC.—See Micro Focus International plc; *Int'l*, pg. 4877
NOVELL DO BRASIL SOFTWARE LTDA—See Micro Focus International plc; *Int'l*, pg. 4877
NOVELL ENTERPRISES, INC.—See Continental Holdings Limited; *Int'l*, pg. 1784
NOVELL FINLAND OY—See Micro Focus International plc; *Int'l*, pg. 4877
NOVEL LIMITED—See Aiphone Co., Ltd.; *Int'l*, pg. 235
NOVELL, INC.—See Micro Focus International plc; *Int'l*, pg. 4877
NOVELL IRELAND SOFTWARE LIMITED—See Micro Focus International plc; *Int'l*, pg. 4877
NOVELL ISRAEL SOFTWARE LIMITED—See Micro Focus International plc; *Int'l*, pg. 4877
NOVELLO & CO. LTD.—See Music Sales Corporation; *U.S. Private*, pg. 2818
NOVELL PORTUGAL INFORMATICA LDA.—See Micro Focus International plc; *Int'l*, pg. 4877
NOVELL SVENSKA AB—See Micro Focus International plc; *Int'l*, pg. 4877
NOVELL UK LIMITED—See Micro Focus International plc; *Int'l*, pg. 4877

NOVELLUS SYSTEMS INTERNATIONAL TRADING (SHANGHAI) CO. LTD—See Lam Research Corporation; *U.S. Public*, pg. 1290
NOVELLUS SYSTEMS ITALY SRL—See Lam Research Corporation; *U.S. Public*, pg. 1290
NOVELLUS SYSTEMS SEMICONDUCTOR EQUIPMENT SHANGHAI CO. LTD.—See Lam Research Corporation; *U.S. Public*, pg. 1290
NOVELSTEM INTERNATIONAL CORP.; *U.S. Public*, pg. 1549
NOVEL TECHNOLOGY LABORATORIES—See A.L. Wilson Chemical Co.; *U.S. Private*, pg. 27
NOVELTEX MIAMI, INC.; *U.S. Private*, pg. 2968
NOVELTY CO.NE CO.—See Joy Cone Company; *U.S. Private*, pg. 2238
NOVELTY LIGHTS, INC.—See Tsinghua Tongfang Co., Ltd.; *Int'l*, pg. 7951
NOVEMBAL—See Tetra Laval International S.A.; *Int'l*, pg. 7577
NOVEMBER AG; *Int'l*, pg. 5462
NOVEM CAR INTERIOR DESIGN GMBH—See Novem Group S.A.; *Int'l*, pg. 5462
NOVEM GROUP GMBH—See Novem Group S.A.; *Int'l*, pg. 5462
NOVEM GROUP S.A.; *Int'l*, pg. 5462
NOVEM PROFESSIONAL SERVICES LLC—See Wolters Kluwer n.v.; *Int'l*, pg. 8445
NOVENCO A/S—See Hi Air Korea Co., Ltd.; *Int'l*, pg. 3379
NOVENCO B.V.—See Hi Air Korea Co., Ltd.; *Int'l*, pg. 3379
NOV ENERFLOW ULC—See NOV, Inc.; *U.S. Public*, pg. 1545
NOVEN PHARMACEUTICALS, INC.—See Hisamitsu Pharmaceutical Co., Inc.; *Int'l*, pg. 3406
NOVENTIS INC.—See WEX, Inc.; *U.S. Public*, pg. 2364
NOVENT REFRIGERANT SERVICES, INC.—See BC Partners LLP; *U.S. Private*, pg. 923
NOVENT REFRIGERANT SERVICES, INC.—See EQT AB; *Int'l*, pg. 2482
NOVENTUS PTY. LTD.—See Pacific Equity Partners Pty. Limited; *Int'l*, pg. 5689
NOVERCO INC.—See Caisse de Depot et Placement du Quebec; *Int'l*, pg. 1255
NOVERGIE—See Veolia Environnement S.A.; *Int'l*, pg. 8155
NOVERKA CONSEIL INC.—See Alan Allman Associates SA; *Int'l*, pg. 290
NOVETHIC—See Caisse des Depots et Consignations; *Int'l*, pg. 1258
NOVETTA SOLUTIONS, LLC—See The Carlyle Group Inc.; *U.S. Public*, pg. 2051
NOVEXCO (CYPRUS) LTD.—See Novolipetski Metallurgicheski Komb OAO; *Int'l*, pg. 5466
NOVEXCO, INC.; *Int'l*, pg. 5462
NOVEXIA; *Int'l*, pg. 5462
NOVEX INSURANCE COMPANY—See Intact Financial Corporation; *Int'l*, pg. 3726
NOVEX TRADING (SWISS) S.A.—See Novolipetski Metallurgicheski Komb OAO; *Int'l*, pg. 5466
NOVEXX SOLUTIONS B.V.—See L. Possehl & Co. mbH; *Int'l*, pg. 4384
NOVEXX SOLUTIONS GMBH—See L. Possehl & Co. mbH; *Int'l*, pg. 4384
NOVEXX SOLUTIONS S.A.S.—See L. Possehl & Co. mbH; *Int'l*, pg. 4384
NOV-FABTECH FZCO—See NOV, Inc.; *U.S. Public*, pg. 1545
NOV FIBER GLASS SYSTEMS—See NOV, Inc.; *U.S. Public*, pg. 1544
NOV FIBER GLASS SYSTEMS—See NOV, Inc.; *U.S. Public*, pg. 1544
NOV FLUID CONTROL—See NOV, Inc.; *U.S. Public*, pg. 1547
NOV HOLDING GERMANY GMBH & CO KG—See NOV, Inc.; *U.S. Public*, pg. 1545
NOVIA ASSOCIATES, INC.—See Hill & Smith PLC; *Int'l*, pg. 3392
NOVIA CORPORATION, INC.—See Hill & Smith PLC; *Int'l*, pg. 3392
NOVIAN SYSTEMS, UAB—See INVL Technology AB; *Int'l*, pg. 3790
NOVIBRA BOSKOVICE S.R.O.—See Rieter Holding Ltd.; *Int'l*, pg. 6338
NOVIBRAMA S.R.L—See Savino Del Bene S.p.A.; *Int'l*, pg. 6600
NOVICA UNITED, INC.; *U.S. Private*, pg. 2968
NOVI CENTAR D.D.; *Int'l*, pg. 5462
NOVICER-CERAMICAS DE ANGOLA, (SU) LIMITADA.—See Mota-Engil SGPS, S.A.; *Int'l*, pg. 5052
NOVICLEAN INC.; *Int'l*, pg. 5462
NOVICLEAN, LLC—See NoviClean Inc.; *Int'l*, pg. 5462
NOVIDAM CAPITAL LLC; *U.S. Private*, pg. 2968
NOVI DOM - PROMET A.D.; *Int'l*, pg. 5462
NOVIDON B.V.—See Royal Cosun U.A.; *Int'l*, pg. 6411
NOVIDON LTD.—See Royal Cosun U.A.; *Int'l*, pg. 6411
NOVI ENERGII OOD—See PCC SE; *Int'l*, pg. 5766
NOVIGO INC.—See ArchLynk, LLC; *U.S. Private*, pg. 311
NOVII PTY. LTD.—See News Corporation; *U.S. Public*, pg. 1519

NOVIK INC.—See Clearview Capital, LLC; *U.S. Private*, pg. 939
NOVIKOMBANK JSCB; *Int'l*, pg. 5462
NOVIK SALES CORP.—See Clearview Capital, LLC; *U.S. Private*, pg. 939
NOVILON LTD.—See Forbo Holding Ltd.; *Int'l*, pg. 2730
NOVILUX—See Sonepar S.A.; *Int'l*, pg. 7091
NOV, INC.; *U.S. Public*, pg. 1543
NOVINGER GROUP, INC.; *U.S. Private*, pg. 2968
NOVINGER'S INC.—See Novinger Group, Inc.; *U.S. Private*, pg. 2968
NOVINIUM, INC.—See Southwire Company, LLC; *U.S. Private*, pg. 3742
NOVINTEL SAS—See VINCI S.A.; *Int'l*, pg. 8224
NOVI PAZAR PUT A.D.; *Int'l*, pg. 5462
NOVIRA THERAPEUTICS, INC.—See Johnson & Johnson; *U.S. Public*, pg. 1200
NOVISBIO CO., LTD.—See Synergy Innovation Co., Ltd.; *Int'l*, pg. 7385
NOVISOL AG—See Indutrade AB; *Int'l*, pg. 3680
NOVISOL GMBH—See Indutrade AB; *Int'l*, pg. 3680
NOVISOURCE N.V.; *Int'l*, pg. 5462
NOVIS S.A.—See SONDA S.A.; *Int'l*, pg. 7089
NOVIS SOFTWARE GMBH—See ICF Kursmakler AG; *Int'l*, pg. 3579
NOVISTA INSURANCE LIMITED—See Novartis AG; *Int'l*, pg. 5460
NOVITA S.A.—See Vaporjet Ltd.; *Int'l*, pg. 8132
NOVITAS SOLUTIONS INC.—See GuideWell Mutual Holding Corporation; *U.S. Private*, pg. 1813
NOVITA TECHNOLOGIES, INC.—See ams AG; *Int'l*, pg. 438
NOVITECH TECHNOLOGIA E SERVICOS LTDA.—See Microsoft Corporation; *U.S. Public*, pg. 1442
NOVITET A.D.; *Int'l*, pg. 5462
NOVITEX ENTERPRISE SOLUTIONS CANADA, INC.—See Exela Technologies, Inc.; *U.S. Public*, pg. 806
NOVITEX ENTERPRISE SOLUTIONS, INC.—See Exela Technologies, Inc.; *U.S. Public*, pg. 806
NOVITEX GOVERNMENT SOLUTIONS, LLC—See Exela Technologies, Inc.; *U.S. Public*, pg. 806
NOVKOL A.D.—See VINCI S.A.; *Int'l*, pg. 8231
NOV KOSTROMA LLC—See NOV, Inc.; *U.S. Public*, pg. 1545
NOVMETAPHARMA CO., LTD.; *Int'l*, pg. 5462
NOVM HOLDING LLC—See NOV, Inc.; *U.S. Public*, pg. 1545
NOV MISSION PRODUCTS UK LIMITED—See NOV, Inc.; *U.S. Public*, pg. 1545
NOVO 1, INC.; *U.S. Private*, pg. 2968
NOVO BANCO BANCO DOS ACORES, S.A.—See Novo Banco, S.A.; *Int'l*, pg. 5462
NOVO BANCO, S.A.; *Int'l*, pg. 5462
NOVO BANCO, S.A. - SUCURSAL EN ESPANA—See Novo Banco, S.A.; *Int'l*, pg. 5462
NOVO BUILDING PRODUCTS, LLC—See Hardwoods Distribution Inc.; *U.S. Public*, pg. 3273
NOVOCAST, S. DE R.L. DE C.V.—See Gamut Capital Management, L.P.; *U.S. Private*, pg. 1641
NOVOCELLUS LIMITED—See ANGLE plc; *Int'l*, pg. 461
NOVOCHEM LTD.—See MCM-Menedzser Kereskedelmi Es Szolgaltato Korlatolt Felelossegu Tarsasag; *Int'l*, pg. 4760
NOVOCHEM ROMANIA CO. LTD.—See MCM-Menedzser Kereskedelmi Es Szolgaltato Korlatolt Felelossegu Tarsasag; *Int'l*, pg. 4760
NOVOCURE GMBH—See NovoCure Limited; *Int'l*, pg. 5465
NOVOCURE LIMITED; *Int'l*, pg. 5465
NOVODIRECT GMBH—See Thermo Fisher Scientific Inc.; *U.S. Public*, pg. 2148
NOVODIRECT GMBH—See Thermo Fisher Scientific Inc.; *U.S. Public*, pg. 2148
NOVO ENVIROTECH (GUANGZHOU) CO. LTD—See CITIC Group Corporation; *Int'l*, pg. 1620
NOVO ENVIROTECH (TIANJIN) CO. LTD—See CITIC Group Corporation; *Int'l*, pg. 1620
NOVOFERM ALSAL S.A.—See Sanwa Holdings Corporation; *Int'l*, pg. 6560
NOVOFERM B.V.—See Sanwa Holdings Corporation; *Int'l*, pg. 6560
NOVOFERM DOOR SP. Z.O.O—See Sanwa Holdings Corporation; *Int'l*, pg. 6560
NOVOFERM EUROPE LTD., UK—See Sanwa Holdings Corporation; *Int'l*, pg. 6560
NOVOFERM FRANCE S.A.—See Sanwa Holdings Corporation; *Int'l*, pg. 6560
NOVOFERM GMBH—See Sanwa Holdings Corporation; *Int'l*, pg. 6560
NOVOFERM GMBH—See Sanwa Holdings Corporation; *Int'l*, pg. 6560
NOVOFERM HELLAS E.M.E.—See Sanwa Holdings Corporation; *Int'l*, pg. 6560
NOVOFERM LUTERMAX S.A.—See Sanwa Holdings Corporation; *Int'l*, pg. 6560
NOVOFERM SCHIEVANO S.R.L.—See Sanwa Holdings Corporation; *Int'l*, pg. 6560

NOVOFERM SCHWEIZ AG—See Sanwa Holdings Corporation; *Int'l*, pg. 6560
NOVOFERM (SHANGHAI) CO., LTD.—See Sanwa Holdings Corporation; *Int'l*, pg. 6560
NOVOFERM TORMATIC GMBH—See Sanwa Holdings Corporation; *Int'l*, pg. 6560
NOVOFERM UK LIMITED—See Sanwa Holdings Corporation; *Int'l*, pg. 6560
NOVOGAMING GHANA LTD.—See Novomatic AG; *Int'l*, pg. 5467
NOVOGENEAIT GENOMICS SINGAPORE PTE. LTD.—See Novogene Co., Ltd.; *Int'l*, pg. 5465
NOVOGENE CO., LTD.; *Int'l*, pg. 5465
NOVOGENE CORPORATION INC.—See Novogene Co., Ltd.; *Int'l*, pg. 5465
NOVOGENE JAPAN K.K.—See Novogene Co., Ltd.; *Int'l*, pg. 5465
NOVOGY, INC.—See Ginkgo Bioworks Holdings, Inc.; *U.S. Public*, pg. 938
NOVO HEALTHNET LIMITED—See Novo Integrated Sciences, Inc.; *U.S. Public*, pg. 1549
NOVOHEART HOLDINGS, INC.; *U.S. Public*, pg. 1549
NOVO HOLDINGS A/S—See Novo Nordisk Fonden; *Int'l*, pg. 5462
NOV OIL & GAS SERVICES SOUTH AFRICA—See NOV, Inc.; *U.S. Public*, pg. 1545
NOVO INTEGRATED SCIENCES, INC.; *U.S. Public*, pg. 1549
NOVO INVEST BULGARIA EOOD—See Novomatic AG; *Int'l*, pg. 5467
NOVO INVEST CO SRL—See Novomatic AG; *Int'l*, pg. 5467
NOVOKRAMATORSKY MASHINOSTROITELNY ZAVOD, PJSC; *Int'l*, pg. 5465
NOVOLEX HOLDINGS, LLC—See Apollo Global Management, Inc.; *U.S. Public*, pg. 153
NOVOLINK COMMUNICATIONS, INC.; *U.S. Private*, pg. 2968
NOVOLIPETSKI METALLURGICHESKI KOMB OAO; *Int'l*, pg. 5465
NOVOLIPETSK STEEL PJSC—See Novolipetski Metallurgicheski Komb OAO; *Int'l*, pg. 5466
NOVOLOGIX INC.; *U.S. Private*, pg. 2968
NOVOLOG (PHARM-UP 1966) LTD.; *Int'l*, pg. 5466
NOVO MAAR SP. Z.O.O.—See Africa Israel Investments Ltd.; *Int'l*, pg. 190
NOVOMATIC AG; *Int'l*, pg. 5466
NOVOMATIC GAMING SPAIN S.A.—See Novomatic AG; *Int'l*, pg. 5467
NOVOMATIC ITALIA S.P.A.—See Novomatic AG; *Int'l*, pg. 5467
NOVOMATRIX INTERNATIONAL TRADING (SHANGHAI) CO. LTD.—See Eastman Chemical Company; *U.S. Public*, pg. 705
NOVOMED GROUP; *Int'l*, pg. 5467
NOVOMER, INC.—See Danimer Scientific, Inc.; *U.S. Public*, pg. 632
NOVOMETAL DOO—See Viohalco SA/NV; *Int'l*, pg. 8243
NOVOMOSKOVSKIY AZOT, OJSC—See EuroChem Mineral Chemical Company, OJSC; *Int'l*, pg. 2534
NOVONESIS A/S; *Int'l*, pg. 5467
NOVONIX LIMITED; *Int'l*, pg. 5469
NOVO NORDISK A/S - ALGERIA—See Novo Nordisk Fonden; *Int'l*, pg. 5463
NOVO NORDISK ASIA PACIFIC PTE. LIMITED—See Novo Nordisk Fonden; *Int'l*, pg. 5463
NOVO NORDISK A/S - KAZAKHSTAN—See Novo Nordisk Fonden; *Int'l*, pg. 5463
NOVO NORDISK A/S - KENYA—See Novo Nordisk Fonden; *Int'l*, pg. 5463
NOVO NORDISK A/S - NORTH MACEDONIA—See Novo Nordisk Fonden; *Int'l*, pg. 5463
NOVO NORDISK A/S - RUSSIA—See Novo Nordisk Fonden; *Int'l*, pg. 5463
NOVO NORDISK A/S - SERBIA—See Novo Nordisk Fonden; *Int'l*, pg. 5463
NOVO NORDISK A/S—See Novo Nordisk Fonden; *Int'l*, pg. 5463
NOVO NORDISK A/S - UKRAINE—See Novo Nordisk Fonden; *Int'l*, pg. 5463
NOVO NORDISK A/S - UZBEKISTAN—See Novo Nordisk Fonden; *Int'l*, pg. 5463
NOVO NORDISK B.V.—See Novo Nordisk Fonden; *Int'l*, pg. 5463
NOVO NORDISK CANADA, INC.—See Novo Nordisk Fonden; *Int'l*, pg. 5463
NOVO NORDISK CHINA—See Novo Nordisk Fonden; *Int'l*, pg. 5463
NOVO NORDISK COMERCIO PRODUTOS FARMACEUTICOS, LDA—See Novo Nordisk Fonden; *Int'l*, pg. 5463
NOVO NORDISK D.O.O.—See Novo Nordisk Fonden; *Int'l*, pg. 5464
NOVO NORDISK FARMACEUTICA DO BRASIL LTDA.—See Novo Nordisk Fonden; *Int'l*, pg. 5463
NOVO NORDISK FARMACEUTICI S.P.A.—See Novo Nordisk Fonden; *Int'l*, pg. 5463
NOVO NORDISK FONDEN; *Int'l*, pg. 5462

NOVO NORDISK HEALTH CARE AG—See Novo Nordisk Fonden; *Int'l*, pg. 5463
NOVO NORDISK HELLAS LTD.—See Novo Nordisk Fonden; *Int'l*, pg. 5464
NOVO NORDISK HRVATSKA D.O.O.—See Novo Nordisk Fonden; *Int'l*, pg. 5464
NOVO NORDISK HUNGARIA KFT.—See Novo Nordisk Fonden; *Int'l*, pg. 5464
NOVO NORDISK, INC. - PUERTO RICO—See Novo Nordisk Fonden; *Int'l*, pg. 5464
NOVO NORDISK, INC.—See Novo Nordisk Fonden; *Int'l*, pg. 5464
NOVO NORDISK INDIA PVT. LTD.—See Novo Nordisk Fonden; *Int'l*, pg. 5464
NOVO NORDISK LTD.—See Novo Nordisk Fonden; *Int'l*, pg. 5464
NOVO NORDISK MAROC—See Novo Nordisk Fonden; *Int'l*, pg. 5464
NOVO NORDISK PHARMA AG—See Novo Nordisk Fonden; *Int'l*, pg. 5464
NOVO NORDISK PHARMA ARGENTINA S.A.—See Novo Nordisk Fonden; *Int'l*, pg. 5464
NOVO NORDISK PHARMACEUTICALS INDUSTRIES, INC.—See Novo Nordisk Fonden; *Int'l*, pg. 5464
NOVO NORDISK PHARMACEUTICALS LTD.—See Novo Nordisk Fonden; *Int'l*, pg. 5464
NOVO NORDISK PHARMACEUTICALS LTD.—See Novo Nordisk Fonden; *Int'l*, pg. 5464
NOVO NORDISK PHARMACEUTICALS PTY. LTD.—See Novo Nordisk Fonden; *Int'l*, pg. 5464
NOVO NORDISK PHARMACEUTIQUE S.A.—See Novo Nordisk Fonden; *Int'l*, pg. 5464
NOVO NORDISK PHARMA EAD—See Novo Nordisk Fonden; *Int'l*, pg. 5464
NOVO NORDISK PHARMA GMBH—See Novo Nordisk Fonden; *Int'l*, pg. 5464
NOVO NORDISK PHARMA GMBH—See Novo Nordisk Fonden; *Int'l*, pg. 5464
NOVO NORDISK PHARMA KOREA LIMITED—See Novo Nordisk Fonden; *Int'l*, pg. 5464
NOVO NORDISK PHARMA LIMITED—See Novo Nordisk Fonden; *Int'l*, pg. 5464
NOVO NORDISK PHARMA LTD.—See Novo Nordisk Fonden; *Int'l*, pg. 5464
NOVO NORDISK PHARMA PRIVATE LIMITED—See Novo Nordisk Fonden; *Int'l*, pg. 5464
NOVO NORDISK PHARMA S.A.—See Novo Nordisk Fonden; *Int'l*, pg. 5464
NOVO NORDISK PHARMA SDN. BHD.—See Novo Nordisk Fonden; *Int'l*, pg. 5464
NOVO NORDISK PHARMA—See Novo Nordisk Fonden; *Int'l*, pg. 5464
NOVO NORDISK PHARMA SP. Z.O.O.—See Novo Nordisk Fonden; *Int'l*, pg. 5464
NOVO NORDISK PHARMA (TAIWAN) LTD.—See Novo Nordisk Fonden; *Int'l*, pg. 5464
NOVO NORDISK PHARMA (THAILAND) LTD.—See Novo Nordisk Fonden; *Int'l*, pg. 5464
NOVO NORDISK PTY LTD.—See Novo Nordisk Fonden; *Int'l*, pg. 5464
NOVO NORDISK REGIONAL OFFICE LATIN AMERICA (LARO)—See Novo Nordisk Fonden; *Int'l*, pg. 5464
NOVO NORDISK SAGLIK URUNLERI TIC LTD STI—See Novo Nordisk Fonden; *Int'l*, pg. 5464
NOVO NORDISK SCANDINAVIA AB—See Novo Nordisk Fonden; *Int'l*, pg. 5464
NOVO NORDISK SCANVINAVIA A/S—See Novo Nordisk Fonden; *Int'l*, pg. 5464
NOVO NORDISK, S.R.O.—See Novo Nordisk Fonden; *Int'l*, pg. 5465
NOVONOR S.A.; *Int'l*, pg. 5469
NOVON PROTECTA (PTY) LTD—See Element Solutions Inc.; *U.S. Public*, pg. 728
NOVO ONBOARD RETAIL LIMITED; *Int'l*, pg. 5465
NOVOPAK A.D.; *Int'l*, pg. 5470
NOVOPAN INDUSTRIES LIMITED; *Int'l*, pg. 5470
NOVOPLAST SCHLAUCHTECHNIK GMBH—See Masterflex SE; *Int'l*, pg. 4725
NOVO PLM—See Sconce Solutions Pte. Ltd.; *U.S. Private*, pg. 3575
NOVORAY CORP.; *Int'l*, pg. 5470
NOVO RESOURCES CORP.; *Int'l*, pg. 5465
NOVO RS D.O.O.—See Novomatic AG; *Int'l*, pg. 5467
NOVOSADSKI SAJAM A.D.; *Int'l*, pg. 5470
NOVOSCO LIMITED—See Telefonica, S.A.; *Int'l*, pg. 7536
NOVOSCO LTD—See Telefonica, S.A.; *Int'l*, pg. 7536
NOVOSIBIRSKENERGO OJSC; *Int'l*, pg. 5470
NOVOTEC CONSULTORES, S.A., SOCIEDAD UNIPERSONAL—See I Squared Capital Advisors (US) LLC; *U.S. Private*, pg. 2023
NOVOTEC CONSULTORES, S.A., SOCIEDAD UNIPERSONAL—See TDR Capital LLP; *Int'l*, pg. 7492
NOVOTECH HOLDINGS PTY LIMITED—See TPG Capital, L.P.; *U.S. Public*, pg. 2175
NOVOTECHNIK MESSWERTAUFNEHMER OHG; *Int'l*, pg. 5470
NOVOTECHNIK SENSORS TRADING (SHANGHAI) CO. LTD.—See Novotechnik Messwertaufnehmer OHG; *Int'l*, pg. 5470

COMPANY NAME INDEX

NOVOTECHNIK U.S., INC.—See Novotechnik Messwertaufnehmer OHG; *Int'l*, pg. 5471
NOVO TECH SP Z.O.O.—See Time Technoplast Limited; *Int'l*, pg. 7751
NOVOTEK AB; *Int'l*, pg. 5471
NOVOTEK A/S—See Novotek AB; *Int'l*, pg. 5471
NOVOTEK B.V.B.A.—See Novotek AB; *Int'l*, pg. 5471
NOVOTEK B.V.—See Novotek AB; *Int'l*, pg. 5471
NOVOTEK OY—See Novotek AB; *Int'l*, pg. 5471
NOVOTEK SVERIGE AB—See Novotek AB; *Int'l*, pg. 5471
NOVOTEK SWITZERLAND AG—See Novotek AB; *Int'l*, pg. 5471
NOVOTEK UK & IRELAND LTD.—See Novotek AB; *Int'l*, pg. 5471
NOVOTEL AMSTERDAM CITY—See Accor S.A.; *Int'l*, pg. 92
NOVOTEL ATHENS S.A.—See Accor S.A.; *Int'l*, pg. 92
NOVOTEL GOTEBORG AB—See Accor S.A.; *Int'l*, pg. 92
NOVO TELLUS CAPITAL PARTNERS PTE. LTD.; *Int'l*, pg. 5465
NOVOTEL PACIFIC BAY COFFS HARBOUR RESORT—See Brookfield Corporation; *Int'l*, pg. 1189
NOVOTEL—See Accor S.A.; *Int'l*, pg. 92
NOVOTEMA SPA—See IDEX Corp; *U.S. Public*, pg. 1091
NOVOTUS, LLC—See L2 Capital Partners; *U.S. Private*, pg. 2367
NOVOTUS, LLC—See Lakewood Capital, LLC; *U.S. Private*, pg. 2379
NOVO WORKSTYLE (CHINA) CO., LTD.—See Itoki Corporation; *Int'l*, pg. 3843
NOVO WORKSTYLE HK LIMITED—See Itoki Corporation; *Int'l*, pg. 3844
NOVO WORKSTYLE (MALAYSIA) SDN. BHD.—See Itoki Corporation; *Int'l*, pg. 3843
NOVOZYMES A/S—See Novonesis A/S; *Int'l*, pg. 5467
NOVOZYMES AUSTRALIA PTY LTD.—See Novonesis A/S; *Int'l*, pg. 5468
NOVOZYMES AUSTRIA GMBH—See Novonesis A/S; *Int'l*, pg. 5468
NOVOZYMES BELGIUM B.V.—See Novonesis A/S; *Int'l*, pg. 5468
NOVOZYMES BERLIN GMBH—See Novonesis A/S; *Int'l*, pg. 5468
NOVOZYMES BIOAG A/S—See Novonesis A/S; *Int'l*, pg. 5468
NOVOZYMES BIOAG LIMITED—See Novonesis A/S; *Int'l*, pg. 5468
NOVOZYMES BIOAG PRODUCTOS PARA AGRICULTURA LTDA.—See Novonesis A/S; *Int'l*, pg. 5468
NOVOZYMES BIOAG S.A.—See Novonesis A/S; *Int'l*, pg. 5468
NOVOZYMES BIOINDUSTRIAL A/S—See Novonesis A/S; *Int'l*, pg. 5468
NOVOZYMES BIOLOGICALS FRANCE S.A.—See Novonesis A/S; *Int'l*, pg. 5468
NOVOZYMES BIOLOGICALS INC.—See Novonesis A/S; *Int'l*, pg. 5468
NOVOZYMES BIOPHARMA DK A/S—See Novonesis A/S; *Int'l*, pg. 5469
NOVOZYMES BLAIR, INC.—See Novonesis A/S; *Int'l*, pg. 5469
NOVOZYMES CANADA LIMITED—See Novonesis A/S; *Int'l*, pg. 5469
NOVOZYMES (CHINA) BIOTECHNOLOGY CO., LTD.—See Novonesis A/S; *Int'l*, pg. 5468
NOVOZYMES (CHINA) INVESTMENT CO., LTD.—See Novonesis A/S; *Int'l*, pg. 5468
NOVOZYMES CHINA—See Novonesis A/S; *Int'l*, pg. 5469
NOVOZYMES DEUTSCHLAND GMBH—See Novonesis A/S; *Int'l*, pg. 5469
NOVOZYMES DO BRASIL LTDA.—See Novonesis A/S; *Int'l*, pg. 5469
NOVOZYMES EENZIM DIS TICARET LIMITED SIRKETI—See Novonesis A/S; *Int'l*, pg. 5469
NOVOZYMES ENZIM DIS TICARET LTD.—See Novonesis A/S; *Int'l*, pg. 5469
NOVOZYMES FRANCE S.A.S.—See Novonesis A/S; *Int'l*, pg. 5469
NOVOZYMES HONG KONG LTD.—See Novonesis A/S; *Int'l*, pg. 5469
NOVOZYMES, INC.—See Novonesis A/S; *Int'l*, pg. 5469
NOVOZYMES JAPAN, LTD.—See Novonesis A/S; *Int'l*, pg. 5469
NOVOZYMES KOREA, LIMITED—See Novonesis A/S; *Int'l*, pg. 5469
NOVOZYMES LATIN AMERICA LTDA.—See Novonesis A/S; *Int'l*, pg. 5469
NOVOZYMES MALAYSIA SDN. BHD.—See Novonesis A/S; *Int'l*, pg. 5469
NOVOZYMES MEXICANA, S.A. DE C.V.—See Novonesis A/S; *Int'l*, pg. 5469
NOVOZYMES MEXICO, S.A. DE C.V.—See Novonesis A/S; *Int'l*, pg. 5469
NOVOZYMES NEDERLAND B.V.—See Novonesis A/S; *Int'l*, pg. 5469
NOVOZYMES NORTH AMERICA, INC.—See Novonesis A/S; *Int'l*, pg. 5469
NOVOZYMES ONEHEALTH BIOTECHNOLOGY (SHANGHAI) CO., LTD.—See Novonesis A/S; *Int'l*, pg. 5469

NOVOZYMES SA ODDZIAL W POLSCE—See Novonesis A/S; *Int'l*, pg. 5469
NOVOZYMES S.A. (PTY) LTD.—See Novonesis A/S; *Int'l*, pg. 5469
NOVOZYMES (SHENYANG) BIOLOGICALS CO., LTD.—See Novonesis A/S; *Int'l*, pg. 5468
NOVOZYMES SINGAPORE PTE. LTD.—See Novonesis A/S; *Int'l*, pg. 5469
NOVOZYMES SOUTH AFRICA (PTY.) LTD.—See Novonesis A/S; *Int'l*, pg. 5469
NOVOZYMES SOUTH ASIA PACIFIC PTE. LTD.—See Novonesis A/S; *Int'l*, pg. 5469
NOVOZYMES SOUTH ASIA PVT. LTD.—See Novonesis A/S; *Int'l*, pg. 5469
NOVOZYMES SWITZERLAND AG—See Novonesis A/S; *Int'l*, pg. 5469
NOVOZYMES SWITZERLAND HOLDING AG—See Novonesis A/S; *Int'l*, pg. 5469
NOVOZYMES UK LTD.—See Novonesis A/S; *Int'l*, pg. 5469
NOVOZYMES US, INC.—See Novonesis A/S; *Int'l*, pg. 5469
NOVRA TECHNOLOGIES INC.; *Int'l*, pg. 5471
NOV RIG SOLUTIONS PTE. LTD.—See NOV, Inc.; *U.S. Public*, pg. 1545
NOV ROLLIGON—See NOV, Inc.; *U.S. Public*, pg. 1545
NOV SARA INDIA PRIVATE LIMITED—See NOV, Inc.; *U.S. Public*, pg. 1545
NOV TUBOSCOPE NL B.V.—See NOV, Inc.; *U.S. Public*, pg. 1545
NOVU, INC.; *U.S. Private*, pg. 2968
NOVUM MEDICAL PRODUCTS, INC.; *U.S. Private*, pg. 2968
NOVUM PHARMACEUTICAL RESEARCH SERVICES, INC.—See Lambda Therapeutic Research Ltd.; *Int'l*, pg. 4400
NOVUS ACQUISITION & DEVELOPMENT CORPORATION; *U.S. Public*, pg. 1549
NOVUS ARGENTINA, S.A.—See Mitsui & Co., Ltd.; *Int'l*, pg. 4979
NOVUS BIOLOGICALS, LLC—See Bio-Techne Corporation; *U.S. Public*, pg. 334
NOVUS CHILE LTDA.—See Mitsui & Co., Ltd.; *Int'l*, pg. 4979
NOVUS DAHLE GMBH & CO. KG—See Erwin Muller Gruppe GmbH; *Int'l*, pg. 2500
NOVUS DE COLOMBIA LTDA.—See Mitsui & Co., Ltd.; *Int'l*, pg. 4979
NOVUS DO BRASIL COMERCIO E IMPORTACAO LTDA.—See Mitsui & Co., Ltd.; *Int'l*, pg. 4979
NOVUS ENERGY INC.—See Yanchang Petroleum International Limited; *Int'l*, pg. 8559
NOVUS ENGINEERING PC—See LaBella Associates, D.P.C.; *U.S. Private*, pg. 2370
NOVUS EUROPE NV—See Mitsui & Co., Ltd.; *Int'l*, pg. 4979
NOVUS INC.; *U.S. Private*, pg. 2968
NOVUS INTERNATIONAL DE MEXICO—See Mitsui & Co., Ltd.; *Int'l*, pg. 4979
NOVUS INTERNATIONAL, INC.—See Mitsui & Co., Ltd.; *Int'l*, pg. 4979
NOVUS INTERNATIONAL PTE. LTD.—See Mitsui & Co., Ltd.; *Int'l*, pg. 4979
NOVUS INTERNATIONAL TRADING (SHANGHAI) CO. LTD.—See Mitsui & Co., Ltd.; *Int'l*, pg. 4979
NOVUS ITALIANA S.R.L.—See Mitsui & Co., Ltd.; *Int'l*, pg. 4979
NOVUS LAW, LLC—See Rock Gate Partners LLC; *U.S. Private*, pg. 3464
NOVUS LEISURE LTD.; *Int'l*, pg. 5471
NOVUS MEDIACORP CO., LTD.—See Spackman Entertainment Group Ltd.; *Int'l*, pg. 7124
NOVUS MEDIA INC—See Omnicom Group Inc.; *U.S. Public*, pg. 1588
NOVUS MEDICAL DETOX CENTER OF PASCO COUNTY, LLC; *U.S. Private*, pg. 2968
NOVUS PROPERTY SOLUTIONS LIMITED; *Int'l*, pg. 5471
NOVUS ROBOTICS INC.; *Int'l*, pg. 5471
NOVUS SPAIN S.A.—See Mitsui & Co., Ltd.; *Int'l*, pg. 4979
NOVUSTERRA INC.; *U.S. Private*, pg. 2968
NOVUS WOOD GROUP, LP; *U.S. Private*, pg. 2968
NOVVIA GROUP—See Kelso & Company, L.P.; *U.S. Private*, pg. 2278
NOV WEST BV—See NOV, Inc.; *U.S. Public*, pg. 1545
NOVX21 INC.; *Int'l*, pg. 5471
NOWACO SLOVAKIA S.R.O.—See The Bidvest Group Limited; *Int'l*, pg. 7623
NOWA ERA SP. Z O.O.—See Sanoma Oyj; *Int'l*, pg. 6553
NOWAK CONSTRUCTION CO. INC.; *U.S. Private*, pg. 2968
NOWAK S.A.S.; *Int'l*, pg. 5471
NOWASTE LOGISTICS AB—See Dole plc; *Int'l*, pg. 2158
NOWATEC CO., LTD.—See Mitsui O.S.K. Lines, Ltd.; *Int'l*, pg. 4989
NOWCOM CORPORATION; *U.S. Private*, pg. 2969
NOW COMMUNICATIONS; *U.S. Private*, pg. 2968
NOW CORPORATION; *Int'l*, pg. 5471
THE NOW CORPORATION; *U.S. Public*, pg. 2117
NOWCOS CO., LTD.; *Int'l*, pg. 5471

NOW COURIER INC.; *U.S. Private*, pg. 2968
NOW COURIERS LIMITED—See Freightways Group Limited; *Int'l*, pg. 2771
NOW DISTRIBUTION INDIA PRIVATE LIMITED—See DNOW Inc.; *U.S. Public*, pg. 671
NOWDOCS INTERNATIONAL, INC.—See Taylor Corporation; *U.S. Private*, pg. 3938
NOWE JAWORZNO GRUPA TAURON SP. Z O.O.—See Tauron Polska Energia S.A.; *Int'l*, pg. 7476
NOW ELECTRONICS, INC.; *U.S. Private*, pg. 2968
NOWFORCE LIMITED—See Verint Systems Inc.; *U.S. Public*, pg. 2281
NOW GMBH—See Bertelsmann SE & Co. KGaA; *Int'l*, pg. 993
NOW HEALTH GROUP, INC.; *U.S. Private*, pg. 2968
NOWILAN GMBH—See Yankuang Group Co., Limited; *Int'l*, pg. 8562
NOWINFINITY PTY. LTD.—See HUB24 Limited; *Int'l*, pg. 3517
NOW MOTOR RETAILING LIMITED—See General Motors Company; *U.S. Public*, pg. 928
NOWNESS LLC—See LVMH Moet Hennessy Louis Vuitton SE; *Int'l*, pg. 4601
NOW NETHERLANDS B.V.—See DNOW Inc.; *U.S. Public*, pg. 671
NOWNEWS DIGITAL MEDIA TECHNOLOGY CO. LTD.; *Int'l*, pg. 5471
NOW NORWAY AS—See DNOW Inc.; *U.S. Public*, pg. 671
NOW: PENSIONS LTD.—See Marsh & McLennan Companies, Inc.; *U.S. Public*, pg. 1384
NOW PREPAY CORP.; *Int'l*, pg. 5471
NOW SOLUTIONS, INC.—See Vertical Computer Systems, Inc.; *U.S. Private*, pg. 4370
NOWSPOTS, INC.—See Marin Software Inc.; *U.S. Public*, pg. 1366
NOWTRANSIT, INC.; *Int'l*, pg. 5471
NOWVERTICAL GROUP INC.; *Int'l*, pg. 5471
NOWY PRZEWOZNIK SP. Z O.O.—See LOT Polish Airlines S.A.; *Int'l*, pg. 4558
NOX BANGKOK COMPANY LIMITED—See Pico (Thailand) Public Company Limited; *Int'l*, pg. 5860
NOX BELLCOW COSMETICS CO., LTD.—See Fujian Green Pine Co., Ltd.; *Int'l*, pg. 2818
NOXBOX LTD.—See Linde plc; *Int'l*, pg. 4509
NOX CORPORATION; *Int'l*, pg. 5471
NOXELL CORPORATION—See The Procter & Gamble Company; *U.S. Public*, pg. 2121
NOXON AB—See Beijer Alma AB; *Int'l*, pg. 943
NOXON STAINLESS B.V.—See Jacquet Metal Service SA; *Int'l*, pg. 3867
NOXOPHARM LIMITED; *Int'l*, pg. 5471
NOX TECHNOLOGIES, INC.—See Nu Skin Enterprises, Inc.; *U.S. Public*, pg. 1552
NOXXON PHARMA N.V.; *Int'l*, pg. 5472
NOYEN CONSTRUCTION LTD.; *Int'l*, pg. 5472
NOYFIL SA—See Radici Partecipazioni S.p.A.; *Int'l*, pg. 6175
NOYFIL SPA—See Radici Partecipazioni S.p.A.; *Int'l*, pg. 6175
NOYLE W. JOHNSON INSURANCE AGENCY, INC.—See Genstar Capital, LLC; *U.S. Private*, pg. 1674
NOZAKI INSATSU SHIGYO CO., LTD.; *Int'l*, pg. 5472
NOZAWA CORPORATION; *Int'l*, pg. 5472
NOZONE, INC.; *U.S. Private*, pg. 2969
NOZSOBE BT.—See PHOENIX Pharmahandel GmbH & Co. KG; *Int'l*, pg. 5854
NP3 FASTIGHETER AB; *Int'l*, pg. 5472
NPA COATINGS INC.—See Nippon Paint Holdings Co., Ltd.; *Int'l*, pg. 5326
NPA DE MEXICO S DE RL DE CV—See Jabil Inc.; *U.S. Public*, pg. 1181
NP AEROSPACE LIMITED—See Morgan Advanced Materials plc; *Int'l*, pg. 5042
NPA SYSTEM CO., LTD.—See NICHIDEN Corporation; *Int'l*, pg. 5268
NP AUTOMOTIVE COATINGS (EUROPE) LTD.—See Nippon Paint Holdings Co., Ltd.; *Int'l*, pg. 5325
NPB AUTOMATION AB—See XANO Industri AB; *Int'l*, pg. 8519
NPB INSURANCE SERVICES, INC.—See ABRY Partners, LLC; *U.S. Private*, pg. 43
NPC AMERICA AUTOMATION INC.—See NPC Incorporated; *Int'l*, pg. 5472
NPC AMERICA CORPORATION—See NPC Incorporated; *Int'l*, pg. 5472
NPCC ENGINEERING LIMITED—See Alpha Dhabi Holding PJSC; *Int'l*, pg. 367
NPC - CIMPOR (PTY) LIMITED—See HUAXIN CEMENT CO., LTD; *Int'l*, pg. 3515
NPC CO., LTD.; *Int'l*, pg. 5472
NPC CORPORATE SERVICES LTD.—See Marsden Maritime Holdings Limited; *Int'l*, pg. 4701
NPC CREATIVE SERVICES, LLC; *U.S. Private*, pg. 2969
NPC GROUP, INC.—See GTCR LLC; *U.S. Private*, pg. 1806
NPC INCORPORATED; *Int'l*, pg. 5472
NPC, INC.; *U.S. Private*, pg. 2969
NPC INDUSTRIAL DE MONTERREY S. A. DE C. V.—See NPC Co., Ltd.; *Int'l*, pg. 5472

NPC, INC.   CORPORATE AFFILIATIONS

NPC INTERNATIONAL, INC.—See Olympus Partners; *U.S. Private*, pg. 3013
N.P. CONSTRUCTION OF NORTH FLORIDA, INC.; *U.S. Private*, pg. 2828
NPC RESOURCES BERHAD; *Int'l*, pg. 5472
NPC RESTAURANT HOLDINGS, LLC; *U.S. Private*, pg. 2969
NPC SAFETY AND ENVIRONMENTAL SERVICE CO., LTD.—See PTT Global Chemical Public Company Limited; *Int'l*, pg. 6091
NPC SANGSENG PTE. LTD.—See NPC Co., Ltd.; *Int'l*, pg. 5472
NPC SERVICES, INC.—See LANXESS AG; *Int'l*, pg. 4415
NPC S&E SECURITY GUARD COMPANY LIMITED—See PTT Global Chemical Public Company Limited; *Int'l*, pg. 6091
NPC SIAM CO., LTD.—See NPC Co., Ltd.; *Int'l*, pg. 5472
NPC SOUTH INC.—See Natco Products Corporation; *U.S. Private*, pg. 2838
NPC VINA CO., LTD.—See NPC Co., Ltd.; *Int'l*, pg. 5472
NPD CO., LTD.—See S&K Polytec Co., Ltd.; *Int'l*, pg. 6445
NPD DISPLAYSEARCH LLC—See The NPD Group, Inc.; *U.S. Private*, pg. 4085
NPDGROUP DEUTSCHLAND GMBH—See The NPD Group, Inc.; *U.S. Private*, pg. 4085
THE NPD GROUP, INC.; *U.S. Private*, pg. 4085
THE NPD GROUP LTD—See The NPD Group, Inc.; *U.S. Private*, pg. 4085
NPD INFORMATION CONSULTING (SHANGHAI) CO., LTD.—See The NPD Group, Inc.; *U.S. Private*, pg. 4085
NPD JAPAN LTD.—See The NPD Group, Inc.; *U.S. Private*, pg. 4085
NPE, LLC; *U.S. Private*, pg. 2969
NPF FIRST INDUSTRIAL ALLIANCE JSC—See KAMAZ Publicly Traded Company; *Int'l*, pg. 4060
NPF GARMONIA—See PJSC VTB Bank; *Int'l*, pg. 5886
NPF FIESTA LLC—See Red Rock Resorts, Inc.; *U.S. Public*, pg. 1770
NPF JAPAN CO., LTD.—See NIPPN Corporation; *Int'l*, pg. 5309
NPF MICROFINANCE BANK PLC; *Int'l*, pg. 5472
NPF TRANSNEFT, JSC—See OAO AK Transneft; *Int'l*, pg. 5505
NPF VTB PENSION FUND JSC—See PJSC VTB Bank; *Int'l*, pg. 5886
NPG ENERGY NV—See Enovos International S.A.; *Int'l*, pg. 2444
NPG HEALTH LLC; *U.S. Private*, pg. 2969
NPG OF OREGON, INC.—See News-Press & Gazette Company; *U.S. Private*, pg. 2917
NPG PRINTING CO.—See News-Press & Gazette Company; *U.S. Private*, pg. 2917
NPG TECHNOLOGY S.A.; *Int'l*, pg. 5472
NP HUNGARIA KFT—See Sintex Industries, Ltd.; *Int'l*, pg. 6957
NP INC.; *Int'l*, pg. 5472
NPINVESTMENT SA—See Neoen SA; *Int'l*, pg. 5197
NPI SOLUTIONS, INC.—See Amphenol Corporation; *U.S. Public*, pg. 131
NPI VENTILATION AB—See Bravida Holding AB; *Int'l*, pg. 1142
NPK CO., LTD. - NANO DIVISION—See NPK Co., Ltd.; *Int'l*, pg. 5472
NPK CO., LTD. - PLASTICS DIVISION—See NPK Co., Ltd.; *Int'l*, pg. 5472
NPK CO., LTD.; *Int'l*, pg. 5472
NPK CONSTRUCTION EQUIPMENT, INC.—See Nippon Pneumatic Mfg. Co., Ltd.; *Int'l*, pg. 5329
NPK DEMTECH B.V.—See Nippon Pneumatic Mfg. Co., Ltd.; *Int'l*, pg. 5329
NPK EUROPE (HOLLAND) BV—See Nippon Pneumatic Mfg. Co., Ltd.; *Int'l*, pg. 5329
NPK EUROPE MANUFACTURING S.R.O.—See Nippon Pneumatic Mfg. Co., Ltd.; *Int'l*, pg. 5329
NPK FRANCE S.A.S.—See Nippon Pneumatic Mfg. Co., Ltd.; *Int'l*, pg. 5329
NPK MANUFACTURING—See Nippon Pneumatic Mfg. Co., Ltd.; *Int'l*, pg. 5329
NPL CANADA LTD.—See Southwest Gas Holdings, Inc.; *U.S. Public*, pg. 1913
NPL CONSTRUCTION CO.—See Southwest Gas Holdings, Inc.; *U.S. Public*, pg. 1913
NP LIFE SCIENCES HEALTH INDUSTRY GROUP INC.; *U.S. Public*, pg. 1549
NPM CAPITAL N.V.—See SHV Holdings N.V.; *Int'l*, pg. 6871
NP MEDICAL INC.—See Jabil Inc.; *U.S. Public*, pg. 1181
NPMIC INSURANCE AGENCY, INC.—See The Doctors Company; *U.S. Private*, pg. 4022
NPM SECURITIES, LLC—See Nasdaq, Inc.; *U.S. Public*, pg. 1492
NP NORD SAS—See Sintex Industries, Ltd.; *Int'l*, pg. 6957
NPO DEVELOPMENT SDN. BHD.—See Titijaya Land Berhad; *Int'l*, pg. 7761
NPO FIZIKA AO; *Int'l*, pg. 5473
NPO SATURN JSC; *Int'l*, pg. 5473
NPO SISTEMI S.R.L.—See Ricoh Company, Ltd.; *Int'l*, pg. 6335

NPO SOLUTIONS—See Health Management Associates, Inc.; *U.S. Private*, pg. 136
NPOWER COGEN—See RWE AG; *Int'l*, pg. 6435
NP PALACE LLC—See Red Rock Resorts, Inc.; *U.S. Public*, pg. 1770
NPPG (THAILAND) PUBLIC COMPANY LIMITED; *Int'l*, pg. 5473
NP RANCHO LLC—See Red Rock Resorts, Inc.; *U.S. Public*, pg. 1770
N P RECORD TRUSTEES LIMITED—See Record plc; *Int'l*, pg. 6238
NP RED ROCK LLC—See Red Rock Resorts, Inc.; *U.S. Public*, pg. 1770
NPR FINANCE LIMITED; *Int'l*, pg. 5473
N.PRIOR ENERGY GMBH; *Int'l*, pg. 5116
NP SANTA FE LLC—See Red Rock Resorts, Inc.; *U.S. Public*, pg. 1770
NP SAVOIE SAS—See Sintex Industries, Ltd.; *Int'l*, pg. 6957
NPS ENERGY INDIA PRIVATE LIMITED—See National Energy Services Reunited Corp.; *U.S. Public*, pg. 1494
NP SERVICE CO., LTD.—See Nihon Plast Co., Ltd.; *Int'l*, pg. 5287
NP SLOVAKIA SRO—See Sintex Industries, Ltd.; *Int'l*, pg. 6957
NPS PHARMA INTERNATIONAL LIMITED—See Takeda Pharmaceutical Company Limited; *Int'l*, pg. 7437
NPS PHARMA SWEDEN AB—See Takeda Pharmaceutical Company Limited; *Int'l*, pg. 7437
N.P. SPINNING MILLS LIMITED; *Int'l*, pg. 5116
NP SUNSET LLC—See Red Rock Resorts, Inc.; *U.S. Public*, pg. 1770
NPS USA INC.—See NPC Co., Ltd.; *Int'l*, pg. 5472
NPS WORLDWIDE-UK LIMITED—See National Packaging Services Corporation; *U.S. Public*, pg. 2860
NP TEXAS LLC—See Red Rock Resorts, Inc.; *U.S. Public*, pg. 1770
NP TRADING CO., LTD.—See Nippon Paper Industries Co., Ltd.; *Int'l*, pg. 5327
NP TUNISIA SARL—See Sintex Industries, Ltd.; *Int'l*, pg. 6957
NP VOSGES SAS—See Sintex Industries, Ltd.; *Int'l*, pg. 6957
NPX CO., LTD.; *Int'l*, pg. 5473
NQA AFRICA—See Sebata Holdings; *Int'l*, pg. 6669
NQL ENERGY SERVICES US, INC.—See NOV, Inc.; *U.S. Public*, pg. 1545
NQ MINERALS PLC; *Int'l*, pg. 5473
NQ RESOURCE RECOVERY PTY LTD—See Cleanaway Waste Management Limited; *Int'l*, pg. 1655
NQUEUE BILLBACK LLC—See Reckon Limited; *Int'l*, pg. 6237
NR 21 SA; *Int'l*, pg. 5473
N.R. AGARWAL INDUSTRIES LTD.; *Int'l*, pg. 5117
N.R. AGARWAL INDUSTRIES LTD. - UNIT III—See N.R. Agarwal Industries Ltd.; *Int'l*, pg. 5117
N.R. AGARWAL INDUSTRIES LTD. - UNIT II—See N.R. Agarwal Industries Ltd.; *Int'l*, pg. 5117
N.R. AGARWAL INDUSTRIES LTD. - UNIT I—See N.R. Agarwal Industries Ltd.; *Int'l*, pg. 5117
N.R. AGARWAL INDUSTRIES LTD. - UNIT IV—See N.R. Agarwal Industries Ltd.; *Int'l*, pg. 5117
NRAY SERVICES, INC.—See I Squared Capital Advisors (US) LLC; *U.S. Private*, pg. 2023
NRAY SERVICES, INC.—See TDR Capital LLP; *Int'l*, pg. 7492
NRB BEARINGS LIMITED; *Int'l*, pg. 5473
NRB INC.—See Dexterra Group Inc.; *Int'l*, pg. 2093
NRB INDUSTRIAL BEARINGS LIMITED; *Int'l*, pg. 5473
NRB (USA), INC.—See Dexterra Group Inc.; *Int'l*, pg. 2093
NRC ELECTRONICS, INC.; *U.S. Private*, pg. 2969
NRC ENVIRONMENTAL SERVICES INC.—See AIP, LLC; *U.S. Private*, pg. 136
NRC ENVIRONMENTAL SERVICES (UK) LIMITED—See Republic Services, Inc.; *U.S. Public*, pg. 1788
NRC GROUP ASA; *Int'l*, pg. 5473
NRC GROUP HOLDINGS CORP.—See Republic Services, Inc.; *U.S. Public*, pg. 1788
NRC GROUP HOLDINGS, LLC—See Republic Services, Inc.; *U.S. Public*, pg. 1788
NRC NY ENVIRONMENTAL SERVICES, INC.—See Republic Services, Inc.; *U.S. Public*, pg. 1788
NRD CAPITAL MANAGEMENT, LLC; *U.S. Private*, pg. 2969
NRDC REAL ESTATE ADVISORS—See National Realty & Development Corp.; *U.S. Private*, pg. 2861
NRD CS UAB—See INVL Technology AB; *Int'l*, pg. 3790
NRD HOLDINGS, LLC—See National Restaurant Development, Inc.; *U.S. Private*, pg. 2862
NRD, LLC—See BAM Enterprises, Inc.; *U.S. Private*, pg. 463
NRD SYSTEMS UAB—See INVL Technology AB; *Int'l*, pg. 3790
NREG TOSHIBA BUILDING CO., LTD.—See Nomura Real Estate Holdings, Inc.; *Int'l*, pg. 5412
NRE POWER SYSTEMS, INC.—See National Railway Equipment Company; *U.S. Private*, pg. 2861
NRE WHEEL WORKS INC.—See National Railway Equipment Company; *U.S. Private*, pg. 2861

NRF BVBA—See Banco Products (I) Ltd.; *Int'l*, pg. 824
NRF DEUTSCHLAND GMBH—See Banco Products (I) Ltd.; *Int'l*, pg. 824
NRF ESPANA S.A.—See Banco Products (I) Ltd.; *Int'l*, pg. 824
NRF FRANCE SAS—See Banco Products (I) Ltd.; *Int'l*, pg. 824
NRF HANDELSGES. GMBH—See Banco Products (I) Ltd.; *Int'l*, pg. 824
NR FINANCE MEXICO, S.A. DE C.V.—See Nissan Motor Co., Ltd.; *Int'l*, pg. 5367
NRF POLAND SPOLKA. Z.O.O—See Banco Products (I) Ltd.; *Int'l*, pg. 824
NRG AUTOMATION LTD.—See Indutrade AB; *Int'l*, pg. 3680
NRG CANAL 3 DEVELOPMENT LLC—See NRG Energy, Inc.; *U.S. Public*, pg. 1550
NRG CURTAILMENT SOLUTIONS, INC.—See NRG Energy, Inc.; *U.S. Public*, pg. 1550
NRG DEVON OPERATIONS INC.—See NRG Energy, Inc.; *U.S. Public*, pg. 1550
NRG DRILLING LTD.; *Int'l*, pg. 5473
NRG DRILLING NIGERIA LIMITED—See Midwestern Oil & Gas Company Limited; *Int'l*, pg. 4887
NRG DUNKIRK OPERATIONS INC.—See NRG Energy, Inc.; *U.S. Public*, pg. 1550
NRG EL SEGUNDO OPERATIONS INC.—See NRG Energy, Inc.; *U.S. Public*, pg. 1550
NRG ENERGY CENTER DOVER LLC—See BlackRock, Inc.; *U.S. Public*, pg. 345
NRG ENERGY CENTER SAN FRANCISCO LLC—See BlackRock, Inc.; *U.S. Public*, pg. 345
NRG ENERGY, INC.; *U.S. Public*, pg. 1549
NRG ENERGY SERVICES LLC—See NRG Energy, Inc.; *U.S. Public*, pg. 1550
NRGENE TECHNOLOGIES LTD.; *Int'l*, pg. 5473
NRG EV SERVICES LLC—See Vision Ridge Partners, LLC; *U.S. Private*, pg. 4391
NRG FLORIDA, LP—See NRG Energy, Inc.; *U.S. Public*, pg. 1550
NRG GLADSTONE OPERATING SERVICES PTY LTD—See NRG Energy, Inc.; *U.S. Public*, pg. 1550
NRG HOMER CITY SERVICES LLC—See NRG Energy, Inc.; *U.S. Public*, pg. 1550
NRG HOME SERVICES LLC—See NRG Energy, Inc.; *U.S. Public*, pg. 1550
NRG HUNTLEY OPERATIONS INC.—See NRG Energy, Inc.; *U.S. Public*, pg. 1550
NRG KENDALL, LLC—See NRG Energy, Inc.; *U.S. Public*, pg. 1550
NRG MANUFACTURING, INC.—See First Reserve Management, L.P.; *U.S. Private*, pg. 1525
NRG MEDIA, LLC; *U.S. Private*, pg. 2969
NRG MIDDLETOWN OPERATIONS INC.—See NRG Energy, Inc.; *U.S. Public*, pg. 1550
NRG MONTVILLE OPERATIONS INC.—See NRG Energy, Inc.; *U.S. Public*, pg. 1550
NRG PIZZA AB—See Katalysator S.A.; *Int'l*, pg. 4089
NR GREENLINES LOGISTICS CO., LTD.—See Nissin Corporation; *Int'l*, pg. 5375
NRG RENEW LLC—See NRG Energy, Inc.; *U.S. Public*, pg. 1550
NRG RESIDENTIAL SOLAR SOLUTIONS LLC—See NRG Energy, Inc.; *U.S. Public*, pg. 1550
NRG REX-ROTARY B.V.—See Ricoh Company, Ltd.; *Int'l*, pg. 6335
NRG SYSTEMS, INC.—See ESCO Technologies, Inc.; *U.S. Public*, pg. 794
NRG TEXAS, LLC—See NRG Energy, Inc.; *U.S. Public*, pg. 1550
NRG THERMAL LLC—See BlackRock, Inc.; *U.S. Public*, pg. 345
NRH LIMITED—See Newell Brands Inc.; *U.S. Public*, pg. 1514
NRI CYBER PATENT LTD.—See Nomura Research Institute, Ltd.; *Int'l*, pg. 5413
NRI DATA ITECH LTD.—See Nomura Research Institute, Ltd.; *Int'l*, pg. 5413
NRI DIGITAL, LTD.—See Nomura Research Institute, Ltd.; *Int'l*, pg. 5413
NRI INC.; *U.S. Private*, pg. 2969
NRI MIRAI, LTD.—See Nomura Research Institute, Ltd.; *Int'l*, pg. 5413
NRI NETCOM, LTD.—See Nomura Research Institute, Ltd.; *Int'l*, pg. 5413
NR INSTANT PRODUCE PUBLIC COMPANY LIMITED; *Int'l*, pg. 5473
N. R. INTERNATIONAL LIMITED; *Int'l*, pg. 5115
N.R. INVESTMENTS INC.; *U.S. Private*, pg. 2828
N.R. INVESTMENTS, INC.—See N.R. Investments Inc.; *U.S. Private*, pg. 2828
NRI PACIFIC INC.—See Nomura Research Institute, Ltd.; *Int'l*, pg. 5413
NRI PROCESS INNOVATION, LTD.—See Nomura Research Institute, Ltd.; *Int'l*, pg. 5413
NRI REAL ESTATE INVESTMENT & TECHNOLOGY, INC.; *U.S. Private*, pg. 2969
NRI RETAIL NEXT, LTD.—See Nomura Research Institute, Ltd.; *Int'l*, pg. 5413

COMPANY NAME INDEX

NRI SECURETECHNOLOGIES LTD.—See Nomura Research Institute, Ltd.; *Int'l*, pg. 5413
NRI SYSTEM TECHNO, LTD.—See Ajinomoto Company, Inc.; *Int'l*, pg. 257
NRI USA LLC; *U.S. Private*, pg. 2969
NRI WORKPLACE SERVICES LTD.—See Nomura Research Institute, Ltd.; *Int'l*, pg. 5413
NRJ 12 SARL—See NRJ Group SA; *Int'l*, pg. 5474
NRJ AUDIO SAS—See NRJ Group SA; *Int'l*, pg. 5474
NRJ BELGIQUE S.A—See NRJ Group SA; *Int'l*, pg. 5474
NRJ BOILEAU 1 SAS—See NRJ Group SA; *Int'l*, pg. 5474
NRJ BOILEAU 2 SAS—See NRJ Group SA; *Int'l*, pg. 5474
NRJ BOILEAU 3 SAS—See NRJ Group SA; *Int'l*, pg. 5474
NRJ ENTERTAINMENT SARL—See NRJ Group SA; *Int'l*, pg. 5474
NRJ EVENTS SARL—See NRJ Group SA; *Int'l*, pg. 5474
NRJ GLOBAL SAS—See NRJ Group SA; *Int'l*, pg. 5474
NRJ GROUP SA; *Int'l*, pg. 5473
NRJ HOLDING SWITZERLAND SA—See NRJ Group SA; *Int'l*, pg. 5474
NRJ MEDIA AB—See NRJ Group SA; *Int'l*, pg. 5474
NRJ NETWORK SAS—See NRJ Group SA; *Int'l*, pg. 5474
NRJ NORDIC AB—See NRJ Group SA; *Int'l*, pg. 5474
NRJ NORGE AS—See NRJ Group SA; *Int'l*, pg. 5474
NRJ SAS—See NRJ Group SA; *Int'l*, pg. 5474
NRL GROUP LTD; *Int'l*, pg. 5474
NRL PHARMA INC.—See Soiken Holdings Inc.; *Int'l*, pg. 7060
NR MOTORS LTD.; *Int'l*, pg. 5473
NRP CONTRACTORS LLC—See The NRP Group, LLC; *U.S. Private*, pg. 4085
THE NRP GROUP, LLC; *U.S. Private*, pg. 4085
NRPL AERO OY—See Goodwin PLC; *Int'l*, pg. 3042
NRP (OPERATING) LLC—See Natural Resource Partners L.P.; *U.S. Public*, pg. 1499
NRP STONE, INC.; *U.S. Public*, pg. 1551
NRS FARMING AS—See Salmar ASA; *Int'l*, pg. 6494
NRS PRINTING SOLUTIONS AG—See Droege Group AG; *Int'l*, pg. 2205
N R SPUNTECH INDUSTRIES LTD.; *Int'l*, pg. 5115
NRT ARIZONA LLC—See Anywhere Real Estate Inc.; *U.S. Public*, pg. 141
NRT AUSTRALIA PTY. LTD.—See Vitura Health Limited; *Int'l*, pg. 8264
NRT DEVELOPMENT ADVISORS LLC—See Anywhere Real Estate Inc.; *U.S. Public*, pg. 141
NRT DEVONSHIRE WEST LLC—See Anywhere Real Estate Inc.; *U.S. Public*, pg. 142
NRT LLC—See Anywhere Real Estate Inc.; *U.S. Public*, pg. 141
NRT MISSOURI LLC—See Anywhere Real Estate Inc.; *U.S. Public*, pg. 141
NRT MISSOURI REFERRAL NETWORK LLC—See Anywhere Real Estate Inc.; *U.S. Public*, pg. 141
NRT PITTSBURGH LLC—See Anywhere Real Estate Inc.; *U.S. Public*, pg. 141
NRT PROPERTY MANAGEMENT ARIZONA LLC—See Anywhere Real Estate Inc.; *U.S. Public*, pg. 141
NRT PROPERTY MANAGEMENT FLORIDA LLC—See Anywhere Real Estate Inc.; *U.S. Public*, pg. 141
NRT PROPERTY MANAGEMENT TEXAS LLC—See Anywhere Real Estate Inc.; *U.S. Public*, pg. 141
NRT REOEXPERTS LLC—See Anywhere Real Estate Inc.; *U.S. Public*, pg. 141
NRT TECHNOLOGIES INC.; *U.S. Private*, pg. 2969
NRT ZIPREALTY LLC—See Anywhere Real Estate Inc.; *U.S. Public*, pg. 142
N.RUNS AG; *Int'l*, pg. 5117
NRV, INC.—See Serval SAS; *Int'l*, pg. 6724
NRW.BANK MUNSTER—See NRW.BANK; *Int'l*, pg. 5475
NRW.BANK; *Int'l*, pg. 5475
NRW.BANK—See NRW.BANK; *Int'l*, pg. 5475
NRW.BANK—See NRW.BANK; *Int'l*, pg. 5475
NRW CONTRACTING PTY. LTD.—See NRW Holdings Limited; *Int'l*, pg. 5475
NRW HOLDINGS LIMITED; *Int'l*, pg. 5475
NRW PTY LTD—See NRW Holdings Limited; *Int'l*, pg. 5475
NRX COMPANY—See IT Link S.A.; *Int'l*, pg. 3827
NRX PHARMACEUTICALS, INC.; *U.S. Public*, pg. 1551
NS ADVANTECH CO., LTD.—See Nippon Seiki Co., Ltd.; *Int'l*, pg. 5329
NSA MEDIA—See The Interpublic Group of Companies, Inc.; *U.S. Public*, pg. 2103
NSA METAALINDUSTRIE BV—See VDL Groep B.V.; *Int'l*, pg. 8140
NSAM US LLC—See DigitalBridge Group, Inc.; *U.S. Public*, pg. 665
NSA OP, LP—See National Storage Affiliates Trust; *U.S. Public*, pg. 1498
NSA SCHIFFFAHRT UND TRANSPORT GMBH—See Caiano AS; *Int'l*, pg. 1252
NSA SOR AS—See NorCom Information Technology GmbH & Co. KGaA; *Int'l*, pg. 5415
NS BANK JSC; *Int'l*, pg. 5475
NSB FUND MANAGEMENT CO. LTD.—See National Savings Bank; *Int'l*, pg. 5163
NS BLUESCOPE (MALAYSIA) SDN BHD—See BlueScope Steel Limited; *Int'l*, pg. 1073
NS BRANDS LTD—See Blue Road Management, L.P.; *U.S. Private*, pg. 592
NSCC AIR WATER, INC.—See Air Water Inc.; *Int'l*, pg. 240
NSC ENVIRONNEMENT SAS—See NSC Groupe SA; *Int'l*, pg. 5476
NSC FLORIVAL—See NSC Groupe SA; *Int'l*, pg. 5476
NSC GROUPE SA; *Int'l*, pg. 5476
N. SCHLUMBERGER DEUTSCHLAND GMBH—See NSC Groupe SA; *Int'l*, pg. 5476
N. SCHLUMBERGER JAPAN KK—See NSC Groupe SA; *Int'l*, pg. 5476
N. SCHLUMBERGER (U.K.) LTD.—See NSC Groupe SA; *Int'l*, pg. 5476
NSC INTERNATIONAL DIVISION - SIEGEL DISPLAY PRODUCTS DIVISION—See EBSCO Industries, Inc.; *U.S. Private*, pg. 1325
NSCOMPANY CO., LTD.; *Int'l*, pg. 5476
N.S. COMPUTER SERVICE CO., LTD.—See Nippon Seiki Co., Ltd.; *Int'l*, pg. 5329
NS CORPORATION CO., LTD.—See NIPPON KANZAI Holdings Co.,Ltd.; *Int'l*, pg. 5319
NSC PACKAGING SAS—See NSC Groupe SA; *Int'l*, pg. 5476
NSCSA (AMERICA) INC.—See National Shipping Company of Saudi Arabia; *Int'l*, pg. 5163
NSC TECHNOLOGIES, INC.; *U.S. Private*, pg. 2970
NSC USA INC.—See NSC Groupe SA; *Int'l*, pg. 5476
NSD ADVANCED TECHNOLOGY RESEARCH INSTITUTE CO., LTD.—See NSD CO., LTD.; *Int'l*, pg. 5476
NSD CO., LTD.; *Int'l*, pg. 5476
NSD INTERNATIONAL, INC.—See NSD CO., LTD.; *Int'l*, pg. 5476
NSE AERO NORTH AMERICA INC.—See NSE Industries SA; *Int'l*, pg. 5477
NSE AUTOMATECH INC.—See NSE Industries SA; *Int'l*, pg. 5477
NSE BRASIL—See NSE Industries SA; *Int'l*, pg. 5477
NSECURE B.V.—See Triton Advisers Limited; *Int'l*, pg. 7935
NSE DATA & ANALYTICS LIMITED—See National Stock Exchange of India Limited; *Int'l*, pg. 5163
NSE INDUSTRIES SA; *Int'l*, pg. 5477
N S E INTEGRATIONS; *Int'l*, pg. 5115
NSE.IT—See National Stock Exchange of India Limited; *Int'l*, pg. 5163
NSE. IT (US) INC.—See National Stock Exchange of India Limited; *Int'l*, pg. 5163
NSE KOREA LTD.—See Nu Skin Enterprises, Inc.; *U.S. Public*, pg. 1551
N.S. ELECTRONICS CO., LTD.—See Nippon Seiki Co., Ltd.; *Int'l*, pg. 5329
N.S. ENGINEERING CO., LTD.—See RAIZNEXT Corporation; *Int'l*, pg. 6192
NS ENVIRONMENTAL SCIENCE CONSULTANT CORPORATION—See OYO Corporation; *Int'l*, pg. 5678
N.S. FARRINGTON & CO.; *U.S. Private*, pg. 2828
NSF ENGAGEMENT CORPORATION—See Nippon Telegraph & Telephone Corporation; *Int'l*, pg. 5343
NS FINANCE, INC.—See Nippon Steel Corporation; *Int'l*, pg. 5336
NS FINANCIAL SERVICES (HOLDINGS) LTD.—See NV Nederlandse Spoorwegen; *Int'l*, pg. 5497
N.S. FLEXIBLES LLC—See St. Johns Packaging Ltd.; *Int'l*, pg. 7159
NSFOCUS, INC.—See NSFOCUS Technologies Group Co., Ltd.; *Int'l*, pg. 5477
NSFOCUS, INC.—See NSFOCUS Technologies Group Co., Ltd.; *Int'l*, pg. 5477
NSFOCUS JAPAN K.K.—See NSFOCUS Technologies Group Co., Ltd.; *Int'l*, pg. 5477
NSFOCUS TECHNOLOGIES GROUP CO., LTD.; *Int'l*, pg. 5477
NSFOCUS TECHNOLOGIES (S) PTE. LTD.—See NSFOCUS Technologies Group Co., Ltd.; *Int'l*, pg. 5477
NSFOCUS TECHNOLOGIES (UK), LIMITED—See NSFOCUS Technologies Group Co., Ltd.; *Int'l*, pg. 5477
NSFX.IT—See FDCTECH, INC.; *U.S. Public*, pg. 825
NSG ASSEMBLY SERVICE CO., LTD.—See Nippon Sheet Glass Co. Ltd.; *Int'l*, pg. 5330
NSG BUILDING PRODUCTS CO., LTD.—See Nippon Sheet Glass Co. Ltd.; *Int'l*, pg. 5330
NSGDATACOM, INC.; *U.S. Private*, pg. 2970
NSG HONG KONG CO., LTD.—See Nippon Sheet Glass Co. Ltd.; *Int'l*, pg. 5330
NSG INTERIOR CO., LTD.—See Nippon Sheet Glass Co. Ltd.; *Int'l*, pg. 5331
NSGOLD CORP.—See St Barbara Limited; *Int'l*, pg. 7157
NSG PRECISION CO., LTD.—See Nippon Sheet Glass Co. Ltd.; *Int'l*, pg. 5330
NSG PURCHASE & SUPPLY CO., LTD.—See Nippon Sheet Glass Co. Ltd.; *Int'l*, pg. 5331
NS GREEN CO., LTD.—See Nippon Shokubai Co., Ltd.; *Int'l*, pg. 5332
NSG TECHNO-RESEARCH CO., LTD.—See Nippon Sheet Glass Co. Ltd.; *Int'l*, pg. 5331
NSG UMU PRODUCTS CO., LTD.—See Nippon Sheet Glass Co. Ltd.; *Int'l*, pg. 5330
NS HANOI STEEL SERVICE CO.,LTD.—See Nippon Steel Corporation; *Int'l*, pg. 5337
NSH NAHVERKEHR SCHLESWIG-HOLSTEIN GMBH—See Deutsche Bahn AG; *Int'l*, pg. 2052
NS HOME SHOPPING CO., LTD.—See Harim Holdings Co., Ltd.; *Int'l*, pg. 3276
NS HOME SHOPPING CO., LTD.; *Int'l*, pg. 5475
NSI ASSET AG; *Int'l*, pg. 5477
NSI BEDRIJFSGEBOUWEN B.V.—See NSI N.V.; *Int'l*, pg. 5477
NSI BEHEER B.V.—See NSI N.V.; *Int'l*, pg. 5477
NSI BVBA—See discoverIE Group plc; *Int'l*, pg. 2133
NSI DEVELOPMENT BV—See NSI N.V.; *Int'l*, pg. 5477
NSI EUROPE GMBH—See Microsoft Corporation; *U.S. Public*, pg. 1442
NSIGHT TELESERVICES—See Northeast Communications of Wisconsin Incorporated; *U.S. Private*, pg. 2949
NSIGHT TELSERVICES—See Northeast Communications of Wisconsin Incorporated; *U.S. Private*, pg. 2949
NSIGHT TELSERVICES—See Northeast Communications of Wisconsin Incorporated; *U.S. Private*, pg. 2949
NSI HOORN B.V.—See NSI N.V.; *Int'l*, pg. 5477
NSI, INC.—See RTX Corporation; *U.S. Public*, pg. 1823
NSI INDUSTRIES, LLC—See Odyssey Investment Partners, LLC; *U.S. Private*, pg. 2995
NSI INSURANCE GROUP; *U.S. Private*, pg. 2970
NSI KANTOREN B.V.—See NSI N.V.; *Int'l*, pg. 5477
NSI LAB SOLUTIONS, INC.; *U.S. Private*, pg. 2970
NSI MANAGEMENT B.V.—See NSI N.V.; *Int'l*, pg. 5477
NSI-MI TECHNOLOGIES, LLC—See AMETEK, Inc.; *U.S. Public*, pg. 121
NSI-MI UK LIMITED—See AMETEK, Inc.; *U.S. Public*, pg. 121
NSI MONUMENT B.V.—See NSI N.V.; *Int'l*, pg. 5477
NS INDIA DESIGN & TRADING PRIVATE LTD.—See Nippon Seiki Co., Ltd.; *Int'l*, pg. 5329
NS INDUSTRIA DE APARELHOS MEDICOS LTDA.—See OMRON Corporation; *Int'l*, pg. 5564
NS INSTRUMENTS INDIA PRIVATE LTD.—See Nippon Seiki Co., Ltd.; *Int'l*, pg. 5329
NS INTERNATIONAL CHINA CO., LTD—See Harim Holdings Co., Ltd.; *Int'l*, pg. 3276
N.S. INTERNATIONAL, LTD.—See Nippon Seiki Co., Ltd.; *Int'l*, pg. 5329
NSI N.V.; *Int'l*, pg. 5477
NSI OVERIG B.V.—See NSI N.V.; *Int'l*, pg. 5477
NSI S.A.—See Capgemini SE; *Int'l*, pg. 1305
NSI TECHNOLOGIES, LLC—See Premier Oilfield Laboratories LLC; *U.S. Private*, pg. 3250
NSI VOLUMINEUZE DETAILHANDEL B.V.—See NSI N.V.; *Int'l*, pg. 5477
NSI WINKELS B.V.—See NSI N.V.; *Int'l*, pg. 5477
NSI WONINGEN B.V.—See NSI N.V.; *Int'l*, pg. 5477
NSJ GOLD CORP.; *Int'l*, pg. 5477
NSJ-US. CO., LTD.; *Int'l*, pg. 5477
NSK AMERICA CORP.—See Nakanishi Inc.; *Int'l*, pg. 5132
NSK AMERICA LATINA LTDA—See Nakanishi Inc.; *Int'l*, pg. 5132
NSK ARGENTINA S.R.L.—See NSK Ltd.; *Int'l*, pg. 5478
NSK ASIA PACIFIC TECHNOLOGY CENTRE (THAILAND) CO., LTD.—See NSK Ltd.; *Int'l*, pg. 5478
NSK ASIA PTE LTD.—See Nakanishi Inc.; *Int'l*, pg. 5132
NSK & ASSOCIATES, INC.; *U.S. Private*, pg. 2970
NSK AUSTRALIA PTY. LTD.—See NSK Ltd.; *Int'l*, pg. 5478
NSK BEARINGS EUROPE LTD. - PETERLEE PLANT—See NSK Ltd.; *Int'l*, pg. 5478
NSK BEARINGS EUROPE LTD.—See NSK Ltd.; *Int'l*, pg. 5478
NSK BEARINGS INDIA PRIVATE LIMITED—See NSK Ltd.; *Int'l*, pg. 5478
NSK BEARINGS (MALAYSIA) SDN. BHD.—See NSK Ltd.; *Int'l*, pg. 5478
NSK BEARINGS MANUFACTURING, MEXICO, S.A. DE C.V.—See NSK Ltd.; *Int'l*, pg. 5478
NSK BEARINGS MANUFACTURING (THAILAND) CO., LTD.—See NSK Ltd.; *Int'l*, pg. 5478
NSK BEARINGS MIDDLE EAST TRADING CO., LTD.—See NSK Ltd.; *Int'l*, pg. 5478
NSK BEARINGS NEW ZEALAND LTD.—See NSK Ltd.; *Int'l*, pg. 5478
NSK BEARINGS POLSKA S.A.—See NSK Ltd.; *Int'l*, pg. 5479
NSK BEARINGS (THAILAND) CO., LTD.—See NSK Ltd.; *Int'l*, pg. 5478
NSK BRASIL LTDA.—See NSK Ltd.; *Int'l*, pg. 5478
NSK CANADA, INC.—See NSK Ltd.; *Int'l*, pg. 5478
NSK (CHINA) INVESTMENT CO.—See NSK Ltd.; *Int'l*, pg. 5478
NSK (CHINA) RESEARCH & DEVELOPMENT CO., LTD.—See NSK Ltd.; *Int'l*, pg. 5478
NSK-CHUGAI, LTD.—See NSK Ltd.; *Int'l*, pg. 5480
NSK CO., LTD.—See Tokai Rika Co., Ltd.; *Int'l*, pg. 7780
NSK DENTAL KOREA CO., LTD—See Nakanishi Inc.; *Int'l*, pg. 5132
NSK DENTAL SPAIN SA—See Nakanishi Inc.; *Int'l*, pg. 5132
NSK DEUTSCHLAND GMBH—See NSK Ltd.; *Int'l*, pg. 5479
NSK EUROPA HOLDING GMBH—See NSK Ltd.; *Int'l*, pg. 5479

NSK & ASSOCIATES, INC.

CORPORATE AFFILIATIONS

NSK EUROPEAN DISTRIBUTION CENTRE B.V.—See NSK Ltd.; *Int'l*, pg. 5479
NSK EUROPE GMBH—See Nakanishi Inc.; *Int'l*, pg. 5132
NSK EUROPE LIMITED—See NSK Ltd.; *Int'l*, pg. 5478
NSK FRANCE S.A.S.—See NSK Ltd.; *Int'l*, pg. 5479
NSK HANGZHOU AUTOMOTIVE COMPONENTS CO., LTD.—See NSK Ltd.; *Int'l*, pg. 5479
NSK HONG KONG LIMITED—See NSK Ltd.; *Int'l*, pg. 5479
NSK HUMAN RESOURCE SERVICES LTD.—See NSK Ltd.; *Int'l*, pg. 5479
NSK INDIA SALES CO. PVT. LTD.—See NSK Ltd.; *Int'l*, pg. 5479
NSK INTERNATIONAL (SINGAPORE) PTE. LTD.—See NSK Ltd.; *Int'l*, pg. 5479
NSK ITALIA S.P.A.—See NSK Ltd.; *Int'l*, pg. 5479
NSK KOREA CO., LTD. - CHANGWON PLANT—See NSK Ltd.; *Int'l*, pg. 5479
NSK KOREA CO., LTD.—See NSK Ltd.; *Int'l*, pg. 5479
NSK KYUSHU CO., LTD.—See NSK Ltd.; *Int'l*, pg. 5479
NSK LOGISTICS CO., LTD.—See NSK Ltd.; *Int'l*, pg. 5479
NSK LTD. - AUTOMOTIVE BUSINESS DIVISION—See NSK Ltd.; *Int'l*, pg. 5479
NSK LTD. - FUJISAWA PLANT—See NSK Ltd.; *Int'l*, pg. 5479
NSK LTD. - FUKUSHIMA PLANT—See NSK Ltd.; *Int'l*, pg. 5479
NSK LTD. - INDUSTRIAL MACHINERY BUSINESS DIVISION—See NSK Ltd.; *Int'l*, pg. 5479
NSK LTD. - ISHIBE PLANT—See NSK Ltd.; *Int'l*, pg. 5479
NSK LTD. - MAEBASHI PRECISION MACHINERY & PARTS PLANT—See NSK Ltd.; *Int'l*, pg. 5479
NSK LTD. - OHTSU PLANT—See NSK Ltd.; *Int'l*, pg. 5479
NSK LTD. - SAITAMA PLANT—See NSK Ltd.; *Int'l*, pg. 5479
NSK LTD.; *Int'l*, pg. 5477
NSK MACHINERY CO., LTD.—See NSK Ltd.; *Int'l*, pg. 5479
NSK MICRO PRECISION CO., LTD. - MATSUKAWA PLANT—See NSK Ltd.; *Int'l*, pg. 5479
NSK MICRO PRECISION CO., LTD.—See NSK Ltd.; *Int'l*, pg. 5479
NSK MICRO PRECISION (M) SDN. BHD.—See NSK Ltd.; *Int'l*, pg. 5479
NSK MIDDLE EAST—See Nakanishi Inc.; *Int'l*, pg. 5132
NSK NEDERLAND B.V.—See NSK Ltd.; *Int'l*, pg. 5479
NSK NEEDLE BEARING KOREA CO., LTD.—See NSK Ltd.; *Int'l*, pg. 5479
NSK NEEDLE BEARING LTD. - HARUNA PLANT—See NSK Ltd.; *Int'l*, pg. 5479
NSK NEEDLE BEARING LTD.—See NSK Ltd.; *Int'l*, pg. 5479
NSK NEEDLE BEARING LTD. - TAKASAKI PLANT—See NSK Ltd.; *Int'l*, pg. 5480
NSK NEEDLE BEARING POLAND SP. Z O.O.—See NSK Ltd.; *Int'l*, pg. 5480
NSK NEW ZEALAND LIMITED—See NSK Ltd.; *Int'l*, pg. 5478
NSK OCEANIA LTD—See Nakanishi Inc.; *Int'l*, pg. 5132
NSK OCEANIA PTY LTD—See Nakanishi Inc.; *Int'l*, pg. 5132
NS KOTE, INC.—See Nippon Steel Corporation; *Int'l*, pg. 5336
NSK PERU S.A.C.—See NSK Ltd.; *Int'l*, pg. 5480
NSK POLSKA SP. Z.O.O.—See NSK Ltd.; *Int'l*, pg. 5479
NSK PRECISION UK LTD.—See NSK Ltd.; *Int'l*, pg. 5479
NSK REAL ESTATE CO., LTD.—See NSK Ltd.; *Int'l*, pg. 5480
NSK RODAMIENTOS MEXICANA, S.A. DE C.V.—See NSK Ltd.; *Int'l*, pg. 5480
NSK RUS & CIS—See Nakanishi Inc.; *Int'l*, pg. 5132
NSK SALES CO., LTD.—See NSK Ltd.; *Int'l*, pg. 5480
NSK SHANGHAI CO., LTD—See Nakanishi Inc.; *Int'l*, pg. 5132
NSK SINGAPORE (PRIVATE) LTD.—See NSK Ltd.; *Int'l*, pg. 5480
NSK SOUTH AFRICA (PTY) LTD.—See NSK Ltd.; *Int'l*, pg. 5480
NSK SPAIN S.A.—See NSK Ltd.; *Int'l*, pg. 5479
NSK STEERING SYSTEMS CO., LTD. - AKAGI PLANT—See NSK Ltd.; *Int'l*, pg. 5480
NSK STEERING SYSTEMS CO., LTD. - SOJA PLANT—See NSK Ltd.; *Int'l*, pg. 5480
NSK STEERING SYSTEMS CO., LTD.—See NSK Ltd.; *Int'l*, pg. 5480
NSK STEERING SYSTEMS DONGGUAN CO., LTD.—See NSK Ltd.; *Int'l*, pg. 5480
NSK STEERING SYSTEMS EUROPE LTD.—See NSK Ltd.; *Int'l*, pg. 5480
NSK STEERING SYSTEMS EUROPE (POLSKA) SP. Z.O.O.—See NSK Ltd.; *Int'l*, pg. 5479
NSK STEERING SYSTEMS—See NSK Ltd.; *Int'l*, pg. 5479
NSK TOYAMA CO., LTD.—See NSK Ltd.; *Int'l*, pg. 5480
NSK UK LTD.—See NSK Ltd.; *Int'l*, pg. 5479
NSK VIETNAM CO., LTD.—See NSK Ltd.; *Int'l*, pg. 5480
NSK-WANDA ELECTRIC POWER ASSISTED STEERING SYSTEMS CO., LTD.—See NSK Ltd.; *Int'l*, pg. 5480
NSK-WARNER KABUSHIKI KAISHA—See BorgWarner Inc.; *U.S. Public*, pg. 371

NSK-WARNER KABUSHIKI KAISHA—See NSK Ltd.; *Int'l*, pg. 5480
NSK-WARNER MEXICO, S.A. DE C.V.—See BorgWarner Inc.; *U.S. Public*, pg. 371
NSK-WARNER (SHANGHAI) CO., LTD.—See BorgWarner Inc.; *U.S. Public*, pg. 371
NSK-WARNER (SHANGHAI) CO., LTD.—See NSK Ltd.; *Int'l*, pg. 5480
NSK-WARNER U.S.A., INC.—See BorgWarner Inc.; *U.S. Public*, pg. 371
NSK-WARNER U.S.A., INC.—See NSK Ltd.; *Int'l*, pg. 5480
NSL CHEMICALS LTD.—See YTL Corporation Berhad; *Int'l*, pg. 8606
NS LEASE CO., LTD.—See ORIX Corporation; *Int'l*, pg. 5634
NS LIFE CORPORATION—See Sumitomo Chemical Company, Limited; *Int'l*, pg. 7267
NSL LIMITED—See YTL Corporation Berhad; *Int'l*, pg. 8606
NSL MINING RESOURCES INDIA (PVT) LTD—See Elmore Ltd.; *Int'l*, pg. 2368
NSL OILCHEM WASTE MANAGEMENT PTE. LTD.—See YTL Corporation Berhad; *Int'l*, pg. 8606
NS MARUWA LOGISTICS CO., LTD.—See AZ-COM MARUWA Holdings Inc.; *Int'l*, pg. 776
NSM COIL CENTER CO., LTD.—See Nippon Steel Corporation; *Int'l*, pg. 5337
NSM HOLDINGS, INC.—See American International Group, Inc.; *U.S. Public*, pg. 106
NSM INSURANCE GROUP, INC.—See The Carlyle Group Inc.; *U.S. Public*, pg. 2050
NSM INSURANCE GROUP, LLC—See The Carlyle Group Inc.; *U.S. Public*, pg. 2050
NSM MAGNETTECHNIK GMBH—See MAX Automation SE; *Int'l*, pg. 4734
N.S. PACKAGING LLC; *U.S. Private*, pg. 2828
NSP CO., LTD.—See The Nisshin OilliO Group, Ltd.; *Int'l*, pg. 7671
NS PHARMA INC.—See Nippon Shinyaku Co., Ltd.; *Int'l*, pg. 5332
NSPHERE INC.; *U.S. Private*, pg. 2970
NSPIRE HEALTH GMBH—See nSpire Health, Inc.; *U.S. Private*, pg. 2970
NSPIRE HEALTH, INC.; *U.S. Private*, pg. 2970
NSPIRE HEALTH LTD.—See nSpire Health, Inc.; *U.S. Private*, pg. 2970
NSPM AG—See Cactus Communications, Inc.; *U.S. Private*, pg. 712
NSP MARITIME LINK INC.—See Emera, Inc.; *Int'l*, pg. 2377
N SPORTS CO., LTD.—See WEDS CO., LTD.; *Int'l*, pg. 8367
NSR SOLUTIONS INC.; *U.S. Private*, pg. 2970
NS SAIGON COIL CENTER CO, LTD.—See Nippon Steel Corporation; *Int'l*, pg. 5337
NS SAO PAULO COMPONENTES AUTOMOTIVOS LTDA.—See Nippon Seiki Co., Ltd.; *Int'l*, pg. 5330
NSSB COIL CENTER CO., LTD.—See Nippon Steel Corporation; *Int'l*, pg. 5337
NSSB MATERIAL CO., LTD.—See Nippon Steel Corporation; *Int'l*, pg. 5337
NSS ENTERPRISES, INC. - NSS EUROPEAN DIVISION—See NSS Enterprises, Inc.; *U.S. Private*, pg. 2970
NSS ENTERPRISES, INC.; *U.S. Private*, pg. 2970
NS SERVICE CO., LTD.—See Mitsubishi Corporation; *Int'l*, pg. 4942
NS SHARED SERVICE. CO., LTD.—See Nippon Shinyaku Co., Ltd.; *Int'l*, pg. 5332
NS-SIAM UNITED STEEL CO., LTD.—See Nippon Steel Corporation; *Int'l*, pg. 5335
NSSLC SERVICE CORPORATION—See Nippon Steel Corporation; *Int'l*, pg. 5335
NSSLGLOBAL APS—See Arendals Fossekompani ASA; *Int'l*, pg. 559
NSSLGLOBAL GMBH—See Arendals Fossekompani ASA; *Int'l*, pg. 559
NSSLGLOBAL LLC—See Arendals Fossekompani ASA; *Int'l*, pg. 559
NSSL GLOBAL LTD—See Arendals Fossekompani ASA; *Int'l*, pg. 559
NSSLGLOBAL POLSKA SP. Z.O.O.—See Arendals Fossekompani ASA; *Int'l*, pg. 559
NSSLGLOBAL PTE LTD.—See Arendals Fossekompani ASA; *Int'l*, pg. 559
NSSLGLOBAL TECHNOLOGIES AS—See Arendals Fossekompani ASA; *Int'l*, pg. 559
NS SOLUTIONS ASIA PACIFIC PTE. LTD.—See Nippon Steel Corporation; *Int'l*, pg. 5334
NS SOLUTIONS CHUBU CORPORATION—See Nippon Steel Corporation; *Int'l*, pg. 5334
NS SOLUTIONS CORPORATION—See Nippon Steel Corporation; *Int'l*, pg. 5334

NS SOLUTIONS KANSAI CORPORATION—See Nippon Steel Corporation; *Int'l*, pg. 5334
NS SOLUTIONS NISHINIHON CORPORATION—See Nippon Steel Corporation; *Int'l*, pg. 5334
NS-STAINLESS CORP.—See Nippon Steel Corporation; *Int'l*, pg. 5337
NS STATIONS RETAILBEDRIJF BV—See NV Nederlandse Spoorwegen; *Int'l*, pg. 5497
NSS TECHNOLOGIES, INC.—See Berkshire Hathaway Inc.; *U.S. Public*, pg. 314
N&S SUPPLY LLC—See Watsco, Inc.; *U.S. Public*, pg. 2336
NST AGENCY CO., LTD.—See Nippon Steel Corporation; *Int'l*, pg. 5337
N-STARCH SDN. BHD.—See Ingredion Incorporated; *U.S. Public*, pg. 1124
NSTAR ELECTRIC & GAS CORPORATION—See Eversource Energy; *U.S. Public*, pg. 801
NSTAR GAS COMPANY—See Eversource Energy; *U.S. Public*, pg. 801
NSTAR GLOBAL SERVICES INC.—See Westerwood (WG) Global Ltd.; *Int'l*, pg. 8390
NSTAR LLC—See Eversource Energy; *U.S. Public*, pg. 801
NST COIL CENTER (THAILAND) LTD.—See Nippon Steel Corporation; *Int'l*, pg. 5337
NSTEIN TECHNOLOGIES INC.—See Open Text Corporation; *Int'l*, pg. 5597
NS TEK—See Nippon Steel Corporation; *Int'l*, pg. 5336
N. STENNING & CO. PTY LTD.; *Int'l*, pg. 5115
NST HANOI STEEL SERVICE CO., LTD.—See Nippon Steel Corporation; *Int'l*, pg. 5337
NST INFORMATION & COMMUNICATION SYSTEMS CO., LTD.—See Nippon Steel Corporation; *Int'l*, pg. 5337
NST LIMITED—See Cox & Kings Limited; *Int'l*, pg. 1822
NST NIHONTEPPAN CO. LTD.—See Nippon Steel Corporation; *Int'l*, pg. 5337
NST OKUHIRA STEEL CO., LTD.—See Nippon Steel Corporation; *Int'l*, pg. 5337
NS TOOL CO., LTD. - SENDAI PLANT—See NS TOOL CO., LTD.; *Int'l*, pg. 5475
NS TOOL CO., LTD.; *Int'l*, pg. 5475
NSTP E-MEDIA SDN BHD—See Media Prima Berhad; *Int'l*, pg. 4771
N&S TRACTOR CO. INC.; *U.S. Private*, pg. 2827
NST SAIGON COIL CENTER CO., LTD.—See Hanwa Co., Ltd.; *Int'l*, pg. 3263
NST SANKOHAN CO., LTD.—See Nippon Steel Corporation; *Int'l*, pg. 5337
NSTS BANCORP, INC.; *U.S. Public*, pg. 1551
NST SYSTEM BUILDINGS CO., LTD.—See Nippon Steel Corporation; *Int'l*, pg. 5337
NST TRADING MALAYSIA SDN. BHD.—See Nippon Steel Corporation; *Int'l*, pg. 5337
NST TRAVEL GROUP LIMITED—See Cox & Kings Limited; *Int'l*, pg. 1822
NST WIRE & WELDING CO., LTD.—See Nippon Steel Corporation; *Int'l*, pg. 5337
N. SUNDIN DOCKSTAVARVET AB—See Saab AB; *Int'l*, pg. 6459
NS UNITED BULK PTE. LTD.—See NS United Kaiun Kaisha, Ltd.; *Int'l*, pg. 5475
NS UNITED BUSINESS CO., LTD.—See NS United Kaiun Kaisha, Ltd.; *Int'l*, pg. 5475
NS UNITED COASTAL TANKER KAISHA, LTD.—See NS United Kaiun Kaisha, Ltd.; *Int'l*, pg. 5475
NS UNITED KAIUN KAISHA, LTD.; *Int'l*, pg. 5475
NS UNITED KAIUN KAISHA, LTD.—See NS United Kaiun Kaisha, Ltd.; *Int'l*, pg. 5475
NS UNITED KAIUN KAISHA, LTD.—See NS United Kaiun Kaisha, Ltd.; *Int'l*, pg. 5475
NS UNITED MARINE SERVICE CORPORATION—See NS United Kaiun Kaisha, Ltd.; *Int'l*, pg. 5475
NS UNITED NAIKO KAIUN KAISHA, LTD.—See NS United Kaiun Kaisha, Ltd.; *Int'l*, pg. 5475
NS UNITED SHIPPING (H.K.) CO., LTD.—See NS United Kaiun Kaisha, Ltd.; *Int'l*, pg. 5475
NS UNITED SHIPPING (U.K.) LTD.—See NS United Kaiun Kaisha, Ltd.; *Int'l*, pg. 5475
NS UNITED SHIPPING (U.S.A.) INC.—See NS United Kaiun Kaisha, Ltd.; *Int'l*, pg. 5475
NS UNITED SYSTEMS CO., LTD.—See NS United Kaiun Kaisha, Ltd.; *Int'l*, pg. 5475
NSV CORPORATION; *Int'l*, pg. 5480
NSW CHINA CO., LTD.—See NSW Inc.; *Int'l*, pg. 5481
NS WEST INC.—See Nippon Seiki Co., Ltd.; *Int'l*, pg. 5330
NSW INC.; *Int'l*, pg. 5480
NSW TECHNOLOGY LIMITED—See Prysmian S.p.A.; *Int'l*, pg. 6011
NSW TECHNO SERVICE CO., LTD.—See NSW Inc.; *Int'l*, pg. 5481
NSW TECHNOSERVICES CO., LTD.—See NSW Inc.; *Int'l*, pg. 5481
NSX LIMITED; *Int'l*, pg. 5481
NSX SERVICES PTY LIMITED—See NSX Limited; *Int'l*, pg. 5481
NSYS CO., LTD.; *Int'l*, pg. 5481
N-SYSTEM CORPORATION—See Cresco, Ltd.; *Int'l*, pg. 1840

COMPANY NAME INDEX

NTACO CORPORATION; *Int'l*, pg. 5481
NTA GRAPHICS INC.; *U.S. Private*, pg. 2970
NTA GRAPHICS SOUTH, INC.—See NTA Graphics Inc.; *U.S. Private*, pg. 2970
NTA LIFE BUSINESS SERVICES GROUP, INC.—See Horace Mann Educators Corporation; *U.S. Public*, pg. 1053
NTA LIFE INSURANCE COMPANY OF NEW YORK—See Horace Mann Educators Corporation; *U.S. Public*, pg. 1053
NTA, LLC—See International Code Council, Inc.; *U.S. Private*, pg. 2115
NTAN, LLC—See Booth Creek Management Corporation; *U.S. Private*, pg. 617
NTA PRECISION AXLE CORP.—See NTN Corporation; *Int'l*, pg. 5481
N-TARA, INC.; *U.S. Private*, pg. 2827
N.T. AUTO SERVICE INC.—See Nissan Tokyo Sales Holdings Co., Ltd.; *Int'l*, pg. 5370
NT BIOPHARMACEUTICALS CHANGSHA CO., LTD.—See China NT Pharma Group Company Limited; *Int'l*, pg. 1536
NT BIOPHARMACEUTICALS JIANGSU CO., LTD.—See China NT Pharma Group Company Limited; *Int'l*, pg. 1536
NTC AMERICA CORPORATION—See Komatsu Ltd.; *Int'l*, pg. 4235
NTC GROUP; *U.S. Private*, pg. 2970
NTC INDUSTRIES LTD.; *Int'l*, pg. 5481
NTC MACHINING CO., LTD. - FUKUOKA PLANT—See Nippon Carbon Co., Ltd.; *Int'l*, pg. 5311
NTC MACHINING CO., LTD. - MIE PLANT—See Nippon Carbon Co., Ltd.; *Int'l*, pg. 5311
NTC MACHINING CO., LTD. - MIYAGI PLANT—See Nippon Carbon Co., Ltd.; *Int'l*, pg. 5311
NTC MACHINING CO., LTD.—See Nippon Carbon Co., Ltd.; *Int'l*, pg. 5311
NTC MAZZUCA CONTRACTING; *U.S. Private*, pg. 2970
NTC NUCLEACTION—See Groupe Gorge S.A.; *Int'l*, pg. 3103
NTC SHANGHAI TRADING CO., LTD.—See Komatsu Ltd.; *Int'l*, pg. 4239
NTC WISMETTAC AUSTRALIA PTY LTD—See Nishimoto Co., Ltd.; *Int'l*, pg. 5365
NTC WISMETTAC EUROPE B.V.—See Nishimoto Co., Ltd.; *Int'l*, pg. 5365
NTC WISMETTAC SINGAPORE PTE. LTD.—See Nishimoto Co., Ltd.; *Int'l*, pg. 5365
N-TECH SOLUTIONS INC.; *U.S. Private*, pg. 2827
NTEC LTD.—See The Furukawa Electric Co., Ltd.; *Int'l*, pg. 7646
NTEGRATOR INTERNATIONAL LTD; *Int'l*, pg. 5481
NTEGRATOR PTE. LTD.—See Ntegrator International Ltd; *Int'l*, pg. 5481
NTEGRATOR (THAILAND) LIMITED—See Ntegrator International Ltd; *Int'l*, pg. 5481
NTELICOR, LP; *U.S. Private*, pg. 2970
NTELS CO., LTD.; *Int'l*, pg. 5481
NTELX, INC.; *U.S. Private*, pg. 2970
NTE MOBILITY PARTNERS LLC—See Ferrovial S.A.; *Int'l*, pg. 2645
NT ENERGIES LLC—See Alpha Dhabi Holding PJSC; *Int'l*, pg. 367
N. TEPPERMAN LTD.; *Int'l*, pg. 5115
NTE SOLUTIONS; *U.S. Private*, pg. 2970
NT FORGING D.O.O.—See Palladio Holding SpA; *Int'l*, pg. 5708
N.T. GAS PTY. LTD.—See APA Group; *Int'l*, pg. 500
NTG CLARITY NETWORKS INC.; *Int'l*, pg. 5481
NTG NORDIC TRANSPORT GROUP A/S—See Nordic Transport Group Holding A/S; *Int'l*, pg. 5423
NTH AG; *Int'l*, pg. 5481
NTH CONSULTANTS, LTD.; *U.S. Private*, pg. 2970
NTH CONSULTANTS, LTD.—See NTH Consultants, Ltd.; *U.S. Private*, pg. 2970
NTH CONSULTANTS, LTD.—See NTH Consultants, Ltd.; *U.S. Private*, pg. 2970
NTH CONSULTANTS, LTD.—See NTH Consultants, Ltd.; *U.S. Private*, pg. 2971
NTH CONSULTANTS, LTD.—See NTH Consultants, Ltd.; *U.S. Private*, pg. 2971
NTH CONSULTANTS, LTD.—See NTH Consultants, Ltd.; *U.S. Private*, pg. 2970
NTH CONSULTANTS, LTD.—See NTH Consultants, Ltd.; *U.S. Private*, pg. 2970
NTH DEGREE EMEA—See MSouth Equity Partners, LLC; *U.S. Private*, pg. 2808
NTH DEGREE GERMANY—See MSouth Equity Partners, LLC; *U.S. Private*, pg. 2808
NTH DEGREE INC.—See Shamrock Capital Advisors, LLC; *U.S. Private*, pg. 3624
NTH DEGREE INC.—See MSouth Equity Partners, LLC; *U.S. Private*, pg. 2808
NTH GENERATION COMPUTING, INCORPORATED; *U.S. Private*, pg. 2971
NTH MEDIA D.O.O.—See NTH AG; *Int'l*, pg. 5481
NTH MEDIA D.O.O.—See NTH AG; *Int'l*, pg. 5481
NTHRIVE, INC.—See Pamplona Capital Management LLP; *Int'l*, pg. 5713
NTI AUDIO AG—See Indutrade AB; *Int'l*, pg. 3680

NTIA ZERUST PHILIPPINES, INC.—See Northern Technologies International Corporation; *U.S. Public*, pg. 1538
NTI BOILERS INC.—See Ariston Holding N.V.; *Int'l*, pg. 567
NTIC EUROPE GMBH—See Northern Technologies International Corporation; *U.S. Public*, pg. 1538
NTI CORPORATION; *U.S. Private*, pg. 2971
NTIC (SHANGHAI) CO., LTD.—See Northern Technologies International Corporation; *U.S. Public*, pg. 1538
N-TIERACTIVE INCORPORATED; *U.S. Private*, pg. 2827
N-TIER SOLUTIONS INC.; *U.S. Private*, pg. 2827
NTI FACILITIES, INC.—See Northern Technologies International Corporation; *U.S. Public*, pg. 1538
NTI LTD.—See Daeyang Electric Co., Ltd.; *Int'l*, pg. 1911
NTI-SKOLAN AB—See AcadeMedia AB; *Int'l*, pg. 77
NTIVA, INC.—See Southfield Capital Advisors, LLC; *U.S. Private*, pg. 3736
NTK CERAMIC CO., LTD.—See Niterra Co., Ltd.; *Int'l*, pg. 5380
NTK CERATEC CO., LTD.—See Niterra Co., Ltd.; *Int'l*, pg. 5380
NTK IMMOBILIEN GMBH & CO. MANAGEMENT KG—See DZ BANK AG Deutsche Zentral-Genossenschaftsbank; *Int'l*, pg. 2244
NTK INTERNATIONAL LIMITED—See Novatek Microelectronics Corporation; *Int'l*, pg. 5461
NTK PRECISION AXLE CORP.—See NTN Corporation; *Int'l*, pg. 5483
NTK TECHNICAL CERAMICS KOREA CO., LTD.—See Niterra Co., Ltd.; *Int'l*, pg. 5380
NTK TECHNICAL CERAMICS (TAIWAN) LTD.—See Niterra Co., Ltd.; *Int'l*, pg. 5380
NTK TECHNOLOGIES, INC.—See Niterra Co., Ltd.; *Int'l*, pg. 5380
NT LIFTEC OY—See Novatech ApS; *Int'l*, pg. 5461
NTL IRISH NETWORKS LTD.—See Liberty Global plc; *Int'l*, pg. 4485
NTL-LOGISTICS (HK) LIMITED—See Naigai Trans Line Ltd.; *Int'l*, pg. 5130
NTL-LOGISTICS (INDIA) PRIVATE LIMITED—See Naigai Trans Line Ltd.; *Int'l*, pg. 5130
NTL-LOGISTICS (SHENZHEN) LIMITED—See Naigai Trans Line Ltd.; *Int'l*, pg. 5130
N.T.L. MARINE COMPANY LIMITED—See Prima Marine PCL; *Int'l*, pg. 5975
NTL NAIGAI TRANS LINE (KOREA) CO., LTD.—See Naigai Trans Line Ltd.; *Int'l*, pg. 5130
NTL NAIGAI TRANS LINE (MYANMAR) CO., LTD.—See Naigai Trans Line Ltd.; *Int'l*, pg. 5130
NTL NAIGAI TRANS LINE (S) PTE. LTD.—See Naigai Trans Line Ltd.; *Int'l*, pg. 5130
NTL NAIGAI TRANS LINE (THAILAND) CO., LTD.—See Naigai Trans Line Ltd.; *Int'l*, pg. 5130
NTL NAIGAI TRANS LINE (USA) INC.—See Naigai Trans Line Ltd.; *Int'l*, pg. 5130
NT MEXICO S. DE R.L. DE C.V.—See Toyo Tire Corporation; *Int'l*, pg. 7859
NTN AKAIWA CORP.—See NTN Corporation; *Int'l*, pg. 5482
NTN ANTRIEBSTECHNIK GMBH—See NTN Corporation; *Int'l*, pg. 5482
NTN-BCA CORP.—See NTN Corporation; *Int'l*, pg. 5483
NTN BEARING CORP. OF AMERICA-ELGIN PLANT—See NTN Corporation; *Int'l*, pg. 5483
NTN BEARING CORP OF AMERICA-SCHILLER PARK PLANT—See NTN Corporation; *Int'l*, pg. 5483
NTN BEARING CORP. OF CANADA LTD.—See NTN Corporation; *Int'l*, pg. 5482
NTN BEARING CORPORATION OF AMERICA—See NTN Corporation; *Int'l*, pg. 5483
NTN BEARING INDIA PRIVATE LTD.—See NTN Corporation; *Int'l*, pg. 5482
NTN BEARING-MALAYSIA SDN. BHD.—See NTN Corporation; *Int'l*, pg. 5482
NTN BEARING MFG. CANADA—See NTN Corporation; *Int'l*, pg. 5482
NTN BEARING SERVICE CORPORATION—See NTN Corporation; *Int'l*, pg. 5482
NTN BEARING-SINGAPORE (PTE) LTD.—See NTN Corporation; *Int'l*, pg. 5482
NTN BEARINGS (UK) LTD.—See NTN Corporation; *Int'l*, pg. 5482
NTN BEARING-THAILAND CO., LTD.—See NTN Corporation; *Int'l*, pg. 5482
NTN BIZEN CORP.—See NTN Corporation; *Int'l*, pg. 5482
NTN-BOWER CORP-HAMILTON PLANT—See NTN Corporation; *Int'l*, pg. 5483
NTN-BOWER CORP-MACOMB PLANT—See NTN Corporation; *Int'l*, pg. 5483
NTN-BOWER CORP.—See NTN Corporation; *Int'l*, pg. 5483
NTN CASTING CORP.—See NTN Corporation; *Int'l*, pg. 5482
NTN-CBC (AUSTRALIA) PTY. LTD.—See NTN Corporation; *Int'l*, pg. 5483
NTN (CHINA) INVESTMENT CORPORATION—See NTN Corporation; *Int'l*, pg. 5481

NTN CHINA LIMITED—See NTN Corporation; *Int'l*, pg. 5482
NTN CORPORATION; *Int'l*, pg. 5481
NTN DE MEXICO, S.A.—See NTN Corporation; *Int'l*, pg. 5483
NTN DE MEXICO, S.A.—See NTN Corporation; *Int'l*, pg. 5483
NTN DO BRASIL LTDA.—See NTN Corporation; *Int'l*, pg. 5483
NTN DO BRASIL PRODUCAO DE SEMI-EIXOS LTDA.—See NTN Corporation; *Int'l*, pg. 5483
NTN DRIVESHAFT ANDERSON, INC.—See NTN Corporation; *Int'l*, pg. 5482
NTN DRIVESHAFT DO BRASIL—See NTN Corporation; *Int'l*, pg. 5482
NTN DRIVESHAFT, INC.—See NTN Corporation; *Int'l*, pg. 5483
NTN ENGINEERING PLASTICS CORP.—See NTN Corporation; *Int'l*, pg. 5482
NT NETWORK SERVICES, LLC—See GTT Communications, Inc.; *U.S. Private*, pg. 1808
NTN FRANCE S.A.—See NTN Corporation; *Int'l*, pg. 5482
NTN FUKUROI CORP.—See NTN Corporation; *Int'l*, pg. 5482
NTN HOUDATSUSHIMIZU CORP.—See NTN Corporation; *Int'l*, pg. 5482
NTN KAMIINA CORP.—See NTN Corporation; *Int'l*, pg. 5482
NTN KAMINA CORP.—See NTN Corporation; *Int'l*, pg. 5482
NTN KINAN CORP.—See NTN Corporation; *Int'l*, pg. 5482
NTN KONGO CORPORATION—See NTN Corporation; *Int'l*, pg. 5482
NTN KOREA CO., LTD.—See NTN Corporation; *Int'l*, pg. 5482
NTN KUGELLAGERFABRIK (DEUTSCHLAND) G.M.B.H.—See NTN Corporation; *Int'l*, pg. 5482
NTN LOGISTICS CO., LTD.—See NTN Corporation; *Int'l*, pg. 5482
NTN-LYC (LUOYANG) PRECISION BEARING CORPORATION—See NTN Corporation; *Int'l*, pg. 5483
NTN MANUFACTURING DE MEXICO, S.A. DE C.V.—See NTN Corporation; *Int'l*, pg. 5482
NTN MANUFACTURING (THAILAND) CO., LTD.—See NTN Corporation; *Int'l*, pg. 5482
NTN METTMANN (DEUTSCHLAND) GMBH—See NTN Corporation; *Int'l*, pg. 5482
NTN MIE CORP.—See NTN Corporation; *Int'l*, pg. 5482
NTN MIKUMO COMPANY LTD.—See NTN Corporation; *Int'l*, pg. 5482
NTN NEI MANUFACTURING INDIA PRIVATE LTD. - CHENNAI PLANT—See NTN Corporation; *Int'l*, pg. 5482
NTN NEI MANUFACTURING INDIA PVT. LTD.—See NTN Corporation; *Int'l*, pg. 5482
NTN NET MANUFACTURING INDIA PRIVATE LTD.—See NTN Corporation; *Int'l*, pg. 5482
NTN NOTO CORP.—See NTN Corporation; *Int'l*, pg. 5482
NTN OMAEZAKI CORP.—See NTN Corporation; *Int'l*, pg. 5482
NTN POWDER METAL CORP.—See NTN Corporation; *Int'l*, pg. 5482
NTN-RAB (CHANGZHOU) CORP.—See NTN Corporation; *Int'l*, pg. 5482
NTN SALES JAPAN CORP.—See NTN Corporation; *Int'l*, pg. 5483
NTN-SNR IBERICA S.A.—See NTN Corporation; *Int'l*, pg. 5483
NTN-SNR MAROC S.A—See NTN Corporation; *Int'l*, pg. 5483
NTN-SNR ROULEMENTS SA—See NTN Corporation; *Int'l*, pg. 5483
NTN-SNR RULMENTI S.R.L—See NTN Corporation; *Int'l*, pg. 5483
NTN SUDAMERICANA, S.A.—See NTN Corporation; *Int'l*, pg. 5483
NTN TADO CORP.—See NTN Corporation; *Int'l*, pg. 5483
NTN TECHNICAL SERVICE CORP.—See NTN Corporation; *Int'l*, pg. 5483
NTN TRANSMISSIONS EUROPE CREZANCY S.A.S.—See NTN Corporation; *Int'l*, pg. 5483
NTN TRANSMISSIONS EUROPE—See NTN Corporation; *Int'l*, pg. 5483
NTN USA CORPORATION—See NTN Corporation; *Int'l*, pg. 5483
NTN WALZLAGER (EUROPA) GMBH—See NTN Corporation; *Int'l*, pg. 5483
NTPC ELECTRIC SUPPLY COMPANY LTD.—See NTPC Limited; *Int'l*, pg. 5484
NTPC GE POWER SERVICES PRIVATE LIMITED—See General Electric Company; *U.S. Public*, pg. 917
NTPC GE POWER SERVICES PRIVATE LIMITED—See NTPC Limited; *Int'l*, pg. 5484
NTP (CHINA) INVESTMENT CO., LTD.—See China NT Pharma Group Company Limited; *Int'l*, pg. 1536
NTPC LIMITED; *Int'l*, pg. 5484
NTPC SAIL POWER COMPANY PVT. LTD—See NTPC Limited; *Int'l*, pg. 5484

Company Index

NTPC LIMITED CORPORATE AFFILIATIONS

NTPC SAIL POWER COMPANY PVT. LTD—See Steel Authority of India Limited; *Int'l*, pg. 7189
NTPC VIDYUT VYAPAR NIGAM LIMITED—See NTPC Limited; *Int'l*, pg. 5484
NTP DISTRIBUTION—See LKQ Corporation; *U.S. Public*, pg. 1334
NT PHARMA (JIANGSU) CO., LTD.—See China NT Pharma Group Company Limited; *Int'l*, pg. 1536
NTPIA CORPORATION CO., LTD. - DONGTAN PLANT—See K&C Global Co., Ltd.; *Int'l*, pg. 4038
NTPM HOLDINGS BERHAD; *Int'l*, pg. 5484
NTPM (SINGAPORE) PTE. LTD.—See NTPM Holdings Berhad; *Int'l*, pg. 5484
NT PORT & MARINE PTY. LTD.—See AusGroup Limited; *Int'l*, pg. 716
NTPT CO., LTD.—See NTN Corporation; *Int'l*, pg. 5483
NTR HOLDING A/S; *Int'l*, pg. 5484
NTRINSIC CONSULTING EUROPE LIMITED—See Bain Capital, LP; *U.S. Private*, pg. 434
NTRINSIC CONSULTING RESOURCES LIMITED—See Bain Capital, LP; *U.S. Private*, pg. 434
N-TRON, CORP.—See Spectris Plc; *Int'l*, pg. 7131
NTR PLC; *Int'l*, pg. 5484
NTR TRANSPORTER CO., LTD.—See Nissan Tokyo Sales Holdings Co., Ltd.; *Int'l*, pg. 5370
NT RURAL PTY. LTD.—See Nutrien Ltd.; *Int'l*, pg. 5493
NT SALES CO., LTD.—See Shinko Shoji Co., Ltd.; *Int'l*, pg. 6846
NT SALES HONG KONG LTD.—See Shinko Shoji Co., Ltd.; *Int'l*, pg. 6846
NTS ASA—See Salmar ASA; *Int'l*, pg. 6494
NTS BOTECH—See NTS Group; *Int'l*, pg. 5484
NTS COMBIMETAAL—See NTS Group; *Int'l*, pg. 5484
NTS COMMUNICATIONS, INC.—See Keystone Group, L.P.; *U.S. Private*, pg. 2297
NTS COMMUNICATIONS, INC.—See Pamlico Capital Management, L.P.; *U.S. Private*, pg. 3083
NTS COMPONENTS SINGAPORE PTE LTD—See NTS Group; *Int'l*, pg. 5484
NTS COMPONENTS (SUZHOU) LTD.—See NTS Group; *Int'l*, pg. 5484
NTS CORPORATION; *U.S. Private*, pg. 2971
NTS DEVELOPMENT COMPANY—See NTS Corporation; *U.S. Private*, pg. 2971
NT. SERVICE CO., LTD.—See Nippon Tungsten Co., Ltd.; *Int'l*, pg. 5357
NTS EUROPEAN DISTRIBUTION AB—See DSV A/S; *Int'l*, pg. 2214
NTS FINISH—See NTS Group; *Int'l*, pg. 5484
NTS GROUP; *Int'l*, pg. 5484
NTS HERMUS—See NTS Group; *Int'l*, pg. 5484
NTS, INC.—See Keystone Group, L.P.; *U.S. Private*, pg. 2297
NTS, INC.—See Pamlico Capital Management, L.P.; *U.S. Private*, pg. 3083
NTS INTERNATIONAL TRANSPORT SERVICES CO. LTD.—See A.P. Moller-Maersk A/S; *Int'l*, pg. 27
NTS LTD.—See Steilmann Holding AG; *Int'l*, pg. 7193
NTS MECHATRONICS BRNO, S.R.O.—See NTS Group; *Int'l*, pg. 5484
NTS MECHATRONICS SHANGHAI—See NTS Group; *Int'l*, pg. 5484
NTS MECHATRONICS—See NTS Group; *Int'l*, pg. 5484
NTS OPTEL—See NTS Group; *Int'l*, pg. 5484
NTS PRECISION—See NTS Group; *Int'l*, pg. 5484
NTS PROMETAL MACHINING, S.R.O.—See NTS Group; *Int'l*, pg. 5484
NTS REALTY CAPITAL, INC.—See NTS Corporation; *U.S. Private*, pg. 2971
NTS REALTY PARTNERS, LLC—See NTS Corporation; *U.S. Private*, pg. 2971
NTS RESIDENTIAL MANAGEMENT COMPANY—See NTS Corporation; *U.S. Private*, pg. 2971
NTS RESIDENTIAL PROPERTIES, INC.—See NTS Corporation; *U.S. Private*, pg. 2971
NTS SHEMER MOTION—See NTS Group; *Int'l*, pg. 5484
NTS SILICON VALLEY—See Aurora Capital Group, LLC; *U.S. Private*, pg. 393
NTS SYSTEMS DEVELOPMENT—See NTS Group; *Int'l*, pg. 5484
NTS TECHNICAL SYSTEMS—See Aurora Capital Group, LLC; *U.S. Private*, pg. 393
NTS TECHNOLOGY SERVICES PRIVATE LIMITED—See News Corporation; *U.S. Public*, pg. 1520
NTT ADVANCED TECHNOLOGY CORPORATION—See Nippon Telegraph & Telephone Corporation; *Int'l*, pg. 5343
NTT ADVERTISING, INC.; *Int'l*, pg. 5484
NTT ADVERTISING, INC.—See NTT Advertising, Inc.; *Int'l*, pg. 5485
NTT ADVERTISING, INC.—See NTT Advertising, Inc.; *Int'l*, pg. 5485
NTT ADVERTISING, INC.—See NTT Advertising, Inc.; *Int'l*, pg. 5485
NTT ADVERTISING, INC.—See NTT Advertising, Inc.; *Int'l*, pg. 5485
NTT AGRI TECHNOLOGY CORPORATION—See Nippon Telegraph & Telephone Corporation; *Int'l*, pg. 5343
NTT AMERICA, INC.—See Nippon Telegraph & Telephone Corporation; *Int'l*, pg. 5344
NTT AMERICA, INC. (WASHINGTON OFFICE)—See Nippon Telegraph & Telephone Corporation; *Int'l*, pg. 5344
NTT ART TECHNOLOGY CORPORATION—See Nippon Telegraph & Telephone Corporation; *Int'l*, pg. 5343
NTT-AT IPS CORPORATION—See Nippon Telegraph & Telephone Corporation; *Int'l*, pg. 5343
NTT-AT MTACK CORPORATION—See Nippon Telegraph & Telephone Corporation; *Int'l*, pg. 5343
NTT-AT SYSTEMS CORPORATION—See Nippon Telegraph & Telephone Corporation; *Int'l*, pg. 5343
NTT-AT TECHNO COMMUNICATIONS INC.—See Nippon Telegraph & Telephone Corporation; *Int'l*, pg. 5343
NTT AUSTRALIA PTY. LTD.—See Nippon Telegraph & Telephone Corporation; *Int'l*, pg. 5344
NTT BIZLINK, INC.—See Nippon Telegraph & Telephone Corporation; *Int'l*, pg. 5344
NTT BROADBAND PLATFORM, INC.—See Nippon Telegraph & Telephone Corporation; *Int'l*, pg. 5343
NTT BUSINESS ASSOCIE CO., LTD.—See Nippon Telegraph & Telephone Corporation; *Int'l*, pg. 5343
NTT BUSINESS ASSOCIE EAST CO., LTD.—See Nippon Telegraph & Telephone Corporation; *Int'l*, pg. 5343
NTT BUSINESS ASSOCIE PARTNERS CO., LTD.—See Nippon Telegraph & Telephone Corporation; *Int'l*, pg. 5343
NTT CARD SOLUTION CORP.—See Nippon Telegraph & Telephone Corporation; *Int'l*, pg. 5354
NTT CENTERSTANCE, INC—See Nippon Telegraph & Telephone Corporation; *Int'l*, pg. 5344
NTT CLARUTY CORPORATION—See Nippon Telegraph & Telephone Corporation; *Int'l*, pg. 5344
NTT COM ASIA LTD.—See Nippon Telegraph & Telephone Corporation; *Int'l*, pg. 5344
NTT COM CHEO CORPORATION—See Nippon Telegraph & Telephone Corporation; *Int'l*, pg. 5344
NTT COM ENGINEERING CORPORATION—See Nippon Telegraph & Telephone Corporation; *Int'l*, pg. 5344
NTT COMMUNICATIONS CHINA CO., LTD.—See Nippon Telegraph & Telephone Corporation; *Int'l*, pg. 5345
NTT COMMUNICATIONS CORPORATION—See Nippon Telegraph & Telephone Corporation; *Int'l*, pg. 5344
NTT COMMUNICATIONS DEUTSCHLAND GMBH—See Nippon Telegraph & Telephone Corporation; *Int'l*, pg. 5345
NTT COMMUNICATIONS PHILIPPINES CORPORATION—See Nippon Telegraph & Telephone Corporation; *Int'l*, pg. 5345
NTT COMMUNICATIONS RUSSIA LLC—See Nippon Telegraph & Telephone Corporation; *Int'l*, pg. 5345
NTT COMMUNICATIONS (THAILAND) CO., LTD.—See Nippon Telegraph & Telephone Corporation; *Int'l*, pg. 5345
NTT COMMUNICATIONS (VIETNAM) LTD.—See Nippon Telegraph & Telephone Corporation; *Int'l*, pg. 5345
NTT COMMUNICATIONS WORLD NETWORK (S) PTE LTD—See Nippon Telegraph & Telephone Corporation; *Int'l*, pg. 5345
NTTCOM ONLINE MARKETING SOLUTIONS CORPORATION—See Nippon Telegraph & Telephone Corporation; *Int'l*, pg. 5354
NTT COM SECURITY AG—See Nippon Telegraph & Telephone Corporation; *Int'l*, pg. 5344
NTT COM SECURITY (AUSTRIA) GMBH—See Nippon Telegraph & Telephone Corporation; *Int'l*, pg. 5344
NTT COM SECURITY (FRANCE) SAS—See Nippon Telegraph & Telephone Corporation; *Int'l*, pg. 5344
NTT COM SECURITY (GERMANY) GMBH—See Nippon Telegraph & Telephone Corporation; *Int'l*, pg. 5344
NTT COM SECURITY (HONG KONG) LTD.—See Nippon Telegraph & Telephone Corporation; *Int'l*, pg. 5344
NTT COM SECURITY (JAPAN) KK—See Nippon Telegraph & Telephone Corporation; *Int'l*, pg. 5345
NTT COM SECURITY (SINGAPORE) PTE LTD.—See Nippon Telegraph & Telephone Corporation; *Int'l*, pg. 5345
NTT COM SECURITY (SWEDEN) AB—See Nippon Telegraph & Telephone Corporation; *Int'l*, pg. 5345
NTT COM SECURITY (SWITZERLAND) AG—See Nippon Telegraph & Telephone Corporation; *Int'l*, pg. 5345
NTT COM SECURITY (UK) LIMITED—See Nippon Telegraph & Telephone Corporation; *Int'l*, pg. 5345
NTT COM SECURITY (US) INC.—See Nippon Telegraph & Telephone Corporation; *Int'l*, pg. 5345
NTT COM SOLUTION & ENGINEERING CORP.—See Nippon Telegraph & Telephone Corporation; *Int'l*, pg. 5345
NTT COMTECHNOLOGY CORPORATION—See Nippon Telegraph & Telephone Corporation; *Int'l*, pg. 5345
NTT COMWARE BILLING SOLUTIONS CORPORATION—See Nippon Telegraph & Telephone Corporation; *Int'l*, pg. 5344
NTT COMWARE CORPORATION—See Nippon Telegraph & Telephone Corporation; *Int'l*, pg. 5344
NTT COMWARE HOKKAIDO CORPORATION—See Nippon Telegraph & Telephone Corporation; *Int'l*, pg. 5344
NTT COMWARE WEST CORPORATION—See Nippon Telegraph & Telephone Corporation; *Int'l*, pg. 5344
NTT DATA 3C CORPORATION—See Nippon Telegraph & Telephone Corporation; *Int'l*, pg. 5346
NTT DATA ABIC CO., LTD.—See Nippon Telegraph & Telephone Corporation; *Int'l*, pg. 5351
NTT DATA AGILENET LLC—See Nippon Telegraph & Telephone Corporation; *Int'l*, pg. 5348
NTT DATA AURORA CORPORATION—See Nippon Telegraph & Telephone Corporation; *Int'l*, pg. 5346
NTT DATA AUSTRIA GMBH—See Nippon Telegraph & Telephone Corporation; *Int'l*, pg. 5346
NTT DATA AUTOMOBILIGENCE RESEARCH CENTER, LTD.—See Nippon Telegraph & Telephone Corporation; *Int'l*, pg. 5351
NTT DATA BCU, INC.—See Nippon Telegraph & Telephone Corporation; *Int'l*, pg. 5351
NTT DATA BEEN (CHINA) INFORMATION TECHNOLOGY CO., LTD.—See Nippon Telegraph & Telephone Corporation; *Int'l*, pg. 5351
NTT DATA BEEN CORPORATION—See Nippon Telegraph & Telephone Corporation; *Int'l*, pg. 5351
NTT DATA BEEN SERVICE CORPORATION—See Nippon Telegraph & Telephone Corporation; *Int'l*, pg. 5351
NTT DATA BELGIQUE, SPRL—See Nippon Telegraph & Telephone Corporation; *Int'l*, pg. 5351
NTT DATA BILLING SERVICE CORPORATION—See Nippon Telegraph & Telephone Corporation; *Int'l*, pg. 5346
NTT DATA BIZ INTEGRAL CORPORATION—See Nippon Telegraph & Telephone Corporation; *Int'l*, pg. 5346
NTT DATA BUSINESS BRAINS CORP.—See Nippon Sheet Glass Co. Ltd.; *Int'l*, pg. 5331
NTT DATA BUSINESS SOLUTIONS AB—See Nippon Telegraph & Telephone Corporation; *Int'l*, pg. 5351
NTT DATA BUSINESS SOLUTIONS AG—See Nippon Telegraph & Telephone Corporation; *Int'l*, pg. 5351
NTT DATA BUSINESS SOLUTIONS A.S.—See Nippon Telegraph & Telephone Corporation; *Int'l*, pg. 5351
NTT DATA BUSINESS SOLUTIONS BILGI SISTEMLERI ANONIM SIRKETI—See Nippon Telegraph & Telephone Corporation; *Int'l*, pg. 5351
NTT DATA BUSINESS SOLUTIONS B.V.—See Nippon Telegraph & Telephone Corporation; *Int'l*, pg. 5351
NTT DATA BUSINESS SOLUTIONS GLOBAL MANAGED SERVICES CO., LTD.—See Nippon Telegraph & Telephone Corporation; *Int'l*, pg. 5351
NTT DATA BUSINESS SOLUTIONS GLOBAL MANAGED SERVICES GMBH—See Nippon Telegraph & Telephone Corporation; *Int'l*, pg. 5351
NTT DATA BUSINESS SOLUTIONS HOLDING B.V.—See Nippon Telegraph & Telephone Corporation; *Int'l*, pg. 5351
NTT DATA BUSINESS SOLUTIONS INCORPORATED—See Nippon Telegraph & Telephone Corporation; *Int'l*, pg. 5351
NTT DATA BUSINESS SOLUTIONS INC.—See Nippon Telegraph & Telephone Corporation; *Int'l*, pg. 5351
NTT DATA BUSINESS SOLUTIONS INTERNATIONAL HOLDING GMBH—See Nippon Telegraph & Telephone Corporation; *Int'l*, pg. 5351
NTT DATA BUSINESS SOLUTIONS KFT.—See Nippon Telegraph & Telephone Corporation; *Int'l*, pg. 5351
NTT DATA BUSINESS SOLUTIONS LIMITED—See Nippon Telegraph & Telephone Corporation; *Int'l*, pg. 5351
NTT DATA BUSINESS SOLUTIONS LTD.—See Nippon Telegraph & Telephone Corporation; *Int'l*, pg. 5351
NTT DATA BUSINESS SOLUTIONS MALAYSIA SDN. BHD.—See Nippon Telegraph & Telephone Corporation; *Int'l*, pg. 5351
NTT DATA BUSINESS SOLUTIONS MSC SDN. BHD.—See Nippon Telegraph & Telephone Corporation; *Int'l*, pg. 5351
NTT DATA BUSINESS SOLUTIONS OY—See Nippon Telegraph & Telephone Corporation; *Int'l*, pg. 5351
NTT DATA BUSINESS SOLUTIONS PARTICIPACOES S.A.—See Nippon Telegraph & Telephone Corporation; *Int'l*, pg. 5351
NTT DATA BUSINESS SOLUTIONS PRIVATE LIMITED—See Nippon Telegraph & Telephone Corporation; *Int'l*, pg. 5351
NTT DATA BUSINESS SOLUTIONS S.A.—See Nippon Telegraph & Telephone Corporation; *Int'l*, pg. 5351
NTT DATA BUSINESS SOLUTIONS S.A.S.—See Nippon Telegraph & Telephone Corporation; *Int'l*, pg. 5351
NTT DATA BUSINESS SOLUTIONS SINGAPORE PTE. LTD.—See Nippon Telegraph & Telephone Corporation; *Int'l*, pg. 5351
NTT DATA BUSINESS SOLUTIONS S.P.R.L.—See Nippon Telegraph & Telephone Corporation; *Int'l*, pg. 5351
NTT DATA BUSINESS SOLUTIONS SP. Z O.O.—See Nippon Telegraph & Telephone Corporation; *Int'l*, pg. 5351
NTT DATA BUSINESS SOLUTIONS S.R.O.—See Nippon Telegraph & Telephone Corporation; *Int'l*, pg. 5351
NTT DATA BUSINESS SOLUTION (THAILAND) LTD.—See Nippon Telegraph & Telephone Corporation; *Int'l*, pg. 5351
NTT DATA BUSINESS SYSTEMS CORPORATION—See Nippon Telegraph & Telephone Corporation; *Int'l*, pg. 5346
NTT DATA CCS CORPORATION—See Nippon Telegraph & Telephone Corporation; *Int'l*, pg. 5346

COMPANY NAME INDEX NTT ADVERTISING, INC.
Company Index

NTT DATA CHILE CENTERS, LTDA.—See Nippon Telegraph & Telephone Corporation; *Int'l*, pg. 5351
NTT DATA (CHINA) CO., LTD.—See Nippon Telegraph & Telephone Corporation; *Int'l*, pg. 5346
NTT DATA (CHINA) INFORMATION TECHNOLOGY CO., LTD.—See Nippon Telegraph & Telephone Corporation; *Int'l*, pg. 5351
NTT DATA CHINA OUTSOURCING CORPORATION—See Nippon Telegraph & Telephone Corporation; *Int'l*, pg. 5346
NTT DATA CHUGOKU CORPORATION—See Nippon Telegraph & Telephone Corporation; *Int'l*, pg. 5346
NTT DATA CUBIT CORPORATION—See Nippon Telegraph & Telephone Corporation; *Int'l*, pg. 5346
NTT DATA CUSTOMER SERVICE CORPORATION—See Nippon Telegraph & Telephone Corporation; *Int'l*, pg. 5346
NTT DATA DAICHI CORPORATION—See Nippon Telegraph & Telephone Corporation; *Int'l*, pg. 5348
NTT DATA DANMARK A/S—See Nippon Telegraph & Telephone Corporation; *Int'l*, pg. 5346
NTT DATA DEUTSCHLAND GMBH—See Nippon Telegraph & Telephone Corporation; *Int'l*, pg. 5346
NTT DATA EMEA LTD.—See Nippon Telegraph & Telephone Corporation; *Int'l*, pg. 5346
NTT DATA ENGINEERING SYSTEMS CORPORATION—See Nippon Telegraph & Telephone Corporation; *Int'l*, pg. 5347
NTT DATA ENTERPRISE SERVICES HOLDING, INC.—See Nippon Telegraph & Telephone Corporation; *Int'l*, pg. 5351
NTT DATA ENTERPRISE SERVICES, INC.—See Nippon Telegraph & Telephone Corporation; *Int'l*, pg. 5348
NTT DATA EUROPE GMBH & CO. KG—See Nippon Telegraph & Telephone Corporation; *Int'l*, pg. 5346
NTT DATA FINANCIAL CORE CORPORATION—See Nippon Telegraph & Telephone Corporation; *Int'l*, pg. 5347
NTT DATA FINANCIAL TECHNOLOGY CORPORATION—See Nippon Telegraph & Telephone Corporation; *Int'l*, pg. 5351
NTT DATA FORCE CORPORATION—See Nippon Telegraph & Telephone Corporation; *Int'l*, pg. 5347
NTT DATA FRONTIER CORPORATION—See Nippon Telegraph & Telephone Corporation; *Int'l*, pg. 5347
NTT DATA GETRONICS CORPORATION—See Nippon Telegraph & Telephone Corporation; *Int'l*, pg. 5347
NTT DATA GLOBAL SOLUTIONS CORPORATION—See Nippon Telegraph & Telephone Corporation; *Int'l*, pg. 5351
NTT DATA GROUP CORPORATION—See Nippon Telegraph & Telephone Corporation; *Int'l*, pg. 5345
NTT DATA HOKKAIDO CORPORATION—See Nippon Telegraph & Telephone Corporation; *Int'l*, pg. 5347
NTT DATA HOKURIKU CORPORATION—See Nippon Telegraph & Telephone Corporation; *Int'l*, pg. 5347
NTT DATA I CORPORATION—See Nippon Telegraph & Telephone Corporation; *Int'l*, pg. 5347
NTT DATA, INC. - FEDERAL SYSTEMS—See Nippon Telegraph & Telephone Corporation; *Int'l*, pg. 5348
NTT DATA, INC.—See Nippon Telegraph & Telephone Corporation; *Int'l*, pg. 5347
NTT DATA INTELLILINK CORPORATION—See Nippon Telegraph & Telephone Corporation; *Int'l*, pg. 5347
NTT DATA INTERNATIONAL LLC—See Nippon Telegraph & Telephone Corporation; *Int'l*, pg. 5348
NTT DATA INTRAMART CORPORATION—See Nippon Telegraph & Telephone Corporation; *Int'l*, pg. 5347
NTT DATA ITALIA S.P.A.—See Nippon Telegraph & Telephone Corporation; *Int'l*, pg. 5352
NTT DATA KANSAI CORPORATION—See Nippon Telegraph & Telephone Corporation; *Int'l*, pg. 5347
NTT DATA KYUSHU CORPORATION—See Nippon Telegraph & Telephone Corporation; *Int'l*, pg. 5347
NTT DATA LUWEAVE CORPORATION—See Nippon Telegraph & Telephone Corporation; *Int'l*, pg. 5352
NTT DATA MALAYSIA SDN. BHD.—See Nippon Telegraph & Telephone Corporation; *Int'l*, pg. 5352
NTT DATA MANAGEMENT SERVICE CORPORATION—See Nippon Telegraph & Telephone Corporation; *Int'l*, pg. 5352
NTT DATA MATHEMATICAL SYSTEMS INC.—See Nippon Telegraph & Telephone Corporation; *Int'l*, pg. 5352
NTT DATA MCS CORPORATION—See Nippon Telegraph & Telephone Corporation; *Int'l*, pg. 5352
NTT DATA MHI SYSTEMS CORPORATION—See Nippon Telegraph & Telephone Corporation; *Int'l*, pg. 5352
NTT DATA MSE CORPORATION—See Nippon Telegraph & Telephone Corporation; *Int'l*, pg. 5347
NTT DATA MSE DALIAN CORPORATION—See Nippon Telegraph & Telephone Corporation; *Int'l*, pg. 5352
NTT DATA MYANMAR CO., LTD.—See Nippon Telegraph & Telephone Corporation; *Int'l*, pg. 5352
NTT DATA NCB CORPORATION—See Nishi-Nippon Financial Holdings, Inc.; *Int'l*, pg. 5364
NTT DATA NEWSON CORPORATION—See Nippon Telegraph & Telephone Corporation; *Int'l*, pg. 5352
NTT DATA NJK CORPORATION—See Nippon Telegraph & Telephone Corporation; *Int'l*, pg. 5352
NTT DATA PAYMENT SERVICES INDIA LIMITED—See Nippon Telegraph & Telephone Corporation; *Int'l*, pg. 5352
NTT DATA PHILIPPINES, INC.—See Nippon Telegraph & Telephone Corporation; *Int'l*, pg. 5352
NTT DATA SBC CORPORATION—See Nippon Telegraph & Telephone Corporation; *Int'l*, pg. 5347
NTT DATA SEKISUI SYSTEMS CORPORATION—See Nippon Telegraph & Telephone Corporation; *Int'l*, pg. 5352
NTT DATA SERVICES COLOMBIA S.A.S.—See Nippon Telegraph & Telephone Corporation; *Int'l*, pg. 5352
NTT DATA SERVICES GERMANY GMBH—See Nippon Telegraph & Telephone Corporation; *Int'l*, pg. 5352
NTT DATA SERVICES, LLC—See Nippon Telegraph & Telephone Corporation; *Int'l*, pg. 5348
NTT DATA SHIKOKU CORPORATION—See Nippon Telegraph & Telephone Corporation; *Int'l*, pg. 5347
NTT DATA SHINETSU CORPORATION—See Nippon Telegraph & Telephone Corporation; *Int'l*, pg. 5347
NTT DATA SINGAPORE PTE. LTD.—See Nippon Telegraph & Telephone Corporation; *Int'l*, pg. 5352
NTT DATA SMART SOURCING CORPORATION—See Nippon Telegraph & Telephone Corporation; *Int'l*, pg. 5352
NTT DATA SMIS CO,. LTD.—See Nippon Telegraph & Telephone Corporation; *Int'l*, pg. 5347
NTT DATA SMS CORPORATION—See Nippon Telegraph & Telephone Corporation; *Int'l*, pg. 5347
NTT DATA SOFIA CORPORATION—See Nippon Telegraph & Telephone Corporation; *Int'l*, pg. 5347
NTT DATA SOLFIS KOREA INC.—See Nippon Telegraph & Telephone Corporation; *Int'l*, pg. 5347
NTT DATA SPAIN, S.L.U.—See Nippon Telegraph & Telephone Corporation; *Int'l*, pg. 5352
NTT DATA SWITZERLAND AG—See Nippon Telegraph & Telephone Corporation; *Int'l*, pg. 5346
NTT DATA SYSTEM TECHNOLOGIES INC.—See Nippon Telegraph & Telephone Corporation; *Int'l*, pg. 5347
NTT DATA TERANOS CO. LTD.—See Nippon Telegraph & Telephone Corporation; *Int'l*, pg. 5347
NTT DATA TOHOKU CORPORATION—See Nippon Telegraph & Telephone Corporation; *Int'l*, pg. 5347
NTT DATA TOKAI CORPORATION—See Nippon Telegraph & Telephone Corporation; *Int'l*, pg. 5347
NTT DATA UK CONSULTING & IT SOLUTIONS LTD.—See Nippon Telegraph & Telephone Corporation; *Int'l*, pg. 5346
NTT DATA UNIVERSITY CORPORATION—See Nippon Telegraph & Telephone Corporation; *Int'l*, pg. 5347
NTT DATA VERTEX SOFTWARE INC.—See Nippon Telegraph & Telephone Corporation; *Int'l*, pg. 5348
NTT DATA WAVE CORPORATION—See Nippon Telegraph & Telephone Corporation; *Int'l*, pg. 5347
NTT DO BRASIL TELECOMUNICACOES LTDA.—See Nippon Telegraph & Telephone Corporation; *Int'l*, pg. 5345
NTT DOCOMO, INC.—See Nippon Telegraph & Telephone Corporation; *Int'l*, pg. 5349
NTT EARL EYE SOCIAL INFORMATION SYSTEM CO., LTD.—See Nomura Research Institute, Ltd.; *Int'l*, pg. 5413
NTT EAST-CHIBA CORPORATION—See Nippon Telegraph & Telephone Corporation; *Int'l*, pg. 5354
NTT EAST-GUNMA CORPORATION—See Nippon Telegraph & Telephone Corporation; *Int'l*, pg. 5354
NTT EAST-HOKKAIDO CORPORATION—See Nippon Telegraph & Telephone Corporation; *Int'l*, pg. 5354
NTT EAST-IBARAKI CORPORATION—See Nippon Telegraph & Telephone Corporation; *Int'l*, pg. 5354
NTT EAST-KANAGAWA CORPORATION—See Nippon Telegraph & Telephone Corporation; *Int'l*, pg. 5354
NTT EAST-NIIGATA CORPORATION—See Nippon Telegraph & Telephone Corporation; *Int'l*, pg. 5354
NTT EAST PROPERTIES, INC.—See Nippon Telegraph & Telephone Corporation; *Int'l*, pg. 5352
NTT EAST-SAITAMA CORPORATION—See Nippon Telegraph & Telephone Corporation; *Int'l*, pg. 5354
NTT EAST-TOCHIGI CORPORATION—See Nippon Telegraph & Telephone Corporation; *Int'l*, pg. 5354
NTT EAST-TOKYO CORPORATION—See Nippon Telegraph & Telephone Corporation; *Int'l*, pg. 5354
NTT EAST-YAMAGATA CORPORATION—See Nippon Telegraph & Telephone Corporation; *Int'l*, pg. 5354
NTT ELECTRONICS AMERICA, INC.—See Nippon Telegraph & Telephone Corporation; *Int'l*, pg. 5352
NTT ELECTRONICS CORPORATION—See Nippon Telegraph & Telephone Corporation; *Int'l*, pg. 5352
NTT ELECTRONICS EUROPE S.R.L.—See Nippon Telegraph & Telephone Corporation; *Int'l*, pg. 5352
NTT ELECTRONICS HONG KONG LIMITED—See Nippon Telegraph & Telephone Corporation; *Int'l*, pg. 5352
NTT ELECTRONICS SHENZHEN LIMITED—See Nippon Telegraph & Telephone Corporation; *Int'l*, pg. 5352
NTT ELECTRONICS TECHNO CORPORATION—See Nippon Telegraph & Telephone Corporation; *Int'l*, pg. 5352
NTT EUROPE LTD.—See Nippon Telegraph & Telephone Corporation; *Int'l*, pg. 5345
NTT EUROPE SRL—See Nippon Telegraph & Telephone Corporation; *Int'l*, pg. 5345
NTT FACILITIES CHUGOKU, INC.—See Nippon Telegraph & Telephone Corporation; *Int'l*, pg. 5352
NTT FACILITIES CHUO, INC.—See Nippon Telegraph & Telephone Corporation; *Int'l*, pg. 5352
NTT FACILITIES ENGINEERING, INC.—See Nippon Telegraph & Telephone Corporation; *Int'l*, pg. 5353
NTT FACILITIES FM ASSIST, INC.—See Nippon Telegraph & Telephone Corporation; *Int'l*, pg. 5352
NTT FACILITIES HOKKAIDO, INC.—See Nippon Telegraph & Telephone Corporation; *Int'l*, pg. 5352
NTT FACILITIES INC - BUSINESS CREATION DIVISION—See Nippon Telegraph & Telephone Corporation; *Int'l*, pg. 5352
NTT FACILITIES, INC.—See Nippon Telegraph & Telephone Corporation; *Int'l*, pg. 5352
NTT FACILITIES KANSAI, INC.—See Nippon Telegraph & Telephone Corporation; *Int'l*, pg. 5352
NTT FACILITIES RESEARCH INSTITUTE INC.—See Nippon Telegraph & Telephone Corporation; *Int'l*, pg. 5352
NTT FACILITIES TOHOKU, INC.—See Nippon Telegraph & Telephone Corporation; *Int'l*, pg. 5352
NTT FACILITIES TOKAI, INC.—See Nippon Telegraph & Telephone Corporation; *Int'l*, pg. 5352
NTT FACILITIES USA, INC.—See Nippon Telegraph & Telephone Corporation; *Int'l*, pg. 5352
NTT FINANCE ASSETS SERVICE CORPORATION—See Nippon Telegraph & Telephone Corporation; *Int'l*, pg. 5353
NTT FINANCE CORPORATION—See Nippon Telegraph & Telephone Corporation; *Int'l*, pg. 5352
NTT GLOBAL DATA CENTERS AMERICAS, INC.—See Nippon Telegraph & Telephone Corporation; *Int'l*, pg. 5353
NTT GLOBAL DATA CENTERS EMEA GMBH—See Nippon Telegraph & Telephone Corporation; *Int'l*, pg. 5353
NTT GLOBAL DATA CENTERS EMEA (PTY.) LTD.—See Nippon Telegraph & Telephone Corporation; *Int'l*, pg. 5353
NTT GLOBAL DATA CENTERS MAD1 S.L.U.—See Nippon Telegraph & Telephone Corporation; *Int'l*, pg. 5353
NTT GLOBAL DATA CENTERS NETHERLANDS B.V.—See Nippon Telegraph & Telephone Corporation; *Int'l*, pg. 5353
NTT GLOBAL DATA CENTERS SWITZERLAND AG—See Nippon Telegraph & Telephone Corporation; *Int'l*, pg. 5353
NTT GLOBAL NETWORKS INC—See Nippon Telegraph & Telephone Corporation; *Int'l*, pg. 5353
NTT GP-ECOCOMMUNICATION, INC.—See Nippon Telegraph & Telephone Corporation; *Int'l*, pg. 5352
NTT HOKKAIDO TELEMART CO., LTD.—See Nippon Telegraph & Telephone Corporation; *Int'l*, pg. 5354
NTT IF CORPORATION—See Nippon Telegraph & Telephone Corporation; *Int'l*, pg. 5345
NTT INFRANET CO., LTD.—See Nippon Telegraph & Telephone Corporation; *Int'l*, pg. 5354
NTT INTELLIGENT PLANNING & DEVELOPMENT CO., LTD.—See Nippon Telegraph & Telephone Corporation; *Int'l*, pg. 5352
NTT INTERNET INC.—See Nippon Telegraph & Telephone Corporation; *Int'l*, pg. 5344
NTT ITALIA S.P.A.—See Nippon Telegraph & Telephone Corporation; *Int'l*, pg. 5353
NTT IT CORPORATION—See Nippon Telegraph & Telephone Corporation; *Int'l*, pg. 5353
NTT KOREA CO., LTD.—See Nippon Telegraph & Telephone Corporation; *Int'l*, pg. 5345
NTT LEARNING SYSTEMS CORPORATION.—See Nippon Telegraph & Telephone Corporation; *Int'l*, pg. 5353
NTT LEPERC CO., LTD.—See Nippon Telegraph & Telephone Corporation; *Int'l*, pg. 5353
NTT LOGISCO INC.—See Nippon Telegraph & Telephone Corporation; *Int'l*, pg. 5353
NTT MALAYSIA SOLUTIONS SDN. BHD.—See Nippon Telegraph & Telephone Corporation; *Int'l*, pg. 5353
NTT MANAGED SERVICES AMERICAS, LLC—See Nippon Telegraph & Telephone Corporation; *Int'l*, pg. 5353
NTT MARKETING ACT CORPORATION—See Nippon Telegraph & Telephone Corporation; *Int'l*, pg. 5353
NTT-ME CORPORATION—See Nippon Telegraph & Telephone Corporation; *Int'l*, pg. 5354
NTT MEDIACROSS, INC.—See Nippon Telegraph & Telephone Corporation; *Int'l*, pg. 5354
NTT MEDIA SUPPLY INC.—See Nippon Telegraph & Telephone Corporation; *Int'l*, pg. 5355
NTT-ME SERVICE CORPORATION—See Nippon Telegraph & Telephone Corporation; *Int'l*, pg. 5354
NTT MSC SDN. BHD.—See Nippon Telegraph & Telephone Corporation; *Int'l*, pg. 5345
NTT MULTIMEDIA COMMUNICATIONS LABORATORIES, INC.—See Nippon Telegraph & Telephone Corporation; *Int'l*, pg. 5344
NTT NAVISPACE CORPORATION—See Nippon Telegraph & Telephone Corporation; *Int'l*, pg. 5345
NTT NEOMEIT CORPORATION—See Nippon Telegraph & Telephone Corporation; *Int'l*, pg. 5355

NTT ADVERTISING, INC.

NTT NETHERLANDS B.V.—See Nippon Telegraph & Telephone Corporation; *Int'l*, pg. 5353
NTT NEXIA CORPORATION—See Nippon Telegraph & Telephone Corporation; *Int'l*, pg. 5353
NT TONG ZHOU (BEIJING) PHARMACEUTICALS CO., LTD.—See China NT Pharma Group Company Limited; *Int'l*, pg. 1536
NTT PC COMMUNICATIONS, INC.—See Nippon Telegraph & Telephone Corporation; *Int'l*, pg. 5345
NTT PLALA INC.—See Nippon Telegraph & Telephone Corporation; *Int'l*, pg. 5354
NTT POLAND SP. Z O.O.—See Nippon Telegraph & Telephone Corporation; *Int'l*, pg. 5353
NTT PRINTING CORPORATION—See Nippon Telegraph & Telephone Corporation; *Int'l*, pg. 5353
NTT PUBLISHING CO., LTD.—See Nippon Telegraph & Telephone Corporation; *Int'l*, pg. 5353
NTT RENTAL ENGINEERING CO., LTD.—See Nippon Telegraph & Telephone Corporation; *Int'l*, pg. 5354
NTT RESEARCH, INC.—See Nippon Telegraph & Telephone Corporation; *Int'l*, pg. 5353
NTT RESONANT INC.—See Nippon Telegraph & Telephone Corporation; *Int'l*, pg. 5345
NTT RISK MANAGER CORPORATION—See Nippon Telegraph & Telephone Corporation; *Int'l*, pg. 5353
NTT SECURITY APPSEC SOLUTIONS INC.—See Synopsys, Inc.; *U.S. Public*, pg. 1970
NTT SECURITY CORP—See Nippon Telegraph & Telephone Corporation; *Int'l*, pg. 5353
NTT SECURITY (GERMANY) GMBH—See Nippon Telegraph & Telephone Corporation; *Int'l*, pg. 5353
NTT SECURITY HOLDINGS CORPORATION—See Nippon Telegraph & Telephone Corporation; *Int'l*, pg. 5353
NTT SECURITY (JAPAN) KK—See Nippon Telegraph & Telephone Corporation; *Int'l*, pg. 5353
NTT SINGAPORE PTE. LTD.—See Nippon Telegraph & Telephone Corporation; *Int'l*, pg. 5345
NTT SINGAPORE SOLUTIONS PTE. LTD.—See Nippon Telegraph & Telephone Corporation; *Int'l*, pg. 5353
NTT SMART CONNECT CORPORATION—See Nippon Telegraph & Telephone Corporation; *Int'l*, pg. 5355
NTT SMARTTRADE INC.—See Nippon Telegraph & Telephone Corporation; *Int'l*, pg. 5345
NTT SMILE ENERGY CO., LTD.—See Nippon Telegraph & Telephone Corporation; *Int'l*, pg. 5353
NTT SOFT SERVICE CORP.—See Nippon Telegraph & Telephone Corporation; *Int'l*, pg. 5353
NTT SOFTWARE CORPORATION—See Nippon Telegraph & Telephone Corporation; *Int'l*, pg. 5353
NTT SOLCO—See Nippon Telegraph & Telephone Corporation; *Int'l*, pg. 5354
NTT SOLMARE CORPORATION—See Nippon Telegraph & Telephone Corporation; *Int'l*, pg. 5355
NTT SOLUTIONS (THAILAND) LIMITED—See Nippon Telegraph & Telephone Corporation; *Int'l*, pg. 5353
NTT SYSTEM S.A.; *Int'l*, pg. 5485
NTT TAIWAN LTD.—See Nippon Telegraph & Telephone Corporation; *Int'l*, pg. 5345
NTT TAIWAN SOLUTIONS LIMITED—See Nippon Telegraph & Telephone Corporation; *Int'l*, pg. 5353
NTT TC LEASING CO., LTD.—See Nippon Telegraph & Telephone Corporation; *Int'l*, pg. 5353
NTT TECHNOCROSS CORPORATION—See Nippon Telegraph & Telephone Corporation; *Int'l*, pg. 5353
NTT TELECON CO., LTD.—See Nippon Telegraph & Telephone Corporation; *Int'l*, pg. 5354
NTT TOWN PAGE CORPORATION—See Nippon Telegraph & Telephone Corporation; *Int'l*, pg. 5353
NTT TRAVEL SERVICE CO., LTD.—See Nippon Telegraph & Telephone Corporation; *Int'l*, pg. 5353
NTT UD REIT INVESTMENT CORPORATION; *Int'l*, pg. 5485
NTT URBAN DEVELOPMENT ASSET MANAGEMENT CORPORATION—See Nippon Telegraph & Telephone Corporation; *Int'l*, pg. 5353
NTT URBAN DEVELOPMENT BUILSERVICE CO.—See Nippon Telegraph & Telephone Corporation; *Int'l*, pg. 5353
NTT URBAN DEVELOPMENT CORPORATION—See Nippon Telegraph & Telephone Corporation; *Int'l*, pg. 5353
NTT URBAN DEVELOPMENT HOKKAIDO BS CO.—See Nippon Telegraph & Telephone Corporation; *Int'l*, pg. 5353
NTT URBAN SOLUTIONS, INC.—See Nippon Telegraph & Telephone Corporation; *Int'l*, pg. 5353
NTT URBAN SOLUTIONS RESEARCH INSTITUTE, INC.—See Nippon Telegraph & Telephone Corporation; *Int'l*, pg. 5353
NTT URBAN VALUE SUPPORT, INC.—See Nippon Telegraph & Telephone Corporation; *Int'l*, pg. 5353
NTT VIETNAM K.K.—See Nippon Telegraph & Telephone Corporation; *Int'l*, pg. 5354
NTT WEST-CHUGOKU CORPORATION—See Nippon Telegraph & Telephone Corporation; *Int'l*, pg. 5355
NTT WEST-HOKURIKU CORPORATION—See Nippon Telegraph & Telephone Corporation; *Int'l*, pg. 5355
NTT WEST-HOMETECHNO KYUSHU CORPORATION—See Nippon Telegraph & Telephone Corporation; *Int'l*, pg. 5355

NTT WEST-HYOGO CORPORATION—See Nippon Telegraph & Telephone Corporation; *Int'l*, pg. 5355
NTT WEST-KANSAI IT-MATE CO., LTD.—See Nippon Telegraph & Telephone Corporation; *Int'l*, pg. 5355
NTT WEST-KYUSHU IT-MATE INC.—See Nippon Telegraph & Telephone Corporation; *Int'l*, pg. 5355
NTT WEST-SHIKOKU CORPORATION—See Nippon Telegraph & Telephone Corporation; *Int'l*, pg. 5355
NTT WEST-SHIKOKU IT-MATE CO LTD.—See Nippon Telegraph & Telephone Corporation; *Int'l*, pg. 5355
NTT WEST-TOKAI CORPORATION—See Nippon Telegraph & Telephone Corporation; *Int'l*, pg. 5355
NTT WEST-TOKAI IT-MATE CORPORATION—See Nippon Telegraph & Telephone Corporation; *Int'l*, pg. 5355
NTT WORLD ENGINEERING MARINE CORPORATION—See Nippon Telegraph & Telephone Corporation; *Int'l*, pg. 5345
NTT WORLDWIDE TELECOMMUNICATIONS CORPORATION—See Nippon Telegraph & Telephone Corporation; *Int'l*, pg. 5345
NTUC FAIRPRICE CO-OPERATIVE LTD.; *Int'l*, pg. 5485
NT VALDOS, UAB—See UAB Ignitis grupe; *Int'l*, pg. 7998
NTV AMERICA COMPANY—See Nippon Television Holdings Inc.; *Int'l*, pg. 5356
NTVB MEDIA, INC.; *U.S. Private*, pg. 2971
NTV EVENTS INC.—See Nippon Television Holdings Inc.; *Int'l*, pg. 5356
NTV GROUP HOLDINGS INC.—See Nippon Television Holdings Inc.; *Int'l*, pg. 5356
NTV INTERNATIONAL CORPORATION—See Nippon Television Holdings Inc.; *Int'l*, pg. 5356
NTV IT PRODUCE CORPORATION—See Nippon Television Holdings Inc.; *Int'l*, pg. 5356
NTV PERSONNEL CENTER CORP—See Nippon Television Holdings Inc.; *Int'l*, pg. 5356
NTV SERVICES INC.—See Nippon Television Holdings Inc.; *Int'l*, pg. 5356
NTV TECHNICAL RESOURCES INC.—See Nippon Television Holdings Inc.; *Int'l*, pg. 5356
NTX HEALTHCARE PROPERTIES, LLC—See Universal Health Realty Income Trust; *U.S. Public*, pg. 2255
NTY FRANCHISE COMPANY; *U.S. Private*, pg. 2971
NTZ INTERNATIONAL HOLDING B.V.—See Frencken Group Limited; *Int'l*, pg. 2773
NU3 GMBH—See Shop Apotheke Europe N.V.; *Int'l*, pg. 6859
NUADI—See Arta Capital SGEIC SA; *Int'l*, pg. 580
NUAER AS—See Nordic Unmanned ASA; *Int'l*, pg. 5423
NUAIRE INC.—See Kewaunee Scientific Corporation; *U.S. Public*, pg. 1225
NUANCE COMMUNICATIONS AUSTRALIA PTY LTD.—See Microsoft Corporation; *U.S. Public*, pg. 1442
NUANCE COMMUNICATIONS AUSTRIA GMBH—See Microsoft Corporation; *U.S. Public*, pg. 1442
NUANCE COMMUNICATIONS CANADA, INC.—See Microsoft Corporation; *U.S. Public*, pg. 1442
NUANCE COMMUNICATIONS GMBH—See Microsoft Corporation; *U.S. Public*, pg. 1442
NUANCE COMMUNICATIONS HEALTHCARE GERMANY GMBH—See Microsoft Corporation; *U.S. Public*, pg. 1442
NUANCE COMMUNICATIONS HONG KONG LIMITED—See Microsoft Corporation; *U.S. Public*, pg. 1442
NUANCE COMMUNICATIONS HUNGARY KFT—See Microsoft Corporation; *U.S. Public*, pg. 1442
NUANCE COMMUNICATIONS IBERICA SA—See Microsoft Corporation; *U.S. Public*, pg. 1442
NUANCE COMMUNICATIONS, INC.—See Microsoft Corporation; *U.S. Public*, pg. 1441
NUANCE COMMUNICATIONS INTERNATIONAL BVBA—See Microsoft Corporation; *U.S. Public*, pg. 1442
NUANCE COMMUNICATIONS ISRAEL, LTD.—See Microsoft Corporation; *U.S. Public*, pg. 1442
NUANCE COMMUNICATIONS JAPAN K.K.—See Microsoft Corporation; *U.S. Public*, pg. 1442
NUANCE COMMUNICATIONS KOREA LTD.—See Microsoft Corporation; *U.S. Public*, pg. 1442
NUANCE COMMUNICATIONS UK LTD.—See Microsoft Corporation; *U.S. Public*, pg. 1442
NUANCE COMMUNICATONS HONG KONG LIMITED—See Microsoft Corporation; *U.S. Public*, pg. 1442
NUANCE DICTAPHONE HEALTHCARE SOLUTIONS—See Microsoft Corporation; *U.S. Public*, pg. 1442
NUANCE DOCUMENT IMAGING SOLUTIONS—See Microsoft Corporation; *U.S. Public*, pg. 1442
NUANCE DOCUMENT IMAGING ULC—See Microsoft Corporation; *U.S. Public*, pg. 1442
NUANCE ENTERPRISE SOLUTIONS & SERVICES CORPORATION—See Microsoft Corporation; *U.S. Public*, pg. 1443
NUANCE ENTERPRISE SOLUTIONS & SERVICES CORPORATION—See Microsoft Corporation; *U.S. Public*, pg. 1442
NUANCE FRANCE—See Microsoft Corporation; *U.S. Public*, pg. 1443

CORPORATE AFFILIATIONS

THE NUANCE GROUP AG—See Avolta AG; *Int'l*, pg. 749
THE NUANCE GROUP (AUSTRALIA) PTY LTD—See Avolta AG; *Int'l*, pg. 749
THE NUANCE GROUP (MALTA) LIMITED—See Avolta AG; *Int'l*, pg. 749
NUANCE INDIA PVT. LTD.—See Microsoft Corporation; *U.S. Public*, pg. 1443
NUANCE JAPAN K.K.—See Microsoft Corporation; *U.S. Public*, pg. 1443
NUANCE RECOGNITA CORP.—See Microsoft Corporation; *U.S. Public*, pg. 1443
NUANCE SOFTWARE TECHNOLOGY (BEIJING) CO., LTD.—See Microsoft Corporation; *U.S. Public*, pg. 1443
NUANCE SYSTEMS, LLC—See Wynnchurch Capital, L.P.; *U.S. Private*, pg. 4577
NUANCE TRANSCRIPTION SERVICES, INC.—See Microsoft Corporation; *U.S. Public*, pg. 1443
NUARC COMPANY, INC.—See M&R Holdings Inc.; *U.S. Private*, pg. 2525
NUARC WESTERN DIV.—See M&R Holdings Inc.; *U.S. Private*, pg. 2525
NUBCO PROPRIETARY LIMITED—See Coventry Group Limited; *Int'l*, pg. 1821
NUBEVA TECHNOLOGIES LTD.; *U.S. Public*, pg. 1553
NUBIAN RESOURCES LTD.; *Int'l*, pg. 5485
NUBIOLA BULGARIA ODD—See American Securities LLC; *U.S. Private*, pg. 252
NUBIOLA COLOMBIA PIGMENTOS S.A.S.—See American Securities LLC; *U.S. Private*, pg. 252
NUBIOLA INDIA PRIVATE, LIMITED—See American Securities LLC; *U.S. Private*, pg. 252
NUBIOLA PIGMENTS (SHANGHAI) CO., LTD.—See American Securities LLC; *U.S. Private*, pg. 252
NUBIOLA ROMANIA SRL—See American Securities LLC; *U.S. Private*, pg. 252
NUBIOLA USA, INC.—See American Securities LLC; *U.S. Private*, pg. 252
NUBON GMBH & CO. KG—See Otto GmbH & Co. KG; *Int'l*, pg. 5663
NUBOON CO., LTD.—See Saha Pathanapibul Public Company Limited; *Int'l*, pg. 6479
NUBREED NUTRITION INC.—See Velocity Data Inc.; *Int'l*, pg. 8150
NUBRIK PTY LTD—See Brickworks Limited; *Int'l*, pg. 1152
NUBURU, INC.; *U.S. Public*, pg. 1553
NUCADVISOR SAS—See VINCI S.A.; *Int'l*, pg. 8224
NU CAL FOODS INC.; *U.S. Private*, pg. 2971
NU-CALGON WHOLESALER INC.; *U.S. Private*, pg. 2971
NUCANA PLC; *Int'l*, pg. 5485
NUCAP INDUSTRIES INC.; *Int'l*, pg. 5485
NUCAP US INC.—See Nucap Industries Inc.; *Int'l*, pg. 5485
NUCAP VEHICLE COMPONENTS (SHANGHAI) COMPANY—See Nucap Industries Inc.; *Int'l*, pg. 5485
NUCCI BROS INC.; *U.S. Private*, pg. 2972
NUC CORPORATION—See ENEOS Holdings, Inc.; *Int'l*, pg. 2417
NUCEDAR MILLS INC—See Jain Irrigation Systems Limited; *Int'l*, pg. 3872
NUCELLSYS GMBH—See Mercedes-Benz Group AG; *Int'l*, pg. 4828
NUCENT CO. LTD.—See EG Systems LLC; *U.S. Private*, pg. 1344
NUCHEM LIMITED; *Int'l*, pg. 5485
NUCHEV LIMITED; *Int'l*, pg. 5485
NUCH OF TEXAS—See Tenet Healthcare Corporation; *U.S. Public*, pg. 2005
NUCIVIC, INC.—See Actua Corporation; *U.S. Private*, pg. 71
NUCKLES OIL COMPANY INC.; *U.S. Private*, pg. 2972
NUCLEACTION—See Groupe Gorge S.A.; *Int'l*, pg. 3103
NUCLEAR CORPORATE FURNITURE (PTY) LIMITED—See The Bidvest Group Limited; *Int'l*, pg. 7625
NUCLEAR DEVELOPMENT CORPORATION—See Mitsubishi Heavy Industries, Ltd.; *Int'l*, pg. 4960
NUCLEAR DIAGNOSIS, INC.—See HCA Healthcare, Inc.; *U.S. Public*, pg. 1005
NUCLEAR ENGINEERING, LTD.—See The Kansai Electric Power Co., Inc.; *Int'l*, pg. 7662
NUCLEAR FUEL INDUSTRIES LTD. - KUMATORI WORKS—See Japan Industrial Partners, Inc.; *Int'l*, pg. 3894
NUCLEAR FUEL INDUSTRIES LTD.—See Japan Industrial Partners, Inc.; *Int'l*, pg. 3894
NUCLEAR FUEL INDUSTRIES LTD. - TOKAI WORKS—See Japan Industrial Partners, Inc.; *Int'l*, pg. 3895
NUCLEAR FUELS CORPORATION—See General Atomics; *U.S. Private*, pg. 1663
NUCLEAR FUEL SERVICES, INC.—See Electricite de France S.A.; *Int'l*, pg. 2351
NUCLEAR FUEL TRANSPORT CO., LTD.—See Tokyo Electric Power Company Holdings, Incorporated; *Int'l*, pg. 7790
NUCLEAR LOGISTICS LLC—See Paragon Energy Solutions, LLC; *U.S. Private*, pg. 3091
NUCLEAR MEDICINE PROFESSIONALS, INC.; *U.S. Private*, pg. 2972

COMPANY NAME INDEX

NUCLEAR PHARMACY SERVICES—See Cardinal Health, Inc.; *U.S. Public*, pg. 434
NUCLEAR PLANT SERVICE ENGINEERING CO., LTD.—See Mitsubishi Heavy Industries, Ltd.; *Int'l*, pg. 4960
NUCLEAR POWER TRAINING CENTER, LTD.—See Mitsubishi Heavy Industries, Ltd.; *Int'l*, pg. 4960
NUCLEO DE COMUNICACIONES Y CONTROL, S.L.—See Amper, S.A.; *Int'l*, pg. 433
NUCLETRON ASIA PACIFIC LTD.—See Elekta AB; *Int'l*, pg. 2356
NUCLETRON A/S—See Elekta AB; *Int'l*, pg. 2356
NUCLETRON B.V.—See Elekta AB; *Int'l*, pg. 2356
NUCLETRON CANADA INC.—See Elekta AB; *Int'l*, pg. 2356
NUCLETRON ELECTRONIC AG; *Int'l*, pg. 5485
NUCLETRON POLAND SP Z.O.O.—See Elekta AB; *Int'l*, pg. 2356
NUCLETRON PTY. LTD.—See Elekta AB; *Int'l*, pg. 2356
NUCLETRON SAS—See Elekta AB; *Int'l*, pg. 2356
NUCLETRON UK LTD.—See Elekta AB; *Int'l*, pg. 2356
NUCLETUDES—See Airbus SE; *Int'l*, pg. 246
NUCLEUS BIOLOGICS LLC; *U.S. Private*, pg. 2972
NUCLEUS FINANCIAL GROUP PLC—See HPS Investment Partners, LLC; *U.S. Private*, pg. 1997
NUCLEUS FINANCIAL PLATFORMS LIMITED; *Int'l*, pg. 5485
NUCLEUS SOFTWARE EXPORTS LIMITED; *Int'l*, pg. 5485
NUCLEUS SOFTWARE JAPAN KABUSHIKI KAISHA—See Nucleus Software Exports Limited; *Int'l*, pg. 5486
NUCLEUS SOFTWARE NETHERLANDS B.V.—See Nucleus Software Exports Limited; *Int'l*, pg. 5486
NUCLEUS SOFTWARE SOLUTIONS PTE. LTD.—See Nucleus Software Exports Limited; *Int'l*, pg. 5486
NUCLEUS SOFTWARE SOUTH AFRICA PTY. LTD.—See Nucleus Software Exports Limited; *Int'l*, pg. 5486
NUCLEUS UNDERWRITING LIMITED—See Brown & Brown, Inc.; *U.S. Public*, pg. 401
NUCO2 INC.—See Linde plc; *Int'l*, pg. 4509
NUCO2 LLC—See Linde plc; *Int'l*, pg. 4509
NUCO LIGHTING TECHNOLOGY LTD. CO.—See ITAB Shop Concept AB; *Int'l*, pg. 3828
NUCOM GROUP SE—See ProSiebenSat.1 Media SE; *Int'l*, pg. 6000
NUCOMPASS MOBILITY SERVICES INC.; *U.S. Private*, pg. 2972
NU-CON SYSTEMS SDN. BHD.—See GEA Group Aktiengesellschaft; *Int'l*, pg. 2903
NUCOR BUILDING SYSTEMS—See Nucor Corporation; *U.S. Public*, pg. 1553
NUCOR BUILDING SYSTEMS UTAH LLC—See Nucor Corporation; *U.S. Public*, pg. 1553
NUCOR CASTRIP ARKANSAS LLC—See Nucor Corporation; *U.S. Public*, pg. 1553
NUCOR COLD FINISH-NEBRASKA—See Nucor Corporation; *U.S. Public*, pg. 1553
NUCOR COLD FINISH-SOUTH CAROLINA—See Nucor Corporation; *U.S. Public*, pg. 1553
NUCOR COLD FINISH WISCONSIN, INC.—See Nucor Corporation; *U.S. Public*, pg. 1553
NUCOR CORPORATION; *U.S. Public*, pg. 1553
NUCOR ENERGY HOLDINGS INC—See Nucor Corporation; *U.S. Public*, pg. 1554
NUCOR FASTENERS—See Nucor Corporation; *U.S. Public*, pg. 1554
NUCOR-LMP INC.—See Nucor Corporation; *U.S. Public*, pg. 1554
NUCOR STEEL - ARKANSAS—See Nucor Corporation; *U.S. Public*, pg. 1554
NUCOR STEEL AUBURN, INC.—See Nucor Corporation; *U.S. Public*, pg. 1554
NUCOR STEEL-BERKELEY—See Nucor Corporation; *U.S. Public*, pg. 1554
NUCOR STEEL BIRMINGHAM, INC.—See Nucor Corporation; *U.S. Public*, pg. 1554
NUCOR STEEL CONNECTICUT INC.—See Nucor Corporation; *U.S. Public*, pg. 1554
NUCOR STEEL DECATUR, LLC—See Nucor Corporation; *U.S. Public*, pg. 1554
NUCOR STEEL GALLATIN, LLC—See Nucor Corporation; *U.S. Public*, pg. 1554
NUCOR STEEL-INDIANA—See Nucor Corporation; *U.S. Public*, pg. 1554
NUCOR STEEL JACKSON, INC.—See Nucor Corporation; *U.S. Public*, pg. 1554
NUCOR STEEL KANKAKEE, INC.—See Nucor Corporation; *U.S. Public*, pg. 1554
NUCOR STEEL KINGMAN, LLC—See Nucor Corporation; *U.S. Public*, pg. 1554
NUCOR STEEL LONGVIEW LLC—See Nucor Corporation; *U.S. Public*, pg. 1554
NUCOR STEEL LOUISIANA LLC—See Nucor Corporation; *U.S. Public*, pg. 1554
NUCOR STEEL MARION, INC.—See Nucor Corporation; *U.S. Public*, pg. 1554
NUCOR STEEL MEMPHIS, INC.—See Nucor Corporation; *U.S. Public*, pg. 1554

NUCOR STEEL-NEBRASKA—See Nucor Corporation; *U.S. Public*, pg. 1554
NUCOR STEEL SEATTLE, INC.—See Nucor Corporation; *U.S. Public*, pg. 1554
NUCOR STEEL-SOUTH CAROLINA—See Nucor Corporation; *U.S. Public*, pg. 1554
NUCOR STEEL-TEXAS—See Nucor Corporation; *U.S. Public*, pg. 1554
NUCOR STEEL TUSCALOOSA, INC.—See Nucor Corporation; *U.S. Public*, pg. 1554
NUCOR STEEL-UTAH—See Nucor Corporation; *U.S. Public*, pg. 1554
NUCOR TUBULAR PRODUCTS, INC.—See Nucor Corporation; *U.S. Public*, pg. 1554
NUCOR TUBULAR PRODUCTS MADISON LLC—See Nucor Corporation; *U.S. Public*, pg. 1554
NUCOR-YAMATO STEEL COMPANY—See Nucor Corporation; *U.S. Public*, pg. 1554
NUCOR-YAMATO STEEL COMPANY—See Yamato Kogyo Co. Ltd.; *Int'l*, pg. 8555
NUCOURSE DISTRIBUTION INC.; *U.S. Private*, pg. 2972
NUCRYST PHARMACEUTICALS CORP.—See The Westaim Corporation; *Int'l*, pg. 7701
NUCSAFE, INC.—See OSI Systems, Inc.; *U.S. Public*, pg. 1621
NUCTECH COMPANY LIMITED—See Tsinghua Tongfang Co., Ltd.; *Int'l*, pg. 7952
NUDE BY NATURE PTY LIMITED—See Crescent Capital Partners Ltd.; *Int'l*, pg. 1839
NUDELMAN KBTOCHMASH JSC—See Russian Technologies State Corporation; *Int'l*, pg. 6431
NUDO PRODUCTS INC.—See RFE Investment Partners; *U.S. Private*, pg. 3419
NUDURA INC.—See RPM International Inc.; *U.S. Public*, pg. 1817
NUECES COUNTY MHMR COMMUNITY CENTER; *U.S. Private*, pg. 2972
NUECES FARM CENTER INC.; *U.S. Private*, pg. 2972
NUENERGY GAS LIMITED; *Int'l*, pg. 5486
NU ENTERPRISES, INC.—See Eversource Energy; *U.S. Public*, pg. 801
NUERA AIR INC—See Nuera Inc.; *Int'l*, pg. 5486
NUERA COMMUNICATIONS SINGAPORE PTE LTD.—See AudioCodes Ltd.; *Int'l*, pg. 702
NUERA INC.; *Int'l*, pg. 5486
NUERA TRANSPORT, INC.—See Nuera Inc.; *Int'l*, pg. 5486
NUERNBERGER BETEILIGUNGS AG; *Int'l*, pg. 5486
NUESOFT TECHNOLOGIES, INC.—See Global Payments Inc.; *U.S. Public*, pg. 943
NUESTRA CLINICA DEL VALLE, INC.; *U.S. Private*, pg. 2972
NUETERRA CAPITAL MANAGEMENT, LLC; *U.S. Private*, pg. 2972
NUEVA CALIFORNIA S.A.—See Jaeger Resources Corp.; *Int'l*, pg. 3869
NUEVA COMUNICACION-WEBER SHANDWICK—See The Interpublic Group of Companies, Inc.; *U.S. Public*, pg. 2105
NUEVA COMUNICACION-WEBER SHANDWICK—See The Interpublic Group of Companies, Inc.; *U.S. Public*, pg. 2105
NUEVA GENERACION MANUFACTURAS S.A DE C.V.; *Int'l*, pg. 5486
NUEVA HERRAMIENTA DE CORTE SA—See Tivoly S.A.; *Int'l*, pg. 7762
NUEVA RIOJA, SA—See Vocento, S.A.; *Int'l*, pg. 8284
NUEVA SIBOL S.L.U.—See Spasciani S.p.a.; *Int'l*, pg. 7128
NUEVO ADVERTISING GROUP, INC.; *U.S. Private*, pg. 2972
NUEVO BANCO SUQUIA S.A.—See Banco Macro S.A.; *Int'l*, pg. 823
NUEVOLUTION A/S; *Int'l*, pg. 5486
NUEVOS ESPACIOS HOTELEROS, S.L.—See Minor International PCL; *Int'l*, pg. 4912
NUFARM AGRICULTURE, INC.—See Nufarm Limited; *Int'l*, pg. 5486
NUFARM AMERICAS INC.—See Nufarm Limited; *Int'l*, pg. 5486
NUFARM (ASIA) PTE LTD—See Nufarm Limited; *Int'l*, pg. 5486
NUFARM AUSTRALIA LIMITED—See Nufarm Limited; *Int'l*, pg. 5486
NUFARM B.V.—See Nufarm Limited; *Int'l*, pg. 5486
NUFARM CHEMICAL (SHANGHAI) CO., LTD.—See Nufarm Limited; *Int'l*, pg. 5486
NUFARM DEUTSCHLAND GMBH—See Nufarm Limited; *Int'l*, pg. 5486
NUFARM ESPANA S.A.—See Nufarm Limited; *Int'l*, pg. 5486
NUFARM EUROPE GMBH—See Nufarm Limited; *Int'l*, pg. 5486
NUFARM GMBH & CO KG—See Nufarm Limited; *Int'l*, pg. 5486
NUFARM GRUPO MEXICO S DE R.L. DE C.V.—See Nufarm Limited; *Int'l*, pg. 5486
NUFARM HUNGARIA KFT—See Nufarm Limited; *Int'l*, pg. 5486

NUINSCO RESOURCES LIMITED

NUFARM ITALIA S.R.L.—See Nufarm Limited; *Int'l*, pg. 5486
NUFARM KK—See Nufarm Limited; *Int'l*, pg. 5486
NUFARM LIMITED; *Int'l*, pg. 5486
NUFARM MALAYSIA—See Nufarm Limited; *Int'l*, pg. 5486
NUFARM NEW ZEALAND TRADING DIVISION—See Nufarm Limited; *Int'l*, pg. 5486
NUFARM NZ LIMITED—See Nufarm Limited; *Int'l*, pg. 5486
NUFARM POLSKA SP. Z O.O.—See Nufarm Limited; *Int'l*, pg. 5487
NUFARM PORTUGAL LDA.—See Nufarm Limited; *Int'l*, pg. 5487
NUFARM ROMANIA S.R.L.—See Nufarm Limited; *Int'l*, pg. 5487
NUFARM SA—See Nufarm Limited; *Int'l*, pg. 5487
NUFARM SA—See Nufarm Limited; *Int'l*, pg. 5487
NUFARM SUISSE S.A.R.L.—See Nufarm Limited; *Int'l*, pg. 5487
NUFARM UK LTD.—See Nufarm Limited; *Int'l*, pg. 5487
NUFARM UKRAINE LLC—See Nufarm Limited; *Int'l*, pg. 5487
NUFERN INC.—See Coherent Corp.; *U.S. Public*, pg. 527
NUFFER SMITH TUCKER, INC.; *U.S. Private*, pg. 2972
NUFFIELD HAYWARDS HEATH HOSPITAL—See Nuffield Health; *Int'l*, pg. 5487
NUFFIELD HEALTH CHICHESTER HOSPITAL—See Nuffield Health; *Int'l*, pg. 5487
NUFFIELD HEALTH; *Int'l*, pg. 5487
NUFFIELD HEALTH TAUNTON HOSPITAL—See Nuffield Health; *Int'l*, pg. 5487
NUFFIELD HEALTH TEES HOSPITAL—See Nuffield Health; *Int'l*, pg. 5487
NUFFIELD HOSPITAL BRIGHTON—See Nuffield Health; *Int'l*, pg. 5487
NUFFIELD HOSPITAL CAMBRIDGE—See Nuffield Health; *Int'l*, pg. 5487
THE NUFFIELD HOSPITAL DERBY—See Nuffield Health; *Int'l*, pg. 5487
NUFFIELD HOSPITAL EXETER—See Nuffield Health; *Int'l*, pg. 5487
NUFFIELD HOSPITAL HARROGATE—See Centene Corporation; *U.S. Public*, pg. 468
THE NUFFIELD HOSPITAL IPSWICH—See Nuffield Health; *Int'l*, pg. 5488
NUFFIELD HOSPITAL LEEDS—See Nuffield Health; *Int'l*, pg. 5487
NUFFIELD HOSPITALS YORK—See Nuffield Health; *Int'l*, pg. 5487
NUFFIELD PROACTIVE HEALTH—See Nuffield Health; *Int'l*, pg. 5487
NUFFNANG LIVE COMMERCE SDN. BHD.—See Xamble Group Limited; *Int'l*, pg. 8519
NUFLARE TECHNOLOGY, INC.—See Japan Industrial Partners, Inc.; *Int'l*, pg. 3894
NU FLOW AMERICA INC.; *U.S. Private*, pg. 2971
NUFLUX LLC—See Speyside Equity LLC; *U.S. Private*, pg. 3756
NUFORD FORD PTY LTD—See Eagers Automotive Limited; *Int'l*, pg. 2263
NUFORMIX PLC; *Int'l*, pg. 5488
NU FRUIT PTY. LTD.—See Metcash Limited; *Int'l*, pg. 4852
NUGAR, S.A. DE C.V.—See Cie Automotive S.A.; *Int'l*, pg. 1605
NUGEN ENERGY, LLC—See REX American Resources Corporation; *U.S. Public*, pg. 1795
NUGENEREX IMMUNO-ONCOLOGY, INC.—See Generex Biotechnology Corporation; *U.S. Public*, pg. 930
NUGEN HOLDINGS, INC.; *U.S. Private*, pg. 2972
NUGENT SAND COMPANY; *U.S. Private*, pg. 2972
NUGENT SHOPPING PARK LIMITED—See The British Land Company PLC; *Int'l*, pg. 7628
NUGG.AD GMBH—See Zalando SE; *Int'l*, pg. 8621
NUGGET MARKET INC.; *U.S. Private*, pg. 2972
NUGL, INC.; *U.S. Public*, pg. 1555
NU/HART HAIR SOLUTIONS LIMITED—See Town Health International Medical Group Limited; *Int'l*, pg. 7851
NUH BETON A.S.—See Nuh Cimento Sanayi A.S.; *Int'l*, pg. 5488
NUH CIMENTO SANAYI A.S.; *Int'l*, pg. 5488
NUHC, INC.—See Arrow Electronics, Inc.; *U.S. Public*, pg. 199
NUHEARA LIMITED; *Int'l*, pg. 5488
NU HOLDINGS LTD.; *Int'l*, pg. 5485
NU HORIZONS ELECTRONICS A/S—See Arrow Electronics, Inc.; *U.S. Public*, pg. 199
NU HORIZONS ELECTRONICS PTY LTD.—See Arrow Electronics, Inc.; *U.S. Public*, pg. 199
NUH YAPI URUNLERI A.S.—See Nuh Cimento Sanayi A.S.; *Int'l*, pg. 5488
NU IMAGE FABRICS, INC.; *U.S. Private*, pg. 2971
NU IMAGE, INC.; *U.S. Private*, pg. 2971
NUI NHO STONE JOINT STOCK COMPANY; *Int'l*, pg. 5488
NUINSCO RESOURCES LIMITED; *Int'l*, pg. 5488
NU INSTRUMENTS LIMITED—See AMETEK, Inc.; *U.S. Public*, pg. 118

NUINSCO RESOURCES LIMITED

CORPORATE AFFILIATIONS

NUINTEK CO., LTD. - CHINA PLANT—See NUINTEK CO., LTD.; *Int'l*, pg. 5488
NUINTEK CO., LTD. - DAMYANG PLANT—See NUINTEK CO., LTD.; *Int'l*, pg. 5488
NUINTEK CO., LTD. - MEXICO PLANT—See NUINTEK CO., LTD.; *Int'l*, pg. 5488
NUINTEK CO., LTD.; *Int'l*, pg. 5488
NUINTEK CO., LTD. - THAILAND PLANT—See NUINTEK CO., LTD.; *Int'l*, pg. 5488
NUI TEC CORPORATION—See Tachi-S Co., Ltd.; *Int'l*, pg. 7402
NUIX LIMITED; *Int'l*, pg. 5488
NUIX USG INC.—See Nuix Limited; *Int'l*, pg. 5488
NUJAK DEVELOPMENT, INC.; *U.S. Private*, pg. 2973
NUJAY TECHNOLOGIES INC.—See ICAPE Holding S.A.; *Int'l*, pg. 3578
NUKEM GMBH—See Cameco Corporation; *Int'l*, pg. 1270
NUKEM, INC.—See Cameco Corporation; *Int'l*, pg. 1270
NUKK-FREEMAN & CERRA, P.C.; *U.S. Private*, pg. 2973
NUKKLEUS INC.; *U.S. Public*, pg. 1555
NULAB, INC.; *U.S. Private*, pg. 2973
NUL ACCESSIBILITY, LTD.—See BIPROGY Inc.; *Int'l*, pg. 1045
NULAID FOODS INC.; *U.S. Private*, pg. 2973
NULANDIS—See AECI Limited; *Int'l*, pg. 171
NULEAF NATURALS, LLC—See High Tide, Inc.; *Int'l*, pg. 3386
NULEGACY GOLD CORPORATION; *Int'l*, pg. 5488
NULEGACY GOLD N.V.—See NuLegacy Gold Corporation; *Int'l*, pg. 5488
NU-LITE ELECTRICAL WHOLESALERS, INC.—See Blackfriars Corp.; *U.S. Private*, pg. 575
THE NULMAN GROUP; *U.S. Private*, pg. 4085
NULOGIX HEALTH, INC.—See RadNet, Inc.; *U.S. Public*, pg. 1761
NU-LOOK COLLISION, INC.—See Boyd Group Services Inc.; *Int'l*, pg. 1125
NUL SYSTEM SERVICES CORPORATION—See BIPROGY Inc.; *Int'l*, pg. 1045
NUM AG; *Int'l*, pg. 5488
NUMARA SOFTWARE (FRANCE) SAS—See KKR & Co. Inc.; *U.S. Public*, pg. 1241
NUMARA SOFTWARE LIMITED—See KKR & Co. Inc.; *U.S. Public*, pg. 1241
NUMARK CREDIT UNION; *U.S. Private*, pg. 2973
NUMARK INDUSTRIES, L.P.—See inMusic, LLC; *U.S. Private*, pg. 2080
NUMARK LABORATORIES, INC.; *U.S. Private*, pg. 2973
NUMATIC ENGINEERING INC.; *U.S. Private*, pg. 2973
NUMA TOOL CO.; *U.S. Private*, pg. 2973
NUMAZU COPPER REFINING & ROLLING CO., LTD.—See Fujikura Ltd.; *Int'l*, pg. 2829
NUMAZU DAIICHI TRAFFIC CO., LTD.—See Daiichi Koutsu Sangyo Co., Ltd.; *Int'l*, pg. 1929
NUMAZU DYNAPAC CO., LTD.—See Dynapac Co., Ltd.; *Int'l*, pg. 2241
NUMBER 1 SHOES LIMITED—See Bapcor Limited; *Int'l*, pg. 857
NUMBER 8 FREIGHT LTD.—See Mullen Group Ltd.; *Int'l*, pg. 5080
NUMBERFIRE, INC.—See Flutter Entertainment plc; *Int'l*, pg. 2715
THE NUMBER UK LTD.—See kgb USA, Inc.; *U.S. Private*, pg. 2301
NUMBERWORKS, LLC; *U.S. Private*, pg. 2973
NUM CNC HIGHEND APPLICATIONS S. A.—See NUM AG; *Int'l*, pg. 5488
NUM CNC KOREA CO. LTD.—See NUM AG; *Int'l*, pg. 5488
NUM CORPORATION—See NUM AG; *Int'l*, pg. 5489
NUMECA INDIA SOFTWARE PRIVATE LIMITED—See Cadence Design Systems, Inc.; *U.S. Public*, pg. 419
NUMECENT HOLDINGS LTD.; *U.S. Private*, pg. 2973
NU-MED PLUS, INC.; *U.S. Public*, pg. 1552
NU-MEGA INGREDIENTS PTY. LTD.—See Clover Corporation Limited; *Int'l*, pg. 1663
NUMEIRA MIXED SALTS & MUD CO.—See Arab Potash Company PLC; *Int'l*, pg. 5
NUMERA SISTEMI E INFORMATICA S.P.A.—See BPER BANCA S.p.A; *Int'l*, pg. 1132
NUMERATIS SP. Z O.O.—See Ergis S.A.; *Int'l*, pg. 2491
NUMERA CORPORATION; *U.S. Private*, pg. 2973
NUMERICA CREDIT UNION; *U.S. Private*, pg. 2973
NUMERICAL APPLICATIONS, INC.—See Zachry Holdings, Inc.; *U.S. Private*, pg. 4596
NUMERICAL CONCEPTS, INC.; *U.S. Private*, pg. 2973
NUMERICAL PRECISION, INC.—See Behrman Brothers Management Corp.; *U.S. Private*, pg. 515
NUMERICAL PRODUCTIONS, INC.—See Paramount Precision Products, Inc.; *U.S. Private*, pg. 3093
NUMERIC INVESTORS LLC—See MAN Group plc; *Int'l*, pg. 4665
NUMERIC SOLAR ENERGY PRIVATE LIMITED—See SWELECT Energy Systems Ltd.; *Int'l*, pg. 7366
NUMERIX LLC—See Genstar Capital, LLC; *U.S. Private*, pg. 1677
NUMERO (NZ) LIMITED—See Rubicor Group Limited; *Int'l*, pg. 6423

NUMERO UNO CREATIVE GROUP PTE LTD—See Nobel Design Holdings Pte Ltd; *Int'l*, pg. 5394
NUMERO UNO MARKETS—See Breco Holdings, Inc; *U.S. Private*, pg. 644
NUMESH, INC.—See Fertek, Inc.; *Int'l*, pg. 2646
NUMET HOLDINGS PTY. LTD.—See Tupperware Brands Corporation; *U.S. Public*, pg. 2204
NUMET MACHINING TECHNIQUES, LLC—See Arlington Capital Partners LLC; *U.S. Private*, pg. 328
NUMFLO SA—See Cadence Design Systems, Inc.; *U.S. Public*, pg. 419
NUM GMBH—See NUM AG; *Int'l*, pg. 5489
NUMIKO; *Int'l*, pg. 5489
NUMIL GIDA URUNLERI SANAYI VE TICARET A.S.—See Danone; *Int'l*, pg. 1966
NUMIL HELLAS S.A.—See Danone; *Int'l*, pg. 1966
NUMIL HUNGARY TAPSZERKERESKEDELNI KFT.—See Danone; *Int'l*, pg. 1966
NUMIL NUTRICION S.R.L.—See Danone; *Int'l*, pg. 1966
NUMINA GROUP, INCORPORATED; *U.S. Private*, pg. 2973
NUMINUS WELLNESS INC.; *Int'l*, pg. 5489
NUMIS CORPORATION LIMITED—See Deutsche Bank Aktiengesellschaft; *Int'l*, pg. 2061
NUMIS SECURITIES INC—See Deutsche Bank Aktiengesellschaft; *Int'l*, pg. 2061
NUM KIJJAKARN CO., LTD.—See Thai Beverage Public Company Limited; *Int'l*, pg. 7591
NUM MUANG CO., LTD.—See Thai Beverage Public Company Limited; *Int'l*, pg. 7591
NUM NAKORN CO., LTD.—See Thai Beverage Public Company Limited; *Int'l*, pg. 7591
NUM NUMERICAL CONTROL TECHNOLOGY (BEIJING) CO LTD.—See NUM AG; *Int'l*, pg. 5489
NUM NUMERICAL CONTROL TECHNOLOGY (CHANGZHOU) CO. LTD.—See NUM AG; *Int'l*, pg. 5489
NUM PALANG CO., LTD.—See Thai Beverage Public Company Limited; *Int'l*, pg. 7591
NUMRUNGROD CO., LTD.—See Thai Beverage Public Company Limited; *Int'l*, pg. 7591
NUM S.A.S.—See NUM AG; *Int'l*, pg. 5489
NUM SERVIS TURKIYE—See NUM AG; *Int'l*, pg. 5489
NUM SPA—See NUM AG; *Int'l*, pg. 5489
NUMSP LLC—See Tonka Bay Equity Partners LLC; *U.S. Private*, pg. 4185
NUM TAIWAN LTD.—See NUM AG; *Int'l*, pg. 5489
NUMTHIP CO., LTD.—See Thai Beverage Public Company Limited; *Int'l*, pg. 7591
NUM THURAKIJ CO., LTD.—See Thai Beverage Public Company Limited; *Int'l*, pg. 7591
NUM (UK) LTD.—See NUM AG; *Int'l*, pg. 5488
NUMULAE GESTION DE SERVICIOS SOCIMI SA; *Int'l*, pg. 5489
NUM YUK CO., LTD.—See Thai Beverage Public Company Limited; *Int'l*, pg. 7591
NUNAMINERALS A/S; *Int'l*, pg. 5489
NUNASI CORPORATION - CORPORATE OFFICE—See Nunasi Corporation; *Int'l*, pg. 5489
NUNASI CORPORATION; *Int'l*, pg. 5489
NUNATAC S.R.L—See Alkemy SpA; *Int'l*, pg. 331
NUNAVUT SEALINK & SUPPLY INCORPORATED—See Arctic Co-Operatives Limited; *Int'l*, pg. 551
NUNC A/S—See Thermo Fisher Scientific Inc.; *U.S. Public*, pg. 2149
NUNHEMS (BEIJING) SEED CO., LTD.—See BASF SE; *Int'l*, pg. 884
NUNHEMS B.V.—See Bayer Aktiengesellschaft; *Int'l*, pg. 903
NUNHEMS CHILE S.A.—See Bayer Aktiengesellschaft; *Int'l*, pg. 903
NUNHEMS DO BRASIL COMERCIO DE SEMENTES LTDA.—See Bayer Aktiengesellschaft; *Int'l*, pg. 903
NUNHEMS FRANCE S.A.R.L.—See Bayer Aktiengesellschaft; *Int'l*, pg. 903
NUNHEMS HUNGARY KFT.—See Bayer Aktiengesellschaft; *Int'l*, pg. 903
NUNHEMS INDIA PRIVATE LIMITED—See Bayer Aktiengesellschaft; *Int'l*, pg. 903
NUNHEMS ITALY S.R.L.—See Bayer Aktiengesellschaft; *Int'l*, pg. 903
NUNHEMS MAROC SARL—See BASF SE; *Int'l*, pg. 884
NUNHEMS MEXICO S.A. DE C.V.—See Bayer Aktiengesellschaft; *Int'l*, pg. 903
NUNHEMS NETHERLANDS B.V.—See Bayer Aktiengesellschaft; *Int'l*, pg. 903
NUNHEMS POLAND SP. Z O.O.—See Bayer Aktiengesellschaft; *Int'l*, pg. 903
NUNHEMS SPAIN, S.A.—See Bayer Aktiengesellschaft; *Int'l*, pg. 903
NUNHEMS TOHUMCULUK A.S.—See BASF SE; *Int'l*, pg. 884
NUNHEMS TOHUMCULUK LIMITED SIRKETI—See Bayer Aktiengesellschaft; *Int'l*, pg. 903
NUNHEMS UKRAINE T.O.V.—See BASF SE; *Int'l*, pg. 884
NUNHEMS USA, INC.—See Bayer Aktiengesellschaft; *Int'l*, pg. 903
NUNN-BUSH SHOE COMPANY—See Weyco Group, Inc.; *U.S. Public*, pg. 2365

NUNWOOD; *Int'l*, pg. 5489
NUNZIA PHARMACEUTICAL CORPORATION; *U.S. Public*, pg. 1555
NUODE INVESTMENT CO., LTD.; *Int'l*, pg. 5489
NUON DEUTSCHLAND GMBH—See Sudwestfalen Energie und Wasser AG; *Int'l*, pg. 7252
NUON ENERGIE UND SERVICE GMBH—See Vattenfall AB; *Int'l*, pg. 8136
NUON EPE GAS SERVICE B.V.—See Vattenfall AB; *Int'l*, pg. 8136
NUON INTERNATIONAL RENEWABLES PROJECTS B.V.—See Vattenfall AB; *Int'l*, pg. 8136
NUON POWER GENERATION B.V.—See Vattenfall AB; *Int'l*, pg. 8136
NUON RETAIL BEVEILIGING SERVICE B.V.—See Vattenfall AB; *Int'l*, pg. 8136
NUON RETAIL B.V.—See Vattenfall AB; *Int'l*, pg. 8136
NUON RETAIL INSTALLATIE SERVICE B.V.—See Vattenfall AB; *Int'l*, pg. 8136
NUON STORAGE B.V.—See Vattenfall AB; *Int'l*, pg. 8136
NUON ZUIDWENDING B.V.—See Vattenfall AB; *Int'l*, pg. 8136
NUORISOKOTI VALOKKI OY—See Humana AB; *Int'l*, pg. 3530
NUO THERAPEUTICS, INC.; *U.S. Public*, pg. 1555
NUOVA CASTELLI SPA—See Groupe Lactalis SA; *Int'l*, pg. 3106
NUOVA CIBA S.P.A.—See Zeppelin GmbH; *Int'l*, pg. 8637
NUOVA FARMEC S.R.L.—See Ecolab Inc.; *U.S. Public*, pg. 716
NUOVA FIMA DO BRASIL LTDA.—See Schaeff Maschinen GmbH & Co. KG; *Int'l*, pg. 6615
NUOVA NICOL S.R.L.—See Pattern SpA; *Int'l*, pg. 5760
NUOVA OMPI S.R.L.—See Stevanato Group S.p.A.; *Int'l*, pg. 7212
NUOVA STIRERIA TAVOLETO SRL—See Aeffe SpA; *Int'l*, pg. 173
NUOVA TKEI S.P.A.—See ThyssenKrupp AG; *Int'l*, pg. 7725
NUOVE ENERGIE SRL—See Enel S.p.A.; *Int'l*, pg. 2414
NUOVO PIGNONE S.P.A.—See General Electric Company; *U.S. Public*, pg. 919
NUPAR MANUFACTURING—See ABB Ltd.; *Int'l*, pg. 51
NUPATHE INC.—See Teva Pharmaceutical Industries, Ltd.; *Int'l*, pg. 7581
NUPATH, INC.; *U.S. Private*, pg. 2973
NUPIK-FLO UK LTD—See FLO S.p.A.; *Int'l*, pg. 2707
NUPIK FRANCE EURL—See FLO S.p.A.; *Int'l*, pg. 2707
NUPIK INTERNACIONAL SL—See FLO S.p.A.; *Int'l*, pg. 2707
NUPLA CORPORATION—See Q.E.P. Co., Inc.; *U.S. Public*, pg. 1741
NUPOWER, LLC; *U.S. Private*, pg. 2973
NUPUR RECYCLERS LIMITED; *Int'l*, pg. 5489
NURAL ENTERPRISE SDN BHD—See Berjaya Corporation Berhad; *Int'l*, pg. 983
NURANI DYEING & SWEATER LTD.; *Int'l*, pg. 5489
NURAN WIRELESS, INC.; *Int'l*, pg. 5489
NURBANK JSC; *Int'l*, pg. 5489
NURCAPITAL CORPORATION LTD.; *Int'l*, pg. 5490
NURECA LIMITED; *Int'l*, pg. 5490
NURIFLEX CO., LTD.; *Int'l*, pg. 5490
NUR INK INNOVATIONS LTD.; *Int'l*, pg. 5489
NURIPLAN CO., LTD.; *Int'l*, pg. 5490
NURISH.ME, INC.; *U.S. Public*, pg. 1555
NURI TELECOM CO., LTD.—See NuriFlex Co., Ltd.; *Int'l*, pg. 5490
NURI TELECOM USA CO., INC.—See NuriFlex Co., Ltd.; *Int'l*, pg. 5490
NURIX THERAPEUTICS, INC.; *U.S. Public*, pg. 1555
NURMINEN LOGISTICS PLC; *Int'l*, pg. 5490
NURMINEN MARITIME LATVIA SIA—See Nurminen Logistics Plc; *Int'l*, pg. 5490
NURNBERGMESSE BRASIL LTDA.—See Messe Munchen GmbH; *Int'l*, pg. 4842
NUROL AVIATION INC.—See Nurol Holding A.S.; *Int'l*, pg. 5490
NUROL BAE SYSTEMS HAVA SISTEMLERI A.S.—See Nurol Holding A.S.; *Int'l*, pg. 5490
NUROL CONSTRUCTION & TRADING CO. INC.—See Nurol Holding A.S.; *Int'l*, pg. 5490
NUROL ENERGY GENERATION & MARKETING INC.—See Nurol Holding A.S.; *Int'l*, pg. 5490
NUROL ENERJI URETIM VE PAZARLAMA A.S.—See Nurol Holding A.S.; *Int'l*, pg. 5490
NUROL GAYRIMENKUL YATIRIM ORTAKLIGI AS; *Int'l*, pg. 5490
NUROL GEORGIA LLC—See Nurol Holding A.S.; *Int'l*, pg. 5490
NUROL GOKSU ELEKTRIK URETIM A.S.—See Nurol Holding A.S.; *Int'l*, pg. 5490
NUROL HAVACILIK A.S.—See Nurol Holding A.S.; *Int'l*, pg. 5490
NUROL HOLDING A.S.; *Int'l*, pg. 5490
NUROL INSAAT VE TICARET A.S.—See Nurol Holding A.S.; *Int'l*, pg. 5490
NUROL INSURANCE BROKERAGE SERVIVES INC.—See Nurol Holding A.S.; *Int'l*, pg. 5490

COMPANY NAME INDEX

NUROL ISLETME VE GAYRIMENKUL YONETIM A.S.—See Nurol Holding A.S.; *Int'l*, pg. 5490
NUROL KONTROL VE AVIYONIK SISTEMLERI A.S.—See Nurol Holding A.S.; *Int'l*, pg. 5490
NUROL LLC—See Nurol Holding A.S.; *Int'l*, pg. 5490
NUROL MAKINA SANAYI A.S.—See Nurol Holding A.S.; *Int'l*, pg. 5490
NUROL MAKINA VE SANAYI A.S.—See Nurol Holding A.S.; *Int'l*, pg. 5491
NUROL PORTFOY YONETIM ANONIM SIRKETI—See Nurol Yatirim Bankasi A.S.; *Int'l*, pg. 5491
NUROL SIGORTA ARACILIK HIZMETLERI A.S.—See Nurol Holding A.S.; *Int'l*, pg. 5491
NUROL SOLAR ENERJI URETIM A.S.—See Nurol Holding A.S.; *Int'l*, pg. 5491
NUROL TEKNOLOJI SANAYI VE MADENCILIK TICARET A.S.—See Nurol Holding A.S.; *Int'l*, pg. 5491
NUROL VARLIK KIRALAMA A.S.; *Int'l*, pg. 5491
NUROL YATIRIM BANKASI A.S.; *Int'l*, pg. 5491
NURSE AUDIT, LLC—See New Mountain Capital, LLC; *U.S. Private*, pg. 2902
NURSE & DOC PARTNER AB—See NGS Group AB; *Int'l*, pg. 5255
NURSEFINDERS, LLC—See AMN Healthcare Services, Inc.; *U.S. Public*, pg. 125
NURSEFINDERSUK LIMITED—See Bain Capital, LP; *U.S. Private*, pg. 434
NURSE ON CALL HOME HEALTHCARE; *U.S. Private*, pg. 2973
NURSE ON CALL, INC.—See Brookdale Senior Living Inc.; *U.S. Public*, pg. 395
NURSE-ON-CALL OF SOUTH FLORIDA, INC.—See Brookdale Senior Living Inc.; *U.S. Public*, pg. 395
NURSERY SUPPLIES INC.—See Guggenheim Partners, LLC; *U.S. Private*, pg. 1812
NURSESRX—See AMN Healthcare Services, Inc.; *U.S. Public*, pg. 125
NURSING2014—See Wolters Kluwer n.v.; *Int'l*, pg. 8444
NURSING AND RETIREMENT CENTER OF THE ANDOVERS, INC.—See Welltower Inc.; *U.S. Public*, pg. 2348
NURSING EMERGENCIES PROPRIETARY LIMITED—See Workforce Holdings Ltd.; *Int'l*, pg. 8455
NUR TOUSHEH INTERNATIONAL COMPANY—See Pars Tousheh Investment Company; *Int'l*, pg. 5746
NURTURE INC.—See Danone; *Int'l*, pg. 1967
NURTURE LANDSCAPES HOLDINGS LIMITED; *Int'l*, pg. 5491
NURTURE LANDSCAPES LIMITED—See Nurture Landscapes Holdings Limited; *Int'l*, pg. 5491
NURUN CHINA—See Publicis Groupe S.A.; *Int'l*, pg. 6104
NURUN INC.—See Publicis Groupe S.A.; *Int'l*, pg. 6104
NURUN INC.—See Publicis Groupe S.A.; *Int'l*, pg. 6104
NURUN SPAIN—See Publicis Groupe S.A.; *Int'l*, pg. 6104
NUSA MARITIME PTE LTD—See Keppel Corporation Limited; *Int'l*, pg. 4132
NUSANTARA RESOURCES LIMITED; *Int'l*, pg. 5491
NU-SASH OF INDIANAPOLIS INCORPORATED; *U.S. Private*, pg. 2974
NUSASIRI PUBLIC COMPANY LIMITED; *Int'l*, pg. 5491
NUSA TENGGARA MINING CORPORATION—See Sumitomo Corporation; *Int'l*, pg. 7269
NUSCALE POWER CORPORATION—See Fluor Corporation; *U.S. Public*, pg. 859
NUSCALE POWER, LLC—See Fluor Corporation; *U.S. Public*, pg. 859
NUS CONSULTING GROUP PTY LIMITED—See National Utility Service, Inc.; *U.S. Private*, pg. 2864
NUS CONSULTING GROUP—See National Utility Service, Inc.; *U.S. Private*, pg. 2864
NUSCO S.P.A.; *Int'l*, pg. 5491
NUS DEUTSCHLAND GMBH—See National Utility Service, Inc.; *U.S. Private*, pg. 2864
NUSEED AMERICAS—See Nufarm Limited; *Int'l*, pg. 5487
NUSEED CENTRAL US—See Nufarm Limited; *Int'l*, pg. 5487
NUSEED PTY. LTD.—See Nufarm Limited; *Int'l*, pg. 5487
NUSEED UKRAINE LLC—See Nufarm Limited; *Int'l*, pg. 5487
NUSENDA CREDIT UNION; *U.S. Private*, pg. 2973
NUSEP HOLDINGS LTD.; *Int'l*, pg. 5491
NUSEP, INC—See Dycent Biotech (Shanghai) Co. Ltd.; *Int'l*, pg. 2238
NUSIL TECHNOLOGY LLC—See New Mountain Capital, LLC; *U.S. Private*, pg. 2903
NUS INTERNATIONAL PTY. LTD.—See National Utility Service, Inc.; *U.S. Private*, pg. 2864
NUS ITALIA, S.R.L.—See National Utility Service, Inc.; *U.S. Private*, pg. 2864
NU SKIN ASIA INVESTMENT, INC.—See Nu Skin Enterprises, Inc.; *U.S. Public*, pg. 1552
NU SKIN BELGIUM, NV—See Nu Skin Enterprises, Inc.; *U.S. Public*, pg. 1552
NU SKIN CANADA, INC.—See Nu Skin Enterprises, Inc.; *U.S. Public*, pg. 1552
NU SKIN (CHINA) DAILY-USE AND HEALTH PRODUCTS CO., LTD.—See Nu Skin Enterprises, Inc.; *U.S. Public*, pg. 1552

NU SKIN EASTERN EUROPE KFT—See Nu Skin Enterprises, Inc.; *U.S. Public*, pg. 1552
NU SKIN ENTERPRISES AUSTRALIA, INC.—See Nu Skin Enterprises, Inc.; *U.S. Public*, pg. 1552
NU SKIN ENTERPRISES HONG KONG, INC.—See Nu Skin Enterprises, Inc.; *U.S. Public*, pg. 1552
NU SKIN ENTERPRISES, INC.; *U.S. Public*, pg. 1551
NU SKIN ENTERPRISES NEW ZEALAND, INC.—See Nu Skin Enterprises, Inc.; *U.S. Public*, pg. 1552
NU SKIN ENTERPRISES PHILIPPINES, INC.—See Nu Skin Enterprises, Inc.; *U.S. Public*, pg. 1552
NU SKIN ENTERPRISES PHILIPPINES LLC—See Nu Skin Enterprises, Inc.; *U.S. Public*, pg. 1552
NU SKIN ENTERPRISES SINGAPORE PTE. LTD.—See Nu Skin Enterprises, Inc.; *U.S. Public*, pg. 1552
NU SKIN ENTERPRISES (THAILAND) LIMITED—See Nu Skin Enterprises, Inc.; *U.S. Public*, pg. 1552
NU SKIN ENTERPRISES (THAILAND), LTD.—See Nu Skin Enterprises, Inc.; *U.S. Public*, pg. 1552
NU SKIN ENTERPRISES UNITED STATES, INC.—See Nu Skin Enterprises, Inc.; *U.S. Public*, pg. 1552
NU SKIN ENTERPRISES VIETNAM, LLC—See Nu Skin Enterprises, Inc.; *U.S. Public*, pg. 1552
NU SKIN FRANCE, SARL—See Nu Skin Enterprises, Inc.; *U.S. Public*, pg. 1552
NU SKIN GERMANY GMBH—See Nu Skin Enterprises, Inc.; *U.S. Public*, pg. 1552
NU SKIN, INC.—See Nu Skin Enterprises, Inc.; *U.S. Public*, pg. 1552
NU SKIN ITALIA, S.R.L.—See Nu Skin Enterprises, Inc.; *U.S. Public*, pg. 1552
NU SKIN JAPAN CO., LTD.—See Nu Skin Enterprises, Inc.; *U.S. Public*, pg. 1552
NU SKIN MALAYSIA HOLDINGS SDN. BHD.—See Nu Skin Enterprises, Inc.; *U.S. Public*, pg. 1552
NU SKIN (MALAYSIA) SDN. BHD.—See Nu Skin Enterprises, Inc.; *U.S. Public*, pg. 1552
NU SKIN MEXICO, S.A. DE C.V.—See Nu Skin Enterprises, Inc.; *U.S. Public*, pg. 1552
NU SKIN NETHERLANDS, B.V.—See Nu Skin Enterprises, Inc.; *U.S. Public*, pg. 1552
NU SKIN NORWAY AS—See Nu Skin Enterprises, Inc.; *U.S. Public*, pg. 1552
NU SKIN PERSONAL CARE (THAILAND), LTD.—See Nu Skin Enterprises, Inc.; *U.S. Public*, pg. 1552
NU SKIN PERU S.A.C.—See Nu Skin Enterprises, Inc.; *U.S. Public*, pg. 1552
NU SKIN SCANDINAVIA A.S.—See Nu Skin Enterprises, Inc.; *U.S. Public*, pg. 1552
NU SKIN SLOVAKIA S.R.O.—See Nu Skin Enterprises, Inc.; *U.S. Public*, pg. 1552
NU SKIN TAIWAN, LLC—See Nu Skin Enterprises, Inc.; *U.S. Public*, pg. 1552
NUSOFT SOLUTIONS INC.—See TTEC Holdings, Inc.; *U.S. Public*, pg. 2203
NU-SONS ELECTRIC INC.; *U.S. Private*, pg. 2971
NUSPHERE CORPORATION—See Progress Software Corporation; *U.S. Public*, pg. 1725
NUSPIRE CORP; *U.S. Private*, pg. 2974
NUSSER INDUSTRIES INC.; *U.S. Private*, pg. 2974
NUS-SOUTH AFRICA—See National Utility Service, Inc.; *U.S. Private*, pg. 2864
NUSS TRUCK GROUP; *U.S. Private*, pg. 2974
NUSTAR EASTHAM LIMITED—See Brookfield Infrastructure Partners L.P.; *Int'l*, pg. 1193
NUSTAR ENERGY L.P.—See Sunoco LP; *U.S. Public*, pg. 1964
NUSTAR ENERGY L.P. - WICHITA—See Sunoco LP; *U.S. Public*, pg. 1964
NUSTAR GP HOLDINGS, LLC—See Sunoco LP; *U.S. Public*, pg. 1964
NUSTAR GRANGEMOUTH LIMITED—See Brookfield Infrastructure Partners L.P.; *Int'l*, pg. 1193
NUSTAR MARKETING LLC—See Sunoco LP; *U.S. Public*, pg. 1964
NUSTAR PIPELINE COMPANY, LLC—See Sunoco LP; *U.S. Public*, pg. 1964
NUSTAR TERMINALS CANADA PARTNERSHIP—See Sunoco LP; *U.S. Public*, pg. 1965
NUSTAR TERMINALS MARINE SERVICES N.V.—See Sunoco LP; *U.S. Public*, pg. 1965
NU-SWIFT INTERNATIONAL LIMITED—See London Security PLC; *Int'l*, pg. 4547
NUTANA AVIATION CAPITAL IFSC PRIVATE LIMITED—See Easy Trip Planners Limited; *Int'l*, pg. 2276
NUTANIX, INC.; *U.S. Public*, pg. 1555
NUTANIX NETHERLANDS B. V.—See Nutanix, Inc.; *U.S. Public*, pg. 1555
NUTEC AS—See Lundbeckfonden; *Int'l*, pg. 4582
NUTECH ENERGY RESOURCES, INC.; *U.S. Public*, pg. 1555
NUTECH ENGINEERING INC.; *Int'l*, pg. 5491
NUTECH GLOBAL LTD.; *Int'l*, pg. 5491
NUTECH SEED LLC—See Corteva, Inc.; *U.S. Public*, pg. 584
NUTECH SYSTEMS INC.; *U.S. Private*, pg. 2974
NU-TEC ROOFING CONTRACTORS LLC; *U.S. Private*, pg. 2971

NUTRICAP LABS

NUTEC SOUTHERN AFRICA (PTY) LTD.—See Astral Foods Limited; *Int'l*, pg. 658
NUTEC SOUTHERN AFRICA (PTY) LTD.—See Cargill, Inc.; *U.S. Private*, pg. 759
NUTEX HEALTH INC.; *U.S. Public*, pg. 1555
NUTEX INVESTMENTS PUBLIC LIMITED COMPANY; *Int'l*, pg. 5491
NUTFIELD TECHNOLOGY, INC.—See FARO Technologies, Inc.; *U.S. Public*, pg. 823
NUTHEN RESTAURIERUNGEN GMBH + CO. KG—See L. Possehl & Co. mbH; *Int'l*, pg. 4384
NUTIS PRESS INC.; *U.S. Private*, pg. 2974
NUTIT A.S.—See Impel S.A.; *Int'l*, pg. 3632
NUTIVA; *U.S. Private*, pg. 2974
NUTLEY HEATING & COOLING SUPPLY CO.; *U.S. Private*, pg. 2974
NUTMEG CONTAINER CORP.—See Connecticut Container Corporation; *U.S. Private*, pg. 1016
NUTMEG INTERNATIONAL TRUCKS INC.; *U.S. Private*, pg. 2974
NUTMEG PAVILION HEALTHCARE—See Apollo Global Management, Inc.; *U.S. Public*, pg. 157
NUTMEG UTILITY PRODUCTS INC.; *U.S. Private*, pg. 2974
NUTRACEUTICAL CORPORATION—See HGGC, LLC; *U.S. Private*, pg. 1930
NUTRACEUTICAL INTERNATIONAL CORPORATION—See HGGC, LLC; *U.S. Private*, pg. 1930
NUTRADINE, LLC—See Archer-Daniels-Midland Company; *U.S. Public*, pg. 185
NUTRA ESSENTIAL OTC SL—See Ascendis Health Limited; *Int'l*, pg. 601
NUTRAFIZZ PRODUCTS CORP.—See National Beverage Corp.; *U.S. Public*, pg. 1494
NUTRAFUR S.A.—See International Flavors & Fragrances Inc.; *U.S. Public*, pg. 1154
NUTRALIFE BIOSCIENCES, INC.; *U.S. Public*, pg. 1556
NUTRA MANUFACTURING, INC.—See Ares Management Corporation; *U.S. Public*, pg. 189
NUTRA MANUFACTURING, INC.—See Ontario Teachers' Pension Plan; *Int'l*, pg. 5589
NUTRAMAX LABORATORIES, INC.; *U.S. Private*, pg. 2974
NUTRAMED, INC.—See Ampersand Management LLC; *U.S. Private*, pg. 265
NUTRA MED PACKAGING, INC.—See GenNx360 Capital Partners, L.P.; *U.S. Private*, pg. 1672
NUTRANEXT, LLC—See The Clorox Company; *U.S. Public*, pg. 2062
NUTRANOMICS INC.; *U.S. Public*, pg. 1556
NUTRA PHARMA CORP.; *U.S. Public*, pg. 1555
NUTRAPLUS INDIA LIMITED; *Int'l*, pg. 5491
NUTRASCIENCE LABS, INC.—See Twinlab Consolidated Holdings, Inc.; *U.S. Public*, pg. 2207
NUTRASTAR INTERNATIONAL INC.; *Int'l*, pg. 5491
NUTRASUN FOODS LTD.—See Paterson GlobalFoods Inc.; *Int'l*, pg. 5756
THE NUTRASWEET COMPANY—See Prospect Hill Growth Partners, L.P.; *U.S. Private*, pg. 3288
NUTRAVEL TECHNOLOGY SOLUTIONS, LLC—See Airlines Reporting Corporation; *U.S. Private*, pg. 141
NUTRAVET (UK) LIMITED—See Swedencare AB; *Int'l*, pg. 7365
NUTRAWISE CORPORATION; *U.S. Private*, pg. 2974
NUTRAWISE HEALTH & BEAUTY LLC—See Jamieson Wellness, Inc.; *Int'l*, pg. 3878
NUTRECO NEDERLAND B.V.—See SHV Holdings N.V.; *Int'l*, pg. 6872
NUTRECO N.V.—See SHV Holdings N.V.; *Int'l*, pg. 6872
NUTRENA FEEDS—See Cargill, Inc.; *U.S. Private*, pg. 759
NUTREND AUTOMOTIVE INC.—See Newegg Commerce, Inc.; *Int'l*, pg. 5234
NUTREX AG—See Coop-Gruppe Genossenschaft; *Int'l*, pg. 1790
NUTREX, INC.—See Cyanotech Corporation; *U.S. Public*, pg. 617
NUTRI ACTIVE PTE LTD—See OSIM International Ltd.; *Int'l*, pg. 5650
NUTRIART INC.; *Int'l*, pg. 5492
NUTRI-ASIA INC.; *Int'l*, pg. 5491
NUTRIBAND INC.; *U.S. Public*, pg. 1556
NUTRICAP LABS; *U.S. Private*, pg. 2974
NUTRICHEM DIAT + PHARMA GMBH—See B. Braun Melsungen AG; *Int'l*, pg. 787
NUTRICIA A/S—See Danone; *Int'l*, pg. 1966
NUTRICIA A.S.—See Danone; *Int'l*, pg. 1967
NUTRICIA AUSTRALIA PTY. LTD.—See Danone; *Int'l*, pg. 1966
NUTRICIA BABY OY—See Danone; *Int'l*, pg. 1966
NUTRICIA BAGO S.A.—See Bago Group; *Int'l*, pg. 799
NUTRICIA BAGO S.A.—See Danone; *Int'l*, pg. 1966
NUTRICIA BELGIE N.V.—See Danone; *Int'l*, pg. 1966
NUTRICIA CUIJK B.V.—See Danone; *Int'l*, pg. 1966
NUTRICIA DEVA A.S.—See ARX Equity Partners s.r.o.; *Int'l*, pg. 588
NUTRICIA FRANCE S.A.—See Danone; *Int'l*, pg. 1966
NUTRICIA GMBH—See Danone; *Int'l*, pg. 1966
NUTRICIA HOLDINGS LTD.—See Danone; *Int'l*, pg. 1966

NUTRICAP LABS CORPORATE AFFILIATIONS

NUTRICIA ITALIA S.P.A.—See Danone; *Int'l*, pg. 1966
NUTRICIA LTD. - ADVANCED MEDICAL NUTRITION—See Danone; *Int'l*, pg. 1966
NUTRICIA LTD. - BABY NUTRITION—See Danone; *Int'l*, pg. 1966
NUTRICIA MEDICAL OY—See Danone; *Int'l*, pg. 1966
NUTRICIA NAHRUNGSMITTEL GMBH & CO. KG—See Danone; *Int'l*, pg. 1966
NUTRICIA NEDERLAND B.V.—See Danone; *Int'l*, pg. 1966
NUTRICIA NETHERLANDS B.V.—See Danone; *Int'l*, pg. 1967
NUTRICIA (NEW ZEALAND) LTD.—See Danone; *Int'l*, pg. 1966
NUTRICIA NORDICA AB—See Danone; *Int'l*, pg. 1967
NUTRICIA NORGE AS—See Danone; *Int'l*, pg. 1967
NUTRICIA N.V.—See Danone; *Int'l*, pg. 1966
NUTRICIA PHARMACEUTICAL (WUXI) CO., LTD.—See Danone; *Int'l*, pg. 1967
NUTRICIA POLSKA SP. Z O.O.—See Danone; *Int'l*, pg. 1967
NUTRICIA PORTUGAL L.D.A.—See Danone; *Int'l*, pg. 1967
NUTRICIA (RUSSIA) LLC—See Danone; *Int'l*, pg. 1966
NUTRICIA S.A.—See Danone; *Int'l*, pg. 1967
NUTRICIA S.R.L.—See Danone; *Int'l*, pg. 1967
NUTRICIA S.R.O.—See Danone; *Int'l*, pg. 1967
NUTRICIRCLE LIMITED; *Int'l*, pg. 5492
NUTRICITY.COM LLC; *U.S. Private*, pg. 2974
NUTRIDAR PLC; *Int'l*, pg. 5492
NUTRIEN AG SOLUTIONS (CANADA) INC.—See Nutrien Ltd.; *Int'l*, pg. 5493
NUTRIEN AG SOLUTIONS, INC.—See Nutrien Ltd.; *Int'l*, pg. 5492
NUTRIEN AG SOLUTIONS LIMITED—See Nutrien Ltd.; *Int'l*, pg. 5492
NUTRIEN DEUTSCHLAND GMBH—See Nutrien Ltd.; *Int'l*, pg. 5492
NUTRIEN EUROPE S.A.—See Nutrien Ltd.; *Int'l*, pg. 5492
NUTRIEN ITALIA S.P.A.—See Nutrien Ltd.; *Int'l*, pg. 5492
NUTRIEN LTD.; *Int'l*, pg. 5492
NUTRIEN PHOSPHATE - AURORA—See Nutrien Ltd.; *Int'l*, pg. 5494
NUTRIEN PHOSPHATE - MARSEILLES—See Nutrien Ltd.; *Int'l*, pg. 5494
NUTRIEN PHOSPHATES - CINCINNATI—See Nutrien Ltd.; *Int'l*, pg. 5494
NUTRIEN POTASH - ALLAN—See Nutrien Ltd.; *Int'l*, pg. 5493
NUTRIEN POTASH - CORY—See Nutrien Ltd.; *Int'l*, pg. 5493
NUTRIEN POTASH - LANIGAN—See Nutrien Ltd.; *Int'l*, pg. 5493
NUTRIEN POTASH - PATIENCE LAKE—See Nutrien Ltd.; *Int'l*, pg. 5493
NUTRIEN POTASH - ROCANVILLE—See Nutrien Ltd.; *Int'l*, pg. 5493
NUTRIENTS FOR LIFE FOUNDATION; *U.S. Private*, pg. 2974
NUTRI FEEDS (PTY) LIMITED - BLOEMFONTEIN FEED MILL—See Country Bird Holdings Limited; *Int'l*, pg. 1818
NUTRI FEEDS (PTY) LIMITED - MAFIKENG FEED MILL—See Country Bird Holdings Limited; *Int'l*, pg. 1818
NUTRI FEEDS (PTY) LIMITED—See Country Bird Holdings Limited; *Int'l*, pg. 1818
NUTRI FEEDS (PTY) LIMITED - VILJOENSKROON FEED MILL—See Country Bird Holdings Limited; *Int'l*, pg. 1818
NUTRI-FORCE NUTRITION, INC.; *U.S. Private*, pg. 2974
NUTRIGOLD LIMITED; *Int'l*, pg. 5494
NUTRI GRANULATIONS, INC.—See IMCD N.V.; *Int'l*, pg. 3622
NUTRILAB, S.L.—See Eurofins Scientific S.E.; *Int'l*, pg. 2551
NUTRIMETICS AUSTRALIA PTY. LTD.—See Tupperware Brands Corporation; *U.S. Public*, pg. 2204
NUTRIMETICS FRANCE SAS—See Tupperware Brands Corporation; *U.S. Public*, pg. 2204
NUTRIMETICS FRANCE SNC—See Tupperware Brands Corporation; *U.S. Public*, pg. 2204
NUTRIMETICS INTERNATIONAL (NZ) LIMITED—See Tupperware Brands Corporation; *U.S. Public*, pg. 2204
NUTRIMIX FEED CO., INC.; *U.S. Private*, pg. 2974
NUTRINE CONFECTIONERY COMPANY PRIVATE LIMITED—See The Hershey Co.; *U.S. Public*, pg. 2089
NUTRINO HEALTH LTD.—See Brookfield Corporation; *Int'l*, pg. 1180
NUTRINO HEALTH LTD.—See Elliott Management Corporation; *U.S. Private*, pg. 1372
NUTRINOR COOPERATIVE AGRO-ALIMENTAIRE DU SAGUENAY LAC ST-JEAN; *Int'l*, pg. 5494
NUTRIO.COM, INC.; *U.S. Private*, pg. 2974
NUTRI PHARMACEUTICALS RESEARCH, INC.; *U.S. Public*, pg. 1556
NUTRIPLANT INDUSTRIA E COMERCIO S.A.; *Int'l*, pg. 5494
NUTRISYSTEM, INC.—See Kainos Capital, LLC; *U.S. Private*, pg. 2255

NUTRITIONAL GROWTH SOLUTIONS LTD.; *Int'l*, pg. 5494
NUTRITIONAL HEALTH INSTITUTE LABORATORIES, LLC; *U.S. Private*, pg. 2974
NUTRITIONAL HOLDINGS, INC; *U.S. Private*, pg. 2974
NUTRITIONAL HOLDINGS LIMITED; *Int'l*, pg. 5494
NUTRITIONAL LABORATORIES INTERNATIONAL, INC.—See Ampersand Management LLC; *U.S. Private*, pg. 265
NUTRITIONAL PRODUCTS INTERNATIONAL INC.; *U.S. Private*, pg. 2974
NUTRITIONAL SUPPORT SERVICES, L.P.—See National HealthCare Corporation; *U.S. Public*, pg. 1496
NUTRITION BUSINESS JOURNAL—See Informa plc; *Int'l*, pg. 3692
NUTRITION DIMENSION, INC.—See TEGNA Inc.; *U.S. Public*, pg. 1990
NUTRITION HOUSE CO., LTD.—See Saha Pathanapibul Public Company Limited; *Int'l*, pg. 6479
NUTRITION INC.; *U.S. Private*, pg. 2974
NUTRITION MANAGEMENT SERVICES COMPANY; *U.S. Public*, pg. 1556
NUTRITION & SANTE BENELUX SA—See Otsuka Holdings Co., Ltd.; *Int'l*, pg. 5658
NUTRITION & SANTE IBERIA SL—See Otsuka Holdings Co., Ltd.; *Int'l*, pg. 5658
NUTRITION & SANTE ITALIA S.P.A.—See Otsuka Holdings Co., Ltd.; *Int'l*, pg. 5659
NUTRITION & SANTE SAS—See Otsuka Holdings Co., Ltd.; *Int'l*, pg. 5659
NUTRITION & SANTE SAS—See Otsuka Holdings Co., Ltd.; *Int'l*, pg. 5659
NUTRITION SC PUBLIC COMPANY LIMITED; *Int'l*, pg. 5494
NUTRI USA, INC.—See Option Care Health, Inc.; *U.S. Public*, pg. 1610
NUTRIUS, LLC—See Cargill, Inc.; *U.S. Private*, pg. 760
NUTRI-VET, LLC—See Imperial Capital Group Ltd.; *Int'l*, pg. 3634
NUTRIXO S.A.S.—See Vivescia; *Int'l*, pg. 8279
NUTROGANICS, INC.; *U.S. Public*, pg. 1556
NUTRONICS, INC.—See nLIGHT, Inc.; *U.S. Public*, pg. 1530
NUTRO PRODUCTS INC.—See Mars, Incorporated; *U.S. Private*, pg. 2590
NUTRYFARM INTERNATIONAL LIMITED; *Int'l*, pg. 5494
NUTSHELL, INC.—See Web FX Inc.; *U.S. Private*, pg. 4463
NUTSTEEL INDUSTRIA METALURGICA LTDA—See Emerson Electric Co.; *U.S. Public*, pg. 750
NUTTALL GEAR LLC—See Regal Rexnord Corporation; *U.S. Public*, pg. 1772
NUTTER CUSTOM CONSTRUCTION, LLC; *U.S. Private*, pg. 2974
THE NUTTING COMPANY, INC.; *U.S. Private*, pg. 4086
NUUDAY A/S—See Arbejdsmarkedets Tillaegspension; *Int'l*, pg. 537
NUUDAY A/S—See Macquarie Group Limited; *Int'l*, pg. 4626
NUUDAY A/S—See PFA Holding A/S; *Int'l*, pg. 5835
NUUDAY A/S—See PKA A/S; *Int'l*, pg. 5887
NUUK IMEQ A/S—See Carlsberg A/S; *Int'l*, pg. 1340
NUUN & CO., INC.—See TSG Consumer Partners LLC; *U.S. Private*, pg. 4253
NUUO, INC.; *Int'l*, pg. 5494
NUUVERA INC.; *Int'l*, pg. 5494
NUVALENT, INC.; *U.S. Public*, pg. 1556
NU VAN TECHNOLOGY INC.; *U.S. Private*, pg. 2971
NUVANT SYSTEMS INC.—See A3 Global, LLC; *U.S. Private*, pg. 29
NUVASIVE (AUS/NZ) PTY. LTD.—See Globus Medical, Inc.; *U.S. Public*, pg. 947
NUVASIVE CLINICAL SERVICES MONITORING, INC.—See Globus Medical, Inc.; *U.S. Public*, pg. 947
NUVASIVE GERMANY, GMBH—See Globus Medical, Inc.; *U.S. Public*, pg. 947
NUVASIVE, INC.—See Globus Medical, Inc.; *U.S. Public*, pg. 947
NUVASIVE ITALIA S.R.L.—See Globus Medical, Inc.; *U.S. Public*, pg. 947
NUVASIVE NETHERLANDS B.V.—See Globus Medical, Inc.; *U.S. Public*, pg. 947
NUVASIVE SPECIALIZED ORTHOPEDICS, INC.—See Globus Medical, Inc.; *U.S. Public*, pg. 947
NUVASIVE UK LIMITED—See Globus Medical, Inc.; *U.S. Public*, pg. 947
NUVATION BIO INC.; *U.S. Public*, pg. 1556
NUVECTIS PHARMA, INC.; *U.S. Public*, pg. 1556
NUVECTRA CORPORATION; *U.S. Private*, pg. 2974
NUVEEN AMT-FREE MUNICIPAL CREDIT INCOME FUND—See Teachers Insurance Association - College Retirement Fund; *U.S. Private*, pg. 3945
NUVEEN AMT-FREE MUNICIPAL VALUE FUND—See Teachers Insurance Association - College Retirement Fund; *U.S. Private*, pg. 3945
NUVEEN AMT-FREE QUALITY MUNICIPAL INCOME FUND—See Teachers Insurance Association - College Retirement Fund; *U.S. Private*, pg. 3945

NUVEEN ARIZONA QUALITY MUNICIPAL INCOME FUND—See Teachers Insurance Association - College Retirement Fund; *U.S. Private*, pg. 3945
NUVEEN ASSET MANAGEMENT, LLC—See Teachers Insurance Association - College Retirement Fund; *U.S. Private*, pg. 3945
NUVEEN CALIFORNIA AMT-FREE QUALITY MUNICIPAL INCOME FUND—See Teachers Insurance Association - College Retirement Fund; *U.S. Private*, pg. 3945
NUVEEN CALIFORNIA MUNICIPAL VALUE FUND 2—See Teachers Insurance Association - College Retirement Fund; *U.S. Private*, pg. 3945
NUVEEN CALIFORNIA MUNICIPAL VALUE FUND, INC.—See Teachers Insurance Association - College Retirement Fund; *U.S. Private*, pg. 3945
NUVEEN CALIFORNIA QUALITY MUNICIPAL INCOME FUND—See Teachers Insurance Association - College Retirement Fund; *U.S. Private*, pg. 3945
NUVEEN CHURCHILL DIRECT LENDING CORP.—See Teachers Insurance Association - College Retirement Fund; *U.S. Private*, pg. 3945
NUVEEN CORE EQUITY ALPHA FUND—See Teachers Insurance Association - College Retirement Fund; *U.S. Private*, pg. 3945
NUVEEN CREDIT STRATEGIES INCOME FUND—See Teachers Insurance Association - College Retirement Fund; *U.S. Private*, pg. 3946
NUVEEN DIVERSIFIED COMMODITY FUND—See Teachers Insurance Association - College Retirement Fund; *U.S. Private*, pg. 3946
NUVEEN DIVERSIFIED DIVIDEND & INCOME FUND—See Teachers Insurance Association - College Retirement Fund; *U.S. Private*, pg. 3946
NUVEEN DOW 30SM DYNAMIC OVERWRITE FUND—See Teachers Insurance Association - College Retirement Fund; *U.S. Private*, pg. 3946
NUVEEN EMERGING MARKETS DEBT 2022 TARGET TERM FUND—See Teachers Insurance Association - College Retirement Fund; *U.S. Private*, pg. 3946
NUVEEN ENHANCED MUNICIPAL VALUE FUND—See Teachers Insurance Association - College Retirement Fund; *U.S. Private*, pg. 3946
NUVEEN FLOATING RATE INCOME FUND—See Teachers Insurance Association - College Retirement Fund; *U.S. Private*, pg. 3946
NUVEEN GLOBAL CITIES REIT, INC.—See Teachers Insurance Association - College Retirement Fund; *U.S. Private*, pg. 3947
NUVEEN GLOBAL HIGH INCOME FUND—See Teachers Insurance Association - College Retirement Fund; *U.S. Private*, pg. 3946
NUVEEN INVESTMENTS, INC.—See Teachers Insurance Association - College Retirement Fund; *U.S. Private*, pg. 3947
NUVEEN LLC—See Teachers Insurance Association - College Retirement Fund; *U.S. Private*, pg. 3945
NUVEEN LONG/SHORT COMMODITY TOTAL RETURN FUND—See Teachers Insurance Association - College Retirement Fund; *U.S. Private*, pg. 3946
NUVEEN MASSACHUSETTS QUALITY MUNICIPAL INCOME FUND—See Teachers Insurance Association - College Retirement Fund; *U.S. Private*, pg. 3946
NUVEEN MICHIGAN QUALITY MUNICIPAL INCOME FUND—See Teachers Insurance Association - College Retirement Fund; *U.S. Private*, pg. 3946
NUVEEN MINNESOTA QUALITY MUNICIPAL INCOME FUND—See Teachers Insurance Association - College Retirement Fund; *U.S. Private*, pg. 3946
NUVEEN MISSOURI QUALITY MUNICIPAL INCOME FUND—See Teachers Insurance Association - College Retirement Fund; *U.S. Private*, pg. 3946
NUVEEN MORTGAGE OPPORTUNITY TERM FUND 2—See Teachers Insurance Association - College Retirement Fund; *U.S. Private*, pg. 3946
NUVEEN MULTI-MARKET INCOME FUND—See Teachers Insurance Association - College Retirement Fund; *U.S. Private*, pg. 3946
NUVEEN MUNICIPAL 2021 TARGET TERM FUND—See Teachers Insurance Association - College Retirement Fund; *U.S. Private*, pg. 3946
NUVEEN MUNICIPAL CREDIT INCOME FUND—See Teachers Insurance Association - College Retirement Fund; *U.S. Private*, pg. 3946
NUVEEN MUNICIPAL HIGH INCOME OPP FUND—See Teachers Insurance Association - College Retirement Fund; *U.S. Private*, pg. 3946
NUVEEN MUNICIPAL INCOME FUND, INC.—See Teachers Insurance Association - College Retirement Fund; *U.S. Private*, pg. 3946
NUVEEN MUNICIPAL VALUE FUND, INC.—See Teachers Insurance Association - College Retirement Fund; *U.S. Private*, pg. 3946
NUVEEN NASDAQ 100 DYNAMIC OVERWRITE FUND—See Teachers Insurance Association - College Retirement Fund; *U.S. Private*, pg. 3946
NUVEEN NEW JERSEY QUALITY MUNICIPAL INCOME FUND—See Teachers Insurance Association - College Retirement Fund; *U.S. Private*, pg. 3946

NUVEEN NEW YORK AMT-FREE QUALITY MUNICIPAL INCOME FUND—See Teachers Insurance Association - College Retirement Fund; *U.S. Private*, pg. 3946
NUVEEN NEW YORK MUNICIPAL VALUE FUND, INC.—See Teachers Insurance Association - College Retirement Fund; *U.S. Private*, pg. 3946
NUVEEN NEW YORK QUALITY MUNICIPAL INCOME FUND—See Teachers Insurance Association - College Retirement Fund; *U.S. Private*, pg. 3946
NUVEEN NEW YORK SELECT TAX-FREE INCOME PORTFOLIO—See Teachers Insurance Association - College Retirement Fund; *U.S. Private*, pg. 3946
NUVEEN NJ MUNICIPAL VALUE FUND—See Teachers Insurance Association - College Retirement Fund; *U.S. Private*, pg. 3946
NUVEEN NY MUNICIPAL VALUE FUND 2—See Teachers Insurance Association - College Retirement Fund; *U.S. Private*, pg. 3946
NUVEEN OHIO QUALITY MUNICIPAL INCOME FUND—See Teachers Insurance Association - College Retirement Fund; *U.S. Private*, pg. 3946
NUVEEN PENNSYLVANIA MUNICIPAL VALUE FUND—See Teachers Insurance Association - College Retirement Fund; *U.S. Private*, pg. 3946
NUVEEN PENNSYLVANIA QUALITY MUNICIPAL INCOME FUND—See Teachers Insurance Association - College Retirement Fund; *U.S. Private*, pg. 3946
NUVEEN PREFERRED & INCOME 2022 TERM—See Teachers Insurance Association - College Retirement Fund; *U.S. Private*, pg. 3947
NUVEEN PREFERRED & INCOME OPPORTUNITIES FUND—See Teachers Insurance Association - College Retirement Fund; *U.S. Private*, pg. 3947
NUVEEN PREFERRED & INCOME TERM FUND—See Teachers Insurance Association - College Retirement Fund; *U.S. Private*, pg. 3947
NUVEEN PREFERRED SECURITIES INCOME FUND—See Teachers Insurance Association - College Retirement Fund; *U.S. Private*, pg. 3947
NUVEEN QUALITY MUNICIPAL INCOME FUND—See Teachers Insurance Association - College Retirement Fund; *U.S. Private*, pg. 3947
NUVEEN REAL ASSET INCOME AND GROWTH FUND—See Teachers Insurance Association - College Retirement Fund; *U.S. Private*, pg. 3947
NUVEEN REAL ESTATE INCOME FUND—See Teachers Insurance Association - College Retirement Fund; *U.S. Private*, pg. 3947
NUVEEN SECURITIES, LLC—See Teachers Insurance Association - College Retirement Fund; *U.S. Private*, pg. 3947
NUVEEN SELECT MATURITIES MUNICIPAL FUND—See Teachers Insurance Association - College Retirement Fund; *U.S. Private*, pg. 3947
NUVEEN SELECT TAX FREE INCOME PORT 2—See Teachers Insurance Association - College Retirement Fund; *U.S. Private*, pg. 3947
NUVEEN SELECT TAX-FREE INCOME PORTFOLIO—See Teachers Insurance Association - College Retirement Fund; *U.S. Private*, pg. 3947
NUVEEN S&P 500 BUY-WRITE INCOME FUND—See Teachers Insurance Association - College Retirement Fund; *U.S. Private*, pg. 3947
NUVEEN S&P 500 DYNAMIC OVERWRITE FUND—See Teachers Insurance Association - College Retirement Fund; *U.S. Private*, pg. 3947
NUVEEN TAXABLE MUNICIPAL INCOME FUND—See Teachers Insurance Association - College Retirement Fund; *U.S. Private*, pg. 3947
NUVEEN TAX-ADVANTAGED DIVIDEND GROWTH FUND—See Teachers Insurance Association - College Retirement Fund; *U.S. Private*, pg. 3947
NUVEEN TAX-ADVANTAGED TOTAL RETURN STRATEGY FUND—See Teachers Insurance Association - College Retirement Fund; *U.S. Private*, pg. 3947
NUVEEN VIRGINIA QUALITY MUNICIPAL INCOME FUND—See Teachers Insurance Association - College Retirement Fund; *U.S. Private*, pg. 3947
NUVEI CORPORATION; *Int'l*, pg. 5494
NUVEI TECHNOLOGIES; *U.S. Private*, pg. 2975
NUVEK LLC—See Varsity Contractors, Inc.; *U.S. Private*, pg. 4347
NUVENTRA, INC.—See Cato SMS; *Int'l*, pg. 1361
NUVERA COMMUNICATIONS, INC.; *U.S. Public*, pg. 1556
NUVERA FUEL CELLS EUROPE SRL—See Hyster-Yale Materials Handling, Inc.; *U.S. Public*, pg. 1080
NUVERA FUEL CELLS, INC.—See Hyster-Yale Materials Handling, Inc.; *U.S. Public*, pg. 1080
NUVERA MEDICAL, INC.—See Johnson & Johnson; *U.S. Public*, pg. 1194
NUVERRA ENVIRONMENTAL SOLUTIONS, INC.—See Select Water Solutions, Inc.; *U.S. Public*, pg. 1862
NUVIA AS—See VINCI S.A.; *Int'l*, pg. 8224
NUVIA CANADA INC.—See VINCI S.A.; *Int'l*, pg. 8224
NUVIA DYNAMICS INC.—See VINCI S.A.; *Int'l*, pg. 8224
NUVIA FRANCE—See VINCI S.A.; *Int'l*, pg. 8233
NUVIA INDIA PVT LTD.—See VINCI S.A.; *Int'l*, pg. 8233
NUVIA INSTRUMENTS GMBH—See VINCI S.A.; *Int'l*, pg. 8224

NUVIA LIMITED—See VINCI S.A.; *Int'l*, pg. 8233
NUVIA NORDIC AB—See VINCI S.A.; *Int'l*, pg. 8233
NUVIA PREVENTION SAS—See VINCI S.A.; *Int'l*, pg. 8224
NUVIA PROCESS SAS—See VINCI S.A.; *Int'l*, pg. 8224
NUVIA PROTECTION SAS—See VINCI S.A.; *Int'l*, pg. 8224
NUVIA SLOVENSKO SRO.—See VINCI S.A.; *Int'l*, pg. 8224
NUVIA STRUCTURE SAS—See VINCI S.A.; *Int'l*, pg. 8225
NUVIA SUPPORT SAS—See VINCI S.A.; *Int'l*, pg. 8225
NUVIA TRADING (SHENZHEN) CO., LTD.—See VINCI S.A.; *Int'l*, pg. 8225
NUVIM, INC.; *U.S. Public*, pg. 1556
NUVISAN PHARMA SERVICES GMBH & CO KG—See ADCURAM Group AG; *Int'l*, pg. 128
NUVISION ENGINEERING, INC.—See Carr's Group PLC; *Int'l*, pg. 1343
NUVISION FINANCIAL CORPORATION, INC.—See Aon plc; *Int'l*, pg. 497
NUVISION INDUSTRIES INC.—See Ag Growth International Inc.; *Int'l*, pg. 198
NUVISTA ENERGY LTD.; *Int'l*, pg. 5494
NUVISTA RESOURCES—See NuVista Energy Ltd.; *Int'l*, pg. 5494
NUVOCO VISTAS CORP. LTD.—See NIRMA LIMITED; *Int'l*, pg. 5363
NUVO GROUP LTD.—See Holdco Nuvo Group D.G Ltd.; *U.S. Public*, pg. 1044
NUVOLO TECHNOLOGIES CORPORATION—See Trane Technologies Plc; *Int'l*, pg. 7891
NUVO MANUFACTURING GMBH—See Searchlight Pharma, Inc.; *Int'l*, pg. 6666
NUVONIC—See Halma plc; *Int'l*, pg. 3231
NUVON, INC.—See Francisco Partners Management, LP; *U.S. Private*, pg. 1589
NUVONYX INCORPORATED—See Coherent Corp.; *U.S. Public*, pg. 527
NUVO PHARMACEUTICALS INC.—See Searchlight Pharma, Inc.; *Int'l*, pg. 6666
NUVO RESEARCH GMBH—See Searchlight Pharma, Inc.; *Int'l*, pg. 6666
NUVOSUN, INC.—See Dow Inc.; *U.S. Public*, pg. 685
NUVOTEC CO., LTD.; *Int'l*, pg. 5494
NUVO TECHNOLOGIES, LLC—See Legrand S.A.; *Int'l*, pg. 4445
NUVOTON ELECTRONICS TECHNOLOGY (H.K.) LTD.—See Nuvoton Technology Corporation; *Int'l*, pg. 5495
NUVOTON ELECTRONICS TECHNOLOGY (SHANGHAI) LTD.—See Nuvoton Technology Corporation; *Int'l*, pg. 5495
NUVOTON ELECTRONICS TECHNOLOGY (SHENZHEN) LTD.—See Nuvoton Technology Corporation; *Int'l*, pg. 5495
NUVOTON TECHNOLOGY CORPORATION; *Int'l*, pg. 5494
NUVOTON TECHNOLOGY CORP.—See Nuvoton Technology Corporation; *Int'l*, pg. 5495
NUVOTON TECHNOLOGY INDIA PRIVATE LIMITED—See Nuvoton Technology Corporation; *Int'l*, pg. 5495
NUVOTON TECHNOLOGY ISRAEL LTD.—See Nuvoton Technology Corporation; *Int'l*, pg. 5495
NUVOTRONICS, INC.—See Elliott Management Corporation; *U.S. Private*, pg. 1368
NUVOTRONICS, INC.—See Veritas Capital Fund Management, LLC; *U.S. Private*, pg. 4362
NU-VU FOODSERVICE SYSTEMS—See The Middleby Corporation; *U.S. Public*, pg. 2115
NUVUS GRO CORP.; *U.S. Private*, pg. 2975
NUVVE HOLDING CORP.; *U.S. Public*, pg. 1556
NU-WA INDUSTRIES, INC.; *U.S. Private*, pg. 2971
NUWAVE SOLUTIONS LLC—See AE Industrial Partners, LP; *U.S. Private*, pg. 112
NU-WAY CONCRETE FORMS INC.; *U.S. Private*, pg. 2972
NUWAY COOPERATIVE INC.; *U.S. Private*, pg. 2975
NU-WAY INDUSTRIES, INC.; *U.S. Private*, pg. 2972
NUWAY ORGANIC NATURALS INDIA LIMITED; *Int'l*, pg. 5495
NU WAY SERVICE STATION INC.—See NW Holding Co.; *U.S. Private*, pg. 2975
NU-WAY SPEAKER PRODUCTS INC.; *U.S. Private*, pg. 2972
NU-WAY SUPPLY COMPANY INC.; *U.S. Private*, pg. 2972
NUWAY TOBACCO COMPANY INC.; *U.S. Private*, pg. 2975
NUWELLIS, INC.; *U.S. Public*, pg. 1556
NU-WORLD HOLDINGS LTD.; *Int'l*, pg. 5485
NUXEO—See Kennet Partners Ltd; *Int'l*, pg. 4127
NUXEO—See The Goldman Sachs Group, Inc.; *U.S. Public*, pg. 2080
NUZEE, INC.; *U.S. Public*, pg. 1557
NUZINC ENTERPRISES, LLC—See AZZ, Inc.; *U.S. Public*, pg. 259
NV5 GEOSPATIAL SOLUTIONS B.V.—See NV5 Global, Inc.; *U.S. Public*, pg. 1557

NV5 GEOSPATIAL SOLUTIONS FRANCE SARL—See NV5 Global, Inc.; *U.S. Public*, pg. 1557
NV5 GEOSPATIAL SOLUTIONS GMBH—See NV5 Global, Inc.; *U.S. Public*, pg. 1557
NV5 GEOSPATIAL SOLUTIONS, INC.—See NV5 Global, Inc.; *U.S. Public*, pg. 1557
NV5 GEOSPATIAL SOLUTIONS ITALIA S.R.L.—See NV5 Global, Inc.; *U.S. Public*, pg. 1557
NV5 GEOSPATIAL SOLUTIONS KK—See NV5 Global, Inc.; *U.S. Public*, pg. 1557
NV5 GEOSPATIAL SOLUTIONS UK LIMITED—See NV5 Global, Inc.; *U.S. Public*, pg. 1557
NV5 GLOBAL, INC.; *U.S. Public*, pg. 1557
NV5, INC.—See NV5 Global, Inc.; *U.S. Public*, pg. 1557
NV5, LLC—See NV5 Global, Inc.; *U.S. Public*, pg. 1557
NV5 LTD.—See NV5 Global, Inc.; *U.S. Public*, pg. 1557
NV5 MALAYSIA, SDN, BHD—See NV5 Global, Inc.; *U.S. Public*, pg. 1557
NV5 NORTHEAST, INC.—See NV5 Global, Inc.; *U.S. Public*, pg. 1557
NV5 WEST, INC.—See NV5 Global, Inc.; *U.S. Public*, pg. 1557
NV ACTIEF NV—See KBC Group NV; *Int'l*, pg. 4106
NV ASTRAZENECA SA—See AstraZeneca PLC; *Int'l*, pg. 661
NV BEKAERT SA; *Int'l*, pg. 5495
N.V. BEKAERT S.A. - ZWEVEGEM—See NV Bekaert SA; *Int'l*, pg. 5496
NV BELIMED SA—See Metall Zug AG; *Int'l*, pg. 4846
NV BELIMED SA—See Miele & Cie KG; *Int'l*, pg. 4890
NV BESIX SA—See Orascom Construction PLC; *Int'l*, pg. 5612
NV BEVER HOLDING; *Int'l*, pg. 5497
N.V. BOWE SYSTEC S.A.—See L. Possehl & Co. mbH; *Int'l*, pg. 4383
NV BROUWERIJEN ALKEN-MAES BRASSERIES SA—See L'Arche Green N.V.; *Int'l*, pg. 4377
N.V.B. UBBENS BOUWSTOFFEN B.V.—See CRH plc; *Int'l*, pg. 1845
NV CARE SDN. BHD.—See NV Multi Asia Sdn. Bhd.; *Int'l*, pg. 5497
NVC INTERNATIONAL HOLDINGS LIMITED; *Int'l*, pg. 5497
NVC LED LIGHTING APS—See NVC International Holdings Limited; *Int'l*, pg. 5497
NVC LIGHTING AB—See NVC International Holdings Limited; *Int'l*, pg. 5497
NVC LIGHTING (BRAZIL) COMMERCIAL IMPORT & EXPORT CO., LTD.—See NVC International Holdings Limited; *Int'l*, pg. 5497
NVC LIGHTING & ELECTRICAL TECHNOLOGY (SINGAPORE) PRIVATE LIMITED—See NVC International Holdings Limited; *Int'l*, pg. 5497
NVC LIGHTING & ELECTRICAL TECHNOLOGY (S) PTE. LTD.—See NVC International Holdings Limited; *Int'l*, pg. 5497
NVC LIGHTING & ELECTRICAL TECHNOLOGY (VIETNAM) PTE. LTD.—See NVC International Holdings Limited; *Int'l*, pg. 5497
NVC LIGHTING FOR ELECTRICAL EQUIPMENT & MACHINES TRADING & CONTRACTING COMPANY WLL—See NVC International Holdings Limited; *Int'l*, pg. 5498
NVC LIGHTING JAPAN CO., LTD.—See NVC International Holdings Limited; *Int'l*, pg. 5497
NVC LIGHTING LIMITED—See NVC International Holdings Limited; *Int'l*, pg. 5497
NVC LIGHTING MIDDLE EAST FZE—See NVC International Holdings Limited; *Int'l*, pg. 5497
N.V. DANFOSS S.A.—See Danfoss A/S; *Int'l*, pg. 1961
N.V. DELI MAATSCHAPPIJ—See Blackstone Inc.; *U.S. Public*, pg. 356
N.V. DRAEGER SAFETY BELGIUM S.A.—See Draegerwerk AG & Co. KGaA; *Int'l*, pg. 2198
N.V. DURACELL BATTERIES, S.A.—See The Procter & Gamble Company; *U.S. Public*, pg. 2124
NVE BANK; *U.S. Private*, pg. 2975
NVE CORPORATION; *U.S. Public*, pg. 1558
NVELO, INC.—See Samsung Group; *Int'l*, pg. 6512
NVELOPE RAINSCREEN SYSTEMS LTD.—See SFS Group AG; *Int'l*, pg. 6739
NV ENERGY, INC.—See Berkshire Hathaway Inc.; *U.S. Public*, pg. 1557
NVENT ELECTRIC PLC; *Int'l*, pg. 5498
NVENT SOLUTIONS (UK) LIMITED—See Pentair plc; *Int'l*, pg. 5790
NVER ENTERPRISES INC.; *U.S. Private*, pg. 2975
NVEST FINANCIAL HOLDINGS LIMITED; *Int'l*, pg. 5498
NVEST, INC.; *U.S. Private*, pg. 2975
NVEST SECURITIES (PTY) LIMITED—See NVest Financial Holdings Limited; *Int'l*, pg. 5498
N-VET AB—See SeQuent Scientific Limited; *Int'l*, pg. 6719
NV GOLD CORPORATION; *Int'l*, pg. 5497
N.V. GRIFFITH LABORATORIES S.A.—See Griffith Laboratories, Inc.; *U.S. Private*, pg. 1789
N.V. GRUNDFOS BELLUX S.A.—See The Poul Due Jensen Foundation; *Int'l*, pg. 7676
NVH ACQUISITION HOLDINGS LLC—See Angeles Equity Partners, LLC; *U.S. Private*, pg. 282

NV GOLD CORPORATION

CORPORATE AFFILIATIONS

N.V. HAKO BELGIUM S.A.—See L. Possehl & Co. mbH; *Int'l*, pg. 4384
N.V. HEATHORN INC.; *U.S. Private*, pg. 2828
NVH KOREA INC.; *Int'l*, pg. 5498
NVH RUS, LLC—See NVH Korea Inc.; *Int'l*, pg. 5498
NVIDIA ARC GMBH—See NVIDIA Corporation; *U.S. Public*, pg. 1558
NVIDIA CORPORATION; *U.S. Public*, pg. 1558
NVIDIA DEVELOPMENT UK LIMITED—See NVIDIA Corporation; *U.S. Public*, pg. 1558
NVIDIA FZ-LLC—See NVIDIA Corporation; *U.S. Public*, pg. 1558
NVIDIA GK—See NVIDIA Corporation; *U.S. Public*, pg. 1558
NVIDIA LTD.—See NVIDIA Corporation; *U.S. Public*, pg. 1558
NVIDIA SEMICONDUCTOR (SHENZHEN) CO., LTD.—See NVIDIA Corporation; *U.S. Public*, pg. 1558
NVIDIA TECHNOLOGY UK LIMITED—See NVIDIA Corporation; *U.S. Public*, pg. 1558
N-VILLAGE CO., LTD.—See Nomura Holdings, Inc.; *Int'l*, pg. 5409
N.V. ISEKI EUROPE S.A.—See Iseki & Co., Ltd.; *Int'l*, pg. 3814
NVISH SOLUTIONS INC.; *U.S. Private*, pg. 2975
NVIS INC.; *U.S. Private*, pg. 2975
NVISION CZECH REPUBLIC A.S.—See Sistema PJSFC; *Int'l*, pg. 6963
NVISION GROUP JSC—See Sistema PJSFC; *Int'l*, pg. 6963
NVISION LASER EYE CENTER, INC.—See Ontario Teachers' Pension Plan; *Int'l*, pg. 5586
NVISION UKRAINE, AO—See Sistema PJSFC; *Int'l*, pg. 6963
NV JEAN WAUTERS - ACIERS SPECIAUX—See Van Leeuwen Pipe & Tube Group B.V.; *Int'l*, pg. 8126
NV KEMA—See DNV GL Group AS; *Int'l*, pg. 2151
N.V. KSB BELGIUM S.A.—See KSB SE & Co. KGaA; *Int'l*, pg. 4313
N.V. MAYEKAWA EUROPE S.A.—See Mayekawa Mfg. Co. Ltd.; *Int'l*, pg. 4744
N.V. MAYEKAWA EUROPE S.A.—See Mayekawa Mfg. Co. Ltd.; *Int'l*, pg. 4744
N.V. MAYEKAWA EUROPE S.A.—See Mayekawa Mfg. Co. Ltd.; *Int'l*, pg. 4744
N.V. MERCEDES-BENZ AALST—See Mercedes-Benz Group AG; *Int'l*, pg. 4828
N.V. MERCEDES-BENZ MECHELEN—See Mercedes-Benz Group AG; *Int'l*, pg. 4828
N.V. METTLER-TOLEDO S.A.—See Mettler-Toledo International, Inc.; *U.S. Public*, pg. 1433
NV MICHEL VAN DE WIELE; *Int'l*, pg. 5497
N.V. MIELE BELGIE—See Miele & Cie KG; *Int'l*, pg. 4889
NVM PRIVATE EQUITY LIMITED; *Int'l*, pg. 5498
N.V. MSE EUROPE S.A.—See Mitsui-Soko Holdings Co., Ltd.; *Int'l*, pg. 4993
NV MULTI ASIA SDN. BHD.; *Int'l*, pg. 5497
NV MULTI (CAMBODIA) CO., LTD.—See NV Multi Asia Sdn. Bhd.; *Int'l*, pg. 5497
N.V. NATIONALE BORG-MAATSCHAPPIJ—See Egeria Capital Management B.V.; *Int'l*, pg. 2323
N.V. NATIONALE BORG-MAATSCHAPPIJ—See HAL Trust N.V.; *Int'l*, pg. 3224
N.V. NEDERLANDSE GASUNIE; *Int'l*, pg. 5117
NV NEDERLANDSE SPOORWEGEN; *Int'l*, pg. 5497
NV NEXANS BENELUX SA—See Nexans S.A.; *Int'l*, pg. 5240
NV NEXANS HARNESSESS SA—See Nexans S.A.; *Int'l*, pg. 5240
N.V. NORSKE SKOG BELGIUM S.A.—See Norske Skog ASA; *Int'l*, pg. 5438
N.V. NOVARTIS CONSUMER HEALTH S.A.—See Novartis AG; *Int'l*, pg. 5457
N.V. NOVARTIS PHARMA S.A.—See Novartis AG; *Int'l*, pg. 5459
N.V. NUON BUSINESS—See Vattenfall AB; *Int'l*, pg. 8136
N.V. NUON CUSTOMER CARE CENTER—See Vattenfall AB; *Int'l*, pg. 8136
N.V. NUON DUURZAME ENERGIE—See Vattenfall AB; *Int'l*, pg. 8136
N.V. NUON ENERGY—See Vattenfall AB; *Int'l*, pg. 8136
N.V. NUON ENERGY SOURCING—See Vattenfall AB; *Int'l*, pg. 8136
NVOICEPAY, INC.—See Corpay, Inc.; *U.S. Public*, pg. 580
NVO NAHVERKEHR OSTWESTFALEN GMBH—See Deutsche Bahn AG; *Int'l*, pg. 2052
N.V. OWENS-CORNING S.A.—See Owens Corning; *U.S. Public*, pg. 1627
N.V. PAUL HARTMANN S.A.—See PAUL HARTMANN AG; *Int'l*, pg. 5761
N.V. PERRICONE LLC—See THG Holdings Plc; *Int'l*, pg. 7708
NVP S.P.A.; *Int'l*, pg. 5499
NVR FUNDING II, INC.—See NVR Incorporated; *U.S. Public*, pg. 1558
NVR INCORPORATED; *U.S. Public*, pg. 1558
NVR MORTGAGE FINANCE, INC.—See NVR Incorporated; *U.S. Public*, pg. 1558
N.V. ROCHE S.A.—See Roche Holding AG; *Int'l*, pg. 6373

N.V. ROTTERDAM-RIJN PIJPLEIDING MAATSCHAPPIJ; *Int'l*, pg. 5117
NVR SERVICES, INC.—See NVR Incorporated; *U.S. Public*, pg. 1558
N.V. SANDOZ S.A.—See Sandoz Group AG; *Int'l*, pg. 6527
NVS AS—See Triton Advisers Limited; *Int'l*, pg. 7933
N.V. SILICAATSTEEN—See Heidelberg Materials AG; *Int'l*, pg. 3318
NVS INSTALLATION AB—See Triton Advisers Limited; *Int'l*, pg. 7933
N.V. SOMFY S.A.—See Somfy SA; *Int'l*, pg. 7085
NV SOUTHWESTERN PETROLEUM EUROPE, SA—See Southwestern Petroleum Corporation; *U.S. Private*, pg. 3742
NV STORAX BENELUX SA—See F. Ramada Investimentos, SGPS, S.A.; *Int'l*, pg. 2596
N.V. STRABAG BELGIUM S.A.—See STRABAG SE; *Int'l*, pg. 7231
N.V. STRABAG BENELUX S.A.—See STRABAG SE; *Int'l*, pg. 7231
N.V. STRATEC MEDICAL S.A.—See Johnson & Johnson; *U.S. Public*, pg. 1195
N.V. STRYKER SA—See Stryker Corporation; *U.S. Public*, pg. 1956
N.V. SUBARU BENELUX—See Subaru Corporation; *Int'l*, pg. 7247
NVT BATTERY DESIGN SOLUTION CO. LTD.—See TDK Corporation; *Int'l*, pg. 7487
N.V. TOYOTA MOTOR EUROPE MARKETING & ENGINEERING S.A.—See Toyota Motor Corporation; *Int'l*, pg. 7872
N.V. VANDEMOORTELE IZEGEM—See Vandemoortele N.V.; *Int'l*, pg. 8128
N.V. VANDEMOORTELE—See Vandemoortele N.V.; *Int'l*, pg. 8128
NV VREDESTEIN SA—See Apollo Tyres Ltd.; *Int'l*, pg. 519
N.V. YOKO CHEESE S.A.—See Zuivelcooperatie FrieslandCampina U.A.; *Int'l*, pg. 8694
N.V. YOKOHAMA BELGIUM S.A.—See The Yokohama Rubber Co., Ltd.; *Int'l*, pg. 7702
NW18 HSN HOLDINGS PLC—See Reliance - ADA Group Limited; *Int'l*, pg. 6262
N'WAVE STUDIOS S.A.—See Vivendi SE; *Int'l*, pg. 8266
N-WAVE VIETNAM COMPANY LIMITED—See Namura Shipbuilding Co., Ltd.; *Int'l*, pg. 5136
NWB NORD- UND WESTDEUTSCHE BUNKER GMBH—See Hoyer GmbH; *Int'l*, pg. 3499
NW COMMUNICATIONS OF AUSTIN, INC.—See Fox Corporation; *U.S. Public*, pg. 876
NW COMMUNICATIONS OF TEXAS, INC.—See Fox Corporation; *U.S. Public*, pg. 876
NW CONSULTANT SERVICE (SHENZHEN) LTD.—See Nagase & Co., Ltd.; *Int'l*, pg. 5126
NWC SERVICES GMBH—See CANCOM SE; *Int'l*, pg. 1289
NWE MANAGEMENT COMPANY—See Northwestern Engineering Company; *U.S. Private*, pg. 2962
NWF AGRICULTURE HOLDINGS LIMITED—See NWF Group Plc; *Int'l*, pg. 5499
NWF AGRICULTURE LIMITED—See NWF Group Plc; pg. 5499
NWF FUELS LIMITED—See NWF Group Plc; *Int'l*, pg. 5499
NWF GROUP PLC; *Int'l*, pg. 5499
NW HOLDING CO.; *U.S. Private*, pg. 2975
NWI DE MEXICO S. DE R.L. DE C.V.—See Gattaca plc; *Int'l*, pg. 2890
NWJ COMPANIES, INC.; *U.S. Private*, pg. 2975
NWL DENMARK SERVICES APS—See Newell Brands Inc.; *U.S. Public*, pg. 1514
NWL FINANCIAL, INC.—See Prosperity Group Holdings, LP; *U.S. Private*, pg. 3289
NWL SERVICES, INC.—See Prosperity Group Holdings, LP; *U.S. Private*, pg. 3289
NWL TRANSFORMERS INC.—See American Superconductor Corporation; *U.S. Public*, pg. 110
NWMC-WINFIELD ANESTHESIA PHYSICIANS, LLC—See Apollo Global Management, Inc.; *U.S. Public*, pg. 158
NWM SOLUTIONS LIMITED; *Int'l*, pg. 5499
NW NATURAL WATER COMPANY, LLC—See Northwest Natural Holding Company; *U.S. Public*, pg. 1542
NWN CORPORATION—See American Securities LLC; *U.S. Private*, pg. 250
NWN CORPORATION—See American Securities LLC; *U.S. Private*, pg. 250
NWN CORPORATION—See American Securities LLC; *U.S. Private*, pg. 250
NWORK CO., LTD.—See EDION Corporation; *Int'l*, pg. 2310
NWPC DE SLRC, S DE RL DE CV—See Northwest Pipe Company; *U.S. Public*, pg. 1542
NWP COAL CANADA LTD.—See Jameson Resources Limited; *Int'l*, pg. 3878
NWP INDUSTRIES SDN. BHD.—See Auro Holdings Berhad; *Int'l*, pg. 711
NWP INTERNATIONAL TRADING (SHENZHEN) CO., LTD.—See Nagase & Co., Ltd.; *Int'l*, pg. 5126
NWP SERVICES CORPORATION—See Thoma Bravo, L.P.; *U.S. Private*, pg. 4153

NWQ INVESTMENT MANAGEMENT COMPANY, LLC—See Teachers Insurance Association - College Retirement Fund; *U.S. Private*, pg. 3947
NW SERVICES CORPORATION; *U.S. Private*, pg. 2975
NWS HOLDINGS LIMITED—See Chow Tai Fook Enterprises Limited; *Int'l*, pg. 1584
NW SIGN INDUSTRIES INC.; *U.S. Private*, pg. 2975
NWS MICHIGAN INC.; *U.S. Private*, pg. 2975
NW TECH CAPITAL, INC.; *U.S. Private*, pg. 2975
NWT HOLDING (HK) LIMITED—See United Investments Ltd.; *Int'l*, pg. 8070
NW TOTAL ENGINEERED SOLUTIONS LTD.—See Carr's Group PLC; *Int'l*, pg. 1343
NW TRUST (SWITZERLAND) SA—See United Investments Ltd.; *Int'l*, pg. 8070
NWTX PHYSICIAN NETWORK, PLLC—See Universal Health Services, Inc.; *U.S. Public*, pg. 2258
N.W. WHITE & COMPANY; *U.S. Private*, pg. 2828
NXC CORPORATION—See Nexon Co., Ltd.; *Int'l*, pg. 5245
NXCHAIN, INC.; *U.S. Private*, pg. 2975
NXC IMAGING; *U.S. Private*, pg. 2975
NX DEVELOPMENT CORP.—See SBI Holdings, Inc.; *Int'l*, pg. 6604
NXEDGE, INC.—See Trive Capital Inc.; *U.S. Private*, pg. 4240
NXERA PHARMA CO., LTD.; *Int'l*, pg. 5499
NX FILTRATION N.V.; *Int'l*, pg. 5499
NXGEN BRANDS LLC; *U.S. Public*, pg. 1558
NXGEN PAYMENT SERVICES; *U.S. Private*, pg. 2975
NXG NEXTGEN INFRASTRUCTURE INCOME FUND—See Swank Capital, LLC; *U.S. Private*, pg. 3890
NXGN, INC.; *U.S. Private*, pg. 2975
NX GOLD S.A.—See Ero Copper Corp.; *Int'l*, pg. 2496
NXH JOINT VENTURE COMPANY LIMITED—See Pico (Thailand) Public Company Limited; *Int'l*, pg. 5860
NXP B.V.—See Silergy Corp.; *Int'l*, pg. 6919
NXP CORP.; *U.S. Private*, pg. 2975
NXP LIMITED—See Platinum Equity, LLC; *U.S. Private*, pg. 3210
NXP SEMICONDUCTORS AUSTRIA GMBH & CO. KG—See NXP Semiconductors N.V.; *Int'l*, pg. 5499
NXP SEMICONDUCTORS FRANCE S.A.S.—See NXP Semiconductors N.V.; *Int'l*, pg. 5499
NXP SEMICONDUCTORS GMBH—See NXP Semiconductors N.V.; *Int'l*, pg. 5499
NXP SEMICONDUCTORS NETHERLANDS B.V.—See NXP Semiconductors N.V.; *Int'l*, pg. 5499
NXP SEMICONDUCTORS N.V.; *Int'l*, pg. 5499
NXP SEMICONDUCTORS SINGAPORE PTE. LTD.—See NXP Semiconductors N.V.; *Int'l*, pg. 5499
NXP SEMICONDUCTORS USA, INC. - CARY—See NXP Semiconductors N.V.; *Int'l*, pg. 5499
NXP SEMICONDUCTORS USA, INC.—See NXP Semiconductors N.V.; *Int'l*, pg. 5499
NXP SEMICONDUCTORS USA, INC. - TEMPE—See NXP Semiconductors N.V.; *Int'l*, pg. 5499
NXP SOFTWARE B.V.—See NXP Semiconductors N.V.; *Int'l*, pg. 5499
NXSTAGE BOSTON NORTH, LLC—See Fresenius Medical Care AG; *Int'l*, pg. 2776
NXSTAGE KIDNEY CARE, INC.—See Fresenius Medical Care AG; *Int'l*, pg. 2777
NXSTAGE MEDICAL, INC.—See Fresenius Medical Care AG; *Int'l*, pg. 2776
NXSTAGE OAK BROOK, LLC—See Fresenius Medical Care AG; *Int'l*, pg. 2777
NXSTAGE ORLANDO NORTH, LLC—See Fresenius Medical Care AG; *Int'l*, pg. 2777
NXTBOOK MEDIA, LLC; *U.S. Private*, pg. 2976
NXT CAPITAL, LLC—See ORIX Corporation; *Int'l*, pg. 5636
NXT CONTROL GMBH—See Schneider Electric SE; *Int'l*, pg. 6624
NXTDIGITAL LIMITED—See Hinduja Global Solutions Ltd.; *Int'l*, pg. 3398
NXT ENERGY SOLUTIONS INC.; *Int'l*, pg. 5499
NXTFIELD, INC.—See Tobishima Corporation; *Int'l*, pg. 7771
NXTKEY CORPORATION; *U.S. Private*, pg. 2976
NXTLVL MARINE, LLC; *U.S. Private*, pg. 2976
NXTSOFT LLC; *U.S. Private*, pg. 2976
NXU INC.; *U.S. Public*, pg. 1558
NYA CHRISTIANSTADS BILLACKERING AB—See LKQ Corporation; *U.S. Public*, pg. 1335
NYADI HYDROPOWER LIMITED—See Butwal Power Company Limited; *Int'l*, pg. 1229
NYANZA BOTTLING COMPANY LIMITED—See Sumaria Group; *Int'l*, pg. 7259
NYBRON FLOORING INTERNATIONAL CORPORATION—See Vestar Capital Partners, LLC; *U.S. Private*, pg. 4372
NYCA; *U.S. Private*, pg. 2976
NYC CONCRETE MATERIALS, LLC—See Vulcan Materials Company; *U.S. Public*, pg. 2314
NYCE PAYMENTS NETWORK, LLC—See Fidelity National Infor; *U.S. Public*, pg. 833
NYCO CO., LTD.; *Int'l*, pg. 5499

COMPANY NAME INDEX

NYCO FLEXIBLE PACKAGING GMBH—See FairCap GmbH; *Int'l*, pg. 2605
NYCOIL COMPANY—See Parker Hannifin Corporation; *U.S. Public*, pg. 1646
NYCO, INC.—See APi Group Corporation; *Int'l*, pg. 514
NYCOM INC.; *U.S. Private*, pg. 2976
NYCO MINERALS, INC.—See RCF Management LLC; *U.S. Private*, pg. 3362
NYCOMM HOLDINGS LIMITED; *Int'l*, pg. 5500
NYCOPAC AB—See SP Group A/S; *Int'l*, pg. 7122
NYDJ APPAREL, LLC—See Falconhead Capital, LLC; *U.S. Private*, pg. 1467
NYDREE FLOORING; *U.S. Private*, pg. 2976
NYE LUBRICANTS, INC.—See FUCHS SE; *Int'l*, pg. 2804
NYEREG CO., LTD.—See Zensho Holdings Co., Ltd.; *Int'l*, pg. 8634
NYESA MELIA ZARAGOZA S.L.—See Melia Hotels International, S.A.; *Int'l*, pg. 4809
NYESA VALORES CORP SA; *Int'l*, pg. 5500
NYFOSA AB; *Int'l*, pg. 5500
NYGARD CAY—See Nygard International Partnership; *Int'l*, pg. 5500
NYGARD INC.—See Nygard International Partnership; *Int'l*, pg. 5500
NYGARD INTERNATIONAL LIMITED, INC.—See Nygard International Partnership; *Int'l*, pg. 5500
NYGARD INTERNATIONAL PARTNERSHIP; *Int'l*, pg. 5500
NYGARD INTERNATIONAL—See Nygard International Partnership; *Int'l*, pg. 5500
THE NYHART COMPANY INC.; *U.S. Private*, pg. 4087
NYHETSBOLAGET SVERIGE AB—See Bonnier AB; *Int'l*, pg. 1109
NYHUS CHEVROLET & BUICK INC.; *U.S. Private*, pg. 2976
NYHUS COMMUNICATIONS LLC; *U.S. Private*, pg. 2976
NYIAX, INC.; *U.S. Public*, pg. 1559
NYK & BLL OF SOUTH AFRICA (PTY) LTD—See Nippon Yusen Kabushiki Kaisha; *Int'l*, pg. 5358
NYK BULK & PROJECTS CARRIERS LTD.—See Nippon Yusen Kabushiki Kaisha; *Int'l*, pg. 5358
NYK BULKSHIP (ASIA) PTE. LTD.—See Nippon Yusen Kabushiki Kaisha; *Int'l*, pg. 5358
NYK BULKSHIP (ATLANTIC) N.V.—See Nippon Yusen Kabushiki Kaisha; *Int'l*, pg. 5358
NYK BULKSHIP (CHINA) LTD.—See Nippon Yusen Kabushiki Kaisha; *Int'l*, pg. 5358
NYK BULKSHIP (EUROPE) LTD.—See Nippon Yusen Kabushiki Kaisha; *Int'l*, pg. 5358
NYK BULKSHIP (USA) INC.—See Nippon Yusen Kabushiki Kaisha; *Int'l*, pg. 5358
NYK BUSINESS SYSTEMS AMERICAS INC.—See Nippon Yusen Kabushiki Kaisha; *Int'l*, pg. 5358
NYK BUSINESS SYSTEMS CO., LTD.—See Nippon Yusen Kabushiki Kaisha; *Int'l*, pg. 5358
NYK CRUISES CO., LTD.—See Nippon Yusen Kabushiki Kaisha; *Int'l*, pg. 5358
NYK DE MEXICO, S.A. DE C.V.—See Nippon Yusen Kabushiki Kaisha; *Int'l*, pg. 5359
NYK-FIL MARITIME E-TRAINING, INC.—See Nippon Yusen Kabushiki Kaisha; *Int'l*, pg. 5359
NYK-FIL SHIP MANAGEMENT, INC.—See Nippon Yusen Kabushiki Kaisha; *Int'l*, pg. 5359
NYK GLOBAL BULK CORPORATION—See Nippon Yusen Kabushiki Kaisha; *Int'l*, pg. 5358
NYK GROUP AMERICAS INC.—See Nippon Yusen Kabushiki Kaisha; *Int'l*, pg. 5358
NYK GROUP EUROPE LTD.—See Nippon Yusen Kabushiki Kaisha; *Int'l*, pg. 5358
NYK GROUP SOUTH ASIA PTE. LTD.—See Nippon Yusen Kabushiki Kaisha; *Int'l*, pg. 5358
NYK-HINODE LINE, LTD.—See Nippon Yusen Kabushiki Kaisha; *Int'l*, pg. 5359
NYK LINE (AUSTRALIA) PTY. LTD.—See Nippon Yusen Kabushiki Kaisha; *Int'l*, pg. 5358
NYK LINE (BENELUX) B.V.—See Nippon Yusen Kabushiki Kaisha; *Int'l*, pg. 5358
NYK LINE (CANADA), INC.—See Nippon Yusen Kabushiki Kaisha; *Int'l*, pg. 5358
NYK LINE (CHINA) CO., LTD.—See Nippon Yusen Kabushiki Kaisha; *Int'l*, pg. 5358
NYK LINE (DEUTSCHLAND) GMBH—See Nippon Yusen Kabushiki Kaisha; *Int'l*, pg. 5358
NYK LINE (EUROPE) LTD.—See Nippon Yusen Kabushiki Kaisha; *Int'l*, pg. 5358
NYK LINE (HONG KONG) LTD.—See Nippon Yusen Kabushiki Kaisha; *Int'l*, pg. 5358
NYK LINE M SDN BHD—See Nippon Yusen Kabushiki Kaisha; *Int'l*, pg. 5358
NYK LINE (NEW ZEALAND) LTD.—See Nippon Yusen Kabushiki Kaisha; *Int'l*, pg. 5358
NYK LINE (NORTH AMERICA) INC.—See Nippon Yusen Kabushiki Kaisha; *Int'l*, pg. 5358
NYK LINE NZ LTD—See Nippon Yusen Kabushiki Kaisha; *Int'l*, pg. 5358
NYK LINE (SVERIGE) AB—See Nippon Yusen Kabushiki Kaisha; *Int'l*, pg. 5358
NYK LINE (THAILAND) CO., LTD.—See Nippon Yusen Kabushiki Kaisha; *Int'l*, pg. 5358
NYK LNG SHIPMANAGEMENT (UK) LTD.—See Nippon Yusen Kabushiki Kaisha; *Int'l*, pg. 5358
NYK LOGISTICS (CHINA) CO., LTD.—See Nippon Yusen Kabushiki Kaisha; *Int'l*, pg. 5358
NYK LOGISTICS (INDIA) INC.—See Nippon Yusen Kabushiki Kaisha; *Int'l*, pg. 5358
NYK LOGISTICS (MIDDLE EAST) L.L.C.—See Nippon Yusen Kabushiki Kaisha; *Int'l*, pg. 5358
NYK LOGISTICS (PHILIPPINES) INC.—See Nippon Yusen Kabushiki Kaisha; *Int'l*, pg. 5358
NYK LOGISTICS (VIETNAM) CO., LTD.—See Nippon Yusen Kabushiki Kaisha; *Int'l*, pg. 5358
NYKOR PILOT PEN ITALIA SRL—See Pilot Corporation; *Int'l*, pg. 5866
NYKO TECHNOLOGIES INC.; *U.S. Private*, pg. 2976
NYKREDIT A/S; *Int'l*, pg. 5500
NYKREDIT BANK A/S—See Nykredit A/S; *Int'l*, pg. 5500
NYKREDIT EJENDOMME A/S—See Nykredit A/S; *Int'l*, pg. 5500
NYKREDIT FORSIKRING A/S—See Nykredit A/S; *Int'l*, pg. 5500
NYKREDIT MAEGLER A/S—See Nykredit A/S; *Int'l*, pg. 5500
NYKREDIT PANTEBREVSINVESTERING A/S—See Nykredit A/S; *Int'l*, pg. 5500
NYKREDIT PORTEFOLJE ADM. A/S—See Nykredit A/S; *Int'l*, pg. 5500
NYKREDIT PORTEFOLJE BANK A/S—See Nykredit A/S; *Int'l*, pg. 5500
NYK RORO (THAILAND) CO., LTD.—See Nippon Yusen Kabushiki Kaisha; *Int'l*, pg. 5359
NYK SHIPMANAGEMENT PTE. LTD.—See Nippon Yusen Kabushiki Kaisha; *Int'l*, pg. 5359
NYK SHIPPING SERVICE (THAILAND) CO., LTD.—See Nippon Yusen Kabushiki Kaisha; *Int'l*, pg. 5359
NYK SUDAMERICA (CHILE) LTDA.—See Nippon Yusen Kabushiki Kaisha; *Int'l*, pg. 5359
NYK TDG PHILIPPINES INC.—See Nippon Yusen Kabushiki Kaisha; *Int'l*, pg. 5359
NYKT ENERGY & TECHNOLOGY (SHANGHAI) CORP.—See Nippon Yusen Kabushiki Kaisha; *Int'l*, pg. 5359
NYK TERMINALS (TAIWAN), INC.—See Nippon Yusen Kabushiki Kaisha; *Int'l*, pg. 5359
NYKT MARINE CO., LTD.—See Nippon Yusen Kabushiki Kaisha; *Int'l*, pg. 5359
NYK TRADING CORPORATION—See Nippon Yusen Kabushiki Kaisha; *Int'l*, pg. 5359
NYK TRADING (SINGAPORE) PTE. LTD.—See Nippon Yusen Kabushiki Kaisha; *Int'l*, pg. 5359
NYLACARB CORPORATION; *U.S. Private*, pg. 2976
NYLE CORPORATION; *U.S. Private*, pg. 2976
NYLECT ENGINEERING PTE. LTD.—See Tai Sin Electric Limited; *Int'l*, pg. 7409
NYLECT TECHNOLOGY (MYANMAR) LTD.—See Tai Sin Electric Limited; *Int'l*, pg. 7409
NYLEVE BRIDGE CORP.—See The Schultz Organization, LLC; *U.S. Private*, pg. 4115
NYLEX CONSUMER PRODUCTS—See Nylex Limited; *Int'l*, pg. 5500
NYLEX INDUSTRIAL PRODUCTS PTY LTD.—See Nylex Limited; *Int'l*, pg. 5500
NYLEX LIMITED; *Int'l*, pg. 5500
NYLEX (MALAYSIA) BERHAD; *Int'l*, pg. 5500
NYLEX SPECIALTY CHEMICALS SDN BHD—See Nylex (Malaysia) Berhad; *Int'l*, pg. 5500
NYLEX WATER SOLUTIONS PTY LTD.—See Nylex Limited; *Int'l*, pg. 5500
NYLIFE DISTRIBUTORS LLC—See New York Life Insurance Company; *U.S. Private*, pg. 2910
NYLIFE INSURANCE COMPANY OF ARIZONA—See New York Life Insurance Company; *U.S. Private*, pg. 2910
NY LNR LUXURY IMPORTS, INC.—See AutoNation, Inc.; *U.S. Public*, pg. 236
NYLO DALLAS SOUTH SIDE—See NYLO Hotels LLC; *U.S. Private*, pg. 2976
NYLO HOTELS LLC; *U.S. Private*, pg. 2976
NYLO IRVING/LAS COLINAS—See NYLO Hotels LLC; *U.S. Private*, pg. 2976
NYLOK CORPORATION; *U.S. Private*, pg. 2976
NYLON CORPORATION OF AMERICA—See Wembly Enterprises LLC; *U.S. Private*, pg. 4480
NYLONCRAFT, INC. - JONESVILLE—See Hammond, Kennedy, Whitney & Company, Inc.; *U.S. Private*, pg. 1850
NYLONCRAFT, INC.—See Hammond, Kennedy, Whitney & Company, Inc.; *U.S. Private*, pg. 1850
NYLONCRAFT, INC.—See Hammond, Kennedy, Whitney & Company, Inc.; *U.S. Private*, pg. 1850
NYLO NEW YORK CITY—See NYLO Hotels LLC; *U.S. Private*, pg. 2976
NYLON, INC.—See Diversis Capital, LLC; *U.S. Private*, pg. 1244
NYLO PLANO/LEGACY—See NYLO Hotels LLC; *U.S. Private*, pg. 2976
NYLOPLAST EUROPE B.V.—See Tessenderlo Group NV; *Int'l*, pg. 7573
NYLO PROVIDENCE/WARWICK—See NYLO Hotels LLC; *U.S. Private*, pg. 2976
NY LUXURY MOTORS OF MT. KISCO, INC.—See AutoNation, Inc.; *U.S. Public*, pg. 236
NYMAN CONSTRUCTION; *U.S. Private*, pg. 2976
NYMBUS, INC.; *U.S. Private*, pg. 2976
NYMOX PHARMACEUTICAL CORPORATION; *Int'l*, pg. 5501
NYMPHEA ENVIRONNEMENT S.A.—See VINCI S.A.; *Int'l*, pg. 8217
NY MT. KISCO LUXURY IMPORTS, INC.—See AutoNation, Inc.; *U.S. Public*, pg. 236
NYM WORLDGROUP, INC.; *U.S. Private*, pg. 2976
NYNAS AB—See Bitumina Industries Ltd.; *Int'l*, pg. 1050
NYNAS ARGENTINA SA—See Bitumina Industries Ltd.; *Int'l*, pg. 1050
NYNAS A/S—See Bitumina Industries Ltd.; *Int'l*, pg. 1050
NYNAS (AUSTRALIA) PTY LTD—See Bitumina Industries Ltd.; *Int'l*, pg. 1050
NYNAS BELGIUM AB—See Bitumina Industries Ltd.; *Int'l*, pg. 1050
NYNAS CANADA INC—See Bitumina Industries Ltd.; *Int'l*, pg. 1051
NYNAS MEXICO SA—See Bitumina Industries Ltd.; *Int'l*, pg. 1051
NYNAS NAPHTHENICS LTD—See Bitumina Industries Ltd.; *Int'l*, pg. 1051
NYNAS OY—See Bitumina Industries Ltd.; *Int'l*, pg. 1051
NYNAS PETROLEO SA—See Bitumina Industries Ltd.; *Int'l*, pg. 1051
NYNAS PTE, LTD—See Bitumina Industries Ltd.; *Int'l*, pg. 1051
NYNAS SA—See Bitumina Industries Ltd.; *Int'l*, pg. 1051
NYNAS SERVICIOS SA—See Bitumina Industries Ltd.; *Int'l*, pg. 1051
NYNAS (SOUTH AFRICA) (PTY) LTD—See Bitumina Industries Ltd.; *Int'l*, pg. 1050
NYNAS SP. Z O.O.—See Bitumina Industries Ltd.; *Int'l*, pg. 1051
NYNAS SRL—See Bitumina Industries Ltd.; *Int'l*, pg. 1051
NYNAS TECHNOL HANDELS GMBH—See Bitumina Industries Ltd.; *Int'l*, pg. 1051
NYNAS UK AB—See Bitumina Industries Ltd.; *Int'l*, pg. 1051
NYNAS USA, INC—See Bitumina Industries Ltd.; *Int'l*, pg. 1051
NYNAS VERWALTUNGS GMBH—See Bitumina Industries Ltd.; *Int'l*, pg. 1051
NYNOMIC AG; *Int'l*, pg. 5501
NYOCOR CO., LTD.; *Int'l*, pg. 5501
NYOO REAL ESTATE GMBH—See Instone Real Estate Group SE; *Int'l*, pg. 3724
NYOTA MINERALS LTD.; *Int'l*, pg. 5501
NYOTA MINERALS (UK) LIMITED—See Nyota Minerals Ltd.; *Int'l*, pg. 5501
NYP INC; *U.S. Private*, pg. 2976
NYP, LLC—See Granite Creek Capital Partners, LLC; *U.S. Private*, pg. 1755
NYPRO ALABAMA LLC—See Jabil Inc.; *U.S. Public*, pg. 1181
NYPRO ASHEVILLE INC.—See Jabil Inc.; *U.S. Public*, pg. 1181
NYPRO CHICAGO—See Jabil Inc.; *U.S. Public*, pg. 1181
NYPRO DE LA FRONTERA, S DE RL DE CV—See Jabil Inc.; *U.S. Public*, pg. 1182
NYPRO DENMARK APS—See Jabil Inc.; *U.S. Public*, pg. 1181
NYPRO DEUTSCHLAND GMBH—See Jabil Inc.; *U.S. Public*, pg. 1181
NYPRO FRANCE SAS—See Jabil Inc.; *U.S. Public*, pg. 1181
NYPRO GLOBAL HOLDINGS CV—See Jabil Inc.; *U.S. Public*, pg. 1181
NYPRO GUADALAJARA—See Jabil Inc.; *U.S. Public*, pg. 1181
NYPRO HEALTHCARE BAJA INC.—See Jabil Inc.; *U.S. Public*, pg. 1181
NYPRO HUNGARY MUANYAGTECHNIKA KFT—See Jabil Inc.; *U.S. Public*, pg. 1181
NYPRO INC.—See Jabil Inc.; *U.S. Public*, pg. 1181
NYPRO IOWA INC.—See Jabil Inc.; *U.S. Public*, pg. 1182
NYPRO KANAAK-ALABAMA LLC—See Jabil Inc.; *U.S. Public*, pg. 1182
NYPRO KANAAK IOWA INC.—See Jabil Inc.; *U.S. Public*, pg. 1181
NYPRO LIMITED—See Jabil Inc.; *U.S. Public*, pg. 1182
NYPROMOLD INC.; *U.S. Private*, pg. 2977
NYPRO NAGYIGMAND VAGYONKEZELO KFT—See Jabil Inc.; *U.S. Public*, pg. 1182
NYPRO PUERTO RICO INC.—See Jabil Inc.; *U.S. Public*, pg. 1182
NYPRO REALTY CORP—See Jabil Inc.; *U.S. Public*, pg. 1182
NYPRO SAN DIEGO INC.—See Jabil Inc.; *U.S. Public*, pg. 1182
NYQUEST TECHNOLOGY CO., LTD.; *Int'l*, pg. 5501
NYRADA INC.; *Int'l*, pg. 5501
NYRSTAR BELGIUM NV—See Nyrstar NV; *Int'l*, pg. 5501
NYRSTAR BUDEL BV—See Nyrstar NV; *Int'l*, pg. 5501
NYRSTAR CLARKSVILLE INC.—See Nyrstar NV; *Int'l*, pg. 5501

NYRADA INC.

CORPORATE AFFILIATIONS

NYRSTAR FINANCE INTERNATIONAL NV—See Nyrstar NV; *Int'l*, pg. 5501
NYRSTAR FRANCE SAS—See Nyrstar NV; *Int'l*, pg. 5501
NYRSTAR GERMANY GMBH—See Nyrstar NV; *Int'l*, pg. 5501
NYRSTAR HOBART PTY LTD—See Nyrstar NV; *Int'l*, pg. 5501
NYRSTAR HOLDINGS INC—See Nyrstar NV; *Int'l*, pg. 5501
NYRSTAR METALS PTY LTD—See Nyrstar NV; *Int'l*, pg. 5501
NYRSTAR NETHERLANDS (HOLDINGS) BV—See Nyrstar NV; *Int'l*, pg. 5501
NYRSTAR NV; *Int'l*, pg. 5501
NYRSTAR PORT PIRIE PTY LTD—See Nyrstar NV; *Int'l*, pg. 5501
NYRSTAR SALES & MARKETING NV—See Nyrstar NV; *Int'l*, pg. 5502
NYRSTAR TENNESSEE MINES - GORDONSVILLE LLC—See Nyrstar NV; *Int'l*, pg. 5502
NYRSTAR TENNESSEE MINES - STRAWBERRY PLAINS LLC—See Nyrstar NV; *Int'l*, pg. 5502
NYSAGAZ SP. Z O.O.—See Polskie Gornictwo Naftowe i Gazownictwo S.A.; *Int'l*, pg. 5912
NYSE AMERICAN LLC—See Intercontinental Exchange, Inc.; *U.S. Public*, pg. 1143
NYSE ARCA, INC.—See Intercontinental Exchange, Inc.; *U.S. Public*, pg. 1143
NYSE CHICAGO HOLDINGS, INC.—See Intercontinental Exchange, Inc.; *U.S. Public*, pg. 1143
NYSE CHICAGO, INC.—See Intercontinental Exchange, Inc.; *U.S. Public*, pg. 1143
NYSE GROUP, INC.—See Intercontinental Exchange, Inc.; *U.S. Public*, pg. 1143
NYSE LIFFE US LLC—See Intercontinental Exchange, Inc.; *U.S. Public*, pg. 1143
NYSE MARKET (DE), INC.—See Intercontinental Exchange, Inc.; *U.S. Public*, pg. 1143
NYSE NATIONAL, INC.—See Intercontinental Exchange, Inc.; *U.S. Public*, pg. 1143
NYSE REGULATION, INC.—See Intercontinental Exchange, Inc.; *U.S. Public*, pg. 1143
NYSE TECHNOLOGIES, INC.—See Intercontinental Exchange, Inc.; *U.S. Public*, pg. 1143
NYSSA CORPORATION LIMITED; *Int'l*, pg. 5502
NYSTROM EDUCATION—See Social Studies School Service; *U.S. Private*, pg. 3703
NYSTROM, INC.; *U.S. Private*, pg. 2977
NYT CAPITAL, LLC—See The New York Times Company; *U.S. Public*, pg. 2116
NYTEC INC.—See Accenture plc; *Int'l*, pg. 87
NYTEF PLASTICS CORP.—See Nytef Plastics Ltd.; *U.S. Private*, pg. 2977
NYTEF PLASTICS LTD.; *U.S. Private*, pg. 2977
NYTIDA AB—See Triton Advisers Limited; *Int'l*, pg. 7929
NYTIS EXPLORATION COMPANY LLC—See Carbon Energy Corporation; *U.S. Public*, pg. 432
NYTIS EXPLORATION (USA) INC.—See Carbon Energy Corporation; *U.S. Public*, pg. 432
NYT MANAGEMENT SERVICES, INC.—See The New York Times Company; *U.S. Public*, pg. 2116
NYT SHARED SERVICE CENTER, INC.—See The New York Times Company; *U.S. Public*, pg. 2117
NYT SINGAPORE PTE. LTD.—See The New York Times Company; *U.S. Public*, pg. 2117
NY WHITE PLAINS LUXURY IMPORTS, INC.—See AutoNation, Inc.; *U.S. Public*, pg. 236
NYWP ENTERPRISE LLC—See New Yung Wah Trading LLC; *U.S. Private*, pg. 2913
NYW TRADING LLC—See New Yung Wah Trading LLC; *U.S. Private*, pg. 2913
NYX FORT WAYNE—See NYX Inc.; *U.S. Private*, pg. 2977
NYX GAMING GROUP LLC—See Light & Wonder, Inc.; *U.S. Public*, pg. 1314
NYX INC.; *U.S. Private*, pg. 2977
NYXIO TECHNOLOGIES CORPORATION; *U.S. Private*, pg. 2977
NYXOAH SA; *Int'l*, pg. 5502
NZAS RETIREMENT FUND TRUSTEE LIMITED—See Rio Tinto plc; *Int'l*, pg. 6346
NZCH CORPORATION—See Spectrum Brands Holdings, Inc.; *U.S. Public*, pg. 1915
NZ FACTORING COMPANY LTD.—See Butn Limited; *Int'l*, pg. 1229
NZ FARMING SYSTEMS URUGUAY LIMITED—See Temasek Holdings (Private) Limited; *Int'l*, pg. 7549
NZF MONEY LIMITED—See RTO Limited; *Int'l*, pg. 6420
NZ GASKETS LIMITED—See Amotiv Limited; *Int'l*, pg. 431
NZJ HOLDINGS, INC.; *U.S. Private*, pg. 1559
NZME LIMITED—See ARN Media Limited; *Int'l*, pg. 576
NZME ONLINE LIMITED—See ARN Media Limited; *Int'l*, pg. 576
NZ NEW IMAGE SDN BHD—See New Image Group Limited; *Int'l*, pg. 5225
NZOOM LIMITED—See TVNZ; *Int'l*, pg. 7988
NZ RURAL PRESS LIMITED—See Nine Entertainment Co. Holdings Limited; *Int'l*, pg. 5299
NZURI COPPER LIMITED—See Chengtun Mining Group Co., Ltd.; *Int'l*, pg. 1470

NZ WINDFARMS LIMITED; *Int'l*, pg. 5502
NZWTA LTD—See Australian Wool Testing Authority Ltd.; *Int'l*, pg. 723
NZX LIMITED; *Int'l*, pg. 5502
NZZ-MEDIENGRUPPE; *Int'l*, pg. 5502

O

O1 COMMUNICATIONS, INC.—See Siris Capital Group, LLC; *U.S. Private*, pg. 3675
O1 GROUP LIMITED; *Int'l*, pg. 5503
O1 PROPERTIES PLC; *Int'l*, pg. 5503
O2 AERO ACQUISITIONS LLC; *U.S. Private*, pg. 2981
O2 AUTO SERVICE MIDCO, LLC—See O2 Investment Partners, LLC; *U.S. Private*, pg. 2982
O2B KIDS; *U.S. Private*, pg. 2982
O2 CAPITAL PARTNERS B.V.; *Int'l*, pg. 5503
O2 CZECH REPUBLIC A.S.—See PPF Group N.V.; *Int'l*, pg. 5950
O2 FITNESS; *U.S. Private*, pg. 2981
O2GOLD INC.; *Int'l*, pg. 5503
O2IDEAS, INC.; *U.S. Private*, pg. 2982
O2I INGENIERIE SAS—See Prologue S.A.; *Int'l*, pg. 5992
O2 INVESTMENT PARTNERS, LLC; *U.S. Private*, pg. 2982
O2I S.A.—See Prologue S.A.; *Int'l*, pg. 5992
O2KL; *U.S. Private*, pg. 2982
O2 KRAFT AB—See OX2 Group AB; *Int'l*, pg. 5674
O2 MARKETING COMMUNICATIONS; *Int'l*, pg. 5503
O2MICRO (CHINA) CO., LTD—See Forebright Capital Management Ltd.; *Int'l*, pg. 2731
O2MICRO INTERNATIONAL LTD.—See Forebright Capital Management Ltd.; *Int'l*, pg. 2731
O2 SLOVAKIA, S.R.O.—See Telefonica, S.A.; *Int'l*, pg. 7535
O2U SOLUTIONS SDN. BHD.—See TFP Solutions Berhad; *Int'l*, pg. 7587
O2 VINDEL AB—See OX2 Group AB; *Int'l*, pg. 5674
O3 MINING INC.; *Int'l*, pg. 5503
O3SIS INFORMATION TECHNOLOGIES AG—See Thales S.A.; *Int'l*, pg. 7600
O3 WORLD, LLC; *U.S. Private*, pg. 2983
OAASIS GROUP LIMITED—See DNOW Inc.; *U.S. Public*, pg. 671
O-A-C CORPORATION—See O-Well Corporation; *Int'l*, pg. 5503
OAE FOOD TRADE FZE—See Ovostar Union N.V.; *Int'l*, pg. 5673
OAE SOFTWARE LLC—See Toast, Inc.; *U.S. Public*, pg. 2161
OAG AG—See Frauenthal Holding AG; *Int'l*, pg. 2767
OAG AVIATION GROUP LIMITED—See Vitruvian Partners LLP; *Int'l*, pg. 8263
OAG AVIATION WORLDWIDE LIMITED—See Vitruvian Partners LLP; *Int'l*, pg. 8263
OAG AVIATION WORLDWIDE LLC—See Vitruvian Partners LLP; *Int'l*, pg. 8263
OAHU PAVING COMPANY, INC—See Alexander & Baldwin, Inc.; *U.S. Public*, pg. 75
OAHU PUBLICATIONS INC.—See Black Press Group Ltd.; *Int'l*, pg. 1059
OAHU TRANSIT SERVICES INC.; *U.S. Private*, pg. 2983
OAI ELECTRONICS INC.—See Rooney Holdings, Inc.; *U.S. Private*, pg. 3479
OAK 1753 B.V.—See JAB Holding Company S.a.r.l.; *Int'l*, pg. 3862
OAK-BARK CORPORATION; *U.S. Private*, pg. 2984
OAKBAY INVESTMENTS (PTY) LTD.; *Int'l*, pg. 5504
OAKBAY RESOURCES & ENERGY LIMITED; *Int'l*, pg. 5504
OAKBRIDGE ADVISORS, INC.—See Kelso & Company, L.P.; *U.S. Private*, pg. 2280
OAKBRIDGE LAWYERS PTY. LTD.—See Credit Clear Limited; *Int'l*, pg. 1835
OAKBRIDGE PTY LIMITED—See Glencore plc; *Int'l*, pg. 2990
OAKBROOK COMPANIES, INC.; *U.S. Private*, pg. 2984
OAKBROOK HOMES INC.; *U.S. Private*, pg. 2984
OAKBROOK PROPERTIES, INC.—See Oakbrook Companies, Inc.; *U.S. Private*, pg. 2984
OAKBROOK SOLUTIONS, INC.—See Renovus Capital Partners; *U.S. Private*, pg. 3399
OAK CENTER HOMES PARTNERS, L.P.; *U.S. Private*, pg. 2983
OAK CONTRACTING, LLC.; *U.S. Private*, pg. 2983
OAK COURT MALL, LLC—See Washington Prime Group Inc.; *U.S. Private*, pg. 4448
OAK CREEK ENERGY SYSTEMS INC.—See Marubeni Corporation; *Int'l*, pg. 4706
OAK CREEK GOLF CLUB—See Apollo Global Management, Inc.; *U.S. Public*, pg. 150
OAKCREEK GOLF & TURF LP—See Connor, Clark & Lunn Financial Group; *Int'l*, pg. 1769
OAKDALE COMMUNITY HOSPITAL—See Progressive Acute Care LLC; *U.S. Private*, pg. 3278
OAKDALE HOMES LIMITED—See Langley Holdings Plc; *Int'l*, pg. 4410
OAK DRY LINING LIMITED—See Galliford Try Holdings plc; *Int'l*, pg. 2874

OAKES AGENCY INC.; *U.S. Private*, pg. 2984
OAKEY BEEF EXPORTS PTY. LTD.—See NH Foods Ltd.; *Int'l*, pg. 5256
OAK FARMS/SCHEPPS DAIRY—See Dean Foods Company; *U.S. Private*, pg. 1183
OAK FIRE PROTECTION LIMITED—See Galliford Try Holdings plc; *Int'l*, pg. 2874
OAKFIRST LIFE INSURANCE CORPORATION—See First United Corporation; *U.S. Public*, pg. 848
OAK FURNITURE LAND LTD—See Jb Global Ltd.; *Int'l*, pg. 3917
THE OAK GROUP, INC.—See Vitalhub Corp.; *Int'l*, pg. 8258
OAK GROVE PETRO TRUCKSTOP—See Iowa 80 Group, Inc.; *U.S. Private*, pg. 2134
OAK HALL INDUSTRIES LP; *U.S. Private*, pg. 2983
OAK HARBOR FREIGHT LINES, INC.; *U.S. Private*, pg. 2983
OAK HARBOR FREIGHT LINES—See Oak Harbor Freight Lines, Inc.; *U.S. Private*, pg. 2983
OAK HARBOUR MARKETING LIMITED; *U.S. Private*, pg. 2983
OAK HC/FT LDI BLOCKER CORP.—See UnitedHealth Group Incorporated; *U.S. Public*, pg. 2247
OAK HILL ADVISORS (AUSTRALIA) PTY. LTD.—See T. Rowe Price Group Inc.; *U.S. Public*, pg. 1978
OAK HILL ADVISORS (EUROPE), LLP—See T. Rowe Price Group Inc.; *U.S. Public*, pg. 1978
OAK HILL ADVISORS (HONG KONG) LIMITED—See T. Rowe Price Group Inc.; *U.S. Public*, pg. 1978
OAK HILL ADVISORS, L.P.; *U.S. Private*, pg. 2983
OAK HILL ADVISORS SARL—See T. Rowe Price Group Inc.; *U.S. Public*, pg. 1978
OAK HILL CAPITAL MANAGEMENT, LLC—See Keystone Group, L.P.; *U.S. Private*, pg. 2299
OAK HILL CAPITAL PARTNERS, L.P.—See Keystone Group, L.P.; *U.S. Private*, pg. 2296
OAK HILL CEMETERY LLC—See Axar Capital Management L.P.; *U.S. Private*, pg. 411
OAK HILL CLINIC CORP.—See Community Health Systems, Inc.; *U.S. Public*, pg. 555
OAK HILL GOLF RANGE—See OnCourse Strategies; *U.S. Private*, pg. 3019
OAK HILL HOSPITAL CORPORATION—See Community Health Systems, Inc.; *U.S. Public*, pg. 555
OAK HILL HOSPITAL—See HCA Healthcare, Inc.; *U.S. Public*, pg. 1005
OAK HILL PROPERTIES LLC; *U.S. Private*, pg. 2983
OAK HILLS CARTON CO.; *U.S. Private*, pg. 2983
OAKHURST DAIRY; *U.S. Private*, pg. 2984
OAKHURST GOLF CLUB—See OnCourse Strategies; *U.S. Private*, pg. 3019
OAKHURST INDUSTRIES; *U.S. Private*, pg. 2984
OAKHURST MEDICAL CENTERS, INC.; *U.S. Private*, pg. 2984
OAKHURST VILLAGE (SHIRLEY) MANAGEMENT COMPANY LIMITED—See Persimmon plc; *Int'l*, pg. 5816
OAK INFORMATION SYSTEM CORPORATION—See Obayashi Corporation; *Int'l*, pg. 5508
OAK INVESTMENT PARTNERS; *U.S. Private*, pg. 2983
OAKLAND ATHLETICS LIMITED PARTNERSHIP—See Athletics Investment Group, LLC; *U.S. Private*, pg. 368
OAKLAND AUTOMATION, LLC - NOVI PLANT—See Oakland Standard Co., LLC; *U.S. Private*, pg. 2985
OAKLAND AUTOMATION, LLC—See Oakland Standard Co., LLC; *U.S. Private*, pg. 2985
THE OAKLAND CA ENDOSCOPY ASC, L.P.—See KKR & Co. Inc.; *U.S. Public*, pg. 1248
OAKLAND CONSULTING GROUP; *U.S. Private*, pg. 2984
OAKLAND DERMATOLOGY ASSOCIATES—See Harvest Partners L.P.; *U.S. Private*, pg. 1876
OAKLAND GARDENS (WILTHORPE) MANAGEMENT COMPANY LIMITED—See Persimmon plc; *Int'l*, pg. 5816
OAKLAND HOLDINGS SDN. BHD.—See DutaLand Berhad; *Int'l*, pg. 2235
OAKLAND INDUSTRIES BLOCKER CORP.—See Oakland Standard Co., LLC; *U.S. Private*, pg. 2985
OAKLAND LIVINGSTON HUMAN SERVICE AGENCY; *U.S. Private*, pg. 2984
OAKLAND MANAGEMENT CORP.; *U.S. Private*, pg. 2984
OAKLAND METAL BUILDINGS, INC.—See Clayton, Dubilier & Rice, LLC; *U.S. Private*, pg. 921
OAKLAND NURSERY INC.; *U.S. Private*, pg. 2984
OAKLAND PACKAGING SUPPLY; *U.S. Private*, pg. 2984
THE OAKLAND RAIDERS, L.P.; *U.S. Private*, pg. 4087
OAKLAND STANDARD CO., LLC; *U.S. Private*, pg. 2984
THE OAKLAND TRIBUNE—See Alden Global Capital LLC; *U.S. Private*, pg. 155
OAK LANE PARTNERS, LLC; *U.S. Private*, pg. 2983
OAKLAWN CEMETERY ASSOCIATION—See Service Corporation International; *U.S. Public*, pg. 1870
OAK LAWN IL ENDOSCOPY ASC, LLC—See KKR & Co. Inc.; *U.S. Public*, pg. 1246
OAKLAWN JOCKEY CLUB, INC.; *U.S. Private*, pg. 2985
OAK LAWN MARKETING CHINA CO., LTD.—See Nippon Telegraph & Telephone Corporation; *Int'l*, pg. 5355
OAK LAWN TOYOTA; *U.S. Private*, pg. 2983

COMPANY NAME INDEX

OAKLEAF CARE (HARTWELL) LIMITED—See Sheikh Holdings Group (Investments) Limited; *Int'l*, pg. 6793
OAK LEAF MANAGEMENT INC.; *U.S. Private*, pg. 2983
OAK LEAF PROPERTIES, LLC; *U.S. Private*, pg. 2983
OAKLEAF SOFTWARE, INC.; *U.S. Private*, pg. 2985
OAKLEAF WASTE MANAGEMENT, LLC—See Waste Management, Inc.; *U.S. Public*, pg. 2331
OAKLEIGH CONSULTING LIMITED; *Int'l*, pg. 5504
OAKLEY CAPITAL CORPORATE FINANCE LIMITED—See Oakley Capital Limited; *Int'l*, pg. 5504
OAKLEY CAPITAL INVESTMENTS LIMITED—See Oakley Capital Limited; *Int'l*, pg. 5504
OAKLEY CAPITAL LIMITED; *Int'l*, pg. 5504
OAKLEY CONSTRUCTION COMPANY, INC.; *U.S. Private*, pg. 2985
OAKLEY GROVES INC.; *U.S. Private*, pg. 2985
OAKLEY, INC.—See EssilorLuxottica SA; *Int'l*, pg. 2515
OAKLEY INDUSTRIES INCORPORATED; *U.S. Private*, pg. 2985
OAKLEY INDUSTRIES INC.; *U.S. Private*, pg. 2985
OAKLEY TRANSPORT, INC.—See Oakley Groves Inc.; *U.S. Private*, pg. 2985
OAKMAN AEROSPACE, INC.—See Redwire Corporation; *U.S. Public*, pg. 1771
OAKMAN TELEPHONE COMPANY, INC.—See Telephone & Data Systems, Inc.; *U.S. Public*, pg. 1998
OAK-MITSUI INC.—See Mitsui & Co., Ltd.; *Int'l*, pg. 4978
OAKMONT CAPITAL CORP.; *Int'l*, pg. 5504
OAKMONT CAPITAL RESOURCES, INC.; *U.S. Private*, pg. 2985
OAKMONT MEMORIAL PARK & MORTUARY—See Carriage Services, Inc.; *U.S. Public*, pg. 439
OAKMONT OF CAMARILLO OPCO, LLC—See Healthpeak Properties, Inc.; *U.S. Public*, pg. 1016
OAKMONT OF CONCORD LLC—See Healthpeak Properties, Inc.; *U.S. Public*, pg. 1016
OAKMONT OF FAIR OAKS LLC—See Healthpeak Properties, Inc.; *U.S. Public*, pg. 1016
OAKMONT OF MARINER POINT LLC—See Healthpeak Properties, Inc.; *U.S. Public*, pg. 1016
OAKMONT OF PACIFIC BEACH OPCO, LLC—See Healthpeak Properties, Inc.; *U.S. Public*, pg. 1016
OAKMONT OF RIVERPARK OPCO, LLC—See Healthpeak Properties, Inc.; *U.S. Public*, pg. 1016
OAK MORTGAGE COMPANY, LLC—See Republic First Bancorp, Inc.; *U.S. Public*, pg. 1785
OAK MOUNTAIN INDUSTRIES, INC.—See Osceola Capital Management, LLC; *U.S. Private*, pg. 3047
OAK PAPER PRODUCTS CO. INC.; *U.S. Private*, pg. 2983
OAK PLAINS ACADEMY OF TENNESSEE, INC.—See Universal Health Services, Inc.; *U.S. Public*, pg. 2258
OAKRIDGE BUILDERS INC.; *U.S. Private*, pg. 2985
OAK RIDGE CAPITAL GROUP, INC.; *U.S. Private*, pg. 2984
OAK RIDGE FINANCIAL SERVICES, INC.; *U.S. Public*, pg. 1560
OAKRIDGE GLOBAL ENERGY SOLUTIONS, INC.; *U.S. Public*, pg. 1560
OAK RIDGE, INC.; *U.S. Private*, pg. 2984
OAKRIDGE INTERNATIONAL LIMITED; *Int'l*, pg. 5505
OAKRIDGE LANDFILL, INC.—See Waste Management, Inc.; *U.S. Public*, pg. 2331
THE OAK RIDGER, LLC—See Gannett Co., Inc.; *U.S. Public*, pg. 904
OAK RIDGE UTILITY DISTRICT; *U.S. Private*, pg. 2984
OAK RIDGE WASTE & RECYCLING OF CT LLC; *U.S. Private*, pg. 2984
OAK RIVER INSURANCE COMPANY—See Berkshire Hathaway Inc.; *U.S. Public*, pg. 313
OAKS CONCRETE PRODUCTS INC—See Brampton Brick Limited; *Int'l*, pg. 1139
OAKS CONCRETE PRODUCTS LTD—See Brampton Brick Limited; *Int'l*, pg. 1139
OAKS CONSTRUCTION INC.; *U.S. Private*, pg. 2985
OAKS CONSULTANCY LTD.—See Aquila Services Group PLC; *Int'l*, pg. 528
OAK SETSUBI CORPORATION—See Obayashi Corporation; *Int'l*, pg. 5508
OAK SHADOWS OF JENNINGS, LLC—See UnitedHealth Group Incorporated; *U.S. Public*, pg. 2246
OAKS HOTELS & RESORTS (CARLYLE MACKAY) PTY. LTD.—See Minor International PCL; *Int'l*, pg. 4913
OAKS HOTELS & RESORTS LEASING (COLLINS) PTY. LTD.—See Minor International PCL; *Int'l*, pg. 4913
OAKS HOTELS & RESORTS LIMITED—See Minor International PCL; *Int'l*, pg. 4913
OAKS HOTELS & RESORTS (MON KOMO) PTY. LTD.—See Minor International PCL; *Int'l*, pg. 4913
OAKS HOTELS & RESORTS (MORANBAH) PTY. LTD.—See Minor International PCL; *Int'l*, pg. 4913
OAKS HOTELS & RESORTS (RIVERMARQUE) PTY. LTD.—See Minor International PCL; *Int'l*, pg. 4913
OAKS HOTELS & RESORTS (VIC) PTY. LTD.—See Minor International PCL; *Int'l*, pg. 4913
OAKS (M ON PALMER) MANAGEMENT PTY. LTD.—See Minor International PCL; *Int'l*, pg. 4913
THE OAKS RESORT & HOTEL MANAGEMENT PTY. LTD.—See Minor International PCL; *Int'l*, pg. 4913

OAKSTAR BANCSHARES, INC.; *U.S. Private*, pg. 2985
OAKSTAR BANK—See Oakstar Bancshares, Inc.; *U.S. Private*, pg. 2985
OAKSTONE PUBLISHING, LLC—See Ebix Inc.; *U.S. Public*, pg. 710
OAK STREET FUNDING LLC—See First Financial Bancorp.; *U.S. Public*, pg. 843
OAK STREET HEALTH, INC.—See CVS Health Corporation; *U.S. Public*, pg. 616
OAK STREET REAL ESTATE CAPITAL, LLC—See Blue Owl Capital Inc.; *U.S. Public*, pg. 364
OAK STREET SERVICING, LLC—See First Financial Bancorp.; *U.S. Public*, pg. 843
OAKSVILLA SDN. BHD.—See Fiamma Holdings Berhad; *Int'l*, pg. 2650
OAK THERAPEUTICS, INC.—See Avenir Wellness Solutions, Inc.; *U.S. Public*, pg. 242
OAKTON CONTRACTING AND RECRUITMENT PTY LTD.—See Nippon Telegraph & Telephone Corporation; *Int'l*, pg. 5341
OAKTON GLOBAL TECHNOLOGY SERVICES CENTRE (INDIA) PVT LTD.—See Nippon Telegraph & Telephone Corporation; *Int'l*, pg. 5341
OAKTON LTD—See Nippon Telegraph & Telephone Corporation; *Int'l*, pg. 5341
OAKTON SERVICES PTY. LTD.—See Nippon Telegraph & Telephone Corporation; *Int'l*, pg. 5341
OAKTREE CAPITAL (AUSTRALIA) PTY. LIMITED—See Brookfield Corporation; *Int'l*, pg. 1182
OAKTREE CAPITAL (BEIJING) LTD.—See Brookfield Corporation; *Int'l*, pg. 1182
OAKTREE CAPITAL (HONG KONG) LTD.—See Brookfield Corporation; *Int'l*, pg. 1182
OAKTREE CAPITAL MANAGEMENT (DUBAI) LIMITED—See Brookfield Corporation; *Int'l*, pg. 1182
OAKTREE CAPITAL MANAGEMENT FUND—See Brookfield Corporation; *Int'l*, pg. 1182
OAKTREE CAPITAL MANAGEMENT LIMITED—See Brookfield Corporation; *Int'l*, pg. 1182
OAKTREE CAPITAL MANAGEMENT, L.P.—See Brookfield Corporation; *Int'l*, pg. 1181
OAKTREE CAPITAL MANAGEMENT PTE. LTD.—See Brookfield Corporation; *Int'l*, pg. 1182
OAKTREE CAPITAL MANAGEMENT (UK) LLP—See Brookfield Corporation; *Int'l*, pg. 1182
OAKTREE CAPITAL (SEOUL) LIMITED—See Brookfield Corporation; *Int'l*, pg. 1182
OAKTREE CAPITAL (SHANGHAI) LTD.—See Brookfield Corporation; *Int'l*, pg. 1182
OAK TREE CO., LTD.—See Veranda Resort Public Company Limited; *Int'l*, pg. 8164
OAKTREE ENTERPRISE SOLUTIONS, INC.; *U.S. Private*, pg. 2985
OAKTREE FRANCE S.A.S.—See Brookfield Corporation; *Int'l*, pg. 1182
OAKTREE FUND ADVISORS, LLC—See Brookfield Corporation; *Int'l*, pg. 1182
OAK TREE GARDENS (AUDLEY) MANAGEMENT COMPANY LIMITED—See Persimmon plc; *Int'l*, pg. 5816
OAKTREE GARDENS OLP, LLC; *U.S. Private*, pg. 2985
OAKTREE GMBH—See Brookfield Corporation; *Int'l*, pg. 1182
OAKTREE JAPAN, GK—See Brookfield Corporation; *Int'l*, pg. 1182
OAKTREE OVERSEAS INVESTMENT FUND MANAGEMENT (SHANGHAI) CO., LTD.—See Brookfield Corporation; *Int'l*, pg. 1182
OAK TREE REALTY CO., LTD.—See Veranda Resort Public Company Limited; *Int'l*, pg. 8164
OAKTREE SPECIALTY LENDING CORPORATION—See Fifth Street Capital LLC; *U.S. Private*, pg. 1505
OAKTREE STRATEGIC INCOME CORPORATION—See Brookfield Corporation; *Int'l*, pg. 1182
OAK VALLEY BANCORP; *U.S. Public*, pg. 1560
OAK VALLEY COMMUNITY BANK—See Oak Valley Bancorp; *U.S. Public*, pg. 1560
OAK VALLEY HOSPITAL DISTRICT—See Catholic Health Initiatives; *U.S. Private*, pg. 790
OAK VALLEY OPERATING, LLC—See Permian Resources Corp; *U.S. Public*, pg. 1677
THE OAKVIEW COMPANIES, INC.; *U.S. Private*, pg. 4087
OAKVIEW CONSTRUCTION, INC.—See The Oakview Companies, Inc.; *U.S. Private*, pg. 4088
OAK VIEW GROUP, LLC—See Silver Lake Group, LLC; *U.S. Private*, pg. 3658
OAK VIEW NATIONAL BANK; *U.S. Private*, pg. 2984
OAKVILLE GROCERY CO.—See Pace Development Corporation Public Co., Ltd.; *Int'l*, pg. 5685
OAKVILLE GROCERY CO—See Pace Development Corporation Public Co., Ltd.; *Int'l*, pg. 5685
OAKVILLE HYDRO CORPORATION; *Int'l*, pg. 5505
OAKVILLE PRODUCE PARTNERS, LLC—See The Chefs' Warehouse, Inc.; *U.S. Public*, pg. 2059
OAKVILLE VOLKSWAGEN INC.; *Int'l*, pg. 5505
OAKWELL DISTRIBUTION (S) PTE. LTD.; *Int'l*, pg. 5505
OAKWELL ENGINEERING INTERNATIONAL PTE LTD—See Oakwell Distribution (S) Pte. Ltd.; *Int'l*, pg. 5505

OAO IRKUTSKENERGO

OAKWELL ENGINEERING (M) SDN BHD—See Oakwell Distribution (S) Pte. Ltd.; *Int'l*, pg. 5505
OAKWELL INTERNATIONAL TRADING (SHANGHAI) CO., LTD.—See Oakwell Distribution (S) Pte. Ltd.; *Int'l*, pg. 5505
OAKWELL SHIPBUILDING ENGINEERING AND CONSTRUCTION PTE. LTD.—See Oakwell Distribution (S) Pte. Ltd.; *Int'l*, pg. 5505
OAKWOOD CONSTRUCTION & RESTORATION SERVICES, INC.—See BlackEagle Partners, LLC; *U.S. Private*, pg. 573
OAKWOOD FUNERALS PTY LIMITED—See TPG Capital, L.P.; *U.S. Public*, pg. 2174
THE OAKWOOD GROUP; *U.S. Private*, pg. 4088
OAKWOOD HOMES LLC—See Berkshire Hathaway Inc.; *U.S. Public*, pg. 304
OAKWOOD INDUSTRIES, INC.; *U.S. Private*, pg. 2985
OAKWOOD LANDFILL, INC.—See Waste Management, Inc.; *U.S. Public*, pg. 2331
OAKWOOD LUTHERAN HOMES ASSOCIATION, INC.; *U.S. Private*, pg. 2985
OAKWOOD MEADOWS (COLCHESTER) RESIDENTS MANAGEMENT COMPANY LIMITED—See Persimmon plc; *Int'l*, pg. 5816
OAK WOODS ACQUISITION CORPORATION; *Int'l*, pg. 5503
OAK WOODS MANAGEMENT COMPANY—See Service Corporation International; *U.S. Public*, pg. 1870
OAKWOOD SURGERY CENTER, LTD., LLP—See HCA Healthcare, Inc.; *U.S. Public*, pg. 1005
OAKWOOD WORLDWIDE, INC.—See Temasek Holdings (Private) Limited; *Int'l*, pg. 7548
OAKWORKS INC.; *U.S. Private*, pg. 2986
OAKY CREEK COAL JOINT VENTURE—See Glencore plc; *Int'l*, pg. 2991
OA LABORATORY CO., LTD. - FUJISAWA PLANT—See FUJISOFT INCORPORATED; *Int'l*, pg. 2830
OA LABORATORY CO., LTD.—See FUJISOFT INCORPORATED; *Int'l*, pg. 2830
OAL INC.—See Canon Inc.; *Int'l*, pg. 1296
OAM ASIA (SINGAPORE) PTE. LTD.—See Oriental Holdings Berhad; *Int'l*, pg. 5624
OAMPS CONSULTING PTY LTD—See Wesfarmers Limited; *Int'l*, pg. 8381
OAMPS CORPORATE RISK PTY LTD—See Wesfarmers Limited; *Int'l*, pg. 8381
OAMPS GAULT ARMSTRONG PTY LTD—See Wesfarmers Limited; *Int'l*, pg. 8381
OAMPS LIFE SOLUTIONS LTD—See Wesfarmers Limited; *Int'l*, pg. 8381
OAMPS LTD—See Wesfarmers Limited; *Int'l*, pg. 8381
OAMPS (UK) LIMITED—See Arthur J. Gallagher & Co.; *U.S. Public*, pg. 203
OANDA CORP.—See CVC Capital Partners SICAV-FIS S.A.; *Int'l*, pg. 1885
OANDO ENERGY SERVICES LTD.—See Oando PLC; *Int'l*, pg. 5505
OANDO EXPLORATION & PRODUCTION LIMITED—See Oando PLC; *Int'l*, pg. 5505
OANDO PLC; *Int'l*, pg. 5505
O.A. NEWTON & SON CO; *U.S. Private*, pg. 2981
OAO AK TRANSNEFT; *Int'l*, pg. 5505
OAO ALFA LAVAL POTOK—See Alfa Laval AB; *Int'l*, pg. 312
OAO ARTELEKOM ARKHANGELSK REGION—See OJSC Svyazinvest; *Int'l*, pg. 5542
OAO BALTIKA BREWERIES—See Carlsberg A/S; *Int'l*, pg. 1340
OAO BOLSHEVIK—See Tactics Group; *Int'l*, pg. 7403
OAO CITY SERVICE—See City Service SE; *Int'l*, pg. 1627
OAO DNEPROMETIZ—See PAO Severstal; *Int'l*, pg. 5731
OAO ELEKTROSVYAZ KALININGRAD REGION—See OJSC Svyazinvest; *Int'l*, pg. 5542
OAO ELEKTROSVYAZ KALUGA REGION—See OJSC Svyazinvest; *Int'l*, pg. 5542
OAO ELEKTROSVYAZ KARELIYA REPUBLIC—See OJSC Svyazinvest; *Int'l*, pg. 5542
OAO ELEKTROSVYAZ KOSTROMA REGION—See OJSC Svyazinvest; *Int'l*, pg. 5542
OAO ELEKTROSVYAZ KURGAN REGION—See OJSC Svyazinvest; *Int'l*, pg. 5542
OAO ELEKTROSVYAZ KURSK REGION—See OJSC Svyazinvest; *Int'l*, pg. 5543
OAO ELEKTROSVYAZ OREL REGION—See OJSC Svyazinvest; *Int'l*, pg. 5543
OAO ELEKTROSVYAZ PSKOV REGION—See OJSC Svyazinvest; *Int'l*, pg. 5543
OAO ELEKTROSVYAZ RYAZAN REGION—See OJSC Svyazinvest; *Int'l*, pg. 5543
OAO ELEKTROSVYAZ TVER REGION—See OJSC Svyazinvest; *Int'l*, pg. 5543
OAO ELEKTROSVYAZ VLADIMIR REGION—See OJSC Svyazinvest; *Int'l*, pg. 5543
OAO ENERGOTERMINAL—See OAO AK Transneft; *Int'l*, pg. 5505
OAO GAZPROMNEFT OMSK—See PJSC Gazprom; *Int'l*, pg. 5879
OAO GROUP OF COMPANIES PIK; *Int'l*, pg. 5506
OAO IRKUTSKENERGO; *Int'l*, pg. 5506

OAO IRKUTSKENERGO

CORPORATE AFFILIATIONS

OAO ISTRA-NUTRICIA—See Danone; *Int'l*, pg. 1966
OAO KAMCHATSVYAZINFORM—See OJSC Svyazinvest; *Int'l*, pg. 5543
OAO KAMOV—See Russian Technologies State Corporation; *Int'l*, pg. 6431
OAO KIVIJARVI OY—See Outokumpu Oyj; *Int'l*, pg. 5668
OAO KRASNOYARSKGAZPROM—See PJSC Gazprom; *Int'l*, pg. 5879
OAO KUZBASSKAYA TOPLIVNAYA COMPANY OJSC; *Int'l*, pg. 5506
OAO LAZURNAYA—See PJSC Gazprom; *Int'l*, pg. 5879
OAO LEBEDINSKIY MINING AND PROCESSING WORKS—See METALLOINVEST JSC; *Int'l*, pg. 4848
OAO LENSVYAZ—See PJSC Rostelecom; *Int'l*, pg. 5884
OAO LIDSKOE PIVO—See Olvi Oyj; *Int'l*, pg. 5554
OAO LIPETSELEKTROSVYAZ—See PJSC Rostelecom; *Int'l*, pg. 5884
OAO METALLURGREMONT—See PAO Severstal; *Int'l*, pg. 5731
OAO MIKHAILOVSKY MINING AND PROCESSING WORKS—See METALLOINVEST JSC; *Int'l*, pg. 4848
OAO MN DRUZHBA—See OAO AK Transneft; *Int'l*, pg. 5505
OAO NOVGORODTELECOM—See PJSC Rostelecom; *Int'l*, pg. 5884
OAO NOVOSHIP—See PAO Sovcomflot; *Int'l*, pg. 5732
OAO NPO PROMAVTOMATIKA; *Int'l*, pg. 5506
OAO OLKON—See PAO Severstal; *Int'l*, pg. 5731
OAO OLONETSLES—See Stora Enso Oyj; *Int'l*, pg. 7225
OAO OSKOL ELECTROMETALLURGICAL PLANT—See METALLOINVEST JSC; *Int'l*, pg. 4848
OAO OSRAM—See ams AG; *Int'l*, pg. 438
OAO OTKRITIE BROKERAGE HOUSE; *Int'l*, pg. 5506
OAO PETERSBURG TELEPHONE NETWORK—See PJSC Rostelecom; *Int'l*, pg. 5884
OAO RASPADSKAYA; *Int'l*, pg. 5507
OAO REMOSPROM—See Renault S.A.; *Int'l*, pg. 6273
OAO ROSNEFT OIL COMPANY—See OJSC Rosneftegaz; *Int'l*, pg. 5541
OAO ROSNITI—See PAO TMK; *Int'l*, pg. 5732
OAO ROSTOVMETALL—See PAO Severstal; *Int'l*, pg. 5732
OAO SHATURSKAYA UPRAVLYAYUSHCHAYA KOMPANIYA—See E.ON SE; *Int'l*, pg. 2258
OAO SIBNEFTEPROVOD—See OAO AK Transneft; *Int'l*, pg. 5505
OAO SIBUR HOLDING; *Int'l*, pg. 5507
OAO SIBUR-PETF—See OAO SIBUR Holding; *Int'l*, pg. 5507
OAO SMOLENSKSVYAZINFORM—See OJSC Svyazinvest; *Int'l*, pg. 5543
OAO SPB-GIPROSHAKHT—See PAO Severstal; *Int'l*, pg. 5732
OAO SUCHOLOSHSKZEMENT—See Buzzi SpA; *Int'l*, pg. 1230
OAO SZMN—See OAO AK Transneft; *Int'l*, pg. 5505
OAO TRANSSIBNEFT—See OAO AK Transneft; *Int'l*, pg. 5505
OAO TSENTRGAZ—See PJSC Gazprom; *Int'l*, pg. 5879
OAO TUIMAZINSKIY ZAVOD AVTOBETONOVOZOV—See KAMAZ Publicly Traded Company; *Int'l*, pg. 4060
OAO URAL STEEL—See METALLOINVEST JSC; *Int'l*, pg. 4848
OAO URALTELECOM SVERDLOVSK REGION—See OJSC Svyazinvest; *Int'l*, pg. 5543
OAO VENA—See Carlsberg A/S; *Int'l*, pg. 1340
OAO VOLGOGRADENERGOSBYT; *Int'l*, pg. 5507
OAO VORONEZHSINTEZKAUCHUK—See OAO SIBUR Holding; *Int'l*, pg. 5507
OAO YAMAL LNG—See PAO Novatek; *Int'l*, pg. 5731
OAO YARTELECOM—See OJSC Svyazinvest; *Int'l*, pg. 5543
OAR RESOURCES LIMITED; *Int'l*, pg. 5507
OARTECH, INC.—See TIS Inc.; *Int'l*, pg. 7757
OAS AG; *Int'l*, pg. 5507
OASE ASIA PACIFIC PTE LTD.—See Argand Partners, LP; *U.S. Private*, pg. 319
OASE CHINA—See Argand Partners, LP; *U.S. Private*, pg. 319
OASE GMBH—See Argand Partners, LP; *U.S. Private*, pg. 319
OASE MIDDLE EAST FZE—See Argand Partners, LP; *U.S. Private*, pg. 319
OASE NORTH AMERICA, INC.—See Argand Partners, LP; *U.S. Private*, pg. 319
OASE TURKIYE—See Argand Partners, LP; *U.S. Private*, pg. 319
OASE (UK) LTD.—See Argand Partners, LP; *U.S. Private*, pg. 319
OASIS-AMERON COMPANY LTD.—See PPG Industries, Inc.; *U.S. Public*, pg. 1709
OASIS ASSET MANAGEMENT LTD.—See ING Groep N.V.; *Int'l*, pg. 3699
OASIS AVIATION INC.; *U.S. Private*, pg. 2986
OASIS BEAUTY COMPANY LIMITED—See Water Oasis Group Limited; *Int'l*, pg. 8356
OASIS BEVERAGES; *Int'l*, pg. 5507
OASIS CONSULTING CO., LTD.—See Samart Corporation Public Company Limited; *Int'l*, pg. 6502

OASIS CRESCENT MANAGEMENT COMPANY LTD.; *Int'l*, pg. 5507
OASIS DENTAL CARE LIMITED—See The British United Provident Association Limited; *Int'l*, pg. 7630
OASIS DIALYSIS, LLC—See DaVita Inc.; *U.S. Public*, pg. 641
OASIS ENERGY CO. LLC; *Int'l*, pg. 5507
OASIS FLORALIFE CENTRAL EUROPE GMBH—See Smithers-Oasis Company; *U.S. Private*, pg. 3697
OASIS FLORALIFE COLOMBIA LTDA.—See Smithers-Oasis Company; *U.S. Private*, pg. 3697
OASIS HEALTHCARE LIMITED—See The British United Provident Association Limited; *Int'l*, pg. 7629
OASIS HOLDING FZC—See Jai Corp Ltd; *Int'l*, pg. 3871
OASIS HOTEL & BEACH CLUB—See Kassem Darwish Fakhro & Sons; *Int'l*, pg. 4088
OASIS INTERNATIONAL LEASING (USA), INC.—See Waha Capital PJSC; *Int'l*, pg. 8330
OASIS INTERNATIONAL—See Patriarch Partners, LLC; *U.S. Private*, pg. 3109
OASIS KAZAKHSTAN—See Oasis Beverages; *Int'l*, pg. 5507
OASIS LEGAL FINANCE LLC; *U.S. Private*, pg. 2986
OASIS MATERIALS CORPORATION—See Arsenal Capital Management LP; *U.S. Private*, pg. 338
OASIS MEDICAL CLINIC COMPANY LIMITED—See Water Oasis Group Limited; *Int'l*, pg. 8356
OASIS MEDICAL SOLUTIONS LIMITED—See Veradigm Inc.; *U.S. Public*, pg. 2280
OASIS MIDSTREAM PARTNERS LP—See Chord Energy Corporation; *U.S. Public*, pg. 490
OASIS MIDSTREAM SERVICES LLC—See Chord Energy Corporation; *U.S. Public*, pg. 490
OASIS NUCLEAR INC.—See Oasis Aviation Inc.; *U.S. Private*, pg. 2986
OASIS OUTSOURCING, INC.—See Paychex, Inc.; *U.S. Public*, pg. 1655
OASIS OUTSOURCING—See Paychex, Inc.; *U.S. Public*, pg. 1655
OASIS PARK CO., LTD.—See Sega Sammy Holdings, Inc.; *Int'l*, pg. 6681
OASIS PETROLEUM LLC—See Chord Energy Corporation; *U.S. Public*, pg. 490
OASIS PETROLEUM NORTH AMERICA LLC—See Chord Energy Corporation; *U.S. Public*, pg. 490
OASIS PIPE LINE COMPANY; *U.S. Private*, pg. 2986
OASIS PIPE LINE COMPANY TEXAS L.P.—See Energy Transfer LP; *U.S. Public*, pg. 763
OASIS POWER, LLC—See Via Renewables, Inc.; *U.S. Public*, pg. 2290
OASIS REPORTING SERVICES LLC—See Apax Partners LLP; *Int'l*, pg. 503
OASIS RESIDENTIAL RESORTS—See SAAD Group; *Int'l*, pg. 6460
OASIS RUSSIA—See Oasis Beverages; *Int'l*, pg. 5507
OASIS SALES CORP.; *U.S. Private*, pg. 2986
OASIS SECURITIES LIMITED; *Int'l*, pg. 5507
OASIS SOUTH INSURANCE SERVICES INC.—See Dowling Capital Management, LLC; *U.S. Private*, pg. 1268
OASIS SOUTH INSURANCE SERVICES INC.—See Keystone Group, L.P.; *U.S. Private*, pg. 2298
OASIS SPA COMPANY LIMITED—See Water Oasis Group Limited; *Int'l*, pg. 8356
OASIS STAFFING, INC.—See Performance Personnel Partners, LLC; *U.S. Private*, pg. 3149
OASIS SYSTEMS, LLC; *U.S. Private*, pg. 2986
OASIS UKRAINE—See Oasis Beverages; *Int'l*, pg. 5507
OASMIA PHARMACEUTICAL AB; *Int'l*, pg. 5507
OASYS AUSTRALIA PTY LTD—See Arup Group Ltd.; *Int'l*, pg. 587
OASYS, INC.; *U.S. Private*, pg. 2986
OASYS LIMITED—See Arup Group Ltd.; *Int'l*, pg. 587
OASYS MOBILE, INC.; *U.S. Private*, pg. 2986
OAT AGRI FRONTIER CO., LTD.—See OAT Agrio Co., Ltd.; *Int'l*, pg. 5507
OAT AGRIO CO., LTD.; *Int'l*, pg. 5507
OAT - BOHR- UND FUGENTECHNIK GESELLSCHAFT M.B.H.—See STRABAG SE; *Int'l*, pg. 7231
OATES & COMPANY, LLC.—See QXO, Inc.; *U.S. Public*, pg. 1758
OATEY COMPANY; *U.S. Private*, pg. 2986
OATEY SUPPLY CHAIN SERVICES, INC.—See Oatey Company; *U.S. Private*, pg. 2986
OATH (AMERICAS) INC.—See Apollo Global Management, Inc.; *U.S. Public*, pg. 167
OATH (CANADA) CORP.—See Apollo Global Management, Inc.; *U.S. Public*, pg. 167
OATH DENMARK APS—See Apollo Global Management, Inc.; *U.S. Public*, pg. 167
OATH JAPAN KK—See Apollo Global Management, Inc.; *U.S. Public*, pg. 167
OATH (UK) LIMITED—See Apollo Global Management, Inc.; *U.S. Public*, pg. 167
OAT KFT.—See STRABAG SE; *Int'l*, pg. 7231
OATLY AB—See Oatly Group AB; *Int'l*, pg. 5508
OATLY GROUP AB; *Int'l*, pg. 5507
OATLY UK LTD.—See Oatly Group AB; *Int'l*, pg. 5508
OATMEAL STUDIOS, INC.—See Biely & Shoaf Co.; *U.S. Private*, pg. 551

OATS, INC.; *U.S. Private*, pg. 2986
QAT S.R.O.—See STRABAG SE; *Int'l*, pg. 7231
OBA BETONDECKEN AUSBAU DEUTSCHLAND GMBH—See PORR AG; *Int'l*, pg. 5923
OBAGI COSMECEUTICALS LLC—See Waldencast plc; *U.S. Public*, pg. 2321
OBALOVNA LETKOV A.S.—See VINCI S.A.; *Int'l*, pg. 8225
OBALOVNA PRIBRAM, S.R.O.—See PORR AG; *Int'l*, pg. 5923
OBAL-SERVIS, A.S. KOSICE—See United States Steel Corporation; *U.S. Public*, pg. 2236
OBAN CO., LTD.—See Showa Sangyo Co., Ltd.; *Int'l*, pg. 6861
OBA - OSTERREICHISCHE BETONDECKEN AUSBAU GMBH—See PORR AG; *Int'l*, pg. 5923
OBARA CORPORATION - KENTUCKY PLANT—See Obara Group Incorporated; *Int'l*, pg. 5508
OBARA CORPORATION—See Obara Group Incorporated; *Int'l*, pg. 5508
OBARA CORPORATION—See Obara Group Incorporated; *Int'l*, pg. 5508
OBARA CORPORATION—See Obara Group Incorporated; *Int'l*, pg. 5508
OBARA GROUP INCORPORATED; *Int'l*, pg. 5508
OBARA INDIA PVT. LTD.—See Obara Group Incorporated; *Int'l*, pg. 5508
OBARA KOREA CORP.—See Obara Group Incorporated; *Int'l*, pg. 5508
OBARA (MALAYSIA) SDN. BHD.—See Obara Group Incorporated; *Int'l*, pg. 5508
OBARA MEXICO S. DE R.L. DE C.V.—See Obara Group Incorporated; *Int'l*, pg. 5508
OBARA (NANJING) MACHINERY & ELECTRIC CO. LTD.—See Obara Group Incorporated; *Int'l*, pg. 5508
OBARA S.A.S.—See Obara Group Incorporated; *Int'l*, pg. 5508
OBARA (SHANGHAI) CO., LTD.—See Obara Group Incorporated; *Int'l*, pg. 5508
OBARA TECNOLOGIAS E PRODUTOS DE SOLDAGEM LTDA.—See Obara Group Incorporated; *Int'l*, pg. 5508
OBARA (THAILAND) CO., LTD.—See Obara Group Incorporated; *Int'l*, pg. 5508
OBART PUMPS LIMITED—See Seika Corporation; *Int'l*, pg. 6685
OBATA CO., LTD.—See Senko Group Holdings Co., Ltd.; *Int'l*, pg. 6710
OBATA DESIGN, INC.; *U.S. Private*, pg. 2986
OBAYASHI CLEAN ENERGY CORPORATION—See Obayashi Corporation; *Int'l*, pg. 5508
OBAYASHI CONSTRUCTION, INC.—See Obayashi Corporation; *Int'l*, pg. 5509
OBAYASHI CORPORATION; *Int'l*, pg. 5508
OBAYASHI ENERGY CONSTRUCTION, LLC—See Obayashi Corporation; *Int'l*, pg. 5508
OBAYASHI FACILITIES CORPORATION—See Obayashi Corporation; *Int'l*, pg. 5508
OBAYASHI MIDDLE EAST CONSTRUCTION, LLC—See Obayashi Corporation; *Int'l*, pg. 5508
OBAYASHI PROPERTIES UK LIMITED—See Obayashi Corporation; *Int'l*, pg. 5508
OBAYASHI QATAR, LLC—See Obayashi Corporation; *Int'l*, pg. 5508
OBAYASHI REAL ESTATE CORPORATION—See Obayashi Corporation; *Int'l*, pg. 5508
OBAYASHI ROAD CORPORATION—See Obayashi Corporation; *Int'l*, pg. 5509
OBAYASHI-SHINSEIWA REAL ESTATE CORPORATION—See Obayashi Corporation; *Int'l*, pg. 5509
OBAYASHI SINGAPORE PRIVATE LIMITED—See Obayashi Corporation; *Int'l*, pg. 5509
OBAYASHI TECHNICAL RESEARCH INSTITUTE—See Obayashi Corporation; *Int'l*, pg. 5509
OBAYASHI USA, LLC—See Obayashi Corporation; *Int'l*, pg. 5509
OBAYASHI VIETNAM CORPORATION—See Obayashi Corporation; *Int'l*, pg. 5509
OBBCO SAFETY & SUPPLY, INC.—See Genuine Parts Company; *U.S. Public*, pg. 933
OBB-HOLDING AG; *Int'l*, pg. 5509
OBB-IMMOBILIENMANAGEMENT GESELLSCHAFT MBH—See OBB-Holding AG; *Int'l*, pg. 5509
OBB-INFRASTRUKTUR AKTIENGESELLSCHAFT—See OBB-Holding AG; *Int'l*, pg. 5509
OBB-PERSONENVERKEHR AKTIENGESELLSCHAFT—See OBB-Holding AG; *Int'l*, pg. 5509
OBB-POSTBUS GMBH—See OBB-Holding AG; *Int'l*, pg. 5509
OBB TELEKOM SERVICE GMBH—See OBB-Holding AG; *Int'l*, pg. 5509
OB CARE S.R.O.—See Centene Corporation; *U.S. Public*, pg. 470
OB COMPANIES—See Brookfield Corporation; *Int'l*, pg. 1189
OBCORP LLC—See AMETEK, Inc.; *U.S. Public*, pg. 121
OBDUCAT AB; *Int'l*, pg. 5510
OBDUCAT EUROPE GMBH—See Obducat AB; *Int'l*, pg. 5510

COMPANY NAME INDEX

OBEGI CHEMICALS GROUP; *Int'l*, pg. 5510
OBEGI CHEMICALS (L.L.C.)—See Obegi Chemicals Group; *Int'l*, pg. 5510
OBEGI CHEMICALS (R)—See Obegi Chemicals Group; *Int'l*, pg. 5510
OBEGI CHEMICALS S.A.S.—See Obegi Chemicals Group; *Int'l*, pg. 5510
OBEGI CHEMICALS S.A.S.—See Obegi Chemicals Group; *Int'l*, pg. 5510
OBEN HOLDING GROUP SAC; *Int'l*, pg. 5510
OBEO, INC.; *U.S. Private*, pg. 2986
OBERBANK AG—See Bank fur Tirol und Vorarlberg Ag; *Int'l*, pg. 838
OBERBANK GESCHAFTSBEREICH TSCHECHIEN SPOL S.R.O.—See Bank fur Tirol und Vorarlberg Ag; *Int'l*, pg. 838
OBERBANK LEASING SPOL S.R.O.—See Bank fur Tirol und Vorarlberg Ag; *Int'l*, pg. 838
OBERBANK LEASING S.R.O.—See Bank fur Tirol und Vorarlberg Ag; *Int'l*, pg. 838
OBERBECK GRAIN CO.; *U.S. Private*, pg. 2986
OBERDORFER, LLC—See Advanced Metals Group, LLC; *U.S. Private*, pg. 91
OBERE DONAU KRAFTWERKE AKTIENGESELLSCHAFT—See E.ON SE; *Int'l*, pg. 2258
OBERER DEVELOPMENT CO.; *U.S. Private*, pg. 2986
OBERFIELDS LLC—See Graycliff Partners LP; *U.S. Private*, pg. 1761
OBERG ARIZONA—See Oberg Industries Corp.; *U.S. Private*, pg. 2986
OBERG COSTA RCA, LTDA—See Oberg Industries Corp.; *U.S. Private*, pg. 2986
OBERG INDUSTRIES CORP.; *U.S. Private*, pg. 2986
OBERG INDUSTRIES EUROPE, GMBH—See Oberg Industries Corp.; *U.S. Private*, pg. 2986
OBERG INDUSTRIES, INC.—See Oberg Industries Corp.; *U.S. Private*, pg. 2986
OBERG INDUSTRIES—See Oberg Industries Corp.; *U.S. Private*, pg. 2986
OBERG INDUSTRIES—See Oberg Industries Corp.; *U.S. Private*, pg. 2986
OBERG MEDICAL—See Oberg Industries Corp.; *U.S. Private*, pg. 2987
OBERG MEXICO—See Oberg Industries Corp.; *U.S. Private*, pg. 2987
OBERGS VENT TEKNIK AB—See Bravida Holding AB; *Int'l*, pg. 1142
OBERHOLZER AG—See Burkhalter Holding AG; *Int'l*, pg. 1225
O. BERK COMPANY - BOTTLESTORE DIVISION—See O. Berk Company L.L.C.; *U.S. Private*, pg. 2981
O. BERK COMPANY L.L.C.; *U.S. Private*, pg. 2981
O. BERK COMPANY OF NEW ENGLAND—See O. Berk Company L.L.C.; *U.S. Private*, pg. 2981
OBERLAND STROMNETZ GMBH & CO. KG—See E.ON SE; *Int'l*, pg. 2258
OBERLE & ASSOCIATES, INC.; *U.S. Private*, pg. 2987
OBERLIN FILTER COMPANY—See Production Service Company; *U.S. Private*, pg. 3273
OBERLIN FILTER GMBH—See Production Service Company; *U.S. Private*, pg. 3273
OBERLIN FILTER LTD.—See Production Service Company; *U.S. Private*, pg. 3273
OBERLIN MARKETING CO., INC.—See Integrity Marketing Group LLC; *U.S. Private*, pg. 2104
OBERMAN TIVOLI MILLER PICKERT; *U.S. Private*, pg. 2987
OBERMILLER NELSON ENGINEERING, INC.; *U.S. Private*, pg. 2987
OBEROI MALL LIMITED—See Oberoi Realty Limited; *Int'l*, pg. 5510
OBEROI REALTY LIMITED; *Int'l*, pg. 5510
OBERON, INC.—See Chatsworth Products Inc.; *U.S. Private*, pg. 868
OBERON INVESTMENTS GROUP PLC; *Int'l*, pg. 5510
OBERON MEDIA, INC; *U.S. Private*, pg. 2987
OBERON SECURITIES, LLC; *U.S. Private*, pg. 2987
OBEROSTERREICHISCHE VERSICHERUNG AG; *Int'l*, pg. 5511
O'BERRY CAVANAUGH; *U.S. Private*, pg. 2977
OBER S.A.; *Int'l*, pg. 5510
OBERTHUR CARD SYSTEMS KART SISTEMLERI. SANAYI VE TICARET LIMITED SIRKETI—See Advent International Corporation; *U.S. Private*, pg. 102
OBERTHUR CARD SYSTEMS KFT.—See Advent International Corporation; *U.S. Private*, pg. 102
OBERTHUR CARD SYSTEMS KK—See Advent International Corporation; *U.S. Private*, pg. 102
OBERTHUR CARD SYSTEMS OOO—See Advent International Corporation; *U.S. Private*, pg. 102
OBERTHUR CARD SYSTEMS PVT. LTD.—See Advent International Corporation; *U.S. Private*, pg. 102
OBERTHUR CARD SYSTEMS ROMANIA S.R.L—See Advent International Corporation; *U.S. Private*, pg. 102
OBERTHUR CARD SYSTEMS SCIENCE & TECHNOLOGY (SHENZHEN) CO. LTD—See Advent International Corporation; *U.S. Private*, pg. 102
OBERTHUR CARD SYSTEMS—See Advent International Corporation; *U.S. Private*, pg. 102
OBERTHUR CARD SYSTEMS SP. Z O.O.—See Advent International Corporation; *U.S. Private*, pg. 102
OBERTHUR CASH PROTECTION S.A.—See Francois-Charles Oberthur Fiduciaire S.A.; *Int'l*, pg. 2760
OBERTHUR CASH PROTECTION UK LIMITED—See Advent International Corporation; *U.S. Private*, pg. 102
OBERTHUR FIDUCIAIRE SAS—See Francois-Charles Oberthur Fiduciaire S.A.; *Int'l*, pg. 2760
OBERTHUR FIDUCIAIRE (UK) LIMITED—See Francois-Charles Oberthur Fiduciaire S.A.; *Int'l*, pg. 2760
OBERTHUR TECHNOLOGIES (BEIJING) CO LTD—See Advent International Corporation; *U.S. Private*, pg. 102
OBERTHUR TECHNOLOGIES COLOMBIA—See Advent International Corporation; *U.S. Private*, pg. 102
OBERTHUR TECHNOLOGIES DE MEXICO, S. DE R.L. DE C.V.—See Advent International Corporation; *U.S. Private*, pg. 103
OBERTHUR TECHNOLOGIES DENMARK A/S—See Advent International Corporation; *U.S. Private*, pg. 102
OBERTHUR TECHNOLOGIES FINLAND SEGENMARK OY—See Advent International Corporation; *U.S. Private*, pg. 102
OBERTHUR TECHNOLOGIES IBERICA—See Advent International Corporation; *U.S. Private*, pg. 102
OBERTHUR TECHNOLOGIES INC.—See Advent International Corporation; *U.S. Private*, pg. 103
OBERTHUR TECHNOLOGIES ITALIA SRL—See Advent International Corporation; *U.S. Private*, pg. 103
OBERTHUR TECHNOLOGIES KFT—See Advent International Corporation; *U.S. Private*, pg. 103
OBERTHUR TECHNOLOGIES KK—See Advent International Corporation; *U.S. Private*, pg. 103
OBERTHUR TECHNOLOGIES KOREA INC.—See Advent International Corporation; *U.S. Private*, pg. 103
OBERTHUR TECHNOLOGIES LATVIA SIA—See Advent International Corporation; *U.S. Private*, pg. 103
OBERTHUR TECHNOLOGIES LTDA—See Advent International Corporation; *U.S. Private*, pg. 103
OBERTHUR TECHNOLOGIES LTD—See Advent International Corporation; *U.S. Private*, pg. 103
OBERTHUR TECHNOLOGIES NORWAY A/S—See Advent International Corporation; *U.S. Private*, pg. 103
OBERTHUR TECHNOLOGIES OF AMERICA CORP—See Advent International Corporation; *U.S. Private*, pg. 103
OBERTHUR TECHNOLOGIES ROMANIA S.R.L.—See Advent International Corporation; *U.S. Private*, pg. 103
OBERTHUR TECHNOLOGIES SOUTH AFRICA (PTY) LTD—See Advent International Corporation; *U.S. Private*, pg. 103
OBERTHUR TECHNOLOGIES SUCURSAL EM PORTUGAL—See Advent International Corporation; *U.S. Private*, pg. 103
OBERTHUR TECHNOLOGIES SWEDEN ACSC AB—See Advent International Corporation; *U.S. Private*, pg. 103
OBERTHUR TECHNOLOGIES TEKNOLOJI SANAYI VE TICARET LTD.—See Advent International Corporation; *U.S. Private*, pg. 103
OBERTHUR TECHNOLOGIES THE NETHERLANDS BV—See Advent International Corporation; *U.S. Private*, pg. 103
OBERTHUR TECHNOLOGIES UK LTD.—See Advent International Corporation; *U.S. Private*, pg. 103
OBERTO SAUSAGE COMPANY INC.—See Premium Brands Holdings Corporation; *Int'l*, pg. 5963
OBERUBER KARGER KOMMUNIKATIONSAGENTUR GMBH—See Bertelsmann SE & Co. KGaA; *Int'l*, pg. 993
OBERWEIS DAIRY, INC.; *U.S. Private*, pg. 2987
OB HEALTHCARE CORPORATION—See InfuSystem Holdings, Inc.; *U.S. Public*, pg. 1118
OB HOSPITALIST GROUP, INC.—See Kohlberg & Company, LLC; *U.S. Private*, pg. 2338
OBIANE—See Orange S.A.; *Int'l*, pg. 5609
OBI BAU-UND HEIMWERKERMAERKTE GMBH & CO. KG—See Tengelmann Warenhandelsgesellschaft KG; *Int'l*, pg. 7560
OBI BAU-UND HEIMWERKERMARKTE SYSTEMZENTRALE GMBH—See Tengelmann Warenhandelsgesellschaft KG; *Int'l*, pg. 7560
OBI B.B.C. S.R.L.—See Tengelmann Warenhandelsgesellschaft KG; *Int'l*, pg. 7560
OBIC BUSINESS CONSULTANTS CO., LTD.; *Int'l*, pg. 5511
OBIC BUSINESS SOLUTION CO., LTD.—See OBIC Co Ltd; *Int'l*, pg. 5511
OBIC CO LTD; *Int'l*, pg. 5511
OBI CENTRALA SYSTEMOWA SP ZOO—See Tengelmann Warenhandelsgesellschaft KG; *Int'l*, pg. 7560
OBI CESKA REPUBLIKA S.R.O.—See Tengelmann Warenhandelsgesellschaft KG; *Int'l*, pg. 7560
OBIC OFFICE AUTOMATION CO., LTD.—See OBIC Co Ltd; *Int'l*, pg. 5511
OBI FRANCHISE CENTER OOO—See Tengelmann Warenhandelsgesellschaft KG; *Int'l*, pg. 7560
OBIGO INC.; *Int'l*, pg. 5511
OBIHAI TECHNOLOGY INC.—See HP Inc.; *U.S. Public*, pg. 1064
OBI HUNGARY RETAIL KFT—See Tengelmann Warenhandelsgesellschaft KG; *Int'l*, pg. 7560
OBI PHARMA, INC.; *Int'l*, pg. 5511
OBI ROMANIA SRL—See Tengelmann Warenhandelsgesellschaft KG; *Int'l*, pg. 7560
OBI SYSTEMOVA CENTRALA SPOL. S.R.O.—See Tengelmann Warenhandelsgesellschaft KG; *Int'l*, pg. 7560
OBI-SYSTEMZENTRALE—See Tengelmann Warenhandelsgesellschaft KG; *Int'l*, pg. 7560
OBI SYSTEMZENTRALE S.R.L.—See Tengelmann Warenhandelsgesellschaft KG; *Int'l*, pg. 7560
O-BIT TELECOM LIMITED—See Daisy Group Limited; *Int'l*, pg. 1943
OBI UKRAINE FRANCHISE CENTRE LLC—See Tengelmann Warenhandelsgesellschaft KG; *Int'l*, pg. 7560
OBIZ SA; *Int'l*, pg. 5511
OBJECT CTALK INC.; *U.S. Private*, pg. 2987
OBJECTIF LUNE ASIA PTY. LTD.—See Upland Software, Inc.; *U.S. Public*, pg. 2264
OBJECTIF LUNE CAPTURE INC.—See Upland Software, Inc.; *U.S. Public*, pg. 2264
OBJECTIF LUNE GMBH—See Upland Software, Inc.; *U.S. Public*, pg. 2264
OBJECTIF LUNE MALAYSIA SDN. BHD.—See Upland Software, Inc.; *U.S. Public*, pg. 2264
OBJECTIVA CHINA—See Allgeier SE; *Int'l*, pg. 337
OBJECTIVA SOFTWARE SOLUTIONS (BEIJING) CO., LTD.—See Allgeier SE; *Int'l*, pg. 337
OBJECTIVA SOFTWARE SOLUTIONS, INC.—See Allgeier SE; *Int'l*, pg. 337
OBJECTIVA SOFTWARE SOLUTIONS (XI'AN) CO., LTD.—See Allgeier SE; *Int'l*, pg. 337
OBJECTIVE CORPORATION LIMITED; *Int'l*, pg. 5511
OBJECTIVE CORPORATION SINGAPORE PTE LIMITED—See OBJECTIVE CORPORATION LIMITED; *Int'l*, pg. 5511
OBJECTIVE CORPORATION UK LIMITED—See OBJECTIVE CORPORATION LIMITED; *Int'l*, pg. 5511
OBJECTIVE INTEGRITY, INC.; *U.S. Private*, pg. 2987
OBJECTIVE MANAGEMENT GROUP, INC.; *U.S. Private*, pg. 2987
OBJECTIVE MEDICAL ASSESSMENTS CORPORATION—See Stone Point Capital LLC; *U.S. Private*, pg. 3824
OBJECTIVE SYSTEMS INTEGRATORS, INC.—See Inflexion Private Equity Partners LLP; *Int'l*, pg. 3689
OBJECTIVITY INC.; *U.S. Private*, pg. 2987
OBJECTONE INFORMATION SYSTEMS LIMITED; *Int'l*, pg. 5511
OBJECT PARTNERS, INC.—See Trinity Hunt Management, L.P.; *U.S. Private*, pg. 4234
OBJECT RESEARCH SYSTEMS (ORS) INC.—See Comet Holding AG; *Int'l*, pg. 1710
OBJECT SOFTWARE (BEIJING) CO., LTD.—See Object Software Limited; *Int'l*, pg. 5511
OBJECT SOFTWARE LIMITED; *Int'l*, pg. 5511
OBJECTSTREAM, INC.; *U.S. Private*, pg. 2987
OBJECT SYSTEMS GROUP INC.; *U.S. Private*, pg. 2987
OBJECT TECHNOLOGY SOLUTIONS, INC.; *U.S. Private*, pg. 2987
OBJECTVIDEO LABS, LLC—See ABS Capital Partners, L.P.; *U.S. Private*, pg. 44
OBJECTWAVE CORPORATION—See AEA Investors LP; *U.S. Private*, pg. 114
OBJECTWAY FINANCIAL SOFTWARE SPA; *Int'l*, pg. 5511
OBJECTWAY LIMITED—See ObjectWay Financial Software SpA; *Int'l*, pg. 5511
OBJECTWIN TECHNOLOGY, INC.; *U.S. Private*, pg. 2987
OBJEKT BURCHARDPLATZ GMBH & CO. KG—See Allianz SE; *Int'l*, pg. 355
OBJEKT CITY-POINT KASSEL GMBH & CO. KG—See Deutsche EuroShop AG; *Int'l*, pg. 2065
OBJEKTVISION AB—See Alma Media Corporation; *Int'l*, pg. 362
OB KLINIKA A.S.—See Centene Corporation; *U.S. Public*, pg. 470
O/B LEASING COMPANY—See Universal Logistics Holdings, Inc.; *U.S. Public*, pg. 2261
OBLOG CONSULTING S.A.—See Novo Banco, S.A.; *Int'l*, pg. 5462
OBLONG FOOD CENTER INC.; *U.S. Private*, pg. 2987
OBLONG, INC.; *U.S. Public*, pg. 1560
OBLONG INDUSTRIES, INC.—See Oblong, Inc.; *U.S. Public*, pg. 1560
OBL SRL—See IDEX Corp; *U.S. Public*, pg. 1091
OB MEDIA LLC—See Enero Group Limited; *Int'l*, pg. 2424
OBM INTERNATIONAL (OBMI); *Int'l*, pg. 5511
OBM LIMITED—See OBM International (OBMI); *Int'l*, pg. 5511
OBM LIMITED—See OBM International (OBMI); *Int'l*, pg. 5511
OBM LIMITED—See OBM International (OBMI); *Int'l*, pg. 5511
OBM MIAMI INC.—See OBM International (OBMI); *Int'l*, pg. 5511
OBN HOLDINGS, INC.; *U.S. Private*, pg. 2987
OBNOVA A.D. ADA; *Int'l*, pg. 5511
OBNOVA A.D. BEOGRAD; *Int'l*, pg. 5511

OBNOVA PROMET MALESEV A.D.

OBNOVA PROMET MALESEV A.D.; *Int'l*, pg. 5511
OBON SAI COSMETICS LTD—See Aurelius Equity Opportunities SE & Co. KGaA; *Int'l*, pg. 710
OBOS BBL; *Int'l*, pg. 5511
OBOUR LAND FOR FOOD INDUSTRIES S.A.E; *Int'l*, pg. 5512
OBO-WERKE GMBH & CO. KG—See MBB SE; *Int'l*, pg. 4751
O'BOYLE PROPERTIES, INC.—See BGC Group, Inc.; *U.S. Public*, pg. 329
OBOZ FOOTWEAR, LLC—See KMD Brands Limited; *Int'l*, pg. 4204
OBRA CAPITAL, INC.; *U.S. Private*, pg. 2987
OBRASCON HUARTE LAIN, CONSTRUCCION INTERNACIONAL S.L.—See Grupo Villar Mir, S.A.U.; *Int'l*, pg. 3139
OBRASCON HUARTE LAIN, DESARROLLOS S. L.—See Grupo Villar Mir, S.A.U.; *Int'l*, pg. 3139
OBRASCON HUARTE LAIN, S.A.—See Grupo Villar Mir, S.A.U.; *Int'l*, pg. 3138
O'BRIEN AUTOMOTIVE TEAM; *U.S. Private*, pg. 2977
O'BRIEN AUTO PARK; *U.S. Private*, pg. 2977
O'BRIEN BVBA—See AMETEK, Inc.; *U.S. Public*, pg. 121
O'BRIEN CONCRETE PUMPING COLORADO, INC.—See Peninsula Pacific Strategic Partners, LLC; *U.S. Private*, pg. 3133
O'BRIEN CORPORATION—See AMETEK, Inc.; *U.S. Public*, pg. 118
THE O'BRIEN & GERE COMPANIES; *U.S. Private*, pg. 4087
O'BRIEN & GERE INC. OF NORTH AMERICA—See The O'Brien & Gere Companies; *U.S. Private*, pg. 4087
O'BRIEN & GERE LABORATORIES, INC.—See The O'Brien & Gere Companies; *U.S. Private*, pg. 4087
O'BRIEN & GERE TECHNICAL SERVICES INC.—See The O'Brien & Gere Companies; *U.S. Private*, pg. 4087
THE O'BRIEN GROUP LIMITED—See Fletcher Building Limited; *Int'l*, pg. 2701
O'BRIEN GROUP; *U.S. Private*, pg. 2977
OBRIEN IMPORTS, INC.; *U.S. Private*, pg. 2987
O'BRIEN INTERNATIONAL, INC.—See Motion Water Sports Inc.; *U.S. Private*, pg. 2796
O'BRIEN SOUTHERN TRENCHING, INC.; *U.S. Private*, pg. 2977
O'BRIEN'S RESPONSE MANAGEMENT INC.—See AIP, LLC; *U.S. Private*, pg. 136
O'BRYAN'S FARM EQUIPMENT LLC—See Tym Corporation; *Int'l*, pg. 7995
O'BRYANT ELECTRIC, INC.; *U.S. Private*, pg. 2977
OBSCURA ANTIQUES & ODDITIES; *U.S. Private*, pg. 2987
OBSCURA DIGITAL, INC.—See Sphere Entertainment Co.; *U.S. Public*, pg. 1918
OBSCURE TECHNOLOGY PROPRIETARY LIMITED—See Alviva Holdings Limited; *Int'l*, pg. 402
OBSED A.S.—See Fomento de Construcciones y Contratas, S.A.; *Int'l*, pg. 2723
OBSERVANT LLC; *U.S. Private*, pg. 2987
OBSERVE MEDICAL ASA; *Int'l*, pg. 5512
OBSERVEPOINT LLC; *U.S. Private*, pg. 2987
OBSERVER CAPITAL LLC; *U.S. Private*, pg. 2987
THE OBSERVER-DISPATCH—See Gannett Co., Inc.; *U.S. Public*, pg. 904
OBSERVER MEDIA GROUP, INC.; *U.S. Private*, pg. 2988
OBSERVER PUBLISHING COMPANY—See The Nutting Company, Inc.; *U.S. Private*, pg. 4086
THE OBSERVER (SARNIA)—See Chatham Asset Management, LLC; *U.S. Private*, pg. 861
THE OBSERVER—See The Scott Trust Limited; *Int'l*, pg. 7680
OBSEVA SA; *Int'l*, pg. 5512
OBS FINANCIAL SERVICES, INC.—See Huatai Securities Co., Ltd.; *Int'l*, pg. 3514
OBSHESTWO S OGRANIZENNOI OTWETSTWENNOS-TJU MOOG—See Moog Inc.; *U.S. Public*, pg. 1470
OBS HYPERMARKET—See Kooperativa Forbundet; *Int'l*, pg. 4279
OBSIDIAN ENERGY LTD.; *Int'l*, pg. 5512
OBSIDIAN ENTERPRISES, INC.; *U.S. Private*, pg. 2988
OBSIDIAN ENTERTAINMENT, INC.—See Microsoft Corporation; *U.S. Public*, pg. 1440
OBSIDIAN HCM MEDICAL HOLDINGS IRELAND LIMITED—See Johnson Controls International plc; *Int'l*, pg. 3987
OBSIDIAN HOLDINGS LLC—See Goff Capital, Inc.; *U.S. Private*, pg. 1726
OBSIDIAN SOLUTIONS GROUP LLC; *U.S. Private*, pg. 2988
OBSIDIAN TECHNOLOGIES, INC.—See Converge Technology Solutions Corp.; *Int'l*, pg. 1787
OBS REIT, LLC—See MetLife, Inc.; *U.S. Public*, pg. 1431
OBS (SINGAPORE) PTE. LTD.—See Oriental Holdings Berhad; *Int'l*, pg. 5624
OBSTETRIX MEDICAL GROUP—See MEDNAX, Inc.; *U.S. Public*, pg. 1413
O.B.SYSTEM INC.; *Int'l*, pg. 5503
OBTECH MEDICAL AG—See Johnson & Johnson; *U.S. Public*, pg. 1200

OBUK HAUSTURFULLUNGEN GMBH & CO. KG—See INDUS Holding AG; *Int'l*, pg. 3663
OBVERSE CORPORATION; *U.S. Private*, pg. 2988
OBVIENT STRATEGIES, INC.—See ABB Ltd.; *Int'l*, pg. 52
OBVION N.V.—See Cooperatieve Centrale Raiffeisen-Boerenleenbank B.A.; *Int'l*, pg. 1791
OBVIUS; *U.S. Private*, pg. 2988
OBV OSTERREICHISCHER BUNDESVERLAG SCHULBUCH GMBH & CO. KG—See Ernst Klett AG; *Int'l*, pg. 2495
OBXTEK INC.; *U.S. Private*, pg. 2988
OBZEE N.Y INC.—See SK Networks Co., Ltd.; *Int'l*, pg. 6974
OBZOR PUTOVANJA D.O.O—See Croatia Airlines d.d.; *Int'l*, pg. 1851
OCA ACQUISITION CORP.; *U.S. Public*, pg. 1560
OCACSA S.A.—See Groupe Egis S.A.; *Int'l*, pg. 3102
OCADO CELL IN ATLAS INSURANCE PCC LIMITED—See Ocado Group plc; *Int'l*, pg. 5515
OCADO GROUP PLC; *Int'l*, pg. 5515
OCADO LIMITED—See Ocado Group plc; *Int'l*, pg. 5515
OCADO RETAIL LIMITED—See Ocado Group plc; *Int'l*, pg. 5515
OCAENLINE (LABUAN) LTD.—See Benalec Holdings Berhad; *Int'l*, pg. 969
OCALA BEHAVIORAL HEALTH, LLC—See Universal Health Services, Inc.; *U.S. Public*, pg. 2258
OCALA BREEDERS' SALES COMPANY; *U.S. Private*, pg. 2988
OCALA BROADCASTING CORPORATION, LLC—See DIX 1898, Inc; *U.S. Private*, pg. 1244
THE OCALA ENDOSCOPY ASC, L.P.—See KKR & Co. Inc.; *U.S. Public*, pg. 1248
OCALA FREIGHTLINER, INC.—See Florida Truck Group; *U.S. Private*, pg. 1550
OCALA HEALTH IMAGING SERVICES, LLC—See HCA Healthcare, Inc.; *U.S. Public*, pg. 1005
OCALA HEALTH SURGICAL GROUP, LLC—See HCA Healthcare, Inc.; *U.S. Public*, pg. 1005
OCALA HEALTH TRAUMA, LLC—See HCA Healthcare, Inc.; *U.S. Public*, pg. 1005
OCALA REGIONAL MEDICAL CENTER—See HCA Healthcare, Inc.; *U.S. Public*, pg. 1005
OCAM JSC—See Hjolle Industries S.A.; *Int'l*, pg. 3401
THE O'CARROLL GROUP; *U.S. Private*, pg. 4087
OCB BERHAD; *Int'l*, pg. 5515
OCBC AL-AMIN BANK BERHAD—See Oversea-Chinese Banking Corporation Limited; *Int'l*, pg. 5672
OCBC ASSET MANAGEMENT—See Oversea-Chinese Banking Corporation Limited; *Int'l*, pg. 5672
OCBC BANK (MALAYSIA) BERHAD—See Oversea-Chinese Banking Corporation Limited; *Int'l*, pg. 5672
OCBC CAPITAL (MALAYSIA) SDN. BHD.—See Oversea-Chinese Banking Corporation Limited; *Int'l*, pg. 5672
OCBC INCHROY CREDIT CORPORATION LIMITED—See Oversea-Chinese Banking Corporation Limited; *Int'l*, pg. 5672
OCBC NOMINEES (HONG KONG) LIMITED—See Oversea-Chinese Banking Corporation Limited; *Int'l*, pg. 5672
OCBC PROPERTY SERVICES PRIVATE LIMITED—See Oversea-Chinese Banking Corporation Limited; *Int'l*, pg. 5672
OCBC SECURITIES (HONG KONG) LIMITED—See Oversea-Chinese Banking Corporation Limited; *Int'l*, pg. 5672
OCBC SECURITIES PRIVATE LIMITED—See Oversea-Chinese Banking Corporation Limited; *Int'l*, pg. 5672
OCBC SECURITIES PTE. LTD.—See Oversea-Chinese Banking Corporation Limited; *Int'l*, pg. 5672
OCBC WING HANG BANK LIMITED (MACAU)—See Oversea-Chinese Banking Corporation Limited; *Int'l*, pg. 5672
OCBC WING HANG BANK LIMITED—See Oversea-Chinese Banking Corporation Limited; *Int'l*, pg. 5672
OCBC WING HANG CREDIT LIMITED—See Oversea-Chinese Banking Corporation Limited; *Int'l*, pg. 5672
OCBC WING HANG INSURANCE AGENCY LIMITED—See Oversea-Chinese Banking Corporation Limited; *Int'l*, pg. 5672
OCBC WING HANG INSURANCE BROKERS LIMITED—See Oversea-Chinese Banking Corporation Limited; *Int'l*, pg. 5672
OCBC WING HANG SHARES BROKERAGE CO. LIMITED—See Oversea-Chinese Banking Corporation Limited; *Int'l*, pg. 5672
OCBC WING HANG (TRUSTEE) LIMITED—See Oversea-Chinese Banking Corporation Limited; *Int'l*, pg. 5672
OC BEVERAGES, INC.; *U.S. Public*, pg. 1560
OCCAMAT SAS—See Societe Anonyme d'Explosifs et de Produits Chimiques; *Int'l*, pg. 7035
OCCAM DM LIMITED—See Kin and Carta plc; *Int'l*, pg. 4164
OCCAM UNDERWRITING LIMITED—See Brown & Brown, Inc.; *U.S. Public*, pg. 401
OCCASIONS CATERERS INC.; *U.S. Private*, pg. 2988
THE OCCASIONS GROUP, INC.—See Taylor Corporation; *U.S. Private*, pg. 3939

CORPORATE AFFILIATIONS

OCC CORPORATION—See Sumitomo Electric Industries, Ltd.; *Int'l*, pg. 7279
OCCHEALTH SYSTEMS, LLC—See MCMC LLC; *U.S. Private*, pg. 2642
OCCIDENTAL CHEMICAL ASIA, LIMITED—See Occidental Petroleum Corporation; *U.S. Public*, pg. 1561
OCCIDENTAL CHEMICAL BELGIUM B.V.B.A.—See Occidental Petroleum Corporation; *U.S. Public*, pg. 1561
OCCIDENTAL CHEMICAL CHILE LIMITADA—See Occidental Petroleum Corporation; *U.S. Public*, pg. 1561
OCCIDENTAL CHEMICAL CORPORATION—See Occidental Petroleum Corporation; *U.S. Public*, pg. 1561
OCCIDENTAL CHEMICAL DE MEXICO, S.A. DE C.V.—See Occidental Petroleum Corporation; *U.S. Public*, pg. 1561
OCCIDENTAL CHEMICAL FAR EAST LIMITED—See Occidental Petroleum Corporation; *U.S. Public*, pg. 1561
OCCIDENTAL CHEMICAL HOLDING CORPORATION—See Occidental Petroleum Corporation; *U.S. Public*, pg. 1561
OCCIDENTAL DE COLOMBIA, INC.—See Occidental Petroleum Corporation; *U.S. Public*, pg. 1562
OCCIDENTAL DE HORMIGONES S.L.—See Camargo Correa S.A.; *Int'l*, pg. 1268
OCCIDENTAL DEVELOPMENT GROUP, INC.; *U.S. Private*, pg. 2988
OCCIDENTAL ENERGY MARKETING, INC.—See Occidental Petroleum Corporation; *U.S. Public*, pg. 1561
OCCIDENTAL ENERGY TRANSPORTATION LLC—See Occidental Petroleum Corporation; *U.S. Public*, pg. 1561
OCCIDENTAL ENERGY VENTURES CORP.—See Occidental Petroleum Corporation; *U.S. Public*, pg. 1561
OCCIDENTAL FIRE & CASUALTY COMPANY OF NORTH CAROLINA INC.—See MCM Corporation; *U.S. Private*, pg. 2642
OCCIDENTAL GOLD SARL—See Perseus Mining Limited; *Int'l*, pg. 5814
OCCIDENTAL INTERNATIONAL CORPORATION—See Occidental Petroleum Corporation; *U.S. Public*, pg. 1561
OCCIDENTAL INTERNATIONAL FOODS LLC; *U.S. Private*, pg. 2988
OCCIDENTAL MANAGEMENT INC.; *U.S. Private*, pg. 2988
OCCIDENTAL OF ELK HILLS, INC.—See Occidental Petroleum Corporation; *U.S. Public*, pg. 1562
OCCIDENTAL OIL & GAS CORPORATION—See Occidental Petroleum Corporation; *U.S. Public*, pg. 1561
OCCIDENTAL PERMIAN LTD.—See Occidental Petroleum Corporation; *U.S. Public*, pg. 1561
OCCIDENTAL PETROLEUM CORPORATION; *U.S. Public*, pg. 1560
OCCIDENTAL PETROLEUM INVESTMENT CO.—See Occidental Petroleum Corporation; *U.S. Public*, pg. 1561
OCCIDENTAL POWER MARKETING, L.P.—See Occidental Petroleum Corporation; *U.S. Public*, pg. 1561
OCCIDENTAL RESEARCH CORPORATION—See Occidental Petroleum Corporation; *U.S. Public*, pg. 1561
OCCIDENTAL TOWER CORPORATION—See Occidental Petroleum Corporation; *U.S. Public*, pg. 1561
OCCI INC.; *U.S. Private*, pg. 2988
OCCITANIE RESTAURATION SAS—See Compass Group PLC; *Int'l*, pg. 1752
O.C. CLUSS LUMBER COMPANY; *U.S. Private*, pg. 2981
OCC PUBLIC COMPANY LIMITED; *Int'l*, pg. 5515
OCCSPECIALISTS CORP., A MEDICAL CORPORATION—See Select Medical Holdings Corporation; *U.S. Public*, pg. 1858
OC&C STRATEGY CONSULTANTS; *Int'l*, pg. 5515
OCCUPATIONAL AND FAMILY MEDICINE OF SOUTH TEXAS—See HCA Healthcare, Inc.; *U.S. Public*, pg. 1005
OCCUPATIONAL HEALTH CENTERS OF CALIFORNIA, A MEDICAL CORPORATION—See Select Medical Holdings Corporation; *U.S. Public*, pg. 1858
OCCUPATIONAL HEALTH CENTERS OF CALIFORNIA, A MEDICAL, CORP.; *U.S. Private*, pg. 2988
OCCUPATIONAL HEALTH CENTERS OF MICHIGAN, P.C.—See Select Medical Holdings Corporation; *U.S. Public*, pg. 1858
OCCUPATIONAL HEALTH CENTERS OF NEBRASKA, P.C.—See Select Medical Holdings Corporation; *U.S. Public*, pg. 1858
OCCUPATIONAL HEALTH CENTERS OF OHIO, P.A., CO.—See Select Medical Holdings Corporation; *U.S. Public*, pg. 1858
OCCUPATIONAL HEALTH CENTERS OF THE SOUTHWEST, P.A.—See Select Medical Holdings Corporation; *U.S. Public*, pg. 1858
OCCUPATIONAL TRAINING CENTER OF BURLINGTON COUNTY, INC.; *U.S. Private*, pg. 2988
OCEAN8; *Int'l*, pg. 5517
OCEANAA BIOTEK INDUSTRIES LIMITED; *Int'l*, pg. 5517
OCEANA BRANDS—See Oceana Group Limited; *Int'l*, pg. 5517
OCEANA COUNTY FREEZER STORAGE, INC.—See Peterson Farms, Inc.; *U.S. Private*, pg. 3160

COMPANY NAME INDEX

OCEAN ACOUSTICAL SERVICES AND INSTRUMENTATION SYSTEMS, INC.—See ThayerMahan, Inc.; *U.S. Private*, pg. 3980
OCEANA FOODS—See Cherry Central Cooperative, Inc.; *U.S. Private*, pg. 874
OCEANAGOLD CORPORATION; *Int'l*, pg. 5517
OCEANA GOLD HOLDINGS (NEW ZEALAND) LIMITED—See OceanaGold Corporation; *Int'l*, pg. 5517
OCEANA GOLD LIMITED—See OceanaGold Corporation; *Int'l*, pg. 5518
OCEANA GOLD (NEW ZEALAND) LTD.—See OceanaGold Corporation; *Int'l*, pg. 5518
OCEANAGOLD (PHILIPPINES) HOLDINGS INC.—See OceanaGold Corporation; *Int'l*, pg. 5518
OCEANAGOLD (PHILIPPINES) INC.—See OceanaGold Corporation; *Int'l*, pg. 5518
OCEANA GOLD (WAIHI) LIMITED—See OceanaGold Corporation; *Int'l*, pg. 5518
OCEAN AGRO (INDIA) LIMITED; *Int'l*, pg. 5515
OCEAN AGRO LLC—See OCEAN AGRO (INDIA) LIMITED; *Int'l*, pg. 5515
OCEANA GROUP LIMITED; *Int'l*, pg. 5517
OCEANA, INC.; *U.S. Private*, pg. 2990
OCEANAIR INC.; *U.S. Private*, pg. 2990
OCEAN AIR INTERNATIONAL, INC.; *U.S. Private*, pg. 2988
OCEANAIR LINHAS AEREAS LTDA.—See Synergy Group; *Int'l*, pg. 7384
OCEANAIR TAXI AEREO LTDA.—See Synergy Group; *Int'l*, pg. 7384
OCEANA LITHIUM LIMITED; *Int'l*, pg. 5517
OCEANA LOBSTER ABALONE & SQUID—See Oceana Group Limited; *Int'l*, pg. 5517
OCEANA LOBSTER LIMITED—See Oceana Group Limited; *Int'l*, pg. 5517
OCEANA RESORTS, LLC—See Travel & Leisure Co.; *U.S. Public*, pg. 2185
OCEANA SPV (PTY) LTD.—See Brimstone Investment Corporation Ltd.; *Int'l*, pg. 1164
OCEAN ATLANTIC DORCOL D.O.O.—See Immofinanz AG; *Int'l*, pg. 3628
OCEAN BANKSHARES, INC.; *U.S. Private*, pg. 2988
OCEAN BANK—See Ocean Bankshares, Inc.; *U.S. Private*, pg. 2988
OCEAN BEAUTY SEAFOODS, INC., *U.S. Private*, pg. 2989
OCEAN BIO-CHEM, LLC—See OneWater Marine Inc.; *U.S. Public*, pg. 1604
OCEAN BIOMEDICAL HOLDINGS, INC.—See Ocean Biomedical, Inc.; *U.S. Public*, pg. 1562
OCEAN BIOMEDICAL, INC.; *U.S. Public*, pg. 1562
OCEAN BRANDS GP—See The Jim Pattison Group; *Int'l*, pg. 7660
OCEAN BRIDGE CO LTD; *Int'l*, pg. 5515
OCEAN BRIDGE GROUP; *U.S. Private*, pg. 2989
OCEAN CADILLAC INC.; *U.S. Private*, pg. 2989
OCEAN & CAPITAL PROPERTIES PTE LTD—See Keppel Corporation Limited; *Int'l*, pg. 4131
OCEANCASH PACIFIC BERHAD; *Int'l*, pg. 5518
OCEAN CENTURY INVESTMENTS LIMITED—See CK Asset Holdings Limited; *Int'l*, pg. 1635
OCEAN CHOICE INTERNATIONAL, K.K.—See Penney Group; *Int'l*, pg. 5786
OCEAN CHOICE INTERNATIONAL LIMITED—See Penney Group; *Int'l*, pg. 5786
OCEAN CHOICE INTERNATIONAL L.P.—See Penney Group; *Int'l*, pg. 5786
OCEAN CITY OUTBACK, INC.—See Bloomin' Brands, Inc.; *U.S. Public*, pg. 363
OCEAN CITY RESEARCH CORPORATION—See New Mountain Capital, LLC; *U.S. Private*, pg. 2900
OCEAN CLOUD TECHNOLOGY CO., LIMITED—See MicroCloud Hologram Inc.; *U.S. Public*, pg. 1437
OCEAN COLD STORAGE (ST. KITTS) LTD.—See S.L. Horsford & Company Limited; *Int'l*, pg. 6456
OCEAN COLLEGE LLC—See TUI AG; *Int'l*, pg. 7965
OCEAN COLONY PARTNERS; *U.S. Private*, pg. 2989
OCEAN COMBUSTION SERVICES N.V.—See Renewi plc; *Int'l*, pg. 6278
OCEAN CONSERVANCY; *U.S. Private*, pg. 2989
OCEAN CONTAINER SERVICE (OCS)—See Albert Ballin KG; *Int'l*, pg. 296
OCEAN CONTRACTORS LIMITED; *Int'l*, pg. 5516
OCEAN CONVERSION (BVI) LTD.—See Consolidated Water Co. Ltd.; *Int'l*, pg. 1771
OCEAN CONVERSION (CAYMAN) LIMITED—See Consolidated Water Co. Ltd.; *Int'l*, pg. 1771
OCEAN COUNTY AUTO WRECKERS, INC.—See Stellex Capital Management LP; *U.S. Private*, pg. 3800
OCEAN COUNTY UTILITIES AUTHORITY; *U.S. Private*, pg. 2989
OCEAN DIAMOND LIMITED—See Sinolink Worldwide Holdings Limited; *Int'l*, pg. 6952
OCEAN DOWNS LLC—See Churchill Downs, Inc.; *U.S. Public*, pg. 494
OCEAN DRIVE ACQUISITION CORP.; *U.S. Private*, pg. 2989
OCEAN DUNES RESORT & VILLAS; *U.S. Private*, pg. 2989

OCEANE DE RESTAURATION SAS—See Compass Group PLC; *Int'l*, pg. 1752
OCEANEERING ANGOLA, S.A.—See Oceaneering International, Inc.; *U.S. Public*, pg. 1562
OCEANEERING ASSET INTEGRITY AS—See Oceaneering International, Inc.; *U.S. Public*, pg. 1562
OCEANEERING AS—See Oceaneering International, Inc.; *U.S. Public*, pg. 1562
OCEANEERING AUSTRALIA PTY, LIMITED—See Oceaneering International, Inc.; *U.S. Public*, pg. 1562
OCEANEERING CANADA LIMITED—See Oceaneering International, Inc.; *U.S. Public*, pg. 1562
OCEANEERING INTERNATIONAL GMBH—See Oceaneering International, Inc.; *U.S. Public*, pg. 1562
OCEANEERING INTERNATIONAL, INC.; *U.S. Public*, pg. 1562
OCEANEERING INTERNATIONAL PTE. LTD.—See Oceaneering International, Inc.; *U.S. Public*, pg. 1562
OCEANEERING INTERNATIONAL SERVICES, LTD.—See Oceaneering International, Inc.; *U.S. Public*, pg. 1563
OCEANEERING INTERVENTION ENGINEERING—See Oceaneering International, Inc.; *U.S. Public*, pg. 1563
OCEANEERING PIPETECH AS—See Oceaneering International, Inc.; *U.S. Public*, pg. 1563
OCEANEERING ROTATOR AS—See Oceaneering International, Inc.; *U.S. Public*, pg. 1562
OCEANEERING SERVICES AUSTRALIA PTY LTD.—See Oceaneering International, Inc.; *U.S. Public*, pg. 1563
OCEANEERING SPACE SYSTEMS—See Oceaneering International, Inc.; *U.S. Public*, pg. 1563
OCEANEERING TECHNOLOGIES—See Oceaneering International, Inc.; *U.S. Public*, pg. 1563
OCEANEERING UMBILICAL SOLUTIONS—See Oceaneering International, Inc.; *U.S. Public*, pg. 1563
OCEAN ELECTRICAL CO. SDN. BHD.—See YFG Berhad; *Int'l*, pg. 8579
OCEAN ENDOSURGERY CENTER—See KKR & Co. Inc.; *U.S. Public*, pg. 1246
OCEAN ENGINEERING CORPORATION—See OYO Corporation; *Int'l*, pg. 5678
OCEANE RE SA—See Electricite de France S.A.; *Int'l*, pg. 2352
OCEANEX INC. - MONTREAL—See Oceanex Inc.; *Int'l*, pg. 5518
OCEANEX INC.; *Int'l*, pg. 5518
OCEAN EXPLORATION TRUST; *U.S. Private*, pg. 2989
OCEANFIRST BANK, NATIONAL ASSOCIATION—See OceanFirst Financial Corp.; *U.S. Public*, pg. 1563
OCEANFIRST FINANCIAL CORP.; *U.S. Public*, pg. 1563
OCEAN FLOW INTERNATIONAL LLC—See Sapura Energy Berhad; *Int'l*, pg. 6574
OCEANFREIGHT INC.—See DryShips Inc.; *Int'l*, pg. 2207
OCEANFRESH SEAFOODS (PTY) LIMITED—See Lonrho Limited; *Int'l*, pg. 4552
OCEAN GARDENS MANAGEMENT COMPANY LIMITED—See Keck Seng Investments (Hong Kong) Limited; *Int'l*, pg. 4114
OCEANGEO B.V.—See ION Geophysical Corporation; *U.S. Public*, pg. 1166
OCEAN GEOLOOP AS; *Int'l*, pg. 5516
OCEAN GLASS PUBLIC COMPANY LIMITED; *Int'l*, pg. 5516
OCEAN GLASS TRADING INDIA PRIVATE LIMITED—See Ocean Glass Public Company Limited; *Int'l*, pg. 5516
OCEAN GLASS TRADING (SHANGHAI) CO., LTD.—See Ocean Glass Public Company Limited; *Int'l*, pg. 5516
OCEAN GOLD SEAFOODS, INC.; *U.S. Private*, pg. 2989
OCEAN GROUP INVESTMENTS LIMITED—See Deutsche Post AG; *Int'l*, pg. 2082
OCEAN GROUP JOINT STOCK COMPANY; *Int'l*, pg. 5516
OCEAN GROVE R.V. SALES INC., OF ST. AUGUSTINE—See Redwood Capital Investments, LLC; *U.S. Private*, pg. 3380
OCEAN HARVEST WHOLESALE INC.; *U.S. Private*, pg. 2989
OCEAN HEALTH PTE. LTD.—See Hyphens Pharma International Limited; *Int'l*, pg. 3553
OCEAN HONDA—See Victory Automotive Group, Inc.; *U.S. Private*, pg. 4378
OCEANHOUSE MEDIA, INC.; *U.S. Private*, pg. 2990
OCEANIA CAPITAL PARTNERS LIMITED; *Int'l*, pg. 5518
OCEANIA DAIRY LIMITED—See Inner Mongolia Yili Industrial Group Co., Ltd.; *Int'l*, pg. 3708
OCEANIA GAS LIMITED; *Int'l*, pg. 5518
OCEANIA HEALTHCARE LIMITED; *Int'l*, pg. 5518
OCEANIA LEASING AGENCIES—See CAI International, Inc.; *U.S. Public*, pg. 421
OCEANICA AG—See BMT Group Limited; *Int'l*, pg. 1077
OCEANIC BEVERAGES CO., INC.; *Int'l*, pg. 5518
OCEANIC CAPITAL MANAGEMENT LLC—See Ecobank Transnational Incorporated; *U.S. Public*, pg. 2294
OCEANIC EXPLORATION COMPANY; *U.S. Private*, pg. 2990
OCEANIC FOODS LIMITED; *Int'l*, pg. 5518
OCEANIC INVESTMENT CORPORATION; *Int'l*, pg. 5518
OCEANIC IRON ORE CORP.; *Int'l*, pg. 5518
OCEANIC OFFSHORE ENGINEERING PTE. LTD.—See KS Energy Limited; *Int'l*, pg. 4309

OCEAN REEF CLUB INC.

OCEANIC REALTY GROUP INTERNATIONAL, INC—See Alliance Global Group, Inc.; *Int'l*, pg. 339
OCEANIC TANKERS AGENCY LTD.—See Valero Energy Corporation; *U.S. Public*, pg. 2272
OCEANIC TIME WARNER CABLE LLC—See Charter Communications, Inc.; *U.S. Public*, pg. 483
OCEANIC WIND ENERGY INC.; *Int'l*, pg. 5518
OCEAN INCORPORATION LTD.—See Keck Seng Investments (Hong Kong) Limited; *Int'l*, pg. 4114
OCEAN INSIGHT, INC.—See Halma plc; *Int'l*, pg. 3232
OCEAN INVESTMENTS CORPORATION—See Irving Oil Limited; *Int'l*, pg. 3811
OCEANIS AUSTRALIA PTY LTD—See Merlin Entertainments plc; *Int'l*, pg. 4838
OCEANIS HOLDINGS LTD.—See Merlin Entertainments plc; *Int'l*, pg. 4837
OCEAN KEY RESORT & SPA—See Noble House Hotels & Resorts, Ltd.; *U.S. Private*, pg. 2932
OCEANLAND SERVICE INC.; *U.S. Private*, pg. 2990
OCEAN LANKA (PRIVATE) LIMITED—See Fountain Set (Holdings) Limited; *Int'l*, pg. 2754
OCEAN LIFE INSURANCE CO., LTD.—See Dai-ichi Life Holdings, Inc.; *Int'l*, pg. 1917
OCEAN LINE PORT DEVELOPMENT LTD.; *Int'l*, pg. 5516
OCEANLINK LTD.—See Fred. Olsen & Co.; *Int'l*, pg. 2769
OCEAN MACHINERY—See Citizen Watch Co., Ltd.; *Int'l*, pg. 1624
OCEAN MARINE GROUP INC.; *U.S. Private*, pg. 2989
OCEAN MAURITIUS LIMITED—See Teejay Lanka PLC; *Int'l*, pg. 7520
OCEAN MAZDA; *U.S. Private*, pg. 2989
OCEAN MEDIA GROUP LIMITED—See Lonsdale Capital Partners LLP; *Int'l*, pg. 4552
OCEAN MEDIA (HONG KONG) LIMITED—See Winto Group (Holdings) Limited; *Int'l*, pg. 8431
OCEAN MEDIA INC.; *U.S. Private*, pg. 2989
OCEAN MEDICAL CENTER—See Hackensack Meridian Health, Inc.; *U.S. Private*, pg. 1838
OCEAN MINDED, INC.—See Crocs, Inc.; *U.S. Public*, pg. 595
OCEAN MIST FARMS CORP.; *U.S. Private*, pg. 2989
OCEAN MOTORS, INC.; *U.S. Private*, pg. 2989
OCEAN NETWORK EXPRESS HOLDINGS, LTD.—See Kawasaki Kisen Kaisha, Ltd.; *Int'l*, pg. 4101
OCEAN NETWORK EXPRESS HOLDINGS, LTD.—See Mitsui O.S.K. Lines, Ltd.; *Int'l*, pg. 4991
OCEAN NETWORK EXPRESS HOLDINGS, LTD.—See Nippon Yusen Kabushiki Kaisha; *Int'l*, pg. 5359
OCEAN NETWORK EXPRESS PTE. LTD.—See Kawasaki Kisen Kaisha, Ltd.; *Int'l*, pg. 4101
OCEAN NETWORK EXPRESS PTE. LTD.—See Mitsui O.S.K. Lines, Ltd.; *Int'l*, pg. 4991
OCEAN NETWORK EXPRESS PTE. LTD.—See Nippon Yusen Kabushiki Kaisha; *Int'l*, pg. 5359
OCEAN NEXUS SDN. BHD.—See I Synergy Group Limited; *Int'l*, pg. 3562
OCEAN NUTRITION CANADA LIMITED—See Koninklijke DSM N.V.; *Int'l*, pg. 4265
OCEANO AGENCIA MARITIMA SA—See Ultramar Ltda.; *Int'l*, pg. 8019
OCEANOGATE ITALIA S.P.A.—See EUROKAI GmbH & Co. KGaA; *Int'l*, pg. 2553
OCEAN OGILVY & MATHER—See WPP plc; *Int'l*, pg. 8484
OCEAN & OIL HOLDINGS LIMITED; *Int'l*, pg. 5515
OCEAN ONE HOLDING LTD.; *Int'l*, pg. 5516
OCEAN OPTICS BV—See Halma plc; *Int'l*, pg. 3232
OCEAN OPTICS GERMANY—See Halma plc; *Int'l*, pg. 3232
OCEANO SEAFOOD SA; *Int'l*, pg. 5518
OCEANOS, INC.; *U.S. Private*, pg. 2990
OCEAN OUTDOOR LIMITED; *Int'l*, pg. 5516
OCEAN OUTDOOR UK LIMITED—See Ocean Outdoor Limited; *Int'l*, pg. 5516
OCEAN PARK FORD SALES LTD.; *Int'l*, pg. 5516
OCEAN PETROLEUM CO. INC.; *U.S. Private*, pg. 2989
OCEAN PLASTICS CO., LTD.; *Int'l*, pg. 5516
OCEAN PLASTICS (HUI ZHOU) CO., LTD.—See Ocean Plastics Co., Ltd.; *Int'l*, pg. 5516
OCEAN POWER TECHNOLOGIES, INC.; *U.S. Public*, pg. 1562
OCEAN POWER TECHNOLOGIES, LTD.—See Ocean Power Technologies, Inc.; *U.S. Public*, pg. 1562
OCEAN PROPERTIES, LTD.; *U.S. Private*, pg. 2989
OCEAN PROPERTIES & MANAGEMENT, INC.; *U.S. Private*, pg. 2989
OCEAN PROPERTIES PTE. LTD.—See Keppel REIT; *Int'l*, pg. 4132
OCEAN REEF CLUB INC.; *U.S. Private*, pg. 2989
OCEAN RIDGE BIOSCIENCES, INC.—See Hangzhou Tigermed Consulting Co., Ltd.; *Int'l*, pg. 3251
OCEAN RIG 1 AS—See DryShips Inc.; *Int'l*, pg. 2207
OCEAN RIG ASA—See DryShips Inc.; *Int'l*, pg. 2207
OCEAN RIG AS—See DryShips Inc.; *Int'l*, pg. 2207
OCEAN RIG NORWAY AS—See DryShips Inc.; *Int'l*, pg. 2207
OCEAN RIG PARTNERS LP—See Transocean Ltd.; *Int'l*, pg. 7903
OCEAN RIG—See DryShips Inc.; *Int'l*, pg. 2207

OCEAN RIG UDW INC.—See Transocean Ltd.; *Int'l*, pg. 7903
OCEAN RIG UK LTD.—See DryShips Inc.; *Int'l*, pg. 2207
OCEANSCIENCE GROUP, LTD.—See Teledyne Technologies Incorporated; *U.S. Public*, pg. 1992
OCEANS FUNDING COMPANY INC.; *U.S. Private*, pg. 2990
OCEAN SHIPHOLDINGS, INC.; *U.S. Private*, pg. 2990
OCEANSHIP OWNERS LIMITED—See DryShips Inc.; *Int'l*, pg. 2207
OCEANSIDE GLASSTILE COMPANY; *U.S. Private*, pg. 2990
OCEANSIDE INSTITUTIONAL INDUSTRIES; *U.S. Private*, pg. 2990
OCEANSIDE PHOTO & TELESCOPE; *U.S. Private*, pg. 2990
OCEAN'S KING LIGHTING SCIENCE & TECHNOLOGY CO., LTD.; *Int'l*, pg. 5517
OCEAN'S KING TECH LIMITED—See Ocean's King Lighting Science & Technology Co., Ltd.; *Int'l*, pg. 5517
OCEAN SKY INTERNATIONAL LIMITED; *Int'l*, pg. 5516
OCEANSOUND PARTNERS, LP; *U.S. Private*, pg. 2990
OCEAN SPRAY CRANBERRIES-BORDENTOWN PLANT—See Ocean Spray Cranberries, Inc.; *U.S. Private*, pg. 2990
OCEAN SPRAY CRANBERRIES, INC.; *U.S. Private*, pg. 2990
OCEAN SPRAY INTERNATIONAL SERVICES, INC.—See Ocean Spray Cranberries, Inc.; *U.S. Private*, pg. 2990
OCEAN SPRAY INTERNATIONAL SERVICES (UK) LIMITED—See Ocean Spray Cranberries, Inc.; *U.S. Private*, pg. 2990
OCEAN SPRINGS SURGICAL AND ENDOSCOPY CENTER, LLC—See KKR & Co. Inc.; *U.S. Public*, pg. 1250
OCEAN STAGE INC.—See Chuo Gyorui Co., Ltd.; *Int'l*, pg. 1598
OCEANSTAR INTERNATIONAL INC.; *U.S. Private*, pg. 2992
OCEAN STAR TECHNOLOGY GROUP LIMITED; *Int'l*, pg. 5516
OCEAN STATE COMMUNITY RESOURCES, INC.; *U.S. Private*, pg. 2990
OCEAN STATE JOBBERS INC.; *U.S. Private*, pg. 2990
OCEAN STATE POWER—See LS Power Development, LLC; *U.S. Private*, pg. 2508
OCEAN STEEL CORP.—See OSCO Construction Group; *Int'l*, pg. 5648
OCEAN SUN AS; *Int'l*, pg. 5516
OCEAN SYSTEM CORPORATION; *Int'l*, pg. 5516
OCEAN TANKERS HOLDINGS PUBLIC COMPANY LIMITED; *Int'l*, pg. 5517
OCEANTEAM ASA—See SoilTech AS; *Int'l*, pg. 7060
OCEANTEAM MEXICO, S.A. DE C.V.—See SoilTech AS; *Int'l*, pg. 7060
OCEANTECH ACQUISITIONS I CORP.; *U.S. Public*, pg. 1563
OCEAN TECHNICAL SYSTEMS LIMITED—See Eaton Corporation plc; *Int'l*, pg. 2282
OCEAN TECHNOLOGIES PTE., LTD.—See PT Samudera Indonesia Tbk; *Int'l*, pg. 6069
OCEAN TECHNOLOGY INC.; *U.S. Private*, pg. 2990
OCEAN TERMINAL LIMITED—See Arcus Infrastructure Partners LLP; *Int'l*, pg. 552
OCEAN TERRACE INN LTD.—See St. Kitts Nevis Anguilla Trading & Development Co., Ltd.; *Int'l*, pg. 7159
OCEAN THERMAL ENERGY CORPORATION; *U.S. Public*, pg. 1562
OCEANUS AQUACULTURE GROUP PTE. LTD.—See Oceanus Group Limited; *Int'l*, pg. 5518
OCEANUS GROUP LIMITED; *Int'l*, pg. 5518
OCEAN VANTAGE HOLDINGS BERHAD; *Int'l*, pg. 5517
OCEANVENTURE OWNERS LIMITED—See DryShips Inc., pg. 2207
OCEANVIEW HEALTHCARE, INC.—See The Ensign Group, Inc.; *U.S. Public*, pg. 2071
OCEANVIEW PRODUCE COMPANY—See Dole plc; *Int'l*, pg. 2157
OCEAN WAY MOTORS INC.; *U.S. Private*, pg. 2990
OCEANWIDE EUROPE LIMITED—See GI Manager L.P.; *U.S. Private*, pg. 1692
OCEANWIDE HOLDINGS CO., LTD.—See China Oceanwide Holdings Group Co., Ltd.; *Int'l*, pg. 1538
OCEANWIDE INC.—See GI Manager L.P.; *U.S. Private*, pg. 1692
OCEANWIDE SECURITIES COMPANY LIMITED—See Quam Plus International Financial Limited; *Int'l*, pg. 6153
OCEAN WILSONS HOLDINGS LIMITED; *Int'l*, pg. 5517
OCEAN WILSONS INVESTMENTS LIMITED—See Ocean Wilsons Holdings Limited; *Int'l*, pg. 5517
OCEAN WISE LIMITED—See Sincere Navigation Corporation; *Int'l*, pg. 6937
OCEAN YIELD ASA—See KKR & Co. Inc.; *U.S. Public*, pg. 1262
OCEASOFT SAS—See May River Capital, LLC; *U.S. Private*, pg. 2620
OCE BIO BVBA—See Perrigo Company plc; *Int'l*, pg. 5813
OCE-CANADA, INC.—See Canon Inc.; *Int'l*, pg. 1297

OCE-DEUTSCHLAND GMBH—See Canon Inc.; *Int'l*, pg. 1294
OCE-DEUTSCHLAND LEASING GMBH—See Canon Inc.; *Int'l*, pg. 1294
OCE-ESPANA S.A.—See Canon Inc.; *Int'l*, pg. 1294
OCE-FINLAND OY—See Canon Inc.; *Int'l*, pg. 1294
OCE-FRANCE FINANCEMENT S.A.—See Canon Inc.; *Int'l*, pg. 1294
OCE-FRANCE S.A.—See Canon Inc.; *Int'l*, pg. 1294
OCE-HUNGARIA KFT.—See Canon Inc.; *Int'l*, pg. 1294
OCENTURE LLC; *U.S. Private*, pg. 2992
OCE PORTUGAL EQUIPAMENTOS GRAFICOS S.A.—See Canon Inc.; *Int'l*, pg. 1295
OCE PRINTING SYSTEMS GMBH—See Canon Inc.; *Int'l*, pg. 1294
OCERA THERAPEUTICS, INC.—See Mallinckrodt Public Limited Company; *Int'l*, pg. 4663
OCE-RENTING S.A.—See Canon Inc.; *Int'l*, pg. 1294
OCEUS NETWORKS INC.—See Battle Investment Group LLC; *U.S. Private*, pg. 489
OC FINANCE CORPORATION—See Obayashi Corporation; *Int'l*, pg. 5508
OCG CONSULTING LTD.—See Recruit Holdings Co., Ltd.; *Int'l*, pg. 6240
OCHANOMIZU SEMINAR CO., LTD.—See EQT AB; *Int'l*, pg. 2467
O'CHARLEY'S INC.—See Fidelity National Financial, Inc.; *U.S. Public*, pg. 830
OCH CO., LTD.—See TECHMATRIX CORPORATION; *Int'l*, pg. 7505
OCH HOSPITALITY AND SERVICE JOINT STOCK COMPANY; *Int'l*, pg. 5518
OCHIAI MANUFACTURING CO., LTD.—See MITSUBA Corporation; *Int'l*, pg. 4929
OCHI HOLDINGS CO., LTD.; *Int'l*, pg. 5518
OCHIN, INC.; *U.S. Private*, pg. 2992
OCHOA AG UNLIMITED FOODS, INC.; *U.S. Private*, pg. 2992
OCHOCO LUMBER COMPANY; *U.S. Private*, pg. 2992
OCH ORTOPEDI AS—See Ossur hf; *Int'l*, pg. 5653
OCHRANA A BEZPECNOST SE AS—See Enel S.p.A.; *Int'l*, pg. 2412
OCHRESOFT TECHNOLOGIES LTD.—See Daily Mail & General Trust plc; *Int'l*, pg. 1938
OCHSNER-ACADIA, LLC—See Acadia Healthcare Company, Inc.; *U.S. Public*, pg. 29
OCHSNER HEALTH SYSTEM; *U.S. Private*, pg. 2992
OCHSNER MEDICAL CENTER-NORTH SHORE LLC—See Ochsner Health System; *U.S. Private*, pg. 2992
OCHSNER SYSTEM PROTECTION COMPANY; *U.S. Private*, pg. 2992
OCHS OIL COMPANY; *U.S. Private*, pg. 2992
OCH-ZIFF CAPITAL MANAGEMENT HONG KONG LIMITED—See Rithm Capital Corp.; *U.S. Public*, pg. 1800
OCH-ZIFF MANAGEMENT EUROPE LIMITED—See Rithm Capital Corp.; *U.S. Public*, pg. 1800
OCI AGRO BV—See OCI N.V.; *Int'l*, pg. 5519
OCI ALABAMA LLC—See OCI Holdings Co., Ltd.; *Int'l*, pg. 5519
OCI ASSOCIATES, INC.—See Blackstone Inc.; *U.S. Public*, pg. 355
OCI CHEMICAL CORPORATION—See OCI Holdings Co., Ltd.; *Int'l*, pg. 5519
OCI CHINA CO., LTD.—See OCI Holdings Co., Ltd.; *Int'l*, pg. 5519
OCI CO., LTD. - GUNSAN PLANT—See OCI Holdings Co., Ltd.; *Int'l*, pg. 5519
OCI CO., LTD. - GWANGYANG PLANT—See OCI Holdings Co., Ltd.; *Int'l*, pg. 5519
OCI CO., LTD. - IKSAN INSULATION PLANT—See OCI Holdings Co., Ltd.; *Int'l*, pg. 5519
OCI CO., LTD. - IKSAN PLANT—See OCI Holdings Co., Ltd.; *Int'l*, pg. 5519
OCI CO., LTD. - INCHEON PLANT—See HJ Shipbuilding & Construction Company, Ltd.; *Int'l*, pg. 3428
OCI CO., LTD. - POHANG PLANT—See OCI Holdings Co., Ltd.; *Int'l*, pg. 5519
OCI CO., LTD.; *Int'l*, pg. 5519
OCI DREAM CO., LTD.—See OCI Co., Ltd.; *Int'l*, pg. 5519
OCI HOLDINGS CO., LTD.; *Int'l*, pg. 5519
OCI INC.; *U.S. Private*, pg. 2992
OCI INFORMATION & COMMUNICATION CO., LTD.—See OCI Holdings Co., Ltd.; *Int'l*, pg. 5519
OCI INTERNATIONAL CYPRUS—See OCI N.V.; *Int'l*, pg. 5519
OCI INTERNATIONAL HOLDINGS LIMITED; *Int'l*, pg. 5519
OCI JAPAN CO., LTD.—See OCI Holdings Co., Ltd.; *Int'l*, pg. 5519
OCI MATERIALS JAPAN CO., LTD.—See SK Materials Co., Ltd.; *Int'l*, pg. 6974
OCI MATERIALS TAIWAN CO., LTD.—See SK Materials Co., Ltd.; *Int'l*, pg. 6974
OCI MELAMINE AMERICAS INC.—See OCI N.V.; *Int'l*, pg. 5519
OCI MELAMINE B.V.—See OCI N.V.; *Int'l*, pg. 5519

OCIM SDN.BHD.—See OCI Holdings Co., Ltd.; *Int'l*, pg. 5519
O.C.I.M. S.R.L.—See Enovis Corporation; *U.S. Public*, pg. 771
OCIMUM BIOSOLUTIONS INC.—See Ocimum Biosolutions Ltd.; *Int'l*, pg. 5520
OCIMUM BIOSOLUTIONS LTD.; *Int'l*, pg. 5519
OCI N.V.; *Int'l*, pg. 5519
OCION WATER SCIENCES GROUP LTD.; *Int'l*, pg. 5520
OCI PARTNERS LP—See OCI N.V.; *Int'l*, pg. 5519
OCI POWER CO., LTD.—See OCI Holdings Co., Ltd.; *Int'l*, pg. 5519
OCI SE CO., LTD.—See OCI Holdings Co., Ltd.; *Int'l*, pg. 5519
OCI-SNF CO. LTD.—See SNF SAS; *Int'l*, pg. 7027
OCI SPECIALTY CO., LTD.—See OCI Holdings Co., Ltd.; *Int'l*, pg. 5519
OCI VIETNAM CO., LTD.—See OCI Holdings Co., Ltd.; *Int'l*, pg. 5519
OCI WYOMING CO.—See OCI Holdings Co., Ltd.; *Int'l*, pg. 5519
OCI WYOMING, L.P.—See OCI Holdings Co., Ltd.; *Int'l*, pg. 5519
O.C. JONES & SONS INC.; *U.S. Private*, pg. 2981
OCKERLUND INDUSTRIES, INC.; *U.S. Private*, pg. 2992
OCK GROUP BERHAD; *Int'l*, pg. 5520
OCK PHNOM PENH PTE. LTD.—See OCK Group Berhad; *Int'l*, pg. 5520
OCLARO, INC.—See Lumentum Holdings Inc.; *U.S. Public*, pg. 1348
OCLARO JAPAN, INC.—See Lumentum Holdings Inc.; *U.S. Public*, pg. 1348
OCLARO JAPAN K.K.—See Lumentum Holdings Inc.; *U.S. Public*, pg. 1348
OCLARO PHOTONICS, INC.—See Lumentum Holdings Inc.; *U.S. Public*, pg. 1348
OCLARO TECHNOLOGY, INC.—See Lumentum Holdings Inc.; *U.S. Public*, pg. 1348
OCLARO TECHNOLOGY LIMITED—See Lumentum Holdings Inc.; *U.S. Public*, pg. 1348
OCLARO TECHNOLOGY (SHENZHEN) CO., LTD.—See Lumentum Holdings Inc.; *U.S. Public*, pg. 1348
OC LATIN AMERICAN HOLDINGS GMBH—See Owens Corning; *U.S. Public*, pg. 1627
OCLC ASIA PACIFIC—See Online Computer Library Center, Inc.; *U.S. Private*, pg. 3026
OCLC B.V.—See Online Computer Library Center, Inc.; *U.S. Private*, pg. 3026
OCLC CANADA—See Online Computer Library Center, Inc.; *U.S. Private*, pg. 3026
OCLC FOREST PRESS—See Online Computer Library Center, Inc.; *U.S. Private*, pg. 3027
OCLC GMBH—See Online Computer Library Center, Inc.; *U.S. Private*, pg. 3027
OCL CHINA LIMITED—See Dalmia Bharat Limited; *Int'l*, pg. 1954
OCLC LATIN AMERICA AND THE CARIBBEAN—See Online Computer Library Center, Inc.; *U.S. Private*, pg. 3027
OCL CORPORATION—See Hitachi Zosen Corporation; *Int'l*, pg. 3412
OCLC PICA—See Online Computer Library Center, Inc.; *U.S. Private*, pg. 3027
OCL FINANCIAL SERVICES LLC—See Adtalem Global Education Inc.; *U.S. Public*, pg. 43
OCL INDIA LIMITED—See Dalmia Bharat Limited; *Int'l*, pg. 1954
OCL IRON AND STEEL LIMITED; *Int'l*, pg. 5520
THE OC LUGO CO., INC.—See Madison Industries Holdings LLC; *U.S. Private*, pg. 2543
OCM HOLDCO, LLC—See Brookfield Corporation; *Int'l*, pg. 1182
OCM, INC.—See Okabe Co., Ltd.; *Int'l*, pg. 5544
OCM INVESTMENTS, LLC—See Brookfield Corporation; *Int'l*, pg. 1181
OCMULGEE ELECTRIC MEMBERSHIP CORPORATION; *U.S. Private*, pg. 2992
OCMULGEE FIELDS INC.; *U.S. Private*, pg. 2992
OC OERLIKON BALZERS AG—See OC Oerlikon Corporation AG; *Int'l*, pg. 5512
OC OERLIKON CORPORATION AG; *Int'l*, pg. 5512
OCONEE ELECTRIC MEMBERSHIP; *U.S. Private*, pg. 2992
OCONEE FEDERAL FINANCIAL CORP.; *U.S. Public*, pg. 1563
OCONEE FEDERAL SAVINGS & LOAN ASSOCIATON, INC.—See Oconee Federal Financial Corp.; *U.S. Public*, pg. 1563
OCONEE FINANCIAL CORP.; *U.S. Public*, pg. 1563
OCONEE PUBLISHING INC.—See Edwards Publications Inc.; *U.S. Private*, pg. 1342
OCONEE STATE BANK; *U.S. Private*, pg. 2992
THE O'CONNELL COMPANIES, INCORPORATED; *U.S. Private*, pg. 4087
THE O'CONNELL COMPANIES, INCORPORATED - UTILITIES DIVISION—See The O'Connell Companies, Incorporated; *U.S. Private*, pg. 4087

COMPANY NAME INDEX

O'CONNELL DEVELOPMENT GROUP INC.—See The O'Connell Companies, Incorporated; *U.S. Private*, pg. 4087
O'CONNELL ELECTRIC COMPANY, INC.; *U.S. Private*, pg. 2977
O'CONNELL ELECTRIC COMPANY, INC.—See O'Connell Electric Company, Inc.; *U.S. Private*, pg. 2977
O'CONNELL & GOLDBERG; *U.S. Private*, pg. 2977
O'CONNELL LANDSCAPE MAINTENANCE; *U.S. Private*, pg. 2977
O'CONNELL OIL ASSOCIATES INC.; *U.S. Private*, pg. 2977
O'CONNELL PROPERTIES INC.—See The O'Connell Companies, Incorporated; *U.S. Private*, pg. 4087
O'CONNOR COMPANY INC.; *U.S. Private*, pg. 2978
O'CONNOR COMPANY; *U.S. Private*, pg. 2978
O'CONNOR CONSTRUCTORS INC.; *U.S. Private*, pg. 2978
O'CONNOR CONTAINER TRANSPORT LIMITED—See DBAY Advisors Limited; *Int'l*, pg. 1986
O'CONNOR DODGE CHRYSLER JEEP; *Int'l*, pg. 5502
O'CONNOR ENGINEERING—See The Carlyle Group Inc.; *U.S. Public*, pg. 2054
O'CONNOR GMC INC.; *U.S. Private*, pg. 2978
THE O'CONNOR GROUP; *U.S. Private*, pg. 4087
O'CONNOR HOSPITAL—See Daughters of Charity Health System; *U.S. Private*, pg. 1167
O'CONNOR OIL CORPORATION; *U.S. Private*, pg. 2978
O'CONNOR & PARTNERS, INC.; *U.S. Private*, pg. 2977
O'CONNOR'S ENGINEERING SDN. BHD.—See Yanlord Land Group Limited; *Int'l*, pg. 8562
O'CONNOR'S SINGAPORE PTE. LTD.—See Yanlord Land Group Limited; *Int'l*, pg. 8562
O'CONNOR TELESERVICES INC.; *U.S. Private*, pg. 2978
O'CONNOR TITLE SERVICES, INC.—See Near North National Title, LLC; *U.S. Private*, pg. 2877
OCONOMOWOC BANCSHARES, INC.; *U.S. Public*, pg. 1563
OCONTO ELECTRIC COOPERATIVE; *U.S. Private*, pg. 2992
OCORIAN ADMINISTRATION (GUERNSEY) LIMITED—See Ocorian Limited; *Int'l*, pg. 5520
OCORIAN LIMITED; *Int'l*, pg. 5520
OCORIAN (UK) LTD.—See Ocorian Limited; *Int'l*, pg. 5520
OCOTILLO WINDPOWER, LP—See Duke Energy Corporation; *U.S. Public*, pg. 691
OCP ASIA, INC.—See Koch Industries, Inc.; *U.S. Private*, pg. 2335
OCP CONTRACTORS, INC.; *U.S. Private*, pg. 2992
OCP GROUP, INC.—See Blackstone Inc.; *U.S. Public*, pg. 355
OCP SA; *Int'l*, pg. 5520
OCP SENIOR CREDIT FUND; *Int'l*, pg. 5520
OCRA AEROSPACE (ISLE OF MAN) LIMITED—See OCRA (Isle of Man) Limited; *Int'l*, pg. 5521
OCRA (AUSTRALIA) HOLDINGS PTY LTD—See OCRA (Isle of Man) Limited; *Int'l*, pg. 5520
OCRA (BRUNEI) LIMITED—See OCRA (Isle of Man) Limited; *Int'l*, pg. 5520
OCRA (CYPRUS) LIMITED—See OCRA (Isle of Man) Limited; *Int'l*, pg. 5520
OCRA (HONG KONG) LIMITED—See OCRA (Isle of Man) Limited; *Int'l*, pg. 5520
OCRA (ISLE OF MAN) LIMITED; *Int'l*, pg. 5520
OCRA (LONDON) LIMITED—See OCRA (Isle of Man) Limited; *Int'l*, pg. 5520
OCRA (LUXEMBOURG) S.A.—See OCRA (Isle of Man) Limited; *Int'l*, pg. 5520
OCRA (MALTA) LIMITED—See OCRA (Isle of Man) Limited; *Int'l*, pg. 5520
OCRA MARINE (ISLE OF MAN) LIMITED—See OCRA (Isle of Man) Limited; *Int'l*, pg. 5521
OCRA (MAURITIUS) LIMITED—See OCRA (Isle of Man) Limited; *Int'l*, pg. 5520
OCRA (SEYCHELLES) LIMITED—See OCRA (Isle of Man) Limited; *Int'l*, pg. 5521
OCRA (SINGAPORE) PTE LIMITED—See OCRA (Isle of Man) Limited; *Int'l*, pg. 5521
OCRA SWITZERLAND SARL—See OCRA (Isle of Man) Limited; *Int'l*, pg. 5521
OC REAL ESTATE MANAGEMENT, LLC—See Obayashi Corporation; *Int'l*, pg. 5509
OCR GROUP BERHAD; *Int'l*, pg. 5520
OCR SERVICES INC.—See The Descartes Systems Group Inc.; *Int'l*, pg. 7636
O.C.S. FORESTRY UK LIMITED—See OCS Group Limited; *Int'l*, pg. 5521
OCS GROUP INTERNATIONAL LIMITED—See OCS Group Limited; *Int'l*, pg. 5521
OCS GROUP IRELAND LTD.—See OCS Group Limited; *Int'l*, pg. 5521
OCS GROUP LIMITED; *Int'l*, pg. 5521
OCS GROUP UK LTD.—See OCS Group Limited; *Int'l*, pg. 5521
OCS KALININGRAD—See Albert Ballin KG; *Int'l*, pg. 296
OCS NETHERLANDS BV—See OCS Group Limited; *Int'l*, pg. 5521
OCS NEW ZEALAND LTD.—See OCS Group Limited; *Int'l*, pg. 5521
OCS OCEAN CONTAINER SERVICES LTD.—See Albert Ballin KG; *Int'l*, pg. 296
OCS OCEAN CONTAINER SERVICES LTD.—See Albert Ballin KG; *Int'l*, pg. 296
OCS ONE COMPLETE SOLUTION LIMITED—See OCS Group Limited; *Int'l*, pg. 5521
OCS ONE COMPLETE SOLUTION LIMITED—See OCS Group Limited; *Int'l*, pg. 5521
OCS ONE COMPLETE SOLUTION LIMITED—See OCS Group Limited; *Int'l*, pg. 5521
OCS SERVICES PTY LIMITED—See OCS Group Limited; *Int'l*, pg. 5521
OCTAGON 88 RESOURCES, INC.; *Int'l*, pg. 5521
OCTAGON ACCESS—See The Interpublic Group of Companies, Inc.; *U.S. Public*, pg. 2103
OCTAGONAL PLC; *Int'l*, pg. 5521
OCTAGON AUTOMOTIVE, LLC—See Octagon Holdings, LLC; *U.S. Private*, pg. 2992
OCTAGON CREDIT INVESTORS, LLC—See Lin Yuan Investment Co., Ltd.; *Int'l*, pg. 4499
OCTAGON DEVELOPMENT CORPORATION—See Penney Group; *Int'l*, pg. 5787
OCTAGON EMEA—See The Interpublic Group of Companies, Inc.; *U.S. Public*, pg. 2103
OCTAGON HOLDINGS, LLC; *U.S. Private*, pg. 2992
OCTAGON PROCESS, L.L.C.—See Clariant AG; *Int'l*, pg. 1647
OCTAGON RESEARCH SOLUTIONS, INC.—See Accenture plc; *Int'l*, pg. 86
OCTAGON RESOURCES INC.; *U.S. Private*, pg. 2992
OCTAGON—See The Interpublic Group of Companies, Inc.; *U.S. Public*, pg. 2103
OCTAGON—See The Interpublic Group of Companies, Inc.; *U.S. Public*, pg. 2103
OCTAGON—See The Interpublic Group of Companies, Inc.; *U.S. Public*, pg. 2103
OCTAGON—See The Interpublic Group of Companies, Inc.; *U.S. Public*, pg. 2103
OCTAGON—See The Interpublic Group of Companies, Inc.; *U.S. Public*, pg. 2103
OCTAGON—See The Interpublic Group of Companies, Inc.; *U.S. Public*, pg. 2103
OCTAGON—See The Interpublic Group of Companies, Inc.; *U.S. Public*, pg. 2103
OCTAGON—See The Interpublic Group of Companies, Inc.; *U.S. Public*, pg. 2103
OCTAGON SYDNEY—See The Interpublic Group of Companies, Inc.; *U.S. Public*, pg. 2103
OCTAL CREDIT CAPITAL LIMITED; *Int'l*, pg. 5521
OCTANE BIOTECH INC.—See Lonza Group AG; *Int'l*, pg. 4554
OCTANE ENERGY, LLC; *U.S. Private*, pg. 2992
OCTANE FITNESS INTERNATIONAL, B.V.—See Johnson Health Tech. Co., Ltd.; *Int'l*, pg. 3991
OCTANE FITNESS, LLC—See Johnson Health Tech. Co., Ltd.; *Int'l*, pg. 3991
OCTANE FITNESS UK LTD—See Johnson Health Tech. Co., Ltd.; *Int'l*, pg. 3991
OCTANE PR; *Int'l*, pg. 5522
OCTANEX LTD; *Int'l*, pg. 5522
O.C. TANNER COMPANY INC.; *U.S. Private*, pg. 2981
O.C. TANNER MANUFACTURING, INC.—See O.C. Tanner Company Inc.; *U.S. Private*, pg. 2981
O.C. TANNER RECOGNITION COMPANY, INC.—See O.C. Tanner Company Inc.; *U.S. Private*, pg. 2981
OCTANTE SECURITIZADORA S.A.; *Int'l*, pg. 5522
OCTAPHARMA AG, O.Z.Z.O.—See Octapharma AG; *Int'l*, pg. 5522
OCTAPHARMA AG; *Int'l*, pg. 5522
OCTAPHARMA AS—See Octapharma AG; *Int'l*, pg. 5522
OCTAPHARMA AUSTRALIA PTY. LTD—See Octapharma AG; *Int'l*, pg. 5522
OCTAPHARMA BENELUX S.A./N.V.—See Octapharma AG; *Int'l*, pg. 5522
OCTAPHARMA BIOPHARMACEUTICALS GMBH—See Octapharma AG; *Int'l*, pg. 5522
OCTAPHARMA BRASIL LTDA—See Octapharma AG; *Int'l*, pg. 5522
OCTAPHARMA CANADA INC.—See Octapharma AG; *Int'l*, pg. 5522
OCTAPHARMA CZ S.R.O.—See Octapharma AG; *Int'l*, pg. 5522
OCTAPHARMA FRANCE S.A.S.—See Octapharma AG; *Int'l*, pg. 5522
OCTAPHARMA GESTAO ESTRATEGICA E OPERACIONAL, LDA.—See Octapharma AG; *Int'l*, pg. 5522
OCTAPHARMA GMBH—See Octapharma AG; *Int'l*, pg. 5522
OCTAPHARMA HANDELSGESELLSCHAFT M.B.H.—See Octapharma AG; *Int'l*, pg. 5522
OCTAPHARMA HELLA SA—See Octapharma AG; *Int'l*, pg. 5522
OCTAPHARMA ITALY SPA—See Octapharma AG; *Int'l*, pg. 5522
OCTAPHARMA LATIN AMERICA—See Octapharma AG; *Int'l*, pg. 5522
OCTAPHARMA LIMITED—See Octapharma AG; *Int'l*, pg. 5522
OCTAPHARMA NORDIC AB—See Octapharma AG; *Int'l*, pg. 5522
OCTAPHARMA NORDIC AB—See Octapharma AG; *Int'l*, pg. 5522
OCTAPHARMA NORDIC AB—See Octapharma AG; *Int'l*, pg. 5522
OCTAPHARMA PHARMAZEUTIKA PRODUKTIONSGES.M.B.H—See Octapharma AG; *Int'l*, pg. 5522
OCTAPHARMA PLASMA, INC.—See Octapharma AG; *Int'l*, pg. 5522
OCTAPHARMA POLAND SP. Z O.O.—See Octapharma AG; *Int'l*, pg. 5522
OCTAPHARMA PRODUKTIONSGESELLSCHAFT DEUTSCHLAND MBH—See Octapharma AG; *Int'l*, pg. 5522
OCTAPHARMA PRODUTOS FARMACEUTICOS, LDA.—See Octapharma AG; *Int'l*, pg. 5522
OCTAPHARMA PTE LTD—See Octapharma AG; *Int'l*, pg. 5522
OCTAPHARMA RUSSIA LLC—See Octapharma AG; *Int'l*, pg. 5522
OCTAPHARMA S.A. DE C.V.—See Octapharma AG; *Int'l*, pg. 5522
OCTAPHARMA S.A.—See Octapharma AG; *Int'l*, pg. 5522
OCTAPHARMA S.A.S.—See Octapharma AG; *Int'l*, pg. 5522
OCTAPHARMA SOUTH AFRICA (PTY) LTD—See Octapharma AG; *Int'l*, pg. 5522
OCTAPHARMA USA, INC.—See Octapharma AG; *Int'l*, pg. 5522
OCTAVA MINERALS LIMITED; *Int'l*, pg. 5522
OCTAVA S.A.; *Int'l*, pg. 5522
OCTAVIAN DE ARGENTINA S.A.—See Novomatic AG; *Int'l*, pg. 5467
OCTAVIUS PLANTATIONS LTD.; *Int'l*, pg. 5523
OCTAVUS GROUP LLC; *U.S. Private*, pg. 2992
OCTAWARE GULF FZE—See Octaware Technologies Limited; *Int'l*, pg. 5523
OCTAWARE TECHNOLOGIES LIMITED - KENT BRANCH—See Octaware Technologies Limited; *Int'l*, pg. 5523
OCTAWARE TECHNOLOGIES LIMITED; *Int'l*, pg. 5523
OCT EQUIPMENT LLC—See Associated Supply Company Inc.; *U.S. Private*, pg. 357
OCTEVA, S.A.S.—See ACS, Actividades de Construccion y Servicios, S.A.; *Int'l*, pg. 115
OCTEX LLC; *U.S. Private*, pg. 2993
OCTFOLIO PTY LTD—See HRL Holdings Limited; *Int'l*, pg. 3501
OCTIEF PTY LTD—See HRL Holdings Limited; *Int'l*, pg. 3501
OCTIO AS—See Equinor ASA; *Int'l*, pg. 2485
THE OCTOBER COMPANY, INC.; *U.S. Private*, pg. 4088
OCTOBER PHARMA; *Int'l*, pg. 5523
OCTO CONSULTING GROUP, INC.—See Arlington Capital Partners LLC; *U.S. Private*, pg. 328
OCTODEC INVESTMENTS LIMITED; *Int'l*, pg. 5523
OCTOPART INC.—See Altium Limited; *Int'l*, pg. 394
OCTOPEPPER SAS—See Symrise AG; *Int'l*, pg. 7380
OCTOPI BREWING, LLC; *U.S. Private*, pg. 2993
OCTOPUS AIM VCT PLC; *Int'l*, pg. 5523
OCTOPUS APOLLO VCT PLC; *Int'l*, pg. 5523
OCTOPUS CAPITAL LTD; *Int'l*, pg. 5523
OCTOPUS CARDS LIMITED—See MTR Corporation Limited; *Int'l*, pg. 5072
OCTOPUS CONNECT LIMITED—See MTR Corporation Limited; *Int'l*, pg. 5072
OCTOPUS ENERGY LTD—See Octopus Capital Ltd; *Int'l*, pg. 5523
OCTOPUS FUTURE GENERATIONS VCT PLC; *Int'l*, pg. 5523
OCTOPUS HOLDINGS LIMITED—See MTR Corporation Limited; *Int'l*, pg. 5072
OCTOPUS INTERNATIONAL PROJECTS LIMITED—See MTR Corporation Limited; *Int'l*, pg. 5072
OCTOPUS INVESTMENTS LIMITED—See MTR Corporation Limited; *Int'l*, pg. 5072
OCTOPUS PUBLISHING GROUP LTD.—See Vivendi SE; *Int'l*, pg. 8274
OCTOPUS REWARDS LIMITED—See MTR Corporation Limited; *Int'l*, pg. 5072
OCTOPUS ROBOTS SA; *Int'l*, pg. 5523
OCTOPUS TITAN VCT PLC; *Int'l*, pg. 5523
OCTOROCKET PTE. LTD.—See Singapore Press Holdings Ltd.; *Int'l*, pg. 6942
OCTO TECHNOLOGY PTY. LTD.—See Accenture plc; *Int'l*, pg. 87
OCTO TECHNOLOGY SA—See Accenture plc; *Int'l*, pg. 87
OCTO TECHNOLOGY SA—See Accenture plc; *Int'l*, pg. 84
OCTO TELEMATICS SPA—See Renova Group; *Int'l*, pg. 6285
OCUGEN, INC.; *U.S. Public*, pg. 1563
OCULAR THERAPEUTIX, INC.; *U.S. Public*, pg. 1563
OCULIS HOLDING AG; *Int'l*, pg. 5523
OCULIS OPERATIONS SARL—See Oculis Holding AG; *Int'l*, pg. 5523

OCULIS HOLDING AG　　　　　　　　　　　　　　　　　　　　　　　　CORPORATE AFFILIATIONS

OCULUS INNOVATIVE SCIENCES NETHERLANDS B.V.—See Sonoma Pharmaceuticals, Inc.; *U.S. Public*, pg. 1909
OCULUS TECHNOLOGIES OF MEXICO, S.A. DE C.V.—See Sonoma Pharmaceuticals, Inc.; *U.S. Public*, pg. 1909
OCULUS VISIONTECH INC.; *Int'l*, pg. 5523
OCULUS VR, LLC—See Meta Platforms, Inc.; *U.S. Public*, pg. 1427
OCUMENSION THERAPEUTICS (SHANGHAI) CO., LTD.; *Int'l*, pg. 6860
OCUPHIRE PHARMA, INC.; *U.S. Public*, pg. 1564
OCUSOFT, INC.; *U.S. Private*, pg. 2993
OCV CHAMBERY INTERNATIONAL—See Owens Corning; *U.S. Public*, pg. 1627
OCV DISTRIBUTION ANZ PTY LTD—See Owens Corning; *U.S. Public*, pg. 1627
OCV FABRICS US, INC.—See Owens Corning; *U.S. Public*, pg. 1627
OCV MEXICO S. DE R.L. DE C.V.—See Owens Corning; *U.S. Public*, pg. 1627
OCV REINFORCEMENTS ALCALA SPAIN, S.L.—See Owens Corning; *U.S. Public*, pg. 1627
OCV REINFORCEMENTS (HANGZHOU) CO., LTD.—See Owens Corning; *U.S. Public*, pg. 1627
OC WEEKLY, LP—See Village Voice Media Holdings, LLC; *U.S. Private*, pg. 4384
O.C. WELCH FORD LINCOLN INC.; *U.S. Private*, pg. 2981
OCWEN LOAN SERVICING, LLC—See Onity Group Inc.; *U.S. Public*, pg. 1604
OCWEN MORTGAGE SERVICING, INC.—See Onity Group Inc.; *U.S. Public*, pg. 1604
OCZ STORAGE SOLUTIONS, INC.—See Japan Industrial Partners, Inc.; *Int'l*, pg. 3891
OCZ TECHNOLOGY LIMITED—See Japan Industrial Partners, Inc.; *Int'l*, pg. 3891
OD6 METALS LIMITED; *Int'l*, pg. 5523
ODAAT OIL CORP.—See Waskahigan Oil & Gas Corp.; *Int'l*, pg. 8352
ODAKYU AGENCY CO., LTD.—See Odakyu Electric Railway Co., Ltd.; *Int'l*, pg. 5524
ODAKYU BUILDING SERVICE CO., LTD—See Odakyu Electric Railway Co., Ltd.; *Int'l*, pg. 5524
ODAKYU DEPARTMENT STORE CO., LTD.—See Odakyu Electric Railway Co., Ltd.; *Int'l*, pg. 5524
ODAKYU ELECTRIC RAILWAY CO., LTD.; *Int'l*, pg. 5523
ODAKYU HAKONE HIGHWAY BUS CO., LTD—See Odakyu Electric Railway Co., Ltd.; *Int'l*, pg. 5524
ODAKYU HOTELS CO., LTD.—See Odakyu Electric Railway Co., Ltd.; *Int'l*, pg. 5524
ODAKYU HOUSING CO., LTD.—See Odakyu Electric Railway Co., Ltd.; *Int'l*, pg. 5524
ODAKYU KOUTSU CO., LTD.—See Odakyu Electric Railway Co., Ltd.; *Int'l*, pg. 5524
ODAKYU LANDFLORA CO., LTD.—See Hibiya-Kadan Floral Co., Ltd.; *Int'l*, pg. 3383
ODAKYU REAL ESTATE CO., LTD—See Odakyu Electric Railway Co., Ltd.; *Int'l*, pg. 5524
ODAKYU RESORTS CO., LTD—See Odakyu Electric Railway Co., Ltd.; *Int'l*, pg. 5524
ODAKYU SHOJI CO., LTD—See Odakyu Electric Railway Co., Ltd.; *Int'l*, pg. 5524
ODAKYU SIGHTSEEING SERVICE CENTER ODAWARA—See Odakyu Electric Railway Co., Ltd.; *Int'l*, pg. 5524
O'DANIEL MOTORSALES INC.; *U.S. Private*, pg. 2978
ODA PRIMARY HEALTH CARE NETWORK; *U.S. Private*, pg. 2993
ODAS ELEKTRIK URETIM VE SANAYI TICARET AS; *Int'l*, pg. 5524
ODATE ECOMANAGE CORPORATION—See Hitachi Zosen Corporation; *Int'l*, pg. 3412
ODAWARA AUTO-MACHINE MFG. CO., LTD; *Int'l*, pg. 5524
ODAWARA AUTOMATION, INC.—See Odawara Engineering Co., Ltd.; *Int'l*, pg. 5524
ODAWARA AUTOMATION NAGAOKA CO., LTD.—See Odawara Engineering Co., Ltd.; *Int'l*, pg. 5524
ODAWARA ENGINEERING CO., LTD.; *Int'l*, pg. 5524
ODAWARA ENGINEERING (GUANGZHOU) CO., LTD.—See Odawara Engineering Co., Ltd.; *Int'l*, pg. 5524
O'DAY EQUIPMENT, INC.; *U.S. Private*, pg. 2978
ODAY PTE. LTD.—See IPC Corporation Ltd.; *Int'l*, pg. 3796
ODC CONSTRUCTION, LLC—See Asahi Kasei Corporation; *Int'l*, pg. 595
ODC NIMBUS INC—See Dubilier & Company, Inc.; *U.S. Private*, pg. 1283
ODCOMBE PRESS LP—See Apax Partners LLP; *Int'l*, pg. 502
ODCOMBE PRESS LP—See TowerBrook Capital Partners, L.P.; *U.S. Private*, pg. 4195
ODCO SAS—See Delta Plus Group; *Int'l*, pg. 2020
ODD BURGER CORPORATION; *Int'l*, pg. 5524
ODDCAST, INC.; *U.S. Private*, pg. 2993
ODDFELLOWS/DENTSU HOLDINGS PTY LTD.—See Dentsu Group Inc.; *Int'l*, pg. 2036

ODD FELLOWS HOME OF PENNSYLVANIA; *U.S. Private*, pg. 2993
ODDITY TECH LTD.; *Int'l*, pg. 5524
ODD LONDON LIMITED—See Next 15 Group plc; *Int'l*, pg. 5246
ODD MOLLY INC.—See Logistea AB; *Int'l*, pg. 4542
ODDO BHF AKTIENGESELLSCHAFT—See ODDO BHF SCA; *Int'l*, pg. 5524
ODDO BHF SCA; *Int'l*, pg. 5524
ODDWAY FILM & TELEVISION AB—See Shortcut Media AB; *Int'l*, pg. 6860
ODEA BANK AS; *Int'l*, pg. 5525
ODEBRECHT ADMINISTRADORA E CORRETORA DE SEGUROS LTDA.—See Novonor S.A.; *Int'l*, pg. 5470
ODEBRECHT ANGOLA LTDA.—See Novonor S.A.; *Int'l*, pg. 5470
ODEBRECHT ANGOLA LTD.—See Novonor S.A.; *Int'l*, pg. 5470
ODEBRECHT ANGOLA - PROJECTOS E SERVICOS LTDA—See Novonor S.A.; *Int'l*, pg. 5470
ODEBRECHT-CASSIDIAN DEFESA S.A—See Airbus SE; *Int'l*, pg. 242
ODEBRECHT CONSTRUCTION, INC.—See Novonor S.A.; *Int'l*, pg. 5470
ODEBRECHT ENGENHARIA DE PROJETOS—See Novonor S.A.; *Int'l*, pg. 5470
ODEBRECHT OIL AND GAS S.A.—See Novonor S.A.; *Int'l*, pg. 5470
ODEBRECHT PERU INGENIERIA Y CONSTRUCCION S.A.C.—See Novonor S.A.; *Int'l*, pg. 5470
ODEBRECHT REALIZACOES IMOBILIARIAS—See Novonor S.A.; *Int'l*, pg. 5470
ODECEE PTY LIMITED—See Cognizant Technology Solutions Corporation; *U.S. Public*, pg. 525
ODELIC COMPANY LIMITED; *Int'l*, pg. 5525
ODELL PUBLISHING INC; *U.S. Private*, pg. 2993
ODELO DEUTSCHLAND GMBH—See Odelo GmbH; *Int'l*, pg. 5525
ODELO GMBH; *Int'l*, pg. 5525
ODELO LED GMBH—See Odelo GmbH; *Int'l*, pg. 5525
ODELO SLOVENIJA D.O.O.—See Odelo GmbH; *Int'l*, pg. 5525
ODENBERG B.V.—See Tomra Systems ASA; *Int'l*, pg. 7802
ODEN MARKETING AND DESIGN; *U.S. Private*, pg. 2993
ODENSE MARCIPAN A/S—See Orkla ASA; *Int'l*, pg. 5638
ODENSE STEEL SHIPYARD LTD.—See A.P. Moller-Maersk A/S; *Int'l*, pg. 27
ODEON CINEMAS LTD.—See Terra Firma Capital Partners Ltd.; *Int'l*, pg. 7566
ODEON FILM AG—See Tele Munchen Fernseh GmbH + Co. Produktionsgesellschaft; *Int'l*, pg. 7528
ODEPREV ODEBRECHT PREVIDENCIA—See Novonor S.A.; *Int'l*, pg. 5470
ODESCO INDUSTRIAL SERVICES, INC.—See Carylon Corporation; *U.S. Private*, pg. 777
THE ODESSA AMERICAN—See AIM Media Texas, LLC; *U.S. Private*, pg. 133
ODESSA CABLE PLANT ODESKABEL PJSC; *Int'l*, pg. 5525
ODESSA MINERALS LIMITED; *Int'l*, pg. 5525
ODESSA PACKER SERVICE, INC.—See Intervale Capital, LLC; *U.S. Private*, pg. 2127
ODESSA PUMPS AND EQUIPMENT INC.—See DNOW Inc.; *U.S. Public*, pg. 671
ODESSA REGIONAL MEDICAL CENTER—See Steward Health Care System LLC; *U.S. Private*, pg. 3810
ODESSA TRADING COMPANY INC.—See Ritzville Warehouse Co. Inc.; *U.S. Private*, pg. 3442
ODESSA UNION WAREHOUSE CO-OP; *U.S. Private*, pg. 2993
ODESSOS SHIPREPAIR YARD S.A.; *Int'l*, pg. 5525
ODESUS INC.; *U.S. Private*, pg. 2993
ODEWALD & COMPAGNIE GESELLSCHAFT FUR BETEILIGUNGEN MBH; *Int'l*, pg. 5525
ODFJELL AHRENKIEL EUROPE GMBH—See Odfjell SE; *Int'l*, pg. 5526
ODFJELL ARABIA DRILLING SERVICES LLC—See Odfjell Technology Ltd.; *Int'l*, pg. 5526
ODFJELL ARGENTINA SA—See Odfjell SE; *Int'l*, pg. 5525
ODFJELL ASIA II PTE. LTD.—See Odfjell SE; *Int'l*, pg. 5525
ODFJELL AUSTRALIA PTY LTD.—See Odfjell SE; *Int'l*, pg. 5525
ODFJELL BRASIL-REPRESENTACOES LTDA—See Odfjell SE; *Int'l*, pg. 5525
ODFJELL CHEMICAL TANKERS AS—See Odfjell SE; *Int'l*, pg. 5526
ODFJELL CHEMICAL TANKERS II AS—See Odfjell SE; *Int'l*, pg. 5526
ODFJELL CHEMICAL TANKERS NETHERLANDS BV—See Odfjell SE; *Int'l*, pg. 5526
ODFJELL DRILLING LTD.; *Int'l*, pg. 5525
ODFJELL DRILLING PHILIPPINES CORPORATION—See Odfjell Drilling Ltd.; *Int'l*, pg. 5525
ODFJELL DRILLING (UK) LTD.—See Odfjell Drilling Ltd.; *Int'l*, pg. 5525
ODFJELL HOLDINGS (US) INC.—See Odfjell SE; *Int'l*, pg. 5526

ODFJELL JAPAN LTD.—See Odfjell SE; *Int'l*, pg. 5526
ODFJELL KOREA LTD.—See Odfjell SE; *Int'l*, pg. 5526
ODFJELL MANAGEMENT CONSULTANCY (SHANGHAI) CO LTD—See Odfjell SE; *Int'l*, pg. 5526
ODFJELL MANAGEMENT PHILIPPINES INC.—See Odfjell SE; *Int'l*, pg. 5526
ODFJELL MARITIME SERVICES AS—See Odfjell SE; *Int'l*, pg. 5526
ODFJELL NETHERLANDS BV—See Odfjell SE; *Int'l*, pg. 5526
ODFJELL OFFSHORE LTD.—See Odfjell Drilling Ltd.; *Int'l*, pg. 5525
ODFJELL PERU S.A.C.—See Odfjell SE; *Int'l*, pg. 5526
ODFJELL PROJECTS AS—See Odfjell SE; *Int'l*, pg. 5526
ODFJELL SEACHEM AS—See Odfjell SE; *Int'l*, pg. 5526
ODFJELL SEACHEM SOUTH AFRICA (PTY) LTD.—See Odfjell SE; *Int'l*, pg. 5526
ODFJELL SE; *Int'l*, pg. 5525
ODFJELL SHIP MANAGEMENT (PHILIPPINES) INC—See Odfjell SE; *Int'l*, pg. 5526
ODFJELL SINGAPORE PTE. LTD.—See Odfjell SE; *Int'l*, pg. 5526
ODFJELL TANKERS EUROPE AS—See Odfjell SE; *Int'l*, pg. 5526
ODFJELL TECHNOLOGY AS—See Odfjell Technology Ltd.; *Int'l*, pg. 5526
ODFJELL TECHNOLOGY LTD.; *Int'l*, pg. 5526
ODFJELL TERMINALS AS—See Odfjell SE; *Int'l*, pg. 5526
ODFJELL TERMINALS B.V.—See Odfjell SE; *Int'l*, pg. 5526
ODFJELL TERMINALS (DALIAN) CO LTD.—See Odfjell SE; *Int'l*, pg. 5526
ODFJELL TERMINALS EMEA B.V.—See Odfjell SE; *Int'l*, pg. 5526
ODFJELL TERMINALS (HOUSTON) INC.—See Odfjell SE; *Int'l*, pg. 5526
ODFJELL TERMINALS (JIANGYIN) CO LTD.—See Yangzijiang Shipbuilding (Holdings) Ltd; *Int'l*, pg. 8561
ODFJELL TERMINALS (ROTTERDAM) B.V.—See Odfjell SE; *Int'l*, pg. 5526
ODFJELL USA (HOUSTON) INC.—See Odfjell SE; *Int'l*, pg. 5526
ODFJELL WELL SERVICES AS—See Odfjell Drilling Ltd.; *Int'l*, pg. 5525
ODFJELL WELL SERVICES COOPERATIEF U.A.—See Odfjell Drilling Ltd.; *Int'l*, pg. 5525
ODFJELL WELL SERVICES EUROPE AS—See Odfjell Drilling Ltd.; *Int'l*, pg. 5525
ODFJELL WELL SERVICES LTD.—See Odfjell Drilling Ltd.; *Int'l*, pg. 5525
ODFJELL WELL SERVICES S.R.L.—See Odfjell Drilling Ltd.; *Int'l*, pg. 5525
ODFJELL WELL SERVICE (UK) LTD.—See Odfjell Drilling Ltd.; *Int'l*, pg. 5525
ODGERS BERNDTSON AG—See International Resources Group Ltd.; *Int'l*, pg. 3752
ODGERS BERNDTSON A/S—See International Resources Group Ltd.; *Int'l*, pg. 3752
ODGERS BERNDTSON RUSSIA—See International Resources Group Ltd.; *Int'l*, pg. 3752
ODGERS BERNDTSON SA (PTY) LTD—See International Resources Group Ltd.; *Int'l*, pg. 3752
ODGERS BERNDTSON UNTERNEHMENSBERATUNG GMBH—See International Resources Group Ltd.; *Int'l*, pg. 3752
ODIER EXCURSIONS, S.A.—See Mobico Group PLC.; *Int'l*, pg. 5009
ODIN BREWING CO.; *U.S. Private*, pg. 2993
ODIN ENERGY LIMITED; *Int'l*, pg. 5526
ODIN METALS LIMITED; *Int'l*, pg. 5526
ODINSA—See Grupo Argos S.A.; *Int'l*, pg. 3121
ODIN TECHNOLOGIES—See Quake Global, Inc.; *U.S. Private*, pg. 3316
ODISHA HYDRO POWER CORPORATION LTD.; *Int'l*, pg. 5526
ODISHA POWER GENERATION CORPORATION LIMITED—See Odisha Hydro Power Corporation Ltd.; *Int'l*, pg. 5526
ODK SOLUTIONS COMPANY, LTD.; *Int'l*, pg. 5526
ODLANDER FREDRIKSON & CO. AB; *Int'l*, pg. 5527
ODLANDER FREDRIKSON SA—See Odlander Fredrikson & Co. AB; *Int'l*, pg. 5527
ODL EUROPE LTD.—See ODL Incorporated; *U.S. Private*, pg. 2993
ODLEWNIA ZELIWA BYDGOSZCZ SP. Z O.O.—See DI-HAG Holding GmbH; *Int'l*, pg. 2124
ODLEWNIE POLSKIE S.A.; *Int'l*, pg. 5527
ODL INCORPORATED; *U.S. Private*, pg. 2993
OD MEDICAL SOLUTIONS LLC—See The ODP Corporation; *U.S. Public*, pg. 2117
ODNEY ADVERTISING-FARGO—See Odney; *U.S. Private*, pg. 2993
ODNEY ADVERTISING-MINOT—See Odney; *U.S. Private*, pg. 2993
ODNEY; *U.S. Private*, pg. 2993
ODOM CONSTRUCTION SERVICES, INC.; *U.S. Private*, pg. 2993
THE ODOM CORPORATION; *U.S. Private*, pg. 4088
ODONATE THERAPEUTICS, INC.; *U.S. Public*, pg. 1564

COMPANY NAME INDEX

O'DONNELL LANDSCAPES, INC.; *U.S. Private*, pg. 2978
O'DONNELL METAL DECK, LLC.—See Slate Capital Group LLC; *U.S. Private*, pg. 3687
O'DONNELL & SONS CONSTRUCTION CO.—See Clarkson Construction Company; *U.S. Private*, pg. 915
O'DONNELL'S TERMITE & PEST CONTROL, INC.; *U.S. Private*, pg. 2978
O'DONNELL STRATEGIC INDUSTRIAL REIT, INC.; *U.S. Private*, pg. 2978
ODONTOPREV S.A.; *Int'l*, pg. 5527
ODOPOD, INC.—See Publicis Groupe S.A.; *Int'l*, pg. 6104
ODORSTAR TECHNOLOGY, LLC—See OneWater Marine Inc.; *U.S. Public*, pg. 1604
ODOR-TECH LLC—See Arkema S.A.; *Int'l*, pg. 569
THE ODP CORPORATION; *U.S. Public*, pg. 2117
ODRA LLOYD SP. Z O.O.—See OT Logistics S.A.; *Int'l*, pg. 5656
ODRA RHEIN LLOYD SP. O.O.—See OT Logistics S.A.; *Int'l*, pg. 5656
ODRATRANS PORTY SP. Z O.O.—See OT Logistics S.A.; *Int'l*, pg. 5656
ODS ELEKTRO-BIJELJINA A.D. BIJELJINA; *Int'l*, pg. 5527
ODS HEALTH PLAN INC.—See Health Services Group, Inc.; *U.S. Private*, pg. 1894
O.D. SNIDER & SON INCORPORATED; *U.S. Private*, pg. 2981
ODS TECHNOLOGIES LP—See Flutter Entertainment plc; *Int'l*, pg. 2715
ODU DENMARK APS—See ODU Steckverbindungssysteme GmbH & Co. KG; *Int'l*, pg. 5527
ODU FRANCE SARL—See ODU Steckverbindungssysteme GmbH & Co. KG; *Int'l*, pg. 5527
ODU ITALIA S.R.L.—See ODU Steckverbindungssysteme GmbH & Co. KG; *Int'l*, pg. 5527
ODU SCANDINAVIA AB—See ODU Steckverbindungssysteme GmbH & Co. KG; *Int'l*, pg. 5527
ODU (SHANGHAI) INTERNATIONAL TRADING CO., LTD.—See ODU Steckverbindungssysteme GmbH & Co. KG; *Int'l*, pg. 5527
ODU STECKVERBINDUNGSSYSTEME GMBH & CO. KG; *Int'l*, pg. 5527
ODU-UK LTD.—See ODU Steckverbindungssysteme GmbH & Co. KG; *Int'l*, pg. 5527
ODU-USA INC.—See ODU Steckverbindungssysteme GmbH & Co. KG; *Int'l*, pg. 5527
ODW LOGISTICS INC.; *U.S. Private*, pg. 2993
ODYNE CORP.; *U.S. Private*, pg. 2993
ODYSIGHT.AI INC.; *Int'l*, pg. 5527
ODYSSEAN INVESTMENT TRUST PLC; *Int'l*, pg. 5527
ODYSSEY AMERICA REINSURANCE CORPORATION—See Fairfax Financial Holdings Limited; *Int'l*, pg. 2607
ODYSSEY CORPORATION LTD.; *Int'l*, pg. 5527
ODYSSEY DEVELOPMENT, INC.; *U.S. Private*, pg. 2993
ODYSSEY ENTERPRISES, INC.; *U.S. Private*, pg. 2993
ODYSSEY EUROPE AS—See Novalpina Capital LLP; *Int'l*, pg. 5455
ODYSSEY FINANCIAL TECHNOLOGIES S.A.—See Temenos AG; *Int'l*, pg. 7554
ODYSSEY GOLD LTD; *Int'l*, pg. 5527
ODYSSEY HEALTHCARE OF SOUTH TEXAS, LLC—See Apollo Global Management, Inc.; *U.S. Public*, pg. 156
ODYSSEY HEALTH, INC.; *U.S. Public*, pg. 1564
ODYSSEY HOUSE; *U.S. Private*, pg. 2994
ODYSSEY INDIA LTD.—See Deccan Chronicle Holdings Ltd.; *Int'l*, pg. 1999
ODYSSEY INDUSTRIES, LLC—See AIP, LLC; *U.S. Private*, pg. 133
ODYSSEY INSURANCE, INC.—See Howden Group Holdings Limited; *Int'l*, pg. 3494
ODYSSEY INTERACTIVE LIMITED—See Hasgrove plc; *Int'l*, pg. 3283
ODYSSEY INTERNATIONAL LLC—See Odyssey Logistics & Technology Corp.; *U.S. Private*, pg. 2996
ODYSSEY INVESTMENT PARTNERS, LLC; *U.S. Private*, pg. 2994
ODYSSEY LOGISTICS EUROPE BVBA—See Odyssey Logistics & Technology Corp.; *U.S. Private*, pg. 2996
ODYSSEY LOGISTICS & TECHNOLOGY CORP.; *U.S. Private*, pg. 2996
ODYSSEY MAGAZINE PUBLISHING GROUP INC.—See Chatham Asset Management, LLC; *U.S. Private*, pg. 860
ODYSSEY MANUFACTURING CO.; *U.S. Private*, pg. 2996
ODYSSEY MARINE ENTERTAINMENT, INC.—See Odyssey Marine Exploration, Inc.; *U.S. Public*, pg. 1564
ODYSSEY MARINE EXPLORATION, INC.; *U.S. Public*, pg. 1564
ODYSSEY OVERLAND—See Odyssey Logistics & Technology Corp.; *U.S. Private*, pg. 2996
ODYSSEY PICTURES CORPORATION; *U.S. Private*, pg. 2996
ODYSSEY RE HOLDINGS CORP.—See Fairfax Financial Holdings Limited; *Int'l*, pg. 2607
ODYSSEY REINSURANCE COMPANY—See Fairfax Financial Holdings Limited; *Int'l*, pg. 2607
ODYSSEY REINSURANCE EUROASIA DIVISION—See Fairfax Financial Holdings Limited; *Int'l*, pg. 2607
ODYSSEY RESOURCES LIMITED; *Int'l*, pg. 5527
ODYSSEY SEMICONDUCTOR TECHNOLOGIES, INC.—See Power Integrations, Inc.; *U.S. Public*, pg. 1705
ODYSSEY SYSTEMS; *U.S. Private*, pg. 2996
ODYSSEY TECHNICAL SOLUTIONS, LLC; *U.S. Private*, pg. 2996
ODYSSEY TECHNOLOGIES LTD.; *Int'l*, pg. 5527
ODYSSEY TELECOMMUNICATIONS, INC.; *U.S. Private*, pg. 2996
ODYSSEY VENTURES, INC.—See Thermo Fisher Scientific Inc.; *U.S. Public*, pg. 2149
ODYSSEYWARE—See Silver Lake Group, LLC; *U.S. Private*, pg. 3661
ODZACAR A.D.; *Int'l*, pg. 5527
ODZACAR A.D.; *Int'l*, pg. 5527
OE AQUITECH (M) SDN. BHD.—See Miyoshi Limited; *Int'l*, pg. 4996
OE AQUITECH (SINGAPORE) PTE. LTD.—See Miyoshi Limited; *Int'l*, pg. 4996
OEC BUSINESS INTERIORS, INC.; *U.S. Private*, pg. 2997
OEC GROUP INC.; *U.S. Private*, pg. 2997
OEC KANAZAWA CO., LTD.—See Osaki Electric Co., Ltd.; *Int'l*, pg. 5647
OEC LTD.—See Cresco, Ltd.; *Int'l*, pg. 1840
OEC MEDICAL SYSTEMS, INC.—See GE HealthCare Technologies Inc.; *U.S. Public*, pg. 909
OECO LLC—See Parker Hannifin Corporation; *U.S. Public*, pg. 1643
OECONNECTION LLC—See Genstar Capital, LLC; *U.S. Private*, pg. 1678
OEC RECORDS MANAGEMENT COMPANY PRIVATE LIMITED—See Iron Mountain Incorporated; *U.S. Public*, pg. 1174
OEG, INC.—See MDU Resources Group, Inc.; *U.S. Public*, pg. 1410
OEGUSSA GMBH—See Umicore S.A./N.V.; *Int'l*, pg. 8024
OEH PERU LTD.—See LVMH Moet Hennessy Louis Vuitton SE; *Int'l*, pg. 4591
OEKB BUSINESS SERVICES GMBH—See Oesterreichische Kontrollbank AG; *Int'l*, pg. 5529
OEKB SUDOSTEUROPA HOLDING GES.M.B.H.—See Oesterreichische Kontrollbank AG; *Int'l*, pg. 5529
OEKB VERSICHERUNG AG—See Oesterreichische Kontrollbank AG; *Int'l*, pg. 5529
OEKOMETRIC GMBH—See Eurofins Scientific S.E.; *Int'l*, pg. 2551
OEM - ALI S.P.A—See Ali Holding S.r.l; *Int'l*, pg. 321
OEM AUTOMATIC AB—See OEM International AB; *Int'l*, pg. 5528
OEM AUTOMATIC AS—See OEM International AB; *Int'l*, pg. 5528
OEM AUTOMATIC A/S—See OEM International AB; *Int'l*, pg. 5528
OEM AUTOMATIC KFT—See OEM International AB; *Int'l*, pg. 5528
OEM AUTOMATIC KLITSO A/S—See OEM International AB; *Int'l*, pg. 5528
OEM AUTOMATIC LTD.—See OEM International AB; *Int'l*, pg. 5528
OEM AUTOMATIC OU—See OEM International AB; *Int'l*, pg. 5528
OEM AUTOMATIC OY—See OEM International AB; *Int'l*, pg. 5528
OEM AUTOMATIC (SHANGHAI) LTD.—See OEM International AB; *Int'l*, pg. 5528
OEM AUTOMATIC SIA—See OEM International AB; *Int'l*, pg. 5528
OEM AUTOMATIC SPOL. S R.O.—See OEM International AB; *Int'l*, pg. 5528
OEM AUTOMATIC SP. Z O. O.—See OEM International AB; *Int'l*, pg. 5528
OEM AUTOMATIC S.R.O.—See OEM International AB; *Int'l*, pg. 5528
OEM AUTOMATIC UAB—See OEM International AB; *Int'l*, pg. 5528
OEM CHINA DEVELOPMENT B.V.—See OEM International AB; *Int'l*, pg. 5528
O.E.M. CONTROLS, INC.; *U.S. Private*, pg. 2981
OEM EESTI OU—See OEM International AB; *Int'l*, pg. 5528
OEM ELECTRONICS AB—See OEM International AB; *Int'l*, pg. 5528
OEM ELECTRONICS OY—See OEM International AB; *Int'l*, pg. 5528
OEM ELECTRONICS PL—See OEM International AB; *Int'l*, pg. 5528
OEM ENERGY SP. Z O.O.—See CEZ, a.s.; *Int'l*, pg. 1428
OEMETA CHEMISCHE WERKE GMBH; *Int'l*, pg. 5528
OEMETA CR S.R.O.—See Oemeta Chemische Werke GmbH; *Int'l*, pg. 5528
OEMETA INC.—See Oemeta Chemische Werke GmbH; *Int'l*, pg. 5528
OEMETA NORTH AMERICA INC.—See Oemeta Chemische Werke GmbH; *Int'l*, pg. 5528
OEMETA POLSKA SP. Z O. O.—See Oemeta Chemische Werke GmbH; *Int'l*, pg. 5529
OEMETA SINGAPORE PTE LTD—See Oemeta Chemische Werke GmbH; *Int'l*, pg. 5529
OEMETA (UK) LIMITED—See Oemeta Chemische Werke GmbH; *Int'l*, pg. 5528
OEMETA (WUHAN) CO., LTD.—See Oemeta Chemische Werke GmbH; *Int'l*, pg. 5528
OE MEYER CO.; *U.S. Private*, pg. 2996
OEM FABRICATORS, INC.; *U.S. Private*, pg. 2997
OEM GROUP AUSTRIA—See OEM Group, Inc.; *U.S. Private*, pg. 2997
OEM GROUP EAST—See OEM Group, Inc.; *U.S. Private*, pg. 2997
OEM GROUP, INC.; *U.S. Private*, pg. 2997
OEM GROUP JAPAN CO., LTD.—See OEM Group, Inc.; *U.S. Private*, pg. 2997
OEM INTERNATIONAL AB; *Int'l*, pg. 5527
OEM MOTOR AB/OEM AUTOMATIC AB—See THK CO., LTD.; *Int'l*, pg. 7712
OEM MOTOR AB—See OEM International AB; *Int'l*, pg. 5528
OEM PRESS SYSTEMS, INC.; *U.S. Private*, pg. 2997
OEM PRESS SYSTEMS (SHENZHEN) CO., LTD.—See OEM Press Systems, Inc.; *U.S. Private*, pg. 2997
OEM REMANUFACTURING COMPANY INC.—See Finning International Inc.; *Int'l*, pg. 2676
OEM SOLUTIONS GROUP—See Caterpillar, Inc.; *U.S. Public*, pg. 453
OEM SOLUTIONS—See Owens Corning; *U.S. Public*, pg. 1627
OEM TRADING (SHANGHAI) CO., LTD.—See OEM International AB; *Int'l*, pg. 5528
OENEO SA; *Int'l*, pg. 5529
OENOLUXE WINES LIMITED—See Royal Century Resources Holdings Limited; *Int'l*, pg. 6411
OENON ASSET CORPORATION—See Oenon Holdings Inc; *Int'l*, pg. 5529
OENON HOLDINGS INC; *Int'l*, pg. 5529
OENON PRODUCT SUPPORT CO., LTD.—See Oenon Holdings Inc; *Int'l*, pg. 5529
OEP CAPITAL ADVISORS, L.P.; *U.S. Private*, pg. 2997
OE PHILIPPINES—See Orient EuroPharma Co., Ltd.; *Int'l*, pg. 5622
OEP, INC.—See Zurn Elkay Water Solutions Corporation; *U.S. Public*, pg. 2413
OE PLUS, LTD.—See Motorcar Parts of America, Inc.; *U.S. Public*, pg. 1477
OERLIKON BALZERS ARGENTINA SA—See OC Oerlikon Corporation AG; *Int'l*, pg. 5512
OERLIKON BALZERS COATING AUSTRIA GMBH—See OC Oerlikon Corporation AG; *Int'l*, pg. 5512
OERLIKON BALZERS COATING BENELUX N.V.—See OC Oerlikon Corporation AG; *Int'l*, pg. 5512
OERLIKON BALZERS COATING FRANCE SAS—See OC Oerlikon Corporation AG; *Int'l*, pg. 5512
OERLIKON BALZERS COATING GERMANY GMBH—See OC Oerlikon Corporation AG; *Int'l*, pg. 5512
OERLIKON BALZERS COATING INDIA LIMITED—See OC Oerlikon Corporation AG; *Int'l*, pg. 5512
OERLIKON BALZERS COATING KOREA CO. LTD.—See OC Oerlikon Corporation AG; *Int'l*, pg. 5512
OERLIKON BALZERS COATING LUXEMBOURG S.A R.L.—See OC Oerlikon Corporation AG; *Int'l*, pg. 5513
OERLIKON BALZERS COATING MEXICO, S.A. DE C.V.—See OC Oerlikon Corporation AG; *Int'l*, pg. 5513
OERLIKON BALZERS COATING POLAND SP. Z.O.O.—See OC Oerlikon Corporation AG; *Int'l*, pg. 5513
OERLIKON BALZERS COATING SA—See OC Oerlikon Corporation AG; *Int'l*, pg. 5513
OERLIKON BALZERS COATING SINGAPORE PTE. LTD.—See OC Oerlikon Corporation AG; *Int'l*, pg. 5513
OERLIKON BALZERS COATING—See OC Oerlikon Corporation AG; *Int'l*, pg. 5512
OERLIKON BALZERS COATING (SUZHOU) CO. LTD.—See OC Oerlikon Corporation AG; *Int'l*, pg. 5512
OERLIKON BALZERS COATING (THAILAND) CO. LTD.—See OC Oerlikon Corporation AG; *Int'l*, pg. 5512
OERLIKON BALZERS COATING UK LTD.—See OC Oerlikon Corporation AG; *Int'l*, pg. 5513
OERLIKON BALZERS COATING USA, INC.—See OC Oerlikon Corporation AG; *Int'l*, pg. 5513
OERLIKON BALZERS-ELAY COATING S.A.—See OC Oerlikon Corporation AG; *Int'l*, pg. 5513
OERLIKON BALZERS HARTEC GMBH—See OC Oerlikon Corporation AG; *Int'l*, pg. 5513
OERLIKON BALZERS KAPLAMA SANAYI VE TICARET LIMITED—See OC Oerlikon Corporation AG; *Int'l*, pg. 5513
OERLIKON BALZERS REVESTIMENTOS METALICOS LTDA—See OC Oerlikon Corporation AG; *Int'l*, pg. 5513
OERLIKON BALZERS SANDVIK COATING AB—See OC Oerlikon Corporation AG; *Int'l*, pg. 5513
OERLIKON BALZERS SANDVIK COATING AB—See Sandvik AB; *Int'l*, pg. 6530
OERLIKON BALZERS SANDVIK COATING OY—See OC Oerlikon Corporation AG; *Int'l*, pg. 5513
OERLIKON BALZERS SANDVIK COATING OY—See Sandvik AB; *Int'l*, pg. 6530

OEP CAPITAL ADVISORS, L.P.

OERLIKON BARMAG—See OC Oerlikon Corporation AG; *Int'l*, pg. 5514
OERLIKON BARMAG-SPINNZWIRN—See OC Oerlikon Corporation AG; *Int'l*, pg. 5514
OERLIKON (CHINA) TECHNOLOGY CO. LTD.—See OC Oerlikon Corporation AG; *Int'l*, pg. 5514
OERLIKON COATING SERVICES AUSTRIA—See OC Oerlikon Corporation AG; *Int'l*, pg. 5514
OERLIKON CONTRAVES GMBH—See Rheinmetall AG; *Int'l*, pg. 6323
OERLIKON CONTRAVES PTE LTD.—See Rheinmetall AG; *Int'l*, pg. 6323
OERLIKON CZECH S.R.O.—See OC Oerlikon Corporation AG; *Int'l*, pg. 5514
OERLIKON DEUTSCHLAND HOLDING GMBH—See OC Oerlikon Corporation AG; *Int'l*, pg. 5514
OERLIKON DEUTSCHLAND VERTRIEBS GMBH—See OC Oerlikon Corporation AG; *Int'l*, pg. 5514
OERLIKON ELDIM (HU) KFT.—See OC Oerlikon Corporation AG; *Int'l*, pg. 5513
OERLIKON ELDIM (NL) B.V.—See OC Oerlikon Corporation AG; *Int'l*, pg. 5513
OERLIKON FRANCE HOLDING SAS—See OC Oerlikon Corporation AG; *Int'l*, pg. 5514
OERLIKON FRICTION SYSTEMS DO BRASIL LTDA.—See OC Oerlikon Corporation AG; *Int'l*, pg. 5513
OERLIKON FRICTION SYSTEMS (GERMANY) GMBH—See OC Oerlikon Corporation AG; *Int'l*, pg. 5513
OERLIKON FRICTION SYSTEMS INDIA LIMITED—See OC Oerlikon Corporation AG; *Int'l*, pg. 5513
OERLIKON FRICTION SYSTEMS (US) INC.—See OC Oerlikon Corporation AG; *Int'l*, pg. 5513
OERLIKON GRAZIANO CZECH REPUBLIC—See OC Oerlikon Corporation AG; *Int'l*, pg. 5514
OERLIKON GRAZIANO GROUP S.P.A.—See OC Oerlikon Corporation AG; *Int'l*, pg. 5514
OERLIKON GRAZIANO S.P.A.—See OC Oerlikon Corporation AG; *Int'l*, pg. 5514
OERLIKON GRAZIANO SPA—See OC Oerlikon Corporation AG; *Int'l*, pg. 5514
OERLIKON GRAZIANO UNITED KINGDOM—See OC Oerlikon Corporation AG; *Int'l*, pg. 5514
OERLIKON IT SOLUTIONS AG—See OC Oerlikon Corporation AG; *Int'l*, pg. 5514
OERLIKON LEYBOLD VACUUM DRESDEN GMBH—See Atlas Copco AB; *Int'l*, pg. 683
OERLIKON LEYBOLD VACUUM GMBH—See Atlas Copco AB; *Int'l*, pg. 683
OERLIKON LEYBOLD VACUUM INDIA PVT. LTD—See Atlas Copco AB; *Int'l*, pg. 683
OERLIKON LEYBOLD VACUUM KOREA LTD.—See Atlas Copco AB; *Int'l*, pg. 684
OERLIKON LEYBOLD VACUUM (TIANJIN) INTERNATIONAL TRADE CO. LTD.—See Atlas Copco AB; *Int'l*, pg. 683
OERLIKON METAPLAS GMBH—See OC Oerlikon Corporation AG; *Int'l*, pg. 5513
OERLIKON METAPLAS GMBH—See OC Oerlikon Corporation AG; *Int'l*, pg. 5513
OERLIKON METCO AG—See OC Oerlikon Corporation AG; *Int'l*, pg. 5513
OERLIKON METCO (AUSTRALIA) PTY. LTD.—See OC Oerlikon Corporation AG; *Int'l*, pg. 5513
OERLIKON METCO (CANADA) INC.—See OC Oerlikon Corporation AG; *Int'l*, pg. 5513
OERLIKON METCO COATINGS GMBH—See OC Oerlikon Corporation AG; *Int'l*, pg. 5513
OERLIKON METCO COATINGS LTD.—See OC Oerlikon Corporation AG; *Int'l*, pg. 5513
OERLIKON METCO EUROPE GMBH—See OC Oerlikon Corporation AG; *Int'l*, pg. 5513
OERLIKON METCO EUROPE GMBH—See OC Oerlikon Corporation AG; *Int'l*, pg. 5513
OERLIKON METCO EUROPE GMBH—See OC Oerlikon Corporation AG; *Int'l*, pg. 5513
OERLIKON METCO (JAPAN) LTD.—See OC Oerlikon Corporation AG; *Int'l*, pg. 5513
OERLIKON METCO (SINGAPORE) PTE LTD.—See OC Oerlikon Corporation AG; *Int'l*, pg. 5513
OERLIKON METCO SURFACE TECHNOLOGY (SHANGHAI) CO. LTD.—See OC Oerlikon Corporation AG; *Int'l*, pg. 5513
OERLIKON METCO (UK) LIMITED—See OC Oerlikon Corporation AG; *Int'l*, pg. 5513
OERLIKON METCO (US) INC.—See OC Oerlikon Corporation AG; *Int'l*, pg. 5513
OERLIKON METCO (US) INC.—See OC Oerlikon Corporation AG; *Int'l*, pg. 5513
OERLIKON METCO (US) INC.—See OC Oerlikon Corporation AG; *Int'l*, pg. 5513
OERLIKON METCO WOKA GMBH—See OC Oerlikon Corporation AG; *Int'l*, pg. 5514
OERLIKON NEOMET LTD.—See OC Oerlikon Corporation AG; *Int'l*, pg. 5514
OERLIKON NEUMAG ZWEIGNIEDERLASSUNG DER OERLIKON TEXTILE GMBH & CO. KG—See OC Oerlikon Corporation AG; *Int'l*, pg. 5514

OERLIKON NIHON BALZERS COATING CO. LTD.—See OC Oerlikon Corporation AG; *Int'l*, pg. 5514
OERLIKON REAL ESTATE GMBH—See OC Oerlikon Corporation AG; *Int'l*, pg. 5514
OERLIKON SAURER ARBON AG—See OC Oerlikon Corporation AG; *Int'l*, pg. 5514
OERLIKON SAURER ARBON AG—See OC Oerlikon Corporation AG; *Int'l*, pg. 5514
OERLIKON SCANDINAVIA AB—See Lincoln Electric Holdings, Inc.; *U.S. Public*, pg. 1317
OERLIKON SCHLAFHORST ZWEIGNIEDERLASSUNG DER SAURER GMBH & CO.KG—See OC Oerlikon Corporation AG; *Int'l*, pg. 5514
OERLIKON SCHWEISSTECHNIK AG—See Lincoln Electric Holdings, Inc.; *U.S. Public*, pg. 1317
OERLIKON SCHWEISSTECHNIK GMBH—See Lincoln Electric Holdings, Inc.; *U.S. Public*, pg. 1317
OERLIKON SEA PTE. LTD.—See OC Oerlikon Corporation AG; *Int'l*, pg. 5514
OERLIKON SEGMENT MANMADE FIBERS CHINA—See OC Oerlikon Corporation AG; *Int'l*, pg. 5514
OERLIKON SINGAPORE PTE. LTD.—See Rheinmetall AG; *Int'l*, pg. 6323
OERLIKON SKANDINAVIEN AB—See Lincoln Electric Holdings, Inc.; *U.S. Public*, pg. 1317
OERLIKON SOLDADURA SA—See Lincoln Electric Holdings, Inc.; *U.S. Public*, pg. 1317
OERLIKON TEXTILE DO BRASIL MAQUINAS LTDA—See OC Oerlikon Corporation AG; *Int'l*, pg. 5515
OERLIKON TEXTILE FAR EAST LTD.—See OC Oerlikon Corporation AG; *Int'l*, pg. 5515
OERLIKON TEXTILE GMBH & CO. KG—See OC Oerlikon Corporation AG; *Int'l*, pg. 5515
OERLIKON TEXTILE INC.—See OC Oerlikon Corporation AG; *Int'l*, pg. 5515
OERLIKON TEXTILE INDIA PVT. LTD.—See OC Oerlikon Corporation AG; *Int'l*, pg. 5515
OERLIKON TRADING AG—See OC Oerlikon Corporation AG; *Int'l*, pg. 5515
OERLIKON USA HOLDING INC.—See OC Oerlikon Corporation AG; *Int'l*, pg. 5515
OERLIKON VACUUM HOLDING GMBH—See Atlas Copco AB; *Int'l*, pg. 684
OERLIKON VACUUM JAPAN—See OC Oerlikon Corporation AG; *Int'l*, pg. 5514
OERLIKON VACUUM ROMANIA KON TRADE SRL—See Atlas Copco AB; *Int'l*, pg. 684
OERLIKON VACUUM RUSSIAN FEDERATION GERTNER SERVICE GMBH—See Atlas Copco AB; *Int'l*, pg. 684
OERLIKON VACUUM TURKEY TEKSER A.S.—See Atlas Copco AB; *Int'l*, pg. 684
OERMESTER VAGYONVEDELMI NYRT; *Int'l*, pg. 5529
OERTEL SHEET METAL, INC.—See McCarthy Bush Corporation; *U.S. Private*, pg. 2626
OERTHER FOODS, INC.; *U.S. Private*, pg. 3000
OE SOLUTIONS AS—See Axel Johnson Gruppen AB; *Int'l*, pg. 763
OE SOLUTIONS CO., LTD.; *Int'l*, pg. 5527
OESTERREICHISCHE BANKNOTEN- UND SICHERHEITSDRUCK GMBH—See Oesterreichische Nationalbank; *Int'l*, pg. 5529
OESTERREICHISCHE KONTROLLBANK AG; *Int'l*, pg. 5529
OESTERREICHISCHE NATIONALBANK; *Int'l*, pg. 5529
OETERBETON N.V.—See CRH plc; *Int'l*, pg. 1845
OETIKER, INC.—See Oetiker Schweiz AG; *Int'l*, pg. 5529
OETIKER NY INC.—See Oetiker Schweiz AG; *Int'l*, pg. 5529
OETIKER SCHWEIZ AG; *Int'l*, pg. 5529
OETKER DATEN- UND INFORMATIONSVERARBEITUNG KG—See Dr. August Oetker KG; *Int'l*, pg. 2190
OETKER HOTEL MANAGEMENT COMPANY GMBH—See Dr. August Oetker KG; *Int'l*, pg. 2190
OETTINGER IMEX AG; *Int'l*, pg. 5529
OEVERMANN HOCHBAU GMBH—See Heijmans N.V.; *Int'l*, pg. 3323
OEVERMANN INGENIEURBAU GMBH—See Heijmans N.V.; *Int'l*, pg. 3323
OEVERMANN VERKEHRSWEGEBAU GMBH—See Heijmans N.V.; *Int'l*, pg. 3323
OEWA WASSER UND ABWASSER GMBH—See E.ON SE; *Int'l*, pg. 2253
O.E. WHEELS, LLC; *U.S. Private*, pg. 2981
OEX S.A.; *Int'l*, pg. 5530
OEZ SLOVAKIA, SPOL. S R.O.—See Siemens Aktiengesellschaft; *Int'l*, pg. 6887
OEZ S.R.O.—See Siemens Aktiengesellschaft; *Int'l*, pg. 6887
OFA BAMBERG GMBH—See INDUS Holding AG; *Int'l*, pg. 3663
O'FALLON CASTING, LLC; *U.S. Private*, pg. 2978
O'FALLON PROGRESS—See Chatham Asset Management, LLC; *U.S. Private*, pg. 866
OFB BETEILIGUNGEN GMBH—See Helaba Landesbank Hessen-Thuringen; *Int'l*, pg. 3328
OFB GKH GESELLSCHAFT FUR KOMMUNALBAU IN HESSEN MBH—See Helaba Landesbank Hessen-Thuringen; *Int'l*, pg. 3328

CORPORATE AFFILIATIONS

OFB PROJEKTENTWICKLUNG GMBH—See Helaba Landesbank Hessen-Thuringen; *Int'l*, pg. 3328
OFB REISEN GMBH—See Global Business Travel Group, Inc.; *U.S. Public*, pg. 941
OFC AVIATION FUEL SERVICES S.A.—See Motor Oil (Hellas) Corinth Refineries S.A.; *Int'l*, pg. 5054
OFD FOODS, LLC; *U.S. Private*, pg. 3000
OFELIA VARD AB—See Lundbeckfonden; *Int'l*, pg. 4583
OFER GROUP; *Int'l*, pg. 5530
OFER HI-TECH LTD.—See Ofer Group; *Int'l*, pg. 5530
OFF CAMPUS PARTNERS—See CoStar Group, Inc.; *U.S. Public*, pg. 586
OFFCN EDUCATION TECHNOLOGY CO., LTD.; *Int'l*, pg. 5530
OFFENBACHER AQUATICS INC.; *U.S. Private*, pg. 3001
OFFENHAUSER COMPANY; *U.S. Private*, pg. 3001
OFFEN PETROLEUM, LLC—See Court Square Capital Partners, L.P.; *U.S. Private*, pg. 1069
OFFENTLICHE LEBENSVERSICHERUNG BRAUNSCHWEIG—See Norddeutsche Landesbank Girozentrale; *Int'l*, pg. 5417
OFFERLE COOPERATIVE GRAIN & SUPPLY COMPANY; *U.S. Private*, pg. 3001
OFFERPAD SOLUTIONS INC.; *U.S. Public*, pg. 1564
OFF HIGHWAY BRAKES AND CONTROLS LTD—See ZF Friedrichshafen AG; *Int'l*, pg. 8641
OFFICE ADVAN INC.—See MITSUBA Corporation; *Int'l*, pg. 4929
OFFICE ANGELS LIMITED—See Adecco Group AG; *Int'l*, pg. 138
OFFICE BEACON LLC; *U.S. Private*, pg. 3001
OFFICE-BOERSE.DE INTERNET GMBH—See Konica Minolta, Inc.; *Int'l*, pg. 4260
OFFICE BRANDS LIMITED; *Int'l*, pg. 5530
OFFICE BUSINESS SYSTEMS, INC.—See BIS Digital, Inc.; *U.S. Private*, pg. 565
OFFICECENTRE EQUIPAMENTOS DE ESCRITORIO LDA—See Sycamore Partners Management, LP; *U.S. Private*, pg. 3897
OFFICE CONCEPTS INC.; *U.S. Private*, pg. 3001
OFFICE DEPOT ASIA HOLDING LIMITED—See The ODP Corporation; *U.S. Public*, pg. 2117
OFFICE DEPOT BS—See Aurelius Equity Opportunities SE & Co. KGaA; *Int'l*, pg. 709
OFFICE DEPOT BUSINESS SOLUTIONS DIVISION-NEW JERSEY—See The ODP Corporation; *U.S. Public*, pg. 2117
OFFICE DEPOT BUSINESS SOLUTIONS DIVISION—See The ODP Corporation; *U.S. Public*, pg. 2117
OFFICE DEPOT B.V.—See Aurelius Equity Opportunities SE & Co. KGaA; *Int'l*, pg. 709
OFFICE DEPOT DE MEXICO S.A. DE C.V.—See Grupo Gigante, S.A.B. de C.V.; *Int'l*, pg. 3130
OFFICE DEPOT DEUTSCHLAND GMBH—See Aurelius Equity Opportunities SE & Co. KGaA; *Int'l*, pg. 709
OFFICE DEPOT EUROPE B.V.—See Aurelius Equity Opportunities SE & Co. KGaA; *Int'l*, pg. 709
OFFICE DEPOT FRANCE SNC—See Aurelius Equity Opportunities SE & Co. KGaA; *Int'l*, pg. 709
OFFICE DEPOT GMBH—See Aurelius Equity Opportunities SE & Co. KGaA; *Int'l*, pg. 709
OFFICE DEPOT INTERNATIONAL BVBA—See Aurelius Equity Opportunities SE & Co. KGaA; *Int'l*, pg. 709
OFFICE DEPOT INTERNATIONAL (UK) LTD—See Aurelius Equity Opportunities SE & Co. KGaA; *Int'l*, pg. 709
OFFICE DEPOT IRELAND LIMITED—See Aurelius Equity Opportunities SE & Co. KGaA; *Int'l*, pg. 709
OFFICE DEPOT ITALIA S.R.L.—See JM Bruneau SAS; *Int'l*, pg. 3974
OFFICE DEPOT KOREA CO., LTD.—See Excelsior Capital Asia (HK) Limited; *Int'l*, pg. 2578
OFFICE DEPOT NETHERLANDS B.V.—See Aurelius Equity Opportunities SE & Co. KGaA; *Int'l*, pg. 709
OFFICE DEPOT OVERSEAS LIMITED—See The ODP Corporation; *U.S. Public*, pg. 2117
OFFICE DEPOT PUERTO RICO, LLC—See The ODP Corporation; *U.S. Public*, pg. 2117
OFFICE DEPOT SERVICE- UND BETEILIGUNGS-GMBH & CO. KG—See Aurelius Equity Opportunities SE & Co. KGaA; *Int'l*, pg. 709
OFFICE DEPOT S.R.O.—See PBS Holding AG; *Int'l*, pg. 5765
OFFICE DEPOT UK LIMITED—See Aurelius Equity Opportunities SE & Co. KGaA; *Int'l*, pg. 709
OFFICE ENVIRONMENTS INC.; *U.S. Private*, pg. 3001
OFFICE EQUIPMENT COMPANY OF MOBILE, INC.; *U.S. Private*, pg. 3001
OFFICE EQUIPMENT & SUPPLY; *U.S. Private*, pg. 3001
OFFICE & FLOORING WORX INC.; *U.S. Private*, pg. 3001
OFFICE FURNITURE CENTER, INC.; *U.S. Private*, pg. 3001
OFFICEFURNITURE.COM—See Franz Haniel & Cie. GmbH; *Int'l*, pg. 2763
OFFICE FURNITURE DEPOT, INC.—See Interior Fusion, LLC; *U.S. Private*, pg. 2111
OFFICE FURNITURE & DESIGN CONCEPTS, INC.; *U.S. Private*, pg. 3001

COMPANY NAME INDEX

OFFICE FURNITURE PARTNERSHIP; *U.S. Private*, pg. 3001
OFFICE FURNITURE RENTAL ALLIANCE LLC; *U.S. Private*, pg. 3001
OFFICE FURNITURE USA—See Business Interiors Inc.; *U.S. Private*, pg. 695
OFFICE GREEN LIMITED—See Restore plc; *Int'l*, pg. 6304
THE OFFICE GROUP LIMITED—See Blackstone Inc.; *U.S. Public*, pg. 361
THE OFFICE GURUS, LTD.—See Superior Group Of Companies, Inc.; *U.S. Public*, pg. 1966
OFFICE INSTALLERS INC.—See The Kane Company; *U.S. Private*, pg. 4064
OFFICE INTERIORS OF VIRGINIA, INC.—See Workplace Install Network, Inc.; *U.S. Private*, pg. 4564
OFFICE MANAGEMENT SYSTEMS INC.; *U.S. Private*, pg. 3001
OFFICEMAN OY—See Wulff-Group Plc; *Int'l*, pg. 8502
OFFICEMART OFFICE PROFESSIONAL SOLUTIONS SA—See AVE S.A.; *Int'l*, pg. 737
OFFICE MASTER INC.; *U.S. Private*, pg. 3001
OFFICE-MATE CORPORATION—See GSI Creos Corporation; *Int'l*, pg. 3145
OFFICEMATE INTERNATIONAL CORPORATION; *U.S. Private*, pg. 3002
OFFICEMATE OMNI FRANCHISES CO., LTD.—See COL Public Company Limited; *Int'l*, pg. 1697
OFFICEMATE SOFTWARE SOLUTIONS—See Vision Service Plan; *U.S. Private*, pg. 4391
OFFICEMAX AUSTRALIA LIMITED—See Platinum Equity, LLC; *U.S. Private*, pg. 3210
OFFICEMAX CANADA—See The ODP Corporation; *U.S. Public*, pg. 2117
OFFICEMAX INCORPORATED—See The ODP Corporation; *U.S. Public*, pg. 2117
OFFICEMAX NEW ZEALAND LIMITED—See Platinum Equity, LLC; *U.S. Private*, pg. 3210
OFFICEMAX NORTH AMERICA, INC.—See The ODP Corporation; *U.S. Public*, pg. 2117
OFFICE MOVERS INC.—See The Kane Company; *U.S. Private*, pg. 4064
OFFICE MOVERS OF FLORIDA LLC; *U.S. Private*, pg. 3001
OFFICE OPERATION CO. LTD.—See JUTEC Holdings Corporation; *Int'l*, pg. 4032
OFFICE & PROFESSIONAL EMPLOYEES INTERNATIONAL UNION; *U.S. Private*, pg. 3001
OFFICE PROPERTIES INCOME TRUST—See The RMR Group Inc.; *U.S. Public*, pg. 2126
OFFICE REMEDIES, INC.; *U.S. Private*, pg. 3001
OFFICE RESOURCES INC.; *U.S. Private*, pg. 3001
OFFICE RESOURCES, INC.; *U.S. Private*, pg. 3001
OFFICESCAPE, INC.; *U.S. Private*, pg. 3002
OFFICE SHARE - GESTAO DE IMOVEIS E SERVICOS, LDA—See Impresa SGPS S.A.; *Int'l*, pg. 3637
OFFICE SOLUTIONS BUSINESS PRODUCTS SERVICES; *U.S. Private*, pg. 3002
OFFICE SOLUTIONS SVENSKA AB—See Wulff-Group Plc; *Int'l*, pg. 8502
OFFICE SOLUTIONS WHY NOT OY—See Wulff-Group Plc; *Int'l*, pg. 8502
OFFICE SUITES PLUS; *U.S. Private*, pg. 3002
OFFICE SUPERSTORE WEST LLC—See Sycamore Partners Management, LP; *U.S. Private*, pg. 3897
OFFICE SUPPLIES CO. LLC—See Omar Zawawi Establishment LLC; *Int'l*, pg. 5561
OFFICESUPPLY.COM; *U.S. Private*, pg. 3002
OFFICE SYSTEMS CO.—See Loffler Companies, Inc.; *U.S. Private*, pg. 2480
OFFICE SYSTEMS OF VERMONT, INC.—See Visual Edge Technology, Inc.; *U.S. Private*, pg. 4404
OFFICETEAM GROUP LIMITED—See Heritage Group Ltd.; *Int'l*, pg. 3361
OFFICE THREE SIXTY, INC.; *U.S. Private*, pg. 3002
OFFICE VAUDOIS DE CAUTIONNEMENT AGRICOLE SA—See Banque Cantonale Vaudoise; *Int'l*, pg. 853
OFFICEWORKS BUSINESSDIRECT PTY LTD—See Coles Group Limited; *Int'l*, pg. 1698
OFFICEWORKS HOLDINGS PTY LTD—See Wesfarmers Limited; *Int'l*, pg. 8381
OFFICEWORKS, INC.; *U.S. Private*, pg. 3002
OFFICEWORKS LLC; *U.S. Private*, pg. 3002
OFFICEWORKS LTD.—See Coles Group Limited; *Int'l*, pg. 1698
OFFICEWORKS NZ LIMITED—See Wesfarmers Limited; *Int'l*, pg. 8381
OFFICE WORLD AG—See Management Trust Holding AG; *Int'l*, pg. 4666
OFFICEXPRESS INC.; *U.S. Private*, pg. 3002
OFFICIA IMAGING INC; *U.S. Private*, pg. 3002
OFFICINA STELLARE S.P.A.; *Int'l*, pg. 5530
OFFICINE AERONAVALI VENEZIA S.P.A.—See Leonardo S.p.A.; *Int'l*, pg. 4458
OFFICINE BRENNERO S.P.A.—See CNH Industrial N.V.; *Int'l*, pg. 1675
OFFICINE LOVATO PRIVATE LTD.—See Landi Renzo S.p.a.; *Int'l*, pg. 4406

OFFICINE MACCAFERRI S.P.A.—See Societa Esercizi Commerciali Industriali; *Int'l*, pg. 7034
OFFICINE MECCANICHE SIRIO S.R.L.—See Dover Corporation; *U.S. Public*, pg. 682
OFFICINE PICCOLI S.P.A.; *Int'l*, pg. 5530
OFFIS SA/NV—See Aubay SA; *Int'l*, pg. 698
OFFIT KURMAN; *U.S. Private*, pg. 3002
OFFIZIN ANDERSEN NEXO LEIPZIG GMBH; *Int'l*, pg. 5530
OFF MADISON AVE, LLC; *U.S. Private*, pg. 3000
OFF MARKET DATA, INC.; *U.S. Private*, pg. 3001
OFF ROAD UNLIMITED; *U.S. Private*, pg. 3001
OFFSET PAPERBACK MFRS., INC. (BPMC)—See Bertelsmann SE & Co. KGaA; *Int'l*, pg. 990
OFFSET PRESS INC.; *Int'l*, pg. 5530
OFFSHORE CLEANING SYSTEMS, LLC.; *U.S. Private*, pg. 3002
OFFSHORE CRANE & SERVICE COMPANY; *U.S. Private*, pg. 3002
OFFSHORE ENERGY SERVICES INC.; *U.S. Private*, pg. 3002
OFFSHORE ENGINEERING EQUIPMENT SUB-CO.—See Taiyuan Heavy Industry Co., Ltd.; *Int'l*, pg. 7427
OFFSHORE ENGINEERING RESOURCES PTE. LTD.—See Vallianz Holdings Limited; *Int'l*, pg. 8117
OFFSHORE ETKS LTD.—See Original Steel Services Limited; *Int'l*, pg. 5630
OFFSHORE HELICOPTER SUPPORT SERVICES, INC.—See Bristow Group, Inc.; *U.S. Public*, pg. 388
OFFSHORE INLAND SERVICES INC.; *U.S. Private*, pg. 3002
OFFSHORE IWAKI PETROLEUM CO., LTD.—See INPEX CORPORATION; *Int'l*, pg. 3717
OFFSHORE JOINT SERVICES, INC.; *U.S. Private*, pg. 3002
OFFSHOREMARINE TRADING LLC—See Daeyang Electric Co., Ltd.; *Int'l*, pg. 1911
OFFSHORE OIL ENGINEERING COMPANY LIMITED; *Int'l*, pg. 5530
OFFSHORE PETROLEUM CORP.; *U.S. Private*, pg. 3003
OFFSHORE SERVICE VESSELS, LLC.; *U.S. Private*, pg. 3003
OFFSHORE SYSTEMS LTD.—See OSI Maritime Systems; *Int'l*, pg. 5650
OFFSHORE TECHNOLOGY DEVELOPMENT PTE LTD—See Keppel Corporation Limited; *Int'l*, pg. 4132
OFFSHORE WINDPARK RIFFGAT GMBH & CO. KG—See EWE Aktiengesellschaft; *Int'l*, pg. 2576
OFFSITE ARCHIVE STORAGE & INTEGRATED SERVICES (IRELAND) LIMITED—See Housatonic Partners Management Co., Inc.; *U.S. Private*, pg. 1991
OFFSITE ARCHIVE STORAGE & INTEGRATED SERVICES (IRELAND) LIMITED—See Sverica Capital Management LP; *U.S. Private*, pg. 3888
OFFSITE ARCHIVE STORAGE & INTEGRATED SERVICES LIMITED—See Housatonic Partners Management Co., Inc.; *U.S. Private*, pg. 1991
OFFSITE ARCHIVE STORAGE & INTEGRATED SERVICES LIMITED—See Sverica Capital Management LP; *U.S. Private*, pg. 3888
OFFSITE VISION HOLDINGS, INC.—See Gathid Ltd.; *Int'l*, pg. 2889
OFFSPRING INC SDN. BHD.—See SEDANIA Innovator Berhad; *Int'l*, pg. 6677
OFFSPRING SOLUTIONS; *U.S. Private*, pg. 3003
OFFTEC HOLDING GROUP, PLC.; *Int'l*, pg. 5530
OFF THE BEATEN PATH, LLC—See Lindblad Expeditions Holdings, Inc.; *U.S. Public*, pg. 1319
OFF THE GRID PUBLIC RELATIONS; *U.S. Private*, pg. 3001
OFG BANCORP; *U.S. Public*, pg. 1564
OFICEA COMPANY LIMITED—See ENL Limited; *Int'l*, pg. 2442
OFICINA DE REPRESENTACION DE CREDIT SUISSE AG—See UBS Group AG; *Int'l*, pg. 8007
OFICINA TECNICA DE ESTUDIOS Y CONTROL DE OBRAS, S.A—See ACS, Actividades de Construccion y Servicios, S.A.; *Int'l*, pg. 115
OFI MARKESA INTERNATIONAL—See Red Chamber Co.; *U.S. Private*, pg. 3373
OFIRA ITALIANA S.R.L.—See Addtech AB; *Int'l*, pg. 134
OFIR A/S—See North Media A/S; *Int'l*, pg. 5441
OFJ AIRLINKS LIMITED—See ABM Industries, Inc.; *U.S. Public*, pg. 26
O'FLYNN MEDICAL LIMITED—See AddLife AB; *Int'l*, pg. 130
OFM COMMUNICATIONS GMBH & CO. KG—See VINCI S.A.; *Int'l*, pg. 8225
OFM, LLC—See HNI Corporation; *U.S. Public*, pg. 1043
O.F. MOSSBERG & SONS, INC.—See Mossberg Corporation; *U.S. Private*, pg. 2794
OFS BRIGHTWAVE CARROLLTON—See The Furukawa Electric Co., Ltd.; *Int'l*, pg. 7646
OFS CAPITAL CORPORATION; *U.S. Public*, pg. 1564
OFSCAP LLC; *U.S. Private*, pg. 3003
OFS CREDIT COMPANY, INC; *U.S. Public*, pg. 1564
OFS FITEL DENMARK APS—See The Furukawa Electric Co., Ltd.; *Int'l*, pg. 7646

OFS FITEL DEUTSCHLAND GMBH—See The Furukawa Electric Co., Ltd.; *Int'l*, pg. 7646
OFS FITEL LLC—See The Furukawa Electric Co., Ltd.; *Int'l*, pg. 7646
OFS INTERNATIONAL LLC; *U.S. Private*, pg. 3003
OFS LABORATORIES, LLC—See The Furukawa Electric Co., Ltd.; *Int'l*, pg. 7646
OFS RUS FIBER OPTIC CABLE COMPANY—See The Furukawa Electric Co., Ltd.; *Int'l*, pg. 7646
OFS—See The Furukawa Electric Co., Ltd.; *Int'l*, pg. 7646
OFS—See The Furukawa Electric Co., Ltd.; *Int'l*, pg. 7646
OFTEDAL CONSTRUCTION INC.; *U.S. Private*, pg. 3003
OFU CO., LTD.; *Int'l*, pg. 5530
OFUNATO POWER INC.—See Taiheiyo Cement Corporation; *Int'l*, pg. 7411
OFUP—See ADLPartner SA; *Int'l*, pg. 151
OFX GROUP LIMITED; *Int'l*, pg. 5530
OFX PAYMENTS IRELAND LIMITED—See OFX Group Limited; *Int'l*, pg. 5531
OFX (SNG) PTE. LIMITED—See OFX Group Limited; *Int'l*, pg. 5531
OGAAN PUBLICATIONS PVT. LTD.—See Vivendi SE; *Int'l*, pg. 8275
OGAKI FUSO SPINNING CO., LTD.—See Toray Industries, Inc.; *Int'l*, pg. 7823
THE OGAKI KYORITSU BANK, LTD.; *Int'l*, pg. 7671
OGAKI MACHINE & TOOLS CO., LTD.—See Yamazen Corporation; *Int'l*, pg. 8558
OGAKI MURATA MANUFACTURING CO., LTD.—See Murata Manufacturing Co., Ltd.; *Int'l*, pg. 5098
OGALLALA ELECTRONICS—See Compass Diversified Holdings; *U.S. Public*, pg. 560
OGAN/DALLAL ASSOCIATES, INC.; *U.S. Private*, pg. 3003
O'GARA COACH COMPANY LLC; *U.S. Private*, pg. 2978
THE O'GARA GROUP, INC.; *U.S. Private*, pg. 4087
OGAWA CONSTRUCTION CO., LTD.—See Shinoken Group Co., Ltd.; *Int'l*, pg. 6847
OGAWA SMART HEALTHCARE TECHNOLOGY GROUP CO., LTD.; *Int'l*, pg. 5531
OGAWA WORLD BERHAD—See Ogawa Smart Healthcare Technology Group Co., Ltd.; *Int'l*, pg. 5531
OGBM DANNY KAYELAAN ZOETERMEER BV—See Minor International PCL; *Int'l*, pg. 4912
OG CAPITAL CO., LTD—See Osaka Gas Co., Ltd.; *Int'l*, pg. 5645
OGCC KAZSTROYSERVICE JSC; *Int'l*, pg. 5531
OGC INVESTMENTS, LLC—See Pace Development Corporation Public Co., Ltd.; *Int'l*, pg. 5685
OGDEN INTERNAL MEDICINE & UROLOGY, LLC—See HCA Healthcare, Inc.; *U.S. Public*, pg. 1005
OGDEN LINCOLN MERCURY INC.; *U.S. Private*, pg. 3003
THE OGDEN NEWSPAPERS, INC.—See The Nutting Company, Inc.; *U.S. Private*, pg. 4086
OGDEN NEWSPAPERS OF OHIO INC.—See The Nutting Company, Inc.; *U.S. Private*, pg. 4086
OGDEN NEWSPAPERS OF PENNSYLVANIA INC.—See The Nutting Company, Inc.; *U.S. Private*, pg. 4086
OGDEN PUBLICATIONS, INC.—See The Nutting Company, Inc.; *U.S. Private*, pg. 4086
OGDEN PUBLISHING CORPORATION—See Sandusky Newspapers Inc.; *U.S. Private*, pg. 3545
OGDEN REGIONAL MEDICAL CENTER—See HCA Healthcare, Inc.; *U.S. Public*, pg. 1005
OGEE LIMITED—See Sally Beauty Holdings, Inc.; *U.S. Public*, pg. 1838
OGE ENERGY CORP.; *U.S. Public*, pg. 1564
OGF, S.A.—See Ontario Teachers' Pension Plan; *Int'l*, pg. 5590
OGH ACQUISITION CORPORATION—See Waste Management, Inc.; *U.S. Public*, pg. 2331
OGIER GROUP L.P.; *Int'l*, pg. 5531
OGIER HONG KONG—See Ogier Group L.P.; *Int'l*, pg. 5531
OGIER LEGAL LIMITED PARTNERSHIP—See Ogier Group L.P.; *Int'l*, pg. 5531
OGIER LUXEMBOURG—See Ogier Group L.P.; *Int'l*, pg. 5531
OGIER SAS—See Grupo Alimentario Argal SA; *Int'l*, pg. 3119
OGIER SERVICES (CAYMAN) LIMITED—See Ogier Group L.P.; *Int'l*, pg. 5531
OGIER SHANGHAI—See Ogier Group L.P.; *Int'l*, pg. 5531
OGI GROUP LTD; *Int'l*, pg. 5531
OGILVIE MOTORS LIMITED; *Int'l*, pg. 5531
OGILVY 4D OXFORD—See WPP plc; *Int'l*, pg. 8489
OGILVYACTION—See WPP plc; *Int'l*, pg. 8464
OGILVYACTION—See WPP plc; *Int'l*, pg. 8464
OGILVYACTION—See WPP plc; *Int'l*, pg. 8464
OGILVYACTION—See WPP plc; *Int'l*, pg. 8464
OGILVYACTION—See WPP plc; *Int'l*, pg. 8464
OGILVYACTION—See WPP plc; *Int'l*, pg. 8464
OGILVYACTION—See WPP plc; *Int'l*, pg. 8464
OGILVYACTION—See WPP plc; *Int'l*, pg. 8464
OGILVYACTION—See WPP plc; *Int'l*, pg. 8464
OGILVYACTION—See WPP plc; *Int'l*, pg. 8464
OGILVYACTION—See WPP plc; *Int'l*, pg. 8464

# OGILVIE MOTORS LIMITED	CORPORATE AFFILIATIONS

OGILVYACTION—See WPP plc; *Int'l*, pg. 8464
OGILVYACTION—See WPP plc; *Int'l*, pg. 8464
OGILVYACTION—See WPP plc; *Int'l*, pg. 8464
OGILVYACTION—See WPP plc; *Int'l*, pg. 8464
OGILVYACTION—See WPP plc; *Int'l*, pg. 8464
OGILVYACTION—See WPP plc; *Int'l*, pg. 8464
OGILVYACTION—See WPP plc; *Int'l*, pg. 8464
OGILVYACTION—See WPP plc; *Int'l*, pg. 8464
OGILVYACTION—See WPP plc; *Int'l*, pg. 8464
OGILVYACTION—See WPP plc; *Int'l*, pg. 8464
OGILVYACTION—See WPP plc; *Int'l*, pg. 8464
OGILVYACTION—See WPP plc; *Int'l*, pg. 8464
OGILVYACTION—See WPP plc; *Int'l*, pg. 8487
OGILVYACTION—See WPP plc; *Int'l*, pg. 8487
OGILVYACTION—See WPP plc; *Int'l*, pg. 8487
OGILVYACTION VIETNAM—See WPP plc; *Int'l*, pg. 8464
OGILVY ACTIVATION—See WPP plc; *Int'l*, pg. 8486
OGILVY ADVERTISING—See WPP plc; *Int'l*, pg. 8486
OGILVY AG—See WPP plc; *Int'l*, pg. 8486
OGILVY ASIA PACIFIC—See WPP plc; *Int'l*, pg. 8486
OGILVY BRASIL—See WPP plc; *Int'l*, pg. 8486
OGILVY CAPE TOWN—See WPP plc; *Int'l*, pg. 8486
OGILVY CID—See WPP plc; *Int'l*, pg. 8486
OGILVY COMMONHEALTH CONSUMER CARE—See WPP plc; *Int'l*, pg. 8489
OGILVY COMMONHEALTH INSIGHTS & ANALYTICS—See WPP plc; *Int'l*, pg. 8489
OGILVY COMMONHEALTH INTERACTIVE MARKETING—See WPP plc; *Int'l*, pg. 8489
OGILVY COMMONHEALTH MEDICAL EDUCATION—See WPP plc; *Int'l*, pg. 8489
OGILVY COMMONHEALTH MEDICAL MARKETING—See WPP plc; *Int'l*, pg. 8489
OGILVY COMMONHEALTH MEDICAL MEDIA—See WPP plc; *Int'l*, pg. 8489
OGILVY COMMONHEALTH PAYER MARKETING—See WPP plc; *Int'l*, pg. 8489
OGILVY COMMONHEALTH SCIENTIFIC COMMUNICATIONS—See WPP plc; *Int'l*, pg. 8489
OGILVY COMMONHEALTH SPECIALTY MARKETING—See WPP plc; *Int'l*, pg. 8489
OGILVY COMMONHEALTH WORLDWIDE GMBH—See WPP plc; *Int'l*, pg. 8489
OGILVY COMMONHEALTH WORLDWIDE LLC—See WPP plc; *Int'l*, pg. 8489
OGILVY COMMUNICACAO & IMAGEM—See WPP plc; *Int'l*, pg. 8490
OGILVY DURBAN—See WPP plc; *Int'l*, pg. 8486
OGILVY GOVERNMENT RELATIONS—See WPP plc; *Int'l*, pg. 8489
THE OGILVY GROUP, INC—See WPP plc; *Int'l*, pg. 8483
OGILVY GROUP ZRT.—See WPP plc; *Int'l*, pg. 8486
OGILVY HEALTHCARE—See WPP plc; *Int'l*, pg. 8486
OGILVYHEALTHCARE—See WPP plc; *Int'l*, pg. 8487
OGILVYHEALTHCARE—See WPP plc; *Int'l*, pg. 8487
OGILVYHEALTHCARE—See WPP plc; *Int'l*, pg. 8487
OGILVYHEALTHCARE—See WPP plc; *Int'l*, pg. 8489
OGILVY HEALTHWORLD BARCELONA—See WPP plc; *Int'l*, pg. 8486
OGILVY HEALTHWORLD/COPENHAGEN—See WPP plc; *Int'l*, pg. 8489
OGILVY HEALTHWORLD EAME—See WPP plc; *Int'l*, pg. 8489
OGILVY HEALTHWORLD INDIA—See WPP plc; *Int'l*, pg. 8489
OGILVY HEALTHWORLD, LLC—See WPP plc; *Int'l*, pg. 8489
OGILVY HEALTHWORLD LONDON—See WPP plc; *Int'l*, pg. 8489
OGILVY HEALTHWORLD MADRID—See WPP plc; *Int'l*, pg. 8489
OGILVY HEALTHWORLD PAYER MARKETING—See WPP plc; *Int'l*, pg. 8489
OGILVY HEALTHWORLD SAO PAULO—See WPP plc; *Int'l*, pg. 8486
OGILVY HEALTHWORLD—See WPP plc; *Int'l*, pg. 8486
OGILVY HEALTHWORLD—See WPP plc; *Int'l*, pg. 8486
OGILVYHEALTHWORLD—See WPP plc; *Int'l*, pg. 8487
OGILVY HEALTHWORLD—See WPP plc; *Int'l*, pg. 8489
OGILVY HEALTHWORLD—See WPP plc; *Int'l*, pg. 8489
OGILVY HEALTHWORLD—See WPP plc; *Int'l*, pg. 8489
OGILVY HEALTHWORLD—See WPP plc; *Int'l*, pg. 8489
OGILVY HEALTHWORLD—See WPP plc; *Int'l*, pg. 8489
OGILVY HEALTHWORLD—See WPP plc; *Int'l*, pg. 8489
OGILVY HEALTHWORLD TAIVAS—See WPP plc; *Int'l*, pg. 8489
OGILVY HEALTHWORLD-TORONTO—See WPP plc; *Int'l*, pg. 8489
OGILVY HEALTHWORLD USA—See WPP plc; *Int'l*, pg. 8489
OGILVY INDIA—See WPP plc; *Int'l*, pg. 8486
OGILVYINTERACTIVE ASIA PACIFIC—See WPP plc; *Int'l*, pg. 8487
OGILVYINTERACTIVE—See WPP plc; *Int'l*, pg. 8487
OGILVYINTERACTIVE—See WPP plc; *Int'l*, pg. 8487
OGILVYINTERACTIVE—See WPP plc; *Int'l*, pg. 8487
OGILVYINTERACTIVE—See WPP plc; *Int'l*, pg. 8487

OGILVYINTERACTIVE—See WPP plc; *Int'l*, pg. 8487
OGILVYINTERACTIVE—See WPP plc; *Int'l*, pg. 8487
OGILVYINTERACTIVE—See WPP plc; *Int'l*, pg. 8487
OGILVYINTERACTIVE—See WPP plc; *Int'l*, pg. 8487
OGILVYINTERACTIVE—See WPP plc; *Int'l*, pg. 8487
OGILVYINTERACTIVE—See WPP plc; *Int'l*, pg. 8487
OGILVYINTERACTIVE—See WPP plc; *Int'l*, pg. 8487
OGILVYINTERACTIVE—See WPP plc; *Int'l*, pg. 8487
OGILVYINTERACTIVE—See WPP plc; *Int'l*, pg. 8487
OGILVYINTERACTIVE—See WPP plc; *Int'l*, pg. 8487
OGILVY INTERACTIVE WORLDWIDE—See WPP plc; *Int'l*, pg. 8489
OGILVY JOHANNESBURG (PTY.) LTD.—See WPP plc; *Int'l*, pg. 8486
OGILVY & MATHER ADVERTISING BEIJING—See WPP plc; *Int'l*, pg. 8485
OGILVY & MATHER ADVERTISING—See WPP plc; *Int'l*, pg. 8485
OGILVY & MATHER ADVERTISING—See WPP plc; *Int'l*, pg. 8485
OGILVY & MATHER ADVERTISING—See WPP plc; *Int'l*, pg. 8485
OGILVY & MATHER ADVERTISING—See WPP plc; *Int'l*, pg. 8485
OGILVY & MATHER ADVERTISING—See WPP plc; *Int'l*, pg. 8485
OGILVY & MATHER ADVERTISING—See WPP plc; *Int'l*, pg. 8485
OGILVY & MATHER ADVERTISING—See WPP plc; *Int'l*, pg. 8485
OGILVY & MATHER AFRICA—See WPP plc; *Int'l*, pg. 8486
OGILVY & MATHER (AMSTERDAM) B.V.—See WPP plc; *Int'l*, pg. 8486
OGILVY & MATHER ARGENTINA—See WPP plc; *Int'l*, pg. 8486
OGILVY & MATHER ASIA/PACIFIC—See WPP plc; *Int'l*, pg. 8486
OGILVY & MATHER CHICAGO—See WPP plc; *Int'l*, pg. 8486
OGILVY & MATHER (CHINA) LTD.—See WPP plc; *Int'l*, pg. 8485
OGILVY & MATHER (EASTERN AFRICA) LTD.—See WPP plc; *Int'l*, pg. 8485
OGILVY & MATHER EMEA—See WPP plc; *Int'l*, pg. 8486
OGILVY & MATHER FRANKFURT—See WPP plc; *Int'l*, pg. 8486
OGILVY & MATHER GES M.B.H.—See WPP plc; *Int'l*, pg. 8486
OGILVY & MATHER INDIA—See WPP plc; *Int'l*, pg. 8486
OGILVY & MATHER JAPAN K.K.—See WPP plc; *Int'l*, pg. 8486
OGILVY & MATHER LOS ANGELES—See WPP plc; *Int'l*, pg. 8486
OGILVY & MATHER, LTD.—See WPP plc; *Int'l*, pg. 8486
OGILVY & MATHER N AMERICA & CORPORATE—See WPP plc; *Int'l*, pg. 8486
OGILVY & MATHER (PHILIPPINES) INC.—See WPP plc; *Int'l*, pg. 8485
OGILVY & MATHER PORTUGAL—See WPP plc; *Int'l*, pg. 8486
OGILVY & MATHER PUBLICIDAD MADRID, SA—See WPP plc; *Int'l*, pg. 8486
OGILVY & MATHER (SINGAPORE) PVT. LTD.—See WPP plc; *Int'l*, pg. 8485
OGILVY & MATHER—See WPP plc; *Int'l*, pg. 8484
OGILVY & MATHER—See WPP plc; *Int'l*, pg. 8485
OGILVY & MATHER—See WPP plc; *Int'l*, pg. 8485
OGILVY & MATHER—See WPP plc; *Int'l*, pg. 8485
OGILVY & MATHER—See WPP plc; *Int'l*, pg. 8485
OGILVY & MATHER—See WPP plc; *Int'l*, pg. 8485
OGILVY & MATHER—See WPP plc; *Int'l*, pg. 8485
OGILVY & MATHER—See WPP plc; *Int'l*, pg. 8485
OGILVY & MATHER—See WPP plc; *Int'l*, pg. 8485
OGILVY & MATHER—See WPP plc; *Int'l*, pg. 8485
OGILVY & MATHER—See WPP plc; *Int'l*, pg. 8485
OGILVY & MATHER—See WPP plc; *Int'l*, pg. 8485
OGILVY & MATHER—See WPP plc; *Int'l*, pg. 8485
OGILVY & MATHER—See WPP plc; *Int'l*, pg. 8485
OGILVY & MATHER—See WPP plc; *Int'l*, pg. 8485
OGILVY & MATHER—See WPP plc; *Int'l*, pg. 8485
OGILVY & MATHER—See WPP plc; *Int'l*, pg. 8485
OGILVY & MATHER—See WPP plc; *Int'l*, pg. 8485
OGILVY & MATHER—See WPP plc; *Int'l*, pg. 8485
OGILVY & MATHER—See WPP plc; *Int'l*, pg. 8485
OGILVY & MATHER—See WPP plc; *Int'l*, pg. 8485
OGILVY & MATHER—See WPP plc; *Int'l*, pg. 8485
OGILVY & MATHER—See WPP plc; *Int'l*, pg. 8485
OGILVY & MATHER—See WPP plc; *Int'l*, pg. 8485
OGILVY & MATHER—See WPP plc; *Int'l*, pg. 8485
OGILVY & MATHER—See WPP plc; *Int'l*, pg. 8485
OGILVY & MATHER—See WPP plc; *Int'l*, pg. 8485
OGILVY & MATHER SOUTH AFRICA (PTY.) LTD.—See WPP plc; *Int'l*, pg. 8486
OGILVY & MATHER S.P.A.—See WPP plc; *Int'l*, pg. 8489

OGILVY & MATHER SP. Z O.O.—See WPP plc; *Int'l*, pg. 8486
OGILVY & MATHER (VIETNAM) LTD.—See WPP plc; *Int'l*, pg. 8485
OGILVY & MATHER WERBEAGENTUR GMBH—See WPP plc; *Int'l*, pg. 8486
OGILVY MONTREAL—See WPP plc; *Int'l*, pg. 8486
OGILVY MOZAMBIQUE—See WPP plc; *Int'l*, pg. 8486
OGILVY NEW ZEALAND—See WPP plc; *Int'l*, pg. 8486
OGILVY NOOR—See WPP plc; *Int'l*, pg. 8489
OGILVYOFFICE—See WPP plc; *Int'l*, pg. 8487
OGILVYONE DOGRUDAN PAZARLAMA A.S.—See WPP plc; *Int'l*, pg. 8487
OGILVYONE EL SALVADOR—See WPP plc; *Int'l*, pg. 8487
OGILVY ONE MIDDLE EAST COMPANY—See WPP plc; *Int'l*, pg. 8486
OGILVYONE PTY LIMITED—See WPP plc; *Int'l*, pg. 8462
OGILVYONE—See WPP plc; *Int'l*, pg. 8487
OGILVYONE—See WPP plc; *Int'l*, pg. 8487
OGILVYONE—See WPP plc; *Int'l*, pg. 8487
OGILVYONE TELESERVICES—See WPP plc; *Int'l*, pg. 8488
OGILVYONE WORLDWIDE ATHENS—See WPP plc; *Int'l*, pg. 8488
OGILVYONE WORLDWIDE-CAPE TOWN—See WPP plc; *Int'l*, pg. 8488
OGILVYONE WORLDWIDE GMBH—See WPP plc; *Int'l*, pg. 8488
OGILVYONE WORLDWIDE LTD.—See WPP plc; *Int'l*, pg. 8488
OGILVYONE WORLDWIDE SA—See WPP plc; *Int'l*, pg. 8488
OGILVYONE WORLDWIDE—See WPP plc; *Int'l*, pg. 8487
OGILVYONE WORLDWIDE—See WPP plc; *Int'l*, pg. 8487
OGILVYONE WORLDWIDE—See WPP plc; *Int'l*, pg. 8487
OGILVYONE WORLDWIDE—See WPP plc; *Int'l*, pg. 8487
OGILVYONE WORLDWIDE—See WPP plc; *Int'l*, pg. 8487
OGILVYONE WORLDWIDE—See WPP plc; *Int'l*, pg. 8487
OGILVYONE WORLDWIDE—See WPP plc; *Int'l*, pg. 8487
OGILVYONE WORLDWIDE—See WPP plc; *Int'l*, pg. 8487
OGILVYONE WORLDWIDE—See WPP plc; *Int'l*, pg. 8487
OGILVYONE WORLDWIDE—See WPP plc; *Int'l*, pg. 8488
OGILVYONE WORLDWIDE—See WPP plc; *Int'l*, pg. 8488
OGILVYONE WORLDWIDE—See WPP plc; *Int'l*, pg. 8488
OGILVYONE WORLDWIDE—See WPP plc; *Int'l*, pg. 8488
OGILVYONE WORLDWIDE—See WPP plc; *Int'l*, pg. 8488
OGILVYONE WORLDWIDE—See WPP plc; *Int'l*, pg. 8488
OGILVYONE WORLDWIDE—See WPP plc; *Int'l*, pg. 8488
OGILVYONE WORLDWIDE—See WPP plc; *Int'l*, pg. 8488
OGILVYONE WORLDWIDE—See WPP plc; *Int'l*, pg. 8488
OGILVYONE WORLDWIDE—See WPP plc; *Int'l*, pg. 8488
OGILVYONE WORLDWIDE—See WPP plc; *Int'l*, pg. 8488
OGILVY PR/ATLANTA—See WPP plc; *Int'l*, pg. 8490
OGILVY PR—See WPP plc; *Int'l*, pg. 8486
OGILVY PR—See WPP plc; *Int'l*, pg. 8490
OGILVY PR—See WPP plc; *Int'l*, pg. 8490
OGILVY PR—See WPP plc; *Int'l*, pg. 8490
OGILVY PR—See WPP plc; *Int'l*, pg. 8490
OGILVY PR—See WPP plc; *Int'l*, pg. 8490
OGILVY PR—See WPP plc; *Int'l*, pg. 8490
OGILVY PR WORLDWIDE, MUMBAI—See WPP plc; *Int'l*, pg. 8490
OGILVY PR WORLDWIDE—See WPP plc; *Int'l*, pg. 8490
OGILVY PR WORLDWIDE—See WPP plc; *Int'l*, pg. 8490
OGILVY PR WORLDWIDE—See WPP plc; *Int'l*, pg. 8490
OGILVY PR WORLDWIDE—See WPP plc; *Int'l*, pg. 8490
OGILVY PR WORLDWIDE—See WPP plc; *Int'l*, pg. 8490
OGILVY PR WORLDWIDE—See WPP plc; *Int'l*, pg. 8490
OGILVY PR WORLDWIDE—See WPP plc; *Int'l*, pg. 8490
OGILVY PR WORLDWIDE—See WPP plc; *Int'l*, pg. 8490
OGILVY PR WORLDWIDE—See WPP plc; *Int'l*, pg. 8490
OGILVY PR WORLDWIDE—See WPP plc; *Int'l*, pg. 8490
OGILVY PR WORLDWIDE—See WPP plc; *Int'l*, pg. 8490
OGILVY PR WORLDWIDE—See WPP plc; *Int'l*, pg. 8490
OGILVY PR WORLDWIDE—See WPP plc; *Int'l*, pg. 8490
OGILVY PR WORLDWIDE—See WPP plc; *Int'l*, pg. 8490
OGILVY PR WORLDWIDE—See WPP plc; *Int'l*, pg. 8490
OGILVY PUBLIC RELATIONS AB—See WPP plc; *Int'l*, pg. 8490
OGILVY PUBLIC RELATIONS—See WPP plc; *Int'l*, pg. 8486
OGILVY PUBLIC RELATIONS—See WPP plc; *Int'l*, pg. 8486
OGILVY PUBLIC RELATIONS—See WPP plc; *Int'l*, pg. 8490
OGILVY PUBLIC RELATIONS WORLDWIDE, INC.—See WPP plc; *Int'l*, pg. 8489
OGILVY PUBLIC RELATIONS WORLDWIDE—See WPP plc; *Int'l*, pg. 8486
OGILVY PUBLIC RELATIONS WORLDWIDE—See WPP plc; *Int'l*, pg. 8487
OGILVY PUBLIC RELATIONS WORLDWIDE—See WPP plc; *Int'l*, pg. 8490

COMPANY NAME INDEX

OGILVY PUBLIC RELATIONS WORLDWIDE—See WPP plc; *Int'l*, pg. 8490
OGILVY PUBLIC RELATIONS WORLDWIDE—See WPP plc; *Int'l*, pg. 8490
OGILVY PUBLIC RELATIONS WORLDWIDE—See WPP plc; *Int'l*, pg. 8490
OGILVY RECRUITMENT ADVERTISING—See WPP plc; *Int'l*, pg. 8490
OGILVY—See WPP plc; *Int'l*, pg. 8484
OGILVY—See WPP plc; *Int'l*, pg. 8484
OGILVY—See WPP plc; *Int'l*, pg. 8490
OGILVYSTREAMLINE/DESIGN DIRECT—See WPP plc; *Int'l*, pg. 8488
OGILVY SYDNEY—See WPP plc; *Int'l*, pg. 8487
OGILVY ZZAD/BEIJING—See WPP plc; *Int'l*, pg. 8489
O&G INDUSTRIES, INC. - HARWINTON CONCRETE PLANT—See O&G Industries, Inc.; *U.S. Private*, pg. 2977
O&G INDUSTRIES, INC.; *U.S. Private*, pg. 2977
OGIN INC.—See Exelon Corporation; *U.S. Public*, pg. 807
OGIO INTERNATIONAL, INC.—See Topgolf Callaway Brands Corp.; *U.S. Public*, pg. 2164
OGIS-RI CO., LTD.—See Osaka Gas Co., Ltd.; *Int'l*, pg. 5645
OGIWARA & CO., LTD.—See Nippon Steel Corporation; *Int'l*, pg. 5338
OGLAEND INDUSTRIER AS—See Segulah Advisor AB; *Int'l*, pg. 6684
OGLAEND INDUSTRIES MIDDLE EAST LLC—See Segulah Advisor AB; *Int'l*, pg. 6684
OGLAEND INDUSTRIES SND BHD—See Segulah Advisor AB; *Int'l*, pg. 6684
OGLAEND INDUSTRIES (SUZHOU) CO., LTD—See Segulah Advisor AB; *Int'l*, pg. 6684
OGLAEND SYSTEM BV—See Segulah Advisor AB; *Int'l*, pg. 6684
OGLAEND SYSTEM KOREA CO LTD—See Segulah Advisor AB; *Int'l*, pg. 6684
OGLAEND SYSTEM RUSSIA LLC—See Segulah Advisor AB; *Int'l*, pg. 6684
OGLAEND SYSTEM SINGAPORE PTE LTD—See Segulah Advisor AB; *Int'l*, pg. 6684
OGLAEND SYSTEM UK LIMITED—See Segulah Advisor AB; *Int'l*, pg. 6684
OGLAEND SYSTEM US LLC—See Segulah Advisor AB; *Int'l*, pg. 6684
OGLAND SYSTEM AB—See Segulah Advisor AB; *Int'l*, pg. 6684
OGLE HAUS, LLC—See PENN Entertainment, Inc.; *U.S. Public*, pg. 1662
OGLESBY & BUTLER GROUP PLC; *Int'l*, pg. 5531
OGLE SCHOOL MANAGEMENT LLC—See The RLJ Companies, LLC; *U.S. Private*, pg. 4111
OGLETHORPE POWER CORPORATION; *U.S. Private*, pg. 3003
OGLETREE, DEAKINS, NASH, SMOAK & STEWART, P.C.; *U.S. Private*, pg. 3003
OGMA - INDUSTRIA AERONAUTICA DE PORTUGAL S.A.—See Embraer S.A.; *Int'l*, pg. 2375
OGM LAND, LLC—See Percheron, LLC; *U.S. Private*, pg. 3146
OGM, LTD.; *U.S. Private*, pg. 3003
OGPC SDN. BHD.—See Dagang NeXchange Berhad; *Int'l*, pg. 1912
OGP MESSTECHNIK GMBH—See Quality Vision International Inc.; *U.S. Private*, pg. 3321
OGP SHANGHAI CO. LTD.—See Quality Vision International Inc.; *U.S. Private*, pg. 3321
OGP TECHNICAL SERVICES SDN BHD—See Petroliam Nasional Berhad; *Int'l*, pg. 5830
O'GRADY-PEYTON INTERNATIONAL (USA), INC.—See AMN Healthcare Services, Inc.; *U.S. Public*, pg. 125
OGRAN JAPAN CO., LTD.—See Katakura Industries Co., Ltd.; *Int'l*, pg. 4089
O GRUPO SWATCH (MACAU) LIMITADA—See The Swatch Group Ltd.; *Int'l*, pg. 7692
OG SPORTS CO., LTD.—See Osaka Gas Co., Ltd.; *Int'l*, pg. 5645
OGSYSTEMS LLC—See Parsons Corporation; *U.S. Public*, pg. 1651
OGUCHI BOOK BINDING & PRINTING CO., LTD.—See Dai Nippon Printing Co., Ltd.; *Int'l*, pg. 1916
OGUNSEN AB; *Int'l*, pg. 5531
OGURA CLUTCH CO., LTD.; *Int'l*, pg. 5531
OGURA CLUTCH DO BRASIL LTDA.—See OGURA CLUTCH CO., LTD.; *Int'l*, pg. 5531
OGURA SHIKI CO., LTD.—See Dynapac Co., Ltd.; *Int'l*, pg. 2241
OGUS NETZE- UND WIRKWAREN GMBH & CO. KG; *Int'l*, pg. 5531
OHA INSTRUMENTS INC—See Wise El Santo Company Inc.; *U.S. Private*, pg. 4549
OHA INVESTMENT CORPORATION—See Portman Ridge Finance Corporation; *U.S. Public*, pg. 1702
OHAL LIMITED—See WPP plc; *Int'l*, pg. 8466
O'HALLORAN ADVERTISING, INC.; *U.S. Private*, pg. 2978
O'HALLORAN INTERNATIONAL INC.; *U.S. Private*, pg. 2978

THE OHANA COMPANIES, LLC—See 360insights.com Canada, Inc.; *Int'l*, pg. 6
OHANA HEALTH PLAN, INC.—See Centene Corporation; *U.S. Public*, pg. 471
OHANA PACIFIC BANK; *U.S. Public*, pg. 1564
OHANA PARTNERS, INC.—See International Holdings Company PJSC; *Int'l*, pg. 3750
O'HANRAHAN CONSULTANTS, INC.—See Washworld, Inc.; *U.S. Private*, pg. 4450
O'HARA CHRYSLER DODGE JEEP RAM; *U.S. Private*, pg. 2978
OHARA CORPORATION—See Ohara Inc.; *Int'l*, pg. 5531
OHARA GMBH—See Ohara Inc.; *Int'l*, pg. 5531
OHARA INC.; *Int'l*, pg. 5531
OHARA TECHNOLOGIES; *Int'l*, pg. 5531
O'HARA VACANCES SAS—See Beneteau S.A.; *Int'l*, pg. 972
O'HARE-MIDWAY LIMOUSINE SERVICE INC.; *U.S. Private*, pg. 2978
O'HARROW CONSTRUCTION COMPANY; *U.S. Private*, pg. 2978
OHASHI GIKEN, INC. - SENDAI PLANT—See Ohashi Technica, Inc.; *Int'l*, pg. 5532
OHASHI GIKEN, INC.—See Ohashi Technica, Inc.; *Int'l*, pg. 5532
OHASHI LOGISTICS, INC.—See Ohashi Technica, Inc.; *Int'l*, pg. 5532
OHASHI NAKAHYO PRECISION PARTS (GUANGZHOU) CO., LTD.—See Ohashi Technica, Inc.; *Int'l*, pg. 5532
OHASHI NAKAHYO USA. INC.—See Ohashi Technica, Inc.; *Int'l*, pg. 5532
OHASHI SATO (THAILAND) CO., LTD.—See Ohashi Technica, Inc.; *Int'l*, pg. 5532
OHASHI TECHNICA, INC.; *Int'l*, pg. 5531
OHASHI TECHNICA MEXICO S.A. DE .C.V.—See Ohashi Technica, Inc.; *Int'l*, pg. 5532
OHASHI TECHNICA PRECISION PARTS (SHANGHAI) CO., LTD.—See Ohashi Technica, Inc.; *Int'l*, pg. 5532
OHASHI TECHNICA (SHANGHAI) CO., LTD.—See Ohashi Technica, Inc.; *Int'l*, pg. 5532
OHASHI TECHNICA TAIWAN CO., LTD.—See Ohashi Technica, Inc.; *Int'l*, pg. 5532
OHASHI TECHNICA (THAILAND) CO., LTD.—See Ohashi Technica, Inc.; *Int'l*, pg. 5532
OHASHI TECHNICA UK, LTD.—See Ohashi Technica, Inc.; *Int'l*, pg. 5532
OHASHI TECHNICA U.S.A., INC.—See Ohashi Technica, Inc.; *Int'l*, pg. 5532
OHASHI TECHNICA U.S.A. MANUFACTURING INC.—See Ohashi Technica, Inc.; *Int'l*, pg. 5532
OHAUS AUSTRALIA PTY. LTD.—See Mettler-Toledo International, Inc.; *U.S. Public*, pg. 1433
OHAUS CORPORATION—See Mettler-Toledo International, Inc.; *U.S. Public*, pg. 1433
OHAUS DE MEXICO S.A. DE C.V.—See Mettler-Toledo International, Inc.; *U.S. Public*, pg. 1433
OHAUS EUROPE GMBH—See Mettler-Toledo International, Inc.; *U.S. Public*, pg. 1433
OHAUS INDOCHINA LIMITED—See Mettler-Toledo International, Inc.; *U.S. Public*, pg. 1433
OHAUS INSTRUMENTS (SHANGHAI) CO. LTD.—See Mettler-Toledo International, Inc.; *U.S. Public*, pg. 1433
OHBA CO., LTD.; *Int'l*, pg. 5532
OHBA SEIKEN CO. LTD.—See Alconix Corporation; *Int'l*, pg. 302
OHB CHILE SPA—See Hiscox Ltd.; *Int'l*, pg. 3407
OHB COSMOS INTERNATIONAL LAUNCH SERVICES GMBH—See Hiscox Ltd.; *Int'l*, pg. 3407
OHB DIGITAL SERVICES GMBH—See Hiscox Ltd.; *Int'l*, pg. 3407
OHB DIGITAL SOLUTIONS GMBH—See Hiscox Ltd.; *Int'l*, pg. 3407
OHB HELLAS MON.E.P.E—See OHB SE; *Int'l*, pg. 5532
OHB ITALIA S.P.A.—See Hiscox Ltd.; *Int'l*, pg. 3407
OHB LOGISTIC SOLUTIONS GMBH—See OHB SE; *Int'l*, pg. 5532
OHB SE; *Int'l*, pg. 5532
OHB SWEDEN AB—See OHB SE; *Int'l*, pg. 5532
OHB SYSTEM AG—See OHB SE; *Int'l*, pg. 5532
OHBUN CO., LTD.—See Yoshimura Food Holdings K.K.; *Int'l*, pg. 8600
O&H DANISH BAKERY; *U.S. Private*, pg. 2977
OHE INDUSTRIES LLC—See Cerberus Capital Management, L.P.; *U.S. Private*, pg. 838
OHES ENVIRONMENTAL LIMITED—See Wesfarmers Limited; *Int'l*, pg. 8381
OH FRIENDLY VILLAGE, LLC—See UMH Properties, Inc.; *U.S. Public*, pg. 2224
OHGA ELECTRONICS CO., LTD.—See Holy Stone Enterprise Co., Ltd.; *Int'l*, pg. 3454
OHGISHIMA OIL TERMINAL CO., LTD.—See Idemitsu Kosan Co., Ltd.; *Int'l*, pg. 3592
OHG REWE-FOODSERVICE GMBH & CO.—See Coop-Gruppe Genossenschaft; *Int'l*, pg. 1790
OHI ASSET (CO) MESA, LLC—See Omega Healthcare Investors, Inc.; *U.S. Public*, pg. 1571
OHI ASSET (IN) GREENSBURG, LLC—See Omega Healthcare Investors, Inc.; *U.S. Public*, pg. 1571

OHIC INSURANCE COMPANY—See The Doctors Company; *U.S. Public*, pg. 4021
OHI CONNECTICUT INC—See Omega Healthcare Investors, Inc.; *U.S. Public*, pg. 1571
OHIGRO INC.; *U.S. Private*, pg. 3003
OHI HEALTHCARE PROPERTIES LIMITED PARTNERSHIP—See Omega Healthcare Investors, Inc.; *U.S. Public*, pg. 1571
OHI HEATH LODGE AND AUTUMN VALE LTD—See Omega Healthcare Investors, Inc.; *U.S. Public*, pg. 1571
OHI HILLINGS LTD—See Omega Healthcare Investors, Inc.; *U.S. Public*, pg. 1571
OHI MAINE; *U.S. Private*, pg. 3003
O.H. INDUSTRI A/S—See VKR Holding A/S; *Int'l*, pg. 8281
OHIO AG EQUIPMENT SALES CO., INC.—See Ohio Machinery Co.; *U.S. Private*, pg. 3004
THE OHIO ART COMPANY, INC.; *U.S. Public*, pg. 2118
OHIO ASSOCIATED ENTERPRISES; *U.S. Private*, pg. 3003
OHIO AUTO KOLOR, INC.; *U.S. Private*, pg. 3003
OHIO AWNING COMPANY—See Ohio Awning & Manufacturing Co.; *U.S. Private*, pg. 3003
OHIO AWNING & MANUFACTURING CO.; *U.S. Private*, pg. 3003
OHIO BAR TITLE INSURANCE COMPANY—See First American Financial Corporation; *U.S. Public*, pg. 838
THE OHIO BELL TELEPHONE COMPANY—See AT&T Inc.; *U.S. Public*, pg. 219
OHIO BLOW PIPE COMPANY; *U.S. Private*, pg. 3003
OHIO BUILDING AUTHORITY; *U.S. Private*, pg. 3004
OHIO CAPITAL CORPORATION FOR HOUSING; *U.S. Private*, pg. 3004
OHIO CARPENTERS' HEALTH FUND; *U.S. Private*, pg. 3004
OHIO CASHFLOW, LLC; *U.S. Private*, pg. 3004
OHIO CASUALTY CORPORATION—See Liberty Mutual Holding Company Inc.; *U.S. Private*, pg. 2446
THE OHIO CASUALTY INSURANCE COMPANY—See Liberty Mutual Holding Company Inc.; *U.S. Private*, pg. 2446
OHIO CAT—See Ohio Machinery Co.; *U.S. Private*, pg. 3004
OHIO CENTRAL RAILROAD, INC.—See Brookfield Infrastructure Partners L.P.; *Int'l*, pg. 1192
OHIO CENTRAL RAILROAD, INC.—See GIC Pte. Ltd.; *Int'l*, pg. 2966
OHIO COUNTY HOSPITAL CORPORATION; *U.S. Private*, pg. 3004
OHIO CUMMUNITY MEDIA LLC—See Independence Capital Partners, LLC; *U.S. Private*, pg. 2057
OHIO DECORATIVE PRODUCTS INC.; *U.S. Private*, pg. 3004
OHIO DESK CO., INC.; *U.S. Private*, pg. 3004
OHIO EDISON COMPANY—See FirstEnergy Corp.; *U.S. Public*, pg. 849
OHIO EDUCATION ASSOCIATION; *U.S. Private*, pg. 3004
OHIO ELECTRIC MOTORS INC.—See HBD Industries, Inc.; *U.S. Private*, pg. 1887
OHIO FARMERS INSURANCE COMPANY; *U.S. Private*, pg. 3004
OHIO GAS COMPANY; *U.S. Private*, pg. 3004
OHIO GRATINGS, INC.; *U.S. Private*, pg. 3004
OHIOGUIDESTONE; *U.S. Private*, pg. 3005
THE OHIO HIGH SCHOOL ATHLETIC ASSOCIATION; *U.S. Private*, pg. 4088
OHIO HISTORY CONNECTION; *U.S. Private*, pg. 3004
THE OHIO HOSPITAL ASSOCIATION; *U.S. Private*, pg. 4088
OHIO HOSPITAL FOR PSYCHIATRY, LLC—See Acadia Healthcare Company, Inc.; *U.S. Public*, pg. 29
OHIO INDEMNITY COMPANY - OIC LENDER SERVICES DIVISION—See BancInsurance Corporation; *U.S. Private*, pg. 464
OHIO INDEMNITY COMPANY—See BancInsurance Corporation; *U.S. Private*, pg. 464
OHIO LOGOS, INC.—See Lamar Advertising Company; *U.S. Public*, pg. 1291
OHIO LUMEX CO., INC.—See Lumex Ltd.; *Int'l*, pg. 4578
OHIO MACHINERY CO. - MANTSINEN USA DIVISION—See Ohio Machinery Co.; *U.S. Private*, pg. 3004
OHIO MACHINERY CO.; *U.S. Private*, pg. 3004
OHIO MAGNETICS, INC. - STEARNS MAGNETICS DIVISION—See HBD Industries, Inc.; *U.S. Private*, pg. 1887
OHIO MEDICAL CORP.—See Barings BDC, Inc.; *U.S. Public*, pg. 276
OHIO MEDICAL TRANSPORTATION; *U.S. Private*, pg. 3004
OHIO MENTOR, INC.—See Centerbridge Partners, L.P.; *U.S. Private*, pg. 814
OHIO METAL TECHNOLOGIES, INC.; *U.S. Private*, pg. 3004
OHIO METAL WORKING PRODUCTS CO., INC.—See Art's-Way Manufacturing Co., Inc.; *U.S. Public*, pg. 201
OHIO & MICHIGAN PAPER CO.—See Bain Capital, LP; *U.S. Private*, pg. 441

OHIO METAL TECHNOLOGIES, INC.   CORPORATE AFFILIATIONS

THE OHIO MOULDING CORPORATION - OMCO SOLAR DIVISION—See The Ohio Moulding Corporation; *U.S. Private*, pg. 4088
THE OHIO MOULDING CORPORATION; *U.S. Private*, pg. 4088
OHIO MULCH SUPPLY INC.; *U.S. Private*, pg. 3005
OHIO MUTUAL INSURANCE GROUP; *U.S. Private*, pg. 3005
OHIO NATIONAL EQUITIES, INC.—See Caisse de Depot et Placement du Quebec; *Int'l*, pg. 1254
OHIO NATIONAL EQUITIES, INC.—See Ontario Teachers' Pension Plan; *Int'l*, pg. 5586
OHIO NATIONAL FINANCIAL SERVICES, INC.—See Caisse de Depot et Placement du Quebec; *Int'l*, pg. 1254
OHIO NATIONAL FINANCIAL SERVICES, INC.—See Ontario Teachers' Pension Plan; *Int'l*, pg. 5586
OHIO NATIONAL HOLDINGS, INC.—See Caisse de Depot et Placement du Quebec; *Int'l*, pg. 1254
OHIO NATIONAL HOLDINGS, INC.—See Ontario Teachers' Pension Plan; *Int'l*, pg. 5586
OHIO NATIONAL INVESTMENTS, INC.—See Caisse de Depot et Placement du Quebec; *Int'l*, pg. 1254
OHIO NATIONAL INVESTMENTS, INC.—See Ontario Teachers' Pension Plan; *Int'l*, pg. 5586
OHIO NATIONAL LIFE ASSURANCE CORPORATION—See Caisse de Depot et Placement du Quebec; *Int'l*, pg. 1254
OHIO NATIONAL LIFE ASSURANCE CORPORATION—See Ontario Teachers' Pension Plan; *Int'l*, pg. 5586
OHIO NUT & BOLT CO—See Fastener Industries Inc.; *U.S. Private*, pg. 1482
OHIO NUT & BOLT OF CANADA, LTD.—See Fastener Industries Inc.; *U.S. Private*, pg. 1482
OHIO/OKLAHOMA HEARST-ARGYLE TELEVISION, INC.—See The Hearst Corporation; *U.S. Private*, pg. 4048
OHIO PACKAGING CO.—See Greif Inc.; *U.S. Public*, pg. 967
OHIO PACKING COMPANY; *U.S. Private*, pg. 3005
OHIO PHASE-IN-RECOVERY FUNDING LLC—See American Electric Power Company, Inc.; *U.S. Public*, pg. 100
OHIO PICKLING & PROCESSING—See MNP Corporation; *U.S. Private*, pg. 2756
OHIO POWER COMPANY—See American Electric Power Company, Inc.; *U.S. Public*, pg. 100
OHIO POWER TOOL; *U.S. Private*, pg. 3005
OHIO PRESBYTERIAN RETIREMENT SERVICE; *U.S. Private*, pg. 3005
OHIO PROCESSORS, INC.—See Instantwhip Foods, Inc.; *U.S. Private*, pg. 2093
OHIO RIVER METAL SERVICES, INC.—See Reliance Steel & Aluminum Co.; *U.S. Public*, pg. 1781
OHIO-SEALY MATTRESS MANUFACTURING - FORT WORTH—See Tempur Sealy International, Inc.; *U.S. Public*, pg. 1999
OHIO SECURITY SYSTEMS INC.; *U.S. Private*, pg. 3005
OHIO SOUTHERN RAILROAD, INC.—See Brookfield Infrastructure Partners L.P.; *Int'l*, pg. 1192
OHIO SOUTHERN RAILROAD, INC.—See GIC Pte. Ltd.; *Int'l*, pg. 2966
OHIO STAR FORGE CO.—See Daido Steel Co., Ltd.; *Int'l*, pg. 1923
OHIO STATE HOME SERVICES INC.; *U.S. Private*, pg. 3005
THE OHIO STATE LIFE INSURANCE COMPANY—See Financial Holding Corp.; *U.S. Private*, pg. 1507
OHIO STEEL INDUSTRIES, INC.; *U.S. Private*, pg. 3005
OHIO TAR ASPHALT—See Central Allied Enterprises; *U.S. Private*, pg. 818
OHIO TOOL SYSTEMS, INC.; *U.S. Private*, pg. 3005
OHIO TRANSMISSION CORPORATION—See Genstar Capital, LLC; *U.S. Private*, pg. 1678
OHIO TRANSPORT CORPORATION; *U.S. Private*, pg. 3005
OHIO VALLEY ALUMINUM COMPANY LLC—See Interlock Industries, Inc.; *U.S. Private*, pg. 2112
OHIO VALLEY ASPHALT, LLC—See Summit Materials, Inc.; *U.S. Public*, pg. 1960
OHIO VALLEY BANC CORP.; *U.S. Public*, pg. 1565
OHIO VALLEY BANCORP, INC.; *U.S. Private*, pg. 3005
THE OHIO VALLEY BANK COMPANY—See Ohio Valley Banc Corp.; *U.S. Public*, pg. 1565
THE OHIO VALLEY COAL COMPANY—See Ohio Valley Resources Inc.; *U.S. Private*, pg. 3005
OHIO VALLEY ELECTRIC CORPORATION; *U.S. Private*, pg. 3005
OHIO VALLEY FINANCIAL GROUP, INC.—See Ohio Valley Bancorp, Inc.; *U.S. Private*, pg. 3005
OHIO VALLEY FLOORING—See Pabco Fluid Power Company; *U.S. Private*, pg. 3063
OHIO VALLEY GOODWILL; *U.S. Private*, pg. 3005
OHIO VALLEY HEALTH SERVICES AND EDUCATION; *U.S. Private*, pg. 3005
OHIO VALLEY MANUFACTURING INC.; *U.S. Private*, pg. 3005
OHIO VALLEY RESOURCES INC.; *U.S. Private*, pg. 3005

OHIO VALLEY SUPERMARKET INC.; *U.S. Private*, pg. 3005
OHIO VALLEY SUPPLY COMPANY; *U.S. Private*, pg. 3005
OHIO VALLEY SUPPLY, INC.—See GMS Inc.; *U.S. Public*, pg. 948
OHI PETROLEUM AND ENERGY SERVICES LLC—See Oman Holdings International Company SAOG; *Int'l*, pg. 5560
OHISHI SANGYO CO., LTD.; *Int'l*, pg. 5532
OHI TELECOMMUNICATIONS COMPANY LLC—See Oman Holdings International Company SAOG; *Int'l*, pg. 5560
OHIZUMI MFG. CO., LTD.—See Ferrotec Holdings Corporation; *Int'l*, pg. 2643
OHIZUMI MFG CO., LTD. - TOWADA PLANT—See Ferrotec Holdings Corporation; *Int'l*, pg. 2643
OHIZUMI MFG (THAILAND) CO., LTD.—See Ferrotec Holdings Corporation; *Int'l*, pg. 2643
OHJI RUBBER & CHEMICALS CO., LTD.—See Kuriyama Holdings Corporation; *Int'l*, pg. 4342
OHKA ERUOPE LTD.—See Tokyo Ohka Kogyo Co., Ltd.; *Int'l*, pg. 7794
OHKA SERVICE CO., LTD.—See Tokyo Ohka Kogyo Co., Ltd.; *Int'l*, pg. 7794
OHKAWA CORP.—See Alconix Corporation; *Int'l*, pg. 302
OHKI CO., LTD.—See Ohki Healthcare Holdings Co., Ltd.; *Int'l*, pg. 5532
OHKI HEALTHCARE HOLDINGS CO., LTD.; *Int'l*, pg. 5532
OHKUCHI ELECTRONICS CO., LTD.—See Sumitomo Metal Mining Co., Ltd.; *Int'l*, pg. 7291
OHKUCHI MATERIALS CO., LTD.—See Sumitomo Metal Mining Co., Ltd.; *Int'l*, pg. 7291
OHKURA PHARMACEUTICAL CO., LTD.—See Meiji Holdings Co., Ltd.; *Int'l*, pg. 4801
OHL ANDINA, S.A.—See Grupo Villar Mir, S.A.U.; *Int'l*, pg. 3139
OHL CENTRAL EUROPE, A.S.—See Grupo Villar Mir, S.A.U.; *Int'l*, pg. 3139
OHL COLOMBIA, S.A.S.—See Grupo Villar Mir, S.A.U.; *Int'l*, pg. 3139
OHL CONCESIONES ARGENTINA, S.A.—See Industry Super Holdings Pty. Ltd.; *Int'l*, pg. 3676
OHL CONCESIONES CHILE, S.A.—See Industry Super Holdings Pty. Ltd.; *Int'l*, pg. 3676
OHL CONCESIONES, S.L.—See Industry Super Holdings Pty. Ltd.; *Int'l*, pg. 3676
OHL CONSTRUCCION NACIONAL EDIFICACION—See Grupo Villar Mir, S.A.U.; *Int'l*, pg. 3138
OHL CONSTRUCCION NACIONAL OBRA CIVIL—See Grupo Villar Mir, S.A.U.; *Int'l*, pg. 3139
OHL CONSTRUCTION CANADA, INC.—See Grupo Villar Mir, S.A.U.; *Int'l*, pg. 3139
OHL CONSTRUCTION NATIONAL SERVICES—See Grupo Villar Mir, S.A.U.; *Int'l*, pg. 3139
OHL CONSTRUCTION PACIFIC PTY LTD—See Grupo Villar Mir, S.A.U.; *Int'l*, pg. 3139
OHL INDUSTRIAL CHILE, S.A.—See Grupo Villar Mir, S.A.U.; *Int'l*, pg. 3139
OHL INDUSTRIAL, S.L.—See Grupo Villar Mir, S.A.U.; *Int'l*, pg. 3139
OHL INDUSTRIAL USA, INC.—See Grupo Villar Mir, S.A.U.; *Int'l*, pg. 3139
OHL INFRASTRUCTURE, INC.—See Industry Super Holdings Pty. Ltd.; *Int'l*, pg. 3676
OHLINS USA, INC.—See Apollo Global Management, Inc.; *U.S. Public*, pg. 162
OHL LOGISTICS AB—See Ohl Logistik GmbH & Co. KG; *Int'l*, pg. 5533
OHL LOGISTICS A/S—See Ohl Logistik GmbH & Co. KG; *Int'l*, pg. 5533
OHL LOGISTICS AS—See Ohl Logistik GmbH & Co. KG; *Int'l*, pg. 5533
OHL LOGISTIK GMBH & CO. KG; *Int'l*, pg. 5532
OHLSON PACKAGING, INC.—See Warburg Pincus LLC; *U.S. Private*, pg. 4438
OHLTHAVER & LIST GROUP OF COMPANIES; *Int'l*, pg. 5533
OHL URUGUAY, S.A.—See Grupo Villar Mir, S.A.U.; *Int'l*, pg. 3139
OHL USA, INC.—See Grupo Villar Mir, S.A.U.; *Int'l*, pg. 3139
OHL US LLC—See Singha Estate PCL; *Int'l*, pg. 6944
OHL ZS, A.S. - OSTRAVA—See Grupo Villar Mir, S.A.U.; *Int'l*, pg. 3139
OHL ZS, A.S.—See Grupo Villar Mir, S.A.U.; *Int'l*, pg. 3139
OHM ASPHALT GMBH—See VINCI S.A.; *Int'l*, pg. 8225
OHMATSU SERVICES CO., LTD.—See Hirayama Holdings Co., Ltd.; *Int'l*, pg. 3404
OH MEADOWS OF PERRYSBURG, LLC—See UMH Properties, Inc.; *U.S. Public*, pg. 2224
OHMEGA TECHNOLOGIES, INC.—See Arcline Investment Management LP; *U.S. Private*, pg. 315
OHMEGI ELEKTRO AB—See Instalco AB; *Int'l*, pg. 3723
OHMI HIGH-TECH CO., LTD.—See Shirai Electronics Industrial Co., Ltd.; *Int'l*, pg. 6853
OHM INTERNATIONAL CORPORATION; *U.S. Private*, pg. 3005

OHMI RAILWAY CO., LTD.—See Seibu Holdings Inc.; *Int'l*, pg. 6685
OHMI SANGYO CO., LTD.—See JFE Holdings, Inc.; *Int'l*, pg. 3937
OHMISHIMA BUSSAN CO., LTD.—See TENOX CO., LTD.; *Int'l*, pg. 7561
OHMITE MANUFACTURING COMPANY; *U.S. Private*, pg. 3005
OHM LABORATORIES, INC.—See Sun Pharmaceutical Industries Ltd.; *Int'l*, pg. 7307
OHMORI CO., LTD.; *Int'l*, pg. 5533
OHMORIYA CO., LTD.; *Int'l*, pg. 5533
OHMOTO GUMI CO., LTD.; *Int'l*, pg. 5533
OHMSTEDE INDUSTRIAL SERVICES—See EMCOR Group, Inc.; *U.S. Public*, pg. 738
OHMSTEDE, LTD.—See EMCOR Group, Inc.; *U.S. Public*, pg. 738
OHMURA SHIGYO CO., LTD.; *Int'l*, pg. 5533
OHMY CO., LTD.—See NIPPN Corporation; *Int'l*, pg. 5310
OH MY CRAFTS, INC.; *U.S. Private*, pg. 3003
OHMYHOME LIMITED; *Int'l*, pg. 5533
OHNAMI CORPORATION—See Hitachi Zosen Corporation; *Int'l*, pg. 3412
OHNISHI DENKI CO., LTD.—See Toyota Tsusho Corporation; *Int'l*, pg. 7877
OHNO PRINTING CO., LTD.—See Crestec Inc.; *Int'l*, pg. 1841
OH NYNAS AB—See Samhallsbyggnadsbolaget I Norden AB; *Int'l*, pg. 6504
OHO INTERACTIVE; *U.S. Private*, pg. 3006
OH PERRYSBURG ESTATES, LLC—See UMH Properties, Inc.; *U.S. Public*, pg. 2224
OH PIKEWOOD MANOR, LLC—See UMH Properties, Inc.; *U.S. Public*, pg. 2225
OHP, INC.—See American Vanguard Corporation; *U.S. Public*, pg. 111
OHRIDSKA BANKA A.D.—See Erste Group Bank AG; *Int'l*, pg. 2499
OHRLINGS PRICEWATERHOUSECOOPERS; *Int'l*, pg. 5533
OHRMANN MONTAGETECHNIK GMBH; *Int'l*, pg. 5533
OHSHO FOOD SERVICE CORP.; *Int'l*, pg. 5533
OHSHU EXPRESS LTD.—See H.I.S. Co., Ltd.; *Int'l*, pg. 3195
OHSMAN & SONS COMPANY INC.; *U.S. Private*, pg. 3006
OHSU FACULTY PRACTICE PLAN; *U.S. Private*, pg. 3006
OHTAKA PRECISION CO., LTD.—See OSG Corporation; *Int'l*, pg. 5649
OHTAKE-MEISHIN CHEMICAL CO., LTD.—See Chugoku Marine Paints, Ltd.; *Int'l*, pg. 1595
OHTAKIJO GOLF CLUB CORPORATION—See Tokyu Fudosan Holdings Corporation; *Int'l*, pg. 7798
OHTL PUBLIC COMPANY LIMITED—See Jardine Matheson Holdings Limited; *Int'l*, pg. 3910
OHTO CO., LTD.; *Int'l*, pg. 5533
OHTOMO-CHEMICAL INS., CORP - SAMMU FACTORY—See Nicca Chemical Co., Ltd.; *Int'l*, pg. 5264
OHTOMO-CHEMICAL INS., CORP.—See Nicca Chemical Co., Ltd.; *Int'l*, pg. 5264
OHTORI CORPORATION—See Ichinen Holdings Co., Ltd.; *Int'l*, pg. 3580
OHWADA CARBON INDUSTRIAL CO., LTD.—See Toyo Tanso Co., Ltd.; *Int'l*, pg. 7858
OIA GLOBAL LOGISTICS—See LDI Ltd., LLC; *U.S. Private*, pg. 2404
OIARSO S.COOP—See Mondragon Corporation; *Int'l*, pg. 5031
O-I ASIA PACIFIC—See O-I Glass, Inc.; *U.S. Public*, pg. 1559
OICCO ACQUISITION III, INC.; *U.S. Private*, pg. 3006
O-I CHINA—See O-I Glass, Inc.; *U.S. Public*, pg. 1559
O.I. CORPORATION—See Xylem Inc.; *U.S. Public*, pg. 2395
O-I CZECH REPUBLIC A.S.—See O-I Glass, Inc.; *U.S. Public*, pg. 1559
OIDC—See China Steel Corporation; *Int'l*, pg. 1556
OI DEVELOPMENT CO LTD—See H2O Retailing Corp.; *Int'l*, pg. 3200
OIDON CO., LTD.; *U.S. Public*, pg. 1565
OID PTE. LTD.—See Oakwell Distribution (S) Pte. Ltd.; *Int'l*, pg. 5505
OIE AS—See JM AB; *Int'l*, pg. 3974
OI ELECTRIC CO., LTD.; *Int'l*, pg. 5533
OIE SANGYO CO., LTD.; *Int'l*, pg. 5533
O-I ESTONIA AS—See O-I Glass, Inc.; *U.S. Public*, pg. 1559
OI FINNISH HOLDINGS OY—See O-I Glass, Inc.; *U.S. Public*, pg. 1560
O-I FRANCE SAS—See O-I Glass, Inc.; *U.S. Public*, pg. 1559
O-I GERMANY GMBH & CO. KG—See O-I Glass, Inc.; *U.S. Public*, pg. 1559
O-I GLASS, INC.; *U.S. Public*, pg. 1559
O-I GLASS LIMITED—See O-I Glass, Inc.; *U.S. Public*, pg. 1559

COMPANY NAME INDEX

O-I GLASS LIMITED—See O-I Glass, Inc.; *U.S. Public*, pg. 1560

O-I GLASSPACK BETEILIGUNGS & VERWALTUNGSGESELLSCHAFT GMBH—See O-I Glass, Inc.; *U.S. Public*, pg. 1559

OI GLASSPACK GMBH & CO. KG—See O-I Glass, Inc.; *U.S. Public*, pg. 1559

OIG OFFSHORE INSTALLATION GROUP ASA; *Int'l*, pg. 5533

OIL AIR HOLDINGS INC.—See Parker Hannifin Corporation; *U.S. Public*, pg. 1643

OIL-AIR PRODUCTS INC.; *U.S. Private*, pg. 3006

OIL ANALYZERS, INC.—See Amsoil Inc.; *U.S. Private*, pg. 267

OIL AND GAS EXPLORATION AND PRODUCTION PLC—See Chimimport AD; *Int'l*, pg. 1479

OIL AND MARINE AGENCIES (GHANA) LTD.—See Albert Ballin KG; *Int'l*, pg. 296

OIL AND MARINE AGENCIES SARL—See Albert Ballin KG; *Int'l*, pg. 296

OIL CASUALTY INSURANCE, LTD.—See Oil Insurance Limited; *Int'l*, pg. 5534

OIL CENTER RESEARCH INTERNATIONAL, LLC; *U.S. Private*, pg. 3006

OIL CHANGER INC.—See Greenbriar Equity Group, L.P.; *U.S. Private*, pg. 1776

OIL-CHEM RESEARCH CORPORATION—See Sonic Financial Corporation; *U.S. Private*, pg. 3713

OIL CHEM TECHNOLOGIES; *U.S. Private*, pg. 3006

OIL CITY DIALYSIS CENTER, LLC—See Nautic Partners, LLC; *U.S. Private*, pg. 2870

OIL COMPANY OF AUSTRALIA (MOURA) PTY LTD.—See Origin Energy Ltd.; *Int'l*, pg. 5629

OIL COMPANY OF AUSTRALIA (MOURA) TRANSMISSIONS PTY LTD.—See Origin Energy Ltd.; *Int'l*, pg. 5629

OILCORP BERHAD; *Int'l*, pg. 5535

OIL COUNTRY TUBULAR LIMITED - NALGONDA WORKS—See Oil Country Tubular Limited; *Int'l*, pg. 5534

OIL COUNTRY TUBULAR LIMITED; *Int'l*, pg. 5534

OILDALE ENERGY LLC—See Enpower Corp.; *U.S. Private*, pg. 1401

OIL DEVELOPMENT COMPANY K.S.C.—See Kuwait Petroleum Corporation; *Int'l*, pg. 4346

OIL-DRI CANADA ULC—See Oil-Dri Corporation of America; *U.S. Public*, pg. 1566

OIL-DRI CORPORATION OF AMERICA - INDUSTRIAL & AUTOMOTIVE DIVISION—See Oil-Dri Corporation of America; *U.S. Public*, pg. 1566

OIL-DRI CORPORATION OF AMERICA; *U.S. Public*, pg. 1565

OIL-DRI CORPORATION OF GEORGIA—See Oil-Dri Corporation of America; *U.S. Public*, pg. 1566

OIL-DRI PRODUCTION COMPANY—See Oil-Dri Corporation of America; *U.S. Public*, pg. 1566

OIL-DRI SARL—See Oil-Dri Corporation of America; *U.S. Public*, pg. 1566

OIL-DRI S.A.—See Oil-Dri Corporation of America; *U.S. Public*, pg. 1566

OIL-DRI (U.K.) LTD.—See Oil-Dri Corporation of America; *U.S. Public*, pg. 1566

OILENNIUM LIMITED—See Petrofac Limited; *Int'l*, pg. 5826

OILES AMERICA CORPORATION—See Oiles Corporation; *Int'l*, pg. 5535

OILES CORPORATION - ASHIKAGA PLANT—See Oiles Corporation; *Int'l*, pg. 5535

OILES CORPORATION - OITA PLANT—See Oiles Corporation; *Int'l*, pg. 5535

OILES CORPORATION - SHIGA PLANT—See Oiles Corporation; *Int'l*, pg. 5535

OILES CORPORATION; *Int'l*, pg. 5535

OILES CZECH MANUFACTURING S.R.O.—See Oiles Corporation; *Int'l*, pg. 5535

OILES DEUTSCHLAND GMBH—See Oiles Corporation; *Int'l*, pg. 5535

OILES ECO CORPORATION—See Oiles Corporation; *Int'l*, pg. 5535

OILES FRANCE SAS—See Oiles Corporation; *Int'l*, pg. 5535

OILES INDIA PRIVATE LIMITED - RAJASTHAN PLANT—See Oiles Corporation; *Int'l*, pg. 5535

OILES INDIA PRIVATE LIMITED—See Oiles Corporation; *Int'l*, pg. 5535

OILES SUZHOU CORPORATION—See Oiles Corporation; *Int'l*, pg. 5535

OILES (THAILAND) CO., LTD.—See Oiles Corporation; *Int'l*, pg. 5535

OILEX (JPDA 06-103) LTD.—See Synergia Energy Ltd; *Int'l*, pg. 7383

OILEX OMAN LIMITED—See Synergia Energy Ltd; *Int'l*, pg. 7383

OILFAB SDN. BHD.—See Oilcorp Berhad; *Int'l*, pg. 5535

OIL FACTORY BANAT AD; *Int'l*, pg. 5534

OILFIELD HIRE & SERVICES LTD.—See L'Air Liquide S.A.; *Int'l*, pg. 4375

OILFIELD SERVICES & SUPPLIES (INDIA) PVT LTD—See Oilfield Services & Supplies Pte. Ltd.; *Int'l*, pg. 5535

OILFIELD SERVICES & SUPPLIES PTE LTD. - KAKINADA FACILITY—See Oilfield Services & Supplies Pte. Ltd.; *Int'l*, pg. 5535

OILFIELD SERVICES & SUPPLIES PTE. LTD.; *Int'l*, pg. 5535

OILFIELD SERVICES & SUPPLIES (THAILAND) CO., LTD.—See Oilfield Services & Supplies Pte. Ltd.; *Int'l*, pg. 5535

OILFIELD SERVICES & SUPPLIES (TIANJIN) CO. LTD—See Oilfield Services & Supplies Pte. Ltd.; *Int'l*, pg. 5535

OILFIELDS SUPPLY CENTRE LLC—See Bhatia Brothers Group; *Int'l*, pg. 1014

OIL FILM BEARING SUB-CO.—See Taiyuan Heavy Industry Co., Ltd.; *Int'l*, pg. 7427

OIL & GAS ASSET CLEARINGHOUSE, LLC—See OFSCap LLC; *U.S. Private*, pg. 3003

OIL & GAS DEVELOPMENT COMPANY LTD.; *Int'l*, pg. 5533

OIL & GAS EQUIPMENT CORP.; *U.S. Private*, pg. 3006

OIL & GAS SOLUTIONS PTE LTD—See BH Global Corporation Limited; *Int'l*, pg. 1009

THE OILGEAR COMPANY - FREMONT—See Wynnchurch Capital, L.P.; *U.S. Private*, pg. 4578

THE OILGEAR COMPANY—See Wynnchurch Capital, L.P.; *U.S. Private*, pg. 4578

OILGEAR TOWLER GMBH—See Wynnchurch Capital, L.P.; *U.S. Private*, pg. 4578

OILGEAR TOWLER LTD.—See Wynnchurch Capital, L.P.; *U.S. Private*, pg. 4578

OILGEAR TOWLER S.A.—See Wynnchurch Capital, L.P.; *U.S. Private*, pg. 4578

OILGEAR TOWLER SAS—See Wynnchurch Capital, L.P.; *U.S. Private*, pg. 4578

OILGEAR TOWLER S.R.L.—See Wynnchurch Capital, L.P.; *U.S. Private*, pg. 4578

OIL INDIA LIMITED; *Int'l*, pg. 5534

OIL INDUSTRIES ENGINEERING & CONSTRUCTION CO.—See Parsian Oil & Gas Development Co.; *Int'l*, pg. 5747

OIL INSURANCE COMPANY—See Chevron Corporation; *U.S. Public*, pg. 487

OIL INSURANCE LIMITED; *Int'l*, pg. 5534

OIL INVESTMENT CORPORATION LTD.—See Oil Insurance Limited; *Int'l*, pg. 5534

OILKO KDA; *Int'l*, pg. 5535

OIL-LAW RECORDS CORP.—See Hellman & Friedman LLC; *U.S. Private*, pg. 1908

OIL LIFT TECHNOLOGY PTY LTD—See Dover Corporation; *U.S. Public*, pg. 682

OIL-LINE ENGINEERING & ASSOCIATES SDN. BHD.—See Oilcorp Berhad; *Int'l*, pg. 5535

OIL-LYMPIA OIL AND GAS INC.—See Petrolympic Ltd.; *Int'l*, pg. 5831

OIL MANAGEMENT SERVICES LTD.—See Oil Insurance Limited; *Int'l*, pg. 5534

OIL & MARINE AGENCIES (O.M.A.) SARL—See Albert Ballin KG; *Int'l*, pg. 296

OILMAX ENERGY PVT. LTD.; *Int'l*, pg. 5536

OILMEN'S EQUIPMENT CORP.; *U.S. Private*, pg. 3006

OIL MOP, L.L.C.—See Macquarie Group Limited; *Int'l*, pg. 4630

OIL & NATURAL GAS CORPORATION LIMITED; *Int'l*, pg. 5534

OIL OPTIMIZATION INC.; *Int'l*, pg. 5534

OIL PATCH FUEL & SUPPLY INC.; *U.S. Private*, pg. 3006

OIL PRICE INFORMATION SERVICE LLC—See News Corporation; *U.S. Public*, pg. 1521

OIL PURIFICATION SYSTEMS, INC.; *U.S. Private*, pg. 3006

OIL REFINERIES LTD.—See Israel Corporation Ltd.; *Int'l*, pg. 3823

OIL REFINERIES LTD.—See Israel Petrochemical Enterprises Ltd.; *Int'l*, pg. 3824

OIL REFINERY BELGRADE; *Int'l*, pg. 5535

OIL REFINERY J.S.C. BROD; *Int'l*, pg. 5535

OIL REFINERY MODRICA; *Int'l*, pg. 5535

OIL SANDS SONOPROCESS SOLUTIONS INC.—See Sonoro Energy Ltd.; *Int'l*, pg. 7100

OIL SEARCH (ALASKA) LLC—See Santos Limited; *Int'l*, pg. 6559

OIL SEARCH (EASTERN DESERT) SAE—See Santos Limited; *Int'l*, pg. 6559

OIL SEARCH LIMITED—See Santos Limited; *Int'l*, pg. 6559

OIL SEARCH (MIDDLE EASTERN) LIMITED—See Santos Limited; *Int'l*, pg. 6559

OIL SEARCH (PNG) LIMITED—See Santos Limited; *Int'l*, pg. 6559

OIL SEARCH (ROY) LIMITED—See Santos Limited; *Int'l*, pg. 6559

OIL SEARCH (TUNISIA) LIMITED—See Santos Limited; *Int'l*, pg. 6559

OIL SEARCH (YEMEN) LIMITED—See Santos Limited; *Int'l*, pg. 6559

OIL WELL SERVICE CO.

OIL SECTOR SERVICES COMPANY—See Kuwait Petroleum Corporation; *Int'l*, pg. 4346

OILSEEDS INTERNATIONAL LTD.—See ITOCHU Corporation; *Int'l*, pg. 3838

OIL SHIPPING (BUNKERING) B.V.—See World Kinect Corporation; *U.S. Public*, pg. 2381

OIL SPILL RESPONSE (AMERICAS) LIMITED—See Oil Spill Response Limited; *Int'l*, pg. 5535

OIL SPILL RESPONSE LIMITED; *Int'l*, pg. 5535

OIL STATES ENERGY SERVICES (CANADA) INC.—See Oil States International, Inc.; *U.S. Public*, pg. 1565

OIL STATES ENERGY SERVICES HOLDING, INC.—See Oil States International, Inc.; *U.S. Public*, pg. 1565

OIL STATES ENERGY SERVICES, INC.—See Oil States International, Inc.; *U.S. Public*, pg. 1565

OIL STATES ENERGY SERVICES, INC.—See Oil States International, Inc.; *U.S. Public*, pg. 1565

OIL STATES ENERGY SERVICES L.L.C.—See Oil States International, Inc.; *U.S. Public*, pg. 1565

OIL STATES HYDROTECH—See Oil States International, Inc.; *U.S. Public*, pg. 1565

OIL STATES HYDROTECH SYSTEMS—See Oil States International, Inc.; *U.S. Public*, pg. 1565

OIL STATES INDUSTRIES (ASIA) PTE LTD.—See Oil States International, Inc.; *U.S. Public*, pg. 1565

OIL STATES INDUSTRIES, INC.—See Oil States International, Inc.; *U.S. Public*, pg. 1565

OIL STATES INDUSTRIES (UK) LTD.—See Oil States International, Inc.; *U.S. Public*, pg. 1565

OIL STATES INTERNATIONAL, INC.; *U.S. Public*, pg. 1565

OIL STATES QCS—See Oil States International, Inc.; *U.S. Public*, pg. 1565

OIL STATES SKAGIT SMATCO L.L.C.—See Oil States International, Inc.; *U.S. Public*, pg. 1565

OIL STATES—See Oil States International, Inc.; *U.S. Public*, pg. 1565

OIL SYSTEMS, INC.—See MetalTek International; *U.S. Private*, pg. 2682

OILTANKING AMSTERDAM B.V.—See Marquard & Bahls AG; *Int'l*, pg. 4700

OILTANKING BULGARIA A.D.—See Marquard & Bahls AG; *Int'l*, pg. 4700

OILTANKING COLOMBIA S. A.—See Marquard & Bahls AG; *Int'l*, pg. 4700

OILTANKING COPENHAGEN A/S—See Marquard & Bahls AG; *Int'l*, pg. 4700

OILTANKING DAYA BAY CO. LTD.—See Marquard & Bahls AG; *Int'l*, pg. 4700

OILTANKING DEUTSCHLAND GMBH & CO. KG—See Marquard & Bahls AG; *Int'l*, pg. 4700

OILTANKING GHENT N.V.—See Marquard & Bahls AG; *Int'l*, pg. 4700

OILTANKING GMBH—See Marquard & Bahls AG; *Int'l*, pg. 4700

OILTANKING HUNGARY KFT.—See Marquard & Bahls AG; *Int'l*, pg. 4700

OILTANKING MALTA LTD—See Marquard & Bahls AG; *Int'l*, pg. 4700

OILTANKING (NANJING) CO., LTD—See Marquard & Bahls AG; *Int'l*, pg. 4700

OILTANKING ODFJELL TERMINALS & CO. LLC—See Marquard & Bahls AG; *Int'l*, pg. 4700

OILTANKING ODFJELL TERMINALS & CO. LLC—See Odfjell SE; *Int'l*, pg. 5526

OILTANKING PERU S. A. C.—See Marquard & Bahls AG; *Int'l*, pg. 4700

OILTANKING PORT NECHES, LLC—See Marquard & Bahls AG; *Int'l*, pg. 4700

OILTANKING SONMARIN OY—See Marquard & Bahls AG; *Int'l*, pg. 4700

OILTANKING STOLTHAVEN ANTWERP N. V.—See Marquard & Bahls AG; *Int'l*, pg. 4700

OILTANKING TALLINN AS—See Olerex AS; *Int'l*, pg. 5553

OILTANKING TERMINAIS LTDA.—See Marquard & Bahls AG; *Int'l*, pg. 4700

OILTANKING TERNEUZEN B.V.—See Marquard & Bahls AG; *Int'l*, pg. 4700

OILTANKING TEXAS CITY, L.P.—See Marquard & Bahls AG; *Int'l*, pg. 4700

OIL! TANKSTELLEN AG—See Marquard & Bahls AG; *Int'l*, pg. 4700

OILTECH LUBES SERVICE GMBH & CO. KG—See Marquard & Bahls AG; *Int'l*, pg. 4700

OILTEK GLOBAL ENERGY SDN. BHD.—See Koh Brothers Eco Engineering Ltd.; *Int'l*, pg. 4228

OILTEK INTERNATIONAL LIMITED; *Int'l*, pg. 5536

OILTEK SDN. BHD.—See Koh Brothers Group Limited; *Int'l*, pg. 4228

OIL TERMINAL S.A; *Int'l*, pg. 5535

OIL TEX (THAILAND) CO. LTD—See Japan Post Holdings Co., Ltd.; *Int'l*, pg. 3900

OIL TRADING IMPORTADORA E EXPORTADORA LTDA.—See Ultrapar Participacoes S.A.; *Int'l*, pg. 8019

OIL TRADING POLAND SP. Z O.O.—See Hinduja Group Ltd.; *Int'l*, pg. 3399

OILWELL INC.; *U.S. Private*, pg. 3006

OIL WELL SERVICE CO.; *U.S. Private*, pg. 3006

OIL WELL SERVICE CO.

CORPORATE AFFILIATIONS

O-I MANUFACTURING CZECH REPUBLIC A.S.—See O-I Glass, Inc.; *U.S. Public*, pg. 1559
O-I MANUFACTURING FRANCE SAS—See O-I Glass, Inc.; *U.S. Public*, pg. 1559
O-I MANUFACTURING ITALY S.P.A.—See O-I Glass, Inc.; *U.S. Public*, pg. 1559
O-I MANUFACTURING LTD.—See O-I Glass, Inc.; *U.S. Public*, pg. 1560
OIMA S.P.A.—See Sacmi Imola S.C.A.R.L.; *Int'l*, pg. 6464
OIMEX ELECTRODE LTD.; *Int'l*, pg. 5536
OINA VV AKTIEBOLAG—See Ingersoll Rand Inc.; *U.S. Public*, pg. 1122
O-I NETHERLANDS B.V.—See O-I Glass, Inc.; *U.S. Public*, pg. 1559
O-I NETHERLANDS B.V.—See O-I Glass, Inc.; *U.S. Public*, pg. 1560
OINTON INTERNATIONAL INC.; *U.S. Private*, pg. 3006
OIO HOLDINGS LIMITED; *Int'l*, pg. 5536
O-I PACKAGING SOLUTIONS, LLC—See O-I Glass, Inc.; *U.S. Public*, pg. 1559
OIP N.V.—See Elbit Systems Limited; *Int'l*, pg. 2345
O-I SALES AND DISTRIBUTION ITALY S.R.L.—See O-I Glass, Inc.; *U.S. Public*, pg. 1559
O-I SALES AND DISTRIBUTION LT—See O-I Glass, Inc.; *U.S. Public*, pg. 1560
OI S.A.; *Int'l*, pg. 5533
OI SEISHI CO., LTD.—See Oji Holdings Corporation; *Int'l*, pg. 5537
O-I (SHANGHAI) GLASS CONTAINER CO., LTD.—See O-I Glass, Inc.; *U.S. Public*, pg. 1559
OISHI F&B (SINGAPORE) PTE. LTD.—See Thai Beverage Public Company Limited; *Int'l*, pg. 7591
OISHI FOOD SERVICES CO., LTD.—See Thai Beverage Public Company Limited; *Int'l*, pg. 7591
OISHI GROUP PUBLIC COMPANY LIMITED—See Thai Beverage Public Company Limited; *Int'l*, pg. 7591
OISHI JAPANESE PIZZA PTE LTD—See ABR Holdings, Ltd.; *Int'l*, pg. 67
OISHI SECURITIES CO., LTD.—See Okasan Securities Group Inc.; *Int'l*, pg. 5545
OISHI TRADING CO., LTD.—See Thai Beverage Public Company Limited; *Int'l*, pg. 7591
OISIX RA DAICHI INC.; *Int'l*, pg. 5536
OISTINS (PTY) LIMITED—See Country Bird Holdings Limited; *Int'l*, pg. 1818
THE OITA BANK, LTD.; *Int'l*, pg. 7671
OITA BUSINESS SERVICE CO., LTD.—See Sankyu, Inc.; *Int'l*, pg. 6544
OITA CANON INC.—See Canon Inc.; *Int'l*, pg. 1298
OITA CANON MATERIALS INC.—See Canon Inc.; *Int'l*, pg. 1298
OITA CHEMICAL CO., LTD.—See Toagosei Co. Ltd.; *Int'l*, pg. 7770
OITA COMPUTER ENGINEERING & CONSULTING, LTD.—See Computer Engineering & Consulting Ltd.; *Int'l*, pg. 1759
OITA GENERAL SERVICE CO., LTD.—See Sumitomo Chemical Company, Limited; *Int'l*, pg. 7264
OITA KOUN CO., LTD.—See Kamigumi Co., Ltd.; *Int'l*, pg. 4062
OITA KYUSEKI HANBAI CO., LTD.—See Itochu Enex Co., Ltd.; *Int'l*, pg. 3842
OITA LIQUEFIED NATURAL GAS CO., INC.—See Kyushu Electric Power Co., Inc.; *Int'l*, pg. 4368
OITA MARINE BIOLOGICAL TECHNOLOGY CENTER—See Nissui Corporation; *Int'l*, pg. 5378
OITA MINING CO., LTD.—See Tokuyama Corporation; *Int'l*, pg. 7787
OITA NS SOLUTIONS CORPORATION—See Nippon Steel Corporation; *Int'l*, pg. 5335
OITA RINKAI KOGYO K.K.—See Nippon Yusen Kabushiki Kaisha; *Int'l*, pg. 5359
OITA TAIHEIYO MINING CORPORATION—See Taiheiyo Cement Corporation; *Int'l*, pg. 7411
OITA TOSTEM CO., LTD.—See LIXIL Group Corporation; *Int'l*, pg. 4535
OI-TECHNO. CO., LTD.—See Oi Electric Co., Ltd.; *Int'l*, pg. 5533
OI WAH PAWNSHOP CREDIT HOLDINGS LIMITED; *Int'l*, pg. 5533
OIZUMI CORPORATION; *Int'l*, pg. 5536
OJAI OIL COMPANY; *U.S. Public*, pg. 1566
OJAI VALLEY INN & SPA; *U.S. Private*, pg. 3006
O.J. COMPANY; *Int'l*, pg. 5503
OJI ASIA HOUSEHOLD PRODUCT SDN. BHD.—See Oji Holdings Corporation; *Int'l*, pg. 5537
OJI ASIA MANAGEMENT SDN. BHD.—See Oji Holdings Corporation; *Int'l*, pg. 5537
OJIBWAY OF THE PIC RIVER FIRST NATION; *Int'l*, pg. 5539
OJI CHIYODA CONTAINER CO., LTD.—See Oji Holdings Corporation; *Int'l*, pg. 5537
OJI CORNSTARCH CO., LTD.—See Oji Holdings Corporation; *Int'l*, pg. 5537
OJI ECO MATERIALS CO., LTD.—See Oji Holdings Corporation; *Int'l*, pg. 5537
OJI ELECTRIC CO., LTD.—See Yaskawa Electric Corporation; *Int'l*, pg. 8569

OJI ENGINEERING CO., LTD.—See Oji Holdings Corporation; *Int'l*, pg. 5537
OJI FIBER CO., LTD.—See Daiwabo Holdings Co., Ltd.; *Int'l*, pg. 1949
OJI FIBRE SOLUTIONS HONG KONG LTD—See Oji Holdings Corporation; *Int'l*, pg. 5537
OJI FIBRE SOLUTIONS MALAYSIA SDN BHD—See Oji Holdings Corporation; *Int'l*, pg. 5537
OJI FIBRE SOLUTIONS (NZ) LTD.—See Oji Holdings Corporation; *Int'l*, pg. 5537
OJI FIBRE SOLUTIONS PTY. LTD.—See Oji Holdings Corporation; *Int'l*, pg. 5537
OJI FOREST & PRODUCTS CO., LTD.—See Oji Holdings Corporation; *Int'l*, pg. 5537
OJI FOREST PRODUCTS VIETNAM CO., LTD.—See Oji Holdings Corporation; *Int'l*, pg. 5537
OJI GS PACKAGING (YANGON) CO., LTD.—See Oji Holdings Corporation; *Int'l*, pg. 5537
OJI HALL CO., LTD.—See Oji Holdings Corporation; *Int'l*, pg. 5537
OJI HOLDINGS CORPORATION; *Int'l*, pg. 5536
OJI INDIA PACKAGING PVT. LTD.—See Oji Holdings Corporation; *Int'l*, pg. 5537
OJI INTERPACK CO., LTD.—See Oji Holdings Corporation; *Int'l*, pg. 5537
OJI INTERPACK INDIA PVT. LTD.—See Oji Holdings Corporation; *Int'l*, pg. 5537
OJI INTERPACK KOREA LTD.—See Oji Holdings Corporation; *Int'l*, pg. 5537
OJI INTERTECH, INC.—See Oji Holdings Corporation; *Int'l*, pg. 5537
OJI KINOCLOTH CO., LTD.—See Oji Holdings Corporation; *Int'l*, pg. 5538
OJI KINOCLOTH (SHANGHAI) CO., LTD.—See Oji Holdings Corporation; *Int'l*, pg. 5538
OJI LABEL (THAILAND) LTD.—See Oji Holdings Corporation; *Int'l*, pg. 5538
OJI LOGISTICS CO., LTD.—See Oji Holdings Corporation; *Int'l*, pg. 5538
OJI-LTOCHU ENEX POWER RETAILING CO., LTD.—See Itochu Enex Co., Ltd.; *Int'l*, pg. 3842
OJI MYANMAR PACKAGING CO., LTD.—See Oji Holdings Corporation; *Int'l*, pg. 5538
O.J. INDUSTRIAL MAINTENANCE—See Quanta Services, Inc.; *U.S. Public*, pg. 1752
OJI NEPIA CO., LTD.—See Oji Holdings Corporation; *Int'l*, pg. 5538
OJ INSULATION CO. INC.; *U.S. Private*, pg. 3006
OJ INSULATION, L.P.—See Installed Building Products, Inc.; *U.S. Public*, pg. 1133
OJI PACKAGING (CAMBODIA) CO., LTD.—See HPI Resources Berhad; *Int'l*, pg. 3501
OJI PACKAGING CO., LTD.—See Oji Holdings Corporation; *Int'l*, pg. 5538
OJI PACKAGING (SHANGHAI) CO., LTD.—See Oji Holdings Corporation; *Int'l*, pg. 5538
OJI PAPEIS ESPECIAIS LTDA.—See Oji Holdings Corporation; *Int'l*, pg. 5538
OJI PAPERBOARD CO., LTD.—See Oji Holdings Corporation; *Int'l*, pg. 5538
OJI PAPER CO., LTD.—See Oji Holdings Corporation; *Int'l*, pg. 5538
OJI PAPER INTERNATIONAL TRADING (SHANGHAI) CO., LTD.—See Oji Holdings Corporation; *Int'l*, pg. 5538
OJI PAPER MANAGEMENT (SHANGHAI) CO., LTD.—See Oji Holdings Corporation; *Int'l*, pg. 5538
OJI PAPER NEPIA (SUZHOU) CO., LTD.—See Oji Holdings Corporation; *Int'l*, pg. 5538
OJI PAPER (THAILAND) LTD.—See Oji Holdings Corporation; *Int'l*, pg. 5538
OJI REAL ESTATE CO., LTD.—See Oji Holdings Corporation; *Int'l*, pg. 5538
OJI SALMON CO., LTD.—See Oji Holdings Corporation; *Int'l*, pg. 5538
OJI SOUTH LAO PLANTATION FOREST CO., LTD.—See Oji Holdings Corporation; *Int'l*, pg. 5538
OJI SPECIALTY PAPER CO., LTD.—See Oji Holdings Corporation; *Int'l*, pg. 5538
OJI TAC CO., LTD.—See Oji Holdings Corporation; *Int'l*, pg. 5538
OJITEX HAIPHONG CO., LTD.—See Oji Holdings Corporation; *Int'l*, pg. 5538
OJITEX HARTA PACKAGING (SIHANOUKVILLE) LIMITED—See HPI Resources Berhad; *Int'l*, pg. 3501
OJITEX (VIETNAM) CO., LTD.—See Oji Holdings Corporation; *Int'l*, pg. 5538
OJI TIMELY CO., LTD.—See Oji Holdings Corporation; *Int'l*, pg. 5538
OJJUS MEDICARE PRIVATE LIMITED; *Int'l*, pg. 5539
OJO LABS, INC.—See The Northwestern Mutual Life Insurance Company; *U.S. Private*, pg. 4085
OJO TECHNOLOGY, INC.—See Ares Management Corporation; *U.S. Public*, pg. 189
O.J. PIPELINES CANADA LIMITED PARTNERSHIP—See Quanta Services, Inc.; *U.S. Public*, pg. 1752
OJS BUILDING SERVICES INC.; *U.S. Private*, pg. 3006
OJSC AK BARS BANK; *Int'l*, pg. 5539

OJSC ALCHEVSK IRON & STEEL WORKS—See Industrial Union of Donbass Corporation; *Int'l*, pg. 3673
OJSC ANK BASHNEFT—See Sistema PJSFC; *Int'l*, pg. 6963
OJSC ARMADA; *Int'l*, pg. 5539
OJSC BANK SAINT PETERSBURG; *Int'l*, pg. 5539
OJSC BASHMETALLOPTORG—See OJSC Magnitogorsk Iron & Steel Works; *Int'l*, pg. 5540
OJSC CARRIAGE REPAIR COMPANY - 2—See JSC Russian Railways; *Int'l*, pg. 4012
OJSC CARRIAGE REPAIR COMPANY - 3—See JSC Russian Railways; *Int'l*, pg. 4012
OJSC CESLA—See Heidelberg Materials AG; *Int'l*, pg. 3318
OJSC CHERKIZOVO GROUP; *Int'l*, pg. 5539
OJSC CONCERN KALASHNIKOV; *Int'l*, pg. 5539
OJSC CONCERN KALINA—See Unilever PLC; *Int'l*, pg. 8044
OJSC CONCERN STROMNEFTEMASH—See Integra Management LLC; *Int'l*, pg. 3729
OJSC DAGNEFTEGAZ—See OJSC Rosneftegaz; *Int'l*, pg. 5541
OJSC DNEPROVSKY IRON & STEEL INTEGRATED WORKS—See Industrial Union of Donbass Corporation; *Int'l*, pg. 3673
OJSC EAST-SIBERIAN OIL AND GAS COMPANY—See OJSC Rosneftegaz; *Int'l*, pg. 5541
OJSC EVRAZ VANADY TULA—See Evraz plc; *Int'l*, pg. 2574
OJSC EXPERIMENTAL DESIGN BUREAU N.A. A.S. YAKOVLEV—See PJSC United Aircraft Corporation; *Int'l*, pg. 5885
OJSC EXPERIMENTAL MACHINE-BUILDING PLANT N.A. V.M. MYASISHCHEV—See PJSC United Aircraft Corporation; *Int'l*, pg. 5885
OJSC EZHK—See Gruppa Kompaniy Rusagro OOO; *Int'l*, pg. 3140
OJSC FEDERAL GRID COMPANY OF UNIFIED ENERGY SYSTEM; *Int'l*, pg. 5539
OJSC FREIGHT ONE—See Universal Cargo Logistics Holding B.V.; *Int'l*, pg. 8077
OJSC GLOBALSTROY-ENGINEERING; *Int'l*, pg. 5539
OJSC HIGH-SPEED RAIL LINES—See JSC Russian Railways; *Int'l*, pg. 4012
OJSC HUMAN STEM CELL INSTITUTE; *Int'l*, pg. 5539
OJSC IG SPASSKIE VOROTA—See OJSC Globalstroy-Engineering; *Int'l*, pg. 5539
OJSC ILYUSHIN AVIATION COMPLEX—See PJSC United Aircraft Corporation; *Int'l*, pg. 5885
OJSC INTERREGIONAL DISTRIBUTION GRID COMPANY OF THE SOUTH—See JSC ROSSETI; *Int'l*, pg. 4010
OJSC INTERREGIONAL DISTRIBUTIVE GRID COMPANY OF URALS—See JSC ROSSETI; *Int'l*, pg. 4010
OJSC IZHORSKIYE ZAVODY—See Gazprombank JSC; *Int'l*, pg. 2892
OJSC KUYBYSHEV REFINERY—See OJSC Rosneftegaz; *Int'l*, pg. 5541
OJSC KUZBASSENERGO; *Int'l*, pg. 5539
OJSC KUZBASSTOPLIVOSBYT—See OAO Kuzbasskaya Toplivnaya Company OJSC; *Int'l*, pg. 5506
OJSC MAGNITOGORSK IRON & STEEL WORKS; *Int'l*, pg. 5539
OJSC MCRW—See OJSC Magnitogorsk Iron & Steel Works; *Int'l*, pg. 5540
OJSC MMK-METIZ—See OJSC Magnitogorsk Iron & Steel Works; *Int'l*, pg. 5540
OJSC MONDI SYKTYVKA—See Mondi plc; *Int'l*, pg. 5027
OJSC MOSCOW EXCHANGE MICEX-RTS; *Int'l*, pg. 5540
OJSC MOSENERGO—See PJSC Gazprom; *Int'l*, pg. 5879
OJSC MOSVODOKANALBANK—See PJSC VTB Bank; *Int'l*, pg. 5886
OJSC MYRONIVSKY HLIBOPRODUCT LEHKO PLANT—See OJSC Myronivsky Hliboprodukt; *Int'l*, pg. 5540
OJSC MYRONIVSKY HLIBOPRODUCT; *Int'l*, pg. 5540
OJSC NAK AKI-OTYR—See RussNeft PJSC; *Int'l*, pg. 6432
OJSC NORILSKO TAIMYRSKAYA ENERGETICHESKAYA KOMPANIYA—See PJSC MMC Norilsk Nickel; *Int'l*, pg. 5883
OJSC NORILSKY KOMBINAT—See PJSC MMC Norilsk Nickel; *Int'l*, pg. 5883
OJSC NORTH-WEST TELECOM—See PJSC Rostelecom; *Int'l*, pg. 5884
OJSC NOVOROSSIYSK SHIPYARD—See PJSC Novorossiysk Commercial Sea Port; *Int'l*, pg. 5883
OJSC NPO BUROVAYA TECHNIKA—See Integra Management LLC; *Int'l*, pg. 3730
OJSC NRI ELECTRON—See Russian Technologies State Corporation; *Int'l*, pg. 6432
OJSC OLMA INVESTMENT FIRM; *Int'l*, pg. 5541
OJSC ORIENBANK; *Int'l*, pg. 5541
OJSC OTP BANK—See OTP Bank Plc; *Int'l*, pg. 5657
OJSC PAVA; *Int'l*, pg. 5541
OJSC PETROLESPORT—See Delo Group; *Int'l*, pg. 2014
OJSC PHARMACY CHAIN 36.6; *Int'l*, pg. 5541
OJSC PLANT OF PURE IRON—See CRONIMET Holding GmbH; *Int'l*, pg. 1855
OJSC POLYUS GOLD—See PJSC Polyus; *Int'l*, pg. 5883

COMPANY NAME INDEX

OJSC POWER MACHINES—See OOO Severgrupp; *Int'l*, pg. 5594
OJSC PROMSVYAZBANK—See PromSvyazCapital B.V.; *Int'l*, pg. 5996
OJSC "BELVNESHECONOMBANK"—See VEB.RF; *Int'l*, pg. 8143
OJSC "FEDERAL CENTER FOR PROJECT FINANCE"—See VEB.RF; *Int'l*, pg. 8143
OJSC "NORTH CAUCASUS DEVELOPMENT CORPORATION"—See VEB.RF; *Int'l*, pg. 8143
OJSC "SME BANK"—See VEB.RF; *Int'l*, pg. 8143
OJSC "VEB-LEASING"—See VEB.RF; *Int'l*, pg. 8143
OJSC RAO NORILSK NICKEL—See PJSC MMC Norilsk Nickel; *Int'l*, pg. 5883
OJSC RESO GARANTIA; *Int'l*, pg. 5541
OJSC ROSGOSSTRAKH BANK—See Central Bank of the Russian Federation; *Int'l*, pg. 1405
OJSC ROSINTER RESTAURANTS HOLDING; *Int'l*, pg. 5541
OJSC ROSNEFTEGAZ; *Int'l*, pg. 5541
OJSC ROSNEFT-KARACHAEVO—See OJSC Rosneftegaz; *Int'l*, pg. 5541
OJSC ROSNEFT-SMOLENSKNEFTEPRODUCT—See OJSC Rosneftegaz; *Int'l*, pg. 5541
OJSC ROSNO—See Allianz SE; *Int'l*, pg. 354
OJSC ROSOBORONEXPORT—See Russian Technologies State Corporation; *Int'l*, pg. 6432
OJSC RT-STANKOINSTRUMENT—See Russian Technologies State Corporation; *Int'l*, pg. 6431
OJSC RUSAL ACHINSK—See United Company RUSAL Plc; *Int'l*, pg. 8066
OJSC RUSAL NOVOKUZNETSK—See United Company RUSAL Plc; *Int'l*, pg. 8066
OJSC RUSSIAN UTILITY SYSTEMS—See Renova Group; *Int'l*, pg. 6285
OJSC SAMARAENERGO; *Int'l*, pg. 5541
OJSC SAMARANEFTEGAZ—See OJSC Rosneftegaz; *Int'l*, pg. 5541
OJSC SARATOVNEFTEGAZ—See RussNeft PJSC; *Int'l*, pg. 6432
OJSC SBERBANK OF RUSSIA; *Int'l*, pg. 5541
OJSC SEA PORT OF SAINT-PETERSBURG—See Universal Cargo Logistics Holding B.V.; *Int'l*, pg. 8077
OJSC SIBERIAN COAL ENERGY COMPANY—See SUEK LTD; *Int'l*, pg. 7253
OJSC SIBIRTELECOM—See PJSC Rostelecom; *Int'l*, pg. 5884
OJSC SOLLERS; *Int'l*, pg. 5542
OJSC SOUTHERN TELECOMMUNICATIONS COMPANY—See PJSC Rostelecom; *Int'l*, pg. 5884
OJSC SVYAZINVEST; *Int'l*, pg. 5542
OJSC TAGANROG SEA COMMERCIAL PORT—See Universal Cargo Logistics Holding B.V.; *Int'l*, pg. 8077
OJSC TAIMYRENERGO—See PJSC MMC Norilsk Nickel; *Int'l*, pg. 5883
OJSC TUAPSE SEA COMMERCIAL PORT—See Universal Cargo Logistics Holding B.V.; *Int'l*, pg. 8077
OJSC ULYANOVSKNEFT—See RussNeft PJSC; *Int'l*, pg. 6432
OJSC URALSIB FINANCIAL CORPORATION; *Int'l*, pg. 5543
OJSC VILYUISKAYA HPP-3—See PJSC Alrosa; *Int'l*, pg. 5878
OJSC VOLGATELECOM—See PJSC Rostelecom; *Int'l*, pg. 5884
OJSC VTB BANK (AZERBAIJAN)—See PJSC VTB Bank; *Int'l*, pg. 5886
OJSC VYSOCHAISHY; *Int'l*, pg. 5543
OJSYS, INC.; *U.S. Public*, pg. 1566
OK3 AIR; *U.S. Private*, pg. 3006
OKAB CONVERT AB; *Int'l*, pg. 5543
OKABE CO., LTD.; *Int'l*, pg. 5543
OKABE COMPANY, INC.—See Okabe Co., Ltd.; *Int'l*, pg. 5544
OKABE KAIYO ENGINEERING CO., LTD.—See Okabe Co., Ltd.; *Int'l*, pg. 5544
OKABE LEASE CO., LTD.—See Okabe Co., Ltd.; *Int'l*, pg. 5544
OKABE NORTH AMERICA, INC.—See APA Holdings Co., Ltd.; *Int'l*, pg. 500
OKABE SHINDENGEN CO., LTD.—See Shindengen Electric Manufacturing Co., Ltd.; *Int'l*, pg. 6842
OKAB FRANCE SAS—See OKAB Convert AB; *Int'l*, pg. 5543
OKAB GERMANY GMBH—See OKAB Convert AB; *Int'l*, pg. 5543
OKA-BUROMOBEL GMBH & CO. KG; *Int'l*, pg. 5543
OKACHI INVESTMENTS LTD—See Keppel Corporation Limited; *Int'l*, pg. 4132
OKA CORPORATION BHD; *Int'l*, pg. 5543
OKADA AIYON CORPORATION; *Int'l*, pg. 5544
OKADA AMERICA, INC.—See Okada Aiyon Corporation; *Int'l*, pg. 5544
OKADA TRUCKING CO. LTD.; *U.S. Private*, pg. 3006
OKA DIRECT LIMITED; *Int'l*, pg. 5543
OKAI INFORMATION SYSTEM CONSULTATION; *Int'l*, pg. 5544
OKALOOSA GAS DISTRICT; *U.S. Private*, pg. 3006

OKALOOSA HOSPITAL, INC.—See HCA Healthcare, Inc.; *U.S. Public*, pg. 1005
OKAMI, INC. - DENVER PLANT—See Meruelo Group LLC; *U.S. Private*, pg. 2677
OKAMI, INC.—See Meruelo Group LLC; *U.S. Private*, pg. 2677
OKAMOTO CORPORATION—See Okamoto Machine Tool Works, Ltd.; *Int'l*, pg. 5545
OKAMOTO GLASS CO., LTD; *Int'l*, pg. 5544
OKAMOTO INDUSTRIES (HONG KONG) LTD.—See Okamoto Industries, Inc.; *Int'l*, pg. 5544
OKAMOTO INDUSTRIES, INC.; *Int'l*, pg. 5544
OKAMOTO INDUSTRIES (SHENZHEN) CO., LTD—See Okamoto Industries, Inc.; *Int'l*, pg. 5544
OKAMOTO MACHINERY CO., LTD. - CHINESE PLANT—See Okamoto Machine Tool Works, Ltd.; *Int'l*, pg. 5545
OKAMOTO MACHINERY CO., LTD. - MATSUNAGA PLANT—See Okamoto Machine Tool Works, Ltd.; *Int'l*, pg. 5545
OKAMOTO MACHINERY CO., LTD. - ONOMICHI PLANT—See Okamoto Machine Tool Works, Ltd.; *Int'l*, pg. 5545
OKAMOTO MACHINERY CO., LTD.—See Okamoto Machine Tool Works, Ltd.; *Int'l*, pg. 5545
OKAMOTO MACHINE TOOL EUROPE GMBH—See Okamoto Machine Tool Works, Ltd.; *Int'l*, pg. 5545
OKAMOTO MACHINE TOOL WORKS, LTD.; *Int'l*, pg. 5544
OKAMOTO OPTECH CO., LTD.—See Okamoto Glass Co., Ltd; *Int'l*, pg. 5544
OKAMOTO RUBBER PRODUCTS CO., LTD.—See Okamoto Industries, Inc.; *Int'l*, pg. 5544
OKAMOTO SANDUSKY MANUFACTURING LLC.—See Okamoto Industries, Inc.; *Int'l*, pg. 5544
OKAMOTO (SINGAPORE) PTE, LTD.—See Okamoto Machine Tool Works, Ltd.; *Int'l*, pg. 5544
OKAMOTO (THAI) COMPANY LTD.—See Okamoto Machine Tool Works, Ltd.; *Int'l*, pg. 5544
OKAMOTO VIETNAM CO., LTD.—See Okamoto Industries, Inc.; *Int'l*, pg. 5544
OKAMURA BUSINESS SUPPORT CORPORATION—See Okamura Corporation; *Int'l*, pg. 5545
OKAMURA CORPORATION; *Int'l*, pg. 5545
ОКАМПА ГООDЕ CO., LTD.; *Int'l*, pg. 5545
OKAMURA INTERNATIONAL (SINGAPORE) PTE LTD.—See Okamura Corporation; *Int'l*, pg. 5545
OKAMURA LOGISTICS CORPORATION—See Okamura Corporation; *Int'l*, pg. 5545
OKAMURA SUPPORT & SERVICE CORPORATION—See Okamura Corporation; *Int'l*, pg. 5545
OKANAGAN SPECIALTY FRUITS INC.—See Precigen, Inc.; *U.S. Public*, pg. 1713
OKANO CABLE CO., LTD.—See The Furukawa Electric Co., Ltd.; *Int'l*, pg. 7646
OKANOGAN DIALYSIS, LLC—See DaVita Inc.; *U.S. Public*, pg. 641
OKANO VALVE MFG. CO.LTD.; *Int'l*, pg. 5545
OKANO VALVE MFG. CO. - YUKUHASHI STEEL FOUNDRY WORKS—See OKANO VALVE MFG. CO.LTD.; *Int'l*, pg. 5545
O&K ANTRIEBSTECHNIK GMBH—See Bonfiglioli Riduttori S.p.A.; *Int'l*, pg. 1106
OKAPI RESOURCES LIMITED; *Int'l*, pg. 5545
OKAPI VENTURE CAPITAL, LLC; *U.S. Private*, pg. 3006
OKASAN ASSET MANAGEMENT CO., LTD.—See Okasan Securities Group Inc.; *Int'l*, pg. 5545
OKASAN BUSINESS SERVICE CO., LTD.—See Okasan Securities Group Inc.; *Int'l*, pg. 5545
OKASAN INTERNATIONAL (ASIA) LIMITED—See Okasan Securities Group Inc.; *Int'l*, pg. 5545
OKASAN KOGYO CO., LTD.—See Okasan Securities Group Inc.; *Int'l*, pg. 5545
OKASAN NIIGATA SECURITIES CO., LTD.—See Okasan Securities Group Inc.; *Int'l*, pg. 5545
OKASAN ONLINE SECURITIES CO., LTD.—See Okasan Securities Group Inc.; *Int'l*, pg. 5545
OKASAN SECURITIES CO., LTD.—See Okasan Securities Group Inc.; *Int'l*, pg. 5545
OKASAN SECURITIES GROUP INC.; *Int'l*, pg. 5545
OKASKI UNITED INTERNATIONAL PTE. LTD.—See Osaki Electric Co., Ltd.; *Int'l*, pg. 5647
OKATIE SURGICAL PARTNERS, L.L.C.—See Tenet Healthcare Corporation; *U.S. Public*, pg. 2008
OK AUTOMOTIVE—See Automotive Parts Headquarters, Inc.; *U.S. Private*, pg. 400
OKAW FARMERS COOPERATIVE, INC.; *U.S. Private*, pg. 3006
OKAW PROPERTIES INC.; *U.S. Private*, pg. 3006
OKAYA AUSTRALIA PTY. LTD.—See Okaya & Co., Ltd.; *Int'l*, pg. 5546
OKAYA (BEIJING) CO., LTD.—See Okaya & Co., Ltd.; *Int'l*, pg. 5546
OKAYA BUILDING CO., LTD.—See Okaya & Co., Ltd.; *Int'l*, pg. 5546
OKAYA BUSINESS SUPPORT CO., LTD.—See Okaya & Co., Ltd.; *Int'l*, pg. 5546
OKAYA (CANADA) CO., LTD.—See Okaya & Co., Ltd.; *Int'l*, pg. 5546

OKAYA & CO., INDIA PVT. LTD.—See Okaya & Co., Ltd.; *Int'l*, pg. 5546
OKAYA & CO., LTD.; *Int'l*, pg. 5545
OKAYA CONSULTANT CO., LTD.—See Okaya & Co., Ltd.; *Int'l*, pg. 5546
OKAYA DO BRASIL COMERCIO LTDA.—See Okaya & Co., Ltd.; *Int'l*, pg. 5546
OKAYA ECO-ASSORT CORP.—See Okaya & Co., Ltd.; *Int'l*, pg. 5546
OKAYA ELECTRIC AMERICA, INC.—See Okaya Electric Industries Co., Ltd.; *Int'l*, pg. 5548
OKAYA ELECTRIC INDUSTRIES CO., LTD.; *Int'l*, pg. 5548
OKAYA ELECTRIC SINGAPORE PTE LTD.—See Okaya Electric Industries Co., Ltd.; *Int'l*, pg. 5548
OKAYA ELECTRIC (THAILAND) CO., LTD.—See Okaya Electric Industries Co., Ltd.; *Int'l*, pg. 5548
OKAYA ELECTRONICS CORP.—See Okaya & Co., Ltd.; *Int'l*, pg. 5546
OKAYA ELECTRONICS (H.K.) LTD.—See Okaya & Co., Ltd.; *Int'l*, pg. 5546
OKAYA ELECTRONICS (SHENZHEN) LTD.—See Okaya & Co., Ltd.; *Int'l*, pg. 5546
OKAYA EUROPE GMBH—See Okaya & Co., Ltd.; *Int'l*, pg. 5546
OKAYA (GUANGZHOU) CO., LTD.—See Okaya & Co., Ltd.; *Int'l*, pg. 5546
OKAYA HOKKAIDO CO., LTD.—See Okaya & Co., Ltd.; *Int'l*, pg. 5546
OKAYA HOMES CO., LTD.—See Okaya & Co., Ltd.; *Int'l*, pg. 5546
OKAYA (HONG KONG) LIMITED - DONGGUAN DONGKENG OKAYA ELECTRONIC FACTORY—See Okaya Electric Industries Co., Ltd.; *Int'l*, pg. 5548
OKAYA (HONG KONG) LIMITED—See Okaya Electric Industries Co., Ltd.; *Int'l*, pg. 5548
OKAYA INTERNATIONAL (H.K.) LTD.—See Okaya & Co., Ltd.; *Int'l*, pg. 5546
OKAYA INTERNATIONAL (MALAYSIA) SDN. BHD.—See Okaya & Co., Ltd.; *Int'l*, pg. 5546
OKAYA IWAI HOKKAIDO CO., LTD.—See Okaya & Co., Ltd.; *Int'l*, pg. 5546
OKAYA KENZAI CO., LTD.—See Okaya & Co., Ltd.; *Int'l*, pg. 5547
OKAYA KENZAI TECH CONSTRUCTION CO., LTD.—See Okaya & Co., Ltd.; *Int'l*, pg. 5547
OKAYA KIDEN CO., LTD.—See Okaya & Co., Ltd.; *Int'l*, pg. 5547
OKAYA KIHAN CO., LTD.—See Okaya & Co., Ltd.; *Int'l*, pg. 5547
OKAYA (KOREA) CO., LTD.—See Okaya & Co., Ltd.; *Int'l*, pg. 5547
OKAYA KYUSHU CO., LTD.—See Okaya & Co., Ltd.; *Int'l*, pg. 5547
OKAYA LANKA (PVT) LTD.—See Okaya Electric Industries Co., Ltd.; *Int'l*, pg. 5548
OKAYA LOGISTICS CO., LTD.—See Okaya & Co., Ltd.; *Int'l*, pg. 5547
OKAYAMA AIR SERVICE CO., LTD.—See Sojitz Corporation; *Int'l*, pg. 7063
OKAYAMA BEAUTY CORPORATION—See HOWA Corporation; *Int'l*, pg. 3492
OKAYAMA EAGLE CO., LTD.—See Eagle Industry Co., Ltd.; *Int'l*, pg. 2266
OKAYAMA ELECTRONIC DATA PROCESSING SYSTEM CENTER CO., LTD.; *Int'l*, pg. 5548
OKAYAMA HARADA PIPE & TUBE CO., LTD.—See Nippon Steel Corporation; *Int'l*, pg. 5338
OKAYAMA KAKO CO., LTD.—See Dai Nippon Toryo Co., Ltd.; *Int'l*, pg. 1916
OKAYAMAKEN FREIGHT TRANSPORTATION CO., LTD.; *Int'l*, pg. 5548
OKAYAMAKEN SHOKUHIN CO., LTD.—See Meiji Holdings Co., Ltd.; *Int'l*, pg. 4801
OKAYAMA KOYU CO., LTD.—See Dowa Holdings Co., Ltd.; *Int'l*, pg. 2183
OKAYAMA MURATA MANUFACTURING CO., LTD.—See Murata Manufacturing Co., Ltd.; *Int'l*, pg. 5098
OKAYAMA PAPER INDUSTRIES CO., LTD.; *Int'l*, pg. 5548
OKAYAMA RINKOH CO., LTD.—See Kuraray Co., Ltd.; *Int'l*, pg. 4338
OKAYA MART CO., LTD.—See Okaya & Co., Ltd.; *Int'l*, pg. 5547
OKAYAMA SANSO ELECTRIC CO., LTD.—See Sanso Electric Co., Ltd.; *Int'l*, pg. 6557
OKAYAMA SENKO TRANSPORT CO., LTD—See Senko Group Holdings Co., Ltd.; *Int'l*, pg. 6710
OKAYAMA SHIZUKI CO., INC.—See Shizuki Electric Company, Inc.; *Int'l*, pg. 6855
OKAYAMA TAIHO PHARMACEUTICAL CO., LTD.—See Otsuka Holdings Co., Ltd.; *Int'l*, pg. 5659
OKAYA MEXICO S.A. DE C.V.—See Okaya & Co., Ltd.; *Int'l*, pg. 5547
OKAYA OLYMPUS CO., LTD.—See Olympus Corporation; *Int'l*, pg. 5556
OKAYA SEIRITSU ENGINEERING CO., LTD.—See Okaya & Co., Ltd.; *Int'l*, pg. 5547

OKAYA SERVICE CO., LTD.—See Okaya & Co., Ltd.; *Int'l*, pg. 5547
OKAYA SERVICE & HOMES CO., LTD.—See Okaya & Co., Ltd.; *Int'l*, pg. 5547
OKAYA (SHANGHAI) CO., LTD.—See Okaya & Co., Ltd.; *Int'l*, pg. 5546
OKAYA SHINNICHI CORPORATION OF AMERICA—See Okaya & Co., Ltd.; *Int'l*, pg. 5546
OKAYA SINGAPORE PTE. LTD.—See Okaya & Co., Ltd.; *Int'l*, pg. 5547
OKAYA SPECIAL STEEL CENTER CO., LTD.—See Okaya & Co., Ltd.; *Int'l*, pg. 5547
OKAYA STEEL CO., LTD.—See Okaya & Co., Ltd.; *Int'l*, pg. 5547
OKAYA STEEL SHEET SALES CO., LTD.—See Okaya & Co., Ltd.; *Int'l*, pg. 5547
OKAYA SYSTEM CO., LTD.—See Okaya & Co., Ltd.; *Int'l*, pg. 5547
OKAYA (TAIWAN) CO., LTD.—See Okaya & Co., Ltd.; *Int'l*, pg. 5546
OKAYA (THAILAND) CO., LTD.—See Okaya & Co., Ltd.; *Int'l*, pg. 5546
OKAYA (TIANJIN) CO., LTD.—See Okaya & Co., Ltd.; *Int'l*, pg. 5546
OKAYA TRADE SERVICE CO., LTD.—See Okaya & Co., Ltd.; *Int'l*, pg. 5547
OKAYA (U.S.A.), INC.—See Okaya & Co., Ltd.; *Int'l*, pg. 5546
OKAY CONSTRUCTION COMPANY—See Quanta Services, Inc.; *U.S. Public*, pg. 1751
OKAZAKI HA CHEMICALS CO. LTD.—See Huettenes-Albertus Chemische Werke GmbH; *Int'l*, pg. 3523
OK BIOTECH CO., LTD.; *Int'l*, pg. 5543
OK BLOCKCHAIN CENTRE SDN. BHD.; *Int'l*, pg. 5543
OKB RESEARCH INSTITUTE CO., LTD.—See The Ogaki Kyoritsu Bank, Ltd.; *Int'l*, pg. 7671
OKB RESTAURANG AB—See New Wave Group AB; *Int'l*, pg. 5230
OKC CLASSEN CURVE, LLC—See Washington Prime Group Inc.; *U.S. Private*, pg. 4449
OK CHEVROLET, INC; *U.S. Private*, pg. 3006
O & K CO., LTD.—See Onward Holdings Co., Ltd.; *Int'l*, pg. 5592
OK CONTAINER EXPRESS CO., LTD.—See The Keihin Co., Ltd.; *Int'l*, pg. 7662
OKDO TECHNOLOGY LIMITED—See RS Group plc; *Int'l*, pg. 6417
OK DRILLING SERVICES L.P.—See Mullen Group Ltd.; *Int'l*, pg. 5080
OKEA ASA; *Int'l*, pg. 5548
OKEANIS ECO TANKERS CORP.; *Int'l*, pg. 5548
OKEANOS FOOD CO., LTD.—See Thai Union Group Public Company Limited; *Int'l*, pg. 7596
OKEANUS SCIENCE & TECHNOLOGY, LLC; *U.S. Private*, pg. 3006
THE OKEECHOBEE NEWS—See Independent Newspapers, Inc.; *U.S. Private*, pg. 2060
O'KEEFE ELEVATOR COMPANY INC.—See Advent International Corporation; *U.S. Private*, pg. 106
O'KEEFE ELEVATOR COMPANY INC.—See Cinven Limited; *Int'l*, pg. 1614
O'KEEFE ELEVATOR COMPANY INC.—See RAG-Stiftung; *Int'l*, pg. 6179
O'KEEFFE & CO.; *U.S. Private*, pg. 2978
O'KEEFFE & CO.—See O'Keeffe & Co.; *U.S. Private*, pg. 2978
O'KEEFFE & CO.—See O'Keeffe & Co.; *U.S. Private*, pg. 2978
O'KEEFFE & CO.—See O'Keeffe & Co.; *U.S. Private*, pg. 2978
O'KEEFFE & CO.—See O'Keeffe & Co.; *U.S. Private*, pg. 2978
O'KEEFFE'S, INC.; *U.S. Private*, pg. 2978
OKEE INDUSTRIES INC.; *U.S. Private*, pg. 3007
OKEELANTA CORPORATION—See Florida Crystals Corporation; *U.S. Private*, pg. 1548
OKEFENOKE RURAL ELECTRIC MEMBERSHIP CORPORATION; *U.S. Private*, pg. 3007
OKE PRECISION CUTTING TOOLS CO., LTD.; *Int'l*, pg. 5548
O&K ESCALATORS S.A.—See KONE Oyj; *Int'l*, pg. 4250
O'KEY GROUP S.A.; *Int'l*, pg. 5502
O.K. FARMS, INC.—See Industrias Bachoco S.A.B. de C.V.; *Int'l*, pg. 3673
OK FOOD INDUSTRY CO., LTD.—See NIPPN Corporation; *Int'l*, pg. 5310
O.K. FOODS, INC.—See Industrias Bachoco S.A.B. de C.V.; *Int'l*, pg. 3673
OKG AB—See E.ON SE; *Int'l*, pg. 2258
OKH GLOBAL LTD.; *Int'l*, pg. 5548
O & K - HILFE GMBH—See CNH Industrial N.V.; *Int'l*, pg. 1674
OKHOTSK NICHIRO CORPORATION—See Maruha Nichiro Corporation; *Int'l*, pg. 4711
OKI AUTO AUCTION, INC.—See Dealer's Auto Auction Group; *U.S. Private*, pg. 1182
OKI BEARING CANADA INC.—See Sycamore Partners Management, LP; *U.S. Private*, pg. 3896

OKI BERING MIDDLE EAST, FZE—See Sycamore Partners Management, LP; *U.S. Private*, pg. 3896
OKI COMMUNICATION SYSTEMS CO., LTD.—See Oki Electric Industry Co., Ltd.; *Int'l*, pg. 5549
OKI COMTEC CO., LTD.—See Oki Electric Industry Co., Ltd.; *Int'l*, pg. 5549
OKI CONSULTING SOLUTIONS CO., LTD.—See Oki Electric Industry Co., Ltd.; *Int'l*, pg. 5549
OKI CUSTOMER ADTECH CO., LTD.—See Oki Electric Industry Co., Ltd.; *Int'l*, pg. 5548
OKI DATA AMERICAS, INC.—See Oki Electric Industry Co., Ltd.; *Int'l*, pg. 5549
OKI DATA DALIAN CO., LTD.—See Oki Electric Industry Co., Ltd.; *Int'l*, pg. 5549
OKI DATA DE MEXICO, S.A. DE C.V.—See Oki Electric Industry Co., Ltd.; *Int'l*, pg. 5549
OKI DATA DO BRASIL, LTDA.—See Oki Electric Industry Co., Ltd.; *Int'l*, pg. 5549
OKI DATA MANUFACTURING (THAILAND) CO., LTD.—See Oki Electric Industry Co., Ltd.; *Int'l*, pg. 5549
OKI DATA (SINGAPORE) PTE. LTD.—See Oki Electric Industry Co., Ltd.; *Int'l*, pg. 5549
OKI ELECTRIC CABLE CO., LTD.—See Oki Electric Industry Co., Ltd.; *Int'l*, pg. 5549
OKI ELECTRIC CABLE SERVICE—See Oki Electric Industry Co., Ltd.; *Int'l*, pg. 5548
OKI ELECTRIC CABLE WIRE HARNESS—See Oki Electric Industry Co., Ltd.; *Int'l*, pg. 5548
OKI ELECTRIC INDUSTRY CO., LTD.; *Int'l*, pg. 5548
OKI ELECTRIC TECHNOLOGY (KUNSHAN) CO., LTD.—See Oki Electric Industry Co., Ltd.; *Int'l*, pg. 5549
OKI ENGINEERING CO., LTD.—See Oki Electric Industry Co., Ltd.; *Int'l*, pg. 5549
OKI EUROPE LTD.—See Oki Electric Industry Co., Ltd.; *Int'l*, pg. 5549
OKI EUROPE LTD. - SPAIN—See Oki Electric Industry Co., Ltd.; *Int'l*, pg. 5549
OKI FURNITURE FAIR INC.; *U.S. Private*, pg. 3007
OKIGIN GENERAL LEASE CO., LTD.—See The Bank of Okinawa, Ltd.; *Int'l*, pg. 7619
OKIGIN JCB CO., LTD.—See The Bank of Okinawa, Ltd.; *Int'l*, pg. 7619
OKIGIN SPO CO., LTD.—See The Bank of Okinawa, Ltd.; *Int'l*, pg. 7619
OKI GLASS CO., LTD.—See Nippon Sheet Glass Co. Ltd.; *Int'l*, pg. 5331
OKI HONG KONG LIMITED—See Oki Electric Industry Co., Ltd.; *Int'l*, pg. 5549
OKI INFORMATION SYSTEMS CO., LTD.—See Oki Electric Industry Co., Ltd.; *Int'l*, pg. 5549
OKIL-HOLDING, JSC—See SATO Holdings Corporation; *Int'l*, pg. 6585
OKIL-SATO X-PACK CO., LTD.—See SATO Holdings Corporation; *Int'l*, pg. 6585
OKIN AMERICA INC.—See Phoenix Mecano AG; *Int'l*, pg. 5852
OKINAWA AIRPORT SERVICE CO., LTD.—See Japan Airlines Co., Ltd.; *Int'l*, pg. 3885
OKINAWA BUNKA SHUTTER CO., LTD—See Bunka Shutter Co., Ltd.; *Int'l*, pg. 1216
OKINAWA BUSINESS FORMS CO., LTD.—See TOPPAN Holdings Inc.; *Int'l*, pg. 7817
OKINAWA CABLE NETWORK INC.—See TOKAI Holdings Corporation; *Int'l*, pg. 7779
OKINAWA CELLULAR TELEPHONE COMPANY; *Int'l*, pg. 5549
OKINAWA COCA-COLA BOTTLING CO., LTD.; *Int'l*, pg. 5549
OKINAWA CREDIT SERVICE CO., LTD.—See Bank of The Ryukyus, Ltd.; *Int'l*, pg. 849
OKINAWA CROSS HEAD CO., LTD.—See TECHMATRIX CORPORATION; *Int'l*, pg. 7505
THE OKINAWA ELECTRIC POWER COMPANY, INCORPORATED; *Int'l*, pg. 7671
OKINAWA FINANCIAL GROUP, INC.; *Int'l*, pg. 5550
OKINAWA FRESH PACK CO., LTD.—See Itoham Yonekyu Holdings Inc.; *Int'l*, pg. 3843
OKINAWA FUELING FACILITIES CO., LTD.—See Japan Airlines Co., Ltd.; *Int'l*, pg. 3885
OKINAWA HITACHI CO., LTD.—See Hitachi, Ltd.; *Int'l*, pg. 3423
OKINAWA HITACHI NETWORK SYSTEMS, LTD.—See Hitachi, Ltd.; *Int'l*, pg. 3423
OKINAWA MARITIME INDUSTRIES CO., LTD.—See Nippon Yusen Kabushiki Kaisha; *Int'l*, pg. 5359
OKINAWA MARUICHI LTD.—See Maruichi Steel Tube Ltd; *Int'l*, pg. 4714
OKINAWA MAZDA SALES CO., LTD.—See Mazda Motor Corporation; *Int'l*, pg. 4749
OKINAWA MEIJI MILK PRODUCTS CO., LTD.—See Meiji Holdings Co., Ltd.; *Int'l*, pg. 4801
OKINAWA MIYAKO HOTEL—See Kintetsu Group Holdings Co., Ltd.; *Int'l*, pg. 4184
OKINAWA NIPPON KANZAI CO., LTD.—See NIPPON KANZAI Holdings Co.,Ltd.; *Int'l*, pg. 5319
OKINAWA POKKA CORPORATION CO., LTD.—See Sapporo Holdings Limited; *Int'l*, pg. 6573

OKINAWA SANWA SHUTTER CORPORATION—See Sanwa Holdings Corporation; *Int'l*, pg. 6560
OKINAWA SEINO TRANSPORTATION CO., LTD.—See Seino Holdings Co., Ltd.; *Int'l*, pg. 6690
OKINAWA SHIBUYA CO., LTD.—See Shibuya Corporation; *Int'l*, pg. 6827
OKINAWA SUNTORY LTD.—See Suntory Holdings Limited; *Int'l*, pg. 7326
OKINAWA TECNOS CO.—See Tecnos Japan Inc.; *Int'l*, pg. 7517
OKINAWA TELECOMMUNICATION NETWORK CO., INC.—See KDDI Corporation; *Int'l*, pg. 4112
OKINAWA UDS CO., LTD.—See Odakyu Electric Railway Co., Ltd.; *Int'l*, pg. 5524
OKINAWA YAMADA DENKI CO., LTD.—See Yamada Holdings Co., Ltd.; *Int'l*, pg. 8548
OKINAWA YAMATO TRANSPORT CO., LTD.—See Yamato Holdings Co., Ltd.; *Int'l*, pg. 8554
OKINAWA YOSHINOYA CO., LTD.—See Yoshinoya Holdings Co., Ltd.; *Int'l*, pg. 8600
O&K INC.; *U.S. Private*, pg. 2977
OK INCURE OU—See B2Holding AS; *Int'l*, pg. 790
O.K. INDUSTRIES INC.—See Industrias Bachoco S.A.B. de C.V.; *Int'l*, pg. 3673
O.K. INDUSTRIES LTD. - DUNCAN PAVING DIVISION—See O.K. Industries Ltd.; *Int'l*, pg. 5503
O.K. INDUSTRIES LTD. - HAYLOCK BROS. PAVING DIVISION—See O.K. Industries Ltd.; *Int'l*, pg. 5503
O.K. INDUSTRIES LTD. - O.K. PAVING DIVISION—See O.K. Industries Ltd.; *Int'l*, pg. 5503
O.K. INDUSTRIES LTD.; *Int'l*, pg. 5503
OKI NETWORKS CO., LTD.—See Oki Electric Industry Co., Ltd.; *Int'l*, pg. 5548
OKIN SCANDINAVIA AB—See Phoenix Mecano AG; *Int'l*, pg. 5852
OKINS ELECTRONICS CO., LTD. - SONGSAN FACTORY—See Okins Electronics Co., Ltd.; *Int'l*, pg. 5550
OKINS ELECTRONICS CO., LTD.; *Int'l*, pg. 5550
OKINS USA INC.—See Okins Electronics Co., Ltd.; *Int'l*, pg. 5550
OK INTERIORS CORP.; *U.S. Private*, pg. 3006
OK INTERNATIONAL, INC.—See Dover Corporation; *U.S. Public*, pg. 680
OK INTERNATIONAL (UK) LTD.—See Dover Corporation; *U.S. Public*, pg. 681
OKIN VIETNAM COMPANY LTD.—See Phoenix Mecano AG; *Int'l*, pg. 5852
OKI POWERTECH HONG KONG CO., LTD.—See Oki Electric Industry Co., Ltd.; *Int'l*, pg. 5549
OKI PRECISION (THAILAND) CO LTD—See Oki Electric Industry Co., Ltd.; *Int'l*, pg. 5548
OKI PRINTED CIRCUITS CO., LTD.—See Oki Electric Industry Co., Ltd.; *Int'l*, pg. 5548
OKI PROSERVE CO., LTD.—See Oki Electric Industry Co., Ltd.; *Int'l*, pg. 5548
OK IRON & METAL CO—See M. Lipsitz & Co., Ltd.; *U.S. Private*, pg. 2527
OKI SEATEC CO., LTD.—See Oki Electric Industry Co., Ltd.; *Int'l*, pg. 5549
OKI SEMICONDUCTOR AMERICA, INC.—See ROHM Co., Ltd.; *Int'l*, pg. 6385
OKI SEMICONDUCTOR CO., LTD.—See ROHM Co., Ltd.; *Int'l*, pg. 6385
OKI SEMICONDUCTOR MIYAZAKI CO., LTD.—See ROHM Co., Ltd.; *Int'l*, pg. 6385
OKI SISTEM VE YAZICI COZUMLERI TICARET LTD STI—See Oki Electric Industry Co., Ltd.; *Int'l*, pg. 5549
OKI SOFTWARE EXPERT SERVICE—See Oki Electric Industry Co., Ltd.; *Int'l*, pg. 5549
OKI SYSTEMS (CZECH AND SLOVAK), S.R.O.—See Oki Electric Industry Co., Ltd.; *Int'l*, pg. 5549
OKI SYSTEMS (DEUTSCHLAND) GMBH—See Oki Electric Industry Co., Ltd.; *Int'l*, pg. 5549
OKI SYSTEMS (HOLLAND) B.V.—See Oki Electric Industry Co., Ltd.; *Int'l*, pg. 5549
OKI SYSTEMS (HONG KONG) LTD—See Oki Electric Industry Co., Ltd.; *Int'l*, pg. 5549
OKI SYSTEMS (IRELAND) LTD.—See Oki Electric Industry Co., Ltd.; *Int'l*, pg. 5549
OKI SYSTEMS (ITALIA) S.P.A.—See Oki Electric Industry Co., Ltd.; *Int'l*, pg. 5549
OKI SYSTEMS KOREA CO., LTD.—See Oki Electric Industry Co., Ltd.; *Int'l*, pg. 5549
OKI SYSTEMS (MAGYARORSZAG) KFT.—See Oki Electric Industry Co., Ltd.; *Int'l*, pg. 5549
OKI SYSTEMS (NORWAY) A/S—See Oki Electric Industry Co., Ltd.; *Int'l*, pg. 5549
OKI SYSTEMS (RUS)—See Oki Electric Industry Co., Ltd.; *Int'l*, pg. 5549
OKI SYSTEMS (SWEDEN) AB—See Oki Electric Industry Co., Ltd.; *Int'l*, pg. 5549
OKI (THAILAND) CO., LTD.—See ROHM Co., Ltd.; *Int'l*, pg. 6385
OKI TRADING (BEIJING) CO., LTD.—See Oki Electric Industry Co., Ltd.; *Int'l*, pg. 5549
OKIURA GOLF CENTER CO., LTD.—See Nippon Kayaku Co., Ltd.; *Int'l*, pg. 5320

COMPANY NAME INDEX

OKI VIETNAM COMPANY LIMITED—See Oki Electric Industry Co., Ltd.; *Int'l*, pg. 5549
OKI WORKWEL CO., LTD.—See Oki Electric Industry Co., Ltd.; *Int'l*, pg. 5549
OKKAR LIFTRYGGINGAR HF.—See Arion Bank hf.; *Int'l*, pg. 565
OKKAR THIRI CO., LTD.—See Ship Healthcare Holdings, Inc.; *Int'l*, pg. 6852
OKK CORPORATION; *Int'l*, pg. 5550
OKK EUROPE GMBH—See OKK Corporation; *Int'l*, pg. 5550
OK KIZAI CO., LTD.—See Daikin Industries, Ltd.; *Int'l*, pg. 1936
OKK (SHANGHAI) CO., LTD.—See OKK Corporation; *Int'l*, pg. 5550
OKK USA CORPORATION—See OKK Corporation; *Int'l*, pg. 5550
OKLAHOMA CENTER FOR ORTHOPEDIC AND MULTI-SPECIALTY SURGERY, LLC—See Tenet Healthcare Corporation; *U.S. Public*, pg. 2005
OKLAHOMA CENTRAL CREDIT UNION; *U.S. Private*, pg. 3007
OKLAHOMA CITY COMMUNITY FOUNDATION, INC.; *U.S. Private*, pg. 3007
OKLAHOMA CITY HOME CARE SERVICES, LLC—See Community Health Systems, Inc.; *U.S. Public*, pg. 555
OKLAHOMA CITY LANDFILL, L.L.C.—See Republic Services, Inc.; *U.S. Public*, pg. 1786
OKLAHOMA CITY OTHER POST EMPLOYMENT BENEFITS; *U.S. Private*, pg. 3007
OKLAHOMA CITY THUNDER—See The Professional Basketball Club, LLC; *U.S. Private*, pg. 4100
OKLAHOMA CITY ZOOLOGICAL PARK; *U.S. Private*, pg. 3007
OKLAHOMA CYBERKNIFE, LLC—See Akumin, Inc.; *U.S. Public*, pg. 70
OKLAHOMA ELECTRICAL SUPPLY COMPANY, INC.; *U.S. Private*, pg. 3007
OKLAHOMA FARM BUREAU MUTUAL INSURANCE CO.; *U.S. Private*, pg. 3007
OKLAHOMA FIDELITY BANK—See Fidelity Financial Corporation; *U.S. Public*, pg. 1503
OKLAHOMA FINANCIAL CENTER, INC.—See Aon plc; *Int'l*, pg. 497
OKLAHOMA FORGE INC.; *U.S. Private*, pg. 3007
OKLAHOMA GAS & ELECTRIC COMPANY—See OGE Energy Corp.; *U.S. Public*, pg. 1564
OKLAHOMA GENERAL AGENCY, INC.; *U.S. Private*, pg. 3007
OKLAHOMA INSTALLATION COMPANY; *U.S. Private*, pg. 3007
OKLAHOMA INVESTMENTS CASTING COMPANY—See Parrish Enterprises, Ltd.; *U.S. Private*, pg. 3100
OKLAHOMA LAND TITLE SERVICES, LLC—See Stewart Information Services Corporation; *U.S. Public*, pg. 1947
OKLAHOMA LOGOS, L.L.C.—See Lamar Advertising Company; *U.S. Public*, pg. 1291
OKLAHOMA MAGIC LP; *U.S. Private*, pg. 3007
OKLAHOMA MUNICIPAL POWER AUTHORITY; *U.S. Private*, pg. 3007
OKLAHOMA NATURAL GAS COMPANY—See ONEOK, Inc.; *U.S. Public*, pg. 1603
THE OKLAHOMAN—See The Anschutz Corporation; *U.S. Private*, pg. 3987
OKLAHOMA PROPERTY & CASUALTY INSURANCE GUARANTY ASSOCIATION; *U.S. Private*, pg. 3007
THE OKLAHOMA PUBLISHING COMPANY—See The Anschutz Corporation; *U.S. Private*, pg. 3987
OKLAHOMA SAFETY EQUIPMENT CO. INC.—See Halma plc; *Int'l*, pg. 3231
OKLAHOMA'S CREDIT UNION; *U.S. Private*, pg. 3007
OKLAHOMA SPINE HOSPITAL, LLC—See Medical Facilities Corporation; *Int'l*, pg. 4775
OKLAHOMA STATE FAIR, INC.; *U.S. Private*, pg. 3007
OKLAHOMA STATE UNIVERSITY MEDICAL CENTER—See Oklahoma State University Medical Center Trust; *U.S. Private*, pg. 3007
OKLAHOMA STATE UNIVERSITY MEDICAL CENTER TRUST; *U.S. Private*, pg. 3007
OKLAHOMA STEEL & WIRE CO. INC.; *U.S. Private*, pg. 3007
OKLAHOMASTONE.COM INC.; *U.S. Private*, pg. 3007
OKLAHOMA SURETY COMPANY—See American Financial Group, Inc.; *U.S. Public*, pg. 103
OKLAHOMA SURGICARE, INC.—See HCA Healthcare, Inc.; *U.S. Public*, pg. 1005
OKLAHOMA TRANSPORTATION AUTHORITY; *U.S. Private*, pg. 3007
OKLAND CONSTRUCTION COMPANY INC.; *U.S. Private*, pg. 3008
OKLO RESOURCES LIMITED—See B2Gold Corp.; *Int'l*, pg. 790
O.K. MAGAZINES LIMITED—See Reach PLC; *Int'l*, pg. 6231
OK! MAGAZINE—See Chatham Asset Management, LLC; *U.S. Private*, pg. 860
OK MARINE AS—See Egersund Group AS; *Int'l*, pg. 2324
OKMETIC INC.—See Okmetic Oyj; *Int'l*, pg. 5550
OKMETIC K.K.—See Okmetic Oyj; *Int'l*, pg. 5550

OKMETIC LIMITED—See Okmetic Oyj; *Int'l*, pg. 5550
OKMETIC OYJ; *Int'l*, pg. 5550
OK MINILAGER AS—See Teachers Insurance Association - College Retirement Fund; *U.S. Private*, pg. 3945
OKMIN RESOURCES, INC.; *U.S. Public*, pg. 1566
OK MONEY POLAND SP. Z.O.O.—See Lone Star Global Acquisitions, LLC; *U.S. Private*, pg. 2487
OKM VALVE (JIANGSU) CO., LTD.—See Okumura Engineering Corp.; *Int'l*, pg. 5551
OKM VALVE (M) SDN. BHD.—See Okumura Engineering Corp.; *Int'l*, pg. 5551
OKOBOJI FINANCIAL SERVICES, INC.; *U.S. Private*, pg. 3008
OKOBOJI GM; *U.S. Private*, pg. 3008
OKOMU OIL PALM PLC; *Int'l*, pg. 5550
OKONG CORPORATION; *Int'l*, pg. 5550
OKONG TS CO., LTD.—See Okong Corporation; *Int'l*, pg. 5550
OKON, INC.—See RPM International Inc.; *U.S. Public*, pg. 1817
THE OKONITE COMPANY; *U.S. Private*, pg. 4088
OKORUSU FLUORSPAR (PTY) LTD—See Solvay S.A.; *Int'l*, pg. 7078
OKOS SOLUTIONS, LLC—See PVA TePla AG; *Int'l*, pg. 6125
OKOTEC ENERGIEMANAGEMENT GMBH—See Veolia Environnement S.A.; *Int'l*, pg. 8153
OKOTECHNA ENTSORGUNGS- UND UMWELTTECHNIK GMBH—See ALPINE Bau GmbH; *Int'l*, pg. 371
OKOV A.D.; *Int'l*, pg. 5550
OKO VENTURE CAPITAL LTD—See OP Financial Group; *Int'l*, pg. 5595
OKOWORLD AG; *Int'l*, pg. 5550
OK PERINTA OY—See B2Holding AS; *Int'l*, pg. 790
O.K. PETROLEUM DISTRIBUTION CORP.; *U.S. Private*, pg. 2981
OKP HOLDINGS LIMITED; *Int'l*, pg. 5550
OK PLAY INDIA LTD; *Int'l*, pg. 5543
OK PROPERTIES I SOCIMI, S.A.U.; *Int'l*, pg. 5543
OKSA KIMYA SANAYI A.S.—See Ecolab Inc.; *U.S. Public*, pg. 716
OK SCIENCE & TECHNOLOGY CO., LTD.; *Int'l*, pg. 5543
O.K.S.M. SP. Z O.O.—See CRH plc; *Int'l*, pg. 1845
OKS OTTO KNAUF GMBH—See Stemcor Holdings Limited; *Int'l*, pg. 7006
OKS SPEZIALSCHMIERSTOFFE GMBH—See Freudenberg SE; *Int'l*, pg. 2790
OKSUT MADENCILIK A.S.—See Centerra Gold Inc.; *Int'l*, pg. 1403
OKTA A.D.—See HELLENiQ ENERGY Holdings S.A.; *Int'l*, pg. 3334
OKTA AUSTRALIA PTY LIMITED—See Okta, Inc.; *U.S. Public*, pg. 1566
OKTA, INC.; *U.S. Public*, pg. 1566
OKTAL PHARMA D.O.O.—See Walgreens Boots Alliance, Inc.; *U.S. Public*, pg. 2322
OKTAL SAS—See Sogeclair; *Int'l*, pg. 7058
OKTAL SYNTHETIC ENVIRONMENT SAS—See Sogeclair; *Int'l*, pg. 7058
OK TEDI MINING LIMITED—See First Quantum Minerals Ltd.; *Int'l*, pg. 2687
OK TIRE STORE INC.; *U.S. Private*, pg. 3006
OKTOPUS S.A./N.V.—See Siemens Aktiengesellschaft; *Int'l*, pg. 6887
OK TRANSPORTATION LIMITED; *Int'l*, pg. 5543
OKUBO DAIICHI TRAFFIC LTD.—See Daiichi Koutsu Sangyo Co., Ltd.; *Int'l*, pg. 1929
OKUDA KINZOKU CO., LTD.—See Okaya & Co., Ltd.; *Int'l*, pg. 5547
OKUMA AMERICA CORPORATION—See Okuma Corporation; *Int'l*, pg. 5550
OKUMA AUSTRALIA PTY LTD—See Okuma Corporation; *Int'l*, pg. 5550
OKUMA BEACH LAND CO., LTD.—See Japan Airlines Co., Ltd.; *Int'l*, pg. 3882
OKUMA BENELUX B.V.—See Okuma Corporation; *Int'l*, pg. 5551
OKUMA (CHANGZHOU) MACHINE TOOL CO., LTD.—See Okuma Corporation; *Int'l*, pg. 5550
OKUMA CORPORATION - KANI PLANT—See Okuma Corporation; *Int'l*, pg. 5551
OKUMA CORPORATION; *Int'l*, pg. 5550
OKUMA DEUTSCHLAND GMBH—See Okuma Corporation; *Int'l*, pg. 5551
OKUMA EUROPE GMBH—See Okuma Corporation; *Int'l*, pg. 5551
OKUMA EUROPE RUS LLC—See Okuma Corporation; *Int'l*, pg. 5551
OKUMA INDIA PVT LTD—See Okuma Corporation; *Int'l*, pg. 5551
OKUMA KOREA CORPORATION—See Okuma Corporation; *Int'l*, pg. 5551
OKUMA LATINO AMERICANA COMERCIO LTDA—See Okuma Corporation; *Int'l*, pg. 5551
OKUMA MACHINE TOOL (SHANGHAI) CORPORATION—See Okuma Corporation; *Int'l*, pg. 5551
OKUMA NEW ZEALAND LTD—See Okuma Corporation; *Int'l*, pg. 5551

OK ZIMBABWE LIMITED

OKUMA TECHNO (THAILAND) LTD. - SINGAPORE BRANCH—See Okuma Corporation; *Int'l*, pg. 5551
OKUMA TECHNO (THAILAND) LTD.—See Okuma Corporation; *Int'l*, pg. 5551
OKUMA TECHNO (THAILAND) LTD.—See Okuma Corporation; *Int'l*, pg. 5551
OKUMA VIETNAM CO., LTD.—See Okuma Corporation; *Int'l*, pg. 5551
OKUMURA CORPORATION—See Senko Group Holdings Co., Ltd.; *Int'l*, pg. 6710
OKUMURA ENGINEERING CORP.; *Int'l*, pg. 5551
OKUMURA MACHINERY CORPORATION—See Senko Group Holdings Co., Ltd.; *Int'l*, pg. 6710
OKUMURA METALS CO., LTD.—See The Furukawa Electric Co., Ltd.; *Int'l*, pg. 7646
OKURA ACT CITY HOTEL HAMAMATSU—See Hotel Okura Co., Ltd.; *Int'l*, pg. 3488
OKURA AKADEMIA PARK HOTEL, CHIBA—See Hotel Okura Co., Ltd.; *Int'l*, pg. 3488
OKURA ART CHINA, INC.—See Noritake Co., Limited; *Int'l*, pg. 5428
OKURA CHIBA HOTEL—See Hotel Okura Co., Ltd.; *Int'l*, pg. 3488
OKURA FOOD SALES CO., LTD.—See Nippi, Inc.; *Int'l*, pg. 5309
OKURA FRONTIER HOTEL EBINA—See Hotel Okura Co., Ltd.; *Int'l*, pg. 3488
OKURA FRONTIER HOTEL TSUKUBA—See Hotel Okura Co., Ltd.; *Int'l*, pg. 3488
OKURA GARDEN HOTEL SHANGHAI—See Hotel Okura Co., Ltd.; *Int'l*, pg. 3488
OKURA HOLDINGS CORPORATION—See GEO Holdings Corporation; *Int'l*, pg. 2932
OKURA HOUSE CO., LTD.—See Okura Industrial Co., Ltd.; *Int'l*, pg. 5551
OKURA INDUSTRIAL CO., LTD. - CHUNAN PLANT—See Okura Industrial Co., Ltd.; *Int'l*, pg. 5551
OKURA INDUSTRIAL CO., LTD. - MARUGAME NO. 4 PLANT—See Okura Industrial Co., Ltd.; *Int'l*, pg. 5551
OKURA INDUSTRIAL CO., LTD. - MARUGAME NO. 5 PLANT—See Okura Industrial Co., Ltd.; *Int'l*, pg. 5551
OKURA INDUSTRIAL CO., LTD. - SAITAMA PLANT—See Okura Industrial Co., Ltd.; *Int'l*, pg. 5551
OKURA INDUSTRIAL CO., LTD.; *Int'l*, pg. 5551
OKURA INDUSTRIAL CO., LTD. - TAKUMA PLANT—See Okura Industrial Co., Ltd.; *Int'l*, pg. 5551
OKURA SANGYO CO., LTD.—See Okura Industrial Co., Ltd.; *Int'l*, pg. 5551
OKURA VIETNAM CO., LTD.—See Okura Industrial Co., Ltd.; *Int'l*, pg. 5551
OKUTAMA KOGYO CO., LTD—See Taiheiyo Cement Corporation; *Int'l*, pg. 7411
OKUTATU (MACAO COMMERCIAL OFFSHORE) LIMITED—See EVA Precision Industrial Holdings Limited; *Int'l*, pg. 2560
OKUWA CO., LTD.; *Int'l*, pg. 5551
OKWAVE INC.; *Int'l*, pg. 5551
OKYO PHARMA LIMITED; *Int'l*, pg. 5551
OK ZIMBABWE LIMITED; *Int'l*, pg. 5543
OLAER AS—See Parker Hannifin Corporation; *U.S. Public*, pg. 1643
OLAER AUSTRALIA PTY LTD—See Parker Hannifin Corporation; *U.S. Public*, pg. 1643
OLAER AUSTRIA GMBH—See Parker Hannifin Corporation; *U.S. Public*, pg. 1643
OLAER HYDRAULICS (INDIA) PVT. LTD—See Parker Hannifin Corporation; *U.S. Public*, pg. 1643
OLAER TIANJIN HYDRAULIC MANUFACTURING CO.,LTD—See Parker Hannifin Corporation; *U.S. Public*, pg. 1643
OLAER USA, INC.—See Parker Hannifin Corporation; *U.S. Public*, pg. 1643
OLAM AGRO PERU S.A.C.—See Temasek Holdings (Private) Limited; *Int'l*, pg. 7549
OLAM AMERICAS, INC.—See Temasek Holdings (Private) Limited; *Int'l*, pg. 7549
OLAM ARGENTINA S.A.—See Temasek Holdings (Private) Limited; *Int'l*, pg. 7549
OLAM BRASIL LTDA.—See Temasek Holdings (Private) Limited; *Int'l*, pg. 7549
OLAM BURKINA S.A.R.L.—See Temasek Holdings (Private) Limited; *Int'l*, pg. 7549
OLAM DAIRY B.V.—See Temasek Holdings (Private) Limited; *Int'l*, pg. 7549
OLAM EGYPT LLC—See Temasek Holdings (Private) Limited; *Int'l*, pg. 7549
OLAM EUROPE B.V.—See Temasek Holdings (Private) Limited; *Int'l*, pg. 7549
OLAM EUROPE LTD—See Temasek Holdings (Private) Limited; *Int'l*, pg. 7549
OLAM EXPORT (INDIA) LIMITED—See Temasek Holdings (Private) Limited; *Int'l*, pg. 7549
OLAM FRANCE S.A.R.L.—See Temasek Holdings (Private) Limited; *Int'l*, pg. 7549
OLAM INFORMATION SERVICES PTE LTD—See Temasek Holdings (Private) Limited; *Int'l*, pg. 7549
OLAM INTERNATIONAL LIMITED—See Temasek Holdings (Private) Limited; *Int'l*, pg. 7549

OK ZIMBABWE LIMITED

CORPORATE AFFILIATIONS

OLAM IVOIRE S.A.R.L.—See Temasek Holdings (Private) Limited; *Int'l*, pg. 7549
OLAM KAZAKHSTAN CO LIMITED—See Temasek Holdings (Private) Limited; *Int'l*, pg. 7549
OLAM MIDDLE EAST LLC—See Temasek Holdings (Private) Limited; *Int'l*, pg. 7549
OLAM MOZAMBIQUE LIMITADA—See Temasek Holdings (Private) Limited; *Int'l*, pg. 7549
OLAM NIGERIA—See Temasek Holdings (Private) Limited; *Int'l*, pg. 7549
OLAM POLSKA SP. Z.O.O.—See Temasek Holdings (Private) Limited; *Int'l*, pg. 7549
OLAM SHANDONG LIMITED—See Temasek Holdings (Private) Limited; *Int'l*, pg. 7549
OLAM SHANGHAI LIMITED—See Temasek Holdings (Private) Limited; *Int'l*, pg. 7549
OLAM SOUTH AFRICA (PROPRIETARY) LIMITED—See Temasek Holdings (Private) Limited; *Int'l*, pg. 7549
OLAM TOMATO PROCESSORS—See Temasek Holdings (Private) Limited; *Int'l*, pg. 7549
OLAM UKRAINE LLC—See Temasek Holdings (Private) Limited; *Int'l*, pg. 7549
OLANDER MEDIA GROUP; *U.S. Private*, pg. 3008
OLANDS BANK AB—See Swedbank AB; *Int'l*, pg. 7364
OLAPLEX HOLDINGS, INC.; *U.S. Public*, pg. 1566
OLAREGEN THERAPEUTIX, INC.—See Generex Biotechnology Corporation; *U.S. Public*, pg. 930
OLAS SOFTWARE TRAINING AND DEVELOPMENT LIMITED—See Fonds de Solidarite des Travailleurs du Quebec; *Int'l*, pg. 2725
OLATECH SOLUTIONS LIMITED; *Int'l*, pg. 5551
OLATHE FORD SALES INC.; *U.S. Private*, pg. 3008
THE OLATHE NEWS—See Chatham Asset Management, LLC; *U.S. Private*, pg. 867
OLAV THON EIENDOMSSELSKAP ASA; *Int'l*, pg. 5552
OLAYAN EUROPE LIMITED—See The Olayan Group; *Int'l*, pg. 7672
OLAYAN FINANCING COMPANY—See The Olayan Group; *Int'l*, pg. 7672
OLAYAN FOOD SERVICES COMPANY—See The Olayan Group; *Int'l*, pg. 7672
THE OLAYAN GROUP; *Int'l*, pg. 7672
OLAY COMPANY, INC.—See The Procter & Gamble Company; *U.S. Public*, pg. 2121
OLBA HEALTHCARE HOLDINGS INC; *Int'l*, pg. 5552
OLB-BETEILIGUNGSGESELLSCHAFT MBH—See Allianz SE; *Int'l*, pg. 354
OLBERSDORFER GUB GMBH.—See BAUER Aktiengesellschaft; *Int'l*, pg. 893
OLBERSDORFER GUSS GMBH—See BAUER Aktiengesellschaft; *Int'l*, pg. 893
THE OLB GROUP, INC.; *U.S. Public*, pg. 2118
OLB-IMMOBILIENDIENST-GMBH—See Allianz SE; *Int'l*, pg. 354
OLBO & MEHLER TEX PORTUGAL, LDA.—See KAP Beteiligungs-AG; *Int'l*, pg. 4076
OLBRICH GMBH—See Matthews International Corporation; *U.S. Public*, pg. 1400
OLB-SERVICE GMBH—See Allianz SE; *Int'l*, pg. 355
O.L.C.I. ENGINEERING INDIA PRIVATE LIMITED—See EFORT Intelligent Equipment Co., Ltd.; *Int'l*, pg. 2321
OLCI ENGINEERING S.R.L.—See EFORT Intelligent Equipment Co., Ltd.; *Int'l*, pg. 2321
OLCO PETROLEUM GROUP INC.—See Morgan Stanley; *U.S. Public*, pg. 1475
OLCOTT PLASTICS, INC.—See Clearlake Capital Group, L.P.; *U.S. Private*, pg. 937
OLC/RIGHTS ENTERTAINMENT (JAPAN) INC—See Oriental Land Co., Ltd.; *Int'l*, pg. 5625
OLDACRE MCDONALD, LLC; *U.S. Private*, pg. 3009
OLD AMERICAN INSURANCE COMPANY—See Kansas City Life Insurance Company; *U.S. Public*, pg. 1214
OLD AUGUSTA RAILROAD COMPANY—See Koch Industries, Inc.; *U.S. Private*, pg. 2329
OLD AYALA, INC.—See Ayala Pharmaceuticals, Inc.; *U.S. Public*, pg. 256
OLD BRIDGE MUNICIPAL UTILITY AUTHORITY; *U.S. Private*, pg. 3008
OLDCASTLE ADAMS PRODUCTS COMPANY—See CRH plc; *Int'l*, pg. 1845
OLDCASTLE APG, INC.—See CRH plc; *Int'l*, pg. 1845
OLDCASTLE APG NORTHEAST, INC.—See CRH plc; *Int'l*, pg. 1846
OLDCASTLE APG SOUTH, INC.—See CRH plc; *Int'l*, pg. 1846
OLDCASTLE APG WEST, INC.—See CRH plc; *Int'l*, pg. 1846
OLDCASTLE ARCHITECTURAL, INC.—See CRH plc; *Int'l*, pg. 1845
OLDCASTLE BUILDING ENVELOP CANADA, INC.—See CRH plc; *Int'l*, pg. 1846
OLDCASTLE BUILDINGENVELOPE, INC. - CHANDLER—See KPS Capital Partners, LP; *U.S. Private*, pg. 2348
OLDCASTLE BUILDINGENVELOPE, INC. - DALLAS—See KPS Capital Partners, LP; *U.S. Private*, pg. 2348
OLDCASTLE BUILDINGENVELOPE, INC.—See KPS Capital Partners, LP; *U.S. Private*, pg. 2348

OLDCASTLE BUILDING PRODUCTS CANADA, INC. - PERMACON DIVISION—See CRH plc; *Int'l*, pg. 1846
OLDCASTLE BUILDING PRODUCTS CANADA, INC.—See CRH plc; *Int'l*, pg. 1846
OLDCASTLE BUILDING PRODUCTS, INC—See CRH plc; *Int'l*, pg. 1846
OLD CASTLE COASTAL INC.; *U.S. Private*, pg. 3008
OLDCASTLE COASTAL, INC.; *U.S. Private*, pg. 3009
OLDCASTLE, INC.—See CRH plc; *Int'l*, pg. 1846
OLDCASTLE INFRASTRUCTURE, INC.—See CRH plc; *Int'l*, pg. 1846
OLDCASTLE LAWN & GARDEN, INC.—See CRH plc; *Int'l*, pg. 1846
OLDCASTLE MATERIALS, INC.-MID-ATLANTIC GROUP—See CRH plc; *Int'l*, pg. 1847
OLDCASTLE MATERIALS, INC.—See CRH plc; *Int'l*, pg. 1846
OLDCASTLE MATERIAL TEXAS INC.—See CRH plc; *Int'l*, pg. 1846
OLDCASTLE PRECAST BUILDING SYSTEMS—See CRH plc; *Int'l*, pg. 1846
OLDCASTLE PRECAST, INC. - PORTLAND—See CRH plc; *Int'l*, pg. 1846
OLDCASTLE SOUTHERN GROUP, INC.—See CRH plc; *Int'l*, pg. 1848
OLDCASTLE SURFACES, INC.—See CRH plc; *Int'l*, pg. 1848
OLDCASTLE SW GROUP, INC.—See CRH plc; *Int'l*, pg. 1848
OLD CHANG KEE LTD; *Int'l*, pg. 5552
OLD CHANG KEE UK LIMITED—See Old Chang Kee Ltd; *Int'l*, pg. 5552
OLD COLONY ELDER SERVICES; *U.S. Private*, pg. 3008
OLD COLONY - GMAC REAL ESTATE; *U.S. Private*, pg. 3008
OLD COLORADO INN HOTEL; *U.S. Private*, pg. 3008
OLD COUNTRY MILLWORK INC.; *U.S. Private*, pg. 3008
THE OLD DEANERY CARE VILLAGE—See August Equity LLP; *Int'l*, pg. 703
OLD DOMINION BRUSH COMPANY, INC.—See Alamo Group Inc.; *U.S. Public*, pg. 71
OLD DOMINION CAPITAL MANAGEMENT, INC.—See Atlantic Union Bankshares Corporation; *U.S. Public*, pg. 223
OLD DOMINION ELECTRIC COOPERATIVE; *U.S. Private*, pg. 3008
OLD DOMINION FREIGHT LINE, INC.; *U.S. Public*, pg. 1566
OLD DOMINION GRAIN CORPORATION—See The Mennel Milling Company; *U.S. Private*, pg. 4077
OLD DOMINION LAND CONSERVANCY, INC.; *U.S. Private*, pg. 3008
OLD DOMINION LIFE INSURANCE CO.—See Shenandoah Life Insurance Company; *U.S. Private*, pg. 3632
OLD DOMINION SUPPLY, INC.—See Ferguson plc; *Int'l*, pg. 2638
OLD DOMINION TOBACCO COMPANY INC. - CAROLINA DIVISION—See Old Dominion Tobacco Company Inc.; *U.S. Private*, pg. 3008
OLD DOMINION TOBACCO COMPANY INC.; *U.S. Private*, pg. 3008
OLD DOMINION TRUCK LEASING INC.; *U.S. Private*, pg. 3008
OLD DOMINION UNIVERSITY; *U.S. Private*, pg. 3008
OLD DOMINION UTILITY SERVICES, INC.—See American States Water Company; *U.S. Public*, pg. 110
OLD DUTCH FOODS, INC.; *U.S. Private*, pg. 3008
OLDEMT LIMITED—See Pitney Bowes Inc.; *U.S. Public*, pg. 1695
OLDENBURG AVIATION INC.—See Oldenburg Group, Inc.; *U.S. Private*, pg. 3009
OLDENBURG GROUP, INC. - DEFENSE DIVISION—See Oldenburg Group, Inc.; *U.S. Private*, pg. 3010
OLDENBURG GROUP, INC.; *U.S. Private*, pg. 3009
OLDENBURGISCHE LANDESBANK AG—See Apollo Global Management, Inc.; *U.S. Public*, pg. 148
OLDENBURGISCHE LANDESBANK AG—See Grovepoint Capital LLP; *Int'l*, pg. 3112
OLDENBURGISCHE LANDESBANK AG—See Teacher Retirement System of Texas; *U.S. Private*, pg. 3944
OLDENDORFF GMBH & CO. KG—See Star Bulk Carriers Corp.; *Int'l*, pg. 7173
OLDE PEKING DINING HALL PTE LTD—See Tung Lok Restaurants (2000) Ltd; *Int'l*, pg. 7971
OLDER & LUNDY; *U.S. Private*, pg. 3010
OLDE THOMPSON, LLC—See Temasek Holdings (Private) Limited; *Int'l*, pg. 7549
OLD EUROPE CHEESE, INC.; *U.S. Private*, pg. 3009
THE OLD EVANGELINE DOWNS, LLC—See Boyd Gaming Corporation; *U.S. Public*, pg. 378
THE OLD FACTORY LIMITED—See ENL Limited; *Int'l*, pg. 2442
OLD FASHIONED FOODS INC.; *U.S. Private*, pg. 3009
OLD FASHION FOODS, INC.; *U.S. Private*, pg. 3009
OLDFIELD DAVIS, INC.; *U.S. Private*, pg. 3010
OLDFIELDS HOLDINGS LIMITED; *Int'l*, pg. 5552
OLDFIELDS PTY LIMITED—See Oldfields Holdings Limited; *Int'l*, pg. 5553
OLD FORGE SPRING HOUSE; *U.S. Private*, pg. 3009

OLD FORT BUILDING SUPPLY OF SOUTH BEND INC—See Hendricks Holding Company, Inc.; *U.S. Private*, pg. 1915
OLD FORT HARLEY DAVIDSON—See Hickingbotham Investments, Inc.; *U.S. Private*, pg. 1933
THE OLD GLOBE; *U.S. Public*, pg. 4088
OLD GRANGONIAN CLUB S.A.; *Int'l*, pg. 5552
OLDHAM CHEMICALS COMPANY INC.; *U.S. Private*, pg. 3010
OLDHAM COLLISION CENTER—See Glaser's Collision Center; *U.S. Private*, pg. 1706
THE OLDHAM GROUP; *U.S. Private*, pg. 4088
OLDHAM LUMBER CO. INC.; *U.S. Private*, pg. 3010
OLDHAM SAS—See Teledyne Technologies Incorporated; *U.S. Public*, pg. 1992
OLDHAM WINTER GMBH—See Teledyne Technologies Incorporated; *U.S. Public*, pg. 1992
OLD HILL PARTNERS INC—See Spouting Rock Financial Partners LLC; *U.S. Private*, pg. 3762
OLD HOME FOODS, INC.; *U.S. Private*, pg. 3009
OLD KEY WEST RESORT—See The Walt Disney Company; *U.S. Public*, pg. 2138
OLD LINE SPIRITS, LLC—See Constellation Brands, Inc.; *U.S. Public*, pg. 571
OLD LYME GOURMET COMPANY; *U.S. Private*, pg. 3009
OLD MASTER PRODUCTS INC.; *U.S. Private*, pg. 3009
OLD MILL MARKETING; *U.S. Private*, pg. 3009
OLD MISSION BANCORP, INC.; *U.S. Private*, pg. 3009
OLD MISSION BANK—See 4Front Credit Union; *U.S. Private*, pg. 15
OLD MISSOURI BANK—See Jamesmark Bancshares, Inc.; *U.S. Private*, pg. 2185
OLD MUTUAL INSURE LIMITED—See Old Mutual Limited; *Int'l*, pg. 5552
OLD MUTUAL LIFE ASSURANCE COMPANY (SOUTH AFRICA) LTD.; *Int'l*, pg. 5552
OLD MUTUAL LIMITED; *Int'l*, pg. 5552
OLD MUTUAL WEALTH LIFE ASSURANCE LTD.—See Phoenix Group Holdings PLC; *Int'l*, pg. 5851
OLD MUTUAL ZIMBABWE LIMITED—See Old Mutual Limited; *Int'l*, pg. 5552
OLD NATIONAL BANCORP; *U.S. Public*, pg. 1566
OLD NATIONAL BANK—See Old National Bancorp; *U.S. Public*, pg. 1567
OLD NAVY (APPAREL), LLC—See The Gap, Inc.; *U.S. Public*, pg. 2074
OLD NAVY (CANADA) INC.—See The Gap, Inc.; *U.S. Public*, pg. 2074
OLD NAVY—See The Gap, Inc.; *U.S. Public*, pg. 2074
OLD NORTH UTILITY SERVICES, INC.—See American States Water Company; *U.S. Public*, pg. 110
OLD OAK HOLDINGS LIMITED; *Int'l*, pg. 5552
OLD OAK PROPERTIES INC.; *Int'l*, pg. 5552
OLD O'BRIEN BANC SHARES, INC.; *U.S. Private*, pg. 3009
OLD ORCHARD BRANDS, LLC—See Lassonde Industries, Inc.; *Int'l*, pg. 4421
OLD PEAK LIMITED—See National Investments Fund Limited; *Int'l*, pg. 5160
OLD PEORIA COMPANY INC.; *U.S. Private*, pg. 3009
OLD PLANK TRAIL COMMUNITY BANK, N.A.—See Wintrust Financial Corporation; *U.S. Public*, pg. 2375
OLD POINT FINANCIAL CORPORATION; *U.S. Public*, pg. 1567
THE OLD POINT NATIONAL BANK OF PHOEBUS—See Old Point Financial Corporation; *U.S. Public*, pg. 1567
OLD POINT TRUST & FINANCIAL SERVICES, N.A.—See Old Point Financial Corporation; *U.S. Public*, pg. 1567
OLD RELIABLE CASUALTY CO.—See Kemper Corporation; *U.S. Public*, pg. 1221
OLD REPUBLIC AEROSPACE, INC.—See Old Republic International Corporation; *U.S. Public*, pg. 1568
OLD REPUBLIC AGRIBUSINESS UNDERWRITERS, INC.—See Old Republic International Corporation; *U.S. Public*, pg. 1568
OLD REPUBLIC CONTRACTORS INSURANCE GROUP, INC.—See Old Republic International Corporation; *U.S. Public*, pg. 1567
OLD REPUBLIC DEALER SERVICE CORPORATION—See Old Republic International Corporation; *U.S. Public*, pg. 1567
OLD REPUBLIC GENERAL INSURANCE CORPORATION—See Old Republic International Corporation; *U.S. Public*, pg. 1568
OLD REPUBLIC GENERAL INSURANCE GROUP, INC.—See Old Republic International Corporation; *U.S. Public*, pg. 1567
OLD REPUBLIC HOME PROTECTION COMPANY, INC.—See Old Republic International Corporation; *U.S. Public*, pg. 1568
OLD REPUBLIC INSURANCE COMPANY OF CANADA—See Old Republic International Corporation; *U.S. Public*, pg. 1568
OLD REPUBLIC INSURANCE COMPANY—See Old Republic International Corporation; *U.S. Public*, pg. 1568
OLD REPUBLIC INSURED AUTOMOTIVE SERVICES, INC.—See Old Republic International Corporation; *U.S. Public*, pg. 1568

COMPANY NAME INDEX

OLD REPUBLIC INTERNATIONAL CORPORATION; *U.S. Public*, pg. 1567
OLD REPUBLIC LIFE INSURANCE COMPANY—See Old Republic International Corporation; *U.S. Public*, pg. 1568
OLD REPUBLIC LIFE INSURANCE GROUP, INC.—See Old Republic International Corporation; *U.S. Public*, pg. 1568
OLD REPUBLIC MORTGAGE GUARANTY GROUP, INC.—See Old Republic International Corporation; *U.S. Public*, pg. 1568
OLD REPUBLIC NATIONAL TITLE HOLDING COMPANY—See Old Republic International Corporation; *U.S. Public*, pg. 1568
OLD REPUBLIC NATIONAL TITLE INSURANCE COMPANY—See Old Republic International Corporation; *U.S. Public*, pg. 1569
OLD REPUBLIC PROFESSIONAL LIABILITY, INC.—See Old Republic International Corporation; *U.S. Public*, pg. 1568
OLD REPUBLIC RISK MANAGEMENT, INC.—See Old Republic International Corporation; *U.S. Public*, pg. 1568
OLD REPUBLIC SPECIALIZED AGENCY SOLUTIONS—See Old Republic International Corporation; *U.S. Public*, pg. 1569
OLD REPUBLIC SPECIALTY INSURANCE UNDERWRITERS, INC.—See Old Republic International Corporation; *U.S. Public*, pg. 1568
OLD REPUBLIC SURETY COMPANY—See Old Republic International Corporation; *U.S. Public*, pg. 1568
OLD REPUBLIC SURETY GROUP, INC.—See Old Republic International Corporation; *U.S. Public*, pg. 1568
OLD REPUBLIC TITLE AND ESCROW OF HAWAII, LTD.—See Old Republic International Corporation; *U.S. Public*, pg. 1569
OLD REPUBLIC TITLE COMPANY OF CONROE—See Old Republic International Corporation; *U.S. Public*, pg. 1569
OLD REPUBLIC TITLE COMPANY OF HOUSTON—See Old Republic International Corporation; *U.S. Public*, pg. 1569
OLD REPUBLIC TITLE COMPANY OF NEVADA—See Old Republic International Corporation; *U.S. Public*, pg. 1569
OLD REPUBLIC TITLE COMPANY OF OKLAHOMA—See Old Republic International Corporation; *U.S. Public*, pg. 1569
OLD REPUBLIC TITLE COMPANY OF ST. LOUIS, INC.—See Old Republic International Corporation; *U.S. Public*, pg. 1569
OLD REPUBLIC TITLE HOLDING COMPANY, INC.—See Old Republic International Corporation; *U.S. Public*, pg. 1569
OLD REPUBLIC TITLE INFORMATION CONCEPTS—See Old Republic International Corporation; *U.S. Public*, pg. 1569
OLD REPUBLIC TITLE INSURANCE AGENCY, INC.—See Old Republic International Corporation; *U.S. Public*, pg. 1569
OLD REPUBLIC TITLE INSURANCE GROUP, INC.—See Old Republic International Corporation; *U.S. Public*, pg. 1568
OLD SALEM MUSEUMS & GARDENS; *U.S. Private*, pg. 3009
OLD SECOND BANCORP, INC.; *U.S. Public*, pg. 1569
OLD SECOND NATIONAL BANK—See Old Second Bancorp, Inc.; *U.S. Public*, pg. 1569
OLD SPAGHETTI FACTORY (CANADA) LTD.—See Cracken, Harkey & Co., LLC; *U.S. Private*, pg. 1081
OLD SPARTAN LIFE INSURANCE CO.—See Continental Holding Company; *U.S. Private*, pg. 1029
OLD TESSON SURGERY CENTER, L.P.—See Tenet Healthcare Corporation; *U.S. Public*, pg. 2012
OLD TIME POTTERY INC.—See Warburg Pincus LLC; *U.S. Private*, pg. 4438
OLD TIME SPORTS, INC.—See '47 Brand, LLC; *U.S. Private*, pg. 1
OLDTOWN BERHAD—See JAB Holding Company S.a.r.l.; *Int'l*, pg. 3863
OLD TOWN CANOE CO.—See Johnson Outdoors Inc.; *U.S. Public*, pg. 1201
OLD TOWN COFFEE & TEA CO INC; *U.S. Private*, pg. 3009
OLD TOWN ENDOSCOPY CENTER, LLC—See KKR & Co. Inc.; *U.S. Public*, pg. 1246
OLD TOWNE PHYSICAL THERAPY, LIMITED PARTNERSHIP—See U.S. Physical Therapy, Inc.; *U.S. Public*, pg. 2215
OLD TOWN IT, LLC; *U.S. Private*, pg. 3009
OLD TOWN S.A.; *Int'l*, pg. 5552
OLD TOWN TROLLEY TOURS OF SAN DIEGO INC—See Historic Tours of America Inc.; *U.S. Private*, pg. 1952
OLD TOWN TROLLEY TOURS OF SAVANNAH INC—See Historic Tours of America Inc.; *U.S. Private*, pg. 1952
OLD TOWN TROLLEY TOURS OF WASHINGTON INC.—See Historic Tours of America Inc.; *U.S. Private*, pg. 1952

OLD TOWN TROLLEY TOURS—See Historic Tours of America Inc.; *U.S. Private*, pg. 1952
THE OLD TRAIL PRINTING CO., INC.; *U.S. Private*, pg. 4088
OLD TUCSON COMPANY; *U.S. Private*, pg. 3009
OLD UNITED CASUALTY COMPANY—See Berkshire Hathaway Inc.; *U.S. Public*, pg. 313
OLD VETERAN CONSTRUCTION, INC.; *U.S. Private*, pg. 3009
OLD VIRGINIA BRICK COMPANY INC.; *U.S. Private*, pg. 3009
OLDWEBSITES.COM, INC.; *U.S. Private*, pg. 3010
OLD WESTBURY GOLF & COUNTRY CLUB; *U.S. Private*, pg. 3009
OLD WEST PROPERTIES LLC; *U.S. Private*, pg. 3009
OLD WISCONSIN SAUSAGE—See Carl Buddig & Company; *U.S. Private*, pg. 762
OLD WORLD INDUSTRIES, LLC; *U.S. Private*, pg. 3009
OLEAN ADVANCED PRODUCTS DIVISION—See KYOCERA Corporation; *Int'l*, pg. 4359
OLEAN WHOLESALE GROCERY COOPERATIVE INC.—See C&S Wholesale Grocers, Inc.; *U.S. Private*, pg. 704
O'LEARY AUTO GROUP; *Int'l*, pg. 5502
O'LEARY INSURANCES GALWAY LIMITED—See Brown & Brown, Inc.; *U.S. Public*, pg. 401
O'LEARY INSURANCES WATERFORD LIMITED—See Brown & Brown, Inc.; *U.S. Public*, pg. 401
O'LEARY'S MATERIAL HANDLING SERVICES PTY LTD—See Cargotec Corporation; *Int'l*, pg. 1329
OLECTRA GREENTECH LTD; *Int'l*, pg. 5553
OLED AOMORI CO., LTD.—See Kaneka Corporation; *Int'l*, pg. 4067
OLEDWORKS LLC; *U.S. Private*, pg. 3010
OLEEO, PLC; *Int'l*, pg. 5553
OLE HENRIKSEN OF DENMARK, INC.—See LVMH Moet Hennessy Louis Vuitton SE; *Int'l*, pg. 4601
OLEKSA ENTERPRISES INCORPORATED; *U.S. Private*, pg. 3010
OLEMA PHARMACEUTICALS, INC.; *U.S. Public*, pg. 1570
OLE MEDIA MANAGEMENT LP; *Int'l*, pg. 5553
OLE MOE AS—See Einhell Germany AG; *Int'l*, pg. 2334
OLEN CORPORATION—See Kokosing Construction Company, Inc.; *U.S. Private*, pg. 2341
OLENEX EDIBLE OIL B.V.—See Wilmar International Limited; *Int'l*, pg. 8421
OLEN PROPERTIES CORP.; *U.S. Private*, pg. 3010
OLEODINAMICA PANNI S.R.L.—See Interpump Group S.p.A.; *Int'l*, pg. 3757
OLEODUCTO BICENTENARIO DE COLOMBIA S.A.S.—See Ecopetrol S.A.; *Int'l*, pg. 2299
OLEO E GAS PARTICIPACOES S.A.—See Petro Rio S.A.; *Int'l*, pg. 5825
OLEO-FATS INC—See D&L Industries, Inc.; *Int'l*, pg. 1899
OLEON N.V.—See Avril SCA; *Int'l*, pg. 750
OLEOQUIMICA INDUSTRIA E COMERCIO DE PRODUTOS QUIMICOS LTDA.—See Ultrapar Participacoes S.A.; *Int'l*, pg. 8019
OLEOS "MENU" INDUSTRIA E COMERCIO LTDA.—See Toyota Tsusho Corporation; *Int'l*, pg. 7877
OLEOTRADE INTERNATIONAL CO., LTD.—See Nippon Fine Chemical Co., Ltd.; *Int'l*, pg. 5318
OLE RED GATLINBURG, LLC—See Ryman Hospitality Properties, Inc.; *U.S. Public*, pg. 1829
OLEREX AS; *Int'l*, pg. 5553
OLERUP GMBH—See CareDx, Inc.; *U.S. Public*, pg. 435
OLERUP SSP AB—See CareDx, Inc.; *U.S. Public*, pg. 435
OLES ENVELOPE CORPORATION; *U.S. Private*, pg. 3010
OLESON'S FOODS INC.; *U.S. Private*, pg. 3010
OLE SOUTH PROPERTIES INC; *U.S. Private*, pg. 3010
OLEUM INSURANCE COMPANY, LIMITED—See Repsol, S.A.; *Int'l*, pg. 6293
OLEX AUSTRALIA PTY. LTD.—See Nexans S.A.; *Int'l*, pg. 5240
OLEX HOLDINGS PTY. LTD.—See Nexans S.A.; *Int'l*, pg. 5240
OLEX NEW ZEALAND LTD.—See Nexans S.A.; *Int'l*, pg. 5240
OLFACTORY BIOSCIENCES CORP.; *U.S. Public*, pg. 1570
OLFA NORTH AMERICA—See Cornell Capital Management LLC; *U.S. Private*, pg. 1051
OLF SA—See Vivendi SE; *Int'l*, pg. 8278
OLGA FILM GMBH—See Highlight Communications AG; *Int'l*, pg. 3388
OLGA'S KITCHEN INC.—See Robert B. Solomon Holding Company, Inc.; *U.S. Private*, pg. 3457
OLGOONIK CORPORATION; *U.S. Private*, pg. 3010
OLGOONIK DEVELOPMENT, LLC—See Olgoonik Corporation; *U.S. Private*, pg. 3010
OLGOONIK MANAGEMENT SERVICES, LLC—See Olgoonik Corporation; *U.S. Private*, pg. 3010
OLHARES.COM - FOTOGRAFIA ONLINE, S.A.—See Impresa SGPS S.A.; *Int'l*, pg. 3637
OLHAUSEN BILLIARD MFG, INC.; *U.S. Private*, pg. 3010
OLI BENELUX B.V.—See WAMGROUP S.p.A.; *Int'l*, pg. 8338

OLIVER OIL COMPANY INC.

OLICAR S.P.A; *Int'l*, pg. 5553
OLIC (THAILAND) LIMITED—See Fuji Pharma Co., Ltd.; *Int'l*, pg. 2816
OLIDATA S.P.A.; *Int'l*, pg. 5553
OLI DO BRASIL EQUIPAMENTOS INDUSTRIAIS LTDA.—See WAMGROUP S.p.A.; *Int'l*, pg. 8338
OLIEHANDEL KLAAS DE BOER B. V.—See Marquard & Bahls AG; *Int'l*, pg. 4700
OLIE, INC.; *Int'l*, pg. 5553
OLI ELECTRICAL VIBRATORS SOUTH AFRICA—See WAMGROUP S.p.A.; *Int'l*, pg. 8338
OLIGO SA—See Huntsman Corporation; *U.S. Public*, pg. 1075
OLI MAKINE SAN.VE TIC. LTD.—See WAMGROUP S.p.A.; *Int'l*, pg. 8338
OLIMAX NT SP. Z .O.O.—See Sativa Wellness Group Inc.; *Int'l*, pg. 6584
OLIMB RORFORNYING HOLDING AS—See Per Aarsleff Holding A/S; *Int'l*, pg. 5796
OLIMPIAS GROUP S.R.L.—See Edizione S.r.l.; *Int'l*, pg. 2312
OLIMPO REAL ESTATE PORTUGAL, SIGI, S.A.; *Int'l*, pg. 5553
OLIMPO REAL ESTATE SOCIMI SA; *Int'l*, pg. 5553
OLIN AUSTRALIA LIMITED—See Olin Corporation; *U.S. Public*, pg. 1570
OLIN BRASS INTERNATIONAL GROUP—See Wieland-Werke AG; *Int'l*, pg. 8403
OLIN CHLOR ALKALI PRODUCTS—See Olin Corporation; *U.S. Public*, pg. 1570
OLIN CORPORATION - CHLOR ALKALI PRODUCTS DIVISION—See Olin Corporation; *U.S. Public*, pg. 1570
OLIN CORPORATION; *U.S. Public*, pg. 1570
OLIN CORPORATION - WINCHESTER DIVISION—See Olin Corporation; *U.S. Public*, pg. 1570
OLINDE'S FURNITURE & APPLIANCES; *U.S. Private*, pg. 3010
OLINK HOLDING AB—See Thermo Fisher Scientific Inc.; *U.S. Public*, pg. 2149
OLIN MEXICO S.A. DE C.V.—See Wieland-Werke AG; *Int'l*, pg. 8403
OLIN OIL CO. INC.; *U.S. Private*, pg. 3010
OLIO OILFIELD SERVICES SDN BHD—See Oilfield Services & Supplies Pte. Ltd.; *Int'l*, pg. 5535
OLIPASS CORPORATION; *Int'l*, pg. 5553
OLI RUSSIA LLC—See WAMGROUP S.p.A.; *Int'l*, pg. 8338
OLI SPAIN 2006, S.L.U.—See WAMGROUP S.p.A.; *Int'l*, pg. 8338
OLI S.P.A.—See WAMGROUP S.p.A.; *Int'l*, pg. 8338
OLITRA INC.—See J.A.G. Mines Ltd.; *Int'l*, pg. 3857
OLIUDREIFING EHF.—See Festi hf; *Int'l*, pg. 2646
OLIUVERZLUN ISLANDS HF.—See Hagar hf.; *Int'l*, pg. 3206
OLIVA PINTO LOGISTICA LTDA.—See Log-In Logistica Intermodal S.A.; *Int'l*, pg. 4541
OLIVA TOBACCO COMPANY; *U.S. Private*, pg. 3010
OLIVE & BETTE'S; *U.S. Private*, pg. 3010
OLIVE BUSINESS SOLUTIONS LIMITED; *Int'l*, pg. 5553
OLIVEDA INTERNATIONAL, INC.; *U.S. Public*, pg. 1570
OLIVE DIALYSIS, LLC—See DaVita Inc.; *U.S. Public*, pg. 641
OLIVE ECOPAK PRIVATE LIMITED—See Rajshree Polypack Ltd.; *Int'l*, pg. 6194
OLIVE GARDEN ITALIAN RESTAURANT—See Darden Restaurants, Inc.; *U.S. Public*, pg. 633
OLIVE INTERACTIVE DESIGN & MARKETING INC.; *U.S. Private*, pg. 3010
OLIVEIRA ENERGIA GERACAO E SERVICOS LTDA.; *Int'l*, pg. 5553
OLIVER CARR COMPANY; *U.S. Private*, pg. 3010
OLIVER C. JOSEPH; *U.S. Private*, pg. 3010
OLIVER DITSON CO.—See Theodore Presser Co.; *U.S. Private*, pg. 4141
OLIVER EXTERMINATING CORP.; *U.S. Private*, pg. 3010
THE OLIVER GROUP, INC.; *U.S. Private*, pg. 4088
THE OLIVER GROUP LLC—See JLL Partners, LLC; *U.S. Private*, pg. 2213
OLIVER HUME CORPORATION PTY. LTD.; *Int'l*, pg. 5553
OLIVER H. VAN HORN CO., LLC; *U.S. Private*, pg. 3011
OLIVERI ARCHITECTS INC.; *U.S. Private*, pg. 3011
OLIVERI INSTRUMENT COMPANY; *U.S. Private*, pg. 3011
OLIVERI SOLUTIONS PTY LIMITED—See Fletcher Building Limited; *Int'l*, pg. 2700
OLIVER JAMES ASSOCIATES; *Int'l*, pg. 5554
OLIVER JAMES ASSOCIATES (SWITZERLAND) AG—See Oliver James Associates; *Int'l*, pg. 5554
OLIVER J. NILSEN (AUSTRALIA) LIMITED; *Int'l*, pg. 5553
OLIVER MACHINERY CO.—See Chiu Ting Machinery Co., Ltd.; *Int'l*, pg. 1574
OLIVER MARKETING, INC.; *U.S. Private*, pg. 3011
OLIVER MARKETING LIMITED—See You & Mr Jones Inc.; *U.S. Private*, pg. 4592
OLIVER M. DEAN, INC.; *U.S. Private*, pg. 3011
OLIVER OIL COMPANY INC.; *U.S. Private*, pg. 3011
OLIVER PRINTING & PACKAGING CO., LLC—See Dunsirn Partners LLC; *U.S. Private*, pg. 1290

OLIVER OIL COMPANY INC.   CORPORATE AFFILIATIONS

OLIVER PRINTING & PACKAGING CO., LLC—See Pfingsten Partners, LLC; *U.S. Private*, pg. 3164
OLIVER PRODUCTS COMPANY INC.—See Berwind Corporation; *U.S. Private*, pg. 541
OLIVER RUBBER COMPANY—See Compagnie Generale des Etablissements Michelin SCA; *Int'l*, pg. 1744
OLIVER RUSSELL & ASSOCIATES LLC; *U.S. Private*, pg. 3011
OLIVER SCHROTT KOMMUNIKATION GMBH; *Int'l*, pg. 5554
OLIVER'S REAL FOOD LIMITED; *Int'l*, pg. 5554
OLIVER STEEL PLATE CO.—See A. M. Castle & Co.; *U.S. Public*, pg. 11
OLIVER STREET DERMATOLOGY HOLDINGS LLC—See ABRY Partners, LLC; *U.S. Private*, pg. 42
OLIVER VALVES LIMITED; *Int'l*, pg. 5554
OLIVER WAREHOUSE INC.—See BASF SE; *Int'l*, pg. 876
OLIVER WYMAN AB—See Marsh & McLennan Companies, Inc.; *U.S. Public*, pg. 1387
OLIVER WYMAN ACTUARIAL CONSULTING, INC.—See Marsh & McLennan Companies, Inc.; *U.S. Public*, pg. 1387
OLIVER WYMAN AG—See Marsh & McLennan Companies, Inc.; *U.S. Public*, pg. 1387
OLIVER WYMAN CONSULTING GMBH—See Marsh & McLennan Companies, Inc.; *U.S. Public*, pg. 1387
OLIVER WYMAN CONSULTING LIMITED—See Marsh & McLennan Companies, Inc.; *U.S. Public*, pg. 1387
OLIVER WYMAN CONSULTING SARL—See Marsh & McLennan Companies, Inc.; *U.S. Public*, pg. 1387
OLIVER WYMAN CONSULTING (SHANGHAI) LTD—See Marsh & McLennan Companies, Inc.; *U.S. Public*, pg. 1386
OLIVER WYMAN CONSULTING SL—See Marsh & McLennan Companies, Inc.; *U.S. Public*, pg. 1387
OLIVER WYMAN CONSULTORIA EM ESTRATEGIA DE NEGOCIOS LTDA.—See Marsh & McLennan Companies, Inc.; *U.S. Public*, pg. 1387
OLIVER WYMAN ENERGY CONSULTING LIMITED—See Marsh & McLennan Companies, Inc.; *U.S. Public*, pg. 1387
OLIVER WYMAN FZ-LLC—See Marsh & McLennan Companies, Inc.; *U.S. Public*, pg. 1387
OLIVER WYMAN GERMANY GMBH—See Marsh & McLennan Companies, Inc.; *U.S. Public*, pg. 1387
OLIVER WYMAN GMBH—See Marsh & McLennan Companies, Inc.; *U.S. Public*, pg. 1387
OLIVER WYMAN GROUP KK—See Marsh & McLennan Companies, Inc.; *U.S. Public*, pg. 1387
OLIVER WYMAN (HONG KONG) LIMITED—See Marsh & McLennan Companies, Inc.; *U.S. Public*, pg. 1386
OLIVER WYMAN, INC.—See Marsh & McLennan Companies, Inc.; *U.S. Public*, pg. 1386
OLIVER WYMAN LIMITED LIABILITY COMPANY—See Marsh & McLennan Companies, Inc.; *U.S. Public*, pg. 1386
OLIVER WYMAN LIMITED—See Marsh & McLennan Companies, Inc.; *U.S. Public*, pg. 1387
OLIVER WYMAN LTD.—See Marsh & McLennan Companies, Inc.; *U.S. Public*, pg. 1387
OLIVER WYMAN PTE. LTD.—See Marsh & McLennan Companies, Inc.; *U.S. Public*, pg. 1387
OLIVER WYMAN PTY. LTD.—See Marsh & McLennan Companies, Inc.; *U.S. Public*, pg. 1387
OLIVER WYMAN PTY. LTD.—See Marsh & McLennan Companies, Inc.; *U.S. Public*, pg. 1387
OLIVER WYMAN (PTY) LTD.—See Marsh & McLennan Companies, Inc.; *U.S. Public*, pg. 1386
OLIVER WYMAN SAS—See Marsh & McLennan Companies, Inc.; *U.S. Public*, pg. 1386
OLIVER WYMAN S.A.S.—See Marsh & McLennan Companies, Inc.; *U.S. Public*, pg. 1386
OLIVER WYMAN, S. DE R.L. DE C.V.—See Marsh & McLennan Companies, Inc.; *U.S. Public*, pg. 1388
OLIVER WYMAN SDN. BHD.—See Marsh & McLennan Companies, Inc.; *U.S. Public*, pg. 1388
OLIVER WYMAN S.L.—See Marsh & McLennan Companies, Inc.; *U.S. Public*, pg. 1387
OLIVER WYMAN SNC—See Marsh & McLennan Companies, Inc.; *U.S. Public*, pg. 1387
OLIVER WYMAN SP. Z O.O.—See Marsh & McLennan Companies, Inc.; *U.S. Public*, pg. 1388
OLIVE SOFTWARE, INC.—See ESW Capital, LLC; *U.S. Private*, pg. 1430
OLIVE; *U.S. Private*, pg. 3010
OLIVE TREE ENERGY, LLC; *U.S. Private*, pg. 3010
OLIVE TREE ESTATES LIMITED; *Int'l*, pg. 5553
OLIVETTI ARGENTINA S.A.—See TIM S.p.A.; *Int'l*, pg. 7749
OLIVETTI DE CHILE S.A.—See TIM S.p.A.; *Int'l*, pg. 7749
OLIVETTI DEUTSCHLAND GMBH—See TIM S.p.A.; *Int'l*, pg. 7749
OLIVETTI DO BRASIL S.A.—See TIM S.p.A.; *Int'l*, pg. 7749
OLIVETTI ENGINEERING S.A.—See TIM S.p.A.; *Int'l*, pg. 7749
OLIVETTI GESTIONI IVREA S.R.L.—See TIM S.p.A.; *Int'l*, pg. 7749
OLIVETTI I-JET S.P.A.—See TIM S.p.A.; *Int'l*, pg. 7749

OLIVETTI LEXIKON ESPANA S.A.—See TIM S.p.A.; *Int'l*, pg. 7749
OLIVETTI S.P.A.—See TIM S.p.A.; *Int'l*, pg. 7749
OLIVETTI TECNOST AFRICA (PTY.) LTD.—See TIM S.p.A.; *Int'l*, pg. 7749
OLIVETTI TECNOST BELUX—See TIM S.p.A.; *Int'l*, pg. 7749
OLIVETTI TECNOST DEUTSCHLAND GMBH—See TIM S.p.A.; *Int'l*, pg. 7749
OLIVETTI UK LIMITED—See TIM S.p.A.; *Int'l*, pg. 7749
OLIVE VISTA BEHAVIORAL HEALTH CENTER—See Formation Capital, LLC; *U.S. Private*, pg. 1570
OLI VIBRA LTD.—See WAMGROUP S.p.A.; *Int'l*, pg. 8338
OLI VIBRA NORDIC AB—See WAMGROUP S.p.A.; *Int'l*, pg. 8338
OLI VIBRATIONSTECHNICK GMBH—See WAMGROUP S.p.A.; *Int'l*, pg. 8339
OLI VIBRATORS INDIA PVT. LTD.—See WAMGROUP S.p.A.; *Int'l*, pg. 8338
OLI VIBRATORS PTY LTD—See WAMGROUP S.p.A.; *Int'l*, pg. 8338
OLI VIBRATOR U.S.A. INC.—See WAMGROUP S.p.A.; *Int'l*, pg. 8338
OLI VIBRA UK LTD.—See WAMGROUP S.p.A.; *Int'l*, pg. 8338
OLIVIERI FOODS LIMITED—See Ebro Foods S.A.; *Int'l*, pg. 2287
OLIVINE INDUSTRIES (PRIVATE) LIMITED—See Cottco Holdings Limited; *Int'l*, pg. 1817
OLIVOTTO GLASS TECHNOLOGIES S.P.A.—See China Glass Holdings Limited; *Int'l*, pg. 1504
OLIVUT RESOURCES LTD.; *Int'l*, pg. 5554
OLI WOLONG COMPANY—See WAMGROUP S.p.A.; *Int'l*, pg. 8338
OLIX PHARMACEUTICALS, INC.; *Int'l*, pg. 5554
OLLIE'S BARGAIN OUTLET HOLDINGS, INC.—See CCMP Capital Advisors, LP; *U.S. Private*, pg. 800
OLLIE'S BARGAIN OUTLET, INC.—See CCMP Capital Advisors, LP; *U.S. Private*, pg. 801
OLL LOGISTICS (MALAYSIA) SDN. BHD.—See China COSCO Shipping Corporation Limited; *Int'l*, pg. 1495
OLLOO JOINT STOCK COMPANY; *Int'l*, pg. 5554
OLLY PUBLIC BENEFIT CORPORATION—See Unilever PLC; *Int'l*, pg. 8048
OLMA, A.S.—See Agrofert Holding, a.s.; *Int'l*, pg. 219
OLMA INVESTMENT COMPANY OJSC; *Int'l*, pg. 5554
OLM DIGITAL, INC.—See Imagica Group Inc.; *Int'l*, pg. 3618
OLMED ORTOPEDISKA AB—See Volati AB; *Int'l*, pg. 8301
OLMERO AG—See TX Group AG; *Int'l*, pg. 7992
OLMIX B.V.—See Olmix S.A.; *Int'l*, pg. 5554
OLMIX CHINA CO., LTD.—See Olmix S.A.; *Int'l*, pg. 5554
OLMIX DO BRASIL SC—See Olmix S.A.; *Int'l*, pg. 5554
OLMIX IBERICA, S.L.—See Olmix S.A.; *Int'l*, pg. 5554
OLMIX INDONESIA NUTRITION P.T.—See Olmix S.A.; *Int'l*, pg. 5554
OLMIX MEXICO—See Olmix S.A.; *Int'l*, pg. 5554
OLMIX NORTH AMERICA—See Olmix S.A.; *Int'l*, pg. 5554
OLMIX OOO—See Olmix S.A.; *Int'l*, pg. 5554
OLMIX SA SITE DE BRAINS—See Olmix S.A.; *Int'l*, pg. 5554
OLMIX SA SITE DE BRENELLE—See Olmix S.A.; *Int'l*, pg. 5554
OLMIX S.A.; *Int'l*, pg. 5554
OLMIX SA—See Olmix S.A.; *Int'l*, pg. 5554
OLMIX SUISSE SA—See Olmix S.A.; *Int'l*, pg. 5554
OLM, LLC; *U.S. Private*, pg. 3011
OLMOS EQUIPMENT INC.; *U.S. Private*, pg. 3011
OLMSTED-KIRK COMPANY OF HOUSTON, INC.—See Olmsted-Kirk Paper Company; *U.S. Private*, pg. 3011
OLMSTED-KIRK EQUIPMENT & SUPPLY CO.—See Olmsted-Kirk Paper Company; *U.S. Private*, pg. 3011
OLMSTED-KIRK PAPER COMPANY; *U.S. Private*, pg. 3011
OLMUKSAN INTERNATIONAL PAPER AMBALAJ SANAYI VE TICARET ANONIM SIRKETI—See Mondi plc; *Int'l*, pg. 5027
OLNEYA RESTORATION GROUP; *U.S. Private*, pg. 3011
OLNEY BANCSHARES OF TEXAS, INC.; *U.S. Private*, pg. 3011
THE OLNEY ENTERPRISE—See Alden Global Capital LLC; *U.S. Private*, pg. 156
OLOF MOBJER ENTREPRENAD AB—See Peab AB; *Int'l*, pg. 5772
OLOFSKAPEL MONUMENTEN, B.V.—See Minor International PCL; *Int'l*, pg. 4912
OLOGIE; *U.S. Private*, pg. 3011
OLO INC.; *U.S. Public*, pg. 1570
OLOL PONTCHARTRAIN SURGERY CENTER, LLC—See Tenet Healthcare Corporation; *U.S. Public*, pg. 2012
OLOMANA LOOMIS ISC, INC.; *U.S. Private*, pg. 3011
OLPIDURR S.P.A.—See Durr AG; *Int'l*, pg. 2233
OLPIDURR S.T.A—See Durr AG; *Int'l*, pg. 2233
OLP SELDEN, INC.—See One Liberty Properties, Inc.; *U.S. Public*, pg. 1602
OLRAC SPS (PTY) LTD.; *Int'l*, pg. 5554
OLSBERG HERMANN EVERKEN GMBH; *Int'l*, pg. 5554
O.L.S. CO., LTD.—See Okura Industrial Co., Ltd.; *Int'l*, pg. 5551

OLSEN/AIRCO HEATING & COOLING PRODUCTS - US—See TerraVest Industries, Inc.; *Int'l*, pg. 7568
OLSEN THIELEN & CO. LTD.; *U.S. Private*, pg. 3011
OLSHAN FOUNDATION REPAIR; *U.S. Private*, pg. 3011
OLSHAN LUMBER CO.; *U.S. Private*, pg. 3011
OLSON CANADA, INC.—See ICF International, Inc.; *U.S. Public*, pg. 1086
THE OLSON COMPANY; *U.S. Private*, pg. 4088
OLSON & CO. STEEL; *U.S. Private*, pg. 3011
OLSON ENGAGE—See ICF International, Inc.; *U.S. Public*, pg. 1086
OLSON IRRIGATION SYSTEMS—See Xylem Inc.; *U.S. Public*, pg. 2394
OLSON MOBECK INVESTMENT ADVISORS INC.—See M&T Bank Corporation; *U.S. Public*, pg. 1351
OLSON OIL CO. INC.; *U.S. Private*, pg. 3011
OLSON OIL CO. INC.; *U.S. Private*, pg. 3011
OLSON PRECAST COMPANY; *U.S. Private*, pg. 3011
OLSON RUG COMPANY; *U.S. Private*, pg. 3011
OLSON TECHNOLOGY INC.; *U.S. Private*, pg. 3012
OLSSON ASSOCIATES, INC.; *U.S. Private*, pg. 3012
OLSSON INDUSTRIAL ELECTRIC, INC.—See ITOCHU Corporation; *Int'l*, pg. 3838
OLSSON & ZARINS BALTINVEST AB—See Peab AB; *Int'l*, pg. 5772
OLSWANG LLP—See CMS Cameron McKenna Nabarro Olswang LLP; *Int'l*, pg. 1672
OLTA PHARMACEUTICALS CORP.—See Akorn, Inc.; *U.S. Private*, pg. 146
OLTCHIM S.A.; *Int'l*, pg. 5554
OL&T INTERNATIONAL (SHANGHAI) COMPANY LTD.—See Odyssey Logistics & Technology Corp.; *U.S. Private*, pg. 2996
OLTIS SOFTWARE, LLC—See Bain Capital, LP; *U.S. Private*, pg. 439
OLTMAN INSURANCE AGENCY, INC.—See S&V Insurance Services LLC; *U.S. Private*, pg. 3514
OLTMANS CONSTRUCTION COMPANY; *U.S. Private*, pg. 3012
OLTON CO-OP GIN—See Ag Producers Co-op; *U.S. Private*, pg. 125
OLUMS OF BINGHAMTON INC.; *U.S. Private*, pg. 3012
OLVE FARMACEUTICA LIMITADA—See FAES Farma, S.A.; *Int'l*, pg. 2601
OLVI OYJ; *Int'l*, pg. 5554
OLX GLOBAL B.V.—See Naspers Limited; *Int'l*, pg. 5148
OLYMEL S.E.C. - BOUCHERVILLE—See Sollio Cooperative Group; *Int'l*, pg. 7074
OLYMEL SOCIETE EN COMMANDITE—See Sollio Cooperative Group; *Int'l*, pg. 7074
OLY/METRO NEW MEXICO LP—See Olympus Real Estate Corp.; *U.S. Private*, pg. 3014
OLYMPIA BENEFITS INC.—See Olympia Financial Group Inc.; *Int'l*, pg. 5555
OLYMPIA BRNO S.R.O.—See Deutsche EuroShop AG; *Int'l*, pg. 2065
OLYMPIA BUILDING SUPPLIES, LLC—See GMS Inc.; *U.S. Public*, pg. 948
OLYMPIA CAPITAL HOLDINGS LIMITED; *Int'l*, pg. 5555
OLYMPIA CAPITAL MANAGEMENT INC.—See Ambroisie Capital Holding S.A.S.; *Int'l*, pg. 416
OLYMPIA CAPITAL MANAGEMENT S.A.—See Ambroisie Capital Holding S.A.S.; *Int'l*, pg. 415
OLYMPIA CAPITAL MANAGMENT INC.—See Starrex International Ltd.; *Int'l*, pg. 7179
OLYMPIA CHIMNEY SUPPLY HOLDINGS, LLC; *U.S. Private*, pg. 3012
OLYMPIA ENTERTAINMENT, INC.—See Ilitch Holdings, Inc.; *U.S. Private*, pg. 2042
OLYMPIA FINANCIAL GROUP INC.; *Int'l*, pg. 5555
OLYMPIA FUEL INC.; *U.S. Private*, pg. 3012
OLYMPIA GROUP SINGLE MEMBER HOLDING CO. S.A.; *Int'l*, pg. 5555
OLYMPIA INDUSTRIES BERHAD; *Int'l*, pg. 5555
OLYMPIA INDUSTRIES LIMITED; *Int'l*, pg. 5555
OLYMPIA KOGYO CO., LTD.—See Mitsui Fudosan Co., Ltd.; *Int'l*, pg. 4988
OLYMPIA LAND BERHAD—See DutaLand Berhad; *Int'l*, pg. 2235
OLYMPIA MANAGEMENT SERVICES LIMITED; *Int'l*, pg. 5555
OLYMPIA MILLS LIMITED; *Int'l*, pg. 5555
THE OLYMPIAN—See Chatham Asset Management, LLC; *U.S. Private*, pg. 867
OLYMPIA RESPIRATORY SERVICES LLC—See AdaptHealth Corp.; *U.S. Public*, pg. 39
OLYMPIA SALES, INC.; *U.S. Private*, pg. 3012
OLYMPIA SPORTS INC.; *U.S. Private*, pg. 3012
OLYMPIA TILE INTERNATIONAL, INC.; *Int'l*, pg. 5555
OLYMPIA TRUST COMPANY—See Olympia Financial Group Inc.; *Int'l*, pg. 5555
OLYMPIC ACCESSORIES LTD.; *Int'l*, pg. 5555
OLYMPIC AIR S.A.—See AEGEAN AIRLINES S.A.; *Int'l*, pg. 173
OLYMPIC BANCORP; *U.S. Private*, pg. 3012
OLYMPIC BRAKE SUPPLY; *U.S. Private*, pg. 3012
OLYMPIC BROADCASTING SERVICES SA—See International Olympic Committee; *Int'l*, pg. 3751

COMPANY NAME INDEX

OLYMPIC CABLE COMPANY SDN. BHD.—See OSK Holdings Berhad; *Int'l*, pg. 5651
OLYMPIC CARDS LIMITED; *Int'l*, pg. 5555
OLYMPIC-CASCADE PUBLISHING, INC.—See Chatham Asset Management, LLC; *U.S. Private*, pg. 867
OLYMPIC CASINO GROUP BALTIJA UAB—See Novalpina Capital LLP; *Int'l*, pg. 5455
OLYMPIC CATERING S.A.; *Int'l*, pg. 5555
OLYMPIC CIRCUIT TECHNOLOGY CO., LTD.; *Int'l*, pg. 5555
OLYMPIC CLUB; *U.S. Private*, pg. 3012
OLYMPIC COMPANIES INC.; *U.S. Private*, pg. 3012
OLYMPIC DAM CORPORATION PTY LTD.—See BHP Group Limited; *Int'l*, pg. 1016
OLYMPIC DIARY PRODUCTS INC.—See Agrifoods International Cooperative LTD; *Int'l*, pg. 217
OLYMPIC ENGINEERING S.A.—See Marfin Investment Group Holdings S.A.; *Int'l*, pg. 4692
OLYMPIC ENTERTAINMENT GROUP AS—See Novalpina Capital LLP; *Int'l*, pg. 5455
OLYMPIC FOUNDRY INC.; *U.S. Private*, pg. 3012
OLYMPIC GROUP CORPORATION; *Int'l*, pg. 5555
OLYMPIC GROUP; *Int'l*, pg. 5555
OLYMPIC HANDLING S.A—See Marfin Investment Group Holdings S.A.; *Int'l*, pg. 4692
OLYMPIC HEALTH MANAGEMENT SERVICES INC.—See Munchener Ruckversicherungs AG; *Int'l*, pg. 5091
OLYMPIC HEALTH MANAGEMENT SYSTEMS, INC.—See Munchener Ruckversicherungs AG; *Int'l*, pg. 5090
OLYMPIC IMPORTED PARTS CORP.; *U.S. Private*, pg. 3012
OLYMPIC INDUSTRIES, INC.—See Forest City Trading Group, LLC; *U.S. Private*, pg. 1566
OLYMPIC INDUSTRIES LIMITED; *Int'l*, pg. 5555
OLYMPIC INTERNATIONAL LTD.; *Int'l*, pg. 5555
OLYMPIC LASER PROCESSING, LLC—See Olympic Steel Inc.; *U.S. Public*, pg. 1570
OLYMPIC LASER PROCESSING, LLC—See United States Steel Corporation; *U.S. Public*, pg. 2236
OLYMPIC MANAGEMENT & FINANCIAL SERVICES LIMITED; *Int'l*, pg. 5555
OLYMPIC METALS, INC.—See Reliance Steel & Aluminum Co.; *U.S. Public*, pg. 1781
OLYMPIC OIL INDUSTRIES LIMITED; *Int'l*, pg. 5556
OLYMPIC OIL, LTD.—See Aurora Capital Group, LLC; *U.S. Private*, pg. 394
OLYMPIC OIL, LTD.—See The Jordan Company, L.P.; *U.S. Private*, pg. 4061
OLYMPIC RESOURCE MANAGEMENT—See Rayonier Inc.; *U.S. Public*, pg. 1765
OLYMPIC RETREADS (M) SDN BHD—See Eversafe Rubber Berhad; *Int'l*, pg. 2568
OLYMPIC SECURITY SERVICES, INC.; *U.S. Private*, pg. 3012
OLYMPIC SEISMIC, LTD.—See ValueAct Capital Management, L.P.; *U.S. Private*, pg. 4338
OLYMPIC STAFFING SERVICES; *U.S. Private*, pg. 3012
OLYMPIC STEEL-CHAMBERSBURG DIVISION—See Olympic Steel Inc.; *U.S. Public*, pg. 1571
OLYMPIC STEEL-CHICAGO DIVISION—See Olympic Steel Inc.; *U.S. Public*, pg. 1571
OLYMPIC STEEL-CLEVELAND DIVISION—See Olympic Steel Inc.; *U.S. Public*, pg. 1571
OLYMPIC STEEL-CONNECTICUT DIVISION—See Olympic Steel Inc.; *U.S. Public*, pg. 1571
OLYMPIC STEEL-DETROIT—See Olympic Steel Inc.; *U.S. Public*, pg. 1571
OLYMPIC STEEL INC. - SILER CITY—See Olympic Steel Inc.; *U.S. Public*, pg. 1570
OLYMPIC STEEL INC.; *U.S. Public*, pg. 1570
OLYMPIC STEEL IOWA, INC.—See Olympic Steel Inc.; *U.S. Public*, pg. 1570
OLYMPIC STEEL LAFAYETTE, INC.—See Olympic Steel Inc.; *U.S. Public*, pg. 1571
OLYMPIC STEEL-MINNEAPOLIS DIVISION—See Olympic Steel Inc.; *U.S. Public*, pg. 1571
OLYMPIC STEEL-SOUTHERN DIVISION—See Olympic Steel Inc.; *U.S. Public*, pg. 1571
OLYMPIC STEEL TRADING, INC.—See Olympic Steel Inc.; *U.S. Public*, pg. 1571
OLYMPUS AMERICA DE MEXICO S.A. DE C.V.—See Olympus Corporation; *Int'l*, pg. 5556
OLYMPUS AMERICA, INC.—See Olympus Corporation; *Int'l*, pg. 5556
OLYMPUS ASIAN PACIFIC LIMITED—See Olympus Corporation; *Int'l*, pg. 5556
OLYMPUS AUSTRALIA PTY. LTD.—See Olympus Corporation; *Int'l*, pg. 5556
OLYMPUS AUSTRIA GES.M.B.H.—See Olympus Corporation; *Int'l*, pg. 5556
OLYMPUS CAPITAL HOLDINGS ASIA; *U.S. Private*, pg. 3012
OLYMPUS CAPITAL INVESTMENTS, LLC—See Olympus Holdings, LLC; *U.S. Private*, pg. 3013
OLYMPUS (CHINA) CO., LTD.—See Olympus Corporation; *Int'l*, pg. 5556
OLYMPUS CO. (EUROPA) GMBH—See Olympus Corporation; *Int'l*, pg. 5556

OLYMPUS CONTROLS CORP.—See Applied Industrial Technologies, Inc.; *U.S. Public*, pg. 171
OLYMPUS CORPORATION OF ASIA PACIFIC LIMITED—See Olympus Corporation; *Int'l*, pg. 5556
OLYMPUS CORPORATION OF THE AMERICAS—See Olympus Corporation; *Int'l*, pg. 5556
OLYMPUS CORPORATION; *Int'l*, pg. 5556
OLYMPUS C&S SPOL. S.R.O.—See Olympus Corporation; *Int'l*, pg. 5556
OLYMPUS DANMARK A/S—See Olympus Corporation; *Int'l*, pg. 5556
OLYMPUS DEUTSCHLAND GMBH—See Olympus Corporation; *Int'l*, pg. 5556
OLYMPUS DIGITAL KG; *Int'l*, pg. 5558
OLYMPUS DIGITAL SYSTEM DESIGN CORP.—See Olympus Corporation; *Int'l*, pg. 5556
OLYMPUS D.O.O. ZA TRGOVINU—See Olympus Corporation; *Int'l*, pg. 5558
OLYMPUS ENGINEERING CO., LTD.—See Olympus Corporation; *Int'l*, pg. 5556
OLYMPUS EUROPA GMBH—See Olympus Corporation; *Int'l*, pg. 5556
OLYMPUS EUROPA HOLDING GMBH—See Olympus Corporation; *Int'l*, pg. 5556
OLYMPUS FINLAND OY—See Olympus Corporation; *Int'l*, pg. 5556
OLYMPUS FRANCE S.A.S.—See Olympus Corporation; *Int'l*, pg. 5556
OLYMPUS GROUP; *U.S. Private*, pg. 3012
OLYMPUS HOLDINGS, LLC; *U.S. Private*, pg. 3012
OLYMPUS HOMES INC.; *U.S. Private*, pg. 3013
OLYMPUS HONG KONG AND CHINA LTD.—See Olympus Corporation; *Int'l*, pg. 5557
OLYMPUS HUNGARY KFT.—See Olympus Corporation; *Int'l*, pg. 5557
OLYMPUS IMAGING AMERICA INC.—See Olympus Corporation; *Int'l*, pg. 5557
OLYMPUS IMAGING CORP - ISHIKAWA FACILITY—See Olympus Corporation; *Int'l*, pg. 5557
OLYMPUS IMAGING CORP.—See Olympus Corporation; *Int'l*, pg. 5557
OLYMPUS IMAGING CORP - UTSUGI FACILITY—See Olympus Corporation; *Int'l*, pg. 5557
OLYMPUS IMAGING INDIA PRIVATE LIMITED—See Olympus Corporation; *Int'l*, pg. 5557
OLYMPUS IMAGING SINGAPORE PTE. LTD.—See Olympus Corporation; *Int'l*, pg. 5557
OLYMPUS IMPORTED AUTO PARTS—See Genuine Parts Company; *U.S. Public*, pg. 932
OLYMPUS IRELAND—See Olympus Corporation; *Int'l*, pg. 5557
OLYMPUS ITALIA S.R.L.—See Olympus Corporation; *Int'l*, pg. 5557
OLYMPUS KEYMED GROUP LIMITED—See Olympus Corporation; *Int'l*, pg. 5557
OLYMPUS KOREA CO., LTD.—See Olympus Corporation; *Int'l*, pg. 5557
OLYMPUS LATIN AMERICA INC.—See Olympus Corporation; *Int'l*, pg. 5557
OLYMPUS LOGITEX CO., LTD.—See Olympus Corporation; *Int'l*, pg. 5557
OLYMPUS MEDICAL ENGINEERING CO., LTD.—See Olympus Corporation; *Int'l*, pg. 5557
OLYMPUS MEDICAL SCIENCE SALES CORP.—See Olympus Corporation; *Int'l*, pg. 5557
OLYMPUS MEDICAL SYSTEMS CORP - HINODE PLANT—See Olympus Corporation; *Int'l*, pg. 5557
OLYMPUS MEDICAL SYSTEMS CORP - ISHIKAWA FACILITY—See Olympus Corporation; *Int'l*, pg. 5557
OLYMPUS MEDICAL SYSTEMS CORP - SHIRAKAWA FACILITY—See Olympus Corporation; *Int'l*, pg. 5557
OLYMPUS MEDICAL SYSTEMS CORP.—See Olympus Corporation; *Int'l*, pg. 5557
OLYMPUS MEDICAL SYSTEMS CORP - UTSUGI FACILITY—See Olympus Corporation; *Int'l*, pg. 5557
OLYMPUS MEDICAL SYSTEMS INDIA PRIVATE LIMITED—See Olympus Corporation; *Int'l*, pg. 5557
OLYMPUS MEDICAL SYSTEMS VIETNAM CO., LTD.—See Olympus Corporation; *Int'l*, pg. 5557
OLYMPUS MEMORY WORKS CORP.—See Olympus Corporation; *Int'l*, pg. 5557
OLYMPUS NDT CANADA INC.—See Olympus Corporation; *Int'l*, pg. 5557
OLYMPUS NDT CORPORATION—See Olympus Corporation; *Int'l*, pg. 5557
OLYMPUS NEW ZEALAND LIMITED—See Olympus Corporation; *Int'l*, pg. 5557
OLYMPUS NORGE A/S—See Olympus Corporation; *Int'l*, pg. 5557
OLYMPUS OPTICAL POLSKA SP. Z.O.O.—See Olympus Corporation; *Int'l*, pg. 5557
OLYMPUS OPTICAL TECHNOLOGY PHILIPPINES, INC.—See Olympus Corporation; *Int'l*, pg. 5557
OLYMPUS OPTO-TECHNOLOGY CO., LTD.- SAKAKI—See Olympus Corporation; *Int'l*, pg. 5557
OLYMPUS OPTO-TECHNOLOGY CO., LTD—See Olympus Corporation; *Int'l*, pg. 5557
OLYMPUS PARTNERS; *U.S. Private*, pg. 3013

OMAHA TRUCK CENTER INC.

OLYMPUS PICTURES, LLC—See Olympus Holdings, LLC; *U.S. Private*, pg. 3013
OLYMPUS POWER, LLC—See Olympus Holdings, LLC; *U.S. Private*, pg. 3013
OLYMPUS PRODUCTIONS, LLC—See Olympus Holdings, LLC; *U.S. Private*, pg. 3013
OLYMPUS REAL ESTATE CORP.; *U.S. Private*, pg. 3014
OLYMPUS (SCHWEIZ) AG—See Olympus Corporation; *Int'l*, pg. 5557
OLYMPUS SCIENTIFIC SOLUTIONS AMERICAS INC.—See Olympus Corporation; *Int'l*, pg. 5557
OLYMPUS (SHENZHEN) INDUSTRIAL LTD.—See Olympus Corporation; *Int'l*, pg. 5556
OLYMPUS SINGAPORE PTE LTD.—See Olympus Corporation; *Int'l*, pg. 5557
OLYMPUS SLOVENIA D.O.O.—See Olympus Corporation; *Int'l*, pg. 5558
OLYMPUS SOFT IMAGING SOLUTIONS GMBH—See Olympus Corporation; *Int'l*, pg. 5558
OLYMPUS SOFTWARE TECHNOLOGY CORP.—See Olympus Corporation; *Int'l*, pg. 5558
OLYMPUS-SUPPORTMATE CORP.—See Olympus Corporation; *Int'l*, pg. 5558
OLYMPUS SURGICAL TECHNOLOGIES AMERICA—See Olympus Corporation; *Int'l*, pg. 5558
OLYMPUS SURGICAL TECHNOLOGIES EUROPE—See Olympus Corporation; *Int'l*, pg. 5558
OLYMPUS SVERIGE AB—See Olympus Corporation; *Int'l*, pg. 5558
OLYMPUS SYSTEMS CORPORATION - ENTERPRISE DIVISION—See Olympus Corporation; *Int'l*, pg. 5558
OLYMPUS SYSTEMS CORPORATION—See Olympus Corporation; *Int'l*, pg. 5558
OLYMPUS SYSTEMS CORPORATION - UVAS DIVISION—See Olympus Corporation; *Int'l*, pg. 5558
OLYMPUS TAIWAN CO., LTD.—See Olympus Corporation; *Int'l*, pg. 5558
OLYMPUS TECHNOLOGIES SINGAPORE PTE. LTD.—See Olympus Corporation; *Int'l*, pg. 5558
OLYMPUS TERUMO BIOMATERIALS CORP.—See Olympus Corporation; *Int'l*, pg. 5558
OLYMPUS (THAILAND) COMPANY LIMITED—See Olympus Corporation; *Int'l*, pg. 5556
OLYMPUS THEATRICALS, LLC—See Olympus Holdings, LLC; *U.S. Private*, pg. 3013
OLYMPUS TRADING (SHANGHAI) LIMITED—See Olympus Corporation; *Int'l*, pg. 5558
OLYMPUS (U.K.) LTD.—See Olympus Corporation; *Int'l*, pg. 5557
OLYMPUS VIETNAM CO., LTD.—See Olympus Corporation; *Int'l*, pg. 5558
OLYMPUS WINTER & IBE GMBH—See Olympus Corporation; *Int'l*, pg. 5558
OLYMPUS WORLDWIDE CHAUFFEURED SERVICES; *U.S. Private*, pg. 3014
OM2NETWORK CO., LTD.; *Int'l*, pg. 5559
OM3 FISH (ASIA) SDN BHD—See IGB Berhad; *Int'l*, pg. 3601
OMAC LABORATORIES LIMITED—See ALS Limited; *Int'l*, pg. 378
OMAC SALES LIMITED—See Hana Microelectronics Public Company Limited; *Int'l*, pg. 3241
OMAEZAKI CABLE TELEVISION—See Chubu Electric Power Co., Inc.; *Int'l*, pg. 1593
OMAGH MINERALS LIMITED—See Galantas Gold Corporation; *Int'l*, pg. 2870
OMAGINE, INC.; *U.S. Public*, pg. 1571
OMAHA AIRPLANE SUPPLY CO.; *U.S. Private*, pg. 3014
OMAHA AUTO AUCTION—See Cox Enterprises, Inc.; *U.S. Private*, pg. 1077
OMAHA BOX COMPANY—See Liberty Diversified International Inc.; *U.S. Private*, pg. 2443
OMAHA COMMUNITY FOUNDATION; *U.S. Private*, pg. 3014
OMAHA CREATIVE GROUP; *U.S. Private*, pg. 3014
OMAHA FASTENER, INC.—See Birmingham Fastener & Supply Inc.; *U.S. Private*, pg. 564
OMAHA HARDWOOD LUMBER CO.; *U.S. Private*, pg. 3014
OMAHA MAGNOLIA HOTEL—See Magnolia Hotels; *U.S. Private*, pg. 2548
OMAHA NEON SIGN CO. INC.; *U.S. Private*, pg. 3014
OMAHA PERFORMING ARTS; *U.S. Private*, pg. 3014
OMAHA PUBLIC POWER DISTRICT; *U.S. Private*, pg. 3014
OMAHA STANDARD, INC.—See Palfinger AG; *Int'l*, pg. 5708
OMAHA STATE BANK INC.; *U.S. Private*, pg. 3014
OMAHASTEAKS.COM, INC.—See Omaha Steaks International, Inc.; *U.S. Private*, pg. 3014
OMAHA STEAKS, INC.—See Omaha Steaks International, Inc.; *U.S. Private*, pg. 3014
OMAHA STEAKS INTERNATIONAL, INC.; *U.S. Private*, pg. 3014
OMAHA STEAKS-RETAIL STORES—See Omaha Steaks International, Inc.; *U.S. Private*, pg. 3014
THE OMAHA THEATER COMPANY; *U.S. Private*, pg. 4088
OMAHA TRUCK CENTER INC.; *U.S. Private*, pg. 3014

OMAHA TRUCK CENTER INC.

CORPORATE AFFILIATIONS

OMAHA WORLD HERALD COMPANY—See Lee Enterprises, Incorporated; *U.S. Public*, pg. 1298
OMAHA ZOOLOGICAL SOCIETY; *U.S. Private*, pg. 3014
OMAI GOLD MINES CORP.; *Int'l*, pg. 5559
OMAI GOLD MINES LIMITED—See IAMGOLD Corporation; *Int'l*, pg. 3568
O'MALIA FOOD MARKETS INC.—See Sun Capital Partners, Inc.; *U.S. Private*, pg. 3860
O'MALLEY HANSEN COMMUNICATIONS; *U.S. Private*, pg. 2978
OMAM INC.—See BrightSphere Investment Group Inc.; *U.S. Public*, pg. 383
OMAN AGRICULTURE DEVELOPMENT COMANY SAOG—See Omar Zawawi Establishment LLC; *Int'l*, pg. 5561
OMAN AIR S.A.O.C.; *Int'l*, pg. 5559
OMAN ALUMINIUM PROCESSING INDUSTRIES LLC—See Prysmian S.p.A.; *Int'l*, pg. 6012
OMAN ARAB BANK S.A.O.C.—See Arab Bank plc; *Int'l*, pg. 529
OMAN ARAB BANK S.A.O.C.—See Oman International Development & Investment Company SAOG; *Int'l*, pg. 5560
OMAN CABLES INDUSTRIES SAOG—See Prysmian S.p.A.; *Int'l*, pg. 6012
OMAN CEMENT COMPANY SAOG—See HUAXIN CEMENT CO., LTD.; *Int'l*, pg. 3515
OMAN CHLORINE S.A.O.G.; *Int'l*, pg. 5559
OMAN CHROMITE COMPANY (SAOG); *Int'l*, pg. 5559
THE OMAN CONSTRUCTION COMPANY LLC—See Primoris Services Corporation; *U.S. Public*, pg. 1719
OMAN DATA PARK LLC—See Oman Telecommunications Company; *Int'l*, pg. 5560
OMAN DATA PARK LLC—See Oman Telecommunications Company; *Int'l*, pg. 5560
OMAN DATA PARK LLC—See Oman Telecommunications Company; *Int'l*, pg. 5560
OMAN DATA PARK LLC—See Oman Telecommunications Company; *Int'l*, pg. 5560
OMAN EDUCATION & TRAINING INVESTMENTS; *Int'l*, pg. 5559
OMAN & EMIRATES INVESTMENT HOLDING COMPANY SAOG; *Int'l*, pg. 5559
OMAN ENTERPRISES INC.; *U.S. Private*, pg. 3014
OMAN EXPO—See Tawoos LLC; *Int'l*, pg. 7477
OMAN FIBER OPTIC CO. S.A.O.G.; *Int'l*, pg. 5559
OMAN FILTERS INDUSTRY COMPANY SAOG; *Int'l*, pg. 5559
OMAN FISHERIES CO. SAOG; *Int'l*, pg. 5559
OMAN FLOUR MILLS CO SAOG; *Int'l*, pg. 5559
OMAN FOODS INTERNATIONAL SAOG; *Int'l*, pg. 5559
OMAN HOLDINGS INTERNATIONAL COMPANY SAOG; *Int'l*, pg. 5559
OMAN HOTELS & TOURISM COMPANY SAOG; *Int'l*, pg. 5560
OMANI EURO FOOD INDUSTRIES SAOG—See Oman & Emirates Investment Holding Company SAOG; *Int'l*, pg. 5559
OMAN INTERNATIONAL CONTAINER TERMINAL L.L.C.—See CK Hutchison Holdings Limited; *Int'l*, pg. 1638
OMAN INTERNATIONAL DEVELOPMENT & INVESTMENT COMPANY SAOG; *Int'l*, pg. 5560
OMAN INVESTMENT AUTHORITY; *Int'l*, pg. 5560
OMAN INVESTMENT & FINANCE CO. SAOG; *Int'l*, pg. 5560
OMANI PACKAGING COMPANY (S.A.O.G); *Int'l*, pg. 5560
OMAN MECHANICAL SERVICES CO. LTD. LLC—See Omar Zawawi Establishment LLC; *Int'l*, pg. 5561
OMAN METHANOL HOLDING CO. LLC—See Omar Zawawi Establishment LLC; *Int'l*, pg. 5561
OMAN MOBILE TELECOMMUNICATIONS COMPANY LLC—See Oman Telecommunications Company; *Int'l*, pg. 5560
OMAN NATIONAL ENGINEERING & INVESTMENT CO. S.A.O.G; *Int'l*, pg. 5560
OMAN QATAR INSURANCE COMPANY S.A.O.G.—See Qatar Insurance Company S.A.Q.; *Int'l*, pg. 6134
OMAN REFRESHMENT COMPANY SAOG; *Int'l*, pg. 5560
OMAN SERVICES & SUPPLY ORGANISATION LLC—See Omar Zawawi Establishment LLC; *Int'l*, pg. 5561
OMAN SHARPOORJI CONSTRUCTION CO. LLC—See Al Yousef Group; *Int'l*, pg. 283
OMANSH ENTERPRISES LIMITED; *Int'l*, pg. 5560
OMAN TELECOMMUNICATIONS COMPANY; *Int'l*, pg. 5560
OMAN TEXTILE MILLS CO. LLC—See Omar Zawawi Establishment LLC; *Int'l*, pg. 5561
OMAN TRADING INTERNATIONAL LIMITED—See OQ S.A.O.C.; *Int'l*, pg. 5607
OMAN UNITED AGENCIES LLC—See The Emirates Group; *Int'l*, pg. 7639
OMAN UNITED INSURANCE COMPANY SAOG; *Int'l*, pg. 5560
O'MARA, INC.—See Aquafin Holding S.p.A.; *Int'l*, pg. 527
OMAREEF SPAIN SL—See Leonard Green & Partners, L.P.; *U.S. Private*, pg. 2424
OMAR MEDICAL SUPPLIES, INC.; *U.S. Private*, pg. 3014

OMAR MINING COMPANY—See Alpha Natural Resources, Inc.; *U.S. Private*, pg. 198
OMAR ZAWAWI ESTABLISHMENT LLC; *Int'l*, pg. 5561
OMA SAASTOPANKKI OYJ; *Int'l*, pg. 5559
OMASA FRANCE—See L'Air Liquide S.A.; *Int'l*, pg. 4375
OMAS SRL—See Apollo Future Mobility Group Limited; *Int'l*, pg. 517
O'MASTER COMMUNICATIONS (HONG KONG) LTD.—See Charm Communications Inc.; *Int'l*, pg. 1450
OMATEK VENTURES PLC; *Int'l*, pg. 5561
OMA-VYNMSA AERO INDUSTRIAL PARK, S.A. DE C.V.—See Grupo Aeroportuario del Centro Norte, S.A.B. de C.V.; *Int'l*, pg. 3118
OMAX AUTOS LTD; *Int'l*, pg. 5561
OMAX CORP; *U.S. Private*, pg. 3015
OMAXE LTD; *Int'l*, pg. 5561
OMAX INTERNATIONAL LIMITED—See Euromax Resources Ltd.; *Int'l*, pg. 2553
OM CARRELLI ELEVATORI S.P.A.—See KKR & Co. Inc.; *U.S. Public*, pg. 1255
OM CARRELLI ELEVATORI S.P.A.—See The Goldman Sachs Group, Inc.; *U.S. Public*, pg. 2079
OMC GROUP CO. LTD.; *Int'l*, pg. 5561
OMC SHIPPING PTE. LTD.—See Mitsui & Co., Ltd.; *Int'l*, pg. 4979
OMDA AS; *Int'l*, pg. 5561
OMDA OIL & GAS, INC.; *U.S. Private*, pg. 3015
OMD ATLANTA—See Omnicom Group Inc.; *U.S. Public*, pg. 1589
OMD AUSTRALIA—See Omnicom Group Inc.; *U.S. Public*, pg. 1588
OMD BEIJING—See Omnicom Group Inc.; *U.S. Public*, pg. 1588
OMD CANADA—See Omnicom Group Inc.; *U.S. Public*, pg. 1588
OMD CHICAGO—See Omnicom Group Inc.; *U.S. Public*, pg. 1589
OMD DALLAS—See Omnicom Group Inc.; *U.S. Public*, pg. 1589
OMD FINLAND OY—See Omnicom Group Inc.; *U.S. Public*, pg. 1588
OMD GERMANY GMBH & OMD DUSSELDORF GMBH—See Omnicom Group Inc.; *U.S. Public*, pg. 1588
OMD GUANGZHOU—See Omnicom Group Inc.; *U.S. Public*, pg. 1588
OMD HONG KONG—See Omnicom Group Inc.; *U.S. Public*, pg. 1589
OMD LATINO—See Omnicom Group Inc.; *U.S. Public*, pg. 1589
OMD LOS ANGELES—See Omnicom Group Inc.; *U.S. Public*, pg. 1589
OMD NEDERLAND—See Omnicom Group Inc.; *U.S. Public*, pg. 1589
OMD NEW ZEALAND/AUCKLAND—See Omnicom Group Inc.; *U.S. Public*, pg. 1589
OMD PHILIPPINES—See Omnicom Group Inc.; *U.S. Public*, pg. 1589
OMD SAN FRANCISCO—See Omnicom Group Inc.; *U.S. Public*, pg. 1589
OMD SEATTLE—See Omnicom Group Inc.; *U.S. Public*, pg. 1589
OMD SHANGHAI—See Omnicom Group Inc.; *U.S. Public*, pg. 1589
OMD SINGAPORE—See Omnicom Group Inc.; *U.S. Public*, pg. 1589
OMD—See Omnicom Group Inc.; *U.S. Public*, pg. 1588
OMD TURKEY—See Omnicom Group Inc.; *U.S. Public*, pg. 1589
OMD UK—See Omnicom Group Inc.; *U.S. Public*, pg. 1589
OMDURMAN NATIONAL BANK; *Int'l*, pg. 5562
OMD-USA—See Omnicom Group Inc.; *U.S. Public*, pg. 1589
OMD VANCOUVER—See Omnicom Group Inc.; *U.S. Public*, pg. 1589
OMD WORLDWIDE—See Omnicom Group Inc.; *U.S. Public*, pg. 1588
O'MEARA-BROWN PUBLICATIONS, INC.; *U.S. Private*, pg. 2979
O'MEARA FORD CENTER INC.; *U.S. Private*, pg. 2979
O'MEARA HOLDINGS LIMITED—See ANSA McAL Limited; *Int'l*, pg. 477
OMEDA COMMUNICATIONS, INC.; *U.S. Private*, pg. 3015
OMEGA3 INNOVATIONS COMPANY; *U.S. Private*, pg. 3015
OMEGA ADVISORS, INC.; *U.S. Private*, pg. 3015
OMEGA AG-SEEDS (PUNJAB) LIMITED; *Int'l*, pg. 5562
OMEGA ALPHA SPAC; *U.S. Public*, pg. 1571
OMEGA BIO-TEK, INC.—See Level Biotechnology, Inc.; *Int'l*, pg. 4470
OMEGA BRANDS INC.; *U.S. Private*, pg. 3015
OMEGA CABINETS, LTD.—See MasterBrand, Inc.; *U.S. Public*, pg. 1394
OMEGA CAPITAL EUROPE PLC—See BNP Paribas SA; *Int'l*, pg. 1092
OMEGA CAPITAL INVESTMENTS PLC—See BNP Paribas SA; *Int'l*, pg. 1092
OMEGA/CINEMA PROPS INC.; *U.S. Private*, pg. 3015

OMEGA COMMERCIAL FINANCE CORPORATION; *U.S. Public*, pg. 1571
OMEGA DEPOT S.L—See Israel Corporation Ltd.; *Int'l*, pg. 3823
OMEGA DIAGNOSTICS LIMITED—See Cambridge Nutritional Sciences Plc; *Int'l*, pg. 1269
OMEGADYNE, INC.—See Arcline Investment Management LP; *U.S. Private*, pg. 315
OMEGA ELECTRIC CONSTRUCTION CO.; *U.S. Private*, pg. 3015
OMEGA ELECTRONICS MANUFACTURING SERVICES; *U.S. Private*, pg. 3015
OMEGA ENGINEERING GMBH—See Arcline Investment Management LP; *U.S. Private*, pg. 314
OMEGA ENGINEERING, INC.—See Arcline Investment Management LP; *U.S. Private*, pg. 314
OMEGA ENGINEERING LTD.—See Arcline Investment Management LP; *U.S. Private*, pg. 314
OMEGA ENTERPRISES INC.; *U.S. Private*, pg. 3015
OMEGA ENVIRONMENTAL, INC.—See Arcline Investment Management LP; *U.S. Private*, pg. 314
OMEGA ENVIRONMENTAL TECHNOLOGIES, INC.—See River Associates Investments, LLC; *U.S. Private*, pg. 3443
OMEGA FINANCIAL, LLC—See GI Manager L.P.; *U.S. Private*, pg. 1694
OMEGA FLEX, INC.; *U.S. Public*, pg. 1571
OMEGA GERACAO S.A.; *Int'l*, pg. 5562
THE OMEGA GROUP, INC.—See Vista Equity Partners, LLC; *U.S. Private*, pg. 4395
OMEGA HEALTHCARE INVESTORS INC.-MARYLAND—See Omega Healthcare Investors, Inc.; *U.S. Public*, pg. 1571
OMEGA HEALTHCARE INVESTORS, INC.; *U.S. Public*, pg. 1571
OMEGAHOLTAN AS—See Rejlers AB; *Int'l*, pg. 6259
OMEGA III INVESTMENT CO.—See Tristar Holdings Inc.; *U.S. Public*, pg. 4238
OMEGA IMMOBILIERE ET FINANCIERE,S.A.—See Vidrala S.A.; *Int'l*, pg. 8192
OMEGA INDUSTRIES INC.; *U.S. Private*, pg. 3015
OMEGA INSURANCE AGENCY, INC.—See HCI Group, Inc.; *U.S. Public*, pg. 1014
OMEGA LABORATORIES, INC.; *U.S. Private*, pg. 3015
OMEGA LABORATORIES LIMITED—See Juno Pharmaceuticals, Inc.; *Int'l*, pg. 4029
OMEGA LEGAL SYSTEMS, INC.; *U.S. Private*, pg. 3015
OMEGA MEATS INC.; *U.S. Private*, pg. 3015
OMEGA METAL INDUSTRIES SDN. BHD.—See Success Transformer Corporation Berhad; *Int'l*, pg. 7250
OMEGA METALS—See STABILIS SOLUTIONS, INC.; *U.S. Public*, pg. 1924
OMEGA OIL & GAS LIMITED; *Int'l*, pg. 5562
OMEGA OPTICAL CO. LP; *U.S. Private*, pg. 3015
OMEGA OPTICAL HOLDINGS INC.—See EssilorLuxottica SA; *Int'l*, pg. 2513
OMEGA OPTICAL, LLC—See Artemis Capital Partners Management Co., LLC; *U.S. Private*, pg. 341
OMEGA OPTIX S.R.O.—See EssilorLuxottica SA; *Int'l*, pg. 2516
OMEGA PACIFIC RESOURCES INC.; *Int'l*, pg. 5562
OMEGA PACKING COMPANY—See Dulcich, Inc.; *U.S. Private*, pg. 1286
OMEGA PARTNERS III LLC; *U.S. Private*, pg. 3015
OMEGA PARTNERS JOLIET LLC—See Omega Partners III LLC; *U.S. Private*, pg. 3015
OMEGA PERFORMANCE CORPORATION—See Moody's Corporation; *U.S. Public*, pg. 1469
OMEGA PHARMA AUSTRIA HEALTHCARE GMBH—See Perrigo Company plc; *Int'l*, pg. 5813
OMEGA PHARMA DEUTSCHLAND GMBH—See Perrigo Company plc; *Int'l*, pg. 5813
OMEGA PHARMA ESPANA SA—See Perrigo Company plc; *Int'l*, pg. 5813
OMEGA PHARMA HOLDING (NEDERLAND) B.V.—See Perrigo Company plc; *Int'l*, pg. 5813
OMEGA PHARMA HUNGARY KFT.—See Perrigo Company plc; *Int'l*, pg. 5813
OMEGA PHARMA KISISEL BAKIM URUNLERI SANAYI VE TICARET LIMITED SIRKETI—See Perrigo Company plc; *Int'l*, pg. 5813
OMEGA PHARMA LIMITED—See Perrigo Company plc; *Int'l*, pg. 5813
OMEGA PHARMA LUXEMBOURG SARL—See Perrigo Company plc; *Int'l*, pg. 5813
OMEGA PHARMA MANUFACTURING GMBH & CO. KG—See Perrigo Company plc; *Int'l*, pg. 5813
OMEGA PHARMA NEDERLAND B.V.—See Perrigo Company plc; *Int'l*, pg. 5813
OMEGA PHARMA NV—See Perrigo Company plc; *Int'l*, pg. 5813
OMEGA PHARMA POLAND SP.Z.O.O.—See Perrigo Company plc; *Int'l*, pg. 5813
OMEGA PIPELINE COMPANY, LLC—See Spire, Inc; *U.S. Public*, pg. 1918
OMEGA PLASTICS, INC.—See TriMas Corporation; *U.S. Public*, pg. 2189
OMEGA PLASTICS—See Alpha Industries, Inc.; *U.S. Private*, pg. 197

COMPANY NAME INDEX

OMEGA PROCESSING SOLUTIONS, LLC—See Independence Capital Partners, LLC; *U.S. Private*, pg. 2056
OMEGA PROTEIN CORPORATION—See Cooke, Inc.; *Int'l*, pg. 1788
OMEGA SANE FOUNDRY MACHINERY PVT. LTD.—See Sintokogio Ltd.; *Int'l*, pg. 6958
OMEGA S.A.—See The Swatch Group Ltd.; *Int'l*, pg. 7692
OMEGA SEMICONDUCTOR SDN. BHD.—See D & O Green Technologies Berhad; *Int'l*, pg. 1898
OMEGA SHIPYARD, INC.—See Cooke, Inc.; *Int'l*, pg. 1788
OMEGA SIMULATION CO., LTD.—See Yokogawa Electric Corporation; *Int'l*, pg. 8592
OMEGA SINTO FOUNDRY MACHINERY LIMITED—See Sintokogio Ltd.; *Int'l*, pg. 6958
OMEGA SINTO FOUNDRY MACHINERY (MALAYSIA) SDN. BHD.—See Sintokogio Ltd.; *Int'l*, pg. 6958
OMEGA SINTO (ITALY) S.R.L.—See Sintokogio Ltd.; *Int'l*, pg. 6958
OMEGA SOFTWARE GMBH—See USU Software AG; *Int'l*, pg. 8099
OMEGA SPORTS INC.; *U.S. Private*, pg. 3015
OMEGA STEEL CO.; *U.S. Private*, pg. 3015
OMEGA STEEL INC.—See Calstrip Industries Inc.; *U.S. Private*, pg. 723
OMEGA STUDIOS-SOUTHWEST INC.—See Chatham Asset Management, LLC; *U.S. Private*, pg. 864
OMEGA SYSTEMS, LLC—See Pfingsten Partners, LLC; *U.S. Private*, pg. 3164
OMEGA THERAPEUTICS, INC.; *U.S. Public*, pg. 1572
OMEGA TRAINING GROUP, INC.—See Valiant Integrated Services LLC; *U.S. Private*, pg. 4331
OMEGA VISION 2000 S.A.—See Hexagon AB; *Int'l*, pg. 3369
OMEGA WATCH COMPANY—See The Swatch Group Ltd.; *Int'l*, pg. 7693
OMEGA WELL MONITORING—See ALS Limited; *Int'l*, pg. 379
OMEGA WELL MONITORING—See ALS Limited; *Int'l*, pg. 379
OMEGA WORLD TRAVEL, INC.; *U.S. Private*, pg. 3015
OME IRON CASTING CO., LTD.—See Harmonic Drive Systems Inc.; *Int'l*, pg. 3277
OME ISUZU CORPORATION—See Mitsubishi Corporation; *Int'l*, pg. 4942
OMELET; *U.S. Private*, pg. 3015
OMELIA LIMITED—See Acsion Limited; *Int'l*, pg. 117
O'MELVENY & MYERS LLP; *U.S. Private*, pg. 2979
OMERA CYLINDERS LIMITED—See MJL Bangladesh Limited; *Int'l*, pg. 5000
OMER-DECUGIS & CIE SA; *Int'l*, pg. 5562
OMERIN USA, INC. - QS TECHNOLOGIES DIVISION—See Groupe OMERIN; *Int'l*, pg. 3109
OMERIN USA, INC.—See Groupe OMERIN; *Int'l*, pg. 3109
OMEROS CORPORATION; *U.S. Public*, pg. 1572
OMERS INFRASTRUCTURE MANAGEMENT INC.—See Ontario Municipal Employees Retirement System; *Int'l*, pg. 5583
OMER S.P.A.; *Int'l*, pg. 5562
OMERS PRIVATE EQUITY INC.—See Ontario Municipal Employees Retirement System; *Int'l*, pg. 5584
OMESTI BERHAD; *Int'l*, pg. 5562
OMEXOM AUSTRIA GMBH—See VINCI S.A.; *Int'l*, pg. 8225
OMEXOM EMOBILITY GMBH—See VINCI S.A.; *Int'l*, pg. 8225
OMEXOM MAGYARORSZAG KFT.—See VINCI S.A.; *Int'l*, pg. 8225
OMEXOM MOBILE ASSETS GMBH—See VINCI S.A.; *Int'l*, pg. 8225
OMEXOM MOBILE POWER GMBH—See VINCI S.A.; *Int'l*, pg. 8225
OMEXOM SCHALTANLAGENBAU GMBH—See VINCI S.A.; *Int'l*, pg. 8225
OMEXOM SERVICE GMBH—See VINCI S.A.; *Int'l*, pg. 8225
OMEXOM SLOVENSKO S.R.O.—See VINCI S.A.; *Int'l*, pg. 8225
OMEXOM—See VINCI S.A.; *Int'l*, pg. 8239
OMEXOM UK LIMITED—See VINCI S.A.; *Int'l*, pg. 8225
OMEXOM UMSPANNWERKE GMBH—See VINCI S.A.; *Int'l*, pg. 8225
OMEXON AS—See VINCI S.A.; *Int'l*, pg. 8238
OMFESA JV—See OYAK Cement Group; *Int'l*, pg. 5678
OM FINANCIAL LIMITED; *Int'l*, pg. 5558
OMFURN INDIA LTD.; *Int'l*, pg. 5562
OMG AMERICAS, INC.—See Apollo Global Management, Inc.; *U.S. Public*, pg. 166
OMG (ASIA) ELECTRONIC CHEMICALS CO. LTD.—See Element Solutions Inc.; *U.S. Public*, pg. 728
OMG, INC.—See Steel Partners Holdings L.P.; *U.S. Public*, pg. 1943
OMG MIDWEST, INC.—See CRH plc; *Int'l*, pg. 1847
OMG NATIONAL; *U.S. Private*, pg. 3016
O&M HALYARD FRANCE—See Owens & Minor, Inc.; *U.S. Public*, pg. 1626
O&M HALYARD HEALTH INDIA PRIVATE LIMITED—See Owens & Minor, Inc.; *U.S. Public*, pg. 1626
O&M HALYARD JAPAN GK—See Owens & Minor, Inc.; *U.S. Public*, pg. 1626

OMH, INC.; *U.S. Private*, pg. 3016
OM HOLDINGS LIMITED; *Int'l*, pg. 5558
OMICIA, INC.; *U.S. Private*, pg. 3016
OMICO CORPORATION; *Int'l*, pg. 5562
OMICO INC.; *U.S. Private*, pg. 3016
OMICRON CONSULTING, LLC; *U.S. Private*, pg. 3016
OMICRON EVEN RIO EMPREENDIMENTOS IMOBILIARIOS LTDA.—See Even Construtora e Incorporadora S.A.; *Int'l*, pg. 2562
OMID HOLDINGS, INC.; *U.S. Public*, pg. 1572
OMID INVESTMENT BANK CO.; *Int'l*, pg. 5563
OMID INVESTMENT MANAGEMENT CORPORATION; *Int'l*, pg. 5563
OMI DO BRASIL TEXTIL S.A.—See Omikenshi Co., Ltd.; *Int'l*, pg. 5563
OMIGRADE SERVIZI S.R.L.—See Sesa S.p.A.; *Int'l*, pg. 6728
OMIHACHIMAN ECO SERVICE CO., LTD.—See Daiei Kankyo Co., Ltd.; *Int'l*, pg. 1924
OMI INDUSTRIES; *U.S. Private*, pg. 3016
OMIKENSHI CO., LTD. - KAKOGAWA PLANT—See Omikenshi Co., Ltd.; *Int'l*, pg. 5563
OMIKENSHI CO., LTD.; *Int'l*, pg. 5563
OMIKENSHI SHANGHAI CO., LTD.—See Omikenshi Co., Ltd.; *Int'l*, pg. 5563
OMIKENSHI SOLUTION CO., LTD.—See Omikenshi Co., Ltd.; *Int'l*, pg. 5563
OMIKRON SYSTEMHAUS GMBH & CO.; *Int'l*, pg. 5563
OMIMEX RESOURCES, INC.; *U.S. Private*, pg. 3016
OMI MINING CO., LTD.—See Aichi Steel Corporation; *Int'l*, pg. 230
O&M INDUSTRIES INC.; *U.S. Private*, pg. 2977
OMINECA MINING AND METALS LTD.; *Int'l*, pg. 5563
OM INFRA LTD.; *Int'l*, pg. 5558
OMINTO, INC.; *U.S. Public*, pg. 1572
OMIP OPERADOR DO MERCADO IBERICO DE ENERGIA S.A.—See REN - Redes Energeticas Nacionais SGPS, S.A.; *Int'l*, pg. 6272
OMIP - 'OPERADOR DO MERCADO IBERICO (PORTUGAL), SGPS, S.A.—See REN - Redes Energeticas Nacionais SGPS, S.A.; *Int'l*, pg. 6272
OMI REFRACTORIES, LLC—See Osceola Capital Management, LLC; *U.S. Private*, pg. 3047
OMISE CO. LTD.; *Int'l*, pg. 5563
OMI—See EssilorLuxottica SA; *Int'l*, pg. 2515
OMIX-ADA, INC.—See CCMP Capital Advisors, LP; *U.S. Private*, pg. 801
OMIX-ADA, INC.—See TA Associates, Inc.; *U.S. Private*, pg. 3919
OMJ PHARMACEUTICALS, INC.—See Johnson & Johnson; *U.S. Public*, pg. 1197
OMKAR OVERSEAS LIMITED; *Int'l*, pg. 5563
OMKAR PHARMACHEM LIMITED; *Int'l*, pg. 5563
OMKAR SPECIALITY CHEMICALS LTD.; *Int'l*, pg. 5563
OMKIRON HUNGARY LTD.—See Omikron Systemhaus GmbH & Co.; *Int'l*, pg. 5563
OMK LTD.—See Daiwabo Holdings Co., Ltd.; *Int'l*, pg. 1949
OMLAND ENGINEERING ASSOCIATES, INC.—See Bowman Consulting Group Ltd.; *U.S. Public*, pg. 376
O-M MACHINERY LTD.—See Daiwabo Holdings Co., Ltd.; *Int'l*, pg. 1949
OM (MANGANESE) LTD—See OM Holdings Limited; *Int'l*, pg. 5558
OMMA S.R.L.—See Chargeurs SA; *Int'l*, pg. 1450
OM MATERIALS (QINZHOU) CO LTD—See OM Holdings Limited; *Int'l*, pg. 5558
OM MATERIALS (S) PTE LTD—See OM Holdings Limited; *Int'l*, pg. 5558
OM METALS AUTO PVT. LTD—See Om Infra Ltd.; *Int'l*, pg. 5558
O&M-MOVIANTO NEDERLAND B.V.—See Owens & Minor, Inc.; *U.S. Public*, pg. 1626
OMNEON, INC.—See Harmonic, Inc.; *U.S. Public*, pg. 986
OMNETRIC GMBH—See Siemens Aktiengesellschaft; *Int'l*, pg. 6887
OMNEX GROUP, INC.—See Nexxar Group Inc.; *U.S. Private*, pg. 2922
OMNIAB, INC.; *U.S. Public*, pg. 1572
OMNIABIOS S.R.L.—See Compagnie des Levures Lesaffre SA; *Int'l*, pg. 1739
OMNIAB OPERATIONS, INC.—See OmniAb, Inc.; *U.S. Public*, pg. 1572
OMNIACTIVE HEALTH TECHNOLOGIES, INC. - PUNE PLANT—See V. Mane Fils SA; *Int'l*, pg. 8105
OMNIACTIVE HEALTH TECHNOLOGIES, INC.—See V. Mane Fils SA; *Int'l*, pg. 8105
OMNIACTIVE HEALTH TECHNOLOGIES, INC.—See V. Mane Fils SA; *Int'l*, pg. 8105
OMNIA DENTAL S.L.—See STERIS plc; *Int'l*, pg. 7209
THE OMNIA GROUP INC.; *U.S. Private*, pg. 4088
OMNIA GROUP SERVICE SRL—See Omnia Network SpA; *Int'l*, pg. 5564
OMNI AIR INTERNATIONAL, LLC—See Air Transport Services Group, Inc.; *U.S. Public*, pg. 68
OMNIA LLC—See STERIS plc; *Int'l*, pg. 7209
OMNI AMERICAN INC.—See Global Capital Corp.; *U.S. Private*, pg. 1712
OMNIA METALS GROUP LIMITED; *Int'l*, pg. 5563

OMNICOM GROUP INC.

OMNIA MOTOR S.A.—See China National Chemical Corporation; *Int'l*, pg. 1528
OMNIA NETWORK SPA; *Int'l*, pg. 5563
OMNIA POWER S.R.L.—See Iren S.p.A.; *Int'l*, pg. 3808
OMNIA SERVICE CENTER SPA—See Omnia Network SpA; *Int'l*, pg. 5564
OMNIASIG ASIGAURARI DE VIATA S.A.—See Vienna Insurance Group AG Wiener Versicherung Gruppe; *Int'l*, pg. 8195
OMNIASIG VIENNA INSURANCE GROUP S.A.—See Vienna Insurance Group AG Wiener Versicherung Gruppe; *Int'l*, pg. 8195
OMNIA SPA—See STERIS plc; *Int'l*, pg. 7209
OMNIA WELLNESS, INC.; *U.S. Public*, pg. 1572
OMNI AX'S SOFTWARE LIMITED; *Int'l*, pg. 5563
OMNI BANCO & FINANCEIRA; *Int'l*, pg. 5563
OMNI BARTON CREEK, INC.—See TRT Holdings, Inc.; *U.S. Private*, pg. 4244
OMNI BIO PHARMACEUTICAL, INC.; *U.S. Private*, pg. 3016
OMNIBLEND PTY. LTD.—See Halo Food Co. Limited; *Int'l*, pg. 3233
OMNIBRIDGE HOLDINGS LIMITED; *Int'l*, pg. 5564
OMNI BRIDGEWAY EMERGING MARKETS LIMITED—See IMF Bentham Limited; *Int'l*, pg. 3624
OMNI BRIDGEWAY HOLDING B.V.—See IMF Bentham Limited; *Int'l*, pg. 3624
OMNIBUILD CONSTRUCTION INC.; *U.S. Private*, pg. 3017
OMNIBUS BB TRANSPORTES, S. A.—See General Motors Company; *U.S. Public*, pg. 926
OMNIBUS JAPAN INC.—See Tohokushinsha Film Corporation; *Int'l*, pg. 7777
OMNIBUS K.K.—See Credit Saison Co., Ltd.; *Int'l*, pg. 1836
OMNIBUS PRESS—See Music Sales Corporation; *U.S. Private*, pg. 2818
OMNIBUSVERKEHR FRANKEN GMBH—See Deutsche Bahn AG; *Int'l*, pg. 2052
OMNI CABLE, LLC—See Dot Family Holdings LLC; *U.S. Private*, pg. 1264
OMNICANE LTD; *Int'l*, pg. 5564
OMNICANNA HEALTH SOLUTIONS, INC.; *U.S. Public*, pg. 1572
OMNICARD, LLC—See P2 Capital Partners, LLC; *U.S. Private*, pg. 3061
OMNICARD, LLC—See Silver Lake Group, LLC; *U.S. Private*, pg. 3656
OMNICARE, INC.—See CVS Health Corporation; *U.S. Public*, pg. 616
OMNICARE PHARMACIES OF PENNSYLVANIA WEST, LLC—See CVS Health Corporation; *U.S. Public*, pg. 616
OMNICARE PHARMACY OF PUEBLO, LLC—See CVS Health Corporation; *U.S. Public*, pg. 616
OMNICAS MANAGEMENT AG—See BAWAG Group AG; *Int'l*, pg. 900
OMNICELL B.V.—See Omnicell, Inc.; *U.S. Public*, pg. 1572
OMNICELL GMBH—See Omnicell, Inc.; *U.S. Public*, pg. 1572
OMNICELL, INC.; *U.S. Public*, pg. 1572
OMNICELL LTD.—See Omnicell, Inc.; *U.S. Public*, pg. 1572
OMNICELL PTY LTD—See Omnicell, Inc.; *U.S. Public*, pg. 1572
OMNICELL S.R.L.—See Omnicell, Inc.; *U.S. Public*, pg. 1573
OMNICHANNEL ACQUISITION CORP.; *U.S. Public*, pg. 1573
OMNICHANNEL SOLUTIONS, LLC—See Thoma Bravo, L.P.; *U.S. Private*, pg. 4149
OMNICHIP SP. Z O.O.—See Atende S.A.; *Int'l*, pg. 668
OMNI CIRCUITS INTERNATIONAL LLC; *U.S. Private*, pg. 3016
OMNICOM CANADA CORP.—See Omnicom Group Inc.; *U.S. Public*, pg. 1589
OMNICOM CAPITAL INC—See Omnicom Group Inc.; *U.S. Public*, pg. 1589
OMNICOM EUROPE LIMITED—See Omnicom Group Inc.; *U.S. Public*, pg. 1589
OMNICOM GROUP INC.; *U.S. Public*, pg. 1573
OMNICOM MEDIA GROUP ASIA PACIFIC PTE LTD—See Omnicom Group Inc.; *U.S. Public*, pg. 1589
OMNICOM MEDIA GROUP HOLDINGS INC—See Omnicom Group Inc.; *U.S. Public*, pg. 1589
OMNICOM MEDIA GROUP—See Omnicom Group Inc.; *U.S. Public*, pg. 1589
OMNICOMM EUROPE GMBH.—See ABRY Partners, LLC; *U.S. Private*, pg. 41
OMNICOMM SPAIN S.L.—See ABRY Partners, LLC; *U.S. Private*, pg. 41
OMNICOMM SYSTEMS B.V.—See ABRY Partners, LLC; *U.S. Private*, pg. 41
OMNICOMM SYSTEMS, INC.—See ABRY Partners, LLC; *U.S. Private*, pg. 41
OMNI COMPONENTS CORP.—See Aterian Investment Management, L.P.; *U.S. Private*, pg. 367
OMNICOM PUBLIC RELATIONS GROUP, INC.—See Omnicom Group Inc.; *U.S. Public*, pg. 1589

OMNICOM GROUP INC.

THE OMNICON GROUP, INC.—See Spectris Plc; *Int'l*, pg. 7131
OMNI CONNECTION INTERNATIONAL, INC.—See Cerberus Capital Management, L.P.; *U.S. Private*, pg. 838
OMNI CONTROL TECHNOLOGY INC—See NIBE Industrier AB; *Int'l*, pg. 5262
OMNICON VERWALTUNGS GMBH—See Starwood Capital Group Global I, LLC; *U.S. Private*, pg. 3789
OMNI CORPORATION; *U.S. Private*, pg. 3016
OMNIDATA GMBH & CO. KG—See Ohl Logistik GmbH & Co. KG; *Int'l*, pg. 5533
OMNI DIRECTIONA BORING LP—See Sage Park, Inc.; *U.S. Private*, pg. 3526
OMNI DIRECTIONAL BORING LP—See Sage Park, Inc.; *U.S. Private*, pg. 3526
OMNI ENERGY SERVICES CORP.—See Gibson Energy Inc.; *Int'l*, pg. 2963
OMNI ENGINEERING INC.—See Omni Holding Company; *U.S. Private*, pg. 3016
OMNI ENGINEERING SHANGHAI CO. LTD—See Adval Tech Holding AG; *Int'l*, pg. 155
OMNI ENTERPRISES INC.; *U.S. Private*, pg. 3016
OMNI ENVIRONMENTAL LLC—See Goldberg Lindsay & Co., LLC; *U.S. Private*, pg. 1730
OMNIFAB LLC; *U.S. Private*, pg. 3017
OMNI FACILITY SERVICES, INC.; *U.S. Private*, pg. 3016
OMNI FACILITY SERVICES—See Omni Facility Services, Inc.; *U.S. Private*, pg. 3016
OMNIFICS INC.; *U.S. Private*, pg. 3017
OMNIFLORA BLUMEN CENTER GMBH—See John Swire & Sons Limited; *Int'l*, pg. 3980
OMNI GLASS AND PAINT INC.; *U.S. Private*, pg. 3016
OMNI GLOBAL SOURCING SOLUTIONS INC.—See Bain Capital, LP; *U.S. Private*, pg. 439
OMNIGO SOFTWARE LLC—See The Riverside Company; *U.S. Private*, pg. 4109
OMNIGRAPHICS, INC.—See Centre Lane Partners, LLC; *U.S. Private*, pg. 827
OMNIGRAPHICS LIMITED—See OPUS Group Limited; *Int'l*, pg. 5606
OMNI GROVE PARK, LLC—See TRT Holdings, Inc.; *U.S. Private*, pg. 4244
OMNI HEALTHCARE INC.—See Lovell Minnick Partners LLC; *U.S. Private*, pg. 2503
OMNI HEALTH, INC.; *U.S. Private*, pg. 3016
OMNI HELICOPTERS INTERNATIONAL S.A.—See Stirling Square Capital Partners LLP; *Int'l*, pg. 7216
OMNI HOLDING COMPANY; *U.S. Private*, pg. 3016
OMNI HOME HEALTH - DISTRICT 1, LLC—See UnitedHealth Group Incorporated; *U.S. Public*, pg. 2244
OMNI HOME HEALTH - DISTRICT 4, LLC—See UnitedHealth Group Incorporated; *U.S. Public*, pg. 2244
OMNI HOME HEALTH - JACKSONVILLE, LLC—See UnitedHealth Group Incorporated; *U.S. Public*, pg. 2246
OMNI HOMESTEAD, INC.—See TRT Holdings, Inc.; *U.S. Private*, pg. 4244
OMNI HOTELS MANAGEMENT CORPORATION—See TRT Holdings, Inc.; *U.S. Private*, pg. 4244
OMNI-ID USA, INC.—See ASSA ABLOY AB; *Int'l*, pg. 637
OMNI INTERNATIONAL, INC.—See Revvity, Inc.; *U.S. Public*, pg. 1794
OMNI INVESTORS PTE. LTD—See Adval Tech Holding AG; *Int'l*, pg. 155
OMNIJOI MEDIA CORP; *Int'l*, pg. 5564
OMNILAB S.R.L.—See Abbott Laboratories; *U.S. Public*, pg. 20
OMNI LA COSTA RESORT & SPA, LLC—See TRT Holdings, Inc.; *U.S. Private*, pg. 4244
OMNILIFE INSURANCE COMPANY, LIMITED—See Reinsurance Group of America, Inc.; *U.S. Public*, pg. 1777
OMNILIFT INC.; *U.S. Private*, pg. 3017
OMNI-LITE INDUSTRIES CANADA INC.; *U.S. Public*, pg. 1572
OMNI LOGISTICS LLC—See Forward Air Corporation; *U.S. Public*, pg. 874
OMNILYTICS, INC.—See Phagelux, Inc.; *Int'l*, pg. 5839
OMNIM2M INC.—See TraQiQ, Inc.; *U.S. Public*, pg. 2185
OMNI MANAGEMENT ACQUISITION CORP.; *U.S. Private*, pg. 3016
OMNI MANUFACTURING INC.; *U.S. Private*, pg. 3016
OMNIMATICS SDN. BHD.—See APM Automotive Holdings Berhad; *Int'l*, pg. 516
OMNIMAX HOLDINGS, INC.; *U.S. Private*, pg. 3017
OMNIMAX INTERNATIONAL, INC.—See Omnimax Holdings, Inc.; *U.S. Private*, pg. 3017
OMNI MOLD LTD.—See Sunningdale Tech Ltd; *Int'l*, pg. 7318
OMNI MOTION, INC.—See Water Street Healthcare Partners, LLC; *U.S. Private*, pg. 4452
OMNINSTAL ELECTRICIDADE, S.A.—See Elecnor, S.A.; *Int'l*, pg. 2347
OMNI OPHTHALMIC MANAGEMENT CONSULTANTS LLC—See NMS Capital Services, LLC; *U.S. Private*, pg. 2931
OMNI OPTICAL LAB—See EssilorLuxottica SA; *Int'l*, pg. 2513
OMNI PACKAGING CORPORATION—See Wellspring Capital Management LLC; *U.S. Private*, pg. 4478
OMNI PARTNERS, LP; *U.S. Private*, pg. 3016
OMNIPHARMA S.A.L.—See HORIBA Ltd; *Int'l*, pg. 3477
OMNI PLASTICS (THAILAND) CO. LTD—See Adval Tech Holding AG; *Int'l*, pg. 155
OMNI PLASTICS (XIAMEN) CO. LTD—See Adval Tech Holding AG; *Int'l*, pg. 155
OMNIPLESS MANUFACTURING (PROPRIETARY) LIMITED—See Advent International Corporation; *U.S. Private*, pg. 100
OMNIPLEX WORLD SERVICES CORPORATION—See Altamont Capital Partners; *U.S. Private*, pg. 205
OMNI-PLUS SYSTEM LIMITED; *Int'l*, pg. 5563
OMNI-PLUS SYSTEM PHILIPINES, INC.—See Omni-Plus System Limited; *Int'l*, pg. 5563
OMNI-PLUS SYSTEM SHANGHAI LIMITED—See Omni-Plus System Limited; *Int'l*, pg. 5563
OMNI PLUS SYSTEM (THAILAND) CO., LTD.—See Omni-Plus System Limited; *Int'l*, pg. 5563
OMNIPOINT, INC.; *U.S. Private*, pg. 3017
OMNIPOTECH, LTD.; *U.S. Private*, pg. 3017
OMNIPOTENT INDUSTRIES PVT. LTD.; *Int'l*, pg. 5564
OMNI PRECISION SDN. BHD.—See Adval Tech Holding AG; *Int'l*, pg. 155
OMNIPRINT INTERNATIONAL INC.; *U.S. Private*, pg. 3017
OMNIPROBE, INC.—See Oxford Instruments Plc; *Int'l*, pg. 5674
OMNIPROCESS AB—See Addtech AB; *Int'l*, pg. 134
OMNI PRODUCTS, INC.; *U.S. Private*, pg. 3016
OMNIPRO GESELLSCHAFT FUR PROJEKTMANAGEMENT MBH—See Starwood Capital Group Global I, LLC; *U.S. Private*, pg. 3789
OMNIPUNKTSE AB—See Schibsted ASA; *Int'l*, pg. 6617
OMNIQ CORP.; *U.S. Public*, pg. 1600
OMNI RANCHO LAS PALMAS, LLC—See TRT Holdings, Inc.; *U.S. Private*, pg. 4244
OMNI RAY AG—See Addtech AB; *Int'l*, pg. 134
OMNI RESOURCES INC.—See Saggezza Inc.; *U.S. Private*, pg. 3528
OMNISENSE SYSTEMS PRIVATE LIMITED—See BH Global Corporation Limited; *Int'l*, pg. 1009
OMNI SERV LIMITED—See ABM Industries, Inc.; *U.S. Public*, pg. 26
OMNIS HEALTH, LLC—See Bertram Capital Management, LLC; *U.S. Private*, pg. 540
OMNISHOP S.A.—See YALCO - SOCRATES D. CONSTANTINOU & SON S.A.; *Int'l*, pg. 8547
OMNI SHRIMP, INC.; *U.S. Public*, pg. 1572
OMNI-SICA OY—See YIT Corporation; *Int'l*, pg. 8586
OMNI SOLID SERVICES INC.—See Solid Group, Inc.; *Int'l*, pg. 7072
OMNISOLIS SAS—See Vivescia; *Int'l*, pg. 8279
OMNISOURCE CORPORATION—See Steel Dynamics, Inc.; *U.S. Public*, pg. 1942
OMNISOURCE, LLC—See Steel Dynamics, Inc.; *U.S. Public*, pg. 1942
OMNISOURCE SOUTHEAST, LLC—See Steel Dynamics, Inc.; *U.S. Public*, pg. 1942
OMNISPHERE CORP.; *U.S. Private*, pg. 3017
OMNI STRUCTURES & MANAGEMENT INC.; *U.S. Private*, pg. 3016
OMNISTUDIO, INC.; *U.S. Private*, pg. 3017
OMNISURE GROUP, LLC—See Milestone Partners Ltd.; *U.S. Private*, pg. 2729
OMNI SYSTEM CO., LTD.; *Int'l*, pg. 5563
OMNI SYSTEMS INC.; *U.S. Private*, pg. 3016
OMNITEAM INC.; *U.S. Private*, pg. 3017
OMNITECH INFOSOLUTIONS LTD; *Int'l*, pg. 5564
OMNI TECH (SUZHOU) CO., LTD.—See Sunningdale Tech Ltd; *Int'l*, pg. 7318
OMNITEC INFORMATIONSTECHNOLOGIE-SYSTEMSERVICE GMBH—See Osterreichische Post AG; *Int'l*, pg. 5654
OMNITEC SOLUTIONS, INC.—See AE Industrial Partners, LP; *U.S. Private*, pg. 112
OMNITEK ENGINEERING CORP.; *U.S. Public*, pg. 1600
OMNITEX INDUSTRIES (INDIA) LIMITED; *Int'l*, pg. 5564
OMNITICKET NETWORK LTD.—See Vivaticket; *Int'l*, pg. 8265
OMNITICKET NETWORK PTE LTD—See Vivaticket; *Int'l*, pg. 8265
OMNITI; *U.S. Private*, pg. 3017
OMNITRACS, LLC—See Vista Equity Partners, LLC; *U.S. Private*, pg. 4399
OMNITRANS; *U.S. Private*, pg. 3017
OMNITRAX CANADA, INC.—See The Broe Companies, Inc.; *U.S. Private*, pg. 4001
OMNITRAX, INC.—See The Broe Companies, Inc.; *U.S. Private*, pg. 4001
OMNIUM ET REALISATION D'EMBALLAGES PLASTIQUES; *Int'l*, pg. 5564
OMNI VALVE COMPANY, LLC.; *U.S. Private*, pg. 3016
OMNI VENTURES, INC.; *U.S. Private*, pg. 3016
OMNIVERE, LLC—See Driven, Inc.; *U.S. Private*, pg. 1278
OMNIVISION TECHNOLOGIES, INC.—See CITIC Group Corporation; *Int'l*, pg. 1619
OMNIVISION TECHNOLOGIES, INC.—See CITIC Securities Co., Ltd.; *Int'l*, pg. 1622
OMNIVISION TECHNOLOGIES, INC.—See Hua Capital Management Co., Ltd.; *Int'l*, pg. 3509

CORPORATE AFFILIATIONS

OMNIVISION TECHNOLOGIES (SHANGHAI) CO., LTD.—See CITIC Group Corporation; *Int'l*, pg. 1619
OMNIVISION TECHNOLOGIES (SHANGHAI) CO., LTD.—See CITIC Securities Co., Ltd.; *Int'l*, pg. 1622
OMNIVISION TECHNOLOGIES (SHANGHAI) CO., LTD.—See Hua Capital Management Co., Ltd.; *Int'l*, pg. 3509
OMNIVISION TECHNOLOGIES SINGAPORE PTE. LTD—See CITIC Group Corporation; *Int'l*, pg. 1619
OMNIVISION TECHNOLOGIES SINGAPORE PTE. LTD—See CITIC Securities Co., Ltd.; *Int'l*, pg. 1622
OMNIVISION TECHNOLOGIES SINGAPORE PTE. LTD—See Hua Capital Management Co., Ltd.; *Int'l*, pg. 3509
OMNIVUE BUSINESS SOLUTIONS; *U.S. Private*, pg. 3017
OMNIWAVE LTD.—See Transition Evergreen; *Int'l*, pg. 7901
OMNI WEALTH ADVISORS, LLC.—See Affiliated Managers Group, Inc.; *U.S. Public*, pg. 56
OMNI WEALTH ADVISORS, LLC.—See HGGC, LLC; *U.S. Private*, pg. 1930
OMNI WORKSPACE COMPANY—See HNI Corporation; *U.S. Public*, pg. 1043
OMNOVA NINGBO CO., LTD.—See OMNOVA Solutions Inc.; *U.S. Private*, pg. 3017
OMNOVA PERFORMANCE CHEMICALS (UK) LTD.—See OMNOVA Solutions Inc.; *U.S. Private*, pg. 3017
OMNOVA SOLUTIONS INC.; *U.S. Private*, pg. 3017
OMNOVA SOLUTIONS PORTUGAL S.A.—See OMNOVA Solutions Inc.; *U.S. Private*, pg. 3017
OMNOVA SOLUTIONS SAS—See OMNOVA Solutions Inc.; *U.S. Private*, pg. 3017
OMNYON LLC—See Alpine Investors; *U.S. Private*, pg. 201
OM OBJEKTMANAGEMENT GMBH—See Erste Group Bank AG; *Int'l*, pg. 2499
OM OF MEDICINE LLC—See 4Front Ventures Corp.; *U.S. Public*, pg. 9
OMPHALOS CORP.; *Int'l*, pg. 5564
OM PHARMA SA; *Int'l*, pg. 5558
OMP INC.; *U.S. Private*, pg. 3017
OMP INSURANCE BROKERS LTD.—See Wesfarmers Limited; *Int'l*, pg. 8382
OMPI OF AMERICA, INC.—See Stevanato Group S.p.A.; *Int'l*, pg. 7212
OM RESIDUAL UK LIMITED; *Int'l*, pg. 5558
OMRIX BIOPHARMACEUTICALS LTD—See Johnson & Johnson; *U.S. Public*, pg. 1196
OMRON ADEPT MOBILEROBOTS, LLC—See OMRON Corporation; *Int'l*, pg. 5567
OMRON ADEPT TECHNOLOGIES FRANCE—See OMRON Corporation; *Int'l*, pg. 5567
OMRON ADEPT TECHNOLOGIES GMBH—See OMRON Corporation; *Int'l*, pg. 5567
OMRON ADEPT TECHNOLOGIES, INC.—See OMRON Corporation; *Int'l*, pg. 5567
OMRON AMUSEMENT HONG KONG CO., LTD.—See OMRON Corporation; *Int'l*, pg. 5564
OMRON ASIA PACIFIC PTE. LTD.—See OMRON Corporation; *Int'l*, pg. 5564
OMRON AUTOMATION PVT LTD—See OMRON Corporation; *Int'l*, pg. 5565
OMRON AUTOMOTIVE COMPONENTS INDIA PVT. LTD—See OMRON Corporation; *Int'l*, pg. 5565
OMRON AUTOMOTIVE ELECTRONICS EUROPE GMBH—See OMRON Corporation; *Int'l*, pg. 5565
OMRON AUTOMOTIVE ELECTRONICS INC. (MANUFACTURING)—See OMRON Corporation; *Int'l*, pg. 5565
OMRON AUTOMOTIVE ELECTRONICS INC. (MARKETING)—See OMRON Corporation; *Int'l*, pg. 5565
OMRON AUTOMOTIVE ELECTRONICS ITALY S.R.L.—See OMRON Corporation; *Int'l*, pg. 5565
OMRON AUTOMOTIVE ELECTRONICS KOREA, CO., LTD.—See OMRON Corporation; *Int'l*, pg. 5565
OMRON AUTOMOTIVE EUROPEAN SERVICE, LTD.—See OMRON Corporation; *Int'l*, pg. 5565
OMRON AUTOMOTIVE TECHNOLOGIES, INC.—See OMRON Corporation; *Int'l*, pg. 5564
OMRON AUTOMOTIVE TECHNOLOGIES, INC.—See OMRON Corporation; *Int'l*, pg. 5565
OMRON CANADA, INC.—See OMRON Corporation; *Int'l*, pg. 5565
OMRON (CHINA) CO., LTD.—See OMRON Corporation; *Int'l*, pg. 5564
OMRON (CHINA) GROUP CO., LTD.—See OMRON Corporation; *Int'l*, pg. 5564
OMRON COMPONENTES AUTOMOTIVOS LTDA.—See OMRON Corporation; *Int'l*, pg. 5565
OMRON CORPORATION; *Int'l*, pg. 5564
OMRON DALIAN CO., LTD.—See OMRON Corporation; *Int'l*, pg. 5565
OMRON ELECTRONIC COMPONENTS CANADA, INC.—See OMRON Corporation; *Int'l*, pg. 5565
OMRON ELECTRONIC COMPONENTS CO., LTD. (OCBTH)—See OMRON Corporation; *Int'l*, pg. 5565

OMRON ELECTRONIC COMPONENTS CO., LTD.—See OMRON Corporation; *Int'l*, pg. 5565
OMRON ELECTRONIC COMPONENTS EUROPE B.V.—See OMRON Corporation; *Int'l*, pg. 5565
OMRON ELECTRONIC COMPONENTS FRANCE S.A.R.L.—See OMRON Corporation; *Int'l*, pg. 5565
OMRON ELECTRONIC COMPONENTS (HONG KONG) LTD.—See OMRON Corporation; *Int'l*, pg. 5565
OMRON ELECTRONIC COMPONENTS LLC—See OMRON Corporation; *Int'l*, pg. 5565
OMRON ELECTRONIC COMPONENTS PTE. LTD.—See OMRON Corporation; *Int'l*, pg. 5565
OMRON ELECTRONIC COMPONENTS SDN. BHD.—See OMRON Corporation; *Int'l*, pg. 5565
OMRON ELECTRONIC COMPONENTS (SHENZHEN) LTD.—See OMRON Corporation; *Int'l*, pg. 5565
OMRON ELECTRONIC COMPONENTS TRADING (SHANGHAI) LTD.—See OMRON Corporation; *Int'l*, pg. 5565
OMRON ELECTRONICS A.B.—See OMRON Corporation; *Int'l*, pg. 5565
OMRON ELECTRONICS AG—See OMRON Corporation; *Int'l*, pg. 5565
OMRON ELECTRONICS ASIA LTD.—See OMRON Corporation; *Int'l*, pg. 5565
OMRON ELECTRONICS A/S—See OMRON Corporation; *Int'l*, pg. 5565
OMRON ELECTRONICS B.V.—See OMRON Corporation; *Int'l*, pg. 5565
OMRON ELECTRONICS CO., LTD.—See OMRON Corporation; *Int'l*, pg. 5565
OMRON ELECTRONICS GES.M.B.H.—See OMRON Corporation; *Int'l*, pg. 5565
OMRON ELECTRONICS GMBH—See OMRON Corporation; *Int'l*, pg. 5565
OMRON ELECTRONICS GMBH—See OMRON Corporation; *Int'l*, pg. 5565
OMRON ELECTRONICS IBERIA SA.—See OMRON Corporation; *Int'l*, pg. 5565
OMRON ELECTRONICS IBERIA SAU—See OMRON Corporation; *Int'l*, pg. 5565
OMRON ELECTRONICS, KFT—See OMRON Corporation; *Int'l*, pg. 5566
OMRON ELECTRONICS KOREA CO., LTD.—See OMRON Corporation; *Int'l*, pg. 5565
OMRON ELECTRONICS LLC—See OMRON Corporation; *Int'l*, pg. 5565
OMRON ELECTRONICS LTD.—See OMRON Corporation; *Int'l*, pg. 5565
OMRON ELECTRONICS LTD.—See OMRON Corporation; *Int'l*, pg. 5566
OMRON ELECTRONICS MANUFACTURING OF GERMANY GMBH—See OMRON Corporation; *Int'l*, pg. 5566
OMRON ELECTRONICS NORWAY A/S—See OMRON Corporation; *Int'l*, pg. 5566
OMRON ELECTRONICS N.V./S.A.—See OMRON Corporation; *Int'l*, pg. 5566
OMRON ELECTRONICS O.Y.—See OMRON Corporation; *Int'l*, pg. 5566
OMRON ELECTRONICS PTE. LTD.—See OMRON Corporation; *Int'l*, pg. 5566
OMRON ELECTRONICS PTY. LTD.—See OMRON Corporation; *Int'l*, pg. 5566
OMRON ELECTRONICS S.A.R.L.—See OMRON Corporation; *Int'l*, pg. 5566
OMRON ELECTRONICS S.A.—See OMRON Corporation; *Int'l*, pg. 5566
OMRON ELECTRONICS S.A.S.—See OMRON Corporation; *Int'l*, pg. 5566
OMRON ELECTRONICS SDN. BHD. (OEP-MY)—See OMRON Corporation; *Int'l*, pg. 5566
OMRON ELECTRONICS SDN. BHD.—See OMRON Corporation; *Int'l*, pg. 5566
OMRON ELECTRONICS S.P.A.—See OMRON Corporation; *Int'l*, pg. 5566
OMRON ELECTRONICS SPOL. S.R.O.—See OMRON Corporation; *Int'l*, pg. 5566
OMRON ELECTRONICS SP.Z.O.O.—See OMRON Corporation; *Int'l*, pg. 5566
OMRON ELECTRONICS S.R.L.—See OMRON Corporation; *Int'l*, pg. 5566
OMRON ELETRONICA DO BRASIL LTDA.—See OMRON Corporation; *Int'l*, pg. 5566
OMRON EUROPE B.V.—See OMRON Corporation; *Int'l*, pg. 5566
OMRON FINANCE CANADA, INC.—See OMRON Corporation; *Int'l*, pg. 5566
OMRON (GUANGZHOU) AUTOMOTIVE ELECTRONICS CO., LTD.—See OMRON Corporation; *Int'l*, pg. 5564
OMRON HEALTHCARE BANGLADESH LTD.—See OMRON Corporation; *Int'l*, pg. 5566
OMRON HEALTHCARE BRAZIL—See OMRON Corporation; *Int'l*, pg. 5566
OMRON HEALTHCARE (CHINA) CO., LTD.—See OMRON Corporation; *Int'l*, pg. 5566

OMRON HEALTHCARE CO., LTD.—See OMRON Corporation; *Int'l*, pg. 5566
OMRON HEALTHCARE EUROPE B.V.—See OMRON Corporation; *Int'l*, pg. 5566
OMRON HEALTHCARE, INC.—See OMRON Corporation; *Int'l*, pg. 5566
OMRON HEALTHCARE INDIA PVT LTD.—See OMRON Corporation; *Int'l*, pg. 5566
OMRON HEALTHCARE KOREA CO., LTD.—See OMRON Corporation; *Int'l*, pg. 5566
OMRON HEALTHCARE MANUFACTURING VIETNAM CO., LTD.—See OMRON Corporation; *Int'l*, pg. 5566
OMRON HEALTHCARE MEXICO S.A DE C.V.—See OMRON Corporation; *Int'l*, pg. 5566
OMRON HEALTHCARE PRODUCT DEVELOPMENT DALIAN CO., LTD.—See OMRON Corporation; *Int'l*, pg. 5566
OMRON HEALTHCARE SINGAPORE PTE LTD.—See OMRON Corporation; *Int'l*, pg. 5566
OMRON HEALTHCARE TAIWAN CO., LTD.—See OMRON Corporation; *Int'l*, pg. 5566
OMRON HEALTHCARE (THAILAND) CO., LTD.—See OMRON Corporation; *Int'l*, pg. 5566
OMRON HEALTHCARE U.K. LTD.—See OMRON Corporation; *Int'l*, pg. 5566
OMRON HONG KONG LIMITED—See OMRON Corporation; *Int'l*, pg. 5566
OMRON IMMOBILIARE S.R.L.—See OMRON Corporation; *Int'l*, pg. 5566
OMRON INDUSTRIAL AUTOMATION (CHINA) CO., LTD.—See OMRON Corporation; *Int'l*, pg. 5566
OMRON INDUSTRY & TRADE (DALIAN) CO., LTD.—See OMRON Corporation; *Int'l*, pg. 5566
OMRON LASERFRONT KOREA INC.—See OMRON Corporation; *Int'l*, pg. 5567
OMRON MALAYSIA SDN. BHD.—See OMRON Corporation; *Int'l*, pg. 5567
OMRON MANAGEMENT CENTER OF AMERICA, INC.—See OMRON Corporation; *Int'l*, pg. 5567
OMRON MANAGEMENT CENTER OF INDIA—See OMRON Corporation; *Int'l*, pg. 5567
OMRON MANUFACTURING OF AMERICA, INC.—See OMRON Corporation; *Int'l*, pg. 5567
OMRON MANUFACTURING OF THE NETHERLANDS B.V.—See OMRON Corporation; *Int'l*, pg. 5567
OMRON MEDICAL (BEIJING) CO., LTD.—See OMRON Corporation; *Int'l*, pg. 5567
OMRON MEDIZINTECHNIK HANDELSGESELLSCHAFT MBH—See OMRON Corporation; *Int'l*, pg. 5567
OMRON MEXICO, S.A. DE C.V.—See OMRON Corporation; *Int'l*, pg. 5567
OMRON MICROSCAN SYSTEMS INC.—See OMRON Corporation; *Int'l*, pg. 5567
OMRON PRECISION TECH HONG KONG—See OMRON Corporation; *Int'l*, pg. 5567
OMRON PRECISION TECHNOLOGY KOREA CO., LTD.—See OMRON Corporation; *Int'l*, pg. 5567
OMRON ROBOTICS & SAFETY TECHNOLOGIES, INC.—See OMRON Corporation; *Int'l*, pg. 5567
OMRON SANTE FRANCE SAS—See OMRON Corporation; *Int'l*, pg. 5567
OMRON (SHANGHAI) CO., LTD.—See OMRON Corporation; *Int'l*, pg. 5564
OMRON (SHANGHAI) CO., LTD.—See OMRON Corporation; *Int'l*, pg. 5564
OMRON TAIWAN ELECTRONICS, INC.—See OMRON Corporation; *Int'l*, pg. 5567
OMRON VIETNAM CO., LTD.—See OMRON Corporation; *Int'l*, pg. 5567
OMSAN LOGISTICA SRL—See OYAK Cement Group; *Int'l*, pg. 5677
OMSAN LOGISTIQUE SARL—See OYAK Cement Group; *Int'l*, pg. 5677
OMSAN LOJISTIK A.S.—See OYAK Cement Group; *Int'l*, pg. 5677
O&M SERVICOS - OPERACAO E MANUTENCAO INDUSTRIAL, S.A.—See EDP - Energias de Portugal, S.A.; *Int'l*, pg. 2314
O-M SHANGHAI CO., LTD.—See Daiwabo Holdings Co., Ltd.; *Int'l*, pg. 1949
OMS KORNYEZETVEDELMI KFT.—See SW Umwelttechnik Stoiser & Wolschner AG; *Int'l*, pg. 7359
OMS MOTION, INC.; *U.S. Private*, pg. 3018
O.M.S. SERVICOS DE PROGRAMACAO, LDA.—See OMRON Corporation; *Int'l*, pg. 5564
OMS TECHNOLOGY SDN. BHD.—See MSM International Limited; *Int'l*, pg. 5069
OMTAS A.S.—See Parsan Makina Parcalari Sanayii AS; *Int'l*, pg. 5747
OMTAS OTOMOTIV SANAYI VE TICARET A.S.—See Parsan Makina Parcalari Sanayii AS; *Int'l*, pg. 5747
OM&T B.V.—See Moser Baer India Limited; *Int'l*, pg. 5051
OMTEC LTD.—See Daiwabo Holdings Co., Ltd.; *Int'l*, pg. 1949
OMTEL ESTRUCTURAS DE COMUNICACOES S.A.—See Cellnex Telecom, S.A.; *Int'l*, pg. 1394
OMTHERA PHARMACEUTICALS, INC.—See AstraZeneca PLC; *Int'l*, pg. 661

O.M.T OFFICINA MECCANICA TARTARINI S.R.L.—See Emerson Electric Co.; *U.S. Public*, pg. 750
OMTOOL, LTD.—See Upland Software, Inc.; *U.S. Public*, pg. 2264
OM TRAX PACKAGING SOLUTIONS LTD.—See Tradia Corporation; *Int'l*, pg. 7889
OMU MILK PRODUCTS CO., LTD.—See Fuji Oil Holdings Inc.; *Int'l*, pg. 2815
O-M (U.S.A.), INC.—See Daiwabo Holdings Co., Ltd.; *Int'l*, pg. 1949
OMUSUBIKORORIN HONPO CO., LTD.—See Yoshimura Food Holdings K.K.; *Int'l*, pg. 8600
OMV AKTIENGESELLSCHAFT; *Int'l*, pg. 5567
OMV AUSTRALIA PTY LTD.—See OMV Aktiengesellschaft; *Int'l*, pg. 5568
OMV AUSTRIA EXPLORATION & PRODUCTION GMBH—See OMV Aktiengesellschaft; *Int'l*, pg. 5568
OMV (BAYERN) EXPLORATION GMBH—See OMV Aktiengesellschaft; *Int'l*, pg. 5567
OMV BULGARIA OOD—See OMV Aktiengesellschaft; *Int'l*, pg. 5568
OMV BULGARIEN OOD EINMANNGESELLSCHAFT MBH—See OMV Aktiengesellschaft; *Int'l*, pg. 5568
OMV CESKA REPUBLIKA, S.R.O.—See OMV Aktiengesellschaft; *Int'l*, pg. 5569
OMV CZECH REPUBLIC SPOL. S.R.O.—See OMV Aktiengesellschaft; *Int'l*, pg. 5568
OMV DEUTSCHLAND GMBH—See OMV Aktiengesellschaft; *Int'l*, pg. 5568
OMV EXPLORATION & PRODUCTION GMBH—See OMV Aktiengesellschaft; *Int'l*, pg. 5568
OMV GAS MARKETING &TRADING GMBH—See OMV Aktiengesellschaft; *Int'l*, pg. 5568
OMV GAS & POWER GMBH—See OMV Aktiengesellschaft; *Int'l*, pg. 5568
OMV GAZ VE ENERJI LIMITED SIRKETI—See OMV Aktiengesellschaft; *Int'l*, pg. 5568
OMV GLOBAL OIL & GAS GMBH—See OMV Aktiengesellschaft; *Int'l*, pg. 5568
OMV INSURANCE BROKER GMBH—See OMV Aktiengesellschaft; *Int'l*, pg. 5568
OMV - INTERNATIONAL SERVICES GES.M.B.H.—See OMV Aktiengesellschaft; *Int'l*, pg. 5569
OMV KIMBERLEY (PTY) LTD.—See Raubex Group Limited; *Int'l*, pg. 6221
OMVL S.P.A.—See Westport Fuel Systems Inc.; *Int'l*, pg. 8393
OMV NEW ZEALAND LIMITED—See OMV Aktiengesellschaft; *Int'l*, pg. 5568
OMV (NORGE) AS—See OMV Aktiengesellschaft; *Int'l*, pg. 5568
OMV OF LIBYA LIMITED ('OLIB')—See OMV Aktiengesellschaft; *Int'l*, pg. 5569
OMV OIL AND GAS EXPLORATION GMBH—See OMV Aktiengesellschaft; *Int'l*, pg. 5568
OMV OIL PRODUCTION GMBH—See OMV Aktiengesellschaft; *Int'l*, pg. 5568
OMV (PAKISTAN) EXPLORATION GMBH—See United Energy Group Limited; *Int'l*, pg. 8067
OMV PETROLEUM EXPLORATION GMBH—See OMV Aktiengesellschaft; *Int'l*, pg. 5568
OMV PETROM GAS SRL—See OMV Aktiengesellschaft; *Int'l*, pg. 5568
OMV PETROM SA—See OMV Aktiengesellschaft; *Int'l*, pg. 5568
OMV POWER & GAS GMBH—See OMV Aktiengesellschaft; *Int'l*, pg. 5568
OMV PROTERRA GMBH—See OMV Aktiengesellschaft; *Int'l*, pg. 5568
OMV REFINING & MARKETING GMBH—See OMV Aktiengesellschaft; *Int'l*, pg. 5568
OMV SAMSUN ELEKTRIK URETIM SANAYI VE TICARET A.S.—See Bilgin Enerji Yatirim Holding A.S.; *Int'l*, pg. 1029
OMV (SLOVAKIA) EXPLORATION GMBH—See OMV Aktiengesellschaft; *Int'l*, pg. 5568
OMV SLOVENIJA TRGOVINA Z NAFTO IN NAFTNIMI DERIVATI, D.O.O.—See OMV Aktiengesellschaft; *Int'l*, pg. 5569
OMV SLOVENSKO S.R.O.—See OMV Aktiengesellschaft; *Int'l*, pg. 5569
OMV SOLUTIONS GMBH—See OMV Aktiengesellschaft; *Int'l*, pg. 5569
OMV SOUTHEAST CASPIAN UPSTREAM GMBH—See OMV Aktiengesellschaft; *Int'l*, pg. 5568
OMV SRBIJA D.O.O.—See OMV Aktiengesellschaft; *Int'l*, pg. 5569
OMV SUPPLY & TRADING AG—See OMV Aktiengesellschaft; *Int'l*, pg. 5568
OMV TARANAKI LIMITED—See OMV Aktiengesellschaft; *Int'l*, pg. 5568
OMV TRADING GMBH—See OMV Aktiengesellschaft; *Int'l*, pg. 5569
OMV TRADING SERVICES LIMITED—See OMV Aktiengesellschaft; *Int'l*, pg. 5569
OMV (TUNESIEN) EXPLORATION GMBH—See OMV Aktiengesellschaft; *Int'l*, pg. 5568
OMV WARME VERTRIEBSGMBH—See OMV Aktiengesellschaft; *Int'l*, pg. 5569

OMV AKTIENGESELLSCHAFT

OMV (YEMEN) AL MABAR EXPLORATION GMBH—See OMV Aktiengesellschaft; *Int'l*, pg. 5568
OMV (YEMEN BLOCK S 2) EXPLORATION GMBH—See OMV Aktiengesellschaft; *Int'l*, pg. 5568
OMV (YEMEN) SOUTH SANAU EXPLORATION GMBH—See OMV Aktiengesellschaft; *Int'l*, pg. 5568
OMW CORPORATION; *U.S. Private*, pg. 3018
OMX TECHNOLOGY AB—See Nasdaq, Inc.; *U.S. Public*, pg. 1492
OMX TECHNOLOGY ITALY SRL—See Nasdaq, Inc.; *U.S. Public*, pg. 1492
OMX TECHNOLOGY LTD.—See Nasdaq, Inc.; *U.S. Public*, pg. 1492
OMYA AB—See Omya (Schweiz) AG; *Int'l*, pg. 5570
OMYA ALABAMA INC.—See Omya (Schweiz) AG; *Int'l*, pg. 5572
OMYA ANDINA S.A.—See Omya (Schweiz) AG; *Int'l*, pg. 5570
OMYA ARGENTINA S.A.—See Omya (Schweiz) AG; *Int'l*, pg. 5570
OMYA ARIZONA INC.—See Omya (Schweiz) AG; *Int'l*, pg. 5570
OMYA A/S—See Omya (Schweiz) AG; *Int'l*, pg. 5570
OMYA AUSTRALIA PTY. LTD.—See Omya (Schweiz) AG; *Int'l*, pg. 5570
OMYA BULGARIA EOOD—See Omya (Schweiz) AG; *Int'l*, pg. 5570
OMYA CALCITA S.R.L.—See Omya (Schweiz) AG; *Int'l*, pg. 5570
OMYA, CALIFORNIA, INC.—See Omya (Schweiz) AG; *Int'l*, pg. 5572
OMYA CANADA INC.—See Omya (Schweiz) AG; *Int'l*, pg. 5570
OMYA CANADA INC. - ST. ARMAND PLANT—See Omya (Schweiz) AG; *Int'l*, pg. 5570
OMYA CHEMICAL MERCHANTS INC.—See Omya (Schweiz) AG; *Int'l*, pg. 5570
OMYA CHILE S.A.—See Omya (Schweiz) AG; *Int'l*, pg. 5570
OMYA CLARIANA S.L.U.—See Omya (Schweiz) AG; *Int'l*, pg. 5570
OMYACOLOR S.A.—See F.I.L.A. - Fabbrica Italiana Lapis ed Affini S.p.A.; *Int'l*, pg. 2597
OMYA CZ, S.R.O.—See Omya (Schweiz) AG; *Int'l*, pg. 5570
OMYA DO BRASIL IMPORTACAO, EXPORTACAO E COMERCIO DE MINERAIS LTDA.—See Omya (Schweiz) AG; *Int'l*, pg. 5572
OMYA EGYPT S.A.E.—See Omya (Schweiz) AG; *Int'l*, pg. 5570
OMYA GMBH - EMDEN PLANT—See Omya (Schweiz) AG; *Int'l*, pg. 5570
OMYA GMBH - GOLLING PLANT—See Omya (Schweiz) AG; *Int'l*, pg. 5570
OMYA GMBH - NEU PIRKA PLANT—See Omya (Schweiz) AG; *Int'l*, pg. 5570
OMYA GMBH—See Omya (Schweiz) AG; *Int'l*, pg. 5570
OMYA GMBH—See Omya (Schweiz) AG; *Int'l*, pg. 5570
OMYA GMBH - ULMERFELD-HAUSMENING PLANT—See Omya (Schweiz) AG; *Int'l*, pg. 5570
OMYA HAIMING (NANCHANG) CHEMICAL CO. LTD.—See Omya (Schweiz) AG; *Int'l*, pg. 5570
OMYA HAMBURG GMBH—See Omya (Schweiz) AG; *Int'l*, pg. 5570
OMYA HANKUK CHEMICAL INC.—See Omya (Schweiz) AG; *Int'l*, pg. 5571
OMYA HELLAS S.A.—See Omya (Schweiz) AG; *Int'l*, pg. 5570
OMYA HUNGARIA KFT.—See Omya (Schweiz) AG; *Int'l*, pg. 5571
OMYA HUSTADMARMOR AS—See Omya (Schweiz) AG; *Int'l*, pg. 5571
OMYA HUSTADMARMOR AS—See Omya (Schweiz) AG; *Int'l*, pg. 5571
OMYA INC. - COLUMBIA RIVER CARBONATES PLANT—See Omya (Schweiz) AG; *Int'l*, pg. 5572
OMYA, INC.—See Omya (Schweiz) AG; *Int'l*, pg. 5572
OMYA INC. - VERPOL PLANT—See Omya (Schweiz) AG; *Int'l*, pg. 5572
OMYA INDIA PVT. LTD.—See Omya (Schweiz) AG; *Int'l*, pg. 5571
OMYA INDUSTRIES, INC.—See Omya (Schweiz) AG; *Int'l*, pg. 5570
OMYA INTERNATIONAL AG—See Omya (Schweiz) AG; *Int'l*, pg. 5571
OMYA JAPAN K.K.—See Omya (Schweiz) AG; *Int'l*, pg. 5571
OMYA KOREA INC. - CHECHON PLANT—See Omya (Schweiz) AG; *Int'l*, pg. 5571
OMYA KOREA INC. - GANGWON-DO PLANT—See Omya (Schweiz) AG; *Int'l*, pg. 5571
OMYA KOREA INC. - GYEONGSANGBUK DO PLANT—See Omya (Schweiz) AG; *Int'l*, pg. 5571
OMYA KOREA INC. - JEOLLABUK-DO PLANT—See Omya (Schweiz) AG; *Int'l*, pg. 5571
OMYA KOREA INC.—See Omya (Schweiz) AG; *Int'l*, pg. 5571
OMYA MADENCILIK A.S.—See Omya (Schweiz) AG; *Int'l*, pg. 5571

OMYA MADENCILIK SANAYI VE TICARET A.S. - GEBZE FACTORY—See Omya (Schweiz) AG; *Int'l*, pg. 5571
OMYA MADENCILIK SANAYI VE TICARET A.S. - KARABIGA FACTORY—See Omya (Schweiz) AG; *Int'l*, pg. 5571
OMYA MADENCILIK SANAYI VE TICARET A.S. - KIRSEHIR FACTORY—See Omya (Schweiz) AG; *Int'l*, pg. 5571
OMYA MADENCILIK SANAYI VE TICARET A.S.—See Omya (Schweiz) AG; *Int'l*, pg. 5571
OMYA MALAYSIA SDN.BHD. - BERCHAM PLANT—See Omya (Schweiz) AG; *Int'l*, pg. 5571
OMYA MALAYSIA SDN.BHD. - IPOH PLANT—See Omya (Schweiz) AG; *Int'l*, pg. 5571
OMYA MALAYSIA SDN BHD. - KERAMAT PLANT—See Omya (Schweiz) AG; *Int'l*, pg. 5571
OMYA MALAYSIA SDN BHD.—See Omya (Schweiz) AG; *Int'l*, pg. 5571
OMYA MEXICO S.A. DE C.V. - MPIO TLAJOMULCO JALISCO PLANT—See Omya (Schweiz) AG; *Int'l*, pg. 5571
OMYA MEXICO S.A. DE C.V. - SAN JUAN DEL RIO PLANT—See Omya (Schweiz) AG; *Int'l*, pg. 5571
OMYA MEXICO SA DE CV—See Omya (Schweiz) AG; *Int'l*, pg. 5571
OMYA MINERAL PORTUGUESA LDA.—See Omya (Schweiz) AG; *Int'l*, pg. 5571
OMYA MINERALS (CHANGSHU) CO., LTD.—See Omya (Schweiz) AG; *Int'l*, pg. 5571
OMYA MINERAL (VIETNAM) INC.—See Omya (Schweiz) AG; *Int'l*, pg. 5571
OMYA NETHERLANDS BV - MOERDIJK PLANT—See Omya (Schweiz) AG; *Int'l*, pg. 5571
OMYA NETHERLANDS BV—See Omya (Schweiz) AG; *Int'l*, pg. 5571
OMYA NEW ZEALAND LTD.—See Omya (Schweiz) AG; *Int'l*, pg. 5571
OMYA NEW ZEALAND LTD. - TE KUITI PLANT—See Omya (Schweiz) AG; *Int'l*, pg. 5571
OMYA OY - FORBY PLANT—See Omya (Schweiz) AG; *Int'l*, pg. 5571
OMYA OY - IMATRA PLANT—See Omya (Schweiz) AG; *Int'l*, pg. 5571
OMYA OY - KEMI PLANT—See Omya (Schweiz) AG; *Int'l*, pg. 5571
OMYA OY—See Omya (Schweiz) AG; *Int'l*, pg. 5571
OMYA PCC USA INC. - HAWESVILLE PLANT—See Omya (Schweiz) AG; *Int'l*, pg. 5571
OMYA PCC USA INC. - KINGSPORT PLANT—See Omya (Schweiz) AG; *Int'l*, pg. 5571
OMYA PCC USA INC.—See Omya (Schweiz) AG; *Int'l*, pg. 5571
OMYA SA/NV - HARMIGNIES PLANT—See Omya (Schweiz) AG; *Int'l*, pg. 5572
OMYA SA/NV—See Omya (Schweiz) AG; *Int'l*, pg. 5571
OMYA SAS - ENTRAINS-SUR-NOHAIN PLANT—See Omya (Schweiz) AG; *Int'l*, pg. 5572
OMYA SAS - OMEY PLANT—See Omya (Schweiz) AG; *Int'l*, pg. 5572
OMYA SAS - ONYX & MARBRES GRANULES PLANT—See Omya (Schweiz) AG; *Int'l*, pg. 5572
OMYA SAS - ORGON PLANT—See Omya (Schweiz) AG; *Int'l*, pg. 5572
OMYA SA—See Omya (Schweiz) AG; *Int'l*, pg. 5571
OMYA S.A.—See Omya (Schweiz) AG; *Int'l*, pg. 5571
OMYA SAS - SALSES LE CHATEAU PLANT—See Omya (Schweiz) AG; *Int'l*, pg. 5572
OMYA SAS—See Omya (Schweiz) AG; *Int'l*, pg. 5572
OMYA (SCHWEIZ) AG; *Int'l*, pg. 5570
OMYA SHUNDA (LINKOU) FINE CHEMICAL CO., LTD.—See Omya (Schweiz) AG; *Int'l*, pg. 5572
OMYA SLOVAKIA S.R.O.—See Omya (Schweiz) AG; *Int'l*, pg. 5572
OMYA SPA - AVENZA PLANT—See Omya (Schweiz) AG; *Int'l*, pg. 5571
OMYA SPA - NOCERA UMBRA PLANT—See Omya (Schweiz) AG; *Int'l*, pg. 5571
OMYA S.P.A.—See Omya (Schweiz) AG; *Int'l*, pg. 5571
OMYA SPA - VIPITENO PLANT—See Omya (Schweiz) AG; *Int'l*, pg. 5571
OMYA SP. Z O.O. - MIELNIK PLANT—See Omya (Schweiz) AG; *Int'l*, pg. 5572
OMYA SP. Z O.O. - ROMANOWO PLANT—See Omya (Schweiz) AG; *Int'l*, pg. 5572
OMYA SP. Z O.O.—See Omya (Schweiz) AG; *Int'l*, pg. 5572
OMYA SP. Z O.O. - WOJCIECHOWICE PLANT—See Omya (Schweiz) AG; *Int'l*, pg. 5572
OMYA S.R.O.—See Omya (Schweiz) AG; *Int'l*, pg. 5572
OMYA UAE FZC—See Omya (Schweiz) AG; *Int'l*, pg. 5572
OMYA UK LTD. - BALLYMENA PLANT—See Omya (Schweiz) AG; *Int'l*, pg. 5572
OMYA UK LTD. - HARTLEPOOL PLANT—See Omya (Schweiz) AG; *Int'l*, pg. 5572
OMYA UK LTD. - HUMBER PLANT—See Omya (Schweiz) AG; *Int'l*, pg. 5572
OMYA UK LTD.—See Omya (Schweiz) AG; *Int'l*, pg. 5572
OMYA UK LTD. - STEEPLE MORDEN PLANT—See Omya (Schweiz) AG; *Int'l*, pg. 5572

CORPORATE AFFILIATIONS

OMYA VENCAC D.O.O.—See Omya (Schweiz) AG; *Int'l*, pg. 5572
OMYA WEIL GMBH—See Omya (Schweiz) AG; *Int'l*, pg. 5570
OMZ FOUNDRY MANUFACTURE LLC—See Gazprombank JSC; *Int'l*, pg. 2892
OMZ-SPECIAL STEELS LLC—See Gazprombank JSC; *Int'l*, pg. 2892
OMZ-SPETSSTAL OOO—See Gazprombank JSC; *Int'l*, pg. 2892
ON24, INC.; *U.S. Public*, pg. 1601
ON24 PTE LTD—See ON24, Inc.; *U.S. Public*, pg. 1601
ON24 UK—See ON24, Inc.; *U.S. Public*, pg. 1601
ON4 COMMUNICATIONS INC.; *U.S. Public*, pg. 1601
ONAFHANKELIJKE THUISZORG VLAANDEREN CVBA—See Clariane SE; *Int'l*, pg. 1643
ONAHAMA PETROLEUM CO., LTD.—See Mitsubishi Corporation; *Int'l*, pg. 4942
ONAHAMA SMELTING AND REFINING CO., LTD.—See Mitsubishi Materials Corporation; *Int'l*, pg. 4965
ONAMAC INDUSTRIES INC.—See Warburg Pincus LLC; *U.S. Private*, pg. 4437
ONAMBA CO., LTD.; *Int'l*, pg. 5573
ONAMBA ELECTRONIC PARTS (KUNSHAN) CO., LTD.—See Onamba Co., Ltd.; *Int'l*, pg. 5573
ONAMBA INTERCONNECT TECHNOLOGY CO., LTD. - ELECTRIC CABLE DIVISION—See Onamba Co., Ltd.; *Int'l*, pg. 5573
ONAMBA INTERCONNECT TECHNOLOGY CO., LTD.—See Onamba Co., Ltd.; *Int'l*, pg. 5573
ONAMBA (M) SDN. BHD.—See Onamba Co., Ltd.; *Int'l*, pg. 5573
ONAMBA (SHANGHAI) TRADING CO., LTD.—See Onamba Co., Ltd.; *Int'l*, pg. 5573
ON ANIMATION STUDIO MONTREAL SADC—See Mediawan SA; *Int'l*, pg. 4774
ONANO CORPORATION; *Int'l*, pg. 5573
ONANON INC.—See Amphenol Corporation; *U.S. Public*, pg. 132
ONA POLYMERS LLC—See CFS Group, Inc.; *Int'l*, pg. 1430
ON APPROACH LLC—See Trellance, Inc.; *U.S. Private*, pg. 4217
ONARA - INDUSTRIA E COMERCIO DE TEXTEIS LDA; *Int'l*, pg. 5573
ON A SHOESTRING, INC.; *U.S. Private*, pg. 3018
ONASSIS HOLDINGS CORP; *U.S. Public*, pg. 1601
ONATEL SA—See Emirates Telecommunications Group Compapny PJSC; *Int'l*, pg. 2382
ONBEYOND LLC; *U.S. Private*, pg. 3019
ONB INVESTMENT SERVICES—See Old National Bancorp; *U.S. Public*, pg. 1567
ON BOARD ENTERTAINMENT, INC.; *U.S. Private*, pg. 3018
ON BOARD MEDIA INC—See LVMH Moet Hennessy Louis Vuitton SE; *Int'l*, pg. 4601
ONBRAND—See Stagwell, Inc.; *U.S. Public*, pg. 1927
ON-BRIGHT ELECTRONICS, INC.; *Int'l*, pg. 5573
ON CALL INTERNATIONAL, LLC—See Tokio Marine Holdings, Inc.; *Int'l*, pg. 7784
ONCALL—See WPP plc; *Int'l*, pg. 8470
ONCAP MANAGEMENT PARTNERS L.P.—See ONEX Corporation; *Int'l*, pg. 5578
ONCARD LTD.—See TasFoods Limited; *Int'l*, pg. 7465
ONCE AGAIN NUT BUTTER COLLECTIVE INC.; *U.S. Private*, pg. 3019
ONCE INNOVATIONS, INC.—See Signify N.V.; *Int'l*, pg. 6912
ON CENTER SOFTWARE, INC.—See Roper Technologies, Inc.; *U.S. Public*, pg. 1812
ONCE UPON A TIME LONDON LTD.; *Int'l*, pg. 5574
ONCIDIUM INC.—See CPS Capital; *Int'l*, pg. 1826
ONCIMMUNE GERMANY GMBH—See Oncimmune Holdings Plc; *Int'l*, pg. 5574
ONCIMMUNE HOLDINGS PLC; *Int'l*, pg. 5574
ONCO360; *U.S. Private*, pg. 3019
ONCOARENDI THERAPEUTICS S.A.; *Int'l*, pg. 5574
ONCOCYTE CORPORATION; *U.S. Public*, pg. 1601
ONCODESIGN PRECISION MEDICINE SACA; *Int'l*, pg. 5574
ONCODESIGN SA—See Edmond de Rothschild Holding S.A.; *Int'l*, pg. 2313
ONCOLIX INC.; *U.S. Public*, pg. 1601
ON COLLABORATIVE LLC—See Anywhere Real Estate Inc.; *U.S. Public*, pg. 142
ONCOLOGICS, INC.—See Kohlberg & Company, LLC; *U.S. Private*, pg. 2339
ONCOLOGIX TECH, INC.; *U.S. Private*, pg. 3019
ONCOLOGY ANALYTICS, INC.; *U.S. Private*, pg. 3019
ONCOLOGY/HEMATOLOGY CARE, INC.—See Bon Secours Mercy Health, Inc.; *U.S. Private*, pg. 612
THE ONCOLOGY INSTITUTE, INC.; *U.S. Public*, pg. 2118
ONCOLOGY NURSING SOCIETY; *U.S. Private*, pg. 3019
ONCOLOGY PHARMA, INC.; *U.S. Public*, pg. 1601
ONCOLOGY PLUS, LLC—See Avella of Deer Valley, Inc.; *U.S. Private*, pg. 405
ONCOLOGY THERAPEUTIC NETWORK CORPORATION—See McKesson Corporation; *U.S. Public*, pg. 1408

COMPANY NAME INDEX

ONCOLOGY THERAPEUTIC NETWORK—See Cardinal Health, Inc.; *U.S. Public*, pg. 434
ON COLORS & CHEMICALS (SHANGHAI) CO., LTD.—See Nagase & Co., Ltd.; *Int'l*, pg. 5128
ONCOLYS BIOPHARMA INC.; *Int'l*, pg. 5574
ONCOLYTICS BIOTECH INC.; *Int'l*, pg. 5574
ONCOMED PHARMACEUTICALS, INC.—See Mereo BioPharma Group plc; *Int'l*, pg. 4834
ONCONTACT SOFTWARE CORP.—See WorkWise, LLC; *U.S. Private*, pg. 4564
ONCOPEPTIDES AB; *Int'l*, pg. 5574
ONCOPEPTIDES, INC.—See Oncopeptides AB; *Int'l*, pg. 5574
ONCORAL PHARMA APS—See Ascelia Pharma AB; *Int'l*, pg. 601
ONCORE AVIATION LLC; *U.S. Private*, pg. 3019
ONCORE CONSULTING, LLC—See Sagewind Capital LLC; *U.S. Private*, pg. 3527
ONCOR ELECTRIC DELIVERY COMPANY LLC—See Sempra; *U.S. Public*, pg. 1863
ON-COR FROZEN FOODS LLC; *U.S. Private*, pg. 3018
ONCOR INTERNATIONAL LLC—See Anywhere Real Estate Inc.; *U.S. Public*, pg. 142
ONCOR NTU HOLDINGS COMPANY LLC—See Sempra; *U.S. Public*, pg. 1863
ONCORUS, INC.; *U.S. Public*, pg. 1601
ONCOSEC MEDICAL INCORPORATED; *U.S. Public*, pg. 1601
ONCOSIL MEDICAL LIMITED; *Int'l*, pg. 5574
ONCOTEAM DIAGNOSTIC SA—See MedLife S.A.; *Int'l*, pg. 4785
ONCOTELIC THERAPEUTICS, INC.; *U.S. Public*, pg. 1602
ONCO THERAPIES LIMITED—See Strides Pharma Science Limited; *Int'l*, pg. 7240
ONCOTHERAPY SCIENCE, INC.; *Int'l*, pg. 5574
ONCOURSE LEARNING CORPORATION—See Bertelsmann SE & Co. KGaA; *Int'l*, pg. 990
ONCOURSE STRATEGIES; *U.S. Private*, pg. 3019
ONCOZENGE AB; *Int'l*, pg. 5574
ONCTERNAL THERAPEUTICS, INC.; *U.S. Public*, pg. 1602
ONCUE MARKETING LLC; *U.S. Private*, pg. 3020
ONCURE HOLDINGS, INC.—See Vestar Capital Partners, LLC; *U.S. Private*, pg. 4371
ONCURE MEDICAL CORPORATION—See Vestar Capital Partners, LLC; *U.S. Private*, pg. 4371
ONDA ENTERTAINMENT CO., LTD.—See CHA Biotech Co., Ltd.; *Int'l*, pg. 1435
ONDAL FRANCE SARL—See The Procter & Gamble Company; *U.S. Public*, pg. 2121
ONDAL MEDICAL SYSTEMS GMBH—See IK Investment Partners Limited; *Int'l*, pg. 3609
ONDAL MEDICAL SYSTEMS OF AMERICA, INC.—See IK Investment Partners Limited; *Int'l*, pg. 3610
ONDAS HOLDINGS, INC.; *U.S. Public*, pg. 1602
ONDAS MEDIA, S.A.—See Aptiv PLC; *Int'l*, pg. 525
ONDAS NETWORKS INC.—See Ondas Holdings, Inc.; *U.S. Public*, pg. 1602
ON DECK CAPITAL INC.—See Enova International, Inc.; *U.S. Public*, pg. 769
ONDECK CO., LTD.; *Int'l*, pg. 5574
ONDEMAND4U GMBH—See Orbis SE; *Int'l*, pg. 5614
ONDEMANDCOMMERCE GMBH—See Otto GmbH & Co. KG; *Int'l*, pg. 5663
ON-DEMAND ENERGY, L.P.—See World Kinect Corporation; *U.S. Public*, pg. 2381
ON DEMAND ICARS, INC.; *U.S. Private*, pg. 3018
ON-DEMAND MAIL SERVICES, LLC; *U.S. Private*, pg. 3018
ON-DEMAND PUBLISHING, LLC—See Amazon.com, Inc.; *U.S. Public*, pg. 91
ONDEO DEGREMONT SA—See Veolia Environnement S.A.; *Int'l*, pg. 8155
ONDEO INDUSTRIAL SOLUTIONS LIMITED—See Veolia Environnement S.A.; *Int'l*, pg. 8155
ONDEO INDUSTRIAL SOLUTIONS—See Veolia Environnement S.A.; *Int'l*, pg. 8155
ONDEO INDUSTRIAL SOLUTIONS SRL—See Veolia Environnement S.A.; *Int'l*, pg. 8155
ONDEO NALCO ENERGY SERVICES—See Ecolab Inc.; *U.S. Public*, pg. 716
ONDE S.A.—See Erbud S.A.; *Int'l*, pg. 2489
ON DESIGN CZECH S.R.O.—See ON Semiconductor Corporation; *U.S. Public*, pg. 1600
ONDINE BIOMEDICAL INC.; *Int'l*, pg. 5574
ONDINE RESEARCH LABORATORIES, INC.—See Ondine Biomedical Inc.; *Int'l*, pg. 5574
ONDISPLAY ADVERTISING LLC—See Federated Media Inc.; *U.S. Private*, pg. 1492
ONDOAN S. COOP.—See Mondragon Corporation; *Int'l*, pg. 5031
ONDO INSURTECH PLC; *Int'l*, pg. 5574
ON DOOR CONCEPTS LIMITED; *Int'l*, pg. 5572
ONDRA-HUYETT ASSOCIATES, INC.; *U.S. Private*, pg. 3020
ONDULINE BELGIQUE SA/NV—See Kingspan Group PLC; *Int'l*, pg. 4179

ONDULINE BUILDING PRODUCTS LIMITED—See Kingspan Group PLC; *Int'l*, pg. 4179
ONDULINE GMBH—See Kingspan Group PLC; *Int'l*, pg. 4179
ONDULINE ITALIA S.P.A.—See Kingspan Group PLC; *Int'l*, pg. 4179
ONDULINE MATERIAIS DE CONSTRUCAO, S.A.—See Kingspan Group PLC; *Int'l*, pg. 4179
ONDULINE MATERIAL DE CONSTRUCTII S.R.L.—See Kingspan Group PLC; *Int'l*, pg. 4179
ONDULINE MATERIALES DE CONSTRUCCION, S.A.—See Kingspan Group PLC; *Int'l*, pg. 4179
ONDULINE POLSKA SP. Z O. O. UL.—See Kingspan Group PLC; *Int'l*, pg. 4179
ONDULINE S.M., S.R.O.—See Kingspan Group PLC; *Int'l*, pg. 4179
ONDULINE—See Kingspan Group PLC; *Int'l*, pg. 4179
ONDULYS INDUSTRIE—See VPK Packaging Group NV; *Int'l*, pg. 8312
ONDULYS SAINT-QUENTIN SAS—See VPK Packaging Group NV; *Int'l*, pg. 8312
ONE15 LUXURY YACHTING PTE. LTD.—See SUTL Enterprise Limited; *Int'l*, pg. 7347
ONE1 FINANCIAL LIMITED—See GraceKennedy Limited; *Int'l*, pg. 3049
ONE2ONE LIVING CORPORATION; *U.S. Private*, pg. 3024
ONE 3 TWO, INC.; *U.S. Private*, pg. 3020
ONE51 ES METALS (NORTH) LTD—See Madison Dearborn Partners, LLC; *U.S. Private*, pg. 2541
ONE51 PLASTICS HOLDINGS LIMITED—See Madison Dearborn Partners, LLC; *U.S. Private*, pg. 2541
ONE80 INTERMEDIARIES LLC; *U.S. Private*, pg. 3024
ONE97 COMMUNICATIONS LIMITED; *Int'l*, pg. 5575
ONEACCESS SA—See Ekinops S.A.; *Int'l*, pg. 2338
ONEACCORD CAPITAL LLC; *U.S. Private*, pg. 3024
THE ONE ACCOUNT LTD.—See NatWest Group plc; *Int'l*, pg. 5172
ONE ACRE FUND; *U.S. Private*, pg. 3020
ONEADVANCED, INC.—See HgCapital Trust plc; *Int'l*, pg. 3377
ONE ADVANTAGE LLC—See RPSG Ventures Limited; *Int'l*, pg. 6416
O'NEAL CONSTRUCTION INC.—See O'Neal, Inc.; *U.S. Private*, pg. 2979
O'NEAL FLAT ROLLED METALS, LLC - MONROE—See O'Neal Industries, Inc.; *U.S. Private*, pg. 2979
O'NEAL FLAT ROLLED METALS, LLC—See O'Neal Industries, Inc.; *U.S. Private*, pg. 2979
O'NEAL, INC.; *U.S. Private*, pg. 2979
O'NEAL INC.; *U.S. Private*, pg. 2979
O'NEAL INDUSTRIES, INC.; *U.S. Private*, pg. 2979
ONE ALLEN CENTER CO. LLC—See Brookfield Corporation; *Int'l*, pg. 1186
ONEALL INTERNATIONAL LIMITED; *Int'l*, pg. 5575
ONE ALLOY CORPORATION—See TCC STEEL CORP.; *Int'l*, pg. 7483
ONE & ALL—See Omnicom Group Inc.; *U.S. Public*, pg. 1589
ONE & ALL—See Omnicom Group Inc.; *U.S. Public*, pg. 1589
O'NEAL MANUFACTURING SERVICES DIVISION—See O'Neal Industries, Inc.; *U.S. Private*, pg. 2979
O'NEAL STEEL, INC.—See O'Neal Industries, Inc.; *U.S. Private*, pg. 2979
ONEAMERICA FINANCIAL PARTNERS, INC.—See American United Mutual Insurance Holding Company; *U.S. Private*, pg. 257
ONE AMERICAN CORP.; *U.S. Private*, pg. 3020
ONEAPEX LIMITED; *Int'l*, pg. 5576
ONE ASSET MANAGEMENT LIMITED—See KGI Financial Holding Co., Ltd.; *Int'l*, pg. 4150
ONE BANK LIMITED - RETAIL BANKING DIVISION—See One Bank PLC; *Int'l*, pg. 5574
ONE BANK PLC; *Int'l*, pg. 5574
ONEBEACON INSURANCE GROUP, LLC—See Intact Financial Corporation; *Int'l*, pg. 3726
ONEBEACON INSURANCE GROUP, LTD.—See Intact Financial Corporation; *Int'l*, pg. 3726
ONEBEACON U.S. HOLDINGS, INC.—See Intact Financial Corporation; *Int'l*, pg. 3726
ONE BEAT CPR LEARNING CENTER, INC.—See Investor AB; *Int'l*, pg. 3787
ONE BIO, CORP.; *U.S. Public*, pg. 1602
ONEBLOOD, INC.; *U.S. Private*, pg. 3024
ONE BRANDS, LLC—See The Hershey Co.; *U.S. Public*, pg. 2089
ONEBRIDGE SOLUTIONS, INC.—See Blackstone Inc.; *U.S. Public*, pg. 355
ONEBRIDGE SOLUTIONS INC.—See Blackstone Inc.; *U.S. Public*, pg. 355
ONE BRYANT PARK LLC—See Bank of America Corporation; *U.S. Public*, pg. 272
ONE CALL CARE MANAGEMENT, INC.—See Apax Partners LLP; *Int'l*, pg. 505
ONE CALL CARE MANAGEMENT, INC.—See Apax Partners LLP; *Int'l*, pg. 505
ONE CALL CARE TRANSPORT + TRANSLATE ENTERPRISES, LLC—See Apax Partners LLP; *Int'l*, pg. 505

ONEIDA MOLDED PLASTICS, LLC

ONE CALL CONCEPTS INCORPORATED; *U.S. Private*, pg. 3020
ONE CARIBBEAN MEDIA LIMITED; *Int'l*, pg. 5574
ONECENT SDN. BHD.—See TFP Solutions Berhad; *Int'l*, pg. 7587
ONECLICKHR PLC—See Automatic Data Processing, Inc.; *U.S. Public*, pg. 230
ONECLICK LOGISTICS INDIA LIMITED; *Int'l*, pg. 5576
ONE CLICK METAL GMBH—See TRUMPF SE + Co. KG; *Int'l*, pg. 7942
ONE CLICK VENTURES; *U.S. Private*, pg. 3020
ONECO AS—See Katalysator S.A.; *Int'l*, pg. 4089
ONECOAST NETWORK CORPORATION; *U.S. Private*, pg. 3024
ONECOMMAND, INC.—See Affinitiv, Inc.; *U.S. Private*, pg. 122
ONE COMMUNICATIONS, LLC—See ATN International, Inc.; *U.S. Public*, pg. 225
ONE COMMUNICATIONS LTD.; *Int'l*, pg. 5575
ONE COMMUNICATION TECHNOLOGY CORPORATION; *Int'l*, pg. 5574
ONECONNECT FINANCIAL TECHNOLOGY CO., LTD.; *Int'l*, pg. 5576
ONE CRANS-MONTANA SA—See CPI Property Group, S.A.; *Int'l*, pg. 1825
ONE CRNA GORA DOO—See 4iG Nyrt.; *Int'l*, pg. 12
ONE CYPRESS ENERGY LLC; *U.S. Private*, pg. 3020
ONE DESIGNS CO., LTD.—See Koyou Rentia Co., Ltd.; *Int'l*, pg. 4295
ONEDEV LLC—See The O'Neil Group Company, LLC; *U.S. Private*, pg. 4087
ONEDIGITAL HEALTH & BENEFITS—See New Mountain Capital, LLC; *U.S. Private*, pg. 2901
ONEDIGITAL INVESTMENT ADVISORS LLC—See New Mountain Capital, LLC; *U.S. Private*, pg. 2901
ONE DIRECT (IRELAND) LIMITED—See An Post LLC; *Int'l*, pg. 443
ONEDIRECT SAS—See Groupe BPCE; *Int'l*, pg. 3095
ONE EARTH ENERGY, LLC—See REX American Resources Corporation; *U.S. Public*, pg. 1795
ONE-EIGHT-ONE HOSPITALITY MANAGEMENT LIMITED—See Liu Chong Hing Investment Limited; *Int'l*, pg. 4529
ONE EMBARCADERO CENTER VENTURE—See Boston Properties, Inc.; *U.S. Public*, pg. 373
ONE EQUITY PARTNERS EUROPE GMBH—See OEP Capital Advisors, L.P.; *U.S. Private*, pg. 2999
ONEE TAX LIMITED; *Int'l*, pg. 5576
ONEEVENT TECHNOLOGIES, INC.—See National Presto Industries, Inc.; *U.S. Public*, pg. 1497
ONE EXAM PREP LLC—See ProBility Media Corporation; *U.S. Public*, pg. 1723
ONE EXPERIENCE S.A.; *Int'l*, pg. 5575
ONE FIVE ONE PROPERTY PTY LTD.—See Blackstone Inc.; *U.S. Public*, pg. 360
ONEFLOW AB; *Int'l*, pg. 5576
ONEFLOW B.V.—See Oneflow AB; *Int'l*, pg. 5576
ONEFLOW ENGLAND LTD.—See Oneflow AB; *Int'l*, pg. 5576
ONEFLOW NORGE AS—See Oneflow AB; *Int'l*, pg. 5576
ONEFLOW S.A.S.—See Oneflow AB; *Int'l*, pg. 5576
ONE FOR ALL IBERIA S.L.—See Universal Electronics, Inc.; *U.S. Public*, pg. 2255
ONEFORCE HOLDINGS LTD.; *Int'l*, pg. 5576
ONE FREEDOM SQUARE, L.L.C.—See Boston Properties, Inc.; *U.S. Public*, pg. 373
ONE GAS, INC.; *U.S. Public*, pg. 1602
ONE GLOBAL SERVICE PROVIDER LTD.; *Int'l*, pg. 5575
ONE GLOVE GROUP BERHAD; *Int'l*, pg. 5575
ONE GREEN BEAN LONDON LIMITED—See Vivendi SE; *Int'l*, pg. 8269
ONE GREEN BEAN PTY. LTD.—See Vivendi SE; *Int'l*, pg. 8269
THE ONE GROUP HOSPITALITY, INC.; *U.S. Public*, pg. 2118
ONEGROUP NY, INC.—See Community Bank System, Inc.; *U.S. Public*, pg. 550
ONEGROUP WEALTH PARTNERS, INC.—See Community Bank System, Inc.; *U.S. Public*, pg. 550
ONE HERITAGE GROUP PLC; *Int'l*, pg. 5575
ONE HOMECARE SOLUTIONS, LLC—See Humana, Inc.; *U.S. Public*, pg. 1070
ONEHOPE WINE; *U.S. Private*, pg. 3025
ONE HORIZON GROUP PLC—See Touchpoint Group Holdings, Inc.; *U.S. Public*, pg. 2165
ONE HUGHES LANDING, LLC—See Howard Hughes Holdings Inc.; *U.S. Public*, pg. 1060
ONEIDA CANADA LTD.—See EveryWare Global, Inc.; *U.S. Private*, pg. 1441
ONEIDA CONSUMER PRODUCTS DIVISION—See EveryWare Global, Inc.; *U.S. Private*, pg. 1441
ONEIDA FOOD SERVICE, INC.—See EveryWare Global, Inc.; *U.S. Private*, pg. 1441
ONEIDA (GUANGZHOU) FOODSERVICE CO. LTD.—See EveryWare Global, Inc.; *U.S. Private*, pg. 1441
ONEIDA LTD.—See EveryWare Global, Inc.; *U.S. Private*, pg. 1441
ONEIDA MOLDED PLASTICS, LLC; *U.S. Private*, pg. 3025

ONEIDA RESEARCH SERVICES, INC.
CORPORATE AFFILIATIONS

ONEIDA RESEARCH SERVICES, INC.; *U.S. Private*, pg. 3025
ONEIDA, S.A. DE C.V.—See EveryWare Global, Inc.; *U.S. Private*, pg. 1441
ONEIDA SILVERSMITHS INC.—See EveryWare Global, Inc.; *U.S. Private*, pg. 1441
ONEIDA TOTAL INTEGRATED ENTERPRISES (OTIE); *U.S. Private*, pg. 3025
ONEIDA WEALTH MANAGEMENT, INC.—See Community Bank System, Inc.; *U.S. Public*, pg. 550
O'NEIL & ASSOCIATES INCORPORATED; *U.S. Private*, pg. 2979
O'NEIL BUICK - GMC INC.; *U.S. Private*, pg. 2979
O'NEIL COLOR & COMPOUNDING CORP. - NORTH FACILITY—See ICC Industries, Inc.; *U.S. Private*, pg. 2030
O'NEIL COLOR & COMPOUNDING CORP. - SOUTH FACILITY—See ICC Industries, Inc.; *U.S. Private*, pg. 2030
O'NEIL & CO. LTD.—See Intact Financial Corporation; *Int'l*, pg. 3726
O'NEIL DATA SYSTEMS, INC.—See William O'Neil & Co., Inc.; *U.S. Private*, pg. 4524
THE O'NEIL GROUP COMPANY, LLC; *U.S. Private*, pg. 4087
O'NEIL INDUSTRIES INC.; *U.S. Private*, pg. 2979
O'NEILL AND ASSOCIATES, LLC—See Blue Engine Message & Media, LLC; *U.S. Private*, pg. 588
O'NEILL AUTOMOTIVE INC.; *U.S. Private*, pg. 2980
O'NEILL ELECTRIC INC.; *U.S. Private*, pg. 2980
O'NEILL INC.; *U.S. Private*, pg. 2980
O'NEILL PROPERTIES GROUP, LP; *U.S. Private*, pg. 2980
O'NEILLS CHEVROLET & BUICK; *U.S. Private*, pg. 2980
O'NEIL SECURITIES, INCORPORATED—See William O'Neil & Co., Inc.; *U.S. Private*, pg. 4524
ONE, INC.—See Great Hill Partners, L.P.; *U.S. Private*, pg. 1763
ONEINDIA BSC PRIVATE LIMITED—See Adani Enterprises Limited; *Int'l*, pg. 125
ONEJOON CO., LTD.; *Int'l*, pg. 5576
ONE KINGS LANE, INC.—See 20230930-DK-Butterfly-1, *U.S. Private*, pg. 5
ONE LAMBDA, INC—See Thermo Fisher Scientific Inc.; *U.S. Public*, pg. 2149
ONE LAZULI SDN. BHD.—See Rhone Ma Holdings Berhad; *Int'l*, pg. 6327
ONELCT AG—See NEXUS AG; *Int'l*, pg. 5251
ONE LEGAL, LLC—See Infotrack Pty Ltd; *Int'l*, pg. 3696
ONE LIBERTY PROPERTIES, INC.; *U.S. Public*, pg. 1602
ONELIFE CAPITAL ADVISORS LIMITED; *Int'l*, pg. 5576
ONELIFE TECHNOLOGIES CORP.; *U.S. Public*, pg. 1602
ONELOGIN, INC.; *U.S. Private*, pg. 3025
ONELOGIX CARGO SOLUTIONS PROPRIETARY LIMITED—See OneLogix Group Limited; *Int'l*, pg. 5576
ONELOGIX GROUP LIMITED; *Int'l*, pg. 5576
ONELOGIX WAREHOUSING PROPRIETARY LIMITED—See OneLogix Group Limited; *Int'l*, pg. 5576
ONE LOVE FOUNDATION; *U.S. Private*, pg. 3020
ONEMAIN ASSURANCE SERVICES, INC.—See SoftBank Group Corp.; *Int'l*, pg. 7053
ONEMAIN FINANCE CORPORATION; *U.S. Private*, pg. 3025
ONEMAIN HOLDINGS, INC.—See SoftBank Group Corp.; *Int'l*, pg. 7053
ONEMARKETDATA, LLC; *U.S. Private*, pg. 3025
ONEMED AS—See Interogo Holding AG; *Int'l*, pg. 3754
ONEMED GROUP OY—See Interogo Holding AG; *Int'l*, pg. 3754
ONEMEDIA FRANCE SARL; *Int'l*, pg. 5576
ONE MEDIA GROUP LIMITED; *Int'l*, pg. 5575
ONE MEDIA IP GROUP PLC; *Int'l*, pg. 5575
ONE MEDIA, LLC—See Sinclair, Inc.; *U.S. Public*, pg. 1885
ONEMEDNET CORPORATION; *Int'l*, pg. 5576
ONEMEDNET SOLUTIONS CORPORATION—See OneMedNet Corporation; *Int'l*, pg. 5576
ONEMED OU—See Interogo Holding AG; *Int'l*, pg. 3754
ONEMED SIA—See Interogo Holding AG; *Int'l*, pg. 3754
ONEMED SVERIGE AB—See Interogo Holding AG; *Int'l*, pg. 3754
ONEMETA, INC.; *U.S. Public*, pg. 1602
ONE MODEL MANAGEMENT LLC; *U.S. Private*, pg. 3020
ONE MORE TIME INC.—See Baker Commodities, Inc.; *U.S. Private*, pg. 455
ONENECK IT SERVICES CORPORATION—See Telephone & Data Systems, Inc.; *U.S. Public*, pg. 1997
ONENECK IT SOLUTIONS LLC—See Mitsubishi UFJ Financial Group, Inc.; *Int'l*, pg. 4971
ONENERGY INC.; *Int'l*, pg. 5576
ON ENERGY INC.—See CGX Energy Inc.; *Int'l*, pg. 1435
ONENESS BIOTECH CO., LTD.; *Int'l*, pg. 5577
ONE NIGHT, LLC—See Sansiri pcl; *Int'l*, pg. 6556
ONE NORTH ENTERTAINMENT LIMITED; *Int'l*, pg. 5575
ONEOK ENERGY MARKETING & TRADING COMPANY, II—See ONEOK, Inc.; *U.S. Public*, pg. 1603
ONEOK ENERGY RESOURCES COMPANY—See ONEOK, Inc.; *U.S. Public*, pg. 1603

ONEOK FIELD SERVICES COMPANY, L.L.C.—See ONEOK, Inc.; *U.S. Public*, pg. 1603
ONEOK FOUNDATION, INC.—See ONEOK, Inc.; *U.S. Public*, pg. 1603
ONEOK GAS PROCESSING, LLC—See ONEOK, Inc.; *U.S. Public*, pg. 1603
ONEOK GAS STORAGE, LLC—See ONEOK, Inc.; *U.S. Public*, pg. 1603
ONEOK GAS TRANSPORTATION, LLC—See ONEOK, Inc.; *U.S. Public*, pg. 1603
ONEOK HYDROCARBON, L.L.C.—See ONEOK, Inc.; *U.S. Public*, pg. 1603
ONEOK, INC.; *U.S. Public*, pg. 1602
ONEOK LEASING COMPANY—See ONEOK, Inc.; *U.S. Public*, pg. 1603
ONEOK PARTNERS, L.P.—See ONEOK, Inc.; *U.S. Public*, pg. 1603
ONEONCOLOGY, INC.—See TPG Capital, L.P.; *U.S. Public*, pg. 2175
ONE ON ONE MARKETING INC.; *U.S. Private*, pg. 3020
ONEONTA-STARR RANCH GROWERS LLC—See Oneonta Trading Corporation; *U.S. Private*, pg. 3025
ONEONTA TRADING CORPORATION; *U.S. Private*, pg. 3025
ONEOTT INTERTAINMENT LIMITED—See Hinduja Global Solutions Ltd.; *Int'l*, pg. 3398
THE ONE-PAGE COMPANY INC.; *U.S. Private*, pg. 4088
ONEPAK, INC.; *U.S. Private*, pg. 3025
ONEPATH FUNDS MANAGEMENT LIMITED—See Australia & New Zealand Banking Group Limited; *Int'l*, pg. 720
ONEPATH SYSTEMS, LLC—See Trivest Partners, LP; *U.S. Private*, pg. 4241
ONE PICA, INC; *U.S. Private*, pg. 3020
ONEPLACE LLC—See Salem Media Group, Inc.; *U.S. Public*, pg. 1836
ONE PLACE LLC—See Salem Media Group, Inc.; *U.S. Public*, pg. 1836
ONE PLANET GROUP LLC; *U.S. Private*, pg. 3020
ONE PLUS CORP.—See ParkerGale, LLC; *U.S. Private*, pg. 3098
ONEPOINTCITY, LLC—See Fidelity National Financial, Inc.; *U.S. Public*, pg. 831
ONE POINT ONE SOLUTIONS LIMITED; *Int'l*, pg. 5575
ONEPOINT SOFTWARE GMBH; *Int'l*, pg. 5577
ONEPOWER SYSTEMS LTD.; *U.S. Private*, pg. 3025
THE O.N. EQUITY SALES COMPANY—See Caisse de Depot et Placement du Quebec; *Int'l*, pg. 1254
THE O.N. EQUITY SALES COMPANY—See Ontario Teachers' Pension Plan; *Int'l*, pg. 5586
ONERAIL GLOBAL HOLDINGS PTY. LTD.—See Amadeus IT Group, S.A.; *Int'l*, pg. 407
ONERAIN, INC.; *U.S. Private*, pg. 3025
ONE REEL INC.; *U.S. Private*, pg. 3020
ONE REIT, INC.; *Int'l*, pg. 5575
ONEREPORT, INC.—See Nasdaq, Inc.; *U.S. Public*, pg. 1492
ONE RESOURCE GROUP, LLC—See Integrity Marketing Group LLC; *U.S. Private*, pg. 2104
ONE RING NETWORKS, INC.—See Trive Capital Inc.; *U.S. Private*, pg. 4239
ONE ROCK CAPITAL PARTNERS, LLC; *U.S. Private*, pg. 3020
ONEROOF ENERGY GROUP, INC.; *U.S. Public*, pg. 1603
ONEROOF ENERGY, INC.—See OneRoof Energy Group, Inc.; *U.S. Public*, pg. 1603
ONESANO S.A.; *Int'l*, pg. 5577
ONE SA; *Int'l*, pg. 5575
ONESAVINGS BANK PLC; *Int'l*, pg. 5577
ONESCREEN, INC.; *U.S. Public*, pg. 1603
ONE SECURITIES LIMITED—See One Bank PLC; *Int'l*, pg. 5574
ONESHIELD, INC.; *U.S. Private*, pg. 3025
ONESHOP RETAIL SDN. BHD.; *Int'l*, pg. 5577
ONESHORE ENERGY GMBH—See BayWa AG; *Int'l*, pg. 918
ONE SHOT LLC—See PPG Industries, Inc.; *U.S. Public*, pg. 1707
ONE SIXTY OVER NINETY, INC.—See William Morris Endeavor Entertainment, LLC; *U.S. Private*, pg. 4523
ONE SKI HILL PLACE, LLC—See Vail Resorts, Inc.; *U.S. Public*, pg. 2271
ONE SKY INC.—See Dentsu Group Inc.; *Int'l*, pg. 2039
ONE'S LIFE HOME, INC—See Sansei Landic Co., Ltd.; *Int'l*, pg. 6555
ONE SMOOTH STONE, INC.—See EagleTree Capital, LP; *U.S. Private*, pg. 1311
ONESOFT SOLUTIONS INC.—See Blackstone Inc.; *U.S. Public*, pg. 355
ONE SOFTWARE HOLDING AS—See Ratos AB; *Int'l*, pg. 6220
ONE SOFTWARE TECHNOLOGIES LTD.; *Int'l*, pg. 5575
ONE SOTHEBY'S INTERNATIONAL REALTY, INC.; *U.S. Private*, pg. 3023
ONE SOURCE ASSOCIATES, INC.; *U.S. Private*, pg. 3023
ONE SOURCE DISTRIBUTORS INC.—See Sonepar S.A.; *Int'l*, pg. 7093

ONESOURCE GENERAL CONTRACTING, INC.; *U.S. Private*, pg. 3025
ONESOURCE IDEAS VENTURE LTD.; *Int'l*, pg. 5577
ONE SOURCE INDUSTRIES, LLC—See Westminster Capital Inc.; *U.S. Private*, pg. 4499
ONESOURCE MANAGED SERVICES, LLC—See Xerox Holdings Corporation; *U.S. Public*, pg. 2388
ONE SOURCE TALENT; *U.S. Private*, pg. 3023
ONESOURCE VIRTUAL; *U.S. Private*, pg. 3025
ONESPAN CANADA INC.—See OneSpan Inc.; *U.S. Public*, pg. 1603
ONESPAN INC.; *U.S. Public*, pg. 1603
ONESPAWORLD HOLDINGS LIMITED; *U.S. Public*, pg. 1604
ONESPRING LLC; *U.S. Private*, pg. 3025
THE ONESTAR FOUNDATION; *U.S. Private*, pg. 4088
ONESTA; *U.S. Private*, pg. 3025
ONESTAT INTERNATIONAL B.V.; *Int'l*, pg. 5577
ONE STEP (SUPPORT) LIMITED—See Sheikh Holdings Group (Investments) Limited; *Int'l*, pg. 6794
ONE STEP VENDING CORP.; *U.S. Public*, pg. 1602
ONE STONE ENERGY PARTNERS, L.P.; *U.S. Private*, pg. 3023
ONE STOP BUSINESS CENTERS INC.; *U.S. Private*, pg. 3023
ONE STOP DISPLAYS, LLC—See New Vision Display, Inc.; *U.S. Private*, pg. 2907
ONE STOP ENVIRONMENTAL, LLC—See Ambipar Participacoes e Empreendimentos SA; *Int'l*, pg. 414
ONESTOPERGONOMICS.COM; *U.S. Private*, pg. 3025
ONESTOP INTERNET, INC.; *U.S. Private*, pg. 3025
ONE STOP STORES LIMITED—See Tesco PLC; *Int'l*, pg. 7571
ONE STOP SYSTEMS, INC.; *U.S. Public*, pg. 1602
ONE STOP UNDERCAR, INC.—See Halla Group; *Int'l*, pg. 3230
ONESTORY INC.—See Yoshimura Food Holdings K.K.; *Int'l*, pg. 8600
ONESUBSEA GMBH—See Schlumberger Limited; *U.S. Public*, pg. 1844
ONESUBSEA LLC—See Schlumberger Limited; *U.S. Public*, pg. 1844
ONESUBSEA MALAYSIA SYSTEMS SDN BHD—See Schlumberger Limited; *U.S. Public*, pg. 1844
ONESUBSEA OPERATIONS LIMITED—See Schlumberger Limited; *U.S. Public*, pg. 1844
ONESUBSEA PROCESSING ASIA PACIFIC SDN. BHD.—See Schlumberger Limited; *U.S. Public*, pg. 1844
ONESUBSEA PROCESSING AS—See Schlumberger Limited; *U.S. Public*, pg. 1844
ONESUBSEA UK LIMITED—See Schlumberger Limited; *U.S. Public*, pg. 1844
ONETA COMPANY; *U.S. Private*, pg. 3026
O-NET COMMUNICATIONS (HK) LIMITED—See O-Net Technologies (Group) Limited; *Int'l*, pg. 5502
O-NET COMMUNICATIONS (USA), INC.—See O-Net Technologies (Group) Limited; *Int'l*, pg. 5502
ONE TECH JAPAN, INC.—See Systena Corporation; *Int'l*, pg. 7393
ONE TECHNOLOGIES, LTD.; *U.S. Private*, pg. 3024
ONETEL TELECOMMUNICATION GMBH—See 3U Holding AG; *Int'l*, pg. 10
O-NET, INC.—See Polaris Capital Group Co., Ltd.; *Int'l*, pg. 5907
ONETONE RESEARCH SRL—See Fullsix S.p.A.; *Int'l*, pg. 2843
ONE TO ONE (CAMBODIA) CO., LTD.—See Samart Corporation Public Company Limited; *Int'l*, pg. 6501
ONE TO ONE CONTACTS PUBLIC CO., LTD.—See Samart Corporation Public Company Limited; *Int'l*, pg. 6501
ONETOUCHPOINT CORP.—See ICV Partners, LLC; *U.S. Private*, pg. 2034
ONETOUCHPOINT EAST CORP.—See ICV Partners, LLC; *U.S. Private*, pg. 2034
ONETOUCHPOINT MIDWEST CORP.—See ICV Partners, LLC; *U.S. Private*, pg. 2034
ONETOUCHPOINT WEST CORP. - TEMPE OFFICE—See ICV Partners, LLC; *U.S. Private*, pg. 2034
ONETREE MICRODEVICES, INC.—See Analog Devices, Inc.; *U.S. Public*, pg. 136
ONETRUST LLC; *U.S. Private*, pg. 3026
ONETRUST TECHNOLOGY LIMITED—See OneTrust LLC; *U.S. Private*, pg. 3026
ONET SA; *Int'l*, pg. 5577
O-NET TECHNOLOGIES (GROUP) LIMITED; *Int'l*, pg. 5502
O-NET TECHNOLOGIES (THAILAND) CO., LTD.—See O-Net Technologies (Group) Limited; *Int'l*, pg. 5502
THE ONE UMBRELLA PTY LIMITED—See Ignite Limited; *Int'l*, pg. 3603
ONE UNITED BANK; *U.S. Private*, pg. 3024
ONEUNITED BANK—See One United Bank; *U.S. Private*, pg. 3024
ONE UP CO., LTD.—See Areeya Property Public Company Limited; *Int'l*, pg. 557
ONE UP ENTERPRISES INC.—See Family Federation for World Peace & Unification; *U.S. Private*, pg. 1469

COMPANY NAME INDEX

ONE UP INNOVATIONS, INC.—See Luvu Brands, Inc.; *U.S. Public*, pg. 1349
ONEVIEW GROUP PLC; *Int'l*, pg. 5577
ONEVIEW HEALTHCARE INC—See Oneview Healthcare Plc; *Int'l*, pg. 5577
ONEVIEW HEALTHCARE PLC; *Int'l*, pg. 5577
ONEVIEW HEALTHCARE PTY LIMITED—See Oneview Healthcare Plc; *Int'l*, pg. 5577
ONEVIEW MIDDLE EAST DMCC—See Oneview Healthcare Plc; *Int'l*, pg. 5577
ONEVOICE COMMUNICATIONS, INC.; *U.S. Private*, pg. 3026
ONEVUE HOLDINGS LIMITED—See IRESS Limited; *Int'l*, pg. 3808
ONEWATER MARINE HOLDINGS LLC; *U.S. Private*, pg. 3026
ONEWATER MARINE INC.; *U.S. Public*, pg. 1604
ONE WAY FURNITURE, INC.; *U.S. Private*, pg. 3024
ONEWEST RESOURCES LLC—See First Citizens BancShares, Inc.; *U.S. Public*, pg. 841
ONEWO INC.; *Int'l*, pg. 5577
ONE WORKPLACE; *U.S. Private*, pg. 3024
ONEWORKS BIM TECHNOLOGIES PRIVATE LIMITED—See Pennar Industries Limited; *Int'l*, pg. 5786
ONEWORLD APPAREL, LLC—See Shangying Global Co., Ltd.; *Int'l*, pg. 6784
ONEWORLD COMMUNICATIONS, INC.; *U.S. Private*, pg. 3026
ONE WORLD ENTERPRISES, LLC—See PepsiCo, Inc.; *U.S. Public*, pg. 1669
ONEWORLD HOTEL DESTINATION SERVICE INC.; *Int'l*, pg. 5577
ONE WORLD INC; *U.S. Private*, pg. 3024
ONE WORLD LITHIUM INC.; *Int'l*, pg. 5575
ONE WORLD LOGISTICS MALDIVES (PVT) LTD.—See Hayleys PLC; *Int'l*, pg. 3292
ONE WORLD PRODUCTS, INC.; *U.S. Public*, pg. 1602
ONE WORLD TECHNOLOGIES, INC.—See Techtronic Industries Co., Ltd.; *Int'l*, pg. 7513
ONE WORLD VENTURES, INC.; *U.S. Public*, pg. 1602
ONEX CORPORATION - HIGASHI MATSUYAMA PLANT—See ONEX Corporation; *Int'l*, pg. 5581
ONEX CORPORATION - NAGANO PLANT—See ONEX Corporation; *Int'l*, pg. 5580
ONEX CORPORATION; *Int'l*, pg. 5580
ONEX CORPORATION; *Int'l*, pg. 5577
ONEX CORPORATION - YAMAGUCHI PLANT—See ONEX Corporation; *Int'l*, pg. 5581
ONEXIM GROUP LIMITED; *Int'l*, pg. 5581
ONEX INC.; *U.S. Private*, pg. 3026
ONE XOX SDN. BHD.—See XOX Bhd; *Int'l*, pg. 8536
ONEX PARTNERS LP—See ONEX Corporation; *Int'l*, pg. 5578
ONEX REAL ESTATE PARTNERS—See ONEX Corporation; *Int'l*, pg. 5580
ONE/X; *U.S. Private*, pg. 3024
ONEX TECHNOLOGY CENTER CO., LTD.—See ONEX Corporation; *Int'l*, pg. 5581
ONEY BANK LLC—See Ozon Holdings PLC; *Int'l*, pg. 5679
ONEY BANK SA—See Groupe BPCE; *Int'l*, pg. 3099
ONEY - INSTITUICAO FINANCEIRA DE CREDITO, S.A.—See Auchan Holding S.A.; *Int'l*, pg. 699
ONEY INSURANCE (PCC) LIMITED—See Groupe BPCE; *Int'l*, pg. 3099
ONEY MAGYARORSZAG ZRT.—See Auchan Holding S.A.; *Int'l*, pg. 699
ONEY POLSKA S.A.—See Groupe BPCE; *Int'l*, pg. 3099
ONE ZERO COMMUNICATIONS PTY. LTD.—See Vita Group Limited; *Int'l*, pg. 8257
ONEZERO COMPANY LTD.—See Commercial Bank of Ceylon PLC; *Int'l*, pg. 1715
ONFIDO LTD; *Int'l*, pg. 5581
ONFIELD APPAREL GROUP LLC—See Leonard Green & Partners, L.P.; *U.S. Private*, pg. 2424
ON FINANCE SA—See EFG International AG; *Int'l*, pg. 2321
ONFOLIO HOLDINGS INC.; *U.S. Public*, pg. 1604
ONFORCE, INC.—See Adecco Group AG; *Int'l*, pg. 141
ONFORCE SOLAR, INC.—See Hanwha Group; *Int'l*, pg. 3264
ON GAME NETWORK INC.—See CJ Corporation; *Int'l*, pg. 1634
ONGC CAMPOS LTDA.—See Oil & Natural Gas Corporation Limited; *Int'l*, pg. 5534
ONGC MANGALORE PETROCHEMICALS LTD.—See Oil & Natural Gas Corporation Limited; *Int'l*, pg. 5534
ONGC NILE GANGA B.V.—See Oil & Natural Gas Corporation Limited; *Int'l*, pg. 5534
ONGC NILE GANGA (SAN CRISTOBAL) B.V.—See Oil & Natural Gas Corporation Limited; *Int'l*, pg. 5534
ONGC VIDESH ATLANTIC INC.—See Oil & Natural Gas Corporation Limited; *Int'l*, pg. 5534
ONGC VIDESH LTD.—See Oil & Natural Gas Corporation Limited; *Int'l*, pg. 5534
ONGC VIDESH SINGAPORE PTE. LTD.—See Oil & Natural Gas Corporation Limited; *Int'l*, pg. 5534

ONGUARD INDUSTRIES LLC—See Ansell Limited; *Int'l*, pg. 478
ONGWEOWEH CORP.; *U.S. Private*, pg. 3026
ON HOLDING AG; *Int'l*, pg. 5572
ONICON INCORPORATED—See Harbour Group Industries, Inc.; *U.S. Private*, pg. 1860
ON IDEAS, INC.; *U.S. Private*, pg. 3018
ONI HOLDINGS AD; *Int'l*, pg. 5581
ONIN STAFFING; *U.S. Private*, pg. 3026
ONION GLOBAL LIMITED; *Int'l*, pg. 5581
ONION, INC.; *U.S. Private*, pg. 3026
ONIONTECH CO. LIMITED—See Edition Ltd.; *Int'l*, pg. 2311
ONI RISK PARTNERS, INC.—See Keystone Group, L.P.; *U.S. Private*, pg. 2299
ONIRIS S.A.—See Perceva SAS; *Int'l*, pg. 5797
ONISI FOODS CO., LTD.—See Kameda Seika Co., Ltd.; *Int'l*, pg. 4061
ONITELECOM - INFOCOMUNICACOES, S.A.—See The Riverside Company; *U.S. Private*, pg. 4109
ONITY CO., LIMITED—See Carrier Global Corporation; *U.S. Public*, pg. 443
ONITY GROUP INC.; *U.S. Public*, pg. 1604
ONITY, INC.—See Carrier Global Corporation; *U.S. Public*, pg. 441
ONITY LIMITED—See Carrier Global Corporation; *U.S. Public*, pg. 443
ONITY LTDA—See Carrier Global Corporation; *U.S. Public*, pg. 443
ONITY PTY LTD—See Carrier Global Corporation; *U.S. Public*, pg. 444
ONITY SAS—See Carrier Global Corporation; *U.S. Public*, pg. 444
ONITY, S.L.U.—See Carrier Global Corporation; *U.S. Public*, pg. 444
ONIVA ONLINE GROUP EUROPE AB; *Int'l*, pg. 5581
ONIX NETWORKING, CORP.—See Tailwind Capital Group, LLC; *U.S. Private*, pg. 3924
ONIX SYSTEMS INC.—See Thermo Fisher Scientific Inc.; *U.S. Public*, pg. 2149
ONKODATAMED GMBH—See IQVIA Holdings Inc.; *U.S. Public*, pg. 1170
ONKO SERVICE GMBH & CO. KG—See Medios AG; *Int'l*, pg. 4778
ONKURE, INC.—See OnKure Therapeutics, Inc.; *U.S. Public*, pg. 1605
ONKURE THERAPEUTICS, INC.; *U.S. Public*, pg. 1605
ONKYO HOME ENTERTAINMENT CORP.; *Int'l*, pg. 5581
ONKYO U.S.A. CORPORATION—See Onkyo Home Entertainment Corp.; *Int'l*, pg. 5581
ONLINE 401(K); *U.S. Private*, pg. 3026
ONLINE BLOCKCHAIN PLC; *Int'l*, pg. 5581
ONLINE BRANDS NORDIC AB; *Int'l*, pg. 5581
ONLINE COMMERCE GROUP, LLC; *U.S. Private*, pg. 3026
ONLINE COMPUTER LIBRARY CENTER, INC.; *U.S. Private*, pg. 3026
ON-LINE COMPUTER PRODUCTS INC.; *U.S. Private*, pg. 3018
ONLINE CONSULTING, INC.; *U.S. Private*, pg. 3027
ONLINE DISRUPTIVE TECHNOLOGIES, INC.; *U.S. Public*, pg. 1605
ONLINE ENGINEERING GMBH—See ELMOS Semiconductor AG; *Int'l*, pg. 2368
ONLINEFORMAPRO S.A.; *Int'l*, pg. 5582
ONLINE INSIGHT INC.—See HealthTrio, LLC; *U.S. Private*, pg. 1898
ON LINE LOTTERY SERVICES (PROPRIETARY) LIMITED—See CONDUIT CAPITAL LIMITED; *Int'l*, pg. 1766
ONLINE MARKETING SOLUTIONS AG; *Int'l*, pg. 5581
ONLINE MEDIA COMMUNICATIONS DESIGN GMBH—See Berndorf AG; *Int'l*, pg. 987
ONLINE MEDIA SOLUTIONS LIMITED—See Brightcom Group Ltd.; *Int'l*, pg. 1162
ONLINE PACKAGING LIMITED—See Macfarlane Group PLC; *Int'l*, pg. 4622
ONLINE POUNDSHOP LIMITED—See Steinhoff International Holdings N.V.; *Int'l*, pg. 7194
ONLINE-REDEFINED, INC.; *U.S. Private*, pg. 3027
ONLINE REWARDS; *U.S. Private*, pg. 3027
ONLINE SAS—See LVMH Moet Hennessy Louis Vuitton SE; *Int'l*, pg. 4592
ONLINE SECURITY SERVICES LIMITED—See Freightways Group Limited; *Int'l*, pg. 2772
ONLINE—See Information Today Inc.; *U.S. Private*, pg. 2073
ONLINE STORES, INC.; *U.S. Private*, pg. 3027
ONLINE TRANSPORT SYSTEM, INC.; *U.S. Private*, pg. 3027
ONLINE VACATION CENTER HOLDINGS CORP.; *U.S. Public*, pg. 1605
ONLINE VACATION CENTER, INC.—See Online Vacation Center Holdings Corp.; *U.S. Public*, pg. 1605
ON LOCATION EVENTS, LLC—See Silver Lake Group, LLC; *U.S. Private*, pg. 3654
ONLOCATION, INC.—See System One Holdings, LLC; *U.S. Private*, pg. 3907
ONLY CORPORATION; *Int'l*, pg. 5582

ONLY THE BEST, INC.; *U.S. Private*, pg. 3027
ONLY THE BEST (PTE) LTD.—See Workforce Holdings Ltd.; *Int'l*, pg. 8455
ONLY WORLD GROUP HOLDINGS BERHAD; *Int'l*, pg. 5582
ONM ENVIRONMENTAL, INC.—See BioLargo, Inc.; *U.S. Public*, pg. 337
ONMOBILE BANGLADESH PRIVATE LIMITED—See OnMobile Global Limited; *Int'l*, pg. 5582
ONMOBILE GLOBAL LIMITED - AUSTRALIA—See OnMobile Global Limited; *Int'l*, pg. 5582
ONMOBILE GLOBAL LIMITED; *Int'l*, pg. 5582
ONMOBILE GLOBAL S.A.—See OnMobile Global Limited; *Int'l*, pg. 5582
ONMOBILE GLOBAL SOLUTIONS CANADA LIMITED—See OnMobile Global Limited; *Int'l*, pg. 5582
ONMOBILE LIVE INC.—See OnMobile Global Limited; *Int'l*, pg. 5582
ONMOBILE S.A.—See OnMobile Global Limited; *Int'l*, pg. 5582
ONMOBILE SERVICIOS CORPORATIVOS DE TELEFONIA S.A. DE C.V.—See OnMobile Global Limited; *Int'l*, pg. 5582
ONMOBILE SINGAPORE PTE. LTD—See OnMobile Global Limited; *Int'l*, pg. 5582
ONMOBILE SYSTEMS, INC.; *U.S. Private*, pg. 3027
ONMOBILE USA LLC—See OnMobile Global Limited; *Int'l*, pg. 5582
ONMOBILE USA—See OnMobile Global Limited; *Int'l*, pg. 5582
ON.NET—See Telekom Slovenije, d.d.; *Int'l*, pg. 7538
ON-NET SURVEILLANCE SYSTEMS INC.—See Hexagon AB; *Int'l*, pg. 3369
ONNINEN AB—See Kesko Corporation; *Int'l*, pg. 4142
ONNINEN AS—See Kesko Corporation; *Int'l*, pg. 4142
ONNINEN AS—See Kesko Corporation; *Int'l*, pg. 4142
ONNINEN OY—See Kesko Corporation; *Int'l*, pg. 4142
ONNINEN SIA—See Kesko Corporation; *Int'l*, pg. 4142
ONNINEN SP. Z O.O.—See Kesko Corporation; *Int'l*, pg. 4142
ONNINEN UAB—See Kesko Corporation; *Int'l*, pg. 4142
ONNO BEHRENDS GMBH & CO. KG—See Laurens Spethmann Holding Aktiengesellschaft & Co. KG; *Int'l*, pg. 4424
ONNURI INDUSTRIAL MACHINERY CO. LTD—See Alfa Laval AB; *Int'l*, pg. 312
ONODA CHEMICAL INDUSTRY CO., LTD—See Taiheiyo Cement Corporation; *Int'l*, pg. 7412
ONODA CHEMICO CO., LTD.—See Taiheiyo Cement Corporation; *Int'l*, pg. 7412
ONODERA GROUP CO., LTD.; *Int'l*, pg. 5582
ONOE ROPE ENGINEERING, LTD.—See Kobelco Wire Co Ltd; *Int'l*, pg. 4221
ONOKEN CO., LTD.; *Int'l*, pg. 5583
ONOKEN OKINAWA CO., LTD.—See Onoken Co., Ltd.; *Int'l*, pg. 5583
ONOMICHI KUMIKA INDUSTRY CO., LTD.—See Kumiai Chemical Industry Co., Ltd.; *Int'l*, pg. 4330
ONOMICHI PRESS KOGYO CO., LTD.—See Press Kogyo Co., Ltd.; *Int'l*, pg. 5964
ONONDAGA COUNTY RESOURCE RECOVERY AGENCY; *U.S. Private*, pg. 3027
ONONDAGA COUNTY WATER AUTHORITY; *U.S. Private*, pg. 3027
ONO PHARMACEUTICAL CO., LTD.; *Int'l*, pg. 5582
ONO PHARMA KOREA CO., LTD.—See Ono Pharmaceutical Co., Ltd.; *Int'l*, pg. 5582
ONO PHARMA TAIWAN CO., LTD.—See Ono Pharmaceutical Co., Ltd.; *Int'l*, pg. 5582
ONO PHARMA UK LTD.—See Ono Pharmaceutical Co., Ltd.; *Int'l*, pg. 5582
ONO PHARMA USA, INC.—See Ono Pharmaceutical Co., Ltd.; *Int'l*, pg. 5582
ONORYO CO., LTD.—See RAITO KOGYO Co., Ltd.; *Int'l*, pg. 6191
ONO SANGYO CO., LTD.—See Takashima & Co., Ltd.; *Int'l*, pg. 7435
ONO SOKKI CO., LTD.; *Int'l*, pg. 5582
ONO SOKKI INDIA PRIVATE LTD.—See Ono Sokki Co., Ltd.; *Int'l*, pg. 5582
ONO SOKKI SHANGHAI TECHNOLOGY CO., LTD.—See Ono Sokki Co., Ltd.; *Int'l*, pg. 5582
ONO SOKKI TECHNOLOGY INC.—See Ono Sokki Co., Ltd.; *Int'l*, pg. 5582
ONO SOKKI (THAILAND) CO., LTD.—See Ono Sokki Co., Ltd.; *Int'l*, pg. 5582
ONO TRANSPORT SERVICES, INC.; *U.S. Private*, pg. 3027
ONPAY SOLUTIONS, INC.—See Medius Sverige AB; *Int'l*, pg. 4784
ONPEAK LLC—See Viad Corp.; *U.S. Public*, pg. 2291
ONPLATINUM ICT PTY. LTD.—See Comms Group Ltd; *Int'l*, pg. 1720
ONPOINT COMMUNITY CREDIT UNION; *U.S. Private*, pg. 3027
ONPOINT CONSULTING, INC.—See Publicis Groupe S.A.; *Int'l*, pg. 6104
ON-POINT GROUP, LLC; *U.S. Private*, pg. 3018

ON-POINT GROUP, LLC CORPORATE AFFILIATIONS

ONPOINT ONCOLOGY, INC.—See RxVantage, Inc.; *U.S. Private*, pg. 3509
ONPOINT UNDERWRITING, INC.—See Brown & Brown, Inc.; *U.S. Public*, pg. 401
ONPOINT WARRANTY SOLUTIONS, LLC; *U.S. Private*, pg. 3027
ONP OWNER LLC—See Ladder Capital Corp.; *U.S. Public*, pg. 1288
ONPRESS PCB LIMITED; *Int'l*, pg. 5583
ONPR GMBH—See OnPR; *U.S. Private*, pg. 3027
ONPR—See OnPR; *U.S. Private*, pg. 3027
ONPR; *U.S. Private*, pg. 3027
ON Q FINANCIAL, INC.; *U.S. Private*, pg. 3018
ON-Q/LEGRAND—See Legrand S.A.; *Int'l*, pg. 4445
ONQ SOLUTIONS, INC.; *U.S. Private*, pg. 3027
ONQUEST CANADA, ULC—See Primoris Services Corporation; *U.S. Public*, pg. 1718
ONQUEST, INC.—See Primoris Services Corporation; *U.S. Public*, pg. 1718
ONQUEST LABORATORIES LTD.; *Int'l*, pg. 5583
ONRAD, INC.; *U.S. Private*, pg. 3028
ONRAMP ACCESS, LLC—See GI Manager L.P.; *U.S. Private*, pg. 1692
ON-RAMP WIRELESS, INC.; *U.S. Private*, pg. 3019
ONS ACQUISITION CORP.; *U.S. Public*, pg. 1605
ON SEMICONDUCTOR CONNECTIVITY SOLUTIONS, INC.—See ON Semiconductor Corporation; *U.S. Public*, pg. 1600
ON SEMICONDUCTOR CORPORATION; *U.S. Public*, pg. 1600
ON SEMICONDUCTOR CZECH REPUBLIC A.S.—See ON Semiconductor Corporation; *U.S. Public*, pg. 1600
ON SEMICONDUCTOR FRANCE SAS—See ON Semiconductor Corporation; *U.S. Public*, pg. 1600
ON SEMICONDUCTOR GERMANY GMBH—See ON Semiconductor Corporation; *U.S. Public*, pg. 1600
ON SEMICONDUCTOR HONG KONG DESIGN LTD.—See ON Semiconductor Corporation; *U.S. Public*, pg. 1600
ON SEMICONDUCTOR IMAGE SENSOR BVBA—See ON Semiconductor Corporation; *U.S. Public*, pg. 1600
ON SEMICONDUCTOR ITALY S.R.L—See ON Semiconductor Corporation; *U.S. Public*, pg. 1600
ON SEMICONDUCTOR LEASING BVBA—See ON Semiconductor Corporation; *U.S. Public*, pg. 1600
ON SEMICONDUCTOR SLOVAKIA A.S.—See ON Semiconductor Corporation; *U.S. Public*, pg. 1600
ON SEMICONDUCTOR—See ON Semiconductor Corporation; *U.S. Public*, pg. 1600
ON SEMICONDUCTOR—See ON Semiconductor Corporation; *U.S. Public*, pg. 1600
ON SEMICONDUCTOR SWITZERLAND S.A.—See ON Semiconductor Corporation; *U.S. Public*, pg. 1600
ON SEMICONDUCTOR TECHNOLOGY INDIA PRIVATE LIMITED—See ON Semiconductor Corporation; *U.S. Public*, pg. 1600
ON SEMICONDUCTOR TECHNOLOGY JAPAN LTD.—See ON Semiconductor Corporation; *U.S. Public*, pg. 1600
ON SERVICES HOUSTON—See Viad Corp.; *U.S. Public*, pg. 2291
ON SERVICES—See Viad Corp.; *U.S. Public*, pg. 2291
ONSET MEDICAL, CORP.—See Terumo Corporation; *Int'l*, pg. 7570
ONSET TECHNOLOGY INC.—See Cukierman & Co. Investment House Ltd.; *Int'l*, pg. 1876
ONSET VENTURES; *U.S. Private*, pg. 3028
ONSHAPE INC.—See PTC Inc.; *U.S. Public*, pg. 1734
ON SIDE RESTORATION SERVICES LTD.; *Int'l*, pg. 5573
ONSIDE SPORTS GMBH—See Vivendi SE; *Int'l*, pg. 8278
ONSITE CENTRAL LIMITED—See Arjun Infrastructure Partners Limited; *Int'l*, pg. 568
ONSITE COMPUTER SERVICES—See Enterprise Onsite Services Co.; *U.S. Private*, pg. 1404
ONSITE ELECTRO SERVICES PVT. LTD.; *Int'l*, pg. 5583
ONSITE ENERGY CORPORATION—See Willdan Group, Inc.; *U.S. Public*, pg. 2371
ONSITE ENERGY, INC.—See NRG Energy, Inc.; *U.S. Public*, pg. 1550
ON-SITE FUEL SERVICE; *U.S. Private*, pg. 3019
ON SITE GAS SYSTEMS, INC.; *U.S. Private*, pg. 3018
ONSITE HOLDING LLC—See Walgreens Boots Alliance, Inc.; *U.S. Public*, pg. 2322
ONSITE INNOVATIONS, INC.—See Athletico Ltd.; *U.S. Private*, pg. 368
ON SITE MANAGEMENT INC.; *U.S. Private*, pg. 3018
ON-SITE MANAGER, INC.—See Thoma Bravo, L.P.; *U.S. Private*, pg. 4153
ONSITE OCCMED, P.A.—See Select Medical Holdings Corporation; *U.S. Public*, pg. 1858
ONSITE OCCUPATIONAL HEALTH & SAFETY, INC.; *U.S. Private*, pg. 3028
ON SITE POWER CO., LTD.—See Idemitsu Kosan Co., Ltd.; *Int'l*, pg. 3592
ON-SITE-SOLUTIONS, INC—See The Judge Group, Inc.; *U.S. Private*, pg. 4063
ONSLOW BAY FINANCIAL LLC—See Annaly Capital Management, Inc.; *U.S. Public*, pg. 138
ONSOLVE, LLC—See BC Partners LLP; *Int'l*, pg. 924

ONSPEX—See CSA Group; *Int'l*, pg. 1861
ONSPOT OF NORTH AMERICA, INC.—See VBG Group AB; *Int'l*, pg. 8138
ONSPOT S.A.R.L.—See VBG Group AB; *Int'l*, pg. 8138
ONSTAR, LLC—See General Motors Company; *U.S. Public*, pg. 926
ONSTREAM MEDIA CORPORATION; *U.S. Private*, pg. 3028
ONSTREAM PIPELINE INSPECTION SERVICES INC.—See Mistras Group, Inc.; *U.S. Public*, pg. 1451
ONTAP—See Decker Creative Marketing; *U.S. Private*, pg. 1187
ON TARGET HEALTH, LLC; *U.S. Private*, pg. 3018
ONTARGETJOBS CANADA, INC.—See Ziff Davis, Inc.; *U.S. Public*, pg. 2404
ONTARGETJOBS, INC.—See Ziff Davis, Inc.; *U.S. Public*, pg. 2404
ON TARGET PROFESSIONALS; *U.S. Private*, pg. 3018
ON-TARGET SUPPLIES & LOGISTICS; *U.S. Private*, pg. 3019
ONTARIO DODGE, INC.—See AutoNation, Inc.; *U.S. Public*, pg. 236
ONTARIO DRIVE & GEAR LIMITED; *Int'l*, pg. 5583
ONTARIO GLOVE & SAFETY, INC.—See Delta Plus Group; *Int'l*, pg. 2020
ONTARIO HOSPITALITY PROPERTIES LIMITED PARTNERSHIP—See InnSuites Hospitality Trust; *U.S. Public*, pg. 1128
ONTARIO HOSPITALITY PROPERTIES L.L.L.P.—See InnSuites Hospitality Trust; *U.S. Public*, pg. 1128
ONTARIO KNIFE COMPANY—See Blue Ridge Knives, Inc.; *U.S. Private*, pg. 592
ONTARIO LIMITED—See Allianz SE; *Int'l*, pg. 355
ONTARIO LOTTERY & GAMING CORPORATION; *Int'l*, pg. 5583
ONTARIO MIDLAND RAILROAD CORP.—See Livonia, Avon & Lakeville Railroad Corp.; *U.S. Public*, pg. 2474
ONTARIO MILLS—See Simon Property Group, Inc.; *U.S. Public*, pg. 1882
ONTARIO MUNICIPAL EMPLOYEES RETIREMENT SYSTEM; *Int'l*, pg. 5583
ONTARIO NISSAN INC.—See New Age Investments Inc.; *U.S. Private*, pg. 2892
ONTARIO NORTHLAND TRANSPORTATION COMMISSION; *Int'l*, pg. 5585
ONTARIO POWER GENERATION, INC.; *Int'l*, pg. 5585
ONTARIO REFRIGERATION SERVICE; *U.S. Private*, pg. 3028
ONTARIO SEED COMPANY LTD.; *Int'l*, pg. 5585
ONTARIO SYSTEMS, LLC—See New Mountain Capital LLC; *U.S. Private*, pg. 2903
ONTARIO TEACHERS' PENSION PLAN; *Int'l*, pg. 5585
ONTARIO TELEPHONE COMPANY, INC.—See Keystone Group, L.P.; *U.S. Private*, pg. 2299
ONTELLUS—See Aquiline Capital Partners LLC; *U.S. Private*, pg. 304
ONTERA MODULAR CARPETS PTY. LIMITED—See Bremworth Limited; *Int'l*, pg. 1145
ONTERRAN LIMITED; *Int'l*, pg. 5591
ONTEX BVBA—See Ontex Group N.V.; *Int'l*, pg. 5591
ONTEX CZ SRO—See Ontex Group N.V.; *Int'l*, pg. 5591
ONTEX FRANCE SAS—See Ontex Group N.V.; *Int'l*, pg. 5591
ONTEX GROUP N.V.; *Int'l*, pg. 5591
ONTEX HEALTHCARE DEUTSCHLAND GMBH—See Ontex Group N.V.; *Int'l*, pg. 5591
ONTEX HYGIENARTIKEL DEUTSCHLAND GMBH—See Ontex Group N.V.; *Int'l*, pg. 5591
ONTEX HYGIENIC DISPOSABLES PLC—See Ontex Group N.V.; *Int'l*, pg. 5591
ONTEX HYGIENIC DISPOSABLES (SHANGHAI) LTD.—See Ontex Group N.V.; *Int'l*, pg. 5591
ONTEX INTERNATIONAL BVBA—See Ontex Group N.V.; *Int'l*, pg. 5591
ONTEX ITALIA S.R.L.—See Ontex Group N.V.; *Int'l*, pg. 5591
ONTEX MANUFACTURING ITALY S.R.L.—See Ontex Group N.V.; *Int'l*, pg. 5591
ONTEX MANUFACTURING PTY LTD—See Ontex Group N.V.; *Int'l*, pg. 5591
ONTEX MAYEN GMBH—See Ontex Group N.V.; *Int'l*, pg. 5591
ONTEX MEXICO OPERATIONS S.A. DE C.V.—See Ontex Group N.V.; *Int'l*, pg. 5591
ONTEX OPERATIONS USA, LCC—See Ontex Group N.V.; *Int'l*, pg. 5591
ONTEX PAKISTAN LTD.—See Ontex Group N.V.; *Int'l*, pg. 5591
ONTEX RETAIL UK LTD.—See Ontex Group N.V.; *Int'l*, pg. 5591
ONTEX RU LLC—See Ontex Group N.V.; *Int'l*, pg. 5591
ON TEXTILE CHEMICALS (SHANGHAI) CO., LTD.—See Nagase & Co., Ltd.; *Int'l*, pg. 5128
ONTEX TUKETIM. URN. SAN. VE TIC. AS—See Ontex Group N.V.; *Int'l*, pg. 5591
ONTEX UKRAINE LLC—See Ontex Group N.V.; *Int'l*, pg. 5591
ON THE BEACH GROUP PLC; *Int'l*, pg. 5573

ON THE BEACH LIMITED—See On the Beach Group plc; *Int'l*, pg. 5573
ONTHEHOUSE HOLDINGS LIMITED; *Int'l*, pg. 5591
ONTHEMARKET PLC—See CoStar Group, Inc.; *U.S. Public*, pg. 586
ON THE MOVE CORP.; *U.S. Private*, pg. 3018
ONTHENET—See Aware Super Pty Ltd; *Int'l*, pg. 752
ONTHENET—See Macquarie Group Limited; *Int'l*, pg. 4629
ON THE SCENE; *U.S. Private*, pg. 3018
ONTIC ENGINEERING & MANUFACTURING, INC.—See CVC Capital Partners SICAV-FIS S.A.; *Int'l*, pg. 1884
ONTIC ENGINEERING & MANUFACTURING UK LIMITED—See CVC Capital Partners SICAV-FIS S.A.; *Int'l*, pg. 1884
ONTIC FINSERVE LIMITED; *Int'l*, pg. 5591
ONTILITY LLC—See N.F. Smith & Associates, LP; *U.S. Private*, pg. 2828
ONTIME AUTOMOTIVE LIMITED—See The Bidvest Group Limited; *Int'l*, pg. 7626
ON TIME EXPRESS, INC.—See Radiant Logistics, Inc.; *U.S. Public*, pg. 1759
ON-TIME PAYROLL, INC.—See DiVirgilio Insurance & Financial Group; *U.S. Private*, pg. 1244
ON-TIME STEEL MANAGEMENT HOLDING, INC.—See INNOVATE Corp.; *U.S. Public*, pg. 1126
ON TIME TRUCKING, INC.—See The RK Logistics Group, Inc.; *U.S. Private*, pg. 4110
ONTODIA, INC.—See Cox Enterprises, Inc.; *U.S. Private*, pg. 1078
ONTO INNOVATION EUROPE, B.V.—See Onto Innovation Inc.; *U.S. Public*, pg. 1605
ONTO INNOVATION INC.; *U.S. Public*, pg. 1605
ONTO INNOVATION SOUTHEAST ASIA PTE. LIMITED—See Onto Innovation Inc.; *U.S. Public*, pg. 1605
ON TOP OF THE WORLD INC.; *U.S. Private*, pg. 3018
ONTOR LTD.; *Int'l*, pg. 5591
ONTOTEXT AD—See Sirma Group Holding JSC; *Int'l*, pg. 6962
ON-TRACK COMPUTER TRAINING LTD—See Quizam Media Corporation; *Int'l*, pg. 6165
ON-TRACK CORPORATE TRAINING LTD.—See Quizam Media Corporation; *Int'l*, pg. 6165
ON-TRACK FINANCIAL SOLUTIONS PTY. LTD.—See Azimut Holding SpA; *Int'l*, pg. 779
ONTRACK GLOBAL SERVICES LTD.—See Ontrack Systems Ltd; *Int'l*, pg. 5591
ON TRACK INNOVATIONS, LTD.; *U.S. Public*, pg. 5573
ONTRACKS EAM CONSULTING LTD.—See Bentley Systems, Inc.; *U.S. Public*, pg. 297
ONTRACK SYSTEMS (AUST.) PTY. LTD.—See Ontrack Systems Ltd; *Int'l*, pg. 5591
ONTRACK SYSTEMS BV.—See Ontrack Systems Ltd; *Int'l*, pg. 5592
ONTRACK SYSTEMS LTD; *Int'l*, pg. 5591
ONTRACK SYSTEMS (UK) LTD—See Ontrack Systems Ltd; *Int'l*, pg. 5591
ONTRAK, INC.; *U.S. Public*, pg. 1605
ONTRAPORT; *U.S. Private*, pg. 3028
ONTRAS GASTRANSPORT GMBH—See EnBW Energie Baden-Wurttemberg AG; *Int'l*, pg. 2400
ONTUSTIK ZHARYK TRANZIT LLP—See Kazakhstan Utility Systems LLP; *Int'l*, pg. 4102
ONVALLA COMPANY LIMITED—See Alla Public Company Limited; *Int'l*, pg. 332
ONVEST OY; *Int'l*, pg. 5592
ONWARD BEACH RESORT GUAM, INC.—See Onward Holdings Co., Ltd.; *Int'l*, pg. 5592
ONWARD CAPITAL LLC; *U.S. Private*, pg. 3028
ONWARD CREATIVE CENTER CO., LTD.—See Onward Holdings Co., Ltd.; *Int'l*, pg. 5592
ONWARD FASHION TRADING CO., LTD.—See Onward Holdings Co., Ltd.; *Int'l*, pg. 5592
ONWARD GOLF RESORT GUAM, INC.—See Onward Holdings Co., Ltd.; *Int'l*, pg. 5592
ONWARD HOLDINGS CO., LTD.; *Int'l*, pg. 5592
ONWARD INTERNATIONAL FASHION CO., LTD.—See Onward Holdings Co., Ltd.; *Int'l*, pg. 5592
ONWARD ITALIA S.P.A.—See Onward Holdings Co., Ltd.; *Int'l*, pg. 5592
ONWARD J BRIDGE CO., LTD.—See Onward Holdings Co., Ltd.; *Int'l*, pg. 5593
ONWARD KASHIYAMA CO., LTD.—See Onward Holdings Co., Ltd.; *Int'l*, pg. 5593
ONWARD KASHIYAMA HONG KONG LTD.—See Onward Holdings Co., Ltd.; *Int'l*, pg. 5593
ONWARD KASHIYAMA KOREA CO., LTD.—See Onward Holdings Co., Ltd.; *Int'l*, pg. 5593
ONWARD KASHIYAMA SINGAPORE PTE. CO., LTD.—See Onward Holdings Co., Ltd.; *Int'l*, pg. 5592
ONWARD KASHIYAMA VIETNAM CO., LTD.—See Onward Holdings Co., Ltd.; *Int'l*, pg. 5593
ONWARD LEASING & CREDIT SDN. BHD.—See Oriental Holdings Berhad; *Int'l*, pg. 5624
ONWARD LIFE DESIGN NETWORK CO., LTD.—See Onward Holdings Co., Ltd.; *Int'l*, pg. 5593
ONWARD LUXURY GROUP S.P.A.; *Int'l*, pg. 5593
ONWARD MEDICAL N.V.; *Int'l*, pg. 5593

ONWARD PERSONAL STYLE CO., LTD.—See Onward Holdings Co., Ltd.; *Int'l*, pg. 5593
ONWARD PERSONAL STYLE CO, LTD—See Onward Holdings Co., Ltd.; *Int'l*, pg. 5593
ONWARD RESORT & GOLF CO., LTD.—See Onward Holdings Co., Ltd.; *Int'l*, pg. 5593
ONWARD RETAIL L.L.C.—See Onward Holdings Co., Ltd.; *Int'l*, pg. 5593
ONWARD—See Richelieu Hardware Ltd.; *Int'l*, pg. 6331
ONWARD TECHNOLOGIES GMBH—See Onward Technologies Ltd.; *Int'l*, pg. 5593
ONWARD TECHNOLOGIES LTD.; *Int'l*, pg. 5593
ONWARD TRADING CO., LTD.—See Onward Holdings Co., Ltd.; *Int'l*, pg. 5593
ONWARD TRADING (SHANGHAI) CO., LTD.—See Onward Holdings Co., Ltd.; *Int'l*, pg. 5593
ONWARD U.S.A. L.L.C.—See Onward Holdings Co., Ltd.; *Int'l*, pg. 5593
ONWERK GMBH—See NFON AG; *Int'l*, pg. 5253
ONX ENTERPRISE SOLUTIONS LTD.—See Macquarie Group Limited; *Int'l*, pg. 4628
ONXEO S.A.; *Int'l*, pg. 5593
ONXEO US INC.—See Onxeo S.A.; *Int'l*, pg. 5593
ON-X LIFE TECHNOLOGIES, INC.—See Artivion, Inc.; *U.S. Public*, pg. 208
ONYX EST S.A.—See Veolia Environnement S.A.; *Int'l*, pg. 8153
ONYX FOR ENGINEERING & INTEGRATED SOLUTIONS PLC—See Endress+Hauser (International) Holding AG; *Int'l*, pg. 2408
THE ONYX GROUP; *U.S. Private*, pg. 4088
ONYX HEALTHCARE EUROPE B.V.—See ASUSTeK Computer Inc.; *Int'l*, pg. 664
ONYX HEALTHCARE USA, INC.—See ASUSTeK Computer Inc.; *Int'l*, pg. 664
ONYX INFOSOFT; *U.S. Private*, pg. 3028
ONYX INTERNET LIMITED; *Int'l*, pg. 5593
ONYX MEDICAL LLC—See TA Associates, Inc.; *U.S. Private*, pg. 3918
ONYX & PEARL SURGICAL SUITES, LLC—See Tenet Healthcare Corporation; *U.S. Public*, pg. 2005
ONYX POWER INC.—See Eaton Corporation plc; *Int'l*, pg. 2282
ONYX ROHR- UND KANAL-SERVICE GMBH & CO. KG—See Veolia Environnement S.A.; *Int'l*, pg. 8160
ONYX SCIENTIFIC LIMITED—See Ipca Laboratories Ltd.; *Int'l*, pg. 3796
ONYX SPECIALTY PAPERS, INC.; *U.S. Private*, pg. 3028
ONYX TA-HO ENVIRONMENTAL SERVICES CO. LTD.—See Taiwan Cement Corporation; *Int'l*, pg. 7419
ONYX TA-HO ENVIRONMENTAL SERVICES CO. LTD.—See Veolia Environnement S.A.; *Int'l*, pg. 8153
ONZIMA VENTURES PLC; *Int'l*, pg. 5593
OOBE, INC.; *U.S. Private*, pg. 3028
OOCL (ASIA PACIFIC) LTD—See China COSCO Shipping Corporation Limited; *Int'l*, pg. 1495
OOCL AUSTRALIA PTY LTD—See China COSCO Shipping Corporation Limited; *Int'l*, pg. 1495
OOCL (BENELUX) NV—See China COSCO Shipping Corporation Limited; *Int'l*, pg. 1495
OOCL (CANADA) INC.—See China COSCO Shipping Corporation Limited; *Int'l*, pg. 1495
OOCL CHINA DOMESTICS LTD—See China COSCO Shipping Corporation Limited; *Int'l*, pg. 1495
OOCL (DENMARK) A/S—See China COSCO Shipping Corporation Limited; *Int'l*, pg. 1495
OOCL (DEUTSCHLAND) GMBH—See China COSCO Shipping Corporation Limited; *Int'l*, pg. 1495
OOCL (EUROPE) LTD—See China COSCO Shipping Corporation Limited; *Int'l*, pg. 1495
OOCL (FINLAND) LTD OY—See China COSCO Shipping Corporation Limited; *Int'l*, pg. 1495
OOCL (FRANCE) S.A.—See China COSCO Shipping Corporation Limited; *Int'l*, pg. 1495
OOCL (INDIA) PRIVATE LTD—See China COSCO Shipping Corporation Limited; *Int'l*, pg. 1495
OOCL (ITALY) S.R.L.—See China COSCO Shipping Corporation Limited; *Int'l*, pg. 1495
OOCL (KOREA) LTD—See China COSCO Shipping Corporation Limited; *Int'l*, pg. 1495
OOCL LOGISTICS (AUSTRALIA) PTY. LTD.—See China COSCO Shipping Corporation Limited; *Int'l*, pg. 1496
OOCL LOGISTICS (CHINA) LTD—See China COSCO Shipping Corporation Limited; *Int'l*, pg. 1496
OOCL LOGISTICS (EUROPE) LTD - BREMEN BRANCH—See China COSCO Shipping Corporation Limited; *Int'l*, pg. 1496
OOCL LOGISTICS (EUROPE) LTD - ROTTERDAM BRANCH—See China COSCO Shipping Corporation Limited; *Int'l*, pg. 1496
OOCL LOGISTICS (EUROPE) LTD—See China COSCO Shipping Corporation Limited; *Int'l*, pg. 1496
OOCL LOGISTICS (INDIA) PRIVATE LIMITED—See China COSCO Shipping Corporation Limited; *Int'l*, pg. 1496
OOCL LOGISTICS (JAPAN) LTD—See China COSCO Shipping Corporation Limited; *Int'l*, pg. 1496
OOCL LOGISTICS (KOREA) LTD—See China COSCO Shipping Corporation Limited; *Int'l*, pg. 1496

OOCL LOGISTICS LIMITED—See China COSCO Shipping Corporation Limited; *Int'l*, pg. 1495
OOCL LOGISTICS PHILIPPINES INC.—See China COSCO Shipping Corporation Limited; *Int'l*, pg. 1495
OOCL LOGISTICS (SINGAPORE) PTE. LTD.—See China COSCO Shipping Corporation Limited; *Int'l*, pg. 1496
OOCL LOGISTICS (TAIWAN) LTD—See China COSCO Shipping Corporation Limited; *Int'l*, pg. 1496
OOCL LOGISTICS (THAILAND) LTD—See China COSCO Shipping Corporation Limited; *Int'l*, pg. 1496
OOCL LOGISTICS (USA) INC.—See China COSCO Shipping Corporation Limited; *Int'l*, pg. 1496
OOCL (PHILIPPINES) INC.—See China COSCO Shipping Corporation Limited; *Int'l*, pg. 1495
OOCL (PORTUGAL) LDA—See China COSCO Shipping Corporation Limited; *Int'l*, pg. 1495
OOCL (RUSSIA) LTD—See China COSCO Shipping Corporation Limited; *Int'l*, pg. 1495
OOCL (SINGAPORE) PTE LTD—See China COSCO Shipping Corporation Limited; *Int'l*, pg. 1495
OOCL (SWEDEN) AB—See China COSCO Shipping Corporation Limited; *Int'l*, pg. 1495
OOCL (TAIWAN) CO LTD—See China COSCO Shipping Corporation Limited; *Int'l*, pg. 1495
OOCL (UAE) LLC—See China COSCO Shipping Corporation Limited; *Int'l*, pg. 1495
OOCL (UK) LTD—See China COSCO Shipping Corporation Limited; *Int'l*, pg. 1495
OOCL (USA) INC.—See China COSCO Shipping Corporation Limited; *Int'l*, pg. 1495
OOEDO ONSEN REIT INVESTMENT CORPORATION; *Int'l*, pg. 5593
OOGC AMERICA LLC—See China National Offshore Oil Corp.; *Int'l*, pg. 1532
OO. GESUNDHEITS- UND SPITALS-AG—See OO. Landesholding GmbH; *Int'l*, pg. 5593
OOGP, INC.—See EssilorLuxottica SA; *Int'l*, pg. 2514
OOH HOLDINGS LIMITED; *Int'l*, pg. 5593
OOH!MEDIA GROUP LIMITED—See oOh!media Limited; *Int'l*, pg. 5594
OOH!MEDIA LIMITED; *Int'l*, pg. 5594
OOH!MEDIA OPERATIONS PTY. LTD.—See oOh!media Limited; *Int'l*, pg. 5594
OOH!MEDIA REGIONAL PTY. LIMITED—See oOh!media Limited; *Int'l*, pg. 5594
OOH MEDIA SOLUTION, INC.—See Dentsu Group Inc.; *Int'l*, pg. 2039
OOI JOO KEE & BROTHERS SDN. BHD.—See Astino Berhad; *Int'l*, pg. 655
OOKA ISLAND INC.—See Scholastic Corporation; *U.S. Public*, pg. 1847
OOKAMI LIMITED; *Int'l*, pg. 5594
OOKAM SOFTWARE GMBH—See MEDIQON Group AG; *Int'l*, pg. 4780
OOKBEE CO., LTD.—See Transcosmos Inc.; *Int'l*, pg. 7898
OO. LANDESHOLDING GMBH; *Int'l*, pg. 5593
O OLIVE OIL, LLC—See Lifecore Biomedical, Inc.; *U.S. Public*, pg. 1312
OOMA, INC.; *U.S. Public*, pg. 1605
OOMBA, INC.; *U.S. Private*, pg. 3028
O.O.M GLOBAL CARE N.V.—See O.O.M. Onderlinge Verzekering-Maatschappij U.A; *Int'l*, pg. 5503
OOMITSU CO., LTD.; *Int'l*, pg. 5594
O.O.M. ONDERLINGE VERZEKERING-MAATSCHAPPIJ U.A; *Int'l*, pg. 5503
OOMURA INDUSTRIAL CO., LTD.—See Bain Capital, LP; *U.S. Private*, pg. 435
OONA HOLDINGS PTE. LTD.—See Warburg Pincus LLC; *U.S. Private*, pg. 4439
OONA INSURANCE PTE LTD—See Warburg Pincus LLC; *U.S. Private*, pg. 4439
OOO AEK—See Samvardhana Motherson International Limited; *Int'l*, pg. 6517
OOO AFIN LEASING VOSTOK LLC—See CNH Industrial N.V.; *Int'l*, pg. 1676
OOO AGROFIRMA MEZHDURECHYE—See Ekosem-Agrar GmbH; *Int'l*, pg. 2339
OOO AGROPROM VOSTOK—See Ecom Agroindustrial Corporation Ltd.; *Int'l*, pg. 2296
OOO AIDA—See AIDA Engineering, Ltd.; *Int'l*, pg. 231
OOO AKZO NOBEL—See Akzo Nobel N.V.; *Int'l*, pg. 274
OOO AKZO NOBEL WOOD COATINGS—See Akzo Nobel N.V.; *Int'l*, pg. 274
OOO ALFA WASSERMANN—See Alfa-Wassermann S.p.A.; *Int'l*, pg. 315
OOO ALKALOID RUS—See Alkaloid A.D. Skopje; *Int'l*, pg. 330
OOO AL-KO KOBER—See PRIMEPULSE SE; *Int'l*, pg. 5979
OOO AMERPLAST—See Chiltern Capital LLP; *Int'l*, pg. 1479
OOO AMREST—See AmRest Holdings SE; *Int'l*, pg. 437
OOO APS ENERGIA RUS—See APS Energia SA; *Int'l*, pg. 523
OOO A.S. CREATION (RUS)—See A.S. Creation Tapeten AG; *Int'l*, pg. 28
OOO ASTRA - 77—See HORIBA Ltd; *Int'l*, pg. 3477

OOO ATOTECH-CHEMETA—See TotalEnergies SE; *Int'l*, pg. 7837
OOO AUDATEX—See Vista Equity Partners, LLC; *U.S. Private*, pg. 4401
OOO AUMAPRIVODSERVICE—See AUMA Riester GmbH & Co. KG; *Int'l*, pg. 705
OOO AURORA—See Ring International Holding AG; *Int'l*, pg. 6343
OOO AUTO.RU—See Yandex N.V.; *Int'l*, pg. 8559
OOO AZO RUS—See AZO GmbH & Co. KG; *Int'l*, pg. 780
OOO BASF STROITELNYE SISTEMY—See BASF SE; *Int'l*, pg. 884
OOO BASF WOSTOK—See BASF SE; *Int'l*, pg. 886
OOO BAUER MASCHINEN RUSSLAND—See BAUER Aktiengesellschaft; *Int'l*, pg. 893
OOO BEKAERT LIPETSK—See NV Bekaert SA; *Int'l*, pg. 5496
OOO BEKAERT WIRE—See NV Bekaert SA; *Int'l*, pg. 5496
OOO BENTELER AUTOMOTIVE—See Benteler International AG; *Int'l*, pg. 977
OOO BENTELER DISTRIBUTION RUSSIA—See Benteler International AG; *Int'l*, pg. 977
O.O.O. BERICAP—See BERICAP GmbH & Co. KG; *Int'l*, pg. 981
O.O.O BERICAP—See BERICAP GmbH & Co. KG; *Int'l*, pg. 981
OOO BIOTRONIK—See Biotronik GmbH & Co.; *Int'l*, pg. 1044
OOO BIOTRONIK URAL—See Biotronik GmbH & Co.; *Int'l*, pg. 1044
OOO BOEHRINGER INGELHEIM—See C.H. Boehringer Sohn AG & Co. KG; *Int'l*, pg. 1243
OOO BOSCH REXROTH—See Robert Bosch GmbH; *Int'l*, pg. 6366
OOO BOSCH THERMOTECHNIK—See Robert Bosch GmbH; *Int'l*, pg. 6364
OOO BRENNTAG—See BRENNTAG SE; *Int'l*, pg. 1149
OOO BWT—See BWT Aktiengesellschaft; *Int'l*, pg. 1233
OOO CAMPOMOS—See Atria Plc; *Int'l*, pg. 694
OOO CARL ZEISS—See Carl-Zeiss-Stiftung; *Int'l*, pg. 1336
OOO CAVERION ELMEK—See Triton Advisers Limited; *Int'l*, pg. 7935
OOO CHEMINOVA—See FMC Corporation; *U.S. Public*, pg. 861
OOO COMPAREX—See SoftwareONE Holding AG; *Int'l*, pg. 7057
OOO CONTINENTAL AUTOMOTIVE RUS—See Continental Aktiengesellschaft; *Int'l*, pg. 1783
OOO CRANE CENTER KAMAZ—See KAMAZ Publicly Traded Company; *Int'l*, pg. 4060
OOO CRIF—See CRIF S.p.A.; *Int'l*, pg. 1849
OOO CSB-SYSTEM—See CSB-System AG; *Int'l*, pg. 1862
OOO CUMMINS—See Cummins Inc.; *U.S. Public*, pg. 609
OOO DALET MEDIA SYSTEMY—See Long Path Partners, LP; *U.S. Private*, pg. 2491
OOO DANFOSS—See Danfoss A/S; *Int'l*, pg. 1961
OOO DBA PROEKT—See DBA Group SRL; *Int'l*, pg. 1986
OOO DEUTSCHE MESSE RUS—See Deutsche Messe AG; *Int'l*, pg. 2071
OOO DIEFFENBACHER MOSCOW—See Dieffenbacher Holding GmbH & Co. KG; *Int'l*, pg. 2114
OOO DOPPELMAYR RUSSIA—See Doppelmayr Group; *Int'l*, pg. 2175
OOO DSD—See OAO AK Transneft; *Int'l*, pg. 5505
OOO DSV TRANSPORT—See DSV A/S; *Int'l*, pg. 2214
OOO DYCKERHOFF KORKINO CEMENT—See Buzzi SpA; *Int'l*, pg. 1230
OOO EADS—See Airbus SE; *Int'l*, pg. 247
OOO EDAG PRODUCTION SOLUTIONS RU—See ATON GmbH; *Int'l*, pg. 689
OOO EGGER DREVPRODUKT GAGARIN—See Fritz Egger GmbH & Co.; *Int'l*, pg. 2794
OOO EGGER DREVPRODUKT SHUYA—See Fritz Egger GmbH & Co.; *Int'l*, pg. 2794
OOO EIRICH MASCHINENTECHNIK—See Maschinenfabrik Gustav Eirich GmbH & Co KG; *Int'l*, pg. 4720
OOO EIRICH MASCHINENTECHNIK—See Maschinenfabrik Gustav Eirich GmbH & Co KG; *Int'l*, pg. 4720
OOO EISENMANN—See Eisenmann AG; *Int'l*, pg. 2336
OOO EISENMANN TOGLIATTI—See Eisenmann AG; *Int'l*, pg. 2336
OOO EKONIVAAGRO—See Ekosem-Agrar GmbH; *Int'l*, pg. 2339
OOO EKONIVA-MEDIA—See Ekosem-Agrar GmbH; *Int'l*, pg. 2339
OOO ELASTOKAM—See BASF SE; *Int'l*, pg. 883
OOO ELEKTROSKANDIA RUS—See Rexel, S.A.; *Int'l*, pg. 6316
OOO ELMETA—See BLRT Grupp AS; *Int'l*, pg. 1066
OOO ELME TRANS UKRAINE—See BLRT Grupp AS; *Int'l*, pg. 1066
OOO ELTEK—See Delta Electronics, Inc.; *Int'l*, pg. 2017
OOO ELUMATEC—See Cifin S.r.l.; *Int'l*, pg. 1606
OOO EMUGE-FRANKEN—See EMUGE-Werk Richard Glimpel GmbH & Co. KG; *Int'l*, pg. 2394
OOO ENI ENERGHIA—See Eni S.p.A.; *Int'l*, pg. 2438
OOO ENI-NEFTO—See PJSC Lukoil; *Int'l*, pg. 5882

O.O.M. ONDERLINGE VERZEKERING-MAATSCHAPPIJ U.A   CORPORATE AFFILIATIONS

OOO ENVIRO-CHEMIE GMBH—See SKion GmbH; *Int'l*, pg. 6990
OOO FESTO-RF—See Festo AG & Co. KG; *Int'l*, pg. 2648
OOO FIDIA—See FIDIA S.p.A.; *Int'l*, pg. 2655
OOO FINNPACK—See Elecster Oyj; *Int'l*, pg. 2348
OOO FIRM PROTEX-SVM—See Protek OAO; *Int'l*, pg. 6004
OOO FISCHER BEFESTIGUNGSSYSTEME RUS—See fischerwerke GmbH & Co. KG; *Int'l*, pg. 2692
OOO FLEXLINK SYSTEMS—See Coesia S.p.A.; *Int'l*, pg. 1689
OOO FM STROIPROJECT—See Sweco AB; *Int'l*, pg. 7363
OOO FRANK RUS—See Gesco AG; *Int'l*, pg. 2946
OOO FUCHS OIL—See FUCHS SE; *Int'l*, pg. 2804
OOO GAMMA INDUSTRIAL COATINGS—See PPG Industries, Inc.; *U.S. Public*, pg. 1710
OOO GAZPROM BURENIE—See PJSC Gazprom; *Int'l*, pg. 5879
OOO GAZPROM DOBYCHA ASTRAKHAN—See PJSC Gazprom; *Int'l*, pg. 5879
OOO GAZPROM DOBYCHA KRASNODAR—See PJSC Gazprom; *Int'l*, pg. 5879
OOO GAZPROM DOBYCHA NADYM—See PJSC Gazprom; *Int'l*, pg. 5879
OOO GAZPROM DOBYCHA NOYABRSK—See PJSC Gazprom; *Int'l*, pg. 5879
OOO GAZPROM DOBYCHA ORENBURG—See PJSC Gazprom; *Int'l*, pg. 5879
OOO GAZPROM DOBYCHA URENGOY—See PJSC Gazprom; *Int'l*, pg. 5879
OOO GAZPROM DOBYCHA YAMBURG—See PJSC Gazprom; *Int'l*, pg. 5879
OOO GAZPROM INFORM—See PJSC Gazprom; *Int'l*, pg. 5879
OOO GAZPROM INVEST ZAPAD—See PJSC Gazprom; *Int'l*, pg. 5879
OOO GAZPROMNEFTFINANS—See PJSC Gazprom; *Int'l*, pg. 5880
OOO GAZPROM PERERABOTKA—See PJSC Gazprom; *Int'l*, pg. 5879
OOO GAZPROM PKHG—See PJSC Gazprom; *Int'l*, pg. 5879
OOO GAZPROM PODZEMREMONT URENGOY—See PJSC Gazprom; *Int'l*, pg. 5879
OOO GAZPROMPURINVEST—See PJSC Gazprom; *Int'l*, pg. 5880
OOO GAZPROM TRANSGAS MOSKVA—See PJSC Gazprom; *Int'l*, pg. 5880
OOO GAZPROM TRANSGAS TCHAIKOVSKY—See PJSC Gazprom; *Int'l*, pg. 5880
OOO GAZPROM TRANSGAS UFA—PJSC Gazprom; *Int'l*, pg. 5880
OOO GAZPROM TRANSGAS VOLGOGRAD—See PJSC Gazprom; *Int'l*, pg. 5880
OOO GAZPROM TRANSGAS YUGORSK—See PJSC Gazprom; *Int'l*, pg. 5880
OOO GAZPROM TRANSGAZ KRASNODAR—See PJSC Gazprom; *Int'l*, pg. 5880
OOO GAZPROM TRANSGAZ MAKHACHKALA—See PJSC Gazprom; *Int'l*, pg. 5880
OOO GAZPROM TRANSGAZ MOSKVA—See PJSC Gazprom; *Int'l*, pg. 5880
OOO GAZPROM TRANSGAZ NIZHNY NOVGOROD—See PJSC Gazprom; *Int'l*, pg. 5880
OOO GAZPROM TRANSGAZ SAMARA—See PJSC Gazprom; *Int'l*, pg. 5880
OOO GAZPROM TRANSGAZ SANKT-PETERBURG—See PJSC Gazprom; *Int'l*, pg. 5880
OOO GAZPROM TRANSGAZ SARATOV—See PJSC Gazprom; *Int'l*, pg. 5880
OOO GAZPROM TRANSGAZ SURGUT—See PJSC Gazprom; *Int'l*, pg. 5880
OOO GAZPROM TRANSGAZ TOMSK—See PJSC Gazprom; *Int'l*, pg. 5880
OOO GAZPROM TRANSGAZ UHTA—See PJSC Gazprom; *Int'l*, pg. 5880
OOO GAZPROM TRANSGAZ YEKATERINBURG—See PJSC Gazprom; *Int'l*, pg. 5880
OOO GEA FARM TECHNOLOGIES RUS—See GEA Group Aktiengesellschaft; *Int'l*, pg. 2899
OOO GEA REFRIGERATION RUS—See GEA Group Aktiengesellschaft; *Int'l*, pg. 2903
OOO GERRY WEBER RUS—See GERRY WEBER International AG; *Int'l*, pg. 2945
OOO GEWISS RUSSIA—See Gewiss S.p.A.; *Int'l*, pg. 2955
OOO GIMATIC RUS—See Barnes Group Inc.; *U.S. Public*, pg. 277
OOO GK SOFTWARE RUS—See Fujitsu Limited; *Int'l*, pg. 2837
OOO GOLDMAN SACHS BANK—See The Goldman Sachs Group, Inc.; *U.S. Public*, pg. 2082
OOO GREINER PACKAGING—See Greiner Holding AG; *Int'l*, pg. 3079
OOO HAARSLEV INDUSTRIES—See Altor Equity Partners AB; *Int'l*, pg. 395
OOO HABASIT LTD.—See Habasit AG; *Int'l*, pg. 3202
OOO HAHN + KOLB—See Wurth Verwaltungsgesellschaft mbH; *Int'l*, pg. 8505

OOO HASCO RU—See Berndorf AG; *Int'l*, pg. 987
OOO HAUNI ST. PETERSBURG—See Korber AG; *Int'l*, pg. 4280
OOO HAY GROUP—See Korn Ferry; *U.S. Public*, pg. 1275
OOO HELLMANN EAST EUROPE—See Hellmann Worldwide Logistics GmbH & Co. KG; *Int'l*, pg. 3336
OOO HEMOFARM—See Bain Capital, LP; *U.S. Private*, pg. 443
OOO HEMOFARM—See Cinven Limited; *Int'l*, pg. 1613
OOO HENKEL BAUTECHNIK—See Henkel AG & Co. KGaA; *Int'l*, pg. 3354
OOO HENKEL RUS—See Henkel AG & Co. KGaA; *Int'l*, pg. 3350
OOO HENKEL RUS—See Henkel AG & Co. KGaA; *Int'l*, pg. 3354
OOO HENKEL SUD—See Henkel AG & Co. KGaA; *Int'l*, pg. 3350
OOO HERMLE VOSTOK—See Maschinenfabrik Berthold Hermle AG; *Int'l*, pg. 4720
OOO HEWLETT-PACKARD RUS—See HP Inc.; *U.S. Public*, pg. 1064
OOO H+H—See PJSC LSR Group; *Int'l*, pg. 5881
OOO HORNSCHUCH RUS—See Continental Aktiengesellschaft; *Int'l*, pg. 1780
OOO HOYER RUS—See Hoyer GmbH; *Int'l*, pg. 3499
OOO HSBC BANK (RR)—See HSBC Holdings plc; *Int'l*, pg. 3506
OOO HUHTAMAKI S.N.G.—See Huhtamaki Oyj; *Int'l*, pg. 3526
OOO HUOLINTAKESKUS—See Nurminen Logistics Plc; *Int'l*, pg. 5490
OOO HYDAC INTERNATIONAL—See Hydac International GmbH; *Int'l*, pg. 3545
OOO HYDRO BUILDING SYSTEMS—See Norsk Hydro ASA; *Int'l*, pg. 5435
OOO IMPERIAL ENERGY—See Oil & Natural Gas Corporation Limited; *Int'l*, pg. 5534
OOO IMPERIAL ENERGY TOMSK GAS—See Oil & Natural Gas Corporation Limited; *Int'l*, pg. 5534
OOO IMPERIAL TOBACCO VOLGA LLC—See Imperial Brands PLC; *Int'l*, pg. 3634
OOO INFORM FUTURE—See Blackstone Inc.; *U.S. Public*, pg. 351
OOO IRIDIUM COMMUNICATIONS—See Iridium Communications Inc.; *U.S. Public*, pg. 1171
OOO IVECO RUSSIA—See CNH Industrial N.V.; *Int'l*, pg. 1676
OOO JET AVIATION VNUKOVO—See General Dynamics Corporation; *U.S. Public*, pg. 916
OOO JJ HOME—See J.J. Exporters Ltd.; *Int'l*, pg. 3858
OOO JOSEF GARTNER—See Atlas Holdings, LLC; *U.S. Private*, pg. 377
OOO KAPSCH CARRIERCOM RUSSIA—See Kontron AG; *Int'l*, pg. 4277
OOO KARL STORZ ENDOSKOPY - WOSTOK—See Karl Storz GmbH & Co.; *Int'l*, pg. 4083
OOO KATKONEF—See Petro Welt Technologies AG; *Int'l*, pg. 5825
OOO KATOBNEFT—See Petro Welt Technologies AG; *Int'l*, pg. 5825
OOO KAT-OIL DRILLING—See Petro Welt Technologies AG; *Int'l*, pg. 5825
OOO KAUKO RUS—See Aspo Oyj; *Int'l*, pg. 631
OOO KAUTEX MASCHINENBAU—See PLASTECH Holding GmbH; *Int'l*, pg. 5892
OOO KEH EKOMMERZ—See Naspers Limited; *Int'l*, pg. 5148
OOO KENNAMETAL—See Kennametal Inc.; *U.S. Public*, pg. 1223
OOO KFO BRAUN—See Ziegelmundstuckbau Braun GmbH; *Int'l*, pg. 8681
OOO KIMBERLY-CLARK—See Kimberly-Clark Corporation; *U.S. Public*, pg. 1231
OOO KNAUF ARMENIA—See Gebr. Knauf KG; *Int'l*, pg. 2908
OOO KNAUF GIPS—See Gebr. Knauf KG; *Int'l*, pg. 2908
OOO KNAUF GIPS TBILISI—See Gebr. Knauf KG; *Int'l*, pg. 2908
OOO KOMPAN—See KOMPAN A/S; *Int'l*, pg. 4243
OOO KOSTER RUS—See INDUS Holding AG; *Int'l*, pg. 3663
OOO KOVYKTANEFTEGAZ—See PJSC Gazprom; *Int'l*, pg. 5880
OOO KRKA FARMA—See Krka, d.d., Novo Mesto; *Int'l*, pg. 4303
OOO KRKA-RUS—See Krka, d.d., Novo Mesto; *Int'l*, pg. 4303
OOO KRONA DESIGN—See Immofinanz AG; *Int'l*, pg. 3628
OOO KUEHNE + NAGEL—See Kuehne + Nagel International AG; *Int'l*, pg. 4325
OOO KURSKKHIMVOLOKNO—See PJSC KuibyshevAzot; *Int'l*, pg. 5881
OOO KURTZ OST—See Kurtz Holding GmbH & Co. Beteiligungs KG; *Int'l*, pg. 4343
O.O.O. KWS RUS—See KWS SAAT SE & Co. KGaA; *Int'l*, pg. 4353

OOO LAHMEYER INTERNATIONAL RUS—See Lahmeyer Holding GmbH; *Int'l*, pg. 4396
OOO LANDI RENZO RUS—See Landi Renzo S.p.A.; *Int'l*, pg. 4406
OOO LANXESS—See LANXESS AG; *Int'l*, pg. 4416
OOO LASSELSBERGER—See Lasselsberger GmbH; *Int'l*, pg. 4421
OOO LAUDA WOSTOK—See Lauda Dr. R. Wobser GmbH & Co. KG; *Int'l*, pg. 4424
OOO LEGION T2—See Siemens Aktiengesellschaft; *Int'l*, pg. 6887
OOO LEGO—See Kirkbi A/S; *Int'l*, pg. 4190
OOO LEIPURIEN TUKKU—See Aspo Oyj; *Int'l*, pg. 631
OOO LEMKEN-RUS—See Lemken GmbH & Co. KG; *Int'l*, pg. 4449
OOO LENZE—See Lenze SE; *Int'l*, pg. 4455
OOO LEONI WIRING SYSTEMS—See LEONI AG; *Int'l*, pg. 4464
OOO LEONI WIRING SYSTEMS—See LEONI AG; *Int'l*, pg. 4464
OOO LEVEL 3 COMMUNICATIONS—See Lumen Technologies, Inc.; *U.S. Public*, pg. 1347
OOO LINAK—See Linak A/S; *Int'l*, pg. 4500
OOO LNR—See Elisa Corporation; *Int'l*, pg. 2361
OOO LOHMANN RUS—See Lohmann GmbH & Co. KG; *Int'l*, pg. 4544
OOO LONZA RUS—See Lonza Group AG; *Int'l*, pg. 4554
OOO LUKOIL-VOLGOGRADNEFTEPERERA—See PJSC Lukoil; *Int'l*, pg. 5882
OOO MANAGEMENT COMPANY METALLOINVEST—See METALLOINVEST JSC; *Int'l*, pg. 4848
OOO M-BRAIN—See M-Brain Oy; *Int'l*, pg. 4614
OOO MEDIA-MARKT-SATURN—See Safmar Industrial & Financial Group; *Int'l*, pg. 6472
OOO MEDIA-SATURN-RUSSLAND—See Safmar Industrial & Financial Group; *Int'l*, pg. 6472
OOO MEFRO WHEELS RUSSIA—See Crestview Partners, L.P.; *U.S. Private*, pg. 1097
OOO MERRILL LYNCH SECURITIES—See Bank of America Corporation; *U.S. Public*, pg. 272
OOO MESSE MUENCHEN CONSULTING—See Messe Munchen GmbH; *Int'l*, pg. 4842
OOO MIELE CIS—See Miele & Cie KG; *Int'l*, pg. 4889
OOO MITAS—See Trelleborg AB; *Int'l*, pg. 7911
OOO MITEL RUS—See Searchlight Capital Partners, L.P.; *U.S. Private*, pg. 3589
OOO MONDI SALES CIS—See Mondi plc; *Int'l*, pg. 5027
OOO MORGAN STANLEY BANK; *Int'l*, pg. 5594
OOO MORON; *Int'l*, pg. 5594
OOO MPS RUS—See Equistone Partners Europe Limited; *Int'l*, pg. 2486
OOO MSC.SOFTWARE RUS—See Hexagon AB; *Int'l*, pg. 3369
OOO MSZ MEKHANIKA—See State Atomic Energy Corporation ROSATOM; *Int'l*, pg. 7181
OOO MT RUSSIA—See Maire Tecnimont S.p.A.; *Int'l*, pg. 4652
OOO MUSIC1—See Enerfund, LLC; *U.S. Private*, pg. 1393
OOO NET ELEMENT RUSSIA—See Mullen Automotive, Inc.; *U.S. Public*, pg. 1486
OOO NETZSCH PUMPS RUS—See Erich Netzsch GmbH & Co. Holding KG; *Int'l*, pg. 2493
OOO NKT CABLES—See NKT A/S; *Int'l*, pg. 5391
OOO NOKIAN SHINA—See Nokian Renkaat Oyj; *Int'l*, pg. 5407
OOO NOKIA—See Nokia Corporation; *Int'l*, pg. 5406
OOO NOMURA—See Nomura Holdings, Inc.; *Int'l*, pg. 5411
OOO NORCEM KOLA—See Heidelberg Materials AG; *Int'l*, pg. 3318
OOO NORD IMPERIAL—See Oil & Natural Gas Corporation Limited; *Int'l*, pg. 5534
OOO NORD PRIVODY—See Getriebebau NORD GmbH & Co. KG; *Int'l*, pg. 2953
OOO NOVGORODPRODUKT; *Int'l*, pg. 5594
OOO NPP SOYUZKARBON—See Schunk GmbH; *Int'l*, pg. 6641
OOO OERLIKON BALZERS RUS—See OC Oerlikon Corporation AG; *Int'l*, pg. 5512
OOO OKA MOLOKO—See Ekosem-Agrar GmbH; *Int'l*, pg. 2339
OOO OMRON ELECTRONICS (OEE-RUS)—See OMRON Corporation; *Int'l*, pg. 5567
OOO OMRON ELECTRONICS—See OMRON Corporation; *Int'l*, pg. 5567
OOO OMYA UKRAINE—See Omya (Schweiz) AG; *Int'l*, pg. 5570
OOO OMYA URAL—See Omya (Schweiz) AG; *Int'l*, pg. 5570
OOO OMYA URAL - SUBUTAK PLANT—See Omya (Schweiz) AG; *Int'l*, pg. 5570
OOO OMYA URAL - SVETOGORSK PLANT—See Omya (Schweiz) AG; *Int'l*, pg. 5570
OOOOO ENTERTAINMENT COMMERCE LTD.; *Int'l*, pg. 5594
OOO OPTEC—See Carl-Zeiss-Stiftung; *Int'l*, pg. 1336
OOO OPTISCAN—See Amplex AB; *Int'l*, pg. 434
OOO ORION PHARMA—See Orion Corporation; *Int'l*, pg. 5631

COMPANY NAME INDEX

OOO OTTO BOCK SERVICE—See Ottobock Holding GmbH & Co. KG; *Int'l*, pg. 5664
OOO OUTOTEC NORILSK—See Metso Oyj; *Int'l*, pg. 4867
OOO PCC CONSUMER PRODUCTS—See PCC SE; *Int'l*, pg. 5766
OOO PETERBURGSKAYA NIVA—See Ekosem-Agrar GmbH; *Int'l*, pg. 2339
OOO PETROKOM-LIPETSK—See Akzo Nobel N.V.; *Int'l*, pg. 274
OOO PETRO WELT TECHNOLOGIES—See Petro Welt Technologies AG; *Int'l*, pg. 5825
OOO PIT-PRODUCT—See PJSC Cherkizovo Group; *Int'l*, pg. 5878
OOO POLYSIUS—See ThyssenKrupp AG; *Int'l*, pg. 7725
OOO PONSSE; *Int'l*, pg. 5594
OOO POSUDA LIMITED—See Turkiye Sise ve Cam Fabrikalari A.S.; *Int'l*, pg. 7977
OOO PRIMA INDUSTRIE—See Prima Industrie SpA; *Int'l*, pg. 5974
OOO PRIMA POWER—See Prima Industrie SpA; *Int'l*, pg. 5974
OOO PRIWODY AUMA—See AUMA Riester GmbH & Co. KG; *Int'l*, pg. 705
OOO PROMOPHARM—See Protek OAO; *Int'l*, pg. 6004
OOO PSI—See PSI Software SE; *Int'l*, pg. 6017
OOO PURCHASE AND LOGISTIC CENTER OF THE HELICOPTER INDUSTRY—See Russian Technologies State Corporation; *Int'l*, pg. 6431
OOO PUTSCH—See Putsch GmbH & Co. KG; *Int'l*, pg. 6124
OOO "BARTEC RUS"—See Charterhouse Capital Partners LLP; *Int'l*, pg. 1455
OOO "BARTEC SB"—See Charterhouse Capital Partners LLP; *Int'l*, pg. 1455
OOO "COPERION"—See Hillenbrand, Inc.; *U.S. Public*, pg. 1036
OOO "RAIL CARGO LOGISTICS - RUS"—See OBB-Holding AG; *Int'l*, pg. 5510
OOO RAIFFEISEN CAPITAL ASSET MANAGEMENT COMPANY—See Raiffeisen Bank International AG; *Int'l*, pg. 6183
OOO RAIFFEISEN-LEASING—See Raiffeisen Bank International AG; *Int'l*, pg. 6183
OOO RAISIO NUTRITION—See Raisio PLC; *Int'l*, pg. 6191
OOO RAMIRENT—See Loxam SAS; *Int'l*, pg. 4566
OOO RAPTECH—See Rapala VMC Oyj; *Int'l*, pg. 6209
OOO REMONDIS SARANSK—See RETHMANN AG & Co. KG; *Int'l*, pg. 6307
OOO RENISHAW—See Renishaw plc; *Int'l*, pg. 6283
OOO RENOLIT-RUS—See RENOLIT SE; *Int'l*, pg. 6284
OOO RETTENMAIER RUS—See J. Rettenmaier & Sohne GmbH & Co. KG; *Int'l*, pg. 3856
OOO RHENUS AUTOMOTIVE—See RETHMANN AG & Co. KG; *Int'l*, pg. 6307
OOO RIMERA-SERVICE—See PAO TMK; *Int'l*, pg. 5732
OOO ROBERT BOSCH SARATOV—See Robert Bosch GmbH; *Int'l*, pg. 6361
OOO ROBERT BOSCH—See Robert Bosch GmbH; *Int'l*, pg. 6361
OOO ROQUETTE RUS—See Roquette Freres SA; *Int'l*, pg. 6398
OOO ROXTEC RU—See Mellby Gard Holding AB; *Int'l*, pg. 4811
OOO R. STAHL—See R. STAHL AG; *Int'l*, pg. 6169
OOO RUSCAM GLASS PACKAGING HOLDING - KIRISHI PLANT—See Turkiye Sise ve Cam Fabrikalari A.S.; *Int'l*, pg. 7977
OOO RUSCAM GLASS PACKAGING HOLDING—See Turkiye Sise ve Cam Fabrikalari A.S.; *Int'l*, pg. 7977
OOO RUSCAM GLASS—See Turkiye Sise ve Cam Fabrikalari A.S.; *Int'l*, pg. 7977
OOO RUSCAM MANAGEMENT COMPANY—See Turkiye Sise ve Cam Fabrikalari A.S.; *Int'l*, pg. 7977
OOO RUSCAM—See Turkiye Sise ve Cam Fabrikalari A.S.; *Int'l*, pg. 7977
OOO RUSFEN—See Tekfen Holding A.S.; *Int'l*, pg. 7526
OOO RUUKKI RUS; *Int'l*, pg. 5594
OOO SABETTA INTERNATIONAL AIRPORT—See PAO Novatek; *Int'l*, pg. 5731
OOO SACMI MOSCA LTD.—See Sacmi Imola S.C.A.R.L.; *Int'l*, pg. 6464
OOO SARPAK—See Sarten Ambalaj Sanayi ve Ticaret A.S.; *Int'l*, pg. 6578
OOO SAVCOR ART RUS—See Trimble, Inc.; *U.S. Public*, pg. 2191
OOO SAVINSKAJA NIVA—See Ekosem-Agrar GmbH; *Int'l*, pg. 2339
OOO SCF GEO—See PAO Sovcomflot; *Int'l*, pg. 5732
OOO SCF MANAGEMENT SERVICES—See PAO Sovcomflot; *Int'l*, pg. 5732
OOO SCHNEIDER ELECTRIC BUILDINGS—See Schneider Electric SE; *Int'l*, pg. 6628
OOO SCHNEIDER ELECTRIC KALININGRAD—See Schneider Electric SE; *Int'l*, pg. 6628
OOO SCHNELLECKE RUS—See Schnellecke Group AG & Co. KG; *Int'l*, pg. 6636
OOO SCHUNK CARBON TECHNOLOGY—See Schunk GmbH; *Int'l*, pg. 6641

OOO SCHUNK KARBON MOSKAU—See Schunk GmbH; *Int'l*, pg. 6641
OOO SEAQUIST CLOSURES—See AptarGroup, Inc.; *U.S. Public*, pg. 174
OOO SEGEZHA PACKAGING—See Sistema PJSFC; *Int'l*, pg. 6963
OOO SEST-LUVE—See LU-VE SpA; *Int'l*, pg. 4572
OOO SETLES—See Stora Enso Oyj; *Int'l*, pg. 7225
OOO SEVERGRUPP; *Int'l*, pg. 5594
OOO SEVERSTAL-PROMSERVIS—See PAO Severstal; *Int'l*, pg. 5732
OOO SIBINTERNEFT—See Oil & Natural Gas Corporation Limited; *Int'l*, pg. 5534
OOO SIBIRSKAYA NIVA—See Ekosem-Agrar GmbH; *Int'l*, pg. 2339
OOO SIBUR—See OAO SIBUR Holding; *Int'l*, pg. 5507
OOO SIEGWERK—See Siegwerk Druckfarben AG & Co. KGaA; *Int'l*, pg. 6884
OOO SIEMENS—See Siemens Aktiengesellschaft; *Int'l*, pg. 6887
OOO SIEMPELKAMP—See G. Siempelkamp GmbH & Co. KG; *Int'l*, pg. 2864
OOO SIMONA RUS—See Simona AG; *Int'l*, pg. 6932
OOO SMT SCHARF—See Yankuang Group Co., Limited; *Int'l*, pg. 8562
OOO SONOCO ALCORE—See Sonoco Products Company; *U.S. Public*, pg. 1904
OOO SONY DADC—See Sony Group Corporation; *Int'l*, pg. 7105
OOO SRV DEVELOPMENT—See SRV Group Plc; *Int'l*, pg. 7153
OOO STILLEYS—See PAO Severstal; *Int'l*, pg. 5732
OOO STORA ENSO FOREST WEST—See Stora Enso Oyj; *Int'l*, pg. 7225
OOO STORA ENSO PACKAGING KG—See Stora Enso Oyj; *Int'l*, pg. 7225
OOO STORCK—See Storck GmbH & Co.; *Int'l*, pg. 7225
OOO STO—See Sto SE & Co. KGaA; *Int'l*, pg. 7219
OOO STUPINSKAYA NIVA—See Ekosem-Agrar GmbH; *Int'l*, pg. 2339
OOO SUNNEN RUS—See Sunnen Products Company; *U.S. Private*, pg. 3868
OOO SURTECO—See Surteco Group SE; *Int'l*, pg. 7345
OOO SURTEC—See Freudenberg SE; *Int'l*, pg. 2790
OOO SWEDISH ORPHAN BIOVITRUM—See Swedish Orphan Biovitrum AB; *Int'l*, pg. 7365
OOO SYMRISE ROGOVO—See Symrise AG; *Int'l*, pg. 7380
O.O.O. SYNGENTA—See China National Chemical Corporation; *Int'l*, pg. 1529
OOO SYSTEMAIR—See Systemair AB; *Int'l*, pg. 7391
OOO TAGANKA MOST—See Mostotrest PAO; *Int'l*, pg. 5051
OOO TALLINK-RU—See AS Infortar; *Int'l*, pg. 590
OOO TANN NEVSKIY—See Mayr-Melnhof Karton AG; *Int'l*, pg. 4747
OOO TECHNOLOGY POLIMERY—See Dohler GmbH; *Int'l*, pg. 2156
OOO TEKMEN SPB—See YIT Corporation; *Int'l*, pg. 8587
OOO TELKO—See JSC GK Khimik; *Int'l*, pg. 4008
OOO TESMEC RUS—See TESMEC S.p.A.; *Int'l*, pg. 7572
OOO THERMON CIS—See Thermon Group Holdings, Inc.; *U.S. Public*, pg. 2155
OOO THYSSENKRUPP BAUTECHNIK TECHNISCHER SERVICE—See ThyssenKrupp AG; *Int'l*, pg. 7725
OOO THYSSENKRUPP INDUSTRIAL SOLUTIONS (RUS)—See ThyssenKrupp AG; *Int'l*, pg. 7725
OOO THYSSENKRUPP INFRASTRUCTURE—See ThyssenKrupp AG; *Int'l*, pg. 7725
OOO THYSSENKRUPP MATERIALS—See ThyssenKrupp AG; *Int'l*, pg. 7725
OOO THYSSENKRUPP SYSTEM ENGINEERING—See ThyssenKrupp AG; *Int'l*, pg. 7725
OOO TIKKURILA—See PPG Industries, Inc.; *U.S. Public*, pg. 1710
OOO TORNUM—See Volati AB; *Int'l*, pg. 8300
OOO TOYOTA MOTOR—See Toyota Motor Corporation; *Int'l*, pg. 7872
OOO TRANSFENNICA RUSSIA—See Spliethoff's Bevrachtingskantoor B.V.; *Int'l*, pg. 7141
OOO TRANSNEFT FINANCE—See OAO AK Transneft; *Int'l*, pg. 5505
OOO TRANSNEFT-SERVIS—See OAO AK Transneft; *Int'l*, pg. 5505
OOO TRANSPRESS—See OAO AK Transneft; *Int'l*, pg. 5505
OOO TRANSSERVICE CUSTOMS WAREHOUSE—See Protek OAO; *Int'l*, pg. 6004
OOO TROSIFOL—See Kuraray Co., Ltd.; *Int'l*, pg. 4337
OOO TRUMPF MED—See Baxter International Inc.; *U.S. Public*, pg. 283
OOO TSUBAKI KABELSCHLEPP—See Tsubakimoto Chain Co.; *Int'l*, pg. 7953
OOO TULIKIVI—See Tulikivi Corporation; *Int'l*, pg. 7969
OOO TUV SUD RUS—See TUV SUD AG; *Int'l*, pg. 7984
OOO UBM RUS—See UBM Holding Public Company Limited; *Int'l*, pg. 8005
OOO UBS BANK—See UBS Group AG; *Int'l*, pg. 8007
OOO UHDE—See ThyssenKrupp AG; *Int'l*, pg. 7725

OOO UNICREDIT LEASING—See UniCredit S.p.A.; *Int'l*, pg. 8036
OOO UNIKRISTALL KOMI—See Omya (Schweiz) AG; *Int'l*, pg. 5570
OOO UNITED GAMING INDUSTRIES—See Novomatic AG; *Int'l*, pg. 5467
OOO UPM-KYMMENE CHUDOVO—See UPM-Kymmene Corporation; *Int'l*, pg. 8092
OOO VAG ARMATUREN RUS—See Zurn Elkay Water Solutions Corporation; *U.S. Public*, pg. 2414
OOO VALIO—See Valio Ltd.; *Int'l*, pg. 8116
OOO VAMED—See Fresenius SE & Co. KGaA; *Int'l*, pg. 2780
OOO VNIIBT DRILLING INSTRUMENTS—See Integra Management LLC; *Int'l*, pg. 3730
OOO VOESTALPINE HIGH PERFORMANCE METALS RUS—See voestalpine AG; *Int'l*, pg. 8289
OOO VON ROLL—See SKion GmbH; *Int'l*, pg. 6987
OOO VOSTOKNEFTEPROVOD—See OAO AK Transneft; *Int'l*, pg. 5505
OOO VOSTOK SOLOD—See Anadolu Efes Biracilik ve Malt Sanayii A.S.; *Int'l*, pg. 445
OOO WAAGNER-BIRO ST. PETERSBURG STAGE SYSTEMS—See Waagner-Biro AG; *Int'l*, pg. 8323
OOO WACKER CHEMIE RUS—See Wacker Chemie AG; *Int'l*, pg. 8323
OOO WAGO—See WAGO Kontakttechnik GmbH & Co. KG; *Int'l*, pg. 8327
OOO WALTER—See Sandvik AB; *Int'l*, pg. 6534
OOO WAM - MOSCOW—See WAMGROUP S.p.A.; *Int'l*, pg. 8338
OOO WAVIN RUS—See Bharti Enterprises Limited; *Int'l*, pg. 1012
OOO WEISS KLIMATECHNIK—See Schunk GmbH; *Int'l*, pg. 6641
OOO WELLPROP—See Petro Welt Technologies AG; *Int'l*, pg. 5825
OOO WITTMANN BATTENFELD—See Wittmann Kunststoffgerate GmbH; *Int'l*, pg. 8439
OOO WK INDUSTRIAL SERVICE—See W&K Gesellschaft fur Industrietechnik mbH; *Int'l*, pg. 8320
OOO WOLGODEMINOIL—See BASF SE; *Int'l*, pg. 885
OOO WOLGODEMINOIL—See PJSC Lukoil; *Int'l*, pg. 5882
OOO YKK—See YKK Corporation; *Int'l*, pg. 8588
OOO YUNISPRING—See PAO Severstal; *Int'l*, pg. 5732
OOO ZARYA—See Gruppa Kompaniy Rusagro OOO; *Int'l*, pg. 3140
OOO ZASCHITNOE—See Ekosem-Agrar GmbH; *Int'l*, pg. 2339
OOO ZENTIS RUSSIA—See Zentis GmbH & Co. KG; *Int'l*, pg. 8635
OOO ZF KAMA—See ZF Friedrichshafen AG; *Int'l*, pg. 8641
OOO ZF RUSSIA—See ZF Friedrichshafen AG; *Int'l*, pg. 8641
OOPARTS, INC.—See Kuriyama Holdings Corporation; *Int'l*, pg. 4342
OORAH, INC.; *U.S. Private*, pg. 3028
OOREDOO MALDIVES PLC—See Ooredoo Q.S.C.; *Int'l*, pg. 5594
OOREDOO MYANMAR LTD.—See Ooredoo Q.S.C.; *Int'l*, pg. 5594
OOREDOO OMAN—See Ooredoo Q.S.C.; *Int'l*, pg. 5594
OOREDOO PALESTINE—See Ooredoo Q.S.C.; *Int'l*, pg. 5594
OOREDOO QATAR—See Ooredoo Q.S.C.; *Int'l*, pg. 5594
OOREDOO Q.S.C.; *Int'l*, pg. 5594
OOSHOP—See Carrefour SA; *Int'l*, pg. 1346
O&O S.R.L.—See Somfy SA; *Int'l*, pg. 7085
OOSTVLAAMS MILIEUBEHEER—See Eiffage S.A.; *Int'l*, pg. 2331
OOT BROS. INC.; *U.S. Private*, pg. 3028
OO. TECHNOLOGIE- UND MARKETINGGESELLSCHAFT M.B.H.—See OO. Landesholding GmbH; *Int'l*, pg. 5593
OOTOYA CO., LTD.—See OOTOYA Holdings Co., Ltd.; *Int'l*, pg. 5595
OOTOYA HOLDINGS CO., LTD.; *Int'l*, pg. 5595
OOYALA, INC.—See Telstra Group Limited; *Int'l*, pg. 7545
OOYALA LIMITED—See Telstra Group Limited; *Int'l*, pg. 7545
OOYALA MEXICO—See Telstra Group Limited; *Int'l*, pg. 7545
OOZLE MEDIA, INC.—See Association Member Benefits Advisors, LLC; *U.S. Private*, pg. 358
OOZX TECHNO INC.—See Fuji Oozx Inc.; *Int'l*, pg. 2816
OPAA FOOD MANAGEMENT INC.; *U.S. Private*, pg. 3028
OPA CO., LTD—See AEON Co., Ltd.; *Int'l*, pg. 177
OPADE ORGANIZAC. Y PROMOC DE ACTIVIDADES DEPORTIVAS, S.A.—See ACS, Actividades de Construccion y Servicios, S.A.; *Int'l*, pg. 115
OPA INTERNATIONAL CORPORATION - HOUSTON—See Alfa; *Int'l*, pg. 307
OPA INTERNATIONAL CORPORATION—See Alfa; *Int'l*, pg. 307
OPAL BALANCE INVESTMENTS LTD.; *Int'l*, pg. 5595
OPALE ENVIRONNEMENT—See Groupe Seche SAS; *Int'l*, pg. 3110
OPAL FUELS INC.; *U.S. Public*, pg. 1606
OPAL HORIZON LIMITED; *Int'l*, pg. 5595

OPAL HORIZON LIMITED / CORPORATE AFFILIATIONS

OPALIA PHARMA S.A.—See Recordati S.p.A.; *Int'l*, pg. 6239
OPALIA RECORDATI S.A R.L.—See Recordati S.p.A.; *Int'l*, pg. 6239
OPALINE S.A.S.—See Thermador Groupe; *Int'l*, pg. 7707
OPAL ISLAND ACQUISITION CORPORATION; *U.S. Private*, pg. 3028
OPALIUM—See Veolia Environnement S.A.; *Int'l*, pg. 8161
OPAL LUXURY TIME PRODUCTS LIMITED; *Int'l*, pg. 5595
OPAL NEL TRANSPORT GMBH—See BASF SE; *Int'l*, pg. 884
O'PAL OPTEX CO., LTD—See Optex Group Co., Ltd.; *Int'l*, pg. 5601
OPAL REAL ESTATE GROUP—See Peter Pan Bus Lines, Inc.; *U.S. Private*, pg. 3159
OPAL SOFTWARE—See General Electric Company; *U.S. Public*, pg. 919
OPALSTAFF; *U.S. Private*, pg. 3028
OPAP SERVICES S.A.—See Greek Organisation of Football Prognostics S.A.; *Int'l*, pg. 3069
OPAQ NETWORKS, INC—See Fortinet, Inc.; *U.S. Public*, pg. 869
OPASNET CO LTD; *Int'l*, pg. 5595
OP ASSET MANAGEMENT LTD—See OP Financial Group; *Int'l*, pg. 5595
OPAS SOFTWARE GMBH—See MEDIQON Group AG; *Int'l*, pg. 4780
OPATHERM A.S.—See Groupe BPCE; *Int'l*, pg. 3094
OPAVIA LU S.R.O.—See Mondelez International, Inc.; *U.S. Public*, pg. 1464
OPAWICA EXPLORATIONS INC.; *Int'l*, pg. 5595
OP BANCORP; *U.S. Public*, pg. 1605
OPB VERWALTUNGS- UND TREUHAND GMBH—See Deutsche Bank Aktiengesellschaft; *Int'l*, pg. 2061
OPCAPITA LLP; *Int'l*, pg. 5595
OPC CORPORATION—See TPG Capital, L.P.; *U.S. Public*, pg. 2175
OPC ENERGY LTD.—See Kenon Holdings Ltd.; *Int'l*, pg. 4127
O. P. CHAINS LTD.; *Int'l*, pg. 5503
OPCOM CABLES SDN. BHD.—See Opcom Holdings Berhad; *Int'l*, pg. 5595
OPCOM CABLES SDN. BHD.—See Telefonaktiebolaget LM Ericsson; *Int'l*, pg. 7534
OPCOM HOLDINGS BERHAD; *Int'l*, pg. 5595
OPCOM NIAGA SDN BHD—See Opcom Holdings Berhad; *Int'l*, pg. 5595
OPCOM VC SDN. BHD.—See Opcom Holdings Berhad; *Int'l*, pg. 5595
OPCON BIOENERGY AB—See Trention AB; *Int'l*, pg. 7916
OPCON TECHNOLOGY SUZHOU CO., LTD—See Trention AB; *Int'l*, pg. 7916
OPC PEST CONTROL, INC.—See Rollins, Inc.; *U.S. Public*, pg. 1809
OPC PHARMACEUTICAL JOINT-STOCK COMPANY; *Int'l*, pg. 5595
OPDENERGY HOLDING SA—See Antin Infrastructure Partners SAS; *Int'l*, pg. 483
OPECO INC.; *U.S. Private*, pg. 3028
OPEL AUSTRIA GMBH—See Stellantis N.V.; *Int'l*, pg. 7202
OPEL AUSTRIA VERTRIEB GMBH—See Stellantis N.V.; *Int'l*, pg. 7200
OPEL AUTOMOBILE GMBH—See Stellantis N.V.; *Int'l*, pg. 7202
OPEL BELGIUM NV—See Stellantis N.V.; *Int'l*, pg. 7202
OPEL BRUN AUTOMOBILES S.A.; *Int'l*, pg. 5595
OPEL DANMARK A/S—See Stellantis N.V.; *Int'l*, pg. 7200
OPEL FRANCE S.A.S.—See Stellantis N.V.; *Int'l*, pg. 7202
OPEL GROUP GMBH—See General Motors Company; *U.S. Public*, pg. 926
OPEL GROUP WAREHOUSING GMBH—See Stellantis N.V.; *Int'l*, pg. 7200
OPELIKA-AUBURN NEWS—See Lee Enterprises, Incorporated; *U.S. Public*, pg. 1298
OPEL IRELAND—See Stellantis N.V.; *Int'l*, pg. 7201
OPEL ITALIA S.R.L.—See Stellantis N.V.; *Int'l*, pg. 7202
OPELLA LIMITED—See Fluidmaster, Inc.; *U.S. Private*, pg. 1552
OPEL LEASING AUSTRIA GMBH—See General Motors Company; *U.S. Public*, pg. 927
OPEL MANUFACTURING POLAND SP.Z O.O.—See Stellantis N.V.; *Int'l*, pg. 7202
OPEL NEDERLAND B.V.—See Stellantis N.V.; *Int'l*, pg. 7202
OPEL NORGE AS—See Stellantis N.V.; *Int'l*, pg. 7201
OPELOUSAS GENERAL HEALTH SYSTEM; *U.S. Private*, pg. 3028
OPEL POLAND SP.Z O.O.—See Stellantis N.V.; *Int'l*, pg. 7202
OPEL PORTUGAL, LDA.—See Stellantis N.V.; *Int'l*, pg. 7202
OPEL SERVICE GMBH—See Stellantis N.V.; *Int'l*, pg. 7201
OPEL SIBIU SRL—See Stellantis N.V.; *Int'l*, pg. 7202
OPEL SVERIGE AB—See Stellantis N.V.; *Int'l*, pg. 7201
OPEL WIEN GMBH—See Stellantis N.V.; *Int'l*, pg. 7201
OPEN 24 S.A.—See Eurobank Ergasias Services and Holdings S.A.; *Int'l*, pg. 2533

OPEN 4 BUSINESS PRODUCTIONS LLC—See Comcast Corporation; *U.S. Public*, pg. 541
OPEN ACCESS TECHNOLOGY INTERNATIONAL, INC.; *U.S. Private*, pg. 3028
OPEN ADVENTURE SDN. BHD.—See Harvest Miracle Capital Berhad; *Int'l*, pg. 3281
OPENAI, INC.; *U.S. Private*, pg. 3030
OPENAI, L.L.C.—See OpenAI, Inc.; *U.S. Private*, pg. 3030
OPENAIR ST.GALLEN AG—See CTS Eventim AG & Co. KGAA; *Int'l*, pg. 1873
OPEN AIRWAY DENTAL SOLUTIONS LTD; *Int'l*, pg. 5596
OPENALPR SOFTWARE SOLUTIONS, LLC—See Rekor Systems, Inc.; *U.S. Public*, pg. 1778
OPEN AMERICA INC.; *U.S. Private*, pg. 3028
OPEN APPLICATIONS CONSULTING LIMITED—See IQVIA Holdings Inc.; *U.S. Public*, pg. 1170
OPEN ARMS CARE CORPORATION; *U.S. Private*, pg. 3029
OPEN ASSOCIATES JAPAN, INC.—See OPEN Group, Inc.; *Int'l*, pg. 5596
OPEN BANK, S.A.—See Banco Santander, S.A.; *Int'l*, pg. 826
OPENBASE INC.; *Int'l*, pg. 5599
OPEN BAY TIMBER LTD.—See Sumitomo Forestry Co., Ltd.; *Int'l*, pg. 7285
OPENBET RETAIL LTD.—See Silver Lake Group, LLC; *U.S. Private*, pg. 3654
OPENBET TECHNOLOGIES LTD.—See Silver Lake Group, LLC; *U.S. Private*, pg. 3654
OPENCAPE CORPORATION; *U.S. Private*, pg. 3030
OPENCELL BIOMED, INC.; *Int'l*, pg. 5599
OPENCFD LTD.—See Keysight Technologies, Inc.; *U.S. Public*, pg. 1227
OPEN CHANNEL SOLUTIONS B.V.—See Steel Connect, Inc.; *U.S. Public*, pg. 1942
OPEN CHANNEL SOLUTIONS—See Steel Connect, Inc.; *U.S. Public*, pg. 1942
OPENCONNECT SYSTEMS, INC.—See Bain Capital, LP; *U.S. Private*, pg. 442
OPENDEAL INC.; *U.S. Private*, pg. 3030
OPEN DENTAL SOFTWARE; *U.S. Private*, pg. 3029
OPENDNS, INC.—See Cisco Systems, Inc.; *U.S. Public*, pg. 499
OPENDOOR BROKERAGE INC.—See Opendoor Technologies, Inc.; *U.S. Public*, pg. 1606
OPEN DOOR FAMILY MEDICAL CENTER, INC.; *U.S. Private*, pg. 3029
OPEN DOOR INC.; *Int'l*, pg. 5596
OPEN DOOR PRODUCTIONS INC.—See National Amusements, Inc.; *U.S. Private*, pg. 2842
OPENDOOR TECHNOLOGIES INC.; *U.S. Public*, pg. 1606
OPENDOR; *Int'l*, pg. 5599
OPENEDGE PAYMENTS LLC—See Global Payments Inc.; *U.S. Public*, pg. 944
OPENEDGE - PLEASANT GROVE—See Global Payments Inc.; *U.S. Public*, pg. 944
OPENEDGES TECHNOLOGY CORP.—See Openedges Technology, Inc.; *Int'l*, pg. 5599
OPENEDGES TECHNOLOGY, INC.; *Int'l*, pg. 5599
OPENET JAPAN—See Amdocs Limited; *Int'l*, pg. 420
OPENET TELECOM, INC.—See Amdocs Limited; *Int'l*, pg. 420
OPENET TELECOM LTD.—See Amdocs Limited; *Int'l*, pg. 420
OPENET TELECOM MALAYSIA SDN BHD.—See Amdocs Limited; *Int'l*, pg. 420
OPENET TELECOM SALES LIMITED—See Amdocs Limited; *Int'l*, pg. 420
OPENEYE SCIENTIFIC SOFTWARE, INC.—See Cadence Design Systems, Inc.; *U.S. Public*, pg. 419
OPENFIBER KENTUCKY CO. LLC; *U.S. Private*, pg. 3030
OPENFIELD AGRICULTURE LIMITED; *Int'l*, pg. 5599
OPENFILM, LLC—See Enerfund, LLC; *U.S. Private*, pg. 1393
OPEN FINANCE SL—See SIX Group AG; *Int'l*, pg. 6966
OPENGATE CAPITAL MANAGEMENT, LLC; *U.S. Private*, pg. 3030
OPENGATE CONSULTING, INC.—See SolomonEdwards-Group, LLC; *U.S. Private*, pg. 3710
OPENGEAR, INC.—See Digi International Inc.; *U.S. Public*, pg. 662
OPENGEAR LIMITED—See Digi International Inc.; *U.S. Public*, pg. 662
OPENGEAR PTY. LTD.—See Digi International Inc.; *U.S. Public*, pg. 662
OPEN GI LIMITED—See Towergate Partnership Limited; *Int'l*, pg. 7850
OPENGOV, INC.—See Cox Enterprises, Inc.; *U.S. Private*, pg. 1078
OPEN GRID EUROPE GMBH—See British Columbia Investment Management Corp.; *Int'l*, pg. 1169
OPEN GRID EUROPE GMBH—See Macquarie Group Limited; *Int'l*, pg. 4626
OPEN GRID SERVICE GMBH—See E.ON SE; *Int'l*, pg. 2258
OPEN GROUP, INC.; *Int'l*, pg. 5596
OPEN HAND; *U.S. Private*, pg. 3029

OPEN HOUSE ARCHITECT CO., LTD.—See Open House Group Co., Ltd.; *Int'l*, pg. 5596
OPEN HOUSE GROUP CO., LTD.; *Int'l*, pg. 5596
OPENJOBMETIS S.P.A.; *Int'l*, pg. 5599
OPEN JOINT-STOCK COMPANY EASTERN ENERGY COMPANY—See JSC INTER RAO UES; *Int'l*, pg. 4009
OPEN JOINT STOCK COMPANY GUROVO-BETON—See Heidelberg Materials AG; *Int'l*, pg. 3318
OPEN JOINT-STOCK COMPANY SLANTSY CEMENT PLANT CESLA—See Heidelberg Materials AG; *Int'l*, pg. 3318
OPEN JOINT-STOCK COMPANY TAMBOV POWER SUPPLY COMPANY—See JSC INTER RAO UES; *Int'l*, pg. 4009
OPEN JOINT-STOCK COMPANY TERRITORIAL GENERATING COMPANY NO. 11—See JSC INTER RAO UES; *Int'l*, pg. 4009
OPEN KERNEL LABS, INC.—See General Dynamics Corporation; *U.S. Public*, pg. 916
OPEN KERNEL LABS PTY LTD—See General Dynamics Corporation; *U.S. Public*, pg. 916
OPEN KITCHENS INC.; *U.S. Private*, pg. 3029
OPENKNOWL CO., LTD.; *Int'l*, pg. 5599
OPENLANE BELGIUM N.V.—See OPENLANE, Inc.; *U.S. Public*, pg. 1607
OPENLANE DEUTSCHLAND GMBH—See OPENLANE, Inc.; *U.S. Public*, pg. 1607
OPENLANE EUROPE N.V.—See OPENLANE, Inc.; *U.S. Public*, pg. 1607
OPENLANE FRANCE S.A.S.—See OPENLANE, Inc.; *U.S. Public*, pg. 1607
OPENLANE, INC.; *U.S. Public*, pg. 1606
OPENLANE ITALIA S.R.L.—See OPENLANE, Inc.; *U.S. Public*, pg. 1607
OPENLANE NEDERLAND B.V.—See OPENLANE, Inc.; *U.S. Public*, pg. 1607
OPENLANE REMARKETING LIMITED—See OPENLANE, Inc.; *U.S. Public*, pg. 1607
OPENLANE SUBASTAS ESPANA, S.L.—See OPENLANE, Inc.; *U.S. Public*, pg. 1607
OPENLANE US, INC.—See OPENLANE, Inc.; *U.S. Public*, pg. 1607
OPEN LEARNING GLOBAL PTY. LTD.—See OpenLearning Limited; *Int'l*, pg. 5599
OPENLEARNING LIMITED; *Int'l*, pg. 5599
OPEN LENDING CORPORATION; *U.S. Public*, pg. 1606
OPEN LENDING, LLC—See Open Lending Corporation; *U.S. Public*, pg. 1606
OPENLIMIT HOLDING AG; *Int'l*, pg. 5599
OPENLIMIT SIGNCUBES GMBH—See OpenLimit Holding AG; *Int'l*, pg. 5599
OPENLINK FINANCIAL LLC—See ION Investment Group Ltd.; *Int'l*, pg. 3794
OPENLOGIX CORP.—See K2 Partnering Solutions, Inc.; *U.S. Private*, pg. 2253
OPEN LOOP ENERGY, INC.; *U.S. Private*, pg. 3029
OPENMAIL LLC; *U.S. Private*, pg. 3031
OPENMARKET, INC.—See Infobip Ltd.; *Int'l*, pg. 3690
OPENMATICS S.R.O.—See ZF Friedrichshafen AG; *Int'l*, pg. 8641
OPEN MIND CAD-CAM TECHNOLOGIES INDIA PRIVATE LTD.—See Mensch und Maschine Software SE; *Int'l*, pg. 4817
OPEN MIND TECHNOLOGIA BRASIL LTDA.—See Mensch und Maschine Software SE; *Int'l*, pg. 4818
OPEN MIND TECHNOLOGIES AG—See Mensch und Maschine Software SE; *Int'l*, pg. 4817
OPEN MIND TECHNOLOGIES ASIA PACIFIC LTD.—See Mensch und Maschine Software SE; *Int'l*, pg. 4817
OPEN MIND TECHNOLOGIES BENELUX B.V.—See Mensch und Maschine Software SE; *Int'l*, pg. 4817
OPEN MIND TECHNOLOGIES CHINA CO.LTD—See Mensch und Maschine Software SE; *Int'l*, pg. 4817
OPEN MIND TECHNOLOGIES FRANCE S.A.R.L.—See Mensch und Maschine Software SE; *Int'l*, pg. 4817
OPEN MIND TECHNOLOGIES IBERIA S.L.—See Mensch und Maschine Software SE; *Int'l*, pg. 4818
OPEN MIND TECHNOLOGIES ITALIA S.R.L.—See Mensch und Maschine Software SE; *Int'l*, pg. 4817
OPEN MIND TECHNOLOGIES JAPAN INC.—See Mensch und Maschine Software SE; *Int'l*, pg. 4817
OPEN MIND TECHNOLOGIES PORTUGAL UNIPESSOAL LDA.—See Mensch und Maschine Software SE; *Int'l*, pg. 4818
OPEN MIND TECHNOLOGIES PTE LTD.—See Mensch und Maschine Software SE; *Int'l*, pg. 4817
OPEN MIND TECHNOLOGIES SCHWEIZ GMBH—See Mensch und Maschine Software SE; *Int'l*, pg. 4817
OPEN MIND TECHNOLOGIES SPAIN S.L.—See Mensch und Maschine Software SE; *Int'l*, pg. 4818
OPEN MIND TECHNOLOGIES S.R.L.—See Mensch und Maschine Software SE; *Int'l*, pg. 4818
OPEN MIND TECHNOLOGIES TAIWAN INC.—See Mensch und Maschine Software SE; *Int'l*, pg. 4817
OPEN MIND TECHNOLOGIES UK LIMITED—See Mensch und Maschine Software SE; *Int'l*, pg. 4817
OPEN MIND TECHNOLOGIES USA INC.—See Mensch und Maschine Software SE; *Int'l*, pg. 4817
OPEN MORTGAGE, LLC; *U.S. Private*, pg. 3029

OPENMOVES LLC—See PopReach Corporation; *Int'l*, pg. 5921
OPENN NEGOTIATION LIMITED; *Int'l*, pg. 5599
OPENONLINE, LLC—See Sackett National Holdings, Inc.; *U.S. Private*, pg. 3522
OPEN OPTIONS L.P.—See ACRE, LLC; *U.S. Private*, pg. 65
OPEN ORPHAN PLC; *Int'l*, pg. 5596
OPEN PANTRY FOOD MARTS OF WISCONSIN INC.; *U.S. Private*, pg. 3029
OPENPAY ARGENTINA, S.A.—See Banco Bilbao Vizcaya Argentaria, S.A.; *Int'l*, pg. 818
OPENPAY COLOMBIA SAS—See Banco Bilbao Vizcaya Argentaria, S.A.; *Int'l*, pg. 818
OPENPAY PERU, S.A.—See Banco Bilbao Vizcaya Argentaria, S.A.; *Int'l*, pg. 818
OPENPAY S.A. DE C.V.—See Banco Bilbao Vizcaya Argentaria, S.A.; *Int'l*, pg. 818
OPEN PLAN SYSTEMS, INC.—See The Supply Room Companies Inc.; *U.S. Private*, pg. 4125
OPENPLAY TECHNOLOGIES PRIVATE LIMITED—See Nazara Technologies Limited; *Int'l*, pg. 5178
OPENREACH—See BT Group plc; *Int'l*, pg. 1203
OPENROAD AUTO GROUP LIMITED; *Int'l*, pg. 5599
OPEN ROAD AUTO GROUP; *U.S. Private*, pg. 3029
OPEN ROAD BMW, INC.—See Open Road Auto Group; *U.S. Private*, pg. 3029
OPEN ROAD FILMS, LLC.—See MetLife, Inc.; *U.S. Public*, pg. 1430
OPEN ROAD OF BRIDGEWATER, LLC—See Open Road Auto Group; *U.S. Private*, pg. 3029
OPEN ROADS CONSULTING, INC.—See Guardian Capital Group Limited; *Int'l*, pg. 3170
OPEN RULE SYSTEMS INC.—See defi SOLUTIONS, Inc.; *U.S. Private*, pg. 1191
OPEN-SILICON, INC.—See SiFive, Inc.; *U.S. Private*, pg. 3648
OPENSKY CORPORATION—See TUV Rheinland Berlin-Brandenburg Pfalz e.V.; *Int'l*, pg. 7982
OPEN SKY MEDIA INC.; *U.S. Private*, pg. 3029
OPEN SOLUTIONS GROUP, INC.—See AE Industrial Partners, LP; *U.S. Private*, pg. 112
OPENSOURCE INTELLIGENT SOLUTIONS PROPRIETARY LIMITED—See Workforce Holdings Ltd.; *Int'l*, pg. 8455
OPENSPACE GMBH—See Commerzbank AG; *Int'l*, pg. 1719
OPENSPAN, INC.—See Pegasystems Inc.; *U.S. Public*, pg. 1660
OPENSYMMETRY-AUSTRALIA—See OpenSymmetry, Inc.; *U.S. Private*, pg. 3031
OPENSYMMETRY-CANADA—See OpenSymmetry, Inc.; *U.S. Private*, pg. 3031
OPENSYMMETRY, INC.; *U.S. Private*, pg. 3031
OPENSYMMETRY-MALAYSIA—See OpenSymmetry, Inc.; *U.S. Private*, pg. 3031
OPENSYMMETRY-SOUTH AFRICA—See OpenSymmetry, Inc.; *U.S. Private*, pg. 3031
OPENSYMMETRY-UK—See OpenSymmetry, Inc.; *U.S. Private*, pg. 3031
OPENSYNERGY GMBH—See Panasonic Holdings Corporation; *Int'l*, pg. 5717
OPENSYS (M) BERHAD; *Int'l*, pg. 5599
OPEN SYSTEMS HEALTHCARE, INC.—See Centerbridge Partners, L.P.; *U.S. Private*, pg. 815
OPEN SYSTEMS HEALTHCARE, INC.—See The Vistria Group, LP; *U.S. Private*, pg. 4132
OPEN SYSTEMS, INC.; *U.S. Private*, pg. 3029
OPEN SYSTEMS INTEGRATORS, INC.—See The Carlyle Group Inc.; *U.S. Public*, pg. 2053
OPEN SYSTEMS INTERNATIONAL AUSTRALIA PTY LTD—See Emerson Electric Co.; *U.S. Public*, pg. 750
OPEN SYSTEMS INTERNATIONAL EUROPE SL—See Emerson Electric Co.; *U.S. Public*, pg. 750
OPEN SYSTEMS INTERNATIONAL, INC.; *U.S. Private*, pg. 3029
OPEN SYSTEMS OF CLEVELAND, INC.; *U.S. Private*, pg. 3029
OPEN SYSTEMS TECHNOLOGIES, INC.; *U.S. Private*, pg. 3029
OPENTABLE, INC.—See Booking Holdings, Inc.; *U.S. Public*, pg. 368
OPENTECH ALLIANCE, INC.; *U.S. Private*, pg. 3031
OPEN TECHNOLOGIES SRL—See FARO Technologies, Inc.; *U.S. Public*, pg. 823
OPENTEC SOLUTIONS PTY LIMITED—See Inventis Limited; *Int'l*, pg. 3773
OPEN TEXT AB—See Open Text Corporation; *Int'l*, pg. 5597
OPEN TEXT AG—See Open Text Corporation; *Int'l*, pg. 5597
OPEN TEXT (ASIA) PTE LTD.—See Open Text Corporation; *Int'l*, pg. 5597
OPEN TEXT A/S—See Open Text Corporation; *Int'l*, pg. 5597
OPEN TEXT BRASIL COMERCIO DE SOFTWARE LTDA.—See Open Text Corporation; *Int'l*, pg. 5597
OPEN TEXT BRASIL COMERICO DE SOFTWARE LTDA.—See Open Text Corporation; *Int'l*, pg. 5597
OPEN TEXT CANADA LTD.—See Open Text Corporation; *Int'l*, pg. 5597
OPEN TEXT CORPORATION INDIA PRIVATE LIMITED—See Open Text Corporation; *Int'l*, pg. 5597
OPEN TEXT CORPORATION; *Int'l*, pg. 5596
OPEN TEXT DOCUMENT TECHNOLOGIES GMBH—See Open Text Corporation; *Int'l*, pg. 5597
OPEN TEXT GMBH—See Open Text Corporation; *Int'l*, pg. 5597
OPEN TEXT (HONG KONG) LIMITED—See Open Text Corporation; *Int'l*, pg. 5597
OPEN TEXT INC.—See Open Text Corporation; *Int'l*, pg. 5597
OPEN TEXT INC.—See Open Text Corporation; *Int'l*, pg. 5597
OPEN TEXT INTERNATIONAL B.V.—See Open Text Corporation; *Int'l*, pg. 5597
OPEN TEXT K.K.—See Open Text Corporation; *Int'l*, pg. 5598
OPEN TEXT KOREA CO., LTD.—See Open Text Corporation; *Int'l*, pg. 5598
OPEN TEXT OY—See Open Text Corporation; *Int'l*, pg. 5598
OPEN TEXT PTY LTD.—See Open Text Corporation; *Int'l*, pg. 5598
OPEN TEXT PUBLIC SECTOR SOLUTIONS, INC.—See Open Text Corporation; *Int'l*, pg. 5598
OPEN TEXT SARL—See Open Text Corporation; *Int'l*, pg. 5598
OPEN TEXT SA—See Open Text Corporation; *Int'l*, pg. 5598
OPEN TEXT SOFTWARE AUSTRIA GMBH—See Open Text Corporation; *Int'l*, pg. 5598
OPEN TEXT SOFTWARE GMBH—See Open Text Corporation; *Int'l*, pg. 5598
OPEN TEXT SOFTWARE S.L.U.—See Open Text Corporation; *Int'l*, pg. 5598
OPEN TEXT—See Open Text Corporation; *Int'l*, pg. 5597
OPEN TEXT—See Open Text Corporation; *Int'l*, pg. 5597
OPEN TEXT—See Open Text Corporation; *Int'l*, pg. 5597
OPEN TEXT—See Open Text Corporation; *Int'l*, pg. 5597
OPEN TEXT SP. Z.O.O.—See Open Text Corporation; *Int'l*, pg. 5598
OPEN TEXT S.R.L.—See Open Text Corporation; *Int'l*, pg. 5598
OPEN TEXT S.R.O.—See Open Text Corporation; *Int'l*, pg. 5598
OPEN TEXT TECHNOLOGIES INDIA PRIVATE LIMITED—See Open Text Corporation; *Int'l*, pg. 5598
OPEN TEXT UK LIMITED—See Open Text Corporation; *Int'l*, pg. 5598
OPEN TEXT USA INC.—See Open Text Corporation; *Int'l*, pg. 5598
OPENTV AUSTRALIA PTY. LTD.—See Kudelski S.A.; *Int'l*, pg. 4323
OPENTV, INC.—See Kudelski S.A.; *Int'l*, pg. 4323
OPEN UP GROUP INC; *Int'l*, pg. 5598
OPEN UP SYSTEM CO., LTD.—See Open Up Group Inc; *Int'l*, pg. 5599
OPENWAVE MOBILITY, INC.—See Enea AB; *Int'l*, pg. 2410
OPENWAVE SYSTEMS BRASIL LTDA—See Forest Investments, Inc.; *U.S. Private*, pg. 1567
OPENWAVE SYSTEMS JAPAN KK—See Forest Investments, Inc.; *U.S. Private*, pg. 1567
OPENWAY SAS—See Arrow Electronics, Inc.; *U.S. Public*, pg. 199
OPEN WINDOW BAKERY LIMITED; *Int'l*, pg. 5599
OPENWORKS; *U.S. Private*, pg. 3031
OPENX TECHNOLOGIES, INC—See Vivendi SE; *Int'l*, pg. 8270
OPENZONE S.P.A.—See Zambon Company S.p.A.; *Int'l*, pg. 8622
OPERACIONES ACCENTURE S.A. DE C.V.—See Accenture plc; *Int'l*, pg. 86
OPERACIONES AL SUR DEL ORINOCO, C.A.—See Tele Plastic, C.A.; *Int'l*, pg. 7528
OPERACIONES ARCOS DORADOS DE PERU, S.A.—See Arcos Dorados Holdings Inc.; *Int'l*, pg. 550
OPERACION Y MANTENIMIENTO ENERGY, S.A.—See Naturgy Energy Group, S.A.; *Int'l*, pg. 5169
OPERA CONTRACT RESEARCH ORGANIZATION SRL.—See Hangzhou Tigermed Consulting Co., Ltd.; *Int'l*, pg. 3251
OPERADORA DE ESTACIONES DE SERVICIO, S.A.—See YPF S.A.; *Int'l*, pg. 8605
OPERADORA DE FRANQUICIAS ALSEA, S. A. DE C. V.—See Alsea, S.A.B. de C.V.; *Int'l*, pg. 379
OPERADORA DE LA AUTOPISTA DEL OCCIDENTE, S.A. DE C.V.—See Empresas ICA S.A.B. de C.V.; *Int'l*, pg. 2391
OPERADORA DE LA SULTANA, S.A. DE C.V.—See Promotora y Operadora de Infraestructura, S.A.B. de C.V.; *Int'l*, pg. 5996
OPERADORA DE SERVICIOS DE PERSONAL, S.A. DE C.V.—See Industrias Bachoco S.A.B. de C.V.; *Int'l*, pg. 3673
OPERADORA PORTUARIA CENTROAMERICANA S.A.—See International Container Terminal Services, Inc.; *Int'l*, pg. 3746
OPERADORA PORTUARIA DEL GOLFO, S.A. DE C.V.—See Grupo TMM, S.A.B.; *Int'l*, pg. 3137
THE OPERA HOUSE INC.—See Live Nation Entertainment, Inc.; *U.S. Public*, pg. 1331
OPERA INVESTMENTS PLC; *Int'l*, pg. 5600
OPERA LIMITED; *Int'l*, pg. 5600
THE OPERAND GROUP II LLC; *U.S. Private*, pg. 4088
OPERAONE AG; *Int'l*, pg. 5600
OPERA RENDEMENT SCPI—See BNP Paribas SA; *Int'l*, pg. 1092
OPERA SGR SPA; *Int'l*, pg. 5600
OPERA SOFTWARE INTERNATIONAL AS—See Otello Corporation ASA; *Int'l*, pg. 5656
OPERA SOLUTIONS, LLC; *U.S. Private*, pg. 3031
OPERATING TAX SYSTEMS, LLC—See The Riverside Company; *U.S. Private*, pg. 4109
OPERATIONAL ENERGY GROUP LIMITED—See Rojana Industrial Park Public Company Limited; *Int'l*, pg. 6388
OPERATIONAL INTELLIGENCE LLC—See NewSpring Capital LLC; *U.S. Private*, pg. 2918
OPERATIONAL RESEARCH CONSULTANTS, INC.—See WidePoint Corporation; *U.S. Public*, pg. 2370
OPERATIONAL SERVICES GMBH & CO. KG—See Fraport AG; *Int'l*, pg. 2764
OPERATIONAL TECHNOLOGIES CORPORATION-MIDWEST REGIONAL OFFICE—See Operational Technologies Corporation; *U.S. Private*, pg. 3032
OPERATIONAL TECHNOLOGIES CORPORATION; *U.S. Private*, pg. 3032
OPERATION COMPASSION; *U.S. Private*, pg. 3031
OPERATION PAR, INC.; *U.S. Private*, pg. 3032
OPERATIONS MANAGEMENT INTERNATIONAL, INC.—See Jacobs Engineering Group, Inc.; *U.S. Public*, pg. 1184
OPERATION TECHNOLOGY, INC.—See Schneider Electric SE; *Int'l*, pg. 6624
OPERATION THRESHOLD; *U.S. Private*, pg. 3032
OPERATIVE MEDIA, INC.—See Francisco Partners Management, LP; *U.S. Private*, pg. 1591
OPERATOR SYSTEMU MAGAZYNOWANIA SP. Z O.O.—See Polskie Gornictwo Naftowe i Gazownictwo S.A.; *Int'l*, pg. 5912
OPERBES, S.A. DE C.V.—See Grupo Televisa, S.A.B.; *Int'l*, pg. 3136
OPERIO GROUP, LLC; *U.S. Private*, pg. 3032
OPERON SYSTEMS, L.L.C.—See Dunsirn Partners LLC; *U.S. Private*, pg. 1291
OPEROSE HEALTH LTD.—See Centene Corporation; *U.S. Public*, pg. 470
OPES ADVISORS, INC.—See New York Community Bancorp, Inc.; *U.S. Public*, pg. 1513
OPET A.S.—See Koc Holding A.S.; *Int'l*, pg. 4223
OPET FUCHS MADENI YAG A.S.—See Koc Holding A.S.; *Int'l*, pg. 4223
OPET PETROLCULUK A.S.; *Int'l*, pg. 5600
OPEX CORPORATION; *U.S. Private*, pg. 3032
OP FINANCIAL GROUP; *Int'l*, pg. 5595
OP FUND MANAGEMENT COMPANY LTD—See OP Financial Group; *Int'l*, pg. 5595
OPGAL - OPTRONICS INDUSTRIES LTD.—See Elbit Systems Limited; *Int'l*, pg. 2345
OPGEN, INC.; *U.S. Public*, pg. 1607
OPG POWER VENTURES PLC; *Int'l*, pg. 5600
OP HAWLER KURDISTAN LIMITED—See Forza Petroleum Limited; *Int'l*, pg. 2748
OPHIR ENERGY INDONESIA—See PT Medco Energi Internasional Tbk; *Int'l*, pg. 6055
OPHIR ENERGY PLC—See PT Medco Energi Internasional Tbk; *Int'l*, pg. 6055
OPHIR GOLD CORP.; *Int'l*, pg. 5600
OPHIR JAPAN LTD.—See MKS Instruments, Inc.; *U.S. Public*, pg. 1453
OPHIR OPTICS, LLC—See MKS Instruments, Inc.; *U.S. Public*, pg. 1453
OPHIR OPTRONICS GMBH—See MKS Instruments, Inc.; *U.S. Public*, pg. 1453
OPHIR OPTRONICS SOLUTIONS LTD.—See MKS Instruments, Inc.; *U.S. Public*, pg. 1453
OPHIR OPTRONICS SOLUTIONS LTD.—See MKS Instruments, Inc.; *U.S. Public*, pg. 1453
OPHIR SERVICES PTY LIMITED—See PT Medco Energi Internasional Tbk; *Int'l*, pg. 6055
OPHIR SPIRICON EUROPE GMBH—See MKS Instruments, Inc.; *U.S. Public*, pg. 1453
OPHIR-SPIRICON, LLC—See MKS Instruments, Inc.; *U.S. Public*, pg. 1453
OPHIUCHUS EVEN EMPREENDIMENTOS IMOBILIARIOS LTDA.—See Even Construtora e Incorporadora S.A.; *Int'l*, pg. 2562
OPHTHALMIC CONSULTANTS OF LONG ISLAND; *U.S. Private*, pg. 3032
OPHTHALMOLOGY SURGERY CENTER OF ORLANDO, LLC—See Tenet Healthcare Corporation; *U.S. Public*, pg. 2005
OPHTHALMOS S/A—See Rohto Pharmaceutical Co. Ltd.; *Int'l*, pg. 6387

OPHTHASWISSMED PHILIPPINES INC.—See EBOS Group Limited; *Int'l*, pg. 2285
OPIA LIMITED—See Village Roadshow Limited; *Int'l*, pg. 8206
OPIANT PHARMACEUTICALS, INC.—See Indivior PLC; *Int'l*, pg. 3656
OPIC AFRICA CORPORATION—See CPC Corporation; *Int'l*, pg. 1824
OPICI WINE COMPANY OF CONNECTICUT—See Opici Wine Group Inc.; *U.S. Private*, pg. 3032
OPICI WINE COMPANY OF NJ - AMERICAN BD—See Opici Wine Group Inc.; *U.S. Private*, pg. 3032
OPICI WINE GROUP INC.; *U.S. Private*, pg. 3032
OPICI WINES—See Opici Wine Group Inc.; *U.S. Private*, pg. 3032
OPICOIL AMERICA, INC.—See CPC Corporation; *Int'l*, pg. 1824
OPICOIL HOUSTON, INC.—See CPC Corporation; *Int'l*, pg. 1824
OPI JAPAN KK—See JAB Holding Company S.a.r.l.; *Int'l*, pg. 3861
OPINAC NORTH AMERICA, INC.—See National Grid plc; *Int'l*, pg. 5158
OPINICUS TEXTRON INC.—See Textron Inc.; *U.S. Public*, pg. 2029
OPINION DYNAMICS CORPORATION; *U.S. Private*, pg. 3032
OPINIONLAB INC.—See Verint Systems Inc.; *U.S. Public*, pg. 2281
OPINION LEADER RESEARCH LIMITED—See Providence Equity Partners L.L.C.; *U.S. Private*, pg. 3292
OPINIONMETER INC.—See PeriscopeIQ, Inc.; *U.S. Private*, pg. 3151
OPINION RESEARCH CORPORATION—See Lake Capital Management LLC; *U.S. Private*, pg. 2374
OPINION SEARCH INC.—See Brookfield Corporation; *Int'l*, pg. 1179
OPINION SEARCH INC.—See Elliott Management Corporation; *U.S. Private*, pg. 1371
OPIN KERFI PLC; *Int'l*, pg. 5600
OPKO BIOLOGICS, LTD—See OPKO Health, Inc.; *U.S. Public*, pg. 1608
OPKO CHILE, S.A.—See OPKO Health, Inc.; *U.S. Public*, pg. 1608
OPKO DIAGNOSTICS, LLC—See OPKO Health, Inc.; *U.S. Public*, pg. 1608
OPKO DO BRASIL COMERCIO DE PRODUTOS FARMACEUTICOS, LTDA—See OPKO Health, Inc.; *U.S. Public*, pg. 1608
OPKO HEALTH EUROPE, S.L.—See OPKO Health, Inc.; *U.S. Public*, pg. 1608
OPKO HEALTH, INC.; *U.S. Public*, pg. 1608
OPKO LAB, LLC—See OPKO Health, Inc.; *U.S. Public*, pg. 1608
OPKO RENAL, LLC—See OPKO Health, Inc.; *U.S. Public*, pg. 1608
OP-KOTIPANKKI OYJ—See OP Financial Group; *Int'l*, pg. 5595
OPLINK COMMUNICATIONS, LLC.—See Koch Industries, Inc.; *U.S. Private*, pg. 2335
OPMEDIC GROUP INC.; *Int'l*, pg. 5600
OPM SP. Z.O.O.—See Impel S.A.; *Int'l*, pg. 3632
OPNET S.P.A.—See Jefferies Financial Group Inc.; *U.S. Public*, pg. 1189
OPODO LIMITED—See Ardian SAS; *Int'l*, pg. 556
OPODO LIMITED—See Permira Advisers LLP; *Int'l*, pg. 5807
OPO, INC.—See Bausch Health Companies Inc.; *Int'l*, pg. 897
OPOLIS DESIGN; *U.S. Private*, pg. 3032
OPONEO.CO.UK LTD.—See OPONEO.PL S.A.; *Int'l*, pg. 5600
OPONEO.DE GMBH—See OPONEO.PL S.A.; *Int'l*, pg. 5600
OPONEO.PL S.A.; *Int'l*, pg. 5600
OPONY.PL SP. Z O.O.—See OPONEO.PL S.A.; *Int'l*, pg. 5600
OPORTUN FINANCIAL CORPORATION; *U.S. Public*, pg. 1608
OPORTUN, INC.; *U.S. Private*, pg. 3032
OPPAMA INDUSTRY CO., LTD.—See Yamabiko Corporation; *Int'l*, pg. 8547
OP PAPIRNA, S.R.O.—See delfortgroup AG; *Int'l*, pg. 2013
OPP CONSTRUCTION LLC; *U.S. Private*, pg. 3032
OPPEDISANO'S BOOTERY; *U.S. Private*, pg. 3033
OPPEIN HOME GROUP INC; *Int'l*, pg. 5600
OPPENHEIM ASSET MANAGEMENT GMBH—See Deutsche Bank Aktiengesellschaft; *Int'l*, pg. 2062
OPPENHEIM CAPITAL ADVISORY GMBH—See Deutsche Bank Aktiengesellschaft; *Int'l*, pg. 2062
OPPENHEIMER ASSET MANAGEMENT INC.—See Oppenheimer Holdings Inc.; *U.S. Public*, pg. 1608
OPPENHEIMER & CO, INC. - NEW YORK, PARK AVE—See Oppenheimer Holdings Inc.; *U.S. Public*, pg. 1608
OPPENHEIMER & CO. INC.—See Oppenheimer Holdings Inc.; *U.S. Public*, pg. 1608
OPPENHEIMER & CO. INC. - TROY—See Oppenheimer Holdings Inc.; *U.S. Public*, pg. 1608

OPPENHEIMER COMPANIES, INC.; *U.S. Private*, pg. 3033
OPPENHEIMER DEVELOPMENT CORPORATION—See Oppenheimer Companies, Inc.; *U.S. Private*, pg. 3033
OPPENHEIMER EUROPE LTD.—See Oppenheimer Holdings Inc.; *U.S. Public*, pg. 1608
OPPENHEIMERFUNDS DISTRIBUTOR, INC.—See Invesco Ltd.; *U.S. Public*, pg. 1163
OPPENHEIMERFUNDS, INC. - ROCHESTER OFFICE—See Invesco Ltd.; *U.S. Public*, pg. 1163
OPPENHEIMERFUNDS, INC.—See Invesco Ltd.; *U.S. Public*, pg. 1163
OPPENHEIMER HOLDINGS INC.; *U.S. Public*, pg. 1608
OPPENHEIM KAPITALANLAGEGESELLSCHAFT MBH—See Deutsche Bank Aktiengesellschaft; *Int'l*, pg. 2062
OPPENHEIM LANDERT FAMILY OFFICE AG—See Deutsche Bank Aktiengesellschaft; *Int'l*, pg. 2062
OPPENHEIM PRAMERICA ASSET MANAGEMENT S.A R.L.—See Fosun International Limited; *Int'l*, pg. 2751
OPPENHEIM PRIVATE EQUITY VERWALTUNGSGESELLSCHAFT MBH—See Deutsche Bank Aktiengesellschaft; *Int'l*, pg. 2062
OPPENHEIM VERMOGENSTREUHAND GMBH—See Deutsche Bank Aktiengesellschaft; *Int'l*, pg. 2062
OPPENHEIM VERWALTUNG VON IMMOBILIENVERMOGEN GMBH—See Deutsche Bank Aktiengesellschaft; *Int'l*, pg. 2062
OPPFI INC.; *U.S. Public*, pg. 1608
OPP FILM ARGENTINA S.A.—See Oben Holding Group SAC; *Int'l*, pg. 5510
OPP FILM CHILE S.A.—See Oben Holding Group SAC; *Int'l*, pg. 5510
OPP FILM S.A.—See Oben Holding Group SAC; *Int'l*, pg. 5510
OPPLE LIGHTING CO., LTD; *Int'l*, pg. 5600
OPPLE LIGHTING SOUTH AFRICA (PTY) LTD—See OPPLE Lighting Co., Ltd; *Int'l*, pg. 5600
OPPLYSNINGEN 1881 AS—See Kistefos AS; *Int'l*, pg. 4193
OPPORTUNE LLP; *U.S. Private*, pg. 3033
OPPORTUNITIES, INC.; *U.S. Private*, pg. 3033
OPPORTUNITIES INDUSTRIALIZATION CENTERS INTERNATIONAL; *U.S. Private*, pg. 3033
THE OPPORTUNITY ALLIANCE; *U.S. Private*, pg. 4088
OPPORTUNITY BANK OF MONTANA—See Eagle Bancorp Montana, Inc.; *U.S. Public*, pg. 701
OPPORTUNITY BULGARIA INVESTMENT AD; *Int'l*, pg. 5600
OPPORTUNITY ENERGIA E PARTICIPACOES S.A.; *Int'l*, pg. 5600
OPPORTUNITY ENTERPRISES, INC.; *U.S. Private*, pg. 3033
OPPORTUNITY FINANCE NETWORK; *U.S. Private*, pg. 3033
OPPORTUNITY INTERNATIONAL, INC.; *U.S. Private*, pg. 3033
OPPORTUNITY INVESTMENT MANAGEMENT PLC; *Int'l*, pg. 5600
OPPORTUNITY PARTNERS, INC.; *U.S. Private*, pg. 3033
OPPRTUNITY, INC.; *U.S. Private*, pg. 3033
OPPSOURCE INC.; *U.S. Private*, pg. 3033
OPPY ARGENTINA—See David Oppenheimer & Company; *Int'l*, pg. 1983
OPPY CHILE—See David Oppenheimer & Company; *Int'l*, pg. 1983
OPPY COSTA RICA—See David Oppenheimer & Company; *Int'l*, pg. 1983
OPPY PERU—See David Oppenheimer & Company; *Int'l*, pg. 1983
OPREMA A.D.; *Int'l*, pg. 5600
OPRESA D.D.—See British American Tobacco plc; *Int'l*, pg. 1168
OPSCODE, INC.; *U.S. Private*, pg. 3033
OPSCOMPASS, LLC; *U.S. Private*, pg. 3033
OPSCO PROCESS CORP.—See Total Energy Services Inc.; *Int'l*, pg. 7834
OPS-CORE INC.—See Gentex Corporation; *U.S. Private*, pg. 1679
OPSEC SECURITY GROUP LTD—See Crane NXT, Co.; *U.S. Public*, pg. 592
OPSEC SECURITY LIMITED—See Crane NXT, Co.; *U.S. Public*, pg. 592
OP-SEED CO., (BD) LTD.—See Tamura Corporation; *Int'l*, pg. 7451
OPS ELECTRONIC (SHENZHEN) LIMITED—See Sigurd Microelectronics Corp.; *Int'l*, pg. 6913
OPSENS INC.—See Haemonetics Corporation; *U.S. Public*, pg. 979
OPSENS SOLUTIONS INC.—See Haemonetics Corporation; *U.S. Public*, pg. 979
OPSEU PENSION TRUST; *Int'l*, pg. 5600
OPSG LTD.—See EssilorLuxottica SA; *Int'l*, pg. 2515
OPSL HUMAN CAPITAL—See Ocean & Oil Holdings Limited; *Int'l*, pg. 5515
OPSMOBIL, INC.; *Int'l*, pg. 5600
OPSONA THERAPEUTICS LIMITED; *Int'l*, pg. 5601
OPSOURCE, INC.—See Nippon Telegraph & Telephone Corporation; *Int'l*, pg. 5342

OPSTALAN BV—See Mohawk Industries, Inc.; *U.S. Public*, pg. 1458
OPS TECHNOLOGIES SDN. BHD.—See Omni-Plus System Limited; *Int'l*, pg. 5563
OPSTECHNOLOGY, INC.—See Thoma Bravo, L.P.; *U.S. Private*, pg. 4153
OPSWAT, INC.; *U.S. Private*, pg. 3034
OPTA GROUP LLC—See Speyside Equity LLC; *U.S. Private*, pg. 3756
OPTAL LIMITED—See WEX, Inc.; *U.S. Public*, pg. 2364
OPTARE GROUP LTD—See Hinduja Group Ltd.; *Int'l*, pg. 3398
OPTARE GROUP LTD.—See Hinduja Group Ltd.; *Int'l*, pg. 3398
OPTARE UK LTD—See Hinduja Group Ltd.; *Int'l*, pg. 3398
OPTAROS, INC.—See The Interpublic Group of Companies, Inc.; *U.S. Public*, pg. 2099
OPTASENSE CANADA LTD.—See Luna Innovations Incorporated; *U.S. Public*, pg. 1349
OPTASENSE LIMITED—See QinetiQ Group plc; *Int'l*, pg. 6141
OPTA SYSTEMS, LLC—See TCL Technology Group Corp.; *Int'l*, pg. 7483
OPTAVIA (HONG KONG) LIMITED—See Medifast, Inc.; *U.S. Public*, pg. 1412
OPTAVIA, LLC—See Medifast, Inc.; *U.S. Public*, pg. 1412
OPTAVIA (SINGAPORE) PTE. LTD.—See Medifast, Inc.; *U.S. Public*, pg. 1412
OPTCONNECT, LLC; *U.S. Private*, pg. 3034
OPTEAM SA; *Int'l*, pg. 5601
OPTECH INC.—See Teledyne Technologies Incorporated; *U.S. Public*, pg. 1993
OPTECH, LLC; *U.S. Private*, pg. 3034
OPTEC INTERNATIONAL, INC.; *U.S. Public*, pg. 1608
OPTEDIS SA—See Randstad N.V.; *Int'l*, pg. 6202
OPTEGO VISION USA INC.—See Windjammer Capital Investors, LLC; *U.S. Private*, pg. 4538
OPTEK TECHNOLOGY INC.—See TT Electronics plc; *Int'l*, pg. 7959
OPTELIAN ACCESS NETWORKS, INC.—See DZS Inc.; *U.S. Public*, pg. 701
OPTEL VISION INC.; *Int'l*, pg. 5601
OPTEON APPRAISAL, INC.—See Opteon Property Group Pty Ltd.; *Int'l*, pg. 5601
OPTEON PROPERTY GROUP PTY LTD.; *Int'l*, pg. 5601
OPTER AB; *Int'l*, pg. 5601
OPTERA, INC.—See Magna International Inc.; *Int'l*, pg. 4639
OPTERNA AM, INC.—See Belden, Inc.; *U.S. Public*, pg. 294
OPTERNA EUROPE LIMITED—See Belden, Inc.; *U.S. Public*, pg. 294
OPTERNA TECHNOLOGY LIMITED—See Belden, Inc.; *U.S. Public*, pg. 294
OPTERNA TRADING—See Belden, Inc.; *U.S. Public*, pg. 294
OPTERNUS COMPONENTS GMBH—See Hexatronic Group AB; *Int'l*, pg. 3371
OPTERNUS GMBH—See Hexatronic Group AB; *Int'l*, pg. 3371
OPTERRA BETON GMBH—See CRH plc; *Int'l*, pg. 1845
OPTERRA GMBH—See CRH plc; *Int'l*, pg. 1845
OPTERRA ZEMENT GMBH—See CRH plc; *Int'l*, pg. 1845
OPTES INC.—See Zeon Corporation; *Int'l*, pg. 8635
OPT EUROPE: OPT MACHINE VISION GMBH—See OPT Machine Vision Technology Co., Ltd.; *Int'l*, pg. 5601
OPTEX CO., LTD.—See Optex Group Co., Ltd.; *Int'l*, pg. 5602
OPTEX DO BRASIL LTDA.—See Optex Group Co., Ltd.; *Int'l*, pg. 5601
OPTEX (DONGGUAN) CO., LTD.—See Optex Group Co., Ltd.; *Int'l*, pg. 5601
OPTEX (EUROPE) LTD.—See Optex Group Co., Ltd.; *Int'l*, pg. 5601
OPTEX FA CO., LTD.—See Optex Group Co., Ltd.; *Int'l*, pg. 5601
OPTEX FA INC.—See Optex Group Co., Ltd.; *Int'l*, pg. 5602
OPTEX GROUP CO., LTD.; *Int'l*, pg. 5601
OPTEX (H.K.) LIMITED—See Optex Group Co., Ltd.; *Int'l*, pg. 5602
OPTEX, INC.—See Optex Group Co., Ltd.; *Int'l*, pg. 5602
OPTEX KOREA CO., LTD.—See Optex Group Co., Ltd.; *Int'l*, pg. 5602
OPTEX MFG CO., LTD.—See Optex Group Co., Ltd.; *Int'l*, pg. 5602
OPTEX PINNACLE INDIA PRIVATE LIMITED—See Optex Group Co., Ltd.; *Int'l*, pg. 5602
OPTEX SECURITY SAS—See Optex Group Co., Ltd.; *Int'l*, pg. 5602
OPTEX SECURITY SP.Z O.O.—See Optex Group Co., Ltd.; *Int'l*, pg. 5602
OPTEX SYSTEMS HOLDINGS, INC.; *U.S. Public*, pg. 1609
OPTEX TECHNOLOGIES B.V.—See Optex Group Co., Ltd.; *Int'l*, pg. 5602
OPTEX TECHNOLOGIES, INC.—See Optex Group Co., Ltd.; *Int'l*, pg. 5602

COMPANY NAME INDEX

OPTEX(THAILAND) CO., LTD.—See Optex Group Co., Ltd.; *Int'l*, pg. 5602
OPTHEA LIMITED; *Int'l*, pg. 5602
OPTIBASE INC.—See Optibase Ltd.; *Int'l*, pg. 5602
OPTIBASE LTD.; *Int'l*, pg. 5602
OPTIBASE TECHNOLOGIES LTD.—See VITEC Multimedia S.A.; *Int'l*, pg. 8259
OPTIBIOTIX HEALTH PLC; *Int'l*, pg. 5602
OPTIC 2000; *Int'l*, pg. 5602
OPTICABLE NV—See Nexans S.A.; *Int'l*, pg. 5240
OPTICAL 88 EYECARE (M) SDN BHD—See Stelux Holdings International Limited; *Int'l*, pg. 7204
OPTICAL 88 LIMITED—See Stelux Holdings International Limited; *Int'l*, pg. 7204
OPTICAL CABLE CORP. - ASHEVILLE—See Optical Cable Corporation; *U.S. Public*, pg. 1609
OPTICAL CABLE CORPORATION; *U.S. Public*, pg. 1609
OPTICAL COATINGS JAPAN—See AGC Inc.; *Int'l*, pg. 204
OPTICAL CONNECTIVITY LLC—See Huber + Suhner AG; *Int'l*, pg. 3519
OPTICAL DIMENSION INC—See EssilorLuxottica SA; *Int'l*, pg. 2514
OPTICAL DISPLAY ENGINEERING LLC—See HEICO Corporation; *U.S. Public*, pg. 1020
OPTICAL DISTRIBUTOR GROUP, LLC—See ABB/Concise Optical Group LLC; *U.S. Private*, pg. 34
OPTICAL GAGING PRODUCTS INC.—See Quality Vision International Inc.; *U.S. Private*, pg. 3321
OPTICAL GAGING (S) PTE, LTD—See Quality Vision International Inc.; *U.S. Private*, pg. 3321
OPTICAL LABORATORIES LTD.—See EssilorLuxottica SA; *Int'l*, pg. 2516
OPTICAL ONE INC—See EssilorLuxottica SA; *Int'l*, pg. 2513
THE OPTICAL SOCIETY OF AMERICA, INC.; *U.S. Private*, pg. 4088
OPTICAL SOLUTIONS AUSTRALIA (ACT) PTY. LIMITED—See Hexatronic Group AB; *Int'l*, pg. 3371
OPTICAL SOLUTIONS AUSTRALIA (QUEENSLAND) PTY LIMITED—See Hexatronic Group AB; *Int'l*, pg. 3371
OPTICAL SOLUTIONS GROUP—See Synopsys, Inc.; *U.S. Public*, pg. 1970
OPTICAL SOLUTIONS (SYDNEY CITY) PTY. LTD.—See Hexatronic Group AB; *Int'l*, pg. 3371
OPTICAL SOLUTIONS (VICTORIA) PTY. LTD.—See Hexatronic Group AB; *Int'l*, pg. 3371
OPTICAL SOLUTIONS (WA) PTY. LTD.—See Hexatronic Group AB; *Int'l*, pg. 3371
OPTICAL SWITCH CORPORATION; *U.S. Private*, pg. 3034
OPTICAL & TELECOMMUNICATION SOLUTIONS, INC.—See Fujikura Ltd.; *Int'l*, pg. 2827
OPTICEPT TECHNOLOGIES AB; *Int'l*, pg. 5602
OPTICHEM (2000) LIMITED—See Saudi Arabian Mining Company (2000) - Ma'aden; *Int'l*, pg. 6589
OPTICIS COMPANY LIMITED; *Int'l*, pg. 5602
OPTIC NERVE STUDIOS, INC.; *U.S. Private*, pg. 3034
OPTI-COATING LABORATORIES, INC.; *Int'l*, pg. 5602
OPTICOLOR, INC.—See Techmer PM, LLC; *U.S. Private*, pg. 3953
OPTICOMM CORPORATION—See EMCORE Corporation; *U.S. Public*, pg. 739
OPTICOMM MEDIA LIMITED—See Arsenal Capital Management LP; *U.S. Private*, pg. 338
OPTICON DANMARK APS—See OPTOELECTRONICS CO., LTD.; *Int'l*, pg. 5605
OPTICON, INC.—See OPTOELECTRONICS CO., LTD.; *Int'l*, pg. 5606
OPTICON LATIN AMERICA—See OPTOELECTRONICS CO., LTD.; *Int'l*, pg. 5605
OPTICON LTD.—See OPTOELECTRONICS CO., LTD.; *Int'l*, pg. 5605
OPTICON S.A.S.—See OPTOELECTRONICS CO., LTD.; *Int'l*, pg. 5605
OPTICON SENSOREN GMBH—See OPTOELECTRONICS CO., LTD.; *Int'l*, pg. 5606
OPTICON SENSORS EUROPE B.V.—See OPTOELECTRONICS CO., LTD.; *Int'l*, pg. 5606
OPTICON SENSORS NORDIC AB—See OPTOELECTRONICS CO., LTD.; *Int'l*, pg. 5606
OPTICON SENSORS PHILIPPINES INC.—See OPTOELECTRONICS CO., LTD.; *Int'l*, pg. 5606
OPTICON SENSORS PTY. LTD.—See OPTOELECTRONICS CO., LTD.; *Int'l*, pg. 5606
OPTICON S.R.L.—See OPTOELECTRONICS CO., LTD.; *Int'l*, pg. 5605
OPTICON VIETNAM LLC—See OPTOELECTRONICS CO., LTD.; *Int'l*, pg. 5606
OPTICONX, INC.—See Belden, Inc.; *U.S. Public*, pg. 294
OPTICORE INC.; *Int'l*, pg. 5603
OPTIC RIVER COMMUNICATION LTD.—See Henan Shijia Photons Technology Co., Ltd.; *Int'l*, pg. 3343
OPTICS1 INC.—See Safran SA; *Int'l*, pg. 6475
OPTICS BALZERS AG—See Materion Corporation; *U.S. Public*, pg. 1396
OPTICS BALZERS GMBH—See Materion Corporation; *U.S. Public*, pg. 1396
OPTICS BALZERS JENA GMBH—See Materion Corporation; *U.S. Public*, pg. 1396

OPTICS BALZERS MALAYSIA SDN. BHD.—See Materion Corporation; *U.S. Public*, pg. 1396
OPTICS BALZERS USA INC.—See Materion Corporation; *U.S. Public*, pg. 1396
OPTIC SECURITY GROUP LIMITED; *Int'l*, pg. 5602
OPTICSPLANET, INC.; *U.S. Private*, pg. 3034
OPTICS TECHNOLOGY HOLDING CO., LTD; *Int'l*, pg. 5603
OPTIEMUS INFRACOM LIMITED; *Int'l*, pg. 5603
OPTIFACTS INC.—See EssilorLuxottica SA; *Int'l*, pg. 2514
OPTIFIN INVEST S.R.O.; *Int'l*, pg. 5603
OPTIFIT JAKA-MOBEL GMBH—See Nobia AB; *Int'l*, pg. 5395
OPTIFY, INC.; *U.S. Private*, pg. 3034
OPTIGENEX, INC.; *U.S. Private*, pg. 3034
OPTIGRATE CORPORATION—See IPG Photonics Corporation; *U.S. Public*, pg. 1167
OPTIGROUP AB—See Altor Equity Partners AB; *Int'l*, pg. 395
OPTIKA A/S—See Aon plc; *Int'l*, pg. 495
OPTIKER CARL GMBH—See Fielmann Group AG; *Int'l*, pg. 2659
OPTIK HESS GMBH & CO. KG—See Fielmann Group AG; *Int'l*, pg. 2659
OPTIK HESS GMBH—See Fielmann Group AG; *Int'l*, pg. 2659
OPTIK HORGER GMBH & CO. OHG—See Fielmann Group AG; *Int'l*, pg. 2659
OPTIK KAPERNICK GMBH & CO. KG—See Fielmann Group AG; *Int'l*, pg. 2659
OPTIK KLUTTERMANN VERWALTUNGS GMBH—See Fielmann Group AG; *Int'l*, pg. 2659
OPTIKOS SP ZOO—See EssilorLuxottica SA; *Int'l*, pg. 2516
OPTIK SCHUPPIN GMBH & CO. OHG—See Fielmann Group AG; *Int'l*, pg. 2659
OPTIK SIMON GMBH—See Fielmann Group AG; *Int'l*, pg. 2659
OPTILEAF, INC.; *U.S. Private*, pg. 3034
OPTILINE ENTERPRISES, LLC; *U.S. Private*, pg. 3034
OPTIMA ASSET MANAGEMENT SERVICES; *U.S. Private*, pg. 3034
OPTIMA AUTOMATION GMBH—See OPTIMA Packaging Group GmbH; *Int'l*, pg. 6603
OPTIMA AUTOMOBILE GROUP HOLDINGS LIMITED; *Int'l*, pg. 5603
OPTIMA BATTERIES AB—See Brookfield Corporation; *Int'l*, pg. 1175
OPTIMA BATTERIES AB—See Caisse de Depot et Placement du Quebec; *Int'l*, pg. 1254
OPTIMA BATTERIES, INC.—See Brookfield Corporation; *Int'l*, pg. 1175
OPTIMA BATTERIES, INC.—See Caisse de Depot et Placement du Quebec; *Int'l*, pg. 1254
OPTIMA BEG D.O.O.—See Sportradar Group AG; *Int'l*, pg. 7142
OPTIMA CAPITAL LIMITED—See Realord Group Holdings Limited; *Int'l*, pg. 6234
OPTIMA CARZ LEASING PTE. LTD.—See Optima Automobile Group Holdings Limited; *Int'l*, pg. 5603
OPTIMA CHEMICAL GROUP, LLC—See Charkit Chemical Company, LLC; *U.S. Private*, pg. 851
OPTIMA CONSUMER GMBH—See OPTIMA Packaging Group GmbH; *Int'l*, pg. 5603
OPTIMA DIRECT, INC.—See Omnicom Group Inc.; *U.S. Public*, pg. 1592
OPTIMA DO BRASIL MAQUINAS DE EMBALAGEM LTDA.—See OPTIMA Packaging Group GmbH; *Int'l*, pg. 5603
OPTIMA EPS CORP—See Elma Electronic AG; *Int'l*, pg. 2367
OPTIMA GRAPHICS, INC.—See Taylor Corporation; *U.S. Private*, pg. 3938
OPTIMA GROUP, INC.; *U.S. Private*, pg. 3034
OPTIMA HEALTHCARE SOLUTIONS, LLC—See Level Equity Management, LLC; *U.S. Private*, pg. 2434
OPTIMA HEALTHCARE SOLUTIONS, LLC—See Silversmith Management, L.P.; *U.S. Private*, pg. 3664
OPTIMA HEALTHCARE SOLUTIONS, LLC—See The Carlyle Group Inc.; *U.S. Private*, pg. 2050
OPTIMA INDIA PACKAGING MACHINES PVT. LTD.—See OPTIMA Packaging Group GmbH; *Int'l*, pg. 5603
OPTIMA JAPAN CO., LTD.—See OPTIMA Packaging Group GmbH; *Int'l*, pg. 5603
OPTIMA KOREA LTD.—See OPTIMA Packaging Group GmbH; *Int'l*, pg. 5603
OPTIMAL AG & CO. KG—See LKQ Corporation; *U.S. Public*, pg. 1336
OPTIMAL BENELUX BVBA—See LKQ Corporation; *U.S. Public*, pg. 1336
OPTIMAL BLUE, LLC—See Constellation Software Inc.; *Int'l*, pg. 1774
OPTIMAL DESIGN CO.—See Deloitte LLP; *U.S. Private*, pg. 1198
OPTIMAL DESIGN CO.—See Deloitte Touche Tohmatsu Limited; *Int'l*, pg. 2015
OPTIMAL LEGAL SERVICES LTD.—See PEXA Group Limited; *Int'l*, pg. 5835

OPTIMAX HOLDINGS BERHAD

OPTIMAL GEO INC.—See Woolpert Inc.; *U.S. Private*, pg. 4562
OPTIMAL GEOMATICS INC.—See Geotech Ltd.; *Int'l*, pg. 2941
OPTIMAL IDM, LLC; *U.S. Private*, pg. 3034
OPTIMA LIFE SCIENCE GMBH—See OPTIMA Packaging Group GmbH; *Int'l*, pg. 5603
OPTIMAL IMX, INC.—See Great Point Partners, LLC; *U.S. Private*, pg. 1767
OPTIMAL INVESTMENT SERVICES S.A.—See Banco Santander, S.A.; *Int'l*, pg. 826
OPTIMAL MEDIA PRODUCTION GMBH—See Edel SE & Co. KGaA; *Int'l*, pg. 2305
OPTIMAL OUTCOMES, LLC; *U.S. Private*, pg. 3034
OPTIMAL PHONE INTERPRETERS, INC.—See Kinderhook Industries, LLC; *U.S. Private*, pg. 2306
OPTIMAL PLUS LTD.—See National Instruments Corporation; *U.S. Private*, pg. 2858
OPTIMAL POLSKA SP. Z O.O.—See LKQ Corporation; *U.S. Public*, pg. 1336
OPTIMAL STEEL SERVICE LLC—See The Thompson Companies; *U.S. Private*, pg. 4126
OPTIMAL STRATEGIX GROUP, INC.; *U.S. Private*, pg. 3034
OPTIMAL TECHNOLOGY LIMITED—See InnoTek Limited; *Int'l*, pg. 3711
OPTIMAL UK DISTRIBUTION LIMITED—See LKQ Corporation; *U.S. Public*, pg. 1336
OPTIMA MACHINERY CORPORATION—See OPTIMA Packaging Group GmbH; *Int'l*, pg. 5603
OPTIMA MATERIALS MANAGEMENT GMBH—See OPTIMA Packaging Group GmbH; *Int'l*, pg. 5603
OPTIMA MEDICAL INNOVATIONS CORP.; *Int'l*, pg. 5603
OPTIMA NEUROSCIENCE, INC.—See Tucker-Davis Technologies, Inc.; *U.S. Private*, pg. 4256
OPTIMA NONWOVENS GMBH—See OPTIMA Packaging Group GmbH; *Int'l*, pg. 5603
OPTIMA PACKAGING FRANCE S.A.R.L.—See OPTIMA Packaging Group GmbH; *Int'l*, pg. 5603
OPTIMA PACKAGING GROUP GMBH; *Int'l*, pg. 5603
OPTIMA PACKAGING MACHINERY PLC—See OPTIMA Packaging Group GmbH; *Int'l*, pg. 5603
OPTIMA PACKAGING MACHINES (M) SDN. BHD.—See OPTIMA Packaging Group GmbH; *Int'l*, pg. 5603
OPTIMA PACKAGING MACHINES, S.A. DE C.V.—See OPTIMA Packaging Group GmbH; *Int'l*, pg. 5603
OPTIMA PACKAGING MACHINES (SHANGHAI) CO., LTD.—See OPTIMA Packaging Group GmbH; *Int'l*, pg. 5603
OPTIMA PHARMA GMBH—See OPTIMA Packaging Group GmbH; *Int'l*, pg. 5603
OPTIMA SGR S.P.A.—See BPER BANCA S.p.A; *Int'l*, pg. 1132
OPTIMAS OE SOLUTIONS GMBH—See AIP, LLC; *U.S. Private*, pg. 134
OPTIMAS OE SOLUTIONS, LLC—See AIP, LLC; *U.S. Private*, pg. 134
OPTIMAS OE SOLUTIONS LTD.—See AIP, LLC; *U.S. Private*, pg. 134
OPTIMA SOLUTIONS U.K. LIMITED—See TETRA Technologies, Inc.; *U.S. Public*, pg. 2024
OPTIMA S.P.A.—See BPER BANCA S.p.A; *Int'l*, pg. 1132
OPTIMA SPECIALTY STEEL, INC.; *U.S. Private*, pg. 3034
OPTIMA STANTRON CORP.—See Elma Electronic AG; *Int'l*, pg. 2367
OPTIMA TECHNOLOGY GROUP LIMITED; *Int'l*, pg. 5603
OPTIMATION TECHNOLOGY, INC.—See Owner Resource Group, LLC; *U.S. Private*, pg. 3055
OPTIMA VERSICHERUNGSBROKER AG—See Wurth Verwaltungsgesellschaft mbH; *Int'l*, pg. 8506
OPTIMAX ENGINE INC.—See Genuine Parts Company; *U.S. Public*, pg. 932
OPTIMAX EYE SPECIALIST CENTRE (BAHAU) SDN. BHD.—See Optimax Holdings Berhad; *Int'l*, pg. 5604
OPTIMAX EYE SPECIALIST CENTRE (KLUANG) SDN. BHD.—See Optimax Holdings Berhad; *Int'l*, pg. 5604
OPTIMAX EYE SPECIALIST CENTRE (KUCHING) SDN. BHD.—See Optimax Healthcare Services Sdn. Bhd.; *Int'l*, pg. 5604
OPTIMAX EYE SPECIALIST CENTRE (MUAR) SDN. BHD.—See Optimax Holdings Berhad; *Int'l*, pg. 5604
OPTIMAX EYE SPECIALIST CENTRE SDN. BHD.—See Optimax Healthcare Services Sdn. Bhd.; *Int'l*, pg. 5604
OPTIMAX EYE SPECIALIST CENTRE (SEGAMAT) SDN. BHD.—See Optimax Holdings Berhad; *Int'l*, pg. 5604
OPTIMAX EYE SPECIALIST CENTRE (SEREMBAN) SDN. BHD.—See Optimax Healthcare Services Sdn. Bhd.; *Int'l*, pg. 5604
OPTIMAX EYE SPECIALIST CENTRE (SHAH ALAM) SDN. BHD.—See Optimax Healthcare Services Sdn. Bhd.; *Int'l*, pg. 5604
OPTIMAX EYE SPECIALIST CENTRE (SUNWAY) SDN. BHD.—See Optimax Healthcare Services Sdn. Bhd.; *Int'l*, pg. 5604
OPTIMAX EYE SPECIALIST CENTRE (SUTERA) SDN. BHD.—See Optimax Holdings Berhad; *Int'l*, pg. 5604
OPTIMAX HEALTHCARE SERVICES SDN. BHD.; *Int'l*, pg. 5604
OPTIMAX HOLDINGS BERHAD; *Int'l*, pg. 5604

OPTIMAX SYSTEMS, INC.   CORPORATE AFFILIATIONS

OPTIMAX SYSTEMS, INC.; *U.S. Private*, pg. 3034
OPTIMAX TECHNOLOGY CORPORATION; *Int'l*, pg. 5604
OPTIM CORPORATION; *Int'l*, pg. 5603
OPTIMECH, LLC—See Ivey Mechanical Company LLC; *U.S. Private*, pg. 2151
OPTIMEDIA-DALLAS—See Publicis Groupe S.A.; *Int'l*, pg. 6113
OPTIMEDIA GESELLSCHAFT FUR MEDIA-SERVICES MBH—See Publicis Groupe S.A.; *Int'l*, pg. 6113
OPTIMEDIA-INDIANAPOLIS—See Publicis Groupe S.A.; *Int'l*, pg. 6114
OPTIMEDIA INTERNATIONAL U.S., INC.—See Publicis Groupe S.A.; *Int'l*, pg. 6113
OPTIMEDIA PERU—See Publicis Groupe S.A.; *Int'l*, pg. 6113
OPTIMEDIA-SAN FRANCISCO—See Publicis Groupe S.A.; *Int'l*, pg. 6114
OPTIMEDIA-SEATTLE—See Publicis Groupe S.A.; *Int'l*, pg. 6114
OPTIMEDIA—See Publicis Groupe S.A.; *Int'l*, pg. 6113
OPTIMEDIA—See Publicis Groupe S.A.; *Int'l*, pg. 6113
OPTIMEDIA—See Publicis Groupe S.A.; *Int'l*, pg. 6113
OPTIMEDIA—See Publicis Groupe S.A.; *Int'l*, pg. 6113
OPTIMEDIA—See Publicis Groupe S.A.; *Int'l*, pg. 6113
OPTIMEDIA—See Publicis Groupe S.A.; *Int'l*, pg. 6113
OPTIMEDIA—See Publicis Groupe S.A.; *Int'l*, pg. 6113
OPTIMEDIA—See Publicis Groupe S.A.; *Int'l*, pg. 6113
OPTIMEDIA—See Publicis Groupe S.A.; *Int'l*, pg. 6113
OPTIMEDIA—See Publicis Groupe S.A.; *Int'l*, pg. 6113
OPTI MEDICAL, INC.—See IDEXX Laboratories, Inc.; *U.S. Public*, pg. 1093
OPTI MEDICAL SYSTEMS, INC.—See IDEXX Laboratories, Inc.; *U.S. Public*, pg. 1093
OPTIMEDI SP. Z.O.O.—See Carl-Zeiss-Stiftung; *Int'l*, pg. 1336
OPTIMED S.A.—See Eurofins Scientific S.E.; *Int'l*, pg. 2543
OPTIMED SOFTWARE CORPORATION—See George Weston Limited; *Int'l*, pg. 2939
OPTIM ENERGY ALTURA COGEN LLC—See BlackRock, Inc.; *U.S. Public*, pg. 346
OPTIMERA A/S—See Compagnie de Saint-Gobain SA; *Int'l*, pg. 1724
OPTIMETRICS, INC.—See DCS Corporation; *U.S. Private*, pg. 1180
OPTIMI HEALTH CORP.; *Int'l*, pg. 5604
OPTIMI HOLDINGS (PTY.) LTD.—See PSG Group Limited; *Int'l*, pg. 6016
OPTIM INCORPORATED—See Juno Investments LLC; *U.S. Private*, pg. 2244
OPTIMIND PHARMA CORP.; *Int'l*, pg. 5604
OPTIMISA PLC; *Int'l*, pg. 5604
OPTIMISE-IT GMBH—See Stroer SE & Co. KGaA; *Int'l*, pg. 7242
OPTIMISE MEDIA GROUP LIMITED—See Clime Investment Management Limited; *Int'l*, pg. 1659
OPTIMISSA CAPITAL MARKETS CONSULTING S.A. DE C.V.—See Alten S.A.; *Int'l*, pg. 390
OPTIMISSA LTD.—See Alten S.A.; *Int'l*, pg. 390
OPTIMISSA PORTUGAL UNIPESSOAL, LDA—See Alten S.A.; *Int'l*, pg. 390
OPTIMISSA SERVICIOS PROFESIONALES SL—See Alten S.A.; *Int'l*, pg. 390
OPTIMIX VERMOGENSBEHEER N.V.—See Svenska Handelsbanken AB; *Int'l*, pg. 7358
OPTIMIZACLICK, S.L.—See Solocal Group; *Int'l*, pg. 7074
OPTIMIZED ENERGY SOLUTIONS, LLC—See Chevron Corporation; *U.S. Public*, pg. 487
OPTIMIZED PROCESS DESIGNS INC.—See Koch Industries, Inc.; *U.S. Private*, pg. 2332
OPTIMIZED SYSTEMS & SOLUTIONS, LLC—See Rolls-Royce Holdings plc; *Int'l*, pg. 6393
OPTIMIZELY, INC.—See Insight Venture Management, LLC; *U.S. Private*, pg. 2090
OPTIMIZERX CORPORATION; *U.S. Public*, pg. 1609
OPTIMODAL, INC.—See Odyssey Logistics & Technology Corp.; *U.S. Private*, pg. 2996
OPTIMO IT; *U.S. Private*, pg. 3034
OPTIMOL OELWERKE INDUSTRIE GMBH & CO. KG—See BP plc; *Int'l*, pg. 1131
OPTIMOS LLC—See MAXIMUS, Inc.; *U.S. Public*, pg. 1402
OPTIMUM ASSET MANAGEMENT INC.—See Optimum Group Inc.; *Int'l*, pg. 5604
OPTIMUMBANK HOLDINGS INC.; *U.S. Public*, pg. 1609
OPTIMUMBANK—See OptimumBank Holdings Inc.; *U.S. Public*, pg. 1609
OPTIMUM BARRIERS—See Hill & Smith PLC; *Int'l*, pg. 3392
OPTIMUM CARAIBES S.A.S.—See Optimum Group Inc.; *Int'l*, pg. 5604
OPTIMUM CHOICE, INC.—See UnitedHealth Group Incorporated; *U.S. Public*, pg. 2243
OPTIMUM CONSULTANTS & ACTUARIES INC—See Optimum Group Inc.; *Int'l*, pg. 5604

OPTIMUM CONTACT LIMITED—See IQVIA Holdings Inc.; *U.S. Public*, pg. 1170
OPTIMUM DESIGN ASSOCIATES, INC.—See Crestview Partners, L.P.; *U.S. Private*, pg. 1098
OPTIMUM GROUP INC.; *Int'l*, pg. 5604
OPTIMUM HEALTHCARE, INC.; *U.S. Private*, pg. 3035
OPTIMUM HEALTHCARE IT, LLC—See Achieve Partners Management, LLC; *U.S. Private*, pg. 59
OPTIMUM INFORMATIQUE INC.—See Optimum Group Inc.; *Int'l*, pg. 5604
OPTIMUM MORTGAGE—See Canadian Western Bank; *Int'l*, pg. 1287
OPTIMUM NETWORKING, INC.—See Vitruvian Partners LLP; *Int'l*, pg. 8263
OPTIMUM OUTSOURCING LLC; *U.S. Private*, pg. 3035
OPTIMUM PLASTICS, INC.—See Bloomer Plastics, Inc.; *U.S. Private*, pg. 584
OPTIMUM REASSURANCE INC.—See Optimum Group Inc.; *Int'l*, pg. 5604
OPTIMUM RE CORPORATION; *U.S. Private*, pg. 3035
OPTIMUM SOLUTIONS INC.—See Hellman & Friedman LLC; *U.S. Private*, pg. 1911
OPTIMUM SOURCE INTERNATIONAL, LTD.; *U.S. Public*, pg. 1609
OPTIMUM SPINE CENTER, LLC—See Tenet Healthcare Corporation; *U.S. Public*, pg. 2005
OPTIMUM SYSTEM PRODUCTS INC.; *U.S. Private*, pg. 3035
OPTIMUM TECHNICAL SERVICES LTD.—See Turner & Co. (Glasgow) Limited; *Int'l*, pg. 7978
OPTIMUM TECHNOLOGY SOLUTIONS INC.; *U.S. Private*, pg. 3035
OPTIMUM VENTURES LTD.—See NexGold Mining Corp.; *Int'l*, pg. 5243
OPTIMUM VIE S.A.—See Optimum Group Inc.; *Int'l*, pg. 5604
OPTIMUS CORPORATION; *U.S. Private*, pg. 3035
OPTIMUS FIDUCIARIES LIMITED; *Int'l*, pg. 5604
OPTIMUS FINANCE LIMITED; *Int'l*, pg. 5604
OPTIMUS GROUP CO., LTD.; *Int'l*, pg. 5604
OPTIMUS HEALTHCARE SERVICES, INC.; *U.S. Public*, pg. 1609
OPTIMUS HEALTH CARE; *U.S. Private*, pg. 3035
OPTIMUS INDUSTRIES, LLC—See Babcock & Wilcox Enterprises, Inc.; *U.S. Public*, pg. 263
OPTIMUS PROFESSIONAL PUBLISHING LIMITED—See Electric Word Plc; *Int'l*, pg. 2349
OPTIMUS S.A.—See Aiphone Co., Ltd.; *Int'l*, pg. 235
OPTIMUS SORTER TECHNOLOGY B.V.—See L. Possehl & Co. mbH; *Int'l*, pg. 4384
OPTIMUS STEEL, LLC - BEAUMONT STEEL MILL—See Optimus Steel, LLC; *U.S. Private*, pg. 3035
OPTIMUS STEEL, LLC; *U.S. Private*, pg. 3035
OPTINOSE AS—See OptiNose, Inc.; *U.S. Public*, pg. 1609
OPTINOSE, INC.; *U.S. Public*, pg. 1609
OPTINOSE US, INC.—See OptiNose, Inc.; *U.S. Public*, pg. 1609
OPTION 1 NUTRITION HOLDINGS, LLC—See Bain Capital, LP; *U.S. Private*, pg. 439
OPTIONABLE, INC.; *U.S. Private*, pg. 3035
OPTION CARE ENTERPRISES, INC.—See Option Care Health, Inc.; *U.S. Public*, pg. 1610
OPTION CARE ENTERPRISES, INC.—See Madison Dearborn Partners, LLC; *U.S. Private*, pg. 2542
OPTION CARE HEALTH, INC.; *U.S. Public*, pg. 1610
OPTION CARE HOME HEALTH, L.L.C.—See Option Care Health, Inc.; *U.S. Public*, pg. 1610
OPTION CARE, INC.—See Option Care Health, Inc.; *U.S. Public*, pg. 1610
OPTION CARE OF NEW YORK, INC.—See Option Care Health, Inc.; *U.S. Public*, pg. 1610
OPTION GERMANY GMBH—See Crescent N.V.; *Int'l*, pg. 1839
OPTION HEALTH, LTD.—See Option Care Health, Inc.; *U.S. Public*, pg. 1610
OPTIONS & CHOICES, INC.—See Stone Point Capital LLC; *U.S. Private*, pg. 3824
OPTIONSCITY SOFTWARE, INC.—See Marlin Equity Partners, LLC; *U.S. Private*, pg. 2584
THE OPTIONS CLEARING CORP.; *U.S. Private*, pg. 4089
OPTIONS CORPORATE PENSIONS UK LIMITED—See STM Group Plc; *Int'l*, pg. 7216
OPTIONS FOR COMMUNITY LIVING, INC.; *U.S. Private*, pg. 3035
OPTIONS FOR LEARNING; *U.S. Private*, pg. 3035
OPTIONS INFORMATION TECHNOLOGY LLC—See ABRY Partners, LLC; *U.S. Private*, pg. 42
OPTION SIX, INC.; *U.S. Private*, pg. 3035
OPTIONS SERVICES, INC.—See Addus HomeCare Corporation; *U.S. Public*, pg. 40
OPTIONS TREATMENT CENTER ACQUISITION CORPORATION—See Acadia Healthcare Company, Inc.; *U.S. Public*, pg. 29
OPTIONS UK PERSONAL PENSIONS LLP—See STM Group Plc; *Int'l*, pg. 7216
OPTIONS UNIVERSITY; *U.S. Private*, pg. 3035
OPTIONSXPRESS HOLDINGS, INC.—See The Charles Schwab Corporation; *U.S. Public*, pg. 2058

OPTIONSXPRESS SINGAPORE PTE LTD.—See The Charles Schwab Corporation; *U.S. Public*, pg. 2058
OPTION WIRELESS HONG KONG LIMITED—See Crescent N.V.; *Int'l*, pg. 1839
OPTION WIRELESS LTD—See Crescent N.V.; *Int'l*, pg. 1839
OPTIPHARM CO., LTD.; *Int'l*, pg. 5605
OPTIPLAN GMBH—See senata GmbH; *Int'l*, pg. 6707
OPTIQUA PIPES AND ELECTRICALS PRIVATE LIMITED—See Kirloskar Oil Engines Limited; *Int'l*, pg. 4191
OPTIQUE CRISTAL INC—See EssilorLuxottica SA; *Int'l*, pg. 2516
OPTIQUE DE L'ESTRIE INC—See EssilorLuxottica SA; *Int'l*, pg. 2516
OPTIQUE LISON INC.—See EssilorLuxottica SA; *Int'l*, pg. 2516
OPTIROC SA—See Compagnie de Saint-Gobain SA; *Int'l*, pg. 1727
OPTISCAN AB—See Amplex AB; *Int'l*, pg. 434
OPTISCAN DENMARK—See Amplex AB; *Int'l*, pg. 434
OPTISCAN IMAGING LIMITED; *Int'l*, pg. 5605
OPTISCAN, INC.; *U.S. Private*, pg. 3035
OPTISCAN OY—See Amplex AB; *Int'l*, pg. 434
OPTISCAN PTY LTD—See Optiscan Imaging Limited; *Int'l*, pg. 5605
OPTIS CN LIMITED—See ANSYS, Inc.; *U.S. Public*, pg. 139
OPTIS JAPAN K.K.—See ANSYS, Inc.; *U.S. Public*, pg. 139
OPTIS KOREA CO., LTD—See ANSYS, Inc.; *U.S. Public*, pg. 139
OPTIS NORTH AMERICA INC.—See ANSYS, Inc.; *U.S. Public*, pg. 139
OPTISOFT NYRT.; *Int'l*, pg. 5605
OPTISPHERE NETWORKS INC.—See Siemens Aktiengesellschaft; *Int'l*, pg. 6889
OPTIS PRISTINE LIMITED—See ANSYS, Inc.; *U.S. Public*, pg. 139
OPTIS SAS—See ANSYS, Inc.; *U.S. Public*, pg. 139
OPTISURE RISK PARTNERS, LLC; *U.S. Private*, pg. 3035
OPTISWISS AG—See Carl-Zeiss-Stiftung; *Int'l*, pg. 1336
OPTISWISS FRANCE SARL—See Carl-Zeiss-Stiftung; *Int'l*, pg. 1336
OPTI-TIME -GEOCONCEPT GROUP—See GeoConcept SA; *Int'l*, pg. 2933
OPTIVA, INC.; *Int'l*, pg. 5605
OPTIVIA BANKING EQUIPMENT & SERVICES—See Loth MBI, Inc.; *U.S. Private*, pg. 2497
OPTIVIA BIOTECHNOLOGY INC.—See BioIVT, LLC; *U.S. Private*, pg. 562
OPTIV INC.; *U.S. Private*, pg. 3035
OPTIV SECURITY, INC.—See KKR & Co. Inc.; *U.S. Public*, pg. 1262
OPTIWA B.V.—See Frencken Group Limited; *Int'l*, pg. 2773
OPTIWORK, INC.—See BizLink Holding Inc.; *Int'l*, pg. 1053
OPTIWORKS, INC.—See BizLink Holding Inc.; *Int'l*, pg. 1053
OPTIXANTHIN SDN. BHD.—See Optimax Holdings Berhad; *Int'l*, pg. 5604
OPTIZ INC.—See China Wafer Level CSP Co., Ltd.; *Int'l*, pg. 1562
OPTIZMO TECHNOLOGIES, LLC; *U.S. Private*, pg. 3035
OPT JAPAN CO., LTD.—See Mitsubishi Research Institute, Inc.; *Int'l*, pg. 4968
OPT JAPAN: OPT MACHINE VISION TECH CO., LTD.—See OPT Machine Vision Technology Co., Ltd.; *Int'l*, pg. 5601
OPT MACHINE VISION GMBH—See OPT Machine Vision Technology Co., Ltd.; *Int'l*, pg. 5601
OPT MACHINE VISION TECHNOLOGY CO., LTD.; *Int'l*, pg. 5601
OPT MACHINE VISION TECH (SUZHOU) LIMITED—See OPT Machine Vision Technology Co., Ltd.; *Int'l*, pg. 5601
OPT MALAYSIA SDN. BHD.—See OPT Machine Vision Technology Co., Ltd.; *Int'l*, pg. 5601
OPTMATE CORPORATION—See Nitto Denko Corporation; *Int'l*, pg. 5387
OPTO 22; *U.S. Private*, pg. 3035
OPTOCAP LIMITED—See TUV NORD AG; *Int'l*, pg. 7979
OPTO CIRCUITS (INDIA) LIMITED; *Int'l*, pg. 5605
OPTO DEVICE TECHNOLOGY CO., LTD. - SEMICONDUCTOR DIVISION—See Opto Device Technology Co., Ltd.; *Int'l*, pg. 5605
OPTO DEVICE TECHNOLOGY CO., LTD.; *Int'l*, pg. 5605
OPTODEV, INC.—See EssilorLuxottica SA; *Int'l*, pg. 2512
OPTODOT CORPORATION—See Meta Materials Inc.; *Int'l*, pg. 4844
OPTOELECTRONICS CO., LTD.; *Int'l*, pg. 5605
OPTO-ELECTRONICS INC.—See Textron Inc.; *U.S. Public*, pg. 2028
OPTOENERGY, INC.—See Fujikura Ltd.; *Int'l*, pg. 2829
OPTOFIDELITY LTD.—See ChangYuan Group Ltd.; *Int'l*, pg. 1445
OPTOFLUX GMBH; *Int'l*, pg. 5606

COMPANY NAME INDEX

OPTO INFRASTRUCTURE LTD—See Opto Circuits (India) Limited; *Int'l*, pg. 5605
OPTOKON CO. LTD.—See Methode Electronics, Inc.; *U.S. Public*, pg. 1429
OPTOKON D.O.O.—See Methode Electronics, Inc.; *U.S. Public*, pg. 1429
OPTOKON POLSKA SP. Z O.O.—See Methode Electronics, Inc.; *U.S. Public*, pg. 1429
OPTOMA BENELUX B.V.—See Coretronic Corporation; *Int'l*, pg. 1800
OPTOMA CANADA—See Coretronic Corporation; *Int'l*, pg. 1800
OPTOMA (CHINA & H.K.) LIMITED—See Coretronic Corporation; *Int'l*, pg. 1800
OPTOMA DEUTSCHLAND GMBH—See Coretronic Corporation; *Int'l*, pg. 1800
OPTOMA ESPANA, S.L.—See Coretronic Corporation; *Int'l*, pg. 1800
OPTOMA EUROPE LIMITED—See Coretronic Corporation; *Int'l*, pg. 1800
OPTOMA FRANCE, S.A.S.—See Coretronic Corporation; *Int'l*, pg. 1800
OPTOMA SCANDINAVIA. A.S.—See Coretronic Corporation; *Int'l*, pg. 1800
OPTOMA TECHNOLOGY, INC.—See Coretronic Corporation; *Int'l*, pg. 1800
OPTOMA USA—See Coretronic Corporation; *Int'l*, pg. 1800
OPTOMEDICAL TECHNOLOGIES GMBH—See Metall Zug AG; *Int'l*, pg. 4847
OPTOMED OYJ; *Int'l*, pg. 5606
OPTOMED SAS—See Mars, Incorporated; *U.S. Private*, pg. 2588
OPTOMETRICS CORPORATION—See Dynasil Corporation of America; *U.S. Private*, pg. 1299
OPTOPLEX CORP.; *U.S. Private*, pg. 3036
OPTO PLUS TECHNOLOGY CO., LTD.—See Star Asia Vision Corporation; *Int'l*, pg. 7173
OPTOPOL TECHNOLOGY S.A.—See Canon Inc.; *Int'l*, pg. 1294
OPTOPRIM GERMANY GMBH—See Optoprim SAS; *Int'l*, pg. 5606
OPTOPRIM SAS; *Int'l*, pg. 5606
OPTOPRIM S.R.L.—See Optoprim SAS; *Int'l*, pg. 5606
OPTORUN CO., LTD.; *Int'l*, pg. 5606
OPTORUN (SHANGHAI) CO., LTD.—See Optorun Co., Ltd.; *Int'l*, pg. 5606
OPTORUN TAIWAN CO., LTD.—See Optorun Co., Ltd.; *Int'l*, pg. 5606
OPTORUN USA, INC.—See Optorun Co., Ltd.; *Int'l*, pg. 5606
OPTOSAT S.R.O.—See TCS TurControlSysteme AG; *Int'l*, pg. 7485
OPTOS AUSTRALIA PTY. LTD.—See Nikon Corporation; *Int'l*, pg. 5294
OPTO SENSORS HONG KONG LIMITED—See OSI Systems, Inc.; *U.S. Public*, pg. 1621
OPTOS GMBH—See Nikon Corporation; *Int'l*, pg. 5294
OPTOSIGMA CORP.; *U.S. Private*, pg. 3036
OPTOS, INC.—See Nikon Corporation; *Int'l*, pg. 5294
OPTOSKAND AB—See Coherent Corp.; *U.S. Public*, pg. 528
OPTOS PLC—See Nikon Corporation; *Int'l*, pg. 5294
OPTOTAL HOYA LIMITADA—See Hoya Corporation; *Int'l*, pg. 3498
OPTOTECH AG—See Schunk GmbH; *Int'l*, pg. 6641
OPTOTECH ASIA LTD.—See Schunk GmbH; *Int'l*, pg. 6641
OPTOTECH INDIA PVT. LTD.—See Schunk GmbH; *Int'l*, pg. 6641
OPTO TECH (MACAO) CO., LTD.—See Star Asia Vision Corporation; *Int'l*, pg. 7173
OPTOTECH OPTICAL MACHINERY INC.—See Schunk GmbH; *Int'l*, pg. 6641
OPTOTECH OPTIKMASCHINEN GMBH; *Int'l*, pg. 5606
OPTO-TECH SRL—See FARO Technologies, Inc.; *U.S. Public*, pg. 823
OPTO TECH (SUZHOU) CO., LTD.—See Star Asia Vision Corporation; *Int'l*, pg. 7173
OPTOTECH TECHNOLOGIES INC.—See Schunk GmbH; *Int'l*, pg. 6641
OPTOTEC S.P.A.—See Sterlite Technologies Limited; *Int'l*, pg. 7212
OPTOWIDE TECHNOLOGIES CO., LTD.; *Int'l*, pg. 5606
OPTREL—See Stevanato Group S.p.A.; *Int'l*, pg. 7213
OPTREX LIMITED—See Reckitt Benckiser Group plc; *Int'l*, pg. 6236
OPTRICON GMBH—See Biosynex SA; *Int'l*, pg. 1042
OPTRONIC AB; *Int'l*, pg. 5606
OPTRONIC PARTNER PR AB—See Nordstjernan AB; *Int'l*, pg. 5424
OPTRON SCIENTIFIC COMPANY INC.—See US Nuclear Corp.; *U.S. Public*, pg. 2267
OPTRONTEC INC.; *Int'l*, pg. 5606
OPT-SCIENCES CORPORATION; *U.S. Public*, pg. 1608
OPTS IDEAS; *U.S. Private*, pg. 3036
OPTSYS SAS—See GIAT Industries S.A.; *Int'l*, pg. 2962
OPT TAIWAN CO., LTD.—See OPT Machine Vision Technology Co., Ltd.; *Int'l*, pg. 5601

OPTUM360, LLC—See UnitedHealth Group Incorporated; *U.S. Public*, pg. 2247
OPTUM360, LLC—See UnitedHealth Group Incorporated; *U.S. Public*, pg. 2247
OPTUM BANK, INC.—See UnitedHealth Group Incorporated; *U.S. Public*, pg. 2248
OPTUM BIOMETRICS, INC.—See UnitedHealth Group Incorporated; *U.S. Public*, pg. 2243
OPTUMCARE FLORIDA, LLC—See UnitedHealth Group Incorporated; *U.S. Public*, pg. 2247
OPTUMCARE MANAGEMENT, LLC—See UnitedHealth Group Incorporated; *U.S. Public*, pg. 2247
OPTUMCARE SOUTH FLORIDA, LLC—See UnitedHealth Group Incorporated; *U.S. Public*, pg. 2248
OPTUM CLINICAL SOLUTIONS, INC.—See UnitedHealth Group Incorporated; *U.S. Public*, pg. 2243
OPTUM CLINICAL SOLUTIONS, LTD.—See UnitedHealth Group Incorporated; *U.S. Public*, pg. 2243
OPTUM FINANCIAL, INC.—See UnitedHealth Group Incorporated; *U.S. Public*, pg. 2248
OPTUM (FRANCE) SAS—See UnitedHealth Group Incorporated; *U.S. Public*, pg. 2243
OPTUM FRONTIER THERAPIES, LLC—See UnitedHealth Group Incorporated; *U.S. Public*, pg. 2247
OPTUM GLOBAL SOLUTIONS (INDIA) PRIVATE LIMITED—See UnitedHealth Group Incorporated; *U.S. Public*, pg. 2243
OPTUM GLOBAL SOLUTIONS INTERNATIONAL B.V.—See UnitedHealth Group Incorporated; *U.S. Public*, pg. 2243
OPTUM GOVERNMENT SOLUTIONS, INC.—See UnitedHealth Group Incorporated; *U.S. Public*, pg. 2243
OPTUMHEALTH ALLIES; *U.S. Private*, pg. 3036
OPTUMHEALTH CARE SOLUTIONS, INC.—See UnitedHealth Group Incorporated; *U.S. Public*, pg. 2248
OPTUMHEALTH HOLDINGS, LLC—See UnitedHealth Group Incorporated; *U.S. Public*, pg. 2248
OPTUMHEALTH INC.—See UnitedHealth Group Incorporated; *U.S. Public*, pg. 2248
OPTUM HEALTH SOLUTIONS (UK) LIMITED—See UnitedHealth Group Incorporated; *U.S. Public*, pg. 2243
OPTUM, INC.—See UnitedHealth Group Incorporated; *U.S. Public*, pg. 2243
OPTUM INFUSION SERVICES 100, INC.—See UnitedHealth Group Incorporated; *U.S. Public*, pg. 2243
OPTUM INFUSION SERVICES 301, LP—See UnitedHealth Group Incorporated; *U.S. Public*, pg. 2243
OPTUM INFUSION SERVICES 551, LLC—See UnitedHealth Group Incorporated; *U.S. Public*, pg. 2247
OPTUM INFUSION SERVICES 553, LLC—See UnitedHealth Group Incorporated; *U.S. Public*, pg. 2247
OPTUMINSIGHT, INC.—See UnitedHealth Group Incorporated; *U.S. Public*, pg. 2248
OPTUMINSIGHT (SWEDEN) AB—See UnitedHealth Group Incorporated; *U.S. Public*, pg. 2248
OPTUM PALLIATIVE AND HOSPICE CARE, INC.—See UnitedHealth Group Incorporated; *U.S. Public*, pg. 2243
OPTUM PERKS LLC—See UnitedHealth Group Incorporated; *U.S. Public*, pg. 2243
OPTUM PHARMACY 701, LLC—See UnitedHealth Group Incorporated; *U.S. Public*, pg. 2243
OPTUM PUBLIC SECTOR SOLUTIONS, INC.—See UnitedHealth Group Incorporated; *U.S. Public*, pg. 2243
OPTUMRX DISCOUNT CARD SERVICES, LLC—See UnitedHealth Group Incorporated; *U.S. Public*, pg. 2247
OPTUMRX HOME DELIVERY OF OHIO, LLC—See UnitedHealth Group Incorporated; *U.S. Public*, pg. 2247
OPTUMRX, INC.—See UnitedHealth Group Incorporated; *U.S. Public*, pg. 2247
OPTUMRX PBM OF ILLINOIS, INC.—See UnitedHealth Group Incorporated; *U.S. Public*, pg. 2247
OPTUMRX PBM OF WISCONSIN, LLC—See UnitedHealth Group Incorporated; *U.S. Public*, pg. 2247
OPTUMRX PD OF PENNSYLVANIA, LLC—See UnitedHealth Group Incorporated; *U.S. Public*, pg. 2247
OPTUMSERVE TECHNOLOGY SERVICES, INC.—See UnitedHealth Group Incorporated; *U.S. Public*, pg. 2248
OPTUM SERVICES (IRELAND) LIMITED—See UnitedHealth Group Incorporated; *U.S. Public*, pg. 2243
OPTUM (SPAIN) S.A.U.—See UnitedHealth Group Incorporated; *U.S. Public*, pg. 2243
OPT USA INC.—See OPT Machine Vision Technology Co., Ltd.; *Int'l*, pg. 5601
OPT USA LIMITED—See OPT Machine Vision Technology Co., Ltd.; *Int'l*, pg. 5601
OPTUS INC.; *U.S. Private*, pg. 3036
OPTUS MOBILE PTY. LTD.—See Temasek Holdings (Private) Limited; *Int'l*, pg. 7553
OPTUS PHARMACEUTICAL CO., LTD.—See Sam Chun Dang Pharm. Co., Ltd.; *Int'l*, pg. 6500
OPTYMA SECURITY SYSTEMS LTD.—See Sdiptech AB; *Int'l*, pg. 6659
OPU INC.; *U.S. Private*, pg. 3036
OPUS 3 ARTISTS GMBH—See Opus 3 Artists LLC; *U.S. Private*, pg. 3036

OPUS 3 ARTISTS LLC - LOS ANGELES—See Opus 3 Artists LLC; *U.S. Private*, pg. 3036
OPUS 3 ARTISTS LLC; *U.S. Private*, pg. 3036
OPUS AE GROUP, INC.—See Opus Holding, LLC; *U.S. Private*, pg. 3036
OPUS BILPROVNING AB—See Searchlight Capital Partners, L.P.; *U.S. Private*, pg. 3590
OPUS CAPITAL LLC; *U.S. Private*, pg. 3036
OPUS DESIGN BUILD, L.L.C.—See Opus Holding, LLC; *U.S. Private*, pg. 3036
OPUS DEVELOPMENT CORPORATION—See Opus Holding, LLC; *U.S. Private*, pg. 3036
OPUS DEVELOPMENT CORPORATION—See Opus Holding, LLC; *U.S. Private*, pg. 3036
OPUS EVENTS AGENCY; *U.S. Private*, pg. 3036
OPUS FOODS MEXICO, S.A. DE C.V.—See SunOpta Inc.; *Int'l*, pg. 7319
OPUS FORMENBAU GMBH & CO. KG—See AdCapital AG; *Int'l*, pg. 126
OPUS GLOBAL HOLDINGS LLC—See GTCR LLC; *U.S. Private*, pg. 1806
OPUS GLOBAL NYRT; *Int'l*, pg. 5606
OPUS GROUP AB—See Searchlight Capital Partners, L.P.; *U.S. Private*, pg. 3590
OPUS GROUP BERHAD—See Khazanah Nasional Berhad; *Int'l*, pg. 4154
OPUS GROUP LIMITED; *Int'l*, pg. 5606
OPUS GROUP NZ HOLDINGS LIMITED—See OPUS Group Limited; *Int'l*, pg. 5606
OPUS HEALTHCARE LIMITED—See Alliance Pharma PLC; *Int'l*, pg. 340
OPUS HOLDING, LLC; *U.S. Private*, pg. 3036
OPUS INSPECTION INC.—See Searchlight Capital Partners, L.P.; *U.S. Private*, pg. 3590
OPUS INSPECTION (PVT) LTD.—See Searchlight Capital Partners, L.P.; *U.S. Private*, pg. 3590
OPUS INSPECTION SA—See Searchlight Capital Partners, L.P.; *U.S. Private*, pg. 3590
OPUS INSPECTION VICS SINDH (PVT) LTD.—See Searchlight Capital Partners, L.P.; *U.S. Private*, pg. 3590
OPUS INTERNATIONAL (M) BERHAD—See Khazanah Nasional Berhad; *Int'l*, pg. 4154
OPUS ONE GOLD CORPORATION; *Int'l*, pg. 5606
OPUS PRINT GROUP (AUSTRALIA) PTY. LIMITED—See Knox Investment Partners Limited; *Int'l*, pg. 4214
OPUS RS EUROPE S.L.—See Searchlight Capital Partners, L.P.; *U.S. Private*, pg. 3590
OPUS SOLUTIONS, LLC; *U.S. Private*, pg. 3036
OPVANTEK, INC.—See Off Market Data, Inc.; *U.S. Private*, pg. 3001
OPW ENGINEERED SYSTEMS, INC.—See Dover Corporation; *U.S. Public*, pg. 679
OPW FLUID TRANSFER GROUP EUROPE B.V.—See Dover Corporation; *U.S. Public*, pg. 679
OPW FLUID TRANSFER SOLUTIONS (JIANG SU) CO., LTD.—See Dover Corporation; *U.S. Public*, pg. 682
OPW FRANCE—See Dover Corporation; *U.S. Public*, pg. 682
OPW FUELING COMPONENTS—See Dover Corporation; *U.S. Public*, pg. 679
OPW FUELING COMPONENTS (SUZHOU) CO., LTD.—See Dover Corporation; *U.S. Public*, pg. 679
OPW FUEL MANAGEMENT SYSTEMS, INC.—See Dover Corporation; *U.S. Public*, pg. 679
OPW MALAYSIA SDN. BHD.—See Dover Corporation; *U.S. Public*, pg. 682
OPW SLOVAKIA S.R.O.—See Dover Corporation; *U.S. Public*, pg. 682
OPW SWEDEN AB—See Dover Corporation; *U.S. Public*, pg. 682
OPX BIOTECHNOLOGIES INC.—See Cargill, Inc.; *U.S. Private*, pg. 759
OPYS PHYSICIAN SERVICES, LLC; *U.S. Private*, pg. 3036
OQ S.A.O.C.; *Int'l*, pg. 5606
ORAB ENTREPRENAD AB—See Instalco AB; *Int'l*, pg. 3722
ORACLE AMERICA, INC.—See Oracle Corporation; *U.S. Public*, pg. 1611
ORACLE ARGENTINA S.A.—See Oracle Corporation; *U.S. Public*, pg. 1611
ORACLE AUSTRIA GMBH—See Oracle Corporation; *U.S. Public*, pg. 1612
ORACLE BELGIUM BVBA—See Oracle Corporation; *U.S. Public*, pg. 1612
ORACLE CANADA - HOSPITALITY - RICHMOND—See Oracle Corporation; *U.S. Public*, pg. 1611
ORACLE CANADA ULC - MARKHAM—See Oracle Corporation; *U.S. Public*, pg. 1611
ORACLE CANADA ULC - MONTREAL—See Oracle Corporation; *U.S. Public*, pg. 1611
ORACLE CANADA ULC—See Oracle Corporation; *U.S. Public*, pg. 1611
ORACLE CARIBBEAN, INC.—See Oracle Corporation; *U.S. Public*, pg. 1611
ORACLE (CHINA) SOFTWARE SYSTEMS CO., LTD.-SHANGHAI—See Oracle Corporation; *U.S. Public*, pg. 1611

OQ S.A.O.C.

ORACLE (CHINA) SOFTWARE SYSTEMS CO., LTD.—See Oracle Corporation; *U.S. Public*, pg. 1611
ORACLE COLOMBIA LIMITADA—See Oracle Corporation; *U.S. Public*, pg. 1611
ORACLE CORPORATION (AUSTRALIA) PTY. LTD.—See Oracle Corporation; *U.S. Public*, pg. 1611
ORACLE CORPORATION JAPAN—See Oracle Corporation; *U.S. Public*, pg. 1612
ORACLE CORPORATION MALAYSIA SDN. BHD.—See Oracle Corporation; *U.S. Public*, pg. 1612
ORACLE CORPORATION (PHILIPPINES), INC.—See Oracle Corporation; *U.S. Public*, pg. 1612
ORACLE CORPORATION SINGAPORE PTE LTD—See Oracle Corporation; *U.S. Public*, pg. 1611
ORACLE CORPORATION; *U.S. Public*, pg. 1610
ORACLE CORPORATION (THAILAND) COMPANY LTD.—See Oracle Corporation; *U.S. Public*, pg. 1612
ORACLE CORPORATION UK LTD.-LONDON—See Oracle Corporation; *U.S. Public*, pg. 1612
ORACLE CORPORATION U.K. LTD.—See Oracle Corporation; *U.S. Public*, pg. 1612
ORACLE DE CENTRO AMERICA S.A.—See Oracle Corporation; *U.S. Public*, pg. 1613
ORACLE DE MEXICO, S.A. DE C.V.—See Oracle Corporation; *U.S. Public*, pg. 1613
ORACLE DENMARK APS—See Oracle Corporation; *U.S. Public*, pg. 1612
ORACLE DEUTSCHLAND B.V. & CO. KG—See Oracle Corporation; *U.S. Public*, pg. 1612
ORACLE DEUTSCHLAND B.V. & CO. KG—See Oracle Corporation; *U.S. Public*, pg. 1612
ORACLE DE VENEZUELA, S.A.—See Oracle Corporation; *U.S. Public*, pg. 1613
ORACLE DO BRASIL SISTEMAS LIMITADA—See Oracle Corporation; *U.S. Public*, pg. 1613
ORACLE EGYPT LTD.—See Oracle Corporation; *U.S. Public*, pg. 1612
ORACLE ELEVATOR COMPANY—See L Squared Capital Management LP; *U.S. Private*, pg. 2362
ORACLE ELEVATOR COMPANY - TORRINGTON—See L Squared Capital Management LP; *U.S. Private*, pg. 2362
ORACLE EMEA LIMITED—See Oracle Corporation; *U.S. Public*, pg. 1612
ORACLE ENERGY CORP.; *Int'l*, pg. 5607
ORACLE FINANCIAL SERVICES SOFTWARE B.V.—See Oracle Corporation; *U.S. Public*, pg. 1613
ORACLE FINANCIAL SERVICES SOFTWARE B.V.—See Oracle Corporation; *U.S. Public*, pg. 1613
ORACLE FINANCIAL SERVICES SOFTWARE, INC-MINNEAPOLIS—See Oracle Corporation; *U.S. Public*, pg. 1613
ORACLE FINANCIAL SERVICES SOFTWARE, INC.—See Oracle Corporation; *U.S. Public*, pg. 1613
ORACLE FINANCIAL SERVICES SOFTWARE LIMITED—See Oracle Corporation; *U.S. Public*, pg. 1612
ORACLE FINANCIAL SERVICES SOFTWARE PTE. LTD.—See Oracle Corporation; *U.S. Public*, pg. 1612
ORACLE FINANCIAL SERVICES SOFTWARE S.A.—See Oracle Corporation; *U.S. Public*, pg. 1613
ORACLE FINLAND OY—See Oracle Corporation; *U.S. Public*, pg. 1612
ORACLE FRANCE S.A.S.—See Oracle Corporation; *U.S. Public*, pg. 1613
ORACLE HARDWARE RUSSIA—See Oracle Corporation; *U.S. Public*, pg. 1611
ORACLE HELLAS, S.A.—See Oracle Corporation; *U.S. Public*, pg. 1613
ORACLE HONG KONG LIMITED—See Oracle Corporation; *U.S. Public*, pg. 1612
ORACLE HOSPITALITY—See Oracle Corporation; *U.S. Public*, pg. 1613
ORACLE IBERICA SA—See Oracle Corporation; *U.S. Public*, pg. 1613
ORACLE INDIA PRIVATE LIMITED—See Oracle Corporation; *U.S. Public*, pg. 1612
ORACLE INDIA PRIVATE LIMITED—See Oracle Corporation; *U.S. Public*, pg. 1612
ORACLE ITALIA S.R.L.—See Oracle Corporation; *U.S. Public*, pg. 1613
ORACLE KOREA LTD.—See Oracle Corporation; *U.S. Public*, pg. 1612
ORACLE NEDERLAND B.V.—See Oracle Corporation; *U.S. Public*, pg. 1613
ORACLE NEW ZEALAND LIMITED—See Oracle Corporation; *U.S. Public*, pg. 1613
ORACLE NEW ZEALAND LIMITED—See Oracle Corporation; *U.S. Public*, pg. 1613
ORACLE NORGE A/S—See Oracle Corporation; *U.S. Public*, pg. 1613
ORACLE NUMETRIX CO.—See Oracle Corporation; *U.S. Public*, pg. 1613
ORACLE (OFSS) BPO SERVICES INC.—See Oracle Corporation; *U.S. Public*, pg. 1612
ORACLE (OFSS) BPO SERVICES LIMITED—See Oracle Corporation; *U.S. Public*, pg. 1612
ORACLE POLSKA SP.Z.O.O.—See Oracle Corporation; *U.S. Public*, pg. 1613

ORACLE PORTUGAL-SISTEMAS DE INFORMACAO LDA.—See Oracle Corporation; *U.S. Public*, pg. 1613
ORACLE POWER PLC; *Int'l*, pg. 5607
ORACLE SOFTWARE D.O.O.—See Oracle Corporation; *U.S. Public*, pg. 1613
ORACLE SOFTWARE (SCHWEIZ) AG—See Oracle Corporation; *U.S. Public*, pg. 1613
ORACLE SOFTWARE TECHNOLOGY GMBH—See Oracle Corporation; *U.S. Public*, pg. 1613
ORACLE SOUTH AFRICA (PTY) LTD.—See Oracle Corporation; *U.S. Public*, pg. 1613
ORACLE SVENSKA AB—See Oracle Corporation; *U.S. Public*, pg. 1613
ORACLE SVENSKA AB—See Oracle Corporation; *U.S. Public*, pg. 1613
ORACLE SVENSKA AB—See Oracle Corporation; *U.S. Public*, pg. 1613
ORACLE TAIWAN, LLC—See Oracle Corporation; *U.S. Public*, pg. 1613
ORACLE TECHNOLOGY COMPANY—See Oracle Corporation; *U.S. Public*, pg. 1613
ORAC PUBLISHING KFT.; *Int'l*, pg. 5607
ORADEA VIE SA—See Societe Generale S.A.; *Int'l*, pg. 7040
ORAD HI-TEC SYSTEMS POLAND SP. Z.O.O.—See Symphony Technology Group, LLC; *U.S. Private*, pg. 3901
ORAD LTD.; *Int'l*, pg. 5607
ORAGENICS, INC.; *U.S. Public*, pg. 1614
ORAGIN FOODS INC; *Int'l*, pg. 5607
ORA GOLD LIMITED; *Int'l*, pg. 5607
ORA HOME LLC—See Idrees Textile Mills Limited; *Int'l*, pg. 3596
ORAHOVO A.D.; *Int'l*, pg. 5607
ORALABS, INC.—See China Precision Steel, Inc.; *Int'l*, pg. 1542
ORAL-B LABORATORIES, G.P.—See The Procter & Gamble Company; *U.S. Public*, pg. 2121
ORALDNA LABS, INC.—See Access Genetics, LLC; *U.S. Private*, pg. 51
ORAL HAMMASLAAKARIT - ITAKESKUS—See Jacobs Holding AG; *Int'l*, pg. 3865
ORAL HAMMASLAAKARIT OYJ—See Jacobs Holding AG; *Int'l*, pg. 3865
ORAL HAMMASLAAKARIT - VANTAA—See Jacobs Holding AG; *Int'l*, pg. 3865
ORAMED LTD—See Oramed Pharmaceuticals Inc.; *U.S. Public*, pg. 1614
ORAMED PHARMACEUTICALS INC.; *U.S. Public*, pg. 1614
ORAMETRIX, INC.—See DENTSPLY SIRONA Inc.; *U.S. Public*, pg. 655
ORANCO, INC.; *U.S. Public*, pg. 1614
ORANGE 1 ELECTRIC MOTORS S.P.A.—See Orange1 Holding; *Int'l*, pg. 5611
ORANGE1 HOLDING; *Int'l*, pg. 5611
ORANGE ARMENIA CJSC—See Orange S.A.; *Int'l*, pg. 5609
ORANGE ASSISTANCE SA—See Orange S.A.; *Int'l*, pg. 5610
ORANGE AUSTRIA TELECOMMUNICATION GMBH—See CK Hutchison Holdings Limited; *Int'l*, pg. 1637
ORANGE BAKERY, INC.—See Rheon Automatic Machinery Co., Ltd.; *Int'l*, pg. 6325
ORANGE BANK SA—See Orange S.A.; *Int'l*, pg. 5609
ORANGE BANK & TRUST COMPANY—See Orange County Bancorp, Inc.; *U.S. Public*, pg. 1614
ORANGE BELGIUM S.A.—See Orange S.A.; *Int'l*, pg. 5609
ORANGE & BLUE DISTRIBUTING CO. INC.; *U.S. Private*, pg. 3036
ORANGEBOX LTD.; *Int'l*, pg. 5611
ORANGEBOX MIDDLE EAST—See Orangebox Ltd.; *Int'l*, pg. 5611
ORANGEBOX US INC—See Orangebox Ltd.; *Int'l*, pg. 5611
ORANGE BUSINESS AUSTRIA GMBH—See Orange S.A.; *Int'l*, pg. 5609
ORANGE BUSINESS BELGIUM NV/SA—See Orange S.A.; *Int'l*, pg. 5609
ORANGE BUSINESS CZECH REPUBLIC S.R.O.—See Orange S.A.; *Int'l*, pg. 5609
ORANGE BUSINESS DENMARK A/S—See Orange S.A.; *Int'l*, pg. 5609
ORANGE BUSINESS FINLAND OY—See Orange S.A.; *Int'l*, pg. 5609
ORANGE BUSINESS GERMANY GMBH—See Orange S.A.; *Int'l*, pg. 5609
ORANGE BUSINESS ITALY S.P.A.—See Orange S.A.; *Int'l*, pg. 5609
ORANGE BUSINESS LUXEMBOURG SA—See Orange S.A.; *Int'l*, pg. 5609
ORANGE BUSINESS NETHERLANDS B.V.—See Orange S.A.; *Int'l*, pg. 5609
ORANGE BUSINESS NORWAY AS—See Orange S.A.; *Int'l*, pg. 5609
ORANGE BUSINESS SERVICES - ARGENTINA—See Orange S.A.; *Int'l*, pg. 5609

CORPORATE AFFILIATIONS

ORANGE BUSINESS SERVICES AUSTRALIA PTY. LTD.—See Orange S.A.; *Int'l*, pg. 5609
ORANGE BUSINESS SERVICES - BRAZIL—See Orange S.A.; *Int'l*, pg. 5609
ORANGE BUSINESS SERVICES CANADA INC.—See Orange S.A.; *Int'l*, pg. 5610
ORANGE BUSINESS SERVICES - CHILE—See Orange S.A.; *Int'l*, pg. 5609
ORANGE BUSINESS SERVICES - CHINA—See Orange S.A.; *Int'l*, pg. 5609
ORANGE BUSINESS SERVICES - COLOMBIA—See Orange S.A.; *Int'l*, pg. 5609
ORANGE BUSINESS SERVICES - DUBAI—See Orange S.A.; *Int'l*, pg. 5609
ORANGE BUSINESS SERVICES - EGYPT—See Orange S.A.; *Int'l*, pg. 5609
ORANGE BUSINESS SERVICES - FRANCE—See Orange S.A.; *Int'l*, pg. 5609
ORANGE BUSINESS SERVICES - ICELAND—See Orange S.A.; *Int'l*, pg. 5609
ORANGE BUSINESS SERVICES - INDIA—See Orange S.A.; *Int'l*, pg. 5609
ORANGE BUSINESS SERVICES - IRELAND—See Orange S.A.; *Int'l*, pg. 5610
ORANGE BUSINESS SERVICES - JAPAN—See Orange S.A.; *Int'l*, pg. 5610
ORANGE BUSINESS SERVICES - MEXICO—See Orange S.A.; *Int'l*, pg. 5610
ORANGE BUSINESS SERVICES PARTICIPATIONS—See Orange S.A.; *Int'l*, pg. 5609
ORANGE BUSINESS SERVICES - PORTUGAL—See Orange S.A.; *Int'l*, pg. 5610
ORANGE BUSINESS SERVICES - ROMANIA—See Orange S.A.; *Int'l*, pg. 5610
ORANGE BUSINESS SERVICES SINGAPORE PTE. LTD.—See Orange S.A.; *Int'l*, pg. 5610
ORANGE BUSINESS SERVICES SLOVAKIA S.R.O.—See Orange S.A.; *Int'l*, pg. 5610
ORANGE BUSINESS SERVICES - SOUTH AFRICA—See Orange S.A.; *Int'l*, pg. 5610
ORANGE BUSINESS SERVICES - TAIWAN—See Orange S.A.; *Int'l*, pg. 5610
ORANGE BUSINESS SERVICES - TURKEY—See Orange S.A.; *Int'l*, pg. 5610
ORANGE BUSINESS SERVICES U.S. INC. - ATLANTA—See Orange S.A.; *Int'l*, pg. 5610
ORANGE BUSINESS SERVICES U.S., INC.—See Orange S.A.; *Int'l*, pg. 5610
ORANGE BUSINESS SERVICES - VIETNAM—See Orange S.A.; *Int'l*, pg. 5610
ORANGE BUSINESS SPAIN SA—See Orange S.A.; *Int'l*, pg. 5610
ORANGE BUSINESS SWITZERLAND AG—See Orange S.A.; *Int'l*, pg. 5610
ORANGE BW—See Orange S.A.; *Int'l*, pg. 5609
ORANGE CANADA—See Orange S.A.; *Int'l*, pg. 5609
ORANGE CAPITAL VENTURES GP, LLC; *U.S. Private*, pg. 3036
ORANGE CATALUNYA XAXET DE TELECOMUNICACIONS S.A.—See Orange S.A.; *Int'l*, pg. 5610
ORANGE CITY SURGERY CENTER, LLC—See Bain Capital, LP; *U.S. Private*, pg. 446
ORANGE CLOVE CATERING PTE. LTD.—See Neo Group Limited; *Int'l*, pg. 5196
ORANGE COAST MAGAZINE, LLC—See Hour Media Group, LLC; *U.S. Private*, pg. 1991
ORANGE COAST TITLE COMPANY INC.; *U.S. Private*, pg. 3036
ORANGE COAST TITLE COMPANY OF LOS ANGELES—See Orange Coast Title Company Inc.; *U.S. Private*, pg. 3037
ORANGE COAST TITLE COMPANY—See Orange Coast Title Company Inc.; *U.S. Private*, pg. 3037
ORANGE COMMERICAL CREDIT, INC.; *U.S. Private*, pg. 3037
ORANGE COMMUNICATIONS LUXEMBOURG S.A.—See Orange S.A.; *Int'l*, pg. 5610
ORANGE COMMUNICATIONS—See WPP plc; *Int'l*, pg. 8472
ORANGE CONSULTING—See Orange S.A.; *Int'l*, pg. 5610
ORANGE CORPSEC SPOL. S R.O.—See Orange S.A.; *Int'l*, pg. 5610
ORANGE COTE D'IVOIRE SA—See Orange S.A.; *Int'l*, pg. 5610
ORANGE COUNTY ADULT ACHIEVEMENT CENTER; *U.S. Private*, pg. 3037
ORANGE COUNTY BANCORP, INC.; *U.S. Public*, pg. 1614
ORANGE COUNTY BUILDING MATERIALS INC.; *U.S. Private*, pg. 3037
ORANGE COUNTY HEAD START, INC.; *U.S. Private*, pg. 3037
ORANGE COUNTY NATIONAL GOLF CENTER & LODGE; *U.S. Private*, pg. 3037
ORANGE COUNTY PRINTING—See Chatham Asset Management, LLC; *U.S. Private*, pg. 863
ORANGE COUNTY RADIATION ONCOLOGY, LLC—See RadNet, Inc.; *U.S. Public*, pg. 1761

COMPANY NAME INDEX

THE ORANGE COUNTY REGISTER—See Alden Global Capital LLC; *U.S. Private*, pg. 159
ORANGE COUNTY REMC; *U.S. Private*, pg. 3037
ORANGE COUNTY SCHOOL READINESS COALITION, INC.; *U.S. Private*, pg. 3037
ORANGE COUNTY'S CREDIT UNION; *U.S. Private*, pg. 3037
ORANGE COUNTY SPEAKER, INC.; *U.S. Private*, pg. 3037
ORANGE COUNTY TRANSPORTATION AUTHORITY; *U.S. Private*, pg. 3037
ORANGE COUNTY WATER DISTRICT; *U.S. Private*, pg. 3037
ORANGE CYBERDEFENSE SA—See Orange S.A.; *Int'l*, pg. 5609
ORANGE DIALYSIS, LLC—See DaVita Inc.; *U.S. Public*, pg. 641
ORANGE DOMINICANA SA—See Altice Europe N.V.; *Int'l*, pg. 392
ORANGE EGYPT FOR TELECOMMUNICATIONS S.A.E.—See Orange S.A.; *Int'l*, pg. 5610
ORANGE ENERGY LIMITED—See PTT Public Company Limited; *Int'l*, pg. 6092
ORANGE ESPANA—See Orange S.A.; *Int'l*, pg. 5610
ORANGEE SRL—See Leonardo S.p.A.; *Int'l*, pg. 4460
ORANGE FOOD COURT—See AEON Co., Ltd.; *Int'l*, pg. 178
ORANGE FRANCE SA—See Orange S.A.; *Int'l*, pg. 5610
ORANGE GROVE CO-OPERATIVE; *U.S. Private*, pg. 3037
ORANGE HEALTH CARE CENTER—See Apollo Global Management, Inc.; *U.S. Public*, pg. 157
ORANGE HOLDING S.A.—See Orange S.A.; *Int'l*, pg. 5609
ORANGEHOOK, INC.; *U.S. Public*, pg. 1614
ORANGE JULIUS OF AMERICA—See Berkshire Hathaway Inc.; *U.S. Public*, pg. 308
ORANGE LABEL ART & ADVERTISING; *U.S. Private*, pg. 3037
ORANGE LAKE COUNTRY CLUB, INC.—See Kemmons Wilson, Inc.; *U.S. Private*, pg. 2281
ORANGE LAKE COUNTRY CLUB REALTY, INC.—See Kemmons Wilson, Inc.; *U.S. Private*, pg. 2281
ORANGE LIFE INSURANCE CO., LTD.—See Shinhan Financial Group Co., Ltd.; *Int'l*, pg. 6843
ORANGE LINE OIL COMPANY, INC.—See AIP, LLC; *U.S. Private*, pg. 136
ORANGE MAISON—See Lassonde Industries, Inc.; *Int'l*, pg. 4421
ORANGE MINERALS NL; *Int'l*, pg. 5607
ORANGE MOLDOVA SA—See Orange S.A.; *Int'l*, pg. 5610
ORANGE MOTOR COMPANY INC.; *U.S. Private*, pg. 3037
ORANGE MOTORS B.V.—See General Motors Company; *U.S. Public*, pg. 927
ORANGE NETWORK SA—See Orange S.A.; *Int'l*, pg. 5610
ORANGE NETWORKS GMBH—See Datatec Limited; *Int'l*, pg. 1981
ORANGE ORTHODONTICS & DENTOFACIAL ORTHOPAEDICS PTE. LTD.—See New Silkroutes Group Limited; *Int'l*, pg. 5227
ORANGE PARK ENDOSCOPY CENTER, LLC—See Tenet Healthcare Corporation; *U.S. Public*, pg. 2006
ORANGE PARK MALL, LLC—See Washington Prime Group Inc.; *U.S. Private*, pg. 4448
ORANGE PARK MEDICAL CENTER, INC.—See HCA Healthcare, Inc.; *U.S. Public*, pg. 1005
ORANGE PARK SURGERY CENTER—See HCA Healthcare, Inc.; *U.S. Public*, pg. 1005
ORANGE PEEL ENTERPRISES, INC.; *U.S. Private*, pg. 3037
ORANGE POLSKA S.A.—See Orange S.A.; *Int'l*, pg. 5610
ORANGE POWER T & D EQUIPMENTS PVT. LTD.—See AT Capital Pte Limited; *Int'l*, pg. 664
ORANGE P.R. LTD.—See Mitsui O.S.K. Lines, Ltd.; *Int'l*, pg. 4991
ORANGE & ROCKLAND UTILITIES, INC.—See Consolidated Edison, Inc.; *U.S. Public*, pg. 570
ORANGE S.A.; *Int'l*, pg. 5607
ORANGE SHIPBUILDING COMPANY, INC.—See Conrad Industries, Inc.; *U.S. Public*, pg. 569
ORANGE SKY GOLDEN HARVEST ENTERTAINMENT (HOLDINGS) LIMITED; *Int'l*, pg. 5611
ORANGE SLOVENSKO, A.S.—See Orange S.A.; *Int'l*, pg. 5610
ORANGESODA, INC.—See Deluxe Corporation; *U.S. Public*, pg. 653
ORANGE SPORT—See Orange S.A.; *Int'l*, pg. 5610
THE ORANGE SQUARE COMPANY LTD.—See Kering S.A.; *Int'l*, pg. 4136
ORANGE SUPPORT SERVICES LIMITED—See Aramark; *U.S. Public*, pg. 178
ORANGE TOUR CULTURAL HOLDING LIMITED; *Int'l*, pg. 5611
ORANGE TREE EMPLOYMENT SCREENING LLC—See Boathouse Capital Management, LLC; *U.S. Private*, pg. 603
ORANGE TREE STAFFING, LLC; *U.S. Private*, pg. 3037

ORANGE VALLEY NURSING HOMES PTE. LTD.—See Singapore Press Holdings Limited; *Int'l*, pg. 6942
ORANGE VEHICLE SALES LLC—See Tesla, Inc.; *U.S. Public*, pg. 2021
ORANGEVILLE CHRYSLER LIMITED; *Int'l*, pg. 5611
ORANGEVILLE RACEWAY LIMITED—See Great Canadian Gaming Corporation; *Int'l*, pg. 3063
ORANGE WATER & SEWER AUTHORITY; *U.S. Private*, pg. 3037
ORANGEWOOD PARTNERS LLC; *U.S. Private*, pg. 3038
ORANGE WORLD INC.; *U.S. Private*, pg. 3038
ORANGINA SCHWEPPES BELGIUM SA/NV—See Suntory Holdings Limited; *Int'l*, pg. 7327
ORANGINA SCHWEPPES HOLDING B.V.—See Suntory Holdings Limited; *Int'l*, pg. 7326
ORANGINA SCHWEPPES INTERNATIONAL—See Suntory Holdings Limited; *Int'l*, pg. 7327
ORANGINA SCHWEPPES S.A.S.—See Suntory Holdings Limited; *Int'l*, pg. 7326
ORANGUTAN HOME SERVICES; *U.S. Private*, pg. 3038
ORANJE-NASSAU GROEP B.V.—See Wendel S.A.; *Int'l*, pg. 8376
ORANJE-NASSAU PARTICIPATIES B.V.—See Wendel S.A.; *Int'l*, pg. 8376
ORANJEWOUD N.V.—See Centric Holding B.V.; *Int'l*, pg. 1412
ORANJTEK CO.; *U.S. Private*, pg. 3038
ORANO CANADA INC.—See Orano SA; *Int'l*, pg. 5611
ORANO CYCLE SA—See Orano SA; *Int'l*, pg. 5611
ORANO JAPAN CO., LTD.—See Orano SA; *Int'l*, pg. 5611
ORANO KOREA LTD.—See Orano SA; *Int'l*, pg. 5611
ORANO PROJECTS LTD.—See Orano SA; *Int'l*, pg. 5611
ORANO SA; *Int'l*, pg. 5611
ORANO USA LLC—See Orano SA; *Int'l*, pg. 5611
ORANZERII HAMZALI AD; *Int'l*, pg. 5612
ORAPHARMA, INC.—See Bausch Health Companies Inc.; *Int'l*, pg. 898
ORAPI APPLIED BELGIUM S.A.—See Orapi S.A.; *Int'l*, pg. 5612
ORAPI APPLIED LTD—See Orapi S.A.; *Int'l*, pg. 5612
ORAPI APPLIED (M) SDN BHD—See Orapi S.A.; *Int'l*, pg. 5612
ORAPI APPLIED NEDERLAND B.V—See Orapi S.A.; *Int'l*, pg. 5612
ORAPI APPLIED (S) PTE LTD—See Orapi S.A.; *Int'l*, pg. 5612
ORAPI APPLIED (T) CO., LTD.—See Orapi S.A.; *Int'l*, pg. 5612
ORAPI CANADA LTD—See Orapi S.A.; *Int'l*, pg. 5612
ORAPI CHILE S.A—See Orapi S.A.; *Int'l*, pg. 5612
ORAPI DRY-SHINE INC.—See Orapi S.A.; *Int'l*, pg. 5612
ORAPI HYGIENE ILE DE FRANCE SASU—See Orapi S.A.; *Int'l*, pg. 5612
ORAPI ITALIA SRL—See Orapi S.A.; *Int'l*, pg. 5612
ORAPI MIDDLE EAST L.L.C.—See Orapi S.A.; *Int'l*, pg. 5612
ORAPI NORDIC OY AB—See Orapi S.A.; *Int'l*, pg. 5612
ORAPI NORDIC OY AB—See Orapi S.A.; *Int'l*, pg. 5612
ORAPI NORWAY OY AB—See Orapi S.A.; *Int'l*, pg. 5612
ORAPI PACIFIC - ORAPI AFRICA LTD.—See Orapi S.A.; *Int'l*, pg. 5612
ORAPI PACIFIC PROLUB CIE LTD—See Orapi S.A.; *Int'l*, pg. 5612
ORAPI PACIFIC SALT (PTY) LDT—See Orapi S.A.; *Int'l*, pg. 5612
ORAPI PACIFIC SFAC SARL—See Orapi S.A.; *Int'l*, pg. 5612
ORAPI PACIFIC TECHNIPAC SARL—See Orapi S.A.; *Int'l*, pg. 5612
ORAPI PACIFIC-VICTORIA LUB PTY LTD—See Orapi S.A.; *Int'l*, pg. 5612
ORAPI S.A.; *Int'l*, pg. 5612
ORAPI TRANSNET ESPANA, SL—See Orapi S.A.; *Int'l*, pg. 5612
ORAPI TRANSNET SP. Z O.O.—See Orapi S.A.; *Int'l*, pg. 5612
ORA RESORT CO., LTD.—See Daelim Industrial Co., Ltd.; *Int'l*, pg. 1908
ORAS AS—See Bravida Holding AB; *Int'l*, pg. 1142
ORASCOM CONSTRUCTION INDUSTRIES ALGERIA SPA—See Orascom Construction PLC; *Int'l*, pg. 5613
ORASCOM CONSTRUCTION INDUSTRIES SAE—See Orascom Construction PLC; *Int'l*, pg. 5613
ORASCOM CONSTRUCTION PLC; *Int'l*, pg. 5612
ORASCOM DEVELOPMENT EGYPT—See Orascom Development Holding AG; *Int'l*, pg. 5613
ORASCOM DEVELOPMENT HOLDING AG; *Int'l*, pg. 5613
ORASCOM E&C USA INC—See Orascom Construction PLC; *Int'l*, pg. 5613
ORASCOM FINANCIAL HOLDING SAE—See B Investments Holding SAE; *Int'l*, pg. 783
ORASCOM HOUSING COMPANY—See Orascom Development Holding AG; *Int'l*, pg. 5613
ORASCOM TELECOM ALGERIE SPA—See Fonds National d'Investissement; *Int'l*, pg. 2725
ORASCOM TELECOM ALGERIE SPA—See VEON Ltd.; *Int'l*, pg. 8163

ORBIS CORPORATION

ORASCOM TELECOM BANGLADESH LTD.—See VEON Ltd.; *Int'l*, pg. 8163
ORASCOM TELECOM MEDIA & TECHNOLOGY HOLDING SAE—See VEON Ltd.; *Int'l*, pg. 8163
ORASCOM TRADING COMPANY—See Orascom Construction PLC; *Int'l*, pg. 5613
ORASI SOFTWARE, INC.; *U.S. Private*, pg. 3038
ORASURE TECHNOLOGIES, INC.; *U.S. Public*, pg. 1614
ORATECH COMPANY—See Raya Holding Company; *Int'l*, pg. 6223
ORAVEIEN INDUSTRIPARK AS—See Orkla ASA; *Int'l*, pg. 5638
ORAVEL STAYS LIMITED; *Int'l*, pg. 5613
ORAZUL ENERGY CERROS COLORADOS, S.A.—See I Squared Capital Advisors (US) LLC; *U.S. Private*, pg. 2026
ORAZUL ENERGY CORPORATION—See I Squared Capital Advisors (US) LLC; *U.S. Private*, pg. 2025
ORAZUL ENERGY EGENOR S. EN C. POR A.—See I Squared Capital Advisors (US) LLC; *U.S. Private*, pg. 2026
ORAZUL ENERGY EL SALVADOR, S. EN C. DE C.V.—See I Squared Capital Advisors (US) LLC; *U.S. Private*, pg. 2026
ORAZUL ENERGY GENERATING S.A.—See I Squared Capital Advisors (US) LLC; *U.S. Private*, pg. 2026
ORAZUL ENERGY GUATEMALA Y COMPANIA SOCIEDAD EN COMANDITA POR ACCIONES—See I Squared Capital Advisors (US) LLC; *U.S. Private*, pg. 2026
ORAZUL ENERGY INTERNATIONAL CHILE C.P.A.—See I Squared Capital Advisors (US) LLC; *U.S. Private*, pg. 2026
ORAZUL ENERGY INTERNATIONAL SOUTHERN CONE S.R.L.—See I Squared Capital Advisors (US) LLC; *U.S. Private*, pg. 2026
ORBAEKVEJ 280 A/S—See Schneider Electric SE; *Int'l*, pg. 6628
ORBAN—See Nabro Able LLC; *U.S. Private*, pg. 2829
ORBCOMM DEUTSCHLAND SATELLITENKOMMUNIKATION AG—See Hiscox Ltd.; *Int'l*, pg. 3407
ORBCOMM EUROPE, B.V.—See ORBCOMM, Inc.; *U.S. Public*, pg. 1614
ORBCOMM EUROPE GMBH—See ORBCOMM, Inc.; *U.S. Public*, pg. 1614
ORBCOMM, INC.; *U.S. Public*, pg. 1614
ORBCOMM IRELAND LTD.—See ORBCOMM, Inc.; *U.S. Public*, pg. 1614
ORBEA S. COOP.—See Mondragon Corporation; *Int'l*, pg. 5031
ORBE CANADA INC.—See AVK Holding A/S; *Int'l*, pg. 748
ORBELAN PLASTICOS, S.A.—See Cie Automotive S.A.; *Int'l*, pg. 1605
ORBEL CORPORATION; *U.S. Private*, pg. 3038
ORB ELECTRICAL STEELS LTD—See Tata Sons Limited; *Int'l*, pg. 7471
ORB ENERGY PVT. LTD.; *Int'l*, pg. 5613
ORBEO CLIMATE CARE S.A.S.—See Solvay S.A.; *Int'l*, pg. 7078
ORBETH, INC.—See MarineMax, Inc.; *U.S. Public*, pg. 1367
ORBE VALVE INC.—See AVK Holding A/S; *Int'l*, pg. 748
ORBIA ADVANCE CORPORATION, S.A.B. DE C.V.—See Grupo Empresarial Kaluz S.A. de C.V.; *Int'l*, pg. 3127
ORBIA ARGENTINA S.A.U.—See Bayer Aktiengesellschaft; *Int'l*, pg. 909
ORBICOM (PTY) LIMITED—See MTN Group Limited; *Int'l*, pg. 5071
ORBICON A/S—See WSP Global, Inc.; *Int'l*, pg. 8497
ORBID S.A. - INDUSTRIA E COMERCIO; *Int'l*, pg. 5613
ORBIMED ADVISORS LLC; *U.S. Private*, pg. 3038
ORBINOX BRASIL INDUSTRIA E COMERCIO LTDA.—See AVK Holding A/S; *Int'l*, pg. 748
ORBINOX COMERCIAL S.L.—See AVK Holding A/S; *Int'l*, pg. 748
ORBINOX DEUTSHLAND GMBH—See AVK Holding A/S; *Int'l*, pg. 748
ORBINOX S.A.—See AVK Holding A/S; *Int'l*, pg. 748
ORBINOX VALVES INTERNATIONAL SA—See AVK Holding A/S; *Int'l*, pg. 748
ORBIS AMERICA INC.—See Orbis SE; *Int'l*, pg. 5614
ORBISAT INDUSTRIA E AEROLEVANTAMENTO S.A.—See Embraer S.A.; *Int'l*, pg. 2376
ORBIS AUSTRIA GMBH—See Orbis SE; *Int'l*, pg. 5614
ORBIS CASCADE ALLIANCE; *U.S. Private*, pg. 3038
ORBIS CLINICAL, LLC—See Webster Equity Partners, LLC; *U.S. Private*, pg. 4467
ORBIS CONSULTING SHANGHAI CO., LTD.—See Orbis SE; *Int'l*, pg. 5614
ORBIS CORPORATION - LEWISBINS+ DIVISION—See Menasha Corporation; *U.S. Private*, pg. 2666
ORBIS CORPORATION—See Menasha Corporation; *U.S. Private*, pg. 2665
ORBIS CORPORATION; *Int'l*, pg. 5613
ORBIS EDUCATION SERVICES, LLC—See Grand Canyon Education, Inc.; *U.S. Public*, pg. 957
ORBIS FRANCE SA—See Orbis SE; *Int'l*, pg. 5614
ORBIS INC.—See Pola Orbis Holdings Inc.; *Int'l*, pg. 5905

ORBIS CORPORATION
CORPORATE AFFILIATIONS

ORBIS (INDIA) PVT. LTD.—See Orbis Systems Oy; *Int'l*, pg. 5614
ORBIS INTERNATIONAL TECHNOLOGIES, INC.—See Orbis Systems Oy; *Int'l*, pg. 5614
ORBIS INVESTMENT LTD.—See Amdocs Limited; *Int'l*, pg. 420
ORBISONIA COMMUNITY BANCORP INC.; *U.S. Private*, pg. 3038
ORBIS OPERATIONS, LLC—See McNally Capital, LLC; *U.S. Private*, pg. 2643
ORBIS OY EESTI FILIAA—See Orbis Oy; *Int'l*, pg. 5613
ORBIS OY; *Int'l*, pg. 5613
ORBIS PROPERTIES SOCIMI, S.A.U.; *Int'l*, pg. 5613
ORBIS PROTECT LIMITED—See Synova Capital LLP; *Int'l*, pg. 7386
ORBIS S.A.—See Accor S.A.; *Int'l*, pg. 92
ORBIS SCHWEIZ AG—See Orbis SE; *Int'l*, pg. 5614
ORBIS SE; *Int'l*, pg. 5614
ORBIS (SHANGHAI) MATERIAL HANDLING CO., LTD.—See Menasha Corporation; *U.S. Private*, pg. 2665
ORBIS SYSTEMS OY; *Int'l*, pg. 5614
ORBIS TECHNOLOGIES, INC.; *U.S. Private*, pg. 3038
ORBIS TRANSPORT SP. Z O.O.—See Accor S.A.; *Int'l*, pg. 92
ORBITA, AGENCIA DE SEGUROS—See Grupo Catalana Occidente, S.A.; *Int'l*, pg. 3124
ORBITA CORPORATION; *U.S. Private*, pg. 3038
ORBITA, INC.; *U.S. Private*, pg. 3038
ORBITAL AUSTRALIA PTY LTD—See Orbital Corporation Limited; *Int'l*, pg. 5614
ORBITAL CORPORATION LIMITED; *Int'l*, pg. 5614
ORBITAL GAS SYSTEMS LTD.—See Orbital Infrastructure Group, Inc.; *U.S. Public*, pg. 1615
ORBITAL GAS SYSTEMS, NORTH AMERICA, INC.—See Orbital Infrastructure Group, Inc.; *U.S. Public*, pg. 1615
ORBITAL INFRASTRUCTURE GROUP, INC.; *U.S. Public*, pg. 1615
ORBITAL MEDIA NETWORKS, INC.—See Satellite Holdings, Inc.; *U.S. Private*, pg. 3553
ORBITAL POWER, INC.—See Orbital Infrastructure Group, Inc.; *U.S. Public*, pg. 1615
ORBITAL RENEWABLES, LLC—See Orbital Infrastructure Group, Inc.; *U.S. Public*, pg. 1615
ORBITAL SATCOM CORP.—See NextPlat Corp.; *U.S. Public*, pg. 1526
ORBITAL SCIENCES CORPORATION—See Northrop Grumman Corporation; *U.S. Public*, pg. 1541
ORBITAL SHOPPING PARK SWINDON LIMITED—See The British Land Company PLC; *Int'l*, pg. 7628
ORBITAL SOLAR SERVICES, LLC—See Orbital Infrastructure Group, Inc.; *U.S. Public*, pg. 1615
ORBITAL SYSTEMS, LTD.—See Odyssey Investment Partners, LLC; *U.S. Private*, pg. 2995
ORBITAL TECHNOLOGIES CORP.—See Sierra Nevada Corporation; *U.S. Private*, pg. 3647
ORBITAL UAV USA, LLC—See Orbital Corporation Limited; *Int'l*, pg. 5614
ORBITALUM TOOLS GMBH—See Illinois Tool Works Inc.; *U.S. Public*, pg. 1109
ORBIT BABY, INC.—See Compass Diversified Holdings; *U.S. Public*, pg. 560
ORBIT BUSINESS TECHNOLOGIES—See Circle Computer Resources, Inc.; *U.S. Private*, pg. 899
ORBIT CORPORATION LTD; *Int'l*, pg. 5614
ORBIT DEVELOPMENTS (SOUTHERN) LIMITED—See Emerson Developments (Holdings) Limited; *Int'l*, pg. 2380
ORBITEC AB—See AFRY AB; *Int'l*, pg. 194
ORBITECH CO., LTD.; *Int'l*, pg. 5614
ORBITEL COMMUNICATIONS, LLC—See Schurz Communications, Inc.; *U.S. Private*, pg. 3571
ORBITEL HOLDINGS, LLC—See Schurz Communications, Inc.; *U.S. Private*, pg. 3571
ORBIT EXPORTS LTD; *Int'l*, pg. 5614
ORBIT EXPORTS LTD.; *U.S. Private*, pg. 3038
ORBITFORM GROUP, LLC; *U.S. Private*, pg. 3038
ORBIT/FR, INC.—See Microwave Vision SA; *Int'l*, pg. 4882
ORBIT GARANT DRILLING INC.; *Int'l*, pg. 5614
ORBIT HOMES AUSTRALIA PTY. LTD.; *Int'l*, pg. 5614
ORBIT INTERNATIONAL CORP.; *U.S. Public*, pg. 1614
ORBIT IRRIGATION PRODUCTS INC.—See Platinum Equity, LLC; *U.S. Private*, pg. 3207
ORBIT LOGIC, INC.—See Enlightenment Capital LLC; *U.S. Private*, pg. 1400
ORBIT MEDIA STUDIOS, INC.; *U.S. Private*, pg. 3038
ORBIT MOVERS & ERECTORS—See Unitize Company Inc.; *U.S. Private*, pg. 4302
ORBIT PROJECTS PRIVATE LIMITED—See Emami Ltd; *Int'l*, pg. 2774
ORBIT SHEET METAL CO. INC.—See Unitize Company Inc.; *U.S. Private*, pg. 4302
ORBIT SINGAPORE PTE. LTD.—See Orbit Technologies Ltd.; *Int'l*, pg. 5614
ORBIT SYSTEMS, INC.; *U.S. Private*, pg. 3038
ORBIT TECHNOLOGIES LTD.; *Int'l*, pg. 5614
ORBITZ WORLDWIDE, LLC—See Expedia Group, Inc.; *U.S. Public*, pg. 809

ORBOGRAPH LTD.—See KLA Corporation; *U.S. Public*, pg. 1268
ORBOTECH ASIA LTD.—See KLA Corporation; *U.S. Public*, pg. 1268
ORBOTECH ELECTRONICS (SHENZHEN) CO., LTD.—See KLA Corporation; *U.S. Public*, pg. 1268
ORBOTECH ELECTRONICS (SUZHOU) CO., LTD.—See KLA Corporation; *U.S. Public*, pg. 1268
ORBOTECH INC.—See KLA Corporation; *U.S. Public*, pg. 1268
ORBOTECH JAPAN CO., LTD.—See KLA Corporation; *U.S. Public*, pg. 1268
ORBOTECH LTD.—See KLA Corporation; *U.S. Public*, pg. 1268
ORBOTECH LT SOLAR, LLC—See KLA Corporation; *U.S. Public*, pg. 1268
ORBOTECH PACIFIC LTD.—See KLA Corporation; *U.S. Public*, pg. 1268
ORBOTECH S.A., EUROPE—See KLA Corporation; *U.S. Public*, pg. 1268
ORBOTECH SINGAPORE CORPORATION PTE. LTD.—See KLA Corporation; *U.S. Public*, pg. 1268
ORBUSNEICH MEDICAL GROUP HOLDINGS LIMITED; *Int'l*, pg. 5614
ORBUSNEICH MEDICAL KK—See OrbusNeich Medical Group Holdings Limited; *Int'l*, pg. 5615
ORBUS PHARMA INC.; *Int'l*, pg. 5614
ORCA BAY SEAFOODS, INC.—See Tokusui Corporation; *Int'l*, pg. 7786
ORCADIAN ENERGY PLC; *Int'l*, pg. 5615
ORCA ENERGY GROUP INC.; *Int'l*, pg. 5615
ORCA GLOBAL DISRUPTION FUND; *Int'l*, pg. 5615
ORCA GOLD, INC.—See Perseus Mining Limited; *Int'l*, pg. 5814
ORCA INVESTMENT PLC; *Int'l*, pg. 5615
ORCA SAND & GRAVEL LTD.—See Vulcan Materials Company; *U.S. Public*, pg. 2314
ORCA SPECIALTY FOODS LTD.; *Int'l*, pg. 5615
ORCAS POWER & LIGHT COOP; *U.S. Private*, pg. 3039
ORC AUS PTY LTD—See Lake Capital Management LLC; *U.S. Private*, pg. 2374
ORC AUSTRALIA PTY LTD.—See Broadridge Financial Solutions, Inc.; *U.S. Public*, pg. 392
ORC EDUCATION AB—See Broadridge Financial Solutions, Inc.; *U.S. Public*, pg. 392
ORC EXNET TRANSACTION SERVICES AB—See Broadridge Financial Solutions, Inc.; *U.S. Public*, pg. 392
ORC GROUP AB—See Broadridge Financial Solutions, Inc.; *U.S. Public*, pg. 392
ORCHARD 290 LTD.—See Singapore Press Holdings Ltd.; *Int'l*, pg. 6942
ORCHARD ADVERTISING—See Publicis Groupe S.A.; *Int'l*, pg. 6101
ORCHARD BOOKS, INC.—See Scholastic Corporation; *U.S. Public*, pg. 1847
ORCHARD CHRYSLER DODGE JEEP; *U.S. Private*, pg. 3039
ORCHARD ENERGY LIMITED—See World Kinect Corporation; *U.S. Public*, pg. 2381
ORCHARD FORD SALES LTD.; *Int'l*, pg. 5615
ORCHARD FUNDING GROUP PLC; *Int'l*, pg. 5615
ORCHARD FUNDING LIMITED—See Orchard Funding Group PLC; *Int'l*, pg. 5615
ORCHARD HEIGHTS, INC.—See The Hamister Group, Inc.; *U.S. Private*, pg. 4042
ORCHARD, HILTZ & MCCLIMENT INC.; *U.S. Private*, pg. 3039
ORCHARD HOLDINGS GROUP LLC; *U.S. Private*, pg. 3039
ORCHARD HOMES AND DEVELOPMENTS LIMITED; *Int'l*, pg. 5615
ORCHARD HOUSE FOODS LIMITED—See Elaghmore GP LLP; *Int'l*, pg. 2342
THE ORCHARD IMAGING CENTRE PTE LTD—See Asia-Medic Ltd.; *Int'l*, pg. 617
ORCHARD INC.; *U.S. Private*, pg. 3039
ORCHARD MANOR (CHEDDINGTON) RESIDENTS MANAGEMENT COMPANY LIMITED—See Persimmon plc; *Int'l*, pg. 5816
ORCHARD MARITIME LOGISTICS PTE LTD—See PT Adaro Energy Indonesia Tbk; *Int'l*, pg. 6019
ORCHARD MEADOWS (IWADE) RESIDENTS MANAGEMENT COMPANY LIMITED—See Persimmon plc; *Int'l*, pg. 5816
THE ORCHARD MEDIA, INC.—See JDS Capital Management, Inc.; *U.S. Private*, pg. 2196
ORCHARD MEWS PERSHORE MANAGEMENT COMPANY LIMITED—See Persimmon plc; *Int'l*, pg. 5816
ORCHARD PARADE HOLDINGS LTD.—See Far East Organization Pte. Ltd.; *Int'l*, pg. 2617
ORCHARD PORTMAN HOSPITAL LIMITED—See Universal Health Services, Inc.; *U.S. Public*, pg. 2258
ORCHARD RIDGE CARE & REHABILITATION CENTER—See Formation Capital, LLC; *U.S. Private*, pg. 1571
ORCHARD SQUARE LIMITED—See London & Associated Properties PLC; *Int'l*, pg. 4546
ORCHARD SUPPLY COMPANY, LLC—See Lowe's Companies, Inc.; *U.S. Public*, pg. 1343

ORCHARD THERAPEUTICS PLC—See Kirin Holdings Company, Limited; *Int'l*, pg. 4189
ORCHARD VALE NATURALS INC.—See EastWest Bioscience, Inc.; *Int'l*, pg. 2275
ORCHARD VALLEY FOODS AUSTRALIA LTD.—See Orkla ASA; *Int'l*, pg. 5638
ORCHARD WORLD LTD—See Argent Group Europe Limited; *Int'l*, pg. 560
ORCHASP LIMITED; *Int'l*, pg. 5615
ORCHESTRA BIOMED HOLDINGS, INC.; *U.S. Public*, pg. 1615
ORCHESTRA HOLDINGS, INC.; *Int'l*, pg. 5615
ORCHESTRA PREMAMAN SA; *Int'l*, pg. 5615
ORCHESTRA SERVICE GMBH—See Avnet, Inc.; *U.S. Public*, pg. 253
ORCHESTRO INC.—See Insight Venture Management, LLC; *U.S. Private*, pg. 2090
ORCHID BIO-COAT—See Nordic Capital AB; *Int'l*, pg. 5420
ORCHID BIOMEDICAL SYSTEMS PVT LTD.—See Revvity, Inc.; *U.S. Public*, pg. 1795
ORCHID CELLMARK LTD.—See Laboratory Corporation of America Holdings; *U.S. Public*, pg. 1287
ORCHID CELLMARK ULC—See Laboratory Corporation of America Holdings; *U.S. Public*, pg. 1287
ORCHID DEVELOPMENTS GROUP LTD.; *Int'l*, pg. 5615
ORCHID FIELD MARKETING LTD—See H2O Creative; *Int'l*, pg. 3200
ORCHID GARDENS VARNA EOOD—See Orchid Developments Group Ltd.; *Int'l*, pg. 5615
THE ORCHID GROUP; *Int'l*, pg. 7672
ORCHID HOTELS PUNE PRIVATE LIMITED—See Kamat Hotels India Ltd; *Int'l*, pg. 4060
ORCHID ISLAND CAPITAL, INC.; *U.S. Public*, pg. 1615
ORCHID ISLAND JUICE COMPANY; *U.S. Private*, pg. 3039
ORCHID KELLER—See Nordic Capital AB; *Int'l*, pg. 5420
ORCHID LOGISTIC CENTERS EOOD—See Orchid Developments Group Ltd.; *Int'l*, pg. 5615
ORCHID MACDEE ORTHOPEDIC SOLUTIONS, LLC—See Nordic Capital AB; *Int'l*, pg. 5420
ORCHID ORTHOPEDIC SOLUTIONS, LLC - ALABAMA—See Nordic Capital AB; *Int'l*, pg. 5420
ORCHID ORTHOPEDIC SOLUTIONS, LLC—See Nordic Capital AB; *Int'l*, pg. 5420
ORCHID ORTHOPEDIC SOLUTIONS SHEFFIELD LTD.—See Nordic Capital AB; *Int'l*, pg. 5420
ORCHID PHARMA LIMITED; *Int'l*, pg. 5615
ORCHIDS PAPER PRODUCTS COMPANY—See Cascades Inc.; *Int'l*, pg. 1351
ORCHID UNDERWRITERS AGENCY, LLC—See Brown & Brown, Inc.; *U.S. Public*, pg. 401
ORCHID VENTURES, INC.; *U.S. Public*, pg. 1615
ORC IMAGE & STRATEGIES D'EMPLOYEUR—See WPP plc; *Int'l*, pg. 8481
ORC IMAGE & STRATEGIES D'EMPLOYEUR—See WPP plc; *Int'l*, pg. 8481
ORC IMAGE & STRATEGIES D'EMPLOYEUR—See WPP plc; *Int'l*, pg. 8481
ORC IMAGE & STRATEGIES D'EMPLOYEUR—See WPP plc; *Int'l*, pg. 8481
ORC IMAGE & STRATEGIES D'EMPLOYEUR—See WPP plc; *Int'l*, pg. 8481
ORC IMAGE & STRATEGIES D'EMPLOYEUR—See WPP plc; *Int'l*, pg. 8481
ORC IMAGE & STRATEGIES D'EMPLOYEUR—See WPP plc; *Int'l*, pg. 8481
ORC INDUSTRIES, INC.; *U.S. Private*, pg. 3038
O.R.C. INTERNATIONAL LTD.—See Lake Capital Management LLC; *U.S. Private*, pg. 2374
ORC ITALY S.R.L.—See Broadridge Financial Solutions, Inc.; *U.S. Public*, pg. 392
ORCKESTRA TECHNOLOGIES INC.—See KKR & Co. Inc.; *U.S. Public*, pg. 1267
ORC NETHERLANDS B.V.—See Broadridge Financial Solutions, Inc.; *U.S. Public*, pg. 392
ORCO BLENDED PRODUCTS, INC.—See Orco Block Company Inc.; *U.S. Private*, pg. 3039
ORCO BLOCK COMPANY INC. - ORCO PAVINGSTONES DIVISION—See Orco Block Company Inc.; *U.S. Private*, pg. 3039
ORCO BLOCK COMPANY INC.; *U.S. Private*, pg. 3039
ORCO BUDAPEST KFT—See CPI Property Group, S.A.; *Int'l*, pg. 1825
ORCODA LIMITED; *Int'l*, pg. 5615
ORCON CORPORATION; *U.S. Private*, pg. 3039
ORCO PAVINGSTONES - COACHELLA / IMPERIAL PLANT—See Orco Block Company Inc.; *U.S. Private*, pg. 3039
ORCO PAVINGSTONES - INLAND EMPIRE PLANT—See Orco Block Company Inc.; *U.S. Private*, pg. 3039
ORCO PAVINGSTONES - ORANGE / LOS ANGELES PLANT—See Orco Block Company Inc.; *U.S. Private*, pg. 3039
ORCO PAVINGSTONES - TEMECULA VALLEY PLANT—See Orco Block Company Inc.; *U.S. Private*, pg. 3039
ORC SOFTWARE GMBH—See Broadridge Financial Solutions, Inc.; *U.S. Public*, pg. 392

ORC SOFTWARE GMBH—See Broadridge Financial Solutions, Inc.; *U.S. Public*, pg. 392
ORC SOFTWARE HK LTD.—See Broadridge Financial Solutions, Inc.; *U.S. Public*, pg. 392
ORC SOFTWARE LTD.—See Broadridge Financial Solutions, Inc.; *U.S. Public*, pg. 392
ORC SOFTWARE STOCKHOLM AB—See Broadridge Financial Solutions, Inc.; *U.S. Public*, pg. 392
ORC USA INC.—See Broadridge Financial Solutions, Inc.; *U.S. Public*, pg. 392
ORCUS TECHNOLOGIES, INC; *U.S. Private*, pg. 3039
ORC UTILITY & INFRASTRUCTURE LAND SERVICES, LLC; *U.S. Private*, pg. 3039
ORDABASY CORPORATION JSC; *Int'l*, pg. 5615
ORDAIN HEALTH CARE PVT. LTD.—See Insud Pharma, S.L.; *Int'l*, pg. 3725
ORDAN ASIA PACIFIC SDN. BHD.—See Orkla ASA; *Int'l*, pg. 5638
ORDERMAN GMBH—See NCR Voyix Corporation.; *U.S. Public*, pg. 1503
ORDERMATE PTY LTD.—See FirstRand Limited; *Int'l*, pg. 2690
ORDERMATIC ELECTRONICS, INC.—See GLORY Ltd.; *Int'l*, pg. 3010
ORDERS CONSTRUCTION COMPANY, INC.; *U.S. Private*, pg. 3039
ORDINA APPLICATION MANAGEMENT B.V.—See Sopra Steria Group S.A.; *Int'l*, pg. 7109
ORDINA APPLICATION OUTSOURCING EN PROJECTEN B.V.—See Sopra Steria Group S.A.; *Int'l*, pg. 7109
ORDINA BELGIUM N.V.—See Sopra Steria Group S.A.; *Int'l*, pg. 7109
ORDINA BUSINESS & ENTERPRISE SOLUTIONS B.V.—See Sopra Steria Group S.A.; *Int'l*, pg. 7109
ORDINA CONSULTING B.V.—See Sopra Steria Group S.A.; *Int'l*, pg. 7109
ORDINA E-CHAIN MANAGEMENT FINANCIALS BVBA—See Sopra Steria Group S.A.; *Int'l*, pg. 7109
ORDINA ENTERPRISE APPLICATIONS B.V.—See Sopra Steria Group S.A.; *Int'l*, pg. 7109
ORDINA ENTERPRISE APPLICATION SERVICES B.V.—See Sopra Steria Group S.A.; *Int'l*, pg. 7109
ORDINA HOLDING B.V.—See Sopra Steria Group S.A.; *Int'l*, pg. 7109
ORDINA ICT B.V.—See Sopra Steria Group S.A.; *Int'l*, pg. 7110
ORDINA J. TECHNOGIES B.V.—See Sopra Steria Group S.A.; *Int'l*, pg. 7110
ORDINA LUXEMBOURG SA—See Sopra Steria Group S.A.; *Int'l*, pg. 7110
ORDINA NEDERLAND B.V.—See Sopra Steria Group S.A.; *Int'l*, pg. 7110
ORDINA N.V.—See Sopra Steria Group S.A.; *Int'l*, pg. 7109
ORDINA—See Sopra Steria Group S.A.; *Int'l*, pg. 7109
ORDINA SYSTEM INTEGRATION & DEVELOPMENT B.V.—See Sopra Steria Group S.A.; *Int'l*, pg. 7110
ORD INVESTMENTS PTY. LTD.—See Lachlan Star Limited; *Int'l*, pg. 4391
ORDISSIMO SA; *Int'l*, pg. 5616
ORDIY CO., LTD.—See Inabata & Co. Ltd.; *Int'l*, pg. 3644
ORD MINNETT FINANCIAL PLANNING PTY LIMITED—See Insignia Financial Ltd.; *Int'l*, pg. 3719
ORD MINNETT HOLDINGS PTY LIMITED—See Insignia Financial Ltd.; *Int'l*, pg. 3719
ORD MINNETT LIMITED; *Int'l*, pg. 5615
ORD MINNETT MANAGEMENT LTD—See Insignia Financial Ltd.; *Int'l*, pg. 3719
ORD MOUNTAIN RESOURCES CORP.; *Int'l*, pg. 5615
ORDNANCE SURVEY PARTNERS LTD—See Ordnance Survey; *Int'l*, pg. 5616
ORDNANCE SURVEY; *Int'l*, pg. 5616
ORDOS YUANSHENG OPTOELECTRONICS CO., LTD.—See BOE Technology Group Co., Ltd.; *Int'l*, pg. 1099
ORDU YARDIMLASMA KURUMU GENEL MUDURLUGU; *Int'l*, pg. 5616
OREA MINING CORP.; *Int'l*, pg. 5616
OREBRO BIDEMONTERING AB—See LKQ Corporation; *U.S. Public*, pg. 1336
OREBRO BILDEMONTERING AB—See LKQ Corporation; *U.S. Public*, pg. 1336
ORE-CAL CORPORATION; *U.S. Private*, pg. 3039
ORECK CORPORATION—See Techtronic Industries Co., Ltd.; *Int'l*, pg. 7513
ORECK FLOOR CARE CENTERS, LTD.—See Techtronic Industries Co., Ltd.; *Int'l*, pg. 7513
ORECK MANUFACTURING COMPANY—See Techtronic Industries Co., Ltd.; *Int'l*, pg. 7513
ORECORP LIMITED; *Int'l*, pg. 5616
ORECX LLC—See CallMiner, Inc.; *U.S. Private*, pg. 722
OREDEV AB—See Devoteam SA; *Int'l*, pg. 2090
OREFINDERS RESOURCES INC.; *Int'l*, pg. 5616
OREFOX EXPLORATION PTY. LTD.—See Q2 Metals Corp.; *Int'l*, pg. 6131
O'REGAN'S CHEVROLET BUICK GMC CADILLAC; *Int'l*, pg. 5502
OREGE SA - SCIENTIFIC DIVISION—See Eren Groupe SA; *Int'l*, pg. 2490

OREGE SA—See Eren Groupe SA; *Int'l*, pg. 2490
OREGON AERO, INC.; *U.S. Private*, pg. 3039
OREGON AFFORDABLE HOUSING ASSISTANCE CORPORATION; *U.S. Private*, pg. 3039
OREGON BANCORP, INC.; *U.S. Public*, pg. 1615
OREGON CANADIAN FOREST PRODUCTS INC.; *U.S. Private*, pg. 3039
OREGON CASCADE PLUMBING & HEATING, INC.; *U.S. Private*, pg. 3039
OREGON CHERRY GROWERS INC.; *U.S. Private*, pg. 3040
OREGON CHERRY GROWERS INC. - THE DALLES PLANT—See Oregon Cherry Growers Inc.; *U.S. Private*, pg. 3040
OREGON CHERRY GROWERS—See Oregon Cherry Growers Inc.; *U.S. Private*, pg. 3040
OREGON CHILD DEVELOPMENT COALITION, INC.; *U.S. Private*, pg. 3040
OREGON COFFEE ROASTER, INC.; *U.S. Private*, pg. 3040
OREGON COMMUNITY CREDIT UNION; *U.S. Private*, pg. 3040
THE OREGON COMMUNITY FOUNDATION; *U.S. Private*, pg. 4089
OREGON DISTRIBUTION LTD—See American Securities LLC; *U.S. Private*, pg. 247
OREGON DISTRIBUTION LTD—See P2 Capital Partners, LLC; *U.S. Private*, pg. 3062
OREGON EDUCATION ASSOCIATION; *U.S. Private*, pg. 3040
OREGON ELECTRIC GROUP; *U.S. Private*, pg. 3040
OREGON FERALLOY PARTNERS—See Evraz plc; *Int'l*, pg. 2574
OREGON FERALLOY PARTNERS—See Reliance Steel & Aluminum Co.; *U.S. Public*, pg. 1780
THE OREGON HISTORICAL SOCIETY; *U.S. Private*, pg. 4089
OREGONIAN PUBLISHING CO.—See Advance Publications, Inc.; *U.S. Private*, pg. 86
OREGONIAN V 5—See Advance Publications, Inc.; *U.S. Private*, pg. 86
OREGON INTERNATIONAL AIR FREIGHT COMPANY INC.; *U.S. Private*, pg. 3040
OREGON MATTRESS COMPANY—See Restonic Mattress Corporation; *U.S. Private*, pg. 3409
OREGON METALLURGICAL, LLC—See ATI Inc.; *U.S. Public*, pg. 222
OREGON MUTUAL INSURANCE COMPANY, INC.; *U.S. Private*, pg. 3040
OREGON NEWSPAPER ADVERTISING CO.; *U.S. Private*, pg. 3040
OREGON OUTPATIENT SURGERY CENTER, LLC—See UnitedHealth Group Incorporated; *U.S. Public*, pg. 2251
OREGON PACIFIC BANCORP; *U.S. Public*, pg. 1615
OREGON PACIFIC BUILDING PRODUCTS EXCHANGE INC.—See OrePac Holding Company Inc.; *U.S. Private*, pg. 3041
OREGON PACIFIC BUILDING PRODUCTS IDAHO INC.—See OrePac Holding Company Inc.; *U.S. Private*, pg. 3041
OREGON PACIFIC BUILDING PRODUCTS MAPLE INC.—See OrePac Holding Company Inc.; *U.S. Private*, pg. 3041
OREGON PACIFIC BUILDING PRODUCTS WASH. INC.—See OrePac Holding Company Inc.; *U.S. Private*, pg. 3041
OREGON PALLET REPAIR, INC.; *U.S. Private*, pg. 3040
OREGON POTATO COMPANY; *U.S. Private*, pg. 3040
OREGON RAIL MARKETING CO.—See Radius Recycling, Inc.; *U.S. Public*, pg. 1760
OREGON RESTAURANT SERVICES, INC.; *U.S. Private*, pg. 3040
OREGON SCIENTIFIC AUSTRALIA PTY LIMITED—See IDT International Limited; *Int'l*, pg. 3596
OREGON SCIENTIFIC BRASIL LTDA—See IDT International Limited; *Int'l*, pg. 3596
OREGON SCIENTIFIC (DEUTSCHLAND) GMBH—See IDT International Limited; *Int'l*, pg. 3596
OREGON SCIENTIFIC ENTERPRISE (SHANGHAI) LIMITED—See IDT International Limited; *Int'l*, pg. 3597
OREGON SCIENTIFIC FRANCE S.A.R.L.—See IDT International Limited; *Int'l*, pg. 3597
OREGON SCIENTIFIC GLOBAL DISTRIBUTION LIMITED—See IDT International Limited; *Int'l*, pg. 3596
OREGON SCIENTIFIC HONG KONG LIMITED—See IDT International Limited; *Int'l*, pg. 3597
OREGON SCIENTIFIC IBERICA, S.A.—See IDT International Limited; *Int'l*, pg. 3597
OREGON SCIENTIFIC, INC.—See IDT International Limited; *Int'l*, pg. 3597
OREGON SCIENTIFIC ITALIA SPA—See IDT International Limited; *Int'l*, pg. 3597
OREGON SCIENTIFIC SOUTH EAST ASIA PTE LIMITED—See IDT International Limited; *Int'l*, pg. 3597
OREGON SCIENTIFIC TRADING (BEIJING) CO., LTD.—See IDT International Limited; *Int'l*, pg. 3597
OREGON SCIENTIFIC (U.K.) LIMITED—See IDT International Limited; *Int'l*, pg. 3596

OREGON SHAKESPEARE FESTIVAL; *U.S. Private*, pg. 3040
OREGON SPINE & PHYSICAL THERAPY, LIMITED PARTNERSHIP—See U.S. Physical Therapy, Inc.; *U.S. Public*, pg. 2215
OREGON STATE UNIVERSITY BOOKSTORE; *U.S. Private*, pg. 3040
OREGON TIMBER FRAME LIMITED—See Barratt Developments PLC; *Int'l*, pg. 868
OREGON TRAIL BANK—See Banner County Ban Corporation; *U.S. Public*, pg. 469
OREGON TRAIL EQUIPMENT LLC; *U.S. Private*, pg. 3040
OREGON TRANSFER CO.; *U.S. Private*, pg. 3040
OREG SITE WORK SERVICES, LLC; *U.S. Private*, pg. 3039
O'REILLY ALPHATECH VENTURES—See O'Reilly Media, Inc.; *U.S. Private*, pg. 2980
O'REILLY AUTOMOTIVE, INC.; *U.S. Public*, pg. 1559
O'REILLY AUTOMOTIVE STORES, INC.—See O'Reilly Automotive, Inc.; *U.S. Public*, pg. 1559
O'REILLY CHINA—See O'Reilly Media, Inc.; *U.S. Private*, pg. 2980
O'REILLY JAPAN—See O'Reilly Media, Inc.; *U.S. Private*, pg. 2980
O'REILLY MEDIA, INC.; *U.S. Private*, pg. 2980
O'REILLY UK—See O'Reilly Media, Inc.; *U.S. Private*, pg. 2980
O'REILLY VERLAG—See O'Reilly Media, Inc.; *U.S. Private*, pg. 2980
ORELL FUSSLI BUCHHANDLUNGS AG—See Orell Fussli Holding AG; *Int'l*, pg. 5616
ORELL FUSSLI HOLDING AG; *Int'l*, pg. 5616
ORELL FUSSLI KARTOGRAPHIE AG; *Int'l*, pg. 5616
ORELL FUSSLI SECURITY PRINTING LTD.—See Orell Fussli Holding AG; *Int'l*, pg. 5616
ORELL FUSSLI SICHERHEITSDRUCK AG—See Orell Fussli Holding AG; *Int'l*, pg. 5616
ORELL FUSSLI THALIA AG—See Orell Fussli Holding AG; *Int'l*, pg. 5616
ORELL FUSSLI THALIA AG—See Thalia Bucher GmbH; *Int'l*, pg. 7607
ORELL FUSSLI VERLAG AG—See Orell Fussli Holding AG; *Int'l*, pg. 5616
OREMCO, INC.—See Tata Sons Limited; *Int'l*, pg. 7473
ORENBURGGAZPROM—See PJSC Gazprom; *Int'l*, pg. 5880
ORENCO STATION SALES LLC—See RAK Development Company; *U.S. Private*, pg. 3349
ORENCO SYSTEMS INC.; *U.S. Private*, pg. 3040
ORENDA INTERNATIONAL, LLC; *U.S. Private*, pg. 3040
OREN INTERNATIONAL INC.; *U.S. Private*, pg. 3040
OREN SPORT (CHERAS) SDN. BHD.—See MBV International Limited; *Int'l*, pg. 4754
OREN SPORT (KEPONG) SDN. BHD.—See MBV International Limited; *Int'l*, pg. 4754
OREN SPORT (KLANG) SDN. BHD.—See MBV International Limited; *Int'l*, pg. 4754
OREN SPORT (PJ) SDN. BHD.—See MBV International Limited; *Int'l*, pg. 4754
OREN SPORT SDN. BHD.—See MBV International Limited; *Int'l*, pg. 4755
OREN SPORT (S) PTE. LTD.—See MBV International Limited; *Int'l*, pg. 4754
OREOVICA A.D.; *Int'l*, pg. 5616
OREPAC HOLDING COMPANY INC.; *U.S. Private*, pg. 3041
ORE PHARMACEUTICALS INC.; *U.S. Private*, pg. 3039
ORESA VENTURES ROMANIA SRL; *Int'l*, pg. 5616
ORESTONE MINING CORP.; *Int'l*, pg. 5616
ORESUNDSVARVET AB; *Int'l*, pg. 5616
ORESUND UNLOADER DESIGN BUREAU AB—See FLSmidth & Co. A/S; *Int'l*, pg. 2712
OREXAD SA—See Rubix Group International Limtied; *Int'l*, pg. 6423
OREX MINERALS INC.; *Int'l*, pg. 5616
OREXO AB; *Int'l*, pg. 5616
OREXPLORE TECHNOLOGIES LIMITED; *Int'l*, pg. 5617
OREY FINANCIAL - INSTITUICAO FINANCEIRA DE CREDITO, SA—See Caixa Geral de Depositos S.A.; *Int'l*, pg. 1260
OREZONE GOLD CORPORATION; *Int'l*, pg. 5617
OREZONE INC.—See Orezone Gold Corporation; *Int'l*, pg. 5617
ORFAGEN—See Pierre Fabre S.A.; *Int'l*, pg. 5864
ORFFA INTERNATIONAL HOLDING B.V.—See Marubeni Corporation; *Int'l*, pg. 4709
ORFI-FARMA S.L.—See Pfizer Inc.; *U.S. Public*, pg. 1680
ORFIN FINANSMAN AS; *Int'l*, pg. 5617
ORF KIRALAMA PAZARLAMA VE PAZARLAMA DANISMANLIGI A.S.—See OYAK Cement Group; *Int'l*, pg. 5678
ORFORD MINING CORPORATION; *Int'l*, pg. 5617
ORGABIO HOLDINGS BERHAD; *Int'l*, pg. 5617
ORGACHIM JSC; *Int'l*, pg. 5617
ORGAIN BUILDING SUPPLY COMPANY; *U.S. Private*, pg. 3041
ORGAIN, LLC—See Butterfly Equity LP; *U.S. Private*, pg. 698

ORGANA TECHNOLOGIES GROUP INC.
CORPORATE AFFILIATIONS

ORGANA TECHNOLOGIES GROUP INC.; *U.S. Public*, pg. 1615
ORGANE DE ASAMBLARE S.A.; *Int'l*, pg. 5617
ORGANIC AGRICULTURAL COMPANY LIMITED; *Int'l*, pg. 5617
ORGANICALLY COATED STEELS LTD.—See Klockner & Co. SE; *Int'l*, pg. 4202
ORGANICALLY GROWN CO.; *U.S. Private*, pg. 3041
ORGANIC COATINGS LIMITED; *Int'l*, pg. 5618
THE ORGANIC CORPORATION B.V.—See SunOpta Inc.; *Int'l*, pg. 7320
ORGANIC DYES AND PIGMENTS, LLC; *U.S. Private*, pg. 3041
ORGANICELL REGENERATIVE MEDICINE, INC.; *U.S. Public*, pg. 1615
ORGANIC FLOWER INVESTMENTS GROUP INC.; *Int'l*, pg. 5618
ORGANIC FOOD BROKERS, LLC—See Innovative Food Holdings, Inc.; *U.S. Public*, pg. 1127
ORGANIC, INC.—See Omnicom Group Inc.; *U.S. Public*, pg. 1589
ORGANIC, INC.—See Omnicom Group Inc.; *U.S. Public*, pg. 1589
ORGANIC, INC.—See Omnicom Group Inc.; *U.S. Public*, pg. 1589
ORGANIC, INC.—See Omnicom Group Inc.; *U.S. Public*, pg. 1589
ORGANIC LAND CORPORATION OOD—See SunOpta Inc.; *Int'l*, pg. 7319
ORGANIC OILS S.P.A.—See Bioera S.p.A.; *Int'l*, pg. 1037
ORGANIC PLANT HEALTH, INC.; *U.S. Private*, pg. 3041
ORGANIC POTASH CORPORATION; *Int'l*, pg. 5618
ORGANIC PRODUCTS TRADING COMPANY, LLC—See Coffee Holding Company, Inc.; *U.S. Public*, pg. 522
ORGANICS BY GOSH—See QSAM Biosciences, Inc.; *U.S. Public*, pg. 1744
ORGANIC TEA COSMETICS HOLDINGS CO LTD; *Int'l*, pg. 5618
ORGANIGRAM HOLDINGS INC.; *Int'l*, pg. 5618
ORGANIX INCORPORATED—See Keensight Capital SAS; *Int'l*, pg. 4115
ORGANIX SOLUTIONS, LLC—See Republic Services, Inc.; *U.S. Public*, pg. 1786
ORGANIX SOUTH, INC.—See HGGC, LLC; *U.S. Private*, pg. 1930
ORGANIZACION BROCKMAN Y SCHUH S.A. DE C.V.—See Marsh & McLennan Companies, Inc.; *U.S. Public*, pg. 1388
ORGANIZACION CORONA SA; *Int'l*, pg. 5618
ORGANIZACION CULTIBA, S.A.B. DE C.V.; *Int'l*, pg. 5618
ORGANIZACION SAHUAYO, S.A.—See Grupo Corvi, S.A.B. de C.V.; *Int'l*, pg. 3125
ORGANIZACION SORIANA, S.A.B. DE C.V.; *Int'l*, pg. 5618
ORGANIZACION TERPEL SA; *Int'l*, pg. 5618
ORGANIZATIONAL DEVELOPMENT INC.; *U.S. Private*, pg. 3041
ORGANIZATIONAL DYNAMICS INC.; *U.S. Private*, pg. 3041
ORGANIZATION AND SOFTWARE GMBH; *Int'l*, pg. 5618
ORGANIZE.COM, INC.; *U.S. Private*, pg. 3041
ORGANIZING FOR ACTION; *U.S. Private*, pg. 3041
ORGAN MEDICAL CO., LTD.—See Ship Healthcare Holdings, Inc.; *Int'l*, pg. 6852
ORGANO (ASIA) SDN. BHD.—See Organo Corporation; *Int'l*, pg. 5618
ORGANOCLICK AB; *Int'l*, pg. 5619
ORGANO CORPORATION; *Int'l*, pg. 5618
ORGANOGENESIS HOLDINGS INC.; *U.S. Public*, pg. 1615
ORGANOGENESIS INC.—See Organogenesis Holdings Inc.; *U.S. Public*, pg. 1615
ORGANOGENESIS SWITZERLAND GMBH—See Organogenesis Holdings Inc.; *U.S. Public*, pg. 1615
ORGANON ARGENTINA S.R.L.—See Organon & Co.; *U.S. Public*, pg. 1616
ORGANON ASIA PACIFIC SERVICES PTE. LTD.—See Organon & Co.; *U.S. Public*, pg. 1616
ORGANON AUSTRIA GMBH—See Organon & Co.; *U.S. Public*, pg. 1616
ORGANON BELGIUM BV—See Organon & Co.; *U.S. Public*, pg. 1616
ORGANON CANADA HOLDINGS LLC—See Organon & Co.; *U.S. Public*, pg. 1616
ORGANON CENTRAL EAST GMBH—See Organon & Co.; *U.S. Public*, pg. 1616
ORGANON COLOMBIA S.A.S.—See Organon & Co.; *U.S. Public*, pg. 1616
ORGANON COMERCIALIZADORA, S. DE R.L. DE C.V.—See Organon & Co.; *U.S. Public*, pg. 1616
ORGANON & CO.; *U.S. Public*, pg. 1616
ORGANON CZECH REPUBLIC S.R.O.—See Organon & Co.; *U.S. Public*, pg. 1616
ORGANON DENMARK APS—See Organon & Co.; *U.S. Public*, pg. 1616
ORGANON - ECUADOR S.A.—See Organon & Co.; *U.S. Public*, pg. 1616

ORGANON EGYPT LTD—See Organon & Co.; *U.S. Public*, pg. 1616
ORGANON FINLAND OY—See Organon & Co.; *U.S. Public*, pg. 1616
ORGANON FRANCE—See Organon & Co.; *U.S. Public*, pg. 1616
ORGANON GLOBAL INC.—See Organon & Co.; *U.S. Public*, pg. 1616
ORGANON GMBH—See Organon & Co.; *U.S. Public*, pg. 1616
ORGANON HEALTHCARE GMBH—See Organon & Co.; *U.S. Public*, pg. 1616
ORGANON HONG KONG LIMITED—See Organon & Co.; *U.S. Public*, pg. 1616
ORGANON INTERNATIONAL SERVICES GMBH—See Organon & Co.; *U.S. Public*, pg. 1616
ORGANON (IRELAND) LTD—See Organon & Co.; *U.S. Public*, pg. 1616
ORGANON ITALIA SPA—See Organon & Co.; *U.S. Public*, pg. 1616
ORGANON ITALIA S.R.L.—See Organon & Co.; *U.S. Public*, pg. 1616
ORGANON KOREA CO. LTD.—See Organon & Co.; *U.S. Public*, pg. 1616
ORGANON KSA GMBH—See Organon & Co.; *U.S. Public*, pg. 1616
ORGANON LLC—See Organon & Co.; *U.S. Public*, pg. 1616
ORGANON MALAYSIA SDN. BHD.—See Organon & Co.; *U.S. Public*, pg. 1616
ORGANON MAROC S.A.R.L.—See Organon & Co.; *U.S. Public*, pg. 1616
ORGANON NEW ZEALAND LIMITED—See Organon & Co.; *U.S. Public*, pg. 1616
ORGANON PHARMA B.V.—See Organon & Co.; *U.S. Public*, pg. 1616
ORGANON PHARMA FZ-LLC—See Organon & Co.; *U.S. Public*, pg. 1616
ORGANON PHARMA HOLDINGS LLC—See Organon & Co.; *U.S. Public*, pg. 1616
ORGANON PHARMA PTY LTD—See Organon & Co.; *U.S. Public*, pg. 1616
ORGANON PHARMA S. DE R.L.—See Organon & Co.; *U.S. Public*, pg. 1616
ORGANON (PHILIPPINES) INC.—See Organon & Co.; *U.S. Public*, pg. 1616
ORGANON POLSKA SP. Z O.O.—See Organon & Co.; *U.S. Public*, pg. 1616
ORGANON PORTUGAL SOCIEDADE UNIPESSOAL LDA—See Organon & Co.; *U.S. Public*, pg. 1616
ORGANON SALUD, S.L.—See Organon & Co.; *U.S. Public*, pg. 1616
ORGANON (SHANGHAI) PHARMACEUTICAL TECHNOLOGY CO., LTD.—See Organon & Co.; *U.S. Public*, pg. 1616
ORGANON SINGAPORE PTE. LTD.—See Organon & Co.; *U.S. Public*, pg. 1616
ORGANON SLOVAKIA S.R.O.—See Organon & Co.; *U.S. Public*, pg. 1616
ORGANON SOUTH AFRICA (PTY) LTD—See Organon & Co.; *U.S. Public*, pg. 1616
ORGANON (THAILAND) LTD.—See Organon & Co.; *U.S. Public*, pg. 1616
ORGANON TRADE LLC—See Organon & Co.; *U.S. Public*, pg. 1616
ORGANON TURKEY ILACLARI LIMITED SIRKETI—See Organon & Co.; *U.S. Public*, pg. 1616
ORGANO (SUZHOU) WATER TREATMENT CO., LTD.—See Organo Corporation; *Int'l*, pg. 5618
ORGANO TECHNOLOGY CO., LTD.—See Organo Corporation; *Int'l*, pg. 5618
ORGANO (THAILAND) CO., LTD.—See Organo Corporation; *Int'l*, pg. 5618
ORGANOTIKI S.A.—See Brookfield Corporation; *Int'l*, pg. 1180
ORGANOTIKI S.A.—See Elliott Management Corporation; *U.S. Private*, pg. 1372
ORGANO (VIETNAM) CO., LTD.—See Organo Corporation; *Int'l*, pg. 5618
ORGANOVO HOLDINGS, INC.; *U.S. Public*, pg. 1616
ORGANOWOOD AB—See OrganoClick AB; *Int'l*, pg. 5619
ORGAN PROCUREMENT AGENCY OF MICHIGAN; *U.S. Private*, pg. 3041
ORGAN TECHNOLOGIES INC.—See Otsuka Holdings Co., Ltd.; *Int'l*, pg. 5659
ORGANTO FOODS INC.; *Int'l*, pg. 5619
ORGAN WORLDWIDE LLC; *U.S. Private*, pg. 3041
ORGAPACK GMBH—See Illinois Tool Works Inc.; *U.S. Public*, pg. 1109
ORGAWORLD B.V.- COMPOSTING PLANT—See Renewi plc; *Int'l*, pg. 6279
ORGAWORLD B.V. - FERMENTATION PLANT—See Renewi plc; *Int'l*, pg. 6279
ORGAWORLD B.V.—See Renewi plc; *Int'l*, pg. 6279
ORGAWORLD CANADA LIMITED—See Renewi plc; *Int'l*, pg. 6279
ORGAWORLD NEDERLAND B.V.—See Renewi plc; *Int'l*, pg. 6278
ORG CHEM GROUP, LLC; *U.S. Private*, pg. 3041

ORGE ENERJI ELEKTRIK TAAHHUT A.S.; *Int'l*, pg. 5619
ORGENESIS INC.; *U.S. Public*, pg. 1616
ORGENICS LTD.—See Abbott Laboratories; *U.S. Public*, pg. 19
ORGENTEC DIAGNOSTIKA GMBH—See Caisse de Depot et Placement du Quebec; *Int'l*, pg. 1255
ORGENTEC DIAGNOSTIKA GMBH—See CVC Capital Partners SICAV-FIS S.A.; *Int'l*, pg. 1884
ORGENTEC DIAGNOSTIKA GMBH—See Tethys Invest SAS; *Int'l*, pg. 7575
ORGHARVEST, INC.—See First Seed Farms Inc.; *U.S. Private*, pg. 1527
ORGILL, INC.; *U.S. Private*, pg. 3041
ORGOSOFT CO., LTD.—See Digital Hearts Holdings Co., Ltd.; *Int'l*, pg. 2122
ORGO-THERMIT, INC.—See Vermogensverwaltung Erben Dr. Karl Goldschmidt GmbH; *Int'l*, pg. 8173
ORGSYNC, INC.—See Leeds Equity Partners, LLC; *U.S. Private*, pg. 2414
ORGSYNC, INC.—See Veritas Capital Fund Management, LLC; *U.S. Private*, pg. 4361
ORGTECHNICA LTD.; *Int'l*, pg. 5619
ORG TECHNOLOGY CO., LTD.; *Int'l*, pg. 5617
ORHP MANAGEMENT COMPANY—See Old Republic International Corporation; *U.S. Public*, pg. 1567
ORHUB, INC.; *U.S. Public*, pg. 1617
ORIAM SA—See Mannai Corporation QPSC; *Int'l*, pg. 4675
ORIANA POWER LIMITED; *Int'l*, pg. 5619
ORIAN SHM LTD.; *Int'l*, pg. 5619
ORIBASE PHARMA SAS—See PPF Group N.V.; *Int'l*, pg. 5951
ORIBE HAIR CARE, LLC—See Kao Corporation; *Int'l*, pg. 4073
ORIBRIGHT SHANGHAI CO., LTD.—See ZEUS CO., Ltd; *Int'l*, pg. 8640
ORICA AFRICA (PTY) LTD.—See Orica Limited; *Int'l*, pg. 5619
ORICA ARGENTINA S.A.I.C.—See Orica Limited; *Int'l*, pg. 5619
ORICA AUSTRALIA PTY. LTD.—See Orica Limited; *Int'l*, pg. 5619
ORICA AUSTRALIA SECURITIES PTY LTD—See Orica Limited; *Int'l*, pg. 5619
ORICA AUSTRALIA—See Orica Limited; *Int'l*, pg. 5619
ORICA BELGIUM S.A.—See Orica Limited; *Int'l*, pg. 5619
ORICA BOLIVIA S.A.—See Orica Limited; *Int'l*, pg. 5619
ORICA CHILE S.A.—See Orica Limited; *Int'l*, pg. 5619
ORICA CIS CJSC—See Orica Limited; *Int'l*, pg. 5619
ORICA COLOMBIA S.A.S.—See Orica Limited; *Int'l*, pg. 5619
ORICA DENMARK A/S—See Orica Limited; *Int'l*, pg. 5620
ORICA DRC S.A.R.L.—See Orica Limited; *Int'l*, pg. 5620
ORICA EUROPE MANAGEMENT GMBH—See Orica Limited; *Int'l*, pg. 5620
ORICA EUROPE PTY LTD & CO. KG—See Orica Limited; *Int'l*, pg. 5620
ORICA EXPLOSIVES HOLDINGS PTY LTD—See Orica Limited; *Int'l*, pg. 5620
ORICA EXPLOSIVES TECHNOLOGY PTY LTD—See Orica Limited; *Int'l*, pg. 5620
ORICA EXPLOSIVOS INDUSTRIALES, S.A.—See Orica Limited; *Int'l*, pg. 5620
ORICA FINANCE LIMITED—See Orica Limited; *Int'l*, pg. 5620
ORICA FINLAND OY—See Orica Limited; *Int'l*, pg. 5620
ORICA GERMANY GMBH—See Orica Limited; *Int'l*, pg. 5620
ORICA GHANA LIMITED—See Orica Limited; *Int'l*, pg. 5620
ORICA INVESTMENTS PTY. LTD.—See Orica Limited; *Int'l*, pg. 5620
ORICA JAPAN CO. LTD.—See Orica Limited; *Int'l*, pg. 5620
ORICA LIMITED; *Int'l*, pg. 5619
ORICA MINING SERVICES (HONG KONG) LTD.—See Orica Limited; *Int'l*, pg. 5620
ORICA MINING SERVICES LATIN AMERICA—See Orica Limited; *Int'l*, pg. 5620
ORICA MINING SERVICES PERU S.A.—See Orica Limited; *Int'l*, pg. 5620
ORICA MINING SERVICES PORTUGAL S.A.—See Orica Limited; *Int'l*, pg. 5620
ORICA MINING SERVICES—See Orica Limited; *Int'l*, pg. 5620
ORICA MINING SERVICES—See Orica Limited; *Int'l*, pg. 5620
ORICA MONGOLIA LLC—See Orica Limited; *Int'l*, pg. 5620
ORICA MOZAMBIQUE LIMITADA—See Orica Limited; *Int'l*, pg. 5620
ORICA NEW ZEALAND LTD—See Orica Limited; *Int'l*, pg. 5620
ORICA NITRO PATLAYICI MADDELER SANAYI VE TICARET ANONIM SIRKETI—See Orica Limited; *Int'l*, pg. 5620
ORICA NOMINEES PTY LTD—See Orica Limited; *Int'l*, pg. 5620
ORICA NORWAY AS—See Orica Limited; *Int'l*, pg. 5620

COMPANY NAME INDEX

ORICA PHILIPPINES INC—See Orica Limited; *Int'l*, pg. 5620
ORICA POLAND SP. Z.O.O.—See Orica Limited; *Int'l*, pg. 5620
ORICA SINGAPORE PTE LTD—See Orica Limited; *Int'l*, pg. 5620
ORICA SOUTH AFRICA (PROPRIETARY) LIMITED—See Orica Limited; *Int'l*, pg. 5620
ORICA SWEDEN AB—See Orica Limited; *Int'l*, pg. 5620
ORICA SWEDEN HOLDINGS AB—See Orica Limited; *Int'l*, pg. 5620
ORICA TANZANIA LIMITED—See Orica Limited; *Int'l*, pg. 5620
ORICA UK LIMITED—See Orica Limited; *Int'l*, pg. 5620
ORICA USA INC.—See Orica Limited; *Int'l*, pg. 5620
ORICA U.S. SERVICES INC.—See Orica Limited; *Int'l*, pg. 5620
ORICA VENEZUELA C.A.—See Orica Limited; *Int'l*, pg. 5620
ORICA WATERCARE INC.—See Orica Limited; *Int'l*, pg. 5620
ORICA ZAMBIA LIMITED—See Orica Limited; *Int'l*, pg. 5620
ORICO AUTO CHUBU CO., LTD.—See Orient Corporation; *Int'l*, pg. 5621
ORICO AUTO HOKKAIDO CO., LTD.—See Orient Corporation; *Int'l*, pg. 5621
ORICO AUTO KANSAI CO., LTD.—See Orient Corporation; *Int'l*, pg. 5621
ORICO AUTO KANTO CO., LTD.—See Orient Corporation; *Int'l*, pg. 5621
ORICO AUTO LEASING CO., LTD.—See Tokyo Century Corporation; *Int'l*, pg. 7789
ORICO AUTO TOHOKU CO., LTD.—See Orient Corporation; *Int'l*, pg. 5621
ORICO BUSINESS & COMMUNICATIONS CO., LTD—See Orient Corporation; *Int'l*, pg. 5621
ORICO CHUBU CO., LTD.—See Orient Corporation; *Int'l*, pg. 5621
ORICO CHUSHIKOKU CO., LTD.—See Orient Corporation; *Int'l*, pg. 5621
ORICO KANSAI CO., LTD—See Orient Corporation; *Int'l*, pg. 5621
ORICO KANTO CO., LTD—See Orient Corporation; *Int'l*, pg. 5622
ORICOM INC.—See Doosan Corporation; *Int'l*, pg. 2174
ORICON ENTERPRISES LTD.; *Int'l*, pg. 5621
ORICON INC; *Int'l*, pg. 5621
ORICON ME INC.—See Oricon Inc; *Int'l*, pg. 5621
ORICOPA OY—See Patria Oyj; *Int'l*, pg. 5758
ORICORP COMERCIAL S.A. DE C.V.—See Orica Limited; *Int'l*, pg. 5620
ORICO SUPPORT CO., LTD.—See Orient Corporation; *Int'l*, pg. 5622
ORICO TOHOKU CO., LTD—See Orient Corporation; *Int'l*, pg. 5622
ORICO TOKYO CO., LTD—See Orient Corporation; *Int'l*, pg. 5622
ORICO TRADING CO., LTD.—See Orient Corporation; *Int'l*, pg. 5622
ORIC PHARMACEUTICALS, INC.; *U.S. Public*, pg. 1617
ORIDION SYSTEMS LTD.—See Medtronic plc; *Int'l*, pg. 4789
ORIEL ASSET MANAGEMENT LLP—See Stifel Financial Corp.; *U.S. Public*, pg. 1950
ORIEL HOLDINGS LTD; *Int'l*, pg. 5621
O'RIELLY CHEVROLET, INC.—See O'Rielly Motor Company; *U.S. Private*, pg. 2980
O'RIELLY MOTOR COMPANY; *U.S. Private*, pg. 2980
ORIEL RESOURCES PLC; *Int'l*, pg. 5621
ORIEM TECHNOLOGY SDN. BHD.; *Int'l*, pg. 5621
ORIENS CO., LTD.—See Dongyang Piston Co., Ltd.; *Int'l*, pg. 2172
ORIENS; *Int'l*, pg. 5621
ORIENT ABRASIVES LIMITED—See Amergeris Wealth Management Group GmbH; *Int'l*, pg. 421
ORIENT ABRASIVES LIMITED—See Ashapura Minechem Limited; *Int'l*, pg. 606
ORIENTAL AROMATICS LTD.; *Int'l*, pg. 5623
ORIENTAL ASIA (MAURITIUS) PTE. LTD.—See Oriental Holdings Berhad; *Int'l*, pg. 5624
ORIENTAL ASSEMBLERS SDN. BHD.—See Berjaya Assets Berhad; *Int'l*, pg. 982
ORIENTAL AVIATION INTERNATIONAL PTE. LTD.—See Will Group, Inc.; *Int'l*, pg. 8412
ORIENTAL BANK—See OFG Bancorp; *U.S. Public*, pg. 1564
ORIENTAL BANK - US VIRGIN ISLANDS—See OFG Bancorp; *U.S. Public*, pg. 1564
ORIENTAL BOON SIEW (MAURITIUS) PTE. LTD.—See Oriental Holdings Berhad; *Int'l*, pg. 5624
ORIENTAL BOON SIEW (M) SDN. BHD.—See Oriental Holdings Berhad; *Int'l*, pg. 5624
ORIENTAL BREWERY CO., LTD.—See Anheuser-Busch InBev SA/NV; *Int'l*, pg. 466
ORIENTAL CARBON & CHEMICALS LIMITED; *Int'l*, pg. 5623
ORIENTAL CHAIN MFG. CO., LTD.; *Int'l*, pg. 5623

ORIENTAL CHEMICAL INDUSTRIAL CORP LTD.—See China National Chemical Corporation; *Int'l*, pg. 1527
ORIENTAL CITY GROUP (THAILAND) COMPANY LIMITED—See China Smartpay Group Holdings Limited; *Int'l*, pg. 1552
ORIENTAL CONSULTANTS HOLDINGS COMPANY LIMITED; *Int'l*, pg. 5623
ORIENTAL CONTAINERS LIMITED—See Oricon Enterprises Ltd.; *Int'l*, pg. 5621
ORIENTAL CULTURE HOLDING LTD.; *Int'l*, pg. 5623
ORIENTAL ELECTRONICS DEVICE CO., LTD.—See Seiko Epson Corporation; *Int'l*, pg. 6687
ORIENTAL ENERGY CO., LTD.; *Int'l*, pg. 5623
ORIENTAL ENTERPRISE HOLDINGS LIMITED; *Int'l*, pg. 5623
ORIENTAL EXPLORER HOLDINGS LTD.; *Int'l*, pg. 5623
ORIENTAL FASTECH MANUFACTURING SDN. BHD.—See YBS International Berhad; *Int'l*, pg. 8574
ORIENTAL FASTECH MANUFACTURING (VIETNAM) CO., LTD.—See YBS International Berhad; *Int'l*, pg. 8574
ORIENTAL FINANCIAL SERVICES LLC—See OFG Bancorp; *U.S. Public*, pg. 1564
ORIENTAL FOOD INDUSTRIES HOLDINGS BERHAD; *Int'l*, pg. 5623
ORIENTAL FOOD INDUSTRIES SDN. BHD.—See Oriental Food Industries Holdings Berhad; *Int'l*, pg. 5623
ORIENTAL FOUNDRY PRIVATE LIMITED—See Oriental Rail Infrastructure Limited; *Int'l*, pg. 5626
ORIENTAL HOLDINGS BERHAD; *Int'l*, pg. 5624
ORIENTAL HOTELS LTD.; *Int'l*, pg. 5625
ORIENTAL INDUSTRIES (SUZHOU) CO., LTD.—See The Far Eastern Group; *Int'l*, pg. 7642
ORIENTAL INDUSTRIES (WUXI) CO., LTD.—See Oriental Holdings Berhad; *Int'l*, pg. 5624
ORIENTAL INSPECTION & SERVICE CO. LTD.—See oriental precision & engineering co., ltd.; *Int'l*, pg. 5626
ORIENTAL INTEREST BERHAD; *Int'l*, pg. 5625
ORIENTAL INTERNATIONAL ENTERPRISE LIMITED; *Int'l*, pg. 5625
ORIENTAL INTERNATIONAL (MAURITIUS) PTE. LTD.—See Oriental Holdings Berhad; *Int'l*, pg. 5624
ORIENTAL INTERNATIONAL SHANGHAI KNITWEAR CO., LTD.—See Oriental International Enterprise Limited; *Int'l*, pg. 5625
ORIENTAL LAND CO., LTD.; *Int'l*, pg. 5625
ORIENTAL LIFE INSURANCE CULTURAL DEVELOPMENT CENTER—See Prudential Financial, Inc.; *U.S. Public*, pg. 1733
ORIENTAL LOTUS HOTEL SUPPLIES PRIVATE LIMITED—See Ming Fai International Holdings Limited; *Int'l*, pg. 4908
ORIENTAL MAGIC SOUP, INC.; *U.S. Public*, pg. 1617
ORIENTAL MERCHANT EUROPE LTD.—See Oriental Merchant Pty. Ltd.; *Int'l*, pg. 5626
ORIENTAL MERCHANT PTY. LTD.; *Int'l*, pg. 5626
ORIENTAL METALS PTE LTD—See HG Metal Manufacturing Limited; *Int'l*, pg. 3375
ORIENTAL MOTOR ASIA PACIFIC PTE. LTD.—See Oriental Motor Co., Ltd.; *Int'l*, pg. 5626
ORIENTAL MOTOR CO., LTD.; *Int'l*, pg. 5626
ORIENTAL MOTOR DO BRASIL LTDA.—See Motor Co., Ltd.; *Int'l*, pg. 5626
ORIENTAL MOTOR (EUROPA) GMBH—See Oriental Motor Co., Ltd.; *Int'l*, pg. 5626
ORIENTAL MOTOR (FRANCE) SARL—See Oriental Motor Co., Ltd.; *Int'l*, pg. 5626
ORIENTAL MOTOR (INDIA) PVT.LTD.—See Oriental Motor Co., Ltd.; *Int'l*, pg. 5626
ORIENTAL MOTOR ITALIA S.R.L.—See Oriental Motor Co., Ltd.; *Int'l*, pg. 5626
ORIENTAL MOTOR (MALAYSIA) SDN. BHD.—See Oriental Motor Co., Ltd.; *Int'l*, pg. 5626
ORIENTAL MOTOR SHANGHAI CO., LTD.—See Oriental Motor Co., Ltd.; *Int'l*, pg. 5626
ORIENTAL MOTOR (THAILAND) CO.,LTD—See Oriental Motor Co., Ltd.; *Int'l*, pg. 5626
ORIENTAL MOTOR (UK) LTD.—See Oriental Motor Co., Ltd.; *Int'l*, pg. 5626
ORIENTAL MOTOR U.S.A. CORP.—See Oriental Motor Co., Ltd.; *Int'l*, pg. 5626
ORIENTAL NICHINAN DESIGN ENGINEERING SDN. BHD.—See Oriental Holdings Berhad; *Int'l*, pg. 5624
ORIENTAL PAYMENT GROUP HOLDINGS LTD.—See China Smartpay Group Holdings Limited; *Int'l*, pg. 1552
ORIENTAL PEARL GROUP CO., LTD.—See New Guomai Digital Culture Co., Ltd.; *Int'l*, pg. 5224
ORIENTAL PENINSULA RESOURCES GROUP, INC.; *Int'l*, pg. 5626
ORIENTAL PENSION CONSULTANTS, INC.—See OFG Bancorp; *U.S. Public*, pg. 1564
ORIENTAL PETROLEUM & MINERALS CORPORATION—See JG Summit Holdings, Inc.; *Int'l*, pg. 3939
ORIENTAL PHARMACEUTICAL & SYNTHETIC CHEMICAL CO., LTD.—See Ono Pharmaceutical Co., Ltd.; *Int'l*, pg. 5582
ORIENTAL PRECISION & ENGINEERING CO., LTD.; *Int'l*, pg. 5626

ORIENT GROUP INCORPORATION

ORIENTAL PRECISION MACHINERY CO., LTD.—See oriental precision & engineering co., ltd.; *Int'l*, pg. 5626
ORIENTAL PRINTED CIRCUITS, INC.—See TTM Technologies, Inc.; *U.S. Public*, pg. 2203
ORIENTAL PRINTED CIRCUITS (USA), INC.—See TTM Technologies, Inc.; *U.S. Public*, pg. 2203
ORIENTAL RAIL INFRASTRUCTURE LIMITED; *Int'l*, pg. 5626
ORIENTAL REALTY SDN. BHD.—See Oriental Holdings Berhad; *Int'l*, pg. 5624
ORIENTAL RESOURCES DEVELOPMENT CO., LTD.—See The Far Eastern Group; *Int'l*, pg. 7642
ORIENTAL RUBBER & PALM OIL SDN. BERHAD—See Oriental Holdings Berhad; *Int'l*, pg. 5624
ORIENTAL SANGYO CO., LTD.—See Tokai Carbon Co., Ltd.; *Int'l*, pg. 7778
ORIENTAL SAN INDUSTRIES SDN. BHD.—See Oriental Holdings Berhad; *Int'l*, pg. 5624
ORIENTAL SHIMOMURA DRAWING (M) SDN. BHD.—See Daido Steel Co., Ltd.; *Int'l*, pg. 1923
ORIENTAL SINO LIMITED—See Danish Crown AmbA; *Int'l*, pg. 1964
ORIENTAL STEEL CO., LTD.—See Toyota Tsusho Corporation; *Int'l*, pg. 7877
ORIENTAL TECHNOLOGIES INVESTMENT LIMITED; *Int'l*, pg. 5626
ORIENTAL TRADING COMPANY, INC.—See Berkshire Hathaway Inc.; *U.S. Public*, pg. 313
ORIENTAL TRIMEX LIMITED; *Int'l*, pg. 5626
ORIENTAL UNION CHEMICAL CORPORATION; *Int'l*, pg. 5626
ORIENTAL UNIVERSITY CITY HOLDINGS (H.K.) LTD.; *Int'l*, pg. 5626
ORIENTAL WATCH (CHINA) COMPANY LIMITED—See Oriental Watch Holdings Limited; *Int'l*, pg. 5627
ORIENTAL WATCH COMPANY LIMITED—See Oriental Watch Holdings Limited; *Int'l*, pg. 5627
ORIENTAL WATCH HOLDINGS LIMITED; *Int'l*, pg. 5627
ORIENTAL WATCH (MACAU) COMPANY LIMITED—See Oriental Watch Holdings Limited; *Int'l*, pg. 5627
ORIENTAL WEAVERS; *Int'l*, pg. 5627
ORIENTAL YEAST CO., LTD.—See Nisshin Seifun Group, Inc.; *Int'l*, pg. 5372
ORIENT BANCORPORATION INC.; *U.S. Private*, pg. 3041
ORIENT BELL LIMITED; *Int'l*, pg. 5621
ORIENT BEVERAGES LIMITED; *Int'l*, pg. 5621
ORIENT BIO INC.; *Int'l*, pg. 5621
ORIENT BLACKSWAN PRIVATE LIMITED; *Int'l*, pg. 5621
ORIENT CAPITAL LIMITED—See Mitsubishi UFJ Financial Group, Inc.; *Int'l*, pg. 4972
ORIENT CAPITAL PTY LTD.—See Pacific Equity Partners Pty. Limited; *Int'l*, pg. 5689
ORIENT CAPITAL VENTURES LIMITED—See AsianLogic Limited; *Int'l*, pg. 620
ORIENT CEMENT LIMITED; *Int'l*, pg. 5621
ORIENT CONTAINERS CO., LTD.—See The Siam Cement Public Company Limited; *Int'l*, pg. 7683
ORIENT CORPORATION; *Int'l*, pg. 5621
ORIENTEC CO., LTD.—See A&D Co., Ltd.; *Int'l*, pg. 19
ORIENT ECOLOGY CO., LTD.—See Toyo Construction Co., Ltd.; *Int'l*, pg. 7852
ORIENT ESCAPE TRAVEL (SABAH) SDN. BHD.—See Advance Synergy Berhad; *Int'l*, pg. 156
ORIENT ESCAPE TRAVEL SDN. BHD.—See Advance Synergy Berhad; *Int'l*, pg. 156
ORIENT EUROPHARMA CO., LTD.; *Int'l*, pg. 5622
ORIENT EUROPHARMA CO. LTD—See Orient EuroPharma Co., Ltd.; *Int'l*, pg. 5622
ORIENT EUROPHARMA (M) SDN BHD—See Orient EuroPharma Co., Ltd.; *Int'l*, pg. 5622
ORIENT EUROPHARMA PTE LTD—See Orient EuroPharma Co., Ltd.; *Int'l*, pg. 5622
ORIENT EXPRESS BANK OJSC; *Int'l*, pg. 5622
ORIENT FLEXI-PAX TOURS—See Isram Wholesale Tours & Travel Ltd.; *U.S. Private*, pg. 2147
ORIENT FUTURES INTERNATIONAL (SINGAPORE) PTE LTD.—See Orient Securities Company Limited; *Int'l*, pg. 5622
ORIENT GREEN POWER LTD.—See SEPC Limited; *Int'l*, pg. 6718
ORIENT GROUP INCORPORATION; *Int'l*, pg. 5622
ORIENT INSURANCE PJSC—See Al-Futtaim Private Company LLC; *Int'l*, pg. 285
ORIENT INTERNATIONAL SHANGAI HOMETEX CO., LTD.—See Oriental International Enterprise Limited; *Int'l*, pg. 5625
ORIENT INTERNATIONAL SHANGHAI TEXTILE CO., LTD.—See Oriental International Enterprise Limited; *Int'l*, pg. 5625
ORIENT INTERNATIONAL TRADING—See Landmark Retail Holdings 1 Limited; *Int'l*, pg. 4407
ORIENT KOKI CO.,LTD—See Toyo Tire Corporation; *Int'l*, pg. 7859
ORIENT MACHINERY CO., LTD.—See Toyo Tire Corporation; *Int'l*, pg. 7859
ORIENT MARINE CO., LTD.—See Mitsui & Co., Ltd.; *Int'l*, pg. 4979
ORIENT MARINE PTE. LTD.—See KS Energy Limited; *Int'l*, pg. 4309

ORIENT GROUP INCORPORATION

ORIENT/MCCANN—See The Interpublic Group of Companies, Inc.; *U.S. Public*, pg. 2102
ORIENT/MCCANN—See The Interpublic Group of Companies, Inc.; *U.S. Public*, pg. 2102
ORIENT MOTOR COMPANY LIMITED—See United Motors Lanka PLC; *Int'l*, pg. 8071
ORIENT MOTORS WLL—See Al Zayani Investments WLL; *Int'l*, pg. 283
ORIENT OVERSEAS CONTAINER LINE (CHINA) CO. LTD - GUANGZHOU BRANCH—See China COSCO Shipping Corporation Limited; *Int'l*, pg. 1495
ORIENT OVERSEAS CONTAINER LINE LIMITED—See China COSCO Shipping Corporation Limited; *Int'l*, pg. 1495
ORIENT OVERSEAS CONTAINER LINE (MALAYSIA) SDN. BHD.—See China COSCO Shipping Corporation Limited; *Int'l*, pg. 1495
ORIENT OVERSEAS CONTAINER LINE (SPAIN) S. L.—See China COSCO Shipping Corporation Limited; *Int'l*, pg. 1495
ORIENT OVERSEAS (INTERNATIONAL) LIMITED—See China COSCO Shipping Corporation Limited; *Int'l*, pg. 1495
ORIENT PAPER & INDUSTRIES LIMITED; *Int'l*, pg. 5622
ORIENT PETROLEUM AND ENERGY, INC.; *Int'l*, pg. 5622
ORIENT PHARMA CO., LTD.; *Int'l*, pg. 5622
ORIENT PLANET; *Int'l*, pg. 5622
ORIENT PRECISION INDUSTRIES INC.; *Int'l*, pg. 5622
ORIENT PRESS LIMITED; *Int'l*, pg. 5622
ORIENT RENTAL MODARABA; *Int'l*, pg. 5622
ORIENT-SALT CHEMICALS PTE. LTD.—See Abundance International Ltd.; *Int'l*, pg. 74
ORIENT-SALT CHEMICALS (SHANGHAI) CO., LTD.—See Abundance International Ltd.; *Int'l*, pg. 74
ORIENT SECURITIES COMPANY LIMITED; *Int'l*, pg. 5622
ORIENT SECURITIES FINANCE LIMITED—See Orient Securities Inter; *Int'l*, pg. 5623
ORIENT SECURITIES INTERNATIONAL HOLDINGS LIMITED; *Int'l*, pg. 5622
ORIENT SECURITIES INVESTMENT BANKING CO., LTD.—See Orient Securities Company Limited; *Int'l*, pg. 5622
ORIENT SEMICONDUCTOR ELECTRONICS INC—See Orient Semiconductor Electronics Limited; *Int'l*, pg. 5623
ORIENT SEMICONDUCTOR ELECTRONICS LIMITED; *Int'l*, pg. 5623
ORIENT SHOPPING CENTRE - HUAIHAI—See Bailian Group Co., Ltd.; *Int'l*, pg. 802
ORIENT SHOPPING CENTRE - JIADING—See Bailian Group Co., Ltd.; *Int'l*, pg. 802
ORIENT SHOPPING CENTRE LTD.—See Bailian Group Co., Ltd.; *Int'l*, pg. 802
ORIENT SHOPPING CENTRE - NANDONG—See Bailian Group Co., Ltd.; *Int'l*, pg. 802
ORIENT SHOPPING CENTRE - NINGBO—See Bailian Group Co., Ltd.; *Int'l*, pg. 802
ORIENT SHOPPING CENTRE - YANGPU—See Bailian Group Co., Ltd.; *Int'l*, pg. 802
ORIENT TAKAFUL PJSC—See Abu Dhabi Commercial Bank PJSC; *Int'l*, pg. 71
ORIENT TELECOMS PLC; *Int'l*, pg. 5623
ORIENT THAI AIRLINES; *Int'l*, pg. 5623
ORIENT TRADELINK LIMITED; *Int'l*, pg. 5623
ORIENT VICTORY SMART URBAN SERVICES HOLDING LIMITED; *Int'l*, pg. 5623
ORIFA SERVICE SERVICER CO., LTD.—See Orient Corporation; *Int'l*, pg. 5621
ORIFAST CONNECTOR SOLUTIONS LLC—See YBS International Berhad; *Int'l*, pg. 8574
ORIFLAME AZERBAIJAN—See Oriflame Cosmetics S.A.; *Int'l*, pg. 5627
ORIFLAME BULGARIA EOOD—See Oriflame Cosmetics S.A.; *Int'l*, pg. 5627
ORIFLAME COSMETICOS LTDA—See Oriflame Cosmetics S.A.; *Int'l*, pg. 5627
ORIFLAME COSMETICOS S.A.—See Oriflame Cosmetics S.A.; *Int'l*, pg. 5627
ORIFLAME COSMETICS AB—See Oriflame Cosmetics S.A.; *Int'l*, pg. 5627
ORIFLAME COSMETICS FOREIGN LLC—See Oriflame Cosmetics S.A.; *Int'l*, pg. 5627
ORIFLAME COSMETICS PAKISTAN (PVT) LTD—See Oriflame Cosmetics S.A.; *Int'l*, pg. 5627
ORIFLAME COSMETICS S.A.; *Int'l*, pg. 5627
ORIFLAME COSMETICS—See Oriflame Cosmetics S.A.; *Int'l*, pg. 5627
ORIFLAME COSMETICS SRL—See Oriflame Cosmetics S.A.; *Int'l*, pg. 5627
ORIFLAME COSMETICS (THAILAND) LTD.—See Oriflame Cosmetics S.A.; *Int'l*, pg. 5627
ORIFLAME CZECH REPUBLIC SRO—See Oriflame Cosmetics S.A.; *Int'l*, pg. 5627
ORIFLAME DE CHILE S.A—See Oriflame Cosmetics S.A.; *Int'l*, pg. 5627
ORIFLAME DE COLOMBIA S.A.—See Oriflame Cosmetics S.A.; *Int'l*, pg. 5628

ORIFLAME DE COSTA RICA S.A.—See Oriflame Cosmetics S.A.; *Int'l*, pg. 5628
ORIFLAME DE EL SALVADOR S.A.—See Oriflame Cosmetics S.A.; *Int'l*, pg. 5628
ORIFLAME DE GUATEMALA S.A.—See Oriflame Cosmetics S.A.; *Int'l*, pg. 5628
ORIFLAME DEL ECUADOR—See Oriflame Cosmetics S.A.; *Int'l*, pg. 5628
ORIFLAME DE NICARAGUA S.A.—See Oriflame Cosmetics S.A.; *Int'l*, pg. 5628
ORIFLAME EESTI OU—See Oriflame Cosmetics S.A.; *Int'l*, pg. 5627
ORIFLAME EGYPT LTD.—See Oriflame Cosmetics S.A.; *Int'l*, pg. 5627
ORIFLAME FINLAND OY—See Oriflame Cosmetics S.A.; *Int'l*, pg. 5627
ORIFLAME GREECE LTD.—See Oriflame Cosmetics S.A.; *Int'l*, pg. 5627
ORIFLAME HUNGARY KFT—See Oriflame Cosmetics S.A.; *Int'l*, pg. 5627
ORIFLAME INDIA PVT. LTD.—See Oriflame Cosmetics S.A.; *Int'l*, pg. 5627
ORIFLAME INDONESIA—See Oriflame Cosmetics S.A.; *Int'l*, pg. 5627
ORIFLAME INTERNATIONAL APS—See Oriflame Cosmetics S.A.; *Int'l*, pg. 5627
ORIFLAME KAZAKHSTAN—See Oriflame Cosmetics S.A.; *Int'l*, pg. 5627
ORIFLAME KOSMETIEK B.V.—See Oriflame Cosmetics S.A.; *Int'l*, pg. 5627
ORIFLAME KOSMETIKA BH D.J.L.—See Oriflame Cosmetics S.A.; *Int'l*, pg. 5627
ORIFLAME KOSMETIKA D.O.O.—See Oriflame Cosmetics S.A.; *Int'l*, pg. 5627
ORIFLAME KOSMETIKA UAB—See Oriflame Cosmetics S.A.; *Int'l*, pg. 5627
ORIFLAME KOZMETIKA CROATIA D.O.O.—See Oriflame Cosmetics S.A.; *Int'l*, pg. 5627
ORIFLAME KOZMETIKA DOOEL—See Oriflame Cosmetics S.A.; *Int'l*, pg. 5627
ORIFLAME KOZMETIKA D.O.O.—See Oriflame Cosmetics S.A.; *Int'l*, pg. 5627
ORIFLAME KOZMETIK URUNLERI TICARET LTD STI.—See Oriflame Cosmetics S.A.; *Int'l*, pg. 5627
ORIFLAME LANKA (PVT.) LTD.—See Oriflame Cosmetics S.A.; *Int'l*, pg. 5628
ORIFLAME LATVIA SIA—See Oriflame Cosmetics S.A.; *Int'l*, pg. 5628
ORIFLAME LLP—See Oriflame Cosmetics S.A.; *Int'l*, pg. 5628
ORIFLAME MARKETING (M) SDN BHD—See Oriflame Cosmetics S.A.; *Int'l*, pg. 5628
ORIFLAME MAROC S.A.R.L.—See Oriflame Cosmetics S.A.; *Int'l*, pg. 5628
ORIFLAME MEXICO S.A. DE C.V.—See Oriflame Cosmetics S.A.; *Int'l*, pg. 5628
ORIFLAME MONGOLIA XXK—See Oriflame Cosmetics S.A.; *Int'l*, pg. 5628
ORIFLAME NORGE A.S.—See Oriflame Cosmetics S.A.; *Int'l*, pg. 5628
ORIFLAME PERU S.A.—See Oriflame Cosmetics S.A.; *Int'l*, pg. 5628
ORIFLAME POLAND SP. Z.O.O.—See Oriflame Cosmetics S.A.; *Int'l*, pg. 5628
ORIFLAME RESEARCH & DEVELOPMENT LTD.—See Oriflame Cosmetics S.A.; *Int'l*, pg. 5628
ORIFLAME SERVICES INTERNATIONAL AB—See Oriflame Cosmetics S.A.; *Int'l*, pg. 5628
ORIFLAME SLOVAKIA SRO—See Oriflame Cosmetics S.A.; *Int'l*, pg. 5628
ORIFLAME—See Oriflame Cosmetics S.A.; *Int'l*, pg. 5627
ORIFLAME SPOL SRO—See Oriflame Cosmetics S.A.; *Int'l*, pg. 5628
ORIFLAME SPOL SRO—See Oriflame Cosmetics S.A.; *Int'l*, pg. 5628
ORIFLAME SP ZOO—See Oriflame Cosmetics S.A.; *Int'l*, pg. 5628
ORIFLAME SUDAN—See Oriflame Cosmetics S.A.; *Int'l*, pg. 5628
ORIFLAME UKRAINE—See Oriflame Cosmetics S.A.; *Int'l*, pg. 5628
ORIFLAME USA—See Oriflame Cosmetics S.A.; *Int'l*, pg. 5628
ORIFLAME UZBEKISTAN—See Oriflame Cosmetics S.A.; *Int'l*, pg. 5628
ORIFLAME VIETNAM LTD.—See Oriflame Cosmetics S.A.; *Int'l*, pg. 5628
ORIG3N INC.—See 180 Degree Capital Corp.; *U.S. Public*, pg. 2
ORIGAMI CREATIVE CONCEPTS PVT. LTD.; *Int'l*, pg. 5628
ORIGAMI FRONTIERS—See Hakuhodo DY Holdings Incorporated; *Int'l*, pg. 3222
ORIGAMI LOGIC LTD.—See Intuit Inc.; *U.S. Public*, pg. 1160
ORIGEN ARGENTINA—See Origen Global; *U.S. Private*, pg. 3041
ORIGEN BRAZIL—See Origen Global; *U.S. Private*, pg. 3041

CORPORATE AFFILIATIONS

ORIGENCE LENDING SERVICES—See CU Direct Corporation; *U.S. Private*, pg. 1119
ORIGEN COLOMBIA—See Origen Global; *U.S. Private*, pg. 3041
ORIGEN COSTA RICA—See Origen Global; *U.S. Private*, pg. 3041
ORIGEN ECUADOR—See Origen Global; *U.S. Private*, pg. 3041
ORIGEN EL SALVADOR—See Origen Global; *U.S. Private*, pg. 3041
ORIGEN ESPANA—See Origen Global; *U.S. Private*, pg. 3041
ORIGENES SEGUROS DE RETIRO, S.A.—See Grupo EMES S.A.; *Int'l*, pg. 3126
ORIGENE TECHNOLOGIES, INC.; *U.S. Private*, pg. 3042
ORIGENE WUXI—See OriGene Technologies, Inc.; *U.S. Private*, pg. 3042
ORIGEN FINANCIAL, INC.; *U.S. Private*, pg. 3041
ORIGEN GLOBAL; *U.S. Private*, pg. 3041
ORIGEN GUATEMALA—See Origen Global; *U.S. Private*, pg. 3041
ORIGEN HONDURAS—See Origen Global; *U.S. Private*, pg. 3041
ORIGEN MEXICO—See Origen Global; *U.S. Private*, pg. 3042
ORIGEN NICARAGUA—See Origen Global; *U.S. Private*, pg. 3042
ORIGEN PANAMA—See Origen Global; *U.S. Private*, pg. 3042
ORIGEN RESOURCES, INC.; *Int'l*, pg. 5628
ORIGIN8 SAATCHI & SAATCHI—See Publicis Groupe S.A.; *Int'l*, pg. 6108
ORIGIN AGRITECH LIMITED; *Int'l*, pg. 5628
ORIGINAL1 GMBH—See Giesecke & Devrient GmbH; *Int'l*, pg. 2970
ORIGINAL1 GMBH—See Nokia Corporation; *Int'l*, pg. 5406
ORIGINAL1 GMBH—See SAP SE; *Int'l*, pg. 6569
ORIGINAL ADDITIONS (BEAUTY PRODUCTS) LTD.—See Yellow Wood Partners LLC; *U.S. Private*, pg. 4587
ORIGINAL APPALACHIAN ARTWORKS, INC.; *U.S. Private*, pg. 3042
ORIGINAL AUSTIN'S GROCERY STORES; *U.S. Private*, pg. 3042
ORIGINAL BRADFORD SOAP WORKS, INC.; *U.S. Private*, pg. 3042
THE ORIGINAL CAST LIGHTING, INC.—See Legrand S.A.; *Int'l*, pg. 4446
THE ORIGINAL CHILI BOWL—See Ajinomoto Company, Inc.; *Int'l*, pg. 257
ORIGINAL CRISPY PIZZA CRUST OF BOSTON CO. INC.; *U.S. Private*, pg. 3042
ORIGINAL ENGINEERING CONSULTANTS CO., LTD.; *Int'l*, pg. 5630
THE ORIGINAL FOOTWEAR CO.—See Brand Velocity Partners; *U.S. Private*, pg. 637
THE ORIGINAL HONEYBAKED HAM CO.; *U.S. Private*, pg. 4089
ORIGINAL IMPRESSIONS, LLC—See Postal Center International; *U.S. Private*, pg. 3234
THE ORIGINAL KEVIN GUIDRY PRODUCE MARKET, INC.; *U.S. Private*, pg. 4089
THE ORIGINAL LONDON SIGHTSEEING TOUR LTD.—See I Squared Capital Advisors (US) LLC; *U.S. Private*, pg. 2025
ORIGINAL MATTRESS FACTORY PTY LTD—See Steinhoff International Holdings N.V.; *Int'l*, pg. 7194
THE ORIGINAL MATTRESS FACTORY; *U.S. Private*, pg. 4089
ORIGINAL NUT HOUSE—See Conagra Brands, Inc.; *U.S. Public*, pg. 564
ORIGINAL PRODUCTIONS LLC—See Bertelsmann SE & Co. KGaA; *Int'l*, pg. 994
ORIGINAL SIXTEEN TO ONE MINE, INC.; *U.S. Public*, pg. 1617
ORIGINAL SMITH PRINTING—See Taylor Corporation; *U.S. Private*, pg. 3938
ORIGINAL SOURCE MUSIC, INC.; *U.S. Private*, pg. 3042
ORIGINAL STEEL SERVICES LIMITED; *Int'l*, pg. 5630
ORIGIN ASSET MANAGEMENT LLP—See Principal Financial Group, Inc.; *U.S. Public*, pg. 1720
ORIGINATE LABS; *U.S. Private*, pg. 3042
ORIGIN BANCORP, INC.; *U.S. Public*, pg. 1617
ORIGIN BANK—See Origin Bancorp, Inc.; *U.S. Public*, pg. 1617
ORIGIN BIOSCIENCES, INC.—See BridgeBio Pharma, Inc.; *U.S. Public*, pg. 382
ORIGINCLEAR, INC.; *U.S. Public*, pg. 1617
ORIGIN CO., LTD.; *Int'l*, pg. 5628
ORIGIN COMMUNICATIONS GROUP FZ LLC; *Int'l*, pg. 5629
ORIGIN DIGITAL, INC.—See Accenture plc; *Int'l*, pg. 86
ORIGIN DIRECT ASIA (SHANGHAI) TRADING CO., LTD.—See Mahindra & Mahindra Limited; *Int'l*, pg. 4646
ORIGIN DONBON PAINTS (DONGGUAN) CO., LTD.—See Origin Co., Ltd.; *Int'l*, pg. 5629
ORIGIN EASON PAINT CO., LTD.—See Origin Co., Ltd.; *Int'l*, pg. 5629

COMPANY NAME INDEX

ORIGIN ELECTRIC AMERICA CO., LTD.—See Origin Co., Ltd.; *Int'l*, pg. 5629
ORIGIN ELECTRIC CO., LTD. - MAMADA PLANT—See Origin Co., Ltd.; *Int'l*, pg. 5629
ORIGIN ELECTRIC CO., LTD. - MIZUHO PLANT—See Origin Co., Ltd.; *Int'l*, pg. 5629
ORIGIN ELECTRIC CO., LTD. - YOSHIMI FACTORY—See Origin Co., Ltd.; *Int'l*, pg. 5629
ORIGIN ENERGY ASSET MANAGEMENT SERVICES PTY LTD.—See Origin Energy Ltd.; *Int'l*, pg. 5629
ORIGIN ENERGY AUSTRALIA HOLDING B.V.—See Origin Energy Ltd.; *Int'l*, pg. 5629
ORIGIN ENERGY BONAPARTE PTY LTD—See Origin Energy Ltd.; *Int'l*, pg. 5629
ORIGIN ENERGY CONTRACTING LTD.—See Origin Energy Ltd.; *Int'l*, pg. 5629
ORIGIN ENERGY CSG LTD.—See Origin Energy Ltd.; *Int'l*, pg. 5629
ORIGIN ENERGY DEVELOPMENTS PTY LTD—See Origin Energy Ltd.; *Int'l*, pg. 5629
ORIGIN ENERGY ELECTRICITY LTD—See Origin Energy Ltd.; *Int'l*, pg. 5629
ORIGIN ENERGY HOLDINGS LTD.—See Origin Energy Ltd.; *Int'l*, pg. 5629
ORIGIN ENERGY LPG LTD.—See Origin Energy Ltd.; *Int'l*, pg. 5629
ORIGIN ENERGY LTD.; *Int'l*, pg. 5629
ORIGIN ENERGY PETROLEUM PTY LTD.—See Origin Energy Ltd.; *Int'l*, pg. 5629
ORIGIN ENERGY PIPELINES PTY LTD—See Origin Energy Ltd.; *Int'l*, pg. 5629
ORIGIN ENERGY PIPELINES (VIC) HOLDINGS PTY LTD—See Origin Energy Ltd.; *Int'l*, pg. 5629
ORIGIN ENERGY PNG LTD.—See Origin Energy Ltd.; *Int'l*, pg. 5629
ORIGIN ENERGY POWER LTD—See Origin Energy Ltd.; *Int'l*, pg. 5629
ORIGIN ENERGY RESOURCES NZ LTD.—See Origin Energy Ltd.; *Int'l*, pg. 5629
ORIGIN ENERGY RETAIL LTD.—See Origin Energy Ltd.; *Int'l*, pg. 5629
ORIGIN ENERGY SA PTY LTD.—See Origin Energy Ltd.; *Int'l*, pg. 5630
ORIGIN ENERGY SOLOMONS LTD—See Origin Energy Ltd.; *Int'l*, pg. 5630
ORIGIN ENERGY SWC LTD.—See Origin Energy Ltd.; *Int'l*, pg. 5630
ORIGIN ENERGY TASMANIA LTD.—See Origin Energy Ltd.; *Int'l*, pg. 5630
ORIGIN ENERGY VIC HOLDINGS PTY LTD—See Origin Energy Ltd.; *Int'l*, pg. 5630
ORIGIN ENERGY (VIC) PTY LTD.—See Origin Energy Ltd.; *Int'l*, pg. 5630
ORIGIN ENERGY WALLUMBILLA TRANSMISSIONS PTY LTD—See Origin Energy Ltd.; *Int'l*, pg. 5630
ORIGIN ENERGY WA PTY LTD.—See Origin Energy Ltd.; *Int'l*, pg. 5630
ORIGIN ENTERPRISES PLC—See ARYZTA AG; *Int'l*, pg. 589
ORIGINES S.A.R.L.—See Symrise AG; *Int'l*, pg. 7380
ORIGIN FERTILISERS (UK) LIMITED—See ARYZTA AG; *Int'l*, pg. 589
ORIGIN FOUNDATION PTY LIMITED—See Origin Energy Ltd.; *Int'l*, pg. 5630
ORIGIN FRUIT DIRECT B.V.—See Mahindra & Mahindra Limited; *Int'l*, pg. 4646
ORIGIN FRUIT SERVICES SOUTH AMERICA SPA—See Mahindra & Mahindra Limited; *Int'l*, pg. 4646
ORIGIN INTERNATIONAL INC.—See Element Alpha SA; *Int'l*, pg. 2358
ORIGIN KOREA CO., LTD.—See Origin Co., Ltd.; *Int'l*, pg. 5629
ORIGIN MATERIALS, INC.; *U.S. Public*, pg. 1617
ORIGIN MERGER SUB II, LLC—See Westrock Coffee Company; *U.S. Public*, pg. 2361
ORIGIN PAINTS (TIANJIN) CO., LTD.—See Origin Co., Ltd.; *Int'l*, pg. 5629
ORIGIN PC, LLC—See EagleTree Capital, LP; *U.S. Private*, pg. 1311
ORIGIN PRECISION MACHINE (SHANGHAI) CO., LTD.—See Origin Co., Ltd.; *Int'l*, pg. 5629
ORIGIN PROPERTY PUBLIC COMPANY LIMITED; *Int'l*, pg. 5630
ORIGIN SOLUTIONS, LTD.—See KKR & Co. Inc.; *U.S. Public*, pg. 1257
ORIGIN STORAGE LTD.; *Int'l*, pg. 5630
ORIGIN TOSHU CO., LTD—See AEON Co., Ltd.; *Int'l*, pg. 178
ORIGIO A/S—See The Cooper Companies, Inc.; *U.S. Public*, pg. 2066
ORIGIO FRANCE SARL—See The Cooper Companies, Inc.; *U.S. Public*, pg. 2066
ORIGIO, INC.—See The Cooper Companies, Inc.; *U.S. Public*, pg. 2066
ORIGIO LTD.—See The Cooper Companies, Inc.; *U.S. Public*, pg. 2066
ORIGO ACQUISITION CORPORATION; *U.S. Private*, pg. 3042

ORIGO DISTRIBUTION LIMITED—See Sicon Ltd.; *Int'l*, pg. 6882
ORIGO HF.; *Int'l*, pg. 5630
ORIGO PARTNERS PLC; *Int'l*, pg. 5631
ORIGO SERVICES LIMITED—See Aviva plc; *Int'l*, pg. 746
ORIGO SOLUTIONS AS—See HitecVision AS; *Int'l*, pg. 3426
ORI GREAT WEST HOLDING, INC.—See Old Republic International Corporation; *U.S. Public*, pg. 1567
ORIHICA INC.—See AOKI Holdings Inc.; *Int'l*, pg. 488
ORILLION CORPORATION; *U.S. Private*, pg. 3042
ORILLION USA INC.—See Orillion Corporation; *U.S. Private*, pg. 3042
ORINKO ADVANCED PLASTICS CO., LTD.; *Int'l*, pg. 5631
ORINOCO GOLD, LTD.; *Int'l*, pg. 5631
ORINOQUIA REAL ESTATE SOCIMI, S.A.; *Int'l*, pg. 5631
ORIN SWIFT CELLARS LLC—See E. & J. Gallo Winery; *U.S. Private*, pg. 1303
ORIN USA; *U.S. Private*, pg. 3042
ORIO AB; *Int'l*, pg. 5631
ORIOLA AB—See Oriola Corporation; *Int'l*, pg. 5631
ORIOLA CORPORATION; *Int'l*, pg. 5631
ORIOLA FINLAND OY—See Oriola Corporation; *Int'l*, pg. 5631
ORIOLA OY GRAPHIC ARTS—See Oriola Corporation; *Int'l*, pg. 5631
ORIOLA OY MEDION—See Oriola Corporation; *Int'l*, pg. 5631
ORIOLA OY REFORMI-KESKUS—See Oriola Corporation; *Int'l*, pg. 5631
ORIOLA OY—See Oriola Corporation; *Int'l*, pg. 5631
ORIOLE RESOURCES PLC; *Int'l*, pg. 5631
ORIOL FIBRA S.L.—See Orange S.A.; *Int'l*, pg. 5609
ORION ACQUISITION CORP.; *U.S. Public*, pg. 1617
ORION ADMINISTRATIVE SERVICES, INC.—See Orion Group Holdings, Inc.; *U.S. Public*, pg. 1618
ORION ADVISOR SOLUTIONS, LLC; *U.S. Private*, pg. 3042
ORION ASSOCIATES; *U.S. Private*, pg. 3042
ORION BIOTECH OPPORTUNITIES CORP.; *U.S. Public*, pg. 1617
ORION BLISS CORP.; *Int'l*, pg. 5631
ORION BUILDING CORPORATION; *U.S. Private*, pg. 3042
ORION CHEMICAL TECHNOLOGIES; *U.S. Private*, pg. 3042
ORION COMMUNICATIONS, INC.—See Fieldware, LLC; *U.S. Private*, pg. 1504
ORION CONSTRUCTION LP—See Orion Group Holdings, Inc.; *U.S. Public*, pg. 1618
ORION CORPORATION - HANKO PLANT—See Orion Corporation; *Int'l*, pg. 5631
ORION CORPORATION - OULU PLANT—See Orion Corporation; *Int'l*, pg. 5631
ORION CORPORATION; *Int'l*, pg. 5631
ORION CORPORATION; *Int'l*, pg. 5632
ORION CUSTOM METAL FABRICATION CORPORATION—See Lincoln Electric Holdings, Inc.; *U.S. Public*, pg. 1318
ORION DIVERSIFIED HOLDINGS CO. INC.; *U.S. Public*, pg. 1617
ORION ENERGY SYSTEMS, INC.; *U.S. Public*, pg. 1617
ORION ENGINEERED CARBONS FRANCE SAS—See Rhone Group, LLC; *U.S. Private*, pg. 3424
ORION ENGINEERED CARBONS GMBH—See Rhone Group, LLC; *U.S. Private*, pg. 3424
ORION ENGINEERED CARBONS HOLDINGS GMBH—See Rhone Group, LLC; *U.S. Private*, pg. 3424
ORION ENGINEERED CARBONS LLC—See Rhone Group, LLC; *U.S. Private*, pg. 3424
ORION ENGINEERED CARBONS TRADING (SHANGHAI) CO., LTD.—See Rhone Group, LLC; *U.S. Private*, pg. 3424
ORION ENGINEERING BV—See Alten S.A.; *Int'l*, pg. 390
ORION ENGINEERING SA (PTY) LTD—See Orion Engineering Services Limited; *Int'l*, pg. 5632
ORION ENGINEERING SERVICES LIMITED; *Int'l*, pg. 5632
ORION ENGINEERING SERVICES MOZAMBIQUE LIMITADA—See Orion Engineering Services Limited; *Int'l*, pg. 5632
ORION ENGINEERING SERVICES NIGERIA LIMITED—See Orion Engineering Services Limited; *Int'l*, pg. 5632
ORION ENTERPRISES, INC.—See Watts Water Technologies, Inc.; *U.S. Public*, pg. 2337
ORION ENTRANCE CONTROL, INC.; *U.S. Private*, pg. 3042
ORION EQUITIES LIMITED; *Int'l*, pg. 5632
ORION EXPEDITION CRUISES PTY. LTD.—See KSL Capital Partners, LLC; *U.S. Private*, pg. 2355
ORION EXPLORATION PTY LTD—See Intiger Group Limited; *Int'l*, pg. 3767
ORION FINANCIAL CORP.; *U.S. Private*, pg. 3043
ORION FINANCIAL GROUP, INC.—See Longshore Capital Partners; *U.S. Private*, pg. 2493

ORION OFFICE REIT, INC.

ORIONFIN UNIPESSOAL LDA—See Orion Corporation; *Int'l*, pg. 5632
ORION FITTINGS INC.—See Watts Water Technologies, Inc.; *U.S. Public*, pg. 2337
ORION FOOD SYSTEMS, LLC—See One Rock Capital Partners, LLC; *U.S. Private*, pg. 3022
ORION FUNDING CREDIT UNION; *U.S. Private*, pg. 3043
ORION GENOMICS, LLC; *U.S. Private*, pg. 3043
ORION GLOBAL CORP.; *U.S. Private*, pg. 3043
ORION GLOBAL SOLUTIONS, LLC; *U.S. Private*, pg. 3043
ORION GROUP HOLDINGS, INC.; *U.S. Public*, pg. 1618
ORION GROUP KZ—See Orion Engineering Services Limited; *Int'l*, pg. 5632
ORION HEALTH GROUP LIMITED; *Int'l*, pg. 5632
ORION INCORPORADORA LTDA—See PDG Realty S.A. Empreendimentos e Participacoes; *Int'l*, pg. 5770
ORION INDUSTRIAL CONSTRUCTION, LLC—See Orion Group Holdings, Inc.; *U.S. Public*, pg. 1618
ORION INFUSION LIMITED; *Int'l*, pg. 5633
ORION INSTRUMENTS, LLC.—See AMETEK, Inc.; *U.S. Public*, pg. 121
ORION INTERNATIONAL CONSULTING GROUP, LLC - GEMINI ENERGY SERVICES DIVISION—See L2 Capital Partners; *U.S. Private*, pg. 2367
ORION INTERNATIONAL CONSULTING GROUP, LLC - GEMINI ENERGY SERVICES DIVISION—See Lakewood Capital, LLC; *U.S. Private*, pg. 2379
ORION INTERNATIONAL CONSULTING GROUP, LLC—See L2 Capital Partners; *U.S. Private*, pg. 2367
ORION INTERNATIONAL CONSULTING GROUP, LLC—See Lakewood Capital, LLC; *U.S. Private*, pg. 2379
ORION INVESTMENT & MANAGEMENT LTD. CORP.; *U.S. Private*, pg. 3043
ORION LABORATORIES (NZ) LTD.—See Perrigo Company plc; *Int'l*, pg. 5813
ORION LABORATORIES PTY LIMITED—See Perrigo Company plc; *Int'l*, pg. 5813
ORION MALL MANAGEMENT COMPANY LIMITED—See Brigade Enterprises Limited; *Int'l*, pg. 1161
ORION MARINE CONSTRUCTION, INC.—See Orion Group Holdings, Inc.; *U.S. Public*, pg. 1618
ORION MARINE CONTRACTORS, INC.—See Orion Group Holdings, Inc.; *U.S. Public*, pg. 1618
ORION MEDIA ASSOCIATES, INC.; *U.S. Private*, pg. 3043
ORION METALS LIMITED; *Int'l*, pg. 5633
ORION MINERALS LTD; *Int'l*, pg. 5633
ORION MOBILITY; *U.S. Private*, pg. 3043
ORION NEW ZEALAND LTD—See Christchurch City Holdings Ltd.; *Int'l*, pg. 1586
ORION NUTRACEUTICALS, INC.; *Int'l*, pg. 5633
ORION OFFICE REIT, INC.; *U.S. Public*, pg. 1618
ORION PERSONNEL PH INC—See Orion Engineering Services Limited; *Int'l*, pg. 5632
ORION PHARMA AB—See Orion Corporation; *Int'l*, pg. 5632
ORION PHARMA AB—See Orion Corporation; *Int'l*, pg. 5632
ORION PHARMA AB—See Orion Corporation; *Int'l*, pg. 5632
ORION PHARMA AB—See Orion Corporation; *Int'l*, pg. 5632
ORION PHARMA AG—See Orion Corporation; *Int'l*, pg. 5632
ORION PHARMA ANIMAL HEALTH—See Orion Corporation; *Int'l*, pg. 5632
ORION PHARMA ANIMAL HEALTH—See Orion Corporation; *Int'l*, pg. 5632
ORION PHARMA A/S—See Orion Corporation; *Int'l*, pg. 5632
ORION PHARMA A/S—See Orion Corporation; *Int'l*, pg. 5632
ORION PHARMA (AUSTRIA) GMBH—See Orion Corporation; *Int'l*, pg. 5632
ORION PHARMA BVBA—See Orion Corporation; *Int'l*, pg. 5632
ORION PHARMA D.O.O.—See Orion Corporation; *Int'l*, pg. 5632
ORION PHARMA GMBH—See Orion Corporation; *Int'l*, pg. 5632
ORION PHARMA HELLAS MEPE—See Orion Corporation; *Int'l*, pg. 5632
ORION PHARMA (IRELAND) LTD.—See Orion Corporation; *Int'l*, pg. 5632
ORION PHARMA KFT.—See Orion Corporation; *Int'l*, pg. 5632
ORION PHARMA POLAND SP. Z.O.O.—See Orion Corporation; *Int'l*, pg. 5632
ORION PHARMA S.L.—See Orion Corporation; *Int'l*, pg. 5632
ORION PHARMA—See Orion Corporation; *Int'l*, pg. 5631
ORION PHARMA (UK) LTD.—See Orion Corporation; *Int'l*, pg. 5632
ORION PROJECT SERVICES B.V—See Orion Engineering Services Limited; *Int'l*, pg. 5632
ORION PROJECT SERVICES (HOUSTON) LLC—See Orion Engineering Services Limited; *Int'l*, pg. 5632

ORION OFFICE REIT, INC.

CORPORATE AFFILIATIONS

ORION PROJECT SERVICES LLC—See Orion Engineering Services Limited; *Int'l*, pg. 5632
ORION PROJECT SERVICES LLC—See Orion Engineering Services Limited; *Int'l*, pg. 5632
ORION PROJECT SERVICES MALAYSIA SDN. BHD.—See Orion Engineering Services Limited; *Int'l*, pg. 5632
ORION PROJECT SERVICES PTE. LTD.—See Orion Engineering Services Limited; *Int'l*, pg. 5632
ORION PROJECT SERVICES SAKHALLIN LLC—See Orion Engineering Services Limited; *Int'l*, pg. 5632
THE ORION PUBLISHING GROUP LIMITED—See Vivendi SE; *Int'l*, pg. 8274
ORION PU SP. Z O.O.—See SELENA FM S.A.; *Int'l*, pg. 6700
ORION RECHTSSCHUTZ VERSICHERUNGSGESELLSCHAFT AG—See Zurich Insurance Group Limited; *Int'l*, pg. 8697
ORION RESOURCE PARTNERS (USA) LP; *U.S. Private*, pg. 3043
ORION RISK MANAGEMENT INSURANCE SERVICES, INC.—See Genstar Capital, LLC; *U.S. Private*, pg. 1674
ORION ROPEWORKS, INC.—See Canada Cordage, Inc.; *Int'l*, pg. 1278
ORION S.A.—See Rhone Group, LLC; *U.S. Private*, pg. 3424
ORION SEAFOOD INTERNATIONAL, INC.; *U.S. Private*, pg. 3043
ORION SOLUTIONS, INC.—See Ayalaland Logistics Holdings Corp.; *Int'l*, pg. 774
ORION SOUTH INC.; *U.S. Private*, pg. 3043
ORION SYSTEMS INTEGRATION PTE. LTD.—See Zicom Group Limited; *Int'l*, pg. 8681
ORION SYSTEMS INTEGRATORS, INC.—See OEP Capital Advisors, L.P.; *U.S. Private*, pg. 2999
ORION TECHNICAL RECRUITMENT SERVICES PVT LTD—See Orion Engineering Services Limited; *Int'l*, pg. 5632
ORION TECHNOLOGY, INC.—See Rolta India Ltd.; *Int'l*, pg. 6394
ORION TOUR CO., LTD.—See H.I.S. Co., Ltd.; *Int'l*, pg. 3196
ORION TRADING CANADA INC.—See The Interpublic Group of Companies, Inc.; *U.S. Public*, pg. 2103
ORION TRADING—See The Interpublic Group of Companies, Inc.; *U.S. Public*, pg. 2103
ORION TRANSPORTATION SERVICES INC.; *U.S. Private*, pg. 3043
ORIOR AG; *Int'l*, pg. 5633
ORIOR FOOD AG—See Orior AG; *Int'l*, pg. 5633
ORIOR MENU AG LE PATRON—See Orior AG; *Int'l*, pg. 5633
ORIOR MENU AG PASTINELLA—See Orior AG; *Int'l*, pg. 5633
ORIOR MENU AG—See Orior AG; *Int'l*, pg. 5633
ORI SERVICES CORPORATION; *U.S. Private*, pg. 3041
ORISKANY FALLS TELEPHONE CORP, INC.—See Telephone & Data Systems, Inc.; *U.S. Public*, pg. 1998
ORISLINE ESPANA S.L.—See Henry Schein, Inc.; *U.S. Public*, pg. 1027
ORISOFT TECHNOLOGY SDN BHD; *Int'l*, pg. 5633
ORISOFT (THAILAND) CO., LTD.—See Orisoft Technology Sdn Bhd; *Int'l*, pg. 5633
ORISSA BENGAL CARRIER LTD.; *Int'l*, pg. 5633
ORISSA MINERALS DEVELOPMENT COMPANY LIMITED; *Int'l*, pg. 5633
ORISSA POWER GENERATION CORPORATION LIMITED—See The AES Corporation; *U.S. Public*, pg. 2032
ORISUN ACQUISITION CORP.—See Ucommune International Ltd.; *U.S. Public*, pg. 2217
ORITANI FINANCIAL CORP.—See Valley National Bancorp; *U.S. Public*, pg. 2273
ORITZ CORPORATION; *U.S. Private*, pg. 3043
ORIWINA SDN. BHD.—See CSH Alliance Berhad; *Int'l*, pg. 1865
ORIX AIRCRAFT CORPORATION—See ORIX Corporation; *Int'l*, pg. 5634
ORIX ALPHA CORPORATION—See ORIX Corporation; *Int'l*, pg. 5634
ORIX ASIA CAPITAL LIMITED—See ORIX Corporation; *Int'l*, pg. 5634
ORIX ASIA LIMITED—See ORIX Corporation; *Int'l*, pg. 5634
ORIX ASSET MANAGEMENT CORPORATION—See ORIX Corporation; *Int'l*, pg. 5634
ORIX ASSET MANAGEMENT & LOAN SERVICES CORPORATION—See ORIX Corporation; *Int'l*, pg. 5634
ORIX ASSET MANAGEMENT MALAYSIA SDN. BHD.—See ORIX Corporation; *Int'l*, pg. 5634
ORIX AUSTRALIA CORPORATION LIMITED—See ORIX Corporation; *Int'l*, pg. 5634
ORIX AUTO CORPORATION—See ORIX Corporation; *Int'l*, pg. 5634
ORIX AUTO FINANCE (INDIA) LIMITED—See ORIX Corporation; *Int'l*, pg. 5634

ORIX AUTO INFRASTRUCTURE SERVICES LIMITED—See ORIX Corporation; *Int'l*, pg. 5634
ORIX AUTO LEASING CORPORATION—See ORIX Corporation; *Int'l*, pg. 5634
ORIX AUTO LEASING MALAYSIA SDN. BHD.—See ORIX Corporation; *Int'l*, pg. 5635
ORIX AUTO LEASING TAIWAN CORPORATION—See ORIX Corporation; *Int'l*, pg. 5634
ORIX AVIATION SYSTEMS LIMITED—See ORIX Corporation; *Int'l*, pg. 5634
ORIX BANK CORPORATION—See ORIX Corporation; *Int'l*, pg. 5634
ORIX BUFFALOES BASEBALL CLUB—See ORIX Corporation; *Int'l*, pg. 5634
ORIX BUSINESS CENTER OKINAWA CORPORATION—See ORIX Corporation; *Int'l*, pg. 5634
ORIX BUSINESS SUPPORT CORPORATION—See ORIX Corporation; *Int'l*, pg. 5634
ORIX CALLCENTER CORPORATION—See ORIX Corporation; *Int'l*, pg. 5634
ORIX CAPITAL CORPORATION—See ORIX Corporation; *Int'l*, pg. 5634
ORIX CAPITAL MALAYSIA SDN. BHD.—See ORIX Corporation; *Int'l*, pg. 5635
ORIX CAPITAL PARTNERS LLC—See ORIX Corporation; *Int'l*, pg. 5636
ORIX CAR RENTALS SDN. BHD.—See ORIX Corporation; *Int'l*, pg. 5634
ORIX CHINA CORPORATION—See ORIX Corporation; *Int'l*, pg. 5634
ORIX (CHINA) INVESTMENT CO., LTD.—See ORIX Corporation; *Int'l*, pg. 5634
ORIX CLUB CARD—See Nippon Telegraph & Telephone Corporation; *Int'l*, pg. 5351
ORIX COMPUTER SYSTEMS CORPORATION—See ORIX Corporation; *Int'l*, pg. 5634
ORIX CORPORATE FINANCE GROUP—See ORIX Corporation; *Int'l*, pg. 5636
ORIX CORPORATION EUROPE N.V.—See ORIX Corporation; *Int'l*, pg. 5634
ORIX CORPORATION; *Int'l*, pg. 5633
ORIX CREATE CORPORATION—See ORIX Corporation; *Int'l*, pg. 5635
ORIX CREDIT CORPORATION—See Nippon Telegraph & Telephone Corporation; *Int'l*, pg. 5351
ORIX ECO SERVICES CORPORATION—See ORIX Corporation; *Int'l*, pg. 5635
ORIX ELECTRIC POWER CORPORATION—See The Kansai Electric Power Co., Inc.; *Int'l*, pg. 7662
ORIX ENVIRONMENTAL RESOURCES MANAGEMENT CORPORATION—See ORIX Corporation; *Int'l*, pg. 5635
ORIX EQUIPMENT FINANCE GROUP—See ORIX Corporation; *Int'l*, pg. 5636
ORIX FACTORING MALAYSIA SDN. BHD.—See ORIX Corporation; *Int'l*, pg. 5635
ORIX GOLF MANAGEMENT CORPORATION—See ORIX Corporation; *Int'l*, pg. 5635
ORIX HOTEL MANAGEMENT CORPORATION—See ORIX Corporation; *Int'l*, pg. 5635
ORIX INSURANCE AGENCIES SDN. BHD.—See ORIX Corporation; *Int'l*, pg. 5635
ORIX INSURANCE CONSULTING CORPORATION—See ORIX Corporation; *Int'l*, pg. 5635
ORIX INSURANCE PLANNING CORPORATION—See ORIX Corporation; *Int'l*, pg. 5635
ORIX INSURANCE SERVICES CORPORATION—See ORIX Corporation; *Int'l*, pg. 5635
ORIX INTERIOR CORPORATION—See ORIX Corporation; *Int'l*, pg. 5635
ORIX INVESTMENT CORPORATION—See ORIX Corporation; *Int'l*, pg. 5635
ORIX INVESTMENT & MANAGEMENT PRIVATE LIMITED—See ORIX Corporation; *Int'l*, pg. 5635
ORIX IRELAND LIMITED—See ORIX Corporation; *Int'l*, pg. 5635
ORIX JREIT INC.; *Int'l*, pg. 5637
ORIX LEASING EGYPT SAE—See ORIX Corporation; *Int'l*, pg. 5635
ORIX LEASING MALAYSIA BERHAD—See ORIX Corporation; *Int'l*, pg. 5635
ORIX LEASING PAKISTAN LIMITED—See ORIX Corporation; *Int'l*, pg. 5635
ORIX LEASING SINGAPORE LIMITED—See ORIX Corporation; *Int'l*, pg. 5635
ORIX LIFE INSURANCE CORPORATION—See ORIX Corporation; *Int'l*, pg. 5635
ORIX LOAN BUSINESS CENTER CORPORATION—See ORIX Corporation; *Int'l*, pg. 5635
ORIX MANAGEMENT INFORMATION CENTER CORPORATION—See ORIX Corporation; *Int'l*, pg. 5635
ORIX MARITIME CORPORATION-SEOUL REPRESENTATIVE OFFICE—See ORIX Corporation; *Int'l*, pg. 5635
ORIX MARITIME CORPORATION—See ORIX Corporation; *Int'l*, pg. 5635
ORIX M&A SOLUTIONS CORPORATION—See ORIX Corporation; *Int'l*, pg. 5635

ORIX METRO LEASING AND FINANCE CORPORATION—See Metropolitan Bank & Trust Company; *Int'l*, pg. 4864
ORIX METRO LEASING AND FINANCE CORPORATION—See ORIX Corporation; *Int'l*, pg. 5635
ORIX NEW ZEALAND (NZ) LIMITED—See ORIX Corporation; *Int'l*, pg. 5635
ORIX POLSKA S.A.—See ORIX Corporation; *Int'l*, pg. 5635
ORIX REAL ESTATE CORPORATION—See ORIX Corporation; *Int'l*, pg. 5635
ORIX REAL ESTATE EQUITIES, INC.—See ORIX Corporation; *Int'l*, pg. 5636
ORIX REAL ESTATE INVESTMENT ADVISORS CORPORATION—See ORIX Corporation; *Int'l*, pg. 5635
ORIX RENEWABLE ENERGY MANAGEMENT CORPORATION—See ORIX Corporation; *Int'l*, pg. 5636
ORIX RENT-A-CAR KAMEI CO., LTD.—See Kamei Corporation; *Int'l*, pg. 4061
ORIX RENTEC CORPORATION—See ORIX Corporation; *Int'l*, pg. 5636
ORIX RENTEC (KOREA) CORPORATION—See ORIX Corporation; *Int'l*, pg. 5636
ORIX RENTEC (SINGAPORE) PTE. LTD.—See ORIX Corporation; *Int'l*, pg. 5636
ORIX RENTEC (TIANJIN) CORPORATION—See ORIX Corporation; *Int'l*, pg. 5636
ORIX RISK MANAGEMENT SDN. BHD.—See ORIX Corporation; *Int'l*, pg. 5635
ORIX TAIWAN ASSET MANAGEMENT COMPANY—See ORIX Corporation; *Int'l*, pg. 5636
ORIX TAIWAN CORPORATION—See ORIX Corporation; *Int'l*, pg. 5636
ORIX TOKUSHIMA CORPORATION—See ORIX Corporation; *Int'l*, pg. 5636
ORIX TRUST & BANKING CORPORATION—See ORIX Corporation; *Int'l*, pg. 5636
ORIX USA CORPORATION-NEW YORK—See ORIX Corporation; *Int'l*, pg. 5636
ORIX USA CORPORATION—See ORIX Corporation; *Int'l*, pg. 5636
ORIX WHOLESALE SECURITIES CORPORATION—See ORIX Corporation; *Int'l*, pg. 5636
ORIZON GMBH—See Bain Capital, LP; *U.S. Private*, pg. 435
ORIZON HOLDING GMBH—See Bain Capital, LP; *U.S. Private*, pg. 435
ORIZON, INC.; *U.S. Private*, pg. 3043
ORIZON S.A.—See AntarChile S.A.; *Int'l*, pg. 482
ORIZON UNDERWRITERS SL—See Marsh & McLennan Companies, Inc.; *U.S. Public*, pg. 1388
ORIZZONTE SGR S.P.A.—See HAT Sicaf S.p.A; *Int'l*, pg. 3284
ORIZZONTE SISTEMI NAVALI S.P.A.—See Fincantieri S.p.A.; *Int'l*, pg. 2671
ORIZZONTE SISTEMI NAVALI S.P.A.—See Leonardo S.p.A.; *Int'l*, pg. 4460
ORIZZONTI CO., LTD.—See TRIP Holdings, Inc.; *Int'l*, pg. 7926
ORIZZONTI HOLDING SPA; *Int'l*, pg. 5637
ORJ INC.—See Bain Capital, LP; *U.S. Private*, pg. 434
ORKA HOLDING AD; *Int'l*, pg. 5637
ORKDALSVEGEN AS—See Skanska AB; *Int'l*, pg. 6978
ORKIM SDN. BHD.—See Ekuiti Nasional Berhad; *Int'l*, pg. 2340
ORKIN CANADA—See Rollins, Inc.; *U.S. Public*, pg. 1809
ORKIN CANADA—See Rollins, Inc.; *U.S. Public*, pg. 1809
ORKIN CANADA—See Rollins, Inc.; *U.S. Public*, pg. 1809
ORKIN, INC.—See Rollins, Inc.; *U.S. Public*, pg. 1809
ORKLA A.S.A. - ORKLA BRANDS INTERNATIONAL UNIT—See Orkla ASA; *Int'l*, pg. 5638
ORKLA ASA; *Int'l*, pg. 5637
ORKLA ASIA HOLDING AS—See Orkla ASA; *Int'l*, pg. 5638
ORKLA ASIA PACIFIC PTE LTD—See Orkla ASA; *Int'l*, pg. 5638
ORKLA BRANDS AS—See Orkla ASA; *Int'l*, pg. 5638
ORKLA CARE OY—See Orkla ASA; *Int'l*, pg. 5637
ORKLA CARE—See Orkla ASA; *Int'l*, pg. 5637
ORKLA CONFECTIONERY & SNACKS SVERIGE AB—See Orkla ASA; *Int'l*, pg. 5638
ORKLA EESTI AS—See Orkla ASA; *Int'l*, pg. 5638
ORKLA ENERGI AS—See Orkla ASA; *Int'l*, pg. 5638
ORKLA ESTI AS—See Orkla ASA; *Int'l*, pg. 5638
ORKLA FINANS A/S—See Orkla ASA; *Int'l*, pg. 5638
ORKLA FOOD INGREDIENTS AS—See Orkla ASA; *Int'l*, pg. 5638
ORKLA FOODS A/S—See Orkla ASA; *Int'l*, pg. 5638
ORKLA FOODS DANMARK AS—See Orkla ASA; *Int'l*, pg. 5639
ORKLA FOODS FINLAND OY—See Orkla ASA; *Int'l*, pg. 5638
ORKLA FOODS NORGE AS—See Orkla ASA; *Int'l*, pg. 5639
ORKLA FOODS NORGE—See Orkla ASA; *Int'l*, pg. 5639

COMPANY NAME INDEX

ORKLA FOODS SVERIGE AB—See Orkla ASA; *Int'l*, pg. 5639
ORKLA HOME & PERSONAL—See Orkla ASA; *Int'l*, pg. 5638
ORKLA INSURANCE COMPANY LTD.—See Orkla ASA; *Int'l*, pg. 5639
ORKLA SHARED SERVICES AS—See Orkla ASA; *Int'l*, pg. 5639
ORKNEY COACHES LIMITED—See Stagecoach Group plc; *Int'l*, pg. 7163
ORKUFJARSKIPTI HF.—See Landsvirkjun - The Na; *Int'l*, pg. 4408
ORKUVEITA REYKJAVIKUR; *Int'l*, pg. 5639
ORKYN—See L'Air Liquide S.A.; *Int'l*, pg. 4374
ORLACO GMBH—See Stoneridge, Inc.; *U.S. Public*, pg. 1951
ORLACO INC.—See Stoneridge, Inc.; *U.S. Public*, pg. 1951
ORLACO PRODUCTS B.V.—See Stoneridge, Inc.; *U.S. Public*, pg. 1951
ORLA MINING LTD.; *Int'l*, pg. 5639
ORLANDINI ENTERPRISES; *U.S. Private*, pg. 3043
ORLANDI S.P.A.; *Int'l*, pg. 5639
THE ORLANDO BAKING COMPANY INC.; *U.S. Private*, pg. 4089
ORLANDO BALLET, INC.; *U.S. Private*, pg. 3043
ORLANDO BUSINESS JOURNAL—See Advance Publications, Inc.; *U.S. Private*, pg. 84
ORLANDO COGEN LIMITED, L.P.—See I Squared Capital Advisors (US) LLC; *U.S. Private*, pg. 2025
ORLANDO DODGE; *U.S. Private*, pg. 3043
THE ORLANDO FL ENDOSCOPY ASC, LLC—See KKR & Co. Inc.; *U.S. Public*, pg. 1248
ORLANDO FREIGHTLINER INC.—See Florida Truck Group; *U.S. Private*, pg. 1551
ORLANDO HEALTH, INC.; *U.S. Private*, pg. 3043
ORLANDO HEARST TELEVISION INC.—See The Hearst Corporation; *U.S. Private*, pg. 4048
ORLANDO INTERNATIONAL RESORT CLUB—See Travel & Leisure Co.; *U.S. Public*, pg. 2186
ORLANDO ITALY MANAGEMENT S.A.—See Orlando Management AG; *Int'l*, pg. 5639
ORLANDO LUTHERAN TOWERS; *U.S. Private*, pg. 3044
ORLANDO MAGIC, LTD.—See RDV Corporation; *U.S. Private*, pg. 3364
ORLANDO MANAGEMENT AG; *Int'l*, pg. 5639
ORLANDO MANAGEMENT SCHWEIZ AG—See Orlando Management AG; *Int'l*, pg. 5640
THE ORLANDO/MILLS FL ENDOSCOPY ASC, LLC—See KKR & Co. Inc.; *U.S. Public*, pg. 1248
ORLANDO OUTPATIENT CENTER FOR SURGERY, LLC—See Tenet Healthcare Corporation; *U.S. Public*, pg. 2006
ORLANDO OUTPATIENT SURGICAL CENTER, INC.—See HCA Healthcare, Inc.; *U.S. Public*, pg. 1005
THE ORLANDO PALM—See Palm Restaurant Group; *U.S. Private*, pg. 3080
ORLANDO SANFORD DOMESTIC INC—See ACS, Actividades de Construccion y Servicios, S.A.; *Int'l*, pg. 112
ORLANDO SANFORD INTERNATIONAL INC.—See ACS, Actividades de Construccion y Servicios, S.A.; *Int'l*, pg. 112
ORLANDO SENTINEL COMMUNICATIONS COMPANY—See Tribune Publishing Company; *U.S. Private*, pg. 4228
ORLANDO UTILITIES COMMISSION; *U.S. Private*, pg. 3044
ORLANDO WYNDHAM—See Pernod Ricard S.A.; *Int'l*, pg. 5810
ORLANE INC.—See Orlane S.A.; *Int'l*, pg. 5640
ORLANE INSTITUT DE BEAUTE—See Orlane S.A.; *Int'l*, pg. 5640
ORLANE JAPON INC—See Pola Orbis Holdings Inc.; *Int'l*, pg. 5905
ORLANE S.A.; *Int'l*, pg. 5640
O.R. LASERTECHNOLOGIE GMBH—See Coherent Corp.; *U.S. Public*, pg. 527
O,R&L COMMERCIAL, LLC—See O,R&L Construction Corp.; *U.S. Private*, pg. 2981
O,R&L CONSTRUCTION CORP.; *U.S. Private*, pg. 2981
ORLEANS CORPORATION—See Orleans Homebuilders, Inc.; *U.S. Private*, pg. 3044
ORLEANS COSMETICS PROPRIETARY LIMITED—See AYO Technology Solutions Ltd.; *Int'l*, pg. 775
ORLEANS FURNITURE INC.; *U.S. Private*, pg. 3044
ORLEANS HOMEBUILDERS, INC.; *U.S. Private*, pg. 3044
ORLEANS INTERNATIONAL; *U.S. Private*, pg. 3044
ORLEANS RH PA-IL, LP—See Orleans Homebuilders, Inc.; *U.S. Private*, pg. 3044
ORLEANS RV; *Int'l*, pg. 5640
ORLEN ADMINISTRACJA SP. Z O.O.—See Orlen S.A.; *Int'l*, pg. 5640
ORLEN ASFALT SP. Z O.O.—See Orlen S.A.; *Int'l*, pg. 5640
ORLEN AVIATION SP. Z O.O.—See Orlen S.A.; *Int'l*, pg. 5640
ORLEN BUDONAFT SP .Z O.O.—See Orlen S.A.; *Int'l*, pg. 5640
ORLEN CAPITAL AB—See Orlen S.A.; *Int'l*, pg. 5640
ORLEN CENTRUM SERWISOWE SP. Z O.O.—See Orlen S.A.; *Int'l*, pg. 5640
ORLEN CENTRUM USLUG KORPORACYJNYCH SP Z O.O.—See Orlen S.A.; *Int'l*, pg. 5640
ORLEN DEUTSCHLAND GMBH—See Orlen S.A.; *Int'l*, pg. 5640
ORLEN EESTI OU—See Orlen S.A.; *Int'l*, pg. 5640
ORLEN EKO LLC—See Orlen S.A.; *Int'l*, pg. 5640
ORLEN GAZ SP. Z O.O.—See Orlen S.A.; *Int'l*, pg. 5640
ORLEN KOLTRANS SP. Z O.O.—See Orlen S.A.; *Int'l*, pg. 5640
ORLEN MEDICA SP. Z O.O.—See Orlen S.A.; *Int'l*, pg. 5640
ORLEN OCHRONA SP. Z O.O.—See Orlen S.A.; *Int'l*, pg. 5641
ORLEN PALIWA SP. Z O.O.—See Orlen S.A.; *Int'l*, pg. 5640
ORLEN PETROCENTRUM SP. Z O.O.—See Orlen S.A.; *Int'l*, pg. 5640
ORLEN PETROTANK SP. Z O.O.—See Orlen S.A.; *Int'l*, pg. 5640
ORLEN POLUDNIE S.A.—See Orlen S.A.; *Int'l*, pg. 5640
ORLEN S.A.; *Int'l*, pg. 5640
ORLEN SERWIS S.A.—See Orlen S.A.; *Int'l*, pg. 5640
ORLEN UPSTREAM CANADA LTD.—See Orlen S.A.; *Int'l*, pg. 5640
ORLEN UPSTREAM SP. Z O.O.—See Orlen S.A.; *Int'l*, pg. 5640
ORLEN USLUGI FINANSOWE SP. Z O.O.—See Orlen S.A.; *Int'l*, pg. 5640
ORLEN WIR SP. Z O.O.—See Orlen S.A.; *Int'l*, pg. 5640
O,R&L FACILITY SERVICES—See O,R&L Construction Corp.; *U.S. Private*, pg. 2981
ORLIMAN SL—See Infarco SA; *Int'l*, pg. 3684
ORLIN, INC.—See Avis Budget Group, Inc.; *U.S. Public*, pg. 249
OR-LIVE, INC.—See BroadcastMed, Inc.; *U.S. Private*, pg. 659
ORLOR INC.; *U.S. Private*, pg. 3044
ORLY AIR TRAITEUR—See Air France-KLM S.A.; *Int'l*, pg. 237
ORLY INTERNATIONAL, INC.; *U.S. Private*, pg. 3044
ORMAN, NORD & HURD, P.L.L.P.—See Beaumier, Trogdon, Orman, Hurd & Viegas, PLLP; *U.S. Private*, pg. 500
ORMA ORMAN MAHSULLERI INTEGRE SANAYI VE TICARET A.S.; *Int'l*, pg. 5641
ORMAT INDUSTRIES LTD.—See Ormat Technologies, Inc.; *U.S. Public*, pg. 1618
ORMAT NEVADA INC.—See Ormat Technologies, Inc.; *U.S. Public*, pg. 1618
ORMAT TECHNOLOGIES, INC.; *U.S. Public*, pg. 1618
ORM BERGOLD CHEMIE GMBH & CO.—See Clean Harbors, Inc.; *U.S. Public*, pg. 510
ORMCO BV—See Danaher Corporation; *U.S. Public*, pg. 629
ORMCO CORPORATION—See Danaher Corporation; *U.S. Public*, pg. 631
ORMCO EUROPE BV—See Danaher Corporation; *U.S. Public*, pg. 629
ORMCO LLC—See Danaher Corporation; *U.S. Public*, pg. 629
ORMED GMBH—See Enovis Corporation; *U.S. Public*, pg. 773
ORMED MEDICAL TECHNOLOGY LTD.—See Opto Circuits (India) Limited; *Int'l*, pg. 5605
ORMESTER SECURITY RO S.R.L.—See Ormester Vagyonvedelmi Nyrt; *Int'l*, pg. 5641
ORMESTER VAGYONVEDELMI NYRT; *Int'l*, pg. 5641
ORMET CORP.; *U.S. Public*, pg. 1618
ORMIC COMPONENTS LTD.—See Avnet, Inc.; *U.S. Public*, pg. 253
ORMIT BELGIUM N.V.; *Int'l*, pg. 5641
ORMONDE MINING PLC; *Int'l*, pg. 5641
ORMSBY TRUCKING INC.; *U.S. Private*, pg. 3044
ORMSRAY CORPORATION PTY LTD.—See Nylex Limited; *Int'l*, pg. 5501
ORM TIMBER FUND II, INC.—See Rayonier Inc.; *U.S. Public*, pg. 1765
ORNAMENTAL PRODUCTS LLC; *U.S. Private*, pg. 3044
ORNAPAPER BERHAD; *Int'l*, pg. 5641
ORNAPAPER INDUSTRY (BATU PAHAT) SDN. BHD.—See Ornapaper Berhad; *Int'l*, pg. 5641
ORNAPAPER INDUSTRY (JOHOR) SDN. BHD.—See Ornapaper Berhad; *Int'l*, pg. 5641
ORNAPAPER INDUSTRY (M) SDN. BHD.—See Ornapaper Berhad; *Int'l*, pg. 5641
ORNAPAPER INDUSTRY (PERAK) SDN. BHD.—See Ornapaper Berhad; *Int'l*, pg. 5641
OR-NA TARIM URUNLERI SAN. VE TIC. A.S. - IZMIR FACTORY—See OR-NA Tarim Urunleri San. ve Tic. A.S.; *Int'l*, pg. 5607
OR-NA TARIM URUNLERI SAN. VE TIC. A.S.; *Int'l*, pg. 5607
ORNDA HOSPITAL CORPORATION—See Tenet Healthcare Corporation; *U.S. Public*, pg. 2005
ORNDORFF & SPAID, INC.; *U.S. Private*, pg. 3044
ORN OMNIBUSVERKEHR RHEIN-NAHE GMBH—See Deutsche Bahn AG; *Int'l*, pg. 2052
ORN OXYCOUPAGE—See Oxymetal SA; *Int'l*, pg. 5676
ORNSBERG EL TELE & DATA AB—See Storskögen Group AB; *Int'l*, pg. 7228
ORNSKOLDSVIKS MEKANISKA VERKSTAD (OMV) AB—See Outokumpu Oyj; *Int'l*, pg. 5668
ORNUA CO-OPERATIVE LIMITED; *Int'l*, pg. 5641
ORNUA NORTH AMERICA INC—See Ornua Co-operative Limited; *Int'l*, pg. 5642
ORNUA (WISCONSIN) INGREDIENTS LLC—See Ornua Co-operative Limited; *Int'l*, pg. 5642
ORO CO., LTD.; *Int'l*, pg. 5642
OROCO RESOURCE CORP.; *Int'l*, pg. 5642
ORODAY, INC.; *U.S. Private*, pg. 3044
ORO DE ALTAR, S.A. DE C.V.—See Alamos Gold Inc.; *Int'l*, pg. 290
ORO DIGITAL ASIA PTE. LTD.—See oRo Co., Ltd.; *Int'l*, pg. 5642
ORO DIGITAL ASIA SDN. BHD.—See oRo Co., Ltd.; *Int'l*, pg. 5642
ORO EAST MINING, INC.; *U.S. Public*, pg. 1618
ORO FINANCECORP PLC.—See CREED Corporation; *Int'l*, pg. 1837
THE OROGEN GROUP; *U.S. Private*, pg. 4089
OROGEN ROYALTIES INC.; *Int'l*, pg. 5642
OROLIA GOVERNMENT SYSTEMS INC.—See Safran SA; *Int'l*, pg. 6473
OROLIA SA—See Eurazeo SE; *Int'l*, pg. 2528
OROLIA SPAIN S.L.—See Safran SA; *Int'l*, pg. 6473
OROLIA SWITZERLAND SA—See Eurazeo SE; *Int'l*, pg. 2528
ORO MALAYSIA SDN. BHD.—See oRo Co., Ltd.; *Int'l*, pg. 5642
ORO MIYAZAKI CO., LTD.—See oRo Co., Ltd.; *Int'l*, pg. 5642
ORON GROUP INVESTMENTS & HOLDINGS LTD.; *Int'l*, pg. 5642
ORONOS GOLD CORP.—See Sonoro Gold Corp.; *Int'l*, pg. 7100
ORONOVA ENERGY INC.; *Int'l*, pg. 5642
OROPEZA INGENIEROS S.A. DE C.V.; *Int'l*, pg. 5642
OROPLATA S.A.—See Newmont Corporation; *U.S. Public*, pg. 1516
ORORA BAGS—See Nippon Paper Industries Co., Ltd.; *Int'l*, pg. 5328
ORORA BEVERAGE CANS - CANNING VALE PLANT—See Nippon Paper Industries Co., Ltd.; *Int'l*, pg. 5328
ORORA BEVERAGE CANS—See Nippon Paper Industries Co., Ltd.; *Int'l*, pg. 5328
ORORA CARTONS—See Nippon Paper Industries Co., Ltd.; *Int'l*, pg. 5328
ORORA FIBRE PACKAGING - SMITHFIELD PLANT—See Nippon Paper Industries Co., Ltd.; *Int'l*, pg. 5328
ORORA FIBRE PACKAGING—See Nippon Paper Industries Co., Ltd.; *Int'l*, pg. 5328
ORORA LIMITED; *Int'l*, pg. 5642
ORORA NORTH AMERICA - LANDSBERG—See Orora Limited; *Int'l*, pg. 5642
ORORA NORTH AMERICA - MANUFACTURED PACKAGING PRODUCTS, BREA—See Orora Limited; *Int'l*, pg. 5643
ORORA NORTH AMERICA - MANUFACTURED PACKAGING PRODUCTS, SAN DIEGO—See Orora Limited; *Int'l*, pg. 5643
ORORA NORTH AMERICA - MANUFACTURED PACKAGING PRODUCTS—See Orora Limited; *Int'l*, pg. 5643
ORORA NORTH AMERICA - MANUFACTURED PACKAGING PRODUCTS, SYCAMORE—See Orora Limited; *Int'l*, pg. 5643
ORORA NORTH AMERICA—See Orora Limited; *Int'l*, pg. 5642
ORORA PACKAGING AUSTRALIA PTY. LTD.—See Nippon Paper Industries Co., Ltd.; *Int'l*, pg. 5328
ORORA PACKAGING NEW ZEALAND LTD. - KIWI PACKAGING—See Nippon Paper Industries Co., Ltd.; *Int'l*, pg. 5328
ORORA PACKAGING NEW ZEALAND LTD.—See Nippon Paper Industries Co., Ltd.; *Int'l*, pg. 5328
ORORA VISUAL - CHICAGO—See Orora Limited; *Int'l*, pg. 5643
ORORA VISUAL LLC—See Orora Limited; *Int'l*, pg. 5643
OROSCIENCE PLC; *Int'l*, pg. 5643
OROS DIVISION—See Linamar Corporation; *Int'l*, pg. 4502
OROSIL SMITHS INDIA LIMITED; *Int'l*, pg. 5643
OROSUR MINING INC.; *Int'l*, pg. 5643
OROSUR MINING INC. - URUGUAY HEAD OFFICE—See Orosur Mining Inc.; *Int'l*, pg. 5643
ORO TAIWAN CO., LTD.—See oRo Co., Ltd.; *Int'l*, pg. 5642
ORO TECHNOLOGY (DALIAN) CO., LTD.—See oRo Co., Ltd.; *Int'l*, pg. 5642
OROTEX BELGIUM NV—See Beaulieu International Group NV; *Int'l*, pg. 934
ORO (THAILAND) CO., LTD.—See oRo Co., Ltd.; *Int'l*, pg. 5642
OROT LIFE INSURANCE AGENCY (2005) LTD.—See Menora Mivtachim Holdings Ltd.; *Int'l*, pg. 4817
OROTONGROUP (AUSTRALIA) PTY LIMITED—See OrotonGroup Limited; *Int'l*, pg. 5643

OROTONGROUP LIMITED; Int'l, pg. 5643
OROTONGROUP (NEW ZEALAND) PTY LIMITED—See OrotonGroup Limited; Int'l, pg. 5643
O'ROURKE DIST. CO., INC.; U.S. Private, pg. 2980
O'ROURKE MEDIA GROUP, LLC; U.S. Private, pg. 2980
O'ROURKE SALES COMPANY; U.S. Private, pg. 2980
ORO VALLEY COUNTRY CLUB, INC.—See Apollo Global Management, Inc.; U.S. Public, pg. 150
ORO VALLEY SURGICAL SUITES, LLC—See Tenet Healthcare Corporation; U.S. Public, pg. 2006
ORO VERDA SPA—See Ionic Rare Earths Limited; Int'l, pg. 3795
ORO VIETNAM CO., LTD.—See oRo Co., Ltd.; Int'l, pg. 5642
OROVILLE MERCURY-REGISTER—See Alden Global Capital LLC; U.S. Private, pg. 156
OROWEAT FOODS—See Grupo Bimbo, S.A.B. de C.V.; Int'l, pg. 3122
OROWEAT—See Grupo Bimbo, S.A.B. de C.V.; Int'l, pg. 3122
ORPAK LATINA S.P.A.—See Vontier Corporation; U.S. Public, pg. 2309
ORPAK ROMANIA S.R.L.—See Vontier Corporation; U.S. Public, pg. 2309
ORPAK SOLUTION CO., LTD.—See Vontier Corporation; U.S. Public, pg. 2309
ORPAK SYSTEMS LTD—See Vontier Corporation; U.S. Public, pg. 2309
ORPEA DEUTSCHLAND GMBH—See Emeis SA; Int'l, pg. 2376
ORPEA IBERICA S.A.U—See Emeis SA; Int'l, pg. 2376
ORPEA POLSKA SP. Z O. O—See Emeis SA; Int'l, pg. 2376
ORPHAMED INC.—See Bausch Health Companies Inc.; Int'l, pg. 897
ORPHAN EUROPE BENELUX BVBA—See Recordati S.p.A.; Int'l, pg. 6239
ORPHAN EUROPE GERMANY GMBH—See Recordati S.p.A.; Int'l, pg. 6239
ORPHAN EUROPE ITALY S.R.L.—See Recordati S.p.A.; Int'l, pg. 6239
ORPHAN EUROPE MIDDLE EAST FZ LLC—See Recordati S.p.A.; Int'l, pg. 6239
ORPHAN EUROPE NORDIC AB—See Recordati S.p.A.; Int'l, pg. 6239
ORPHAN EUROPE PORTUGAL LDA.—See Recordati S.p.A.; Int'l, pg. 6239
ORPHAN EUROPE S.A.R.L.—See Recordati S.p.A.; Int'l, pg. 6239
ORPHAN EUROPE SPAIN S.L.—See Recordati S.p.A.; Int'l, pg. 6239
ORPHAN EUROPE UK LTD.—See Recordati S.p.A.; Int'l, pg. 6239
ORPHANPACIFIC, INC.—See Medipal Holdings Corporation; Int'l, pg. 4779
ORPHAN TRUST JAPAN CO., LTD.—See Toho Holdings Co., Ltd.; Int'l, pg. 7776
ORPHEUM PROPERTY, INC.; U.S. Public, pg. 1618
ORPHEUS CLUB WELLNESS PLC; Int'l, pg. 5643
ORPHEUS MEDICAL GMBH—See Intuitive Surgical, Inc.; U.S. Public, pg. 1160
ORPHEUS MEDICAL LTD.—See Intuitive Surgical, Inc.; U.S. Public, pg. 1160
ORPHEUS MEDICAL USA INC.—See Intuitive Surgical, Inc.; U.S. Public, pg. 1161
ORPHEUS URANIUM LIMITED; Int'l, pg. 5643
OR PJSC; Int'l, pg. 5607
ORRADA CO., LTD.—See DCON Products Public Company Limited; Int'l, pg. 1993
ORRCON OPERATIONS PTY. LTD.—See BlueScope Steel Limited; Int'l, pg. 1074
ORR CORPORATION; U.S. Private, pg. 3044
ORREFORS KOSTA BODA AB—See New Wave Group AB; Int'l, pg. 5230
ORREFORS KOSTA BODA HOLDING AB—See New Wave Group AB; Int'l, pg. 5230
ORREFORS KOSTA BODA, INC.—See Axcel Management A/S; Int'l, pg. 762
ORREFORS KOSTA BODA LLC—See New Wave Group AB; Int'l, pg. 5230
ORREGENT AB—See Svedbergs i Dalstorp AB; Int'l, pg. 7356
ORRELL'S FOOD SERVICE, INC.—See Ben E. Keith Company; U.S. Private, pg. 522
ORRICK, HERRINGTON & SUTCLIFFE LLP; U.S. Private, pg. 3044
ORRIDGE & CO LTD.—See Blackstone Inc.; U.S. Public, pg. 357
ORRIDGE SA—See Blackstone Inc.; U.S. Public, pg. 357
ORRIN B HAYES INC.; U.S. Private, pg. 3044
ORR INC.; U.S. Private, pg. 3044
ORR INDUSTRIES OF PENNSYLVANIA, LLC—See Installed Building Products, Inc.; U.S. Public, pg. 1133
ORRISON DISTRIBUTING LTD.; U.S. Private, pg. 3045
ORR SAFETY CORPORATION—See Wurth Verwaltungsgesellschaft mbH; Int'l, pg. 8511
ORRSTOWN BANK—See Orrstown Financial Services, Inc.; U.S. Public, pg. 1618

ORRSTOWN FINANCIAL SERVICES, INC.; U.S. Public, pg. 1618
ORR TOYOTA; U.S. Private, pg. 3044
ORRU SAS—See Bunzl plc; Int'l, pg. 1219
ORRVILLE COMPOSITE CONTAINER PLANT—See Greif Inc.; U.S. Public, pg. 966
ORSCHELN EUROPE ULC—See Orscheln Group; U.S. Private, pg. 3045
ORSCHELN FARM & HOME LLC—See Orscheln Group; U.S. Private, pg. 3045
ORSCHELN GROUP; U.S. Private, pg. 3045
ORSCHELN INDUSTRIES PLATING DIVISION—See Orscheln Group; U.S. Private, pg. 3045
ORSCHELN MANAGEMENT CO.—See Orscheln Group; U.S. Private, pg. 3045
ORSCHELN PRODUCTS LLC—See Orscheln Group; U.S. Private, pg. 3045
ORSCHELN PRODUCTS TRADING CO. LTD—See Orscheln Group; U.S. Private, pg. 3045
ORSCHELN PROPERTIES CO. L.L.C.—See Orscheln Group; U.S. Private, pg. 3045
ORSCHELN TECHNOLOGIES PVT LTD—See Orscheln Group; U.S. Private, pg. 3045
ORS CORPORATION—See OSG Corporation; Int'l, pg. 5649
ORSERO S.P.A.; Int'l, pg. 5644
OR SHAY GS LTD.; Int'l, pg. 5607
ORSINI NURSING AGENCY, INC.; U.S. Private, pg. 3045
ORS NASCO, INC.—See Sycamore Partners Management, LP; U.S. Private, pg. 3897
ORSTED AB—See Orsted AS; Int'l, pg. 5644
ORSTED AS; Int'l, pg. 5644
ORSTED HORNSEA PROJECT THREE (UK) LIMITED—See Orsted AS; Int'l, pg. 5644
ORSTED LONDON ARRAY LIMITED—See Orsted AS; Int'l, pg. 5644
ORSTED MARKETS GMBH—See Orsted AS; Int'l, pg. 5644
ORSTED NETHERLANDS B.V.—See Orsted AS; Int'l, pg. 5644
ORSTED ONSHORE IRELAND GREEN ENERGY LIMITED—See Orsted AS; Int'l, pg. 5644
ORSTED POLSKA SP. Z O.O.—See Orsted AS; Int'l, pg. 5644
ORSTED SERVICES MALAYSIA SDN. BHD.—See Orsted AS; Int'l, pg. 5644
ORSTED TAIWAN LTD.—See Orsted AS; Int'l, pg. 5644
ORSTED WIND POWER GERMANY GMBH—See Orsted AS; Int'l, pg. 5644
ORSTED WIND POWER NORTH AMERICA LLC—See Orsted AS; Int'l, pg. 5644
ORSUS XELENT TECHNOLOGIES, INC,; Int'l, pg. 5644
ORTAK VARLIK YONETIM ANONIM SIRKETI—See Nurol Yatirim Bankasi A.S.; Int'l, pg. 5491
ORT AMERICA, INC.; U.S. Private, pg. 3045
ORTECH CONSULTING INC.—See Kontrol Technologies Corp.; Int'l, pg. 4276
ORTECH MALAYSIA SDN. BHD.—See Minebea Mitsumi Inc.; Int'l, pg. 4905
ORTEC MESSE UND KONGRESS GMBH—See Bertelsmann SE & Co. KGaA; Int'l, pg. 993
ORTEC SPORTS B.V.—See Sportradar Group AG; Int'l, pg. 7142
ORTEGO OIL & SUPPLY CO. INC.; U.S. Private, pg. 3045
ORTEL COMMUNICATIONS LTD; Int'l, pg. 5644
ORTEL MOBILE HOLDING B.V.—See CVC Capital Partners SICAV-FIS S.A.; Int'l, pg. 1884
ORTEP OF PENNSYLVANIA INC.—See Star Group, L.P.; U.S. Public, pg. 1937
ORTHEX SWEDEN AB—See Intera Equity Partners Oy; Int'l, pg. 3735
ORTHOARIZONA SURGERY CENTER GILBERT, LLC—See Tenet Healthcare Corporation; U.S. Public, pg. 2006
ORTHOBANC LLC; U.S. Private, pg. 3045
ORTHOBAND CO., INC.—See Barnhart Industries, Inc.; U.S. Private, pg. 478
ORTHO BIOLOGICS, LLC—See Johnson & Johnson; U.S. Public, pg. 1197
ORTHOCELL LIMITED; Int'l, pg. 5644
ORTHOCENTER GOTEBORG AB—See Apax Partners LLP; Int'l, pg. 502
ORTHO-CLINICAL DIAGNOSTICS GMBH—See QuidelOrtho Corporation; U.S. Public, pg. 1756
ORTHO CLINICAL DIAGNOSTICS HOLDINGS PLC—See QuidelOrtho Corporation; U.S. Public, pg. 1756
ORTHO-CLINICAL DIAGNOSTICS, INC. - ROCHESTER—See QuidelOrtho Corporation; U.S. Public, pg. 1757
ORTHO-CLINICAL DIAGNOSTICS, INC.—See QuidelOrtho Corporation; U.S. Public, pg. 1756
ORTHO-CLINICAL DIAGNOSTICS K.K.—See QuidelOrtho Corporation; U.S. Public, pg. 1756
ORTHO-CLINICAL DIAGNOSTICS N.V.—See QuidelOrtho Corporation; U.S. Public, pg. 1756
ORTHO-CLINICAL DIAGNOSTICS S.A.—See QuidelOrtho Corporation; U.S. Public, pg. 1756
ORTHO-CLINICAL DIAGNOSTICS—See QuidelOrtho Corporation; U.S. Public, pg. 1756

ORTHO-CLINICAL DIAGNOSTICS S.P.A.—See QuidelOrtho Corporation; U.S. Public, pg. 1756
ORTHOCOR MEDICAL, INC.—See Caerus Corporation; U.S. Private, pg. 714
ORTHODENTAL INTERNATIONAL, INC.—See DENTSPLY SIRONA Inc.; U.S. Public, pg. 655
ORTHO DEVELOPMENT CORPORATION; U.S. Private, pg. 3045
THE ORTHODONTIC STORE, INC.—See The Jordan Company, L.P.; U.S. Private, pg. 4063
ORTHOFIX AG—See Orthofix Medical Inc.; U.S. Public, pg. 1619
ORTHOFIX AUSTRALIA PTY LIMITED—See Orthofix Medical Inc.; U.S. Public, pg. 1619
ORTHOFIX DO BRASIL LTDA.—See Orthofix Medical Inc.; U.S. Public, pg. 1619
ORTHOFIX GMBH—See Orthofix Medical Inc.; U.S. Public, pg. 1619
ORTHOFIX INC.—See Orthofix Medical Inc.; U.S. Public, pg. 1619
ORTHOFIX LIMITED—See Orthofix Medical Inc.; U.S. Public, pg. 1619
ORTHOFIX MEDICAL INC.; U.S. Public, pg. 1619
ORTHOFIX ORTHOPEDICS NORTH AMERICA—See Orthofix Medical Inc.; U.S. Public, pg. 1619
ORTHOFIX ORTHOPEDICS—See Orthofix Medical Inc.; U.S. Public, pg. 1619
ORTHOFIX SA—See Orthofix Medical Inc.; U.S. Public, pg. 1619
ORTHOFIX SPINE G.M.B.H.—See Orthofix Medical Inc.; U.S. Public, pg. 1619
ORTHOFIX SPORTS MEDICINE BREG, INC. - MANUFACTURING FACILITY—See Orthofix Medical Inc.; U.S. Public, pg. 1619
ORTHOFIX SPORTS MEDICINE BREG, INC.—See Orthofix Medical Inc.; U.S. Public, pg. 1619
ORTHOFIX S.R.L.—See Orthofix Medical Inc.; U.S. Public, pg. 1619
ORTHOFIX UK LIMITED—See Orthofix Medical Inc.; U.S. Public, pg. 1619
ORTHOHUB S.R.L.—See SOL S.p.A.; Int'l, pg. 7067
ORTHOLOGY INC.—See UnitedHealth Group Incorporated; U.S. Public, pg. 2249
ORTHO-MCNEIL PHARMACEUTICAL, INC.—See Johnson & Johnson; U.S. Public, pg. 1197
ORTHOMED MEDIZINTECHNIK GMBH—See Enovis Corporation; U.S. Public, pg. 773
ORTHOMED S.A.S—See Apposite Capital LLP; Int'l, pg. 522
ORTHOMERICA PRODUCTS INC.; U.S. Private, pg. 3045
ORTHONET LLC—See UnitedHealth Group Incorporated; U.S. Public, pg. 2248
ORTHOPADIETECHNIK MAYER & BEHNSEN GMBH—See Sonic Healthcare Limited; Int'l, pg. 7098
THE ORTHOPAEDIC CENTRE (FARRER) PTE. LTD.—See Doctor Anywhere Pte Ltd.; Int'l, pg. 2153
THE ORTHOPAEDIC CENTRE (GLENEAGLES) PTE. LTD.—See Doctor Anywhere Pte Ltd.; Int'l, pg. 2153
THE ORTHOPAEDIC CENTRE (NOVENA) PTE. LTD.—See Doctor Anywhere Pte Ltd.; Int'l, pg. 2153
THE ORTHOPAEDIC CENTRE (ORCHARD) PTE. LTD.—See Doctor Anywhere Pte Ltd.; Int'l, pg. 2153
ORTHOPAEDIC HOSPITAL; U.S. Private, pg. 3045
ORTHOPAEDIC SURGERY CENTER OF ASHEVILLE, L.P.—See Bain Capital, LP; U.S. Private, pg. 447
ORTHOPEDIATRICS CORP.; U.S. Public, pg. 1619
ORTHOPEDIC AND SURGICAL SPECIALTY COMPANY, LLC—See Tenet Healthcare Corporation; U.S. Public, pg. 2012
ORTHOPEDIC ASSOCIATES OF THE LOWCOUNTRY, L.L.C.—See Tenet Healthcare Corporation; U.S. Public, pg. 2008
ORTHOPEDIC BIOMET CENTROAMERICANA SA—See Zimmer Biomet Holdings, Inc.; U.S. Public, pg. 2406
ORTHOPEDIC REHABILITATION PRODUCTS, LTD.—See Patient Square Capital, L.P.; U.S. Private, pg. 3107
ORTHOPEDIC SOUTH SURGICAL PARTNERS, LLC—See Tenet Healthcare Corporation; U.S. Public, pg. 2012
ORTHOPEDIC & SPINE SURGICAL HOSPITAL OF SOUTH TEXAS LP—See Bain Capital, LP; U.S. Private, pg. 445
ORTHOPEDICS SPECIALISTS, LLC—See HCA Healthcare, Inc.; U.S. Public, pg. 1005
ORTHOPEDIE INVESTMENTS EUROPE B.V.—See HAL Trust N.V.; Int'l, pg. 3224
ORTHOPY HEALTH GMBH—See Enovis Corporation; U.S. Public, pg. 773
ORTHOSCAN, INC.—See ATON GmbH; Int'l, pg. 689
ORTHOSENSOR, INC.—See Stryker Corporation; U.S. Public, pg. 1956
ORTHOSONICS LTD.—See Orthofix Medical Inc.; U.S. Public, pg. 1619
ORTHOSPACE, LTD.—See Stryker Corporation; U.S. Public, pg. 1956
ORTHOSYNETICS, INC.; U.S. Private, pg. 3045
ORTHO TECHNOLOGY, INC.—See Henry Schein, Inc.; U.S. Public, pg. 1027

COMPANY NAME INDEX

ORTHOTIC CENTRE (MIDLANDS) LIMITED—See Orthotic Centre (NZ) Limited; *Int'l*, pg. 5644
ORTHOTIC CENTRE (NZ) LIMITED; *Int'l*, pg. 5644
ORTHOTIC CENTRE (WELLINGTON) LIMITED—See Orthotic Centre (NZ) Limited; *Int'l*, pg. 5644
THE ORTHOTIC GROUP INC.; *Int'l*, pg. 7672
ORTHOTIC & PROSTHETIC TECHNOLOGIES, INC.—See Patient Square Capital, L.P.; *U.S. Private*, pg. 3107
ORTHOVITA, INC.—See Stryker Corporation; *U.S. Public*, pg. 1956
ORTHOVITA—See Stryker Corporation; *U.S. Public*, pg. 1956
ORTIN LABORATORIES LIMITED; *Int'l*, pg. 5644
ORTITLAN LIMITADA—See Ormat Technologies, Inc.; *U.S. Public*, pg. 1618
ORTIVUS AB; *Int'l*, pg. 5644
ORTIVUS UK LTD.—See Ortivus AB; *Int'l*, pg. 5645
ORTIZ ENGINEERED PRODUCTS, INC.—See Insteel Industries, Inc.; *U.S. Public*, pg. 1134
ORTLINGHAUS-WERKE GMBH—See Brd. Klee A/S; *Int'l*, pg. 1143
ORTLOFF ENGINEERS, LTD.—See Torgo, Ltd.; *U.S. Private*, pg. 4189
ORTOFON A/S; *Int'l*, pg. 5645
ORTOFON, INC.—See Ortofon A/S; *Int'l*, pg. 5645
ORTON MOTORS INC.; *U.S. Private*, pg. 3045
ORTON SRL—See IMI plc; *Int'l*, pg. 3626
ORTO PARQUES Y JARDINES, S.L.—See ACS, Actividades de Construccion y Servicios, S.A.; *Int'l*, pg. 115
ORTOPEDIO.PL SP. Z O.O.—See NEUCA S.A.; *Int'l*, pg. 5218
ORTOPRO TIBBI ALETLER SAN. TIC. A.S.—See Turkiye Is Bankasi A.S.; *Int'l*, pg. 7976
ORTOVOX CANADA LTD—See Schwan-STABILO Cosmetics GmbH & Co. KG; *Int'l*, pg. 6644
ORTOVOX SPORTARTIKEL GMBH—See Schwan-STABILO Cosmetics GmbH & Co. KG; *Int'l*, pg. 6644
ORTOVOX VERTRIEBS GMBH—See Schwan-STABILO Cosmetics GmbH & Co. KG; *Int'l*, pg. 6644
ORTRONICS/LEGRAND—See Legrand S.A.; *Int'l*, pg. 4445
ORT TOOL & DIE CORPORATION; *U.S. Private*, pg. 3045
ORTUS TECHNOLOGY CO., LTD.—See TOPPAN Holdings Inc.; *Int'l*, pg. 7817
ORU KAYAK INC.; *U.S. Private*, pg. 3045
ORUM OY AB—See Helvar Merca Oy AB; *Int'l*, pg. 3339
ORVANA MINERALS CORP.; *Int'l*, pg. 5645
ORVIANDE INC.; *Int'l*, pg. 5645
THE ORVIS COMPANY, INC.; *U.S. Private*, pg. 4089
THE ORVIS COMPANY—See The Orvis Company, Inc.; *U.S. Private*, pg. 4089
ORVIS CORPORATION; *Int'l*, pg. 5645
ORWAK AB—See Accent Equity Partners AB; *Int'l*, pg. 81
ORWAK GROUP AB—See Accent Equity Partners AB; *Int'l*, pg. 81
ORWAK LLC—See Tomra Systems ASA; *Int'l*, pg. 7803
ORWAK POLSKA SP. Z O.O.—See Accent Equity Partners AB; *Int'l*, pg. 81
ORWAY MINERAL CONSULTANTS (WA) PTY LTD—See Lycopodium Limited; *Int'l*, pg. 4605
ORW IMPORT PARTS & MACHINE; *U.S. Private*, pg. 3046
ORYON TECHNOLOGIES, INC.; *U.S. Private*, pg. 3046
ORYX INTERNATIONAL GROWTH FUND LIMITED—See Harwood Capital LLP; *Int'l*, pg. 3282
ORYX PETROLEUM SERVICES SA—See Forza Petroleum Limited; *Int'l*, pg. 2748
ORYX PROPERTIES LIMITED; *Int'l*, pg. 5645
ORYX TECHNOLOGY CORP.; *U.S. Public*, pg. 1619
ORYZON GENOMICS SA; *Int'l*, pg. 5645
ORZEL BIALY S.A.; *Int'l*, pg. 5645
OS ACQUISITION CORP.; *U.S. Public*, pg. 1619
OSA DOOR PARTS LIMITED—See ARGENT INDUSTRIAL LIMITED; *Int'l*, pg. 561
OSAGE BANCSHARES, INC.—See American Heritage Bank; *U.S. Private*, pg. 236
OSAGE DIALYSIS, LLC—See DaVita Inc.; *U.S. Public*, pg. 641
OSAGE FEDERAL BANK—See American Heritage Bank; *U.S. Private*, pg. 236
OSAGE LANDFILL, INC.—See Waste Connections, Inc.; *Int'l*, pg. 8353
OSAGE VALLEY ELECTRIC COOP ASSOCIATION; *U.S. Private*, pg. 3046
OSAI AUTOMATION SYSTEM S.P.A.; *Int'l*, pg. 5645
OSAI AUTOMATION SYSTEM USA CORPORATION—See Osai Automation System S.p.A.; *Int'l*, pg. 5645
OSAIR INC.; *U.S. Private*, pg. 3046
OSAI-UK LTD.—See Prima Industrie SpA; *Int'l*, pg. 5974
OSAI-USA LLC—See Prima Industrie SpA; *Int'l*, pg. 5974
OSAKA ADVANCED MEDICAL IMAGE CENTER, INC.—See Ship Healthcare Holdings, Inc.; *Int'l*, pg. 6852
OSAKA AIRPORT TRANSPORT CO., LTD.—See Japan Airlines Co., Ltd.; *Int'l*, pg. 3885
OSAKA AQUARIUM KAIYUKAN CO., LTD.—See Kintetsu Group Holdings Co.,Ltd.; *Int'l*, pg. 4184
OSAKA CONTAINER SERVICE CO.,LTD.—See Taiyo Kogyo Corporation; *Int'l*, pg. 7425
OSAKA DAIICHI TRAFFIC CO., LTD.—See Daiichi Koutsu Sangyo Co., Ltd.; *Int'l*, pg. 1929
OSAKA DIA BUIL-TECH CO.,LTD.—See Mitsubishi Logistics Corporation; *Int'l*, pg. 4963
OSAKA DIAMOND CHIKAGAI CO., LTD.—See Hankyu Hanshin Holdings Inc.; *Int'l*, pg. 3256
OSAKA FOOTBALL CLUB CO., LTD—See NH Foods Ltd.; *Int'l*, pg. 5256
OSAKA FUSE CO., LTD.—See Daihen Corporation; *Int'l*, pg. 1926
OSAKA GAS AUSTRALIA PTY. LTD.—See Osaka Gas Co., Ltd.; *Int'l*, pg. 5645
OSAKA GAS AUTOSERVICE CO., LTD—See Osaka Gas Co., Ltd.; *Int'l*, pg. 5645
OSAKA GAS BUSINESS CREATE CO., LTD.—See Osaka Gas Co., Ltd.; *Int'l*, pg. 5645
OSAKA GAS CHEMICALS CO., LTD.—See Osaka Gas Co., Ltd.; *Int'l*, pg. 5645
OSAKA GAS CHEMICALS CO., LTD. - TOKYO OFFICE—See Osaka Gas Co., Ltd.; *Int'l*, pg. 5646
OSAKA GAS CO., LTD.; *Int'l*, pg. 5645
OSAKA GAS CUSTOMER RELATIONS CO., LTD.—See Osaka Gas Co., Ltd.; *Int'l*, pg. 5646
OSAKA GAS FINANCE CO., LTD.—See Osaka Gas Co., Ltd.; *Int'l*, pg. 5646
OSAKA GAS GORGON PTY. LTD.—See Osaka Gas Co., Ltd.; *Int'l*, pg. 5646
OSAKA GAS HOUSING & EQUIPMENT CO., LTD.—See Osaka Gas Co., Ltd.; *Int'l*, pg. 5646
OSAKA GAS INTERNATIONAL TRANSPORT INC.—See Osaka Gas Co., Ltd.; *Int'l*, pg. 5646
OSAKA GAS LPG CO., LTD.—See Osaka Gas Co., Ltd.; *Int'l*, pg. 5646
OSAKA GAS SUMMIT RESOURCES CO., LTD.—See Osaka Gas Co., Ltd.; *Int'l*, pg. 5646
OSAKA GAS URBAN DEVELOPMENT CO., LTD.—See Osaka Gas Co., Ltd.; *Int'l*, pg. 5646
OSAKA GAS USA CORPORATION—See Osaka Gas Co., Ltd.; *Int'l*, pg. 5646
OSAKA GENERAL SERVICE CO., LTD.—See Sumitomo Chemical Company, Limited; *Int'l*, pg. 5646
OSAKA HEAVY ION ADMINISTRATION COMPANY—See Ship Healthcare Holdings, Inc.; *Int'l*, pg. 6852
OSAKA HINO MOTOR LTD.—See Toyota Motor Corporation; *Int'l*, pg. 7871
OSAKA INTERNATIONAL REFINING COMPANY, LIMITED—See ENEOS Holdings, Inc.; *Int'l*, pg. 2418
OSAKA KAMI KYODO SOKO CO., LTD.—See Japan Pulp and Paper Company Limited; *Int'l*, pg. 3904
OSAKA MARUBIRU CO., LTD.—See Daiwa House Industry Co., Ltd.; *Int'l*, pg. 1947
OSAKA NAIGAI EKIYU CO., LTD.—See Mitsubishi Gas Chemical Company, Inc.; *Int'l*, pg. 4950
OSAKA NICHIREI SERVICE INC.—See Nichirei Corporation; *Int'l*, pg. 5270
OSAKA ORGANIC CHEMICAL INDUSTRY LTD. - SAKATA PLANT—See Osaka Organic Chemical Industry Ltd.; *Int'l*, pg. 5646
OSAKA ORGANIC CHEMICAL INDUSTRY LTD.; *Int'l*, pg. 5646
THE OSAKA PACKING & TRANSPORTATION CO., LTD.—See The Sumitomo Warehouse Co. Ltd.; *Int'l*, pg. 7690
OSAKA PAPER CO., LTD.—See Rengo Co., Ltd.; *Int'l*, pg. 6280
OSAKA PETROCHEMICAL INDUSTRIES, LTD.—See Mitsui Chemicals, Inc.; *Int'l*, pg. 4983
OSAKA RECTIFIER CO., LTD.—See Kyosan Electric Manufacturing Co., Ltd.; *Int'l*, pg. 4365
OSAKA SANEI LOGISTICS CORPORATION—See Kewpie Corporation; *Int'l*, pg. 4144
OSAKA SECURITIES EXCHANGE CO., LTD.—See Japan Exchange Group, Inc.; *Int'l*, pg. 3888
OSAKA SEKISUI HEIM REAL ESTATE CO., LTD.—See Sekisui Chemical Co., Ltd.; *Int'l*, pg. 6694
OSAKA SENKO TRANSPORT CO., LTD.—See Senko Group Holdings Co., Ltd.; *Int'l*, pg. 6710
OSAKA SHIPPING CO., LTD.—See Mitsui O.S.K. Lines, Ltd.; *Int'l*, pg. 4991
OSAKA SODA CO., LTD.; *Int'l*, pg. 5646
OSAKA STEEL CO., LTD.—See Nippon Steel Corporation; *Int'l*, pg. 5339
OSAKA SUBARU INC.—See Subaru Corporation; *Int'l*, pg. 7247
OSAKA SYNTHETIC CHEMICAL LABORATORIES, INC.—See Kaneka Corporation; *Int'l*, pg. 4067
OSAKA TECHNOCRAT. CO., LTD.—See Chofu Seisakusho Co., Ltd.; *Int'l*, pg. 1577
OSAKA TERMINAL BUILDING COMPANY—See West Japan Railway Company; *Int'l*, pg. 8385
OSAKA TIGERS KOUHAN CO., LTD.—See Tigers Polymer Corporation; *Int'l*, pg. 7746
OSAKA TITANIUM TECHNOLOGIES CO., LTD.; *Int'l*, pg. 5646
OSAKA UOICHIBA CO LTD—See OUG Holdings Inc.; *Int'l*, pg. 5666
OSAKA YUKA INDUSTRY, LTD.; *Int'l*, pg. 5646
OSAKI DATATECH CO., LTD.—See Osaki Electric Co., Ltd.; *Int'l*, pg. 5647

OSCAR INVESTMENTS LIMITED.

OSAKI ELECTRIC CO., LTD. - SAITAMA PLANT—See Osaki Electric Co., Ltd.; *Int'l*, pg. 5647
OSAKI ELECTRIC CO., LTD.; *Int'l*, pg. 5647
OSAKI ELECTRIC SYSTEMS CO., LTD. - CHIBA PLANT—See Osaki Electric Co., Ltd.; *Int'l*, pg. 5647
OSAKI ELECTRIC SYSTEMS CO., LTD.—See Osaki Electric Co., Ltd.; *Int'l*, pg. 5647
OSAKI ESTATE CO., LTD.—See Osaki Electric Co., Ltd.; *Int'l*, pg. 5647
OSAKI INDUSTRY CO., LTD.—See Sakai Chemical Industry Co., Ltd.; *Int'l*, pg. 6486
OSAKI PLATECH CO., LTD.—See Osaki Electric Co., Ltd.; *Int'l*, pg. 5647
OSAKI TECH-SERVICE CO., LTD.—See Osaki Electric Co., Ltd.; *Int'l*, pg. 5647
OS ALLE 3 AS—See BNP Paribas SA; *Int'l*, pg. 1092
OSA LOGISTIK GMBH—See Die Schweizerische Post AG; *Int'l*, pg. 2113
OSA MACHINERY CO., LTD.—See General Packer Co., Ltd.; *Int'l*, pg. 2919
OSANGJAIEL CO., LTD.; *Int'l*, pg. 5647
OSAN PETROLEUM COMPANY INC.; *U.S. Private*, pg. 3046
THE OSAWATOMIE AGENCY INC.; *U.S. Private*, pg. 4089
OSB GROUP PLC; *Int'l*, pg. 5647
OSB INDIA PRIVATE LIMITED—See OneSavings Bank plc; *Int'l*, pg. 5577
OSBORN & BARR COMMUNICATIONS; *U.S. Private*, pg. 3046
OSBORN & BARR—See Osborn & Barr Communications; *U.S. Private*, pg. 3046
THE OSBORNE ASSOCIATION, INC.; *U.S. Private*, pg. 4089
OSBORNE BOOKS LIMITED—See Graham Holdings Company; *U.S. Public*, pg. 956
THE OSBORNE COINAGE COMPANY—See Groep Heylen Business & Building BV; *U.S. Public*, pg. 3087
OSBORNE CONSTRUCTION COMPANY; *U.S. Private*, pg. 3046
OSBORNE PROPERTIES CORP.; *U.S. Private*, pg. 3046
OSBORNE INTERNATIONAL AB—See Jason Industries, Inc.; *U.S. Private*, pg. 2190
OSBORN INTERNATIONAL GMBH—See Jason Industries, Inc.; *U.S. Private*, pg. 2190
OSBORN INTERNATIONAL GMBH—See Jason Industries, Inc.; *U.S. Private*, pg. 2190
OSBORN INTERNATIONAL LTDA—See Jason Industries, Inc.; *U.S. Private*, pg. 2190
OSBORN INTERNATIONAL—See Jason Industries, Inc.; *U.S. Private*, pg. 2190
OSBORN INTERNATIONAL SRL—See Jason Industries, Inc.; *U.S. Private*, pg. 2190
OSBORN LIPPERT PVT. LTD.—See Jason Industries, Inc.; *U.S. Private*, pg. 2190
OSBORN METALS LIMITED; *Int'l*, pg. 5647
OSBORN METALS SA—See Osborn Metals Limited; *Int'l*, pg. 5648
OSBORN SINGAPORE PTE LTD.—See Jason Industries, Inc.; *U.S. Private*, pg. 2190
THE OSBORN; *U.S. Private*, pg. 4089
OSBORN STRATA PRODUCTS LIMITED—See Osborn Metals Limited; *Int'l*, pg. 5648
OSBORN TRANSPORTATION, INC.; *U.S. Private*, pg. 3046
OSBORN TUBES SAS—See Osborn Metals Limited; *Int'l*, pg. 5648
OSBORN UNIPOL LDA.—See Jason Industries, Inc.; *U.S. Private*, pg. 2190
OSBORN UNIPOL SAS—See Jason Industries, Inc.; *U.S. Private*, pg. 2190
OSBORN-UNIPOL SL—See Jason Industries, Inc.; *U.S. Private*, pg. 2190
OSBORN UNIPOL (UK) LTD.—See Jason Industries, Inc.; *U.S. Private*, pg. 2190
OSBURN ASSOCIATES INC.; *U.S. Private*, pg. 3046
OSBURN BUICK PONTIAC GMC TRUCK; *U.S. Private*, pg. 3046
OSBY PARCA AB—See NIBE Industrier AB; *Int'l*, pg. 5262
OSCAGAS HOGAR SLU—See Brookfield Corporation; *Int'l*, pg. 1188
O & S CALIFORNIA, INC.—See Sumitomo Electric Industries, Ltd.; *Int'l*, pg. 7279
OS CAPITAL PARTNERS INC.—See Bain Capital, LP; *U.S. Private*, pg. 434
OSCAR A/S—See Nestle S.A.; *Int'l*, pg. 5211
OSCAR DE LA RENTA LTD.; *U.S. Private*, pg. 3046
OSCAR ESTATE MANAGEMENT CO., LTD.—See TEE International Limited; *Int'l*, pg. 7519
OSCAR FAH AG—See Addtech AB; *Int'l*, pg. 134
OSCAR G CARLSTEDT CO. INC.; *U.S. Private*, pg. 3046
OSCAR GLOBAL LIMITED; *Int'l*, pg. 5648
OSCAR GRUSS & SON INCORPORATED; *U.S. Private*, pg. 3046
OSCAR HEALTH AGENCY INC.; *U.S. Private*, pg. 3046
OSCAR HEALTH, INC.; *U.S. Public*, pg. 1619
OSCAR HEYMAN & BROTHERS, INC.; *U.S. Private*, pg. 3046
OSCAR INVESTMENTS LIMITED.; *Int'l*, pg. 5648

OSCAR INVESTMENTS LIMITED.

CORPORATE AFFILIATIONS

OSCAR JACOBSON AB—See Mellby Gard Holding AB; *Int'l*, pg. 4811
OSCAR J. BOLDT CONSTRUCTION CO. INC.—See The Boldt Group Inc.; *U.S. Private*, pg. 3996
OSCAR MEDTEC AB—See Indutrade AB; *Int'l*, pg. 3680
OSCAR ORDUNO, INC.; *U.S. Private*, pg. 3046
OSCAR PROPERTIES AB; *Int'l*, pg. 5648
OSCAR PROPERTIES HOLDING AB; *Int'l*, pg. 5648
OSCAR RENDA CONTRACTING INC.; *U.S. Private*, pg. 3046
OSCAR SAVREUX SAS—See VINCI S.A.; *Int'l*, pg. 8225
OSCAR TECHNOLOGY CORPORATION—See Fixstars Corporation; *Int'l*, pg. 2696
OSCAR WEALTH ADVISORY SDN BHD; *Int'l*, pg. 5648
OSCAR WINSKI CO. INC.—*U.S. Private*, pg. 3046
THE OSCAR W. LARSON COMPANY INC.; *U.S. Private*, pg. 4089
OSC, A.S.—See CEZ, a.s.; *Int'l*, pg. 1428
OSCEOLA CAPITAL MANAGEMENT, LLC; *U.S. Private*, pg. 3046
OSCEOLA COUNTY EXPRESSWAY AUTHORITY; *U.S. Private*, pg. 3047
OSCEOLA FARMS CO. INC.—See Florida Crystals Corporation; *U.S. Private*, pg. 1548
OSCEOLA FOODS, INC.—See Hormel Foods Corporation; *U.S. Public*, pg. 1054
OSCEOLA GOLD, INC.; *U.S. Public*, pg. 1619
OSCEOLA NEWS-GAZETTE—See West End Holdings LLC; *U.S. Private*, pg. 4485
OSCEOLA REGIONAL MEDICAL CENTER—See HCA Healthcare, Inc.; *U.S. Public*, pg. 1005
OSCEOLA SURGICAL ASSOCIATES, LLC—See HCA Healthcare, Inc.; *U.S. Public*, pg. 1005
OSCEOLA SURGICAL ASSOCIATES, LLC—See HCA Healthcare, Inc.; *U.S. Public*, pg. 1005
OSC GOLF WORLD CORPORATION—See Olympic Group Corporation; *Int'l*, pg. 5555
OSCILLATE PLC—See Gunsynd plc; *Int'l*, pg. 3185
OSCILLATING SYSTEMS TECHNOLOGY AFRICA (PTY) LTD.—See Invicta Holdings Limited; *Int'l*, pg. 3788
OSCILLOQUARTZ FINLAND OY—See ADTRAN Holdings, Inc.; *U.S. Public*, pg. 44
OSCILLOQUARTZ S.A.—See ADTRAN Holdings, Inc.; *U.S. Public*, pg. 44
OSCO AGGREGATES LIMITED—See OSCO Construction Group; *Int'l*, pg. 5648
OSCO CONSTRUCTION GROUP - ANNAPOLIS VALLEY READY-MIX PLANT—See OSCO Construction Group; *Int'l*, pg. 5648
OSCO CONSTRUCTION GROUP - BEDFORD READY-MIX PLANT—See OSCO Construction Group; *Int'l*, pg. 5648
OSCO CONSTRUCTION GROUP - CHARLOTTETOWN PLANT—See OSCO Construction Group; *Int'l*, pg. 5648
OSCO CONSTRUCTION GROUP - GLENHOLME READY-MIX PLANT—See OSCO Construction Group; *Int'l*, pg. 5648
OSCO CONSTRUCTION GROUP - MONCTON PLANT—See OSCO Construction Group; *Int'l*, pg. 5648
OSCO CONSTRUCTION GROUP - MONTAGUE PLANT—See OSCO Construction Group; *Int'l*, pg. 5648
OSCO CONSTRUCTION GROUP - SACKVILLE PLANT—See OSCO Construction Group; *Int'l*, pg. 5648
OSCO CONSTRUCTION GROUP; *Int'l*, pg. 5648
OSCO CONSTRUCTION GROUP - SOURIS PLANT—See OSCO Construction Group; *Int'l*, pg. 5648
OSCO CONSTRUCTION GROUP - SUMMERSIDE PLANT—See OSCO Construction Group; *Int'l*, pg. 5648
OSCO CONSTRUCTION GROUP - TRISTAR CONCRETE PLANT—See OSCO Construction Group; *Int'l*, pg. 5648
OSCODA PLASTICS, INC.; *U.S. Private*, pg. 3047
OSCO GMBH—See Orbis SE; *Int'l*, pg. 5614
OSCO INDUSTRIES INC.; *U.S. Private*, pg. 3047
OSCO INTERNATIONAL CO., LTD.—See THK CO., LTD.; *Int'l*, pg. 7712
OS CO., LTD.; *Int'l*, pg. 5645
O'S COMPANIES INC.; *U.S. Private*, pg. 2980
OSCOR INC.; *U.S. Private*, pg. 3047
OSCOTEC INC.; *Int'l*, pg. 5648
OSDA, INC.—See Foxtronics EMS; *U.S. Private*, pg. 1585
OSDC CO., LTD.—See Bain Capital, LP; *U.S. Private*, pg. 435
O & S DESIGNS INC.—See MGS Manufacturing Group, Inc.; *U.S. Private*, pg. 2695
OSD GMBH—See BKW AG; *Int'l*, pg. 1055
OSD SCHAFER GMBH & CO. KG—See KOTTER Gmbh & Co. KG; *Int'l*, pg. 4293
OSEASPRE CONSULTANTS LIMITED; *Int'l*, pg. 5648
OSE CONSULTING SARL—See Scientific Brain Training SA; *Int'l*, pg. 6648
OSE IMMUNOTHERAPEUTICS SA; *Int'l*, pg. 5648
OSEM GROUP—See Nestle S.A.; *Int'l*, pg. 5211

O.S. ENGINES MFG. CO., LTD.—See Futaba Corporation; *Int'l*, pg. 2851
OSE PHILIPPINES INC.—See Orient Semiconductor Electronics Limited; *Int'l*, pg. 5623
OSES INTERNATIONAL, LLC—See Oil States International, Inc.; *U.S. Public*, pg. 1565
OSEVA, A.S.—See Agrofert Holding, a.s.; *Int'l*, pg. 219
OS FACILITIES CO., LTD.—See Bain Capital, LP; *U.S. Private*, pg. 434
OSF HEALTHCARE SYSTEM—See The Sisters of the Third Order of St. Francis; *U.S. Private*, pg. 4118
OSF INTERNATIONAL, INC.; *U.S. Private*, pg. 3047
OSG AMERICA, L.P.—See Saltchuk Resources Inc.; *U.S. Private*, pg. 3534
OSG ASIA PTE. LTD.—See OSG Corporation; *Int'l*, pg. 5649
OSG BELUX S.A.N.V.—See OSG Corporation; *Int'l*, pg. 5649
OSG CANADA LTD.—See OSG Corporation; *Int'l*, pg. 5649
OSG COATING SERVICE CO., LTD.—See OSG Corporation; *Int'l*, pg. 5649
OSG CORPORATION CO., LTD.; *Int'l*, pg. 5649
OSG CORPORATION; *Int'l*, pg. 5648
OSG DAVID GRINDING SERVICES B.V.—See OSG Corporation; *Int'l*, pg. 5649
OSG ENVIRONMENTAL TECHNOLOGY (SUZHOU) CO., LTD.—See OSG Corporation Co., Ltd.; *Int'l*, pg. 5650
OSG EUROPE LOGISTICS S.A.—See OSG Corporation; *Int'l*, pg. 5649
OSG FRANCE S.A.S.—See OSG Corporation; *Int'l*, pg. 5649
OSG GMBH—See OSG Corporation; *Int'l*, pg. 5649
OSG IBERICA TOOLING, S.L.U.—See OSG Corporation; *Int'l*, pg. 5649
OSG (INDIA) PVT. LTD.—See OSG Corporation; *Int'l*, pg. 5649
OSG ITALIA S.R.L.—See OSG Corporation; *Int'l*, pg. 5649
OSG KOREA CORPORATION—See OSG Corporation; *Int'l*, pg. 5649
OSGLEN PTY. LIMITED—See Petsec Energy Ltd.; *Int'l*, pg. 5834
OSG LIGHTERING LLC—See Saltchuk Resources Inc.; *U.S. Private*, pg. 3534
OSG LIMITED LIABILITY COMPANY—See OSG Corporation; *Int'l*, pg. 5649
OSG NEDERLAND B.V.—See OSG Corporation; *Int'l*, pg. 5649
OSGOOD INDUSTRIES, INC.—See CVC Capital Partners SICAV-FIS S.A.; *Int'l*, pg. 1884
OSG PHILIPPINES CORPORATION—See OSG Corporation; *Int'l*, pg. 5649
OSG RECORDS MANAGEMENT CRYPTO LLC—See Iron Mountain Incorporated; *U.S. Public*, pg. 1174
OSG RECORDS MANAGEMENT LLC—See Iron Mountain Incorporated; *U.S. Public*, pg. 1174
OSG RECORDS MANAGEMENT LLC—See Iron Mountain Incorporated; *U.S. Public*, pg. 1174
OSG RECORDS MANAGEMENT LLC—See Iron Mountain Incorporated; *U.S. Public*, pg. 1174
OSG RECORDS MANAGEMENT LLP—See Iron Mountain Incorporated; *U.S. Public*, pg. 1174
OSG ROYCO, S.A. DE C.V.—See OSG Corporation; *Int'l*, pg. 5649
OSG SCANDINAVIA A/S—See OSG Corporation; *Int'l*, pg. 5649
OSG (SHANGHAI) CO., LTD.—See OSG Corporation; *Int'l*, pg. 5649
OSG (SHANGHAI) PRECISION TOOLS CO., LTD.—See OSG Corporation; *Int'l*, pg. 5649
OSG SHIP MANAGEMENT INC.—See Saltchuk Resources Inc.; *U.S. Private*, pg. 3534
OSG SHIP MANAGEMENT, MANILA INC.—See Saltchuk Resources Inc.; *U.S. Private*, pg. 3534
OSG SHIP MANAGEMENT (UK) LTD.—See Saltchuk Resources Inc.; *U.S. Private*, pg. 3534
OSG SULAMERICANA DE FERRAMENTAS LTDA.—See OSG Corporation; *Int'l*, pg. 5649
OSG SYSTEM PRODUCTS CO., LTD.—See OSG Corporation; *Int'l*, pg. 5649
OSG THAI CO., LTD.—See OSG Corporation; *Int'l*, pg. 5649
OSG TURKEY KESICI TAKIMLAR SANAYI VE TICARET ANONIM SIRKETI—See OSG Corporation; *Int'l*, pg. 5649
OSG U.K. LIMITED—See OSG Corporation; *Int'l*, pg. 5649
OSG USA, INC.—See OSG Corporation; *Int'l*, pg. 5649
OSG VIETNAM CO., LTD.—See OSG Corporation; *Int'l*, pg. 5649
OSHAMANBE AGRI CO., LTD.—See ASTMAX Trading, Inc.; *Int'l*, pg. 655
OSHIDORI INTERNATIONAL HOLDINGS LIMITED; *Int'l*, pg. 5650
OSHIKA FORMALIN CO., LTD.—See Mitsubishi Gas Chemical Company, Inc.; *Int'l*, pg. 4950
OSHIMA KOGYO CO., LTD.—See Nakano Corporation; *Int'l*, pg. 5132
OSHIMAONO SHOJI CO., LTD.—See Kamei Corporation; *Int'l*, pg. 4061

OSHITARI LABORATORY, INC.—See Freudenberg SE; *Int'l*, pg. 2790
OSHKOSH AIRPORT PRODUCTS, LLC—See Oshkosh Corporation; *U.S. Public*, pg. 1621
OSHKOSH B'GOSH, INC.—See Carter's, Inc.; *U.S. Public*, pg. 445
OSHKOSH COMMERCIAL (BEIJING) CO., LIMITED—See Oshkosh Corporation; *U.S. Public*, pg. 1621
OSHKOSH CORPORATION; *U.S. Public*, pg. 1619
OSHKOSH DEFENSE CANADA INCORPORATED—See Oshkosh Corporation; *U.S. Public*, pg. 1621
OSHKOSH DEFENSE, LLC—See Oshkosh Corporation; *U.S. Public*, pg. 1621
OSHKOSH EUROPE B.V.—See Oshkosh Corporation; *U.S. Public*, pg. 1621
OSHKOSH FLOOR DESIGNS, INC.—See FCF Partners, LP; *U.S. Public*, pg. 1485
OSHKOSH ITALY B.V.—See Oshkosh Corporation; *U.S. Public*, pg. 1621
OSHKOSH-JLG (SHANGHAI) ENTERPRISE DEVELOPMENT CO., LTD.—See Oshkosh Corporation; *U.S. Public*, pg. 1621
OSHKOSH-JLG (SINGAPORE) TECHNOLOGY EQUIPMENT PRIVATE LIMITED—See Oshkosh Corporation; *U.S. Public*, pg. 1621
OSHKOSH JLG (TIANJIN) EQUIPMENT TECHNOLOGY CO. LIMITED—See Oshkosh Corporation; *U.S. Public*, pg. 1620
OSHKOSH LOGISTICS CORPORATION—See Oshkosh Corporation; *U.S. Public*, pg. 1621
OSHKOSH/MCNEILUS FINANCIAL SERVICES PARTNERSHIP—See Bank of America Corporation; *U.S. Public*, pg. 272
OSHKOSH NORTHWESTERN—See Gannett Co., Inc.; *U.S. Public*, pg. 899
OSHKOSH SPECIALTY VEHICLES—See Oshkosh Corporation; *U.S. Public*, pg. 1621
OSHMAN FAMILY JEWISH COMMUNITY CENTER; *U.S. Private*, pg. 3047
O S HOLDINGS, INC.; *U.S. Private*, pg. 2977
OS HRS INDIA PRIVATE LIMITED—See Bain Capital, LP; *U.S. Private*, pg. 434
OS HRS JAPAN INC.—See Bain Capital, LP; *U.S. Private*, pg. 434
OS HRS SDN BHD—See Bain Capital, LP; *U.S. Private*, pg. 434
OSIA HYPER RETAIL LTD.; *Int'l*, pg. 5650
OSIAJEE TEXFAB LIMITED; *Int'l*, pg. 5650
OSIATIS BELGIUM NV—See Econocom Group SA; *Int'l*, pg. 2298
OSIATIS COMPUTER SERVICES GMBH—See Econocom Group SA; *Int'l*, pg. 2298
OSIATIS INGENIERIE S.A.S.—See Econocom Group SA; *Int'l*, pg. 2298
OSIATIS SA—See Econocom Group SA; *Int'l*, pg. 2298
OSI AUTOMATION SOFTWARE SYSTEMS (BEIJING) CO., LTD.—See Emerson Electric Co.; *U.S. Public*, pg. 750
OSIBODU & ASSOCIATES EXPORTING USA, LLC; *U.S. Private*, pg. 3047
OSIB OPERATIONS HOLDING B.V.—See KRC Capital B.V.; *Int'l*, pg. 4300
OSI DU CANADA INC.—See Emerson Electric Co.; *U.S. Public*, pg. 750
OSIEDLE TECZOWY LAS PD DEVELOPMENT SP. Z O.O. S.K.A.—See Polnord S.A.; *Int'l*, pg. 5911
OSI ELECTRONICS, INC.—See OSI Systems, Inc.; *U.S. Public*, pg. 1621
OSI ELECTRONICS (UK) LTD.—See OSI Systems, Inc.; *U.S. Public*, pg. 1621
OSI ENERGY AUTOMATION INDIA PRIVATE LIMITED—See Emerson Electric Co.; *U.S. Public*, pg. 750
OSI/FLEMING'S, LLC—See Bloomin' Brands, Inc.; *U.S. Public*, pg. 363
OSI GROUP, LLC; *U.S. Private*, pg. 3047
OSIGURANJE HELIOS D.D.—See Vienna Insurance Group AG Wiener Versicherung Gruppe; *Int'l*, pg. 8195
OSIGURUVANE MAKEDONIJA AD—See Vienna Insurance Group AG Wiener Versicherung Gruppe; *Int'l*, pg. 8195
OSI, INC.; *U.S. Private*, pg. 3047
OSI INDIA PRIVATE LIMITED—See Inflexion Private Equity Partners LLP; *Int'l*, pg. 3689
OSI LASER DIODE, INC.—See OSI Systems, Inc.; *U.S. Public*, pg. 1621
OSILOVAC D.O.O.—See Nexe Grupa d.d.; *Int'l*, pg. 5243
OSI MARITIME SYSTEMS; *Int'l*, pg. 5650
OSIM CAMBODIA—See OSIM International Ltd.; *Int'l*, pg. 5650
OSIM (CHINA) CO., LTD.-BEIJING—See OSIM International Ltd.; *Int'l*, pg. 5650
OSIM (CHINA) CO., LTD.—See OSIM International Ltd.; *Int'l*, pg. 5650
OSIM (GUANGZHOU) CO. LTD.—See OSIM International Ltd.; *Int'l*, pg. 5650
OSIM (HK) CO. LTD.—See OSIM International Ltd.; *Int'l*, pg. 5650
OSIM INTERNATIONAL LTD.; *Int'l*, pg. 5650

COMPANY NAME INDEX — OSPREY'S DOMINION VINEYARDS LTD.

OSIM INTERNATIONAL TRADING (SHANGHAI) CO. LTD.—See OSIM International Ltd.; *Int'l*, pg. 5650
OSIM (M) SDN BHD—See OSIM International Ltd.; *Int'l*, pg. 5650
OSIM MYANMAR—See OSIM International Ltd.; *Int'l*, pg. 5650
OSIM (TAIWAN) CO. LTD.—See OSIM International Ltd.; *Int'l*, pg. 5650
OSI ONCOLOGY DEVELOPMENT—See Astellas Pharma Inc.; *Int'l*, pg. 653
OSI OPTOELECTRONICS AS—See OSI Systems, Inc.; *U.S. Public*, pg. 1621
OSI OPTOELECTRONICS INC.—See OSI Systems, Inc.; *U.S. Public*, pg. 1621
OSI OPTOELECTRONICS LIMITED—See OSI Systems, Inc.; *U.S. Public*, pg. 1621
OSI PHARMACEUTICALS, INC.—See Astellas Pharma Inc.; *Int'l*, pg. 653
OSIRIS ACQUISITION CORP.; *U.S. Public*, pg. 1622
OSIRIS CORP.; *U.S. Public*, pg. 1622
OSIRIS THERAPEUTICS, INC.—See Smith & Nephew plc; *Int'l*, pg. 7007
OSIRIUM LIMITED—See Thoma Bravo, L.P.; *U.S. Private*, pg. 4153
OSIRIUM TECHNOLOGIES PLC—See Thoma Bravo, L.P.; *U.S. Private*, pg. 4153
OSI SINGAPORE PRIVATE LIMITED—See Inflexion Private Equity Partners LLP; *Int'l*, pg. 3689
OSISKO DEVELOPMENT CORP.; *Int'l*, pg. 5650
OSISKO GOLD ROYALTIES LTD.; *Int'l*, pg. 5650
OSISKO METALS INC.; *Int'l*, pg. 5651
OSISKO MINING INC.—See Gold Fields Limited; *Int'l*, pg. 3024
OSISOFT, LLC; *U.S. Private*, pg. 3047
OSI SYSTEMS, INC.; *U.S. Public*, pg. 1621
OSIVO 2 AS; *Int'l*, pg. 5651
OSIVO AS; *Int'l*, pg. 5651
OSJB HOLDINGS CORPORATION; *Int'l*, pg. 5651
OSK AIMAL SDN. BHD.—See OSK Holdings Berhad; *Int'l*, pg. 5651
OSKALOOSA CONCRETE PRODUCTS—See Johnson Holding Co.; *U.S. Private*, pg. 2228
OSKAR BLUES BREWING COMPANY; *U.S. Private*, pg. 3047
OSKAR FRECH GMBH + CO. KG, *Int'l*, pg. 5051
OSKAR HUBER INC.; *U.S. Private*, pg. 3047
OSKAR KETTERER DRUCKGIESSEREI GMBH; *Int'l*, pg. 5652
OSKAR NOLTE GMBH—See The Sherwin-Williams Company; *U.S. Public*, pg. 2128
OSKAR—See Marcegaglia S.p.A.; *Int'l*, pg. 4689
OSK CAPITAL SDN. BHD.—See OSK Holdings Berhad; *Int'l*, pg. 5651
OSK CO., LTD.—See OTSUKA CORPORATION; *Int'l*, pg. 5658
OSK ECAPITAL SDN. BHD.—See OSK Holdings Berhad; *Int'l*, pg. 5651
THE O.S. KELLY COMPANY—See Paulson & Co. Inc.; *U.S. Private*, pg. 3114
OSK HOLDINGS BERHAD; *Int'l*, pg. 5651
OSK INTERNATIONAL INVESTMENTS HONG KONG LIMITED—See RHB Bank Berhad; *Int'l*, pg. 6320
OSK LLC—See OJSC Magnitogorsk Iron & Steel Works; *Int'l*, pg. 5540
OSK MUMAWAL SDN. BHD.—See OSK Holdings Berhad; *Int'l*, pg. 5651
OSKO INC.—See Rayence Co., Ltd.; *Int'l*, pg. 6224
OSK PROPERTY HOLDINGS BERHAD—See OSK Holdings Berhad; *Int'l*, pg. 5651
OSK TRUSTEES BERHAD—See RHB Bank Berhad; *Int'l*, pg. 6320
OSKUTEX GMBH—See Clayton, Dubilier & Rice, LLC; *U.S. Private*, pg. 926
OSK VENTURES INTERNATIONAL BERHAD; *Int'l*, pg. 5651
OSK VENTURES SDN. BHD.—See OSK Holdings Berhad; *Int'l*, pg. 5651
OSL COMMUNICATIONS; *Int'l*, pg. 5652
OSLER HMA MEDICAL GROUP, LLC—See Community Health Systems, Inc.; *U.S. Public*, pg. 555
OSL HOLDINGS INC.; *U.S. Private*, pg. 3048
OSLIN NATION CO.—See HTS Engineering Ltd.; *Int'l*, pg. 3509
OSLO BORS ASA—See Euronext N.V.; *Int'l*, pg. 2554
OSLO BORS VPS HOLDING ASA—See Euronext N.V.; *Int'l*, pg. 2554
OSLO BRANNSIKRING AS—See AF Gruppen ASA; *Int'l*, pg. 184
OSLO CLEARING ASA—See SIX Group AG; *Int'l*, pg. 6966
OSLOFJORD VARME AS—See Groupe BPCE; *Int'l*, pg. 3096
OSLOFJORD VARME AS—See Infranode Holding AB; *Int'l*, pg. 3697
OSLOFJORD VARME AS—See Kommunal Landspensjonskasse gjensidig forsikringsselskap; *Int'l*, pg. 4242
OS LOGITEC CO., LTD.—See Bain Capital, LP; *U.S. Private*, pg. 434
OSLO ITALIA S.R.L.—See GPI S.p.A.; *Int'l*, pg. 3046

OSLO KINO AS—See Egmont Fonden; *Int'l*, pg. 2326
OSLO LUFTHAVN AS—See Avinor AS; *Int'l*, pg. 744
OSLO NYE HOYSKOLE AS—See Lumi Gruppen AS; *Int'l*, pg. 4578
OSLO PROSJEKTBYGG AS—See AF Gruppen ASA; *Int'l*, pg. 184
OSLO REINSURANCE COMPANY AS—See Storebrand ASA; *Int'l*, pg. 7226
OSLO STILLASUTLEIE AS—See AF Gruppen ASA; *Int'l*, pg. 184
OS MACHINERY CORP.—See Hokkan Holdings Limited; *Int'l*, pg. 3443
OSMANLI MENKUL DEGERLER A.S.; *Int'l*, pg. 5652
OSMOFLO ENGINEERING SERVICES PVT. LTD.—See Hitachi Zosen Corporation; *Int'l*, pg. 3412
OSMOFLO HOLDINGS PTY LTD—See Hitachi Zosen Corporation; *Int'l*, pg. 3412
OSMOFLO INTERNATIONAL FZE—See Hitachi Zosen Corporation; *Int'l*, pg. 3412
OSMOND RESOURCES LIMITED; *Int'l*, pg. 5652
OSMOSE CHILE LIMITADA—See Koppers Holdings Inc.; *U.S. Public*, pg. 1272
OSMOSE UTILITIES SERVICES, INC.—See EQT AB; *Int'l*, pg. 2479
OSMOSE UTILITIES SERVICES, INC.—See EQT AB; *Int'l*, pg. 2479
OSMOSE UTILITIES SERVICES, INC. - SYRACUSE—See EQT AB; *Int'l*, pg. 2479
OSMOSUN SA; *Int'l*, pg. 5652
OSMOTICA ARGENTINA, S.A.—See RVL Pharmaceuticals plc; *U.S. Public*, pg. 1827
OSMOTICA KERESKEDELMI ES SZOLGALTATO KFT—See RVL Pharmaceuticals plc; *U.S. Public*, pg. 1827
OSMOTICS CORP.—See BHMS Investments LP; *U.S. Private*, pg. 549
OSMOZIS SA; *Int'l*, pg. 5652
OSM WORLDWIDE; *U.S. Private*, pg. 3048
OSNABRUCKER WOHNUNGSBAUGESELLSCHAFT MIT BESCHRANKTER HAFTUNG—See Vonovia SE; *Int'l*, pg. 8305
OS NANO TECHNOLOGY CO., LTD.—See Bain Capital, LP; *U.S. Private*, pg. 434
OS NATIONAL LLC—See Opendoor Technologies Inc.; *U.S. Public*, pg. 1606
OSNOVA PROJEKT A.D.; *Int'l*, pg. 5652
OSNOVA SOLSIF LLC—See VINCI S.A.; *Int'l*, pg. 8225
OSN TEXAS LLC—See Opendoor Technologies Inc.; *U.S. Public*, pg. 1606
O SORBET D'AMOUR SA; *Int'l*, pg. 5502
OSOTH INTER LABORATORIES CO., LTD.—See Saha Pathanapibul Public Company Limited; *Int'l*, pg. 6479
OSOTSPA CO., LTD.; *Int'l*, pg. 5652
OSOTSPA INSURANCE PUBLIC COMPANY LIMITED—See Osotspa Co., Ltd.; *Int'l*, pg. 5652
OSOTSPA TAISHO CO., LTD.—See Osotspa Co., Ltd.; *Int'l*, pg. 5652
OSOTSPA TAISHO CO., LTD.—See Taisho Pharmaceutical Holdings Co., Ltd; *Int'l*, pg. 7417
OSOTSPA TAISHO PHARMACEUTICAL CO., LTD.—See Osotspa Co., Ltd.; *Int'l*, pg. 5652
OSOUL INVESTMENT COMPANY KSCC; *Int'l*, pg. 5652
OSPAP AS—See KPP Group Holdings Co., Ltd.; *Int'l*, pg. 4298
OSP CO., LTD.; *Int'l*, pg. 5652
OSPEDALE DEL MARE SOCIETA CONSORTILE A.R.L.—See Salini Costruttori S.p.A.; *Int'l*, pg. 6493
OSPEDALI PRIVATI RIUNITI S.R.L.—See Garofalo Health Care SpA; *Int'l*, pg. 2886
OSPELT HAUSTECHNIK AG—See Poenina Holding AG; *Int'l*, pg. 5903
OSP GROUP MANAGEMENT SERVICES, L.P.—See Charlesbank Capital Partners, LLC; *U.S. Private*, pg. 855
OSP GROUP MANAGEMENT SERVICES, L.P.—See Webster Equity Partners, LLC; *U.S. Private*, pg. 4467
OS PLATINUM CO., LTD.—See Bain Capital, LP; *U.S. Private*, pg. 434
OS POWER VIETNAM CO., LTD.—See Bain Capital, LP; *U.S. Private*, pg. 435
OSPRAIE MANAGEMENT, LLC; *U.S. Private*, pg. 3048
OSPREY BIOTECHNICS, INC.—See Phibro Animal Health Corporation; *U.S. Public*, pg. 1685
OSPREY CAPITAL LLC; *U.S. Private*, pg. 3048
OSPREYDEEPCLEAN INTERNATIONAL LIMITED—See OspreyFrank plc; *Int'l*, pg. 5652
OSPREYDEEPCLEAN LIMITED—See OspreyFrank plc; *Int'l*, pg. 5652
OSPREYFRANK PLC; *Int'l*, pg. 5652
OSPREY INSURANCE BROKERS CO. LTD.—See Tangiers Group Plc; *Int'l*, pg. 7458
OSPREY LINE, LLC—See Kirby Corporation; *U.S. Public*, pg. 1236
OSPREY MANAGEMENT, LLC; *U.S. Private*, pg. 3048
OSPREY MEDICAL INC.; *U.S. Public*, pg. 1622
OSPREY PUBLISHING LIMITED—See Bloomsbury Publishing Plc; *Int'l*, pg. 1065
OSPREY REAL ESTATE SERVICES, LLC—See Osprey S.A. Limited; *U.S. Private*, pg. 3048

OSPREY S.A. LIMITED; *U.S. Private*, pg. 3048
OSPREY'S DOMINION VINEYARDS LTD.; *U.S. Private*, pg. 3048
OSRAM AB—See ams AG; *Int'l*, pg. 438
OSRAM AMPUL TICARET A.S.—See ams AG; *Int'l*, pg. 438
OSRAM ARGENTINA S.A.C.I.—See ams AG; *Int'l*, pg. 440
OSRAM ASIA PACIFIC LTD. (OAPAC)—See ams AG; *Int'l*, pg. 438
OSRAM ASIA PACIFIC LTD.—See ams AG; *Int'l*, pg. 438
OSRAM ASIA PACIFIC MANAGEMENT COMPANY LTD.—See ams AG; *Int'l*, pg. 439
OSRAM, A.S.—See ams AG; *Int'l*, pg. 440
OSRAM A/S—See ams AG; *Int'l*, pg. 438
OSRAM AS—See ams AG; *Int'l*, pg. 438
OSRAM AUSTRALIA PTY. LTD.—See ams AG; *Int'l*, pg. 440
OSRAM AUTOMOTIVE LAMPS PRIVATE LIMITED—See ams AG; *Int'l*, pg. 439
OSRAM BENELUX B.V.—See ams AG; *Int'l*, pg. 439
OSRAM CESKA REPUBLIKA S.R.O.—See ams AG; *Int'l*, pg. 439
OSRAM CHILE LTDA.—See ams AG; *Int'l*, pg. 439
OSRAM CHINA LIGHTING LTD.—See ams AG; *Int'l*, pg. 439
OSRAM COMERCIO DE SOLUCOES DE ILUMINACAO LTDA.—See ams AG; *Int'l*, pg. 439
OSRAM CONTINENTAL GMBH—See ams AG; *Int'l*, pg. 439
OSRAM CONTINENTAL ROMANIA S.R.L.—See ams AG; *Int'l*, pg. 438
OSRAM DE COLOMBIA ILUMINACIONES S.A.—See ams AG; *Int'l*, pg. 439
OSRAM DEL ECUADOR S.A.—See ams AG; *Int'l*, pg. 440
OSRAM DE MEXICO S.A. DE C.V.—See ams AG; *Int'l*, pg. 440
OSRAM DE PERU S.A.C.—See ams AG; *Int'l*, pg. 439
OSRAM DO BRASIL COMPANHIA DE LAMPADAS ELETRICAS S.A.—See ams AG; *Int'l*, pg. 440
OSRAM DO BRASIL LAMPADAS ELETRICAS LTDA.—See ams AG; *Int'l*, pg. 440
OSRAM D.O.O.—See ams AG; *Int'l*, pg. 439
OSRAM D.O.O.—See ams AG; *Int'l*, pg. 439
OSRAM D.O.O—See ams AG; *Int'l*, pg. 439
OSRAM EMPRESA DE APARELHAGEM ELECTRICA LDA.—See ams AG; *Int'l*, pg. 439
OSRAM EOOD—See ams AG; *Int'l*, pg. 439
OSRAM GMBH—See ams AG; *Int'l*, pg. 439
OSRAM KOREA CO. LTD.—See ams AG; *Int'l*, pg. 439
OSRAM KUNSHAN DISPLAY OPTIC CO., LTD.—See ams AG; *Int'l*, pg. 439
OSRAM, LDA.—See ams AG; *Int'l*, pg. 440
OSRAM LICHT AG—See ams AG; *Int'l*, pg. 438
OSRAM LIGHTING CONTROL SYSTEMS LTD.—See ams AG; *Int'l*, pg. 439
OSRAM LIGHTING MIDDLE EAST FZE—See ams AG; *Int'l*, pg. 439
OSRAM LIGHTING PRIVATE LIMITED—See ams AG; *Int'l*, pg. 439
OSRAM LIGHTING PTE. LTD.—See ams AG; *Int'l*, pg. 439
OSRAM LIGHTING S.A.S.U.—See ams AG; *Int'l*, pg. 439
OSRAM LIGHTING S.L.—See ams AG; *Int'l*, pg. 439
OSRAM LTD.—See ams AG; *Int'l*, pg. 439
OSRAM LTD.—See ams AG; *Int'l*, pg. 440
OSRAM (MALAYSIA) SDN. BHD.—See ams AG; *Int'l*, pg. 438
OSRAM-MELCO TOSHIBA LIGHTING LTD.—See ams AG; *Int'l*, pg. 440
OSRAM MIDDLE EAST FZE—See ams AG; *Int'l*, pg. 439
OSRAM OPTO SEMICONDUCTORS ASIA LTD.—See ams AG; *Int'l*, pg. 439
OSRAM OPTO SEMICONDUCTORS (CHINA) CO., LTD.—See ams AG; *Int'l*, pg. 439
OSRAM OPTO SEMICONDUCTORS GMBH—See ams AG; *Int'l*, pg. 439
OSRAM OPTO SEMICONDUCTORS, INC.—See ams AG; *Int'l*, pg. 439
OSRAM OPTO SEMICONDUCTORS (JAPAN) LTD.—See ams AG; *Int'l*, pg. 439
OSRAM OPTO SEMICONDUCTORS (MALAYSIA) SDN BHD—See ams AG; *Int'l*, pg. 439
OSRAM PTE. LTD.—See ams AG; *Int'l*, pg. 439
OSRAM (PTY.) LTD.—See ams AG; *Int'l*, pg. 438
OSRAM ROMANIA S.R.L.—See ams AG; *Int'l*, pg. 439
OSRAM S.A. DE C.V.—See ams AG; *Int'l*, pg. 439
OSRAM SALES EOOD—See ams AG; *Int'l*, pg. 439
OSRAM S.A.—See ams AG; *Int'l*, pg. 439
OSRAM S.A.—See ams AG; *Int'l*, pg. 439
OSRAM S.A.—See ams AG; *Int'l*, pg. 440
OSRAM SL GMBH—See ams AG; *Int'l*, pg. 438
OSRAM SOCIETA RIUNITE OSRAM-EDISON-CLERICI S.P.A.—See ams AG; *Int'l*, pg. 440
OSRAM S.P.A.—See ams AG; *Int'l*, pg. 439
OSRAM SP. Z O.O.—See ams AG; *Int'l*, pg. 439
OSRAM SYLVANIA, INC.—See ams AG; *Int'l*, pg. 440
OSRAM SYLVANIA LTD.—See ams AG; *Int'l*, pg. 440
OSRAM SYLVANIA PUERTO RICO—See ams AG; *Int'l*, pg. 440

OSRAM TAIWAN COMPANY LTD.—See ams AG; *Int'l*, pg. 439
OSRAM TEKNOLOJILERI TICARET ANONIM SIRKETI—See ams AG; *Int'l*, pg. 439
OSRAM (THAILAND) CO., LTD.—See ams AG; *Int'l*, pg. 438
OSRA SPA—See Wolters Kluwer n.v.; *Int'l*, pg. 8445
OS RECRUITMENT (THAILAND) CO., LTD.—See Bain Capital, LP; *U.S. Private*, pg. 434
OSR LOUISIANA, LLC—See Select Medical Holdings Corporation; *U.S. Public*, pg. 1858
OSR PHYSICAL THERAPY, LIMITED PARTNERSHIP—See U.S. Physical Therapy, Inc.; *U.S. Public*, pg. 2215
OSRP, LLC—See Insight Enterprises, Inc.; *U.S. Public*, pg. 1130
OSSDSIGN AB; *Int'l*, pg. 5652
OSSDSIGN USA INC.—See OssDsign AB; *Int'l*, pg. 5652
OSSEN INNOVATION CO. LTD.—See Pujiang International Group; *Int'l*, pg. 6116
OSSIA (HK) COMPANY LIMITED; *Int'l*, pg. 5652
OSSIA INTERNATIONAL LIMITED; *Int'l*, pg. 5652
OSSIAM SA—See Groupe BPCE; *Int'l*, pg. 3099
OSSIAN FINANCIAL SERVICES, INC.—See Farmers & Merchants Bancorp, Inc.; *U.S. Public*, pg. 822
OSSIA WORLD OF GOLF (M) SDN. BHD.—See Ossia International Limited; *Int'l*, pg. 5652
OSSID LLC—See Leonard Green & Partners, L.P.; *U.S. Private*, pg. 2428
OSS IM VIEW INC.—See Creative Vistas Inc.; *Int'l*, pg. 1834
OSSIPEE AGGREGATES CORP—See Boston Sand & Gravel Company; *U.S. Public*, pg. 373
OSSIPEE CORPORATION—See Zimmer Biomet Holdings, Inc.; *U.S. Public*, pg. 2406
OS SOLUTIONS SDN. BHD.—See Evd Berhad; *Int'l*, pg. 2561
OSSTEM AUTRALIA PTY. LTD.—See MBK Partners Ltd.; *Int'l*, pg. 4753
OSSTEM AUTRALIA PTY. LTD.—See Unison Capital, Inc.; *Int'l*, pg. 8061
OSSTEM BANGLADESH LTD.—See MBK Partners Ltd.; *Int'l*, pg. 4753
OSSTEM BANGLADESH LTD.—See Unison Capital, Inc.; *Int'l*, pg. 8061
OSSTEM CHINA CO., LTD.—See MBK Partners Ltd.; *Int'l*, pg. 4753
OSSTEM CHINA CO., LTD.—See Unison Capital, Inc.; *Int'l*, pg. 8061
OSSTEM CO., LTD.—See MBK Partners Ltd.; *Int'l*, pg. 4753
OSSTEM CO., LTD.—See Unison Capital, Inc.; *Int'l*, pg. 8061
OSSTEM CORPORATION—See MBK Partners Ltd.; *Int'l*, pg. 4753
OSSTEM CORPORATION—See Unison Capital, Inc.; *Int'l*, pg. 8061
OSSTEM HONG KONG LTD.—See MBK Partners Ltd.; *Int'l*, pg. 4753
OSSTEM HONG KONG LTD.—See Unison Capital, Inc.; *Int'l*, pg. 8061
OSSTEM IMPLANT BRASIL LTDA.—See MBK Partners Ltd.; *Int'l*, pg. 4753
OSSTEM IMPLANT BRASIL LTDA.—See Unison Capital, Inc.; *Int'l*, pg. 8061
OSSTEM IMPLANT CO., LTD.—See MBK Partners Ltd.; *Int'l*, pg. 4753
OSSTEM IMPLANT CO., LTD.—See Unison Capital, Inc.; *Int'l*, pg. 8061
OSSTEM IMPLANT DIS TIC. A.S.—See MBK Partners Ltd.; *Int'l*, pg. 4753
OSSTEM IMPLANT DIS TIC. A.S.—See Unison Capital, Inc.; *Int'l*, pg. 8061
OSSTEM IMPLANT INDIA PVT. LTD.—See MBK Partners Ltd.; *Int'l*, pg. 4753
OSSTEM IMPLANT INDIA PVT. LTD.—See Unison Capital, Inc.; *Int'l*, pg. 8061
OSSTEM IMPLANT LLP—See MBK Partners Ltd.; *Int'l*, pg. 4753
OSSTEM IMPLANT LLP—See Unison Capital, Inc.; *Int'l*, pg. 8061
OSSTEM IMPLANT SPAIN S.L.—See MBK Partners Ltd.; *Int'l*, pg. 4753
OSSTEM IMPLANT SPAIN S.L.—See Unison Capital, Inc.; *Int'l*, pg. 8061
OSSTEM IMPLANT VINA CO., LTD.—See MBK Partners Ltd.; *Int'l*, pg. 4753
OSSTEM IMPLANT VINA CO., LTD.—See Unison Capital, Inc.; *Int'l*, pg. 8061
OSSTEM JAPAN CORP.—See MBK Partners Ltd.; *Int'l*, pg. 4753
OSSTEM JAPAN CORP.—See Unison Capital, Inc.; *Int'l*, pg. 8061
OSSTEM LLC—See MBK Partners Ltd.; *Int'l*, pg. 4753
OSSTEM LLC—See Unison Capital, Inc.; *Int'l*, pg. 8061
OSSTEM MALAYSIA SDN. BHD.—See MBK Partners Ltd.; *Int'l*, pg. 4753
OSSTEM MALAYSIA SDN. BHD.—See Unison Capital, Inc.; *Int'l*, pg. 8061

OSSTEM MIDDLE EAST FZCO—See MBK Partners Ltd.; *Int'l*, pg. 4753
OSSTEM MIDDLE EAST FZCO—See Unison Capital, Inc.; *Int'l*, pg. 8061
OSSTEM MONGOL LLC—See MBK Partners Ltd.; *Int'l*, pg. 4753
OSSTEM MONGOL LLC—See Unison Capital, Inc.; *Int'l*, pg. 8061
OSSTEM NEW ZEALAND LIMITED—See MBK Partners Ltd.; *Int'l*, pg. 4753
OSSTEM NEW ZEALAND LIMITED—See Unison Capital, Inc.; *Int'l*, pg. 8061
OSSTEM PHILIPPINES INC.—See MBK Partners Ltd.; *Int'l*, pg. 4753
OSSTEM PHILIPPINES INC.—See Unison Capital, Inc.; *Int'l*, pg. 8061
OSSTEM SINGAPORE PTE. LTD.—See MBK Partners Ltd.; *Int'l*, pg. 4753
OSSTEM SINGAPORE PTE. LTD.—See Unison Capital, Inc.; *Int'l*, pg. 8061
OSSTEM SOUTH CHINA CO., LTD.—See MBK Partners Ltd.; *Int'l*, pg. 4753
OSSTEM SOUTH CHINA CO., LTD.—See Unison Capital, Inc.; *Int'l*, pg. 8061
OSSTEM UAH LLC—See MBK Partners Ltd.; *Int'l*, pg. 4753
OSSTEM UAH LLC—See Unison Capital, Inc.; *Int'l*, pg. 8061
OS SUPPORT CO., LTD.—See Bain Capital, LP; *U.S. Private*, pg. 434
OS SUPPORT, INC.; *U.S. Private*, pg. 3046
OSSUR ASIA PACIFIC PTY. LTD.—See Ossur hf; *Int'l*, pg. 5653
OSSUR CANADA, INC—See Ossur hf; *Int'l*, pg. 5653
OSSUR EUROPE B.V.—See Ossur hf; *Int'l*, pg. 5653
OSSUR HF; *Int'l*, pg. 5652
OSSUR IBERIA S.A.—See Ossur hf; *Int'l*, pg. 5653
OSSUR ICELAND EHF—See Ossur hf; *Int'l*, pg. 5653
OSSUR INDIA PVT. LTD.—See Ossur hf; *Int'l*, pg. 5653
OSSUR JAPAN G.K.—See Ossur hf; *Int'l*, pg. 5653
OSSUR NEW ZEALAND LIMITED—See Ossur hf; *Int'l*, pg. 5653
OSSUR NORDIC, AB—See Ossur hf; *Int'l*, pg. 5653
OSSUR RETAIL—See Ossur hf; *Int'l*, pg. 5653
OSSUR SCHWEIZ AG—See Ossur hf; *Int'l*, pg. 5653
OSSUR SOUTH AFRICA PTY. LTD.—See Ossur hf; *Int'l*, pg. 5653
OSTANKINSKY MEAT PROCESSING PLANT OJSC; *Int'l*, pg. 5653
OSTARA LLC—See Onexim Group Limited; *Int'l*, pg. 5581
OSTARA GRUPO HOTELERO—See Grupo Carso, S.A.B. de C.V.; *Int'l*, pg. 3123
OST AS—See Veidekke ASA; *Int'l*, pg. 8148
O.S.T.C LIMITED—See BGC Group, Inc.; *U.S. Public*, pg. 330
OSTEC ENTERPRISE LTD.—See ESPEC Corp.; *Int'l*, pg. 2505
O'STEEL BUILDINGS, INC.; *U.S. Private*, pg. 2980
O'STEEN BROTHERS INC.; *U.S. Private*, pg. 2980
OSTEEN PUBLISHING COMPANY; *U.S. Private*, pg. 3048
O'STEEN VOLVO; *U.S. Private*, pg. 2980
OSTEOMED CORPORATION—See Berkshire Hathaway Inc.; *U.S. Public*, pg. 308
OSTEOMETER MEDITECH, INC.—See OSI Systems, Inc.; *U.S. Public*, pg. 1621
OSTEONIC CO., LTD.; *Int'l*, pg. 5653
OSTEOPORE INTERNATIONAL PTE LTD.—See Osteopore Limited; *Int'l*, pg. 5653
OSTEOPORE LIMITED; *Int'l*, pg. 5653
OSTEOTECH, INC.—See Medtronic plc; *Int'l*, pg. 4790
OSTER COMMUNICATIONS INC.; *U.S. Private*, pg. 3048
OSTERGAARD A/S—See Per Aarsleff Holding A/S; *Int'l*, pg. 5796
OSTER GMBH—See Newell Brands Inc.; *U.S. Public*, pg. 1514
OSTERIA GAMBERONI SDN. BHD.—See Advance Synergy Berhad; *Int'l*, pg. 166
THE OSTERKAMP GROUP; *U.S. Private*, pg. 4089
OSTERKAMP TRUCKING INC.—See The Osterkamp Group; *U.S. Private*, pg. 4089
OSTERLINDS EL-AGENTUR AB—See Amplex AB; *Int'l*, pg. 434
OSTERMAN & CO. INC.; *U.S. Private*, pg. 3048
OSTERMANCRON, INC.; *U.S. Private*, pg. 3048
OSTERMAN PROPANE, LLC—See NGL Energy Partners LP; *U.S. Public*, pg. 1527
OSTERMAN'S INC.—See Signet Jewelers Limited; *Int'l*, pg. 6911
OSTERNA LIMITED—See Places for People Group Limited; *Int'l*, pg. 5888
OSTERN FOODS CO., LTD.—See Kobe Bussan Co., Ltd.; *Int'l*, pg. 4217
OSTERREICHISCHE BETEILIGUNGS AG; *Int'l*, pg. 5653
OSTERREICHISCHE POST AG; *Int'l*, pg. 5653
OSTERREICHISCHE RUBENSAMENZUCHT GESELLSCHAFT M.B.H.—See AGRANA Beteiligungs-AG; *Int'l*, pg. 214
OSTERREICHISCHE STAATSDRUCKEREI GMBH; *Int'l*, pg. 5654

OSTERREICHISCHES VERKEHRSBURO AKTIENGESELLSCHAFT—See Vienna Insurance Group AG Wiener Versicherung Gruppe; *Int'l*, pg. 8195
OSTERREICHISCHE VOLKSBANKEN AG; *Int'l*, pg. 5654
OSTFRIESISCHE TEE GESELLSCHAFT LAURENS SPETHMANN GMBH & CO. KG—See Laurens Spethmann Holding Aktiengesellschaft & Co. KG; *Int'l*, pg. 4424
OS (THAILAND) CO., LTD.—See Bain Capital, LP; *U.S. Private*, pg. 434
OSTIM ENDUSTRIYEL YATIRIMLAR VE ISLETME AS; *Int'l*, pg. 5654
OSTIN TECHNOLOGY GROUP CO., LTD.; *Int'l*, pg. 5655
OST JAPAN GROUP INC.—See Fuji Yakuhin Co., Ltd.; *Int'l*, pg. 2817
OSTNOR AB; *Int'l*, pg. 5655
OSTNOR ASIA LTD—See Ostnor AB; *Int'l*, pg. 5655
OSTNOR DANMARK A/S—See Ostnor AB; *Int'l*, pg. 5655
OSTNOR FINLAND OY—See Ostnor AB; *Int'l*, pg. 5655
OSTNOR NORGE AS—See Ostnor AB; *Int'l*, pg. 5655
OSTOMYCURE AS—See Kistefos AS; *Int'l*, pg. 4193
OSTOOL AL-NAQIL CO.—See Saudi Automotive Services Co.; *Int'l*, pg. 6590
OSTOOL FOR LAND TRANSPORT COMPANY—See Raya Holding Company; *Int'l*, pg. 6223
OST PROSJEKT AS—See Sparebanken Ost; *Int'l*, pg. 7125
OSTRAKON CAPITAL LTD.; *Int'l*, pg. 5655
OSTRODA YACHT SP. Z O.O.—See Beneteau S.A; *Int'l*, pg. 972
OSTROM CLIMATE SOLUTIONS INC.; *Int'l*, pg. 5655
OSTROM MUSHROOM FARMS LLC—See AGF Management Limited; *Int'l*, pg. 207
OSTROM MUSHROOM FARMS LLC—See Instar Group Inc.; *Int'l*, pg. 3723
OSTROW ELECTRICAL CO. INC.; *U.S. Private*, pg. 3048
OSTROW REISIN BERK & ABRAMS, LTD.—See Lingaro Sp z o.o; *Int'l*, pg. 4512
OSTSEE FISCH GMBH—See Thai Union Group Public Company Limited; *Int'l*, pg. 7596
OSTSEE MINERALOL-BUNKER GMBH—See Marquard & Bahls AG; *Int'l*, pg. 4700
OSTSEE RESORT DAMP GMBH—See Fresenius SE & Co. KGaA; *Int'l*, pg. 2780
OST S.R.L.—See WAMGROUP S.p.A.; *Int'l*, pg. 8338
OSTTHURINGER WASSER UND ABWASSER GMBH—See Veolia Environnement S.A.; *Int'l*, pg. 8153
OST TRUCKING COMPANY INC.; *U.S. Private*, pg. 3048
OST-WEST CARGO BALTIC UAB—See Die Schweizerische Post AG; *Int'l*, pg. 2113
OST-WEST CARGO EUROPE GMBH—See Die Schweizerische Post AG; *Int'l*, pg. 2113
OST-WEST CARGO TRANSPORT UAB—See Die Schweizerische Post AG; *Int'l*, pg. 2113
OSUDIO NORDICS APS—See DBAY Advisors Limited; *Int'l*, pg. 1987
OSUGA GAS SERVICE, LTD.—See TOKAI Holdings Corporation; *Int'l*, pg. 7779
O'SULLIVAN COMMUNICATIONS; *U.S. Private*, pg. 2981
O'SULLIVAN FILMS, INC.—See Continental Aktiengesellschaft; *Int'l*, pg. 1780
OSVAH PHARMACEUTICAL COMPANY; *Int'l*, pg. 5655
OS VIETNAM CO., LTD.—See Bain Capital, LP; *U.S. Private*, pg. 435
OSWAL AGRO MILLS LTD.; *Int'l*, pg. 5655
OSWALD COMPANIES; *U.S. Private*, pg. 3048
OSWALD HOMES PTY LTD—See JWH Group Pty Ltd; *Int'l*, pg. 4035
OSWALD METZEN GMBH; *Int'l*, pg. 5655
OSWALD TILLOTSON LIMITED—See Heidelberg Materials AG; *Int'l*, pg. 3318
OSWAL GREENTECH LIMITED; *Int'l*, pg. 5655
O.S. WALKER CO. INC.—See Alliance Holdings, Inc.; *U.S. Private*, pg. 183
OSWAL LEASING LIMITED—See Oswal Woollen Mills Limited; *Int'l*, pg. 5655
OSWAL OVERSEAS LIMITED; *Int'l*, pg. 5655
OSWAL SPINNING & WEAVING MILLS LIMITED; *Int'l*, pg. 5655
OSWAL WOOLLEN MILLS LIMITED; *Int'l*, pg. 5655
OSWAL YARNS LIMITED; *Int'l*, pg. 5655
OSWEGO HARBOR POWER LLC—See NRG Energy, Inc.; *U.S. Public*, pg. 1550
OSWEGO VALLEY INSURANCE AGENCIES LLC; *U.S. Private*, pg. 3048
OSW EQUIPMENT & REPAIR, LLC—See Federal Signal Corporation; *U.S. Public*, pg. 826
OSWORTH NIGERIA LIMITED—See May & Baker Nigeria Plc.; *Int'l*, pg. 4743
OSX BRASIL SA—See EBX Group Ltd.; *Int'l*, pg. 2287
OSYKA CORPORATION; *U.S. Public*, pg. 1622
OTA BROADCASTING, LLC; *U.S. Private*, pg. 3048
OTACO SEATING CO.—See American Seating Company; *U.S. Private*, pg. 247
OTA DANBORU CO., LTD.—See Tomoku Co., Ltd.; *Int'l*, pg. 7801
OTA FLORICULTURE AUCTION CO., LTD.; *Int'l*, pg. 5656
OTAGO SOUTHLAND WASTE SERVICES LTD—See Trojan Holdings Ltd.; *Int'l*, pg. 7938

COMPANY NAME INDEX

OTAKE CORPORATION; *Int'l*, pg. 5656
OTAKI GAS CO., LTD.—See K&O Energy Group Inc.; *Int'l*, pg. 4038
OTAK, INC.; *U.S. Private*, pg. 3048
OTAKI SANGYO CO., LTD.—See K&O Energy Group Inc.; *Int'l*, pg. 4038
OTAK JAPAN INC.—See HanmiGlobal Co., LTD.; *Int'l*, pg. 3257
OTANI KOGYO CO., LTD.; *Int'l*, pg. 5656
OTANI STEEL CORPORATION INC.—See SEC Carbon, Limited; *Int'l*, pg. 6670
O-TA PRECISION INDUSTRY CO., LTD.; *Int'l*, pg. 5502
OTARI GAC CO., LTD—See Denso Corporation; *Int'l*, pg. 2032
OTARI, INC. - MATSUMOTO FACTORY—See Otari, Inc.; *Int'l*, pg. 5656
OTARI, INC.; *Int'l*, pg. 5656
OTARITEC CORPORATION—See Otari, Inc.; *Int'l*, pg. 5656
O'TASTY FOODS, INC.; *U.S. Private*, pg. 2981
OTAVA BOOK PRINTING LTD—See Otava Ltd.; *Int'l*, pg. 5656
OTAVA, LLC—See Schurz Communications, Inc.; *U.S. Private*, pg. 3571
OTAVA LTD.; *Int'l*, pg. 5656
OTAY LAND COMPANY, LLC—See Jefferies Financial Group Inc.; *U.S. Public*, pg. 1188
OTAY TENANT LLC—See Welltower Inc.; *U.S. Public*, pg. 2349
OTBASY BANK JSC; *Int'l*, pg. 5656
OTC BRANDS, INC.—See Berkshire Hathaway Inc.; *U.S. Public*, pg. 313
OTC COMMODITY MARKETS, LLC—See Intercontinental Exchange, Inc.; *U.S. Public*, pg. 1143
OTC DAIHEN ASIA CO., LTD.—See Daihen Corporation; *Int'l*, pg. 1926
OTC DAIHEN EUROPE GMBH—See Daihen Corporation; *Int'l*, pg. 1926
OTC DAIHEN INDIA PVT. LTD.—See Daihen Corporation; *Int'l*, pg. 1926
OTC DIRECT LTD.—See Walgreens Boots Alliance, Inc.; *U.S. Public*, pg. 2322
OTC EXCHANGE OF INDIA; *Int'l*, pg. 5656
OTC INDUSTRIAL (QINGDAO) CO., LTD.—See Daihen Corporation; *Int'l*, pg. 1926
OTC INDUSTRIAL (SHANGHAI) CO., LTD.—See Daihen Corporation; *Int'l*, pg. 1926
OTC INTERNATIONAL, LTD.; *U.S. Private*, pg. 3049
OTC MARKETS GROUP INC.; *U.S. Public*, pg. 1622
OTCO INTERNATIONAL LTD.; *Int'l*, pg. 5656
OTC PHARMA-VERTRIEB GMBH; *Int'l*, pg. 5656
OTC (TAIWAN) CO., LTD.—See Daihen Corporation; *Int'l*, pg. 1926
O.T. DRESCHER AG—See Exela Technologies, Inc.; *U.S. Public*, pg. 806
OTE ACADEMY S.A.—See Hellenic Telecommunications Organization S.A.; *Int'l*, pg. 3333
OTEAC LIMITED—See Lonsdale Capital Partners LLP; *Int'l*, pg. 4552
OTEC CORPORATION; *Int'l*, pg. 5656
OTEC (THAILAND) CO., LTD.—See Mitsubishi Materials Corporation; *Int'l*, pg. 4965
OTE ESTATE S.A.—See Hellenic Telecommunications Organization S.A.; *Int'l*, pg. 3334
O.T.E INGENIERIE; *Int'l*, pg. 5503
OTE INTERNATIONAL SOLUTIONS S.A.—See Hellenic Telecommunications Organization S.A.; *Int'l*, pg. 3334
OTEKS AD; *Int'l*, pg. 5656
OTELCO INC.—See Keystone Group, L.P.; *U.S. Private*, pg. 2299
OTELCO TELECOMMUNICATIONS LLC—See Keystone Group, L.P.; *U.S. Private*, pg. 2299
OTELLO CORPORATION ASA; *Int'l*, pg. 5656
OTEMACHI FIRST SQUARE INC.—See Nippon Telegraph & Telephone Corporation; *Int'l*, pg. 5355
OT ENERGY SERVICES A.S.; *Int'l*, pg. 5655
OTE PLUS TECHNICAL & BUSINESS SOLUTIONS S.A.—See Hellenic Telecommunications Organization S.A.; *Int'l*, pg. 3334
OTERA CAPITAL, INC.—See Caisse de Depot et Placement du Quebec; *Int'l*, pg. 1254
OTERO COUNTY ELECTRIC COOP; *U.S. Private*, pg. 3049
OTESSA—See Groupe Crit, S.A.; *Int'l*, pg. 3101
OTEY WHITE & ASSOCIATES; *U.S. Private*, pg. 3049
OTG EXP, INC.; *U.S. Private*, pg. 3049
OT HAPAG-LLOYD FINLAND AB—See Albert Ballin KG; *Int'l*, pg. 296
OTHELLO INC.—See Allied Architects, Inc.; *Int'l*, pg. 356
O, THE OPRAH MAGAZINE—See The Hearst Corporation; *U.S. Private*, pg. 4046
OTHER ART FAIRS AUSTRALIA PTY LTD—See Graham Holdings Company; *U.S. Public*, pg. 956
OTHER ART FAIRS LTD—See Graham Holdings Company; *U.S. Public*, pg. 956
OTHERLEVELS HOLDINGS LIMITED; *Int'l*, pg. 5656
OTHERLEVELS PTY LIMITED—See OtherLevels Holdings Limited; *Int'l*, pg. 5657

THE OTHER ROOF PTE. LTD.—See TSH Corporation Limited; *Int'l*, pg. 7950
THE OTHER ROOM PTE. LTD.—See TSH Corporation Limited; *Int'l*, pg. 7950
OTHER WORLD COMPUTING; *U.S. Private*, pg. 3049
OTHMARSCHEN PARK HAMBURG GMBH & CO. CENTERPARK KG—See UniCredit S.p.A.; *Int'l*, pg. 8035
OTHMARSCHEN PARK HAMBURG GMBH & CO. GEWERBEPARK KG—See UniCredit S.p.A.; *Int'l*, pg. 8035
OTI AFRICA (PTY) LTD.—See On Track Innovations, Ltd.; *Int'l*, pg. 5573
OTI AMERICA INC.—See On Track Innovations, Ltd.; *Int'l*, pg. 5573
OTICON AB—See Demant A/S; *Int'l*, pg. 2024
OTICON AS—See Demant A/S; *Int'l*, pg. 2024
OTICON A/S—See Demant A/S; *Int'l*, pg. 2024
OTICON AUSTRALIA PTY. LTD.—See Demant A/S; *Int'l*, pg. 2024
OTICON CANADA LTD.—See Demant A/S; *Int'l*, pg. 2024
OTICON DENMARK A/S—See Demant A/S; *Int'l*, pg. 2024
OTICON ESPANA S.A.—See Demant A/S; *Int'l*, pg. 2024
OTICON GMBH—See Demant A/S; *Int'l*, pg. 2024
OTICON, INC.—See Demant A/S; *Int'l*, pg. 2024
OTICON ITALIA S.R.L.—See Demant A/S; *Int'l*, pg. 2024
OTICON K.K.—See Demant A/S; *Int'l*, pg. 2024
OTICON KOREA CO. LTD.—See Demant A/S; *Int'l*, pg. 2024
OTICON LIMITED—See Demant A/S; *Int'l*, pg. 2024
OTICON MALAYSIA SDN—See Demant A/S; *Int'l*, pg. 2024
OTICON MEDICAL AB—See Demant A/S; *Int'l*, pg. 2024
OTICON MEDICAL A/S—See Demant A/S; *Int'l*, pg. 2024
OTICON MEDICAL MAROC—See Demant A/S; *Int'l*, pg. 2024
OTICON NEDERLAND B.V.—See Demant A/S; *Int'l*, pg. 2024
OTICON NEW ZEALAND LTD.—See Demant A/S; *Int'l*, pg. 2024
OTICON POLSKA PRODUCTION SP. Z O.O.—See Demant A/S; *Int'l*, pg. 2024
OTICON POLSKA SP. Z O.O.—See Demant A/S; *Int'l*, pg. 2024
OTICON S.A.—See Demant A/S; *Int'l*, pg. 2024
OTICON SHANGHAI HEARING TECHNOLOGY CO. LTD.—See Demant A/S; *Int'l*, pg. 2024
OTICON SINGAPORE PTE. LTD.—See Demant A/S; *Int'l*, pg. 2024
OTICON SOUTH AFRICA (PTY) LTD.—See Demant A/S; *Int'l*, pg. 2024
OTI GREENTECH AG; *Int'l*, pg. 5657
OT INDUSTRIES-DKG MACHINE MANUFACTURING CO. LTD.—See MOL Magyar Olaj- es Gazipari Nyrt.; *Int'l*, pg. 5021
OT INDUSTRIES ENGINEERING CO. LTD.—See MOL Magyar Olaj- es Gazipari Nyrt.; *Int'l*, pg. 5021
OT INDUSTRIES-KVV CONTRACTOR CO. LTD.—See MOL Magyar Olaj- es Gazipari Nyrt.; *Int'l*, pg. 5021
OT INDUSTRIES ZRT.—See MOL Magyar Olaj- es Gazipari Nyrt.; *Int'l*, pg. 5021
OTI OPERATING, INC.—See L.B. Foster Company; *U.S. Public*, pg. 1279
OTI PETROSMART (PTY) LTD.—See On Track Innovations, Ltd.; *Int'l*, pg. 5573
OTIS AB—See Otis Worldwide Corporation; *U.S. Public*, pg. 1623
OTIS & AHEARN INC.; *U.S. Private*, pg. 3049
OTIS A.S.—See Otis Worldwide Corporation; *U.S. Public*, pg. 1623
OTIS CANADA, INC.—See Otis Worldwide Corporation; *U.S. Public*, pg. 1623
OTIS EASTERN SERVICE, INC.—See Clayton, Dubilier & Rice, LLC; *U.S. Private*, pg. 919
OTIS ELEVATOR (CHINA) COMPANY LIMITED—See Otis Worldwide Corporation; *U.S. Public*, pg. 1623
OTIS ELEVATOR (CHINA) INVESTMENT COMPANY LIMITED—See Otis Worldwide Corporation; *U.S. Public*, pg. 1623
OTIS ELEVATOR COMPANY (INDIA) LIMITED—See Otis Worldwide Corporation; *U.S. Public*, pg. 1623
OTIS ELEVATOR COMPANY - PITTSBURGH—See Otis Worldwide Corporation; *U.S. Public*, pg. 1623
OTIS ELEVATOR COMPANY—See Otis Worldwide Corporation; *U.S. Public*, pg. 1622
OTIS ELEVATOR COMPANY (TAIWAN) LIMITED—See Otis Worldwide Corporation; *U.S. Public*, pg. 1623
OTIS ELEVATOR CO. PTY. LTD.—See Otis Worldwide Corporation; *U.S. Public*, pg. 1623
OTIS ELEVATOR LIMITED—See Otis Worldwide Corporation; *U.S. Public*, pg. 1623
OTIS GESELLSCHAFT M.B.H.—See Otis Worldwide Corporation; *U.S. Public*, pg. 1623
OTIS GMBH & CO. OHG—See Otis Worldwide Corporation; *U.S. Public*, pg. 1623
OTIS GMBH & CO. OHG—See Otis Worldwide Corporation; *U.S. Public*, pg. 1623
OTIS GOLD CORP.—See Excellon Resources Inc.; *Int'l*, pg. 2578
OTIS HOLDINGS GMBH & CO. OHG—See Otis Worldwide Corporation; *U.S. Public*, pg. 1623

OTP BANK PLC

OTISIFARM AO; *Int'l*, pg. 5657
OTIS INTERNATIONAL HOLDINGS GMBH—See Otis Worldwide Corporation; *U.S. Public*, pg. 1623
OTIS INVESTMENTS LIMITED—See Otis Worldwide Corporation; *U.S. Public*, pg. 1623
OTIS LIMITED—See Otis Worldwide Corporation; *U.S. Public*, pg. 1623
OTIS-MAGIE INSURANCE AGENCY, INC.—See Marsh & McLennan Companies, Inc.; *U.S. Public*, pg. 1381
OTIS PACIFIC HOLDINGS B.V.—See Otis Worldwide Corporation; *U.S. Public*, pg. 1623
OTIS S.A.—See Otis Worldwide Corporation; *U.S. Public*, pg. 1623
OTIS S.C.S.—See Otis Worldwide Corporation; *U.S. Public*, pg. 1623
OTIS SERVIZ, S.R.L.—See Otis Worldwide Corporation; *U.S. Public*, pg. 1623
OTIS TECHNOLOGY, INC.; *U.S. Private*, pg. 3049
OTIS WORLDWIDE CORPORATION; *U.S. Public*, pg. 1622
OTIX GLOBAL, INC.—See Demant A/S; *Int'l*, pg. 2024
OTKRITIE HOLDING JSC—See Central Bank of the Russian Federation; *Int'l*, pg. 1405
OTL ASIA SDN. BHD.—See Yamato Holdings Co., Ltd.; *Int'l*, pg. 8554
OT-LAS SRL—See El.En. S.p.A.; *Int'l*, pg. 2342
OT LOGISTICS S.A.; *Int'l*, pg. 5655
THE O.T. MINING CORPORATION; *U.S. Public*, pg. 2117
OT MOBILITY, INC.—See General Motors Company; *U.S. Public*, pg. 926
OTN SYSTEMS NV—See Belden, Inc.; *U.S. Public*, pg. 294
OTO DEVELOPMENT; *U.S. Private*, pg. 3049
O.T. OIL TECHNOLOGY S.R.L.—See Dana Incorporated; *U.S. Public*, pg. 623
OTOKAR EUROPE FILIALA BUCURESTI SRL—See Otokar Otomotiv ve Savunma Sanayi A.S.; *Int'l*, pg. 5657
OTOKAR EUROPE SAS—See Koc Holding A.S.; *Int'l*, pg. 4223
OTOKAR OTOBUS KAROSERI SAN AS—See Koc Holding A.S.; *Int'l*, pg. 4223
OTOKAR OTOMOTIV VE SAVUNMA SANAYI A.S.; *Int'l*, pg. 5657
OTOKOC HUNGARY KFT.—See Koc Holding A.S.; *Int'l*, pg. 4224
OTOKOC OTOMOTIV TIC. VE SAN. A.S.—See Koc Holding A.S.; *Int'l*, pg. 4224
OTOKOC SIGORTA ARACILIK HIZMETLERI A.S.—See Koc Holding A.S.; *Int'l*, pg. 4224
OTO MELARA IBERICA SA—See Leonardo S.p.A.; *Int'l*, pg. 4460
OTO MELARA NORTH AMERICA INC—See Leonardo S.p.A.; *Int'l*, pg. 4460
OTO MELARA SPA—See Leonardo S.p.A.; *Int'l*, pg. 4460
OTOMETRICS A/S—See ArchiMed SAS; *Int'l*, pg. 549
OTOMETRICS FRANCE—See ArchiMed SAS; *Int'l*, pg. 549
OTOMETRICS GMBH—See ArchiMed SAS; *Int'l*, pg. 549
OTO MILLS USA—See Marcegaglia S.p.A.; *Int'l*, pg. 4689
OTOMIX, INC.; *U.S. Private*, pg. 3049
OTOMOTIV LASTIKLERI TEVZI AS—See Continental Aktiengesellschaft; *Int'l*, pg. 1783
OTONOMO TECHNOLOGIES LTD.—See Urgent.ly, Inc.; *U.S. Public*, pg. 2266
OTONOMY, INC.; *U.S. Public*, pg. 1623
OT-OPTIMA TELEKOM D.D.; *Int'l*, pg. 5656
OTORIO LTD.—See ANDRITZ AG; *Int'l*, pg. 456
OTORI TECH CO., LTD.—See Konoike Transport Co., Ltd.; *Int'l*, pg. 4275
OTOSENSE INC.—See Analog Devices, Inc.; *U.S. Public*, pg. 136
OTOVO ASA; *Int'l*, pg. 5657
OTOYOL YATIRIM VE ISLETME A.S.—See Nurol Holding A.S.; *Int'l*, pg. 5491
OTP ASSET MANAGEMENT SAI S.A.—See OTP Bank Plc; *Int'l*, pg. 5657
OTP BANKA DIONICKO DRUSTVO—See OTP Bank Plc; *Int'l*, pg. 5658
OTP BANKA HRVATSKA D.D—See OTP Bank Plc; *Int'l*, pg. 5658
OTP BANKA SLOVENSKO, A.S.—See KBC Group NV; *Int'l*, pg. 4106
OTP BANKA SRBIJA A.D—See OTP Bank Plc; *Int'l*, pg. 5658
OTP BANK PLC; *Int'l*, pg. 5657
OTP BANK ROMANIA S.A.—See Banca Transilvania S.A.; *Int'l*, pg. 816
OTP BANK S.A.—See OTP Bank Plc; *Int'l*, pg. 5657
OTP BANK UKRAINE—See OTP Bank Plc; *Int'l*, pg. 5657
OTP BUILDING SOCIETY LTD.—See OTP Bank Plc; *Int'l*, pg. 5657
OTP FACTORING ASSET MANAGEMENT LTD.—See OTP Bank Plc; *Int'l*, pg. 5657
OTP FACTORING LTD.—See OTP Bank Plc; *Int'l*, pg. 5657
OTP FACTORING ROMANIA LLC—See OTP Bank Plc; *Int'l*, pg. 5657
OTP FACTORING UKRAINE LLC—See OTP Bank Plc; *Int'l*, pg. 5657

OTP BANK PLC

CORPORATE AFFILIATIONS

OTP FUND MANAGEMENT LTD.—See OTP Bank Plc; *Int'l*, pg. 5657
OTP GEOTHERMAL POWER—See Origin Energy Ltd.; *Int'l*, pg. 5629
OTP GEOTHERMAL POWER—See Tata Power Company Limited; *Int'l*, pg. 7468
OTP HUNGARO-PROJEKT LTD.—See OTP Bank Plc; *Int'l*, pg. 5658
OTP LEASING D.O.O.—See OTP Bank Plc; *Int'l*, pg. 5658
OTP LEASING ROMANIA IFN S.A.—See OTP Bank Plc; *Int'l*, pg. 5658
OTP LIFE ANNUITY LTD.—See OTP Bank Plc; *Int'l*, pg. 5658
OTP MORTGAGE BANK LTD—See OTP Bank Plc; *Int'l*, pg. 5658
OTP OSIGURANJE AKCIONARSKO DRUSTVO ZA LLC.—See OTP Bank Plc; *Int'l*, pg. 5658
OTP REAL ESTATE LEASING LTD.—See OTP Bank Plc; *Int'l*, pg. 5658
OTP REAL ESTATE LTD.—See OTP Bank Plc; *Int'l*, pg. 5658
OTP S.A.—See Trans Polonia S.A.; *Int'l*, pg. 7894
OTP TRAVEL LTD.—See OTP Bank Plc; *Int'l*, pg. 5658
OTRACO INTERNATIONAL PTY LIMITED—See Bridgestone Corporation; *Int'l*, pg. 1159
OTRACOM PTY LTD.—See Downer EDI Limited; *Int'l*, pg. 2186
OTR ACQUISITION CORP.; *U.S. Public*, pg. 1623
OTRA NV—See Sonepar S.A.; *Int'l*, pg. 7092
OTRA VASTGOED—See Sonepar S.A.; *Int'l*, pg. 7092
O. TREVINO CONSTRUCTION, LLC.; *U.S. Private*, pg. 2981
OTR GLOBAL LLC—See Infinedi Partners LP; *U.S. Private*, pg. 2070
OT-RHEIN-MAIN GMBH—See Asklepios Kliniken GmbH & Co. KGaA; *Int'l*, pg. 624
OTR MAKINA SANAYI VE TICARET LTD STI.—See Okuma Corporation; *Int'l*, pg. 5550
OTR OBERFLACHENTECHNIK GMBH—See Fielmann Group AG; *Int'l*, pg. 2659
OTRS AG; *Int'l*, pg. 5658
OTRS INC.—See OTRS AG; *Int'l*, pg. 5658
OTRS LTD.—See OTRS AG; *Int'l*, pg. 5658
OTRS S.A. DE C.V.—See OTRS AG; *Int'l*, pg. 5658
OTRS SDN. BHD.—See OTRS AG; *Int'l*, pg. 5658
OTR WHEEL ENGINEERING, INC.; *U.S. Private*, pg. 3049
OTS BRATISLAVA, SPOL. S.R.O.—See Loxam SAS; *Int'l*, pg. 4566
OTS CO., LTD.—See Origin Co., Ltd.; *Int'l*, pg. 5629
OTS CORPORATION—See Patient Square Capital, L.P.; *U.S. Private*, pg. 3107
OTSEGO MEMORIAL HOSPITAL ASSOCIATION; *U.S. Private*, pg. 3049
OTSEGO PAPER, INC.—See Gebr. Knauf KG; *Int'l*, pg. 2908
OTS GESELLSCHAFT ZUM VERTRIEB ELEKTRONISCHER EINTRITTSKARTEN MBH—See CTS Eventim AG & Co. KGAA; *Int'l*, pg. 1873
OTS INC.—See Bain Capital, LP; *U.S. Private*, pg. 435
OTS INTERNATIONAL, INC.—See J Fitzgibbons LLC; *U.S. Private*, pg. 2153
OTSO GOLD CORP; *Int'l*, pg. 5658
OTSUKA AMERICA FOODS INC.—See Otsuka Holdings Co., Ltd.; *Int'l*, pg. 5660
OTSUKA AMERICA, INC.—See Otsuka Holdings Co., Ltd.; *Int'l*, pg. 5660
OTSUKA AMERICA MANUFACTURING, LLC—See Otsuka Holdings Co., Ltd.; *Int'l*, pg. 5660
OTSUKA AMERICA PHARMACEUTICAL, INC.—See Otsuka Holdings Co., Ltd.; *Int'l*, pg. 5659
OTSUKA CANADA PHARMACEUTICAL INC—See Otsuka Holdings Co., Ltd.; *Int'l*, pg. 5660
OTSUKA CHEMICAL CO., LTD.—See Otsuka Holdings Co., Ltd.; *Int'l*, pg. 5659
OTSUKA CHEMICAL DO BRASIL LTDA.—See Otsuka Holdings Co., Ltd.; *Int'l*, pg. 5659
OTSUKA CHEMICAL (INDIA) PRIVATE LIMITED—See Otsuka Holdings Co., Ltd.; *Int'l*, pg. 5659
OTSUKA CHILLED FOODS CO., LTD.—See Otsuka Holdings Co., Ltd.; *Int'l*, pg. 5659
OTSUKA (CHINA) INVESTMENT CO., LTD.—See Otsuka Holdings Co., Ltd.; *Int'l*, pg. 5659
OTSUKA CORPORATION; *Int'l*, pg. 5658
OTSUKA ELECTRIC CO., LTD.—See Kaga Electronics Co., Ltd.; *Int'l*, pg. 4049
OTSUKA ELECTRONICS CO., LTD.—See Otsuka Holdings Co., Ltd.; *Int'l*, pg. 5660
OTSUKA ELECTRONICS KOREA CO., LTD.—See Otsuka Holdings Co., Ltd.; *Int'l*, pg. 5660
OTSUKA ELECTRONICS (SUZHOU) CO., LTD.—See Otsuka Holdings Co., Ltd.; *Int'l*, pg. 5660
OTSUKA FOODS CO., LTD.—See Otsuka Holdings Co., Ltd.; *Int'l*, pg. 5659
OTSUKA FRANKFURT RESEARCH INSTITUTE GMBH—See Otsuka Holdings Co., Ltd.; *Int'l*, pg. 5660
OTSUKA HOLDINGS CO., LTD.; *Int'l*, pg. 5658
OTSUKA INFORMATION TECHNOLOGY CORP.; *Int'l*, pg. 5661

OTSUKA KAGU, LTD.—See Yamada Holdings Co., Ltd.; *Int'l*, pg. 8548
OTSUKA MARYLAND MEDICINAL LABORATORIES, INC.—See Otsuka Holdings Co., Ltd.; *Int'l*, pg. 5660
OTSUKA MEDICAL DEVICES CO., LTD.—See Earth Corporation; *Int'l*, pg. 2268
OTSUKA-MGC CHEMICAL COMPANY, INC.—See Earth Corporation; *Int'l*, pg. 2268
OTSUKA NOVEL PRODUCTS GMBH—See Otsuka Holdings Co., Ltd.; *Int'l*, pg. 5659
OTSUKA OHMI CERAMICS CO., LTD.—See Otsuka Holdings Co., Ltd.; *Int'l*, pg. 5660
OTSUKA PACKAGING INDUSTRIES CO., LTD.—See Otsuka Holdings Co., Ltd.; *Int'l*, pg. 5660
OTSUKA PACKAGING INDUSTRIES LTD.—See Otsuka Holdings Co., Ltd.; *Int'l*, pg. 5660
OTSUKA PAKISTAN LTD.—See Otsuka Holdings Co., Ltd.; *Int'l*, pg. 5659
OTSUKA PHARMACEUTICAL CO., LTD.—See Otsuka Holdings Co., Ltd.; *Int'l*, pg. 5659
OTSUKA PHARMACEUTICAL DEVELOPMENT & COMMERCIALIZATION, INC.—See Otsuka Holdings Co., Ltd.; *Int'l*, pg. 5660
OTSUKA PHARMACEUTICAL EUROPE, LTD.—See Otsuka Holdings Co., Ltd.; *Int'l*, pg. 5660
OTSUKA PHARMACEUTICAL FACTORY, INC.—See Otsuka Holdings Co., Ltd.; *Int'l*, pg. 5660
OTSUKA PHARMACEUTICAL FRANCE SAS—See Otsuka Holdings Co., Ltd.; *Int'l*, pg. 5660
OTSUKA PHARMACEUTICAL (H.K.) LTD.—See Otsuka Holdings Co., Ltd.; *Int'l*, pg. 5660
OTSUKA PHARMACEUTICAL INDIA PRIVATE LIMITED—See Otsuka Holdings Co., Ltd.; *Int'l*, pg. 5660
OTSUKA PHARMACEUTICAL ITALY S.R.L.—See Otsuka Holdings Co., Ltd.; *Int'l*, pg. 5660
OTSUKA PHARMACEUTICAL, S.A.—See Otsuka Holdings Co., Ltd.; *Int'l*, pg. 5660
OTSUKA PHARMACEUTICALS (U.K.) LTD.—See Otsuka Holdings Co., Ltd.; *Int'l*, pg. 5661
OTSUKA PHARMA GMBH—See Otsuka Holdings Co., Ltd.; *Int'l*, pg. 5660
OTSUKA PHARMA SCANDINAVIA AB—See Otsuka Holdings Co., Ltd.; *Int'l*, pg. 5660
OTSUKA (PHILIPPINES) PHARMACEUTICAL, INC.—See Otsuka Holdings Co., Ltd.; *Int'l*, pg. 5659
OTSUKA RIDGE CO., LTD.—See Otsuka Holdings Co., Ltd.; *Int'l*, pg. 5661
OTSUKA S.A.—See Otsuka Holdings Co., Ltd.; *Int'l*, pg. 5661
OTSUKA (SHANGHAI) FOODS SAFETY RESEARCH & DEVELOPMENT CO., LTD.—See Otsuka Holdings Co., Ltd.; *Int'l*, pg. 5659
OTSUKA SIMS (GUANGDONG) BEVERAGE CO., LTD—See Otsuka Holdings Co., Ltd.; *Int'l*, pg. 5661
OTSUKA TECH ELECTRONICS CO., LTD.—See Otsuka Holdings Co., Ltd.; *Int'l*, pg. 5661
OTSUKA TECHNO CO., LTD.—See Otsuka Holdings Co., Ltd.; *Int'l*, pg. 5661
OTSUKA TURFTECH CO., LTD.—See Otsuka Holdings Co., Ltd.; *Int'l*, pg. 5661
OTSUKA WAREHOUSE CO., LTD.—See Otsuka Holdings Co., Ltd.; *Int'l*, pg. 5661
OTSUKA WELLNESS VENDING CO., LTD.—See Earth Corporation; *Int'l*, pg. 2268
OTSU PAPER BOARD CO., LTD.—See Daio Paper Corporation; *Int'l*, pg. 1940
OTSU SEIKAN CO., LTD.—See Rengo Co., Ltd.; *Int'l*, pg. 6280
OTTAKRINGER GETRANKE AG; *Int'l*, pg. 5661
OTTAUQUECHEE HYDRO COMPANY INC.—See Enel S.p.A.; *Int'l*, pg. 2414
OTTAWA AVENUE PRIVATE CAPITAL, LLC—See RDV Corporation; *U.S. Private*, pg. 3364
OTTAWA BANCORP, INC.; *U.S. Public*, pg. 1623
THE OTTAWA CITIZEN—See Chatham Asset Management, LLC; *U.S. Private*, pg. 861
OTTAWA COOPERATIVE ASSOCIATION; *U.S. Private*, pg. 3049
OTTAWA HONDA; *Int'l*, pg. 5661
OTTAWA-KENT INSURANCE AGENCY, INC.—See ABRY Partners, LLC; *U.S. Private*, pg. 42
OTTAWA MAGAZINE—See St. Joseph Communications Inc.; *Int'l*, pg. 7159
OTTAWA OIL COMPANY—See Jay Petroleum, Inc.; *U.S. Private*, pg. 2192
OTTAWA PUBLISHING CO., LLC—See Small Newspaper Group Inc.; *U.S. Private*, pg. 3690
OTTAWA RUBBER COMPANY; *U.S. Private*, pg. 3049
OTTAWA SENATORS HOCKEY CLUB—See Capital Sports Group of Companies; *Int'l*, pg. 1312
THE OTTAWA SUN—See Chatham Asset Management, LLC; *U.S. Private*, pg. 861
OTTAWA VALLEY RAILWAY—See Brookfield Infrastructure Partners L.P.; *Int'l*, pg. 1192
OTTAWA VALLEY RAILWAY—See GIC Pte. Ltd.; *Int'l*, pg. 2966
OTT COMMUNICATIONS—See Keystone Group, L.P.; *U.S. Private*, pg. 2299

OTT CONSULTING INC.; *U.S. Private*, pg. 3049
OTT CONSULTING INC.—See Ott Consulting Inc.; *U.S. Private*, pg. 3049
OTTENBERGS BAKERS INC.; *U.S. Private*, pg. 3049
OTTERBASE TECHNICAL SERVICES, INC.; *U.S. Private*, pg. 3049
OTTERBEIN SENIOR LIFESTYLE CHOICES; *U.S. Private*, pg. 3049
OTTERBOX PRODUCTS LLC; *U.S. Private*, pg. 3050
OTTER CREEK COAL, LLC—See Arch Resources, Inc.; *U.S. Public*, pg. 180
OTTER FARM & HOME COOPERATIVE; *Int'l*, pg. 5661
OTTERSTEDT INSURANCE AGENCY, INC.—See Sasco Insurance Services Inc.; *U.S. Private*, pg. 3552
OTTER TAIL CORPORATION; *U.S. Public*, pg. 1624
OTTER TAIL POWER COMPANY—See Otter Tail Corporation; *U.S. Public*, pg. 1624
OTTER TAIL VALLEY RAILROAD COMPANY, INC.—See Brookfield Infrastructure Partners L.P.; *Int'l*, pg. 1192
OTTER TAIL VALLEY RAILROAD COMPANY, INC.—See GIC Pte. Ltd.; *Int'l*, pg. 2966
OTTER-WESTELAKEN GROEP B.V.—See Randstad N.V.; *Int'l*, pg. 6202
OTT FOOD PRODUCTS—See Westin Foods, Inc.; *U.S. Private*, pg. 4498
OTT HYDROMET CORP.—See Danaher Corporation; *U.S. Public*, pg. 629
OTT HYDROMET GMBH—See Danaher Corporation; *U.S. Public*, pg. 629
OTT-JAKOB SPANNTECHNIK GMBH—See Fukuda Corporation; *Int'l*, pg. 2839
OTTO BAIER ITALIANA S.R.L.—See Maschinenfabrik OTTO BAIER GmbH; *Int'l*, pg. 4721
OTTO BAUM COMPANY, INC.; *U.S. Private*, pg. 3050
OTTO BIHLER MASCHINENFABRIK GMBH & CO. KG; *Int'l*, pg. 5662
OTTO BOCK ADRIA D.O.O.—See Ottobock Holding GmbH & Co. KG; *Int'l*, pg. 5664
OTTO BOCK ADRIA SARAJEWO D.O.O.—See Ottobock Holding GmbH & Co. KG; *Int'l*, pg. 5664
OTTO BOCK ALGERIE E.U.R.L.—See Ottobock Holding GmbH & Co. KG; *Int'l*, pg. 5664
OTTO BOCK ANKARA REGIONAL OFFICE—See Ottobock Holding GmbH & Co. KG; *Int'l*, pg. 5664
OTTO BOCK ARGENTINA S.A.—See Ottobock Holding GmbH & Co. KG; *Int'l*, pg. 5664
OTTO BOCK ASIA PACIFIC LIMITED—See Ottobock Holding GmbH & Co. KG; *Int'l*, pg. 5664
OTTO BOCK AUSTRALIA PTY. LTD.—See Ottobock Holding GmbH & Co. KG; *Int'l*, pg. 5664
OTTO BOCK BULGARIA LTD.—See Ottobock Holding GmbH & Co. KG; *Int'l*, pg. 5664
OTTO BOCK CHILE S.P.A.—See Ottobock Holding GmbH & Co. KG; *Int'l*, pg. 5664
OTTOBOCK (CHINA) INDUSTRIES CO., LTD.—See Ottobock Holding GmbH & Co. KG; *Int'l*, pg. 5665
OTTO BOCK CR S.R.O.—See Ottobock Holding GmbH & Co. KG; *Int'l*, pg. 5664
OTTO BOCK DE MEXICO, S.A. DE C.V.—See Ottobock Holding GmbH & Co. KG; *Int'l*, pg. 5665
OTTO BOCK DO BRASIL TECNICA ORTOPEDICA LTDA—See Ottobock Holding GmbH & Co. KG; *Int'l*, pg. 5665
OTTO BOCK EGYPT S.A.E.—See Ottobock Holding GmbH & Co. KG; *Int'l*, pg. 5664
OTTO BOCK FRANCE S.A.R.L.—See Ottobock Holding GmbH & Co. KG; *Int'l*, pg. 5664
OTTO BOCK HEALTHCARE ANDINA LTDA.—See Ottobock Holding GmbH & Co. KG; *Int'l*, pg. 5664
OTTO BOCK HEALTHCARE CANADA LTD.—See Ottobock Holding GmbH & Co. KG; *Int'l*, pg. 5664
OTTO BOCK HEALTH CARE ECUADOR—See Ottobock Holding GmbH & Co. KG; *Int'l*, pg. 5664
OTTO BOCK HEALTHCARE GMBH—See Ottobock Holding GmbH & Co. KG; *Int'l*, pg. 5664
OTTO BOCK HEALTHCARE INDIA PVT. LTD.—See Ottobock Holding GmbH & Co. KG; *Int'l*, pg. 5664
OTTO BOCK HEALTHCARE LP—See Nader Holding GmbH & Co. KG; *Int'l*, pg. 5123
OTTO BOCK HEALTH CARE PERU—See Ottobock Holding GmbH & Co. KG; *Int'l*, pg. 5664
OTTO BOCK HEALTHCARE PLC—See Ottobock Holding GmbH & Co. KG; *Int'l*, pg. 5664
OTTO BOCK HEALTHCARE PRODUCTS GMBH—See Ottobock Holding GmbH & Co. KG; *Int'l*, pg. 5664
OTTO BOCK HEALTHCARE—See Ottobock Holding GmbH & Co. KG; *Int'l*, pg. 5664
OTTO BOCK HOLDING GMBH & CO. KG—See Ottobock Holding GmbH & Co. KG; *Int'l*, pg. 5664
OTTOBOCK HOLDING GMBH & CO. KG; *Int'l*, pg. 5664
OTTO BOCK HUNGARIA KFT.—See Ottobock Holding GmbH & Co. KG; *Int'l*, pg. 5664
OTTO BOCK IBERICA S.A.—See Ottobock Holding GmbH & Co. KG; *Int'l*, pg. 5664
OTTO BOCK ITALIA S.R.L.—See Ottobock Holding GmbH & Co. KG; *Int'l*, pg. 5664
OTTOBOCK IZMIR REGIONAL OFFICE—See Ottobock Holding GmbH & Co. KG; *Int'l*, pg. 5665

OTTO BOCK JAPAN K. K.—See Ottobock Holding GmbH & Co. KG; *Int'l*, pg. 5664
OTTOBOCK KENYA LIMITED—See Nader Holding GmbH & Co. KG; *Int'l*, pg. 5123
OTTO BOCK KOREA HEALTHCARE INC.—See Ottobock Holding GmbH & Co. KG; *Int'l*, pg. 5664
OTTOBOCK LANKA (PRIVATE) LIMITED—See Nader Holding GmbH & Co. KG; *Int'l*, pg. 5123
OTTO BOCK MANUFACTURING KONIGSEE GMBH—See Ottobock Holding GmbH & Co. KG; *Int'l*, pg. 5664
OTTO BOCK MAROC SARL—See Ottobock Holding GmbH & Co. KG; *Int'l*, pg. 5664
OTTOBOCK (MAURITIUS) LTD.—See Nader Holding GmbH & Co. KG; *Int'l*, pg. 5123
OTTO BOCK MIDDLE EAST FZ-LLC—See Nader Holding GmbH & Co. KG; *Int'l*, pg. 5123
OTTO BOCK MOSCOW—See Ottobock Holding GmbH & Co. KG; *Int'l*, pg. 5664
OTTO BOCK ORTOPEDI VE REHABILITASYON TEKNIGI LTD. STI.—See Ottobock Holding GmbH & Co. KG; *Int'l*, pg. 5664
OTTO BOCK PHILIPPINES CORP.—See Nader Holding GmbH & Co. KG; *Int'l*, pg. 5123
OTTO BOCK POLSKA SP. Z O.O—See Ottobock Holding GmbH & Co. KG; *Int'l*, pg. 5665
OTTO BOCK ROMANIA SRL—See Nader Holding GmbH & Co. KG; *Int'l*, pg. 5123
OTTO BOCK SAVA D.O.O.—See Ottobock Holding GmbH & Co. KG; *Int'l*, pg. 5665
OTTO BOCK SCANDINAVIA AB—See Ottobock Holding GmbH & Co. KG; *Int'l*, pg. 5665
OTTOBOCK SE & CO. KGAA—See Nader Holding GmbH & Co. KG; *Int'l*, pg. 5123
OTTO BOCK SLOVAKIA S.R.O.—See Ottobock Holding GmbH & Co. KG; *Int'l*, pg. 5665
OTTO BOCK SOUTH EAST ASIA CO., LTD.—See Nader Holding GmbH & Co. KG; *Int'l*, pg. 5123
OTTO BOCK SOUTHEAST ASIA CO. LTD.—See Ottobock Holding GmbH & Co. KG; *Int'l*, pg. 5665
OTTO BOCK SUISSE AG—See Ottobock Holding GmbH & Co. KG; *Int'l*, pg. 5665
OTTO BOCK VIETNAM CO., LTD.—See Nader Holding GmbH & Co. KG; *Int'l*, pg. 5123
OTTO BUCK BENELUX B.V.—See Ottobock Holding GmbH & Co. KG; *Int'l*, pg. 5665
OTTO ENERGY LIMITED; *Int'l*, pg. 5662
OTTO ENERGY (USA) INC.—See Otto Energy Limited; *Int'l*, pg. 5662
OTTO GANTER GMBH & CO. KG; *Int'l*, pg. 5662
OTTOGI AMERICA INC.—See Ottogi Corporation; *Int'l*, pg. 5665
OTTOGI CORPORATION; *Int'l*, pg. 5665
OTTOGI NEW ZEALAND LTD.—See Ottogi Corporation; *Int'l*, pg. 5665
OTTO GMBH & CO. KG; *Int'l*, pg. 5662
OTTO GROUP DIGITAL SOLUTIONS GMBH—See Otto GmbH & Co. KG; *Int'l*, pg. 5663
OTTO GROUP MEDIA GMBH—See Otto GmbH & Co. KG; *Int'l*, pg. 5663
OTTO GROUP RUSSIA OOO—See Otto GmbH & Co. KG; *Int'l*, pg. 5663
OTTO HAAS KG; *Int'l*, pg. 5664
OTTO HAUENSTEIN SAMEN AG—See Omya (Schweiz) AG; *Int'l*, pg. 5572
OTTO HEALTH, LLC—See Thoma Bravo, L.P.; *U.S. Private*, pg. 4150
OTTO INTERNATIONAL HONG KONG LTD—See Otto GmbH & Co. KG; *Int'l*, pg. 5663
OTTO INTERNATIONAL INC.; *U.S. Private*, pg. 3050
OTTO JAPAN INC.—See Otto GmbH & Co. KG; *Int'l*, pg. 5663
OTTO JUNKER GMBH; *Int'l*, pg. 5664
OTTO JUNKER METALLURGICAL EQUIPMENT (SHANGHAI) CO., LTD.—See Otto Junker GmbH; *Int'l*, pg. 5664
OTTO JUNKER (UK) LTD.—See Otto Junker GmbH; *Int'l*, pg. 5664
OTTO KUHMANN—See Sonepar S.A.; *Int'l*, pg. 7092
OTTO MANNER GMBH—See Barnes Group Inc.; *U.S. Public*, pg. 277
OTTO MANNER PRAZISIONSFORMENBAU AG, SCHWEIZ—See Barnes Group Inc.; *U.S. Public*, pg. 277
OTTOMOTORES DO BRASIL ENERGIA LTDA.—See Generac Holdings Inc.; *U.S. Public*, pg. 912
OTTOMOTORES S.A. DE C.V.—See Generac Holdings Inc.; *U.S. Public*, pg. 912
OTT-ONE PLC.; *Int'l*, pg. 5661
OTTONIA MEDIA GMBH—See Bavaria Film GmbH; *Int'l*, pg. 899
OTTO REISEN GMBH—See Otto GmbH & Co. KG; *Int'l*, pg. 5663
OTTO SCHMIDT AG—See Die Schweizerische Post AG; *Int'l*, pg. 2113
OTTO SCHNEIDER GMBH UND CO. KG; *Int'l*, pg. 5664
OTTO; *U.S. Private*, pg. 3050
OTTO—See Otto; *U.S. Private*, pg. 3050
OTTO VERSAND GMBH—See Otto GmbH & Co. KG; *Int'l*, pg. 5663

OTTO VISION TECHNOLOGY GMBH—See Jenoptik AG; *Int'l*, pg. 3929
OTTOWAY ENGINEERING PTY. LTD.—See E&A Limited; *Int'l*, pg. 2247
OTTO WOLFF U.S. SALES GMBH—See ThyssenKrupp AG; *Int'l*, pg. 7725
OTTO WORK FORCE B.V.—See Bain Capital, LP; *U.S. Private*, pg. 435
OTTO WORK FORCE CZECH S.R.O.—See Bain Capital, LP; *U.S. Private*, pg. 435
OTTO WORK FORCE ROM S.R.L.—See Bain Capital, LP; *U.S. Private*, pg. 435
OTTR, INC.—See CareDx, Inc.; *U.S. Public*, pg. 435
OTTRINGHAM LIMITED—See Hang Lung Group Limited; *Int'l*, pg. 3245
OTTUMWA COURIER—See The Retirement Systems of Alabama; *U.S. Private*, pg. 4105
OTTUMWA REGIONAL HEALTH CENTER, INC.—See Apollo Global Management, Inc.; *U.S. Public*, pg. 159
OTUS—See Veolia Environnement S.A.; *Int'l*, pg. 8153
OTUWHERO TRUSTEE LIMITED—See Marlborough Wine Estates Group Limited; *Int'l*, pg. 4698
OTV FRANCE S.N.C.—See Veolia Environnement S.A.; *Int'l*, pg. 8161
OTV TURKEY ARITMA INS.SAN.VE TIC.A.S—See Veolia Environnement S.A.; *Int'l*, pg. 8161
OTWAY ENERGY LIMITED—See Lakes Blue Energy NL; *Int'l*, pg. 4397
THE OTWAY FLY PTY. LTD.—See Merlin Entertainments plc; *Int'l*, pg. 4838
OTWAY LOGISTICS PTY. LTD.—See Singapore Post Limited; *Int'l*, pg. 6942
O TWELVE ESTATES LIMITED; *Int'l*, pg. 5502
OU AVENA NORDIC GRAIN—See Apetit Plc; *Int'l*, pg. 509
OU BALTIC WIND ENERGY—See Eolus Vind AB; *Int'l*, pg. 2457
OU BALTIKA TAILOR—See KJK Capital Oy; *Int'l*, pg. 4197
OU BALTMAN—See KJK Capital Oy; *Int'l*, pg. 4197
OUB CENTRE LIMITED—See OUE Limited; *Int'l*, pg. 5666
OU BO-SOFT—See Bang & Olufsen a/s; *Int'l*, pg. 831
OU CATELLA CORPORATE FINANCE TALLIN—See Catella AB; *Int'l*, pg. 1359
O-UCCINO INC.—See Kufu Company Inc.; *Int'l*, pg. 4326
OUDART GESTION SA—See EFG International AG; *Int'l*, pg. 2320
OUDART PATRIMOINE—See EFG International AG; *Int'l*, pg. 2320
OUDART SA—See EFG International AG; *Int'l*, pg. 2320
THE OUDH SUGAR MILLS LIMITED—See K.K. Birla Group; *Int'l*, pg. 4044
OUE COMMERCIAL REAL ESTATE INVESTMENT TRUST—See OUE Limited; *Int'l*, pg. 5666
OUE HEALTHCARE LIMITED—See OUE Limited; *Int'l*, pg. 5666
OUE HOSPITALITY TRUST—See OUE Limited; *Int'l*, pg. 5666
OU ELEKTROSKANDIA BALTICS—See Rexel, S.A.; *Int'l*, pg. 6316
OUE LIMITED; *Int'l*, pg. 5665
OUELLET CANADA INC.—See Groupe Ouellet Canada Inc.; *Int'l*, pg. 3109
OUEST BOULANGERE; *Int'l*, pg. 5666
OUEST CROISSANCE SCR SAS—See Groupe BPCE; *Int'l*, pg. 3099
OU FARBAHOUSE; *Int'l*, pg. 5665
OU FORT EHITUS—See AS Merko Ehitus; *Int'l*, pg. 590
OU FRESENIUS MEDICAL CARE ESTONIA—See Fresenius Medical Care AG; *Int'l*, pg. 2777
OUG HOLDINGS INC.; *Int'l*, pg. 5666
OU GUSTAF TALLINN—See AS Merko Ehitus; *Int'l*, pg. 590
OU HANSATEE KINNISVARA—See AS Infortar; *Int'l*, pg. 590
OU HERA SALONGID—See AS Infortar; *Int'l*, pg. 590
OU HT LAEVATEENINDUS—See AS Infortar; *Int'l*, pg. 590
OU HT MEELELAHUTUS—See AS Infortar; *Int'l*, pg. 590
OUHUA ENERGY HOLDINGS LIMITED; *Int'l*, pg. 5666
OUJOT EESTI—See Head Invest Oy; *Int'l*, pg. 3301
OU KLIIMASEADE—See NIBE Industrier AB; *Int'l*, pg. 5262
OU KOLLEGE BELEGGINGS LTD—See PSG Group Limited; *Int'l*, pg. 6016
OULA FUEL MARKETING COMPANY K.S.C.; *Int'l*, pg.
OU LOHKETOOD—See YIT Corporation; *Int'l*, pg. 8586
OULUN GALLERIA KOY—See Citycon Oyj; *Int'l*, pg. 1629
OULUN LVI-YKKONEN OY—See YIT Corporation; *Int'l*, pg. 8586
OU MEDICAL CENTER EDMOND—See HCA Healthcare, Inc.; *U.S. Public*, pg. 1005
OU MEDICAL CENTER—See HCA Healthcare, Inc.; *U.S. Public*, pg. 1005
OU MEEDIA MONITOORING—See UP Invest OU; *Int'l*, pg. 8087
OUME ELECTRONICS CO., LTD.—See AOI Electronics Co., Ltd.; *Int'l*, pg. 488
OU NOVITER EESTI—See Valmet Oyj; *Int'l*, pg. 8119
OU ORION PHARMA EESTI—See Orion Corporation; *Int'l*, pg. 5631

OU PISTRIK IV; *Int'l*, pg. 5665
OU PLAYTECH (ESTONIA)—See Playtech plc; *Int'l*, pg. 5894
OURAY SILVER MINES, INC.—See Aurcana Silver Corporation; *Int'l*, pg. 707
OURAY SPORTSWEAR, LLC; *U.S. Private*, pg. 3050
OUR CHILDREN OUR FUTURE; *U.S. Private*, pg. 3050
OUR CITY READING; *U.S. Private*, pg. 3050
OUR COMMUNITY BANK—See Crane Credit Union; *U.S. Private*, pg. 1085
OUR DAILY BREAD MINISTRIES; *U.S. Private*, pg. 3050
OURGAME INTERNATIONAL HOLDINGS LTD; *Int'l*, pg. 5666
OUR HEALTHY CIRCLE—See Quorum Health Corporation; *U.S. Private*, pg. 3330
OUR HOSPICE OF SOUTH CENTRAL INDIANA, INC.; *U.S. Private*, pg. 3050
OURINVEST SECURITIZADORA S.A.; *Int'l*, pg. 5666
OURISMAN AUTOMOTIVE GROUP; *U.S. Private*, pg. 3050
OURISMAN CHEVROLET COMPANY, INC.—See Ourisman Automotive Group; *U.S. Private*, pg. 3050
OURISMAN CHRYSLER DODGE JEEP RAM OF CLARKSVILLE—See Ourisman Automotive Group; *U.S. Private*, pg. 3050
OURISMAN DODGE, INC.—See Ourisman Automotive Group; *U.S. Private*, pg. 3050
OURISMAN MITSUBISHI—See Ourisman Automotive Group; *U.S. Private*, pg. 3050
OUR IT DEPARTMENT LIMITED—See Macquarie Group Limited; *Int'l*, pg. 4631
OUR KIDS OF MIAMI-DADE/MONROE, INC.; *U.S. Private*, pg. 3050
OUR LADY OF CONSOLATION NURSING & REHABILITATIVE CARE CENTER—See Catholic Health Services of Long Island; *U.S. Private*, pg. 791
OUR LADY OF LOURDES WOMEN'S & CHILDREN'S HOSPITAL—See HCA Healthcare, Inc.; *U.S. Public*, pg. 1005
OUR MAN IN HAVANA LLC; *U.S. Private*, pg. 3050
OURNETT HOLDINGS, INC.; *U.S. Private*, pg. 3050
OURO FINO SAUDE ANIMAL PARTICIPACOES S.A; *Int'l*, pg. 5666
OURO VERDE LOCACAO E SERVICO S.A.; *Int'l*, pg. 5667
OURPALM CO., LTD.; *Int'l*, pg. 5667
OURPET'S COMPANY—See Hyper Pet, LLC; *U.S. Private*, pg. 2019
OUR SUNDAY VISITOR, INC.; *U.S. Private*, pg. 3050
OUR TOWN AMERICA, INC.; *U.S. Private*, pg. 3050
OUSA-F LLP—See ForteBank JSC; *Int'l*, pg. 2737
OU SCANPIX BALTICS—See UP Invest OU; *Int'l*, pg. 8086
OU SKIP BELEGGINGS PROPRIETARY LIMITED—See Barclays PLC; *Int'l*, pg. 862
THE OUSSET AGENCY, INC.; *U.S. Private*, pg. 4089
OUSTER, INC.; *U.S. Public*, pg. 1624
OUSYSTEM CO., LTD.—See Uchida Yoko Co., Ltd.; *Int'l*, pg. 8012
OUTAGAMIE CO-OP SERVICES; *U.S. Private*, pg. 3051
OU TALLINK TRAVEL CLUB—See AS Infortar; *Int'l*, pg. 590
OUTAREX; *Int'l*, pg. 5667
OU TARTU KAUBAMAJA KINNISVARA—See Tallinna Kaubamaja AS; *Int'l*, pg. 7447
OUTBACK CATERING, INC.—See Bloomin' Brands, Inc.; *U.S. Public*, pg. 363
OUTBACK GOLDFIELDS CORP.; *Int'l*, pg. 5667
OUTBACK KANSAS LLC—See Bloomin' Brands, Inc.; *U.S. Public*, pg. 363
OUTBACK OF ASPEN HILL, INC.—See Bloomin' Brands, Inc.; *U.S. Public*, pg. 363
OUTBACK OF GERMANTOWN, INC.—See Bloomin' Brands, Inc.; *U.S. Public*, pg. 363
OUTBACK OF LA PLATA, INC.—See Bloomin' Brands, Inc.; *U.S. Public*, pg. 363
OUTBACK OF WALDORF, INC.—See Bloomin' Brands, Inc.; *U.S. Public*, pg. 363
OUTBACK OIL & MINERAL EXPLORATION CORP.; *U.S. Public*, pg. 1624
OUTBACK POWER TECHNOLOGIES, INC.—See EnerSys; *U.S. Public*, pg. 767
OUTBACK SOLAR, LLC—See Constellation Energy Corporation; *U.S. Public*, pg. 572
OUTBACK/SOUTHFIELD, LIMITED PARTNERSHIP—See Bloomin' Brands, Inc.; *U.S. Public*, pg. 363
OUTBACK STEAKHOUSE INTERNATIONAL, LLC—See Bloomin' Brands, Inc.; *U.S. Public*, pg. 363
OUTBACK STEAKHOUSE JAPAN CO., LTD.—See Bloomin' Brands, Inc.; *U.S. Public*, pg. 363
OUTBACK STEAKHOUSE KOREA, LTD.—See Bloomin' Brands, Inc.; *U.S. Public*, pg. 363
OUTBACK STEAKHOUSE OF BOWIE, INC.—See Bloomin' Brands, Inc.; *U.S. Public*, pg. 363
OUTBACK STEAKHOUSE OF CANTON, INC.—See Bloomin' Brands, Inc.; *U.S. Public*, pg. 363
OUTBACK STEAKHOUSE OF HOWARD COUNTY, INC.—See Bloomin' Brands, Inc.; *U.S. Public*, pg. 363

OUTBACK STEAKHOUSE OF JONESBORO, INC.—See Bloomin' Brands, Inc.; *U.S. Public*, pg. 363
OUTBACK STEAKHOUSE OF ST. MARY'S COUNTY, INC.—See Bloomin' Brands, Inc.; *U.S. Public*, pg. 363
OUTBACK STEAKHOUSE WEST VIRGINIA, INC.—See Bloomin' Brands, Inc.; *U.S. Public*, pg. 363
OUTBOX SYSTEMS, INC.—See Infosys Limited; *Int'l*, pg. 3696
OUTBRAIN AUSTRALIA PTY LTD—See Outbrain Inc.; *U.S. Public*, pg. 1624
OUTBRAIN BELGIUM BVBA—See Outbrain Inc.; *U.S. Public*, pg. 1624
OUTBRAIN FRANCE SAS—See Outbrain Inc.; *U.S. Public*, pg. 1624
OUTBRAIN GERMANY GMBH—See Outbrain Inc.; *U.S. Public*, pg. 1624
OUTBRAIN INC.; *U.S. Public*, pg. 1624
OUTBRAIN INDIA PRIVATE LIMITED—See Outbrain Inc.; *U.S. Public*, pg. 1624
OUTBRAIN ISRAEL LTD.—See Outbrain Inc.; *U.S. Public*, pg. 1624
OUTBRAIN ITALY SRL—See Outbrain Inc.; *U.S. Public*, pg. 1624
OUTBRAIN JAPAN KK—See Outbrain Inc.; *U.S. Public*, pg. 1624
OUTBRAIN NETHERLANDS B.V.—See Outbrain Inc.; *U.S. Public*, pg. 1624
OUTBRAIN SERVICES MONETIZACAO DE CONTEUDO LTDA—See Outbrain Inc.; *U.S. Public*, pg. 1624
OUTBRAIN SINGAPORE PTE. LTD.—See Outbrain Inc.; *U.S. Public*, pg. 1624
OUTBRAIN SPAIN S.L.—See Outbrain Inc.; *U.S. Public*, pg. 1624
OUTBRAIN UK LIMITED—See Outbrain Inc.; *U.S. Public*, pg. 1624
THE OUTCAST AGENCY LLC - NEW YORK—See Next 15 Group plc; *Int'l*, pg. 5247
THE OUTCAST AGENCY LLC—See Next 15 Group plc; *Int'l*, pg. 5247
THE OUTCAST AGENCY—See Next 15 Group plc; *Int'l*, pg. 5247
OUTCOME SCIENCES, LLC—See IQVIA Holdings Inc.; *U.S. Public*, pg. 1170
OUTCOMES INCORPORATED—See Cardinal Health, Inc.; *U.S. Public*, pg. 434
OUTCROP SILVER & GOLD CORPORATION; *Int'l*, pg. 5667
OUTDOOR ADVERTISING GROUP - DETROIT OFFICE—See The Interpublic Group of Companies, Inc.; *U.S. Public*, pg. 2096
OUTDOOR ADVERTISING GROUP - LOS ANGELES OFFICE—See The Interpublic Group of Companies, Inc.; *U.S. Public*, pg. 2096
OUTDOOR ADVERTISING GROUP—See The Interpublic Group of Companies, Inc.; *U.S. Public*, pg. 2096
OUTDOOR CAP COMPANY INC.; *U.S. Private*, pg. 3051
OUTDOOR CHANNEL HOLDINGS, INC.—See Kroenke Sports & Entertainment, LLC; *U.S. Private*, pg. 2352
THE OUTDOOR CHANNEL, INC.—See Kroenke Sports & Entertainment, LLC; *U.S. Private*, pg. 2352
OUTDOOR CONSTRUCTION INC.—See Munie Outdoor Services, Inc.; *U.S. Private*, pg. 2814
OUTDOOR FIRST, INC.—See Wilkins Media Company; *U.S. Private*, pg. 4520
THE OUTDOOR FOOTWEAR COMPANY—See V. F. Corporation; *U.S. Public*, pg. 2268
OUTDOOR LIVING PTE LTD—See Koda Ltd.; *Int'l*, pg. 4225
OUTDOOR LIVING SUPPLY LLC—See Trilantic Capital Management L.P.; *U.S. Private*, pg. 4231
OUTDOOR POWER PRODUCTS HUSQVARNA KENYA LTD.—See Husqvarna AB; *Int'l*, pg. 3539
OUTDOOR RESEARCH INCORPORATED; *U.S. Private*, pg. 3051
OUTDOOR RESORTS OF AMERICA; *U.S. Private*, pg. 3051
OUTDOOR SERVICES, LLC—See Cerberus Capital Management, L.P.; *U.S. Private*, pg. 838
OUTDOOR SPECIALTY PRODUCTS, INC.; *U.S. Public*, pg. 1624
OUTDOOR & SPORTS COMPANY (HOLDINGS) LIMITED—See Bollin Group Ltd.; *Int'l*, pg. 1103
OUTDOOR TRAVELER DESTINATIONS, LLC—See Hilton Grand Vacations Inc.; *U.S. Public*, pg. 1040
OUTDOOR VENTURE CORP.; *U.S. Private*, pg. 3051
OUTDOOR WORLD INC.; *U.S. Private*, pg. 3051
OUTDOOR WORLD OF NEW ENGLAND, INC.—See Boston Sand & Gravel Company; *U.S. Public*, pg. 373
OUTDRY TECHNOLOGIES S.R.L.—See Columbia Sportswear Company; *U.S. Public*, pg. 535
OUTER BANKS BLUE REALTY SERVICES; *U.S. Private*, pg. 3051
OUTERBOX LLC—See WILsquare Capital LLC; *U.S. Private*, pg. 4532
OUTER DRIVE HOLDINGS INC.—See Mercedes-Benz Group AG; *Int'l*, pg. 4823
OUTERSTUFF, LTD.; *U.S. Private*, pg. 3051
OUTFRONT MEDIA CANADA LP—See OUTFRONT Media Inc.; *U.S. Public*, pg. 1625
OUTFRONT MEDIA CHICAGO LLC—See OUTFRONT Media Inc.; *U.S. Public*, pg. 1625
OUTFRONT MEDIA INC.; *U.S. Public*, pg. 1624
OUTFRONT MEDIA LLC—See OUTFRONT Media Inc.; *U.S. Public*, pg. 1625
OUTFRONT MEDIA - PHOENIX—See OUTFRONT Media Inc.; *U.S. Public*, pg. 1625
OUTFRONT MEDIA VW COMMUNICATIONS LLC—See OUTFRONT Media Inc.; *U.S. Public*, pg. 1625
OUTIN FUTURES CO., LTD.; *Int'l*, pg. 5667
OUT INTERNATIONAL INC.—See NCH Corporation; *U.S. Private*, pg. 2876
OUTKUMPU - MINERALS PROCESSING—See Metso Oyj; *Int'l*, pg. 4867
OUTLAND REFORESTATION INC.; *Int'l*, pg. 5667
OUTLET ARENA MORAVIA, S.R.O.—See CPI Property Group, S.A.; *Int'l*, pg. 1825
OUTLET MALL OF SAVANNAH, LLC—See Tanger Inc.; *U.S. Public*, pg. 1980
OUTLETS AT WESTGATE, LLC—See Tanger Inc.; *U.S. Public*, pg. 1980
OU TLG HOTELL—See AS Infortar; *Int'l*, pg. 590
OUTLINE I SVERIGE AB—See Ratos AB; *Int'l*, pg. 6220
OUTLINE SYSTEMS LLC—See Vista Equity Partners, LLC; *U.S. Private*, pg. 4396
OUTLINE VINDUER A/S—See Ratos AB; *Int'l*, pg. 6220
OUTLOOK FOSTERING SERVICES LIMITED—See Sheikh Holdings Group (Investments) Limited; *Int'l*, pg. 6793
OUTLOOK GROUP CORP.—See Aterian Investment Management, L.P.; *U.S. Private*, pg. 366
OUTLOOK NEBRASKA, INC.; *U.S. Public*, pg. 3051
OUTLOOKSOFT CORPORATION—See SAP SE; *Int'l*, pg. 6567
OUTLOOK THERAPEUTICS, INC.; *U.S. Public*, pg. 1625
OUTMATCH INC.—See Rubicon Technology Partners, LLC; *U.S. Private*, pg. 3499
OUT OF THE BOXTECHNOLOGY; *U.S. Private*, pg. 3050
OUTOKUMPU ASIA PACIFIC LTD—See Outokumpu Oyj; *Int'l*, pg. 5667
OUTOKUMPU A/S—See Outokumpu Oyj; *Int'l*, pg. 5667
OUTOKUMPU AS—See Outokumpu Oyj; *Int'l*, pg. 5667
OUTOKUMPU AUSTRIA—See Outokumpu Oyj; *Int'l*, pg. 5667
OUTOKUMPU BALTIC—See Outokumpu Oyj; *Int'l*, pg. 5667
OUTOKUMPU BENELUX B.V.—See Outokumpu Oyj; *Int'l*, pg. 5667
OUTOKUMPU BRASIL COMERCIO DE METAIS LTDA.—See Outokumpu Oyj; *Int'l*, pg. 5667
OUTOKUMPU BUSINESS SUPPORT UNIT AB—See Outokumpu Oyj; *Int'l*, pg. 5667
OUTOKUMPU BV—See Outokumpu Oyj; *Int'l*, pg. 5667
OUTOKUMPU CHROME OY—See Outokumpu Oyj; *Int'l*, pg. 5668
OUTOKUMPU DISTRIBUTION OY—See Outokumpu Oyj; *Int'l*, pg. 5667
OUTOKUMPU ESPANA S.A.—See Outokumpu Oyj; *Int'l*, pg. 5667
OUTOKUMPU GES.M.B.H—See Outokumpu Oyj; *Int'l*, pg. 5667
OUTOKUMPU INDIA PRIVATE LIMITED—See Outokumpu Oyj; *Int'l*, pg. 5668
OUTOKUMPU ISTANBUL DIS TICARET LIMITED SIRKETI—See Outokumpu Oyj; *Int'l*, pg. 5668
OUTOKUMPU KFT.—See Outokumpu Oyj; *Int'l*, pg. 5668
OUTOKUMPU K.K.—See Outokumpu Oyj; *Int'l*, pg. 5668
OUTOKUMPU LDA.—See Outokumpu Oyj; *Int'l*, pg. 5668
OUTOKUMPU LTD.—See Outokumpu Oyj; *Int'l*, pg. 5668
OUTOKUMPU METALS OFF-TAKE OY—See UPM-Kymmene Corporation; *Int'l*, pg. 8090
OUTOKUMPU MINING OY—See Outokumpu Oyj; *Int'l*, pg. 5668
OUTOKUMPU MINING OY—See Outokumpu Oyj; *Int'l*, pg. 5668
OUTOKUMPU MINING OY—See Outokumpu Oyj; *Int'l*, pg. 5668
OUTOKUMPU NICKEL RESOURCES B.V.—See Outokumpu Oyj; *Int'l*, pg. 5667
OUTOKUMPU NIROSTA GMBH—See Outokumpu Oyj; *Int'l*, pg. 5668
OUTOKUMPU NORDIC AB—See Outokumpu Oyj; *Int'l*, pg. 5668
OUTOKUMPU N.V.—See Outokumpu Oyj; *Int'l*, pg. 5668
OUTOKUMPU OYJ; *Int'l*, pg. 5667
OUTOKUMPU POLAND SP.Z.O.O.—See Outokumpu Oyj; *Int'l*, pg. 5668
OUTOKUMPU PREFAB AB—See Outokumpu Oyj; *Int'l*, pg. 5668
OUTOKUMPU PRESS PLATE AB—See Outokumpu Oyj; *Int'l*, pg. 5668
OUTOKUMPU PRESS PLATE AB—See Outokumpu Oyj; *Int'l*, pg. 5668
OUTOKUMPU PSC BENELUX B.V.—See Outokumpu Oyj; *Int'l*, pg. 5667
OUTOKUMPU PSC GERMANY GMBH—See Outokumpu Oyj; *Int'l*, pg. 5668
OUTOKUMPU PTY. LTD.—See Outokumpu Oyj; *Int'l*, pg. 5668
OUTOKUMPU (PTY) LTD—See Outokumpu Oyj; *Int'l*, pg. 5667
OUTOKUMPU RESEARCH OY—See Outokumpu Oyj; *Int'l*, pg. 5668
OUTOKUMPU ROSSIJA OY—See Outokumpu Oyj; *Int'l*, pg. 5668
OUTOKUMPU SALES NORWAY—See Outokumpu Oyj; *Int'l*, pg. 5668
OUTOKUMPU S.A.—See Outokumpu Oyj; *Int'l*, pg. 5668
OUTOKUMPU S.A.S.—See Outokumpu Oyj; *Int'l*, pg. 5668
OUTOKUMPU (S.E.A.) PTE. LTD.—See Outokumpu Oyj; *Int'l*, pg. 5667
OUTOKUMPU SHIPPING OY—See Outokumpu Oyj; *Int'l*, pg. 5668
OUTOKUMPU S.P.A.—See Outokumpu Oyj; *Int'l*, pg. 5668
OUTOKUMPU SP. Z O.O.—See Outokumpu Oyj; *Int'l*, pg. 5668
OUTOKUMPU S.R.L.—See Outokumpu Oyj; *Int'l*, pg. 5668
OUTOKUMPU S.R.O.—See Outokumpu Oyj; *Int'l*, pg. 5669
OUTOKUMPU STAINLESS AB—See Outokumpu Oyj; *Int'l*, pg. 5668
OUTOKUMPU STAINLESS AB—See Outokumpu Oyj; *Int'l*, pg. 5668
OUTOKUMPU STAINLESS AB—See Outokumpu Oyj; *Int'l*, pg. 5668
OUTOKUMPU STAINLESS BAR—See Outokumpu Oyj; *Int'l*, pg. 5668
OUTOKUMPU STAINLESS B.V.—See Outokumpu Oyj; *Int'l*, pg. 5669
OUTOKUMPU STAINLESS COIL, INC.—See Outokumpu Oyj; *Int'l*, pg. 5668
OUTOKUMPU STAINLESS HOLDING GMBH—See Outokumpu Oyj; *Int'l*, pg. 5669
OUTOKUMPU STAINLESS HOLDINGS LTD—See Outokumpu Oyj; *Int'l*, pg. 5669
OUTOKUMPU STAINLESS, INC.—See Outokumpu Oyj; *Int'l*, pg. 5669
OUTOKUMPU STAINLESS LTD. - ALLOY STEEL RODS MILL—See Outokumpu Oyj; *Int'l*, pg. 5669
OUTOKUMPU STAINLESS LTD.—See Outokumpu Oyj; *Int'l*, pg. 5669
OUTOKUMPU STAINLESS OY—See Outokumpu Oyj; *Int'l*, pg. 5668
OUTOKUMPU STAINLESS PIPE, INC.—See Outokumpu Oyj; *Int'l*, pg. 5669
OUTOKUMPU STAINLESS PLATE, INC.—See Outokumpu Oyj; *Int'l*, pg. 5669
OUTOKUMPU STAINLESS (PTY.) LTD, SOUTH AFRICA—See Outokumpu Oyj; *Int'l*, pg. 5668
OUTOKUMPU STAINLESS—See Outokumpu Oyj; *Int'l*, pg. 5668
OUTOKUMPU STAINLESS STEEL (CHINA) CO. LTD.—See Outokumpu Oyj; *Int'l*, pg. 5669
OUTOKUMPU STAINLESS TUBULAR PRODUCTS AB—See Outokumpu Oyj; *Int'l*, pg. 5669
OUTOKUMPU STAINLESS TUBULAR PRODUCTS AB—See Outokumpu Oyj; *Int'l*, pg. 5669
OUTOKUMPU STAINLESS TUBULAR PRODUCTS AB—See Outokumpu Oyj; *Int'l*, pg. 5669
OUTOKUMPU STAINLESS TUBULAR PRODUCTS AB—See Outokumpu Oyj; *Int'l*, pg. 5668
OUTOKUMPU STAINLESS TUBULAR PRODUCTS AS—See Outokumpu Oyj; *Int'l*, pg. 5669
OUTOKUMPU STAINLESS TUBULAR PRODUCTS OY AB—See Outokumpu Oyj; *Int'l*, pg. 5669
OUTOKUMPU STAINLESS TUBULAR PRODUCTS—See Outokumpu Oyj; *Int'l*, pg. 5669
OUTOKUMPU STAINLESS TUBULAR PRODUCTS—See Outokumpu Oyj; *Int'l*, pg. 5669
OUTOKUMPU STAINLESS USA, LLC—See Outokumpu Oyj; *Int'l*, pg. 5669
OUTOKUMPU STAINLESS USA, LLC—See ThyssenKrupp AG; *Int'l*, pg. 7725
OUTOKUMPU (THAILAND) CO., LTD.—See Outokumpu Oyj; *Int'l*, pg. 5668
OUTOKUMPU UAB—See Outokumpu Oyj; *Int'l*, pg. 5669
OUTOKUMPU (U.K.) LTD.—See Outokumpu Oyj; *Int'l*, pg. 5667
OUTOKUMPU WENMEC AB—See Metso Oyj; *Int'l*, pg. 4867
OUTOKUMPU ZINC AUSTRALIA PTY. LTD.—See Outokumpu Oyj; *Int'l*, pg. 5669
OUTOTEC AUSMELT PTY. LTD.—See Metso Oyj; *Int'l*, pg. 4867
OUTOTEC (AUSTRALASIA) PTY. LTD.—See Metso Oyj; *Int'l*, pg. 4867
OUTOTEC (CERAMICS) OY—See Metso Oyj; *Int'l*, pg. 4867
OUTOTEC (CHILE) LTDA.—See Metso Oyj; *Int'l*, pg. 4867
OUTOTEC DEUTSCHLAND GMBH—See Metso Oyj; *Int'l*, pg. 4867
OUTOTEC ENERGY PRODUCTS—See Metso Oyj; *Int'l*, pg. 4868
OUTOTEC FILTERS AUSTRALIA PTY. LTD.—See Metso Oyj; *Int'l*, pg. 4868
OUTOTEC (FILTERS) GMBH—See Metso Oyj; *Int'l*, pg. 4867

COMPANY NAME INDEX

OUTOTEC (FILTERS) OY—See Metso Oyj; *Int'l*, pg. 4867
OUTOTEC (FINLAND) OY—See Metso Oyj; *Int'l*, pg. 4867
OUTOTEC (GHANA) LIMITED—See Metso Oyj; *Int'l*, pg. 4867
OUTOTEC GMBH—See Metso Oyj; *Int'l*, pg. 4868
OUTOTEC HOLDING GMBH—See Metso Oyj; *Int'l*, pg. 4868
OUTOTEC INDIA PRIVATE LTD.—See Metso Oyj; *Int'l*, pg. 4868
OUTOTEC (KAZAKHSTAN) LLP—See Metso Oyj; *Int'l*, pg. 4867
OUTOTEC (MEXICO), S.A. DE C.V.—See Metso Oyj; *Int'l*, pg. 4867
OUTOTEC (NORWAY) AS—See Metso Oyj; *Int'l*, pg. 4867
OUTOTEC (PERTH)—See Metso Oyj; *Int'l*, pg. 4867
OUTOTEC (PERU) S.A.C.—See Metso Oyj; *Int'l*, pg. 4867
OUTOTEC (POLSKA) SP. Z.O.O.—See Metso Oyj; *Int'l*, pg. 4867
OUTOTEC PTY LTD. - MELBOURNE—See Metso Oyj; *Int'l*, pg. 4868
OUTOTEC PTY LTD—See Metso Oyj; *Int'l*, pg. 4868
OUTOTEC (RSA) (PTY) LTD.—See Metso Oyj; *Int'l*, pg. 4867
OUTOTEC (SHANGHAI) CO. LTD.—See Metso Oyj; *Int'l*, pg. 4867
OUTOTEC ST. PETERSBURG—See Metso Oyj; *Int'l*, pg. 4868
OUTOTEC (SWEDEN) AB—See Metso Oyj; *Int'l*, pg. 4867
OUTOTEC (SYDNEY)—See Metso Oyj; *Int'l*, pg. 4867
OUTOTEC TECNOLOGIA BRASIL LTDA.—See Metso Oyj; *Int'l*, pg. 4868
OUTOTEC TURULA OY—See Metso Oyj; *Int'l*, pg. 4868
OUTOTEC (USA) INC.—See Metso Oyj; *Int'l*, pg. 4867
OUTOTEC (ZAMBIA) LTD.—See Metso Oyj; *Int'l*, pg. 4867
OUTPATIENT INFUSION SYSTEMS, INC.—See McKesson Corporation; *U.S. Public*, pg. 1408
OUTPATIENT SURGERY CENTER OF HILTON HEAD, LLC—See UnitedHealth Group Incorporated; *U.S. Public*, pg. 2249
OUTPATIENT SURGICAL SERVICES, LTD.—See HCA Healthcare, Inc.; *U.S. Public*, pg. 1005
OUTPOST NATURAL FOODS COOP; *U.S. Private*, pg. 3051
OUTPOST WINES LLC—See AXA S.A.; *Int'l*, pg. 759
OUTPUT PHARMA SERVICES GMBH—See Esperite N.V.; *Int'l*, pg. 2506
OUTPUT SERVICES GROUP, INC.—See Aquiline Capital Partners LLC; *U.S. Private*, pg. 304
OUTRAGEOUS INC.; *U.S. Private*, pg. 3051
OUTRAGEOUS VENTURES, INC.; *U.S. Private*, pg. 3051
OUTREACH COMMUNITY HEALTH CENTERS, INC.; *U.S. Private*, pg. 3051
OUTREACH HEALTH SERVICES OF NORTH TEXAS, LLC—See Apollo Global Management, Inc.; *U.S. Public*, pg. 157
OUTREACH ORGANISATION LTD.—See Bergman & Beving AB; *Int'l*, pg. 980
OUTREACH TECHNOLOGY LLC; *U.S. Private*, pg. 3051
OUTREAU TECHNOLOGIES SAS—See Vossloh AG; *Int'l*, pg. 8308
OUTRIDER—See WPP plc; *Int'l*, pg. 8477
OUTRIGGER HOTELS HAWAII—See KSL Capital Partners, LLC; *U.S. Private*, pg. 2355
OUTRIGGER LODGING SERVICES LIMITED PARTNERSHIP; *U.S. Private*, pg. 3051
OUTRIGHT, INC.—See KKR & Co. Inc.; *U.S. Public*, pg. 1252
OUTRIGHT, INC.—See Silver Lake Group, LLC; *U.S. Private*, pg. 3657
OUTRIGHT, INC.—See TCMI, Inc.; *U.S. Private*, pg. 3943
OUTSCALE SAS—See Dassault Systemes S.A.; *Int'l*, pg. 1975
OUTSELL, INC.; *U.S. Private*, pg. 3051
OUTSELL, LLC; *U.S. Private*, pg. 3051
OUTSET MEDICAL, INC.; *U.S. Public*, pg. 1625
OUTSIDE INTERACTIVE, INC.; *U.S. Private*, pg. 3051
THE OUTSIDE LINE LTD.—See Publicis Groupe S.A.; *Int'l*, pg. 6109
OUTSIDE LIVING INDUSTRIES BELUX BVNR—See Outside Living Industries France SARL; *Int'l*, pg. 5669
OUTSIDE LIVING INDUSTRIES FRANCE SARL; *Int'l*, pg. 5669
OUTSIDE LIVING INDUSTRIES NEDERLAND B.V.—See Outside Living Industries France SARL; *Int'l*, pg. 5669
OUTSIDE LIVING INDUSTRIES SA—See Outside Living Industries France SARL; *Int'l*, pg. 5669
OUTSIDE THE LINES, INC; *U.S. Private*, pg. 3051
OUTSITE MEDIA GMBH—See Stroer SE & Co. KGaA; *Int'l*, pg. 7242
OUTSKIRTS PRESS INC.; *U.S. Private*, pg. 3052
OUTSOURCE CONSULTANTS, LLC; *U.S. Private*, pg. 3052
OUTSOURCE ELECTRONICS LIMITED—See Season Group International Co., Ltd.; *Int'l*, pg. 6666
THE OUTSOURCE GROUP, INC.—See HCA Healthcare, Inc.; *U.S. Public*, pg. 1006
OUTSOURCE INC.; *U.S. Private*, pg. 3052
OUTSOURCE IT CORP; *U.S. Private*, pg. 3052

OUTSOURCE PARTNERS INTERNATIONAL SDN BHD—See ExlService Holdings, Inc.; *U.S. Public*, pg. 808
OUTSOURCE TECHNICAL; *U.S. Private*, pg. 3052
OUTSOURCING APPLICATIVO E SERVIZI INNOVATIVI S.P.A.—See Nexi SpA; *Int'l*, pg. 5244
OUTSOURCING BUSINESS SERVICE INC.—See Bain Capital, LP; *U.S. Private*, pg. 435
OUTSOURCING (CAMBODIA) INC.—See Bain Capital, LP; *U.S. Private*, pg. 435
OUTSOURCING COMMUNICATIONS CO., LTD.—See Bain Capital, LP; *U.S. Private*, pg. 435
OUTSOURCING INC.—See Bain Capital, LP; *U.S. Private*, pg. 433
OUTSOURCING OCEANIA PTY LTD.—See Bain Capital, LP; *U.S. Private*, pg. 435
OUTSOURCING PARTNERS N.V—See Intrum AB; *Int'l*, pg. 3771
OUT-SOURCING SYSTEM CONSULTING INC.—See Bain Capital, LP; *U.S. Private*, pg. 435
OUTSOURCING TECHNOLOGY INC.—See Bain Capital, LP; *U.S. Private*, pg. 435
OUTSOURCING UNLIMITED, INC.—See ScanSource, Inc.; *U.S. Public*, pg. 1843
OUTSURANCE GROUP LIMITED; *Int'l*, pg. 5669
OUTSURANCE INSURANCE COMPANY LIMITED—See OUTsurance Group Limited; *Int'l*, pg. 5669
OUTSURANCE LIMITED—See FirstRand Limited; *Int'l*, pg. 2690
OUTTEN CHEVROLET INC.; *U.S. Private*, pg. 3052
OUTWATER PLASTIC INDUSTRIES, INC.—See Foga System International AB; *Int'l*, pg. 2721
OUTWORX GROUP—See Guggenheim Partners, LLC; *U.S. Private*, pg. 1811
OU VIKING LINE EESTI—See Viking Line Abp; *Int'l*, pg. 8205
OU VILMIX—See Orkla ASA; *Int'l*, pg. 5638
OUVRIE PMC, SAS—See PMC Group, Inc.; *U.S. Private*, pg. 3218
OU WAM BALTIC—See WAMGROUP S.p.A.; *Int'l*, pg. 8338
OV2 INVESTMENT 1, INC.; *Int'l*, pg. 5669
OVAB OPTIMAL VENTILATION AB—See Instalco AB; *Int'l*, pg. 3722
OVAIR FREIGHT SERVICE, INC.—See Bruzzone Shipping, Inc.; *U.S. Private*, pg. 673
OVAKO AB—See Nippon Steel Corporation; *Int'l*, pg. 5340
OVAKO BAR AB—See Nippon Steel Corporation; *Int'l*, pg. 5340
OVAKO BAR BENELUX—See Ovako Holdings AB; *Int'l*, pg. 5669
OVAKO CROMAX AB—See Ovako Holdings AB; *Int'l*, pg. 5670
OVAKO FRANCE S.A.S.—See Ovako Holdings AB; *Int'l*, pg. 5670
OVAKO GMBH—See Ovako Holdings AB; *Int'l*, pg. 5670
OVAKO HALLSTAHAMMAR AB—See Ovako Holdings AB; *Int'l*, pg. 5670
OVAKO HOFORS AB—See Ovako Holdings AB; *Int'l*, pg. 5670
OVAKO HOLDINGS AB; *Int'l*, pg. 5669
OVAKO IMATRA OY AB—See Ovako Holdings AB; *Int'l*, pg. 5670
OVAKO LTD—See Ovako Holdings AB; *Int'l*, pg. 5670
OVAKO MOLINELLA S.P.A.—See Ovako Holdings AB; *Int'l*, pg. 5670
OVAKO MORA AB—See Ovako Holdings AB; *Int'l*, pg. 5670
OVAKO NORTH AMERICA INC—See Ovako Holdings AB; *Int'l*, pg. 5670
OVAKO POLSKA SP. Z.O.O.—See Ovako Holdings AB; *Int'l*, pg. 5670
OVAKO REDON S.A.—See Ovako Holdings AB; *Int'l*, pg. 5670
OVAKO SALES UNIT SCANDINAVIA AB—See Ovako Holdings AB; *Int'l*, pg. 5670
OVAKO (SHANGHAI) SPECIAL STEEL TRADING CO., LTD.—See Ovako Holdings AB; *Int'l*, pg. 5669
OVAKO STEEL MARKETING AB—See Ovako Holdings AB; *Int'l*, pg. 5670
OVAKO TWENTE B.V—See Ovako Holdings AB; *Int'l*, pg. 5670
OVAL ASIA PACIFIC PTE. LTD.—See OVAL Corporation; *Int'l*, pg. 5670
OVAL CORPORATION; *Int'l*, pg. 5670
OVAL ENGINEERING INC.—See OVAL Corporation; *Int'l*, pg. 5670
OVAL ENGINEERING SDN BHD—See OVAL Corporation; *Int'l*, pg. 5670
OVALO GMBH—See Nabtesco Corporation; *Int'l*, pg. 5120
OVAL PARTNERS; *U.S. Private*, pg. 3052
OVALSTRAPPING INC.—See Enterprises International Inc.; *U.S. Private*, pg. 1404
OVAL TAIWAN CO., LTD.—See OVAL Corporation; *Int'l*, pg. 5670
OVAL THAILAND LTD.—See OVAL Corporation; *Int'l*, pg. 5670
OVAL VIETNAM JVC, LTD.—See OVAL Corporation; *Int'l*, pg. 5670

OVERGROUP CONSULTING LLC

OVARO KIINTEISTOSIJOITUS OYJ; *Int'l*, pg. 5670
OVARPACK - EMBALAGENS S.A.—See Strategic Value Partners, LLC; *U.S. Private*, pg. 3836
OVATION ADVERTISING—See Omnicom Group Inc.; *U.S. Public*, pg. 1576
OVATION BRANDS, INC.—See Food Management Partners, Inc.; *U.S. Private*, pg. 1561
OVATION CREDIT SERVICES, INC.—See LendingTree, Inc.; *U.S. Public*, pg. 1305
OVATION ENTERPRISES, INC.; *U.S. Private*, pg. 3052
OVATION HOLDINGS, INC.; *U.S. Private*, pg. 3052
OVATION INSTRUMENTS—See Arcline Investment Management LP; *U.S. Private*, pg. 314
OVATION MUSIC & STUDIOS, INC.; *U.S. Private*, pg. 3052
OVATION SCIENCE, INC.; *Int'l*, pg. 5670
OVATIONS FOOD SERVICES LP; *U.S. Private*, pg. 3052
OVATIONS MANAGEMENT SOLUTIONS, LLC—See Cendyn Corp.; *U.S. Private*, pg. 808
OVATION TRAVEL GROUP, INC.—See Global Business Travel Group, Inc.; *U.S. Public*, pg. 941
OVATION TRAVEL GROUP UK LIMITED—See Global Business Travel Group, Inc.; *U.S. Public*, pg. 941
OVATION TRAVEL, LLC—See Global Business Travel Group, Inc.; *U.S. Public*, pg. 941
OVATO LIMITED—See IVE Group Limited; *Int'l*, pg. 3846
OVATO PACKAGING PTY LTD—See IVE Group Limited; *Int'l*, pg. 3847
OVB ALLFINANZ A.S.—See OVB Holding AG; *Int'l*, pg. 5670
OVB ALLFINANZ CROATIA D.O.O.—See OVB Holding AG; *Int'l*, pg. 5670
OVB ALLFINANZ ESPANA, S.A.—See OVB Holding AG; *Int'l*, pg. 5670
OVB ALLFINANZ POLSKA SPOLKA FINANSOWA SP. Z.O.O.—See OVB Holding AG; *Int'l*, pg. 5670
OVB ALLFINANZ SLOVENSKO A.S.—See OVB Holding AG; *Int'l*, pg. 5670
OVB ALLFINANZVERMITTLUNGS GMBH—See OVB Holding AG; *Int'l*, pg. 5670
OVB CONSEILS EN PATRIMOINE FRANCE SARL—See OVB Holding AG; *Int'l*, pg. 5670
OVB-CONSULENZA PATRIMONIALE SRL—See OVB Holding AG; *Int'l*, pg. 5671
OVB HOLDING AG; *Int'l*, pg. 5670
OVB VERMOGENSBERATUNG A.P.K. KFT.—See OVB Holding AG; *Int'l*, pg. 5671
OVB VERMOGENSBERATUNG (SCHWEIZ) AG—See OVB Holding AG; *Int'l*, pg. 5670
OVCON HOLDINGS (PTY) LIMITED—See Wilson Bayly Holmes-Ovcon Limited; *Int'l*, pg. 8422
OVCTEK CHINA, INC.; *Int'l*, pg. 5671
OVD KINEGRAM AG—See Leonhard Kurz GmbH & Co. KG; *Int'l*, pg. 4462
OVE ARUP & PARTNERS DANMARK A/S—See Arup Group Ltd.; *Int'l*, pg. 587
OVE ARUP & PARTNERS HONG KONG LIMITED—See Arup Group Ltd.; *Int'l*, pg. 587
OVE ARUP & PARTNERS INTERNATIONAL LIMITED—See Arup Group Ltd.; *Int'l*, pg. 587
OVE ARUP & PARTNERS IRELAND LIMITED—See Arup Group Ltd.; *Int'l*, pg. 587
OVE ARUP & PARTNERS POLAND SP. ZO.O—See Arup Group Ltd.; *Int'l*, pg. 587
OVE ARUP & PARTNERS SCOTLAND LIMITED—See Arup Group Ltd.; *Int'l*, pg. 587
OVE ARUP (THAILAND) LIMITED—See Arup Group Ltd.; *Int'l*, pg. 587
OVE DESIGN & COMMUNICATIONS LTD.—See Publicis Groupe S.A.; *Int'l*, pg. 6104
OVELIA SAS—See VINCI S.A.; *Int'l*, pg. 8225
OVENTUS MEDICAL LIMITED—See Open Airway Dental Solutions Ltd; *Int'l*, pg. 5596
OVENTUS MEDICAL USA, INC.—See Open Airway Dental Solutions Ltd; *Int'l*, pg. 5596
OVERACTIVE MEDIA CORP.; *Int'l*, pg. 5671
OVERALL FORGE NOMINEES PTY LTD—See Berkshire Hathaway Inc.; *U.S. Public*, pg. 314
OVERALL FORGE PTY LTD—See Berkshire Hathaway Inc.; *U.S. Public*, pg. 314
OVERBECK GMBH—See Mondragon Corporation; *Int'l*, pg. 5028
OVERBURY PLC—See Morgan Sindall Group Plc; *Int'l*, pg. 5045
THE OVERBY GROUP INC.—See Bischof + Klein GmbH & Co. KG; *Int'l*, pg. 1049
OVERBY-SEAWELL COMPANY—See W.R. Berkley Corporation; *U.S. Public*, pg. 2318
OVERCASH ELECTRIC INC.; *U.S. Private*, pg. 3052
OVERDRIVE, INC.—See KKR & Co. Inc.; *U.S. Public*, pg. 1262
OVERDRIVE INTERACTIVE; *U.S. Private*, pg. 3052
OVEREEM B.V.—See Hadley Industries PLC; *Int'l*, pg. 3205
OVER FIFTY FUNDS MANAGEMENT PTY LTD—See Centuria Capital Limited; *Int'l*, pg. 1416
OVER FIFTY SENIORS EQUITY RELEASE PTY LTD—See Centuria Capital Limited; *Int'l*, pg. 1416
OVERGROUP CONSULTING LLC; *U.S. Private*, pg. 3052

2037

OVERHEAD CONVEYOR CO.
CORPORATE AFFILIATIONS

OVERHEAD CONVEYOR CO.; *U.S. Private*, pg. 3053
OVERHEAD DOOR COMPANY OF ALBUQUERQUE—See E.E. Newcomer Enterprises Inc.; *U.S. Private*, pg. 1305
OVERHEAD DOOR COMPANY OF ATLANTA—See E.E. Newcomer Enterprises Inc.; *U.S. Private*, pg. 1305
OVERHEAD DOOR COMPANY OF CENTRAL ARIZONA—See E.E. Newcomer Enterprises Inc.; *U.S. Private*, pg. 1305
OVERHEAD DOOR COMPANY OF CENTRAL MISSOURI—See E.E. Newcomer Enterprises Inc.; *U.S. Private*, pg. 1305
OVERHEAD DOOR COMPANY OF KANSAS CITY—See E.E. Newcomer Enterprises Inc.; *U.S. Private*, pg. 1305
OVERHEAD DOOR COMPANY OF SANTA FE—See E.E. Newcomer Enterprises Inc.; *U.S. Private*, pg. 1305
OVERHEAD DOOR COMPANY OF SPRINGFIELD—See E.E. Newcomer Enterprises Inc.; *U.S. Private*, pg. 1305
OVERHEAD DOOR COMPANY OF ST. LOUIS—See E.E. Newcomer Enterprises Inc.; *U.S. Private*, pg. 1305
OVERHEAD DOOR COMPANY OF THE FOUR CORNERS—See E.E. Newcomer Enterprises Inc.; *U.S. Private*, pg. 1305
OVERHEAD DOOR COMPANY OF WICHITA—See E.E. Newcomer Enterprises Inc.; *U.S. Private*, pg. 1305
OVERHEAD DOOR CO OF NEW ORLEANS, INC.—See DuraServ Corp; *U.S. Private*, pg. 1293
OVERHEAD DOOR CO OF SOUTHWEST LOUISIANA INC.—See Sanwa Holdings Corporation; *Int'l*, pg. 6561
OVERHEAD DOOR CORPORATION—See Sanwa Holdings Corporation; *Int'l*, pg. 6560
OVERHEAD DOOR CORP. - THERMACORE PRODUCTS—See Sanwa Holdings Corporation; *Int'l*, pg. 6561
OVERHEAD DOOR OF CASPER, INC.—See Sanwa Holdings Corporation; *Int'l*, pg. 6561
OVERHILL FARMS, INC.—See Charoen Pokphand Foods Public Company Limited; *Int'l*, pg. 1451
OVERHOFF TECHNOLOGY CORPORATION—See US Nuclear Corp.; *U.S. Public*, pg. 2267
OVERIIT S.P.A.—See Bain Capital, LP; *U.S. Private*, pg. 442
OVERIIT S.P.A.—See Neuberger Berman Group LLC; *U.S. Private*, pg. 2890
OVERIJSE AUTOMOTIVE N.V.—See s.a. D'Ieteren n.v.; *Int'l*, pg. 6448
OVERIT MEDIA INC.; *U.S. Private*, pg. 3053
OVERLACK FURNIERE GMBH & CO. KG; *Int'l*, pg. 5671
OVERLACK FURNIERE POLSKA SP. Z O.O.—See Overlack Furniere GmbH & Co. KG; *Int'l*, pg. 5671
OVERLAKE HOSPITAL MEDICAL CENTER; *U.S. Private*, pg. 3053
OVERLAND CONTRACTING INC.—See Black & Veatch Holding Company; *U.S. Private*, pg. 569
OVERLANDERS MANUFACTURING LP—See Exchange Income Corporation; *Int'l*, pg. 2579
OVERLAND INC; *U.S. Private*, pg. 3053
THE OVERLAND PARK KS ENDOSCOPY ASC, LLC—See KKR & Co. Inc.; *U.S. Public*, pg. 1248
OVERLAND PARK MEDICAL SPECIALISTS, LLC—See HCA Healthcare, Inc.; *U.S. Public*, pg. 1005
OVERLAND PARK ORTHOPEDICS, LLC—See HCA Healthcare, Inc.; *U.S. Public*, pg. 1005
OVERLAND PARK REGIONAL MEDICAL CENTER—See HCA Healthcare, Inc.; *U.S. Public*, pg. 1003
OVERLAND PARK SURGERY CENTER—See HCA Healthcare, Inc.; *U.S. Public*, pg. 1005
OVERLAND PARK SURGICAL SPECIALTIES, LLC—See HCA Healthcare, Inc.; *U.S. Public*, pg. 1005
OVERLAND PASS PIPELINE COMPANY LLC—See The Williams Companies, Inc.; *U.S. Public*, pg. 2142
OVERLAND PRODUCTS COMPANY, INC.—See Quanex Building Products Corp.; *U.S. Public*, pg. 1749
OVERLAND SHEEPSKIN CO. INC; *U.S. Private*, pg. 3053
OVERLAND STORAGE (EUROPE) LTD.—See Overland Storage, Inc.; *U.S. Private*, pg. 3053
OVERLAND STORAGE GMBH—See Overland Storage, Inc.; *U.S. Private*, pg. 3053
OVERLAND STORAGE, INC.; *U.S. Private*, pg. 3053
OVERLAND STORAGE SARL—See Overland Storage, Inc.; *U.S. Private*, pg. 3053
OVERLAND TANK, INC.—See Tenex Capital Management, L.P.; *U.S. Private*, pg. 3966
OVERLAND TOTAL LOGISTIC SERVICES (M) SDN. BHD.—See Yamato Holdings Co., Ltd.; *Int'l*, pg. 8554
OVERLAND TOTAL LOGISTICS SERVICES VIETNAM JOINT STOCK COMPANY—See Yamato Holdings Co., Ltd.; *Int'l*, pg. 8554
OVERLAND TOTAL LOGISTICS (THAILAND) CO., LTD.—See Yamato Holdings Co., Ltd.; *Int'l*, pg. 8554
OVERLAND WEST FREIGHT LINES LTD.; *Int'l*, pg. 5671
OVERLAND WEST, INC. - BILLINGS OFFICE—See Overland West, Inc.; *U.S. Private*, pg. 3053
OVERLAND WEST, INC.; *U.S. Private*, pg. 3053
OVERLY DOOR COMPANY; *U.S. Private*, pg. 3053
OVERLY MANUFACTURING COMPANY—See Overly Door Company; *U.S. Private*, pg. 3053
OVERMACH SPA.—See Nicolas Correa S.A.; *Int'l*, pg. 5273

OVERMYER & ASSOCIATES INC.; *U.S. Private*, pg. 3053
OVERNIGHT SERVICES GMBH VERMITTLUNG UEBER-REGIONALER KURIERDIENSTE—See International Distributions Services plc; *Int'l*, pg. 3748
OVERON S.L—See WPP plc; *Int'l*, pg. 8477
OVERSEA-CHINESE BANKING CORPORATION LIMITED; *Int'l*, pg. 5671
OVERSEAS ENTERPRISE BERHAD; *Int'l*, pg. 5671
OVERSEAS ADJUSTERS AND SURVEYORS CO—See Lovell Minnick Partners LLC; *U.S. Private*, pg. 2502
THE OVERSEAS ASSURANCE CORPORATION LIMITED—See Oversea-Chinese Banking Corporation Limited; *Int'l*, pg. 5672
OVERSEAS ASSURANCE CORPORATION (MALAYSIA) BERHAD—See Oversea-Chinese Banking Corporation Limited; *Int'l*, pg. 5671
OVERSEAS CHINESE TOWN (ASIA) HOLDINGS LIMITED; *Int'l*, pg. 5672
OVERSEAS COMMODEX CORP.—See Ferd AS; *Int'l*, pg. 2636
OVERSEAS CONTAINER FORWARDING INC.; *Int'l*, pg. 5672
OVERSEAS CONTAINER FORWARDING INC.—See Overseas Container Forwarding Inc.; *Int'l*, pg. 5672
OVERSEAS CONTAINER LINE LIMITED - JAPAN BRANCH—See China COSCO Shipping Corporation Limited; *Int'l*, pg. 1495
OVERSEAS COURIER SERVICE CO., LTD.—See Nikkei Inc.; *Int'l*, pg. 5290
OVERSEAS DEVELOPMENT CORP.; *U.S. Private*, pg. 3053
OVERSEAS EDUCATION LIMITED; *Int'l*, pg. 5672
OVERSEAS EMPLOYMENT SERVICES—See Fauji Foundation; *Int'l*, pg. 2623
OVERSEAS ENTERPRISES—See BELIMO Holding AG; *Int'l*, pg. 965
OVERSEAS HARDWOODS COMPANY; *U.S. Private*, pg. 3053
OVERSEAS MARKETING CORPORATION(PVT.) LTD.; *Int'l*, pg. 5672
OVERSEAS MILITARY SALES CORPORATION; *U.S. Private*, pg. 3053
OVERSEAS PETROLEUM AND INVESTMENT CORPORATION—See CPC Corporation; *Int'l*, pg. 1824
OVERSEAS PRINTING CORPORATION—See HH Global Group Limited; *Int'l*, pg. 3379
OVERSEAS PROJECTS AND EQUIPMENT CO. LLC—See Oman Holdings International Company SAOG; *Int'l*, pg. 5560
OVERSEAS REALTY (CEYLON) PLC; *Int'l*, pg. 5673
OVERSEAS SERVICE CORPORATION-EXCHANGE DIV—See Overseas Service Corporation; *U.S. Private*, pg. 3053
OVERSEAS SERVICE CORPORATION; *U.S. Private*, pg. 3053
OVERSEAS SHIPHOLDING GROUP, INC.—See Saltchuk Resources Inc.; *U.S. Private*, pg. 3534
OVERSEAS TECHNICAL ENGINEERING AND CONSTRUCTION PTE. LTD.—See Dialog Group Berhad; *Int'l*, pg. 2104
OVERSEAS TRADE CO LTD D.O.O.—See Osterreichische Post AG; *Int'l*, pg. 5654
OVERSEAS TRANSPORT UKRAINE LTD.—See Albert Ballin KG; *Int'l*, pg. 296
OVERSEAS WIBORG CHARTERING CO.—See Clarkson PLC; *Int'l*, pg. 1651
OVERSEE.NET; *U.S. Private*, pg. 3053
OVERSIGHT SYSTEMS, INC.—See TCMI, Inc.; *U.S. Private*, pg. 3943
OVERSTOCK ART, LLC.; *U.S. Private*, pg. 3053
OVERSTOCK.COM REAL ESTATE LLC—See Beyond, Inc.; *U.S. Public*, pg. 327
OVERSTOCKDEALS LLC; *U.S. Private*, pg. 3053
OVERSTREET-HUGHES CO., INC.—See Lincoln Electric Holdings, Inc.; *U.S. Public*, pg. 1318
OVERSTREET PAVING COMPANY; *U.S. Private*, pg. 3053
OVER THE WIRE HOLDINGS LIMITED; *Int'l*, pg. 5671
OVERTON CHICAGO GEAR INC.—See Hicks Holdings, LLC; *U.S. Private*, pg. 1934
OVERTON CHICAGO GEAR INC.—See The Riverside Company; *U.S. Private*, pg. 4108
OVERTON CHICAGO GEAR INC.—See Weinberg Capital Group, Inc.; *U.S. Private*, pg. 4471
OVERTON ENTERPRISES, LLC; *U.S. Private*, pg. 3054
OVERTON FINANCIAL CORPORATION; *U.S. Private*, pg. 3054
OVERTON MOORE PROPERTIES; *U.S. Private*, pg. 3054
OVERTON POWER DISTRICT NO 5; *U.S. Private*, pg. 3054
OVERTON'S INC.—See Gander Mountain Company; *U.S. Private*, pg. 1641
OVERTOOM INTERNATIONAL BELGIUM NV—See Manutan International SA; *Int'l*, pg. 4680
OVERTURE PARTNERS; *U.S. Private*, pg. 3054
OVERTURF MOTOR CO. INC.; *U.S. Private*, pg. 3054
OVERUMANS FISK AB—See PRFoods AS; *Int'l*, pg. 5968
OVERUM INDUSTRIES AB—See FairCap GmbH; *Int'l*, pg. 2605

OVERWAITEA FOOD GROUP—See The Jim Pattison Group; *Int'l*, pg. 7660
OVERWATCH LEAGUE, LLC—See Microsoft Corporation; *U.S. Public*, pg. 1439
OVERWATCH SYSTEMS, LTD.—See Textron Inc.; *U.S. Public*, pg. 2028
OVG-PROXY A/S—See The Character Group plc; *Int'l*, pg. 7631
OVH GROUPE SA; *Int'l*, pg. 5673
OVHTECH R&D (INDIA) PRIVATE LIMITED—See OVH Groupe SA; *Int'l*, pg. 5673
OVIDEO—See WPP plc; *Int'l*, pg. 8477
OVIDIAN GROUP LLC—See Pendrell Corporation; *U.S. Public*, pg. 1661
OVID TECHNOLOGIES, INC.—See Wolters Kluwer n.v.; *Int'l*, pg. 8444
OVID TECHNOLOGIES SARL—See Wolters Kluwer n.v.; *Int'l*, pg. 8444
OVID TECHNOLOGIES—See Wolters Kluwer n.v.; *Int'l*, pg. 8444
OVID THERAPEUTICS INC.; *U.S. Public*, pg. 1625
OVID WIND LLC—See Parsan Makina Parcalari Sanayii AS; *Int'l*, pg. 5747
OVIEDO MEDICAL CENTER, LLC—See HCA Healthcare, Inc.; *U.S. Public*, pg. 1005
OVIK LASTEKNIK AB—See Kesko Corporation; *Int'l*, pg. 4142
OV INTERNATIONAL PTE LTD—See Asiatravel.com Holdings Limited; *Int'l*, pg. 620
OVINTIV INC.; *U.S. Public*, pg. 1625
OVISA PAVIMENTOS Y OBRAS SA—See VINCI S.A.; *Int'l*, pg. 8220
OVITEC GMBH—See Jenoptik AG; *Int'l*, pg. 3929
OVIVO AQUA AUSTRIA GMBH—See SKion GmbH; *Int'l*, pg. 6990
OVIVO CHINA CO., LTD.—See SKion GmbH; *Int'l*, pg. 6990
OVIVO DEUTSCHLAND GMBH—See SKion GmbH; *Int'l*, pg. 6990
OVIVO HOLLAND B.V.—See SKion GmbH; *Int'l*, pg. 6990
OVIVO INC.—See SKion GmbH; *Int'l*, pg. 6990
OVIVO MIDDLE EAST L.L.C.—See SKion GmbH; *Int'l*, pg. 6990
OVIVO SINGAPORE PTE. LTD.—See SKion GmbH; *Int'l*, pg. 6990
OVIVO UK LIMITED - INDUSTRIAL DIVISION, COLCHESTER—See SKion GmbH; *Int'l*, pg. 6990
OVIVO UK LIMITED - INDUSTRIAL DIVISION, WOLVERHAMPTON—See SKion GmbH; *Int'l*, pg. 6990
OVIVO UK LIMITED—See SKion GmbH; *Int'l*, pg. 6990
OVIVO USA, LLC - HOUSTON—See SKion GmbH; *Int'l*, pg. 6990
OVIVO USA, LLC—See SKion GmbH; *Int'l*, pg. 6990
OV LOOP, INC.; *U.S. Private*, pg. 3052
OVL OVERSEAS IFSC LIMITED—See Oil & Natural Gas Corporation Limited; *Int'l*, pg. 5534
OVOBEL FOODS LIMITED; *Int'l*, pg. 5673
OVOCA BIO PLC; *Int'l*, pg. 5673
OVODAN FOODS (CHINA) LTD.—See Thornico A/S; *Int'l*, pg. 7720
OVO ENERGY PTY. LIMITED—See AGL Energy Limited; *Int'l*, pg. 211
OVOL ICT SOLUTIONS CO., LTD.—See Japan Pulp and Paper Company Limited; *Int'l*, pg. 3904
OVOL MALAYSIA SDN. BHD.—See Japan Pulp and Paper Company Limited; *Int'l*, pg. 3904
OVOL SINGAPORE PTE. LTD.—See Japan Pulp and Paper Company Limited; *Int'l*, pg. 3904
OVONIC BATTERY COMPANY, INC.—See BASF SE; *Int'l*, pg. 876
OVOPRO—See FPS Food Processing Systems B.V.; *Int'l*, pg. 2757
OVOSTAR UNION N.V.; *Int'l*, pg. 5673
OVPS - OBERELBISCHE VERKEHRSGESELLSCHAFT PIRNA-SEBNITZ MBH; *Int'l*, pg. 5673
OVS INDIA SOURCING PRIVATE LTD.—See OVS S.p.A.; *Int'l*, pg. 5673
OV SMITH & SONS INC.; *U.S. Private*, pg. 3052
OVS OPEL VERSICHERUNGSSERVICE GMBH—See Maiden Holdings, Ltd.; *Int'l*, pg. 4649
OVS S.P.A.; *Int'l*, pg. 5673
OVULINE, INC.—See Laboratory Corporation of America Holdings; *U.S. Public*, pg. 1287
OVUM AUSTRALIA—See Informa plc; *Int'l*, pg. 3693
OVUM HONG KONG—See Informa plc; *Int'l*, pg. 3693
OVUM, INC.—See Informa plc; *Int'l*, pg. 3693
OVUM KOREA LIMITED—See Informa plc; *Int'l*, pg. 3693
OVUM LIMITED—See Informa plc; *Int'l*, pg. 3692
OVUM-RHK—See Informa plc; *Int'l*, pg. 3693
OVUM-RHK—See Informa plc; *Int'l*, pg. 3693
OVZON AB; *Int'l*, pg. 5673
OVZON SWEDEN AB—See Ovzon AB; *Int'l*, pg. 5673
OVZON US, LLC.—See Ovzon AB; *Int'l*, pg. 5673
OWA HAGANE INDUSTRY CO., LTD.—See TORQ Inc.; *Int'l*, pg. 7829
OWANDY IBERIA SL—See Villa Sistemi Medicali S.p.A.; *Int'l*, pg. 8206
OWANDY RADIOLOGIE ITALIA SRL—See Villa Sistemi Medicali S.p.A.; *Int'l*, pg. 8206

COMPANY NAME INDEX

OWANDY SAS—See Villa Sistemi Medicali S.p.A.; *Int'l*, pg. 8206
OWANO SHOTEN CO., LTD.—See Hanwa Co., Ltd.; *Int'l*, pg. 3263
OWARI PRECISE PRODUCTS CO., LTD.; *Int'l*, pg. 5673
OWASCO BEVERAGE INC.; *U.S. Private*, pg. 3054
OWASCO VOLKSWAGEN; *Int'l*, pg. 5673
OWASSO DIALYSIS, LLC—See DaVita Inc.; *U.S. Public*, pg. 641
OWATONNA FORD CHRYSLER; *U.S. Private*, pg. 3054
OW BROTHERS PTE LTD—See Singapore Shipping Corporation Limited; *Int'l*, pg. 6943
OWC PHARMACEUTICAL RESEARCH CORP.; *Int'l*, pg. 5673
O-WELL COLOR CENTER CORPORATION—See O-Well Corporation; *Int'l*, pg. 5503
O-WELL CORPORATION; *Int'l*, pg. 5502
O-WELL (DALIAN) CORPORATION—See O-Well Corporation; *Int'l*, pg. 5503
O-WELL GERMANY GMBH—See O-Well Corporation; *Int'l*, pg. 5503
O-WELL KOREA CORPORATION—See O-Well Corporation; *Int'l*, pg. 5503
O-WELL MEXICO COATINGS & ELECTRONICS S.A. DE C.V.—See O-Well Corporation; *Int'l*, pg. 5503
O-WELL (SHANGHAI) CORPORATION—See O-Well Corporation; *Int'l*, pg. 5503
O-WELL SUPER BUILD CORPORATION—See O-Well Corporation; *Int'l*, pg. 5503
O-WELL (THAILAND) COMPANY LIMITED—See O-Well Corporation; *Int'l*, pg. 5503
O-WELL VIETNAM COMPANY LIMITED—See O-Well Corporation; *Int'l*, pg. 5503
OWEN-AMES-KIMBALL COMPANY; *U.S. Private*, pg. 3054
OWEN-AMES-KIMBALL COMPANY—See Owen-Ames-Kimball Company; *U.S. Private*, pg. 3054
OWEN-AMES-KIMBALL ENGINEERING, INC.—See Owen-Ames-Kimball Company; *U.S. Private*, pg. 3055
OWEN AYRES & ASSOCIATES, INC.; *U.S. Private*, pg. 3054
OWEN & CO. LTD.; *Int'l*, pg. 5673
OWEN COUNTY STATE BANK—See Owen Financial Corporation; *U.S. Private*, pg. 3054
OWENDO CONTAINER TERMINAL SARL—See Financiere de L'Odet; *Int'l*, pg. 2667
OWEN ELECTRIC COOPERATIVE INC.; *U.S. Private*, pg. 3054
OWEN ELECTRIC STEEL COMPANY OF SOUTH CAROLINA—See Commercial Metals Company; *U.S. Public*, pg. 547
OWEN ELECTRIC SUPPLY INC.; *U.S. Private*, pg. 3054
OWEN FINANCIAL CORPORATION; *U.S. Private*, pg. 3054
OWEN INDUSTRIES, INC. - NORTHERN PLAINS FINISHING DIVISION—See Owen Industries, Inc.; *U.S. Private*, pg. 3054
OWEN INDUSTRIES, INC.; *U.S. Private*, pg. 3054
OWEN MUMFORD GMBH—See Owen Mumford Ltd.; *Int'l*, pg. 5673
OWEN MUMFORD INC—See Owen Mumford Ltd.; *Int'l*, pg. 5673
OWEN MUMFORD LTD. - COTSWOLD DIVISION—See Owen Mumford Ltd.; *Int'l*, pg. 5673
OWEN MUMFORD LTD.; *Int'l*, pg. 5673
OWEN MUMFORD—See Owen Mumford Ltd.; *Int'l*, pg. 5673
OWEN OIL TOOLS LP—See Core Laboratories N.V.; *Int'l*, pg. 1798
OWEN PACIFIC; *U.S. Private*, pg. 3054
OWENSBORO GRAIN BIODIESEL, LLC—See Cargill, Inc.; *U.S. Private*, pg. 759
OWENSBORO GRAIN COMPANY, LLC—See Cargill, Inc.; *U.S. Private*, pg. 759
OWENSBORO MANUFACTURING LLC—See The Hines Group, Inc.; *U.S. Private*, pg. 4053
OWENS COMPANIES, INC.; *U.S. Private*, pg. 3055
OWENS CORNING AUSTRALIA PTY LTD—See Owens Corning; *U.S. Public*, pg. 1627
OWENS CORNING CANADA GP INC.—See Owens Corning; *U.S. Public*, pg. 1628
OWENS-CORNING CANADA—See Owens Corning; *U.S. Public*, pg. 1628
OWENS CORNING COMPOSITES (BEIJING) CO., LTD.—See Owens Corning; *U.S. Public*, pg. 1628
OWENS CORNING COMPOSITES (CHINA) CO., LTD.—See Owens Corning; *U.S. Public*, pg. 1628
OWENS-CORNING COMPOSITE SOLUTIONS—See Owens Corning; *U.S. Public*, pg. 1628
OWENS CORNING FIBERGLAS A.S. LIMITADA—See Owens Corning; *U.S. Public*, pg. 1628
OWENS-CORNING FIBERGLAS FRANCE—See Owens Corning; *U.S. Public*, pg. 1628
OWENS-CORNING FIBERGLASS FRANCE S.A.—See Owens Corning; *U.S. Public*, pg. 1628
OWENS-CORNING (GUANGZHOU) FIBERGLAS CO. LTD.—See Owens Corning; *U.S. Public*, pg. 1628
OWENS CORNING HOLDINGS HOLLAND B.V.—See Owens Corning; *U.S. Public*, pg. 1628
OWENS-CORNING (INDIA) LIMITED—See Owens Corning; *U.S. Public*, pg. 1628
OWENS CORNING JAPAN LLC—See Owens Corning; *U.S. Public*, pg. 1628
OWENS CORNING KOREA—See Owens Corning; *U.S. Public*, pg. 1628
OWENS CORNING MEXICO S. DE RL DE C.V.—See Owens Corning; *U.S. Public*, pg. 1628
OWENS CORNING NETHERLAND—See Owens Corning; *U.S. Public*, pg. 1628
OWENS CORNING OCV TECHNICAL FABRICS—See Owens Corning; *U.S. Public*, pg. 1627
OWENS CORNING - OEM SOLUTIONS GROUP—See Owens Corning; *U.S. Public*, pg. 1627
OWENS-CORNING ONTARIO HOLDINGS INC.—See Owens Corning; *U.S. Public*, pg. 1628
OWENS-CORNING (SHANGHAI) TRADING CO., LTD.—See Owens Corning; *U.S. Public*, pg. 1627
OWENS CORNING; *U.S. Public*, pg. 1626
OWENS-CORNING VEIL U.K. LIMITED—See Owens Corning; *U.S. Public*, pg. 1628
OWENS DDB—See Omnicom Group Inc.; *U.S. Public*, pg. 1582
OWEN SECURITY SOLUTIONS INC.; *U.S. Private*, pg. 3054
OWENS GROUP LTD.—See Mainfreight Ltd.; *Int'l*, pg. 4651
OWENS-ILLINOIS GENERAL INC.—See O-I Glass, Inc.; *U.S. Public*, pg. 1559
OWENS-ILLINOIS GROUP, INC.—See O-I Glass, Inc.; *U.S. Public*, pg. 1559
OWENS-ILLINOIS INTERNATIONAL B.V.—See O-I Glass, Inc.; *U.S. Public*, pg. 1559
OWENS-ILLINOIS PERU S.A.—See O-I Glass, Inc.; *U.S. Public*, pg. 1560
OWENS-ILLINOIS POLSKA S.A.—See O-I Glass, Inc.; *U.S. Public*, pg. 1560
OWENS & MINOR DISTRIBUTION, INC.—See Owens & Minor, Inc.; *U.S. Public*, pg. 1626
OWENS & MINOR GLOBAL SERVICES—See Owens & Minor, Inc.; *U.S. Public*, pg. 1626
OWENS & MINOR, INC.; *U.S. Public*, pg. 1625
OWENSMORRIS COMMUNICATIONS, INC.; *U.S. Private*, pg. 3055
OWENC MORTGAGE INVESTMENT FUND, A CALIFORNIA LIMITED PARTNERSHIP; *U.S. Private*, pg. 3055
OWENS REALTY MORTGAGE, INC.—See Waterfall Asset Management LLC; *U.S. Private*, pg. 4453
OWENS TRANSPORT LTD.—See Mainfreight Ltd.; *Int'l*, pg. 4651
OWENS TRANSPORT PTY LTD.—See Mainfreight Ltd.; *Int'l*, pg. 4651
OWENSVILLE SUPPLY, INC.; *U.S. Private*, pg. 3055
OWEN TAYLOR & SONS LTD; *Int'l*, pg. 5673
OWENTON CENTER—See Formation Capital, LLC; *U.S. Private*, pg. 1571
O'WILL CORPORATION; *Int'l*, pg. 5502
OWIN INDUSTRIAL SDN. BHD.—See Aimflex Berhad; *Int'l*, pg. 233
OWL COMPANIES; *U.S. Private*, pg. 3055
OWL COMPUTER SL—See CompuGroup Medical SE & Co. KGaA; *Int'l*, pg. 1757
OWL CYBER DEFENSE SOLUTIONS, LLC—See D.C. Capital Partners, LLC; *U.S. Private*, pg. 1141
OWL EDUCATION & TRAINING, INC.—See Owl Companies; *U.S. Private*, pg. 3055
OWL ENERGY RESOURCES, INC.—See Owl Companies; *U.S. Private*, pg. 3055
OWLER INC.—See Meltwater N.V.; *Int'l*, pg. 4814
OWLET, INC.; *U.S. Public*, pg. 1628
OWLIENT SAS—See Ubisoft Entertainment S.A.; *Int'l*, pg. 8003
OWL LOGISTICS SHANGHAI LIMITED—See XPO, Inc.; *U.S. Public*, pg. 2392
OWL MARINE INSURANCE-BROKERS GMBH & CO. KG—See Marsh & McLennan Companies, Inc.; *U.S. Public*, pg. 1386
OWL OCEAN WORLD LINES EUROPE GMBH—See XPO, Inc.; *U.S. Public*, pg. 2392
OWL OIL INC.; *U.S. Private*, pg. 3055
OWL SERVICES, INC.; *U.S. Private*, pg. 3055
OWLS HEAD TRANSPORTATION MUSEUM; *U.S. Private*, pg. 3055
OWLS, INC.—See en-japan Inc.; *Int'l*, pg. 2395
OWL WIRE & CABLE, LLC—See Atlas Holdings, LLC; *U.S. Private*, pg. 376
OWN A HOLIDAY HOME LIMITED—See Cox & Kings Limited; *Int'l*, pg. 1822
OWNCLOUD GMBH; *Int'l*, pg. 5674
OWNCLOUD, INC.—See ownCloud GmbH; *Int'l*, pg. 5674
OWNENERGY, INC.—See Electricite de France S.A.; *Int'l*, pg. 2350
OWNEN MUMFORD (SHANGHAI) MEDICAL DEVICE COMPANY LTD—See Owen Mumford Ltd.; *Int'l*, pg. 5673
OWNERGUARD CORPORATION—See Stone Point Capital LLC; *U.S. Private*, pg. 3821
OWNERIQ, INC.—See Ontario Municipal Employees Retirement System; *Int'l*, pg. 5584

OXFORD BANK AND TRUST

OWNER RESOURCE GROUP, LLC; *U.S. Private*, pg. 3055
OWNERSEDGE INC.; *U.S. Private*, pg. 3055
OWNERS INSURANCE COMPANY—See Auto-Owners Insurance Company; *U.S. Private*, pg. 398
OWNIT MORTGAGE SOLUTIONS OAKMONT; *U.S. Private*, pg. 3055
OWNLOCAL, INC.; *U.S. Private*, pg. 3055
OWN: OPRAH WINFREY NETWORK LLC—See Warner Bros. Discovery, Inc.; *U.S. Public*, pg. 2327
OWS RAIL CAR, INC.—See Milman Industries Inc.; *Int'l*, pg. 4897
OWT INDUSTRIES, INC.—See Techtronic Industries Co., Ltd.; *Int'l*, pg. 7513
OWT OIL-WATER TREATMENT SERVICES B.V.—See Ecolab Inc.; *U.S. Public*, pg. 716
OWYHEE DIALYSIS, LLC—See DaVita Inc.; *U.S. Public*, pg. 641
OWYHEE GROUP COMPANIES; *U.S. Private*, pg. 3055
OX2 GROUP AB; *Int'l*, pg. 5674
OXADIS S.L.—See Groupe Limagrain Holding SA; *Int'l*, pg. 3108
OXADIS S.R.L.—See Groupe Limagrain Holding SA; *Int'l*, pg. 3108
OXAGILE LLC; *U.S. Private*, pg. 3056
OXAGILE LLC—See Oxagile LLC; *U.S. Private*, pg. 3056
OXALIS CHEMICALS LTD.—See Uyeno Kosan Ltd.; *Int'l*, pg. 8103
OXAMEDIA CORPORATION; *U.S. Private*, pg. 3056
OXARC INC.; *U.S. Private*, pg. 3056
OXATIS SA; *Int'l*, pg. 5674
OXBLUE CORPORATION—See Hexagon AB; *Int'l*, pg. 3369
OX BODIES, INC.—See Federal Signal Corporation; *U.S. Public*, pg. 826
OXBO INTERNATIONAL CORPORATION—See Ploeger Machines B.V.; *Int'l*, pg. 5897
OXBOW CALCINING LLC—See Oxbow Corporation; *U.S. Private*, pg. 3056
OXBOW CARBON BATON ROUGE—See Oxbow Corporation; *U.S. Private*, pg. 3056
OXBOW CARBON & MINERALS INTERNATIONAL GMBH—See Oxbow Corporation; *U.S. Private*, pg. 3056
OXBOW CARBON & MINERALS LLC—See Oxbow Corporation; *U.S. Private*, pg. 3056
OXBOW COAL B.V.—See Oxbow Corporation; *U.S. Private*, pg. 3056
OXBOW COAL B.V.—See Oxbow Corporation; *U.S. Private*, pg. 3056
OXBOW COAL LTD.—See Oxbow Corporation; *U.S. Private*, pg. 3056
OXBOW COAL S.A.R.L.—See Oxbow Corporation; *U.S. Private*, pg. 3056
OXBOW CORPORATION; *U.S. Private*, pg. 3056
OXBOW GMBH—See Oxbow Corporation; *U.S. Private*, pg. 3056
OXBOW MACHINE PRODUCTS INC.; *U.S. Private*, pg. 3056
OXBOW MARKETING COMPANY—See Simplicity Financial Marketing Holdings Inc.; *U.S. Private*, pg. 3667
OXBOW MIDWEST CALCINING LLC—See Oxbow Corporation; *U.S. Private*, pg. 3056
OXBOW MINING, LLC—See Oxbow Corporation; *U.S. Private*, pg. 3056
OXBOW SULPHUR CANADA ULC—See H.J. Baker & Bro., Inc.; *U.S. Private*, pg. 1834
OXBOW SULPHUR & FERTILISER (BRAZIL) LTDA—See Oxbow Corporation; *U.S. Private*, pg. 3056
OXBOW SULPHUR & FERTILISER (SINGAPORE) PTE LTD—See Oxbow Corporation; *U.S. Private*, pg. 3056
OXBOW SULPHUR & FERTILISER (UK) LIMITED—See Oxbow Corporation; *U.S. Private*, pg. 3056
OXBRIDGE ACADEMY (PTY) LTD.—See ADvTECH Limited; *Int'l*, pg. 169
OXBRIDGE RE HOLDINGS LIMITED; *Int'l*, pg. 5674
OXCYON, INC.; *U.S. Private*, pg. 3056
OXEA BISHOP, LLC—See OQ S.A.O.C.; *Int'l*, pg. 5607
OXEA CORPORATION—See OQ S.A.O.C.; *Int'l*, pg. 5607
OXEA GMBH—See OQ S.A.O.C.; *Int'l*, pg. 5607
OXEA HOLDING GMBH—See OQ S.A.O.C.; *Int'l*, pg. 5607
OXEA JAPAN KK—See OQ S.A.O.C.; *Int'l*, pg. 5607
OXEA (NANJING) ADVANCED DERIVATIVES LTD.—See OQ S.A.O.C.; *Int'l*, pg. 5607
OXEA NEDERLAND B.V.—See OQ S.A.O.C.; *Int'l*, pg. 5607
OXEA PTE. LTD.—See OQ S.A.O.C.; *Int'l*, pg. 5607
OXEA S.A R.L.—See OQ S.A.O.C.; *Int'l*, pg. 5607
OXEIA BIOPHARMACEUTICALS, INC.; *U.S. Private*, pg. 3056
OXENDALE CHRYSLER DODGE JEEP; *U.S. Private*, pg. 3056
OXENDALE & CO. LIMITED—See N Brown Group plc; *Int'l*, pg. 5115
OXFORD APPAREL—See Li & Fung Limited; *Int'l*, pg. 4480
OXFORD AVIATION ACADEMY LIMITED—See CAE Inc.; *Int'l*, pg. 1249
OXFORD BANK AND TRUST; *U.S. Private*, pg. 3056

OXFORD BANK CORPORATION

OXFORD BANK CORPORATION; *U.S. Public*, pg. 1628
OXFORD BANK—See Oxford Bank Corporation; *U.S. Public*, pg. 1628
OXFORD BIODYNAMICS PLC; *Int'l*, pg. 5674
OXFORD BIOMEDICA PLC; *Int'l*, pg. 5674
OXFORD BUILDERS SUPPLIES—See EllisDon Corporation; *Int'l*, pg. 2367
THE OXFORD BUS COMPANY LTD—See GLOBALVIA Inversiones, S.A.U.; *Int'l*, pg. 3005
THE OXFORD BUS COMPANY LTD—See Kinetic Group Services Pty Ltd.; *Int'l*, pg. 4168
OXFORD CANNABINOID HOLDINGS PLC; *Int'l*, pg. 5674
OXFORD CANNABINOID TECHNOLOGIES LTD.—See Oxford Cannabinoid Holdings Plc; *Int'l*, pg. 5674
OXFORD CARIBBEAN, INC.—See Oxford Industries, Inc.; *U.S. Public*, pg. 1629
OXFORD COMMUNICATIONS, INC.; *U.S. Private*, pg. 3056
OXFORD CONSTRUCTION COMPANY; *U.S. Private*, pg. 3057
OXFORD CONSULTING GROUP, INC.; *U.S. Private*, pg. 3057
OXFORD CRYOSYSTEMS LTD.—See Judges Scientific plc; *Int'l*, pg. 4021
OXFORD DEVELOPMENT COMPANY; *U.S. Private*, pg. 3057
OXFORD DODGE CHRYSLER JEEP LTD; *Int'l*, pg. 5674
OXFORD FAJAR SDN. BHD.—See Oxford University Press; *Int'l*, pg. 5675
OXFORD FINANCIAL GROUP LTD.; *U.S. Private*, pg. 3057
OXFORD FORGE, INC.—See American Axle & Manufacturing Holdings, Inc.; *U.S. Public*, pg. 97
OXFORD FROZEN FOODS LIMITED—See Bragg Group of Companies; *Int'l*, pg. 1136
OXFORD GARMENT, INC.—See Oxford Industries, Inc.; *U.S. Public*, pg. 1629
OXFORD GENE TECHNOLOGY INC.—See Sysmex Corporation; *Int'l*, pg. 7388
OXFORD GENE TECHNOLOGY (OPERATIONS) LIMITED—See Sysmex Corporation; *Int'l*, pg. 7388
OXFORD GLOBAL RESOURCES, INC.—See H.I.G. Capital, LLC; *U.S. Private*, pg. 1831
OXFORD HEALTH PLANS (CT)—See UnitedHealth Group Incorporated; *U.S. Public*, pg. 2249
OXFORD HEALTH PLANS LLC—See UnitedHealth Group Incorporated; *U.S. Public*, pg. 2249
OXFORD HEALTH PLANS (NY), INC.—See UnitedHealth Group Incorporated; *U.S. Public*, pg. 2249
OXFORD HOLDINGS INC.; *U.S. Private*, pg. 3057
OXFORD HOTEL PTE LTD—See Koh Brothers Group Limited; *Int'l*, pg. 4228
OXFORD IMMUNOTEC GLOBAL LIMITED—See Revvity, Inc.; *U.S. Public*, pg. 1794
OXFORD IMMUNOTEC, INC.—See Revvity, Inc.; *U.S. Public*, pg. 1794
OXFORD IMMUNOTEC K.K.—See Revvity, Inc.; *U.S. Public*, pg. 1794
OXFORD IMMUNOTEC LTD—See Revvity, Inc.; *U.S. Public*, pg. 1794
OXFORD INDUSTRIES, INC.; *U.S. Public*, pg. 1629
OXFORD INSTRUMENTS AMERICA, INC.—See Oxford Instruments Plc; *Int'l*, pg. 5674
OXFORD INSTRUMENTS-ANALYTICAL—See Oxford Instruments Plc; *Int'l*, pg. 5675
OXFORD INSTRUMENTS GMBH—See Oxford Instruments Plc; *Int'l*, pg. 5674
OXFORD INSTRUMENTS KK—See Oxford Instruments Plc; *Int'l*, pg. 5674
OXFORD INSTRUMENTS MOLECULAR BIOTOOLS LTD—See Oxford Instruments Plc; *Int'l*, pg. 5674
OXFORD INSTRUMENTS OVERSEAS HOLDINGS 2008 LTD—See Oxford Instruments Plc; *Int'l*, pg. 5674
OXFORD INSTRUMENTS OVERSEAS MARKETING LTD—See Oxford Instruments Plc; *Int'l*, pg. 5674
OXFORD INSTRUMENTS PLASMA TECHNOLOGY LTD—See Oxford Instruments Plc; *Int'l*, pg. 5674
OXFORD INSTRUMENTS PLC; *Int'l*, pg. 5674
OXFORD INSTRUMENTS PTE LTD—See Oxford Instruments Plc; *Int'l*, pg. 5674
OXFORD INSTRUMENTS SAS—See Oxford Instruments Plc; *Int'l*, pg. 5675
OXFORD INSTRUMENTS-SUPERCONDUCTIVITY—See Oxford Instruments Plc; *Int'l*, pg. 5675
OXFORD INSTRUMENTS-X-RAY TECHNOLOGY GROUP—See Oxford Instruments Plc; *Int'l*, pg. 5674
THE OXFORD INVESTMENT GROUP, INC.; *U.S. Private*, pg. 4089
OXFORD INVESTMENTS HOLDINGS INC.; *Int'l*, pg. 5675
OXFORD LANE CAPITAL CORP.; *U.S. Public*, pg. 1629
OXFORD LIFE INSURANCE COMPANY—See U-Haul Holding Company; *U.S. Public*, pg. 2211
OXFORD METRICS PLC; *Int'l*, pg. 5675
OXFORD MINING COMPANY, LLC; *U.S. Private*, pg. 3057
OXFORD MUSIC ONLINE—See Oxford University Press; *Int'l*, pg. 5675
OXFORD NANOPORE TECHNOLOGIES PLC; *Int'l*, pg. 5675
OXFORD NORTHEAST, LTD.; *U.S. Private*, pg. 3057

OXFORD PHARMAGENESIS AG—See Oxford PharmaGenesis Ltd.; *Int'l*, pg. 5675
OXFORD PHARMAGENESIS INC.—See Oxford PharmaGenesis Ltd.; *Int'l*, pg. 5675
OXFORD PHARMAGENESIS LTD.; *Int'l*, pg. 5675
OXFORD PHOTOVOLTAICS LIMITED; *Int'l*, pg. 5675
OXFORD PRODUCTS (INTERNATIONAL) LIMITED—See Oxford Industries, Inc.; *U.S. Public*, pg. 1629
OXFORD PROPERTIES GROUP, INC.—See Ontario Municipal Employees Retirement System; *Int'l*, pg. 5585
OXFORD PROPERTIES, LLC; *U.S. Private*, pg. 3057
OXFORD REALTY FINANCIAL GROUP; *U.S. Private*, pg. 3057
OXFORD REALTY, INC.; *U.S. Private*, pg. 3057
OXFORD SCIENTIFIC FILMS LIMITED—See ITV plc; *Int'l*, pg. 3845
OXFORD SQUARE CAPITAL CORP.; *U.S. Public*, pg. 1629
OXFORD TECHNOLOGY 2 VENTURE CAPITAL TRUST PLC; *Int'l*, pg. 5675
OXFORD TECHNOLOGY VENTURE CAPITAL TRUST PLC; *Int'l*, pg. 5675
OXFORD THAMES HOTEL OPCO LIMITED—See InterContinental Hotels Group PLC; *Int'l*, pg. 3739
OXFORD TRANSFER STATION, LLC—See Casella Waste Systems, Inc.; *U.S. Public*, pg. 446
OXFORD TREATMENT CENTER, LLC—See AAC Holdings, Inc.; *U.S. Private*, pg. 30
OXFORD UNIVERSITY PRESS ARGENTINA SA—See Oxford University Press; *Int'l*, pg. 5675
OXFORD UNIVERSITY PRESS CANADA—See Oxford University Press; *Int'l*, pg. 5675
OXFORD UNIVERSITY PRESS CHINA LTD—See Oxford University Press; *Int'l*, pg. 5675
OXFORD UNIVERSITY PRESS DO BRASIL PUBLICACOES LTDA—See Oxford University Press; *Int'l*, pg. 5676
OXFORD UNIVERSITY PRESS EAST AFRICA LTD.—See Oxford University Press; *Int'l*, pg. 5675
OXFORD UNIVERSITY PRESS ECUADOR SA—See Oxford University Press; *Int'l*, pg. 5675
OXFORD UNIVERSITY PRESS ESPANA S.A.—See Oxford University Press; *Int'l*, pg. 5675
OXFORD UNIVERSITY PRESS, INC.—See Oxford University Press; *Int'l*, pg. 5675
OXFORD UNIVERSITY PRESS (INDIA)—See Oxford University Press; *Int'l*, pg. 5675
OXFORD UNIVERSITY PRESS K.K.—See Oxford University Press; *Int'l*, pg. 5675
OXFORD UNIVERSITY PRESS (MACAU) LTD.—See Oxford University Press; *Int'l*, pg. 5675
OXFORD UNIVERSITY PRESS MEXICO S.A. DE C.V.—See Oxford University Press; *Int'l*, pg. 5675
OXFORD UNIVERSITY PRESS PAKISTAN LTD.—See Oxford University Press; *Int'l*, pg. 5676
OXFORD UNIVERSITY PRESS POLSKA SP. Z O.O.—See Oxford University Press; *Int'l*, pg. 5676
OXFORD UNIVERSITY PRESS—See Oxford University Press; *Int'l*, pg. 5675
OXFORD UNIVERSITY PRESS—See Oxford University Press; *Int'l*, pg. 5675
OXFORD UNIVERSITY PRESS—See Oxford University Press; *Int'l*, pg. 5676
OXFORD UNIVERSITY PRESS; *Int'l*, pg. 5675
OXFORD UNIVERSITY PRESS (SOUTH AFRICA)—See Oxford University Press; *Int'l*, pg. 5675
OXFORD UNIVERSITY PRESS TANZANIA LTD—See Oxford University Press; *Int'l*, pg. 5676
OXFORD VILLAGE LTD—See UMH Properties, Inc.; *U.S. Public*, pg. 2225
OXIDE CORPORATION; *Int'l*, pg. 5676
OXIEM, LLC; *U.S. Private*, pg. 3057
OXIGENO DEL NORTE S.A.—See Mitsubishi Chemical Group Corporation; *Int'l*, pg. 4937
OXIGENOS DE COLOMBIA LTDA.—See Linde plc; *Int'l*, pg. 4509
OXIGENOS DE COLOMBIA LTDA.—See Linde plc; *Int'l*, pg. 4509
OXIMESA, S.L.—See Mitsubishi Chemical Group Corporation; *Int'l*, pg. 4937
OXIMET S.R.L.—See American Securities LLC; *U.S. Private*, pg. 252
OXINOVA C.A.—See GrupoNueva S.A.; *Int'l*, pg. 3140
OXIQUIM SA; *Int'l*, pg. 5676
OXIRANE CHEMICAL CORPORATION—See Adeka Corporation; *Int'l*, pg. 142
OXITEC DO BRASIL TECNOLOGIA DE INSETOS LTDA—See Precigen, Inc.; *U.S. Public*, pg. 1713
OXITEC LTD.—See Precigen, Inc.; *U.S. Public*, pg. 1713
OXITENO ANDINA, C.A.—See Ultrapar Participacoes S.A.; *Int'l*, pg. 8019
OXITENO COLOMBIA S.A.S—See Ultrapar Participacoes S.A.; *Int'l*, pg. 8019
OXITENO EUROPE SPRL—See Ultrapar Participacoes S.A.; *Int'l*, pg. 8019
OXITENO MEXICO S.A. DE C.V.—See Ultrapar Participacoes S.A.; *Int'l*, pg. 8019

CORPORATE AFFILIATIONS

OXITENO NORDESTE S.A. INDUSTRIA E COMERCIO—See Ultrapar Participacoes S.A.; *Int'l*, pg. 8019
OXITENO SERVICIOS CORPORATIVOS S.A. DE C.V.—See Ultrapar Participacoes S.A.; *Int'l*, pg. 8019
OXITENO USA LLC—See Ultrapar Participacoes S.A.; *Int'l*, pg. 8019
OXLEY DEVELOPMENT PTE LTD—See Tuan Sing Holdings Limited; *Int'l*, pg. 7962
OXLEY HOLDINGS LIMITED; *Int'l*, pg. 5676
OXLEY HOLDINGS (MALAYSIA) SDN. BHD.—See Oxley Holdings Limited; *Int'l*, pg. 5676
OXLEY-WORLDBRIDGE (CAMBODIA) CO., LTD.—See Oxley Holdings Limited; *Int'l*, pg. 5676
OXLO SYSTEMS, INC.—See Dura Software Series A Qof LLC; *U.S. Private*, pg. 1292
OXMOOR CRA-B1, LLC—See Independence Realty Trust, Inc.; *U.S. Public*, pg. 1116
OXMOOR FORD LINCOLN MERCURY, INC.; *U.S. Private*, pg. 3057
OXMOOR TOYOTA; *U.S. Private*, pg. 3057
OXOID AB—See Thermo Fisher Scientific Inc.; *U.S. Public*, pg. 2150
OXOID AG—See Thermo Fisher Scientific Inc.; *U.S. Public*, pg. 2150
OXOID AS—See Thermo Fisher Scientific Inc.; *U.S. Public*, pg. 2150
OXOID A/S—See Thermo Fisher Scientific Inc.; *U.S. Public*, pg. 2149
OXOID AUSTRALIA PTY. LIMITED—See Thermo Fisher Scientific Inc.; *U.S. Public*, pg. 2150
OXOID BRAZIL LTDA—See Thermo Fisher Scientific Inc.; *U.S. Public*, pg. 2150
OXOID BV—See Thermo Fisher Scientific Inc.; *U.S. Public*, pg. 2150
OXOID COMPANY—See Thermo Fisher Scientific Inc.; *U.S. Public*, pg. 2150
OXOID CZ S.R.O.—See Thermo Fisher Scientific Inc.; *U.S. Public*, pg. 2150
OXOID DEUTSCHLAND GMBH—See Thermo Fisher Scientific Inc.; *U.S. Public*, pg. 2150
OXOID INVESTMENTS GMBH—See Thermo Fisher Scientific Inc.; *U.S. Public*, pg. 2154
OXOID LIMITED—See Thermo Fisher Scientific Inc.; *U.S. Public*, pg. 2150
OXOID LIMITED—See Thermo Fisher Scientific Inc.; *U.S. Public*, pg. 2150
OXOID N.V.—See Thermo Fisher Scientific Inc.; *U.S. Public*, pg. 2150
OXOID S.P.A—See Thermo Fisher Scientific Inc.; *U.S. Public*, pg. 2150
OXO INTERNATIONAL INC.—See Helen of Troy Limited; *Int'l*, pg. 3329
OXONICA LIMITED; *Int'l*, pg. 5676
OX PAPERBOARD LLC—See Ox Paper Tube & Core, Inc.; *U.S. Private*, pg. 3056
OX PAPER TUBE & CORE, INC.; *U.S. Private*, pg. 3055
OXPAY FINANCIAL LIMITED; *Int'l*, pg. 5676
OXPAY (M) SDN. BHD.—See OxPay Financial Limited; *Int'l*, pg. 5676
OXPAY SG PTE. LTD.—See OxPay Financial Limited; *Int'l*, pg. 5676
OXPLUS B.V.—See Bentley Systems, Inc.; *U.S. Public*, pg. 297
OXURION NV; *Int'l*, pg. 5676
OXXIIUS SA—See BNP Paribas SA; *Int'l*, pg. 1089
OXXO SA—See Cevital S.p.A.; *Int'l*, pg. 1425
OXXY GROUP PLC; *Int'l*, pg. 5676
OXXYNOVA GMBH; *Int'l*, pg. 5676
OXYA CONSULTING BENELUX NV—See Hitachi, Ltd.; *Int'l*, pg. 3423
OXYA CORPORATION—See Hitachi, Ltd.; *Int'l*, pg. 3423
OXYA UK LIMITED—See Hitachi, Ltd.; *Int'l*, pg. 3423
OXYBOT, INC—See TBS Holdings, Inc.; *Int'l*, pg. 7481
OXYCHEM DO BRASIL LTDA.—See Occidental Petroleum Corporation; *U.S. Public*, pg. 1562
OXYCHEM - LUDINGTON—See Occidental Petroleum Corporation; *U.S. Public*, pg. 1561
OXYCOUPAGE CHAMPAGNE—See Oxymetal SA; *Int'l*, pg. 5676
OXYDE BELGIUM BVBA—See Oxyde Chemicals, Inc.; *U.S. Private*, pg. 3057
OXYDE CHEMICALS, INC.; *U.S. Private*, pg. 3057
OXYFRESH WORLDWIDE, INC.—See Young Living Essential Oils, LC; *U.S. Private*, pg. 4593
OXYGAS LTD.—See Alam Group of Companies; *Int'l*, pg. 289
OXYGEN ADVERTISING, INC.; *U.S. Private*, pg. 3057
OXYGEN & ARGON WORKS, LTD.—See Air Products & Chemicals, Inc.; *U.S. Public*, pg. 66
OXYGEN BUSINESS SOLUTIONS PTY. LTD—See DXC Technology Company; *U.S. Public*, pg. 695
OXYGEN CAPITAL CORPORATION; *Int'l*, pg. 5676
OXYGEN CONSULTANCY—See Allgeier SE; *Int'l*, pg. 337
OXYGENE INDUSTRIEL GIRARDIN, INC.—See Linde plc; *Int'l*, pg. 4509
OXYGEN FINANCE AMERICAS, INC.—See TruFin plc; *Int'l*, pg. 7941

COMPANY NAME INDEX

OXYGEN FINANCE LIMITED—See TruFin plc; *Int'l*, pg. 7941
OXYGEN FREEJUMPING LTD.—See Literacy Capital Plc; *Int'l*, pg. 4526
OXYGEN LEARNING PTY LIMITED—See WPP plc; *Int'l*, pg. 8462
OXYGEN MEDIA LLC—See Comcast Corporation; *U.S. Public*, pg. 540
OXYGEN ONE, INC.—See AdaptHealth Corp.; *U.S. Public*, pg. 39
OXYGEN—See Robert Kennedy Publishing; *Int'l*, pg. 6368
OXYLION S.A.—See Cyber_Folks S.A.; *Int'l*, pg. 1892
OXYMASTER S.A.—See L'Air Liquide S.A.; *Int'l*, pg. 4375
OXYMETAL BOURGOGNE—See Oxymetal SA; *Int'l*, pg. 5676
OXYMETAL EST—See Oxymetal SA; *Int'l*, pg. 5676
OXYMETAL NORMANDIE—See Oxymetal SA; *Int'l*, pg. 5676
OXYMETAL OUEST—See Oxymetal SA; *Int'l*, pg. 5676
OXYMETAL PARIS EST—See Oxymetal SA; *Int'l*, pg. 5676
OXYMETAL SA; *Int'l*, pg. 5676
OXYNORD SA—See Oxymetal SA; *Int'l*, pg. 5676
OXYON PEOPLES SOLUTIONS PROPRIETARY LIMITED—See Workforce Holdings Ltd.; *Int'l*, pg. 8455
OXYPLAST BELGIUM NV—See Protech Chemicals Ltd.; *Int'l*, pg. 6004
OXYPLAST MAROC S.A.R.L.—See Protech Chemicals Ltd.; *Int'l*, pg. 6004
OXYPLAST TAIWAN CO. LTD.—See Protech Chemicals Ltd.; *Int'l*, pg. 6004
OXYPLAST UK LIMITED—See Protech Chemicals Ltd.; *Int'l*, pg. 6004
OXY RECKITT BENCKISER LLC—See Reckitt Benckiser Group plc; *Int'l*, pg. 6236
OXY USA INC.—See Occidental Petroleum Corporation; *U.S. Public*, pg. 1561
OXY VINYLS CANADA CO.—See Occidental Petroleum Corporation; *U.S. Public*, pg. 1562
OXY VINYLS EXPORT SALES, LLC—See Occidental Petroleum Corporation; *U.S. Public*, pg. 1562
OXY VINYLS, LP—See Occidental Petroleum Corporation; *U.S. Public*, pg. 1562
OXYVIT KIMYA SANAYII VE TIC. A.S.—See Soda Sanayii A.S.; *Int'l*, pg. 7045
OYAK CEMENT GROUP; *Int'l*, pg. 5677
OYAK GIRISIM DANISMANLIGI A.S.—See OYAK Cement Group; *Int'l*, pg. 5678
OYAK-RENAULT OTOMOBIL FABRIKALARI AS—See Renault S.A.; *Int'l*, pg. 6274
OYAK SAVUNMA VE GUVENLIK SISTEMLERI A.S.—See OYAK Cement Group; *Int'l*, pg. 5678
OYAK YATIRIM MENKUL DEGERLER A.S.; *Int'l*, pg. 5678
OYAK YATIRIM ORTAKLIGI AS; *Int'l*, pg. 5678
OY ALFA-KEM AB—See Panostaja Oyj; *Int'l*, pg. 5729
OY ALFRED A. PALMBERG AB—See YIT Corporation; *Int'l*, pg. 8586
OY ATLAS COPCO AB—See Atlas Copco AB; *Int'l*, pg. 684
OY ATLAS COPCO KOMPRESSORIT AB—See Atlas Copco AB; *Int'l*, pg. 684
OY ATLAS COPCO LOUHINTATEKNIIKKA AB—See Atlas Copco AB; *Int'l*, pg. 684
OY ATLAS COPCO ROTEX AB—See Atlas Copco AB; *Int'l*, pg. 684
OY ATLAS COPCO TOOLS AB—See Atlas Copco AB; *Int'l*, pg. 684
OY AURINKOMATKAT-SUNTOURS LTD. AB—See Finnair Plc; *Int'l*, pg. 8586
OY AUTOCARRERA AB—See Kesko Corporation; *Int'l*, pg. 4142
OY. AVANE TRADING LTD.—See Dainichiseika Color & Chemicals Mfg. Co., Ltd.; *Int'l*, pg. 1939
OY BALTINIA AB—See KJK Capital Oy; *Int'l*, pg. 4197
OY BENZLER AB—See Elecon Engineering Company Ltd.; *Int'l*, pg. 2348
OY BIOMAR AB—See Aktieselskabet Schouw & Co.; *Int'l*, pg. 265
OY BMW SUOMI AB—See Bayerische Motoren Werke Aktiengesellschaft; *Int'l*, pg. 912
OY BRISTOL-MYERS SQUIBB (FINLAND) AB—See Bristol-Myers Squibb Company; *U.S. Public*, pg. 387
OY CENTER-INN AB—See Suomen Osuuskauppojen Keskuskunta; *Int'l*, pg. 7333
OY COLLY COMPANY AB—See Indutrade AB; *Int'l*, pg. 3680
OY COMBI COOL AB—See Beijer Ref AB; *Int'l*, pg. 945
OY CONAXESS TRADE FINLAND AB—See Aurelius Equity Opportunities SE & Co. KGaA; *Int'l*, pg. 709
OY DAT - SCHAUB FINLAND AB—See Danish Crown AmbA; *Int'l*, pg. 1964
OY DELL A.B.—See Dell Technologies Inc.; *U.S. Public*, pg. 556
OY EBOOKERS FINLAND LTD—See Expedia Group, Inc.; *U.S. Public*, pg. 809
OY ECOLAB AB—See Ecolab Inc.; *U.S. Public*, pg. 716
OY EKORNES AB—See QuMei Home Furnishings Group Co., Ltd.; *Int'l*, pg. 6166
OY ELECTROLUX AB—See AB Electrolux; *Int'l*, pg. 41

OY ELECTROLUX KOTITALOUSKONEET AB—See AB Electrolux; *Int'l*, pg. 41
OY ELI LILLY FINLAND AB—See Eli Lilly & Company; *U.S. Public*, pg. 733
OYER INC.; *U.S. Private*, pg. 3057
OY ESSITY FINLAND AB—See Essity Aktiebolag; *Int'l*, pg. 2517
OY ETRA AB; *Int'l*, pg. 5676
OYEX HANDELS GMBH—See AG Anadolu Grubu Holding A.S.; *Int'l*, pg. 197
OY FARNELL AB—See Avnet, Inc.; *U.S. Public*, pg. 254
OY FENNOSCANDIAN RESOURCES AB—See Beowulf Mining plc; *Int'l*, pg. 978
OY FERROSAN AB—See Altor Equity Partners AB; *Int'l*, pg. 394
OY FG-NAXOS AB—See HNH International Ltd.; *Int'l*, pg. 3434
OY FINN-GAMEC AB—See K-Develop Oy; *Int'l*, pg. 4042
OY FINNISH PEROXIDES AB—See Solvay S.A.; *Int'l*, pg. 7078
OY FINNMATKAT AB—See TUI AG; *Int'l*, pg. 7965
OY FINNROCK AB—See Oy Forcit AB; *Int'l*, pg. 5677
OY FORCIT AB; *Int'l*, pg. 5676
OY FORD AB—See Ford Motor Company; *U.S. Public*, pg. 867
OY. GAMBRO—See Baxter International Inc.; *U.S. Public*, pg. 282
OY GAMECLUSTER LTD.—See G-cluster Global Corporation; *Int'l*, pg. 2862
OY GRUNDFOS ENVIRONMENTAL FINLAND AB—See The Poul Due Jensen Foundation; *Int'l*, pg. 7676
OY GRUNDFOS PUMPUT AB—See The Poul Due Jensen Foundation; *Int'l*, pg. 7676
OY HAKO GROUND & GARDEN AB—See L. Possehl & Co. mbH; *Int'l*, pg. 4384
OY HALTON GROUP LTD.; *Int'l*, pg. 5677
OY HARTWALL AB—See Royal Unibrew A/S; *Int'l*, pg. 6414
OY H.B. FULLER NORDIC AB—See H.B. Fuller Company; *U.S. Public*, pg. 978
OY HEDENGREN SECURITY AB—See Aiphone Co., Ltd.; *Int'l*, pg. 235
OY H. LUNDBECK AB—See Lundbeckfonden; *Int'l*, pg. 4582
OY HUSQVARNA COMMERCIAL SOLUTIONS FINI AND AB—See Husqvarna AB; *Int'l*, pg. 3539
OY IBM FINLAND AB—See International Business Machines Corporation; *U.S. Public*, pg. 1149
OY IBM FINLAND AB—See International Business Machines Corporation; *U.S. Public*, pg. 1149
OY INNOTEAM OY AB—See REHAU Verwaltungszentrale AG; *Int'l*, pg. 6256
OY INTERCARRIERS AB—See Grimaldi Group SpA; *Int'l*, pg. 3085
OY JENS S. AB—See Axel Johnson Gruppen AB; *Int'l*, pg. 763
OY J-TRADING AB—See Iseki & Co., Ltd.; *Int'l*, pg. 3814
OY KAHA AB; *Int'l*, pg. 5677
OYKA KAGIT AMBALAJ SAN. A.S.—See OYAK Cement Group; *Int'l*, pg. 5678
OY KARL FAZER AB; *Int'l*, pg. 5677
OY KELLFRI AB—See Volati Ab; *Int'l*, pg. 8301
OY KOKKO-FIBER AB—See IMCD N.V.; *Int'l*, pg. 3622
OY KONTE AB—See YIT Corporation; *Int'l*, pg. 8586
OY KOPPERS FINLAND AB—See Koppers Holdings Inc.; *U.S. Public*, pg. 1272
OY KUEHNE + NAGEL LTD.—See Kuehne + Nagel International AG; *Int'l*, pg. 4325
OY LEIRAS TAKEDA PHARMACEUTICALS AB—See Takeda Pharmaceutical Company Limited; *Int'l*, pg. 7439
OY LESJOFORS AB—See Beijer Alma AB; *Int'l*, pg. 943
OY LINDAB AB—See Lindab International AB; *Int'l*, pg. 4504
OY LINDE GAS AB—See Linde plc; *Int'l*, pg. 4506
OY LINING AB—See Indutrade AB; *Int'l*, pg. 3680
O.Y.L. MANUFACTURING COMPANY SDN. BHD. (OYLM)—See Daikin Industries, Ltd.; *Int'l*, pg. 1936
OY LM ERICSSON AB—See Telefonaktiebolaget LM Ericsson; *Int'l*, pg. 7534
OYLUM SINAI YATIRIMLAR A.S.; *Int'l*, pg. 5678
OY LUXOTTICA FINLAND AB—See EssilorLuxottica SA; *Int'l*, pg. 2515
OY MAANTERA AB—See Indutrade AB; *Int'l*, pg. 3680
OY MARITIM AB—See Oy Etra AB; *Int'l*, pg. 5676
OY MEDIX BIOCHEMICA AB—See DevCo Partners Oy; *Int'l*, pg. 2086
OY MERCANTILE AB—See BASF SE; *Int'l*, pg. 880
OY METRORADIO FINLAND AB—See Communicorp Group Ltd.; *Int'l*, pg. 1721
OY NEFAB AB—See Nefab AB; *Int'l*, pg. 5191
OY NIS - NORDIC INDUSTRIAL SALES AB—See Oy Karl Fazer Ab; *Int'l*, pg. 5677
OY NORDISK FILM AB—See Egmont Fonden; *Int'l*, pg. 2326
OYOCAR GROUP, INC.; *Int'l*, pg. 5678
OYO CORPORATION, PACIFIC—See OYO Corporation; *Int'l*, pg. 5678
OYO CORPORATION; *Int'l*, pg. 5678

OYO CORPORATION U.S.A.—See OYO Corporation; *Int'l*, pg. 5678
OYO GEOSPACE CHINA—See GEOSPACE TECHNOLOGIES CORPORATION; *U.S. Public*, pg. 934
OYO GEOTECHNICAL CORPORATION—See OYO Corporation; *Int'l*, pg. 5678
OYO RESOURCES MANAGEMENT CORPROATION—See OYO Corporation; *Int'l*, pg. 5678
OYO RMS CORPORATION—See Moody's Corporation; *U.S. Public*, pg. 1469
OYO SEISMIC INSTRUMENTATION CORPROATION—See OYO Corporation; *Int'l*, pg. 5678
OY OSRAM AB—See ams AG; *Int'l*, pg. 440
OY OTICON AB—See Demant A/S; *Int'l*, pg. 2024
OY PUKKILA AB—See QuattroR SGR S.p.A.; *Int'l*, pg. 6157
OY RAUMA STEVEDORING LTD.—See Brookfield Infrastructure Partners L.P.; *Int'l*, pg. 1190
OY RENTOKIL INITIAL AB—See Rentokil Initial plc; *Int'l*, pg. 6287
OYSA CIMENTO SANAYII A.S.—See Haci Omer Sabanci Holding A.S.; *Int'l*, pg. 3203
OYSA CIMENTO SANAYII A.S.—See OYAK Cement Group; *Int'l*, pg. 5678
OY SAMLINK AB—See Cognizant Technology Solutions Corporation; *U.S. Public*, pg. 525
OY SCA HYGIENE PRODUCTS AB—See Svenska Cellulosa Aktiebolaget SCA; *Int'l*, pg. 7356
OY SCHENKER EAST AB—See Deutsche Bahn AG; *Int'l*, pg. 2053
OY SELECTA AB—See Allianz SE; *Int'l*, pg. 355
OY SHERWIN-WILLIAMS FINLAND AB—See The Sherwin-Williams Company; *U.S. Public*, pg. 2128
OYSHO CESKA REPUBLICA, SRO—See Industria de Diseno Textil, S.A.; *Int'l*, pg. 3666
OYSHO CIS LTD.—See Industria de Diseno Textil, S.A.; *Int'l*, pg. 3666
OYSHO ESPANA S.A.—See Industria de Diseno Textil, S.A.; *Int'l*, pg. 3666
OYSHO FRANCE, S.A.R.L.—See Industria de Diseno Textil, S.A.; *Int'l*, pg. 3666
OYSHO GIYIM ITHALAT IHRACAT VE TICARET LTD—See Industria de Diseno Textil, S.A.; *Int'l*, pg. 3666
OYSHO HELLAS S.A.—See Industria de Diseno Textil, S.A.; *Int'l*, pg. 3666
OYSHO ITALIA, S.R.L.—See Industria de Diseno Textil, S.A.; *Int'l*, pg. 3666
OYSHO LOGISTICA, S.A.—See Industria de Diseno Textil, S.A.; *Int'l*, pg. 3666
OYSHO MAGYARORSZAG, KFT—See Industria de Diseno Textil, S.A.; *Int'l*, pg. 3666
OYSHO MEXICO, S.A. DE C.V.—See Industria de Diseno Textil, S.A.; *Int'l*, pg. 3666
OYSHO POLSKA SP ZO.O.—See Industria de Diseno Textil, S.A.; *Int'l*, pg. 3667
OYSHO PORTUGAL CONF. LDA.—See Industria de Diseno Textil, S.A.; *Int'l*, pg. 3667
OYSHO RO, SRL—See Industria de Diseno Textil, S.A.; *Int'l*, pg. 3667
OYSHO SERBIA, D.O.O.—See Industria de Diseno Textil, S.A.; *Int'l*, pg. 3667
OY SIKA FINLAND AB—See Sika AG; *Int'l*, pg. 6915
OY SINEBRYCHOFF AB—See Carlsberg A/S; *Int'l*, pg. 1340
OY SISU AUTO AB—See Oy Suomen Autoteollisuus Ab; *Int'l*, pg. 5677
OY SKF AB—See SKF AB; *Int'l*, pg. 6981
OYSTAR HOLDING GMBH—See Odewald & Compagnie Gesellschaft fur Beteiligungen mbH; *Int'l*, pg. 5525
OYSTER BAY WIND FARM (RF) (PTY.) LTD.—See Enel S.p.A.; *Int'l*, pg. 2414
OYSTER BAY WINES AUSTRALIA PTY LIMITED—See Delegat's Group Limited; *Int'l*, pg. 2011
OYSTER BAY WINES USA, INC—See Delegat's Group Limited; *Int'l*, pg. 2011
OYSTER ENTERPRISES ACQUISITION CORP.; *U.S. Public*, pg. 1629
OYSTER MARINE LTD.—See H.T.P. Investments BV; *Int'l*, pg. 3196
OYSTER MEDISAFE PRIVATE LTD.—See B. Braun Melsungen AG; *Int'l*, pg. 788
OYSTER POINT APARTMENTS VIRGINIA, LLC—See RAIT Financial Trust; *U.S. Private*, pg. 3349
OYSTER POINT PHARMA, INC.—See Viatris Inc.; *U.S. Public*, pg. 2294
OYSTER YACHTS LTD.—See H.T.P. Investments BV; *Int'l*, pg. 3196
OYSTER YACHTS SOUTHAMPTON—See H.T.P. Investments BV; *Int'l*, pg. 3196
OYSTER YACHTS USA—See H.T.P. Investments BV; *Int'l*, pg. 3196
OY SUOMEN AUTOTEOLLISUUS AB; *Int'l*, pg. 5677
OY SUOMEN LEGO AB—See Kirkbi A/S; *Int'l*, pg. 4190

OY SWEDISH ORPHAN BIOVITRUM AB—See Swedish Orphan Biovitrum AB; *Int'l*, pg. 7365
OY SWEGON AB—See Investment AB Latour; *Int'l*, pg. 3783
OY TEBOIL AB—See PJSC Lukoil; *Int'l*, pg. 5882
OY TEOLLISUUSAPU AB—See Indutrade AB; *Int'l*, pg. 3680
OY TOMRA AB—See Tomra Systems ASA; *Int'l*, pg. 7802
OY TREXET FINLAND AB—See New Wave Group AB; *Int'l*, pg. 5230
OY TUMLARE CORPORATION AB—See JTB Corp.; *Int'l*, pg. 4016
OY UDDEHOLM AB—See voestalpine AG; *Int'l*, pg. 8292
OYU TOLGOI LLC—See Rio Tinto plc; *Int'l*, pg. 6348
OY VALITUT PALAT - READER'S DIGEST AB—See CIL Group SL; *Int'l*, pg. 1607
OY VALORA TRADE FINLAND AB—See Fomento Economico Mexicano, S.A.B. de C.V.; *Int'l*, pg. 2724
OY VIASAT FINLAND AB—See Modern Times Group MTG AB; *Int'l*, pg. 5015
OY WENNERCO AB—See Altia Oyj; *Int'l*, pg. 392
OZAK GYO A.S.; *Int'l*, pg. 5679
OZALID SOUTH AFRICA (PTY) LIMITED—See The Bidvest Group Limited; *Int'l*, pg. 7626
OZANAM HALL OF QUEENS NURSING HOME; *U.S. Private*, pg. 3057
OZANNE CONSTRUCTION COMPANY; *U.S. Private*, pg. 3057
OZARK AUTOMOTIVE DISTRIBUTORS, INC.—See O'Reilly Automotive, Inc.; *U.S. Public*, pg. 1559
OZARKA WATER—See Metropoulos & Co.; *U.S. Private*, pg. 2690
OZARKA WATER—See One Rock Capital Partners, LLC; *U.S. Private*, pg. 3021
OZARKA WATER—See Metropoulos & Co.; *U.S. Private*, pg. 2690
OZARKA WATER—See One Rock Capital Partners, LLC; *U.S. Private*, pg. 3021
OZARK BORDER ELECTRIC COOP ASSOCIATION; *U.S. Private*, pg. 3057
OZARK FOAM INSEALATORS, INC.—See TopBuild Corp.; *U.S. Public*, pg. 2163
OZARK KENWORTH INC.—See Murphy-Hoffman Company; *U.S. Private*, pg. 2816
OZARK MOTOR LINES INC.; *U.S. Private*, pg. 3057
OZARK MOUNTAIN BANK—See Central Bancompany, Inc.; *U.S. Public*, pg. 473
OZARK MOUNTAIN POULTRY, INC.—See George's Inc.; *U.S. Private*, pg. 1684
OZARK MOUNTAIN TECHNOLOGIES, LLC—See SONACA S.A; *Int'l*, pg. 7088
OZARK NATIONAL LIFE INSURANCE COMPANY—See Prosperity Group Holdings, LP; *U.S. Private*, pg. 3289
OZARK NEWS DISTRIBUTION INC.; *U.S. Private*, pg. 3058
OZARK RIDGE LANDFILL, INC.—See Waste Management, Inc.; *U.S. Public*, pg. 2331
OZARKS COCA COLA/DR PEPPER BOTTLING COMPANY; *U.S. Private*, pg. 3058
OZARKS ELECTRIC COOPERATIVE CORPORATION; *U.S. Private*, pg. 3058
OZARKS FEDERAL SAVINGS & LOAN ASSOCIATION; *U.S. Private*, pg. 3058
OZARKS OPTICAL LABORATORIES INC—See EssilorLuxottica SA; *Int'l*, pg. 2513
OZARK STEEL, LLC.—See International Chemical Company; *U.S. Private*, pg. 2115
OZARK STRUCTURES, INC.; *U.S. Private*, pg. 3058
OZARK SUPERMARKET INC.; *U.S. Private*, pg. 3058
OZARK TRUCKING INC.; *U.S. Private*, pg. 3058
OZARK WAFFLES LLC; *U.S. Private*, pg. 3058
OZARK WAREHOUSES, INC.; *U.S. Private*, pg. 3058
OZAROW BIZNES PARK SP.Z.O.O.—See SEGRO plc; *Int'l*, pg. 6683
OZAURUM RESOURCES LIMITED; *Int'l*, pg. 5679
OZAWA CORPORATION—See UBE Corporation; *Int'l*, pg. 8001
OZBAL CELIK BORU SANAYI TICARET VE TAAHHUT AS; *Int'l*, pg. 5679
OZBAL CELIK BORU SAN. TIC. VE TAAHHUT A.S.; *Int'l*, pg. 5679
OZCARE; *Int'l*, pg. 5679
OZDEMIR ANTIMUAN MADENLERI A.S.—See Ipek Dogal Enerji Kaynaklari Arastirma ve Uretim AS; *Int'l*, pg. 3796
OZDERICI GAYRIMENKUL YATIRIM ORTAKLIGI A.S.; *Int'l*, pg. 5679
OZEKI CO., LTD.; *Int'l*, pg. 5679
OZEKI SAKE (U.S.A.) INC.—See Ozeki Co., Ltd.; *Int'l*, pg. 5679
OZERDEN PLASTIK SANAYI VE TICARET AS; *Int'l*, pg. 5679
OZERY BAKERY INC.; *Int'l*, pg. 5679
OZFOREX LIMITED—See OFX Group Limited; *Int'l*, pg. 5531
O-Z GEDNEY COMPANY LLC—See Emerson Electric Co.; *U.S. Public*, pg. 740
OZGRAF S.A.—See Przedsiebiorstwo Produkcyjno Handlowe Kompap S.A.; *Int'l*, pg. 6014

OZGROWTH LIMITED—See WAM Capital Limited; *Int'l*, pg. 8337
OZINCA PERU SAC—See Oar Resources Limited; *Int'l*, pg. 5507
OZINGA BROS., INC.; *U.S. Private*, pg. 3058
OZINGA CHICAGO RMC, INC.—See Ozinga Bros., Inc.; *U.S. Private*, pg. 3058
OZINGA SOUTH SUBURBAN RMC, INC.—See Ozinga Bros., Inc.; *U.S. Private*, pg. 3058
OZITO INDUSTRIES PTY. LTD.—See Einhell Germany AG; *Int'l*, pg. 2334
OZKOSEOGLU ISI SANAYI VE TICARET A.S.; *Int'l*, pg. 5679
OZMA INC.; *Int'l*, pg. 5679
OZ MANAGEMENT II LP—See Rithm Capital Corp.; *U.S. Public*, pg. 1800
OZMA OSAKA—See Ozma Inc.; *Int'l*, pg. 5679
OZMAYA SANAYI A.S.—See Compagnie des Levures Lesaffre SA; *Int'l*, pg. 1739
OZMAYA SANAYI A.S. - YEAST & INGREDIENT FACTORY—See Compagnie des Levures Lesaffre SA; *Int'l*, pg. 1739
OZMEN TIBBI LABORATUAR TESHISLERI A.S.—See Revvity, Inc.; *U.S. Public*, pg. 1794
OZ MINERALS INSURANCE PTE. LTD.—See BHP Group Limited; *Int'l*, pg. 1016
OZ MINERALS LIMITED—See BHP Group Limited; *Int'l*, pg. 1016
OZ MINERALS PROMINENT HILL PTY LTD—See BHP Group Limited; *Int'l*, pg. 1016
OZNER WATER INTERNATIONAL HOLDING LIMITED; *Int'l*, pg. 5679
OZON D.D.; *Int'l*, pg. 5679
OZON HOLDINGS PLC; *Int'l*, pg. 5679
OZONIA INTERNATIONAL HOLDING S.A—See Veolia Environnement S.A.; *Int'l*, pg. 8154
OZONIA KOREA CO., LTD—See Veolia Environnement S.A.; *Int'l*, pg. 8154
OZONIA NORTH AMERICA, LLC—See Veolia Environnement S.A.; *Int'l*, pg. 8154
OZONIA OOO—See Veolia Environnement S.A.; *Int'l*, pg. 8154
OZOP ENERGY SOLUTIONS, INC.; *U.S. Public*, pg. 1629
OZ OPTICS A.S.—See OZ Optics Limted; *Int'l*, pg. 5678
OZ OPTICS LIMTED; *Int'l*, pg. 5678
OZREN BOROVNO A.D.; *Int'l*, pg. 5679
OZTEK CORP.—See Trystar, LLC; *U.S. Private*, pg. 4252
OZTIRYAKILER MADENI ESYA SANAYI VE TICARET ANONIM SIRKETI—See Hoshizaki Corporation; *Int'l*, pg. 3484
OZU CORPORATION; *Int'l*, pg. 5679
OZUKI STEEL INDUSTRIES CO LTD—See Shinko Ind. Ltd.; *Int'l*, pg. 6846
OZU (SHANGHAI) TRADING CO., LTD.—See Ozu Corporation; *Int'l*, pg. 5679
OZU SHOTEN CO., LTD.—See Ozu Corporation; *Int'l*, pg. 5679
OZU TECHNO CO., LTD.—See Ozu Corporation; *Int'l*, pg. 5680
OZU (THAILAND) CO., LTD.—See Ozu Corporation; *Int'l*, pg. 5680
OZZIE'S PIPELINE PADDER, INC.; *U.S. Private*, pg. 3058
OZZ RESOURCES LTD.; *Int'l*, pg. 5680

P

P10 HOLDINGS, INC.—See P10, Inc.; *U.S. Public*, pg. 1630
P10, INC.; *U.S. Public*, pg. 1630
P1 GROUP, INC.; *U.S. Private*, pg. 3061
P2BINVESTOR INC.; *U.S. Private*, pg. 3062
P2 CAPITAL PARTNERS, LLC; *U.S. Private*, pg. 3061
P2C, INC.—See Perrigo Company plc; *Int'l*, pg. 5813
P2 ENERGY SOLUTIONS, INC. - LIVINGSTON—See Advent International Corporation; *U.S. Private*, pg. 105
P2 ENERGY SOLUTIONS, INC. - SAN ANTONIO—See Advent International Corporation; *U.S. Private*, pg. 105
P2 ENERGY SOLUTIONS, INC.—See Advent International Corporation; *U.S. Private*, pg. 105
P2 ENERGY SOLUTIONS PTY LTD—See Advent International Corporation; *U.S. Private*, pg. 105
P2 GOLD INC.; *Int'l*, pg. 5684
P2I FIRE PROTECTION SYSTEMS, LDA.—See Johnson Controls International plc; *Int'l*, pg. 3987
P2, INC.—See Markel Group Inc.; *U.S. Public*, pg. 1368
P2 LED CUBE—See Heerim Architects & Planners Co., Ltd.; *Int'l*, pg. 3307
P2P HOLDINGS LLC—See System One Holdings, LLC; *Int'l*, pg. 3907
P2 PLANT & PIPELINE ENGINEERING GMBH—See EnBW Energie Baden-Wurttemberg AG; *Int'l*, pg. 2399
P2P STAFFING CORP.; *U.S. Private*, pg. 3062
P2P TRANSPORT LIMITED; *Int'l*, pg. 5684
P2SAMPLE, INC.—See Nordic Capital AB; *Int'l*, pg. 5420
P2S INC.—See Blackstone Inc.; *U.S. Public*, pg. 355
P3 HEALTH PARTNERS INC.; *U.S. Public*, pg. 1630
P3I INC.; *U.S. Private*, pg. 3062
P3 PULLEN POLYURETHANE PRODUCTS B.V.—See Team, Inc.; *U.S. Public*, pg. 1988

P3S CORPORATION; *U.S. Private*, pg. 3062
P4G CAPITAL MANAGEMENT, LLC; *U.S. Private*, pg. 3062
P4 HEALTHCARE, LLC—See Cardinal Health, Inc.; *U.S. Public*, pg. 434
P4 RADIO HELE NORGE—See Modern Times Group MTG AB; *Int'l*, pg. 5014
P4 SP. Z O.O.—See Iliad S.A.; *Int'l*, pg. 3614
P5 RADIO HALVE NORGE AS—See Modern Times Group MTG AB; *Int'l*, pg. 5014
P97 NETWORKS INC.—See Corpay, Inc.; *U.S. Public*, pg. 580
PAACO AUTOMOTIVE GROUP LP; *U.S. Private*, pg. 3062
PA ACQUISITION CORP.; *U.S. Private*, pg. 3062
PAA INTERNATIONAL ENGINEERING CORP.—See Per Aarsleff Holding A/S; *Int'l*, pg. 5796
PAAMCO PRISMA HOLDINGS, LLC; *U.S. Private*, pg. 3062
PA AMERICA, INC.—See PA Power Automation AG; *Int'l*, pg. 5684
PAA NATURAL GAS STORAGE, L.P.—See Plains All American Pipeline, L.P.; *U.S. Public*, pg. 1696
PAA PROJECT FINANCE A/S—See Per Aarsleff Holding A/S; *Int'l*, pg. 5796
PAA RIVER CONSTRUCTION, LLC—See Nana Regional Corporation, Inc.; *U.S. Private*, pg. 2833
P.A. BACHKE AS—See Nicolas Correa S.A.; *Int'l*, pg. 5273
PABCO BUILDING PRODUCTS, LLC - H.C. MUDDOX DIVISION—See Pacific Coast Building Products, Inc.; *U.S. Private*, pg. 3066
PABCO BUILDING PRODUCTS, LLC - INTERSTATE BRICK DIVISION—See Pacific Coast Building Products, Inc.; *U.S. Private*, pg. 3066
PABCO BUILDING PRODUCTS, LLC - PABCO GYPSUM DIVISION—See Pacific Coast Building Products, Inc.; *U.S. Private*, pg. 3066
PABCO BUILDING PRODUCTS, LLC - PABCO PAPER DIVISION—See Pacific Coast Building Products, Inc.; *U.S. Private*, pg. 3066
PABCO BUILDING PRODUCTS, LLC - PABCO ROOFING PRODUCTS DIVISION—See Pacific Coast Building Products, Inc.; *U.S. Private*, pg. 3066
PABCO CO., LTD.—See Mercedes-Benz Group AG; *Int'l*, pg. 4828
PABCO FLUID POWER COMPANY; *U.S. Private*, pg. 3062
PABCO SENDAI CO., LTD.—See Mercedes-Benz Group AG; *Int'l*, pg. 4828
THE PABLOVE FOUNDATION; *U.S. Private*, pg. 4090
P/A BOHEMIA S.R.O.—See P/A Industries, Inc.; *U.S. Private*, pg. 3061
PABOR ARCHER DANIELS MIDLAND COMPANY—See Archer-Daniels-Midland Company; *U.S. Public*, pg. 185
P/A BRASIL LTDA—See P/A Industries, Inc.; *U.S. Private*, pg. 3061
PABRIK KERTAS TJIWI KIMIA TBK; *Int'l*, pg. 5684
PABST BREWING COMPANY—See TSG Consumer Partners LLC; *U.S. Private*, pg. 4253
PABST & RICHARZ VERTRIEBS GMBH—See Berentzen-Gruppe AG; *Int'l*, pg. 978
PABTEX, INC.—See Canadian Pacific Kansas City Limited; *Int'l*, pg. 1285
PAC-12 CONFERENCE; *U.S. Private*, pg. 3063
PACA ASCENSEURS SERVICES SARL—See KONE Oyj; *Int'l*, pg. 4250
PACA ASCENSEURS SERVICES SAS—See ASSA ABLOY AB; *Int'l*, pg. 638
PACAL INDUSTRIES, LLC—See Pacal LLC; *U.S. Private*, pg. 3063
PACAL LLC; *U.S. Private*, pg. 3063
P&A CAPITAL ADVISORS, INC.—See Aon plc; *Int'l*, pg. 497
PACCAR AUSTRALIA PTY. LTD.—See PACCAR Inc.; *U.S. Public*, pg. 1630
PACCAR ENGINE COMPANY—See PACCAR Inc.; *U.S. Public*, pg. 1630
PACCAR FINANCIAL BELUX BVBA—See PACCAR Inc.; *U.S. Public*, pg. 1630
PACCAR FINANCIAL CORP.—See PACCAR Inc.; *U.S. Public*, pg. 1630
PACCAR FINANCIAL DEUTSCHLAND GMBH—See PACCAR Inc.; *U.S. Public*, pg. 1630
PACCAR FINANCIAL ESPANA S.R.L.—See PACCAR Inc.; *U.S. Public*, pg. 1630
PACCAR FINANCIAL EUROPE B.V.—See PACCAR Inc.; *U.S. Public*, pg. 1630
PACCAR FINANCIAL FRANCE S.A.S.—See PACCAR Inc.; *U.S. Public*, pg. 1630
PACCAR FINANCIAL ITALIA SRL—See PACCAR Inc.; *U.S. Public*, pg. 1630
PACCAR FINANCIAL LTD.—See PACCAR Inc.; *U.S. Public*, pg. 1630
PACCAR FINANCIAL MEXICO, S.A. DE C.V., SOFOM, E.N.R.—See PACCAR Inc.; *U.S. Public*, pg. 1631
PACCAR FINANCIAL MEXICO—See PACCAR Inc.; *U.S. Public*, pg. 1631
PACCAR FINANCIAL PLC—See PACCAR Inc.; *U.S. Public*, pg. 1631

COMPANY NAME INDEX

PACCAR FINANCIAL PTY. LTD.—See PACCAR Inc.; *U.S. Public*, pg. 1631
PACCAR FINANCIAL PTY. LTD.—See PACCAR Inc.; *U.S. Public*, pg. 1631
PACCAR FINANCIAL SERVICES CORP.—See PACCAR Inc.; *U.S. Public*, pg. 1631
PACCAR FINANCIAL SERVICES LTD.—See PACCAR Inc.; *U.S. Public*, pg. 1631
PACCAR GLOBAL SALES—See PACCAR Inc.; *U.S. Public*, pg. 1631
PACCAR INC.; *U.S. Public*, pg. 1630
PACCAR LEASING CO.—See PACCAR Inc.; *U.S. Public*, pg. 1631
PACCAR LEASING GMBH—See PACCAR Inc.; *U.S. Public*, pg. 1631
PACCAR MEXICO, S.A. DE C.V.—See PACCAR Inc.; *U.S. Public*, pg. 1631
PACCAR OF CANADA LTD.—See PACCAR Inc.; *U.S. Public*, pg. 1631
PACCAR PARTS MEXICO, S.A. DE C.V.—See PACCAR Inc.; *U.S. Public*, pg. 1631
PACCAR PARTS—See PACCAR Inc.; *U.S. Public*, pg. 1631
PACCAR PARTS U.K. LIMITED—See PACCAR Inc.; *U.S. Public*, pg. 1631
PACCAR SALES NORTH AMERICA, INC.—See PACCAR Inc.; *U.S. Public*, pg. 1631
PACCAR TECHNICAL CENTER—See PACCAR Inc.; *U.S. Public*, pg. 1631
PACCAR TRUCKS U.K. LTD.—See PACCAR Inc.; *U.S. Public*, pg. 1631
PACCAR WINCH DIVISION—See PACCAR Inc.; *U.S. Public*, pg. 1631
PACCAR WINCH INC.—See The Black Phoenix Group; *U.S. Private*, pg. 3995
PACCESS LLC; *U.S. Private*, pg. 3063
PACC OFFSHORE SERVICES HOLDINGS LTD; *Int'l*, pg. 5684
PACC SHIP MANAGERS (BEIJING) CO LTD—See Kuok (Singapore) Limited; *Int'l*, pg. 4334
PACC SHIPPING PHILS., INC—See Kuok (Singapore) Limited; *Int'l*, pg. 4334
PACCSHIP (UK) LIMITED—See Kuok (Singapore) Limited; *Int'l*, pg. 4334
PACE ADVERTISING—See WPP plc; *Int'l*, pg. 8483
PACE AMERICAN ENTERPRISES INC.-FITZGERALD—See LGS Industries, Inc.; *U.S. Private*, pg. 2441
PACE AMERICAN ENTERPRISES INC.—See LGS Industries, Inc.; *U.S. Private*, pg. 2441
PACE AMERICAN ENTERPRISES INC.-SPRINGVILLE—See LGS Industries, Inc.; *U.S. Private*, pg. 2441
PACE ANALYTICAL LIFE SCIENCES LLC—See Leonard Green & Partners, L.P.; *U.S. Private*, pg. 2426
PACE ANALYTICAL SERVICES, INC. - ASHEVILLE ENVIRONMENTAL LABORATORY—See Leonard Green & Partners, L.P.; *U.S. Private*, pg. 2427
PACE ANALYTICAL SERVICES, INC. - GREEN BAY ENVIRONMENTAL LABORATORY—See Leonard Green & Partners, L.P.; *U.S. Private*, pg. 2427
PACE ANALYTICAL SERVICES, INC. - GREENSBURG ENVIRONMENTAL LABORATORY—See Leonard Green & Partners, L.P.; *U.S. Private*, pg. 2427
PACE ANALYTICAL SERVICES, INC. - HOUSTON LABORS/SERVICE CENTER—See Leonard Green & Partners, L.P.; *U.S. Private*, pg. 2427
PACE ANALYTICAL SERVICES, INC. - HUNTERSVILLE ENVIRONMENTAL LABORATORY—See Leonard Green & Partners, L.P.; *U.S. Private*, pg. 2427
PACE ANALYTICAL SERVICES, INC. - INDIANAPOLIS ENVIRONMENTAL LABORATORY—See Leonard Green & Partners, L.P.; *U.S. Private*, pg. 2427
PACE ANALYTICAL SERVICES, INC. - LENEXA ENVIRONMENTAL LABORATORY—See Leonard Green & Partners, L.P.; *U.S. Private*, pg. 2427
PACE ANALYTICAL SERVICES, INC. - MINNEAPOLIS ENVIRONMENTAL LABORATORY—See Leonard Green & Partners, L.P.; *U.S. Private*, pg. 2427
PACE ANALYTICAL SERVICES, LLC—See Leonard Green & Partners, L.P.; *U.S. Private*, pg. 2426
PACECO CORP.—See Mitsui E&S Holdings Co., Ltd.; *Int'l*, pg. 4986
PACE COMMUNICATIONS INC.; *U.S. Private*, pg. 3063
PACE COMPUTER SOLUTIONS INC; *U.S. Private*, pg. 3063
PACE CONSTRUCTION COMPANY INC.—See Lionmark Inc.; *U.S. Private*, pg. 2464
PACE CONTRACTING, LLC—See LPX, Inc.; *U.S. Private*, pg. 2507
PACE DAIRY FOODS COMPANY—See The Kroger Co.; *U.S. Public*, pg. 2109
PACE DAIRY FOODS—See The Kroger Co.; *U.S. Public*, pg. 2109
PACE DEVELOPMENT CORPORATION PUBLIC CO., LTD.; *Int'l*, pg. 5684
PACE E-COMMERCE VENTURES LIMITED; *Int'l*, pg. 5685
PACE EDITIONS INC.; *U.S. Private*, pg. 3063

PACE ELECTRONICS INC.; *U.S. Private*, pg. 3063
PACE ENGINEERING INC.; *U.S. Private*, pg. 3063
PACE ENGINEERS, INC.; *U.S. Private*, pg. 3063
PACE EUROPE, LTD.—See PACE Inc.; *U.S. Private*, pg. 3063
PACE FARM PTY LTD—See ROC Partners Pty Ltd; *Int'l*, pg. 6372
PACE FUELCARE LIMITED—See DCC plc; *Int'l*, pg. 1991
PACE GLOBAL ENERGY SERVICES, LLC—See Siemens Aktiengesellschaft; *Int'l*, pg. 6889
PACE GMBH—See TXT e-Solutions S.p.A.; *Int'l*, pg. 7993
PACE HARMON, LLC—See West Monroe Partners, LLC; *U.S. Private*, pg. 4486
PACE INC.; *U.S. Private*, pg. 3063
PACE, INC.—See Integrated Communications Corp.; *U.S. Private*, pg. 2099
PACE INDUSTRIES - B & C DIVISION—See Kenner & Company, Inc.; *U.S. Private*, pg. 2286
PACE INDUSTRIES DE CHIHUAHUA, S.A. DE C.V.—See Kenner & Company, Inc.; *U.S. Private*, pg. 2286
PACE INDUSTRIES DE MEXICO, S.A. DE C.V.—See Kenner & Company, Inc.; *U.S. Private*, pg. 2286
PACE INDUSTRIES, INC.—See Kenner & Company, Inc.; *U.S. Private*, pg. 2286
PACE INDUSTRIES INC.; *U.S. Private*, pg. 3063
PACE INDUSTRIES - ST. PAUL DIVISION—See Kenner & Company, Inc.; *U.S. Private*, pg. 2286
PACE INTERNATIONAL, LLC—See Paine Schwartz Partners, LLC; *U.S. Private*, pg. 3075
PACEJET LOGISTICS, INC.—See Sumeru Equity Partners LLC; *U.S. Private*, pg. 3852
PACELINE EQUITY PARTNERS LLC; *U.S. Private*, pg. 3064
PACELINE, INC.; *U.S. Private*, pg. 3064
PACEMAKER SILVER MINING, S.A. DE C.V.—See Silver Tiger Metals Inc.; *Int'l*, pg. 6924
PACEMAKER STEEL AND PIPING CO.; *U.S. Private*, pg. 3064
PACE MATERIAL HANDLING, INC.—See On-Point Group, LLC; *U.S. Private*, pg. 3019
PACE MECHANICAL SERVICES II, INC.—See EMCOR Group, Inc.; *U.S. Public*, pg. 738
PACE METALS LTD.; *Int'l*, pg. 5685
PACE MOTOR LINES INC.; *U.S. Private*, pg. 3063
PACE ORGANIZATION OF RHODE ISLAND; *U.S. Private*, pg. 3063
PACE (PAKISTAN) LIMITED; *Int'l*, pg. 5684
PACE PAPARAZZI CATERING & EVENT GMBH—See Axel Springer SE; *Int'l*, pg. 766
PACE POLYETHYLENE MFG. CO. INC.; *U.S. Private*, pg. 3063
PACE PRESS, INC.; *U.S. Private*, pg. 3063
PACE PROFESSIONAL SERVICES, LTD.—See Kelso & Company, L.P.; *U.S. Private*, pg. 2280
PACER BUILDING COMPONENTS INC.—See Atlas Engineered Products Ltd.; *Int'l*, pg. 685
PACER COMPONENTS LTD.; *Int'l*, pg. 5685
PACER CORPORATION; *U.S. Private*, pg. 3064
PACE REGISTRARS LIMITED—See Sterling Bank Plc; *Int'l*, pg. 7211
PACER ELECTRONICS OF FLORIDA, INC.; *U.S. Private*, pg. 3064
PACE RESOURCES, INC.; *U.S. Private*, pg. 3064
PACER HEALTH CORPORATION—See Pacer Corporation; *U.S. Private*, pg. 3064
PACE ROOFING SUPPLY COMPANY—See Leonard Green & Partners, L.P.; *U.S. Private*, pg. 2429
PACER PROPANE LLC—See NGL Energy Partners LP; *U.S. Public*, pg. 1527
PACERS BASKETBALL, LLC; *U.S. Private*, pg. 3064
PACER TECHNOLOGY—See AC MARCA, S.A; *Int'l*, pg. 74
PACER USA LLC—See Pacer Components Ltd.; *Int'l*, pg. 5685
PACESETTER CAPITAL GROUP; *U.S. Private*, pg. 3064
PACESETTER CLAIMS SERVICE; *U.S. Private*, pg. 3064
PACESETTER GRAPHIC SERVICE; *U.S. Private*, pg. 3065
PACESETTERS, INC; *U.S. Private*, pg. 3065
PACESETTER STEEL SERVICE, INC.—See Flack Steel LLC; *U.S. Private*, pg. 1538
PACES, INC.; *U.S. Private*, pg. 3064
PACE—See Regional Transportation Authority; *U.S. Private*, pg. 3389
PACE—See New Zealand Post Limited; *Int'l*, pg. 5232
PACE SUBURBAN BUS; *U.S. Private*, pg. 3064
PACE SUPPLY CORP.; *U.S. Private*, pg. 3064
PACE SYSTEMS, INC.; *U.S. Private*, pg. 3064
PACE TRANSPORTATION—See Warren Distribution, Inc.; *U.S. Private*, pg. 4443
PACGEN LIFE SCIENCE CORPORATION—See General Biologicals Corporation; *Int'l*, pg. 2918
PACGOLD LIMITED; *Int'l*, pg. 5685
PACHECO DIALYSIS, LLC—See DaVita Inc.; *U.S. Public*, pg. 641
PACHECO RANCH WINERY; *U.S. Private*, pg. 3065
PACHELI INDUSTRIAL FINANCE LTD.; *Int'l*, pg. 5685
PACHEM DISTRIBUTION INC.—See BRENNTAG SE; *Int'l*, pg. 1149

PACHMAS PACKAGING LTD—See Greif Inc.; *U.S. Public*, pg. 968
PACHMAYR—See Lyman Products Corporation; *U.S. Private*, pg. 2520
THE PACIELLO GROUP, LLC—See Freedom Scientific Inc.; *U.S. Private*, pg. 1604
PACIFICA COMPANIES, LLC; *U.S. Private*, pg. 3071
PACIFICA ENGINEERING, INC.—See MTorres Disenos Industriales SAU; *Int'l*, pg. 5071
PACIFIC AEROSPACE & ELECTRONICS, INC. - BONDED METALS—See TransDigm Group Incorporated; *U.S. Public*, pg. 2181
PACIFIC AEROSPACE & ELECTRONICS, INC.—See TransDigm Group Incorporated; *U.S. Public*, pg. 2181
PACIFICA FOODS LLC—See Wind Point Advisors LLC; *U.S. Private*, pg. 4534
PACIFIC AG, LLC; *U.S. Private*, pg. 3065
PACIFIC AG. PRODUCTS, LLC—See Alto Ingredients, Inc.; *U.S. Public*, pg. 88
PACIFIC AGRICULTURAL SALES & SERVICES, INC.—See J.R. Simplot Company; *U.S. Public*, pg. 2171
PACIFIC AGRI-PRODUCTS INC.; *U.S. Private*, pg. 3065
PACIFICA GROUP LIMITED—See Robert Bosch GmbH; *Int'l*, pg. 6362
PACIFICA HOLDINGS INC.; *Int'l*, pg. 5692
PACIFICA HOST HOTELS—See Pacifica Companies, LLC; *U.S. Private*, pg. 3072
PACIFICA HOTEL COMPANY—See Invest West Financial Corporation; *U.S. Private*, pg. 2131
PACIFIC AIR CONTROLS CO., LTD.—See PACIFIC INDUSTRIAL CO. LTD.; *Int'l*, pg. 5690
PACIFIC AIR & ENVIRONMENT PTY LTD—See Enviro-Suite Limited; *Int'l*, pg. 2455
PACIFIC ALASKA SHELLFISH CO—See Dulcich, Inc.; *U.S. Private*, pg. 1286
PACIFIC ALLIANCE BANK; *U.S. Public*, pg. 1631
PACIFIC ALLIANCE CAPITAL, INC.—See Craftsman Capital Partners, LLC; *U.S. Private*, pg. 1082
PACIFIC ALLIANCE GROUP—See PAG Capital; *Int'l*, pg. 5697
PACIFIC ALLIANCE MEDICAL CENTER, INC.—See PAMC, Ltd.; *U.S. Private*, pg. 3083
PACIFIC ALLIANCE REAL ESTATE LIMITED; *Int'l*, pg. 5685
PACIFIC ALLIANCE TECHNOLOGIES INC.—See StarDyne Technologies Inc.; *Int'l*, pg. 7176
PACIFIC ALLIANCE USA, INC.—See Li & Fung Limited; *Int'l*, pg. 4480
PACIFIC ALTERNATIVE ASSET MANAGEMENT COMPANY—See PAAMCO Prisma Holdings, LLC; *U.S. Private*, pg. 3062
PACIFIC ALUMINIUM PTY LIMITED—See Rio Tinto plc; *Int'l*, pg. 6346
PACIFIC AMERICAN FISH CO., INC.; *U.S. Private*, pg. 3065
PACIFIC AMERICAN GROUP, LLC; *U.S. Private*, pg. 3065
PACIFIC ANDES INTERNATIONAL HOLDINGS LIMITED; *Int'l*, pg. 5685
PACIFIC AQUACULTURE, INC.—See Dulcich, Inc.; *U.S. Private*, pg. 1286
PACIFIC ARCHITECTS & ENGINEERS, INC.—See Amentum Services, Inc.; *U.S. Private*, pg. 219
PACIFIC ARCHITECTURAL PRODUCTS, INC.—See Tumac Lumber Co. Inc.; *U.S. Private*, pg. 4258
PACIFIC ARC RESOURCES LTD.; *Int'l*, pg. 5685
PACIFICA REAL ESTATE GROUP, LLC; *U.S. Private*, pg. 3072
PACIFICARE DENTAL—See UnitedHealth Group Incorporated; *U.S. Public*, pg. 2249
PACIFICARE LIFE & HEALTH INSURANCE COMPANY—See UnitedHealth Group Incorporated; *U.S. Public*, pg. 2249
PACIFICARE OF COLORADO, INC.—See UnitedHealth Group Incorporated; *U.S. Public*, pg. 2249
PACIFICARE OF OKLAHOMA, INC.—See UnitedHealth Group Incorporated; *U.S. Public*, pg. 2249
PACIFICARE OF TEXAS, INC.—See UnitedHealth Group Incorporated; *U.S. Public*, pg. 2249
PACIFICA SENIOR LIVING; *U.S. Private*, pg. 3072
PACIFICA SERVICES, INC.; *U.S. Private*, pg. 3072
PACIFICA SHIPPING LIMITED—See Skeggs Group Limited; *Int'l*, pg. 6980
PACIFIC ASIAN CONSORTIUM IN EMPLOYMENT; *U.S. Private*, pg. 3065
PACIFIC ATHLETIC CLUB - SAN DIEGO—See KKR & Co. Inc.; *U.S. Public*, pg. 1264
PACIFIC ATHLETIC CLUB—See KKR & Co. Inc.; *U.S. Public*, pg. 1264
PACIFICA TRIBUNE—See Alden Global Capital LLC; *U.S. Private*, pg. 155
PACIFIC AUTO BODY; *U.S. Private*, pg. 3065
PACIFIC AUTO PARTS TECHNOLOGY (CHANGSHU) CO., LTD.—See PACIFIC INDUSTRIAL CO. LTD.; *Int'l*, pg. 5690
PACIFIC AUTO PARTS (THAILAND) CO., LTD.—See PACIFIC INDUSTRIAL CO. LTD.; *Int'l*, pg. 5690
PACIFIC AUXILIARY FIRE ALARM COMPANY—See Financial Investments Corporation; *U.S. Private*, pg. 1507

PACIFIC AVENUE CAPITAL PARTNERS, LLC   CORPORATE AFFILIATIONS

PACIFIC AVENUE CAPITAL PARTNERS, LLC; *U.S. Private*, pg. 3065
PACIFIC AVIATION CORPORATION—See Woodlawn Partners, Inc.; *U.S. Private*, pg. 4559
PACIFIC AWARDS METALS, INC.—See Gibraltar Industries, Inc.; *U.S. Public*, pg. 936
PACIFIC BASIN IHC LIMITED—See Pacific Basin Shipping Limited; *Int'l*, pg. 5686
PACIFIC BASIN IHC (UK) LIMITED—See Pacific Basin Shipping Limited; *Int'l*, pg. 5686
PACIFIC BASIN SHIPPING (BRASIL) LTDA.—See Pacific Basin Shipping Limited; *Int'l*, pg. 5686
PACIFIC BASIN SHIPPING (CANADA) LIMITED—See Pacific Basin Shipping Limited; *Int'l*, pg. 5686
PACIFIC BASIN SHIPPING (CHILE) LIMITADA—See Pacific Basin Shipping Limited; *Int'l*, pg. 5686
PACIFIC BASIN SHIPPING (HK) LIMITED—See Pacific Basin Shipping Limited; *Int'l*, pg. 5686
PACIFIC BASIN SHIPPING LIMITED; *Int'l*, pg. 5685
PACIFIC BASIN SHIPPING (NEW ZEALAND) LIMITED—See Pacific Basin Shipping Limited; *Int'l*, pg. 5686
PACIFIC BASIN SHIPPING (UK) LIMITED—See Pacific Basin Shipping Limited; *Int'l*, pg. 5686
PACIFIC BAUXITE LIMITED; *Int'l*, pg. 5686
PACIFIC BAY HOMES, LLC—See Ford Motor Company; *U.S. Public*, pg. 867
PACIFIC BAY MINERALS LTD.; *Int'l*, pg. 5686
PACIFIC BEACH HOTEL—See HTH Corporation; *U.S. Private*, pg. 1999
PACIFIC BELLS, LLC—See Partners Group Holding AG; *Int'l*, pg. 5750
PACIFIC BELL TELEPHONE COMPANY—See AT&T Inc.; *U.S. Public*, pg. 219
PACIFIC BENEFITS CONSULTANTS, INC.—See ABRY Partners, LLC; *U.S. Private*, pg. 42
PACIFIC BEST INC; *U.S. Private*, pg. 3065
PACIFIC BEVERAGE CO. INC.—See Jordano's, Inc.; *U.S. Private*, pg. 2236
PACIFIC BIO CO., LTD.; *Int'l*, pg. 5686
PACIFIC BIOCONTROL CORPORATION—See Shin-Etsu Chemical Co. Ltd.; *Int'l*, pg. 6839
PACIFIC BIOENERGY CORPORATION—See Sumitomo Corporation; *Int'l*, pg. 7269
PACIFIC BIOSCIENCE LABORATORIES, INC.—See L'Oreal S.A.; *Int'l*, pg. 4380
PACIFIC BIOSCIENCES OF CALIFORNIA, INC.; *U.S. Public*, pg. 1631
PACIFIC BOOKER MINERALS INC.; *Int'l*, pg. 5686
PACIFIC BUILDERS SUPPLIES; *Int'l*, pg. 5686
PACIFIC BUILDING GROUP; *U.S. Private*, pg. 3065
PACIFIC BUSINESS GROUP ON HEALTH; *U.S. Private*, pg. 3065
PACIFIC BUSINESS NEWS INC.—See Advance Publications, Inc.; *U.S. Private*, pg. 84
PACIFIC CANCER CENTRE PTE. LTD.; *Int'l*, pg. 5686
PACIFIC CANCER INSTITUTE, LLC—See Akumin, Inc.; *U.S. Public*, pg. 70
PACIFIC CARDIOVASCULAR ASSOCIATES MEDICAL GROUP, INC.—See UnitedHealth Group Incorporated; *U.S. Public*, pg. 2249
PACIFIC CARPETS, INC.—See The Sterling Group, L.P.; *U.S. Private*, pg. 4122
PACIFIC CARRIERS LIMITED—See Kuok (Singapore) Limited; *Int'l*, pg. 4334
PACIFIC CAST TECHNOLOGIES, INC.—See Warburg Pincus LLC; *U.S. Private*, pg. 4437
PACIFIC CEMENT PTE LIMITED—See Fijian Holdings Limited; *Int'l*, pg. 2662
PACIFIC CENTURY GROUP HOLDINGS LIMITED; *Int'l*, pg. 5686
PACIFIC CENTURY MOTORS—See Aviation Industry Corporation of China; *Int'l*, pg. 742
PACIFIC CENTURY PREMIUM DEVELOPMENTS LTD.—See Pacific Century Group Holdings Limited; *Int'l*, pg. 5687
PACIFIC CENTURY REGIONAL DEVELOPMENTS LTD.; *Int'l*, pg. 5687
PACIFIC CHEVROLET BUICK GMC LTD; *Int'l*, pg. 5687
PACIFIC CHOICE BRANDS, INC.; *U.S. Private*, pg. 3065
PACIFIC CHOICE SEAFOOD COMPANY—See Dulcich, Inc.; *U.S. Private*, pg. 1286
PACIFIC CITY (ASIA PACIFIC) PTE. LTD.—See VSTECS Holdings Limited; *Int'l*, pg. 8315
PACIFIC CITY BANK—See PCB Bancorp; *U.S. Public*, pg. 1658
PACIFIC CLAY PRODUCTS, INC.—See Murdock Holdings, LLC; *U.S. Private*, pg. 2814
PACIFIC COASTAL AIRLINES LIMITED; *Int'l*, pg. 5687
PACIFIC COAST BUILDING PRODUCTS, INC.; *U.S. Private*, pg. 3065
PACIFIC COAST CABLING INC.; *U.S. Private*, pg. 3066
PACIFIC COAST CAPITAL PARTNERS, LLC; *U.S. Private*, pg. 3066
PACIFIC COAST CARE CENTER, L.L.C.—See Apollo Global Management, Inc.; *U.S. Public*, pg. 157
PACIFIC COAST CHEMICALS CO.; *U.S. Private*, pg. 3066

PACIFIC COAST COMPANIES, INC.—See Pacific Coast Building Products, Inc.; *U.S. Private*, pg. 3066
PACIFIC COAST COMPOSITES, INC.—See Carl Marks & Co., Inc.; *U.S. Private*, pg. 763
PACIFIC COAST ENERGY COMPANY LP; *U.S. Private*, pg. 3066
PACIFIC COAST EVERGREEN INC; *U.S. Private*, pg. 3066
PACIFIC COAST EXPRESS LIMITED—See Mullen Group Ltd.; *Int'l*, pg. 5080
PACIFIC COAST FEATHER COMPANY—See Centre Lane Partners, LLC; *U.S. Private*, pg. 827
PACIFIC COAST FEATHER CUSHION CO.—See Centre Lane Partners, LLC; *U.S. Private*, pg. 827
PACIFIC COAST FIELD SERVICES, INC.—See New Mountain Capital, LLC; *U.S. Private*, pg. 2900
PACIFIC COAST GROUP INC.; *U.S. Private*, pg. 3066
PACIFIC COAST LIGHTING INC.; *U.S. Private*, pg. 3066
PACIFIC COAST OIL TRUST—See Pacific Coast Energy Company LP; *U.S. Private*, pg. 3066
PACIFIC COAST PRODUCERS - LODI PLANT—See Pacific Coast Producers; *U.S. Private*, pg. 3066
PACIFIC COAST PRODUCERS - OROVILLE PLANT—See Pacific Coast Producers; *U.S. Private*, pg. 3066
PACIFIC COAST PRODUCERS; *U.S. Private*, pg. 3066
PACIFIC COAST PRODUCERS - WOODLAND PLANT—See Pacific Coast Producers; *U.S. Private*, pg. 3066
PACIFIC COAST RECYCLING, LLC—See Sims Limited; *U.S. Public*, pg. 1883
PACIFIC COAST RESTAURANTS, INC.—See Sun Capital Partners, Inc.; *U.S. Private*, pg. 3860
PACIFIC COAST SALES & SERVICE, INC.—See Trane Technologies Plc; *Int'l*, pg. 7892
PACIFIC COAST SEAFOODS COMPANY, INC.—See Dulcich, Inc.; *U.S. Private*, pg. 1286
PACIFIC COAST SHOWCASE, INC.—See UFP Industries, Inc.; *U.S. Public*, pg. 2219
PACIFIC COAST SUPPLY, LLC - ANDERSON LUMBER DIVISION—See Pacific Coast Building Products, Inc.; *U.S. Private*, pg. 3066
PACIFIC COAST SUPPLY, LLC - DIAMOND PACIFIC DIVISION—See Pacific Coast Building Products, Inc.; *U.S. Private*, pg. 3066
PACIFIC COAST SUPPLY, LLC - PACIFIC SUPPLY DIVISION—See Pacific Coast Building Products, Inc.; *U.S. Private*, pg. 3066
PACIFIC COAST SUPPLY, LLC - P.C. WHOLESALE DIVISION—See Pacific Coast Building Products, Inc.; *U.S. Private*, pg. 3066
PACIFIC COAST SUPPLY, LLC—See Pacific Coast Building Products, Inc.; *U.S. Private*, pg. 3066
PACIFIC COAST WAREHOUSE CO—See Weber Distribution, LLC; *U.S. Private*, pg. 4465
PACIFIC COLUMNS, INC.; *U.S. Private*, pg. 3066
PACIFIC COMMUNICATIONS PTY. LTD.—See Hills Limited; *Int'l*, pg. 3393
PACIFIC COMMUNICATIONS, INC.; *U.S. Private*, pg. 3066
PACIFIC COMPENSATION INSURANCE COMPANY—See CopperPoint Mutual Insurance Holding Company; *U.S. Private*, pg. 1045
PACIFIC COMPOSITES PTY. LTD—See Exel Composites Oyj; *Int'l*, pg. 2582
PACIFIC CONCEPT INDUSTRIES (USA) LLC—See Illinois Tool Works Inc.; *U.S. Public*, pg. 1110
PACIFIC CONQUEST HOLDINGS, INC.; *Int'l*, pg. 5687
PACIFIC CONSTRUCTION CO., LTD.; *Int'l*, pg. 5687
PACIFIC CONSTRUCTION GROUP COMPANY LIMITED; *Int'l*, pg. 5687
PACIFIC CONSTRUCTION SYSTEMS INC.; *U.S. Private*, pg. 3067
PACIFIC CONTAINERBAG CO. LTD.—See Greif Inc.; *U.S. Public*, pg. 967
PACIFIC CONTINENTAL TEXTILE, INC.—See Edmund Kim International Inc.; *U.S. Private*, pg. 1338
PACIFIC CONTINENTAL TEXTILES, INC, APPAREL DIVISION (PCT-A)—See Edmund Kim International Inc.; *U.S. Private*, pg. 1338
PACIFIC CONTROLS CLOUD SERVICES FZE—See Pacific Controls Inc.; *Int'l*, pg. 5687
PACIFIC CONTROLS INC.; *Int'l*, pg. 5687
PACIFIC CONTROLS INC.—See Pacific Controls Inc.; *Int'l*, pg. 5687
PACIFIC CONTROLS INC.—See Pacific Controls Inc.; *Int'l*, pg. 5688
PACIFIC CONTROLS SMART GRID SERVICES—See Pacific Controls Inc.; *Int'l*, pg. 5688
PACIFIC CONVEYOR SYSTEMS, INC.—See Blower Dempsay Corporation; *U.S. Private*, pg. 584
PACIFIC CORNERSTONE ARCHITECTS INC.—See Harley Ellis Devereaux Corporation; *U.S. Private*, pg. 1865
PACIFIC CREST BANCORP, INC.; *U.S. Private*, pg. 3067
PACIFIC CREST SAVINGS BANK—See Pacific Crest Bancorp, Inc.; *U.S. Private*, pg. 3067
PACIFIC CREST SECURITIES LLC—See KeyCorp; *U.S. Public*, pg. 1226
PACIFIC CRYSTAL TEXTILES LIMITED—See Pacific Textiles Holdings Limited; *Int'l*, pg. 5692

PACIFIC CURRENT GROUP LIMITED; *Int'l*, pg. 5688
PACIFIC CUSTODIANS PTY LIMITED—See Pacific Equity Partners Pty. Limited; *Int'l*, pg. 5689
PACIFIC CUSTOMS BROKERS LTD.; *Int'l*, pg. 5688
PACIFIC CYCLE INC.—See Dorel Industries, Inc.; *Int'l*, pg. 2176
PACIFIC CYCLE INC.—See Dorel Industries, Inc.; *Int'l*, pg. 2176
PACIFIC DAILY NEWS—See Gannett Co., Inc.; *U.S. Public*, pg. 898
PACIFIC DAIRIES LIMITED; *Int'l*, pg. 5688
PACIFIC DENIMS LTD.; *Int'l*, pg. 5688
PACIFIC DENTAL SERVICES, INC.; *U.S. Private*, pg. 3067
PACIFIC DEPT STORES (DALIAN) CO. LTD.—See The Far Eastern Group; *Int'l*, pg. 7641
PACIFIC DESIGN TECHNOLOGIES, INC.—See AMETEK, Inc.; *U.S. Public*, pg. 116
PACIFIC DIGITAL USA CORPORATION, INC.; *U.S. Private*, pg. 3067
PACIFIC DRILLING S.A.; *Int'l*, pg. 5688
PACIFIC DRILLING SERVICES, INC.—See Pacific Drilling S.A.; *Int'l*, pg. 5688
PACIFIC DRILLING SERVICES PTE. LTD.—See Pacific Drilling S.A.; *Int'l*, pg. 5688
PACIFIC EAGLE HOLDINGS CORPORATION—See Great Eagle Holdings Limited; *Int'l*, pg. 3064
PACIFIC EDGE DIAGNOSTICS NEW ZEALAND LIMITED—See Pacific Edge Limited; *Int'l*, pg. 5688
PACIFIC EDGE DIAGNOSTICS SINGAPORE PTE LIMITED—See Pacific Edge Limited; *Int'l*, pg. 5688
PACIFIC EDGE DIAGNOSTICS USA LIMITED—See Pacific Edge Limited; *Int'l*, pg. 5688
PACIFIC EDGE LIMITED; *Int'l*, pg. 5688
PACIFIC EMBEDDED PRODUCTS—See Clark Pacific; *U.S. Private*, pg. 913
PACIFIC EMERGING TECHNOLOGIES LIMITED—See Fiji National Provident Fund; *Int'l*, pg. 2661
PACIFIC EMPIRE MINERALS CORP.; *Int'l*, pg. 5688
PACIFIC EMPLOYERS INSURANCE COMPANY—See Chubb Limited; *Int'l*, pg. 1593
PACIFIC ENDOSCOPY & SURGERY CENTER, LLC—See Tenet Healthcare Corporation; *U.S. Public*, pg. 2005
PACIFIC ENDO-SURGICAL CENTER, L.P.—See Tenet Healthcare Corporation; *U.S. Public*, pg. 2012
PACIFIC ENERGY LIMITED—See QIC Limited; *Int'l*, pg. 6141
PACIFIC ENGINE DEVELOPMENT & CONSULTING, INC.—See Mitsubishi Heavy Industries, Ltd.; *Int'l*, pg. 4957
PACIFIC ENGINEERS & CONSTRUCTORS, LTD.—See Bechtel Group, Inc.; *U.S. Private*, pg. 510
PACIFIC ENTERPRISE BANCORP; *U.S. Public*, pg. 1631
PACIFIC ENTERPRISE BANK—See Pacific Enterprise Bancorp; *U.S. Public*, pg. 1631
PACIFIC EQUITY PARTNERS PTY. LIMITED; *Int'l*, pg. 5688
PACIFIC ESTATE DEVELOPMENT LIMITED—See Thai Property Public Company Limited; *Int'l*, pg. 7595
PACIFIC ETHANOL AURORA EAST, LLC—See Alto Ingredients, Inc.; *U.S. Public*, pg. 88
PACIFIC ETHANOL CENTRAL, LLC—See Alto Ingredients, Inc.; *U.S. Public*, pg. 88
PACIFIC ETHANOL COLUMBIA, LLC—See Alto Ingredients, Inc.; *U.S. Public*, pg. 88
PACIFIC ETHANOL MADERA LLC—See Alto Ingredients, Inc.; *U.S. Public*, pg. 88
PACIFIC ETHANOL MAGIC VALLEY, LLC—See Alto Ingredients, Inc.; *U.S. Public*, pg. 88
PACIFIC ETHANOL PEKIN, INC.—See Alto Ingredients, Inc.; *U.S. Public*, pg. 88
PACIFIC EVENT PRODUCTIONS; *U.S. Private*, pg. 3067
PACIFIC EXPORT RESOURCES, LLC—See Peabody Energy Corporation; *U.S. Public*, pg. 1659
PACIFIC FIBRE PRODUCTS INC.; *U.S. Private*, pg. 3067
PACIFIC FINANCIAL CORPORATION; *U.S. Public*, pg. 1631
PACIFIC FIRE AND SECURITY, INC.—See Pye-Barker Fire & Safety, LLC; *U.S. Private*, pg. 3309
PACIFIC FLOW TECHNOLOGY PTY. LTD.; *Int'l*, pg. 5689
PACIFIC FOOD IMPORTERS INC.; *U.S. Private*, pg. 3067
PACIFIC FOODS OF OREGON, INC.—See Campbell Soup Company; *U.S. Public*, pg. 427
PACIFIC FORGE, INC.—See Avis Industrial Corporation; *U.S. Private*, pg. 407
PACIFIC FRESH SEAFOOD—See Dulcich, Inc.; *U.S. Private*, pg. 1286
PACIFIC GAS CENTER CO., LTD.—See Pacific Metals Co., Ltd.; *Int'l*, pg. 5690
PACIFIC GAS & ELECTRIC COMPANY—See PG&E Corporation; *U.S. Public*, pg. 1684
PACIFIC GIANT, INC.—See Han Sung Enterprise Co., Ltd.; *Int'l*, pg. 3240
PACIFIC GLOBAL INC.; *U.S. Private*, pg. 3067
PACIFIC GLOBAL ONE AVIATION COMPANY, INC.—See PLDT Inc.; *Int'l*, pg. 5896
PACIFIC GRAIN & FOODS; *U.S. Private*, pg. 3067
PACIFIC GRAIN TERMINAL, CO., LTD.—See Marubeni Corporation; *Int'l*, pg. 4709

COMPANY NAME INDEX

PACIFIC GREEN ENERGY STORAGE TECHNOLOGIES INC.—See PACIFIC GREEN TECHNOLOGIES INC.; *U.S. Public*, pg. 1631
PACIFIC GREEN MARINE TECHNOLOGIES INC.—See PACIFIC GREEN TECHNOLOGIES INC.; *U.S. Public*, pg. 1631
PACIFIC GREEN TECHNOLOGIES INC.; *U.S. Public*, pg. 1631
PACIFIC GROSERVICE, INC.; *U.S. Private*, pg. 3067
PACIFIC GROUP TRANSPORT CO., INC.—See Dulcich, Inc.; *U.S. Private*, pg. 1286
PACIFIC GUARDIAN LIFE INSURANCE CO., LTD.—See Meiji Yasuda Life Insurance Company; *Int'l*, pg. 4802
PACIFIC GUARDIAN LIFE INSURANCE CO., LTD.—See Meiji Yasuda Life Insurance Company; *Int'l*, pg. 4802
PACIFIC HANDY CUTTER, INC.—See Levine Leichtman Capital Partners, LLC; *U.S. Private*, pg. 2436
PACIFIC HEALTHCARE HOLDINGS LTD.; *Int'l*, pg. 5689
PACIFIC HEALTH CARE ORGANIZATION, INC.; *U.S. Public*, pg. 1632
PACIFIC HEALTHCARE SPECIALIST SERVICES PTE. LTD.—See Pacific Healthcare Holdings Ltd.; *Int'l*, pg. 5689
PACIFICHEALTH LABORATORIES, INC.; *U.S. Public*, pg. 1632
PACIFIC HELIPORT SERVICES—See Helijet International Inc.; *Int'l*, pg. 3330
PACIFIC HIDE & FUR DEPOT; *U.S. Private*, pg. 3067
PACIFIC HILL MANAGEMENT INC.; *Int'l*, pg. 5689
PACIFIC HOME SALES INC.—See Pacific Housing Group, LLC; *U.S. Private*, pg. 3067
PACIFIC HORIZON LIMITED—See Hinduja Global Solutions Ltd.; *Int'l*, pg. 3398
PACIFIC HOSPITALITY GROUP, INC.; *U.S. Private*, pg. 3067
PACIFIC HOSPITAL SUPPLY CO., LTD.; *Int'l*, pg. 5689
PACIFIC HOUSING GROUP, LLC; *U.S. Private*, pg. 3067
PACIFIC HYDRO AUSTRALIA—See State Power Investment Corporation; *Int'l*, pg. 7184
PACIFIC HYPERMARKET PROPERTIES SDN. BHD.—See The Store Corporation Berhad; *Int'l*, pg. 7689
PACIFIC IMAGE ELECTRONICS CO., LTD.; *Int'l*, pg. 5690
PACIFIC IMPERIAL MINES INC.; *Int'l*, pg. 5690
PACIFIC INCOME ADVISERS INC.; *U.S. Private*, pg. 3067
PACIFIC, INC.—See Hines Corporation; *U.S. Private*, pg. 1949
PACIFIC INDUSTRIAL CO., LTD. - HIGASHI OGAKI PLANT—See PACIFIC INDUSTRIAL CO. LTD.; *Int'l*, pg. 5690
PACIFIC INDUSTRIAL CO., LTD. - KYUSHU PLANT—See PACIFIC INDUSTRIAL CO. LTD.; *Int'l*, pg. 5690
PACIFIC INDUSTRIAL CO., LTD. - MINO PLANT—See PACIFIC INDUSTRIAL CO. LTD.; *Int'l*, pg. 5690
PACIFIC INDUSTRIAL CO. LTD.; *Int'l*, pg. 5690
PACIFIC INDUSTRIAL CO., LTD. - YORO PLANT—See PACIFIC INDUSTRIAL CO. LTD.; *Int'l*, pg. 5690
PACIFIC INDUSTRIES CHINA CORPORATION—See PACIFIC INDUSTRIAL CO. LTD.; *Int'l*, pg. 5690
PACIFIC INDUSTRIES EUROPE NV/SA—See PACIFIC INDUSTRIAL CO. LTD.; *Int'l*, pg. 5690
PACIFIC INDUSTRIES INC.; *U.S. Private*, pg. 3067
PACIFIC INDUSTRIES LTD.; *Int'l*, pg. 5690
PACIFIC INDUSTRIES (THAILAND) CO., LTD.—See PACIFIC INDUSTRIAL CO. LTD.; *Int'l*, pg. 5690
PACIFIC INDUSTRIES USA INC.—See PACIFIC INDUSTRIAL CO. LTD.; *Int'l*, pg. 5690
PACIFIC INFRASTRUCTURE PROJECT DEVELOPMENT AND INVESTMENT CORPORATION; *Int'l*, pg. 5690
PACIFIC INSIGHT ELECTRONICS CORP.—See Methode Electronics, Inc.; *U.S. Public*, pg. 1429
PACIFIC INSTITUTE FOR RESEARCH & EVALUATION; *U.S. Private*, pg. 3067
PACIFIC INSTRUMENTS, INC.—See Vishay Precision Group, Inc.; *U.S. Public*, pg. 2303
PACIFIC INSULATING MATERIAL (THAILAND) LIMITED—See Kingboard Holdings Limited; *Int'l*, pg. 4171
THE PACIFIC INSURANCE BERHAD—See Fairfax Financial Holdings Limited; *Int'l*, pg. 2608
PACIFIC INTEGRATED HANDLING INC.; *U.S. Private*, pg. 3067
PACIFIC INTER-LINK SDN BHD—See Hayel Saeed Anam Group of Companies; *Int'l*, pg. 3291
PACIFIC INTERNATIONAL GROUT COMPANY—See Cematrix Corporation; *Int'l*, pg. 1396
PACIFIC INTERNATIONAL MARKETING, INC.; *U.S. Private*, pg. 3068
PACIFIC INTERNATIONAL RICE MILLS—See Anheuser-Busch InBev SA/NV; *Int'l*, pg. 465
PACIFIC INVESTMENT MANAGEMENT COMPANY LLC—See Allianz SE; *Int'l*, pg. 346
PACIFIC ISLANDS DEVELOPMENT CORP.—See Tokyu Fudosan Holdings Corporation; *Int'l*, pg. 7798
PACIFIC LANGUAGE INSTITUTE, INC.—See Graham Holdings Company; *U.S. Public*, pg. 955
PACIFIC LEGEND GROUP LTD.; *Int'l*, pg. 5690

PACIFIC LEISURE (AUSTRALIA) PTY LTD—See Ossia International Limited; *Int'l*, pg. 5652
PACIFIC LIFE & ANNUITY COMPANY—See Pacific Mutual Holding Company; *U.S. Private*, pg. 3069
PACIFIC LIFECORP—See Pacific Mutual Holding Company; *U.S. Private*, pg. 3068
PACIFIC LIFE FUND ADVISORS LLC—See Pacific Mutual Holding Company; *U.S. Private*, pg. 3069
PACIFIC LIFE INSURANCE COMPANY—See Pacific Mutual Holding Company; *U.S. Private*, pg. 3068
PACIFIC LIFE RE LIMITED—See Pacific Mutual Holding Company; *U.S. Private*, pg. 3069
PACIFIC LIFE RE LIMITED—See Pacific Mutual Holding Company; *U.S. Private*, pg. 3069
PACIFICLIGHT POWER PTE. LTD.—See First Pacific Company Limited; *Int'l*, pg. 2686
PACIFIC LINK MINING CORP.; *Int'l*, pg. 5690
PACIFIC LIQUID AND AIR SYSTEMS—See Solaray Corporation; *U.S. Private*, pg. 3707
PACIFIC LOGISTICS CORP.; *U.S. Private*, pg. 3068
PACIFIC LUMBER & SHIPPING CO.; *U.S. Private*, pg. 3068
PACIFIC MAGAZINES PTY. LTD.—See Heinrich Bauer Verlag KG; *Int'l*, pg. 3324
PACIFIC MAGNETICS INC.—See Careen, Inc.; *U.S. Private*, pg. 752
PACIFIC MANUFACTURING OHIO, INC.—See PACIFIC INDUSTRIAL CO. LTD.; *Int'l*, pg. 5690
PACIFIC MANUFACTURING TENNESSEE, INC.—See PACIFIC INDUSTRIAL CO. LTD.; *Int'l*, pg. 5690
PACIFIC MARINE BATTERIES PTY. LTD.; *Int'l*, pg. 5690
PACIFIC MARINE CREDIT UNION; *U.S. Private*, pg. 3068
PACIFIC MARINE SERVICES CO., LTD.—See Tokyo Kisen Co., Ltd.; *Int'l*, pg. 7793
PACIFIC MARINE & SUPPLY CO. LTD. INC.; *U.S. Private*, pg. 3068
PACIFIC MARKETING GROUP INC.—See Dulcich, Inc.; *U.S. Private*, pg. 1286
PACIFIC MARKETING; *U.S. Private*, pg. 3068
PACIFIC MARKET INTERNATIONAL, LLC; *U.S. Private*, pg. 3068
PACIFIC MATERIAL HOLDING SOLUTIONS, INC.; *U.S. Private*, pg. 3068
PACIFIC MECHANICAL SUPPLY; *U.S. Private*, pg. 3068
PACIFIC MEDICAL CENTERS; *U.S. Private*, pg. 3068
PACIFIC MEDICAL CENTRES PTY LTD—See Healius Limited; *Int'l*, pg. 3303
PACIFIC MEDICAL MANAGEMENT SERVICES, INC—See Constellation Software Inc.; *Int'l*, pg. 1774
PACIFIC MERCANTILE BANCORP—See Banc of California, Inc.; *U.S. Public*, pg. 269
PACIFIC MERCANTILE BANK—See Banc of California, Inc.; *U.S. Public*, pg. 269
PACIFIC METAL CO—See Reliance Steel & Aluminum Co.; *U.S. Public*, pg. 1781
PACIFIC METALS CO., LTD.; *Int'l*, pg. 5690
PACIFIC MICRO-TECH; *U.S. Private*, pg. 3068
PACIFIC MILLENNIUM PACKAGING GROUP CORPORATION; *Int'l*, pg. 5691
PACIFIC MOBILE STRUCTURES INC.; *U.S. Private*, pg. 3068
PACIFIC MOBILE STRUCTURES INC.—See Pacific Mobile Structures Inc.; *U.S. Private*, pg. 3068
PACIFIC MOTOR GROUP PTY. LTD.; *Int'l*, pg. 5691
PACIFIC MOTOR TRUCKING COMPANY INC.—See Jack Cooper Transport Co., Inc.; *U.S. Private*, pg. 2173
PACIFIC MUNICIPAL CONSULTANTS; *U.S. Private*, pg. 3068
PACIFIC MUTUAL DOOR COMPANY—See Hardwoods Distribution Inc.; *Int'l*, pg. 3273
PACIFIC MUTUAL FUND BHD.—See Oversea-Chinese Banking Corporation Limited; *Int'l*, pg. 5671
PACIFIC MUTUAL HOLDING COMPANY; *U.S. Private*, pg. 3068
PACIFIC NATIONAL GROUP; *U.S. Private*, pg. 3069
PACIFIC NATIONAL PTY. LTD.; *Int'l*, pg. 5691
PACIFIC NATIONAL PTY. LTD.; *Int'l*, pg. 5691
PACIFICNET BEIJING LIMITED—See PacificNet Inc.; *Int'l*, pg. 5692
PACIFICNET CLICKCOM LIMITED—See PacificNet Inc.; *Int'l*, pg. 5692
PACIFIC NET CO., LTD.; *Int'l*, pg. 5691
PACIFICNET INC.; *Int'l*, pg. 5692
PACIFICNET POWER LIMITED—See PacificNet Inc.; *Int'l*, pg. 5692
PACIFICNET SOLUTIONS LIMITED—See PacificNet Inc.; *Int'l*, pg. 5692
PACIFICNET VENTURES LIMITED—See PacificNet Inc.; *Int'l*, pg. 5692
PACIFIC NEWSPAPER GROUP INC.—See Chatham Asset Management, LLC; *U.S. Private*, pg. 861
PACIFIC-NGIU KEE SDN. BHD.—See Ngiu Kee Corporation (M) Berhad; *Int'l*, pg. 5254
PACIFIC NICKEL MINES LIMITED; *Int'l*, pg. 5691
PACIFIC NISSAN INC.; *U.S. Private*, pg. 3069
PACIFIC NORTHERN ENVIRONMENTAL CORP; *U.S. Private*, pg. 3069
PACIFIC NORTHERN GAS LTD.—See AltaGas Ltd.; *Int'l*, pg. 384

PACIFIC PIPE PUBLIC COMPANY LIMITED

PACIFIC NORTHWEST CAPITAL CORP.; *U.S. Private*, pg. 3069
PACIFIC NORTHWEST FARMERS COOPERATIVE-GENESEE—See Pacific Northwest Farmers Cooperative; *U.S. Private*, pg. 3069
PACIFIC NORTHWEST FARMERS COOPERATIVE; *U.S. Private*, pg. 3069
PACIFIC NORTHWEST NATIONAL LABORATORY—See Battelle Memorial Institute; *U.S. Public*, pg. 487
PACIFICO ACQUISITION CORP.—See Caravelle International Group; *Int'l*, pg. 1320
PACIFIC OAK RESIDENTIAL TRUST, INC.—See Pacific Oak Strategic Opportunity REIT, Inc.; *U.S. Public*, pg. 1632
PACIFIC OAK STRATEGIC OPPORTUNITY REIT, INC.; *U.S. Public*, pg. 1632
PACIFIC OCEAN BREEDING CO., LTD.—See Prima Meat Packers Ltd.; *Int'l*, pg. 5975
PACIFICO COMPANIA DE SEGUROS Y REASEGUROS S.A.—See Credicorp Ltd.; *Int'l*, pg. 1834
PACIFICO ENTERPRISES, INC.; *U.S. Private*, pg. 3072
PACIFIC OFFICE AUTOMATION, INC.; *U.S. Private*, pg. 3069
PACIFIC OFFICE INTERIORS; *U.S. Private*, pg. 3069
PACIFICO FORD, INC.; *U.S. Private*, pg. 3072
PACIFIC OIL & CHEMICAL COMPANY LIMITED—See Yips Chemical Holdings Limited; *Int'l*, pg. 8585
PACIFIC OIL COMPANY LLC; *U.S. Private*, pg. 3069
PACIFIC OLEOCHEMICALS SDN BHD.—See Akzo Nobel N.V.; *Int'l*, pg. 274
PACIFIC ONLINE LIMITED; *Int'l*, pg. 5691
PACIFIC ONLINE SYSTEMS CORPORATION—See Belle Corporation; *Int'l*, pg. 966
PACIFIC & ORIENT BERHAD; *Int'l*, pg. 5685
PACIFIC & ORIENT CAPITAL SDN. BHD.—See Pacific & Orient Berhad; *Int'l*, pg. 5685
PACIFIC & ORIENT INSURANCE CO. BERHAD—See Pacific & Orient Berhad; *Int'l*, pg. 5685
PACIFIC & ORIENT INSURANCE CO. BERHAD—See Sanlam Limited; *Int'l*, pg. 6545
PACIFIC & ORIENT PROPERTIES LTD.—See Pacific & Orient Berhad; *Int'l*, pg. 5685
PACIFIC OROVILLE POWER, INC.—See EQT AB; *Int'l*, pg. 2474
PACIFICORP INTERNATIONAL HOTEL MANAGEMENT, INC.; *Int'l*, pg. 5693
PACIFICORP—See Berkshire Hathaway Inc.; *U.S. Public*, pg. 301
PACIFICO S.A. ENTIDAD PRESTADORA DE SALUD—See UnitedHealth Group Incorporated; *U.S. Public*, pg. 2249
PACIFIC OUTDOOR LIVING; *U.S. Private*, pg. 3069
PACIFIC OVERSEAS TEXTILES MACAO COMMERCIAL OFFSHORE LIMITED—See Pacific Textiles Holdings Limited; *Int'l*, pg. 5692
PACIFICO V REGION S.A.; *Int'l*, pg. 5692
PACIFIC OYSTER CO., INC.—See Dulcich, Inc.; *U.S. Private*, pg. 1286
PACIFIC OZONE TECHNOLOGY INC.—See Xylem Inc.; *U.S. Public*, pg. 2394
PACIFIC PACKAGING MACHINERY, INC.—See Leonard Green & Partners, L.P.; *U.S. Private*, pg. 2428
PACIFIC PACKAGING PRODUCTS, INC.; *U.S. Private*, pg. 3069
PACIFIC PALISADES POST INC.—See Small Newspaper Group Inc.; *U.S. Private*, pg. 3690
PACIFIC (PANYU) TEXTILES LIMITED—See Pacific Textiles Holdings Limited; *Int'l*, pg. 5692
PACIFIC PAPER—See Salt Creek Capital Management, LLC; *U.S. Private*, pg. 3533
PACIFIC PAPER TUBE, INC.—See Sky Island Capital LLC; *U.S. Private*, pg. 3684
PACIFIC PARADISE FOODS, INC.—See JFLA Holdings Inc.; *Int'l*, pg. 3939
PACIFIC PARADYM ENERGY INC.; *Int'l*, pg. 5691
PACIFIC PARTNERSHIPS PTY LTD—See ACS, Actividades de Construccion y Servicios, S.A.; *Int'l*, pg. 115
PACIFIC PARTNERS INSULATION NORTH, A BDI COMPANY, LLC—See Installed Building Products, Inc.; *U.S. Public*, pg. 1133
PACIFIC PARTNERS INSULATION SOUTH, A BDI COMPANY, LLC—See Installed Building Products, Inc.; *U.S. Public*, pg. 1133
PACIFIC PARTNERS MANAGEMENT SERVICES, INC.—See HCA Healthcare, Inc.; *U.S. Public*, pg. 1005
PACIFIC PARTS & CONTROLS INC.; *U.S. Private*, pg. 3069
PACIFIC PAVINGSTONE, INC.; *U.S. Private*, pg. 3070
PACIFIC PAVINGSTONE—See Pacific Outdoor Living; *U.S. Private*, pg. 3069
PACIFIC PETRO IMPORT & EXPORT TRADING JOINT STOCK COMPANY—See Air Water Inc.; *Int'l*, pg. 240
PACIFIC PILOTAGE AUTHORITY CANADA; *Int'l*, pg. 5691
PACIFIC PIONEER INSURANCE GROUP INC.; *U.S. Private*, pg. 3070
PACIFIC PIPE PUBLIC COMPANY LIMITED; *Int'l*, pg. 5691

2045

PACIFIC PIPE PUBLIC COMPANY LIMITED — CORPORATE AFFILIATIONS

PACIFIC PLASTICS & ENGINEERING INC.—See The Cretex Companies, Inc.; *U.S. Private*, pg. 4016
PACIFIC PLUMBING CO.—See Jarboe's Plumbing, Heating & Cooling, Inc.; *U.S. Private*, pg. 2188
PACIFIC PLUMBING SUPPLY CO.; *U.S. Private*, pg. 3070
PACIFIC POTENTIAL TRADING COMPANY LIMITED—See Glorious Sun Enterprises Limited; *Int'l*, pg. 3009
PACIFIC POWER PRODUCTS COMPANY; *U.S. Private*, pg. 3070
PACIFIC POWER SERVICES CORP.—See Andrews Group; *U.S. Private*, pg. 280
PACIFIC POWER SOURCE, INC.; *U.S. Private*, pg. 3070
PACIFIC POWER & SYSTEMS, INC.—See White Wolf Capital LLC; *U.S. Private*, pg. 4510
PACIFIC PRECISION LABORATORIES, INC.; *U.S. Private*, pg. 3070
PACIFIC PRECISION METALS, INC.; *U.S. Private*, pg. 3070
PACIFIC PREMIER BANCORP, INC.; *U.S. Public*, pg. 1632
PACIFIC PREMIER BANK—See Pacific Premier Bancorp, Inc.; *U.S. Public*, pg. 1632
PACIFIC PREMIER TRUST—See Pacific Premier Bancorp, Inc.; *U.S. Public*, pg. 1632
PACIFIC PRESS PUBLISHING ASSOCIATION; *U.S. Private*, pg. 3070
PACIFIC PRIDE SEAFOOD INC.; *U.S. Private*, pg. 3070
PACIFIC PRIDE SERVICES, LLC—See WEX, Inc.; *U.S. Public*, pg. 2364
PACIFIC PROPERTIES III; *U.S. Private*, pg. 3070
PACIFIC PROPERTY AND CASUALTY COMPANY—See Brookfield Corporation; *Int'l*, pg. 1174
PACIFIC PULMONARY SERVICE—See PPSC, Inc.; *U.S. Private*, pg. 3241
PACIFIC PULP MOLDING, INC—See Altamont Capital Partners; *U.S. Private*, pg. 205
PACIFIC RADIANCE LTD.; *Int'l*, pg. 5691
PACIFIC RAIL SERVICES LLC; *U.S. Private*, pg. 3070
PACIFIC RARE SPECIALTY METALS & CHEMICALS, INC.—See Coherent Corp.; *U.S. Public*, pg. 529
PACIFIC REAL ESTATE CO., LTD.—See Land & Houses Public Company Limited; *Int'l*, pg. 4403
PACIFIC REALTY ASSOCIATES, LP; *U.S. Private*, pg. 3070
PACIFIC REALTY COMMERCIAL, LLC—See Colliers International Group Inc.; *Int'l*, pg. 1701
PACIFIC REDWOOD INSURANCE AGENCY, INC.—See Inszone Insurance Services, LLC; *U.S. Private*, pg. 2096
PACIFIC REGISTER CO, INC—See Cottonwood Acquisitions LLC; *U.S. Private*, pg. 1064
PACIFIC RESIDENTIAL SERVICE, INC.—See Relo Group, Inc.; *Int'l*, pg. 6265
PACIFIC RESOURCES BENEFITS ADVISORS, LLC—See Brown & Brown, Inc.; *U.S. Public*, pg. 401
PACIFIC RIDGE EXPLORATION LTD.; *Int'l*, pg. 5691
PACIFIC RIM CAPITAL, INC.—See Fuyo General Lease Co., Ltd.; *Int'l*, pg. 2859
PACIFIC RUBBER & PACKING, INC.; *U.S. Private*, pg. 3070
PACIFIC RUBIALES ENERGY CORP.—See Frontera Energy Corporation; *Int'l*, pg. 2794
PACIFIC RUNDUM CO., LTD.—See Pacific Metals Co., Ltd.; *Int'l*, pg. 5690
PACIFIC SALES KITCHEN AND BATH CENTERS, LLC—See Best Buy Co., Inc.; *U.S. Public*, pg. 326
PACIFIC SALON SYSTEMS INC.—See Sally Beauty Holdings, Inc.; *U.S. Public*, pg. 1839
PACIFIC SANDS, INC.; *U.S. Private*, pg. 3070
PACIFIC SCIENTIFIC AVIATION SERVICES COMPANY—See Parker Hannifin Corporation; *U.S. Public*, pg. 1643
PACIFIC SCIENTIFIC ENERGETIC MATERIALS COMPANY (ARIZONA) LLC—See Fortive Corporation; *U.S. Public*, pg. 871
PACIFIC SCIENTIFIC ENERGETIC MATERIALS COMPANY (CALIFORNIA) LLC—See Fortive Corporation; *U.S. Public*, pg. 871
PACIFIC SCIENTIFIC HTL—See Parker Hannifin Corporation; *U.S. Public*, pg. 1643
PACIFIC SEAFOOD CO., INC.—See Dulcich, Inc.; *U.S. Private*, pg. 1286
PACIFIC SEAFOOD OF WASHINGTON—See Dulcich, Inc.; *U.S. Private*, pg. 1286
THE PACIFIC SECURITIES CO., LTD.; *Int'l*, pg. 7672
PACIFIC SEEDS (THAI) LTD.—See UPL Limited; *Int'l*, pg. 8088
PACIFIC SELECT DISTRIBUTORS, INC.—See Pacific Mutual Holding Company; *U.S. Private*, pg. 3069
PACIFIC SERVICE CREDIT UNION; *U.S. Private*, pg. 3070
PACIFIC SERVICES AND DEVELOPMENT CORPORATION—See Xerox Holdings Corporation; *U.S. Public*, pg. 2388
PACIFIC SERVICES CANADA LIMITED—See Pacific Mutual Holding Company; *U.S. Private*, pg. 3069
PACIFIC SHIP-MANAGERS SDN BHD—See Malaysian Bulk Carriers Berhad; *Int'l*, pg. 4662

PACIFIC SHIP REPAIR & FABRICATION; *U.S. Private*, pg. 3070
PACIFIC SHIPYARDS INTERNATIONAL, LLC—See Pacific Marine & Supply Co. Ltd. Inc.; *U.S. Private*, pg. 3068
PACIFIC SHORE HOLDINGS, INC.—See Med-X, Inc.; *U.S. Private*, pg. 2650
PACIFIC SHORE STONES; *U.S. Private*, pg. 3070
PACIFIC SHRIMP COMPANY—See Dulcich, Inc.; *U.S. Private*, pg. 1286
PACIFIC SHUANGLIN BIO-PHARMACY CO., LTD.; *Int'l*, pg. 5691
PACIFIC SILK ROAD RESOURCES GROUP INC.; *Int'l*, pg. 5691
PACIFIC SMILES GROUP LIMITED; *Int'l*, pg. 5692
PACIFIC SOFTWARE PUBLISHING, INC.; *U.S. Private*, pg. 3070
PACIFIC SOGO DEPARTMENT STORES LTD.—See The Far Eastern Group; *Int'l*, pg. 7641
PACIFICSOURCE HEALTH PLANS; *U.S. Private*, pg. 3072
PACIFIC SOURCE INC.; *U.S. Private*, pg. 3070
PACIFIC & SOUTHERN, LLC—See TEGNA Inc.; *U.S. Public*, pg. 1990
PACIFIC SOUTHWEST COMMUNITY DEVELOPMENT CORPORATION; *U.S. Private*, pg. 3070
PACIFIC SPECIALITY INSURANCE COMPANY—See The McGraw Company; *U.S. Private*, pg. 4077
PACIFIC SPORTS EXCHANGE, INC.; *U.S. Public*, pg. 1632
PACIFIC SPORTS INC.—See Peace Textile America Inc.; *U.S. Private*, pg. 3122
PACIFIC STAINLESS PRODUCTS; *U.S. Private*, pg. 3070
PACIFIC STANDARD—See Grist Magazine, Inc.; *U.S. Private*, pg. 1790
PACIFIC STAR COMMUNICATIONS, INC.; *U.S. Private*, pg. 3071
PACIFIC STAR DEVELOPMENT LIMITED; *Int'l*, pg. 5692
PACIFIC STAR DEVELOPMENT (MALAYSIA) SDN. BHD.—See Pacific Star Development Limited; *Int'l*, pg. 5692
PACIFIC STAR DEVELOPMENT (THAILAND) CO., LTD.—See Pacific Star Development Limited; *Int'l*, pg. 5692
PACIFIC STAR NETWORK LIMITED; *Int'l*, pg. 5692
PACIFIC STAR SPORTS SERVICES L.L.C.—See Toyam Sports Limited; *Int'l*, pg. 7851
PACIFIC STATES CAST IRON PIPE COMPANY—See McWane, Inc.; *U.S. Private*, pg. 2645
PACIFIC STATES INDUSTRIES INCORPORATED; *U.S. Private*, pg. 3071
PACIFIC STEEL CASTING COMPANY; *U.S. Private*, pg. 3071
PACIFIC STEEL (NZ) LIMITED—See BlueScope Steel Limited; *Int'l*, pg. 1074
PACIFIC STRATEGIC FINANCIAL TBK; *Int'l*, pg. 5692
PACIFIC STRATEGIC INVESTMENTS PTY LIMITED—See BKI Investment Company Limited; *Int'l*, pg. 1054
PACIFIC SUMMIT ENERGY LLC—See Sumitomo Corporation; *Int'l*, pg. 7273
PACIFIC SUNWEAR OF CALIFORNIA, LLC—See Golden Gate Capital Management II, LLC; *U.S. Private*, pg. 1731
PACIFIC SUNWEAR STORES LLC—See Golden Gate Capital Management II, LLC; *U.S. Private*, pg. 1731
PACIFIC SUPERMARKET INC.; *U.S. Private*, pg. 3071
PACIFIC SUPPLY COMPANY; *U.S. Private*, pg. 3071
PACIFIC SURGICAL & ENDOSCOPY CENTRE PTE. LTD.—See Pacific Healthcare Holdings Ltd.; *Int'l*, pg. 5689
PACIFIC SYMPHONY; *U.S. Private*, pg. 3071
PACIFIC SYSTEMS CORPORATION—See Taiheiyo Cement Corporation; *Int'l*, pg. 7412
PACIFIC TELEVISION CENTER—See Tata Sons Limited; *Int'l*, pg. 7469
PACIFIC TEXTILES HOLDINGS LIMITED; *Int'l*, pg. 5692
PACIFIC TEXTILES LIMITED—See Pacific Textiles Holdings Limited; *Int'l*, pg. 5692
PACIFIC THEATERS ENTERTAINMENT CORP.—See Decurion Corp.; *U.S. Private*, pg. 1188
PACIFIC THEATRES CORPORATION—See Decurion Corp.; *U.S. Private*, pg. 1188
PACIFIC TIME CO., LTD.—See Cortina Holdings Limited; *Int'l*, pg. 1808
PACIFIC TIME PTE LTD.—See Cortina Holdings Limited; *Int'l*, pg. 1808
PACIFIC TIRE DISTRIBUTORS—See U.S. Venture, Inc.; *U.S. Private*, pg. 4272
PACIFIC TOLL PROCESSING, INC.; *U.S. Private*, pg. 3071
PACIFIC TOMATO GROWERS LTD.; *U.S. Private*, pg. 3071
PACIFIC TOPSOILS INC.—See GRO-WELL Brands Inc.; *U.S. Private*, pg. 1791
PACIFIC TOWER PROPERTIES INC.—See Cook Inlet Region, Inc.; *U.S. Private*, pg. 1038
PACIFIC TOWING (PNG) LIMITED—See Steamships Trading Company Limited; *Int'l*, pg. 7189
PACIFIC TRADING CO., LTD.—See Kikkoman Corporation; *Int'l*, pg. 4161

PACIFIC TRAIL CORPORATION—See Columbia Sportswear Company; *U.S. Public*, pg. 535
PACIFIC TRAIL INC.—See Columbia Sportswear Company; *U.S. Public*, pg. 535
PACIFIC TRANS ENVIRONMENTAL SERVICES, INC.—See Aurora Capital Group, LLC; *U.S. Private*, pg. 394
PACIFIC TRANSPORTATION FEDERAL CREDIT UNION—See Credit Union of Southern California; *U.S. Private*, pg. 1091
PACIFIC TRANSPORTATION LINES, INC.; *U.S. Private*, pg. 3071
PACIFIC TRELLIS FRUIT LLC—See Arable Capital Partners LLC; *U.S. Private*, pg. 307
PACIFIC TRUCK CENTERS—See Pacific Power Products Company; *U.S. Private*, pg. 3070
PACIFIC TRUCK & TRAILER—See Great Western Leasing & Sales, LLC; *U.S. Private*, pg. 1768
PACIFIC TURBINE USA, LLC—See PTB Group Limited; *Int'l*, pg. 6090
PACIFIC UNDERWRITING CORPORATION PTY LTD—See The Hanover Insurance Group, Inc.; *U.S. Public*, pg. 2087
PACIFIC UNION INTERNATIONAL, INC.; *U.S. Private*, pg. 3071
PACIFIC VALLEY BANK; *U.S. Public*, pg. 1632
PACIFIC VALLEY FOODS INC.; *U.S. Private*, pg. 3071
PACIFIC VALLEY INVESTORS INC.; *U.S. Private*, pg. 3071
PACIFIC VALVE INDUSTRIAL CO., LTD.—See PACIFIC INDUSTRIAL CO. LTD.; *Int'l*, pg. 5690
PACIFIC VALVES—See Crane NXT, Co.; *U.S. Public*, pg. 590
PACIFIC VALVE (TAIWAN) CO., LTD.—See PACIFIC INDUSTRIAL CO. LTD.; *Int'l*, pg. 5690
PACIFIC VEGAS GLOBAL STRATEGIES, INC.; *Int'l*, pg. 5692
PACIFIC VENTILATION PTY. LTD.—See Systemair AB; *Int'l*, pg. 7391
PACIFIC VENTURES GROUP, INC.; *U.S. Private*, pg. 1632
PACIFIC WEST BANK; *U.S. Public*, pg. 1632
PACIFIC WESTERN AGENCIES, INC.; *U.S. Private*, pg. 3071
PACIFIC WESTERN BANK—See Banc of California, Inc.; *U.S. Public*, pg. 269
PACIFIC WESTERN CONTAINER CORP.—See Blower Dempsay Corporation; *U.S. Private*, pg. 584
PACIFIC WESTERN INSURANCE, LLC—See Essex Property Trust, Inc.; *U.S. Public*, pg. 796
PACIFIC WESTERN TRAINING COMPANY—See Oppenheimer Companies, Inc.; *U.S. Private*, pg. 3033
PACIFIC WESTERN TRANSPORTATION LTD; *Int'l*, pg. 5692
PACIFIC WEST SYSTEMS SUPPLY LTD.; *Int'l*, pg. 5692
PACIFIC WHEEL INC.—See Zhejiang Jingu Co., Ltd.; *Int'l*, pg. 8657
PACIFICWIDE BUSINESS GROUP, INC.; *U.S. Private*, pg. 3072
PACIFIC WILDCAT RESOURCES CORP.; *Int'l*, pg. 5692
PACIFIC WINE DISTRIBUTORS—See Epic Wine & Spirits; *U.S. Private*, pg. 1413
PACIFIC WOOD LAMINATES INC.; *U.S. Private*, pg. 3071
PACIFIC WOOD PRESERVING OF BAKERSFIELD, INC.; *U.S. Private*, pg. 3071
PACIFIC WOODTECH CORPORATION—See Daiken Corporation; *Int'l*, pg. 1931
PACIFIC WORLD (BEIJING) TRAVEL AGENCY CO., LTD.—See TUI AG; *Int'l*, pg. 7966
PACIFIC WORLD CORPORATION—See Levine Leichtman Capital Partners, LLC; *U.S. Private*, pg. 2436
PACIFIC WORLD DESTINATION EAST SDN. BHD.—See TUI AG; *Int'l*, pg. 7966
PACIFIC WORLD MEETINGS & EVENTS HELLAS TRAVEL LIMITED—See TUI AG; *Int'l*, pg. 7966
PACIFIC WORLD MEETINGS & EVENTS HONG KONG, LIMITED—See TUI AG; *Int'l*, pg. 7966
PACIFIC WORLD MEETINGS & EVENTS SAM—See TUI AG; *Int'l*, pg. 7966
PACIFIC WORLD MEETINGS & EVENTS SINGAPORE PTE. LTD.—See TUI AG; *Int'l*, pg. 7966
PACIFIC WORLD (SHANGHAI) TRAVEL AGENCY CO. LIMITED—See TUI AG; *Int'l*, pg. 7966
PACIFIC WORLD TRADE INC.—See Cummins Inc.; *U.S. Public*, pg. 609
PACIFIC YGNACIO CORPORATION—See Great Eagle Holdings Limited; *Int'l*, pg. 3064
PAC INDUSTRIES, LLC—See EVI Industries, Inc.; *U.S. Public*, pg. 803
PAC INSTRUMENTS (THAILAND) COMPANY LIMITED—See Roper Technologies, Inc.; *U.S. Public*, pg. 1812
PACIOLAN, INC.—See Comcast Corporation; *U.S. Public*, pg. 537
PACIRA BIOSCIENCES, INC.; *U.S. Public*, pg. 1632
PACIRA CRYOTECH, INC.—See Pacira BioSciences, Inc.; *U.S. Public*, pg. 1632
PACIRA PHARMACEUTICALS, INC.—See Pacira BioSciences, Inc.; *U.S. Public*, pg. 1632

COMPANY NAME INDEX

PACT

PACIRA - SAN DIEGO—See Pacira BioSciences, Inc.; *U.S. Public*, pg. 1632
PACIUGO FRANCHISING, LP; *U.S. Private*, pg. 3072
PACIV, INC.—See Blackford Capital LLC; *U.S. Private*, pg. 574
PACJETS FINANCIAL LTD.—See Nordic Group of Companies, Ltd.; *U.S. Private*, pg. 2937
PACK2PACK GROUP N.V.—See Greif Inc.; *U.S. Public*, pg. 969
PACK2PACK HALSTEREN B.V.—See Gilde Buy Out Partners B.V.; *Int'l*, pg. 2975
PACK2PACK ZWOLLE B.V.—See Greif Inc.; *U.S. Public*, pg. 969
PACKABLE HOLDINGS, LLC; *U.S. Private*, pg. 3072
PACKAGE ALL CORP.—See Ares Management Corporation; *U.S. Public*, pg. 191
PACKAGE ALL CORP.—See Ontario Teachers' Pension Plan; *Int'l*, pg. 5590
PACKAGE CONCIERGE, INC.—See Gibraltar Industries, Inc.; *U.S. Public*, pg. 936
PACKAGED GOODS LTD—See The Quarto Group, Inc.; *Int'l*, pg. 7677
PACKAGE MACHINERY COMPANY, INC.; *U.S. Private*, pg. 3072
PACKAGEONE, INC.—See Goldberg Lindsay & Co., LLC; *U.S. Private*, pg. 1729
PACKAGES CONVERTORS LIMITED—See Packages Ltd.; *Int'l*, pg. 5693
PACKAGES LTD.; *Int'l*, pg. 5693
PACKAGING 2 BUY LIMITED—See Bunzl plc; *Int'l*, pg. 1219
THE PACKAGING CAFE—See Lawrence Paper Company; *U.S. Private*, pg. 2401
PACKAGING CO., LTD. SAOG; *Int'l*, pg. 5693
THE PACKAGING COMPANY—See Visy Industries Holdings Pty. Ltd.; *Int'l*, pg. 8256
PACKAGING CONCEPTS ASSOC., LLC; *U.S. Private*, pg. 3072
PACKAGING CONCEPTS INC.; *U.S. Private*, pg. 3072
PACKAGING COORDINATORS, INC.—See Kohlberg & Company, LLC; *U.S. Private*, pg. 2338
PACKAGING CORPORATION OF AMERICA - CHICAGO FULL-LINE PLANT—See Packaging Corporation of America; *U.S. Public*, pg. 1633
PACKAGING CORPORATION OF AMERICA - HUNTSVILLE SHEET PLANT—See Packaging Corporation of America; *U.S. Public*, pg. 1633
PACKAGING CORPORATION OF AMERICA; *U.S. Public*, pg. 1632
PACKAGING CORPORATION OF ILLINOIS—See Packaging Corporation of America; *U.S. Public*, pg. 1633
PACKAGING FILM SALES, INC.—See Bunzl plc; *Int'l*, pg. 1217
PACKAGING FIRST LTD.—See Bong AB; *Int'l*, pg. 1107
THE PACKAGING HOUSE, INC.; *U.S. Private*, pg. 4090
PACKAGING INCORPORATED—See TruArc Partners, L.P.; *U.S. Private*, pg. 4245
PACKAGING INNOVATORS, LLC—See Goldberg Lindsay & Co., LLC; *U.S. Private*, pg. 1729
PACKAGING LEASING SYSTEMS INC.—See Illinois Tool Works Inc.; *U.S. Public*, pg. 1110
PACKAGING MACHINERY MANUFACTURERS INSTITUTE, INC.; *U.S. Private*, pg. 3072
PACKAGING PERSONIFIED, INC.; *U.S. Private*, pg. 3072
PACKAGING PERSONIFIED, INC.—See Packaging Personified, Inc.; *U.S. Private*, pg. 3072
PACKAGING PROGRESSIONS, INC.—See The Middleby Corporation; *U.S. Public*, pg. 2115
PACKAGING RESOURCES, INC.; *U.S. Private*, pg. 3072
PACKAGING SPECIALTIES INC.; *U.S. Private*, pg. 3072
PACKAGING SYSTEMS, LLC; *U.S. Private*, pg. 3072
PACKAGING TAPE INC.; *U.S. Private*, pg. 3072
PACKAGING UNLIMITED, LLC; *U.S. Private*, pg. 3073
PACKAGING UNLIMITED LLC—See Hood Industries Inc.; *U.S. Private*, pg. 1977
THE PACK AMERICA CORP.—See The Pack Corporation; *Int'l*, pg. 7672
PACKARD BELL BELGIUM BVBA—See Acer Incorporated; *Int'l*, pg. 100
PACKARD BELL DEUTSCHLAND GMBH—See Acer Incorporated; *Int'l*, pg. 100
PACKARD BELL (UK) LTD.—See Acer Incorporated; *Int'l*, pg. 100
PACKARD ELECTRIC DIVISION MEXICAN OPERATIONS—See General Motors Company; *U.S. Public*, pg. 928
PACKARD ELECTRIC EUROPA GES.M.B.H.—See General Motors Company; *U.S. Public*, pg. 928
PACKARD, INC.—See Partners Group Holding AG; *Int'l*, pg. 5749
PACKARD MOTOR CAR CO. INC.; *U.S. Private*, pg. 3073
PACKARD TRANSPORT INC.; *U.S. Private*, pg. 3073
THE PACK (CHANGSHU) CORPORATION—See The Pack Corporation; *Int'l*, pg. 7672
THE PACK CORPORATION; *Int'l*, pg. 7672
PACKER CITY INTERNATIONAL TRUCKS INC.; *U.S. Private*, pg. 3073
THE PACKER GROUP INC.; *U.S. Private*, pg. 4090

PACKERS HOLDINGS, LLC—See Harvest Partners L.P.; *U.S. Private*, pg. 1877
PACKERS PROVISION CO. OF PUERTO RICO INC.—See TraFon Group; *U.S. Private*, pg. 4203
PACKERS SANITATION SERVICES, INC.—See Blue Point Capital Partners, LLC; *U.S. Private*, pg. 590
PACKERWARE, LLC—See Berry Global Group, Inc; *U.S. Public*, pg. 321
PACKESTATE LIMITED—See ENL Limited; *Int'l*, pg. 2441
PACKETFABRIC, INC; *U.S. Private*, pg. 3073
PACKET FUSION, INC.; *U.S. Private*, pg. 3073
PACKETLIGHT NETWORKS LTD.—See RAD Group; *Int'l*, pg. 6172
PACKET NEWSPAPERS LIMITED—See Gannett Co., Inc.; *U.S. Public*, pg. 899
PACKET ONE NETWORKS (MALAYSIA) SDN. BHD.—See Green Packet Berhad; *Int'l*, pg. 3072
PACKET ONE SDN. BHD.—See Green Packet Berhad; *Int'l*, pg. 3072
PACKETVIDEO CORPORATION—See Nippon Telegraph & Telephone Corporation; *Int'l*, pg. 5351
PACKFILM LTDA—See Oben Holding Group SAC; *Int'l*, pg. 5510
PACK HEALTH, LLC—See Quest Diagnostics, Inc.; *U.S. Public*, pg. 1755
PACK'INDUSTRIE—See NSC Groupe SA; *Int'l*, pg. 5476
PACKING MATERIAL COMPANY INC.; *U.S. Private*, pg. 3073
PACKINOX MOSCOW—See Alfa Laval AB; *Int'l*, pg. 311
PAC-KIT SAFETY EQUIPMENT—See Acme United Corporation; *U.S. Public*, pg. 35
PACKLESS METAL HOSE INC.; *U.S. Private*, pg. 3073
PACK-LINE HOLDINGS (PTY) LTD—See Berry Global Group, Inc; *U.S. Public*, pg. 324
PACKNET, LTD.—See UFP Industries, Inc.; *U.S. Public*, pg. 2219
PACK PLASTICS LIMITED—See ENL Limited; *Int'l*, pg. 2441
PACKPOOL MEDIEN GMBH—See Janoschka GmbH; *Int'l*, pg. 3880
PACKPOOL SWISS GMBH—See Janoschka GmbH; *Int'l*, pg. 3880
PACKRITE, LLC; *U.S. Private*, pg. 3073
THE PACK (SHANGHAI) CORPORATION—See The Pack Corporation; *Int'l*, pg. 7672
PACKSIZE INTERNATIONAL, LLC; *U.S. Private*, pg. 3073
PACK TAKEYAMA CO., LTD—See The Pack Corporation; *Int'l*, pg. 7672
PACK-TIGER GMBH—See Sealed Air Corporation; *U.S. Public*, pg. 1854
PACKTIME INNOVATIONS PRIVATE LIMITED—See Mankind Pharma Ltd.; *Int'l*, pg. 4673
PACLEASE MEXICANA, S.A. DE C.V.—See PACCAR Inc.; *U.S. Public*, pg. 1631
PACMARINE SERVICES CO., LTD.—See Pacific Basin Shipping Limited; *Int'l*, pg. 5685
PACMARINE SERVICES (HK) LIMITED—See Pacific Basin Shipping Limited; *Int'l*, pg. 5685
PACMARINE SERVICES LLC—See Pacific Basin Shipping Limited; *Int'l*, pg. 5685
PACMARINE SERVICES PTE. LTD.—See Pacific Basin Shipping Limited; *Int'l*, pg. 5685
PAC-MARU, INC.—See Toyo Suisan Kaisha, Ltd.; *Int'l*, pg. 7858
PAC NATIONAL INC.—See PAC Worldwide Corporation; *U.S. Private*, pg. 3063
PACNET LIMITED—See Telstra Group Limited; *Int'l*, pg. 7545
PACNET THAILAND—See Telstra Group Limited; *Int'l*, pg. 7546
PACO ASSURANCE COMPANY, INC.—See ProAssurance Corporation; *U.S. Public*, pg. 1723
PA CO., LTD.; *Int'l*, pg. 5684
PACOM GROUP AB—See Stanley Black & Decker, Inc.; *U.S. Public*, pg. 1933
PACOM SYSTEMS ESPANA SL—See Stanley Black & Decker, Inc.; *U.S. Public*, pg. 1933
PACOM SYSTEMS (NORTH AMERICA) INC.—See Stanley Black & Decker, Inc.; *U.S. Public*, pg. 1933
PACOM SYSTEMS PTY LIMITED—See Stanley Black & Decker, Inc.; *U.S. Public*, pg. 1933
PACON CORPORATION—See F.I.L.A. - Fabbrica Italiana Lapis ed Affini S.p.A.; *Int'l*, pg. 2596
PA CONSULTING GROUP AB—See The Carlyle Group Inc.; *U.S. Public*, pg. 2051
PA CONSULTING GROUP A/S—See The Carlyle Group Inc.; *U.S. Public*, pg. 2051
PA CONSULTING GROUP AS—See The Carlyle Group Inc.; *U.S. Public*, pg. 2051
PA CONSULTING GROUP GMBH—See The Carlyle Group Inc.; *U.S. Public*, pg. 2051
PA CONSULTING GROUP INC—See The Carlyle Group Inc.; *U.S. Public*, pg. 2051
PA CONSULTING HOLDINGS LIMITED—See The Carlyle Group Inc.; *U.S. Public*, pg. 2051
PA CONSULTING SERVICES (INDIA) PRIVATE LIMITED—See The Carlyle Group Inc.; *U.S. Public*, pg. 2052

PA CONSULTING SERVICES LIMITED—See The Carlyle Group Inc.; *U.S. Public*, pg. 2052
PACOR, INC. - FABRICATING DIVISION—See Pacor, Inc.; *U.S. Private*, pg. 3073
PACOR, INC.; *U.S. Private*, pg. 3073
PACORINI BEO D.O.O.—See B. Pacorini S.p.A.; *Int'l*, pg. 789
PACORINI CUSTOMS & FORWARDING LLC—See B. Pacorini S.p.A.; *Int'l*, pg. 789
PACORINI DMCC—See B. Pacorini S.p.A.; *Int'l*, pg. 789
PACORINI FORWARDING S.R.L.—See Crane Worldwide Logistics LLC; *U.S. Private*, pg. 1085
PACORINI GLOBAL SERVICES LLC—See B. Pacorini S.p.A.; *Int'l*, pg. 789
PACORINI IBERICA SAU—See B. Pacorini S.p.A.; *Int'l*, pg. 789
PACORINI KOPER D.O.O—See B. Pacorini S.p.A.; *Int'l*, pg. 789
PACORINI METALS ITALIA S.R.L—See B. Pacorini S.p.A.; *Int'l*, pg. 789
PACORINI METALS USA LLC—See B. Pacorini S.p.A.; *Int'l*, pg. 789
PACORINI MONTENEGRO D.O.O.—See B. Pacorini S.p.A.; *Int'l*, pg. 789
PACORINI ROTTERDAM B.V.—See B. Pacorini S.p.A.; *Int'l*, pg. 789
PACORINI SILOCAF S.R.L.—See B. Pacorini S.p.A.; *Int'l*, pg. 789
PACORINI TOLL PTE. LTD.—See B. Pacorini S.p.A.; *Int'l*, pg. 789
PACORINI TOLL (SHANGHAI) WAREHOUSING LIMITED—See B. Pacorini S.p.A.; *Int'l*, pg. 789
PACORINI VIETNAM LTD—See B. Pacorini S.p.A.; *Int'l*, pg. 789
PACORINI VLISSINGEN B.V.—See B. Pacorini S.p.A.; *Int'l*, pg. 789
PACO SPORT LTD. INC.; *U.S. Private*, pg. 3073
PACO STEELE & ENGINEERING CORP.; *U.S. Private*, pg. 3073
PACOVSKE STROJIRNY, A.S.—See Safichem Group AG; *Int'l*, pg. 6471
PAC PAPER, LLC—See Apollo Global Management, Inc.; *U.S. Public*, pg. 154
PAC PARKSIDE AT THE BEACH, LLC—See Blackstone Inc.; *U.S. Public*, pg. 351
PACPARTS INC.; *U.S. Private*, pg. 3073
PACPIZZA LLC; *U.S. Private*, pg. 3073
PACPROJECT GMBH—See Mayr-Melnhof Karton AG; *Int'l*, pg. 4747
PACRAFT CO., LTD.—See Nabtesco Corporation; *Int'l*, pg. 5120
PACRAY INTERNATIONAL HOLDINGS LIMITED; *Int'l*, pg. 5693
PACRIM HOSPITALITY SERVICES INC.—See Pacrim International Capital Inc.; *Int'l*, pg. 5693
PACRIM INTERNATIONAL CAPITAL INC.; *Int'l*, pg. 5693
PACRIM INTERNATIONAL CAPITAL INC.—See Pacrim International Capital Inc.; *Int'l*, pg. 5693
PACRIM MARKETING GROUP INC.—See Vector Inc.; *Int'l*, pg. 8144
PACSA, SERVICIOS URBANOS Y DEL MEDIO NATURAL, S.L.—See Grupo Villar Mir, S.A.U.; *Int'l*, pg. 3139
PACSCI MOTION CONTROL, INC.—See Fortive Corporation; *U.S. Public*, pg. 871
PAC/SIB L.L.C.—See Pacific Realty Associates, LP; *U.S. Private*, pg. 3070
PACS INDUSTRIES INC.; *U.S. Private*, pg. 3073
PAC STRAPPING PRODUCTS INC.; *U.S. Private*, pg. 3063
PAC TECH ASIA SDN. BHD.—See Nagase & Co., Ltd.; *Int'l*, pg. 5128
PAC TECH-PACKAGING TECHNOLOGIES GMBH—See Nagase & Co., Ltd.; *Int'l*, pg. 5128
PAC TECH USA-PACKAGING TECHNOLOGIES INC.—See Nagase & Co., Ltd.; *Int'l*, pg. 5128
PACTERA TECHNOLOGY JAPAN CO., LTD.—See China Electronics Corporation; *Int'l*, pg. 1499
PACTERA TECHNOLOGY NA, INC.—See China Electronics Corporation; *Int'l*, pg. 1499
PACT GROUP HOLDINGS (AUSTRALIA) PTY. LTD.—See Pact Group Holdings Ltd.; *Int'l*, pg. 5693
PACT GROUP HOLDINGS LTD.; *Int'l*, pg. 5693
PACTIMO LLC; *U.S. Private*, pg. 3073
PACTIV CORP. - BEECH ISLAND—See Pactiv Evergreen Inc.; *U.S. Public*, pg. 1633
PACTIV CORP. - BELVIDERE—See Pactiv Evergreen Inc.; *U.S. Public*, pg. 1633
PACTIV EVERGREEN INC.; *U.S. Public*, pg. 1633
PACTIV LLC—See Pactiv Evergreen Inc.; *U.S. Public*, pg. 1633
PACT-ONE SOLUTIONS, INC.—See Executech Utah, LLC; *U.S. Private*, pg. 1447
PACTON GOLD INC.—See Renegade Gold Inc.; *Int'l*, pg. 6275
PACTROL CONTROLS LTD.—See Emerson Electric Co.; *U.S. Public*, pg. 751
PACT; *U.S. Private*, pg. 3073
PAC-VAN, INC.—See United Rentals, Inc.; *U.S. Public*, pg. 2235

PACT — CORPORATE AFFILIATIONS

PACWEST BANCORP—See Banc of California, Inc.; *U.S. Public*, pg. 268
PACWEST DISTRIBUTING, INC.; *U.S. Private*, pg. 3073
PACWEST EQUITIES, INC.; *U.S. Public*, pg. 1634
PACWEST FINANCIAL MANAGEMENT, INC.—See Clayton, Dubilier & Rice, LLC; *U.S. Private*, pg. 923
PACWEST FINANCIAL MANAGEMENT, INC.—See Stone Point Capital LLC; *U.S. Private*, pg. 3824
PAC-WEST TELECOMM, INC.; *U.S. Private*, pg. 3063
PAC WORLDWIDE CORPORATION; *U.S. Private*, pg. 3063
PAC WORLDWIDE MEXICO, S. DE R.L. DE C.V.—See PAC Worldwide Corporation; *U.S. Private*, pg. 3063
PADAENG INDUSTRY PCL; *Int'l*, pg. 5693
PADAENG INDUSTRY—See Padaeng Industry pcl; *Int'l*, pg. 5693
PADAENG INDUSTRY—See Padaeng Industry pcl; *Int'l*, pg. 5693
PADAENG INTERNATIONAL MINING CO., LTD.—See Padaeng Industry pcl; *Int'l*, pg. 5693
PADAENG POONGSAN METALS CO., LTD.—See Padaeng Industry pcl; *Int'l*, pg. 5693
PADAENG PROPERTIES CO., LTD.—See Padaeng Industry pcl; *Int'l*, pg. 5693
PADAM COTTON YARNS LIMITED; *Int'l*, pg. 5693
PADANAPLAST S.P.A.—See Solvay S.A.; *Int'l*, pg. 7078
PADANAPLAST S.R.L.—See Finproject S.p.A.; *Int'l*, pg. 2676
PADAUK TECHNOLOGY CO., LTD.; *Int'l*, pg. 5694
THE PADDED WAGON INC.; *U.S. Private*, pg. 4090
PADDINGTON GOLD PTY. LTD.—See Zijin Mining Group Company Limited; *Int'l*, pg. 8683
PADDINGTON—See Mondelez International, Inc.; *U.S. Public*, pg. 1464
PADDOCK CHEVROLET INC.; *U.S. Private*, pg. 3073
PADDOCK LABORATORIES, LLC—See Perrigo Company plc; *Int'l*, pg. 5813
PADDOCK MALL, LLC—See Washington Prime Group Inc.; *U.S. Private*, pg. 4448
PADDOCK PUBLICATIONS, INC.; *U.S. Private*, pg. 3073
PADDOCK SWIMMING POOL COMPANY—See Colliers International Group Inc.; *Int'l*, pg. 1701
PADENGA HOLDINGS LIMITED; *Int'l*, pg. 5694
PADERBORNER BRAUEREI HAUS CRAMER GMBH & CO. KG—See Warsteiner Brauerei Haus Cramer KG; *Int'l*, pg. 8346
PADERBORNER TRANSPORT-BETON-GESELLSCHAFT MIT BESCHRANKTER HAFTUNG & CO. K.-G.—See Heidelberg Materials AG; *Int'l*, pg. 3318
PADERBORNER TRANSPORT-BETON-GESELLSCHAFT MIT BESCHRANKTER HAFTUNG—See Heidelberg Materials AG; *Int'l*, pg. 3318
PADES PERSONALSERVICE GMBH—See E.ON SE; *Int'l*, pg. 2258
PADGETT COMMUNICATIONS, INC.; *U.S. Private*, pg. 3073
PADI AMERICAS—See Capital Investments & Ventures Corp.; *U.S. Private*, pg. 741
PADI ASIA PACIFIC PTY LTD—See Capital Investments & Ventures Corp.; *U.S. Private*, pg. 741
PADIBERAS NASIONAL BERHAD - KBB BAGAN TERAP MILL—See Padiberas Nasional Berhad; *Int'l*, pg. 5694
PADIBERAS NASIONAL BERHAD - KBB BUKIT BESAR MILL—See Padiberas Nasional Berhad; *Int'l*, pg. 5694
PADIBERAS NASIONAL BERHAD - KBB BUKIT KENAK MILL—See Padiberas Nasional Berhad; *Int'l*, pg. 5694
PADIBERAS NASIONAL BERHAD - KBB BUKIT RAYA MILL—See Padiberas Nasional Berhad; *Int'l*, pg. 5694
PADIBERAS NASIONAL BERHAD - KBB CHANGKAT LADA MILL—See Padiberas Nasional Berhad; *Int'l*, pg. 5694
PADIBERAS NASIONAL BERHAD - KBB GUAR CHEMPEDAK MILL—See Padiberas Nasional Berhad; *Int'l*, pg. 5694
PADIBERAS NASIONAL BERHAD - KBB JERLUN MILL—See Padiberas Nasional Berhad; *Int'l*, pg. 5694
PADIBERAS NASIONAL BERHAD - KBB JITRA MILL—See Padiberas Nasional Berhad; *Int'l*, pg. 5694
PADIBERAS NASIONAL BERHAD - KBB KANGKONG MILL—See Padiberas Nasional Berhad; *Int'l*, pg. 5694
PADIBERAS NASIONAL BERHAD - KBB KERPAN MILL—See Padiberas Nasional Berhad; *Int'l*, pg. 5694
PADIBERAS NASIONAL BERHAD - KBB KODIANG MIILL—See Padiberas Nasional Berhad; *Int'l*, pg. 5694
PADIBERAS NASIONAL BERHAD - KBB KUALA PERLIS MILL—See Padiberas Nasional Berhad; *Int'l*, pg. 5694
PADIBERAS NASIONAL BERHAD - KBB KUALA ROMPIN MILL—See Padiberas Nasional Berhad; *Int'l*, pg. 5694
PADIBERAS NASIONAL BERHAD - KBB LANGGAR MILL—See Padiberas Nasional Berhad; *Int'l*, pg. 5694
PADIBERAS NASIONAL BERHAD - KBB MEGAT DEWA MILL—See Padiberas Nasional Berhad; *Int'l*, pg. 5694
PADIBERAS NASIONAL BERHAD - KBB PASIR PUTIH MILL—See Padiberas Nasional Berhad; *Int'l*, pg. 5694
PADIBERAS NASIONAL BERHAD - KBB PAYA KELADI MILL—See Padiberas Nasional Berhad; *Int'l*, pg. 5694
PADIBERAS NASIONAL BERHAD - KBB PERINGAT MILL—See Padiberas Nasional Berhad; *Int'l*, pg. 5694

PADIBERAS NASIONAL BERHAD - KBB PERING MILL—See Padiberas Nasional Berhad; *Int'l*, pg. 5694
PADIBERAS NASIONAL BERHAD - KBB SERI TIRAM JAYA MILL—See Padiberas Nasional Berhad; *Int'l*, pg. 5694
PADIBERAS NASIONAL BERHAD - KBB SIMPANG EMPAT MILL—See Padiberas Nasional Berhad; *Int'l*, pg. 5694
PADIBERAS NASIONAL BERHAD - KBB SIMPANG LIMA MILL—See Padiberas Nasional Berhad; *Int'l*, pg. 5694
PADIBERAS NASIONAL BERHAD - KBB SUNGAI BARU MILL—See Padiberas Nasional Berhad; *Int'l*, pg. 5694
PADIBERAS NASIONAL BERHAD - KBB SUNGAI BESAR MILL—See Padiberas Nasional Berhad; *Int'l*, pg. 5694
PADIBERAS NASIONAL BERHAD - KBB SUNGAI LIMAU MILL—See Padiberas Nasional Berhad; *Int'l*, pg. 5694
PADIBERAS NASIONAL BERHAD - KBB SUNGAI MANIK MILL—See Padiberas Nasional Berhad; *Int'l*, pg. 5694
PADIBERAS NASIONAL BERHAD - KBB SUNGAI RANGGAM MILL—See Padiberas Nasional Berhad; *Int'l*, pg. 5694
PADIBERAS NASIONAL BERHAD - KBB TELUK KECHAI MILL—See Padiberas Nasional Berhad; *Int'l*, pg. 5694
PADIBERAS NASIONAL BERHAD - KBB UTAN AJI MILL—See Padiberas Nasional Berhad; *Int'l*, pg. 5694
PADIBERAS NASIONAL BERHAD; *Int'l*, pg. 5694
PADI CANADA LIMITED—See Capital Investments & Ventures Corp.; *U.S. Private*, pg. 741
PADI JAPAN, INC.—See Capital Investments & Ventures Corp.; *U.S. Private*, pg. 741
PADILLACRT - LOS ANGELES—See Padilla Speer Beardsley Inc.; *U.S. Private*, pg. 3074
PADILLACRT - NEW YORK—See Padilla Speer Beardsley Inc.; *U.S. Private*, pg. 3074
PADILLACRT - NORFOLK—See Padilla Speer Beardsley Inc.; *U.S. Private*, pg. 3074
PADILLACRT - RICHMOND—See Padilla Speer Beardsley Inc.; *U.S. Private*, pg. 3074
PADILLA SPEER BEARDSLEY INC.; *U.S. Private*, pg. 3073
PADINI DOT COM SDN. BHD.—See Padini Holdings Berhad; *Int'l*, pg. 5694
PADINI HOLDINGS BERHAD; *Int'l*, pg. 5694
PADI—See Lincolnshire Management, Inc.; *U.S. Private*, pg. 2459
PA DISTRIBUTION LLC; *U.S. Private*, pg. 3062
PADMA ISLAMI LIFE INSURANCE LIMITED; *Int'l*, pg. 5694
PADMALAYA TELEFILMS LIMITED; *Int'l*, pg. 5695
PADMANABH ALLOYS & POLYMERS LTD.; *Int'l*, pg. 5695
PADMA OIL COMPANY LIMITED; *Int'l*, pg. 5694
PADNOS LEITELT, INC.—See Louis Padnos Iron & Metal Company; *U.S. Private*, pg. 2498
PADNOS-SUMMIT—See Louis Padnos Iron & Metal Company; *U.S. Private*, pg. 2499
PADO CORPORATION—See RIZAP GROUP, Inc.; *Int'l*, pg. 6354
PADRES L.P.; *U.S. Private*, pg. 3074
PADTEC HOLDING S.A.; *Int'l*, pg. 5695
PADUCAH BANK SHARES, INC.; *U.S. Private*, pg. 3074
PADUCAH BANK & TRUST CO., INC.—See Paducah Bank Shares, Inc.; *U.S. Private*, pg. 3074
PADUCAH & LOUISVILLE RAILWAY, INC.; *U.S. Private*, pg. 3074
THE PADUCAH OPHTHALMOLOGY ASC, LLC—See KKR & Co. Inc.; *U.S. Public*, pg. 1248
THE PADUCAH SUN NEWSPAPER—See Paxton Media Group LLC; *U.S. Private*, pg. 3116
PADUS GRUNDSTUCKS-VERMIETUNGSGESELLSCHAFT MBH—See Deutsche Bank Aktiengesellschaft; *Int'l*, pg. 2061
PAE CONSTRUCTION RESOURCES COMPANY LIMITED—See PAE (Thailand) Public Company Limited; *Int'l*, pg. 5695
PAEDAE, INC.; *U.S. Private*, pg. 3074
PAE INCORPORATED—See Amentum Services, Inc.; *U.S. Private*, pg. 219
PAE LIMITED; *Int'l*, pg. 5695
PAE (NEW ZEALAND) LIMITED—See Amentum Services, Inc.; *U.S. Private*, pg. 219
PAE (THAILAND) PUBLIC COMPANY LIMITED; *Int'l*, pg. 5695
P.A. EXTRUSION (M) SDN. BHD.—See P.A. Resources Berhad; *Int'l*, pg. 5682
PAFCO GENERAL INSURANCE COMPANY—See Goran Capital Inc.; *Int'l*, pg. 3042
PAFCO INSURANCE COMPANY—See The Allstate Corporation; *U.S. Public*, pg. 2034
PAFF LANDSCAPE, INC.; *U.S. Private*, pg. 3074
PAF (NEW ZEALAND) LTD—See Wesfarmers Limited; *Int'l*, pg. 8380
PAFU AUSTRALIA PTY LTD.—See ST Group Food Industries Holdings Limited; *Int'l*, pg. 7158
PAGARIA ENERGY LIMITED; *Int'l*, pg. 5697
PAGAR.ME PAGAMENTOS S.A.—See StoneCo Ltd.; *Int'l*, pg. 7222
PAGASA PHILIPPINES FINANCE CORPORATION, INC.—See ASA International Group plc; *Int'l*, pg. 592

PAG ASIA CAPITAL LTD.; *Int'l*, pg. 5695
PAGAYA TECHNOLOGIES LTD.; *U.S. Public*, pg. 1634
P.A.G. CAPITAL PARTNERS, LLC; *U.S. Private*, pg. 3060
PAG CAPITAL; *Int'l*, pg. 5697
PAG DALY CITY LLC; *U.S. Private*, pg. 3074
PAGEANT HOLDINGS LIMITED; *Int'l*, pg. 5697
PAGEANT MEDIA LTD.; *Int'l*, pg. 5697
PAGE BROS ENTERPRISES LTD.; *U.S. Private*, pg. 3074
PAGED S.A.; *Int'l*, pg. 5697
PAGEFLEX INC.; *U.S. Private*, pg. 3075
PAGEGROUP PLC; *Int'l*, pg. 5697
PAGE INDUSTRIES LIMITED; *Int'l*, pg. 5697
PAGE INTERIM BV—See PageGroup plc; *Int'l*, pg. 5698
PAGEL S.A.S.—See L. Possehl & Co. mbH; *Int'l*, pg. 4384
PAGEL SPEZIAL-BETON GMBH & CO. KG—See L. Possehl & Co. mbH; *Int'l*, pg. 4384
PAGEL TECHNISCHE MORTEL GMBH & CO. KG—See L. Possehl & Co. mbH; *Int'l*, pg. 4384
PAGE MANAGEMENT CO., INC.; *U.S. Private*, pg. 3074
PAGEMASTERS PTY LTD.—See Australian Associated Press Pty Ltd; *Int'l*, pg. 721
PAGE MECHANICAL GROUP, INC.—See Partners Group Holding AG; *Int'l*, pg. 5750
PAGEONE COMMUNICATIONS LIMITED—See Erisbeg Holdings Limited; *Int'l*, pg. 2493
PAGE.ONE CONSULTANTS, INC.—See NV5 Global, Inc.; *U.S. Public*, pg. 1557
PAGE ONE PR, LLC; *U.S. Private*, pg. 3074
PAGEPATH TECHNOLOGIES, INC.—See Print Reach, Inc.; *U.S. Private*, pg. 3265
PAGE PERSONNEL BV—See PageGroup plc; *Int'l*, pg. 5698
PAGE PERSONNEL (DEUTSCHLAND) GMBH—See PageGroup plc; *Int'l*, pg. 5698
PAGE PERSONNEL DO BRASIL - RECRUTAMENTO ESPECIALIZADO E SERVIGOS CORPORATIVOS LTDA.—See PageGroup plc; *Int'l*, pg. 5698
PAGE PERSONNEL ETT SA—See PageGroup plc; *Int'l*, pg. 5698
PAGE PERSONNEL INTERNATIONAL CHILE LTDA.—See PageGroup plc; *Int'l*, pg. 5698
PAGE PERSONNEL ITALY S.P.A.—See PageGroup plc; *Int'l*, pg. 5699
PAGE PERSONNEL LTD—See PageGroup plc; *Int'l*, pg. 5699
PAGE PERSONNEL RECRUITMENT PTE. LTD.—See PageGroup plc; *Int'l*, pg. 5699
PAGE PERSONNEL SAS—See PageGroup plc; *Int'l*, pg. 5699
PAGE PERSONNEL SELECCION SA—See PageGroup plc; *Int'l*, pg. 5699
PAGERDUTY, INC.; *U.S. Public*, pg. 1634
PAGERO FRANCE S.A.S.—See Thomson Reuters Corporation; *Int'l*, pg. 7715
PAGERO GMBH—See Thomson Reuters Corporation; *Int'l*, pg. 7715
PAGERO GROUP AB—See Thomson Reuters Corporation; *Int'l*, pg. 7715
PAGERO GULF FZ-LLC—See Thomson Reuters Corporation; *Int'l*, pg. 7715
PAGERO IBERICA S.L.—See Thomson Reuters Corporation; *Int'l*, pg. 7715
PAGERO INC.—See Thomson Reuters Corporation; *Int'l*, pg. 7715
PAGERO ITALY S.R.L.—See Thomson Reuters Corporation; *Int'l*, pg. 7715
PAGERO NORWAY AS—See Thomson Reuters Corporation; *Int'l*, pg. 7715
PAGERO OY—See Thomson Reuters Corporation; *Int'l*, pg. 7715
PAGERO POLAND SP. Z O.O.—See Thomson Reuters Corporation; *Int'l*, pg. 7715
PAGERO (PTY.) LTD.—See Thomson Reuters Corporation; *Int'l*, pg. 7715
PAGERO S.R.L.—See Thomson Reuters Corporation; *Int'l*, pg. 7715
PAGERO UK LTD.—See Thomson Reuters Corporation; *Int'l*, pg. 7715
PAGES BBDO—See Omnicom Group Inc.; *U.S. Public*, pg. 1576
THE PAGE SEED CO.; *U.S. Private*, pg. 4090
PAGESJAUNES—See Solocal Group; *Int'l*, pg. 7074
PAGE SOUTHERLAND PAGE, INC.; *U.S. Private*, pg. 3074
PAGE'S PRODUCE COMPANY; *U.S. Private*, pg. 3075
PAGES S.A.S.—See Laurens Spethmann Holding Aktiengesellschaft & Co. KG; *Int'l*, pg. 4424
PAGE + STEELE / IBI GROUP ARCHITECTS—See ARCADIS N.V.; *Int'l*, pg. 542
PAGE STEEL, INC.; *U.S. Private*, pg. 3074
PAGE THEUS FUNERAL HOME—See NorthStar Memorial Group, LLC; *U.S. Private*, pg. 2958
PAGET MINERALS CORP.; *Int'l*, pg. 5699
PAGE TOYOTA, INC.; *U.S. Private*, pg. 3074
PAGE TRANSPORTATION INC.—See Keith Titus Corporation; *U.S. Private*, pg. 2274
PAGET REINSURANCE LTD—See Chubb Limited; *Int'l*, pg. 1590
PAGE ZERO MEDIA INC.; *Int'l*, pg. 5697

COMPANY NAME INDEX

PAG GREENWICH M1, LLC—See Penske Automotive Group, Inc.; *U.S. Public*, pg. 1665
PAG HOLDINGS, INC.—See Metals and Additives; *U.S. Private*, pg. 2682
PAGINAS AMARELAS S.A.—See Apax Partners LLP; *Int'l*, pg. 507
PAGINAS AMARELAS S.A.—See Cinven Limited; *Int'l*, pg. 1615
PAGLIERI SPA; *Int'l*, pg. 5699
PAG MADISON L1, LLC—See Penske Automotive Group, Inc.; *U.S. Public*, pg. 1665
PAG MADISON T1, LLC—See Penske Automotive Group, Inc.; *U.S. Public*, pg. 1665
P/A GMBH—See P/A Industries, Inc.; *U.S. Private*, pg. 3061
P. AGNES INC.; *U.S. Private*, pg. 3059
PAGNOSSIN S.P.A.; *Int'l*, pg. 5699
PAGNOTTI ENTERPRISES INC.; *U.S. Private*, pg. 3075
PAGO AG—See Fuji Seal International, Inc.; *Int'l*, pg. 2816
PAGO CROATIA D.O.O.—See Eckes AG; *Int'l*, pg. 2291
PAGODA INTERNATIONAL FOOTWEAR LIMITED—See Caleres, Inc.; *U.S. Public*, pg. 422
PAGO ETIKETTIERSYSTEME GMBH—See Fuji Seal International, Inc.; *Int'l*, pg. 2817
PAGO INTERNATIONAL GMBH—See Eckes AG; *Int'l*, pg. 2290
PAG ORLANDO PARTNERSHIP, LTD.—See Penske Automotive Group, Inc.; *U.S. Public*, pg. 1665
PAGOSA SPRINGS SUN PUBLISHING, INC.—See O'Rourke Media Group, LLC; *U.S. Private*, pg. 2980
PAGO S.R.L.—See Fuji Seal International, Inc.; *Int'l*, pg. 2817
PAG SANTA ANA AVW, INC.—See Penske Automotive Group, Inc.; *U.S. Public*, pg. 1665
PAGSEGURO DIGITAL LTD.; *Int'l*, pg. 5699
PAGSEGURO INTERNET SA—See PagSeguro Digital Ltd.; *Int'l*, pg. 5699
PAG WEST, LLC—See Penske Automotive Group, Inc.; *U.S. Public*, pg. 1665
PAHA MEHR PERSIAN CO.—See TCS TurControlSysteme AG; *Int'l*, pg. 7485
PAHANG SPECIALIST HOSPITAL SDN BHD—See KPJ Healthcare Berhad; *Int'l*, pg. 4297
PAHLAWAN POWER SDN BHD—See Powertek Energy Sdn Bhd; *Int'l*, pg. 5948
PAHLEN AB—See Litorina Capital Management AB; *Int'l*, pg. 4528
PAHL & MCCAY A PROFESSIONAL CORPORATION—See Spencer Fane LLP; *U.S. Private*, pg. 3755
PAHLMEYER, LLC—See E. & J. Gallo Winery; *U.S. Private*, pg. 1303
PAH LUXEMBOURG 2 SARL—See Zoetis, Inc.; *U.S. Public*, pg. 2409
THE P.A. HUTCHISON COMPANY; *U.S. Private*, pg. 4089
PAID, INC.; *U.S. Public*, pg. 1634
PAIFAT HONG LTD.—See Toyota Motor Corporation; *Int'l*, pg. 7870
PAIGE BUS ENTERPRISES INC.—See Cook-Illinois Corp.; *U.S. Private*, pg. 1039
PAIGE DENIM—See TSG Consumer Partners LLC; *U.S. Private*, pg. 4253
PAIGE ELECTRIC COMPANY, LLP—See Audax Group, Limited Partnership; *U.S. Private*, pg. 390
THE PAIGE GROUP; *U.S. Private*, pg. 4090
PAIGE HENDRICKS PUBLIC RELATIONS INC; *U.S. Private*, pg. 3075
PAIHO EUROPE S.A.—See Taiwan Paiho Limited; *Int'l*, pg. 7422
PAIHO NORTH AMERICA CORPORATION—See Taiwan Paiho Limited; *Int'l*, pg. 7422
PAIHO SHIH HOLDINGS CORPORATION—See Taiwan Paiho Limited; *Int'l*, pg. 7422
PAI INDUSTRIES INC.; *U.S. Private*, pg. 3075
PAIK KWANG INDUSTRIAL CO., LTD.; *Int'l*, pg. 5702
PAILLARD AUTOMOBILES ABBEVILLE; *Int'l*, pg. 5702
PAIM COMUNICACAO—See The Interpublic Group of Companies, Inc.; *U.S. Public*, pg. 2100
PAIMION TEURASTAMO OY—See HKFoods Plc; *Int'l*, pg. 3429
PAIMPOLDIS; *Int'l*, pg. 5702
PAINCARE CENTER PTE. LTD.—See Singapore Paincare Holdings Limited; *Int'l*, pg. 6941
PAINCHEK LTD.; *Int'l*, pg. 5702
PA INC.; *U.S. Private*, pg. 3062
PAIN DIAGNOSTIC AND TREATMENT CENTER, L.P.—See Tenet Healthcare Corporation; *U.S. Public*, pg. 2012
PAINDOR PROVENCE FRAIS SAS—See Vandemoortele N.V.; *Int'l*, pg. 8128
PAINDOR SAS—See Vandemoortele N.V.; *Int'l*, pg. 8128
P/A INDUSTRIES, INC.; *U.S. Private*, pg. 3061
P&A INDUSTRIES, INC.—See Midway Products Group, Inc.; *U.S. Private*, pg. 2719
P/A INDUSTRIES-METAL STAMPING EQUIPMENT—See P/A Industries, Inc.; *U.S. Private*, pg. 3061
P/A INDUSTRIES—See P/A Industries, Inc.; *U.S. Private*, pg. 3061

PAINE SCHWARTZ PARTNERS, LLC; *U.S. Private*, pg. 3075
PAIN JACQUET—See Groupe Limagrain Holding SA; *Int'l*, pg. 3107
PAINREFORM LTD.; *Int'l*, pg. 5702
PAINT AND PLASTIC JOINT STOCK COMPANY—See Masan Consumer Corp.; *Int'l*, pg. 4719
PAINTED PONY ENERGY LTD.—See Canadian Natural Resources Ltd.; *Int'l*, pg. 1284
PAINTER BROTHERS LTD.—See Balfour Beatty plc; *Int'l*, pg. 808
PAINTER & JOHNSON FINANCIAL—See Galiot Insurance Services, Inc.; *U.S. Private*, pg. 1638
PAINTERS ON DEMAND, LLC; *U.S. Private*, pg. 3076
PAINTER'S SUN COUNTRY MITSUBISHI; *U.S. Private*, pg. 3076
PAINTERS SUPPLY & EQUIPMENT CO.—See Odyssey Investment Partners, LLC; *U.S. Private*, pg. 2995
PAINTERS USA, INC.; *U.S. Private*, pg. 3076
PAINT MARKETING CO (M) SDN. BHD.—See Nippon Paint Holdings Co., Ltd.; *Int'l*, pg. 5326
PAINTORY INC.—See Giftee, Inc.; *Int'l*, pg. 2970
PAINT OVER RUST PRODUCTS, INC.—See CapVest Limited; *Int'l*, pg. 1318
PAIN TREATMENT CENTERS OF MICHIGAN, LLC—See Tenet Healthcare Corporation; *U.S. Public*, pg. 2012
PAINTS AND CHEMICALS INDUSTRIES COMPANY S.A.E. - ALEXANDRIA FACTORY—See Paints and Chemicals Industries Company S.A.E.; *Int'l*, pg. 5702
PAINTS AND CHEMICALS INDUSTRIES COMPANY S.A.E. - ELOBOUR FACTORY—See Paints and Chemicals Industries Company S.A.E.; *Int'l*, pg. 5703
PAINTS AND CHEMICALS INDUSTRIES COMPANY S.A.E. - LIBYA FACTORY—See Paints and Chemicals Industries Company S.A.E.; *Int'l*, pg. 5703
PAINTS AND CHEMICALS INDUSTRIES COMPANY S.A.E.; *Int'l*, pg. 5702
PAINTSVILLE HMA PHYSICIAN MANAGEMENT, LLC—See Quorum Health Corporation; *U.S. Private*, pg. 3330
PAINTSVILLE HOSPITAL COMPANY, LLC—See Quorum Health Corporation; *U.S. Private*, pg. 3330
PAINTZEN INC.—See PPG Industries, Inc.; *U.S. Public*, pg. 1710
PAION AG; *Int'l*, pg. 5703
PAION DEUTSCHLAND GMBH—See Paion AG; *Int'l*, pg. 5703
PAION HOLDINGS UK LTD.—See Paion AG; *Int'l*, pg. 5703
PAION SCANDIC APS—See Paion AG; *Int'l*, pg. 5703
PAION UK LIMITED—See Paion AG; *Int'l*, pg. 5703
PAI PARTNERS AB—See PAI Partners S.A.S.; *Int'l*, pg. 5701
PAI PARTNERS GMBH—See PAI Partners S.A.S.; *Int'l*, pg. 5701
PAI PARTNERS S.A.R.L.—See PAI Partners S.A.S.; *Int'l*, pg. 5701
PAI PARTNERS S.A.S.; *Int'l*, pg. 5699
PAIRI DAIZA SA; *Int'l*, pg. 5703
PAIR NETWORKS, INC.—See Liberated Syndication Inc.; *U.S. Public*, pg. 1310
PAISABAZAAR MARKETING AND CONSULTING PRIVATE LIMITED—See PB Fintech Limited; *Int'l*, pg. 5764
PAISALO DIGITAL LIMITED; *Int'l*, pg. 5703
PAISANO PUBLICATIONS, LLC; *U.S. Private*, pg. 3076
PAI SERVICES LLC; *U.S. Private*, pg. 3075
PAISLEY CONSULTING INC.—See Thomson Reuters Corporation; *Int'l*, pg. 7716
PAISLEY FARM, INC.—See The Fremont Company; *U.S. Private*, pg. 4030
PAISLEY-MANOR INSURANCE BROKERS INC.; *Int'l*, pg. 5703
PAISLEY PRODUCTS OF CANADA INCORPORATED; *Int'l*, pg. 5703
PAIUTE PIPELINE COMPANY—See Southwest Gas Holdings, Inc.; *U.S. Public*, pg. 1913
PAIZO PUBLISHING LLC; *U.S. Private*, pg. 3076
PAJAK GADAI BERTUAH SDN. BHD.—See Pappajack Berhad; *Int'l*, pg. 5734
PAJAK GADAI BT CLEANING SDN. BHD.—See Pappajack Berhad; *Int'l*, pg. 5734
PAJAK GADAI CONSISTENT REACH SDN. BHD.—See Pappajack Berhad; *Int'l*, pg. 5734
PAJAK GADAI PAPPAJACK SDN. BHD.—See Pappajack Berhad; *Int'l*, pg. 5734
PAJAK GADAI PAPPAJACK SEHATI SDN. BHD.—See Pappajack Berhad; *Int'l*, pg. 5734
PAJAK GADAI PASIR GUDANG SDN. BHD.—See MoneyMax Financial Services Ltd.; *Int'l*, pg. 5033
PAJAK GADAI PPJACK SDN. BHD.—See Pappajack Berhad; *Int'l*, pg. 5734
PAJAK GADAI PPJ SDN. BHD.—See Pappajack Berhad; *Int'l*, pg. 5734
PAJAK GADAI PPJ SEHATI SDN. BHD.—See Pappajack Berhad; *Int'l*, pg. 5734
PAJAK GADAI TETAP SEJIWA SDN. BHD.—See Pappajack Berhad; *Int'l*, pg. 5734

PAKISTAN TELECOMMUNICATION COMPANY LIMITED

PAJAK GADAI TMI SDN. BHD.—See Pappajack Berhad; *Int'l*, pg. 5734
PAJAK GADAI TSE SDN. BHD.—See Pappajack Berhad; *Int'l*, pg. 5734
PAJERO MANUFACTURING CO., LTD.—See Mitsubishi Motors Corporation; *Int'l*, pg. 4967
PAJU ELECTRIC GLASS CO., LTD.—See Nippon Electric Glass Co., Ltd.; *Int'l*, pg. 5314
PAJURA S.A.; *Int'l*, pg. 5703
PAK 2000 (PTY) LTD—See Berry Global Group, Inc; *U.S. Public*, pg. 324
PAK AGRO PACKAGING (PRIVATE) LIMITED—See Hi-Tech Lubricants Ltd.; *Int'l*, pg. 3381
PAKARAB FERTILIZERS LIMITED—See Aisha Steel Mills Limited; *Int'l*, pg. 251
PAK-ARAB REFINERY LTD.; *Int'l*, pg. 5703
PAKAR ANGSANA SDN BHD—See Berjaya Corporation Berhad; *Int'l*, pg. 983
PAK BRUNEI INVESTMENT COMPANY LIMITED—See KASB Modaraba; *Int'l*, pg. 4087
PAKCEM LIMITED—See Bestway (Holdings) Limited; *Int'l*, pg. 1001
PAK DATACOM LIMITED; *Int'l*, pg. 5703
PAKEA - RIXHEIM PLANT—See NSC Groupe SA; *Int'l*, pg. 5476
PAKEA—See NSC Groupe SA; *Int'l*, pg. 5476
PAKEA - TRAINEL PLANT—See NSC Groupe SA; *Int'l*, pg. 5476
PAKEDGE DEVICE & SOFTWARE INC.—See Resideo Technologies, Inc.; *U.S. Public*, pg. 1790
PAK ELEKTRON LTD.; *Int'l*, pg. 5703
PAKERS CO., LTD.; *Int'l*, pg. 5703
PAKETERIA GMBH—See Acorn Energy, Inc.; *U.S. Public*, pg. 36
PAKETPLUS MARKETING GMBH—See Hubert Burda Media Holding Kommanditgesellschaft; *Int'l*, pg. 3520
PAK FAH YEOW INTERNATIONAL LIMITED; *Int'l*, pg. 5703
PAKFOOD PLC—See Thai Union Group Public Company Limited; *Int'l*, pg. 7596
PAKGEN POWER LTD.; *Int'l*, pg. 5703
PAK GORNICTWO SP. Z O.O.—See Zespol Elektrowni Patnow-Adamow-Konin S.A.; *Int'l*, pg. 8639
PAK-GULF LEASING COMPANY LIMITED; *Int'l*, pg. 5703
PAKHSH ALBORZ COMPANY—See Alborz Investment Company; *Int'l*, pg. 299
PAKISTAN CABLES LIMITED; *Int'l*, pg. 5704
PAKISTAN ENGINEERING COMPANY LIMITED; *Int'l*, pg. 5704
THE PAKISTAN GENERAL INSURANCE COMPANY LIMITED; *Int'l*, pg. 7672
PAKISTAN GUM & CHEMICALS LIMITED; *Int'l*, pg. 5704
PAKISTAN GUM INDUSTRIES LIMITED—See Ashland Inc.; *U.S. Public*, pg. 212
PAKISTAN HOTELS DEVELOPERS LIMITED; *Int'l*, pg. 5704
PAKISTAN INDUSTRIAL AIDS (PRIVATE) LIMITED—See House of Habib; *Int'l*, pg. 3491
PAKISTAN INDUSTRIAL & COMMERCIAL LEASING LTD.; *Int'l*, pg. 5704
PAKISTAN INTERNATIONAL AIRLINES CORPORATION; *Int'l*, pg. 5704
PAKISTAN INTERNATIONAL BULK TERMINAL LIMITED; *Int'l*, pg. 5704
PAKISTAN INTERNATIONAL CONTAINER TERMINAL LIMITED—See International Container Terminal Services, Inc.; *Int'l*, pg. 3746
PAKISTAN KUWAIT INVESTMENT COMPANY (PRIVATE) LIMITED; *Int'l*, pg. 5704
PAKISTAN NATIONAL SHIPPING CORPORATION; *Int'l*, pg. 5704
PAKISTAN OILFIELDS LIMITED—See Attock Refinery Ltd; *Int'l*, pg. 697
PAKISTAN OPPORTUNITIES LIMITED—See Aisha Steel Mills Limited; *Int'l*, pg. 251
PAKISTAN OXYGEN LIMITED; *Int'l*, pg. 5704
PAKISTAN PAPER PRODUCTS LIMITED; *Int'l*, pg. 5704
PAKISTAN PETROLEUM LTD.; *Int'l*, pg. 5704
THE PAKISTAN PETROLEUM PROVIDENT FUND TRUST COMPANY (PRIVATE) LIMITED—See Pakistan Petroleum Ltd.; *Int'l*, pg. 5704
PAKISTAN RAHMAN TYRES INTERNATIONAL PVT. LTD.—See Bridgestone Corporation; *Int'l*, pg. 1160
PAKISTAN REFINERY LIMITED; *Int'l*, pg. 5704
PAKISTAN REINSURANCE CO. LTD.; *Int'l*, pg. 5704
PAKISTAN RUBBER & TYRE CO.—See Bridgestone Corporation; *Int'l*, pg. 1160
PAKISTAN SERVICES LIMITED; *Int'l*, pg. 5704
PAKISTAN STATE OIL LTD.; *Int'l*, pg. 5704
PAKISTAN SYNTHETICS LTD; *Int'l*, pg. 5704
PAKISTAN TELECOMMUNICATION COMPANY LIMITED; *Int'l*, pg. 5704
PAKISTAN TOBACCO CO. LTD.—See British American Tobacco plc; *Int'l*, pg. 1168
PAKISTAN TOURISM DEVELOPMENT CORPORATION—See Sui Southern Gas Company Limited; *Int'l*, pg. 7255
PAKKA IMPACT LIMITED—See Yash Pakka Limited; *Int'l*, pg. 8568

PAKISTAN TELECOMMUNICATION COMPANY LIMITED / CORPORATE AFFILIATIONS

PAK KOPALNIA WEGLA BRUNATNEGO KONIN S.A.—See Zespol Elektrowni Patnow-Adamow-Konin S.A.; *Int'l*, pg. 8639
PAK LEATHER CRAFTS LIMITED; *Int'l*, pg. 5703
PAK LIGHTING AUSTRALIA PTY LTD—See Guangdong PAK Corporation Co. Ltd.; *Int'l*, pg. 3158
PAKMARKAS LTD.; *Int'l*, pg. 5705
PAK MEDIACOM (PVT.) LTD.—See WPP plc; *Int'l*, pg. 8466
PAKNET LIMITED—See Pakistan Telecommunication Company Limited; *Int'l*, pg. 5705
PAK 'N SAVE, INC.—See Cerberus Capital Management, L.P.; *U.S. Private*, pg. 836
PA KOMPETENS LON AB—See TowerBrook Capital Partners, L.P.; *U.S. Private*, pg. 4195
PAK PETROLEUM MARKETING INC.; *U.S. Private*, pg. 3076
PAK-RITE, LTD.—See UFP Industries, Inc.; *U.S. Public*, pg. 2219
PAKSI TEGUH SDN BHD—See IOI Corporation Berhad; *Int'l*, pg. 3792
PAK STEEL; *Int'l*, pg. 5703
PAK SUZUKI MOTOR CO., LTD.—See Suzuki Motor Corporation; *Int'l*, pg. 7354
PAK TAK INTERNATIONAL LIMITED; *Int'l*, pg. 5703
PAK TAK KNITTING & GARMENT FACTORY LIMITED—See Pak Tak International Limited; *Int'l*, pg. 5703
PAKTRON CAPACITORS—See Milestone Partners Ltd.; *U.S. Private*, pg. 2729
PAKURANGA PLAZA LIMITED—See Rumah & Co. Pte. Ltd.; *Int'l*, pg. 6427
PAKUWON JATI FINANCE, B.V.—See PT. PAKUWON JATI Tbk; *Int'l*, pg. 6088
PAK-VOLT S.A.—See Zespol Elektrowni Patnow-Adamow-Konin S.A.; *Int'l*, pg. 8639
PAK WEST PAPER & PACKAGING LLC—See Blower Dempsay Corporation; *U.S. Private*, pg. 584
PALABORA ASIA PTE LIMITED—See General Nice Development Limited; *Int'l*, pg. 2919
PALABORA ASIA PTE LIMITED—See HBIS Group Co., Ltd.; *Int'l*, pg. 3296
PALABORA ASIA PTE LIMITED—See Tewoo Group Co., Ltd.; *Int'l*, pg. 7581
PALABORA EUROPE LIMITED—See General Nice Development Limited; *Int'l*, pg. 2919
PALABORA EUROPE LIMITED—See HBIS Group Co., Ltd.; *Int'l*, pg. 3296
PALABORA EUROPE LIMITED—See Tewoo Group Co., Ltd.; *Int'l*, pg. 7581
PALABORA HOLDINGS LTD.—See Rio Tinto plc; *Int'l*, pg. 6346
PALABORA MINING CO. LTD.—See General Nice Development Limited; *Int'l*, pg. 2919
PALABORA MINING CO. LTD.—See HBIS Group Co., Ltd.; *Int'l*, pg. 3296
PALABORA MINING CO. LTD.—See Tewoo Group Co., Ltd.; *Int'l*, pg. 7581
PALABORA US—See General Nice Development Limited; *Int'l*, pg. 2919
PALABORA US—See HBIS Group Co., Ltd.; *Int'l*, pg. 3296
PALABORA US—See Tewoo Group Co., Ltd.; *Int'l*, pg. 7581
THE PALACE AMUSEMENT COMPANY (1921) LIMITED; *Int'l*, pg. 7672
PALACE CAPITAL (MANCHESTER) LIMITED—See Palace Capital plc; *Int'l*, pg. 5705
PALACE CAPITAL PLC; *Int'l*, pg. 5705
PALACE ENTERTAINMENT HOLDINGS, INC.—See Newgate Private Equity LLP; *Int'l*, pg. 5234
PALACE GATE PRACTICE LIMITED—See HCA Healthcare, Inc.; *U.S. Public*, pg. 1005
PALACE HOTEL ZAGREB D.D; *Int'l*, pg. 5705
PALACE LAUNDRY INC.; *U.S. Private*, pg. 3076
PALACE SPORTS & ENTERTAINMENT, INC.—See Platinum Equity, LLC; *U.S. Private*, pg. 3206
PALACE THEATER LONDON LIMITED—See Nimax Theatres Limited; *Int'l*, pg. 5295
PALADEX LTD.—See Avrot Industries Ltd.; *Int'l*, pg. 750
PALADIN BRANDS, LLC—See Stanley Black & Decker, Inc.; *U.S. Public*, pg. 1933
PALADIN COMMERCIAL PRINTERS, LLC—See Marketing Solutions Unlimited, LLC; *U.S. Private*, pg. 2580
PALADIN COMPANIES INC.—See Adecco Group AG; *Int'l*, pg. 141
PALADIN CONSULTING, INC.—See GEE Group Inc.; *U.S. Public*, pg. 910
PALADIN ENERGY LTD.; *Int'l*, pg. 5705
PALADIN HEALTHCARE CAPITAL, LLC; *U.S. Private*, pg. 3076
PALADIN HEALTHCARE MANAGEMENT, LLC—See Paladin Healthcare Capital, LLC; *U.S. Private*, pg. 3076
PALADIN LABS INC.—See Endo International plc; *Int'l*, pg. 2404
PALADIN LIMITED; *Int'l*, pg. 5705
PALADIN SECURITY SYSTEMS LTD; *Int'l*, pg. 5706
PALADION NETWORKS PRIVATE LIMITED—See Atos SE; *Int'l*, pg. 692
PALAGAN LIMITED—See Synnovia Plc; *Int'l*, pg. 7386

PALAGONIA BAKERY, INC.; *U.S. Private*, pg. 3076
PALA GROUP, INC.; *U.S. Private*, pg. 3076
PALA HOLDING, B.V.—See LKQ Corporation; *U.S. Public*, pg. 1336
PALA-INTERSTATE, INC.; *U.S. Private*, pg. 3076
PALA INTERSTATE, LLC—See Pala Group, Inc.; *U.S. Private*, pg. 3076
PALA INVESTMENTS HOLDINGS LIMITED—See Pala Investments Limited; *Int'l*, pg. 5705
PALA INVESTMENTS LIMITED; *Int'l*, pg. 5705
PALAIS HANSEN IMMOBILIENENTWICKLUNG GMBH—See Vienna Insurance Group AG Wiener Versicherung Gruppe; *Int'l*, pg. 8195
PALAMIDA, INC.—See Ontario Teachers' Pension Plan; *Int'l*, pg. 5589
PALAMIDA, INC.—See TA Associates, Inc.; *U.S. Private*, pg. 3915
PALAMINA CORP.; *Int'l*, pg. 5706
PALAMON CAPITAL PARTNERS, LP; *Int'l*, pg. 5706
PALAMY STE; *Int'l*, pg. 5706
P.A. LANDERS INC.; *U.S. Private*, pg. 3060
PALANGNGAN PATTANA CO., LTD.—See PTG Energy Public Company Limited; *Int'l*, pg. 6090
PALANTIR TECHNOLOGIES INC.; *U.S. Public*, pg. 1634
PALAQAR FOR REAL ESTATE DEVELOPMENT & MANAGEMENT COMPANY; *Int'l*, pg. 5706
PALAS GMBH—See Brockhaus Private Equity GmbH; *Int'l*, pg. 1172
PALASH SECURITIES LTD.; *Int'l*, pg. 5706
PALATIA INGENIEUR- UND STADTEBAU GMBH—See BKW AG; *Int'l*, pg. 1055
PALATINE ASSET MANAGEMENT SA—See Groupe BPCE; *Int'l*, pg. 3099
PALATINE HILLS LEASING INC.—See Schneider Electric SE; *Int'l*, pg. 6633
PALATINE PRIVATE EQUITY LLP; *Int'l*, pg. 5706
PALATINIT GMBH—See Suddeutsche Zuckerruben-Verwertungs-Genossenschaft eG; *Int'l*, pg. 7252
PALATIN TECHNOLOGIES INC.; *U.S. Public*, pg. 1634
PALATKA DAILY NEWS—See Community Newspapers Inc.; *U.S. Private*, pg. 996
PALAU NATIONAL COMMUNICATIONS CORPORATION; *U.S. Private*, pg. 3076
PALAVERSICH Y CIA S.A.—See Barenbrug Holding B.V.; *Int'l*, pg. 864
PALAYAN RESOURCES, INC.; *U.S. Public*, pg. 1634
PALAZZO, INC.—See Greener Pastures Group LLC; *U.S. Private*, pg. 1777
PALAZZO PRODUCTIES B.V.—See CTS Eventim AG & Co. KGAA; *Int'l*, pg. 1873
PALAZZO PRODUKTIONEN BERLIN GMBH—See CTS Eventim AG & Co. KGAA; *Int'l*, pg. 1873
PALAZZO PRODUKTIONEN GMBH—See CTS Eventim AG & Co. KGAA; *Int'l*, pg. 1873
PALAZZO PRODUKTIONEN GMBH—See CTS Eventim AG & Co. KGAA; *Int'l*, pg. 1873
PALCO LIMITED; *Int'l*, pg. 5706
PALCO LLC—See Rouse's Enterprises LLC; *U.S. Private*, pg. 3489
PALCO METALS LIMITED; *Int'l*, pg. 5706
PALCO RECYCLE INDUSTRIES LIMITED—See Palco Metals Limited; *Int'l*, pg. 5706
PAL-DO COMPANY INC.; *U.S. Private*, pg. 3076
PALECEK IMPORTS INC.; *U.S. Private*, pg. 3076
PALEMO CO., LTD—See Phoenix Capital Co., Ltd.; *Int'l*, pg. 5849
PALEMO HOLDINGS CO., LTD.—See Phoenix Capital Co., Ltd.; *Int'l*, pg. 5849
PALEO RESOURCES, INC.; *U.S. Public*, pg. 1634
PALERO CAPITAL GMBH; *Int'l*, pg. 5706
PALESTINE CELLULAR COMMUNICATIONS COMPANY—See Palestine Telecommunications Company P.L.C.; *Int'l*, pg. 5707
PALESTINE COMMERCIAL BANK; *Int'l*, pg. 5706
PALESTINE CONCRETE TILE COMPANY, L.P.—See Seven Group Holdings Limited; *Int'l*, pg. 6733
PALESTINE DEVELOPMENT & INVESTMENT LTD.—See Arab Supply & Trading Co.; *Int'l*, pg. 532
PALESTINE HOTEL; *Int'l*, pg. 5706
PALESTINE INDUSTRIAL INVESTMENT CO. LTD.—See Arab Supply & Trading Co.; *Int'l*, pg. 532
PALESTINE INSURANCE COMPANY; *Int'l*, pg. 5706
PALESTINE INVESTMENT BANK; *Int'l*, pg. 5706
PALESTINE INVESTMENT & DEVELOPMENT CO.; *Int'l*, pg. 5706
PALESTINE ISLAMIC BANK; *Int'l*, pg. 5706
PALESTINE PLASTIC INDUSTRIES CO. LTD.—See Arab Supply & Trading Co.; *Int'l*, pg. 532
PALESTINE POULTRY CO. LTD.—See Arab Supply & Trading Co.; *Int'l*, pg. 532
PALESTINE REAL ESTATE INVESTMENT CO.; *Int'l*, pg. 5707
THE PALESTINE SECURITIES EXCHANGE, LTD.—See Arab Supply & Trading Co.; *Int'l*, pg. 532
PALESTINE TELECOMMUNICATIONS COMPANY P.L.C.; *Int'l*, pg. 5707
PALETTENFABRIK BASSUM GMBH; *Int'l*, pg. 5707
PALETTES GESTION SERVICES; *Int'l*, pg. 5707

PALEX LIMITED—See Hang Lung Group Limited; *Int'l*, pg. 3245
THE PALEY CENTER FOR MEDIA; *U.S. Private*, pg. 4090
PALFINGER AG; *Int'l*, pg. 5707
PALFINGER AREA UNITS GMBH—See Palfinger AG; *Int'l*, pg. 5707
PALFINGER ASIA PACIFIC PTE LTD—See Palfinger AG; *Int'l*, pg. 5707
PALFINGER CIS GMBH—See Palfinger AG; *Int'l*, pg. 5707
PALFINGER CRANES INDIA PVT. LTD.—See Palfinger AG; *Int'l*, pg. 5707
PALFINGER DREGGEN AS—See Palfinger AG; *Int'l*, pg. 5707
PALFINGER EUROPEAN UNITS GMBH—See Palfinger AG; *Int'l*, pg. 5707
PALFINGER EUROPE GMBH—See Palfinger AG; *Int'l*, pg. 5707
PALFINGER GMBH—See Palfinger AG; *Int'l*, pg. 5707
PALFINGER GRU IDRAULICHE SRL—See Palfinger AG; *Int'l*, pg. 5707
PALFINGER INC.—See Palfinger AG; *Int'l*, pg. 5707
PALFINGER INDUSTRIEANLAGEN GMBH—See Palfinger AG; *Int'l*, pg. 5707
PALFINGER LIFTGATES, LLC—See Palfinger AG; *Int'l*, pg. 5707
PALFINGER MARINE PTE. LTD.—See Palfinger AG; *Int'l*, pg. 5707
PALFINGER MARINE- UND BETEILIGUNGS-GMBH—See Palfinger AG; *Int'l*, pg. 5707
PALFINGER NED-DECK BV—See Palfinger AG; *Int'l*, pg. 5707
PALFINGER PLATFORMS GMBH—See Palfinger AG; *Int'l*, pg. 5707
PALFINGER PLATFORMS ITALY S.R.L.—See Palfinger AG; *Int'l*, pg. 5708
PALFINGER PRODUKCIONSTECHNIK BULGARIA EOOD—See Palfinger AG; *Int'l*, pg. 5708
PALFINGER PRODUKTIONSTECHNIK BULGARIA EOOD—See Palfinger AG; *Int'l*, pg. 5707
PALFINGER PROIZVODNA TEHNOLOGIJA HRVATSKA D.O.O.—See Palfinger AG; *Int'l*, pg. 5707
PALFINGER PROIZVODNJA D.O.O.—See Palfinger AG; *Int'l*, pg. 5707
PALFINGER RUSSLAND GMBH—See Palfinger AG; *Int'l*, pg. 5707
PALFINGER SERVICE S.A.—See Palfinger AG; *Int'l*, pg. 5708
PALFINGER SERVICE-UND BETEILIGUNGS-GMBH—See Palfinger AG; *Int'l*, pg. 5708
PALFINGER (SHENZHEN) LTD.—See Palfinger AG; *Int'l*, pg. 5707
PALFINGER TAIL LIFTS GMBH—See Palfinger AG; *Int'l*, pg. 5708
PALFINGER USA INC—See Palfinger AG; *Int'l*, pg. 5708
PALFLEET TRUCK EQUIPMENT, CO.—See Palfinger AG; *Int'l*, pg. 5708
PALGAZ DOGALGAZ DAGITIM TICARET VE SANAYI A.S.; *Int'l*, pg. 5708
PAL GENERAL ENGINEERING INC.; *U.S. Private*, pg. 3076
PALGEY MAIM LTD.—See Kardan N.V.; *Int'l*, pg. 4079
PAL GROUP HOLDINGS CO., LTD.; *Int'l*, pg. 5705
PAL HOLDINGS, INC.; *Int'l*, pg. 5705
PALIBURG HOLDINGS LIMITED—See Century City International Holdings Ltd; *Int'l*, pg. 1417
PAL IFM S.R.L.—See Sesa S.p.A.; *Int'l*, pg. 6728
PALINDA GROUP HOLDINGS LIMITED; *Int'l*, pg. 5708
PALINE PIPELINE COMPANY, LLC—See Delek Group Ltd.; *Int'l*, pg. 2012
PALING INDUSTRIES SDN. BHD.—See Aliaxis S.A./N.V.; *Int'l*, pg. 325
PAL INTERNATIONAL LTD.; *Int'l*, pg. 5705
PALINTEST LIMITED—See Halma plc; *Int'l*, pg. 3232
PALIO + IGNITE, LLC—See Elliott Management Corporation; *U.S. Private*, pg. 1366
PALIO + IGNITE, LLC—See Patient Square Capital, L.P.; *U.S. Private*, pg. 3108
PALIO + IGNITE, LLC—See Veritas Capital Fund Management, LLC; *U.S. Private*, pg. 4365
PALISAD A.D.; *Int'l*, pg. 5708
PALISADE BIO, INC.; *U.S. Public*, pg. 1634
PALISADE CAPITAL MANAGEMENT, LLC; *U.S. Private*, pg. 3077
PALISADE INVESTMENT PARTNERS LIMITED; *Int'l*, pg. 5708
PALISADES ASSOCIATES, INC.; *U.S. Private*, pg. 3077
PALISADES CHILD CARE CENTER INC.—See New York-Presbyterian Healthcare System, Inc.; *U.S. Private*, pg. 2913
PALISADES COLLECTION, LLC—See Asta Funding, Inc.; *U.S. Private*, pg. 360
PALISADES GOLDCORP LTD.; *Int'l*, pg. 5708
THE PALISADES GROUP LLC; *U.S. Private*, pg. 4090
PALISADES GROWTH CAPITAL, LLC; *U.S. Private*, pg. 3077
PALISADES MEDIA GROUP, INC.; *U.S. Private*, pg. 3077
PALISADES MEDICAL CENTER—See New York-Presbyterian Healthcare System, Inc.; *U.S. Private*, pg. 2913

COMPANY NAME INDEX

PALISADES RANCH, INC.—See Sysco Corporation; *U.S. Public*, pg. 1975

PALITAL GMBH & CO. KG.—See Bewital GmbH & Co. KG; *Int'l*, pg. 1004

PALITALSOFT SRL—See Sesa S.p.A.; *Int'l*, pg. 6729

PALIWAL DIAGNOSTICS PRIVATE LIMITED—See Dr. Lal PathLabs Ltd.; *Int'l*, pg. 2194

PALKAR INC.; *U.S. Private*, pg. 3077

PALLACANESTRO TREVISO SOCIETA SPORTIVA DILETTANTISTICA A R.L.—See Edizione S.r.l.; *Int'l*, pg. 2312

PALLADIA, INC.; *U.S. Private*, pg. 3077

PALLADIAN CAPITAL PARTNERS LLC; *U.S. Private*, pg. 3077

PALLADIAN LAND DEVELOPMENT INC—See ATN Holdings, Inc.; *Int'l*, pg. 687

PALLADIN CONSUMER RETAIL PARTNERS, LLC; *U.S. Private*, pg. 3077

PALLADIO HOLDING SPA; *Int'l*, pg. 5708

PALLADIUM EQUITY PARTNERS, LLC; *U.S. Private*, pg. 3077

PALLADIUM GROUP, INC.; *U.S. Private*, pg. 3079

PALLADIUM GROUP LIMITED—See Next 15 Group plc; *Int'l*, pg. 5246

PALLADIUM-ITEM—See Gannett Co., Inc.; *U.S. Public*, pg. 899

PALLADIUM ONE MINING INC.; *Int'l*, pg. 5708

PALLADIUM PRAHA S.R.O.—See Helaba Landesbank Hessen-Thuringen; *Int'l*, pg. 3328

PALLADIUS AG; *Int'l*, pg. 5708

PALLADIUS, INC.—See Rockwell Automation, Inc.; *U.S. Public*, pg. 1805

PALLADON VENTURES LTD.; *Int'l*, pg. 5709

PALLADYNE AI CORP.; *U.S. Public*, pg. 1634

PALL AEROPOWER CORPORATION—See Danaher Corporation; *U.S. Public*, pg. 629

PALLA PHARMA LTD.; *Int'l*, pg. 5708

PALLAS FOODS FARM FRESH UNLIMITED COMPANY—See Sysco Corporation; *U.S. Public*, pg. 1975

PALLAS FOODS—See Sysco Corporation; *U.S. Public*, pg. 1975

PALLAS FOODS UNLIMITED COMPANY—See Sysco Corporation; *U.S. Public*, pg. 1975

PALL ASIA INTERNATIONAL LTD.—See Danaher Corporation; *U.S. Public*, pg. 629

PALLAS TEXTILES—See Krueger International, Inc.; *U.S. Private*, pg. 2353

PALLAS VERSICHERUNG AG—See Bayer Aktiengesellschaft; *Int'l*, pg. 910

PALL AUSTRALIA PTY LTD—See Danaher Corporation; *U.S. Public*, pg. 629

PALL AUSTRIA FILTER GMBH—See Danaher Corporation; *U.S. Public*, pg. 629

PALL BIOMEDICAL, INC.—See Danaher Corporation; *U.S. Public*, pg. 629

PALL (CANADA) LIMITED—See Danaher Corporation; *U.S. Public*, pg. 629

PALL CORPORATION FILTRATION & SEPARATIONS LTD.—See Danaher Corporation; *U.S. Public*, pg. 629

PALL CORPORATION—See Danaher Corporation; *U.S. Public*, pg. 629

PALL CORTLAND—See Danaher Corporation; *U.S. Public*, pg. 629

PALL DO BRASIL LTDA.—See Danaher Corporation; *U.S. Public*, pg. 630

PALL ESPANA S.A.U.—See Danaher Corporation; *U.S. Public*, pg. 629

PALLET CONSULTANTS CORP.; *U.S. Private*, pg. 3079

PALLET DIRECT, INC.; *U.S. Private*, pg. 3079

PALLETMAXX, INC.; *U.S. Private*, pg. 3079

PALLETONE, INC.—See UFP Industries, Inc.; *U.S. Public*, pg. 2219

PALLETONE OF ALABAMA, LLC—See UFP Industries, Inc.; *U.S. Public*, pg. 2219

PALLET SERVICES INC.; *U.S. Private*, pg. 3079

PALLETS, INC.—See Damabois, Inc.; *Int'l*, pg. 1955

PALLETTE STONE CORPORATION—See The D.A. Collins Construction Co., Inc.; *U.S. Private*, pg. 4017

PALLETWAYS GROUP LIMITED—See Dubai World Corporation; *Int'l*, pg. 2221

PALL EUROPE LTD.—See Danaher Corporation; *U.S. Public*, pg. 629

PALL FILTER (BEIJING) CO., LTD.—See Danaher Corporation; *U.S. Public*, pg. 629

PALL FILTERSYSTEMS GMBH—See Danaher Corporation; *U.S. Public*, pg. 629

PALL FILTRATION AND SEPARATIONS GROUP—See Danaher Corporation; *U.S. Public*, pg. 629

PALL FILTRATION PTE LTD—See Danaher Corporation; *U.S. Public*, pg. 629

PALL FRANCE—See Danaher Corporation; *U.S. Public*, pg. 629

PALL GMBH—See Danaher Corporation; *U.S. Public*, pg. 629

PALLIATIVE CARECENTER & HOSPICE OF CATAWBA VALLEY, INC.; *U.S. Private*, pg. 3079

PAL LIFE CO., LTD.—See Sumitomo Mitsui Financial Group, Inc.; *Int'l*, pg. 7294

PALL INDIA PVT. LTD.—See Danaher Corporation; *U.S. Public*, pg. 629

PALLINGHURST ADVISORS LLP—See Gemfields Group Limited; *Int'l*, pg. 2916

PALLINGHURST ADVISORS (PTY) LIMITED—See Gemfields Group Limited; *Int'l*, pg. 2916

PALL INTERNATIONAL SARL—See Danaher Corporation; *U.S. Public*, pg. 630

PALLIOS BROS. INC.; *U.S. Public*, pg. 3079

PALLISER FURNITURE LTD.; *Int'l*, pg. 5709

PALL ITALIA S.R.L—See Danaher Corporation; *U.S. Public*, pg. 630

PALL KOREA LIMITED—See Danaher Corporation; *U.S. Public*, pg. 630

PALL LIFE SCIENCES BELGIUM BVBA—See Danaher Corporation; *U.S. Public*, pg. 630

PALL LIFE SCIENCES PUERTO RICO, LLC—See Danaher Corporation; *U.S. Public*, pg. 630

PALLMANN GMBH—See Uzin Utz AG; *Int'l*, pg. 8103

PALLMANN MASCHINENFABRIK GMBH & CO. KG—See G. Siempelkamp GmbH & Co. KG; *Int'l*, pg. 2864

PALL MANUFACTURING UK LIMITED—See Danaher Corporation; *U.S. Public*, pg. 630

PALL MEDISTAD BV—See Danaher Corporation; *U.S. Public*, pg. 630

PALL NEW ZEALAND LTD.—See Danaher Corporation; *U.S. Public*, pg. 630

PALL NORDEN AB—See Danaher Corporation; *U.S. Public*, pg. 630

PALL NORGE A/S—See Danaher Corporation; *U.S. Public*, pg. 630

PALL POLAND LTD.—See Danaher Corporation; *U.S. Public*, pg. 630

PALL SAS—See Danaher Corporation; *U.S. Public*, pg. 630

PALL (SCHWEIZ) AG—See Danaher Corporation; *U.S. Public*, pg. 629

PALL SINGAPORE TAIWAN BRANCH HOLDING COMPANY PTE LTD.—See Danaher Corporation; *U.S. Public*, pg. 630

PALL SOUTH AFRICA (PTY) LIMITED—See Danaher Corporation; *U.S. Public*, pg. 630

PALL TECHNOLOGIES SA—See Danaher Corporation; *U.S. Public*, pg. 630

PALL TECHNOLOGY UK LIMITED—See Danaher Corporation; *U.S. Public*, pg. 630

PALMA A.S.—See SLAVIA CAPITAL Group, a.s.; *Int'l*, pg. 6996

PALMA BEE'Z RESEARCH INSTITUTE CO., LTD.—See Eisai Co., Ltd.; *Int'l*, pg. 2335

PALMA CO., LTD.; *Int'l*, pg. 5709

PALMAJU EDIBLE OIL SDN. BHD.—See Fuji Oil Holdings Inc.; *Int'l*, pg. 2815

PALMAM DPL LTD.—See Palram Industries Ltd.; *Int'l*, pg. 5710

PALMA MEXICO INC.—See Palram Industries Ltd.; *Int'l*, pg. 5710

PALMAMIDE SDN BHD—See Kuala Lumpur Kepong Berhad; *Int'l*, pg. 4318

PALMAR GERMANY GMBH—See Palram Industries Ltd.; *Int'l*, pg. 5710

PALMARIS CAPITAL PLC; *Int'l*, pg. 5709

THE PALM AT THE HUNTTING INN—See Palm Restaurant Group; *U.S. Private*, pg. 3080

PALM AUTOMOTIVE GROUP; *U.S. Private*, pg. 3079

PALM BAY INTERNATIONAL, INC.; *U.S. Private*, pg. 3079

PALM BEACH CAPITAL PARTNERS LLC; *U.S. Private*, pg. 3079

PALM BEACH GARDENS COMMUNITY HOSPITAL, INC.—See Tenet Healthcare Corporation; *U.S. Public*, pg. 2008

PALM BEACH HOSPITALISTS PROGRAM, LLC—See HCA Healthcare, Inc.; *U.S. Public*, pg. 1005

PALM BEACH ILLUSTRATED—See Hour Media Group, LLC; *U.S. Private*, pg. 1991

PALM BEACH IMPORTS INC.; *U.S. Private*, pg. 3079

PALM BEACH IMPORTS, INC.; *U.S. Private*, pg. 3079

PALM BEACH INTERNATIONAL SURGERY CENTER, LLC—See Tenet Healthcare Corporation; *U.S. Public*, pg. 2006

PALM BEACH MEDIA GROUP INC—See Hour Media Group, LLC; *U.S. Private*, pg. 1991

PALM BEACH MOTORING ACCESSORIES, INC.—See Vision Investments, LLC; *U.S. Private*, pg. 4391

PALM BEACH MOTOR YACHT CO. PTY. LTD.—See Grand Banks Yachts Limited; *Int'l*, pg. 3054

PALM BEACH NEWSPAPERS, LLC—See Gannett Co., Inc.; *U.S. Public*, pg. 906

PALM BEACH RESOURCE RECOVERY CORPORATION—See EQT AB; *Int'l*, pg. 2474

PALM BEACH SPORTS CLUB, LLC—See Town Sports International Holdings, Inc.; *U.S. Private*, pg. 4197

PALM BEACH TAN, INC.; *U.S. Private*, pg. 3079

PALM BEACH TOWERS—See Viking Yacht Company; *U.S. Private*, pg. 4383

PALM BEACH TOYOTA—See Penske Automotive Group, Inc.; *U.S. Public*, pg. 1665

PALMBERG-RAKENNUS OY—See YIT Corporation; *Int'l*, pg. 8586

PALMBERG-URAKOITSIJAT OY—See YIT Corporation; *Int'l*, pg. 8586

PALM CARE LIMITED—See Sheikh Holdings Group (Investments) Limited; *Int'l*, pg. 6794

PALM CHEVROLET OF GAINESVILLE; *U.S. Private*, pg. 3079

PALM CHRYSLER JEEP DODGE RAM; *U.S. Private*, pg. 3079

PALM CITY MILLWORK, INC.—See Glenn Rieder, Inc.; *U.S. Private*, pg. 1711

PALM COAST DATA HOLDCO, INC.—See AMREP Corporation; *U.S. Public*, pg. 133

PALM COAST DATA, LLC—See Irish Studio, LLC; *U.S. Private*, pg. 2138

PALM COAST HOLDINGS, INC.—See ALLETE, Inc.; *U.S. Public*, pg. 79

PALM COMERCIO DE APARELHOS ELETRONICOS LTDA.—See HP Inc.; *U.S. Public*, pg. 1064

PALM COMMODITIES INTERNATIONAL, LLC—See Umicore S.A./N.V.; *Int'l*, pg. 8025

PALM CREEK HOLDINGS LLC—See Sun Communities, Inc.; *U.S. Public*, pg. 1961

PALMDALE OIL COMPANY, INC.; *U.S. Private*, pg. 3080

PALM DESIGN CO., LTD.—See Palm Eco-Town Development Co., Ltd.; *Int'l*, pg. 5709

PALM ECO-TOWN DEVELOPMENT CO., LTD. - CONSTRUCTION DIVISION—See Palm Eco-Town Development Co., Ltd.; *Int'l*, pg. 5709

PALM ECO-TOWN DEVELOPMENT CO., LTD. - DESIGN DIVISION—See Palm Eco-Town Development Co., Ltd.; *Int'l*, pg. 5709

PALM ECO-TOWN DEVELOPMENT CO., LTD. - MUNICIPAL UTILITY DIVISION—See Palm Eco-Town Development Co., Ltd.; *Int'l*, pg. 5709

PALM ECO-TOWN DEVELOPMENT CO., LTD.; *Int'l*, pg. 5709

PALMEDIA LTD.—See Palestine Telecommunications Company P.L.C.; *Int'l*, pg. 5707

PAL-MED, LLC—See AdaptHealth Corp.; *U.S. Public*, pg. 39

PALMEN AUTOMOTIVE GROUP INC.; *U.S. Private*, pg. 3080

PALMEN DODGE CHRYSLER JEEP OF RACINE—See Palmen Automotive Group Inc.; *U.S. Private*, pg. 3080

PALMEN KIA; *U.S. Private*, pg. 3080

PALM ENTERTAINMENT PROPERTIES LLC; *U.S. Private*, pg. 3079

PALMER AND SICARD INC.; *U.S. Private*, pg. 3080

PALMER AUTO GROUP; *U.S. Private*, pg. 3080

PALMER BANCSHARES, INC.; *U.S. Private*, pg. 3080

PALMER CANDY COMPANY; *U.S. Private*, pg. 3080

PALMER CAPITAL CZECH REPUBLIC, S.R.O.—See Fiera Capital Corporation; *Int'l*, pg. 2660

PALMER CAPITAL FONDSENBEHEER B.V.—See Fiera Capital Corporation; *Int'l*, pg. 2660

PALMER CAPITAL NEDERLAND N.V.—See Fiera Capital Corporation; *Int'l*, pg. 2660

PALMER CAPITAL PARTNERS LIMITED—See Fiera Capital Corporation; *Int'l*, pg. 2659

PALMER CONTINUUM OF CARE, INC.; *U.S. Private*, pg. 3080

PALMER DISTRIBUTION SERVICES, INC.; *U.S. Private*, pg. 3081

THE PALMER-DONAVIN MANUFACTURING COMPANY, INC.; *U.S. Private*, pg. 4090

PALMER ELECTRIC CO.; *U.S. Private*, pg. 3081

PALMER ENVIRONMENTAL LIMITED—See Halma plc; *Int'l*, pg. 3232

PALMER GOTHEIM SKIFERBRUDD AS—See AF Gruppen ASA; *Int'l*, pg. 184

PALMER & HARVEY MCLANE (HOLDINGS) LIMITED; *Int'l*, pg. 5709

PALMERHOUSE PROPERTIES, LLC- DULUTH—See HomeSmart International LLC; *U.S. Private*, pg. 1974

PALMERHOUSE PROPERTIES, LLC.—See HomeSmart International LLC; *U.S. Private*, pg. 1974

PALMER INTERNATIONAL, INC.; *U.S. Private*, pg. 3081

PALMER JOHNSON ENTERPRISES, INC.; *U.S. Private*, pg. 3081

PALMER JOHNSON POWER SYSTEMS LLC—See Palmer Johnson Enterprises, Inc.; *U.S. Private*, pg. 3081

PALMER MOVING & STORAGE CO.; *U.S. Private*, pg. 3081

PALMER OF TEXAS TANKS, INC.—See Ascent Industries Co.; *U.S. Public*, pg. 210

PALMER OIL CO. INCORPORATED; *U.S. Private*, pg. 3081

PALMER PAVING CORP.—See Peckham Industries, Inc.; *U.S. Private*, pg. 3127

PALMER RANCH HOLDINGS LTD.; *U.S. Private*, pg. 3081

PALMER SNYDER FURNITURE CO.; *U.S. Private*, pg. 3081

PALMER SQUARE CAPITAL BDC INC.; *U.S. Public*, pg. 1634

PALMER SQUARE CAPITAL BDC INC.   CORPORATE AFFILIATIONS

PALMERS TEXTIL AG—See Quadriga Capital Beteiligungsberatung GmbH; *Int'l*, pg. 6150
PALMERTON LUMBER CO., INC.—See Your Building Centers, Inc.; *U.S. Private*, pg. 4594
PALMER (UK) LIMITED—See Palmer International, Inc.; *U.S. Private*, pg. 3081
PALMETAL ARMAZENAGEM E SERVICOS S.A.—See ThyssenKrupp AG; *Int'l*, pg. 7725
PALMETAL CONTROLO E ARMAZENAGEM S.A.—See ThyssenKrupp AG; *Int'l*, pg. 7725
PALMETTO BEHAVIORAL HEALTH SYSTEM, L.L.C.—See Universal Health Services, Inc.; *U.S. Public*, pg. 2259
PALMETTO CAR & TRUCK GROUP; *U.S. Private*, pg. 3081
PALMETTO CHEVROLET CO., INC.; *U.S. Private*, pg. 3081
PALMETTO DIALYSIS, LLC—See DaVita Inc.; *U.S. Public*, pg. 641
PALMETTO ELECTRIC COOPERATIVE; *U.S. Private*, pg. 3081
PALMETTO ENTERPRISES LLC—See PT Sinar Mas Group; *Int'l*, pg. 6073
PALMETTO GBA, LLC—See Blue Cross & Blue Shield of South Carolina; *U.S. Private*, pg. 587
PALMETTO HEALTH BAPTIST EASLEY—See Palmetto Health; *U.S. Private*, pg. 3081
PALMETTO HEALTH; *U.S. Private*, pg. 3081
PALMETTO HOSPITAL TRUST; *U.S. Private*, pg. 3081
PALMETTO INC.—See Greene, Tweed & Co.; *U.S. Private*, pg. 1777
PALMETTO MINING CORPORATION—See Pancontinental Resources Corporation; *Int'l*, pg. 5726
PALMETTO OXYGEN, LLC—See AdaptHealth Corp.; *U.S. Public*, pg. 39
PALMETTO PAVING CORPORATION; *U.S. Private*, pg. 3081
PALMETTO PEE DEE BEHAVIORAL HEALTH, L.L.C.—See Universal Health Services, Inc.; *U.S. Public*, pg. 2259
PALMETTO REAL ESTATE TRUST; *U.S. Public*, pg. 1635
PALMETTO RESIDENTIAL RENTALS, LLC—See Berkshire Hathaway Inc.; *U.S. Public*, pg. 304
PALMETTO RURAL TELEPHONE COOPERATIVE, INC.; *U.S. Private*, pg. 3081
THE PALMETTOS OF PARKLANE, LLC—See National HealthCare Corporation; *U.S. Public*, pg. 1497
PALMETTO STATE BANKSHARES, INC.; *U.S. Private*, pg. 3081
PALMETTO STATE BANK—See Palmetto State Bankshares, Inc.; *U.S. Private*, pg. 3082
PALMETTO STATE UTILITY SERVICES, INC.—See American States Water Company; *U.S. Public*, pg. 110
PALMETTO TRI-COUNTY MEDICAL SPECIALISTS, LLC—See Community Health Systems, Inc.; *U.S. Public*, pg. 555
PALM EUROPE LIMITED—See HP Inc.; *U.S. Public*, pg. 1064
PALMEX ALIMENTOS SA DE CV—See Wind Point Advisors LLC; *U.S. Private*, pg. 4534
PALMEX INDUSTRIES SDN BERHAD—See IOI Corporation Berhad; *Int'l*, pg. 3792
PALMGREN STEEL PRODUCTS, INC.—See Colovos Company; *U.S. Private*, pg. 975
PALM HARBOR DERMATOLOGY, P.A.; *U.S. Private*, pg. 3079
PALM HARBOR HEATING & AIR CONDITIONING, INC.—See Northside Services, Inc.; *U.S. Private*, pg. 2957
PALM HARBOR HOMES, INC.—See Cavco Industries, Inc.; *U.S. Public*, pg. 455
PALM HARBOR VILLAGES REAL ESTATE, LLC—See Cavco Industries, Inc.; *U.S. Public*, pg. 455
PALM + HAVAS; *Int'l*, pg. 5709
PALM HILLS DEVELOPMENT SAE; *Int'l*, pg. 5709
PALM HOLDINGS INC.; *Int'l*, pg. 5709
PALM HOLDINGS UK—See Palm Holdings Inc.; *Int'l*, pg. 5709
PALMITECO ENGINEERING SDN. BHD.—See CB Industrial Product Holding Berhad; *Int'l*, pg. 1364
PALM JEWELS LTD.; *Int'l*, pg. 5709
PALM MORTUARY INC.—See Service Corporation International; *U.S. Public*, pg. 1870
PALM-OLEO (KLANG) SDN BHD—See Kuala Lumpur Kepong Berhad; *Int'l*, pg. 4318
PALM-OLEO SDN BHD—See Kuala Lumpur Kepong Berhad; *Int'l*, pg. 4318
PALM PETERBILT-GMC TRUCKS INC.; *U.S. Private*, pg. 3079
PALM PICTURES, LLC—See Palm Entertainment Properties LLC; *U.S. Private*, pg. 3079
PALM POINT BEHAVIORAL HEALTH, LLC—See Universal Health Services, Inc.; *U.S. Public*, pg. 2259
PALM RESTAURANT GROUP; *U.S. Private*, pg. 3079
THE PALM RESTAURANT—See Palm Restaurant Group; *U.S. Private*, pg. 3080
THE PALM RESTAURANT—See Palm Restaurant Group; *U.S. Private*, pg. 3080
PALMS AGRO PRODUCTION CO; *Int'l*, pg. 5709

PALMS AT PECCOLE RANCH—See Kennedy-Wilson Holdings, Inc.; *U.S. Public*, pg. 1223
PALMS & COMPANY INC.; *U.S. Private*, pg. 3082
PALMS CROSSING TOWN CENTER, LLC—See Washington Prime Group Inc.; *U.S. Private*, pg. 4448
PALM SHADOWS MOBILE HOME & RV RESORT—See Manufactured Housing Properties Inc.; *U.S. Public*, pg. 1362
PALMS OF PASADENA HOSPITAL—See HCA Healthcare, Inc.; *U.S. Public*, pg. 1005
PALM SPRINGS FBO TWO LLC—See Macquarie Group Limited; *Int'l*, pg. 4627
PALM SPRINGS RESORT BERHAD—See Tanco Holdings Berhad; *Int'l*, pg. 7456
PALM SPRINGS RESORT (MM2H) SDN. BHD.—See Tanco Holdings Berhad; *Int'l*, pg. 7456
PALM SPRINGS TREATMENT CENTERS, LLC—See Universal Health Services, Inc.; *U.S. Public*, pg. 2259
PALMS SC INSURANCE COMPANY, LLC—See NextEra Energy, Inc.; *U.S. Public*, pg. 1526
PALMS SPECIALTY INSURANCE COMPANY, INC.—See NextEra Energy, Inc.; *U.S. Public*, pg. 1526
PALMSTIERNA INTERNATIONAL AB—See Flowserve Corporation; *U.S. Public*, pg. 857
PALMSTIERNAS SVENSKA AB—See Indutrade AB; *Int'l*, pg. 3680
PALMSVILLE INVESTMENT PTE LTD—See Keppel Corporation Limited; *Int'l*, pg. 4132
PALMS WEST HOSPITAL—See HCA Healthcare, Inc.; *U.S. Public*, pg. 1005
PALMS WEST SURGICENTER—See HCA Healthcare, Inc.; *U.S. Public*, pg. 1005
PALMTOP SDN BHD—See C.I. Holdings Berhad; *Int'l*, pg. 1243
PALM USA INC.; *U.S. Private*, pg. 3080
PALMYRA BOLOGNA CO.; *U.S. Private*, pg. 3082
PALMYRA DO BRASIL INDUSTRIA E COMERCIO DE SILICIO METALICO E RECURSOS NATURAIS LTDA.—See Dow Inc.; *U.S. Public*, pg. 685
PALO ALTO NETWORKS DENMARK APS—See Palo Alto Networks, Inc.; *U.S. Public*, pg. 1635
PALO ALTO NETWORKS (EU) B.V.—See Palo Alto Networks, Inc.; *U.S. Public*, pg. 1635
PALO ALTO NETWORKS, INC.; *U.S. Public*, pg. 1635
PALO ALTO NETWORKS (ISRAEL ANALYTICS) LTD.—See Palo Alto Networks, Inc.; *U.S. Public*, pg. 1635
PALO ALTO NETWORKS SAUDI ARABIAN LIMITED COMPANY—See Palo Alto Networks, Inc.; *U.S. Public*, pg. 1635
PALO ALTO PARTNERS, LLC—See Wells Fargo & Company; *U.S. Public*, pg. 2345
PALO ALTO RESEARCH CENTER INCORPORATED—See Xerox Holdings Corporation; *U.S. Public*, pg. 2388
PALO ALTO SANITATION COMPANY—See Waste Management, Inc.; *U.S. Public*, pg. 2331
PALO ALTO VETERANS INSTITUTE FOR RESEARCH; *U.S. Private*, pg. 3082
PALODEX GROUP OY—See Danaher Corporation; *U.S. Public*, pg. 630
PALODEX HOLDING OY—See Danaher Corporation; *U.S. Public*, pg. 630
PALO DURO CAPITAL, LLC; *U.S. Private*, pg. 3082
PALO DURO HARDWOODS INC.; *U.S. Private*, pg. 3082
PALOMA INDUSTRIES LIMITED; *Int'l*, pg. 5709
PALOMA PARTNERS VI HOLDINGS, LLC—See EnCap Investments L.P.; *U.S. Private*, pg. 1390
PALOMAR DISPLAY PRODUCTS, INC.; *U.S. Private*, pg. 3082
PALOMA RESOURCES, LLC; *U.S. Public*, pg. 1635
PALOMAR HOLDINGS, INC.; *U.S. Public*, pg. 1635
PALOMAR INSURANCE CORP; *U.S. Private*, pg. 3082
PALOMAR MEDICAL PRODUCTS, LLC—See Clayton, Dubilier & Rice, LLC; *U.S. Private*, pg. 922
PALOMAR MEDICAL TECHNOLOGIES, LLC—See Clayton, Dubilier & Rice, LLC; *U.S. Private*, pg. 922
PALOMAR MOUNTAIN PREMIUM SPRING WATER; *U.S. Private*, pg. 3082
PALOMAR PRODUCTS INC.—See TransDigm Group Incorporated; *U.S. Public*, pg. 1870
PALOMAR S.P.A.—See Mediawan SA; *Int'l*, pg. 4774
PALOMAR TECHNOLOGIES COMPANIES, LLC; *U.S. Private*, pg. 3082
PALOMAR TECHNOLOGIES GMBH—See Palomar Technologies Companies, LLC; *U.S. Private*, pg. 3082
PALOMAR TECHNOLOGIES INC.—See Palomar Technologies Companies, LLC; *U.S. Private*, pg. 3082
PALOMAR TECHNOLOGIES PTE LTD.—See Palomar Technologies Companies, LLC; *U.S. Private*, pg. 3082
PALOMAR VISTA HEALTHCARE CENTER—See The Ensign Group, Inc.; *U.S. Public*, pg. 2071
PALOMA SUMMIT APARTMENTS—See Sequoia Equities Inc.; *U.S. Private*, pg. 3612
PALOMA SYSTEMS, INC.; *U.S. Private*, pg. 3082
PALOS CAPITAL CORPORATION; *Int'l*, pg. 5710
PALOS COMMUNITY HOSPITAL; *U.S. Private*, pg. 3082

PALOS HEALTH SURGERY CENTER, LLC—See Tenet Healthcare Corporation; *U.S. Public*, pg. 2006
PALOS VERDES BUILDING CORP.; *U.S. Private*, pg. 3082
PALPLINTAR I SVERIGE AB—See AF Gruppen ASA; *Int'l*, pg. 184
PALRAM 4U LTD.—See Palram Industries Ltd.; *Int'l*, pg. 5710
PALRAM AMERICAS INC.—See Palram Industries Ltd.; *Int'l*, pg. 5710
PALRAM AUSTRALIA PTY LTD.—See Palram Industries Ltd.; *Int'l*, pg. 5710
PALRAM BEIJING LTD.—See Palram Industries Ltd.; *Int'l*, pg. 5710
PALRAM EUROPE LTD.—See Palram Industries Ltd.; *Int'l*, pg. 5710
PALRAM FRANCE LTD.—See Palram Industries Ltd.; *Int'l*, pg. 5710
PALRAM INDIA LTD.—See Palram Industries Ltd.; *Int'l*, pg. 5710
PALRAM INDUSTRIES LTD.; *Int'l*, pg. 5710
PALRAM SOUTH-AFRICA PTY. LTD.—See Palram Industries Ltd.; *Int'l*, pg. 5710
PALRED TECHNOLOGIES LIMITED; *Int'l*, pg. 5710
PAL SALES LLC—See Asia Tele-Net & Technology Corporation Limited; *Int'l*, pg. 615
PALSGAARD ASIA-PACIFIC PTE LTD—See Palsgaard A/S; *Int'l*, pg. 5710
PALSGAARD A/S; *Int'l*, pg. 5710
PALSGAARD CHINA LTD—See Palsgaard A/S; *Int'l*, pg. 5710
PALSGAARD DO BRASIL LTDA—See Palsgaard A/S; *Int'l*, pg. 5710
PALSGAARD DWC-LLC—See Palsgaard A/S; *Int'l*, pg. 5710
PALSGAARD FRANCE S.A.S.—See Palsgaard A/S; *Int'l*, pg. 5710
PALSGAARD NETHERLANDS B.V.—See Palsgaard A/S; *Int'l*, pg. 5710
PALSGAARD POLSKA SP. Z O. O.—See Palsgaard A/S; *Int'l*, pg. 5710
PALSGAARD SOUTH AFRICA (PTY) LTD.—See Palsgaard A/S; *Int'l*, pg. 5710
PALSGAARD VERKAUFSGESELLSCHAFT MBH & CO KG—See Palsgaard A/S; *Int'l*, pg. 5710
PALS, INC.; *U.S. Private*, pg. 3082
PALSOFT INFOSYSTEMS LIMITED; *Int'l*, pg. 5710
PALSYS DIGITAL TECHNOLOGY CORP.—See SYSTEX Corporation; *Int'l*, pg. 7393
PALTAC CORPORATION—See Medipal Holdings Corporation; *Int'l*, pg. 4779
PALTALK, INC.; *U.S. Private*, pg. 3082
PALTALK, INC.; *U.S. Public*, pg. 1635
PALTALK; *U.S. Private*, pg. 3082
PALTEK CORPORATION; *Int'l*, pg. 5710
PALTEK HONG KONG LIMITED—See PALTEK CORPORATION; *Int'l*, pg. 5710
PALUEL-MARMONT CAPITAL SA—See Compagnie Lebon SA; *Int'l*, pg. 1745
PALUMBO GROUP S.P.A; *Int'l*, pg. 5710
PALUMBO LUMBER & MANUFACTURING CO.; *U.S. Private*, pg. 3082
PAMAG ENGINEERING AG—See ROCKWOOL A/S; *Int'l*, pg. 6380
PAMAL BROADCASTING LTD.; *U.S. Private*, pg. 3082
PAMALICAN ISLAND HOLDINGS, INC.—See A. Soriano Corporation; *Int'l*, pg. 22
PAMANTASAN NG ARAULLO (ARAULLO UNIVERSITY), INC.—See PHINMA Corporation; *Int'l*, pg. 5848
PAMAPOL S.A.; *Int'l*, pg. 5711
PAMARCO GLOBAL GRAPHICS (PGG)—See J.P. Kotts & Co.; *U.S. Private*, pg. 2170
PAMARCO GLOBAL GRAPHICS—See J.P. Kotts & Co.; *U.S. Private*, pg. 2170
PAMARCO, INCORPORATED—See J.P. Kotts & Co.; *U.S. Private*, pg. 2170
PAMA SHOPPING VILLAGE LIMITED—See PG PLC; *Int'l*, pg. 5837
PAMBILI NATURAL RESOURCES CORPORATION; *Int'l*, pg. 5711
PAMBY MOTORS INCORPORATED; *U.S. Private*, pg. 3083
PAMC, LTD.; *U.S. Private*, pg. 3083
PAMCO LABEL COMPANY; *U.S. Private*, pg. 3083
PAM COLOMBIA SA—See Compagnie de Saint-Gobain SA; *Int'l*, pg. 1724
P.A.M. DEDICATED SERVICES, INC.—See P.A.M. Transportation Services, Inc.; *U.S. Public*, pg. 1630
PAMELA LOREN LIMITED, INC.—See Loren Communications International Ltd., Inc.; *U.S. Private*, pg. 2495
PAMEL YENILENEBILIR ELEKTRIK URETIM A.S.—See Verusa Holding A.S.; *Int'l*, pg. 8175
P-AMERICAS, LLC—See PepsiCo, Inc.; *U.S. Public*, pg. 1669
PAM FASTENING TECHNOLOGY, INC.—See Steel Partners Holdings L.P.; *U.S. Public*, pg. 1943
PAMLICO CAPITAL MANAGEMENT, L.P.; *U.S. Private*, pg. 3083

COMPANY NAME INDEX

PAMLICO PACKING COMPANY INCORPORATED; U.S. Private, pg. 3083
PAMOCO SPA—See Nanjing Estun Automation Co., Ltd.; Int'l, pg. 5140
PAMODZI INVESTMENT HOLDINGS; Int'l, pg. 5711
PAMODZI UNIQUE ENGINEERING PTY LTD—See Pamodzi Investment Holdings; Int'l, pg. 5711
PAMOL PLANTATIONS SDN BHD—See IOI Corporation Berhad; Int'l, pg. 3792
PAMO PROMET A.D.; Int'l, pg. 5711
PA-MORNING CALL, LLC—See Nexstar Media Group, Inc.; U.S. Public, pg. 1524
PAMPA CONCRETE CO; U.S. Private, pg. 3083
PAMPA ENERGIA S.A.—See Grupo EMES S.A.; Int'l, pg. 3126
PAMPA METALS CORPORATION; Int'l, pg. 5711
PAM PANORAMA S.P.A.—See GECOS S.p.A.; Int'l, pg. 2909
THE PAMPERED CHEF, LTD.—See Berkshire Hathaway Inc.; U.S. Public, pg. 319
PAMPLIN COMMUNICATIONS CORPORATION—See R.B. Pamplin Corporation; U.S. Private, pg. 3334
PAMPLONA CAPITAL MANAGEMENT LLP; Int'l, pg. 5711
PAMPR'OEUF DISTRIBUTION; Int'l, pg. 5713
PAM REHABILITATION HOSPITAL OF BEAUMONT—See Post Acute Medical, LLC; U.S. Private, pg. 3234
PAMS, INC.—See Key Impact & Sales Systems, Inc.; U.S. Private, pg. 2293
P.A.M. TRANSPORTATION SERVICES, INC.; U.S. Public, pg. 1629
P.A.M. TRANSPORT, INC.—See P.A.M. Transportation Services, Inc.; U.S. Public, pg. 1630
PAMUKOVA ELEKTRIK URETIM A.S.—See Verusaturk Girisim Sermayesi Yatirim Ortakligi A.S.; Int'l, pg. 8176
PAMUKOVA YENILENEBILR ELEKTRIK RETIM A.S.; Int'l, pg. 5713
PAN-ABODE INTERNATIONAL LTD.—See Mill & Timber Products Ltd; Int'l, pg. 4895
PANACEA BIOTEC LIMITED; Int'l, pg. 5716
PANACEA GLOBAL, INC.; Int'l, pg. 5716
PANACEA INC; Int'l, pg. 5716
PANACEA LIFE SCIENCES HOLDINGS, INC.; U.S. Public, pg. 1635
PANACEA PRODUCTS CORPORATION; U.S. Private, pg. 3084
PANACHE DIGILIFE LTD.; Int'l, pg. 5716
PANACHE INNOVATIONS LIMITED; Int'l, pg. 5716
PANACOL-ELOSOL GMBH—See Dr. Honle AG; Int'l, pg. 2192
PANACOL-KOREA CO., LTD.—See Dr. Honle AG; Int'l, pg. 2192
PANA COMMUNITY HOSPITAL; U.S. Private, pg. 3084
PANACON CORP.—See InterContinental Hotels Group PLC; Int'l, pg. 3738
PANADIS, S.A. DE C.V.—See Compagnie des Levures Lesaffre SA; Int'l, pg. 1739
PANAFIC INDUSTRIALS LIMITED; Int'l, pg. 5716
PANAFLO CONTROLS PTE. LTD.—See Pantech Group Holdings Berhad; Int'l, pg. 5730
PAN AFRICAN AIRLINES (NIGERIA) LIMITED—See Bristow Group, Inc.; U.S. Public, pg. 387
PANAFRICAN ENERGY TANZANIA LIMITED—See Orca Energy Group Inc.; Int'l, pg. 5615
PAN AFRICAN RESOURCES PLC; Int'l, pg. 5713
PAN-AFRICAN SAVINGS & LOANS GHANA LIMITED—See Ecobank Transnational Incorporated; Int'l, pg. 2294
PANAGORA ASSET MANAGEMENT, INC.—See Power Corporation of Canada; Int'l, pg. 5943
PANAGO; Int'l, pg. 5716
PANAH JAYA SERVICES SDN. BHD.—See Annica Holdings Limited; Int'l, pg. 474
PANALI CO., LTD.—See Hotel Royal Limited; Int'l, pg. 3489
PANALOG SAS—See Vandemoortele N.V.; Int'l, pg. 8128
PANALOK LIMITED—See Stanley Black & Decker, Inc.; U.S. Public, pg. 1933
PANALPINA AB—See DSV A/S; Int'l, pg. 2214
PANALPINA AG—See DSV A/S; Int'l, pg. 2214
PANALPINA ASIA-PACIFIC SERVICES LTD.—See DSV A/S; Int'l, pg. 2214
PANALPINA ASIA-PACIFIC SERVICES (THAILAND) LTD.—See DSV A/S; Int'l, pg. 2214
PANALPINA A/S—See DSV A/S; Int'l, pg. 2214
PANALPINA BAHRAIN W.L.L.—See DSV A/S; Int'l, pg. 2214
PANALPINA BEVERWIJK B.V.—See DSV A/S; Int'l, pg. 2214
PANALPINA C.A.—See DSV A/S; Int'l, pg. 2214
PANALPINA CENTRAL ASIA AZERBAIJAN—See DSV A/S; Int'l, pg. 2214
PANALPINA CHILE TRANSPORTES MUNDIALES LTDA.—See DSV A/S; Int'l, pg. 2214
PANALPINA CHINA LIMITED—See DSV A/S; Int'l, pg. 2214
PANALPINA CZECH SRO.—See DSV A/S; Int'l, pg. 2214
PANALPINA DENMARK—See DSV A/S; Int'l, pg. 2214
PANALPINA ECUADOR S.A.—See DSV A/S; Int'l, pg. 2214
PANALPINA FINLAND—See DSV A/S; Int'l, pg. 2214
PANALPINA FREIGHT LLC—See DSV A/S; Int'l, pg. 2214
PANALPINA (GHANA) LIMITED—See DSV A/S; Int'l, pg. 2214
PANALPINA GRIEG AS—See DSV A/S; Int'l, pg. 2214
PANALPINA GULF LLC—See DSV A/S; Int'l, pg. 2214
PANALPINA HASSI MESSAOUD—See DSV A/S; Int'l, pg. 2214
PANALPINA IAF (KOREA) LTD.—See DSV A/S; Int'l, pg. 2214
PANALPINA, INC.—See DSV A/S; Int'l, pg. 2216
PANALPINA, INC.—See DSV A/S; Int'l, pg. 2216
PANALPINA INSURANCE BROKER LTD.—See DSV A/S; Int'l, pg. 2214
PANALPINA KOREA LTD.—See DSV A/S; Int'l, pg. 2214
PANALPINA LOGISTICS (WUHAN) LTD.—See DSV A/S; Int'l, pg. 2214
PANALPINA LTDA.—See DSV A/S; Int'l, pg. 2214
PANALPINA S.A.—See DSV A/S; Int'l, pg. 2214
PANALPINA LUXEMBOURG S.A.—See DSV A/S; Int'l, pg. 2214
PANALPINA MACAU EMPRESA TRANSITARIA LIMITADA—See DSV A/S; Int'l, pg. 2214
PANALPINA MAGYARORSZAG KFT.—See DSV A/S; Int'l, pg. 2214
PANALPINA MANAGEMENT LTD.—See DSV A/S; Int'l, pg. 2215
PANALPINA POLSKA SP. Z O.O.—See DSV A/S; Int'l, pg. 2215
PANALPINA QATAR W.L.L.—See DSV A/S; Int'l, pg. 2215
PANALPINA ROMANIA S.R.L.—See DSV A/S; Int'l, pg. 2215
PANALPINA S.A.—See DSV A/S; Int'l, pg. 2215
PANALPINA S.A.—See DSV A/S; Int'l, pg. 2215
PANALPINA SLOVAKIA S.R.O.—See DSV A/S; Int'l, pg. 2215
PANALPINA TAIWAN LTD.—See DSV A/S; Int'l, pg. 2215
PANALPINA TRANSPORTES MUNDIAIS LDA.—See DSV A/S; Int'l, pg. 2215
PANALPINA TRANSPORTES MUNDIAIS, NAVEGACAO & TRANSISTOS S.A.R.L.—See DSV A/S; Int'l, pg. 2215
PANALPINA TRANSPORTES MUNDIALES C.A.—See DSV A/S; Int'l, pg. 2215
PANALPINA TRANSPORTES MUNDIALES S.A. DE C.V.—See DSV A/S; Int'l, pg. 2215
PANALPINA TRANSPORTES MUNDIALES S.A.—See DSV A/S; Int'l, pg. 2215
PANALPINA TRANSPORTES MUNDIALES S.A.—See DSV A/S; Int'l, pg. 2215
PANALPINA TRANSPORTES MUNDIALES S.A.—See DSV A/S; Int'l, pg. 2215
PANALPINA TRANSPORTES MUNDIALES S.A.—See DSV A/S; Int'l, pg. 2215
PANALPINA TRANSPORTES MUNDIALES S.A.—See DSV A/S; Int'l, pg. 2215
PANALPINA TRANSPORTI MONDIALI S.P.A.—See DSV A/S; Int'l, pg. 2215
PANALPINA TRANSPORT (MALAYSIA) SDN. BHD.—See DSV A/S; Int'l, pg. 2215
PANALPINA TRANSPORT MONDIAUX SARL—See DSV A/S; Int'l, pg. 2215
PANALPINA TRANSPORTS INTERNATIONAUX S.A.—See DSV A/S; Int'l, pg. 2215
PANALPINA TRANSPORTS MONDIAUX CAMEROON S.A.—See DSV A/S; Int'l, pg. 2215
PANALPINA TRANSPORTS MONDIAUX CONGO S.A.R.L.—See DSV A/S; Int'l, pg. 2215
PANALPINA TRANSPORTS MONDIAUX GABON S.A.—See DSV A/S; Int'l, pg. 2215
PANALPINA URUGUAY TRANSPORTES MUNDIALES S.A.—See DSV A/S; Int'l, pg. 2215
PANALPINA WELTTRANSPORT (DEUTSCHLAND) GMBH—See DSV A/S; Int'l, pg. 2215
PANALPINA WELTTRANSPORT GMBH—See DSV A/S; Int'l, pg. 2215
PANALPINA WELTTRANSPORT GMBH—See DSV A/S; Int'l, pg. 2215
PANALPINA WELTTRANSPORT GMBH—See DSV A/S; Int'l, pg. 2215
PANALPINA WELTTRANSPORT GMBH—See DSV A/S; Int'l, pg. 2215
PANALPINA WELTTRANSPORT GMBH—See DSV A/S; Int'l, pg. 2215
PANALPINA WELTTRANSPORT GMBH—See DSV A/S; Int'l, pg. 2215
PANALPINA WORLD TRANSPORT B.V.—See DSV A/S; Int'l, pg. 2216
PANALPINA WORLD TRANSPORT (DUBAI) DWC-LLC—See DSV A/S; Int'l, pg. 2215
PANALPINA WORLD TRANSPORT GMBH—See DSV A/S; Int'l, pg. 2215
PANALPINA WORLD TRANSPORT HOLDING LTD.—See DSV A/S; Int'l, pg. 2214
PANALPINA WORLD TRANSPORT (INDIA) PVT. LTD.—See DSV A/S; Int'l, pg. 2215
PANALPINA WORLD TRANSPORT (IRELAND) LTD.—See DSV A/S; Int'l, pg. 2215
PANALPINA WORLD TRANSPORT (JAPAN) LTD.—See DSV A/S; Int'l, pg. 2215
PANALPINA WORLD TRANSPORT LLP—See DSV A/S; Int'l, pg. 2216
PANALPINA WORLD TRANSPORT LTD.—See DSV A/S; Int'l, pg. 2216
PANALPINA WORLD TRANSPORT LTD.—See DSV A/S; Int'l, pg. 2216
PANALPINA WORLD TRANSPORT LTD.—See DSV A/S; Int'l, pg. 2216
PANALPINA WORLD TRANSPORT NAKLIYAT LTD. STI.—See DSV A/S; Int'l, pg. 2216
PANALPINA WORLD TRANSPORT NIGERIA LTD.—See DSV A/S; Int'l, pg. 2216
PANALPINA WORLD TRANSPORT N.V.—See DSV A/S; Int'l, pg. 2216
PANALPINA WORLD TRANSPORT N.V.—See DSV A/S; Int'l, pg. 2216
PANALPINA WORLD TRANSPORT (PHILS.) INC.—See DSV A/S; Int'l, pg. 2215
PANALPINA WORLD TRANSPORT (PRC) LTD.—See DSV A/S; Int'l, pg. 2215
PANALPINA WORLD TRANSPORT PTY. LTD.—See DSV A/S; Int'l, pg. 2216
PANALPINA WORLD TRANSPORT PTY. LTD.—See DSV A/S; Int'l, pg. 2216
PANALPINA WORLD TRANSPORT (SAUDI ARABIA) LTD.—See DSV A/S; Int'l, pg. 2216
PANALPINA WORLD TRANSPORT (SINGAPORE) PTE. LTD.—See DSV A/S; Int'l, pg. 2216
PANALPINA WORLD TRANSPORT (THAILAND) LIMITED—See DSV A/S; Int'l, pg. 2216
PANALPINA WORLD TRANSPORT ZAO—See DSV A/S; Int'l, pg. 2216
PANALYTICAL B.V.—See Spectris Plc; Int'l, pg. 7131
PANALYTICAL, INC.—See Spectris Plc; Int'l, pg. 7131
PANAMA CANAL RAILWAY COMPANY—See Canadian Pacific Kansas City Limited; Int'l, pg. 1285
PANAMA CITY NURSING CENTER LLC—See Omega Healthcare Investors, Inc.; U.S. Public, pg. 1571
PANAMA CITY SURGERY CENTER, LLC—See UnitedHealth Group Incorporated; U.S. Public, pg. 2249
PANAMA PETROCHEM LTD. - PLANT 4—See Panama Petrochem Ltd.; Int'l, pg. 5717
PANAMA PETROCHEM LTD.; Int'l, pg. 5716
PANAMA PORTS COMPANY, S.A.—See CK Hutchison Holdings Limited; Int'l, pg. 1638
PANAMA POWER HOLDINGS, INC.; Int'l, pg. 5717
PANAMAX AG; Int'l, pg. 5717
PANAMAX LLC—See Melrose Industries PLC; Int'l, pg. 4813
PAN-AM EQUITIES, INC.; U.S. Private, pg. 3084
PANAMERA HOLDINGS CORPORATION; U.S. Public, pg. 1635
PANAMERICA COMPUTERS INC.; U.S. Private, pg. 3085
PAN AMERICAN COFFEE COMPANY INC.; U.S. Private, pg. 3083
PAN AMERICAN DEVELOPMENT FOUNDATION; U.S. Private, pg. 3083
PAN AMERICAN ENERGY CORP.; Int'l, pg. 5713
PAN AMERICAN ENERGY LLC—See BP plc; Int'l, pg. 1131
PAN AMERICAN ENERGY LLC—See Bridas Corporation; Int'l, pg. 1152
PAN AMERICAN EXPRESS INC.; U.S. Private, pg. 3083
PAN AMERICAN FINANCE CORPORATION—See MAPFRE S.A.; Int'l, pg. 4684
PAN AMERICAN GRAIN COMPANY; U.S. Private, pg. 3083
PAN AMERICAN INSURANCE COMPANY—See MAPFRE S.A.; Int'l, pg. 4683
PAN AMERICAN LABORATORIES INC.; U.S. Private, pg. 3084
PAN-AMERICAN LIFE INSURANCE DE COSTA RICA, S.A.—See Pan-American Life Insurance Group, Inc.; U.S. Private, pg. 3084
PAN-AMERICAN LIFE INSURANCE GROUP, INC.; U.S. Private, pg. 3084
PAN AMERICAN PAPERS, INC.; U.S. Private, pg. 3084
PANAMERICAN SEED CO.—See Ball Horticultural Company; U.S. Private, pg. 460
PAN AMERICAN SILVER BOLIVIA S.A.—See Pan American Silver Corp.; Int'l, pg. 5713
PAN AMERICAN SILVER CORP.; Int'l, pg. 5713
PAN AMERICAN SILVER PERU S.A.C.—See Pan American Silver Corp.; Int'l, pg. 5713
PAN AMERICAN TOOL CORPORATION; U.S. Private, pg. 3084
PANAMEX NEW ZEALAND—See Panamex Pacific, Inc; U.S. Private, pg. 3085
PANAMEX PACIFIC, INC; U.S. Private, pg. 3085
PAN AM RAILWAYS, INC.—See CSX Corporation; U.S. Public, pg. 602
PAN ARAB RESEARCH CENTER (PARC); Int'l, pg. 5713
PAN ARAB RESEARCH CENTER (PARC) W.L.L.—See Pan Arab Research Center (PARC); Int'l, pg. 5714

PAN ARCTIC INUIT LOGISTICS CORPORATION—See Nunasi Corporation; *Int'l*, pg. 5489
PANA R&D CO., LTD.—See Altech Corporation; *Int'l*, pg. 389
PANARIAGROUP INDIA PVT. LTD.—See Panariagroup Industrie Ceramiche S.p.A.; *Int'l*, pg. 5717
PANARIAGROUP INDUSTRIE CERAMICHE S.P.A.; *Int'l*, pg. 5717
PANARMENIAN BANK OJSC—See Central Bank of Armenia; *Int'l*, pg. 1404
PANARMEN SAS—See Vandemoortele N.V.; *Int'l*, pg. 8128
PAN ASIA BANKING CORPORATION PLC; *Int'l*, pg. 5714
PAN ASIA CORPORATION LTD.; *Int'l*, pg. 5714
PAN ASIA DATA HOLDINGS INC.; *Int'l*, pg. 5714
PANASIA ENTERPRISES GROUP LIMITED—See PanAsialum Holdings Company Limited; *Int'l*, pg. 5717
PAN ASIA FOOTWEAR PUBLIC COMPANY LIMITED; *Int'l*, pg. 5714
PANASIALUM HOLDINGS COMPANY LIMITED; *Int'l*, pg. 5717
PAN ASIA METALS LIMITED; *Int'l*, pg. 5714
PAN ASIAN CURRENCY EXCHANGE CORP.; *U.S. Private*, pg. 3084
PAN ASIAN MICROVENT TECHNOLOGY (JIANGSU) CORPORATION; *Int'l*, pg. 5714
PAN ASIAN PLASTICS CORP.—See Shin Kong Group; *Int'l*, pg. 6837
PANASIAN POWER PLC—See RIL Property PLC; *Int'l*, pg. 6341
PAN ASIA PACKING LTD.—See Sumitomo Forestry Co., Ltd.; *Int'l*, pg. 7286
PAN ASIA TECHNICAL AUTOMOTIVE CENTER CO., LTD.—See General Motors Company; *U.S. Public*, pg. 928
PAN ASIA TECHNICAL AUTOMOTIVE CENTER CO., LTD.—See Shanghai Automotive Industry Corporation; *Int'l*, pg. 6762
PAN ASIA WATERWORKS CO., LTD.—See Yunnan Water Investment Co., Limited; *Int'l*, pg. 8616
PANASONIC APPLIANCES FOUNDRY MALAYSIA SDN. BHD.—See Panasonic Holdings Corporation; *Int'l*, pg. 5722
PANASONIC APPLIANCES INDIA COMPANY LIMITED—See Panasonic Holdings Corporation; *Int'l*, pg. 5717
PANASONIC APPLIANCES MOTOR (THAILAND) CO., LTD.—See Panasonic Holdings Corporation; *Int'l*, pg. 5718
PANASONIC APPLIANCES REFRIGERATION DEVICES MALAYSIA SDN. BHD.—See Panasonic Holdings Corporation; *Int'l*, pg. 5718
PANASONIC APPLIANCES VIETNAM CO., LTD.—See Panasonic Holdings Corporation; *Int'l*, pg. 5718
PANASONIC APPLIANCES WASHING MACHINE (HANGZHOU) CO., LTD.—See Panasonic Holdings Corporation; *Int'l*, pg. 5719
PANASONIC A.P. SALES (THAILAND) CO., LTD.—See Panasonic Holdings Corporation; *Int'l*, pg. 5717
PANASONIC ASIA PACIFIC PTE. LTD. - CONSUMER ELECTRONICS DIVISION—See Panasonic Holdings Corporation; *Int'l*, pg. 5718
PANASONIC ASIA PACIFIC PTE. LTD. - PANASONIC SINGAPORE DIVISION—See Panasonic Holdings Corporation; *Int'l*, pg. 5718
PANASONIC AUSTRALIA PTY. LTD.; *Int'l*, pg. 5717
PANASONIC AUTOMOTIVE ELECTRONICS CO.—See Panasonic Holdings Corporation; *Int'l*, pg. 5720
PANASONIC AUTOMOTIVE & INDUSTRIAL SYSTEMS EUROPE GMBH - OTTOBRUNN—See Panasonic Holdings Corporation; *Int'l*, pg. 5718
PANASONIC AUTOMOTIVE SYSTEMS ASIA PACIFIC (THAILAND) CO., LTD—See Panasonic Holdings Corporation; *Int'l*, pg. 5718
PANASONIC AUTOMOTIVE SYSTEMS COMPANY OF AMERICA—See Panasonic Holdings Corporation; *Int'l*, pg. 5720
PANASONIC AUTOMOTIVE SYSTEMS CZECH, S.R.O.—See Panasonic Holdings Corporation; *Int'l*, pg. 5718
PANASONIC AUTOMOTIVE SYSTEMS DEVELOPMENT TIANJIN CO., LTD.—See Panasonic Holdings Corporation; *Int'l*, pg. 5719
PANASONIC AVC AMERICAN CO.—See Panasonic Holdings Corporation; *Int'l*, pg. 5720
PANASONIC AVC NETWORKS KUALA LUMPUR MALAYSIA SDN. BHD.—See Panasonic Holdings Corporation; *Int'l*, pg. 5722
PANASONIC AVC NETWORKS SHANDONG CO., LTD.—See Panasonic Holdings Corporation; *Int'l*, pg. 5719
PANASONIC AVC NETWORKS SINGAPORE PTE. LTD.—See Panasonic Holdings Corporation; *Int'l*, pg. 5718
PANASONIC AVC NETWORKS SLOVAKIA S.R.O.—See Panasonic Holdings Corporation; *Int'l*, pg. 5717
PANASONIC AVC NETWORKS TAIWAN CO., LTD.—See Panasonic Holdings Corporation; *Int'l*, pg. 5723

PANASONIC AVC NETWORKS (THAILAND) CO., LTD.—See Panasonic Holdings Corporation; *Int'l*, pg. 5717
PANASONIC AVC NETWORKS XIAMEN CO., LTD.—See Panasonic Holdings Corporation; *Int'l*, pg. 5719
PANASONIC AVIONICS CORPORATION—See Panasonic Holdings Corporation; *Int'l*, pg. 5720
PANASONIC AVIONICS CORPORATION—See Panasonic Holdings Corporation; *Int'l*, pg. 5720
PANASONIC BIOMEDICAL SALES EUROPE B.V.—See Panasonic Holdings Corporation; *Int'l*, pg. 5718
PANASONIC BIOMEDICAL SALES EUROPE BV - UK—See Panasonic Holdings Corporation; *Int'l*, pg. 5718
PANASONIC BROADCAST & TELEVISION SYSTEMS COMPANY—See Panasonic Holdings Corporation; *Int'l*, pg. 5720
PANASONIC BROADCAST & TV SYSTEMS—See Panasonic Holdings Corporation; *Int'l*, pg. 5720
PANASONIC CANADA, INC.—See Panasonic Holdings Corporation; *Int'l*, pg. 5720
PANASONIC CANADA INC.—See Panasonic Holdings Corporation; *Int'l*, pg. 5720
PANASONIC CARBON (ANYANG) CO., LTD.—See Panasonic Holdings Corporation; *Int'l*, pg. 5719
PANASONIC CARBON INDIA CO. LIMITED—See Panasonic Holdings Corporation; *Int'l*, pg. 5718
PANASONIC CHILE LIMITADA—See Panasonic Holdings Corporation; *Int'l*, pg. 5720
PANASONIC (CIS) OY—See Panasonic Holdings Corporation; *Int'l*, pg. 5717
PANASONIC COMMUNICATIONS CO. LTD.—See Panasonic Holdings Corporation; *Int'l*, pg. 5718
PANASONIC COMMUNICATIONS SYSTEM CO. LTD.—See Panasonic Holdings Corporation; *Int'l*, pg. 5718
PANASONIC CORP OF NORTH AMERICA—See Panasonic Holdings Corporation; *Int'l*, pg. 5721
PANASONIC CORPORATION ECO SOLUTIONS COMPANY—See Panasonic Holdings Corporation; *Int'l*, pg. 5718
PANASONIC CORPORATION OF CHINA—See Panasonic Holdings Corporation; *Int'l*, pg. 5719
PANASONIC CORPORATION OF LATIN AMERICA—See Panasonic Holdings Corporation; *Int'l*, pg. 5720
PANASONIC CORPORATION OF NORTH AMERICA—See Panasonic Holdings Corporation; *Int'l*, pg. 5720
PANASONIC CZECH REPUBLIC, S.R.O.—See Panasonic Holdings Corporation; *Int'l*, pg. 5721
PANASONIC DE MEXICO, S.A. DE C.V.—See Panasonic Holdings Corporation; *Int'l*, pg. 5723
PANASONIC DIGITAL SERVICE CENTER—See Panasonic Holdings Corporation; *Int'l*, pg. 5721
PANASONIC DISC MANUFACTURING CORPORATION OF AMERICA—See Panasonic Holdings Corporation; *Int'l*, pg. 5721
PANASONIC DO BRASIL LIMITADA—See Panasonic Holdings Corporation; *Int'l*, pg. 5720
PANASONIC ECOLOGY SYSTEMS CO., LTD.—See Panasonic Holdings Corporation; *Int'l*, pg. 5721
PANASONIC ECOLOGY SYSTEMS GUANGDONG CO., LTD.—See Panasonic Holdings Corporation; *Int'l*, pg. 5719
PANASONIC ECOLOGY SYSTEMS KYOEI CO., LTD.—See Panasonic Holdings Corporation; *Int'l*, pg. 5719
PANASONIC ECOLOGY SYSTEMS VENTEC CO., LTD.—See Panasonic Holdings Corporation; *Int'l*, pg. 5719
PANASONIC ECO SOLUTIONS ASAHI CO., LTD.—See Panasonic Holdings Corporation; *Int'l*, pg. 5718
PANASONIC ECO SOLUTIONS AWE CO., LTD.—See Panasonic Holdings Corporation; *Int'l*, pg. 5718
PANASONIC ECO SOLUTIONS CANADA INC.—See Panasonic Holdings Corporation; *Int'l*, pg. 5718
PANASONIC ECO SOLUTIONS CHEMICAL CO., LTD.—See Panasonic Holdings Corporation; *Int'l*, pg. 5718
PANASONIC ECO SOLUTIONS CREATES CO., LTD.—See Panasonic Holdings Corporation; *Int'l*, pg. 5718
PANASONIC ECO SOLUTIONS ELECTRICAL CONSTRUCTION MATERIALS MIE CO., LTD.—See Panasonic Holdings Corporation; *Int'l*, pg. 5718
PANASONIC ECO SOLUTIONS ELECTRICAL CONSTRUCTION MATERIALS TAIWAN CO., LTD.—See Panasonic Holdings Corporation; *Int'l*, pg. 5719
PANASONIC ECO SOLUTIONS ENERGY MANAGEMENT NORTH AMERICA—See Panasonic Holdings Corporation; *Int'l*, pg. 5719
PANASONIC ECO SOLUTIONS FACILITY MANAGEMENT CO., LTD.—See Panasonic Holdings Corporation; *Int'l*, pg. 5719
PANASONIC ECO SOLUTIONS (HONG KONG) CO., LTD.—See Panasonic Holdings Corporation; *Int'l*, pg. 5718

PANASONIC ECO SOLUTIONS IKEDA ELECTRIC CO., LTD.—See Panasonic Holdings Corporation; *Int'l*, pg. 5719
PANASONIC ECO SOLUTIONS INFORMATION EQUIPMENT (SHANGHAI) CO., LTD.—See Panasonic Holdings Corporation; *Int'l*, pg. 5719
PANASONIC ECO SOLUTIONS LOGISTICS CO., LTD.—See Panasonic Holdings Corporation; *Int'l*, pg. 5719
PANASONIC ECO SOLUTIONS NETWORKS CO., LTD.—See Panasonic Holdings Corporation; *Int'l*, pg. 5719
PANASONIC ECO SOLUTIONS NORDIC AB—See Panasonic Holdings Corporation; *Int'l*, pg. 5719
PANASONIC ECO SOLUTIONS POWER TOOLS (SHANGHAI) CO., LTD.—See Panasonic Holdings Corporation; *Int'l*, pg. 5719
PANASONIC ECO SOLUTIONS SALES TAIWAN CO., LTD.—See Panasonic Holdings Corporation; *Int'l*, pg. 5719
PANASONIC ECO SOLUTIONS SHIN DONG-A CO., LTD.—See Panasonic Holdings Corporation; *Int'l*, pg. 5719
PANASONIC ECO SOLUTIONS TECHNO SERVICE CO., LTD.—See Panasonic Holdings Corporation; *Int'l*, pg. 5719
PANASONIC ELECTRIC WORKS AUSTRIA GMBH—See Panasonic Holdings Corporation; *Int'l*, pg. 5721
PANASONIC ELECTRIC WORKS ESPANA S.A.—See Panasonic Holdings Corporation; *Int'l*, pg. 5721
PANASONIC ELECTRIC WORKS EUROPE AG—See Panasonic Holdings Corporation; *Int'l*, pg. 5721
PANASONIC ELECTRIC WORKS ITALIA S.R.L.—See Panasonic Holdings Corporation; *Int'l*, pg. 5721
PANASONIC ELECTRIC WORKS KOREA CO. LTD.—See Panasonic Holdings Corporation; *Int'l*, pg. 5721
PANASONIC ELECTRIC WORKS POLSKA SP. Z.O.O.—See Panasonic Holdings Corporation; *Int'l*, pg. 5721
PANASONIC ELECTRIC WORKS SALES WESTERN EUROPE B.V.—See Panasonic Holdings Corporation; *Int'l*, pg. 5721
PANASONIC ELECTRIC WORKS SCHWEIZ AG—See Panasonic Holdings Corporation; *Int'l*, pg. 5721
PANASONIC ELECTRIC WORKS TAIKO DEVICE (SHENZHEN) CO., LTD.—See Panasonic Holdings Corporation; *Int'l*, pg. 5719
PANASONIC ELECTRIC WORKS UK LTD.—See Panasonic Holdings Corporation; *Int'l*, pg. 5721
PANASONIC ELECTRONIC DEVICE COMPANY CO. LTD.—See Panasonic Holdings Corporation; *Int'l*, pg. 5721
PANASONIC ELECTRONIC DEVICES (JIANGMEN) CO., LTD.—See Panasonic Holdings Corporation; *Int'l*, pg. 5719
PANASONIC ELECTRONIC DEVICES (QINGDAO) CO., LTD.—See Panasonic Holdings Corporation; *Int'l*, pg. 5719
PANASONIC ELECTRONIC DEVICES SINGAPORE PTE. LTD.—See Panasonic Holdings Corporation; *Int'l*, pg. 5718
PANASONIC ELECTRONIC DEVICES SLOVAKIA S.R.O.—See Panasonic Holdings Corporation; *Int'l*, pg. 5721
PANASONIC ELECTRONIC DEVICES (THAILAND) CO., LTD.—See Panasonic Holdings Corporation; *Int'l*, pg. 5721
PANASONIC ELECTRONIC DEVICES (TIANJIN) CO., LTD.—See Panasonic Holdings Corporation; *Int'l*, pg. 5719
PANASONIC ELECTRONIC DEVICES VIETNAM CO., LTD.—See Panasonic Holdings Corporation; *Int'l*, pg. 5721
PANASONIC ELEKTRONIK SATIS A.S.—See Panasonic Holdings Corporation; *Int'l*, pg. 5721
PANASONIC ENERGY BELGIUM N.V.—See Panasonic Holdings Corporation; *Int'l*, pg. 5721
PANASONIC ENERGY CORPORATION OF AMERICA—See Panasonic Holdings Corporation; *Int'l*, pg. 5721
PANASONIC ENERGY INDIA COMPANY LTD.—See Panasonic Holdings Corporation; *Int'l*, pg. 5721
PANASONIC ENERGY POLAND S.A.—See Panasonic Holdings Corporation; *Int'l*, pg. 5721
PANASONIC ENERGY (SHANGHAI) CO., LTD.—See Panasonic Holdings Corporation; *Int'l*, pg. 5719
PANASONIC ENERGY TANZANIA CO., LTD.—See Panasonic Holdings Corporation; *Int'l*, pg. 5721
PANASONIC ENERGY (THAILAND) CO., LTD.—See Panasonic Holdings Corporation; *Int'l*, pg. 5721
PANASONIC ENERGY (WUXI) CO., LTD.—See Panasonic Holdings Corporation; *Int'l*, pg. 5721
PANASONIC ENVIRONMENTAL SYSTEMS & ENGINEERING CO., LTD.—See Panasonic Holdings Corporation; *Int'l*, pg. 5721
PANASONIC ESPANA S.A.—See Panasonic Holdings Corporation; *Int'l*, pg. 5721
PANASONIC FACTORY AUTOMATION CO.—See Panasonic Holdings Corporation; *Int'l*, pg. 5721

COMPANY NAME INDEX

PANASONIC FACTORY SOLUTIONS ASIA PACIFIC PTE. LTD.—See Panasonic Holdings Corporation; *Int'l*, pg. 5719
PANASONIC FACTORY SOLUTIONS CO., LTD.—See Panasonic Holdings Corporation; *Int'l*, pg. 5722
PANASONIC FACTORY SOLUTIONS SUZHOU CO., LTD.—See Panasonic Holdings Corporation; *Int'l*, pg. 5719
PANASONIC FACTORY SOLUTIONS - WELDING ROBOTICS GROUP—See Panasonic Holdings Corporation; *Int'l*, pg. 5721
PANASONIC FINANCIAL CENTRE (M) SDN BHD—See Panasonic Holdings Corporation; *Int'l*, pg. 5722
PANASONIC FOUNDRY MALAYSIA SDN BHD—See Panasonic Holdings Corporation; *Int'l*, pg. 5722
PANASONIC GERMANY—See Panasonic Holdings Corporation; *Int'l*, pg. 5722
PANASONIC GULF FZE—See Panasonic Holdings Corporation; *Int'l*, pg. 5722
PANASONIC HEALTHCARE SINGAPORE PTE. LTD.—See PHC Holdings Corporation; *Int'l*, pg. 5843
PANASONIC HOLDINGS CORPORATION; *Int'l*, pg. 5717
PANASONIC HOME ELEVATOR CO., LTD.—See Panasonic Holdings Corporation; *Int'l*, pg. 5722
PANASONIC HOMES CO., LTD.—See Panasonic Holdings Corporation; *Int'l*, pg. 5722
PANASONIC HONG KONG CO., LTD.—See Panasonic Holdings Corporation; *Int'l*, pg. 5719
PANASONIC INDUSTRIAL ASIA PTE. LTD.—See Panasonic Holdings Corporation; *Int'l*, pg. 5718
PANASONIC INDUSTRIAL (CHINA) CO., LTD.—See Panasonic Holdings Corporation; *Int'l*, pg. 5719
PANASONIC INDUSTRIAL COMPANY—See Panasonic Holdings Corporation; *Int'l*, pg. 5721
PANASONIC INDUSTRIAL CO., (M) SDN BHD—See Panasonic Holdings Corporation; *Int'l*, pg. 5722
PANASONIC INDUSTRIAL CO.—See Panasonic Holdings Corporation; *Int'l*, pg. 5721
PANASONIC INDUSTRIAL DEVICES CORPORATION OF AMERICA—See Panasonic Holdings Corporation; *Int'l*, pg. 5721
PANASONIC INDUSTRIAL DEVICES EUROPE GMBH—See Panasonic Holdings Corporation; *Int'l*, pg. 5721
PANASONIC INDUSTRIAL DEVICES MATERIALS EUROPE GMBH—See Panasonic Holdings Corporation; *Int'l*, pg. 5722
PANASONIC INDUSTRIAL DEVICES MATERIALS (GUANGZHOU) CO., LTD.—See Panasonic Holdings Corporation; *Int'l*, pg. 5718
PANASONIC INDUSTRIAL DEVICES MATERIALS SALES CO., LTD.—See Panasonic Holdings Corporation; *Int'l*, pg. 5722
PANASONIC INDUSTRIAL DEVICES MATERIALS (SHANGHAI) CO., LTD.—See Panasonic Holdings Corporation; *Int'l*, pg. 5718
PANASONIC INDUSTRIAL DEVICES MATERIALS TAIWAN CO., LTD.—See Panasonic Holdings Corporation; *Int'l*, pg. 5718
PANASONIC INDUSTRIAL DEVICES SALES (CHINA) CO., LTD.—See Panasonic Holdings Corporation; *Int'l*, pg. 5720
PANASONIC INDUSTRIAL DEVICES SALES KOREA CO., LTD.—See Panasonic Holdings Corporation; *Int'l*, pg. 5722
PANASONIC INDUSTRIAL DEVICES SALES (M) SDN. BHD.—See Panasonic Holdings Corporation; *Int'l*, pg. 5722
PANASONIC INDUSTRIAL DEVICES SALES (TAIWAN) CO., LTD.—See Panasonic Holdings Corporation; *Int'l*, pg. 5723
PANASONIC INDUSTRIAL DEVICES SALES (THAILAND) CO., LTD.—See Panasonic Holdings Corporation; *Int'l*, pg. 5718
PANASONIC INDUSTRIAL DEVICES (SHANGHAI) CO., LTD.—See Panasonic Holdings Corporation; *Int'l*, pg. 5720
PANASONIC INDUSTRIAL DEVICES SUNX CO., LTD.—See Panasonic Holdings Corporation; *Int'l*, pg. 5722
PANASONIC INDUSTRIAL DEVICES (THAILAND) CO., LTD.—See Panasonic Holdings Corporation; *Int'l*, pg. 5718
PANASONIC INDUSTRIAL SYSTEMS—See Panasonic Holdings Corporation; *Int'l*, pg. 5721
PANASONIC INFORMATION SYSTEMS CO., LTD.—See Panasonic Holdings Corporation; *Int'l*, pg. 5722
PANASONIC INSURANCE SERVICE BROKER (THAILAND) CO., LTD.—See Panasonic Holdings Corporation; *Int'l*, pg. 5722
PANASONIC INTERIOR LIGHTING CO., LTD.—See Panasonic Holdings Corporation; *Int'l*, pg. 5722
PANASONIC INTERNATIONAL TRADING CORPORATION OF AMERICA—See Panasonic Holdings Corporation; *Int'l*, pg. 5721
PANASONIC IRELAND LTD.—See Panasonic Holdings Corporation; *Int'l*, pg. 5722
PANASONIC ITALIA S.P.A.—See Panasonic Holdings Corporation; *Int'l*, pg. 5722
PANASONIC KOREA LTD.—See Panasonic Holdings Corporation; *Int'l*, pg. 5722
PANASONIC LATIN AMERICA, S.A.—See Panasonic Holdings Corporation; *Int'l*, pg. 5722
PANASONIC LIFE SOLUTIONS INDIA PRIVATE LIMITED—See Panasonic Holdings Corporation; *Int'l*, pg. 5722
PANASONIC LIGHTING AMERICAS, INC.—See Panasonic Holdings Corporation; *Int'l*, pg. 5722
PANASONIC LIGHTING (BEIJING) CO.,LTD—See Panasonic Holdings Corporation; *Int'l*, pg. 5722
PANASONIC LIGHTING DEVICE MARKETING CO., LTD.—See Panasonic Holdings Corporation; *Int'l*, pg. 5722
PANASONIC LIGHTING DEVICES SERBIA D. O. O.—See Panasonic Holdings Corporation; *Int'l*, pg. 5722
PANASONIC LIGHTING EUROPE GMBH—See Panasonic Holdings Corporation; *Int'l*, pg. 5722
PANASONIC LIGHTING SYSTEMS CO., LTD.—See Panasonic Holdings Corporation; *Int'l*, pg. 5722
PANASONIC LIVING CHUBU CO., LTD.—See Panasonic Holdings Corporation; *Int'l*, pg. 5719
PANASONIC LIVING CHUSHIKOKU CO., LTD.—See Panasonic Holdings Corporation; *Int'l*, pg. 5719
PANASONIC LIVING HOKKAIDO TOHOKU CO., LTD.—See Panasonic Holdings Corporation; *Int'l*, pg. 5719
PANASONIC LIVING KINKI CO., LTD.—See Panasonic Holdings Corporation; *Int'l*, pg. 5719
PANASONIC LIVING KYUSHU CO., LTD.—See Panasonic Holdings Corporation; *Int'l*, pg. 5719
PANASONIC LIVING SHUTOKEN KANTOH CO., LTD.—See Panasonic Holdings Corporation; *Int'l*, pg. 5719
PANASONIC LOGISTICS ASIA—See Panasonic Holdings Corporation; *Int'l*, pg. 5718
PANASONIC MALAYSIA SDN. BHD.—See Panasonic Holdings Corporation; *Int'l*, pg. 5722
PANASONIC MANUFACTURING (AYUTHAYA) CO., LTD.—See Panasonic Holdings Corporation; *Int'l*, pg. 5723
PANASONIC MANUFACTURING MALAYSIA BERHAD—See Panasonic Holdings Corporation; *Int'l*, pg. 5722
PANASONIC MANUFACTURING PHILIPPINES CORPORATION—See Panasonic Holdings Corporation; *Int'l*, pg. 5719
PANASONIC MANUFACTURING U.K. LTD.—See Panasonic Holdings Corporation; *Int'l*, pg. 5723
PANASONIC MARKETING EUROPE G.M.B.H. - PANASONIC DEUTSCHLAND DIVISION—See Panasonic Holdings Corporation; *Int'l*, pg. 5723
PANASONIC MARKETING EUROPE GMBH - ROMANIA—See Panasonic Holdings Corporation; *Int'l*, pg. 5723
PANASONIC MARKETING EUROPE G.M.B.H.—See Panasonic Holdings Corporation; *Int'l*, pg. 5723
PANASONIC MARKETING MIDDLE EAST & AFRICA FZE—See Panasonic Holdings Corporation; *Int'l*, pg. 5722
PANASONIC MOBILE COMMUNICATIONS CO., LTD.—See Panasonic Holdings Corporation; *Int'l*, pg. 5723
PANASONIC MOBILE COMMUNICATIONS DEVELOPMENT OF EUROPE LIMITED—See Panasonic Holdings Corporation; *Int'l*, pg. 5723
PANASONIC N.A—See Panasonic Holdings Corporation; *Int'l*, pg. 5723
PANASONIC NEW ZEALAND LIMITED—See Panasonic Holdings Corporation; *Int'l*, pg. 5723
PANASONIC NORDIC AB—See Panasonic Holdings Corporation; *Int'l*, pg. 5723
PANASONIC PERUANA S.A.—See Panasonic Holdings Corporation; *Int'l*, pg. 5720
PANASONIC PHOTO & LIGHTING CO., LTD.—See Panasonic Holdings Corporation; *Int'l*, pg. 5719
PANASONIC PHOTO & LIGHTING HONG KONG CO., LTD.—See Panasonic Holdings Corporation; *Int'l*, pg. 5723
PANASONIC PHOTO & LIGHTING KUMIHAMA CO., LTD.—See Panasonic Holdings Corporation; *Int'l*, pg. 5719
PANASONIC PLASMA DISPLAY CO., LTD.—See Panasonic Holdings Corporation; *Int'l*, pg. 5723
PANASONIC R&D CENTER CHINA CO., LTD.—See Panasonic Holdings Corporation; *Int'l*, pg. 5720
PANASONIC R&D CENTER GERMANY GMBH—See Panasonic Holdings Corporation; *Int'l*, pg. 5723
PANASONIC R&D CENTER SUZHOU CO., LTD.—See Panasonic Holdings Corporation; *Int'l*, pg. 5720
PANASONIC R&D CENTRE MALAYSIA SDN. BHD.—See Panasonic Holdings Corporation; *Int'l*, pg. 5722
PANASONIC REFRIGERATION DEVICES (WUXI) CO., LTD.—See Panasonic Holdings Corporation; *Int'l*, pg. 5720
PANASONIC RUSSIA, LTD.—See Panasonic Holdings Corporation; *Int'l*, pg. 5723
PANASONIC SEMICONDUCTOR ASIA PTE. LTD.—See Panasonic Holdings Corporation; *Int'l*, pg. 5718

PANCHMAHAL STEEL LIMITED

PANASONIC SEMICONDUCTOR DISCRETE DEVICES (M) SDN BHD—See Panasonic Holdings Corporation; *Int'l*, pg. 5722
PANASONIC SEMICONDUCTOR (SUZHOU) CO., LTD.—See Panasonic Holdings Corporation; *Int'l*, pg. 5720
PANASONIC SHIKOKU EECTRONICS (S) PTE LTD—See Panasonic Holdings Corporation; *Int'l*, pg. 5718
PANASONIC—See Panasonic Holdings Corporation; *Int'l*, pg. 5720
PANASONIC—See Panasonic Holdings Corporation; *Int'l*, pg. 5720
PANASONIC—See Panasonic Holdings Corporation; *Int'l*, pg. 5720
PANASONIC SOUTH-EAST EUROPE LTD.—See Panasonic Holdings Corporation; *Int'l*, pg. 5723
PANASONIC SYSTEM NETWORKS CO., LTD.—See Panasonic Holdings Corporation; *Int'l*, pg. 5723
PANASONIC SYSTEM NETWORKS (DALIAN) CO., LTD.—See Panasonic Holdings Corporation; *Int'l*, pg. 5720
PANASONIC SYSTEM NETWORKS MALAYSIA SDN. BHD.—See Panasonic Holdings Corporation; *Int'l*, pg. 5722
PANASONIC SYSTEM NETWORKS (SUZHOU) CO., LTD.—See Panasonic Holdings Corporation; *Int'l*, pg. 5720
PANASONIC SYSTEM NETWORKS (ZHUHAI) CO., LTD.—See Panasonic Holdings Corporation; *Int'l*, pg. 5720
PANASONIC SYSTEMS ASIA PACIFIC PTE. LTD.—See Panasonic Holdings Corporation; *Int'l*, pg. 5718
PANASONIC TAIWAN CO., LTD.—See Panasonic Holdings Corporation; *Int'l*, pg. 5723
PANASONIC TECHNOLOGIES INC.—See Panasonic Holdings Corporation; *Int'l*, pg. 5721
PANASONIC TRADING MALAYSIA SDN BHD—See Panasonic Holdings Corporation; *Int'l*, pg. 5722
PANASONIC TREASURY CENTER (THAILAND) CO., LTD.—See Panasonic Holdings Corporation; *Int'l*, pg. 5723
PANASONIC (U.K.) LTD—See Panasonic Holdings Corporation; *Int'l*, pg. 5717
PANASONIC VIETNAM CO., LTD.—See Panasonic Holdings Corporation; *Int'l*, pg. 5723
PANASONIC WELDING SYSTEMS CO., LTD.—See Panasonic Holdings Corporation; *Int'l*, pg. 5723
PANATLANTICA CATARINENSE S.A.—See Panatlantica S.A.; *Int'l*, pg. 5725
PANATLANTICA SAO FRANCISCO DO SUL—See Panatlantica S.A.; *Int'l*, pg. 5725
PANATLANTICA S.A.; *Int'l*, pg. 5725
PANATON INC.—See Sirma Group Holding JSC; *Int'l*, pg. 6962
PANATTONI CONSTRUCTION, INC.—See Panattoni Development Company; *U.S. Private*, pg. 3085
PANATTONI DEVELOPMENT COMPANY; *U.S. Private*, pg. 3085
PANATTONI DEVELOPMENT COMPANY—See Panattoni Development Company; *U.S. Private*, pg. 3085
PANATTONI LUXEMBOURG SERVICES S.A.R.L—See Panattoni Development Company; *U.S. Private*, pg. 3085
PANAUST LIMITED—See Guangdong Rising Assets Management Co., Ltd.; *Int'l*, pg. 3159
PANAVIA AIRCRAFT GMBH—See Airbus SE; *Int'l*, pg. 247
PANAVIA AIRCRAFT GMBH—See BAE Systems plc; *Int'l*, pg. 798
PANAVI SAS—See Vandemoortele N.V.; *Int'l*, pg. 8128
PANAVISE PRODUCTS, INC.; *U.S. Private*, pg. 3085
PANAVISE TOOL (CHANGZHOU), LLC—See Panavise Products, Inc.; *U.S. Private*, pg. 3085
PANAVISION (CANADA) CORP.—See Cerberus Capital Management, L.P.; *U.S. Private*, pg. 839
PANAVISION INC.—See Cerberus Capital Management, L.P.; *U.S. Private*, pg. 839
PANAVISION INTERNATIONAL, LP—See Cerberus Capital Management, L.P.; *U.S. Private*, pg. 839
PANAVISTA PROMOTIONS—See Ryan Partnership, LLC; *U.S. Private*, pg. 3510
PANAYA INC.—See Infosys Limited; *Int'l*, pg. 3696
PANAYA LTD.—See Infosys Limited; *Int'l*, pg. 3696
PANBELA THERAPEUTICS, INC.; *U.S. Public*, pg. 1635
PANCARE OF FLORIDA, INC.; *U.S. Private*, pg. 3085
PANCELTICA HOLDINGS LIMITED; *Int'l*, pg. 5725
PAN-CENTURY EDIBLE OILS SDN BHD—See IOI Corporation Berhad; *Int'l*, pg. 3792
PAN-CENTURY OLEOCHEMICALS SDN BHD—See IOI Corporation Berhad; *Int'l*, pg. 3792
PAN CENTURY SURFACTANTS INC.—See The Aditya Birla Group; *Int'l*, pg. 7612
PANCEVAC A.D.; *Int'l*, pg. 5726
PANCHAKANYA MAI HYDROPOWER LTD.; *Int'l*, pg. 5726
PANCHMAHAL PROPERTIES LTD.—See Bengal & Assam Company Ltd.; *Int'l*, pg. 973
PANCHMAHAL STEEL LIMITED; *Int'l*, pg. 5726
PANCHOS MEXICAN FOODS, INC.—See Centre Partners Management LLC; *U.S. Private*, pg. 828

PANCHSHEEL ORGANICS LIMITED

PANCHSHEEL ORGANICS LIMITED; *Int'l*, pg. 5726
PANCO HEALTHCARE CO., LTD.—See PharmaEssentia Corp.; *Int'l*, pg. 5840
PANCOLOUR INK CO., LTD.; *Int'l*, pg. 5726
PANCOM INTERNATIONAL, INC.; *U.S. Private*, pg. 3085
PAN COMMUNICATIONS; *U.S. Private*, pg. 3084
PANCON CONNECTORS—See Milestone Partners Ltd.; *U.S. Private*, pg. 2729
PANCON CORPORATION—See Milestone Partners Ltd.; *U.S. Private*, pg. 2728
PANCONTINENTAL ENERGY NL; *Int'l*, pg. 5726
PANCONTINENTAL RESOURCES CORPORATION; *Int'l*, pg. 5726
PAN CONTINENTAL RESOURCES, INC.; *U.S. Private*, pg. 3084
PANCOSMA SA—See Archer-Daniels-Midland Company; *U.S. Public*, pg. 185
PANCREATIC CANCER ACTION NETWORK; *U.S. Private*, pg. 3085
PANCYPRIAN INSURANCE COMPANY LTD—See Hellenic Bank Public Company Ltd.; *Int'l*, pg. 3333
PANDAAMERICA CORP.; *U.S. Private*, pg. 3085
PANDA DAIRY CORPORATION; *Int'l*, pg. 5726
PANDA ENERGY INTERNATIONAL INC.; *U.S. Private*, pg. 3085
PANDA EXPRESS INC.—See Panda Restaurant Group, Inc.; *U.S. Private*, pg. 3085
PANDA FINANCIAL HOLDING CORP., LTD.; *Int'l*, pg. 5726
PANDA FYRVERKERIER I SVERIGE AB—See Panda Financial Holding Corp., Ltd.; *Int'l*, pg. 5726
PANDA PLACE MANAGEMENT LIMITED—See Hopewell Holdings Limited; *Int'l*, pg. 3473
PANDA POWER CORP.—See Panda Energy International Inc.; *U.S. Private*, pg. 3085
PANDA RESTAURANT GROUP, INC.; *U.S. Private*, pg. 3085
PANDA SECURITY, INC.—See Francisco Partners Management, LP; *U.S. Private*, pg. 1593
PANDA SECURITY, S.L.—See Francisco Partners Management, LP; *U.S. Private*, pg. 1593
PANDEE SERVICES PTY LTD—See ALS Limited; *Int'l*, pg. 378
PANDERA SYSTEMS, LLC—See Sunstone Partners Management LLC; *U.S. Private*, pg. 3873
PANDIAS RE AG—See Bayer Aktiengesellschaft; *Int'l*, pg. 910
PANDION THERAPEUTICS, INC.—See Merck & Co., Inc.; *U.S. Public*, pg. 1420
PANDORA A/S; *Int'l*, pg. 5726
PANDORA CONSULTANCY SERVICES PLC; *Int'l*, pg. 5727
PANDORA DO BRASIL COMERCIO E IMPORTACAO LTDA.—See PANDORA A/S; *Int'l*, pg. 5727
PANDORA ECOMM LLC—See PANDORA A/S; *Int'l*, pg. 5726
PANDORA FRANCE SAS—See PANDORA A/S; *Int'l*, pg. 5726
PANDORA INT. APS—See PANDORA A/S; *Int'l*, pg. 5726
PANDORA ITALIA SRL—See PANDORA A/S; *Int'l*, pg. 5726
PANDORA JEWELLERY UK LTD.—See PANDORA A/S; *Int'l*, pg. 5726
PANDORA JEWELRY ASIA-PACIFIC LIMITED—See PANDORA A/S; *Int'l*, pg. 5726
PANDORA JEWELRY B.V.—See PANDORA A/S; *Int'l*, pg. 5726
PANDORA JEWELRY CEE SP. Z.O.O.—See PANDORA A/S; *Int'l*, pg. 5726
PANDORA JEWELRY CR, S.R.O.—See PANDORA A/S; *Int'l*, pg. 5726
PANDORA JEWELRY GMBH—See PANDORA A/S; *Int'l*, pg. 5726
PANDORA JEWELRY HUNGARY KFT.—See PANDORA A/S; *Int'l*, pg. 5726
PANDORA JEWELRY JAPAN LTD.—See PANDORA A/S; *Int'l*, pg. 5726
PANDORA JEWELRY LLC—See PANDORA A/S; *Int'l*, pg. 5726
PANDORA JEWELRY PTY. LTD.—See PANDORA A/S; *Int'l*, pg. 5726
PANDORA JEWELRY ROMANIA SRL—See PANDORA A/S; *Int'l*, pg. 5726
PANDORA JEWELRY (SHANGHAI) COMPANY LTD.—See PANDORA A/S; *Int'l*, pg. 5726
PANDORA JEWELRY SHARED SERVICES CEE SP Z.O.O.—See PANDORA A/S; *Int'l*, pg. 5726
PANDORA MEDIA, LLC—See Liberty Media Corporation; *U.S. Public*, pg. 1311
PANDORA/OGILVY & MATHER—See WPP plc; *Int'l*, pg. 8488
PANDORA OSTERREICH GMBH—See PANDORA A/S; *Int'l*, pg. 5726
PANDORA PRODUCTION CO. LTD.—See PANDORA A/S; *Int'l*, pg. 5726
PANDORA RETAIL PTY. LTD.—See PANDORA A/S; *Int'l*, pg. 5727
PANDORA SCHWEIZ AG—See PANDORA A/S; *Int'l*, pg. 5726

PANDORA TV CO., LTD.; *Int'l*, pg. 5727
PANDOX AB—See Eiendomsspar ASA; *Int'l*, pg. 2329
PANDROL AUSTRALIA PTY LIMITED—See CVC Capital Partners SICAV-FIS S.A.; *Int'l*, pg. 1887
PANDUIT AUST, PTY. LTD.—See Panduit Corp.; *U.S. Private*, pg. 3086
PANDUIT CANADA CORP.—See Panduit Corp.; *U.S. Private*, pg. 3086
PANDUIT CORP. JAPAN BRANCH—See Panduit Corp.; *U.S. Private*, pg. 3086
PANDUIT CORP.; *U.S. Private*, pg. 3085
PANDUIT EUROPE LTD.—See Panduit Corp.; *U.S. Private*, pg. 3085
PANDUIT EUROPE LTD.—See Panduit Corp.; *U.S. Private*, pg. 3085
PANDUIT GMBH—See Panduit Corp.; *U.S. Private*, pg. 3086
PANDUIT HONG KONG—See Panduit Corp.; *U.S. Private*, pg. 3086
PANDUIT INT—See Panduit Corp.; *U.S. Private*, pg. 3085
PANDUIT KOREA LTD.—See Panduit Corp.; *U.S. Private*, pg. 3086
PANDUIT LIMITED—See Panduit Corp.; *U.S. Private*, pg. 3085
PANDUIT MEXICO S, EN N.C.—See Panduit Corp.; *U.S. Private*, pg. 3086
PANDUIT NEDERLAND—See Panduit Corp.; *U.S. Private*, pg. 3086
PANDUIT SINGAPORE PTE. LTD.—See Panduit Corp.; *U.S. Private*, pg. 3086
PANEFFORT (CAMBODIA) GARMENT CO., LTD.—See Roo Hsing Co., Ltd.; *Int'l*, pg. 6397
PANEF, INC.; *U.S. Private*, pg. 3086
PANELCLAW, INC.—See Esdec BV; *Int'l*, pg. 2502
PANELCO S.A.—See SIDMA Steel S.A.; *Int'l*, pg. 6884
PAN ELECTRICS SDN BHD—See M+W Group GmbH; *Int'l*, pg. 4614
PAN ELECTRONICS (INDIA) LIMITED; *Int'l*, pg. 5714
PANELES NAPSA, S.A.—See Clear Channel Outdoor Holdings, Inc.; *U.S. Public*, pg. 512
PANELFOLD INC.; *U.S. Private*, pg. 3086
PANELIZED STRUCTURES, INC.; *U.S. Private*, pg. 3086
PANELLING CENTRE LIMITED—See Grafton Group plc; *Int'l*, pg. 3051
PANELMATIC INC.; *U.S. Private*, pg. 3086
PANEL PLUS CO., LTD.—See Mitr Phol Sugar Corporation Limited; *Int'l*, pg. 4927
PANEL PROCESSING, INC.; *U.S. Private*, pg. 3086
PANEL PROCESSING OF COLDWATER, INC.—See Panel Processing, Inc.; *U.S. Private*, pg. 3086
PANEL PROCESSING OF INDIANA, INC.—See Panel Processing, Inc.; *U.S. Private*, pg. 3086
PANEL PROCESSING OF OREGON, INC.—See Panel Processing, Inc.; *U.S. Private*, pg. 3086
PANEL PROCESSING OF TEXAS, INC.—See Panel Processing, Inc.; *U.S. Private*, pg. 3086
PANEL SPECIALISTS INC.—See Markel Group Inc.; *U.S. Public*, pg. 1369
PANELTECH INTERNATIONAL HOLDINGS, INC.; *U.S. Public*, pg. 1635
PANEL WORLD CO., LTD.—See The Siam Cement Public Company Limited; *Int'l*, pg. 7683
PAN ENTERTAINMENT CO., LTD.; *Int'l*, pg. 5714
PANERA BREAD COMPANY—See JAB Holding Company S.a.r.l.; *Int'l*, pg. 3863
PANERA BREAD COMPANY—See JAB Holding Company S.a.r.l.; *Int'l*, pg. 3863
PANERA BREAD COMPANY—See JAB Holding Company S.a.r.l.; *Int'l*, pg. 3863
PANERA BREAD COMPANY—See JAB Holding Company S.a.r.l.; *Int'l*, pg. 3863
PANERA BREAD COMPANY—See JAB Holding Company S.a.r.l.; *Int'l*, pg. 3863
PANERA BREAD COMPANY—See JAB Holding Company S.a.r.l.; *Int'l*, pg. 3863
PANERA BREAD COMPANY—See JAB Holding Company S.a.r.l.; *Int'l*, pg. 3863
PANERA BREAD ULC—See JAB Holding Company S.a.r.l.; *Int'l*, pg. 3863
PANERGON S.A.—See SFAKIANAKIS S.A.; *Int'l*, pg. 6738
PAN EUROPEAN TERMINALS LIMITED—See Belphar Ltd.; *Int'l*, pg. 968
PANEVEZIO STATYBOS TRESTAS AB; *Int'l*, pg. 5727
PAN FOOD JOINT STOCK COMPANY—See The Pan Group Joint Stock Company; *Int'l*, pg. 7673
PANFORA OIL & GAS S.R.L.—See MOL Magyar Olaj- es Gazipari Nyrt.; *Int'l*, pg. 5021
PANGAEA CONNECTIVITY TECHNOLOGY LIMITED; *Int'l*, pg. 5727
PANGAEA LOGISTICS SOLUTIONS LTD.; *U.S. Public*, pg. 1635
PANGAEA ONCOLOGY SA; *Int'l*, pg. 5727
PANGANG GROUP VANADIUM TITANIUM AND RESOURCES CO., LTD.; *Int'l*, pg. 5727
PANGANG GROUP VANADIUM TITANIUM & RESOURCES CO., LTD.; *Int'l*, pg. 5727
PANGAS AG—See Linde plc; *Int'l*, pg. 4506
PANG DA AUTOMOBILE TRADE CO., LTD.; *Int'l*, pg. 5727

PANGEA3 LEGAL DATABASE SYSTEMS PVT. LTD.—See Ernst & Young Pvt Ltd.; *Int'l*, pg. 2494
PANGEA3, LLC—See Ernst & Young LLP; *U.S. Private*, pg. 1422
PANGEA GROUP; *U.S. Private*, pg. 3086
PANGEA NATURAL FOODS INC.; *Int'l*, pg. 5727
PANGEA REAL ESTATE; *U.S. Private*, pg. 3086
PANGEN BIOTECH INC.; *Int'l*, pg. 5727
PANGENOMIC HEALTH INC.; *Int'l*, pg. 5727
PANGERE CORPORATION; *U.S. Private*, pg. 3086
PANGKALAN BEKALAN KEMAMAN SDN BHD—See Terengganu Incorporated Sdn. Bhd.; *Int'l*, pg. 7564
PANGLIMA POWER SDN BHD—See Powertek Energy Sdn Bhd; *Int'l*, pg. 5948
PAN GLOBAL RESOURCES INC.; *Int'l*, pg. 5714
PANGOLIN DIAMONDS CORP.; *Int'l*, pg. 5727
PANGRIM CO., LTD. - ANSAN FACTORY—See PangRim Co., Ltd.; *Int'l*, pg. 5727
PANGRIM CO., LTD. - KUMI FACTORY—See PangRim Co., Ltd.; *Int'l*, pg. 5727
PANGRIM CO., LTD.; *Int'l*, pg. 5727
PANGRIO SUGAR MILLS LIMITED; *Int'l*, pg. 5727
THE PAN GROUP JOINT STOCK COMPANY; *Int'l*, pg. 7672
PANHANDLE BUILDERS & EXCAVATING INC.; *U.S. Private*, pg. 3086
PANHANDLE COMMUNITY SERVICES; *U.S. Private*, pg. 3086
PANHANDLE EASTERN PIPE LINE COMPANY, LP—See Energy Transfer LP; *U.S. Public*, pg. 763
PANHANDLE ENERGY—See Energy Transfer LP; *U.S. Public*, pg. 763
PANHANDLE NORTHERN RAILROAD—See The Broe Companies, Inc.; *U.S. Private*, pg. 806
PANHANDLE OILFIELD SERVICE COMPANIES, INC.—See Argosy Capital Group, LLC; *U.S. Private*, pg. 321
PANHANDLE-PLAINS HIGHER EDUCATION AUTHORITY INC; *U.S. Private*, pg. 3086
PANHANDLE PLAINS MANAGEMENT AND SERVICING CORPORATION; *U.S. Private*, pg. 3086
PANHANDLE TELEPHONE COOP; *U.S. Private*, pg. 3086
PANHANDLE VALVE, FABRICATION & MACHINE—See D.E. Rice Construction Co., Inc.; *U.S. Private*, pg. 1142
P.A.N. HEATING SYSTEMS LTD.—See Max Weishaupt GmbH; *Int'l*, pg. 4735
PAN HONG HOLDINGS GROUP LIMITED; *Int'l*, pg. 5714
PANHUIZEN GRAVEERINDUSTRIE B.V.—See Apex International Co., Ltd.; *Int'l*, pg. 511
PAN INDIA CORPORATION LTD.; *Int'l*, pg. 5714
PAN INDIA PARYATAN LIMITED—See Essel Corporate Resources Pvt. Ltd.; *Int'l*, pg. 2509
PANINI AMERICA, INC.—See Panini S.p.A.; *Int'l*, pg. 5727
PANINI BRASIL LTDA.—See Panini S.p.A.; *Int'l*, pg. 5728
PANINI CHILE LTDA—See Panini S.p.A.; *Int'l*, pg. 5728
PANINI ESPANA SA—See Panini S.p.A.; *Int'l*, pg. 5728
PANINI FRANCE SA—See Panini S.p.A.; *Int'l*, pg. 5728
PANINI MEDYA YAYINCILIK VE TICARET A.S.—See Panini S.p.A.; *Int'l*, pg. 5728
PANINI MEXICO SA—See Panini S.p.A.; *Int'l*, pg. 5728
PANINI NEDERLAND B.V.—See Panini S.p.A.; *Int'l*, pg. 5728
PANINI S.P.A.; *Int'l*, pg. 5727
PANINI SUISSE AG—See Panini S.p.A.; *Int'l*, pg. 5728
PANINI VERLAGS GMBH—See Panini S.p.A.; *Int'l*, pg. 5728
PAN-INTERNATIONAL CORPORATION (S) PTE. LTD.—See P.I.E. Industrial Berhad; *Int'l*, pg. 5682
PAN-INTERNATIONAL ELECTRONICS (MALAYSIA) SDN.BHD—See Pan-International Industrial Corporation; *Int'l*, pg. 5715
PAN-INTERNATIONAL ELECTRONICS (THAILAND) CO., LTD.—See Pan-International Industrial Corporation; *Int'l*, pg. 5715
PAN-INTERNATIONAL ELECTRONICS (U.S.A), INC.—See Pan-International Industrial Corporation; *Int'l*, pg. 5715
PAN-INTERNATIONAL INDUSTRIAL CORPORATION - PCB DIVISION—See Pan-International Industrial Corporation; *Int'l*, pg. 5716
PAN-INTERNATIONAL INDUSTRIAL CORPORATION; *Int'l*, pg. 5715
PAN-INTERNATIONAL INDUSTRY CO., LTD.—See Pan-International Industrial Corporation; *Int'l*, pg. 5716
PAN-INTERNATIONAL PRECISION ELECTRONIC CO., LTD.—See Pan-International Industrial Corporation; *Int'l*, pg. 5716
PAN INTERNATIONAL (THAILAND) CO., LTD.—See Thai Beverage Public Company Limited; *Int'l*, pg. 7591
PAN-INTERNATIONAL (USA), INC.—See Pan-International Industrial Corporation; *Int'l*, pg. 5715
PAN-INTERNATIONAL WIRE & CABLE (MALAYSIA) SDN.BHD—See Pan-International Industrial Corporation; *Int'l*, pg. 5716
PANION & BF BIOTECH, INC.; *Int'l*, pg. 5728
THE PAN ISLAMIC STEAMSHIP COMPANY LTD.; *Int'l*, pg. 7673
PAN-ISLAND INDUSTRIAL(S) PTE LTD.—See A.A.G. STUCCHI s.r.l.; *Int'l*, pg. 23

COMPANY NAME INDEX

PANI TERESA MEDICA S.A.—See Sigvaris Holding AG; *Int'l*, pg. 6913
PANITZKY GESELLSCHAFT M.B.H.—See PORR AG; *Int'l*, pg. 5923
PANJAM INVESTMENT LIMITED; *Int'l*, pg. 5728
PANJAWATTANA PLASTIC PUBLIC COMPANY LIMITED; *Int'l*, pg. 5728
PANJIN AOXIN QUANMIN STOMATOLOGY HOSPITAL CO., LTD.—See Aoxin Q & M Dental Group Limited; *Int'l*, pg. 498
PANJIN JINGCHENG Q & M STOMATOLOGY CO., LTD.—See Aoxin Q & M Dental Group Limited; *Int'l*, pg. 498
PANJIN JINSAI Q & M STOMATOLOGY CO., LTD.—See Aoxin Q & M Dental Group Limited; *Int'l*, pg. 498
PANJIT AMERICAS, INC.—See Pan Jit International Inc.; *Int'l*, pg. 5714
PANJIT ELECTRONICS (SHANDONG) CO., LTD.—See Pan Jit International Inc.; *Int'l*, pg. 5714
PANJIT ELECTRONICS (SHEN ZHEN) CO., LTD.—See Pan Jit International Inc.; *Int'l*, pg. 5714
PAN JIT EUROPE GMBH—See Pan Jit International Inc.; *Int'l*, pg. 5714
PANJIT INTERNATIONAL (H.K.) CO., LTD.—See Pan Jit International Inc.; *Int'l*, pg. 5714
PAN JIT INTERNATIONAL INC.; *Int'l*, pg. 5714
PANJIT KOREA CO., LTD.—See Pan Jit International Inc.; *Int'l*, pg. 5714
PANJIT SEMICONDUCTOR (XUZHOU) CO., LTD.—See Pan Jit International Inc.; *Int'l*, pg. 5714
PANJIVA, INC.—See S&P Global Inc.; *U.S. Public*, pg. 1831
PANJON LIMITED; *Int'l*, pg. 5728
PANKAJ PIYUSH TRADE & INVESTMENT LIMITED; *Int'l*, pg. 5728
PANKAJ POLYMERS LIMITED; *Int'l*, pg. 5728
PANKL AEROSPACE INNOVATIONS, LLC—See Pierer Konzerngesellschaft mbH; *Int'l*, pg. 5863
PANKL AEROSPACE SYSTEMS EUROPE GMBH—See Pierer Konzerngesellschaft mbH; *Int'l*, pg. 5863
PANKL AEROSPACE SYSTEMS INC.—See Pierer Konzerngesellschaft mbH; *Int'l*, pg. 5863
PANKL - APC TURBOSYSTEMS GMBH—See Pierer Konzerngesellschaft mbH; *Int'l*, pg. 5863
PANKL AUTOMOTIVE SLOVAKIA S.R.O.—See Pierer Konzerngesellschaft mbH; *Int'l*, pg. 5863
PANKL DRIVETRAIN SYSTEMS GMBH AND CO KG—See Pierer Konzerngesellschaft mbH; *Int'l*, pg. 5863
PANKL ENGINE SYSTEMS AG—See Pierer Konzerngesellschaft mbH; *Int'l*, pg. 5863
PANKL HIGH PERFORMANCE PISTONS GMBH—See Pierer Konzerngesellschaft mbH; *Int'l*, pg. 5863
PANKL INC—See Pierer Konzerngesellschaft mbH; *Int'l*, pg. 5863
PANKL JAPAN INC.—See Pierer Konzerngesellschaft mbH; *Int'l*, pg. 5863
PANKL RACING SYSTEMS AG—See Pierer Konzerngesellschaft mbH; *Int'l*, pg. 5863
PANKL RACING SYSTEMS UK LTD—See Pierer Konzerngesellschaft mbH; *Int'l*, pg. 5863
PANKL SCHMIEDETECHNIK GMBH & CO KG—See Pierer Konzerngesellschaft mbH; *Int'l*, pg. 5863
PANKOW SPECIAL PROJECTS; *U.S. Private*, pg. 3086
PANLAB S.L.—See Harvard Bioscience, Inc.; *U.S. Public*, pg. 987
PAN LEE SDN BHD; *Int'l*, pg. 5714
PANLOGIC; *Int'l*, pg. 5728
PAN MACHINE IMPORT AND EXPORT TRADE—See Quaser Machine Tools, Inc.; *Int'l*, pg. 6157
PAN MACMILLAN AUSTRALIA PTY LTD—See Verlagsgruppe Georg von Holtzbrinck GmbH; *Int'l*, pg. 8171
PAN MACMILLAN LTD.—See Verlagsgruppe Georg von Holtzbrinck GmbH; *Int'l*, pg. 8171
PAN MACMILLAN SA (PTY) LTD—See Verlagsgruppe Georg von Holtzbrinck GmbH; *Int'l*, pg. 8171
PAN-MALAYAN PHARMACEUTICALS PTE LTD—See Hyphens Pharma International Limited; *Int'l*, pg. 3553
PAN MALAYSIA CORPORATION BERHAD—See Malayan United Industries Berhad; *Int'l*, pg. 4661
PAN MALAYSIA HOLDINGS BERHAD; *Int'l*, pg. 5714
PAN MALAYSIAN INDUSTRIES BERHAD; *Int'l*, pg. 5715
PAN MALAYSIAN POOLS SDN BHD—See Tanjong Plc; *Int'l*, pg. 7459
PAN-MAR CORPORATION; *U.S. Private*, pg. 3084
PAN MARINE DO BRASIL LTDA.—See Tidewater Inc.; *U.S. Public*, pg. 2158
PANMERIDIAN TUBULAR—See SeAH Holdings Corp.; *Int'l*, pg. 6664
PANMURE GORDON (BROKING) LIMITED—See Atlas Merchant Capital LLC; *U.S. Private*, pg. 379
PANMURE GORDON (BROKING) LIMITED—See Qatar Islamic Bank (S.A.Q.); *Int'l*, pg. 6134
PANMURE GORDON & CO. LIMITED—See Atlas Merchant Capital LLC; *U.S. Private*, pg. 379
PANMURE GORDON & CO. LIMITED—See Qatar Islamic Bank (S.A.Q.); *Int'l*, pg. 6134
PANMURE GORDON (UK) LIMITED—See Atlas Merchant Capital LLC; *U.S. Private*, pg. 379

PANMURE GORDON (UK) LIMITED—See Qatar Islamic Bank (S.A.Q.); *Int'l*, pg. 6134
PANNELL KERR FORSTER OF TEXAS, P.C.; *U.S. Private*, pg. 3086
PANNERGY NYRT.; *Int'l*, pg. 5728
PANNESMA COMPANY LTD.—See Atheeb Group; *Int'l*, pg. 669
PANNIER CORPORATION - PANNIER GRAPHICS DIVISION—See Pannier Corporation; *U.S. Private*, pg. 3087
PANNIER CORPORATION; *U.S. Private*, pg. 3087
PANNON ANTENNA, KFT—See EQT AB; *Int'l*, pg. 2479
PANNON ANTENNA, KFT—See Public Sector Pension Investment Board; *Int'l*, pg. 6096
PANNON-EFFEKT PLASTICS LTD.—See PannErgy Nyrt.; *Int'l*, pg. 5728
PANNONFACILITY PROPERTY MANAGEMENT KFT.—See Videoton Holding Zrt.; *Int'l*, pg. 8191
PANNON-FLAX LINEN WEAVING CO; *Int'l*, pg. 5729
PANNON FREYSSINET LTD—See VINCI S.A.; *Int'l*, pg. 8233
PANNONIA HOTELS RT—See Accor S.A.; *Int'l*, pg. 92
PANNONMILL MALOMIPARI ZRT.—See Raiffeisen-Holding Niederosterreich-Wien reg. Gen.m.b.H.; *Int'l*, pg. 6185
PANNUNION PACKAGING PLC—See PannErgy Nyrt.; *Int'l*, pg. 5728
PAN OCEAN (AMERICA), INC.—See Pan Ocean Co., Ltd.; *Int'l*, pg. 5715
PAN OCEAN BRASIL APOIO MARITIMO LTDA.—See Pan Ocean Co., Ltd.; *Int'l*, pg. 5715
PAN OCEAN (CHINA) CO., LTD.—See Pan Ocean Co., Ltd.; *Int'l*, pg. 5715
PAN OCEAN CO., LTD.; *Int'l*, pg. 5715
PANOCEANIC ENERGY LIMITED—See PGS ASA; *Int'l*, pg. 5839
PAN OCEANIC EYEWEAR LTD.; *U.S. Private*, pg. 3084
PAN OCEANIC JAPAN CORPORATION—See Pan Ocean Co., Ltd.; *Int'l*, pg. 5715
PAN OCEAN SINGAPORE BULK CARRIER PTE. LTD.—See Pan Ocean Co., Ltd.; *Int'l*, pg. 5715
PANOFINA AG—See Coop-Gruppe Genossenschaft; *Int'l*, pg. 1790
PAN-O-GOLD BAKING CO.; *U.S. Private*, pg. 3084
PANOLAM INDUSTRIES INTERNATIONAL, INC.—See Insight Equity Holdings LLC; *U.S. Private*, pg. 2086
THE PANOLA WATCHMAN—See Texas Community Media LLC; *U.S. Private*, pg. 3975
PANONIJA A.D.; *Int'l*, pg. 5729
PANONKA A.D.; *Int'l*, pg. 5729
PANOPLY GROUP CORP.; *Int'l*, pg. 5729
PANOPTA LLC—See Fortinet, Inc.; *U.S. Public*, pg. 869
PANOPTES PHARMA GES.M.B.H.—See Kiora Pharmaceuticals, Inc.; *U.S. Public*, pg. 1235
PANOPTO, INC.—See K1 Investment Management, LLC; *U.S. Private*, pg. 2252
PANORA GAYRIMENKUL YATIRIM ORTAKLIGI AS; *Int'l*, pg. 5729
PANORAMA CAPITAL CORP.; *U.S. Public*, pg. 1636
PANORAMA CAPITAL, LLC; *U.S. Private*, pg. 3087
PANORAMA CATERING—See Wurth Verwaltungsgesellschaft mbH; *Int'l*, pg. 8506
PANORAMA DESTINATION (VIETNAM) JV LTD.—See PT Destinasi Tirta Nusantara Tbk; *Int'l*, pg. 6036
PANORAMA EYE CARE LLC; *U.S. Private*, pg. 3087
PANORAMA FIRM SP. Z O.O.; *Int'l*, pg. 5729
PANORAMA HOTEL- UND SERVICE GMBH—See Wurth Verwaltungsgesellschaft mbH; *Int'l*, pg. 8506
PANORAMAHOTEL WALDENBURG—See Wurth Verwaltungsgesellschaft mbH; *Int'l*, pg. 8506
PANORAMA; *U.S. Private*, pg. 3087
PANORAMA STUDIOS INTERNATIONAL LIMITED; *Int'l*, pg. 5729
PANORAMIC RENTAL CORP.—See The Jordan Company, L.P.; *U.S. Private*, pg. 4063
PANORAMIC RESOURCES LIMITED; *Int'l*, pg. 5729
PANORAMIC UNIVERSAL LIMITED; *Int'l*, pg. 5729
PAN ORIENT ENERGY CORP.—See Dialog Group Berhad; *Int'l*, pg. 2104
PANORO ENERGY ASA; *Int'l*, pg. 5729
PANORO ENERGY LIMITED—See Panoro Energy ASA; *Int'l*, pg. 5729
PANORO MINERALS LTD.; *Int'l*, pg. 5729
PANOS BRANDS LLC—See Hammond, Kennedy, Whitney & Company, Inc.; *U.S. Private*, pg. 1850
PANOSTAJA OYJ; *Int'l*, pg. 5729
PAN-OSTON CO.—See Houchens Industries, Inc.; *U.S. Private*, pg. 1990
PANOS UTP A.D.; *Int'l*, pg. 5729
PA NOVA S.A.; *Int'l*, pg. 5684
PAN OVERSEAS (GUANGZHOU) ELECTRONIC CO., LTD.—See Walsin Technology Corporation; *Int'l*, pg. 8335
PAN PAC FOREST PRODUCTS LIMITED—See Nippon Paper Industries Co., Ltd.; *Int'l*, pg. 5328
PAN PAC FOREST PRODUCTS LTD.—See Oji Holdings Corporation; *Int'l*, pg. 5538
PAN-PACIFIC CO., LTD.; *Int'l*, pg. 5716
PAN PACIFIC COPPER CO., LTD.—See ENEOS Holdings, Inc.; *Int'l*, pg. 2416

PANTEX SA

PAN PACIFIC COPPER SHANGHAI CO., LTD.—See ENEOS Holdings, Inc.; *Int'l*, pg. 2416
PAN PACIFIC EXPRESS CORP.; *U.S. Private*, pg. 3084
PAN PACIFIC HOTELS GROUP LTD.—See UOL Group Limited; *Int'l*, pg. 8086
PAN PACIFIC HOTELS GROUP—See UOL Group Limited; *Int'l*, pg. 8086
PAN PACIFIC HOTELS & RESORTS SEATTLE LIMITED LIABILITY CO.—See UOL Group Limited; *Int'l*, pg. 8086
PAN PACIFIC INTERNATIONAL HOLDINGS CORPORATION; *Int'l*, pg. 5715
PAN PACIFIC INTERNATIONAL TRADING CO., LTD.—See Pan Pacific International Holdings Corporation; *Int'l*, pg. 5715
PAN PACIFIC METAL MINING CORP.—See Korea Zinc Company, Ltd.; *Int'l*, pg. 4287
PAN PACIFIC RV CENTERS INC.; *U.S. Private*, pg. 3084
PAN PACIFIC STRAPTEX SDN. BHD.—See Scientex Berhad; *Int'l*, pg. 6648
PAN-PACIFIC TELECOMMUNICATION COMPANY LIMITED—See Telestone Technologies Corporation; *Int'l*, pg. 7542
PAN PAN DOOR CO LTD—See ASSA ABLOY AB; *Int'l*, pg. 640
PAN PEPIN INC.; *U.S. Private*, pg. 3084
PAN PROBE BIOTECH, INC.—See EarlyDETECT Inc.; *U.S. Private*, pg. 1314
PANRAM INTERNATIONAL CORP.; *Int'l*, pg. 5730
PANRUSGAS GAS TRADING PLC.—See MVM Magyar Villamos Muvek Zrt.; *Int'l*, pg. 5108
PANSAR BERHAD; *Int'l*, pg. 5730
PANSAR COMPANY SDN BHD—See Pansar Berhad; *Int'l*, pg. 5730
PANSARI DEVELOPERS LIMITED; *Int'l*, pg. 5730
PANSARI SINGAPORE PTE LTD—See Pansar Berhad; *Int'l*, pg. 5730
PANSEND, LLC—See INNOVATE Corp.; *U.S. Public*, pg. 1126
PANSING DISTRIBUTION PTE LTD—See Thai Beverage Public Company Limited; *Int'l*, pg. 7590
PANSING MARKETING SDN BHD—See Thai Beverage Public Company Limited; *Int'l*, pg. 7590
PANSMART PROPRIETARY LIMITED—See Huge Group Limited; *Int'l*, pg. 3524
PANSOFT COMPANY LIMITED; *Int'l*, pg. 5730
PANSOLUTIONS HOLDINGS LIMITED—See Reunert Limited; *Int'l*, pg. 6312
PANSTAR ENTERPRISE CO., LTD.; *Int'l*, pg. 5730
PANSUEVIA GMBH & CO. KG—See STRABAG SE; *Int'l*, pg. 7231
PANSYSTEM S.R.L.—See Arrow Electronics, Inc.; *U.S. Public*, pg. 199
PANTA DISTRIBUZIONE SPA—See MOL Magyar Olaj- es Gazipari Nyrt.; *Int'l*, pg. 5020
PANTAFLEX B.V.—See TKH Group N.V.; *Int'l*, pg. 7764
PANTAFLIX AG; *Int'l*, pg. 5730
PANTAFLIX TECHNOLOGIES GMBH—See Pantaflix AG; *Int'l*, pg. 5730
PANTAGRAPH PUBLISHING CO.—See Lee Enterprises, Incorporated; *U.S. Public*, pg. 1300
PANTA HOLDINGS B.V.; *Int'l*, pg. 5730
PANTAI DALIT BEACH RESORT SDN BERHAD—See Shangri-La Asia Limited; *Int'l*, pg. 6783
PANTAI HOLDINGS BERHAD—See Khazanah Nasional Berhad; *Int'l*, pg. 4152
PANTAI MEDIVEST SDN. BHD.—See Khazanah Nasional Berhad; *Int'l*, pg. 4152
PANTALHA, LDA.—See Transition Evergreen; *Int'l*, pg. 7901
PANTEBREVSSELSKABET AF 8/8 1995 A/S—See Nykredit A/S; *Int'l*, pg. 5500
PANTECH CORPORATION SDN. BHD.—See Pantech Group Holdings Berhad; *Int'l*, pg. 5730
PANTECH GROUP HOLDINGS BERHAD; *Int'l*, pg. 5730
PANTECH (KUANTAN) SDN. BHD.—See Pantech Group Holdings Berhad; *Int'l*, pg. 5730
PAN TECHNOLOGY INC.; *U.S. Private*, pg. 3084
PANTECH STEEL INDUSTRIES SDN. BHD.—See Pantech Group Holdings Berhad; *Int'l*, pg. 5730
PANTECNIKI SA—See ELLAKTOR S.A.; *Int'l*, pg. 2365
PANTEK TECHNOLOGY CORP.—See Alltek Technology Corporation; *Int'l*, pg. 360
PANTELAKIS SECURITIES S.A.—See HSBC Holdings plc; *Int'l*, pg. 3506
PANTELION LLC—See Grupo Televisa, S.A.B.; *Int'l*, pg. 3137
PANTEL TECHNOLOGIES PVT. LTD.; *Int'l*, pg. 5730
PANTENE INDUSTRIAL CO., LIMITED—See Sinohope Technology Holdings Limited; *Int'l*, pg. 6952
PANTERA MINERALS LIMITED; *Int'l*, pg. 5730
PANTER B.V.—See Akzo Nobel N.V.; *Int'l*, pg. 274
PANTERO CORPORATION—See Progress Software Corporation; *U.S. Public*, pg. 1725
PANTERRA GOLD (PERU) S.A.—See Antilles Gold Limited; *Int'l*, pg. 483
PANTERRA NETWORKS INC.; *U.S. Private*, pg. 3087
PANTEX SA; *Int'l*, pg. 5730

PANTHEON CAPITAL (ASIA) LIMITED—See Affiliated Managers Group, Inc.; *U.S. Public*, pg. 55
PANTHEON HOLDINGS LIMITED—See Affiliated Managers Group, Inc.; *U.S. Public*, pg. 55
PANTHEON INFRASTRUCTURE PLC; *Int'l*, pg. 5730
PANTHEON INTERNATIONAL PLC; *Int'l*, pg. 5730
PANTHEON KOREA INC.—See Affiliated Managers Group, Inc.; *U.S. Public*, pg. 55
PANTHEON LEISURE PLC—See Insig AI plc; *Int'l*, pg. 3718
PANTHEON RESOURCES PLC; *Int'l*, pg. 5730
PANTHEON SECURITIES LLC—See Affiliated Managers Group, Inc.; *U.S. Public*, pg. 55
PANTHEON (US) LLC—See Affiliated Managers Group, Inc.; *U.S. Public*, pg. 55
PANTHEON VENTURES (HK) LLP—See Affiliated Managers Group, Inc.; *U.S. Public*, pg. 55
PANTHEON VENTURES (UK) LLP—See Affiliated Managers Group, Inc.; *U.S. Public*, pg. 55
PANTHERCORP CST PTY LTD—See Sequoia Financial Group Limited; *Int'l*, pg. 6719
PANTHER EXPEDITED SERVICES, INC.—See ArcBest Corporation; *U.S. Public*, pg. 180
PANTHER II TRANSPORTATION, INC.—See ArcBest Corporation; *U.S. Public*, pg. 180
PANTHER INDUSTRIAL PRODUCTS LIMITED; *Int'l*, pg. 5731
PANTHER INDUSTRIES INC.—See Pic Investment Group Inc.; *Int'l*, pg. 5859
PANTHER METALS PLC; *Int'l*, pg. 5731
PANTHER MOTOR GROUP INC.; *U.S. Private*, pg. 3087
PANTHER PREMIUM LOGISTICS, INC.—See ArcBest Corporation; *U.S. Public*, pg. 180
PANTHER SECURITIES PLC; *Int'l*, pg. 5731
PANTHERS FOOTBALL, LLC; *U.S. Private*, pg. 3087
PANTHER SUMMIT INDUSTRIES INC.; *U.S. Private*, pg. 3087
PANTHER VAT PROPERTIES LIMITED—See Panther Securities PLC; *Int'l*, pg. 5731
PANTHERX SPECIALTY, LLC—See General Atlantic Service Company, L.P.; *U.S. Private*, pg. 1663
PANTHERX SPECIALTY, LLC—See Nautic Partners, LLC; *U.S. Private*, pg. 2871
PANTHERX SPECIALTY, LLC—See The Vistria Group, LP; *U.S. Private*, pg. 4132
PANTONE, INC.—See Danaher Corporation; *U.S. Public*, pg. 632
PANTOP CORPORATION; *Int'l*, pg. 5731
PANTORAMA INDUSTRIES INC.; *Int'l*, pg. 5731
PANTORO LIMITED; *Int'l*, pg. 5731
PANTOS LOGISTICS (CHINA) CO., LTD.—See LX Holdings Corp.; *Int'l*, pg. 4604
PANTOS LOGISTICS FRANCE SARL—See LX Holdings Corp.; *Int'l*, pg. 4604
PANTOS LOGISTICS LLC—See LX Holdings Corp.; *Int'l*, pg. 4604
PANTOS LOGISTICS SWEDAN AB—See LX Holdings Corp.; *Int'l*, pg. 4604
PANTOS NORTH AMERICA INC.—See LX Holdings Corp.; *Int'l*, pg. 4604
PANTRAC GMBH—See Westinghouse Air Brake Technologies Corporation; *U.S. Public*, pg. 2359
PANTROPIC POWER PRODUCTS INC.; *U.S. Private*, pg. 3087
PANTURIST DIONICKO DRUSTVO ZA PRIJEVOZ PUTNIKA I TURIZAM D.D.—See Deutsche Bahn AG; *Int'l*, pg. 2052
PANU HARMONY PTE. LTD.—See Pan-United Corporation Ltd.; *Int'l*, pg. 5716
PANUM TELECOMMUNICATIONS, LLC—See Renovus Capital Partners; *U.S. Private*, pg. 3399
PAN-UNITED CONCRETE PTE LTD—See Pan-United Corporation Ltd.; *Int'l*, pg. 5716
PAN-UNITED CORPORATION LTD.; *Int'l*, pg. 5716
PAN-UNITED INDUSTRIES PTE LTD—See Pan-United Corporation Ltd.; *Int'l*, pg. 5716
PAN WEST CORP.; *U.S. Private*, pg. 3084
PAN-WEST (PRIVATE) LIMITED—See Tuan Sing Holdings Limited; *Int'l*, pg. 7962
PANW (PORTUGAL) UNIPESSOAL, LDA—See Palo Alto Networks, Inc.; *U.S. Public*, pg. 1635
PANYAM CEMENTS & MINERAL INDUSTRIES LIMITED; *Int'l*, pg. 5731
PANYATARA CO., LTD.—See C.P. All Public Company Limited; *Int'l*, pg. 1244
PANYU CHU KONG STEEL PIPE (LIANYUNGANG) CO., LTD.—See Chu Kong Petroleum and Natural Gas Steel Pipe Holdings Limited; *Int'l*, pg. 1589
PANYU CHU KONG STEEL PIPE (ZHUHAI) CO., LTD.—See Chu Kong Petroleum and Natural Gas Steel Pipe Holdings Limited; *Int'l*, pg. 1589
PANYU KYOKUTO SAKATA ELECTRONICS LTD.—See SIIX CORPORATION; *Int'l*, pg. 6913
PANYU TRIO MICROTRONICS CO., LTD.—See Trio Industrial Electronics Group Limited; *Int'l*, pg. 7925
PANZANI, S.A.S.—See Ebro Foods S.A.; *Int'l*, pg. 2287
PANZHIHUA TOLEDO ELECTRONIC SCALE LTD.—See Mettler-Toledo International, Inc.; *U.S. Public*, pg. 1433
PANZURA, INC.; *U.S. Private*, pg. 3087

PAO ARSENYEV AVIATION COMPANY PROGRESS—See Russian Technologies State Corporation; *Int'l*, pg. 6431
PAOFOONG INSURANCE COMPANY (HONG KONG) LIMITED—See Shanghai Commercial Bank Limited; *Int'l*, pg. 6763
PAO FORTUM—See Fortum Oyj; *Int'l*, pg. 2742
PAO KAZAN HELICOPTER PLANT—See Russian Technologies State Corporation; *Int'l*, pg. 6431
PAOLETTI AMERICA S.A.—See Corporacion America Airports S.A.; *Int'l*, pg. 1803
PAOLETTI SRL—See Kering S.A.; *Int'l*, pg. 4136
PAOLICELLI & ASSOCIATES, INC.—See One Source Associates, Inc.; *U.S. Private*, pg. 3023
PAOLI LLC—See HNI Corporation; *U.S. Public*, pg. 1043
PAOLINO INSURANCE AGENCY, INC.—See Starkweather & Shepley Insurance Brokerage, Inc.; *U.S. Private*, pg. 3787
PAOLI PEAKS INC.—See Vail Resorts, Inc.; *U.S. Public*, pg. 2271
PAOLO MEDIC CO., LTD.—See Bangkok Dusit Medical Services Public Company Limited; *Int'l*, pg. 834
PAO NOVATEK; *Int'l*, pg. 5731
PAO ROSTVERTOL—See Russian Technologies State Corporation; *Int'l*, pg. 6431
PAO RUSCAM POKROVSKY—See Turkiye Sise ve Cam Fabrikalari A.S.; *Int'l*, pg. 7977
PAO SEVERSTAL; *Int'l*, pg. 5731
PAOS HOLDINGS BERHAD; *Int'l*, pg. 5733
PAOS INDUSTRIES LTD.; *Int'l*, pg. 5733
PAOS INDUSTRIES SDN. BHD.—See Paos Holdings Berhad; *Int'l*, pg. 5733
PAO SOVCOMFLOT; *Int'l*, pg. 5732
PAO TMK; *Int'l*, pg. 5732
PAO ZAWOLZHSKY MOTORNY ZAWOD; *Int'l*, pg. 5733
PAPA GINOS-DEANGELO HOLDING CORPORATION, INC.; *U.S. Private*, pg. 3087
PAPAGO BREWING CO. INC.—See Huss Brewing Co. LLC; *U.S. Private*, pg. 2014
PAPA JOHN'S INTERNATIONAL, INC.; *U.S. Public*, pg. 1636
PAPA JOHN'S OF IOWA LLC; *U.S. Private*, pg. 3087
PAPA MURPHY'S HOLDINGS, INC.—See MTY Food Group Inc.; *Int'l*, pg. 5073
PAPA MURPHY'S INTERNATIONAL, INC.—See MTY Food Group Inc.; *Int'l*, pg. 5073
PAPANETS CO., LTD.; *Int'l*, pg. 5733
PAPAS DODGE INC.; *U.S. Private*, pg. 3087
P.A.P A/S—See AFRY AB; *Int'l*, pg. 194
PAPASTRATOS CIGARETTE MANUFACTURING COMPANY—See Philip Morris International Inc.; *U.S. Public*, pg. 1685
PAPASTRATOS CIGARETTES MANUFACTURING COMPANY S.A.—See Philip Morris International Inc.; *U.S. Public*, pg. 1685
PAPASU CO., LTD.—See MatsukiyoCocokara & Co.; *Int'l*, pg. 4730
PAPCO, INC.—See World Kinect Corporation; *U.S. Public*, pg. 2381
PAPE CHEVROLET INC.; *U.S. Private*, pg. 3087
PAPE-DAWSON ENGINEERS, LLC—See Palm Beach Capital Partners LLC; *U.S. Private*, pg. 3079
PAPE D.W., INC.—See The Pape Group, Inc.; *U.S. Private*, pg. 4090
PAPEETE SEIRLAND TRANSPORTS (PST)—See Albert Ballin KG; *Int'l*, pg. 296
THE PAPE GROUP, INC.; *U.S. Private*, pg. 4090
PAPE KENWORTH—See The Pape Group, Inc.; *U.S. Private*, pg. 4090
PAPE KENWORTH—See The Pape Group, Inc.; *U.S. Private*, pg. 4090
PAPELERA DE CHIHUAHUA, S.A. DE C.V.—See Corporativo Copamex, S.A. de C.V.; *Int'l*, pg. 1806
PAPELERA GUIPUZCOANA DE ZICUNAGA, S.A.—See Iberpapel Gestion SA; *Int'l*, pg. 3574
PAPELERA MEXICANA SA DE CV, INDUSTRIAL—See Corporativo Copamex, S.A. de C.V.; *Int'l*, pg. 1806
PAPELES ANOIA S.A.—See Miquel y Costas & Miquel, S.A.; *Int'l*, pg. 4915
PAPELES BIO BIO S.A.; *Int'l*, pg. 5733
PAPELES CORDILLERA SPA—See Empresas CMPC S.A.; *Int'l*, pg. 2389
PAPELES CORRUGADOS, S.A. DE C.V.—See Grupo La Moderna, S.A.B. de C.V.; *Int'l*, pg. 3131
PAPELES NORSKE SKOG BIO BIO S.A.—See Norske Skog ASA; *Int'l*, pg. 5438
PAPELES VENEZOLANOS, S.A.—See Kruger Inc.; *Int'l*, pg. 4308
PAPELES Y CARTONES DE EUROPA SA; *Int'l*, pg. 5733
PAPEL MEDIA NETWORK; *U.S. Private*, pg. 3087
PAPEL PRENSA S.A.I.C.F. Y DE M.—See Grupo Clarin S.A.; *Int'l*, pg. 3124
PAPE MACHINERY, INC.—See The Pape Group, Inc.; *U.S. Private*, pg. 4090
PAPE MACHINERY—See The Pape Group, Inc.; *U.S. Private*, pg. 4090
PAPE MACHINERY—See The Pape Group, Inc.; *U.S. Private*, pg. 4090
PAPE MATERIAL HANDLING—See The Pape Group, Inc.; *U.S. Private*, pg. 4090

PAPER AGENTS LTD.—See Norske Skog ASA; *Int'l*, pg. 5438
PAPER AUSTRALIA PTY. LTD.—See Nippon Paper Industries Co., Ltd.; *Int'l*, pg. 5328
PAPER BOAT APPS PRIVATE LIMITED—See Nazara Technologies Limited; *Int'l*, pg. 5178
PAPERCHASE PRODUCTS LIMITED—See Primary Capital Limited; *Int'l*, pg. 5975
PAPER CHEMICAL SUPPLY COMPANY; *U.S. Private*, pg. 3087
PAPER & CHEMICAL SUPPLY CO.; *U.S. Private*, pg. 3087
PAPERCLIP INC.; *U.S. Public*, pg. 1636
PAPER CONVERTING MACHINE COMPANY FAR EAST—See Barry-Wehmiller Companies, Inc.; *U.S. Private*, pg. 482
PAPER CONVERTING MACHINE COMPANY FAR EAST—See Barry-Wehmiller Companies, Inc.; *U.S. Private*, pg. 482
PAPER CONVERTING MACHINE COMPANY, LTD.—See Barry-Wehmiller Companies, Inc.; *U.S. Private*, pg. 482
PAPER CONVERTING MACHINE COMPANY—See Barry-Wehmiller Companies, Inc.; *U.S. Private*, pg. 482
PAPER CONVERTING MACHINE EUROPE GMBH—See Barry-Wehmiller Companies, Inc.; *U.S. Private*, pg. 482
PAPERCOREA CO., LTD.; *Int'l*, pg. 5733
PAPERCOREA INC.—See PAPERCOREA CO., LTD.; *Int'l*, pg. 5733
PAPERCRAFT SDN. BHD.—See Lion Rock Group Ltd; *Int'l*, pg. 4519
PAPER CUTTERS INC.; *U.S. Private*, pg. 3088
PAPER ENTERPRISES, INC.; *U.S. Private*, pg. 3088
PAPER EXCELLENCE B.V.—See PT Sinar Mas Group; *Int'l*, pg. 6072
PAPER EXCELLENCE CANADA HOLDINGS CORPORATION—See PT Sinar Mas Group; *Int'l*, pg. 6072
PAPER EXCELLENCE CANADA - SKOOKUMCHUCK NBSK PULP MILL—See PT Sinar Mas Group; *Int'l*, pg. 6074
PAPER FORCE OCEANIA PTY. LTD.—See Pabrik Kertas Tjiwi Kimia Tbk; *Int'l*, pg. 5684
PAPERFREE MEDICAL SOLUTIONS, INC.; *U.S. Public*, pg. 1636
PAPERG; *U.S. Private*, pg. 3088
PAPERICH PTE. LTD.—See Nippecraft Limited; *Int'l*, pg. 5309
PAPERLESS BUSINESS SYSTEMS, INC.; *U.S. Private*, pg. 3088
PAPERLESS OFFICE SOLUTIONS, INC.—See New York Community Bancorp, Inc.; *U.S. Public*, pg. 1513
PAPERLESS TRANSACTION CORPORATION; *U.S. Private*, pg. 3088
PAPERLINX AUSTRALIA PTY. LTD.—See KPP Group Holdings Co., Ltd.; *Int'l*, pg. 4298
PAPERLINX BV—See KPP Group Holdings Co., Ltd.; *Int'l*, pg. 4298
PAPERLINX DENMARK HOLDINGS APS—See KPP Group Holdings Co., Ltd.; *Int'l*, pg. 4298
PAPERLINX DIEMEN—See KPP Group Holdings Co., Ltd.; *Int'l*, pg. 4298
PAPERLINX HOLDINGS (ASIA) PTE LTD—See KPP Group Holdings Co., Ltd.; *Int'l*, pg. 4298
PAPERLINX INVESTMENTS PTY LTD—See KPP Group Holdings Co., Ltd.; *Int'l*, pg. 4298
PAPERLINX IRELAND LTD—See KPP Group Holdings Co., Ltd.; *Int'l*, pg. 4298
PAPERLINX NETHERLANDS BV—See KPP Group Holdings Co., Ltd.; *Int'l*, pg. 4298
PAPERLINX NETHERLANDS HOLDINGS BV—See KPP Group Holdings Co., Ltd.; *Int'l*, pg. 4298
PAPERLINX SERVICES PTY. LTD.—See KPP Group Holdings Co., Ltd.; *Int'l*, pg. 4298
PAPERLINX SPS TRUST—See KPP Group Holdings Co., Ltd.; *Int'l*, pg. 4298
PAPERLINX (UK) LIMITED—See KPP Group Holdings Co., Ltd.; *Int'l*, pg. 4298
PAPERLY, INC.—See JRjr33, Inc.; *U.S. Private*, pg. 2240
PAPER MACHINERY CORPORATION; *U.S. Private*, pg. 3088
PAPER MACHINERY GROUP—See Mitsubishi Heavy Industries, Ltd.; *Int'l*, pg. 4957
PAPER MAGIC GROUP, INC.—See IG Design Group Plc; *Int'l*, pg. 3600
PAPERMILLDIRECT.COM LIMITED—See James Cropper Plc; *Int'l*, pg. 3875
PAPER ONE S.R.L.—See Artinova AB; *Int'l*, pg. 584
PAPERPACK PRINTING, BOX - MANUFACTURING & PAPER PACKAGING INDUSTRIAL S.A.; *Int'l*, pg. 5733
PAPERPLUS—See Clayton, Dubilier & Rice, LLC; *U.S. Private*, pg. 929
PAPERPLUS—See Clayton, Dubilier & Rice, LLC; *U.S. Private*, pg. 929
PAPERPLUS—See Clayton, Dubilier & Rice, LLC; *U.S. Private*, pg. 929
PAPERPLUS—See Clayton, Dubilier & Rice, LLC; *U.S. Private*, pg. 929

COMPANY NAME INDEX

PAPERPLUS—See Clayton, Dubilier & Rice, LLC; *U.S. Private*, pg. 929
PAPERPLUS—See Clayton, Dubilier & Rice, LLC; *U.S. Private*, pg. 929
PAPERPLUS—See Clayton, Dubilier & Rice, LLC; *U.S. Private*, pg. 929
PAPER PRODUCTS CO. INC.; *U.S. Private*, pg. 3088
THE PAPER PRODUCTS LTD.—See Huhtamaki Oyj; *Int'l*, pg. 3526
PAPER PRODUCTS MARKETING EUROPE GMBH—See Nippon Paper Industries Co., Ltd.; *Int'l*, pg. 5328
PAPER PRODUCTS MARKETING INC—See KPP Group Holdings Co., Ltd.; *Int'l*, pg. 4298
PAPER PRODUCTS MARKETING (MALAYSIA BRANCH) PTE. LTD.—See Nippon Paper Industries Co., Ltd.; *Int'l*, pg. 5328
PAPER PRODUCTS MARKETING (TAIWAN) LTD.—See Nippon Paper Industries Co., Ltd.; *Int'l*, pg. 5328
PAPER SACKS FACTORY—See Sharjah Cement & Industrial Development Company P.S.C.; *Int'l*, pg. 6790
PAPERSAVE; *U.S. Private*, pg. 3088
PAPER SOURCE, INC.—See Elliott Management Corporation; *U.S. Private*, pg. 1373
PAPER STORE INCORPORATED; *U.S. Private*, pg. 3088
PAPER SYSTEMS INC.; *U.S. Private*, pg. 3088
PAPERTECH SL—See Sonoco Products Company; *U.S. Public*, pg. 1904
PAPER TIGERS INC.; *U.S. Private*, pg. 3088
PAPER VALLEY CORPORATION—See The Boldt Group Inc.; *U.S. Private*, pg. 3996
PAPERWEIGHT DEVELOPMENT CORP.; *U.S. Private*, pg. 3088
PAPERWISE, INC.—See Dura Software Series A Qof LLC; *U.S. Private*, pg. 1292
PAPERWORKS INC.—See Diversified Chemical Technologies Inc.; *U.S. Private*, pg. 1241
PAPERWORKS INDUSTRIES, INC. - BALDWINSVILLE—See Sun Capital Partners, Inc.; *U.S. Private*, pg. 3860
PAPERWORKS INDUSTRIES, INC. - DALLAS PLANT—See Sun Capital Partners, Inc.; *U.S. Private*, pg. 3860
PAPERWORKS INDUSTRIES, INC. - HASTINGS—See Sun Capital Partners, Inc.; *U.S. Private*, pg. 3860
PAPERWORKS INDUSTRIES, INC. - MENDON PLANT—See Sun Capital Partners, Inc.; *U.S. Private*, pg. 3860
PAPERWORKS INDUSTRIES, INC. - MOUNT GILEAD—See Sun Capital Partners, Inc.; *U.S. Private*, pg. 3860
PAPERWORKS INDUSTRIES, INC. - PHILADELPHIA MILL—See Sun Capital Partners, Inc.; *U.S. Private*, pg. 3860
PAPERWORKS INDUSTRIES, INC. - RICHMOND PLANT—See Sun Capital Partners, Inc.; *U.S. Private*, pg. 3860
PAPERWORKS INDUSTRIES, INC.—See Sun Capital Partners, Inc.; *U.S. Private*, pg. 3860
PAPERWORKS INDUSTRIES, INC. - WABASH MILL—See Sun Capital Partners, Inc.; *U.S. Private*, pg. 3860
PAPERWORKS INDUSTRIES, INC. - WILKES-BARRE PLANT—See Sun Capital Partners, Inc.; *U.S. Private*, pg. 3860
PAPETERIES DE GASCOGNE GMBH—See Gascogne SA; *Int'l*, pg. 2888
PAPETERIES DE MALAUCENE S.A.S—See Mativ Holdings, Inc.; *U.S. Public*, pg. 1396
PAPETERIES DE SAINT-GIRONS S.A.S.—See Mativ Holdings, Inc.; *U.S. Public*, pg. 1396
PAPETERIES DE VIZILLE—See Vicat S.A.; *Int'l*, pg. 8186
PAPETERIES PICHON SAS—See Manutan International SA; *Int'l*, pg. 4680
PAPETTI'S HYGRADE EGG PRODUCTS, INC.—See Post Holdings, Inc.; *U.S. Public*, pg. 1703
PAPFEN JOINT STOCK COMPANY—See Tekfen Holding A.S.; *Int'l*, pg. 7526
PAPHOS STONE C. ESTATES PLC; *Int'l*, pg. 5733
PAPIERFABRIK LOUISENTHAL GMBH—See Giesecke & Devrient GmbH; *Int'l*, pg. 2970
PAPIERFABRIK SCHEUFELEN GMBH + CO. KG—See Schaeff Maschinen GmbH & Co. KG; *Int'l*, pg. 6615
PAPIERFABRIK WATTENS GMBH & CO. KG—See delfortgroup AG; *Int'l*, pg. 2013
PAPIER MASSON WB L.P.—See Black Diamond Capital Holdings, L.P.; *U.S. Private*, pg. 570
PAPIERSACKFABRIK TENAX GMBH & CO. KG; *Int'l*, pg. 5733
PAPIER UNION GMBH—See Inapa - Investimentos, Participacoes e Gestao, SA; *Int'l*, pg. 3645
PAPILLON AIRWAYS INC.; *U.S. Private*, pg. 3088
PAPILON SAVUNMA-GUVENLIK SISTEMLERI BILISIM MUHENDISLIK HIZMETLERI ITHALAT IHRACAT SANAYI VE TICARET A.S.; *Int'l*, pg. 5733
PAPINEAU INTERNATIONAL L.P.—See TFI International Inc.; *Int'l*, pg. 7586
PAPIRBREDDEN EIENDOM AS—See Entra ASA; *Int'l*, pg. 2452

PAPIRNICA VEVCE D. O. O.—See Roxcel Handelsges.m.b.H.; *Int'l*, pg. 6408
P.A. POST AGENCY, LLC—See ABRY Partners, LLC; *U.S. Private*, pg. 43
PAPOULI'S GREEK GRILL RESTAURANTS; *U.S. Private*, pg. 3088
PAPOUTSANIS S.A.; *Int'l*, pg. 5733
PA POWER AUTOMATION AG; *Int'l*, pg. 5684
PAPPAJACK BERHAD; *Int'l*, pg. 5733
PAPPARICH OUTLETS PTY LTD.—See ST Group Food Industries Holdings Limited; *Int'l*, pg. 7158
PAPPAS ENTERPRISES INC.; *U.S. Private*, pg. 3088
THE PAPPAS GROUP, INC.—See OceanSound Partners, LP; *U.S. Private*, pg. 2991
PAPPAS PARTNERS LP; *U.S. Private*, pg. 3088
PAPPAS REALTY CO.; *U.S. Private*, pg. 3088
PAPPAS RESTAURANTS INC.—See Pappas Partners LP; *U.S. Private*, pg. 3088
PAPPAS TELECASTING COMPANIES; *U.S. Private*, pg. 3088
PAPPAS VENTURES; *U.S. Private*, pg. 3088
PAPRIKA STUDIOS KFT.; *Int'l*, pg. 5734
P. A. PROJECTS SDN. BHD.—See P.A. Resources Berhad; *Int'l*, pg. 5682
PAP-R PRODUCTS COMPANY; *U.S. Private*, pg. 3087
PAP SAC MAGHREB SA—See Mondi plc; *Int'l*, pg. 5027
PAPUAN OIL SEARCH LIMITED—See Santos Limited; *Int'l*, pg. 6559
PA PUBS INC.; *U.S. Private*, pg. 3062
PAPYLESS CO., LTD.; *Int'l*, pg. 5734
PAPYRO-TEX A/S—See ConvaTec Group PLC; *Int'l*, pg. 1786
PAPYRUS ALTPAPIERSERVICE HANDELSGESELLSCHAFT M.B.H.—See Mayr-Melnhof Karton AG; *Int'l*, pg. 4747
PAPYRUS AS—See Altor Equity Partners AB; *Int'l*, pg. 395
PAPYRUS A/S—See Altor Equity Partners AB; *Int'l*, pg. 395
PAPYRUS AUSTRALIA LIMITED; *Int'l*, pg. 5734
PAPYRUS DEUTSCHLAND GMBH & CO. KG—See Inapa - Investimentos, Participacoes e Gestao, SA; *Int'l*, pg. 3645
PAPYRUS FINLAND OY—See Altor Equity Partners AB; *Int'l*, pg. 395
PAPYRUS GROEP NEDERLAND B.V.—See Altor Equity Partners AB; *Int'l*, pg. 395
PAPYRUS HUNGARIA ZRT.—See Altor Equity Partners AB; *Int'l*, pg. 395
PAPYRUS NORGE AS—See Altor Equity Partners AB; *Int'l*, pg. 395
PAPYRUS-RECYCLED GREETINGS, INC.—See Clayton, Dubilier & Rice, LLC; *U.S. Private*, pg. 919
PAPYRUS SCHWEIZ AG—See Altor Equity Partners AB; *Int'l*, pg. 395
PAPYRUS SIA—See Altor Equity Partners AB; *Int'l*, pg. 395
PAPYRUS SP. Z O.O.—See Altor Equity Partners AB; *Int'l*, pg. 395
PAPYRUS SVERIGE AB—See Altor Equity Partners AB; *Int'l*, pg. 395
PAPYRUS WERTSTOFF SERVICE GMBH—See Mayr-Melnhof Karton AG; *Int'l*, pg. 4747
PAQ, INC.; *U.S. Private*, pg. 3088
PARABEAM B.V.—See ShawCor Ltd.; *Int'l*, pg. 6791
PARABEL INC.; *U.S. Private*, pg. 3089
PARABELLUM ACQUISITION CORP.; *U.S. Public*, pg. 1636
PARABELLUM LIMITED; *Int'l*, pg. 5734
PARAB INFRA LIMITED; *Int'l*, pg. 5734
PAR AB—See Ratos AB; *Int'l*, pg. 6217
PARACA INC.; *Int'l*, pg. 5734
PARACHUTE DESIGN, INC.—See Clarity Coverdale Fury Advertising, Inc.; *U.S. Private*, pg. 911
PARACHUTES INDUSTRIES SOUTHERN AFRICA PTY LTD.—See Safran SA; *Int'l*, pg. 6473
PARACO GAS CORPORATION; *U.S. Private*, pg. 3089
PARACOM LLC—See Colliers International Group Inc.; *Int'l*, pg. 1701
PARACON HOLDINGS LIMITED—See Adcorp Holdings Limited; *Int'l*, pg. 127
PARACON SA (PTY) LIMITED—See Adcorp Holdings Limited; *Int'l*, pg. 127
PARACO SOUTH LLC—See Paraco Gas Corporation; *U.S. Private*, pg. 3089
PAR ACTIVE TECHNOLOGIES PRIVATE LIMITED—See Endo International plc; *Int'l*, pg. 2404
PARADATA FINANCIAL SYSTEMS—See World Acceptance Corporation; *U.S. Public*, pg. 2379
PARADEE GAS COMPANY—See UGI Corporation; *U.S. Public*, pg. 2222
PARADEEP PHOSPHATES LTD—See Adventz Group; *Int'l*, pg. 167
PARADEEP PHOSPHATES LTD—See OCP SA; *Int'l*, pg. 5520
PARADE MAGAZINE—See Advance Publications, Inc.; *U.S. Private*, pg. 86
PARADE PUBLICATIONS INC.—See Advance Publications, Inc.; *U.S. Private*, pg. 86

PARADE TECHNOLOGIES, INC.—See Parade Technologies, Ltd.; *Int'l*, pg. 5734
PARADE TECHNOLOGIES, LTD.; *Int'l*, pg. 5734
PAR-A-DICE GAMING CORPORATION—See Boyd Gaming Corporation; *U.S. Public*, pg. 378
PARADIES LAGARDERE—See Vivendi SE; *Int'l*, pg. 8276
PARADIES LAGARDERE—See Vivendi SE; *Int'l*, pg. 8276
PARADIGMA DIGITAL, S.L.—See Indra Sistemas, S.A.; *Int'l*, pg. 3661
PARADIGM AEROSPACE CORPORATION—See Metro Aviation, Inc.; *U.S. Private*, pg. 2685
PARADIGM ASSOCIATES; *U.S. Private*, pg. 3089
PARADIGM BIOPHARMACEUTICALS LIMITED; *Int'l*, pg. 5735
PARADIGM B.V.—See Apax Partners LLP; *Int'l*, pg. 505
PARADIGM B.V.—See JMI Services, Inc.; *U.S. Private*, pg. 2216
PARADIGM CAPITAL PARTNERS; *U.S. Private*, pg. 3089
PARADIGM CONVERGENCE TECHNOLOGIES CORPORATION—See PCT LTD; *U.S. Public*, pg. 1658
PARADIGM DKD GROUP, L.L.C.—See Ryan, LLC; *U.S. Private*, pg. 3511
PARADIGM ENERGY, INC.—See Ares Management Corporation; *U.S. Public*, pg. 188
PARADIGM ENTERPRISES, INC.—See Babcock Power, Inc.; *U.S. Private*, pg. 422
PARADIGM FRANCE S.A.—See Emerson Electric Co.; *U.S. Public*, pg. 751
PARADIGM FZ-LLC—See Apax Partners LLP; *Int'l*, pg. 505
PARADIGM FZ-LLC—See JMI Services, Inc.; *U.S. Private*, pg. 2216
PARADIGM GEOPHYSICAL CANADA LIMITED—See Apax Partners LLP; *Int'l*, pg. 505
PARADIGM GEOPHYSICAL CANADA LIMITED—See JMI Services, Inc.; *U.S. Private*, pg. 2216
PARADIGM GEOPHYSICAL CORP.—See Apax Partners LLP; *Int'l*, pg. 505
PARADIGM GEOPHYSICAL CORP.—See JMI Services, Inc.; *U.S. Private*, pg. 2216
PARADIGM GEOPHYSICAL LLC—See Apax Partners LLP; *Int'l*, pg. 505
PARADIGM GEOPHYSICAL LLC—See JMI Services, Inc.; *U.S. Private*, pg. 2216
PARADIGM GEOPHYSICAL S.A.—See Apax Partners LLP; *Int'l*, pg. 505
PARADIGM GEOPHYSICAL S.A.—See JMI Services, Inc.; *U.S. Private*, pg. 2216
PARADIGM GEOPHYSICAL SDN BHD—See Apax Partners LLP; *Int'l*, pg. 505
PARADIGM GEOPHYSICAL SDN BHD—See JMI Services, Inc.; *U.S. Private*, pg. 2216
PARADIGM GEOPHYSICAL (UK) LIMITED—See Apax Partners LLP; *Int'l*, pg. 505
PARADIGM GEOPHYSICAL (UK) LIMITED—See JMI Services, Inc.; *U.S. Private*, pg. 2216
PARADIGM GROUP, LLC—See New Mountain Capital, LLC; *U.S. Private*, pg. 2901
PARADIGM INFOTECH, INC.; *U.S. Private*, pg. 3089
PARADIGM LABEL, INC—See Genstar Capital, LLC; *U.S. Private*, pg. 1676
PARADIGM LEARNING, INC.—See Hammond, Kennedy, Whitney & Company, Inc.; *U.S. Private*, pg. 1850
PARADIGM MANAGEMENT SERVICES, LLC—See Summit Partners, L.P.; *U.S. Private*, pg. 3855
PARADIGM MEDICAL INDUSTRIES, INC.; *U.S. Public*, pg. 1636
PARADIGM METAL INDUSTRIES SDN. BHD—See Kobay Technology Bhd.; *Int'l*, pg. 4216
PARADIGM METALS INC.; *U.S. Private*, pg. 3089
PARADIGM PACKAGING, INC.—See Linsalata Capital Partners, Inc.; *U.S. Private*, pg. 2463
PARADIGM PARTNERS LIMITED—See Tatton Asset Management plc; *Int'l*, pg. 7475
PARADIGM PARTNERS; *U.S. Private*, pg. 3089
PARADIGM PRECISION - BERLIN—See AeroEquity Partners, LLC; *U.S. Private*, pg. 118
PARADIGM PRECISION - BERLIN—See The Carlyle Group Inc.; *U.S. Public*, pg. 2046
PARADIGM PRECISION BURNLEY LTD—See General Electric Company; *U.S. Public*, pg. 919
PARADIGM PRECISION COMPONENTS SDN. BHD—See Kobay Technology Bhd.; *Int'l*, pg. 4216
PARADIGM PRECISION HOLDINGS, LLC—See AeroEquity Partners, LLC; *U.S. Private*, pg. 118
PARADIGM PRECISION HOLDINGS, LLC—See The Carlyle Group Inc.; *U.S. Public*, pg. 2046
PARADIGM PRECISION MACHINING SDN. BHD—See Kobay Technology Bhd.; *Int'l*, pg. 4216
PARADIGM PRECISION - MALDEN—See AeroEquity Partners, LLC; *U.S. Private*, pg. 118
PARADIGM PRECISION - MALDEN—See The Carlyle Group Inc.; *U.S. Public*, pg. 2046
PARADIGM PRECISION - TEMPE—See AeroEquity Partners, LLC; *U.S. Private*, pg. 118
PARADIGM PRECISION - TEMPE—See The Carlyle Group Inc.; *U.S. Public*, pg. 2046
PARADIGM PRECISION - TUNIS—See AeroEquity Partners, LLC; *U.S. Private*, pg. 119

PARADIGM PARTNERS

CORPORATE AFFILIATIONS

PARADIGM PRECISION - TUNIS—See The Carlyle Group Inc.; *U.S. Public*, pg. 2046
PARADIGM RECOVERY SOLUTIONS, LLC; *U.S. Private*, pg. 3089
PARADIGM SERVICES LLC; *U.S. Private*, pg. 3089
PARADIGM SERVICES LTD.—See Airbus SE; *Int'l*, pg. 245
PARADIGM SPINE, LLC—See Surgalign Holdings, Inc.; *U.S. Public*, pg. 1967
PARADIGM SYSTEM SOLUTIONS, INC.; *U.S. Public*, pg. 1636
PARADIGM TAX GROUP—See The Riverside Company; *U.S. Private*, pg. 4109
PARADIGM TECHNOLOGY (BEIJING) CO., LTD.—See Apax Partners LLP; *Int'l*, pg. 505
PARADIGM TECHNOLOGY (BEIJING) CO., LTD.—See JMI Services, Inc.; *U.S. Private*, pg. 2216
PARADIGM TECHNOLOGY CONSULTING, LLC—See Geisinger Health System; *U.S. Private*, pg. 1656
PARADISE ADVERTISING & MARKETING, INC.; *U.S. Private*, pg. 3090
PARADISE ADVERTISING & MARKETING-NAPLES—See Paradise Advertising & Marketing, Inc.; *U.S. Private*, pg. 3090
PARADISE BAKERY & CAFE, INC.—See JAB Holding Company S.a.r.l.; *Int'l*, pg. 3863
PARADISE BEVERAGES (FIJI) LIMITED—See COCA-COLA EUROPACIFIC PARTNERS PLC; *Int'l*, pg. 1684
PARADISE BEVERAGES, INC.; *U.S. Private*, pg. 3090
PARADISE CASINO INCHEON—See Paradise Co. Ltd.; *Int'l*, pg. 5735
PARADISE CHAPEL FUNERAL HOME, INC.—See Security National Financial Corporation; *U.S. Public*, pg. 1856
PARADISE CHEVROLET; *U.S. Private*, pg. 3090
PARADISE CO. LTD.; *Int'l*, pg. 5735
PARADISE CRUISES LTD.; *U.S. Private*, pg. 3090
PARADISE DATACOM LLC—See Teledyne Technologies Incorporated; *U.S. Public*, pg. 1994
PARADISE DATACOM LTD—See Teledyne Technologies Incorporated; *U.S. Public*, pg. 1994
PARADISE ENTERTAINMENT LIMITED; *Int'l*, pg. 5735
PARADISE EXTERIORS LLC; *U.S. Private*, pg. 3090
PARADISE FUNERAL HOME, INC.—See Service Corporation International; *U.S. Public*, pg. 1870
PARADISE GALLERIES, INC.; *U.S. Private*, pg. 3090
PARADISE GLOBAL CASINO DIVISION CO., LTD.—See Paradise Co. Ltd.; *Int'l*, pg. 5735
PARADISE GRAND CASINO—See Paradise Co. Ltd.; *Int'l*, pg. 5735
PARADISE GROUP SP. Z O. O.—See Alma Market S.A.; *Int'l*, pg. 361
PARADISE HOME IMPROVEMENT LLC—See York Capital Management Global Advisors, LLC; *U.S. Private*, pg. 4590
PARADISE ICE PLANT; *U.S. Private*, pg. 3090
PARADISE, INC.; *U.S. Private*, pg. 3090
PARADISE ISLAND FOODS INC.; *Int'l*, pg. 5735
PARADISE LOTTE CASINO—See Paradise Co. Ltd.; *Int'l*, pg. 5735
PARADISE PLASTIC COMPANY LIMITED—See SNC Holding Company Limited; *Int'l*, pg. 7025
PARADISE PLASTICS, INC.—See Paradise, Inc.; *U.S. Private*, pg. 3090
PARADISE POST—See Alden Global Capital LLC; *U.S. Private*, pg. 156
PARADISE ROAD LLC—See ONEX Corporation; *Int'l*, pg. 5578
PARADISE ROAD LLC—See Surf City Garage, LLC; *U.S. Private*, pg. 3883
PARADISE STREAM RESORT—See Mcsam Hotel Group LLC; *U.S. Private*, pg. 2644
PARADISE TOMATO KITCHENS, INC.; *U.S. Private*, pg. 3090
PARADISE VACATION ADVENTURES, LLC—See Marriott Vacations Worldwide Corporation; *U.S. Public*, pg. 1374
PARADOX ENGINEERING S.A.; *Int'l*, pg. 5735
PARADOX INTERACTIVE AB; *Int'l*, pg. 5735
PARADY FINANCIAL GROUP, INC.—See Kelso & Company, L.P.; *U.S. Private*, pg. 2280
PARADYSZ MATERA COMPANY, INC.; *U.S. Private*, pg. 3090
PARAFIN CORP.; *U.S. Public*, pg. 1636
PARAFLUID GMBH—See FUCHS SE; *Int'l*, pg. 2804
PARAFLUID MINERALOELGESELLSCHAFT MBH—See FUCHS SE; *Int'l*, pg. 2804
PARAG BREWERIES LTD—See Carlsberg A/S; *Int'l*, pg. 1340
PARAGEM PTY LTD—See HUB24 Limited; *Int'l*, pg. 3517
PARAG MILK FOODS LTD; *Int'l*, pg. 5735
PARAGON 28, INC.; *U.S. Public*, pg. 1636
PARAGON ACURA; *U.S. Private*, pg. 3090
PARAGON ADVERTISING; *U.S. Private*, pg. 3090
PARAGON ADVERTISING; *U.S. Private*, pg. 3090
PARAGON ADVISOR PARTNERS LLP; *Int'l*, pg. 5735
PARAGON AGGREGATE PRODUCTS INC.—See Paragon Building Products Inc.; *U.S. Private*, pg. 3090
PARAGON AQUATICS—See Pentair plc; *Int'l*, pg. 5791

PARAGON BANKING GROUP PLC; *Int'l*, pg. 5735
PARAGON BIOSERVICES, INC.—See Catalent, Inc.; *U.S. Public*, pg. 449
PARAGON BROKERS (BERMUDA) LTD.—See PSC Insurance Group Limited; *Int'l*, pg. 6016
PARAGON BUILDING PRODUCTS INC. - NEVADA PREMIX DIVISION—See Paragon Building Products Inc.; *U.S. Private*, pg. 3090
PARAGON BUILDING PRODUCTS INC. - PARAGON CONCRETE PRODUCTS DIVISION—See Paragon Building Products Inc.; *U.S. Private*, pg. 3090
PARAGON BUILDING PRODUCTS INC.; *U.S. Private*, pg. 3090
PARAGON CARE GROUP AUSTRALIA PTY. LTD.—See Paragon Care Limited; *Int'l*, pg. 5736
PARAGON CARE GROUP NEW ZEALAND LTD.—See Paragon Care Limited; *Int'l*, pg. 5736
PARAGON CARE LIMITED; *Int'l*, pg. 5736
PARAGON CAR FINANCE (1) LIMITED—See Paragon Banking Group PLC; *Int'l*, pg. 5735
PARAGON CAR FINANCE LIMITED—See Paragon Banking Group PLC; *Int'l*, pg. 5735
PARAGON CERTIFIED RESTORATION; *U.S. Private*, pg. 3090
PARAGON CEYLON PLC; *Int'l*, pg. 5736
PARAGON COMMUNICATIONS SDN. BHD.—See WPP plc; *Int'l*, pg. 8492
PARAGON COMPUTER PROFESSIONALS INC.—See CGI Inc.; *Int'l*, pg. 1434
PARAGON CUSTOMER COMMUNICATIONS LIMITED—See SS&C Technologies Holdings, Inc.; *U.S. Public*, pg. 1923
PARAGON CUSTOMER COMMUNICATIONS SCHWANDORF GMBH—See Paragon Group Limited; *Int'l*, pg. 5737
PARAGON DATA ANALYTICS LIMITED—See SS&C Technologies Holdings, Inc.; *U.S. Public*, pg. 1923
PARAGON DECORS INC.; *U.S. Private*, pg. 3090
PARAGON DEVELOPMENT SYSTEMS, INC.—See Converge Technology Solutions Corp.; *Int'l*, pg. 1787
PARAGON DIE & ENGINEERING COMPANY; *U.S. Private*, pg. 3091
PARAGON DOOR DESIGNS, INC.—See True Home Value, Inc.; *U.S. Private*, pg. 4247
PARAGON DYNAMICS INC.—See Mercury Systems, Inc.; *U.S. Public*, pg. 1422
PARAGON ELECTROACOUSIC GMBH—See Paragon GmbH & Co. KGaA; *Int'l*, pg. 5736
PARAGON ELECTRONIC SYSTEMS INC.; *U.S. Private*, pg. 3091
PARAGON ENERGY SOLUTIONS, LLC; *U.S. Private*, pg. 3091
PARAGON ENTERTAINMENT LIMITED; *Int'l*, pg. 5736
PARAGON FILMS, INC.—See Wellspring Capital Management LLC; *U.S. Private*, pg. 4477
PARAGON FINANCE LTD.; *Int'l*, pg. 5736
PARAGON FINANCE PLC—See Paragon Banking Group PLC; *Int'l*, pg. 5735
PARAGON FINANCIAL SOLUTIONS, INC.; *U.S. Public*, pg. 1637
PARAGON FINE & SPECIALITY CHEMICAL LIMITED; *Int'l*, pg. 5736
PARAGON FOOD SERVICE; *U.S. Private*, pg. 3091
PARAGON GLOBAL RESOURCES, INC.; *U.S. Private*, pg. 3091
PARAGON GLOBE BERHAD; *Int'l*, pg. 5736
PARAGON GLOBE PROPERTIES SDN. BHD.—See Paragon Globe Berhad; *Int'l*, pg. 5736
PARAGON GMBH & CO. KGAA; *Int'l*, pg. 5736
PARAGON GROUP LIMITED - CORPORATE OFFICE—See Paragon Group Limited; *Int'l*, pg. 5737
PARAGON GROUP LIMITED; *Int'l*, pg. 5736
PARAGON GROUP UK LIMITED—See Paragon Group Limited; *Int'l*, pg. 5737
PARAGON HEALTHCARE, INC.—See Elevance Health, Inc.; *U.S. Public*, pg. 730
PARAGON HOTELBETRIEBS GMBH—See Erste Group Bank AG; *Int'l*, pg. 2499
PARAGON IDENTIFICATION SAS—See Paragon Banking Group PLC; *Int'l*, pg. 5735
PARAGON INDUSTRIES, INC.; *U.S. Private*, pg. 3091
PARAGON INDUSTRIES INC.; *U.S. Private*, pg. 3091
PARAGON INSURANCE HOLDINGS, LLC; *U.S. Private*, pg. 3091
PARAGON INTERNATIONAL, INC.; *U.S. Private*, pg. 3091
PARAGON INTERNATIONAL INSURANCE BROKERS LTD.—See PSC Insurance Group Limited; *Int'l*, pg. 6016
PARAGON LEGAL GROUP, P.C.; *U.S. Private*, pg. 3091
PARAGON MECHANICAL INC.; *U.S. Private*, pg. 3091
PARAGON MEDICAL, DEVICE (CHANGZHOU) CO., LTD.—See AMETEK, Inc.; *U.S. Public*, pg. 121
PARAGON MEDICAL EUROPE SARL—See AMETEK, Inc.; *U.S. Public*, pg. 121
PARAGON MEDICAL, INC.—See AMETEK, Inc.; *U.S. Public*, pg. 121
PARAGON MEDICAL INTERNATIONAL, INC.—See AMETEK, Inc.; *U.S. Public*, pg. 121

PARAGON METALS—See Stellex Capital Management LP; *U.S. Private*, pg. 3800
PARAGON MICRO, INC.; *U.S. Private*, pg. 3091
PARAGON MORTGAGES LIMITED—See Paragon Banking Group PLC; *Int'l*, pg. 5735
PARAGON MOTORS OF WOODSIDE, INC.; *U.S. Private*, pg. 3091
PARAGON PARK (COVENTRY) MANAGEMENT COMPANY LIMITED—See Persimmon plc; *Int'l*, pg. 5816
PARAGON PARTNERS GMBH; *Int'l*, pg. 5737
PARAGON PERSONAL FINANCE LIMITED—See Paragon Banking Group PLC; *Int'l*, pg. 5735
PARAGON PLASTICS, INC.; *U.S. Private*, pg. 3091
PARAGON PLUS INC.; *U.S. Private*, pg. 3091
PARAGON REIT; *Int'l*, pg. 5737
PARAGON ROMANIA S.R.L.—See Paragon Group Limited; *Int'l*, pg. 5737
PARAGON SECOND FUNDING LIMITED—See Paragon Banking Group PLC; *Int'l*, pg. 5735
PARAGON SEMVOX GMBH—See Porsche Automobil Holding SE; *Int'l*, pg. 5926
PARAGON SIECHNICE SP. Z O.O.—See AMETEK, Inc.; *U.S. Public*, pg. 121
PARAGON SOFTWARE SYSTEMS INC—See TA Associates, Inc.; *U.S. Private*, pg. 3914
PARAGON SOFTWARE SYSTEMS PLC—See TA Associates, Inc.; *U.S. Private*, pg. 3914
PARAGON SPACE DEVELOPMENT CORPORATION; *U.S. Private*, pg. 3091
PARAGON SPORTS CONSTRUCTORS LLC.; *U.S. Private*, pg. 3091
PARAGON STEEL ENTERPRISES LLC; *U.S. Private*, pg. 3091
PARAGON STEEL INC—See Midwest Pipe & Steel Inc.; *U.S. Private*, pg. 2722
PARAGON STRATEGIC SOLUTIONS INC.—See Aon plc; *Int'l*, pg. 490
PARAGON SURGERY CENTERS OF TEXAS, INC.—See HCA Healthcare, Inc.; *U.S. Public*, pg. 1005
PARAGON SYSTEMS, INC.—See Securitas AB; *Int'l*, pg. 6676
PARAGON TECHNICAL SERVICES, INC.—See Ergon, Inc.; *U.S. Private*, pg. 1418
PARAGON TECHNOLOGIES CO., LTD.; *Int'l*, pg. 5737
PARAGON TECHNOLOGIES, INC.; *U.S. Public*, pg. 1637
PARAGON TECHNOLOGIES INC.; *U.S. Private*, pg. 3092
PARAGON TECHNOLOGY GROUP, INC.—See Independence Capital Partners, LLC; *U.S. Private*, pg. 2056
PARAGON TRANSACTION S.A.—See Paragon Group Limited; *Int'l*, pg. 5737
PARAGON TUBE CORP.—See Midwest Pipe & Steel Inc.; *U.S. Private*, pg. 2722
PARAGON UNDERWRITERS, INC.—See ABRY Partners, LLC; *U.S. Private*, pg. 42
PARAGON UNION BERHAD; *Int'l*, pg. 5737
PARAGON VEHICLE CONTRACTS LIMITED—See Paragon Banking Group PLC; *Int'l*, pg. 5736
PARAGON VISION SCIENCES, INC.—See The Cooper Companies, Inc.; *U.S. Public*, pg. 2066
PARAGON WATER SYSTEMS, INC.—See BDT Capital Partners, LLC; *U.S. Private*, pg. 502
PARAGON WHOLESALE FOODS CORP.—See Sysco Corporation; *U.S. Public*, pg. 1975
PARAGON WOOD PRODUCT (DALIAN) CO., LTD.—See Sumitomo Forestry Co., Ltd.; *Int'l*, pg. 7286
PARAGON WOOD PRODUCT (SHANGHAI) CO., LTD.—See Sumitomo Forestry Co., Ltd.; *Int'l*, pg. 7286
PARAGON YACHTS OY—See R12 Kapital Fund I AB; *Int'l*, pg. 6171
PARAGOULD DAILY PRESS—See Paxton Media Group LLC; *U.S. Private*, pg. 3116
PARAGUS STRATEGIC IT; *U.S. Private*, pg. 3092
PARA LIGHT CORP.—See Para Light Electronics Co., Ltd.; *Int'l*, pg. 5734
PARA LIGHT ELECTRONICS CO., LTD.; *Int'l*, pg. 5734
PARA LIGHT ELECTRONICS HK LIMITED—See Para Light Electronics Co., Ltd.; *Int'l*, pg. 5734
PARA LIGHT INDIA PVT. LTD.—See Para Light Electronics Co., Ltd.; *Int'l*, pg. 5734
PARA LIGHT KOREA CO., LTD.—See Para Light Electronics Co., Ltd.; *Int'l*, pg. 5734
PARA LIGHT (QINGDAO) ELECTRONICS CO., LTD.—See Para Light Electronics Co., Ltd.; *Int'l*, pg. 5734
PARALLAX CAPITAL PARTNERS, LLC; *U.S. Private*, pg. 3092
PARALLAX CENTER, LLC—See AAC Holdings, Inc.; *U.S. Private*, pg. 30
PARALLAX HEALTH SCIENCES, INC.; *U.S. Private*, pg. 3092
PARALLAX POWER SUPPLIES LLC; *U.S. Private*, pg. 3092
PARALLEL49 EQUITY—See Tricor Pacific Capital, Inc.; *Int'l*, pg. 7920
PARALLEL 6, INC.—See ICON plc; *Int'l*, pg. 3585
PARALLEL GRAPHICS LTD.—See Siemens Aktiengesellschaft; *Int'l*, pg. 6887
PARALLEL INVESTMENT PARTNERS LLC; *U.S. Private*, pg. 3092
PARALLEL MINING CORP.; *Int'l*, pg. 5737

COMPANY NAME INDEX — PARATECH, INC.

PARALLEL PETROLEUM LLC—See Samsung Group; *Int'l*, pg. 6511
PARALLEL PRODUCTS OF KENTUCKY, INC.; *U.S. Private*, pg. 3092
PARALLELS, INC.—See KKR & Co. Inc.; *U.S. Public*, pg. 1243
PARALLEL TELEVISION (2001) LTD—See Live Company Group Plc; *Int'l*, pg. 4530
PARALLO LIMITED—See Crayon Group Holding ASA; *Int'l*, pg. 1829
PARALLON BUSINESS SOLUTIONS, LLC—See HCA Healthcare, Inc.; *U.S. Public*, pg. 1005
PARALLON TECHNOLOGY SOLUTIONS, LLC—See HCA Healthcare, Inc.; *U.S. Public*, pg. 1006
PARALLON WORKFORCE MANAGEMENT SOLUTIONS, LLC—See HCA Healthcare, Inc.; *U.S. Public*, pg. 1006
PARAMEDICS PLUS LLC—See Alvarez & Marsal, Inc.; *U.S. Private*, pg. 213
PARAMETRIC PORTFOLIO ASSOCIATES LLC—See Morgan Stanley; *U.S. Public*, pg. 1471
PARAMETRIC SOLUTIONS, INC.; *U.S. Private*, pg. 3092
PARAMETRIC TECH BRASIL LTDA.—See PTC Inc.; *U.S. Public*, pg. 1734
PARAMETRIC TECHNOLOGY AUSTRALIA PTY. LIMITED—See PTC Inc.; *U.S. Public*, pg. 1735
PARAMETRIC TECHNOLOGY (CANADA) LTD. - WATERLOO—See PTC Inc.; *U.S. Public*, pg. 1734
PARAMETRIC TECHNOLOGY CORPORATION (MALAYSIA) SDN. BHD.—See PTC Inc.; *U.S. Public*, pg. 1735
PARAMETRIC TECHNOLOGY (DENMARK) A/S—See PTC Inc.; *U.S. Public*, pg. 1734
PARAMETRIC TECHNOLOGY ESPANA, S.A.—See PTC Inc.; *U.S. Public*, pg. 1735
PARAMETRIC TECHNOLOGY EUROPE B.V.—See PTC Inc.; *U.S. Public*, pg. 1735
PARAMETRIC TECHNOLOGY GESELLSCHAFT, M.B.H.—See PTC Inc.; *U.S. Public*, pg. 1735
PARAMETRIC TECHNOLOGY GMBH - SINDELFINGEN—See PTC Inc.; *U.S. Public*, pg. 1735
PARAMETRIC TECHNOLOGY GMBH—See PTC Inc.; *U.S. Public*, pg. 1735
PARAMETRIC TECHNOLOGY (HONG KONG) LIMITED—See PTC Inc.; *U.S. Public*, pg. 1734
PARAMETRIC TECHNOLOGY (INDIA) PRIVATE LTD.—See PTC Inc.; *U.S. Public*, pg. 1734
PARAMETRIC TECHNOLOGY ISRAEL LTD.—See PTC Inc.; *U.S. Public*, pg. 1735
PARAMETRIC TECHNOLOGY MEXICO, S.A. DE C.V.—See PTC Inc.; *U.S. Public*, pg. 1735
PARAMETRIC TECHNOLOGY S.A.—See PTC Inc.; *U.S. Public*, pg. 1735
PARAMETRIC TECHNOLOGY (SCHWEIZ) AG—See PTC Inc.; *U.S. Public*, pg. 1735
PARAMETRIC TECHNOLOGY SINGAPORE PTE. LTD.—See PTC Inc.; *U.S. Public*, pg. 1735
PARAMETRIC TECHNOLOGY (UK) LTD.—See PTC Inc.; *U.S. Public*, pg. 1735
PARAMETRIX, INC.; *U.S. Private*, pg. 3092
PARAMIT CORPORATION—See Tecan Group AG; *Int'l*, pg. 7501
PARAMIT MALAYSIA SDN. BHD—See Tecan Group AG; *Int'l*, pg. 7502
PARAMIT MALYSIA SDN. BHD.—See Tecan Group AG; *Int'l*, pg. 7502
PARAMO, A.S.—See Orlen S.A.; *Int'l*, pg. 5641
PARAMODEN SDN. BHD.—See M K Land Holdings Berhad; *Int'l*, pg. 4610
PARAMONT CONTURA, LLC—See Alpha Metallurgical Resources, Inc.; *U.S. Public*, pg. 82
PARAMONT MACHINE COMPANY, INC.—See A. M. Castle & Co.; *U.S. Public*, pg. 11
PARAMORE THE DIGITAL AGENCY LLC—See Osborn & Barr Communications; *U.S. Private*, pg. 3046
PARAMOUNT ADVERTISER SERVICES INC.—See National Amusements, Inc.; *U.S. Private*, pg. 2843
PARAMOUNT APPAREL INTERNATIONAL INC.; *U.S. Private*, pg. 3092
PARAMOUNT BEAUTY DISTRIBUTING ASSOCIATES INC.; *U.S. Private*, pg. 3092
PARAMOUNT BED ASIA PACIFIC PTE. LTD.—See Paramount Bed Holdings Co., Ltd.; *Int'l*, pg. 5737
PARAMOUNT BED (CHINA) CO., LTD.—See Paramount Bed Holdings Co., Ltd.; *Int'l*, pg. 5737
PARAMOUNT BED DO BRASIL LTDA.—See Paramount Bed Holdings Co., Ltd.; *Int'l*, pg. 5737
PARAMOUNT BED HOLDINGS CO., LTD.; *Int'l*, pg. 5737
PARAMOUNT BED INDIA PVT. LTD.—See Paramount Bed Holdings Co., Ltd.; *Int'l*, pg. 5737
PARAMOUNT BED MEXICO S.A. DE C.V.—See Paramount Bed Holdings Co., Ltd.; *Int'l*, pg. 5737
PARAMOUNT BED VIETNAM CO., LTD.—See Paramount Bed Holdings Co., Ltd.; *Int'l*, pg. 5737
PARAMOUNT BRITISH PICTURES LIMITED—See National Amusements, Inc.; *U.S. Private*, pg. 2843
PARAMOUNT BUILDERS INC.; *U.S. Private*, pg. 3092
PARAMOUNT BUILDING SOLUTIONS, LLC—See GDI Integrated Facility Services Inc.; *Int'l*, pg. 2896
PARAMOUNT BUSINESS JETS; *U.S. Private*, pg. 3092

PARAMOUNT CAN COMPANY INC.; *U.S. Private*, pg. 3092
PARAMOUNT CENTRE, INC.—See Susquehanna International Group, LLP; *U.S. Private*, pg. 3885
PARAMOUNT COMEDY CHANNEL ESPANA S.L.—See National Amusements, Inc.; *U.S. Private*, pg. 2842
PARAMOUNT COMMUNICATIONS LIMITED - DHARUHERA PLANT—See Paramount Communications Limited; *Int'l*, pg. 5737
PARAMOUNT COMMUNICATIONS LIMITED; *Int'l*, pg. 5737
PARAMOUNT CONTRACTING, INC.; *U.S. Private*, pg. 3092
PARAMOUNT CORPORATION BERHAD; *Int'l*, pg. 5737
PARAMOUNT COSMETICS INDIA LIMITED; *Int'l*, pg. 5738
PARAMOUNT DRILLING U.S. LLC—See Paramount Resources Ltd.; *Int'l*, pg. 5738
PARAMOUNT ENGINEERING & CONSTRUCTION SDN. BHD.—See Paramount Corporation Berhad; *Int'l*, pg. 5738
PARAMOUNT EQUIPMENT LLC; *U.S. Private*, pg. 3092
PARAMOUNT EQUITY MORTGAGE, LLC; *U.S. Private*, pg. 3093
PARAMOUNT FOODS INC.; *U.S. Private*, pg. 3093
PARAMOUNT GLASS MANUFACTURING CO., LTD.—See NITTO BOSEKI CO., LTD.; *Int'l*, pg. 5384
PARAMOUNT GLOBAL—See National Amusements, Inc.; *U.S. Private*, pg. 2839
PARAMOUNT GLOBAL SURFACES—See Platinum Equity, LLC; *U.S. Private*, pg. 3206
PARAMOUNT GOLD NEVADA CORP.; *U.S. Public*, pg. 1637
PARAMOUNT GROUP INC.; *U.S. Public*, pg. 1637
PARAMOUNT GROUP REAL ESTATE ADVISOR LLC—See Paramount Group Inc.; *U.S. Public*, pg. 1637
PARAMOUNT HEALTH SYSTEMS—See American Healthcare Systems Corp., Inc.; *U.S. Private*, pg. 236
PARAMOUNT HOLDINGS LTD—See Silverfleet Capital Limited; *Int'l*, pg. 6925
PARAMOUNT HOME ENTERTAINMENT (AUSTRALASIA) PTY. LIMITED—See National Amusements, Inc.; *U.S. Private*, pg. 2843
PARAMOUNT HOME ENTERTAINMENT (BRAZIL) LIMITADA—See National Amusements, Inc.; *U.S. Private*, pg. 2843
PARAMOUNT HOME ENTERTAINMENT (DENMARK) I/S—See National Amusements, Inc.; *U.S. Private*, pg. 2843
PARAMOUNT HOME ENTERTAINMENT (FINLAND) OY—See National Amusements, Inc.; *U.S. Private*, pg. 2843
PARAMOUNT HOME ENTERTAINMENT (GERMANY) GMBH—See National Amusements, Inc.; *U.S. Private*, pg. 2843
PARAMOUNT HOME ENTERTAINMENT INTERNATIONAL LIMITED—See National Amusements, Inc.; *U.S. Private*, pg. 2843
PARAMOUNT HOME ENTERTAINMENT (MEXICO) S. DE R.L. DE C.V.—See National Amusements, Inc.; *U.S. Private*, pg. 2843
PARAMOUNT HOME ENTERTAINMENT (NORWAY) ANS—See National Amusements, Inc.; *U.S. Private*, pg. 2843
PARAMOUNT HOME ENTERTAINMENT (SWEDEN) AB—See National Amusements, Inc.; *U.S. Private*, pg. 2843
PARAMOUNT HOMES LLC; *U.S. Private*, pg. 3093
PARAMOUNT HOTEL GROUP, LLC; *U.S. Private*, pg. 3093
PARAMOUNT HOTELS LLC; *U.S. Private*, pg. 3093
PARAMOUNT INSURANCE COMPANY LIMITED; *Int'l*, pg. 5738
PARAMOUNT INSURANCE REPAIR SERVICE; *U.S. Private*, pg. 3093
PARAMOUNT INTERNATIONAL NETHERLANDS B.V.—See National Amusements, Inc.; *U.S. Private*, pg. 2843
PARAMOUNT LIFE & GENERAL INSURANCE CORPORATION; *Int'l*, pg. 5738
PARAMOUNT MANUFACTURING LLC; *U.S. Private*, pg. 3093
PARAMOUNT METALIZING DIV.—See Koller Enterprises, Inc.; *U.S. Private*, pg. 2341
PARAMOUNT-NEVADA ASPHALT COMPANY, LLC—See Marathon Petroleum Corporation; *U.S. Public*, pg. 1363
PARAMOUNT PAINTING & INDUSTRIAL SERVICES, INC.—See Tailwind Capital Group, LLC; *U.S. Private*, pg. 3924
PARAMOUNT PICTURES AUSTRALIA PTY.—See National Amusements, Inc.; *U.S. Private*, pg. 2843
PARAMOUNT PICTURES CORPORATION—See National Amusements, Inc.; *U.S. Private*, pg. 2842
PARAMOUNT PICTURES ENTERTAINMENT CANADA INC.—See National Amusements, Inc.; *U.S. Private*, pg. 2843
PARAMOUNT PICTURES FRANCE SARL—See National Amusements, Inc.; *U.S. Private*, pg. 2843

PARAMOUNT PICTURES INTERNATIONAL LIMITED—See National Amusements, Inc.; *U.S. Private*, pg. 2843
PARAMOUNT PICTURES MEXICO S. DE R.L. DE C.V.—See National Amusements, Inc.; *U.S. Private*, pg. 2843
PARAMOUNT PICTURES NZ—See National Amusements, Inc.; *U.S. Private*, pg. 2843
PARAMOUNT PRECISION PRODUCTS, INC.; *U.S. Private*, pg. 3093
PARAMOUNT PRINTING COMPANY LIMITED—See Next Digital Limited; *Int'l*, pg. 5248
PARAMOUNT PRINTPACKAGING LTD; *Int'l*, pg. 5738
PARAMOUNT PRODUCTION SUPPORT INC.—See National Amusements, Inc.; *U.S. Private*, pg. 2843
PARAMOUNT PRODUCTION SUPPORT INC.—See National Amusements, Inc.; *U.S. Private*, pg. 2843
PARAMOUNT PROPERTY (CITYVIEW) SDN. BHD.—See Paramount Corporation Berhad; *Int'l*, pg. 5738
PARAMOUNT PROPERTY FUND LIMITED—See Growthpoint Properties Limited; *Int'l*, pg. 3113
PARAMOUNT PROPERTY HOLDINGS SDN. BHD.—See Paramount Corporation Berhad; *Int'l*, pg. 5738
PARAMOUNT PROPERTY (SEKITAR 26 ENTERPRISE) SDN. BHD.—See Paramount Corporation Berhad; *Int'l*, pg. 5738
PARAMOUNT PROPERTY (UTARA) SDN. BHD.—See Paramount Corporation Berhad; *Int'l*, pg. 5738
PARAMOUNT RESEARCH, INC.—See Colgate-Palmolive Company; *U.S. Public*, pg. 533
PARAMOUNT RESIDENTIAL MORTGAGE GROUP, INC.; *U.S. Private*, pg. 3093
PARAMOUNT RESOURCES (ACL) LTD.—See Paramount Resources Ltd.; *Int'l*, pg. 5738
PARAMOUNT RESOURCES LTD.; *Int'l*, pg. 5738
PARAMOUNT RESTAURANT SUPPLY CORPORATION; *U.S. Private*, pg. 3093
PARAMOUNT SPAIN S.L.—See National Amusements, Inc.; *U.S. Private*, pg. 2843
PARAMOUNT SPINNING MILLS LIMITED—See Gulistan Group; *Int'l*, pg. 3182
PARAMOUNT SUPPLY CO. INC.; *U.S. Private*, pg. 3093
PARAMOUNT TECHNICAL PRODUCTS—See RPM International Inc.; *U.S. Public*, pg. 1818
PARAMOUNT TECHNOLOGIES, INC.—See PaperSave, Inc.; *U.S. Private*, pg. 3088
PARAMOUNT THEATER SCP L.P.—See Wells Fargo & Company; *U.S. Public*, pg. 2345
PARAMOUNT TRADING (JAMAICA) LIMITED; *Int'l*, pg. 5738
PARAMOUNT TUBE—See Auxo Investment Partners, LLC; *U.S. Private*, pg. 402
PARAMOUNT VENTURES SDN. BHD.—See Stella Holdings Berhad; *Int'l*, pg. 7195
PARAMOUNT WINDOWS, INC.—See Altamont Capital Partners; *U.S. Private*, pg. 205
PARAMOUNT WINDOWS INC.; *Int'l*, pg. 5738
PARAMOUNT WORLDWIDE PRODUCTIONS INC.—See National Amusements, Inc.; *U.S. Private*, pg. 2843
PARAMUS AUTO MALL CHEVROLET-HUMMER; *U.S. Private*, pg. 3093
PARAMUS ENDOSCOPY, LLC—See Tenet Healthcare Corporation; *U.S. Public*, pg. 2012
PARANA BANCO SA—See J. Malucelli Holding SA; *Int'l*, pg. 3856
PARANA BCO S.A.; *Int'l*, pg. 5738
PARANAPANEMA S.A.; *Int'l*, pg. 5739
PARANET SOLUTIONS, LLC; *U.S. Private*, pg. 3093
PARANGUL SA; *Int'l*, pg. 5739
PARANOVUS ENTERTAINMENT TECHNOLOGY LTD.; *Int'l*, pg. 5739
PARA-PLUS TRANSLATIONS, INC.; *U.S. Private*, pg. 3089
PARASCRIPT LLC; *U.S. Private*, pg. 3093
PARAS DEFENCE & SPACE TECHNOLOGIES LTD.; *Int'l*, pg. 5739
PARAS FLOWFORM ENGINEERING LIMITED; *Int'l*, pg. 5739
PARASOLE RESTAURANT HOLDINGS, INC.; *U.S. Private*, pg. 3093
PARASOL TAHOE COMMUNITY FOUNDATION; *U.S. Private*, pg. 3093
PARASTAR, INC.—See Beaumont Health; *U.S. Private*, pg. 508
PARASTEK OY AB—See Bain Capital, LP; *U.S. Private*, pg. 438
PARASUCO JEANS INC.; *Int'l*, pg. 5739
PARASYN LTD.—See Synergon Holding PLC; *Int'l*, pg. 7384
PARA SYSTEMS INC.—See Components Corporation of America, Inc.; *U.S. Private*, pg. 1002
PARATA SYSTEMS, LLC—See Becton, Dickinson & Company; *U.S. Public*, pg. 292
PARATECH CO., LTD. - SEOSAN PLANT—See Paratech Co., Ltd.; *Int'l*, pg. 5739
PARATECH CO., LTD.; *Int'l*, pg. 5739
PARATECH, INC.; *U.S. Private*, pg. 3093
PARATECHNO CO., LTD.—See Paramount Bed Holdings Co., Ltd.; *Int'l*, pg. 5737

PARATECH, INC.   CORPORATE AFFILIATIONS

PARATEK PHARMACEUTICALS, INC.—See Gurnet Point Capital LLC; *U.S. Private*, pg. 1819
PARATEK PHARMACEUTICALS, INC.—See Novo Nordisk Fonden; *Int'l*, pg. 5465
PARATEK PHARMACEUTICALS, LLC—See Gurnet Point Capital LLC; *U.S. Private*, pg. 1819
PARATEK PHARMACEUTICALS, LLC—See Novo Nordisk Fonden; *Int'l*, pg. 5465
PARATI INDUSTRIA E COMERCIO DE ALIMENTOS LTDA—See Kellanova; *U.S. Public*, pg. 1218
PARATRANSIT SERVICES; *U.S. Private*, pg. 3093
PARATURE, INC.—See Microsoft Corporation; *U.S. Public*, pg. 1443
PARA. TV INC.—See Avex Inc.; *Int'l*, pg. 740
PARA USA, LLC—See Cerberus Capital Management, L.P.; *U.S. Private*, pg. 839
PARAVION TECHNOLOGIES INC.—See TransDigm Group Incorporated; *U.S. Public*, pg. 2181
PAR AVION TRAVEL, INC.; *U.S. Private*, pg. 3089
PARAYTEC LIMITED—See Braveheart Investment Group Plc; *Int'l*, pg. 1141
PARAZUL LLC—See LVMH Moet Hennessy Louis Vuitton SE; *Int'l*, pg. 4601
PAR BIOSCIENCES PRIVATE LIMITED—See Endo International plc; *Int'l*, pg. 2404
PAR CAPITAL MANAGEMENT, INC.; *U.S. Private*, pg. 3089
PARC ASTERIX SAS—See Compagnie des Alpes S.A.; *Int'l*, pg. 1738
PARC AT MAUMELLE, LP—See American Realty Investors, Inc.; *U.S. Public*, pg. 109
PARC AT METRO CENTER, LP—See American Realty Investors, Inc.; *U.S. Public*, pg. 109
PARC AT ROGERS, LP—See American Realty Investors, Inc.; *U.S. Public*, pg. 109
PARC AVIATION, LTD.—See CAE Inc.; *Int'l*, pg. 1249
PARCEL DIRECTGROUP PTY LIMITED—See New Zealand Post Limited; *Int'l*, pg. 5232
PARCELFORCE LTD—See International Distributions Services plc; *Int'l*, pg. 3748
PARCELL STEEL CO., INC.; *U.S. Private*, pg. 3094
PARCELPAL LOGISTICS INC.; *Int'l*, pg. 5739
PARCEL PENDING INC.—See Quadient SA; *Int'l*, pg. 6149
PARCEL PRO, INC.—See United Parcel Service, Inc.; *U.S. Public*, pg. 2233
PARCHEM CONSTRUCTION SUPPLIES PTY LIMITED—See Nippon Paint Holdings Co., Ltd.; *Int'l*, pg. 5325
PARCHMENT LLC—See KKR & Co. Inc.; *U.S. Public*, pg. 1253
PARC, INC.; *U.S. Private*, pg. 3094
PARC LOGISTIC TRANSILVANIA SRL; *Int'l*, pg. 5739
PARCO CO., LTD.—See J. Front Retailing Co., Ltd.; *Int'l*, pg. 3855
PARCO DIGITAL MARKETING CO., LTD.—See J. Front Retailing Co., Ltd.; *Int'l*, pg. 3855
PARCO EOLICO DEL SAN GOTTARDO SA—See Azienda Elettrica Ticinese; *Int'l*, pg. 779
PARCO INC.—See Pema Holding AG; *Int'l*, pg. 5784
PARCOM CAPITAL MANAGEMENT B.V.; *Int'l*, pg. 5739
PARCO PEARL GAS LIMITED—See Pak-Arab Refinery Ltd.; *Int'l*, pg. 5703
PARCO (SINGAPORE) PTE LTD.—See J. Front Retailing Co., Ltd.; *Int'l*, pg. 3855
PARCO SPACE SYSTEMS CO., LTD.—See J. Front Retailing Co., Ltd.; *Int'l*, pg. 3855
PARCUS MEDICAL, LLC—See Anika Therapeutics, Inc.; *U.S. Public*, pg. 137
PARDEE HOMES—See Tri Pointe Homes, Inc.; *U.S. Public*, pg. 2188
PARDEE RESOURCES COMPANY; *U.S. Public*, pg. 1637
PARDES BIOSCIENCES, INC.—See Foresite Capital Management, LLC; *U.S. Private*, pg. 1566
PARDIOR, S.A. DE C.V.—See LVMH Moet Hennessy Louis Vuitton SE; *Int'l*, pg. 4598
PARDIS INVESTMENT COMPANY; *Int'l*, pg. 5741
PARDIS PETROCHEMICAL COMPANY; *Int'l*, pg. 5741
PARDOT EMEA—See Salesforce, Inc.; *U.S. Public*, pg. 1837
PARDOT LLC—See Salesforce, Inc.; *U.S. Public*, pg. 1837
PARDOT NORDIC—See Salesforce, Inc.; *U.S. Public*, pg. 1837
PAR DRUGS & CHEMICALS LIMITED; *Int'l*, pg. 5734
PARECO S.N.C.—See Savencia Fromage & Dairy; *Int'l*, pg. 6597
PAREF SA—See Fosun International Limited; *Int'l*, pg. 2752
PAREKH ALUMINEX LIMITED; *Int'l*, pg. 5741
PAREK PAPIERVERWERTUNGS GESELLSCHAFT M.B.H.—See Mayr-Melnhof Karton AG; *Int'l*, pg. 4747
PAR ELECTRICAL CONTRACTORS, INC.—See Quanta Services, Inc.; *U.S. Public*, pg. 1752
PARENCO B.V.—See H2 Equity Partners B.V.; *Int'l*, pg. 3199
PARENT CAPITAL CORP.; *Int'l*, pg. 5741
THE PARENT COMPANY, INC.; *U.S. Private*, pg. 4090
PARENTECH HEALTHCARE LIMITED—See Parenteral Drugs (India) Limited; *Int'l*, pg. 5741

PARENTERAL DRUG ASSOCIATION, INC.; *U.S. Private*, pg. 3094
PARENTERAL DRUGS (INDIA) LIMITED; *Int'l*, pg. 5741
PAR ENTERPRISES, INC.; *U.S. Private*, pg. 3089
PARENTGIVING, INC.—See Santex S.p.a.; *Int'l*, pg. 6558
PARENTHESIS, INC.; *U.S. Private*, pg. 3094
THE PARENTING GROUP, INC.—See Bonnier AB; *Int'l*, pg. 1109
PARENT PETROLEUM INC.; *U.S. Private*, pg. 3094
PARENTS IN COMMUNITY ACTION, INC.; *U.S. Private*, pg. 3094
PARENTS MAGAZINE—See Meredith Corporation; *U.S. Public*, pg. 1423
PARESKY FLITT & COMPANY, LLP—See UHY LLP; *U.S. Private*, pg. 4275
PA RESOURCES AB; *Int'l*, pg. 5684
P.A. RESOURCES BERHAD; *Int'l*, pg. 5682
PARETEUM CORPORATION; *U.S. Public*, pg. 1637
PARETO BANK ASA; *Int'l*, pg. 5741
PARETO CORPORATION—See The Riverside Company; *U.S. Private*, pg. 4109
PARETO GROUP; *Int'l*, pg. 5741
PARETO INVESTMENT MANAGEMENT LIMITED—See The Bank of New York Mellon Corporation; *U.S. Public*, pg. 2038
PARETO LAW LTD—See Randstad N.V.; *Int'l*, pg. 6202
PARETO PHONE PTY LIMITED—See IVE Group Limited; *Int'l*, pg. 3847
PARETO SECURITIES AS—See Pareto Group; *Int'l*, pg. 5741
PARETTI IMPORTS INC.; *U.S. Private*, pg. 3094
PARETTI MAZDA; *U.S. Private*, pg. 3094
PAREX ASSET MANAGEMENT RUSSIA—See AS Reverta; *Int'l*, pg. 591
PAREX ASSET MANAGEMENT—See AS Reverta; *Int'l*, pg. 591
PAREX ASSET MANAGEMENT UKRAINE—See AS Reverta; *Int'l*, pg. 591
PAREX BANK SWEIGNIEDERLASSUNG BERLIN—See AS Reverta; *Int'l*, pg. 591
PAREX BROKERAGE SYSTEM—See AS Reverta; *Int'l*, pg. 591
PAREXEL BELGIUM SPRL—See Pamplona Capital Management LLP; *Int'l*, pg. 5712
PAREXEL DENMARK A/S—See Pamplona Capital Management LLP; *Int'l*, pg. 5712
PAREXEL FINLAND OY—See Pamplona Capital Management LLP; *Int'l*, pg. 5712
PAREXEL HUNGARY LIMITED—See Pamplona Capital Management LLP; *Int'l*, pg. 5712
PAREXEL INTERNATIONAL CLINICAL RESEARCH (ISRAEL) LTD.—See Pamplona Capital Management LLP; *Int'l*, pg. 5712
PAREXEL INTERNATIONAL CO. LTD.—See Pamplona Capital Management LLP; *Int'l*, pg. 5712
PAREXEL INTERNATIONAL CORPORATION—See Pamplona Capital Management LLP; *Int'l*, pg. 5712
PAREXEL INTERNATIONAL CZECH REPUBLIC S.R.O.—See Pamplona Capital Management LLP; *Int'l*, pg. 5712
PAREXEL INTERNATIONAL D.O.O.—See Pamplona Capital Management LLP; *Int'l*, pg. 5712
PAREXEL INTERNATIONAL GMBH—See Pamplona Capital Management LLP; *Int'l*, pg. 5712
PAREXEL INTERNATIONAL HOLDING GERMANY GMBH—See Pamplona Capital Management LLP; *Int'l*, pg. 5712
PAREXEL INTERNATIONAL HOLDING UK LIMITED—See Pamplona Capital Management LLP; *Int'l*, pg. 5712
PAREXEL INTERNATIONAL (HONG KONG) COMPANY LIMITED—See Pamplona Capital Management LLP; *Int'l*, pg. 5712
PAREXEL INTERNATIONAL INC.—See Pamplona Capital Management LLP; *Int'l*, pg. 5712
PAREXEL INTERNATIONAL (INDIA) PRIVATE LIMITED—See Pamplona Capital Management LLP; *Int'l*, pg. 5712
PAREXEL INTERNATIONAL (IRL) LIMITED—See Pamplona Capital Management LLP; *Int'l*, pg. 5712
PAREXEL INTERNATIONAL LIMITED—See Pamplona Capital Management LLP; *Int'l*, pg. 5712
PAREXEL INTERNATIONAL, LLC—See Pamplona Capital Management LLP; *Int'l*, pg. 5712
PAREXEL INTERNATIONAL, LLC—See Pamplona Capital Management LLP; *Int'l*, pg. 5712
PAREXEL INTERNATIONAL, LLC—See Pamplona Capital Management LLP; *Int'l*, pg. 5712
PAREXEL INTERNATIONAL (MALAYSIA) SDN BHD—See Pamplona Capital Management LLP; *Int'l*, pg. 5712
PAREXEL INTERNATIONAL MEXICO S.A. DE C.V.—See Pamplona Capital Management LLP; *Int'l*, pg. 5712
PAREXEL INTERNATIONAL PESQUISAS CLINICAS LTDA.—See Pamplona Capital Management LLP; *Int'l*, pg. 5712
PAREXEL INTERNATIONAL PTY LTD.—See Pamplona Capital Management LLP; *Int'l*, pg. 5712
PAREXEL INTERNATIONAL ROMANIA SRL—See Pamplona Capital Management LLP; *Int'l*, pg. 5712

PAREXEL INTERNATIONAL SARL—See Pamplona Capital Management LLP; *Int'l*, pg. 5712
PAREXEL INTERNATIONAL SARL—See Pamplona Capital Management LLP; *Int'l*, pg. 5712
PAREXEL INTERNATIONAL, S.A.—See Pamplona Capital Management LLP; *Int'l*, pg. 5712
PAREXEL INTERNATIONAL (SINGAPORE) PTE. LTD.—See Pamplona Capital Management LLP; *Int'l*, pg. 5712
PAREXEL INTERNATIONAL S.L.—See Pamplona Capital Management LLP; *Int'l*, pg. 5712
PAREXEL INTERNATIONAL—See Pamplona Capital Management LLP; *Int'l*, pg. 5712
PAREXEL INTERNATIONAL—See Pamplona Capital Management LLP; *Int'l*, pg. 5713
PAREXEL INTERNATIONAL SRL—See Pamplona Capital Management LLP; *Int'l*, pg. 5712
PAREXEL INTERNATIONAL (THAILAND) CO., LTD.—See Pamplona Capital Management LLP; *Int'l*, pg. 5712
PAREXEL INTERNATIONAL (UK) LIMITED—See Pamplona Capital Management LLP; *Int'l*, pg. 5712
PAREXEL KOREA CO., LTD.—See Pamplona Capital Management LLP; *Int'l*, pg. 5713
PAREXEL MMS EUROPE LIMITED—See Pamplona Capital Management LLP; *Int'l*, pg. 5713
PAREXEL NEDERLAND B.V.—See Pamplona Capital Management LLP; *Int'l*, pg. 5713
PAREXEL POLSKA SP Z.O.O.—See Pamplona Capital Management LLP; *Int'l*, pg. 5713
PAREXEL RUSSIA A/S—See Pamplona Capital Management LLP; *Int'l*, pg. 5713
PAREXEL UKRAINE LLC—See Pamplona Capital Management LLP; *Int'l*, pg. 5713
PAREXGROUP SA—See Sika AG; *Int'l*, pg. 6915
PAREX, INC.—See Sika AG; *Int'l*, pg. 6915
PAREX INDUSTRIES LIMITED—See Emerson Electric Co.; *U.S. Public*, pg. 751
PAREXKLAUKOL S.A.—See Sika AG; *Int'l*, pg. 6915
PAREXLANKO—See Sika AG; *Int'l*, pg. 6915
PAREX LEASING & FACTORING—See AS Reverta; *Int'l*, pg. 591
PAREX LTD.—See Sika AG; *Int'l*, pg. 6915
PAREX OPEN PENSION FUND—See AS Reverta; *Int'l*, pg. 591
PAREX RESOURCES (COLOMBIA) LTD.—See Parex Resources Inc.; *Int'l*, pg. 5741
PAREX RESOURCES INC.; *Int'l*, pg. 5741
PAREX USA, INC.—See Sika AG; *Int'l*, pg. 6915
PARFAS LIMITED; *Int'l*, pg. 5741
PARFETTS; *Int'l*, pg. 5741
PARFIPAR SA—See Belfius Bank SA/NV; *Int'l*, pg. 963
PAR FORMULATIONS PRIVATE LIMITED—See Endo International plc; *Int'l*, pg. 2404
PARFUMERIE DOUGLAS AG—See CVC Capital Partners SICAV-FIS S.A.; *Int'l*, pg. 1883
PARFUMERIE DOUGLAS GES.M.B.H.—See CVC Capital Partners SICAV-FIS S.A.; *Int'l*, pg. 1883
PARFUMERIE DOUGLAS GMBH—See CVC Capital Partners SICAV-FIS S.A.; *Int'l*, pg. 1883
PARFUMERIE DOUGLAS INTERNATIONAL GMBH—See CVC Capital Partners SICAV-FIS S.A.; *Int'l*, pg. 1883
PARFUMERIE DOUGLAS MONACO S.A.M.—See CVC Capital Partners SICAV-FIS S.A.; *Int'l*, pg. 1883
PARFUMERIE DOUGLAS NEDERLAND B.V.—See CVC Capital Partners SICAV-FIS S.A.; *Int'l*, pg. 1883
PARFUMERIE DOUGLAS S.R.O.—See CVC Capital Partners SICAV-FIS S.A.; *Int'l*, pg. 1883
PARFUMES GIVENCHY—See LVMH Moet Hennessy Louis Vuitton SE; *Int'l*, pg. 4593
PARFUMS CACHAREL & CIE SNC—See L'Oreal S.A.; *Int'l*, pg. 4381
PARFUMS CACHREL & CIE—See L'Oreal S.A.; *Int'l*, pg. 4381
PARFUMS CARON—See Impala SAS; *Int'l*, pg. 3631
PARFUMS CHRISTIAN DIOR AB—See LVMH Moet Hennessy Louis Vuitton SE; *Int'l*, pg. 4598
PARFUMS CHRISTIAN DIOR AG—See LVMH Moet Hennessy Louis Vuitton SE; *Int'l*, pg. 4598
PARFUMS CHRISTIAN DIOR A/S LTD—See LVMH Moet Hennessy Louis Vuitton SE; *Int'l*, pg. 4600
PARFUMS CHRISTIAN DIOR A/S—See LVMH Moet Hennessy Louis Vuitton SE; *Int'l*, pg. 4598
PARFUMS CHRISTIAN DIOR (AUSTRALIA) PTY LTD—See LVMH Moet Hennessy Louis Vuitton SE; *Int'l*, pg. 4598
PARFUMS CHRISTIAN DIOR BV—See LVMH Moet Hennessy Louis Vuitton SE; *Int'l*, pg. 4598
PARFUMS CHRISTIAN DIOR CANADA INC.—See LVMH Moet Hennessy Louis Vuitton SE; *Int'l*, pg. 4598
PARFUMS CHRISTIAN DIOR GMBH—See LVMH Moet Hennessy Louis Vuitton SE; *Int'l*, pg. 4598
PARFUMS CHRISTIAN DIOR GMBH—See LVMH Moet Hennessy Louis Vuitton SE; *Int'l*, pg. 4598
PARFUMS CHRISTIAN DIOR HELLAS S.A.—See LVMH Moet Hennessy Louis Vuitton SE; *Int'l*, pg. 4598
PARFUMS CHRISTIAN DIOR HONG KONG LTD—See LVMH Moet Hennessy Louis Vuitton SE; *Int'l*, pg. 4600
PARFUMS CHRISTIAN DIOR, INC—See LVMH Moet Hennessy Louis Vuitton SE; *Int'l*, pg. 4598

COMPANY NAME INDEX

PARFUMS CHRISTIAN DIOR JAPAN KK—See LVMH Moet Hennessy Louis Vuitton SE; *Int'l*, pg. 4598
PARFUMS CHRISTIAN DIOR LTD.—See LVMH Moet Hennessy Louis Vuitton SE; *Int'l*, pg. 4598
PARFUMS CHRISTIAN DIOR NEW ZEALAND LTD.—See LVMH Moet Hennessy Louis Vuitton SE; *Int'l*, pg. 4598
PARFUMS CHRISTIAN DIOR OSTERREICH GMBH—See LVMH Moet Hennessy Louis Vuitton SE; *Int'l*, pg. 4598
PARFUMS CHRISTIAN DIOR SAB—See LVMH Moet Hennessy Louis Vuitton SE; *Int'l*, pg. 4598
PARFUMS CHRISTIAN DIOR SA—See LVMH Moet Hennessy Louis Vuitton SE; *Int'l*, pg. 4598
PARFUMS CHRISTIAN DIOR SINGAPORE PTE. LTD.—See LVMH Moet Hennessy Louis Vuitton SE; *Int'l*, pg. 4598
PARFUMS CHRISTIAN DIOR—See LVMH Moet Hennessy Louis Vuitton SE; *Int'l*, pg. 4598
PARFUMS CHRISTIAN DIOR—See LVMH Moet Hennessy Louis Vuitton SE; *Int'l*, pg. 4598
PARFUMS CHRISTIAN DIOR SPA—See LVMH Moet Hennessy Louis Vuitton SE; *Int'l*, pg. 4598
PARFUMS CHRISTINA DIOR ARGENTINA SA—See LVMH Moet Hennessy Louis Vuitton SE; *Int'l*, pg. 4598
PARFUMS DE COEUR LTD.—See Yellow Wood Partners LLC; *U.S. Private*, pg. 4587
PARFUMS ET BEAUTE FRANCE & CIE.—See L'Oreal S.A.; *Int'l*, pg. 4381
PARFUMS GIVENCHY ARGENTINE SA—See LVMH Moet Hennessy Louis Vuitton SE; *Int'l*, pg. 4593
PARFUMS GIVENCHY ASIA PACIFIC PTE. LTD.—See LVMH Moet Hennessy Louis Vuitton SE; *Int'l*, pg. 4593
PARFUMS GIVENCHY BENELUX—See LVMH Moet Hennessy Louis Vuitton SE; *Int'l*, pg. 4593
PARFUMS GIVENCHY GMBH—See LVMH Moet Hennessy Louis Vuitton SE; *Int'l*, pg. 4593
PARFUMS GIVENCHY INC.—See LVMH Moet Hennessy Louis Vuitton SE; *Int'l*, pg. 4593
PARFUMS GIVENCHY ITALIA S.R.L.—See LVMH Moet Hennessy Louis Vuitton SE; *Int'l*, pg. 4593
PARFUMS GIVENCHY KK—See LVMH Moet Hennessy Louis Vuitton SE; *Int'l*, pg. 4593
PARFUMS GIVENCHY MEXICO—See LVMH Moet Hennessy Louis Vuitton SE; *Int'l*, pg. 4593
PARFUMS GIVENCHY S.A.—See LVMH Moet Hennessy Louis Vuitton SE; *Int'l*, pg. 4593
PARFUMS GIVENCHY—See LVMH Moet Hennessy Louis Vuitton SE; *Int'l*, pg. 4593
PARFUMS GIVENCHY SPAIN—See LVMH Moet Hennessy Louis Vuitton SE; *Int'l*, pg. 4593
PARFUMS GIVENCHY UK LTD.—See LVMH Moet Hennessy Louis Vuitton SE; *Int'l*, pg. 4593
PARFUMS GRES SA—See Lalique Group S.A.; *Int'l*, pg. 4399
PARFUMS NINA RICCI—See Puig Brands S.A.; *Int'l*, pg. 6115
PARGA PARK- UND GARTENTECHNIK GESELLSCHAFT M.B.H—See BayWa AG; *Int'l*, pg. 918
PARGESA HOLDING S.A.—See BNP Paribas SA; *Int'l*, pg. 1090
PARGESA HOLDING S.A.—See Frere-Bourgeois; *Int'l*, pg. 2773
PARGESA HOLDING S.A.—See Power Corporation of Canada; *Int'l*, pg. 5944
PAR GOVERNMENT SYSTEMS CORPORATION—See Booz Allen Hamilton Holding Corporation; *U.S. Public*, pg. 369
PARGREEN SALES ENGINEERING CORP.; *U.S. Private*, pg. 3094
PARHAM CONSTRUCTION CO.; *U.S. Private*, pg. 3094
PARHAM DOCTORS' HOSPITAL—See HCA Healthcare, Inc.; *U.S. Public*, pg. 997
PAR HAWAII, INC.—See Par Pacific Holdings, Inc.; *U.S. Public*, pg. 1636
PAR HAWAII REFINING, LLC—See Par Pacific Holdings, Inc.; *U.S. Public*, pg. 1636
PARIBAS ASIA EQUITY LTD.—See BNP Paribas SA; *Int'l*, pg. 1092
PARI CAPITAL GMBH; *Int'l*, pg. 5741
PARIC CORP.; *U.S. Private*, pg. 3094
PARIC HOLDINGS, INC.; *U.S. Private*, pg. 3094
PARICOLA ELECTRICAL ENGINEERING SDN. BHD.—See Pico Far East Holdings Limited; *Int'l*, pg. 5861
PARICOMI 2 (EX-PARICOMI)—See BNP Paribas SA; *Int'l*, pg. 1092
PARIGI GROUP LTD; *U.S. Private*, pg. 3094
PARIGI INTERNATIONAL INC.; *U.S. Private*, pg. 3094
PARI JAPAN KK—See PARI Medical Holding GmbH; *Int'l*, pg. 5741
PARIKSHA FIN-INVEST-LEASE LIMITED; *Int'l*, pg. 5741
PARILEASE SAS—See BNP Paribas SA; *Int'l*, pg. 1092
PARI MEDICAL HOLDING GMBH; *Int'l*, pg. 5741
PARI MEDICAL LTD.—See PARI Medical Holding GmbH; *Int'l*, pg. 5741
PARIMETAL—See Prysmian S.p.A.; *Int'l*, pg. 6012
PARI MUTUEL URBAIN; *Int'l*, pg. 5741
PAR, INC.—See OPENLANE, Inc.; *U.S. Public*, pg. 1607
PARIN FURNITURE LTD.; *Int'l*, pg. 5742
PARINGA RESOURCES LIMITED; *U.S. Private*, pg. 3094

PARI PHARMA GMBH—See PARI Medical Holding GmbH; *Int'l*, pg. 5741
PARI PULMOMED S.A.R.L.—See PARI Medical Holding GmbH; *Int'l*, pg. 5741
PARI RESPIRATORY EQUIPMENT, INC.—See PARI Medical Holding GmbH; *Int'l*, pg. 5741
PARIS ACCESSORIES, INC.; *U.S. Private*, pg. 3094
PARIS ART LABEL CO., INC.—See WestRock Company; *U.S. Public*, pg. 2362
PARIS BLUES, INC.; *U.S. Private*, pg. 3094
PARIS BROTHERS INC.; *U.S. Private*, pg. 3094
PARIS BUSINESS PRODUCTS, INC.; *U.S. Private*, pg. 3094
PARIS CHEVROLET BUICK GMC; *U.S. Private*, pg. 3095
PARIS CLEANERS INC.; *U.S. Private*, pg. 3095
PARIS FARMERS UNION; *U.S. Private*, pg. 3095
PARIS FOODS CORPORATION; *U.S. Private*, pg. 3095
PARIS GLOVE OF CANADA INC.—See New Wave Group AB; *Int'l*, pg. 5230
PARIS GOURMET OF NEW YORK INC.; *U.S. Private*, pg. 3095
PARIS GROUP INTERNATIONAL LLC; *Int'l*, pg. 5742
PARISH GROUP LIMITED—See APQ Global Limited; *Int'l*, pg. 522
PARISH OIL CO. INC.; *U.S. Private*, pg. 3095
PARISHRAM TRADING CO.—See SACHETA METALS LIMITED; *Int'l*, pg. 6463
PARISHSOFT LLC—See Site Organic, LLC; *U.S. Private*, pg. 3676
PARISH WATER COMPANY, INC.—See Baton Rouge Water Works Company; *U.S. Private*, pg. 487
PARISI GRAND SMOOTH LOGISTICS LTD.—See Francesco Parisi S.p.A.; *Int'l*, pg. 2759
PARIS LAS VEGAS OPERATING COMPANY, LLC—See Caesars Entertainment, Inc.; *U.S. Public*, pg. 420
PARIS MAINTENANCE CO. INC.; *U.S. Private*, pg. 3095
PARIS MAINTENANCE CO. INC.—See Paris Maintenance Co. Inc.; *U.S. Private*, pg. 3095
PARIS MIKI HOLDINGS INC.; *Int'l*, pg. 5742
PARIS MIKI INC.—See PARIS MIKI HOLDINGS Inc.; *Int'l*, pg. 5742
PARIS OXYGEN COMPANY—See BBHC, Inc.; *U.S. Public*, pg. 281
PARIS PREMIERE SAS—See Metropole Television SA; *Int'l*, pg. 4863
PARIS PRESENTS, INC.—See Yellow Wood Partners LLC; *U.S. Private*, pg. 4587
PARIS SECURITIES CORP—See Paris Foods Corporation; *U.S. Private*, pg. 3095
PARI SYNERGY IN MEDICINE OOO—See PARI Medical Holding GmbH; *Int'l*, pg. 5741
PARITEC GMBH—See PARI Medical Holding GmbH; *Int'l*, pg. 5741
PARITY GROUP PLC; *Int'l*, pg. 5742
PARITY HEALTHCARE, INC.—See KKR & Co. Inc.; *U.S. Public*, pg. 1246
PARITY HOLDINGS LIMITED—See Parity Group Plc; *Int'l*, pg. 5742
PARITY SOFTWARE GMBH—See MEDIQON Group AG; *Int'l*, pg. 4780
PARITY SOLUTIONS LIMITED—See Parity Group Plc; *Int'l*, pg. 5742
PARITY TRAINING LIMITED—See ECS Limited; *Int'l*, pg. 2301
PARIVEDA SOLUTIONS, INC.; *U.S. Private*, pg. 3095
PARJOINTCO N.V.—See BNP Paribas SA; *Int'l*, pg. 1090
PARJOINTCO N.V.—See Frere-Bourgeois; *Int'l*, pg. 2773
PARJOINTCO N.V.—See Power Corporation of Canada; *Int'l*, pg. 5944
PARK 100 FOODS INC.—See OSI Group, LLC; *U.S. Private*, pg. 3047
PARK24 BUSINESS SUPPORT CO., LTD.—See PARK24 Co. Ltd.; *Int'l*, pg. 5742
PARK24 CO. LTD.; *Int'l*, pg. 5742
PARKADEN AB—See L. E. Lundbergforetagen AB; *Int'l*, pg. 4381
PARK AEROSPACE CORPORATION; *U.S. Public*, pg. 1637
PARK AEROSPACE TECHNOLOGIES ASIA PTE. LTD.—See Park Aerospace Corporation; *U.S. Public*, pg. 1637
PARK AIR SYSTEMS LIMITED—See Indra Sistemas, S.A.; *Int'l*, pg. 3661
PARK AMERICA INC.; *U.S. Private*, pg. 3095
PARKANON LISTATEHDAS OY; *Int'l*, pg. 5743
PARK ASSIST LLC—See TKH Group N.V.; *Int'l*, pg. 7764
PARK ASSIST PTY. LTD.—See TKH Group N.V.; *Int'l*, pg. 7764
THE PARK AT ONE RIVERFRONT, LLC—See Goff Capital, Inc.; *U.S. Private*, pg. 1726
PARK AVENUE ARMORY; *U.S. Private*, pg. 3095
PARK AVENUE BBQ & GRILLE INC.; *U.S. Private*, pg. 3095
PARK AVENUE EQUITY PARTNERS, L.P.; *U.S. Private*, pg. 3095
PARK AVENUE FUNDING, LLC—See The Lightstone Group, LLC; *U.S. Private*, pg. 4070

PARKER CASSIDY SUPPLY CO.

PARK AVENUE LIFE INSURANCE COMPANY—See The Guardian Life Insurance Company of America; *U.S. Private*, pg. 4040
PARK AVENUE MOTORS CORP; *U.S. Private*, pg. 3095
PARK AVENUE SERVICE CORPORATION—See Great American Bancorp, Inc.; *U.S. Public*, pg. 961
PARK BANK—See Old National Bancorp; *U.S. Public*, pg. 1567
THE PARK BANK; *U.S. Private*, pg. 4091
PARK & BELLHEIMER AG; *Int'l*, pg. 5742
PARK B SMITH, LTD.; *U.S. Private*, pg. 3095
PARK CAKE BAKERIES LTD.—See Vision Capital, LLP; *Int'l*, pg. 8252
PARK CAKE BAKERIES—See Vision Capital, LLP; *Int'l*, pg. 8252
PARK CENTRAL HOTEL SAN FRANCISCO—See Pebblebrook Hotel Trust; *U.S. Public*, pg. 1660
PARK CENTRAL SURGICAL CENTER, LTD.—See HCA Healthcare, Inc.; *U.S. Public*, pg. 1006
PARK CHEESE COMPANY INC.; *U.S. Private*, pg. 3095
PARK CHRISTMAS SAVINGS CLUB LIMITED—See PayPoint plc; *Int'l*, pg. 5763
PARK CHRYSLER JEEP; *U.S. Private*, pg. 3095
THE PARK CIRCLE MOTOR CO.; *U.S. Private*, pg. 4091
PARK CITIES ASSET MANAGEMENT LLC; *U.S. Private*, pg. 3095
PARK CITIES QUAIL; *U.S. Private*, pg. 3096
PARK CITIES SURGERY CENTER, LLC—See Tenet Healthcare Corporation; *U.S. Public*, pg. 2012
PARK CITY FORD; *U.S. Private*, pg. 3096
PARK CITY MOUNTAIN RESORT—See Vail Resorts, Inc.; *U.S. Public*, pg. 2271
PARK CONSTRUCTION COMPANY; *U.S. Private*, pg. 3096
PARK CONSTRUCTION CORP.; *U.S. Private*, pg. 3096
PARK CORP.; *U.S. Private*, pg. 3096
PARKCREEK ASC, LLC—See Tenet Healthcare Corporation; *U.S. Public*, pg. 2006
PARKDALE AMERICA, LLC—See Parkdale, Inc.; *U.S. Private*, pg. 3097
PARKDALE, INC.; *U.S. Private*, pg. 3097
PARKDALE MALL, LLC—See CBL & Associates Properties, Inc.; *U.S. Public*, pg. 458
PARKDALE MILLS INC.; *U.S. Private*, pg. 3097
PARKDEAN HOLIDAYS LIMITED—See Alchemy Partners LLP; *Int'l*, pg. 300
PARKDEAN RESORTS UK LIMITED—See Alchemy Partners LLP; *Int'l*, pg. 300
PARK DIRECT CREDIT LIMITED—See PayPoint plc; *Int'l*, pg. 5763
PARK DISTRIBUTORS, INC.; *U.S. Private*, pg. 3096
PARKD LTD.; *Int'l*, pg. 5743
PARKE BANCORP, INC.; *U.S. Public*, pg. 1640
PARKE BANK—See Parke Bancorp, Inc.; *U.S. Public*, pg. 1640
PARKE-BELL LTD., INC.; *U.S. Private*, pg. 3097
PARKE-DAVIS & COMPANY LIMITED—See Pfizer Inc.; *U.S. Public*, pg. 1680
PARK ELEKTRIK URETIM MADENCILIK SANAYI VE TICARET AS; *Int'l*, pg. 5742
PARKELL INC.—See Carl Bennet AB; *Int'l*, pg. 1332
PARK ENERGY SERVICES, LLC—See Rock Hill Capital Group, LLC; *U.S. Private*, pg. 3464
PARKEN SPORT & ENTERTAINMENT A/S; *Int'l*, pg. 5743
PARKEON GMBH—See Astorg Partners S.A.S.; *Int'l*, pg. 657
PARKEON, INC.—See Astorg Partners S.A.S.; *Int'l*, pg. 657
PARKEON PTY LTD.—See Astorg Partners S.A.S.; *Int'l*, pg. 657
PARKEON S.A.S.—See Astorg Partners S.A.S.; *Int'l*, pg. 656
PARKEON S.A.S.—See Astorg Partners S.A.S.; *Int'l*, pg. 657
PARKEON S.L.U.—See Astorg Partners S.A.S.; *Int'l*, pg. 657
PARKEON S.P.A—See Astorg Partners S.A.S.; *Int'l*, pg. 657
PARKER AEROSPACE CUSTOMER SUPPORT INC.—See Parker Hannifin Corporation; *U.S. Public*, pg. 1643
PARKER AEROSPACE, SAO PAULO CUSTOMER SERVICE CENTER—See Parker Hannifin Corporation; *U.S. Public*, pg. 1643
PARKER AEROSPACE—See Parker Hannifin Corporation; *U.S. Public*, pg. 1643
PARKER AGROCHEM EXPORTS LIMITED; *Int'l*, pg. 5743
PARKER AIRCRAFT CONTROL SYSTEMS DIV.—See Parker Hannifin Corporation; *U.S. Public*, pg. 1648
PARKER AIRTEK—See Parker Hannifin Corporation; *U.S. Public*, pg. 1645
PARKER ASSURANCE, LTD.—See Sentry Insurance Group; *U.S. Private*, pg. 3610
PARKER AUTO GROUP; *U.S. Private*, pg. 3097
PARKER CANADA HOLDING CO.—See Parker Hannifin Corporation; *U.S. Public*, pg. 1644
PARKER CANADA—See Parker Hannifin Corporation; *U.S. Public*, pg. 1645
PARKER CASSIDY SUPPLY CO.; *U.S. Private*, pg. 3097

PARKER CASSIDY SUPPLY CO.

CORPORATE AFFILIATIONS

PARKER CENTENNIAL ASSURANCE COMPANY—See Sentry Insurance Group; *U.S. Private*, pg. 3610
PARKER CHEVROLET OLDS PONTIAC GEO INC.; *U.S. Private*, pg. 3097
PARKER CHOMERICS OPTICAL PRODUCTS—See Parker Hannifin Corporation; *U.S. Public*, pg. 1643
PARKER CHOMERICS—See Parker Hannifin Corporation; *U.S. Public*, pg. 1643
PARKER CHOMERICS—See Parker Hannifin Corporation; *U.S. Public*, pg. 1643
PARKER COMPANY, INC—See Ariens Company Inc.; *U.S. Private*, pg. 322
PARKER & COMPANY INC.; *U.S. Private*, pg. 3097
PARKER CONTROLS SYSTEMS DIVISION—See Parker Hannifin Corporation; *U.S. Public*, pg. 1648
PARKER CORPORATION; *Int'l*, pg. 5743
PARKER DIALYSIS, LLC—See DaVita Inc.; *U.S. Public*, pg. 641
PARKER DRILLING ALASKA SERVICES, LTD—See Parker Wellbore Company; *U.S. Public*, pg. 1650
PARKER DRILLING ARCTIC OPERATING INC.—See Parker Wellbore Company; *U.S. Public*, pg. 1650
PARKER DRILLING CANADA COMPANY—See Parker Wellbore Company; *U.S. Public*, pg. 1650
PARKER DRILLING COMPANY INTERNATIONAL LIMITED—See Parker Wellbore Company; *U.S. Public*, pg. 1650
PARKER DRILLING COMPANY—See Parker Wellbore Company; *U.S. Public*, pg. 1650
PARKER DRILLING MANAGEMENT SERVICES, INC.—See Parker Wellbore Company; *U.S. Public*, pg. 1650
PARKER DRILLING NETHERLANDS BV—See Parker Wellbore Company; *U.S. Public*, pg. 1650
PARKER ENGINEERING CO., LTD.—See Nihon Parkerizing Co., Ltd.; *Int'l*, pg. 5286
PARKER ENGINEERING (INDIA) PVT. LTD.—See Nihon Parkerizing Co., Ltd.; *Int'l*, pg. 5286
PARKER ENGINEERING (SHANGHAI) CO., LTD.—See Nihon Parkerizing Co., Ltd.; *Int'l*, pg. 5286
PARKER ENGINEERING (THAILAND) CO., LTD.—See Nihon Parkerizing Co., Ltd.; *Int'l*, pg. 5286
PARKER FILTRATION B.V.—See Parker Hannifin Corporation; *U.S. Public*, pg. 1644
PARKER FILTRATION & SEPARATION BV—See Parker Hannifin Corporation; *U.S. Public*, pg. 1644
PARKER FLUID CONNECTORS DE MEXICO—See Parker Hannifin Corporation; *U.S. Public*, pg. 1645
PARKER FURNITURE INCORPORATED; *U.S. Private*, pg. 3097
PARKERGALE, LLC; *U.S. Private*, pg. 3098
PARKER GAS COMPANY INC.; *U.S. Private*, pg. 3097
THE PARKER GROUP, INC.—See Diploma PLC; *Int'l*, pg. 2129
PARKER HANNIFIN ADVANCED PRODUCTS COMPANY—See Parker Hannifin Corporation; *U.S. Public*, pg. 1648
PARKER HANNIFIN AFRICA PTY LTD.—See Parker Hannifin Corporation; *U.S. Public*, pg. 1644
PARKER HANNIFIN AKTIEBOLAG—See Parker Hannifin Corporation; *U.S. Public*, pg. 1644
PARKER HANNIFIN ALMELO—See Parker Hannifin Corporation; *U.S. Public*, pg. 1645
PARKER HANNIFIN ARGENTINA SAIC—See Parker Hannifin Corporation; *U.S. Public*, pg. 1644
PARKER HANNIFIN A/S—See Parker Hannifin Corporation; *U.S. Public*, pg. 1645
PARKER HANNIFIN A/S—See Parker Hannifin Corporation; *U.S. Public*, pg. 1645
PARKER HANNIFIN A/S—See Parker Hannifin Corporation; *U.S. Public*, pg. 1645
PARKER HANNIFIN AUSTRALIA PTY. LTD.—See Parker Hannifin Corporation; *U.S. Public*, pg. 1644
PARKER HANNIFIN AUTOMATION GROUP—See Parker Hannifin Corporation; *U.S. Public*, pg. 1644
PARKER HANNIFIN AUTOMOTIVE CONNECTORS DO BRAZIL—See Parker Hannifin Corporation; *U.S. Public*, pg. 1645
PARKER HANNIFIN BRASS PRODUCTS DIV.—See Parker Hannifin Corporation; *U.S. Public*, pg. 1645
PARKER HANNIFIN BV, NETHERLANDS SALES & SERVICE—See Parker Hannifin Corporation; *U.S. Public*, pg. 1645
PARKER HANNIFIN B.V.—See Parker Hannifin Corporation; *U.S. Public*, pg. 1646
PARKER HANNIFIN (CANADA) INC., CYLINDER DIVISION—See Parker Hannifin Corporation; *U.S. Public*, pg. 1647
PARKER HANNIFIN CHILE LIMITADA—See Parker Hannifin Corporation; *U.S. Public*, pg. 1645
PARKER HANNIFIN CHOMERICS (M) SDN, BHD.—See Parker Hannifin Corporation; *U.S. Public*, pg. 1644
PARKER HANNIFIN CLIMATE & INDUSTRIAL CONTROLS GROUP—See Parker Hannifin Corporation; *U.S. Public*, pg. 1644
PARKER HANNIFIN CO., LTD.-AEROSPACE CUSTOMER SUPPORT—See Parker Hannifin Corporation; *U.S. Public*, pg. 1644

PARKER HANNIFIN COMPOSITE SEALING SYSTEMS DIVISION—See Parker Hannifin Corporation; *U.S. Public*, pg. 1643
PARKER HANNIFIN COMPUMOTOR CORP.—See Parker Hannifin Corporation; *U.S. Public*, pg. 1644
PARKER HANNIFIN CONNECTORS, LTD.—See Parker Hannifin Corporation; *U.S. Public*, pg. 1645
PARKER HANNIFIN, CONTROL SYSTEMS DIVISION—See Parker Hannifin Corporation; *U.S. Public*, pg. 1649
PARKER HANNIFIN CORP., AIRCRAFT WHEEL & BRAKE DIVISION—See Parker Hannifin Corporation; *U.S. Public*, pg. 1648
PARKER HANNIFIN CORP, FILTRATION & SEPARATION DIVISION—See Parker Hannifin Corporation; *U.S. Public*, pg. 1645
PARKER HANNIFIN CORP. - FLUID SYSTEMS DIVISION—See Parker Hannifin Corporation; *U.S. Public*, pg. 1648
PARKER HANNIFIN CORP., GAS TURBINE FUEL SYSTEMS DIV.—See Parker Hannifin Corporation; *U.S. Public*, pg. 1648
PARKER HANNIFIN CORPORATION, AIRBORNE DIVISION—See Parker Hannifin Corporation; *U.S. Public*, pg. 1648
PARKER HANNIFIN CORPORATION CHILE LTDA—See Parker Hannifin Corporation; *U.S. Public*, pg. 1645
PARKER HANNIFIN CORPORATION-EAST EUROPEAN SALES OFFICE—See Parker Hannifin Corporation; *U.S. Public*, pg. 1646
PARKER HANNIFIN CORPORATION, ENGINEERED SEALS DIVISION, SYRACUSE—See Parker Hannifin Corporation; *U.S. Public*, pg. 1643
PARKER HANNIFIN CORPORATION; *U.S. Public*, pg. 1640
PARKER HANNIFIN CORP., SLOVENIA—See Parker Hannifin Corporation; *U.S. Public*, pg. 1646
PARKER HANNIFIN CORP., TECHSEAL DIV.—See Parker Hannifin Corporation; *U.S. Public*, pg. 1643
PARKER HANNIFIN CUSTOM CYLINDER OPERATIONS—See Parker Hannifin Corporation; *U.S. Public*, pg. 1647
PARKER HANNIFIN CUSTOMER SUPPORT COMMERCIAL DIVISION—See Parker Hannifin Corporation; *U.S. Public*, pg. 1648
PARKER HANNIFIN CYLINDER DIVISION—See Parker Hannifin Corporation; *U.S. Public*, pg. 1647
PARKER HANNIFIN CYLINDER DIVISION—See Parker Hannifin Corporation; *U.S. Public*, pg. 1647
PARKER HANNIFIN CYLINDER DIVISION, SWEDEN—See Parker Hannifin Corporation; *U.S. Public*, pg. 1647
PARKER HANNIFIN CZECH REPUBLIC SRO—See Parker Hannifin Corporation; *U.S. Public*, pg. 1645
PARKER HANNIFIN DAEDAL DIVISION—See Parker Hannifin Corporation; *U.S. Public*, pg. 1644
PARKER HANNIFIN DANMARK A/S—See Parker Hannifin Corporation; *U.S. Public*, pg. 1646
PARKER HANNIFIN DE MEXICO S.A. DE C.V.—See Parker Hannifin Corporation; *U.S. Public*, pg. 1649
PARKER HANNIFIN DE MEXICO-SEAL DE MATAMOROS FACILITY—See Parker Hannifin Corporation; *U.S. Public*, pg. 1649
PARKER HANNIFIN DE MEXICO—See Parker Hannifin Corporation; *U.S. Public*, pg. 1646
PARKER HANNIFIN ELECTRONIC SYSTEMS DIV.—See Parker Hannifin Corporation; *U.S. Public*, pg. 1648
PARKER HANNIFIN EMEA S.A.R.L.—See Parker Hannifin Corporation; *U.S. Public*, pg. 1645
PARKER HANNIFIN ENGINEERED POLYMER SYSTEMS DIVISION—See Parker Hannifin Corporation; *U.S. Public*, pg. 1643
PARKER HANNIFIN ENGINEERED POLYMER SYSTEMS DIV.—See Parker Hannifin Corporation; *U.S. Public*, pg. 1643
PARKER HANNIFIN ENGINEERED SEALS DIVISION—See Parker Hannifin Corporation; *U.S. Public*, pg. 1643
PARKER HANNIFIN ESPANA SA—See Parker Hannifin Corporation; *U.S. Public*, pg. 1645
PARKER HANNIFIN (ESPANA) S.A.—See Parker Hannifin Corporation; *U.S. Public*, pg. 1644
PARKER HANNIFIN ESSC SP Z.O.O.—See Parker Hannifin Corporation; *U.S. Public*, pg. 1645
PARKER HANNIFIN FILTRATION GROUP—See Parker Hannifin Corporation; *U.S. Public*, pg. 1645
PARKER HANNIFIN FILTRATION PRODUCTS AND SYSTEMS (SHANGHAI) CO., LTD.—See Parker Hannifin Corporation; *U.S. Public*, pg. 1645
PARKER HANNIFIN FILTRATION & SEPARATION DIVISION-BALSTON PRODUCTS—See Parker Hannifin Corporation; *U.S. Public*, pg. 1645
PARKER HANNIFIN FLUID CONNECTORS & SEAL GROUP—See Parker Hannifin Corporation; *U.S. Public*, pg. 1649
PARKER HANNIFIN FLUID CONTROL DIVISION—See Parker Hannifin Corporation; *U.S. Public*, pg. 1644

PARKER HANNIFIN FLUID POWER SYSTEMS & COMPONENTS CO., LTD.—See Parker Hannifin Corporation; *U.S. Public*, pg. 1645
PARKER HANNIFIN FLUID SYSTEM CONNECTORS GROUP—See Parker Hannifin Corporation; *U.S. Public*, pg. 1645
PARKER HANNIFIN FRANCE SAS—See Parker Hannifin Corporation; *U.S. Public*, pg. 1646
PARKER HANNIFIN FRANCE SAS—See Parker Hannifin Corporation; *U.S. Public*, pg. 1646
PARKER HANNIFIN GB LTD.—See Parker Hannifin Corporation; *U.S. Public*, pg. 1646
PARKER HANNIFIN GEAR PUMP DIVISION—See Parker Hannifin Corporation; *U.S. Public*, pg. 1647
PARKER HANNIFIN GENERAL VALVE OPERATION PNEUTRONICS DIVISION—See Parker Hannifin Corporation; *U.S. Public*, pg. 1647
PARKER HANNIFIN GES.M.B.H.—See Parker Hannifin Corporation; *U.S. Public*, pg. 1646
PARKER HANNIFIN GLOBAL CAPITAL MANAGEMENT S.A.R.L.—See Parker Hannifin Corporation; *U.S. Public*, pg. 1647
PARKER HANNIFIN GMBH & CO. KG ELECTROMECHANICAL AUTOMATION—See Parker Hannifin Corporation; *U.S. Public*, pg. 1644
PARKER HANNIFIN GMBH & CO. KG HOSE PRODUCTS DIVISION EUROPE—See Parker Hannifin Corporation; *U.S. Public*, pg. 1646
PARKER HANNIFIN GMBH & CO. KG HYDRAULIC CONTROLS DIVISION EUROPE—See Parker Hannifin Corporation; *U.S. Public*, pg. 1647
PARKER HANNIFIN GMBH & CO. KG O-RING DIVISION EUROPE—See Parker Hannifin Corporation; *U.S. Public*, pg. 1649
PARKER HANNIFIN GMBH & CO. KG PACKING DIVISION EUROPE—See Parker Hannifin Corporation; *U.S. Public*, pg. 1649
PARKER HANNIFIN GMBH & CO. KG POLYFLEX DIVISION—See Parker Hannifin Corporation; *U.S. Public*, pg. 1646
PARKER HANNIFIN GMBH & CO. KG VERTRIEBS- UND SERVICEZENTRALE—See Parker Hannifin Corporation; *U.S. Public*, pg. 1647
PARKER HANNIFIN GMBH & CO.—See Parker Hannifin Corporation; *U.S. Public*, pg. 1644
PARKER HANNIFIN GMBH—See Parker Hannifin Corporation; *U.S. Public*, pg. 1646
PARKER HANNIFIN GMBH—See Parker Hannifin Corporation; *U.S. Public*, pg. 1646
PARKER HANNIFIN GMBH—See Parker Hannifin Corporation; *U.S. Public*, pg. 1647
PARKER HANNIFIN HOLDING, S. DE R.L. DE C.V.—See Parker Hannifin Corporation; *U.S. Public*, pg. 1647
PARKER HANNIFIN HONG KONG LTD.—See Parker Hannifin Corporation; *U.S. Public*, pg. 1647
PARKER HANNIFIN HOOGEZAND B.V.—See Parker Hannifin Corporation; *U.S. Public*, pg. 1646
PARKER HANNIFIN HOSE PRODUCTS DIVISION—See Parker Hannifin Corporation; *U.S. Public*, pg. 1646
PARKER HANNIFIN HYDRAULIC ACCUMULATOR DIVISION—See Parker Hannifin Corporation; *U.S. Public*, pg. 1647
PARKER HANNIFIN HYDRAULIC FILTER DIVISION—See Parker Hannifin Corporation; *U.S. Public*, pg. 1645
PARKER HANNIFIN HYDRAULIC PUMP & MOTOR DIV.—See Parker Hannifin Corporation; *U.S. Public*, pg. 1647
PARKER HANNIFIN HYDRAULICS DIVISION, BRAZIL—See Parker Hannifin Corporation; *U.S. Public*, pg. 1647
PARKER HANNIFIN-HYDRAULICS DIVISION—See Parker Hannifin Corporation; *U.S. Public*, pg. 1646
PARKER HANNIFIN HYDRAULICS GROUP—See Parker Hannifin Corporation; *U.S. Public*, pg. 1647
PARKER HANNIFIN HYDRAULICS SYSTEMS DIVISION—See Parker Hannifin Corporation; *U.S. Public*, pg. 1649
PARKER HANNIFIN HYDRAULIC VALVE DIV.—See Parker Hannifin Corporation; *U.S. Public*, pg. 1647
PARKER HANNIFIN INDIA PVT. LTD.—See Parker Hannifin Corporation; *U.S. Public*, pg. 1644
PARKER HANNIFIN INDUSTRIA E COMERCIO, LTDA.—See Parker Hannifin Corporation; *U.S. Public*, pg. 1644
PARKER HANNIFIN INDUSTRIAL HOSE PRODUCTS DIVISION—See Parker Hannifin Corporation; *U.S. Public*, pg. 1646
PARKER HANNIFIN INDUSTRIAL HOSE PRODUCTS DIVISION—See Parker Hannifin Corporation; *U.S. Public*, pg. 1646
PARKER HANNIFIN INDUSTRIAL S.R.O.—See Parker Hannifin Corporation; *U.S. Public*, pg. 1647
PARKER HANNIFIN INSTRUMENTATION GROUP—See Parker Hannifin Corporation; *U.S. Public*, pg. 1647
PARKER HANNIFIN - INSTRUMENTATION PRODUCTS DIV—See Parker Hannifin Corporation; *U.S. Public*, pg. 1647

COMPANY NAME INDEX

PARKER HANNIFIN INTEGRATED HYDRAULICS DIVISION—See Parker Hannifin Corporation; *U.S. Public*, pg. 1647
PARKER-HANNIFIN INTERNATIONAL CORP.—See Parker Hannifin Corporation; *U.S. Public*, pg. 1649
PARKER HANNIFIN ITALY SRL—See Parker Hannifin Corporation; *U.S. Public*, pg. 1648
PARKER HANNIFIN ITALY SRL SUCURSAL EN ESPANA—See Parker Hannifin Corporation; *U.S. Public*, pg. 1648
PARKER HANNIFIN JAPAN HOLDINGS GK—See Parker Hannifin Corporation; *U.S. Public*, pg. 1648
PARKER HANNIFIN JAPAN LTD.—See Parker Hannifin Corporation; *U.S. Public*, pg. 1648
PARKER HANNIFIN JAPAN LTD.—See Parker Hannifin Corporation; *U.S. Public*, pg. 1648
PARKER HANNIFIN KIT OPERATIONS—See Parker Hannifin Corporation; *U.S. Public*, pg. 1646
PARKER HANNIFIN KOREA—See Parker Hannifin Corporation; *U.S. Public*, pg. 1648
PARKER HANNIFIN LIMITED—See Parker Hannifin Corporation; *U.S. Public*, pg. 1648
PARKER HANNIFIN LLC—See Parker Hannifin Corporation; *U.S. Public*, pg. 1648
PARKER HANNIFIN MALAYSIA SDN. BHD—See Parker Hannifin Corporation; *U.S. Public*, pg. 1648
PARKER HANNIFIN MANUFACTURING BELGIUM BVBA—See Parker Hannifin Corporation; *U.S. Public*, pg. 1648
PARKER HANNIFIN MANUFACTURING FINLAND OY—See Parker Hannifin Corporation; *U.S. Public*, pg. 1648
PARKER HANNIFIN MANUFACTURING FRANCE S.A.S.—See Parker Hannifin Corporation; *U.S. Public*, pg. 1646
PARKER HANNIFIN MANUFACTURING GERMANY GMBH & CO. KG AEROSPACE HYDRAULIC DIVISION—See Parker Hannifin Corporation; *U.S. Public*, pg. 1643
PARKER HANNIFIN MANUFACTURING GERMANY GMBH & CO. KG—See Parker Hannifin Corporation; *U.S. Public*, pg. 1648
PARKER HANNIFIN MANUFACTURING LTD.-CYLINDER DIVISION—See Parker Hannifin Corporation; *U.S. Public*, pg. 1647
PARKER HANNIFIN MANUFACTURING NETHERLANDS (FILTRATION AND SEPARATION) B.V.—See Parker Hannifin Corporation; *U.S. Public*, pg. 1648
PARKER HANNIFIN MANUFACTURING NETHERLANDS (FILTRATION) B.V.—See Parker Hannifin Corporation; *U.S. Public*, pg. 1648
PARKER HANNIFIN MANUFACTURING NETHERLANDS (HOSE) B.V.—See Parker Hannifin Corporation; *U.S. Public*, pg. 1648
PARKER HANNIFIN MANUFACTURING NETHERLANDS (PNEUMATIC) B.V.—See Parker Hannifin Corporation; *U.S. Public*, pg. 1648
PARKER HANNIFIN MANUFACTURING POLAND SP Z.O.O.—See Parker Hannifin Corporation; *U.S. Public*, pg. 1648
PARKER HANNIFIN MANUFACTURING SPAIN SL—See Parker Hannifin Corporation; *U.S. Public*, pg. 1648
PARKER HANNIFIN MANUFACTURING SRL—See Parker Hannifin Corporation; *U.S. Public*, pg. 1648
PARKER HANNIFIN MANUFACTURING SRL—See Parker Hannifin Corporation; *U.S. Public*, pg. 1648
PARKER HANNIFIN MANUFACTURING (UK) LIMITED—See Parker Hannifin Corporation; *U.S. Public*, pg. 1648
PARKER HANNIFIN MFG POLAND SP. Z.O.O.—See Parker Hannifin Corporation; *U.S. Public*, pg. 1646
PARKER HANNIFIN MOBILE BUSINESS UNIT—See Parker Hannifin Corporation; *U.S. Public*, pg. 1644
PARKER HANNIFIN MOBILE CYLINDER DIVISION—See Parker Hannifin Corporation; *U.S. Public*, pg. 1647
PARKER HANNIFIN MOBILE SYSTEMS DIVISION—See Parker Hannifin Corporation; *U.S. Public*, pg. 1647
PARKER HANNIFIN MOSCOW—See Parker Hannifin Corporation; *U.S. Public*, pg. 1646
PARKER HANNIFIN MOTION AND CONTROL—See Parker Hannifin Corporation; *U.S. Public*, pg. 1647
PARKER HANNIFIN MOTION & CONTROL SALES DIVISION CANADA—See Parker Hannifin Corporation; *U.S. Public*, pg. 1647
PARKER HANNIFIN MOTION & CONTROL (SHANGHAI) CO. LTD.—See Parker Hannifin Corporation; *U.S. Public*, pg. 1648
PARKER HANNIFIN NETHERLANDS HOLDINGS 2 B.V.—See Parker Hannifin Corporation; *U.S. Public*, pg. 1648
PARKER HANNIFIN NETHERLANDS HOLDINGS B.V.—See Parker Hannifin Corporation; *U.S. Public*, pg. 1648
PARKER HANNIFIN NICHOLS AIRBORNE DIV—See Parker Hannifin Corporation; *U.S. Public*, pg. 1649
PARKER HANNIFIN (NZ) LTD.—See Parker Hannifin Corporation; *U.S. Public*, pg. 1644
PARKER HANNIFIN (NZ) LTD.—See Parker Hannifin Corporation; *U.S. Public*, pg. 1644

PARKER HANNIFIN OILDYNE DIVISION—See Parker Hannifin Corporation; *U.S. Public*, pg. 1647
PARKER HANNIFIN OY FILTER DIVISION EUROPE—See Parker Hannifin Corporation; *U.S. Public*, pg. 1645
PARKER HANNIFIN PAN AMERICAN DIVISION—See Parker Hannifin Corporation; *U.S. Public*, pg. 1643
PARKER HANNIFIN PARFLEX DIVISION - PARKER-TEXLOC—See Parker Hannifin Corporation; *U.S. Public*, pg. 1646
PARKER HANNIFIN PARFLEX DIV., RAVENNA PLANT—See Parker Hannifin Corporation; *U.S. Public*, pg. 1646
PARKER HANNIFIN PARTNER B LLC—See Parker Hannifin Corporation; *U.S. Public*, pg. 1648
PARKER HANNIFIN PLC - INSTRUMENTATION DIVISION—See Parker Hannifin Corporation; *U.S. Public*, pg. 1648
PARKER HANNIFIN PLC—See Parker Hannifin Corporation; *U.S. Public*, pg. 1646
PARKER HANNIFIN PLC—See Parker Hannifin Corporation; *U.S. Public*, pg. 1644
PARKER HANNIFIN PNEUMATIC DIVISION-NORTH AMERICA—See Parker Hannifin Corporation; *U.S. Public*, pg. 1644
PARKER HANNIFIN PNEUMATIC DIVISION NORTH AMERICA WATTS FLUIDAIR—See Parker Hannifin Corporation; *U.S. Public*, pg. 1644
PARKER HANNIFIN PNEUMATIC DIVISION—See Parker Hannifin Corporation; *U.S. Public*, pg. 1644
PARKER HANNIFIN POLYFLEX—See Parker Hannifin Corporation; *U.S. Public*, pg. 1646
PARKER HANNIFIN PORTUGAL, LDA—See Parker Hannifin Corporation; *U.S. Public*, pg. 1646
PARKER HANNIFIN PORTUGAL UNIPESSOAL LDA—See Parker Hannifin Corporation; *U.S. Public*, pg. 1648
PARKER HANNIFIN POWER TRAIN DIVISION—See Parker Hannifin Corporation; *U.S. Public*, pg. 1643
PARKER HANNIFIN PRECISION FLUIDICS DIVISION—See Parker Hannifin Corporation; *U.S. Public*, pg. 1647
PARKER HANNIFIN PROCESS ADVANCED FILTRATION DIVISION—See Parker Hannifin Corporation; *U.S. Public*, pg. 1645
PARKER HANNIFIN, QUICK COUPLING DIV.—See Parker Hannifin Corporation; *U.S. Public*, pg. 1646
PARKER HANNIFIN RACOR - FILTERS—See Parker Hannifin Corporation; *U.S. Public*, pg. 1645
PARKER HANNIFIN RACOR—See Parker Hannifin Corporation; *U.S. Public*, pg. 1645
PARKER HANNIFIN REFRIGERATING SPECIALTIES DIV.—See Parker Hannifin Corporation; *U.S. Public*, pg. 1644
PARKER HANNIFIN REFRIGERATION & AIR CONDITIONING DIVISION—See Parker Hannifin Corporation; *U.S. Public*, pg. 1644
PARKER HANNIFIN REFRIGERATION & AIR CONDITIONING DIV.—See Parker Hannifin Corporation; *U.S. Public*, pg. 1644
PARKER HANNIFIN REFRIGERATION & AIR CONDITIONING (WUXI) CO., LTD.—See Parker Hannifin Corporation; *U.S. Public*, pg. 1648
PARKER HANNIFIN SA CLIMATE & INDUSTRIAL CONTROLS—See Parker Hannifin Corporation; *U.S. Public*, pg. 1644
PARKER HANNIFIN S.A.—See Parker Hannifin Corporation; *U.S. Public*, pg. 1647
PARKER HANNIFIN, SA—See Parker Hannifin Corporation; *U.S. Public*, pg. 1647
PARKER HANNIFIN SEAL GROUP - ENGINEERED POLYMER SYSTEMS DIVISION—See Parker Hannifin Corporation; *U.S. Public*, pg. 1649
PARKER HANNIFIN SEAL GROUP—See Parker Hannifin Corporation; *U.S. Public*, pg. 1648
PARKER HANNIFIN SINGAPORE PTE. LTD.—See Parker Hannifin Corporation; *U.S. Public*, pg. 1649
PARKER HANNIFIN—See Crane NXT, Co.; *U.S. Public*, pg. 590
PARKER HANNIFIN—See Parker Hannifin Corporation; *U.S. Public*, pg. 1645
PARKER HANNIFIN SPA CYLINDER DIVISION—See Parker Hannifin Corporation; *U.S. Public*, pg. 1647
PARKER HANNIFIN SPA FLUID CONTROL DIVISION—See Parker Hannifin Corporation; *U.S. Public*, pg. 1646
PARKER HANNIFIN SP. Z.O.O.—See Parker Hannifin Corporation; *U.S. Public*, pg. 1648
PARKER HANNIFIN SRL—See Parker Hannifin Corporation; *U.S. Public*, pg. 1649
PARKER HANNIFIN S.R.O., PACKING DIVISION—See Parker Hannifin Corporation; *U.S. Public*, pg. 1649
PARKER HANNIFIN S.R.O.—See Parker Hannifin Corporation; *U.S. Public*, pg. 1649
PARKER HANNIFIN STRATOFLEX PRODUCTS DIVISION-MANSFIELD HOSE PLANT—See Parker Hannifin Corporation; *U.S. Public*, pg. 1646
PARKER HANNIFIN STRATOFLEX PRODUCTS DIV—See Parker Hannifin Corporation; *U.S. Public*, pg. 1646
PARKER HANNIFIN STRATOFLEX—See Parker Hannifin Corporation; *U.S. Public*, pg. 1646

PARKER'S CORPORATION

PARKER HANNIFIN SWEDEN SALES AB—See Parker Hannifin Corporation; *U.S. Public*, pg. 1649
PARKER HANNIFIN TAIWAN CO. LTD.—See Parker Hannifin Corporation; *U.S. Public*, pg. 1649
PARKER HANNIFIN THAILAND CO. LTD.—See Parker Hannifin Corporation; *U.S. Public*, pg. 1649
PARKER HANNIFIN TUBE FITTINGS DIVISION-CUSTOM MANUFACTURING BUSINESS UNIT—See Parker Hannifin Corporation; *U.S. Public*, pg. 1646
PARKER HANNIFIN TUBE FITTINGS DIV.—See Parker Hannifin Corporation; *U.S. Public*, pg. 1646
PARKER HANNIFIN VERIFLO DIVISION—See Parker Hannifin Corporation; *U.S. Public*, pg. 1647
PARKER HANNIFIN VERWALTUNGS-GMBH—See Parker Hannifin Corporation; *U.S. Public*, pg. 1649
PARKER HANNIFIN WATTS FLUID AIR—See Parker Hannifin Corporation; *U.S. Public*, pg. 1643
PARKER HAREKET VE KONTROL SISTEMLERI TIC. A.S.—See Parker Hannifin Corporation; *U.S. Public*, pg. 1649
PARKER-HELAC DIVISION—See Parker Hannifin Corporation; *U.S. Public*, pg. 1647
PARKER HOLDING COMPANY, INC.; *U.S. Private*, pg. 3097
PARKER HOSE BV—See Parker Hannifin Corporation; *U.S. Public*, pg. 1649
PARKER HOUSE SAUSAGE COMPANY; *U.S. Private*, pg. 3097
PARKER INDUSTRIES, INC.—See Nihon Parkerizing Co., Ltd.; *Int'l*, pg. 5286
PARKER INSULATION AND BUILDING PRODUCTS, LLC—See Installed Building Products, Inc.; *U.S. Public*, pg. 1133
PARKER INTERIOR PLANTSCAPE, INC.; *U.S. Private*, pg. 3097
PARKER ITALY HOLDING S.R.L.—See Parker Hannifin Corporation; *U.S. Public*, pg. 1649
PARKER JEWISH INSTITUTE FOR HEALTH CARE & REHABILITATION; *U.S. Private*, pg. 3097
PARKER KIDNEY CENTER, LLC—See Nautic Partners, LLC; *U.S. Private*, pg. 2870
PARKER KOREA LTD.—See Parker Hannifin Corporation; *U.S. Public*, pg. 1649
PARKER LKLIM KONTROL SISTEMLERI SANAYI VE TIC AS—See Parker Hannifin Corporation; *U.S. Public*, pg. 1649
PARKER LUMBER; *U.S. Private*, pg. 3097
PARKER & LYNCH—See Adecco Group AG; *Int'l*, pg. 136
PARKER MARITIME AS—See Parker Hannifin Corporation; *U.S. Public*, pg. 1649
PARKER-MCCRORY MANUFACTURING CO.; *U.S. Private*, pg. 3098
PARKER MERCHANTING—See Rexel, S.A.; *Int'l*, pg. 6317
PARKER MIDDLE EAST FZE—See Parker Hannifin Corporation; *U.S. Public*, pg. 1649
PARKER OIL COMPANY, INC. - ENVIRONMENTAL MANAGEMENT SERVICES DIVISION—See Parker Holding Company, Inc.; *U.S. Private*, pg. 3097
PARKER OIL COMPANY, INC.—See AIP, LLC; *U.S. Private*, pg. 136
PARKER OIL COMPANY, INC.—See Parker Holding Company, Inc.; *U.S. Private*, pg. 3097
PARKER ONTARIO HOLDING INC.—See Parker Hannifin Corporation; *U.S. Public*, pg. 1649
PARKER & ORLEANS HOMEBUILDERS, INC.—See Orleans Homebuilders, Inc.; *U.S. Private*, pg. 3044
PARKER PACIFIC—See The Inland Group; *Int'l*, pg. 7656
PARKER & PARTNERS MARKETING RESOURCES, LLC; *U.S. Private*, pg. 3097
PARKER PGI—See HM International; *U.S. Private*, pg. 1954
PARKER POLYFLEX BV—See Parker Hannifin Corporation; *U.S. Public*, pg. 1649
PARKER PROCESSING VIETNAM CO., LTD.—See Nihon Parkerizing Co., Ltd.; *Int'l*, pg. 5286
PARKER PRODUCTS, LLC—See The Riverside Company; *U.S. Private*, pg. 4109
PARKER RD. HOOTERS, INC.—See Restaurants of America, Inc.; *U.S. Private*, pg. 3408
PARKER SALES (IRELAND) LIMITED—See Parker Hannifin Corporation; *U.S. Public*, pg. 1649
PARKERSBURG TREATMENT CENTER, LLC—See Acadia Healthcare Company, Inc.; *U.S. Public*, pg. 29
PARKER SCAFFOLDING CO LIMITED—See Enviri Corporation; *U.S. Public*, pg. 781
PARKERS CHRYSLER DODGE JEEP; *Int'l*, pg. 5743
PARKER'S CORPORATION; *U.S. Private*, pg. 3097
PARKER SEAL DE MEXICO, S.A.—See Parker Hannifin Corporation; *U.S. Public*, pg. 1649
PARKER SEAL O-RING DIVISION—See Parker Hannifin Corporation; *U.S. Public*, pg. 1643
PARKER SEALS—See Parker Hannifin Corporation; *U.S. Public*, pg. 1649
PARKER SERVICES, L.L.C.—See Sentry Insurance Group; *U.S. Private*, pg. 3610
PARKER SERVICIO'S DE MEXICO, S.A. DE C.V.—See Parker Hannifin Corporation; *U.S. Public*, pg. 1649

PARKER, SMITH & FEEK, INC.—See IMA Financial Group, Inc.; *U.S. Private*, pg. 2043
PARKER SOFTWARE INC.—See Parker Software Ltd; *Int'l*, pg. 5743
PARKER SOFTWARE LTD; *Int'l*, pg. 5743
PARKER SPORLAN DIVISION—See Parker Hannifin Corporation; *U.S. Public*, pg. 1644
PARKER STEVENS AGENCY, L.L.C.—See Sentry Insurance Group; *U.S. Private*, pg. 3611
PARKER SURFACE TECHNOLOGIES (SHANGHAI) CO., LTD.—See Nihon Parkerizing Co., Ltd.; *Int'l*, pg. 5287
PARKER TECH SEAL DIVISION—See Parker Hannifin Corporation; *U.S. Public*, pg. 1649
PARKER TOWING COMPANY, INC.; *U.S. Private*, pg. 3097
PARKER TRUTEC INC.—See Nihon Parkerizing Co., Ltd.; *Int'l*, pg. 5287
PARKER TRUTEC INC. - URBANA PLANT—See Nihon Parkerizing Co., Ltd.; *Int'l*, pg. 5287
PARKER TRUTEC MEXICANA S.A DE C.V. - AGUASCALIENTES PLANT—See Nihon Parkerizing Co., Ltd.; *Int'l*, pg. 5287
PARKER TRUTEC MEXICANA S.A DE C.V.—See Nihon Parkerizing Co., Ltd.; *Int'l*, pg. 5287
PARKER TRUTEC MMI INC. - ARKANSAS PLANT—See Nihon Parkerizing Co., Ltd.; *Int'l*, pg. 5287
PARKER TRUTEC MMI INC.—See Nihon Parkerizing Co., Ltd.; *Int'l*, pg. 5287
PARKER UNIFORMS INC.; *U.S. Private*, pg. 3097
PARKER USA DRILLING COMPANY—See Parker Wellbore Company; *U.S. Public*, pg. 1650
PARKER VANSCO ELECTRONIC CONTROLS DIVISION—See Parker Hannifin Corporation; *U.S. Public*, pg. 1647
PARKERVISION, INC.; *U.S. Public*, pg. 1650
PARKER WELLBORE COMPANY; *U.S. Public*, pg. 1650
PARKER WILLIAMS DESIGN LTD.—See DIC Corporation; *Int'l*, pg. 2109
PARK FAMILY PRACTICE SERVICES PTY LTD—See Healius Limited; *Int'l*, pg. 3303
PARK FAST OF MARYLAND—See Edison Properties, LLC; *U.S. Private*, pg. 1337
PARK FINANCIAL GROUP, INC.; *U.S. Private*, pg. 3096
PARK FINANCIAL SERVICES LIMITED—See PayPoint plc; *Int'l*, pg. 5763
PARK FOSTER CARE LIMITED—See Sheikh Holdings Group (Investments) Limited; *Int'l*, pg. 6794
PARK GEORGIA REALTY LTD; *Int'l*, pg. 5742
PARKHAUS PROHLIS GMBH—See Vonovia SE; *Int'l*, pg. 8305
PARK HAVEN APARTMENTS; *U.S. Private*, pg. 3096
PARK HILL GROUP LLC—See Blackstone Inc.; *U.S. Public*, pg. 356
PARK HILL REAL ESTATE GROUP L.L.C.—See Blackstone Inc.; *U.S. Public*, pg. 350
PARKHILL, SMITH & COOPER, INC.; *U.S. Private*, pg. 3098
PARK HONDA; *U.S. Private*, pg. 3096
PARK HOTELS & RESORTS INC.; *U.S. Public*, pg. 1637
PARKHOUSE RECRUITMENT—See Randstad N.V.; *Int'l*, pg. 6204
PARKHOUSE TIRE SERVICE INC.; *U.S. Private*, pg. 3098
PARKHURST HOUSE, LLC—See TPG Capital, L.P.; *U.S. Public*, pg. 2168
PARK HYATT HAMBURG GMBH—See Hyatt Hotels Corporation; *U.S. Public*, pg. 1078
PARK HYATT HOTEL GMBH—See Hyatt Hotels Corporation; *U.S. Public*, pg. 1078
PARK HYATT WATER TOWER ASSOCIATES, L.L.C.—See Hyatt Hotels Corporation; *U.S. Public*, pg. 1078
PARK-IN COMMERCIAL CENTRE—See Hang Lung Group Limited; *Int'l*, pg. 3245
PARKING 4040—See Indigo Group S.A.S.; *Int'l*, pg. 3655
PARKING COMPANY OF AMERICA AIRPORTS, LLC—See Macquarie Group Limited; *Int'l*, pg. 4627
PARKING COMPANY OF AMERICA, HOTEL DIVISION—See PCA Management; *U.S. Private*, pg. 3119
PARKING COMPANY OF AMERICA, LLC—See Macquarie Group Limited; *Int'l*, pg. 4627
PARKING COMPANY OF AMERICA, PARKING MANAGEMENT DIVISION—See PCA Management; *U.S. Private*, pg. 3119
PARKING CONCEPTS INC.; *U.S. Private*, pg. 3098
PARKING FACILITIES LTD.—See Hill & Smith PLC; *Int'l*, pg. 3392
PARKING GARE DE LAUSANNE SA—See Indigo Group S.A.S.; *Int'l*, pg. 3655
PARKING MANAGEMENT, INC.; *U.S. Private*, pg. 3098
PARKING MANAGEMENT ORGANIZATION, LTD.—See Aspirant Group, Inc.; *Int'l*, pg. 631
PARKING PANDA CORP.—See SpotHero, Inc.; *U.S. Private*, pg. 3761
PARKING PARTNERS NV—See Indigo Group S.A.S.; *Int'l*, pg. 3655
PARKING SOLUTIONS CO., LTD.—See Daiwa House Industry Co., Ltd.; *Int'l*, pg. 1947
PARKING STRUCTURES, INC.—See R.W. Sidley, Incorporated; *U.S. Private*, pg. 3340

PARKING SUPPORT CENTER CORPORATION—See Tokyo Tatemono Co. Ltd.; *Int'l*, pg. 7796
PARKING VENTILATION EQUIPMENT LIMITED—See SIG plc; *Int'l*, pg. 6906
PARK INN HOTELS—See Carlson Companies Inc.; *U.S. Private*, pg. 764
PARK INN & SUITES—See Northampton Group Inc.; *Int'l*, pg. 5442
PARKINSON'S FOUNDATION, INC.; *U.S. Private*, pg. 3098
PARKINSON TECHNOLOGIES, INC.; *U.S. Private*, pg. 3098
PARKIT ENTERPRISE INC.; *Int'l*, pg. 5743
PARKIT NASHVILLE LLC—See Parkit Enterprise Inc.; *Int'l*, pg. 5743
PARK JEFFERSON SPEEDWAY INC.—See Heroes, Inc.; *U.S. Private*, pg. 1926
PARK-KRANKENHAUS LEIPZIG-SUDOST GMBH—See Asklepios Kliniken GmbH & Co. KGaA; *Int'l*, pg. 624
PARKLAND CORPORATION; *Int'l*, pg. 5743
PARKLAND GOLF CLUB, INC.—See Toll Brothers, Inc.; *U.S. Public*, pg. 2162
PARKLAND MEDICAL CENTER—See HCA Healthcare, Inc.; *U.S. Public*, pg. 1006
PARKLAND ONCOLOGY, LLC—See HCA Healthcare, Inc.; *U.S. Public*, pg. 1006
PARKLAND PHYSICIAN SERVICES, INC.—See HCA Healthcare, Inc.; *U.S. Public*, pg. 1006
PARKLAND PIPELINE CONTRACTORS LTD—See Tetra Tech, Inc.; *U.S. Public*, pg. 2023
PARKLAND PLASTICS—See Patrick Industries, Inc.; *U.S. Public*, pg. 1653
PARKLAND PROJECTS LTD.—See Tetra Tech, Inc.; *U.S. Public*, pg. 2023
PARKLAND SENIOR HOUSING, LP—See Wells Fargo & Company; *U.S. Public*, pg. 2345
PARKLANDS (HESSLE) RESIDENTS MANAGEMENT COMPANY LIMITED—See Persimmon plc; *Int'l*, pg. 5816
PARKLAND (USA) LLC—See Parkland Corporation; *Int'l*, pg. 5743
PARK LANE CONSTRUCTION INC.; *U.S. Private*, pg. 3096
PARK LANE DRIVE HOTEL DEVELOPMENT, LLC—See Choice Hotels International, Inc.; *U.S. Public*, pg. 490
PARK LANE FOODS LLC; *U.S. Private*, pg. 3096
PARKLANE LIMOUSINE SERVICE LIMITED—See Brockman Mining Limited; *Int'l*, pg. 1173
PARKLANE LIMOUSINE SERVICE (SHANGHAI) LTD—See Brockman Mining Limited; *Int'l*, pg. 1173
PARK LANE LTD.—See Bayerische Motoren Werke Aktiengesellschaft; *Int'l*, pg. 913
PARK LANE RETIREMENT VILLAGE LIMITED—See Arvida Group Limited; *Int'l*, pg. 587
PARK LAWN CEMETERY INC.—See Inglewood Park Cemetery Inc.; *U.S. Private*, pg. 2076
PARK LAWN COMPANY LIMITED; *Int'l*, pg. 5742
PARK LAWN CORPORATION—See Birch Hill Equity Partners Management Inc.; *Int'l*, pg. 1046
PARK LAWN CORPORATION—See Homesteaders Life Co. Inc.; *U.S. Private*, pg. 1974
PARKLEA CORRECTIONAL CENTRE—See The GEO Group, Inc.; *U.S. Public*, pg. 2075
PARKLEY HOLDING INC.; *U.S. Private*, pg. 3098
PARKLOT SP. Z O.O.—See Wirtualna Polska Holding S.A.; *Int'l*, pg. 8434
PARK L PROJECTS LTD.—See Tetra Tech, Inc.; *U.S. Public*, pg. 2023
PARK MANAGEMENT GROUP—See J.E. Robert Company; *U.S. Private*, pg. 2162
THE PARKMEAD GROUP PLC; *Int'l*, pg. 7673
PARK MEDIA—See WPP plc; *Int'l*, pg. 8477
PARKMOBILE USA, INC.—See BCD Holdings N.V.; *Int'l*, pg. 926
PARKMOTIVE GMBH—See ATON GmbH; *Int'l*, pg. 689
THE PARK NATIONAL BANK—See Park National Corporation; *U.S. Public*, pg. 1638
PARK NATIONAL CORPORATION; *U.S. Public*, pg. 1638
PARK 'N FLY, INC.—See Green Courte Partners, LLC; *U.S. Private*, pg. 1772
PARKNOW AUSTRIA GMBH—See Bayerische Motoren Werke Aktiengesellschaft; *Int'l*, pg. 913
PARKNSHOP (HK) LIMITED—See CK Hutchison Holdings Limited; *Int'l*, pg. 1638
PARK OF HOLDING INC.; *U.S. Private*, pg. 3096
PARK-OHIO HOLDINGS CORP.; *U.S. Public*, pg. 1638
PARK-OHIO INDUSTRIES, INC. - OHIO CRANKSHAFT DIVISION—See Park-Ohio Holdings Corp.; *U.S. Public*, pg. 1640
PARK-OHIO INDUSTRIES, INC.—See Park-Ohio Holdings Corp.; *U.S. Public*, pg. 1639
PARK-OHIO INDUSTRIES (SHANGHAI) CO. LTD.—See Park-Ohio Holdings Corp.; *U.S. Public*, pg. 1639
PARK-OHIO PRODUCTS, INC.—See Park-Ohio Holdings Corp.; *U.S. Public*, pg. 1640
PARKOMAT INTERNATIONAL LTD.; *Int'l*, pg. 5744
PARK ONE INCORPORATED; *U.S. Private*, pg. 3096
PARK PLACE CORPORATION; *U.S. Private*, pg. 3096
PARK PLACE HOTEL; *U.S. Private*, pg. 3096

PARK PLACE MOTORCARS, LTD.; *U.S. Private*, pg. 3096
PARK PLACE TECHNOLOGIES, LLC—See Charlesbank Capital Partners, LLC; *U.S. Private*, pg. 856
PARK PLACE TECHNOLOGIES, LLC—See GTCR LLC; *U.S. Private*, pg. 1806
PARK PLACE VOLVO; *U.S. Private*, pg. 3096
PARK PLAZA BLOOMINGTON—See Carlson Companies Inc.; *U.S. Private*, pg. 764
PARK PLAZA GERMANY HOLDINGS GMBH—See PPHE Hotel Group Limited; *Int'l*, pg. 5951
PARK PLAZA HOSPITAL BILLING CENTER, L.L.C.—See HCA Healthcare, Inc.; *U.S. Public*, pg. 1006
PARK PLAZA HOTELS EUROPE B.V.—See PPHE Hotel Group Limited; *Int'l*, pg. 5951
PARK PLAZA NURNBERG GMBH—See PPHE Hotel Group Limited; *Int'l*, pg. 5951
PARK REGIS CAIRNS PTY. LTD.—See Seibu Holdings Inc.; *Int'l*, pg. 6685
PARK REGIS GRIFFIN PTY. LTD.—See Seibu Holdings Inc.; *Int'l*, pg. 6685
PARK REIT; *Int'l*, pg. 5742
PARK RETAIL LIMITED—See PayPoint plc; *Int'l*, pg. 5763
PARKRIDGE EAST HOSPITAL—See HCA Healthcare, Inc.; *U.S. Public*, pg. 1012
PARK RIDGE HEALTH; *U.S. Private*, pg. 3096
PARKRIDGE MEDICAL CENTER, INC.—See HCA Healthcare, Inc.; *U.S. Public*, pg. 1012
PARK RIDGE SURGERY CENTER, LLC—See HCA Healthcare, Inc.; *U.S. Public*, pg. 1006
PARKRIDGE VALLEY HOSPITAL—See HCA Healthcare, Inc.; *U.S. Public*, pg. 1012
PARKRIDGE WEST HOSPITAL—See HCA Healthcare, Inc.; *U.S. Public*, pg. 1012
PARKROSE HARDWARE, INC.—See Tyndale Advisors, LLC; *U.S. Private*, pg. 4268
PARKROSE HARDWARE WASHINGTON, INC.—See Tyndale Advisors, LLC; *U.S. Private*, pg. 4268
PARK RUG COMPANY INC.; *U.S. Private*, pg. 3096
PARKS! AMERICA, INC.; *U.S. Public*, pg. 1650
PARKS AUTOMOTIVE INC.; *U.S. Private*, pg. 3098
PARKS AUTO PARTS INC.; *U.S. Private*, pg. 3098
PARK & SHOP FOOD MART; *U.S. Private*, pg. 3095
PARKSHOPPING CAMPO GRANDE LTDA.—See Multiplan Empreendimentos Imobiliarios S.A.; *Int'l*, pg. 5084
PARK SHORE RESORT—See SunStream, Inc.; *U.S. Private*, pg. 3873
PARKSIDE DIALYSIS, LLC—See DaVita Inc.; *U.S. Public*, pg. 641
PARKSIDE FORD LINCOLN LTD.; *Int'l*, pg. 5744
PARKSIDE HEALTHCARE, INC.—See The Ensign Group, Inc.; *U.S. Public*, pg. 2072
PARKSIDE MANAGEMENT SERVICES, LLC; *U.S. Private*, pg. 3098
PARKSIDE PACKAGING LTD—See Sequana SA; *Int'l*, pg. 6719
PARKSIDE RESOURCES CORPORATION; *Int'l*, pg. 5744
PARKSIDE SURGERY CENTER, INC.—See HCA Healthcare, Inc.; *U.S. Public*, pg. 1006
PARKSIDE TOWNHOMES, LLC—See Goff Capital, Inc.; *U.S. Private*, pg. 1726
PARKSIDE UTILITY CONSTRUCTION CORP.—See Dycom Industries, Inc.; *U.S. Public*, pg. 699
PARKSIDE UTILITY CONSTRUCTION, LLC—See Dycom Industries, Inc.; *U.S. Public*, pg. 699
PARKS INSURANCE PTY LTD—See Wesfarmers Limited; *Int'l*, pg. 8382
THE PARKSITE GROUP; *U.S. Private*, pg. 4091
PARKSITE PLUNKETT-WEBSTER—See The Parksite Group; *U.S. Private*, pg. 4091
PARKS KOUSHINETSU CO., LTD.—See Sumitomo Heavy Industries, Ltd.; *Int'l*, pg. 7287
PARK'S MOTOR GROUP; *Int'l*, pg. 5742
PARKSON CANADA CORPORATION—See Axel Johnson Gruppen AB; *Int'l*, pg. 765
PARKSON CORPORATION SDN BHD—See Parkson Holdings Berhad; *Int'l*, pg. 5744
PARKSON CORPORATION—See Axel Johnson Gruppen AB; *Int'l*, pg. 765
PARKSON CREDIT SDN. BHD.—See Parkson Retail Group Limited; *Int'l*, pg. 5744
PARKSON HANOI CO LTD—See Parkson Holdings Berhad; *Int'l*, pg. 5744
PARKSON HOLDINGS BERHAD; *Int'l*, pg. 5744
PARKSON RETAIL ASIA LIMITED; *Int'l*, pg. 5744
PARKSON RETAIL DEVELOPMENT CO., LTD.—See Parkson Holdings Berhad; *Int'l*, pg. 5744
PARKSON RETAIL GROUP LIMITED; *Int'l*, pg. 5744
PARKSONS CARTAMUNDI PVT. LTD.—See Cartamundi N.V.; *Int'l*, pg. 1348
PARKSONS PACKAGING LTD.—See Warburg Pincus LLC; *U.S. Private*, pg. 4439
PARK SOUND ACQUISITION CORPORATION; *U.S. Private*, pg. 3096
PARK SQUARE ENTERPRISES INC.; *U.S. Private*, pg. 3097
PARK STATE BANK, INC.—See Park Financial Group, Inc.; *U.S. Private*, pg. 3096
PARK STREET NORDICOM A/S; *Int'l*, pg. 5742

COMPANY NAME INDEX

PARK SUANPLU HOLDINGS CO. LTD.—See Oriental Holdings Berhad; *Int'l*, pg. 5625
PARK SUNSET, LLC—See Pebblebrook Hotel Trust; *U.S. Public*, pg. 1660
PARK SURGICAL CO, INC.—See Dealmed Medical Supplies LLC; *U.S. Private*, pg. 1183
PARKSVILLE CHRYSLER LTD.; *Int'l*, pg. 5744
PARK SYSTEMS CORP.; *Int'l*, pg. 5742
PARK SYSTEMS EUROPE GMBH—See Park Systems Corp.; *Int'l*, pg. 5742
PARK SYSTEMS FRANCE SARL—See Park Systems Corp.; *Int'l*, pg. 5742
PARK SYSTEMS INC.—See Park Systems Corp.; *Int'l*, pg. 5742
PARK SYSTEMS JAPAN INC.—See Park Systems Corp.; *Int'l*, pg. 5742
PARK SYSTEMS MICROSCOPY S.A. DE C.V.—See Park Systems Corp.; *Int'l*, pg. 5742
PARK SYSTEMS PTE. LTD.—See Park Systems Corp.; *Int'l*, pg. 5742
PARKTRON MALAYSIA SDH BHD—See Chung-Hsin Electric & Machinery Manufacturing Corp.; *Int'l*, pg. 1597
PARKTRON TECHNOLOGY CO., LTD—See Chung-Hsin Electric & Machinery Manufacturing Corp.; *Int'l*, pg. 1597
PARK VENTURA ENDOSCOPY CENTER, LLC—See KKR & Co. Inc.; *U.S. Public*, pg. 1246
PARKVIEW ACRES CURE & REHABILITATION CENTER—See Apollo Global Management, Inc.; *U.S. Public*, pg. 157
PARKVIEW CAPITAL CREDIT, INC.; *U.S. Private*, pg. 3098
PARKVIEW COMMUNTY HOSPITAL MEDICAL CENTER; *U.S. Private*, pg. 3098
PARKVIEW MEDICAL CENTER, INC.—See University of Colorado Health; *U.S. Private*, pg. 4308
PARKVIEW - SKILLED NURSING, INC.—See Omega Healthcare Investors, Inc.; *U.S. Public*, pg. 1571
PARKVIEW TRANSIT—See Caisse de Depot et Placement du Quebec; *Int'l*, pg. 1255
PARKVIEW TRANSIT—See Ullico Inc.; *U.S. Private*, pg. 4276
PARKWALK ADVISORS LIMITED—See IP Group plc; *Int'l*, pg. 3795
PARK WAVERLY HEALTHCARE LLC—See The Ensign Group, Inc.; *U.S. Public*, pg. 2071
PARKWAY BANCORP, INC.; *U.S. Private*, pg. 3098
PARKWAY BANK & TRUST COMPANY - ARIZONA DIVISION—See Parkway Bancorp, Inc.; *U.S. Private*, pg. 3098
PARKWAY BANK & TRUST COMPANY—See Parkway Bancorp, Inc.; *U.S. Private*, pg. 3098
PARKWAY BUICK GMC; *U.S. Private*, pg. 3098
PARKWAY CHRYSLER DODGE JEEP RAM; *Int'l*, pg. 5744
PARKWAY CONSTRUCTION & ASSOCIATES LP; *U.S. Private*, pg. 3098
PARKWAY CORPORATE LIMITED; *Int'l*, pg. 5744
PARKWAY CORPORATION; *U.S. Private*, pg. 3099
PARKWAY ELECTRIC & COMMUNICATIONS LLC—See Huizenga Manufacturing Group, Inc.; *U.S. Private*, pg. 2004
PARKWAY FINANCIAL GROUP, LLC—See Century Communities, Inc.; *U.S. Public*, pg. 475
PARKWAY FORD SALES 1996 LTD.—See Ford Motor Company; *U.S. Public*, pg. 865
PARKWAY GROUP HEALTHCARE PTE LTD—See Khazanah Nasional Berhad; *Int'l*, pg. 4152
PARKWAY HOLDINGS LIMITED—See Khazanah Nasional Berhad; *Int'l*, pg. 4152
PARKWAY, INC.; *U.S. Public*, pg. 1650
PARKWAY INTERNATIONAL CONTRACTING L.L.C.—See Al Shafar Group; *Int'l*, pg. 282
PARKWAY LABORATORY SERVICES LTD—See Khazanah Nasional Berhad; *Int'l*, pg. 4152
PARKWAY LIFE REAL ESTATE INVESTMENT TRUST; *Int'l*, pg. 5744
PARKWAY MOTORCARS; *U.S. Private*, pg. 3099
PARKWAY MOTORS OF LEONIA INC.; *U.S. Private*, pg. 3099
PARKWAY PANTAI LIMITED—See Khazanah Nasional Berhad; *Int'l*, pg. 4152
PARKWAY PAVILION HEALTHCARE—See Apollo Global Management, Inc.; *U.S. Public*, pg. 157
PARKWAY PRODUCTS, LLC - ATLANTA FACILITY—See Heartwood Partners, LLC; *U.S. Private*, pg. 1901
PARKWAY PRODUCTS, LLC - LOVELAND FACILITY—See Heartwood Partners, LLC; *U.S. Private*, pg. 1901
PARKWAY PRODUCTS, LLC - MARIETTA FACILITY—See Heartwood Partners, LLC; *U.S. Private*, pg. 1901
PARKWAY PRODUCTS, LLC - SALTILLO FACILITY—See Heartwood Partners, LLC; *U.S. Private*, pg. 1901
PARKWAY PRODUCTS, LLC - SENECA FACILITY—See Heartwood Partners, LLC; *U.S. Private*, pg. 1901
PARKWAY PRODUCTS, LLC—See Heartwood Partners, LLC; *U.S. Private*, pg. 1901
PARKWAY PROPERTIES LP—See Parkway, Inc.; *U.S. Public*, pg. 1650

PARKWAY PROPERTY INVESTMENTS, LLC—See Parkway, Inc.; *U.S. Public*, pg. 1650
PARKWAY RECOVERY CARE CENTER, LLC—See Tenet Healthcare Corporation; *U.S. Public*, pg. 2006
PARKWAY REGIONAL MEDICAL CLINIC, INC.—See Community Health Systems, Inc.; *U.S. Public*, pg. 555
PARKWAY SHENTON PTE LTD—See Khazanah Nasional Berhad; *Int'l*, pg. 4152
PARKWAY SURGERY CENTER, LLC—See Tenet Healthcare Corporation; *U.S. Public*, pg. 2012
PARK WEST HEALTH SYSTEM; *U.S. Private*, pg. 3097
PARK WEST LANDSCAPE INC.—See Tracy Industries Inc.; *U.S. Private*, pg. 4201
PARK WEST LANDSCAPE INC.—See Tracy Industries Inc.; *U.S. Private*, pg. 4201
PARK WEST LANDSCAPE—See Tracy Industries Inc.; *U.S. Private*, pg. 4201
PARKWEST MEDICAL CENTER; *U.S. Private*, pg. 3099
PARKWEST SURGERY CENTER, L.P.—See Tenet Healthcare Corporation; *U.S. Public*, pg. 2012
THE PARKWOOD CEMETERY COMPANY—See Service Corporation International; *U.S. Public*, pg. 1871
PARKWOOD COMMUNITY LEISURE LIMITED—See Parkwood Holdings Limited; *Int'l*, pg. 5745
PARKWOOD CONSULTANCY SERVICES (PCS)—See Parkwood Holdings Limited; *Int'l*, pg. 5745
PARKWOOD DEVELOPMENTS SDN. BHD.—See Parkwood Holdings Berhad; *Int'l*, pg. 5744
PARKWOOD GROUP LIMITED—See KKR & Co. Inc.; *U.S. Public*, pg. 1266
PARKWOOD GROUP TRUSTEES LIMITED—See Parkwood Holdings Limited; *Int'l*, pg. 5745
PARKWOOD HEALTHCARE LIMITED—See Parkwood Holdings Limited; *Int'l*, pg. 5745
PARKWOOD HEALTH & FITNESS LIMITED—See Parkwood Holdings Limited; *Int'l*, pg. 5745
PARKWOOD HOLDINGS BERHAD; *Int'l*, pg. 5744
PARKWOOD HOLDINGS LIMITED; *Int'l*, pg. 5744
PARKWOOD LEISURE LIMITED—See Parkwood Holdings Limited; *Int'l*, pg. 5745
PARKWOOD PROJECT MANAGEMENT LIMITED—See Parkwood Holdings Limited; *Int'l*, pg. 5745
PARLANCE SYSTEMS, INC.—See PLDT Inc.; *Int'l*, pg. 5896
PARLAY ENTERTAINMENT—See Backstageplay Inc.; *Int'l*, pg. 795
PARLE FREUND MACHINERY PRIVATE LIMITED—See Freund Corporation; *Int'l*, pg. 2791
PARLE INDUSTRIES LTD.; *Int'l*, pg. 5745
PARLEM TELECOM CO DE TELECOMUNICACIONS SA; *Int'l*, pg. 5745
PARLEX DYNAFLEX CORPORATION—See Johnson Electric Holdings Limited; *Int'l*, pg. 3991
PARLEX (SHANGHAI) ELECTRONICS CO. LTD.—See Johnson Electric Holdings Limited; *Int'l*, pg. 3991
PARLEX USA—See Johnson Electric Holdings Limited; *Int'l*, pg. 3991
PARLO BERHAD; *Int'l*, pg. 5745
PARLOPHONE RECORDS LIMITED—See Access Industries, Inc.; *U.S. Private*, pg. 52
PARLUX FRAGRANCES, LLC—See Perfumania Holdings, Inc.; *U.S. Private*, pg. 3150
PARMAC AIR CONDITIONING & MECHANICAL SERVICES PTY. LTD.—See BlueNRGY Group Limited; *Int'l*, pg. 1072
PARMACOTTO SPA—See UniCredit S.p.A.; *Int'l*, pg. 8035
PARMALAT AUSTRALIA LTD.—See Groupe Lactalis SA; *Int'l*, pg. 3106
PARMALAT SOUTH AFRICA (PTY) LTD.—See Groupe Lactalis SA; *Int'l*, pg. 3106
PARMALAT S.P.A.—See Groupe Lactalis SA; *Int'l*, pg. 3106
PARMAN ENERGY CORPORATION—See Parman Holding Corporation; *U.S. Private*, pg. 3099
PARMAN HOLDING CORPORATION; *U.S. Private*, pg. 3099
PARMA OY—See Bain Capital, LP; *U.S. Private*, pg. 438
PARMARINE LTD—See YTL Corporation Berhad; *Int'l*, pg. 8606
PAR MAR OIL COMPANY—See Croton Holding Company; *U.S. Private*, pg. 1108
PARMATECH CORPORATION—See ATW Companies Inc.; *U.S. Private*, pg. 384
PARMAX PHARMA LIMITED; *Int'l*, pg. 5745
PARMED PHARMACEUTICALS, INC.—See Cardinal Health, Inc.; *U.S. Public*, pg. 434
PARMELEE INDUSTRIES, INC.—See Bunzl plc; *Int'l*, pg. 1219
PARMELEE LIMITED—See Bunzl plc; *Int'l*, pg. 1219
PARMENION CAPITAL PARTNERS LLP—See Preservation Capital Partners Ltd.; *Int'l*, pg. 5964
PARMENTER, INC.; *U.S. Private*, pg. 3099
PARMENTER REALTY & INVESTMENT COMPANY; *U.S. Private*, pg. 3099
PARMESHWARI SILK MILLS LIMITED; *Int'l*, pg. 5745
PARNAS HOTEL CO., LTD.—See GS Holdings Corp.; *Int'l*, pg. 3142
PARNASSOS ENTERPRISES S.A.; *Int'l*, pg. 5745
PARNASSUS BOOKS LLC; *U.S. Private*, pg. 3099

PARNAV SPORTS ACADEMY LIMITED; *Int'l*, pg. 5745
PARNAX LAB LTD.; *Int'l*, pg. 5745
PARNELL FISHER CHILD & CO LIMITED—See The Skipton Building Society; *Int'l*, pg. 7687
PARNELL PHARMACEUTICALS HOLDINGS LTD.; *Int'l*, pg. 5745
PARNU POSTIMEES—See UP Invest OU; *Int'l*, pg. 8086
PAROC AB—See Owens Corning; *U.S. Public*, pg. 1628
PAROC GMBH—See Owens Corning; *U.S. Public*, pg. 1628
PAROC GROUP OY—See Owens Corning; *U.S. Public*, pg. 1628
PAROC LIMITED—See Owens Corning; *U.S. Public*, pg. 1628
PAROC OY AB—See Owens Corning; *U.S. Public*, pg. 1628
PAROC POLSKA SP. Z O.O.—See Owens Corning; *U.S. Public*, pg. 1628
PARON AG—See APG/SGA SA; *Int'l*, pg. 513
PARO SERVICES CORP. - ROYAL CHEMICAL CHATTANOOGA PLANT—See Paro Services Corp.; *U.S. Private*, pg. 3099
PARO SERVICES CORP. - ROYAL CHEMICAL DALLAS PLANT—See Paro Services Corp.; *U.S. Private*, pg. 3099
PARO SERVICES CORP. - ROYAL CHEMICAL EAST STROUDSBURG PLANT—See Paro Services Corp.; *U.S. Private*, pg. 3099
PARO SERVICES CORP. - ROYAL CHEMICAL MACEDONIA PLANT—See Paro Services Corp.; *U.S. Private*, pg. 3099
PARO SERVICES CORP.; *U.S. Private*, pg. 3099
PAROS SHIPPING (PTE.) LTD.—See Minerva Bunkering; *Int'l*, pg. 4908
P.A. ROSS LTD.; *Int'l*, pg. 5682
PAR PACIFIC HOLDINGS, INC.; *U.S. Public*, pg. 1636
PAR PHARMACEUTICAL COMPANIES, INC.—See Endo International plc; *Int'l*, pg. 2404
PAR PHARMACEUTICAL HOLDINGS, INC.—See Endo International plc; *Int'l*, pg. 2404
PAR PHARMACEUTICAL, INC.—See Endo International plc; *Int'l*, pg. 2404
PAR PICEANCE ENERGY EQUITY, LLC—See Par Pacific Holdings, Inc.; *U.S. Public*, pg. 1636
PAR PLUMBING CO. INC.; *U.S. Private*, pg. 3089
PARPRO CORPORATION; *Int'l*, pg. 5745
PARPRO (NEVADA), INC.—See PARPRO Corporation; *Int'l*, pg. 5745
PARQUE ARAUCO S.A.; *Int'l*, pg. 5745
PARQUE EOLICO PAMPA SA—See Enel S.p.A.; *Int'l*, pg. 2414
PARQUE SAN ANTONIO, S.A.—See Melia Hotels International, S.A.; *Int'l*, pg. 4809
PARQUES EOLICOS DEL CANTABRICO S.A.—See EDP - Energias de Portugal, S.A.; *Int'l*, pg. 2315
PARQUES REUNIDOS SERVICIOS CENTRALES SA—See Newgate Private Equity LLP; *Int'l*, pg. 5234
PARQUEST CAPITAL SAS; *Int'l*, pg. 5745
THE PARQUET GROUP; *U.S. Private*, pg. 4091
PARQUET PUBLIC AFFAIRS, LLC—See The Parquet Group; *U.S. Private*, pg. 4091
PARRAGON BOOKS LTD—See D.C. Thomson & Co. Ltd.; *Int'l*, pg. 1900
PARRATT-WOLFF, INC.; *U.S. Private*, pg. 3099
PARR CREDIT S.R.L.—See Arrow Global Group PLC; *Int'l*, pg. 579
PARRETT WINDOWS & DOORS, INC.; *U.S. Private*, pg. 3099
PARR INSTRUMENT COMPANY; *U.S. Private*, pg. 3099
PARRISH & COMPANY INC.; *U.S. Private*, pg. 3099
PARRISH ENTERPRISES, LTD.; *U.S. Private*, pg. 3100
PARRISH EQUIPMENT SUPPLY INC.; *U.S. Private*, pg. 3100
PARRISH-HARE ELECTRICAL SUPPLY CORPORATION; *U.S. Private*, pg. 3100
PARRISH & HEIMBECKER, LIMITED - P&H FOODS HANOVER PROCESSING PLANT—See Exceldor Cooperative Avicole; *Int'l*, pg. 2578
PARRISH & HEIMBECKER, LIMITED—See Exceldor Co-operative Avicole; *Int'l*, pg. 2577
PARRISH HOME MEDICAL INC—See AdaptHealth Corp.; *U.S. Public*, pg. 39
PARRISH-MCCALL CONSTRUCTORS, INC.; *U.S. Private*, pg. 3100
PARRISH & PARTNERS, LLC; *U.S. Private*, pg. 3100
PARRISH TIRE COMPANY, INC. - COMMERCIAL DIVISION—See Parrish Tire Company, Inc.; *U.S. Private*, pg. 3100
PARRISH TIRE COMPANY, INC.; *U.S. Private*, pg. 3100
PARRISH TIRE COMPANY, INC. - WHOLESALE DIVISION—See Parrish Tire Company, Inc.; *U.S. Private*, pg. 3100
PARRIZIA ACTIVOS INMOBILIARIOS ESPANA S.L.U.—See PATRIZIA SE; *U.S. Private*, pg. 5758
PARR LUMBER COMPANY INC.; *U.S. Private*, pg. 3099
PARR MEDIA GROUP; *U.S. Private*, pg. 3099
PARR METAL FABRICATORS LTD—See Dynamic Technologies Group Inc.; *Int'l*, pg. 2241

PARR MEDIA GROUP / CORPORATE AFFILIATIONS

PARROT ASIA PACIFIC LTD.—See Parrot S.A.; *Int'l*, pg. 5746
PARROT DRONES S.A.S.—See Parrot S.A.; *Int'l*, pg. 5746
PARROT S.A.; *Int'l*, pg. 5746
PARR TECHNOLOGIES, LLC—See Gladstone Management Corporation; *U.S. Private*, pg. 1705
PARRY AGRO INDUSTRIES LTD—See The Murugappa Group, Ltd.; *Int'l*, pg. 7668
PARRY AMERICA INC—See The Murugappa Group, Ltd.; *Int'l*, pg. 7668
PARRY INFRASTRUCTURE COMPANY PRIVATE LIMITED—See The Murugappa Group, Ltd.; *Int'l*, pg. 7668
PARRY PHYTOREMEDIES PRIVATE LIMITED—See The Murugappa Group, Ltd.; *Int'l*, pg. 7668
PARRY SUGAR INDUSTRIES LIMITED—See The Murugappa Group, Ltd.; *Int'l*, pg. 7668
PARS ANIMAL FEED COMPANY; *Int'l*, pg. 5746
PARSAN MAKINA PARCALARI SANAYII AS; *Int'l*, pg. 5746
PARS CARTON COMPANY; *Int'l*, pg. 5746
PARS DAROU COMPANY; *Int'l*, pg. 5746
PARS DRILLING KISH CO., LTD.—See Japan Drilling Co., Ltd.; *Int'l*, pg. 3888
PARSEC CAPITAL ACQUISITION CORP.; *U.S. Public*, pg. 1650
PARSEC COMPUTER CORP.; *U.S. Private*, pg. 3100
PARSEC FINANCIAL MANAGEMENT, INC.—See Modera Wealth Management, LLC; *U.S. Private*, pg. 2759
PARSEC INC.—See Universal Logistics Holdings, Inc.; *U.S. Public*, pg. 2261
PARSEC INNOVATION LABS LLC—See Golden Agri-Resources Ltd.; *Int'l*, pg. 3028
PARS ELECTRIC MANUFACTURING COMPANY PJSC; *Int'l*, pg. 5746
PARSE, LLC—See Meta Platforms, Inc.; *U.S. Public*, pg. 1427
PARSELY, INC.—See Automattic Inc.; *U.S. Private*, pg. 400
PARS ENVIRONMENTAL, INC.—See Montrose Environmental Group, Inc.; *U.S. Public*, pg. 1466
PARSEPORT APS—See Workiva Inc.; *U.S. Public*, pg. 2379
PARSEQ LIMITED—See Parseq plc; *Int'l*, pg. 5747
PARSEQ PLC; *Int'l*, pg. 5747
PARSHIP ELITE GROUP GMBH—See ProSiebenSat.1 Media SE; *Int'l*, pg. 6000
PARSHIP GROUP GMBH—See ProSiebenSat.1 Media SE; *Int'l*, pg. 6000
PARSHVA ENTERPRISES LIMITED; *Int'l*, pg. 5747
PARSHWANATH CORPORATION LIMITED; *Int'l*, pg. 5747
PARSIAN BANK; *Int'l*, pg. 5747
PARSIAN BROKERAGE COMPANY—See Parsian Bank; *Int'l*, pg. 5747
PARSIAN CATALYST CHEMICAL COMPANY LTD.—See National Iranian Lead & Zinc Company; *Int'l*, pg. 5160
PARSIAN CONSTRUCTION DEVELOPMENT COMPANY—See Parsian Bank; *Int'l*, pg. 5747
PARSIAN E-COMMERCE COMPANY—See Parsian Bank; *Int'l*, pg. 5747
PARSIAN EXCHANGE COMPANY—See Parsian Bank; *Int'l*, pg. 5747
PARSIAN INSURANCE COMPANY; *Int'l*, pg. 5747
PARSIAN OIL & GAS DEVELOPMENT CO.; *Int'l*, pg. 5747
PARSIAN OIL & GAS DEVELOPMENT GROUP COMPANY; *Int'l*, pg. 5748
PARSIENA DESIGN, INC.; *Int'l*, pg. 5748
PARS INTERNATIONAL CORP.; *U.S. Private*, pg. 3100
PARS KHAZAR DISTRIBUTION COMPANY—See Pars Tousheh Investment Company; *Int'l*, pg. 5746
PARS KHAZAR INDUSTRIAL COMPANY; *Int'l*, pg. 5746
PARS KHAZAR NOGHREH COMPANY—See Pars Tousheh Investment Company; *Int'l*, pg. 5746
PARSLEY ENERGY, LLC—See Pioneer Natural Resources Company; *U.S. Public*, pg. 1693
PARSLEY ENERGY MANAGEMENT, LLC—See Pioneer Natural Resources Company; *U.S. Public*, pg. 1693
PARSLEY ENERGY OPERATIONS, LLC—See Pioneer Natural Resources Company; *U.S. Public*, pg. 1693
PARSLEY FINANCE CORP.—See Pioneer Natural Resources Company; *U.S. Public*, pg. 1693
PARS OIL & GAS COMPANY; *Int'l*, pg. 5746
PARSONS BRINCKERHOFF GROUP INC.—See WSP Global, Inc.; *Int'l*, pg. 8497
PARSONS CHEVROLET-BUICK INC.; *U.S. Private*, pg. 3100
PARSONS CONSTRUCTION GROUP INC.—See Parsons Corporation; *U.S. Public*, pg. 1651
PARSONS CORPORATION; *U.S. Public*, pg. 1650
PARSONS-EAGLE PACKAGING SYSTEMS—See Campbell Wrapper Corporation; *U.S. Private*, pg. 731
PARSONS-EAGLE PACKAGING SYSTEMS—See Campbell Wrapper Corporation; *U.S. Private*, pg. 731
PARSONS ELECTRIC LLC; *U.S. Private*, pg. 3100
PARSONS FORD LINCOLN MERCURY; *U.S. Private*, pg. 3100
PARSONS GROUP INTERNATIONAL LIMITED—See Parsons Corporation; *U.S. Public*, pg. 1651

PARSONS INFRASTRUCTURE & TECHNOLOGY GROUP INC.—See Parsons Corporation; *U.S. Public*, pg. 1651
PARSONS OIL COMPANY INC—See Kent Distributors Inc.; *U.S. Private*, pg. 2287
PARSONS ROOFING COMPANY, INC.; *U.S. Private*, pg. 3100
PARSONS TRANSPORTATION GROUP INC.—See Parsons Corporation; *U.S. Public*, pg. 1651
PARSONS & WHITTEMORE, INC.; *U.S. Private*, pg. 3100
PARSONS XTREME GOLF, LLC; *U.S. Private*, pg. 3100
PARS PAMCHAL CHEMICAL COMPANY; *Int'l*, pg. 5746
PARS PETROCHEMICAL CO.—See Persian Gulf Petrochemical Industry Commercial Company; *Int'l*, pg. 5815
PARS PRODUTOS PROCES. DE DATOS LTDA.—See SONDA S.A.; *Int'l*, pg. 7089
PARS PUMP MANUFACTURING CO.; *Int'l*, pg. 5746
PARS REFRACTORIES CO; *Int'l*, pg. 5746
PARS SHAHAB LAMP COMPANY; *Int'l*, pg. 5746
PARS SHAHAB NOGHREH COMPANY—See Pars Tousheh Investment Company; *Int'l*, pg. 5746
PARS SWITCH COMPANY; *Int'l*, pg. 5746
PAR STERILE PRODUCTS, LLC—See Endo International plc; *Int'l*, pg. 2404
PARS TILE COMPANY; *Int'l*, pg. 5746
PARS TOUSHEH INVESTMENT COMPANY; *Int'l*, pg. 5746
PARSVNATH DEVELOPERS LTD.; *Int'l*, pg. 5748
PARSVNATH ESTATE DEVELOPERS PVT. LTD.; *Int'l*, pg. 5748
PARSVNATH LANDMARK DEVELOPERS PRIVATE LIMITED—See Parsvnath Developers Ltd.; *Int'l*, pg. 5748
PARSVNATH RAIL LAND PROJECT PRIVATE LIMITED—See Parsvnath Developers Ltd.; *Int'l*, pg. 5748
PAR SYSTEMS, LLC—See Pohlad Companies; *U.S. Private*, pg. 3220
PARS ZARASA HOME APPLIANCES DESIGN & INDUSTRIAL COMPANY—See Pars Tousheh Investment Company; *Int'l*, pg. 5746
PARTANI APPLIANCES LTD.; *Int'l*, pg. 5748
PARTEC AG; *Int'l*, pg. 5748
PARTECH, INC.—See PAR Technology Corporation; *U.S. Public*, pg. 1636
PAR TECHNOLOGY CORPORATION; *U.S. Public*, pg. 1636
PARTEK CARGOTEC S.R.L.—See Komatsu Ltd.; *Int'l*, pg. 4237
PARTENON M.A.M. SISTEM A.D.; *Int'l*, pg. 5748
PARTENOPEA FINANZA DI PROGETTO SPA—See Salini Costruttori S.p.A.; *Int'l*, pg. 6493
PARTER CAPITAL GROUP GMBH; *Int'l*, pg. 5748
PARTES DE PRECISION MITSUBA DE MEXICO S.A. DE C.V.—See MITSUBA Corporation; *Int'l*, pg. 4928
PARTEX BRASIL LTDA.—See PTT Public Company Limited; *Int'l*, pg. 6092
PARTEX BRASIL SERVICOS PETROLIFEROS LTD—See PTT Public Company Limited; *Int'l*, pg. 6092
PARTEX GAS CORPORATION—See PTT Public Company Limited; *Int'l*, pg. 6092
PARTEX OIL & GAS (HOLDINGS) CORP.—See PTT Public Company Limited; *Int'l*, pg. 6092
PARTEX (OMAN) CORPORATION—See PTT Public Company Limited; *Int'l*, pg. 6092
PARTEX SERVICES PORTUGAL, S.A.—See PTT Public Company Limited; *Int'l*, pg. 6092
PART GMBH—See Robert Bosch GmbH; *Int'l*, pg. 6364
PART GMBH—See Sika AG; *Int'l*, pg. 6916
PARTHENON CAPITAL PARTNERS - WEST COAST OFFICE—See PCP Enterprise, L.P.; *U.S. Private*, pg. 3121
PARTHENON METAL WORKS, INC.—See Crowne Group LLC; *U.S. Private*, pg. 1112
PARTHENON PAVILION INC.—See HCA Healthcare, Inc.; *U.S. Public*, pg. 992
PARTHOLON CDO 1 PLC—See Bank of Ireland Group plc; *Int'l*, pg. 845
PARTICIPANT MEDIA, LLC—See Apollo Global Management, Inc.; *U.S. Public*, pg. 167
PARTICIPANT PRODUCTIONS, LLC; *U.S. Private*, pg. 3100
PARTICIPATIE MAATSCHAPPIJ GRAAFSCHAP HOLLAND N.V.—See Assicurazioni Generali S.p.A.; *Int'l*, pg. 647
PARTICIPATIE MAATSCHAPPIJ TRANSHOL B.V.—See Assicurazioni Generali S.p.A.; *Int'l*, pg. 648
PARTICIPATIEMAATSCHAPPIJ VLAANDEREN; *Int'l*, pg. 5748
PARTICIPATIONS DES ARDENNES—See Compagnie de Saint-Gobain SA; *Int'l*, pg. 1724
PARTICIPATIONS INDUSTRIELLES ET MINIERES SA; *Int'l*, pg. 5748
PARTICLE DRILLING TECHNOLOGIES, LLC; *U.S. Private*, pg. 3101
PARTICLE ENGINEERING SOLUTIONS, LLC—See Ion Beam Applications, S.A.; *Int'l*, pg. 3793
PARTICLE MEASURING SYSTEMS, INC.—See Spectris Plc; *Int'l*, pg. 7131

PARTICLE MEASURING SYSTEMS S.R.L.—See Spectris Plc; *Int'l*, pg. 7131
PARTICLE PLANNER CO., LTD.—See Vanachai Group Public Company Limited; *Int'l*, pg. 8128
PARTICLE SCIENCES INC.—See Agno Pharma; *U.S. Private*, pg. 128
PARTICLE SIZING SYSTEMS, LLC—See Entegris, Inc.; *U.S. Public*, pg. 777
PARTICULAR SCIENCES LTD.—See HORIBA Ltd; *Int'l*, pg. 3478
PARTIDA TEQUILA, LLC; *U.S. Private*, pg. 3101
PARTIDIS S.A.S.—See Compagnie de Saint-Gobain SA; *Int'l*, pg. 1724
PARTIES THAT COOK LLC; *U.S. Private*, pg. 3101
PARTINGTON ENGINEERING LIMITED—See ARGENT INDUSTRIAL LIMITED; *Int'l*, pg. 561
PARTIOAITTA OY—See Fenix Outdoor International AG; *Int'l*, pg. 2634
PARTIR SERVICE CO., LTD.—See PT Bank JTrust Indonesia Tbk.; *Int'l*, pg. 6026
PARTIZANSKE BUILDING COMPONENTS-SK S.R.O.—See VKR Holding A/S; *Int'l*, pg. 8281
PARTMAKER, INC.—See Autodesk, Inc.; *U.S. Public*, pg. 229
PARTMASTER (PTY) LTD.—See AFGRI Limited; *Int'l*, pg. 188
PARTMINER DIRECT—See PartMiner, Inc.; *U.S. Private*, pg. 3101
PARTMINER, INC.; *U.S. Private*, pg. 3101
PARTNERA OYJ; *Int'l*, pg. 5749
PARTNERBUD S.A.; *Int'l*, pg. 5749
PARTNERCENTRIC, INC.—See Schaaf Consulting; *U.S. Private*, pg. 3562
PARTNER CO., LTD.—See Willtec Co., Ltd.; *Int'l*, pg. 8420
PARTNER COMMUNICATIONS COMPANY LTD.; *Int'l*, pg. 5748
PARTNER ENGINEERING & SCIENCE, INC; *U.S. Private*, pg. 3101
PARTNERFONDS AG; *Int'l*, pg. 5749
PARTNER IN PET FOOD CZ S.R.O—See Cinven Limited; *Int'l*, pg. 1613
PARTNER IN PET FOOD HUNGARIA KFT.—See Cinven Limited; *Int'l*, pg. 1613
PARTNER IN PET FOOD SK S.R.O—See Cinven Limited; *Int'l*, pg. 1613
PARTNERMD, LLC—See Markel Group Inc.; *U.S. Public*, pg. 1369
PARTNER ONE CAPITAL, INC.; *Int'l*, pg. 5748
PARTNER ONE SOFTWARE INC.—See Fonds de Solidarite des Travailleurs du Quebec; *Int'l*, pg. 2725
PARTNERPATH, LLC; *U.S. Private*, pg. 3101
PARTNERPEDIA SOLUTIONS INC.; *Int'l*, pg. 5749
PARTNERRE ASSET MANAGEMENT CORPORATION—See Covea Groupe S.A.S.; *Int'l*, pg. 1820
PARTNERRE CONNECTICUT INC.—See Covea Groupe S.A.S.; *Int'l*, pg. 1820
PARTNERRE FINANCE A LLC—See Covea Groupe S.A.S.; *Int'l*, pg. 1820
PARTNERRE FINANCE B LLC—See Covea Groupe S.A.S.; *Int'l*, pg. 1820
PARTNER REGNSKAP AS—See TowerBrook Capital Partners, L.P.; *U.S. Private*, pg. 4195
PARTNERRE HOLDINGS EUROPE LIMITED—See Covea Groupe S.A.S.; *Int'l*, pg. 1820
PARTNERRE HOLDINGS SA—See Covea Groupe S.A.S.; *Int'l*, pg. 1820
PARTNERRE HOLDINGS SWITZERLAND GMBH—See Covea Groupe S.A.S.; *Int'l*, pg. 1820
PARTNER REINSURANCE ASIA PTE. LTD.—See Covea Groupe S.A.S.; *Int'l*, pg. 1820
PARTNER REINSURANCE COMPANY LTD.—See Covea Groupe S.A.S.; *Int'l*, pg. 1820
PARTNERRE INSURANCE COMPANY OF NEW YORK—See Employers Holdings, Inc.; *U.S. Public*, pg. 754
PARTNER REINSURANCE COMPANY OF THE U.S.—See Covea Groupe S.A.S.; *Int'l*, pg. 1820
PARTNER REINSURANCE EUROPE SE—See Covea Groupe S.A.S.; *Int'l*, pg. 1820
PARTNERRE LIFE REINSURANCE COMPANY OF CANADA—See Covea Groupe S.A.S.; *Int'l*, pg. 1820
PARTNERRE LTD.—See Covea Groupe S.A.S.; *Int'l*, pg. 1820
PARTNERRE MIAMI INC.—See Covea Groupe S.A.S.; *Int'l*, pg. 1820
PARTNERRE U.S. CORPORATION—See Covea Groupe S.A.S.; *Int'l*, pg. 1820
PARTNERS ADVANTAGE INSURANCE SERVICES—See AMZ Financial Insurance Services, LLC; *U.S. Private*, pg. 270
PARTNERS ANDREWS ALDRIDGE—See The Engine Group; *Int'l*, pg. 7640
PARTNERS BANK OF CALIFORNIA; *U.S. Public*, pg. 1651
PARTNERS BANK OF WISCONSIN—See Stratford Bancshares, Inc.; *U.S. Private*, pg. 3837
PARTNERS BOOK DISTRIBUTING; *U.S. Private*, pg. 3101

COMPANY NAME INDEX

PARTNERS BOOK DISTRIBUTING-WEST—See Partners Book Distributing; *U.S. Private*, pg. 3101
PARTNERS COMMUNITY HEALTHCARE, INC.—See Partners HealthCare System, Inc.; *U.S. Private*, pg. 3101
PARTNER'S CONSULTING, INC.; *U.S. Private*, pg. 3101
PARTNERS CONSULTING SERVICES, INC.—See Calance Corporation; *Int'l*, pg. 1261
PARTNERS CONTINUING CARE, INC.—See Partners HealthCare System, Inc.; *U.S. Private*, pg. 3101
PARTNERS FOR INCENTIVES INC.; *U.S. Private*, pg. 3101
PARTNERS GROUP ADVISORS (DIFC) LIMITED—See Partners Group Holding AG; *Int'l*, pg. 5750
PARTNERS GROUP (BRAZIL) INVESTIMENTOS LTDA.—See Partners Group Holding AG; *Int'l*, pg. 5750
PARTNERS GROUP (CANADA) INC.—See Partners Group Holding AG; *Int'l*, pg. 5750
PARTNERS GROUP (FRANCE) SAS—See Partners Group Holding AG; *Int'l*, pg. 5750
PARTNERS GROUP GLOBAL OPPORTUNITIES LTD.—See Partners Group Holding AG; *Int'l*, pg. 5750
PARTNERS GROUP (GUERNSEY) LTD.—See Partners Group Holding AG; *Int'l*, pg. 5750
PARTNERS GROUP HOLDING AG; *Int'l*, pg. 5749
PARTNERS GROUP (INDIA) PRIVATE LIMITED—See Partners Group Holding AG; *Int'l*, pg. 5750
PARTNERS GROUP JAPAN KABUSHIKI KAISHA—See Partners Group Holding AG; *Int'l*, pg. 5750
THE PARTNERS GROUP, LTD.; *U.S. Private*, pg. 4091
PARTNERS GROUP (LUXEMBOURG) S.A.R.L.—See Partners Group Holding AG; *Int'l*, pg. 5750
PARTNERS GROUP PRIME SERVICES SOLUTIONS (PHILIPPINES), INC.—See Partners Group Holding AG; *Int'l*, pg. 5750
PARTNERS GROUP PRIVATE MARKETS (AUSTRALIA) PTY. LTD.—See Partners Group Holding AG; *Int'l*, pg. 5750
PARTNERS GROUP (SHANGHAI) CO., LTD.—See Partners Group Holding AG; *Int'l*, pg. 5750
PARTNERS GROUP (SINGAPORE) PTE. LIMITED—See Partners Group Holding AG; *Int'l*, pg. 5750
PARTNERS GROUP SOLIS SARL—See Partners Group Holding AG; *Int'l*, pg. 5750
PARTNERS GROUP (UK) LIMITED—See Partners Group Holding AG; *Int'l*, pg. 5750
PARTNERS GROUP (USA) INC.—See Partners Group Holding AG; *Int'l*, pg. 5750
PARTNERS HARVARD MEDICAL INTERNATIONAL—See Partners HealthCare System, Inc.; *U.S. Private*, pg. 3101
PARTNERS HEALTHCARE SYSTEM, INC.; *U.S. Private*, pg. 3101
PARTNERSHIP ASSURANCE GROUP LIMITED—See Permira Advisers LLP; *Int'l*, pg. 5807
PARTNERSHIP CAPITAL GROWTH LLC; *U.S. Private*, pg. 3103
PARTNERSHIP EMPLOYMENT; *U.S. Private*, pg. 3103
PARTNERSHIP FOR CHILDREN OF CUMBERLAND COUNTY, INC.; *U.S. Private*, pg. 3103
PARTNERSHIP FOR STRONG FAMILIES, INC.; *U.S. Private*, pg. 3103
PARTNERSHIP HEALTH GROUP LIMITED—See Bridgepoint Group Plc; *Int'l*, pg. 1154
PARTNERSHIP OF PACKER, OESTERLING & SMITH (PPO&S); *U.S. Private*, pg. 3103
PARTNERSHIPS IN CARE LIMITED—See Acadia Healthcare Company, Inc.; *U.S. Public*, pg. 29
PARTNERS HOME CARE INC.—See Partners HealthCare System, Inc.; *U.S. Private*, pg. 3101
PARTNERS IMAGING CENTER OF CHARLOTTE, LLC—See Medical Imaging Corp.; *U.S. Public*, pg. 1411
PARTNERS IMAGING CENTER OF NAPLES, LLC—See Medical Imaging Corp.; *U.S. Public*, pg. 1412
PARTNERS IMAGING CENTER OF VENICE, LLC—See Medical Imaging Corp.; *U.S. Public*, pg. 1412
PARTNERS IN ASSOCIATION MANAGEMENT, INC.; *U.S. Private*, pg. 3102
PARTNERS IN BOUWEN—See Heijmans N.V.; *Int'l*, pg. 3323
PARTNERS IN CARE INC.—See Visiting Nurse Service of New York; *U.S. Private*, pg. 4393
PARTNERS IN CARE MARYLAND, INC.—See Visiting Nurse Service of New York; *U.S. Private*, pg. 4393
PARTNERS IN CARE; *U.S. Private*, pg. 3102
PARTNERS IN COSTS LIMITED—See Frenkel Topping Group plc; *Int'l*, pg. 2773
PARTNERS IN HEALTHCARE, INC.; *U.S. Private*, pg. 3102
PARTNERS IN HEALTH; *U.S. Private*, pg. 3102
PARTNERS IN INTEGRATED CARE, INC.—See Humana, Inc.; *U.S. Public*, pg. 1070
PARTNERS INSURANCE GROUP LLC—See Narragansett Financial Corp.; *U.S. Private*, pg. 2835
PARTNERS/JWT BUDAPEST—See WPP plc; *Int'l*, pg. 8481
PARTNERS MUTUAL INSURANCE CO.; *U.S. Private*, pg. 3102

PARTNERS + NAPIER INC. - ATLANTA OFFICE—See Project: Worldwide, Inc.; *U.S. Private*, pg. 3281
PARTNERS + NAPIER INC.—See Project: Worldwide, Inc.; *U.S. Private*, pg. 3281
PARTNERS OGILVYINTERACTIVE—See WPP plc; *Int'l*, pg. 8488
PARTNERS OGILVY & MATHER—See WPP plc; *Int'l*, pg. 8488
PARTNERS OGILVYONE—See WPP plc; *Int'l*, pg. 8488
PARTNERS PHARMACY, LLC; *U.S. Private*, pg. 3102
PARTNERS REAL ESTATE INVESTMENT TRUST—See McCowan and Associates Ltd.; *Int'l*, pg. 4757
PARTNERS RX MANAGEMENT, LLC—See Centene Corporation; *U.S. Public*, pg. 470
THE PARTNERS—See WPP plc; *Int'l*, pg. 8467
PARTNERS SPECIALTY GROUP LLC—See AmWINS Group, Inc.; *U.S. Private*, pg. 269
PARTNERS TWO INC.; *U.S. Private*, pg. 3103
PARTNERS UNITED FINANCIAL, LLC—See Rithm Capital Corp.; *U.S. Public*, pg. 1800
PARTNERS VALUE INVESTMENTS INC.; *Int'l*, pg. 5751
PARTNERS VALUE SPLIT CORPORATION; *Int'l*, pg. 5751
PARTNERS WEALTH MANAGEMENT LLP—See Caledonia Investments plc; *Int'l*, pg. 1262
PARTNER TECH CORP.—See Qisda Corporation; *Int'l*, pg. 6146
PARTNER TECH UK CORP., LTD.—See Qisda Corporation; *Int'l*, pg. 6146
PARTNERWINNER AG—See TX Group AG; *Int'l*, pg. 7992
PARTRIDGE CREEK FASHION PARK LLC—See Simon Property Group, Inc.; *U.S. Public*, pg. 1881
PARTRON CO., LTD.; *Int'l*, pg. 5751
PARTRON PRECISION—See Partron Co., Ltd.; *Int'l*, pg. 5751
PARTS ADVANTAGE, LLC—See HEICO Corporation; *U.S. Public*, pg. 1019
PARTS ALLIANCE GROUP LIMITED—See LKQ Corporation; *U.S. Public*, pg. 1336
PARTS AUTHORITY INC.; *U.S. Private*, pg. 3103
PARTSEARCH TECHNOLOGIES; *U.S. Private*, pg. 3103
PARTS EXPRESS INTERNATIONAL; *U.S. Private*, pg. 3103
PARTSFLEET, INC.—See Harbour Group Industries, Inc.; *U.S. Private*, pg. 1860
PARTS FOR TRUCKS, INC.; *Int'l*, pg. 5751
PARTS ID, INC.; *U.S. Public*, pg. 1651
PARTSLIFE GMBH—See ZF Friedrichshafen AG; *Int'l*, pg. 8641
PARTSMASTER, INC.—See Distribution Solutions Group, Inc.; *U.S. Public*, pg. 669
PARTS NOW LLC—See CounterPoint Capital Partners, LLC; *U.S. Private*, pg. 1066
PARTS PLUS OF NEW MEXICO INCORPORATED; *U.S. Private*, pg. 3103
THE PARTS PROS AUTOMOTIVE WAREHOUSE, INC.—See TPH Acquisition, LLLP; *U.S. Private*, pg. 4200
PARTS SERVICES INTERNATIONAL LLC—See Industrial Distribution Resources, LLC; *U.S. Private*, pg. 2065
PARTSSOURCE, INC.—See Great Hill Partners, L.P.; *U.S. Private*, pg. 1763
PARTS TOWN LLC—See Berkshire Partners LLC; *U.S. Private*, pg. 535
PARTS WAREHOUSE INC.—See Replacement Parts Inc.; *U.S. Private*, pg. 3401
PARTS WHOLESALERS INC.; *U.S. Private*, pg. 3103
PARTY CITY CORPORATION—See Thomas H. Lee Partners, L.P.; *U.S. Private*, pg. 4156
PARTY CITY HOLDCO, INC.—See Thomas H. Lee Partners, L.P.; *U.S. Private*, pg. 4156
PARTY CITY HOLDINGS, INC.—See Thomas H. Lee Partners, L.P.; *U.S. Private*, pg. 4156
PARTY CITY OF BIRMINGHAM INC.; *U.S. Private*, pg. 3103
PARTY CITY OF PUERTO RICO INC.; *U.S. Private*, pg. 3103
PARTY CRUISERS LIMITED; *Int'l*, pg. 5751
PARTYLITE GIFTS, INC.—See The Carlyle Group Inc.; *U.S. Public*, pg. 2052
PARTYLITE GIFTS, LTD.—See The Carlyle Group Inc.; *U.S. Public*, pg. 2052
PARTYLITE GMBH—See The Carlyle Group Inc.; *U.S. Public*, pg. 2052
PARTYLITE HANDELSGESELLSCHAFT M.B.H.—See The Carlyle Group Inc.; *U.S. Public*, pg. 2052
PARTYLITE, INC.—See The Carlyle Group Inc.; *U.S. Public*, pg. 2052
PARTYLITE OY—See The Carlyle Group Inc.; *U.S. Public*, pg. 2052
PARTYLITE TRADING S.A.—See The Carlyle Group Inc.; *U.S. Public*, pg. 2052
PARTYLITE UK LTD—See The Carlyle Group Inc.; *U.S. Public*, pg. 2052
PARTY RENTAL LTD.; *U.S. Private*, pg. 3103
PARTY TIME RENTALS, INC.—See Premiere Events; *U.S. Private*, pg. 3251
PARU CO., LTD.; *Int'l*, pg. 5751
PARVATI SWEETNERS & POWER LTD.; *Int'l*, pg. 5751

PASEK CORPORATION

PARVUS CORP.—See Curtiss-Wright Corporation; *U.S. Public*, pg. 611
PAR-WAY TRYSON COMPANY; *U.S. Private*, pg. 3089
PARX CONSULTING GMBH—See Persistent Systems Ltd.; *Int'l*, pg. 5818
PARX MATERIALS N.V.; *Int'l*, pg. 5751
PARX WERK AG—See Persistent Systems Ltd.; *Int'l*, pg. 5818
PASABAHCE GLASS GMBH—See Türkiye Sise ve Cam Fabrikalari A.S.; *Int'l*, pg. 7977
PASABAHCE INVESTMENT B.V.—See Turkiye Sise ve Cam Fabrikalari A.S.; *Int'l*, pg. 7977
PASABAHCE MAGAZALARI A.S.—See Turkiye Sise ve Cam Fabrikalari A.S.; *Int'l*, pg. 7977
PASABAHCE USA INC.—See Turkiye Sise ve Cam Fabrikalari A.S.; *Int'l*, pg. 7977
PASA CUERNAVACA, S.A. DE C.V.—See Promotora Ambiental S.A.B de C.V.; *Int'l*, pg. 5994
PASADENA EYE CENTER; *U.S. Private*, pg. 3103
PASADENA FUNERAL HOME, INC.—See Service Corporation International; *U.S. Public*, pg. 1871
PASADENA LIQUORS AND FINE WINES; *U.S. Private*, pg. 3103
PASADENA PLAYHOUSE; *U.S. Private*, pg. 3103
PASADENA STAR-NEWS—See Alden Global Capital LLC; *U.S. Private*, pg. 156
PASAL DEVELOPMENT S.A.; *Int'l*, pg. 5751
PASAN SA—See Meyer Burger Technology AG; *Int'l*, pg. 4869
PASARAYA JAYA GADING SDN. BHD.—See Cab Cakaran Corporation Berhad; *Int'l*, pg. 1245
PASARGAD GROUP INTERNATIONAL TRADING COMPANY—See Bank Pasargad; *Int'l*, pg. 849
PASAR GROUP—See Glencore plc; *Int'l*, pg. 2991
PASARI SPINNING MILLS LIMITED; *Int'l*, pg. 5752
PASCAL BIOSCIENCES, INC.; *Int'l*, pg. 5752
PASCALE SERVICE CORPORATION—See Platinum Equity, LLC; *U.S. Private*, pg. 3209
PASCALL ELECTRONICS LTD.—See TransDigm Group Incorporated; *U.S. Public*, pg. 2182
PASCHAL AG—See PASCHAL-Werk G. Maier GmbH; *Int'l*, pg. 5752
PASCHAL CONCRETE FORMS CO. W.L.L.—See PASCHAL-Werk G. Maier GmbH; *Int'l*, pg. 5752
PASCHAL-DANMARK A/S—See PASCHAL-Werk G. Maier GmbH; *Int'l*, pg. 5752
PASCHAL EMIRATES CO. L.L.C—See PASCHAL-Werk G. Maier GmbH; *Int'l*, pg. 5752
PASCHAL EMIRATES L.L.C.—See PASCHAL-Werk G. Maier GmbH; *Int'l*, pg. 5752
PASCHAL FORM WORK (INDIA) PVT. LTD—See PASCHAL-Werk G. Maier GmbH; *Int'l*, pg. 5752
PASCHAL HOME SERVICES, LLC; *U.S. Private*, pg. 3103
PASCHAL SARL—See PASCHAL-Werk G. Maier GmbH; *Int'l*, pg. 5752
PASCHAL SPOL.S.R.O—See PASCHAL-Werk G. Maier GmbH; *Int'l*, pg. 5752
PASCHAL-WERK G. MAIER GMBH; *Int'l*, pg. 5752
PASCH CONSULTING GROUP, LLC; *U.S. Private*, pg. 3103
PASCHEN MANAGEMENT CORPORATION; *U.S. Private*, pg. 3104
PASCOAG UTILITY DISTRICT; *U.S. Private*, pg. 3104
PASCO BROKERAGE, INC.; *U.S. Private*, pg. 3104
PASCO CHINA CORPORATION—See SECOM Co., Ltd.; *Int'l*, pg. 6671
PASCO COGEN, LTD.—See Quantum Energy Partners, LLC; *U.S. Private*, pg. 3323
PASCO CORPORATION—See SECOM Co., Ltd.; *Int'l*, pg. 6671
PASCO ECONOMIC DEVELOPMENT COUNCIL, INC.; *U.S. Private*, pg. 3104
PASCO ENGINEERING CO., LTD.—See SECOM Co., Ltd.; *Int'l*, pg. 6671
PASCO PHILIPPINES CORPORATION—See SECOM Co., Ltd.; *Int'l*, pg. 6671
PASCO SPECIALTY & MANUFACTURING INC.; *U.S. Private*, pg. 3104
PASCO THAILAND CO., LTD.—See SECOM Co., Ltd.; *Int'l*, pg. 6671
PASDEC BINA SDN. BHD.—See Pasdec Holdings Berhad; *Int'l*, pg. 5752
PASDEC CORPORATION SDN.BHD.—See Pasdec Holdings Berhad; *Int'l*, pg. 5752
PASDEC HOLDINGS BERHAD; *Int'l*, pg. 5752
PASDEC LAND SDN. BHD.—See Pasdec Holdings Berhad; *Int'l*, pg. 5752
PASDEC PUTRA SDN. BHD.—See Pasdec Holdings Berhad; *Int'l*, pg. 5752
PASDEC TRADING SDN. BHD.—See Pasdec Holdings Berhad; *Int'l*, pg. 5752
PASECO CO., LTD.; *Int'l*, pg. 5752
PASEK CORPORATION; *U.S. Private*, pg. 3104
THE PAS GROUP PTY LTD—See Queens Lane Capital Pty Ltd; *Int'l*, pg. 6159
PASHA DISTRIBUTION SERVICES LLC—See The Pasha Group; *U.S. Private*, pg. 4091

PASEK CORPORATION   CORPORATE AFFILIATIONS

THE PASHA GROUP - AUTOMOTIVE AND LOGISTICS DIVISION—See The Pasha Group; *U.S. Private*, pg. 4091
THE PASHA GROUP; *U.S. Private*, pg. 4091
PASHA STEVEDORING & TERMINALS L.P.—See The Pasha Group; *U.S. Private*, pg. 4091
PASHA YATIRIM BANKASI A.S.; *Int'l*, pg. 5752
PASHUPATI COTSPIN LTD.; *Int'l*, pg. 5752
PASINEX RESOURCES LIMITED - NEVADA BRANCH—See Pasinex Resources Limited; *Int'l*, pg. 5752
PASINEX RESOURCES LIMITED; *Int'l*, pg. 5752
PASIN SDN. BHD.—See Ta Ann Holdings Berhad; *Int'l*, pg. 7398
PASIR GUDANG SPECIALIST HOSPITAL SDN BHD—See KPJ Healthcare Berhad; *Int'l*, pg. 4297
PASIR MAS HOLDINGS SDN. BHD.—See Sunway Berhad; *Int'l*, pg. 7328
PASITHEA THERAPEUTICS CORP.; *U.S. Public*, pg. 1651
PASKAL LIGHTING, INC.—See The Jordan Company, L.P.; *U.S. Private*, pg. 4061
PASKERT DISTRIBUTING COMPANY; *U.S. Private*, pg. 3104
PASKEWITZ ASSET MANAGEMENT LLC; *U.S. Private*, pg. 3104
PASKOLU KLUBAS UAB—See NEO Finance AB; *Int'l*, pg. 5195
THE PASLIN COMPANY—See Wanfeng Auto Holding Group Co., Ltd.; *Int'l*, pg. 8340
PASLIN DIGITAL TECHNOLOGY CO., LTD.; *Int'l*, pg. 5752
PASLODE FASTENERS (SHANGHAI) CO., LTD.—See Illinois Tool Works Inc.; *U.S. Public*, pg. 1110
PASLODE—See Illinois Tool Works Inc.; *U.S. Public*, pg. 1110
PASOFINO GOLD LIMITED; *Int'l*, pg. 5752
PASONA AGRI-PARTNERS INC.—See Pasona Group Inc.; *Int'l*, pg. 5753
PASONA ART NOW INC.—See Pasona Group Inc.; *Int'l*, pg. 5753
PASONA ASIA CO., LIMITED—See Pasona Group Inc.; *Int'l*, pg. 5753
PASONA CANADA, INC.—See Pasona Group Inc.; *Int'l*, pg. 5753
PASONA CAREER INC.—See Pasona Group Inc.; *Int'l*, pg. 5753
PASONA EDUCATION CO. LIMITED—See Pasona Group Inc.; *Int'l*, pg. 5753
PASONA EMPOWER INC.—See Pasona Group Inc.; *Int'l*, pg. 5753
PASONA FORTUNE INC.—See Pasona Group Inc.; *Int'l*, pg. 5753
PASONA FOSTER INC.—See Pasona Group Inc.; *Int'l*, pg. 5753
PASONA GROUP INC.; *Int'l*, pg. 5753
PASONA HEARTFUL INC.—See Pasona Group Inc.; *Int'l*, pg. 5753
PASONA HR CONSULTING INC.—See Pasona Group Inc.; *Int'l*, pg. 5753
PASONA HR CONSULTING & RECRUITMENT (THAILAND) CO., LTD.—See Pasona Group Inc.; *Int'l*, pg. 5753
PASONA HR CONSULTING (THAILAND) CO., LTD.—See Pasona Group Inc.; *Int'l*, pg. 5753
PASONA HR MALAYSIA SDN. BHD.—See Pasona Group Inc.; *Int'l*, pg. 5753
PASONA HS INC.—See Pasona Group Inc.; *Int'l*, pg. 5753
PASONA HUMAN RESOURCES (SHANGHAI) CO., LTD.—See Pasona Group Inc.; *Int'l*, pg. 5753
PASONA HUMAN SOLUTIONS INC.—See Pasona Group Inc.; *Int'l*, pg. 5753
PASONA INDIA PRIVATE LIMITED—See Pasona Group Inc.; *Int'l*, pg. 5754
PASONA JOB HUB INC.—See Pasona Group Inc.; *Int'l*, pg. 5754
PASONA KNOWLEDGE PARTNER INC.—See Pasona Group Inc.; *Int'l*, pg. 5754
PASONA KOREA CO., LTD.—See Pasona Group Inc.; *Int'l*, pg. 5754
PASONA KYOTO INC.—See Pasona Group Inc.; *Int'l*, pg. 5754
PASONA LIFE CARE INC.—See Pasona Group Inc.; *Int'l*, pg. 5754
PASONA LOGICOM INC.—See Pasona Group Inc.; *Int'l*, pg. 5754
PASONA MASTERS INC.—See Pasona Group Inc.; *Int'l*, pg. 5754
PASONA NA, INC.—See Pasona Group Inc.; *Int'l*, pg. 5754
PASONA OKAYAMA INC.—See Pasona Group Inc.; *Int'l*, pg. 5754
PASONA PANASONIC BUSINESS SERVICE CO., LTD.—See Pasona Group Inc.; *Int'l*, pg. 5754
PASONA SINGAPORE PTE.LTD.—See Pasona Group Inc.; *Int'l*, pg. 5754
PASONA SOURCING INC.—See Pasona Group Inc.; *Int'l*, pg. 5754
PASONA TAIWAN CO., LTD.—See Pasona Group Inc.; *Int'l*, pg. 5754

PASONA TECH, INC.—See Pasona Group Inc.; *Int'l*, pg. 5754
PASONA TECH VIETNAM CO.,LTD.—See Pasona Group Inc.; *Int'l*, pg. 5753
PASONA YASKAWA BUSINESS STAFF INC.—See Pasona Group Inc.; *Int'l*, pg. 5754
PASON DE MEXICO S.A. DE C.V.—See Pason Systems Inc.; *Int'l*, pg. 5752
PASON DGS BRASIL SERVICOS - PETROLIFEROS LTDA—See Pason Systems Inc.; *Int'l*, pg. 5752
PASON DGS COLOMBIA LTDA—See Pason Systems Inc.; *Int'l*, pg. 5752
PASON DGS PERU S.A.C—See Pason Systems Inc.; *Int'l*, pg. 5753
PASON DGS S.A.—See Pason Systems Inc.; *Int'l*, pg. 5753
PASON OFFSHORE CORP.—See Pason Systems Inc.; *Int'l*, pg. 5753
PASON SYSTEMS CORP.—See Pason Systems Inc.; *Int'l*, pg. 5753
PASON SYSTEMS INC.; *Int'l*, pg. 5752
PASON SYSTEMS USA CORP.—See Pason Systems Inc.; *Int'l*, pg. 5753
PASON SYSTEMS USA CORP.—See Pason Systems Inc.; *Int'l*, pg. 5753
PASOTEC GMBH—See Allient Inc.; *U.S. Public*, pg. 80
PASQUARELLI AUTO S.P.A.; *Int'l*, pg. 5754
PASQUINELLI CONSTRUCTION CO., INC.; *U.S. Private*, pg. 3104
PAS REFORM HATCHERY TECHNOLOGIES BV—See Hydratec Industries NV; *Int'l*, pg. 3546
PASSAGE BIO, INC.; *U.S. Public*, pg. 1651
PASSAGE CO., LTD.—See Crestec Inc.; *Int'l*, pg. 1841
PASSAGE SERVICES HOLDING GMBH—See Deutsche Lufthansa AG; *Int'l*, pg. 2070
PASSAGES TO RECOVERY, LLC—See Acadia Healthcare Company, Inc.; *U.S. Public*, pg. 29
PASSAGEWAYS, LLC; *U.S. Private*, pg. 3104
PASSAIC VALLEY WATER COMMISSION; *U.S. Private*, pg. 3104
PASSAT SA; *Int'l*, pg. 5754
PASSAUERHOF BETRIEBS-GES.M.B.H.—See UNIQA Insurance Group AG; *Int'l*, pg. 8058
PASSAVANT ENERGY & ENVIRONMENT GMBH—See Drake & Scull International PJSC; *Int'l*, pg. 2200
PASSAVANT MEMORIAL HOMES; *U.S. Private*, pg. 3104
PASSAVANT MEMORIAL HOSPITAL ASSOCIATION; *U.S. Private*, pg. 3104
PASSAVANT-ROEDIGER GMBH—See Drake & Scull International PJSC; *Int'l*, pg. 2200
PASS CREEK RESOURCES LLC; *U.S. Private*, pg. 3104
PASSERELLE—See Air France-KLM S.A.; *Int'l*, pg. 237
PASSERO ASSOCIATES; *U.S. Private*, pg. 3104
PASSFORT LIMITED—See Moody's Corporation; *U.S. Public*, pg. 1469
PASSINI GROUP; *Int'l*, pg. 5754
THE PASSION GROUP; *U.S. Private*, pg. 4091
PASSION HOLDINGS LIMITED; *Int'l*, pg. 5754
PASSIVSYSTEMS GROUP PLC; *Int'l*, pg. 5754
PASSKEY, INC.—See SK Inc.; *Int'l*, pg. 6972
PASSLOGIX, INC.—See Oracle Corporation; *U.S. Public*, pg. 1613
PASSLOGY CO., LTD.; *Int'l*, pg. 5754
PASS MEXICO S.A. DE C.V.; *Int'l*, pg. 5754
PASSPORT FOOD GROUP, LLC—See Swander Pace Capital, LLC; *U.S. Private*, pg. 3890
PASSPORT GLOBAL INC.; *U.S. Private*, pg. 3104
PASSPORT HEALTH COMMUNICATIONS, INC.—See Experian plc; *Int'l*, pg. 2587
PASSPORT HEALTH; *U.S. Private*, pg. 3104
PASS & SEYMOUR/LEGRAND—See Legrand S.A.; *Int'l*, pg. 4445
PASSTECH CO., LTD.—See Itochu Enex Co., Ltd.; *Int'l*, pg. 3842
PASSTECH MACHINE TOOLS M.E.—See Nicolas Correa S.A.; *Int'l*, pg. 5273
PASSUMPSIC BANCORP INC.; *U.S. Private*, pg. 3104
PASSUMPSIC SAVINGS BANK—See Passumpsic Bancorp Inc.; *U.S. Private*, pg. 3104
PASSUR AEROSPACE, INC.; *U.S. Public*, pg. 1651
PASSUS SA; *Int'l*, pg. 5754
PASTA GALA SA—See Coop-Gruppe Genossenschaft; *Int'l*, pg. 1790
THE PASTA HOUSE COMPANY FRANCHISES, INC.—See The Pasta House Co.; *U.S. Private*, pg. 4091
THE PASTA HOUSE CO.; *U.S. Private*, pg. 4091
PASTA LENSI, S.R.L.—See Conagra Brands, Inc.; *U.S. Public*, pg. 563
PASTA MONTANA, LLC—See NIPPN Corporation; *Int'l*, pg. 5310
PASTAS COMARRICO S.A.S—See Ihlas Holding A.S.; *Int'l*, pg. 3606
PASTA SHOP; *U.S. Private*, pg. 3104
PAS TECHNOLOGIES INC.—See The Carlyle Group Inc.; *U.S. Public*, pg. 2054
PASTEJKOKET AB—See Atria Plc; *Int'l*, pg. 694
PASTEL GLOVE SDN. BHD.—See Enviro-Hub Holdings Ltd.; *Int'l*, pg. 2454

THE PASTENE COMPANIES, LTD.; *U.S. Private*, pg. 4091
PASTENE INC.—See The Pastene Companies, Ltd.; *U.S. Private*, pg. 4091
PASTERNACK ENTERPRISES, INC.—See Windjammer Capital Investors, LLC; *U.S. Private*, pg. 4538
PASTEUR MEDICAL CENTER, LLC—See Elevance Health, Inc.; *U.S. Public*, pg. 730
PASTIFICIO LUCIO GAROFALO S.P.A.—See Ebro Foods S.A.; *Int'l*, pg. 2287
PASTORELLI FOOD PRODUCTS, INC.; *U.S. Private*, pg. 3104
PASTRY GLOBAL FOOD SERVICE LIMITED—See The Bidvest Group Limited; *Int'l*, pg. 7626
PASTURAL—See Compagnie de Saint-Gobain SA; *Int'l*, pg. 1724
PASTURE GENETICS PTY LTD—See S&W Seed Co.; *U.S. Public*, pg. 1832
PASTURE HOLDINGS LTD.; *Int'l*, pg. 5754
PASUKHAS GROUP BERHAD; *Int'l*, pg. 5754
PASUPATI ACRYLON LTD.; *Int'l*, pg. 5754
PASUPATI FINCAP LIMITED; *Int'l*, pg. 5754
PASUPATI SPINNING & WEAVING MILLS LIMITED; *Int'l*, pg. 5755
PAS US, INC.—See Queens Lane Capital Pty Ltd; *Int'l*, pg. 6159
PATAGON BANK, S.A.—See Banco Santander, S.A.; *Int'l*, pg. 826
PATAGONIA GOLD CORP.; *Int'l*, pg. 5755
PATAGONIA GOLD LTD—See Patagonia Gold Corp.; *Int'l*, pg. 5755
PATAGONIA, INC.—See Patagonia Works, Inc.; *U.S. Private*, pg. 3105
PATAGONIA LITHIUM LIMITED; *Int'l*, pg. 5755
PATAGONIA WORKS, INC.; *U.S. Private*, pg. 3105
PATAGONIK FILM GROUP S.A.—See Grupo Clarin S.A.; *Int'l*, pg. 3125
PATANA INTERCOOL CO., LTD.—See Univentures Public Company Limited; *Int'l*, pg. 8077
PATANJALI AYURVED LIMITED; *Int'l*, pg. 5755
PATANJALI FOODS LIMITED—See Patanjali Ayurved Limited; *Int'l*, pg. 5755
PATARA (GENEVA) SA—See S&P Syndicate Public Company Limited; *Int'l*, pg. 6445
PATARA INTERNATIONAL RESTAURANT MANAGEMENT (BEIJING) CO., LTD.—See S&P Syndicate Public Company Limited; *Int'l*, pg. 6445
PATARA RESTAURANT, VIENNA GMBH—See S&P Syndicate Public Company Limited; *Int'l*, pg. 6445
PATA SALDUS AS; *Int'l*, pg. 5755
PATCHETT'S MOTORS INCORPORATED; *U.S. Private*, pg. 3105
PATCH RUBBER COMPANY—See Myers Industries, Inc.; *U.S. Public*, pg. 1488
PAT CLEMONS INC.; *U.S. Private*, pg. 3104
PATCO ELECTRONICS, INC.—See Southwire Company, LLC; *U.S. Private*, pg. 3742
PATCO INDUSTRIES, INC.; *U.S. Private*, pg. 3105
PATCON LIMITED—See Hadco Limited; *Int'l*, pg. 3205
PAT COOK CONSTRUCTION, INC.; *U.S. Private*, pg. 3105
PATDAN LLC; *U.S. Private*, pg. 3105
PAT DAVIE LIMITED—See Shui On Company Limited; *Int'l*, pg. 6869
PATDIAM JEWELLERY LTD.; *Int'l*, pg. 5755
PATEC PRECISION INDUSTRY CO., LTD.; *Int'l*, pg. 5755
PATEC PRECISION KFT—See Patec Precision Industry Co., Ltd.; *Int'l*, pg. 5755
PATE-DAWSON COMPANY; *U.S. Private*, pg. 3105
PA-TED SPRING CO. INC.; *U.S. Private*, pg. 3062
PATEK PHILIPPE GENEVA; *Int'l*, pg. 5755
PATEK PHILIPPE—See Patek Philippe Geneva; *Int'l*, pg. 5755
PATEL CONSULTANTS CORPORATION; *U.S. Private*, pg. 3105
PATEL CONVENIENCE STORES INC.; *U.S. Private*, pg. 3105
PATEL ENGINEERING INC—See Patel Engineering Ltd.; *Int'l*, pg. 5755
PATEL ENGINEERING LTD.; *Int'l*, pg. 5755
PATEL HYDRO POWER PVT. LTD.—See Patel Engineering Ltd.; *Int'l*, pg. 5755
PATEL INTEGRATED LOGISTICS LIMITED; *Int'l*, pg. 5755
PATEL REALTY (INDIA) LTD.—See Patel Engineering Ltd.; *Int'l*, pg. 5755
PATELS AIRTEMP (INDIA) LTD.; *Int'l*, pg. 5755
PATELS AIRTEMP (USA) INC.—See Patels Airtemp (India) Ltd.; *Int'l*, pg. 5756
PATENT CO., DOO LAKTASI—See BayWa AG; *Int'l*, pg. 918
PATENT CO. DOO—See BayWa AG; *Int'l*, pg. 918
PATENTES TALGO S.L.; *Int'l*, pg. 5756
PATENTUS S.A.; *Int'l*, pg. 5756
PATERSON CARD & PAPER CO.; *U.S. Private*, pg. 3105
PATERSON GLOBALFOODS INC.; *Int'l*, pg. 5756
PATERSON GRAIN LTD.—See Paterson GlobalFoods Inc.; *Int'l*, pg. 5756
PATERSON PACIFIC PARCHMENT CO—See Wellspring Capital Management LLC; *U.S. Private*, pg. 4477

COMPANY NAME INDEX

PATERSON RESOURCES LIMITED—See Carling Capital Partners Pty Ltd.; *Int'l*, pg. 1338
PATERSON SECURITIES PVT LTD—See Hinduja Group Ltd.; *Int'l*, pg. 3399
PATERSONS FINANCIAL SERVICES LTD.—See Security Research Group plc; *Int'l*, pg. 6677
PATERSON STAMP WORKS—See American Marking Systems, Inc.; *U.S. Private*, pg. 241
PATEU ET ROBERT SAS—See VINCI S.A.; *Int'l*, pg. 8235
PATHABLE, INC.—See Insight Venture Management, LLC; *U.S. Private*, pg. 2088
PATH CORPORATION; *Int'l*, pg. 5756
PATHE ENTERTAINMENT LTD—See Pathe SA; *Int'l*, pg. 5756
PATHE FINANCE SARL—See Pathe SA; *Int'l*, pg. 5756
PATHE MOTORWAY S.A.; *Int'l*, pg. 5756
PATHEON API MANUFACTURING INC.—See Thermo Fisher Scientific Inc.; *U.S. Public*, pg. 2151
PATHEON API SERVICES, INC.—See Thermo Fisher Scientific Inc.; *U.S. Public*, pg. 2151
PATHEON BIOLOGICS B.V.—See Thermo Fisher Scientific Inc.; *U.S. Public*, pg. 2151
PATHEON BURLINGTON CENTURY OPERATIONS—See Thermo Fisher Scientific Inc.; *U.S. Public*, pg. 2151
PATHEON FLORENCE - EAST—See Thermo Fisher Scientific Inc.; *U.S. Public*, pg. 2151
PATHEON FRANCE S.A.S.—See Thermo Fisher Scientific Inc.; *U.S. Public*, pg. 2151
PATHEON GMBH—See Thermo Fisher Scientific Inc.; *U.S. Public*, pg. 2151
PATHEON INC.—See Thermo Fisher Scientific Inc.; *U.S. Public*, pg. 2151
PATHEON INC TORONTO YORK MILLS OPERATIONS—See Thermo Fisher Scientific Inc.; *U.S. Public*, pg. 2151
PATHEON ITALIA S.P.A.—See Thermo Fisher Scientific Inc.; *U.S. Public*, pg. 2151
PATHEON KK—See Thermo Fisher Scientific Inc.; *U.S. Public*, pg. 2151
PATHEON MOVA—See Thermo Fisher Scientific Inc.; *U.S. Public*, pg. 2151
PATHEON N.V.—See Thermo Fisher Scientific Inc.; *U.S. Public*, pg. 2151
PATHEON PUERTO RICO, INC.—See Thermo Fisher Scientific Inc.; *U.S. Public*, pg. 2151
PATHEON REGENSBURG GMBH—See Thermo Fisher Scientific Inc.; *U.S. Public*, pg. 2151
PATHEON SOFTGELS B.V.—See Thermo Fisher Scientific Inc.; *U.S. Public*, pg. 2151
PATHEON SOFTGELS INC.—See Thermo Fisher Scientific Inc.; *U.S. Public*, pg. 2151
PATHEON UK LIMITED—See Thermo Fisher Scientific Inc.; *U.S. Public*, pg. 2151
PATHEOS, INC.—See BN Media LLC; *U.S. Private*, pg. 601
PATHE PRODUCTIONS LTD—See Pathe SA; *Int'l*, pg. 5756
PATHE SA; *Int'l*, pg. 5756
PATHFINDER - A SCHLUMBERGER COMPANY—See Schlumberger Limited; *U.S. Public*, pg. 1844
PATHFINDER AVIATION, LLC—See Dios Rios Partners, LP; *U.S. Private*, pg. 1234
PATHFINDER BANCORP, INC.; *U.S. Public*, pg. 1651
PATHFINDER BANK—See Pathfinder Bancorp, Inc.; *U.S. Public*, pg. 1651
PATHFINDER CELL THERAPY, INC.; *U.S. Public*, pg. 1651
PATHFINDER COMMUNICATIONS CORPORATION—See Federated Media Inc.; *U.S. Private*, pg. 1492
PATHFINDER CONSULTANTS LLC; *U.S. Private*, pg. 3105
PATHFINDER ENERGY SERVICES, CANADA LTD.—See Schlumberger Limited; *U.S. Public*, pg. 1844
PATHFINDER, INC.; *U.S. Private*, pg. 3105
PATHFINDERS ADVERTISING & MARKETING GROUP; *U.S. Private*, pg. 3105
PATHFINDER—See Schlumberger Limited; *U.S. Public*, pg. 1844
PATHFINDERS; *U.S. Private*, pg. 3105
PATHFINDR LTD.; *Int'l*, pg. 5756
PATHFIVE LTD—See StarDyne Technologies Inc.; *Int'l*, pg. 7176
PATHGROUP; *U.S. Private*, pg. 3106
PATH IMAGING INC.—See inspec Inc.; *Int'l*, pg. 3719
PATH, INC.; *U.S. Private*, pg. 3105
PATHLINE, INC.—See Gwin Dobson & Foreman Inc.; *U.S. Private*, pg. 1821
PATHLOCK, INC.; *U.S. Private*, pg. 3106
PATHMARK STORES, INC.—See The Great Atlantic & Pacific Tea Company, Inc.; *U.S. Private*, pg. 4038
PATHMARK TRANSPORTATION MARKETING CO.; *U.S. Private*, pg. 3106
PATH.NET S.P.A.—See TIM S.p.A.; *Int'l*, pg. 7749
PATHOLOGY ASSOCIATES—See Charles River Laboratories International, Inc.; *U.S. Public*, pg. 480
PATHOLOGY CONSULTANTS, INC.—See PathGroup; *U.S. Private*, pg. 3106
PATHOLOGY LABORATORIES, INC.—See Sonic Healthcare Limited; *Int'l*, pg. 7098
PATHOLOGY LAB SOLUTIONS, INC.—See Harol Brothers LLC; *U.S. Private*, pg. 1866
PATHOS AI, INC.; *U.S. Private*, pg. 3106
PATHSENSORS, INC.—See Smiths Group plc; *Int'l*, pg. 7011
PATHSTONE CORPORATION; *U.S. Private*, pg. 3106
PATHSTONE FAMILY OFFICE, LLC—See Lovell Minnick Partners LLC; *U.S. Private*, pg. 2503
PATH-TEC; *U.S. Private*, pg. 3105
PATHUMTHANI GLASS INDUSTRY CO., LTD.—See BG Container Glass Public Company Limited; *Int'l*, pg. 1006
PATHUM THANI WATER COMPANY LIMITED—See TTW Public Company Limited; *Int'l*, pg. 7961
PATHWARD FINANCIAL, INC.; *U.S. Public*, pg. 1652
PATHWARD, N.A.—See Pathward Financial, Inc.; *U.S. Public*, pg. 1652
PATHWAY COMMUNITIES INC.; *U.S. Private*, pg. 3106
PATHWAYS COMMUNITY HEALTH; *U.S. Private*, pg. 3106
PATHWAYS COMMUNITY SERVICES LLC—See ATAR Capital, LLC; *U.S. Private*, pg. 364
PATHWAYS COMMUNITY SERVICES LLC—See ATAR Capital, LLC; *U.S. Private*, pg. 364
PATHWAYS FINANCIAL CREDIT UNION, INC.; *U.S. Private*, pg. 3106
PATHWAYS HEALTH AND COMMUNITY SUPPORT LLC—See ATAR Capital, LLC; *U.S. Private*, pg. 364
PATHWAYS HOSPICE; *U.S. Private*, pg. 3106
PATHWAYS OF ARIZONA, INC.—See ATAR Capital, LLC; *U.S. Private*, pg. 364
PATHWAYS OF DELAWARE, INC.—See ATAR Capital, LLC; *U.S. Private*, pg. 364
PATHWAYS OF MAINE, INC.—See ATAR Capital, LLC; *U.S. Private*, pg. 364
PATHWAYS OF MASSACHUSETTS, LLC—See ATAR Capital, LLC; *U.S. Private*, pg. 364
PATHWAYS OF WASHINGTON, INC.—See ATAR Capital, LLC; *U.S. Private*, pg. 364
PATHWAYS; *U.S. Private*, pg. 3106
PATIDAR BUILDCON LIMITED; *Int'l*, pg. 5756
PATIENCE BREWSTER, INC.—See EagleTree Capital, LP; *U.S. Private*, pg. 1311
PATIENT ACCESS NETWORK FOUNDATION; *U.S. Private*, pg. 3106
PATIENT ACCESS SOLUTIONS, INC.; *U.S. Public*, pg. 1652
PATIENT-AIDS, INC.—See Quipt Home Medical Corp.; *U.S. Public*, pg. 1757
PATIENTBOND, LLC—See Upfront Healthcare Services, Inc.; *U.S. Private*, pg. 4311
PATIENT CARE ASSOCIATES, L.L.C.—See UnitedHealth Group Incorporated; *U.S. Public*, pg. 2249
PATIENTCARE EMS SOLUTIONS—See Alvarez & Marsal, Inc.; *U.S. Private*, pg. 213
PATIENT CARE, INC.—See UnitedHealth Group Incorporated; *U.S. Public*, pg. 2244
PATIENT CARE MEDICAL SERVICES, INC.—See UnitedHealth Group Incorporated; *U.S. Public*, pg. 2244
PATIENT CARE NEW JERSEY, INC.—See UnitedHealth Group Incorporated; *U.S. Public*, pg. 2244
PATIENT CARE PENNSYLVANIA, INC.—See UnitedHealth Group Incorporated; *U.S. Public*, pg. 2244
PATIENTCO HOLDINGS, INC.; *U.S. Private*, pg. 3109
PATIENT CONVERSATION MEDIA, INC.; *U.S. Private*, pg. 3106
PATIENT EDUCATION CONCEPTS, INC—See Bain Capital, LP; *U.S. Private*, pg. 446
PATIENTKEEPER, INC.—See HCA Healthcare, Inc.; *U.S. Public*, pg. 1006
PATIENTLINE EXPLOITATIE BV—See Marlin Equity Partners, LLC; *U.S. Private*, pg. 2584
PATIENT PARTNERS, LLC—See Tenet Healthcare Corporation; *U.S. Public*, pg. 2012
PATIENT PATHWAYS, LLC—See DaVita Inc.; *U.S. Public*, pg. 641
PATIENT PLATFORM LIMITED—See EMIS Group plc; *Int'l*, pg. 2383
PATIENT PLUS LIMITED—See Crawford Healthcare Holdings Limited; *Int'l*, pg. 1829
PATIENTPOINT NETWORK SOLUTIONS, LLC—See Catterton Management Company, LLC; *U.S. Private*, pg. 793
PATIENT PORTAL TECHNOLOGIES, INC.; *U.S. Public*, pg. 1652
THE PATIENT RECRUITING AGENCY; *U.S. Private*, pg. 4091
PATIENTSAFE SOLUTIONS, INC.; *U.S. Private*, pg. 3109
PATIENT'S CHOICE HOSPICE AND PALLIATIVE CARE OF LOUISIANA, LLC—See UnitedHealth Group Incorporated; *U.S. Public*, pg. 2246
PATIENT'S CHOICE HOSPICE, LLC—See UnitedHealth Group Incorporated; *U.S. Public*, pg. 2246
PATIENTSKY GROUP AS; *Int'l*, pg. 5756
PATIENTSLIKEME, LLC—See UnitedHealth Group Incorporated; *U.S. Public*, pg. 2249
PATIENTS PENDING LTD.—See Abbott Laboratories; *U.S. Public*, pg. 20
PATIENTS & PROVIDERS TO PROTECT ACCESS & CONTAIN HEALTH COSTS; *U.S. Private*, pg. 3109
PATIENTS & PURPOSE, LLC—See Omnicom Group Inc.; *U.S. Public*, pg. 1579
PATIENT SQUARE CAPITAL, L.P.; *U.S. Private*, pg. 3106
PATIENTYS SAS—See Concentrix Corporation; *U.S. Public*, pg. 565
PATIMAS COMPUTERS BERHAD; *Int'l*, pg. 5756
PATIMAS COMPUTER SECURITY SDN BHD—See Patimas Computers Berhad; *Int'l*, pg. 5756
PATIMAS COMPUTER SYSTEMS SDN BHD—See Patimas Computers Berhad; *Int'l*, pg. 5756
PATIMAS-HPD SYSTEMS SDN BHD—See Patimas Computers Berhad; *Int'l*, pg. 5757
PATIMAS OUTSOURCING SERVICES SDN BHD—See Patimas Computers Berhad; *Int'l*, pg. 5757
PATINA GROUP—See Delaware North Companies, Inc.; *U.S. Private*, pg. 1195
PATINA RESTAURANT GROUP LLC—See Delaware North Companies, Inc.; *U.S. Private*, pg. 1195
PATINA SOLUTIONS GROUP INC.—See Korn Ferry; *U.S. Public*, pg. 1275
PATINA SOLUTIONS GROUP INC.—See Korn Ferry; *U.S. Public*, pg. 1275
PATINA SOLUTIONS GROUP INC.—See Korn Ferry; *U.S. Public*, pg. 1275
PATINA SOLUTIONS GROUP INC.—See Korn Ferry; *U.S. Public*, pg. 1275
PATINA SOLUTIONS GROUP INC.—See Korn Ferry; *U.S. Public*, pg. 1275
PATINA SOLUTIONS GROUP INC.—See Korn Ferry; *U.S. Public*, pg. 1275
PATINA SOLUTIONS GROUP INC.—See Korn Ferry; *U.S. Public*, pg. 1275
PATINA SOLUTIONS GROUP INC.—See Korn Ferry; *U.S. Public*, pg. 1275
PATINA—See Delaware North Companies, Inc.; *U.S. Private*, pg. 1195
PATINA-V—See Norlaine Inc.; *U.S. Private*, pg. 2938
PATINA WELLNESS LIMITED—See Chinachem Group; *Int'l*, pg. 1568
PATIO INTERNATIONAL COMPANY LIMITED—See S&P Syndicate Public Company Limited; *Int'l*, pg. 6445
PATIO POOLS OF TUCSON INC.; *U.S. Private*, pg. 3109
PATIO SAVASSI ADMINISTRACAO DE SHOPPING CENTER LTDA.—See Multiplan Empreendimentos Imobiliarios S.A.; *Int'l*, pg. 5084
PATIOSHOPPERS INC.; *U.S. Private*, pg. 3109
PATI PAVE SDN BHD—See Khazanah Nasional Berhad; *Int'l*, pg. 4153
PATISSERIE HOLDINGS PLC; *Int'l*, pg. 5757
PATISSERIE VALERIE LIMITED—See Patisserie Holdings plc; *Int'l*, pg. 5757
PATKOL PUBLIC COMPANY LIMITED; *Int'l*, pg. 5757
PAT-KRUGER TRAFFIC B.V.—See Quarterhill Inc.; *Int'l*, pg. 6155
PATLITE(CHINA) CORPORATION—See Inaba Denki Sangyo Co., Ltd.; *Int'l*, pg. 3643
PATLITE CORPORATION—See Inaba Denki Sangyo Co., Ltd.; *Int'l*, pg. 3643
PATLITE EUROPE GMBH—See Inaba Denki Sangyo Co., Ltd.; *Int'l*, pg. 3643
PATLITE KOREA CO., LTD.—See Inaba Denki Sangyo Co., Ltd.; *Int'l*, pg. 3643
PATLITE(SINGAPORE) PTE LTD—See Inaba Denki Sangyo Co., Ltd.; *Int'l*, pg. 3643
PATLITE USA CORP.—See Inaba Denki Sangyo Co., Ltd.; *Int'l*, pg. 3643
PATLON AIRCRAFT & INDUSTRIES, LTD.; *Int'l*, pg. 5757
PAT MCGRATH DODGE COUNTRY; *U.S. Private*, pg. 3105
PAT MILLIKEN FORD; *U.S. Private*, pg. 3105
PATNA SIGNALIZATSIA I SAORAZHENIA JSC—See Trace Group Hold PLC; *Int'l*, pg. 7886
PATO CHEMICAL INDUSTRY PUBLIC CO., LTD.; *Int'l*, pg. 5757
PATOKA DIALYSIS, LLC—See DaVita Inc.; *U.S. Public*, pg. 642
PATOL LTD.—See Sdiptech AB; *Int'l*, pg. 6659
PATON - MILLER LLC—See H2I Group, Inc.; *U.S. Private*, pg. 1837
PAT PECK NISSAN GULFPORT; *U.S. Private*, pg. 3105
PAT PECK NISSAN; *U.S. Private*, pg. 3105
PATRIA AEROSTRUCTURES OY—See Patria Oyj; *Int'l*, pg. 5758
PATRIA AVIATION OY—See Patria Oyj; *Int'l*, pg. 5758
PATRIA BANK S.A.; *Int'l*, pg. 5757
PATRIA CORPORATE FINANCE, A.S.—See KBC Group NV; *Int'l*, pg. 4106
PATRIA CZECH S.R.O.—See Patria Oyj; *Int'l*, pg. 5758
PATRIA DIRECT, A.S.—See KBC Group NV; *Int'l*, pg. 4106
PATRIA FINANCE A.S.—See KBC Group NV; *Int'l*, pg. 4106
PATRIA FINANCE CF A.S.—See KBC Group NV; *Int'l*, pg. 4106
PATRIA HELICOPTERS AB—See Patria Oyj; *Int'l*, pg. 5758
PATRIA HELICOPTERS AS—See Patria Oyj; *Int'l*, pg. 5758

PATRIA INVESTIMENTOS SA

PATRIA INVESTIMENTOS SA; *Int'l*, pg. 5757
PATRIA INVESTMENTS LIMITED; *Int'l*, pg. 5757
PATRIA LAND SERVICES OY—See Patria Oyj; *Int'l*, pg. 5758
PATRIA LATIN AMERICAN OPPORTUNITY ACQUISITION CORP.; *Int'l*, pg. 5757
PATRIA OYJ; *Int'l*, pg. 5757
PATRIA PILOT TRAINING OY—See Patria Oyj; *Int'l*, pg. 5758
PATRIA POLSKA SP. Z O.O.—See Patria Oyj; *Int'l*, pg. 5758
PATRIARCH PARTNERS, LLC; *U.S. Private*, pg. 3109
PATRICIA ACQUISITION CORP.; *U.S. Private*, pg. 3110
PATRICIA FIELD BOUTIQUE; *U.S. Private*, pg. 3110
PATRICIA GRAND RESORT, LLC—See Travel & Leisure Co.; *U.S. Public*, pg. 2185
PATRICIA INDUSTRIES AB—See Investor AB; *Int'l*, pg. 3786
PATRICK ADORN MANUFACTURING—See Patrick Industries, Inc.; *U.S. Public*, pg. 1653
PATRICK CUDAHY INC.—See WH Group Limited; *Int'l*, pg. 8395
PATRICK EXTERMINATING, INC.—See Certus Pest, Inc.; *U.S. Private*, pg. 842
PATRICK GALLAGHER TRUCKING INC.; *U.S. Private*, pg. 3110
PATRICK INDUSTRIES, INC.; *U.S. Public*, pg. 1652
PATRICK JAMES INC.; *U.S. Private*, pg. 3110
PATRICK LUMBER COMPANY, INC.; *U.S. Private*, pg. 3110
PATRICK MALLOY COMMUNITIES, INC.; *U.S. Private*, pg. 3110
PATRICK MECHANICAL LLC—See The Aleut Corporation; *U.S. Private*, pg. 3984
PATRICK MOTORS INC.; *U.S. Private*, pg. 3110
PATRICKORTMAN, INC.; *U.S. Private*, pg. 3110
PATRICK PLASTICS INC.—See Season Group International Co., Ltd.; *Int'l*, pg. 6666
PATRICK PONTIAC INC.; *U.S. Private*, pg. 3110
PATRICK PRODUCTS, INC.—See Clearlake Capital Group, L.P.; *U.S. Private*, pg. 937
PATRICK T. OTTUSO, M.D., F.A.A.D., P.A.—See Harvest Partners L.P.; *U.S. Private*, pg. 1876
PATRICK YARN MILL, INC.—See Coats Group plc; *Int'l*, pg. 1682
PATRIMOINE ET COMMERCE; *Int'l*, pg. 5758
PATRIMONY 1873 SA—See EFG International AG; *Int'l*, pg. 2321
PATRIOT ADVERTISING INC.; *U.S. Private*, pg. 3110
PATRIOT BANK MORTGAGE, INC.—See Veritex Holdings, Inc.; *U.S. Public*, pg. 2283
PATRIOT BANK, N.A.—See Patriot National Bancorp, Inc.; *U.S. Public*, pg. 1653
PATRIOT BANK—See Security BanCorp of Tennessee, Inc.; *U.S. Private*, pg. 3595
PATRIOT BATTERY METALS INC.; *Int'l*, pg. 5758
PATRIOT CARE, INC.—See Patriot National, Inc.; *U.S. Private*, pg. 3110
PATRIOT CHEVROLET GEO INC.; *U.S. Private*, pg. 3110
PATRIOT CHEVROLET, INC.—See General Motors Company; *U.S. Public*, pg. 928
PATRIOT CONTRACTORS, INC; *U.S. Private*, pg. 3110
PATRIOT CONVERTING, INC.—See Brixey & Meyer, Inc.; *U.S. Private*, pg. 658
PATRIOT ENVIRONMENTAL SERVICES, INC.—See J.F. Lehman & Company, Inc.; *U.S. Private*, pg. 2163
PATRIOT FINANCIAL PARTNERS, L.P.—See Independence Capital Partners, LLC; *U.S. Private*, pg. 2056
PATRIOT FIRE PROTECTION INC.; *U.S. Private*, pg. 3110
PATRIOT FLOORING SUPPLY, INC.—See The Belknap White Group, LLC; *U.S. Private*, pg. 3993
PATRIOT FORGE CO.; *Int'l*, pg. 5758
PATRIOT FORGE—See Patriot Forge Co.; *Int'l*, pg. 5758
PATRIOT FORWARDERS INC.—See Stevens Group, Inc.; *U.S. Private*, pg. 3809
PATRIOT FRIEGHT SERVICES INC.—See TFI International, Inc.; *Int'l*, pg. 7586
PATRIOT FUELS BIODIESEL, LLC—See CHS INC.; *U.S. Public*, pg. 492
PATRIOT GENERAL INSURANCE CO.—See Sentry Insurance Group; *U.S. Private*, pg. 3611
PATRIOT GOLD CORP.; *U.S. Public*, pg. 1653
PATRIOT GROWTH PARTNERS, LLC—See GI Manager L.P.; *U.S. Private*, pg. 1693
PATRIOT GROWTH PARTNERS, LLC—See Summit Partners, L.P.; *U.S. Private*, pg. 3856
PATRIOT HARLEY-DAVIDSON, INC.—See Sheehy Auto Stores, Inc.; *U.S. Private*, pg. 3629
THE PATRIOT LEDGER—See Gannett Co., Inc.; *U.S. Public*, pg. 903
PATRIOT LITHIUM LIMITED; *Int'l*, pg. 5758
PATRIOT LOGISTICS, INC.—See US 1 Industries, Inc.; *U.S. Private*, pg. 4317
PATRIOT LOGISTICS; *U.S. Private*, pg. 3110
PATRIOT MEDIA CONSULTING LLC; *U.S. Private*, pg. 3110
PATRIOT MEMORY—See Peripheral Devices & Products Systems Inc.; *U.S. Private*, pg. 3151
PATRIOT MINING COMPANY INC.—See Arch Resources, Inc.; *U.S. Public*, pg. 180
PATRIOT MORTGAGE CORPORATION; *U.S. Private*, pg. 3110
PATRIOT NATIONAL BANCORP, INC.; *U.S. Public*, pg. 1653
PATRIOT NATIONAL, INC.; *U.S. Private*, pg. 3110
PATRIOT-NEWS CO. INC.—See Advance Publications, Inc.; *U.S. Private*, pg. 86
PATRIOT-NEWS CO—See Advance Publications, Inc.; *U.S. Private*, pg. 86
PATRIOT PICKLE CO.—See Swander Pace Capital, LLC; *U.S. Private*, pg. 3890
PATRIOT PONTIAC GMC BUICK LTD PARTNERSHIP; *U.S. Private*, pg. 3110
PATRIOT PREMIUM THREADING SERVICES, LLC—See United States Steel Corporation; *U.S. Public*, pg. 2237
PATRIOT RAIL COMPANY LLC—See Mitsubishi UFJ Financial Group, Inc.; *Int'l*, pg. 4971
PATRIOT RENEWABLE FUELS, LLC—See CHS INC.; *U.S. Public*, pg. 492
PATRIOT SERVICES, INC.—See Patriot National, Inc.; *U.S. Private*, pg. 3110
PATRIOT SPECIAL METALS, INC.—See Patriot Forge Co.; *Int'l*, pg. 5758
PATRIOT TECHNOLOGIES, INC.—See L3Harris Technologies, Inc.; *U.S. Public*, pg. 1284
PATRIOT TRANSPORTATION HOLDING, INC.—See Gregmar, Inc.; *U.S. Private*, pg. 1783
PATRIOT UNDERWRITERS, INC.—See Patriot National, Inc.; *U.S. Private*, pg. 3110
PATRIOT WEALTH MANAGEMENT, INC.—See Mariner Wealth Advisors, LLC; *U.S. Private*, pg. 2576
PATRIS INVESTIMENTOS SGPS, S.A.; *Int'l*, pg. 5758
PATRIZIA ACQUISITION & CONSULTING GMBH.—See PATRIZIA SE; *Int'l*, pg. 5758
PATRIZIA AUGSBURG KAPITALVERWALTUNGSGESELLSCHAFT MBH—See PATRIZIA SE; *Int'l*, pg. 5758
PATRIZIA DENMARK A/S—See PATRIZIA SE; *Int'l*, pg. 5758
PATRIZIA DEUTSCHLAND GMBH—See PATRIZIA SE; *Int'l*, pg. 5758
PATRIZIA FINLAND OY—See PATRIZIA SE; *Int'l*, pg. 5758
PATRIZIA FRANCE SAS—See PATRIZIA SE; *Int'l*, pg. 5758
PATRIZIA HONG KONG LIMITED—See PATRIZIA SE; *Int'l*, pg. 5758
PATRIZIA IMMOBILIEN KAPITALANLAGEGESELLSCHAFT MBH.—See PATRIZIA SE; *Int'l*, pg. 5759
PATRIZIA IMMOBILIEN KAPITALVERWALTUNGSGESELLSCHAFT MBH—See PATRIZIA SE; *Int'l*, pg. 5759
PATRIZIA IMMOBILIENMANAGEMENT GMBH.—See PATRIZIA SE; *Int'l*, pg. 5759
PATRIZIA INFRASTRUCTURE LTD.—See PATRIZIA SE; *Int'l*, pg. 5759
PATRIZIA INVESTMENTMANAGEMENT GMBH.—See PATRIZIA SE; *Int'l*, pg. 5759
PATRIZIA IRELAND LTD.—See PATRIZIA SE; *Int'l*, pg. 5759
PATRIZIA JAPAN KK—See PATRIZIA SE; *Int'l*, pg. 5759
PATRIZIA MULTI MANAGERS A/S—See PATRIZIA SE; *Int'l*, pg. 5759
PATRIZIA NETHERLANDS B.V.—See PATRIZIA SE; *Int'l*, pg. 5759
PATRIZIA PROJEKT 110 GMBH.—See PATRIZIA SE; *Int'l*, pg. 5759
PATRIZIA PROJEKT 180 GMBH.—See PATRIZIA SE; *Int'l*, pg. 5759
PATRIZIA PROJEKT 240 GMBH.—See PATRIZIA SE; *Int'l*, pg. 5759
PATRIZIA PROJEKT 280 VERWALTUNGS GMBH.—See PATRIZIA SE; *Int'l*, pg. 5759
PATRIZIA PROJEKTENTWICKLUNG GMBH.—See PATRIZIA SE; *Int'l*, pg. 5759
PATRIZIA PTY. LTD.—See PATRIZIA SE; *Int'l*, pg. 5759
PATRIZIA REAL ESTATE INVESTMENT MANAGEMENT S.A.R.L.—See PATRIZIA SE; *Int'l*, pg. 5759
PATRIZIA SE; *Int'l*, pg. 5758
PATRIZIA SWEDEN AB—See PATRIZIA SE; *Int'l*, pg. 5759
PATRIZIA UK LIMITED—See PATRIZIA SE; *Int'l*, pg. 5759
PATRIZIA WOHNEN GMBH.—See PATRIZIA SE; *Int'l*, pg. 5759
PATRONALE LIFE NV; *Int'l*, pg. 5759
PATRONAS FINANCIAL SYSTEMS GMBH—See Niiio Finance Group AG; *Int'l*, pg. 5288
PATRON CAPITAL ADVISERS LLP; *Int'l*, pg. 5759
PATRON CAPITAL EUROPE S.A.R.L—See Patron Capital Advisers LLP; *Int'l*, pg. 5759
PATRON CAPITAL IBERIA—See Patron Capital Advisers LLP; *Int'l*, pg. 5759
PATRON CAPITAL ITALIA SRL—See Patron Capital Advisers LLP; *Int'l*, pg. 5759
PATRON EXIM LIMITED; *Int'l*, pg. 5759
PATRON SOLUTIONS, L.P.—See Comcast Corporation; *U.S. Public*, pg. 541
PATRONS OXFORD INSURANCE COMPANY—See Quincy Mutual Fire Insurance Company; *U.S. Private*, pg. 3327

CORPORATE AFFILIATIONS

THE PATRON SPIRITS COMPANY; *U.S. Private*, pg. 4091
PATRONUS RESOURCES LIMITED; *Int'l*, pg. 5759
PATRYS GMBH—See Patrys Limited; *Int'l*, pg. 5760
PATRYS LIMITED; *Int'l*, pg. 5759
PAT SALMON & SONS, INC.; *U.S. Private*, pg. 3105
PATS N.V.—See TUI AG; *Int'l*, pg. 7965
PATSON INC.; *U.S. Private*, pg. 3111
PATSON'S MEDIA GROUP; *U.S. Private*, pg. 3111
PATSPIN INDIA LTD.; *Int'l*, pg. 5760
PAT'S PLACE CHILD ADVOCACY CENTER INC.; *U.S. Private*, pg. 3105
PATSTROYINJENERING JSC—See Stara Planina Hold Plc; *Int'l*, pg. 7175
PATSY LOU BUICK GMC INC.; *U.S. Private*, pg. 3111
PATSY'S BUS SALES & SERVICE—See Patsy's, Inc.; *U.S. Private*, pg. 3111
PATSY'S, INC.; *U.S. Private*, pg. 3111
PATSYSTEMS HONG KONG LIMITED—See ION Investment Group Ltd.; *Int'l*, pg. 3794
PATSYSTEMS (JAPAN) KK—See ION Investment Group Ltd.; *Int'l*, pg. 3794
PATSYSTEMS LIMITED—See ION Investment Group Ltd.; *Int'l*, pg. 3794
PATSYSTEMS (NA) LLC—See ION Investment Group Ltd.; *Int'l*, pg. 3794
PATSYSTEMS (UK) LTD—See ION Investment Group Ltd.; *Int'l*, pg. 3794
PATSY STROCCHIA & SONS IRON WORKS, INC.; *U.S. Private*, pg. 3111
PATTANA AGRO FUTURES CO., LTD.—See Sri Trang Agro-Industry Public Company Limited; *Int'l*, pg. 7150
PAT TECH FITWELL TUBE COMPONENTS LIMITED; *Int'l*, pg. 5755
PATTEN AND PATTEN, INC.; *U.S. Private*, pg. 3111
PATTEN ENERGY ENTERPRISES, INC.—See Patten Energy Solutions Group, Inc.; *U.S. Public*, pg. 1653
PATTEN ENERGY SOLUTIONS GROUP, INC.; *U.S. Public*, pg. 1653
PATTEN INDUSTRIES, INC.; *U.S. Private*, pg. 3111
PATTEN POWER SYSTEMS INC.—See Patten Industries, Inc.; *U.S. Private*, pg. 3111
PATTEN SALES & MARKETING, LLC; *U.S. Private*, pg. 3111
PATTEN SEED COMPANY INC. - SOIL3 DIVISION—See Patten Seed Company Inc.; *U.S. Private*, pg. 3111
PATTEN SEED COMPANY INC.; *U.S. Private*, pg. 3111
PATTEN SEED COMPANY INC. - SUPER-SOD DIVISION—See Patten Seed Company Inc.; *U.S. Private*, pg. 3111
PATTEN SEED COMPANY INC. - SUPER-SOD TREES DIVISION—See Patten Seed Company Inc.; *U.S. Private*, pg. 3111
PATTERN ENERGY GROUP LP—See Canada Pension Plan Investment Board; *Int'l*, pg. 1281
PATTERN LIMITED—See Messe Munchen GmbH; *Int'l*, pg. 4842
PATTERN SPA; *Int'l*, pg. 5760
PATTERSON BELKNAP WEBB & TYLER LLP; *U.S. Private*, pg. 3111
THE PATTERSON CAPITAL CORPORATION—See Estancia Capital Management, LLC; *U.S. Private*, pg. 1428
PATTERSON COMPANIES, INC.; *U.S. Public*, pg. 1653
PATTERSON DENTAL CANADA INC.—See Patterson Companies, Inc.; *U.S. Public*, pg. 1654
PATTERSON DENTAL—See Patterson Companies, Inc.; *U.S. Public*, pg. 1654
PATTERSON DENTAL SUPPLY, INC.—See Patterson Companies, Inc.; *U.S. Public*, pg. 1654
PATTERSON-ERIE CORPORATION; *U.S. Private*, pg. 3111
PATTERSON FUEL OIL INC.; *U.S. Private*, pg. 3111
PATTERSON GARNET CORP.—See Peckham Industries, Inc.; *U.S. Private*, pg. 3127
PATTERSON GLOBAL LIMITED—See Patterson Companies, Inc.; *U.S. Public*, pg. 1654
PATTERSON LOGISTICS SERVICES, INC.—See Patterson Companies, Inc.; *U.S. Public*, pg. 1654
PATTERSON MEDICAL CANADA, INC.—See Madison Dearborn Partners, LLC; *U.S. Private*, pg. 2542
PATTERSON OFFICE SUPPLIES, INC.—See Patterson Companies, Inc.; *U.S. Public*, pg. 1654
PATTERSON OIL COMPANY; *U.S. Private*, pg. 3111
PATTERSON OLDSMOBILE-GMC-TOYOTA—See Foundation Automotive Corp; *U.S. Private*, pg. 1579
PATTERSON POWER ENGINEERS LLC—See New Mountain Capital, LLC; *U.S. Private*, pg. 2903
PATTERSON PUMP COMPANY—See The Gorman-Rupp Company; *U.S. Public*, pg. 2085
PATTERSON PUMP IRELAND LIMITED—See The Gorman-Rupp Company; *U.S. Public*, pg. 2085
PATTERSON-SCHWARTZ & ASSOCIATES INC.; *U.S. Private*, pg. 3111
PATTERSON SERVICES, INC.—See RPC, Inc.; *U.S. Public*, pg. 1816
PATTERSON TECHNOLOGY CENTER, INC.—See Patterson Companies, Inc.; *U.S. Public*, pg. 1654
PATTERSON THUENTE PEDERSEN, P.A.—See Husch Blackwell LLP; *U.S. Private*, pg. 2013

COMPANY NAME INDEX

PATTERSON TRAVEL SERVICE—See ZZLL Information Technology, Inc.; *Int'l*, pg. 8701
PATTERSON TRAVEL SERVICES—See ZZLL Information Technology, Inc.; *Int'l*, pg. 8701
PATTERSON TRUCK LINE, INC.—See RPC, Inc.; *U.S. Public*, pg. 1816
PATTERSON-UTI DRILLING CANADA LIMITED—See Patterson-UTI Energy, Inc.; *U.S. Public*, pg. 1654
PATTERSON-UTI DRILLING COMPANY, LLC—See Patterson-UTI Energy, Inc.; *U.S. Public*, pg. 1654
PATTERSON-UTI ENERGY, INC.; *U.S. Public*, pg. 1654
PATTERSON-UTI MANAGEMENT SERVICES, LLC—See Patterson-UTI Energy, Inc.; *U.S. Public*, pg. 1654
PATTERSON VETERINARY SUPPLY, INC.—See Patterson Companies, Inc.; *U.S. Public*, pg. 1654
PATTIES FOODS PTY LIMITED—See PAG Capital; *Int'l*, pg. 5697
PATTISON AGRICULTURE LIMITED—See The Jim Pattison Group; *Int'l*, pg. 7660
PATTISON OUTDOOR ADVERTISING—See The Jim Pattison Group; *Int'l*, pg. 7660
PATTISON SIGN GROUP (NE) INC.—See The Jim Pattison Group; *Int'l*, pg. 7660
PATTISON SIGN GROUP—See The Jim Pattison Group; *Int'l*, pg. 7660
PATTISON SIGN GROUP—See The Jim Pattison Group; *Int'l*, pg. 7660
PATTLEN ENTERPRISES INC.; *U.S. Private*, pg. 3111
PATTONAIR DERBY LIMITED—See Platinum Equity, LLC; *U.S. Private*, pg. 3207
PATTONAIR LIMITED—See Platinum Equity, LLC; *U.S. Private*, pg. 3206
PATTONAIR SAS—See Platinum Equity, LLC; *U.S. Private*, pg. 3207
PATTONAIR—See Platinum Equity, LLC; *U.S. Private*, pg. 3207
PATTON ALBERTSON & MILLER GROUP, LLC—See Clayton, Dubilier & Rice, LLC; *U.S. Private*, pg. 923
PATTON ALBERTSON & MILLER GROUP, LLC—See Stone Point Capital LLC; *U.S. Private*, pg. 3824
PATTON & COOKE CO; *Int'l*, pg. 5760
PATTON ELECTRONICS CO.; *U.S. Private*, pg. 3111
PATTON INDUSTRIAL PRODUCTS; *U.S. Private*, pg. 3111
PATTON MUSIC CO., INC.; *U.S. Private*, pg. 3111
PATTON PICTURE COMPANY—See Kohlberg & Company, LLC; *U.S. Private*, pg. 2338
PATTON SALES CORPORATION; *U.S. Private*, pg. 3112
PATTON'S, INC.—See ELGI Equipments Limited; *Int'l*, pg. 2360
PATTON WALLCOVERINGS, INC.—See Norwall Group Inc.; *Int'l*, pg. 5448
PAT TRAFFIC LTDA.—See Quarterhill Inc.; *Int'l*, pg. 6155
PAT TRAFFIC SISTEMAS DE TRANSPORTE INTELIGENTE LTDA—See Quarterhill Inc.; *Int'l*, pg. 6155
PATTYN BELGIUM NV; *Int'l*, pg. 5760
PATTY PECK HONDA; *U.S. Private*, pg. 3112
PATUS 216 GMBH—See Barclays PLC; *Int'l*, pg. 862
PATUXENT ROOFING & CONTRACTING, LLC—See New State Capital Partners LLC; *U.S. Private*, pg. 2907
PATXI'S PIZZA; *U.S. Private*, pg. 3112
PATZ & HALL WINE COMPANY—See Altria Group, Inc.; *U.S. Public*, pg. 89
PAUL A. DE JESSE, INC. ADVERTISING; *U.S. Private*, pg. 3112
PAULANER BRAUEREI GMBH & CO. KG—See L'Arche Green N.V.; *Int'l*, pg. 4376
PAULANER BRAUEREI GMBH & CO. KG—See Schorghuber Stiftung & Co. Holding KG; *Int'l*, pg. 6639
PAUL ARGOE SCREENS, INC.; *U.S. Private*, pg. 3112
PAUL ARPIN VAN LINES, INC.; *U.S. Private*, pg. 3112
PAUL A. SCHMITT MUSIC COMPANY; *U.S. Private*, pg. 3112
PAULA'S CHOICE LLC—See TA Associates, Inc.; *U.S. Private*, pg. 3917
PAULAUR CORPORATION; *U.S. Private*, pg. 3114
PAUL AYOTTE INSURANCE BROKER LTD.; *Int'l*, pg. 5760
PAULA YOUNG CATALOG—See EdgeStone Capital Partners Inc.; *Int'l*, pg. 2309
PAULBECKS INC.; *U.S. Private*, pg. 3114
PAUL BEIER GMBH WERKZEUG- UND MASCHINENBAU & CO. KG—See Gesco AG; *Int'l*, pg. 2946
PAUL BELLACK INC.; *U.S. Private*, pg. 3112
PAUL BROWN MOTORS, INC.; *U.S. Private*, pg. 3112
PAUL BUNYAN COMMUNICATIONS; *U.S. Private*, pg. 3112
PAUL B. ZIMMERMAN INC.; *U.S. Private*, pg. 3112
PAULCAMPER GMBH—See Camplify Holdings Limited; *Int'l*, pg. 1275
PAUL CERAME FORD; *U.S. Private*, pg. 3112
PAUL CONTE CADILLAC, INC.; *U.S. Private*, pg. 3112
PAUL C. RIZZO ASSOCIATES, INC.; *U.S. Private*, pg. 3112
PAUL DAVIS RESTORATION, INC.—See FirstService Corporation; *Int'l*, pg. 2691
PAUL DE LIMA CO. INC.; *U.S. Private*, pg. 3112
PAULDING WIND FARM II, L.L.C.—See EDP - Energias de Portugal, S.A.; *Int'l*, pg. 2314

PAUL DINTO ELECTRICAL CONTRS; *U.S. Private*, pg. 3112
PAUL DPOINT TECHNOLOGIES GMBH—See Zehnder Group AG; *Int'l*, pg. 8630
PAUL ECKE RANCH; *U.S. Private*, pg. 3112
PAUL ERNST VERSICHERUNGSVERMITTLUNGS MBH—See DZ BANK AG Deutsche Zentral-Genossenschaftsbank; *Int'l*, pg. 2244
PAULETTE CARTER DESIGN INC.; *U.S. Private*, pg. 3114
PAUL EVERTS RV COUNTRY; *U.S. Private*, pg. 3112
PAULEY CONSTRUCTION INC.—See Dycom Industries, Inc.; *U.S. Public*, pg. 699
PAUL FIEREK SPEDITION GMBH; *Int'l*, pg. 5760
PAUL FISHER OIL COMPANY INC.; *U.S. Private*, pg. 3112
PAUL FRANK INDUSTRIES, INC.—See Saban Capital Group, Inc.; *U.S. Private*, pg. 3520
PAUL FREDRICK MENSTYLE INC.—See SECOM Co., Ltd.; *Int'l*, pg. 6671
PAUL GRANDJOUAN SACO—See Veolia Environnement S.A.; *Int'l*, pg. 8153
PAUL G. WHITE TILE CO., INC.; *U.S. Private*, pg. 3112
PAUL HARTMANN ADRIATIC D.O.O.—See PAUL HARTMANN AG; *Int'l*, pg. 5761
PAUL HARTMANN AG & CO. LOGISTIKZENTRUM SUD OHG—See PAUL HARTMANN AG; *Int'l*, pg. 5761
PAUL HARTMANN AG (SHANGHAI) TRADE CO., LTD.—See PAUL HARTMANN AG; *Int'l*, pg. 5761
PAUL HARTMANN AG; *Int'l*, pg. 5760
PAUL HARTMANN ASIA-PACIFIC LTD.—See PAUL HARTMANN AG; *Int'l*, pg. 5761
PAUL HARTMANN A/S—See PAUL HARTMANN AG; *Int'l*, pg. 5761
PAUL HARTMANN AS—See PAUL HARTMANN AG; *Int'l*, pg. 5761
PAUL HARTMANN B.V.—See PAUL HARTMANN AG; *Int'l*, pg. 5761
PAUL HARTMANN CHILE SPA—See PAUL HARTMANN AG; *Int'l*, pg. 5761
PAUL HARTMANN D.O.O.—See PAUL HARTMANN AG; *Int'l*, pg. 5761
PAUL HARTMANN EGYPT S.A.E.—See PAUL HARTMANN AG; *Int'l*, pg. 5761
PAUL HARTMANN FINANCE B.V.—See PAUL HARTMANN AG; *Int'l*, pg. 5761
PAUL HARTMANN GMBH—See PAUL HARTMANN AG; *Int'l*, pg. 5761
PAUL HARTMANN HELLAS A.E.—See PAUL HARTMANN AG; *Int'l*, pg. 5761
PAUL HARTMANN LDA—See PAUL HARTMANN AG; *Int'l*, pg. 5761
PAUL HARTMANN LTD.—See PAUL HARTMANN AG; *Int'l*, pg. 5761
PAUL HARTMANN LTD. STI.—See PAUL HARTMANN AG; *Int'l*, pg. 5761
PAUL HARTMANN MEDICAL PRIVATE LTD.—See PAUL HARTMANN AG; *Int'l*, pg. 5761
PAUL HARTMANN MIDDLE EAST FZE—See PAUL HARTMANN AG; *Int'l*, pg. 5761
PAUL HARTMANN OOO—See PAUL HARTMANN AG; *Int'l*, pg. 5761
PAUL HARTMANN POLSKA—See PAUL HARTMANN AG; *Int'l*, pg. 5761
PAUL HARTMANN PTY. LTD.—See PAUL HARTMANN AG; *Int'l*, pg. 5761
PAUL HARTMANN S.A.R.L.—See PAUL HARTMANN AG; *Int'l*, pg. 5761
PAUL HARTMANN S.A.R.L.—See PAUL HARTMANN AG; *Int'l*, pg. 5761
PAUL HARTMANN S.A—See PAUL HARTMANN AG; *Int'l*, pg. 5761
PAUL HARTMANN (SHANGHAI) TRADE CO., LTD.—See PAUL HARTMANN AG; *Int'l*, pg. 5761
PAUL HARTMANN S.P.A.—See PAUL HARTMANN AG; *Int'l*, pg. 5761
PAUL HARTMANN TAIWAN LIMITED—See PAUL HARTMANN AG; *Int'l*, pg. 5761
PAUL HASTINGS LLP; *U.S. Private*, pg. 3112
PAUL HEMMER CONSTRUCTION COMPANY; *U.S. Private*, pg. 3113
PAUL HENKE GMBH & CO. KG; *Int'l*, pg. 5762
PAUL HETTICH GMBH & CO. KG—See Hettich Holding GmbH & Co. oHG; *Int'l*, pg. 3366
PAUL HEURING MOTORS INC.; *U.S. Private*, pg. 3113
PAULIC MEUNERIE SA; *Int'l*, pg. 5762
PAULI ELEKTRO AG—See Burkhalter Holding AG; *Int'l*, pg. 1225
PAULIG TEPPICHWEBEREI GMBH; *Int'l*, pg. 5762
PAUL INFOTECH PRIVATE LIMITED—See Paul Merchants Limited; *Int'l*, pg. 5762
PAULIN INDUSTRIES INC.—See Hillman Solutions Corp.; *U.S. Public*, pg. 1038
PAUL JARDIN OF USA INC.; *U.S. Private*, pg. 3113
PAUL J. KREZ COMPANY; *U.S. Private*, pg. 3113
PAUL JOHNSON DRYWALL, INC.; *U.S. Private*, pg. 3113
PAUL KELLER GARTEN- LANDSCHAFTS- SPORTPLATZ- UND TIEFBAU GMBH; *Int'l*, pg. 5762

PAUSHAK LIMITED

PAUL KELLER INGENIEURE AG—See AFRY AB; *Int'l*, pg. 195
PAUL KEMPOWSKI GMBH & CO. KG—See Dole plc; *Int'l*, pg. 2157
PAUL & MARLENE INC.; *U.S. Private*, pg. 3112
PAULMAY CO., INC.; *U.S. Private*, pg. 3114
PAUL MERCHANTS LIMITED; *Int'l*, pg. 5762
PAUL MILLER AUTO GROUP; *U.S. Private*, pg. 3113
PAUL MUELLER COMPANY; *U.S. Public*, pg. 1655
PAUL N. GARDNER COMPANY, INC.—See SKion GmbH; *Int'l*, pg. 6989
PAUL OIL COMPANY INC.; *U.S. Private*, pg. 3113
PAULO PRODUCTS COMPANY INC.; *U.S. Private*, pg. 3114
PAUL PAULET S.A.S.—See Thai Union Group Public Company Limited; *Int'l*, pg. 7596
PAUL PETERS AGENCY INC.; *U.S. Private*, pg. 3113
PAUL PIAZZA & SON INC.; *U.S. Private*, pg. 3113
PAUL POLLRICH GMBH—See GEA Group Aktiengesellschaft; *Int'l*, pg. 2903
PAUL PON POLSKA SP.Z.O.O.—See Koepon Holdings B.V.; *Int'l*, pg. 4227
PAUL R. BRILES INC.—See Berkshire Hathaway Inc.; *U.S. Public*, pg. 315
PAUL REED SMITH GUITARS; *U.S. Private*, pg. 3113
THE PAUL REVERE LIFE INSURANCE COMPANY—See Unum Group; *U.S. Public*, pg. 2263
PAUL RISK ASSOCIATES, INC.; *U.S. Private*, pg. 3113
PAUL'S ACE HARDWARE STORES; *U.S. Private*, pg. 3113
PAULSBORO NATURAL GAS PIPELINE COMPANY LLC—See PBF Energy Inc.; *U.S. Public*, pg. 1657
PAULSBORO PACKAGING CO.—See The Clorox Company; *U.S. Public*, pg. 2062
PAULSBORO REFINING COMPANY LLC—See PBF Energy Inc.; *U.S. Public*, pg. 1657
PAULSCORP, LLC; *U.S. Private*, pg. 3114
PAULSEN FOOD GMBH—See Charoen Pokphand Foods Public Company Limited; *Int'l*, pg. 1453
PAULSEN, INC.; *U.S. Private*, pg. 3114
PAULSEN MARKETING COMMUNICATIONS, INC.; *U.S. Private*, pg. 3114
PAUL SHERRY CHRYSLER-DODGE-JEEP INC.; *U.S. Private*, pg. 3113
PAULSON & CO. INC.; *U.S. Private*, pg. 3114
PAULSON INVESTMENT COMPANY, LLC; *U.S. Private*, pg. 3114
PAULSON OIL COMPANY INC.—See Berkshire Hathaway Inc.; *U.S. Public*, pg. 313
PAULSTRA CRC CORP.—See TotalEnergies SE; *Int'l*, pg. 7837
PAULSTRA S.N.C.—See TotalEnergies SE; *Int'l*, pg. 7837
PAUL STUART, INC.—See Mitsui & Co., Ltd.; *Int'l*, pg. 4975
PAUL SUSTEK COMPANY INC.; *U.S. Private*, pg. 3113
PAULS VALLEY LANDFILL, LLC—See BC Partners LLP; *Int'l*, pg. 924
PAUL THIGPEN CHEVROLET BUICK GMC; *U.S. Private*, pg. 3113
PAULUS, SOKOLOWSKI & SARTOR LLC; *U.S. Private*, pg. 3114
PAUL & VIRGINE HOTEL—See Rogers & Company Limited; *Int'l*, pg. 6383
PAUL WAGNER ET FILS—See Electricite de France S.A.; *Int'l*, pg. 2352
PAUL WALSH NISSAN, INC.; *U.S. Private*, pg. 3113
PAUL WARMERUCKGEWINNUNG GMBH—See Zehnder Group AG; *Int'l*, pg. 8630
PAUL, WEISS, RIFKIND, WHARTON & GARRISON LLP; *U.S. Private*, pg. 3113
PAUL WINSTON FINE JEWELRY GROUP; *U.S. Private*, pg. 3113
PAUL WURTH DO BRASIL LTDA.—See SMS Holding GmbH; *Int'l*, pg. 7015
PAUL WURTH IHI CO., LTD.—See IHI Corporation; *Int'l*, pg. 3606
PAUL WURTH INC.—See SMS Holding GmbH; *Int'l*, pg. 7015
PAUL WURTH S.A.—See SMS Holding GmbH; *Int'l*, pg. 7015
PAUL Y. CONSTRUCTION & ENGINEERING PTE LIMITED—See South Shore Holdings Ltd.; *Int'l*, pg. 7116
PAUL Y. ENGINEERING GROUP LIMITED—See South Shore Holdings Ltd.; *Int'l*, pg. 7116
PAULY JAIL BUILDING COMPANY, INC.; *U.S. Private*, pg. 3114
PAUMIER SAS—See VINCI S.A.; *Int'l*, pg. 8225
PAUSHAK LIMITED; *Int'l*, pg. 5762
PAUWELS TRANSFORMERS N.V.—See Electrical Industries Company; *Int'l*, pg. 2349
PAVA-EXPORT LLC—See OJSC Pava; *Int'l*, pg. 5541
PAVAGE ROLLAND FORTIER INC.—See VINCI S.A.; *Int'l*, pg. 8219
PAVAILLER S.A.S.—See Ali Holding S.r.l; *Int'l*, pg. 322
PAVANA GMBH—See PNE AG; *Int'l*, pg. 5900
PAVANA POLSKA SP. Z O.O.—See PNE AG; *Int'l*, pg. 5900

PAUSHAK LIMITED — CORPORATE AFFILIATIONS

PAVANA POWER CORPORATION—See First National Energy Corporation; *Int'l*, pg. 2686
PAVAN S.P.A.—See GEA Group Aktiengesellschaft; *Int'l*, pg. 2903
PAVAN U.S.A., INC.—See GEA Group Aktiengesellschaft; *Int'l*, pg. 2903
PAVARINI CONSTRUCTION CO. INC.—See STO Building Group Inc.; *U.S. Private*, pg. 3813
PAVARINI CONSTRUCTION CO. INC.-STAMFORD—See STO Building Group Inc.; *U.S. Private*, pg. 3814
PAVARINI MCGOVERN LLC—See STO Building Group Inc.; *U.S. Private*, pg. 3814
PAVCO DE VENEZUELA, S.A.—See Grupo Empresarial Kaluz S.A. de C.V.; *Int'l*, pg. 3128
PAVCO, INC.; *U.S. Private*, pg. 3115
PAVECON INC.; *U.S. Private*, pg. 3115
PAVECON UTILITIES INC.—See Pavecon Inc.; *U.S. Private*, pg. 3115
PAVEMENT MANAGEMENT SERVICES PTY LTD.; *Int'l*, pg. 5762
PAVES COSSUTTA—See VINCI S.A.; *Int'l*, pg. 8225
PAVESE-MCCORMICK AGENCY, INC.—See King Insurance Partners, LLC; *U.S. Private*, pg. 2309
PAVE-TAR CONSTRUCTION LTD.; *Int'l*, pg. 5762
PAVETEX ENGINEERING LLC—See GI Manager L.P.; *U.S. Private*, pg. 1691
PAVEX INC.; *U.S. Private*, pg. 3115
THE PAVILION AT HEALTHPARK, LLC—See Acadia Healthcare Company, Inc.; *U.S. Public*, pg. 31
PAVILION BOOKS COMPANY LIMITED—See News Corporation; *U.S. Public*, pg. 1521
THE PAVILION CARE CENTER, LLC—See Regional Health Properties, Inc.; *U.S. Public*, pg. 1776
THE PAVILION CLINIC LTD.—See Centene Corporation; *U.S. Public*, pg. 470
PAVILION PRIVATE EQUITY CO., LTD.; *Int'l*, pg. 5762
PAVILION REAL ESTATE INVESTMENT TRUST—See Pavilion REIT Management Sdn. Bhd.; *Int'l*, pg. 5762
PAVILION REIT MANAGEMENT SDN. BHD.; *Int'l*, pg. 5762
PAVILIONS—See Cerberus Capital Management, L.P.; *U.S. Private*, pg. 836
PAVILLION BANK—See AmTex Bancshares Inc.; *U.S. Private*, pg. 268
PAVILLION NURSING CENTER NORTH, INC.—See Omega Healthcare Investors, Inc.; *U.S. Public*, pg. 1571
PAVILLION, S.A. DE C.V.—See Grupo Lamosa S.A. de C.V.; *Int'l*, pg. 3132
PAVIMENTAL POLSKA SP Z.O.O.—See Edizione S.r.l.; *Int'l*, pg. 2312
PAVIMENTAL SPA—See Edizione S.r.l.; *Int'l*, pg. 2312
PAVING MAINTENANCE SUPPLY, INC.—See Ergon, Inc.; *U.S. Private*, pg. 1418
PAVION CORP.—See Wind Point Advisors LLC; *U.S. Private*, pg. 4535
PAVI SHOPPING COMPLEX PLC—See PG PLC; *Int'l*, pg. 5837
PAVLODARENERGO JSC; *Int'l*, pg. 5762
PAVLODAR HEATING NETWORKS LLP—See Central-Asian Power Energy Company JSC; *Int'l*, pg. 1410
PAVLODAR OIL CHEMISTRY REFINERY JSC; *Int'l*, pg. 5762
PAVLODAR REGIONAL ELECTRIC DISTRIBUTION COMPANY JSC—See Pavlodarenergo JSC; *Int'l*, pg. 5762
PAVLOVO BUS AO; *Int'l*, pg. 5762
PAVMED INC.; *U.S. Public*, pg. 1655
PAVNA INDUSTRIES LIMITED; *Int'l*, pg. 5762
PAVONE; *U.S. Private*, pg. 3115
PAVONIA HOLDINGS (US), INC.—See Eli Global, LLC; *U.S. Private*, pg. 1360
PAVONINE CO., LTD. - GWANGJU DIVISION—See Pavonine Co., Ltd.; *Int'l*, pg. 5762
PAVONINE CO., LTD. - SONGDO DIVISION—See Pavonine Co., Ltd.; *Int'l*, pg. 5762
PAVONINE CO., LTD.; *Int'l*, pg. 5762
PAVO PFERDENAHRUNG GMBH—See ForFarmers Group B.V; *Int'l*, pg. 2732
PAVO TEKNIK SERVIS ELEKTRIK ELEKTRONIK SANAYI VE TICARET A.S.—See Aktif Yatirim Bankasi A.S.; *Int'l*, pg. 267
PAWAA SOFTWARE PRIVATE LIMITED—See Cisco Systems, Inc.; *U.S. Public*, pg. 500
PAWANSUT HOLDINGS LIMITED; *Int'l*, pg. 5762
PAWLING CORPORATION-ARCHITECTURAL PRODUCTS DIVISION—See Pawling Corporation; *U.S. Private*, pg. 3115
PAWLING CORPORATION; *U.S. Private*, pg. 3115
PAWN CO., LTD.—See King Co., Ltd.; *Int'l*, pg. 4168
PAWNEE COUNTY COOPERATIVE ASSOCIATION; *U.S. Private*, pg. 3115
PAWNEE LEASING CORPORATION—See Chesswood Group Limited; *Int'l*, pg. 1472
PAWNEE VALLEY COMMUNITY HOSPITAL INC.; *U.S. Private*, pg. 3115
PAW-PAW'S CAMPER CITY INC.; *U.S. Private*, pg. 3115
PAW PAW WINE DISTRIBUTORS COMPANY; *U.S. Private*, pg. 3115
PAWS/LA; *U.S. Private*, pg. 3115

PAWTUCKET CREDIT UNION; *U.S. Private*, pg. 3115
PAWTUCKET TIMES—See R.I.S.N. Operations Inc.; *U.S. Private*, pg. 3336
PAX8, INC.—See Arrow Electronics, Inc.; *U.S. Public*, pg. 199
PAXAN. CO; *Int'l*, pg. 5763
PAX ANLAGE AG—See Baloise Holding AG; *Int'l*, pg. 811
PAXAN YEREVAN CO.—See Behshahr Industrial Development Corp.; *Int'l*, pg. 942
PAXAR CORPORATION PTY. LTD.—See Avery Dennison Corporation; *U.S. Public*, pg. 244
PAXATA, INC.—See Right Side Capital Management, LLC; *U.S. Private*, pg. 3436
PAX COMPUTER TECHNOLOGY (SHENZHEN) CO., LTD—See PAX Global Technology Limited; *Int'l*, pg. 5763
PAX CONSTRUCTION LTD.; *Int'l*, pg. 5762
PAX CORRUGATED PRODUCTS, INC.—See Welch Packaging Group, Inc.; *U.S. Private*, pg. 4473
PAX DISTRIBUTION, LLC—See World Kinect Corporation; *U.S. Public*, pg. 2381
PAX ELECTRO PRODUCTS AB—See Litorina Capital Management AB; *Int'l*, pg. 4528
PAXEN LEARNING CORPORATION; *U.S. Private*, pg. 3115
PAX FORLAG AS; *Int'l*, pg. 5762
PAX GLOBAL TECHNOLOGY LIMITED; *Int'l*, pg. 5763
PAXIO INC.; *U.S. Private*, pg. 3115
PAXION CAPITAL, LP; *U.S. Private*, pg. 3115
PAX ITALIA S.R.L.—See PAX Global Technology Limited; *Int'l*, pg. 5763
PAX JAPAN KABUSHIKI KAISHA—See PAX Global Technology Limited; *Int'l*, pg. 5763
PAX MACHINE WORKS INC.; *U.S. Private*, pg. 3115
PAXMAN AB; *Int'l*, pg. 5763
PAXMAN COOLERS LIMITED—See Paxman AB; *Int'l*, pg. 5763
PAXMEDICA, INC.; *U.S. Public*, pg. 1655
PAXNET INC.—See KX Innovation Co Ltd; *Int'l*, pg. 4353
PAX POS SOLUTIONS INDIA PRIVATE LTD.—See PAX Global Technology Limited; *Int'l*, pg. 5763
PAXSAL BUSINESS PROCESS OUTSOURCING (PTY) LTD—See Adcorp Holdings Limited; *Int'l*, pg. 127
PAXSAL PAYROLL OUTSOURCING (PTY) LTD—See Adcorp Holdings Limited; *Int'l*, pg. 127
PAX SCANDINAVIA AB—See New Wave Group AB; *Int'l*, pg. 5230
PAX TECHNOLOGY, INC.—See PAX Global Technology Limited; *Int'l*, pg. 5763
PAX TECHNOLOGY LIMITED—See PAX Global Technology Limited; *Int'l*, pg. 5763
PAXTER SECURITY & AUTOMATION SDN BHD—See ASSA ABLOY AB; *Int'l*, pg. 638
PAXTON & BALL INC.; *U.S. Private*, pg. 3115
PAXTON COMPANY; *U.S. Private*, pg. 3115
PAXTON MEDIA GROUP LLC; *U.S. Private*, pg. 3115
PAXTON-MITCHELL COMPANY; *U.S. Private*, pg. 3116
PAXTON VAN LINES INCORPORATED; *U.S. Private*, pg. 3116
PAXTON & VIERLING STEEL COMPANY- A DIV OF OWEN INDUSTRIES INC—See Owen Industries, Inc.; *U.S. Private*, pg. 3054
PAXUS AUSTRALIA PTY. LIMITED—See Adcorp Holdings Limited; *Int'l*, pg. 127
PAX WORLD FUNDS; *U.S. Public*, pg. 3115
PAXYS, INC.; *Int'l*, pg. 5763
PAYABILITY, LLC; *U.S. Private*, pg. 3116
PAYACCSYS SERVICES (PTY) LTD—See Adcorp Holdings Limited; *Int'l*, pg. 127
PAYA HOLDINGS INC.—See Nuvei Corporation; *Int'l*, pg. 5494
PAYA, INC.—See Nuvei Corporation; *Int'l*, pg. 5494
PAYBACK AUSTRIA GMBH—See American Express Company; *U.S. Public*, pg. 102
PAYBACK GMBH—See American Express Company; *U.S. Public*, pg. 102
PAYBAY NETWORKS SRL—See Qui! Group S.p.A.; *Int'l*, pg. 6161
PAYBOX CORP—See Aquiline Capital Partners LLC; *U.S. Private*, pg. 305
PAYBRIGHT INC.—See Affirm Holdings, Inc.; *U.S. Public*, pg. 57
PAYCE CONSOLIDATED LIMITED; *Int'l*, pg. 5763
PAYCE, INC.—See Deluxe Corporation; *U.S. Public*, pg. 653
PAYCHEST, INC.; *Int'l*, pg. 5763
PAYCHEX, INC.; *U.S. Public*, pg. 1655
PAYCHEX MANAGEMENT CORP.—See Paychex, Inc.; *U.S. Public*, pg. 1656
PAYCHEX SECURITIES CORPORATION—See Paychex, Inc.; *U.S. Public*, pg. 1656
PAYCHEX TIME & ATTENDANCE INC.—See Paychex, Inc.; *U.S. Public*, pg. 1656
PAYCO FOODS CORPORATION—See Nestle S.A.; *Int'l*, pg. 5211
PAYCOM SOFTWARE, INC.—See Welsh, Carson, Anderson & Stowe; *U.S. Private*, pg. 4480
PAYCOR HCM, INC.; *U.S. Public*, pg. 1656
PAYCOR, INC.; *U.S. Private*, pg. 3116

PAYCOR, INC.—See Paycor, Inc.; *U.S. Private*, pg. 3116
PAYCORP PAYMENT SOLUTIONS PTY LTD—See General Atlantic Service Company, L.P.; *U.S. Private*, pg. 1661
PAYDAY LLC—See Hilan Ltd.; *Int'l*, pg. 3390
PAYDAY PAYROLL SERVICES; *U.S. Private*, pg. 3116
PAYDEE SDN. BHD.—See Advance Synergy Berhad; *Int'l*, pg. 157
PAYDEN & RYGEL GLOBAL LIMITED—See Payden & Rygel; *U.S. Private*, pg. 3117
PAYDEN & RYGEL; *U.S. Private*, pg. 3116
PAYDIANT, INC.—See PayPal Holdings, Inc.; *U.S. Public*, pg. 1657
PAYER COMPASS, LLC—See PCP Enterprise, L.P.; *U.S. Private*, pg. 3121
PAYER SCIENCES LLC—See Publicis Groupe S.A.; *Int'l*, pg. 6104
PAYETTE ASSOCIATES INC.; *U.S. Private*, pg. 3117
PAYETTE SHIPS INC.—See Payette Associates Inc.; *U.S. Private*, pg. 3117
PAYFACTO INC.; *Int'l*, pg. 5763
PAYFARE INC.; *Int'l*, pg. 5763
PAYFLEX HOLDINGS, INC.—See ABRY Partners, LLC; *U.S. Private*, pg. 42
PAYFLEX SYSTEMS USA, INC.—See ABRY Partners, LLC; *U.S. Private*, pg. 42
PAYGENT CO., LTD.—See DeNA Co., Ltd.; *Int'l*, pg. 2026
PAYGRO—See Hendricks Holding Company, Inc.; *U.S. Private*, pg. 1915
PAYGROUP LIMITED—See Deel, Inc.; *U.S. Private*, pg. 1189
PAYK12, LLC—See Raptor Technologies, Inc; *U.S. Private*, pg. 3356
PAYLEASE LLC—See Global Payments Inc.; *U.S. Public*, pg. 944
PAYLESS BUILDING CENTER INC.; *U.S. Private*, pg. 3117
PAYLESS CAR RENTAL CANADA INC.—See Avis Budget Group, Inc.; *U.S. Public*, pg. 249
PAYLESS CAR RENTAL, INC.—See Avis Budget Group, Inc.; *U.S. Public*, pg. 249
PAYLESS DRUG STORES INC.; *U.S. Private*, pg. 3117
PAYLESS HOLDINGS LLC; *U.S. Private*, pg. 3117
PAYLESS PARKING, LLC—See Avis Budget Group, Inc.; *U.S. Public*, pg. 249
PAYLESS SHOESOURCE DE GUATEMALA LTDA.—See Payless Holdings LLC; *U.S. Private*, pg. 3117
PAYLESS SHOESOURCE, INC.—See Payless Holdings LLC; *U.S. Private*, pg. 3117
PAYLESS SHOESOURCE WORLDWIDE, LLC—See Payless Holdings LLC; *U.S. Private*, pg. 3117
PAYLESS TIRE & EXHAUST—See Condon Oil Company, Inc.; *U.S. Private*, pg. 1012
PAYLIFE BANK GMBH—See SIX Group AG; *Int'l*, pg. 6966
PAYLIFE SERVICE GMBH—See SIX Group AG; *Int'l*, pg. 6966
PAYLINK PAYMENT PLANS, LLC—See Milestone Partners Ltd.; *U.S. Private*, pg. 2729
PAYLOCITY CORPORATION—See Paylocity Holding Corporation; *U.S. Public*, pg. 1656
PAYLOCITY HOLDING CORPORATION; *U.S. Public*, pg. 1656
PAYMENT ALLIANCE INTERNATIONAL, INC.—See Further Global Capital Management, L.P.; *U.S. Private*, pg. 1625
PAYMENTCLOUD INC.—See BharCap Partners, LLC; *U.S. Private*, pg. 549
PAYMENTECH SALEM SERVICES, LLC—See JPMorgan Chase & Co.; *U.S. Public*, pg. 1209
PAYMENTMAX PROCESSING INC.; *U.S. Private*, pg. 3117
PAYMENTONE CORPORATION; *U.S. Private*, pg. 3117
PAYMENT RESOLUTION SERVICES, LLC—See UnitedHealth Group Incorporated; *U.S. Public*, pg. 2249
PAYMENT SOFTWARE COMPANY LIMITED—See NCC Group Plc; *Int'l*, pg. 5181
PAYMENT SOLUTION AG—See Mountain Capital Management AG; *Int'l*, pg. 5057
PAYMENTSPRING, LLC—See Nelnet, Inc.; *U.S. Public*, pg. 1504
PAYMENTUS CORPORATION; *U.S. Public*, pg. 3117
PAYMENTUS HOLDINGS, INC.; *U.S. Public*, pg. 1656
PAYMERANG, LLC—See Aldrich Capital Partners, LLC; *U.S. Private*, pg. 160
PAYMETRIC INC.—See GTCR LLC; *U.S. Private*, pg. 1806
PAY MY TIME LTD; *Int'l*, pg. 5763
PAYNE & DOLAN, INC.; *U.S. Private*, pg. 3117
THE PAYNE INVESTMENT COMPANY—See Brittany Stamping, LLC; *U.S. Private*, pg. 657
PAYNE-PIKE DEVELOPMENT CO.; *U.S. Private*, pg. 3117
PAYNET. INC.—See Equifax Inc.; *U.S. Public*, pg. 786
PAYNE TRANSPORTATION L.P.—See Mullen Group Ltd.; *Int'l*, pg. 5080
PAYNEWEST INSURANCE, INC. - HELENA, CEDAR STREET—See Marsh & McLennan Companies, Inc.; *U.S. Public*, pg. 1381

PAYNEWEST INSURANCE, INC. - KALISPELL—See Marsh & McLennan Companies, Inc.; *U.S. Public*, pg. 1382
PAYNEWEST INSURANCE, INC. - MISSOULA, FRONT STREET—See Marsh & McLennan Companies, Inc.; *U.S. Public*, pg. 1382
PAYNEWEST INSURANCE, INC. - MISSOULA (PALMER STREET) CORPORATE OFFICE—See Marsh & McLennan Companies, Inc.; *U.S. Public*, pg. 1381
PAYNEWEST INSURANCE, INC.—See Marsh & McLennan Companies, Inc.; *U.S. Public*, pg. 1381
PAYNODE AB—See World Kinect Corporation; *U.S. Public*, pg. 2381
PAYNOVA AB; *Int'l*, pg. 5763
PAY-O-MATIC CHECK CASHING CORP.—See Founders Equity, Inc.; *U.S. Private*, pg. 1581
THE PAY-O-MATIC CORP.—See Founders Equity, Inc.; *U.S. Private*, pg. 1581
THE PAY-O-MATIC CORP.—See Founders Equity, Inc.; *U.S. Private*, pg. 1581
PAYONEER GLOBAL INC.; *U.S. Public*, pg. 1656
PAYONEER, INC.—See Payoneer Global Inc.; *U.S. Public*, pg. 1656
PAYOT NAVILLE DISTRIBUTION SA—See Vivendi SE; *Int'l*, pg. 8276
PAYPAL ASSET MANAGEMENT, INC.—See PayPal Holdings, Inc.; *U.S. Public*, pg. 1656
PAYPAL AUSTRALIA PTY LIMITED—See PayPal Holdings, Inc.; *U.S. Public*, pg. 1656
PAYPAL CANADA CO.—See PayPal Holdings, Inc.; *U.S. Public*, pg. 1656
PAYPAL CHARITABLE GIVING FUND—See PayPal Holdings, Inc.; *U.S. Public*, pg. 1656
PAYPAL HOLDINGS, INC.; *U.S. Public*, pg. 1656
PAYPAL, INC.—See PayPal Holdings, Inc.; *U.S. Public*, pg. 1656
PAYPAL NEDERLANDS B.V.—See PayPal Holdings, Inc.; *U.S. Public*, pg. 1656
PAYPAL POLSKA SP Z O.O.—See PayPal Holdings, Inc.; *U.S. Public*, pg. 1656
PAYPAL PTE. LTD.—See PayPal Holdings, Inc.; *U.S. Public*, pg. 1656
PAYPAL (UK) LIMITED—See PayPal Holdings, Inc.; *U.S. Public*, pg. 1656
PAYPAL U.K. LTD.—See PayPal Holdings, Inc.; *U.S. Public*, pg. 1656
PAYPLUG SAS—See Groupe BPCE; *Int'l*, pg. 3099
PAYPLUS, LLC; *U.S. Private*, pg. 3117
PAYPOINT COLLECTIONS LIMITED—See PayPoint plc; *Int'l*, pg. 5763
PAYPOINT.NET LIMITED—See PayPoint plc; *Int'l*, pg. 5764
PAYPOINT NETWORK LIMITED—See PayPoint plc; *Int'l*, pg. 5763
PAYPOINT PLC; *Int'l*, pg. 5763
PAYPOINT RETAIL SOLUTIONS LIMITED—See PayPoint plc; *Int'l*, pg. 5764
PAYPOINT SERVICES ROMANIA SRL—See PayPoint plc; *Int'l*, pg. 5764
PAYPOP CO., LTD.—See Energy Absolute Public Company Limited; *Int'l*, pg. 2422
PAYPROS LLC—See Global Payments Inc.; *U.S. Public*, pg. 944
PAYRED CARD SERVICES AG—See Metro AG; *Int'l*, pg. 4859
PAYROC LLC—See PCP Enterprise, L.P.; *U.S. Private*, pg. 3121
PAYROLL 1, INC.—See Global Payments Inc.; *U.S. Public*, pg. 944
PAYROLL MANAGEMENT, INC.; *U.S. Private*, pg. 3117
PAYROLL MAXX, LLC—See Asure Software, Inc.; *U.S. Public*, pg. 218
PAYROLL SERVICES PLUS, INC.; *U.S. Private*, pg. 3117
PAYROLL TAX FILING SERVICES, INC.—See NCR Voyix Corporation; *U.S. Public*, pg. 1502
PAYSAFE GROUP PLC—See Paysafe Limited; *Int'l*, pg. 5764
PAYSAFE LIMITED; *Int'l*, pg. 5764
PAYSAFE - MONTREAL—See Paysafe Limited; *Int'l*, pg. 5764
PAYSAUCE LIMITED; *Int'l*, pg. 5764
PAYSBUY CO., LTD.—See Omise Co. Ltd.; *Int'l*, pg. 5563
PAYSCALE, INC.—See Francisco Partners Management, LP; *U.S. Private*, pg. 1590
PAYSCAPE ADVISORS; *U.S. Private*, pg. 3117
PAYSIGN, INC.; *U.S. Public*, pg. 1657
PAYSON BRONCO, INC.—See Payson Casters, Inc.; *U.S. Private*, pg. 3117
PAYSON CASTERS, INC.; *U.S. Private*, pg. 3117
PAYSON HOSPITAL CORPORATION—See Banner Health System; *U.S. Private*, pg. 469
PAYSON NORCROSS—See Payson Casters, Inc.; *U.S. Private*, pg. 3117
PAYSON PARK THOROUGHBRED TRAINING CENTER INC.; *U.S. Private*, pg. 3117
PAYSON ROUNDUP—See The World Company; *U.S. Private*, pg. 4139
PAYSON TEXAS, INC.—See Payson Casters, Inc.; *U.S. Private*, pg. 3117

PAYSPOT, LLC—See Euronet Worldwide, Inc.; *U.S. Public*, pg. 798
PAY SYSTEMS OF AMERICA INC.—See Asure Software, Inc.; *U.S. Public*, pg. 218
PAYTABS—See EFG Holding; *Int'l*, pg. 2319
PAY TEL COMMUNICATIONS, INC.; *U.S. Private*, pg. 3116
PAYTM INSURANCE BROKING PRIVATE LIMITED—See One97 Communications Limited; *Int'l*, pg. 5575
PAYTM MONEY LIMITED—See One97 Communications Limited; *Int'l*, pg. 5575
PAYTON AMERICA INC.—See Payton Planar Magnetics Ltd.; *Int'l*, pg. 5764
PAYTON CONSTRUCTION CORP.; *U.S. Private*, pg. 3118
PAYTON INDUSTRIES LTD.; *Int'l*, pg. 5764
PAYTON PLANAR MAGNETICS LTD.; *Int'l*, pg. 5764
PAYTRONIX SYSTEMS, INC.—See Access Technology Group Limited; *Int'l*, pg. 89
PAYU PAYMENTS PRIVATE LIMITED—See Prosus N.V.; *Int'l*, pg. 6003
PAYVISION CANADA SERVICES LTD.—See ING Groep N.V.; *Int'l*, pg. 3701
PAYZER, INC.—See WEX, Inc.; *U.S. Public*, pg. 2364
PAYZONE DIRECTIONAL SERVICES; *U.S. Private*, pg. 3118
PAYZONE IRELAND LIMITED—See AIB Group plc; *Int'l*, pg. 228
PAYZONE IRELAND LIMITED—See First Data Corporation; *U.S. Private*, pg. 1517
PAYZONE UK LIMITED—See Grovepoint Capital LLP; *Int'l*, pg. 3112
PAZARDZHIK BTM AD; *Int'l*, pg. 5764
PAZ AVIATION ASSETS LTD.—See Paz Oil Company Ltd.; *Int'l*, pg. 5764
PAZ AVIATION SERVICES LTD.—See Paz Oil Company Ltd.; *Int'l*, pg. 5764
PAZ CORP S.A.; *Int'l*, pg. 5764
PAZGAS LTD.—See Paz Oil Company Ltd.; *Int'l*, pg. 5764
PAZIEN, INC.—See GTCR LLC; *U.S. Private*, pg. 1806
PAZIM—See Polska Zegluga Morska; *Int'l*, pg. 5911
PAZKAR LTD.—See Paz Oil Company Ltd.; *Int'l*, pg. 5764
PAZ LUBRICANTS & CHEMICALS LTD.—See Paz Oil Company Ltd.; *Int'l*, pg. 5764
PAZ OIL COMPANY LTD.; *Int'l*, pg. 5764
PAZOO, INC.; *U.S. Public*, pg. 1657
PAZZO CO., LTD.—See KOMATSU MATERE Co.,Ltd.; *Int'l*, pg. 4239
PBA HOLDINGS BHD.; *Int'l*, pg. 5764
PBA INFRASTRUCTURE LIMITED; *Int'l*, pg. 5765
P-BAN.COM, CORP.; *Int'l*, pg. 5681
PB ANIMAL HEALTH DE MEXICO S. DE R.L. DE C.V.—See Phibro Animal Health Corporation; *U.S. Public*, pg. 1685
PB BANCORP, INC.—See Centreville Bank; *U.S. Private*, pg. 829
PB BANKSHARES, INC.; *U.S. Public*, pg. 1657
PBBPOLISUR S.R.L.—See Dow Inc.; *U.S. Public*, pg. 685
PBBS EQUIPMENT CORPORATION; *U.S. Private*, pg. 3118
PBC HEALTH BENEFITS SOCIETY; *Int'l*, pg. 5765
PBC LIMITED—See Ghana Cocoa Board; *Int'l*, pg. 2958
PBC—See Imperial Brands PLC; *Int'l*, pg. 3633
P.B. DEVELOPMENTS LIMITED—See Pochin's Ltd.; *Int'l*, pg. 5902
PBD, INC.; *U.S. Private*, pg. 3118
PB DOMESTA SP. Z O.O.—See INPRO S.A.; *Int'l*, pg. 3717
PBE COMPANIES, LLC—See Banco Santander, S.A.; *Int'l*, pg. 827
PBE JOBBERS WAREHOUSE INC.; *U.S. Private*, pg. 3118
PBEL (PTY) LIMITED—See Lesaka Technologies, Inc.; *Int'l*, pg. 4469
PBE WAREHOUSE INC.; *U.S. Private*, pg. 3118
PBE WAREHOUSE SALES INC.; *U.S. Private*, pg. 3118
PBEX, LLC; *U.S. Private*, pg. 3118
PB EXPRESS INC.; *U.S. Private*, pg. 3118
PBEX RESOURCES, LLC—See PBEX, LLC; *U.S. Private*, pg. 3118
P&B FABRICS INC.; *U.S. Private*, pg. 3058
PB FACTORING GMBH—See Deutsche Bank Aktiengesellschaft; *Int'l*, pg. 2061
PBF ENERGY COMPANY LLC—See PBF Energy Inc.; *U.S. Public*, pg. 1657
PBF ENERGY INC.; *U.S. Public*, pg. 1657
PBF ENERGY WESTERN REGION LLC—See PBF Energy Inc.; *U.S. Public*, pg. 1657
PBF FINANCE CORPORATION—See PBF Energy Inc.; *U.S. Public*, pg. 1657
PBF GROUP B. V.—See SFC Energy AG; *Int'l*, pg. 6738
PBF HOLDING COMPANY LLC—See PBF Energy Inc.; *U.S. Public*, pg. 1657
P. B. FILMS LTD.; *Int'l*, pg. 5682
PB FINANCIAL CORPORATION; *U.S. Public*, pg. 1657
PB FINTECH LIMITED; *Int'l*, pg. 5764
PBF LOGISTICS LP—See PBF Energy Inc.; *U.S. Public*, pg. 1657
PBF POWER SRL—See SFC Energy AG; *Int'l*, pg. 6738

P.B. GAST & SONS INCORPORATED; *U.S. Private*, pg. 3060
PBG BUILDERS, INC.; *U.S. Private*, pg. 3118
PBG CONSULTING, LLC; *U.S. Private*, pg. 3118
PBG DOM SP. Z O.O.—See PBG S.A.; *Int'l*, pg. 5765
PB GELATINS GMBH—See Tessenderlo Group NV; *Int'l*, pg. 7573
PB GELATINS (PINGYANG) CO, LTD.—See Tessenderlo Group NV; *Int'l*, pg. 7573
PB GELATINS UK LTD.—See Tessenderlo Group NV; *Int'l*, pg. 7574
PB GLOBAL LTD.; *Int'l*, pg. 5764
P&B GMBH—See Industria de Diseno Textil, S.A.; *Int'l*, pg. 3667
PB GROUP LTD.; *Int'l*, pg. 5764
PBG S/A; *Int'l*, pg. 5765
PBG S.A.; *Int'l*, pg. 5765
PB HEAT, LLC—See Noritz Corporation; *Int'l*, pg. 5430
PB HOIDALE CO. INC.; *U.S. Private*, pg. 3118
PB HOLDING NV; *Int'l*, pg. 5764
P&B HOLDINGS, INC.; *U.S. Private*, pg. 3058
PBI BANK—See Peoples Bancorp Inc.; *U.S. Public*, pg. 1667
P.B.I. FRUIT JUICE COMPANY BVBA—See PepsiCo, Inc.; *U.S. Public*, pg. 1669
PBI/GORDON CORPORATION; *U.S. Private*, pg. 3118
PBI MARKET EQUIPMENT INC.; *U.S. Private*, pg. 3118
PB INDUSTRIES INC.; *U.S. Private*, pg. 3118
PB ISSUER LIMITED—See Pacific Basin Shipping Limited; *Int'l*, pg. 5685
PB&J RESTAURANTS INC.; *U.S. Private*, pg. 3118
PBJS, INC.—See Publicis Groupe S.A.; *Int'l*, pg. 6104
PBJV GROUP SDN. BHD—See Barakah Offshore Petroleum Berhad; *Int'l*, pg. 858
PB LEINER ARGENTINA S.A.—See Tessenderlo Group NV; *Int'l*, pg. 7573
PB LEINER USA—See Tessenderlo Group NV; *Int'l*, pg. 7574
PBL EXCHANGE (UK) LTD.—See Prime Bank PLC.; *Int'l*, pg. 5976
PBL FINANCE (HONG KONG) LIMITED—See Prime Bank PLC.; *Int'l*, pg. 5976
PBL MANAGEMENT PTY LIMITED—See News Corporation; *U.S. Public*, pg. 1521
PBMARES, LLP; *U.S. Private*, pg. 3118
PBM CAPITAL GROUP, LLC; *U.S. Private*, pg. 3118
PBM GRAPHICS, INC - PACKAGING DIVISION—See Chatham Asset Management, LLC; *U.S. Private*, pg. 863
PBM GRAPHICS INC.—See Chatham Asset Management, LLC; *U.S. Private*, pg. 863
PBM GRAPHICS, INC - TRIAD DIVISION—See Chatham Asset Management, LLC; *U.S. Private*, pg. 863
PBM, INC.—See IMI plc; *Int'l*, pg. 3626
PBM NUTRITIONALS, LLC—See Perrigo Company plc; *Int'l*, pg. 5813
PBM-PLUS, INC.—See Consonance Capital Partners LLC; *U.S. Private*, pg. 1023
PBM POLYTEX LIMITED; *Int'l*, pg. 5765
PBM PRODUCTS, LLC—See Perrigo Company plc; *Int'l*, pg. 5813
PBNA, LLC—See Peoples Bancorp Inc.; *U.S. Public*, pg. 1667
PBO ANIOTA S.A.; *Int'l*, pg. 5765
P&B PETROLEUM CO. INC.; *U.S. Private*, pg. 3058
PBP ORBIS SP. Z O.O.—See Accor S.A.; *Int'l*, pg. 92
PBR HOLSCHER BRANDSCHUTZ GMBH—See pbr Planungsbüro Rohling AG; *Int'l*, pg. 5765
PBR LTD.—See The Orchid Group; *Int'l*, pg. 7672
PBR PLANUNGSBURO ROHLING AG; *Int'l*, pg. 5765
PBS COALS, INC.—See Quintana Capital Group, L.P.; *U.S. Private*, pg. 3328
PBS CONSTRUCTION INC.; *U.S. Private*, pg. 3119
PBS ENGINEERING & ENVRNMNTL; *U.S. Private*, pg. 3119
PBS ENTERPRISES, INC.—See Public Broadcasting Service; *U.S. Public*, pg. 3298
PBS FINANSE S.A.; *Int'l*, pg. 5765
PBS HOLDING AG; *Int'l*, pg. 5765
PBS HOLDING, INC.; *U.S. Public*, pg. 1657
PBSR DEVELOPERS PVT. LTD.—See Patel Engineering Ltd.; *Int'l*, pg. 5755
PBT BANCSHARES, INC.; *U.S. Private*, pg. 3119
PBT ENGINEERING PTE LTD—See TEE International Limited; *Int'l*, pg. 7519
PBT ENGINEERING SDN BHD—See TEE International Limited; *Int'l*, pg. 7519
PB TRUSTEE SERVICES BERHAD—See Public Bank Berhad; *Int'l*, pg. 6094
PB TRUST (L) LTD.—See Public Bank Berhad; *Int'l*, pg. 6094
PB TUB SARL—See Thermador Groupe; *Int'l*, pg. 7707
PBU CAD-SYSTEME GMBH—See Sesa S.p.A.; *Int'l*, pg. 6729
PB VENTURE CAPITAL SDN. BHD.—See Public Bank Berhad; *Int'l*, pg. 6094
PB VESSELS HOLDING LIMITED—See Pacific Basin Shipping Limited; *Int'l*, pg. 5685

PBT BANCSHARES, INC.

PBW LLC—See Willis Towers Watson Public Limited Company; *Int'l*, pg. 8414
PBZ INVEST D.O.O.—See Intesa Sanpaolo S.p.A.; *Int'l*, pg. 3766
PBZ LEASING D.O.O.—See Intesa Sanpaolo S.p.A.; *Int'l*, pg. 3766
PCA AUTOMOBILES INDIA PRIVATE LIMITED—See Stellantis N.V.; *Int'l*, pg. 7202
PCA CORPORATION; *Int'l*, pg. 5766
PC ACOUSTIC CO., LTD.—See Nihon Parkerizing Co., Ltd.; *Int'l*, pg. 5286
PCA-ECHOLOGICS PTY LTD.—See Mueller Water Products, Inc.; *U.S. Public*, pg. 1485
PC AGE, INC.; *U.S. Private*, pg. 3119
PCA INTERNATIONAL S.A.—See Molinos Rio de la Plata S.A.; *Int'l*, pg. 5022
PCA, LLC—See Chatham Asset Management, LLC; *U.S. Private*, pg. 863
PCA MANAGEMENT; *U.S. Private*, pg. 3119
PCAMERICA, LLC—See Global Payments Inc.; *U.S. Public*, pg. 944
PC APPLEWOOD LLC—See Varia US Properties AG; *Int'l*, pg. 8132
PCAS AMERICA INC.—See Eurazeo SE; *Int'l*, pg. 2530
PCAS CHINA—See Eurazeo SE; *Int'l*, pg. 2530
PCAS FINLAND OY—See Eurazeo SE; *Int'l*, pg. 2530
PCAS GMBH—See Eurazeo SE; *Int'l*, pg. 2530
PCA SOUTHERN INDIANA CORRUGATED, LLC—See Packaging Corporation of America; *U.S. Public*, pg. 1633
PCAS SA—See Eurazeo SE; *Int'l*, pg. 2530
PCA TECHNOLOGY LIMITED; *Int'l*, pg. 5766
PCA TECHNOLOGY (M) SDN. BHD - TAMPOI PLANT—See PCA Technology Limited; *Int'l*, pg. 5766
PC AVENUE 8 MESA LLC—See Varia US Properties AG; *Int'l*, pg. 8132
PCB APPS, LLC; *U.S. Private*, pg. 3119
PCB BANCORP; *U.S. Public*, pg. 1658
P.C.B. CENTER (THAILAND) CO., LTD.—See Aspocomp Group Oyj; *Int'l*, pg. 632
PCB FINANCLAL, INC; *U.S. Private*, pg. 3119
PCB GROUP, INC.—See Amphenol Corporation; *U.S. Public*, pg. 131
PCBL LIMITED; *Int'l*, pg. 5766
PCB LOAD & TORQUE, INC.—See Amphenol Corporation; *U.S. Public*, pg. 131
PCBL (TN) LIMITED—See PCBL Limited; *Int'l*, pg. 5766
PCB PIEZOTRONICS BVBA—See Amphenol Corporation; *U.S. Public*, pg. 131
PCB PIEZOTRONICS EUROPE GMBH—See Amphenol Corporation; *U.S. Public*, pg. 131
PCB PIEZOTRONICS GMBH—See Amphenol Corporation; *U.S. Public*, pg. 132
PCB PIEZOTRONICS INC—See Amphenol Corporation; *U.S. Public*, pg. 131
PCB PIEZOTRONICS LTD—See Amphenol Corporation; *U.S. Public*, pg. 131
PCB PIEZOTRONICS S.A.—See Amphenol Corporation; *U.S. Public*, pg. 131
PCB PIEZOTRONICS SRL—See Amphenol Corporation; *U.S. Public*, pg. 131
PCB-PRECICAST BILBAO S.A.—See Bain Capital, LP; *U.S. Private*, pg. 433
PCB SA; *Int'l*, pg. 5766
PCB SYNOTECH GMBH—See Amphenol Corporation; *U.S. Public*, pg. 131
PCB TECHNOLOGIES LTD.; *Int'l*, pg. 5766
PCB TRANSPORTATION TRAVEL & TOURS SDN. BHD.—See Perak Corporation Berhad; *Int'l*, pg. 5796
PCC AEROSTRUCTURES AUBURN—See Berkshire Hathaway Inc.; *U.S. Public*, pg. 314
PCC AEROSTRUCTURES DORVAL INC.—See Berkshire Hathaway Inc.; *U.S. Public*, pg. 314
PCC AIRFOILS, LLC—See Berkshire Hathaway Inc.; *U.S. Public*, pg. 314
PCC AIRFOILS LLC—See Berkshire Hathaway Inc.; *U.S. Public*, pg. 314
PCC AIRFOILS S.A. DE C.V.—See Berkshire Hathaway Inc.; *U.S. Public*, pg. 314
P.C. CAMPANA INC.; *U.S. Private*, pg. 3060
PCC CHEMAX, INC.—See PCC SE; *Int'l*, pg. 5767
PCC CONSUMER PRODUCTS CZECHOWICE S.A.—See PCC SE; *Int'l*, pg. 5767
PCC CONSUMER PRODUCTS S.A.—See PCC SE; *Int'l*, pg. 5767
PCC DIRECT DELIVERY—See PCC Logistics; *U.S. Private*, pg. 3119
PCC DISTRIBUTION JAPAN K. K.—See Berkshire Hathaway Inc.; *U.S. Public*, pg. 315
PCC ENERGETYKA BLACHOWNIA SP. Z O.O.—See PCC SE; *Int'l*, pg. 5767
PCC ENERGIA EOOD—See PCC SE; *Int'l*, pg. 5767
PCC ENERGY GROUP—See Berkshire Hathaway Inc.; *U.S. Public*, pg. 314
PCC ENERGY TRADING GMBH—See PCC SE; *Int'l*, pg. 5767
PCC EXOL KIMYA SAN.VE TIC. LTD.—See PCC SE; *Int'l*, pg. 5767
PCC EXOL SA; *Int'l*, pg. 5766

PCC HYDRO DOOEL SKOPJE—See PCC SE; *Int'l*, pg. 5767
PCC INSULATIONS GMBH—See PCC SE; *Int'l*, pg. 5767
PCC INTERMODAL GMBH—See PCC SE; *Int'l*, pg. 5767
PCC INTERMODAL S.A; *Int'l*, pg. 5766
PCC INTERMODAL S.A.—See PCC SE; *Int'l*, pg. 5767
PCC LOGISTICS; *U.S. Private*, pg. 3119
PCC LOGISTICS—See PCC Logistics; *U.S. Private*, pg. 3119
PCC LOGISTICS—See PCC Logistics; *U.S. Private*, pg. 3119
PCC LOGISTICS—See PCC Logistics; *U.S. Private*, pg. 3119
PCC LOGISTICS—See PCC Logistics; *U.S. Private*, pg. 3119
PCC LOGISTICS - WATSON CENTER RD. FACILITY—See PCC Logistics; *U.S. Private*, pg. 3119
PCC MORAVA - CHEM S.R.O.—See PCC SE; *Int'l*, pg. 5767
PC CONNECTION, INC.; *U.S. Public*, pg. 1658
PC CONNECTION SALES CORPORATION—See PC Connection, Inc.; *U.S. Public*, pg. 1658
PC CONSTRUCTION COMPANY; *U.S. Private*, pg. 3119
P&C CONSTRUCTION INC.; *U.S. Private*, pg. 3058
PCC ORGANIC OILS GHANA LTD.—See PCC SE; *Int'l*, pg. 5767
PC CORP; *Int'l*, pg. 5765
PCC PRODEX SP. Z O.O.—See PCC SE; *Int'l*, pg. 5767
PCC ROKITA SA—See PCC SE; *Int'l*, pg. 5767
PCC ROLLMET, INC.—See Berkshire Hathaway Inc.; *U.S. Public*, pg. 314
PCC SEAVIEW RESIDENCES EHF.—See PCC SE; *Int'l*, pg. 5767
PCC SE; *Int'l*, pg. 5766
PCCS GARMENTS LIMITED—See PCCS Group Berhad; *Int'l*, pg. 5767
PCCS GARMENTS (SUZHOU) LTD.—See PCCS Group Berhad; *Int'l*, pg. 5767
PCCS GROUP BERHAD; *Int'l*, pg. 5767
PCCS (HONG KONG) LIMITED—See PCCS Group Berhad; *Int'l*, pg. 5767
PCC SILICIUM S.A.—See PCC SE; *Int'l*, pg. 5767
PCC SLOVAKIA S.R.O.—See PCC SE; *Int'l*, pg. 5767
PCC SPECIALTIES GMBH—See PCC SE; *Int'l*, pg. 5767
PCC STRUCTURALS (FRANCE)—See Berkshire Hathaway Inc.; *U.S. Public*, pg. 314
PCC STRUCTURALS, INC.—See Berkshire Hathaway Inc.; *U.S. Public*, pg. 314
PCC SYSTEMS LLC—See Professional Control Corporation; *U.S. Private*, pg. 3274
PCC TECHNOLOGY GROUP, LLC—See Government Contracting Resources, Inc.; *U.S. Private*, pg. 1746
PCC THERM SP. Z O.O.—See PCC SE; *Int'l*, pg. 5767
PCC TRANSLOAD SYSTEM—See PCC Logistics; *U.S. Private*, pg. 3120
PCCW (BEIJING) LTD.—See Pacific Century Group Holdings Limited; *Int'l*, pg. 5686
PCCW CASCADE TECHNOLOGY (GUANGZHOU) LIMITED—See Pacific Century Group Holdings Limited; *Int'l*, pg. 5686
PCCW GLOBAL B.V.—See Pacific Century Group Holdings Limited; *Int'l*, pg. 5687
PCCW GLOBAL (HELLAS) TELECOMMUNICATIONS SERVICES S.A.—See Pacific Century Group Holdings Limited; *Int'l*, pg. 5686
PCCW GLOBAL, INC.—See Pacific Century Group Holdings Limited; *Int'l*, pg. 5687
PCCW GLOBAL (JAPAN) K.K.—See Pacific Century Group Holdings Limited; *Int'l*, pg. 5686
PCCW GLOBAL KOREA LIMITED—See Pacific Century Group Holdings Limited; *Int'l*, pg. 5687
PCCW GLOBAL LIMITED—See Pacific Century Group Holdings Limited; *Int'l*, pg. 5687
PCCW GLOBAL (UK) LTD.—See Pacific Century Group Holdings Limited; *Int'l*, pg. 5686
PCCW LIMITED—See Pacific Century Group Holdings Limited; *Int'l*, pg. 5686
PCCW LIMITED VENTURES—See Pacific Century Group Holdings Limited; *Int'l*, pg. 5687
PCCW SOLUTIONS LIMITED—See Pacific Century Group Holdings Limited; *Int'l*, pg. 5687
PCCW SOLUTIONS (XI'AN) LIMITED—See Pacific Century Group Holdings Limited; *Int'l*, pg. 5687
PCCW TECHNOLOGY (BEIJING) LIMITED—See Pacific Century Group Holdings Limited; *Int'l*, pg. 5687
PCCW TELESERVICES—See Pacific Century Group Holdings Limited; *Int'l*, pg. 5687
PCD ENGINEERING SERVICES, INC.—See Bowman Consulting Group Ltd.; *U.S. Public*, pg. 376
PC DEPOT CORPORATION; *Int'l*, pg. 5765
PC DEVONSHIRE GARDENS LLC—See Varia US Properties AG; *Int'l*, pg. 8132
PC DEVONSHIRE PLACE LLC—See Varia US Properties AG; *Int'l*, pg. 8132
PC DIESEL PTY. LTD.—See Engenco Limited; *Int'l*, pg. 2427
PC DIRECT, INC.; *Int'l*, pg. 5766
P&C DISTRIBUTORS INC.; *U.S. Private*, pg. 3058

CORPORATE AFFILIATIONS

PCD REALTY LLC—See PulteGroup, Inc.; *U.S. Public*, pg. 1737
PCD STORES (GROUP) LIMITED; *Int'l*, pg. 5767
PCE CONSTRUCTORS, INC.; *U.S. Private*, pg. 3120
PCE, INC.; *U.S. Private*, pg. 3120
PC&E INC.—See Emerson Electric Co.; *U.S. Public*, pg. 750
PC ELECTRIC GMBH—See Berndorf AG; *Int'l*, pg. 987
PCF ASSET FINANCE LIMITED—See PCF Group plc; *Int'l*, pg. 5767
PCF EQUIPMENT LEASING LIMITED—See PCF Group plc; *Int'l*, pg. 5768
PCF FRONTEO INC.—See Fronteo, Inc.; *Int'l*, pg. 2794
PCF GROUP LIMITED—See PCF Group plc; *Int'l*, pg. 5768
PCF GROUP PLC; *Int'l*, pg. 5767
PCF GROUP SA; *Int'l*, pg. 5768
PCF INSURANCE SERVICES OF THE WEST, LLC; *U.S. Private*, pg. 3120
PCF LEASING LIMITED—See PCF Group plc; *Int'l*, pg. 5768
PCG AGENCIES, INC.—See Berkshire Hathaway Inc.; *U.S. Public*, pg. 313
PCGCAMPBELL; *U.S. Private*, pg. 3120
P&C GENERAL CONTRACTING LTD.; *Int'l*, pg. 5681
PCG PARENT CORP.—See Arrow Electronics, Inc.; *U.S. Public*, pg. 199
P&C GROUP, INC.; *U.S. Private*, pg. 3058
PC GROUP, INC.; *U.S. Private*, pg. 3119
PCG TRADING, LLC—See Arrow Electronics, Inc.; *U.S. Public*, pg. 199
PC GUARD S.A.; *Int'l*, pg. 5766
P C HENDERSON (IRELAND) LIMITED—See ASSA ABLOY AB; *Int'l*, pg. 640
P.C. HENDERSON (IRELAND) LTD.—See ASSA ABLOY AB; *Int'l*, pg. 635
P C HENDERSON LTD.—See ASSA ABLOY AB; *Int'l*, pg. 635
PCH GROUP PTY LTD.—See Altrad Investment Authority SAS; *Int'l*, pg. 398
PCH INNOVATION HUB-SHENZHEN—See PCH International Ltd.; *Int'l*, pg. 5768
PCH INTEGRATED FACILITY MANAGEMENT & SERVICES B.V.—See Koninklijke VolkerWessels N.V.; *Int'l*, pg. 4272
PCH INTERNATIONAL LTD. - SEOUL—See PCH International Ltd.; *Int'l*, pg. 5768
PCH INTERNATIONAL LTD.; *Int'l*, pg. 5768
PCH INTERNATIONAL LTD.—See PCH International Ltd.; *Int'l*, pg. 5768
PCH INTERNATIONAL LTD.—See PCH International Ltd.; *Int'l*, pg. 5768
PCH METALS S.A.S.—See Callista Private Equity GmbH & Co. KG; *Int'l*, pg. 1265
PCHOME BIBIAN INC.—See PChome Online, Inc.; *Int'l*, pg. 5768
PCHOME ONLINE, INC.; *Int'l*, pg. 5768
PCI AIOS CO., LTD.—See Restar Holdings Corporation; *Int'l*, pg. 6303
PCI ARDMAC—See Performance Contracting Group; *U.S. Private*, pg. 3148
PCI AUGSBURG GMBH—See BASF SE; *Int'l*, pg. 875
PCI BAUPRODUKTE AG—See BASF SE; *Int'l*, pg. 884
PCI BIOTECH HOLDING ASA; *Int'l*, pg. 5768
PCIB SECURITIES, INC.—See BDO Unibank, Inc.; *Int'l*, pg. 930
PCI GAMING AUTHORITY; *U.S. Private*, pg. 3120
PCI GEOMATICS GROUP INC; *Int'l*, pg. 5768
PCI GEOMATICS USA INC.—See Pci Geomatics Group Inc; *Int'l*, pg. 5768
PCI HOLDINGS INC.—See Restar Holdings Corporation; *Int'l*, pg. 6303
PCI HONG KONG LIMITED—See PCI Technology Group Co., Ltd; *Int'l*, pg. 5768
PCI, INC.—See Lewis & Clark Capital LLC; *U.S. Private*, pg. 2437
PCI INC.—See Advanced Horizons Inc.; *U.S. Private*, pg. 90
PCI INDUSTRIES INC.; *U.S. Private*, pg. 3120
PCI INSUL-ENERGY INC.—See Performance Contracting Group; *U.S. Private*, pg. 3148
PCI-JIANXUN XINJIANG TECHNOLOGY CO., LTD.—See PCI Technology Group Co., Ltd; *Int'l*, pg. 5768
PCI LIMITED—See Platinum Equity, LLC; *U.S. Private*, pg. 3206
PCI LLC; *U.S. Private*, pg. 3120
PCI MEDIA, INC.; *U.S. Private*, pg. 3120
PCI MILLWORK; *U.S. Private*, pg. 3120
PCI-PAL LIMITED—See PCI-PAL PLC; *Int'l*, pg. 5768
PCI-PAL PLC; *Int'l*, pg. 5768
PCI, PAPER CONVERSION INC.—See Matt Industries Inc.; *U.S. Public*, pg. 2613
PCI PEST CONTROL PRIVATE LIMITED—See Rentokil Initial plc; *Int'l*, pg. 6287
PCI PHARMA SERVICES - ROCKFORD—See Kohlberg & Company, LLC; *U.S. Private*, pg. 2339
PCI PHARMA SERVICES—See Kohlberg & Company, LLC; *U.S. Private*, pg. 2339

COMPANY NAME INDEX

PCI PHARMA SERVICES—See Kohlberg & Company, LLC; *U.S. Private*, pg. 2339
PCI PROMATEC—See Performance Contracting Group; *U.S. Private*, pg. 3148
PCI ROADS; *U.S. Private*, pg. 3120
PCI SERVICE SUPPORT TECHNOLOGY CO., LTD.—See PCI Technology Group Co., Ltd; *Int'l*, pg. 5768
PCI-SHANGHAI ELECTRONIC COMPANY LTD.—See Platinum Equity, LLC; *U.S. Private*, pg. 3206
PCI SKANSKA INC.—See Salas O'Brien Engineers, Inc.; *U.S. Private*, pg. 3530
PCI STRATEGIC MANAGEMENT, LLC; *U.S. Private*, pg. 3120
PCI-SUNTEK PAYMENT TECHNOLOGY CO., LTD.—See PCI Technology Group Co., Ltd; *Int'l*, pg. 5768
PCI TECHNOLOGY GROUP CO., LTD; *Int'l*, pg. 5768
PCI TECHNOLOGY&SERVICE CO., LTD.—See PCI Technology Group Co., Ltd; *Int'l*, pg. 5768
PC JEWELLER LIMITED; *Int'l*, pg. 5766
PCL CIVIL CONSTRUCTORS, INC.-SE—See PCL Employees Holdings Ltd.; *Int'l*, pg. 5769
PCL CIVIL CONSTRUCTORS, INC.; *U.S. Private*, pg. 3120
PCL CIVIL CONSTRUCTORS, INC.-SW—See PCL Employees Holdings Ltd.; *Int'l*, pg. 5769
PCL CONSTRUCTION ENTERPRISES, INC.—See PCL Employees Holdings Ltd.; *Int'l*, pg. 5769
PCL CONSTRUCTION, INC.—See PCL Employees Holdings Ltd.; *Int'l*, pg. 5769
PCL CONSTRUCTION MANAGEMENT INC.-CALGARY—See PCL Employees Holdings Ltd.; *Int'l*, pg. 5769
PCL CONSTRUCTION MANAGEMENT INC.-SASKATOON—See PCL Employees Holdings Ltd.; *Int'l*, pg. 5769
PCL CONSTRUCTION RESOURCES INC.—See PCL Employees Holdings Ltd.; *Int'l*, pg. 5769
PCL CONSTRUCTION SERVICES, INC.—See PCL Employees Holdings Ltd.; *Int'l*, pg. 5769
PCL CONSTRUCTORS CANADA INC.-ATLANTIC CANADA—See PCL Employees Holdings Ltd.; *Int'l*, pg. 5769
PCL CONSTRUCTORS CANADA INC.-OTTAWA—See PCL Employees Holdings Ltd.; *Int'l*, pg. 5769
PCL CONSTRUCTORS CANADA INC.-TORONTO—See PCL Employees Holdings Ltd.; *Int'l*, pg. 5769
PCL CONSTRUCTORS CANADA INC.-WINNIPEG—See PCL Employees Holdings Ltd.; *Int'l*, pg. 5769
PCL CONSTRUCTORS INC.—See PCL Employees Holdings Ltd.; *Int'l*, pg. 5769
PCL CONSTRUCTORS NORTHERN INC.—See PCL Employees Holdings Ltd.; *Int'l*, pg. 5769
PCL CONSTRUCTORS PACIFIC RIM PTY LTD.—See PCL Employees Holdings Ltd.; *Int'l*, pg. 5769
PCL CONSTRUCTORS WESTCOAST INC.—See PCL Employees Holdings Ltd.; *Int'l*, pg. 5769
PCL CONTAINER SERVICES LIMITED—See Eng Kong Holdings Pte Ltd.; *Int'l*, pg. 2426
PCL EMPLOYEES HOLDINGS LTD.; *Int'l*, pg. 5769
PCL ENERGY INC.—See PCL Employees Holdings Ltd.; *Int'l*, pg. 5769
PCL FIXTURES, INC.; *U.S. Private*, pg. 3120
PCL INC; *Int'l*, pg. 5769
PCL INDUSTRIAL CONSTRUCTORS INC.—See PCL Employees Holdings Ltd.; *Int'l*, pg. 5769
PCL INDUSTRIAL MANAGEMENT INC.—See PCL Employees Holdings Ltd.; *Int'l*, pg. 5769
PCL INDUSTRIAL SERVICES, INC.—See PCL Employees Holdings Ltd.; *Int'l*, pg. 5769
PCL INTRACON POWER INC.—See PCL Employees Holdings Ltd.; *Int'l*, pg. 5769
PCL JAPAN, INC.—See BML, Inc.; *Int'l*, pg. 1076
PCL (PTE) LTD—See Eng Kong Holdings Pte Ltd.; *Int'l*, pg. 2426
PCL SHIPPING INC.—See Kuok (Singapore) Limited; *Int'l*, pg. 4334
PCL SHIPPING PRIVATE LIMITED—See Kuok (Singapore) Limited; *Int'l*, pg. 4334
PCL (SHIPPING) PTE. LTD.—See Kuok (Singapore) Limited; *Int'l*, pg. 4334
PCL (SUZHOU) CO., LTD.—See PCL Technologies Trading, Inc.; *Int'l*, pg. 5769
PCL TECHNOLOGIES (TAIWAN) CO., LTD.—See PCL Technologies Trading, Inc.; *Int'l*, pg. 5769
PCL TECHNOLOGIES TRADING, INC.; *Int'l*, pg. 5769
PC MAGAZINE—See Ziff Davis, Inc.; *U.S. Public*, pg. 2404
PC MALL CANADA, INC.—See Insight Enterprises, Inc.; *U.S. Public*, pg. 1130
PC MALL GOV, INC.—See Insight Enterprises, Inc.; *U.S. Public*, pg. 1130
PC MALL SERVICES, INC.—See Insight Enterprises, Inc.; *U.S. Public*, pg. 1130
PCM DEUTSCHLAND GMBH—See Gevelot S.A.; *Int'l*, pg. 2954
PCME LTD.—See The Carlyle Group Inc.; *U.S. Public*, pg. 2046
PCM EUROPE S.A.S.—See Gevelot S.A.; *Int'l*, pg. 2954
PCM FLOW TECHNOLOGY INC—See Gevelot S.A.; *Int'l*, pg. 2954

PCM FUND, INC.; *U.S. Public*, pg. 1658
PCMG INC.—See Insight Enterprises, Inc.; *U.S. Public*, pg. 1130
PCM GROUP ITALIA SRL—See Gevelot S.A.; *Int'l*, pg. 2954
PCM GROUP UK LTD—See Gevelot S.A.; *Int'l*, pg. 2954
PCM, INC.—See Insight Enterprises, Inc.; *U.S. Public*, pg. 1130
PCM-LOGISTICS, LLC—See Insight Enterprises, Inc.; *U.S. Public*, pg. 1130
PCM MANUFACTURING FRANCE S.A.S.—See Gevelot S.A.; *Int'l*, pg. 2954
PCM POMEROY CONSTRUCTION & MAINTENANCE LTD.; *Int'l*, pg. 5769
PCM POMPES—See Gevelot S.A.; *Int'l*, pg. 2954
PCM PROCESSING (THAILAND) LTD.—See Hanwa Co., Ltd.; *Int'l*, pg. 3263
PCM PROPERTIES LLC—See Invesco Ltd.; *U.S. Public*, pg. 1163
PCM PUMPS LTD.—See Gevelot S.A.; *Int'l*, pg. 2954
PCM S.A.—See Gevelot S.A.; *Int'l*, pg. 2954
PCM SERVICES INC.; *U.S. Private*, pg. 3120
PCM TECHNOLOGIES S.A.S.—See Gevelot S.A.; *Int'l*, pg. 2954
PCM TECHNOLOGY SOLUTIONS UK, LTD.—See Insight Enterprises, Inc.; *U.S. Public*, pg. 1130
PCM TRADING (SHANGHAI) CO. LTD—See Gevelot S.A.; *Int'l*, pg. 2954
PCM TRANSPORT AND INDUSTRIAL SUPPLIES LIMITED—See B. Grimm Group; *Int'l*, pg. 788
PCM USA INC.—See Gevelot S.A.; *Int'l*, pg. 2954
PC/NAMETAG, INC.—See CCL Industries Inc.; *Int'l*, pg. 1367
PCNET INC.; *U.S. Private*, pg. 3120
PCN NETWORK; *U.S. Private*, pg. 3120
PCO ACQUISITIONS, INC.—See Rollins, Inc.; *U.S. Public*, pg. 1809
PCO AG; *Int'l*, pg. 5769
PCO INCORPORATED; *U.S. Private*, pg. 3121
PCORE ELECTRIC COMPANY, INC.—See Hubbell Incorporated; *U.S. Public*, pg. 1067
PCO-TECH INC.—See PCO AG; *Int'l*, pg. 5769
PCO TRADING LTD—See Harbour Energy plc; *Int'l*, pg. 3271
PC PARKWAY SQUARE LLC—See Varia US Properties AG; *Int'l*, pg. 8132
PC PARTNER GROUP LIMITED; *Int'l*, pg. 5766
PC PARTS, INC.—See GreenLoop IT, Inc.; *U.S. Private*, pg. 1779
PCP. A/S—See Maj Invest Holding A/S; *Int'l*, pg. 4653
PCPC DIRECT, LTD.; *U.S. Private*, pg. 3121
PCP. DANMARK A/S—See Lagercrantz Group AB; *Int'l*, pg. 4394
PCP ENTERPRISE, L.P.; *U.S. Private*, pg. 3121
PCP NEDERLAND B.V.—See Lagercrantz Group AB; *Int'l*, pg. 4394
PCP. NORGE AS—See Lagercrantz Group AB; *Int'l*, pg. 4394
PC PRODUCTS & SERVICES INC—See UCA Group Component Specialty Inc.; *U.S. Private*, pg. 4273
PCP. SVERIGE AB—See Lagercrantz Group AB; *Int'l*, pg. 4394
PCQUOTE.COM, INC.—See Money.net, Inc.; *U.S. Private*, pg. 2770
PC QUOTE (M) SDN BHD—See Phillip Capital Pte. Ltd.; *Int'l*, pg. 5846
PCRC CORP.; *U.S. Private*, pg. 3121
P.C. RICHARD & SON LONG ISLAND CORP.—See P.C. Richard & Son; *U.S. Private*, pg. 3060
P.C. RICHARD & SON; *U.S. Private*, pg. 3060
PC ROLLING HILLS LOUISVILLE LLC—See Varia US Properties AG; *Int'l*, pg. 8132
PCS ADMINISTRATION (USA), INC.—See Nutrien Ltd.; *Int'l*, pg. 5493
PCSB BANK—See Brookline Bancorp, Inc.; *U.S. Public*, pg. 396
PCSB FINANCIAL CORPORATION—See Brookline Bancorp, Inc.; *U.S. Public*, pg. 396
PC SCALE, INC.—See Advanced Manufacturing Control Systems Ltd.; *Int'l*, pg. 160
P.C.S. COMPANY—See MISUMI Group Inc.; *Int'l*, pg. 4922
PCS DEVELOPMENT CORPORATION—See Public Communications Services, Inc.; *U.S. Private*, pg. 3298
P.C.S. DIE CASTING CO., LTD.—See P.C.S. Machine Group Holding Public Company Limited; *Int'l*, pg. 5682
PCS EDVENTURES!.COM, INC.; *U.S. Public*, pg. 1658
PCS FERGUSON CANADA INC.—See Dover Corporation; *U.S. Public*, pg. 682
P.C.S. FORGING CO., LTD.—See P.C.S. Machine Group Holding Public Company Limited; *Int'l*, pg. 5682
PCS HOLDING AG; *Int'l*, pg. 5769
P.C.S. MACHINE GROUP HOLDING PUBLIC COMPANY LIMITED; *Int'l*, pg. 5682
PCS NITROGEN FERTILIZER, L.P.—See Nutrien Ltd.; *Int'l*, pg. 5493
PCS NITROGEN FERTILIZER OPERATIONS, INC.—See Nutrien Ltd.; *Int'l*, pg. 5493
PCS NITROGEN, INC.—See Nutrien Ltd.; *Int'l*, pg. 5493

PDC FACILITIES INC.

PCS NITROGEN OHIO, L.P.—See Nutrien Ltd.; *Int'l*, pg. 5493
PCS NITROGEN TRINIDAD CORPORATION—See Nutrien Ltd.; *Int'l*, pg. 5493
PCS NITROGEN TRINIDAD LIMITED—See Nutrien Ltd.; *Int'l*, pg. 5493
PC SPECIALISTS, INC.—See Converge Technology Solutions Corp.; *Int'l*, pg. 1787
PCS PHOSPHATE COMPANY, INC.—See Nutrien Ltd.; *Int'l*, pg. 5494
PC SPLASH WATER PUBLIC COMPANY LTD.; *Int'l*, pg. 5766
PCS PROFESSIONAL CLINICAL SOFTWARE GMBH—See GPI S.p.A.; *Int'l*, pg. 3046
PCS RETIREMENT, LLC; *U.S. Private*, pg. 3121
PCS SALES (USA), INC.—See Nutrien Ltd.; *Int'l*, pg. 5494
PC&S TECHNOLOGIES GMBH—See Berndorf AG; *Int'l*, pg. 987
PCS TECHNOLOGY LIMITED; *Int'l*, pg. 5770
PC SYNERGY, INC.—See A.P. Moller-Maersk A/S; *Int'l*, pg. 28
PC SYSTEMS S.A.; *Int'l*, pg. 5766
PC TALLY SQUARE LLC—See Varia US Properties AG; *Int'l*, pg. 8132
PCT CO., LTD.—See Bain Capital, LP; *U.S. Private*, pg. 435
PC-TECH S.A.—See Klockner & Co. SE; *Int'l*, pg. 4203
PCTEL EUROPE AB—See Amphenol Corporation; *U.S. Public*, pg. 132
PCTEL, INC.—See Amphenol Corporation; *U.S. Public*, pg. 132
PCTEL RF SOLUTIONS INC.—See Amphenol Corporation; *U.S. Public*, pg. 132
PCTEL (TIANJIN) ELECTRONICS COMPANY LTD.—See Amphenol Corporation; *U.S. Public*, pg. 132
PCTEST ENGINEERING LABORATORY, INC.—See Temasek Holdings (Private) Limited; *Int'l*, pg. 7547
PCT-GW CARBIDE TOOLS USA, INC—See PLANSEE Holding AG; *Int'l*, pg. 5890
PC THE RIDGE ON SPRING VALLEY LLC—See Varia US Properties AG; *Int'l*, pg. 8132
PCT, LLC—See Resonac Holdings Corporation; *Int'l*, pg. 6299
PCT LTD; *U.S. Public*, pg. 1658
PCTV SYSTEMS—See HAUPPAUGE DIGITAL, INC.; *U.S. Public*, pg. 988
PCUBED AUSTRALIA PTY LTD—See Alten S.A.; *Int'l*, pg. 390
PCU, INC.—See ITT Inc.; *U.S. Public*, pg. 1178
PC-WARE (BEIJING) LTD.—See Raiffeisen Bank International AG; *Int'l*, pg. 6184
PC-WARE (BEIJING) LTD.—See Raiffeisen-Holding Niederosterreich-Wien reg. Gen.m.b.H.; *Int'l*, pg. 6186
PC WAREHOUSE INVESTMENT INC.; *U.S. Private*, pg. 3119
PC-WARE INFORMATION TECHNOLOGIES (PTY) LTD.—See Raiffeisen Bank International AG; *Int'l*, pg. 6184
PC-WARE INFORMATION TECHNOLOGIES (PTY) LTD.—See Raiffeisen-Holding Niederosterreich-Wien reg. Gen.m.b.H.; *Int'l*, pg. 6186
PC-WARE OOO—See Raiffeisen Bank International AG; *Int'l*, pg. 6184
PC-WARE OOO—See Raiffeisen-Holding Niederosterreich-Wien reg. Gen.m.b.H.; *Int'l*, pg. 6186
PC WHOLESALE CANADA—See TD Synnex Corp; *U.S. Public*, pg. 1984
PC WHOLESALE LTD.; *U.S. Private*, pg. 3119
PCX AEROSTRUCTURES, LLC—See Greenbriar Equity Group, L.P.; *U.S. Private*, pg. 1776
PCX AEROSYSTEMS - MANCHESTER LLC—See Greenbriar Equity Group, L.P.; *U.S. Private*, pg. 1776
PCX CORP.—See Hubbell Incorporated; *U.S. Public*, pg. 1067
PC ZONA VILLAGETUCSON LLC—See Varia US Properties AG; *Int'l*, pg. 8133
PC ZONE COMPUTER TRADING (M) SDN. BHD.—See Harvest Miracle Capital Berhad; *Int'l*, pg. 3281
P & D BUILDERS, LTD.; *U.S. Private*, pg. 3058
PDC BIOLOGICAL HEALTH GROUP CORPORATION; *Int'l*, pg. 5770
PDC BRAZELETES Y PRODUCTOS S. DE R.L. DE C.V.—See Brady Corporation; *U.S. Public*, pg. 379
PDC CONSULTANTS PTY. LTD.; *Int'l*, pg. 5770
PDC DRILLING PTY. LTD.—See Dynamic Group Holdings Limited; *Int'l*, pg. 2240
PDC ENERGY, INC.—See Chevron Corporation; *U.S. Public*, pg. 487
PDC ENGINEERING, INC.—See RESPEC Inc.; *U.S. Private*, pg. 3407
PDC EUROPE SPRL—See Brady Corporation; *U.S. Public*, pg. 379
PDC FACILITIES INC.; *U.S. Private*, pg. 3121
PDC INC.—See Pola Orbis Holdings Inc.; *Int'l*, pg. 5905
P.D.C. LABORATORIES INC—See Peoria Disposal Company/Area Disposal Service, Inc.; *U.S. Private*, pg. 3143
PDC LOGIC, LLC—See Intervale Capital, LLC; *U.S. Private*, pg. 2127

PDC FACILITIES INC.

PDC LOGISTICS—See Product Development Corporation; *U.S. Private*, pg. 3273
P.D. (CONTRACTORS) LIMITED—See Shui On Company Limited; *Int'l*, pg. 6869
P.D.C. TECHNICAL SERVICES INC.—See Peoria Disposal Company/Area Disposal Service, Inc.; *U.S. Private*, pg. 3143
PD DEVELOPMENT SP. Z O. O.—See Polnord S.A.; *Int'l*, pg. 5911
PDD HOLDINGS INC.; *Int'l*, pg. 5770
PD ENERGY GMBH—See Stadtwerke Hannover AG; *Int'l*, pg. 7161
PD ENERGY INTERNATIONAL CORPORATION—See Prysmian S.p.A.; *Int'l*, pg. 6011
PD EROZIJA A.D.; *Int'l*, pg. 5770
PDF SOLUTIONS GMBH—See PDF Solutions, Inc.; *U.S. Public*, pg. 1658
PDF SOLUTIONS, INC.; *U.S. Public*, pg. 1658
PDF SOLUTIONS KK—See PDF Solutions, Inc.; *U.S. Public*, pg. 1658
PDG BARAO GERALDO—See PDG Realty S.A. Empreendimentos e Participacoes; *Int'l*, pg. 5770
PDG REALTY S.A. EMPREENDIMENTOS E PARTICIPACOES; *Int'l*, pg. 5770
PDH MUSIC A/S—See Live Nation Entertainment, Inc.; *U.S. Public*, pg. 1330
PD HOLDINGS, LLC—See Edgewater Capital Partners, L.P.; *U.S. Private*, pg. 1335
PDI COMMUNICATION SYSTEMS INC.; *U.S. Private*, pg. 3121
PDI GRAPHICA—See Phipps Dickson Integria Inc.; *Int'l*, pg. 5848
PDI GROUP INC.; *U.S. Private*, pg. 3122
PDK REGENCY HOME FASHIONS INC.; *U.S. Private*, pg. 3122
PDL BIOPHARMA INC.; *U.S. Private*, pg. 3122
PDL COMMUNITY BANCORP; *U.S. Public*, pg. 1658
PD LOGISTICS LLP—See Kazakhstan Kagazy JSC; *Int'l*, pg. 4102
PD LOGISTICS—See Brookfield Infrastructure Partners L.P.; *Int'l*, pg. 1190
PDM COMPANY INC.; *U.S. Private*, pg. 3122
PD MEXICANA, S. DE R.L. DE C.V.—See Weatherford International plc; *U.S. Public*, pg. 2339
PDM INTERNATIONAL (BEIJING) LIMITED—See Jones Lang LaSalle Incorporated; *U.S. Public*, pg. 1205
PDM INTERNATIONAL (CHENGDU) LIMITED—See Jones Lang LaSalle Incorporated; *U.S. Public*, pg. 1205
PDM INTERNATIONAL CHINA LIMITED—See Jones Lang LaSalle Incorporated; *U.S. Public*, pg. 1205
PDM INTERNATIONAL LIMITED—See Jones Lang LaSalle Incorporated; *U.S. Public*, pg. 1205
PDM LTD.—See Compagnie de Saint-Gobain SA; *Int'l*, pg. 1733
PDM PRECAST, INC.; *U.S. Private*, pg. 3122
PDMS LTD.; *Int'l*, pg. 5770
PDM STEEL SERVICE CENTER-FRESNO—See Reliance Steel & Aluminum Co.; *U.S. Public*, pg. 1781
PDM STEEL SERVICE CENTER-SANTA CLARA—See Reliance Steel & Aluminum Co.; *U.S. Public*, pg. 1781
PDM STEEL SERVICE CENTERS, INC.—See Reliance Steel & Aluminum Co.; *U.S. Public*, pg. 1781
PDM STEEL SERVICE CENTER-SPANISH FORK—See Reliance Steel & Aluminum Co.; *U.S. Public*, pg. 1781
PDM STEEL SERVICE CENTER-SPARKS—See Reliance Steel & Aluminum Co.; *U.S. Public*, pg. 1781
PDM - WOODLAND—See Reliance Steel & Aluminum Co.; *U.S. Public*, pg. 1781
PD OMOLJICA AD; *Int'l*, pg. 5770
PDP GROUP, INCORPORATED—See Stone Point Capital LLC; *U.S. Private*, pg. 3821
PDP HOLDINGS, INC.—See Stone Point Capital LLC; *U.S. Private*, pg. 3821
PD PORT SERVICES LTD.—See Brookfield Infrastructure Partners L.P.; *Int'l*, pg. 1190
PD PORTS GROUP LIMITED—See Brookfield Infrastructure Partners L.P.; *Int'l*, pg. 1190
PD PORTS LTD.—See Brookfield Infrastructure Partners L.P.; *Int'l*, pg. 1190
PDP WINE CORPORATION—See Sajodongaone Co., Ltd.; *Int'l*, pg. 6486
PDQ FOOD STORES, INC.; *U.S. Private*, pg. 3122
PDQ MANUFACTURING, INC.—See Dover Corporation; *U.S. Public*, pg. 679
PDQ PRINT CENTER, INC.; *U.S. Private*, pg. 3122
PDQ TEMPORARIES INCORPORATED; *U.S. Private*, pg. 3122
PDR CERTIFIED PUBLIC ACCOUNTANTS; *U.S. Private*, pg. 3122
PD-RX PHARMACEUTICALS, INC.; *U.S. Public*, pg. 1658
PDS BIOTECHNOLOGY CORPORATION.; *U.S. Public*, pg. 1658
PDS ENTWICKLUNGS- UND SERVICE GMBH—See NORD Holding Unternehmensbeteiligungsgesellschaft mbH; *Int'l*, pg. 5416
PDS GAMING CORPORATION—See Northlight Financial LLC; *U.S. Private*, pg. 2956
PDSI B.V.—See Avnet, Inc.; *U.S. Public*, pg. 253
PDSI SINGAPORE PTE. LTD.—See Avnet, Inc.; *U.S. Public*, pg. 253
PDS LIMITED; *Int'l*, pg. 5770
PDS SERVICES, LLC; *U.S. Private*, pg. 3122
PDS TECH, INC.—See Adecco Group AG; *Int'l*, pg. 140
PDS TECHNICAL SERVICES, SEATTLE BRANCH—See Adecco Group AG; *Int'l*, pg. 140
PDS TECHNICAL SERVICES—See Adecco Group AG; *Int'l*, pg. 140
PDS TECHNICAL SERVICES—See Adecco Group AG; *Int'l*, pg. 140
PDS TECHNICAL SERVICES, WICHITA BRANCH—See Adecco Group AG; *Int'l*, pg. 140
PDS TRADING (SHANGHAI) CO., LIMITED—See PDS Limited; *Int'l*, pg. 5770
PDT COMMUNICATIONS, LTD.—See Waterfield Technologies, Inc.; *U.S. Private*, pg. 4453
PD TECHNOLOGY LTD.—See Somfy SA; *Int'l*, pg. 7085
P-DUKE TECHNOLOGY CO., LTD.; *Int'l*, pg. 5681
P. DUSSMANN EESTI OU—See Dussmann Stiftung & Co. KGaA; *Int'l*, pg. 2234
P. DUSSMANN EOOD—See Dussmann Stiftung & Co. KGaA; *Int'l*, pg. 2234
P. DUSSMANN GES.M.B.H.—See Dussmann Stiftung & Co. KGaA; *Int'l*, pg. 2234
P. DUSSMANN GUVENLIK, TEMIZLIK, BAKIM, ONARIM, HIZMET LIMITED SIRKETI—See Dussmann Stiftung & Co. KGaA; *Int'l*, pg. 2234
P. DUSSMANN HONG KONG LTD.—See Dussmann Stiftung & Co. KGaA; *Int'l*, pg. 2234
P. DUSSMANN KFT.—See Dussmann Stiftung & Co. KGaA; *Int'l*, pg. 2234
P. DUSSMANN ROMANIA S.R.L.—See Dussmann Stiftung & Co. KGaA; *Int'l*, pg. 2234
P. DUSSMANN SPOL. S.R.O.—See Dussmann Stiftung & Co. KGaA; *Int'l*, pg. 2235
P. DUSSMANN SPOL. S.R.O.—See Dussmann Stiftung & Co. KGaA; *Int'l*, pg. 2234
P. DUSSMANN SP.Z.O.O.—See Dussmann Stiftung & Co. KGaA; *Int'l*, pg. 2234
P. DUSSMANN TNHH—See Dussmann Stiftung & Co. KGaA; *Int'l*, pg. 2234
P. DUSSMANN UAB—See Dussmann Stiftung & Co. KGaA; *Int'l*, pg. 2234
PDV BRASIL COMBUSTIBLES E LUBRIFICANTES LTDA—See Petroleos de Venezuela S.A.; *Int'l*, pg. 5828
PDV ECUADOR S.A.—See Petroleos de Venezuela S.A.; *Int'l*, pg. 5828
PDV LTD—See DM plc; *Int'l*, pg. 2142
PDV MARINA, S.A.—See Petroleos de Venezuela S.A.; *Int'l*, pg. 5828
PDVSA ARGENTINA S.A.—See Petroleos de Venezuela S.A.; *Int'l*, pg. 5828
PDVSA CUBA SA—See Petroleos de Venezuela S.A.; *Int'l*, pg. 5828
PDVSA DO BRASIL LTDA.—See Petroleos de Venezuela S.A.; *Int'l*, pg. 5828
PDVSA ECUADOR SA—See Petroleos de Venezuela S.A.; *Int'l*, pg. 5828
PDVSA SERVICES B.V.—See Petroleos de Venezuela S.A.; *Int'l*, pg. 5828
PDVSA SERVICES, INC.—See Petroleos de Venezuela S.A.; *Int'l*, pg. 5828
PDVSA URUGUAY SA—See Petroleos de Venezuela S.A.; *Int'l*, pg. 5828
PDVSA USA, INC.—See Petroleos de Venezuela S.A.; *Int'l*, pg. 5828
PDX INC.—See UnitedHealth Group Incorporated; *U.S. Public*, pg. 2248
PD ZAJECAR A.D.; *Int'l*, pg. 5770
PDZ HOLDINGS BERHAD; *Int'l*, pg. 5771
PDZ PERSONALDIENSTE & ZEITARBEIT GMBH—See DZ BANK AG Deutsche Zentral-Genossenschaftsbank; *Int'l*, pg. 2244
PDZ SHIPPING AGENCY (BINTULU) SDN. BHD.—See PDZ Holdings Berhad; *Int'l*, pg. 5771
PDZ SHIPPING AGENCY (JOHOR) SDN.BHD.—See PDZ Holdings Berhad; *Int'l*, pg. 5771
PDZ SHIPPING AGENCY (KUCHING) SDN.BHD.—See PDZ Holdings Berhad; *Int'l*, pg. 5771
PDZ SHIPPING AGENCY (SABAH) SDN.BHD.—See PDZ Holdings Berhad; *Int'l*, pg. 5771
PDZ SHIPPING AGENCY (SIBU) SDN.BHD.—See PDZ Holdings Berhad; *Int'l*, pg. 5771
PDZ SHIPPING AGENCY (TAWAU) SDN. BHD.—See PDZ Holdings Berhad; *Int'l*, pg. 5771
PEAB AB; *Int'l*, pg. 5771
PEAB ASFALT AB—See Peab AB; *Int'l*, pg. 5772
PEAB ASFALT A/S—See Peab AB; *Int'l*, pg. 5772
PEAB ASFALT NORDEN AB—See Peab AB; *Int'l*, pg. 5772
PEAB ASFALT NORGE AS—See Peab AB; *Int'l*, pg. 5772
PEAB ASFALT SYD AB—See Peab AB; *Int'l*, pg. 5772
PEAB AS—See Peab AB; *Int'l*, pg. 5772
PEAB BILDRIFT AB—See Peab AB; *Int'l*, pg. 5772
PEAB BOLIG AS—See Peab AB; *Int'l*, pg. 5772
PEAB BOLIG PROSJEKT AS—See Peab AB; *Int'l*, pg. 5772
PEAB BOSTAD AB—See Peab AB; *Int'l*, pg. 5772

CORPORATE AFFILIATIONS

PEAB BYGGKONSTRUKTION AB—See Peab AB; *Int'l*, pg. 5772
PEAB CONSTRUCTION I GOTEBORG AB—See Peab AB; *Int'l*, pg. 5772
PEAB ELEVBYGGEN AB—See Peab AB; *Int'l*, pg. 5772
PEAB ENERGI AB—See Peab AB; *Int'l*, pg. 5772
PEABERRY THAI COMPANY LIMITED—See PTT Public Company Limited; *Int'l*, pg. 6093
PEAB EXPLOATERING AB—See Peab AB; *Int'l*, pg. 5772
PEAB FASTIGHETSUTVECKLING SVERIGE AB—See Peab AB; *Int'l*, pg. 5772
PEAB FORVALTNING NYKOPING AB—See Peab AB; *Int'l*, pg. 5772
PEAB GRUNDLAGGNING AB—See Peab AB; *Int'l*, pg. 5772
PEAB GRUNDLAGGNING NORDEN AB—See Peab AB; *Int'l*, pg. 5772
PEAB I 5 AB—See Peab AB; *Int'l*, pg. 5772
PEAB INDUSTRI AB—See Peab AB; *Int'l*, pg. 5772
PEAB INDUSTRI B.V.—See Peab AB; *Int'l*, pg. 5772
PEAB INDUSTRI NORGE AS—See Peab AB; *Int'l*, pg. 5772
PEAB INDUSTRI SVERIGE AB—See Peab AB; *Int'l*, pg. 5772
PEAB INFRA OY—See Peab AB; *Int'l*, pg. 5772
PEAB INVEST AS—See Peab AB; *Int'l*, pg. 5772
PEAB KIINTEISTOKEHITYS OY—See Peab AB; *Int'l*, pg. 5772
PEAB NORGE AS—See Peab AB; *Int'l*, pg. 5772
PEABODY AUSTRALIA HOLDCO PTY LTD.—See Peabody Energy Corporation; *U.S. Public*, pg. 1659
PEABODY (BOWEN) PTY LTD.—See Peabody Energy Corporation; *U.S. Public*, pg. 1659
PEABODY CAPRICORN PTY LTD—See Peabody Energy Corporation; *U.S. Public*, pg. 1659
PEABODY COALTRADE ASIA PRIVATE LTD.—See Peabody Energy Corporation; *U.S. Public*, pg. 1659
PEABODY COALTRADE GMBH—See Peabody Energy Corporation; *U.S. Public*, pg. 1659
PEABODY COALTRADE, LLC—See Peabody Energy Corporation; *U.S. Public*, pg. 1659
PEABODY COPPABELLA PTY LTD—See Peabody Energy Corporation; *U.S. Public*, pg. 1659
PEABODY DEVELOPMENT COMPANY, LLC—See Peabody Energy Corporation; *U.S. Public*, pg. 1659
PEABODY ENERGY AUSTRALIA COAL PTY LTD—See Peabody Energy Corporation; *U.S. Public*, pg. 1659
PEABODY ENERGY AUSTRALIA PCI LIMITED—See Peabody Energy Corporation; *U.S. Public*, pg. 1659
PEABODY ENERGY CORPORATION; *U.S. Public*, pg. 1658
PEABODY ENERGY MIDWEST GROUP—See Peabody Energy Corporation; *U.S. Public*, pg. 1659
THE PEABODY ESSEX MUSEUM; *U.S. Private*, pg. 4091
PEABODY GROUP MAINTENANCE LTD—See Peabody; *Int'l*, pg. 5773
PEABODY HOLDING COMPANY INC.—See Peabody Energy Corporation; *U.S. Public*, pg. 1659
PEABODY HOTEL GROUP, INC.—See Belz Enterprises; *U.S. Private*, pg. 522
PEABODY INVESTMENT & DEVELOPMENT BUSINESS SERVICES BEIJING CO. LTD.—See Peabody Energy Corporation; *U.S. Public*, pg. 1659
PEABODY MIDWEST MINING, LLC—See Peabody Energy Corporation; *U.S. Public*, pg. 1659
PEABODY OFFICE FURNITURE CORPORATION; *U.S. Private*, pg. 3122
PEABODY PENSION TRUST LIMITED—See Peabody; *Int'l*, pg. 5773
PEABODY & PLUM REALTORS, INC.—See Century 21 Hometown Realty; *U.S. Private*, pg. 831
PEABODY PROPERTIES, INC.; *U.S. Private*, pg. 3122
PEABODY PROPERTIES SOUTH, LLC—See Peabody Properties, Inc.; *U.S. Private*, pg. 3122
PEABODY; *Int'l*, pg. 5773
PEABODY SUPPLY COMPANY INC.; *U.S. Private*, pg. 3122
PEABODY (WILKIE CREEK) PTY LTD.—See Peabody Energy Corporation; *U.S. Public*, pg. 1659
PEABODY-WINSWAY RESOURCES BV—See Peabody Energy Corporation; *U.S. Public*, pg. 1659
PEAB OY—See Peab AB; *Int'l*, pg. 5773
PEAB PARK AB—See Peab AB; *Int'l*, pg. 5773
PEAB PROJEKTFASTIGHETER AB—See Peab AB; *Int'l*, pg. 5773
PEAB PROJEKTUTVECKLING NORD AB—See Peab AB; *Int'l*, pg. 5773
PEAB SEICON OY—See Peab AB; *Int'l*, pg. 5773
PEABSKOLAN I ANGELHOLM AB—See Peab AB; *Int'l*, pg. 5773
PEAB SP.Z.O.O—See Peab AB; *Int'l*, pg. 5773
PEAB SVERIGE AB, FINSK FILIAL—See Peab AB; *Int'l*, pg. 5773
PEAB SVERIGE AB—See Peab AB; *Int'l*, pg. 5773
PEAB SVERIGE AB—See Peab AB; *Int'l*, pg. 5773
PEAB TRANSPORT & MASKIN AB—See Peab AB; *Int'l*, pg. 5773
PEAB UGGLARP AB—See Peab AB; *Int'l*, pg. 5773
PEAB UTVECKLINGS AB—See Peab AB; *Int'l*, pg. 5773

COMPANY NAME INDEX

THE PEACEABLE KINGDOM PRESS, INC.—See GL Group, Inc.; *U.S. Private*, pg. 1704
PEACE ARCH ENTERTAINMENT GROUP INC.; *Int'l*, pg. 5773
PEACE CEREAL—See Attune Foods, Inc.; *U.S. Private*, pg. 383
PEACE FAMILY CLINIC & SURGERY (AMK) PTE. LTD.—See OUE Limited; *Int'l*, pg. 5666
PEACE FAMILY CLINIC & SURGERY (SEMBAWANG) PTE LTD—See OUE Limited; *Int'l*, pg. 5666
PEACEHEALTH; *U.S. Private*, pg. 3123
PEACE HILLS GENERAL INSURANCE COMPANY; *Int'l*, pg. 5773
PEACE INDUSTRIES INC. - SPOTNAILS DIVISION—See Peace Industries Ltd.; *U.S. Private*, pg. 3122
PEACE INDUSTRIES LTD.; *U.S. Private*, pg. 3122
PEACE IN MEDICINE; *U.S. Private*, pg. 3122
PEACE LIVING CO., LTD.; *Int'l*, pg. 5773
PEACE RIVER CITRUS PRODUCTS INC.; *U.S. Private*, pg. 3122
PEACE RIVER ELECTRIC COOPERATIVE, INC.; *U.S. Private*, pg. 3122
PEACE TEXTILE AMERICA INC.; *U.S. Private*, pg. 3122
PEACHES INSURANCE AGENCY INC—See Align Financial Group, LLC; *U.S. Private*, pg. 168
PEACHES INSURANCE AGENCY INC—See Excellere Capital Management LLC; *U.S. Private*, pg. 1446
THE PEACH FOUNDATION; *U.S. Private*, pg. 4091
PEACH GARDEN @33 PTE LTD—See Select Group Limited; *Int'l*, pg. 6699
PEACH GARDEN @OCC PTE LTD—See Select Group Limited; *Int'l*, pg. 6699
PEACH GARDEN RESTAURANT PTE LTD—See Select Group Limited; *Int'l*, pg. 6699
PEACH JOHN CO., LTD.—See Wacoal Holdings Corp.; *Int'l*, pg. 8326
PEACH JOHN HONG KONG COMPANY LIMITED—See Wacoal Holdings Corp.; *Int'l*, pg. 8326
PEACH JOHN SHANGHAI CO.,LTD.—See Wacoal Holdings Corp.; *Int'l*, pg. 8326
PEACHMAC; *U.S. Private*, pg. 3123
PEACH PROPERTY GROUP AG; *Int'l*, pg. 5773
PEACH PROPERTY GROUP (DEUTSCHLAND) GMBH—See Peach Property Group AG; *Int'l*, pg. 5773
PEACH STATE FEDERAL CREDIT UNION.; *U.S. Private*, pg. 3123
PEACH STATE FORD TRUCK SALES, INC.; *U.S. Private*, pg. 3123
PEACH STATE FREIGHTLINER—See Mercedes-Benz Group AG; *Int'l*, pg. 4823
PEACH STATE HEALTH PLAN INC.—See Centene Corporation; *U.S. Public*, pg. 470
PEACH STATE INTEGRATED TECHNOLOGIES INC.—See Toyota Industries Corporation; *Int'l*, pg. 7869
PEACH STATE LAB, LLC—See Arsenal Capital Management LP; *U.S. Private*, pg. 339
PEACH STATE ROOFING INC.; *U.S. Private*, pg. 3123
PEACH STATE TRUCK CENTERS LLC; *U.S. Private*, pg. 3123
PEACH TELECOM LTD.; *Int'l*, pg. 5773
PEACHTREE CASUALTY INSURANCE COMPANY—See Align Financial Group, LLC; *U.S. Private*, pg. 168
PEACHTREE CASUALTY INSURANCE COMPANY—See Excellere Capital Management LLC; *U.S. Private*, pg. 1446
PEACHTREE COMMUNITIES, LLC—See Century Communities, Inc.; *U.S. Public*, pg. 475
PEACHTREE FABRICS INC.; *U.S. Private*, pg. 3123
PEACH TREE HEALTH; *U.S. Private*, pg. 3123
PEACHTREE METALS CO.—See Ta Chen International Inc; *U.S. Private*, pg. 3919
PEACHTREE SPECIAL RISK BROKERS, LLC—See Brown & Brown, Inc.; *U.S. Public*, pg. 401
PEACHTREE SURGICAL & BARIATRIC, PC—See WellStar Health System, Inc.; *U.S. Private*, pg. 4478
PEACHTREE TENTS AND EVENTS, LLC—See Quest Events, LLC; *U.S. Private*, pg. 3325
PEACOCK ALLEY, INC.; *U.S. Private*, pg. 3123
PEACOCK, LTD.—See Fox Powersports LLC; *U.S. Private*, pg. 1584
PEACOCK OIL CO. OF BAXLEY INC.; *U.S. Private*, pg. 3123
PEA ENCOM INTERNATIONAL CO., LTD; *Int'l*, pg. 5771
PEA JAPAN—See AIRTECH JAPAN, LTD.; *Int'l*, pg. 249
PEAK 10, INC.—See GI Manager L.P.; *U.S. Private*, pg. 1693
PEAKAVENUE GMBH—See Main Capital Partners B.V.; *Int'l*, pg. 4650
PEAK BEHAVIORAL HEALTH SERVICES, LLC—See Universal Health Services, Inc.; *U.S. Public*, pg. 2259
PEAKBIETY INC.; *U.S. Private*, pg. 3124
PEAK BIO, INC.—See Akari Therapeutics, Plc; *Int'l*, pg. 259
PEAK-CATALYST—See Sole Source Capital LLC; *U.S. Private*, pg. 3708
PEAK CIVIL CONSULTANTS INC.—See Atwell, LLC; *U.S. Private*, pg. 384
PEAK CONSTRUCTION, INC.—See The Ensign Group, Inc.; *U.S. Public*, pg. 2072
PEAK DRINK DISPENSE LIMITED—See The Middleby Corporation; *U.S. Public*, pg. 2115
PEAKE BMW; *U.S. Private*, pg. 3124
PEAK ENERGY SERVICES LTD.—See Clean Harbors, Inc.; *U.S. Public*, pg. 510
PEAK ENERGY; *U.S. Private*, pg. 3123
PEAK ENGINEERING & CONSTRUCTION LTD.; *Int'l*, pg. 5773
PEAKE PRINTERS, INC.; *U.S. Private*, pg. 3125
PEAKEQUITY PARTNERS; *U.S. Private*, pg. 3125
PEAK FOODS, LLC—See Lakeside Foods, Inc.; *U.S. Private*, pg. 2377
PEAK GLOBAL CONSULTANCY LTD.; *Int'l*, pg. 5774
PEAK GLOBAL HOLDINGS, LLC; *U.S. Private*, pg. 3123
PEAK HEALTH SOLUTIONS, INC.—See AMN Healthcare Services, Inc.; *U.S. Public*, pg. 125
PEAK INSURANCE ADVISORS, LLC—See Yardi Systems, Inc.; *U.S. Private*, pg. 4586
PEAK INTERNATIONAL, INC.—See Daewon Semiconductor Packaging Industrial Corporation; *Int'l*, pg. 1910
PEAK INTERNATIONAL, INC.—See Daewon Semiconductor Packaging Industrial Corporation; *Int'l*, pg. 1910
PEAK INTERNATIONAL SINGAPORE—See Daewon Semiconductor Packaging Industrial Corporation; *Int'l*, pg. 1910
PEAK INVESTMENT SOLUTIONS, LLC; *U.S. Private*, pg. 3123
PEAKLOGIX, INC.—See Alta Equipment Group Inc.; *U.S. Public*, pg. 86
PEAK MATERIALS, LLC—See Summit Materials, Inc.; *U.S. Public*, pg. 1959
PEAK MEDICAL - BEAR CREEK CENTER—See Formation Capital, LLC; *U.S. Private*, pg. 1570
PEAK MEDICAL IDAHO OPERATIONS, INC.—See Formation Capital, LLC; *U.S. Private*, pg. 1570
PEAK MEDICAL - MCKINLEY CENTER—See Formation Capital, LLC; *U.S. Private*, pg. 1570
PEAK MEDICAL OF IDAHO, INC.—See Formation Capital, LLC; *U.S. Private*, pg. 1570
PEAK MEDICAL - PIKES PEAK CENTER—See Formation Capital, LLC; *U.S. Private*, pg. 1570
PEAK METHODS, INC.; *U.S. Private*, pg. 3123
PEAK MINERALS LIMITED; *Int'l*, pg. 5774
PEAK NANO OPTICS, LLC—See L3Harris Technologies, Inc.; *U.S. Public*, pg. 1284
PEAKNET, LLC—See Duke Energy Corporation; *U.S. Public*, pg. 691
PEAK OILFIELD SERVICES COMPANY—See Cook Inlet Region, Inc.; *U.S. Private*, pg. 1038
PEAK OILFIELD SERVICES COMPANY—See Nabors Industries Ltd.; *U.S. Public*, pg. 5119
PEAK OILFIELD SERVICES, LLC—See Select Water Solutions, Inc.; *U.S. Public*, pg. 1862
PEAKO LIMITED; *Int'l*, pg. 5774
PEAK PERFORMANCE PRODUCTION AB—See ANTA Sports Products Limited; *Int'l*, pg. 481
PEAK POWER ENGINEERING, INC.—See Atwell, LLC; *U.S. Private*, pg. 384
PEAK PROFESSIONAL CONTRACTORS INC.—See CUSITech, LLC; *U.S. Private*, pg. 1127
PEAK PROPERTY AND CASUALTY INSURANCE CORP.—See Sentry Insurance Group; *U.S. Private*, pg. 3611
PEAK RARE EARTHS LIMITED; *Int'l*, pg. 5774
PEAK REINSURANCE COMPANY LIMITED—See Fosun International Limited; *Int'l*, pg. 2752
PEAK RESORTS, INC.—See Vail Resorts, Inc.; *U.S. Public*, pg. 2271
PEAK RESOURCE GROUP, INC.; *U.S. Private*, pg. 3123
PEAK RESOURCES, INC.; *U.S. Private*, pg. 3123
PEAK ROCK CAPITAL LLC; *U.S. Private*, pg. 3123
PEAKS & PLAINS MEDICAL, INC.—See Mi-Med Supply Co. Inc.; *U.S. Private*, pg. 2696
PEAKSTONE REALTY TRUST—See Griffin Capital Corporation; *U.S. Private*, pg. 1787
PEAKSWARE, LLC.; *U.S. Private*, pg. 3125
PEAK TECHNICAL SERVICES, INC.; *U.S. Private*, pg. 3124
PEAK TECHNICAL SERVICES, IRVINE—See Peak Technical Services, Inc.; *U.S. Private*, pg. 3124
PEAK TECHNICAL SERVICES, NATIONAL DIVISON—See Peak Technical Services, Inc.; *U.S. Private*, pg. 3124
PEAK TECHNICAL SERVICES, TROY—See Peak Technical Services, Inc.; *U.S. Private*, pg. 3124
PEAK TECHNOLOGIES, INC.—See Sole Source Capital LLC; *U.S. Private*, pg. 3708
THE PEAK TOWER LIMITED—See The Hongkong and Shanghai Hotels Limited; *Int'l*, pg. 7653
PEAK TRAMWAYS COMPANY, LIMITED—See The Hongkong and Shanghai Hotels Limited; *Int'l*, pg. 7653
PEAK TRAVEL GROUP, INC.—See ABRY Partners, LLC; *U.S. Private*, pg. 41
PEAK USA ENERGY SERVICES LTD.—See Nabors Industries Ltd.; *U.S. Public*, pg. 5119
PEAK UTILITY SERVICES GROUP—See ORIX Corporation; *Int'l*, pg. 5636
PEAK VISTA COMMUNITY HEALTH CENTERS; *U.S. Private*, pg. 3124
PEANUT BUTTER & CO.; *U.S. Private*, pg. 3125
PEANUT COMPANY OF AUSTRALIA LIMITED; *Int'l*, pg. 5774
PEANUT PROCESSORS INC.; *U.S. Private*, pg. 3125
PEAPACK-GLADSTONE BANK—See Peapack-Gladstone Financial Corporation; *U.S. Public*, pg. 1659
PEAPACK-GLADSTONE FINANCIAL CORPORATION; *U.S. Public*, pg. 1659
PEAPOD, LLC—See Koninklijke Ahold Delhaize N.V.; *Int'l*, pg. 4260
PEARCE INDUSTRIES INC.; *U.S. Private*, pg. 3125
PEARCE RENEWABLES LLC—See Willcrest Partners; *U.S. Private*, pg. 4521
PEARCE SERVICES, LLC—See Willcrest Partners; *U.S. Private*, pg. 4521
PEAR COMMERCIAL INTERIORS INC.; *U.S. Private*, pg. 3125
PEARL ABRASIVE COMPANY—See Harbour Group Industries, Inc.; *U.S. Private*, pg. 1860
PEARL ABYSS CORP.; *Int'l*, pg. 5774
PEARL AGENCY ALLGEMEINE VERMITTLUNGSGESELLSCHAFT MBH; *Int'l*, pg. 5774
PEARLAND AMBULATORY SURGERY CENTER, LP—See Tenet Healthcare Corporation; *U.S. Public*, pg. 2012
PEARLAND SUNRISE MEDICAL CENTER LLC—See Adeptus Health Inc.; *U.S. Private*, pg. 78
PEARLAND TOWN CENTER HOTEL/RESIDENTIAL CONDOMINIUM ASSOCIATION, INC.—See CBL & Associates Properties, Inc.; *U.S. Public*, pg. 459
PEARL ARTIST & CRAFT SUPPLY; *U.S. Private*, pg. 3125
PEARL CITY ELEVATOR INC.; *U.S. Private*, pg. 3125
PEARL COMPANIES; *U.S. Private*, pg. 3125
PEARL CORPORATION—See Pearl Musical Instrument Co. Ltd.; *Int'l*, pg. 5774
PEARL (CRAWLEY) LIMITED—See General Motors Company; *U.S. Public*, pg. 928
PEARL & DEAN CINEMAS LIMITED; *Int'l*, pg. 5774
PEARL DIALYSIS, LLC—See DaVita Inc.; *U.S. Public*, pg. 642
PEARL ENERGY PHILIPPINES OPERATING, INC.—See Electricity Generating Public Co., Ltd.; *Int'l*, pg. 2352
PEARL ENGINEERED SOLUTIONS PTE. LTD.—See Platinum Equity, LLC; *U.S. Private*, pg. 3207
PEARL ENGINEERING POLYMERS LIMITED—See Pearl Polymers Limited; *Int'l*, pg. 5775
PEARL E&P CANADA LTD.—See Lundin Group of Companies; *Int'l*, pg. 4583
PEARLFISHER; *U.S. Private*, pg. 3125
PEARL GLOBAL INDUSTRIES LIMITED; *Int'l*, pg. 5774
PEARL GOLD AG; *Int'l*, pg. 5774
PEARL GREEN CLUBS & RESORTS LIMITED; *Int'l*, pg. 5774
PEARL GULL IRON LIMITED; *Int'l*, pg. 5774
PEARL HEALTHCARE LIMITED; *Int'l*, pg. 5774
PEARL HOLDINGS ACQUISITION CORP.; *U.S. Public*, pg. 1660
PEARL INSULATIONS PRIVATE LTD—See SKion GmbH; *Int'l*, pg. 6987
PEARL LAW GROUP; *U.S. Private*, pg. 3125
PEAR, LLC—See Merchants Office Furniture Company; *U.S. Private*, pg. 2670
PEARL LIFE HOLDINGS LIMITED—See Phoenix Group Holdings PLC; *Int'l*, pg. 5851
PEARLMAN CORPORATION—See Harbour Group Industries, Inc.; *U.S. Private*, pg. 1860
PEARLMAN GROUP—See The Stephens Group, LLC; *U.S. Private*, pg. 4121
PEARL MARINA ESTATES LIMITED—See Centum Investment Company Limited; *Int'l*, pg. 1416
PEARLMARK REAL ESTATE PARTNERS LLC; *U.S. Private*, pg. 3125
PEARL MEDIA LLC; *U.S. Private*, pg. 3125
PEARL METAL PRODUCTS (BANGALORE) PVT. LTD.—See SKion GmbH; *Int'l*, pg. 6987
PEARL MEYER & PARTNERS, LLC; *U.S. Private*, pg. 3125
PEARL MUSICAL INSTRUMENT CO. LTD.; *Int'l*, pg. 5774
PEARL MUSIC EUROPE B.V.—See Pearl Musical Instrument Co. Ltd.; *Int'l*, pg. 5774
PEARL OF KUWAIT REAL ESTATE COMPANY K.S.C.C.; *Int'l*, pg. 5774
PEARL PAINT CO. INC.; *U.S. Private*, pg. 3125
PEARL POLYMERS LIMITED; *Int'l*, pg. 5775
PEARL-PRESSMAN-LIBERTY COMMUNICATIONS GROUP; *U.S. Private*, pg. 3125
PEARL RIVER HOLDINGS LIMITED; *Int'l*, pg. 5775
PEARL RIVER SHOP RITE ASSOCIATES INC.—See Glass Gardens Inc.; *U.S. Private*, pg. 1706
PEARL RIVER VALLEY ELECTRIC POWER ASSOCIATION; *U.S. Private*, pg. 3125
PEARL RIVER VALLEY OPPORTUNITY, INC.; *U.S. Private*, pg. 3125
PEARL SANITARY PAPER CONVERTING CO. PLC; *Int'l*, pg. 5775
PEARL STREET HEALTHCARE CENTER, LLC—See National HealthCare Corporation; *U.S. Public*, pg. 1496

PEARL SANITARY PAPER CONVERTING CO. PLC

PEARL UNLIMITED INC.—See Pearl Global Industries Limited; *Int'l*, pg. 5774
PEARLWATER MINERALQUELLEN AG—See Coop-Gruppe Genossenschaft; *Int'l*, pg. 1790
PEARPOINT, INC.—See SPX Technologies, Inc.; *U.S. Public*, pg. 1921
PEARSANTA, INC.—See Aditxt, Inc.; *U.S. Public*, pg. 41
PEARSE-PEARSON COMPANY INC.; *U.S. Private*, pg. 3126
PEARSON AMSTERDAM BV—See Pearson plc; *Int'l*, pg. 5776
PEARSON ASSESSMENT & INFORMATION BV—See Pearson plc; *Int'l*, pg. 5776
PEARSON ASSESSMENT & INFORMATION GMBH—See Pearson plc; *Int'l*, pg. 5776
PEARSON AUSTRALIA GROUP PTY. LTD.—See Pearson plc; *Int'l*, pg. 5776
PEARSON AUSTRALIA-SCHOOLS DIVISION—See Pearson plc; *Int'l*, pg. 5776
PEARSON BENELUX—See Pearson plc; *Int'l*, pg. 5776
PEARSON BUICK GMC; *U.S. Private*, pg. 3126
PEARSON BUSINESS SERVICES INC—See Pearson plc; *Int'l*, pg. 5776
PEARSON CANADA ASSESSMENT INC.—See Pearson plc; *Int'l*, pg. 5776
PEARSON CANADA FINANCE UNLIMITED—See Pearson plc; *Int'l*, pg. 5776
PEARSON CANADA INC - PENGUIN GROUP (CANADA) DIVISION—See Pearson plc; *Int'l*, pg. 5776
PEARSON CANADA INC.—See Pearson plc; *Int'l*, pg. 5776
PEARSON CANDY COMPANY—See Brynwood Partners Management LLC; *U.S. Private*, pg. 674
PEARSON COLLEGE LIMITED—See Pearson plc; *Int'l*, pg. 5776
THE PEARSON COMPANY—See Heritage Home Group, LLC; *U.S. Private*, pg. 1924
PEARSON CONSTRUCTION COMPANY, INC.; *U.S. Private*, pg. 3126
PEARSON DENTAL SUPPLIES INC.; *U.S. Private*, pg. 3126
PEARSON DEUTSCHLAND GMBH—See Pearson plc; *Int'l*, pg. 5776
PEARSON DRIVING ASSESSMENTS LTD—See Pearson plc; *Int'l*, pg. 5776
PEARSON EDUCACION DE CHILE—See Pearson plc; *Int'l*, pg. 5776
PEARSON EDUCACION DE COLOMBIA LTDA—See Pearson plc; *Int'l*, pg. 5776
PEARSON EDUCACION DE MEXICO SA DE CV—See Pearson plc; *Int'l*, pg. 5776
PEARSON EDUCACION DE PERU SA—See Pearson plc; *Int'l*, pg. 5776
PEARSON EDUCACION DE VENEZUELA—See Pearson plc; *Int'l*, pg. 5776
PEARSON EDUCACION LATINOAMERICA—See Pearson plc; *Int'l*, pg. 5776
PEARSON EDUCACION S.A—See Pearson plc; *Int'l*, pg. 5776
PEARSON EDUCATION ASIA LTD—See Pearson plc; *Int'l*, pg. 5777
PEARSON EDUCATION AUSTRALIA PTY. LTD.—See Pearson plc; *Int'l*, pg. 5776
PEARSON EDUCATION BOTSWANA (PROPRIETARY) LTD—See Pearson plc; *Int'l*, pg. 5777
PEARSON EDUCATION CANADA—See Pearson plc; *Int'l*, pg. 5776
PEARSON EDUCATION CENTRAL EUROPE SPZOO—See Pearson plc; *Int'l*, pg. 5777
PEARSON EDUCATION DO BRASIL—See Pearson plc; *Int'l*, pg. 5777
PEARSON EDUCATION - EUROPE, MIDDLE EAST & AFRICA—See Pearson plc; *Int'l*, pg. 5776
PEARSON EDUCATION HELLAS SA—See Pearson plc; *Int'l*, pg. 5777
PEARSON EDUCATION HOLDINGS INC—See Pearson plc; *Int'l*, pg. 5777
PEARSON EDUCATION HOLDINGS LTD—See Pearson plc; *Int'l*, pg. 5777
PEARSON EDUCATION, INC.—See Pearson plc; *Int'l*, pg. 5777
PEARSON EDUCATION INDOCHINA LTD—See Pearson plc; *Int'l*, pg. 5777
PEARSON EDUCATION ITALIA S.R.L.—See Pearson plc; *Int'l*, pg. 5776
PEARSON EDUCATION KOREA LTD—See Pearson plc; *Int'l*, pg. 5777
PEARSON EDUCATION LTD.—See Pearson plc; *Int'l*, pg. 5777
PEARSON EDUCATION (SINGAPORE) PTE LTD—See Pearson plc; *Int'l*, pg. 5777
PEARSON EDUCATION (SOUTH AFRICA) PTY LTD—See Pearson plc; *Int'l*, pg. 5777
PEARSON EDUCATION SOUTH ASIA PTE LTD—See Pearson plc; *Int'l*, pg. 5777
PEARSON EDUCATION TAIWAN LTD—See Pearson plc; *Int'l*, pg. 5777
PEARSON EDUCATION YAYINCILIK SIRKETI—See Pearson plc; *Int'l*, pg. 5777

PEARSON EGITIM COZUMLERI TIKARET LIMITED SIRKETI—See Pearson plc; *Int'l*, pg. 5777
PEARSON FORD; *U.S. Private*, pg. 3126
PEARSON FRANCE SAS—See Pearson plc; *Int'l*, pg. 5777
PEARSON HEINEMANN LTD—See Pearson plc; *Int'l*, pg. 5777
PEARSON HOLDING COMPANY INC.; *U.S. Private*, pg. 3126
PEARSON HOLDINGS INC—See Pearson plc; *Int'l*, pg. 5777
PEARSON HOLDINGS SOUTHERN AFRICA (PTY) LTD.—See Pearson plc; *Int'l*, pg. 5777
PEARSON-HUGGINS COMPANIES INC.; *U.S. Private*, pg. 3126
PEARSON, INC.—See Pearson plc; *Int'l*, pg. 5777
PEARSON INDIA PVT LTD—See Pearson plc; *Int'l*, pg. 5777
PEARSON INSURANCE COMPANY, LTD—See TPG Capital, L.P.; *U.S. Public*, pg. 2168
PEARSON INTERNATIONAL FINANCE LTD—See Pearson plc; *Int'l*, pg. 5777
PEARSON IOKI SPOLKA Z OGRANICZONA ODPOWIEDZIALNOSCIA—See Pearson plc; *Int'l*, pg. 5777
PEARSON ITALY SRL—See Pearson plc; *Int'l*, pg. 5777
PEARSON JAPAN K.K.—See Pearson plc; *Int'l*, pg. 5777
PEARSON JONES PLC—See abrdn PLC; *Int'l*, pg. 69
PEARSON LESOTHO (PROPRIETARY) LTD—See Pearson plc; *Int'l*, pg. 5777
PEARSON LOAN FINANCE UNLIMITED—See Pearson plc; *Int'l*, pg. 5777
PEARSON LUXEMBOURG HOLDINGS LTD—See Pearson plc; *Int'l*, pg. 5777
PEARSON LUXEMBOURG HOLDINGS NO.2 LTD—See Pearson plc; *Int'l*, pg. 5777
PEARSON MALAYSIA SDN BHD—See Pearson plc; *Int'l*, pg. 5777
PEARSON MANAGEMENT SERVICES LTD—See Pearson plc; *Int'l*, pg. 5777
PEARSON NEW ZEALAND—See Pearson plc; *Int'l*, pg. 5776
PEARSON OVERSEAS HOLDINGS LTD—See Pearson plc; *Int'l*, pg. 5777
PEARSON PACKAGING SYSTEMS; *U.S. Private*, pg. 3126
PEARSON PENGUIN CANADA INC.—See Pearson plc; *Int'l*, pg. 5776
PEARSON PLC; *Int'l*, pg. 5775
PEARSON REAL ESTATE HOLDINGS INC—See Pearson plc; *Int'l*, pg. 5777
PEARSON SCHWEIZ AG—See Pearson plc; *Int'l*, pg. 5777
PEARSON SHARED SERVICES LTD—See Pearson plc; *Int'l*, pg. 5777
PEARSON (SINGAPORE) PTE LTD—See Pearson plc; *Int'l*, pg. 5776
PEARSON'S KNOWLEDGE TECHNOLOGIES LLC—See Pearson plc; *Int'l*, pg. 5778
PEARSON SMITH REALTY, LLC—See United Real Estate Group, LLC; *U.S. Private*, pg. 4296
PEARSON SOUTH AFRICA (PTY) LTD.—See Pearson plc; *Int'l*, pg. 5777
PEARSON SWEDEN AB—See Pearson plc; *Int'l*, pg. 5777
PEARSON TECHNOLOGY CENTRE INC—See Pearson plc; *Int'l*, pg. 5777
PEAR THERAPEUTICS, INC.; *U.S. Public*, pg. 1659
PEART INSURANCE BROKERS LIMITED—See Marsh & McLennan Companies, Inc.; *U.S. Public*, pg. 1388
PEASE & CURREN INCORPORATED; *U.S. Private*, pg. 3126
PEASE & SONS INC.; *U.S. Private*, pg. 3126
PEATY MILLS PLC; *Int'l*, pg. 5778
PEAVEY COMMERCIAL AUDIO—See Peavey Electronics Corporation; *U.S. Private*, pg. 3126
PEAVEY ELECTRONICS CORPORATION; *U.S. Private*, pg. 3126
PEAVEY ELECTRONICS LTD.—See Peavey Electronics Corporation; *U.S. Private*, pg. 3126
PEAVEY INDUSTRIES LP; *Int'l*, pg. 5778
PEAXY, INC.; *U.S. Private*, pg. 3126
PEBBLE BEACH COMPANY; *U.S. Private*, pg. 3126
PEBBLE BEACH SYSTEMS GROUP PLC; *Int'l*, pg. 5778
PEBBLE BEACH SYSTEMS LIMITED—See Pebble Beach Systems Group PLC; *Int'l*, pg. 5778
PEBBLEBROOK HOTEL TRUST; *U.S. Public*, pg. 1660
THE PEBBLE GROUP PLC; *Int'l*, pg. 7673
PEBBLE LIMITED PARTNERSHIP—See Northern Dynasty Minerals Ltd.; *Int'l*, pg. 5443
PEBBLES IN MY POCKET, INC.; *U.S. Private*, pg. 3126
PEBBLE SPRINGS WIND LLC—See Iberdrola, S.A.; *Int'l*, pg. 3571
PEBBLE TECHNOLOGY, INC.—See Graycliff Partners LP; *Int'l*, pg. 1761
PE BEN INDUSTRIES COMPANY LTD.—See Mullen Group Ltd.; *Int'l*, pg. 5080
PE BEN OILFIELD SERVICES LP—See Mullen Group Ltd.; *Int'l*, pg. 5080

CORPORATE AFFILIATIONS

PEBMIS PTY LTD—See KPP Group Holdings Co., Ltd.; *Int'l*, pg. 4298
THE PECAN DELUXE CANDY COMPANY INC.; *U.S. Private*, pg. 4091
PECANLAND MALL—See Brookfield Corporation; *Int'l*, pg. 1185
PECAN PIPELINE (NORTH DAKOTA), INC.—See EOG Resources, Inc.; *U.S. Public*, pg. 782
PECCA GROUP BERHAD; *Int'l*, pg. 5779
PECCOLE NEVADA CORP; *U.S. Private*, pg. 3126
PECHANGA RESORTS & CASINOS; *U.S. Private*, pg. 3126
PECHTER INC.; *U.S. Private*, pg. 3126
PECHTERS BAKING GROUP LLC; *U.S. Private*, pg. 3126
PECKHAM ASPHALT RESALE CORP.—See Peckham Industries, Inc.; *U.S. Private*, pg. 3127
PECKHAM INDUSTRIES, INC.; *U.S. Private*, pg. 3126
PECKHAM MATERIALS CORPORATION—See Peckham Industries, Inc.; *U.S. Private*, pg. 3127
PECKHAM ROAD CORPORATION—See Peckham Industries, Inc.; *U.S. Private*, pg. 3127
THE PECK-HANNAFORD & BRIGGS CO. INC.; *U.S. Private*, pg. 4091
PECK-HANNAFORD & BRIGGS SERVICE CORP.—See The Peck-Hannaford & Briggs Co. Inc.; *U.S. Private*, pg. 4092
PECK TECH CONSULTING LTD.—See Caterpillar, Inc.; *U.S. Public*, pg. 453
PECKVILLE HOSPITAL COMPANY, LLC—See Community Health Systems, Inc.; *U.S. Public*, pg. 555
PEC LTD.; *Int'l*, pg. 5778
PEC LTD.; *Int'l*, pg. 5778
PECO CONSTRUCTION COMPANY; *U.S. Private*, pg. 3127
PECO ENERGY COMPANY—See Exelon Corporation; *U.S. Public*, pg. 807
PECO FARMS INC.—See Peco Foods Inc.; *U.S. Private*, pg. 3127
PECO FARMS OF MISSISSIPPI, LLC.—See Peco Foods Inc.; *U.S. Private*, pg. 3127
PECO FOODS INC. - BATESVILLE PROCESSING PLANT—See Peco Foods Inc.; *U.S. Private*, pg. 3127
PECO FOODS INC. - BROOKSVILLE PROCESSING PLANT—See Peco Foods Inc.; *U.S. Private*, pg. 3127
PECO FOODS INC. - CANTON FEATHER LANE PROCESSING PLANT—See Peco Foods Inc.; *U.S. Private*, pg. 3127
PECO FOODS INC. - CANTON WEST FULTON STREET PROCESSING PLANT—See Peco Foods Inc.; *U.S. Private*, pg. 3127
PECO FOODS INC.; *U.S. Private*, pg. 3127
PECO FOODS INC.—See Peco Foods Inc.; *U.S. Private*, pg. 3127
PECO FOODS INC. - TUSCALOOSA PROCESSING PLANT—See Peco Foods Inc.; *U.S. Private*, pg. 3127
PECO, INC.—See Astronics Corporation; *U.S. Public*, pg. 217
PECO INSPX; *U.S. Private*, pg. 3127
PECONIC LAND TRUST, INCORPORATED; *U.S. Private*, pg. 3127
PECO PALLET, INC.—See The Pritzker Group - Chicago, LLC; *U.S. Private*, pg. 4099
PECORA CORPORATION—See Navigation Capital Partners, Inc.; *U.S. Private*, pg. 2873
PECOS HOTELS & PUBS LTD.; *Int'l*, pg. 5779
PECOS VALLEY OF NEW MEXICO, LLC—See Community Health Systems, Inc.; *U.S. Public*, pg. 555
PEC SAFETY OPERATIONS LLC—See Thoma Bravo, L.P.; *U.S. Private*, pg. 4150
PECTEN TRADING COMPANY—See Shell plc; *Int'l*, pg. 6796
PECUARIUS LABORATORIOS, S.A. DE C.V.—See Industrias Bachoco S.A.B. de C.V.; *Int'l*, pg. 3674
PECVAL INDUSTRIA LTDA.—See Toyoda Gosei Co., Ltd.; *Int'l*, pg. 7861
PEDATA RESALES, INC.; *U.S. Private*, pg. 3127
PEDCO E&A SERVICES, INC.; *U.S. Private*, pg. 3127
PEDDINGHAUS CORPORATION; *U.S. Private*, pg. 3127
PEDDLER'S VILLAGE, INC.; *U.S. Private*, pg. 3127
PEDERNALES DIALYSIS, LLC—See DaVita Inc.; *U.S. Public*, pg. 642
PEDERNALES ELECTRIC COOPERATIVE INC.; *U.S. Private*, pg. 3127
PEDERSEN TOYOTA-VOLVO INC.; *U.S. Private*, pg. 3127
PEDERSEN WORLDWIDE; *U.S. Private*, pg. 3127
PEDERSHAAB A/S—See FLSmidth & Co. A/S; *Int'l*, pg. 2711
PEDERSHAAB CONCRETE TECHNOLOGIES A/S—See Kohlberg & Company, LLC; *U.S. Private*, pg. 2337
PEDESTAL BANCSHARES, INC.—See Business First Bancshares, Inc.; *U.S. Public*, pg. 413
PEDESTAL BANK—See Business First Bancshares, Inc.; *U.S. Public*, pg. 413
PEDESTRIAN GROUP PTY LIMITED—See Nine Entertainment Co. Holdings Limited; *Int'l*, pg. 5300
PEDEVCO CORP; *U.S. Public*, pg. 1660
PEDEX GMBH—See Global Equity Partners Beteiligungs-Management AG; *Int'l*, pg. 2996

COMPANY NAME INDEX

PEGASUSTSI, INC.

Company Index

PEDIATRIC ACADEMIC ASSOCIATION INC.; *U.S. Private*, pg. 3128
PEDIATRIC CARDIAC INTENSIVISTS OF NORTH TEXAS, PLLC—See HCA Healthcare, Inc.; *U.S. Public*, pg. 1006
PEDIATRIC HOME RESPIRATORY SERVICES, LLC—See InTandem Capital Partners, LLC; *U.S. Private*, pg. 2097
PEDIATRIC HOSPITALISTS OF CONROE, PLLC—See HCA Healthcare, Inc.; *U.S. Public*, pg. 1006
PEDIATRIC INTENSIVIST GROUP, LLC—See HCA Healthcare, Inc.; *U.S. Public*, pg. 1006
PEDIATRICS & ADOLESCENT MEDICINE, PC—See American Medical Administrators, Inc.; *U.S. Private*, pg. 241
PEDIATRIC SERVICES OF AMERICA, INC.—See Bain Capital, LP; *U.S. Private*, pg. 439
PEDIATRICS OF GREATER HOUSTON, PLLC—See HCA Healthcare, Inc.; *U.S. Public*, pg. 1006
PEDIATRIC SPECIALISTS OF CLEAR LAKE, PLLC—See HCA Healthcare, Inc.; *U.S. Public*, pg. 1006
PEDIATRIC SPECIALTY CLINIC LLC—See HCA Healthcare, Inc.; *U.S. Public*, pg. 1006
PEDIATRIC SURGERY CENTER - ODESSA, LLC—See Tenet Healthcare Corporation; *U.S. Public*, pg. 2005
PEDIATRIC SURGERY CENTERS, LLC—See Tenet Healthcare Corporation; *U.S. Public*, pg. 2005
PEDIATRIC THERAPEUTIC SERVICES, INC.—See Kelly Services, Inc.; *U.S. Public*, pg. 1220
PEDIATRIX MEDICAL GROUP, INC.—See MEDNAX, Inc.; *U.S. Public*, pg. 1413
PEDIAVASCULAR INC.—See Medikit Co., Ltd.; *Int'l*, pg. 4777
PE DIGITAL GMBH—See ProSiebenSat.1 Media SE; *Int'l*, pg. 6000
PEDIGREE TECHNOLOGIES L.L.C.; *U.S. Private*, pg. 3128
PEDIGREE WHOLESALE LTD.; *Int'l*, pg. 5779
PEDIMENT GOLD LLC—See Nevada Exploration Inc.; *Int'l*, pg. 5221
PEDLEY PROPANE—See UGI Corporation; *U.S. Public*, pg. 2222
PEDONE; *U.S. Private*, pg. 3128
THE PEDRO COMPANIES, INC.; *U.S. Private*, pg. 4092
PEDRO FALCON ELECTRICAL CONTRACTORS INC.; *U.S. Private*, pg. 3128
PEDRO LAND INC.—See The Schafer Company Inc.; *U.S. Private*, pg. 4114
PEDRO RESOURCES LTD.; *Int'l*, pg. 5779
PEDRO'S LIST, INC.; *U.S. Public*, pg. 1660
PEDS LEGWEAR INC.—See Gildan Activewear Inc.; *Int'l*, pg. 2973
PEDUS FOOD SERVICES INC.—See Dussmann Stiftung & Co. KGaA; *Int'l*, pg. 2235
PEDUS SERVICE S.A.R.L.—See Dussmann Stiftung & Co. KGaA; *Int'l*, pg. 2235
THE PEEBLES CORPORATION; *U.S. Private*, pg. 4092
PEE CEE COSMA SOPE LTD.; *Int'l*, pg. 5779
PEE DEE ELECTRIC COOPERATIVE INC.; *U.S. Private*, pg. 3128
PEE DEE PATHOLOGY ASSOCIATES, INC.—See Laboratory Corporation of America Holdings; *U.S. Public*, pg. 1287
PEEK & CLOPPENBURG KG; *Int'l*, pg. 5779
PEEK'N PEAK RECREATION INC.; *U.S. Private*, pg. 3128
PEEK PACKAGING SOLUTIONS; *U.S. Private*, pg. 3128
PEEK PROMET D.O.O.—See Egeria Capital Management B.V.; *Int'l*, pg. 2323
PEEL AIRPORTS LTD.—See Peel Holdings Ltd.; *Int'l*, pg. 5779
PEEL ALEHOUSE (WA) PTY LTD—See Woolworths Group Limited; *Int'l*, pg. 8451
PEEL CHRYSLER JEEP DODGE; *Int'l*, pg. 5779
PEELED INC; *U.S. Private*, pg. 3128
PEEL HOLDINGS LTD.; *Int'l*, pg. 5779
PEEL HOTELS PLC; *Int'l*, pg. 5779
PEEL HUNT INC.—See Peel Hunt LLP; *Int'l*, pg. 5779
PEEL HUNT LLP; *Int'l*, pg. 5779
PEEL LAND AND PROPERTY HOLDINGS LTD.—See Peel Holdings Ltd.; *Int'l*, pg. 5779
PEELLE ASIA PACIFIC, PTE. LTD.—See The Peelle Company; *U.S. Private*, pg. 4092
THE PEELLE COMPANY LTD.—See The Peelle Company; *U.S. Private*, pg. 4092
THE PEELLE COMPANY; *U.S. Private*, pg. 4092
PEEL MEDIA LIMITED—See Peel Holdings Ltd.; *Int'l*, pg. 5779
PEEL MINING LTD.; *Int'l*, pg. 5779
PEEL MUTUAL INSURANCE COMPANY; *Int'l*, pg. 5779
PEEL PORTS LTD—See Peel Holdings Ltd.; *Int'l*, pg. 5779
PEEL'S BEAUTY SUPPLY INC.; *U.S. Private*, pg. 3128
PE ENERGY LIMITED—See Endress+Hauser (International) Holding AG; *Int'l*, pg. 2408
PEEPLES INDUSTRIES INC.; *U.S. Private*, pg. 3128
PEER 1 NETWORK ENTERPRISES, INC.—See DigitalBridge Group, Inc.; *U.S. Public*, pg. 664
PEER 1 NETWORK (TORONTO) INC.—See DigitalBridge Group, Inc.; *U.S. Public*, pg. 664
PEER 1 NETWORK (USA), INC.—See DigitalBridge Group, Inc.; *U.S. Public*, pg. 664
PEERAGE REALTY PARTNERS, INC.; *Int'l*, pg. 5779
PEERAPAT TECHNOLOGY PUBLIC COMPANY LIMITED; *Int'l*, pg. 5779
PEER BEARING COMPANY—See SKF AB; *Int'l*, pg. 6985
PEER BEARING GMBH—See SKF AB; *Int'l*, pg. 6981
PEER+ B.V.—See Merck KGaA; *Int'l*, pg. 4832
PEER CHAIN COMPANY; *U.S. Private*, pg. 3128
PEER FOODS GROUP, INC.; *U.S. Private*, pg. 3128
PEERFORM, INC.—See Versara Lending LLC; *U.S. Private*, pg. 4369
PEER INC.—See Peer Chain Company; *U.S. Private*, pg. 3128
PEERLESS AEROSPACE FASTENER CORP.—See Diploma PLC; *Int'l*, pg. 2129
PEERLESS ASIA PACIFIC PTE. LTD.—See CECO Environmental Corp.; *U.S. Public*, pg. 464
PEERLESS BLOWERS—See HBD Industries, Inc.; *U.S. Private*, pg. 1887
PEERLESS CHAIN COMPANY—See The Carlyle Group Inc.; *U.S. Public*, pg. 2055
PEERLESS CHINA MANUFACTURING CO. LTD.—See CECO Environmental Corp.; *U.S. Public*, pg. 464
PEERLESS CONVEYOR & MANUFACTURING CO.—See The G.W. Van Keppel Company; *U.S. Private*, pg. 4031
PEERLESS DISTRIBUTING CO.; *U.S. Private*, pg. 3128
PEERLESS ELECTRIC—See HBD Industries, Inc.; *U.S. Private*, pg. 1887
PEERLESS ELECTRONICS INC.; *U.S. Private*, pg. 3128
PEERLESS ENGINEERING SALES LTD.; *Int'l*, pg. 5780
PEERLESS ENTERPRISES INC.; *U.S. Private*, pg. 3128
PEERLESS EUROPE LTD.—See CECO Environmental Corp.; *U.S. Public*, pg. 464
PEERLESS FAUCET CORPORATION—See Masco Corporation; *U.S. Public*, pg. 1391
PEERLESS FOOD EQUIPMENT LLC—See Hillenbrand, Inc.; *U.S. Public*, pg. 1037
PEERLESS GARMENTS INC.—See Unisync Corp.; *Int'l*, pg. 8062
PEERLESS GARMENTS LP—See Unisync Corp.; *Int'l*, pg. 8062
PEERLESS GEAR LLC—See Certified Parts Corporation; *U.S. Private*, pg. 841
THE PEERLESS GROUP—See Illinois Tool Works Inc.; *U.S. Public*, pg. 1111
PEERLESS INDUSTRIAL GROUP, INC.—See The Carlyle Group Inc.; *U.S. Public*, pg. 2055
PEERLESS INDUSTRIES INC.; *U.S. Private*, pg. 3128
PEERLESS INSTRUMENT CO., INC.—See Curtiss-Wright Corporation; *U.S. Public*, pg. 612
PEERLESS INSURANCE COMPANY—See Liberty Mutual Holding Company Inc.; *U.S. Private*, pg. 2446
PEERLESS LIGHTING CORP.—See Acuity Brands, Inc.; *U.S. Public*, pg. 37
PEERLESS LIMITED—See Placements CMI Inc.; *Int'l*, pg. 5888
PEERLESS MANUFACTURING CO.—See CECO Environmental Corp.; *U.S. Public*, pg. 464
PEERLESS MIDWEST INC.; *U.S. Private*, pg. 3128
PEERLESS NETWORK, INC.—See Infobip Ltd.; *Int'l*, pg. 3690
PEERLESS PUMP COMPANY—See The Poul Due Jensen Foundation; *Int'l*, pg. 7675
PEERLESS SAW CO.; *U.S. Private*, pg. 3128
PEERLESS STEEL COMPANY INC.; *U.S. Private*, pg. 3128
PEERLESS SUPPLY INC.; *U.S. Private*, pg. 3129
PEERLESS SYSTEMS CORPORATION—See LCV Capital Management, LLC; *U.S. Private*, pg. 2404
PEERLESS TECHNOLOGIES CORPORATION; *U.S. Private*, pg. 3129
PEERLESS TYRE CO.; *U.S. Private*, pg. 3129
PEERLESS UMBRELLA CO., INC.; *U.S. Private*, pg. 3129
PEERLESS VALUE OPPORTUNITY FUND; *U.S. Private*, pg. 3129
PEERLESS-WINSMITH, INC.—See HBD Industries, Inc.; *U.S. Private*, pg. 1887
PEERLOGIX, INC.; *U.S. Private*, pg. 3129
PEER TO PEER NETWORK; *U.S. Private*, pg. 3128
PEET ESTATES (QLD) PTY LIMITED—See Peet Limited; *Int'l*, pg. 5780
PEET ESTATES (VIC) PTY LIMITED—See Peet Limited; *Int'l*, pg. 5780
PEET ESTATES (WA) PTY LIMITED—See Peet Limited; *Int'l*, pg. 5780
PEETI SECURITIES LIMITED; *Int'l*, pg. 5780
PEET LIMITED; *Int'l*, pg. 5780
PEET NO 72 AVOCA PTY. LIMITED—See Peet Limited; *Int'l*, pg. 5780
PEET NO 77 PTY. LIMITED—See Peet Limited; *Int'l*, pg. 5780
PEET QUEENS PARK JV PTY. LIMITED—See Peet Limited; *Int'l*, pg. 5780
PEET'S COFFEE & TEA, INC.—See JAB Holding Company S.a.r.l.; *Int'l*, pg. 3863
PEET SOUTHERN JV PTY. LIMITED—See Peet Limited; *Int'l*, pg. 5780
PE.FIBEROPTICS LIMITED—See Judges Scientific plc; *Int'l*, pg. 4021
PEFIPRESA S.A.—See Intermediate Capital Group plc; *Int'l*, pg. 3743
PEFIPRESA S.A.—See Kirkbi A/S; *Int'l*, pg. 4190
PEGA INTERNATIONAL LIMITED—See Pegatron Corporation; *Int'l*, pg. 5781
PEGA JAPAN K.K.—See Pegasystems Inc.; *U.S. Public*, pg. 1660
PEGASI ENERGY RESOURCES CORPORATION; *U.S. Private*, pg. 3129
PEGASO S.R.L.—See Cellularline SpA; *Int'l*, pg. 1395
PEGASUS ADVANCE ENGINEERING (US) INC.—See Mun Siong Engineering Limited; *Int'l*, pg. 5085
PEGASUS ADVANCE INDUSTRIAL COMPANY LTD.—See Mun Siong Engineering Limited; *Int'l*, pg. 5085
PEGASUS ASIA; *Int'l*, pg. 5780
PEGASUS AUTO RACING SUPPLIES, INC.; *U.S. Private*, pg. 3129
PEGASUS AVIATION SERVICES, LLC—See Nana Regional Corporation, Inc.; *U.S. Private*, pg. 2832
PEGASUS BANK—See BancFirst Corporation; *U.S. Public*, pg. 269
PEGASUS CAPITAL ADVISORS, L.P.; *U.S. Private*, pg. 3129
PEGASUS COMMERCIAL & RESIDENTIAL CLEANING LLC; *U.S. Private*, pg. 3129
PEGASUS COMMUNICATIONS—See Daniel J. Edelman, Inc.; *U.S. Private*, pg. 1155
PEGASUS CORPORATION OF AMERICA—See Pegasus Sewing Machine Manufacturing Co., Ltd.; *Int'l*, pg. 5780
PEGASUS DIGITAL MOBILITY ACQUISITION CORP.; *Int'l*, pg. 5780
PEGASUS ENTERPRISE CO., LTD.—See Nippon Yusen Kabushiki Kaisha; *Int'l*, pg. 5359
PEGASUS EUROPA GMBH—See Pegasus Sewing Machine Manufacturing Co., Ltd.; *Int'l*, pg. 5780
PEGASUS FUNDING, LLC—See Asta Funding, Inc.; *U.S. Private*, pg. 360
PEGASUS GLOBAL EXPRESS CO., LTD.—See Kanda Holdings Co., Ltd.; *Int'l*, pg. 4065
THE PEGASUS GROUP; *U.S. Private*, pg. 4092
PEGASUS HAVA TASIMACILIGI A.S.—See ESAS Holding A.S.; *Int'l*, pg. 2501
PEGASUS HEALTH GROUP PTY. LTD.—See H&G High Conviction Limited; *Int'l*, pg. 3191
PEGASUS HEIGHTS BERHAD; *Int'l*, pg. 5780
PEGASUS HOTELS OF CEYLON PLC—See Carson Cumberbatch PLC; *Int'l*, pg. 1347
PEGASUS IMAGING CORPORATION; *U.S. Private*, pg. 3129
PEGASUS INDUSTRIAL MIDWEST LIMITED LIABILITY COMPANY—See Mun Siong Engineering Limited; *Int'l*, pg. 5085
PEGASUS INTERNATIONAL HOLDINGS LIMITED; *Int'l*, pg. 5780
PEGASUS INVESTMENT COMPANY LIMITED—See Centremanor Ltd.; *Int'l*, pg. 1412
PEGASUS LABORATORIES INC.—See PBI/Gordon Corporation; *U.S. Private*, pg. 3118
PEGASUS LINK CONSTRUCTORS, LLC—See Fluor Corporation; *U.S. Public*, pg. 859
PEGASUS LOGISTICS GROUP; *U.S. Private*, pg. 3129
PEGASUS MARITIME CO., LTD.—See Nippon Yusen Kabushiki Kaisha; *Int'l*, pg. 5359
PEGASUS ORGANIZATION INTERNATIONAL INC.; *U.S. Private*, pg. 3129
PEGASUS PHARMACEUTICALS, INC.; *U.S. Public*, pg. 1660
PEGASUS POLYMERS MARKETING GMBH—See Ravago Holding S.A.; *Int'l*, pg. 6222
PEGASUS PRINTING—See AAB Holdings Pty Limited; *Int'l*, pg. 30
PEGASUS RESOURCES INC.; *Int'l*, pg. 5780
PEGASUS SEWING MACHINE MANUFACTURING CO., LTD. - SHIGA FACTORY—See Pegasus Sewing Machine Manufacturing Co., Ltd.; *Int'l*, pg. 5780
PEGASUS SEWING MACHINE MANUFACTURING CO., LTD.; *Int'l*, pg. 5780
PEGASUS SEWING MACHINE PTE LTD.—See Pegasus Sewing Machine Manufacturing Co., Ltd.; *Int'l*, pg. 5780
PEGASUS-SHIMAMOTO AUTO PARTS (VIETNAM) CO., LTD.—See Pegasus Sewing Machine Manufacturing Co., Ltd.; *Int'l*, pg. 5780
PEGASUS SOLUTIONS COMPANIES—See Travel Tripper, LLC; *U.S. Private*, pg. 4213
PEGASUS STEEL, LLC—See Arlington Capital Partners LLC; *U.S. Private*, pg. 328
PEGASUS TECHNOLOGY SOLUTIONS, LLC; *U.S. Private*, pg. 3129
PEGASUS TRANSPORTATION GROUP, INC.; *U.S. Private*, pg. 3129
PEGASUS TRANSPORTATION, INC.—See CRST International, Inc.; *U.S. Private*, pg. 1113
PEGASUS TRANSTECH, LLC; *U.S. Private*, pg. 3129
PEGASUSTSI, INC.; *U.S. Private*, pg. 3130
PEGASUS VIETNAM SEWING MACHINE CO., LTD.—See Pegasus Sewing Machine Manufacturing Co., Ltd.; *Int'l*, pg. 5780
PEGASYSTEMS AG—See Pegasystems Inc.; *U.S. Public*, pg. 1660

PEGASYSTEMS BILGI TEKNOLOJILERI ANONIM SIRKETI—See Pegasystems Inc.; *U.S. Public*, pg. 1661
PEGASYSTEMS B.V.—See Pegasystems Inc.; *U.S. Public*, pg. 1660
PEGASYSTEMS CANADA INC.—See Pegasystems Inc.; *U.S. Public*, pg. 1661
PEGASYSTEMS FRANCE, S.A.R.L.—See Pegasystems Inc.; *U.S. Public*, pg. 1661
PEGASYSTEMS GMBH—See Pegasystems Inc.; *U.S. Public*, pg. 1661
PEGASYSTEMS INC.; *U.S. Public*, pg. 1660
PEGASYSTEMS JAPAN K.K.—See Pegasystems Inc.; *U.S. Public*, pg. 1661
PEGASYSTEMS LIMITED—See Pegasystems Inc.; *U.S. Public*, pg. 1661
PEGASYSTEMS PRIVATE LIMITED—See Pegasystems Inc.; *U.S. Public*, pg. 1661
PEGASYSTEMS PROPRIETARY LIMITED—See Pegasystems Inc.; *U.S. Public*, pg. 1661
PEGASYSTEMS SPAIN, S.L.—See Pegasystems Inc.; *U.S. Public*, pg. 1661
PEGASYSTEMS SP. ZOO—See Pegasystems Inc.; *U.S. Public*, pg. 1661
PEGASYSTEMS THAILAND LIMITED—See Pegasystems Inc.; *U.S. Public*, pg. 1661
PEGASYSTEMS WORLDWIDE INC.—See Pegasystems Inc.; *U.S. Public*, pg. 1661
PEGASYSTEMS WORLDWIDE INDIA PRIVATE LIMITED—See Pegasystems Inc.; *U.S. Public*, pg. 1661
PEGATRON CORPORATION; *Int'l*, pg. 5780
PEGATRON CZECH S.R.O.—See Pegatron Corporation; *Int'l*, pg. 5781
PEGATRON TECHNOLOGY SERVICE INC—See Pegatron Corporation; *Int'l*, pg. 5781
PEGAVISION CORP.; *Int'l*, pg. 5781
PEG BANDWIDTH, LLC—See Uniti Group Inc.; *U.S. Public*, pg. 2253
PEGBOARD SOFTWARE PTY LTD; *Int'l*, pg. 5781
PEG BROADCASTING, LLC; *U.S. Private*, pg. 3129
PEG BROADCASTING - MCMINNVILLE/MANCHESTER—See PEG Broadcasting, LLC; *U.S. Private*, pg. 3129
PEG BROADCASTING - SPARTA—See PEG Broadcasting, LLC; *U.S. Private*, pg. 3129
PE GENERATORS LTD—See Turner & Co. (Glasgow) Limited; *Int'l*, pg. 7978
PEGGY ADAMS ANIMAL RESCUE LEAGUE OF THE PALM BEACHES, INCORPORATED; *U.S. Private*, pg. 3130
PEG INFRASTRUKTUR AG—See E.ON SE; *Int'l*, pg. 2258
PEGLER & LOUDEN—See Travis Perkins plc; *Int'l*, pg. 7908
PEGLER YORKSHIRE GROUP LTD.—See Aalberts N.V.; *Int'l*, pg. 35
PEG, LLC—See Installed Building Products, Inc.; *U.S. Public*, pg. 1133
PEGMONT MINES LIMITED; *Int'l*, pg. 5781
PEGOP - ENERGIA ELECTRICA, S.A.—See ENGIE SA; *Int'l*, pg. 2434
PEG PEREGO SPA; *Int'l*, pg. 5780
PEG PEREGO USA INC.—See Peg Perego SpA; *Int'l*, pg. 5780
PEGUES-HURST MOTOR COMPANY; *U.S. Private*, pg. 3130
PEH WERTPAPIER AG; *Int'l*, pg. 5781
PEI-GENESIS INC.; *U.S. Private*, pg. 3130
PEI GROUP, LLC—See Electricite de France S.A.; *Int'l*, pg. 2352
PEI, INC.; *U.S. Private*, pg. 3130
PEIJIA MEDICAL LIMITED; *Int'l*, pg. 5781
PEI LICENSING, INC.—See Perry Ellis International, Inc.; *U.S. Private*, pg. 3154
PEI LOGISTICS, INC.—See PEI, Inc.; *U.S. Private*, pg. 3130
PEINER TRAGER GMBH—See Salzgitter AG; *Int'l*, pg. 6498
PEINER UMFORMTECHNIK GMBH—See TV Sundram Iyengar & Sons Limited; *Int'l*, pg. 7987
PEINTURE DE PARIS SAS—See PPG Industries, Inc.; *U.S. Public*, pg. 1710
PEINTURES COULEURS DECORATION S.A.S.—See Akzo Nobel N.V.; *Int'l*, pg. 274
PEINTURES DE PARIS; *Int'l*, pg. 5781
PEIPORT HOLDINGS LTD.; *Int'l*, pg. 5781
PEIRCE PARK GROUP, INC.—See Marquette Associates, Inc.; *U.S. Private*, pg. 2587
PEIRCE-PHELPS, INC.; *U.S. Private*, pg. 3130
PEIRONE PRODUCE COMPANY—See URM Stores, Inc.; *U.S. Private*, pg. 4316
PEISELER GMBH & CO. KG—See INDUS Holding AG; *Int'l*, pg. 3664
PEISELER LLC—See INDUS Holding AG; *Int'l*, pg. 3664
PEISSENBERGER KRAFTWERKSGESELLSCHAFT MIT BESCHRANKTER HAFTUNG—See E.ON SE; *Int'l*, pg. 2258
PEI WEI ASIAN DINER, LLC; *U.S. Private*, pg. 3130

PEI WEI ASIAN DINER TWO (DALLAS) LLP—See Pei Wei Asian Diner, LLC; *U.S. Private*, pg. 3130
PEI WEI HOUSTON, INC.—See Pei Wei Asian Diner, LLC; *U.S. Private*, pg. 3130
PEI WORLDWIDE HOLDINGS, INC.; *U.S. Private*, pg. 1661
PEIXIN INTERNATIONAL GROUP N.V.; *Int'l*, pg. 5781
PEKABESKO AD; *Int'l*, pg. 5781
PEKAES SP. Z O.O.—See SNCF; *Int'l*, pg. 7026
PEKAO BANK HIPOTECZNY S.A.—See Bank Polska Kasa Opieki Spolka Akcyjna; *Int'l*, pg. 849
PEKAO DIRECT SP. Z O.O—See Bank Polska Kasa Opieki Spolka Akcyjna; *Int'l*, pg. 850
PEKAO FAKTORING SP. ZOO—See Bank Polska Kasa Opieki Spolka Akcyjna; *Int'l*, pg. 849
PEKAO FINANCIAL SERVICES SP. Z O.O.—See Bank Polska Kasa Opieki Spolka Akcyjna; *Int'l*, pg. 850
PEKAO FUNDUSZ KAPITALOWY SP. Z O.O.—See Bank Polska Kasa Opieki Spolka Akcyjna; *Int'l*, pg. 850
PEKAO INVESTMENT BANKING S.A.—See Bank Polska Kasa Opieki Spolka Akcyjna; *Int'l*, pg. 850
PEKAO INVESTMENT MANAGEMENT S.A.—See Bank Polska Kasa Opieki Spolka Akcyjna; *Int'l*, pg. 850
PEKAO LEASING HOLDING S.A.—See Bank Polska Kasa Opieki Spolka Akcyjna; *Int'l*, pg. 849
PEKAO LEASING SP. Z O.O.—See Bank Polska Kasa Opieki Spolka Akcyjna; *Int'l*, pg. 850
PEKAO PIONEER POWSZECHNED TOWARZYSTWO EMERYTALNE S.A.—See Bank Polska Kasa Opieki Spolka Akcyjna; *Int'l*, pg. 850
PEKAO PROPERTY SA—See Bank Polska Kasa Opieki Spolka Akcyjna; *Int'l*, pg. 849
PEKAO TFI S.A.—See Bank Polska Kasa Opieki Spolka Akcyjna; *Int'l*, pg. 850
PEKARA 1 MAJ A.D.; *Int'l*, pg. 5781
PEKARA A.D.; *Int'l*, pg. 5781
PEKARNA GROSUPLJE, D.D.—See Fortenova Group d.d.; *Int'l*, pg. 2738
PEKARSKA INDUSTRIJA A.D.; *Int'l*, pg. 5781
PEKAT S.R.O.—See Datalogic S.p.A.; *Int'l*, pg. 1978
PEK CO., LTD.—See Japan Material Co., Ltd.; *Int'l*, pg. 3899
PEKER GAYRIMENKUL YATIRIM ORTAKLIGI AS; *Int'l*, pg. 5781
PEKIN DIALYSIS, LLC—See DaVita Inc.; *U.S. Public*, pg. 642
PEK INDUSTRY CO., LTD.—See Saha Pathanapibul Public Company Limited; *Int'l*, pg. 6479
PEKING HANDICRAFT INC.; *U.S. Private*, pg. 3130
PEKING TONGRENTANG (M) SDN. BHD.—See Beijing Tong Ren Tang Chinese Medicine Company Limited; *Int'l*, pg. 959
PEKING UNIVERSITY RESOURCES HOLDINGS COMPANY LIMITED; *Int'l*, pg. 5781
PEKIN HOSPITAL—See Progressive Health Systems Inc.; *U.S. Public*, pg. 3279
PEKIN LIFE INSURANCE CO; *U.S. Public*, pg. 1661
PEKM KABELTECHNIK S.R.O.—See Commercial Vehicle Group, Inc.; *U.S. Public*, pg. 547
PEKO PRECISION PRODUCTS INC.; *U.S. Private*, pg. 3130
P.E. KRAMME INC.—See Kramme Consolidated Inc.; *U.S. Private*, pg. 2349
PELABUHAN TANJUNG PELEPAS SDN. BHD.—See MMC Corporation Berhad; *Int'l*, pg. 5005
PELABURAN HARTANAH NASIONAL BERHAD—See Permodalan Nasional Berhad; *Int'l*, pg. 5809
PELADON SOFTWARE INC.—See The Software Construction Co. Inc.; *U.S. Private*, pg. 4119
PELAGIA AS—See Austevoll Seafood ASA; *Int'l*, pg. 718
PELAGIA AS—See Kverva AS; *Int'l*, pg. 4349
PELAGIA SHETLAND LIMITED; *Int'l*, pg. 5781
PELAGOS CAPITAL MANAGEMENT, LLC—See Franklin Resources, Inc.; *U.S. Public*, pg. 883
PEL-AIR AVIATION PTY LIMITED—See REGIONAL EXPRESS HOLDINGS LIMITED; *Int'l*, pg. 6254
PELANGI EDUCATION SDN. BHD.—See Pelangi Publishing Group Bhd; *Int'l*, pg. 5782
PELANGI FORMPRESS SDN. BHD.—See Pelangi Publishing Group Bhd; *Int'l*, pg. 5782
PELANGI INDAH CANINDO TBK; *Int'l*, pg. 5781
PELANGI MULTIMEDIA TECHNOLOGIES SDN. BHD.—See Pelangi Publishing Group Bhd; *Int'l*, pg. 5782
PELANGIO EXPLORATION INC.; *Int'l*, pg. 5782
PELANGI PUBLISHING GROUP BHD; *Int'l*, pg. 5781
PELANGI PUBLISHING (THAILAND) CO. LTD.—See Pelangi Publishing Group Bhd; *Int'l*, pg. 5782
PELANGI SDN. BERHAD—See S P Setia Berhad; *Int'l*, pg. 6443
PELANGI SEMENYIH SDN. BHD.—See MKH Berhad; *Int'l*, pg. 5002
PELATRO PLC; *Int'l*, pg. 5782
PELAWAN INVESTMENTS (PROPRIETARY) LIMITED—See Atlatsa Resources Corporation; *Int'l*, pg. 687
PELCO EUROPE BV—See Schneider Electric SE; *Int'l*, pg. 6628

PELCO INC.—See Motorola Solutions, Inc.; *U.S. Public*, pg. 1479
PELCO PRODUCTS, INC.; *U.S. Private*, pg. 3130
PELCO STRUCTURAL, LLC; *U.S. Private*, pg. 3130
PELCO SWEDEN AB—See Schneider Electric SE; *Int'l*, pg. 6628
PELCO UK LTD—See Schneider Electric SE; *Int'l*, pg. 6628
PELE DIAMOND CORPORATION—See Bhang Inc.; *U.S. Public*, pg. 1010
PELEGOL LTD.—See Golan Plastic Products Ltd.; *Int'l*, pg. 3023
PELEPHONE COMMUNICATIONS, LTD.—See Bezeq - The Israel Telecommunication Corp. Limited; *Int'l*, pg. 1006
PELE SECURITY AB—See Schneider Electric SE; *Int'l*, pg. 6628
PELESYS LEARNING SYSTEMS INC.—See CAE Inc.; *Int'l*, pg. 1249
PELEUS REINSURANCE, LTD.—See Brookfield Reinsurance Ltd.; *Int'l*, pg. 1194
PELHAMS LIMITED; *Int'l*, pg. 5782
PELIA GEBAEUDESYSTEME GMBH—See 3U Holding AG; *Int'l*, pg. 10
PELIAS NORSK SKADEDYRKONTROLL AS—See Rentokil Initial plc; *Int'l*, pg. 6289
PELICAN CHEMICAL TRADERS LTD.—See BRENNTAG SE; *Int'l*, pg. 1149
PELICAN DELIVERS, INC.; *U.S. Private*, pg. 3130
PELICAN ENERGY PARTNERS LP; *U.S. Private*, pg. 3130
PELICAN ENGINEERING CONSULTANTS LLC; *U.S. Private*, pg. 3130
PELICAN EXPRESSION TECHNOLOGY—See Ligand Pharmaceuticals Incorporated; *U.S. Public*, pg. 1314
PELICAN INTERNATIONAL INC.; *Int'l*, pg. 5782
PELICAN MARSH GOLF CLUB—See Lennar Corporation; *U.S. Public*, pg. 1307
PELICAN MIDCO LIMITED—See Oakley Capital Limited; *Int'l*, pg. 5504
PELICAN OFFSHORE SERVICES PTE LTD—See Dymon Asia Capital (Singapore) Pte. Ltd; *Int'l*, pg. 2238
PELICAN OIL INC.; *U.S. Private*, pg. 3130
PELICAN PROCUREMENT SERVICES LIMITED—See Aramark; *U.S. Public*, pg. 178
PELICAN PRODUCTS AUSTRALIA PTY LTD—See Platinum Equity, LLC; *U.S. Private*, pg. 3207
PELICAN PRODUCTS, INC.—See Platinum Equity, LLC; *U.S. Private*, pg. 3207
PELICAN PRODUCTS, INC.—See Platinum Equity, LLC; *U.S. Private*, pg. 3207
PELICAN PRODUCTS K.K.—See Platinum Equity, LLC; *U.S. Private*, pg. 3207
PELICAN PRODUCTS KOREA LTD—See Platinum Equity, LLC; *U.S. Private*, pg. 3207
PELICAN PRODUCTS SINGAPORE PTE LTD—See Platinum Equity, LLC; *U.S. Private*, pg. 3207
PELICAN PRODUCTS ULC—See Platinum Equity, LLC; *U.S. Private*, pg. 3207
PELICAN RESOURCES LIMITED; *Int'l*, pg. 5782
PELICAN SHIP MANAGEMENT SERVIES PTE LTD—See Dymon Asia Capital (Singapore) Pte. Ltd; *Int'l*, pg. 2238
PELICAN STATE CREDIT UNION; *U.S. Private*, pg. 3130
PELICAN STATE PHYSICAL THERAPY, LIMITED PARTNERSHIP—See U.S. Physical Therapy, Inc.; *U.S. Public*, pg. 2215
PELICAN WASTE & DEBRIS, LLC; *U.S. Private*, pg. 3131
PELICAN WIRE COMPANY, INC.; *U.S. Private*, pg. 3131
PELICAN WORLDWIDE; *U.S. Private*, pg. 3131
PELICULAS PLASTICAS, S.A. DE C.V.—See Grupo La Moderna, S.A.B. de C.V.; *Int'l*, pg. 3131
PELIKAN AG—See Pelikan International Corporation Berhad; *Int'l*, pg. 5782
PELIKAN ARGENTINA S.A.—See Pelikan International Corporation Berhad; *Int'l*, pg. 5782
PELIKAN-ARTLINE PTY., LTD.—See ACCO Brands Corporation; *U.S. Public*, pg. 32
PELIKAN-ARTLINE PTY., LTD.—See Pelikan International Corporation Berhad; *Int'l*, pg. 5783
PELIKAN ASIA SDN. BHD.—See Pelikan International Corporation Berhad; *Int'l*, pg. 5783
PELIKAN AUSTRIA GESMBH—See Pelikan International Corporation Berhad; *Int'l*, pg. 5783
PELIKAN BENELUX N.V./S.A.—See Pelikan International Corporation Berhad; *Int'l*, pg. 5783
PELIKAN COLOMBIA S.A.S.—See Pelikan International Corporation Berhad; *Int'l*, pg. 5783
PELIKAN HARDCOPY HOLDING AG—See Pelikan International Corporation Berhad; *Int'l*, pg. 5782
PELIKAN HARDCOPY PRODUCTION AG—See Pelikan International Corporation Berhad; *Int'l*, pg. 5782
PELIKAN HOLDING AG—See Pelikan International Corporation Berhad; *Int'l*, pg. 5782
PELIKAN INTERNATIONAL CORPORATION BERHAD; *Int'l*, pg. 5782
PELIKAN ITALIA S.P.A.—See Pelikan International Corporation Berhad; *Int'l*, pg. 5783
PELIKAN JAPAN K.K.—See Pelikan International Corporation Berhad; *Int'l*, pg. 5783

COMPANY NAME INDEX

PELIKAN MEXICO S.A. DE C.V.—See Pelikan International Corporation Berhad; *Int'l*, pg. 5783
PELIKAN MIDDLE EAST FZE—See Pelikan International Corporation Berhad; *Int'l*, pg. 5783
PELIKAN N.V./S.A—See Pelikan International Corporation Berhad; *Int'l*, pg. 5783
PELIKAN PBS-PRODUKTIONSGESELLSCHAFT MBH & CO. KG—See Pelikan International Corporation Berhad; *Int'l*, pg. 5783
PELIKAN PBS-PRODUKTION VERWALTUNGS-GMBH—See Pelikan International Corporation Berhad; *Int'l*, pg. 5783
PELIKAN (SCHWEIZ) AG—See Pelikan International Corporation Berhad; *Int'l*, pg. 5782
PELIKAN SINGAPORE PTE. LTD.—See Pelikan International Corporation Berhad; *Int'l*, pg. 5783
PELIKAN TAIWAN CO., LTD.—See Pelikan International Corporation Berhad; *Int'l*, pg. 5783
PELIKAN (THAILAND) CO. LTD.—See Pelikan International Corporation Berhad; *Int'l*, pg. 5782
PELIKAN VERTRIEBSGESELLSCHAFT MBH & CO. KG—See Pelikan International Corporation Berhad; *Int'l*, pg. 5783
P.E.L., INC.; *U.S. Private*, pg. 3060
PELION GREEN FUTURE GMBH; *Int'l*, pg. 5783
PELION S.A.; *Int'l*, pg. 5783
PELI PRODUCTS, S.L.U.—See Platinum Equity, LLC; *U.S. Private*, pg. 3207
PELISTERKA AD; *Int'l*, pg. 5783
PELLA CORPORATION; *U.S. Private*, pg. 3131
PELLA FINANCIAL GROUP, INC.; *U.S. Private*, pg. 3131
PELLA PRODUCTS OF KANSAS CITY; *U.S. Private*, pg. 3131
PELLA REGIONAL HEALTH CENTER; *U.S. Private*, pg. 3131
PELLA TRAVEL INC.; *U.S. Private*, pg. 3131
PELLA WINDOW & DOOR LLC; *U.S. Private*, pg. 3131
PELLA WINDOWS & DOORS, INC. - BOSTON; *U.S. Private*, pg. 3131
PELLA WINDOWS & DOORS, INC. - COLORADO—See Pella Corporation; *U.S. Private*, pg. 3131
PELLA WINDOWS & DOORS, INC. - DETROIT—See Pella Corporation; *U.S. Private*, pg. 3131
PELLA WINDOWS & DOORS, INC.; *U.S. Private*, pg. 3131
PELLA WINDOWS & DOORS, INC.—See Pella Corporation; *U.S. Private*, pg. 3131
PELLEGRINI S.A—See Banco de la Nacion Argentina; *Int'l*, pg. 820
PELLEGRINO DISTRIBUIDORA AUTOPECAS LTDA.—See The Cypress Group LLC; *U.S. Private*, pg. 4017
PELLERIN MILNOR CORPORATION; *U.S. Private*, pg. 3131
PELLICANO BUILDERS PTY LTD—See Pellicano Pty Ltd; *Int'l*, pg. 5783
PELLICANO PTY LTD; *Int'l*, pg. 5783
PELLUX GMBH—See NIBE Industrier AB; *Int'l*, pg. 5262
PELLY INDUSTRI HOLDING AB—See Litorina Capital Management AB; *Int'l*, pg. 4528
PELMAC THAI LIMITED—See Minebea Mitsumi Inc.; *Int'l*, pg. 4905
PELNOX, LTD.—See Arakawa Chemical Industries, Ltd.; *Int'l*, pg. 535
PELORUS PRIVATE EQUITY LIMITED; *Int'l*, pg. 5783
PELOTON CAPITAL MANAGEMENT, INC.; *Int'l*, pg. 5783
PELOTON EQUITY LLC; *U.S. Private*, pg. 3131
PELOTON INTERACTIVE, INC.; *U.S. Public*, pg. 1661
PELOTON MINERALS CORPORATION; *Int'l*, pg. 5784
PELOTON THERAPEUTICS, INC.; *U.S. Private*, pg. 3131
PELSIS HOLDING (UK) LIMITED; *Int'l*, pg. 5784
PELSIS LIMITED—See Lloyds Banking Group plc; *Int'l*, pg. 4537
PELSIS LIMITED—See Pelsis Holding (UK) Limited; *Int'l*, pg. 5784
PELTON & CRANE GROUP—See Nakanishi Inc.; *Int'l*, pg. 5132
PELTONEN SKI OY—See Rapala VMC Oyj; *Int'l*, pg. 6209
PELTOURS INSURANCE AGENCIES LTD.—See Assicurazioni Generali S.p.A.; *Int'l*, pg. 647
PELWATTE DAIRY INDUSTRIES LIMITED; *Int'l*, pg. 5784
PEMA 2B; *Int'l*, pg. 5784
PEMAC PTE. LTD.—See MTQ Corporation Limited; *Int'l*, pg. 5072
PEMA HOLDING AG; *Int'l*, pg. 5784
PEMASARAN ALAT GANTI SDN. BHD.—See Tan Chong Motor Holdings Berhad; *Int'l*, pg. 7453
PEMBA CAPITAL PARTNERS PTY. LTD.—See FirstRand Limited; *Int'l*, pg. 2690
PEMBANGUNAN BANDAR MUTIARA SDN. BHD.—See Nadayu Properties Berhad; *Int'l*, pg. 5123
PEMBERTON MARKETING INTERNATIONAL LIMITED—See Clayton, Dubilier & Rice, LLC; *U.S. Private*, pg. 928
PEMBINAAN HUA YANG SDN. BHD.—See Hua Yang Berhad; *Int'l*, pg. 3510
PEMBINAAN MITRAJAYA SDN. BHD.—See Mitrajaya Holdings Berhad; *Int'l*, pg. 4928

PEMBINA COUNTY MEMORIAL HOSPITAL; *U.S. Private*, pg. 3131
PEMBINA MIDSTREAM LIMITED PARTNERSHIP—See Pembina Pipeline Corporation; *Int'l*, pg. 5785
PEMBINA NGL CORPORATION—See Pembina Pipeline Corporation; *Int'l*, pg. 5785
PEMBINA PIPELINE CORPORATION; *Int'l*, pg. 5785
PEMBRIDGE INSURANCE COMPANY—See The Allstate Corporation; *U.S. Public*, pg. 2034
PEMBRIDGE RESOURCES PLC; *Int'l*, pg. 5785
PEMBROKE COMMUNICATIONS—See QMP Publicis; *Int'l*, pg. 6147
PEMBROKE MANAGING AGENCY LIMITED—See Hamilton Insurance Group, Ltd.; *Int'l*, pg. 3238
PEMBROKE MARINER & REPORTER—See Gannett Co., Inc.; *U.S. Public*, pg. 902
PEMBROKE MOTORS, INC.—See AutoNation, Inc.; *U.S. Public*, pg. 236
PEMBROKE VCT PLC; *Int'l*, pg. 5785
PEMBROKE OCCUPATIONAL HEALTH, INC.—See Abbott Laboratories; *U.S. Public*, pg. 19
PEMBROOK REALTY CAPITAL LLC; *U.S. Private*, pg. 3131
PEMCO BRUGGE BVBA—See American Securities LLC; *U.S. Private*, pg. 253
PEMCO CORPORATION—See American Securities LLC; *U.S. Private*, pg. 253
PEMCO EMELIER S.A.—See American Securities LLC; *U.S. Private*, pg. 253
PEMCO, INC.; *U.S. Private*, pg. 3132
PEMCO INSURANCE COMPANY INC.—See PEMCO Mutual Insurance Co. Inc.; *U.S. Private*, pg. 3132
PEMCO MUTUAL INSURANCE CO. INC.; *U.S. Private*, pg. 3132
PEMCO WORLD AIR SERVICES INC.—See Air Transport Services Group, Inc.; *U.S. Public*, pg. 67
PEMEC, S.A.—See Mondragon Corporation; *Int'l*, pg. 5029
PEMEX EXPLORACION Y PRODUCCION—See Petroleos Mexicanos; *Int'l*, pg. 5828
PEMEX FINANCE, LTD.—See Petroleos Mexicanos; *Int'l*, pg. 5828
PEMEX GAS Y PETROQUIMICA BASICA—See Petroleos Mexicanos; *Int'l*, pg. 5829
PEMEX PROCUREMENT INTERNATIONAL, INC.—See Petroleos Mexicanos; *Int'l*, pg. 5829
PEMEX REFINACION—See Petroleos Mexicanos; *Int'l*, pg. 5829
PEMISCOT MEMORIAL HEALTH SYSTEMS; *U.S. Private*, pg. 3132
PEMI VENTILATION & MONTAGE AB—See Instalco AB; *Int'l*, pg. 3722
PEMKO MANUFACTURING COMPANY; *U.S. Private*, pg. 3132
PEMKO MANUFACTURING COMPANY—See Pemko Manufacturing Company; *U.S. Private*, pg. 3132
PEMTRON CORPORATION; *Int'l*, pg. 5785
PEMTRON EUROPE GMBH—See Pemtron Corporation; *Int'l*, pg. 5785
PEMTRON TECHNOLOGIES ASIA PTE. LIMITED—See Pemtron Corporation; *Int'l*, pg. 5785
PEMTRON TECHNOLOGIES CO., LTD.—See Pemtron Corporation; *Int'l*, pg. 5785
PEMTRON TECHNOLOGY, CORP.—See Pemtron Corporation; *Int'l*, pg. 5785
PEMTRON TECHNOLOGY MEXICO, S DE R.L. DE C.V.—See Pemtron Corporation; *Int'l*, pg. 5785
PEMTRON VINA CO., LTD.—See Pemtron Corporation; *Int'l*, pg. 5785
PENACOOK PLACE; *U.S. Private*, pg. 3132
PENAFLOR S.A.; *Int'l*, pg. 5785
PENAGA DRESSER SDN. BHD.—See Deleum Berhad; *Int'l*, pg. 2012
PENAM, A.S.—See Agrofert Holding, a.s.; *Int'l*, pg. 219
PENAM SLOVAKIA, A.S.—See Agrofert Holding, a.s.; *Int'l*, pg. 219
PENANG PORT SDN. BHD.—See MMC Corporation Berhad; *Int'l*, pg. 5005
PENANG SEAGATE INDUSTRIES (M) SDN. BHD.—See Seagate Technology Holdings PLC; *Int'l*, pg. 6663
PENANG SENTRAL DCS SDN. BHD.—See Malaysian Resources Corporation Berhad; *Int'l*, pg. 4662
PENANG SENTRAL SDN. BHD.—See Malaysian Resources Corporation Berhad; *Int'l*, pg. 4662
PENANG SPECIALIST HOSPITAL SDN BHD—See KPJ Healthcare Berhad; *Int'l*, pg. 4297
PENBAY SOLUTIONS LLC—See Pamlico Capital Management, L.P.; *U.S. Private*, pg. 3083
PEN BOUTIQUE LIMITED; *U.S. Private*, pg. 3132
PEN-CAL ADMINISTRATORS, INC.—See Voya Financial, Inc.; *U.S. Public*, pg. 2311
PENCE BRIGGS INC.; *U.S. Private*, pg. 3132
PENCHEM TECHNOLOGIES SDN. BHD.—See Frencken Group Limited; *Int'l*, pg. 2773
PENCILS.COM—See California Cedar Products Company; *U.S. Private*, pg. 718
PENCOA; *U.S. Private*, pg. 3132
PENCO CORPORATION; *U.S. Private*, pg. 3132
PENCOM SYSTEMS INCORPORATED; *U.S. Private*, pg. 3132

PENCO PRODUCTS, INC.—See Summa Holdings, Inc.; *U.S. Private*, pg. 3852
PENCOR SERVICES INC.; *U.S. Private*, pg. 3132
PENCRETE LIMITED—See Heidelberg Materials AG; *Int'l*, pg. 3318
PENDA CORPORATION—See Kruger Brown Holdings, LLC; *U.S. Private*, pg. 2353
PENDAFORM CORPORATION—See Kruger Brown Holdings, LLC; *U.S. Private*, pg. 2353
PENDAL GROUP LIMITED—See Perpetual Limited; *Int'l*, pg. 5812
PENDANT AUTOMATION, INC.; *U.S. Private*, pg. 3132
PENDER FINANCIAL GROUP CORPORATION; *Int'l*, pg. 5785
PENDERFUND CAPITAL MANAGEMENT LTD.; *Int'l*, pg. 5785
PENDER GROWTH FUND INC.; *Int'l*, pg. 5785
PENDLETON ASSOCIATES INC; *U.S. Private*, pg. 3132
PENDLETON FLOUR MILLS, LLC.; *U.S. Private*, pg. 3132
PENDLETON GRAIN GROWERS INC.; *U.S. Private*, pg. 3132
PENDLETON WOOLEN MILLS, INC.; *U.S. Private*, pg. 3132
PENDO.IO, INC.; *U.S. Private*, pg. 3132
PENDOPHARM—See Pharmascience Inc.; *Int'l*, pg. 5841
PEND OREILLE PRINTERS INC.—See The Hagadone Corporation; *U.S. Private*, pg. 4041
PENDRAGON CONTRACTS LIMITED—See Pinewood Technologies Group PLC; *Int'l*, pg. 5869
PENDRAGON FINANCE & INSURANCE LIMITED—See Pinewood Technologies Group PLC; *Int'l*, pg. 5869
PENDRAGON JAVELIN LIMITED—See Pinewood Technologies Group PLC; *Int'l*, pg. 5869
PENDRAGON MOTORCYCLES LIMITED—See Pinewood Technologies Group PLC; *Int'l*, pg. 5869
PENDRAGON MOTOR GROUP LIMITED—See Pinewood Technologies Group PLC; *Int'l*, pg. 5869
PENDRAGON PROFESSIONAL INFORMATION LIMITED—See Wilmington plc; *Int'l*, pg. 8422
PENDRAGON VEHICLE MANAGEMENT LIMITED—See Pinewood Technologies Group PLC; *Int'l*, pg. 5869
PENDRELL CORPORATION; *U.S. Public*, pg. 1661
PENDSTER DIALYSIS, LLC—See DaVita Inc.; *U.S. Public*, pg. 642
PENDU MANUFACTURING INC.; *U.S. Private*, pg. 3132
PENDUM LLC—See Marlin Equity Partners, LLC; *U.S. Private*, pg. 2584
PENEGON PROPERTIES, INC.—See Pinewood Technologies Group PLC; *Int'l*, pg. 5869
PENEQUITY REALTY CORPORATION; *Int'l*, pg. 5785
PENERBANGAN MALAYSIA BHD—See Khazanah Nasional Berhad; *Int'l*, pg. 4153
PENERBITAN PELANGI SDN. BHD.—See Pelangi Publishing Group Bhd; *Int'l*, pg. 5782
PENETONE CORPORATION—See Wechco, Inc.; *U.S. Private*, pg. 4468
PENFABRIC SDN. BERHAD—See Toray Industries, Inc.; *Int'l*, pg. 7823
PENFIBRE SDN. BERHAD—See Toray Industries, Inc.; *Int'l*, pg. 7823
PENFUND MANAGEMENT LTD.; *Int'l*, pg. 5785
PENGANA CAPITAL GROUP LIMITED; *Int'l*, pg. 5785
PENGANA INTERNATIONAL EQUITIES LTD—See Pengana Capital Group Limited; *Int'l*, pg. 5785
PENGANGKUTAN COGENT SDN. BHD.—See Ancom Logistics Berhad; *Int'l*, pg. 449
PENGATE HANDLING SYSTEMS INC.; *U.S. Private*, pg. 3132
PENGATE HANDLING SYSTEMS OF NY—See Pengate Handling Systems Inc.; *U.S. Private*, pg. 3133
PENGDU AGRICULTURE & ANIMAL HUSBANDRY CO., LTD.; *Int'l*, pg. 5785
PENGELUARAN GETAH BANDO (MALAYSIA) SDN. BHD.—See Bando Chemical Industries, Ltd.; *Int'l*, pg. 830
PENGER:NO AS—See Schibsted ASA; *Int'l*, pg. 6617
PENGG DRAT S.R.O.—See Berndorf AG; *Int'l*, pg. 987
PENG KOON HEAVY MACHINERY PTE LTD—See Affirma Capital Limited; *Int'l*, pg. 187
PENGLAI JUTAL OFFSHORE ENGINEERING HEAVY INDUSTRIES COMPANY LIMITED—See Jutal Offshore Oil Services Limited; *Int'l*, pg. 4031
PENGO ATTACHMENTS, INC. - COKATO—See Stanley Black & Decker, Inc.; *U.S. Public*, pg. 1933
PENGO ATTACHMENTS, INC.—See Stanley Black & Decker, Inc.; *U.S. Public*, pg. 1933
PENGQI TECHNOLOGY DEVELOPMENT CO., LTD.; *Int'l*, pg. 5786
PENGROWTH ENERGY CORP.—See Waterous Energy Fund; *Int'l*, pg. 8357
PENGUEN GIDA SANAYI A.S.; *Int'l*, pg. 5786
PENGUIN AIR CONDITIONING CORP.—See EMCOR Group, Inc.; *U.S. Public*, pg. 738
PENGUIN AUSTRALIA PTY LTD—See Bertelsmann SE & Co. KGaA; *Int'l*, pg. 991
PENGUIN AUSTRALIA PTY. LTD.—See Pearson plc; *Int'l*, pg. 5776

PENGUEN GIDA SANAYI A.S.

PENGUIN BOOKS BENELUX BV—See Bertelsmann SE & Co. KGaA; *Int'l*, pg. 991
PENGUIN BOOKS DEUTSCHLAND GMBH—See Bertelsmann SE & Co. KGaA; *Int'l*, pg. 991
PENGUIN BOOKS LTD—See Bertelsmann SE & Co. KGaA; *Int'l*, pg. 991
PENGUIN BOOKS (NZ) LTD—See Pearson plc; *Int'l*, pg. 5776
PENGUIN BOOKS, S.A.—See Bertelsmann SE & Co. KGaA; *Int'l*, pg. 991
PENGUIN BOOKS SOUTH AFRICA—See Bertelsmann SE & Co. KGaA; *Int'l*, pg. 991
PENGUIN COMPUTING INC.—See Penguin Solutions, Inc.; *U.S. Public*, pg. 1661
PENGUIN ENGINEERING LIMITED—See Daikin Industries, Ltd.; *Int'l*, pg. 1936
PENGUIN GROUP (NZ) LTD—See Pearson plc; *Int'l*, pg. 5776
PENGUIN GROUP UK—See Bertelsmann SE & Co. KGaA; *Int'l*, pg. 991
PENGUIN GROUP (USA) INC.—See Bertelsmann SE & Co. KGaA; *Int'l*, pg. 991
PENGUIN INTERNATIONAL LIMITED—See Dymon Asia Capital (Singapore) Pte. Ltd; *Int'l*, pg. 2238
PENGUIN IRELAND—See Bertelsmann SE & Co. KGaA; *Int'l*, pg. 991
PENGUIN MARINE BOATS SERVICES L.L.C.—See Dymon Asia Capital (Singapore) Pte. Ltd; *Int'l*, pg. 2238
PENGUIN POINT FRANCHISE SYSTEMS INC; *U.S. Private*, pg. 3133
PENGUIN PUMPS, INC.—See Finish Thompson, Inc.; *U.S. Private*, pg. 1510
PENGUIN RANDOM HOUSE GRUPO EDITORIAL, S.A. DE C.V.—See Bertelsmann SE & Co. KGaA; *Int'l*, pg. 993
PENGUIN RANDOM HOUSE GRUPO EDITORIAL, S.A.—See Bertelsmann SE & Co. KGaA; *Int'l*, pg. 993
PENGUIN RANDOM HOUSE GRUPO EDITORIAL S.A.—See Bertelsmann SE & Co. KGaA; *Int'l*, pg. 993
PENGUIN RANDOM HOUSE GRUPO EDITORIAL S.A.S.—See Bertelsmann SE & Co. KGaA; *Int'l*, pg. 993
PENGUIN RANDOM HOUSE GRUPO EDITORIAL—See Bertelsmann SE & Co. KGaA; *Int'l*, pg. 991
PENGUIN RANDOM HOUSE LLC - CANADA—See Bertelsmann SE & Co. KGaA; *Int'l*, pg. 991
PENGUIN RANDOM HOUSE LLC—See Bertelsmann SE & Co. KGaA; *Int'l*, pg. 990
PENGUIN RANDOM HOUSE LTD.—See Bertelsmann SE & Co. KGaA; *Int'l*, pg. 991
PENGUIN RANDOM HOUSE SOUTH AFRICA (PTY) LTD.—See Bertelsmann SE & Co. KGaA; *Int'l*, pg. 993
PENGUIN RANDOM HOUSE VERLAGSGRUPPE GMBH—See Bertelsmann SE & Co. KGaA; *Int'l*, pg. 993
PENGUIN SHIPYARD INTERNATIONAL PTE LTD—See Dymon Asia Capital (Singapore) Pte. Ltd; *Int'l*, pg. 2238
PENGUIN SOLUTIONS, INC.; *U.S. Public*, pg. 1661
PENGUIN VENTURES B.V.; *Int'l*, pg. 5786
PENGURUSAN PELABURAN ASW 2020 BERHAD—See Permodalan Nasional Berhad; *Int'l*, pg. 5809
PENG USHA MARTIN PVT. LTD.—See Berndorf AG; *Int'l*, pg. 987
PENG USHA MARTIN PVT. LTD.—See Usha Martin Limited; *Int'l*, pg. 8097
PENHALIGON'S LIMITED—See Paine Schwartz Partners, LLC; *U.S. Private*, pg. 3076
PENHALL COMPANY—See H.I.G. Capital, LLC; *U.S. Private*, pg. 1833
PENHALL CO.—See H.I.G. Capital, LLC; *U.S. Private*, pg. 1833
PENINSULA AIRWAYS INC.—See J.F. Lehman & Company, Inc.; *U.S. Private*, pg. 2163
PENINSULA CAPITAL ADVISORS LLP; *Int'l*, pg. 5786
PENINSULA CAPITAL PARTNERS LLC; *U.S. Private*, pg. 3133
PENINSULA CHICAGO LLC—See The Hongkong and Shanghai Hotels Limited; *Int'l*, pg. 7653
THE PENINSULA CHITTAGONG LTD.; *Int'l*, pg. 7673
THE PENINSULA CLARION—See Gannett Co., Inc.; *U.S. Public*, pg. 905
PENINSULA CLEANING SERVICE INC; *U.S. Private*, pg. 3133
PENINSULA CLUBS AND CONSULTANCY SERVICES LIMITED—See The Hongkong and Shanghai Hotels Limited; *Int'l*, pg. 7653
PENINSULA COMMUNITY HEALTH SERVICES OF ALASKA, INC.; *U.S. Private*, pg. 3133
PENINSULA COMMUNITY HEALTH SERVICES; *U.S. Private*, pg. 3133
PENINSULA COMPONENTS INC.; *U.S. Private*, pg. 3133
PENINSULA CONSUMER SERVICES CO-OP ASSOCIATION LTD; *Int'l*, pg. 5786
PENINSULA COPPER INDUSTRIES; *U.S. Private*, pg. 3133
PENINSULA ENERGY LIMITED; *Int'l*, pg. 5786
PENINSULA ENERGY SERVICES COMPANY, INC.—See Chesapeake Utilities Corporation; *U.S. Public*, pg. 486

PENINSULA EYE SURGERY CENTER, LLC—See UnitedHealth Group Incorporated; *U.S. Public*, pg. 2249
PENINSULA FIBER NETWORK, LLC; *U.S. Private*, pg. 3133
PENINSULA FINANCE LLC—See Elliott Management Corporation; *U.S. Private*, pg. 1367
PENINSULA FINANCE LLC—See Vista Equity Partners, LLC; *U.S. Private*, pg. 4396
PENINSULA FLOORS, INC.; *U.S. Private*, pg. 3133
PENINSULA FORD LINCOLN; *Int'l*, pg. 5786
PENINSULA GENERATION COOPERATIVE; *U.S. Private*, pg. 3133
THE PENINSULA GROUP LTD.; *Int'l*, pg. 7673
THE PENINSULA HOTEL LIMITED—See The Hongkong and Shanghai Hotels Limited; *Int'l*, pg. 7653
PENINSULA INDEMNITY COMPANY—See Donegal Group Inc.; *U.S. Public*, pg. 676
PENINSULA INSURANCE COMPANY—See Donegal Group Inc.; *U.S. Public*, pg. 676
PENINSULA LAND LIMITED—See Ashok Piramal Group; *Int'l*, pg. 608
PENINSULA LIGHT COMPANY; *U.S. Private*, pg. 3133
PENINSULA MERCHANDISING LIMITED—See The Hongkong and Shanghai Hotels Limited; *Int'l*, pg. 7653
PENINSULA NEWS—See Alden Global Capital LLC; *U.S. Private*, pg. 158
PENINSULA OF NEW YORK, INC.—See The Hongkong and Shanghai Hotels Limited; *Int'l*, pg. 7653
PENINSULA OF TOKYO LIMITED—See The Hongkong and Shanghai Hotels Limited; *Int'l*, pg. 7653
PENINSULA OIL & PROPANE COMPANY; *U.S. Private*, pg. 3133
PENINSULA PACIFIC STRATEGIC PARTNERS, LLC; *U.S. Private*, pg. 3133
PENINSULA PACKAGING, LLC—See Sonoco Products Company; *U.S. Public*, pg. 1904
PENINSULA PETROLEUM AS—See Gibunco Group Limited; *Int'l*, pg. 2963
PENINSULA PETROLEUM (BROKERS) LTD—See Gibunco Group Limited; *Int'l*, pg. 2963
PENINSULA PETROLEUM DMCC—See Gibunco Group Limited; *Int'l*, pg. 2963
PENINSULA PETROLEUM EPE—See Gibunco Group Limited; *Int'l*, pg. 2963
PENINSULA PETROLEUM FAR EAST PTE LTD—See Gibunco Group Limited; *Int'l*, pg. 2963
PENINSULA PETROLEUM INC—See Gibunco Group Limited; *Int'l*, pg. 2963
PENINSULA PETROLEUM (MONACO) S.A.R.L—See Gibunco Group Limited; *Int'l*, pg. 2963
PENINSULA PETROLEUM PANAMA INC.—See Gibunco Group Limited; *Int'l*, pg. 2963
PENINSULA PETROLEUM SA—See Gibunco Group Limited; *Int'l*, pg. 2963
PENINSULA PETROLEUM SL—See Gibunco Group Limited; *Int'l*, pg. 2963
PENINSULA PETROLEUM SOUTH AMERICA SA—See Gibunco Group Limited; *Int'l*, pg. 2963
PENINSULAR AVIATION SERVICES CO. LTD.—See BP plc; *Int'l*, pg. 1131
PENINSULAR AVIATION SERVICES CO. LTD.—See Saudi Arabian Markets Ltd.; *Int'l*, pg. 6588
PENINSULAR AVIATION SERVICES CO. LTD.—See Shell plc; *Int'l*, pg. 6797
PENINSULAR CYLINDER CO.—See Avis Industrial Corporation; *U.S. Private*, pg. 408
PENINSULAR GOLD LIMITED; *Int'l*, pg. 5786
PENINSULAR HOME SDN BHD—See United Overseas Australia Ltd; *Int'l*, pg. 8071
PENINSULAR PAPER COMPANY, INC.—See Bain Capital, LP; *U.S. Private*, pg. 440
PENINSULA TAVERN (WA) PTY LTD—See Woolworths Group Limited; *Int'l*, pg. 8451
PENINSULATORS, INC.—See The Courtney Group, Incorporated; *U.S. Private*, pg. 4015
PENINSULA TRUCK LINES INC.; *U.S. Private*, pg. 3133
PENLINK AB—See Addtech AB; *Int'l*, pg. 134
PEN-LINK, LTD.; *U.S. Private*, pg. 3132
PENLON LIMITED—See The Goldman Sachs Group, Inc.; *U.S. Public*, pg. 2076
PENNACO ENERGY, INC.—See ConocoPhillips; *U.S. Public*, pg. 569
PENNA CONSULTING LIMITED—See Adecco Group AG; *Int'l*, pg. 139
PENN-AIRE AVIATION INC.; *U.S. Private*, pg. 3135
PENN-AIR & HYDRAULICS CORP.; *U.S. Private*, pg. 3135
PENN A KEM, LLC—See Minafin Sarl; *Int'l*, pg. 4899
PENN ALUMINUM INTERNATIONAL, INC.—See Berkshire Hathaway Inc.; *U.S. Public*, pg. 310
PENN-AMERICA GROUP, INC.—See Paine Schwartz Partners, LLC; *U.S. Private*, pg. 3075
PENN-AMERICA INSURANCE COMPANY—See Paine Schwartz Partners, LLC; *U.S. Private*, pg. 3075
PENNANT AUSTRALASIA PTY LTD.—See Pennant International Group plc; *Int'l*, pg. 5786
PENNANT CANADA LIMITED—See Pennant International Group plc; *Int'l*, pg. 5786

CORPORATE AFFILIATIONS

PENNANT CONSTRUCTION MANAGEMENT, INC.—See McWhorter Capital Partners, LLC; *U.S. Private*, pg. 2645
THE PENNANT GROUP, INC.; *U.S. Public*, pg. 2118
PENNANT INFORMATION SERVICES LIMITED—See Pennant International Group plc; *Int'l*, pg. 5786
PENNANT INTERNATIONAL GROUP PLC; *Int'l*, pg. 5786
PENNANTPARK FLOATING RATE CAPITAL LTD.; *U.S. Public*, pg. 1663
PENNANTPARK INVESTMENT CORPORATION; *U.S. Public*, pg. 1663
PENNANTPARK SBIC GP, LLC—See PennantPark Investment Corporation; *U.S. Public*, pg. 1663
PENNANT SOFTWARE SERVICES LIMITED—See Pennant International Group plc; *Int'l*, pg. 5786
PENNANT SPORTS INC.; *U.S. Public*, pg. 3135
PENNANT TRAINING SYSTEMS LIMITED—See Pennant International Group plc; *Int'l*, pg. 5786
PENNA POWERS BRIAN HAYNES; *U.S. Private*, pg. 3135
PENNAR ENGINEERED BUILDING SYSTEMS LIMITED—See Pennar Industries Limited; *Int'l*, pg. 5786
PENNAR GLOBAL INC.—See Pennar Industries Limited; *Int'l*, pg. 5786
PENNAR INDUSTRIES LIMITED; *Int'l*, pg. 5786
PENN BANCSHARES, INC.; *U.S. Public*, pg. 1661
PENNBARRY—See Canada Pension Plan Investment Board; *Int'l*, pg. 1278
PENN CECIL MARYLAND, INC.—See PENN Entertainment, Inc.; *U.S. Public*, pg. 1662
PENN CENTER INC.—See UnityPoint Health; *U.S. Private*, pg. 4303
PENN CENTER MANAGEMENT CORP.; *U.S. Private*, pg. 3133
PENN CENTRAL COMMUNICATIONS CORP.—See CSX Corporation; *U.S. Public*, pg. 602
PENN CENTRAL COMMUNICATIONS CORP.—See Norfolk Southern Corporation; *U.S. Public*, pg. 1535
PENN-CO CONSTRUCTION CANADA (2003) LTD; *Int'l*, pg. 5786
PENN COLOR INC. - ELMWOOD PARK FACILITY—See Penn Color Inc.; *U.S. Private*, pg. 3133
PENN COLOR INC. - MILTON FACILITY—See Penn Color Inc.; *U.S. Private*, pg. 3133
PENN COLOR INC. - RINGGOLD FACILITY—See Penn Color Inc.; *U.S. Private*, pg. 3133
PENN COLOR INC.; *U.S. Private*, pg. 3133
PENN COLOR INTERNATIONAL BV—See Penn Color Inc.; *U.S. Private*, pg. 3133
PENN COMMUNITY BANK—See Penn Community Financial Corporation; *U.S. Private*, pg. 3134
PENN COMMUNITY FINANCIAL CORPORATION; *U.S. Private*, pg. 3134
THE PENN COMPANIES - IMPRINTSUSA—See The Penn Companies; *U.S. Private*, pg. 4092
THE PENN COMPANIES; *U.S. Private*, pg. 4092
PENNCORP LLC; *U.S. Private*, pg. 3135
PENNCORP LIFE INSURANCE COMPANY—See La Capitale Civil Service Mutual; *Int'l*, pg. 4387
PENNDEL MENTAL HEALTH CENTER, INC.; *U.S. Private*, pg. 3135
PENNEBAKER LLC—See Comcast Corporation; *U.S. Public*, pg. 541
PENNECON ENERGY LTD.—See Penney Group; *Int'l*, pg. 5787
PENNECON HEAVY CIVIL LIMITED—See Penney Group; *Int'l*, pg. 5787
PENNECON HEAVY CIVIL LIMITED—See Penney Group; *Int'l*, pg. 5787
PENNECON LIMITED—See Penney Group; *Int'l*, pg. 5786
PENNE INTERNATIONAL NV—See BNP Paribas SA; *Int'l*, pg. 1092
PENN ELASTIC GMBH—See Sherpa Capital SL; *Int'l*, pg. 6826
PENN EMBLEM CO.—See The Penn Companies; *U.S. Private*, pg. 4092
PENN ENERGY RESOURCES, LLC; *U.S. Private*, pg. 3134
PENNENGINEERING FASTENING TECHNOLOGIES—See Tinicum Enterprises, Inc.; *U.S. Private*, pg. 4174
PENN ENGINEERING & MANUFACTURING CORP.—See Tinicum Enterprises, Inc.; *U.S. Private*, pg. 4174
PENNENGINEERING & MANUFACTURING CORP.—See Tinicum Enterprises, Inc.; *U.S. Private*, pg. 4174
PENN ENTERTAINMENT, INC.; *U.S. Public*, pg. 1661
PENN ENVIRONMENTAL & REMEDIATION, INC.—See Penn Color Inc.; *U.S. Private*, pg. 3133
PENNEO A/S; *Int'l*, pg. 5786
PENN ERIE DIVISION—See The Plastek Group; *U.S. Private*, pg. 4096
PENNER INTERNATIONAL INC.; *Int'l*, pg. 5786
PENNEXX FOODS, INC.; *U.S. Public*, pg. 1663
PENNEY GROUP; *Int'l*, pg. 5786
PENNFIELD CORPORATION; *U.S. Private*, pg. 3136
PENNFIELD PRECISION INCORPORATED; *U.S. Private*, pg. 3136

COMPANY NAME INDEX

PENN FISHING TACKLE MANUFACTURING COMPANY—See Sycamore Partners Management, LP; *U.S. Private*, pg. 3896
PENN FLORIDA CAPITAL CORP.; *U.S. Private*, pg. 3134
PENN FOSTER, INC.—See IAC Inc.; *U.S. Public*, pg. 1083
PENN GARRITANO DIRECT RESPONSE MARKETING; *U.S. Private*, pg. 3134
PENNG AUSTRIA GMBH—See Berndorf AG; *Int'l*, pg. 987
PENN GLOBAL MARKETING, LLC—See Integrity Marketing Group LLC; *U.S. Private*, pg. 2104
PENN HIGHLANDS BROOKVILLE—See Penn Highlands Healthcare; *U.S. Private*, pg. 3134
PENN HIGHLANDS HEALTHCARE; *U.S. Private*, pg. 3134
PENNICHUCK CORPORATION; *U.S. Private*, pg. 3136
PENNICHUCK EAST UTILITY, INC.—See Pennichuck Corporation; *U.S. Private*, pg. 3136
PENNICHUCK WATER SERVICE CORP.—See Pennichuck Corporation; *U.S. Private*, pg. 3136
PENNICHUCK WATER WORKS, INC.—See Pennichuck Corporation; *U.S. Private*, pg. 3136
PENNINE FOODS—See Boparan Holdings Limited; *Int'l*, pg. 1111
PENNINE TELECOM LTD.; *Int'l*, pg. 5787
PENNINGTON GAP HMA, INC.—See Community Health Systems, Inc.; *U.S. Public*, pg. 555
PENNINGTON'S ADDITIONELLE LTD.—See Reitmans (Canada) Limited; *Int'l*, pg. 6259
PENNINGTON SEED INC.—See Central Garden & Pet Company; *U.S. Public*, pg. 473
PENNINGTONS INC.; *U.S. Private*, pg. 3136
PENN INSURANCE & ANNUITY CO.—See The Penn Mutual Life Insurance Company; *U.S. Private*, pg. 4092
PENN JERSEY PAPER CO.; *U.S. Private*, pg. 3134
PENN LINE CORP.; *U.S. Private*, pg. 3134
PENN LINE SERVICE, INC.—See Penn Line Corp.; *U.S. Private*, pg. 3134
PENN LOCOMOTIVE GEAR—See Berkshire Hathaway Inc.; *U.S. Public*, pg. 311
PENN LYON HOMES INC.; *U.S. Private*, pg. 3134
PENN MACHINE COMPANY—See Berkshire Hathaway Inc.; *U.S. Public*, pg. 311
PENN MARITIME INC.—See Kirby Corporation; *U.S. Public*, pg. 1236
PENN-MAR ORGANIZATION, INC.; *U.S. Private*, pg. 3135
PENN-MAR ORGANIZATION, INC.—See Penn-Mar Organization, Inc.; *U.S. Private*, pg. 3135
PENN/MD MATERIALS—See Haines & Kibblehouse Inc.; *U.S. Private*, pg. 1841
THE PENN MUTUAL LIFE INSURANCE COMPANY; *U.S. Private*, pg. 4092
PENN NATIONAL HOLDING CORP.—See Pennsylvania National Mutual Casualty Insurance Company; *U.S. Private*, pg. 3137
PENN NATIONAL SECURITY INSURANCE COMPANY—See Pennsylvania National Mutual Casualty Insurance Company; *U.S. Private*, pg. 3137
PENN NON-DESTRUCTIVE TESTING, LLC—See Mistras Group, Inc.; *U.S. Public*, pg. 1451
PENNOCK COMPANY; *U.S. Private*, pg. 3136
PENN-OHIO COAL CO.—See Kimble Companies Inc.; *U.S. Private*, pg. 2305
PENNON GROUP PLC; *Int'l*, pg. 5787
PENNONI ASSOCIATES INC. - NEW YORK—See Pennoni Associates Inc.; *U.S. Private*, pg. 3136
PENNONI ASSOCIATES INC.; *U.S. Private*, pg. 3136
PENNON WATER SERVICES LIMITED—See Pennon Group PLC; *Int'l*, pg. 5787
THE PENNOYER GROUP, INC.—See ABRY Partners, LLC; *U.S. Private*, pg. 43
PENNPETRO ENERGY PLC; *Int'l*, pg. 5787
PENN-PLAX, INC.; *U.S. Private*, pg. 3135
PENN POWER GROUP, LLC; *U.S. Private*, pg. 3134
PENN POWER SYSTEMS—See Penn Power Group, LLC; *U.S. Private*, pg. 3134
PENN PRIDE INC—See Alexa Energy Ltd.; *U.S. Private*, pg. 163
PENN'S BEST INC.; *U.S. Private*, pg. 3135
PENN SCHOEN BERLAND ASSOCIATES INC.; *U.S. Private*, pg. 3134
PENN SCHOEN & BERLAND—See Penn Schoen Berland Associates Inc.; *U.S. Private*, pg. 3134
PENN SHORE WINERY & VINEYARDS; *U.S. Private*, pg. 3134
PENNSPRING CAPITAL, LLC; *U.S. Private*, pg. 3136
PENN-STAR INSURANCE COMPANY—See Paine Schwartz Partners, LLC; *U.S. Private*, pg. 3075
PENN STATE HEALTH; *U.S. Private*, pg. 3134
PENN STATE SEED CO. INC.; *U.S. Private*, pg. 3135
PENN STATE TOOL & DIE CORPORATION; *U.S. Private*, pg. 3135
PENNSUCO CEMENT CO. LLC—See Titan Cement Company S.A.; *Int'l*, pg. 7760
PENNS WOOD PHYSICAL THERAPY, LIMITED PARTNERSHIP—See U.S. Physical Therapy, Inc.; *U.S. Public*, pg. 2215
PENNS WOODS BANCORP, INC.; *U.S. Public*, pg. 1663

PENNSYLVANIA AGRICULTURAL COMMODITIES MARKETING ASSOCIATION—See Perdue Farms Incorporated; *U.S. Private*, pg. 3147
PENNSYLVANIA AMERICAN WATER—See American Water Works Company, Inc.; *U.S. Public*, pg. 112
PENNSYLVANIA BALLET; *U.S. Private*, pg. 3136
PENNSYLVANIA BAR INSTITUTE; *U.S. Private*, pg. 3136
THE PENNSYLVANIA COALITION AGAINST DOMESTIC VIOLENCE; *U.S. Private*, pg. 4092
PENNSYLVANIA COMPENSATION RATING BUREAU; *U.S. Private*, pg. 3136
PENNSYLVANIA CVS PHARMACY, L.L.C.—See CVS Health Corporation; *U.S. Public*, pg. 616
PENNSYLVANIA ELECTRIC COMPANY—See FirstEnergy Corp.; *U.S. Public*, pg. 849
THE PENNSYLVANIA EMPLOYEES BENEFIT TRUST FUND; *U.S. Private*, pg. 4093
PENNSYLVANIA EXTRUDED TUBE CO.—See Sandvik AB; *Int'l*, pg. 6535
PENNSYLVANIA GENERAL ENERGY; *U.S. Private*, pg. 3136
PENNSYLVANIA GLASS SAND CORPORATION—See Apollo Global Management, Inc.; *U.S. Public*, pg. 165
PENNSYLVANIA GRANITE CORP.—See TorQuest Partners Inc.; *Int'l*, pg. 7830
PENNSYLVANIA HEALTH & WELLNESS, INC.—See Centene Corporation; *U.S. Public*, pg. 470
PENNSYLVANIA INTERACTIVE, LLC—See Tyler Technologies, Inc.; *U.S. Public*, pg. 2209
PENNSYLVANIA LIBRARY ASSOCIATION.; *U.S. Private*, pg. 3136
PENNSYLVANIA LUMBERMENS MUTUAL INSURANCE COMPANY; *U.S. Public*, pg. 1663
PENNSYLVANIA MACARONI COMPANY; *U.S. Private*, pg. 3137
PENNSYLVANIA MACHINE WORKS, LLC—See Wynnchurch Capital, L.P.; *U.S. Private*, pg. 4577
PENNSYLVANIA MANUFACTURERS' ASSOCIATION INSURANCE COMPANY—See Old Republic International Corporation; *U.S. Public*, pg. 1568
PENNSYLVANIA MANUFACTURERS INDEMNITY COMPANY—See Old Republic International Corporation; *U.S. Public*, pg. 1568
PENNSYLVANIA MEDIA ASSOCIATES—See Salem Media Group, Inc.; *U.S. Public*, pg. 1836
PENNSYLVANIA NATIONAL MUTUAL CASUALTY INSURANCE COMPANY; *U.S. Private*, pg. 3137
PENNSYLVANIA NATIONAL TURF CLUB, LLC—See PENN Entertainment, Inc.; *U.S. Public*, pg. 1662
PENNSYLVANIA POWER COMPANY—See FirstEnergy Corp.; *U.S. Public*, pg. 849
PENNSYLVANIA PROFESSIONAL LIABILITY JOINT UNDERWRITING ASSOCIATION; *U.S. Private*, pg. 3137
PENNSYLVANIA PROPERTIES, INC.—See Senvest Capital, Inc.; *Int'l*, pg. 6715
PENNSYLVANIA PROPERTY AND CASUALTY INSURANCE GUARANTY ASSOCIATION; *U.S. Private*, pg. 3137
PENNSYLVANIA PSYCHIATRIC INSTITUTE; *U.S. Private*, pg. 3137
PENNSYLVANIA REAL ESTATE INVESTMENT TRUST; *U.S. Public*, pg. 1663
PENNSYLVANIA RESOURCES CORP.; *U.S. Private*, pg. 3137
PENNSYLVANIA SCALE COMPANY—See The A.H. Emery Company; *U.S. Private*, pg. 3980
PENNSYLVANIA SCHOOL OF BUSINESS, INC.—See EVCI Career Colleges Holding Corp.; *U.S. Private*, pg. 1436
PENNSYLVANIA SLING CO. INC.—See ALP Industries, Inc.; *U.S. Private*, pg. 196
PENNSYLVANIA STATE EMPLOYEES CREDIT UNION; *U.S. Private*, pg. 3137
PENNSYLVANIA STEEL COMPANY - ALLENTOWN DIVISION—See Pennsylvania Steel Company, Inc; *U.S. Private*, pg. 3137
PENNSYLVANIA STEEL COMPANY - CONNECTICUT DIVISION—See Pennsylvania Steel Company, Inc; *U.S. Private*, pg. 3137
PENNSYLVANIA STEEL COMPANY, INC; *U.S. Private*, pg. 3137
PENNSYLVANIA STEEL COMPANY - LONG ISLAND DIVISION—See Pennsylvania Steel Company, Inc; *U.S. Private*, pg. 3137
PENNSYLVANIA STEEL COMPANY, LUCAS STEEL DIVISION—See Pennsylvania Steel Company, Inc; *U.S. Private*, pg. 3137
PENNSYLVANIA STEEL COMPANY - RICHMOND DIVISION—See Pennsylvania Steel Company, Inc; *U.S. Private*, pg. 3137
PENNSYLVANIA TOOL SALES & SERVICE; *U.S. Private*, pg. 3137
PENNSYLVANIA TRANSFORMER TECHNOLOGY INC.—See Quanta Services, Inc.; *U.S. Public*, pg. 1752
PENNSYLVANIA TRUCK CENTERS, INC.; *U.S. Private*, pg. 3137
PENNSYLVANIA TRUST CO.—See Fiduciary Company Incorporated; *U.S. Private*, pg. 1503

PENSERRA SECURITIES LLC

PENNSYLVANIA TURNPIKE COMMISSION; *U.S. Private*, pg. 3137
PENNSY SUPPLY, INC.—See CRH plc; *Int'l*, pg. 1847
PENN TANK LINES INC.; *U.S. Private*, pg. 3135
PENN TERMINALS INC.—See Temasek Holdings (Private) Limited; *Int'l*, pg. 7549
PENN TREATY AMERICAN CORPORATION; *U.S. Private*, pg. 3135
PENN TREATY NETWORK AMERICA INSURANCE COMPANY—See Penn Treaty American Corporation; *U.S. Private*, pg. 3135
PENN UNITED COSTA RICA SA—See Penn United Technologies, Inc.; *U.S. Private*, pg. 3135
PENN UNITED TECHNOLOGIES, INC. - CARBIDE DIVISION—See Penn United Technologies, Inc.; *U.S. Private*, pg. 3135
PENN UNITED TECHNOLOGIES, INC.; *U.S. Private*, pg. 3135
PENN VIRGINIA MC ENERGY LLC—See Baytex Energy Corp.; *Int'l*, pg. 915
PENN VIRGINIA OIL & GAS CORP.—See Baytex Energy Corp.; *Int'l*, pg. 915
PENN VIRGINIA OIL & GAS GP LLC—See Baytex Energy Corp.; *Int'l*, pg. 915
PENN VIRGINIA OIL & GAS LP LLC—See Baytex Energy Corp.; *Int'l*, pg. 915
PENN VIRGINIA OIL & GAS, L.P.—See Baytex Energy Corp.; *Int'l*, pg. 915
PENN WARRANTY CORPORATION; *U.S. Private*, pg. 3135
PENN WOOD PRODUCTS INC.; *U.S. Private*, pg. 3135
PENNY AUCTION SOLUTIONS, INC.; *U.S. Private*, pg. 3137
PENNY & GILES AEROSPACE LTD.—See Curtiss-Wright Corporation; *U.S. Public*, pg. 611
PENNY & GILES CONTROLS INC—See Curtiss-Wright Corporation; *U.S. Public*, pg. 611
PENNY & GILES CONTROLS LTD.—See Curtiss-Wright Corporation; *U.S. Public*, pg. 611
PENNY & GILES CONTROLS LTD.—See Curtiss-Wright Corporation; *U.S. Public*, pg. 611
PENNY & GILES GMBH—See Curtiss-Wright Corporation; *U.S. Public*, pg. 612
PENNY HYDRAULICS LTD.; *Int'l*, pg. 5787
PENNYMAC CORP.—See PennyMac Mortgage Investment Trust; *U.S. Public*, pg. 1664
PENNYMAC FINANCIAL SERVICES, INC.; *U.S. Public*, pg. 1664
PENNYMAC LOAN SERVICES, LLC—See PennyMac Financial Services, Inc.; *U.S. Public*, pg. 1664
PENNYMAC MORTGAGE INVESTMENT TRUST; *U.S. Public*, pg. 1664
PENNY NEWMAN GRAIN COMPANY; *U.S. Private*, pg. 3137
PENNY/OHLMANN/NEIMAN, INC.; *U.S. Private*, pg. 3138
PENNY PLATE, INC.; *U.S. Private*, pg. 3137
PENNY PUBLICATIONS, LLC; *U.S. Private*, pg. 3137
PENNYRILE FORD; *U.S. Private*, pg. 3138
PENNYRILE RURAL ELECTRIC COOPERATIVE CORPORATION; *U.S. Private*, pg. 3138
PENNYROYAL REGIONAL MENTAL HEALTH, MENTAL RETARDATION BOARD, INC.; *U.S. Private*, pg. 3138
PENNYSAVER GROUP INC—See SV Investment Partners; *U.S. Private*, pg. 3888
PENNY'S CONCRETE INC.; *U.S. Private*, pg. 3137
PENNYWORTH HOMES INCORPORATED; *U.S. Private*, pg. 3138
PENOBSCOT MCCRUM LLC; *U.S. Private*, pg. 3138
PENOBSCOT RIVER RESTORATION TRUST; *U.S. Private*, pg. 3138
PENOLES METALS & CHEMICALS INC—See Grupo BAL; *Int'l*, pg. 3121
PENPOWER TECHNOLOGY LTD.; *Int'l*, pg. 5787
PENRAD TECHNOLOGIES, INC.—See HgCapital Trust plc; *Int'l*, pg. 3376
THE PENRAY COMPANIES, INC.—See The Pritzker Group - Chicago, LLC; *U.S. Private*, pg. 4099
PENRECO—See Calumet, Inc.; *U.S. Public*, pg. 425
PENRITH MEDICAL CENTRE NO. 2 PTY LIMITED—See Sonic Healthcare Limited; *Int'l*, pg. 7098
THE PENROD COMPANY INC.; *U.S. Private*, pg. 4093
PENSACOLA GLASS COMPANY—See Dothan Glass Co. Inc.; *U.S. Private*, pg. 1265
PENSACOLA NEWS-JOURNAL—See Gannett Co., Inc.; *U.S. Public*, pg. 899
PENSACOLA READY MIX, LLC.; *U.S. Private*, pg. 3138
PENSAFE INC.; *Int'l*, pg. 5787
PENSALAB SA—See HORIBA Ltd; *Int'l*, pg. 3478
PENSAM CAPITAL, LLC; *U.S. Private*, pg. 3138
PENSANA METALS LTD.; *Int'l*, pg. 5787
PENSANA PLC; *Int'l*, pg. 5787
PENSAR DEVELOPMENT INC; *U.S. Private*, pg. 3138
PENSER MAITRISER TECHNICITE LOGISTIQUE P.M.T.L S.A.S.—See HENSOLDT AG; *Int'l*, pg. 3356
PENSERRA SECURITIES LLC; *U.S. Private*, pg. 3138
PENSERSC—See The Suddath Companies; *U.S. Private*, pg. 4124
PENSIA ELECTRONIC SDN. BHD.—See Pensonic Holdings Berhad; *Int'l*, pg. 5788

PENSIOEN ESC—See Swiss Life Holding; *Int'l*, pg. 7368
PENSION ASSURANCE COMPANY DOVERIE AD—See Vienna Insurance Group AG Wiener Versicherung Gruppe; *Int'l*, pg. 8195
PENSIONBEE GROUP PLC; *Int'l*, pg. 5787
PENSIONBEE LIMITED—See PensionBee Group Plc; *Int'l*, pg. 5787
PENSION BENEFITS UNLIMITED, INC.—See Lightyear Capital LLC; *U.S. Private*, pg. 2454
PENSION CONSULT-BERATUNGSGESELLSCHAFT FUR ALTERSVORSORGE MBH—See DZ BANK AG Deutsche Zentral-Genossenschaftsbank; *Int'l*, pg. 2244
PENSION INSURANCE COMPANY DOVERIE AD—See Vienna Insurance Group AG Wiener Versicherung Gruppe; *Int'l*, pg. 8195
PENSION INSURANCE CORPORATION; *Int'l*, pg. 5787
PENSIONMARK RETIREMENT GROUP LLC—See World Insurance Associates LLC; *U.S. Private*, pg. 4566
PENSIONS & INVESTMENTS—See Crain Communications, Inc.; *U.S. Private*, pg. 1084
PENSKE AUSTRALIA PTY. LTD.—See Penske Automotive Group, Inc.; *U.S. Public*, pg. 1665
PENSKE AUTOMOTIVE EUROPE GMBH—See Penske Automotive Group, Inc.; *U.S. Public*, pg. 1665
PENSKE AUTOMOTIVE GROUP, INC. - ARIZONA—See Penske Automotive Group, Inc.; *U.S. Public*, pg. 1665
PENSKE AUTOMOTIVE GROUP, INC.; *U.S. Public*, pg. 1664
PENSKE AUTOMOTIVE GROUP, INC. - SOUTHERN CALIFORNIA—See Penske Automotive Group, Inc.; *U.S. Public*, pg. 1665
PENSKE BUICK-GMC TRUCKS, INC.; *U.S. Private*, pg. 3138
PENSKE CADILLAC OF CALIFORNIA, INC.—See Penske Automotive Group, Inc.; *U.S. Public*, pg. 1665
PENSKE CAR RENTAL MEMPHIS, LLC—See Penske Automotive Group, Inc.; *U.S. Public*, pg. 1665
PENSKE COMMERCIAL VEHICLES INVESTMENTS NZ PTY LTD.—See Penske Automotive Group, Inc.; *U.S. Public*, pg. 1665
PENSKE COMMERCIAL VEHICLES NZ—See Penske Automotive Group, Inc.; *U.S. Public*, pg. 1665
PENSKE CORPORATION; *U.S. Private*, pg. 3138
PENSKE HONDA OF INDIANAPOLIS—See Penske Automotive Group, Inc.; *U.S. Public*, pg. 1665
PENSKE LOGISTICS, LLC—See Penske Corporation; *U.S. Private*, pg. 3138
PENSKE MEDIA CORPORATION; *U.S. Private*, pg. 3139
PENSKE NEW ZEALAND—See Penske Automotive Group, Inc.; *U.S. Public*, pg. 1665
PENSKE POWER SYSTEMS PTY LTD—See Penske Automotive Group, Inc.; *U.S. Public*, pg. 1665
PENSKE RACING, INC.—See Penske Corporation; *U.S. Private*, pg. 3138
PENSKE SPORTWAGEN HAMBURG GMBH—See Penske Automotive Group, Inc.; *U.S. Public*, pg. 1665
PENSKE SPORTWAGENZENTRUM GMBH—See Penske Automotive Group, Inc.; *U.S. Public*, pg. 1665
PENSKE TRUCK LEASING COMPANY, L.P.—See Mitsui & Co., Ltd.; *Int'l*, pg. 4979
PENSKE TRUCK LEASING COMPANY, L.P.—See Penske Automotive Group, Inc.; *U.S. Public*, pg. 1665
PENSKE TRUCK LEASING COMPANY, L.P.—See Penske Corporation; *U.S. Private*, pg. 3139
PENSKE TRUCK RENTAL—See Mitsui & Co., Ltd.; *Int'l*, pg. 4980
PENSKE TRUCK RENTAL—See Penske Automotive Group, Inc.; *U.S. Public*, pg. 1666
PENSKE TRUCK RENTAL—See Penske Corporation; *U.S. Private*, pg. 3139
PENSLER CAPITAL CORPORATION; *U.S. Private*, pg. 3139
PENSLOW MEDICAL CENTER—See Wilmington Health Associates, Pa.; *U.S. Private*, pg. 4529
PENS N MORE; *U.S. Private*, pg. 3138
PENSONIC (CAMBODIA) CO., LTD.—See Pensonic Holdings Berhad; *Int'l*, pg. 5788
PENSONIC (H.K.) CORPORATION LIMITED—See Pensonic Holdings Berhad; *Int'l*, pg. 5788
PENSONIC HOLDINGS BERHAD; *Int'l*, pg. 5787
PENSONIC INDUSTRIES SDN. BHD.—See Pensonic Holdings Berhad; *Int'l*, pg. 5788
PENSONIC SALES & SERVICE SDN. BHD.—See Pensonic Holdings Berhad; *Int'l*, pg. 5788
PENS & PLASTICS (GHANA) LTD.—See Toyota Tsusho Corporation; *Int'l*, pg. 7876
PENTA-91 OOO—See Illinois Tool Works Inc.; *U.S. Public*, pg. 1109
PENTA CAPITAL LLP; *Int'l*, pg. 5788
PENTACON GMBH—See Jos. Schneider Optische Werke GmbH; *Int'l*, pg. 4000
THE PENTAD GROUP PTY. LTD.—See Capricorn Investment Partners Limited; *Int'l*, pg. 1316
PENTA DON OOO—See Illinois Tool Works Inc.; *U.S. Public*, pg. 1110
PENTA ELECTROMEC PVT. LTD.—See Daeyang Electric Co.; *Int'l*, pg. 1911
PENTA EXIM PVT. LTD.—See Gravita India Limited; *Int'l*, pg. 3062

PENTAFOUR SOLUTIONS, LLC; *U.S. Private*, pg. 3139
PENTA GOLD LTD.; *Int'l*, pg. 5788
PENTAGON CHEMICAL SPECIALTIES LTD.; *Int'l*, pg. 5788
PENTAGON COATING TECHNOLOGIES SDN. BHD.—See HPMT Holding Berhad; *Int'l*, pg. 3501
PENTAGON FEDERAL CREDIT UNION FOUNDATION—See Pentagon Federal Credit Union; *U.S. Private*, pg. 3140
PENTAGON FEDERAL CREDIT UNION; *U.S. Private*, pg. 3139
PENTAGON FINE CHEMICALS LTD.—See Pentagon Chemical Specialties Ltd.; *Int'l*, pg. 5789
PENTAGON FREIGHT SERVICES, INC.; *U.S. Private*, pg. 3140
PENTAGON TECHNOLOGIES GROUP, INC.—See Kurita Water Industries Ltd.; *Int'l*, pg. 4340
PENTAGRAM DESIGN, INC.; *U.S. Private*, pg. 3140
PENTAHO CORPORATION—See Hitachi, Ltd.; *Int'l*, pg. 3414
PENTAHO UK—See Hitachi, Ltd.; *Int'l*, pg. 3414
PENTA INTERNATIONAL CORP.; *U.S. Private*, pg. 3139
PENTA INVESTMENTS LIMITED; *Int'l*, pg. 5788
PENTA INVESTMENTS LTD.—See Penta Investments Limited; *Int'l*, pg. 5788
PENTAIR CANADA, INC.—See Pentair plc; *Int'l*, pg. 5789
PENTAIR CLEAN PROCESS TECHNOLOGIES INDIA PRIVATE LIMITED—See Pentair plc; *Int'l*, pg. 5789
PENTAIR CONTROL BEIJING CO., LTD.—See Pentair plc; *Int'l*, pg. 5789
PENTAIR EUROPEAN INVESTMENTS (DEUTSCHLAND) GMBH—See Pentair plc; *Int'l*, pg. 5789
PENTAIR EUROPEAN SECURITY HOLDINGS SA—See Pentair plc; *Int'l*, pg. 5789
PENTAIR FLOW CONTROL INTERNATIONAL PTY. LIMITED—See Pentair plc; *Int'l*, pg. 5789
PENTAIR FLOW CONTROL PACIFIC PTY. LIMITED—See Pentair plc; *Int'l*, pg. 5789
PENTAIR FRANCE SARL—See Pentair plc; *Int'l*, pg. 5789
PENTAIR, INC.—See Pentair plc; *Int'l*, pg. 5790
PENTAIR INTERNATIONAL ARMATUREN HOLDING GMBH—See Pentair plc; *Int'l*, pg. 5789
PENTAIR INTERNATIONAL PLT DEUTSCHLAND GMBH—See Pentair plc; *Int'l*, pg. 5789
PENTAIR INTERNATIONAL PLT KLARTECHNIK GMBH—See Pentair plc; *Int'l*, pg. 5789
PENTAIR INTERNATIONAL PLT UMWELTTECHNIK GMBH—See Pentair plc; *Int'l*, pg. 5789
PENTAIR MANUFACTURING BELGIUM BVBA—See Pentair plc; *Int'l*, pg. 5789
PENTAIR PLC; *Int'l*, pg. 5789
PENTAIR PRIVATE, LIMITED—See Pentair plc; *Int'l*, pg. 5790
PENTAIR PUMP GROUP, INC.—See Pentair plc; *Int'l*, pg. 5790
PENTAIR TECHNICAL PRODUCTS CHINA—See Pentair plc; *Int'l*, pg. 5790
PENTAIR TECHNICAL PRODUCTS, INC.—See Pentair plc; *Int'l*, pg. 5790
PENTAIR TECHNICAL PRODUCTS INDIA PRIVATE LIMITED—See Pentair plc; *Int'l*, pg. 5790
PENTAIR THAILAND LTD.—See Pentair plc; *Int'l*, pg. 5790
PENTAIR THERMAL CONTROLS NORWAY AS—See Pentair plc; *Int'l*, pg. 5790
PENTAIR THERMAL MANAGEMENT CANADA LTD.—See Pentair plc; *Int'l*, pg. 5790
PENTAIR THERMAL MANAGEMENT HOLDINGS B LLC—See Pentair plc; *Int'l*, pg. 5790
PENTAIR THERMAL MANAGEMENT HOLDINGS LLC—See Pentair plc; *Int'l*, pg. 5790
PENTAIR THERMAL MANAGEMENT INDIA PRIVATE LIMITED—See Pentair plc; *Int'l*, pg. 5790
PENTAIR THERMAL MANAGEMENT JAPAN CO., LTD.—See Pentair plc; *Int'l*, pg. 5790
PENTAIR THERMAL MANAGEMENT KOREA LTD.—See Pentair plc; *Int'l*, pg. 5790
PENTAIR THERMAL MANAGEMENT KZ LLP—See Pentair plc; *Int'l*, pg. 5790
PENTAIR THERMAL MANAGEMENT LLC—See Pentair plc; *Int'l*, pg. 5790
PENTAIR THERMAL MANAGEMENT NORDIC AB—See Pentair plc; *Int'l*, pg. 5790
PENTAIR THERMAL MANAGEMENT NORWAY AS—See Pentair plc; *Int'l*, pg. 5790
PENTAIR THERMAL MANAGEMENT POLSKA SP. Z O.O.—See Pentair plc; *Int'l*, pg. 5790
PENTAIR UMWELTTECHNIK GMBH—See Pentair plc; *Int'l*, pg. 5790
PENTAIR VALVES & CONTROLS BRASIL LTDA.—See Emerson Electric Co.; *U.S. Public*, pg. 751
PENTAIR VALVES & CONTROLS CANADA INC. - BURLINGTON OFFICE—See Emerson Electric Co.; *U.S. Public*, pg. 751
PENTAIR VALVES & CONTROLS CANADA INC.—See Emerson Electric Co.; *U.S. Public*, pg. 751
PENTAIR VALVES & CONTROLS DISTRIBUTION CZECH S.R.O.—See Emerson Electric Co.; *U.S. Public*, pg. 751

PENTAIR VALVES & CONTROLS (FRANCE) S.C.A.—See Emerson Electric Co.; *U.S. Public*, pg. 751
PENTAIR VALVES & CONTROLS, INC. - BATON ROUGE—See Emerson Electric Co.; *U.S. Public*, pg. 751
PENTAIR VALVES & CONTROLS, INC. - BRIDGEPORT—See Emerson Electric Co.; *U.S. Public*, pg. 751
PENTAIR VALVES & CONTROLS, INC. - CORONA—See Emerson Electric Co.; *U.S. Public*, pg. 751
PENTAIR VALVES & CONTROLS, INC. - PROPHETSTOWN—See Emerson Electric Co.; *U.S. Public*, pg. 751
PENTAIR VALVES & CONTROLS, INC.—See Emerson Electric Co.; *U.S. Public*, pg. 751
PENTAIR VALVES & CONTROLS, INC. - STAFFORD—See Emerson Electric Co.; *U.S. Public*, pg. 751
PENTAIR VALVES & CONTROLS INDIA PVT. LTD.—See Emerson Electric Co.; *U.S. Public*, pg. 751
PENTAIR VALVES & CONTROLS ITALIA S.R.L.—See Emerson Electric Co.; *U.S. Public*, pg. 751
PENTAIR VALVES & CONTROLS (M) SDN. BHD.—See Emerson Electric Co.; *U.S. Public*, pg. 751
PENTAIR VALVES & CONTROLS POLSKA SP. Z O.O.—See Emerson Electric Co.; *U.S. Public*, pg. 751
PENTAIR VALVES & CONTROLS SINGAPORE PTE. LTD.—See Emerson Electric Co.; *U.S. Public*, pg. 751
PENTAIR VALVES & CONTROLS (TAIWAN) LTD.—See Emerson Electric Co.; *U.S. Public*, pg. 751
PENTAIR VALVES & CONTROLS (THAILAND) LTD.—See Emerson Electric Co.; *U.S. Public*, pg. 751
PENTAIR WATER BELGIUM N.V.—See Pentair plc; *Int'l*, pg. 5791
PENTAIR WATER GERMANY GMBH—See Pentair plc; *Int'l*, pg. 5790
PENTAIR WATER GROUP, INC. - DOVER—See Pentair plc; *Int'l*, pg. 5791
PENTAIR WATER GROUP, INC.—See Pentair plc; *Int'l*, pg. 5791
PENTAIR WATER ITALY S.R.L.—See Pentair plc; *Int'l*, pg. 5791
PENTAIR WATER LATINAMERICA S.A.—See Pentair plc; *Int'l*, pg. 5790
PENTAIR WATER POLSKA SP.Z.O.O.—See Pentair plc; *Int'l*, pg. 5790
PENTAIR WATER POOL & SPA, INC. - CALIFORNIA—See Pentair plc; *Int'l*, pg. 5791
PENTAIR WATER POOL & SPA, INC.—See Pentair plc; *Int'l*, pg. 5791
PENTAIR WATER (SUZHOU) CO. LTD.—See Pentair plc; *Int'l*, pg. 5791
PENTAIR WATER TREATMENT—See Pentair plc; *Int'l*, pg. 5791
PENTA LAS AMERICAS ADMINISTRADORA DE FONDOS DE INVERSION SA—See Empresas Penta S.A.; *Int'l*, pg. 2391
PENTA LASER ZHEJIANG CO., LTD.—See El.En. S.p.A.; *Int'l*, pg. 2342
PENTA LATEX LLP—See Mankind Pharma Ltd.; *Int'l*, pg. 4673
PENTAL GRANITE & MARBLE, LLC—See Architectural Surfaces Group, LLC; *U.S. Private*, pg. 311
PENTAL LIMITED; *Int'l*, pg. 5791
PENTALVER CANNOCK LIMITED—See Brookfield Infrastructure Partners L.P.; *Int'l*, pg. 1192
PENTALVER CANNOCK LIMITED—See GIC Pte. Ltd.; *Int'l*, pg. 2966
PENTALVER TRANSPORT LIMITED—See Brookfield Infrastructure Partners L.P.; *Int'l*, pg. 1192
PENTALVER TRANSPORT LIMITED—See GIC Pte. Ltd.; *Int'l*, pg. 2966
PENTAMASTER AUTOMATION (GERMANY) GMBH—See Pentamaster Corporation Berhad; *Int'l*, pg. 5791
PENTAMASTER AUTOMATION (JAPAN) CO., LTD.—See Pentamaster Corporation Berhad; *Int'l*, pg. 5791
PENTAMASTER CORPORATION BERHAD; *Int'l*, pg. 5791
PENTAMASTER EQUIPMENT MANUFACTURING SDN. BHD.—See Pentamaster Corporation Berhad; *Int'l*, pg. 5791
PENTAMASTER INTERNATIONAL LTD.—See Pentamaster Corporation Berhad; *Int'l*, pg. 5791
PENTAMEDIA GRAPHICS LIMITED; *Int'l*, pg. 5791
PENTANA INC.—See HgCapital Trust plc; *Int'l*, pg. 3377
PENTANA LIMITED—See HgCapital Trust plc; *Int'l*, pg. 3377
PENTANET LIMITED; *Int'l*, pg. 5792
PENTA-OCEAN CONSTRUCTION CO., LTD.; *Int'l*, pg. 5788
PENTA-OCEAN CONSTRUCTION (HONG KONG) LTD.—See Penta-Ocean Construction Co., Ltd.; *Int'l*, pg. 5788
PENTA-OCEAN CONSTRUCTION (INDIA) PVT. LTD.—See Penta-Ocean Construction Co., Ltd.; *Int'l*, pg. 5788
PENTA-OCEAN DREDGING CO., LTD.—See Penta-Ocean Construction Co., Ltd.; *Int'l*, pg. 5788

COMPANY NAME INDEX

PENTA PAINTS CARIBBEAN LIMITED—See ANSA McAL Limited; *Int'l*, pg. 476
PENTAPHARM AG—See Koninklijke DSM N.V.; *Int'l*, pg. 4265
PENTASTAR AVIATION LLC; *U.S. Private*, pg. 3140
PENTASYS AG—See Randstad N.V.; *Int'l*, pg. 6201
PENTA TECHNO SERVICE K.K.—See Penta-Ocean Construction Co., Ltd.; *Int'l*, pg. 5788
PENTAX CANADA INC.—See Hoya Corporation; *Int'l*, pg. 3495
PENTAX EUROPE GMBH—See Hoya Corporation; *Int'l*, pg. 3495
PENTAX FRANCE LIFE CARE S.A.S.—See Hoya Corporation; *Int'l*, pg. 3495
PENTAX ITALIA S.R.L.—See Hoya Corporation; *Int'l*, pg. 3498
PENTAX MEDICAL BULGARIA EOOD—See Hoya Corporation; *Int'l*, pg. 3495
PENTAX MEDICAL RUS LLC—See Hoya Corporation; *Int'l*, pg. 3498
PENTAX MEDICAL (SHANGHAI) CO., LTD.—See Hoya Corporation; *Int'l*, pg. 3495
PENTAX MEDICAL SINGAPORE PTE. LTD.—See Hoya Corporation; *Int'l*, pg. 3495
PENTAX MEDICAL—See Hoya Corporation; *Int'l*, pg. 3495
PENTAX NEDERLAND B.V.—See Hoya Corporation; *Int'l*, pg. 3495
PENTAX OF AMERICA, INC.—See Hoya Corporation; *Int'l*, pg. 3495
PENTAX SINTAI HOLDING CO., LTD.—See Hoya Corporation; *Int'l*, pg. 3495
PENTAX SINTAI OPTICAL INSTRUMENT (SHENZHEN) CO., LTD.—See Hoya Corporation; *Int'l*, pg. 3495
PENTAX U.K. LIMITED—See Hoya Corporation; *Int'l*, pg. 3495
PENTEC ENVIRONMENTAL—See Haley & Aldrich Inc.; *U.S. Private*, pg. 1842
PENTEC HEALTH, INC.—See Wellspring Capital Management LLC; *U.S. Private*, pg. 4477
PENTECH FINANCIAL SERVICES; *U.S. Private*, pg. 3140
PENTEGRA RETIREMENT SERVICES; *U.S. Private*, pg. 3140
PENTEGRA RETIREMENT SERVICES—See Pentegra Retirement Services; *U.S. Private*, pg. 3140
PENTEK SYSTEMS, INC.—See Mercury Systems, Inc.; *U.S. Public*, pg. 1422
PENTEL CO., LTD.; *Int'l*, pg. 5792
PENTEL OF AMERICA, LTD.—See Pentel Co., Ltd.; *Int'l*, pg. 5792
PENTEL OF AMERICA—See Pentel Co., Ltd.; *Int'l*, pg. 5792
PENTEST LIMITED—See Shearwater Group plc; *Int'l*, pg. 6792
PENTEX SDN. BERHAD—See Toray Industries, Inc.; *Int'l*, pg. 7823
PENTIUM HYDRO PTY. LTD.—See Vysarn Limited; *Int'l*, pg. 8319
PENTIUM TEST PUMPING PTY. LTD.—See Vysarn Limited; *Int'l*, pg. 8319
PENTIUM WATER PTY. LTD.—See Vysarn Limited; *Int'l*, pg. 8319
PENTIXAPHARM GMBH—See Eckert & Ziegler Strahlen- und Medizintechnik AG; *Int'l*, pg. 2290
PENTLAND ASIA BANGKOK (THAILAND)—See Pentland Group Limited; *Int'l*, pg. 5792
PENTLAND ASIA HO CHI MINH CITY (VIETNAM) LTD—See Pentland Group Limited; *Int'l*, pg. 5792
PENTLAND ASIA PACIFIC LTD—See Pentland Group Limited; *Int'l*, pg. 5792
PENTLAND ASIA SHENZHEN (CHINA) CO LTD—See Pentland Group Limited; *Int'l*, pg. 5792
PENTLAND ASIA—See Pentland Group Limited; *Int'l*, pg. 5792
PENTLAND BRANDS PLC—See Pentland Group Limited; *Int'l*, pg. 5792
PENTLAND GROUP LIMITED; *Int'l*, pg. 5792
PENTLAND GROUP PLC - PENTLAND DISTRIBUTION GREAT HARWOOD UNIT—See Pentland Group Limited; *Int'l*, pg. 5792
PENTLAND GROUP PLC - PENTLAND DISTRIBUTION WASHINGTON UNIT—See Pentland Group Limited; *Int'l*, pg. 5792
PENTLAND GROUP PLC - PENTLAND SHIPPING UNIT—See Pentland Group Limited; *Int'l*, pg. 5792
PENTLAND LIMITED—See Galliford Try Holdings plc; *Int'l*, pg. 2874
PENTLAND SHIPPING SERVICES, LTD.—See Pentland Group Limited; *Int'l*, pg. 5792
PENTLAND TRADING PRIVATE LTD—See Pentland Group Limited; *Int'l*, pg. 5792
PENTLAND USA INC.—See Pentland Group Limited; *Int'l*, pg. 5792
PENTLAND VETS4PETS LIMITED—See Pets at Home Group Plc; *Int'l*, pg. 5834
PENTOKEY ORGANY (INDIA) LIMITED - RATNAGIRI FACTORY—See PENTOKEY ORGANY (INDIA) LIMITED; *Int'l*, pg. 5792
PENTOKEY ORGANY (INDIA) LIMITED; *Int'l*, pg. 5792

PENTRAVEL (PTY) LTD—See Cullinan Holdings Limited; *Int'l*, pg. 1877
PENTRON CORPORATION; *U.S. Private*, pg. 3140
PENTRONIC AB—See Indutrade AB; *Int'l*, pg. 3680
PENTUCKET BANK; *U.S. Private*, pg. 3140
PENTWATER CABINETRY, INC.; *U.S. Private*, pg. 3140
PENUMBRA EUROPE GMBH—See Penumbra, Inc.; *U.S. Public*, pg. 1667
PENUMBRA, INC.; *U.S. Public*, pg. 1666
PENUMBRA LATIN AMERICA DISTRIBUIDORA DE EQUIPAMENTOS E PRODUCTOS MEDICOS LTDA—See Penumbra, Inc.; *U.S. Public*, pg. 1667
PENUMBRA NEURO AUSTRALIA PTY. LTD.—See Penumbra, Inc.; *U.S. Public*, pg. 1667
PENUNDERWRITING GROUP PTY LTD.—See Arthur J. Gallagher & Co.; *U.S. Public*, pg. 203
PEN UNDERWRITING LIMITED—See Arthur J. Gallagher & Co.; *U.S. Public*, pg. 207
PENYAO ENVIRONMENTAL PROTECTION CO., LTD.; *Int'l*, pg. 5792
PENZIJNI FOND CESKE SPORITELNY, A.S—See Erste Group Bank AG; *Int'l*, pg. 2498
PEO CO., LTD.—See Bain Capital, LP; *U.S. Private*, pg. 435
PEO CONSTRUCTION MACHINERY OPERATORS TRAINING CENTER CO., LTD.—See Bain Capital, LP; *U.S. Private*, pg. 435
PEONY GROVE ACQUISITION CORP; *U.S. Private*, pg. 3140
PE OP CO.—See Alto Ingredients, Inc.; *U.S. Public*, pg. 88
PEOPLE 2.0 GLOBAL, LLC—See TPG Capital, L.P.; *U.S. Public*, pg. 2177
PEOPLE2PEOPLE GROUP INC.—See The Phoenix Media/Communications Group; *U.S. Private*, pg. 4095
PEOPLEADMIN, INC.—See ONEX Corporation; *Int'l*, pg. 5579
PEOPLEADMIN, INC.—See Vista Equity Partners, LLC; *U.S. Private*, pg. 4399
PEOPLEBANK AUSTRALIA LTD.—See Recruit Holdings Co., Ltd.; *Int'l*, pg. 6240
PEOPLEBIO CO.; *Int'l*, pg. 5793
PEOPLE.CN CO., LTD.; *Int'l*, pg. 5793
PEOPLE CO., LTD.; *Int'l*, pg. 5793
PEOPLECO. PTY LTD—See Persol Holdings Co., Ltd.; *Int'l*, pg. 5920
PEOPLE CORPORATION; *Int'l*, pg. 5793
PEOPLE CREATING SUCCESS, INC.; *U.S. Private*, pg. 3140
PEOPLEDOC, INCORPORATED—See Hellman & Friedman LLC; *U.S. Private*, pg. 1911
PEOPLE, DREAMS & TECHNOLOGIES GROUP CO., LTD.; *Int'l*, pg. 5793
PEOPLEFINDERS.COM; *U.S. Private*, pg. 3141
PEOPLE FIRST BANCSHARES, INC.; *U.S. Private*, pg. 3140
PEOPLEFIRST HOMECARE & HOSPICE OF INDIANA, LLC—See Apollo Global Management, Inc.; *U.S. Public*, pg. 157
PEOPLEFIRST HOMECARE & HOSPICE OF OHIO, LLC—See Apollo Global Management, Inc.; *U.S. Public*, pg. 157
PEOPLE FIRST HR SERVICES LTD.—See People Corporation; *Int'l*, pg. 5793
PEOPLEFIRST VIRGINIA, LLC—See Apollo Global Management, Inc.; *U.S. Public*, pg. 157
PEOPLEFLUENT, INC. - RALEIGH—See Learning Technologies Group plc; *Int'l*, pg. 4435
PEOPLEFLUENT INC.—See Learning Technologies Group plc; *Int'l*, pg. 4435
PEOPLEFORBIKES COALITION LTD; *U.S. Private*, pg. 3141
PEOPLEFORBIKES FOUNDATION—See PeopleForBikes Coalition LTD; *U.S. Private*, pg. 3141
PEOPLEG2; *U.S. Private*, pg. 3141
PEOPLE & GRIT (M) SDN. BHD.—See Oji Holdings Corporation; *Int'l*, pg. 5538
PEOPLE INC.; *U.S. Public*, pg. 3140
PEOPLE INC.; *U.S. Private*, pg. 3140
PEOPLEIN LIMITED; *Int'l*, pg. 5794
PEOPLELINK INC.—See Groupe Crit, S.A.; *Int'l*, pg. 3101
PEOPLELINK STAFFING SOLUTIONS INC.—See Groupe Crit, S.A.; *Int'l*, pg. 3101
PEOPLELINX, LLC; *U.S. Private*, pg. 3141
PEOPLE MAGAZINE—See Meredith Corporation; *U.S. Public*, pg. 1423
PEOPLEMARK, INC.—See Allied Universal Manager LLC; *U.S. Private*, pg. 190
PEOPLENET COMMUNICATIONS CORPORATION—See Trimble, Inc.; *U.S. Public*, pg. 2190
PEOPLE OF COLOR NETWORK, INC.; *U.S. Private*, pg. 3140
PEOPLE & PARTNERS PTY. LTD.—See Azimut Holding SpA; *Int'l*, pg. 779
PEOPLE & PARTNERS WEALTH MANAGEMENT PTY. LTD.—See Azimut Holding SpA; *Int'l*, pg. 779
PEOPLEPLUS GROUP LIMITED—See Staffline Group PLC; *Int'l*, pg. 7162
PEOPLE PREMIER, INC.; *U.S. Private*, pg. 3140
PEOPLES ADVERTISING; *Int'l*, pg. 5794

PEOPLE'S GARMENT PUBLIC COMPANY LIMITED

PEOPLES BANCORP INC.; *U.S. Public*, pg. 1667
PEOPLES BANCORP OF MT. PLEASANT, INC.—See Consumers Bancorp, Inc.; *U.S. Public*, pg. 573
PEOPLES BANCORP OF NORTH CAROLINA, INC.; *U.S. Public*, pg. 1667
PEOPLES BANCORP; *U.S. Private*, pg. 3141
PEOPLES BANCORP WASH; *U.S. Public*, pg. 1667
PEOPLES BANCSHARES-POINTE COUPEE, INC.—See Synergy Bancshares Inc.; *U.S. Private*, pg. 3904
PEOPLESBANK, A CODORUS VALLEY COMPANY—See Orrstown Financial Services, Inc.; *U.S. Public*, pg. 1619
PEOPLES BANK AND TRUST; *U.S. Private*, pg. 3141
THE PEOPLES BANK CO. INC.; *U.S. Private*, pg. 4093
PEOPLES BANK OF ALABAMA—See Altrust Financial Services, Inc.; *U.S. Public*, pg. 89
PEOPLE'S BANK OF CHINA; *Int'l*, pg. 5793
PEOPLES BANK OF COMMERCE; *U.S. Private*, pg. 3141
PEOPLES BANK OF NORTH ALABAMA; *U.S. Private*, pg. 3141
PEOPLES BANKSHARES, INC.; *U.S. Private*, pg. 3141
THE PEOPLE'S BANK; *U.S. Public*, pg. 4093
PEOPLES BANK—See Peoples Bancorp of North Carolina, Inc.; *U.S. Public*, pg. 1667
PEOPLES BANK—See Peoples Bancorp; *U.S. Private*, pg. 3141
THE PEOPLES BANK—See Peoples Financial Corporation; *U.S. Public*, pg. 1667
PEOPLES BANK—See Texas Peoples National Bancshares, Inc.; *U.S. Private*, pg. 3976
PEOPLESBANK; *U.S. Private*, pg. 3142
PEOPLES BANK—See NorthWest Indiana Bancorp; *U.S. Public*, pg. 1542
PEOPLES BANK—See Peoples Bancorp Inc.; *U.S. Public*, pg. 1667
PEOPLES BANK & TRUST COMPANY OF MADISON COUNTY—See Whitaker Bank Corporation of Kentucky; *U.S. Private*, pg. 4507
PEOPLES BANK & TRUST COMPANY; *U.S. Private*, pg. 3141
PEOPLES BANK & TRUST CO.—See Lincoln County Bancorp., Inc.; *U.S. Private*, pg. 2457
PEOPLES BANK & TRUST—See People First Bancshares, Inc.; *U.S. Private*, pg. 3140
PEOPLESCAPE COMPANY LIMITED—See Major Development Public Company Limited; *Int'l*, pg. 4654
PEOPLE'S CAPITAL & LEASING CORP.—See M&T Bank Corporation; *U.S. Public*, pg. 1351
PEOPLES CARE, INC.; *U.S. Private*, pg. 3141
PEOPLES CARTAGE INC—See Peoples Services Inc.; *U.S. Private*, pg. 3142
PEOPLES CHOICE AB—See Celsius Holdings, Inc.; *U.S. Public*, pg. 466
PEOPLES COMMUNICATIONS SYSTEM—See Peoples Electric Contractor, Inc.; *U.S. Private*, pg. 3141
PEOPLE'S COMMUNITY BANK; *U.S. Private*, pg. 3140
PEOPLE SCOUT INC.—See TrueBlue, Inc.; *U.S. Public*, pg. 2198
PEOPLESCOUT LIMITED—See TrueBlue, Inc.; *U.S. Public*, pg. 2198
PEOPLESCOUT PTY, LTD—See TrueBlue, Inc.; *U.S. Public*, pg. 2198
PEOPLE'S CREDIT UNION; *U.S. Private*, pg. 3140
PEOPLESEARCH PTE. LTD.—See HRnetGroup Limited; *Int'l*, pg. 3501
PEOPLES ELECTRIC CONTRACTOR, INC.; *U.S. Private*, pg. 3141
PEOPLES ELECTRIC COOPERATIVE; *U.S. Private*, pg. 3142
PEOPLES ENERGY, LLC—See WEC Energy Group, Inc.; *U.S. Public*, pg. 2342
THE PEOPLE-SENTINEL—See Shivers Trading & Operating Company; *U.S. Private*, pg. 3638
PEOPLE'S EQUAL ACTION AND COMMUNITY EFFORT, INC.; *U.S. Private*, pg. 3141
PEOPLESERVE, INC.—See Staffing 360 Solutions, Inc.; *U.S. Public*, pg. 1925
PEOPLES EXCHANGE BANCSHARES, INC.; *U.S. Private*, pg. 3142
PEOPLES EXCHANGE BANK OF MONROE COUNTY—See Peoples Exchange Bancshares, Inc.; *U.S. Private*, pg. 3142
PEOPLES EXCHANGE BANK—See American State Bancshares, Inc.; *U.S. Private*, pg. 255
PEOPLES FEDERAL SAVINGS & LOAN ASSOCIATION OF SIDNEY—See Farmers & Merchants Bancorp, Inc.; *U.S. Public*, pg. 822
PEOPLES FINANCIAL CORPORATION; *U.S. Public*, pg. 1667
PEOPLES FINANCIAL SERVICES CORP.; *U.S. Public*, pg. 1667
PEOPLES FIRST PROPERTIES INC.; *U.S. Private*, pg. 3142
PEOPLE'S GARMENT PUBLIC COMPANY LIMITED; *Int'l*, pg. 5793
THE PEOPLES GAS LIGHT AND COKE COMPANY—See WEC Energy Group, Inc.; *U.S. Public*, pg. 2342
PEOPLES GAS SYSTEM (FLORIDA), INC.—See Emera, Inc.; *Int'l*, pg. 2377

PEOPLE'S GARMENT PUBLIC COMPANY LIMITED — CORPORATE AFFILIATIONS

PEOPLESHARE CHERRY HILL—See Proman SAS; *Int'l*, pg. 5992
PEOPLESHARE DELAWARE—See Proman SAS; *Int'l*, pg. 5992
PEOPLESHARE, LLC—See Proman SAS; *Int'l*, pg. 5992
PEOPLES HEALTH, INC.—See UnitedHealth Group Incorporated; *U.S. Public*, pg. 2249
PEOPLES INDEPENDENT BANCSHARES, INC.; *U.S. Private*, pg. 3142
PEOPLES INDEPENDENT BANK—See Peoples Independent Bancshares, Inc.; *U.S. Private*, pg. 3142
PEOPLES INSURANCE AGENCY, LLC—See Peoples Bancorp Inc.; *U.S. Public*, pg. 1667
PEOPLE'S INSURANCE COMPANY (GROUP) OF CHINA LIMITED; *Int'l*, pg. 5793
PEOPLES INSURANCE COMPANY LIMITED; *Int'l*, pg. 5794
PEOPLE'S INSURANCE PLC—See Peoples Leasing & Finance PLC; *Int'l*, pg. 5794
PEOPLES INVESTMENTS LIMITED; *Int'l*, pg. 5794
PEOPLE'S JEWELRY COMPANY, INC; *U.S. Private*, pg. 3141
PEOPLE'S LEASING AND FINANCIAL SERVICES LIMITED; *Int'l*, pg. 5793
PEOPLES LEASING & FINANCE PLC; *Int'l*, pg. 5794
PEOPLE'S LEASING FLEET MANAGEMENT LIMITED—See Peoples Leasing & Finance PLC; *Int'l*, pg. 5794
PEOPLE'S LEASING PROPERTY DEVELOPMENT LIMITED—See Peoples Leasing & Finance PLC; *Int'l*, pg. 5794
PEOPLES LTD.; *U.S. Public*, pg. 1667
PEOPLES MARKET, INCORPORATED—See United Natural Foods, Inc.; *U.S. Public*, pg. 2232
PEOPLES MORTGAGE COMPANY; *U.S. Private*, pg. 3142
THE PEOPLES NATIONAL BANK OF MOUNT PLEASANT—See Consumers Bancorp, Inc.; *U.S. Public*, pg. 573
PEOPLES NATURAL GAS CO. LLC—See Essential Utilities Inc.; *U.S. Public*, pg. 795
PEOPLES NATURAL GAS COMPANY, LLC—See SteelRiver Infrastructure Partners LP; *U.S. Private*, pg. 3797
PEOPLESOLVE PTE. LTD.—See Raffles Medical Group Ltd; *Int'l*, pg. 6177
PEOPLE SOURCE CONSULTING LIMITED—See ManpowerGroup Inc.; *U.S. Public*, pg. 1361
PEOPLES RURAL TELEPHONE COOPERATIVE; *U.S. Private*, pg. 3142
PEOPLES SECURITY BANK AND TRUST COMPANY—See Peoples Financial Services Corp.; *U.S. Public*, pg. 1667
PEOPLES SERVICES INC.; *U.S. Private*, pg. 3142
PEOPLES-SIDNEY FINANCIAL CORPORATION—See Farmers & Merchants Bancorp, Inc.; *U.S. Public*, pg. 822
PEOPLESSOUTH BANCSHARES, INC.; *U.S. Private*, pg. 3142
PEOPLESSOUTH BANK—See PeoplesSouth Bancshares, Inc.; *U.S. Private*, pg. 3142
PEOPLES STATE BANK OF PLAINVIEW—See WRZ Bankshares, Inc.; *U.S. Private*, pg. 4574
THE PEOPLES STATE BANK; *U.S. Private*, pg. 4093
PEOPLES STATE BANK—See AmTex Bancshares Inc.; *U.S. Private*, pg. 268
PEOPLES STATE BANK—See PSB Holdings, Inc.; *U.S. Public*, pg. 1734
PEOPLES TELEPHONE CO., INC.—See Telephone Electronics Corporation; *U.S. Private*, pg. 3961
PEOPLE'S TELEPHONE COOPERATIVE, INC.; *U.S. Private*, pg. 3141
PEOPLES TRUST COMPANY OF ST. ALBANS; *U.S. Public*, pg. 1667
PEOPLES TRUST COMPANY; *Int'l*, pg. 5794
PEOPLES TWP LLC—See SteelRiver Infrastructure Partners LP; *U.S. Private*, pg. 3797
PEOPLE'S UNITED ADVISORS, INC.—See M&T Bank Corporation; *U.S. Public*, pg. 1351
PEOPLE'S UNITED BANK, N.A.—See M&T Bank Corporation; *U.S. Public*, pg. 1351
PEOPLE'S UNITED EQUIPMENT FINANCE CORP.—See M&T Bank Corporation; *U.S. Public*, pg. 1351
PEOPLE'S UNITED FINANCIAL, INC.—See M&T Bank Corporation; *U.S. Public*, pg. 1351
PEOPLE'S UNITED INSURANCE AGENCY, INC.—See GTCR LLC; *U.S. Private*, pg. 1803
PEOPLES WATER SERVICE COMPANY; *U.S. Private*, pg. 3142
PEOPLESWAY.COM, INC.; *U.S. Public*, pg. 1668
PEOPLE & TECHNOLOGY INC. - 2TH FACTORY—See People & Technology Inc.; *Int'l*, pg. 5793
PEOPLE & TECHNOLOGY INC.; *Int'l*, pg. 5792
PEOPLE&TECHNOLOGY MS, INC.; *Int'l*, pg. 5793
PEOPLETEC, INC.; *U.S. Private*, pg. 3142
PEOPLETOMYSITE.COM, LLC; *U.S. Private*, pg. 3143
PEOPULSE—See Groupe Crit, S.A.; *Int'l*, pg. 3101
PEORIA DISPOSAL COMPANY/AREA DISPOSAL SERVICE, INC.; *U.S. Private*, pg. 3143

PEORIA INDEPENDENT—See Independent Newspapers, Inc.; *U.S. Private*, pg. 2060
THE PEORIA JOURNAL STAR, INC.—See Gannett Co., Inc.; *U.S. Public*, pg. 905
PEORIA PACKING LTD.; *U.S. Private*, pg. 3143
PEORIA & PEKIN UNION RAILWAY CO.—See CSX Corporation; *U.S. Public*, pg. 602
PEORIA & PEKIN UNION RAILWAY CO.—See Norfolk Southern Corporation; *U.S. Public*, pg. 1535
PEORIA ROOFING AND RESTORATION COMPANY—See Western Construction Group; *U.S. Private*, pg. 4492
PEORIA TOYOTA SCION; *U.S. Private*, pg. 3143
PEORIA TUBE FORMING CORP.—See Wind Point Advisors LLC; *U.S. Private*, pg. 4534
PEPARLET CO., LTD.—See Unicharm Corporation; *Int'l*, pg. 8032
THE PEP BOYS MANNY MOE & JACK OF CALIFORNIA—See Icahn Enterprises L.P.; *U.S. Public*, pg. 1085
THE PEP BOYS - MANNY, MOE & JACK—See Icahn Enterprises L.P.; *U.S. Public*, pg. 1085
PEPCAP RESOURCES INC.; *Int'l*, pg. 5794
PEP CENTRAL PTY LTD—See IVE Group Limited; *Int'l*, pg. 3847
PEPCO GROUP LIMITED—See Steinhoff International Holdings N.V.; *Int'l*, pg. 7194
PEPCO HOLDINGS LLC—See Exelon Corporation; *U.S. Public*, pg. 807
PEPCO MANUFACTURING COMPANY; *U.S. Private*, pg. 3143
PEPCOM GMBH—See Morgan Stanley; *U.S. Public*, pg. 1473
PEPCO POLAND SP. Z O.O.—See Steinhoff International Holdings N.V.; *Int'l*, pg. 7195
PEPCO SLOVAKIA S.R.O.—See Steinhoff International Holdings N.V.; *Int'l*, pg. 7194
PEP DIRECT, LLC; *U.S. Private*, pg. 3143
PEPEMOBILE, S.L.—See Orange S.A.; *Int'l*, pg. 5609
PEPE MOTORS CORP.; *U.S. Private*, pg. 3143
PEPE'S INC.; *U.S. Private*, pg. 3143
PEP FILTERS, INC.—See Amiad Water Systems Ltd.; *Int'l*, pg. 427
PEPGEN INC.; *U.S. Public*, pg. 1668
PEPICA INC.—See SANYEI CORPORATION; *Int'l*, pg. 6563
PEPIN DISTRIBUTING COMPANY; *U.S. Private*, pg. 3144
PEP INDUSTRIES LLC—See Nautic Partners, LLC; *U.S. Private*, pg. 2871
PEP INDUSTRIES LLC—See The Jordan Company, L.P.; *U.S. Private*, pg. 4061
PEPINE REALTY, LLC; *U.S. Private*, pg. 3144
PEPINIERES JEAN REY; *Int'l*, pg. 5794
PEPINNINI RESOURCES CURNAMONA PTY LTD.—See Power Minerals Limited; *Int'l*, pg. 5946
PEPITONE PROPERTIES CORP.; *U.S. Private*, pg. 3144
PEPKOR HOLDINGS LIMITED—See Steinhoff International Holdings N.V.; *Int'l*, pg. 7194
PEPKOR RETAIL LIMITED—See Steinhoff International Holdings N.V.; *Int'l*, pg. 7195
PEPLIN, INC.—See LEO Pharma A/S; *Int'l*, pg. 4456
PEPLIN LIMITED—See LEO Pharma A/S; *Int'l*, pg. 4456
PEPLIN OPERATIONS PTY LTD—See LEO Pharma A/S; *Int'l*, pg. 4457
PEPPERCOM, INC.; *U.S. Private*, pg. 3144
PEPPERCOM—See Peppercom, Inc.; *U.S. Private*, pg. 3144
PEPPERCOM UK LTD.—See Peppercom, Inc.; *U.S. Private*, pg. 3144
PEPPER CONSTRUCTION COMPANY OF OHIO—See Pepper Construction Group, LLC; *U.S. Private*, pg. 3144
PEPPER CONSTRUCTION CO. OF INDIANA, LLC—See Pepper Construction Group, LLC; *U.S. Private*, pg. 3144
PEPPER CONSTRUCTION CO.—See Pepper Construction Group, LLC; *U.S. Private*, pg. 3144
PEPPER CONSTRUCTION GROUP, LLC; *U.S. Private*, pg. 3144
PEPPERCORN PRODUCTIONS, INC.—See National Amusements, Inc.; *U.S. Private*, pg. 2842
PEPPERDASH TECHNOLOGY CORP.; *U.S. Private*, pg. 3145
PEPPER DINING INC.—See Brinker International, Inc.; *U.S. Public*, pg. 384
PEPPERELL NEWS—See Alden Global Capital LLC; *U.S. Private*, pg. 157
PEPPER ENVIRONMENTAL TECHNOLOGIES, INC.—See Pepper Construction Group, LLC; *U.S. Private*, pg. 3144
PEPPER FOOD SERVICE CO., LTD.; *Int'l*, pg. 5794
PEPPER GROUP LIMITED—See KKR & Co. Inc.; *U.S. Public*, pg. 1262
THE PEPPER GROUP; *U.S. Private*, pg. 4093
PEPPER HAMILTON LLP; *U.S. Private*, pg. 3144
PEPPERIDGE FARM, INC.—See Campbell Soup Company; *U.S. Public*, pg. 427
PEPPERL+FUCHS INC; *U.S. Private*, pg. 3145
PEPPERLIME HEALTH ACQUISITION CORPORATION; *U.S. Public*, pg. 1668

PEPPERMILL CASINOS, INC.; *U.S. Private*, pg. 3145
PEPPERMILL HOTEL CASINO—See Peppermill Casinos, Inc.; *U.S. Private*, pg. 3145
PEPPER MILL INC.; *U.S. Private*, pg. 3144
PEPPERMINT BIZMOTO INC.—See Peppermint Innovation Limited; *Int'l*, pg. 5795
PEPPERMINT INNOVATION LIMITED; *Int'l*, pg. 5794
PEPPERMINT PR; *Int'l*, pg. 5795
PEPPERS AUTOMOTIVE GROUP, INC.; *U.S. Private*, pg. 3145
PEPPERS LEISURE PTY. LTD.—See Accor S.A.; *Int'l*, pg. 92
PEPPER SOURCE, LTD.; *U.S. Private*, pg. 3144
PEPPERS & ROGERS GROUP - BELGIUM—See TTEC Holdings, Inc.; *U.S. Public*, pg. 2202
PEPPERSTONE GROUP LIMITED—See CHAMP Private Equity Pty. Ltd.; *Int'l*, pg. 1439
PEPPERS UNLIMITED OF LOUISIANA, INC.; *U.S. Private*, pg. 3145
PEPPERTREE CAPITAL MANAGEMENT, INC.; *U.S. Private*, pg. 3145
PEPPER TREE INC.; *U.S. Private*, pg. 3144
PEPPERTREE VILLAGE OF AVON PARK, LIMITED—See Apartment Investment and Management Company; *U.S. Public*, pg. 144
PEPPO FASHIONS GROUP COMPANY LMD—See FJ Benjamin Holdings Ltd.; *Int'l*, pg. 2697
PEP PRINTING, INC.; *U.S. Private*, pg. 3143
PEPR INC.—See Caterpillar, Inc.; *U.S. Public*, pg. 453
PE PROJEKT-ENTWICKLUNGSGESELLSCHAFT MBH—See Erste Abwicklungsanstalt AoR; *Int'l*, pg. 2497
PEPROTECH ASIA LTD.—See Thermo Fisher Scientific Inc.; *U.S. Public*, pg. 2151
PEPROTECH EC LTD.—See Thermo Fisher Scientific Inc.; *U.S. Public*, pg. 2151
PEPROTECH FRANCE S.A.S—See Thermo Fisher Scientific Inc.; *U.S. Public*, pg. 2151
PEPROTECH GMBH—See Thermo Fisher Scientific Inc.; *U.S. Public*, pg. 2151
PEPROTECH, INC.—See Thermo Fisher Scientific Inc.; *U.S. Public*, pg. 2151
PEPSI BEVERAGES COMPANY MEXICO—See PepsiCo, Inc.; *U.S. Public*, pg. 1669
PEPSI BEVERAGES COMPANY—See PepsiCo, Inc.; *U.S. Public*, pg. 1669
THE PEPSI BOTTLING GROUP (CANADA) ULC—See PepsiCo, Inc.; *U.S. Public*, pg. 1672
PEPSI BOTTLING - RALEIGH—See PepsiCo, Inc.; *U.S. Public*, pg. 1669
PEPSI BOTTLING - RALEIGH—See Suntory Holdings Limited; *Int'l*, pg. 7327
PEPSI BOTTLING VENTURES LLC—See PepsiCo, Inc.; *U.S. Public*, pg. 1669
PEPSI BOTTLING VENTURES LLC—See Suntory Holdings Limited; *Int'l*, pg. 7327
PEPSICO AMACOCO BEBIDAS DO BRASIL LTDA.—See PepsiCo, Inc.; *U.S. Public*, pg. 1669
PEPSICO AMERICAS BEVERAGES—See PepsiCo, Inc.; *U.S. Public*, pg. 1669
PEPSICO AMERICAS FOODS—See PepsiCo, Inc.; *U.S. Public*, pg. 1670
PEPSICO AUSTRALIA HOLDINGS PTY LIMITED—See PepsiCo, Inc.; *U.S. Public*, pg. 1670
PEPSICO AZERBAIJAN LIMITED LIABILITY COMPANY—See PepsiCo, Inc.; *U.S. Public*, pg. 1670
PEPSICO BELUX BVBA—See PepsiCo, Inc.; *U.S. Public*, pg. 1670
PEPSICO BEVERAGES AMERICAS—See PepsiCo, Inc.; *U.S. Public*, pg. 1670
PEPSICO BEVERAGES CANADA—See PepsiCo, Inc.; *U.S. Public*, pg. 1671
PEPSICO BEVERAGES ITALIA S.R.L.—See PepsiCo, Inc.; *U.S. Public*, pg. 1670
PEPSICO BEVERAGES SWITZERLAND GMBH—See PepsiCo, Inc.; *U.S. Public*, pg. 1670
PEPSICO CANADA ULC—See PepsiCo, Inc.; *U.S. Public*, pg. 1671
PEPSICO (CHINA) CO., LTD.—See PepsiCo, Inc.; *U.S. Public*, pg. 1669
PEPSICO CZ S.R.O.—See PepsiCo, Inc.; *U.S. Public*, pg. 1671
PEPSICO DE ARGENTINA S.R.L.—See PepsiCo, Inc.; *U.S. Public*, pg. 1671
PEPSICO DEUTSCHLAND GMBH—See PepsiCo, Inc.; *U.S. Public*, pg. 1671
PEPSICO DEUTSCHLAND GMBH—See PepsiCo, Inc.; *U.S. Public*, pg. 1671
PEPSICO DO BRASIL HOLDING LTDA.—See PepsiCo, Inc.; *U.S. Public*, pg. 1671
PEPSICO DO BRASIL LTDA.—See PepsiCo, Inc.; *U.S. Public*, pg. 1671
PEPSICO EESTI—See PepsiCo, Inc.; *U.S. Public*, pg. 1671
PEPSICO FINANCE (ANTILLES B) N.V.—See PepsiCo, Inc.; *U.S. Public*, pg. 1671
PEPSICO FOODS, A.I.E.—See PepsiCo, Inc.; *U.S. Public*, pg. 1671

COMPANY NAME INDEX

PEPSICO FOODS CANADA - PETERBOROUGH PLANT—See PepsiCo, Inc.; *U.S. Public*, pg. 1671
PEPSICO FOODS CANADA—See PepsiCo, Inc.; *U.S. Public*, pg. 1671
PEPSICO FRANCE SNC—See PepsiCo, Inc.; *U.S. Public*, pg. 1671
PEPSICO, INC.; *U.S. Public*, pg. 1668
PEPSICO INDIA HOLDINGS PRIVATE LIMITED—See PepsiCo, Inc.; *U.S. Public*, pg. 1671
PEPSICO INDIA HOLDINGS PRIVATE LIMITED—See PepsiCo, Inc.; *U.S. Public*, pg. 1671
PEPSICO INTERNATIONAL LTD.—See PepsiCo, Inc.; *U.S. Public*, pg. 1671
PEPSICO IRELAND FOOD & BEVERAGES—See PepsiCo, Inc.; *U.S. Public*, pg. 1671
PEPSICO (IRELAND)—See PepsiCo, Inc.; *U.S. Public*, pg. 1669
PEPSI-COLA BOTTLING COMPANY OF ESTERVILLE INC.—See Pohlad Companies; *U.S. Private*, pg. 3220
PEPSI-COLA BOTTLING COMPANY OF FARGO INC.—See Pohlad Companies; *U.S. Private*, pg. 3220
PEPSI-COLA BOTTLING COMPANY OF FT. LAUDERDALE-PALM BEACH, LLC—See PepsiCo, Inc.; *U.S. Public*, pg. 1669
PEPSI-COLA BOTTLING CO. OF ABERDEEN, LLC—See Pohlad Companies; *U.S. Private*, pg. 3220
PEPSI COLA BOTTLING CO. OF CENTRAL VIRGINIA INC.; *U.S. Private*, pg. 3145
PEPSI COLA BOTTLING CO. OF GREENVILLE, SOUTH CAROLINA—See Carolina Canners Inc.; *U.S. Private*, pg. 767
PEPSI-COLA BOTTLING CO. OF LA CROSSE; *U.S. Private*, pg. 3145
PEPSI-COLA BOTTLING CO. OF NEW YORK, INC.—See Pepsi-Cola & National Brand Beverages, Ltd.; *U.S. Private*, pg. 3145
PEPSI-COLA BOTTLING CO. OF NORTON, VIRGINIA; *U.S. Private*, pg. 3145
PEPSI-COLA BOTTLING CO OF ROXBORO, NC, INC.—See PepsiCo, Inc.; *U.S. Public*, pg. 1670
PEPSI-COLA BOTTLING CO OF ROXBORO, NC, INC.—See Suntory Holdings Limited; *Int'l*, pg. 7327
PEPSI-COLA BOTTLING CO. OF SALINA INC.—See Mahaska Bottling Company Inc.; *U.S. Private*, pg. 2550
PEPSI-COLA BOTTLING OF CORBIN, KENTUCKY INC.; *U.S. Private*, pg. 3145
PEPSI-COLA BOTTLING OF HICKORY, NORTH CAROLINA INC.; *U.S. Private*, pg. 3145
PEPSI-COLA BOTTLING OF WORCESTER; *U.S. Private*, pg. 3145
PEPSI-COLA COMPANY NEW HAVEN; *U.S. Private*, pg. 3145
PEPSI-COLA GENERAL BOTTLERS POLAND SP, Z.O.O.—See PepsiCo, Inc.; *U.S. Public*, pg. 1669
PEPSI-COLA GMBH—See PepsiCo, Inc.; *U.S. Public*, pg. 1669
PEPSI-COLA INTERAMERICANA DE GUATEMALA S.A.—See PepsiCo, Inc.; *U.S. Public*, pg. 1669
PEPSI-COLA INTERNATIONAL (PVT) LIMITED—See PepsiCo, Inc.; *U.S. Public*, pg. 1669
PEPSI-COLA MANUFACTURING INTERNATIONAL LTD.—See PepsiCo, Inc.; *U.S. Public*, pg. 1670
PEPSI-COLA MANUFACTURING (IRELAND) UNLIMITED COMPANY—See PepsiCo, Inc.; *U.S. Public*, pg. 1669
PEPSI-COLA MEMPHIS BOTTLING CO., INC.; *U.S. Private*, pg. 3145
PEPSI-COLA MEXICANA, S. DE R.L. DE C.V.—See PepsiCo, Inc.; *U.S. Public*, pg. 1669
PEPSI-COLA & NATIONAL BRAND BEVERAGES, LTD.; *U.S. Private*, pg. 3145
PEPSI-COLA NORTH AMERICA—See PepsiCo, Inc.; *U.S. Public*, pg. 1670
PEPSI-COLA OF CORVALLIS, INC.—See PepsiCo, Inc.; *U.S. Public*, pg. 1669
PEPSI-COLA OF FLORENCE, LLC; *U.S. Private*, pg. 3146
PEPSI COLA OGDENSBURG BOTTLERS; *U.S. Private*, pg. 3145
PEPSI-COLA OPERATING COMPANY OF CHESAPEAKE & INDIANAPOLIS—See PepsiCo, Inc.; *U.S. Public*, pg. 1669
PEPSI-COLA PRODUCTS PHILIPPINES, INC.—See PepsiCo, Inc.; *U.S. Public*, pg. 1669
PEPSI-COLA SR, S.R.O.—See PepsiCo, Inc.; *U.S. Public*, pg. 1669
PEPSI-COLA (THAI) TRADING COMPANY LIMITED—See PepsiCo, Inc.; *U.S. Public*, pg. 1669
PEPSICO NEDERLAND B.V.—See PepsiCo, Inc.; *U.S. Public*, pg. 1671
PEPSICO NEDERLAND B.V.—See PepsiCo, Inc.; *U.S. Public*, pg. 1671
PEPSICO NORDIC FINLAND OY—See PepsiCo, Inc.; *U.S. Public*, pg. 1671
PEPSICO PUERTO RICO, INC.—See PepsiCo, Inc.; *U.S. Public*, pg. 1671
PEPSICO SERVICES ASIA LTD.—See PepsiCo, Inc.; *U.S. Public*, pg. 1671
PEPSI FOODS PRIVATE LIMITED—See PepsiCo, Inc.; *U.S. Public*, pg. 1669

PEPSI LOGISTICS COMPANY, INC.—See PepsiCo, Inc.; *U.S. Public*, pg. 1669
PEPSI MIDAMERICA CO.; *U.S. Private*, pg. 3145
PEPSI NORTHWEST BEVERAGES LLC—See PepsiCo, Inc.; *U.S. Public*, pg. 1669
PEPS-JV (KEDAH) SDN. BHD.—See EP Manufacturing Bhd.; *Int'l*, pg. 2458
PEPS - JV (M) SDN BHD—See EP Manufacturing Bhd.; *Int'l*, pg. 2458
PEP STORES (PTY) LTD—See Steinhoff International Holdings N.V.; *Int'l*, pg. 7195
PEPTIDES INTERNATIONAL, INC.—See Ampersand Management LLC; *U.S. Private*, pg. 266
PEPTIDREAM INC.; *Int'l*, pg. 5795
PEPTISYNTHA S.A.—See Astorg Partners S.A.S.; *Int'l*, pg. 656
PEPTONIC MEDICAL AB; *Int'l*, pg. 5795
PEPTRON, INC.; *Int'l*, pg. 5795
PEP-UP, INC.; *U.S. Private*, pg. 3143
PEQUANNOCK DISPOSAL, INC.—See Interstate Waste Services, Inc.; *U.S. Private*, pg. 2126
PEQUOT CAPITAL MANAGEMENT INC.; *U.S. Private*, pg. 3146
PEQUOT PHARMACEUTICAL NETWORK MANAGEMENT SERVICES—See Mashantucket Pequot Gaming Enterprise Inc.; *U.S. Private*, pg. 2601
PER AARSLEFF GRONLAND APS—See Per Aarsleff Holding A/S; *Int'l*, pg. 5796
PER AARSLEFF HOLDING A/S; *Int'l*, pg. 5795
PER AARSLEFF OY—See Per Aarsleff Holding A/S; *Int'l*, pg. 5796
PER AARSLEFF POLSKA SP. Z O.O.—See Per Aarsleff Holding A/S; *Int'l*, pg. 5796
PER AARSLEFF ZAO—See Per Aarsleff Holding A/S; *Int'l*, pg. 5796
PERA GAYRIMENKUL YATIRIM ORTAKLIGI A.S.; *Int'l*, pg. 5796
PERAGO FINANCIAL SYSTEMS ENABLERS (PTY) LTD—See Cassa Depositi e Prestiti S.p.A.; *Int'l*, pg. 1354
PERAHARTA SDN BHD—See KUB Malaysia Berhad; *Int'l*, pg. 4320
PERAK CORPORATION BERHAD; *Int'l*, pg. 5796
PERAK TRANSIT BERHAD; *Int'l*, pg. 5796
PERALTASTRAWBERRYFROG—See APCO Worldwide; *U.S. Private*, pg. 291
PERASO INC.; *U.S. Public*, pg. 1672
PERATON CORP.—See Veritas Capital Fund Management, LLC; *U.S. Private*, pg. 4363
PERATON GOVERNMENT COMMUNICATIONS, INC.; *U.S. Private*, pg. 3146
PERAZIO ENGINEERING SAS—See VINCI S.A.; *Int'l*, pg. 8225
PERBADANAN BEKALAN AIR PULAU PINANG SDN. BHD.—See PBA Holdings Bhd.; *Int'l*, pg. 5765
PERBIO SCIENCE AB—See Thermo Fisher Scientific Inc.; *U.S. Public*, pg. 2147
PERBIO SCIENCE BVBA—See Thermo Fisher Scientific Inc.; *U.S. Public*, pg. 2151
PERBIO SCIENCE DEUTSCHLAND—See Thermo Fisher Scientific Inc.; *U.S. Public*, pg. 2154
PERBIO SCIENCE FRANCE—See Thermo Fisher Scientific Inc.; *U.S. Public*, pg. 2154
PERBIO SCIENCE NEDERLAND BV—See Thermo Fisher Scientific Inc.; *U.S. Public*, pg. 2154
PERBIO SCIENCE PROJEKT AB—See Thermo Fisher Scientific Inc.; *U.S. Public*, pg. 2151
PERBIO SCIENCE UK LTD—See Thermo Fisher Scientific Inc.; *U.S. Public*, pg. 2154
PERBIX MACHINE COMPANY, INC.—See Tesla, Inc.; *U.S. Public*, pg. 2021
PER BURELL—See Thames & Hudson Ltd; *Int'l*, pg. 7607
PERCEPTA LLC—See Ford Motor Company; *U.S. Public*, pg. 867
PERCEPTA LLC—See TTEC Holdings, Inc.; *U.S. Public*, pg. 2202
PERCEPTA UK LIMITED—See TTEC Holdings, Inc.; *U.S. Public*, pg. 2203
PERCEPT GULF—See Percept Holdings Pvt. Ltd.; *Int'l*, pg. 5796
PERCEPT HOLDINGS PVT. LTD.; *Int'l*, pg. 5796
PERCEPT / H—See Percept Holdings Pvt. Ltd.; *Int'l*, pg. 5796
PERCEPTICS, LLC; *U.S. Private*, pg. 3146
PERCEPTION CAPITAL CORP. III; *U.S. Public*, pg. 1673
PERCEPTION DIGITAL TECHNOLOGY (SHENZHEN) LIMITED—See HongDa Financial Holding Limited; *Int'l*, pg. 3470
PERCEPTIONS, INC.; *U.S. Private*, pg. 3146
PERCEPTION UK LLP—See Rentokil Initial plc; *Int'l*, pg. 6287
PERCEPTIVE ADVISORS, LLC; *U.S. Private*, pg. 3146
PERCEPTIVE ENGINEERING LIMITED—See Applied Materials, Inc.; *U.S. Public*, pg. 172
PERCEPTIVE ENGINEERING PTE. LTD.—See Applied Materials, Inc.; *U.S. Public*, pg. 172
PERCEPTIVE INFORMATICS, INC.—See Pamplona Capital Management LLP; *Int'l*, pg. 5713

PEREGRINE ENERGY CORP.

PERCEPTIVE INFORMATICS, LLC—See Pamplona Capital Management LLP; *Int'l*, pg. 5713
PERCEPTIVE INFORMATICS UK LIMITED—See Pamplona Capital Management LLP; *Int'l*, pg. 5713
PERCEPTIVE INSTRUMENTS LIMITED—See ArchiMed SAS; *Int'l*, pg. 548
PERCEPTIVE RECRUITING, LLC; *U.S. Private*, pg. 3146
PERCEPT OOH—See Percept Holdings Pvt. Ltd.; *Int'l*, pg. 5797
PERCEPT PROFILE—See Percept Holdings Pvt. Ltd.; *Int'l*, pg. 5797
PERCEPTRON ASIA PACIFIC LTD.—See Atlas Copco AB; *Int'l*, pg. 680
PERCEPTRON ASIA PTE. LTD.—See Atlas Copco AB; *Int'l*, pg. 680
PERCEPTRON DO BRASIL LTDA.—See Atlas Copco AB; *Int'l*, pg. 680
PERCEPTRON (EUROPE) GMBH—See Atlas Copco AB; *Int'l*, pg. 680
PERCEPTRONICS SOLUTIONS, INC.; *U.S. Private*, pg. 3146
PERCEPTRONICS SOLUTIONS, INC.—See Perceptronics Solutions, Inc.; *U.S. Private*, pg. 3146
PERCEPTRONICS SOLUTIONS, INC.—See Perceptronics Solutions, Inc.; *U.S. Private*, pg. 3146
PERCEPTRON, INC.—See Atlas Copco AB; *Int'l*, pg. 680
PERCEPTRON ITALIA, S.R.L—See Atlas Copco AB; *Int'l*, pg. 680
PERCEPTRON METROLOGY TECHNOLOGY (SHANGHAI) CO. LTD.—See Atlas Copco AB; *Int'l*, pg. 680
PERCEPTRON METROLOGY UK LTD.—See Atlas Copco AB; *Int'l*, pg. 680
PERCEPTRON NON CONTACT METROLOGY SOLUTIONS PVT LTD.—See Atlas Copco AB; *Int'l*, pg. 680
PERCEPTRON TRADING (SHANGHAI) CO., LTD.—See Atlas Copco AB; *Int'l*, pg. 680
PERCEPT SWIFT ADVERTISING PRIVATE LIMITED—See Percept Holdings Pvt. Ltd.; *Int'l*, pg. 5797
PERCEPTYX, INC.; *U.S. Private*, pg. 3146
PERCETAKAN KESELAMATAN NASIONAL SDN. BHD.—See Kumpulan Fima Berhad; *Int'l*, pg. 4331
PERCEVA SAS; *Int'l*, pg. 5797
PERCHA DIALYSIS, LLC—See DaVita Inc.; *U.S. Public*, pg. 642
PERCHERON INVESTMENT MANAGEMENT LP; *U.S. Private*, pg. 3146
PERCHERON, LLC—See Percheron, LLC; *U.S. Private*, pg. 3146
PERCHERON, LLC; *U.S. Private*, pg. 3146
PERCHERON THERAPEUTICS LIMITED; *Int'l*, pg. 5797
PERCH SOLUTIONS OY—See Bruker Corporation; *U.S. Public*, pg. 407
PERCIER PUBLICATIONS SNC—See LVMH Moet Hennessy Louis Vuitton SE; *Int'l*, pg. 4600
PERCISION GMBH—See adesso SE; *Int'l*, pg. 145
PERCISION SERVICES GMBH—See adesso SE; *Int'l*, pg. 144
PERCIVIA LLC—See Johnson & Johnson; *U.S. Public*, pg. 1195
PERCOLATE INDUSTRIES, INC.—See Seismic Software, Inc.; *U.S. Private*, pg. 3600
PERCONA LLC; *U.S. Private*, pg. 3146
PERCON CONSTRUCTION INC.; *Int'l*, pg. 5797
PERCUSSION SOFTWARE INC.; *U.S. Private*, pg. 3147
PERC WATER CORPORATION—See Consolidated Water Co. Ltd.; *U.S. Public*, pg. 1771
PERCY DALTON'S FAMOUS PEANUT COMPANY LIMITED; *Int'l*, pg. 5797
PERDANA MARINE OFFSHORE PTE LTD—See Dayang Enterprise Holdings Berhad; *Int'l*, pg. 1985
PERDANA PETROLEUM BERHAD—See Dayang Enterprise Holdings Berhad; *Int'l*, pg. 1985
PERDANA SPECIALIST HOSPITAL SDN BHD—See KPJ Healthcare Berhad; *Int'l*, pg. 4297
PERDIGAO AGROINDUSTRIAL S.A.—See BRF S.A.; *Int'l*, pg. 1151
PERDIGAO HOLLAND B.V.—See BRF S.A.; *Int'l*, pg. 1151
PERDIGAO INTERNATIONAL LTD.—See BRF S.A.; *Int'l*, pg. 1151
PERDIGAO UK LTD.—See BRF S.A.; *Int'l*, pg. 1151
PERDOCEO EDUCATION CORPORATION; *U.S. Public*, pg. 1673
THE PERDUCO GROUP, INC.—See KBR, Inc.; *U.S. Public*, pg. 1216
PERDUE FARMS HATCHERY, INC.—See Perdue Farms Incorporated; *U.S. Private*, pg. 3147
PERDUE FARMS INCORPORATED; *U.S. Private*, pg. 3147
PERDUE INC.; *U.S. Private*, pg. 3147
PERDUE ADVENTURES PTY LTD—See TUI AG; *Int'l*, pg. 7966
PEREGRINE AVIATION SERVICES; *U.S. Private*, pg. 3147
PEREGRINE CAPITAL MANAGEMENT, INC.—See Wells Fargo & Company; *U.S. Public*, pg. 2345
PEREGRINE CORPORATION; *Int'l*, pg. 5797
PEREGRINE ENERGY CORP.; *U.S. Private*, pg. 3147

PEREGRINE ENERGY CORP.

PEREGRINE FINANCIAL GROUP, INC. - CHICAGO—See Peregrine Financial Group, Inc.; *U.S. Private*, pg. 3147
PEREGRINE FINANCIAL GROUP, INC.; *U.S. Private*, pg. 3147
PEREGRINE FINANCIAL PRODUCTS (PTY) LTD—See Peregrine Holdings Limited; *Int'l*, pg. 5797
PEREGRINE GOLD LIMITED; *Int'l*, pg. 5797
PEREGRINE HOLDINGS LIMITED; *Int'l*, pg. 5797
PEREGRINE INDUSTRIES, INC.; *U.S. Public*, pg. 1673
PEREGRINE MANAGEMENT SERVICES (PTY) LTD—See Peregrine Holdings Limited; *Int'l*, pg. 5797
PEREGRINE SEMICONDUCTOR CORPORATION—See Murata Manufacturing Co., Ltd.; *Int'l*, pg. 5097
PEREGRINE TECHNICAL SERVICES, LLC—See Gold Belt Incorporated; *U.S. Private*, pg. 1727
PEREGRIN TECHNOLOGIES INC; *U.S. Private*, pg. 3147
PEREIRA & COMPANY LIMITED—See Massy Holdings Ltd.; *Int'l*, pg. 4724
PEREIRA & O'DELL; *U.S. Private*, pg. 3147
PEREKOP BROMINE; *Int'l*, pg. 5797
PEREL EESTI AS—See P-Duke Technology Co., Ltd.; *Int'l*, pg. 5681
PERELLA WEINBERG PARTNERS LP; *U.S. Public*, pg. 1674
PERELLA WEINBERG UK LIMITED—See Perella Weinberg Partners LP; *U.S. Public*, pg. 1674
PERELLI ENTERPRISES, INC.; *U.S. Private*, pg. 3147
PEREL OY—See P-Duke Technology Co., Ltd.; *Int'l*, pg. 5681
PEREMEX COMPUTER SYSTEMS PVT LTD—See Digilife Technologies Limited; *Int'l*, pg. 2119
PEREMEX PTE. LTD.—See Digilife Technologies Limited; *Int'l*, pg. 2119
PERENCE COLOMBIA LIMITED—See Perenco Gas Ltd.; *Int'l*, pg. 5797
PERENCO GAS LTD.; *Int'l*, pg. 5797
PERENCO SA—See Perenco Gas Ltd.; *Int'l*, pg. 5797
PERENNIAL ENERGY HOLDINGS LIMITED; *Int'l*, pg. 5797
PERENNIAL ENERGY, LLC—See Commerce Bancshares, Inc.; *U.S. Public*, pg. 544
PERENNIAL ENVIRONMENTAL SERVICES—See Eagle Infrastructure Services, Inc.; *U.S. Private*, pg. 1309
PERENNIAL INC.—See DATA Communications Management Corp.; *Int'l*, pg. 1976
PERENNIAL INTERNATIONAL LIMITED; *Int'l*, pg. 5797
PERENNIAL INVESTMENT PARTNERS LIMITED—See Insignia Financial Ltd.; *Int'l*, pg. 3719
PERENNIAL REAL ESTATE HOLDINGS LIMITED; *Int'l*, pg. 5797
PERENNIUS CAPITAL PARTNERS SGR S.P.A.—See Partners Group Holding AG; *Int'l*, pg. 5750
PERENTI GLOBAL LIMITED; *Int'l*, pg. 5797
PERESEC PRIME BROKERS (PTY) LTD—See Peresec South Africa Proprietary Limited; *Int'l*, pg. 5798
PERESEC SOUTH AFRICA PROPRIETARY LIMITED; *Int'l*, pg. 5798
PERESEC TECHNOLOGY SOLUTIONS PROPRIETARY LIMITED—See Zarclear Holdings Limited; *Int'l*, pg. 8625
PEREZ & MORRIS LLC; *U.S. Private*, pg. 3147
PEREZ TRADING CO. INC.; *U.S. Private*, pg. 3147
PEREZ Y CIA JAMAICA LTD.—See Albert Ballin KG; *Int'l*, pg. 296
PEREZ Y VILLA BBDO—See Omnicom Group Inc.; *U.S. Public*, pg. 1576
PERFECBORE AG—See Fuji Corporation; *Int'l*, pg. 2810
PERFECSEAL, INC.—See Amcor plc; *Int'l*, pg. 418
PERFECT AIR & HOME IMPROVEMENT INC.; *U.S. Private*, pg. 3148
PERFECT AUTOMATION PRIVATE LIMITED—See M2I Corporation; *Int'l*, pg. 4617
PERFECT BAR, LLC—See Mondelez International, Inc.; *U.S. Public*, pg. 1464
PERFECT CALL (NETHERLANDS) BV—See Teleperformance SE; *Int'l*, pg. 7540
PERFECT CARE INC.; *U.S. Private*, pg. 3148
PERFECT COMBO LIMITED—See North Asia Strategic Holdings Limited; *Int'l*, pg. 5440
PERFECT COMMERCE HOLDINGS, LLC.; *U.S. Private*, pg. 3148
PERFECT COMMERCE, LLC—See Pollen Street Limited; *Int'l*, pg. 5910
PERFECT COMPANION GROUP COMPANY LIMITED—See Charoen Pokphand Group Co., Ltd.; *Int'l*, pg. 1453
PERFECT CONTROL PANELS PRIVATE LIMITED—See Perfect Infraengineers Limited; *Int'l*, pg. 5798
PERFECT CORP.; *Int'l*, pg. 5798
PERFECTECH COLOUR CENTRE LIMITED—See Perfectech International Holdings Limited; *Int'l*, pg. 5799
PERFECTECH INTERNATIONAL HOLDINGS LIMITED; *Int'l*, pg. 5799
PERFECTECH INTERNATIONAL TRADING LTD—See Perfectech International Holdings Limited; *Int'l*, pg. 5799
PERFECTENERGY GMBH—See PERFECTENERGY INTERNATIONAL LIMITED; *Int'l*, pg. 5799

PERFECTENERGY INTERNATIONAL LIMITED; *Int'l*, pg. 5799
PERFECT EQUIPMENT CO., LLC - MURFREESBORO—See Berwind Corporation; *U.S. Private*, pg. 541
PERFECT EQUIPMENT CO., LLC - MURFREESBORO—See Berwind Corporation; *U.S. Private*, pg. 541
PERFECT EQUIPMENT CO., LLC - SNUGL MANUFACTURING DIVISION—See Berwind Corporation; *U.S. Private*, pg. 541
PERFECT EQUIPMENT CO., LLC - SNUGL MANUFACTURING DIVISION—See Berwind Corporation; *U.S. Private*, pg. 541
PERFECT EQUIPMENT COMPANY, LLC—See Berwind Corporation; *U.S. Private*, pg. 541
PERFECT EQUIPMENT COMPANY, LLC—See Berwind Corporation; *U.S. Private*, pg. 541
PERFECT EQUIPMENT COMPANY, LLC—See Berwind Corporation; *U.S. Private*, pg. 541
PERFECT EQUIPMENT COMPANY, LLC—See Berwind Corporation; *U.S. Private*, pg. 541
PERFECT EQUIPMENT COMPANY, LLC—See Berwind Corporation; *U.S. Private*, pg. 541
PERFECT EVENT SERVICES LIMITED—See FSE Services Group Limited; *Int'l*, pg. 2798
PERFECT FIT INDUSTRIES, LLC—See The Anderson Group, LLC; *U.S. Private*, pg. 3986
PERFECT FOOLS AB—See The Interpublic Group of Companies, Inc.; *U.S. Public*, pg. 2098
PERFECTFORM—See Lady Ester Lingerie Corp.; *U.S. Private*, pg. 2372
PERFECT FRY COMPANY LCC—See The Middleby Corporation; *U.S. Public*, pg. 2115
PERFECT GROUP CORP., LTD.; *Int'l*, pg. 5798
PERFECT GROUP INTERNATIONAL HOLDINGS LTD. - CHINA FACTORY—See Perfect Group International Holdings Ltd.; *Int'l*, pg. 5798
PERFECT GROUP INTERNATIONAL HOLDINGS LTD.; *Int'l*, pg. 5798
PERFECT HOLDING SA; *Int'l*, pg. 5798
PERFECT INFORMATION LTD—See ION Investment Group Ltd.; *Int'l*, pg. 3794
PERFECT INFRAENGINEERS LIMITED; *Int'l*, pg. 5798
PERFECTION CLUTCH—See Berkshire Hathaway Inc.; *U.S. Public*, pg. 310
PERFECTION FOODS COMPANY, INC.; *U.S. Private*, pg. 3148
PERFECTION GEAR, INC.—See HBD Industries, Inc.; *U.S. Private*, pg. 1887
PERFECTION GROUP, INC.; *U.S. Private*, pg. 3148
PERFECTION LEARNING CORPORATION; *U.S. Private*, pg. 3148
PERFECTION MACHINERY SALES, INC.; *U.S. Private*, pg. 3148
PERFECTION PACKAGING PTY. LTD.—See Pro-Pac Packaging Limited; *Int'l*, pg. 5985
PERFECTION STEEL TREATING—See MNP Corporation; *U.S. Private*, pg. 2756
PERFECTION STRUCTURAL COMPONENTS LLC—See Star Lumber & Supply Company, Inc.; *U.S. Private*, pg. 3785
THE PERFECTLY SAFE CATALOG—See Kids Stuff, Inc.; *U.S. Private*, pg. 2303
PERFECT MARKETING CORPORATION; *U.S. Private*, pg. 3148
PERFECT MEDICAL HEALTH MANAGEMENT LIMITED; *Int'l*, pg. 5798
PERFECT MOMENT LTD.; *Int'l*, pg. 5799
PERFECT-OCTAVE MEDIA PROJECTS LTD.; *Int'l*, pg. 5799
PERFECTO INDUSTRIES INC.; *U.S. Private*, pg. 3148
PERFECT OPTRONICS LTD; *Int'l*, pg. 5799
PERFECTPAC LIMITED; *Int'l*, pg. 5799
PERFECT PRESENTATION FOR COMMERCIAL SERVICES COMPANY; *Int'l*, pg. 5799
THE PERFECT PUREE OF NAPA VALLEY, LLC.; *U.S. Private*, pg. 4093
PERFECT RELATIONS PVT. LTD.—See Dentsu Group Inc.; *Int'l*, pg. 2036
PERFECT SEAMLESS GARMENTS (CAMBODIA) LTD.—See PCCS Group Berhad; *Int'l*, pg. 5767
PERFECT SHAPE & SKIN LIMITED—See Perfect Medical Health Management Limited; *Int'l*, pg. 5799
PERFECT SHAPE & SKIN MANAGEMENT CO. LIMITED—See Perfect Medical Health Management Limited; *Int'l*, pg. 5799
PERFECT SHAPE & SKIN (YL) LIMITED—See Perfect Medical Health Management Limited; *Int'l*, pg. 5798
PERFECT SHAPE & SPA (CWB) LIMITED—See Perfect Medical Health Management Limited; *Int'l*, pg. 5799
PERFECT SHUTTERS INC.; *U.S. Private*, pg. 3148
PERFECT SPORT CLUB CO., LTD.—See Property Perfect Public Company Limited; *Int'l*, pg. 5998
PERFECT TIMING, INC.—See Sun Capital Partners, Inc.; *U.S. Private*, pg. 3860
PERFECT WORLD CO., LTD.; *Int'l*, pg. 5799
PERFECT WORLD ENTERTAINMENT INC.—See Perfect World Co., Ltd.; *Int'l*, pg. 5799
PERFECT WORLD EUROPE B.V.—See Perfect World Co., Ltd.; *Int'l*, pg. 5799

CORPORATE AFFILIATIONS

PERFEKTA HOLDING JOSSEFORS AB; *Int'l*, pg. 5799
PERFEKTA INC.—See Arlington Capital Partners LLC; *U.S. Private*, pg. 327
PERFEKT ZRT—See DPG Media Group NV; *Int'l*, pg. 2188
PERFERX OPTICAL CO. INC.—See EssilorLuxottica SA; *Int'l*, pg. 2513
PERFETTI CONFECTIONERY VIETNAM LTD.—See Perfetti Van Melle Holding B.V.; *Int'l*, pg. 5800
PERFETTI CR S.R.O.—See Perfetti Van Melle Holding B.V.; *Int'l*, pg. 5800
PERFETTIE VAN MELLE BRASIL LTDA—See Perfetti Van Melle Holding B.V.; *Int'l*, pg. 5801
PERFETTI S.A.—See Perfetti Van Melle Holding B.V.; *Int'l*, pg. 5800
PERFETTI VAN MELLE ASIA PACIFIC PTE LTD—See Perfetti Van Melle Holding B.V.; *Int'l*, pg. 5800
PERFETTI VAN MELLE BENELUX B.V.—See Perfetti Van Melle Holding B.V.; *Int'l*, pg. 5799
PERFETTI VAN MELLE BRASIL LTDA.—See Perfetti Van Melle Holding B.V.; *Int'l*, pg. 5800
PERFETTI VAN MELLE B.V.—See Perfetti Van Melle Holding B.V.; *Int'l*, pg. 5800
PERFETTI VAN MELLE CANADA LTD.—See Perfetti Van Melle Holding B.V.; *Int'l*, pg. 5800
PERFETTI VAN MELLE CONFECTIONERY CHINA CO LTD—See Perfetti Van Melle Holding B.V.; *Int'l*, pg. 5800
PERFETTI VAN MELLE CONFECTIONERY (SHENZHEN) CO., LTD.—See Perfetti Van Melle Holding B.V.; *Int'l*, pg. 5800
PERFETTI VAN MELLE EXPORT FAR EAST LTD—See Perfetti Van Melle Holding B.V.; *Int'l*, pg. 5800
PERFETTI VAN MELLE GIDA SANAYI VE TICARET A.S.—See Perfetti Van Melle Holding B.V.; *Int'l*, pg. 5800
PERFETTI VAN MELLE HELLAS S.A.—See Perfetti Van Melle Holding B.V.; *Int'l*, pg. 5800
PERFETTI VAN MELLE HOLDING B.V.; *Int'l*, pg. 5799
PERFETTI VAN MELLE INDIA PVT. LTD. - CHENNAI FACTORY—See Perfetti Van Melle Holding B.V.; *Int'l*, pg. 5800
PERFETTI VAN MELLE INDIA PVT. LTD. - MANESAR FACTORY—See Perfetti Van Melle Holding B.V.; *Int'l*, pg. 5800
PERFETTI VAN MELLE INDIA PVT. LTD. - RUDRAPUR FACTORY—See Perfetti Van Melle Holding B.V.; *Int'l*, pg. 5800
PERFETTI VAN MELLE INDIA PVT. LTD.—See Perfetti Van Melle Holding B.V.; *Int'l*, pg. 5800
PERFETTI VAN MELLE INDONESIA - CIKAMPEK FACTORY—See Perfetti Van Melle Holding B.V.; *Int'l*, pg. 5800
PERFETTI VAN MELLE INDONESIA—See Perfetti Van Melle Holding B.V.; *Int'l*, pg. 5800
PERFETTI VAN MELLE INTERNATIONAL HOLDING B.V.—See Perfetti Van Melle Holding B.V.; *Int'l*, pg. 5800
PERFETTI VAN MELLE INTERNATIONAL TRUST B.V.—See Perfetti Van Melle Holding B.V.; *Int'l*, pg. 5800
PERFETTI VAN MELLE OOO—See Perfetti Van Melle Holding B.V.; *Int'l*, pg. 5800
PERFETTI VAN MELLE PHILS., INC.—See Perfetti Van Melle Holding B.V.; *Int'l*, pg. 5800
PERFETTI VAN MELLE POLSKA SP. Z.O.O.—See Perfetti Van Melle Holding B.V.; *Int'l*, pg. 5800
PERFETTI VAN MELLE ROMANIA SRL—See Perfetti Van Melle Holding B.V.; *Int'l*, pg. 5800
PERFETTI VAN MELLE SLOVAKIA S.R.O.—See Perfetti Van Melle Holding B.V.; *Int'l*, pg. 5801
PERFETTI VAN MELLE USA, INC.—See Perfetti Van Melle Holding B.V.; *Int'l*, pg. 5800
PERF-FORM PRODUCTS, INC.; *U.S. Private*, pg. 3148
PERF GO-GREEN HOLDINGS, INC.; *U.S. Public*, pg. 1674
PERFICIENT CANADA CORP.—See EQT AB; *Int'l*, pg. 2483
PERFICIENT D.O.O.—See EQT AB; *Int'l*, pg. 2483
PERFICIENT, INC. - ATLANTA—See EQT AB; *Int'l*, pg. 2483
PERFICIENT, INC. - CHICAGO—See EQT AB; *Int'l*, pg. 2483
PERFICIENT, INC. - DENVER—See EQT AB; *Int'l*, pg. 2483
PERFICIENT, INC. - NEW ORLEANS—See EQT AB; *Int'l*, pg. 2483
PERFICIENT, INC. - NEW YORK—See EQT AB; *Int'l*, pg. 2483
PERFICIENT, INC. - PLANO—See EQT AB; *Int'l*, pg. 2483
PERFICIENT, INC. - SAN FRANCISCO—See EQT AB; *Int'l*, pg. 2483
PERFICIENT, INC.—See EQT AB; *Int'l*, pg. 2483
PERFICIENT UK LTD.—See EQT AB; *Int'l*, pg. 2483
PERFILES ARAGON S.A.—See Klockner & Co. SE; *Int'l*, pg. 4202
PERFOLINE—See DMC Global Inc.; *U.S. Public*, pg. 671
PERFORCE SOFTWARE, INC.-OHIO—See Clearlake Capital Group, L.P.; *U.S. Private*, pg. 936

COMPANY NAME INDEX

PERFORCE SOFTWARE, INC.-OHIO—See Francisco Partners Management, LP; *U.S. Private*, pg. 1591
PERFORCE SOFTWARE, INC.—See Clearlake Capital Group, L.P.; *U.S. Private*, pg. 936
PERFORCE SOFTWARE, INC.—See Francisco Partners Management, LP; *U.S. Private*, pg. 1591
PERFORCE SOFTWARE PTY. LTD.—See Clearlake Capital Group, L.P.; *U.S. Private*, pg. 936
PERFORCE SOFTWARE PTY. LTD.—See Francisco Partners Management, LP; *U.S. Private*, pg. 1591
PERFORCE SOFTWARE UK LTD.—See Clearlake Capital Group, L.P.; *U.S. Private*, pg. 936
PERFORCE SOFTWARE UK LTD.—See Francisco Partners Management, LP; *U.S. Private*, pg. 1591
PERFORMANCE ABATEMENT SERVICES, INC.—See Performance Contracting Group; *U.S. Private*, pg. 3149
PERFORMANCE ADDITIVES OF AMERICA, LLC—See Behn Meyer (D) Holding AG & Co.; *Int'l*, pg. 941
PERFORMANCE ARCHITECTS INC.; *U.S. Private*, pg. 3148
PERFORMANCE AUTO GROUP; *Int'l*, pg. 5801
PERFORMANCE AUTOMOTIVE NETWORK; *U.S. Private*, pg. 3148
PERFORMANCE AVIATION AUSTRALIA—See Experience Co Limited; *Int'l*, pg. 2588
PERFORMANCE AVIATION (NEW ZEALAND) LIMITED—See Experience Co Limited; *Int'l*, pg. 2588
PERFORMANCE AWARDS INC.—See ITAGroup, Inc.; *U.S. Private*, pg. 2148
PERFORMANCE BROKERAGE SERVICES, INC.; *U.S. Private*, pg. 3148
PERFORMANCE CAPTURE STUDIOS—See Motion Analysis Corporation; *U.S. Private*, pg. 2795
PERFORMANCE CARS (ST. CATHARINES) LTD.; *Int'l*, pg. 5801
PERFORMANCE CHEMISERVE LIMITED—See Deepak Fertilisers & Petrochemicals Corporation Limited; *Int'l*, pg. 2003
PERFORMANCE CHEVROLET LLC; *U.S. Private*, pg. 3148
PERFORMANCE COAL COMPANY—See Alpha Natural Resources, Inc.; *U.S. Private*, pg. 199
PERFORMANCE COATINGS INTERNATIONAL LABORATORIES, LLC; *U.S. Private*, pg. 3148
PERFORMANCE COMMUNICATIONS LTD—See Performance PR Ltd.; *Int'l*, pg. 5801
PERFORMANCE COMPANIES, INC.; *U.S. Private*, pg. 3148
THE PERFORMANCE COMPANIES INC.; *U.S. Private*, pg. 4093
PERFORMANCE CONTRACTING GROUP, INC.—See Performance Contracting Group; *U.S. Private*, pg. 3149
PERFORMANCE CONTRACTING GROUP; *U.S. Private*, pg. 3148
PERFORMANCE CONTRACTING, INC. - ISS DIVISION—See Performance Contracting Group; *U.S. Private*, pg. 3149
PERFORMANCE CONTRACTORS INC.; *U.S. Private*, pg. 3149
PERFORMANCE CYCLING LIMITED—See Halfords Group plc; *Int'l*, pg. 3229
PERFORMANCE DESIGNED PRODUCTS, LLC—See Diversis Capital, LLC; *U.S. Private*, pg. 1244
PERFORMANCE DOOR & HARDWARE, INC.; *U.S. Private*, pg. 3149
PERFORMANCE DOORSET SOLUTIONS, INC.—See Owens Corning; *U.S. Public*, pg. 1627
PERFORMANCE ELECTRICAL PRODUCTS,INC.—See Emek Elektrik Endustrisi A.S.; *Int'l*, pg. 2377
PERFORMANCE ENERGY SERVICES, L.L.C.—See Quanta Services, Inc.; *U.S. Public*, pg. 1752
PERFORMANCE ENGINEERED PRODUCTS INC.; *U.S. Private*, pg. 3149
PERFORMANCE ENHANCEMENTS INC.—See Trinity Hunt Management, L.P.; *U.S. Private*, pg. 4234
PERFORMANCE EQUIPMENT LTD.; *Int'l*, pg. 5801
PERFORMANCE EQUITY MANAGEMENT, LLC; *U.S. Private*, pg. 3149
PERFORMANCE FABRICS, INC.—See UVEX Winter Holding GmbH & Co KG; *Int'l*, pg. 8102
PERFORMANCE FIBERS OPERATIONS MEXICO, S. DE R.L. DE C.V.—See Indorama Ventures Public Company Limited; *Int'l*, pg. 3659
PERFORMANCE FOOD GROUP AFI—See Performance Food Group Company; *U.S. Public*, pg. 1675
PERFORMANCE FOOD GROUP COMPANY; *U.S. Public*, pg. 1674
PERFORMANCE FOOD GROUP, INC. - BROADLINE DIVISION—See Performance Food Group Company; *U.S. Public*, pg. 1675
PERFORMANCE FOOD GROUP, INC. - CUSTOMIZED DISTRIBUTION—See Performance Food Group Company; *U.S. Public*, pg. 1675
PERFORMANCE FOOD GROUP, INC. - PHOENIX SPECIALTY DISTRIBUTION CENTER—See Performance Food Group Company; *U.S. Public*, pg. 1675
PERFORMANCE FOOD GROUP, INC.—See Performance Food Group Company; *U.S. Public*, pg. 1675

PERFORMANCE FOOD GROUP LITTLE ROCK—See Performance Food Group Company; *U.S. Public*, pg. 1675
PERFORMANCE FOOD GROUP OF TEXAS, LP—See Performance Food Group Company; *U.S. Public*, pg. 1675
PERFORMANCE FOOD GROUP—See Performance Food Group Company; *U.S. Public*, pg. 1675
PERFORMANCE FOOD GROUP VICTORIA—See Performance Food Group Company; *U.S. Public*, pg. 1675
PERFORMANCE FOODSERVICE-SOMERSET, LLC—See Performance Food Group Company; *U.S. Public*, pg. 1675
PERFORMANCE FRICTION CORP.; *U.S. Private*, pg. 3149
PERFORMANCE GROUP, INC.; *U.S. Private*, pg. 3149
PERFORMANCE HEALTH FRANCE—See Patterson Companies, Inc.; *U.S. Public*, pg. 1654
PERFORMANCE HEALTH HOLDINGS, INC.—See Madison Dearborn Partners, LLC; *U.S. Private*, pg. 2542
PERFORMANCE HEALTH INTERNATIONAL LIMITED—See Madison Dearborn Partners, LLC; *U.S. Private*, pg. 2542
PERFORMANCE HEALTH (PTY) LTD—See Lesaka Technologies, Inc.; *Int'l*, pg. 4469
PERFORMANCE HEALTH SUPPLY, INC.—See Madison Dearborn Partners, LLC; *U.S. Private*, pg. 2542
PERFORMANCE IMPROVEMENTS (PI) GROUP LIMITED—See John Wood Group PLC; *Int'l*, pg. 3983
PERFORMANCE IMPROVEMENTS (PI) LIMITED—See John Wood Group PLC; *Int'l*, pg. 3983
PERFORMANCE INCORPORATED—See Automatic Data Processing, Inc.; *U.S. Public*, pg. 230
PERFORMANCE INDICATOR, LLC; *U.S. Private*, pg. 3149
PERFORMANCE INDUSTRIES INC.; *U.S. Private*, pg. 3149
PERFORMANCE INTERACTIVE ALLIANCE GMBH—See Equistone Partners Europe Limited; *Int'l*, pg. 2487
PERFORMANCE LIVESTOCK ANALYTICS, INC.—See Zoetis, Inc.; *U.S. Public*, pg. 2409
PERFORMANCE MARKETING OF IOWA, INC.; *U.S. Private*, pg. 3149
PERFORMANCE MATTERS ASSOCIATES OF TEXAS, INC.—See CNO Financial Group, Inc.; *U.S. Public*, pg. 520
PERFORMANCE MECHANICAL, INC.—See EMCOR Group, Inc.; *U.S. Public*, pg. 737
PERFORMANCE MEDICAL GROUP; *U.S. Private*, pg. 3149
PERFORMANCE MUNICH AUTOS PTE. LTD.—See Sime Darby Berhad; *Int'l*, pg. 6928
PERFORMANCE ONE AG; *Int'l*, pg. 5801
PERFORMANCE OPPORTUNITIES FUND, L.P.—See General Motors Company; *U.S. Public*, pg. 928
PERFORMANCE PACKAGING INC.—See Alpha Industries, Inc.; *U.S. Private*, pg. 197
PERFORMANCE PACKAGING; *U.S. Private*, pg. 3149
PERFORMANCE PAPER LLC; *U.S. Private*, pg. 3149
PERFORMANCE PERSONNEL PARTNERS, LLC; *U.S. Private*, pg. 3149
PERFORMANCE PET PRODUCTS, LLC—See Rosens Diversified, Inc.; *U.S. Private*, pg. 3484
PERFORMANCE PETROPLEX INC.; *U.S. Private*, pg. 3149
PERFORMANCE PLASTICS INC.—See Rock West Composites, Inc.; *U.S. Private*, pg. 3465
PERFORMANCE PLASTICS, LTD.—See Odyssey Investment Partners, LLC; *U.S. Private*, pg. 2995
PERFORMANCE PLUS CARTS—See Morgan Stanley; *U.S. Public*, pg. 1474
PERFORMANCE PLUS—See The Performance Companies Inc.; *U.S. Private*, pg. 4093
PERFORMANCE POLYMER SOLUTIONS INC.—See Proof Research, Inc.; *U.S. Private*, pg. 3284
PERFORMANCE PRESS, INC.; *U.S. Private*, pg. 3149
PERFORMANCE PR LTD.; *Int'l*, pg. 5801
PERFORMANCE PR MIDDLE EAST—See Performance PR Ltd.; *Int'l*, pg. 5801
PERFORMANCE PROCESS, INC.; *U.S. Private*, pg. 3149
PERFORMANCE PRODUCTS LIMITED—See In Phase International Ltd.; *Int'l*, pg. 3639
PERFORMANCE RETREADS SDN. BHD.—See Tuan Sing Holdings Limited; *Int'l*, pg. 7962
PERFORMANCE REVIEW INSTITUTE, INC.; *U.S. Private*, pg. 3149
PERFORMANCE SHIPPING INC.; *Int'l*, pg. 5801
PERFORMANCE SOFTWARE CORPORATION; *U.S. Private*, pg. 3149
PERFORMANCE SPECIALTY PRODUCTS (INDIA) PRIVATE LIMITED—See DuPont de Nemours, Inc.; *U.S. Public*, pg. 694
PERFORMANCE SPECIALTY PRODUCTS (SINGAPORE) PTE. LTD.—See DuPont de Nemours, Inc.; *U.S. Public*, pg. 694
PERFORMANCE SPORTS SYSTEMS, INC.—See Gen Cap America, Inc.; *U.S. Private*, pg. 1660
PERFORMANCES S.A.—See Vivendi SE; *Int'l*, pg. 8275

PERFORMANCE STAMPING CO., INC.—See Willis & Smith Capital, Inc.; *U.S. Public*, pg. 4527
PERFORMANCE STRENGTH DESIGNS, INC.; *U.S. Private*, pg. 3150
PERFORMANCE SUPERSTORE; *U.S. Private*, pg. 3150
PERFORMANCE SYSTEMATIX, INC.—See Henry Crown & Company; *U.S. Private*, pg. 1918
PERFORMANCE SYSTEMS INTEGRATION, LLC; *U.S. Private*, pg. 3150
PERFORMANCE TEAM, LLC—See A.P. Moller-Maersk A/S; *Int'l*, pg. 26
PERFORMANCE TEXTILES, INC.—See Praesidian Capital Corp.; *U.S. Private*, pg. 3241
PERFORMANCE TOYOTA; *U.S. Private*, pg. 3150
PERFORMANCE TRUCK PRODUCTS; *U.S. Private*, pg. 3150
PERFORMANCE VALIDATION, INC.; *U.S. Private*, pg. 3150
PERFORMANCE WAREHOUSE COMPANY, INC.—See National Auto Parts Warehouse, LLC; *U.S. Private*, pg. 2847
PERFORMANCE WAREHOUSE—See National Auto Parts Warehouse, LLC; *U.S. Private*, pg. 2847
PERFORMANCE WHOLESALE PTY. LTD.—See HKS CO., LTD.; *Int'l*, pg. 3429
PERFORMANT FINANCIAL CORPORATION; *U.S. Public*, pg. 1676
PERFORMANT MANAGEMENT COMPANY, LLC; *U.S. Private*, pg. 3150
PERFORMANT RECOVERY, INC.—See Performant Financial Corporation; *U.S. Public*, pg. 1676
PERFORMA PARTNERS; *Int'l*, pg. 5801
PERFORM DUE DILIGENCE SERVICES LIMITED—See JTC PLC; *Int'l*, pg. 4017
PERFORM GROUP, LLC - ALPHA FACTOR DIVISION—See Perform Group, LLC; *U.S. Private*, pg. 3148
PERFORM GROUP, LLC; *U.S. Private*, pg. 3148
PERFORM'HABITAT SAS—See AST GROUPE SA; *Int'l*, pg. 651
PERFORMICS—See Publicis Groupe S.A.; *Int'l*, pg. 6104
PERFORMLINE INC.; *U.S. Private*, pg. 3150
PERFORM MEDIA ASIA PTE LTD—See Vista Equity Partners, LLC; *U.S. Private*, pg. 4401
PERFORM MEDIA DEUTSCHLAND GMBH—See Vista Equity Partners, LLC; *U.S. Private*, pg. 4401
PERFORM MEDIA INC—See Vista Equity Partners, LLC; *U.S. Private*, pg. 4401
PERFORM MEDIA JAPAN KK—See Vista Equity Partners, LLC; *U.S. Private*, pg. 4401
PERFORM MEDIA POLAND ZOO—See Vista Equity Partners, LLC; *U.S. Private*, pg. 4401
PERFORM MEDIA SERVICES SRL—See Vista Equity Partners, LLC; *U.S. Private*, pg. 4401
PERFUMANIA HOLDINGS, INC.; *U.S. Private*, pg. 3150
PERFUMANIA, INC.—See Perfumania Holdings, Inc.; *U.S. Private*, pg. 3150
PERFUMANIA PUERTO RICO, INC.—See Perfumania Holdings, Inc.; *U.S. Private*, pg. 3150
PERFUMARIA DOUGLAS PORTUGAL LDA.—See CVC Capital Partners SICAV-FIS S.A.; *Int'l*, pg. 1883
PERFUME HOLDING ASIA PTE LTD—See BI-Invest Advisors S.A.; *Int'l*, pg. 1017
PERFUME HOLDING CORP.—See BI-Invest Advisors S.A.; *Int'l*, pg. 1017
PERFUME HOLDING LLC—See BI-Invest Advisors S.A.; *Int'l*, pg. 1017
PERFUME HOLDING SAS—See BI-Invest Advisors S.A.; *Int'l*, pg. 1017
PERFUME HOLDING S.P.A.—See BI-Invest Advisors S.A.; *Int'l*, pg. 1017
PERFUMERIA JULIA, S.A.; *Int'l*, pg. 5801
THE PERFUME SHOP LIMITED—See CK Hutchison Holdings Limited; *Int'l*, pg. 1636
PERFUMES LOEWE S.A—See LVMH Moet Hennessy Louis Vuitton SE; *Int'l*, pg. 4602
PERGAMON STATUS DIS TICARET AS; *Int'l*, pg. 5801
PERGA-PLASTIC GMBH—See Serafin Unternehmensgruppe GmbH; *Int'l*, pg. 6720
PERGO AB—See Mohawk Industries, Inc.; *U.S. Public*, pg. 1458
PERGO ASIA CO. LTD.—See Mohawk Industries, Inc.; *U.S. Public*, pg. 1458
PERGO (EUROPE) AB—See Mohawk Industries, Inc.; *U.S. Public*, pg. 1458
PERGO (FRANCE) S. A. S.—See Mohawk Industries, Inc.; *U.S. Public*, pg. 1458
PERGO GMBH—See Mohawk Industries, Inc.; *U.S. Public*, pg. 1458
PERGO HOLDING B. V.—See Mohawk Industries, Inc.; *U.S. Public*, pg. 1458
PERGO INC.—See Mohawk Industries, Inc.; *U.S. Public*, pg. 1458
PERHAM PHYSICAL THERAPY, LTD.—See UnitedHealth Group Incorporated; *U.S. Public*, pg. 4168
PERHENTIAN ISLAND RESORT SDN. BHD.—See Inch Kenneth Kajang Rubber Public Limited Company; *Int'l*, pg. 3646
PERHOPOLIS S.R.L.—See Camfin S.p.A.; *Int'l*, pg. 1272

THE PERIA KARAMALAI TEA & PRODUCE COMPANY LIMITED — CORPORATE AFFILIATIONS

THE PERIA KARAMALAI TEA & PRODUCE COMPANY LIMITED; *Int'l*, pg. 7673
PERICEYL (PVT) LTD.—See Melstacorp PLC; *Int'l*, pg. 4813
PERICH ADVERTISING + DESIGN; *U.S. Private*, pg. 3150
PERI-DENT LTD.—See Platinum Equity, LLC; *U.S. Private*, pg. 3205
PERIDIAN ASIA PTE LTD.—See Downer EDI Limited; *Int'l*, pg. 2186
PERIDOT CORPORATION—See Genstar Capital, LLC; *U.S. Private*, pg. 1679
PERIGEE HOLDINGS INC.; *U.S. Public*, pg. 1676
PERIGEN INC.—See Halma plc; *Int'l*, pg. 3232
PERIGON GROUP PTY. LTD.—See PeopleIn Limited; *Int'l*, pg. 5794
PERIGON PARTNERS LLC; *U.S. Private*, pg. 3150
PERIGON WEALTH MANAGEMENT LLC; *U.S. Private*, pg. 3150
PERIHELION CAPITAL LTD.; *Int'l*, pg. 5801
PERILLON SOFTWARE, INC—See Lisam Systems Inc.; *Int'l*, pg. 4523
PERILS AG—See Marsh & McLennan Companies, Inc.; *U.S. Public*, pg. 1388
PERILYA BROKEN HILL LIMITED—See Shenzhen Zhongjin Lingnan Nonfemet Co., Ltd.; *Int'l*, pg. 6825
PERILYA LIMITED—See Shenzhen Zhongjin Lingnan Nonfemet Co., Ltd.; *Int'l*, pg. 6825
PERIMETER AVIATION LP—See Exchange Income Corporation; *Int'l*, pg. 2579
PERIMETER MALL—See Brookfield Corporation; *Int'l*, pg. 1185
PERIMETER MEDICAL IMAGING AI, INC.; *Int'l*, pg. 5801
PERIMETER OFFICE PRODUCTS, INC.—See The ODP Corporation; *U.S. Public*, pg. 2117
PERIMETER ROAD SURGICAL HOSPITAL, LLC—See Nobilis Health Corp.; *U.S. Private*, pg. 2932
PERIMETER SECURITY PARTNERS, LLC; *U.S. Private*, pg. 3150
PERIMETER SOLUTIONS LP—See EverArc Holdings Limited; *Int'l*, pg. 2563
PERIMETER SOLUTIONS, SA; *U.S. Public*, pg. 1676
PERIMETER TERMINAL, LLC; *U.S. Private*, pg. 3150
PERINI BUILDING COMPANY, INC.—See Tutor Perini Corporation; *U.S. Public*, pg. 2206
PERINI COMERCIAL DE ALIMENTOS LTDA.—See Cencosud S.A.; *Int'l*, pg. 1401
PERINI MANAGEMENT SERVICES, INC.—See Tutor Perini Corporation; *U.S. Public*, pg. 2206
PERIODICAL MANAGEMENT GROUP INTERNATIONAL LTD.; *U.S. Private*, pg. 3150
PERIODICAL PUBLISHERS' SERVICE BUREAU, LLC—See Subco Inc.; *U.S. Private*, pg. 3847
PERION NETWORK LTD.; *Int'l*, pg. 5801
PERIOPTIX, INC.—See Centre Partners Management LLC; *U.S. Private*, pg. 828
PERIOPTIX, INC.—See Mill Street Partners LLC; *U.S. Private*, pg. 2730
PERIPHAS CAPITAL PARTNERING CORPORATION; *U.S. Public*, pg. 1676
PERIPHERAL COMPANY, INC.—See Black River Computer, LLC; *U.S. Private*, pg. 572
PERIPHERAL COMPUTER SUPPORT, INC.—See Lincolnshire Management, Inc.; *U.S. Private*, pg. 2459
PERIPHERAL DEVICES & PRODUCTS SYSTEMS INC.; *U.S. Private*, pg. 3151
PERIPHONICS CORPORATION—See Nortel Networks Corporation; *Int'l*, pg. 5438
PERISAI PETROLEUM TEKNOLOGI BHD.; *Int'l*, pg. 5801
PERIS COMPANIES INC.; *U.S. Private*, pg. 3151
PERISCOPE (ASIA) LIMITED—See Quad/Graphics, Inc.; *U.S. Public*, pg. 1744
PERISCOPE EQUITY LLC; *U.S. Private*, pg. 3151
PERISCOPE HOLDINGS INC.—See KKR & Co. Inc.; *U.S. Public*, pg. 1267
PERISCOPE, INC.—See Quad/Graphics, Inc.; *U.S. Public*, pg. 1744
PERISCOPE INTERMEDIATE CORP.—See KKR & Co. Inc.; *U.S. Public*, pg. 1267
PERISCOPEIQ, INC.; *U.S. Private*, pg. 3151
PERISCOPE PRINTING & PACKAGING INDIA PRIVATE LIMITED.—See Quad/Graphics, Inc.; *U.S. Public*, pg. 1744
PERISHABLE CENTER GMBH + CO. BETRIEBS KG—See Fraport AG; *Int'l*, pg. 2764
PERISHABLE DISTRIBUTORS OF IA—See Hy-Vee, Inc.; *U.S. Private*, pg. 2016
THE PERISHABLES GROUP, INC.—See Brookfield Corporation; *Int'l*, pg. 1180
THE PERISHABLES GROUP, INC.—See Elliott Management Corporation; *U.S. Private*, pg. 1373
PERISHABLE SHIPPING SOLUTIONS, LLC—See Bay Grove Capital LLC; *U.S. Private*, pg. 493
PERISHIP LLC—See VerifyMe, Inc.; *U.S. Public*, pg. 2280
PERISSON PETROLEUM CORPORATION; *Int'l*, pg. 5801
PERISTEL S.A.—See Getinge AB; *Int'l*, pg. 2952
PERITEC CORPORATION—See Techno Alpha Co., Ltd.; *Int'l*, pg. 7509
PERITUS INC.; *U.S. Private*, pg. 3151

PERITUS INTERNATIONAL SDN. BHD.—See Sapura Energy Berhad; *Int'l*, pg. 6574
PERIYA CORP.; *Int'l*, pg. 5801
PERKAPALAN DAI ZHUN SDN. BHD.; *Int'l*, pg. 5802
PERKASIE INDUSTRIES CORPORATION; *U.S. Private*, pg. 3151
PERK.COM, INC.; *Int'l*, pg. 5801
PERK HERO SOFTWARE INC.—See Perk Labs, Inc.; *Int'l*, pg. 5801
PERKHIDMATAN KOMPUTER PERLADANGAN SDN. BHD.—See Sime Darby Berhad; *Int'l*, pg. 6929
PERK INC.—See Nexxen International Ltd.; *Int'l*, pg. 5251
PERKINELMER BIOSIGNAL, INC.—See Revvity, Inc.; *U.S. Public*, pg. 1794
PERKINELMER CHEMAGEN TECHNOLOGIE GMBH—See Revvity, Inc.; *U.S. Public*, pg. 1795
PERKINELMER DANMARK A/S—See Revvity, Inc.; *U.S. Public*, pg. 1794
PERKIN ELMER DE MEXICO, S.A.—See Revvity, Inc.; *U.S. Public*, pg. 1794
PERKINELMER ESPANA, S.L.—See Revvity, Inc.; *U.S. Public*, pg. 1794
PERKINELMER FINLAND OY—See Revvity, Inc.; *U.S. Public*, pg. 1794
PERKINELMER GENOMICS, INC.—See Revvity, Inc.; *U.S. Public*, pg. 1794
PERKINELMER HEALTHCARE DIAGNOSTICS (SHANGHAI) CO., LTD.—See Revvity, Inc.; *U.S. Public*, pg. 1795
PERKINELMER HEALTH SCIENCES CANADA INC.—See Revvity, Inc.; *U.S. Public*, pg. 1794
PERKINELMER HEALTH SCIENCES, INC.—See Revvity, Inc.; *U.S. Public*, pg. 1794
PERKINELMER HOLDING GMBH—See Revvity, Inc.; *U.S. Public*, pg. 1795
PERKINELMER (HONG KONG) LTD.—See Revvity, Inc.; *U.S. Public*, pg. 1794
PERKINELMER INFORMATICS, INC.—See Revvity, Inc.; *U.S. Public*, pg. 1795
PERKIN-ELMER INSTRUMENTS (PHILIPPINES) CORPORATION—See Revvity, Inc.; *U.S. Public*, pg. 1794
PERKINELMER INSTRUMENTS (SHANGHAI) CO. LTD.—See Revvity, Inc.; *U.S. Public*, pg. 1795
PERKINELMER JAPAN CO. LTD.—See Revvity, Inc.; *U.S. Public*, pg. 1795
PERKINELMER MEDICAL IMAGING, LLC—See Varex Imaging Corporation; *U.S. Public*, pg. 2275
PERKINELMER NEDERLAND B.V.—See Revvity, Inc.; *U.S. Public*, pg. 1795
PERKINELMER PTY. LTD.—See Revvity, Inc.; *U.S. Public*, pg. 1795
PERKINELMER SAGLIK VE CEVRE BILIMLERI LTD.—See Revvity, Inc.; *U.S. Public*, pg. 1795
PERKINELMER SAOLYK VE CEVRE BILIMLERI LTD.—See Revvity, Inc.; *U.S. Public*, pg. 1795
PERKINELMER SINGAPORE PTE LTD.—See Revvity, Inc.; *U.S. Public*, pg. 1795
PERKINELMER SOUTH AFRICA (PTY) LTD.—See Revvity, Inc.; *U.S. Public*, pg. 1795
PERKINELMER TAIWAN CORPORATION—See Revvity, Inc.; *U.S. Public*, pg. 1795
PERKINELMER VERTRIEBS GMBH—See Revvity, Inc.; *U.S. Public*, pg. 1795
PERKINS COIE LLP; *U.S. Private*, pg. 3151
PERKINS & COMPANY, P.C.; *U.S. Private*, pg. 3151
PERKINS EASTMAN ARCHITECTS P.C.; *U.S. Private*, pg. 3151
PERKINS ENGINES COMPANY LTD.—See Caterpillar, Inc.; *U.S. Public*, pg. 453
PERKINS ENGINES INC—See Caterpillar, Inc.; *U.S. Public*, pg. 453
PERKINS FRANCE (S.A.S.)—See Caterpillar, Inc.; *U.S. Public*, pg. 453
PERKINS GROUP SERVICES—See Cathay Investments Limited; *Int'l*, pg. 1360
PERKINS HOME CENTER, INC.; *U.S. Public*, pg. 3151
PERKINS INDIA PRIVATE LIMITED—See Caterpillar, Inc.; *U.S. Public*, pg. 453
PERKINS INTERNATIONAL INC.—See Caterpillar, Inc.; *U.S. Public*, pg. 453
PERKINS INVESTMENT MANAGEMENT LLC—See Janus Henderson Group plc; *Int'l*, pg. 3881
PERKINS LLC—See Huddle House, Inc.; *U.S. Private*, pg. 2001
PERKINS LUMBER CO. INC.; *U.S. Private*, pg. 3151
PERKINS MOTOR COMPANY; *U.S. Private*, pg. 3151
PERKINS MOTOREN GMBH—See Caterpillar, Inc.; *U.S. Public*, pg. 453
PERKINS NICHOLS MEDIA—See Young & Laramore; *U.S. Private*, pg. 4592
PERKINS OIL & GAS, INC.; *U.S. Private*, pg. 3152
PERKINS POWER CORP.—See Southeast Diesel Corp.; *U.S. Private*, pg. 3725
THE PERKINS + WILL GROUP, LTD.; *U.S. Private*, pg. 4093
PERKINS + WILL - RESEARCH TRIANGLE PARK—See The Perkins + Will Group, Ltd.; *U.S. Private*, pg. 4093

PERKINS + WILL - WASHINGTON, DC—See The Perkins + Will Group, Ltd.; *U.S. Private*, pg. 4093
PERK LABS, INC.; *Int'l*, pg. 5801
PERKO WORLDWIDE CORP.; *U.S. Private*, pg. 3152
PERKUMPULAN EKONOMI INDONESIA JERMAN—See Messe Munchen GmbH; *Int'l*, pg. 4842
PERLAGONIA 1 HOLDING GMBH—See Immofinanz AG; *Int'l*, pg. 3628
PERLA GREEK SALT LTD.—See Dem. Th. Bertzeletos & Bros. SA; *Int'l*, pg. 2022
PERLA GREEK SALT LTD.—See GIC Pte. Ltd.; *Int'l*, pg. 2968
PERLA GREEK SALT LTD.—See The Carlyle Group Inc.; *U.S. Public*, pg. 2051
PERLAVITA ROSENAU AG—See Swiss Prime Site AG; *Int'l*, pg. 7370
PERLECTRIC, INC.—See MDU Resources Group, Inc.; *U.S. Public*, pg. 1411
PERLEGEN SCIENCES, INC.; *U.S. Private*, pg. 3152
PERLEN CONVERTING AG—See CPH Chemie + Papier Holding AG; *Int'l*, pg. 1824
PERLEN CONVERTING L.L.C.—See CPH Chemie + Papier Holding AG; *Int'l*, pg. 1824
PERLEN DEUTSCHLAND GMBH—See CPH Chemie + Papier Holding AG; *Int'l*, pg. 1824
PERLEN FRANCE SARL—See CPH Chemie + Papier Holding AG; *Int'l*, pg. 1824
PERLEN IMMOBILIEN AG—See CPH Chemie + Papier Holding AG; *Int'l*, pg. 1824
PERLEN PACKAGING AG—See CPH Chemie + Papier Holding AG; *Int'l*, pg. 1824
PERLEN PACKAGING ANAPOLIS INDUSTRIA E COMERCIO LTDA.—See CPH Chemie + Papier Holding AG; *Int'l*, pg. 1824
PERLEN PACKAGING GMBH—See CPH Chemie + Papier Holding AG; *Int'l*, pg. 1824
PERLEN PACKAGING L.L.C.—See CPH Chemie + Papier Holding AG; *Int'l*, pg. 1824
PERLEN PACKAGING (SUZHOU) CO., LTD.—See CPH Chemie + Papier Holding AG; *Int'l*, pg. 1824
PERLEN PAPIER AG—See CPH Chemie + Papier Holding AG; *Int'l*, pg. 1824
PERLES MERKUR ITALIA, S.R.L.—See Merkur, d.d.; *Int'l*, pg. 4837
PERLE SYSTEMS ASIA PACIFIC (PTE) LTD.—See PHOENIX CONTACT GmbH & Co. KG; *Int'l*, pg. 5850
PERLE SYSTEMS EUROPE LIMITED—See PHOENIX CONTACT GmbH & Co. KG; *Int'l*, pg. 5850
PERLE SYSTEMS GMBH—See PHOENIX CONTACT GmbH & Co. KG; *Int'l*, pg. 5850
PERLE SYSTEMS INC.—See PHOENIX CONTACT GmbH & Co. KG; *Int'l*, pg. 5850
PERLE SYSTEMS K.K.—See PHOENIX CONTACT GmbH & Co. KG; *Int'l*, pg. 5850
PERLE SYSTEMS LIMITED—See PHOENIX CONTACT GmbH & Co. KG; *Int'l*, pg. 5850
PERLE SYSTEMS S.A.R.L.—See PHOENIX CONTACT GmbH & Co. KG; *Int'l*, pg. 5850
PERLICK CORPORATION; *U.S. Private*, pg. 3152
PERLIS SPECIALIST HOSPITAL SDN BHD—See KPJ Healthcare Berhad; *Int'l*, pg. 4297
PERLITA Y VERMICULITA, S.L.U.—See RPM International Inc.; *U.S. Public*, pg. 1818
PERLITE CANADA, INC.; *Int'l*, pg. 5802
PERLIT THERMOPUTZ ERSEN GMBH—See Compagnie de Saint-Gobain SA; *Int'l*, pg. 1726
PERLMART DRUGS OF LACEY INC.—See Perlmart Inc.; *U.S. Private*, pg. 3152
PERLMART DRUGS OF TOMS RIVER INC.—See Perlmart Inc.; *U.S. Private*, pg. 3152
PERLMART INC.; *U.S. Private*, pg. 3152
PERLMART MANAGEMENT CO. INC.—See Perlmart Inc.; *U.S. Private*, pg. 3152
PERLMART OF LACEY TOWNSHIP INC.—See Perlmart Inc.; *U.S. Private*, pg. 3152
PERLO MCCORMACK PACIFIC—See W.L. McCormack & Co. Inc.; *U.S. Private*, pg. 4421
PERLON-MONOFIL GMBH—See Serafin Unternehmensgruppe GmbH; *Int'l*, pg. 6720
PERLOS ASIA PTE. LTD.—See Lite-On Technology Corporation; *Int'l*, pg. 4526
PERLOS (BEIJING) ELECTRONIC & TELECOMMUNICATION COMPONENTS CO., LTD.—See Lite-On Technology Corporation; *Int'l*, pg. 4525
PERLOS (GUANGZHOU) ENGINEERING PLASTICS CO., LTD.—See Lite-On Technology Corporation; *Int'l*, pg. 4526
PERLOS JAPAN—See Lite-On Technology Corporation; *Int'l*, pg. 4526
PERLOS PRECISION MOLDS (SHENZHEN) CO. LTD.—See Lite-On Technology Corporation; *Int'l*, pg. 4525
PERLOS PRECISION PLASTICS MOULDING LLC—See Lite-On Technology Corporation; *Int'l*, pg. 4526
PERLOS TELECOMMUNICATION & ELECTRONIC COMPONENTS INDIA PVT. LTD.—See Lite-On Technology Corporation; *Int'l*, pg. 4526
PERLOWIN DEVELOPMENT CORP.; *U.S. Private*, pg. 3152

COMPANY NAME INDEX

PERL-POOL AG—See Burkhalter Holding AG; *Int'l*, pg. 1225
PERMA-FIX ENVIRONMENTAL SERVICES, INC.; *U.S. Public*, pg. 1676
PERMA-FIX ENVIRONMENTAL SERVICES UK LIMITED—See Perma-Fix Environmental Services, Inc.; *U.S. Public*, pg. 1676
PERMA-FIX MEDICAL S.A—See Perma-Fix Environmental Services, Inc.; *U.S. Public*, pg. 1676
PERMA-FIX NORTHWEST, INC.—See Perma-Fix Environmental Services, Inc.; *U.S. Public*, pg. 1676
PERMA-FIX OF FLORIDA, INC.—See Perma-Fix Environmental Services, Inc.; *U.S. Public*, pg. 1676
PERMA-FLEX/ESI—See Perma-Flex Roller Technology LLC; *U.S. Private*, pg. 3152
PERMA-FLEX ROLLER TECHNOLOGY LLC; *U.S. Private*, pg. 3152
PERMA FUNDS MANAGEMENT; *Int'l*, pg. 5802
PERMAJU INDUSTRIES BERHAD; *Int'l*, pg. 5802
PERMAL CAPITAL MANAGEMENT, LLC; *U.S. Private*, pg. 3152
PERMAL GROUP LTD.—See Franklin Resources, Inc.; *U.S. Public*, pg. 882
PERMALOK CORPORATION—See Northwest Pipe Company; *U.S. Public*, pg. 1542
PERMANENCE EUROPEENNE SAS—See Synergie SA; *Int'l*, pg. 7383
PERMANENTE DENTAL ASSOCIATES, PC—See Kaiser Permanente; *U.S. Private*, pg. 2256
THE PERMANENTE FEDERATION, LLC—See Kaiser Permanente; *U.S. Private*, pg. 2256
THE PERMANENTE MEDICAL GROUP, INC.—See Kaiser Permanente; *U.S. Private*, pg. 2256
PERMANENT EQUITY MANAGEMENT, LLC; *U.S. Private*, pg. 3152
PERMANENT MAGNETS LIMITED; *Int'l*, pg. 5802
PERMANENT TECHNOLOGIES, INC.; *U.S. Public*, pg. 1676
PERMANENT TSB GROUP HOLDINGS PLC; *Int'l*, pg. 5802
PERMANENT TSB PLC—See permanent tsb Group Holdings plc; *Int'l*, pg. 5802
PERMA-PIPE CANADA, LTD.—See Perma-Pipe International Holdings, Inc.; *U.S. Public*, pg. 1676
PERMA-PIPE EGYPT FOR METAL FABRICATION & INSULATION INDUSTRIES (PERMA-PIPE EGYPT) S.A.E—See Perma-Pipe International Holdings, Inc.; *U.S. Public*, pg. 1676
PERMA-PIPE, INC.—See Perma-Pipe International Holdings, Inc.; *U.S. Public*, pg. 1676
PERMA-PIPE INTERNATIONAL HOLDINGS, INC.; *U.S. Public*, pg. 1676
PERMA-PIPE MIDDLE EAST FZC—See Perma-Pipe International Holdings, Inc.; *U.S. Public*, pg. 1676
PERMA PURE INC. LLC—See Halma plc; *Int'l*, pg. 3232
PERMARK INTERNATIONAL (PTY.) LTD.; *Int'l*, pg. 5802
PERMAROCK PRODUCTS LIMITED—See Carillion plc; *Int'l*, pg. 1330
PERMA R PRODUCTS INC.—See Industrial Development Company sal; *Int'l*, pg. 3671
PERMA R PRODUCTS INC.—See Le Clair Industries Inc.; *U.S. Private*, pg. 2405
PER MAR SECURITY SERVICES; *U.S. Private*, pg. 3146
PERMAR SISTEMAS DE ALMACENAJE S.A.—See Whittan Storage Systems Ltd.; *Int'l*, pg. 8400
PERMASCAND AB—See Norvestor Equity AS; *Int'l*, pg. 5447
PERMASCAND TOP HOLDING AB—See Altor Equity Partners AB; *Int'l*, pg. 395
PERMASENSE LIMITED—See Emerson Electric Co.; *U.S. Public*, pg. 751
PERMAS JAYA SDN. BHD.—See Bandar Raya Developments Berhad; *Int'l*, pg. 829
PERMASTEELISA CLADDING TECHNOLOGIES—See Atlas Holdings, LLC; *U.S. Private*, pg. 377
PERMASTEELISA CLADDING TECH—See Atlas Holdings, LLC; *U.S. Private*, pg. 377
PERMASTEELISA ESPANA S.A.U—See Atlas Holdings, LLC; *U.S. Private*, pg. 377
PERMASTEELISA FRANCE S.A.S.—See Atlas Holdings, LLC; *U.S. Private*, pg. 377
PERMASTEELISA-GARTNER TAIWAN LTD.—See Atlas Holdings, LLC; *U.S. Private*, pg. 378
PERMASTEELISA HONG KONG LTD.—See Atlas Holdings, LLC; *U.S. Private*, pg. 378
PERMASTEELISA IMPIANTI S.R.L.- FCC PLANTERM DIVISION—See Atlas Holdings, LLC; *U.S. Private*, pg. 377
PERMASTEELISA (INDIA) PRIVATE LIMITED—See Atlas Holdings, LLC; *U.S. Private*, pg. 378
PERMASTEELISA INTERIORS S.R.L.—See Atlas Holdings, LLC; *U.S. Private*, pg. 377
PERMASTEELISA IRELAND LTD.—See Atlas Holdings, LLC; *U.S. Private*, pg. 377
PERMASTEELISA NORTH AMERICA CORP. - MIAMI—See Atlas Holdings, LLC; *U.S. Private*, pg. 377
PERMASTEELISA NORTH AMERICA CORP.—See Atlas Holdings, LLC; *U.S. Private*, pg. 377

PERMASTEELISA PACIFIC HOLDINGS LTD.—See Atlas Holdings, LLC; *U.S. Private*, pg. 377
PERMASTEELISA PTY LTD—See Atlas Holdings, LLC; *U.S. Private*, pg. 378
PERMASTEELISA S.P.A.—See Atlas Holdings, LLC; *U.S. Private*, pg. 377
PERMASTEELISA TAIWAN LTD.—See Atlas Holdings, LLC; *U.S. Private*, pg. 378
PERMASTEELISA (THAILAND) LTD.—See Atlas Holdings, LLC; *U.S. Private*, pg. 378
PERMASTEELISA UK LTD.—See Atlas Holdings, LLC; *U.S. Private*, pg. 378
PERMASTEELISA (VICTORIA) PTY LTD.—See Atlas Holdings, LLC; *U.S. Private*, pg. 377
PERMASWAGE HOLDINGS, INC.—See Berkshire Hathaway Inc.; *U.S. Public*, pg. 314
PERMASWAGE S.A.—See Berkshire Hathaway Inc.; *U.S. Public*, pg. 314
PERMATECH ELECTRONIC CORPORATION—See ZTEST Electronics Inc.; *Int'l*, pg. 8692
PERMATECH, INC.; *U.S. Private*, pg. 3152
PERMATREAT PEST CONTROL COMPANY INC.—See Rollins, Inc.; *U.S. Public*, pg. 1809
PERMAWICK COMPANY INC-INDIANA PLANT—See Permawick Company, Inc.; *U.S. Private*, pg. 3152
PERMAWICK COMPANY, INC.; *U.S. Private*, pg. 3152
PERMEA CHINA, LTD.—See Air Products & Chemicals, Inc.; *U.S. Public*, pg. 67
PERMEA INC.—See Air Products & Chemicals, Inc.; *U.S. Public*, pg. 67
PERMEDION INC.—See Veritas Capital Fund Management, LLC; *U.S. Private*, pg. 4362
PERM ENERGY RETAIL COMPANY OJSC; *Int'l*, pg. 5802
PERMEX PETROLEUM CORPORATION; *U.S. Public*, pg. 1677
PERMEX PETROLEUM CORP.; *Int'l*, pg. 5802
PERMIAN BASIN AREA FOUNDATION; *U.S. Private*, pg. 3152
PERMIAN BASIN RAILWAYS—See Iowa Pacific Holdings, LLC; *U.S. Private*, pg. 2135
PERMIAN BASIN ROYALTY TRUST; *U.S. Public*, pg. 1677
PERMIAN RESOURCES CORP; *U.S. Public*, pg. 1677
PERMIAN TANK & MANUFACTURING, INC.; *U.S. Private*, pg. 3152
PERMIANVILLE ROYALTY TRUST; *U.S. Public*, pg. 1677
PERMINTEX FURUKAWA AUTOPARTS MALAYSIA SDN. BHD.—See The Furukawa Electric Co., Ltd.; *Int'l*, pg. 7646
PERMINTEX SANKO TECHNOLOGIES SDN BHD.—See Sanko Gosei Ltd.; *Int'l*, pg. 6541
PERMINT GRANITE-HCM SDN BHD—See Protasco Berhad; *Int'l*, pg. 6003
PERMINT PLYWOOD SDN BHD—See Golden Pharos Berhad; *Int'l*, pg. 3031
PERMINT TIMBER CORPORATION SDN BHD—See Golden Pharos Berhad; *Int'l*, pg. 3030
PERMIRA ADVISERS LLC—See Permira Advisers LLP; *Int'l*, pg. 5808
PERMIRA ADVISERS LLP; *Int'l*, pg. 5802
PERMIRA BETEILIGUNGSBERATUNG GMBH—See Permira Advisers LLP; *Int'l*, pg. 5808
PERMIRA (GUERNSEY) LIMITED—See Permira Advisers LLP; *Int'l*, pg. 5807
PERMIRA LUXEMBOURG S.AR.L.—See Permira Advisers LLP; *Int'l*, pg. 5808
PERMIT CAPITAL ADVISORS, LLC—See Genstar Capital, LLC; *U.S. Private*, pg. 1676
PERMOBIL AB—See Investor AB; *Int'l*, pg. 3787
PERMOBIL AUSTRALIA PTY. LTD.—See Investor AB; *Int'l*, pg. 3787
PERMOBIL, INC.—See Investor AB; *Int'l*, pg. 3787
PERMOBIL, LTD.—See Investor AB; *Int'l*, pg. 3787
PERMODALAN NASIONAL BERHAD; *Int'l*, pg. 5809
PERMODO GMBH—See Stroer SE & Co. KGaA; *Int'l*, pg. 7242
PERMROCK ROYALTY TRUST; *U.S. Public*, pg. 1677
PERMSINPATTANA CO., LTD.—See Kaset Thai International Sugar Corporation Public Company Limited; *Int'l*, pg. 4087
PERMSIN STEEL WORKS PLC; *Int'l*, pg. 5809
PERNAS ELECTRONICS CO., LTD.—See WPG Holdings Limited; *Int'l*, pg. 8461
PERNEC CORPORATION BHD.—See NEC Corporation; *Int'l*, pg. 5186
PERNIX GROUP, INC.; *U.S. Public*, pg. 1677
PERNIX THERAPEUTICS HOLDINGS, INC.; *U.S. Private*, pg. 3152
PERNIX THERAPEUTICS, LLC—See Pernix Therapeutics Holdings, Inc.; *U.S. Private*, pg. 3152
PERNOD RICARD AFRICA & MIDDLE EAST—See Pernod Ricard S.A.; *Int'l*, pg. 5810
PERNOD RICARD ARGENTINA CORP.—See Pernod Ricard S.A.; *Int'l*, pg. 5810
PERNOD RICARD ARMENIA—See Pernod Ricard S.A.; *Int'l*, pg. 5810
PERNOD RICARD ASIA DUTY FREE LTD—See Pernod Ricard S.A.; *Int'l*, pg. 5810

PERNOD RICARD S.A.

PERNOD RICARD AUSTRALIA PTY LTD—See Pernod Ricard S.A.; *Int'l*, pg. 5810
PERNOD RICARD AUSTRIA GMBH—See Pernod Ricard S.A.; *Int'l*, pg. 5810
PERNOD RICARD BELGIUM SA—See Pernod Ricard S.A.; *Int'l*, pg. 5810
PERNOD RICARD BULGARIA EOOD—See Pernod Ricard S.A.; *Int'l*, pg. 5810
PERNOD RICARD CHILE SA—See Pernod Ricard S.A.; *Int'l*, pg. 5810
PERNOD RICARD (CHINA) TRADING CO LTD—See Pernod Ricard S.A.; *Int'l*, pg. 5810
PERNOD RICARD COLOMBIA SA—See Pernod Ricard S.A.; *Int'l*, pg. 5810
PERNOD RICARD CROATIA D.O.O.—See Pernod Ricard S.A.; *Int'l*, pg. 5811
PERNOD RICARD DENMARK A/S—See Pernod Ricard S.A.; *Int'l*, pg. 5810
PERNOD RICARD DEUTSCHLAND GMBH—See Pernod Ricard S.A.; *Int'l*, pg. 5810
PERNOD RICARD ESPANA S.A—See Pernod Ricard S.A.; *Int'l*, pg. 5810
PERNOD RICARD ESTONIA OU—See Pernod Ricard S.A.; *Int'l*, pg. 5810
PERNOD RICARD EUROPE SA—See Pernod Ricard S.A.; *Int'l*, pg. 5810
PERNOD RICARD FINANCE SA—See Pernod Ricard S.A.; *Int'l*, pg. 5811
PERNOD RICARD FINLAND OY—See Pernod Ricard S.A.; *Int'l*, pg. 5810
PERNOD RICARD GULF—See Pernod Ricard S.A.; *Int'l*, pg. 5810
PERNOD RICARD (HOLDING)—See Pernod Ricard S.A.; *Int'l*, pg. 5810
PERNOD RICARD HONG KONG LTD—See Pernod Ricard S.A.; *Int'l*, pg. 5811
PERNOD RICARD INDIA PTE LTD—See Pernod Ricard S.A.; *Int'l*, pg. 5811
PERNOD RICARD ISTANBUL—See Pernod Ricard S.A.; *Int'l*, pg. 5810
PERNOD RICARD ITALIA S.P.A.—See Pernod Ricard S.A.; *Int'l*, pg. 5810
PERNOD RICARD JAPAN K.K.—See Pernod Ricard S.A.; *Int'l*, pg. 5811
PERNOD RICARD KAZAKHSTAN LLP—See Pernod Ricard S.A.; *Int'l*, pg. 5811
PERNOD RICARD KOREA LTD—See Pernod Ricard S.A.; *Int'l*, pg. 5811
PERNOD RICARD MINSK LLC—See Pernod Ricard S.A.; *Int'l*, pg. 5811
PERNOD RICARD NEDERLAND BV—See Pernod Ricard S.A.; *Int'l*, pg. 5810
PERNOD RICARD NEW ZEALAND LIMITED—See Pernod Ricard S.A.; *Int'l*, pg. 5811
PERNOD RICARD NORDIC—See Pernod Ricard S.A.; *Int'l*, pg. 5810
PERNOD RICARD NORTH AMERICA SAS—See Pernod Ricard S.A.; *Int'l*, pg. 5811
PERNOD-RICARD NORWAY A/S—See Pernod Ricard S.A.; *Int'l*, pg. 5810
PERNOD RICARD PACIFIC HOLDING PTY LTD—See Pernod Ricard S.A.; *Int'l*, pg. 5811
PERNOD RICARD PACIFIC TRAVEL RETAIL—See Pernod Ricard S.A.; *Int'l*, pg. 5811
PERNOD RICARD PHILIPPINES INC.—See Pernod Ricard S.A.; *Int'l*, pg. 5811
PERNOD RICARD ROUSS CJSC—See Pernod Ricard S.A.; *Int'l*, pg. 5811
PERNOD RICARD S.A.; *Int'l*, pg. 5809
PERNOD RICARD SERBIA D.O.O.—See Pernod Ricard S.A.; *Int'l*, pg. 5811
PERNOD RICARD SINGAPORE PTE LTD—See Pernod Ricard S.A.; *Int'l*, pg. 5811
PERNOD RICARD SLOVENJA D.O.O.—See Pernod Ricard S.A.; *Int'l*, pg. 5811
PERNOD RICARD SOUTH AFRICA PTY LTD—See Pernod Ricard S.A.; *Int'l*, pg. 5810
PERNOD RICARD SOUTHERN CENTRAL EUROPE—See Pernod Ricard S.A.; *Int'l*, pg. 5811
PERNOD RICARD SWEDEN AB—See Pernod Ricard S.A.; *Int'l*, pg. 5810
PERNOD RICARD SWISS S.A.—See Pernod Ricard S.A.; *Int'l*, pg. 5810
PERNOD RICARD TAIWAN LTD—See Pernod Ricard S.A.; *Int'l*, pg. 5811
PERNOD RICARD THAILAND LTD—See Pernod Ricard S.A.; *Int'l*, pg. 5811
PERNOD RICARD UK LIMITED—See Pernod Ricard S.A.; *Int'l*, pg. 5811
PERNOD RICARD UKRAINE—See Pernod Ricard S.A.; *Int'l*, pg. 5811
PERNOD RICARD URUGUAY SA—See Pernod Ricard S.A.; *Int'l*, pg. 5811
PERNOD RICARD USA, INC.—See Pernod Ricard S.A.; *Int'l*, pg. 5811
PERNOD RICARD USA LLC - CONTINENTAL DIVISION—See Pernod Ricard S.A.; *Int'l*, pg. 5811
PERNOD RICARD USA LLC - EAST DIVISION—See Pernod Ricard S.A.; *Int'l*, pg. 5811

PERNOD RICARD S.A. — CORPORATE AFFILIATIONS

PERNOD RICARD USA LLC. - WEST DIVISION—See Pernod Ricard S.A.; *Int'l*, pg. 5811
PERNOD RICARD WINEMAKERS PTY LTD—See Pernod Ricard S.A.; *Int'l*, pg. 5810
PERNOD—See Pernod Ricard S.A.; *Int'l*, pg. 5810
PERN S.A.; *Int'l*, pg. 5809
PEROBOT CO., LTD.—See Hon Hai Precision Industry Co., Ltd.; *Int'l*, pg. 3457
PERO ENGINEERING & SALES COMPANY, INC.; *U.S. Private*, pg. 3152
PERONNE MANUFACTURING COMPANY LTD—See Barbados Shipping & Trading Co. Ltd.; *Int'l*, pg. 858
PEROXIDOS DO BRAZIL LTDA—See Solvay S.A.; *Int'l*, pg. 7078
PEROXYCHEM LLC—See RAG-Stiftung; *Int'l*, pg. 6179
PERPETUAL CAPITAL, LLC; *U.S. Private*, pg. 3152
PERPETUAL CORPORATION—See Sinclair, Inc.; *U.S. Public*, pg. 1885
PERPETUAL ENERGY INC.—See Rubellite Energy Corp.; *Int'l*, pg. 6422
PERPETUAL ENERGY OPERATING CORP.—See Rubellite Energy Corp.; *Int'l*, pg. 6422
PERPETUAL EQUITY INVESTMENT COMPANY LIMITED; *Int'l*, pg. 5812
PERPETUAL FEDERAL SAVINGS BANK, INC.—See Farmers & Merchants Bancorp, Inc.; *U.S. Public*, pg. 822
PERPETUAL GLOBAL LIMITED; *Int'l*, pg. 5812
PERPETUAL INCOME & GROWTH INVESTMENT TRUST PLC; *Int'l*, pg. 5812
PERPETUAL INDUSTRIES INC.; *U.S. Public*, pg. 1677
PERPETUAL INSIGHTS LLC; *U.S. Private*, pg. 3153
PERPETUAL INVESTMENT MANAGEMENT LIMITED—See Perpetual Limited; *Int'l*, pg. 5812
PERPETUAL LEGAL SERVICES PTY LIMITED—See Perpetual Limited; *Int'l*, pg. 5812
PERPETUAL LIMITED; *Int'l*, pg. 5812
PERPETUAL MACHINE COMPANY—See Textile Rubber & Chemical Co., Inc.; *U.S. Private*, pg. 3978
PERPETUAL MORTGAGE SERVICES PTY LIMITED—See Perpetual Limited; *Int'l*, pg. 5812
PERPETUAL MOTION ENTERPRISES LIMITED—See Invacare Corporation; *U.S. Private*, pg. 2131
PERPETUAL NOMINEES LIMITED—See Perpetual Limited; *Int'l*, pg. 5812
PERPETUAL RESOURCES LIMITED; *Int'l*, pg. 5812
PERPETUAL SUPERANNUATION LTD—See Perpetual Limited; *Int'l*, pg. 5812
PERPETUAL TRUSTEE COMPANY (CANBERRA) LIMITED—See Perpetual Limited; *Int'l*, pg. 5812
PERPETUAL TRUSTEE COMPANY LIMITED—See Perpetual Limited; *Int'l*, pg. 5812
PERPETUAL TRUSTEES QUEENSLAND LIMITED—See Perpetual Limited; *Int'l*, pg. 5812
PERPETUAL TRUSTEES VICTORIA LIMITED—See Perpetual Limited; *Int'l*, pg. 5812
PERPETUAL TRUSTEES WA LIMITED—See Perpetual Limited; *Int'l*, pg. 5812
PERPETUAL TRUST LIMITED—See Bath Street Capital Limited; *Int'l*, pg. 889
PERPETUAL TRUST SERVICES LIMITED—See Perpetual Limited; *Int'l*, pg. 5812
PERPETUA RESOURCES CORP.; *U.S. Public*, pg. 1677
PERRAM ELECTRIC, INC.; *U.S. Private*, pg. 3153
PERRARD S.A.—See Eiffage S.A.; *Int'l*, pg. 2330
PERRECA ELECTRIC CO. INC.; *U.S. Private*, pg. 3153
PERRIER GROUP OF AMERICA INC.—See Nestle S.A.; *Int'l*, pg. 5210
PERRIER GROUP OF AMERICA INC.—See Nestle S.A.; *Int'l*, pg. 5210
PERRIGO COMPANY OF SOUTH CAROLINA, INC.—See Perrigo Company plc; *Int'l*, pg. 5813
PERRIGO COMPANY PLC; *Int'l*, pg. 5812
PERRIGO COMPANY—See Perrigo Company plc; *Int'l*, pg. 5813
PERRIGO DE MEXICO S.A. DE C.V.—See Perrigo Company plc; *Int'l*, pg. 5813
PERRIGO INTERNATIONAL, INC.—See Perrigo Company plc; *Int'l*, pg. 5813
PERRIGO ISRAEL AGENCIES LTD.—See Perrigo Company plc; *Int'l*, pg. 5813
PERRIGO ISRAEL PHARMACEUTICALS LTD.—See Perrigo Company plc; *Int'l*, pg. 5813
PERRIGO NEW YORK, INC.—See Perrigo Company plc; *Int'l*, pg. 5813
PERRIGO NORGE AS—See Perrigo Company plc; *Int'l*, pg. 5813
PERRIGO PHARMACEUTICALS COMPANY—See Perrigo Company plc; *Int'l*, pg. 5813
PERRIGO RESEARCH & DEVELOPMENT COMPANY—See Perrigo Company plc; *Int'l*, pg. 5813
PERRIGO SALES CORPORATION—See Perrigo Company plc; *Int'l*, pg. 5813
PERRIGO UK ACQUISITION LIMITED—See Perrigo Company plc; *Int'l*, pg. 5813
PERRIN BERNARD SUPOWITZ, LLC—See Kelso & Company, L.P.; *U.S. Private*, pg. 2278
PERRIN GMBH—See KITZ CORPORATION; *Int'l*, pg. 4196

PERROT DUVAL HOLDING S.A.; *Int'l*, pg. 5814
PERROT DUVAL MANAGEMENT S.A—See Perrot Duval Holding S.A.; *Int'l*, pg. 5814
PERROTT ENGINEERING GROUP LTD.; *Int'l*, pg. 5814
PERRY AUTO MALL; *U.S. Private*, pg. 3153
PERRY BALLARD INCORPORATED; *U.S. Private*, pg. 3153
PERRY BROTHERS, INC.; *U.S. Private*, pg. 3153
PERRY BROTHERS TIRE SERVICE, INC.; *U.S. Private*, pg. 3153
PERRY BUICK CO.; *U.S. Private*, pg. 3153
PERRY CHEMICAL & MANUFACTURING CO. INC.; *U.S. Private*, pg. 3153
PERRY CHRYSLER DODGE JEEP RAM; *U.S. Private*, pg. 3153
PERRY COMMUNICATIONS GROUP, INC.; *U.S. Private*, pg. 3153
THE PERRY COMPANY; *U.S. Private*, pg. 4093
PERRY CONSTRUCTION GROUP INC.; *U.S. Private*, pg. 3153
PERRY CORPORATION; *U.S. Private*, pg. 3153
PERRY COUNTY HEALTH SYSTEM; *U.S. Private*, pg. 3153
PERRY & DERRICK CO.; *U.S. Private*, pg. 3153
PERRY ELLIS EUROPE LIMITED—See Perry Ellis International, Inc.; *U.S. Private*, pg. 3154
PERRY ELLIS INTERNATIONAL EUROPE LIMITED—See Perry Ellis International, Inc.; *U.S. Private*, pg. 3154
PERRY ELLIS INTERNATIONAL HK LIMITED—See Perry Ellis International, Inc.; *U.S. Private*, pg. 3154
PERRY ELLIS INTERNATIONAL, INC.; *U.S. Private*, pg. 3153
PERRY ELLIS MENSWEAR, LLC—See Perry Ellis International, Inc.; *U.S. Private*, pg. 3154
PERRY ENGINEERING COMPANY, INC.; *U.S. Private*, pg. 3154
PERRY FOAM PRODUCTS INC.; *U.S. Private*, pg. 3154
PERRY FORD; *U.S. Private*, pg. 3154
PERRY HALL OUTBACK, INC.—See Bloomin' Brands, Inc.; *U.S. Public*, pg. 363
PERRY HILL ACQUISITION CORPORATION; *U.S. Private*, pg. 3154
PERRY HOMES INC.; *U.S. Private*, pg. 3154
PERRY LINCOLN MERCURY MAZDA; *U.S. Private*, pg. 3154
PERRY MACHINERY CZECH REPUBLIC S.R.O.—See Perry Videx LLC; *U.S. Private*, pg. 3154
PERRY MACHINERY POLAND LTD—See Perry Videx LLC; *U.S. Private*, pg. 3154
THE PERRYMAN COMPANY; *U.S. Private*, pg. 4093
THE PERRYMAN CO. - PITTSBURGH PLANT—See The Perryman Company; *U.S. Private*, pg. 4093
PERRY MCCALL CONSTRUCTION INC.; *U.S. Private*, pg. 3154
PERRY PARK VIEW (PERRY BARR) MANAGEMENT COMPANY LIMITED—See Persimmon plc; *Int'l*, pg. 5816
PERRY PRINTING CO.—See Hot Frog Print Media LLC; *U.S. Private*, pg. 1988
PERRY PROCESS EQUIPMENT LTD.—See Perry Videx LLC; *U.S. Private*, pg. 3154
PERRY PRODUCTIONS; *U.S. Private*, pg. 3154
PERRY PRODUCTS CORPORATION—See Perry Videx LLC; *U.S. Private*, pg. 3154
PERRY'S AUTO PARTS & SERVICE; *U.S. Private*, pg. 3154
PERRY'S ICE CREAM CO., INC.; *U.S. Private*, pg. 3154
PERRY'S OIL SERVICE INC.—See NGL Energy Partners LP; *U.S. Public*, pg. 1527
THE PERRY SOUTH BEACH HOTEL—See Coral Hospitality, LLC; *U.S. Private*, pg. 1046
PERRY SPORT BV—See CVC Capital Partners SICAV-FIS S.A.; *Int'l*, pg. 1886
PERRY SUPPLY COMPANY INCORPORATED; *U.S. Private*, pg. 3154
PERRY SUPPLY INC.—See Drummond Company, Inc.; *U.S. Private*, pg. 1280
PERRYTON EQUITY; *U.S. Private*, pg. 3154
PERRYTON FEEDERS INC.; *U.S. Private*, pg. 3154
PERRY VIDEX LLC; *U.S. Private*, pg. 3154
PERSAUD COMPANIES INC.; *U.S. Private*, pg. 3154
PERSEID THERAPEUTICS LLC—See Astellas Pharma Inc.; *Int'l*, pg. 653
PERSEPHONE CAPITAL PARTNERS LLC; *U.S. Private*, pg. 3154
THE PERSE SCHOOL (SINGAPORE) PTE. LTD.—See Chip Eng Seng Corporation Ltd.; *Int'l*, pg. 1572
PERSEU COMERCIO DE EQUIPAMENTO PARA INFORMATICA E ASTRONOMICA S.A.—See SDI Group plc; *Int'l*, pg. 6658
PERSEUS BOOKS, INC.—See Perseus Books, LLC; *U.S. Private*, pg. 3155
PERSEUS BOOKS, LLC; *U.S. Private*, pg. 3155
PERSEUS DISTRIBUTION, INC.—See Perseus Books, LLC; *U.S. Private*, pg. 3155
PERSEUS FINTECH SA; *Int'l*, pg. 5814
PERSEUS INVESTMENTS LIMITED—See VTech Holdings Ltd.; *Int'l*, pg. 8316
PERSEUS LLC; *U.S. Private*, pg. 3155

PERSEUS MINING COTE D'IVOIRE SA—See Perseus Mining Limited; *Int'l*, pg. 5814
PERSEUS MINING LIMITED; *Int'l*, pg. 5814
PERSEUS OPERATING GROUP—See Constellation Software Inc.; *Int'l*, pg. 1774
PERSEUS PROTEOMICS INC.; *Int'l*, pg. 5814
PERSEUS SPECIALTY FOOD PRODUCTS S.A.; *Int'l*, pg. 5814
PERSHA EQUIPMENT SALES INC—See Tym Corporation; *Int'l*, pg. 7995
PERSHIMEX RESOURCES CORPORATION—See Abcourt Mines Inc.; *Int'l*, pg. 58
PERSHING ASSOCIATES LP—See InterContinental Hotels Group PLC; *Int'l*, pg. 3738
PERSHING GROUP LLC—See The Bank of New York Mellon Corporation; *U.S. Public*, pg. 2038
PERSHING LIMITED—See The Bank of New York Mellon Corporation; *U.S. Public*, pg. 2038
PERSHING LLC—See The Bank of New York Mellon Corporation; *U.S. Public*, pg. 2038
PERSHING RESOURCES COMPANY, INC.; *U.S. Public*, pg. 1677
PERSHING SQUARE CAPITAL MANAGEMENT, L.P.; *U.S. Private*, pg. 3155
PERSHING SQUARE HOLDINGS, LTD.; *Int'l*, pg. 5815
PERSHING SQUARE SPARC HOLDINGS, LTD.; *U.S. Private*, pg. 3155
PERSHING SQUARE TONTINE HOLDINGS, LTD.; *U.S. Public*, pg. 1677
PERSIA INTERNATIONAL BANK PLC LONDON—See Bank Mellat; *Int'l*, pg. 839
PERSIAN GULF FAJR ENERGY COMPANY; *Int'l*, pg. 5815
PERSIAN GULF PETROCHEMICAL INDUSTRY COMMERCIAL COMPANY; *Int'l*, pg. 5815
PERSIKA SA—See Biokarpet S.A.; *Int'l*, pg. 1038
PERSIL-ALTERSUNTERSTUTZUNG GMBH—See Henkel AG & Co. KGaA; *Int'l*, pg. 3354
PERSIMMON CAPITAL MANAGEMENT, LP—See Dakota Wealth Management LLC; *U.S. Private*, pg. 1148
PERSIMMON FINANCE LTD.—See Persimmon plc; *Int'l*, pg. 5816
PERSIMMON GOLF CLUB LLC—See Drive Shack Inc.; *U.S. Public*, pg. 688
THE PERSIMMON GROUP LLC; *U.S. Private*, pg. 4093
PERSIMMON HOLDINGS LIMITED—See Persimmon plc; *Int'l*, pg. 5816
PERSIMMON HOMES (ANGLIA) LTD.—See Persimmon plc; *Int'l*, pg. 5817
PERSIMMON HOMES (EAST MIDLANDS) LTD.—See Persimmon plc; *Int'l*, pg. 5817
PERSIMMON HOMES (EAST YORKSHIRE) LTD.—See Persimmon plc; *Int'l*, pg. 5817
PERSIMMON HOMES (ESSEX) LTD.—See Persimmon plc; *Int'l*, pg. 5817
PERSIMMON HOMES (LANCASHIRE) LTD—See Persimmon plc; *Int'l*, pg. 5817
PERSIMMON HOMES (MERCIA) LTD.—See Persimmon plc; *Int'l*, pg. 5817
PERSIMMON HOMES (MIDLANDS) LTD.—See Persimmon plc; *Int'l*, pg. 5817
PERSIMMON HOMES (NORTH EAST) LTD.—See Persimmon plc; *Int'l*, pg. 5817
PERSIMMON HOMES (NORTH MIDLANDS) LTD.—See Persimmon plc; *Int'l*, pg. 5817
PERSIMMON HOMES (NORTH WEST) LTD.—See Persimmon plc; *Int'l*, pg. 5817
PERSIMMON HOMES (SOUTH COAST) LTD.—See Persimmon plc; *Int'l*, pg. 5817
PERSIMMON HOMES (SOUTH EAST) LTD.—See Persimmon plc; *Int'l*, pg. 5817
PERSIMMON HOMES (SOUTH MIDLANDS) LTD.—See Persimmon plc; *Int'l*, pg. 5817
PERSIMMON HOMES (SOUTH WEST) LTD.—See Persimmon plc; *Int'l*, pg. 5817
PERSIMMON HOMES (SOUTH YORKSHIRE) LTD.—See Persimmon plc; *Int'l*, pg. 5817
PERSIMMON HOMES (TEESSIDE) LTD—See Persimmon plc; *Int'l*, pg. 5817
PERSIMMON HOMES (THAMES VALLEY) LTD.—See Persimmon plc; *Int'l*, pg. 5817
PERSIMMON HOMES (WALES) LTD.—See Persimmon plc; *Int'l*, pg. 5817
PERSIMMON HOMES (WESSEX) LTD.—See Persimmon plc; *Int'l*, pg. 5817
PERSIMMON HOMES (WEST MIDLANDS) LTD—See Persimmon plc; *Int'l*, pg. 5817
PERSIMMON HOMES (WEST YORKSHIRE) LTD.—See Persimmon plc; *Int'l*, pg. 5817
PERSIMMON HOMES (YORKSHIRE) LTD.—See Persimmon plc; *Int'l*, pg. 5817
PERSIMMON NORTH DIVISION—See Persimmon plc; *Int'l*, pg. 5816
PERSIMMON PARTNERSHIPS (SCOTLAND) LIMITED—See Persimmon plc; *Int'l*, pg. 5817
PERSIMMON PLC; *Int'l*, pg. 5815
PERSIMMON SOUTH DIVISION—See Persimmon plc; *Int'l*, pg. 5817

COMPANY NAME INDEX

PERSIMMON TECHNOLOGIES CORPORATION—See Sumitomo Heavy Industries, Ltd.; *Int'l*, pg. 7287
PERSIS CORPORATION; *U.S. Private*, pg. 3155
PERSIS HOLDINGS LIMITED; *Int'l*, pg. 5818
PERSISTENCE CAPITAL PARTNERS LP; *Int'l*, pg. 5818
PERSISTENT SYSTEMS AND SOLUTIONS LIMITED—See Persistent Systems Ltd.; *Int'l*, pg. 5818
PERSISTENT SYSTEMS AUSTRALIA PTY. LTD.—See Persistent Systems Ltd.; *Int'l*, pg. 5818
PERSISTENT SYSTEMS FRANCE S.A.S.—See Persistent Systems Ltd.; *Int'l*, pg. 5818
PERSISTENT SYSTEMS GERMANY GMBH—See Persistent Systems Ltd.; *Int'l*, pg. 5818
PERSISTENT SYSTEMS, INC.—See Persistent Systems Ltd.; *Int'l*, pg. 5818
PERSISTENT SYSTEMS INC. USA—See Persistent Systems Ltd.; *Int'l*, pg. 5818
PERSISTENT SYSTEMS LANKA (PRIVATE) LIMITED—See Persistent Systems Ltd.; *Int'l*, pg. 5818
PERSISTENT SYSTEMS LTD.; *Int'l*, pg. 5818
PERSISTENT SYSTEMS MALAYSIA SDN. BHD.—See Persistent Systems Ltd.; *Int'l*, pg. 5818
PERSISTENT SYSTEMS PTE. LTD.—See Persistent Systems Ltd.; *Int'l*, pg. 5818
PERSISTENT SYSTEMS SWITZERLAND AG—See Persistent Systems Ltd.; *Int'l*, pg. 5818
PERSIST OIL AND GAS INC.; *Int'l*, pg. 5818
PERSITY RESOURCING B.V.—See Ctac N.V.; *Int'l*, pg. 1869
PERSIVIA, INC.; *U.S. Private*, pg. 3155
PERSOL AVC TECHNOLOGY CO., LTD.—See Persol Holdings Co., Ltd.; *Int'l*, pg. 5818
PERSOL BUSINESS EXPERT CO., LTD.—See Persol Holdings Co., Ltd.; *Int'l*, pg. 5818
PERSOL CAREER CO., LTD.—See Persol Holdings Co., Ltd.; *Int'l*, pg. 5819
PERSOL CAREER CONSULTING CO., LTD.—See Persol Holdings Co., Ltd.; *Int'l*, pg. 5818
PERSOL EXCEL ASSOCIATES CO., LTD.—See Persol Holdings Co., Ltd.; *Int'l*, pg. 5818
PERSOL EXCEL HR PARTNERS CO., LTD.—See Persol Holdings Co., Ltd.; *Int'l*, pg. 5818
PERSOL FACILITY MANAGEMENT CO., LTD.—See Persol Holdings Co., Ltd.; *Int'l*, pg. 5818
PERSOL FACTORY PARTNERS CO., LTD.—See Persol Holdings Co., Ltd.; *Int'l*, pg. 5819
PERSOL FIELD STAFF CO., LTD.—See Persol Holdings Co., Ltd.; *Int'l*, pg. 5819
PERSOL HOLDINGS CO., LTD.; *Int'l*, pg. 5818
PERSOL NEXTAGE CO., LTD.—See Persol Holdings Co., Ltd.; *Int'l*, pg. 5819
PERSOL PROCESS & TECHNOLOGY CO., LTD.—See Persol Holdings Co., Ltd.; *Int'l*, pg. 5819
PERSOL PROCESS & TECHNOLOGY VIETNAM CO., LTD.—See Persol Holdings Co., Ltd.; *Int'l*, pg. 5819
PERSOL RESEARCH & DEVELOPMENT CO., LTD.—See Persol Holdings Co., Ltd.; *Int'l*, pg. 5819
PERSOL TECHNOLOGY STAFF CO., LTD.—See Persol Holdings Co., Ltd.; *Int'l*, pg. 5819
PERSOL TEMPSTAFF CO., LTD.—See Persol Holdings Co., Ltd.; *Int'l*, pg. 5819
PERSOL TEMPSTAFF KAMEI CORPORATION—See Kamei Corporation; *Int'l*, pg. 4061
PERSOL THANKS CO., LTD.—See Persol Holdings Co., Ltd.; *Int'l*, pg. 5819
PERSOL WORKS DESIGN CO., LTD.—See Persol Holdings Co., Ltd.; *Int'l*, pg. 5820
PERSONABLE GENERAL INSURANCE AGENCY, INC.—See Align Financial Group, LLC; *U.S. Private*, pg. 168
PERSONABLE GENERAL INSURANCE AGENCY, INC.—See Excellere Capital Management LLC; *U.S. Private*, pg. 1446
PERSONACARE OF OHIO, LLC—See Apollo Global Management, Inc.; *U.S. Public*, pg. 157
PERSONA INC.—See Holien Inc.; *U.S. Private*, pg. 1963
PERSONAL ASSETS TRUST PLC; *Int'l*, pg. 5820
PERSONAL ASSURANCE PLC—See Personal Group Holdings plc; *Int'l*, pg. 5820
PERSONAL ASSURANCE SERVICES LIMITED—See Personal Group Holdings plc; *Int'l*, pg. 5820
PERSONAL BEST S.A.—See SFAKIANAKIS S.A.; *Int'l*, pg. 6738
PERSONAL CARE PRODUCTS COUNCIL FOUNDATION, INC.; *U.S. Private*, pg. 3155
PERSONAL COMMUNICATION CENTER; *U.S. Private*, pg. 3155
PERSONAL COMPUTER SYSTEMS, INC.; *U.S. Private*, pg. 3155
PERSONAL CREATIONS INC.—See Claranova SA; *Int'l*, pg. 1642
PERSONAL ENRICHMENT THROUGH MENTAL HEALTH SERVICES; *U.S. Private*, pg. 3155
PERSONAL FINANCE COMPANY, LLC—See Warburg Pincus LLC; *U.S. Private*, pg. 4439
PERSONAL GROUP BENEFITS LIMITED—See Personal Group Holdings plc; *Int'l*, pg. 5820
PERSONAL GROUP HOLDINGS PLC; *Int'l*, pg. 5820

PERSONAL GROUP TRUSTEES LIMITED—See Personal Group Holdings plc; *Int'l*, pg. 5820
PERSONAL HEALTHCARE TELEMEDICINE SERVICES B.V.—See SHL Telemedicine Limited; *Int'l*, pg. 6857
PERSONALHUSET STAFFING GROUP—See The Adolfsen Group; *Int'l*, pg. 7612
PERSONAL INC.—See Persol Holdings Co., Ltd.; *Int'l*, pg. 5819
THE PERSONAL INSURANCE COMPANY—See Mouvement des caisses Desjardins; *Int'l*, pg. 5058
PERSONALIS, INC.; *U.S. Public*, pg. 1677
PERSONALIS (UK) LTD.—See Personalis, Inc.; *U.S. Public*, pg. 1677
PERSONALITY HOTELS INC.; *U.S. Private*, pg. 3155
PERSONALITY IT PEOPLE POWER GMBH—See Adecco Group AG; *Int'l*, pg. 140
PERSONALITY SOFTWARE SYSTEMS, INC.; *U.S. Private*, pg. 3155
PERSONALIZATIONMALL.COM, LLC—See 1-800-FLOWERS.COM, Inc.; *U.S. Public*, pg. 1
PERSONALIZED AIR CONDITIONING, INC.—See Air Pros; *U.S. Private*, pg. 139
PERSONALIZED BEAUTY DISCOVERY, INC.; *U.S. Private*, pg. 3156
PERSONALIZED BROKERAGE SERVICE LLC—See Allianz SE; *Int'l*, pg. 355
PERSONALLY YOURS STAFFING; *U.S. Private*, pg. 3156
PERSONAL MANAGEMENT SOLUTIONS LIMITED—See Personal Group Holdings plc; *Int'l*, pg. 5820
PERSONAL MARKETING RESEARCH; *U.S. Private*, pg. 3155
PERSONAL SELLING POWER INC.; *U.S. Private*, pg. 3155
PERSONAL STRENGTHS PUBLISHING, INC.—See Leeds Equity Partners, LLC; *U.S. Private*, pg. 2415
PERSONAL TECHNOLOGY SOLUTIONS LLC; *U.S. Private*, pg. 3155
PERSONAL-TOUCH HOME CARE, INC.; *U.S. Private*, pg. 3155
PERSONAL TOUCH HOME CARE OF BALTIMORE INC.—See Personal-Touch Home Care, Inc.; *U.S. Private*, pg. 3155
PERSONAL TOUCH HOME CARE OF VA. INC.—See Personal-Touch Home Care, Inc.; *U.S. Private*, pg. 3155
PERSONAS SOCIAL INCORPORATED; *Int'l*, pg. 5820
PERSONEELSVERENIGING LUFKIN COOPER TOOLS—See Bain Capital, LP; *U.S. Private*, pg. 430
PERSONIFILRX, LLC—See Nautic Partners, LLC; *U.S. Private*, pg. 2871
PERSONIFY INC.—See Pamlico Capital Management, L.P.; *U.S. Private*, pg. 3083
PERSONNA AMERICAN SAFETY RAZOR COMPANY—See Edgewell Personal Care Company; *U.S. Public*, pg. 718
PERSONNA INTERNATIONAL DE MEXICO, S.A. DE C.V.—See Edgewell Personal Care Company; *U.S. Public*, pg. 718
PERSONNA INTERNATIONAL ISRAEL LTD.—See Edgewell Personal Care Company; *U.S. Public*, pg. 718
PERSONNA INTERNATIONAL UK LIMITED—See Edgewell Personal Care Company; *U.S. Public*, pg. 718
PERSONNEL DECISIONS INTERNATIONAL SCANDINAVIA A.B.—See Korn Ferry; *U.S. Public*, pg. 1274
PERSONNEL HEALTH & SAFETY CONSULTANTS LTD.—See PHSC plc; *Int'l*, pg. 5857
PERSONNEL MANAGEMENT SYSTEMS, INC.—See Asure Software, Inc.; *U.S. Public*, pg. 218
PERSONNEL PARTNERS INC.; *U.S. Private*, pg. 3156
PERSONNEL PLACEMENTS LLC; *U.S. Private*, pg. 3156
PERSONNEL PLUS, INC.; *U.S. Private*, pg. 3156
PERSONNEL SERVICES; *U.S. Private*, pg. 3156
PERSONNEL SOURCE INC.; *U.S. Private*, pg. 3156
PERSPECTA INC.—See Veritas Capital Fund Management, LLC; *U.S. Public*, pg. 4363
PERSPECTA LLC; *U.S. Private*, pg. 3156
PERSPECTICS—See EssilorLuxottica SA; *Int'l*, pg. 2516
PERSPECTIVE PARTNERS, LLC—See Callodine Acquisition Corporation; *U.S. Private*, pg. 424
PERSPECTIVE RESEARCH SERVICES—See The BDRC Group; *Int'l*, pg. 7620
PERSPECTIVE THERAPEUTICS, INC.; *U.S. Public*, pg. 1678
PERSPECTUM GROUP PLC; *Int'l*, pg. 5820
PERSPEX DISTRIBUTION LIMITED—See Schweiter Technologies AG; *Int'l*, pg. 6645
PERSPEX INTERNATIONAL LIMITED—See Schweiter Technologies AG; *Int'l*, pg. 6645
PERSTIMA (VIETNAM) CO., LTD.—See Perusahaan Sadur Timah Malaysia (Perstima) Berhad; *Int'l*, pg. 5822
PERSTORP AB—See PAI Partners S.A.S.; *Int'l*, pg. 5702
PERSTORP CHEMICALS ASIA PTE. LTD.—See PAI Partners S.A.S.; *Int'l*, pg. 5702
PERSTORP CHEMICALS GMBH—See PAI Partners S.A.S.; *Int'l*, pg. 5702
PERSTORP CHEMICALS INDIA PRIVATE LIMITED, MUMBAI—See PAI Partners S.A.S.; *Int'l*, pg. 5702

PERSTORP CHEMICALS—See PAI Partners S.A.S.; *Int'l*, pg. 5702
PERSTORP FRANCE SAS—See PAI Partners S.A.S.; *Int'l*, pg. 5702
PERSTORP HOLDING AB—See PAI Partners S.A.S.; *Int'l*, pg. 5701
PERSTORP POLYOLS INC.—See PAI Partners S.A.S.; *Int'l*, pg. 5702
PERSTORP QUIMICA DO BRASIL LTDA.—See PAI Partners S.A.S.; *Int'l*, pg. 5702
PERSTORP SPA—See PAI Partners S.A.S.; *Int'l*, pg. 5702
PERSTORP SPECIALTY CHEMICALS AB—See PAI Partners S.A.S.; *Int'l*, pg. 5702
PERSTORP UK LTD.—See Ingevity Corporation; *U.S. Public*, pg. 1122
PERSTRUP BETON INDUSTRI A/S—See Industri Beton AS; *Int'l*, pg. 3665
PERTAMA DIGITAL BERHAD; *Int'l*, pg. 5821
PERTAMA HOLDINGS LIMITED—See Harvey Norman Holdings Ltd; *Int'l*, pg. 3281
PERTAMA LAND & DEVELOPMENT SDN. BHD.—See DutaLand Berhad; *Int'l*, pg. 2235
PERTAMINA ENERGY SERVICES PTE. LIMITED—See PT Pertamina (Persero); *Int'l*, pg. 6064
PERTAMINA ENERGY TRADING LIMITED—See PT Pertamina (Persero); *Int'l*, pg. 6064
PERTAMINA HULU ENERGI AUSTRALIA PTY. LTD.—See PT Pertamina (Persero); *Int'l*, pg. 6064
PERTAMINA TRANS KONTINENTAL—See PT Pertamina (Persero); *Int'l*, pg. 6064
PERTEN INSTRUMENTS AB—See Revvity, Inc.; *U.S. Public*, pg. 1795
PERTEN INSTRUMENTS FRANCE SASU—See Revvity, Inc.; *U.S. Public*, pg. 1795
PERTEN INSTRUMENTS GMBH—See Revvity, Inc.; *U.S. Public*, pg. 1795
PERTEN INSTRUMENTS, INC.—See Revvity, Inc.; *U.S. Public*, pg. 1795
PERTEN INSTRUMENTS INC.—See Revvity, Inc.; *U.S. Public*, pg. 1795
PERTEN INSTRUMENTS INC.—See Revvity, Inc.; *U.S. Public*, pg. 1795
PERTEN INSTRUMENTS ITALIA SRL—See Revvity, Inc.; *U.S. Public*, pg. 1795
PERTEN INSTRUMENTS OF AUSTRALIA PTY LTD—See Revvity, Inc.; *U.S. Public*, pg. 1795
THE PERT GROUP; *U.S. Private*, pg. 4093
PERTH ENERGY PTY. LIMITED—See AGL Energy Limited; *Int'l*, pg. 211
PERTH INSURANCE COMPANY—See The Economical Insurance Group; *Int'l*, pg. 7637
PERTH INTERNATIONAL EXCHANGE PTY LTD—See Aware Super Pty Ltd; *Int'l*, pg. 752
PERTH INTERNATIONAL EXCHANGE PTY LTD—See Macquarie Group Limited; *Int'l*, pg. 4629
THE PERTH MINT; *Int'l*, pg. 7673
PERTH VETS4PETS LIMITED—See Pets at Home Group Plc; *Int'l*, pg. 5834
PERTINI VISTA SDN. BHD.—See Shell plc; *Int'l*, pg. 6795
PERTINO, INC.—See Telefonaktiebolaget LM Ericsson; *Int'l*, pg. 7531
PERTRONIX, LLC—See Charger Investment Partners LP; *U.S. Private*, pg. 850
PERTUY CONSTRUCTION SA—See Bouygues S.A.; *Int'l*, pg. 1123
PERU DAILY TRIBUNE PUBLISHING CO. INC.—See Paxton Media Group LLC; *U.S. Private*, pg. 3116
PERUMAHAN KINRARA BERHAD—See S P Setia Berhad; *Int'l*, pg. 6443
PERUMAHAN SLG SELATAN SDN. BHD.—See Sim Lian Group Limited; *Int'l*, pg. 6926
PERUN CAPITAL GMBH & CO KG—See Raiffeisen Bank International AG; *Int'l*, pg. 6183
PERU PIZZA CO. INC.—See Daland Corporation; *U.S. Private*, pg. 1148
PERUPLAST S.A.—See Quinenco S.A.; *Int'l*, pg. 6164
PERUSA GMBH; *Int'l*, pg. 5821
PERUSAHAAN CHAN CHOO SING SDN BHD—See PCCS Group Berhad; *Int'l*, pg. 5767
PERUSAHAAN JAYA PLASTIK (M) SDN. BHD.—See CYL Corporation Berhad; *Int'l*, pg. 1896
PERUSAHAAN KIMIA GEMILANG (VIETNAM) COMPANY LTD.—See Nylex (Malaysia) Berhad; *Int'l*, pg. 5500
PERUSAHAAN OTOMOBIL NASIONAL SDN. BHD.—See DRB-HICOM Berhad; *Int'l*, pg. 2202
PERUSAHAAN PERSEROAN INDONESIA TBK; *Int'l*, pg. 5821
PERUSAHAAN SADUR TIMAH MALAYSIA (PERSTIMA) BERHAD; *Int'l*, pg. 5822
PERUSA PARTNERS MANAGEMENT LIMITED—See Perusa GmbH; *Int'l*, pg. 5821
PERUTNINA PTUJ D.D.—See MHP SE; *Int'l*, pg. 4873
PERUTNINA PTUJ-PIPO D.O.O.—See MHP SE; *Int'l*, pg. 4873
PERUVIAN CONNECTION, LTD.; *U.S. Private*, pg. 3156
PERUVIAN LATIN RESOURCES SAC—See Latin Resources Limited; *Int'l*, pg. 4423
PERUVIAN METALS CORP.; *Int'l*, pg. 5822
PERUZZI BUICK GMC; *U.S. Private*, pg. 3156

PERUZZI PONTIAC GMC TRUCK, INC.   CORPORATE AFFILIATIONS

PERUZZI PONTIAC GMC TRUCK, INC.; *U.S. Private*, pg. 3156
PERVASIP CORP.; *U.S. Private*, pg. 3156
PERVASIVE COMMODITIES LTD.; *Int'l*, pg. 5822
PERVEZ AHMED CONSULTANCY SERVICES LTD.; *Int'l*, pg. 5822
PERVEZ AHMED SECURITIES LIMITED—See D.S. Industries Limited; *Int'l*, pg. 1901
PERVIGIL, INC.—See Mobius Partners Enterprise Solutions; *U.S. Private*, pg. 2758
PERVOICE S.P.A.—See Almawave S.p.A.; *Int'l*, pg. 363
THE PERVO PAINT COMPANY; *U.S. Private*, pg. 4093
PERWANAL SAATCHI & SAATCHI—See Publicis Groupe S.A.; *Int'l*, pg. 6108
PERWIRA ERICSSON SDN. BHD.—See Telefonaktiebolaget LM Ericsson; *Int'l*, pg. 7534
PERWYN LLP; *Int'l*, pg. 5822
PERYAM & KROLL RESEARCH CORP.; *U.S. Private*, pg. 3156
PESACARA A.D.; *Int'l*, pg. 5822
PESADO CONSTRUCTION COMPANY; *U.S. Private*, pg. 3156
PESA ENGINEERING, S.A.—See BAUER Aktiengesellschaft; *Int'l*, pg. 893
PESAKA INSPECTION SERVICES SDN.BHD.—See NOV, Inc.; *U.S. Public*, pg. 1546
PESAKA TERENGGANU BERHAD—See Golden Pharos Berhad; *Int'l*, pg. 3031
PESAMA TIMBER CORPORATION SDN BHD—See Golden Pharos Berhad; *Int'l*, pg. 3031
PESCANOVA S.A.—See Tiger Brands Ltd.; *Int'l*, pg. 7746
PES ENVIRONMENTAL, INC.—See NV5 Global, Inc.; *U.S. Public*, pg. 1557
PESHTIGO TIMES PRINTERS & PUBLISHERS—See Multi Media Channels, LLC; *U.S. Private*, pg. 2812
PESNELL-COTTON; *U.S. Private*, pg. 3156
PESONA METRO HOLDINGS BHD; *Int'l*, pg. 5822
PESONA SAFERAY SDN. BHD.—See Pesona Metro Holdings Bhd; *Int'l*, pg. 5822
PESQUERA EXALMAR SAA; *Int'l*, pg. 5822
PESQUERA IQUIQUE-GUANAYE S.A.—See AntarChile S.A.; *Int'l*, pg. 482
PESQUERA JARAMILLO LTDA; *Int'l*, pg. 5823
PESQUERA VERAZ S.A.; *Int'l*, pg. 5823
PESTCO HOLDINGS, LLC—See Thompson Street Capital Manager LLC; *U.S. Private*, pg. 4161
PESTCO, LLC—See Thompson Street Capital Manager LLC; *U.S. Private*, pg. 4161
PESTECH (CAMBODIA) PLC—See PESTECH International Berhad; *Int'l*, pg. 5823
PESTECH ENERGY SDN. BHD.—See PESTECH International Berhad; *Int'l*, pg. 5823
PESTECH INTERNATIONAL BERHAD; *Int'l*, pg. 5823
PESTECH TECHNOLOGY SDN. BHD.—See PESTECH International Berhad; *Int'l*, pg. 5823
PESTELL NUTRITION INC.; *Int'l*, pg. 5823
PESTELL PET PRODUCTS—See Pestell Nutrition Inc.; *Int'l*, pg. 5823
PESTER MARKETING COMPANY—See Phillips 66 Company; *U.S. Public*, pg. 1688
PESTER MARKETING COMPANY—See SoftBank Group Corp.; *Int'l*, pg. 7053
PESTINGER GMBH—See Droege Group AG; *Int'l*, pg. 2205
PESTOVO LLC—See Onexim Group Limited; *Int'l*, pg. 5581
PESTPROOF LIMITED—See Rollins, Inc.; *U.S. Public*, pg. 1809
PEST PULSE LIMITED—See Rentokil Initial plc; *Int'l*, pg. 6289
PEST PULSE UK LIMITED—See Rentokil Initial plc; *Int'l*, pg. 6289
P.E. STRUCTURAL CONSULTANTS, INC.—See Hardesty & Hanover, LLC; *U.S. Private*, pg. 1863
PEST SOLUTIONS, LLC—See Roark Capital Group Inc.; *U.S. Private*, pg. 3456
PET ACCIDENT & EMERGENCY PTY LTD—See TPG Capital, L.P.; *U.S. Public*, pg. 2176
PETAG, INC.—See PBI/Gordon Corporation; *U.S. Private*, pg. 3118
PETALING GARDEN SDN BHD—See S P Setia Berhad; *Int'l*, pg. 6443
PETALING TIN BERHAD; *Int'l*, pg. 5823
PETAL S.A.; *Int'l*, pg. 5823
PETALS NETWORK PTY. LTD.—See The Wonderful Company LLC; *U.S. Private*, pg. 4138
PETALUMA HOME LOANS—See American Pacific Mortgage; *U.S. Private*, pg. 242
PETALUMA POULTRY—See Perdue Farms Incorporated; *U.S. Private*, pg. 3147
PETAQUILLA MINERALS LTD.; *Int'l*, pg. 5823
PETARDS EIMC LTD.—See Petards Group Plc; *Int'l*, pg. 5823
PETARDS GROUP PLC; *Int'l*, pg. 5823
PETARDS INC.—See Petards Group Plc; *Int'l*, pg. 5823
PETARDS INTERNATIONAL LTD.—See Petards Group Plc; *Int'l*, pg. 5823
PETARDS JOYCE-LOEBL LTD.—See Petards Group Plc; *Int'l*, pg. 5823

PETARDS LTD.—See Petards Group Plc; *Int'l*, pg. 5823
PETARDS—See Petards Group Plc; *Int'l*, pg. 5823
PETAR KARAMINCHEV PLC.—See Synergon Holding PLC; *Int'l*, pg. 7384
PET ASSISTANT HOLDINGS, LLC; *U.S. Private*, pg. 3156
PETCARERX.COM—See PetMed Express, Inc.; *U.S. Public*, pg. 1678
PET CAROUSEL INC.—See Cargill, Inc.; *U.S. Private*, pg. 759
PETCHSIAM (THAILAND) COMPANY LIMITED—See Salee Industry Public Company Limited; *Int'l*, pg. 6492
PET CITY LIMITED—See Pets at Home Group Plc; *Int'l*, pg. 5834
PETCO ANIMAL SUPPLIES, INC.—See Canada Pension Plan Investment Board; *Int'l*, pg. 1281
PETCO ANIMAL SUPPLIES, INC.—See CVC Capital Partners SICAV-FIS S.A.; *Int'l*, pg. 1885
PETCO HEALTH AND WELLNESS COMPANY, INC.; *U.S. Public*, pg. 1678
PETCO HOLDINGS, INC.—See Canada Pension Plan Investment Board; *Int'l*, pg. 1281
PETCO HOLDINGS, INC.—See CVC Capital Partners SICAV-FIS S.A.; *Int'l*, pg. 1885
PETCOM LIMITED—See Petroleum Corporation of Jamaica Limited; *Int'l*, pg. 5829
PETCO PETROLEUM CORPORATION; *U.S. Private*, pg. 3156
PETCOSKY & SONS PLUMBING, HEATING & A/C INC.—See Morgan Stanley; *U.S. Public*, pg. 1474
PETCO WELLNESS, LLC—See Canada Pension Plan Investment Board; *Int'l*, pg. 1281
PETCO WELLNESS, LLC—See CVC Capital Partners SICAV-FIS S.A.; *Int'l*, pg. 1885
THE PET CREMATORIUM LIMITED—See CVS Group Plc; *Int'l*, pg. 1890
PETDINE, LLC—See Archer-Daniels-Midland Company; *U.S. Public*, pg. 185
PET DOCTORS OF AMERICA; *U.S. Private*, pg. 3156
PETE BAUR BUICK GMC INC.; *U.S. Private*, pg. 3157
PET ECOLOGY BRANDS, INC.; *U.S. Public*, pg. 1678
PETEDGE; *U.S. Private*, pg. 3157
PETE & GERRY'S ORGANICS, LLC—See Butterfly Equity LP; *U.S. Private*, pg. 698
PETE HARKNESS AUTO GROUP, INC.; *U.S. Private*, pg. 3157
PETE HARKNESS CHEVROLET BUICK, INC.—See Pete Harkness Auto Group, Inc.; *U.S. Private*, pg. 3157
PETE HARKNESS CHEVROLET—See Pete Harkness Auto Group, Inc.; *U.S. Private*, pg. 3157
PETE HONNEN EQUIPMENT CO. INC.; *U.S. Private*, pg. 3157
PETE KING CORPORATION—See JVPK Inc.; *U.S. Private*, pg. 2246
PETE LIEN & SONS INC.; *U.S. Private*, pg. 3157
PETE MANKINS AUTO; *U.S. Private*, pg. 3157
PETE MOORE CHEVROLET INC.; *U.S. Private*, pg. 3157
PETE & PETE CONTAINER SERVICE, INC.; *U.S. Private*, pg. 3157
PETER A. BASILE SONS, INC.; *U.S. Private*, pg. 3157
PETER ALEXANDER SLEEPWEAR PTY. LIMITED—See Premier Investments Limited; *Int'l*, pg. 5960
PETER A. MAYER ADVERTISING, INC.; *U.S. Private*, pg. 3157
PETER ANDERSSON AB—See Addtech AB; *Int'l*, pg. 134
PETER BAKER & SON CO. INC.; *U.S. Private*, pg. 3157
PETER & BARBISCH AG—See Burkhalter Holding AG; *Int'l*, pg. 1225
PETER BENESCH GMBH—See Hutter & Schrantz PMS Ges.m.b.H; *Int'l*, pg. 3540
PETERBILT CAROLINA INC.; *U.S. Private*, pg. 3159
PETERBILT MOTORS CO.—See PACCAR Inc.; *U.S. Public*, pg. 1631
PETERBILT NORTHERN ILLINOIS—See JX Enterprises Inc.; *U.S. Private*, pg. 2247
PETERBILT OF CANADA—See PACCAR Inc.; *U.S. Public*, pg. 1631
PETERBILT OF LOUISIANA LLC; *U.S. Private*, pg. 3159
PETERBILT OF MEMPHIS—See Daco Corporation; *U.S. Private*, pg. 1144
PETERBILT OF ONTARIO INC.—See Brandt Industries Ltd.; *Int'l*, pg. 1140
PETERBILT OF WISCONSIN INC—See JX Enterprises Inc.; *U.S. Private*, pg. 2247
PETERBILT SPRINGFIELD INC.—See The Larson Group; *U.S. Private*, pg. 4067
THE PETERBILT STORE - KNOXVILLE—See The Pete Store, LLC; *U.S. Private*, pg. 4093
PETER BLACK FOOTWEAR & ACCESSORIES LIMITED—See Li & Fung Limited; *Int'l*, pg. 4480
PETERBOROUGH EXAMINER—See Torstar Corporation; *Int'l*, pg. 7831
PETERBOROUGH GREEN ENERGY LTD.—See KNM Group Berhad; *Int'l*, pg. 4209
PETERBORO WEB LTD—See JPIMedia Holdings Limited; *Int'l*, pg. 4006
PETERBROOKE CHOCOLATIER, INC.—See Hickory Foods, Inc.; *U.S. Private*, pg. 1933
PETER C. FOY & ASSOCIATES INSURANCE SERVICES, INC.; *U.S. Private*, pg. 3157

PETER COLLIN PUBLISHING LIMITED—See Bloomsbury Publishing Plc; *Int'l*, pg. 1065
PETER & COMPANY LIMITED—See Goddard Enterprises Limited; *Int'l*, pg. 3019
PETER CONDAKES COMPANY INC.; *U.S. Private*, pg. 3158
PETER-DE FRIES INCORPORATED; *U.S. Private*, pg. 3159
PETER D. JAMES LIMITED—See White Mountains Insurance Group, Ltd.; *U.S. Public*, pg. 2369
PETER DUSSMANN - VOSTOK—See Dussmann Stiftung & Co. KGaA; *Int'l*, pg. 2235
PETER E HAAS JR FAMILY FUND; *U.S. Private*, pg. 3158
PETER E. KLEINE CO.—See American Solutions for Business; *U.S. Private*, pg. 254
PETER FREY GMBH—See BayWa AG; *Int'l*, pg. 918
THE PETER GROUP, INC.; *U.S. Private*, pg. 4094
PETER HAHN GMBH—See Equistone Partners Europe Limited; *Int'l*, pg. 2487
PETER HENNINGSEN S.A.C.—See BERICAP GmbH & Co. KG; *Int'l*, pg. 981
PETER HODGE TRANSPORT LIMITED—See TFI International Inc.; *Int'l*, pg. 7586
PETER HONEY PUBLICATIONS LIMITED—See Pearson plc; *Int'l*, pg. 5778
PETERHOUSE CORPORATE FINANCE LIMITED; *Int'l*, pg. 5824
PETER HYDE ASSOCIATES—See Thames & Hudson Ltd; *Int'l*, pg. 7607
PETER J. SOLOMON COMPANY—See Groupe BPCE; *Int'l*, pg. 3095
PETER KIEWIT SONS', INC.; *U.S. Private*, pg. 3158
THE PETER KITTLE MOTOR COMPANY; *Int'l*, pg. 7673
PETERLABS HOLDINGS BHD; *Int'l*, pg. 5824
PETERLABS SDN BHD—See Peterlabs Holdings Bhd; *Int'l*, pg. 5824
PETER LANE CONCRETE LTD; *Int'l*, pg. 5823
PETER LEHMANN WINES LIMITED—See Casella Wines Pty. Ltd.; *Int'l*, pg. 1351
PETER LI EDUCATION GROUP; *U.S. Private*, pg. 3158
PETER LI, INC.—See Peter Li Education Group; *U.S. Private*, pg. 3158
PETER LUMBER COMPANY; *U.S. Private*, pg. 3158
PETER MARSHALL STEEL STAIRS LIMITED—See Billington Holdings Plc; *Int'l*, pg. 1031
PETER MILLAR INC.—See Compagnie Financiere Richemont S.A.; *Int'l*, pg. 1741
PETER MUELLER, INC.; *U.S. Private*, pg. 3158
PETER NERO & THE PHILLY POPS—See The Philadelphia Orchestra Association; *U.S. Private*, pg. 4094
PETER NITSCHKE DOSIERANLAGEN UND SERVICE GMBH—See NORD Holding Unternehmensbeteiligungsgesellschaft mbH; *Int'l*, pg. 5416
PETER OGNIBENE ASSOCIATES; *U.S. Private*, pg. 3159
PETE ROSE, INC.—See SiteOne Landscape Supply, Inc.; *U.S. Public*, pg. 1889
PETER PAN BUS LINES, INC.; *U.S. Private*, pg. 3159
PETER PAN SEAFOODS, INC.—See Maruha Nichiro Corporation; *Int'l*, pg. 4711
PETER PARTS ELECTRONICS INC.; *U.S. Private*, pg. 3159
PETER P. BOLLINGER INVESTMENT CO.; *U.S. Private*, pg. 3159
PETER PEPPER PRODUCTS, INC.; *U.S. Private*, pg. 3159
PETER PIPER, INC.—See Apollo Global Management, Inc.; *U.S. Public*, pg. 148
PETER RIEGER KONZERTAGENTUR GMBH & CO. KG—See CTS Eventim AG & Co. KGAA; *Int'l*, pg. 1873
PETER RIEGER KONZERTAGENTUR HOLDING GMBH—See CTS Eventim AG & Co. KGAA; *Int'l*, pg. 1873
PETER RIEGER VERWALTUNGS GMBH—See CTS Eventim AG & Co. KGAA; *Int'l*, pg. 1873
PETER RUPPEL GMBH & CO. KG; *Int'l*, pg. 5823
PETERS AUTO SALES INC.; *U.S. Private*, pg. 3159
PETERSBURG CLINIC COMPANY, LLC—See Community Health Systems, Inc.; *U.S. Public*, pg. 555
PETERSBURG HOSPITAL COMPANY, LLC—See Bon Secours Mercy Health, Inc.; *U.S. Private*, pg. 612
PETERSBURG MOTOR COMPANY INC.; *U.S. Private*, pg. 3159
PETERSBURG SOCIAL COMMERCIAL BANK, JSC; *Int'l*, pg. 5824
PETER SCHOENFELD S.A.—See ED&F Man Holdings Limited; *Int'l*, pg. 2303
PETERS CONCRETE; *U.S. Private*, pg. 3159
PETERS CONSTRUCTION CORPORATION; *U.S. Private*, pg. 3159
PETERS CORPORATION; *U.S. Private*, pg. 3159
PETERSEN ALUMINUM CORPORATION—See Carlisle Companies Incorporated; *U.S. Public*, pg. 437
PETERSEN-DEAN INC.; *U.S. Private*, pg. 3159
PETERS ENGINEERING AG—See Bilfinger SE; *Int'l*, pg. 1026
PETERSEN HEALTH CARE, INC.; *U.S. Private*, pg. 3159

COMPANY NAME INDEX

PETERSEN HEALTH CARE - PALM TERRACE OF MATTOON—See Petersen Health Care, Inc.; *U.S. Private*, pg. 3159
PETERSEN INC.—See Bain Capital, LP; *U.S. Private*, pg. 442
PETERSEN INC.—See Compass Advisers Group LLC; *U.S. Private*, pg. 998
PETERSEN INC.—See Pine Island Capital Partners LLC; *U.S. Private*, pg. 3182
PETERSEN MARINE SUPPLY INC.; *U.S. Private*, pg. 3159
PETERSEN PONTIAC BUICK GMC; *Int'l*, pg. 5824
PETER'S FOOD SERVICE LTD.—See National Bank of Greece S.A.; *Int'l*, pg. 5153
PETERS HEATING & AC; *U.S. Private*, pg. 3159
PETERSHILL PARTNERS PLC; *Int'l*, pg. 5824
PETERSIME N.V.—See FPS Food Processing Systems B.V.; *Int'l*, pg. 2757
PETERS IMPORTS, INC.—See KeHE Distributors, LLC; *U.S. Private*, pg. 2273
PETERS MACGREGOR INVESTMENTS LIMITED; *Int'l*, pg. 5824
PETERS MANUFACTURED HOMES; *U.S. Private*, pg. 3159
PETER SMITH GM; *Int'l*, pg. 5823
PETERSON AMERICAN CORPORATION—See MiddleGround Management, LP; *U.S. Private*, pg. 2712
PETERSON BECKNER INDUSTRIES; *U.S. Private*, pg. 3160
PETERSON BRUSTAD INC.—See Sterling Investment Partners, L.P.; *U.S. Private*, pg. 3806
PETERSON COMPANY INC.; *U.S. Private*, pg. 3160
PETERSON CONTRACTORS, INC.; *U.S. Private*, pg. 3160
PETERSON ENERGY—See Integrated Petroleum Technologies, Inc.; *U.S. Private*, pg. 2100
PETERSON FARMS FRESH, INC.—See Peterson Farms, Inc.; *U.S. Private*, pg. 3160
PETERSON FARMS, INC.; *U.S. Private*, pg. 3160
PETERSON GMC-KENWORTH INC.; *U.S. Private*, pg. 3160
PETERSON INDUSTRIES LLC; *U.S. Private*, pg. 3160
PETERSON MANUFACTURING COMPANY INC.; *U.S. Private*, pg. 3160
PETERSON MILLA HOOKS; *U.S. Private*, pg. 3160
PETERSON MOTOR COMPANY; *U.S. Private*, pg. 3160
PETERSON PACIFIC CORP.—See Astec Industries, Inc.; *U.S. Public*, pg. 216
PETERSON PACIFIC INC.; *U.S. Private*, pg. 3160
PETERSON PARTNERS, INC.; *U.S. Private*, pg. 3160
PETERSON PROBST; *U.S. Private*, pg. 3160
PETERSON'S NELNET, LLC—See Nelnet, Inc.; *U.S. Public*, pg. 1504
PETERSON SPRING-CIMA PLANT—See MiddleGround Management, LP; *U.S. Private*, pg. 2712
PETERSON SPRING-COMMONWEALTH PLANT—See MiddleGround Management, LP; *U.S. Private*, pg. 2712
PETERSON SPRING EUROPE LTD.—See MiddleGround Management, LP; *U.S. Private*, pg. 2712
PETERSON SPRING-GEORGIA PLANT—See MiddleGround Management, LP; *U.S. Private*, pg. 2712
PETERSON SPRING-GREENVILLE PLANT—See MiddleGround Management, LP; *U.S. Private*, pg. 2712
PETERSON SPRING-KINGSVILLE PLANT—See MiddleGround Management, LP; *U.S. Private*, pg. 2712
PETERSON SPRING-MADISON HEIGHTS PLANT—See MiddleGround Management, LP; *U.S. Private*, pg. 2712
PETERSON SPRING-MAUMEE PLANT—See MiddleGround Management, LP; *U.S. Private*, pg. 2712
PETERSON SPRING-PACKAGING & DISTRIBUTION—See MiddleGround Management, LP; *U.S. Private*, pg. 2712
PETERSON SPRING-THREE RIVERS PLANT—See MiddleGround Management, LP; *U.S. Private*, pg. 2712
PETERSON SPRING-WINDSOR PLANT—See MiddleGround Management, LP; *U.S. Private*, pg. 2712
PETERSON STAMPEDE DODGE CHRYSLER JEEP; *U.S. Private*, pg. 3160
PETERSON TOYOTA; *U.S. Private*, pg. 3160
PETERSON TRACTOR COMPANY; *U.S. Private*, pg. 3160
PETERS-REVINGTON CORP.—See Sport Haley Holdings, Inc.; *U.S. Private*, pg. 3760
PETERS SURGICAL SASU—See Eurazeo SE; *Int'l*, pg. 2529
PETERSVILLE AUSTRALIA LTD.—See Nestle S.A.; *Int'l*, pg. 5204
PETER THOMAS ROTH LABS LLC; *U.S. Private*, pg. 3159
PETER WARREN AUTOMOTIVE HOLDINGS LTD.; *Int'l*, pg. 5823
PETER WOLTERS JAPAN CO., LTD.—See Angeles Equity Partners, LP; *U.S. Private*, pg. 282
PETER WOLTERS JAPAN CO., LTD.—See Bison Capital Asset Management, LLC; *U.S. Private*, pg. 566
PETE'S CAR SMART KIA; *U.S. Private*, pg. 3157
PETES CONNECTION INC.; *U.S. Private*, pg. 3160
PETE'S FRESH MARKET; *U.S. Private*, pg. 3157
PETE'S ROAD SERVICE, INC.; *U.S. Private*, pg. 3157

PETES SAKE CANCER RESPITE FOUNDATION; *U.S. Private*, pg. 3160
PETE'S TIRE BARNS, INC.; *U.S. Private*, pg. 3157
THE PETE STORE, LLC; *U.S. Private*, pg. 4093
PET FACTORY—See Alvarez & Marsal, Inc.; *U.S. Private*, pg. 213
PET & FAMILY INSURANCE CO., LTD.—See T&D Holdings, Inc.; *Int'l*, pg. 7395
PET & FAMILY SMALL-AMOUNT SHORT-TERM INSURANCE COMPANY—See T&D Holdings, Inc.; *Int'l*, pg. 7395
PET FIRST CO., LTD.—See Senshukai Co., Ltd.; *Int'l*, pg. 6713
PETFIRST HEALTHCARE; *U.S. Private*, pg. 3160
PETFOODDIRECT.COM; *U.S. Private*, pg. 3161
PET FOOD EXPERTS INC.; *U.S. Private*, pg. 3156
PET FOOD WHOLESALE INC.; *U.S. Private*, pg. 3156
PETFORM (THAILAND) LTD.—See Indorama Ventures Public Company Limited; *Int'l*, pg. 3659
PETGO CORPORATION; *Int'l*, pg. 5824
PETHEALTH INC.—See Fairfax Financial Holdings Limited; *Int'l*, pg. 2608
PETHERWICK INSURANCE BROKERS LIMITED—See Brown & Brown, Inc.; *U.S. Public*, pg. 402
PET HOUSE; *U.S. Private*, pg. 3156
PETILLO, INC.—See Sterling Infrastructure, Inc.; *U.S. Public*, pg. 1946
PETIQ, INC.—See Bansk Group LLC; *U.S. Private*, pg. 469
PETIT BATEAU UK LIMITED—See Groupe Rocher Operations SAS; *Int'l*, pg. 3110
PETIT JEAN ELECTRIC COOPERATIVE; *U.S. Private*, pg. 3161
PETITS-FILS DEVELOPPEMENT JSC—See Clariane SE; *Int'l*, pg. 1643
PETIT—See VINCI S.A.; *Int'l*, pg. 8225
PETIT VEHICULE S.A.—See Fast Retailing Co., Ltd.; *Int'l*, pg. 2621
PETKIM PETROKIMYA HOLDING A.S.; *Int'l*, pg. 5824
PETLAND DISCOUNTS INC.; *U.S. Private*, pg. 3161
PETLIFE PHARMACEUTICALS, INC.; *U.S. Public*, pg. 1678
PETLIM LIMANCILIK TICARET A.S.—See PETKIM Petrokimya Holding A.S.; *Int'l*, pg. 5824
PETLINE INSURANCE COMPANY—See The Economical Insurance Group; *Int'l*, pg. 7637
THE PET LOSS CENTER - AUSTIN LLC; *U.S. Private*, pg. 4093
PETMED EXPRESS, INC.; *U.S. Public*, pg. 1678
PETMIN; *Int'l*, pg. 5824
PETNET SOLUCIONES, S.L.—See Siemens Aktiengesellschaft; *Int'l*, pg. 6887
PETNET SOLUTIONS CLEVELAND, LLC—See Siemens Aktiengesellschaft; *Int'l*, pg. 6889
PETOBEL GMBH—See ProSiebenSat.1 Media SE; *Int'l*, pg. 6000
PETO MACCALLUM LTD.; *Int'l*, pg. 5824
PETON DISTRIBUTORS INC.—See Roark Capital Group Inc.; *U.S. Private*, pg. 3455
PETOSKEY PLASTICS INC.; *U.S. Private*, pg. 3161
PETPAL PET NUTRITION TECHNOLOGY CO., LTD.; *Int'l*, pg. 5824
PET PARADISE RESORT—See Centripetal Capital Partners, LLC; *U.S. Private*, pg. 830
PETPARTNERS, INC.; *U.S. Private*, pg. 3161
PET PLAN LTD.—See Allianz SE; *Int'l*, pg. 355
PET PLASTICS LIMITED; *Int'l*, pg. 5823
PET POWER BV—See Berry Global Group, Inc; *U.S. Public*, pg. 322
PET-POWER DEUTSCHLAND GMBH—See Berry Global Group, Inc; *U.S. Public*, pg. 322
PET POWER HANDELS GMBH—See Berry Global Group, Inc; *U.S. Public*, pg. 322
PET PROCESSORS, LLC—See Diefenthal Holdings, LLC; *U.S. Private*, pg. 1228
PET PROTECT LIMITED; *Int'l*, pg. 5823
PET QWERKS, INC.—See Platinum Equity, LLC; *U.S. Private*, pg. 3202
PETRA ACQUISITION, INC.; *U.S. Private*, pg. 3161
PETRA CAPITAL MANAGEMENT LLC; *U.S. Private*, pg. 3161
PETRA CAPITAL PARTNERS, LLC; *U.S. Private*, pg. 3161
PETRACCA & SONS INC.; *U.S. Private*, pg. 3161
PETRA DIAMONDS LIMITED; *Int'l*, pg. 5824
PETRA EDUCATION COMPANY; *Int'l*, pg. 5824
PETRA ENERGY BERHAD; *Int'l*, pg. 5825
PETRA FABRICATORS SDN BHD—See Petra Energy Berhad; *Int'l*, pg. 5825
PETRA FASHIONS INC.—See Pure Romance Parties, Inc.; *U.S. Private*, pg. 3306
PETRA GEOTECHNICAL, INC.; *U.S. Private*, pg. 3161
PETRA INCORPORATED; *U.S. Private*, pg. 3161
PETRA INVESTMENT COMPANY—See Severson Group Incorporated; *U.S. Private*, pg. 3619
PETR-ALL CORPORATION; *U.S. Private*, pg. 3161
PETRA MARINE SDN. BHD.—See Petra Energy Berhad; *Int'l*, pg. 5825

PETRA NOVA PARISH HOLDINGS LLC—See ENEOS Holdings, Inc.; *Int'l*, pg. 2417
PETRA PET, INC.—See Imperial Capital Group Ltd.; *Int'l*, pg. 3634
PETRA QUARRY (PTY) LIMITED—See Raubex Group Limited; *Int'l*, pg. 6221
PETRA RESOURCES SDN BHD—See Petra Energy Berhad; *Int'l*, pg. 5825
PETRA ROOFING COMPANY, LLC; *U.S. Private*, pg. 3161
PETRASCO SERVICES LTD—See J&J Denholm Ltd.; *Int'l*, pg. 3853
PETRATHERM LIMITED; *Int'l*, pg. 5825
PETRAYS; *U.S. Private*, pg. 3161
PET RECYCLING TEAM GMBH—See Alpla-Werke Alwin Lehner GmbH & Co. KG; *Int'l*, pg. 374
PETREL LIMITED—See Chamberlin plc; *Int'l*, pg. 1439
PETRELOCATION INC.; *U.S. Private*, pg. 3161
PETREL RESOURCES PLC; *Int'l*, pg. 5825
PET REPUBLIC SP. Z O.O.—See Charoen Pokphand Foods Public Company Limited; *Int'l*, pg. 1453
PETREX S.A.—See Eni S.p.A.; *Int'l*, pg. 2438
PETRI BAKING PRODUCTS, INC.—See Conagra Brands, Inc.; *U.S. Public*, pg. 564
PETRICCA INDUSTRIES, INC.; *U.S. Private*, pg. 3161
PETRICHOR ENERGY INC.; *Int'l*, pg. 5825
PETRI & HAUGSTED AS—See Per Aarsleff Holding A/S; *Int'l*, pg. 5796
PETRIN CORP.—See Bernhard Capital Partners Management, LP; *U.S. Private*, pg. 537
PETRIN CORP.—See KBR, Inc.; *U.S. Public*, pg. 1216
PETRIS TECHNOLOGY, INC.—See Halliburton Company; *U.S. Public*, pg. 980
PETRO AIR, CORP.—See World Kinect Corporation; *U.S. Public*, pg. 2381
PETRO AMIGOS SUPPLY, INC.; *U.S. Private*, pg. 3161
PETRO AUTOMOTIVE GROUP, INC.; *U.S. Private*, pg. 3161
PETROBAS TRANSPORTE S.A.—See Petroleo Brasileiro S.A. - PETROBRAS; *Int'l*, pg. 5827
PETROBRAS AMERICA INC.—See Petroleo Brasileiro S.A. - PETROBRAS; *Int'l*, pg. 5827
PETROBRAS ARGENTINA S.A.—See Grupo EMES S.A.; *Int'l*, pg. 3126
PETROBRAS BOLIVIA INTERNACIONAL S.A—See Petroleo Brasileiro S.A. - PETROBRAS; *Int'l*, pg. 5827
PETROBRAS BOLIVIA S.A.—See Petroleo Brasileiro S.A. - PETROBRAS; *Int'l*, pg. 5827
PETROBRAS COMERCIALIZADORA DE ENERGIA LTDA.—See Petroleo Brasileiro S.A. - PETROBRAS; *Int'l*, pg. 5827
PETROBRAS ENERGIA DE MEXICO S.A. DE C.V.—See Petroleo Brasileiro S.A. - PETROBRAS; *Int'l*, pg. 5827
PETROBRAS ENERGIA INTERNACIONAL S.A.—See Grupo EMES S.A.; *Int'l*, pg. 3126
PETROBRAS GAS S.A.—See Cosan S.A.; *Int'l*, pg. 1809
PETROBRAS GAS S.A.—See Mitsui & Co., Ltd.; *Int'l*, pg. 4978
PETROBRAS INTERNACIONAL S.A.—See Petroleo Brasileiro S.A. - PETROBRAS; *Int'l*, pg. 5827
PETROBRAS QUIMICA S.A.—See Petroleo Brasileiro S.A. - PETROBRAS; *Int'l*, pg. 5827
PETROBRESS; *Int'l*, pg. 5826
PETROCAM—See Sonepar S.A.; *Int'l*, pg. 7091
PETRO-CANADA EUROPE LUBRICANTS LIMITED—See HF Sinclair Corporation; *U.S. Public*, pg. 1034
PETRO-CANADA LUBRICANTS INC.—See HF Sinclair Corporation; *U.S. Public*, pg. 1034
PETROCAPITA INCOME TRUST; *Int'l*, pg. 5826
PETRO CARABOBO GANGA B.V.—See Oil & Natural Gas Corporation Limited; *Int'l*, pg. 5534
PETROCARD, INC.—See Bristol Bay Native Corporation; *U.S. Private*, pg. 656
PETROCARD SYSTEMS INC. - FUEL DIVISION—See Bristol Bay Native Corporation; *U.S. Private*, pg. 656
PETROCARD SYSTEMS INC. - FUEL & LUBRICANT DIVISION—See Bristol Bay Native Corporation; *U.S. Private*, pg. 656
PETROCARD SYSTEMS INC. - LUBRICANT DIVISION—See Bristol Bay Native Corporation; *U.S. Private*, pg. 656
PETROCARGO MINERALOL-LOGISTIK GMBH—See Marquard & Bahls AG; *Int'l*, pg. 4700
PETROCART SA; *Int'l*, pg. 5826
PETROCEL - TEMEX, S.A. DE C.V.—See ALFA, S.A.B. de C.V.; *Int'l*, pg. 313
PETROCELTIC AFRICAN HOLDINGS LIMITED—See Sunny Hill Energy; *Int'l*, pg. 7318
PETROCELTIC ELSA S.R.L.—See Sunny Hill Energy; *Int'l*, pg. 7318
PETROCELTIC ERRIS LIMITED—See Sunny Hill Energy; *Int'l*, pg. 7318
PETROCELTIC INVESTMENTS LIMITED—See Sunny Hill Energy; *Int'l*, pg. 7318
PETROCELTIC ISARENE LIMITED—See Sunny Hill Energy; *Int'l*, pg. 7318
PETROCELTIC KSAR HADADA LIMITED—See Sunny Hill Energy; *Int'l*, pg. 7318

PETROCART SA — CORPORATE AFFILIATIONS

PETROCHEM CARLESS BVBA—See H.I.G. Capital, LLC; *U.S. Private*, pg. 1828
PETRO-CHEM DEVELOPMENT COMPANY, INC.—See Heurtey Petrochem SA; *Int'l*, pg. 3366
PETRO-CHEM DEVELOPMENT COMPANY, INC.—See Heurtey Petrochem SA; *Int'l*, pg. 3366
PETROCHEMICAL CORPORATION OF SINGAPORE (PTE.) LTD.—See Sumitomo Chemical Company, Limited; *Int'l*, pg. 7264
PETROCHEMICAL INDUSTRIES COMPANY K.S.C.—See Kuwait Petroleum Corporation; *Int'l*, pg. 4346
PETROCHEMICAL INDUSTRIES INVESTMENT CO.; *Int'l*, pg. 5826
PETROCHEMICAL PIPELINE SERVICES B.V.—See Saudi Basic Industries Corporation; *Int'l*, pg. 6590
PETROCHEMICAL SERVICES INC.; *U.S. Private*, pg. 3162
PETROCHEMICALS INDUSTRIES COMPANY—See Kuwait Petroleum Corporation; *Int'l*, pg. 4346
PETROCHEMICALS (MALAYSIA) SDN. BHD.—See Idemitsu Kosan Co., Ltd.; *Int'l*, pg. 3592
PETROCHEMICAL TRANSPORTATION ENGINEERING CO.; *Int'l*, pg. 5826
PETRO-CHEMICAL TRANSPORT—See Rhone Group, LLC; *U.S. Private*, pg. 3424
PETRO-CHEMICAL TRANSPORT—See The Goldman Sachs Group, Inc.; *U.S. Public*, pg. 2080
PETROCHEM INSULATION, INC.—See Arctic Slope Regional Corporation; *U.S. Private*, pg. 316
PETRO-CHEM KOREA CO. LTD.—See Heurtey Petrochem SA; *Int'l*, pg. 3366
PETROCHEM RECOVERY SERVICES, INC.—See Gryphon Investors, LLC; *U.S. Private*, pg. 1798
PETROCHINA COMPANY LIMITED—See China National Petroleum Corporation; *Int'l*, pg. 1533
PETROCHINA & CRM OIL MARKETING CO., LTD.—See China Railway Materials Co., Ltd.; *Int'l*, pg. 1544
PETROCHINA INTERNATIONAL (AMERICA) INC.—See China National Petroleum Corporation; *Int'l*, pg. 1533
PETROCHINA INTERNATIONAL CO. LTD.—See China National Petroleum Corporation; *Int'l*, pg. 1533
PETROCHINA INTERNATIONAL (INDONESIA)—See China National Petroleum Corporation; *Int'l*, pg. 1533
PETROCHINA INTERNATIONAL (JAPAN) CO., LTD.—See China National Petroleum Corporation; *Int'l*, pg. 1533
PETROCHINA INTERNATIONAL (KAZAKHSTAN) CO., LTD—See China National Petroleum Corporation; *Int'l*, pg. 1533
PETROCHINA INTERNATIONAL (LONDON) CO., LIMITED—See China National Petroleum Corporation; *Int'l*, pg. 1533
PETROCHINA INTERNATIONAL (MIDDLE EAST) COMPANY LIMITED—See China National Petroleum Corporation; *Int'l*, pg. 1533
PETROCHINA INTERNATIONAL (RUS) CO., LTD—See China National Petroleum Corporation; *Int'l*, pg. 1533
PETROCHINA INTERNATIONAL (TURKMENISTAN) LTD.—See China National Petroleum Corporation; *Int'l*, pg. 1533
PETROCHOICE LLC; *U.S. Private*, pg. 3162
PETRO-CYBERWORKS INFORMATION TECHNOLOGY CO., LTD.—See China Petrochemical Corporation; *Int'l*, pg. 1539
PETRODATA AS—See Halliburton Company; *U.S. Public*, pg. 980
PETRODATA AS—See International Business Machines Corporation; *U.S. Public*, pg. 1149
PETRO-DIAMOND, INC.—See Mitsubishi Corporation; *Int'l*, pg. 4942
PETRO-DIAMOND SINGAPORE (PTE) LTD.—See Mitsubishi Corporation; *Int'l*, pg. 4942
PETROENERGY RESOURCES CORPORATION; *Int'l*, pg. 5826
PETRO ENVIRONMENTAL TECHNOLOGIES INC.; *U.S. Private*, pg. 3161
PETROFAC ENERGY LIMITED—See Petrofac Limited; *Int'l*, pg. 5826
PETROFAC ENGINEERING INDIA PRIVATE LIMITED—See Petrofac Limited; *Int'l*, pg. 5826
PETROFAC ENGINEERING SERVICES INDIA PRIVATE LIMITED—See Petrofac Limited; *Int'l*, pg. 5826
PETROFAC INC.—See Petrofac Limited; *Int'l*, pg. 5826
PETROFAC INTERNATIONAL, DAMASCUS—See Petrofac Limited; *Int'l*, pg. 5826
PETROFAC INTERNATIONAL LTD.—See Petrofac Limited; *Int'l*, pg. 5826
PETROFAC INTERNATIONAL LTD.—See Petrofac Limited; *Int'l*, pg. 5826
PETROFAC INTERNATIONAL LTD—See Petrofac Limited; *Int'l*, pg. 5826
PETROFAC LIMITED; *Int'l*, pg. 5826
PETROFAC MEXICO SA DE CV—See Petrofac Limited; *Int'l*, pg. 5826
PETROFAC SOUTH EAST ASIA PTE LTD—See Petrofac Limited; *Int'l*, pg. 5826
PETROFERM CLEANING PRODUCTS—See H.I.G. Capital, LLC; *U.S. Private*, pg. 1832
PETROFIELD INDUSTRIES INC—See Dynamic Technologies Group Inc.; *Int'l*, pg. 2241

PETROFLEX NORTH AMERICA, LTD.; *U.S. Private*, pg. 3162
PETROFLOW ENERGY CORPORATION; *U.S. Private*, pg. 3162
PETROFRONTIER CORP.; *Int'l*, pg. 5826
PETRO FUEL CO. INC.—See Star Group, L.P.; *U.S. Public*, pg. 1937
PETROGAL BRASIL, LDA.—See Galp Energia SGPS, S.A.; *Int'l*, pg. 2875
PETROGAL CABO VERDE, LDA.—See Galp Energia SGPS, S.A.; *Int'l*, pg. 2875
PETROGAL - COUNSELHO FISCAL—See Galp Energia SGPS, S.A.; *Int'l*, pg. 2875
PETROGAS (BASIN) LTD—See RH Petrogas Limited; *Int'l*, pg. 6319
PETROGAS COMPANY; *U.S. Public*, pg. 1678
PETROGAS ENERGY CORPORATION—See AltaGas Ltd.; *Int'l*, pg. 384
PETROGAS E&P LLC—See MB Holding Company LLC; *Int'l*, pg. 4750
PETROGAS E&P NETHERLANDS B.V.—See MB Holding Company LLC; *Int'l*, pg. 4750
PETROGAS LLC—See MB Holding Company LLC; *Int'l*, pg. 4750
PETROGAS RIMA LLC—See MB Holding Company LLC; *Int'l*, pg. 4750
PETROGLYPH ENERGY, INC.—See Intermountain Industries, Inc.; *U.S. Private*, pg. 2113
PETROGRESS, INC.; *Int'l*, pg. 5826
PETROGULF CORPORATION; *U.S. Private*, pg. 3162
PETROGULF WLL—See Bhatia Brothers Group; *Int'l*, pg. 1014
PETRO HOLDINGS, INC.—See Star Group, L.P.; *U.S. Public*, pg. 1937
PETRO-HUNT, L.L.C.; *U.S. Private*, pg. 3161
PETRO IVOIRE S.A.; *Int'l*, pg. 5825
PETROKAZAKHSTAN INC.—See China National Petroleum Corporation; *Int'l*, pg. 1533
PETROKAZAKHSTAN INC.—See JSC National Company KazMunayGas; *Int'l*, pg. 4010
PETROKEMIJA D.D.; *Int'l*, pg. 5826
PETROKEMIJA D.O.O. NOVI SAD—See PETROKEMIJA d.d.; *Int'l*, pg. 5826
PETROKEN PETROQUIMICA ENSENADA SA—See YPF S.A.; *Int'l*, pg. 8605
PETROKENT TURIZM A.S.; *Int'l*, pg. 5826
PETRO-KING GROUP MIDDLE EAST CORPORATION FZCO—See Petro-King Oilfield Services Limited; *Int'l*, pg. 5825
PETRO-KING INTERNATIONAL COMPANY LIMITED—See Petro-King Oilfield Services Limited; *Int'l*, pg. 5826
PETRO-KING OILFIELD SERVICES LIMITED; *Int'l*, pg. 5825
PETRO-KING OILFIELD TECHNOLOGY LIMITED—See Petro-King Oilfield Services Limited; *Int'l*, pg. 5826
PETROL AD-SOFIA; *Int'l*, pg. 5826
PETROL ADVERTISING, INC.—See Toadman Interactive AB; *Int'l*, pg. 7769
PETROLANE, INC.—See UGI Corporation; *U.S. Public*, pg. 2222
PETROL BH OIL COMPANY D.O.O.—See Petrol, Slovenska energetska druzba, d.d.; *Int'l*, pg. 5827
PETROL CRNA GORA MNE D.O.O.—See Petrol, Slovenska energetska druzba, d.d.; *Int'l*, pg. 5827
PETROL D.O.O. BEOGRAD—See Petrol, Slovenska energetska druzba, d.d.; *Int'l*, pg. 5827
PETROL D.O.O.—See Petrol, Slovenska energetska druzba, d.d.; *Int'l*, pg. 5827
PETROL D.O.O.—See Petrol, Slovenska energetska druzba, d.d.; *Int'l*, pg. 5827
PETROLEDGER LLC—See Avisto Capital Partners, LLC; *U.S. Private*, pg. 409
PETROLEO BRASILEIRO NIGERIA LIMITED—See Petroleo Brasileiro S.A. - PETROBRAS; *Int'l*, pg. 5827
PETROLEO BRASILEIRO S.A. - PETROBRAS; *Int'l*, pg. 5827
PETROLEOS DE CANARIAS, S.A.—See Mubadala Investment Company PJSC; *Int'l*, pg. 5074
PETROLEOS DEL NORTE S.A.—See Gran Tierra Energy Inc.; *Int'l*, pg. 3053
PETROLEOS DEL NORTE, S.A.—See Repsol, S.A.; *Int'l*, pg. 6292
PETROLEOS DEL PERU S.A. - CONCHAN REFINERY—See Petroleos del Peru S.A.; *Int'l*, pg. 5828
PETROLEOS DEL PERU S.A. - EL MILAGRO REFINERY—See Petroleos del Peru S.A.; *Int'l*, pg. 5828
PETROLEOS DEL PERU S.A. - IQUITOS REFINERY—See Petroleos del Peru S.A.; *Int'l*, pg. 5828
PETROLEOS DEL PERU S.A.; *Int'l*, pg. 5828
PETROLEOS DEL PERU S.A. - TALARA REFINERY—See Petroleos del Peru S.A.; *Int'l*, pg. 5828
PETROLEOS DELTA, S.A.; *Int'l*, pg. 5828
PETROLEOS DE VALENCIA, S.A.—See Galp Energia SGPS, S.A.; *Int'l*, pg. 2875
PETROLEOS DE VENEZUELA S.A.; *Int'l*, pg. 5828

PETROLEOS DE VENEZUELA—See Petroleos de Venezuela S.A.; *Int'l*, pg. 5828
PETROLEOS MEXICANOS; *Int'l*, pg. 5828
PETROLEOS TRANSANDINOS YPF S.A.—See Repsol, S.A.; *Int'l*, pg. 6292
PETROLERA LF COMPANY S.R.L.—See YPF S.A.; *Int'l*, pg. 8605
PETROLERA TRANSOCEANICA S.A—See Ultramar Ltda.; *Int'l*, pg. 8019
PETROLEUM ADVISORY FORUM; *Int'l*, pg. 5829
PETROLEUM AGENCY SA—See CEF (SOC) Limited; *Int'l*, pg. 1389
THE PETROLEUM ALLIANCE OF OKLAHOMA; *U.S. Private*, pg. 4094
PETROLEUM ANALYZER COMPANY—See Roper Technologies, Inc.; *U.S. Public*, pg. 1812
PETROLEUM CORPORATION OF JAMAICA LIMITED; *Int'l*, pg. 5829
PETROLEUM DEVELOPMENT OMAN LLC—See PTT Public Company Limited; *Int'l*, pg. 6092
PETROLEUM DEVELOPMENT OMAN LLC—See Shell plc; *Int'l*, pg. 6795
PETROLEUM DEVELOPMENT OMAN LLC—See TotalEnergies SE; *Int'l*, pg. 7837
THE PETROLEUM ECONOMIST LIMITED—See Main Street Capital Corporation; *U.S. Public*, pg. 1355
PETROLEUM ENGINEERING & DEVELOPMENT COMPANY—See National Iranian Oil Company; *Int'l*, pg. 5160
PETROLEUM ENGINEERS, INC.—See Harlow Aerostructures, LLC; *U.S. Private*, pg. 1865
PETROLEUM EQUIPMENT ASSEMBLY & METAL STRUCTURE JOINT STOCK COMPANY—See Vietnam Oil and Gas Group; *Int'l*, pg. 8202
PETROLEUM EQUIPMENT CO., INC.—See The Rosewood Corporation; *U.S. Private*, pg. 4112
PETROLEUM EQUIPMENT INSTITUTE; *U.S. Private*, pg. 3162
PETROLEUM EQUIPMENT & SERVICE, INC.; *U.S. Private*, pg. 3162
PETROLEUM FUEL & TERMINAL COMPANY—See Apex Oil Company, Inc.; *U.S. Private*, pg. 293
PETROLEUM GEO-SERVICES ASIA PACIFIC PTE. LTD.—See PGS ASA; *Int'l*, pg. 5839
PETROLEUM GEO-SERVICES ASIA PACIFIC PTE. LTD.—See PGS ASA; *Int'l*, pg. 5839
PETROLEUM GEO-SERVICES EXPLORATION (M) SDN. BHD.—See PGS ASA; *Int'l*, pg. 5839
PETROLEUM GEO-SERVICES, INC.—See PGS ASA; *Int'l*, pg. 5839
PETROLEUM GEO-SERVICES—See PGS ASA; *Int'l*, pg. 5839
PETROLEUM GEO-SERVICES (UK) LTD.—See PGS ASA; *Int'l*, pg. 5839
PETROLEUM HEAT & POWER CO. INC.—See Star Group, L.P.; *U.S. Public*, pg. 1938
PETROLEUM HEAT & POWER CO.—See Star Group, L.P.; *U.S. Public*, pg. 1938
PETROLEUM HELICOPTERS INTERNATIONAL, INC.—See PHI, Inc.; *U.S. Private*, pg. 3168
PETROLEUM INC.; *U.S. Private*, pg. 3162
PETROLEUM INDUSTRY RESEARCH ASSOCIATES, INC.—See S&P Global Inc.; *U.S. Public*, pg. 1831
PETROLEUM INTERIOR DECORATION JOINT STOCK COMPANY; *Int'l*, pg. 5829
PETROLEUM LOGISTIC SERVICE AND INVESTMENT JOINT STOCK COMPANY—See Vietnam National Petroleum Corporation; *Int'l*, pg. 8201
PETROLEUM MARKETERS, INC.—See CrossAmerica Partners LP; *U.S. Public*, pg. 596
PETROLEUM MARKETING GROUP INC.; *U.S. Private*, pg. 3162
THE PETROLEUM OIL & GAS CORPORATION OF SOUTH AFRICA (SOC) LIMITED—See CEF (SOC) Limited; *Int'l*, pg. 1389
PETROLEUM PHUONGDONG TOURISM JOINST-STOCK COMPANY; *Int'l*, pg. 5829
PETROLEUM PIPELINE & TANK CONSTRUCTION JOINT STOCK COMPANY—See Vietnam Oil and Gas Group; *Int'l*, pg. 8202
PETROLEUM PRODUCTS CORP.; *U.S. Private*, pg. 3162
PETROLEUM PRODUCTS INC.; *U.S. Private*, pg. 3162
PETROLEUM REAL ESTATE JSC; *Int'l*, pg. 5829
PETROLEUM SALES INC.; *U.S. Private*, pg. 3162
PETROLEUM SALES INC.; *U.S. Private*, pg. 3162
PETROLEUM SEALS & SYSTEMS LTD.—See Tailwind Capital Group, LLC; *U.S. Private*, pg. 3924
PETROLEUM SOLUTIONS INC.—See MidOcean Partners, LLP; *U.S. Private*, pg. 2716
PETROLEUM TRADERS CORPORATION; *U.S. Private*, pg. 3162
PETROLEUM TRANSPORT COMPANY; *U.S. Private*, pg. 3162
PETROLEUM WHOLESALE, LP; *U.S. Private*, pg. 3162
PETROLEUM WORLD, INC.—See Cleveland Capital Holdings, Inc.; *U.S. Private*, pg. 940
PETROLEXPORTIMPORT S.A.; *Int'l*, pg. 5829
PETROL GAS GROUP D.O.O.—See Petrol, Slovenska energetska druzba, d.d.; *Int'l*, pg. 5827

COMPANY NAME INDEX PETROSAUDI INTERNATIONAL LTD.

Company Index

PETROL GEO D.O.O.—See Petrol, Slovenska energetska druzba, d.d.; *Int'l*, pg. 5827
PETROL HIDROENERGIJA D.O.O.—See Petrol, Slovenska energetska druzba, d.d.; *Int'l*, pg. 5827
PETROLIA ENERGY CORPORATION; *U.S. Public*, pg. 1678
PETROLIAM NASIONAL BERHAD; *Int'l*, pg. 5829
PETROLIANCE LLC - CHICAGO—See PetroLiance LLC; *U.S. Private*, pg. 3162
PETROLIANCE LLC - CLEVELAND—See PetroLiance LLC; *U.S. Private*, pg. 3162
PETROLIANCE LLC; *U.S. Private*, pg. 3162
PETROLIA SE; *Int'l*, pg. 5829
PETROLIG SRL—See Eni S.p.A.; *Int'l*, pg. 2438
PETROLIMEX ANGIANG—See Vietnam National Petroleum Corporation; *Int'l*, pg. 8201
PETROLIMEX BARIAVUNGTAU CO., LTD.—See Vietnam National Petroleum Corporation; *Int'l*, pg. 8201
PETROLIMEX BEN TRE CO., LTD.—See Vietnam National Petroleum Corporation; *Int'l*, pg. 8201
PETROLIMEX CAMAU CO., LTD—See Vietnam National Petroleum Corporation; *Int'l*, pg. 8201
PETROLIMEX CANTHO CO., LTD—See Vietnam National Petroleum Corporation; *Int'l*, pg. 8201
PETROLIMEX CAOBANG CO., LTD—See Vietnam National Petroleum Corporation; *Int'l*, pg. 8201
PETROLIMEX DAKLAK—See Vietnam National Petroleum Corporation; *Int'l*, pg. 8201
PETROLIMEX DA NANG TRANSPORTATION AND SERVICE JSC—See Vietnam National Petroleum Corporation; *Int'l*, pg. 8201
PETROLIMEX DONGNAI—See Vietnam National Petroleum Corporation; *Int'l*, pg. 8201
PETROLIMEX DONGTHAP—See Vietnam National Petroleum Corporation; *Int'l*, pg. 8201
PETROLIMEX EQUIPMENT JOINT STOCK COMPANY—See Vietnam National Petroleum Corporation; *Int'l*, pg. 8201
PETROLIMEX GIA LAI CO., LTD—See Vietnam National Petroleum Corporation; *Int'l*, pg. 8201
PETROLIMEX HABAC—See Vietnam National Petroleum Corporation; *Int'l*, pg. 8201
PETROLIMEX HAGIANG CO., LTD—See Vietnam National Petroleum Corporation; *Int'l*, pg. 8201
PETROLIMEX HANOI CO., LTD—See Vietnam National Petroleum Corporation; *Int'l*, pg. 8201
PETROLIMEX HANOI TRANSPORTATION & TRADING JSC—See Vietnam National Petroleum Corporation; *Int'l*, pg. 8201
PETROLIMEX HATAY CO., LTD.—See Vietnam National Petroleum Corporation; *Int'l*, pg. 8201
PETROLIMEX HUE CO., LTD—See Vietnam National Petroleum Corporation; *Int'l*, pg. 8201
PETROLIMEX INSTALLATION NO. III JOINT STOCK COMPANY; *Int'l*, pg. 5831
PETROLIMEX INSURANCE CORPORATION—See Vietnam National Petroleum Corporation; *Int'l*, pg. 8201
PETROLIMEX INTERNATIONAL TRADING JSC; *Int'l*, pg. 5831
PETROLIMEX KHANHHOA CO., LTD—See Vietnam National Petroleum Corporation; *Int'l*, pg. 8201
PETROLIMEX LAMDONG—See Vietnam National Petroleum Corporation; *Int'l*, pg. 8201
PETROLIMEX LAOCAI CO., LTD.—See Vietnam National Petroleum Corporation; *Int'l*, pg. 8201
PETROLIMEX (LAO) LTD—See Vietnam National Petroleum Corporation; *Int'l*, pg. 8201
PETROLIMEX LONGAN—See Vietnam National Petroleum Corporation; *Int'l*, pg. 8201
PETROLIMEX NAMDINH CO., LTD—See Vietnam National Petroleum Corporation; *Int'l*, pg. 8201
PETROLIMEX NGHEAN—See Vietnam National Petroleum Corporation; *Int'l*, pg. 8201
PETROLIMEX PETROCHEMICAL CORPORATION—See Vietnam National Petroleum Corporation; *Int'l*, pg. 8201
PETROLIMEX PHUTHO CO., LTD.—See Vietnam National Petroleum Corporation; *Int'l*, pg. 8201
PETROLIMEX QUANG BINH CO., LTD—See Vietnam National Petroleum Corporation; *Int'l*, pg. 8201
PETROLIMEX QUANGNINH CO., LTD.—See Vietnam National Petroleum Corporation; *Int'l*, pg. 8201
PETROLIMEX QUANG TRI CO., LTD.—See Vietnam National Petroleum Corporation; *Int'l*, pg. 8201
PETROLIMEX SAIGON CO., LTD.—See Vietnam National Petroleum Corporation; *Int'l*, pg. 8201
PETROLIMEX SAIGON TRANSPORTATION & SERVICE JSC; *Int'l*, pg. 5831
PETROLIMEX SINGAPORE PTE. LTD.—See Vietnam National Petroleum Corporation; *Int'l*, pg. 8201
PETROLIMEX SONGBE—See Vietnam National Petroleum Corporation; *Int'l*, pg. 8201
PETROLIMEX TAY NINH CO., LTD—See Vietnam National Petroleum Corporation; *Int'l*, pg. 8202
PETROLIMEX THAIBINH CO., LTD—See Vietnam National Petroleum Corporation; *Int'l*, pg. 8202
PETROLIMEX THAINGUYEN—See Vietnam National Petroleum Corporation; *Int'l*, pg. 8202
PETROLIMEX THANHHOA—See Vietnam National Petroleum Corporation; *Int'l*, pg. 8202
PETROLIMEX THUA THIEN HUE TRANSPORTATION AND SERVICE JOINT STOCK COMPANY—See Vietnam National Petroleum Corporation; *Int'l*, pg. 8202
PETROLIMEX TIENGIANG CO., LTD—See Vietnam National Petroleum Corporation; *Int'l*, pg. 8202
PETROLIMEX TRAVINH—See Vietnam National Petroleum Corporation; *Int'l*, pg. 8202
PETROLIMEX TUYEN QUANG—See Vietnam National Petroleum Corporation; *Int'l*, pg. 8202
PETROLIMEX VINH LONG CO., LTD.—See Vietnam National Petroleum Corporation; *Int'l*, pg. 8201
PETROLIMEX YENBAI—See Vietnam National Petroleum Corporation; *Int'l*, pg. 8202
PETROLINA (HOLDINGS) PUBLIC LTD; *Int'l*, pg. 5831
PETRO-LINK, INC.; *U.S. Private*, pg. 3162
PETROLINVEST D.D.; *Int'l*, pg. 5831
PETROL - INVEST D.O.O.—See Petrol, Slovenska energetska druzba, d.d.; *Int'l*, pg. 5827
PETROLINVEST S.A.; *Int'l*, pg. 5831
PETROLMECS LDA—See Sebata Holdings; *Int'l*, pg. 6669
PETRO-LOCK INC.; *U.S. Private*, pg. 3162
PETROL OFISI AKDENIZ RAFINERISI SANAYI VE TICARET A.S.—See Vitol Holding B.V.; *Int'l*, pg. 8260
PETROL OFISI A.S.—See Vitol Holding B.V.; *Int'l*, pg. 8260
PETROLOG AUTOMATION, INC.; *U.S. Private*, pg. 3162
PETROLOT SP. Z O.O. (LTD.)—See Orlen S.A.; *Int'l*, pg. 5641
PETROL POWER D.O.O.—See Petrol, Slovenska energetska druzba, d.d.; *Int'l*, pg. 5827
PETROL SIGN GMBH—See MS International plc; *Int'l*, pg. 5065
PETROL SIGN LTD.—See MS International plc; *Int'l*, pg. 5065
PETROL, SLOVENSKA ENERGETSKA DRUZBA, D.D.; *Int'l*, pg. 5827
PETROLSZOLG KFT.—See MOL Magyar Olaj- es Gazipari Nyrt.; *Int'l*, pg. 5021
PETROL TRADE HANDELSGESELLSCHAFT M.B.H.—See Petrol, Slovenska energetska druzba, d.d.; *Int'l*, pg. 5827
PETROL-TRADE HANDELSGES.M.B.H.—See Petrol, Slovenska energetska druzba, d.d.; *Int'l*, pg. 5827
PETROL TRGOVINA D.O.O.—See Petrol, Slovenska energetska druzba, d.d.; *Int'l*, pg. 5827
PETROLYMPIC LTD.; *Int'l*, pg. 5831
PETROMAR ENERGY SERVICES LLC—See Daeyang Electric Co., Ltd.; *Int'l*, pg. 1911
PETRO MARINE SERVICES; *U.S. Private*, pg. 3161
PETROMARK INC.; *U.S. Private*, pg. 3162
PETROMAR LIMITED—See Saltchuk Resources Inc.; *U.S. Private*, pg. 3534
PETROMAROC CORPORATION; *Int'l*, pg. 5831
PETRO MATAD LIMITED; *Int'l*, pg. 5825
PETROMAX OPERATING CO., INC.; *U.S. Private*, pg. 3163
PETROM DISTRIBUTIE GAZE SRL—See OMV Aktiengesellschaft; *Int'l*, pg. 5569
PETROMEL 1 LTD.—See Synergon Holding PLC; *Int'l*, pg. 7384
PETROMIN CORPORATION—See Dabbagh Group Holding Company Ltd.; *Int'l*, pg. 1902
PETROMIN EGYPT—See Dabbagh Group Holding Company Ltd.; *Int'l*, pg. 1902
PETROMINERALS CORPORATION; *U.S. Private*, pg. 3163
PETROMIN RESOURCES LTD.; *Int'l*, pg. 5831
PETROM-MOLDOVA S.R.L.—See OMV Aktiengesellschaft; *Int'l*, pg. 5570
PETROM NADLAC SRL—See OMV Aktiengesellschaft; *Int'l*, pg. 5570
PETRONAS ARGENTINA S.A.—See Petroliam Nasional Berhad; *Int'l*, pg. 5830
PETRONAS AVIATION SDN BHD—See Petroliam Nasional Berhad; *Int'l*, pg. 5830
PETRONAS BASE OIL (M) SDN BHD—See Petroliam Nasional Berhad; *Int'l*, pg. 5830
PETRONAS CAPITAL LIMITED—See Petroliam Nasional Berhad; *Int'l*, pg. 5830
PETRONAS CARIGALI OVERSEAS SDN. BHD.—See Petroliam Nasional Berhad; *Int'l*, pg. 5830
PETRONAS CARIGALI SDN. BDH.—See Petroliam Nasional Berhad; *Int'l*, pg. 5830
PETRONAS CHEMICALS AMMONIA SDN BHD—See Petroliam Nasional Berhad; *Int'l*, pg. 5830
PETRONAS CHEMICALS DERIVATIVES SDN BHD—See Petroliam Nasional Berhad; *Int'l*, pg. 5830
PETRONAS CHEMICALS FERTILISER KEDAH SDN BHD—See Petroliam Nasional Berhad; *Int'l*, pg. 5830
PETRONAS CHEMICALS GLYCOLS SDN BHD—See Petroliam Nasional Berhad; *Int'l*, pg. 5830
PETRONAS CHEMICALS GROUP BERHAD—See Petroliam Nasional Berhad; *Int'l*, pg. 5830
PETRONAS CHEMICALS MARKETING SDN BHD—See Petroliam Nasional Berhad; *Int'l*, pg. 5830
PETRONAS CHEMICALS METHANOL SDN BHD—See Petroliam Nasional Berhad; *Int'l*, pg. 5830
PETRONAS CHEMICALS MTBE SDN BHD—See Petroliam Nasional Berhad; *Int'l*, pg. 5830
PETRONAS CHEMICALS POLYETHYLENE SDN BHD—See Petroliam Nasional Berhad; *Int'l*, pg. 5830
PETRONAS DAGANGAN BERHAD—See Petroliam Nasional Berhad; *Int'l*, pg. 5830
PETRONAS FERTILIZER (KEDAH) SDN. BHD.—See Petroliam Nasional Berhad; *Int'l*, pg. 5830
PETRONAS GAS BERHAD—See Petroliam Nasional Berhad; *Int'l*, pg. 5830
PETRONAS INDIA (HOLDINGS) COMPANY PTE LTD—See Petroliam Nasional Berhad; *Int'l*, pg. 5830
PETRONAS MARITIME SERVICES SDN. BHD.—See Petroliam Nasional Berhad; *Int'l*, pg. 5829
PETRONAS METHANOL (LABUAN) SDN. BHD.—See Petroliam Nasional Berhad; *Int'l*, pg. 5830
PETRONAS NGV SDN. BHD.—See Petroliam Nasional Berhad; *Int'l*, pg. 5830
PETRONAS PENAPISAN (MELAKA) SDN. BHD.—See Petroliam Nasional Berhad; *Int'l*, pg. 5830
PETRONAS PENAPISAN (TERENGGANU) SDN BHD—See Petroliam Nasional Berhad; *Int'l*, pg. 5830
PETRONAS PHILIPPINES, INC.—See Petroliam Nasional Berhad; *Int'l*, pg. 5830
PETRONAS SOUTH AFRICA (PTY) LTD—See Petroliam Nasional Berhad; *Int'l*, pg. 5830
PETRONAS TECHNICAL SERVICES SDN. BHD.—See Petroliam Nasional Berhad; *Int'l*, pg. 5830
PETRONAS TECHNOLOGY VENTURES SDN BHD—See Petroliam Nasional Berhad; *Int'l*, pg. 5830
PETRONAS TRADING CORPORATION SDN. BHD. (PETCO)—See Petroliam Nasional Berhad; *Int'l*, pg. 5830
PETRONCINI IMPIANTI S.P.A.—See I.M.A. Industria Macchine Automatiche S.p.A.; *Int'l*, pg. 3566
PETRON CORPORATION; *Int'l*, pg. 5831
PETRON CORPORATION—See Wechco, Inc.; *U.S. Private*, pg. 4468
PETRONEFT RESOURCES PLC; *Int'l*, pg. 5831
PETRONE GROUP S.R.L.; *Int'l*, pg. 5831
PETRON ENERGY II, INC.; *U.S. Private*, pg. 3163
PETRONET LNG LIMITED - KOCHI LNG TERMINAL FACILITY—See Petronet LNG Limited; *Int'l*, pg. 5831
PETRONET LNG LIMITED; *Int'l*, pg. 5831
PETRONET MHB LTD.—See Oil & Natural Gas Corporation Limited; *Int'l*, pg. 5534
PETRONE WORLDWIDE, INC.; *U.S. Public*, pg. 1678
PETRON FREEPORT CORPORATION—See Petron Corporation; *Int'l*, pg. 5831
PETRON, LLC—See Lykins Companies, Inc.; *U.S. Private*, pg. 2520
PETRON MALAYSIA REFINING & MARKETING BHD.—See Top Frontier Investment Holdings, Inc.; *Int'l*, pg. 7811
PETRON MARKETING CORPORATION—See Petron Corporation; *Int'l*, pg. 5831
PETRONOR E&P AS—See PetroNor E&P Limited; *Int'l*, pg. 5831
PETRONOR E&P LIMITED; *Int'l*, pg. 5831
PETRO OIL INC.—See Star Group, L.P.; *U.S. Public*, pg. 1938
PETRO OIL—See Star Group, L.P.; *U.S. Public*, pg. 1938
PETROPAC LTDA—See CAP S.A.; *Int'l*, pg. 1301
PETROPAVLOVSK HEATING NETWORKS LLP—See SevKazEnergo JSC; *Int'l*, pg. 6736
PETROPAVLOVSK PLC; *Int'l*, pg. 5831
PETROPESCA SL—See Mubadala Investment Company PJSC; *Int'l*, pg. 5074
PETRO-PIPE INDUSTRIES (M) SDN. BHD.—See Wah Seong Corporation Berhad; *Int'l*, pg. 8329
PETROPLAN LIMITED; *Int'l*, pg. 5832
PETRO PROCESS SYSTEM PTE. LTD.—See Technics Oil & Gas Limited; *Int'l*, pg. 7506
PETRO PROGRESS, INC.—See Fuji Oil Company, Ltd.; *Int'l*, pg. 2815
PETRO PROGRESS PTE LTD—See Fuji Oil Company, Ltd.; *Int'l*, pg. 2815
PETRO Q8 CO.(W.L.L)—See Osoul Investment Company KSCC; *Int'l*, pg. 5652
PETROQUEST ENERGY, INC.; *U.S. Private*, pg. 3163
PETROQUEST ENERGY, L.L.C.—See PetroQuest Energy, Inc.; *U.S. Private*, pg. 3163
PETRORECONCAVO S.A.; *Int'l*, pg. 5832
PETRO RIO S.A.; *Int'l*, pg. 5825
PETRO RIVER OIL CORP.; *U.S. Public*, pg. 1678
PETROSAB PETROLEUM ENGINEERING SDN. BHD.—See KNM Group Berhad; *Int'l*, pg. 4209
PETROSA EUROPE BV—See CEF (SOC) Limited; *Int'l*, pg. 1389
PETROSAHARA PTE LTD—See Mitsui & Co., Ltd.; *Int'l*, pg. 4980
PETROSAINS SDN BHD—See Petroliam Nasional Berhad; *Int'l*, pg. 5830
PETROSANTANDER - COLUMBIA INC.—See Petrosantander Inc.; *U.S. Private*, pg. 3163
PETROSANTANDER INC.; *U.S. Private*, pg. 3163
PETROSANTANDER USA INC.—See Petrosantander Inc.; *U.S. Private*, pg. 3163
PETROSAUDI ENERGY & TRADING (UK) LTD—See PetroSaudi International Ltd.; *Int'l*, pg. 5832
PETROSAUDI INTERNATIONAL LTD.; *Int'l*, pg. 5832

PETROSAUDI INTERNATIONAL LTD. CORPORATE AFFILIATIONS

PETROSAUDI INTERNATIONAL SA—See PetroSaudi International Ltd.; *Int'l*, pg. 5832
PETRO SERVICE INC.; *U.S. Private*, pg. 3161
PETROSERVICIOS DE COSTA RICA, S.R.L.—See World Kinect Corporation; *U.S. Public*, pg. 2381
PETROSERVICIOS DE MEXICO S.A. DE C.V.—See World Kinect Corporation; *U.S. Public*, pg. 2381
PETROSHALE, INC.; *U.S. Public*, pg. 1678
PETROSHARE CORP.; *U.S. Private*, pg. 3163
PETROSIBIR AB; *Int'l*, pg. 5832
PETROSKILLS, LLC; *U.S. Private*, pg. 3163
PETRO—See Star Group, L.P.; *U.S. Public*, pg. 1937
PETROSOUTH ENERGY CORPORATION SUCURSAL COLOMBIA—See ROK Resources Inc.; *Int'l*, pg. 6388
PETROSOUTH INC.; *U.S. Private*, pg. 3163
PETROS PACE FINANCE, LLC—See Apollo Global Management, Inc.; *U.S. Public*, pg. 147
PETROS PETROPOULOS S.A.; *Int'l*, pg. 5832
PETROS PHARMACEUTICALS, INC.; *U.S. Public*, pg. 1678
PETRO STAR INC.—See Arctic Slope Regional Corporation; *U.S. Private*, pg. 316
PETRO SUMMIT PTE. LTD.—See Sumitomo Corporation; *Int'l*, pg. 7269
PETROSUN, INC.; *U.S. Public*, pg. 1678
PETROTAL CORP.; *U.S. Public*, pg. 1678
PETROTAL LLC—See PetroTal Corp.; *U.S. Public*, pg. 1678
PETROTAL PERU S.R.L.—See PetroTal Corp.; *U.S. Public*, pg. 1678
PETROTEC AG—See Chevron Corporation; *U.S. Public*, pg. 487
PETROTEC BIODIESEL GMBH—See Chevron Corporation; *U.S. Public*, pg. 487
PETROTECH SOUTHEAST, INC.; *U.S. Private*, pg. 3163
PETROTEL-LUKOIL S.A.—See PJSC Lukoil; *Int'l*, pg. 5882
PETROTEL SP. Z O.O.—See Cyfrowy Polsat S.A.; *Int'l*, pg. 1895
PETROTEQ ENERGY INC.; *U.S. Public*, pg. 1678
PETROTEX; *U.S. Private*, pg. 3163
PETRO TOWER LTD.—See Keppel Corporation Limited; *Int'l*, pg. 4132
PETROTRANS S.R.O.—See Orlen S.A.; *Int'l*, pg. 5641
PETROTX LP; *Int'l*, pg. 5832
PETRO USA, INC.; *U.S. Public*, pg. 1678
PETROVALVE, INC.—See Flotek Industries, Inc.; *U.S. Public*, pg. 853
PETRO VEND SP. Z O.O.—See Dover Corporation; *U.S. Public*, pg. 682
PETROVIC FINANCIAL SOLUTIONS LLC; *U.S. Private*, pg. 3163
PETRO-VICTORY ENERGY CORP.; *U.S. Public*, pg. 1678
PETROVIETNAM CAMAU FERTILIZER COMPANY LIMITED—See Vietnam Oil and Gas Group; *Int'l*, pg. 8203
PETROVIETNAM CHEMICAL AND SERVICES CORPORATION—See Vietnam Oil and Gas Group; *Int'l*, pg. 8203
PETROVIETNAM COATING JOINT STOCK COMPANY; *Int'l*, pg. 5832
PETROVIETNAM CONSTRUCTION JOINT STOCK CORPORATION—See Vietnam Oil and Gas Group; *Int'l*, pg. 8202
PETROVIETNAM DRILLING AND WELL SERVICE CORPORATION—See Vietnam Oil and Gas Group; *Int'l*, pg. 8202
PETROVIETNAM ENGINEERING CONSULTANCY JSC; *Int'l*, pg. 5832
PETROVIETNAM EXPLORATION PRODUCTION CORPORATION—See Vietnam Oil and Gas Group; *Int'l*, pg. 8203
PETROVIETNAM FERTILIZER AND CHEMICALS CORPORATION - JSC—See Vietnam Oil and Gas Group; *Int'l*, pg. 8202
PETROVIETNAM GAS JOINT STOCK CORPORATION—See Vietnam Oil and Gas Group; *Int'l*, pg. 8203
PETROVIETNAM GENERAL SERVICES JOINT STOCK COMPANY—See Vietnam Oil and Gas Group; *Int'l*, pg. 8203
PETROVIETNAM LOW PRESSURE GAS DISTRIBUTION JOINT STOCK COMPANY—See Vietnam Oil and Gas Group; *Int'l*, pg. 8203
PETROVIETNAM - NGHE AN CONSTRUCTION JOINT STOCK CORPORATION—See Vietnam Oil and Gas Group; *Int'l*, pg. 8202
PETRO VIETNAM OIL CORPORATION BA RIA VUNG TAU UNIT—See Petro Vietnam Oil Corporation; *Int'l*, pg. 5825
PETRO VIETNAM OIL CORPORATION DINH VU UNIT—See Petro Vietnam Oil Corporation; *Int'l*, pg. 5825
PETRO VIETNAM OIL CORPORATION HA TINH UNIT—See Petro Vietnam Oil Corporation; *Int'l*, pg. 5825
PETRO VIETNAM OIL CORPORATION MIEN DONG UNIT—See Petro Vietnam Oil Corporation; *Int'l*, pg. 5825

PETRO VIETNAM OIL CORPORATION NHA BE UNIT—See Petro Vietnam Oil Corporation; *Int'l*, pg. 5825
PETRO VIETNAM OIL CORPORATION PV TECH PRO UNIT—See Petro Vietnam Oil Corporation; *Int'l*, pg. 5825
PETROVIETNAM OIL CORPORATION—See Vietnam Oil and Gas Group; *Int'l*, pg. 8203
PETRO VIETNAM OIL CORPORATION; *Int'l*, pg. 5825
PETROVIETNAM OIL PHU YEN JOINT STOCK COMPANY; *Int'l*, pg. 5832
PETROVIETNAM PACKAGING JOINT STOCK COMPANY; *Int'l*, pg. 5832
PETROVIETNAM PETROCHEMICALS AND FIBRE JOINT STOCK COMPANY—See Vietnam Oil and Gas Group; *Int'l*, pg. 8203
PETROVIETNAM PHUOC AN PORT INVESTMENT AND OPERATION JOINT STOCK COMPANY—See Vietnam Oil and Gas Group; *Int'l*, pg. 8203
PETROVIETNAM POWER CORPORATION—See Vietnam Oil and Gas Group; *Int'l*, pg. 8203
PETROVIETNAM POWER ENGINEERING CONSULTING JSC; *Int'l*, pg. 5832
PETROVIETNAM POWER NHON TRACH 2 JOINT STOCK COMPANY; *Int'l*, pg. 5832
PETROVIETNAM PREMIER RECREATION JOINT STOCK COMPANY—See Vietnam Oil and Gas Group; *Int'l*, pg. 8202
PETROVIETNAM SECURITIES INCORPORATED; *Int'l*, pg. 5832
PETROVIETNAM TECHNICAL SERVICES CORPORATION—See Vietnam Oil and Gas Group; *Int'l*, pg. 8202
PETROVIETNAM TRANSPORTATION CORPORATION—See Vietnam Oil and Gas Group; *Int'l*, pg. 8202
PETRO VIKING ENERGY INC.; *Int'l*, pg. 5825
PETROVSKY FORT LLC—See ENR Russia Invest SA; *Int'l*, pg. 2445
PETROVSKY MLYN A.D.; *Int'l*, pg. 5832
PETROWEB, INC.—See Thoma Bravo, L.P.; *U.S. Private*, pg. 4152
PETRO WELT TECHNOLOGIES AG; *Int'l*, pg. 5825
PETROWEST CIVIL SERVICES LP—See Petrowest Corp.; *Int'l*, pg. 5832
PETROWEST CONSTRUCTION LP—See Petrowest Corp.; *Int'l*, pg. 5832
PETROWEST CORP. - CIVIL DIVISION—See Petrowest Corp.; *Int'l*, pg. 5833
PETROWEST CORP.; *Int'l*, pg. 5832
PETROWEST CORP. - TRANSPORTATION & HAULING DIVISION—See Petrowest Corp.; *Int'l*, pg. 5833
PETROX RESOURCES CORP.; *Int'l*, pg. 5833
PETRUS BRANDS, INC.; *U.S. Private*, pg. 3163
PETRUS RESOURCES CORPORATION; *U.S. Private*, pg. 3163
PETRUS RESOURCES LTD.; *Int'l*, pg. 5833
PETRUZALEK COM S.R.L.—See Zeus Packaging Group Ltd.; *Int'l*, pg. 8640
PETRUZALEK D.O.O.—See Zeus Packaging Group Ltd.; *Int'l*, pg. 8640
PETRUZALEK D.O.O.—See Zeus Packaging Group Ltd.; *Int'l*, pg. 8640
PETRUZALEK E.O.O.D.—See Zeus Packaging Group Ltd.; *Int'l*, pg. 8640
PETRUZALEK GES.M.B.H.—See Zeus Packaging Group Ltd.; *Int'l*, pg. 8640
PETRUZALEK ITALIA S.R.L.—See Italmobiliare S.p.A.; *Int'l*, pg. 3829
PETRUZALEK KFT—See Zeus Packaging Group Ltd.; *Int'l*, pg. 8640
PETRUZALEK O.O.O.—See Zeus Packaging Group Ltd.; *Int'l*, pg. 8640
PETRUZALEK S.R.O.—See Zeus Packaging Group Ltd.; *Int'l*, pg. 8640
PETRY MEDIA CORPORATION—See Patriarch Partners, LLC; *U.S. Private*, pg. 3109
PETRY TELEVISION INC.—See Patriarch Partners, LLC; *U.S. Private*, pg. 3109
PETS AT HOME GROUP PLC; *Int'l*, pg. 5833
PETS AT HOME LTD.—See KKR & Co. Inc.; *U.S. Public*, pg. 1262
PETS BEST INSURANCE SERVICES, LLC—See JAB Holding Company S.a.r.l.; *Int'l*, pg. 3861
PETSEC AMERICA PTY. LIMITED—See Petsec Energy Ltd.; *Int'l*, pg. 5834
PETSEC ENERGY, INC.—See Petsec Energy Ltd.; *Int'l*, pg. 5834
PETSEC ENERGY LTD.; *Int'l*, pg. 5834
PETSEC INVESTMENTS PTY LIMITED—See Petsec Energy Ltd.; *Int'l*, pg. 5834
PETSEC (U.S.A.) INC.—See Petsec Energy Ltd.; *Int'l*, pg. 5834
PETSENSE STORE—See Tractor Supply Company; *U.S. Public*, pg. 2178
PETSERVICE HOLDING N.V.; *Int'l*, pg. 5834
PETSKY PRUNIER, LLC—See Canaccord Genuity Group Inc.; *Int'l*, pg. 1277
PETSMART, INC.—See BC Partners LLP; *Int'l*, pg. 925

PETSMART, INC.—See Caisse de Depot et Placement du Quebec; *Int'l*, pg. 1254
PETSMART, INC.—See StepStone Group LP; *U.S. Private*, pg. 3803
PET SPECIALTIES LLC; *U.S. Private*, pg. 3156
PETS RIP PTY. LTD.—See Propel Funeral Partners Limited; *Int'l*, pg. 5997
PETSTAGES, INC.—See Prospect Hill Growth Partners, L.P.; *U.S. Private*, pg. 3288
PETSTAR, S.A. DE C.V.—See Arca Continental, S.A.B. de C.V.; *Int'l*, pg. 540
PET STUFF ILLINOIS, LLC; *U.S. Private*, pg. 3156
PET SUPERMARKET INC.—See Roark Capital Group Inc.; *U.S. Private*, pg. 3455
PETTENATI S.A. INDUSTRIA TEXTI; *Int'l*, pg. 5834
PETTIBONE, LLC—See The Heico Companies, L.L.C.; *U.S. Private*, pg. 4050
PETTIBONE TRAVERSE LIST LLC—See The Heico Companies, L.L.C.; *U.S. Private*, pg. 4050
PETTICOAT-SCHMITT CIVIL CONTRACTORS, INC.; *U.S. Private*, pg. 3163
PETTIGREW REHABILITATION & HEALTHCARE CENTER—See Apollo Global Management, Inc.; *U.S. Public*, pg. 157
PETTIJOHN AUTO CENTER INC.; *U.S. Private*, pg. 3163
PETTISVILLE GRAIN CO.; *U.S. Private*, pg. 3163
PETTIT MACHINERY INC.; *U.S. Private*, pg. 3163
PETTIT PAINT COMPANY—See RPM International Inc.; *U.S. Public*, pg. 1819
PETTUS OFFICE PRODUCTS, INC.; *U.S. Private*, pg. 3163
PETTUS PLUMBING & PIPING INC.; *U.S. Private*, pg. 3163
PETTY HOLDINGS LLC—See BV Investment Partners, LLC; *U.S. Private*, pg. 699
PETTY WOOD & CO. LTD.; *Int'l*, pg. 5834
PETULA ASSOCIATES, LLC—See Principal Financial Group, Inc.; *U.S. Public*, pg. 1720
PETUNA PTY. LTD.—See Sealord Group Ltd.; *Int'l*, pg. 6665
PETUNIA PICKLE BOTTOM CORPORATION; *U.S. Private*, pg. 3163
PET VALU CANADA, INC.—See Roark Capital Group Inc.; *U.S. Private*, pg. 3455
PET VALU INC.—See Roark Capital Group Inc.; *U.S. Private*, pg. 3455
PETVIVO HOLDINGS, INC.; *U.S. Public*, pg. 1679
PETWELL PARTNERS LLC; *U.S. Private*, pg. 3163
PET WORLD INC.; *U.S. Private*, pg. 3156
PEUGEOT AUTOHAUS GMBH—See Stellantis N.V.; *Int'l*, pg. 7202
PEUGEOT BELGIQUE-LUXEMBOURG SA—See Stellantis N.V.; *Int'l*, pg. 7202
PEUGEOT BRATISLAVA S.R.O.—See Stellantis N.V.; *Int'l*, pg. 7202
PEUGEOT CITROEN ARGENTINA S.A.—See Stellantis N.V.; *Int'l*, pg. 7203
PEUGEOT CITROEN AUTOMOBILES S.A.—See Stellantis N.V.; *Int'l*, pg. 7203
PEUGEOT CITROEN AUTOMOVEIS PORTUGAL S.A.—See Stellantis N.V.; *Int'l*, pg. 7203
PEUGEOT CITROEN AUTOMOVILES ESPANA S.A—See Stellantis N.V.; *Int'l*, pg. 7203
PEUGEOT CITROEN MECANIQUE DU NORD OUEST S.N.C.—See Stellantis N.V.; *Int'l*, pg. 7203
PEUGEOT-CITROEN MOTEURS—See Stellantis N.V.; *Int'l*, pg. 7203
PEUGEOT CITROEN PIECES DE RECHANGE S.N.C.—See Stellantis N.V.; *Int'l*, pg. 7203
PEUGEOT CITROEN POISSY S.N.C.—See Stellantis N.V.; *Int'l*, pg. 7203
PEUGEOT CITROEN RENNES S.N.C.—See Stellantis N.V.; *Int'l*, pg. 7203
PEUGEOT CITROEN RETAIL ITALIA S.P.A.—See Stellantis N.V.; *Int'l*, pg. 7202
PEUGEOT CITROEN RUS LLC—See Stellantis N.V.; *Int'l*, pg. 7202
PEUGEOT CITROEN SOCHAUX S.N.C.—See Stellantis N.V.; *Int'l*, pg. 7203
PEUGEOT DELEGATION OFFICE—See Stellantis N.V.; *Int'l*, pg. 7202
PEUGEOT DEUTSCHLAND GMBH—See Stellantis N.V.; *Int'l*, pg. 7202
PEUGEOT MILAN—See Stellantis N.V.; *Int'l*, pg. 7202
PEUGEOT MOTOCYCLES DEUTSCHLAND GMBH—See Stellantis N.V.; *Int'l*, pg. 7202
PEUGEOT MOTOCYCLES S.A.—See Mahindra & Mahindra Limited; *Int'l*, pg. 4646
PEUGEOT MOTOR CO. PLC—See Stellantis N.V.; *Int'l*, pg. 7202
PEUGEOT MOTORS OF AMERICA INC.—See Stellantis N.V.; *Int'l*, pg. 7202
PEUGEOT MOTORS SOUTH AFRICA LTD—See Stellantis N.V.; *Int'l*, pg. 7202
PEUGEOT POLSKA S.P. Z.O.O.—See Stellantis N.V.; *Int'l*, pg. 7202
PEUGEOT RHEINLAND GMBH—See Stellantis N.V.; *Int'l*, pg. 7202

COMPANY NAME INDEX

PEUGEOT SAINT-DENIS AUTOMOBILES—See Stellantis N.V.; *Int'l*, pg. 7203
PEUGEOT S.A.—See Stellantis N.V.; *Int'l*, pg. 7200
PEUGEOT SODEXA—See Stellantis N.V.; *Int'l*, pg. 7203
PEUGEOT SUDBADEN GMBH—See Stellantis N.V.; *Int'l*, pg. 7202
PEUGEOT TOKYO CO., LTD—See Stellantis N.V.; *Int'l*, pg. 7203
PEUGEOT WESER-EMS GMBH—See Stellantis N.V.; *Int'l*, pg. 7202
PEUTE BAUSTOFF GMBH—See Aurubis AG; *Int'l*, pg. 715
PEVESA BIOTECH, S.A.U.—See Kerry Group plc; *Int'l*, pg. 4139
PEVETO COMPANIES LTD.; *U.S. Private*, pg. 3163
PEVIANI S.P.A.—See Dole plc; *Int'l*, pg. 2158
PEVONIA INTERNATIONAL, LLC; *U.S. Private*, pg. 3163
PEVONIA INTERNATIONAL WEST—See Pevonia International, LLC; *U.S. Private*, pg. 3164
THE PEW CHARITABLE TRUSTS; *U.S. Private*, pg. 4094
PEWO AUSTRIA GMBH—See PEWO Energietechnik GmbH; *Int'l*, pg. 5835
PEWO D.O.O.—See PEWO Energietechnik GmbH; *Int'l*, pg. 5835
PEWO ENERGIETECHNIK GMBH; *Int'l*, pg. 5835
PEWO ENERGIETECHNIK SCHWEIZ GMBH—See PEWO Energietechnik GmbH; *Int'l*, pg. 5835
PEWO ENERGITEKNIK AB—See PEWO Energietechnik GmbH; *Int'l*, pg. 5835
PEW RESEARCH CENTER—See The Pew Charitable Trusts; *U.S. Private*, pg. 4094
PEXA AB; *Int'l*, pg. 5835
PEXA GROUP LIMITED; *Int'l*, pg. 5835
PEX AUTOMOTIVE GMBH—See Shanghai Baolong Automotive Corporation; *Int'l*, pg. 6762
PEXCO AEROSPACE, INC.—See TransDigm Group Incorporated; *U.S. Public*, pg. 2183
PEXCO LLC - MONTERREY—See Odyssey Investment Partners, LLC; *U.S. Private*, pg. 2995
PEXCO LLC - MORRISVILLE—See Odyssey Investment Partners, LLC; *U.S. Private*, pg. 2995
PEXCO LLC—See Odyssey Investment Partners, LLC; *U.S. Private*, pg. 2995
PEXCO LLC - TACOMA—See Odyssey Investment Partners, LLC; *U.S. Private*, pg. 2995
PEXCOR MANUFACTURING CO., INC.—See Mueller Industries, Inc.; *U.S. Public*, pg. 1485
PEX HOLDING INC.; *U.S. Private*, pg. 3164
PEXIP HOLDING ASA; *Int'l*, pg. 5835
PEX SOFTWARE AUSTRALIA PTY. LTD.—See Thoma Bravo, L.P.; *U.S. Private*, pg. 4153
PEX SOFTWARE LIMITED—See Thoma Bravo, L.P.; *U.S. Private*, pg. 4153
PEYMA CHR. HANSEN'S PEYNIR MAYASI SANAYI VE TICARET A.S.—See Novonesis A/S; *Int'l*, pg. 5468
PEYOTE BIRD DESIGNS; *U.S. Private*, pg. 3164
PEYTO EXPLORATION & DEVELOPMENT CORP.; *Int'l*, pg. 5835
PEYTON CRAMER AUTOMOTIVE—See AutoNation, Inc.; *U.S. Public*, pg. 237
PEYTON CRAMER FORD—See AutoNation, Inc.; *U.S. Public*, pg. 237
PEYTON CRAMER INFINITI—See AutoNation, Inc.; *U.S. Public*, pg. 237
PEYTON'S-SOUTHEASTERN, INC.—See The Kroger Co.; *U.S. Public*, pg. 2109
PEZ CANDY, INC.; *U.S. Private*, pg. 3164
PEZM GOLD, INC.; *Int'l*, pg. 5835
PEZOLD MANAGEMENT ASSOCIATES; *U.S. Private*, pg. 3164
PFAFF BETEILIGUNGS GMBH—See Columbus McKinnon Corporation; *U.S. Public*, pg. 536
PFAFF INDUSTRIAL SEWING MACHINE (ZHANGJIAGANG) CO., LTD.—See Shang Gong Group Co., Ltd.; *Int'l*, pg. 6760
PFAFF MASCHINENBAU GMBH—See FLSmidth & Co. A/S; *Int'l*, pg. 2711
PFAFF-SILBERBLAU HEBEZEUGFABRIK GMBH—See Columbus McKinnon Corporation; *U.S. Public*, pg. 536
PFA HOLDING A/S; *Int'l*, pg. 5835
PFANNI GMBH & CO. OHG—See Unilever PLC; *Int'l*, pg. 8045
PFANNI WERKE GRUNDSTUCKSVERWALTUNG GMBH & CO. OHG—See Unilever PLC; *Int'l*, pg. 8045
PFA PENSION FORSIKRINGSAKTIESELSKAB—See PFA Holding A/S; *Int'l*, pg. 5835
P/F ATLANTIC PETROLEUM; *Int'l*, pg. 5683
P/F BAKKAFROST; *Int'l*, pg. 5683
P/F BANKNORDIK; *Int'l*, pg. 5683
PFB CORP.—See The Riverside Company; *U.S. Private*, pg. 4109
PFBS HOLDINGS, INC.; *U.S. Private*, pg. 3164
PFCCB EQUIPMENT LLC—See Centerbridge Partners, L.P.; *U.S. Private*, pg. 815
PFC CONSULTING LTD.—See Power Finance Corporation Limited; *Int'l*, pg. 5945
PFC DEVICE INC. - SHUNDE FACTORY—See PFC Device Inc.; *Int'l*, pg. 5835
PFC DEVICE INC.; *Int'l*, pg. 5835

PFC FLEXIBLE CIRCUITS LIMITED—See OSI Systems, Inc.; *U.S. Public*, pg. 1622
PFC FURNITURE INDUSTRIES; *U.S. Private*, pg. 3164
P.F. CHANG'S CHINA BISTRO, INC.—See Centerbridge Partners, L.P.; *U.S. Private*, pg. 815
PFC HAWAII LLC—See Centerbridge Partners, L.P.; *U.S. Private*, pg. 815
PF COLLINS CUSTOMS BROKER LTD.; *Int'l*, pg. 5835
PF CONCEPT INTERNATIONAL B.V.—See Charlesbank Capital Partners, LLC; *U.S. Private*, pg. 855
PF CONCEPT UK OPERATIONS LTD—See Charlesbank Capital Partners, LLC; *U.S. Private*, pg. 856
P/F DEMICH—See Skeljungur hf; *Int'l*, pg. 6980
PF DERRY LLC—See Planet Fitness, Inc.; *U.S. Public*, pg. 1697
PFD FOOD SERVICES PTY., LTD.—See Woolworths Group Limited; *Int'l*, pg. 8452
PFEIFER LINCOLN-MERCURY INC.; *U.S. Private*, pg. 3164
PFEIFFER & SON LTD.; *U.S. Private*, pg. 3164
PFEIFFER VACUUM AUSTRIA GMBH—See Dr. Ing. K. Busch GmbH; *Int'l*, pg. 2194
PFEIFFER VACUUM BENELUX B.V.—See Dr. Ing. K. Busch GmbH; *Int'l*, pg. 2193
PFEIFFER VACUUM BENELUX B. V.—See Dr. Ing. K. Busch GmbH; *Int'l*, pg. 2193
PFEIFFER VACUUM BRASIL LTDA—See Dr. Ing. K. Busch GmbH; *Int'l*, pg. 2194
PFEIFFER VACUUM COMPONENTS & SOLUTIONS GMBH—See Dr. Ing. K. Busch GmbH; *Int'l*, pg. 2194
PFEIFFER VACUUM GMBH—See Dr. Ing. K. Busch GmbH; *Int'l*, pg. 2194
PFEIFFER VACUUM GMBH—See Dr. Ing. K. Busch GmbH; *Int'l*, pg. 2194
PFEIFFER VACUUM INC.—See Dr. Ing. K. Busch GmbH; *Int'l*, pg. 2194
PFEIFFER VACUUM INDIA LTD.—See Dr. Ing. K. Busch GmbH; *Int'l*, pg. 2194
PFEIFFER VACUUM ITALIA S.P.A.—See Dr. Ing. K. Busch GmbH; *Int'l*, pg. 2194
PFEIFFER VACUUM KOREA LTD.—See Dr. Ing. K. Busch GmbH; *Int'l*, pg. 2194
PFEIFFER VACUUM LTD.—See Dr. Ing. K. Busch GmbH; *Int'l*, pg. 2194
PFEIFFER VACUUM ROMANIA S.R.L.—See Dr. Ing. K. Busch GmbH; *Int'l*, pg. 2194
PFEIFFER VACUUM SAS—See Dr. Ing. K. Busch GmbH; *Int'l*, pg. 2194
PFEIFFER VACUUM SCANDINAVIA AB—See Dr. Ing. K. Busch GmbH; *Int'l*, pg. 2194
PFEIFFER VACUUM (SCHWEIZ) AG—See Dr. Ing. K. Busch GmbH; *Int'l*, pg. 2194
PFEIFFER VACUUM (SHANGHAI) CO., LTD.—See Dr. Ing. K. Busch GmbH; *Int'l*, pg. 2194
PFEIFFER VACUUM SINGAPORE PTE. LTD.—See Dr. Ing. K. Busch GmbH; *Int'l*, pg. 2194
PFEIFFER VACUUM TAIWAN CORPORATION LTD.—See Dr. Ing. K. Busch GmbH; *Int'l*, pg. 2193
PFEIFFER VACUUM TAIWAN CORPORATION LTD.—See Dr. Ing. K. Busch GmbH; *Int'l*, pg. 2194
PFEIFFER VACUUM TECHNOLOGY AG—See Dr. Ing. K. Busch GmbH; *Int'l*, pg. 2193
PFEILER & ASSOCIATES ENGINEER INC.—See Psomas; *U.S. Private*, pg. 3297
PFERD AUSTRALIA (PTY.) LTD.—See August Rueggeberg GmbH & Co. KG PFERD-Werkzeuge; *Int'l*, pg. 703
PFERD CANADA INC.—See August Rueggeberg GmbH & Co. KG PFERD-Werkzeuge; *Int'l*, pg. 703
PFERDEWETTEN.DE AG; *Int'l*, pg. 5835
PFERDEWETTEN-SERVICE.DE GMBH—See mybet Holding SE; *Int'l*, pg. 5111
PFERD, INC.—See August Rueggeberg GmbH & Co. KG PFERD-Werkzeuge; *Int'l*, pg. 703
PFERD-RUEGGEBERG BVBA—See August Rueggeberg GmbH & Co. KG PFERD-Werkzeuge; *Int'l*, pg. 703
PFERD-RUEGGEBERG B.V.—See August Rueggeberg GmbH & Co. KG PFERD-Werkzeuge; *Int'l*, pg. 703
PFERD RUEGGEBERG FRANCE—See August Rueggeberg GmbH & Co. KG PFERD-Werkzeuge; *Int'l*, pg. 703
PFERD-RUEGGEBERG GES.M.B.H—See August Rueggeberg GmbH & Co. KG PFERD-Werkzeuge; *Int'l*, pg. 703
PFERD-TOOLS PVT. LTD.—See August Rueggeberg GmbH & Co. KG PFERD-Werkzeuge; *Int'l*, pg. 703
PFERD-VSM SP.Z.O.O.—See August Rueggeberg GmbH & Co. KG PFERD-Werkzeuge; *Int'l*, pg. 703
PF ERIE LLC—See Planet Fitness, Inc.; *U.S. Public*, pg. 1697
PFG FLORIDA, LLC—See Performance Food Group Company; *U.S. Public*, pg. 1675
PFG GLASS INDUSTRIES; *Int'l*, pg. 5835
PFG-LESTER BROADLINE INC.—See Performance Food Group Company; *U.S. Public*, pg. 1675
PFG-MIDDENDORF—See Performance Food Group Company; *U.S. Public*, pg. 1675
PFG MILTONS—See Performance Food Group Company; *U.S. Public*, pg. 1675

PFG-POWELL—See Performance Food Group Company; *U.S. Public*, pg. 1675
PF GREENSBURG LLC—See Planet Fitness, Inc.; *U.S. Public*, pg. 1697
PF GROUP A/S—See Maj Invest Holding A/S; *Int'l*, pg. 4653
PF GROUP HOLDINGS LIMITED; *Int'l*, pg. 5835
PFG-THOMS PROESTLER COMPANY—See Performance Food Group Company; *U.S. Public*, pg. 1675
PFG VENTURES L.P.; *U.S. Private*, pg. 3164
P/F HAVSBRUN—See P/F Bakkafrost; *Int'l*, pg. 5683
PFIFFNER INTERNATIONAL AG; *Int'l*, pg. 5835
PFI, LLC—See Dot Family Holdings LLC; *U.S. Private*, pg. 1264
P&F INDUSTRIES, INC.—See ShoreView Industries, LLC; *U.S. Private*, pg. 3642
PFINGSTEN PARTNERS, LLC; *U.S. Private*, pg. 3164
P F INNI—See Eik Bank P/F; *Int'l*, pg. 2332
PFISTER ENERGY INC.; *U.S. Private*, pg. 3165
PFISTER HOLDING GMBH—See FLSmidth & Co. A/S; *Int'l*, pg. 2712
THE PFISTER HOTEL—See The Marcus Corporation; *U.S. Public*, pg. 2112
PFISTER, LLC—See The Marcus Corporation; *U.S. Public*, pg. 2112
PFISTER SEEDS LLC—See Corteva, Inc.; *U.S. Public*, pg. 584
PFIZER AB—See Pfizer Inc.; *U.S. Public*, pg. 1680
PFIZER AG—See Pfizer Inc.; *U.S. Public*, pg. 1680
PFIZER ANIMAL PHARMA PRIVATE LIMITED—See Zoetis, Inc.; *U.S. Public*, pg. 2409
PFIZER APS—See Pfizer Inc.; *U.S. Public*, pg. 1680
PFIZER ARGENTINA—See Pfizer Inc.; *U.S. Public*, pg. 1680
PFIZER ASIA INTERNATIONAL B.V.—See Pfizer Inc.; *U.S. Public*, pg. 1680
PFIZER ASIA PACIFIC PTE LTD.—See Pfizer Inc.; *U.S. Public*, pg. 1680
PFIZER A/S—See Pfizer Inc.; *U.S. Public*, pg. 1680
PFIZER AS—See Pfizer Inc.; *U.S. Public*, pg. 1680
PFIZER AUSTRALIA HOLDINGS PTY LIMITED—See Pfizer Inc.; *U.S. Public*, pg. 1680
PFIZER AUSTRALIA INVESTMENTS PTY. LTD.—See Pfizer Inc.; *U.S. Public*, pg. 1680
PFIZER AUSTRALIA PTY LIMITED—See Pfizer Inc.; *U.S. Public*, pg. 1680
PFIZER BIOTECH CORPORATION—See Pfizer Inc.; *U.S. Public*, pg. 1681
PFIZER BIOTECHNOLOGY IRELAND—See Pfizer Inc.; *U.S. Public*, pg. 1681
PFIZER B.V.—See Pfizer Inc.; *U.S. Public*, pg. 1681
PFIZER CANADA INC.—See Pfizer Inc.; *U.S. Public*, pg. 1681
PFIZER CHILE S.A.—See Pfizer Inc.; *U.S. Public*, pg. 1681
PFIZER (CHINA) RESEARCH AND DEVELOPMENT CO. LTD.—See Pfizer Inc.; *U.S. Public*, pg. 1680
PFIZER CIA. LTDA.—See Pfizer Inc.; *U.S. Public*, pg. 1681
PFIZER CONSUMER HEALTHCARE GMBH—See Pfizer Inc.; *U.S. Public*, pg. 1681
PFIZER CORPORATION AUSTRIA GESELLSCHAFT M.B.H.—See Pfizer Inc.; *U.S. Public*, pg. 1681
PFIZER CORPORATION HONG KONG LIMITED—See Pfizer Inc.; *U.S. Public*, pg. 1681
PFIZER CORPORATION—See Pfizer Inc.; *U.S. Public*, pg. 1681
PFIZER CROATIA D.O.O.—See Pfizer Inc.; *U.S. Public*, pg. 1681
PFIZER CROATIA D.O.O.—See Pfizer Inc.; *U.S. Public*, pg. 1681
PFIZER DEUTSCHLAND GMBH—See Pfizer Inc.; *U.S. Public*, pg. 1681
PFIZER DOMINICANA, S.A.—See Pfizer Inc.; *U.S. Public*, pg. 1681
PFIZER ENTERPRISES SARL—See Pfizer Inc.; *U.S. Public*, pg. 1681
PFIZER ESBJERG A/S—See Pfizer Inc.; *U.S. Public*, pg. 1681
PFIZER EUROPEAN SERVICE CENTER BVBA—See Pfizer Inc.; *U.S. Public*, pg. 1681
PFIZER EXPORT COMPANY—See Pfizer Inc.; *U.S. Public*, pg. 1681
PFIZER FRANCE INTERNATIONAL INVESTMENTS SAS—See Pfizer Inc.; *U.S. Public*, pg. 1681
PFIZER GERMANY B.V. & CO. KG—See Pfizer Inc.; *U.S. Public*, pg. 1681
PFIZER GLOBAL SUPPLY JAPAN INC.—See Pfizer Inc.; *U.S. Public*, pg. 1681
PFIZER GROUP LIMITED—See Pfizer Inc.; *U.S. Public*, pg. 1681
PFIZER GULF FZ-LLC—See Pfizer Inc.; *U.S. Public*, pg. 1681
PFIZER GYOGYSZERKERESKEDELMI KFT.—See Pfizer Inc.; *U.S. Public*, pg. 1681
PFIZER HEALTH AB—See Pfizer Inc.; *U.S. Public*, pg. 1681
PFIZER HEALTHCARE INDIA PRIVATE LIMITED—See Pfizer Inc.; *U.S. Public*, pg. 1681

PFISTER ENERGY INC.   CORPORATE AFFILIATIONS

PFIZER HEALTHCARE IRELAND—See Pfizer Inc.; *U.S. Public*, pg. 1681
PFIZER HEALTH SOLUTIONS INC.—See Pfizer Inc.; *U.S. Public*, pg. 1681
PFIZER HELLAS, A.E.—See Pfizer Inc.; *U.S. Public*, pg. 1681
PFIZER HK SERVICE COMPANY LIMITED—See Pfizer Inc.; *U.S. Public*, pg. 1681
PFIZER HOLDING FRANCE (S.C.A.)—See Pfizer Inc.; *U.S. Public*, pg. 1681
PFIZER HOLDING ITALY S.P.A.—See Pfizer Inc.; *U.S. Public*, pg. 1681
PFIZER HOLDINGS INTERNATIONAL LUXEMBOURG (PHIL) SARL—See Pfizer Inc.; *U.S. Public*, pg. 1681
PFIZER ILACLARI, A.S.—See Pfizer Inc.; *U.S. Public*, pg. 1681
PFIZER ILACLARI LIMITED SIRKETI—See Pfizer Inc.; *U.S. Public*, pg. 1681
PFIZER INC.; *U.S. Public*, pg. 1679
PFIZER, INC.—See Pfizer Inc.; *U.S. Public*, pg. 1683
PFIZER INTERNATIONAL CORPORATION—See Pfizer Inc.; *U.S. Public*, pg. 1681
PFIZER INTERNATIONAL LLC—See Pfizer Inc.; *U.S. Public*, pg. 1681
PFIZER INTERNATIONAL TRADING (SHANGHAI) LIMITED—See Pfizer Inc.; *U.S. Public*, pg. 1681
PFIZER IRELAND PHARMACEUTICALS—See Pfizer Inc.; *U.S. Public*, pg. 1681
PFIZER ITALIA S.R.L.—See Pfizer Inc.; *U.S. Public*, pg. 1681
PFIZER JAPAN INC.—See Pfizer Inc.; *U.S. Public*, pg. 1681
PFIZER LABORATORIES PFE (PTY) LTD—See Pfizer Inc.; *U.S. Public*, pg. 1681
PFIZER LABORATORIES (PTY) LIMITED—See Pfizer Inc.; *U.S. Public*, pg. 1681
PFIZER LIMITED—See Pfizer Inc.; *U.S. Public*, pg. 1682
PFIZER LIMITED—See Pfizer Inc.; *U.S. Public*, pg. 1682
PFIZER LIMITED—See Pfizer Inc.; *U.S. Public*, pg. 1682
PFIZER LIMITED (TAIWAN)—See Pfizer Inc.; *U.S. Public*, pg. 1682
PFIZER LOGISTICS CENTER—See Pfizer Inc.; *U.S. Public*, pg. 1682
PFIZER LUXEMBOURG SARL—See Pfizer Inc.; *U.S. Public*, pg. 1682
PFIZER MALAYSIA SDN BHD—See Pfizer Inc.; *U.S. Public*, pg. 1682
PFIZER MANUFACTURING AUSTRIA G.M.B.H.—See Pfizer Inc.; *U.S. Public*, pg. 1682
PFIZER MANUFACTURING BELGIUM N.V.—See Pfizer Inc.; *U.S. Public*, pg. 1682
PFIZER MANUFACTURING DEUTSCHLAND GMBH—See Pfizer Inc.; *U.S. Public*, pg. 1682
PFIZER MANUFACTURING DEUTSCHLAND PFE GMBH—See Pfizer Inc.; *U.S. Public*, pg. 1682
PFIZER MEDICAL SYSTEMS, INC.—See Pfizer Inc.; *U.S. Public*, pg. 1682
PFIZER MEDICAL TECHNOLOGY GROUP (NETHERLANDS) B.V.—See Pfizer Inc.; *U.S. Public*, pg. 1682
PFIZER MEDICAMENTOS GENERICOS E PARTICIPACOES LTDA.—See Pfizer Inc.; *U.S. Public*, pg. 1682
PFIZER - MIDDLETON—See Pfizer Inc.; *U.S. Public*, pg. 1680
PFIZER NETHERLANDS B.V.—See Pfizer Inc.; *U.S. Public*, pg. 1682
PFIZER NEW ZEALAND LIMITED—See Pfizer Inc.; *U.S. Public*, pg. 1682
PFIZER NORGE AS—See Pfizer Inc.; *U.S. Public*, pg. 1682
PFIZER N.V./S.A.—See Pfizer Inc.; *U.S. Public*, pg. 1682
PFIZER OVERSEAS LLC—See Pfizer Inc.; *U.S. Public*, pg. 1681
PFIZER OY—See Pfizer Inc.; *U.S. Public*, pg. 1682
PFIZER PAKISTAN LIMITED—See Pfizer Inc.; *U.S. Public*, pg. 1682
PFIZER (PERTH) PTY LIMITED—See Pfizer Inc.; *U.S. Public*, pg. 1680
PFIZER PFE ILACLARI ANONIM SIRKETI—See Pfizer Inc.; *U.S. Public*, pg. 1682
PFIZER PFE (MALAYSIA) SDN. BHD.—See Pfizer Inc.; *U.S. Public*, pg. 1682
PFIZER PFE NEW ZEALAND HOLDING B.V.—See Pfizer Inc.; *U.S. Public*, pg. 1682
PFIZER PFE, SPOL. S R.O.—See Pfizer Inc.; *U.S. Public*, pg. 1682
PFIZER PHARMACEUTICALS ISRAEL LTD.—See Pfizer Inc.; *U.S. Public*, pg. 1682
PFIZER PHARMACEUTICALS KOREA LTD.—See Pfizer Inc.; *U.S. Public*, pg. 1682
PFIZER PHARMACEUTICALS LTD.—See Pfizer Inc.; *U.S. Public*, pg. 1682
PFIZER PHARMACEUTICALS TUNISIE SARL—See Pfizer Inc.; *U.S. Public*, pg. 1682
PFIZER PHARMACEUTICAL (WUXI) CO., LTD.—See Pfizer Inc.; *U.S. Public*, pg. 1682
PFIZER PHARMA GMBH—See Pfizer Inc.; *U.S. Public*, pg. 1682
PFIZER PHARMA PFE GMBH—See Pfizer Inc.; *U.S. Public*, pg. 1682

PFIZER POLSKA SP. Z O.O.—See Pfizer Inc.; *U.S. Public*, pg. 1682
PFIZER PREV-SOCIEDADE DE PREVIDENCIA PRIVADA—See Pfizer Inc.; *U.S. Public*, pg. 1682
PFIZER PRODUCTS INC.—See Pfizer Inc.; *U.S. Public*, pg. 1682
PFIZER PRODUCTS INDIA PRIVATE LIMITED—See Pfizer Inc.; *U.S. Public*, pg. 1682
PFIZER PTE. LTD.—See Pfizer Inc.; *U.S. Public*, pg. 1682
PFIZER RESEARCH & DEVELOPMENT—See Pfizer Inc.; *U.S. Public*, pg. 1682
PFIZER RESEARCH TECHNOLOGY CENTER—See Pfizer Inc.; *U.S. Public*, pg. 1682
PFIZER ROMANIA SRL—See Pfizer Inc.; *U.S. Public*, pg. 1682
PFIZER SA (BELGIUM)—See Pfizer Inc.; *U.S. Public*, pg. 1683
PFIZER, S.A. DE C.V.—See Pfizer Inc.; *U.S. Public*, pg. 1683
PFIZER S.A.—See Pfizer Inc.; *U.S. Public*, pg. 1683
PFIZER S.A.S.—See Pfizer Inc.; *U.S. Public*, pg. 1683
PFIZER SAUDI LIMITED—See Pfizer Inc.; *U.S. Public*, pg. 1683
PFIZER SERVICE COMPANY BVBA—See Pfizer Inc.; *U.S. Public*, pg. 1683
PFIZER SERVICE COMPANY IRELAND—See Pfizer Inc.; *U.S. Public*, pg. 1683
PFIZER S.G.P.S. LDA.—See Pfizer Inc.; *U.S. Public*, pg. 1683
PFIZER SHARED SERVICES—See Pfizer Inc.; *U.S. Public*, pg. 1683
PFIZER, S.L.—See Pfizer Inc.; *U.S. Public*, pg. 1683
PFIZER—See Pfizer Inc.; *U.S. Public*, pg. 1680
PFIZER SPAIN S.A.—See Pfizer Inc.; *U.S. Public*, pg. 1683
PFIZER SPECIALTIES LIMITED—See Pfizer Inc.; *U.S. Public*, pg. 1683
PFIZER, SPOL. S R.O.—See Pfizer Inc.; *U.S. Public*, pg. 1683
PFIZER SRB D.O.O.—See Pfizer Inc.; *U.S. Public*, pg. 1683
PFIZER S.R.L.—See Pfizer Inc.; *U.S. Public*, pg. 1683
PFIZER S.R.L.—See Pfizer Inc.; *U.S. Public*, pg. 1683
PFIZER S.R.O.—See Pfizer Inc.; *U.S. Public*, pg. 1683
PFIZER TAIWAN LTD.—See Pfizer Inc.; *U.S. Public*, pg. 1683
PFIZER (THAILAND) LIMITED—See Pfizer Inc.; *U.S. Public*, pg. 1680
PFIZER TRADING POLSKA SP. Z.O.O.—See Pfizer Inc.; *U.S. Public*, pg. 1683
PFIZER VENEZUELA, S.A.—See Pfizer Inc.; *U.S. Public*, pg. 1683
PFIZER (VIETNAM) LIMITED COMPANY—See Pfizer Inc.; *U.S. Public*, pg. 1680
PFK ELECTRONICS (PTY) LTD.; *Int'l*, pg. 5836
THE P.F. LABORATORIES INC.—See Purdue Pharma LP; *U.S. Private*, pg. 3305
P. FLANIGAN & SONS INC.; *U.S. Private*, pg. 3059
P-FLEET INC.; *U.S. Private*, pg. 3059
PFLEGE AUS EINER HAND GMBH—See Clariane SE; *Int'l*, pg. 1643
PFLEGEN & WOHNEN HAMBURG GMBH—See Deutsche Wohnen SE; *Int'l*, pg. 2085
PFLEGIA AG—See U.C.A. AG; *Int'l*, pg. 7998
PFLEIDERER ACCESSORIES AND SERVICES GMBH—See Pfleiderer GmbH; *Int'l*, pg. 5836
PFLEIDERER BENELUX B.V.—See Pfleiderer GmbH; *Int'l*, pg. 5836
PFLEIDERER DRITTE ERWERBERGESELLSCHAFT MBH & CO—See Pfleiderer GmbH; *Int'l*, pg. 5836
PFLEIDERER EUROPOLS GMBH & CO. KG-WERK REGENSBURG—See Pfleiderer GmbH; *Int'l*, pg. 5836
PFLEIDERER FRANCE S. A. S.—See Pfleiderer GmbH; *Int'l*, pg. 5836
PFLEIDERER GMBH; *Int'l*, pg. 5836
PFLEIDERER GRAJEWO S.A.—See Pfleiderer GmbH; *Int'l*, pg. 5836
PFLEIDERER HOLZWERKSTOFFE GMBH & CO. KG—See Pfleiderer GmbH; *Int'l*, pg. 5836
PFLEIDERER HOLZWERKSTOFFE GMBH & CO. KG-WERK ARNSBERG—See Pfleiderer GmbH; *Int'l*, pg. 5836
PFLEIDERER HOLZWERKSTOFFE NIDDA VERWALTUNGS-GMBH—See Pfleiderer GmbH; *Int'l*, pg. 5836
PFLEIDERER HOLZWERKSTOFFE VERWALTUNGS GMBH—See Pfleiderer GmbH; *Int'l*, pg. 5836
PFLEIDERER INDUSTRIE LTD.—See Pfleiderer GmbH; *Int'l*, pg. 5836
PFLEIDERER INFRASTRUKTURTECHNIK GMBH & CO. KG—See Pfleiderer GmbH; *Int'l*, pg. 5836
PFLEIDERER INFRASTRUKTURTECHNIK GMBH & CO. KG—See Pfleiderer GmbH; *Int'l*, pg. 5836
PFLEIDERER INFRASTRUKTURTECHNOLOGY GMBH & CO. KG—See Pfleiderer GmbH; *Int'l*, pg. 5836
PFLEIDERER LEUTKIRCH GMBH—See Pfleiderer GmbH; *Int'l*, pg. 5836
PFLEIDERER MDF SP. Z O.O.—See Pfleiderer GmbH; *Int'l*, pg. 5836

PFLEIDERER PROSPAN S. A.—See Pfleiderer GmbH; *Int'l*, pg. 5836
PFLEIDERER SERVICE SP. Z O.O.—See Pfleiderer GmbH; *Int'l*, pg. 5836
P-FLEX—See Randstad N.V.; *Int'l*, pg. 6202
PFL INFOTECH LTD.; *Int'l*, pg. 5836
PFLUEGER KOPERTY SP Z O.O.—See Bong AB; *Int'l*, pg. 1107
PFM FINANCIAL ADVISORS LLC—See Public Financial Management, Inc.; *U.S. Private*, pg. 3299
PFMG SOLAR TUSTIN, LLC—See Primoris Services Corporation; *U.S. Public*, pg. 1718
PF MOON AND COMPANY INC.; *U.S. Private*, pg. 3164
PFNONWOVENS A.S.; *Int'l*, pg. 5836
PFNONWOVENS CZECH S.R.O.—See PFNonwovens a.s.; *Int'l*, pg. 5836
PFNONWOVENS EGYPT LLC—See PFNonwovens a.s.; *Int'l*, pg. 5836
PFNONWOVENS HOLDING S.R.O.; *Int'l*, pg. 5836
PFO GLOBAL, INC.; *U.S. Public*, pg. 1683
PFP CAPITAL LIMITED—See Places for People Group Limited; *Int'l*, pg. 5888
PFP COLUMBUS, LLC—See Washington Prime Group Inc.; *U.S. Private*, pg. 4448
PFP (NZ) LIMITED—See Propel Funeral Partners Limited; *Int'l*, pg. 5997
PFP/SCHMITT-SUSSMAN ENTERPRISES; *U.S. Private*, pg. 3165
PFS DISTRIBUTION COMPANY—See JBS S.A.; *Int'l*, pg. 3919
PFS INVESTMENTS, INC.—See Primerica, Inc.; *U.S. Public*, pg. 1717
P/F SKYN—See P/F BankNordik; *Int'l*, pg. 5683
PFSL INVESTMENTS CANADA LTD.—See Primerica, Inc.; *U.S. Public*, pg. 1717
PFS SALES COMPANY—See Kelso & Company, L.P.; *U.S. Private*, pg. 2279
PFS SALES COMPANY—See Warburg Pincus LLC; *U.S. Private*, pg. 4437
PFSWEB, INC.—See GXO Logistics, Inc.; *U.S. Public*, pg. 975
P/F TJALDUR; *Int'l*, pg. 5683
PFU APPLICATIONS LIMITED—See Ricoh Company, Ltd.; *Int'l*, pg. 6333
PFU CREATIVE SERVICES LIMITED—See Ricoh Company, Ltd.; *Int'l*, pg. 6333
PFU EAST JAPAN LIMITED—See Ricoh Company, Ltd.; *Int'l*, pg. 6333
P-FUEL LIMITED—See SECOS Group Limited; *Int'l*, pg. 6673
PFU HOKKAIDO LIMITED—See Ricoh Company, Ltd.; *Int'l*, pg. 6333
PFU HUMAN DESIGN LIMITED—See Ricoh Company, Ltd.; *Int'l*, pg. 6333
PFU IMAGING SOLUTIONS EUROPE LIMITED—See Ricoh Company, Ltd.; *Int'l*, pg. 6333
PFU JIANGSU NANTONG INFORMATION SYSTEMS CO., LTD.—See Ricoh Company, Ltd.; *Int'l*, pg. 6333
PFU LIFE AGENCY LIMITED—See Ricoh Company, Ltd.; *Int'l*, pg. 6333
PFU LIMITED—See Ricoh Company, Ltd.; *Int'l*, pg. 6333
PFU QUALITY SERVICE LIMITED—See Ricoh Company, Ltd.; *Int'l*, pg. 6333
P&F USA—See Funai Electric Co., Ltd.; *Int'l*, pg. 2844
PFU SHANGHAI CO., LTD.—See Ricoh Company, Ltd.; *Int'l*, pg. 6333
PFU SHANGHAI INFORMATION SYSTEMS CO., LTD.—See Ricoh Company, Ltd.; *Int'l*, pg. 6333
PFU SOFTWARE LIMITED—See Ricoh Company, Ltd.; *Int'l*, pg. 6333
PFU SYSTEMS, INC.—See Ricoh Company, Ltd.; *Int'l*, pg. 6333
PFU TECHNOCONSUL LIMITED—See Ricoh Company, Ltd.; *Int'l*, pg. 6333
PFU TECHNOLOGY SINGAPORE PTE LTD—See Ricoh Company, Ltd.; *Int'l*, pg. 6333
PFU TECHNO WISE LIMITED—See Ricoh Company, Ltd.; *Int'l*, pg. 6333
PFU TOHTO LIMITED—See Ricoh Company, Ltd.; *Int'l*, pg. 6333
PF VALLEJO, LLC—See Planet Fitness, Inc.; *U.S. Public*, pg. 1697
PFW AEROSPACE GMBH—See Airbus SE; *Int'l*, pg. 244
PGA ELECTRONIC S.A.—See Astronics Corporation; *U.S. Public*, pg. 217
PGAM ADVANCED TECHNOLOGIES LTD.—See Farmingtons Holding GmbH; *Int'l*, pg. 2620
PGA PROFESSIONAL CENTER PROPERTY OWNERS ASSOCIATION—See LXP Industrial Trust; *U.S. Public*, pg. 1349
PGA RESORTS LTD; *U.S. Private*, pg. 3165
PGA SOMPO INSURANCE CORPORATION—See Prudential Guarantee & Assurance Inc.; *Int'l*, pg. 6008
PGA SOMPO INSURANCE CORPORATION—See Sompo Holdings, Inc.; *Int'l*, pg. 7087
PGA TOUR, INC.; *U.S. Private*, pg. 3165
PGAV INC.; *U.S. Private*, pg. 3165
PG BISON HOLDINGS (PTY) LIMITED—See Steinhoff International Holdings N.V.; *Int'l*, pg. 7194

COMPANY NAME INDEX

PGB TRUST AND INVESTMENTS OF DELAWARE—See Peapack-Gladstone Financial Corporation; *U.S. Public*, pg. 1659

PG CALC, INC.—See GTCR LLC; *U.S. Private*, pg. 1805

P.G.C. HAJENIUS BV—See Skandinavisk Holding A/S; *Int'l*, pg. 6977

P & G CHEVROLET, INC.; *U.S. Private*, pg. 3058

PGC WIRE AND CABLE, LLC—See Proto Labs, Inc.; *U.S. Public*, pg. 1729

PG DEVELOPMENTS LIMITED—See PG PLC; *Int'l*, pg. 5837

P&G DISTRIBUTION EAST AFRICA LIMITED—See The Procter & Gamble Company; *U.S. Public*, pg. 2121

PG DRIVES TECHNOLOGY INC.—See Curtiss-Wright Corporation; *U.S. Public*, pg. 612

PG DRIVES TECHNOLOGY LTD.—See Curtiss-Wright Corporation; *U.S. Public*, pg. 612

PGE BALTICA SP. Z O.O.—See PGE Polska Grupa Energetyczna S.A.; *Int'l*, pg. 5837

PG&E CORPORATION; *U.S. Public*, pg. 1683

PGED CORP.—See Fire & Flower Holdings Corp.; *Int'l*, pg. 2678

PGE DOM MAKLERSKI S.A.—See PGE Polska Grupa Energetyczna S.A.; *Int'l*, pg. 5837

PGE EKOSERWIS SP. Z O.O.—See PGE Polska Grupa Energetyczna S.A.; *Int'l*, pg. 5837

PGE ELEKTROWNIA OPOLE S.A.—See PGE Polska Grupa Energetyczna S.A.; *Int'l*, pg. 5837

PGE ENERGETYKA KOLEJOWA SA—See PGE Polska Grupa Energetyczna S.A.; *Int'l*, pg. 5837

PGE ENERGIA CIEPLA S.A.—See PGE Polska Grupa Energetyczna S.A.; *Int'l*, pg. 5837

PGE ENERGIA JADROWA S.A.—See PGE Polska Grupa Energetyczna S.A.; *Int'l*, pg. 5837

PGE ENERGIA ODNAWIALNA S.A.—See PGE Polska Grupa Energetyczna S.A.; *Int'l*, pg. 5837

PG&E ENERGY RECOVERY FUNDING LLC—See PG&E Corporation; *U.S. Public*, pg. 1684

PG&E GENERATING COMPANY—See PG&E Corporation; *U.S. Public*, pg. 1684

PGE GORNICTWO I ENERGETYKA KONWENCJONALNA S.A.—See PGE Polska Grupa Energetyczna S.A.; *Int'l*, pg. 5837

PG ELECTROPLAST LIMITED; *Int'l*, pg. 5836

PGEO BIOPRODUCTS SDN BHD—See Wilmar International Limited; *Int'l*, pg. 8421

PGE OBROT S.A.—See PGE Polska Grupa Energetyczna S.A.; *Int'l*, pg. 5837

PGEO EDIBLE OILS SDN BHD—See Wilmar International Limited; *Int'l*, pg. 8421

PGEO GROUP SDN. BHD.—See Wilmar International Limited; *Int'l*, pg. 8421

PGE POLSKA GRUPA ENERGETYCZNA S.A.; *Int'l*, pg. 5837

P. GEROLEMOU CONSTRUCTION (PTY) LIMITED—See Basil Read Holdings Limited; *Int'l*, pg. 887

PGE SYSTEMY S.A.—See PGE Polska Grupa Energetyczna S.A.; *Int'l*, pg. 5837

PGE VENTURES SP. Z O.O.—See PGE Polska Grupa Energetyczna S.A.; *Int'l*, pg. 5837

PGF APTEKARZ SP. Z O.O.—See Pelion S.A.; *Int'l*, pg. 5783

PGF - BYDGASZCZ S.A.—See Pelion S.A.; *Int'l*, pg. 5783

PGF CAPITAL BHD; *Int'l*, pg. 5837

PGF CEFARM KRAKOW SP. Z O.O.—See Pelion S.A.; *Int'l*, pg. 5783

PGF CEFARM LUBLIN SP. Z O.O.—See Pelion S.A.; *Int'l*, pg. 5783

PGF CEFARM POZNAN SP. Z O.O.—See Pelion S.A.; *Int'l*, pg. 5783

PGF CEFARM SP. Z O.O.—See Pelion S.A.; *Int'l*, pg. 5783

PGF CONSULTANTS INC.; *Int'l*, pg. 5838

PGF - LODZ SP. Z O.O.—See Pelion S.A.; *Int'l*, pg. 5783

P G FOILS LIMITED; *Int'l*, pg. 5681

PGF POLSKA GRUPA FOTOWOLTAICZNA S.A.; *Int'l*, pg. 5838

PGF SP. Z O.O.—See Pelion S.A.; *Int'l*, pg. 5783

PGF URTICA SP. Z O.O.—See Pelion S.A.; *Int'l*, pg. 5783

PGG HSC FEED COMPANY, LLC—See CHS INC.; *U.S. Public*, pg. 492

PGGM VERMOGENSBEHEER B.V.; *Int'l*, pg. 5838

PGG WRIGHTSON LIMITED—See Agria Corporation; *Int'l*, pg. 216

PGG WRIGHTSON SEEDS (AUSTRALIA) PTY LIMITED—See Agria Corporation; *Int'l*, pg. 216

PGG WRIGHTSON SEEDS LIMITED—See DLF Seeds A/S; *Int'l*, pg. 2141

PGH BRICKS & PAVERS PTY LIMITED—See CSR Limited; *Int'l*, pg. 1867

PGH CONNECT, INC.—See Ad-Base Group, Inc.; *U.S. Private*, pg. 72

P.G.H., LTD.—See Salini Costruttori S.p.A.; *Int'l*, pg. 6493

PG HOLDINGS PTE LTD—See Select Group Limited; *Int'l*, pg. 6699

PG HOME GROUP SPA—See PDS Limited; *Int'l*, pg. 5770

PGH SERVICES LLC—See Pact Group Holdings Ltd.; *Int'l*, pg. 5693

PGI ACQUISITION LIMITED—See Berry Global Group, Inc; *U.S. Public*, pg. 322

PGI COLUMBIA LTDA—See Berry Global Group, Inc; *U.S. Public*, pg. 322

PGI INCORPORATED; *U.S. Public*, pg. 1684

PGI INTERNATIONAL, LTD.—See Parker Hannifin Corporation; *U.S. Public*, pg. 1643

PGIM (AUSTRALIA) PTY. LTD.—See Prudential Financial, Inc.; *U.S. Public*, pg. 1731

PGIM GLOBAL HIGH YIELD FUND, INC.; *U.S. Public*, pg. 1684

PGIM HIGH YIELD BOND FUND, INC.; *U.S. Public*, pg. 1684

PGIM (HONG KONG) LTD.—See Prudential Financial, Inc.; *U.S. Public*, pg. 1731

PGIM, INC.—See Prudential Financial, Inc.; *U.S. Public*, pg. 1731

PGIM INDIA ASSET MANAGEMENT PRIVATE LIMITED—See Prudential Financial, Inc.; *U.S. Public*, pg. 1731

PGIM IRELAND LIMITED—See Prudential Financial, Inc.; *U.S. Public*, pg. 1731

PGIM JAPAN CO., LTD.—See Prudential Financial, Inc.; *U.S. Public*, pg. 1732

PGIM LIMITED—See Prudential Financial, Inc.; *U.S. Public*, pg. 1731

PGIM QUANTITATIVE SOLUTIONS LLC—See Prudential Financial, Inc.; *U.S. Public*, pg. 1731

PGIM REAL ESTATE FRANCE SAS—See Prudential Financial, Inc.; *U.S. Public*, pg. 1731

PGIM REAL ESTATE GERMANY AG—See Prudential Financial, Inc.; *U.S. Public*, pg. 1731

PGIM REAL ESTATE (JAPAN) LTD.—See Prudential Financial, Inc.; *U.S. Public*, pg. 1731

PGIM REAL ESTATE LUXEMBOURG S.A.—See Prudential Financial, Inc.; *U.S. Public*, pg. 1731

PGIM REAL ESTATE MEXICO S.C.—See Prudential Financial, Inc.; *U.S. Public*, pg. 1731

PGIM REAL ESTATE S. DE R.L. DE C.V.—See Prudential Financial, Inc.; *U.S. Public*, pg. 1731

PGIM REAL ESTATE (UK) LIMITED—See Prudential Financial, Inc.; *U.S. Public*, pg. 1731

PGIM (SHANGHAI) COMPANY LTD.—See Prudential Financial, Inc.; *U.S. Public*, pg. 1731

PGIM (SINGAPORE) PTE. LTD.—See Prudential Financial, Inc.; *U.S. Public*, pg. 1731

PGIM WADHWANI LLP—See Prudential Financial, Inc.; *U.S. Public*, pg. 1731

P-G INDUSTRIES INC.; *U.S. Private*, pg. 3059

PG INDUSTRIES (ZIMBABWE) LIMITED; *Int'l*, pg. 5836

P G INDUSTRY LIMITED - ALWAR FACTORY—See Marble City India Limited; *Int'l*, pg. 4688

P&G INNOVATION GODO KAISHA—See The Procter & Gamble Company; *U.S. Public*, pg. 2122

PGI NONWOVENS B.V.—See Berry Global Group, Inc; *U.S. Public*, pg. 322

P. GIOIOSO & SONS, INC.; *U.S. Private*, pg. 3060

PGIO S.A. AGENCIA EN CHILE—See The Procter & Gamble Company; *U.S. Public*, pg. 2121

P&G ISRAEL M.D.O. LTD.—See The Procter & Gamble Company; *U.S. Public*, pg. 2121

P&G K.K.—See The Procter & Gamble Company; *U.S. Public*, pg. 2122

PGL ADVENTURE LIMITED—See Cox & Kings Limited; *Int'l*, pg. 1823

P. G. LAWTON (INDUSTRIAL SERVICES) LTD.—See SGL Carbon SE; *Int'l*, pg. 6741

PGL GROUP LIMITED—See Cox & Kings Limited; *Int'l*, pg. 1823

PGL TRAVEL LIMITED—See Cox & Kings Limited; *Int'l*, pg. 1823

PGMB BUDOPOL S.A.—See Herkules S.A.; *Int'l*, pg. 3362

PGM BUDUCNOST AD; *Int'l*, pg. 5838

PGMD CONSULTING S.R.L.—See TXT e-Solutions S.p.A.; *Int'l*, pg. 7993

PGM EUROPEAN LOGISTICS CENTER—See Pfizer Inc.; *U.S. Public*, pg. 1682

PGM GROUP SP. Z O.O.—See Elemental Holding S.A.; *Int'l*, pg. 2358

PGM HOLDINGS K.K.—See Heiwa Corporation; *Int'l*, pg. 3327

PGM INCORPORATED; *U.S. Private*, pg. 3165

PGM OF TEXAS LLC—See Elemental Holding S.A.; *Int'l*, pg. 2358

PGM PRODUCTS, LLC; *U.S. Private*, pg. 3165

PGM PROMOTERS GROUP MUNICH KONZERTAGENTUR GMBH—See CTS Eventim AG & Co. KGAA; *Int'l*, pg. 1873

PGM PROMOTORS GROUP MUNICH KONZERTAGENTUR GMBH—See CTS Eventim AG & Co. KGAA; *Int'l*, pg. 1873

PGNIG ENERGIA SA—See Polskie Gornictwo Naftowe i Gazownictwo S.A.; *Int'l*, pg. 5912

PGNIG GAZOPROJEKT S.A.—See Polskie Gornictwo Naftowe i Gazownictwo S.A.; *Int'l*, pg. 5912

PGNIG NORWAY AS—See Polskie Gornictwo Naftowe i Gazownictwo S.A.; *Int'l*, pg. 5912

PGNIG OBROT DETALICZNY SP. Z O.O.—See Polskie Gornictwo Naftowe i Gazownictwo S.A.; *Int'l*, pg. 5912

PGNIG SUPPLY & TRADING GMBH—See Polskie Gornictwo Naftowe i Gazownictwo S.A.; *Int'l*, pg. 5912

PGNIG TECHNOLOGIE SP. Z O.O.—See Polskie Gornictwo Naftowe i Gazownictwo S.A.; *Int'l*, pg. 5912

PGNIG UPSTREAM NORTH AFRICA B.V.—See Polskie Gornictwo Naftowe i Gazownictwo S.A.; *Int'l*, pg. 5912

PGNIG UPSTREAM NORWAY AS—See Polskie Gornictwo Naftowe i Gazownictwo S.A.; *Int'l*, pg. 5912

P.G. NIKAS S.A.; *Int'l*, pg. 5682

PGO AUTOMOBILES; *Int'l*, pg. 5838

PGO S.A.—See TDJ S.A.; *Int'l*, pg. 7487

PGP GLASS CEYLON PLC; *Int'l*, pg. 5838

PGP INTERNATIONAL, INC.—See The Garfield Weston Foundation; *Int'l*, pg. 7649

PG PLC; *Int'l*, pg. 5837

P&G PRESTIGE PRODUCTS N.V.—See The Procter & Gamble Company; *U.S. Public*, pg. 2122

P&G PRESTIGE PRODUCTS—See The Procter & Gamble Company; *U.S. Public*, pg. 2121

P&G PRESTIGE SERVICE GMBH—See The Procter & Gamble Company; *U.S. Public*, pg. 2121

PG PUBLISHING COMPANY—See Block Communications, Inc.; *U.S. Private*, pg. 582

PGR OPERATING LLC—See Phoenix Global Resources Plc; *Int'l*, pg. 5851

PGS AMERICAS, INC.—See PGS ASA; *Int'l*, pg. 5838

PGS ANGOLA LTD.—See PGS ASA; *Int'l*, pg. 5838

PGS ASA; *Int'l*, pg. 5838

PGS AUSTRALIA PTY. LTD.—See PGS ASA; *Int'l*, pg. 5838

PGS BERGEN WAREHOUSE—See PGS ASA; *Int'l*, pg. 5838

PGS DATA PROCESSING, INC.—See PGS ASA; *Int'l*, pg. 5838

PGS DATA PROCESSING MIDDLE EAST SAE—See PGS ASA; *Int'l*, pg. 5838

PGS DATA PROCESSING & TECHNOLOGY SDN. BHD.—See PGS ASA; *Int'l*, pg. 5838

PGS DATA PROCESSING & TECHNOLOGY—See PGS ASA; *Int'l*, pg. 5838

PGS EXPLORATION (NORWAY) AS—See PGS ASA; *Int'l*, pg. 5838

PGS EXPLORATION (UK) LTD.—See PGS ASA; *Int'l*, pg. 5838

PGS EXPLORATION (US), INC.—See PGS ASA; *Int'l*, pg. 5838

PGS FALCON AS—See PGS ASA; *Int'l*, pg. 5838

PGS GEOPHYSICAL AS—See PGS ASA; *Int'l*, pg. 5838

PGS GEOPHYSICAL (NETHERLANDS) B.V.—See PGS ASA; *Int'l*, pg. 5838

PGS GEOPHYSICAL NIGERIA LTD.—See PGS ASA; *Int'l*, pg. 5838

PGS GHANA LIMITED—See PGS ASA; *Int'l*, pg. 5838

PGS INTERNATIONAL N.V.—See Bayer Aktiengesellschaft; *Int'l*, pg. 910

PGS INVESTIGACAO PETROLIFERA LIMITADA—See PGS ASA; *Int'l*, pg. 5838

PGS JAPAN K.K.—See PGS ASA; *Int'l*, pg. 5838

PGS-KAZAKHSTAN LLP—See PGS ASA; *Int'l*, pg. 5839

PGS MARINE GEOPHYSICAL GROUP—See PGS ASA; *Int'l*, pg. 5838

PGS MULTICLIENT—See PGS ASA; *Int'l*, pg. 5838

PGS MULTI TRANSIENT EM—See PGS ASA; *Int'l*, pg. 5838

PGS ONSHORE, INC.—See PGS ASA; *Int'l*, pg. 5839

P&G SOUTH AFRICAN TRADING (PTY.) LTD.—See The Procter & Gamble Company; *U.S. Public*, pg. 2121

PGS OVERSEAS AS—See PGS ASA; *Int'l*, pg. 5838

PGS PENSION TRUSTEE LTD.—See PGS ASA; *Int'l*, pg. 5838

PGS PRODUCTION AS—See PGS ASA; *Int'l*, pg. 5838

PGS PROGISOFTWARE—See Teleperformance SE; *Int'l*, pg. 7540

PGS SHIPPING AS—See PGS ASA; *Int'l*, pg. 5839

PGS SUPORTE LOGISTICO E SERVICOS LTDA.—See PGS ASA; *Int'l*, pg. 5839

PGS TANKER AS—See PGS ASA; *Int'l*, pg. 5839

PGS VENTURE AS—See PGS ASA; *Int'l*, pg. 5839

PGT CEEWRITE LTD—See PG Technology, Ltd.; *Int'l*, pg. 5837

PGS TECHNOLOGIES, LLC—See Linde plc; *Int'l*, pg. 4509

PG TECHNOLOGY, LTD.; *Int'l*, pg. 5837

PGT HOLDINGS JSC; *Int'l*, pg. 5839

PGT INDUSTRIES, INC.—See Koch Industries, Inc.; *U.S. Private*, pg. 2333

PGT INNOVATIONS, INC.—See Koch Industries, Inc.; *U.S. Private*, pg. 2332

PG-TRADING (HANGZHOU) CO., LTD.—See Piala, Inc.; *Int'l*, pg. 5859

PGT SOLUTIONS JSC—See PGT Holdings JSC; *Int'l*, pg. 5839

PGV AUSTRIA TRUNK GMBH—See Presse-Vertrieb Hermann Trunk GmbH & Co. KG; *Int'l*, pg. 5965

PGW AUTO GLASS, LLC—See OEP Capital Advisors, L.P.; *U.S. Private*, pg. 2999

PHAARMASIA LIMITED; *Int'l*, pg. 5839

PHA BODY SYSTEMS, LLC—See Pyeong Hwa Automotive Co., Ltd; *Int'l*, pg. 6127

PHACIL FORT MONMOUTH (CECOM) OFFICE—See Sagewind Capital LLC; *U.S. Private*, pg. 3527

PHAARMASIA LIMITED

PHACIL, INC.—See Sagewind Capital LLC; *U.S. Private*, pg. 3527
PHACIL-WASHINGTON, DC—See Sagewind Capital LLC; *U.S. Private*, pg. 3527
PHACIL-WEST COAST—See Sagewind Capital LLC; *U.S. Private*, pg. 3527
PHA CZECH S.R.O—See Pyeong Hwa Automotive Co., Ltd; *Int'l*, pg. 6127
PHADIA AB—See Thermo Fisher Scientific Inc.; *U.S. Public*, pg. 2147
PHADIA AG—See Thermo Fisher Scientific Inc.; *U.S. Public*, pg. 2147
PHADIA APS—See Thermo Fisher Scientific Inc.; *U.S. Public*, pg. 2147
PHADIA AS—See Thermo Fisher Scientific Inc.; *U.S. Public*, pg. 2153
PHADIA AUSTRIA GMBH—See Thermo Fisher Scientific Inc.; *U.S. Public*, pg. 2147
PHADIA B.V.—See Thermo Fisher Scientific Inc.; *U.S. Public*, pg. 2147
PHADIA DIAGNOSTICOS LTDA.—See Thermo Fisher Scientific Inc.; *U.S. Public*, pg. 2147
PHADIA GMBH—See Thermo Fisher Scientific Inc.; *U.S. Public*, pg. 2147
PHADIA K.K.—See Thermo Fisher Scientific Inc.; *U.S. Public*, pg. 2147
PHADIA KOREA CO. LTD.—See Thermo Fisher Scientific Inc.; *U.S. Public*, pg. 2147
PHADIA LTD.—See Thermo Fisher Scientific Inc.; *U.S. Public*, pg. 2147
PHADIA MULTIPLEXING DIAGNOSTICS GMBH—See Thermo Fisher Scientific Inc.; *U.S. Public*, pg. 2147
PHADIA NV/SA—See Thermo Fisher Scientific Inc.; *U.S. Public*, pg. 2147
PHADIA OY—See Thermo Fisher Scientific Inc.; *U.S. Public*, pg. 2148
PHADIA SOCIEDADE UNIPESSOAL LDA—See Thermo Fisher Scientific Inc.; *U.S. Public*, pg. 2148
PHADIA SOCIEDAD UNIPESSOAL LDA.—See Thermo Fisher Scientific Inc.; *U.S. Public*, pg. 2153
PHADIA SPAIN S.L.—See Thermo Fisher Scientific Inc.; *U.S. Public*, pg. 2148
PHADIA S.R.O.—See Thermo Fisher Scientific Inc.; *U.S. Public*, pg. 2148
PHADIA TAIWAN INC.—See Thermo Fisher Scientific Inc.; *U.S. Public*, pg. 2148
PHADIA US INC.—See Thermo Fisher Scientific Inc.; *U.S. Public*, pg. 2148
PHA EDSCHA LTD.—See Pyeong Hwa Automotive Co., Ltd; *Int'l*, pg. 6127
PHA E&E INC.—See Pyeong Hwa Automotive Co., Ltd; *Int'l*, pg. 6127
PHAGELUX, INC.; *Int'l*, pg. 5839
PHA INDIA (PVT), LTD.—See Pyeong Hwa Automotive Co., Ltd; *Int'l*, pg. 6127
PHALANXBIO, INC.—See Win Semiconductors Corp.; *Int'l*, pg. 8424
PHA LIMITED—See Grainger plc; *Int'l*, pg. 3052
PHANALEE ESTATE CO., LTD.—See Pruksa Real Estate Public Company Limited; *Int'l*, pg. 6010
PHANG-NGA FISHING CO., LTD—See Thai Union Group Public Company Limited; *Int'l*, pg. 7597
PHANSRI CO., LTD.—See United Palm Oil Industry Public Company Limited; *Int'l*, pg. 8072
PHANTOM DIGITAL EFFECTS LIMITED; *Int'l*, pg. 5839
PHANTOM EFX, LLC—See Light & Wonder, Inc.; *U.S. Public*, pg. 1315
PHANTOM INDUSTRIES INC; *Int'l*, pg. 5839
PHANTOM MFG. (INTL.) LTD.; *Int'l*, pg. 5839
PHANTOM SCREENS (MFG) AUSTRALIA PTY LTD—See Phantom Mfg. (Intl.) Ltd.; *Int'l*, pg. 5839
PHANTOM SCREENS (UK) LTD—See Phantom Mfg. (Intl.) Ltd.; *Int'l*, pg. 5839
PHANTOMS HOCKEY, LLC—See Comcast Corporation; *U.S. Public*, pg. 538
PHANTOM TECHNICAL SERVICES, INC.—See Hamilton Robinson LLC; *U.S. Private*, pg. 1848
PHAN VU INVESTMENT CORPORATION—See ASIA PILE HOLDINGS CORPORATION; *Int'l*, pg. 614
PHARAOH GOLD MINES NL—See Centamin plc; *Int'l*, pg. 1402
PHARMA AIDS LIMITED; *Int'l*, pg. 5839
PHARMABCINE INC.; *Int'l*, pg. 5840
PHARMA BELGIUM FLANDRIA—See McKesson Corporation; *U.S. Public*, pg. 1408
PHARMA BELGIUM SA—See McKesson Corporation; *U.S. Public*, pg. 1408
PHARMA-BIO SERV, INC.; *U.S. Public*, pg. 1684
PHARMA-BIO SERV LTD.—See PHARMA-BIO SERV, INC.; *U.S. Public*, pg. 1684
PHARMA-BIO SERV PR, INC.—See PHARMA-BIO SERV, INC.; *U.S. Public*, pg. 1684
PHARMA-BIO SERV, S.L.—See PHARMA-BIO SERV, INC.; *U.S. Public*, pg. 1684
PHARMA-BIO SERV US, INC.—See PHARMA-BIO SERV, INC.; *U.S. Public*, pg. 1684
PHARMABLOCK SCIENCES (NANJING), INC.; *Int'l*, pg. 5840
PHARMABLOCK (USA), INC.—See PharmaBlock Sciences (Nanjing), Inc.; *Int'l*, pg. 5840
PHARMACA INTEGRATIVE PHARMACY INC.; *U.S. Private*, pg. 3165
PHARMACARE LABORATORIES PTY. LTD.; *Int'l*, pg. 5840
PHARMACARE LLC; *U.S. Private*, pg. 3165
PHARMACARE LTD—See Aspen Pharmacare Holdings Limited; *Int'l*, pg. 629
PHARMACEUTICAL ASSOCIATES, INC.—See Beach Products, Inc.; *U.S. Private*, pg. 503
PHARMACEUTICAL CARE MANAGEMENT ASSOCIATION; *U.S. Private*, pg. 3165
PHARMACEUTICAL INSTITUTE, LLC—See Elliott Management Corporation; *U.S. Private*, pg. 1365
PHARMACEUTICAL INSTITUTE, LLC—See Patient Square Capital, L.P.; *U.S. Private*, pg. 3108
PHARMACEUTICAL INSTITUTE, LLC—See Veritas Capital Fund Management, LLC; *U.S. Private*, pg. 4365
PHARMACEUTICAL PRODUCT DEVELOPMENT, LLC - AUSTIN—See Thermo Fisher Scientific Inc.; *U.S. Public*, pg. 2150
PHARMACEUTICAL PRODUCT DEVELOPMENT, LLC - BLUE BELL—See Thermo Fisher Scientific Inc.; *U.S. Public*, pg. 2151
PHARMACEUTICAL PRODUCT DEVELOPMENT, LLC - HAMILTON—See Thermo Fisher Scientific Inc.; *U.S. Public*, pg. 2151
PHARMACEUTICAL PRODUCT DEVELOPMENT, LLC - MIDDLETON—See Thermo Fisher Scientific Inc.; *U.S. Public*, pg. 2151
PHARMACEUTICAL PRODUCT DEVELOPMENT, LLC - MORRISVILLE—See Thermo Fisher Scientific Inc.; *U.S. Public*, pg. 2151
PHARMACEUTICAL PRODUCT DEVELOPMENT, LLC - RICHMOND BIOANALYTICAL LABORATORY—See Thermo Fisher Scientific Inc.; *U.S. Public*, pg. 2151
PHARMACEUTICAL PRODUCT DEVELOPMENT, LLC - SAN DIEGO—See Thermo Fisher Scientific Inc.; *U.S. Public*, pg. 2151
PHARMACEUTICAL PRODUCT DEVELOPMENT SOUTH AFRICA (PROPRIETARY) LTD.—See Thermo Fisher Scientific Inc.; *U.S. Public*, pg. 2151
PHARMACEUTICAL PRODUCT DEVELOPMENT SPAIN SL—See Thermo Fisher Scientific Inc.; *U.S. Public*, pg. 2150
PHARMACEUTICAL RESEARCH ASSOCIATES ISRAEL LTD.—See ICON plc; *Int'l*, pg. 3585
PHARMACEUTICAL RESEARCH ASSOCIATES LTDA.—See ICON plc; *Int'l*, pg. 3586
PHARMACEUTICAL RESEARCH ASSOCIATES ROMANIA S.R.L.—See ICON plc; *Int'l*, pg. 3586
PHARMACEUTICAL RESEARCH ASSOCIATES TAIWAN, INC.—See ICON plc; *Int'l*, pg. 3586
PHARMACEUTICAL SPECIALTIES LLC—See Maxor National Pharmacy Services Corporation; *U.S. Private*, pg. 2619
PHARMACEUTIC LITHO & LABEL COMPANY, INC.—See Ares Management Corporation; *U.S. Public*, pg. 191
PHARMACHEMIE B.V.—See Teva Pharmaceutical Industries, Ltd.; *Int'l*, pg. 7580
PHARMACHEM LABORATORIES, LLC—See Ashland Inc.; *U.S. Public*, pg. 213
PHARMACIA LLC—See Pfizer Inc.; *U.S. Public*, pg. 1683
PHARMACIA (SOUTH AFRICA) (PTY) LTD—See Pfizer Inc.; *U.S. Public*, pg. 1683
PHARMACIA & UPJOHN LLC—See Pfizer Inc.; *U.S. Public*, pg. 1683
PHARMACIELO LTD.; *Int'l*, pg. 5840
PHARMACIES BENU S.A.—See PHOENIX Pharmahandel GmbH & Co. KG; *Int'l*, pg. 5854
PHARMACIN B.V.—See Aurobindo Pharma Ltd.; *Int'l*, pg. 712
THE PHARMACISTS LIFE INSURANCE COMPANY INC.—See Pharmacists Mutual Companies; *U.S. Private*, pg. 3165
PHARMACISTS MUTUAL COMPANIES; *U.S. Private*, pg. 3165
PHARMACISTS MUTUAL INSURANCE CO., INC.—See Pharmacists Mutual Companies; *U.S. Private*, pg. 3165
PHARMAC LTD.—See PNC Process Systems Co Ltd; *Int'l*, pg. 5900
PHARMACLUSTER CO., LTD.—See Toho Holdings Co., Ltd.; *Int'l*, pg. 7776
PHARMACOLOGY DISCOVERY SERVICES TAIWAN, LTD.—See Eurofins Scientific S.E.; *Int'l*, pg. 2551
PHARMACONTROL ELECTRONIC GMBH—See Mettler-Toledo International, Inc.; *U.S. Public*, pg. 1433
PHARMACO NZ LTD.; *Int'l*, pg. 5840
PHARMACORE, INC.—See Permira Advisers LLP; *Int'l*, pg. 5803
PHARMACOR PTY LIMITED—See Alkem Laboratories Ltd.; *Int'l*, pg. 330
PHARMACOS EXAKTA S.A. DE C.V.—See OPKO Health, Inc.; *U.S. Public*, pg. 1608
PHARMACOSMOS A/S; *Int'l*, pg. 5840
PHARMACOSMOS THERAPEUTICS INC.—See Pharmacosmos A/S; *Int'l*, pg. 5840

CORPORATE AFFILIATIONS

PHARMACY BUSINESS ASSOCIATION; *U.S. Private*, pg. 3165
PHARMACYCLICS LLC—See AbbVie Inc.; *U.S. Public*, pg. 24
PHARMACYCLICS (SHANGHAI) MANAGEMENT CONSULTING SERVICE LIMITED—See AbbVie Inc.; *U.S. Public*, pg. 24
THE PHARMACY DEVELOPMENT ACADEMY PROPRIETARY LIMITED—See Dis-Chem Pharmacies Ltd.; *Int'l*, pg. 2131
PHARMACY, INC.—See AdaptHealth Corp.; *U.S. Public*, pg. 39
PHARMACY ONESOURCE, INC.—See Wolters Kluwer n.v.; *Int'l*, pg. 8444
PHARMACY RETAILING NZ LIMITED—See EBOS Group Limited; *Int'l*, pg. 2285
PHARMACYTE BIOTECH, INC.; *U.S. Public*, pg. 1684
PHARMACY TECHNICIAN CERTIFICATION BOARD; *U.S. Private*, pg. 3165
PHARMACY WHOLESALERS (WELLINGTON) LIMITED—See Sigma Healthcare Ltd.; *Int'l*, pg. 6907
PHARMACY WON INC.; *Int'l*, pg. 5840
PHARMA DAIWA CO., LTD.—See Toho Holdings Co., Ltd.; *Int'l*, pg. 7776
PHARMA DEKO PLC; *Int'l*, pg. 5839
PHARMADERM LABORATORIES LTD.—See Helix Bio-Pharma Corp.; *Int'l*, pg. 3331
PHARMA DERM SAE CO.—See Emami Ltd; *Int'l*, pg. 2374
PHARMADERM—See Sandoz Group AG; *Int'l*, pg. 6527
PHARMADRUG INC.; *Int'l*, pg. 5840
PHARMADULE MORIMATSU AB—See Morimatsu International Holdings Company Limited; *Int'l*, pg. 5045
PHARMAENGINE, INC.; *Int'l*, pg. 5840
PHARMAESSENTIA ASIA (HONG KONG) LIMITED—See PharmaEssentia Corp.; *Int'l*, pg. 5840
PHARMAESSENTIA BIOTECHNOLOGY (BEIJING) LIMITED—See PharmaEssentia Corp.; *Int'l*, pg. 5840
PHARMAESSENTIA CORP.; *Int'l*, pg. 5840
PHARMAESSENTIA JAPAN KK—See PharmaEssentia Corp.; *Int'l*, pg. 5840
PHARMAESSENTIA KOREA CORPORATION—See PharmaEssentia Corp.; *Int'l*, pg. 5840
PHARMAESSENTIA USA CORPORATION—See PharmaEssentia Corp.; *Int'l*, pg. 5840
PHARMAFLORE SA—See Fagron NV; *Int'l*, pg. 2603
PHARMA FOODS INTERNATIONAL CO., LTD.; *Int'l*, pg. 5839
PHARMAFOODS PTY LTD—See Blackmores Limited; *Int'l*, pg. 1061
PHARMAFORCE INTERNATIONAL INC.—See Northlane Capital Partners, LLC; *U.S. Private*, pg. 2956
PHARMAGABON S.A.S.—See Toyota Tsusho Corporation; *Int'l*, pg. 7876
PHARMAGEST INTERACTIVE SA—See La Cooperative WELCOOP SA; *Int'l*, pg. 4387
PHARMAGG SYSTEMTECHNIK GMBH—See Hebert Kannegiesser GmbH; *Int'l*, pg. 3306
PHARMAGRA HOLDING COMPANY, LLC—See Zhejiang Jiuzhou Pharmaceutical Co., Ltd.; *Int'l*, pg. 8658
PHARMAGRA LABS INC.—See Zhejiang Jiuzhou Pharmaceutical Co., Ltd.; *Int'l*, pg. 8658
PHARMAHEALTH; *U.S. Private*, pg. 3165
PHARMAIDS PHARMACEUTICALS LIMITED; *Int'l*, pg. 5840
PHARMA INTELLIGENCE U.K. LIMITED—See Informa plc; *Int'l*, pg. 3693
PHARMA INTERNATIONAL S.A.—See Abbott Laboratories; *U.S. Public*, pg. 20
PHARMA IXIR CO. LTD.—See Hikma Pharmaceuticals PLC; *Int'l*, pg. 3390
PHARMALA BIOTECH HOLDINGS INC.; *Int'l*, pg. 5840
PHARMALEX GMBH—See AUCTUS Capital Partners AG; *Int'l*, pg. 700
PHARMALINK CONSULTING INC.—See Genpact Limited; *Int'l*, pg. 2927
PHARMALINK CONSULTING LTD.—See Genpact Limited; *Int'l*, pg. 2927
PHARMALINK CONSULTING OPERATIONS LTD.—See Genpact Limited; *Int'l*, pg. 2927
PHARMALINK CONSULTING OPERATIONS PVT. LTD.—See Genpact Limited; *Int'l*, pg. 2927
PHARMALINK CONSULTING PTE. LTD.—See Genpact Limited; *Int'l*, pg. 2927
PHARMALINK SP. Z O.O.—See CEPD N.V.; *Int'l*, pg. 1420
PHARM-ALLERGAN GMBH—See AbbVie Inc.; *U.S. Public*, pg. 23
PHARM-ALLERGAN GMBH—See AbbVie Inc.; *U.S. Public*, pg. 24
PHARMALLY INTERNATIONAL HOLDING CO., LTD.; *Int'l*, pg. 5840
PHARMALOGICALS RESEARCH PTE. LTD.—See Roche Holding AG; *Int'l*, pg. 6372
PHARMALOGIC HOLDINGS CORP.—See Webster Equity Partners, LLC; *U.S. Private*, pg. 4467
PHARMALOGICS RECRUITING LLC—See Webster Equity Partners, LLC; *U.S. Private*, pg. 4467
PHARMA LOGISTICS NV—See Deutsche Post AG; *Int'l*, pg. 2082

COMPANY NAME INDEX

PHARMALOZ MANUFACTURING INC.—See ProPhase Labs, Inc.; *U.S. Public*, pg. 1727
PHARMALUNDENSIS AB; *Int'l*, pg. 5840
PHARMA MAR S.A.U.—See Zeltia, S.A.; *Int'l*, pg. 8631
PHARMA MEDICA RESEARCH INC.—See Ontario Municipal Employees Retirement System; *Int'l*, pg. 5584
PHARMAMED INC.; *U.S. Private*, pg. 3165
PHARMANEST AB—See Karolinska Development AB; *Int'l*, pg. 4084
PHARMANEX, LLC—See Nu Skin Enterprises, Inc.; *U.S. Public*, pg. 1552
PHARMANIAGA BERHAD—See Lembaga Tabung Angkatan Tentera; *Int'l*, pg. 4448
PHARMANIAGA BIOMEDICAL SDN BHD—See Lembaga Tabung Angkatan Tentera; *Int'l*, pg. 4448
PHARMANIAGA BIOVENTION SDN BHD—See Lembaga Tabung Angkatan Tentera; *Int'l*, pg. 4448
PHARMANIAGA INTERNATIONAL CORPORATION SDN BHD—See Lembaga Tabung Angkatan Tentera; *Int'l*, pg. 4448
PHARMANIAGA LIFESCIENCE SDN BHD—See Lembaga Tabung Angkatan Tentera; *Int'l*, pg. 4448
PHARMANIAGA LOGISTICS SDN BHD-JURU—See Lembaga Tabung Angkatan Tentera; *Int'l*, pg. 4448
PHARMANIAGA LOGISTICS SDN BHD—See Lembaga Tabung Angkatan Tentera; *Int'l*, pg. 4448
PHARMANIAGA MANUFACTURING BERHAD—See Lembaga Tabung Angkatan Tentera; *Int'l*, pg. 4448
PHARMANIAGA MARKETING SDN BHD—See Lembaga Tabung Angkatan Tentera; *Int'l*, pg. 4448
PHARMANIAGA RESEARCH CENTRE SDN BHD—See Lembaga Tabung Angkatan Tentera; *Int'l*, pg. 4448
PHARMANUTRA S.P.A.; *Int'l*, pg. 5840
PHARMA PACIFIC MANAGEMENT PTY. LTD.—See Nufarm Limited; *Int'l*, pg. 5487
PHARMAPACKS, LLC—See Packable Holdings, LLC; *U.S. Private*, pg. 3072
PHARMAPAR INC.—See Strides Pharma Science Limited; *Int'l*, pg. 7240
PHARMAPOD LTD.—See Beedie Capital Partners; *Int'l*, pg. 939
PHARMAPOINT SP. Z O.O.—See Pelion S.A.; *Int'l*, pg. 5783
PHARMAPOLAR AS—See Volati AB; *Int'l*, pg. 8301
PHARMAPORTS LLC—See Chunghwa Chemical Synthesis & Biotech Co., Ltd.; *Int'l*, pg. 1598
PHARMAQ ANALYTIQ AS—See Zoetis, Inc.; *U.S. Public*, pg. 2409
PHARMAQ AS CHILE LIMITADA—See Zoetis, Inc.; *U.S. Public*, pg. 2409
PHARMAQ AS—See Zoetis, Inc.; *U.S. Public*, pg. 2409
PHARMAQ CA PANAMA INC.—See Zoetis, Inc.; *U.S. Public*, pg. 2409
PHARMAQ HONG KONG LIMITED—See Zoetis, Inc.; *U.S. Public*, pg. 2409
PHARMAQ LTD—See Zoetis, Inc.; *U.S. Public*, pg. 2409
PHARMAQ SPAIN AQUA SL—See Zoetis, Inc.; *U.S. Public*, pg. 2409
PHARMAQ VETERINAR ECZA DEPOSU VE SU URUNLERI TICARET LTD SKI—See Zoetis, Inc.; *U.S. Public*, pg. 2409
PHARMAQ VIETNAM COMPANY LIMITED—See Zoetis, Inc.; *U.S. Public*, pg. 2409
PHARMA RESEARCH BIO CO., LTD.; *Int'l*, pg. 5840
PHARMARESEARCH CO., LTD.; *Int'l*, pg. 5840
PHARMA RESEARCH TORONTO—See Roche Holding AG; *Int'l*, pg. 6373
PHARMARESOURCES (CHENGDU) CO., LTD.—See PharmaResources (Shanghai) Co., Ltd.; *Int'l*, pg. 5841
PHARMARESOURCES CMC CO., LTD.—See PharmaResources (Shanghai) Co., Ltd.; *Int'l*, pg. 5841
PHARMARESOURCES (KAIYUAN) CO., LTD.—See PharmaResources (Shanghai) Co., Ltd.; *Int'l*, pg. 5841
PHARMARESOURCES (SHANGHAI) CO., LTD.; *Int'l*, pg. 5841
PHARMAREVIEW LIMITED—See IQVIA Holdings Inc.; *U.S. Public*, pg. 1170
PHARMARISE HOLDINGS CORPORATION; *Int'l*, pg. 5841
PHARMARON BEIJING CO., LTD.; *Int'l*, pg. 5841
PHARMARON, INC.—See Pharmaron Beijing Co., Ltd.; *Int'l*, pg. 5841
PHARMARON - RADIOLABELLED SCIENCES—See Pharmaron Beijing Co., Ltd.; *Int'l*, pg. 5841
PHARMASAVE ALBERTA DIVISION—See Pharmasave Drugs (National) Ltd.; *Int'l*, pg. 5841
PHARMASAVE ATLANTIC CANADA DIVISION—See Pharmasave Drugs (National) Ltd.; *Int'l*, pg. 5841
PHARMASAVE BRITISH COLUMBIA DIVISION—See Pharmasave Drugs (National) Ltd.; *Int'l*, pg. 5841
PHARMASAVE CENTRAL DIVISION—See Pharmasave Drugs (National) Ltd.; *Int'l*, pg. 5841
PHARMASAVE DRUGS (NATIONAL) LTD.; *Int'l*, pg. 5841
PHARMASAVE DRUGS (PACIFIC) LTD.—See Pharmasave Drugs (National) Ltd.; *Int'l*, pg. 5841
PHARMASAVE ONTARIO DIVISION—See Pharmasave Drugs (National) Ltd.; *Int'l*, pg. 5841
PHARMASCENT—See IT Ascent, Inc.; *U.S. Private*, pg. 2148
PHARMASCIENCE INC.; *Int'l*, pg. 5841
PHARMAS D.O.O.—See LURA Grupa doo; *Int'l*, pg. 4586
PHARMASERV ALLIANCES SDN BHD—See KPJ Healthcare Berhad; *Int'l*, pg. 4297
PHARMASERVE-LILLY S.A.C.I.—See Eli Lilly & Company; *U.S. Public*, pg. 733
PHARMASERVICE AB—See ITAB Shop Concept AB; *Int'l*, pg. 3828
PHARMASERVICE AS—See ITAB Shop Concept AB; *Int'l*, pg. 3828
PHARMASGP HOLDING SE; *Int'l*, pg. 5841
PHARMASIENA SERVICE S.R.L.—See I.M.A. Industria Macchine Automatiche S.p.A.; *Int'l*, pg. 3566
PHARMASIMPLE SA; *Int'l*, pg. 5841
PHARMASITE RESEARCH INC.—See KKR & Co. Inc.; *U.S. Public*, pg. 1252
PHARMASMART INTERNATIONAL INC; *U.S. Private*, pg. 3165
PHARMASOL CORPORATION; *U.S. Private*, pg. 3165
PHARMA SQUARE CO. LTD.—See Toho Holdings Co., Ltd.; *Int'l*, pg. 7776
PHARM ASSESS, INC.—See BlackRock, Inc.; *U.S. Public*, pg. 347
PHARMASTOCK—See Cegedim S.A.; *Int'l*, pg. 1390
PHARMA STRIDES CANADA CORPORATION—See Strides Pharma Science Limited; *Int'l*, pg. 7240
PHARMASWISS BH D.O.O.—See Bausch Health Companies Inc.; *Int'l*, pg. 897
PHARMASWISS CESKA REPUBLIKA S.R.O.—See Bausch Health Companies Inc.; *Int'l*, pg. 897
PHARMASWISS DOO—See Bausch Health Companies Inc.; *Int'l*, pg. 897
PHARMASWISS D.O.O.—See Bausch Health Companies Inc.; *Int'l*, pg. 897
PHARMASWISS DRUSTVO S OGRANICENOM ODGOVORNOSCU ZA TRGOVINU I USLUGE—See Bausch Health Companies Inc.; *Int'l*, pg. 897
PHARMASWISS HELLAS S.A.—See Bausch Health Companies Inc.; *Int'l*, pg. 897
PHARMASWISS S.A.—See Bausch Health Companies Inc.; *Int'l*, pg. 897
PHARMASYNTHESE S.A.S.—See Inabata & Co. Ltd.; *Int'l*, pg. 3644
PHARMATEC GMBH—See Robert Bosch GmbH; *Int'l*, pg. 6361
PHARMATECH, INC.—See Caris Life Sciences, Ltd.; *U.S. Private*, pg. 761
PHARMA TECH INDUSTRIES INC.; *U.S. Private*, pg. 3165
PHARMATEK PMC S.R.L.—See Fine Foods & Pharmaceuticals N.T.M. S.p.A.; *Int'l*, pg. 2673
PHARMATEL FRESENIUS KABI PTY LTD—See Fresenius SE & Co. KGaA; *Int'l*, pg. 2778
PHARMATHENE US CORPORATION—See Altimmune, Inc; *U.S. Public*, pg. 88
PHARMATON S.A.—See C.H. Boehringer Sohn AG & Co. KG; *Int'l*, pg. 1241
PHARMAUST LTD.; *Int'l*, pg. 5841
PHARMAVET MAROC S.A.—See Merck & Co., Inc.; *U.S. Public*, pg. 1420
PHARMAVITE LLC - BENTONVILLE—See Otsuka Holdings Co., Ltd.; *Int'l*, pg. 5660
PHARMAVITE LLC—See Otsuka Holdings Co., Ltd.; *Int'l*, pg. 5660
PHARMA WALDHOF GMBH—See Aceto Corporation; *U.S. Private*, pg. 58
PHARMAWORKS INC.; *U.S. Private*, pg. 3165
PHARMAXIS LTD.; *Int'l*, pg. 5841
PHARMAXIS PHARMACEUTICALS LIMITED—See Pharmaxis Ltd.; *Int'l*, pg. 5841
PHARMAX LIMITED; *Int'l*, pg. 5841
PHARMAZAM S.A.—See Zambon Company S.p.A.; *Int'l*, pg. 8622
PHARMAZELL GMBH—See Groupe Bruxelles Lambert SA; *Int'l*, pg. 3099
PHARMAZELL GMBH—See Parcom Capital Management B.V.; *Int'l*, pg. 5739
PHARMAZEN MEDICALS PTE. LTD.—See Meiji Holdings Co., Ltd.; *Int'l*, pg. 4801
PHARMCO-AAPER—See GreenField Specialty Alcohols Inc.; *Int'l*, pg. 3074
PHARMCON, INC.—See Moelis Asset Management LP; *U.S. Public*, pg. 2764
PHARMDATA S.R.O.—See Walgreens Boots Alliance, Inc.; *U.S. Public*, pg. 2322
PHARMEDIC PHARMACEUTICAL MEDICINAL JSC; *Int'l*, pg. 5841
PHARMEDIUM SERVICES, LLC—See Cencora, Inc.; *U.S. Public*, pg. 467
PHARMENA S.A.—See CEPD N.V.; *Int'l*, pg. 1420
PHARMERICA CORPORATION—See KKR & Co. Inc.; *U.S. Public*, pg. 1262
PHARMESIS INTERNATIONAL LTD.; *Int'l*, pg. 5842
PHARMETICS - BURLINGTON OPERATIONS—See Monitor Clipper Partners, LLC; *U.S. Public*, pg. 2771
PHARMETICS, INC.—See Monitor Clipper Partners, LLC; *U.S. Public*, pg. 2771
PHARMEXX UK LTD.—See Clayton, Dubilier & Rice, LLC; *U.S. Public*, pg. 928
PHARMGATE LLC—See Jinhe Biotechnology Co., Ltd.; *Int'l*, pg. 3968
PHARMGEN SCIENCE INC.; *Int'l*, pg. 5842
PHARMHOLD AD; *Int'l*, pg. 5842
PHARMICELL CO., LTD.; *Int'l*, pg. 5842
PHARMICELL CO., LTD. - ULSAN PLANT—See PHARMICELL CO., LTD.; *Int'l*, pg. 5842
PHARMING GROUP N.V.; *Int'l*, pg. 5842
PHARMIVA AB—See Peptonic Medical AB; *Int'l*, pg. 5795
PHARMLOG PHARMA LOGISTIK GMBH—See GSK plc; *Int'l*, pg. 3149
PHARM-MART PHARMACY OF WARREN, INC.—See Walgreens Boots Alliance, Inc.; *U.S. Public*, pg. 2323
PHARMMD SOLUTIONS, LLC—See The Riverside Company; *U.S. Public*, pg. 4110
PHARMOCANN GLOBAL LTD.; *Int'l*, pg. 5842
PHARMOPTIMA, LLC—See Genesis Biotechnology Group, LLC; *U.S. Public*, pg. 1669
PHARMORAGE PTY. LIMITED—See Noxopharm Limited; *Int'l*, pg. 5472
PHARMORE INGREDIENTS INC.; *U.S. Private*, pg. 3166
PHARM PLUS ACQUISITION, INC.—See Cencora, Inc.; *U.S. Public*, pg. 467
PHARMSTANDARD-UFAVITA JSC—See JSC Pharmstandard; *Int'l*, pg. 4010
PHARMSVILLE CO., LTD.; *Int'l*, pg. 5842
PHARMSYNTHEZ PJSC; *Int'l*, pg. 5842
PHARNEXT SAS; *Int'l*, pg. 5842
PHAROL SGPS, S.A.; *Int'l*, pg. 5842
PHAROS CAPITAL GROUP, LLC; *U.S. Private*, pg. 3166
PHAROS ENERGY PLC; *Int'l*, pg. 5842
PHAROS IBIO CO., LTD.; *Int'l*, pg. 5842
PHARR R.V 'S, INC.; *U.S. Private*, pg. 3166
PHARUMO, INC.—See MTI Ltd.; *Int'l*, pg. 5070
PHARVARIS N.V.; *Int'l*, pg. 5842
PHASE 1 TECHNOLOGY CORP.; *U.S. Private*, pg. 3166
PHASE 2 COMPANY; *U.S. Private*, pg. 3166
PHASE2 TECHNOLOGY, LLC; *U.S. Private*, pg. 3166
PHASE 3 MEDIA, LLC; *U.S. Private*, pg. 3166
PHASE 3 TECHNOLOGIES INC.—See NCAB Group AB; *Int'l*, pg. 5180
PHASE ANALYZER COMPANY LTD.—See Roper Technologies, Inc.; *U.S. Public*, pg. 1812
PHASEBIO PHARMACEUTICALS, INC.; *U.S. Public*, pg. 1684
PHASECOM, INC.; *U.S. Private*, pg. 3166
PHASE EIGHT (FASHION & DESIGNS) LIMITED—See The Foschini Group Limited; *Int'l*, pg. 7643
PHASE ELECTRONICS LTD.—See Everspring Industry Co., Ltd.; *Int'l*, pg. 2569
PHASE FIVE COMMUNICATIONS—See WPP plc; *Int'l*, pg. 8470
PHASE FORWARD EUROPE LIMITED—See Oracle Corporation; *U.S. Public*, pg. 1613
PHASE FORWARD PTY LIMITED—See Oracle Corporation; *U.S. Public*, pg. 1613
PHASE HOLOGRAPHIC IMAGING PHI AB; *Int'l*, pg. 5842
PHASE II PRODUCTS INC.; *U.S. Private*, pg. 3166
PHASE LINEAR—See VOXX International Corporation; *U.S. Public*, pg. 2311
PHASE MATRIX, INC.—See National Instruments Corporation; *U.S. Private*, pg. 2858
PHASERX, INC.; *U.S. Private*, pg. 3166
PHASES ACCOUNTING & TAX SERVICES—See Apex Accounting And Tax, Inc.; *U.S. Public*, pg. 291
PHA SLOVAKIA S.R.O.—See Pyeong Hwa Automotive Co., Ltd; *Int'l*, pg. 6127
PHASOR ENGINEERING INC.—See Quanta Services, Inc.; *U.S. Public*, pg. 1753
PHASYA S.A.—See Tobii AB; *Int'l*, pg. 7771
PHAT DAT INDUSTRIAL PARK INVESTMENT & DEVELOPMENT JSC—See Phat Dat Real Estate Development Corporation; *Int'l*, pg. 5842
PHAT DAT REAL ESTATE DEVELOPMENT CORPORATION; *Int'l*, pg. 5842
PHAT FASHIONS, LLC—See Sun Capital Partners, Inc.; *U.S. Private*, pg. 3859
PHATHOM PHARMACEUTICALS, INC.; *U.S. Public*, pg. 1684
PHATISA GROUP LIMITED; *Int'l*, pg. 5842
PHAT PANDA LLC; *U.S. Private*, pg. 3166
PHATRA ASSET MANAGEMENT COMPANY LIMITED—See Kiatnakin Bank Public Company Limited; *Int'l*, pg. 4157
PHATRA CAPITAL PUBLIC COMPANY LIMITED—See Kiatnakin Bank Public Company Limited; *Int'l*, pg. 4157
PHATRA LEASING PUBLIC COMPANY LIMITED; *Int'l*, pg. 5843
PHATRA SECURITIES PUBLIC COMPANY LIMITED—See Kiatnakin Bank Public Company Limited; *Int'l*, pg. 4157
PHA USA, LLC—See Pyeong Hwa Automotive Co., Ltd; *Int'l*, pg. 6127
PHAXIAM THERAPEUTICS S.A.; *Int'l*, pg. 5843
PHAZAR ANTENNA CORP.—See Phazar Corp.; *U.S. Private*, pg. 3166
PHAZAR CORP.; *U.S. Private*, pg. 3166
PH BEAUTY LABS, INC.—See Yellow Wood Partners LLC; *U.S. Public*, pg. 4587
PHB INC.; *U.S. Private*, pg. 3166

PHB INC. — CORPORATE AFFILIATIONS

Company Index

PHB MACHINING DIVISION—See PHB Inc.; *U.S. Private*, pg. 3166
PHB MOLDING DIVISION—See PHB Inc.; *U.S. Private*, pg. 3167
PHB TOOL & DIE—See PHB Inc.; *U.S. Private*, pg. 3167
PH BYG FAABORG A/S—See Per Aarsleff Holding A/S; *Int'l*, pg. 5796
P.H. CAPITAL LIMITED; *Int'l*, pg. 5682
PHC CO., LTD; *Int'l*, pg. 5843
PHC CORPORATION—See PHC Holdings Corporation; *Int'l*, pg. 5843
PHC-FORT MOHAVE, INC.—See Apollo Global Management, Inc.; *U.S. Public*, pg. 158
PHC HOLDINGS CORPORATION; *Int'l*, pg. 5843
PHC HOTELS SDN. BHD.—See Aspial Corporation Limited; *Int'l*, pg. 630
PHC-LOS ALAMOS, INC.—See Apollo Global Management, Inc.; *U.S. Public*, pg. 158
PHC MEADOWWOOD, LLC—See Acadia Healthcare Company, Inc.; *U.S. Public*, pg. 29
PHC MEDICAL DIAGNOSTIC CENTRE LIMITED—See China Biotech Services Holdings Limited; *Int'l*, pg. 1487
PHC-MINDEN, L.P.—See Apollo Global Management, Inc.; *U.S. Public*, pg. 158
PHC OF MICHIGAN, INC.—See Acadia Healthcare Company, Inc.; *U.S. Public*, pg. 29
PHC OF NEVADA, INC.—See Acadia Healthcare Company, Inc.; *U.S. Public*, pg. 29
PHC OF UTAH, INC.—See Acadia Healthcare Company, Inc.; *U.S. Public*, pg. 29
PHC OF VIRGINIA, INC.—See Acadia Healthcare Company, Inc.; *U.S. Public*, pg. 29
PH COPPER COUNTRY APOTHECARIES, LLC—See Apollo Global Management, Inc.; *U.S. Public*, pg. 158
PHD CANADA—See Omnicom Group Inc.; *U.S. Public*, pg. 1590
PHD CHICAGO—See Omnicom Group Inc.; *U.S. Public*, pg. 1589
PHD CHINA—See Omnicom Group Inc.; *U.S. Public*, pg. 1589
PHD DETROIT—See Omnicom Group Inc.; *U.S. Public*, pg. 1589
PHD INC.; *U.S. Private*, pg. 3167
PHD LOS ANGELES—See Omnicom Group Inc.; *U.S. Public*, pg. 1589
PHD MANUFACTURING INC.; *U.S. Private*, pg. 3167
PHD MEDIA UK—See Omnicom Group Inc.; *U.S. Public*, pg. 1590
PHD NEW YORK—See Omnicom Group Inc.; *U.S. Public*, pg. 1590
PHD NEW ZEALAND—See Omnicom Group Inc.; *U.S. Public*, pg. 1590
PHD SAN FRANCISCO—See Omnicom Group Inc.; *U.S. Public*, pg. 1590
PHD—See Omnicom Group Inc.; *U.S. Public*, pg. 1589
PHD TORONTO—See Omnicom Group Inc.; *U.S. Public*, pg. 1590
PHEASANT LANE MALL MANAGEMENT—See S.R. Weiner & Associates Inc.; *U.S. Private*, pg. 3518
PHEDINA HYPOTHEKEN 2010 BV—See BNP Paribas SA; *Int'l*, pg. 1092
PHELIA, LLC—See Hawk Auto Group; *U.S. Private*, pg. 1882
PHELPS DODGE INTERNATIONAL CORPORATION—See Prysmian S.p.A.; *Int'l*, pg. 6011
PHELPS DODGE INTERNATIONAL PHILIPPINES, INC.—See Prysmian S.p.A.; *Int'l*, pg. 6011
PHELPS DODGE INTERNATIONAL (THAILAND) LIMITED—See Prysmian S.p.A.; *Int'l*, pg. 6011
PHELPS DODGE NATIONAL CABLES CORPORATION—See Prysmian S.p.A.; *Int'l*, pg. 6011
PHELPS DODGE PHILIPPINES ENERGY PRODUCTS CORPORATION—See Prysmian S.p.A.; *Int'l*, pg. 6011
PHELPS DODGE YANTAI CABLE CO., LTD.—See Prysmian S.p.A.; *Int'l*, pg. 6011
PHELPS DRILLING CO.—See Patterson-UTI Energy, Inc.; *U.S. Public*, pg. 1654
PHELPS DUNBAR LLP; *U.S. Private*, pg. 3167
THE PHELPS GROUP; *U.S. Private*, pg. 4094
PHELPS IMPLEMENT CORPORATION; *U.S. Private*, pg. 3167
PHELPS MEMORIAL HEALTH CENTER; *U.S. Private*, pg. 3167
PHELPS MEMORIAL HOSPITAL CENTER; *U.S. Private*, pg. 3167
PHELPS TOINTON INC.; *U.S. Private*, pg. 3167
PHEM TECHNOLOGIES S.A.—See Orapi S.A.; *Int'l*, pg. 5612
PHEND & BROWN INC.; *U.S. Private*, pg. 3167
PHENITEC SEMICONDUCTOR CORP - 1ST FACTORY—See Torex Semiconductor Ltd.; *Int'l*, pg. 7827
PHENITEC SEMICONDUCTOR CORP—See Torex Semiconductor Ltd.; *Int'l*, pg. 7827
PHENITEC SEMICONDUCTOR - KAGOSHIMA FACTORY—See Torex Semiconductor Ltd.; *Int'l*, pg. 7827
PHENIX COMPAGNIE D'ASSURANCES—See Allianz SE; *Int'l*, pg. 342

PHENIXCOM SA; *Int'l*, pg. 5843
PHENIXFIN CORP.; *U.S. Public*, pg. 1684
PHENIX GOURMET, LLC.; *U.S. Private*, pg. 3167
PHENIXID AB—See Clavister Holding AB; *Int'l*, pg. 1653
PHENIX JET HONG KONG, LTD.—See Sojitz Corporation; *Int'l*, pg. 7063
PHENIX JET INTERNATIONAL, LLC—See Sojitz Corporation; *Int'l*, pg. 7063
PHENIX OPTICAL COMPANY LIMITED; *Int'l*, pg. 5843
PHENIX OPTICS JAPAN CO., LTD.—See Phenix Optical Company Limited; *Int'l*, pg. 5843
PHENIX-ROUSIES INDUSTRIES, S.A.—See Chief Industries, Inc.; *U.S. Private*, pg. 881
PHENIX SALON LLC; *U.S. Private*, pg. 3167
PHENIX SALON SUITES FRANCHISING LLC—See Phenix Salon LLC; *U.S. Private*, pg. 3167
PHENIX SUPPLY COMPANY INC.; *U.S. Private*, pg. 3167
PHENIX SYSTEMS SA—See 3D Systems Corporation; *U.S. Public*, pg. 4
PHENIX TECHNOLOGY, INC.—See ESCO Technologies, Inc.; *U.S. Public*, pg. 794
PHENOMENA MOTION PICTURES CO. LTD—See GMM Grammy Public Company Limited; *Int'l*, pg. 3013
PHENOMENEX, INC.—See Danaher Corporation; *U.S. Public*, pg. 630
PHENOMENON; *U.S. Private*, pg. 3167
PHENOM RESOURCES CORP.; *Int'l*, pg. 5843
PHENOPATH LABORATORIES, PLLC—See Quest Diagnostics, Inc.; *U.S. Public*, pg. 1755
PHERECYDES PHARMA SA—See PHAXIAM Therapeutics S.A.; *Int'l*, pg. 5843
PHERIN PHARMACEUTICALS, INC.—See VistaGen Therapeutics, Inc.; *U.S. Public*, pg. 2305
PHERMPEP BIOTECHNOLOGY CO., LTD.—See China Chemical & Pharmaceutical Co., Ltd.; *Int'l*, pg. 1488
PHETHAI ASSET MANAGEMENT CO. LTD.—See Kasikornbank Public Company Limited; *Int'l*, pg. 4087
P. H. GLATFELTER COMPANY—See Glatfelter Corporation; *U.S. Public*, pg. 939
PHH CORPORATION—See Onity Group Inc.; *U.S. Public*, pg. 1604
PHH HOME LOANS, LLC—See Onity Group Inc.; *U.S. Public*, pg. 1605
PHH INVESTMENTS, LTD.; *U.S. Private*, pg. 3167
PHH MORTGAGE CAPITAL LLC—See Onity Group Inc.; *U.S. Public*, pg. 1605
PHH MORTGAGE CORPORATION—See Onity Group Inc.; *U.S. Public*, pg. 1605
THE PHIA GROUP LLC; *U.S. Private*, pg. 4094
PHI AIR MEDICAL, L.L.C.—See PHI, Inc.; *U.S. Private*, pg. 3168
PHI ASSET MANAGEMENT PARTNERS SGEIC S.A. - BARCELONA—See PHI Asset Management Partners SGEIC S.A.; *Int'l*, pg. 5843
PHI ASSET MANAGEMENT PARTNERS SGEIC S.A.; *Int'l*, pg. 5843
PHIBOR ENTREPRISES—See VINCI S.A.; *Int'l*, pg. 8237
PHIBRO ANIMAL HEALTH CORPORATION; *U.S. Public*, pg. 1684
PHIBRO ANIMAL HEALTH DE ARGENTINA SRL—See Phibro Animal Health Corporation; *U.S. Public*, pg. 1685
PHIBRO ANIMAL HEALTH LTD.—See Phibro Animal Health Corporation; *U.S. Public*, pg. 1685
PHIBRO ANIMAL HEALTH LTD.—See Phibro Animal Health Corporation; *U.S. Public*, pg. 1685
PHIBRO ANIMAL HEALTH (PROPRIETARY) LIMITED—See Phibro Animal Health Corporation; *U.S. Public*, pg. 1685
PHIBRO ANIMAL PTY LIMITED—See Phibro Animal Health Corporation; *U.S. Public*, pg. 1685
PHIBRO HAYVAN SAGLIGI URUNLERI SANAYI VE TICARET A.S.—See Phibro Animal Health Corporation; *U.S. Public*, pg. 1685
PHIBRO LLC; *U.S. Private*, pg. 3168
PHIBRO-TECH, INC.—See Phibro Animal Health Corporation; *U.S. Public*, pg. 1685
PHI CAPITAL HOLDINGS, INC.—See Philux Global Group Inc; *U.S. Public*, pg. 1689
PHICHEM AMERICA, INC.—See PhiChem Corporation; *Int'l*, pg. 5844
PHICHEM CORPORATION; *Int'l*, pg. 5844
PHIDEB PARTNERSHIP; *U.S. Private*, pg. 3168
P.H.I. DIVISION—See Tulip Corporation; *U.S. Private*, pg. 4257
PHIDS, INC.; *U.S. Private*, pg. 3168
PHIFER WIRE PRODUCTS INC.; *U.S. Private*, pg. 3168
PHI GROUP - RETAINING STRUCTURES—See Keller Group plc; *Int'l*, pg. 4120
PHIHONG TECHNOLOGY CO., LTD.; *Int'l*, pg. 5844
PHIHONG TECHNOLOGY JAPAN CO., LTD.—See Phihong Technology Co., Ltd.; *Int'l*, pg. 5844
PHIHONG USA CORP.—See Phihong Technology Co., Ltd.; *Int'l*, pg. 5844
PHIHONG VIETNAM CO., LTD.—See Phihong Technology Co., Ltd.; *Int'l*, pg. 5844
PHI, INC.; *U.S. Private*, pg. 3168
PHILADELPHIA 76ERS, L.P.; *U.S. Private*, pg. 3168

PHILADELPHIA AMERICAN LIFE INSURANCE—See New Era Life Insurance Company of the Midwest; *U.S. Private*, pg. 2896
PHILADELPHIA AVENUE ASSOCIATES—See Welltower Inc.; *U.S. Public*, pg. 2349
PHILADELPHIA BEER WORKS INC.; *U.S. Private*, pg. 3168
THE PHILADELPHIA BOURSE, INC.; *U.S. Private*, pg. 4094
PHILADELPHIA-CAMDEN INTEGRATED KIDNEY CARE, LLC.—See DaVita Inc.; *U.S. Public*, pg. 642
PHILADELPHIA CHEESESTEAK COMPANY—See Tyson Foods, Inc.; *U.S. Public*, pg. 2210
PHILADELPHIA COCA-COLA BOTTLING CO.—See The Coca-Cola Company; *U.S. Public*, pg. 2065
PHILADELPHIA CONSOLIDATED HOLDING CORPORATION—See Tokio Marine Holdings, Inc.; *Int'l*, pg. 7782
THE PHILADELPHIA CONTRIBUTIONSHIP; *U.S. Private*, pg. 4094
PHILADELPHIA COUNTRY CLUB; *U.S. Private*, pg. 3168
PHILADELPHIA CRICKET CLUB; *U.S. Private*, pg. 3168
PHILADELPHIA CRISIS RESPONSE CENTER, LLC—See Acadia Healthcare Company, Inc.; *U.S. Public*, pg. 29
PHILADELPHIA DAILY NEWS—See Philadelphia Media Holdings, LLC; *U.S. Private*, pg. 3169
PHILADELPHIA EAGLES FOOTBALL CLUB, INC.; *U.S. Private*, pg. 3168
PHILADELPHIA ENERGY SOLUTIONS INC.—See Energy Transfer LP; *U.S. Public*, pg. 764
PHILADELPHIA ENERGY SOLUTIONS, LLC—See Energy Transfer LP; *U.S. Public*, pg. 764
PHILADELPHIA FEDERATION OF TEACHERS HEALTH AND WELFARE FUND; *U.S. Private*, pg. 3169
PHILADELPHIA FIGHT; *U.S. Private*, pg. 3169
PHILADELPHIA FINANCIAL GROUP, INC.—See Blackstone Inc.; *U.S. Public*, pg. 356
PHILADELPHIA FLYERS, LLC—See Comcast Corporation; *U.S. Public*, pg. 538
PHILADELPHIA FLYERS, L.P.—See Comcast Corporation; *U.S. Public*, pg. 538
PHILADELPHIA FOODS INC.; *U.S. Private*, pg. 3169
THE PHILADELPHIA FOUNDATION; *U.S. Private*, pg. 4094
PHILADELPHIA GEAR CORPORATION—See The Timken Company; *U.S. Public*, pg. 2133
PHILADELPHIA INDEMNITY INSURANCE COMPANY—See Tokio Marine Holdings, Inc.; *Int'l*, pg. 7783
PHILADELPHIA INDUSTRIES, INC.—See IG Design Group Plc; *Int'l*, pg. 3600
THE PHILADELPHIA INQUIRER—See Philadelphia Media Holdings, LLC; *U.S. Private*, pg. 3169
PHILADELPHIA INSURANCE COMPANIES—See Tokio Marine Holdings, Inc.; *Int'l*, pg. 7783
PHILADELPHIA INSURANCE COMPANY LTD.; *Int'l*, pg. 5844
PHILADELPHIA INTERNATIONAL EDUCATIONAL INVESTMENT COMPANY PLC; *Int'l*, pg. 5844
PHILADELPHIA MACARONI CO. INC.; *U.S. Private*, pg. 3169
PHILADELPHIA MEDIA HOLDINGS, LLC; *U.S. Private*, pg. 3169
PHILADELPHIA MIXING SOLUTIONS LTD.—See Lone Star Funds; *U.S. Private*, pg. 2485
PHILADELPHIA MUSEUM OF ART; *U.S. Private*, pg. 3169
PHILADELPHIA NEWSPAPERS, LLC—See Philadelphia Media Holdings, LLC; *U.S. Private*, pg. 3169
THE PHILADELPHIA ORCHESTRA ASSOCIATION; *U.S. Private*, pg. 4094
THE PHILADELPHIA ORCHESTRA—See The Philadelphia Orchestra Association; *U.S. Private*, pg. 4094
THE PHILADELPHIA PALM—See Palm Restaurant Group; *U.S. Private*, pg. 3080
PHILADELPHIA PARENT CHILD CENTER; *U.S. Private*, pg. 3169
THE PHILADELPHIA PARKING AUTHORITY INC.; *U.S. Private*, pg. 4094
PHILADELPHIA PHARMACEUTICALS; *Int'l*, pg. 5844
PHILADELPHIA PRE-COOKED STEAK, INC.—See Tyson Foods, Inc.; *U.S. Public*, pg. 2210
PHILADELPHIA PRISON SYSTEM; *U.S. Private*, pg. 3169
THE PHILADELPHIA PROTESTANT HOME; *U.S. Private*, pg. 4094
PHILADELPHIA RESERVE SUPPLY COMPANY; *U.S. Private*, pg. 3169
PHILADELPHIA SIGN COMPANY - LITTLETON PLANT—See Philadelphia Sign Company; *U.S. Private*, pg. 3169
PHILADELPHIA SIGN COMPANY; *U.S. Private*, pg. 3169
PHILADELPHIA SKATING CLUB & HUMANE SOCIETY; *U.S. Private*, pg. 3169
PHILADELPHIA WEEKLY—See Broad Street Media, LLC; *U.S. Public*, pg. 658
PHILAGRO FRANCE S.A.S.—See Sumitomo Chemical Company, Limited; *Int'l*, pg. 7266
PHILAGRO SOUTH AFRICA (PTY) LTD.—See Sumitomo Chemical Company, Limited; *Int'l*, pg. 7264

COMPANY NAME INDEX

PHILIPPOS NAKAS S.A.

Company Index

PHILANTHROPIC VENTURES FOUNDATION; *U.S. Private*, pg. 3169

PHILCEMENT CORPORATION—See PHINMA Corporation; *Int'l*, pg. 5848

PHILCO HOLDINGS INC.—See Rizal Resources Corporation; *Int'l*, pg. 6354

PHIL COMPANY, INC.; *Int'l*, pg. 5844

PHILCOMSAT HOLDINGS CORPORATION; *Int'l*, pg. 5844

PHILCORR LLC—See McLean Packaging Corporation; *U.S. Private*, pg. 2641

PHIL DILL BOATS, INC.—See Singleton Marine Group; *U.S. Private*, pg. 3670

PHILENERGY CO., LTD.; *Int'l*, pg. 5844

PHILEO 303 COLLINS PTY LTD—See Phileo Australia Limited; *Int'l*, pg. 5844

PHILEO AUSTRALIA LIMITED; *Int'l*, pg. 5844

PHILEQUITY MANAGEMENT, INC.—See Vantage Equities, Inc.; *Int'l*, pg. 8130

PHILEX MINING CORPORATION; *Int'l*, pg. 5844

PHIL-GOOD PRODUCTS INCORPORATED; *U.S. Public*, pg. 1685

PHILHARMONIC SYMPHONY SOCIETY OF NEW YORK INC.; *U.S. Private*, pg. 3169

PHIL HUGHES AUTO SALES INC.; *U.S. Private*, pg. 3168

PHILIBERT SARL—See Carrefour SA; *Int'l*, pg. 1346

PHILILPS LIFELINE—See Koninklijke Philips N.V.; *Int'l*, pg. 4270

PHILION SE; *Int'l*, pg. 5845

PHILI-ORIENT AIRFREIGHT (MALAYSIA) SDN BHD—See Phili-Orient Lines (Penang) Sdn. Bhd.; *Int'l*, pg. 5844

PHILI-ORIENT AIRFREIGHT (PENANG) SDN BHD—See Phili-Orient Lines (Penang) Sdn. Bhd.; *Int'l*, pg. 5844

PHILI-ORIENT LINES (PENANG) SDN. BHD.; *Int'l*, pg. 5844

PHILIP/ANDREWS DESIGN; *U.S. Private*, pg. 3170

PHILIP LEONG STORES PTY LIMITED—See Woolworths Group Limited; *Int'l*, pg. 8452

PHILIP MORRIS APS—See Philip Morris International Inc.; *U.S. Public*, pg. 1685

PHILIP MORRIS ARMENIA LIMITED LIABILITY COMPANY—See Philip Morris International Inc.; *U.S. Public*, pg. 1686

PHILIP MORRIS ASIA LIMITED—See Philip Morris International Inc.; *U.S. Public*, pg. 1000

PHILIP MORRIS (AUSTRALIA) LTD—See Philip Morris International Inc.; *U.S. Public*, pg. 1685

PHILIP MORRIS AUSTRIA GMBH—See Philip Morris International Inc.; *U.S. Public*, pg. 1686

PHILIP MORRIS BENELUX B.V.B.A.—See Philip Morris International Inc.; *U.S. Public*, pg. 1686

PHILIP MORRIS BRANDS S.A.R.L.—See Philip Morris International Inc.; *U.S. Public*, pg. 1686

PHILIP MORRIS BRASIL INDUSTRIA E COMERCIO LTDA.—See Philip Morris International Inc.; *U.S. Public*, pg. 1686

PHILIP MORRIS BULGARIA EOOD—See Philip Morris International Inc.; *U.S. Public*, pg. 1686

PHILIP MORRIS CAPITAL CORP.—See Altria Group, Inc.; *U.S. Public*, pg. 89

PHILIP MORRIS CHILE COMERCIALIZADORA LIMITADA—See Philip Morris International Inc.; *U.S. Public*, pg. 1686

PHILIP MORRIS COSTA RICA, SOCIEDAD ANONIMA—See Philip Morris International Inc.; *U.S. Public*, pg. 1686

PHILIP MORRIS CR AS; *Int'l*, pg. 5845

PHILIP MORRIS DOMINICANA, S.A.—See Philip Morris International Inc.; *U.S. Public*, pg. 1686

PHILIP MORRIS EESTI OSAUHING—See Philip Morris International Inc.; *U.S. Public*, pg. 1686

PHILIP MORRIS EGYPT LIMITED LIABILITY COMPANY—See Philip Morris International Inc.; *U.S. Public*, pg. 1686

PHILIP MORRIS FINLAND OY—See Philip Morris International Inc.; *U.S. Public*, pg. 1686

PHILIP MORRIS FRANCE S.A.S.—See Philip Morris International Inc.; *U.S. Public*, pg. 1686

PHILIP MORRIS GMBH—See Philip Morris International Inc.; *U.S. Public*, pg. 1686

PHILIP MORRIS INTERNATIONAL INC.; *U.S. Public*, pg. 1685

PHILIP MORRIS INTERNATIONAL MANAGEMENT SA—See Philip Morris International Inc.; *U.S. Public*, pg. 1686

PHILIP MORRIS INVESTMENTS B.V.—See Philip Morris International Inc.; *U.S. Public*, pg. 1686

PHILIP MORRIS ITALIA S.R.L.—See Philip Morris International Inc.; *U.S. Public*, pg. 1686

PHILIP MORRIS JAPAN GODO-KAISHA INC.—See Philip Morris International Inc.; *U.S. Public*, pg. 1686

PHILIP MORRIS JAPAN KABUSHIKI KAISHA—See Philip Morris International Inc.; *U.S. Public*, pg. 1686

PHILIP MORRIS KAZAKHSTAN LLP—See Philip Morris International Inc.; *U.S. Public*, pg. 1686

PHILIP MORRIS KOREA INC.—See Philip Morris International Inc.; *U.S. Public*, pg. 1686

PHILIP MORRIS KOREA INC.—See Philip Morris International Inc.; *U.S. Public*, pg. 1686

PHILIP MORRIS LATIN AMERICA SERVICES S.R.L.—See Philip Morris International Inc.; *U.S. Public*, pg. 1686

PHILIP MORRIS LIMITED—See Philip Morris International Inc.; *U.S. Public*, pg. 1686

PHILIP MORRIS LJUBLJANA, STORITVENO PODJETJE, D.O.O.—See Philip Morris International Inc.; *U.S. Public*, pg. 1686

PHILIP MORRIS LTD.—See Philip Morris International Inc.; *U.S. Public*, pg. 1686

PHILIP MORRIS MAGHREB SARL—See Philip Morris International Inc.; *U.S. Public*, pg. 1686

PHILIP MORRIS MALAYSIA SDN. BHD.—See Philip Morris International Inc.; *U.S. Public*, pg. 1686

PHILIP MORRIS MANAGEMENT SERVICES (MIDDLE EAST) LIMITED—See Philip Morris International Inc.; *U.S. Public*, pg. 1686

PHILIP MORRIS MANUFACTURING GMBH—See Philip Morris International Inc.; *U.S. Public*, pg. 1686

PHILIP MORRIS MANUFACTURING SENEGAL S.A.R.L.—See Philip Morris International Inc.; *U.S. Public*, pg. 1686

PHILIP MORRIS MANUFACTURING & TECHNOLOGY BOLOGNA S.P.A.—See Philip Morris International Inc.; *U.S. Public*, pg. 1686

PHILIP MORRIS MEXICO PRODUCTOS Y SERVICIOS, S. DE R.L. DE C.V.—See Philip Morris International Inc.; *U.S. Public*, pg. 1686

PHILIP MORRIS (NEW ZEALAND) LIMITED—See Philip Morris International Inc.; *U.S. Public*, pg. 1685

PHILIP MORRIS NORTH AFRICA SARL—See Philip Morris International Inc.; *U.S. Public*, pg. 1686

PHILIP MORRIS NORWAY AS—See Philip Morris International Inc.; *U.S. Public*, pg. 1686

PHILIP MORRIS OPERATIONS A.D.—See Philip Morris International Inc.; *U.S. Public*, pg. 1686

PHILIP MORRIS (PAKISTAN) LIMITED—See Philip Morris International Inc.; *U.S. Public*, pg. 1685

PHILIP MORRIS PANAMA SOCIEDAD EN COMANDITA POR ACCIONES—See Philip Morris International Inc.; *U.S. Public*, pg. 1686

PHILIP MORRIS PAZARLAMA VE SATIS A.S.—See Philip Morris International Inc.; *U.S. Public*, pg. 1686

PHILIP MORRIS POLSKA DISTRIBUTION SP. Z O.O.—See Philip Morris International Inc.; *U.S. Public*, pg. 1686

PHILIP MORRIS POLSKA S.A.—See Philip Morris International Inc.; *U.S. Public*, pg. 1686

PHILIP MORRIS POLSKA TOBACCO SPOLKA Z OGRANICZONA ODPOWIEDZIALNOSCIA—See Philip Morris International Inc.; *U.S. Public*, pg. 1686

PHILIP MORRIS PRODUCTS S.A.—See Philip Morris International Inc.; *U.S. Public*, pg. 1686

PHILIP MORRIS REUNION S.A.R.L.—See Philip Morris International Inc.; *U.S. Public*, pg. 1686

PHILIP MORRIS ROMANIA S.R.L.—See Philip Morris International Inc.; *U.S. Public*, pg. 1686

PHILIP MORRIS SABANCI PAZARLAMA VE SATIS A.S.—See Philip Morris International Inc.; *U.S. Public*, pg. 1687

PHILIP MORRIS SABANCI SIGARA VE TUTUNCULUK A.S.—See Philip Morris International Inc.; *U.S. Public*, pg. 1687

PHILIP MORRIS SALES AND MARKETING LTD.—See Philip Morris International Inc.; *U.S. Public*, pg. 1687

PHILIP MORRIS SA PHILIP MORRIS SABANCI PAZARLAMA VE SATIS A.S.—See Philip Morris International Inc.; *U.S. Public*, pg. 1686

PHILIP MORRIS SERVICES D.O.O.—See Philip Morris International Inc.; *U.S. Public*, pg. 1687

PHILIP MORRIS SEYAHAT PERAKENDE SATIS ANONIM SIRKETI—See Philip Morris International Inc.; *U.S. Public*, pg. 1687

PHILIP MORRIS SINGAPORE PTE. LTD.—See Philip Morris International Inc.; *U.S. Public*, pg. 1687

PHILIP MORRIS SOUTH AFRICA (PROPRIETARY) LIMITED—See Philip Morris International Inc.; *U.S. Public*, pg. 1687

PHILIP MORRIS SPAIN, S.L.—See Philip Morris International Inc.; *U.S. Public*, pg. 1687

PHILIP MORRIS SWITZERLAND SARL—See Philip Morris International Inc.; *U.S. Public*, pg. 1687

PHILIP MORRIS TRADING S.R.L.—See Philip Morris International Inc.; *U.S. Public*, pg. 1687

PHILIP MORRIS TRADING (THAILAND) COMPANY LIMITED—See Philip Morris International Inc.; *U.S. Public*, pg. 1687

PHILIP MORRIS TUTUN MAMULLERI SANAYI VE TICARET A.S.—See Philip Morris International Inc.; *U.S. Public*, pg. 1687

PHILIP MORRIS USA INC.—See Altria Group, Inc.; *U.S. Public*, pg. 89

PHILIP MORRIS USA—See Altria Group, Inc.; *U.S. Public*, pg. 89

PHILIP MORRIS VIETNAM LIMITED LIABILITY COMPANY—See Philip Morris International Inc.; *U.S. Public*, pg. 1687

PHILIP MORRIS ZAGREB D.O.O.—See Philip Morris International Inc.; *U.S. Public*, pg. 1687

PHILIP PAYNE LIMITED—See F.W. Thorpe plc; *Int'l*, pg. 2597

PHILIPPEBECKER; *U.S. Private*, pg. 3170

PHILIPPE LEVESQUE SA; *Int'l*, pg. 5845

PHILIP PELUSI SALONS; *U.S. Private*, pg. 3169

PHILIPP HOLZMANN AG; *Int'l*, pg. 5845

PHILIPPINE AIRLINES, INC.—See PAL Holdings, Inc.; *Int'l*, pg. 5705

PHILIPPINE ALLIED ENTERPRISES CORPORATION—See Bridgestone Corporation; *Int'l*, pg. 1160

THE PHILIPPINE AMERICAN LIFE & GENERAL INSURANCE COMPANY—See AIA Group Limited; *Int'l*, pg. 227

PHILIPPINE ANIMATION STUDIO INC—See Astro All Asia Networks plc; *Int'l*, pg. 662

PHILIPPINE ASSOCIATED SMELTING & REFINING CORPORATION—See Glencore plc; *Int'l*, pg. 2991

PHILIPPINE AUTO COMPONENTS, INC.—See Denso Corporation; *Int'l*, pg. 2032

PHILIPPINE BANK OF COMMUNICATIONS; *Int'l*, pg. 5845

PHILIPPINE BELT MANUFACTURING CORP.—See Bando Chemical Industries, Ltd.; *Int'l*, pg. 830

PHILIPPINE BELT MFG. CORP.—See Bando Chemical Industries, Ltd.; *Int'l*, pg. 831

PHILIPPINE BOBBIN CORPORATION—See Imperial Brands PLC; *Int'l*, pg. 3634

PHILIPPINE BUSINESS BANK INC.; *Int'l*, pg. 5845

PHILIPPINE COMPUTER ASSOCIATES INTERNATIONAL, INC.—See Broadcom Inc.; *U.S. Public*, pg. 390

PHILIPPINE ESTATES CORPORATION; *Int'l*, pg. 5845

PHILIPPINE FAMILYMART CVS, INC.—See Phoenix Petroleum Philippines, Inc.; *Int'l*, pg. 5854

PHILIPPINE GAMING MANAGEMENT CORPORATION.—See Berjaya Corporation Berhad; *Int'l*, pg. 983

PHILIPPINE H2O VENTURES CORP.—See Jolliville Holdings Corporation; *Int'l*, pg. 3996

PHILIPPINE IINO CORPORATION—See Daido Metal Corporation; *Int'l*, pg. 1922

PHILIPPINE INFRADEV HOLDINGS INC.; *Int'l*, pg. 5845

PHILIPPINE MANUFACTURING CO. OF MURATA, INC.—See Murata Manufacturing Co., Ltd.; *Int'l*, pg. 5098

PHILIPPINE METALS CORP.—See ReVolve Renewable Power Corp.; *Int'l*, pg. 6314

PHILIPPINE NATIONAL BANK; *Int'l*, pg. 5845

PHILIPPINE NATIONAL OIL COMPANY; *Int'l*, pg. 5845

PHILIPPINE PARKERIZING INC.—See Nihon Parkerizing Co., Ltd.; *Int'l*, pg. 5287

PHILIPPINE RACING CLUB, INC.; *Int'l*, pg. 5846

PHILIPPINE REALTY & HOLDINGS CORPORATION; *Int'l*, pg. 5846

PHILIPPINE RESINS INDUSTRIES, INC.—See Mitsubishi Corporation; *Int'l*, pg. 4943

PHILIPPINE RESINS INDUSTRIES, INC.—See Tosoh Corporation; *Int'l*, pg. 7832

PHILIPPINE SAVINGS BANK—See Metropolitan Bank & Trust Company; *Int'l*, pg. 4864

PHILIPPINES EPSON OPTICAL INC.—See Seiko Epson Corporation; *Int'l*, pg. 6687

PHILIPPINE SEVEN CORPORATION; *Int'l*, pg. 5846

PHILIPPINES INNOREV AUTOMATION INC.—See Shenzhen Colibri Technologies Co., Ltd.; *Int'l*, pg. 6807

PHILIPPINE SINTER CORPORATION—See JFE Holdings, Inc.; *Int'l*, pg. 3938

PHILIPPINE STANDARD SHIPMANAGEMENT INC.—See NS United Kaiun Kaisha, Ltd.; *Int'l*, pg. 5475

PHILIPPINE STOCK EXCHANGE, INC.; *Int'l*, pg. 5846

PHILIPPINES URBAN LIVING SOLUTIONS, INC.—See SM Investments Corporation; *Int'l*, pg. 6998

PHILIPPINE TAIYO AQUA FARMING CORP.—See Maruha Nichiro Corporation; *Int'l*, pg. 4712

PHILIPPINE TELEGRAPH & TELEPHONE CORPORATION; *Int'l*, pg. 5846

PHILIPPINE TOWNSHIPS INC—See RFM Corporation; *Int'l*, pg. 6319

PHILIPPINE TRUST COMPANY; *Int'l*, pg. 5846

PHILIPPINE WACOAL CORP.—See Wacoal Holdings Corp.; *Int'l*, pg. 8326

PHILIPPINE WELDING EQUIPMENT, INC.—See Enovis Corporation; *U.S. Public*, pg. 771

PHILIPPI, PRIETOCARRIZOSA & URIA; *Int'l*, pg. 5845

PHILIPP LITHOGRAPHING COMPANY; *U.S. Private*, pg. 3170

PHILIPPOS NAKAS S.A.; *Int'l*, pg. 5846

PHILIPP UND KEUNTJE GMBH—See fischerAppelt AG; *Int'l*, pg. 2692

PHILIP ROSENAU CO., INC.—See Bain Capital, LP; *U.S. Private*, pg. 440

PHILIPS AB—See Koninklijke Philips N.V.; *Int'l*, pg. 4268

PHILIPS ACCESSORIES & COMPUTER PERIPHERALS N.A.—See Koninklijke Philips N.V.; *Int'l*, pg. 4269

PHILIPS ADAC—See Koninklijke Philips N.V.; *Int'l*, pg. 4270

PHILIPS AG—See Koninklijke Philips N.V.; *Int'l*, pg. 4268

PHILIPS ARGENTINA SOCIEDAD ANONIMA—See Koninklijke Philips N.V.; *Int'l*, pg. 4268
PHILIPS AVENT—See Koninklijke Philips N.V.; *Int'l*, pg. 4268
PHILIPS BALTIC SIA—See Koninklijke Philips N.V.; *Int'l*, pg. 4268
PHILIPS BELGUIM N.V.—See Koninklijke Philips N.V.; *Int'l*, pg. 4268
PHILIPS BULGARIA EOOD—See Koninklijke Philips N.V.; *Int'l*, pg. 4268
PHILIPS CARIBBEAN PANAMA, INC.—See Koninklijke Philips N.V.; *Int'l*, pg. 4268
PHILIPS CESKA REPUBLIKA S.R.O.—See Koninklijke Philips N.V.; *Int'l*, pg. 4268
PHILIPS CHILENA S.A.—See Koninklijke Philips N.V.; *Int'l*, pg. 4268
PHILIPS COLOMBIANA S.A.S.—See Koninklijke Philips N.V.; *Int'l*, pg. 4268
PHILIPS CONSUMER COMMUNICATIONS B.V.—See Koninklijke Philips N.V.; *Int'l*, pg. 4268
PHILIPS CONSUMER ELECTRONIC SERVICES B.V.—See Koninklijke Philips N.V.; *Int'l*, pg. 4269
PHILIPS CONSUMER ELECTRONICS—See Koninklijke Philips N.V.; *Int'l*, pg. 4269
PHILIPS CONSUMER ELECTRONICS—See Koninklijke Philips N.V.; *Int'l*, pg. 4269
PHILIPS CONSUMER LIFESTYLE INTERNATIONAL B.V.—See Koninklijke Philips N.V.; *Int'l*, pg. 4268
PHILIPS CONSUMER LUMINAIRES CORPORATION—See Signify N.V.; *Int'l*, pg. 6912
PHILIPS CONSUMER PRODUCTS NV—See Koninklijke Philips N.V.; *Int'l*, pg. 4268
PHILIPS CONSUMER RELATIONS B.V.—See Koninklijke Philips N.V.; *Int'l*, pg. 4268
PHILIPS CREDIT CORPORATION—See Koninklijke Philips N.V.; *Int'l*, pg. 4269
PHILIPS DANMARK A/S—See Koninklijke Philips N.V.; *Int'l*, pg. 4268
PHILIPS DICTATION SYSTEMS—See Koninklijke Philips N.V.; *Int'l*, pg. 4269
PHILIPS DIGITAL MAMMOGRAPHY SWEDEN AB—See Koninklijke Philips N.V.; *Int'l*, pg. 4268
PHILIPS DO BRASIL-WALITA DIV.—See Koninklijke Philips N.V.; *Int'l*, pg. 4271
PHILIPS DO BRAZIL LTDA.—See Koninklijke Philips N.V.; *Int'l*, pg. 4271
PHILIPS DUNLEE—See Koninklijke Philips N.V.; *Int'l*, pg. 4269
PHILIPS EGYPT (LIMITED LIABILITY COMPANY)—See Koninklijke Philips N.V.; *Int'l*, pg. 4268
PHILIPS ELECTRONIC COMPONENTS (SHANGHAI) CO., LTD.—See Koninklijke Philips N.V.; *Int'l*, pg. 4268
PHILIPS ELECTRONICS ASIA PACIFIC PTE LTD—See Koninklijke Philips N.V.; *Int'l*, pg. 4268
PHILIPS ELECTRONICS AUSTRALIA LIMITED—See Koninklijke Philips N.V.; *Int'l*, pg. 4268
PHILIPS ELECTRONICS BANGLADESH PRIVATE LIMITED—See Koninklijke Philips N.V.; *Int'l*, pg. 4268
PHILIPS ELECTRONICS CHINA B.V.—See Koninklijke Philips N.V.; *Int'l*, pg. 4268
PHILIPS ELECTRONICS HONG KONG LIMITED—See Koninklijke Philips N.V.; *Int'l*, pg. 4268
PHILIPS ELECTRONICS IRELAND LIMITED—See Koninklijke Philips N.V.; *Int'l*, pg. 4268
PHILIPS ELECTRONICS JAPAN, LTD.—See Koninklijke Philips N.V.; *Int'l*, pg. 4268
PHILIPS ELECTRONICS KOREA—See Koninklijke Philips N.V.; *Int'l*, pg. 4269
PHILIPS ELECTRONICS LTD.—See Koninklijke Philips N.V.; *Int'l*, pg. 4269
PHILIPS ELECTRONICS NEDERLAND B.V.—See Koninklijke Philips N.V.; *Int'l*, pg. 4269
PHILIPS ELECTRONICS NORTH AMERICA CORPORATION—See Koninklijke Philips N.V.; *Int'l*, pg. 4269
PHILIPS ELECTRONICS NORTH AMERICA—See Koninklijke Philips N.V.; *Int'l*, pg. 4269
PHILIPS ELECTRONICS NORTH AMERICA—See Koninklijke Philips N.V.; *Int'l*, pg. 4269
PHILIPS ELECTRONICS NORTH AMERICA—See Koninklijke Philips N.V.; *Int'l*, pg. 4269
PHILIPS ELECTRONICS NORTH AMERICA—See Koninklijke Philips N.V.; *Int'l*, pg. 4269
PHILIPS ELECTRONICS (SHENZHEN) CO., LTD.—See Koninklijke Philips N.V.; *Int'l*, pg. 4268
PHILIPS ELECTRONICS SINGAPORE PTE LTD—See Koninklijke Philips N.V.; *Int'l*, pg. 4269
PHILIPS ELECTRONICS (SUZHOU) CO., LTD.—See Koninklijke Philips N.V.; *Int'l*, pg. 4268
PHILIPS ELECTRONICS TECHNOLOGY (SHANGHAI) CO., LTD.—See Koninklijke Philips N.V.; *Int'l*, pg. 4269
PHILIPS ELECTRONICS TECHNOLOGY SHANGHAI HOLDING B.V.—See Koninklijke Philips N.V.; *Int'l*, pg. 4269
PHILIPS ELECTRONICS (THAILAND) LTD.—See Koninklijke Philips N.V.; *Int'l*, pg. 4268
PHILIPS ELECTRONICS UK LIMITED—See Koninklijke Philips N.V.; *Int'l*, pg. 4269

PHILIPS ELECTRONICS VIETNAM LIMITED—See Koninklijke Philips N.V.; *Int'l*, pg. 4269
PHILIPS ELETRONICA DO NORDESTE S.A.—See Koninklijke Philips N.V.; *Int'l*, pg. 4269
PHILIPS ENTERTAINMENT LIGHTING ASIA LIMITED—See Koninklijke Philips N.V.; *Int'l*, pg. 4269
PHILIPS EXPORT B.V.—See Koninklijke Philips N.V.; *Int'l*, pg. 4269
PHILIPS HEALTHCARE INFORMATICS LIMITED—See Koninklijke Philips N.V.; *Int'l*, pg. 4269
PHILIPS HEALTHCARE INFORMATICS-RIS—See Koninklijke Philips N.V.; *Int'l*, pg. 4270
PHILIPS HEALTHCARE INFORMATICS—See Koninklijke Philips N.V.; *Int'l*, pg. 4270
PHILIPS HELLAS S.A.—See Koninklijke Philips N.V.; *Int'l*, pg. 4269
PHILIPS INDIA LIMITED—See Koninklijke Philips N.V.; *Int'l*, pg. 4269
PHILIPS INDUSTRIES HUNGARY ELECTRONICAL MECHANICAL MANUFACTURING AND TRADING LIMITED LIABILITY COMPANY—See Koninklijke Philips N.V.; *Int'l*, pg. 4268
PHILIPS INNOVATIVE APPLICATIONS N.V.—See Koninklijke Philips N.V.; *Int'l*, pg. 4269
PHILIPS INTERNATIONAL B.V.—See Koninklijke Philips N.V.; *Int'l*, pg. 4269
PHILIPS INTERNATIONAL REALTY CORP.; *U.S. Private*, pg. 3170
PHILIPS IPSC TAMASI KFT.—See Koninklijke Philips N.V.; *Int'l*, pg. 4269
PHILIPS LIFELINE—See Koninklijke Philips N.V.; *Int'l*, pg. 4270
PHILIPS LIGHTING ELECTRONICS—See Koninklijke Philips N.V.; *Int'l*, pg. 4269
PHILIPS LIGHTING LTD.—See Koninklijke Philips N.V.; *Int'l*, pg. 4269
PHILIPS LIGHTING—See Signify N.V.; *Int'l*, pg. 6912
PHILIPS LIGHT ON DIGITAL SOLUTIONS—See Koninklijke Philips N.V.; *Int'l*, pg. 4269
PHILIPS & LITE-ON DIGITAL SOLUTIONS CORPORATION—See Lite-On Technology Corporation; *Int'l*, pg. 4526
PHILIPS LUMILEDS LIGHTING COMPANY SDN. BHD.—See Apollo Global Management, Inc.; *U.S. Public*, pg. 153
PHILIPS LUXEMBOURG SA—See Koninklijke Philips N.V.; *Int'l*, pg. 4268
PHILIPS LYS A/S—See Koninklijke Philips N.V.; *Int'l*, pg. 4268
PHILIPS MAGYARORSZAG KERESKEDELMI KFT.—See Koninklijke Philips N.V.; *Int'l*, pg. 4269
PHILIPS MEDICAL SYSTEMS DMC GMBH—See Koninklijke Philips N.V.; *Int'l*, pg. 4270
PHILIPS MEDICAL SYSTEMS MR, INC.—See Koninklijke Philips N.V.; *Int'l*, pg. 4270
PHILIPS MEDICAL SYSTEMS NEDERLAND B.V.—See Koninklijke Philips N.V.; *Int'l*, pg. 4270
PHILIPS MEDICAL SYSTEMS—See Koninklijke Philips N.V.; *Int'l*, pg. 4270
PHILIPS MEDICAL SYSTEMS—See Koninklijke Philips N.V.; *Int'l*, pg. 4270
PHILIPS MEDICAL SYSTEMS—See Koninklijke Philips N.V.; *Int'l*, pg. 4269
PHILIPS MEDICAL SYSTEMS—See Koninklijke Philips N.V.; *Int'l*, pg. 4270
PHILIPS MEDICAL SYSTEMS—See Koninklijke Philips N.V.; *Int'l*, pg. 4270
PHILIPS MEDICAL SYSTEMS—See Koninklijke Philips N.V.; *Int'l*, pg. 4270
PHILIPS MEDIZIN SYSTEME BOBLINGEN GMBH—See Koninklijke Philips N.V.; *Int'l*, pg. 4270
PHILIPS MEXICANA, S.A. DE C.V.—See Koninklijke Philips N.V.; *Int'l*, pg. 4270
PHILIPS NEDERLAND B.V.—See Koninklijke Philips N.V.; *Int'l*, pg. 4270
PHILIPS NORGE AS—See Koninklijke Philips N.V.; *Int'l*, pg. 4270
PHILIPSON & SODERBERG AB—See Altia Oyj; *Int'l*, pg. 392
PHILIPS OVERSEAS HOLDINGS CORPORATION—See Koninklijke Philips N.V.; *Int'l*, pg. 4270
PHILIPS OY—See Koninklijke Philips N.V.; *Int'l*, pg. 4270
PHILIPS PATIENT MONITORING SYSTEMS CHINA HOLDING B.V.—See Koninklijke Philips N.V.; *Int'l*, pg. 4270
PHILIPS PERUANA S.A.—See Koninklijke Philips N.V.; *Int'l*, pg. 4270
PHILIPS PROPERTIES NV—See Koninklijke Philips N.V.; *Int'l*, pg. 4270
PHILIPS' RADIO B.V.—See Koninklijke Philips N.V.; *Int'l*, pg. 4271
PHILIPS REMOTE CARDIAC SERVICES—See Koninklijke Philips N.V.; *Int'l*, pg. 4270
PHILIPS RESEARCH—See Koninklijke Philips N.V.; *Int'l*, pg. 4269
PHILIPS RESPIRONICS HONG KONG—See Koninklijke Philips N.V.; *Int'l*, pg. 4270

PHILIPS ROMANIA S.R.L.—See Koninklijke Philips N.V.; *Int'l*, pg. 4270
PHILIPS SC UNTERSTUTZUNGSKASSE GMBH—See Koninklijke Philips N.V.; *Int'l*, pg. 4270
PHILIPS SLOVAKIA S.R.O.—See Koninklijke Philips N.V.; *Int'l*, pg. 4270
PHILIPS SLOVENIJA TRGOVINA, D.O.O.—See Koninklijke Philips N.V.; *Int'l*, pg. 4270
PHILIPS SOLID-STATE LIGHTING SOLUTIONS, INC.—See Signify N.V.; *Int'l*, pg. 6912
PHILIP'S—See Vivendi SE; *Int'l*, pg. 8274
PHILIPS SOUTH AFRICA (PROPRIETARY) LIMITED—See Koninklijke Philips N.V.; *Int'l*, pg. 4270
PHILIPS TRUSTEE COMPANY LIMITED—See Koninklijke Philips N.V.; *Int'l*, pg. 4270
PHILIPS U.K. LIMITED—See Koninklijke Philips N.V.; *Int'l*, pg. 4270
PHILIPS URUGUAY S.A.—See Koninklijke Philips N.V.; *Int'l*, pg. 4270
PHILIPS VENTURE CAPITAL FUND B.V.—See Koninklijke Philips N.V.; *Int'l*, pg. 4271
PHILIPS X RAY—See Koninklijke Philips N.V.; *Int'l*, pg. 4270
PHILIPS & YAMING LIGHTING CO., LTD.—See Signify N.V.; *Int'l*, pg. 6912
PHILKOEI INTERNATIONAL, INC.—See Nippon Koei Co., Ltd.; *Int'l*, pg. 5322
PHILKO PEROXIDE CORPORATION—See OCI Holdings Co., Ltd.; *Int'l*, pg. 5519
THE PHILLIES, L.P.; *U.S. Private*, pg. 4095
PHIL LIFE INC.—See Livesense Inc.; *Int'l*, pg. 4530
PHILLIP ASSET MANAGEMENT (HK) LTD—See Phillip Capital Pte. Ltd.; *Int'l*, pg. 5846
PHILLIP BANK PLC—See Phillip Capital Pte. Ltd.; *Int'l*, pg. 5846
PHILLIPCAPITAL ASSET MANAGEMENT K.K.—See Phillip Capital Pte. Ltd.; *Int'l*, pg. 5847
PHILLIPCAPITAL CKS JAPAN K.K.—See Phillip Capital Pte. Ltd.; *Int'l*, pg. 5847
PHILLIPCAPITAL (INDIA) PVT. LTD—See Phillip Capital Pte. Ltd.; *Int'l*, pg. 5847
PHILLIP CAPITAL LIMITED—See Phillip Capital Pte. Ltd.; *Int'l*, pg. 5847
PHILLIP CAPITAL MANAGEMENT SDN BHD—See Phillip Capital Pte. Ltd.; *Int'l*, pg. 5847
PHILLIP CAPITAL MANAGEMENT (S) LTD—See Phillip Capital Pte. Ltd.; *Int'l*, pg. 5847
PHILLIP CAPITAL MENKUL DEGERLER A.S.—See Phillip Capital Pte. Ltd.; *Int'l*, pg. 5847
PHILLIP CAPITAL PTE. LTD.; *Int'l*, pg. 5846
PHILLIPCAPITAL UK—See Phillip Capital Pte. Ltd.; *Int'l*, pg. 5847
PHILLIP COMMODITIES (HK) LTD—See Phillip Capital Pte. Ltd.; *Int'l*, pg. 5847
PHILLIP COMMODITIES PTE. LTD.—See Phillip Capital Pte. Ltd.; *Int'l*, pg. 5847
PHILLIP COMMODITIES VIETNAM COMPANY LIMITED—See Phillip Capital Pte. Ltd.; *Int'l*, pg. 5847
PHILLIP FINANCE (HK) LTD—See Phillip Capital Pte. Ltd.; *Int'l*, pg. 5847
PHILLIP FINANCE & INVESTMENT SERVICES INDIA PVT. LTD.—See Phillip Capital Pte. Ltd.; *Int'l*, pg. 5847
PHILLIP FINANCIAL ADVISORS (HK) LTD—See Phillip Capital Pte. Ltd.; *Int'l*, pg. 5847
PHILLIP FINANCIAL ADVISORY (GUANGZHOU) CO. LTD—See Phillip Capital Pte. Ltd.; *Int'l*, pg. 5847
PHILLIP FINANCIAL ADVISORY (SHANGHAI) CO. LTD—See Phillip Capital Pte. Ltd.; *Int'l*, pg. 5847
PHILLIP FINANCIAL PTE LTD—See Phillip Capital Pte. Ltd.; *Int'l*, pg. 5847
PHILLIP FINANCIALS K.K.—See Phillip Capital Pte. Ltd.; *Int'l*, pg. 5847
PHILLIP FUTURES DMCC—See Phillip Capital Pte. Ltd.; *Int'l*, pg. 5847
PHILLIP FUTURES INC—See Phillip Capital Pte. Ltd.; *Int'l*, pg. 5847
PHILLIP FUTURES PTE LTD—See Phillip Capital Pte. Ltd.; *Int'l*, pg. 5847
PHILLIP FUTURES SDN. BHD.—See Phillip Capital Pte. Ltd.; *Int'l*, pg. 5847
PHILLIP LIFE ASSURANCE (THAILAND) PUBLIC CO., LTD—See Phillip Capital Pte. Ltd.; *Int'l*, pg. 5847
PHILLIP MUTUAL BERHAD—See Phillip Capital Pte. Ltd.; *Int'l*, pg. 5847
PHILLIPPI EQUIPMENT CO.; *U.S. Private*, pg. 3170
THE PHILLIPPINES THERMOPOWER CLIMATE CONTROL CORPORATION—See Hongfa Technology Co Ltd; *Int'l*, pg. 3470
PHILLIP PRIVATE EQUITY PTE. LTD.—See Phillip Capital Pte. Ltd.; *Int'l*, pg. 5847
PHILLIPS 66 BANTRY BAY TERMINAL LIMITED—See Phillips 66 Company; *U.S. Public*, pg. 1688
PHILLIPS 66 CANADA LTD.—See Phillips 66 Company; *U.S. Public*, pg. 1688
PHILLIPS 66 COMPANY—See Phillips 66 Company; *U.S. Public*, pg. 1688
PHILLIPS 66 COMPANY; *U.S. Public*, pg. 1688
PHILLIPS 66 GMBH—See Phillips 66 Company; *U.S. Public*, pg. 1688

COMPANY NAME INDEX

PHILLIPS 66 INTERNATIONAL TRADING PTE. LTD.—See Phillips 66 Company; *U.S. Public*, pg. 1688
PHILLIPS 66 LIMITED—See Phillips 66 Company; *U.S. Public*, pg. 1688
PHILLIPS 66 PARTNERS LP—See Phillips 66 Company; *U.S. Public*, pg. 1688
PHILLIPS 66 POLYPROPYLENE CANADA INC.—See Phillips 66 Company; *U.S. Public*, pg. 1688
PHILLIPS ARCHITECTURE PA—See Redline Design Group, P.A.; *U.S. Private*, pg. 3379
PHILLIPS BUICK PONTIAC GMC; *U.S. Private*, pg. 3170
PHILLIPS BUILDING SUPPLY OF GULFPORT; *U.S. Private*, pg. 3170
PHILLIPS CHRYSLER JEEP DODGE RAM; *U.S. Private*, pg. 3170
PHILLIPS CLINIC CORP.—See Quorum Health Corporation; *U.S. Private*, pg. 3330
PHILLIPS & COHEN ASSOCIATES LTD.; *U.S. Private*, pg. 3170
PHILLIPS COMMUNICATION & EQUIPMENT CO.; *U.S. Private*, pg. 3170
PHILLIPS CORPORATION; *U.S. Private*, pg. 3170
PHILLIPS DE PURY & COMPANY; *U.S. Private*, pg. 3170
PHILLIPS DEVELOPMENT CORP.; *U.S. Private*, pg. 3170
PHILLIPS DEVELOPMENT & REALTY, LLC; *U.S. Private*, pg. 3170
PHILLIPS DISTRIBUTING CORP; *U.S. Private*, pg. 3170
PHILLIP SECURITIES (HK) LTD—See Phillip Capital Pte. Ltd.; *Int'l*, pg. 5847
PHILLIP SECURITIES JAPAN LTD.—See Phillip Capital Pte. Ltd.; *Int'l*, pg. 5847
PHILLIP SECURITIES PTE. LTD.—See Phillip Capital Pte. Ltd.; *Int'l*, pg. 5847
PHILLIP SECURITIES RESEARCH PTE LTD—See Phillip Capital Pte. Ltd.; *Int'l*, pg. 5847
PHILLIP SECURITIES (THAILAND) PUBLIC CO. LTD—See Phillip Capital Pte. Ltd.; *Int'l*, pg. 5847
PHILLIPS EDISON & COMPANY INC.—See Phillips Edison & Company LLC; *U.S. Private*, pg. 3170
PHILLIPS EDISON & COMPANY LLC; *U.S. Private*, pg. 3170
PHILLIPS EDISON GROCERY CENTER REIT II, INC.—See Phillips Edison & Company LLC; *U.S. Private*, pg. 3170
PHILLIPS' FLOORS, INC.; *U.S. Private*, pg. 3171
PHILLIPS FOODS ASIA CO., LTD.—See Phillips Foods Inc.; *U.S. Private*, pg. 3171
PHILLIPS FOODS INC.; *U.S. Private*, pg. 3171
PHILLIPS GAS COMPANY—See Phillips 66 Company; *U.S. Public*, pg. 1688
PHILLIPS GOURMET, INC.—See Phillips Mushroom Farms; *U.S. Private*, pg. 3171
PHILLIPS HOSPITAL CORPORATION—See Quorum Health Corporation; *U.S. Private*, pg. 3330
PHILLIPS INDUSTRIES; *U.S. Private*, pg. 3171
PHILLIPS INSURANCE ASSOCIATES, INC.; *U.S. Private*, pg. 3171
PHILLIPS & JORDAN INCORPORATED; *U.S. Private*, pg. 3170
PHILLIPS KILN SERVICES LTD.—See FLSmidth & Co. A/S; *Int'l*, pg. 2712
PHILLIPS LIFT SYSTEMS, INC.—See Homecare Products, Inc.; *U.S. Private*, pg. 1973
PHILLIPS MACHINE SERVICE INC.; *U.S. Private*, pg. 3171
PHILLIPS MANUFACTURING INC.; *U.S. Private*, pg. 3171
PHILLIPS-MEDISIZE, LLC—See Koch Industries, Inc.; *U.S. Private*, pg. 2335
PHILLIPS MUSHROOM FARMS; *U.S. Private*, pg. 3171
PHILLIPS OFFICE SOLUTIONS, INC.—See Wells Fargo & Company; *U.S. Public*, pg. 2344
PHILLIPS PAINTING; *U.S. Private*, pg. 3171
PHILLIPS PET FOOD & SUPPLIES; *U.S. Private*, pg. 3171
PHILLIPS RIVER MINING LTD.; *Int'l*, pg. 5847
PHILLIPS SEAFOOD RESTAURANT—See Phillips Foods Inc.; *U.S. Private*, pg. 3171
PHILLIPS SERVICE INDUSTRIES, INC. (PSI); *U.S. Private*, pg. 3171
PHILLIPS SERVICES, LLC; *U.S. Private*, pg. 3171
PHILLIPS SUPPLY CO. INC.; *U.S. Private*, pg. 3171
PHILLIPS & TEMRO INDUSTRIES, INC.—See Harbour Group Industries, Inc.; *U.S. Private*, pg. 1860
PHILLIP STEPHENS FUNERAL SERVICES PTY LTD—See Propel Funeral Partners Limited; *Int'l*, pg. 5997
PHILLIPS UTILITY GAS CORPORATION—See Phillips 66 Company; *U.S. Public*, pg. 1688
PHILLIPS-VAN HEUSEN CANADA, INC.—See PVH Corp.; *U.S. Public*, pg. 1739
PHILLIP TRADING PTE LTD—See Phillip Capital Pte. Ltd.; *Int'l*, pg. 5847
PHILLIP VENTURES IFSC PVT. LTD.—See Phillip Capital Pte. Ltd.; *Int'l*, pg. 5847
PHILLIP WEALTH PLANNER SDN. BHD.—See Phillip Capital Pte. Ltd.; *Int'l*, pg. 5847
PHIL LONG DENVER VALUCAR, LLC.; *U.S. Private*, pg. 3168
PHIL LONG LLC; *U.S. Private*, pg. 3168

PHILLY'S FAMOUS WATER ICE, INC.—See J&J Snack Foods Corporation; *U.S. Public*, pg. 1180
PHILLY SHIPYARD, INC.—See Aker ASA; *Int'l*, pg. 262
PHILMAC PTY. LTD.—See Aliaxis S.A./N.V.; *Int'l*, pg. 325
PHIL MEADOR TOYOTA, INC.; *U.S. Private*, pg. 3168
THE PHILODRILL CORPORATION; *Int'l*, pg. 7673
PHILOKTIMATIKI ERGOLIPTIKI LTD.—See Piraeus Financial Holdings S.A.; *Int'l*, pg. 5873
PHILÖKTIMATIKI PUBLIC LTD; *Int'l*, pg. 5847
PHILOMAXCAP AG; *Int'l*, pg. 5847
PHILOPTICS; *Int'l*, pg. 5847
PHILOPTICS USA INC.—See Philoptics; *Int'l*, pg. 5847
PHILOSOPHY IB, LLP—See Heidrick & Struggles International, Inc.; *U.S. Public*, pg. 1023
PHILOSOPHY INC.—See JAB Holding Company S.a.r.l.; *Int'l*, pg. 3861
PHILOTECH FRANCE S.A.S.—See Bertrandt AG; *Int'l*, pg. 998
PHILOTECH IBERICA SISTEMAS Y LOGISTICA S.L.—See Bertrandt AG; *Int'l*, pg. 998
PHILPOT DAIRY PRODUCTS LIMITED—See Saputo Inc.; *Int'l*, pg. 6575
PHILPOTT MOTORS, LLC—See Sonic Automotive, Inc.; *U.S. Public*, pg. 1902
PHILPOTT MOTORS, LTD.—See Sonic Automotive, Inc.; *U.S. Public*, pg. 1902
PHILSA PHILIP MORRIS SABANCI SIGARA VE TUTUNCULUK SANAYI VE TICARET A.S.—See Philip Morris International Inc.; *U.S. Public*, pg. 1685
PHIL SMITH AUTOMOTIVE GROUP; *U.S. Private*, pg. 3168
PHILSON, INC.—See AptarGroup, Inc.; *U.S. Public*, pg. 174
PHILTER COMMUNICATIONS INC.; *Int'l*, pg. 5848
PHILUX GLOBAL GROUP INC; *U.S. Public*, pg. 1688
PHILWAY PRODUCTS, INC.; *U.S. Private*, pg. 3171
PHILWEB CORPORATION; *Int'l*, pg. 5848
PHIL WRIGHT AUTOPLEX CO.; *U.S. Private*, pg. 3168
PHI MU FRATERNITY; *U.S. Private*, pg. 3168
PHINERGY LTD.; *Int'l*, pg. 5848
PHINMA CORPORATION; *Int'l*, pg. 5848
PHINMA EDUCATION HOLDINGS, INC.—See PHINMA Corporation; *Int'l*, pg. 5848
PHINMA PROPERTY HOLDINGS CORPORATION—See PHINMA Corporation; *Int'l*, pg. 5848
PHINMA SOLAR ENERGY CORPORATION—See PHINMA Corporation; *Int'l*, pg. 5848
PHINMA UNIVERSITY OF ILOILO—See PHINMA Corporation; *Int'l*, pg. 5848
P-H INVESTMENTS INC.; *U.S. Private*, pg. 3059
PHIO PHARMACEUTICALS CORP.; *U.S. Public*, pg. 1689
PHIPPS & BIRD, INC.; *U.S. Private*, pg. 3171
PHIPPS DICKSON INTEGRIA INC.; *Int'l*, pg. 5848
PHIPPS HOUSES; *U.S. Private*, pg. 3172
PHIPPS REPORTING, INC.—See Trinity Hunt Management, L.P.; *U.S. Private*, pg. 4234
PHIPPS VENTURES INC.; *U.S. Private*, pg. 3172
PHIROZE SETHNA PRIVATE LIMITED—See Chembond Chemicals Ltd; *Int'l*, pg. 1461
PHI SEEDS PRIVATE LIMITED—See Corteva, Inc.; *U.S. Public*, pg. 582
PHI SERVICE COMPANY—See Exelon Corporation; *U.S. Public*, pg. 807
PHISON ELECTRONICS CORPORATION; *Int'l*, pg. 5848
PHI; *U.S. Private*, pg. 3167
PHIVETOL SA—See Carrefour SA; *Int'l*, pg. 1346
PHK ENGINEERING LIMITED—See Propak Systems Ltd.; *Int'l*, pg. 5997
PHLEXGLOBAL, INC—See Vitruvian Partners LLP; *Int'l*, pg. 8263
PHLEXGLOBAL LTD.—See Vitruvian Partners LLP; *Int'l*, pg. 8263
PHL SA; *Int'l*, pg. 5848
PHL VARIABLE INSURANCE COMPANY—See Golden Gate Capital Management II, LLC; *U.S. Private*, pg. 1731
PHMC, INC.; *U.S. Private*, pg. 3172
PHM GROUP HOLDING OYJ; *Int'l*, pg. 5848
P&H MILLING GROUP—See Exceldor Cooperative Avicole; *Int'l*, pg. 2578
P&H MILLING GROUP—See Exceldor Cooperative Avicole; *Int'l*, pg. 2578
P&H MINEPRO DO BRASIL COMERCIO E INDUSTRIA LTDA.—See Komatsu Ltd.; *Int'l*, pg. 4236
PHM MULTIDISCIPLINARY CLINIC ARECIBO LLC—See Elevance Health, Inc.; *U.S. Public*, pg. 730
PHM MULTIDISCIPLINARY CLINIC CABO ROJO LLC—See Elevance Health, Inc.; *U.S. Public*, pg. 730
PHM MULTISALUD, LLC—See Elevance Health, Inc.; *U.S. Public*, pg. 730
P.H.M. PEHAMET SP.Z.O.O.—See Intek Group S.p.A.; *Int'l*, pg. 3782
PHN INDUSTRY SDN. BHD.—See DRB-HICOM Berhad; *Int'l*, pg. 2202
PHNTUS CREEKSIDE LLC—See Brookdale Senior Living Inc.; *U.S. Public*, pg. 395
PHNTUS PINEHURST LLC—See Brookdale Senior Living Inc.; *U.S. Public*, pg. 395

PHOENIX CHILDREN'S FOUNDATION

PHNTUS QUAIL RIDGE LLC—See Brookdale Senior Living Inc.; *U.S. Public*, pg. 395
PHOAM STUDIO APS—See Park Street Nordicom A/S; *Int'l*, pg. 5742
PHOBIO, LLC; *U.S. Private*, pg. 3172
PHOCEENNE ASIA PTE. LTD.—See Groupe BPCE; *Int'l*, pg. 3095
PHOCEENNE CHILI LTDA.—See Groupe BPCE; *Int'l*, pg. 3095
PHOCEENNE S.A.—See Groupe BPCE; *Int'l*, pg. 3095
PHOCEENNE SAS—See Groupe BPCE; *Int'l*, pg. 3095
PHOCOMEX; *Int'l*, pg. 5848
PHOCUSWRIGHT INC.—See EagleTree Capital, LP; *U.S. Private*, pg. 1312
PHOEBUS HOLDINGS LTD.; *Int'l*, pg. 5848
PHOEBUS SOFTWARE LIMITED—See NorthEdge Capital LLP; *Int'l*, pg. 5442
PHOEBUS—See Rubis SCA; *Int'l*, pg. 6423
PHOENICIA FINANCE COMPANY PLC; *Int'l*, pg. 5848
PHOENICIA LTD.—See Fortissimo Capital Management Ltd.; *Int'l*, pg. 2740
PHOENICIAN OPERATING LLC—See Host Hotels & Resorts, Inc.; *U.S. Public*, pg. 1055
PHOENICIAN PROPERTIES REALTY; *U.S. Private*, pg. 3172
THE PHOENICIAN—See Marriott International, Inc.; *U.S. Public*, pg. 1372
PHOENICS ELECTRONICS CORPORATION—See Avnet, Inc.; *U.S. Public*, pg. 253
PHOENITRON HOLDINGS LIMITED; *Int'l*, pg. 5848
PHOENIX ACQUISITION LIMITED; *Int'l*, pg. 5849
PHOENIX AIR GROUP INC.; *U.S. Private*, pg. 3172
PHOENIX AIR RACING INC—See Phoenix Air Group Inc.; *U.S. Private*, pg. 3172
PHOENIX ALUMINIUM 2011 LIMITED—See Fletcher Building Limited; *Int'l*, pg. 2700
PHOENIX A.M.D. INTERNATIONAL INC.; *Int'l*, pg. 5849
PHOENIX AMERICA, INC.—See discoverIE Group plc; *Int'l*, pg. 2133
PHOENIX AMERICAN FINANCIAL SERVICES, INC.—See Phoenix American Incorporated; *U.S. Private*, pg. 3172
PHOENIX AMERICAN INCORPORATED; *U.S. Private*, pg. 3172
PHOENIX AMERICAN SALESFOCUS SOLUTIONS, INC.—See Phoenix American Incorporated; *U.S. Private*, pg. 3172
PHOENIX ANUSA, LLC—See AutoNation, Inc.; *U.S. Public*, pg. 237
PHOENIX APPS INC.; *Int'l*, pg. 5849
PHOENIX ARENA GP, LLC—See Suns Legacy Partners, LLC; *U.S. Private*, pg. 3870
PHOENIX AROMAS & ESSENTIAL OILS, INC.—See SK Capital Partners, LP; *U.S. Private*, pg. 3679
PHOENIX ARZNEIWAREN- GROSSHANDLUNG GES.M.B.H.—See PHOENIX Pharmahandel GmbH & Co. KG; *Int'l*, pg. 5854
PHOENIX ASSET MANAGEMENT, LLC; *U.S. Private*, pg. 3172
PHOENIX ASSET MANAGEMENT LLC; *U.S. Private*, pg. 3172
PHOENIX ASSET MANAGEMENT PARTNERS LTD.; *Int'l*, pg. 5849
PHOENIX ASSOCIATES OF SOUTH FLORIDA, INC.; *U.S. Private*, pg. 3172
PHOENIX AT AVONDALE APARTMENTS—See Olympus Real Estate Corp.; *U.S. Private*, pg. 3014
PHOENIX AVIATION LIMITED—See Frontier Services Group Limited; *Int'l*, pg. 2796
PHOENIX AVONDALE ANUSA, LLC—See AutoNation, Inc.; *U.S. Public*, pg. 237
PHOENIX BATTERY CO., LTD.—See Phoenix Silicon International Corp.; *Int'l*, pg. 5855
PHOENIX BEARINGS, LTD.—See RBC Bearings Incorporated; *U.S. Public*, pg. 1766
PHOENIX BEVERAGES, INC.; *U.S. Private*, pg. 3172
PHOENIX BEVERAGES LIMITED; *Int'l*, pg. 5849
PHOENIX BIG CINEMAS MANAGEMENT LLC—See Reliance - ADA Group Limited; *Int'l*, pg. 6263
PHOENIXBIO CO., LTD.; *Int'l*, pg. 5855
PHOENIX BIOTECH ACQUISITION CORP.; *U.S. Public*, pg. 1689
PHOENIXBIO USA CORPORATION—See PhoenixBio Co., Ltd.; *Int'l*, pg. 5855
PHOENIX BOOKS LTD.—See Jiangsu Phoenix Publishing & Media Corporation Ltd.; *Int'l*, pg. 3952
PHOENIX BULK CARRIERS (US) LLC—See Pangaea Logistics Solutions, Inc.; *U.S. Public*, pg. 1635
PHOENIX BUSINESS JOURNAL—See Advance Publications, Inc.; *U.S. Private*, pg. 84
PHOENIX CABLE TV CO., LTD.—See Taiwan Mobile Co., Ltd.; *Int'l*, pg. 7422
PHOENIX CANADA OIL COMPANY LIMITED; *Int'l*, pg. 5849
PHOENIX CAPITAL CO., LTD.; *Int'l*, pg. 5849
PHOENIX CAPITAL HOLDING AD; *Int'l*, pg. 5849
PHOENIX CENTRAL LABORATORY FOR VETERINARIANS, INC.—See Zoetis, Inc.; *U.S. Public*, pg. 2409
PHOENIX CHILDREN'S FOUNDATION; *U.S. Private*, pg. 3172

2109

PHOENIX CHILDREN'S FOUNDATION / CORPORATE AFFILIATIONS

PHOENIX CHINESE NEWS & ENTERTAINMENT LIMITED—See Phoenix Media Investment (Holdings) Limited; *Int'l*, pg. 5853

PHOENIX COAL COMPANY, INC.; *U.S. Private*, pg. 3172

PHOENIX COATING RESOURCES, INC.—See Compagnie de Saint-Gobain SA; *Int'l*, pg. 1732

PHOENIX COCA-COLA BOTTLING COMPANY—See The Coca-Cola Company; *U.S. Public*, pg. 2065

PHOENIX COLOR CORP.—See Atlas Holdings, LLC; *U.S. Private*, pg. 376

PHOENIX COMMERCIAL COLLECTIONS LIMITED—See Bain Capital, LP; *U.S. Private*, pg. 435

THE PHOENIX COMPANIES, INC.—See Golden Gate Capital Management II, LLC; *U.S. Private*, pg. 1731

PHOENIX COMPOUNDING TECHNOLOGY GMBH—See Continental Aktiengesellschaft; *Int'l*, pg. 1781

PHOENIX CONTACT AB—See PHOENIX CONTACT GmbH & Co. KG; *Int'l*, pg. 5849

PHOENIX CONTACT AS—See PHOENIX CONTACT GmbH & Co. KG; *Int'l*, pg. 5849

PHOENIX CONTACT A/S—See PHOENIX CONTACT GmbH & Co. KG; *Int'l*, pg. 5849

PHOENIX CONTACT B.V.—See PHOENIX CONTACT GmbH & Co. KG; *Int'l*, pg. 5849

PHOENIX CONTACT D.O.O.—See PHOENIX CONTACT GmbH & Co. KG; *Int'l*, pg. 5850

PHOENIX CONTACT ELECTRICAL EQUIPMENT TRADING LLC—See PHOENIX CONTACT GmbH & Co. KG; *Int'l*, pg. 5850

PHOENIX CONTACT ELEKTRONIK TIC. LTD. STI.—See PHOENIX CONTACT GmbH & Co. KG; *Int'l*, pg. 5850

PHOENIX CONTACT E-MOBILITY GMBH—See PHOENIX CONTACT GmbH & Co. KG; *Int'l*, pg. 5850

PHOENIX CONTACT GMBH & CO. KG; *Int'l*, pg. 5849

PHOENIX CONTACT GMBH—See PHOENIX CONTACT GmbH & Co. KG; *Int'l*, pg. 5849

PHOENIX CONTACT, INC—See PHOENIX CONTACT GmbH & Co. KG; *Int'l*, pg. 5850

PHOENIX CONTACT IND. COM. LTDA.—See PHOENIX CONTACT GmbH & Co. KG; *Int'l*, pg. 5849

PHOENIX CONTACT (IRELAND) LTD—See PHOENIX CONTACT GmbH & Co. KG; *Int'l*, pg. 5849

PHOENIX CONTACT (ISRAEL) LTD—See PHOENIX CONTACT GmbH & Co. KG; *Int'l*, pg. 5849

PHOENIX CONTACT KFT.—See PHOENIX CONTACT GmbH & Co. KG; *Int'l*, pg. 5850

PHOENIX CONTACT LTD—See PHOENIX CONTACT GmbH & Co. KG; *Int'l*, pg. 5849

PHOENIX CONTACT MIDDLE EAST FZ LLC—See PHOENIX CONTACT GmbH & Co. KG; *Int'l*, pg. 5849

PHOENIX CONTACT NV/SA—See PHOENIX CONTACT GmbH & Co. KG; *Int'l*, pg. 5850

PHOENIX CONTACT OY—See PHOENIX CONTACT GmbH & Co. KG; *Int'l*, pg. 5850

PHOENIX CONTACT POWER SUPPLIES GMBH—See PHOENIX CONTACT GmbH & Co. KG; *Int'l*, pg. 5850

PHOENIX CONTACT (PTY) LTD.—See PHOENIX CONTACT GmbH & Co. KG; *Int'l*, pg. 5849

PHOENIX CONTACT PTY. LTD.—See PHOENIX CONTACT GmbH & Co. KG; *Int'l*, pg. 5850

PHOENIX CONTACT S.A. DE C.V.—See PHOENIX CONTACT GmbH & Co. KG; *Int'l*, pg. 5850

PHOENIX CONTACT S.A R.L.—See PHOENIX CONTACT GmbH & Co. KG; *Int'l*, pg. 5850

PHOENIX CONTACT S.A.—See PHOENIX CONTACT GmbH & Co. KG; *Int'l*, pg. 5850

PHOENIX CONTACT S.A.—See PHOENIX CONTACT GmbH & Co. KG; *Int'l*, pg. 5850

PHOENIX CONTACT SAS—See PHOENIX CONTACT GmbH & Co. KG; *Int'l*, pg. 5850

PHOENIX CONTACT, S.A.U.—See PHOENIX CONTACT GmbH & Co. KG; *Int'l*, pg. 5850

PHOENIX CONTACT SEA PTE. LTD.—See PHOENIX CONTACT GmbH & Co. KG; *Int'l*, pg. 5850

PHOENIX CONTACT SOFTWARE GMBH—See PHOENIX CONTACT GmbH & Co. KG; *Int'l*, pg. 5850

PHOENIX CONTACT SOFTWARE—See PHOENIX CONTACT GmbH & Co. KG; *Int'l*, pg. 5850

PHOENIX CONTACT SOFTWARE—See PHOENIX CONTACT GmbH & Co. KG; *Int'l*, pg. 5850

PHOENIX CONTACT SOFTWARE—See PHOENIX CONTACT GmbH & Co. KG; *Int'l*, pg. 5850

PHOENIX CONTACT—See PHOENIX CONTACT GmbH & Co. KG; *Int'l*, pg. 5850

PHOENIX CONTACT S.P.A.—See PHOENIX CONTACT GmbH & Co. KG; *Int'l*, pg. 5850

PHOENIX CONTACT SP. Z O.O—See PHOENIX CONTACT GmbH & Co. KG; *Int'l*, pg. 5850

PHOENIX CONTACT SRL—See PHOENIX CONTACT GmbH & Co. KG; *Int'l*, pg. 5850

PHOENIX CONTACT, S.R.O.—See PHOENIX CONTACT GmbH & Co. KG; *Int'l*, pg. 5850

PHOENIX CONTACT, S.R.O.—See PHOENIX CONTACT GmbH & Co. KG; *Int'l*, pg. 5850

PHOENIX CONTACT UAB—See PHOENIX CONTACT GmbH & Co. KG; *Int'l*, pg. 5850

PHOENIX CONTACT WIELKOPOLSKA SP. Z O.O.—See PHOENIX CONTACT GmbH & Co. KG; *Int'l*, pg. 5850

PHOENIX CONTROLS CORPORATION—See Honeywell International Inc.; *U.S. Public*, pg. 1047

PHOENIX CORPORATION—See Reliance Steel & Aluminum Co.; *U.S. Public*, pg. 1781

PHOENIX CREATIVE CO.; *U.S. Private*, pg. 3172

PHOENIX DIGITAL MEDIA LTD.—See Jiangsu Phoenix Publishing & Media Corporation Ltd.; *Int'l*, pg. 3952

PHOENIX DIGITAL PRINTING LTD.—See Jiangsu Phoenix Publishing & Media Corporation Ltd.; *Int'l*, pg. 3952

PHOENIX DIGITAL TECHNOLOGIES PRIVATE LIMITED—See The Phoenix Mills Limited; *Int'l*, pg. 7673

PHOENIX DOOR PANELS LIMITED—See Masco Corporation; *U.S. Public*, pg. 1391

PHOENIX EDUCATION DEVELOPMENT LTD.—See Jiangsu Phoenix Publishing & Media Corporation Ltd.; *Int'l*, pg. 3952

PHOENIX EDUCATION PUBLISHING LTD.—See Jiangsu Phoenix Publishing & Media Corporation Ltd.; *Int'l*, pg. 3952

PHOENIX ELECTRIC CO., LTD.—See Helios Techno Holding Co., Ltd.; *Int'l*, pg. 3330

PHOENIX EMERGENCY SERVICES OF INVERNESS, LLC—See KKR & Co. Inc.; *U.S. Public*, pg. 1250

PHOENIX ENDOSCOPY, L.L.C.—See KKR & Co. Inc.; *U.S. Public*, pg. 1246

PHOENIX ENERGY TECHNOLOGIES; *U.S. Private*, pg. 3172

PHOENIX EQUITY PARTNERS LTD.; *Int'l*, pg. 5850

PHOENIX FABRICATORS & ERECTORS INC.; *U.S. Private*, pg. 3172

PHOENIX FARMACIJA D.D.—See PHOENIX Pharmahandel GmbH & Co. KG; *Int'l*, pg. 5854

PHOENIX FEINBAU GMBH & CO KG—See PHOENIX CONTACT GmbH & Co. KG; *Int'l*, pg. 5850

PHOENIX FILMS & VIDEO—See The Phoenix Learning Group, Inc.; *U.S. Private*, pg. 4095

PHOENIX FINANCE & INVESTMENTS LIMITED; *Int'l*, pg. 5850

PHOENIX FINANCIAL SERVICES, LLC; *U.S. Private*, pg. 3172

PHOENIX FINE ARTS PUBLISHING LTD.—See Jiangsu Phoenix Publishing & Media Corporation Ltd.; *Int'l*, pg. 3952

PHOENIX FIRE SERVICES LTD.—See Interserve Plc; *Int'l*, pg. 3759

PHOENIX FIRE SYSTEMS, INC.—See Pye-Barker Fire & Safety, LLC; *U.S. Private*, pg. 3309

PHOENIX FOODS, INC.—See Specialty Powders Holdings Ltd.; *Int'l*, pg. 7129

PHOENIX FOOTWEAR GROUP, INC.; *U.S. Public*, pg. 1689

PHOENIX FOREST PRODUCTS; *Int'l*, pg. 5850

PHOENIX FORGING COMPANY, INC.; *U.S. Private*, pg. 3172

PHOENIX FOUNDERS, INC.—See Golden Gate Capital Management II, LLC; *U.S. Private*, pg. 1731

PHOENIX GLOBAL RESOURCES PLC; *Int'l*, pg. 5850

PHOENIX GOLD—See PHX AP Acquisitions LLC; *U.S. Private*, pg. 3174

THE PHOENIX GRILL COMPANY—See American Performance Industries; *U.S. Private*, pg. 243

PHOENIX GROUP HOLDINGS LLC; *U.S. Private*, pg. 3173

PHOENIX GROUP HOLDINGS PLC; *Int'l*, pg. 5851

PHOENIX HEALTH CARE INC.—See Constellation Healthcare Technologies, Inc.; *U.S. Private*, pg. 1023

PHOENIX HEALTH PLANS, INC.—See Tenet Healthcare Corporation; *U.S. Public*, pg. 2014

THE PHOENIX HOLDINGS LTD.—See Delek Group Ltd.; *Int'l*, pg. 2011

PHOENIX HOOTERS, INC.—See Restaurants of America, Inc.; *U.S. Private*, pg. 3408

PHOENIX HOUSE FOUNDATION, INC.; *U.S. Private*, pg. 3173

PHOENIX HOUSES OF LOS ANGELES, INC.; *U.S. Private*, pg. 3173

PHOENIX INDUSTRIES LIMITED—See Phoenix International Ltd.; *Int'l*, pg. 5851

PHOENIX INDUSTRIES, LLC; *U.S. Private*, pg. 3173

PHOENIX INSURANCE BROKERS PTY LTD—See Steadfast Group Limited; *Int'l*, pg. 7187

PHOENIX INSURANCE CO. LTD.; *Int'l*, pg. 5851

THE PHOENIX INSURANCE COMPANY LTD.—See Delek Group Ltd.; *Int'l*, pg. 2011

PHOENIX INTEGRATION, INC. - NORTH AMERICA—See ANSYS, Inc.; *U.S. Public*, pg. 139

PHOENIX INTEGRATION, INC.—See ANSYS, Inc.; *U.S. Public*, pg. 139

PHOENIX INTERACTIVE DESIGN INC.—See Diebold Nixdorf, Inc.; *U.S. Public*, pg. 661

PHOENIX INTERNATIONAL, INC.—See JMC Capital Partners LLC; *U.S. Private*, pg. 2215

PHOENIX INTERNATIONAL LTD.; *Int'l*, pg. 5851

PHOENIX INTERNATIONAL PUBLICATIONS INC.—See Jiangsu Phoenix Publishing & Media Corporation Ltd.; *Int'l*, pg. 3952

PHOENIX JUVENILE & CHILDREN'S PUBLISHING LTD.—See Jiangsu Phoenix Publishing & Media Corporation Ltd.; *Int'l*, pg. 3952

PHOENIX LAMPS DIVISION—See Suprajit Engineering Limited; *Int'l*, pg. 7340

THE PHOENIX LEARNING GROUP, INC.; *U.S. Private*, pg. 4095

PHOENIX LEARNING RESOURCES—See The Phoenix Learning Group, Inc.; *U.S. Private*, pg. 4095

PHOENIX LEASING BANK SERVICES—See Phoenix American Incorporated; *U.S. Private*, pg. 3172

PHOENIX LEASING PORTFOLIO SERVICES, INC.—See Phoenix American Incorporated; *U.S. Private*, pg. 3172

PHOENIX LEGEND FILMS LTD.—See Jiangsu Phoenix Publishing & Media Corporation Ltd.; *Int'l*, pg. 3952

PHOENIX LEKARENSKY VELKOOBCHOD A.S—See PHOENIX Pharmahandel GmbH & Co. KG; *Int'l*, pg. 5854

PHOENIX LIFE ASSURANCE LIMITED—See Phoenix Group Holdings PLC; *Int'l*, pg. 5851

PHOENIX LIFE HOLDINGS LIMITED—See Phoenix Group Holdings PLC; *Int'l*, pg. 5851

PHOENIX LIFE LIMITED—See Phoenix Group Holdings PLC; *Int'l*, pg. 5851

PHOENIX LIVING SPACES PVT. LTD.; *Int'l*, pg. 5851

PHOENIX LLC—See SHINE Medical Technologies, LLC; *U.S. Private*, pg. 3637

PHOENIX LOGISTICS, INC.; *U.S. Private*, pg. 3173

PHOENIX LPG PHILIPPINES, INC.—See Phoenix Petroleum Philippines, Inc.; *Int'l*, pg. 5854

PHOENIX MANAGEMENT INC.; *U.S. Private*, pg. 3173

PHOENIX MANUFACTURING, INC.—See Bee Street Holdings LLC; *U.S. Private*, pg. 518

PHOENIX MANUFACTURING SERVICES PTY, LTD.—See Dart Container Corporation; *U.S. Private*, pg. 1160

PHOENIX MARKETING GROUP, INC.; *U.S. Private*, pg. 3173

PHOENIX MARKETING INTERNATIONAL, INC.; *U.S. Private*, pg. 3173

PHOENIX MARKETING SOLUTIONS LLC—See Phoenix Group Holdings LLC; *U.S. Private*, pg. 3173

PHOENIX MECANO AG; *Int'l*, pg. 5851

PHOENIX MECANO APS—See Phoenix Mecano AG; *Int'l*, pg. 5852

PHOENIX MECANO BETEILIGUNGEN AG—See Phoenix Mecano AG; *Int'l*, pg. 5852

PHOENIX MECANO B.V.—See Phoenix Mecano AG; *Int'l*, pg. 5852

PHOENIX MECANO COMERCIAL E TECNICA LTDA.—See Phoenix Mecano AG; *Int'l*, pg. 5852

PHOENIX MECANO COMPONENTS (SHANGHAI) CO. LTD.—See Phoenix Mecano AG; *Int'l*, pg. 5853

PHOENIX MECANO DIGITAL ELEKTRONIK GMBH—See Phoenix Mecano AG; *Int'l*, pg. 5853

PHOENIX MECANO ELCOM S.A.R.L.—See Phoenix Mecano AG; *Int'l*, pg. 5853

PHOENIX MECANO HARTU S.A.R.L.—See Phoenix Mecano AG; *Int'l*, pg. 5853

PHOENIX MECANO HOLDING LTDA.—See Phoenix Mecano AG; *Int'l*, pg. 5853

PHOENIX MECANO HONG KONG LTD.—See Phoenix Mecano AG; *Int'l*, pg. 5853

PHOENIX MECANO INC.—See Phoenix Mecano AG; *Int'l*, pg. 5853

PHOENIX MECANO (INDIA) LTD.—See Phoenix Mecano AG; *Int'l*, pg. 5852

PHOENIX MECANO KECSKEMET KFT—See Phoenix Mecano AG; *Int'l*, pg. 5853

PHOENIX MECANO KOMPONENTEN AG—See Phoenix Mecano AG; *Int'l*, pg. 5853

PHOENIX MECANO KOREA CO. LTD.—See Phoenix Mecano AG; *Int'l*, pg. 5853

PHOENIX MECANO LTD.—See Phoenix Mecano AG; *Int'l*, pg. 5853

PHOENIX MECANO MANAGEMENT AG—See Phoenix Mecano AG; *Int'l*, pg. 5853

PHOENIX MECANO N.V.—See Phoenix Mecano AG; *Int'l*, pg. 5853

PHOENIX MECANO OOO—See Phoenix Mecano AG; *Int'l*, pg. 5853

PHOENIX MECANO PLASTIC S.R.L.—See Phoenix Mecano AG; *Int'l*, pg. 5853

PHOENIX MECANO S.A.R.L.—See Phoenix Mecano AG; *Int'l*, pg. 5853

PHOENIX MECANO SAUDI ARABIA LLC—See Phoenix Mecano AG; *Int'l*, pg. 5853

PHOENIX MECANO S.E. ASIA PTE LTD.—See Phoenix Mecano AG; *Int'l*, pg. 5853

PHOENIX MECANO S.R.L.—See Phoenix Mecano AG; *Int'l*, pg. 5853

PHOENIX MECANO TRADING AG—See Phoenix Mecano AG; *Int'l*, pg. 5853

PHOENIX MECANO TUNISIE S.A.R.L.—See Phoenix Mecano AG; *Int'l*, pg. 5853

THE PHOENIX MEDIA/COMMUNICATIONS GROUP; *U.S. Private*, pg. 4095

PHOENIX MEDIA INVESTMENT (HOLDINGS) LIMITED; *Int'l*, pg. 5853

COMPANY NAME INDEX

PHOENIX MEDIA PUBLISHING LTD.—See Jiangsu Phoenix Publishing & Media Corporation Ltd.; *Int'l*, pg. 3952
PHOENIX MEDICAL GROUP PTE. LTD.—See Livingstone Health Holdings Limited; *Int'l*, pg. 4532
PHOENIX MEDICAL SOFTWARE, INC.; *U.S. Private*, pg. 3173
PHOENIX MEDICAL SUPPLIES LTD.—See PHOENIX Pharmahandel GmbH & Co. KG; *Int'l*, pg. 5854
PHOENIX MEMORIAL PARK ASSOCIATION—See Service Corporation International; *U.S. Public*, pg. 1870
PHOENIX MERCURY—See Suns Legacy Partners, LLC; *U.S. Private*, pg. 3871
PHOENIX METAL CORP.—See Rever Holdings Corporation; *Int'l*, pg. 6313
PHOENIX METALLICS, INC.—See John S. Frey Enterprises; *U.S. Private*, pg. 2224
PHOENIX METALS COMPANY—See Reliance Steel & Aluminum Co.; *U.S. Public*, pg. 1781
PHOENIX METALS COMPANY—See Reliance Steel & Aluminum Co.; *U.S. Public*, pg. 1781
PHOENIX METROPOLIS MEDIA (BEIJING) COMPANY LIMITED—See Phoenix Media Investment (Holdings) Limited; *Int'l*, pg. 5853
PHOENIX METROPOLIS MEDIA (SHANGHAI) COMPANY LIMITED—See Phoenix Media Investment (Holdings) Limited; *Int'l*, pg. 5853
THE PHOENIX MILLS LIMITED; *Int'l*, pg. 7673
PHOENIX MOTOR INC.; *U.S. Public*, pg. 1689
PHOENIX NEW MEDIA LIMITED—See Phoenix Media Investment (Holdings) Limited; *Int'l*, pg. 5853
PHOENIX NEWSPAPERS, INC.—See Gannett Co., Inc.; *U.S. Public*, pg. 899
PHOENIX NEW TIMES, LLC—See Village Voice Media Holdings, LLC; *U.S. Private*, pg. 4384
PHOENIX OFFSHORE CO. LTD—See AMOS Group Limited; *Int'l*, pg. 430
PHOENIX OF TANZANIA COMPANY LIMITED—See MUA Ltd.; *Int'l*, pg. 5073
PHOENIX OIL, INC.—See Adams Resources & Energy, Inc.; *U.S. Public*, pg. 38
PHOENIX O&M (PVT.) LTD.—See WPP plc; *Int'l*, pg. 8488
PHOENIX ONE SALES, MARKETING, MANAGEMENT + COMMUNICATIONS LLC; *U.S. Private*, pg. 3173
THE PHOENIX OPHTHALMOLOGY ASC, LLC—See KKR & Co. Inc.; *U.S. Public*, pg. 1248
PHOENIX ORTHOPAEDIC AMBULATORY CENTER, L.L.C.—See KKR & Co. Inc.; *U.S. Public*, pg. 1246
PHOENIX PACKAGING CARIBE S.A.S.—See Genstar Capital, LLC; *U.S. Private*, pg. 1679
PHOENIX PACKAGING INC.; *U.S. Private*, pg. 3173
PHOENIX PACKAGING LLC—See Genstar Capital, LLC; *U.S. Private*, pg. 1679
PHOENIX PACKAGING MEXICO, S.A. DE C.V.—See Genstar Capital, LLC; *U.S. Private*, pg. 1679
PHOENIX PAPER PACKAGING COLOMBIA S.A.S.—See Genstar Capital, LLC; *U.S. Private*, pg. 1679
PHOENIX PAPER PACKAGING MEXICO, S. DE R.L. DE C.V.—See Genstar Capital, LLC; *U.S. Private*, pg. 1679
PHOENIX PARTNERS INC.; *U.S. Private*, pg. 3173
PHOENIX PEACH, LLC—See Baum Capital Partners Management LLC; *U.S. Private*, pg. 490
PHOENIX PERSONNEL; *U.S. Private*, pg. 3173
PHOENIX PETROLEUM PHILIPPINES, INC.; *Int'l*, pg. 5854
PHOENIX PHARMA DOOEL—See PHOENIX Pharmahandel GmbH & Co. KG; *Int'l*, pg. 5854
PHOENIX PHARMA D.O.O.—See PHOENIX Pharmahandel GmbH & Co. KG; *Int'l*, pg. 5854
PHOENIX PHARMAHANDEL GMBH & CO. KG; *Int'l*, pg. 5854
PHOENIX PHARMA POLSKA SP. Z O.O.—See PHOENIX Pharmahandel GmbH & Co. KG; *Int'l*, pg. 5854
PHOENIX PHARMA S.A.S.—See PHOENIX Pharmahandel GmbH & Co. KG; *Int'l*, pg. 5854
PHOENIX PHARMA ZRT.—See PHOENIX Pharmahandel GmbH & Co. KG; *Int'l*, pg. 5854
PHOENIX PICTURES INC.; *U.S. Private*, pg. 3173
PHOENIX PLUS CORP.; *Int'l*, pg. 5855
PHOENIX POWER CO SAOG; *Int'l*, pg. 5855
PHOENIX-POWER CULTURAL DEVELOPMENT LTD.—See Jiangsu Phoenix Publishing & Media Corporation Ltd.; *Int'l*, pg. 3952
PHOENIX POWER GROUP, INC.—See Quanta Services, Inc.; *U.S. Public*, pg. 1752
PHOENIX PRESS LTD L.P.—See Heinrich Bauer Verlag KG; *Int'l*, pg. 3324
PHOENIX PROCESS EQUIPMENT; *U.S. Private*, pg. 3173
PHOENIX PRODUCTS COMPANY, INC.—See JMC Capital Partners LLC; *U.S. Private*, pg. 2215
PHOENIX REHABILITATION & HEALTH SERVICES, INC.—See Audax Group, Limited Partnership; *U.S. Private*, pg. 389
PHOENIX RESORT CO., LTD.—See Sega Sammy Holdings, Inc.; *Int'l*, pg. 6681
PHOENIX RESOURCES, INC.—See Waste Management, Inc.; *U.S. Public*, pg. 2331
PHOENIX RETAIL GROUP; *U.S. Private*, pg. 3173
PHOENIX RISING AVIATION INC.—See Saker Aviation Services, Inc.; *U.S. Public*, pg. 1836

PHOENIX RISING COMPANIES, INC.; *Int'l*, pg. 5855
PHOENIX ROOFING, INC.; *U.S. Private*, pg. 3173
PHOENIX SATELLITE TELEVISION COMPANY LIMITED—See Phoenix Media Investment (Holdings) Limited; *Int'l*, pg. 5854
PHOENIX SATELLITE TELEVISION (U.S.) INC.—See Phoenix Media Investment (Holdings) Limited; *Int'l*, pg. 5854
PHOENIX SCIENCE PRESS LTD.—See Jiangsu Phoenix Publishing & Media Corporation Ltd.; *Int'l*, pg. 3952
PHOENIX SHIPPING (WUHAN) CO., LTD.; *Int'l*, pg. 5855
PHOENIX SILICON INTERNATIONAL CORP.; *Int'l*, pg. 5855
PHOENIX SOIL, LLC—See Enviri Corporation; *U.S. Public*, pg. 780
PHOENIX SOLAR AG; *Int'l*, pg. 5855
PHOENIX SOLAR E.P.E.—See Phoenix Solar AG; *Int'l*, pg. 5855
PHOENIX SOLAR PTY LTD.—See Phoenix Solar AG; *Int'l*, pg. 5855
PHOENIX SOLAR S.L.—See Phoenix Solar AG; *Int'l*, pg. 5855
PHOENIX SOLAR S.R.L.—See Phoenix Solar AG; *Int'l*, pg. 5855
PHOENIX SOLUTIONS CO.; *U.S. Private*, pg. 3173
PHOENIX SPREE DEUTSCHLAND LIMITED; *Int'l*, pg. 5855
PHOENIX SUNS—See Suns Legacy Partners, LLC; *U.S. Private*, pg. 3870
PHOENIX SURGERY CENTER, LLC—See Nobilis Health Corp.; *U.S. Private*, pg. 2932
PHOENIX SYNERGISTICS—See Phoenix Marketing International, Inc.; *U.S. Private*, pg. 3173
PHOENIX SYSTEMS SP. Z O.O.—See Atende S.A.; *Int'l*, pg. 668
PHOENIX TANKERS PTE. LTD.—See Mitsui O.S.K. Lines, Ltd.; *Int'l*, pg. 4991
PHOENIX TECHNOLOGIES KK—See Marlin Equity Partners, LLC; *U.S. Private*, pg. 2585
PHOENIX TECHNOLOGIES (KOREA) LTD.—See Marlin Equity Partners, LLC; *U.S. Private*, pg. 2584
PHOENIX TECHNOLOGIES LTD.—See Marlin Equity Partners, LLC; *U.S. Private*, pg. 2584
PHOENIX TECHNOLOGIES (TAIWAN) LTD.—See Marlin Equity Partners, LLC; *U.S. Private*, pg. 2584
PHOENIX TECHNOLOGY LTD; *U.S. Private*, pg. 3173
PHOENIX TECHNOLOGY SERVICES INC.—See PHX Energy Services Corp.; *Int'l*, pg. 5858
PHOENIX TECHNOLOGY SERVICES LP—See PHX Energy Services Corp.; *Int'l*, pg. 5858
PHOENIX TELECOMMUNICATIONS, INC.—See Level 4 Telcom; *U.S. Private*, pg. 2434
PHOENIX TELECOM SOLUTIONS, INC.; *U.S. Private*, pg. 3174
PHOENIX TEXTILE CORPORATION; *U.S. Private*, pg. 3174
PHOENIX THERAPY & CARE LIMITED—See Sheikh Holdings Group (Investments) Limited; *Int'l*, pg. 6794
PHOENIX TIMBER FACTORY LLC—See Alpha Dhabi Holding PJSC; *Int'l*, pg. 367
PHOENIX-T, INC.—See Lithia Motors, Inc.; *U.S. Public*, pg. 1326
PHOENIX TISSUE REPAIR, INC.—See BridgeBio Pharma, Inc.; *U.S. Public*, pg. 382
PHOENIX TOURS INTERNATIONAL, INC.; *Int'l*, pg. 5855
PHOENIX TOWER INTERNATIONAL LLC—See Blackstone Inc.; *U.S. Public*, pg. 356
PHOENIX TOWNSHIP LTD.; *Int'l*, pg. 5855
PHOENIX TRADING CORP.—See 3G Capital Partners L.P.; *U.S. Private*, pg. 13
PHOENIX TRADING INC.; *U.S. Private*, pg. 3174
PHOENIX TRANSPORTATION SERVICES LLC; *U.S. Private*, pg. 3174
PHOENIX TREE HOLDINGS LIMITED; *Int'l*, pg. 5855
PHOENIX VENEZUELA—See Genstar Capital, LLC; *U.S. Private*, pg. 1679
PHOENIXVILLE FEDERAL BANK & TRUST; *U.S. Private*, pg. 3174
PHOENIXVILLE HOSPITAL COMPANY, LLC—See Tower Health; *U.S. Public*, pg. 4193
PHOENIXVILLE NEWSPAPERS, INC.—See Alden Global Capital LLC; *U.S. Private*, pg. 157
PHOENIX VINTNERS, LLC; *U.S. Private*, pg. 3174
PHOENIX VOCATIONAL EDUCATION BOOKS LTD.—See Jiangsu Phoenix Publishing & Media Corporation Ltd.; *Int'l*, pg. 3952
PHOENIX WEALTH SERVICES LIMITED—See Phoenix Group Holdings PLC; *Int'l*, pg. 5851
PHOENIX WELDING SUPPLY, CO.; *U.S. Private*, pg. 3174
PHOENIX XINHUA PRINTING LTD.—See Jiangsu Phoenix Publishing & Media Corporation Ltd.; *Int'l*, pg. 3952
PHOENIX ZOO; *U.S. Private*, pg. 3174
PHOENX PLM PTY. LTD.—See Schneider Electric SE; *Int'l*, pg. 6625
PHO HOI AN LIMITED—See Tonking New Energy Group Holdings Limited; *Int'l*, pg. 7809
PHOINIX GLOBAL LLC—See Forum Energy Technologies, Inc.; *U.S. Public*, pg. 874

PHONG PHU PHARMACEUTICAL JSC

PHOLA COACHES PROPRIETARY LIMITED—See Super Group Limited; *Int'l*, pg. 7334
PHOL DHANYA PUBLIC COMPANY LIMITED; *Int'l*, pg. 5855
PHOL WATER COMPANY LIMITED—See Phol Dhanya Public Company Limited; *Int'l*, pg. 5856
PHONAG RECORDS AG—See Edel SE & Co. KGaA; *Int'l*, pg. 2305
PHONAK AB—See Sonova Holding AG; *Int'l*, pg. 7100
PHONAK ACOUSTIC IMPLANTS SA—See Sonova Holding AG; *Int'l*, pg. 7100
PHONAK AG—See Sonova Holding AG; *Int'l*, pg. 7100
PHONAK AS—See Sonova Holding AG; *Int'l*, pg. 7100
PHONAK BELGIUM S.A./N.V.—See Sonova Holding AG; *Int'l*, pg. 7100
PHONAK B.V.—See Sonova Holding AG; *Int'l*, pg. 7100
PHONAK CANADA LIMITED—See Sonova Holding AG; *Int'l*, pg. 7100
PHONAK CIS LTD.—See Sonova Holding AG; *Int'l*, pg. 7100
PHONAK COMMUNICATIONS AG—See Sonova Holding AG; *Int'l*, pg. 7100
PHONAK DANMARK A/S—See Sonova Holding AG; *Int'l*, pg. 7100
PHONAK DO BRASIL SISTEMAS AUDIOLOGICOS LTDA.—See Sonova Holding AG; *Int'l*, pg. 7100
PHONAK DUYU SISTEMLERI ITHALAT IHRACAT TICARET PAZARLAMA LIMITED SIRKETI—See Sonova Holding AG; *Int'l*, pg. 7100
PHONAK FINLAND OY—See Sonova Holding AG; *Int'l*, pg. 7101
PHONAK GMBH—See Sonova Holding AG; *Int'l*, pg. 7101
PHONAK GROUP LTD.—See Sonova Holding AG; *Int'l*, pg. 7101
PHONAK HEARING SYSTEMS AG—See Sonova Holding AG; *Int'l*, pg. 7101
PHONAK INDIA PVT. LTD.—See Sonova Holding AG; *Int'l*, pg. 7101
PHONAK ITALIA S.R.L.—See Sonova Holding AG; *Int'l*, pg. 7101
PHONAK JAPAN CO., LTD.—See Sonova Holding AG; *Int'l*, pg. 7101
PHONAK KOREA LTD.—See Sonova Holding AG; *Int'l*, pg. 7101
PHONAK LLC—See Sonova Holding AG; *Int'l*, pg. 7101
PHONAK MEXICANA S.A. DE C.V.—See Sonova Holding AG; *Int'l*, pg. 7101
PHONAK NEW ZEALAND LTD.—See Sonova Holding AG; *Int'l*, pg. 7101
PHONAK OPERATION CENTER VIETNAM CO., LTD.—See Sonova Holding AG; *Int'l*, pg. 7101
PHONAK POLSKA SP. Z O.O.—See Sonova Holding AG; *Int'l*, pg. 7101
PHONAK PTY. LTD.—See Sonova Holding AG; *Int'l*, pg. 7101
PHONAK (SHANGHAI) CO. LTD.—See Sonova Holding AG; *Int'l*, pg. 7100
PHONAK SINGAPORE PTE. LTD.—See Sonova Holding AG; *Int'l*, pg. 7101
PHONAK TAIWAN PTE. LTD.—See Sonova Holding AG; *Int'l*, pg. 7101
PHONECARD EXPRESS, LLC—See Magnet LLC; *U.S. Private*, pg. 2547
PHONE.COM INC.; *U.S. Private*, pg. 3174
PH ONE DEVELOPMENT (CAMBODIA) LTD.—See Hong Lai Huat Group Limited; *Int'l*, pg. 3467
PHONE DIRECTORIES COMPANY—See Kainos Capital, LLC; *U.S. Private*, pg. 2255
PHONE POWER, LLC; *U.S. Private*, pg. 3174
PHONERO AS—See Telia Company AB; *Int'l*, pg. 7543
PHONES 4U LTD.—See BC Partners LLP; *Int'l*, pg. 925
THE PHONE SHOPPE; *U.S. Private*, pg. 4095
PHONETEC LP; *U.S. Private*, pg. 3174
PHONETICS, INC.; *U.S. Private*, pg. 3174
PHONETIME INC.—See Mexedia S.p.A.; *Int'l*, pg. 4869
PHONETIME NETWORKS, INC.—See Tellza Inc.; *U.S. Public*, pg. 1999
PHONET & JOHNSON—See Whippoorwill Associates, Inc.; *U.S. Private*, pg. 4507
PHONEVALLEY—See Publicis Groupe S.A.; *Int'l*, pg. 6104
PHONE WEB SA; *Int'l*, pg. 5856
PHONEX COMMUNICATIONS INC.—See Tose Co., Ltd.; *Int'l*, pg. 7832
PHONEX-GEMA AG—See Armstrong World Industries, Inc.; *U.S. Public*, pg. 194
PHONEX HOLDINGS, INC; *U.S. Public*, pg. 1689
PHONG PHU PHARMACEUTICAL JSC; *Int'l*, pg. 5856
PHONIC EAR A/S—See Demant A/S; *Int'l*, pg. 2023
PHONIC EAR INC.—See Demant A/S; *Int'l*, pg. 2024
PHONIX-HAUS AM STEINSGRABEN SENIOREN- UND PFLEGEZENTRUM GMBH—See Clariane SE; *Int'l*, pg. 1643
PHONIX - HAUS ROGGENBERG - PFLEGEHEIM GMBH—See Clariane SE; *Int'l*, pg. 1643
PHONIX-HAUS ROSMARIN SENIOREN- UND PFLEGEZENTRUM GMBH—See Clariane SE; *Int'l*, pg. 1643
PHONIX - HAUS SILBERDISTEL - ALTEN- U.PFLEGEHEIM GMBH—See Clariane SE; *Int'l*, pg. 1643

PHONIX-SENIORENRESIDENZ AM TEICHBERG GMBH—See Clariane SE; *Int'l*, pg. 1643
PHONIX SENIORENRESIDENZ ELSTERTALBLICK GMBH—See Clariane SE; *Int'l*, pg. 1643
PHONIX-SENIORENZENTRUM AHORNHOF GMBH—See Clariane SE; *Int'l*, pg. 1643
PHONIX-SENIORENZENTRUM AM BODENSEERING GMBH—See Clariane SE; *Int'l*, pg. 1643
PHONIX-SENIORENZENTRUM AM MUPPBERG GMBH—See Clariane SE; *Int'l*, pg. 1643
PHONIX-SENIORENZENTRUM AM SCHLOSSTEICH GMBH—See Clariane SE; *Int'l*, pg. 1643
PHONIX-SENIORENZENTRUM EVERGREEN GMBH—See Clariane SE; *Int'l*, pg. 1643
PHONIX-SENIORENZENTRUM EVERGREEN MAXHUTTE GMBH—See Clariane SE; *Int'l*, pg. 1644
PHONIX-SENIORENZENTRUM GARTENSTADT GMBH—See Clariane SE; *Int'l*, pg. 1644
PHONIX - SENIORENZENTRUM GRAF TILLY GMBH—See Clariane SE; *Int'l*, pg. 1643
PHONIX-SENIORENZENTRUM HERZOG ALBRECHT GMBH—See Clariane SE; *Int'l*, pg. 1643
PHONIX - SENIORENZENTRUM HESSENALLEE GMBH—See Clariane SE; *Int'l*, pg. 1643
PHONIX-SENIORENZENTRUM IM BRUHL GMBH—See Clariane SE; *Int'l*, pg. 1644
PHONIX-SENIORENZENTRUM MAINPARKSEE GMBH—See Clariane SE; *Int'l*, pg. 1644
PHONIX-SENIORENZENTRUM NEUPERLACH GMBH—See Clariane SE; *Int'l*, pg. 1644
PHONIX-SENIORENZENTRUM ST HEDWIG GMBH—See Clariane SE; *Int'l*, pg. 1644
PHONIX-SENIORENZENTRUM TAUNUSBLICK GMBH—See Clariane SE; *Int'l*, pg. 1644
PHONIX-SENIORENZENTRUM ULMENHOF GMBH—See Clariane SE; *Int'l*, pg. 1644
PHONIX-SENIORENZENTRUM ZWEI LINDEN GMBH—See Clariane SE; *Int'l*, pg. 1644
PHONIX SOZIALZENTRUM WINDSBACH GMBH—See Clariane SE; *Int'l*, pg. 1643
PHORUS, INC—See Xperi Inc.; *U.S. Public*, pg. 2392
PHOSAGRO BALKANS DOO—See PJSC PhosAgro; *Int'l*, pg. 5883
PHOSAGRO-CHEREPOVETS, OJSC—See PJSC PhosAgro; *Int'l*, pg. 5883
PHOSAGRO DEUTSCHLAND GMBH—See PJSC PhosAgro; *Int'l*, pg. 5883
PHOSAGRO FRANCE SAS—See PJSC PhosAgro; *Int'l*, pg. 5883
PHOSAGRO-KURSK, LLC—See PJSC PhosAgro; *Int'l*, pg. 5883
PHOSAGRO POLSKA SP.Z O.O—See PJSC RusHydro; *Int'l*, pg. 5884
PHOSAGRO TRADING SA—See PJSC PhosAgro; *Int'l*, pg. 5883
PHOSAGRO-TRANS, LLC—See PJSC PhosAgro; *Int'l*, pg. 5883
PHOSCO LTD; *Int'l*, pg. 5856
PHOSEON TECHNOLOGY, INC.—See AEA Investors LP; *U.S. Private*, pg. 113
PHOSFONIA, S.L.—See UPL Limited; *Int'l*, pg. 8089
PHOSINT TRADING LIMITED—See PJSC PhosAgro; *Int'l*, pg. 5883
PHOSLOCK (BEIJING) ECOLOGICAL ENGINEERING TECHNOLOGY CO., LTD.—See Phoslock Environmental Technologies Limited; *Int'l*, pg. 5856
PHOSLOCK ENVIRONMENTAL TECHNOLOGIES LIMITED; *Int'l*, pg. 5856
THE PHOSPHATE COMPANY LIMITED; *Int'l*, pg. 7673
PHOSPHATE RESOURCES LIMITED—See CI Resources Limited; *Int'l*, pg. 1601
PHOSPHATE RESOURCES (SINGAPORE) PTE LTD—See CI Resources Limited; *Int'l*, pg. 1601
PHOSPHORE SARL; *Int'l*, pg. 5856
PHOSPHORIT INDUSTRIAL GROUP, LLC—See EuroChem Mineral Chemical Company, OJSC; *Int'l*, pg. 2534
PHOSPHOSOLUTIONS, LLC—See Janel Corporation; *U.S. Public*, pg. 1187
PHOSTECH LITHIUM INC.—See Clariant AG; *Int'l*, pg. 1645
PHOTEL INC.—See Teleperformance SE; *Int'l*, pg. 7540
PHOTIZO CO., LTD.—See Nepes Corporation Limited; *Int'l*, pg. 5200
PHOTIZO GROUP; *U.S. Private*, pg. 3174
PHOTOBUCKET CORPORATION; *U.S. Private*, pg. 3174
PHOTOCAT A/S; *Int'l*, pg. 5856
PHOTOCHEMICAL CO., LTD.—See Hamamatsu Photonics K.K.; *Int'l*, pg. 3235
PHOTOCHEMIE AG—See Cicor Technologies Ltd.; *Int'l*, pg. 1603
PHOTOCRAFT, INC.—See Taylor Corporation; *U.S. Private*, pg. 3938
PHOTOCREATE CO., LTD.—See Culture Convenience Club Co., Ltd.; *Int'l*, pg. 1877
PHOTOCURE ASA; *Int'l*, pg. 5856
PHOTO ETCH TECHNOLOGY—See Align Capital Partners, LLC; *U.S. Private*, pg. 167

PHOTOGENIC, INC.—See Keystone Capital, Inc.; *U.S. Private*, pg. 2295
PHOTOGENIC PROFESSIONAL LIGHTING—See Promark International Inc.; *U.S. Private*, pg. 3282
PHOTOGLOB AG; *Int'l*, pg. 5856
PHOTOLINK CREATIVE GROUP; *Int'l*, pg. 5856
PHOTOMATICO (SINGAPORE) PTE. LIMITED—See ME Group International plc; *Int'l*, pg. 4762
PHOTOMATON SA—See ME Group International plc; *Int'l*, pg. 4762
PHOTOMATON S.A.S.—See ME Group International plc; *Int'l*, pg. 4762
PHOTO-ME CR SRO—See ME Group International plc; *Int'l*, pg. 4762
PHOTO-ME FRANCE / KIS—See ME Group International plc; *Int'l*, pg. 4762
PHOTO ME HOLDING FRANCE S.A.S.—See ME Group International plc; *Int'l*, pg. 4762
PHOTO-ME IRELAND LTD—See ME Group International plc; *Int'l*, pg. 4762
PHOTO-ME NORTHERN IRELAND LTD—See ME Group International plc; *Int'l*, pg. 4762
PHOTO-ME SHANGHAI—See ME Group International plc; *Int'l*, pg. 4762
PHOTOMETRICS—See Teledyne Technologies Incorporated; *U.S. Public*, pg. 1992
PHOTOMETRICS UK LIMITED—See Roper Technologies, Inc.; *U.S. Public*, pg. 1812
PHOTOMYNE LTD.; *Int'l*, pg. 5856
PHOTON CAPITAL ADVISORS LIMITED; *Int'l*, pg. 5856
PHOTON CONTROL INC.—See MKS Instruments, Inc.; *U.S. Public*, pg. 1453
PHOTON DYNAMICS, INC.—See KLA Corporation; *U.S. Public*, pg. 1268
PHOTON ENERGY AUSTRALIA PTY. LTD.—See Photon Energy N.V.; *Int'l*, pg. 5856
PHOTON ENERGY N.V.; *Int'l*, pg. 5856
PHOTON ENERGY OPERATIONS CZ S.R.O.—See Photon Energy N.V.; *Int'l*, pg. 5856
PHOTON ENERGY OPERATIONS SK S.R.O.—See Photon Energy N.V.; *Int'l*, pg. 5856
PHOTON GROUP SINGAPORE PTE LIMITED—See Enero Group Limited; *Int'l*, pg. 2424
PHOTONICORE TECHNOLOGIES CO., LTD.—See Largan Precision Co., Ltd.; *Int'l*, pg. 4418
PHOTONIC SENSE GMBH—See Hellma GmbH & Co. KG; *Int'l*, pg. 3334
PHOTONICS HEALTHCARE B.V.—See SBI Holdings, Inc.; *Int'l*, pg. 6604
PHOTONICS MANAGEMENT CORP.—See Hamamatsu Photonics K.K.; *Int'l*, pg. 3235
PHOTONIKA LLC—See Endress+Hauser (International) Holding AG; *Int'l*, pg. 2409
PHOTON INFOTECH PRIVATE LIMITED; *Int'l*, pg. 5856
PHOTONIS FRANCE S.A.S.—See Ardian SAS; *Int'l*, pg. 556
PHOTONIS NETHERLANDS B.V.—See Ardian SAS; *Int'l*, pg. 556
PHOTONIS TECHNOLOGIES S.A.S.—See Ardian SAS; *Int'l*, pg. 556
PHOTONIS USA, INC.—See Ardian SAS; *Int'l*, pg. 556
PHOTONIS USA PENNSYLVANIA, INC.—See Ardian SAS; *Int'l*, pg. 556
PHOTON MACHINES INC; *U.S. Private*, pg. 3174
PHOTON POWER PLC—See Borealis Exploration Limited; *Int'l*, pg. 1113
PHOTON SYSTEMS, INC.—See Dow Inc.; *U.S. Public*, pg. 685
PHOTON-TECH INSTRUMENTS CO., LTD.—See Basler AG; *Int'l*, pg. 887
PHOTON WATER TECHNOLOGY S.R.O.—See Photon Energy N.V.; *Int'l*, pg. 5856
PHOTOP TECHNOLOGIES, INC.—See Coherent Corp.; *U.S. Public*, pg. 529
PHOTOQUIP INDIA LTD.; *Int'l*, pg. 5856
PHOTOREFLECT, LLC; *U.S. Private*, pg. 3174
PHOTOSOL—See Rubis SCA; *Int'l*, pg. 6423
PHOTO-SONICS INC.; *U.S. Private*, pg. 3174
PHOTOSOUND COMMUNICATIONS—See HealthSTAR Communications, Inc.; *U.S. Private*, pg. 1898
PHOTOSOUND COMMUNICATIONS—See HealthSTAR Communications, Inc.; *U.S. Private*, pg. 1898
PHOTO SYSTEMS INC.; *U.S. Private*, pg. 3174
PHOTOVAC—See INFICON Holding AG; *Int'l*, pg. 3684
PHOTOVOLTECH N.V.; *Int'l*, pg. 5856
PHOTO WORKS CO., LTD.—See Oriental Land Co., Ltd.; *Int'l*, pg. 5625
PHOTOWORKS, INC.—See Clayton, Dubilier & Rice, LLC; *U.S. Private*, pg. 919
PHOTOZOU HOLDINGS, INC.; *Int'l*, pg. 5856
PHOTRON EUROPE LIMITED—See Imagica Group Inc.; *Int'l*, pg. 3618
PHOTRONICS CALIFORNIA, INC.—See Photronics, Inc.; *U.S. Public*, pg. 1689
PHOTRONICS IDAHO, INC.—See Photronics, Inc.; *U.S. Public*, pg. 1689
PHOTRONICS, INC.; *U.S. Public*, pg. 1689
PHOTRONICS KOREA, LTD.—See Photronics, Inc.; *U.S. Public*, pg. 1689

PHOTRONICS MZD, GMBH—See Photronics, Inc.; *U.S. Public*, pg. 1689
PHOTRONICS SINGAPORE PTE, LTD.—See Photronics, Inc.; *U.S. Public*, pg. 1689
PHOTRONICS UK, LTD.—See Photronics, Inc.; *U.S. Public*, pg. 1689
PHOTRON LIMITED—See Imagica Group Inc.; *Int'l*, pg. 3618
PHOTRON M&E SOLUTIONS INC.—See Imagica Group Inc.; *Int'l*, pg. 3618
PHOTRON USA, INC.—See Imagica Group Inc.; *Int'l*, pg. 3619
PHPC CO. LTD. INC.—See Hitachi, Ltd.; *Int'l*, pg. 3424
PHP FIBERS GMBH—See Indorama Ventures Public Company Limited; *Int'l*, pg. 3659
PHP FIBERS INC.—See Indorama Ventures Public Company Limited; *Int'l*, pg. 3659
PHP HYOGO CO., LTD.—See Pigeon Corporation; *Int'l*, pg. 5865
PHP IBARAKI CO., LTD.—See Pigeon Corporation; *Int'l*, pg. 5865
PHP MERCUS SP. Z.O.O.—See KGHM Polska Miedz S.A.; *Int'l*, pg. 4149
PHP VENTURES ACQUISITION CORP.; *Int'l*, pg. 5856
PHRATRA SDN. BHD—See Nam Heng Oil Mill Co. Sdn. Bhd.; *Int'l*, pg. 5134
PHREESIA, INC.; *U.S. Public*, pg. 1689
PHRIKOLAT CHEMISCHE ERZEUGNISSE GMBH; *Int'l*, pg. 5857
PHRIKOLAT DRILLING SPECIALTIES GMBH—See Phrikolat Chemische Erzeugnisse GmbH; *Int'l*, pg. 5857
PHRIKOLAT DRILLING SPECIALTIES GMBH—See Phrikolat Chemische Erzeugnisse GmbH; *Int'l*, pg. 5857
PHS ALL CLEAR LIMITED—See The Bidvest Group Limited; *Int'l*, pg. 7622
PHS BESAFE LTD—See The Bidvest Group Limited; *Int'l*, pg. 7622
PHSC PLC; *Int'l*, pg. 5857
PHS DATASHRED LTD—See The Bidvest Group Limited; *Int'l*, pg. 7622
PHS DIRECT LTD—See The Bidvest Group Limited; *Int'l*, pg. 7622
PHS GROUP LIMITED—See The Bidvest Group Limited; *Int'l*, pg. 7626
PHS GROUP PLC—See The Bidvest Group Limited; *Int'l*, pg. 7622
PHS INVESTMENTS LIMITED—See The Bidvest Group Limited; *Int'l*, pg. 7622
PHS LAUNDRYSERV LTD.—See The Bidvest Group Limited; *Int'l*, pg. 7622
PHS/MWA—See HEICO Corporation; *U.S. Public*, pg. 1021
PHS PHYSICAL THERAPY, LLC—See Select Medical Holdings Corporation; *U.S. Public*, pg. 1858
P.H. S.R.L.—See TUV SUD AG; *Int'l*, pg. 7985
PHS-TOMSKHIMPHARM JSC—See JSC Pharmstandard; *Int'l*, pg. 4010
PHS TREADSMART LTD—See The Bidvest Group Limited; *Int'l*, pg. 7622
PHS WASTEKIT—See The Bidvest Group Limited; *Int'l*, pg. 7622
PHS WASTEMANAGEMENT LTD.—See The Bidvest Group Limited; *Int'l*, pg. 7622
PHS WATERLOGIC LTD—See The Bidvest Group Limited; *Int'l*, pg. 7622
P&H TECH CO., LTD - JINCHEON FACTORY—See P&H TECH Co., Ltd; *Int'l*, pg. 5681
P&H TECH CO., LTD; *Int'l*, pg. 5681
PHT INC.—See Kobayashi Travel Service Ltd. Inc.; *U.S. Private*, pg. 2326
PH TRADING LIMITED; *Int'l*, pg. 5839
PH TRADING W.L.L.—See Endress+Hauser (International) Holding AG; *Int'l*, pg. 2409
P&H TRANSPORTATION—See Bradford Oil Company, Inc.; *U.S. Private*, pg. 632
PHT SERVICES LTD.—See Palmetto Hospital Trust; *U.S. Private*, pg. 3081
PHU BIA MINING LIMITED—See Guangdong Rising Assets Management Co., Ltd.; *Int'l*, pg. 3159
PHUC HUNG HOLDINGS CONSTRUCTION JOINT STOCK COMPANY; *Int'l*, pg. 5857
PHUC LOC ENGINEERING & TRADING CO., LTD.—See CHINO Corporation; *Int'l*, pg. 1571
PHUC SON TECHNOLOGY CO., LTD.—See Adtec Plasma Technology Co., Ltd.; *Int'l*, pg. 154
PHUC THINH DESIGN CONSTRUCTION TRADING CORPORATION; *Int'l*, pg. 5857
PHU ELMAR SP. Z.O.O.—See BRENNTAG SE; *Int'l*, pg. 1149
PHU HOA TAN WATER SUPPLY JSC; *Int'l*, pg. 5857
PHU HUNG REAL ESTATE INVESTMENT CO., LTD.—See Phat Dat Real Estate Development Corporation; *Int'l*, pg. 5842
PHUKET FUTURE PLAN CO., LTD.—See Land & Houses Public Company Limited; *Int'l*, pg. 4403
PHUMELELA GAMING AND LEISURE LIMITED; *Int'l*, pg. 5858
PHU MY ONE MEMBER LIMITED LIABILITIES COMPANY—See Hoa Sen Group; *Int'l*, pg. 3436

COMPANY NAME INDEX

PHU NHAT CANNING COMPANY LIMITED—See Viet Nhat Seafood Corporation; *Int'l*, pg. 8197
PHU NHUAN JEWELRY JOINT STOCK COMPANY; *Int'l*, pg. 5857
PHUNWARE, INC.; *U.S. Public*, pg. 1689
PHUNWARE OPCO, INC.—See Phunware, Inc.; *U.S. Public*, pg. 1689
PHUOC HOA RUBBER JOINT STOCK COMPANY; *Int'l*, pg. 5858
PHUOC LONG PORT CO., LTD.—See Gemadept Corporation; *Int'l*, pg. 2915
PHUONG NAM CULTURAL JOINT STOCK CORPORATION; *Int'l*, pg. 5858
PHUONG NAM EDUCATION INVESTMENT & DEVELOPMENT JSC; *Int'l*, pg. 5858
PHU PHONG PRODUCTION - TRADE - SERVICE - STOCK COMPANY; *Int'l*, pg. 5857
PHU QUOC HOUSING & URBAN DEVELOPMENT JSC—See C.E.O Group Joint Stock Company; *Int'l*, pg. 1240
PHU QUOC INVESTMENT & DEVELOPMENT JSC—See C.E.O Group Joint Stock Company; *Int'l*, pg. 1240
PHUSION IM LTD.—See Sword Group SE; *Int'l*, pg. 7376
PHU TAI DONG NAI COMPANY LIMITED—See Phu Tai Joint Stock Company; *Int'l*, pg. 5857
PHU TAI JOINT STOCK COMPANY; *Int'l*, pg. 5857
PHU TAI NINH THUAN STONE JSC—See Phu Tai Joint Stock Company; *Int'l*, pg. 5857
PHUTAI QUARTZ STONE COMPANY LIMITED—See Phu Tai Joint Stock Company; *Int'l*, pg. 5857
PHU TAI REAL ESTATES COMPANY LIMITED—See Phu Tai Joint Stock Company; *Int'l*, pg. 5857
PHU THINH - NHA BE GARMENT JSC; *Int'l*, pg. 5857
PHU YEN CONSTRUCTION MATERIALS JSC—See Phu Tai Joint Stock Company; *Int'l*, pg. 5857
PH VICTORIA JUNCTION (PTY) LTD—See Marriott International, Inc.; *U.S. Public*, pg. 1371
PH VINEX SLAVIANTSI POLAND SP. Z O.O.—See Schloss Wachenheim AG; *Int'l*, pg. 6622
PH VITRES D'AUTOS; *Int'l*, pg. 5839
PHW LAS VEGAS, LLC—See Caesars Entertainment, Inc.; *U.S. Public*, pg. 420
PHX AP ACQUISITIONS LLC; *U.S. Private*, pg. 3174
PHX ENERGY SERVICES CORP.; *Int'l*, pg. 5858
PHX MINERALS INC.; *U.S. Public*, pg. 1690
PHYATHAI 1 HOSPITAL CO., LTD.—See Bangkok Dusit Medical Services Public Company Limited; *Int'l*, pg. 834
PHYATHAI 2 HOSPITAL CO., LTD.—See Bangkok Dusit Medical Services Public Company Limited; *Int'l*, pg. 834
THE PHYA THAI II HOSPITAL CO., LTD.—See Bangkok Dusit Medical Services Public Company Limited; *Int'l*, pg. 834
PHYN LLC—See Hon Hai Precision Industry Co., Ltd.; *Int'l*, pg. 3457
PHYNOVA GROUP LTD.; *Int'l*, pg. 5858
PHYS HOLDING CORP.—See UnitedHealth Group Incorporated; *U.S. Public*, pg. 2249
PHYSICAL ACOUSTICS B.V.—See Mistras Group, Inc.; *U.S. Public*, pg. 1451
PHYSICAL ACOUSTICS CORP.—See Mistras Group, Inc.; *U.S. Public*, pg. 1451
PHYSICAL ACOUSTICS SOUTH AMERICA LTDA.—See Mistras Group, Inc.; *U.S. Public*, pg. 1451
PHYSICAL DISTRIBUTION SERVICES; *U.S. Private*, pg. 3174
PHYSICAL ELECTRONICS GMBH—See ULVAC, Inc.; *Int'l*, pg. 8021
PHYSICAL ELECTRONICS INC.—See ULVAC, Inc.; *Int'l*, pg. 8021
PHYSICAL OPTICS CORPORATION—See Mercury Systems, Inc.; *U.S. Public*, pg. 1422
PHYSICAL PROPERTY HOLDINGS INC.; *Int'l*, pg. 5858
PHYSICAL REHABILITATION NETWORK, LLC—See Gryphon Investors, LLC; *U.S. Private*, pg. 1799
PHYSICAL SCIENCES INC.; *U.S. Private*, pg. 3174
THE PHYSICAL THERAPY CONNECTION, INC.—See Audax Group, Limited Partnership; *U.S. Private*, pg. 389
PHYSICAL THERAPY ETC.—See Audax Group, Limited Partnership; *U.S. Private*, pg. 389
PHYSICAL THERAPY NORTHWEST, LIMITED PARTNERSHIP—See U.S. Physical Therapy, Inc.; *U.S. Public*, pg. 2215
PHYSICAL THERAPY & SPINE INSTITUTE, LIMITED PARTNERSHIP—See U.S. Physical Therapy, Inc.; *U.S. Public*, pg. 2215
PHYSICIAN ALLIANCE OF THE ROCKIES, LLC—See UnitedHealth Group Incorporated; *U.S. Public*, pg. 2249
PHYSICIAN BILLING PARTNERS LLC—See Medstreaming, LLC; *U.S. Private*, pg. 2659
PHYSICIAN CARE PARTNERS, INC.—See UnitedHealth Group Incorporated; *U.S. Public*, pg. 2249
PHYSICIAN OFFICE PARTNERS, INC.—See KKR & Co. Inc.; *U.S. Public*, pg. 1246
PHYSICIAN PARTNERS OF AMERICA, LLC; *U.S. Private*, pg. 3175

PHYSICIAN PERFORMANCE NETWORK OF GEORGIA, L.L.C.—See Tenet Healthcare Corporation; *U.S. Public*, pg. 2008
PHYSICIAN PRACTICE SUPPORT, INC.—See Community Health Systems, Inc.; *U.S. Public*, pg. 555
PHYSICIANS BILLING & SUPPORT SERVICES—See Central Georgia Health System Inc.; *U.S. Private*, pg. 821
THE PHYSICIANS' CENTER, L.P.—See Tenet Healthcare Corporation; *U.S. Public*, pg. 2013
PHYSICIANS CHOICE DIALYSIS, LLC—See DaVita Inc.; *U.S. Public*, pg. 642
PHYSICIANS CHOICE INSURANCE SERVICE, LLC—See UnitedHealth Group Incorporated; *U.S. Public*, pg. 2249
THE PHYSICIANS CLINIC LIMITED—See HCA Healthcare, Inc.; *U.S. Public*, pg. 1012
PHYSICIANS DAY SURGERY CENTER, LLC—See UnitedHealth Group Incorporated; *U.S. Public*, pg. 2249
PHYSICIANS DEVELOPMENT GROUP LLC; *U.S. Private*, pg. 3175
PHYSICIANS DIALYSIS OF LANCASTER, LLC—See DaVita Inc.; *U.S. Public*, pg. 642
PHYSICIANS ENDOSCOPY CENTER—See HCA Healthcare, Inc.; *U.S. Public*, pg. 1006
PHYSICIANS ENDOSCOPY CENTER—See HCA Healthcare, Inc.; *U.S. Public*, pg. 1006
PHYSICIANS ENDOSCOPY, LLC—See Kelso & Company, L.P.; *U.S. Private*, pg. 2279
PHYSICIANS EXCLUSIVE LLC—See Novonesis A/S; *Int'l*, pg. 5469
PHYSICIANS' EYE SURGERY CENTER, LLC—See KKR & Co. Inc.; *U.S. Public*, pg. 1246
PHYSICIANS FORMULA COSMETICS, INC.—See Markwins International Corporation; *U.S. Private*, pg. 2582
PHYSICIANS FORMULA HOLDINGS, INC.—See Markwins International Corporation; *U.S. Private*, pg. 2582
PHYSICIANS GROUP MANAGEMENT, INC.; *U.S. Private*, pg. 3175
PHYSICIANS HEALTH CHOICE OF TEXAS, LLC—See UnitedHealth Group Incorporated; *U.S. Public*, pg. 2249
PHYSICIANS INSURANCE, A MUTUAL COMPANY; *U.S. Private*, pg. 3175
PHYSICIANS INTERACTIVE INC.—See KKR & Co. Inc.; *U.S. Public*, pg. 1253
PHYSICIANS INTERACTIVE INDIA PRIVATE LIMITED—See Merck & Co., Inc.; *U.S. Public*, pg. 1421
PHYSICIANS LIFE INSURANCE COMPANY—See Physicians Mutual Insurance Co.; *U.S. Private*, pg. 3175
PHYSICIANS MEDICAL CENTER, LLC—See Bain Capital, LP; *U.S. Private*, pg. 447
PHYSICIANS MUTUAL INSURANCE CO.; *U.S. Private*, pg. 3175
PHYSICIANS PAVILION, L.P.—See Tenet Healthcare Corporation; *U.S. Public*, pg. 2012
PHYSICIANS' PHARMACEUTICAL CORPORATION; *U.S. Private*, pg. 3175
PHYSICIANS PHARMACY ALLIANCE, INC.—See The Riverside Company; *U.S. Private*, pg. 4110
THE PHYSICIAN & SPORTSMEDICINE—See JTE Multimedia, LLC; *U.S. Private*, pg. 2242
PHYSICIAN'S PRACTICE ORGANIZATION INC.; *U.S. Private*, pg. 3175
PHYSICIANS REALTY TRUST—See Healthpeak Properties, Inc.; *U.S. Public*, pg. 1016
PHYSICIANS RECIPROCAL INSURERS—See Administrators for the Professions, Inc.; *U.S. Private*, pg. 81
PHYSICIANS REGIONAL MARCO ISLAND, LLC—See Community Health Systems, Inc.; *U.S. Public*, pg. 556
PHYSICIANS SPECIALTY HOSPITAL, LLC—See Community Health Systems, Inc.; *U.S. Public*, pg. 556
PHYSICIANS SURGERY CENTER AT GOOD SAMARITAN, LLC—See Tenet Healthcare Corporation; *U.S. Public*, pg. 2012
PHYSICIANS SURGERY CENTER, LLC; *U.S. Private*, pg. 3175
PHYSICIAN'S SURGERY CENTER OF CHATTANOOGA, L.L.C.—See Tenet Healthcare Corporation; *U.S. Public*, pg. 2006
PHYSICIAN'S SURGERY CENTER OF KNOXVILLE, LLC—See Tenet Healthcare Corporation; *U.S. Public*, pg. 2012
PHYSICIAN'S SURGERY CENTER OF TEMPE, LLC—See Tenet Healthcare Corporation; *U.S. Public*, pg. 2006
PHYSICIANS SURGICAL CARE, INC—See Bain Capital, LP; *U.S. Private*, pg. 446
PHYSICIANS WEIGHT LOSS CENTERS, INC.—See The Health Management Group, Inc.; *U.S. Private*, pg. 4043
PHYSICIANS WORLD, LLC—See Veeva Systems, Inc.; *U.S. Public*, pg. 2277
PHYSIK INSTRUMENTE (PI) GMBH & CO. KG; *Int'l*, pg. 5858
PHYSIK INSTRUMENTE (PI SHANGHAI) CO., LTD.—See Physik Instrumente (PI) GmbH & Co. KG; *Int'l*, pg. 5858

PHYSIK INSTRUMENTE (PI) S. R. L.—See Physik Instrumente (PI) GmbH & Co. KG; *Int'l*, pg. 5858
PHYSIK INSTRUMENTE (PI) TAIWAN LTD.—See Physik Instrumente (PI) GmbH & Co. KG; *Int'l*, pg. 5858
PHYSIO AT HAMMONDS CENTRE, LLC—See Select Medical Holdings Corporation; *U.S. Public*, pg. 1858
PHYSIO-CONTROL CANADA SALES LTD.—See Stryker Corporation; *U.S. Public*, pg. 1956
PHYSIO-CONTROL, INC.—See Stryker Corporation; *U.S. Public*, pg. 1956
PHYSIO-CONTROL MANUFACTURING, INC.—See Stryker Corporation; *U.S. Public*, pg. 1956
PHYSIO-CONTROL OPERATIONS NETHERLANDS B.V.—See Stryker Corporation; *U.S. Public*, pg. 1956
PHYSIO-CONTROL SINGAPORE PTE. LTD.—See Stryker Corporation; *U.S. Public*, pg. 1956
PHYSIO-CONTROL UK SALES LTD.—See Stryker Corporation; *U.S. Public*, pg. 1956
PHYSIOMICS PLC; *Int'l*, pg. 5858
PHYSIOTHERAPY ASSOCIATES, INC.—See Select Medical Holdings Corporation; *U.S. Public*, pg. 1858
PHYSIOTHERAPY ASSOCIATES NRH REHAB, LLC—See Select Medical Holdings Corporation; *U.S. Public*, pg. 1858
PHYSIOTHERM GMBH; *Int'l*, pg. 5858
PHYSIQUE 57; *U.S. Private*, pg. 3175
PHYSMED INC.—See Pharos Capital Group, LLC; *U.S. Private*, pg. 3166
PHYSPEED, LLC—See MaxLinear, Inc.; *U.S. Public*, pg. 1403
PHYSTECH II JSC; *Int'l*, pg. 5858
PHYTEL, INC.—See International Business Machines Corporation; *U.S. Public*, pg. 1148
PHYTO CHEM INDIA LTD; *Int'l*, pg. 5858
PHYTOCHEM TECHNOLOGIES, INC.—See Nutralife Biosciences, Inc.; *U.S. Public*, pg. 1556
PHYTOHEALTH CORPORATION—See Maywufa Company Limited; *Int'l*, pg. 4748
PHYTON BIOTECH GMBH—See DFB Pharmaceuticals, Inc.; *U.S. Private*, pg. 1220
PHYTON BIOTECH, INC.—See DFB Pharmaceuticals, Inc.; *U.S. Private*, pg. 1220
PHYTONE LIMITED—See FMC Corporation; *U.S. Public*, pg. 862
PHYTOTHERAPIC SOLUTIONS S.L.—See SeQuent Scientific Limited; *Int'l*, pg. 6719
PHYZ HOLDINGS INC.—See AZ-COM MARUWA Holdings Inc.; *Int'l*, pg. 776
PHZ BALTONA S.A.; *Int'l*, pg. 5859
PI 2 PELICAN STATE LLC—See Kinder Morgan, Inc.; *U.S. Public*, pg. 1234
PIAA CORPORATION—See Valeo S.A.; *Int'l*, pg. 8113
PIAB AB—See Investor AB; *Int'l*, pg. 3787
PIACELABO CORPORATION—See Mandom Corporation; *Int'l*, pg. 4668
PIA CORPORATION; *Int'l*, pg. 5859
PI ADVANCED MATERIALS CO., LTD—See Arkema S.A.; *Int'l*, pg. 569
PIAGET S.A.—See Compagnie Financière Richemont S.A.; *Int'l*, pg. 1741
PIAGGIO & C. SPA—See Immsi S.p.a.; *Int'l*, pg. 3628
PIAGGIO DEUTSCHLAND GMBH—See Immsi S.p.a.; *Int'l*, pg. 3629
PIAGGIO GROUP AMERICAS, INC.—See Immsi S.p.a.; *Int'l*, pg. 3628
PIAGGIO USA, INC.—See Immsi S.p.a.; *Int'l*, pg. 3628
PIAGGIO VEHICLES PRIVATE LIMITED—See Immsi S.p.a.; *Int'l*, pg. 3629
PIALAB, INC.—See Piala, Inc.; *Int'l*, pg. 5859
PIALA, INC.; *Int'l*, pg. 5859
PIALA VENTURES INC.—See Piala, Inc.; *Int'l*, pg. 5859
PIAL CONSULT GMBH—See msg group GmbH; *Int'l*, pg. 5067
PIANA LEASING GESELLSCHAFT M.B.H.—See UniCredit S.p.A.; *Int'l*, pg. 8037
PIANEGONDA CORP.—See Pianegonda Srl; *Int'l*, pg. 5859
PIANEGONDA FRANCE S.A.—See Pianegonda Srl; *Int'l*, pg. 5859
PIANEGONDA SRL; *Int'l*, pg. 5859
PIANO SOFTWARE B.V.; *Int'l*, pg. 5859
PIANTEDOSI BAKING CO. INC.; *U.S. Private*, pg. 3175
PIASA MOTOR FUELS LLC; *U.S. Private*, pg. 3175
PIASA OIL TRANSPORT LLC—See Piasa Motor Fuels LLC; *U.S. Private*, pg. 3175
PIASA REAL ESTATE, INC.—See Piasa Motor Fuels LLC; *U.S. Private*, pg. 3175
PIASAU GAS SDN. BHD.—See Shin Yang Shipping Corporation Berhad; *Int'l*, pg. 6838
PIASAU SLIPWAYS SDN. BHD.—See Shin Yang Shipping Corporation Berhad; *Int'l*, pg. 6838
P.I. ASSISTANCE (THAILAND) CO., LTD.—See Prestige International Inc.; *Int'l*, pg. 5966
PIASTEN GMBH—See Xaver Fassin GmbH; *Int'l*, pg. 8520
PIATEC (THAILAND) CO., LTD.—See Piala, Inc.; *Int'l*, pg. 5859
PIATT COUNTY SERVICE CO.; *U.S. Private*, pg. 3175
PIAZAR AGRO INDUSTRIAL COMPANY; *Int'l*, pg. 5859
PIAZZA ACURA OF ARDMORE; *U.S. Private*, pg. 3175

PIAZZA ACURA OF ARDMORE

CORPORATE AFFILIATIONS

PIAZZA AG—See TX Group AG; *Int'l*, pg. 7992
PIAZZA HONDA OF PHILADELPHIA; *U.S. Private*, pg. 3175
PIAZZA PRODUCE INC.—See Wind Point Advisors LLC; *U.S. Private*, pg. 4534
PIAZZO ROSA S.R.L.—See Standex International; *U.S. Public*, pg. 1930
PI BENELUX B.V.—See Physik Instrumente (PI) GmbH & Co. KG; *Int'l*, pg. 5858
PIB GROUP LIMITED—See Apax Partners LLP; *Int'l*, pg. 505
PIBIVIESSE S.R.L.—See Certina Holding AG; *Int'l*, pg. 1423
PIBLE DIALYSIS, LLC—See DaVita Inc.; *U.S. Public*, pg. 642
PIBOON CONCRETE CO., LTD.—See Thanachart Capital PCL; *Int'l*, pg. 7607
PICABOO CORPORATION—See Reischling Press, Inc.; *U.S. Private*, pg. 3392
PICA CO., LTD.—See Fuji Kyuko Co., Ltd.; *Int'l*, pg. 2813
PIC ANDINA S.A.—See Genus Plc; *Int'l*, pg. 2931
PICANOL DE MEXICO SA DE CV—See Tessenderlo Group NV; *Int'l*, pg. 7574
PICANOL DO BRASIL LTDA—See Tessenderlo Group NV; *Int'l*, pg. 7574
PICANOL INDIA PRIVATE LIMITED—See Tessenderlo Group NV; *Int'l*, pg. 7574
PICANOL NV—See Tessenderlo Group NV; *Int'l*, pg. 7573
PICANOL OF AMERICA INC.—See Tessenderlo Group NV; *Int'l*, pg. 7574
PICANOL (SUZHOU IND. PARK) TEXTILE MACHINERY CO. LTD.—See Tessenderlo Group NV; *Int'l*, pg. 7574
PICANOL TEKSTIL MAKINALARI TICARET LIMITED SIRKET—See Tessenderlo Group NV; *Int'l*, pg. 7574
PICARD AUTOS 33; *Int'l*, pg. 5859
PICARD AUTOS RAMONVILLE; *Int'l*, pg. 5859
PICARD SERRURES—See Groupe SFPI SA; *Int'l*, pg. 3111
PICARD SURGELES S.A.—See Lion Capital LLP; *Int'l*, pg. 4517
PIC ARGENTINA—See Genus Plc; *Int'l*, pg. 2931
PICAR S.A—See Piraeus Financial Holdings S.A.; *Int'l*, pg. 5873
PIC AUSTRALIA—See Genus Plc; *Int'l*, pg. 2931
PICAYUNE HOMECARE, LLC—See UnitedHealth Group Incorporated; *U.S. Public*, pg. 2246
PIC BENELUX BV—See Genus Plc; *Int'l*, pg. 2931
PICCADILLY AD; *Int'l*, pg. 5860
PICCADILLY RESTAURANTS, LLC—See The Yucaipa Companies LLC; *U.S. Private*, pg. 4140
PICCADILY AGRO INDUSTRIES LTD.; *Int'l*, pg. 5860
PICCADILLY SUGAR & ALLIED INDUSTRIES LIMITED; *Int'l*, pg. 5860
PIC CANADA LTD.—See Genus Plc; *Int'l*, pg. 2931
PICCARD SURGERY CENTER, LLC—See Tenet Healthcare Corporation; *U.S. Public*, pg. 2006
PICC ASSET MANAGEMENT COMPANY LIMITED—See People's Insurance Company (Group) of China Limited; *Int'l*, pg. 5793
PICC CAPITAL INSURANCE ASSET MANAGEMENT CO., LTD.—See People's Insurance Company (Group) of China Limited; *Int'l*, pg. 5793
PICC CAPITAL INVESTMENT MANAGEMENT COMPANY LIMITED—See People's Insurance Company (Group) of China Limited; *Int'l*, pg. 5793
PICC HEALTH INSURANCE COMPANY LIMITED—See People's Insurance Company (Group) of China Limited; *Int'l*, pg. 5793
PICC (HONG KONG) LIMITED—See People's Insurance Company (Group) of China Limited; *Int'l*, pg. 5793
PICC INVESTMENT HOLDING COMPANY LIMITED—See People's Insurance Company (Group) of China Limited; *Int'l*, pg. 5793
PICCO ENTERPRISE PTE. LTD.—See Beng Kuang Marine Limited; *Int'l*, pg. 973
PICCOLLO S.R.O.—See Columbia Sportswear Company; *U.S. Public*, pg. 535
PIC COLOMBIA S.A.—See Genus Plc; *Int'l*, pg. 2931
PICCOLO SP. Z O.O.—See Emperia Holding S.A; *Int'l*, pg. 2386
PICC PROPERTY & CASUALTY COMPANY LIMITED—See People's Insurance Company (Group) of China Limited; *Int'l*, pg. 5793
PIC DENMARK A/S—See Genus Plc; *Int'l*, pg. 2931
PIC DESIGN INC.—See RBC Bearings Incorporated; *U.S. Public*, pg. 1766
PIC DEUTSCHLAND GMBH—See Genus Plc; *Int'l*, pg. 2931
PI CERAMIC GMBH—See Physik Instrumente (PI) GmbH & Co. KG; *Int'l*, pg. 5858
PICERNE CONSTRUCTION CORP.—See Picerne Real Estate Group; *U.S. Private*, pg. 3176
PICERNE DEVELOPMENT CORP.—See Picerne Real Estate Group; *U.S. Private*, pg. 3176
THE PICERNE GROUP, INC.; *U.S. Private*, pg. 4095
PICERNE INVESTMENT CORPORATION; *U.S. Private*, pg. 3176
PICERNE REAL ESTATE GROUP; *U.S. Private*, pg. 3176
PIC ESPANA—See Genus Plc; *Int'l*, pg. 2931

PICEU GROUP LIMITED, INC.; *U.S. Private*, pg. 3176
PIC FRANCE—See Genus Plc; *Int'l*, pg. 2931
PIC GENETICS LLC—See Genus Plc; *Int'l*, pg. 2930
PIC GROUP, INC.—See Marubeni Corporation; *Int'l*, pg. 4707
PICHARD PERE ET FILS S.A.S.; *Int'l*, pg. 5860
PICHIT INDUSTRIAL WORKS CO. LTD.—See Schunk GmbH; *Int'l*, pg. 6641
PICHLINGERHOF LIEGENSCHAFTSVERWERTUNGS GMBH & CO KG—See PORR AG; *Int'l*, pg. 5923
PICHLINGERHOF LIEGENSCHAFTSVERWERTUNGS GMBH—See PORR AG; *Int'l*, pg. 5923
PIC INVESTMENT GROUP INC.; *Int'l*, pg. 5859
PIC IRELAND GTC—See Genus Plc; *Int'l*, pg. 2931
PICIS CLINICAL SOLUTIONS, INC.—See Constellation Software Inc.; *Int'l*, pg. 1774
PICIS CLINICAL SOLUTIONS, LTD.—See Constellation Software Inc.; *Int'l*, pg. 1774
PICIS CLINICAL SOLUTIONS S.A.—See Constellation Software Inc.; *Int'l*, pg. 1774
PIC ITALIA S.P.A.—See Genus Plc; *Int'l*, pg. 2931
PICKALBATROS HOTELS & NILE CRUISES; *Int'l*, pg. 5860
PICKARD CHRYSLER DODGE JEEP; *U.S. Private*, pg. 3176
PICKAWAY DIALYSIS CENTER LLC—See Nautic Partners, LLC; *U.S. Private*, pg. 2870
PICKAWAY PLAINS AMBULANCE SERVICE, INC.—See Source Capital, LLC; *U.S. Private*, pg. 3718
PICKELNER FUEL CO. INC.; *U.S. Private*, pg. 3176
PICKENS COUNTY PORTS INC.—See Parker Towing Company, Inc.; *U.S. Private*, pg. 3097
PICKERING CREATIVE GROUP; *U.S. Private*, pg. 3176
PICKERINGS AUTO GROUP PTY. LTD.; *Int'l*, pg. 5860
PICKERSGILL RETIREMENT COMMUNITY; *U.S. Private*, pg. 3176
PICKFORD REALTY INC.; *U.S. Private*, pg. 3176
PICKFORDS LIMITED—See Madison Dearborn Partners, LLC; *U.S. Private*, pg. 2542
PICKHARDT & GERLACH GMBH & CO. KG—See Gesco AG; *Int'l*, pg. 2946
PICKHARDT SARASOTA, INC.—See Rentokil Initial plc; *Int'l*, pg. 6286
PICKLES CORPORATION; *Int'l*, pg. 5860
PICK N PAY FRANCHISE FINANCING (PTY) LIMITED—See Pink n Pay Holdings Limited RF; *Int'l*, pg. 5870
PICK N PAY GARAGES (PTY) LIMITED—See Pink n Pay Holdings Limited RF; *Int'l*, pg. 5870
PICK N PAY HOLDINGS LIMITED—See Pink n Pay Holdings Limited RF; *Int'l*, pg. 5870
PICK N PAY STORES LTD.; *Int'l*, pg. 5860
PICK N PAY WHOLESALERS (PTY) LIMITED—See Pink n Pay Holdings Limited RF; *Int'l*, pg. 5870
PICK-N-PULL AUTO DISMANTLERS—See Radius Recycling, Inc.; *U.S. Public*, pg. 1760
PICK-N-PULL AUTO & TRUCK DISMANTLERS—See Radius Recycling, Inc.; *U.S. Public*, pg. 1760
PIC KOREA INC.—See Genus Plc; *Int'l*, pg. 2931
PICK QUICK FOODS; *U.S. Private*, pg. 3176
PICKSEED WEST INC.—See DLF AmbA; *Int'l*, pg. 2140
PICKSTOCK ASHBY LTD.; *Int'l*, pg. 5860
PICKUP OUTFITTERS—See The Perry Company; *U.S. Private*, pg. 4093
PICK-UPS PLUS, INC.; *U.S. Public*, pg. 1690
PICK UP STIX—See West Coast Capital LLC; *U.S. Private*, pg. 4484
PICKWICK COMPANY INC.; *U.S. Private*, pg. 3176
PICKWICK ELECTRIC COOPERATIVE; *U.S. Private*, pg. 3176
PICK-YOUR-PART AUTO WRECKING INC.—See LKQ Corporation; *U.S. Public*, pg. 1336
PICL (INDIA) PRIVATE LIMITED—See Prataap Snacks Limited; *Int'l*, pg. 5955
PIC MEXICO—See Genus Plc; *Int'l*, pg. 2931
PICMONIC, INC.—See TrueLearn, LLC; *U.S. Private*, pg. 4248
PIC NEW ZEALAND—See Genus Plc; *Int'l*, pg. 2931
PICNIC CORPORATION PUBLIC CO. LTD.; *Int'l*, pg. 5860
PICO ART EXHIBIT, INC.—See Pico Far East Holdings Limited; *Int'l*, pg. 5861
PICO ART INTERNATIONAL PTE. LTD.—See Pico Far East Holdings Limited; *Int'l*, pg. 5861
PICO CHICAGO, INC.—See Pico Far East Holdings Limited; *Int'l*, pg. 5861
PICO CONCEPTS INDIA PRIVATE LTD.—See Pico Far East Holdings Limited; *Int'l*, pg. 5861
PICO CONTRACTS LIMITED—See Pico Far East Holdings Limited; *Int'l*, pg. 5861
PICO DIGITAL INC.—See H.I.G. Capital, LLC; *U.S. Private*, pg. 1828
PICO FAR EAST HOLDINGS LIMITED; *Int'l*, pg. 5861
PICO GLOBAL SERVICES LTD.—See Pico Far East Holdings Limited; *Int'l*, pg. 5861
PICO GLOBAL SERVICES LTD.—See Pico Far East Holdings Limited; *Int'l*, pg. 5861
PICOGRAM CO., LTD.; *Int'l*, pg. 5862
PICOGRAM MALAYSIA SDN. BHD.—See Picogram Co., Ltd.; *Int'l*, pg. 5862

PICO HANOI LIMITED—See Pico Far East Holdings Limited; *Int'l*, pg. 5861
PICO HOCHIMINH CITY LTD.—See Pico Far East Holdings Limited; *Int'l*, pg. 5861
PICOI CO., LTD.—See Freesia Macross Corporation; *Int'l*, pg. 2771
PICO IES GROUP (CHINA) CO., LTD.—See Pico Far East Holdings Limited; *Int'l*, pg. 5861
PICO IES GROUP LTD.—See Pico Far East Holdings Limited; *Int'l*, pg. 5861
PICO INTERNATIONAL (DUBAI) LLC—See Pico Far East Holdings Limited; *Int'l*, pg. 5861
PICO INTERNATIONAL (HENAN) EXHIBITION SERVICES COMPANY, LIMITED—See Pico Far East Holdings Limited; *Int'l*, pg. 5861
PICO INTERNATIONAL (HK) LIMITED—See Pico Far East Holdings Limited; *Int'l*, pg. 5861
PICO INTERNATIONAL, INC.—See Pico Far East Holdings Limited; *Int'l*, pg. 5861
PICO INTERNATIONAL (LA) INC.—See Pico Far East Holdings Limited; *Int'l*, pg. 5861
PICO INTERNATIONAL LIMITED—See Pico Far East Holdings Limited; *Int'l*, pg. 5861
PICO INTERNATIONAL (MACAO) LTD.—See Pico Far East Holdings Limited; *Int'l*, pg. 5861
PICO INTERNATIONAL (M) SDN. BHD.—See Pico Far East Holdings Limited; *Int'l*, pg. 5861
PICO INTERNATIONAL (QATAR) WLL—See Pico Far East Holdings Limited; *Int'l*, pg. 5861
PICO INTERNATIONAL TAIWAN LTD.—See Pico Far East Holdings Limited; *Int'l*, pg. 5861
PICOLEAD (BEIJING) WATER TREATMENT TECHNOLOGY CO., LTD.—See Picogram Co., Ltd.; *Int'l*, pg. 5862
PICOMETRIX, LLC—See Luna Innovations Incorporated; *U.S. Public*, pg. 1349
PI COMPANY; *U.S. Private*, pg. 3175
P.I. COMPONENTS CORP.; *U.S. Private*, pg. 3060
PICO MYANMAR COMPANY LIMITED—See Pico Far East Holdings Limited; *Int'l*, pg. 5861
PICO NORTH ASIA LTD.—See Pico Far East Holdings Limited; *Int'l*, pg. 5861
PICO PETROLEUM PRODUCTS LTD.—See Meritum Energy Holdings, LP; *U.S. Private*, pg. 2675
PICOP RESOURCES INC; *Int'l*, pg. 5862
PICO PROJECTS (INTERNATIONAL) LIMITED—See Pico Far East Holdings Limited; *Int'l*, pg. 5861
PICOSPIN, LLC—See Thermo Fisher Scientific Inc.; *U.S. Public*, pg. 2155
PICOTECH LTD.—See Disco Corporation; *Int'l*, pg. 2132
PICO (THAILAND) PUBLIC COMPANY LIMITED; *Int'l*, pg. 5860
PI COUNTY CDB VILLAGE BANK CO., LTD.—See China Development Bank Corporation; *Int'l*, pg. 1497
PICOWAY TECHNOLOGY INC.—See Promate Electronic Co., Ltd.; *Int'l*, pg. 5992
PIC PHILIPPINES INC.—See Genus Plc; *Int'l*, pg. 2931
PIC POLSKA SP. Z.O.O.—See Genus Plc; *Int'l*, pg. 2931
PIC PORTUGAL—See Genus Plc; *Int'l*, pg. 2931
PIC QUIK STORES INC.; *U.S. Private*, pg. 3176
PICRIC LIMITED—See A.K. Al-Muhaidib & Sons Group of Companies; *Int'l*, pg. 25
PIC RIVER DEVELOPMENT CORP—See Ojibway Of The Pic River First Nation; *Int'l*, pg. 5539
PI-CRYSTAL INC.—See Daicel Corporation; *Int'l*, pg. 1919
P.I.C.S. CO., LTD.—See Imagica Group Inc.; *Int'l*, pg. 3618
PICSCOUT LTD.—See CC Capital Partners, LLC; *U.S. Private*, pg. 797
PIC SIAM CO., LTD.—See Genus Plc; *Int'l*, pg. 2931
PICS LTD.; *Int'l*, pg. 5862
PICSOLVE INTERNATIONAL LTD.—See Pomvom Ltd.; *Int'l*, pg. 5918
PICTET & CIE; *Int'l*, pg. 5862
PICT INC.—See Dentsu Group Inc.; *Int'l*, pg. 2039
PICTOMETRY INTERNATIONAL CORP.; *U.S. Private*, pg. 3176
PICTON CAPITAL LIMITED—See Picton Property Income Limited; *Int'l*, pg. 5862
PICTON MAHONEY TACTICAL INCOME FUND; *Int'l*, pg. 5862
PICTON MEDICAL CENTRE PTE LTD—See OUE Limited; *Int'l*, pg. 5666
PICTON PROPERTY INCOME LIMITED; *Int'l*, pg. 5862
PICTORIAL OFFSET CORPORATION; *U.S. Private*, pg. 3176
THE PICTSWEET COMPANY; *U.S. Private*, pg. 4095
THE PICTURE FACTORY—See Millimages S.A.; *Int'l*, pg. 4896
PICTUREHOUSE CINEMAS LIMITED—See Cineworld Group plc; *Int'l*, pg. 1610
PICTUREHOUSE MEDIA LIMITED; *Int'l*, pg. 5862
PICTURE MARKETING, INC.; *U.S. Private*, pg. 3176
PICTURE PEOPLE INC.—See Hallmark Cards, Inc.; *U.S. Private*, pg. 1845
PICTUREPHONE, INC.—See AMETEK, Inc.; *U.S. Public*, pg. 121
PIC UK—See Genus Plc; *Int'l*, pg. 2930
PIC USA, INC.—See Genus Plc; *Int'l*, pg. 2931

COMPANY NAME INDEX

PICUT ACQUISITION CORP—See Picut Manufacturing Company; *U.S. Private*, pg. 3176
PICUT MANUFACTURING COMPANY; *U.S. Private*, pg. 3176
PIDC - REGIONAL DEVELOPMENT CORPORATION—See Wells Fargo & Company; *U.S. Public*, pg. 2344
PIDILITE BAMCO LTD.—See Pidilite Industries Limited; *Int'l*, pg. 5862
PIDILITE INDUSTRIES EGYPT SAE—See Pidilite Industries Limited; *Int'l*, pg. 5862
PIDILITE INDUSTRIES LIMITED; *Int'l*, pg. 5862
PIDILITE INNOVATION CENTRE PTE LTD.—See Pidilite Industries Limited; *Int'l*, pg. 5862
PIDILITE LANKA (PVT) LTD.—See Pidilite Industries Limited; *Int'l*, pg. 5862
PIDILITE MIDDLE EAST LTD.—See Pidilite Industries Limited; *Int'l*, pg. 5862
PIDILITE SPECIALITY CHEMICALS BANGLADESH PVT. LTD.—See Pidilite Industries Limited; *Int'l*, pg. 5862
PIDILITE USA INC.—See Pidilite Industries Limited; *Int'l*, pg. 5862
PIECE OF CAKE, INC—See Brentwood Associates; *U.S. Private*, pg. 646
PIECLEX CO., LTD.—See Murata Manufacturing Co., Ltd.; *Int'l*, pg. 5098
PIE CONSULTING & ENGINEERING, INC.—See Lerch Bates Inc.; *U.S. Private*, pg. 2431
PIEDADE PIETEC S.A.—See OENEO SA; *Int'l*, pg. 5529
PIEDMONT AIR CONDITIONING CO.; *U.S. Private*, pg. 3176
PIEDMONT AIRLINES, INC.—See American Airlines Group Inc.; *U.S. Public*, pg. 96
PIEDMONT APPAREL CORPORATION—See Oxford Industries, Inc.; *U.S. Public*, pg. 1629
PIEDMONT AUTOMOTIVE OF ANDERSON; *U.S. Private*, pg. 3176
PIEDMONT AVIATION COMPONENT SERVICES LLC—See First Israel Mezzanine Investors Ltd.; *Int'l*, pg. 2685
PIEDMONT BANCORP, INC.; *U.S. Private*, pg. 3176
THE PIEDMONT BANK—See Piedmont Bancorp, Inc.; *U.S. Private*, pg. 3177
PIEDMONT BEHAVIORAL MEDICINE ASSOCIATES, L.L.C.—See Tenet Healthcare Corporation; *U.S. Public*, pg. 2008
PIEDMONT BOBCAT LLC; *U.S. Private*, pg. 3177
PIEDMONT BOTTLING & VENDING, INC.; *U.S. Private*, pg. 3177
PIEDMONT CAROLINA OB/GYN OF YORK COUNTY, L.L.C.—See Tenet Healthcare Corporation; *U.S. Public*, pg. 2008
PIEDMONT/CAROLINA—See Tenet Healthcare Corporation; *U.S. Public*, pg. 2008
PIEDMONT/CAROLINAS RADIATION THERAPY, LLC—See Tenet Healthcare Corporation; *U.S. Public*, pg. 2006
PIEDMONT CHEMICAL INDUSTRIES I, LLC—See Piedmont Chemical Industries, Inc.; *U.S. Private*, pg. 3177
PIEDMONT CHEMICAL INDUSTRIES, INC.; *U.S. Private*, pg. 3177
PIEDMONT COMMUNITY BANK GROUP, INC.; *U.S. Public*, pg. 1690
PIEDMONT CONSTRUCTION GROUP LLC; *U.S. Private*, pg. 3177
PIEDMONT EAST URGENT CARE CENTER, L.L.C.—See Tenet Healthcare Corporation; *U.S. Public*, pg. 2008
PIEDMONT ELECTRIC MEMBERSHIP CORP.; *U.S. Private*, pg. 3177
PIEDMONT ENERGY PARTNERS, INC.—See Duke Energy Corporation; *U.S. Public*, pg. 691
PIEDMONT FAMILY PRACTICE AT ROCK HILL, L.L.C.—See Tenet Healthcare Corporation; *U.S. Public*, pg. 2008
PIEDMONT FAMILY PRACTICE AT TEGA CAY, L.L.C.—See Tenet Healthcare Corporation; *U.S. Public*, pg. 2008
PIEDMONT FEDERAL SAVINGS BANK—See Piedmont Financial Holding Company; *U.S. Private*, pg. 3177
PIEDMONT FINANCIAL HOLDING COMPANY; *U.S. Private*, pg. 3177
PIEDMONT GOVERNMENT SERVICES, LLC—See Piedmont Office Realty Trust, Inc.; *U.S. Public*, pg. 1690
PIEDMONT HEALTHCARE, INC.; *U.S. Private*, pg. 3177
PIEDMONT HEALTH, INC.; *U.S. Private*, pg. 3177
PIEDMONT INTERNATIONAL TRUCKS, LLC—See Carolina International Trucks Inc.; *U.S. Private*, pg. 768
PIEDMONT INTERSTATE PIPELINE COMPANY—See Duke Energy Corporation; *U.S. Public*, pg. 691
PIEDMONT INVESTMENT ADVISORS, LLC; *U.S. Private*, pg. 3177
PIEDMONT LIMOUSINE; *U.S. Private*, pg. 3177
PIEDMONT LITHIUM INC.; *U.S. Public*, pg. 1690
PIEDMONT MANUFACTURING GROUP LLC—See Berkshire Hathaway Inc.; *U.S. Public*, pg. 298
PIEDMONT MECHANICAL, INC. - LAGRANGE—See Piedmont Mechanical, Inc.; *U.S. Private*, pg. 3177
PIEDMONT MECHANICAL, INC.; *U.S. Private*, pg. 3177
PIEDMONT METAL PRODUCTS, INC.—See Williams Industries, Inc.; *U.S. Public*, pg. 4526
PIEDMONT MINERALS DIVISION—See Balmoral Funds LLC; *U.S. Private*, pg. 461
PIEDMONT MINERALS—See Thiele Kaolin Company; *U.S. Private*, pg. 4144
PIEDMONT NATIONAL CORPORATION; *U.S. Private*, pg. 3177
PIEDMONT NATURAL GAS COMPANY, INC.—See Duke Energy Corporation; *U.S. Public*, pg. 691
PIEDMONT NEWNAN HOSPITAL; *U.S. Private*, pg. 3177
PIEDMONT OFFICE REALTY TRUST, INC.; *U.S. Public*, pg. 1690
PIEDMONT PETERBILT, LLC—See The Larson Group, Inc.; *U.S. Private*, pg. 4067
PIEDMONT PETROLEUM CORP.; *U.S. Private*, pg. 3178
PIEDMONT PHYSICIAN NETWORK, LLC—See Tenet Healthcare Corporation; *U.S. Public*, pg. 2006
PIEDMONT PLASTICS, INC.; *U.S. Private*, pg. 3178
PIEDMONT POWER, LLC—See Piedmont Office Realty Trust, Inc.; *U.S. Public*, pg. 1690
PIEDMONT REGIONAL HEALTH; *U.S. Private*, pg. 3178
PIEDMONT RURAL TELEPHONE COOPERATIVE INC.; *U.S. Private*, pg. 3178
PIEDMONT SURGICAL CENTER OF EXCELLENCE, LLC—See Community Health Systems, Inc.; *U.S. Public*, pg. 556
PIEDMONT TRUCK TIRES INC.—See McCarthy Tire Service Company; *U.S. Private*, pg. 2628
PIEDMONT URGENT CARE CENTER AT BAXTER VILLAGE, LLC—See Tenet Healthcare Corporation; *U.S. Public*, pg. 2008
PIEDMONT WEST URGENT CARE CENTER LLC—See Tenet Healthcare Corporation; *U.S. Public*, pg. 2008
PIED PIPER PET & WILDLIFE, INC.; *U.S. Private*, pg. 3176
PIEDRAS HEADWATERS, S. DE RL DE CV—See Seven Group Holdings Limited; *Int'l*, pg. 6733
PIE ENTERPRISE (M) SDN. BHD.—See P.I.E. Industrial Berhad; *Int'l*, pg. 5682
PIE FACE HOLDINGS PTY LTD; *Int'l*, pg. 5862
PIE FIVE PIZZA COMPANY, INC.—See Rave Restaurant Group, Inc.; *U.S. Public*, pg. 1763
PIEGE CO. INC.; *U.S. Private*, pg. 3178
PIEHLER PONTIAC CORP.; *U.S. Private*, pg. 3178
P.I.E. INDUSTRIAL BERHAD; *Int'l*, pg. 5682
P I E INDUSTRIAL BHD; *Int'l*, pg. 5681
PI EIS INSURANCE TECHNOLOGY INC.—See Prestige International Inc.; *Int'l*, pg. 5966
PIELET BROS TRADING INC.; *U.S. Private*, pg. 3178
PIELMEIER MEDIZINTECHNIK GMBH—See SOL S.p.A.; *Int'l*, pg. 7067
PIEMME SPA—See Caltagirone Editore S.p.A.; *Int'l*, pg. 1266
PIENO ZVAIGZDES AB; *Int'l*, pg. 5862
PIEPER ELECTRIC INC.; *U.S. Private*, pg. 3178
PIEPER GMBH—See Moog Inc.; *U.S. Public*, pg. 1471
PIE PIPER PRODUCTS, LTD.—See Vienna Sausage Mfg. Co.; *U.S. Private*, pg. 4381
PIEPS GMBH—See Clarus Corporation; *U.S. Public*, pg. 508
PIER 1 IMPORTS, INC.; *U.S. Public*, pg. 1690
PIER 1 IMPORTS (U.S.), INC.—See Pier 1 Imports, Inc.; *U.S. Public*, pg. 1690
PIER 1 SERVICES COMPANY—See Pier 1 Imports, Inc.; *U.S. Public*, pg. 1690
PIER 39 L.P.; *U.S. Private*, pg. 3178
PIER 4 LLC—See UDR, Inc.; *U.S. Public*, pg. 2218
PIER 8 GROUP—See 2Gen Net; *Int'l*, pg. 5
PIERATTS INC.; *U.S. Private*, pg. 3178
PIERBRIDGE INC.—See WiseTech Global Limited; *Int'l*, pg. 8437
PIERBURG CHINA LTD.—See Rheinmetall AG; *Int'l*, pg. 6322
PIERBURG GESTION S.L.—See Rheinmetall AG; *Int'l*, pg. 6322
PIERBURG GMBH—See Rheinmetall AG; *Int'l*, pg. 6322
PIERBURG INC.—See Rheinmetall AG; *Int'l*, pg. 6323
PIERBURG MIKUNI PUMP TECHNOLOGY CORPORATION—See Rheinmetall AG; *Int'l*, pg. 6322
PIERBURG PUMP TECHNOLOGIE US LLC—See Rheinmetall AG; *Int'l*, pg. 6323
PIERBURG PUMP TECHNOLOGY FRANCE S A R.L.—See Rheinmetall AG; *Int'l*, pg. 6322
PIERBURG PUMP TECHNOLOGY GMBH—See Rheinmetall AG; *Int'l*, pg. 6322
PIERBURG PUMP TECHNOLOGY INDIA PRIVATE LIMITED—See Rheinmetall AG; *Int'l*, pg. 6322
PIERBURG PUMP TECHNOLOGY ITALY S.P.A.—See Rheinmetall AG; *Int'l*, pg. 6322
PIERBURG PUMP TECHNOLOGY MEXICO S.A. DE C.V.—See Rheinmetall AG; *Int'l*, pg. 6322
PIERBURG PUMP TECHNOLOGY US LLC—See Rheinmetall AG; *Int'l*, pg. 6322
PIERBURG S.A.—See Rheinmetall AG; *Int'l*, pg. 6322
PIERBURG S.P.A.—See Rheinmetall AG; *Int'l*, pg. 6322
PIERBURG S.R.O.—See Rheinmetall AG; *Int'l*, pg. 6322
PIERBURG SYSTEMS S.L.—See Rheinmetall AG; *Int'l*, pg. 6322
PIERCE ALUMINUM COMPANY INC.; *U.S. Private*, pg. 3178
PIERCE ASSOCIATES INC.; *U.S. Private*, pg. 3178
PIERCE BIOTECHNOLOGY, INC.—See Thermo Fisher Scientific Inc.; *U.S. Public*, pg. 2151
PIERCE BOX & PAPER CORP.—See Welch Packaging Group, Inc.; *U.S. Private*, pg. 4473
THE PIERCE CO., INC.—See Avis Industrial Corporation; *U.S. Private*, pg. 408
PIERCE COMMUNICATIONS, INC.; *U.S. Private*, pg. 3178
PIERCE-COTE ADVERTISING, INC.—See Regan Communications Group, Inc.; *U.S. Private*, pg. 3386
PIERCE COUNTY PUBLIC TRANSPORTATION BENEFIT AREA CORPORATION; *U.S. Private*, pg. 3178
PIERCE COUNTY RECYCLING, COMPOSTING AND DISPOSAL, LLC—See Waste Connections, Inc.; *Int'l*, pg. 8353
PIERCE EISLEN, INC.—See Yardi Systems, Inc.; *U.S. Private*, pg. 4586
PIERCE ENTERPRISES INC.; *U.S. Private*, pg. 3178
PIERCE EQUIPMENT—See Ram Consolidated Industries, Inc.; *U.S. Private*, pg. 3350
PIERCE FITTINGS—See Fresno Valves & Castings Inc.; *U.S. Private*, pg. 1610
PIERCE FLOORING & DESIGN; *U.S. Private*, pg. 3178
PIERCE GROUP BENEFITS, LLC—See GTCR LLC; *U.S. Private*, pg. 1804
PIERCE, LLC—See AutoNation, Inc.; *U.S. Public*, pg. 237
PIERCE MANAGEMENT GROUP; *U.S. Private*, pg. 3178
PIERCE MANUFACTURING, INC.—See Oshkosh Corporation; *U.S. Public*, pg. 1621
PIERCE MATTIE COMMUNICATIONS; *U.S. Private*, pg. 3178
PIERCE MEMORIAL BAPTIST HOME, INC.; *U.S. Private*, pg. 3178
PIERCE-PACIFIC MANUFACTURING INC.; *U.S. Private*, pg. 3179
PIERCE PACKAGING CO.; *U.S. Private*, pg. 3178
PIERCE PROMOTIONS & EVENT MANAGEMENT—See Omnicom Group Inc.; *U.S. Public*, pg. 1593
PIERCE PUMP—See Applied Industrial Technologies, Inc.; *U.S. Public*, pg. 171
PIERCE'S FLOORING; *U.S. Private*, pg. 3178
PIERCING PAGODA—See Signet Jewelers Limited; *Int'l*, pg. 6911
PIERER INDUSTRIE AG—See Pierer Konzerngesellschaft mbH; *Int'l*, pg. 5863
PIERER KONZERNGESELLSCHAFT MBH; *Int'l*, pg. 5862
PIERER MOBILITY AG—See Pierer Konzerngesellschaft mbH; *Int'l*, pg. 5862
PIERIANDX, INC.; *U.S. Private*, pg. 3179
PIERIDAE ENERGY (CANADA) LIMITED; *Int'l*, pg. 5864
PIERIS AUSTRALIA PTY LIMITED—See Pieris Pharmaceuticals, Inc.; *U.S. Public*, pg. 1690
PIERIS PHARMACEUTICALS GMBH—See Pieris Pharmaceuticals, Inc.; *U.S. Public*, pg. 1690
PIERIS PHARMACEUTICALS, INC.; *U.S. Public*, pg. 1690
PIERLESS FISH CORP.—See Baldor Specialty Foods Inc.; *U.S. Private*, pg. 458
PIERLITE AUSTRALIA PTY LIMITED—See Bain Capital, LP; *U.S. Private*, pg. 439
PIERLITE AUSTRALIA PTY LIMITED—See Investec Limited; *Int'l*, pg. 3777
PIERMONT WEALTH MANAGEMENT, INC.—See TA Associates, Inc.; *U.S. Private*, pg. 3919
PIEROS CONSTRUCTION CO, INC.—See Altas Partners LP; *Int'l*, pg. 386
PIER PARK, LLC; *U.S. Private*, pg. 3178
PIERPOINT CAPITAL LLC; *U.S. Private*, pg. 3179
PIERPONT COMMUNICATIONS, INC.; *U.S. Private*, pg. 3179
PIERPONT COMMUNICATIONS, INC.—See Pierpont Communications, Inc.; *U.S. Private*, pg. 3179
PIERPONT INN, INC.—See DKN Hotel LLC; *U.S. Private*, pg. 1247
PIERRE BALMAIN MONTRES AG—See The Swatch Group Ltd.; *Int'l*, pg. 7692
PIERRE BOSSIER MALL, LLC—See Brookfield Corporation; *Int'l*, pg. 1185
PIERRE DEUX FRENCH COUNTRY; *U.S. Private*, pg. 3179
PIERRE ENTREPRENAD I GAVLE AB—See Storskogen Group AB; *Int'l*, pg. 7228
PIERRE FABRE DERMO-COSMETIQUE ARGENTINA S.A.—See Pierre Fabre S.A.; *Int'l*, pg. 5864
PIERRE FABRE DERMO-COSMETIQUE, S.A.—See Pierre Fabre S.A.; *Int'l*, pg. 5864
PIERRE FABRE IBERICA, S.A.—See Pierre Fabre S.A.; *Int'l*, pg. 5864
PIERRE FABRE ITALIA SPA—See Pierre Fabre S.A.; *Int'l*, pg. 5864
PIERRE FABRE MEDICAMENT S.A.—See Pierre Fabre S.A.; *Int'l*, pg. 5864
PIERRE FABRE PHARMACEUTICALS INC—See Pierre Fabre S.A.; *Int'l*, pg. 5864
PIERRE FABRE S.A.; *Int'l*, pg. 5864
PIERRE FABRE (SWITZERLAND) S.A.—See Pierre Fabre S.A.; *Int'l*, pg. 5864

PIERRE FABRE S.A. CORPORATE AFFILIATIONS

PIERRE FABRE USA KLORANE—See Pierre Fabre S.A.; *Int'l*, pg. 5864
THE PIERRE HOTEL—See Tata Sons Limited; *Int'l*, pg. 7468
PIERREL S.P.A.—See Petrone Group S.r.l.; *Int'l*, pg. 5831
PIERRE ROBERT GROUP AB—See Orkla ASA; *Int'l*, pg. 5639
PIERRE ROBERT GROUP AS—See Orkla ASA; *Int'l*, pg. 5639
PIERRE'S FRENCH ICE CREAM COMPANY; *U.S. Private*, pg. 3179
PIER RESTAURANTS L.P.—See PIER 39 L.P.; *U.S. Private*, pg. 3178
PIERRE & VACANCES DEVELOPPEMENT SA—See Pierre & Vacances SA; *Int'l*, pg. 5864
PIERRE & VACANCES SA; *Int'l*, pg. 5864
PIERRY INC.—See WPP plc; *Int'l*, pg. 8481
PIERS 92/94 LLC—See Vornado Realty Trust; *U.S. Public*, pg. 2310
PIERSON AUTOMOTIVE INC.; *U.S. Private*, pg. 3179
PIERSON DIFFUSION; *Int'l*, pg. 5864
PIERSON FORD LINCOLN MERCURY INC.; *U.S. Private*, pg. 3179
PIERSON-GIBBS HOMES INC.; *U.S. Private*, pg. 3179
PIERSON INDUSTRIES INC.; *U.S. Private*, pg. 3179
PIESAT INFORMATION TECHNOLOGY CO., LTD.; *Int'l*, pg. 5864
PIESYNC NV—See HubSpot, Inc.; *U.S. Public*, pg. 1068
PIE TNUFA LTD.—See Haulotte Group SA; *Int'l*, pg. 3285
PIETRO CO., LTD.; *Int'l*, pg. 5864
PIETTE & PARTNERS NV—See P&V Assurances SCRL; *Int'l*, pg. 5681
PIEZAS Y RODAJES SA—See Titan International, Inc.; *U.S. Public*, pg. 2160
PIEZO KINETICS INC.—See Crest Group Inc.; *U.S. Private*, pg. 1096
PIEZO MOTION CORP.; *U.S. Private*, pg. 3179
PIEZOTECH, LLC—See Amphenol Corporation; *U.S. Public*, pg. 132
PIFCO LTD.—See Spectrum Brands Holdings, Inc.; *U.S. Public*, pg. 1916
PI FRANCE S.A.S.—See Physik Instrumente (PI) GmbH & Co. KG; *Int'l*, pg. 5858
PIGCHAMP INC.—See Farms.com Ltd.; *Int'l*, pg. 2620
PIGEON CORPORATION; *Int'l*, pg. 5864
PIGEON FALLS STATE BANK; *U.S. Private*, pg. 3179
PIGEON HEARTS CORPORATION—See Pigeon Corporation; *Int'l*, pg. 5865
PIGEON HOME PRODUCTS CORPORATION—See Pigeon Corporation; *Int'l*, pg. 5865
PIGEON INDIA PVT. LTD.—See Pigeon Corporation; *Int'l*, pg. 5865
PIGEON INDUSTRIES (THAILAND) CO., LTD.—See Pigeon Corporation; *Int'l*, pg. 5865
PIGEON MANUFACTURING HYOGO CORPORATION—See Pigeon Corporation; *Int'l*, pg. 5865
PIGEON SINGAPORE PTE. LTD.—See Pigeon Corporation; *Int'l*, pg. 5865
PIGGLY WIGGLY ALABAMA DISTRIBUTING CO.; *U.S. Private*, pg. 3179
PIGGLY WIGGLY CAROLINA COMPANY; *U.S. Private*, pg. 3179
PIGGLY WIGGLY CENTRAL INC.; *U.S. Private*, pg. 3179
PIGGLY WIGGLY FOOD STORES OF JEFFERSON COUNTY, INC.; *U.S. Private*, pg. 3179
PIGGLY WIGGLY HALEYVILLE INC.; *U.S. Private*, pg. 3179
PIGGLY WIGGLY, LLC—See C&S Wholesale Grocers, Inc.; *U.S. Private*, pg. 704
PIGGLY WIGGLY MIDWEST, LLC—See C&S Wholesale Grocers, Inc.; *U.S. Private*, pg. 704
PIGGLY WIGGLY OF CRYSTAL SPRING INC; *U.S. Private*, pg. 3179
PIG IMPROVEMENT COMPANY DEUTSCHLAND GMBH—See Genus Plc; *Int'l*, pg. 2931
PIG IMPROVEMENT COMPANY UK LIMITED—See Genus Plc; *Int'l*, pg. 2931
PIGINI S.R.L.—See Kering S.A.; *Int'l*, pg. 4136
PIGOTT INC.; *U.S. Private*, pg. 3179
PIGOTT OIL COMPANY INC.; *U.S. Private*, pg. 3179
PIGROL FARBEN GMBH—See PPG Industries, Inc.; *U.S. Public*, pg. 1710
PIGUET GALLAND & CIE SA—See Banque Cantonale Vaudoise; *Int'l*, pg. 853
PIGUET GRAPHIC & PRINTS COMPANY LIMITED—See Hung Hing Printing Group Limited; *Int'l*, pg. 3535
PIHA PTY LTD—See Mineral Resources Limited; *Int'l*, pg. 4907
PI HEALTH SCIENCES LTD.—See PI Industries Ltd.; *Int'l*, pg. 5859
PIHER INTERNATIONAL CORPORATION—See Parker Hannifin Corporation; *U.S. Public*, pg. 1642
PIHER INTERNATIONAL GMBH—See Parker Hannifin Corporation; *U.S. Public*, pg. 1643
PIHER INTERNATIONAL LTD.—See Parker Hannifin Corporation; *U.S. Public*, pg. 1643
PIHER SENSORS & CONTROLS S.A.—See Amphenol Corporation; *U.S. Public*, pg. 132

PIH HEALTH HOSPITAL - DOWNEY—See Presbyterian Intercommunity Hospital, Inc.; *U.S. Private*, pg. 3253
PIHLAJALINNA IKIOMA OY—See Pihlajalinna Oy; *Int'l*, pg. 5865
PIHLAJALINNA OY; *Int'l*, pg. 5865
PIHLAJALINNA TERVEYS OY—See Pihlajalinna Oy; *Int'l*, pg. 5865
PIHLAVAN IKKUNAT OY—See Ratos AB; *Int'l*, pg. 6220
PIH LTD.—See Stanley Black & Decker, Inc.; *U.S. Public*, pg. 1933
PIH SERVICES ME LLC—See Stanley Black & Decker, Inc.; *U.S. Public*, pg. 1933
PIH SERVICES ME LTD.—See Stanley Black & Decker, Inc.; *U.S. Public*, pg. 1933
PIH SERVICES ME LTD.—See Stanley Black & Decker, Inc.; *U.S. Public*, pg. 1933
PIHSIANG ENERGY TECHNOLOGY CO., LTD.—See Pihsiang Machinery MFG. Co., Ltd.; *Int'l*, pg. 5865
PIHSIANG MACHINERY MFG. CO., LTD.; *Int'l*, pg. 5865
PIIDEA CANADA LTD.—See Henkel AG & Co. KGaA; *Int'l*, pg. 3354
PIIKKIO WORKS OY—See MEYER WERFT GmbH; *Int'l*, pg. 4870
PI INC.; *U.S. Private*, pg. 3175
PI, INC.; *U.S. Private*, pg. 3175
PI INDUSTRIES LTD.; *Int'l*, pg. 5859
PI INNOVO LLC—See Dana Incorporated; *U.S. Public*, pg. 623
PIIPPO OYJ; *Int'l*, pg. 5865
PI JAPAN CO.LTD.—See PI Industries Ltd.; *Int'l*, pg. 5859
PI-JAPAN CO., LTD.—See Physik Instrumente (PI) GmbH & Co. KG; *Int'l*, pg. 5858
PIKA AUTOTEILE GMBH—See LKQ Corporation; *U.S. Public*, pg. 1336
PIKA EDITION SAS—See Vivendi SE; *Int'l*, pg. 8278
PIKA ENERGY, INC.—See Generac Holdings Inc.; *U.S. Public*, pg. 912
PIK D.D.; *Int'l*, pg. 5865
THE PIKE COMPANY INC.; *U.S. Private*, pg. 4095
PIKE CORPORATION—See Goldberg Lindsay & Co., LLC; *U.S. Private*, pg. 1729
PIKE COUNTY LIGHT & POWER COMPANY—See Argo Infrastructure Partners LLC; *U.S. Private*, pg. 320
PIKE ELECTRIC, LLC—See Goldberg Lindsay & Co., LLC; *U.S. Private*, pg. 1729
PIKE INDUSTRIES, INC.—See CRH plc; *Int'l*, pg. 1847
PIKE INDUSTRIES—See CRH plc; *Int'l*, pg. 1847
PIKE NURSERIES ACQUISITION, LLC—See Armstrong Garden Centers, Inc.; *U.S. Private*, pg. 331
PIKES CREEK ASPHALT & CRUSHED STONE—See Haines & Kibblehouse Inc.; *U.S. Private*, pg. 1841
PIKES PEAK COMMUNITY FOUNDATION; *U.S. Private*, pg. 3180
PIKES PEAK DISTRIBUTORS LLC; *U.S. Private*, pg. 3180
PIKES PEAK HARLEY DAVIDSON; *U.S. Private*, pg. 3180
PIKES PEAK IMPORTS LTD.; *U.S. Private*, pg. 3180
PIKES PEAK LIBRARY DISTRICT; *U.S. Private*, pg. 3180
PIKES PEAK OF TEXAS INC.; *U.S. Private*, pg. 3180
PIKES PEAK SOLAR GARDEN I LLC—See BlackRock, Inc.; *U.S. Public*, pg. 345
PIKES PEAK TELEVISION, INC.—See News-Press & Gazette Company; *U.S. Private*, pg. 2917
PIKE STREET CAPITAL, LP; *U.S. Private*, pg. 3179
PIKESVILLE ASSISTED LIVING, LLC—See Healthpeak Properties, Inc.; *U.S. Public*, pg. 1016
THE PIKESVILLE MD ENDOSCOPY ASC, LLC—See KKR & Co. Inc.; *U.S. Public*, pg. 1248
PIKETEC GMBH—See Synopsys, Inc.; *U.S. Public*, pg. 1970
PIKE WHEATON; *Int'l*, pg. 5865
PIK GROUP OF COMPANIES PJSC; *Int'l*, pg. 5865
PIKO A.D.; *Int'l*, pg. 5865
PIKOLIN S.A.; *Int'l*, pg. 5865
PI KOREA LTD—See Physik Instrumente (PI) GmbH & Co. KG; *Int'l*, pg. 5858
PIK PESTER A.D.; *Int'l*, pg. 5865
PIK PROFILE OOO—See OAO Group of Companies PIK; *Int'l*, pg. 5506
PIKSEL, INC.; *U.S. Private*, pg. 3180
PIKSEL INDUSTRY SOLUTIONS LTD.—See Redcentric plc; *Int'l*, pg. 6246
PIKSIK, LLC—See Nana Regional Corporation, Inc.; *U.S. Private*, pg. 2833
PIKS PORSCHE INFORMATION KOMMUNIKATION SERVICES GMBH—See Porsche Automobil Holding SE; *Int'l*, pg. 5927
PIK VRBAS A.D.; *Int'l*, pg. 5865
PIK WIRTGEN UKRAINE—See Deere & Company; *U.S. Public*, pg. 647
PIK-ZAPAD ZAO—See OAO Group of Companies PIK; *Int'l*, pg. 5506
PILANI INVESTMENT & INDUSTRIES CORPORATION LIMITED; *Int'l*, pg. 5866
PILA PHARMA AB; *Int'l*, pg. 5866
PILAT INC.—See Galileo Tech Ltd.; *Int'l*, pg. 2873
PILAT ISRAEL—See Galileo Tech Ltd.; *Int'l*, pg. 2873
PILATUS AIRCRAFT LTD.; *Int'l*, pg. 5866

PILATUS AUSTRALIA PTY LTD—See Pilatus Aircraft Ltd.; *Int'l*, pg. 5866
PILATUS BUSINESS AIRCRAFT LTD—See Pilatus Aircraft Ltd.; *Int'l*, pg. 5866
PILBARA GOLD GROUP PTY. LTD.—See Australian Goldfields Limited; *Int'l*, pg. 721
THE PILBARA INFRASTRUCTURE PTY LIMITED—See Fortescue Ltd; *Int'l*, pg. 2738
PILBARA MINERALS LIMITED; *Int'l*, pg. 5866
PILERSUISOQ; *Int'l*, pg. 5866
PILES CHEVROLET-OLDS-PONTIAC-BUICK, INC.; *U.S. Private*, pg. 3180
PILET INTERSISTEMAS S.R.L—See Doppelmayr Group; *Int'l*, pg. 2175
PILEUM IMPORT & MANUFACTURING CO., LTD.—See Young An Hat Co., Ltd.; *Int'l*, pg. 8602
PILGRIM CAPITAL PARTNERS, LLC; *U.S. Private*, pg. 3180
PILGRIM CLEANERS INC.; *U.S. Private*, pg. 3180
PILGRIM FURNITURE CITY; *U.S. Private*, pg. 3180
PILGRIM INSURANCE COMPANY—See The Plymouth Rock Co.; *U.S. Private*, pg. 4097
PILGRIM INTERNATIONAL LTD.—See SKF AB; *Int'l*, pg. 6981
PILGRIM MEDIA GROUP, LLC—See Lions Gate Entertainment Corp.; *Int'l*, pg. 4521
PILGRIM MINING COMPANY, INC.—See Alpha Natural Resources, Inc.; *U.S. Private*, pg. 199
PILGRIM PARKING INC.—See Propark, Inc.; *U.S. Private*, pg. 3284
PILGRIM PETROLEUM CORP.; *U.S. Private*, pg. 3180
PILGRIM PLASTIC PRODUCTS COMPANY; *U.S. Private*, pg. 3180
PILGRIM QUALITY SOLUTIONS EMEA BV—See Riverside Partners, LLC; *U.S. Private*, pg. 3446
PILGRIM SCREW CORPORATION—See MEIDOH Co., Ltd; *Int'l*, pg. 4799
PILGRIM SOFTWARE INC.—See Riverside Partners, LLC; *U.S. Private*, pg. 3446
PILGRIM'S PRIDE - ATHENS—See JBS S.A.; *Int'l*, pg. 3919
PILGRIM'S PRIDE - CANTON—See JBS S.A.; *Int'l*, pg. 3919
PILGRIM'S PRIDE - CHATTANOOGA—See JBS S.A.; *Int'l*, pg. 3919
PILGRIM'S PRIDE CORPORATION OF WEST VIRGINIA, INC.—See JBS S.A.; *Int'l*, pg. 3919
PILGRIM'S PRIDE CORPORATION—See JBS S.A.; *Int'l*, pg. 3919
PILGRIM'S PRIDE CORP.—See JBS S.A.; *Int'l*, pg. 3919
PILGRIM'S PRIDE - ELBERTON—See JBS S.A.; *Int'l*, pg. 3919
PILGRIM'S PRIDE - ENTERPRISE—See JBS S.A.; *Int'l*, pg. 3919
PILGRIM'S PRIDE - GAINESVILLE—See JBS S.A.; *Int'l*, pg. 3919
PILGRIM'S PRIDE - MOUNT PLEASANT—See JBS S.A.; *Int'l*, pg. 3919
PILGRIM'S PRIDE - NATCHITOCHES—See JBS S.A.; *Int'l*, pg. 3919
PILGRIM VAN LINES, LLC—See UniGroup, Inc.; *U.S. Private*, pg. 4283
PILI INTERNATIONAL MULTIMEDIA CO., LTD.; *Int'l*, pg. 5866
PILING CONTRACTORS PTY LTD—See Keller Group plc; *Int'l*, pg. 4121
PILIPINAS KAO, INC.—See Kao Corporation; *Int'l*, pg. 4075
PILIPINAS KYOHRITSU INC.—See Sumitomo Electric Industries, Ltd.; *Int'l*, pg. 7279
PILIPINAS SHELL FOUNDATION, INC.—See Shell plc; *Int'l*, pg. 6797
PILIPINAS SHELL PETROLEUM CORPORATION; *Int'l*, pg. 5866
PIL ITALICA LIFESTYLE LTD.; *Int'l*, pg. 5865
PILKINGTON AGR AUSTRIA GMBH—See Nippon Sheet Glass Co. Ltd.; *Int'l*, pg. 5331
PILKINGTON AGR CZECH SPOL S.R.O.—See Nippon Sheet Glass Co. Ltd.; *Int'l*, pg. 5331
PILKINGTON AGR DANMARK A/S—See Nippon Sheet Glass Co. Ltd.; *Int'l*, pg. 5331
PILKINGTON AGR HUNGARY KFT.—See Nippon Sheet Glass Co. Ltd.; *Int'l*, pg. 5331
PILKINGTON AUSTRIA GMBH—See Nippon Sheet Glass Co. Ltd.; *Int'l*, pg. 5331
PILKINGTON AUSTRIA GMBH—See Nippon Sheet Glass Co. Ltd.; *Int'l*, pg. 5331
PILKINGTON AUTOMOTIVE ARGENTINA SA—See Nippon Sheet Glass Co. Ltd.; *Int'l*, pg. 5331
PILKINGTON AUTOMOTIVE DEUTSCHLAND GMBH—See Nippon Sheet Glass Co. Ltd.; *Int'l*, pg. 5331
PILKINGTON AUTOMOTIVE FINLAND OY—See Nippon Sheet Glass Co. Ltd.; *Int'l*, pg. 5331
PILKINGTON AUTOMOTIVE FRANCE SA—See Nippon Sheet Glass Co. Ltd.; *Int'l*, pg. 5331
PILKINGTON AUTOMOTIVE INDIA PRIVATE LIMITED—See Nippon Sheet Glass Co. Ltd.; *Int'l*, pg. 5331

PILKINGTON AUTOMOTIVE LIMITED—See Nippon Sheet Glass Co. Ltd.; *Int'l*, pg. 5331
PILKINGTON AUTOMOTIVE MANAGEMENT SERVICES LIMITED—See Nippon Sheet Glass Co. Ltd.; *Int'l*, pg. 5331
PILKINGTON AUTOMOTIVE POLAND SP. Z O.O.—See Nippon Sheet Glass Co. Ltd.; *Int'l*, pg. 5331
PILKINGTON BENELUX AGR B.V.—See Nippon Sheet Glass Co. Ltd.; *Int'l*, pg. 5331
PILKINGTON BENELUX BV—See Nippon Sheet Glass Co. Ltd.; *Int'l*, pg. 5331
PILKINGTON BRASIL LTDA—See Nippon Sheet Glass Co. Ltd.; *Int'l*, pg. 5331
PILKINGTON DANMARK A/S—See Nippon Sheet Glass Co. Ltd.; *Int'l*, pg. 5331
PILKINGTON FINANCE LIMITED—See Nippon Sheet Glass Co. Ltd.; *Int'l*, pg. 5331
PILKINGTON FLOATGLAS AB—See Nippon Sheet Glass Co. Ltd.; *Int'l*, pg. 5331
PILKINGTON (FOREX) LIMITED—See Nippon Sheet Glass Co. Ltd.; *Int'l*, pg. 5331
PILKINGTON GLASS INDIA PVT. LTD.—See Nippon Sheet Glass Co. Ltd.; *Int'l*, pg. 5332
PILKINGTON GLASS LLC—See Nippon Sheet Glass Co. Ltd.; *Int'l*, pg. 5332
PILKINGTON GLASS OF CANADA LIMITED—See Nippon Sheet Glass Co. Ltd.; *Int'l*, pg. 5332
PILKINGTON GLASS SERVICE SAS—See Nippon Sheet Glass Co. Ltd.; *Int'l*, pg. 5332
PILKINGTON GROUP LIMITED—See Nippon Sheet Glass Co. Ltd.; *Int'l*, pg. 5331
PILKINGTON HOLDING GMBH—See Nippon Sheet Glass Co. Ltd.; *Int'l*, pg. 5332
PILKINGTON IGP SP. Z O.O.—See Nippon Sheet Glass Co. Ltd.; *Int'l*, pg. 5332
PILKINGTON ITALIA SPA—See Nippon Sheet Glass Co. Ltd.; *Int'l*, pg. 5332
PILKINGTON LAHDEN LASITEHDAS OY—See Nippon Sheet Glass Co. Ltd.; *Int'l*, pg. 5332
PILKINGTON METAL FINISHING LLC—See Aterian Investment Management, L.P.; *U.S. Private*, pg. 366
PILKINGTON NORGE AS—See Nippon Sheet Glass Co. Ltd.; *Int'l*, pg. 5332
PILKINGTON NORTH AMERICA, INC.—See Nippon Sheet Glass Co. Ltd.; *Int'l*, pg. 5332
PILKINGTON POLSKA SP. Z O.O.—See Nippon Sheet Glass Co. Ltd.; *Int'l*, pg. 5332
PILKINGTON PROPERTIES LIMITED—See Nippon Sheet Glass Co. Ltd.; *Int'l*, pg. 5332
PILKINGTON SOLAR (TAICANG), LTD.—See Nippon Sheet Glass Co. Ltd.; *Int'l*, pg. 5332
PILKINGTON'S TILES GROUP PLC; *Int'l*, pg. 5866
PILKINGTON'S TILES LTD.—See Pilkington's Tiles Group Plc; *Int'l*, pg. 5866
PILKINGTON SVERIGE AB—See Nippon Sheet Glass Co. Ltd.; *Int'l*, pg. 5332
PILKINGTON UNITED KINGDOM LTD.—See Nippon Sheet Glass Co. Ltd.; *Int'l*, pg. 5332
PILLAR 5 PHARMA INC.—See ANJAC SAS; *Int'l*, pg. 472
PILLAR CAPITAL MANAGEMENT LIMITED—See Marsh & McLennan Companies, Inc.; *U.S. Public*, pg. 1388
PILLAR CONSTRUCTION INC.; *U.S. Private*, pg. 3180
PILLAR ENTERPRISE LTD.—See The Berlin Steel Construction Company; *U.S. Private*, pg. 3994
PILLAR RESOURCE SERVICES, INC. - EDMONTON FACILITY—See Pillar Resource Services, Inc.; *Int'l*, pg. 5866
PILLAR RESOURCE SERVICES, INC.; *Int'l*, pg. 5866
PILLAR SEALS & GASKETS LIMITED—See Inflexion Private Equity Partners LLP; *Int'l*, pg. 3688
PILLARSTONE CAPITAL REIT; *U.S. Private*, pg. 3180
PILLARSTONE EUROPE LLP—See KKR & Co. Inc.; *U.S. Public*, pg. 1263
PILLARSTONE GREECE—See KKR & Co. Inc.; *U.S. Public*, pg. 1263
PILLARSTONE ITALY S.P.A.—See KKR & Co. Inc.; *U.S. Public*, pg. 1263
PILLAR TECHNOLOGIES—See Illinois Tool Works Inc.; *U.S. Public*, pg. 1110
PILLAR TECHNOLOGY GROUP, LLC—See Accenture plc; *Int'l*, pg. 87
PILLER AUSTRALIA PTY LTD—See Langley Holdings Plc; *Int'l*, pg. 4410
PILLER BC SHANGHAI LTD.—See Piller Industrieventilatoren GmbH; *Int'l*, pg. 5866
PILLER DENMARK A/S—See Langley Holdings Plc; *Int'l*, pg. 4410
PILLER FRANCE SAS—See Langley Holdings Plc; *Int'l*, pg. 4410
PILLER GERMANY GMBH & CO KG—See Langley Holdings Plc; *Int'l*, pg. 4410
PILLER GROUP GMBH—See Langley Holdings Plc; *Int'l*, pg. 4410
PILLER IBERICA S.L.U—See Langley Holdings Plc; *Int'l*, pg. 4410
PILLER INDUSTRIEVENTILATOREN GMBH; *Int'l*, pg. 5866
PILLER ITALIA S.R.L.—See Langley Holdings Plc; *Int'l*, pg. 4410

PILLER POWER BEIJING CO. LTD.—See Langley Holdings Plc; *Int'l*, pg. 4410
PILLER POWER SINGAPORE PTE. LTD.—See Langley Holdings Plc; *Int'l*, pg. 4410
PILLER SAUSAGES & DELICATESSENS LTD.—See Premium Brands Holdings Corporation; *Int'l*, pg. 5963
PILLER SEA PTE. LTD.—See Piller Industrieventilatoren GmbH; *Int'l*, pg. 5866
PILLER (THAILAND) CO. LTD—See Langley Holdings Plc; *Int'l*, pg. 4410
PILLER TSC BLOWER CORPORATION—See Piller Industrieventilatoren GmbH; *Int'l*, pg. 5866
PILLER UK LIMITED—See Langley Holdings Plc; *Int'l*, pg. 4410
PILLER USA INC—See Langley Holdings Plc; *Int'l*, pg. 4410
PILLO HOTELS LIMITED—See Dalata Hotel Group plc; *Int'l*, pg. 1950
PILLOW KINGDOM INC.—See Funiture Row LLC; *U.S. Private*, pg. 1623
THE PILLSBURY COMPANY—See General Mills, Inc.; *U.S. Public*, pg. 922
PILLSBURY WINTHROP SHAW PITTMAN LLP; *U.S. Private*, pg. 3180
PILMICO FOODS CORPORATION—See Aboitiz Equity Ventures, Inc.; *Int'l*, pg. 67
PILOMAT S.R.L.—See Hormann KG Verkaufsgesellschaf; *Int'l*, pg. 3481
PILOT AIR FREIGHT, LLC—See A.P. Moller-Maersk A/S; *Int'l*, pg. 27
PILOT AND ASSOCIATES INC.—See Pilot Catastrophe Services Inc.; *U.S. Private*, pg. 3181
PILOT BANCSHARES, INC.—See Lake Michigan Credit Union; *U.S. Private*, pg. 2375
PILOT BANK—See Lake Michigan Credit Union; *U.S. Private*, pg. 2375
PILOT BLANKENFELDE MEDIZINISCH-ELEKTRONISCHE GERATE GMBH—See Amplifon S.p.A.; *Int'l*, pg. 435
PILOT CATASTROPHE SERVICES INC.; *U.S. Private*, pg. 3181
PILOT CHEMICAL COMPANY; *U.S. Private*, pg. 3181
PILOT CHEMICAL CO. OF CALIFORNIA, INC.—See Pilot Chemical Company; *U.S. Private*, pg. 3181
PILOT CHEMICAL CO. OF OHIO INC.—See Pilot Chemical Company; *U.S. Private*, pg. 3181
THE PILOT CORPORATION OF AMERICA—See Pilot Corporation; *Int'l*, pg. 5867
THE PILOT CORPORATION OF AMERICA—See Pilot Corporation; *Int'l*, pg. 5867
THE PILOT CORPORATION OF AMERICA—See Pilot Corporation; *Int'l*, pg. 5867
PILOT CORPORATION OF EUROPE S.A. - BENELUX DIVISION—See Pilot Corporation; *Int'l*, pg. 5866
PILOT CORPORATION OF EUROPE S.A.—See Pilot Corporation; *Int'l*, pg. 5866
PILOT CORPORATION; *Int'l*, pg. 5866
PILOT CORPORATION; *U.S. Private*, pg. 3181
PILOT ENERGY LTD.; *Int'l*, pg. 5867
PILOTES TERRATEST PERU S.A.C.—See Echeverria Izquierdo S.A.; *Int'l*, pg. 2289
PILOTES TERRATEST S.A.—See Echeverria Izquierdo S.A.; *Int'l*, pg. 2289
PILOT GROUP, LLC; *U.S. Private*, pg. 3181
PILOT GROUP—See Hakuhodo DY Holdings Incorporated; *Int'l*, pg. 3221
PILOT GROVE SAVINGS BANK; *U.S. Private*, pg. 3181
PILOT HOUSEWARES (U.K.) LIMITED—See Herald Holdings Limited; *Int'l*, pg. 3358
PILOT INDUSTRIES OF TEXAS INC.—See Pilot Chemical Company; *U.S. Private*, pg. 3181
PILOT INSURANCE COMPANY—See Aviva plc; *Int'l*, pg. 745
PILOT LABORATORIES INC.—See Pilot Chemical Company; *U.S. Private*, pg. 3181
THE PILOT LLC; *U.S. Private*, pg. 4095
PILOTMALL.COM, INC.; *U.S. Private*, pg. 3181
PILOT NORDIC AB—See Pilot Corporation; *Int'l*, pg. 5866
PILOT PEN AUSTRALIA PTY. LTD.—See Pilot Corporation; *Int'l*, pg. 5867
PILOT PEN (DEUTSCHLAND) GMBH—See Pilot Corporation; *Int'l*, pg. 5867
PILOT PEN FRANCE, SA—See Pilot Corporation; *Int'l*, pg. 5867
PILOTPEN IBERICA, UNIPESSOAL, LDA—See Pilot Corporation; *Int'l*, pg. 5867
PILOT PEN (MALAYSIA) SDN. BHD.—See Pilot Corporation; *Int'l*, pg. 5867
PILOT PEN NORSK AS—See Pilot Corporation; *Int'l*, pg. 5867
PILOT PEN PETERSBURG LTD.—See Pilot Corporation; *Int'l*, pg. 5867
PILOT PEN SOUTH AFRICA (PTY) LTD.—See Pilot Corporation; *Int'l*, pg. 5867
PILOT PEN (S) PTE. LTD.—See Pilot Corporation; *Int'l*, pg. 5867
PILOT PEN UK LTD.—See Pilot Corporation; *Int'l*, pg. 5867

PILOT POLYMER TECHNOLOGIES, INC.—See Pilot Chemical Company; *U.S. Private*, pg. 3181
PILOT POWER GROUP, INC.—See Boyne Capital Management, LLC; *U.S. Private*, pg. 629
PILOT TRADING COMPANY INC.; *U.S. Private*, pg. 3181
PILOT TRAINING NETWORK GMBH—See Deutsche Lufthansa AG; *Int'l*, pg. 2068
PILOT TRAVEL CENTERS LLC—See Berkshire Hathaway Inc.; *U.S. Public*, pg. 313
PILOT TRUCK BROKERAGE, LLC—See A.P. Moller-Maersk A/S; *Int'l*, pg. 27
PILSEN STEEL S.R.O.; *Int'l*, pg. 5867
PILTZ GLASS AND MIRROR, INC.—See Brin Northwestern Glass Company Inc.; *U.S. Private*, pg. 654
PIMACO AUTOADESIVOS LTDA.—See Grupo CCRR; *Int'l*, pg. 3124
PIMA-MPU GMBH—See TUV SUD AG; *Int'l*, pg. 7984
PIMAS PLASTIK INSAAT MALZEMELERI A.S.—See Deceuninck NV; *Int'l*, pg. 2000
PIMA VALVE, INC.—See Arcline Investment Management LP; *U.S. Private*, pg. 313
PIMA ZINC CORP.; *Int'l*, pg. 5867
PIM BRANDS, LLC—See Promotion In Motion, Inc.; *U.S. Private*, pg. 3283
PIMCO ADVISORY—See Allianz SE; *Int'l*, pg. 346
PIMCO ASIA LTD.—See Allianz SE; *Int'l*, pg. 346
PIMCO ASIA PTE. LTD.—See Allianz SE; *Int'l*, pg. 346
PIMCO AUSTRALIA PTY LTD.—See Allianz SE; *Int'l*, pg. 346
PIMCO CA MUNI INCOME FUND II; *U.S. Public*, pg. 1690
PIMCO CANADA CORP.—See Allianz SE; *Int'l*, pg. 346
PIMCO CAPITAL SOLUTIONS BDC CORP.; *U.S. Private*, pg. 3181
PIMCO CORPORATE & INCOME OPPORTUNITY FUND; *U.S. Public*, pg. 1690
PIMCO CORPORATE & INCOME STRATEGY FUND; *U.S. Public*, pg. 1690
PIMCO DEUTSCHLAND GMBH—See Allianz SE; *Int'l*, pg. 347
PIMCO DYNAMIC CREDIT INCOME FUND; *U.S. Private*, pg. 3181
PIMCO DYNAMIC INCOME FUND; *U.S. Public*, pg. 1690
PIMCO EUROPE GMBH—See Allianz SE; *Int'l*, pg. 355
PIMCO EUROPE LTD.—See Allianz SE; *Int'l*, pg. 346
PIMCO GLOBAL ADVISORS (IRELAND) LTD.—See Allianz SE; *Int'l*, pg. 355
PIMCO GLOBAL ADVISORS LLC—See Allianz SE; *Int'l*, pg. 347
PIMCO GLOBAL STOCKSPLUS & INCOME FUND; *U.S. Public*, pg. 1690
PIMCO INCOME OPPORTUNITY FUND; *U.S. Public*, pg. 1690
PIMCO INCOME STRATEGY FUND II; *U.S. Public*, pg. 1690
PIMCO INVESTMENTS LLC—See Allianz SE; *Int'l*, pg. 347
PIMCO JAPAN LTD.—See Allianz SE; *Int'l*, pg. 346
PIMCO MORTGAGE INCOME TRUST INC.; *U.S. Public*, pg. 1690
PIMCO MUNICIPAL INCOME FUND II; *U.S. Public*, pg. 1690
PIMCO NEW YORK MUNICIPAL INCOME FUND III; *U.S. Public*, pg. 1691
PIMCO NEW YORK MUNICIPAL INCOME FUND; *U.S. Public*, pg. 1691
PIMCO REIT, INC.; *U.S. Private*, pg. 3181
PIMCO (SCHWEIZ) GMBH—See Allianz SE; *Int'l*, pg. 355
PIMCO (SWITZERLAND) LLC—See Allianz SE; *Int'l*, pg. 347
PIMCO TAIWAN LTD.—See Allianz SE; *Int'l*, pg. 355
PIM FINANCIAL SERVICES INC.—See Centurion Counsel, Inc.; *U.S. Private*, pg. 831
PI MICOS GMBH—See Physik Instrumente (PI) GmbH & Co. KG; *Int'l*, pg. 5858
PIM KOREA CO., LTD.; *Int'l*, pg. 5867
PIMLICO RACING ASSOCIATION, INC.—See The Stronach Group Inc.; *Int'l*, pg. 7689
PIM LIMITED; *Int'l*, pg. 5867
PI MLINPRODUKT AD ADA; *Int'l*, pg. 5859
PIM MULIER B.V.—See Achmea B.V.; *Int'l*, pg. 103
P.I MYANMAR PTE. LIMITED—See Prestige International Inc.; *Int'l*, pg. 5966
PINAR ENTEGRE ET VE UN SANAYI AS; *Int'l*, pg. 5867
PINAR SU SANAYI VE TICARET AS; *Int'l*, pg. 5867
PINAR SUT MAMULLERI SANAYII AS; *Int'l*, pg. 5867
PIN BUSINESS NETWORK; *U.S. Private*, pg. 3181
PINC FINSERVE PRIVATE LIMITED—See Pioneer Investcorp Ltd; *Int'l*, pg. 5872
PINCH A PENNY, INC.; *U.S. Private*, pg. 3181
PINCHERS CRAB SHACK, INC.; *U.S. Private*, pg. 3181
PINCHIN LTD; *Int'l*, pg. 5867
PINCHME.COM, INC.; *U.S. Private*, pg. 3181
PINCKNEY HUGO GROUP; *U.S. Private*, pg. 3181
PINCOCK, ALLEN & HOLT—See Runge ICT Group Pty Limited; *Int'l*, pg. 6427
PINCON LIFESTYLE LTD.; *Int'l*, pg. 5867
PINCOTT INTERNATIONAL PTY LIMITED—See Elgi Rubber Company Limited; *Int'l*, pg. 2360

PINCOTT SALES COMPANY INC—See Elgi Rubber Company Limited; *Int'l*, pg. 2360
PINDAO HOLDINGS LIMITED; *Int'l*, pg. 5867
PINDAR SCARBOROUGH LIMITED—See York Mailing Limited; *Int'l*, pg. 8599
THE PINDEN PLANT & PROCESSING CO. LIMITED—See Heidelberg Materials AG; *Int'l*, pg. 3320
PINDERS PROFESSIONAL & CONSULTANCY SERVICES LTD.—See Christie Group plc; *Int'l*, pg. 1587
PINDLER & PINDLER INC.; *U.S. Private*, pg. 3182
PINEAPPLE ENERGY INC.; *U.S. Public*, pg. 1691
PINEAPPLE EXPRESS CANNABIS COMPANY; *Int'l*, pg. 5868
PINEAPPLE EXPRESS DELIVERY INC.—See Fire & Flower Holdings Corp.; *Int'l*, pg. 2678
PINEAPPLE FINANCIAL INC.; *Int'l*, pg. 5868
PINEAPPLE HOUSE OF BREVARD, INC.—See The Goldfield Corporation; *U.S. Public*, pg. 2075
PINEAPPLE, INC.; *U.S. Public*, pg. 1691
PINEAPPLE PAYMENTS, LLC—See Global Payments Inc.; *U.S. Public*, pg. 943
PINEAPPLE POWER CORPORATION PLC; *Int'l*, pg. 5868
PINEAPPLE RESOURCES BERHAD; *Int'l*, pg. 5868
PINE BELT ENTERPRISES; *U.S. Private*, pg. 3182
PINE BELT NISSAN OF TOMS RIVER; *U.S. Private*, pg. 3182
PINE BLUFF CABLE TELEVISION INC.—See Wehco Media, Inc.; *U.S. Private*, pg. 4469
PINE BLUFF SAND AND GRAVEL CO; *U.S. Private*, pg. 3182
PINE BRANCH COAL SALES INC.; *U.S. Private*, pg. 3182
PINEBRIDGE BENSON ELLIOT LLP—See Pacific Century Group Holdings Limited; *Int'l*, pg. 5687
PINEBRIDGE INVESTMENTS ASIA LTD.—See Pacific Century Group Holdings Limited; *Int'l*, pg. 5687
PINEBRIDGE INVESTMENTS (CENTRAL EUROPE) SP. Z O.O.—See Pacific Century Group Holdings Limited; *Int'l*, pg. 5687
PINEBRIDGE INVESTMENTS EUROPE LTD.—See Pacific Century Group Holdings Limited; *Int'l*, pg. 5687
PINEBRIDGE INVESTMENTS JAPAN CO., LTD.—See Pacific Century Group Holdings Limited; *Int'l*, pg. 5687
PINEBRIDGE INVESTMENTS LLC—See Pacific Century Group Holdings Limited; *Int'l*, pg. 5687
PINEBRIDGE INVESTMENTS MIDDLE EAST B.S.C. (C)—See Pacific Century Group Holdings Limited; *Int'l*, pg. 5687
PINEBROOK CARE & REHABILITATION CENTER—See Formation Capital, LLC; *U.S. Private*, pg. 1571
PINEBROOK IMAGING, INC.—See Applied Materials, Inc.; *U.S. Public*, pg. 172
PINE BROOK PARTNERS, LLC; *U.S. Private*, pg. 3182
PINE BROOK ROAD PARTNERS, LLC; *U.S. Private*, pg. 3182
PINE BUSH EQUIPMENT CO. INC.; *U.S. Private*, pg. 3182
PINE CAPITAL GROUP LIMITED; *Int'l*, pg. 5867
PINE CARE GROUP LIMITED—See Chinachem Group; *Int'l*, pg. 1568
PINE CLIFF ENERGY LTD.; *Int'l*, pg. 5867
PINE CREEK BREWING COMPANY LTD—See Big Rock Brewery Inc.; *Int'l*, pg. 1021
PINE CREEK GOLF CLUB—See Escalante Golf, Inc.; *U.S. Private*, pg. 1424
PINE CREEK PARTNERS, LLC; *U.S. Private*, pg. 3182
PINECREST CAPITAL PARTNERS, LLC; *U.S. Private*, pg. 3183
PINEDALE TRADING PTE LIMITED—See General Mills, Inc.; *U.S. Public*, pg. 922
PINE DECALS—See PPS, Inc.; *U.S. Private*, pg. 3240
PINE ENVIRONMENTAL SERVICES, LLC—See ACON Investments, LLC; *U.S. Private*, pg. 62
PINE GATE RENEWABLES LLC; *U.S. Private*, pg. 3182
PINE GROUP HONG KONG LIMITED—See PINE Technology Holdings Limited; *Int'l*, pg. 5868
PINE GROVE HOLDINGS, LLC; *U.S. Private*, pg. 3182
PINE GROVE LANDFILL, INC.—See Waste Management, Inc.; *U.S. Public*, pg. 2331
PINE HALL BRICK CO. INC.; *U.S. Private*, pg. 3182
PINE HILL FARMS LANDFILL TX, LP—See Republic Services, Inc.; *U.S. Public*, pg. 1786
PINE HILL GROUP LLC—See The Carlyle Group Inc.; *U.S. Public*, pg. 2045
PINEHILL PACIFIC BERHAD; *Int'l*, pg. 5868
THE PINEHILL PARTNERSHIP LTD—See Vorwerk & Co. KG; *Int'l*, pg. 8307
PINEHURST, LLC; *U.S. Private*, pg. 3183
PINE INSTRUMENT COMPANY; *U.S. Private*, pg. 3182
PINE ISLAND ACQUISITION CORP.; *U.S. Public*, pg. 1691
PINE ISLAND CAPITAL PARTNERS LLC; *U.S. Private*, pg. 3182
PINE ISLAND TELEPHONE COMPANY—See Arvig Enterprises, Inc.; *U.S. Private*, pg. 344
PINE ISLAND TELEPHONE COMPANY—See Blue Earth Valley Communications; *U.S. Private*, pg. 588
PINE ISLAND TELEPHONE COMPANY—See Nuvera Communications, Inc.; *U.S. Public*, pg. 1556

PINE LAB TW CO. LTD.—See PINE Technology Holdings Limited; *Int'l*, pg. 5868
PINELAND COGENTES, INC.—See Pineland Telephone Cooperative, Inc.; *U.S. Private*, pg. 3183
PINELAND FARMS POTATO COMPANY, INC.—See Post Holdings, Inc.; *U.S. Public*, pg. 1704
PINELANDS GROUP HOMES, INC.—See Bain Capital, LP; *U.S. Private*, pg. 431
PINELANDS WATER COMPANY—See Middlesex Water Company; *U.S. Public*, pg. 1445
PINELAND TELEPHONE COOPERATIVE, INC.; *U.S. Private*, pg. 3183
PINELLAS COUNTY ANESTHESIA ASSOCIATES LLC—See WELL Health Technologies Corp.; *Int'l*, pg. 8372
THE PINELLAS COUNTY EMERGENCY MEDICAL SERVICES AUTHORITY; *U.S. Private*, pg. 4095
PINELLAS COUNTY HOUSING AUTHORITY; *U.S. Private*, pg. 3183
PINELLAS COUNTY UTILITIES; *U.S. Private*, pg. 3183
PINELLAS HEALTH CARE NEWS—See Florida Health Care News, Inc.; *U.S. Private*, pg. 1548
PINELLAS OPPORTUNITY COUNCIL INC; *U.S. Private*, pg. 3183
PINELLAS SUNCOAST TRANSIT AUTHORITY; *U.S. Private*, pg. 3183
PINELLI UNIVERSAL, S DE R.L. DE C.V.—See UFP Industries, Inc.; *U.S. Public*, pg. 2219
PINE MANOR INC.; *U.S. Private*, pg. 3182
PINE NEEDLE OPERATING COMPANY—See The Williams Companies, Inc.; *U.S. Public*, pg. 2143
PINENEX CO., LTD.; *Int'l*, pg. 5868
PINENO LEVIN & FORD ASSET MANAGEMENT, INC.—See Dakota Wealth Management LLC; *U.S. Private*, pg. 1148
PINE-O-PINE LP—See Industrias Alen S.A. de C.V.; *Int'l*, pg. 3673
PINE PACKAGING (M) SDN. BHD.—See Jaycorp Berhad; *Int'l*, pg. 3915
PINE POINT MINING LIMITED—See Osisko Metals Inc.; *Int'l*, pg. 5651
PINE PRAIRIE ENERGY CENTER, LLC—See Plains All American Pipeline, L.P.; *U.S. Public*, pg. 1696
PINE PROPERTIES SDN BHD—See IOI Corporation Berhad; *Int'l*, pg. 3792
PINERIDGE FOODS INC.—See Swander Pace Capital, LLC; *U.S. Private*, pg. 3890
PINERIDGE FOODS INC.—See The Bank of Nova Scotia; *Int'l*, pg. 7617
PINE RIDGE WINERY, LLC—See Crimson Wine Group, Ltd.; *U.S. Public*, pg. 594
PINE RIVER CAPITAL MANAGEMENT, LP; *U.S. Private*, pg. 3183
THE PINES AT DAVIDSON; *U.S. Private*, pg. 4095
THE PINES AT WHITING; *U.S. Private*, pg. 4095
PINES HEALTH SERVICES; *U.S. Private*, pg. 3183
PINES INTERNATIONAL, INC.; *U.S. Private*, pg. 3183
PINES OF SARASOTA, INC.; *U.S. Private*, pg. 3184
PINESOLUTIONS.CO.UK; *Int'l*, pg. 5868
PINE STATE BEVERAGE CO.—See Pine State Trading Co.; *U.S. Private*, pg. 3183
PINE STATE TRADING CO.; *U.S. Private*, pg. 3183
PINESTONE CAPITAL LIMITED; *Int'l*, pg. 5868
PINE STREET ALTERNATIVE ASSET MANAGEMENT LP; *U.S. Private*, pg. 3183
PINE STREET INN INC.; *U.S. Private*, pg. 3183
PINE TECHNOLOGY ACQUISITION CORP.; *U.S. Public*, pg. 1691
PINE TECHNOLOGY HOLDINGS LIMITED; *Int'l*, pg. 5868
PINE TECHNOLOGY LIMITED—See PINE Technology Holdings Limited; *Int'l*, pg. 5868
PINE TECHNOLOGY (MACAO COMMERCIAL OFFSHORE) LTD—See PINE Technology Holdings Limited; *Int'l*, pg. 5868
PINE TRAIL REAL ESTATE INVESTMENT TRUST; *Int'l*, pg. 5868
PINE TREE ACRES, INC.—See Waste Management, Inc.; *U.S. Public*, pg. 2331
PINETREE CAPITAL LTD.; *Int'l*, pg. 5868
PINE TREE EQUITY MANAGEMENT, LP; *U.S. Private*, pg. 3183
PINE TREE FORD LINCOLN; *Int'l*, pg. 5868
PINE TREE LUMBER CO. INC.; *U.S. Private*, pg. 3183
PINETREE RESOURCE PARTNERSHIP—See Pinetree Capital Ltd.; *Int'l*, pg. 5868
PINE TREE SOCIETY FOR HANDICAPPED CHILDREN AND ADULTS, INC.; *U.S. Private*, pg. 3183
PINE TREE WASTE, INC.—See Casella Waste Systems, Inc.; *U.S. Public*, pg. 446
PINE VALLEY FOODS, INC.; *U.S. Private*, pg. 3183
PINEVIEW INDUSTRIES LIMITED—See PINE Technology Holdings Limited; *Int'l*, pg. 5868
PINEVIEW MEMORIAL PARK, INC.—See Service Corporation International; *U.S. Public*, pg. 1870
PINEWELL CAPITAL LLC; *U.S. Private*, pg. 3184
PINEWOOD GROUP LIMITED—See Aermont Capital LLP; *Int'l*, pg. 180
PINEWOOD HEALTHCARE LIMITED—See Wockhardt Limited; *Int'l*, pg. 8441

PINEWOOD HEALTHCARE REALTY, L.P.—See Acadia Healthcare Company, Inc.; *U.S. Public*, pg. 29
PINEWOOD LABORATORIES LTD.—See Wockhardt Limited; *Int'l*, pg. 8441
PINEWOOD PARK APARTMENTS, A LIMITED PARTNERSHIP—See Apartment Investment and Management Company; *U.S. Public*, pg. 144
PINEWOOD STUDIOS LIMITED—See Aermont Capital LLP; *Int'l*, pg. 180
PINEWOOD TECHNOLOGIES GROUP PLC; *Int'l*, pg. 5868
PINEWOOD TECHNOLOGIES PLC—See Pinewood Technologies Group PLC; *Int'l*, pg. 5869
PINEY LUFKIN HEALTHCARE, INC.—See The Ensign Group, Inc.; *U.S. Public*, pg. 2072
PINFENG (SHANGHAI) INFORMATION TECHNOLOGY CO., LTD.—See Dayforce, Inc.; *U.S. Public*, pg. 645
PINFRA US, LLC—See Promotora y Operadora de Infraestructura, S.A.B. de C.V.; *Int'l*, pg. 5996
PING AN ANNUITY INSURANCE COMPANY OF CHINA, LTD—See Ping An Insurance (Group) Company of China, Ltd.; *Int'l*, pg. 5869
PING AN ASSET MANAGEMENT CO., LTD.—See Ping An Insurance (Group) Company of China, Ltd.; *Int'l*, pg. 5869
PING AN BANK CO., LTD.—See Ping An Insurance (Group) Company of China, Ltd.; *Int'l*, pg. 5869
PING AN HEALTHCARE & TECHNOLOGY COMPANY LIMITED; *Int'l*, pg. 5869
PING AN INSURANCE (GROUP) COMPANY OF CHINA, LTD.; *Int'l*, pg. 5869
PING AN LIFE INSURANCE COMPANY OF CHINA, LTD.—See Ping An Insurance (Group) Company of China, Ltd.; *Int'l*, pg. 5869
PING AN OF CHINA ASSET MANAGEMENT (HONG KONG) COMPANY LIMITED—See Ping An Insurance (Group) Company of China, Ltd.; *Int'l*, pg. 5869
PING AN PROPERTY & CASUALTY INSURANCE COMPANY OF CHINA, LTD.—See Ping An Insurance (Group) Company of China, Ltd.; *Int'l*, pg. 5869
PING AN SECURITIES CO., LTD.—See Ping An Insurance (Group) Company of China, Ltd.; *Int'l*, pg. 5869
PING AN TRADITION INTERNATIONAL MONEY BROKING CO. LTD.—See Ping An Insurance (Group) Company of China, Ltd.; *Int'l*, pg. 5869
PING CANADA CORPORATION—See Karsten Manufacturing Corporation; *U.S. Private*, pg. 2263
PINGDINGSHAN RAIL SLEEPER COMPANY—See China Railway Materials Co., Ltd.; *Int'l*, pg. 1544
PINGDINGSHAN TIANAN COAL MINING CO. LTD.; *Int'l*, pg. 5870
PINGDOM AB—See Silver Lake Group, LLC; *U.S. Private*, pg. 3661
PINGDOM AB—See Thoma Bravo, L.P.; *U.S. Private*, pg. 4153
PINGER PR AT POWERS—See Powers Agency; *U.S. Private*, pg. 3240
PINGGAO GROUP CO., LTD.—See State Grid Corporation of China; *Int'l*, pg. 7183
PING HD LLC—See The Jordan Company, L.P.; *U.S. Private*, pg. 4062
PINGHU CITY JING XING PACKING MATERIAL LIMITED COMPANY—See Zhejiang Jingxing Paper Joint Stock Co., Ltd.; *Int'l*, pg. 8658
PINGHU KIBING GLASS CO., LTD.—See Zhuzhou Kibing Group Co., Ltd.; *Int'l*, pg. 8680
PING IDENTITY AUSTRALIA PTY. LTD.—See Vista Equity Partners, LLC; *U.S. Private*, pg. 4399
PING IDENTITY CANADA INC.—See Thoma Bravo, L.P.; *U.S. Private*, pg. 4150
PING IDENTITY CORPORATION—See Vista Equity Partners, LLC; *U.S. Private*, pg. 4399
PING IDENTITY CORPORATION—See Vista Equity Partners, LLC; *U.S. Private*, pg. 4399
PING IDENTITY FRANCE, SAS—See Thoma Bravo, L.P.; *U.S. Private*, pg. 4150
PING IDENTITY HOLDING CORP.—See Thoma Bravo, L.P.; *U.S. Private*, pg. 4150
PING IDENTITY ISRAEL, LTD.—See Thoma Bravo, L.P.; *U.S. Private*, pg. 4150
PING IDENTITY UK LIMITED—See Thoma Bravo, L.P.; *U.S. Private*, pg. 4150
PING INC.—See Karsten Manufacturing Corporation; *U.S. Private*, pg. 2263
PINGLIANG JINGCHUAN HUITONG VILLAGE BANK CO., LTD.—See China Development Bank Corporation; *Int'l*, pg. 1497
PINGO DOCE-DISTRIBUICAO ALIMENTAR, S.A.—See Jeronimo Martins SGPS SA; *Int'l*, pg. 3931
PING PETROLEUM UK PLC—See Dagang NeXchange Berhad; *Int'l*, pg. 1912
PINGPROPERTIES BV; *Int'l*, pg. 5870
PINGTAN MARINE ENTERPRISE LTD.; *Int'l*, pg. 5870
PING YUE TECHNOLOGIES SDN. BHD.—See TOPCO Scientific Co., Ltd.; *Int'l*, pg. 7814
PININFARINA DEUTSCHLAND GMBH—See Mahindra & Mahindra Limited; *Int'l*, pg. 4646
PININFARINA EXTRA S.R.L.—See Mahindra & Mahindra Limited; *Int'l*, pg. 4646

COMPANY NAME INDEX

PININFARINA S.P.A.—See Mahindra & Mahindra Limited; *Int'l*, pg. 4646
PINKARD CONSTRUCTION COMPANY; *U.S. Private*, pg. 3184
PINKERTON CHEVROLET-GEO, INC.; *U.S. Private*, pg. 3184
PINKERTON GOVERNMENT SERVICES, INC.—See Securitas AB; *Int'l*, pg. 6676
PINKERTON & LAWS INC.; *U.S. Private*, pg. 3184
PINK HOMELOANS LTD.—See The Skipton Building Society; *Int'l*, pg. 7687
PINKI A.D.; *Int'l*, pg. 5870
PINKIE'S INC.; *U.S. Private*, pg. 3184
PINK JEEP TOURS, INC.—See Herschend Family Entertainment Corp.; *U.S. Private*, pg. 1926
PINK N PAY HOLDINGS LIMITED RF; *Int'l*, pg. 5870
PINKO CREATIVE SDN. BHD.—See Sasbadi Holdings Berhad; *Int'l*, pg. 6582
PINK SHELL BEACH RESORT & MARINA—See Boykin Management Company, LLC; *U.S. Private*, pg. 628
PINKS ORIGINAL BAKERY, INC.; *U.S. Private*, pg. 3184
PINKSTON-HOLLAR CONSTRUCTION SERVICES INC.—See Altas Partners LP; *Int'l*, pg. 386
PINLIVE FOODS CO., LTD.; *Int'l*, pg. 5870
PINMAR USA, INC.—See GYG plc; *Int'l*, pg. 3191
PINMAR YACHT SUPPLY, S.L.—See GYG plc; *Int'l*, pg. 3191
PINNACLE 21, LLC—See Certara, Inc.; *U.S. Public*, pg. 476
PINNACLE ACQUISITIONS LLC—See ModivCare, Inc.; *U.S. Public*, pg. 1456
PINNACLE ADVISORY GROUP; *U.S. Private*, pg. 3184
PINNACLE AMS DEVELOPMENT COMPANY LLC—See American Management Services LLC; *U.S. Private*, pg. 240
PINNACLE ARCHITECTURAL LIGHTING, INC.—See Legrand S.A.; *Int'l*, pg. 4445
PINNACLEART INTERNATIONAL, LLC; *U.S. Private*, pg. 3186
PINNACLE ASSET MANAGEMENT, L.P.; *U.S. Private*, pg. 3184
PINNACLE ASSOCIATES, LTD.; *U.S. Private*, pg. 3184
PINNACLE AT UNION HILLS LLC—See Greystar Real Estate Partners, LLC; *U.S. Private*, pg. 1785
PINNACLE BANCORP, INC.; *U.S. Private*, pg. 3184
PINNACLE BANCSHARES, INC.; *U.S. Public*, pg. 1691
PINNACLE BANK OF OREGON; *U.S. Public*, pg. 1691
PINNACLE BANKSHARES CORP.; *U.S. Public*, pg. 1691
PINNACLE BANK SIOUX CITY—See Pinnacle Bancorp, Inc.; *U.S. Private*, pg. 3184
PINNACLE BANK; *U.S. Public*, pg. 1691
PINNACLE BANK—See Iowa River Bancorp, Inc.; *U.S. Private*, pg. 2135
PINNACLE BANK—See Pinnacle Bancorp, Inc.; *U.S. Private*, pg. 3184
PINNACLE BANK—See Pinnacle Bancorp, Inc.; *U.S. Private*, pg. 3184
PINNACLE BANK—See Pinnacle Bancshares, Inc.; *U.S. Public*, pg. 1691
PINNACLE BANK—See Pinnacle Financial Corporation; *U.S. Private*, pg. 3185
PINNACLE BANK—See Pinnacle Financial Partners, Inc.; *U.S. Public*, pg. 1692
PINNACLE BANK - WYOMING—See Pinnacle Bancorp, Inc.; *U.S. Private*, pg. 3184
THE PINNACLE BENEFITS GROUP, LLC.—See Integrity Marketing Group LLC; *U.S. Private*, pg. 2104
PINNACLE BIOLOGICS, INC.—See Advanz Pharma Corp.; *Int'l*, pg. 166
PINNACLE BUSINESS SYSTEMS, INC.; *U.S. Private*, pg. 3184
PINNACLE CAPITAL PARTNERS, LLC—See Alliance Funding Group, Inc.; *U.S. Private*, pg. 182
PINNACLE CARE INTERNATIONAL, LLC—See Sun Life Financial Inc.; *Int'l*, pg. 7305
PINNACLE CENTRAL COMPANY, INC.—See Source Capital, LLC; *U.S. Private*, pg. 3718
PINNACLE COATING & CONVERTING, INC.; *U.S. Private*, pg. 3184
PINNACLE COMMUNICATION SERVICES; *U.S. Private*, pg. 3184
PINNACLE CONSTRUCTION GROUP; *U.S. Private*, pg. 3185
PINNACLE DATA SYSTEMS, LLC—See GI Manager L.P.; *U.S. Private*, pg. 1692
PINNACLE DERMATOLOGY LLC; *U.S. Private*, pg. 3185
PINNACLE DOOR & HARDWARE, INC.—See Platinum Equity, LLC; *U.S. Private*, pg. 3209
PINNACLE ELECTRONIC SYSTEMS—See Construction Management Service; *U.S. Private*, pg. 1024
PINNACLE ENTERTAINMENT, INC.—See PENN Entertainment, Inc.; *U.S. Public*, pg. 1662
PINNACLE ENVIRONMENTAL CORPORATION; *U.S. Private*, pg. 3185
PINNACLE EXHIBITS, INC.; *U.S. Private*, pg. 3185
PINNACLE FIBRE PVT LTD—See Premium Textile Mills Limited; *Int'l*, pg. 5963
PINNACLE FINANCIAL CORPORATION; *U.S. Private*, pg. 3185

PINNACLE FINANCIAL PARTNERS, INC.; *U.S. Public*, pg. 1691
PINNACLE FOODS CANADA CORPORATION—See Conagra Brands, Inc.; *U.S. Public*, pg. 564
PINNACLE FOODS FINANCE LLC—See Conagra Brands, Inc.; *U.S. Public*, pg. 564
PINNACLE FOODS FORT MADISON LLC—See Conagra Brands, Inc.; *U.S. Public*, pg. 564
PINNACLE FOODS GROUP LLC—See Conagra Brands, Inc.; *U.S. Public*, pg. 564
PINNACLE FOODS INC.—See Conagra Brands, Inc.; *U.S. Public*, pg. 564
PINNACLE FOODS INTERNATIONAL CORP.—See Conagra Brands, Inc.; *U.S. Public*, pg. 564
PINNACLE FRAMES & ACCENTS, INC.—See Newcastle Partners LP; *U.S. Private*, pg. 2914
PINNACLE FRAMES AND ACCENTS, INC.—See Newcastle Partners LP; *U.S. Private*, pg. 2914
PINNACLE GALLERIA LLC—See FPI Management, Inc.; *U.S. Private*, pg. 1586
PINNACLE GAS TREATING LLC—See Western Midstream Partners, LP; *U.S. Public*, pg. 2356
PINNACLE HEALTH CARE; *U.S. Private*, pg. 3185
PINNACLE HEALTH PARTNERSHIP LLP—See EMIS Group plc; *Int'l*, pg. 2383
PINNACLE HOLDINGS LIMITED—See Alviva Holdings Limited; *Int'l*, pg. 402
PINNACLE INSURANCE & FINANCIAL SERVICES, LLC; *U.S. Private*, pg. 3185
PINNACLE INSURANCE PLC—See BNP Paribas SA; *Int'l*, pg. 1092
PINNACLE INVESTMENT MANAGEMENT GROUP LIMITED; *Int'l*, pg. 5870
PINNACLE INVESTMENT MANAGEMENT LTD.—See SinoPac Financial Holdings Company Ltd.; *Int'l*, pg. 6954
PINNACLE INVESTMENT SERVICES, INC.—See Pinnacle Financial Corporation; *U.S. Private*, pg. 3185
PINNACLE LIFE SCIENCE PRIVATE LIMITED—See Aarti Drugs Ltd.; *Int'l*, pg. 38
PINNACLE MACHINE TOOLS, INC.; *U.S. Private*, pg. 3185
PINNACLE MACHINE TOOLS, INC.—See Pinnacle Machine Tools, Inc.; *U.S. Private*, pg. 3185
PINNACLE MATERIALS, INC.; *U.S. Private*, pg. 3185
PINNACLE MEDICAL SOLUTIONS LLC—See AdaptHealth Corp.; *U.S. Public*, pg. 39
PINNACLE MICRO NAMIBIA (PTY) LIMITED—See Alviva Holdings Limited; *Int'l*, pg. 402
PINNACLE MICRO (PTY) LIMITED—See Alviva Holdings Limited; *Int'l*, pg. 402
PINNACLE MINERALS LIMITED; *Int'l*, pg. 5870
PINNACLE MOUNTAIN HOMES, INC.; *U.S. Private*, pg. 3185
PINNACLE NISSAN; *U.S. Private*, pg. 3185
PINNACLE OILFIELD SERVICES, INC.—See J Fitzgibbons LLC; *U.S. Private*, pg. 2153
PINNACLE PHYSICIAN NETWORK, LLC—See HCA Healthcare, Inc.; *U.S. Public*, pg. 1006
PINNACLE PLATFORM SDN BHD—See Johor Corporation; *Int'l*, pg. 3994
PINNACLE PRECISION SHEET METAL; *U.S. Private*, pg. 3185
PINNACLE PROPANE, LLC—See SHV Holdings N.V.; *Int'l*, pg. 6873
PINNACLE PUBLIC FINANCE, INC.—See BankUnited, Inc.; *U.S. Public*, pg. 274
PINNACLE RENEWABLE ENERGY, INC.—See Drax Group plc; *Int'l*, pg. 2200
PINNACLE RESTAURANT GROUP LLC; *U.S. Private*, pg. 3185
PINNACLE RETAMA PARTNERS, LLC—See PENN Entertainment, Inc.; *U.S. Public*, pg. 1662
PINNACLE RISK MANAGEMENT SERVICES, INC.; *U.S. Private*, pg. 3185
PINNACLE SENIOR LIVING LLC—See The Pennant Group, Inc.; *U.S. Public*, pg. 2118
PINNACLE SERVICES, INC.; *U.S. Private*, pg. 3185
PINNACLE SOLUTIONS, INC.—See Nana Regional Corporation, Inc.; *U.S. Private*, pg. 2832
PINNACLE STAFFING INC.; *U.S. Private*, pg. 3185
PINNACLE SUMMER INVESTMENTS, INC.—See Lee Equity Partners LLC; *U.S. Private*, pg. 2412
PINNACLE SYSTEMS, INC.—See Symphony Technology Group, LLC; *U.S. Private*, pg. 3901
PINNACLE SYSTEMS LTD.—See Symphony Technology Group, LLC; *U.S. Private*, pg. 3902
PINNACLE TALENT INC.—See ASM Technologies Limited; *Int'l*, pg. 627
PINNACLE TECHNICAL RESOURCES, INC.; *U.S. Private*, pg. 3185
PINNACLE TEK, INC.—See Scienture Holdings, Inc.; *U.S. Public*, pg. 1849
PINNACLE TELECOMMUNICATIONS, INC.; *U.S. Private*, pg. 3185
PINNACLE TEXTILE INDUSTRIES, LLC; *U.S. Private*, pg. 3186
PINNACLE TREATMENT CENTERS—See Linden LLC; *U.S. Private*, pg. 2460

PIONEER AGRO EXTRACTS LIMITED

PINNACLE UNDERWRITING LIMITED—See BNP Paribas SA; *Int'l*, pg. 1092
PINNACLE VACATIONS, INC.—See Hilton Grand Vacations Inc.; *U.S. Public*, pg. 1040
PINNACLE WEST CAPITAL CORPORATION; *U.S. Public*, pg. 1692
PINNACOL ASSURANCE; *U.S. Private*, pg. 3186
PINNAFRICA INSURANCE—See BNP Paribas SA; *Int'l*, pg. 1092
PINN BROTHERS CONSTRUCTION; *U.S. Private*, pg. 3184
PINOLE VALLEY TRUCKING, INC.; *U.S. Private*, pg. 3186
PINO TILE HOLDINGS LLC; *U.S. Private*, pg. 3186
PINOT PROVENCE—See Delaware North Companies, Inc.; *U.S. Private*, pg. 1195
PINOVA CAPITAL GMBH; *Int'l*, pg. 5870
PINPROS; *U.S. Private*, pg. 3186
PINSLY RAILROAD CO. INC.; *U.S. Private*, pg. 3186
PINSTRIPE MARKETING, INC.; *U.S. Private*, pg. 3186
PINTAIL CORPORATION—See Tech Agricultural, Inc.; *U.S. Private*, pg. 3951
PINTARAS GEOTECHNICS SDN. BHD.—See Pintaras Jaya Berhad; *Int'l*, pg. 5870
PINTARAS JAYA BERHAD; *Int'l*, pg. 5870
PINTARMAS SDN BHD—See Venture Corporation Limited; *Int'l*, pg. 8151
PINTEC CORPORATION—See Punch Industry Co., Ltd.; *Int'l*, pg. 6119
PINTECO OY—See Indutrade AB; *Int'l*, pg. 3682
PINTEC TECHNOLOGY HOLDINGS LIMITED; *Int'l*, pg. 5871
PINTEL CO., LTD.; *Int'l*, pg. 5871
PINTEREST, INC.; *U.S. Public*, pg. 1692
PINT, INC.; *U.S. Private*, pg. 3186
PINTSCH B.V.—See The Carlyle Group Inc.; *U.S. Public*, pg. 2053
PINTSCH GMBH—See The Carlyle Group Inc.; *U.S. Public*, pg. 2053
PINTSCH TIEFENBACH US INC.—See The Carlyle Group Inc.; *U.S. Public*, pg. 2053
PINT SIZE CORPORATION; *U.S. Private*, pg. 3186
PINTURA, ESTAMPADO Y MONTAJE, S.A.P.I. DE C.V.—See Cie Automotive S.A.; *Int'l*, pg. 1605
PINTURAS BENICARLO, S.L.—See American Securities LLC; *U.S. Private*, pg. 252
PINTURAS CORAL DE BOLIVIA LTDA—See Akzo Nobel N.V.; *Int'l*, pg. 274
PINTURAS DYRUP, S.A.—See PPG Industries, Inc.; *U.S. Public*, pg. 1707
PINTURAS INCA S.A.—See Akzo Nobel N.V.; *Int'l*, pg. 271
PINUS SP. Z O.O.—See Norvik hf; *Int'l*, pg. 5448
P.I OF EUROPE NV.—See Nihon Parkerizing Co., Ltd.; *Int'l*, pg. 5286
PIOLAX BUSINESS SERVICE CO., LTD.—See Piolax Inc.; *Int'l*, pg. 5871
PIOLAX (CHINA) CO., LTD.—See Piolax Inc.; *Int'l*, pg. 5871
PIOLAX CO., LTD.—See Piolax Inc.; *Int'l*, pg. 5871
PIOLAX CORPORATION—See Piolax Inc.; *Int'l*, pg. 5871
PIOLAX HARNESS FASTENING SYSTEMS, INC.—See Piolax Inc.; *Int'l*, pg. 5871
PIOLAX INC. - FUJI PLANT—See Piolax Inc.; *Int'l*, pg. 5871
PIOLAX INC. - MOKA PLANT—See Piolax Inc.; *Int'l*, pg. 5871
PIOLAX INC.; *Int'l*, pg. 5871
PIOLAX INDIA PRIVATE LIMITED—See Piolax Inc.; *Int'l*, pg. 5871
PIOLAX KYUSYU CO., LTD.—See Piolax Inc.; *Int'l*, pg. 5871
PIOLAX LTD.—See Piolax Inc.; *Int'l*, pg. 5871
PIOLAX MEDICAL DEVICES, INC.—See Piolax Inc.; *Int'l*, pg. 5871
PIOLAX MEXICANA S. A. DE C. V.—See Piolax Inc.; *Int'l*, pg. 5871
PIOLAX (THAILAND) LTD.—See Piolax Inc.; *Int'l*, pg. 5871
PIOLINK CHINA—See Piolink Inc.; *Int'l*, pg. 5871
PIOLINK INC.; *Int'l*, pg. 5871
PIOLINK JAPAN—See Piolink Inc.; *Int'l*, pg. 5871
PIOLI S.R.L.—See Interpump Group S.p.A.; *Int'l*, pg. 3757
PIONEER AEROSPACE CORPORATION—See Space Exploration Technologies Corp.; *U.S. Private*, pg. 3744
PIONEER AG-CHEM INC.; *U.S. Private*, pg. 3186
PIONEER AGGREGATES (UK) LIMITED—See Heidelberg Materials AG; *Int'l*, pg. 3318
PIONEER AGRO EXTRACTS LIMITED; *Int'l*, pg. 5871
PIONEER AMERICAN INSURANCE COMPANY—See iA Financial Corporation Inc.; *U.S. Public*, pg. 3567
PIONEER AMERICAS LLC—See Olin Corporation; *U.S. Public*, pg. 1570
PIONEER ARGENTINA, S.R.L.—See Corteva, Inc.; *U.S. Public*, pg. 582
PIONEER ASPHALTS (U.K.) LIMITED—See Heidelberg Materials AG; *Int'l*, pg. 3318
PIONEER ASSET MANAGEMENT S.A.—See UniCredit S.p.A.; *Int'l*, pg. 8035
PIONEER AUTOMOTIVE TECHNOLOGY—See EQT AB; *Int'l*, pg. 2470

2119

PIONEER BANCORP, INC.

CORPORATE AFFILIATIONS

PIONEER BANCORP, INC.; *U.S. Public*, pg. 1692
PIONEER BANCSHARES, INC.—See FirstSun Capital Bancorp; *U.S. Public*, pg. 850
PIONEER BANKCORP, INC.; *U.S. Public*, pg. 1692
PIONEER BANKSHARES, INC.; *U.S. Public*, pg. 1692
PIONEER BANK—See Pioneer Bankshares, Inc.; *U.S. Public*, pg. 1692
PIONEER BANK; *U.S. Private*, pg. 3186
PIONEER BUILDERS SUPPLY CO.; *U.S. Private*, pg. 3186
PIONEER CEMENT INDUSTRIES LLC—See RAYSUT CEMENT COMPANY SAOG; *Int'l*, pg. 6225
PIONEER CEMENT LTD.; *Int'l*, pg. 5871
PIONEER CENTER FOR HUMAN SERVICES; *U.S. Private*, pg. 3186
PIONEER CENTRES INC.; *U.S. Private*, pg. 3186
PIONEER CHINA HOLDING CO LTD—See EQT AB; *Int'l*, pg. 2470
PIONEER COILED TUBING SERVICES, LLC—See Patterson-UTI Energy, Inc.; *U.S. Public*, pg. 1654
PIONEER COMMERCIAL BANK—See Pioneer Savings Bank; *U.S. Private*, pg. 3188
PIONEER COMMODITY INTERMEDIARIES PVT. LTD.—See Pioneer Investcorp Ltd; *Int'l*, pg. 5872
PIONEER COMMUNICATIONS CORP—See EQT AB; *Int'l*, pg. 2470
PIONEER CONCRETE PUMPING SERVICE; *U.S. Private*, pg. 3186
PIONEER CORPORATION - KAWAGOE PLANT—See EQT AB; *Int'l*, pg. 2470
PIONEER CORPORATION—See EQT AB; *Int'l*, pg. 2470
PIONEER COVER-ALL—See H.I.G. Capital, LLC; *U.S. Private*, pg. 1832
PIONEER CREDIT COMPANY INC.; *U.S. Private*, pg. 3186
PIONEER CREDIT LIMITED; *Int'l*, pg. 5871
PIONEER CREDIT RECOVERY, INC.—See SLM Corporation; *U.S. Public*, pg. 1894
PIONEER CRITICAL POWER INC.—See CleanSpark, Inc.; *U.S. Public*, pg. 511
PIONEER CUSTOM ELECTRICAL PRODUCTS CORP.—See Guggenheim Partners, LLC; *U.S. Private*, pg. 1812
PIONEER CUT STOCK INC.—See Bright Wood Corp.; *U.S. Private*, pg. 651
PIONEER DISTILLERIES LIMITED—See Diageo plc; *Int'l*, pg. 2103
PIONEER DIVERSIFIED HIGH INCOME FUND, INC; *U.S. Public*, pg. 1692
PIONEER DO BRASIL LTDA—See EQT AB; *Int'l*, pg. 2471
PIONEER ECLIPSE CORPORATION—See Amano Corporation; *Int'l*, pg. 411
PIONEER ELECTRIC COOPERATIVE; *U.S. Private*, pg. 3186
PIONEER ELECTRONICS ASIACENTRE PTE. LTD.—See EQT AB; *Int'l*, pg. 2470
PIONEER ELECTRONICS AUSTRALIA PTY LTD—See EQT AB; *Int'l*, pg. 2470
PIONEER ELECTRONICS OF CANADA INC.—See EQT AB; *Int'l*, pg. 2470
PIONEER ELECTRONICS SERVICE—See EQT AB; *Int'l*, pg. 2470
PIONEER ELECTRONICS TECHNOLOGY—See EQT AB; *Int'l*, pg. 2470
PIONEER ELECTRONICS(THAILAND) CO LTD—See EQT AB; *Int'l*, pg. 2470
PIONEER ELECTRONICS (USA) INC.—See EQT AB; *Int'l*, pg. 2470
PIONEER EMBROIDERIES LIMITED; *Int'l*, pg. 5871
PIONEER ENERGY SERVICES CORP. - COILED TUBING SERVICES—See Patterson-UTI Energy, Inc.; *U.S. Public*, pg. 1654
PIONEER ENERGY SERVICES CORP.—See Patterson-UTI Energy, Inc.; *U.S. Public*, pg. 1654
PIONEER ENVIRONMENTAL TECHNOLOGY PTE LTD—See AnnAik Limited; *Int'l*, pg. 473
PIONEER EUROPE N.V—See EQT AB; *Int'l*, pg. 2471
PIONEER EXPLORATION COMPANY; *U.S. Private*, pg. 3187
PIONEER FA CORPORATION—See Yamaha Corporation; *Int'l*, pg. 8550
PIONEERFA CORP—See EQT AB; *Int'l*, pg. 2471
PIONEER FARM EQUIPMENT CO.; *U.S. Private*, pg. 3187
PIONEER FINANCIAL SERVICES, INC.—See MidCountry Financial Corp.; *U.S. Private*, pg. 2711
PIONEER FLOAT GLASS MFG INC.—See TQMP Glass Manufacturing Corp.; *Int'l*, pg. 7885
PIONEER FLOATING RATE FUND, INC; *U.S. Public*, pg. 1692
PIONEER FOOD CANNERY LIMITED—See Thai Union Group Public Company Limited; *Int'l*, pg. 7596
PIONEER FOOD GROUP LIMITED—See PepsiCo, Inc.; *U.S. Public*, pg. 1671
PIONEER FOODS (UK) LIMITED—See PepsiCo, Inc.; *U.S. Public*, pg. 1672
PIONEER FOODS UK LTD.—See PepsiCo, Inc.; *U.S. Public*, pg. 1671
PIONEER FORGE DIVISION—See Letts Industries, Inc.; *U.S. Private*, pg. 2433

PIONEER FRICTION LIMITED—See Westinghouse Air Brake Technologies Corporation; *U.S. Public*, pg. 2359
PIONEER FROZEN FOODS LLC—See The Pritzker Group - Chicago, LLC; *U.S. Private*, pg. 4098
PIONEER GARAGE; *U.S. Private*, pg. 3187
PIONEER GARAGE LTD; *Int'l*, pg. 5871
PIONEER GLOBAL GROUP LIMITED; *Int'l*, pg. 5872
THE PIONEER GROUP, INC.; *U.S. Private*, pg. 4096
PIONEER GROUP, INC.—See Full House Resorts, Inc.; *U.S. Public*, pg. 892
PIONEER GULF, FZE—See EQT AB; *Int'l*, pg. 2471
PIONEER HEALTH RESOURCES—See ATAR Capital, LLC; *U.S. Private*, pg. 364
PIONEER HI-BRED AUSTRALIA, PTY LTD.—See Corteva, Inc.; *U.S. Public*, pg. 582
PIONEER HI-BRED CANADA COMPANY—See Corteva, Inc.; *U.S. Public*, pg. 582
PIONEER HI-BRED INTERNATIONAL, INC.—See Corteva, Inc.; *U.S. Public*, pg. 582
PIONEER HI-BRED INTERNATIONAL—See Corteva, Inc.; *U.S. Public*, pg. 583
PIONEER HI-BRED INTERNATIONAL—See Corteva, Inc.; *U.S. Public*, pg. 583
PIONEER HI-BRED INTERNATIONAL—See Corteva, Inc.; *U.S. Public*, pg. 583
PIONEER HI-BRED INTERNATIONAL—See Corteva, Inc.; *U.S. Public*, pg. 583
PIONEER HI-BRED INTERNATIONAL—See Corteva, Inc.; *U.S. Public*, pg. 583
PIONEER HI-BRED INTERNATIONAL—See Corteva, Inc.; *U.S. Public*, pg. 583
PIONEER HI-BRED INTERNATIONAL—See Corteva, Inc.; *U.S. Public*, pg. 583
PIONEER HI-BRED INTERNATIONAL—See Corteva, Inc.; *U.S. Public*, pg. 583
PIONEER HI-BRED INTERNATIONAL—See Corteva, Inc.; *U.S. Public*, pg. 583
PIONEER HI-BRED INTERNATIONAL—See Corteva, Inc.; *U.S. Public*, pg. 583
PIONEER HI-BRED INTERNATIONAL—See Corteva, Inc.; *U.S. Public*, pg. 583
PIONEER HI-BRED INTERNATIONAL—See Corteva, Inc.; *U.S. Public*, pg. 583
PIONEER HI-BRED INTERNATIONAL—See Corteva, Inc.; *U.S. Public*, pg. 583
PIONEER HI-BRED INTERNATIONAL—See Corteva, Inc.; *U.S. Public*, pg. 583
PIONEER HI-BRED INTERNATIONAL—See Corteva, Inc.; *U.S. Public*, pg. 583
PIONEER HI-BRED INTERNATIONAL—See Corteva, Inc.; *U.S. Public*, pg. 583
PIONEER HI-BRED INTERNATIONAL—See Corteva, Inc.; *U.S. Public*, pg. 583
PIONEER HI-BRED INTERNATIONAL—See Corteva, Inc.; *U.S. Public*, pg. 583
PIONEER HI-BRED INTERNATIONAL—See Corteva, Inc.; *U.S. Public*, pg. 583
PIONEER HI-BRED INTERNATIONAL—See Corteva, Inc.; *U.S. Public*, pg. 583
PIONEER HI-BRED INTERNATIONAL—See Corteva, Inc.; *U.S. Public*, pg. 583
PIONEER HI-BRED INTERNATIONAL—See Corteva, Inc.; *U.S. Public*, pg. 583
PIONEER HI-BRED INTERNATIONAL—See Corteva, Inc.; *U.S. Public*, pg. 583
PIONEER HI-BRED INTERNATIONAL—See Corteva, Inc.; *U.S. Public*, pg. 583
PIONEER HI-BRED INTERNATIONAL—See Corteva, Inc.; *U.S. Public*, pg. 583
PIONEER HI-BRED INTERNATIONAL—See Corteva, Inc.; *U.S. Public*, pg. 583
PIONEER HI-BRED INTERNATIONAL—See Corteva, Inc.; *U.S. Public*, pg. 583
PIONEER HI-BRED INTERNATIONAL—See Corteva, Inc.; *U.S. Public*, pg. 583
PIONEER HI-BRED ITALIA SRL—See Corteva, Inc.; *U.S. Public*, pg. 583
PIONEER HI-BRED LTD.—See Corteva, Inc.; *U.S. Public*, pg. 582
PIONEER HI-BRED MAGYARORSZAG KFT—See Corteva, Inc.; *U.S. Public*, pg. 584

PIONEER HI-BRED NORTHERN EUROPE SERVICE DIVISION GMBH—See Corteva, Inc.; *U.S. Public*, pg. 584
PIONEER HI-BRED POLAND SP Z O.O.—See Corteva, Inc.; *U.S. Public*, pg. 584
PIONEER HI-BRED PRODUCTION COMPANY—See Corteva, Inc.; *U.S. Public*, pg. 583
PIONEER HI-BRED PUERTO RICO—See Corteva, Inc.; *U.S. Public*, pg. 583
PIONEER HI-BRED RESEARCH CENTER—See Corteva, Inc.; *U.S. Public*, pg. 583
PIONEER HI-BRED ROMANIA S.R.L.—See Corteva, Inc.; *U.S. Public*, pg. 584
PIONEER HI-BRED R.S.A. (PTY) LTD.—See Corteva, Inc.; *U.S. Public*, pg. 584
PIONEER HI-BRED SERVICES GMBH—See Corteva, Inc.; *U.S. Public*, pg. 583
PIONEER HI-BRED (THAILAND) CO. LIMITED—See Corteva, Inc.; *U.S. Public*, pg. 582
PIONEER HIGH FIDELITY TAIWAN CO.,LTD—See EQT AB; *Int'l*, pg. 2471
PIONEER HIGH INCOME FUND, INC.; *U.S. Public*, pg. 1692
PIONEER (HK) LTD.—See EQT AB; *Int'l*, pg. 2470
PIONEER HOMES AUSTRALIA PTY LTD—See ACS, Actividades de Construccion y Servicios, S.A.; *Int'l*, pg. 113
PIONEER HOMES, INC.; *U.S. Private*, pg. 3187
PIONEER HOTEL INC.—See Archon Corporation; *U.S. Public*, pg. 185
PIONEER HUMAN SERVICES, INC.; *U.S. Private*, pg. 3187
PIONEER INDIA ELECTRONICS PRIVATE LTD—See EQT AB; *Int'l*, pg. 2471
PIONEER INDUSTRIAL COMPONENTS (HONG KONG) CO., LTD.—See EQT AB; *Int'l*, pg. 2471
PIONEER INDUSTRIAL CORPORATION; *U.S. Private*, pg. 3187
PIONEER INDUSTRIES (HOLDINGS) LIMITED—See Pioneer Global Group Limited; *Int'l*, pg. 5872
PIONEER INDUSTRIES, INC. - BATLINER CONVERTING DIVISION—See Pioneer Industries, Inc.; *U.S. Private*, pg. 3187
PIONEER INDUSTRIES, INC.; *U.S. Private*, pg. 3187
PIONEERING TECHNOLOGY CORP.; *Int'l*, pg. 5872
PIONEER INSURANCE COMPANY LIMITED; *Int'l*, pg. 5872
PIONEER INTERNATIONAL INVESTMENTS LIMITED—See Heidelberg Materials AG; *Int'l*, pg. 3318
PIONEER INVESTCORP LTD; *Int'l*, pg. 5872
PIONEER INVESTMENT, INC.—See NCS Multistage Holdings, Inc.; *U.S. Public*, pg. 1503
PIONEER INVESTMENTS—See UniCredit S.p.A.; *Int'l*, pg. 8035
PIONEER JELLICE INDIA PVT. LTD.; *Int'l*, pg. 5872
PIONEER LANDSCAPING MATERIALS; *U.S. Private*, pg. 3187
PIONEER MAGNETICS INC.—See Greenbriar Equity Group, L.P.; *U.S. Private*, pg. 1776
PIONEER MANUFACTURING COMPANY; *U.S. Private*, pg. 3187
PIONEER MANUFACTURING (THAILAND) CO., LTD.—See EQT AB; *Int'l*, pg. 2471
PIONEER MARKETING CORP—See EQT AB; *Int'l*, pg. 2471
PIONEER MATERIALS, INC.—See GMS Inc.; *U.S. Public*, pg. 948
PIONEER MATERIALS WEST, INC.—See GMS Inc.; *U.S. Public*, pg. 948
PIONEER MEDIA HOLDINGS INC.; *Int'l*, pg. 5872
PIONEER MEDICAL GROUP, INC.—See Presbyterian Intercommunity Hospital, Inc.; *U.S. Private*, pg. 3253
PIONEER MERGER CORP.; *U.S. Public*, pg. 1693
PIONEER METAL FINISHING LLC - ANODIZING & PLATING FACILITY—See Aterian Investment Management, L.P.; *U.S. Private*, pg. 366
PIONEER METAL FINISHING LLC - GAFFNEY DIVISION—See Aterian Investment Management, L.P.; *U.S. Private*, pg. 367
PIONEER METAL FINISHING LLC - MINNEAPOLIS DIVISION—See Aterian Investment Management, L.P.; *U.S. Private*, pg. 367
PIONEER METAL FINISHING LLC - MONROE DIVISION—See Aterian Investment Management, L.P.; *U.S. Private*, pg. 367
PIONEER METAL FINISHING LLC - OSHKOSH DIVISION—See Aterian Investment Management, L.P.; *U.S. Private*, pg. 367
PIONEER METAL FINISHING LLC—See Aterian Investment Management, L.P.; *U.S. Private*, pg. 366
PIONEER METAL FINISHING LLC - SOUTH BEND DIVISION—See Aterian Investment Management, L.P.; *U.S. Private*, pg. 367
PIONEER MOTOR PCL; *Int'l*, pg. 5872
PIONEER MUNICIPAL HIGH INCOME ADVANTAGE FUND, INC.; *U.S. Public*, pg. 1693
PIONEER MUNICIPAL HIGH INCOME FUND, INC.; *U.S. Public*, pg. 1693

COMPANY NAME INDEX

PIONEER MUTUAL LIFE INSURANCE COMPANY—See American United Mutual Insurance Holding Company; *U.S. Private*, pg. 258

PIONEER NATIONAL LATEX COMPANY—See Continental American Corporation; *U.S. Private*, pg. 1028

PIONEER NATURAL RESOURCES COMPANY; *U.S. Public*, pg. 1693

PIONEER NATURAL RESOURCES TUNISIA LTD.—See Pioneer Natural Resources Company; *U.S. Public*, pg. 1693

PIONEER NATURAL RESOURCES USA, INC.—See Pioneer Natural Resources Company; *U.S. Public*, pg. 1693

PIONEER NEWSPAPERS INC.; *U.S. Private*, pg. 3187

THE PIONEER NEWSPAPER—See The Pioneer Group, Inc.; *U.S. Private*, pg. 4096

PIONEER NEWSPAPERS—See Chicago Public Media, Inc.; *U.S. Private*, pg. 879

PIONEER NORTH AMERICA INC.—See EQT AB; *Int'l*, pg. 2470

PIONEER NORTHERN INC.—See Pioneer Packing Inc.; *U.S. Private*, pg. 3188

PIONEER NORTH QUEENSLAND PTY LTD—See Heidelberg Materials AG; *Int'l*, pg. 3311

PIONEER OIL & GAS; *U.S. Public*, pg. 1693

PIONEER OIL LLC; *U.S. Private*, pg. 3187

PIONEER OPTICAL INC.—See EssilorLuxottica SA; *Int'l*, pg. 2516

PIONEER PACKAGING INC.—See Pioneer Packing Inc.; *U.S. Private*, pg. 3188

PIONEER PACKING INC.; *U.S. Private*, pg. 3187

PIONEER PAPER CORPORATION—See Vidya Brands Group LLC; *U.S. Private*, pg. 4381

PIONEER PAPER STOCK COMPANY—See Pioneer Industries, Inc.; *U.S. Private*, pg. 3187

PIONEER PAPER STOCK CO. OF TEXAS, INC.—See Pioneer Industries, Inc.; *U.S. Private*, pg. 3187

PIONEER PE HOLDING LLC—See Pioneer Natural Resources Company; *U.S. Public*, pg. 1693

PIONEER PEKAO INVESTMENT MANAGEMENT S.A.—See Bank Polska Kasa Opieki Spolka Akcyjna; *Int'l*, pg. 850

PIONEER PETROTECH SERVICES INC.—See SPT Energy Group Inc.; *Int'l*, pg. 7146

PIONEER PHARMA (HONG KONG) COMPANY LIMITED—See Shanghai Pioneer Holding Ltd.; *Int'l*, pg. 6776

PIONEER PHOTO ALBUMS INC.; *U.S. Private*, pg. 3188

PIONEER PHYSICAL THERAPY, LIMITED PARTNERSHIP—See U.S. Physical Therapy, Inc.; *U.S. Public*, pg. 2215

PIONEER PIPE, INC.; *U.S. Private*, pg. 3188

PIONEER PIPE LINE COMPANY—See Phillips 66 Company; *U.S. Public*, pg. 1688

PIONEER POWER SOLUTIONS, INC.; *U.S. Public*, pg. 1693

PIONEER PRESS - WEST GROUP—See Chicago Public Media, Inc.; *U.S. Private*, pg. 879

PIONEER PRODUCTS, INC.; *U.S. Private*, pg. 3188

PIONEER PROPANE—See UGI Corporation; *U.S. Public*, pg. 2222

PIONEER PROPERTY GROUP ASA; *Int'l*, pg. 5872

PIONEER PUMP HOLDINGS, INC.—See Franklin Electric Co., Inc.; *U.S. Public*, pg. 878

PIONEER PUMP HOLDINGS PTY.—See Franklin Electric Co., Inc.; *U.S. Public*, pg. 878

PIONEER PUMP LTD.—See Franklin Electric Co., Inc.; *U.S. Public*, pg. 879

PIONEER PUMP PTY. LTD.—See Franklin Electric Co., Inc.; *U.S. Public*, pg. 879

PIONEER PUMP SOLUTIONS LTD.—See Franklin Electric Co., Inc.; *U.S. Public*, pg. 879

PIONEER RAILCORP; *U.S. Private*, pg. 3188

PIONEER REAL ESTATE SERVICES INC.—See Dickerson & Nieman Realtors, Inc.; *U.S. Private*, pg. 1226

PIONEER RESEARCH CENTER USA INC.—See EQT AB; *Int'l*, pg. 2470

PIONEER RIM AND WHEEL COMPANY; *U.S. Private*, pg. 3188

PIONEER ROAD SERVICES PTY. LTD.—See Fulton Hogan Limited; *Int'l*, pg. 2843

PIONEER ROAD SERVICES PTY. LTD.—See Shell plc; *Int'l*, pg. 6797

PIONEER ROOFING, LLC—See Altas Partners LP; *Int'l*, pg. 386

PIONEER RURAL ELECTRIC COOPERATIVE INC.; *U.S. Private*, pg. 3188

PIONEER RUS LIMITED LIABILITY COMPANY—See EQT AB; *Int'l*, pg. 2471

PIONEER SALES GROUP, INC.; *U.S. Private*, pg. 3188

PIONEER SAND COMPANY INC.—See SiteOne Landscape Supply, Inc.; *U.S. Public*, pg. 1889

PIONEER SAVINGS BANK; *U.S. Private*, pg. 3188

PIONEER SECURITY LIFE INSURANCE COMPANY—See iA Financial Corporation Inc.; *U.S. Private*, pg. 3567

PIONEER SEEDS INC.—See Corteva, Inc.; *U.S. Public*, pg. 583

PIONEER SEMENCES S.A.S—See Corteva, Inc.; *U.S. Public*, pg. 583

PIONEER SERVICE NETWORK CORP—See EQT AB; *Int'l*, pg. 2471

PIONEER SERVICES CORP.—See MidCountry Acquisition Corp.; *U.S. Private*, pg. 2711

PIONEER SERVICES SALES FINANCE, INC.—See MidCountry Acquisition Corp.; *U.S. Private*, pg. 2711

PIONEERS HEALTHCARE PARS PRIVATE JOINT STOCK COMPANY—See PAUL HARTMANN AG; *Int'l*, pg. 5761

PIONEERS HOLDING COMPANY; *Int'l*, pg. 5872

PIONEER SPECIALTY INSURANCE COMPANY—See Western National Mutual Insurance Co.; *U.S. Private*, pg. 4494

PIONEERS SECURITIES CO.—See Pioneers Holding Company; *Int'l*, pg. 5872

PIONEER STATE BANK—See NBE Bancshares, Inc.; *U.S. Private*, pg. 2875

PIONEER STATE MUTUAL INSURANCE CO.; *U.S. Private*, pg. 3188

PIONEER STEEL CORPORATION; *U.S. Private*, pg. 3188

PIONEER STEEL & TUBE CORP.—See Russel Metals Inc.; *Int'l*, pg. 6430

PIONEER SUPPLY COMPANY INC.; *U.S. Private*, pg. 3188

PIONEER SURGICAL TECHNOLOGY B.V—See Montagu Private Equity LLP; *Int'l*, pg. 5036

PIONEER TECHNOLOGY (DONGGUAN) CO., LTD.—See EQT AB; *Int'l*, pg. 2471

PIONEER TECHNOLOGY (MALAYSIA) SDN. BHD.—See EQT AB; *Int'l*, pg. 2471

PIONEER TECHNOLOGY (SHANGHAI) CO., LTD.—See EQT AB; *Int'l*, pg. 2471

PIONEER TELEPHONE ASSOCIATION INC.; *U.S. Private*, pg. 3188

PIONEER TELEPHONE COOPERATIVE INC.; *U.S. Private*, pg. 3188

PIONEER TELEPHONE COOPERATIVE; *U.S. Private*, pg. 3188

PIONEER TELEPHONE; *U.S. Private*, pg. 3188

PIONEER TITLE COMPANY OF ADA COUNTY; *U.S. Private*, pg. 3188

PIONEER TITLE COMPANY; *U.S. Private*, pg. 3188

PIONEER TITLE COMPANY—See First American Financial Corporation; *U.S. Public*, pg. 837

PIONEER TOHUMCULUK A.S.—See Corteva, Inc.; *U.S. Public*, pg. 583

PIONEER TRANSFER, LLC—See Refrigerated Food Express Inc.; *U.S. Private*, pg. 3384

PIONEER TRANSFORMERS LTD.—See Guggenheim Partners, LLC; *U.S. Private*, pg. 1812

PIONEER TRANSPORTATION CORP.; *U.S. Private*, pg. 3188

PIONEER TRUCK LINES LTD.; *Int'l*, pg. 5872

PIONEER TRUST BANK NA INC—See Planet Trust Bank Corporation; *U.S. Private*, pg. 3196

PIONEER VALLEY BOOKS; *U.S. Private*, pg. 3188

PIONEER VALLEY RAILROAD—See Pinsly Railroad Co. Inc.; *U.S. Private*, pg. 3186

PIONEER VALLEY SURGICENTER, LLC—See KKR & Co. Inc.; *U.S. Public*, pg. 1246

PIONEER VENTURE PTE LTD—See Advanced Systems Automation Limited; *Int'l*, pg. 162

PIONEER WATER TANKS (AUSTRALIA) PTY LTD.—See BlueScope Steel Limited; *Int'l*, pg. 1074

PIONEER WINDOW & DOOR MFG. LTD.—See Pioneer Window Holdings Inc.; *U.S. Private*, pg. 3189

PIONEER WINDOW HOLDINGS INC.; *U.S. Private*, pg. 3189

PIONEER WINDOWS INC.—See Pioneer Window Holdings Inc.; *U.S. Private*, pg. 3189

PIONEER WIRELINE SERVICES, L.L.C.—See Patterson-UTI Energy, Inc.; *U.S. Public*, pg. 1654

PIONER BOAT AS—See XANO Industri AB; *Int'l*, pg. 8519

PION GROUP AB; *Int'l*, pg. 5871

PIONIR AD; *Int'l*, pg. 5872

PIONJAREN FASTIGHETS AB—See Peab AB; *Int'l*, pg. 5773

PIOTEK COMPUTER CORP.—See Kinsus Interconnect Technology Corp.; *Int'l*, pg. 4182

PIOVAN ASIA PACIFIC LTD.—See Piovan SpA; *Int'l*, pg. 5872

PIOVAN CANADA LTD.—See Piovan SpA; *Int'l*, pg. 5872

PIOVAN CENTRAL EUROPE GMBH—See Piovan SpA; *Int'l*, pg. 5872

PIOVAN CZECH REPUBLIC S.R.O.—See Piovan SpA; *Int'l*, pg. 5873

PIOVAN DO BRASIL LTDA.—See Piovan SpA; *Int'l*, pg. 5873

PIOVAN FRANCE SAS—See Piovan SpA; *Int'l*, pg. 5873

PIOVAN GMBH—See Piovan SpA; *Int'l*, pg. 5873

PIOVAN GULF FZE—See Piovan SpA; *Int'l*, pg. 5873

PIOVAN HUNGARY KFT.—See Piovan SpA; *Int'l*, pg. 5873

PIOVAN INDIA PRIVATE LIMITED—See Piovan SpA; *Int'l*, pg. 5873

PIOVAN JAPAN INC.—See Piovan SpA; *Int'l*, pg. 5873

PIOVAN MAROC SARL. AU—See Piovan SpA; *Int'l*, pg. 5873

PIOVAN MEXICO S.A. DE C.V.—See Piovan SpA; *Int'l*, pg. 5873

PIOVAN MUHENDSLIK LIMITED SIRKETI—See Piovan SpA; *Int'l*, pg. 5873

PIOVAN SPA; *Int'l*, pg. 5872

PIOVAN UK LIMITED—See Piovan SpA; *Int'l*, pg. 5873

PIOVAN VIETNAM COMPANY LIMITED—See Piovan SpA; *Int'l*, pg. 5873

PIPAL RESEARCH CORPORATION—See S&P Global Inc.; *U.S. Public*, pg. 1831

THE PIPCO COMPANIES LTD.; *U.S. Private*, pg. 4096

PIPE COIL TECHNOLOGY LTD.—See Reece Group Ltd.; *Int'l*, pg. 6249

PIPECO SERVICES; *U.S. Private*, pg. 3189

PIPED BITS CO., LTD.; *Int'l*, pg. 5873

PIPE DISTRIBUTORS INC.—See PDI Group Inc.; *U.S. Private*, pg. 3122

PIPEDO HD, INC.—See Advantage Partners LLP; *Int'l*, pg. 164

PIPEDRIVE INC.; *U.S. Private*, pg. 3189

PIPE EQUIPMENT SPECIALISTS LIMITED—See Indutrade AB; *Int'l*, pg. 3680

PIPE EXCHANGE INC.—See Corpac Steel Products Corp.; *U.S. Private*, pg. 1053

PIPE FABRICATING & SUPPLY COMPANY; *U.S. Private*, pg. 3189

PIPE FABRICATING & SUPPLY COMPANY - UTAH PLANT—See Pipe Fabricating & Supply Company; *U.S. Private*, pg. 3189

PIPE FREEZING SERVICES, INC.—See N2 Solutions LLC; *U.S. Private*, pg. 2829

PIPEHAWK PLC; *Int'l*, pg. 5873

PIPE JACKING TRENCHLESS, INC.—See Primoris Services Corporation; *U.S. Public*, pg. 1719

PIPELIFE AUSTRIA GMBH & CO. KG—See Wienerberger AG; *Int'l*, pg. 8405

PIPELIFE BELGIUM NV—See Wienerberger AG; *Int'l*, pg. 8405

PIPELIFE BULGARIA EOOD—See Wienerberger AG; *Int'l*, pg. 8405

PIPELIFE CZECH S.R.O.—See Wienerberger AG; *Int'l*, pg. 8405

PIPELIFE DEUTSCHLAND GMBH & CO.KG—See Wienerberger AG; *Int'l*, pg. 8405

PIPELIFE EESTI AS—See Wienerberger AG; *Int'l*, pg. 8405

PIPELIFE FINLAND OY—See Wienerberger AG; *Int'l*, pg. 8405

PIPELIFE FRANCE S.A.—See Wienerberger AG; *Int'l*, pg. 8405

PIPELIFE HAFAB AB—See Wienerberger AG; *Int'l*, pg. 8405

PIPELIFE HELLAS S.A.—See Wienerberger AG; *Int'l*, pg. 8405

PIPELIFE-HRVATSKA CIJEVNI SUSTAVI D.O.O.—See Wienerberger AG; *Int'l*, pg. 8405

PIPELIFE HUNGARIA MUANYAGIPARI KFT.—See Wienerberger AG; *Int'l*, pg. 8405

PIPELIFE INTERNATIONAL GMBH—See Wienerberger AG; *Int'l*, pg. 8405

PIPELIFE IRELAND LTD.—See Wienerberger AG; *Int'l*, pg. 8405

PIPELIFE JET STREAM INC.—See Wienerberger AG; *Int'l*, pg. 8405

PIPELIFE LATVIA SIA—See Wienerberger AG; *Int'l*, pg. 8405

PIPELIFE NEDERLAND B.V.—See Wienerberger AG; *Int'l*, pg. 8405

PIPELIFE NORGE AS—See Wienerberger AG; *Int'l*, pg. 8405

PIPELIFE POLSKA SP. Z.O.O.—See Wienerberger AG; *Int'l*, pg. 8405

PIPELIFE ROMANIA S.R.L.—See Wienerberger AG; *Int'l*, pg. 8405

PIPELIFE RUS LLC—See Wienerberger AG; *Int'l*, pg. 8405

PIPELIFE SERBIA D.O.O.—See Wienerberger AG; *Int'l*, pg. 8405

PIPELIFE SLOVAKIA S R.O.—See Wienerberger AG; *Int'l*, pg. 8405

PIPELIFE SLOVENIJA D.O.O.—See Wienerberger AG; *Int'l*, pg. 8405

PIPELIFE SVERIGE AB—See Wienerberger AG; *Int'l*, pg. 8405

PIPELIFE UK LTD.—See Wienerberger AG; *Int'l*, pg. 8405

PIPELINE AND DRAINAGE SYSTEMS LIMITED—See RPM International Inc.; *U.S. Public*, pg. 1817

PIPELINE BRICKELL; *U.S. Private*, pg. 3189

THE PIPE LINE DEVELOPMENT COMPANY; *U.S. Private*, pg. 4096

PIPELINE ENGINEERING LTD—See KKR & Co. Inc.; *U.S. Public*, pg. 1242

PIPELINE INDUCTION HEAT LIMITED—See CRC-Evans International, Inc.; *U.S. Private*, pg. 1087

PIPELINE INDUSTRIES, INC.—See CIVC Partners LLC; *U.S. Private*, pg. 908

PIPELINE OIL SALES INC.; *U.S. Private*, pg. 3189

PIPELINE OPERATIONS EQUISTAR CHEMICALS, LP—See LyondellBasell Industries N.V.; *Int'l*, pg. 4608

PIPELINE PACKAGING CORPORATION—See Cleveland Steel Container Corporation; *U.S. Private*, pg. 941

PIPELINE PETROLEUM, INC.; *U.S. Private*, pg. 3189

PIPELINE PUBLIC RELATIONS & MARKETING CORPORATE AFFILIATIONS

Company Index

PIPELINE PUBLIC RELATIONS & MARKETING; *U.S. Private*, pg. 3189
PIPELINE RENEWAL TECHNOLOGIES LIMITED LIABILITY COMPANY—See IDEX Corp; *U.S. Public*, pg. 1091
PIPELINE RESEARCH COUNCIL INTERNATIONAL; *U.S. Private*, pg. 3189
PIPELINERX; *U.S. Private*, pg. 3189
PIPELINES AND PRODUCT MARKETING COMPANY—See Nigerian National Petroleum Corporation; *Int'l*, pg. 5282
THE PIPELINES OF PUERTO RICO, INC.—See Chevron Corporation; *U.S. Public*, pg. 488
PIPELINE SUPPLY INCORPORATED; *U.S. Private*, pg. 3189
PIPELINE SUPPLY & SERVICE HOLDINGS, LLC—See Cadent Energy Partners, LLC; *U.S. Private*, pg. 713
PIPELINE TECHNIQUE LTD.—See Blue Water Energy LLP; *Int'l*, pg. 1070
PIPELINE TECHNOLOGIES PHILIPPINES CORP.—See Xylem Inc.; *U.S. Public*, pg. 2394
PIPELINE TESTING SERVICES—See J. Murphy & Sons Limited; *Int'l*, pg. 3856
THE PIPELINE TRANSPORT INSTITUTE, LLC—See OAO AK Transneft; *Int'l*, pg. 5505
PIPELINE VIDEO INSPECTIONS & CLEANING LLC—See Mack Operations LLC; *U.S. Private*, pg. 2536
PIPENET PTE LTD—See Keppel Corporation Limited; *Int'l*, pg. 4130
PIPER AIRCRAFT, INC.; *U.S. Private*, pg. 3189
PIPER FIRE PROTECTION, INC.—See Fortis Fire & Safety, Inc.; *U.S. Private*, pg. 1576
PIPERGY, INC.; *U.S. Private*, pg. 3190
PIPER JAFFRAY COMPANIES-SEATTLE—See Piper Sandler Companies; *U.S. Public*, pg. 1694
PIPER JAFFRAY LTD.—See Piper Sandler Companies; *U.S. Public*, pg. 1694
PIPER JORDAN, LLC—See Brown & Brown, Inc.; *U.S. Public*, pg. 402
PIPER PLASTICS INC; *U.S. Private*, pg. 3189
PIPER PRODUCTS, INC.—See The Jordan Company, L.P.; *U.S. Private*, pg. 4060
PIPER SANDLER COMPANIES; *U.S. Public*, pg. 1693
PIPER SANDLER & CO.—See Piper Sandler Companies; *U.S. Public*, pg. 1694
PIPERS CRISPS LIMITED—See PepsiCo, Inc.; *U.S. Public*, pg. 1671
P&I PERSONAL & INFORMATIK AG—See HgCapital Trust plc; *Int'l*, pg. 3377
P&I PERSONAL & INFORMATIK AG—See HgCapital Trust plc; *Int'l*, pg. 3377
P&I PERSONAL & INFORMATIK GMBH—See HgCapital Trust plc; *Int'l*, pg. 3377
P&I PERSONAL & INFORMATIK S.R.O.—See HgCapital Trust plc; *Int'l*, pg. 3377
PIPESHIELD INTERNATIONAL LIMITED—See Tekmar Group plc; *Int'l*, pg. 7527
PIPE SHIELDS, INC.—See Piping Technology & Products Inc.; *U.S. Private*, pg. 3190
PIPESTONE ENERGY CORP.—See Waterous Energy Fund; *Int'l*, pg. 8358
PIPESTONE EQUIPMENT LLC—See Pike Street Capital, LP; *U.S. Private*, pg. 3180
PIPE SUPPORTS ASIA LTD—See Hill & Smith PLC; *Int'l*, pg. 3392
PIPE SUPPORTS LTD—See Hill & Smith PLC; *Int'l*, pg. 3392
PIPE SYSTEMS INC.; *U.S. Private*, pg. 3189
PIPETECH DESIGN & CONSTRUCTION LTD; *Int'l*, pg. 5873
PIPE TRANSMISSION PTY LTD—See CK Hutchison Holdings Limited; *Int'l*, pg. 1638
PIPE TRANSMISSION PTY LTD—See Vodafone Group Plc; *Int'l*, pg. 8285
PIPETTE CALIBRATION SERVICES, INC.—See Mettler-Toledo International, Inc.; *U.S. Public*, pg. 1433
PIPE WELDERS INC.; *U.S. Private*, pg. 3189
PIPEX DEUTSCHLAND GMBH—See Zeleziarne Podbrezova a.s.; *Int'l*, pg. 8631
PIPEX ITALIA S.P.A.—See Zeleziarne Podbrezova a.s.; *Int'l*, pg. 8631
PIPEX LIMITED—See NOV, Inc.; *U.S. Public*, pg. 1546
PIPEX PX (SCOTLAND) LIMITED—See NOV, Inc.; *U.S. Public*, pg. 1546
P. I. PHILIPPINES, INC.—See Prestige International Inc.; *Int'l*, pg. 5966
PI (PHYSIK INSTRUMENTE) L.P.—See Physik Instrumente (PI) GmbH & Co. KG; *Int'l*, pg. 5858
PI (PHYSIK INSTRUMENTE) LTD.—See Physik Instrumente (PI) GmbH & Co. KG; *Int'l*, pg. 5858
PI (PHYSIK INSTRUMENTE) SINGAPORE LLP—See Physik Instrumente (PI) GmbH & Co. KG; *Int'l*, pg. 5858
PIPING ALLOYS INC.; *U.S. Private*, pg. 3190
PIPING & EQUIPMENT CO., INC.; *U.S. Private*, pg. 3190
PIPING ROCK CLUB; *U.S. Private*, pg. 3190
PIPING SYSTEM INDONESIA PT.—See BELIMO Holding AG; *Int'l*, pg. 965
PIPING TECHNOLOGY & PRODUCTS INC.; *U.S. Private*, pg. 3190
PIPIS BROS FARM PUBLIC COMPANY LIMITED; *Int'l*, pg. 5873
PIPITONE GROUP; *U.S. Private*, pg. 3190
PIPOL A/S—See Telefonica, S.A.; *Int'l*, pg. 7535
PIP PRINTING, INC.—See KOA Holdings Inc.; *U.S. Private*, pg. 2325
P.I. PRESTIGE INTERNATIONAL (CAMBODIA) CO., LTD.—See Prestige International Inc.; *Int'l*, pg. 5966
P.I. PRESTIGE INTERNATIONAL INDIA PRIVATE LIMITED—See Prestige International Inc.; *Int'l*, pg. 5966
PIQUADRO RETAIL SAN MARINO SRL—See Piquadro SpA; *Int'l*, pg. 5873
PIQUADRO SPA; *Int'l*, pg. 5873
PIQUADRO UK LIMITED—See Piquadro SpA; *Int'l*, pg. 5873
PIQUNIQ MANAGEMENT CORP.—See Arctic Slope Regional Corporation; *U.S. Private*, pg. 316
PIRACLE, INC.—See AvidXchange Holdings, Inc.; *U.S. Public*, pg. 246
PIRAEUS ASSET MANAGEMENT MUTUAL FUNDS S.A.—See Piraeus Financial Holdings S.A.; *Int'l*, pg. 5873
PIRAEUS ASSET MANAGEMENT SINGLE MEMBER S.A.—See Piraeus Financial Holdings S.A.; *Int'l*, pg. 5873
PIRAEUS BANK BULGARIA AD—See Eurobank Ergasias Services and Holdings S.A.; *Int'l*, pg. 2532
PIRAEUS BANK S.A.—See Piraeus Financial Holdings S.A.; *Int'l*, pg. 5874
PIRAEUS BEST LEASING S.A.—See Piraeus Financial Holdings S.A.; *Int'l*, pg. 5874
PIRAEUS CAPITAL MANAGEMENT S.A.—See Piraeus Financial Holdings S.A.; *Int'l*, pg. 5874
PIRAEUS CARD SERVICES S.A—See Piraeus Financial Holdings S.A.; *Int'l*, pg. 5874
PIRAEUS DATA LLC.; *U.S. Private*, pg. 3190
PIRAEUS DIRECT SERVICES S.A.—See Piraeus Financial Holdings S.A.; *Int'l*, pg. 5874
PIRAEUS DIRECT SOLUTIONS SINGLE MEMBER S.A.—See Piraeus Financial Holdings S.A.; *Int'l*, pg. 5874
PIRAEUS FACTORING S.A.—See Piraeus Financial Holdings S.A.; *Int'l*, pg. 5874
PIRAEUS FINANCIAL HOLDINGS S.A.; *Int'l*, pg. 5873
PIRAEUS INSURANCE AND REINSURANCE BROKERAGE SA—See Piraeus Financial Holdings S.A.; *Int'l*, pg. 5874
PIRAEUS LEASING S.A.—See Piraeus Financial Holdings S.A.; *Int'l*, pg. 5874
PIRAEUS MULTIFIN S.A.—See Piraeus Financial Holdings S.A.; *Int'l*, pg. 5874
PIRAEUS PORT AUTHORITY S.A.—See China COSCO Shipping Corporation Limited; *Int'l*, pg. 1496
PIRAEUS REAL ESTATE S.A—See Piraeus Financial Holdings S.A.; *Int'l*, pg. 5874
PIRAEUS SECURITIES S.A.—See Piraeus Financial Holdings S.A.; *Int'l*, pg. 5874
PIRA INTERNATIONAL LIMITED—See The Smithers Group; *U.S. Private*, pg. 4118
PIRAMAL CAPITAL & HOUSING FINANCE LIMITED—See Piramal Enterprises Ltd.; *Int'l*, pg. 5874
PIRAMAL CONSUMER PRODUCTS PRIVATE LIMITED—See Piramal Enterprises Ltd.; *Int'l*, pg. 5874
PIRAMAL CRITICAL CARE B.V.—See Piramal Enterprises Ltd.; *Int'l*, pg. 5874
PIRAMAL CRITICAL CARE DEUTSCHLAND GMBH—See Piramal Enterprises Ltd.; *Int'l*, pg. 5874
PIRAMAL CRITICAL CARE, INC.—See Piramal Enterprises Ltd.; *Int'l*, pg. 5874
PIRAMAL CRITICAL CARE ITALIA, S.P.A.—See Piramal Enterprises Ltd.; *Int'l*, pg. 5874
PIRAMAL CRITICAL CARE LIMITED—See Piramal Enterprises Ltd.; *Int'l*, pg. 5874
PIRAMAL CRITICAL CARE SOUTH AFRICA (PTY) LTD.—See Piramal Enterprises Ltd.; *Int'l*, pg. 5874
PIRAMAL ENTERPRISES LTD.; *Int'l*, pg. 5874
PIRAMAL FUND MANAGEMENT PRIVATE LIMITED—See Piramal Enterprises Ltd.; *Int'l*, pg. 5874
PIRAMAL GLASS FLAT RIVER LLC—See Piramal Glass Limited; *Int'l*, pg. 5874
PIRAMAL GLASS LIMITED; *Int'l*, pg. 5874
PIRAMAL GLASS - USA, INC.—See Piramal Glass Limited; *Int'l*, pg. 5874
PIRAMAL GLASS WILLIAMSTOWN LLC—See Piramal Glass Limited; *Int'l*, pg. 5874
PIRAMAL HEALTHCARE (CANADA) LIMITED—See Piramal Enterprises Ltd.; *Int'l*, pg. 5874
PIRAMAL HEALTHCARE LIMITED—See Piramal Enterprises Ltd.; *Int'l*, pg. 5874
PIRAMAL HEALTHCARE UK LIMITED—See Piramal Enterprises Ltd.; *Int'l*, pg. 5874
PIRAMAL PHARMA LIMITED—See Piramal Enterprises Ltd.; *Int'l*, pg. 5874
PIRAMAL PHYTOCARE LIMITED; *Int'l*, pg. 5875
PIRANHA HOSE PRODUCTS, INC.—See Kuriyama Holdings Corporation; *Int'l*, pg. 4342
PIRANSHAHR SUGAR COMPANY; *Int'l*, pg. 5875
PIRATE ADVENTURE GOLF LIMITED—See Merlin Entertainments plc; *Int'l*, pg. 4838
PIREAN LTD.—See Arlington Capital Partners LLC; *U.S. Private*, pg. 327
PIRELLI AMBIENTE S.R.L.—See China National Chemical Corporation; *Int'l*, pg. 1528
PIRELLI ASIA PTE. LIMITED—See China National Chemical Corporation; *Int'l*, pg. 1529
PIRELLI CHINA TYRE N.V.—See China National Chemical Corporation; *Int'l*, pg. 1528
PIRELLI COMERCIAL DE PNEUS BRASIL LTDA—See China National Chemical Corporation; *Int'l*, pg. 1528
PIRELLI & C. S.P.A.—See China National Chemical Corporation; *Int'l*, pg. 1528
PIRELLI DEUTSCHLAND GMBH—See China National Chemical Corporation; *Int'l*, pg. 1528
PIRELLI DE VENEZUELA, C.A.; *Int'l*, pg. 5875
PIRELLI GMBH—See China National Chemical Corporation; *Int'l*, pg. 1529
PIRELLI INDUSTRIE PNEUMATICI S.R.L.—See China National Chemical Corporation; *Int'l*, pg. 1528
PIRELLI JAPAN K.K.—See China National Chemical Corporation; *Int'l*, pg. 1528
PIRELLI MOTORSPORT SERVICES LTD—See China National Chemical Corporation; *Int'l*, pg. 1528
PIRELLI NEUMATICOS DE MEXICO S.A. DE C.V.—See China National Chemical Corporation; *Int'l*, pg. 1528
PIRELLI NEUMATICOS S.A. DE C.V.—See China National Chemical Corporation; *Int'l*, pg. 1528
PIRELLI NEUMATICOS S.A.I.C—See China National Chemical Corporation; *Int'l*, pg. 1528
PIRELLI NEUMATICOS S.A.—See China National Chemical Corporation; *Int'l*, pg. 1528
PIRELLI NORTH AMERICA INC.—See China National Chemical Corporation; *Int'l*, pg. 1528
PIRELLI PERSONAL SERVICE GMBH—See China National Chemical Corporation; *Int'l*, pg. 1528
PIRELLI PNEUS LTDA—See China National Chemical Corporation; *Int'l*, pg. 1528
PIRELLI POLSKA SP. Z.O.O.—See China National Chemical Corporation; *Int'l*, pg. 1528
PIRELLI SERVIZI FINANZIARI S.P.A.—See China National Chemical Corporation; *Int'l*, pg. 1528
PIRELLI SISTEMI INFORMATIVI S.R.L.—See China National Chemical Corporation; *Int'l*, pg. 1528
PIRELLI SLOVAKIA S.R.O.—See China National Chemical Corporation; *Int'l*, pg. 1529
PIRELLI TIRE, INC.—See China National Chemical Corporation; *Int'l*, pg. 1529
PIRELLI TIRE LLC—See China National Chemical Corporation; *Int'l*, pg. 1528
PIRELLI TYRE CO., LTD—See China National Chemical Corporation; *Int'l*, pg. 1528
PIRELLI TYRE NORDIC AB—See China National Chemical Corporation; *Int'l*, pg. 1529
PIRELLI TYRE (PTY) LTD—See China National Chemical Corporation; *Int'l*, pg. 1529
PIRELLI TYRES ALEXANDRIA CO.—See China National Chemical Corporation; *Int'l*, pg. 1529
PIRELLI TYRES AUSTRALIA PTY. LTD.—See China National Chemical Corporation; *Int'l*, pg. 1529
PIRELLI TYRES BELUX S.A.—See China National Chemical Corporation; *Int'l*, pg. 1529
PIRELLI TYRES LTD—See China National Chemical Corporation; *Int'l*, pg. 1529
PIRELLI TYRES NEDERLAND B.V.—See China National Chemical Corporation; *Int'l*, pg. 1529
PIRELLI TYRE S.P.A.—See China National Chemical Corporation; *Int'l*, pg. 1528
PIRELLI TYRE (SUISSE) S.A. - CZECH—See China National Chemical Corporation; *Int'l*, pg. 1529
PIRELLI TYRE (SUISSE) SA—See China National Chemical Corporation; *Int'l*, pg. 1529
PIRELLI UK LIMITED—See China National Chemical Corporation; *Int'l*, pg. 1529
PIRELLI UK TYRES LIMITED—See China National Chemical Corporation; *Int'l*, pg. 1529
PIRIE STREET CUSTODIAN LTD.—See Bendigo & Adelaide Bank Ltd.; *Int'l*, pg. 970
PIRIFORM LTD.—See Gen Digital Inc.; *U.S. Public*, pg. 910
PIRIFORM SOFTWARE LTD.—See Gen Digital Inc.; *U.S. Public*, pg. 910
PIRIOU SAS; *Int'l*, pg. 5875
PIRISTEEL OY—See SSAB AB; *Int'l*, pg. 7153
P.I. ROOF MAINTENANCE, INC.; *U.S. Private*, pg. 3060
PIROVANO STELVIO SPA—See Banca Popolare di Sondrio S.p.A.; *Int'l*, pg. 816
PIRS CAPITAL, LLC; *U.S. Private*, pg. 3190
PIRSON MONTAGE SA; *Int'l*, pg. 5875
PIRSON REFRACTORIES B.V.—See Pirson Montage SA; *Int'l*, pg. 5875
PIRTAKOTI OY—See Humana AB; *Int'l*, pg. 3530
PIRTEK ASIA PTE LTD—See Pirtek Fluid Systems Pty. Ltd.; *Int'l*, pg. 5875
PIRTEK B.V—See Pirtek Fluid Systems Pty. Ltd.; *Int'l*, pg. 5875
PIRTEK DEUTSCHLAND (GERMANY) GMBH—See Pirtek Fluid Systems Pty. Ltd.; *Int'l*, pg. 5875

COMPANY NAME INDEX

PIRTEK EUROPE LTD.—See Pirtek Fluid Systems Pty. Ltd.; *Int'l*, pg. 5875
PIRTEK FLUID SYSTEMS (DELTA) LTD—See Pirtek Fluid Systems Pty. Ltd.; *Int'l*, pg. 5875
PIRTEK FLUID SYSTEMS PTY. LTD.; *Int'l*, pg. 5875
PIRTEK (MONGOLIA) LLC—See Pirtek Fluid Systems Pty. Ltd.; *Int'l*, pg. 5875
PIRTEK (NEW ZEALAND) LTD—See Pirtek Fluid Systems Pty. Ltd.; *Int'l*, pg. 5875
PIRTEK SOUTHERN AFRICA (PTY) LTD—See Pirtek Fluid Systems Pty. Ltd.; *Int'l*, pg. 5875
PIRTEK USA LLC—See Pirtek Fluid Systems Pty. Ltd.; *Int'l*, pg. 5875
PISANI & RICKERTSEN GMBH; *Int'l*, pg. 5875
PISARA AB—See Schneider Electric SE; *Int'l*, pg. 6628
PISCATAQUA LANDSCAPIING & TREE SERVICE; *U.S. Private*, pg. 3190
PISCES EVEN EMPREENDIMENTOS IMOBILIARIOS LTDA.—See Even Construtora e Incorporadora S.A.; *Int'l*, pg. 2562
PISCES NOMINEES LIMITED—See Commerzbank AG; *Int'l*, pg. 1719
PISCHKE MOTORS, INC.; *U.S. Private*, pg. 3190
PISCINES DESJOYAUX SA; *Int'l*, pg. 5875
PISCINES GROUPE GA SA; *Int'l*, pg. 5876
PISCINES MAGILINE SAS; *Int'l*, pg. 5876
PISEC GROUP GMBH; *Int'l*, pg. 5876
PISGAH INSULATION AND FIREPLACES OF NC, LLC—See Installed Building Products, Inc.; *U.S. Public*, pg. 1133
PISGAH LABS, INC.—See Ipca Laboratories Ltd.; *Int'l*, pg. 3796
PISHAHANG COMMUNICATIONS NETWORKS DEVELOPMENT COMPANY—See Nokia Corporation; *Int'l*, pg. 5406
PISIFFIK A/S—See NorgesGruppen ASA; *Int'l*, pg. 5427
PISMO COAST VILLAGE, INC.; *U.S. Private*, pg. 3190
PI SOUTHEAST LLC—See The Predictive Index LLC; *U.S. Private*, pg. 4097
PI SP.Z.O.O.—See Impel S.A.; *Int'l*, pg. 3632
PISTOLSTAR, INC.—See BIO-key International, Inc.; *U.S. Public*, pg. 332
PISTON AGENCY—See LEWIS Communications Limited; *Int'l*, pg. 4471
PISTON AUTOMOTIVE—See Piston Group, LLO; *U.S. Private*, pg. 3190
PISTON GROUP, LLC; *U.S. Private*, pg. 3190
PISTORA OY—See Illinois Tool Works Inc.; *U.S. Public*, pg. 1110
P&I SYSTEM CO LTD; *Int'l*, pg. 5681
PI SYSTEM CO., LTD.—See PACIFIC INDUSTRIAL CO. LTD.; *Int'l*, pg. 5690
PI-SYSTEM GMBH—See BKW AG; *Int'l*, pg. 1056
PITACOLUMN CO.,LTD.—See Yahagi Construction Co., Ltd.; *Int'l*, pg. 8546
PITAGORA INFORMATIONS MANAGEMENT GMBH—See VINCI S.A.; *Int'l*, pg. 8225
PITAGORA SRL—See Acciona, S.A.; *Int'l*, pg. 90
PITAKKIJ THAILAND CO., LTD.—See SECOM Co., Ltd.; *Int'l*, pg. 6671
PITANCE—See VINCI S.A.; *Int'l*, pg. 8225
PITANGO VENTURE CAPITAL; *Int'l*, pg. 5876
PIT ANTWERPEN NV—See Eiffage S.A.; *Int'l*, pg. 2330
PITA PIT USA, INC.; *U.S. Private*, pg. 3190
PITCAIRN FINANCIAL GROUP; *U.S. Private*, pg. 3190
PITCHBOOK DATA, INC.—See Morningstar, Inc.; *U.S. Public*, pg. 1476
PITCHBOOK DATA INC.—See Morningstar, Inc.; *U.S. Public*, pg. 1476
PITCHER AND LE QUESNE LIMITED—See Dignity plc; *Int'l*, pg. 2124
PITCHMASTIC PMB LIMITED—See RPM International Inc.; *U.S. Public*, pg. 1817
PITCH PROMOTION SNC—See Altarea SCA; *Int'l*, pg. 385
PITCH TECHNOLOGIES AB—See BAE Systems plc; *Int'l*, pg. 798
PITCH TECHNOLOGIES LIMITED—See BAE Systems plc; *Int'l*, pg. 798
PITCO FRIALATOR INC.—See The Middleby Corporation; *U.S. Public*, pg. 2113
PITCREW CO., LTD.—See Pole To Win Holdings, Inc.; *Int'l*, pg. 5908
PITECO S.P.A.—See Zucchetti Group S.p.A.; *Int'l*, pg. 8692
PITER TRUST INVESTMENT COMPANY JSC; *Int'l*, pg. 5876
PITLIK & WICK, INC.; *U.S. Private*, pg. 3190
PITLOCHRY CARE HOME—See Balhousie Holdings Limited; *Int'l*, pg. 808
PITMON OIL & GAS CO.; *U.S. Private*, pg. 3191
PITNEY BOWES (ASIA PACIFIC) PTE. LTD—See Pitney Bowes Inc.; *U.S. Public*, pg. 1694
PITNEY BOWES ASTERION SAS—See Pitney Bowes Inc.; *U.S. Public*, pg. 1694
PITNEY BOWES AUSTRALIA FAS PTY. LIMITED—See Pitney Bowes Inc.; *U.S. Public*, pg. 1694
PITNEY BOWES AUSTRALIA PTY LIMITED—See Pitney Bowes Inc.; *U.S. Public*, pg. 1694

PITNEY BOWES BRASIL EQUIPAMENTOS E SERVICOS LTDA—See Pitney Bowes Inc.; *U.S. Public*, pg. 1694
PITNEY BOWES BUSINESS SUPPLIES & SERVICES—See Pitney Bowes Inc.; *U.S. Public*, pg. 1694
PITNEY BOWES BUSINESS SYSTEMS-INTERNATIONAL—See Pitney Bowes Inc.; *U.S. Public*, pg. 1695
PITNEY BOWES CANADA LP—See Pitney Bowes Inc.; *U.S. Public*, pg. 1695
PITNEY BOWES CREDIT AUSTRALIA LIMITED—See Pitney Bowes Inc.; *U.S. Public*, pg. 1694
PITNEY BOWES DANMARK A/S—See Pitney Bowes Inc.; *U.S. Public*, pg. 1694
PITNEY BOWES DEUTSCHLAND G.M.B.H.—See Pitney Bowes Inc.; *U.S. Public*, pg. 1694
PITNEY BOWES FRANCE—See Pitney Bowes Inc.; *U.S. Public*, pg. 1694
PITNEY BOWES INC.; *U.S. Public*, pg. 1694
PITNEY BOWES INTERNATIONAL HOLDINGS, INC.—See Pitney Bowes Inc.; *U.S. Public*, pg. 1695
PITNEY BOWES (IRELAND) LIMITED—See Pitney Bowes Inc.; *U.S. Public*, pg. 1694
PITNEY BOWES ITALIA S.R.L.—See Pitney Bowes Inc.; *U.S. Public*, pg. 1695
PITNEY BOWES JAPAN—See Pitney Bowes Inc.; *U.S. Public*, pg. 1695
PITNEY BOWES LIMITED—See Pitney Bowes Inc.; *U.S. Public*, pg. 1695
PITNEY BOWES OF CANADA LTD.-LEASING DIVISION—See Pitney Bowes Inc.; *U.S. Public*, pg. 1695
PITNEY BOWES OF CANADA LTD.—See Pitney Bowes Inc.; *U.S. Public*, pg. 1695
PITNEY BOWES OY—See Pitney Bowes Inc.; *U.S. Public*, pg. 1695
PITNEY BOWES PRESORT SERVICES, INC.—See Pitney Bowes Inc.; *U.S. Public*, pg. 1695
PITNEY BOWES SOFTWARE AUSTRALIA PTY. LTD.—See Pitney Bowes Inc.; *U.S. Public*, pg. 1695
PITNEY BOWES SOFTWARE EUROPE LIMITED—See Pitney Bowes Inc.; *U.S. Public*, pg. 1695
PITNEY BOWES SOFTWARE GMBH—See Pitney Bowes Inc.; *U.S. Public*, pg. 1695
PITNEY BOWES SOFTWARE INC.—See Pitney Bowes Inc.; *U.S. Public*, pg. 1695
PITNEY BOWES SOFTWARE K. K.—See Pitney Bowes Inc.; *U.S. Public*, pg. 1695
PITNEY BOWES SOFTWARE LIMITED—See Pitney Bowes Inc.; *U.S. Public*, pg. 1695
PITNEY BOWES SVENSKA AB—See Pitney Bowes Inc.; *U.S. Public*, pg. 1695
PITNEY BOWES (SWITZERLAND) AG—See Pitney Bowes Inc.; *U.S. Public*, pg. 1694
PITNEY BOWES TECHNOLOGY CENTER—See Pitney Bowes Inc.; *U.S. Public*, pg. 1695
PITNEY BOWES (THAILAND) LIMITED—See Pitney Bowes Inc.; *U.S. Public*, pg. 1694
PITNEY BOWES UK LP—See Pitney Bowes Inc.; *U.S. Public*, pg. 1695
PIT N PORTAL MINING SERVICES PTY LTD—See Emeco Holdings Limited; *Int'l*, pg. 2376
PITOMETER LOG DIV.—See The Dewey Electronics Corporation; *U.S. Public*, pg. 2067
PITSANULOKE MEDICAL CO., LTD.—See Principal Capital Company Public Company Limited; *Int'l*, pg. 5981
PITSCO INC.; *U.S. Private*, pg. 3191
PITS NV—See Koninklijke Philips N.V.; *Int'l*, pg. 4268
PITSS AMERICA LLC; *U.S. Private*, pg. 3191
PIT-STOP AUTO SERVICE GMBH—See BLUO SICAV-SIF; *Int'l*, pg. 1075
PIT-STOP CREDIT (SG) PTE. LTD.—See Aspial Lifestyle Limited; *Int'l*, pg. 630
PIT STOP GAS INC.; *U.S. Private*, pg. 3190
PITTARDS GROUP LIMITED—See Pittards plc; *Int'l*, pg. 5876
PITTARDS PLC; *Int'l*, pg. 5876
PITT AUTO ELECTRIC COMPANY; *U.S. Private*, pg. 3191
PITT CAPITAL PARTNERS LIMITED—See Washington H. Soul Pattinson & Company Limited; *Int'l*, pg. 8351
PITTCON INDUSTRIES; *U.S. Private*, pg. 3191
PITTI CASTINGS PVT LTD—See Pitti Engineering Limited; *Int'l*, pg. 5876
PITTI ENGINEERING LIMITED; *Int'l*, pg. 5876
PITTJES VERTRIEBS GMBH—See Intersnack Group GmbH & Co. KG; *Int'l*, pg. 3761
PITTLER MASCHINENFABRIK AG; *Int'l*, pg. 5876
PITTMAN CONSTRUCTION COMPANY; *U.S. Private*, pg. 3191
PITTMAN—See AMETEK, Inc.; *U.S. Public*, pg. 116
PITT-OHIO EXPRESS INC.; *U.S. Private*, pg. 3191
PITTSBURG DIALYSIS PARTNERS, LLC—See DaVita Inc.; *U.S. Public*, pg. 642
PITTSBURGH ARENA OPERATING LP—See Sports & Exhibition Authority of Pittsburgh & Allegheny County; *U.S. Private*, pg. 3761
THE PITTSBURGH BAGEL FACTORY INC.; *U.S. Private*, pg. 4096

PIVOTAL GROUP, INC.

PITTSBURGH BASEBALL HOLDINGS, INC.—See The Nutting Company, Inc.; *U.S. Private*, pg. 4086
PITTSBURGH BASEBALL PARTNERSHIP—See The Nutting Company, Inc.; *U.S. Private*, pg. 4086
PITTSBURGH BREWING COMPANY—See Uni-World Capital, L.P.; *U.S. Private*, pg. 4281
PITTSBURGH BUSINESS TIMES—See Advance Publications, Inc.; *U.S. Private*, pg. 84
PITTSBURGH COMMERCIAL REAL ESTATE, INC.—See Colliers International Group Inc.; *Int'l*, pg. 1701
PITTSBURGH CORNING CR, S.R.O.—See Owens Corning; *U.S. Public*, pg. 1628
PITTSBURGH CORNING EUROPE, N.V.—See Owens Corning; *U.S. Public*, pg. 1628
PITTSBURGH CORNING FRANCE—See Owens Corning; *U.S. Public*, pg. 1628
PITTSBURGH CORNING GESELLSCHAFT M.B.H.—See Owens Corning; *U.S. Public*, pg. 1628
PITTSBURGH CORNING, LLC—See Owens Corning; *U.S. Public*, pg. 1628
PITTSBURGH CORNING NEDERLAND B.V.—See Owens Corning; *U.S. Public*, pg. 1628
PITTSBURGH CORNING SUISSE SA—See Owens Corning; *U.S. Public*, pg. 1628
PITTSBURGH CORNING (UNITED KINGDOM) LIMITED—See Owens Corning; *U.S. Public*, pg. 1628
PITTSBURGH CULTURAL TRUST; *U.S. Private*, pg. 3191
PITTSBURGH ELECTRIC ENGINES, INC.—See Watt Fuel Cell Corp.; *U.S. Private*, pg. 4456
PITTSBURGH FOUNDATION; *U.S. Private*, pg. 3191
PITTSBURGH GLASS WORKS (GERMANY) GMBH—See Vitro, S.A.B. de C.V.; *Int'l*, pg. 8262
PITTSBURGH GLASS WORKS, LLC—See Vitro, S.A.B. de C.V.; *Int'l*, pg. 8262
PITTSBURGH GLASS WORKS POLAND SP. Z O.O.—See Vitro, S.A.B. de C.V.; *Int'l*, pg. 8262
PITTSBURGH HISTORY & LANDMARKS FOUNDATION; *U.S. Private*, pg. 3191
PITTSBURGH LOGISTICS SYSTEMS, INC.—See Quadrivius, Inc.; *U.S. Private*, pg. 3316
PITTSBURGH MACK SALES & SERVICE INC.—See Allentown Mack Sales & Service, Inc.; *U.S. Public*, pg. 180
PITTSBURGH MERCY HEALTH SYSTEM, INC.; *U.S. Private*, pg. 3191
THE PITTSBURGH & OHIO CENTRAL RAILROAD COMPANY—See Brookfield Infrastructure Partners L.P.; *Int'l*, pg. 1193
THE PITTSBURGH & OHIO CENTRAL RAILROAD COMPANY—See GIC Pte. Ltd.; *Int'l*, pg. 2967
PITTSBURGH OPERA; *U.S. Private*, pg. 3191
PITTSBURGH PENGUINS LLC—See Lemieux Group L.P.; *U.S. Private*, pg. 2421
PITTSBURGH PIPE & SUPPLY CORP; *U.S. Private*, pg. 3191
PITTSBURGH PLUMBING & HEATING CORP.—See Famous Enterprises Inc.; *U.S. Private*, pg. 1472
PITTSBURGH POND CO.; *U.S. Private*, pg. 3191
PITTSBURGH STEELERS SPORTS INC.; *U.S. Private*, pg. 3191
PITTSBURGH WATER & SEWER AUTHORITY; *U.S. Private*, pg. 3191
PITTSBURGH & WEST VIRGINIA RAILROAD—See Power REIT; *U.S. Public*, pg. 1705
PITTSBURG TANK & TOWER CO., INC.; *U.S. Private*, pg. 3191
PITTSFIELD AQUEDUCT COMPANY INC.—See Pennichuck Corporation; *U.S. Private*, pg. 3136
PITTSFIELD CO-OPERATIVE BANK; *U.S. Private*, pg. 3192
PITTSFIELD PRODUCTS INC.; *U.S. Private*, pg. 3192
PITTS SAND & GRAVEL, INC.—See Smith's Greenhouses, Inc.; *U.S. Private*, pg. 3696
PITTSTON COAL COMPANY—See The Brink's Company; *U.S. Public*, pg. 2043
PITTSTON COAL MANAGEMENT COMPANY—See The Brink's Company; *U.S. Public*, pg. 2043
PITTS TOYOTA INC.; *U.S. Private*, pg. 3191
PITTWAY 3 GMBH—See Resideo Technologies, Inc.; *U.S. Public*, pg. 1789
PITTWAY BVBA—See Resideo Technologies, Inc.; *U.S. Public*, pg. 1789
PITTWAY HOMES SYSTEMS, S.L.—See Resideo Technologies, Inc.; *U.S. Public*, pg. 1789
PITZER TRANSFER & STORAGE—See Peoples Services Inc.; *U.S. Private*, pg. 3142
PIVARA TUZLA D.D.; *Int'l*, pg. 5876
PIV DRIVES GMBH—See Dana Incorporated; *U.S. Public*, pg. 623
PIVOT3, INC.; *U.S. Private*, pg. 3192
PIVOTAL ACQUISITION CORP.; *U.S. Private*, pg. 3192
PIVOTAL CAPITAL CORP.—See Axis Auto Finance Inc.; *Int'l*, pg. 769
PIVOTAL CORPORATION—See TA Associates, Inc.; *U.S. Private*, pg. 3914
PIVOTAL FINANCIAL ADVISERS LIMITED—See Dai-ichi Life Holdings, Inc.; *Int'l*, pg. 1918
PIVOTAL GROUP, INC.; *U.S. Private*, pg. 3192
PIVOTAL GROUP, INC.; *U.S. Private*, pg. 3192

PIVOTAL GROUP, INC.

PIVOTAL HOME SOLUTIONS, LLC—See American Water Works Company, Inc.; *U.S. Public*, pg. 112
PIVOTAL POWER, INC.—See Leonardo S.p.A.; *Int'l*, pg. 4460
PIVOTAL RESEARCH CENTERS LLC—See Metalmark Capital Holdings LLC; *U.S. Private*, pg. 2681
PIVOTAL RESOURCES, INC.; *U.S. Private*, pg. 3192
PIVOTAL SOFTWARE, INC.—See Broadcom Inc.; *U.S. Public*, pg. 390
PIVOTAL SYSTEMS CORPORATION; *U.S. Private*, pg. 3192
PIVOTAL THERAPEUTICS INC.; *Int'l*, pg. 5876
PIVOT COMPANIES, LLC—See GEE Group Inc.; *U.S. Public*, pg. 910
PIVOT HEALTH SOLUTIONS—See Athletico Ltd.; *U.S. Private*, pg. 368
PIVOT, INC.—See CME Group, Inc.; *U.S. Public*, pg. 518
PIVOT INTERIORS INC.; *U.S. Private*, pg. 3192
PIVOT INTERNATIONAL, INC.; *U.S. Private*, pg. 3192
PIVOT LEARNING, LLC—See Korn Ferry; *U.S. Public*, pg. 1273
PIVOT MEDICAL, INC.—See Stryker Corporation; *U.S. Public*, pg. 1956
PIVOTRAC—See Valmont Industries, Inc.; *U.S. Public*, pg. 2274
PIVOTREE INC.; *Int'l*, pg. 5876
PIVOT REMESYS LIMITED—See K1 Investment Management, LLC; *U.S. Private*, pg. 2252
PIVOT REMESYS PTY, LIMITED—See K1 Investment Management, LLC; *U.S. Private*, pg. 2252
PIVOTSHARE INC.—See Chicken Soup for the Soul Entertainment, Inc.; *U.S. Public*, pg. 488
PIVOT TECHNOLOGY SOLUTIONS, INC.; *U.S. Public*, pg. 1695
PIVOT TECHNOLOGY SOLUTIONS, LTD.—See Pivot Technology Solutions, Inc.; *U.S. Public*, pg. 1695
PIVOVARNA LASKO D.D.—See L'Arche Green N.V.; *Int'l*, pg. 4377
PIVOVAR SAMSON A.S.—See Anheuser-Busch InBev SA/NV; *Int'l*, pg. 466
PIVOVARY STAROPRAMEN A.S.—See Molson Coors Beverage Company; *U.S. Public*, pg. 1460
PIWATTANA COMPANY LIMITED—See Sansiri pcl; *Int'l*, pg. 6556
PIX4D ESPAGNE SL—See Parrot S.A.; *Int'l*, pg. 5746
PIX4D GMBH—See Parrot S.A.; *Int'l*, pg. 5746
PIX4D INC.—See Parrot S.A.; *Int'l*, pg. 5746
PIX4D SA—See Parrot S.A.; *Int'l*, pg. 5746
PIXAFY, INC.—See Net@Work, Inc.; *U.S. Private*, pg. 2886
PIXAR—See The Walt Disney Company; *U.S. Public*, pg. 2139
PIXART IMAGING, INC.; *Int'l*, pg. 5876
PIXART IMAGING (PENANG) SDN. BHD.—See PixArt Imaging, Inc.; *Int'l*, pg. 5876
PIXART IMAGING (USA), INC.—See PixArt Imaging, Inc.; *Int'l*, pg. 5877
PIXARTPRINTING S.P.A.—See Cimpress plc; *Int'l*, pg. 1609
PIXART TECHNOLOGY (SHENZHEN) CO., LTD.—See PixArt Imaging, Inc.; *Int'l*, pg. 5877
PIXCELL MEDICAL TECHNOLOGIES LTD.—See KLA Corporation; *U.S. Public*, pg. 1269
PIXDIX CO., LTD.—See LG Corp.; *Int'l*, pg. 4477
PIXELA CORPORATION; *Int'l*, pg. 5877
PIXEL COMPANYZ INC.; *Int'l*, pg. 5877
PIXELCREEK TECHNOLOGY INC.—See Adams Remco Inc.; *U.S. Private*, pg. 75
PIXEL DIGITAL LTD.—See LeoVegas AB; *Int'l*, pg. 4466
PIXELED BUSINESS SYSTEMS; *U.S. Private*, pg. 3192
PIXELINK, INC.—See AMETEK, Inc.; *U.S. Public*, pg. 121
PIXELLE ANDROSCOGGIN LLC—See Goldberg Lindsay & Co., LLC; *U.S. Private*, pg. 1729
PIXELLE SPECIALTY SOLUTIONS LLC—See Goldberg Lindsay & Co., LLC; *U.S. Private*, pg. 1729
PIXELPLUS CO., LTD.; *Int'l*, pg. 5877
PIXELPLUS SHANGHAI CO., LTD.—See Pixelplus Co., Ltd.; *Int'l*, pg. 5877
PIXELPLUS TECHNOLOGY INC.—See Pixelplus Co., Ltd.; *Int'l*, pg. 5877
PIXELPUSHERS, INC.—See Events.com, Inc.; *U.S. Private*, pg. 1437
PIXELWORKS CORPORATION—See Pixelworks, Inc.; *U.S. Public*, pg. 1695
PIXELWORKS, INC.; *U.S. Public*, pg. 1695
PIXELWORKS SEMICONDUCTOR TECHNOLOGY (SHANGHAI) CO. LTD.—See Pixelworks, Inc.; *U.S. Public*, pg. 1695
PIXELWORKS SEMICONDUCTOR TECHNOLOGY (TAIWAN) INC.—See Pixelworks, Inc.; *U.S. Public*, pg. 1696
PIX EUROPE LIMITED—See PIX Transmissions Limited; *Int'l*, pg. 5876
PIX GERMANY GMBH—See PIX Transmissions Limited; *Int'l*, pg. 5876
PIX HYDRAULICS EUROPE LIMITED—See PIX Transmissions Limited; *Int'l*, pg. 5876
PIXIA CORP.—See Elliott Management Corporation; *U.S. Private*, pg. 1368

PIXIA CORP.—See Veritas Capital Fund Management, LLC; *U.S. Private*, pg. 4362
PIXIDIS SARL—See Ardian SAS; *Int'l*, pg. 555
PIXID S.N.C.—See ManpowerGroup Inc.; *U.S. Public*, pg. 1360
PIXIE DUST TECHNOLOGIES, INC.; *Int'l*, pg. 5877
PIXIO SDN. BHD.—See mDR Limited; *Int'l*, pg. 4762
PIXIUM VISION; *Int'l*, pg. 5877
PIXLEE, INC.; *U.S. Private*, pg. 3193
PIX MIDDLE EAST FZC—See PIX Transmissions Limited; *Int'l*, pg. 5876
PIXTA INC.; *Int'l*, pg. 5877
PIX TRANSMISSIONS LIMITED; *Int'l*, pg. 5876
PIZU GROUP HOLDING LIMITED; *Int'l*, pg. 5877
PIZZA BLENDS INC.—See The Pritzker Group - Chicago, LLC; *U.S. Private*, pg. 4098
PIZZACO INC.; *U.S. Private*, pg. 3193
PIZZAEXPRESS LTD.—See Legend Holdings Corporation; *Int'l*, pg. 4443
THE PIZZA FACTORY—See Boparan Holdings Limited; *Int'l*, pg. 1111
PIZZA HUT, INC.—See Yum! Brands, Inc.; *U.S. Public*, pg. 2400
PIZZA HUT OF AMERICA, INC.—See Yum! Brands, Inc.; *U.S. Public*, pg. 2400
PIZZA HUT OF ARIZONA INC.; *U.S. Private*, pg. 3193
PIZZA HUT OF IDAHO INC.; *U.S. Private*, pg. 3193
PIZZA HUT OF MARYLAND INC.; *U.S. Private*, pg. 3193
PIZZA HUT OF PUERTO RICO INC.—See Encanto Restaurants, Inc; *U.S. Private*, pg. 1389
PIZZA HUT RESTAURANTS SDN. BHD.—See Johor Corporation; *Int'l*, pg. 3994
PIZZA HUT SINGAPORE PTE. LTD.—See Johor Corporation; *Int'l*, pg. 3994
PIZZA HUT (UK) LIMITED—See Rutland Partners LLP; *Int'l*, pg. 6432
PIZZA INN, INC.—See Rave Restaurant Group, Inc.; *U.S. Public*, pg. 1763
PIZZA KING INC.; *U.S. Private*, pg. 3193
PIZZA OF SCOTLAND INC.—See ZV Pate Inc.; *U.S. Private*, pg. 4610
PIZZA PAN GROUP PTY. LTD.—See Allegro Funds Pty. Ltd.; *Int'l*, pg. 336
PIZZA PIZZA ROYALTY CORP.; *Int'l*, pg. 5877
PIZZA VENTURE SAN ANTONIO LLC; *U.S. Private*, pg. 3193
PIZZA VENTURES WEST TEXAS LLC—See Pizza Venture San Antonio LLC; *U.S. Private*, pg. 3193
PIZZA WHOLESALE LEXINGTON INC.; *U.S. Private*, pg. 3193
THE PIZZERIA—See Bakkavor Group plc; *Int'l*, pg. 806
PIZZEYS PTE. LTD.—See IPH Limited; *Int'l*, pg. 3797
PJA ADVERTISING & MARKETING, INC. - SAN FRANCISCO—See PJA Advertising & Marketing, Inc.; *U.S. Private*, pg. 3193
PJA ADVERTISING & MARKETING, INC.; *U.S. Private*, pg. 3193
PJ ALTEK CO., LTD.—See PJ Metal Co., Ltd.; *Int'l*, pg. 5877
P & J ARCOMET LLC—See Arcomet & Co.; *Int'l*, pg. 550
PJB BETEILIGUNGS-GMBH—See Bilfinger SE; *Int'l*, pg. 1028
PJB MANAGEMENT-GMBH—See Bilfinger SE; *Int'l*, pg. 1028
PJBUMI BERHAD; *Int'l*, pg. 5877
P.J. CARROLL & CO. LTD.—See British American Tobacco plc; *Int'l*, pg. 1167
PJ CHEMTEK CO., LTD.—See PJ Metal Co., Ltd.; *Int'l*, pg. 5877
P. J. DALY CONTRACTING LTD.; *Int'l*, pg. 5682
P.J. DICK INCORPORATED; *U.S. Private*, pg. 3060
P.J. DICK-TRUMBULL-LINDY - HOMER CITY PLANT—See P.J. Dick Incorporated; *U.S. Private*, pg. 3060
P.J. DICK-TRUMBULL-LINDY - KOPPEL PLANT—See P.J. Dick Incorporated; *U.S. Private*, pg. 3060
P.J. DICK-TRUMBULL-LINDY - NEVILLE ISLAND PLANT—See P.J. Dick Incorporated; *U.S. Private*, pg. 3060
P.J. DICK-TRUMBULL-LINDY - NEW KENSINGTON PLANT—See P.J. Dick Incorporated; *U.S. Private*, pg. 3060
P.J. DICK-TRUMBULL-LINDY - SECOND AVENUE PLANT—See P.J. Dick Incorporated; *U.S. Private*, pg. 3060
P.J. DOHERTY & ASSOCIATES CO. LTD.—See AGF Management Limited; *Int'l*, pg. 207
PJ ELECTRONICS CO., LTD. - FACTORY II—See PJ Electronics Co Ltd; *Int'l*, pg. 5877
PJ ELECTRONICS CO LTD; *Int'l*, pg. 5877
P.J. HAYES, INC.; *U.S. Private*, pg. 3060
P.J. HELICOPTERS, INC.—See Quanta Services, Inc.; *U.S. Public*, pg. 1752
PJH GROUP LTD.—See Globe Union Industrial Corp.; *Int'l*, pg. 3007
P.J. HOERR, INC.; *U.S. Private*, pg. 3060
P.J. INDAH SDN. BHD.—See YFG Berhad; *Int'l*, pg. 8579
PJJ ENTERPRISES INC.—See John Lenore & Company, Inc.; *U.S. Private*, pg. 2223

CORPORATE AFFILIATIONS

PJ&J, INC.; *U.S. Private*, pg. 3193
P.J. KEATING COMPANY—See CRH plc; *Int'l*, pg. 1847
PJLM SOFTWARE INC.—See Apax Partners LLP; *Int'l*, pg. 503
PJ METAL CO., LTD.; *Int'l*, pg. 5877
PJMS—See Solocal Group; *Int'l*, pg. 7074
PJP MAKRUM S.A.; *Int'l*, pg. 5877
PJSC AEROFLOT RUSSIAN AIRLINES; *Int'l*, pg. 5877
PJSC ALCHEVSKKOKS; *Int'l*, pg. 5878
PJSC ALROSA; *Int'l*, pg. 5878
PJSC ARCELORMITTAL KRYVYI RIH—See ArcelorMittal S.A.; *Int'l*, pg. 546
PJSC AUTOKRAZ; *Int'l*, pg. 5878
PJSC BROVARY PLASTICS PLANT—See VBH Holding AG; *Int'l*, pg. 8139
PJSC CENTER FOR CARGO CONTAINER TRAFFIC TRANSCONTAINER—See Delo Group; *Int'l*, pg. 2014
PJSC CENTRENERGO; *Int'l*, pg. 5878
PJSC CHERKIZOVO GROUP; *Int'l*, pg. 5878
PJSC CONCERN GALNAFTOGAZ; *Int'l*, pg. 5878
PJSC CONCERN KHLIBPROM; *Int'l*, pg. 5878
PJSC CREDIT EUROPE BANK—See Fiba Holding A.S.; *Int'l*, pg. 2651
PJSC DNIPROSPETSSTAL; *Int'l*, pg. 5878
PJSC DOROGOBUZH—See Public Joint Stock Company Acron; *Int'l*, pg. 6095
PJSC EFES UKRAINE—See Anadolu Efes Biracilik ve Malt Sanayii A.S.; *Int'l*, pg. 445
PJSC EL5-ENERGO—See PJSC Lukoil; *Int'l*, pg. 5882
PJSC EL5-ENERGO; *Int'l*, pg. 5878
PJSC ENERGOMASHINOSTROITELNY ALLIANCE; *Int'l*, pg. 5878
PJSC FEDERAL GRID COMPANY ROSSETI—See JSC ROSSETI; *Int'l*, pg. 4010
PJSC FIDOBANK; *Int'l*, pg. 5879
PJSC FLEET OF NCSP—See PJSC Novorossiysk Commercial Sea Port; *Int'l*, pg. 5883
PJSC GAZPROM; *Int'l*, pg. 5879
PJSC GIPROSVYAZ—See PJSC Rostelecom; *Int'l*, pg. 5884
PJSC IC RUSS-INVEST; *Int'l*, pg. 5880
PJSC IDGC OF NORTHERN CAUCASUS—See JSC ROSSETI; *Int'l*, pg. 4010
PJSC IDGC OF SIBERIA—See JSC ROSSETI; *Int'l*, pg. 4010
PJSC ING BANK—See ING Groep N.V.; *Int'l*, pg. 3700
PJSC INSURANCE COMPANY—See Vienna Insurance Group AG Wiener Versicherung Gruppe; *Int'l*, pg. 8195
PJSC IZHNEFTEMASH—See PAO-TMK; *Int'l*, pg. 5732
PJSC JUPITER LIFE INSURANCE—See Vienna Insurance Group AG Wiener Versicherung Gruppe; *Int'l*, pg. 8195
PJSC KAZANORGSINTEZ—See PSC TAIF; *Int'l*, pg. 6016
PJSC KHIMPROM; *Int'l*, pg. 5881
PJSC KUIBYSHEVAZOT; *Int'l*, pg. 5881
PJSC LSR GROUP; *Int'l*, pg. 5881
PJSC LUKOIL; *Int'l*, pg. 5881
PJSC M2M PRIVATE BANK; *Int'l*, pg. 5882
PJSC MAGNITOGORSK IRON & STEEL WORKS; *Int'l*, pg. 5882
PJSC MEGAFON; *Int'l*, pg. 5882
PJSC MMC NORILSK NICKEL; *Int'l*, pg. 5882
PJSC MOESK; *Int'l*, pg. 5883
PJSC MTS BANK—See MOBILE TELESYSTEMS PUBLIC JOINT STOCK COMPANY; *Int'l*, pg. 5011
PJSC M.VIDEO—See Safmar Industrial & Financial Group; *Int'l*, pg. 6472
PJSC MYKOLAIVCEMENT—See CRH plc; *Int'l*, pg. 1848
PJSC NADEZHDA—See Compagnie des Levures Lesaffre SA; *Int'l*, pg. 1739
PJSC NOVOROSSIYSK COMMERCIAL SEA PORT; *Int'l*, pg. 5883
PJSC PHOSAGRO; *Int'l*, pg. 5883
PJSC POLYUS; *Int'l*, pg. 5883
PJSC "LINDE GAS UKRAINE"—See Linde plc; *Int'l*, pg. 4506
PJSC RAO ENERGY SYSTEM OF EAST; *Int'l*, pg. 5883
PJSC ROSSETI MOSCOW REGION—See JSC ROSSETI; *Int'l*, pg. 4010
PJSC ROSTELECOM; *Int'l*, pg. 5883
PJSC RUSHYDRO; *Int'l*, pg. 5884
PJSC RUSPOLYMET; *Int'l*, pg. 5884
PJSC SAFMAR FINANCIAL INVESTMENTS—See Safmar Industrial & Financial Group; *Int'l*, pg. 6472
PJSC SAROVBUSINESSBANK—See PJSC VTB Bank; *Int'l*, pg. 5886
PJSC SCIENTIFIC & PRODUCTION CORPORATION—See PJSC United Aircraft Corporation; *Int'l*, pg. 5885
PJSC SEVERALMAZ—See PJSC Alrosa; *Int'l*, pg. 5878
PJSC S.P. KOROLEV ROCKET & SPACE CORPORATION ENERGIA; *Int'l*, pg. 5885
PJSC STROYTRANSGAZ; *Int'l*, pg. 5885
PJSC TAGANROG AVIATION SCIENTIFIC-TECHNICAL COMPLEX N.A. G.M. BERIEV—See PJSC United Aircraft Corporation; *Int'l*, pg. 5885
PJSC TATNEFT; *Int'l*, pg. 5885
PJSC TERRITORIAL GENERATING COMPANY NO 1; *Int'l*, pg. 5885

COMPANY NAME INDEX

PJSC TKZ KRASNY KOTELSHCHIK—See OOO Severgrupp; *Int'l*, pg. 5594
PJSC TRANSCONTAINER; *Int'l*, pg. 5885
PJSC TUPOLEV—See PJSC United Aircraft Corporation; *Int'l*, pg. 5885
PJSC UIC KNIAZHA—See Vienna Insurance Group AG Wiener Versicherung Gruppe; *Int'l*, pg. 8195
PJSC UKRSOTSBANK—See Alfa Group; *Int'l*, pg. 308
PJSC UKRTRANSGAS—See National Joint-Stock Company Naftogaz of Ukraine; *Int'l*, pg. 5160
PJSC UNITED AIRCRAFT CORPORATION; *Int'l*, pg. 5885
PJSC VSEUKRAINSKYI AKSIONERNYI BANK; *Int'l*, pg. 5885
PJSC VTB BANK; *Int'l*, pg. 5886
PJSC YUZHNIIGIPROGAZ; *Int'l*, pg. 5886
PJSC ZAPOROZHYE FERRO ALLOYS PLANT; *Int'l*, pg. 5886
P.J. SERVICES PTE LTD—See Annica Holdings Limited; *Int'l*, pg. 474
PJSOC BASHNEFT—See OJSC Rosneftegaz; *Int'l*, pg. 5541
P & J SPRINKLER COMPANY, INC.—See TruArc Partners, L.P.; *U.S. Private*, pg. 4244
P&J TEAM AMERICA INC.; *U.S. Private*, pg. 3059
PJT PARTNERS (FRANCE) SAS—See PJT Partners Inc.; *U.S. Public*, pg. 1696
PJT PARTNERS INC.; *U.S. Public*, pg. 1696
PJT PARTNERS JAPAN K.K.—See PJT Partners Inc.; *U.S. Public*, pg. 1696
PJT PARTNERS (UK) LIMITED—See PJT Partners Inc.; *U.S. Public*, pg. 1696
PJ TRAILERS, INC.—See Bain Capital, LP; *U.S. Private*, pg. 436
PJ TRAILERS INC.; *U.S. Private*, pg. 3193
PJT TECHNOLOGY CO. LTD. - PHUKET GREEN INCINERATOR PLANT—See Yunnan Water Investment Co., Limited; *Int'l*, pg. 8616
PJT TECHNOLOGY CO. LTD.—See Yunnan Water Investment Co., Limited; *Int'l*, pg. 8616
PJ WHITE HARDWOODS LTD—See Richelieu Hardware Ltd.; *Int'l*, pg. 6331
PJX RESOURCES INC.; *Int'l*, pg. 5886
PKA A/S; *Int'l*, pg. 5886
PK AIR FINANCE FRANCE SAS—See Apollo Global Management, Inc.; *U.S. Public*, pg. 154
PK AIRFINANCE JAPAN G.K.—See Apollo Global Management, Inc.; *U.S. Public*, pg. 154
PKA KLOCKER GMBH—See Bunzl plc; *Int'l*, pg. 1219
P. KAUFMANN INC.; *U.S. Private*, pg. 3060
P. KAY METAL SUPPLY INC.; *U.S. Private*, pg. 3060
PKB ENTERPRISE CO., LTD.—See Patkol Public Company Limited; *Int'l*, pg. 5757
PKB PRIVATBANK SA—See Compagnie de l'Occident pour la Finance et l'Industrie S.A.; *Int'l*, pg. 1722
PKB VELEPRODAJA PRODUKT AD; *Int'l*, pg. 5887
PK CABLES DO BRASIL LTDA.—See Samvardhana Motherson International Limited; *Int'l*, pg. 6517
PKC ADVISORY SERVICES JLT—See Kuwait Projects Company (Holding) K.S.C.P.; *Int'l*, pg. 4346
PKC ADVISORY—See Kuwait Projects Company (Holding) K.S.C.P.; *Int'l*, pg. 4346
PKC CABLES DO BRASIL INDUSTRIA E COMERCIO LTDA—See Samvardhana Motherson International Limited; *Int'l*, pg. 6517
PKC CO., LTD.—See Press Kogyo Co., Ltd.; *Int'l*, pg. 5964
PKC CONSTRUCTION; *U.S. Private*, pg. 3193
PKC EESTI AS—See Samvardhana Motherson International Limited; *Int'l*, pg. 6517
PKC GROUP DE PIEDRAS NEGRAS, S. DE R.L. DE C.V.—See Samvardhana Motherson International Limited; *Int'l*, pg. 6517
PKC GROUP LITHUANIA UAB—See Samvardhana Motherson International Limited; *Int'l*, pg. 6517
PKC GROUP LTD.—See Samvardhana Motherson International Limited; *Int'l*, pg. 6517
PKC GROUP MEXICO S.A. DE C.V.—See Samvardhana Motherson International Limited; *Int'l*, pg. 6517
PKC GROUP POLAND SP. Z.O.O—See Samvardhana Motherson International Limited; *Int'l*, pg. 6517
PKC GROUP USA INC.—See Samvardhana Motherson International Limited; *Int'l*, pg. 6517
PKC INC.—See Loeb Holding Corporation; *U.S. Private*, pg. 2479
PK CONTRACTING, INC.—See The Sterling Group, L.P.; *U.S. Private*, pg. 4123
PKC SEGU SYSTEMELEKTRIK GMBH—See Samvardhana Motherson International Limited; *Int'l*, pg. 6517
PKC VEHICLE TECHNOLOGY (SUZHOU) CO. LTD—See Samvardhana Motherson International Limited; *Int'l*, pg. 6517
PKC WIRING SYSTEMS D.O.O.—See Samvardhana Motherson International Limited; *Int'l*, pg. 6517
PKC WIRING SYSTEMS OY—See Samvardhana Motherson International Limited; *Int'l*, pg. 6517
PKDM HOLDINGS, INC.; *U.S. Private*, pg. 3193
PKDW EQUITY PARTNERS, LLC; *U.S. Private*, pg. 3193
P&K EQUIPMENT INC.; *U.S. Private*, pg. 3059
PKF CONSULTING, INC.—See CBRE Group, Inc.; *U.S. Public*, pg. 460
PK FERTILIZERS (SARAWAK) SDN. BHD.—See Hextar Industries Berhad; *Int'l*, pg. 3373
PKF-MARK III, INC.; *U.S. Private*, pg. 3194
PKF O'CONNOR DAVIES CAPITAL, LLC—See PKF O'Connor Davies, LLP; *U.S. Private*, pg. 3193
PKF O'CONNOR DAVIES, LLP; *U.S. Private*, pg. 3193
P.K. GARMENT (IMPORT-EXPORT) CO., LTD.—See MC Group Public Company Limited; *Int'l*, pg. 4755
PK HOTELES, S.L.—See MERLIN Properties, SOCIMI, S.A.; *Int'l*, pg. 4838
PKI MANUFACTURING & TECHNOLOGY, INC.—See Konoike Transport Co., Ltd.; *Int'l*, pg. 4275
PK INTERNATIONAL INC.; *U.S. Private*, pg. 3193
PKI PREDOM SP. Z O.O.—See PROCHEM S.A.; *Int'l*, pg. 5987
PK KOPERTY SP. Z. O—See Bong AB; *Int'l*, pg. 1107
PKL GROUP (UK) LTD—See Perwyn LLP; *Int'l*, pg. 5822
PK, LTD.—See Photronics, Inc.; *U.S. Public*, pg. 1689
PKLT—See Photronics, Inc.; *U.S. Public*, pg. 1689
PK MANUFACTURING (SUZHOU) CO., LTD.—See Press Kogyo Co., Ltd.; *Int'l*, pg. 5964
PK MECHATRONIC CO., LTD.—See Pungkang Co., Ltd; *Int'l*, pg. 6119
PKM - MULDENZENTRALE GMBH—See PORR AG; *Int'l*, pg. 5923
PKO BANK HIPOTECZNY SA—See PKO Bank Polski SA; *Int'l*, pg. 5887
PKO BANK POLSKI SA; *Int'l*, pg. 5887
PKO BP FAKTORING SA—See PKO Bank Polski SA; *Int'l*, pg. 5887
PKO/CREDIT SUISSE TOWARZYSTWO FUNDUSZY INWESTYCYJ-NYCH S.A.—See PKO Bank Polski SA; *Int'l*, pg. 5887
PKO INWESTYCJE SP. Z O.O.—See PKO Bank Polski SA; *Int'l*, pg. 5887
PKO LEASING SA—See PKO Bank Polski SA; *Int'l*, pg. 5887
P'KOLINO LLC; *U.S. Private*, pg. 3059
PKO TOWARZYSTWO FUNDUSZY INWESTYCYJNYCH SA—See PKO Bank Polski SA; *Int'l*, pg. 5887
PKO ZYCIE TOWARZYSTWO UBEZPIECZEN SA—See PKO Bank Polski SA; *Int'l*, pg. 5887
PKP BBDO—See Omnicom Group Inc.; *U.S. Public*, pg. 1576
PKP CARGO, S.A.—See Polskie Koleje Panstwowe S.A.; *Int'l*, pg. 5913
PKP LINIA HUTNICZA SZEROKOTOROWA SP. Z O.O.—See Polskie Koleje Panstwowe S.A.; *Int'l*, pg. 5913
PKP POLSKIE LINIE KOLEJOWE S.A.—See Polskie Koleje Panstwowe S.A.; *Int'l*, pg. 5913
PKP ROHSTOFFE GMBH—See L. Possehl & Co. mbH; *Int'l*, pg. 4384
PK SERVICE CO., LTD.—See Press Kogyo Co., Ltd.; *Int'l*, pg. 5964
PKSHA TECHNOLOGY, INC.; *Int'l*, pg. 5887
P&K SKIN RESEARCH CENTER CO., LTD.—See Daebong LS Co., Ltd.; *Int'l*, pg. 1906
PKS OSTROLEKA S.A.—See Egged Israel Transport Cooperative Society Ltd.; *Int'l*, pg. 2324
PKS PLOCK S.A.—See Egged Israel Transport Cooperative Society Ltd.; *Int'l*, pg. 2324
PKS PRIVATKLINIK SALZBURG GMBH & CO KG—See Fresenius SE & Co. KGaA; *Int'l*, pg. 2780
PKS SDN BHD—See Tai Sin Electric Limited; *Int'l*, pg. 7409
PKS TARNOBRZEG SP. Z O.O.—See Accor S.A.; *Int'l*, pg. 92
PK STUDIOS INC.; *U.S. Private*, pg. 3193
PKT LOGISTICS GROUP SDN. BHD.—See Mitsui O.S.K. Lines, Ltd.; *Int'l*, pg. 4991
P-K TOOL & MANUFACTURING CO.; *U.S. Private*, pg. 3059
PKU HEALTHCARE CORP., LTD.; *Int'l*, pg. 5887
PK U.S.A., INC.—See Press Kogyo Co., Ltd.; *Int'l*, pg. 5964
PKWARE, INC.—See Thompson Street Capital Manager LLC; *U.S. Private*, pg. 4161
PLACACENTRO MASISA MEXICO S.A. DE C.V.—See AntarChile S.A.; *Int'l*, pg. 481
PLACE2B SERVICOS IMOBILIARIOS LTDA.—See Companhia Brasileira de Distribuicao; *Int'l*, pg. 1746
THE PLACE HOLDINGS LIMITED; *Int'l*, pg. 7673
PLACEIQ, INC.—See Clearlake Capital Group, L.P.; *U.S. Private*, pg. 936
PLACEIQ, INC.—See TA Associates, Inc.; *U.S. Private*, pg. 3917
PLACEMAKERS LIMITED—See Fletcher Building Limited; *Int'l*, pg. 2701
THE PLACEMAKING GROUP; *U.S. Private*, pg. 4096
PLACEMENT DIRECT SAS—See Swiss Life Holding; *Int'l*, pg. 7368
PLACEMENT PROS—See Randstad N.V.; *Int'l*, pg. 6204
PLACEMENTS CMI INC.; *Int'l*, pg. 5887
PLACE MOTOR INC.; *U.S. Private*, pg. 3194
PLACENTIA-LINDA HOSPITAL, INC.—See UCI Health; *U.S. Private*, pg. 4274
PLACER COUNTY WATER AGENCY; *U.S. Private*, pg. 3194

PLAINS GP HOLDINGS, L.P.

PLACER ELECTRIC INCORPORATED; *U.S. Private*, pg. 3194
PLACER SOLAR, LLC—See Trina Solar Limited; *Int'l*, pg. 7924
PLACER TITLE CO. INC.—See First American Financial Corporation; *U.S. Public*, pg. 838
PLACER TITLE INSURANCE AGENCY OF UTAH, INC.—See First American Financial Corporation; *U.S. Public*, pg. 838
PLACES FOR PEOPLE CAPITAL MARKETS PLC—See Places for People Group Limited; *Int'l*, pg. 5888
PLACES FOR PEOPLE DEVELOPMENTS LIMITED—See Places for People Group Limited; *Int'l*, pg. 5888
PLACES FOR PEOPLE GROUP LIMITED; *Int'l*, pg. 5888
PLACES FOR PEOPLE HOMES LIMITED—See Places for People Group Limited; *Int'l*, pg. 5888
PLACES FOR PEOPLE INDIVIDUAL SUPPORT LIMITED—See Places for People Group Limited; *Int'l*, pg. 5888
PLACES FOR PEOPLE LANDSCAPES LIMITED—See Places for People Group Limited; *Int'l*, pg. 5888
PLACES FOR PEOPLE LEISURE MANAGEMENT LIMITED—See Places for People Group Limited; *Int'l*, pg. 5888
PLACESTER, INC.; *U.S. Private*, pg. 3194
PLACID HOLDING COMPANY; *U.S. Private*, pg. 3194
PLACID REFINING COMPANY LLC—See Placid Holding Company; *U.S. Private*, pg. 3194
PLACO ARGENTINA S.A.—See Compagnie de Saint-Gobain SA; *Int'l*, pg. 1725
PLACO CO., LTD; *Int'l*, pg. 5888
PLACO DO BRASIL LTDA.—See Compagnie de Saint-Gobain SA; *Int'l*, pg. 1725
PLACON CORPORATION; *U.S. Private*, pg. 3194
PLACOPLATRE SA—See Compagnie de Saint-Gobain SA; *Int'l*, pg. 1733
PLAFACTORY CO., LTD.—See Daiei Kankyo Co., Ltd.; *Int'l*, pg. 1924
PLA-FIT HOLDINGS, LLC—See Planet Fitness, Inc.; *U.S. Public*, pg. 1697
PLAFOMETAL SAS—See Compagnie de Saint-Gobain SA; *Int'l*, pg. 1726
PLAFOND FIT OUT LLC—See The Emirates Group; *Int'l*, pg. 7639
PLAGEMAN ASSOCIATES INC.; *U.S. Private*, pg. 3194
PLAID ENTERPRISES, INC.—See The Dyson-Kissner-Moran Corporation; *U.S. Private*, pg. 4024
PLAID INC.; *U.S. Private*, pg. 3194
PLAID PANTRIES, INC.; *U.S. Private*, pg. 3194
PLAINBRIDGE LLC—See The Great Atlantic & Pacific Tea Company, Inc.; *U.S. Private*, pg. 4038
PLAIN DEALER PUBLISHING CO.—See Advance Publications, Inc.; *U.S. Public*, pg. 87
PLAIN DEALER PUBLISHING CO.—See Advance Publications, Inc.; *U.S. Public*, pg. 87
PLAIN DEALER PUBLISHING CO.—See Advance Publications, Inc.; *U.S. Public*, pg. 87
PLAINE DIALYSIS, LLC—See DaVita Inc.; *U.S. Public*, pg. 642
PLAINFIELD LUMBER COMPANY; *U.S. Private*, pg. 3194
PLAINFIELD MOLDING, INC.—See Plainfield Precision Companies; *U.S. Private*, pg. 3194
PLAINFIELD PRECISION COMPANIES; *U.S. Private*, pg. 3194
PLAINFIELD STAMPING TEXAS, INC.—See Plainfield Precision Companies; *U.S. Private*, pg. 3194
PLAINFIELD TOBACCO & CANDY INC.; *U.S. Private*, pg. 3194
PLAIN 'N FANCY KITCHENS INC.; *U.S. Private*, pg. 3194
PLAINS ALL AMERICAN, INC.—See Plains All American Pipeline, L.P.; *U.S. Public*, pg. 1696
PLAINS ALL AMERICAN PIPELINE, L.P.; *U.S. Public*, pg. 1696
PLAINSCAPITAL BANK—See Hilltop Holdings Inc.; *U.S. Public*, pg. 1039
PLAINSCAPITAL CORPORATION—See Hilltop Holdings Inc.; *U.S. Public*, pg. 1039
PLAINS CHEVROLET, LTD.—See AutoNation, Inc.; *U.S. Public*, pg. 237
PLAINS COMMERCE BANK; *U.S. Private*, pg. 3195
PLAINS COTTON COOPERATIVE ASSOCIATION - ALTUS WAREHOUSE—See Plains Cotton Cooperative Association; *U.S. Private*, pg. 3195
PLAINS COTTON COOPERATIVE ASSOCIATION; *U.S. Private*, pg. 3195
PLAINS COTTON COOPERATIVE ASSOCIATION - SWEETWATER WAREHOUSE—See Plains Cotton Cooperative Association; *U.S. Private*, pg. 3195
PLAINS DAIRY—See Affiliated Foods, Inc.; *U.S. Private*, pg. 122
PLAINS EQUITY EXCHANGE & COOPERATIVE UNION; *U.S. Private*, pg. 3195
PLAINS GAS SOLUTIONS, LLC—See Plains GP Holdings, L.P.; *U.S. Public*, pg. 1697
PLAINS GAS SOLUTIONS, LLC—See Plains All American Pipeline, L.P.; *U.S. Public*, pg. 1696
PLAINS GP HOLDINGS, L.P.; *U.S. Public*, pg. 1696
PLAINS LPG SERVICES GP LLC—See Plains All American Pipeline, L.P.; *U.S. Public*, pg. 1696

PLAINSMAN TIRE CO. INC.   CORPORATE AFFILIATIONS

PLAINSMAN TIRE CO. INC.; *U.S. Private,* pg. 3195
PLAINS MARKETING GP INC.—See Plains All American Pipeline, L.P.; *U.S. Public,* pg. 1696
PLAINS MARKETING, LP—See Plains All American Pipeline, L.P.; *U.S. Public,* pg. 1696
PLAINS MARKETING, L.P.—See Plains GP Holdings, L.P.; *U.S. Public,* pg. 1697
PLAINS MIDSTREAM CANADA ULC—See Plains All American Pipeline, L.P.; *U.S. Public,* pg. 1696
PLAINS TRANSPORTATION INC.; *U.S. Private,* pg. 3195
PLAINTREE SYSTEMS INC.; *Int'l,* pg. 5888
PLAINVIEW AGRI POWER INC.—See Minnesota Ag Group Inc.; *U.S. Private,* pg. 2743
PLAINVIEW DAILY HERALD—See The Hearst Corporation; *U.S. Private,* pg. 4047
PLAINVIEW MILK PRODUCTS ASSOCIATION; *U.S. Private,* pg. 3195
PLAINVILLE FARMS, LLC—See The Hain Celestial Group, Inc.; *U.S. Public,* pg. 2087
PLAINVILLE GAMING AND REDEVELOPMENT, LLC—See PENN Entertainment, Inc.; *U.S. Public,* pg. 1662
PLAINVILLE STOCK COMPANY, INC.; *U.S. Private,* pg. 3195
PLAISANCE AIR TRANSPORT SERVICES LIMITED—See Rogers & Company Limited; *Int'l,* pg. 6383
PLAISIMMO S.A.R.L.—See Vastned Retail N.V.; *Int'l,* pg. 8134
PLAISIO COMPUTERS S.A.; *Int'l,* pg. 5888
PLAKABETON FRANCE S.A.—See CRH plc; *Int'l,* pg. 1844
PLAKABETON N.V.—See CRH plc; *Int'l,* pg. 1848
PLAKA IRELAND LIMITED—See CRH plc; *Int'l,* pg. 1848
PLAKOR CO., LTD.—See Sambo Motors Co., Ltd.; *Int'l,* pg. 6502
PLALLOY MTD B.V.—See Dainichiseika Color & Chemicals Mfg. Co., Ltd.; *Int'l,* pg. 1939
PLALOC ASIA (THAILAND) CO., LTD.—See Idemitsu Kosan Co., Ltd.; *Int'l,* pg. 3592
PLA-MA BELGIUM NV—See Arplama N.V.; *Int'l,* pg. 578
PLAMA-PUR D.D.; *Int'l,* pg. 5888
PLA MATELS CORPORATION—See Sojitz Corporation; *Int'l,* pg. 7065
PLA MATELS (DALIAN) CO., LTD.—See Sojitz Corporation; *Int'l,* pg. 7065
PLA MATELS (HONG KONG) CO., LTD.—See Sojitz Corporation; *Int'l,* pg. 7065
PLA MATELS (INDIA) PVT. LTD.—See Sojitz Corporation; *Int'l,* pg. 7065
PLA MATELS (PHILIPPINES) CORPORATION—See Sojitz Corporation; *Int'l,* pg. 7065
PLA MATELS (SHANGHAI) CO., LTD.—See Sojitz Corporation; *Int'l,* pg. 7065
PLA MATELS (SHENZHEN) CO., LTD.—See Sojitz Corporation; *Int'l,* pg. 7065
PLA MATELS (THAILAND) CO., LTD.—See Sojitz Corporation; *Int'l,* pg. 7065
PLAMBECK NEUE ENERGIEN BETRIEBS- UND BETEILIGUNGSGESELLSCHAFT MBH—See PNE AG; *Int'l,* pg. 5900
PLAMBECK NEUE ENERGIEN BIOMASSE AG—See PNE AG; *Int'l,* pg. 5900
PLAMBECK NEUE ENERGIEN BIOMASSE BETRIEBSGESELLSCHAFT MBH—See PNE AG; *Int'l,* pg. 5900
PLAMBECK NEUE ENERGIEN GRUNDSTUCKS GMBH—See PNE AG; *Int'l,* pg. 5901
PLAMED INC.—See Nippon Telegraph & Telephone Corporation; *Int'l,* pg. 5350
PLAMEKS TREJD DOO SKOPJE—See Max Weishaupt GmbH; *Int'l,* pg. 4735
PLAMEX, S.A. DE C.V.—See HP Inc.; *U.S. Public,* pg. 1064
PLAMONDON ENTERPRISES INC.; *U.S. Private,* pg. 3195
PLAN1 HEALTH S.R.L.—See Poly Medicure Ltd.; *Int'l,* pg. 5914
PLAN 365, INC.—See BCD Holdings N.V.; *Int'l,* pg. 926
PLAN4DEMAND SOLUTIONS, INC.—See Spinnaker Management Group, LLC; *U.S. Private,* pg. 3757
PLANACO SA—See Folli Follie S.A.; *Int'l,* pg. 2721
PLAN ADMINISTRATORS, INC.—See Aquiline Capital Partners LLC; *U.S. Private,* pg. 304
PLAN ADMINISTRATORS, INC.—See Genstar Capital, LLC; *U.S. Private,* pg. 1675
PLANA-INNOVA AG—See plana-innova GmbH; *Int'l,* pg. 5889
PLANA-INNOVA GMBH; *Int'l,* pg. 5889
PLANALYTICS, INC.; *U.S. Private,* pg. 3195
PLANAR MONOLITHICS INDUSTRIES, INC.—See Arcline Investment Management LP; *U.S. Private,* pg. 315
PLANAR SYSTEMS, INC.—See Leyard Optoelectronic Co., Ltd.; *Int'l,* pg. 4472
PLAN ASIA, INC.; *U.S. Private,* pg. 3195
PLAN A SP. Z O.O.—See Agora S.A.; *Int'l,* pg. 212
PLANATOL GMBH—See Blue Cap AG; *Int'l,* pg. 1067
PLANATOL SYSTEM GMBH—See Blue Cap AG; *Int'l,* pg. 1067

PLAN B MEDIA PUBLIC COMPANY LIMITED; *Int'l,* pg. 5888
PLANBOX, INC.—See Main Capital Partners B.V.; *Int'l,* pg. 4650
PLANB TECHNOLOGIES, INC.—See Berkshire Partners LLC; *U.S. Private,* pg. 534
PLAN B (THE AGENCY ALTERNATIVE); *U.S. Private,* pg. 3195
PLANCAL GMBH—See Trimble, Inc.; *U.S. Public,* pg. 2190
PLANCONNECT, LLC—See Equitable Holdings, Inc.; *U.S. Public,* pg. 790
PLANDAI BIOTECHNOLOGY, INC.; *Int'l,* pg. 5889
PLANDIT CO., LTD.—See EQT AB; *Int'l,* pg. 2467
PLANES MOVING & STORAGE COMPANY OF COLUMBUS—See Planes Moving & Storage, Inc.; *U.S. Private,* pg. 3195
PLANES MOVING & STORAGE, INC.; *U.S. Private,* pg. 3195
PLANES MOVING & STORAGE OF CHICAGO, LLC—See Planes Moving & Storage, Inc.; *U.S. Private,* pg. 3195
PLANES MOVING & STORAGE OF DAYTON, INC.—See Planes Moving & Storage, Inc.; *U.S. Private,* pg. 3195
PLANES MOVING & STORAGE OF INDIANAPOLIS, INC.—See Planes Moving & Storage, Inc.; *U.S. Private,* pg. 3195
PLANET 13 HOLDINGS, INC.; *U.S. Public,* pg. 1697
PLANET 9—See Telekom Slovenije, d.d.; *Int'l,* pg. 7538
PLANETA CORPORACION SRL; *Int'l,* pg. 5889
PLANET ACP, INC.; *U.S. Private,* pg. 3195
PLANET AID, INC.; *U.S. Private,* pg. 3195
PLANETARIO ALFA—See ALFA, S.A.B. de C.V.; *Int'l,* pg. 313
PLANETART, LLC—See Claranova SA; *Int'l,* pg. 1642
PLANETARY SYSTEMS CORP.—See Rocket Lab USA, Inc.; *U.S. Public,* pg. 1804
PLANET BASED FOODS GLOBAL INC.; *Int'l,* pg. 5889
PLANET BEACH FRANCHISING CORPORATION; *U.S. Private,* pg. 3195
PLANETBIDS INC—See The CapStreet Group LLC; *U.S. Private,* pg. 4005
PLANET CHRYSLER JEEP; *U.S. Private,* pg. 3195
PLANET CLOUD COMPANY LIMITED—See Planet Communications Asia Public Company Limited; *Int'l,* pg. 5889
PLANET COMMUNICATIONS ASIA PUBLIC COMPANY LIMITED; *Int'l,* pg. 5889
PLANET DATA SOLUTIONS, INC.—See Veristar LLC; *U.S. Private,* pg. 4360
PLANET DDS, INC.—See Level Equity Management, LLC; *U.S. Private,* pg. 2434
PLANET DEPOS, LLC; *U.S. Private,* pg. 3196
PLANETECHS, LLC—See The Argentum Group; *U.S. Private,* pg. 3988
PLANETE INTERACTIVE—See Dentsu Group Inc.; *Int'l,* pg. 2037
PLANETEL S.P.A.; *Int'l,* pg. 5889
PLANET EVENTS S.A.—See Live Nation Entertainment, Inc.; *U.S. Public,* pg. 1330
PLANET FINANCIAL GROUP, LLC; *U.S. Private,* pg. 3196
PLANET FITNESS HOLDINGS, LLC—See Planet Fitness, Inc.; *U.S. Public,* pg. 1697
PLANET FITNESS, INC.; *U.S. Public,* pg. 1697
PLANET GREEN HOLDINGS CORP.; *U.S. Public,* pg. 1697
THE PLANET GROUP LLC—See Odyssey Investment Partners, LLC; *U.S. Private,* pg. 2996
PLANET HOLLYWOOD HOTELS-ADULT SCENE-CANCUN—See Sunwing Travel Group, Inc.; *Int'l,* pg. 7332
PLANET HOLLYWOOD HOTELS-CANCUN—See Sunwing Travel Group, Inc.; *Int'l,* pg. 7332
PLANET HOLLYWOOD HOTELS-COSTA RICA—See Sunwing Travel Group, Inc.; *Int'l,* pg. 7332
PLANET HOLLYWOOD INTERNATIONAL, INC.; *U.S. Private,* pg. 3196
PLANETHOME AG—See UniCredit S.p.A.; *Int'l,* pg. 8039
PLANETHOME GMBH—See UniCredit S.p.A.; *Int'l,* pg. 8039
PLANET HOME LENDING, LLC—See Planet Financial Group, LLC; *U.S. Private,* pg. 3196
PLANET HONDA—See Lithia Motors, Inc.; *U.S. Public,* pg. 1326
PLANET HYUNDAI SAHARA; *U.S. Private,* pg. 3196
PLANET IMAGE INTERNATIONAL LIMITED; *Int'l,* pg. 5889
PLANET, INC.—See Lion Corporation; *Int'l,* pg. 4518
PLANET LABS PBC; *U.S. Public,* pg. 1697
PLANET LOGISTICS CO., LTD.—See Lion Corporation; *Int'l,* pg. 4518
PLANETMEDIA SA; *Int'l,* pg. 5889
PLANET METRIX—See Warranty Corporation America; *U.S. Private,* pg. 4443
PLANET NETWORKS, INC.—See Nippon Telegraph & Telephone Corporation; *Int'l,* pg. 5348
PLANETONE COMMUNICATIONS INC.—See Avant Communications, Inc.; *U.S. Private,* pg. 404
PLANET ORGANIC HEALTH CORP.—See The Catalyst Capital Group Inc.; *Int'l,* pg. 7630

PLANET ORGANIC MARKET LTD.—See The Catalyst Capital Group Inc.; *Int'l,* pg. 7631
PLANETOUT, INC.—See Here Media Inc.; *U.S. Private,* pg. 1921
PLANET PAYMENT AUSTRIA GMBH—See Eurazeo SE; *Int'l,* pg. 2529
PLANET PAYMENT BELGIUM SA—See Eurazeo SE; *Int'l,* pg. 2529
PLANET PAYMENT DENMARK APS—See Eurazeo SE; *Int'l,* pg. 2529
PLANET PAYMENT FINLAND OY—See Eurazeo SE; *Int'l,* pg. 2529
PLANET PAYMENT FRANCE SAS—See Eurazeo SE; *Int'l,* pg. 2529
PLANET PAYMENT GERMANY GMBH—See Eurazeo SE; *Int'l,* pg. 2529
PLANET PAYMENT (GREECE) TAX SERVICES SINGLE PARTNER LIMITED—See Eurazeo SE; *Int'l,* pg. 2529
PLANET PAYMENT GROUP HOLDINGS LTD.; *Int'l,* pg. 5889
PLANET PAYMENT ICELAND EHF.—See Eurazeo SE; *Int'l,* pg. 2529
PLANET PAYMENT INC.—See Planet Payment Group Holdings Ltd.; *Int'l,* pg. 5889
PLANET PAYMENT IRELAND LIMITED—See Eurazeo SE; *Int'l,* pg. 2529
PLANET PAYMENT ITALY S.R.L.—See Eurazeo SE; *Int'l,* pg. 2529
PLANET PAYMENT LUXEMBOURG SARL—See Eurazeo SE; *Int'l,* pg. 2529
PLANET PAYMENT MALTA LIMITED—See Eurazeo SE; *Int'l,* pg. 2529
PLANET PAYMENT NETHERLANDS B.V.—See Eurazeo SE; *Int'l,* pg. 2529
PLANET PAYMENT NORWAY A/S—See Eurazeo SE; *Int'l,* pg. 2529
PLANET PAYMENT POLAND SP. Z O.O.—See Eurazeo SE; *Int'l,* pg. 2529
PLANET PAYMENT PORTUGAL UNIPESSOAL LDA.—See Eurazeo SE; *Int'l,* pg. 2529
PLANET PAYMENT SWEDEN AB—See Eurazeo SE; *Int'l,* pg. 2529
PLANET PAYMENT SWITZERLAND GMBH—See Eurazeo SE; *Int'l,* pg. 2529
PLANET PAYMENT UK LIMITED—See Eurazeo SE; *Int'l,* pg. 2529
PLANET PRODUCTS CORPORATION; *U.S. Private,* pg. 3196
PLANETPRO, INC.—See Kellton Tech Solutions Ltd.; *Int'l,* pg. 4121
PLANET RECRUITMENT LIMITED—See Reach PLC; *Int'l,* pg. 6231
PLANETREE INTERNATIONAL DEVELOPMENT LIMITED; *Int'l,* pg. 5889
PLANET RESOURCE RECOVERY, INC.; *U.S. Public,* pg. 1697
PLANETRISK, INC.; *U.S. Private,* pg. 3196
PLANETROLL GMBH & CO. KG—See INDUS Holding AG; *Int'l,* pg. 3664
PLANET SHOES; *U.S. Private,* pg. 3196
PLANET SIGNAL, INC.; *U.S. Public,* pg. 1697
PLANETSOFTWARE GMBH—See Bechtle AG; *Int'l,* pg. 938
PLANET SOLAR INC.; *U.S. Private,* pg. 3196
PLANETSPARK PTE. LTD.—See WT Microelectronics Co., Ltd.; *Int'l,* pg. 8498
PLANET SUBARU CAR DEALER; *U.S. Private,* pg. 3196
PLANET TOYOTA-SCION; *U.S. Private,* pg. 3196
PLANETTRAN; *U.S. Private,* pg. 3196
PLANET TRUST BANK CORPORATION; *U.S. Private,* pg. 3196
PLANET T&S CO., LTD.—See Saha Pathanapibul Public Company Limited; *Int'l,* pg. 6479
PLANET VENTURES INC.; *Int'l,* pg. 5889
PLANET-WATTOHM SNC—See Legrand S.A.; *Int'l,* pg. 4446
PLANETWIDE LIMITED—See Braemar PLC; *Int'l,* pg. 1135
PLANFURO GLOBAL, S.A.—See F. Ramada Investimentos, SGPS, S.A.; *Int'l,* pg. 2596
PLANGLASTEKNIK STOCKHOLM AB—See Lindengruppen AB; *Int'l,* pg. 4511
PLANGRID, INC.—See Autodesk, Inc.; *U.S. Public,* pg. 229
PLAN GROUP INC.—See Bouygues S.A.; *Int'l,* pg. 1122
PLANIGRUPO LATAM SAB DE CV; *Int'l,* pg. 5889
PLANI JACAREI DIAGNOSTICOS MEDICOS LTDA.—See Centro de Imagem Diagnosticos S.A.; *Int'l,* pg. 1413
PLANINKA A.D.; *Int'l,* pg. 5889
PLANINSKO DOBRO GACKO A.D.; *Int'l,* pg. 5889
PLAN INTERNATIONAL USA; *U.S. Private,* pg. 3195
PLANIT, INCORPORATED—See Dohmen Co.; *U.S. Private,* pg. 1254
PLANIT TEST MANAGEMENT SOLUTIONS PTY. LTD.—See Nomura Research Institute, Ltd.; *Int'l,* pg. 5413
PLANK ENTERPRISES INC.; *U.S. Private,* pg. 3196
PLANLOC PTY LTD—See Pelorus Private Equity Limited; *Int'l,* pg. 5783
PLANMILL LTD.—See CapMan PLC; *Int'l,* pg. 1315

COMPANY NAME INDEX

PLANMILL LTD.—See Osprey Capital LLC; *U.S. Private*, pg. 3048
PLANNED ADMINISTRATORS INC.—See Blue Cross & Blue Shield of South Carolina; *U.S. Private*, pg. 587
PLANNED COMMUNITY DEVELOPERS LTD; *U.S. Private*, pg. 3196
PLANNED & ENGINEERED CONSTRUCTION, INC.—See Vortex Company, LLC; *U.S. Private*, pg. 4413
PLANNED FURNITURE PROMOTIONS, LLC; *U.S. Private*, pg. 3196
PLANNED PARENTHOOD GREAT PLAINS; *U.S. Private*, pg. 3196
PLANNED SYSTEMS INTERNATIONAL, INC.; *U.S. Private*, pg. 3196
PLANNED TELEVISION ARTS—See Ruder Finn Group, Inc.; *U.S. Private*, pg. 3501
PLAN.NET—See The Interpublic Group of Companies, Inc.; *U.S. Public*, pg. 2097
THE PLANNING COUNCIL; *U.S. Private*, pg. 4096
PLANNING-INC LIMITED—See Next 15 Group plc; *Int'l*, pg. 5246
PLANNJA SIBA—See SSAB AB; *Int'l*, pg. 7153
PLANO ANUSA, LLC—See AutoNation, Inc.; *U.S. Public*, pg. 237
PLANO COLLISION, INC.—See AutoNation, Inc.; *U.S. Public*, pg. 237
PLANO DE SAUDE ANA COSTA LTDA.—See UnitedHealth Group Incorporated; *U.S. Public*, pg. 2249
PLANO ER CARE CENTER LLC—See Adeptus Health Inc.; *U.S. Private*, pg. 78
PLANO MARINE SERVICE; *U.S. Private*, pg. 3197
PLANO MOLDING COMPANY, INC.—See Ontario Teachers' Pension Plan; *Int'l*, pg. 5590
PLAN ONE (PTY) LTD—See Marriott International, Inc.; *U.S. Public*, pg. 1371
PLANO PITANGUEIRAS EMPREENDIMENTOS IMOBILIARIOS LTDA.—See Cyrela Brazil Realty S.A.; *Int'l*, pg. 1897
PLAN OPTIK AG; *Int'l*, pg. 5888
PLANPAY PTY. LTD.—See Touch Ventures Limited; *Int'l*, pg. 7847
PLANPRESCRIBER, INC.—See eHealth, Inc.; *U.S. Public*, pg. 721
PLAN SAS; *Int'l*, pg. 5888
PLANSEE BONDINGSHOP K.K.—See PLANSEE Holding AG; *Int'l*, pg. 5890
PLANSEE CHINA LTD.—See PLANSEE Holding AG; *Int'l*, pg. 5890
PLANSEE COMPOSITE MATERIALS GMBH—See PLANSEE Holding AG; *Int'l*, pg. 5890
PLANSEE HOLDING AG; *Int'l*, pg. 5889
PLANSEE INDIA HPM PVT. LTD.—See PLANSEE Holding AG; *Int'l*, pg. 5890
PLANSEE JAPAN LTD.—See PLANSEE Holding AG; *Int'l*, pg. 5890
PLANSEE KOREA HPM INC.—See PLANSEE Holding AG; *Int'l*, pg. 5890
PLANSEE MEXICO S.A. DE C.V.—See PLANSEE Holding AG; *Int'l*, pg. 5890
PLANSEE MITSUBISHI MATERIALS GLOBAL SINTER HOLDING, S.A.—See PLANSEE Holding AG; *Int'l*, pg. 5890
PLANSEE MW GMBH—See PLANSEE Holding AG; *Int'l*, pg. 5890
PLANSEE NEDERLAND—See PLANSEE Holding AG; *Int'l*, pg. 5890
PLANSEE POWERTECH AG—See PLANSEE Holding AG; *Int'l*, pg. 5890
PLANSEE SE—See PLANSEE Holding AG; *Int'l*, pg. 5890
PLANSEE SHANGHAI HIGH PERFORMANCE MATERIALS LTD.—See PLANSEE Holding AG; *Int'l*, pg. 5890
PLANSEE SOUTH AMERICA LTDA.—See PLANSEE Holding AG; *Int'l*, pg. 5890
PLANSEE TAIWAN CO., LTD.—See PLANSEE Holding AG; *Int'l*, pg. 5890
PLANSEE THERMAL MANAGEMENT SOLUTIONS INC.—See PLANSEE Holding AG; *Int'l*, pg. 5890
PLANSEE TUNGSTEN ALLOYS SAS—See PLANSEE Holding AG; *Int'l*, pg. 5890
PLANSEE USA LLC—See PLANSEE Holding AG; *Int'l*, pg. 5890
PLANSOURCE BENEFITS ADMINISTRATION, INC.—See Vista Equity Partners, LLC; *U.S. Private*, pg. 4399
PLANTAARDIG FARM CO., LTD.—See Tokyu Construction Co., Ltd.; *Int'l*, pg. 7797
PLANTABBS PRODUCTS COMPANY—See Tango Industries Ltd.; *U.S. Private*, pg. 3931
PLANTA CREST MONTERREY—See Grupo Lamosa S.A. de C.V.; *Int'l*, pg. 3131
PLANT ADVANCED TECHNOLOGIES SA; *Int'l*, pg. 5890
PLANTA EOLICA EUROPEA SA—See Enel S.p.A.; *Int'l*, pg. 2414
PLANTAIN PRODUCTS COMPANY; *U.S. Private*, pg. 3197
PLANTA MONTERREY, S.A. DE C.V.—See Grupo Lamosa S.A. de C.V.; *Int'l*, pg. 3132
PLANTARC BIO LTD.; *Int'l*, pg. 5891

PLANTA SAN JUAN DEL RIO UNIDAD DE NEGOCIOS IMPRESION COMERCIAL—See Atlas Holdings, LLC; *U.S. Private*, pg. 377
PLANTATION CORP.; *U.S. Private*, pg. 3197
PLANTATION GENERAL HOSPITAL—See HCA Healthcare, Inc.; *U.S. Public*, pg. 1006
PLANTATION PATTERNS, LLC—See Sycamore Partners Management, LP; *U.S. Private*, pg. 3896
PLANTATION PETROLEUM HOLDINGS IV, LLC (PPH); *U.S. Private*, pg. 3197
PLANTATION PIPE LINE COMPANY—See Kinder Morgan, Inc.; *U.S. Public*, pg. 1233
PLANTATION PRODUCTS INC; *U.S. Private*, pg. 3197
PLANT-BASED INVESTMENT CORP.; *Int'l*, pg. 5891
PLANT CO., LTD.; *Int'l*, pg. 5890
PLANT DESIGN ENGINEERS SDN BHD—See I Squared Capital Advisors (US) LLC; *U.S. Private*, pg. 2023
PLANT DESIGN ENGINEERS SDN BHD—See TDR Capital LLP; *Int'l*, pg. 7493
PLANTE & MORAN, PLLC—See Aquiline Capital Partners LLC; *U.S. Private*, pg. 304
PLANT ENGTECH PRIVATE LIMITED—See PEC Ltd.; *Int'l*, pg. 5778
PLANTERS BANK, INC.—See Planters Financial Group, Inc.; *U.S. Private*, pg. 3197
PLANTERS BANK & TRUST COMPANY—See Planters Holding Company Inc.; *U.S. Private*, pg. 3197
PLANTERS COOPERATIVE ASSOCIATION; *U.S. Private*, pg. 3197
PLANTERS COTTON OIL MILL INC.; *U.S. Private*, pg. 3197
PLANTERS ELECTRIC MEMBERSHIP CORP; *U.S. Private*, pg. 3197
PLANTERS EQUIPMENT CO.—See Ayres-Delta Implement, Inc.; *U.S. Private*, pg. 415
PLANTERS FINANCIAL GROUP, INC.; *U.S. Private*, pg. 3197
PLANTERS GRAIN COOP ODEM TEXAS; *U.S. Private*, pg. 3197
PLANTERS HOLDING COMPANY INC.; *U.S. Private*, pg. 3197
PLANTERS RICE MILL LLC.; *U.S. Private*, pg. 3197
PLANTERS WAREHOUSE & LOAN CO.; *U.S. Private*, pg. 3198
PLANT FANTASIES INCORPORATED; *U.S. Private*, pg. 3197
PLANT HEALTH CARE PLC—See PI Industries Ltd.; *Int'l*, pg. 5859
PLANTFUEL LIFE INC.; *Int'l*, pg. 5891
PLANTHEON CO., LTD.; *Int'l*, pg. 5891
PLANTIC TECHNOLOGIES LTD—See Kuraray Co., Ltd.; *Int'l*, pg. 4338
PLANT IMPACT PLC - MORRISVILLE BRANCH—See Croda International plc; *Int'l*, pg. 1852
PLANT IMPACT PLC—See Croda International plc; *Int'l*, pg. 1852
PLANT IMPACT TECNOLOGIA EM NUTRICAO LTDA—See Croda International plc; *Int'l*, pg. 1852
PLANT IMPROVEMENT CO. INC.; *U.S. Private*, pg. 3197
PLANTIN BVBA—See CoBe Capital LLC; *U.S. Private*, pg. 957
THE PLANTING HOPE COMPANY INC.; *Int'l*, pg. 7674
PLANT MAINTENANCE CORPORATION—See Kyokuto Boeki Kaisha, Ltd.; *Int'l*, pg. 4362
PLANT MAINTENANCE, INC.; *U.S. Private*, pg. 3197
PLANT MAINTENANCE SERVICE CORPORATION - FIELD CONSTRUCTION DIVISION—See Plant Maintenance Service Corporation; *U.S. Private*, pg. 3197
PLANT MAINTENANCE SERVICE CORPORATION; *U.S. Private*, pg. 3197
PLANT MARKETING LLC; *U.S. Private*, pg. 3197
PLANT NUTRIENT GROUP—See The Andersons Incorporated; *U.S. Public*, pg. 2034
PLANT PERFORMANCE SERVICES INC; *U.S. Private*, pg. 3197
PLANT POWER & CONTROL SYSTEMS, LLC—See IES Holdings, Inc.; *U.S. Public*, pg. 1094
PLANT PROCESS EQUIPMENT INC.; *U.S. Private*, pg. 3197
PLAN TRACKER PTY. LTD.—See McMillan Shakespeare Limited; *Int'l*, pg. 4760
PLANT RECLAMATION; *U.S. Private*, pg. 3197
PLANTRONICS ACOUSTICS ITALIA, S.R.L.—See HP Inc.; *U.S. Public*, pg. 1064
PLANTRONICS B.V.—See HP Inc.; *U.S. Public*, pg. 1064
PLANTRONICS CANADA LIMITED—See HP Inc.; *U.S. Public*, pg. 1064
PLANTRONICS GMBH—See HP Inc.; *U.S. Public*, pg. 1064
PLANTRONICS, INC.—See HP Inc.; *U.S. Public*, pg. 1064
PLANTRONICS INTERNATIONAL DO BRASIL, LTDA.—See HP Inc.; *U.S. Public*, pg. 1064
PLANTRONICS INTERNATIONAL—See HP Inc.; *U.S. Public*, pg. 1064
PLANTRONICS JAPAN LTD.—See HP Inc.; *U.S. Public*, pg. 1064
PLANTRONICS LIMITED—See HP Inc.; *U.S. Public*, pg. 1064

PLANTRONICS PTY. LIMITED—See HP Inc.; *U.S. Public*, pg. 1064
PLANTRONICS RUS LLC—See HP Inc.; *U.S. Public*, pg. 1064
PLANTRONICS SINGAPORE PTE. LTD.—See HP Inc.; *U.S. Public*, pg. 1064
PLANTRON, INC.; *U.S. Private*, pg. 3198
PLANTSCAPES, INC.; *U.S. Private*, pg. 3198
PLANT SCIENCES INC.; *U.S. Private*, pg. 3197
PLANT SCIENCE SWEDEN AB—See BASF SE; *Int'l*, pg. 877
PLANTS & GOODWIN, INC.—See Zefiro Methane Corp; *Int'l*, pg. 8629
PLANT SOLUTIONS NOORD-OOST BV—See VINCI S.A.; *Int'l*, pg. 8225
PLANTSTREAM INC.—See Chiyoda Corporation; *Int'l*, pg. 1575
PLANT SYSTEMS & SERVICES PSS GMBH—See ELKA Beteiligungs GmbH; *Int'l*, pg. 2364
PLANT TELEPHONE COMPANY; *U.S. Private*, pg. 3197
PLANT VEDA FOODS LTD.; *Int'l*, pg. 5891
PLANTX LIFE INC.; *Int'l*, pg. 5891
PLANTX LIVING INC.—See PlantX Life Inc.; *Int'l*, pg. 5891
PLANTYNET CO. LTD.; *Int'l*, pg. 5891
PLANUM CYPRUS LIMITED—See GP PLANUM AD; *Int'l*, pg. 3046
PLAN USA, INC.; *U.S. Private*, pg. 3195
PLANVIEW, INC.—See TA Associates, Inc.; *U.S. Private*, pg. 3917
PLANVIEW, INC.—See TPG Capital, L.P.; *U.S. Public*, pg. 2175
PLANVISTA CORPORATION; *U.S. Private*, pg. 3198
PLANWELL, LLC—See ARC DOCUMENT SOLUTIONS, INC.; *U.S. Public*, pg. 179
PLAQUEMINE REMEDIATION SERVICES, LLC—See Clean Harbors, Inc.; *U.S. Public*, pg. 510
PLARAD BOLTING TECHNOLOGY, LLC—See Maschinenfabrik Wagner GmbH & Co. KG; *Int'l*, pg. 4721
PLARAD ITALY SRL—See Maschinenfabrik Wagner GmbH & Co. KG; *Int'l*, pg. 4721
PLARAD TORK ANAHTARLAN VE GERDIRME SISTEMLERI SAN.DIS.TIC.LTD.STI.—See Maschinenfabrik Wagner GmbH & Co. KG; *Int'l*, pg. 4721
PLARAD UK LTD—See Maschinenfabrik Wagner GmbH & Co. KG; *Int'l*, pg. 4721
PLARIUM GLOBAL LIMITED—See Aristocrat Leisure Limited; *Int'l*, pg. 566
PLASAN NORTH AMERICA, INC.—See Plasan Sasa Ltd.; *Int'l*, pg. 5891
PLASAN SASA LTD.; *Int'l*, pg. 5891
PLASAN USA; INC.—See Plasan Sasa Ltd.; *Int'l*, pg. 5891
PLASCAL CORPORATION; *U.S. Private*, pg. 3198
PLASCAR PARTICIPACOES INDUSTRIAIS S.A.; *Int'l*, pg. 5891
PLASCOAT EUROPE BV—See International Process Technologies Limited; *Int'l*, pg. 3752
PLASCOAT SYSTEMS LIMITED—See Axalta Coating Systems Ltd.; *U.S. Public*, pg. 255
PLASCOBEL BVBA; *Int'l*, pg. 5891
PLASCO INC.; *U.S. Private*, pg. 3198
PLASCO, LLC—See Odyssey Investment Partners, LLC; *U.S. Private*, pg. 2994
PLASCON CAPE (PTY) LIMITED—See Kansai Paint Co., Ltd.; *Int'l*, pg. 4072
PLASCON GROUP; *U.S. Private*, pg. 3198
THE PLASENCIA GROUP, INC.; *U.S. Private*, pg. 4096
PLASGOM S.A.U.—See OpenGate Capital Management, LLC; *U.S. Private*, pg. 3031
PLASGRAN LIMITED—See Berry Global Group, Inc; *U.S. Public*, pg. 322
PLAS INDUSTRIES SDN. BHD.—See Techbase Industries Berhad; *Int'l*, pg. 7503
PLASIS LTD.—See OTP Bank Plc; *Int'l*, pg. 5658
PLASKOLITE, LLC—See The Pritzker Group - Chicago, LLC; *U.S. Private*, pg. 4099
PLASMA AUTOMATION, INC.; *U.S. Private*, pg. 3198
PLASMA BIOLOGICAL SERVICES, LLC—See Grifols, S.A.; *Int'l*, pg. 3085
PLASMABIOTICS S.A.S.—See Hoya Corporation; *Int'l*, pg. 3498
PLASMACARE, INC.—See Grifols, S.A.; *Int'l*, pg. 3084
PLASMA COMPUTING GROUP, INC.; *U.S. Private*, pg. 3198
PLASMADIENST TIROL GMBH—See Biotest AG; *Int'l*, pg. 1043
PLASMAPP CO., LTD.; *Int'l*, pg. 5891
PLASMART, INC.—See MKS Instruments, Inc.; *U.S. Public*, pg. 1453
PLASMA SERVICE EUROPE GMBH—See Biotest AG; *Int'l*, pg. 1043
PLASMA SYSTEMS GMBH.—See PVA TePla AG; *Int'l*, pg. 6125
PLASMA TECHNOLOGY, INCORPORATED - EAST COAST FACILITY—See Plasma Technology, Incorporated; *U.S. Private*, pg. 3198
PLASMA TECHNOLOGY, INCORPORATED; *U.S. Private*, pg. 3198
PLASMA-THERM, LLC; *U.S. Private*, pg. 3198
PLASMEQ PJSC; *Int'l*, pg. 5891

PLASMET CORP.
CORPORATE AFFILIATIONS

PLASMET CORP.; *U.S. Private*, pg. 3198
PLASMINE TECHNOLOGY, INC. - BAY MINETTE—See Harima Chemicals Group, Inc.; *Int'l*, pg. 3276
PLASMINE TECHNOLOGY, INC.—See Harima Chemicals Group, Inc.; *Int'l*, pg. 3276
PLASMO INDUSTRIETECHNIK GMBH—See Berndorf AG; *Int'l*, pg. 987
PLASMOTECH PTE. LTD.—See Amphenol Corporation; *U.S. Public*, pg. 132
PLAS-PAK INDUSTRIES, INC.—See Nordson Corporation; *U.S. Public*, pg. 1534
PLASS APPLIANCES AND FURNITURE INC.; *U.S. Private*, pg. 3198
PLASSON INDUSTRIES LTD.; *Int'l*, pg. 5891
PLASSON ITALIA S.R.L.—See Plasson Industries Ltd.; *Int'l*, pg. 5891
PLASSON POLSKA SP. Z O.O.—See Plasson Industries Ltd.; *Int'l*, pg. 5891
PLASSON (QINGDAO) LIVESTOCK TECHNOLOGY CO., LTD.—See Plasson Industries Ltd.; *Int'l*, pg. 5891
PLASSON ROMANIA SRL—See Plasson Industries Ltd.; *Int'l*, pg. 5891
PLASTAKET MANUFACTURING COMPANY INC.; *U.S. Private*, pg. 3198
PLASTAL INDUSTRI AB—See Insight Equity Holdings LLC; *U.S. Public*, pg. 2086
PLASTATECH ENGINEERING LTD.; *U.S. Private*, pg. 3198
PLASTECH BETEILIGUNGS GMBH—See PLASTECH Holding GmbH; *Int'l*, pg. 5891
PLAS-TECH CORPORATION—See Tosoh Corporation; *Int'l*, pg. 7833
PLASTECH CORPORATION—See Frandsen Corporation; *U.S. Private*, pg. 1593
PLASTECH HOLDING GMBH; *Int'l*, pg. 5891
PLASTECH MOULDERS (PTY) LTD—See Berry Global Group, Inc; *U.S. Public*, pg. 324
PLASTEC TECHNOLOGIES, LTD.; *Int'l*, pg. 5891
PLASTEC TECHNOLOGY GMBH—See L. Possehl & Co. mbH; *Int'l*, pg. 4384
THE PLASTEK GROUP - ENGINEERED PLASTICS DIVISION—See The Plastek Group; *U.S. Private*, pg. 4096
THE PLASTEK GROUP - PLASTEK DO BRASIL DIVISION—See The Plastek Group; *U.S. Private*, pg. 4096
THE PLASTEK GROUP; *U.S. Private*, pg. 4096
PLASTEK INDUSTRIES, INC.—See The Plastek Group; *U.S. Private*, pg. 4096
PLASTEKOL ORGANIZACJA ODZYSKU S.A.—See Grupa LOTOS S.A.; *Int'l*, pg. 3117
PLASTEK UK LTD—See The Plastek Group; *U.S. Private*, pg. 4096
PLASTENE INDIA LIMITED; *Int'l*, pg. 5892
PLASTER CASTER, INC.; *U.S. Private*, pg. 3198
PLASTERER EQUIPMENT CO, INC.; *U.S. Private*, pg. 3198
PLASTEX EXTRUDERS, INC.USA—See Enterprises International Inc.; *U.S. Private*, pg. 1404
PLASTI-APE S.P.A.—See Berry Global Group, Inc; *U.S. Public*, pg. 322
PLASTIAPE SP. Z O.O.—See Berry Global Group, Inc; *U.S. Public*, pg. 322
PLASTIBELL SAS—See PSB Industries SA; *Int'l*, pg. 6014
PLASTIBENACO SRL—See Camozzi Group; *Int'l*, pg. 1274
PLASTIBERT & CIE NV—See Duroc AB; *Int'l*, pg. 2230
PLASTIBLENDS INDIA LIMITED; *Int'l*, pg. 5892
PLASTIBLENDS INDIA LIMITED - WORKS II—See Plastiblends India Limited; *Int'l*, pg. 5892
PLASTIBLENDS INDIA LIMITED - WORKS I—See Plastiblends India Limited; *Int'l*, pg. 5892
PLASTIC2OIL, INC.; *U.S. Private*, pg. 1697
PLASTICARD - LOCKTECH INTERNATIONAL—See Platinum Equity, LLC; *U.S. Private*, pg. 3207
PLASTICAST HUNGARY KORLATOLT FELELOSSEGU TARSASAG—See Jabil Inc.; *U.S. Public*, pg. 1182
PLASTIC COATINGS LTD—See International Process Technologies Limited; *Int'l*, pg. 3752
PLASTIC COLOR CORPORATION, INC.—See PMC Capital Partners, LLC; *U.S. Private*, pg. 3218
PLASTIC COMPONENTS AND MODULES HOLDING S.P.A.—See Stellantis N.V.; *Int'l*, pg. 7203
PLASTIC COMPONENTS AND MODULES POLAND S.A.—See Stellantis N.V.; *Int'l*, pg. 7203
PLASTIC COMPONENTS FUEL SYSTEMS POLAND SP. Z O.O.—See Stellantis N.V.; *Int'l*, pg. 7203
PLASTIC COMPONENTS, INC.; *U.S. Private*, pg. 3198
PLASTIC COMPONENTS, INC.—See Nordstjernan AB; *Int'l*, pg. 5426
PLASTIC DISTRIBUTORS & FABRICATORS, INC.—See Edgewater Capital Partners, L.P.; *U.S. Private*, pg. 1334
PLASTIC INGENUITY INC.; *U.S. Private*, pg. 3198
PLASTIC MOLD TECHNOLOGY, INC.; *U.S. Private*, pg. 3198
PLASTICOLOR HUNGARY KFT—See Nexam Chemical Holding AB; *Int'l*, pg. 5239

PLASTICOLOR POLSKA SP. Z O.O.—See Nexam Chemical Holding AB; *Int'l*, pg. 5239
PLASTIC OMNIUM AB—See Burelle S.A.; *Int'l*, pg. 1222
PLASTIC OMNIUM AG—See Burelle S.A.; *Int'l*, pg. 1223
PLASTIC OMNIUM AUTO EXTERIEUR SA—See Burelle S.A.; *Int'l*, pg. 1223
PLASTIC OMNIUM AUTOMOTIVE LTD—See Burelle S.A.; *Int'l*, pg. 1223
PLASTIC OMNIUM BV—See Burelle S.A.; *Int'l*, pg. 1223
PLASTIC OMNIUM DO BRASIL LTDA—See Burelle S.A.; *Int'l*, pg. 1223
PLASTIC OMNIUM ENTSORGUNGSTECHNIK GMBH—See Burelle S.A.; *Int'l*, pg. 1223
PLASTIC OMNIUM EQUIPAMIENTOS EXTERIORES SA—See Burelle S.A.; *Int'l*, pg. 1223
PLASTIC OMNIUM, INC—See Burelle S.A.; *Int'l*, pg. 1223
PLASTIC OMNIUM INDUSTRIES INC.—See Burelle S.A.; *Int'l*, pg. 1223
PLASTIC OMNIUM MEDICAL SA—See Burelle S.A.; *Int'l*, pg. 1223
PLASTIC OMNIUM SA—See Burelle S.A.; *Int'l*, pg. 1223
PLASTIC OMNIUM SISTEMAS URBANOS SA—See Burelle S.A.; *Int'l*, pg. 1223
PLASTIC OMNIUM SYSTEMES URBAINS SA—See Burelle S.A.; *Int'l*, pg. 1223
PLASTICOMP, INC.—See Avient Corporation; *U.S. Public*, pg. 248
PLASTICON ASIA CO., LTD.—See Nimbus B.V.; *Int'l*, pg. 5296
PLASTICON AUBERT SAS—See Nimbus B.V.; *Int'l*, pg. 5296
PLASTICON CANADA INC.—See Nimbus B.V.; *Int'l*, pg. 5296
PLASTICON CHINA CO., LTD.—See Nimbus B.V.; *Int'l*, pg. 5296
PLASTICON COMPOSITES LLC—See Nimbus B.V.; *Int'l*, pg. 5296
PLASTICON EUROPE B.V.—See Nimbus B.V.; *Int'l*, pg. 5296
PLASTICON FRANCE SA—See Nimbus B.V.; *Int'l*, pg. 5296
PLASTICON GERMANY GMBH—See Nimbus B.V.; *Int'l*, pg. 5296
PLASTICON NORTH AMERICA INC.—See Nimbus B.V.; *Int'l*, pg. 5296
PLASTICON POLAND S.A.—See Nimbus B.V.; *Int'l*, pg. 5296
PLASTICON SOUTH AFRICA (PTY)—See Nimbus B.V.; *Int'l*, pg. 5296
PLASTICON THE NETHERLANDS B.V.—See Nimbus B.V.; *Int'l*, pg. 5296
PLASTICON UK LTD.—See Nimbus B.V.; *Int'l*, pg. 5296
PLASTICOS AMC, DE MEXICO, S.A. DE C.V.—See Power-Sonic Corporation; *U.S. Private*, pg. 3239
PLASTICOS COMPUESTOS, S.A.; *Int'l*, pg. 5892
PLASTICOS ENVOLVENTES, S.A. DE C.V.—See PPG Industries, Inc.; *U.S. Public*, pg. 1710
PLASTICOS NOVEL DO NORDESTE S.A.—See Myers Industries, Inc.; *U.S. Public*, pg. 1488
PLASTICOS NOVEL DO PARANA S.A.—See Myers Industries, Inc.; *U.S. Public*, pg. 1488
PLASTIC PACKAGING TECHNOLOGIES, LLC—See GTCR LLC; *U.S. Private*, pg. 1806
PLASTIC PLATE, INC.—See Lacks Enterprises, Inc.; *U.S. Private*, pg. 2371
PLASTIC PRINTING PROFESSIONALS, INC.—See Bristol ID Technologies, Inc.; *U.S. Private*, pg. 656
PLASTIC PRODUCTS COMPANY, INC. - GREENFIELD FACILITY—See Plastic Products Company, Inc.; *U.S. Private*, pg. 3199
PLASTIC PRODUCTS COMPANY, INC. - GREENVILLE FACILITY—See Plastic Products Company, Inc.; *U.S. Private*, pg. 3199
PLASTIC PRODUCTS COMPANY, INC. - LEBANON FACILITY—See Plastic Products Company, Inc.; *U.S. Private*, pg. 3199
PLASTIC PRODUCTS COMPANY, INC. - MOLINE FACILITY—See Plastic Products Company, Inc.; *U.S. Private*, pg. 3199
PLASTIC PRODUCTS COMPANY, INC. - PRINCETON FACILITY—See Plastic Products Company, Inc.; *U.S. Private*, pg. 3199
PLASTIC PRODUCTS COMPANY, INC.; *U.S. Private*, pg. 3199
PLASTIC PRODUCTS COMPANY, INC. - WEST BRANCH FACILITY—See Plastic Products Company, Inc.; *U.S. Private*, pg. 3199
PLASTICRAFT MANUFACTURING COMPANY, INC.; *U.S. Private*, pg. 3199
PLASTIC RECYCLING, INC.; *U.S. Private*, pg. 3199
PLASTIC RECYCLING SA—See Veolia Environnement S.A.; *Int'l*, pg. 8159
PLASTIC RESEARCH AND DEVELOPMENT CORPORATION - COMMONWEALTH PRODUCTIONS DIVISION—See EBSCO Industries, Inc.; *U.S. Private*, pg. 1325
PLASTIC RESEARCH AND DEVELOPMENT CORPORATION—See EBSCO Industries, Inc.; *U.S. Private*, pg. 1325

PLASTIC REVOLUTIONS, INC.; *U.S. Private*, pg. 3199
PLASTICS DECEUNINCK NV—See Deceuninck NV; *Int'l*, pg. 2000
PLASTICS DESIGN & MANUFACTURING, INC.—See Tide Rock Holdings, LLC; *U.S. Private*, pg. 4167
PLASTICS ENGINEERING COMPANY INC.; *U.S. Private*, pg. 3199
PLASTIC SERVICES, INC.—See Laser Excel, Inc.; *U.S. Private*, pg. 2395
PLASTICS GROUP INC.; *U.S. Private*, pg. 3199
PLASTICS NEWS—See Crain Communications, Inc.; *U.S. Private*, pg. 1084
PLASTICS NEW ZEALAND—See O-I Glass, Inc.; *U.S. Public*, pg. 1559
PLASTICS RESEARCH CORPORATION; *U.S. Private*, pg. 3199
PLASTIC SUPPLIERS, INC.; *U.S. Private*, pg. 3199
PLASTIC SYSTEMS, LLC; *U.S. Private*, pg. 3199
PLASTIC TECHNOLOGY INC.—See Hickory Springs Manufacturing Company; *U.S. Private*, pg. 1933
PLASTICTECNIC (M) SDN. BERHAD—See SKP Resources Bhd; *Int'l*, pg. 6991
PLASTICWELD SYSTEMS INC.—See Forsyth Capital Investors LLC; *U.S. Private*, pg. 1574
PLASTI-FAB, INC.; *U.S. Private*, pg. 3198
PLASTIFAB INDUSTRIES, INC.—See Regimen Equity Partners Inc.; *Int'l*, pg. 6253
PLASTI-FAB LTD. - CROSSFIELD PLANT—See The Riverside Company; *U.S. Private*, pg. 4109
PLASTI-FAB LTD. - DELTA PLANT—See The Riverside Company; *U.S. Private*, pg. 4109
PLASTI-FAB LTD.—See The Riverside Company; *U.S. Private*, pg. 4109
PLASTIFORM, INC.—See Nefab AB; *Int'l*, pg. 5191
PLASTIGRAY; *Int'l*, pg. 5892
PLASTIKA A.S.; *Int'l*, pg. 5892
PLASTIKA KRITIS S.A.; *Int'l*, pg. 5892
PLASTIKKART AKILLI KART ILETISIM SISTEMLERI SANAYI VE TICARET A.S.—See Thales S.A.; *Int'l*, pg. 7600
PLASTI-KOTE COMPANY INC.—See The Sherwin-Williams Company; *U.S. Public*, pg. 2129
PLASTIK STC SDN BHD—See Kumpulan H & L High-Tech Berhad; *Int'l*, pg. 4332
PLASTILITE CORPORATION; *U.S. Private*, pg. 3199
PLASTIMAYD CORPORATION; *U.S. Private*, pg. 3199
PLASTIMO AMS—See Navimo International; *Int'l*, pg. 5175
PLASTIMO MARINE ROUMANIE SRL—See Navimo International; *Int'l*, pg. 5175
PLASTIMO USA, INC.—See Navimo International; *Int'l*, pg. 5175
PLASTINAX AUSTRAL LIMITEE—See ENL Limited; *Int'l*, pg. 2441
PLASTINAX MADAGASCAR LTD.—See ENL Limited; *Int'l*, pg. 2441
PLASTINTCO INTERNATIONAL LTD.—See ENL Limited; *Int'l*, pg. 2441
PLASTIPAK ARGENTINA SA—See Plastipak Holdings, Inc.; *U.S. Private*, pg. 3199
PLASTIPAK BELGIUM—See Plastipak Holdings, Inc.; *U.S. Private*, pg. 3199
PLASTIPAK CZECH REPUBLIC S.R.O.—See Plastipak Holdings, Inc.; *U.S. Private*, pg. 3199
PLASTIPAK DEUTSCHLAND GMBH—See Plastipak Holdings, Inc.; *U.S. Private*, pg. 3199
PLASTIPAK EUROPE—See Plastipak Holdings, Inc.; *U.S. Private*, pg. 3199
PLASTIPAK HOLDINGS, INC.; *U.S. Private*, pg. 3199
PLASTIPAK IBERIA—See Plastipak Holdings, Inc.; *U.S. Private*, pg. 3199
PLASTIPAK MAROC—See Plastipak Holdings, Inc.; *U.S. Private*, pg. 3199
PLASTIPAK PACKAGING DA AMAZONIA—See Plastipak Holdings, Inc.; *U.S. Private*, pg. 3200
PLASTIPAK PACKAGING DO BRASIL LTDA.—See Plastipak Holdings, Inc.; *U.S. Private*, pg. 3200
PLASTIPAK PACKAGING FRANCE—See Plastipak Holdings, Inc.; *U.S. Private*, pg. 3199
PLASTIPAK PACKAGING INC. - JACKSON CENTER—See Plastipak Holdings, Inc.; *U.S. Private*, pg. 3200
PLASTIPAK PACKAGING, INC.—See Plastipak Holdings, Inc.; *U.S. Private*, pg. 3199
PLASTIPAK UK LTD.—See Plastipak Holdings, Inc.; *U.S. Private*, pg. 3200
PLASTIPRINT INC.; *U.S. Private*, pg. 3200
PLASTIQUE HOLDINGS LIMITED—See Sonoco Products Company; *U.S. Public*, pg. 1904
PLASTIQUE LIMITED—See Sonoco Products Company; *U.S. Public*, pg. 1904
PLASTIQUE MICRON INC.—See Loews Corporation; *U.S. Public*, pg. 1339
PLASTIQUE ROYAL INC.—See LKQ Corporation; *U.S. Public*, pg. 1336
PLASTIQUES CASCADES, INC.—See Cascades Inc.; *Int'l*, pg. 1350
PLASTIQUES DU VAL DE LOIRE S.A.; *Int'l*, pg. 5892
PLASTIQUE SP. Z O.O.—See Sonoco Products Company; *U.S. Public*, pg. 1904

COMPANY NAME INDEX

PLASTIROUTE FORGALOMTECHNIKAI KFT.—See Solix Group AB; *Int'l*, pg. 7074
PLASTISHELLS LTD.—See Richard Pieris & Co. Ltd.; *Int'l*, pg. 6330
PLASTIVAL INC.—See Cyprium Investment Partners LLC; *U.S. Private*, pg. 1135
PLASTLES D.O.O.—See Inles d.d.; *Int'l*, pg. 3705
PLASTMO LTD.; *Int'l*, pg. 5892
PLASTO CARGAL GROUP LTD.; *Int'l*, pg. 5892
PLASTOCHEM BRNO, SPOL. S R.O.—See Omya (Schweiz) AG; *Int'l*, pg. 5572
PLASTOCHEM KIEV T.O.V.—See Omya (Schweiz) AG; *Int'l*, pg. 5572
PLASTOFORM HOLDINGS LIMITED; *Int'l*, pg. 5892
PLASTOMER CORP.; *U.S. Private*, pg. 3200
PLASTOMER TECHNOLOGIES—See Enpro Inc.; *U.S. Public*, pg. 775
PLASTOPIL BV—See Plastopil Hazorea Company Ltd.; *Int'l*, pg. 5892
PLASTOPIL HAZOREA COMPANY LTD.; *Int'l*, pg. 5892
PLASTOPIL INC.—See Plastopil Hazorea Company Ltd.; *Int'l*, pg. 5892
PLASTOP KWAZULU-NATAL (PTY) LTD—See Berry Global Group, Inc; *U.S. Public*, pg. 324
PLAS-TOP (PTY) LTD—See Berry Global Group, Inc; *U.S. Public*, pg. 324
PLASTOREG SMIDT GMBH (OFFICE SUPPLIES DIVISION)—See Asia File Corporation Bhd.; *Int'l*, pg. 612
PLASTOREG SMIDT GMBH (SPECIALS DIVISION)—See Asia File Corporation Bhd.; *Int'l*, pg. 612
PLASTO-TEC GMBH—See Nimbus B.V.; *Int'l*, pg. 5296
PLASTO-TECH CORPORATION—See Magni-Power Company Inc.; *U.S. Private*, pg. 2548
PLASTPRO, INC.; *U.S. Private*, pg. 3200
PLASTRIBUTION LIMITED—See ITOCHU Corporation; *Int'l*, pg. 3841
THE PLASTRIDGE AGENCY, INC.; *U.S. Private*, pg. 4096
PLASTRO MAYER GMBH; *Int'l*, pg. 5892
PLASTRON ELECTRONIC TECHNOLOGY (ANHUI) CO., LTD.—See Plastron Presicion Co., Ltd.; *Int'l*, pg. 5893
PLASTRON ELECTRONIC TECHNOLOGY (SUZHOU) CO., LTD.—See Plastron Presicion Co., Ltd.; *Int'l*, pg. 5893
PLASTRONICS SOCKET PARTNERS, LTD.—See Smiths Group plc; *Int'l*, pg. 7012
PLASTRON PRESICION CO., LTD.; *Int'l*, pg. 5892
PLASTRON TECHNOLOGY (SHENZHEN) CO., LTD.—See Plastron Presicion Co., Ltd.; *Int'l*, pg. 5893
PLASTSVEIS AS—See Egersund Group AS; *Int'l*, pg. 2324
PLASTUBE INC.—See CAI Private Equity; *Int'l*, pg. 1252
PLASTYC INC.; *U.S. Private*, pg. 3200
PLATAFORMA EUROPA S.A.—See Industria de Diseno Textil, S.A.; *Int'l*, pg. 3667
PLATAFORMA LOGISTICA MECO S.A.—See Industria de Diseno Textil, S.A.; *Int'l*, pg. 3667
PLATA LATINA MINERALS CORPORATION; *Int'l*, pg. 5893
PLATA MANAGEMENT PUBLIC LTD.; *Int'l*, pg. 5893
PLATA PANAMERICANA S.A. DE C.V.—See Pan American Silver Corp.; *Int'l*, pg. 5713
PLATA & PUNTA SDN BHD—See Xamble Group Limited; *Int'l*, pg. 8519
PLATEAU ELECTRIC COOPERATIVE; *U.S. Private*, pg. 3200
PLATEAU ENERGY METALS INC.—See American Lithium Corp.; *Int'l*, pg. 422
PLATEAU EXCAVATION, INC.—See Sterling Infrastructure, Inc.; *U.S. Public*, pg. 1946
PLATEAU FOREST PRODUCTS, LLC—See Forest City Trading Group, LLC; *U.S. Private*, pg. 1566
PLATEAU GROUP INC.; *U.S. Private*, pg. 3200
PLATEAU MINERAL DEVELOPMENT, INC.; *U.S. Public*, pg. 1697
PLATEAU RESOURCES (PROPRIETARY) LIMITED—See Atlatsa Resources Corporation; *Int'l*, pg. 687
PLATEAU SYSTEMS, LTD.—See SAP SE; *Int'l*, pg. 6568
PLATEAU SYSTEMS UK LTD—See SAP SE; *Int'l*, pg. 6568
PLATEDEPAN AB—See SSAB AB; *Int'l*, pg. 7155
PLATEER CO., LTD.; *Int'l*, pg. 5893
PLATEG GMBH—See PVA TePla AG; *Int'l*, pg. 6125
PLATENO GROUP CO. LTD.—See CDC Group plc; *Int'l*, pg. 1370
PLATENO GROUP CO. LTD.—See Sequoia Capital Operations, LLC; *U.S. Private*, pg. 3612
PLATENO GROUP CO. LTD.—See The Carlyle Group Inc.; *U.S. Public*, pg. 2052
PLATEPASS, L.L.C.—See Verra Mobility Corporation; *U.S. Public*, pg. 2286
PLATEPLUS, INC. - HOUSTON—See Mitsubishi Corporation; *Int'l*, pg. 4940
PLATEPLUS, INC. - HOUSTON—See Sojitz Corporation; *Int'l*, pg. 7062
PLATEPLUS, INC.—See Mitsubishi Corporation; *Int'l*, pg. 4940
PLATEPLUS, INC.—See Sojitz Corporation; *Int'l*, pg. 7062
PLATFORM 9 CORPORATION—See PlayAGS, Inc.; *U.S. Public*, pg. 1697

PLATFORMA ELEVADORAS JLG IBERICA S.L.—See Oshkosh Corporation; *U.S. Public*, pg. 1620
PLATFORMAS ELEVADORAS JLG IBERICA S.L—See Oshkosh Corporation; *U.S. Public*, pg. 1621
PLATFORM CAPITAL, LLC; *U.S. Private*, pg. 3200
PLATFORM COMPUTING INC.—See International Business Machines Corporation; *U.S. Public*, pg. 1148
PLATFORM CONSOLIDATED GROUP PTY LIMITED—See Consolidated Operations Group Limited; *Int'l*, pg. 1771
PLATFORM CRANE SERVICES MEXICO S. DE. R.L.—See Cargotec Corporation; *Int'l*, pg. 1329
PLATFORM DELAWARE HOLDINGS, INC—See Element Solutions Inc.; *U.S. Public*, pg. 728
PLATFORM FUNDING LIMITED—See Co-operative Group Limited; *Int'l*, pg. 1679
THE PLATFORM GROUP AG; *Int'l*, pg. 7674
THE PLATFORM GROUP AG—See Benner Holding GmbH; *Int'l*, pg. 974
PLATFORM HOME LOANS LIMITED—See Co-operative Group Limited; *Int'l*, pg. 1679
PLATFORM PARTNERS LLC; *U.S. Private*, pg. 3200
PLATFORMQ, LLC; *U.S. Private*, pg. 3200
PLATFORM SECURITIES LLP—See Fidelity National Infor; *U.S. Public*, pg. 833
PLATFORM SERVICE AND REPAIR LIMITED—See Terex Corporation; *U.S. Public*, pg. 2019
PLATFORM SPECIALISTS, LLC—See Accordion Partners LLC; *U.S. Private*, pg. 53
PLATFORM WASTE SOLUTIONS, LLC—See Platform Capital, LLC; *U.S. Private*, pg. 3200
PLAT'HOME CO., LTD.; *Int'l*, pg. 5893
PLATHUSET I MALARDALEN AB—See Storskogen Group AB; *Int'l*, pg. 7228
PLATI ELETTROFORNITURE S.P.A.—See Accursia Capital GmbH; *Int'l*, pg. 94
PLATIGE IMAGE S.A.; *Int'l*, pg. 5893
PLATI MOROCCO SARL.—See Shenzhen Deren Electronic Co., Ltd.; *Int'l*, pg. 6808
PLATINA PARTNERS LLP; *Int'l*, pg. 5893
PLATINA RESOURCES LIMITED; *Int'l*, pg. 5893
PLATING FOR ELECTRONICS, LLC—See AOTCO Metal Finishing LLC; *U.S. Private*, pg. 289
PLATING TECHNOLOGY INC.; *U.S. Private*, pg. 3200
PLATINIA VERWALTUNGS-GMBH—See Munchener Ruckversicherungs AG; *Int'l*, pg. 5091
PLATINIUM M.M. SPOLKA Z OGRANICZONA ODPOWIEDZIALNOSCIA SP.K.—See Elemental Holding S.A.; *Int'l*, pg. 2358
PLATINOVA SARL—See Einhell Germany AG; *Int'l*, pg. 2334
PLATINUM ASIA INVESTMENTS LIMITED; *Int'l*, pg. 5893
PLATINUM ASSET MANAGEMENT LTD.; *Int'l*, pg. 5893
PLATINUM ASSET PTY LIMITED—See Platinum Asset Management Ltd.; *Int'l*, pg. 5893
PLATINUM BANK; *U.S. Private*, pg. 3200
PLATINUM BLASTING SERVICES PTY. LIMITED—See Deepak Fertilisers & Petrochemicals Corporation Limited; *Int'l*, pg. 2003
PLATINUM CAPITAL LIMITED; *Int'l*, pg. 5893
PLATINUM DATA SOLUTIONS, INC.—See Insight Venture Management, LLC; *U.S. Private*, pg. 2089
PLATINUM DATA SOLUTIONS, INC.—See Stone Point Capital LLC; *U.S. Private*, pg. 3822
PLATINUM EAGLE MORTGAGE, LLC—See Rithm Capital Corp.; *U.S. Public*, pg. 1800
PLATINUM ENERGY RESOURCES, INC.; *U.S. Private*, pg. 3200
PLATINUM ENERGY SDN. BHD.—See Fintec Global Berhad; *Int'l*, pg. 2677
PLATINUM ENERGY SERVICES LTD.—See TerraVest Industries, Inc.; *Int'l*, pg. 7568
PLATINUM ENERGY SERVICES ULC—See Trinity Industries, Inc.; *U.S. Public*, pg. 2193
PLATINUM EQUITY ADVISORS, LLC—See Platinum Equity, LLC; *U.S. Private*, pg. 3207
PLATINUM EQUITY, LLC - NEW YORK—See Platinum Equity, LLC; *U.S. Private*, pg. 3207
PLATINUM EQUITY, LLC; *U.S. Private*, pg. 3207
PLATINUM EVENT TRAVEL LIMITED—See TUI AG; *Int'l*, pg. 7968
PLATINUM GMBH I.I.—See Mutares SE & Co. KGaA; *Int'l*, pg. 5105
PLATINUM GROUP METALS LTD.; *Int'l*, pg. 5893
PLATINUM GROUP METALS RSA PTY LTD—See Platinum Group Metals Ltd.; *Int'l*, pg. 5893
THE PLATINUM GROUP PUBLIC COMPANY LIMITED; *Int'l*, pg. 7674
PLATINUM GUILD INTERNATIONAL (USA) JEWELRY, INC.; *U.S. Private*, pg. 3210
PLATINUM HEALTHCARE PTY. LTD.—See ComfortDelGro Corporation Limited; *Int'l*, pg. 1713
PLATINUM HOME MORTGAGE CORPORATION—See Planet Financial Group, LLC; *U.S. Public*, pg. 3196
PLATINUM INSURANCE COMPANY LIMITED; *Int'l*, pg. 5893
PLATINUM INVESTMENT MANAGEMENT LIMITED—See Platinum Asset Management Ltd.; *Int'l*, pg. 5893

THE PLATINUM MEDICAL CENTRE—See HCA Healthcare, Inc.; *U.S. Public*, pg. 1012
PLATINUM ONE BUSINESS SERVICES LIMITED; *Int'l*, pg. 5893
PLATINUM PERFORMANCE, INC.—See Zoetis, Inc.; *U.S. Public*, pg. 2409
PLATINUM PLACEMENT SOLUTIONS PTY LTD—See Steadfast Group Limited; *Int'l*, pg. 7187
PLATINUM PRESSURE SERVICES, INC.—See Basic Energy Services Inc.; *U.S. Public*, pg. 279
PLATINUM PROPERTIES, LLC.; *U.S. Private*, pg. 3210
PLATINUM REALTY, LLC—See United Real Estate Group, LLC; *U.S. Private*, pg. 4296
PLATINUM REALTY R.E. SERVICES—See United Real Estate Group, LLC; *U.S. Private*, pg. 4296
PLATINUM STUDIOS, INC.; *U.S. Public*, pg. 1697
PLATINUM TAX DEFENDERS, LLC—See Cardiff Lexington Corporation; *U.S. Public*, pg. 433
PLATINUM TOOLS INC.—See Odyssey Investment Partners, LLC; *U.S. Private*, pg. 2995
PLATINUM TRAFFIC SERVICES PTY LTD.—See AVADA Group Limited; *Int'l*, pg. 734
PLATINUM WARRANTY CORPORATION; *U.S. Private*, pg. 3210
PLATINUM WEALTH PARTNERS, INC.; *U.S. Private*, pg. 3210
PLATNICK STEEL & ENGINEERING, INC.—See Spencer Mac Corporation; *U.S. Private*, pg. 3755
PLATO BIO PHARMA INC.—See Inotiv, Inc.; *U.S. Public*, pg. 1128
PLATO CAPITAL LIMITED; *Int'l*, pg. 5893
PLATOGO INTERACTIVE ENTERTAINMENT GMBH—See Novomatic AG; *Int'l*, pg. 5467
PLATO GOLD CORP.; *Int'l*, pg. 5893
PLATO INCOME MAXIMISER LIMITED; *Int'l*, pg. 5893
PLATO INVESTMENT MANAGEMENT LIMITED; *Int'l*, pg. 5893
PLAT & SPIRALTEKNIK I TORSAS AB—See Lagercrantz Group AB; *Int'l*, pg. 4394
THE PLATT BROTHERS & COMPANY, INC.; *U.S. Private*, pg. 4096
PLATT CONSTRUCTION, INC.; *U.S. Private*, pg. 3210
PLATTE-CLAY ELECTRIC COOP; *U.S. Private*, pg. 3212
PLATTE DIALYSIS, LLC—See DaVita Inc.; *U.S. Public*, pg. 642
PLATTE GMBH—See Recticel S.A.; *Int'l*, pg. 6241
PLATTE RIVER INSURANCE COMPANY—See Berkshire Hathaway Inc.; *U.S. Public*, pg. 298
PLATTE RIVER NETWORKS INC.; *U.S. Private*, pg. 3211
PLATTE RIVER POWER AUTHORITY; *U.S. Public*, pg. 3211
PLATTE RIVER VENTURES, LLC; *U.S. Private*, pg. 3211
PLATTE VALLEY AG CREDIT CO.—See Platte Valley Financial Service Companies Inc.; *U.S. Private*, pg. 3211
PLATTE VALLEY BANK NEBRASKA—See Platte Valley Financial Service Companies Inc.; *U.S. Private*, pg. 3211
PLATTE VALLEY BANK—See Platte Valley Financial Service Companies Inc.; *U.S. Private*, pg. 3211
PLATTE VALLEY BANK WYOMING—See Platte Valley Financial Service Companies Inc.; *U.S. Private*, pg. 3211
PLATTE VALLEY FINANCIAL SERVICE COMPANIES INC.; *U.S. Private*, pg. 3211
PLATTE VALLEY INVESTMENT CENTER INC.—See Platte Valley Financial Service Companies Inc.; *U.S. Private*, pg. 3212
PLATTFORM ADVERTISING, INC.—See Arlington Capital Partners LLC; *U.S. Private*, pg. 328
PLATT NERA INTERNATIONAL LIMITED; *Int'l*, pg. 5893
PLATTNER AUTOMOTIVE GROUP, INC.; *U.S. Private*, pg. 3212
PLATTNER'S WINTER PARK SUPERSTORE—See Plattner Automotive Group, Inc.; *U.S. Private*, pg. 3212
PLATTSBURGH DISTRIBUTING CO, INC.—See Try-It Distributing Co. Inc.; *U.S. Private*, pg. 4251
PLATTS HARRIS LIMITED—See Lookers plc; *Int'l*, pg. 4555
THE PLATTSMOUTH JOURNAL—See Lee Enterprises, Incorporated; *U.S. Public*, pg. 1299
PLATYNOWE INWESTYCJE S.A.; *Int'l*, pg. 5894
PLATYPUS ADVERTISING + DESIGN; *U.S. Private*, pg. 3212
PLATZ CO., LTD.; *Int'l*, pg. 5894
PLATZER FASTIGHETER HOLDING AB; *Int'l*, pg. 5894
PLAUEN STAHL TECHNOLOGIE GMBH—See L'Air Liquide S.A.; *Int'l*, pg. 4375
PLAUT AG—See msg group GmbH; *Int'l*, pg. 5068
PLAUT BUSINESS CONSULTING GMBH—See msg group GmbH; *Int'l*, pg. 5068
PLAUT CONSULTING CZ, S.R.O.—See msg group GmbH; *Int'l*, pg. 5067
PLAUT CONSULTING LLC—See msg group GmbH; *Int'l*, pg. 5067
PLAUT CONSULTING LTD.—See msg group GmbH; *Int'l*, pg. 5068
PLAUT CONSULTING POLSKA SP.Z.O.O.—See msg group GmbH; *Int'l*, pg. 5067

PLAUT CONSULTING ROMANIA, S.R.L.—See msg group GmbH; *Int'l*, pg. 5067
PLAUT DEUTSCHLAND GMBH—See msg group GmbH; *Int'l*, pg. 5068
PLAUT MANAGEMENT & IT CONSULTING AG—See msg group GmbH; *Int'l*, pg. 5067
PLAUT (SCHWEIZ) CONSULTING AG—See msg group GmbH; *Int'l*, pg. 5067
PLAUT (SWITZERLAND) CONSULTING AG—See msg group GmbH; *Int'l*, pg. 5068
PLAVA LAGUNA DD; *Int'l*, pg. 5894
PLAXO, INC.—See Comcast Corporation; *U.S. Public*, pg. 541
PLAXTON LIMITED—See NFI Group Inc.; *Int'l*, pg. 5252
PLAY ADVERTISING; *Int'l*, pg. 5894
PLAYAGS, INC.; *U.S. Public*, pg. 1697
PLAYAGS MEXICO, S. DE R.L. DE C.V.—See PlayAGS, Inc.; *U.S. Public*, pg. 1697
PLAYA HOTELS & RESORTS N.V.; *Int'l*, pg. 5894
PLAYBILL INCORPORATED; *U.S. Private*, pg. 3212
PLAYBOY ENTERPRISES, INC.—See PLBY Group, Inc.; *U.S. Public*, pg. 1698
PLAYBOY ENTERTAINMENT GROUP, INC.—See PLBY Group, Inc.; *U.S. Public*, pg. 1698
PLAYBOY FRANCHISINGS INC.—See PLBY Group, Inc.; *U.S. Public*, pg. 1698
PLAYBOY SPECIAL EDITIONS—See PLBY Group, Inc.; *U.S. Public*, pg. 1698
PLAYBOY STUDIO WEST—See PLBY Group, Inc.; *U.S. Public*, pg. 1698
PLAYBOY TV & VIDEO ENTERPRISES, INC.—See PLBY Group, Inc.; *U.S. Public*, pg. 1698
PLAYCADE INTERACTIVE GMBH—See Azerion Group N.V.; *Int'l*, pg. 778
PLAY COMMUNICATIONS S.A.—See Iliad S.A.; *Int'l*, pg. 3614
PLAYCORE HOLDINGS, INC.—See Court Square Capital Partners, L.P.; *U.S. Private*, pg. 1069
PLAYCORE, INC.—See Court Square Capital Partners, L.P.; *U.S. Private*, pg. 1069
PLAYCORE WISCONSIN, INC.—See Court Square Capital Partners, L.P.; *U.S. Private*, pg. 1069
PLAYCYBERGAMES COMPANY LIMITED—See Asphere Innovations Public Company Limited; *Int'l*, pg. 630
PLAYD CO., LTD.; *Int'l*, pg. 5894
PLAYDOM, INC.—See The Walt Disney Company; *U.S. Public*, pg. 2139
PLAYER & CORNISH LIMITED—See Enpro Inc.; *U.S. Public*, pg. 775
PLAYER ONE AMUSEMENT GROUP INC.—See OpenGate Capital Management, LLC; *U.S. Private*, pg. 3031
PLAYERS HEALTH COVER USA INC.; *U.S. Private*, pg. 3212
PLAYERS NETWORK; *U.S. Public*, pg. 1698
PLAYFAIR MINING LTD.; *Int'l*, pg. 5894
PLAYFIELD INTERNATIONAL, INC.; *U.S. Private*, pg. 3212
PLAYFISH, INC.—See Electronic Arts Inc.; *U.S. Public*, pg. 724
PLAYFLY SPORTS PROPERTIES, LLC; *U.S. Private*, pg. 3212
PLAYFORD TAVERN PTY LTD—See Woolworths Group Limited; *Int'l*, pg. 8452
PLAYGIRL INDUSTRIES, INC.; *U.S. Private*, pg. 3212
PLAYGON GAMES, INC.; *Int'l*, pg. 5894
PLAYGRAM CO., LTD.; *Int'l*, pg. 5894
PLAYGREEN FINLAND OY—See Kingspan Group PLC; *Int'l*, pg. 4178
PLAYGROUND GROUP INC; *U.S. Private*, pg. 3212
PLAYGROUND MUSIC SCANDINAVIA AB - COPENHAGEN BRANCH—See Edel SE & Co. KGaA; *Int'l*, pg. 2305
PLAYGROUND MUSIC SCANDINAVIA AB - OSLO BRANCH—See Edel SE & Co. KGaA; *Int'l*, pg. 2305
PLAYGROUND MUSIC SCANDINAVIA AB—See Edel SE & Co. KGaA; *Int'l*, pg. 2305
PLAYGROUND VENTURES INC; *Int'l*, pg. 5894
PLAYHOUSE SQUARE FOUNDATION; *U.S. Private*, pg. 3212
PLAYIGNITE LTD.—See TruFin plc; *Int'l*, pg. 7941
PLAY IT AGAIN SPORTS; *U.S. Private*, pg. 3212
PLAYJAM LTD.; *Int'l*, pg. 5894
PLAYLAND INC.—See Pfingsten Partners, LLC; *U.S. Private*, pg. 3165
PLAYMAKER CAPITAL INC.—See Better Collective A/S; *Int'l*, pg. 1003
PLAYMATES HOLDINGS, LTD.; *Int'l*, pg. 5894
PLAYMATES TOYS INC—See Playmates Holdings, Ltd.; *Int'l*, pg. 5894
PLAYMATES TOYS LIMITED—See Playmates Holdings, Ltd.; *Int'l*, pg. 5894
PLAYMOBIL AUSTRIA GMBH—See Geobra Brandstatter GmbH & Co. KG; *Int'l*, pg. 2932
PLAYMOBIL CANADA INC.—See Geobra Brandstatter GmbH & Co. KG; *Int'l*, pg. 2932
PLAYMOBIL FRANCE SARL—See Geobra Brandstatter GmbH & Co. KG; *Int'l*, pg. 2932
PLAYMOBIL FUNPARK ORLANDO—See Geobra Brandstatter GmbH & Co. KG; *Int'l*, pg. 2932

PLAYMOBIL HELLAS S.A.—See Geobra Brandstatter GmbH & Co. KG; *Int'l*, pg. 2932
PLAYMOBIL IBERICA S.A.U.—See Geobra Brandstatter GmbH & Co. KG; *Int'l*, pg. 2932
PLAYMOBIL MALTA LTD—See Geobra Brandstatter GmbH & Co. KG; *Int'l*, pg. 2932
PLAYMOBIL MERCHANDISING MEXICANA, S.A. DE C.V.—See Geobra Brandstatter GmbH & Co. KG; *Int'l*, pg. 2932
PLAYMOBIL SWISS GMBH—See Geobra Brandstatter GmbH & Co. KG; *Int'l*, pg. 2932
PLAYMOBIL UK LTD.—See Geobra Brandstatter GmbH & Co. KG; *Int'l*, pg. 2932
PLAYMOBIL USA INC.—See Geobra Brandstatter GmbH & Co. KG; *Int'l*, pg. 2932
PLAYMONSTER LLC—See Audax Group, Limited Partnership; *U.S. Private*, pg. 390
PLAYNETWORK, INC.—See Vector Capital Management, L.P.; *U.S. Private*, pg. 4351
PLAYNEXT, INC.; *U.S. Private*, pg. 3212
PLAY & PARK STRUCTURES—See Court Square Capital Partners, L.P.; *U.S. Private*, pg. 1069
PLAYPHONE, INC.—See GungHo Online Entertainment, Inc.; *Int'l*, pg. 3183
PLAYPOWER CANADA—See Littlejohn & Co., LLC; *U.S. Private*, pg. 2471
PLAYPOWER, INC.—See Littlejohn & Co., LLC; *U.S. Private*, pg. 2471
PLAYPOWER LT FARMINGTON, INC.—See Littlejohn & Co., LLC; *U.S. Private*, pg. 2471
THE PLAY PRACTICE LTD.—See KOMPAN A/S; *Int'l*, pg. 4243
PLAYSCRIPTS INC.; *U.S. Private*, pg. 3212
PLAYSIDE STUDIOS LIMITED; *Int'l*, pg. 5894
PLAYSPAN, INC.—See Visa, Inc.; *U.S. Public*, pg. 2302
PLAY SPORTS NETWORK LIMITED—See Warner Bros. Discovery, Inc.; *U.S. Public*, pg. 2327
PLAYSTUDIOS, INC.; *U.S. Public*, pg. 1698
PLAYSTUDIOS, INC.—See PlayStudios, Inc.; *U.S. Public*, pg. 1698
PLAYTECH BULGARIA—See Playtech plc; *Int'l*, pg. 5894
PLAYTECH PLC; *Int'l*, pg. 5894
PLAYTEX APPAREL, INC.—See Hanesbrands Inc.; *U.S. Public*, pg. 983
PLAYTEX MARKETING CORP.—See Edgewell Personal Care Company; *U.S. Public*, pg. 718
PLAYTEX PRODUCTS, LLC—See Edgewell Personal Care Company; *U.S. Public*, pg. 718
PLAYTIKA HOLDING CORP.; *Int'l*, pg. 5894
PLAYTIKA LTD.—See Playtika Holding Corp.; *Int'l*, pg. 5895
PLAY VISIONS, INC.; *U.S. Private*, pg. 3212
PLAYWAY SA; *Int'l*, pg. 5895
PLAYWIRE, LLC—See FreakOut Holdings, Inc.; *Int'l*, pg. 2767
PLAYWIRE MEDIA, LLC; *U.S. Private*, pg. 3212
PLAYWITH INC.; *Int'l*, pg. 5895
PLAYWIZE PLC; *Int'l*, pg. 5895
PLAYWORLD SYSTEMS, INC.—See Littlejohn & Co., LLC; *U.S. Private*, pg. 2471
PLAZA ADVISORS, INC.; *U.S. Private*, pg. 3212
PLAZA ANTOFAGASTA S.A.—See Falabella S.A.; *Int'l*, pg. 2610
PLAZA APPLIANCE MART INC.; *U.S. Private*, pg. 3212
PLAZA ASSET MANAGEMENT CO., LTD.—See Sumitomo Corporation; *Int'l*, pg. 7270
PLAZA AT NORTHWOOD, LLC—See Washington Prime Group Inc.; *U.S. Private*, pg. 4448
PLAZA BELMONT MANAGEMENT GROUP II LLC; *U.S. Private*, pg. 3212
PLAZA CENTERS N.V.; *Int'l*, pg. 5895
PLAZA CENTRAL DENTISTS PTY. LTD.—See BGH Capital Pty Ltd; *Int'l*, pg. 1007
PLAZA CENTRAL DENTISTS PTY. LTD.—See Ontario Teachers' Pension Plan; *Int'l*, pg. 5585
PLAZA CENTRES P.L.C.; *Int'l*, pg. 5895
THE PLAZA CLUB; *U.S. Private*, pg. 4096
PLAZA CREATE HONSHA CO., LTD.; *Int'l*, pg. 5895
PLAZA CREATE MOBILING CO., LTD.—See Plaza Create Honsha Co., Ltd.; *Int'l*, pg. 5895
PLAZA DEL TREBOL SPA—See Falabella S.A.; *Int'l*, pg. 2610
PLAZA FOOD SYSTEMS—See Plaza Provision Company; *U.S. Private*, pg. 3213
PLAZA FORD SALES LIMITED; *U.S. Private*, pg. 5895
THE PLAZA GROUP INC.; *U.S. Private*, pg. 4096
PLAZA GUARANTEE CO., LTD.—See Leopalace21 Corporation; *Int'l*, pg. 4465
PLAZA HEART CO., LTD.—See Plaza Create Honsha Co., Ltd.; *Int'l*, pg. 5895
PLAZA HOTEL & CASINO—See Tamares Group; *Int'l*, pg. 7449
PLAZA HOUSE INC.—See Grandy House Corporation; *Int'l*, pg. 3058
PLAZA INSURANCE COMPANY—See State Automobile Mutual Insurance Company; *U.S. Private*, pg. 3791
PLAZA KIA; *U.S. Private*, pg. 5895
PLAZA LINCOLN MERCURY INC.; *U.S. Private*, pg. 3212

PLAZA MAKOTI EQUITY ELEVATOR; *U.S. Private*, pg. 3212
PLAZAMEDIA GMBH—See Sport1 Medien AG; *Int'l*, pg. 7142
PLAZA MEDICAL CENTER OF FORT WORTH—See HCA Healthcare, Inc.; *U.S. Public*, pg. 1006
PLAZA MEDICAL SPECIALISTS, PLLC—See HCA Healthcare, Inc.; *U.S. Public*, pg. 1006
PLAZAMERICAS MALL TEXAS, LLC—See RAIT Financial Trust; *U.S. Private*, pg. 3349
PLAZA MOTORS COMPANY; *U.S. Private*, pg. 3213
PLAZA MOTORS OF BROOKLYN; *U.S. Private*, pg. 3213
PLAZA OESTE SPA—See Falabella S.A.; *Int'l*, pg. 2610
PLAZA PROPERTIES INC.; *U.S. Private*, pg. 3213
PLAZA PROVISION COMPANY; *U.S. Private*, pg. 3213
PLAZA RECOVERY, INC.—See Audax Group, Limited Partnership; *U.S. Private*, pg. 390
PLAZA RESORT CLUB INC.—See World Holdings Inc.; *U.S. Private*, pg. 4565
PLAZA RETAIL REIT; *Int'l*, pg. 5895
PLAZA SPECIALTY HOSPITAL, LLC—See HCA Healthcare, Inc.; *U.S. Public*, pg. 1006
PLAZASTYLE CORPORATION—See TBS Holdings, Inc.; *Int'l*, pg. 7481
PLAZA SURGERY CENTER II—See HCA Healthcare, Inc.; *U.S. Public*, pg. 1006
PLAZA SURGERY CENTER, LIMITED PARTNERSHIP—See Universal Health Services, Inc.; *U.S. Public*, pg. 2259
PLAZA SWEETS, INC.; *U.S. Private*, pg. 3213
PLAZA TIRE SERVICE INC.; *U.S. Private*, pg. 3213
PLAZA TOBALABA SPA—See Falabella S.A.; *Int'l*, pg. 2610
PLAZA TRANSPLANT CENTER, PLLC—See HCA Healthcare, Inc.; *U.S. Public*, pg. 1006
PLAZA TRAVEL, INC.—See BCD Holdings N.V.; *Int'l*, pg. 926
PLAZA VESPUCIO SPA—See Falabella S.A.; *Int'l*, pg. 2610
PLAZA WAREHOUSING & REALTY CORPORATION—See Plaza Provision Company; *U.S. Private*, pg. 3213
PLAZA WIRES LIMITED; *Int'l*, pg. 5895
PLAZE, INC.—See The Pritzker Group - Chicago, LLC; *U.S. Private*, pg. 4099
PLAZMAFERIS ALLOMAS NONPROFIT KFT.—See Kedrion S.p.A.; *Int'l*, pg. 4115
PLAZMASZOLGALAT KFT.—See Biotest AG; *Int'l*, pg. 1043
PLAZZA AG—See Bystronic AG; *Int'l*, pg. 1236
PLB ENGINEERING BERHAD; *Int'l*, pg. 5895
PL-BITUNOVA SP. Z O.O.—See STRABAG SE; *Int'l*, pg. 7231
PLBY GROUP, INC.; *U.S. Public*, pg. 1698
PLC ENTERPRISES INC.; *U.S. Private*, pg. 3213
PLC FINANCIAL SOLUTIONS LIMITED; *Int'l*, pg. 5895
PLC HOLDING CO.; *Int'l*, pg. 5895
PLC MEDICAL SYSTEMS, INC.; *U.S. Private*, pg. 3213
PLC S.P.A.; *Int'l*, pg. 5895
PLC S.P.A.; *Int'l*, pg. 5895
PLCS PLUS INTERNATIONAL, INC.; *U.S. Private*, pg. 3213
PLC TRENCHING CO., LLC.; *U.S. Private*, pg. 3213
PL CUSTOM BODY & EQUIPMENT CO.; *U.S. Private*, pg. 3194
PLC UUTECHNIC GROUP OYJ—See Lone Star Funds; *U.S. Private*, pg. 2486
PL DEVELOPMENT, INC. - LYNWOOD PLANT—See PL Development, Inc.; *U.S. Private*, pg. 3194
PL DEVELOPMENT, INC.; *U.S. Private*, pg. 3194
PLD FINLAND OY—See Addtech AB; *Int'l*, pg. 134
PLDT CLARK TELECOM, INC.—See PLDT Inc.; *Int'l*, pg. 5896
PLDT COMMUNICATIONS AND ENERGY VENTURES, INC.—See PLDT Inc.; *Int'l*, pg. 5896
PLDT INC.; *Int'l*, pg. 5895
PLDT-PHILCOM, INC.—See PLDT Inc.; *Int'l*, pg. 5896
PLDT SINGAPORE PTE LTD.—See PLDT Inc.; *Int'l*, pg. 5896
PLDT US—See PLDT Inc.; *Int'l*, pg. 5896
THE PLEASANT HILL BANK—See Goppert Financial Corp.; *U.S. Private*, pg. 1741
PLEASANT HILL GRAIN LLC; *U.S. Private*, pg. 3213
PLEASANT HOLIDAYS LLC; *U.S. Private*, pg. 3213
PLEASANT HOTELS INTERNATIONAL; *Int'l*, pg. 5896
PLEASANT MATTRESS CO., INC.; *U.S. Private*, pg. 3213
PLEASANT OAKS LANDFILL TX, LP—See Republic Services, Inc.; *U.S. Public*, pg. 1786
PLEASANTON DIAGNOSTIC IMAGING, INC.—See Tenet Healthcare Corporation; *U.S. Public*, pg. 2003
PLEASANT RIDGE MANOR; *U.S. Private*, pg. 3213
PLEASANT STREET APOTHECARY—See A C Center, Inc.; *U.S. Private*, pg. 18
PLEASANT STREET HOMES LLC; *U.S. Private*, pg. 3213
PLEASANT VALLEY HOSPITAL, INC.—See Cabell Huntington Hospital, Inc.; *U.S. Private*, pg. 710
PLEASANT VIEW RETIREMENT COMMUNITY; *U.S. Private*, pg. 3213
PLEASANTVILLE FORD INC.; *U.S. Private*, pg. 3213

COMPANY NAME INDEX

PLEAS A.S.—See GMM Capital LLC; *U.S. Private*, pg. 1722
PLEA SDN. BHD.—See FoundPac Group Berhad; *Int'l*, pg. 2754
PLEASS GLOBAL LTD.; *Int'l*, pg. 5896
PLEASURE CAST CO., LTD.—See BANDAI NAMCO Holdings Inc.; *Int'l*, pg. 829
PLEASURECRAFT ENGINE GROUP—See Correct Craft, Inc.; *U.S. Private*, pg. 1058
PLEASURELAND INCORPORATED; *U.S. Private*, pg. 3213
PLEASUREWOOD HILLS LTD—See Compagnie des Alpes S.A.; *Int'l*, pg. 1738
PLEATCO, LLC—See Align Capital Partners, LLC; *U.S. Private*, pg. 167
PLECIA CO., LTD.—See Air Water Inc.; *Int'l*, pg. 240
PLEDGED PROPERTY LLC—See Credit-Based Asset Servicing & Securitization LLC; *U.S. Private*, pg. 1092
PLEDGE PETROLEUM CORP.; *U.S. Private*, pg. 3213
PLEDOC GESELLSCHAFT FUR DOKUMENTATIONSERSTELLUNG UND -PFLEGE MBH—See British Columbia Investment Management Corp.; *Int'l*, pg. 1169
PLEDOC GESELLSCHAFT FUR DOKUMENTATIONSERSTELLUNG UND -PFLEGE MBH—See Macquarie Group Limited; *Int'l*, pg. 4626
PLEISSNER GUSS GMBH—See Georgsmarienhutte Holding GmbH; *Int'l*, pg. 2941
PLEJD AB; *Int'l*, pg. 5896
PLEK VOOR KINDEREN B.V.—See AcadeMedia AB; *Int'l*, pg. 77
PLEMET ENROBES SAS—See VINCI S.A.; *Int'l*, pg. 8225
P LEMMENS COMPANY S.A.—See Investment AB Latour; *Int'l*, pg. 3784
PL ENGINEERING LIMITED—See Punj Lloyd Ltd.; *Int'l*, pg. 6119
PLENITUDE BANGSAR RESIDENCES SDN BHD—See Plenitude Berhad; *Int'l*, pg. 5896
PLENITUDE BAYU SDN BHD—See Plenitude Berhad; *Int'l*, pg. 5896
PLENITUDE BERHAD; *Int'l*, pg. 5896
PLENITUDE BUILDERS SDN. BHD.—See Plenitude Berhad; *Int'l*, pg. 5896
PLENITUDE HEIGHTS SDN. BHD.—See Plenitude Berhad; *Int'l*, pg. 5896
PLENITUDE PERMAI SDN. BHD.—See Plenitude Berhad, *Int'l*, pg. 5896
PLENITUDE TEBRAU SDN. BHD.—See Plenitude Berhad; *Int'l*, pg. 5896
PLENO INTERNACIONAL, SPA—See Promotora de Informaciones S.A.; *Int'l*, pg. 5995
P & L ENTERPRISES OF NAPLES, INC.; *U.S. Private*, pg. 3058
PLENTEX LIMITED; *Int'l*, pg. 5897
PLENTI GROUP LTD.; *Int'l*, pg. 5897
PLENTY CO., LTD.; *Int'l*, pg. 5897
PLENTY ISLAND (THAI) CO., LTD.—See Aurotek Corporation; *Int'l*, pg. 714
PLENUM AG; *Int'l*, pg. 5897
PLENUM INTERNATIONAL MANAGEMENT CONSULTING GMBH—See Plenum AG; *Int'l*, pg. 5897
PLENUM MANAGEMENT CONSULTING GMBH—See Plenum AG; *Int'l*, pg. 5897
PLENUS AUST PTY. LTD.—See Plenus Company Limited; *Int'l*, pg. 5897
PLENUS COMPANY LIMITED; *Int'l*, pg. 5897
PLENUS GROUP INC.; *U.S. Private*, pg. 3213
PLENUS, INC.—See Plenus Company Limited; *Int'l*, pg. 5897
PLEON IMPACT—See Omnicom Group Inc.; *U.S. Public*, pg. 1576
PLE PIPELINE ENGINEERING GMBH—See E.ON SE; *Int'l*, pg. 2255
PLESK INTERNATIONAL GMBH—See Oakley Capital Limited; *Int'l*, pg. 5504
PLESO PRIJEVOZ D.O.O.—See Croatia Airlines d.d.; *Int'l*, pg. 1851
PLESSER HOLLAND ASSOCIATES; *U.S. Private*, pg. 3213
PLETHICO GLOBAL HOLDINGS BV—See Plethico Pharmaceuticals Ltd.; *Int'l*, pg. 5897
PLETHICO PHARMACEUTICALS LTD. - MANGLIA PLANT—See Plethico Pharmaceuticals Ltd.; *Int'l*, pg. 5897
PLETHICO PHARMACEUTICALS LTD.; *Int'l*, pg. 5897
PLETHORA SOLUTIONS HOLDINGS PLC—See Regent Pacific Group Limited; *Int'l*, pg. 6252
PLETHORA SOLUTIONS LIMITED—See Regent Pacific Group Limited; *Int'l*, pg. 6252
PLETTNER & BRECHT IMMOBILIEN GMBH—See Deutsche Grundstuecksauktionen AG; *Int'l*, pg. 2065
PLEUNE SERVICE COMPANY; *U.S. Private*, pg. 3214
PLEVEN-BT AD—See Bulgarian Investment Holding; *Int'l*, pg. 1213
PLEWS, INC.; *U.S. Private*, pg. 3214
PLEXBIO CO., LTD.; *Int'l*, pg. 5897
PLEXBOND QUIMICA S/A—See H.B. Fuller Company; *U.S. Public*, pg. 978
PLEX CO., LTD.—See BANDAI NAMCO Holdings Inc.; *Int'l*, pg. 829

PLEXENT; *U.S. Private*, pg. 3214
PLEXIAN AB; *Int'l*, pg. 5897
PLEXIS SERVICES INC.—See Japan Post Holdings Co., Ltd.; *Int'l*, pg. 3901
PLEX SYSTEMS, INC.—See Francisco Partners Management, LP; *U.S. Private*, pg. 1591
PLEXUS AEROSPACE, DEFENSE & SECURITY SERVICES, LLC—See Plexus Corp.; *U.S. Public*, pg. 1698
PLEXUS ASIA, LTD.—See Plexus Corp.; *U.S. Public*, pg. 1698
PLEXUS CAPITAL, LLC; *U.S. Private*, pg. 3214
PLEXUS CORP. LIMITED—See Plexus Corp.; *U.S. Public*, pg. 1698
PLEXUS CORP. SERVICES (UK) LIMITED—See Plexus Corp.; *U.S. Public*, pg. 1698
PLEXUS CORP.; *U.S. Public*, pg. 1698
PLEXUS CORP. (UK) LIMITED—See Plexus Corp.; *U.S. Public*, pg. 1698
PLEXUS COTTON LIMITED; *Int'l*, pg. 5897
PLEXUS DEUTSCHLAND GMBH—See Plexus Corp.; *U.S. Public*, pg. 1698
THE PLEXUS GROUPE, INC.; *U.S. Private*, pg. 4096
PLEXUS (HANGZHOU) CO., LTD.—See Plexus Corp.; *U.S. Public*, pg. 1698
PLEXUS HOLDINGS PLC; *Int'l*, pg. 5897
PLEXUS INTERNATIONAL SERVICES, INC.—See Plexus Corp.; *U.S. Public*, pg. 1698
PLEXUS MANUFACTURING SDN. BHD.—See Plexus Corp.; *U.S. Public*, pg. 1698
PLEXUS OCEAN SYSTEMS LIMITED—See Plexus Holdings PLC; *Int'l*, pg. 5897
PLEXUS OCEAN SYSTEMS (MALAYSIA) SDN BHD—See Plexus Holdings PLC; *Int'l*, pg. 5897
PLEXUS SCIENTIFIC CORPORATION; *U.S. Private*, pg. 3214
PLEXUS SERVICES CORP.—See Plexus Corp.; *U.S. Public*, pg. 1698
PLEXUS SERVICES RO S.R.L.—See Plexus Corp.; *U.S. Public*, pg. 1699
PLEXUS SERVICIOS S. DE R.L. DE C.V.—See Plexus Corp.; *U.S. Public*, pg. 1698
PLEXUS—See Plexus Corp.; *U.S. Public*, pg. 1698
PLEXUS (XIAMEN) CO., LTD.—See Plexus Corp.; *U.S. Public*, pg. 1698
PLEYADE PENINSULAR CORREDURIA DE SEGUROS DEL GRUPO TELEFONICA, S.A.—See Telefonica, S.A.; *Int'l*, pg. 7535
PLEZ U STORES INC.; *U.S. Private*, pg. 3214
PL FINLAND OY—See Proto Labs, Inc.; *U.S. Public*, pg. 1729
PLF INTERNATIONAL LIMITED—See John Bean Technologies Corporation; *U.S. Public*, pg. 1192
PLH GROUP, INC.—See Primoris Services Corporation; *U.S. Public*, pg. 1718
PLH PRODUCTS, INC.; *U.S. Private*, pg. 3214
PLIANT THERAPEUTICS, INC.; *U.S. Private*, pg. 1699
PLIBRICO CO. LLC; *U.S. Private*, pg. 3214
PLICO, INC.—See Berkshire Hathaway Inc.; *U.S. Public*, pg. 313
PLIM COOPERATION AG; *Int'l*, pg. 5897
PLIMPTON & HILLS CORPORATION; *U.S. Private*, pg. 3214
PLIMSOLL PRODUCTIONS LIMITED—See ITV plc; *Int'l*, pg. 3845
PL INDUSTRIES, LLC; *U.S. Private*, pg. 3194
PLIN SARAJEVO D.D.—See Messer Group GmbH; *Int'l*, pg. 4842
PLITEK, LLC; *U.S. Private*, pg. 3214
PLITRON MANUFACTURING INCORPORATED—See discoverIE Group plc; *Int'l*, pg. 2133
PLIVA CROATIA LTD.—See Teva Pharmaceutical Industries, Ltd.; *Int'l*, pg. 7579
PLIVA D.D.—See Teva Pharmaceutical Industries, Ltd.; *Int'l*, pg. 7579
PLIVA HRVATSKA D.O.O.—See Teva Pharmaceutical Industries, Ltd.; *Int'l*, pg. 7579
PLIVA, INC.—See Teva Pharmaceutical Industries, Ltd.; *Int'l*, pg. 7579
PLIVA LJUBLJANA D.O.O.—See Teva Pharmaceutical Industries, Ltd.; *Int'l*, pg. 7579
PLIXER INTERNATIONAL, INC.—See Battery Ventures, L.P.; *U.S. Private*, pg. 489
PLIXXENT GMBH & CO. KG—See Bayer Aktiengesellschaft; *Int'l*, pg. 907
PLJ INFORMATION SYSTEMS, INC.; *U.S. Private*, pg. 3214
PLLYPORE K.K.—See Asahi Kasei Corporation; *Int'l*, pg. 597
PL MANAGEMENT LTD—See Harrods Ltd.; *Int'l*, pg. 3279
PLM FLEET, LLC—See Mizuho Leasing Company, Limited; *Int'l*, pg. 4999
PLM JAPAN INC.—See Business Brain Showa-Ota Inc.; *Int'l*, pg. 1228
PLM OPERATIONS, LLC—See Wind Point Advisors LLC; *U.S. Private*, pg. 4536
PLM TRAILER LEASING—See Marubeni Corporation; *Int'l*, pg. 4707
PLN CONSTRUCTION LTD—See Punj Lloyd Ltd.; *Int'l*, pg. 6119

PLN CONTRACTING INC.; *U.S. Private*, pg. 3214
PLOCHMAN, INC.; *U.S. Private*, pg. 3214
PLOCKMATIC INTERNATIONAL AB—See Grimaldi Industri AB; *Int'l*, pg. 3086
PLOEGER AGRO B.V.—See Ploeger Machines B.V.; *Int'l*, pg. 5897
PLOEGER MACHINES B.V.; *Int'l*, pg. 5897
PLOIESTI SHOPPING CITY SRL—See NEPI Rockcastle N.V.; *Int'l*, pg. 5200
PLOMBCO INC.; *Int'l*, pg. 5897
PLOMIN HOLDING D.O.O.—See Hrvatska elektroprivreda d.d.; *Int'l*, pg. 3502
PLOOIJER ZAANDAM B.V.—See Indutrade AB; *Int'l*, pg. 3680
PLOTECH CO., LTD.; *Int'l*, pg. 5897
PLOTECH TECHNOLOGY (KUNSHAN) CO., LTD.—See Plotech Co., Ltd.; *Int'l*, pg. 5897
PLOTE CONSTRUCTION, INC.; *U.S. Private*, pg. 3214
PLOTINUS NYRT; *Int'l*, pg. 5897
PLOTUN D.O.O.—See Delivery Hero SE; *Int'l*, pg. 2013
PLOTWATT, INC.—See American Efficient LLC; *U.S. Private*, pg. 231
PLOVDIV TECH PARK AD; *Int'l*, pg. 5897
PLOVER BAY TECHNOLOGIES LIMITED; *Int'l*, pg. 5898
PLOW & HEARTH, LLC—See Evergreen Enterprises, Inc.; *U.S. Private*, pg. 1439
PL&P ADVERTISING; *U.S. Private*, pg. 3194
PLP ARGENTINA SRL—See Preformed Line Products Company; *U.S. Public*, pg. 1714
P.L. PORTER CONTROLS, INC.—See Crane NXT, Co.; *U.S. Public*, pg. 589
PLP PRODUTOS PARA LINHAS PROFORMADOS LTDA.—See Preformed Line Products Company; *U.S. Public*, pg. 1714
PLP RUSSIA LTD.—See Preformed Line Products Company; *U.S. Public*, pg. 1714
P & LS BETEILIGUNGS GMBH—See BWT Aktiengesellschaft; *Int'l*, pg. 1233
P & LS HOLDING GMBH—See BWT Aktiengesellschaft; *Int'l*, pg. 1233
PLS LOGISTICS SERVICES; *U.S. Private*, pg. 3214
PLS PACIFIC LASER SYSTEMS LLC—See Danaher Corporation; *U.S. Public*, pg. 629
PLS PLANTATIONS BERHAD; *Int'l*, pg. 5898
PLT CONSTRUCTION CO., INC.—See Construction Partners, Inc.; *U.S. Public*, pg. 572
P&L TECHNOLOGY, INC.—See Transom Capital Group, LLC; *U.S. Private*, pg. 4210
P&L TRANSPORTATION, INC.; *U.S. Private*, pg. 3059
PLUGG—See Andrew Sports Club Inc.; *U.S. Private*, pg. 280
PLUG-INS ELECTRONIX—See Al-Futtaim Private Company LLC; *Int'l*, pg. 285
PLUG POWER INC.; *U.S. Public*, pg. 1699
PLUGSURFING GMBH—See Corpay, Inc.; *U.S. Public*, pg. 580
PLUKON FOOD GROUP BV; *Int'l*, pg. 5898
PLUM ACQUISITION CORP. III; *U.S. Public*, pg. 1699
PLUMA FLEISCHWARENVERTRIEB GMBH—See What's Cooking Group NV; *Int'l*, pg. 8396
PLUMA NV—See What's Cooking Group NV; *Int'l*, pg. 8396
PLUMAS BANCORP; *U.S. Public*, pg. 1699
PLUMAS BANK—See Plumas Bancorp; *U.S. Public*, pg. 1699
PLUMBASE LTD.; *Int'l*, pg. 5898
PLUM BENEFITS, LLC—See Entertainment Benefits Group, LLC; *U.S. Private*, pg. 1404
PLUMBERS SUPPLY CO. INC.; *U.S. Private*, pg. 3214
PLUMBERS SUPPLY COMPANY; *U.S. Private*, pg. 3215
THE PLUMBERY INC.—See Slakey Brothers Inc.; *U.S. Private*, pg. 3687
PLUMBEX UK LTD.—See Norcros plc; *Int'l*, pg. 5415
PLUMBFAST CO., LTD.; *Int'l*, pg. 5898
PLUMB HOUSE INC.; *U.S. Private*, pg. 3214
PLUMB INC.; *U.S. Private*, pg. 3214
PLUMBING DISTRIBUTORS INC.; *U.S. Private*, pg. 3215
PLUMBING & DRAINAGE MERCHANTS LTD.—See Grafton Group plc; *Int'l*, pg. 3051
PLUMBING-HEATING-COOLING CONTRACTORS ASSOCIATION; *U.S. Private*, pg. 3215
PLUMBING & INDUSTRIAL SUPPLY CO.; *U.S. Private*, pg. 3215
PLUMBING N' THINGS, INC.—See Slakey Brothers Inc.; *U.S. Private*, pg. 3687
THE PLUMBING SOURCE, INC.—See Ferguson plc; *Int'l*, pg. 2638
PLUMBING SPECIALTIES & SUPPLIES, INC.—See Ferguson plc; *Int'l*, pg. 2638
PLUMBLINE LIFE SCIENCES, INC.; *Int'l*, pg. 5898
PLUMB LINE MECHANICAL, INC.; *U.S. Private*, pg. 3214
PLUMBLINE SUPPLIES LTD.—See Grafton Group plc; *Int'l*, pg. 3051
PLUMBLINK (SA) PROPRIETARY LIMITED—See The Bidvest Group Limited; *Int'l*, pg. 7626
PLUMBMASTER INC.—See Dunes Point Capital, LLC; *U.S. Private*, pg. 1289
PLUMB SHOP—See Masco Corporation; *U.S. Public*, pg. 1392

PLUMB LINE MECHANICAL, INC.
CORPORATE AFFILIATIONS

PLUMB SUPPLY COMPANY, INC.—See Templeton Coal Company, Inc.; *U.S. Private*, pg. 3963
PLUMCHOICE, INC.—See The Allstate Corporation; *U.S. Public*, pg. 2032
PLUM FINANCIAL SERVICES LIMITED—See Nippon Life Insurance Company; *Int'l*, pg. 5322
PLUMGOOD FOOD, LLC; *U.S. Private*, pg. 3215
THE PLUM GROUP, INC.—See Teleo Capital Management, LLC; *U.S. Private*, pg. 3961
PLUM GROVE PTY LTD.—See Seaboard Corporation; *U.S. Public*, pg. 1850
PLUM HEALTHCARE GROUP, LLC; *U.S. Private*, pg. 3214
PLUM LOGIC, LLC; *U.S. Private*, pg. 3214
PLUMMERS INC.; *U.S. Private*, pg. 3215
PLUMOR-NOVIMEX AG—See Pilot Corporation; *Int'l*, pg. 5867
PLUM, PBC—See Campbell Soup Company; *U.S. Public*, pg. 2427
PLUMROSE CARACAS C.A.—See EAC Invest AS; *Int'l*, pg. 2262
PLUMROSE LATINOAMERICANA C.A.—See EAC Invest AS; *Int'l*, pg. 2262
PLUMROSE USA INC.—See JBS S.A.; *Int'l*, pg. 3918
PLUM SOFTWARE LIMITED—See Praemium Limited; *Int'l*, pg. 5953
PLUMTREE GROUP LIMITED—See HgCapital Trust plc; *Int'l*, pg. 3378
PLUM UNDERWRITING LIMITED—See Brown & Brown, Inc.; *U.S. Public*, pg. 402
PLUNKETT HOMES PTY LTD—See JWH Group Pty Ltd; *Int'l*, pg. 4035
PLUNKETT & LYNCH ASSOCIATES; *U.S. Private*, pg. 3215
PLUNKETT OPTICAL, INC.—See EssilorLuxottica SA; *Int'l*, pg. 2514
PLUNKETT'S PEST CONTROL, INC.; *U.S. Private*, pg. 3215
PLURADENT AG & CO. KG—See Deutsche Mittelstandsholding GmbH; *Int'l*, pg. 2071
PLURAL ENTERTAINMENT PORTUGAL, S.A.—See Promotora de Informaciones S.A.; *Int'l*, pg. 5995
PLURAL GRAFICA E EDITORA LTDA—See Quad/Graphics, Inc.; *U.S. Public*, pg. 1744
PLURAL SERVICEPOOL GMBH—See Compass Group PLC; *Int'l*, pg. 1752
PLURALSIGHT, INC.; *U.S. Public*, pg. 1699
PLURALSIGHT, LLC—See Pluralsight, Inc.; *U.S. Public*, pg. 1699
PLUREL BV—See DEKRA e.V.; *Int'l*, pg. 2008
PLURIBUS CAPITAL MANAGEMENT LLC; *U.S. Private*, pg. 3215
PLURIBUS DIALISE - BENFICA, S.A.—See DaVita Inc.; *U.S. Public*, pg. 642
PLURIBUS DIALISE - CASCAIS, S.A.—See DaVita Inc.; *U.S. Public*, pg. 642
PLURIBUS DIALISE - SACAVEM, S.A.—See DaVita Inc.; *U.S. Public*, pg. 642
PLURIBUS INTERNATIONAL CORPORATION—See Amentum Services, Inc.; *U.S. Private*, pg. 219
PLURIBUS TECHNOLOGIES INC.; *Int'l*, pg. 5898
PLURICANAL SANTAREM TELEVISAO POR CABO, S.A.—See NOS SGPS, S.A.; *Int'l*, pg. 5448
PLURICO S.R.L.—See Vittoria Assicurazioni S.p.A.; *Int'l*, pg. 8264
PLURIDIS—See AXA S.A.; *Int'l*, pg. 754
PLURIFILTER D.O.O.—See Ingersoll Rand Inc.; *U.S. Public*, pg. 1122
PLURI INC.; *Int'l*, pg. 5898
PLURILOCK SECURITY, INC.; *Int'l*, pg. 5898
PLURIMARKETING (PORTUGAL)—See Teleperformance SE; *Int'l*, pg. 7540
PLURIMEDIA SA—See The European Metadata Group; *Int'l*, pg. 7641
PLURITEC LTD.; *Int'l*, pg. 5898
PLUS500UK LTD.; *Int'l*, pg. 5899
PLUS ALPHA CONSULTING CO., LTD.; *Int'l*, pg. 5898
PLUS A/S—See Maj Invest Holding A/S; *Int'l*, pg. 4653
PLUS BANK PJSC; *Int'l*, pg. 5898
PLUS CARGO SERVICE CO., LTD.—See PLUS Corporation; *Int'l*, pg. 5898
PLUS CHEMICALS S.A—See Teva Pharmaceutical Industries, Ltd.; *Int'l*, pg. 7580
PLUS CONSULTING LLC—See iVision Scale, LLC; *U.S. Private*, pg. 2151
PLUS CORPORATION; *Int'l*, pg. 5898
PLUS DELTA CONSULTING, LLC; *U.S. Private*, pg. 3215
PLUS EUROPE GMBH—See PLUS Corporation; *Int'l*, pg. 5898
PLUS FITNESS (NZ) LIMITED—See Viva Leisure Limited; *Int'l*, pg. 8264
PLUS FITNESS PTY. LIMITED—See Viva Leisure Limited; *Int'l*, pg. 8264
PLUSFOOD HOLLAND B.V.—See BRF S.A.; *Int'l*, pg. 1150
PLUSFOOD HUNGARY TRADE AND SERVICE LLC—See BRF S.A.; *Int'l*, pg. 1150
PLUSFOOD ITALY SRL—See BRF S.A.; *Int'l*, pg. 1150
PLUSFOOD UK LTD.—See BRF S.A.; *Int'l*, pg. 1151

PLUSFOOD WREXHAM LTD.—See BRF S.A.; *Int'l*, pg. 1151
PLUSFORTA GMBH—See Advent International Corporation; *U.S. Private*, pg. 97
PLUSFORTA GMBH—See Centerbridge Partners, L.P.; *U.S. Private*, pg. 813
PLUSGRADE PARENT L.P.—See General Atlantic Service Company, L.P.; *U.S. Private*, pg. 1663
PLUS GROUP HOLDINGS INC.; *Int'l*, pg. 5899
PLUS GROUP INC.; *U.S. Private*, pg. 3215
PLUSHCARE, INC.—See Accolade, Inc.; *U.S. Public*, pg. 33
PLUSH - THINK SOFAS PTY LTD—See Steinhoff International Holdings N.V.; *Int'l*, pg. 7194
PLUSINE SYSTEMS BV—See VINCI S.A.; *Int'l*, pg. 8225
PLUS KALYAN (MAURITIUS) PRIVATE LIMITED—See Khazanah Nasional Berhad; *Int'l*, pg. 4153
PLUS LIGHT TECH FZE—See Focus Lighting & Fixtures Limited; *Int'l*, pg. 2719
PLUS LOGISTICS CORP.—See PLUS Corporation; *Int'l*, pg. 5898
PLUS MALAYSIA BERHAD—See Khazanah Nasional Berhad; *Int'l*, pg. 4153
PLUS MARK LLC—See Clayton, Dubilier & Rice, LLC; *U.S. Private*, pg. 919
PLUS MOBILE COMMUNICATIONS CO., LTD.—See CYBIRD Holdings Co., Ltd.; *Int'l*, pg. 1894
PLUSNET INFRASTRUKTUR GMBH & CO. KG—See EnBW Energie Baden-Wurttemberg AG; *Int'l*, pg. 2399
PLUSNET PLC—See BT Group plc; *Int'l*, pg. 1203
PLUS ONE HEALTH MANAGEMENT, INC.; *U.S. Private*, pg. 3215
PLUSPACK S.A.—See KARATZIS S.A.; *Int'l*, pg. 4079
PLUSPETROL RESOURCES CORPORATION BV; *Int'l*, pg. 5899
PLUSPETROL S.A.—See Pluspetrol Resources Corporation BV; *Int'l*, pg. 5899
PLUSPETROL VENEZUELA S.A.—See Pluspetrol Resources Corporation BV; *Int'l*, pg. 5899
PLUS PHARMACIE SA—See PHOENIX Pharmahandel GmbH & Co. KG; *Int'l*, pg. 5854
PLUSPHARMA, INC.; *U.S. Private*, pg. 3215
PLUS PRODUCTS INC; *U.S. Public*, pg. 1699
PLUS PROPERTY COMPANY LIMITED—See Sansiri pcl; *Int'l*, pg. 6556
PLUS PROPERTY PARTNERS CO., LTD.—See Sansiri pcl; *Int'l*, pg. 6556
PLUS PROPERTY SPACE CO., LTD.—See Sansiri pcl; *Int'l*, pg. 6556
PLUS PROPERTY VENTURE COMPANY LIMITED—See Sansiri pcl; *Int'l*, pg. 6556
PLUS RELOCATION MORTGAGE, LLC—See Rithm Capital Corp.; *U.S. Public*, pg. 1800
PLUS RELOCATION SERVICES, INC.; *U.S. Private*, pg. 3215
PLUS STATIONERY SHANGHAI CO., LTD.—See PLUS Corporation; *Int'l*, pg. 5898
PLUSTECH INC.—See Yamazen Corporation; *Int'l*, pg. 8558
PLUS TECH INNOVATION PUBLIC COMPANY LIMITED—See T.K.S. Technologies Public Company Limited; *Int'l*, pg. 7397
PLUSTECH SINGAPORE PTE., LTD.—See Sodick Co., Ltd.; *Int'l*, pg. 7048
PLUS TEN STAINLESS, INC.—See O'Neal Industries, Inc.; *U.S. Private*, pg. 2979
PLUS THERAPEUTICS, INC.; *U.S. Public*, pg. 1699
PLUS VIETNAM INDUSTRIAL CO., LTD. - NHON TRACH FACTORY—See PLUS Corporation; *Int'l*, pg. 5898
PLUS VIETNAM INDUSTRIAL CO., LTD.—See PLUS Corporation; *Int'l*, pg. 5898
PLUS VISION CORP. OF JAPAN—See PLUS Corporation; *Int'l*, pg. 5898
PLUS VISON CORP. OF AMERICA—See PLUS Corporation; *Int'l*, pg. 5898
PLUTOLIFE AS—See Primary Opinion Limited; *Int'l*, pg. 5976
PLUTON BIOSCIENCES LLC; *U.S. Private*, pg. 3215
PLUTONIAN ACQUISITION CORP.; *U.S. Public*, pg. 1699
PLUTON RESOURCES LIMITED; *Int'l*, pg. 5899
PLUTORA, INC.—See TA Associates, Inc.; *U.S. Private*, pg. 3917
PLUTORA, INC.—See TPG Capital, L.P.; *U.S. Public*, pg. 2175
PLUTUS POWERGEN PLC; *Int'l*, pg. 5899
PLUZYNSKI/ASSOCIATES; *U.S. Private*, pg. 3215
PLX, INC.—See Edgewater Capital Partners, L.P.; *U.S. Private*, pg. 1335
PLX, INC.—See SK Capital Partners, LP; *U.S. Private*, pg. 3679
PLX OPCO INC.—See PLx Pharma Inc.; *U.S. Public*, pg. 1699
PLX PHARMA INC.; *U.S. Public*, pg. 1699
PLYCEM—See Grupo Empresarial Kaluz S.A. de C.V.; *Int'l*, pg. 3127
PLYCO CORPORATION; *U.S. Private*, pg. 3215
PLYCRETE, INC.; *Int'l*, pg. 5899
PLY GEM HOLDINGS, INC.—See Clayton, Dubilier & Rice, LLC; *U.S. Private*, pg. 921

PLY GEM INDUSTRIES, INC.—See Clayton, Dubilier & Rice, LLC; *U.S. Private*, pg. 921
PLY GEM PACIFIC WINDOWS CORPORATION—See Clayton, Dubilier & Rice, LLC; *U.S. Private*, pg. 921
PLYMKRAFT, INC.—See Unicord Corporation; *U.S. Private*, pg. 4282
PLYMOUTH CITY AIRPORT LIMITED—See Sutton Harbour Group PLC; *Int'l*, pg. 7347
PLYMOUTH CITYBUS LIMITED—See GLOBALVIA Inversiones, S.A.U.; *Int'l*, pg. 3005
PLYMOUTH CITYBUS LIMITED—See Kinetic Group Services Pty Ltd.; *Int'l*, pg. 4168
PLYMOUTH FISHERIES LIMITED—See Sutton Harbour Group PLC; *Int'l*, pg. 7347
PLYMOUTH FOAM, INC. - MINNESOTA—See Plymouth Foam Incorporated; *U.S. Private*, pg. 3216
PLYMOUTH FOAM INCORPORATED; *U.S. Private*, pg. 3215
PLYMOUTH HARBOR INC.; *U.S. Private*, pg. 3216
PLYMOUTH HEALTH—See CareNex Health Services; *U.S. Private*, pg. 753
PLYMOUTH INDUSTRIAL REIT, INC.; *U.S. Public*, pg. 1699
PLYMOUTH INDUSTRIES INC.—See Hines Corporation; *U.S. Private*, pg. 1949
THE PLYMOUTH NUFFIELD HOSPITAL—See Nuffield Health; *Int'l*, pg. 5488
PLYMOUTH PACKAGING, INC.—See WestRock Company; *U.S. Public*, pg. 2362
PLYMOUTH PARK TAX SERVICES LLC—See JPMorgan Chase & Co.; *U.S. Public*, pg. 1210
PLYMOUTH PHYSICAL THERAPY SPECIALISTS, LIMITED PARTNERSHIP—See U.S. Physical Therapy, Inc.; *U.S. Public*, pg. 2215
PLYMOUTH PLACE INC.; *U.S. Private*, pg. 3216
PLYMOUTH PRINTING CO. INC.; *U.S. Private*, pg. 3216
PLYMOUTH REALTY CAPITAL CORP.; *Int'l*, pg. 5899
PLYMOUTH ROCK ASSURANCE; *U.S. Private*, pg. 3216
THE PLYMOUTH ROCK CO.; *U.S. Private*, pg. 4096
PLYMOUTH ROCK MANAGEMENT COMPANY OF NEW JERSEY—See The Plymouth Rock Co.; *U.S. Private*, pg. 4097
PLYMOUTH RUBBER EUROPA, S.A.—See Talde Gestion, S.G.E.I.C., S.A; *Int'l*, pg. 7446
PLYMOUTH SPRING COMPANY, INC.—See Beijer Alma AB; *Int'l*, pg. 943
PLYMOUTH TUBE COMPANY - CHICAGO PROCESSING MILL—See Plymouth Tube Company; *U.S. Private*, pg. 3216
PLYMOUTH TUBE COMPANY - EAST TROY MILL—See Plymouth Tube Company; *U.S. Private*, pg. 3216
PLYMOUTH TUBE COMPANY - EUPORA MILL—See Plymouth Tube Company; *U.S. Private*, pg. 3216
PLYMOUTH TUBE COMPANY - HOPKINSVILLE MILL—See Plymouth Tube Company; *U.S. Private*, pg. 3216
PLYMOUTH TUBE COMPANY - SALISBURY MILL—See Plymouth Tube Company; *U.S. Private*, pg. 3216
PLYMOUTH TUBE COMPANY; *U.S. Private*, pg. 3216
PLYMOUTH TUBE COMPANY - STREATOR MILL—See Plymouth Tube Company; *U.S. Private*, pg. 3216
PLYMOUTH TUBE COMPANY - THE WINAMAC COLD DRAW MILL—See Plymouth Tube Company; *U.S. Private*, pg. 3216
PLYMOUTH TUBE COMPANY - TRENT MILL—See Plymouth Tube Company; *U.S. Private*, pg. 3216
PLYMOUTH TUBE COMPANY - WEST MONROE MILL—See Plymouth Tube Company; *U.S. Private*, pg. 3216
PLYTECH INTERNATIONAL LIMITED—See Big River Industries Limited; *Int'l*, pg. 1021
PLY-TRIM INC.; *U.S. Private*, pg. 3215
PLYWOOD & DOOR MANUFACTURERS; *U.S. Private*, pg. 3216
PLYWOOD & LUMBER SALES INCORPORATED; *U.S. Private*, pg. 3216
PLYZER TECHNOLOGIES INC.; *Int'l*, pg. 5899
PLZ CORP.—See The Pritzker Group - Chicago, LLC; *U.S. Private*, pg. 4099
PLZENSKA ENERGETIKA A.S.—See Energeticky a Prumyslovy Holding, a.s.; *Int'l*, pg. 2420
PLZENSKE STERKOPISKY S.R.O.—See Heidelberg Materials AG; *Int'l*, pg. 3319
PLZENSKY PRAZDROJ A.S.—See Asahi Group Holdings Ltd.; *Int'l*, pg. 594
PLZENSKY PRAZDROJ SLOVENSKO, A.S.—See Asahi Group Holdings Ltd.; *Int'l*, pg. 594
PM2 BUILDING SYSTEM SDN. BHD.—See Pasona Metro Holdings Bhd; *Int'l*, pg. 5822
PMA COMPANIES, INC.—See Old Republic International Corporation; *U.S. Public*, pg. 1568
PM ADVERTISING; *U.S. Private*, pg. 3216
PM ADVERTISING—See PM Advertising; *U.S. Private*, pg. 3216
PMA FINANCIAL NETWORK, LLC; *U.S. Private*, pg. 3217
PMA INDUSTRIES—See Ancor Holdings, L.P.; *U.S. Private*, pg. 275
PMALLIANCE, INC.; *U.S. Private*, pg. 3217

COMPANY NAME INDEX

PMA MANAGEMENT CORPORATION OF NEW ENGLAND—See Old Republic International Corporation; *U.S. Public*, pg. 1568
PMA MANAGEMENT CORP.—See Old Republic International Corporation; *U.S. Public*, pg. 1568
PM ARGENTINA SISTEMAS DE ELEVACION S.A.—See Manitex International, Inc.; *U.S. Public*, pg. 1356
PMB ALUMINIUM SABAH SDN. BHD.—See Press Metal Aluminium Holdings Bhd; *Int'l*, pg. 5965
PMB CENTRAL SDN. BHD.—See PMB Technology Berhad; *Int'l*, pg. 5899
PMB-CYBERWALL LIMITED—See PMB Technology Berhad; *Int'l*, pg. 5900
PMB EASTERN SDN. BHD.—See PMB Technology Berhad; *Int'l*, pg. 5899
PMB FACADE TECHNOLOGY SDN. BHD.—See PMB Technology Berhad; *Int'l*, pg. 5900
PMB NORTHERN SDN. BHD.—See PMB Technology Berhad; *Int'l*, pg. 5899
PMB QUICK ACCESS SDN. BHD.—See PMB Technology Berhad; *Int'l*, pg. 5899
PMB REAL ESTATE SERVICES LLC—See Ventas, Inc.; *U.S. Public*, pg. 2278
PMB TECHNOLOGY BERHAD; *Int'l*, pg. 5899
PMB-UVA INTERNATIONAL BV—See VDL Groep B.V.; *Int'l*, pg. 8140
PM CABIN MANUFACTURING CO., LTD.—See Press Kogyo Co., Ltd.; *Int'l*, pg. 5964
PMC ACQUISITION COMPANY, INC.—See NN, Inc.; *U.S. Public*, pg. 1531
PM CAPITAL ASIAN OPPORTUNITIES FUND LIMITED; *Int'l*, pg. 5899
PM CAPITAL GLOBAL OPPORTUNITIES FUND LIMITED; *Int'l*, pg. 5899
PM CARE SDN. BHD.—See Sumitomo Corporation; *Int'l*, pg. 7269
PMC BEIJING—See PMC Communications Co., Ltd.; *Int'l*, pg. 5900
PMC BIOGENIX, INC.—See PMC Group, Inc.; *U.S. Private*, pg. 3218
PMC BIOGENIX KOREA LTD.—See PMC Group, Inc.; *U.S. Private*, pg. 3218
PMC CAPITAL PARTNERS, LLC; *U.S. Private*, pg. 3217
PMC-COLINET, INC.—See Park-Ohio Holdings Corp.; *U.S. Public*, pg. 1639
PMC CO., LTD.—See CDS Co., Ltd.; *Int'l*, pg. 1371
PMC COMMUNICATIONS CO., LTD.; *Int'l*, pg. 5900
PMC CYLINDERS OY—See Nordstjernan AB; *Int'l*, pg. 5424
PM CENTER CO., LTD.—See CMO Public Company Limited; *Int'l*, pg. 1671
PMC ESPO, LLC—See OAO AK Transneft; *Int'l*, pg. 5505
PMC FINANCIAL SERVICE GROUP LLC—See PMC Capital Partners, LLC; *U.S. Private*, pg. 3217
PMC FINCORP LIMITED; *Int'l*, pg. 5900
PMC GROUP - CINCINNATI—See PMC Group, Inc.; *U.S. Private*, pg. 3218
PMC GROUP, INC.; *U.S. Private*, pg. 3218
PM CHILE S.P.A.—See Manitex International, Inc.; *U.S. Public*, pg. 1356
PMC HOMES CORPORATION; *U.S. Private*, pg. 3218
PMC HONG KONG—See PMC Communications Co., Ltd.; *Int'l*, pg. 5900
PMC HYDRAULICS AB—See Nordstjernan AB; *Int'l*, pg. 5424
PMC HYDRAULICS GROUP AB—See Nordstjernan AB; *Int'l*, pg. 5424
PMC HYDRAULICS LLC—See Nordstjernan AB; *Int'l*, pg. 5424
PMC HYDRAULICS OY—See Nordstjernan AB; *Int'l*, pg. 5424
PMC HYDRAULIKA SP.Z O.O.—See Nordstjernan AB; *Int'l*, pg. 5425
PMC, INC.—See PMC Capital Partners, LLC; *U.S. Private*, pg. 3217
PMC INDUSTRIES INC.—See Park-Ohio Holdings Corp.; *U.S. Public*, pg. 1639
PMC LABEL MATERIALS CO., LTD.—See Selic Corp PCL; *Int'l*, pg. 6701
PMC LABEL MATERIALS (MALAYSIA) SDN. BHD.—See Selic Corp PCL; *Int'l*, pg. 6701
PMC LABEL MATERIALS PTE. LTD.—See Selic Corp PCL; *Int'l*, pg. 6701
PM COMPANY LLC; *U.S. Private*, pg. 3216
PM CONSTRUCTION CO. INC.; *U.S. Private*, pg. 3216
PM CONSTRUCTION—See J.F. Lehman & Company, Inc.; *U.S. Private*, pg. 2163
PM CONTROL SYSTEMS (AUST) PTY. LTD.—See Woodward, Inc.; *U.S. Public*, pg. 2377
PM CONTROL SYSTEMS (INDIA) PRIVATE LTD.—See Woodward, Inc.; *U.S. Public*, pg. 2377
PM CONTROL SYSTEMS PTE. LTD.—See Woodward, Inc.; *U.S. Public*, pg. 2377
PMC ORGANOMETALLIX, INC.—See PMC Group, Inc.; *U.S. Private*, pg. 3218
PMC PERFORMANCE MATERIALS (GUANGZHOU) LTD.—See Toray Industries, Inc.; *Int'l*, pg. 7823
PMC PHARMACY INC.—See Portage Pharma Ltd.; *U.S. Private*, pg. 3231

PMC PHYSICIAN NETWORK, L.L.C.—See Tenet Healthcare Corporation; *U.S. Public*, pg. 2008
PMC POLARTEKNIK AS—See Nordstjernan AB; *Int'l*, pg. 5424
PMC QINGDAO CO. LTD.—See Nordstjernan AB; *Int'l*, pg. 5425
PMC RUBBER CHEMICALS INDIA PRIVATE LIMITED—See PMC Group, Inc.; *U.S. Private*, pg. 3218
PMC SCIENCE-TECH INDUSTRIES (NANJING) CO LTD—See PMC Capital Partners, LLC; *U.S. Private*, pg. 3217
PMC SHANGHAI—See PMC Communications Co., Ltd.; *Int'l*, pg. 5900
PMCS. HELPLINE SOFTWARE S.L.—See Serviceware SE; *Int'l*, pg. 6726
PMC SMART SOLUTIONS, LLC; *U.S. Private*, pg. 3218
PMC SPECIALTIES GROUP, CO., INC.—See PMC Capital Partners, LLC; *U.S. Private*, pg. 3217
PMC SPECIALTIES GROUP, INC.—See PMC Capital Partners, LLC; *U.S. Private*, pg. 3217
PMC SPECIALTY LEADERS IN CHEMICALS, INC.—See PMC Capital Partners, LLC; *U.S. Private*, pg. 3217
PMC TECHNOLOGY A/S—See Segulah Advisor AB; *Int'l*, pg. 6684
PMC WINSTAR HYDRAULICS PVT. LTD.—See Nordstjernan AB; *Int'l*, pg. 5425
PMD ACADEMY CORP; *Int'l*, pg. 5900
PM DATA SDN BHD.—See Powermatic Data Systems Limited; *Int'l*, pg. 5947
PMDCA, LLC—See The Ensign Group, Inc.; *U.S. Public*, pg. 3217
PMD PROPERTIES, LLC—See Laboratory Corporation of America Holdings; *U.S. Public*, pg. 1287
PMDSOFT INC.; *U.S. Private*, pg. 3218
PME AFRICAN INFRASTRUCTURE OPPORTUNITIES PLC; *Int'l*, pg. 5900
P.MEIDELL AS—See Quaser Machine Tools, Inc.; *Int'l*, pg. 6157
PM&E, INC.; *Int'l*, pg. 5899
PM ENGINEERING SRL; *Int'l*, pg. 5899
PME PROJEKMANAGEMENT & ENGINEERING GMBH—See Stadtwerke Hannover AG; *Int'l*, pg. 7161
PM EQUIPMENT TRADING FZE—See Manitex International, Inc.; *U.S. Public*, pg. 1356
PM EQUITY PARTNER SARL—See Philip Morris International Inc.; *U.S. Public*, pg. 1685
PME S.A.; *Int'l*, pg. 5900
PMFG, INC.—See CECO Environmental Corp.; *U.S. Public*, pg. 464
P.M. FOOD CO., LTD.—See Premier Marketing Public Company Limited; *Int'l*, pg. 5960
PM FOODS INC.—See CrossAmerica Partners LP; *U.S. Public*, pg. 596
PM FRANCHISING, LLC—See Fog Cutter Capital Group Inc.; *U.S. Private*, pg. 1557
PMGC TECHNOLOGY GROUP LIMITED; *Int'l*, pg. 5900
PMG WORLDWIDE INC.; *U.S. Private*, pg. 3218
PMG WORLDWIDE LLC; *U.S. Private*, pg. 3218
PMHCC INC; *U.S. Private*, pg. 3218
PMH DRUCKLUFT GMBH—See Atlas Copco AB; *Int'l*, pg. 684
PMH INTERNATIONAL AB—See Indutrade AB; *Int'l*, pg. 3680
PM HOSPITALITY STRATEGIES, INC.—See The Buccini/Pollin Group, Inc.; *U.S. Private*, pg. 4002
P.M.I. COMERCIO INTERNACIONAL, S.A. DE C.V.—See Petroleos Mexicanos; *Int'l*, pg. 5828
PMI GLOBAL SERVICES, INC.—See Philip Morris International Inc.; *U.S. Public*, pg. 1685
PMI HEALTH GROUP LIMITED—See Willis Towers Watson Public Limited Company; *Int'l*, pg. 8414
P.M.I. HOLDINGS PETROLEOS ESPANA, S.L.—See Petroleos Mexicanos; *Int'l*, pg. 5828
PMI INDUSTRIES, INC.—See BAM Enterprises, Inc.; *U.S. Public*, pg. 463
PMI LUBRICANTS, INC.; *U.S. Private*, pg. 3218
PM INTERNATIONAL B.V.—See Phoenix Mecano AG; *Int'l*, pg. 5852
PMI OPERATING COMPANY, LTD.—See DXP Enterprises, Inc.; *U.S. Public*, pg. 697
PMI SERVICE CENTER EUROPE SPOLKA Z OGRANICZONA ODPOWIEDZIALNOSCIA—See Philip Morris International Inc.; *U.S. Public*, pg. 1685
P.M.I. SERVICES NORTH AMERICA, INC.—See Petroleos Mexicanos; *Int'l*, pg. 5828
P.M.I. TRADING LIMITED—See Petroleos Mexicanos; *Int'l*, pg. 5828
PMK-BNC, INC.—See The Interpublic Group of Companies, Inc.; *U.S. Public*, pg. 2103
PMK*BNC—See The Interpublic Group of Companies, Inc.; *U.S. Public*, pg. 2102
PMK*BNC—See The Interpublic Group of Companies, Inc.; *U.S. Public*, pg. 2102
PM KOMPONENTEN B.V.—See Phoenix Mecano AG; *Int'l*, pg. 5852
PM KOMPONENTEN N.V.—See Phoenix Mecano AG; *Int'l*, pg. 5852

PMX COMMUNITIES, INC.

PM LINK PTE LTD—See China Architecture Design & Research Group; *Int'l*, pg. 1483
PML SERVICES LLC—See InterContinental Hotels Group PLC; *Int'l*, pg. 3738
PM MACKAY GROUP; *U.S. Private*, pg. 3216
PM & M ELECTRIC, INC.; *U.S. Private*, pg. 3216
PMM, INC.—See HCA Healthcare, Inc.; *U.S. Public*, pg. 1005
PMOA, INC.—See Stone Point Capital LLC; *U.S. Private*, pg. 3824
PMOD TECHNOLOGIES LLC—See Bruker Corporation; *U.S. Public*, pg. 407
PM OIL & STEEL IBERICA S.L.—See Manitex International, Inc.; *U.S. Public*, pg. 1356
PM OIL & STEEL S.P.A.—See Manitex International, Inc.; *U.S. Public*, pg. 1356
PMOLINK LLC; *U.S. Private*, pg. 3218
PMO SERVICES, SA—See PTT Public Company Limited; *Int'l*, pg. 6092
PM PARTIES INC.; *U.S. Private*, pg. 3216
PMP AUTO COMPONENTS PVT. LTD.—See Ashok Piramal Group; *Int'l*, pg. 608
PMP DISTRIBUTION—See IVE Group Limited; *Int'l*, pg. 3847
PM PEDIATRICS; *U.S. Private*, pg. 3216
PMP FERMENTATION PRODUCTS, INC.—See Fuso Chemical Co., Ltd.; *Int'l*, pg. 2850
PMPG POLSKIE MEDIA S.A.; *Int'l*, pg. 5900
PMPKONMET SP. Z O.O.—See Valmet Oyj; *Int'l*, pg. 8119
PMP MAXUM—See IVE Group Limited; *Int'l*, pg. 3847
PMP MICROMARKETING—See IVE Group Limited; *Int'l*, pg. 3847
PMP (NZ) LIMITED—See IVE Group Limited; *Int'l*, pg. 3847
PMP PRINT—See IVE Group Limited; *Int'l*, pg. 3847
PM PROPERTIES INC.—See CrossAmerica Partners LP; *U.S. Public*, pg. 596
PM PUBLICIDAD; *U.S. Private*, pg. 3216
P&M QUALITY SMALLGOODS PTY LTD.—See JBS S.A.; *Int'l*, pg. 3918
PM REALTY GROUP LP; *U.S. Private*, pg. 3217
PM RECOVERY INCORPORATED; *U.S. Private*, pg. 3217
PM RETAIL AS—See FSN Capital Partners AS; *Int'l*, pg. 2799
PMS-BERCHEM GMBH—See KSB SE & Co. KGaA; *Int'l*, pg. 4313
PMSE CO., LTD.—See Premier Marketing Public Company Limited; *Int'l*, pg. 5960
PM SECURITIES SDN BHD—See Pan Malaysian Industries Berhad; *Int'l*, pg. 5715
PMS ELEKTRO- UND AUTOMATIONSTECHNIK GMBH—See Christof Holding AG; *Int'l*, pg. 1587
PM SERVICES COMPANY; *U.S. Private*, pg. 3217
PMSI, LLC—See UnitedHealth Group Incorporated; *U.S. Public*, pg. 2249
PMSLIC INSURANCE COMPANY—See ProAssurance Corporation; *U.S. Public*, pg. 1723
PMS MARKETING SDN. BHD.—See Press Metal Aluminium Holdings Bhd; *Int'l*, pg. 5965
P&M SOLUTIONS, LLC; *U.S. Private*, pg. 3059
PM SPECIAL MEASURING SYSTEMS B.V.—See Phoenix Mecano AG; *Int'l*, pg. 5852
PMS PUMPEN- UND MOTOREN SERVICE GMBH—See KSB SE & Co. KGaA; *Int'l*, pg. 4313
PMSQUARE LLC; *U.S. Private*, pg. 3218
PMSR ELECTRO SI AUTOMATIZARE S.R.L.—See Christof Holding AG; *Int'l*, pg. 1587
PMS S.A.—See Petros Petropoulos S.A.; *Int'l*, pg. 5832
PM TECHNOLOGIES; *U.S. Private*, pg. 3217
P. M. TELELINNKS LTD.; *Int'l*, pg. 5682
PM TERMINALS, INC.—See CrossAmerica Partners LP; *U.S. Public*, pg. 596
PMT GROUP INC; *U.S. Private*, pg. 3219
PM THORESEN ASIA HOLDINGS PUBLIC COMPANY LIMITED—See Thoresen Thai Agencies Public Company Limited; *Int'l*, pg. 7718
P.M.T. INC.—See Piolax Inc.; *Int'l*, pg. 5871
PMT INDUSTRIES SDN. BHD.—See Wah Seong Corporation Berhad; *Int'l*, pg. 8329
PMT PHOENIX INDUSTRIES SDN. BHD.—See Wah Seong Corporation Berhad; *Int'l*, pg. 8330
P.M. TSERIOTIS LTD.; *Int'l*, pg. 5900
PMV AUTOMATION AB—See Flowserve Corporation; *U.S. Public*, pg. 857
PMV CONSUMER ACQUISITION CORP.; *U.S. Public*, pg. 1700
PMV PHARMACEUTICALS, INC.; *U.S. Public*, pg. 1700
PMX COMMUNITIES, INC.; *U.S. Private*, pg. 3219
PMX INDUSTRIES, INC.—See Poongsan Holdings Corporation; *Int'l*, pg. 5920
PNA HOLDINGS MEXICO S.A. DE C.V.—See General Plastic Industrial Co., Ltd.; *Int'l*, pg. 2919
PNB ASSET MANAGEMENT (JAPAN) CO LTD—See Permodalan Nasional Berhad; *Int'l*, pg. 5809
PNB CAPITAL & INVESTMENT CORPORATION—See Philippine National Bank; *Int'l*, pg. 5845
PNB CORPORATION—See Philippine National Bank; *Int'l*, pg. 5845

PNB EQUITY RESOURCE CORPORATION SDN. BHD.—See Permodalan Nasional Berhad; *Int'l*, pg. 5809
PNB EUROPE PLC—See Philippine National Bank; *Int'l*, pg. 5845
PNB FOREX, INCORPORATED—See Philippine National Bank; *Int'l*, pg. 5845
PNB GILTS LTD.—See Punjab National Bank; *Int'l*, pg. 6120
PNB GLOBAL REMITTANCE & FINANCIAL COMPANY (HK) LIMITED—See Philippine National Bank; *Int'l*, pg. 5845
PNB HOLDINGS CORPORATION—See Philippine National Bank; *Int'l*, pg. 5845
PNB HOUSING FINANCE LTD.—See Punjab National Bank; *Int'l*, pg. 6120
PNB-IBJL EQUIPMENT RENTALS CORPORATION—See Philippine National Bank; *Int'l*, pg. 5845
PNB INTERNATIONAL INVESTMENTS CORPORATION—See Philippine National Bank; *Int'l*, pg. 5845
PNB INTERNATIONAL LTD—See Punjab National Bank; *Int'l*, pg. 6120
PNB INVESTMENT INSTITUTE SDN. BERHAD—See Permodalan Nasional Berhad; *Int'l*, pg. 5809
PNB INVESTMENT SERVICES LTD—See Punjab National Bank; *Int'l*, pg. 6120
PNB MANAGEMENT SERVICES SDN. BERHAD—See Permodalan Nasional Berhad; *Int'l*, pg. 5809
PNB MERDEKA VENTURES SDN BHD—See Permodalan Nasional Berhad; *Int'l*, pg. 5809
PNB METLIFE INDIA INSURANCE COMPANY LIMITED—See MetLife, Inc.; *U.S. Public*, pg. 1431
PNB-MIZUHO EQUIPMENT RENTALS CORPORATION—See Philippine National Bank; *Int'l*, pg. 5845
PNB-MIZUHO LEASING & FINANCE CORPORATION—See Mizuho Leasing Company, Limited; *Int'l*, pg. 4999
PNB NJI HOLDINGS SDN. BERHAD—See Permodalan Nasional Berhad; *Int'l*, pg. 5809
PNB NOMURA JAFCO MANAGEMENT SDN. BERHAD—See Permodalan Nasional Berhad; *Int'l*, pg. 5809
PNB PROPERTY MANAGEMENT SDN. BERHAD—See Permodalan Nasional Berhad; *Int'l*, pg. 5809
PNB RCI HOLDING CO., LTD.—See Philippine National Bank; *Int'l*, pg. 5845
PNB REMITTANCE CENTERS, INC.—See Philippine National Bank; *Int'l*, pg. 5845
PNB REMITTANCE CO.—See Philippine National Bank; *Int'l*, pg. 5845
PNB SECURITIES INC.—See Philippine National Bank; *Int'l*, pg. 5845
PNB (UK) LIMITED—See Permodalan Nasional Berhad; *Int'l*, pg. 5809
PNC BANCORP, INC.—See The PNC Financial Services Group, Inc.; *U.S. Public*, pg. 2119
PNC BANK, CENTRAL PENNSYLVANIA—See The PNC Financial Services Group, Inc.; *U.S. Public*, pg. 2119
PNC BANK, GREATER MARYLAND—See The PNC Financial Services Group, Inc.; *U.S. Public*, pg. 2119
PNC BANK, GREATER WASHINGTON, D.C. AREA—See The PNC Financial Services Group, Inc.; *U.S. Public*, pg. 2119
PNC BANK, KENTUCKY & INDIANA—See The PNC Financial Services Group, Inc.; *U.S. Public*, pg. 2119
PNC BANK, NATIONAL ASSOCIATION—See The PNC Financial Services Group, Inc.; *U.S. Public*, pg. 2119
PNC BANK, NORTHEAST PENNSYLVANIA—See The PNC Financial Services Group, Inc.; *U.S. Public*, pg. 2119
PNC BANK, NORTHWEST PENNSYLVANIA—See The PNC Financial Services Group, Inc.; *U.S. Public*, pg. 2119
PNC BANK, OHIO & NORTHERN KENTUCKY—See The PNC Financial Services Group, Inc.; *U.S. Public*, pg. 2119
PNC BANK, PHILADELPHIA & SOUTHERN NEW JERSEY—See The PNC Financial Services Group, Inc.; *U.S. Public*, pg. 2119
PNC BANK—See The PNC Financial Services Group, Inc.; *U.S. Public*, pg. 2119
PNC CAPITAL ADVISORS, LLC—See The PNC Financial Services Group, Inc.; *U.S. Public*, pg. 2119
PNC CAPITAL FINANCE, LLC—See The PNC Financial Services Group, Inc.; *U.S. Public*, pg. 2119
PNC CAPITAL MARKETS LLC—See The PNC Financial Services Group, Inc.; *U.S. Public*, pg. 2120
PNC COMMERCIAL CORPORATION—See The PNC Financial Services Group, Inc.; *U.S. Public*, pg. 2120
PNC COMMUNITY DEVELOPMENT CORP.—See The PNC Financial Services Group, Inc.; *U.S. Public*, pg. 2120
PNC DELAWARE TRUST COMPANY—See The PNC Financial Services Group, Inc.; *U.S. Public*, pg. 2119
PNC DELHI INDUSTRIALINFRA PRIVATE LIMITED—See PNC Infratech Limited; *Int'l*, pg. 5900

THE PNC FINANCIAL SERVICES GROUP, INC.; *U.S. Public*, pg. 2118
PNC INFRATECH LIMITED; *Int'l*, pg. 5900
PNC INVESTMENT CORP.—See The PNC Financial Services Group, Inc.; *U.S. Public*, pg. 2120
PNC LEASING LLC—See The PNC Financial Services Group, Inc.; *U.S. Public*, pg. 2120
PNC LIFE INSURANCE COMPANY—See The PNC Financial Services Group, Inc.; *U.S. Public*, pg. 2120
PNC NORGE AS—See PORR AG; *Int'l*, pg. 5923
P&N COAL CO. INC.; *U.S. Public*, pg. 3059
PNC PROCESS SYSTEMS CO LTD; *Int'l*, pg. 5900
PNC REALTY SERVICES—See The PNC Financial Services Group, Inc.; *U.S. Public*, pg. 2120
PNC RIVERARCH CAPITAL—See The PNC Financial Services Group, Inc.; *U.S. Public*, pg. 2119
PNC TECH CO LTD; *Int'l*, pg. 5900
PNE AG; *Int'l*, pg. 5900
PNE BENELUX BV—See Print N Etch Pte. Ltd.; *Int'l*, pg. 5981
PNE BIOGAS OHRETAL GMBH—See Enovos International S.A.; *Int'l*, pg. 2444
PNE ELECTRIC SDN BHD—See Print N Etch Pte. Ltd.; *Int'l*, pg. 5981
PNE ELECTRONICS (DONG GUAN) CORPORATION LIMITED—See PNE PCB Berhad; *Int'l*, pg. 5901
PNE INDUSTRIES LTD—See Print N Etch Pte. Ltd.; *Int'l*, pg. 5981
PNE INTERNATIONAL LLC—See Print N Etch Pte. Ltd.; *Int'l*, pg. 5981
PNE MICRON ENGINEERING PTE LTD—See Print N Etch Pte. Ltd.; *Int'l*, pg. 5981
PNE MICRON ENGINEERING SDN BHD—See Print N Etch Pte. Ltd.; *Int'l*, pg. 5981
PNE MICRON (KUALA LUMPUR) SDN BHD—See Print N Etch Pte. Ltd.; *Int'l*, pg. 5981
PNEO LLC; *U.S. Private*, pg. 3219
PNE PCB BERHAD; *Int'l*, pg. 5901
PNE PCB PTE. LTD.—See PNE PCB Berhad; *Int'l*, pg. 5901
PNE PRECISION SDN BHD—See Print N Etch Pte. Ltd.; *Int'l*, pg. 5981
PNE SVERIGE AB—See PNE AG; *Int'l*, pg. 5900
PNE SYSTEMS CO., LTD.—See Wonik Corporation; *Int'l*, pg. 8448
PNE SYSTEMS SDN BHD—See Print N Etch Pte. Ltd.; *Int'l*, pg. 5981
PNE TRANSLITE PTE LTD—See Print N Etch Pte. Ltd.; *Int'l*, pg. 5981
PNEUDRAULICS, INC.—See TransDigm Group Incorporated; *U.S. Public*, pg. 2183
PNEU-FORCE—See Penn-Air & Hydraulics Corp.; *U.S. Private*, pg. 3135
PNEU LAURENT S.N.C—See Compagnie Generale des Etablissements Michelin SCA; *Int'l*, pg. 1745
PNEUMADYNE, INC.—See IMI plc; *Int'l*, pg. 3624
PNEUMAFIL CORPORATION—See Nederman Holding AB; *Int'l*, pg. 5188
PNEUMATIC PRODUCTS CORP.—See SPX Technologies, Inc.; *U.S. Public*, pg. 1921
PNEUMATICSCALEANGELUS—See Barry-Wehmiller Companies, Inc.; *U.S. Private*, pg. 482
PNEUMATICSCALEANGELUS—See Barry-Wehmiller Companies, Inc.; *U.S. Private*, pg. 482
PNEUMATIC SCALE CORPORATION—See Barry-Wehmiller Companies, Inc.; *U.S. Private*, pg. 482
PNEUMATIQUES KLEBER S.A—See Compagnie Generale des Etablissements Michelin SCA; *Int'l*, pg. 1745
PNEUMAX CO. LTD—See Atlas Copco AB; *Int'l*, pg. 684
PNEUMAX SOUTHERN AFRICA (PTY) LIMITED—See Set Point Group Limited; *Int'l*, pg. 6730
PNEU-MECH SYSTEMS MFG. LLC; *U.S. Private*, pg. 3219
PNEUMEC KONTROLLS PRIVATE LIMITED—See Convum Ltd.; *Int'l*, pg. 1788
PNEUMOTEC CORP.—See SMC Corporation; *Int'l*, pg. 7003
PNEURON CORP.—See UST Global Inc.; *U.S. Private*, pg. 4324
PNEUSMARKET S.P.A.—See Marangoni S.p.A.; *Int'l*, pg. 4688
PNEUS PIRELLI SAS—See China National Chemical Corporation; *Int'l*, pg. 1529
PNE WIND YENILENEBILIR ENERJILER LTD.—See PNE AG; *Int'l*, pg. 5900
PNG AIR LTD.; *Int'l*, pg. 5901
PNGI CHARLES TOWN GAMING, LLC—See PENN Entertainment, Inc.; *U.S. Public*, pg. 1662
PNG RECYCLING LIMITED—See Sims Limited; *U.S. Public*, pg. 1884
PNGS GARGI FASHION JEWELLERY LTD.; *Int'l*, pg. 5901
PNG-TAIHEIYO CEMENT LIMITED—See Taiheiyo Cement Corporation; *Int'l*, pg. 7412
PN HOFFMAN INC.; *U.S. Private*, pg. 3219
PN HOLDINGS INC—See Pearson plc; *Int'l*, pg. 5777
P&N HOMAG IMPORTACAO E COMERCIO LTDA.—See Cifin S.r.l.; *Int'l*, pg. 1606

PNI DIGITAL MEDIA ULC—See Sycamore Partners Management, LP; *U.S. Private*, pg. 3897
PNJ JEWELRY PRODUCTION & TRADING COMPANY LIMITED—See Phu Nhuan Jewelry Joint Stock Company; *Int'l*, pg. 5857
PNJ LABORATORY LIMITED COMPANY—See Phu Nhuan Jewelry Joint Stock Company; *Int'l*, pg. 5857
PNMSOFT LTD.—See Genpact Limited; *Int'l*, pg. 2927
PNMSOFT PORTUGAL SOC UNIPESSOAL, LDA.—See Genpact Limited; *Int'l*, pg. 2927
PNMSOFT UK LIMITED—See Genpact Limited; *Int'l*, pg. 2927
PNMSOFT USA INC.INC...—See Genpact Limited; *Int'l*, pg. 2927
PNOC ALTERNATIVE FUELS CORPORATION—See Philippine National Oil Company; *Int'l*, pg. 5845
PNOC DEVELOPMENT & MANAGEMENT CORPORATION—See Philippine National Oil Company; *Int'l*, pg. 5845
PNOC EXPLORATION CORPORATION—See Philippine National Oil Company; *Int'l*, pg. 5845
PNOC RENEWABLES CORPORATION—See Philippine National Oil Company; *Int'l*, pg. 5846
PN POONGNYUN CO. LTD.; *Int'l*, pg. 5900
PNR RAILWORKS INC - SIGNALS & COMMUNICATIONS DIVISION—See Wind Point Advisors LLC; *U.S. Private*, pg. 4535
PNR RAILWORKS INC—See Wind Point Advisors LLC; *U.S. Private*, pg. 4535
P.N.S. INC.—See Piolax Inc.; *Int'l*, pg. 5871
PNS STORES, INC.—See Big Lots, Inc.; *U.S. Public*, pg. 330
PNST CO., LTD.—See STI CO. LTD.; *Int'l*, pg. 7214
PNUCOR LLC—See Voigt-Abernathy Company, Inc.; *U.S. Private*, pg. 4409
PNW CASCADIAN COMPANY, L.L.C.—See Brookfield Corporation; *Int'l*, pg. 1183
PNW RAILCARS, INC.—See Mitsubishi HC Capital Inc.; *Int'l*, pg. 4952
PNX ENERGY INTERNATIONAL HOLDINGS, PTE. LTD.—See Phoenix Petroleum Philippines, Inc.; *Int'l*, pg. 5854
PNX METALS LIMITED—See Patronus Resources Limited; *Int'l*, pg. 5759
PNY TECHNOLOGIES, INC.; *U.S. Private*, pg. 3219
POAG SHOPPING CENTERS, LLC; *U.S. Private*, pg. 3219
POA PHARMA SCANDINAVIA AB—See Almac Sciences Group Ltd.; *Int'l*, pg. 363
POBAD INTERNATIONAL LTD.—See Nayax Ltd.; *Int'l*, pg. 5178
POBAL DEVICE KOREA CO., LTD.—See Poval Kogyo Co., Ltd.; *Int'l*, pg. 5942
POBEDA A.D.; *Int'l*, pg. 5901
POBEDA A.D.; *Int'l*, pg. 5901
POBEDA METALAC A.D.; *Int'l*, pg. 5901
POBEDA ZARA A.D.; *Int'l*, pg. 5901
POBELLO DIALYSIS, LLC—See DaVita Inc.; *U.S. Public*, pg. 642
POBJEDA D.D.; *Int'l*, pg. 5901
POBJEDA-RUDET D.D.; *Int'l*, pg. 5901
POBJEDA TECHNOLOGY D.O.O. GORAZDE; *Int'l*, pg. 5901
POBJOY MINT LTD.—See Derek Pobjoy Investments Ltd.; *Int'l*, pg. 2041
POBLOCKI SIGN COMPANY, LLC; *U.S. Private*, pg. 3219
POBOGEL & PARTNER STRASSEN- UND TIEFBAU GMBH HERMDORF/THUR—See STRABAG SE; *Int'l*, pg. 7231
POB:S ELEKTRISKA AB—See Instalco AB; *Int'l*, pg. 3722
POCAHONTAS DEVELOPMENT CORPORATION—See Norfolk Southern Corporation; *U.S. Public*, pg. 1536
POCAHONTAS LAND CORPORATION—See Norfolk Southern Corporation; *U.S. Public*, pg. 1536
POCAHONTAS STATE BANK—See Dentel Bancorporation; *U.S. Public*, pg. 1206
POCALITON LIMITED—See Hang Lung Group Limited; *Int'l*, pg. 3245
POC AUSTRIA—See Clarus Corporation; *U.S. Public*, pg. 508
THE POCA VALLEY BANKSHARES; *U.S. Private*, pg. 4097
POCHET S.A.; *Int'l*, pg. 5901
POCHIN CONSTRUCTION LIMITED—See Pochin's Ltd.; *Int'l*, pg. 5902
POCHIN (CONTRACTORS) LIMITED—See Pochin's Ltd.; *Int'l*, pg. 5902
POCHIN DEVELOPMENTS LIMITED—See Pochin's Ltd.; *Int'l*, pg. 5902
POCHIN HOMES LIMITED—See Pochin's Ltd.; *Int'l*, pg. 5902
POCHIN PLANT LIMITED—See Pochin's Ltd.; *Int'l*, pg. 5902
POCHIN'S LTD.; *Int'l*, pg. 5902
POCHIRAJU INDUSTRIES LIMITED; *Int'l*, pg. 5902
POCH PERSONNEL, INC.; *U.S. Private*, pg. 3219
POCKET ACES PICTURES PRIVATE LIMITED—See Saregama India Limited; *Int'l*, pg. 6577

POCKET CARD CO., LTD.—See ITOCHU Corporation; Int'l, pg. 3841
POCKET GAMES, INC.; U.S. Private, pg. 3219
POCKET GEMS, INC.; U.S. Private, pg. 3219
POCKET HERCULES; U.S. Private, pg. 3219
POCKETINET COMMUNICATIONS INC.—See Columbia Ventures Corporation; U.S. Private, pg. 978
POCKETMOBILE COMMUNICATIONS AB—See Trimble, Inc.; U.S. Public, pg. 2190
POCKETMOBILE NORGE AS—See Trimble, Inc.; U.S. Public, pg. 2190
POCKET OUTDOOR MEDIA, INC.; U.S. Private, pg. 3219
POCL ENTERPRISES LIMITED; Int'l, pg. 5902
POCO GRAPHITE INC.—See Entegris, Inc.; U.S. Public, pg. 777
POCO GRAPHITE SARL—See Entegris, Inc.; U.S. Public, pg. 777
POCO HOLDING CO., LTD.; Int'l, pg. 5902
POCONO AMBULATORY SURGERY CENTER, LIMITED—See UnitedHealth Group Incorporated; U.S. Public, pg. 2249
POCONO MANOR GOLF RESORT & SPA; U.S. Private, pg. 3219
POCONO PALACE, INC.—See Mcsam Hotel Group LLC; U.S. Private, pg. 2644
POCONO PHARMACEUTICALS INC.—See NutriBand Inc.; U.S. Public, pg. 1556
POCONO PRODUCE CO. INC.; U.S. Private, pg. 3219
POCONO RV SALES & SERVICE INC.; U.S. Private, pg. 3219
P&O CRUISES LIMITED—See Carnival Corporation; U.S. Public, pg. 438
POC SWEDEN AB—See Clarus Corporation; U.S. Public, pg. 508
POC USA LLC—See Clarus Corporation; U.S. Public, pg. 508
PODAK CO., LTD.; Int'l, pg. 5902
PODCASTONE, INC.—See LiveOne, Inc.; U.S. Public, pg. 1332
PODDAR HOUSING AND DEVELOPMENT LIMITED; Int'l, pg. 5902
PODDAR PIGMENTS LTD.; Int'l, pg. 5902
P&O DEVELOPMENTS LTD.—See Dubai World Corporation; Int'l, pg. 2222
PODGORICKA BANKA SG GROUP—See Societe Generale S.A.; Int'l, pg. 7040
PODIATRY INSURANCE COMPANY OF AMERICA—See ProAssurance Corporation; U.S. Public, pg. 1723
PODILSKY CEMENT PJSC—See CRH plc; Int'l, pg. 1848
PODIO APS—See Elliott Management Corporation; U.S. Private, pg. 1367
PODIO APS—See Vista Equity Partners, LLC; U.S. Private, pg. 4396
PODIUM MINERALS LIMITED; Int'l, pg. 5902
POD PACK INTERNATIONAL, LTD.; U.S. Private, pg. 3220
POD POINT GROUP HOLDINGS PLC; Int'l, pg. 5902
POD POINT LIMITED—See Pod Point Group Holdings Plc; Int'l, pg. 5902
POD POINT NORGE AS—See Pod Point Group Holdings Plc; Int'l, pg. 5902
PODRAVKA D.D.; Int'l, pg. 5902
PODRAVKA DOOEL—See Podravka d.d.; Int'l, pg. 5903
PODRAVKA D.O.O—See Podravka d.d.; Int'l, pg. 5903
PODRAVKA D.O.O—See Podravka d.d.; Int'l, pg. 5903
PODRAVKA D.O.O—See Podravka d.d.; Int'l, pg. 5903
PODRAVKA EOOD—See Podravka d.d.; Int'l, pg. 5903
PODRAVKA GULF FZE—See Podravka d.d.; Int'l, pg. 5903
PODRAVKA- INT DEUTSCHLAND - KONAR GMBH—See Podravka d.d.; Int'l, pg. 5903
PODRAVKA INTERNATIONAL KFT.—See Podravka d.d.; Int'l, pg. 5903
PODRAVKA INTERNATIONAL PTY LTD—See Podravka d.d.; Int'l, pg. 5903
PODRAVKA-INTERNATIONAL S.R.L.—See Podravka d.d.; Int'l, pg. 5903
PODRAVKA - INTERNATIONAL S.R.O.—See Podravka d.d.; Int'l, pg. 5903
PODRAVKA INTERNATIONAL USA INC—See Podravka d.d.; Int'l, pg. 5903
PODRAVKA INZENJERING D.O.O—See Podravka d.d.; Int'l, pg. 5903
PODRAVKA-LAGRIS A.S.—See Podravka d.d.; Int'l, pg. 5903
PODRAVKA POLSKA SP. Z.O.O.—See Podravka d.d.; Int'l, pg. 5903
PODRAVKA TRGOVACKO PODUZECE D.O.O.—See Podravka d.d.; Int'l, pg. 5903
PODRAVSKA BANKA D.D.; Int'l, pg. 5903
PODS ENTERPRISES, LLC—See Ontario Teachers' Pension Plan; Int'l, pg. 5590
PODUFAL-WIEHOFSKY GENERALPLANUNG GMBH—See BKW AG; Int'l, pg. 1056
PODUNAVLJE A.D.; Int'l, pg. 5903
PODUNAVLJE A.D.; Int'l, pg. 5903
PODUNAVLJE A.D.; Int'l, pg. 5903
PODVIS TERM A.D.; Int'l, pg. 5903
POE ASPHALT PAVING INC.; U.S. Private, pg. 3220

POEMA GLOBAL HOLDINGS CORP.; U.S. Public, pg. 1700
POENINA HOLDING AG; Int'l, pg. 5903
P&O ESTATES LTD.—See Dubai World Corporation; Int'l, pg. 2222
POETICGEM LTD.—See Pearl Global Industries Limited; Int'l, pg. 5774
POET, LLC; U.S. Private, pg. 3220
POET RESEARCH, INC.—See POET, LLC; U.S. Private, pg. 3220
POET TECHNOLOGIES INC.; Int'l, pg. 5903
P&O FERRIES HOLDINGS LIMITED—See Dubai World Corporation; Int'l, pg. 2220
P&O FERRIES LTD.—See Dubai World Corporation; Int'l, pg. 2220
P&O FERRYMASTERS LIMITED—See Dubai World Corporation; Int'l, pg. 2220
POGAGNA; Int'l, pg. 5904
POGGENPOHL AB—See Nobia AB; Int'l, pg. 5395
POGGENPOHL A/S—See Nobia AB; Int'l, pg. 5395
POGGENPOHL AUSTRIA GMBH—See Nobia AB; Int'l, pg. 5395
POGGENPOHL FORUM GMBH.—See Nobia AB; Int'l, pg. 5395
POGGENPOHL FRANCE S.A.R.L.—See Nobia AB; Int'l, pg. 5395
POGGENPOHL GMBH—See Nobia AB; Int'l, pg. 5395
POGGENPOHL GROUP SCHWEIZ AG—See Nobia AB; Int'l, pg. 5395
POGGENPOHL GROUP UK LTD.—See Nobia AB; Int'l, pg. 5395
POGGENPOHL JAPAN CO. LTD.—See Nobia AB; Int'l, pg. 5396
POGGENPOHL MOBELWERKE GMBH—See Lux Group Holdings Limited; Int'l, pg. 4587
POGGENPOHL NEDERLAND B.V.—See Nobia AB; Int'l, pg. 5396
POGGENPOHL U.S., INC.—See Nobia AB; Int'l, pg. 5396
P & O GLOBAL TECHNOLOGIES, INC.—See Pacific & Orient Berhad; Int'l, pg. 5685
P & O GLOBAL TECHNOLOGIES SDN. BHD.—See Pacific & Orient Berhad; Int'l, pg. 5685
POGO.COM—See Electronic Arts Inc.; U.S. Public, pg. 724
POGOTEC, INC.; U.S. Private, pg. 3220
POGUE LABEL & SCREEN, INC.; U.S. Private, pg. 3220
POHANKA AUTO IMPORTS INC.—See Pohanka Auto North Inc.; U.S. Private, pg. 3220
POHANKA AUTO NORTH INC.; U.S. Private, pg. 3220
POHANKA HONDA; U.S. Private, pg. 3220
POHANKA OF SALISBURY—See Pohanka Auto North Inc.; U.S. Private, pg. 3220
POHANKA PROPERTIES INC.—See Pohanka Auto North Inc.; U.S. Private, pg. 3220
POHANKA TOYOTA SERVICE DEPARTMENT; U.S. Private, pg. 3220
POH HUAT FURNITURE INDUSTRIES (M) SDN. BHD.—See Poh Huat Resources Holdings Berhad; Int'l, pg. 5904
POH HUAT FURNITURE INDUSTRIES VIETNAM JOINT STOCK COMPANY - DONG NAI FACTORY—See Poh Huat Resources Holdings Berhad; Int'l, pg. 5904
POH HUAT FURNITURE INDUSTRIES VIETNAM JOINT STOCK COMPANY—See Poh Huat Resources Holdings Berhad; Int'l, pg. 5904
POH HUAT INTERNATIONAL FURNITURE S.A. (PROPRIETARY) LIMITED—See Poh Huat Resources Holdings Berhad; Int'l, pg. 5904
POH HUAT RESOURCES HOLDINGS BERHAD; Int'l, pg. 5904
POHIVORK OU—See Eesti Energia AS; Int'l, pg. 2318
POHJANMAAN LAHISANOMAT OY—See Ilkka Yhtymae Oyj; Int'l, pg. 3615
POHJOLA BANK PLC—See OP Financial Group; Int'l, pg. 5595
POHJOLA INSURANCE COMPANY LTD—See OP Financial Group; Int'l, pg. 5595
POHJOLAN DESIGN-TALO OY—See Afarak Group SE; Int'l, pg. 185
POHJOLAN VOIMA OY; Int'l, pg. 5904
POH KEONG INDUSTRIES SDN. BHD.—See SWS Capital Berhad; Int'l, pg. 7376
POH KONG HOLDINGS BERHAD; Int'l, pg. 5904
POH KONG JEWELLERY MANUFACTURER SDN. BHD.—See Poh Kong Holdings Berhad; Int'l, pg. 5904
POHLAD COMPANIES; U.S. Private, pg. 3220
POHLAND-HERRENKLEIDUNG GMBH & CO. KG—See Aurelius Equity Opportunities SE & Co. KGaA; Int'l, pg. 709
POHLMAN, LLC; U.S. Private, pg. 3221
PO HONG SERVICES LTD—See Rentokil Initial plc; Int'l, pg. 6287
POH TIONG CHOON LOGISTICS LIMITED—See Tower Capital Asia Pte. Ltd.; Int'l, pg. 7849
POIANA BRASOV SA; Int'l, pg. 5904
POINCARE CAPITAL MANAGEMENT LTD.—See Groupe BPCE; Int'l, pg. 3099
POINCARE GESTION SAS; Int'l, pg. 5904
POINDEXTER EXCAVATING, INC.; U.S. Private, pg. 3221

POINDUS SYSTEMS CORP.—See Flytech Technology Co., Ltd.; Int'l, pg. 2716
POINDUS SYSTEMS UK LIMITED—See Compal Electronics, Inc.; Int'l, pg. 1746
POINSETT FERTILIZER INC.; U.S. Private, pg. 3221
POINSETTIA GROVES INC.; U.S. Private, pg. 3221
POINSETT RICE & GRAIN, INC. - CHERRY VALLEY—See Poinsett Rice & Grain, Inc.; U.S. Private, pg. 3221
POINSETT RICE & GRAIN, INC. - MARKED TREE—See Poinsett Rice & Grain, Inc.; U.S. Private, pg. 3221
POINSETT RICE & GRAIN, INC.; U.S. Private, pg. 3221
POINT.360-HIGHLAND—See Point.360; U.S. Public, pg. 1700
POINT.360; U.S. Public, pg. 1700
POINT4 DATA CORPORATION; U.S. Private, pg. 3222
POINT72 ASSET MANAGEMENT, L.P.; U.S. Private, pg. 3222
POINT BANCORP INC.; U.S. Private, pg. 3221
POINT B COMMUNICATIONS; U.S. Private, pg. 3221
POINT BIOPHARMA GLOBAL INC.—See Eli Lilly & Company; U.S. Public, pg. 734
POINT BLANK BODY ARMOR INC.—See JLL Partners, LLC; U.S. Public, pg. 2213
POINT BLANK ENTERPRISES, INC.—See JLL Partners, LLC; U.S. Public, pg. 2213
POINT BREAK HOLDINGS LLC—See INSPIRATO INCORPORATED; U.S. Public, pg. 1131
POINT BREEZE CREDIT UNION; U.S. Private, pg. 3221
POINT BROADCASTING COMPANY; U.S. Private, pg. 3221
POINT B; U.S. Private, pg. 3221
POINT BUILDERS, LLC; U.S. Private, pg. 3221
POINTCLEAR, LLC; U.S. Private, pg. 3222
POINTCLICKCARE CORP.; Int'l, pg. 5904
POINT COMM, INC.—See RCM Technologies, Inc.; U.S. Public, pg. 1767
THE POINT COMMUNITY DEVELOPMENT CORPORATION; U.S. Private, pg. 4097
POINTE AT CANYON RIDGE, LLC—See Independence Realty Trust, Inc.; U.S. Public, pg. 1116
POINTE BUILDERS—See Pointe Group Ltd.; U.S. Private, pg. 3222
POINTE DIALYSIS, LLC—See DaVita Inc.; U.S. Public, pg. 642
POINTE EAST CONDOMINIUM, LLC—See Equity Residential; U.S. Public, pg. 792
POINTE ESTERO BEACH RESORT—See SunStream, Inc.; U.S. Private, pg. 3873
POINTE GROUP LTD.; U.S. Private, pg. 3222
POINTE HILTON TAPATIO CLIFFS RESORT—See Hilton Worldwide Holdings Inc.; U.S. Public, pg. 1041
POINT EIGHT POWER INC.—See Mission Critical Group; U.S. Private, pg. 2747
POINT ELECTRIC—See Swivelier Co., Inc.; U.S. Private, pg. 3894
POINT ENGINEERING CO., LTD.; Int'l, pg. 5904
POINTENORTH INSURANCE GROUP LLC; U.S. Private, pg. 3222
POINTE PEST CONTROL-ID LLC—See Thompson Street Capital Manager LLC; U.S. Private, pg. 4161
POINTE PEST CONTROL-IL, LLC—See Thompson Street Capital Manager LLC; U.S. Private, pg. 4161
POINTER ARGENTINA S.A.—See PowerFleet, Inc.; U.S. Public, pg. 1706
POINTER ASIA LIMITED—See Pointer Limited; Int'l, pg. 5904
POINTER DO BRASIL COMERCIAL LTDA.—See PowerFleet, Inc.; U.S. Public, pg. 1706
POINTER, INC.—See PowerFleet, Inc.; U.S. Public, pg. 1706
POINTER LIMITED; Int'l, pg. 5904
POINTER LLC—See Pointer Limited; Int'l, pg. 5904
POINTER LOCALIZACION Y ASISTENCIA S.A—See PowerFleet, Inc.; U.S. Public, pg. 1706
POINTER LOGISTICA Y MONITOREO, S.A. DE C.V.—See PowerFleet, Inc.; U.S. Public, pg. 1706
POINTER PR LLC; U.S. Private, pg. 3222
POINTERRA LIMITED; Int'l, pg. 5904
POINTERRA US, INC.—See Pointerra Limited; Int'l, pg. 5904
POINTER RECUPERACION DE MEXICO S.A. DE C.V.—See PowerFleet, Inc.; U.S. Public, pg. 1706
POINTER SA (PTY) LTD.—See PowerFleet, Inc.; U.S. Public, pg. 1706
POINTER TELOCATION LTD.—See PowerFleet, Inc.; U.S. Public, pg. 1706
POINTE SCIENTIFIC, INC.—See MedTest DX, Inc.; U.S. Private, pg. 2659
POINTE VISTA DEVELOPMENT LLC; U.S. Private, pg. 3222
POINT FIVE WINDOWS, INC.—See Kolbe & Kolbe Millwork Co., Inc.; U.S. Private, pg. 2341
THE POINT GROUP; U.S. Private, pg. 4097
POINT GUARD PARTNERS LLC; U.S. Private, pg. 3222
POINT HEALTH TECH, INC.; U.S. Private, pg. 3222
POINTILLIST, INC.—See Altisource Portfolio Solutions S.A.; U.S. Public, pg. 393
POINT INSIDE, INC.—See MapsPeople A/S; Int'l, pg. 4687

POINT INSURANCE AGENCY, LLC—See Sentry Insurance Group; *U.S. Private*, pg. 3611
POINT INTERNATIONAL AS—See British Columbia Investment Management Corp.; *Int'l*, pg. 1170
POINT INTERNATIONAL AS—See Francisco Partners Management, LP; *U.S. Private*, pg. 1592
POINT IT INC.—See Add3, LLC; *U.S. Private*, pg. 77
POINT JUDITH CAPITAL PARTNERS, LLC; *U.S. Private*, pg. 3222
POINT LIGHTING CORPORATION; *U.S. Private*, pg. 3222
POINT LISAS INDUSTRIAL PORT DEVELOPMENT CORPORATION LIMITED; *Int'l*, pg. 5904
POINT LISAS NITROGEN LIMITED—See CF Industries Holdings, Inc.; *U.S. Public*, pg. 477
POINT LISAS NITROGEN LIMITED—See Koch Industries, Inc.; *U.S. Private*, pg. 2333
POINTLOGIC USA INC.—See Brookfield Corporation; *Int'l*, pg. 1180
POINTLOGIC USA INC.—See Elliott Management Corporation; *U.S. Private*, pg. 1372
POINT LOMA CREDIT UNION; *U.S. Private*, pg. 3222
POINT LOMA RESOURCES LTD.; *Int'l*, pg. 5904
POINT MARINE, L.L.C.—See Tidewater Inc.; *U.S. Public*, pg. 2158
POINT MOBILE CO., LTD.—See BG T&A Co.; *Int'l*, pg. 1007
POINT OF CARE NANO-TECHNOLOGY, INC.; *U.S. Private*, pg. 3222
THE POINT-OF-SALE CENTRE (NEW ZEALAND) LTD—See Hancock & Gore Ltd.; *Int'l*, pg. 3242
POINT OF VIEW DESIGN PTY LIMITED—See Firefly Point of View Ltd.; *Int'l*, pg. 2679
POINT ONE, LLC—See FedCap Partners, LLC; *U.S. Private*, pg. 1486
POINTON YORK GROUP LIMITED; *Int'l*, pg. 5905
POINTPACK SA; *Int'l*, pg. 5905
POINT & PAY LLC; *U.S. Private*, pg. 3221
POINT P DEVELOPPEMENT—See Compagnie de Saint-Gobain SA; *Int'l*, pg. 1724
POINT PLACE CENTER—See Formation Capital, LLC; *U.S. Private*, pg. 1571
POINT PLEASANT REGISTER—See Heartland Publications, LLC; *U.S. Private*, pg. 1900
POINT PROJECT MANAGEMENT (PNG) LTD.—See RPS Group plc; *Int'l*, pg. 6415
POINT P SA—See Compagnie de Saint-Gobain SA; *Int'l*, pg. 1724
POINT P—See Compagnie de Saint-Gobain SA; *Int'l*, pg. 1724
POINT P—See Compagnie de Saint-Gobain SA; *Int'l*, pg. 1724
POINT P—See Compagnie de Saint-Gobain SA; *Int'l*, pg. 1724
POINT P TROUILLARD—See Compagnie de Saint-Gobain SA; *Int'l*, pg. 1725
POINT RECOGNITION; *U.S. Private*, pg. 3222
POINTRED TELECOM PVT. LTD.—See Gemini Communication Ltd.; *Int'l*, pg. 2916
POINTRIGHT, INC.—See Level Equity Management, LLC; *U.S. Private*, pg. 2434
POINTRIGHT, INC.—See Silversmith Management, L.P.; *U.S. Private*, pg. 3664
POINTRIGHT, INC.—See The Carlyle Group Inc.; *U.S. Public*, pg. 2050
POINT ROLL, INC. - CHICAGO—See TEGNA Inc.; *U.S. Public*, pg. 1990
POINT ROLL, INC. - DETROIT—See TEGNA Inc.; *U.S. Public*, pg. 1990
POINT ROLL, INC.—See TEGNA Inc.; *U.S. Public*, pg. 1990
POINTSBET HOLDINGS LIMITED; *Int'l*, pg. 5905
POINTS.COM INC.—See General Atlantic Service Company, L.P.; *U.S. Private*, pg. 1663
POINTSEC MOBILE TECHNOLOGIES AB—See Check Point Software Technologies Ltd.; *Int'l*, pg. 1459
POINTSEC MOBILE TECHNOLOGIES LIMITED—See Check Point Software Technologies Ltd.; *Int'l*, pg. 1459
POINT (SHANGHAI) CO., LTD.—See Adastria Co., Ltd.; *Int'l*, pg. 126
POINTS NORTH CONTRACTING, LTD.; *Int'l*, pg. 5905
POINTS OF COLORADO, INC.—See Marriott Vacations Worldwide Corporation; *U.S. Public*, pg. 1374
POINT SPRING & DRIVESHAFT COMPANY; *U.S. Private*, pg. 3222
POINT TO POINT COMMUNICATIONS, INC.—See Dycom Industries, Inc.; *U.S. Public*, pg. 699
POINT TO POINT INC.; *U.S. Private*, pg. 3222
POINT TO POINT METHODICS, INC.; *U.S. Public*, pg. 1700
POINT TO POINT TRANSPORTATION SERVICES INC.; *U.S. Private*, pg. 3222
POINTWISE, INC.—See Cadence Design Systems, Inc.; *U.S. Public*, pg. 419
POIRIER SERVICE CORPORATION; *U.S. Private*, pg. 3222
POISTOVNA CARDIF SLOVAKIA AS—See BNP Paribas SA; *Int'l*, pg. 1092

POISTOVNA SLOVENSKEJ SPORITEL'NE A.S.—See Vienna Insurance Group AG Wiener Versicherung Gruppe; *Int'l*, pg. 8195
POITOU CARBURANTS SAE DES ETS TABAUD; *Int'l*, pg. 5905
POJAZDY SZYNOWE PESA BYDGOSZCZ S.A. HOLDING; *Int'l*, pg. 5905
POJISTOVNA CESKE SPORITELNY, A.S.—See Vienna Insurance Group AG Wiener Versicherung Gruppe; *Int'l*, pg. 8195
POKAGON BAND OF POTAWATOMI INDIANS; *U.S. Private*, pg. 3222
POKAGON DIALYSIS, LLC—See DaVita Inc.; *U.S. Public*, pg. 642
POKARNA LIMITED; *Int'l*, pg. 5905
POK BROTHERS SDN. BHD.—See Envictus International Holdings Limited; *Int'l*, pg. 2453
POKE LONDON LTD.—See Publicis Groupe S.A.; *Int'l*, pg. 6104
THE POKEMON COMPANY; *Int'l*, pg. 7674
POKERVISION MEDIA INC.—See ePlay Digital Inc.; *Int'l*, pg. 2463
POKFULAM DEVELOPMENT COMPANY LIMITED; *Int'l*, pg. 5905
POKHARA FINANCE LIMITED; *Int'l*, pg. 5905
POKITDOK, INC.—See McKesson Corporation; *U.S. Public*, pg. 1407
POKKA CORPORATION (SINGAPORE) PTE. LTD.—See Sapporo Holdings Limited; *Int'l*, pg. 6573
POKKA CORPORATION—See Sapporo Holdings Limited; *Int'l*, pg. 6573
POKKA CREATE CO., LTD.—See Sapporo Holdings Limited; *Int'l*, pg. 6573
POKKA PTE. LTD.—See Sapporo Holdings Limited; *Int'l*, pg. 6573
POKKA SAPPORO OFFICE SUPPORT LTD.—See Sapporo Holdings Limited; *Int'l*, pg. 6573
POKO REKORDS—See Universal Music Group N.V.; *Int'l*, pg. 8080
P.O. KORHONEN OY—See Martela Oyj; *Int'l*, pg. 4703
POKUT ELEKTRIK URETIM A.S.—See Parsan Makina Parcalari Sanayii AS; *Int'l*, pg. 5747
POLA CHEMICAL INDUSTRIES, INC. - FUKUROI PLANT—See Pola Orbis Holdings Inc.; *Int'l*, pg. 5905
POLA CHEMICAL INDUSTRIES, INC.—See Pola Orbis Holdings Inc.; *Int'l*, pg. 5905
POLA COSMETICS (HONGKONG) CO., LTD—See Pola Orbis Holdings Inc.; *Int'l*, pg. 5905
POLA COSMETICS (THAILAND) CO., LTD—See Pola Orbis Holdings Inc.; *Int'l*, pg. 5905
POLA INC.—See Pola Orbis Holdings Inc.; *Int'l*, pg. 5905
POLAMCO LTD; *Int'l*, pg. 5905
POLAMER INC.; *U.S. Private*, pg. 3223
POLAND CURT GEORGI POLAND—See Curt Georgi GmbH & Co. KG; *Int'l*, pg. 1880
POLAND SMELTING TECHNOLOGIES SP. Z.O.O.—See Toyota Tsusho Corporation; *Int'l*, pg. 7877
POLAND SPRING BOTTLING—See Metropoulos & Co.; *U.S. Private*, pg. 2690
POLAND SPRING BOTTLING—See One Rock Capital Partners, LLC; *U.S. Private*, pg. 3021
POLAND SPRING CORPORATION—See Metropoulos & Co.; *U.S. Private*, pg. 2691
POLAND SPRING CORPORATION—See One Rock Capital Partners, LLC; *U.S. Private*, pg. 3021
POLAND SPRING CORPORATION—See Metropoulos & Co.; *U.S. Private*, pg. 2690
POLAND SPRING CORPORATION—See Metropoulos & Co.; *U.S. Private*, pg. 2690
POLAND SPRING CORPORATION—See One Rock Capital Partners, LLC; *U.S. Private*, pg. 3021
POLAND SPRING CORPORATION—See One Rock Capital Partners, LLC; *U.S. Private*, pg. 3021
POLAND TOKAI OKAYA MANUFACTURING SP. Z O.O.—See Okaya & Co., Ltd.; *Int'l*, pg. 5547
POLA ORBIS HOLDINGS INC.; *Int'l*, pg. 5905
POLA ORBIS TRAVEL RETAIL LIMITED—See Pola Orbis Holdings Inc.; *Int'l*, pg. 5905
POLA PHARMA INC.—See Sun Pharmaceutical Industries Ltd.; *Int'l*, pg. 7307
POLAR AIR CARGO INC.—See Apollo Global Management, Inc.; *U.S. Public*, pg. 148
POLAR AIR CARGO INC.—See J.F. Lehman & Company, Inc.; *U.S. Private*, pg. 2163
POLAR AIR CARGO WORLDWIDE, INC.—See Apollo Global Management, Inc.; *U.S. Public*, pg. 148
POLAR AIR CARGO WORLDWIDE, INC.—See J.F. Lehman & Company, Inc.; *U.S. Private*, pg. 2162
POLARAY OPTOELECTRONICS CO., LTD.; *Int'l*, pg. 5906
POLAR BEVERAGE INC.; *U.S. Private*, pg. 3223
POLAR BEVERAGES; *U.S. Private*, pg. 3223
POLAR CAPITAL (AMERICA) CORPORATION—See Polar Capital Holdings plc; *Int'l*, pg. 5906
POLAR CAPITAL GLOBAL FINANCIALS TRUST PLC; *Int'l*, pg. 5905
POLAR CAPITAL GLOBAL HEALTHCARE TRUST PLC; *Int'l*, pg. 5906
POLAR CAPITAL HOLDINGS PLC; *Int'l*, pg. 5906

POLAR CAPITAL PARTNERS (JERSEY) LIMITED—See Polar Capital Holdings plc; *Int'l*, pg. 5906
POLAR CAPITAL TECHNOLOGY TRUST PLC; *Int'l*, pg. 5906
POLARCOOL AB; *Int'l*, pg. 5906
POLAR CORPORATION—See Questor Management Company, LLC; *U.S. Private*, pg. 3326
POLAR COVE, INC.; *U.S. Private*, pg. 3223
POLAR CRUISES; *U.S. Private*, pg. 3223
POLARCUS DMCC—See Polarcus Limited; *Int'l*, pg. 5906
POLARCUS LIMITED; *Int'l*, pg. 5906
POLARCUS SEISMIC LIMITED—See Polarcus Limited; *Int'l*, pg. 5906
POLAREAN IMAGING PLC—See Amphion Innovations plc; *Int'l*, pg. 433
POLAREAN, INC.—See Amphion Innovations plc; *Int'l*, pg. 433
POLAR ELECTRO AUSTRIA GMBH—See Polar Electro Oy; *Int'l*, pg. 5906
POLAR ELECTRO BELGIUM NV—See Polar Electro Oy; *Int'l*, pg. 5906
POLAR ELECTRO CANADA INC—See Polar Electro Oy; *Int'l*, pg. 5906
POLAR ELECTRO DANMARK APS—See Polar Electro Oy; *Int'l*, pg. 5906
POLAR ELECTRO EUROPE AG—See Polar Electro Oy; *Int'l*, pg. 5906
POLAR ELECTRO FRANCE S.A.S.—See Polar Electro Oy; *Int'l*, pg. 5906
POLAR ELECTRO GMBH—See Polar Electro Oy; *Int'l*, pg. 5906
POLAR ELECTRO IBERICA S.A—See Polar Electro Oy; *Int'l*, pg. 5906
POLAR ELECTRO INC.—See Polar Electro Oy; *Int'l*, pg. 5906
POLAR ELECTRO ITALIA SRL—See Polar Electro Oy; *Int'l*, pg. 5906
POLAR ELECTRO NORGE AS—See Polar Electro Oy; *Int'l*, pg. 5906
POLAR ELECTRO OY; *Int'l*, pg. 5906
POLAR ELECTRO SINGAPORE PTE LTD—See Polar Electro Oy; *Int'l*, pg. 5906
POLAR ELECTRO SVERIGE AB—See Polar Electro Oy; *Int'l*, pg. 5906
POLAR ELECTRO (UK) LTD—See Polar Electro Oy; *Int'l*, pg. 5906
POLAR EXPLOSIVES LTD.—See Incitec Pivot Limited; *Int'l*, pg. 3648
POLARION AG—See Siemens Aktiengesellschaft; *Int'l*, pg. 6887
POLARIS ACCEPTANCE INC.—See Polaris, Inc.; *U.S. Public*, pg. 1700
POLARIS AI CO., LTD.; *Int'l*, pg. 5906
POLARIS AI CO., LTD.; *Int'l*, pg. 5906
POLARIS ALI SPA.—See Ali Holding S.r.l.; *Int'l*, pg. 321
POLARIS ALPHA ADVANCED SYSTEMS, INC.—See Parsons Corporation; *U.S. Public*, pg. 1651
POLARIS - ANSERV S.R.L.—See RINA S.p.A.; *Int'l*, pg. 6342
POLARIS BANK LIMITED; *Int'l*, pg. 5906
POLARIS BRITAIN LIMITED—See Polaris, Inc.; *U.S. Public*, pg. 1700
POLARIS CAPITAL (ASIA) LTD.—See Yuanta Financial Holding Co., Ltd.; *Int'l*, pg. 8608
POLARIS CAPITAL GROUP CO., LTD.; *Int'l*, pg. 5906
POLARIS CAPITAL PUBLIC COMPANY LIMITED; *Int'l*, pg. 5907
POLARIS CHEMICALS SPRL—See Bunzl plc; *Int'l*, pg. 1219
POLARIS CONSULTING AND SERVICES JAPAN, K.K.—See EQT AB; *Int'l*, pg. 2472
POLARIS CONSULTING & SERVICES B.V.—See EQT AB; *Int'l*, pg. 2472
POLARIS CONSULTING & SERVICES FZ LLC—See EQT AB; *Int'l*, pg. 2472
POLARIS CONSULTING & SERVICES GMBH—See EQT AB; *Int'l*, pg. 2472
POLARIS CONSULTING & SERVICES INC.—See EQT AB; *Int'l*, pg. 2472
POLARIS CONSULTING & SERVICES IRELAND LTD.—See EQT AB; *Int'l*, pg. 2472
POLARIS CONSULTING & SERVICES LIMITED—See EQT AB; *Int'l*, pg. 2471
POLARIS CONSULTING & SERVICES LIMITED—See EQT AB; *Int'l*, pg. 2472
POLARIS CONSULTING & SERVICES LTD—See EQT AB; *Int'l*, pg. 2472
POLARIS CONSULTING & SERVICES PTE. LTD.—See EQT AB; *Int'l*, pg. 2472
POLARIS CONSULTING & SERVICES PTY LTD—See EQT AB; *Int'l*, pg. 2472
POLARIS CONSULTING & SERVICES SA—See EQT AB; *Int'l*, pg. 2472
POLARIS CONTRACT MANUFACTURING, INC.—See Lockheed Martin Corporation; *U.S. Public*, pg. 1338
POLARIS DIRECT INC.—See Polaris, Inc.; *U.S. Public*, pg. 1700
POLARIS ELECTRONICS INC.—See Primax Electronics Ltd.; *Int'l*, pg. 5976

COMPANY NAME INDEX

POLARIS FASHION PLACE REIT, LLC—See Washington Prime Group Inc.; *U.S. Private*, pg. 4448
POLARIS FINLAND OY—See Polaris, Inc.; *U.S. Public*, pg. 1700
POLARIS FRANCE S.A.—See Polaris, Inc.; *U.S. Public*, pg. 1700
POLARIS GROWTH MANAGEMENT, LLC; *U.S. Private*, pg. 3223
POLARIS HOLDING COMPANY LIMITED; *Int'l*, pg. 5907
POLARIS HOLDINGS CO., LTD.; *Int'l*, pg. 5907
POLARIS, INC.; *U.S. Public*, pg. 1700
POLARIS INDUSTRIES LTD.—See Polaris, Inc.; *U.S. Public*, pg. 1700
POLARIS INDUSTRIES MANUFACTURING LLC—See Polaris, Inc.; *U.S. Public*, pg. 1700
POLARIS INDUSTRIES OF CANADA—See Polaris, Inc.; *U.S. Public*, pg. 1700
POLARIS INTERNATIONAL HOLDINGS, INC.; *U.S. Public*, pg. 1700
POLARIS LABORATORIES; *U.S. Private*, pg. 3223
POLARIS LOGISTICS GROUP, INC.; *U.S. Private*, pg. 3223
POLARIS LTD.; *Int'l*, pg. 5907
POLARIS MANAGEMENT A/S; *Int'l*, pg. 5908
POLARIS MATERIALS CORPORATION—See Vulcan Materials Company; *U.S. Public*, pg. 2314
POLARIS MEDIA ASA; *Int'l*, pg. 5908
POLARIS NORTHSTAR CAPITAL CORP; *Int'l*, pg. 5908
POLARIS NORWAY AS—See Polaris, Inc.; *U.S. Public*, pg. 1701
POLARIS OFFICE CORP.; *Int'l*, pg. 5908
POLARIS PACIFIC; *U.S. Private*, pg. 3223
POLARIS PLASTICS LIMITED—See IG Design Group Plc; *Int'l*, pg. 3600
POLARIS RECRUITMENT COMMUNICATIONS; *U.S. Private*, pg. 3223
POLARIS RENEWABLE ENERGY INC.; *Int'l*, pg. 5908
POLARIS RENEWABLE ENERGY S.A.—See Polaris Renewable Energy Inc.; *Int'l*, pg. 5908
POLARIS SALES AUSTRALIA PTY LTD.—See Polaris, Inc.; *U.S. Public*, pg. 1701
POLARIS SALES, CO., INC.—See Odyssey Investment Partners, LLC; *U.S. Private*, pg. 2995
POLARIO SALES INC.—See Polaris, Inc.; *U.S. Public*, pg. 1701
POLARIS SCANDINAVIA AB—See Polaris, Inc.; *U.S. Public*, pg. 1701
POLARIS SECURITIES CO., LTD.—See Yuanta Financial Holding Co., Ltd.; *Int'l*, pg. 8608
POLARIS SHIPMANAGEMENT CO. LTD.—See Rickmers Holding AG; *Int'l*, pg. 6333
POLARIS SOFTWARE CONSULTING & SERVICES SDN BHD—See EQT AB; *Int'l*, pg. 2472
POLARIS SOFTWARE (SHANGHAI) COMPANY LIMITED—See EQT AB; *Int'l*, pg. 2472
POLARIS STAINLESS STEEL TECHNOLOGY (KUNSHAN) CO., LTD—See Kunshan Kinglai Hygienic Materials Co., Ltd.; *Int'l*, pg. 4333
POLARIS TECHNOLOGIES; *U.S. Private*, pg. 3223
POLARIS UNO, INC.—See Polaris Office Corp.; *Int'l*, pg. 5908
POLARIS VENTURE MANAGEMENT CO., LLC; *U.S. Private*, pg. 3223
POLARIS VENTURE PARTNERS—See Polaris Venture Management Co., LLC; *U.S. Private*, pg. 3223
POLARIS WIRELESS; *U.S. Private*, pg. 3223
POLARIS WORKS, INC.; *Int'l*, pg. 5908
POLARIT WELDING, INC—See Outokumpu Oyj; *Int'l*, pg. 5669
POLARITYTE, INC.; *U.S. Public*, pg. 1701
POLARIZED MEAT CO., INC.; *U.S. Private*, pg. 3223
POLAR MINING OY—See Dragon Mining; *Int'l*, pg. 2199
POLARN O. PYRET AB—See Procuritas Partners AB; *Int'l*, pg. 5988
POLAROID CORPORATION—See Gordon Brothers Group, LLC; *U.S. Private*, pg. 1742
POLAROID CORPORATION—See Hilco Trading, LLC; *U.S. Private*, pg. 1943
POLAROID DE MEXICO S.A. DE C.V.—See Gordon Brothers Group, LLC; *U.S. Private*, pg. 1742
POLAROID DE MEXICO S.A. DE C.V.—See Hilco Trading, LLC; *U.S. Private*, pg. 1943
POLAROID (ESPANA) S.A.—See Gordon Brothers Group, LLC; *U.S. Private*, pg. 1742
POLAROID (ESPANA) S.A.—See Hilco Trading, LLC; *U.S. Private*, pg. 1943
POLAROID GMBH—See Gordon Brothers Group, LLC; *U.S. Private*, pg. 1742
POLAROID GMBH—See Hilco Trading, LLC; *U.S. Private*, pg. 1943
POLAROID (U.K.) LIMITED—See Gordon Brothers Group, LLC; *U.S. Private*, pg. 1742
POLAROID (U.K.) LIMITED—See Hilco Trading, LLC; *U.S. Private*, pg. 1943
POLARON SOLARTECH CORPORATION—See Xinyi Solar Holdings Limited; *Int'l*, pg. 8534
POLAR PAK INC—See Apollo Global Management, Inc.; *U.S. Public*, pg. 154
POLAR PARTS CO.—See Road Machinery & Supplies Company; *U.S. Private*, pg. 3453
POLAR POWER, INC.; *U.S. Public*, pg. 1700
POLAR PROPERTY HOLDINGS CORP.—See Land & Houses Public Company Limited; *Int'l*, pg. 4403
POLARPUMPEN AB—See BHG Group AB; *Int'l*, pg. 1014
POLAR SEMICONDUCTOR, LLC—See Sanken Electric Co., Ltd.; *Int'l*, pg. 6541
POLAR SERVICE CENTERS, INC.—See Questor Management Company, LLC; *U.S. Private*, pg. 3326
POLAR STAR CANADIAN OIL & GAS, INC.—See Tourmaline Oil Corp.; *Int'l*, pg. 7848
POLAR TANKERS, INC.—See ConocoPhillips; *U.S. Public*, pg. 569
POLARTEC LLC—See Milliken & Company; *U.S. Private*, pg. 2737
POLAR VISION CENTRES LTD.—See Nunasi Corporation; *Int'l*, pg. 5489
POLAR WARE COMPANY; *U.S. Private*, pg. 3223
POLAR WINDOWS OF CANADA LTD.; *Int'l*, pg. 5906
POLARX LIMITED—See PolarX Limited; *Int'l*, pg. 5908
POLARX LIMITED; *Int'l*, pg. 5908
POLATECHNO CO., LTD. - NAKADAHARA FACTORY—See Nippon Kayaku Co., Ltd.; *Int'l*, pg. 5321
POLATECHNO CO., LTD.—See Nippon Kayaku Co., Ltd.; *Int'l*, pg. 5320
POLATECHNO (HONG KONG) CO. LIMITED—See Nippon Kayaku Co., Ltd.; *Int'l*, pg. 5320
POLATIS INCORPORATED—See Huber + Suhner AG; *Int'l*, pg. 3519
POLA TRADING (SHANGHAI) CO., LTD.—See Pola Orbis Holdings Inc.; *Int'l*, pg. 5905
POLA U.S.A. INC—See Pola Orbis Holdings Inc.; *Int'l*, pg. 5905
POLBALTICA A/B—See Polska Zegluga Morska; *Int'l*, pg. 5911
POLBANK EFG—See Raiffeisen Bank International AG; *Int'l*, pg. 6183
POLBRUK S.A.—See CRH plc; *Int'l*, pg. 1848
POL-BUD TECHNOLOGIA WODY SP.Z.O.O—See BAUER Aktiengesellschaft; *Int'l*, pg. 893
POLCOLORIT S.A.; *Int'l*, pg. 5908
POLCO METAL FINISHING CO.—See Meridian International Group, Inc.; *U.S. Private*, pg. 2673
POLCOMMERCE GMBH—See Kulczyk Investments S.A.; *Int'l*, pg. 4328
POLDER PRODUCTS, LLC—See Topspin Partners, L.P.; *U.S. Private*, pg. 4188
POLDIS; *Int'l*, pg. 5908
POLDMIR LTD.—See Lesico Ltd; *Int'l*, pg. 4469
POLE ARNOLD FINANCIAL MANAGEMENT LIMITED—See Pollen Street Limited; *Int'l*, pg. 5910
POLEN CAPITAL MANAGEMENT, INC.; *U.S. Private*, pg. 3223
POLENERGIA S.A.; *Int'l*, pg. 5909
POLENZANI BENEFITS & INSURANCE SERVICES, LLC—See IMA Financial Group, Inc.; *U.S. Private*, pg. 2043
POLE POSITION RACEWAY, INC.—See K1 Speed, LLC; *U.S. Private*, pg. 2253
POLESTAR APPLIED SOLUTIONS LIMITED—See Sun Capital Partners, Inc.; *U.S. Private*, pg. 3862
POLESTAR APPLIED SOLUTIONS LTD. - LEEDS—See Sun Capital Partners, Inc.; *U.S. Private*, pg. 3862
POLESTAR AUTOMOTIVE HOLDING UK PLC; *Int'l*, pg. 5909
POLESTAR BICESTER LTD—See Sun Capital Partners, Inc.; *U.S. Private*, pg. 3862
POLESTAR CHANTRY LIMITED—See Sun Capital Partners, Inc.; *U.S. Private*, pg. 3862
POLESTAR CHROMOWORKS LIMITED—See Sun Capital Partners, Inc.; *U.S. Private*, pg. 3862
POLESTAR COLCHESTER LIMITED—See Sun Capital Partners, Inc.; *U.S. Private*, pg. 3862
POLESTAR LABS, INC.; *U.S. Private*, pg. 3224
POLESTAR PETTY LIMITED—See Sun Capital Partners, Inc.; *U.S. Private*, pg. 3862
POLESTAR PURNELL LIMITED—See Sun Capital Partners, Inc.; *U.S. Private*, pg. 3862
POLESTAR SHEFFIELD LIMITED—See Sun Capital Partners, Inc.; *U.S. Private*, pg. 3862
POLESTAR STONES—See Sun Capital Partners, Inc.; *U.S. Private*, pg. 3862
POLE STAR TRANSPORT INC—See Armour Transportation Systems; *Int'l*, pg. 575
POLESTAR UK PRINT LIMITED—See Sun Capital Partners, Inc.; *U.S. Private*, pg. 3862
POLET A.D.; *Int'l*, pg. 5909
POLET A.D.—See Nexe Grupa d.d.; *Int'l*, pg. 5243
POLETAEVSKOE LLC—See Gruppa Kompaniy Rusagro OOO; *Int'l*, pg. 3140
POLET IGK A.D; *Int'l*, pg. 5909
POLET KERAMIKA D.O.O.—See Nexe Grupa d.d.; *Int'l*, pg. 5243
POLE TO WIN AMERICA HUNT VALLEY INC.—See Pole To Win Holdings, Inc.; *Int'l*, pg. 5908
POLE TO WIN AMERICA, INC.—See Pole To Win Holdings, Inc.; *Int'l*, pg. 5908
POLE TO WIN CO., LTD.—See Pole To Win Holdings, Inc.; *Int'l*, pg. 5908
POLE TO WIN HOLDINGS, INC.; *Int'l*, pg. 5908
POLE TO WIN INDIA LTD.—See Pole To Win Holdings, Inc.; *Int'l*, pg. 5908
POLE TO WIN VIET NAM JOINT STOCK COMPANY—See Pole To Win Holdings, Inc.; *Int'l*, pg. 5909
POLFA SP. Z O.O.—See Kulczyk Investments S.A.; *Int'l*, pg. 4328
POLHANSA SHIPPING GMBH—See Polska Zegluga Morska; *Int'l*, pg. 5911
POLHEM INFRA AB—See Fjarde AP-fonden; *Int'l*, pg. 2697
POLHEM INFRA AB—See Forsta AP-fonden; *Int'l*, pg. 2737
POLHEM INFRA AB—See Tredje AP-fonden; *Int'l*, pg. 7909
POLI ALPES SAS—See PAI Partners S.A.S.; *Int'l*, pg. 5699
POLIAMBULATORIO DALLA ROSA PRATI S.R.L.—See Garofalo Health Care SpA; *Int'l*, pg. 2886
POLIAN FINANCIAL SERVICES SP. Z O.O.; *Int'l*, pg. 5909
POLICLINICA DE DIAGNOSTIC RAPID SA—See MedLife S.A.; *Int'l*, pg. 4785
POLICOM AB—See Hafslund ASA; *Int'l*, pg. 3206
POLI COMPUTER PC KFT. LTD.—See 4iG Nyrt.; *Int'l*, pg. 12
POLICY ADM SOLUTIONS INC.; *U.S. Private*, pg. 3224
P.O.L.I.C.Y. LIMITED; *Int'l*, pg. 5682
POLICYSTAT, LLC—See Rothschild & Co SCA; *Int'l*, pg. 6403
POLICYSTAT, LLC—See TA Associates, Inc.; *U.S. Private*, pg. 3918
POLIDUX, S.A.—See Repsol, S.A.; *Int'l*, pg. 6293
POLIFOAM PLASTIC PROCESSING CO., LTD.—See PannErgy Nyrt.; *Int'l*, pg. 5729
POLIFORM USA, INC.; *U.S. Private*, pg. 3224
POLIGHT ASA; *Int'l*, pg. 5909
POLIGOF SPA—See 21 Investimenti Societa' di Gestione del Risparmio S.p.A.; *Int'l*, pg. 4
POLIGRAFICA S. FAUSTINO S.P.A.; *Int'l*, pg. 5909
POLIGRAFICI EDITORIALE S.P.A.—See Monrif S.p.A.; *Int'l*, pg. 5035
POLIGRAFICI PRINTING S.P.A.—See Monrif S.p.A.; *Int'l*, pg. 5035
POLIGRAFICI REAL ESTATE SRL—See Monrif S.p.A.; *Int'l*, pg. 5035
POLIKLINIK CENTRAL & SURGERI SDN. BHD.—See Qualitas Medical Group Limited; *Int'l*, pg. 6151
POLIKLINIK PUTERI DAN SURGERI SDN. BHD.—See Qualitas Medical Group Limited; *Int'l*, pg. 6151
POLIKLINIK SIMPANG PULAI SDN. BHD.—See Qualitas Medical Group Limited; *Int'l*, pg. 6151
POLIMERI EUROPA GMBH—See Eni S.p.A.; *Int'l*, pg. 2438
POLIMERI EUROPA SPA—See Eni S.p.A.; *Int'l*, pg. 2438
POLIMERI EUROPA UK LTD—See Eni S.p.A.; *Int'l*, pg. 2438
POLIMEX BUDOWNICTWO SP. Z O.O. SP.K.—See Polimex-Mostostal S.A.; *Int'l*, pg. 5909
POLIMEX ENERGETYKA SP. Z O.O.—See Polimex-Mostostal S.A.; *Int'l*, pg. 5909
POLIMEX INFRASTRUKTURA SP. Z O.O.—See Polimex-Mostostal S.A.; *Int'l*, pg. 5909
POLIMEX-MOSTOSTAL S.A.; *Int'l*, pg. 5909
POLIMEX OPERATOR SP. Z O.O. SP.K.—See Polimex-Mostostal S.A.; *Int'l*, pg. 5909
POLIMEX POWER ENGINEERING SP Z.O.O.—See Polimex-Mostostal S.A.; *Int'l*, pg. 5909
POL. IND. SON NOGUERA—See Mondragon Corporation; *Int'l*, pg. 5029
POLINGER SHANNON & LUCHS COMPANY; *U.S. Private*, pg. 3224
POLIN POULTRY COMPANY INC.; *U.S. Private*, pg. 3224
POLIOLEFINAS BOREALIS ESPANA S.A.—See OMV Aktiengesellschaft; *Int'l*, pg. 5569
POLIOLES S.A. DE C.V.—See ALFA, S.A.B. de C.V.; *Int'l*, pg. 313
POLIOLES S.A. DE C.V.—See BASF SE; *Int'l*, pg. 876
POLIPAK SP. Z O.O.—See Gr. Sarantis S.A.; *Int'l*, pg. 3047
POLISAN HELLAS S.A.—See Polisan Holding A.S.; *Int'l*, pg. 5909
POLISAN HOLDING A.S.; *Int'l*, pg. 5909
POLISAN KANSAI BOYA SANAYI VE TICARET A.S.—See Kansai Paint Co., Ltd.; *Int'l*, pg. 4073
POLISAN KIMYA SANAYII A.S.—See Polisan Holding A.S.; *Int'l*, pg. 5909
POLISA - ZYCIE UBEZPIECZENIA SP.Z.O.O.—See Vienna Insurance Group AG Wiener Versicherung Gruppe; *Int'l*, pg. 8195
POLISEEK AIS INSURANCE SOLUTIONS, INC.—See Mercury General Corporation; *U.S. Public*, pg. 1422
POLISERVICE B.V.—See ASR Nederland N.V.; *Int'l*, pg. 632
POLISHED METALS LTD INC—See Sky Island Capital LLC; *U.S. Private*, pg. 3684

POLISH NATIONAL ALLIANCE OF US CORPORATE AFFILIATIONS

POLISH NATIONAL ALLIANCE OF US; *U.S. Private*, pg. 3224
POLISH NATIONAL CREDIT UNION; *U.S. Private*, pg. 3224
POLISH NATIONAL UNION OF AMERICA; *U.S. Private*, pg. 3224
POLISH ROMAN CATHOLIC UNION OF AMERICA; *U.S. Private*, pg. 3224
POLISH STEM CELL BANK S.A.—See Enterprise Investors Sp. z o.o.; *Int'l*, pg. 2452
POLISIN OVERSEAS SHIPPING LTD—See Kulczyk Investments S.A.; *Int'l*, pg. 4328
POLI S.P.A—See Westinghouse Air Brake Technologies Corporation; *U.S. Public*, pg. 2359
POLI S.R.L.—See Westinghouse Air Brake Technologies Corporation; *U.S. Public*, pg. 2359
POLITECH SAS—See PAI Partners S.A.S.; *Int'l*, pg. 5699
POLITEKNIK METAL SANAYI VE TICARET A.S.—See Silverfleet Capital Limited; *Int'l*, pg. 6925
POLITEX S.A.S. DI FREUDENBERG POLITEX S.R.L.—See Freudenberg SE; *Int'l*, pg. 2790
POLITIKA A.D.; *Int'l*, pg. 5909
POLITO FORD LINCOLN SALES; *Int'l*, pg. 5909
POLITUB SA—See Teraplast S.A.; *Int'l*, pg. 7563
POLJOOPREMA D.D.; *Int'l*, pg. 5909
POLJOPRIVREDA NOVO SELO A.D.; *Int'l*, pg. 5909
POLJOPRIVREDNA STRUCNA SLUZBA SUBOTICA A.D.; *Int'l*, pg. 5910
POLJOPROMET A.D.; *Int'l*, pg. 5910
POLKA DOT DAIRY; *U.S. Private*, pg. 3224
POL-KA PRODUCCIONES S.A.—See Grupo Clarin S.A.; *Int'l*, pg. 3125
POLK AUDIO, INC.—See Charlesbank Capital Partners, LLC; *U.S. Private*, pg. 855
POLK-BURNETT ELECTRIC COOPERATIVE; *U.S. Private*, pg. 3224
POLK COUNTY FARMERS CO-OP INC; *U.S. Private*, pg. 3224
POLK MECHANICAL COMPANY, LLC.; *U.S. Private*, pg. 3224
POLK MEDICAL CENTER—See HCA Healthcare, Inc.; *U.S. Public*, pg. 1006
POLK OIL COMPANY INC.; *U.S. Private*, pg. 3224
POLKOMTEL S.A.—See Cyfrowy Polsat S.A.; *Int'l*, pg. 1895
POLKSI BANK KOMOREK MACIERZYSTYCH SP. Z.O.O.—See VITA 34 AG; *Int'l*, pg. 8257
POLK'S MEAT PRODUCTS; *U.S. Private*, pg. 3224
POLKTON MANUFACTURING COMPANY; *U.S. Private*, pg. 3224
POLLACK CORPORATION; *U.S. Private*, pg. 3224
POLLACK SHORES REAL ESTATE GROUP, LLC; *U.S. Private*, pg. 3224
POLLACK; *U.S. Private*, pg. 3224
POLLARD ADVISORY SERVICES PTY. LTD.—See Steadfast Group Limited; *Int'l*, pg. 7187
POLLARD BANKNOTE LIMITED; *Int'l*, pg. 5910
POLLARD ENTERPRISES INC.; *U.S. Private*, pg. 3224
POLLARD FRIENDLY FORD; *U.S. Private*, pg. 3225
POLLARD WINDOWS INC.; *Int'l*, pg. 5910
POLLENA AROMA SP. Z O.O.—See Turpaz Industries Ltd; *Int'l*, pg. 7979
POLLEN GEAR LLC—See Greenlane Holdings, Inc.; *U.S. Public*, pg. 965
POLLEN STREET CAPITAL LIMITED—See Pollen Street Limited; *Int'l*, pg. 5910
POLLEN STREET LIMITED; *Int'l*, pg. 5910
POLLER & JORDAN ADVERTISING AGENCY, INC.; *U.S. Private*, pg. 3225
POLLINI AUSTRIA GMBH—See Aeffe SpA; *Int'l*, pg. 173
POLLINI FRANCE S.A.R.L.—See Aeffe SpA; *Int'l*, pg. 173
POLLINI RETAIL S.R.L.—See Aeffe SpA; *Int'l*, pg. 173
POLLINI SPA—See Aeffe SpA; *Int'l*, pg. 173
POLLOCK COMMUNICATIONS; *U.S. Private*, pg. 3225
POLLOCK CORPORATION; *U.S. Private*, pg. 3225
POLLOCK INVESTMENTS INC; *U.S. Private*, pg. 3225
POLLO OPERATIONS, INC.—See Garnett Station Partners, LLC; *U.S. Private*, pg. 1645
POLLUTION MANAGEMENT, INC.—See Terracon Consultants, Inc.; *U.S. Private*, pg. 3971
POLLUTION & PROTECTION SERVICES LIMITED—See PPS International (Holdings) Limited; *Int'l*, pg. 5951
POLLUX BV; *Int'l*, pg. 5910
POLLUX IMMOBILIEN GMBH—See UniCredit S.p.A.; *Int'l*, pg. 8040
POLLUX MANUFACTURING, INC.—See Dale Tile Company; *U.S. Private*, pg. 1149
POLLUX PROPERTIES LTD.; *Int'l*, pg. 5910
THE POLLY HILL ARBORETUM; *U.S. Private*, pg. 4097
POLLY'S FOOD SERVICE INC.; *U.S. Private*, pg. 3225
POLLY'S INC.—See EDD Investment Co.; *U.S. Private*, pg. 1332
POLMED S.A.; *Int'l*, pg. 5910
POLMED ZDROWIE SP. Z O.O.—See Polmed S.A.; *Int'l*, pg. 5910
POLMERIC MOULDINGS LIMITED—See Kingspan Group PLC; *Int'l*, pg. 4179
POL-MIEDZ TRANS SP. Z O.O.—See KGHM Polska Miedz S.A.; *Int'l*, pg. 4149

POL-MIEDZ TRANS SP. Z O.O.—See KGHM Polska Miedz S.A.; *Int'l*, pg. 4149
POLMOS LANCUT S.A.—See Marie Brizard Wine & Spirits S.A.; *Int'l*, pg. 4693
POLNAD CORPORATION OF SHINSUNG AUTOMOTIVE CO,LTD.—See Shinsung Delta Tech Co., Ltd.; *Int'l*, pg. 6849
POLNET ID SPOLKA Z OGRANICZONA ODPOWIEDZIALNOSCIA—See Merck & Co., Inc.; *U.S. Public*, pg. 1421
POLNOC NIERUCHOMOSCI S.A.; *Int'l*, pg. 5910
POLNONAKUP SARIS AS; *Int'l*, pg. 5911
POLNORD - APARTAMENTY SP. Z O.O.—See Polnord S.A.; *Int'l*, pg. 5911
POLNORD INZYNIERIA SP. Z O.O.—See Polnord S.A.; *Int'l*, pg. 5911
POLNORD - LODZ II SP. Z O.O.—See Polnord S.A.; *Int'l*, pg. 5911
POLNORD - LODZ I SP. Z O.O.—See Polnord S.A.; *Int'l*, pg. 5911
POLNORD S.A.; *Int'l*, pg. 5911
POLNORD SOPOT II SP. Z O.O.—See Polnord S.A.; *Int'l*, pg. 5911
POLNORD SZCZECIN I SP. Z O.O.—See Polnord S.A.; *Int'l*, pg. 5911
POLNORD WARSZAWA - WILANOW III SP. Z O.O.—See Polnord S.A.; *Int'l*, pg. 5911
POLNORD WARSZAWA - WILANOW II SP. Z O.O.—See Polnord S.A.; *Int'l*, pg. 5911
POLNORD WARSZAWA - WILANOW I SP. Z O.O.—See Polnord S.A.; *Int'l*, pg. 5911
POLNORD - WYDAWNICTWO OSKAR SP. Z O.O.—See Polnord S.A.; *Int'l*, pg. 5911
POLOCO USA, INC.—See Ralph Lauren Corporation; *U.S. Public*, pg. 1761
POLO CUSTOM PRODUCTS—See M-C Industries Inc.; *U.S. Private*, pg. 2525
POLO HOTELS LIMITED; *Int'l*, pg. 5911
POLOMEX S.A. DE C.V.—See Marcopolo S.A.; *Int'l*, pg. 4690
POLO QUEEN INDUSTRIAL & FINTECH LIMITED; *Int'l*, pg. 5911
POLO RALPH LAUREN AUSTRALIA PTY LIMITED—See OrotonGroup Limited; *Int'l*, pg. 5643
POLO RALPH LAUREN MILAN S.R.L.—See Ralph Lauren Corporation; *U.S. Public*, pg. 1761
POLO/RALPH LAUREN—See Ralph Lauren Corporation; *U.S. Public*, pg. 1761
POLO RESOURCES LIMITED; *Int'l*, pg. 5911
POLPAR S.A.; *Int'l*, pg. 5911
POL PERFECT SP. Z O.O.—See Penta Investments Limited; *Int'l*, pg. 5788
POLSEMANNEN AB—See Danish Crown AmbA; *Int'l*, pg. 1965
POLSERV S.A. DE C.V.—See Host Hotels & Resorts, Inc.; *U.S. Public*, pg. 1055
POLSIB SA; *Int'l*, pg. 5911
POLSINELLI PC; *U.S. Private*, pg. 3225
POLSINELLO FUELS INC.; *U.S. Private*, pg. 3225
POLSIN PRIVATE LTD—See Kulczyk Investments S.A.; *Int'l*, pg. 4328
POLSKA ENERGIA PIERWSZA KOMPANIA HANDLOWA SP. Z O.O—See Tauron Polska Energia S.A.; *Int'l*, pg. 7476
POLSKA ENERGIA - PIERWSZA KOMPANIA HANDLOW SP. Z O.O.—See Poludniowy Koncern Energetyczny S.A.; *Int'l*, pg. 5913
POLSKA GRUPA FARMACEUTYCZNA - HURT SP. Z O.O.—See Pelion S.A.; *Int'l*, pg. 5783
POLSKA PRESS SP. Z O.O.—See Orlen S.A.; *Int'l*, pg. 5641
POLSKA SMURFIT KAPPA POLSKA SP. Z.O.O.—See Smurfit Kappa Group plc; *Int'l*, pg. 7022
POLSKA SPOLKA GAZOWNICTWA SP. Z O.O.—See Polskie Gornictwo Naftowe i Gazownictwo S.A.; *Int'l*, pg. 5912
POLSKA TECHNIKA ZABEZPIECZEN SP. Z O. O.—See Stalprodukt S.A.; *Int'l*, pg. 7164
POLSKA ZEGLUGA MORSKA; *Int'l*, pg. 5911
POLSKI ASFALT SP. Z O. O.—See STRABAG SE; *Int'l*, pg. 7231
POLSKI BANK KOMOREK MACIERZYSTYCH SA; *Int'l*, pg. 5912
POLSKIE BADANIA INTERNETU SP. Z O. O.—See Agora S.A.; *Int'l*, pg. 213
POLSKIE CENTRUM PROMOCJI MIEDZI SP. Z O.O.—See KGHM Polska Miedz S.A.; *Int'l*, pg. 4149
POLSKIE GORNICTWO NAFTOWE I GAZOWNICTWO S.A.; *Int'l*, pg. 5912
POLSKIE KOLEJE PANSTWOWE S.A.; *Int'l*, pg. 5912
POLSKIE LINIE OCEANICZNE S.A.—See Stocznia Gdynia S.A.; *Int'l*, pg. 7220
POLSKIE TOWARZYSTWO REASEKURACJI SPOLKA AKCYJNA—See Fairfax Financial Holdings Limited; *Int'l*, pg. 2608
POLSKIE ZAKLADY LOTNICZE SP. ZO.O.—See RTX Corporation; *U.S. Public*, pg. 1823
POLSKI HOLDING NIERUCHOMOSCI S.A.; *Int'l*, pg. 5912

POLSKI KOKS S.A.—See Jastrzebska Spolka Weglowa S.A.; *Int'l*, pg. 3913
POLSON LIMITED; *Int'l*, pg. 5913
POLSTEAM BENELUX B.V.—See Polska Zegluga Morska; *Int'l*, pg. 5911
POLSTEAM BROKERS GDYNIA LTD.—See Polska Zegluga Morska; *Int'l*, pg. 5911
POLSTEAM BROKERS—See Polska Zegluga Morska; *Int'l*, pg. 5911
POLSTEAM (IBERIA) S.A.—See Polska Zegluga Morska; *Int'l*, pg. 5911
POLSTEAM (LUXEMBOURG) S.A.—See Polska Zegluga Morska; *Int'l*, pg. 5911
POLSTEAM SHIPPING AGENCY LTD.—See Polska Zegluga Morska; *Int'l*, pg. 5911
POLSTEAM (UK) LTD.—See Polska Zegluga Morska; *Int'l*, pg. 5911
POLSTEAM USA INC.—See Polska Zegluga Morska; *Int'l*, pg. 5911
POLSTEAM ZEGLUGA SZCZECINSKA SP. Z O.O.—See Polska Zegluga Morska; *Int'l*, pg. 5911
POLSTEAM ZELUGA SZCZECINSKA LTD.—See Polska Zegluga Morska; *Int'l*, pg. 5911
POLSTIERNAN INDUSTRI AB—See Ledstiernan AB; *Int'l*, pg. 4439
POL-SUPPLY SP. Z O.O.—See Stocznia Gdynia S.A.; *Int'l*, pg. 7220
POLTANK, S.A.U.—See Fluidra SA; *Int'l*, pg. 2714
POLTAVA AUTOMOBILE UNIT PLANT, PJSC; *Int'l*, pg. 5913
POLTAVA PETROLEUM COMPANY—See JKX Oil & Gas Plc; *Int'l*, pg. 3973
POLTEXTIL SP.Z.O.O.—See Hollywood SA; *Int'l*, pg. 3452
POLTRANS GMBH—See OT Logistics S.A.; *Int'l*, pg. 5656
POLTRONA FRAU S.P.A.—See Haworth, Inc.; *U.S. Private*, pg. 1883
POLTRONESOFA HOLDING SRL; *Int'l*, pg. 5913
POLTRONESOFA SPA—See Poltronesofa Holding Srl; *Int'l*, pg. 5913
POLTTIMO OY; *Int'l*, pg. 5913
POLUDNIOWY KONCERN ENERGETYCZNY S.A.; *Int'l*, pg. 5913
POLU KAI SERVICES LLC; *U.S. Private*, pg. 3225
POLUS A.S.—See Immofinanz AG; *Int'l*, pg. 3628
POLUS BIOPHARM INC.; *Int'l*, pg. 5913
POLWAX S.A.; *Int'l*, pg. 5913
POLYAD SERVICES GMBH—See BASF SE; *Int'l*, pg. 884
POLYAD SERVICES LLC—See SKion GmbH; *Int'l*, pg. 6989
POLYAIR INTER PACK, ATLANTA—See Clearlake Capital Group, L.P.; *U.S. Private*, pg. 935
POLYAIR INTER PACK, BARDSTOWN—See Clearlake Capital Group, L.P.; *U.S. Private*, pg. 935
POLYAIR INTER PACK, CHICAGO—See Clearlake Capital Group, L.P.; *U.S. Private*, pg. 935
POLYAIR INTER PACK, CORONA—See Clearlake Capital Group, L.P.; *U.S. Private*, pg. 935
POLYAIR INTER PACK, DALLAS—See Clearlake Capital Group, L.P.; *U.S. Private*, pg. 935
POLYAIR INTER PACK INC. - SACRAMENTO DIVISION—See Clearlake Capital Group, L.P.; *U.S. Private*, pg. 935
POLYAIR INTER PACK INC.—See Clearlake Capital Group, L.P.; *U.S. Private*, pg. 935
POLYAIR INTER PACK, NEW JERSEY—See Clearlake Capital Group, L.P.; *U.S. Private*, pg. 935
POLY-AMERICA LP; *U.S. Private*, pg. 3225
POLYANALYTIC S.A.—See Sonic Healthcare Limited; *Int'l*, pg. 7098
POLYARD PETROLEUM INTERNATIONAL COMPANY LIMITED—See Polyard Petroleum International Group Limited; *Int'l*, pg. 5914
POLYARD PETROLEUM INTERNATIONAL GROUP LIMITED; *Int'l*, pg. 5914
POLYBAND MEDIEN GMBH.—See Splendid Medien AG; *Int'l*, pg. 7141
POLY (BAOTOU) REAL ESTATE DEVELOPMENT CO., LTD.—See China Poly Group Corporation; *Int'l*, pg. 1541
POLY (BEIJING) REAL ESTATE DEVELOPMENT CO., LTD.—See China Poly Group Corporation; *Int'l*, pg. 1541
POLY (BEIJING) THEATRE CONSTRUCTION ENGINEERING CONSULTING CORPORATION LIMITED—See Poly Culture Group Corporation Limited; *Int'l*, pg. 5914
POLYBIA STUDIOS PTY, LTD—See Tautachrome Inc.; *U.S. Public*, pg. 1983
POLYBLEND GMBH—See TotalEnergies SE; *Int'l*, pg. 7837
POLYBOIS INC.; *Int'l*, pg. 5914
POLY BUILDING CORPORATION—See China Poly Group Corporation; *Int'l*, pg. 1541
POLYBUS CORPORATION PTE. LTD.—See TSRC Corporation; *Int'l*, pg. 7952
POLYCAB INDIA LIMITED; *Int'l*, pg. 5914
POLY-CARB, INC.—See Dow Inc.; *U.S. Public*, pg. 685
POLYCASA FRANCE SA—See Schweiter Technologies AG; *Int'l*, pg. 6645

COMPANY NAME INDEX

POLYCASA GMBH—See Schweiter Technologies AG; *Int'l*, pg. 6645
POLYCASA NISCHWITZ GMBH—See Schweiter Technologies AG; *Int'l*, pg. 6645
POLYCASA N.V.—See Schweiter Technologies AG; *Int'l*, pg. 6645
POLYCASA SLOVAKIA SRO—See Schweiter Technologies AG; *Int'l*, pg. 6645
POLYCASA SPAIN S.A.U.—See Schweiter Technologies AG; *Int'l*, pg. 6645
POLYCASA S.R.O.—See Schweiter Technologies AG; *Int'l*, pg. 6645
POLYCEL HOLDINGS INC.; *U.S. Private*, pg. 3225
POLYCEL STRUCTURAL FOAM, INC.—See Polycel Holdings Inc.; *U.S. Private*, pg. 3225
POLYCHARGE AMERICA, INC.—See BorgWarner Inc.; *U.S. Public*, pg. 371
POLYCHEM CORPORATION—See The Sterling Group, L.P.; *U.S. Private*, pg. 4123
POLYCHEMIE GMBH—See SNF SAS; *Int'l*, pg. 7027
POLYCHEM LIMITED; *Int'l*, pg. 5914
POLYCHEM SYSTEMS—See Brentwood Industries Inc.; *U.S. Private*, pg. 646
POLYCHIM INDUSTRIE SAS—See Beaulieu International Group NV; *Int'l*, pg. 934
POLY-CHOKE—See Nitram, LLC; *U.S. Private*, pg. 2929
POLY (CHONGQING) GOLF MANAGEMENT CO., LTD.—See China Poly Group Corporation; *Int'l*, pg. 1541
POLY (CHONGQING) INVESTMENT INDUSTRY CO., LTD.—See China Poly Group Corporation; *Int'l*, pg. 1541
POLYCLEAN INNOVATIONS, LLC; *U.S. Private*, pg. 3225
THE POLYCLINIC—See UnitedHealth Group Incorporated; *U.S. Public*, pg. 2251
POLYCLINIQUE DU PARC DREVON, SA—See Eurazeo SE; *Int'l*, pg. 2529
POLYCLINIQUE DU VAL DE SAONE SAS—See Eurazeo SE; *Int'l*, pg. 2529
POLYCLINIQUE SAINT-ODILON, SA—See Eurazeo SE; *Int'l*, pg. 2529
POLY-CLIP SYSTEM GMBH & CO. KG; *Int'l*, pg. 5914
POLYCOM AG—See HP Inc.; *U.S. Public*, pg. 1064
POLYCOM ASIA PACIFIC PTE LTD.—See HP Inc.; *U.S. Public*, pg. 1064
POLYCOM DANMARK APS—See HP Inc.; *U.S. Public*, pg. 1064
POLYCOM (FRANCE), S.A.R.L.—See HP Inc.; *U.S. Public*, pg. 1064
POLYCOM GLOBAL LIMITED—See HP Inc.; *U.S. Public*, pg. 1064
POLYCOM GMBH—See HP Inc.; *U.S. Public*, pg. 1064
POLYCOM, INC. - AUSTIN—See HP Inc.; *U.S. Public*, pg. 1065
POLYCOM, INC. - BOSTON—See HP Inc.; *U.S. Public*, pg. 1065
POLYCOM, INC.—See HP Inc.; *U.S. Public*, pg. 1064
POLYCOM, INC. - WESTMINSTER—See HP Inc.; *U.S. Public*, pg. 1065
POLYCOM ISRAEL LTD.—See HP Inc.; *U.S. Public*, pg. 1064
POLYCOM (JAPAN) K.K.—See HP Inc.; *U.S. Public*, pg. 1064
POLYCOM NORWAY AS—See HP Inc.; *U.S. Public*, pg. 1065
POLYCOMP ADMINISTRATIVE SERVICES, INC.—See Aquiline Capital Partners LLC; *U.S. Private*, pg. 304
POLYCOMP ADMINISTRATIVE SERVICES, INC.—See Genstar Capital, LLC; *U.S. Private*, pg. 1675
POLYCOM RUSSIA—See HP Inc.; *U.S. Public*, pg. 1065
POLYCOM TECHNOLOGY (R&D) CENTER PRIVATE LIMITED—See HP Inc.; *U.S. Public*, pg. 1065
POLYCOM TELECOMUNICACOES DO BRASIL LTDA.—See HP Inc.; *U.S. Public*, pg. 1065
POLYCOM UK LTD.—See HP Inc.; *U.S. Public*, pg. 1065
POLYCOM UNIFIED COMMUNICATIONS SOLUTIONS PVT. LTD.—See HP Inc.; *U.S. Public*, pg. 1065
POLYCOM UNIFIED ILETISIM SANAYI VE TICARET LIMITED SIRKETI—See HP Inc.; *U.S. Public*, pg. 1065
POLYCON INDUSTRIES INC.—See Crown Packaging International Inc.; *U.S. Public*, pg. 1111
POLYCON INTERNATIONAL LIMITED; *Int'l*, pg. 5914
POLYCOR INC.—See TorQuest Partners Inc.; *Int'l*, pg. 7830
POLYCORP LTD.—See Arsenal Capital Management LP; *U.S. Private*, pg. 339
POLY CULTURE GROUP CORPORATION LIMITED; *Int'l*, pg. 5913
POLYDAKIS LTD.—See BERICAP GmbH & Co. KG; *Int'l*, pg. 5914
POLYDESIGN SYSTEMS S.A.R.L.—See Exco Technologies Limited; *Int'l*, pg. 2580
POLY DEVELOPMENTS AND HOLDINGS GROUP CO., LTD.—See China Poly Group Corporation; *Int'l*, pg. 1541
POLYDEX PHARMACEUTICALS LIMITED—See Biospectra Inc.; *U.S. Private*, pg. 563
POLYDOR LTD.—See Universal Music Group N.V.; *Int'l*, pg. 8080

POLYEDRA AG—See KPP Group Holdings Co., Ltd.; *Int'l*, pg. 4298
POLYEDRA SPA—See CVC Capital Partners SICAV-FIS S.A.; *Int'l*, pg. 1887
POLY EXPLOSIVES CO., LTD.—See China Poly Group Corporation; *Int'l*, pg. 1541
POLYFAB CORPORATION; *U.S. Private*, pg. 3225
POLYFAIR HOLDINGS LTD.; *Int'l*, pg. 5915
POLY FILM INVESTMENT CORPORATION LIMITED—See Poly Culture Group Corporation Limited; *Int'l*, pg. 5914
POLYFIRST PACKAGING, INC.—See The Pritzker Group - Chicago, LLC; *U.S. Private*, pg. 4099
POLY-FLEX CORP; *U.S. Private*, pg. 3225
POLYFLEX PRODUCTS, INC.—See Nefab AB; *Int'l*, pg. 5191
POLYFLON COMPANY—See Crane NXT, Co.; *U.S. Public*, pg. 590
POLYFLOR CANADA INC.—See James Halstead PLC; *Int'l*, pg. 3877
POLYFLOR FZE—See James Halstead PLC; *Int'l*, pg. 3877
POLYFLOR INDIA PVT LIMITED—See James Halstead PLC; *Int'l*, pg. 3877
POLYFLOR LIMITED—See James Halstead PLC; *Int'l*, pg. 3877
POLYFLOR (M) SDN BHD—See James Halstead PLC; *Int'l*, pg. 3877
POLYFLOR NEW ZEALAND LIMITED—See James Halstead PLC; *Int'l*, pg. 3877
POLYFLOW PIPES SDN. BHD.—See Quality Concrete Holdings Berhad; *Int'l*, pg. 6152
POLYFOAM ASIA PTE LTD.—See INOAC Corporation; *Int'l*, pg. 3714
POLY FOAM, INC.—See The Riverside Company; *U.S. Private*, pg. 4109
POLYFORM PRODUCTS COMPANY, INC.—See CNL Strategic Capital Management LLC; *U.S. Private*, pg. 952
POLYFORM S.R.O.—See Hirsch Servo AG; *Int'l*, pg. 3406
POLYGENTA TECHNOLOGIES LIMITED - NASHIK FACTORY—See Polygenta Technologies Limited; *Int'l*, pg. 5915
POLYGENTA TECHNOLOGIES LIMITED; *Int'l*, pg. 5915
POLYGIENE GROUP AB; *Int'l*, pg. 5915
POLYGLASS GREAT BRITAIN LTD—See Mapei SpA; *Int'l*, pg. 4683
POLYGLASS ROMANIA SRL—See Mapei SpA; *Int'l*, pg. 4683
POLYGLASS S.P.A.—See Mapei SpA; *Int'l*, pg. 4683
POLYGLASS USA, INC.—See Mapei SpA; *Int'l*, pg. 4683
POLYGON AB—See Triton Advisers Limited; *Int'l*, pg. 7933
POLYGON AS—See Triton Advisers Limited; *Int'l*, pg. 7933
POLYGON COMPANY; *U.S. Private*, pg. 3225
POLYGONE INTERNATIONAL SA; *Int'l*, pg. 5915
POLYGON GLOBAL PARTNERS LLP; *Int'l*, pg. 5915
POLYGON REAL ESTATE LTD.; *Int'l*, pg. 5915
POLYGON SOLUTIONS, INC.; *U.S. Private*, pg. 3225
POLYGON US CORPORATION—See Triton Advisers Limited; *Int'l*, pg. 7933
POLYGREEN RESOURCES CO., LTD.; *Int'l*, pg. 5915
POLY (GUANGZHOU) INTERNATIONAL TRADE INVESTMENT CO., LTD.—See China Poly Group Corporation; *Int'l*, pg. 1541
POLY (GUANGZHOU) PROPERTY MANAGEMENT CO., LTD.—See China Poly Group Corporation; *Int'l*, pg. 1541
POLY (GUANGZHOU) REAL ESTATE CLUB MANAGEMENT CO., LTD.—See China Poly Group Corporation; *Int'l*, pg. 1541
POLY (GUANGZHOU) REAL ESTATE DEVELOPMENT CO., LTD.—See China Poly Group Corporation; *Int'l*, pg. 1541
POLY GUIZHOU REAL ESTATE DEVELOPMENT CO., LTD.—See China Poly Group Corporation; *Int'l*, pg. 1541
POLY (HONG KONG) HOLDINGS LIMITED—See China Poly Group Corporation; *Int'l*, pg. 1541
POLYHOSE INDIA (RUBBER) PRIVATE LIMITED—See Caterpillar, Inc.; *U.S. Public*, pg. 453
POLYHOSE SATO SHOJI METAL WORKS PRIVATE LIMITED—See Sato shoji Corporation; *Int'l*, pg. 6586
POLY (HU'NAN) REAL ESTATE DEVELOPMENT CO., LTD.—See China Poly Group Corporation; *Int'l*, pg. 1541
POLY INSULATION SOLUTIONS SDN BHD—See PGF Capital Bhd; *Int'l*, pg. 5838
POLY JILIN AMMUNITION MANUFACTURING CO., LTD.—See China Poly Group Corporation; *Int'l*, pg. 1541
POLYKETTING B.V.—See XANO Industri AB; *Int'l*, pg. 8519
POLYKING SERVICES LIMITED—See Allied Group Limited; *Int'l*, pg. 357
POLYLINK POLYMERS (INDIA) LTD.; *Int'l*, pg. 5915
POLYLITE TAIWAN CO., LTD.; *Int'l*, pg. 5915
POLYLOOM CORPORATION OF AMERICA—See ABN AMRO Group N.V.; *Int'l*, pg. 64

POLYLOOM CORPORATION OF AMERICA—See Gilde Buy Out Partners B.V.; *Int'l*, pg. 2974
POLYLOOM CORPORATION OF AMERICA—See Parcom Capital Management B.V.; *Int'l*, pg. 5740
POLYMAC THERMOFORMERS LTD.; *Int'l*, pg. 5915
POLYMAG AG—See REHAU Verwaltungszentrale AG; *Int'l*, pg. 6256
POLYMECHPLAST MACHINES LTD.; *Int'l*, pg. 5915
POLYMEDCO, INC.; *U.S. Private*, pg. 3225
POLYMEDIA S.P.A.—See Piksel, Inc.; *U.S. Private*, pg. 3180
POLY MEDICURE LTD.; *Int'l*, pg. 5914
POLYMED THERAPEUTICS, INC.—See Athenex, Inc.; *U.S. Public*, pg. 221
POLYMEM S.A.—See Repligen Corporation; *U.S. Public*, pg. 1784
POLYMER ADDITIVES, INC.—See H.I.G. Capital, LLC; *U.S. Private*, pg. 1831
POLYMER COMPOSITE ASIA SDN. BHD.—See Hexagon Holdings Berhad; *Int'l*, pg. 3370
POLYMER COMPOSITE ASIA (SHANGHAI) CO. LTD—See Hexagon Holdings Berhad; *Int'l*, pg. 3370
POLYMER ENGINEERED PRODUCTS; *U.S. Private*, pg. 3226
POLYMER ENTERPRISES INC.; *U.S. Private*, pg. 3226
POLYMER FUSION EDUCATION PTY LTD—See Fletcher Building Limited; *Int'l*, pg. 2701
POLYMER GIKEN CO., LTD.—See Fukoku Co., Ltd.; *Int'l*, pg. 2839
POLYMERIC RESOURCES CORP.; *U.S. Public*, pg. 1701
POLYMERICS, INC.; *U.S. Private*, pg. 3226
POLYMERIC SYSTEMS, INC.—See PPG Industries, Inc.; *U.S. Public*, pg. 1711
POLYMER INDUSTRIES; *U.S. Private*, pg. 3226
POLYMER INSTITUTE BRNO, SPOL. S R O.—See Orlen S.A.; *Int'l*, pg. 5641
POLYMER LINK HOLDINGS BHD; *Int'l*, pg. 5915
POLYMER LINK INDIA PVT. LTD.—See Polymer Link Holdings Bhd; *Int'l*, pg. 5915
POLYMER LINK PHILIPPINES INC.—See Polymer Link Holdings Bhd; *Int'l*, pg. 5915
POLYMER LINK SDN. BHD.—See Polymer Link Holdings Bhd; *Int'l*, pg. 5915
POLYMER LOGISTICS, INC.—See Polymer Logistics N.V.; *Int'l*, pg. 5915
POLYMER LOGISTICS N.V.; *Int'l*, pg. 5915
POLYMER PRODUCTS COMPANY, INC.—See PMC Group, Inc.; *U.S. Private*, pg. 3218
POLYMER SEALING SOLUTIONS—See Trelleborg AB; *Int'l*, pg. 7912
POLYMERSHAPES LLC—See Blackfriars Corp.; *U.S. Private*, pg. 575
POLYMER SOLUTIONS GROUP LLC—See The Jordan Company, L.P.; *U.S. Private*, pg. 4061
POLYMER SOLUTIONS IBERICA S.L.U.—See Celanese Corporation; *U.S. Public*, pg. 465
POLYMER SOLUTIONS INTERNATIONAL, INC.; *U.S. Private*, pg. 3226
POLYMER SOLUTIONS (PSI); *U.S. Private*, pg. 3226
POLYMER-TECHNIK ELBE GMBH—See Woco Industrietechnik GmbH; *Int'l*, pg. 8442
POLYMER TECHNOLOGY SYSTEMS, INC.—See Sinocare Inc.; *Int'l*, pg. 6949
POLYMETA CO., LTD.—See Nicolas Correa S.A.; *Int'l*, pg. 5273
POLY METAL AND MINERALS LIMITED—See GT Group Holdings Limited; *Int'l*, pg. 3151
POLYMETAL EURASIA LLC—See Solidcore Resources plc; *Int'l*, pg. 7073
POLYMETALLURGICAL LLC—See NN, Inc.; *U.S. Public*, pg. 1531
POLYMETALS RESOURCES LTD.; *Int'l*, pg. 5915
POLYMET CORPORATION; *U.S. Private*, pg. 3226
POLYMET MINING CORP.—See Glencore plc; *Int'l*, pg. 2991
POLYMET MINING, INC.—See Glencore plc; *Int'l*, pg. 2991
POLYMICRO TECHNOLOGIES, LLC—See Koch Industries, Inc.; *U.S. Private*, pg. 2335
POLYMIRAE CO., LTD.—See LyondellBasell Industries N.V.; *Int'l*, pg. 4608
POLYMIX; *Int'l*, pg. 5915
POLY NDT PTE. LTD.—See Centre Testing International Corporation; *Int'l*, pg. 1411
POLYNESIAN ADVENTURE TOURS INC.—See Norwegian Cruise Line Holdings Ltd.; *U.S. Public*, pg. 1543
POLYNESIAN CULTURAL CENTER; *U.S. Private*, pg. 3226
POLYNESIAN LIMITED; *Int'l*, pg. 5916
POLYNET PUBLIC COMPANY LIMITED; *Int'l*, pg. 5916
POLYNORM GMBH—See voestalpine AG; *Int'l*, pg. 8293
POLYNORM IMMOBILIEN BETEILIGUNGS-GMBH—See voestalpine AG; *Int'l*, pg. 8294
POLYNORM IMMOBILIEN GMBH & CO. KG—See voestalpine AG; *Int'l*, pg. 8293
POLYNOVO BIOMATERIALS PTY LTD.—See PolyNovo Limited; *Int'l*, pg. 5916
POLYNOVO LIMITED—See PolyNovo Limited; *Int'l*, pg. 5916

POLYNOVO LIMITED

CORPORATE AFFILIATIONS

POLYNOVO LIMITED; *Int'l*, pg. 5916
POLYNT CHEMICAL (CHANGZHOU) CO. LTD.—See Reichhold, Inc.; *U.S. Private*, pg. 3390
POLYNT COMPOSITES AUSTRALIA PTY LTD.—See Reichhold, Inc.; *U.S. Private*, pg. 3390
POLYNT COMPOSITES BRAZIL LTDA.—See Reichhold, Inc.; *U.S. Private*, pg. 3390
POLYNT COMPOSITES CANADA INC.—See Reichhold, Inc.; *U.S. Private*, pg. 3390
POLYNT COMPOSITES CANADA INC.—See Reichhold, Inc.; *U.S. Private*, pg. 3390
POLYNT COMPOSITES FRANCE S.A.—See Reichhold, Inc.; *U.S. Private*, pg. 3390
POLYNT COMPOSITES GERMANY GMBH—See Reichhold, Inc.; *U.S. Private*, pg. 3390
POLYNT COMPOSITES KOREA CO. LTD—See Reichhold, Inc.; *U.S. Private*, pg. 3390
POLYNT COMPOSITES MALAYSIA SDN. BHD.—See Reichhold, Inc.; *U.S. Private*, pg. 3390
POLYNT COMPOSITES POLAND SP. Z O.O.—See Reichhold, Inc.; *U.S. Private*, pg. 3390
POLYNT COMPOSITES SPAIN, S.L.—See Reichhold, Inc.; *U.S. Private*, pg. 3390
POLYNT COMPOSITES UK LTD—See Reichhold, Inc.; *U.S. Private*, pg. 3390
POLYNT COMPOSITES USA INC.—See Reichhold, Inc.; *U.S. Private*, pg. 3390
POLYNT GMBH—See Reichhold, Inc.; *U.S. Private*, pg. 3390
POLYNT GROUP HOLDING INC.—See Reichhold, Inc.; *U.S. Private*, pg. 3390
POLYNT HONG KONG CO., LIMITED—See Reichhold, Inc.; *U.S. Private*, pg. 3390
POLYNT IBERICA, S.L.—See Reichhold, Inc.; *U.S. Private*, pg. 3390
POLYNT S.P.A. - BREMBATE DI SOPRA PLANT—See Reichhold, Inc.; *U.S. Private*, pg. 3391
POLYNT S.P.A. - CAVAGLIA PLANT—See Reichhold, Inc.; *U.S. Private*, pg. 3391
POLYNT S.P.A. - RAVENNA PLANT—See Reichhold, Inc.; *U.S. Private*, pg. 3391
POLYNT S.P.A. - SAN GIOVANNI VALDARNO PLANT—See Reichhold, Inc.; *U.S. Private*, pg. 3391
POLYNT S.P.A.—See Reichhold, Inc.; *U.S. Private*, pg. 3390
POLYNT SP. Z O.O.—See Reichhold, Inc.; *U.S. Private*, pg. 3391
POLYNT UK LTD.—See Reichhold, Inc.; *U.S. Private*, pg. 3391
POLYOIL LTD.—See Emerson Electric Co.; *U.S. Public*, pg. 751
THE POLYOLEFIN COMPANY (SINGAPORE) PTE. LTD.—See Sumitomo Chemical Company, Limited; *Int'l*, pg. 7267
POLYOLS ASIA COMPANY, INC.—See Mitsubishi Gas Chemical Company, Inc.; *Int'l*, pg. 4950
POLYONE CORP. - LONG BEACH PLANT—See Avient Corporation; *U.S. Public*, pg. 248
POLYONE CORPORATION UK LIMITED - TRADING COMPANY—See Avient Corporation; *U.S. Public*, pg. 248
POLYONE CORP. - WICHITA—See Avient Corporation; *U.S. Public*, pg. 248
POLYONE DE MEXICO DISTRIBUTION, S. DE R.L. DE C.V.—See Avient Corporation; *U.S. Public*, pg. 248
POLYONE DSS CANADA INC.—See Avient Corporation; *U.S. Public*, pg. 248
POLYONE JAPAN K.K.—See Avient Corporation; *U.S. Public*, pg. 248
POLYONE MANAGEMENT (SHANGHAI) CO. LTD.—See Avient Corporation; *U.S. Public*, pg. 248
POLYONE POLYMERS INDIA PVT. LTD.—See Avient Corporation; *U.S. Public*, pg. 248
POLYONE SHANGHAI, CHINA—See Avient Corporation; *U.S. Public*, pg. 248
POLYONE SHENZHEN CO. LTD.—See Avient Corporation; *U.S. Public*, pg. 248
POLYONE SINGAPORE, LTD.—See Avient Corporation; *U.S. Public*, pg. 248
POLYONE SUZHOU, CHINA—See Avient Corporation; *U.S. Public*, pg. 248
POLYPACIFIC POLYMERS SDN. BHD.—See LyondellBasell Industries N.V.; *Int'l*, pg. 4608
POLYPACIFIC PTY. LTD.—See Mirlex Pty. Ltd.; *Int'l*, pg. 4919
POLYPACIFIC PTY. LTD.—See Viva Energy Group Limited; *Int'l*, pg. 8264
POLYPAC SPA—See Trelleborg AB; *Int'l*, pg. 7911
POLYPAG AG—See Sika AG; *Int'l*, pg. 6915
POLY PAK AMERICA, INC.; *U.S. Private*, pg. 3225
POLY-PAK INDUSTRIES, INC.; *U.S. Private*, pg. 3225
POLYPAL FRANCE SNC—See Whittan Storage Systems Ltd.; *Int'l*, pg. 8400
POLYPAL GERMANY GMBH—See Whittan Storage Systems Ltd.; *Int'l*, pg. 8400
POLYPAL NETHERLANDS BV—See Whittan Storage Systems Ltd.; *Int'l*, pg. 8400
POLYPAL SA—See Whittan Storage Systems Ltd.; *Int'l*, pg. 8400

POLYPAL—See Whittan Storage Systems Ltd.; *Int'l*, pg. 8400
POLYPATHS, LLC—See Genstar Capital, LLC; *U.S. Private*, pg. 1678
POLYPENCO LTD.—See Mitsubishi Chemical Group Corporation; *Int'l*, pg. 4930
POLYPEPTIDE LABORATORIES AB; *Int'l*, pg. 5916
POLYPHASER CORPORATION—See Smiths Group plc; *Int'l*, pg. 7011
POLYPHENOLICS LLC—See Constellation Brands, Inc.; *U.S. Public*, pg. 571
POLYPID INC.—See PolyPid Ltd.; *Int'l*, pg. 5916
POLYPID LTD.; *Int'l*, pg. 5916
POLYPIPE FRANCE SAS—See Groupe ELYDAN; *Int'l*, pg. 3102
POLYPIPE GULF FZ LLC—See Genuit Group plc; *Int'l*, pg. 2930
POLYPIPE GULF FZ LLC—See Genuit Group plc; *Int'l*, pg. 2930
POLYPIPE ITALIA S.R.L.—See Genuit Group plc; *Int'l*, pg. 2930
POLYPIPE LIMITED - POLYPIPE BUILDING PRODUCTS DIVISION—See Genuit Group plc; *Int'l*, pg. 2930
POLYPIPE LIMITED - POLYPIPE CIVILS DIVISION—See Genuit Group plc; *Int'l*, pg. 2930
POLYPIPE LIMITED - POLYPIPE TDI DIVISION—See Genuit Group plc; *Int'l*, pg. 2930
POLYPIPE LIMITED - POLYPIPE TERRAIN DIVISION—See Genuit Group plc; *Int'l*, pg. 2930
POLYPIPE LIMITED - POLYPIPE VENTILATION DIVISION—See Genuit Group plc; *Int'l*, pg. 2930
POLYPIPE LIMITED—See Genuit Group plc; *Int'l*, pg. 2930
POLYPIPE, LLC—See Grupo Empresarial Kaluz S.A. de C.V.; *Int'l*, pg. 3127
POLYPLAS EXTRUSIONS LTD.—See Surteco Group SE; *Int'l*, pg. 7345
POLYPLAS SDN. BHD.—See Ge-Shen Corporation Berhad; *Int'l*, pg. 2897
POLYPLASTIC B.V.—See LCI Industries; *U.S. Public*, pg. 1296
POLY PLASTIC MASTERBATCH (SUZHOU) CO., LTD.; *Int'l*, pg. 5914
POLY PLASTIC PRODUCTS INC—See Alpha Industries, Inc.; *U.S. Private*, pg. 197
POLY PLASTIC PRODUCTS OF NORTH CAROLINA, INC—See Alpha Industries, Inc.; *U.S. Private*, pg. 198
POLYPLASTICS ASIA PACIFIC SDN. BHD.—See Daicel Corporation; *Int'l*, pg. 1919
POLYPLASTICS ASIA PACIFIC SINGAPORE PTE. LTD.—See Daicel Corporation; *Int'l*, pg. 1919
POLYPLASTICS CHINA LTD.—See Daicel Corporation; *Int'l*, pg. 1919
POLYPLASTICS CO., LTD.—See Daicel Corporation; *Int'l*, pg. 1919
POLYPLASTICS EUROPE GMBH—See Daicel Corporation; *Int'l*, pg. 1920
POLYPLASTICS KOREA LTD.—See Daicel Corporation; *Int'l*, pg. 1920
POLYPLASTICS MARKETING (INDIA) PVT LTD—See Daicel Corporation; *Int'l*, pg. 1920
POLYPLASTICS MARKETING MEXICO, S.A. DE C.V.—See Daicel Corporation; *Int'l*, pg. 1920
POLYPLASTICS MARKETING (T) LTD.—See Daicel Corporation; *Int'l*, pg. 1920
POLYPLASTICS (NANTONG) LTD.—See Daicel Corporation; *Int'l*, pg. 1919
POLYPLASTICS SHANGHAI LTD.—See Daicel Corporation; *Int'l*, pg. 1920
POLYPLASTICS TAIWAN CO., LTD.—See Daicel Corporation; *Int'l*, pg. 1920
POLYPLASTICS TRADING (SHANGHAI) LTD.—See Daicel Corporation; *Int'l*, pg. 1920
POLYPLASTICS USA, INC.—See Daicel Corporation; *Int'l*, pg. 1920
POLYPLEX (AMERICAS) INC.—See Polyplex Corporation Limited; *Int'l*, pg. 5916
POLYPLEX (ASIA) PTE. LTD.—See Polyplex Corporation Limited; *Int'l*, pg. 5916
POLYPLEX CORPORATION LIMITED; *Int'l*, pg. 5916
POLYPLEX EUROPA POLYESTER FILM SAN VE TIC A.S.—See Polyplex Corporation Limited; *Int'l*, pg. 5916
POLYPLEX (SINGAPORE) PTE. LIMITED—See Polyplex Corporation Limited; *Int'l*, pg. 5916
POLYPLEX (THAILAND) PUBLIC COMPANY LIMITED—See Polyplex Corporation Limited; *Int'l*, pg. 5916
POLYPLEX TRADING (SHENZHEN) COMPANY LIMITED—See Polyplex Corporation Limited; *Int'l*, pg. 5916
POLY-PLY INDUSTRIES SDN. BHD.—See ANNUM BERHAD; *Int'l*, pg. 474
POLYPORE INTERNATIONAL, LP—See Asahi Kasei Corporation; *Int'l*, pg. 597
POLYPORE K.K.—See Asahi Kasei Corporation; *Int'l*, pg. 596
POLYPORE (SHANGHAI) MEMBRANE PRODUCTS CO., LTD.—See Asahi Kasei Corporation; *Int'l*, pg. 597
POLY PORTABLES INC.; *U.S. Private*, pg. 3225

POLYPRIDE, INC.—See Sealed Air Corporation; *U.S. Public*, pg. 1854
POLYPRINT LTD.—See BERICAP GmbH & Co. KG; *Int'l*, pg. 981
POLYPROJECT ENVIRONMENT AB—See Sdiptech AB; *Int'l*, pg. 6659
POLY PROPERTY GROUP CO., LIMITED; *Int'l*, pg. 5914
POLY PROPERTY SERVICES CO., LTD.—See China Poly Group Corporation; *Int'l*, pg. 1541
POLYPROPLYENE MALAYSIA SDN. BHD.—See Petroliam Nasional Berhad; *Int'l*, pg. 5830
POLYRAM PLASTIC INDUSTRIES LTD.; *Int'l*, pg. 5916
POLY-REK D.O.O.—See Systemair AB; *Int'l*, pg. 7391
POLYREY BENELUX—See International Paper Company; *U.S. Public*, pg. 1157
POLYRIGHT SA—See Adon Production AG; *Int'l*, pg. 152
POLYRIGHT SA—See Mountain Capital Management AG; *Int'l*, pg. 5057
POLYROCKS CHEMICAL CO., LTD.; *Int'l*, pg. 5916
POLY SAGAWA LOGISTIC CO., LTD.—See China Poly Group Corporation; *Int'l*, pg. 1541
POLY (SCIENCE CITY, GUANGZHOU) REAL ESTATE DEVELOPMENT CO., LTD.—See China Poly Group Corporation; *Int'l*, pg. 1541
POLYSCIENCES INC.; *U.S. Private*, pg. 3226
POLY (SHANGHAI) REAL ESTATE DEVELOPMENT CO., LTD.—See China Poly Group Corporation; *Int'l*, pg. 1541
POLY (SHENYANG) REAL ESTATE DEVELOPMENT CO., LTD.—See China Poly Group Corporation; *Int'l*, pg. 1541
POLYSIUS CORP.—See ThyssenKrupp AG; *Int'l*, pg. 7732
POLYSIUS DE ARGENTINA S.A.—See ThyssenKrupp AG; *Int'l*, pg. 7725
POLYSIUS DEL PERU S.A.—See ThyssenKrupp AG; *Int'l*, pg. 7725
POLYSIUS DE MEXICO S.A. DE C.V.—See ThyssenKrupp AG; *Int'l*, pg. 7725
POLYSIUS DO BRASIL LTDA.—See ThyssenKrupp AG; *Int'l*, pg. 7725
POLYSIUS ENGINEERING SDN. BHD.—See ThyssenKrupp AG; *Int'l*, pg. 7725
POLYSIUS INGENIERIA Y SERVICIOS DEL PERU S.A.—See ThyssenKrupp AG; *Int'l*, pg. 7725
POLYSIUS LTD.—See ThyssenKrupp AG; *Int'l*, pg. 7725
POLYSIUS S.A.—See ThyssenKrupp AG; *Int'l*, pg. 7725
POLYSIUS S.A.S.—See ThyssenKrupp AG; *Int'l*, pg. 7728
POLYSIUS (SHANGHAI) CO., LTD.—See ThyssenKrupp AG; *Int'l*, pg. 7725
POLYSIUS VIETNAM LTD.—See ThyssenKrupp AG; *Int'l*, pg. 7725
POLYSONICS CORPORATION; *U.S. Private*, pg. 3226
POLYSOURCE, LLC; *U.S. Private*, pg. 3226
POLY SOUTH CHINA INDUSTRY CO., LTD.—See China Poly Group Corporation; *Int'l*, pg. 1541
POLY SOUTHERN GROUP CO., LTD.—See China Poly Group Corporation; *Int'l*, pg. 1541
POLYSPIN EXPORTS LIMITED; *Int'l*, pg. 5916
POLYSTAN A/S—See Getinge AB; *Int'l*, pg. 2952
POLYSTAR ASIA PRIVATE LTD.—See Elisa Corporation; *Int'l*, pg. 2361
POLYSTAR INSTRUMENTS INC.—See Elisa Corporation; *Int'l*, pg. 2361
POLYSTAR OSIX AB—See Elisa Corporation; *Int'l*, pg. 2361
POLYSTAR RYSSLAND LLC—See Elisa Corporation; *Int'l*, pg. 2361
POLYSUTURE INDUSTRIA E COMERCIO LTDA.—See Medtronic plc; *Int'l*, pg. 4787
POLYSYSTEMS INC.; *U.S. Private*, pg. 3226
POLY-TAINER INC.; *U.S. Private*, pg. 3225
POLYTAINERS INC.; *Int'l*, pg. 5916
POLYTEC ASSET HOLDINGS LIMITED; *Int'l*, pg. 5916
POLYTEC AUTOMOTIVE GMBH & CO KG—See POLYTEC Holding AG; *Int'l*, pg. 5916
POLYTEC AVO NV—See POLYTEC Holding AG; *Int'l*, pg. 5916
POLYTEC CAR STYLING BROMYARD LTD.—See POLYTEC Holding AG; *Int'l*, pg. 5916
POLYTEC COMPOSITES BOHEMIA S.R.O.—See POLYTEC Holding AG; *Int'l*, pg. 5917
POLYTEC COMPOSITES GERMANY GMBH & CO KG—See POLYTEC Holding AG; *Int'l*, pg. 5917
POLYTEC COMPOSITES SWEDEN AB—See POLYTEC Holding AG; *Int'l*, pg. 5916
POLYTEC COMPOSITES VERWALTUNGS GMBH—See POLYTEC Holding AG; *Int'l*, pg. 5917
POLYTEC COMPOSITES WEIDEN GMBH—See POLYTEC Holding AG; *Int'l*, pg. 5917
POLYTEC COMPOUNDS GMBH & CO. KG—See POLYTEC Holding AG; *Int'l*, pg. 5917
POLYTEC DEUTSCHLAND VERWALTUNGS GMBH—See POLYTEC Holding AG; *Int'l*, pg. 5917
POLYTEC ELASTOFORM GMBH & CO KG—See POLYTEC Holding AG; *Int'l*, pg. 5917
POLYTEC EMC ENGINEERING GMBH & CO KG—See POLYTEC Holding AG; *Int'l*, pg. 5917
POLYTEC EMC ENGINEERING GMBH—See POLYTEC Holding AG; *Int'l*, pg. 5917

COMPANY NAME INDEX

POLYTEC FOHA CORP—See POLYTEC Holding AG; *Int'l*, pg. 5917
POLYTEC FOHA INC.—See POLYTEC Holding AG; *Int'l*, pg. 5917
POLYTEC FOR CAR STYLING GMBH & CO KG—See POLYTEC Holding AG; *Int'l*, pg. 5917
POLYTECH ELECTRONICS TECHNOLOGY (DONG GUAN) CO.,LTD—See Shun On Electronic Co, Ltd.; *Int'l*, pg. 6869
THE POLYTECHNIC CLUB, INC.—See Munchener Ruckversicherungs AG; *Int'l*, pg. 5092
POLYTEC HOLDING AG; *Int'l*, pg. 5916
POLYTEC INDUSTRIAL PLASTICS GMBH—See POLYTEC Holding AG; *Int'l*, pg. 5917
POLYTEC INDUSTRIELACKIERUNG GMBH & CO. KG—See POLYTEC Holding AG; *Int'l*, pg. 5917
POLYTEC INDUSTRIELACKIERUNG WEIDEN GMBH—See POLYTEC Holding AG; *Int'l*, pg. 5917
POLYTEC INTERIOR GMBH—See POLYTEC Holding AG; *Int'l*, pg. 5917
POLYTEC INTERIOR POLSKA SP. Z O.O.—See POLYTEC Holding AG; *Int'l*, pg. 5917
POLYTEC INTERIOR SOUTH AFRICA (PTY) LTD.—See POLYTEC Holding AG; *Int'l*, pg. 5917
POLYTEC INTERIOR ZARAGOZA S.L.—See POLYTEC Holding AG; *Int'l*, pg. 5917
POLYTEC PLASTICS GERMANY GMBH & CO KG—See POLYTEC Holding AG; *Int'l*, pg. 5917
POLYTEC PLASTICS IDSTEIN GMBH & CO. KG—See POLYTEC Holding AG; *Int'l*, pg. 5917
POLYTEC PROPERTY (SHENYANG) HIGH CHEER COMPANY LIMITED—See Kowloon Development Company Limited; *Int'l*, pg. 4295
POLYTEC PROPERTY (WUXI) LIMITED—See Kowloon Development Company Limited; *Int'l*, pg. 4295
POLYTEC THELEN GMBH—See POLYTEC Holding AG; *Int'l*, pg. 5917
POLYTEK DEVELOPMENT CORP.—See Arsenal Capital Management LP; *U.S. Private*, pg. 339
POLYTEX FIBERS CORPORATION—See ZL Star Inc.; *U.S. Private*, pg. 4606
POLYTEX INDIA LIMITED; *Int'l*, pg. 5917
POLYTOOL INTEGRATION SDN. BHD.—See Kobay Technology Bhd.; *Int'l*, pg. 4216
POLYTOOL TECHNOLOGIES SDN. BHD.—See Kobay Technology Bhd.; *Int'l*, pg. 4216
POLYTRON GMBH—See Mitsubishi Chemical Group Corporation; *Int'l*, pg. 4930
POLYTRONICS TECHNOLOGY CORP.; *Int'l*, pg. 5917
POLYU GMBH—See PCC SE; *Int'l*, pg. 5767
POLY UNION CHEMICAL HOLDING GROUP CO.,LTD.; *Int'l*, pg. 5914
POLYURETHANE FOAM SYSTEMS INC.; *Int'l*, pg. 5917
POLYURETHANE MACHINERY CORPORATION—See PMC Capital Partners, LLC; *U.S. Private*, pg. 3218
POLYVENTIVE LLC; *U.S. Private*, pg. 3226
POLY VINYL CO.; *U.S. Private*, pg. 3225
POLY VINYL CREATIONS, INC.; *U.S. Private*, pg. 3225
POLYVINYL FILMS, INC.; *U.S. Private*, pg. 3226
POLYVISION CORPORATION-BEAVERTON—See Industrial Opportunity Partners, LLC; *U.S. Private*, pg. 2067
POLYVISION CORPORATION—See Industrial Opportunity Partners, LLC; *U.S. Private*, pg. 2067
POLYVISION NV—See Steelcase Inc.; *U.S. Public*, pg. 1944
POLY VISIONS, INC.—See Bemis Associates Inc.; *U.S. Private*, pg. 522
POLYWELL COMPUTERS, INC.; *U.S. Private*, pg. 3226
POLYWERT GMBH; *Int'l*, pg. 5917
POLYWIN COMPUTER LIMITED—See China Bester Group Telecom Co., Ltd.; *Int'l*, pg. 1486
POLYWOOD PROFILES PRIVATE LIMITED—See Dhabriya Polywood Limited; *Int'l*, pg. 2097
POLY (WUHAN) REAL ESTATE DEVELOPMENT CO., LTD.—See China Poly Group Corporation; *Int'l*, pg. 1541
POLYXYLENOL SINGAPORE PTE. LTD.—See Asahi Kasei Corporation; *Int'l*, pg. 597
POLYZEN, LLC—See Altaris Capital Partners, LLC; *U.S. Private*, pg. 206
POMA AUTOMATED FUELING INC.; *U.S. Private*, pg. 3226
POMAC, LLC—See Lennar Corporation; *U.S. Public*, pg. 1307
POMA-OTIS TRANSPORTATION SYSTEMS—See Otis Worldwide Corporation; *U.S. Public*, pg. 1623
POMARE INTERNATIONAL CORP.—See Pomare Ltd.; *U.S. Private*, pg. 3226
POMARE LTD.; *U.S. Private*, pg. 3226
P&O MARITIME FZE—See Dubai World Corporation; *Int'l*, pg. 2222
P&O MARITIME SERVICES PTY LTD—See Dubai World Corporation; *Int'l*, pg. 2222
POMAROM S.R.L.—See Floridienne SA; *Int'l*, pg. 2708
POMBURAPA CO., LTD.—See Thai Beverage Public Company Limited; *Int'l*, pg. 7591
POMCHAROEN CO., LTD.—See Thai Beverage Public Company Limited; *Int'l*, pg. 7591

POMCHOK CO., LTD.—See Thai Beverage Public Company Limited; *Int'l*, pg. 7591
POMCO, INC.—See UnitedHealth Group Incorporated; *U.S. Public*, pg. 2249
POM-COLLEGE STATION, LLC—See CBL & Associates Properties, Inc.; *U.S. Public*, pg. 458
P.O. MEDIA SERVICE INC—See Pola Orbis Holdings Inc.; *Int'l*, pg. 5905
POMEL (ETABLISSEMENTS)—See Groupe Bruxelles Lambert SA; *Int'l*, pg. 3100
POMELLATO SWITZERLAND S.A.—See Kering S.A.; *Int'l*, pg. 4136
POME ON THE RANGE, LLC—See Louisburg Cider Mill, Inc.; *U.S. Private*, pg. 2499
POMERANKA SP. Z O.O.—See PKO Bank Polski SA; *Int'l*, pg. 5887
POMERLEAU INC.; *Int'l*, pg. 5917
THE POMEROY COLLECTION LTD.—See ELK Group International, Inc.; *U.S. Private*, pg. 1362
POMEROY IT SOLUTIONS SALES COMPANY, INC.—See Aurelius Equity Opportunities SE & Co. KGaA; *Int'l*, pg. 708
POMGRAD INZENJERING D.O.O.—See STRABAG SE; *Int'l*, pg. 7231
POMIFRUTAS S/A; *Int'l*, pg. 5917
POMINA STEEL CORPORATION; *Int'l*, pg. 5917
POMINA STEEL JOINT STOCK COMPANY 2—See Pomina Steel Corporation; *Int'l*, pg. 5918
POMINI RUBBER & PLASTICS S.R.L.—See L. Possehl & Co. MbH; *Int'l*, pg. 4383
POMINVEST DD—See UniCredit S.p.A.; *Int'l*, pg. 8040
POMIRAN METALIZATION RESEARCH CO., LTD.—See Taimide Tech. Inc.; *Int'l*, pg. 7415
POMKIT CO., LTD.—See Thai Beverage Public Company Limited; *Int'l*, pg. 7591
POMKLUNG CO., LTD.—See Thai Beverage Public Company Limited; *Int'l*, pg. 7591
POMMERAIE PARC SC—See BNP Paribas SA; *Int'l*, pg. 1092
POMNAKORN CO., LTD.—See Thai Beverage Public Company Limited; *Int'l*, pg. 7591
POMOCO NISSAN; *U.S. Private*, pg. 3226
POMONA ACQUISITION LTD.; *Int'l*, pg. 5918
POMONA CAPITAL; *U.S. Private*, pg. 3226
POMONA GRUPPEN AB; *Int'l*, pg. 5918
POMONA VALLEY HOSPITAL MEDICAL CENTER; *U.S. Private*, pg. 3226
POMORAVLJE A.D.; *Int'l*, pg. 5918
POMORAVLJE A.D.; *Int'l*, pg. 5918
POMORAVLJE TERM A.D.; *Int'l*, pg. 5918
POMORSKA SPOLKA GAZOWNICTWA SP. Z O.O.—See Polskie Gornictwo Naftowe i Gazownictwo S.A.; *Int'l*, pg. 5912
POMORSKIE BIURO PROJEKTOW GEL SP. Z O.O.—See Polnord S.A.; *Int'l*, pg. 5911
POMPALANG CO., LTD.—See Thai Beverage Public Company Limited; *Int'l*, pg. 7591
POMPANETTE COMPANY LLC; *U.S. Private*, pg. 3227
POMPANO NISSAN; *U.S. Private*, pg. 3226
POMPANOOSUC MILLS CORPORATION; *U.S. Private*, pg. 3227
POMPEIAN, INC.; *U.S. Private*, pg. 3227
POMPES FRISTAM S.N.C.—See FRISTAM Pumpen F. Stamp GmbH & Co. KG; *Int'l*, pg. 2793
POMPES GRUNDFOS DISTRIBUTION S.A.S.—See The Poul Due Jensen Foundation; *Int'l*, pg. 7676
POMPES GRUNDFOS S.A.—See The Poul Due Jensen Foundation; *Int'l*, pg. 7676
POMPES RUTSCHI SAS; *Int'l*, pg. 5918
POMP'S TIRE SERVICE INC.; *U.S. Private*, pg. 3227
POMPTON CARE, L.L.C.—See Welltower Inc.; *U.S. Public*, pg. 2349
POMS & ASSOCIATES INSURANCE BROKERS, INC.; *U.S. Private*, pg. 3227
POMS CORP.—See Constellation Software Inc.; *Int'l*, pg. 1772
POMTHIP (2012) CO., LTD.—See Thai Beverage Public Company Limited; *Int'l*, pg. 7591
POMVOM LTD.; *Int'l*, pg. 5918
POMVOM UK LIMITED—See Pomvom Ltd.; *Int'l*, pg. 5918
POM WONDERFUL LLC—See The Wonderful Company LLC; *U.S. Private*, pg. 4138
PON BICYCLE GROUP—See Pon Holdings B.V.; *Int'l*, pg. 5918
PONCA CITY HOME CARE SERVICES, INC.—See Community Health Systems, Inc.; *U.S. Public*, pg. 556
PONCA DIALYSIS, LLC—See DaVita Inc.; *U.S. Public*, pg. 642
PONCA IRON & METAL INC.—See Yaffe Iron & Metal Company Inc.; *U.S. Private*, pg. 4584
PONCE BUENOS AIRES—See The Interpublic Group of Companies, Inc.; *U.S. Public*, pg. 2092
PONCE CARIBBEAN DISTRIBUTORS—See Able Sales Company, Inc.; *U.S. Private*, pg. 39
PONCE CASH & CARRY INC.; *U.S. Private*, pg. 3227
PONCE DE LEON FEDERAL BANK; *U.S. Private*, pg. 3227
POND5 INC.—See Shutterstock, Inc.; *U.S. Public*, pg. 1876

PONDELWILKINSON INC.; *U.S. Private*, pg. 3227
PONDER & CO.—See Vizient, Inc.; *U.S. Private*, pg. 4407
PONDER IDEAWORKS; *U.S. Private*, pg. 3227
PONDEROSA STEAKHOUSE—See Fog Cutter Capital Group Inc.; *U.S. Private*, pg. 1557
PONDEROSA STEAKHOUSE—See Fog Cutter Capital Group Inc.; *U.S. Private*, pg. 1557
PONDEROSA TELEPHONE CO; *U.S. Private*, pg. 3227
POND NATURALS INC.—See Pond Technologies Holdings Inc.; *Int'l*, pg. 5919
POND SECURITY SERVICE GMBH; *Int'l*, pg. 5919
POND'S EXPORTS LIMITED—See Unilever PLC; *Int'l*, pg. 8044
PONDS & SONS CONSTRUCTION COMPANY, INC.; *U.S. Private*, pg. 3227
POND TECHNICS & TRAINING B.V.B.A.—See Kingspan Group PLC; *Int'l*, pg. 4178
POND TECHNOLOGIES HOLDINGS INC.; *Int'l*, pg. 5919
POND TECHNOLOGIES INC.—See Pond Technologies Holdings Inc.; *Int'l*, pg. 5919
PONDY OXIDES & CHEMICALS LIMITED; *Int'l*, pg. 5919
PONEL BAU GMBH—See Per Aarsleff Holding A/S; *Int'l*, pg. 5796
PON FOOD CORP—See Alvarez & Marsal, Inc.; *U.S. Private*, pg. 213
PON FOOD CORP—See Highview Capital, LLC; *U.S. Private*, pg. 1942
PONG MARKETING & PROMOTIONS INC.; *Int'l*, pg. 5919
PONGO RESUME; *U.S. Private*, pg. 3227
PONGRATZ TRAILER-GROUP GMBH—See Unternehmens Invest AG; *Int'l*, pg. 8085
PON HOLDINGS B.V.; *Int'l*, pg. 5918
PONIARD PHARMACEUTICALS, INC.; *U.S. Public*, pg. 1701
PONISAVLJE A.D.; *Int'l*, pg. 5919
PONMART; *Int'l*, pg. 5919
PONNI SUGARS ERODE LIMITED—See Seshasayee Paper & Boards Ltd; *Int'l*, pg. 6729
PON NORTH AMERICA, INC.—See Pon Holdings B.V.; *Int'l*, pg. 5918
PONO CAPITAL TWO, INC.; *U.S. Public*, pg. 1701
PONOKA FORD SALES; *Int'l*, pg. 5919
PONSSE AB—See Ponsse Oyj; *Int'l*, pg. 5919
PONSSE AS—See Ponsse Oyj; *Int'l*, pg. 5919
PONSSE CHILE SPA—See Ponsse Oyj; *Int'l*, pg. 5919
PONSSE CHINA LTD.—See Ponsse Oyj; *Int'l*, pg. 5919
PONSSE CZECH S.R.O.—See Ponsse Oyj; *Int'l*, pg. 5919
PONSSE NORTH AMERICA, INC.—See Ponsse Oyj; *Int'l*, pg. 5920
PONSSE OYJ; *Int'l*, pg. 5919
PONSSE S.A.S.—See Ponsse Oyj; *Int'l*, pg. 5920
PONSSE UK LTD.—See Ponsse Oyj; *Int'l*, pg. 5920
PONSSE URUGUAY S.A.—See Ponsse Oyj; *Int'l*, pg. 5920
PONTCHARTRAIN FOODS INC.; *U.S. Private*, pg. 3227
PONTEGGI DALMINE—See Marcegaglia S.p.A.; *Int'l*, pg. 4689
PONTEGGI DALMINE—See Marcegaglia S.p.A.; *Int'l*, pg. 4689
PONT EMBALLAGE SAS—See Newship Ltd; *Int'l*, pg. 5238
PONTEM CORPORATION; *U.S. Public*, pg. 1701
PONTETORTO S.P.A.—See Daidoh Limited; *Int'l*, pg. 1924
PONTE VEDRA BEACH INN & CLUB—See Gate Petroleum Company; *U.S. Private*, pg. 1649
PONTE VEDRA LODGE & CLUB—See Gate Petroleum Company; *U.S. Private*, pg. 1649
PONTE VEDRA PLASTIC SURGERY—See Ascend Plastic Surgery Partners; *U.S. Private*, pg. 346
PONTEX POLYBLEND CO., LTD.; *Int'l*, pg. 5920
PONTEX (Q.Y) POLYBLEND CO., LTD.—See Pontex Polyblend Co., Ltd.; *Int'l*, pg. 5920
PONTEX (THAILAND) CO., LTD.—See Saha Pathanapibul Public Company Limited; *Int'l*, pg. 6479
PONTIAC BANCORP, INC.; *U.S. Public*, pg. 1701
PONTIAC CEILING & PARTITION CO. LLC—See National Construction Enterprises Inc.; *U.S. Private*, pg. 2851
PONTIAC COIL INC.—See Sumida Corporation; *Int'l*, pg. 7261
PONTIAC FOODS, INC.—See The Kroger Co.; *U.S. Public*, pg. 2109
PONTIAC IGA FOOD CENTER; *U.S. Private*, pg. 3227
PONTIAC RV INC.; *U.S. Private*, pg. 3227
PONTIAN ICE FACTORY SDN. BHD.—See Haisan Resources Berhad; *Int'l*, pg. 3217
PONTIAN UNITED PLANTATIONS BERHAD—See FGV Holdings Bhd; *Int'l*, pg. 2650
PONTICELLI S.R.L.—See Biancamano S.p.A.; *Int'l*, pg. 1017
PONTIFF & ASSOCIATES, P.C.—See Aprio, LLP; *U.S. Private*, pg. 301
PONTIFLEX INC.; *U.S. Private*, pg. 3227
PONTIGGIA SARL; *Int'l*, pg. 5920
PONTIVY AUTOMOBILES; *Int'l*, pg. 5920
PONTMEYER B.V.—See HAL Trust N.V.; *Int'l*, pg. 3224
PONTOON BOAT, LLC; *U.S. Private*, pg. 3227
PONTOS GROUP; *Int'l*, pg. 5920
PONTOTOC ELECTRIC POWER ASSOCIATION; *U.S. Private*, pg. 3227

PONTOTOC ELECTRIC POWER ASSOCIATION — CORPORATE AFFILIATIONS

PONTOTOC SPRING—See American Securities LLC; *U.S. Private*, pg. 250
PONT PACKAGING B.V.—See Newship Ltd; *Int'l*, pg. 5238
PONT PACKAGING GMBH—See Newship Ltd; *Int'l*, pg. 5238
PONTUS PROTEIN LTD.; *Int'l*, pg. 5920
PONY CANYON ENTERPRISE INC.—See Memory-Tech Corporation; *Int'l*, pg. 4814
PONY CANYON INC.—See Fuji Media Holdings, Inc.; *Int'l*, pg. 2814
PONY CANYON MUSIC INC.—See Fuji Media Holdings, Inc.; *Int'l*, pg. 2814
PONY CANYON PLANNING INC.—See Fuji Media Holdings, Inc.; *Int'l*, pg. 2814
PONY EXPRESS BANCORP, INC.; *U.S. Private*, pg. 3227
PONY EXPRESS COMMUNITY BANK—See Pony Express Bancorp, Inc.; *U.S. Private*, pg. 3227
PONY GROUP INC.; *Int'l*, pg. 5920
PONYLINK CO., LTD; *Int'l*, pg. 5920
PONY TESTING CO., LTD.; *Int'l*, pg. 5920
PONZANO CHILDREN S.R.L.—See Edizione S.r.l.; *Int'l*, pg. 2312
POOF-SLINKY, LLC—See Propel Equity Partners, LLC; *U.S. Private*, pg. 3284
POOJAWESTERN METALIKS LIMITED; *Int'l*, pg. 5920
POOL AND PATIO WORKS INC.—See Anchor Industries, Inc.; *U.S. Private*, pg. 273
POOL ARABIA COMPANY LTD.—See Nabors Industries Ltd.; *Int'l*, pg. 5119
POOLBEG PHARMA (IRELAND) LIMITED—See Poolbeg Pharma Plc; *Int'l*, pg. 5920
POOLBEG PHARMA PLC; *Int'l*, pg. 5920
POOL CITY INC.; *U.S. Private*, pg. 3228
POOL CORPORATION; *U.S. Public*, pg. 1701
POOL COVERS, INC.; *U.S. Private*, pg. 3228
POOL COVER SPECIALIST NATIONAL, INC.—See Pamplona Capital Management LLP; *Int'l*, pg. 5711
POOLDAWG.COM, INC.; *U.S. Private*, pg. 3228
POOL DISTRIBUTORS COLOMBIA S.A.S.—See Pool Corporation; *U.S. Public*, pg. 1701
POOLE & ASSOCIATES, INC.—See Jacobs Engineering Group, Inc.; *U.S. Public*, pg. 1186
POOLE CHEMICAL CO. INC.; *U.S. Private*, pg. 3228
THE POOLE & KENT COMPANY OF FLORIDA—See EMCOR Group, Inc.; *U.S. Public*, pg. 739
THE POOLE & KENT CORPORATION—See EMCOR Group, Inc.; *U.S. Public*, pg. 739
POOL & ELECTRICAL PRODUCTS INC.; *U.S. Private*, pg. 3227
POOLE & POOLE ARCHITECTURE, LLC; *U.S. Private*, pg. 3228
POOLE PROFESSIONAL LTD.—See Brown & Brown, Inc.; *U.S. Public*, pg. 399
POOLE & SHAFFERY, LLP; *U.S. Private*, pg. 3228
POOLIESTUDIOS GMBH—See Allgeier SE; *Int'l*, pg. 337
POOL INTERNATIONAL—See Nabors Industries Ltd.; *Int'l*, pg. 5119
POOL SUPPLIER, S.L.—See Fluidra SA; *Int'l*, pg. 2714
POOL SYSTEMS PTY. LTD.—See Pool Corporation; *U.S. Public*, pg. 1701
POOL WATER PRODUCTS INC.; *U.S. Private*, pg. 3228
POONA DAL & OIL INDUSTRIES LTD.; *Int'l*, pg. 5920
POONAWALLA FINCORP LIMITED; *Int'l*, pg. 5920
POONG JEON NONFERROUS METAL. CO. LTD.—See PJ Metal Co., Ltd.; *Int'l*, pg. 5877
POONGSAN CORP. - BUSAN PLANT—See Poongsan Holdings Corporation; *Int'l*, pg. 5920
POONGSAN CORPORATION—See Poongsan Holdings Corporation; *Int'l*, pg. 5920
POONGSAN CORP. - ULSAN PLANT—See Poongsan Holdings Corporation; *Int'l*, pg. 5920
POONGSAN (H.K.) LTD.—See Poongsan Holdings Corporation; *Int'l*, pg. 5920
POONGSAN HOLDINGS CORP. - BUSAN PLANT—See Poongsan Holdings Corporation; *Int'l*, pg. 5921
POONGSAN HOLDINGS CORP. - CHANGWON PLANT—See Poongsan Holdings Corporation; *Int'l*, pg. 5921
POONGSAN HOLDINGS CORPORATION; *Int'l*, pg. 5920
POONGSAN METAL SERVICE CORPORATION—See Poongsan Holdings Corporation; *Int'l*, pg. 5921
POONGSAN SPECIAL METAL CORPORATION—See Poongsan Holdings Corporation; *Int'l*, pg. 5921
POONGSAN VALINOX CORPORATION—See Poongsan Holdings Corporation; *Int'l*, pg. 5921
POONGSAN VALINOX CORPORATION—See Vallourec SA; *Int'l*, pg. 8118
POONGWON PRECISION CO., LTD.; *Int'l*, pg. 5921
POONSAP CO LTD.—See Loxley Public Company Limited; *Int'l*, pg. 4567
POORT VAN WIJK BV—See Clariane SE; *Int'l*, pg. 1644
POP2LIFE LLC; *U.S. Private*, pg. 3228
PO PARTICIPATIONS S.A.—See Rothschild & Co SCA; *Int'l*, pg. 6403
POPCAP GAMES, LLC—See Electronic Arts Inc.; *U.S. Public*, pg. 724
POP CAPITAL LLC; *U.S. Private*, pg. 3228
POPCHIPS, INC.—See VMG Partners, LLC; *U.S. Private*, pg. 4408

THE POPCORN FACTORY, INC.—See 1-800-FLOWERS.COM, Inc.; *U.S. Public*, pg. 1
POPCORN, INDIANA LLC; *U.S. Private*, pg. 3228
POPCORN MEDIA SA—See Ipsos S.A.; *Int'l*, pg. 3802
POPCORN PALACE; *U.S. Private*, pg. 3228
POP CULTURE GROUP CO., LTD.; *Int'l*, pg. 5921
POP DISPLAYS USA, LLC—See CounterPoint Capital Partners, LLC; *U.S. Private*, pg. 1066
POPE GOLF, LLC; *U.S. Private*, pg. 3228
POPEJOY CONSTRUCTION COMPANY INC.; *U.S. Private*, pg. 3228
POPE RESOURCES LIMITED PARTNERSHIP—See Rayonier Inc.; *U.S. Public*, pg. 1765
POPE WOODHEAD AND ASSOCIATES—See Huron Consulting Group Inc.; *U.S. Public*, pg. 1076
POPEYES LIMITED PARTNERSHIP I; *U.S. Private*, pg. 3228
POP GESELLSCHAFT FUR PROZESSLOGISTIK MBH—See DSV A/S; *Int'l*, pg. 2214
POP LABS, INC; *U.S. Private*, pg. 3228
POPLAR BLUFF REGIONAL MEDICAL CENTER, INC.—See Community Health Systems, Inc.; *U.S. Public*, pg. 556
POPLAR CAPITAL PARTNERS LLC; *U.S. Private*, pg. 3228
POPLAR CO., LTD.; *Int'l*, pg. 5921
POPLAR CREEK RESOURCES INC.; *Int'l*, pg. 5921
POPLAR HEALTHCARE, PLLC; *U.S. Private*, pg. 3228
POPMAIL.COM, INC.; *U.S. Private*, pg. 3228
POP MART INTERNATIONAL GROUP LIMITED; *Int'l*, pg. 5921
POP MART JAPAN, INC.—See Pop Mart International Group Limited; *Int'l*, pg. 5921
POP MART KOREA CO., LTD.—See Pop Mart International Group Limited; *Int'l*, pg. 5921
POPOVA KULA WINERY; *Int'l*, pg. 5921
POPOVO POLJE A.D.; *Int'l*, pg. 5921
POPOWCER KATTEN LTD.—See Kutchins, Robbins & Diamond, Ltd.; *U.S. Private*, pg. 2358
POPPER AND COMPANY LLC; *U.S. Private*, pg. 3228
POPPIN, INC.—See HNI Corporation; *U.S. Public*, pg. 1043
POPPINS CORP.; *Int'l*, pg. 5921
POPPINS HOLDINGS, INC.; *Int'l*, pg. 5921
POPPINS SITTER CO., LTD.—See Poppins Holdings, Inc.; *Int'l*, pg. 5921
POPPLE CONSTRUCTION, INC.; *U.S. Private*, pg. 3229
POPPY MOBILITY NV—See s.a. D'Ieteren n.v.; *Int'l*, pg. 6448
POP RADIO, LP—See Cumulus Media Inc.; *U.S. Public*, pg. 610
POPREACH CORPORATION; *Int'l*, pg. 5921
P&O PRINCESS CRUISES INTERNATIONAL LIMITED—See Carnival Corporation; *U.S. Public*, pg. 438
POPS ACADEMY AB—See AcadeMedia AB; *Int'l*, pg. 77
POPS MART FUELS, LLC; *U.S. Private*, pg. 3229
POPSY—See Softimat SA; *Int'l*, pg. 7055
POPULAR AUTO LLC—See Popular, Inc.; *U.S. Public*, pg. 1702
POPULAR BANK—See Popular, Inc.; *U.S. Public*, pg. 1702
POPULAR DENTAL (WOODLANDS) PTE LTD—See OUE Limited; *Int'l*, pg. 5666
POPULAR ESTATE MANAGEMENT LIMITED; *Int'l*, pg. 5921
POPULAR FORD SALES INC.; *U.S. Private*, pg. 3229
POPULAR GESTION SGIIC, S.A.—See Allianz SE; *Int'l*, pg. 355
POPULAR HOLDINGS LIMITED—See ZQ Capital Management Limited; *Int'l*, pg. 8691
POPULAR, INC.; *U.S. Public*, pg. 1702
POPULAR LIFE INSURANCE COMPANY LIMITED; *Int'l*, pg. 5921
POPULAR MECHANICS—See The Hearst Corporation; *U.S. Private*, pg. 4046
POPULAR PRODUCTIONS, INC.—See The Walt Disney Company; *U.S. Public*, pg. 2140
POPULAR SCIENCE MAGAZINE—See Bonnier AB; *Int'l*, pg. 1108
POPULAR-SOFT CO., LTD.—See T-Gaia Corp.; *Int'l*, pg. 7396
POPULATE SOCIAL LTD.—See The Mission Group Public Limited Company; *Int'l*, pg. 7667
POPULATION HEALTH INVESTMENT CO., INC.; *U.S. Public*, pg. 1702
POPULATION SERVICES INTERNATIONAL; *U.S. Private*, pg. 3229
POPULUS, LLC.—See TPG Capital, L.P.; *U.S. Public*, pg. 2176
POP WARNER LITTLE SCHOLARS INC.; *U.S. Private*, pg. 3229
PORCARO COMMUNICATIONS; *U.S. Private*, pg. 3229
PORCARO VANCOUVER—See Porcaro Communications; *U.S. Private*, pg. 3229
PORCELAIN INDUSTRIES, INC.—See Incline MGMT Corp.; *U.S. Private*, pg. 2054
PORCELAIN PRODUCTS CO., LTD—See The Riverside Company; *U.S. Private*, pg. 4110

PORCELANITE LAMOSA, S.A. DE C.V.—See Grupo Lamosa S.A. de C.V.; *Int'l*, pg. 3132
PORCELANITE SA DE CV—See Grupo Lamosa S.A. de C.V.; *Int'l*, pg. 3132
PORCELANIZADOS ENASA, S.A. DE C.V.—See Grupo Industrial Saltillo S.A. de C.V.; *Int'l*, pg. 3130
PORCELANOSA NEW YORK INC.; *U.S. Private*, pg. 3229
PORCELEN LIMITED CONNECTICUT LLC—See G&S Metal Products Co. Inc.; *U.S. Private*, pg. 1629
PORCHER DO BRASIL TECIDOS DE VIDROS LTDA.—See Groupe Porcher Industries; *Int'l*, pg. 3110
PORCHER INDUSTRIES ASIA-PACIFIC—See Groupe Porcher Industries; *Int'l*, pg. 3109
PORCHER INDUSTRIES, RUSSIA—See Groupe Porcher Industries; *Int'l*, pg. 3109
PORCHER INDUSTRIES SA—See Warwick Capital Partners LLP; *Int'l*, pg. 8350
PORCHER INDUSTRIES, UK—See Groupe Porcher Industries; *Int'l*, pg. 3110
PORCHER ITALIANA—See Groupe Porcher Industries; *Int'l*, pg. 3110
PORCHER LUXURY DESIGNS—See Sun Capital Partners, Inc.; *U.S. Private*, pg. 3858
PORCHER & MEFFERT GRUNDSTUCKS-GESELLSCHAFT MBH & CO. STUTTGART OHG—See Mercedes-Benz Group AG; *Int'l*, pg. 4828
PORCH GROUP, INC.; *U.S. Public*, pg. 1702
PORDA HAVAS INTERNATIONAL FINANCE COMMUNICATIONS GROUP HOLDINGS CO., LTD.—See Vivendi SE; *Int'l*, pg. 8268
P.O. REAL ESTATE INC.—See Pola Orbis Holdings Inc.; *Int'l*, pg. 5905
POREX CORPORATION—See Madison Industries Holdings LLC; *U.S. Private*, pg. 2543
POREXTHERM DAMMSTOFFE GMBH—See Morgan Advanced Materials plc; *Int'l*, pg. 5044
PORGE LTD.—See TruFin plc; *Int'l*, pg. 7941
PORIN ASEMA-AUKIO KOY—See Citycon Oyj; *Int'l*, pg. 1629
PORIN ISOLINNANKATU 18 KOY—See Citycon Oyj; *Int'l*, pg. 1629
PORIN LAAKERI OY—See Axel Johnson Gruppen AB; *Int'l*, pg. 763
PORIN PROSESSIVOIMA OY—See Pohjolan Voima Oy; *Int'l*, pg. 5904
PORK FARMS LIMITED - PALETHORPES—See Vision Capital, LLP; *Int'l*, pg. 8252
PORK FARMS LIMITED—See Vision Capital, LLP; *Int'l*, pg. 8252
PORK FARMS - RIVERSIDE—See Vision Capital, LLP; *Int'l*, pg. 8252
PORKIE COMPANY OF WISCONSIN—See Pork King Good; *U.S. Private*, pg. 3229
PORK KING GOOD; *U.S. Private*, pg. 3229
PORK KING PACKING, INC.; *U.S. Private*, pg. 3229
PORKY PRODUCTS INC.; *U.S. Private*, pg. 3229
PORN PROM METAL PUBLIC COMPANY LIMITED; *Int'l*, pg. 5921
POROCEL CORP.—See Porocel Industries, LLC; *U.S. Private*, pg. 3229
POROCEL INDUSTRIES, LLC; *U.S. Private*, pg. 3229
POROTECHNOLOGY, INC.—See Micromeritics Instrument Corporation, Inc.; *U.S. Private*, pg. 2704
POROWNEO.PL SP. Z O.O—See Aviva plc; *Int'l*, pg. 746
PORR AG; *Int'l*, pg. 5922
PORR ALPHA BAUGESELLSCHAFT MBH—See PORR AG; *Int'l*, pg. 5924
PORR A.S.—See PORR AG; *Int'l*, pg. 5923
PORR AUSTRIARAIL GMBH—See PORR AG; *Int'l*, pg. 5924
PORR BAU GMBH—See PORR AG; *Int'l*, pg. 5924
PORR BETEILIGUNGEN UND MANAGEMENT GMBH—See PORR AG; *Int'l*, pg. 5924
PORR BETEILIGUNGSVERWALTUNGS GMBH—See PORR AG; *Int'l*, pg. 5924
PORR CONSTRUCT S.R.L.—See PORR AG; *Int'l*, pg. 5924
PORR DESIGN & ENGINEERING DEUTSCHLAND GMBH—See PORR AG; *Int'l*, pg. 5924
PORR DESIGN & ENGINEERING GMBH—See PORR AG; *Int'l*, pg. 5924
PORR DEUTSCHLAND GMBH—See PORR AG; *Int'l*, pg. 5924
PORREAL CESKO, S.R.O.—See PORR AG; *Int'l*, pg. 5924
PORREAL GMBH—See Triton Advisers Limited; *Int'l*, pg. 7935
PORREAL IMMOBILIEN MANAGEMENT GMBH—See PORR AG; *Int'l*, pg. 5925
PORRECO NISSAN; *U.S. Private*, pg. 3229
PORR EQUIPMENT SERVICES CESKO S.R.O.—See PORR AG; *Int'l*, pg. 5924
PORR EQUIPMENT SERVICES GMBH—See PORR AG; *Int'l*, pg. 5924
PORR FINANCIAL SERVICES AG—See PORR AG; *Int'l*, pg. 5923
PORR GMBH—See PORR AG; *Int'l*, pg. 5924
PORR HRVATSKA D.O.O. ZA GRADITELJSTVO—See PORR AG; *Int'l*, pg. 5924

PORR INDUSTRIEBAU GMBH—See PORR AG; Int'l, pg. 5924
PORR INFRASTRUKTUR INVESTMENT AG—See PORR AG; Int'l, pg. 5924
PORR INTERNATIONAL GMBH—See PORR AG; Int'l, pg. 5924
PORR - LIVING SOLUTIONS GMBH—See PORR AG; Int'l, pg. 5923
PORR OEVERMANN GMBH—See PORR AG; Int'l, pg. 5924
PORR (POLSKA) S.A.—See PORR AG; Int'l, pg. 5923
PORR PROJEKT UND HOCHBAU AKTIENGESELLSCHAFT—See PORR AG; Int'l, pg. 5924
PORR (SLOVENSKO) A.S.—See PORR AG; Int'l, pg. 5923
PORR SOLUTIONS DEUTSCHLAND GMBH—See PORR AG; Int'l, pg. 5924
PORR SOLUTIONS IMMOBILIEN- UND INFRASTRUKTURPROJEKTE GMBH—See PORR AG; Int'l, pg. 5924
PORR SOLUTIONS S.R.L.—See PORR AG; Int'l, pg. 5924
PORR SUISSE AG—See PORR AG; Int'l, pg. 5924
PORR TECHNICS AND SERVICES GMBH AND CO KG—See PORR AG; Int'l, pg. 5924
PORR TECHNOBAU UND UMWELT GMBH—See PORR AG; Int'l, pg. 5924
PORR TUNNELBAU GMBH—See PORR AG; Int'l, pg. 5924
PORR UK LTD.—See PORR AG; Int'l, pg. 5924
PORR UMWELTTECHNIK DEUTSCHLAND GMBH—See PORR AG; Int'l, pg. 5924
PORR UMWELTTECHNIK GMBH—See PORR AG; Int'l, pg. 5924
PORSACENTRE BARCELONA S.L.—See Porsche Automobil Holding SE; Int'l, pg. 5927
PORSAMADRID S.L.—See Porsche Automobil Holding SE; Int'l, pg. 5927
PORSCHE ASIA PACIFIC PTE. LTD.—See Porsche Automobil Holding SE; Int'l, pg. 5928
PORSCHE AUSTRIA GMBH & CO. OG—See Porsche Automobil Holding SE; Int'l, pg. 5927
PORSCHE AUTOMOBIL HOLDING SE; Int'l, pg. 5925
PORSCHE AVIATION PRODUCTS INC.—See Porsche Automobil Holding SE; Int'l, pg. 5927
PORSCHE CARS AUSTRALIA PTY. LTD.—See Porsche Automobil Holding SE; Int'l, pg. 5927
PORSCHE CARS CANADA—See Porsche Automobil Holding SE; Int'l, pg. 5927
PORSCHE CARS GREAT BRITAIN LTD—See Porsche Automobil Holding SE; Int'l, pg. 5927
PORSCHE CARS NORTH AMERICA, INC.—See Porsche Automobil Holding SE; Int'l, pg. 5927
PORSCHE CENTRE MELBOURNE PTY. LTD.—See Porsche Automobil Holding SE; Int'l, pg. 5927
PORSCHE CLASSIC GMBH—See Porsche Automobil Holding SE; Int'l, pg. 5927
PORSCHE CONSULTING BRASIL LTDA.—See Porsche Automobil Holding SE; Int'l, pg. 5928
PORSCHE CONSULTING GMBH—See Porsche Automobil Holding SE; Int'l, pg. 5927
PORSCHE DESIGN ITALIA S.R.L.—See Porsche Automobil Holding SE; Int'l, pg. 5928
PORSCHE DEUTSCHLAND GMBH—See Porsche Automobil Holding SE; Int'l, pg. 5928
PORSCHE DIENSTLEISTUNGS GMBH—See Porsche Automobil Holding SE; Int'l, pg. 5928
PORSCHE ENGINEERING GROUP GMBH—See Porsche Automobil Holding SE; Int'l, pg. 5928
PORSCHE ENGINEERING JAPAN CO. LTD.—See Porsche Automobil Holding SE; Int'l, pg. 5927
PORSCHE ENGINEERING SERVICES GMBH—See Porsche Automobil Holding SE; Int'l, pg. 5927
PORSCHE ENTERPRISES, INC.—See Porsche Automobil Holding SE; Int'l, pg. 5927
PORSCHE ERSTE VERMOGENSVERWALTUNG GMBH—See Porsche Automobil Holding SE; Int'l, pg. 5927
PORSCHE FINANCIAL MANAGEMENT SERVICES LTD.—See Porsche Automobil Holding SE; Int'l, pg. 5927
PORSCHE FINANCIAL SERVICES AUSTRALIA, PTY. LTD.—See Porsche Automobil Holding SE; Int'l, pg. 5928
PORSCHE FINANCIAL SERVICES FRANCE S.A.—See Porsche Automobil Holding SE; Int'l, pg. 5927
PORSCHE FINANCIAL SERVICES GMBH & CO. KG—See Porsche Automobil Holding SE; Int'l, pg. 5928
PORSCHE FINANCIAL SERVICES GMBH—See Porsche Automobil Holding SE; Int'l, pg. 5927
PORSCHE FINANCIAL SERVICES GREAT BRITAIN LTD.—See Porsche Automobil Holding SE; Int'l, pg. 5928
PORSCHE FINANCIAL SERVICES ITALIA S.P.A.—See Porsche Automobil Holding SE; Int'l, pg. 5927
PORSCHE FINANCIAL SERVICES JAPAN K.K.—See Porsche Automobil Holding SE; Int'l, pg. 5927
PORSCHE FINANCIAL SERVICES—See Porsche Automobil Holding SE; Int'l, pg. 5927

PORSCHE FINANCIAL SERVICES VERWALTUNGS- GESELLSCHAFT MBH—See Porsche Automobil Holding SE; Int'l, pg. 5928
PORSCHE FRANCE S.A.—See Porsche Automobil Holding SE; Int'l, pg. 5927
PORSCHE FUNDING LLC—See Porsche Automobil Holding SE; Int'l, pg. 5928
PORSCHE FUNDING LTD. PARTNERSHIP—See Porsche Automobil Holding SE; Int'l, pg. 5928
PORSCHE IBERICA S.A.—See Porsche Automobil Holding SE; Int'l, pg. 5927
PORSCHE INTERNATIONAL FINANCING LTD.—See Porsche Automobil Holding SE; Int'l, pg. 5927
PORSCHE INTERNATIONAL INSURANCE LTD.—See Porsche Automobil Holding SE; Int'l, pg. 5927
PORSCHE ITALIA S.P.A—See Porsche Automobil Holding SE; Int'l, pg. 5927
PORSCHE JAPAN KK—See Porsche Automobil Holding SE; Int'l, pg. 5927
PORSCHE LATIN AMERICA—See Porsche Automobil Holding SE; Int'l, pg. 5927
PORSCHE LEASING GMBH—See Porsche Automobil Holding SE; Int'l, pg. 5928
PORSCHE LEASING LTD.—See Porsche Automobil Holding SE; Int'l, pg. 5928
PORSCHE LEIPZIG GMBH—See Porsche Automobil Holding SE; Int'l, pg. 5928
PORSCHE LIZENZ- UND HANDELSGESELLSCHAFT MBH & CO. KG—See Porsche Automobil Holding SE; Int'l, pg. 5928
PORSCHE LOGISTIK GMBH—See Porsche Automobil Holding SE; Int'l, pg. 5928
PORSCHE MIDDLE EAST—See Porsche Automobil Holding SE; Int'l, pg. 5928
PORSCHE MOTORSPORTS—See Porsche Automobil Holding SE; Int'l, pg. 5927
PORSCHE NIEDERLASSUNG BERLIN GMBH—See Porsche Automobil Holding SE; Int'l, pg. 5928
PORSCHE NIEDERLASSUNG BERLIN-POTSDAM GMBH—See Porsche Automobil Holding SE; Int'l, pg. 5928
PORSCHE NIEDERLASSUNG HAMBURG GMBH—See Porsche Automobil Holding SE; Int'l, pg. 5928
PORSCHE NIEDERLASSUNG LEIPZIG GMBH—See Porsche Automobil Holding SE; Int'l, pg. 5928
PORSCHE NIEDERLASSUNG STUTTGART GMBH—See Porsche Automobil Holding SE; Int'l, pg. 5928
PORSCHE RETAIL GROUP AUSTRALIA PTY. LTD.—See Porsche Automobil Holding SE; Int'l, pg. 5928
PORSCHE SCHWEIZ AG—See Porsche Automobil Holding SE; Int'l, pg. 5928
PORSCHE SERVICES ESPANA—See Porsche Automobil Holding SE; Int'l, pg. 5927
PORSCHE SLOVAKIA—See Porsche Automobil Holding SE; Int'l, pg. 5928
PORSCHE ZWISCHENHOLDING GMBH—See Porsche Automobil Holding SE; Int'l, pg. 5928
PORTABLE CHURCH INDUSTRIES, INC.; U.S. Private, pg. 3231
PORTABLE COMPUTER SYSTEMS, INC.—See Route1 Inc.; Int'l, pg. 6407
PORTABLE FOODS MANUFACTURING COMPANY LIMITED—See Kellanova; U.S. Public, pg. 1218
PORTABLE PRACTICAL EDUCATIONAL PREPARATION, INC; U.S. Private, pg. 3231
PORTABLES UNLIMITED INC.; U.S. Private, pg. 3231
PORTABRANDS LIMITED—See Bunzl plc; Int'l, pg. 1219
PORTA CABOS INDUSTRIA E COMERCIO LTDA.—See Tsubakimoto Chain Co.; Int'l, pg. 7954
PORTACO, INC.—See Vermogensverwaltung Erben Dr. Karl Goldschmidt GmbH; Int'l, pg. 8173
PORTAFEU SAS—See ASSA ABLOY AB; Int'l, pg. 640
PORTAGAS, INC.—See Celanese Corporation; U.S. Public, pg. 465
PORTAGE BIOTECH INC.; Int'l, pg. 5933
PORTAGE, INC.—See Cook Inlet Region, Inc.; U.S. Private, pg. 1038
PORTAGE LUMBER COMPANY, INC.—See Bliffert Lumber & Fuel Co. Inc.; U.S. Private, pg. 581
PORTAGE PATH BEHAVIORAL HEALTH; U.S. Private, pg. 3231
PORTAGE PHARMACY INC.—See Portage Pharma Ltd.; U.S. Private, pg. 3231
PORTAGE PHARMA LTD.; U.S. Private, pg. 3231
PORTAGE PRECISION POLYMERS, INC.—See HEXPOL AB; Int'l, pg. 3372
PORTAGE RESOURCES INC.; Int'l, pg. 5933
PORTAL DE DOCUMENTOS S.A—See B3 S.A.; Int'l, pg. 791
PORTALE SARDEGNA S.P.A.; Int'l, pg. 5933
THE PORTAL GROUP CONSULTING LLC—See Beyondsoft Corporation; Int'l, pg. 1005
PORTALNET CO., LTD.—See Samart Corporation Public Company Limited; Int'l, pg. 6501
PORTAL PARTNERSHIP INCORPORATED—See Basil Read Holdings Limited; Int'l, pg. 887
PORTAL SERVICE CO.; U.S. Private, pg. 3231
PORTAL SOLUTIONS, LLC; U.S. Private, pg. 3231

PORTALTECH REPLY LTD.—See Reply S.p.A.; Int'l, pg. 6291
PORTA MALLORQUINA REAL ESTATE S.L.U.—See Homes & Holiday AG; Int'l, pg. 3455
PORT AMHERST, LTD.; U.S. Private, pg. 3229
PORTA PUMPER PTE LTD—See Sim Lian Group Limited; Int'l, pg. 6926
PORT AUTHORITY OF ALLEGHENY COUNTY INC.; U.S. Private, pg. 3229
PORT AUTHORITY OF NEW YORK & NEW JERSEY; U.S. Private, pg. 3229
PORT AUTHORITY TRANS-HUDSON CORP.—See Port Authority of New York & New Jersey; U.S. Private, pg. 3229
PORT AUTHORITY TRANSIT CORP. OF PENNSYLVANIA AND NEW JERSEY INC.—See Delaware River Port Authority of Pennsylvania & New Jersey; U.S. Private, pg. 1195
PORT AVENTURA ENTERTAINMENT, S.A.U.—See BI-Invest Advisors S.A.; Int'l, pg. 1017
PORTAVITA B.V.—See PAO Severstal; Int'l, pg. 5732
PORT BOUVARD MARINA PTY LTD—See Tian An Australia Limited; Int'l, pg. 7737
PORT BROKERS INC.; U.S. Private, pg. 3229
PORTCEMEN S.A.—See Cementos Molins S.A.; Int'l, pg. 1397
PORT CHARLOTTE MALL LLC—See Washington Prime Group Inc.; U.S. Private, pg. 4448
PORT CITY BAKERY INC.; U.S. Private, pg. 3230
PORT CITY IMPORTS, INC.—See AutoNation, Inc.; U.S. Public, pg. 237
PORT CITY NITROGEN INC.—See Carolina Eastern Inc.; U.S. Private, pg. 768
PORT CITY PHYSICAL THERAPY, LIMITED PARTNERSHIP—See U.S. Physical Therapy, Inc.; U.S. Public, pg. 2215
PORT CITY PRESS, INC.—See Cenveo, Inc.; U.S. Private, pg. 835
PORT CLINTON LANDFILL, INC.—See Republic Services, Inc.; U.S. Public, pg. 1786
PORTCO CORPORATION; U.S. Private, pg. 3231
PORT COLBORNE DROP FORGE—See Mission Essential Personnel, LLC; U.S. Private, pg. 2747
PORT CO., LTD.; Int'l, pg. 5933
PORT CONSOLIDATED INC.; U.S. Private, pg. 3230
PORT DENARAU MARINA LIMITED—See Skeggs Group Limited; Int'l, pg. 6980
PORTE ADVERTISING, INC.; U.S. Private, pg. 3231
PORTE BROWN LLC; U.S. Private, pg. 3231
PORTEC VETERINARY SERVICES PTY. LTD.—See Apiam Animal Health Limited; Int'l, pg. 515
PORTE KANAZAWA CO., LTD.—See Hulic Co., Ltd.; Int'l, pg. 3528
PORTEK CHINA LTD.—See Mitsui & Co., Ltd.; Int'l, pg. 4980
PORTEK ENGINEERING HOLDINGS PTE LTD—See Mitsui & Co., Ltd.; Int'l, pg. 4980
PORTEK INTERNATIONAL PTE LTD.—See Mitsui & Co., Ltd.; Int'l, pg. 4980
PORTEK NORTH ASIA LIMITED—See Mitsui & Co., Ltd.; Int'l, pg. 4980
PORTEK SYSTEMS & EQUIPMENT PTE LTD—See Mitsui & Co., Ltd.; Int'l, pg. 4980
PORTELL FINANCIAL SERVICES, INC.—See Aon plc; Int'l, pg. 497
PORT ENTERPRISES (GUAM) INC.—See Daikin Industries, Ltd.; Int'l, pg. 1936
PORTENT, INC.—See Creadev SAS; Int'l, pg. 1831
PORTEOUS FASTENER COMPANY INC.; U.S. Private, pg. 3231
PORT EQUIPMENT SOUTHERN AFRICA (PTY) LTD.—See Konecranes Plc; Int'l, pg. 4253
PORTER AIRLINES INC.—See Porter Aviation Holdings Inc.; Int'l, pg. 5934
PORTER AND HAYLETT LIMITED—See TUI AG; Int'l, pg. 7966
PORTER ATHLETIC EQUIPMENT COMPANY—See Litania Sports Group, Inc.; U.S. Private, pg. 2467
PORTER AVIATION HOLDINGS INC.; Int'l, pg. 5934
PORTERBROOK LEASING COMPANY LIMITED—See Alberta Investment Management Corporation; Int'l, pg. 298
PORTERBROOK LEASING COMPANY LIMITED—See Allianz SE; Int'l, pg. 344
PORTERBROOK LEASING COMPANY LIMITED—See Electricite de France S.A.; Int'l, pg. 2352
PORTERBROOK LEASING COMPANY LIMITED—See Westpac Banking Corporation; Int'l, pg. 8391
PORTER BURGESS COMPANY; U.S. Private, pg. 3231
PORTER CAPITAL CORPORATION; U.S. Private, pg. 3231
PORTER CHEVROLET HYUNDAI; U.S. Private, pg. 3231
PORTER COMPANY/MECHANICAL CONTRACTORS; U.S. Private, pg. 3231
PORTERCO OILFIELD SERVICES INC.—See New West Energy Services Inc.; Int'l, pg. 5231
PORTER CORP.—See Court Square Capital Partners, L.P.; U.S. Private, pg. 1070

PORTER COUNTY SCHOOL EMPLOYEES' INSURANCE TRUST **CORPORATE AFFILIATIONS**

PORTER COUNTY SCHOOL EMPLOYEES' INSURANCE TRUST; *U.S. Private*, pg. 3231
PORTER DAVIS HOMES; *Int'l*, pg. 5934
PORTER ENGINEERED SYSTEMS INC—See KP Holdings LLC; *U.S. Private*, pg. 2345
PORTERET ET GOBILLOT SA; *Int'l*, pg. 5934
PORTER EXCAVATIONS PTY. LTD.—See Kanamoto Co., Ltd.; *Int'l*, pg. 4064
PORTER GROUP, INC.; *U.S. Private*, pg. 3231
PORTER HOLDING INTERNATIONAL, INC.; *Int'l*, pg. 5934
PORT ERIE PLASTICS, INC.; *U.S. Private*, pg. 3230
PORTER-LEATH; *U.S. Private*, pg. 3232
PORTER, LEVAY & ROSE, INC.; *U.S. Private*, pg. 3232
PORTER NISSAN INFINITI; *U.S. Private*, pg. 3231
PORTER NOVELLI-AUSTIN—See Omnicom Group Inc.; *U.S. Public*, pg. 1591
PORTER NOVELLI AUSTRALIA-MELBOURNE—See Omnicom Group Inc.; *U.S. Public*, pg. 1591
PORTER NOVELLI-BAY AREA-SAN FRANCISCO—See Omnicom Group Inc.; *U.S. Public*, pg. 1591
PORTER NOVELLI-BEIJING—See Omnicom Group Inc.; *U.S. Public*, pg. 1591
PORTER NOVELLI-BOSTON—See Omnicom Group Inc.; *U.S. Public*, pg. 1591
PORTER NOVELLI CANADA-MONTREAL—See Omnicom Group Inc.; *U.S. Public*, pg. 1591
PORTER NOVELLI-CHICAGO—See Omnicom Group Inc.; *U.S. Public*, pg. 1591
PORTER NOVELLI-FT. LAUDERDALE—See Omnicom Group Inc.; *U.S. Public*, pg. 1591
PORTER NOVELLI-IRVINE—See Omnicom Group Inc.; *U.S. Public*, pg. 1591
PORTER NOVELLI-LONDON—See Omnicom Group Inc.; *U.S. Public*, pg. 1591
PORTER NOVELLI-LOS ANGELES—See Omnicom Group Inc.; *U.S. Public*, pg. 1591
PORTER NOVELLI NEW ZEALAND-AUCKLAND—See Omnicom Group Inc.; *U.S. Public*, pg. 1591
PORTER NOVELLI-PARIS—See Omnicom Group Inc.; *U.S. Public*, pg. 1591
PORTER NOVELLI PTE. LTD. - SINGAPORE—See Omnicom Group Inc.; *U.S. Public*, pg. 1591
PORTER NOVELLI-SAN DIEGO—See Omnicom Group Inc.; *U.S. Public*, pg. 1591
PORTER NOVELLI-SEATTLE—See Omnicom Group Inc.; *U.S. Public*, pg. 1591
PORTER NOVELLI—See Omnicom Group Inc.; *U.S. Public*, pg. 1590
PORTER NOVELLI—See Omnicom Group Inc.; *U.S. Public*, pg. 1591
PORTER NOVELLI—See Omnicom Group Inc.; *U.S. Public*, pg. 1591
PORTER NOVELLI—See Omnicom Group Inc.; *U.S. Public*, pg. 1591
PORTER NOVELLI—See Omnicom Group Inc.; *U.S. Public*, pg. 1591
PORTER NOVELLI—See Omnicom Group Inc.; *U.S. Public*, pg. 1591
PORTER NOVELLI—See Omnicom Group Inc.; *U.S. Public*, pg. 1591
PORTER NOVELLI—See Omnicom Group Inc.; *U.S. Public*, pg. 1591
PORTER NOVELLI SYDNEY—See Omnicom Group Inc.; *U.S. Public*, pg. 1591
PORTER NOVELLI TASMANIA—See Omnicom Group Inc.; *U.S. Public*, pg. 1591
PORTER NOVELLI-TORONTO—See Omnicom Group Inc.; *U.S. Public*, pg. 1591
PORTER NOVELLI-WASHINGTON—See Omnicom Group Inc.; *U.S. Public*, pg. 1591
PORTER PIPE & SUPPLY COMPANY; *U.S. Private*, pg. 3232
PORTER PRECISION PRODUCTS COMPANY; *U.S. Private*, pg. 3232
PORTER ROOFING CONTRACTORS; *U.S. Private*, pg. 3232
PORTERS BUILDING CENTER; *U.S. Private*, pg. 3232
PORTERS CORPORATION; *Int'l*, pg. 5934
PORTER'S GROUP, LLC—See Littlejohn & Co., LLC; *U.S. Private*, pg. 2471
PORTER TRUCK SALES INC.; *U.S. Private*, pg. 3232
PORTER UTILITIES PTY LTD—See Kanamoto Co., Ltd.; *Int'l*, pg. 4064
PORTER VALLEY SOFTWARE, INC.—See Environmental Service Professionals, Inc.; *U.S. Public*, pg. 781
PORTERVILLE RECORDER—See Horizon Publications Inc.; *U.S. Private*, pg. 1982
PORTER WARNER INDUSTRIES LLC; *U.S. Private*, pg. 3232
PORTER WRIGHT MORRIS & ARTHUR LLP; *U.S. Private*, pg. 3232
PORTESCAP CO., LTD.—See Regal Rexnord Corporation; *U.S. Public*, pg. 1772
PORTESCAP INDIA PRIVATE LIMITED—See Danaher Corporation; *U.S. Public*, pg. 626

PORTESCAP SA—See Danaher Corporation; *U.S. Public*, pg. 626
PORTESCAP SINGAPORE PTE. LTD.—See Danaher Corporation; *U.S. Public*, pg. 626
PORTESCAP—See Danaher Corporation; *U.S. Public*, pg. 626
PORTESCAP—See Danaher Corporation; *U.S. Public*, pg. 626
PORTESCAP—See Danaher Corporation; *U.S. Public*, pg. 626
PORTESCAP—See Danaher Corporation; *U.S. Public*, pg. 626
PORTES NOUVELLES DIMENSIONS INC; *Int'l*, pg. 5934
PORT EVERGLADES ENVIRONMENTAL CORP.—See Marathon Petroleum Corporation; *U.S. Public*, pg. 1364
PORT FACILITIES—See National Aluminium Company Limited; *Int'l*, pg. 5150
PORTFOLIO BUREAU PROPRIETARY LIMITED—See Anchor Group Limited; *Int'l*, pg. 448
PORTFOLIO COFFEE INC.—See PlantX Life Inc.; *Int'l*, pg. 5891
PORTFOLIO CREATIVE; *U.S. Private*, pg. 3232
PORTFOLIO INVESTMENT ICAV—See Intrum AB; *Int'l*, pg. 3771
PORTFOLIO MANAGEMENT CONSULTANTS, INC.—See Bain Capital, LP; *U.S. Private*, pg. 439
PORTFOLIO MARKETING GROUP; *U.S. Private*, pg. 3232
PORTFOLIO MEDIA, INC.—See RELX plc; *Int'l*, pg. 6267
PORTFOLIO METRICA LTD.—See Exponent Private Equity LLP; *Int'l*, pg. 2589
PORTFOLIO PUBLICIS MODEM—See Publicis Groupe S.A.; *Int'l*, pg. 6106
PORTFOLIOS FINANCIAL SERVICES, INC.; *U.S. Private*, pg. 3232
PORTFOLIO SOLUTIONS, LLC.; *U.S. Private*, pg. 3232
PORTFOLIO STRATEGIES CORP; *Int'l*, pg. 5934
PORTGAS-SOCIEDADE DE PRODUCAO E DISTRIBUICAO DE GAS SA—See EDP - Energias de Portugal, S.A.; *Int'l*, pg. 2315
PORTGAS—See ENGIE SA; *Int'l*, pg. 2434
PORT GMBH—See Belden, Inc.; *U.S. Public*, pg. 294
PORT HANDLOWY SWINOUJSCIE SP. Z O.O.—See OT Logistics S.A.; *Int'l*, pg. 5656
PORT HARBOR MARINE INC.; *U.S. Private*, pg. 3230
PORT HARCOURT REFINING COMPANY LIMITED—See Nigerian National Petroleum Corporation; *Int'l*, pg. 5282
PORT HAWKESBURY PAPER LIMITED PARTNERSHIP—See Stern Partners Inc.; *Int'l*, pg. 7212
PORT HOPE EVENING GUIDE—See Chatham Asset Management, LLC; *U.S. Private*, pg. 861
PORTICO BED & BATH INCORPORATED; *U.S. Private*, pg. 3232
PORTICO INTERNATIONAL HOLDINGS LTD.; *Int'l*, pg. 5934
PORTICO SERVICES, LLC—See Nana Regional Corporation, Inc.; *U.S. Private*, pg. 2832
PORTICO SYSTEMS, INC.—See McKesson Corporation; *U.S. Public*, pg. 1408
PORTIGON AG - MILAN BRANCH—See Portigon AG; *Int'l*, pg. 5934
PORTIGON AG; *Int'l*, pg. 5934
PORTIGON AG - SYDNEY BRANCH—See Portigon AG; *Int'l*, pg. 5934
PORTIGON AG - TOKYO BRANCH—See Portigon AG; *Int'l*, pg. 5934
PORTIGON FINANCIAL SERVICES GMBH—See Erste Abwicklungsanstalt AoR; *Int'l*, pg. 2497
PORTIGON SECURITIES INC.—See Portigon AG; *Int'l*, pg. 5934
PORTIGON UK LIMITED—See Portigon AG; *Int'l*, pg. 5934
PORTILLOS HOT DOGS INCORPORATED; *U.S. Private*, pg. 3232
PORTILLO'S, INC.; *U.S. Public*, pg. 1702
PORT IMPERIAL SOUTH 15, L.L.C.—See Veris Residential, Inc.; *U.S. Public*, pg. 2281
PORT INC.—See Targus Group International, Inc.; *U.S. Private*, pg. 3934
PORTIONPAC CHEMICAL CORP.; *U.S. Private*, pg. 3232
PORTION PAC—See 3G Capital Inc.; *U.S. Private*, pg. 10
PORTION PAC—See Berkshire Hathaway Inc.; *U.S. Public*, pg. 318
PORT JEFF CHRYSLER PLYMOUTH JEEP EAGLE INC.; *U.S. Private*, pg. 3230
PORT JERSEY LOGISTICS; *U.S. Private*, pg. 3230
PORT KAMBARKA OAO—See Mechel PAO; *Int'l*, pg. 4766
PORT KLANG—See Stonepeak Partners L.P.; *U.S. Private*, pg. 3829
PORTLAND AIR FREIGHT, INC.; *U.S. Private*, pg. 3232
PORTLAND ART MUSEUM; *U.S. Private*, pg. 3232
PORTLAND BOLT & MANUFACTURING CO., LLC; *U.S. Private*, pg. 3232
PORTLAND BOTTLING COMPANY—See Limnes Bottling Acquisition Co.; *U.S. Private*, pg. 2456
PORTLAND BUNKERS INTERNATIONAL LTD.—See Minerva Bunkering; *U.S. Private*, pg. 4908
PORTLAND CEMENT ASSOCIATION; *U.S. Private*, pg. 3232
PORTLAND CHAIN MANUFACTURING CO.—See MPE Partners, LLC; *U.S. Private*, pg. 2804

PORTLAND CONTRACTORS SUPPLY, INC.—See Mallory Safety & Supply LLC; *U.S. Private*, pg. 2558
PORTLAND GENERAL ELECTRIC COMPANY; *U.S. Public*, pg. 1702
PORTLAND GROUP INC. - NEWTON—See Portland Group Inc.; *U.S. Private*, pg. 3233
THE PORTLAND GROUP, INC.—See NVIDIA Corporation; *U.S. Public*, pg. 1558
PORTLAND GROUP INC.; *U.S. Private*, pg. 3233
PORTLAND HOLDINGS INC.—See Portland Investment Counsel Inc.; *Int'l*, pg. 5934
PORTLAND INVESTMENT COUNSEL INC.; *Int'l*, pg. 5934
PORTLAND LIGHTING LIMITED—See F.W. Thorpe plc; *Int'l*, pg. 2597
PORTLAND NATURAL GAS TRANSMISSION SYSTEM—See BlackRock, Inc.; *U.S. Public*, pg. 346
PORTLAND NATURAL GAS TRANSMISSION SYSTEM—See Morgan Stanley; *U.S. Public*, pg. 1475
PORTLAND PAINTS & PRODUCTS NIGERIA PLC—See UAC of Nigeria Plc; *Int'l*, pg. 7999
PORTLAND PIPE LINE CORPORATION—See Exxon Mobil Corporation; *U.S. Public*, pg. 816
PORTLAND PIPE LINE CORPORATION—See Suncor Energy Inc.; *Int'l*, pg. 7311
PORTLAND PRESS HERALD—See MaineToday Media, Inc.; *U.S. Private*, pg. 2553
PORTLAND PRIVATE EQUITY, L.P.—See Portland Investment Counsel Inc.; *Int'l*, pg. 5934
PORTLAND SEAFOOD COMPANY—See Sun Capital Partners, Inc.; *U.S. Private*, pg. 3860
PORTLAND STREET HONDA; *Int'l*, pg. 5934
PORTLAND TRAIL BLAZERS—See Vulcan Inc.; *U.S. Private*, pg. 4416
PORTLAND UTILITIES CONSTRUCTION COMPANY, LLC—See New Mountain Capital, LLC; *U.S. Private*, pg. 2900
PORTLAND VALVE & FITTING COMPANY; *U.S. Private*, pg. 3233
PORTLAND WATER DISTRICT; *U.S. Private*, pg. 3233
PORTLAND & WESTERN RAILROAD INC—See Brookfield Infrastructure Partners L.P.; *Int'l*, pg. 1192
PORTLAND & WESTERN RAILROAD INC—See GIC Pte. Ltd.; *Int'l*, pg. 2966
PORTLAND WILLAMETTE—See Cardinal Aluminum Co.; *U.S. Private*, pg. 749
PORTLAND YACHT SERVICES, INC.; *U.S. Private*, pg. 3233
PORT LINCOLN TIMES PTY LTD—See Nine Entertainment Co. Holdings Limited; *Int'l*, pg. 5299
PORTLINE-TRANSPORTES MARITIMOS INTERNACIONAIS SA—See Compagnie Maritime Belge S.A.; *Int'l*, pg. 1746
PORTLINK INTERNATIONAL SERVICES (PRIVATE) LIMITED—See Pakistan International Bulk Terminal Limited; *Int'l*, pg. 5704
PORTLOGIC SYSTEMS INC.; *Int'l*, pg. 5934
PORT LOGISTICS GROUP, INC.; *U.S. Private*, pg. 3230
PORTLYN, LLC—See Integer Holdings Corporation; *U.S. Public*, pg. 1135
PORT MACHINERY EQUIPMENT SUB-CO.—See Taiyuan Heavy Industry Co., Ltd.; *Int'l*, pg. 7427
PORT MACQUARIE HOSPITAL PTY LIMITED—See Ramsay Health Care Limited; *Int'l*, pg. 6199
PORTMAN RIDGE FINANCE CORPORATION; *U.S. Public*, pg. 1702
PORTMANS PTY. LIMITED—See Premier Investments Limited; *Int'l*, pg. 5960
PORTMAN SQUARE PROPERTIES LIMITED—See Great Portland Estates Plc; *Int'l*, pg. 3065
PORT MECHEL TEMRYUK OOO—See Mechel PAO; *Int'l*, pg. 4766
PORTMEIRION CANADA INC.—See Portmeirion Group Plc; *Int'l*, pg. 5934
PORTMEIRION ENTERPRISES LIMITED—See Portmeirion Group Plc; *Int'l*, pg. 5935
PORTMEIRION GROUP DESIGNS, LLC—See Portmeirion Group Plc; *Int'l*, pg. 5935
PORTMEIRION GROUP PLC; *Int'l*, pg. 5934
PORTMEIRION GROUP UK LIMITED—See Portmeirion Group Plc; *Int'l*, pg. 5935
PORTMEIRION GROUP USA, INC.—See Portmeirion Group Plc; *Int'l*, pg. 5935
PORTMEIRION POTTERIES LIMITED—See Portmeirion Group Plc; *Int'l*, pg. 5935
PORT MILFORD LLC—See Sun Communities, Inc.; *U.S. Public*, pg. 1961
PORT MORESBY STOCK EXCHANGE LIMITED; *Int'l*, pg. 5933
PORT MORRIS TILE & MARBLE; *U.S. Private*, pg. 3230
PORT NECHES FUELS, LLC—See First Reserve Management, L.P.; *U.S. Private*, pg. 1526
PORT NECHES FUELS, LLC—See SK Capital Partners, LP; *U.S. Private*, pg. 3680
PORTO AVIATION GROUP S.P.A.; *Int'l*, pg. 5935
PORTOBELLO CAPITAL ADVISORS SL; *Int'l*, pg. 5935
PORTOBELLO S.P.A.; *Int'l*, pg. 5935
PORTO CARRAS S.A.—See Technical Olympic SA; *Int'l*, pg. 7506

COMPANY NAME INDEX

PORTOCORK AMERICA, INC.—See CORTICEIRA AMORIM, S.G.P.S., S.A.; *Int'l*, pg. 1808
PORTOCORK FRANCE, S.A.S.—See CORTICEIRA AMORIM, S.G.P.S., S.A.; *Int'l*, pg. 1808
PORTOCORK ITALIA, S.R.L.—See CORTICEIRA AMORIM, S.G.P.S., S.A.; *Int'l*, pg. 1808
PORTO EDITORA LDA.; *Int'l*, pg. 5935
PORTO ENERGY CORP.; *U.S. Private*, pg. 3233
PORT OF CORK COMPANY LTD.; *Int'l*, pg. 5933
PORT OF DUNDEE LTD—See Arcus Infrastructure Partners LLP; *Int'l*, pg. 553
PORT OF EVERETT; *U.S. Private*, pg. 3230
PORT OF FELIXSTOWE LIMITED—See CK Hutchison Holdings Limited; *Int'l*, pg. 1638
PORT OF GALVESTON; *U.S. Private*, pg. 3230
PORT OF HAI PHONG JOINT STOCK COMPANY; *Int'l*, pg. 5933
PORT OF HOUSTON AUTHORITY; *U.S. Private*, pg. 3230
PORTOFINO RESOURCES INC.; *Int'l*, pg. 5935
PORT OF MIAMI TERMINAL OPERATING COMPANY, LC; *U.S. Private*, pg. 3230
PORT OF OAKLAND; *U.S. Private*, pg. 3230
PORT OF PORTLAND; *U.S. Private*, pg. 3230
PORT OF ROTTERDAM AUTHORITY NV; *Int'l*, pg. 5933
PORT OF SUBS INC.; *U.S. Private*, pg. 3230
PORT OF TACOMA; *U.S. Private*, pg. 3231
PORT OF TAURANGA LIMITED; *Int'l*, pg. 5933
PORT OF TILBURY LONDON LIMITED—See Arcus Infrastructure Partners LLP; *Int'l*, pg. 553
PORT OF TYNE DISTRIBUTION LTD; *Int'l*, pg. 5933
PORTOLA DIALYSIS, LLC—See DaVita Inc.; *U.S. Public*, pg. 642
PORTOLA ITALIA S.R.L.—See AstraZeneca PLC; *Int'l*, pg. 659
PORTOLAN COMMERCE SOLUTIONS GMBH; *Int'l*, pg. 5935
PORTOLA OSTERREICH GMBH—See AstraZeneca PLC; *Int'l*, pg. 659
PORTOLA PHARMACEUTICALS ESPANA S.L.—See AstraZeneca PLC; *Int'l*, pg. 659
PORTOLA PHARMACEUTICALS, LLC—See AstraZeneca PLC; *Int'l*, pg. 659
PORTOLA PHARMA UK LTD.—See AstraZeneca PLC; *Int'l*, pg. 659
PORTOLA REPORTER—See Feather Publishing Co., Inc.; *U.S. Private*, pg. 1486
PORTOLA SCHWEIZ GMBH—See AstraZeneca PLC; *Int'l*, pg. 659
PORTON BIOLOGICS LTD.—See Porton Pharma Solutions Ltd.; *Int'l*, pg. 5935
PORTON PHARMA SOLUTIONS LTD.; *Int'l*, pg. 5935
PORT ORANGE PHYSICAL THERAPY, LIMITED PARTNERSHIP—See U.S. Physical Therapy, Inc.; *U.S. Public*, pg. 2215
PORT ORCHARD SAND & GRAVEL COMPANY, INC.—See Miles Sand & Gravel Company; *U.S. Private*, pg. 2727
PORTO SEGURO SA; *Int'l*, pg. 5935
PORTO VELHO TRANSMISSORA DE ENERGIA S.A.—See Centrais Eletricas Brasileiras S.A.; *Int'l*, pg. 1403
PORTOVESME S.R.L.—See Salini Costruttori S.p.A.; *Int'l*, pg. 6493
PORT PLASTIC INC.—See Blackfriars Corp.; *U.S. Private*, pg. 574
PORTPLUS (NZ) LIMITED—See Onthehouse Holdings Limited; *Int'l*, pg. 5591
PORTPLUS PTY LIMITED—See Onthehouse Holdings Limited; *Int'l*, pg. 5591
PORT POLNOCNY SP. Z O.O.—See SEA-invest Group; *Int'l*, pg. 6661
PORT POSIET OAO—See Mechel PAO; *Int'l*, pg. 4766
PORTRAIT INNOVATIONS HOLDING COMPANY; *U.S. Private*, pg. 3233
PORTS 1961 USA INC.—See Portico International Holdings Ltd.; *Int'l*, pg. 5934
PORTS AMERICA, INC.—See Canada Pension Plan Investment Board; *Int'l*, pg. 1281
PORTSEA HARBOUR COMPANY LIMITED—See FIH group plc; *Int'l*, pg. 2661
PORTSERCO LOGISTICS JOINT STOCK COMPANY; *Int'l*, pg. 5935
PORT SERVICES CORPORATION SAOG; *Int'l*, pg. 5933
PORTSIDE APARTMENT DEVELOPERS, L.L.C.—See Veris Residential, Inc.; *U.S. Public*, pg. 2282
PORTSIDE BUILDERS, INC.; *U.S. Private*, pg. 3233
PORTSIDE ENERGY CORP.—See EPCOR Utilities, Inc.; *Int'l*, pg. 2459
PORTSIDE HEALTHCARE, INC.—See The Ensign Group, Inc.; *U.S. Public*, pg. 2072
PORTSMOUTH CHEVROLET, INC.—See Key Auto Group; *U.S. Private*, pg. 2292
PORTSMOUTH PUBLISHING & PRINTING LTD—See JPI-Media Holdings Limited; *Int'l*, pg. 4006
PORTSMOUTH REGIONAL AMBULATORY SURGERY CENTER, LLC—See HCA Healthcare, Inc.; *U.S. Public*, pg. 1006
PORTSMOUTH REGIONAL HOSPITAL—See HCA Healthcare, Inc.; *U.S. Public*, pg. 1006

PORTSMOUTH SQUARE, INC.—See InterGroup Corporation; *U.S. Public*, pg. 1144
PORTS OF AUCKLAND LTD.; *Int'l*, pg. 5935
PORT SOLENT MARINA LIMITED—See BAE Systems plc; *Int'l*, pg. 798
PORT ST. JOE MARINA INC.—See The St. Joe Company; *U.S. Public*, pg. 2131
PORT ST. LUCIE SURGERY CENTER, LTD.—See HCA Healthcare, Inc.; *U.S. Public*, pg. 1006
PORT SUTTON BRIDGE LTD.—See Simon Group plc; *Int'l*, pg. 6932
PORT TECHNOLOGY PTE LTD—See Mitsui & Co., Ltd.; *Int'l*, pg. 4980
PORT & TERMINAL MULTISERVICES LIMITED—See Grimaldi Group SpA; *Int'l*, pg. 3085
PORT TO PORT INTERNATIONAL CORP.; *U.S. Private*, pg. 3231
PORT TORREDEMBARRA, S.A.—See Industry Super Holdings Pty. Ltd.; *Int'l*, pg. 3676
PORTUARIA CABO FROWARD SA—See Grupo Empresas Navieras S.A.; *Int'l*, pg. 3128
PORTUGAL TELECOM - ASSOCIACAO DE CUIDADOS DE SAUDE—See Altice Europe N.V.; *Int'l*, pg. 393
PORTUGESE BAKING COMPANY LP; *U.S. Private*, pg. 3233
PORTUS HOLDINGS INC.; *U.S. Private*, pg. 3233
PORTU-SUNBERG & ASSOCIATES INC.—See Brass Ring Capital Inc.; *U.S. Private*, pg. 640
PORTWARE, LLC—See FactSet Research Systems Inc.; *U.S. Public*, pg. 820
PORTWAY INTERNATIONAL INC.—See Vista Equity Partners, LLC; *U.S. Private*, pg. 4395
PORTWAY SA—See VINCI S.A.; *Int'l*, pg. 8225
PORTWELL INC.—See Posiflex Technology Inc.; *Int'l*, pg. 5938
PORTWELL INDIA TECHNOLOGY PRIVATE LIMITED—See Posiflex Technology Inc.; *Int'l*, pg. 5938
PORTWELL JAPAN, INC.—See Posiflex Technology Inc.; *Int'l*, pg. 5938
PORTWELL KOREA, INC.—See Posiflex Technology Inc.; *Int'l*, pg. 5938
PORTWELL SINGAPORE PTE LTD—See ISDN Holdings Limited; *Int'l*, pg. 3813
PORTWELL (UK) LTD.—See Posiflex Technology Inc.; *Int'l*, pg. 5938
PORTZAMPARC GESTION—See BNP Paribas SA; *Int'l*, pg. 1092
PORTZAMPARC SOCIETE DE BOURSE S.A.—See BNP Paribas SA; *Int'l*, pg. 1080
PORVAIR FILTRATION GROUP INC.—See Porvair plc; *Int'l*, pg. 5935
PORVAIR FILTRATION GROUP LTD—See Porvair plc; *Int'l*, pg. 5935
PORVAIR FILTRATION INDIA PRIVATE LIMITED—See Porvair plc; *Int'l*, pg. 5935
PORVAIR PLC; *Int'l*, pg. 5935
PORVAIR SCIENCES LIMITED—See Porvair plc; *Int'l*, pg. 5935
PORVAIR SCIENCES LIMITED—See Porvair plc; *Int'l*, pg. 5935
PORVAIR SELEE ADVANCED MATERIALS WUHAN CO LTD—See Porvair plc; *Int'l*, pg. 5936
PORVAIR SELEE FILTRATION TECHNOLOGY (HUBEI) COMPANY LIMITED—See Porvair plc; *Int'l*, pg. 5935
PORVOON KIRJAKESKUS OY—See Bonnier AB; *Int'l*, pg. 1109
PORWAL AUTO COMPONENTS LTD.; *Int'l*, pg. 5936
PORZELLANMANUFAKTUR FURSTENBERG GMBH—See Norddeutsche Landesbank Girozentrale; *Int'l*, pg. 5417
POSABIT SYSTEMS CORP.; *U.S. Public*, pg. 1703
POSADA HOLDING B.V.—See Envipco Holding N.V.; *Int'l*, pg. 2453
POSADAS DE MEXICO, S.A. DE C.V.—See Grupo Posadas S.A.B. de C.V.; *Int'l*, pg. 3134
POSADAS DE SAN JUAN ASSOCIATES—See Blackstone Inc.; *U.S. Public*, pg. 357
POSADAS USA INC.—See Grupo Posadas S.A.B. de C.V.; *Int'l*, pg. 3134
POSADOS CAFE INC.; *U.S. Private*, pg. 3233
POSATO LEASING GESELLSCHAFT M.B.H.—See UniCredit S.p.A.; *Int'l*, pg. 8036
POS-AUSTEM KUNSHAN AUTOMOTIVE CO., LTD.—See Austem Co., Ltd.; *Int'l*, pg. 717
POS-AUSTEM SUZHOU AUTOMOTIVE CO., LTD.—See Austem Co., Ltd.; *Int'l*, pg. 717
POS-AUSTEM WUHAN AUTOMOTIVE CO., LTD.—See Austem Co., Ltd.; *Int'l*, pg. 717
POS-AUSTEM YANTAI AUTOMOTIVE CO., LTD.—See Austem Co., Ltd.; *Int'l*, pg. 717
POS AVIATION SDN. BHD.—See DRB-HICOM Berhad; *Int'l*, pg. 2202
POSAVINA A.D.; *Int'l*, pg. 5936
POSBAU S.A.—See CVC Capital Partners SICAV-FIS S.A.; *Int'l*, pg. 1881
POSCO A&C CO., LTD.—See POSCO Holdings Inc.; *Int'l*, pg. 5936
POSCO AMERICA CORPORATION—See POSCO Holdings Inc.; *Int'l*, pg. 5936

POSEIDON NICKEL LIMITED

POSCO ASIA CO., LTD.—See POSCO Holdings Inc.; *Int'l*, pg. 5936
POSCO AST CO., LTD.—See POSCO Holdings Inc.; *Int'l*, pg. 5936
POSCO AUSTRALIA PTY. LTD.—See POSCO Holdings Inc.; *Int'l*, pg. 5936
POSCO CANADA LTD.—See POSCO Holdings Inc.; *Int'l*, pg. 5936
POSCO CHINA DALIAN PLATE PROCESSING CENTER LTD.—See POSCO Holdings Inc.; *Int'l*, pg. 5936
POSCO-CHINA HOLDING CORP.—See POSCO Holdings Inc.; *Int'l*, pg. 5936
POSCO COATED & COLOR STEEL CO., LTD.—See POSCO Holdings Inc.; *Int'l*, pg. 5936
POSCO-CTPC CO., LTD.—See POSCO Holdings Inc.; *Int'l*, pg. 5937
POSCO DX CO LTD—See POSCO Holdings Inc.; *Int'l*, pg. 5937
POSCO E&C CO., LTD.—See POSCO Holdings Inc.; *Int'l*, pg. 5936
POSCO E&E CO., LTD.—See POSCO Holdings Inc.; *Int'l*, pg. 5936
POSCO ENGINEERING CO., LTD.—See POSCO Holdings Inc.; *Int'l*, pg. 5936
POSCO-FOSHAN STEEL PROCESSING CENTER CO., LTD.—See POSCO Holdings Inc.; *Int'l*, pg. 5937
POSCO FUTURE M CO., LTD.—See POSCO Holdings Inc.; *Int'l*, pg. 5936
POSCO HOLDINGS INC.; *Int'l*, pg. 5936
POSCO-INDIA PRIVATE LTD.—See POSCO Holdings Inc.; *Int'l*, pg. 5937
POSCO INTERNATIONAL CORPORATION—See POSCO Holdings Inc.; *Int'l*, pg. 5937
POSCO INTERNATIONAL OSAKA—See POSCO Holdings Inc.; *Int'l*, pg. 5937
POSCO INVESTMENT CO., LTD.—See POSCO Holdings Inc.; *Int'l*, pg. 5937
POSCO-JAPAN CO., LTD.—See POSCO Holdings Inc.; *Int'l*, pg. 5937
POSCO-JKPC CO., LTD.—See POSCO Holdings Inc.; *Int'l*, pg. 5937
POSCO-JOPC CO., LTD.—See POSCO Holdings Inc.; *Int'l*, pg. 5937
POSCO (LIAONING) AUTOMOTIVE PROCESSING CENTER LTD.—See POSCO Holdings Inc.; *Int'l*, pg. 5936
POSCO LTD. - POHANG WORKS—See POSCO Holdings Inc.; *Int'l*, pg. 5937
POSCO MC MATERIALS CO., LTD.—See POSCO Holdings Inc.; *Int'l*, pg. 5937
POSCO-MEXICO CO., LTD.—See POSCO Holdings Inc.; *Int'l*, pg. 5937
POSCO M-TECH CO., LTD.—See POSCO Holdings Inc.; *Int'l*, pg. 5937
POSCO MVWPC S.A. DE C.V.—See DHSteel; *Int'l*, pg. 2100
POSCO P&S CO., LTD.—See POSCO Holdings Inc.; *Int'l*, pg. 5937
POSCO SILICON SOLUTION CO LTD.—See POSCO Holdings Inc.; *Int'l*, pg. 5938
POSCO (SUZHOU) AUTOMOTIVE PROCESSING CENTER CO., LTD.—See POSCO Holdings Inc.; *Int'l*, pg. 5936
POSCO (THAILAND) CO., LTD. - WELLGROW FACTORY 3—See POSCO Holdings Inc.; *Int'l*, pg. 5936
POSCO-THAINOX PUBLIC COMPANY LIMITED—See POSCO Holdings Inc.; *Int'l*, pg. 5937
POSCO TMC CO., LTD - CHINESE FACTORY—See POSCO Holdings Inc.; *Int'l*, pg. 5937
POSCO TMC CO., LTD. - POHANG FACTORY—See POSCO Holdings Inc.; *Int'l*, pg. 5937
POSCO TMC CO., LTD.—See POSCO Holdings Inc.; *Int'l*, pg. 5937
POSCO-VIETNAM CO., LTD—See POSCO Holdings Inc.; *Int'l*, pg. 5937
POSCO-VIETNAM PROCESSING CENTER CO., LTD.—See POSCO Holdings Inc.; *Int'l*, pg. 5937
POSCO WA PTY. LTD.—See POSCO Holdings Inc.; *Int'l*, pg. 5937
POS DIGICERT SDN. BHD—See Pos Malaysia Berhad; *Int'l*, pg. 5936
POS DIGICERT SDN. BHD.—See DRB-HICOM Berhad; *Int'l*, pg. 2202
POSEDO CO., LTD.—See Burelle S.A.; *Int'l*, pg. 1223
POSEIDA THERAPEUTICS, INC.; *U.S. Public*, pg. 1703
POSEIDON CONCEPTS CORP.; *Int'l*, pg. 5938
POSEIDON CONCEPTS INC.—See Poseidon Concepts Corp.; *Int'l*, pg. 5938
POSEIDON CONCEPTS LTD.—See Poseidon Concepts Corp.; *Int'l*, pg. 5938
POSEIDON CONTAINERS HOLDINGS LLC—See Global Ship Lease, Inc.; *U.S. Public*, pg. 3001
THE POSEIDON GROUP, INC.—See Thoma Bravo, L.P.; *U.S. Private*, pg. 4150
POSEIDON INTERNATIONAL LIMITED—See Siemens Aktiengesellschaft; *Int'l*, pg. 6887
POSEIDON MARINE LTD.—See Sincere Navigation Corporation; *Int'l*, pg. 6937
POSEIDON NICKEL LIMITED; *Int'l*, pg. 5938

POSEIDON NICKEL LIMITED / CORPORATE AFFILIATIONS

POSEIDON OIL PIPELINE COMPANY, LLC—See Enterprise Products Partners L.P.; *U.S. Public*, pg. 779
POSEIDON OIL PIPELINE COMPANY, LLC—See Genesis Energy, L.P.; *U.S. Public*, pg. 930
POSEIDON OIL PIPELINE COMPANY, LLC—See Shell plc; *Int'l*, pg. 6795
P&O SERVICES, INC.—See Select Medical Holdings Corporation; *U.S. Public*, pg. 1858
POSEY COUNTY FARM BUREAU COOP ASSOCIATION; *U.S. Private*, pg. 3233
POSH BOUTIQUE; *U.S. Private*, pg. 3233
POSH CONCEPT MANNEQUINS CO., LTD.—See Cosmos Machinery Enterprises Limited; *Int'l*, pg. 1813
POS-HIMETAL CO., LTD.—See POSCO Holdings Inc.; *Int'l*, pg. 5936
POSHMARK, INC.—See NAVER Corporation; *Int'l*, pg. 5174
POSH OFFICE SYSTEMS (HK) LTD.—See MillerKnoll, Inc.; *U.S. Public*, pg. 1447
POSH PROPERTIES DEVELOPMENT CORPORATION—See Anchor Land Holdings, Inc.; *Int'l*, pg. 448
POSIFLEX BUSINESS MACHINES (BEIJING) CO., LTD.—See Posiflex Technology Inc.; *Int'l*, pg. 5938
POSIFLEX BUSINESS MACHINES, INC.—See Posiflex Technology Inc.; *Int'l*, pg. 5938
POSIFLEX BUSINESS MACHINES SDN. BHD.—See Posiflex Technology Inc.; *Int'l*, pg. 5938
POSIFLEX GMBH—See Posiflex Technology Inc.; *Int'l*, pg. 5938
POSIFLEX TECHNOLOGIES SOUTH CONE—See Posiflex Technology Inc.; *Int'l*, pg. 5938
POSIFLEX TECHNOLOGY INC.; *Int'l*, pg. 5938
POSIFLEX TECHNOLOGY (INDIA) PVT LTD.—See Posiflex Technology Inc.; *Int'l*, pg. 5938
POSIFLEX TECHNOLOGY PTE. LTD.—See Posiflex Technology Inc.; *Int'l*, pg. 5938
POSIGEN LLC; *U.S. Private*, pg. 3233
POSILLICO CIVIL, INC.—See Posillico, Inc.; *U.S. Private*, pg. 3233
POSILLICO, INC.; *U.S. Private*, pg. 3233
POSILLICO MATERIALS, LLC—See Posillico, Inc.; *U.S. Private*, pg. 3233
POSIM MARKETING SDN BHD—See Lion Industries Corporation Berhad; *Int'l*, pg. 4519
POSIM PETROLEUM MARKETING SDN BHD—See Lion Industries Corporation Berhad; *Int'l*, pg. 4519
POSITECH SRL—See Alten S.A.; *Int'l*, pg. 390
POSITEK LIMITED—See discoverIE Group plc; *Int'l*, pg. 2133
POSITION2, INC.—See thismoment, Inc.; *U.S. Private*, pg. 4145
POSITION LOGIC, LLC—See The Graham Group, Inc.; *U.S. Private*, pg. 4037
POSITION RESEARCH—See Etica Entertainment Inc.; *U.S. Private*, pg. 1432
POSITIVE-A JSC; *Int'l*, pg. 5938
POSITIVE FOOD VENTURES PRIVATE LIMITED—See Food Empire Holdings Limited; *Int'l*, pg. 2727
POSITIVEID CORPORATION; *U.S. Private*, pg. 3233
POSITIVE PHYSICIANS HOLDINGS, INC.; *U.S. Public*, pg. 1703
POSITIVE PHYSICIANS INSURANCE COMPANY—See Positive Physicians Holdings, Inc.; *U.S. Public*, pg. 1703
POSITIVE SOFTWARE USA LLC—See LSI Software S.A.; *Int'l*, pg. 4570
POSITIVE THINKING; *Int'l*, pg. 5938
POSITIVO INFORMATICA DA AMAZONIA LTDA—See Positivo Tecnologia S.A.; *Int'l*, pg. 5939
POSITIVO TECNOLOGIA S.A.; *Int'l*, pg. 5938
POSITOUCH, LLC—See Shift4 Payments, Inc.; *U.S. Public*, pg. 1875
POSITRON CORP.; *U.S. Private*, pg. 3234
POSITRON GROUP PTY LTD—See RCR Tomlinson Ltd.; *Int'l*, pg. 6228
POSITRONIC ASIA PTE LTD.—See Positronic Industries, Inc.; *U.S. Private*, pg. 3234
POSITRONIC INDUSTRIES CARIBE, INC.—See Positronic Industries, Inc.; *U.S. Private*, pg. 3234
POSITRONIC INDUSTRIES, INC.; *U.S. Private*, pg. 3234
POSITRONIC INDUSTRIES S.A.S.—See Positronic Industries, Inc.; *U.S. Private*, pg. 3234
POSITRONIC INTERCONNECTS PVT. LTD.—See Positronic Industries, Inc.; *U.S. Private*, pg. 3234
POSITRONIC JAPAN CO LTD—See Positronic Industries, Inc.; *U.S. Private*, pg. 3234
POSK (PINGHU) STEEL PROCESSING CENTER CO., LTD.—See SK Inc.; *Int'l*, pg. 6972
POSLAB TECHNOLOGY CORPORATION—See Ennoconn Corporation; *Int'l*, pg. 2443
POS LOGISTICS BERHAD—See DRB-HICOM Berhad; *Int'l*, pg. 2202
POSLOVNI OBJEKTI A.D.; *Int'l*, pg. 5939
POSLOVNI SISTEM MERCATOR, D.D.—See Fortenova Group d.d.; *Int'l*, pg. 2738
POSLOVNI SISTEM RMK D.D.; *Int'l*, pg. 5939
POS MALAYSIA BERHAD; *Int'l*, pg. 5936

POSMAN COLLEGIATE STORES INC.; *U.S. Private*, pg. 3234
POSMATIC GMBH—See Shift4 Payments, Inc.; *U.S. Public*, pg. 1875
POSMETAL—See POSCO Holdings Inc.; *Int'l*, pg. 5937
POS-MPC S.A. DE C.V.—See POSCO Holdings Inc.; *Int'l*, pg. 5936
POS NATION—See Crimson Solutions, LLC; *U.S. Private*, pg. 1101
POSNAVITAS RETAIL SERVICES, INC.; *U.S. Private*, pg. 3234
POSNER ADVERTISING; *U.S. Private*, pg. 3234
POSNER ADVERTISING—See Posner Advertising; *U.S. Private*, pg. 3234
POSNER INDUSTRIES INC.; *U.S. Private*, pg. 3234
POS-NP PTY. LTD.—See POSCO Holdings Inc.; *Int'l*, pg. 5936
POS-ORE PTY. LTD.—See POSCO Holdings Inc.; *Int'l*, pg. 5936
POS PORTAL, INC.—See ScanSource, Inc.; *U.S. Public*, pg. 1843
POS-QINGDAO COIL CENTER CO., LTD.—See POSCO Holdings Inc.; *Int'l*, pg. 5936
POS-SEAH STEEL WIRE (NANTONG) CO. LTD.—See SeAH Holdings Corp.; *Int'l*, pg. 6664
POS-SEAH STEEL WIRE (THAILAND) CO., LTD.—See SeAH Holdings Corp.; *Int'l*, pg. 6664
POS-SEAH STEEL WIRE (TIANJIN) CO., LTD.—See SeAH Holdings Corp.; *Int'l*, pg. 6664
THE POSSE FOUNDATION, INC.; *U.S. Private*, pg. 4097
POSSEHL AANNEMINGSMAATSCHAPPIJ BV—See L. Possehl & Co. mbH; *Int'l*, pg. 4384
POSSEHL CONNECTOR SERVICES SC, INC—See L. Possehl & Co. mbH; *Int'l*, pg. 4384
POSSEHL CONNECTOR SERVICES—See L. Possehl & Co. mbH; *Int'l*, pg. 4384
POSSEHL ELECTRONICS CZECH REPUBLIC S.R.O.—See L. Possehl & Co. mbH; *Int'l*, pg. 4384
POSSEHL ELECTRONICS DEUTSCHLAND GMBH—See L. Possehl & Co. mbH; *Int'l*, pg. 4384
POSSEHL ELECTRONICS FRANCE S.A.S.—See L. Possehl & Co. mbH; *Int'l*, pg. 4384
POSSEHL ELECTRONICS HONG KONG LTD.—See L. Possehl & Co. mbH; *Int'l*, pg. 4384
POSSEHL ELECTRONICS MALAYSIA SDN BHD—See L. Possehl & Co. mbH; *Int'l*, pg. 4384
POSSEHL ELECTRONICS NETHERLANDS B.V.—See L. Possehl & Co. mbH; *Int'l*, pg. 4384
POSSEHL ELECTRONICS N.V.—See L. Possehl & Co. mbH; *Int'l*, pg. 4384
POSSEHL ELECTRONICS PUEBLA S. DE R.L. DE C.V.—See L. Possehl & Co. mbH; *Int'l*, pg. 4384
POSSEHL ELECTRONICS SINGAPORE PTE. LTD.—See L. Possehl & Co. mbH; *Int'l*, pg. 4384
POSSEHL ELECTRONICS WACKERSDORF GMBH—See L. Possehl & Co. mbH; *Int'l*, pg. 4384
POSSEHL ERZKONTOR GMBH—See L. Possehl & Co. mbH; *Int'l*, pg. 4384
POSSEHL ERZKONTOR HONG KONG LIMITED—See L. Possehl & Co. mbH; *Int'l*, pg. 4384
POSSEHL (HK) HOLDINGS LTD.—See L. Possehl & Co. mbH; *Int'l*, pg. 4384
POSSEHL ING.—See L. Possehl & Co. mbH; *Int'l*, pg. 4384
POSSEHL LAMINATES LIMITED—See L. Possehl & Co. mbH; *Int'l*, pg. 4384
POSSEHL (MALAYSIA) SDN. BHD.—See L. Possehl & Co. mbH; *Int'l*, pg. 4384
POSSEHL MEXICO, S.A. DE C.V.—See Scully Royalty Ltd.; *Int'l*, pg. 6656
POSSEHL MITTELSTANDSBETEILIGUNGEN GMBH—See L. Possehl & Co. mbH; *Int'l*, pg. 4384
POSSEHL POSEBNE GRADNJE D.O.O.—See L. Possehl & Co. mbH; *Int'l*, pg. 4385
POSSEHL PRECISION TOOLINGS (SHENZHEN) CO. LTD.—See L. Possehl & Co. mbH; *Int'l*, pg. 4384
POSSEHL SPEZIALBAU GESMBH—See L. Possehl & Co. mbH; *Int'l*, pg. 4385
POSSEHL SPEZIALBAU GMBH—See L. Possehl & Co. mbH; *Int'l*, pg. 4384
POSSEHL UMWELTSCHUTZ GMBH—See L. Possehl & Co. mbH; *Int'l*, pg. 4385
POSSIBLE SINGAPORE—See WPP plc; *Int'l*, pg. 8483
POSSIBLE WORLDWIDE, INC.—See WPP plc; *Int'l*, pg. 8483
POSSIBLE WORLDWIDE—See WPP plc; *Int'l*, pg. 8483
POS SM CO., LTD.—See Pan Ocean Co., Ltd.; *Int'l*, pg. 5715
P-OSS SOLUTIONS S.L.U.—See Elisa Corporation; *Int'l*, pg. 2361
POSSUM BOURNE RETIREMENT VILLAGE LIMITED—See Ryman Healthcare Ltd.; *Int'l*, pg. 6439
POSTAC LLC—See Bong AB; *Int'l*, pg. 1107
POST ACUTE MEDICAL, LLC; *U.S. Private*, pg. 3234
POST ACUTE PARTNERS, LLC; *U.S. Private*, pg. 3234
POST ADVISORY GROUP, LLC—See Principal Financial Group, Inc.; *U.S. Public*, pg. 1721
POSTAKERIET SVERIGE AB—See PostNord AB; *Int'l*, pg. 5940

POSTAL CENTER INTERNATIONAL; *U.S. Private*, pg. 3234
POSTAL COMMEMORATIVE SOCIETY COLLECTION—See MBI, Inc.; *U.S. Private*, pg. 2624
POSTAL CONNECTIONS OF AMERICA, INC.; *U.S. Private*, pg. 3234
POSTAL PRESENTS PROPRIETARY LTD—See Bowler Metcalf Limited; *Int'l*, pg. 1124
POSTAL REALTY TRUST, INC.; *U.S. Public*, pg. 1704
POSTAL SAVINGS BANK OF CHINA CO., LTD.; *Int'l*, pg. 5939
POSTAS CO., LTD.—See Persol Holdings Co., Ltd.; *Int'l*, pg. 5820
POST-ATHENIAN COMPANY LLC—See Adams Publishing Group, LLC; *U.S. Private*, pg. 75
POSTAUTO LIECHTENSTEIN ANSTALT—See Die Schweizerische Post AG; *Int'l*, pg. 2113
POSTBANK IMMOBILIEN GMBH—See Deutsche Bank Aktiengesellschaft; *Int'l*, pg. 2061
POSTBANK LEASING GMBH—See Deutsche Bank Aktiengesellschaft; *Int'l*, pg. 2061
POST+BEAM; *U.S. Private*, pg. 3234
POST BRANDS PET CARE, LLC—See Post Holdings, Inc.; *U.S. Public*, pg. 1704
POST BULLETIN COMPANY LLC—See Forum Communications Company; *U.S. Private*, pg. 1577
POST CAPITAL PARTNERS, LLC; *U.S. Private*, pg. 3234
POSTCARD INN ON THE BEACH; *U.S. Private*, pg. 3235
POSTCARDMANIA; *U.S. Private*, pg. 3235
POST CH NETWORK LTD.—See Die Schweizerische Post AG; *Int'l*, pg. 2113
POST COMPANY CARS AG—See Die Schweizerische Post AG; *Int'l*, pg. 2113
THE POST COMPANY; *U.S. Private*, pg. 4097
POST CONSUMER BRANDS, LLC—See Post Holdings, Inc.; *U.S. Public*, pg. 1704
THE POST & COURIER, LLC—See Evening Post Publishing Co.; *U.S. Private*, pg. 1436
POST & CO VERMIETUNGS OEG—See Osterreichische Post AG; *Int'l*, pg. 5654
THE POST-CRESCENT—See Gannett Co., Inc.; *U.S. Public*, pg. 900
POST DANMARK A/S—See PostNord AB; *Int'l*, pg. 5940
POST D.O.O.—See Osterreichische Post AG; *Int'l*, pg. 5654
POSTEF DEVELOPMENT ENERGY SYSTEM COMPANY LIMITED—See Post & Telecommunication Equipment Joint Stock Company; *Int'l*, pg. 5939
POSTE IMMO S.A.—See La Poste S.A.; *Int'l*, pg. 4388
POSTE INSURANCE BROKER SRL—See Poste Italiane S.p.A.; *Int'l*, pg. 5939
POSTE ITALIANE S.P.A.; *Int'l*, pg. 5939
POSTEL SPA—See Poste Italiane S.p.A.; *Int'l*, pg. 5939
POSTEN FORSAKRINGS AB—See PostNord AB; *Int'l*, pg. 5940
POSTEN LEASING AB—See PostNord AB; *Int'l*, pg. 5940
POSTEN LOGISTIK AB—See PostNord AB; *Int'l*, pg. 5940
POSTEN LOGISTIK SCM OY—See PostNord AB; *Int'l*, pg. 5940
POSTEN MEDDELANDE AB—See PostNord AB; *Int'l*, pg. 5940
POSTEN NORGE AS; *Int'l*, pg. 5939
POSTERLOID CORPORATION—See Visual Graphics Systems, Inc.; *U.S. Private*, pg. 4404
POSTER ONE—See WPP plc; *Int'l*, pg. 8488
POSTER PROPERTY LIMITED—See DigitalBridge Group, Inc.; *U.S. Public*, pg. 665
POSTERSELECT MEDIA-AGENTUR FUR AUBENWERBUNG GMBH—See Stroer SE & Co. KGaA; *Int'l*, pg. 7242
POSTER STORE SVERIGE AB—See Desenio Group AB; *Int'l*, pg. 2044
POSTE SRPSKE; *Int'l*, pg. 5939
POSTE VITA SPA—See Poste Italiane S.p.A.; *Int'l*, pg. 5939
POSTE WELFARE SERVIZI SRL—See Poste Italiane S.p.A.; *Int'l*, pg. 5939
POSTFINANCE AG—See Die Schweizerische Post AG; *Int'l*, pg. 2113
POST FOODS CANADA CORP.—See Post Holdings, Inc.; *U.S. Public*, pg. 1704
POST FOODS, LLC - BATTLE CREEK PLANT—See Post Holdings, Inc.; *U.S. Public*, pg. 1704
POST FOODS, LLC - JONESBORO PLANT—See Post Holdings, Inc.; *U.S. Public*, pg. 1704
POST FOODS, LLC - MODESTO PLANT—See Post Holdings, Inc.; *U.S. Public*, pg. 1704
POST FOODS, LLC - PARSIPPANY ADMINISTRATIVE OFFICE—See Post Holdings, Inc.; *U.S. Public*, pg. 1704
POST FOODS, LLC—See Post Holdings, Inc.; *U.S. Public*, pg. 1704
POST GLOVER LIFELINK INC.; *U.S. Private*, pg. 3234
POST GLOVER RESISTORS INC.—See Telema S.p.A.; *Int'l*, pg. 7538
POSTGRADUATE CENTER FOR MENTAL HEALTH; *U.S. Private*, pg. 3235

COMPANY NAME INDEX

POSTGRADUATE HEALTHCARE EDUCATION, LLC—See The Wicks Group of Companies, LLC; *U.S. Private*, pg. 4135

POST GRADUATE INSTITUTE FOR MEDICINE (PIM)—See The Wicks Group of Companies, LLC; *U.S. Private*, pg. 4135

POSTGRADUATE MEDICINE—See JTE Multimedia, LLC; *U.S. Private*, pg. 2242

THE POST GROUP PRODUCTION SUITES; *U.S. Private*, pg. 4097

POS-THAI STEEL SERVICE CENTER CO., LTD.—See POSCO Holdings Inc.; *Int'l*, pg. 5936

POST HARDWOODS, INC—See Littlejohn & Co., LLC; *U.S. Private*, pg. 2471

POST HASTE LIMITED—See Freightways Group Limited; *Int'l*, pg. 2772

POST HOLDINGS, INC.; *U.S. Public*, pg. 1703

POST HOLDINGS PARTNERING CORPORATION; *U.S. Public*, pg. 1703

POSTIE PLUS GROUP LIMITED—See Steinhoff International Holdings N.V.; *Int'l*, pg. 7195

POSTI GROUP OYJ; *Int'l*, pg. 5940

POST IMMOBILIEN MANAGEMENT UND SERVICES AG—See Die Schweizerische Post AG; *Int'l*, pg. 2113

POST INDEPENDENT—See Swift Communications, Inc.; *U.S. Private*, pg. 3893

POST INTERNATIONAL MEDIA CO., LTD.—See Vivendi SE; *Int'l*, pg. 8275

POSTITUSPOJAT OY—See Sanoma Oyj; *Int'l*, pg. 6553

POST JET SYSTEMS LTD.—See Brother Industries, Ltd.; *Int'l*, pg. 1198

POSTLE ALUMINUM CO. LLC—See Strength Capital Partners, LLC; *U.S. Private*, pg. 3839

POSTLER & JAECKLE CORP.; *U.S. Private*, pg. 3235

POSTLIGHT LLC—See Nippon Telegraph & Telephone Corporation; *Int'l*, pg. 5355

POSTLOGISTICS AG—See Die Schweizerische Post AG; *Int'l*, pg. 2113

POSTMA HEERENVEEN BV—See VDL Groep B.V.; *Int'l*, pg. 8140

POSTMAIL AG—See Die Schweizerische Post AG; *Int'l*, pg. 2113

POST.MAINTAIN MANAGEMENT OBJEKTVERWALTUNGS- UND INSTANDIHALTUNGS GMBH—See Osterreichische Post AG; *Int'l*, pg. 5654

POSTMATES INC.—See Uber Technologies, Inc.; *U.S. Public*, pg. 2217

POSTMEDIA NETWORK CANADA CORP.—See Chatham Asset Management, LLC; *U.S. Private*, pg. 860

POSTMEDIA NETWORK INC.—See Chatham Asset Management, LLC; *U.S. Private*, pg. 861

POST MERIDIEM PLASTICS LTD—See KB Components AB; *Int'l*, pg. 4103

POST MODERN EDIT, LLC—See PAR Capital Management, Inc.; *U.S. Private*, pg. 3089

POSTNET INTERNATIONAL FRANCHISE CORPORATION—See MBE Worldwide S.p.A.; *Int'l*, pg. 4751

POST NEUN BETEILIGUNGS GMBH—See Osterreichische Post AG; *Int'l*, pg. 5654

POST-NEWSWEEK MEDIA, LLC—See Nash Holdings LLC; *U.S. Private*, pg. 2835

POSTNL N.V.; *Int'l*, pg. 5940

POSTNORD AB; *Int'l*, pg. 5940

POSTNORD AS—See PostNord AB; *Int'l*, pg. 5940

POSTNORD LOGISTICS GMBH—See PostNord AB; *Int'l*, pg. 5940

POSTNORD LOGISTICS—See PostNord AB; *Int'l*, pg. 5940

POSTNORD OY—See PostNord AB; *Int'l*, pg. 5940

POST OAK GRAPHICS—See Gulf International Corporation; *U.S. Private*, pg. 1816

POST OFFICE FINANCIAL & TRAVEL SERVICES—See Bank of Ireland Group plc; *Int'l*, pg. 844

POST OFFICE LTD.; *Int'l*, pg. 5939

POSTON OF DALTON INC.; *U.S. Private*, pg. 3235

POSTPATH LLC—See Cisco Systems, Inc.; *U.S. Public*, pg. 500

POSTPAY SDN. BHD.—See Advance Synergy Berhad; *Int'l*, pg. 157

POSTPOINT SERVICES LIMITED—See An Post LLC; *Int'l*, pg. 443

POST PRINTING CO. INC.; *U.S. Private*, pg. 3234

THE POST PUBLISHING COMPANY LTD.—See GMM Grammy Public Company Limited; *Int'l*, pg. 3012

POST PUBLISHING COMPANY—See Evening Post Publishing Co.; *U.S. Private*, pg. 1436

POSTROM MASKINER AS—See BOWE SYSTEC AG; *Int'l*, pg. 1123

POSTRONIC AB—See Amplex AB; *Int'l*, pg. 433

THE POST—See Chatham Asset Management, LLC; *U.S. Private*, pg. 861

POST SOUTH END, L.P.—See Mid-America Apartment Communities, Inc.; *U.S. Public*, pg. 1445

POST & TELECOMMUNICATION EQUIPMENT JOINT STOCK COMPANY - BAC NINH FACTORY—See Post & Telecommunication Equipment Joint Stock Company; *Int'l*, pg. 5939

POST & TELECOMMUNICATION EQUIPMENT JOINT STOCK COMPANY - DA NANG FACTORY—See Post & Telecommunication Equipment Joint Stock Company; *Int'l*, pg. 5939

POST & TELECOMMUNICATION EQUIPMENT JOINT STOCK COMPANY - HO CHI MINH FACTORY—See Post & Telecommunication Equipment Joint Stock Company; *Int'l*, pg. 5939

POST & TELECOMMUNICATION EQUIPMENT JOINT STOCK COMPANY; *Int'l*, pg. 5939

POST & TELECOMMUNICATIONS INVESTMENT & CONSTRUCTION JOINT STOCK COMPANY; *Int'l*, pg. 5939

POST & TELECOMMUNICATONS INSURANCE JSC; *Int'l*, pg. 5939

POST & TELEKOM IMMOBILIENGESELLSCHAFT MBH—See Osterreichische Post AG; *Int'l*, pg. 5654

THE POST-TRIBUNE—See Chicago Public Media, Inc.; *U.S. Private*, pg. 879

POST-UP STAND, INC.—See Franz Haniel & Cie. GmbH; *Int'l*, pg. 2763

POST WERTLOGISTIK GMBH—See Osterreichische Post AG; *Int'l*, pg. 5654

POST WORKS; *U.S. Private*, pg. 3234

POSTWORTH LTD—See Carillion plc; *Int'l*, pg. 1330

PO SUN PIECE GOODS COMPANY LIMITED—See Carnival Group International Holdings Limited; *Int'l*, pg. 1342

POSVINA CO., LTD.—See POSCO Holdings Inc.; *Int'l*, pg. 5937

POS WORLD, INC.; *U.S. Private*, pg. 3233

POS-X, LLC—See Custom SpA; *Int'l*, pg. 1881

POSZUKIWANIA NAFTOWE DIAMENT SP. Z O.O.—See Polskie Gornictwo Naftowe i Gazownictwo S.A.; *Int'l*, pg. 5912

POSZUKIWANIA NAFTY I GAZU JASLO SP. Z O.O.—See Polskie Gornictwo Naftowe i Gazownictwo S.A.; *Int'l*, pg. 5912

POSZUKIWANIA NAFTY I GAZU NAFTA SP. Z O.O.—See Polskie Gornictwo Naftowe i Gazownictwo S.A.; *Int'l*, pg. 5912

POTAIN INDIA PVT. LTD.—See The Manitowoc Company, Inc.; *U.S. Public*, pg. 2111

POTAIN S.A.—See The Manitowoc Company, Inc.; *U.S. Public*, pg. 2111

POTAMKIN MANHATTAN CORP; *U.S. Private*, pg. 3235

POTAMKIN NEW YORK L.P.; *U.S. Private*, pg. 3235

POTASH BROS INC.; *U.S. Private*, pg. 3235

POTASH CORPORATION OF SASKATCHEWAN INC.—See Nutrien Ltd.; *Int'l*, pg. 5493

POTASH RIDGE CORPORATION; *Int'l*, pg. 5941

POTASIOS DE CHILE SA; *Int'l*, pg. 5941

POTATO DELICA CO., LTD.—See Kewpie Corporation; *Int'l*, pg. 4144

POTATO KAITSUKA CO. LTD.—See Calbee, Inc.; *Int'l*, pg. 1261

POTBELLY CORPORATION; *U.S. Public*, pg. 1704

POTBELLY FRANCHISING, LLC—See Potbelly Corporation; *U.S. Public*, pg. 1704

POTBELLY SANDWICH WORKS, LLC—See Potbelly Corporation; *U.S. Public*, pg. 1704

POTCHEFSTROOM MEDI-CLINIC (PROPRIETARY) LIMITED—See Remgro Limited; *Int'l*, pg. 6270

P & O TECHNOLOGIES SDN. BHD.—See Pacific & Orient Berhad; *Int'l*, pg. 5685

P.O. TECHNO SERVICE INC.—See Pola Orbis Holdings Inc.; *Int'l*, pg. 5905

POTELCO, INC.—See Quanta Services, Inc.; *U.S. Public*, pg. 1752

POTEL ET CHABOT SAS—See 21 Investimenti Societa' di Gestione del Risparmio S.p.A.; *Int'l*, pg. 4

POTEN ENVIRONMENT GROUP CO LTD; *Int'l*, pg. 5941

POTEN & PARTNERS (AUSTRALIA) PTY. LTD.—See BGC Group, Inc.; *U.S. Public*, pg. 330

POTEN & PARTNERS (HELLAS) LTD.—See BGC Group, Inc.; *U.S. Public*, pg. 330

POTEN & PARTNERS, INC.—See BGC Group, Inc.; *U.S. Public*, pg. 330

POTEN & PARTNERS PTE. LTD.—See BGC Group, Inc.; *U.S. Public*, pg. 330

POTEN & PARTNERS (UK) LTD.—See BGC Group, Inc.; *U.S. Public*, pg. 330

POTENTIAL INDUSTRIES INC.; *U.S. Private*, pg. 3235

POTENTIA PHARMACEUTICALS, INC.—See Apellis Pharmaceuticals, Inc.; *U.S. Public*, pg. 144

POTENTIA RENEWABLES INC—See Power Corporation of Canada; *Int'l*, pg. 5943

POTENT MECHANICAL & INDUSTRIAL (XIAMEN) CO., LTD.—See Xiamen Zhongchuang Environmental Technology Co., Ltd.; *Int'l*, pg. 8526

POTENZA TECHNOLOGY LIMITED—See CNH Industrial N.V.; *Int'l*, pg. 1676

POTEX INDUSTRIES SDN. BHD.—See C.I. Holdings Berhad; *Int'l*, pg. 1243

POTHIER MOTORS LIMITED; *Int'l*, pg. 5941

POTHOS, INC.; *U.S. Private*, pg. 3235

POTIS CAPITAL SA; *Int'l*, pg. 5941

POTI SEA PORT CORPORATION—See A.P. Moller-Maersk A/S; *Int'l*, pg. 27

POU CHEN CORPORATION

POTISJE KANJIZA D.D.—See Wienerberger AG; *Int'l*, pg. 8406

POTISJE PRECIZNI LIV A.D.; *Int'l*, pg. 5941

POTKOZARJE A.D.; *Int'l*, pg. 5941

POTLATCH CORPORATION WOOD PRODUCTS GROUP—See PotlatchDeltic Corporation; *U.S. Public*, pg. 1704

POTLATCHDELTIC CORPORATION; *U.S. Public*, pg. 1704

POTLATCH MINNESOTA TIMBERLANDS, LLC—See PotlatchDeltic Corporation; *U.S. Public*, pg. 1704

POT LUCK F & B SINGAPORE PTE. LTD.—See Soup Holdings Limited; *Int'l*, pg. 7114

POTNETWORK HOLDINGS, INC.; *U.S. Private*, pg. 3235

POTOMAC BANCSHARES INC.; *U.S. Public*, pg. 1705

POTOMAC BASIN GROUP ASSOCIATES, LLC—See Aon plc; *U.S. Public*, pg. 497

POTOMAC CORPORATION; *U.S. Private*, pg. 3235

THE POTOMAC EDISON COMPANY—See FirstEnergy Corp.; *U.S. Public*, pg. 849

POTOMAC ELECTRIC POWER COMPANY—See Exelon Corporation; *U.S. Public*, pg. 807

POTOMAC EQUITY PARTNERS, LLC; *U.S. Private*, pg. 3235

POTOMAC GERMAN AUTO, INC.—See LKQ Corporation; *U.S. Public*, pg. 1336

POTOMAC MORTGAGE GROUP, INC.—See Intercoastal Mortgage, LLC; *U.S. Private*, pg. 2109

POTOMAC PHYSICIANS PRACTICE ASSOCIATION—See CareFirst, Inc.; *U.S. Private*, pg. 753

POTOMAC RIVER GROUP, LLC; *U.S. Private*, pg. 3235

POTOMAC RIVER HOLDINGS, LLC—See Veritex Holdings, Inc.; *U.S. Public*, pg. 2283

POTOMAC SUPPLY, LLC—See AIP, LLC; *U.S. Private*, pg. 134

POTOMAC VALLEY PROPERTIES INC.; *U.S. Private*, pg. 3235

POTOMAC VIEW SURGERY CENTER, LLC—See Tenet Healthcare Corporation; *U.S. Public*, pg. 2006

POTPOURRI GROUP INC.—See Northlane Capital Partners, LLC; *U.S. Private*, pg. 2956

POTRANCO MEDICAL CENTER LLC—See Adeptus Health Inc.; *U.S. Private*, pg. 78

POTTER & BRUMFIELD DE MEXICO, S.A. DE C.V.—See TE Connectivity Ltd.; *Int'l*, pg. 7495

POTTER CONCRETE LTD; *U.S. Private*, pg. 3235

POTTER DISTRIBUTING INCORPORATED; *U.S. Private*, pg. 3235

POTTER ELECTRIC SIGNAL COMPANY, LLC—See KKR & Co. Inc.; *U.S. Public*, pg. 1263

POTTER EQUIPMENT CO—See Machine Maintenance, Inc.; *U.S. Private*, pg. 2535

POTTER-HOLDEN & CO.—See Arthur J. Gallagher & Co.; *U.S. Public*, pg. 207

POTTER INTERIOR SYSTEMS LTD.—See CSR Limited; *Int'l*, pg. 1837

POTTER & MOORE INNOVATIONS LIMITED—See Creightons plc; *Int'l*, pg. 1837

POTTER ROEMER DIV.—See Jay R. Smith Mfg. Co.; *U.S. Private*, pg. 2192

POTTERS BALLOTINI LTD.—See Ecovyst Inc.; *U.S. Public*, pg. 717

POTTERS BALLOTINI S.A.S.—See Ecovyst Inc.; *U.S. Public*, pg. 717

POTTER & SIMS FOODS, INC.; *U.S. Private*, pg. 3235

POTTERS INDUSTRIAL LIMITADA—See Ecovyst Inc.; *U.S. Public*, pg. 717

POTTERS INDUSTRIES, LLC—See The Jordan Company, L.P.; *U.S. Private*, pg. 4061

POTTERS LIMITED—See CSL Limited; *Int'l*, pg. 1866

POTTER'S MILL, INC.—See Apollo Global Management, Inc.; *U.S. Public*, pg. 150

POTTER'S MILL, INC.—See Reverence Capital Partners LLC; *U.S. Private*, pg. 3415

POTTERY BARN OUTLET—See Williams-Sonoma, Inc.; *U.S. Public*, pg. 2371

POTTERY GARDENS (CHEADLE) RESIDENTS MANAGEMENT COMPANY LIMITED—See Persimmon plc; *Int'l*, pg. 5817

POTTINGER STEEL WORKS, INC.—See Alro Steel Corporation; *U.S. Private*, pg. 202

POTTLE'S TRANSPORTATION INC.—See James Richardson & Sons, Limited; *Int'l*, pg. 3878

POTTON LIMITED—See Kingspan Group PLC; *Int'l*, pg. 4179

POTTS & CALLAHAN INC.; *U.S. Private*, pg. 3235

POTTS COMPANY INC.; *U.S. Private*, pg. 3235

POTTSTOWN AUTO SALES INC.; *U.S. Private*, pg. 3235

POTTSTOWN HOSPITAL COMPANY, LLC—See Tower Health; *U.S. Private*, pg. 4193

THE POTTSVILLE PA ENDOSCOPY ASC, L.P.—See KKR & Co. Inc.; *U.S. Public*, pg. 1248

POU CHEN CORPORATION; *Int'l*, pg. 5941

POUCHFILL PACKAGING, LLC—See TOPPAN Holdings Inc.; *Int'l*, pg. 7817

POU CHIEN CHEMICAL CO., LTD.—See Evermore Chemical Industry Co., Ltd.; *Int'l*, pg. 2568

POUCHTEC INDUSTRIES, LLC—See Kent Corporation; *U.S. Private*, pg. 2287

POUDRE VALLEY TRUSS, INC.

POUDRE VALLEY TRUSS, INC.; *U.S. Private*, pg. 3236
POUGHKEEPSIE-HIGHLAND RAILROAD BRIDGE CO. INC.; *U.S. Private*, pg. 3236
POUGHKEEPSIE JOURNAL—See Gannett Co., Inc.; *U.S. Public*, pg. 899
POUJAUD SAS—See Altrad Investment Authority SAS; *Int'l*, pg. 398
POUJOULAT BELUX S.A.—See Poujoulat SA; *Int'l*, pg. 5942
POUJOULAT BV—See Poujoulat SA; *Int'l*, pg. 5942
POUJOULAT SA; *Int'l*, pg. 5942
POUJOULAT SP. Z O.O.—See Poujoulat SA; *Int'l*, pg. 5942
POULAILLON SA; *Int'l*, pg. 5942
POULAIN DISTRIBUTION—See Carrefour SA; *Int'l*, pg. 1346
THE POUL DUE JENSEN FOUNDATION; *Int'l*, pg. 7674
POULET ARC-EN-CIEL LTEE—See Innodis Ltd; *Int'l*, pg. 3709
POULINA GROUP HOLDING S.A.; *Int'l*, pg. 5942
POULIN GRAIN INC.; *U.S. Private*, pg. 3236
POULIN LUMBER INC.; *U.S. Private*, pg. 3236
POULIN VENTURES LLC; *U.S. Private*, pg. 3236
POULOS INSURANCE, INC.—See Aon plc; *Int'l*, pg. 497
POULTRY PRODUCTS COMPANY INC.; *U.S. Private*, pg. 3236
POUNCE TECHNOLOGIES INC.—See Anzu Partners, LLC; *U.S. Private*, pg. 289
POUNDFIELD PRECAST LIMITED—See SigmaRoc Plc; *Int'l*, pg. 6909
POUNDLAND GROUP LIMITED—See Steinhoff International Holdings N.V.; *Int'l*, pg. 7195
POUNDLAND LIMITED—See Steinhoff International Holdings N.V.; *Int'l*, pg. 7195
POUNDLAND STORES LTD.—See Steinhoff International Holdings N.V.; *Int'l*, pg. 7194
POUNDS PHOTOGRAPHIC LABS, INC.; *U.S. Private*, pg. 3236
POUNDSTRETCHER LIMITED—See Poundstretcher Ltd.; *Int'l*, pg. 5942
POUNDSTRETCHER LTD.; *Int'l*, pg. 5942
POUNDWORLD RETAIL LIMITED—See TPG Capital, L.P.; *U.S. Public*, pg. 2175
POUPART LTD—See Argent Group Europe Limited; *Int'l*, pg. 560
POURSHINS LTD.—See RRJ Capital Ltd.; *Int'l*, pg. 6417
POUSCHINE COOK CAPITAL MANAGEMENT LLC; *U.S. Private*, pg. 3236
POU SHENG INTERNATIONAL (HOLDINGS) LIMITED; *Int'l*, pg. 5941
POUYOUKAS FOODS (PROPRIETARY) LIMITED—See Famous Brands Limited; *Int'l*, pg. 2612
POU YU BIOTECHNOLOGY CO., LTD.—See Pou Chen Corporation; *Int'l*, pg. 5941
POVAL KOBASHI (THAILAND) CO., LTD.—See Poval Kogyo Co., Ltd.; *Int'l*, pg. 5942
POVAL KOGYO CO., LTD. - DAIAN FACTORY—See Poval Kogyo Co., Ltd.; *Int'l*, pg. 5942
POVAL KOGYO CO., LTD.; *Int'l*, pg. 5942
POVAL KUSHAN CO., LTD.—See Poval Kogyo Co., Ltd.; *Int'l*, pg. 5942
PO VALLEY ENERGY LIMITED; *Int'l*, pg. 5901
POVAZSKA CEMENTAREN A.S.—See BERGER Holding GmbH; *Int'l*, pg. 979
POVAZSKY CUKOR A.S.—See Nordzucker AG; *Int'l*, pg. 5427
POVERTY SOLUTIONS, INC.; *U.S. Private*, pg. 3236
POWDERCOAT SERVICES, INC.—See Meridian General, LLC; *U.S. Private*, pg. 2672
POWDER COTE II INC.; *U.S. Private*, pg. 3236
POWDERHORN AGENCY, INC.—See GTCR LLC; *U.S. Private*, pg. 1804
POWDERLY TRANSPORTATION, INC.—See Martin Marietta Materials, Inc.; *U.S. Public*, pg. 1389
POWDERMET, INC.—See ABAKAN INC.; *U.S. Private*, pg. 34
POWDER PAINTS AND VARNISHES PLANT LTD.—See Fabryka Farb i Lakierow Sniezka S.A.; *Int'l*, pg. 2600
POWDER PHARMACEUTICALS INCORPORATED—See Lee's Pharmaceutical Holdings Limited; *Int'l*, pg. 4441
POWDER PROCESSING AND TECHNOLOGY, LLC—See E.J. Vestco Industries, LLC; *U.S. Private*, pg. 1306
POWDER RIVER COAL, LLC—See Peabody Energy Corporation; *U.S. Public*, pg. 1659
POWDER RIVER ENERGY CORPORATION; *U.S. Private*, pg. 3236
POWDER RIVER INC.; *U.S. Private*, pg. 3236
POWDERTECH CO., LTD.; *Int'l*, pg. 5942
POWDERTECH INTERNATIONAL CORPORATION—See Powdertech Co., Ltd.; *Int'l*, pg. 5942
POWDERTECH, LLC—See Great Plains Ventures, Inc.; *U.S. Private*, pg. 1767
POWDR CORP.; *U.S. Private*, pg. 3236
POWEL AB—See Powel AS; *Int'l*, pg. 5942
POWEL AG—See Arendals Fossekompani ASA; *Int'l*, pg. 559
POWEL ASA—See Arendals Fossekompani ASA; *Int'l*, pg. 559
POWEL AS; *Int'l*, pg. 5942

POWEL DANMARK A/S—See Powel AS; *Int'l*, pg. 5942
POWEL ENERJI COZUMLERI LIMITED SIRKETI—See Powel AS; *Int'l*, pg. 5942
POWELL CANADA INC.—See Powell Industries, Inc.; *U.S. Public*, pg. 1705
POWELL, CARNEY, MALLER, P.A.; *U.S. Private*, pg. 3237
POWELL CLINCH GAS UTILITY DISTRIBUTION; *U.S. Private*, pg. 3236
POWELL COMPANIES INC.; *U.S. Private*, pg. 3236
POWELL ELECTRICAL MANUFACTURING COMPANY—See Powell Industries, Inc.; *U.S. Public*, pg. 1705
POWELL ELECTRICAL SYSTEMS, INC.—See Powell Industries, Inc.; *U.S. Public*, pg. 1705
POWELL ELECTRONICS EUROPE BV—See Powell Electronics Inc.; *U.S. Private*, pg. 3237
POWELL ELECTRONICS INC.; *U.S. Private*, pg. 3236
POWELL ENGINEERING UK LIMITED—See VINCI S.A.; *Int'l*, pg. 8225
POWELL ESCO COMPANY—See Powell Industries, Inc.; *U.S. Public*, pg. 1705
POWELL GROUP INC.; *U.S. Private*, pg. 3237
POWELL INDUSTRIES ASIA, PTE. LTD.—See Powell Industries, Inc.; *U.S. Public*, pg. 1705
POWELL INDUSTRIES, INC.; *U.S. Public*, pg. 1705
POWELL & MAHONEY LLC—See Fevertree Drinks plc; *Int'l*, pg. 2649
POWELL MOTORS LTD; *Int'l*, pg. 5942
POWELL PINE, INC.—See InterContinental Hotels Group PLC; *Int'l*, pg. 3738
POWELL SALES INC.; *U.S. Private*, pg. 3237
POWELL'S BOOKS INC.; *U.S. Private*, pg. 3237
POWELL'S TRUCK & EQUIPMENT INC.—See K. Neal International Trucks, Inc.; *U.S. Private*, pg. 2251
POWELL TATE-WEBER SHANDWICK—See The Interpublic Group of Companies, Inc.; *U.S. Public*, pg. 2105
POWELL (UK) LIMITED—See Powell Industries, Inc.; *U.S. Public*, pg. 1705
POWELL VALLEY ELECTRIC COOPERATIVE; *U.S. Private*, pg. 3237
POWELL VALLEY HEALTHCARE; *U.S. Private*, pg. 3237
POWELL-WATSON MOTORS INC.; *U.S. Private*, pg. 3237
POWEL SP. Z.O.O.—See Powel AS; *Int'l*, pg. 5942
POW! ENTERTAINMENT, INC.—See Camsing International Holding Limited; *Int'l*, pg. 1275
POWER ADS CORP.; *U.S. Private*, pg. 3237
POWER ADVOCATE, INC.—See Veritas Capital Fund Management, LLC; *U.S. Private*, pg. 4366
POWERAMP TECHNOLOGY LIMITED—See TDK Corporation; *Int'l*, pg. 7487
POWER ANALYTICS CORPORATION—See WaveTech Global, Inc.; *U.S. Private*, pg. 4458
POWER AND SIGNAL GROUP GMBH—See Arrow Electronics, Inc.; *U.S. Public*, pg. 199
POWER ASIA MOTORSPORT COMPANY LIMITED—See China Environmental Resources Group Limited; *Int'l*, pg. 1500
POWER ASSETS HOLDINGS LIMITED; *Int'l*, pg. 5942
POWER ASSOCIATES INTERNATIONAL, INC.—See Crossplane Capital Management LP; *U.S. Private*, pg. 1107
POWER AUTO GROUP; *U.S. Private*, pg. 3237
POWER AUTOMATION FRANCE S.A.R.L.—See PA Power Automation AG; *Int'l*, pg. 5684
POWER AUTOMATION GMBH—See PA Power Automation AG; *Int'l*, pg. 5684
POWERBAND INDUSTRIES PRIVATE LIMITED—See Clearlake Capital Group, L.P.; *U.S. Private*, pg. 935
POWERBAND SOLUTIONS INC.; *Int'l*, pg. 5947
POWERBAR INC.—See Post Holdings, Inc.; *U.S. Public*, pg. 1704
POWERBOX INTERNATIONAL AB—See COSEL Co., Ltd.; *Int'l*, pg. 1810
POWERBRACE CORPORATION—See Miner Enterprises, Inc.; *U.S. Private*, pg. 2741
POWER CABLES MALAYSIA SDN BHD—See Prysmian S.p.A.; *Int'l*, pg. 6012
POWER CAPITAL GLOBAL LIMITED; *Int'l*, pg. 5943
POWERCART SYSTEMS INC.—See Active Control Technology Inc.; *Int'l*, pg. 120
POWERCELL DEUTSCHLAND GMBH—See PowerCell Sweden AB; *Int'l*, pg. 5947
POWERCELL SWEDEN AB; *Int'l*, pg. 5947
POWER CEMENT LIMITED; *Int'l*, pg. 5943
POWERCHIP TECHNOLOGY CORPORATION; *Int'l*, pg. 5947
POWERCHORD, INC.; *U.S. Private*, pg. 3239
POWERCOAL PTY LIMITED—See Banpu Public Company Limited; *Int'l*, pg. 852
POWERCOM AMERICA INC—See Powercom Co., Ltd.; *Int'l*, pg. 5947
POWERCOM CO., LTD.; *Int'l*, pg. 5947
POWERCOM INC.—See SESCO Electrical Services Group; *U.S. Private*, pg. 3617
POWERCOMM HOLDINGS INC.; *U.S. Private*, pg. 3239
POWER CONSTRUCTION COMPANY; *U.S. Private*, pg. 3237

CORPORATE AFFILIATIONS

POWER CONSTRUCTION CORPORATION OF CHINA; *Int'l*, pg. 5943
POWER CONTROLS, INC.—See Braemont Capital Management LLC; *U.S. Private*, pg. 633
POWERCOR AUSTRALIA LIMITED—See CK Hutchison Holdings Limited; *Int'l*, pg. 1637
POWERCOR AUSTRALIA LIMITED—See Power Assets Holdings Limited; *Int'l*, pg. 5943
POWER CORPORATION OF AMERICA—See The Goldfield Corporation; *U.S. Public*, pg. 2075
POWER CORPORATION OF CANADA; *Int'l*, pg. 5943
POWER CREATIVE; *U.S. Private*, pg. 3237
POWER CURBERS INC.; *U.S. Private*, pg. 3237
POWERDB, INC.—See Megger Group Limited; *Int'l*, pg. 4795
POWER DESIGN, INC.; *U.S. Private*, pg. 3237
POWER DESIGN INC.; *U.S. Private*, pg. 3237
POWER DEVELOPMENT SERVICES (PTY) LIMITED; *Int'l*, pg. 5945
POWER DIGITAL COMMUNICATION CO., LTD.—See Cal-Comp Electronics (Thailand) pcl; *Int'l*, pg. 1261
POWER & DIGITAL INFRASTRUCTURE ACQUISITION CORP.; *U.S. Public*, pg. 1705
POWERDIRECT PTY LTD—See AGL Energy Limited; *Int'l*, pg. 211
POWER DIRECT; *U.S. Private*, pg. 3237
POWER DISTRIBUTION, INC.—See Eaton Corporation plc; *Int'l*, pg. 2282
POWER DISTRIBUTORS, LLC; *U.S. Private*, pg. 3237
POWERDMS, INC.; *U.S. Private*, pg. 3239
POWER DRIVES INC.; *U.S. Private*, pg. 3238
POWERDYNE INTERNATIONAL, INC.; *U.S. Public*, pg. 1705
POWER-DYNE—See Bidwell Industrial Group, Inc.; *U.S. Private*, pg. 551
POWERED BRANDS; *U.S. Public*, pg. 1705
POWER EFFICIENCY CORPORATION; *U.S. Private*, pg. 3238
POWER ELECTRONICS, INC.—See AZZ, Inc.; *U.S. Public*, pg. 259
POWER ENERGY CORPORATION—See Power Corporation of Canada; *Int'l*, pg. 5943
POWER & ENERGY, INC.; *U.S. Private*, pg. 3237
POWER ENGINEERING CONSULTING JOINT STOCK COMPANY 2; *Int'l*, pg. 5945
POWER ENGINEERING CONSULTING JOINT STOCK COMPANY 3; *Int'l*, pg. 5945
POWER ENGINEERING CONSULTING JOINT STOCK COMPANY 4; *Int'l*, pg. 5945
POWER ENGINEERING, INC.; *U.S. Private*, pg. 3238
POWER ENGINEERING TRANSFORMATORY SP. Z O.O.—See KONCAR - Electrical Industry Inc; *Int'l*, pg. 4246
POWER ENGINEERS, INC.—See WSP Global, Inc.; *Int'l*, pg. 8497
POWER EQUIPMENT CO. MEMPHIS; *U.S. Private*, pg. 3238
POWER EQUIPMENT COMPANY INC; *U.S. Private*, pg. 3238
POWER EQUIPMENT COMPANY; *U.S. Private*, pg. 3238
POWER EQUIPMENT DIRECT INC.—See Ferguson plc; *Int'l*, pg. 2638
POWER EQUIPMENT LEASING COMPANY—See Utility Sales & Service, Inc.; *U.S. Private*, pg. 4326
POWER-EQUIP SALES REPS, LTD.—See Emek Elektrik Endustrisi A.S.; *Int'l*, pg. 2377
POWEREX CORP.—See B.C. Hydro; *Int'l*, pg. 789
POWEREX INC.—See Mitsubishi Electric Corporation; *Int'l*, pg. 4944
POWEREX IWATA AIR TECHNOLOGY, INC.—See ANEST IWATA Corporation; *Int'l*, pg. 458
POWERFIL AUTO PARTS SDN. BHD.—See PT Selamat Sempurna Tbk; *Int'l*, pg. 6071
POWERFILM, INC.; *U.S. Private*, pg. 3239
POWER FINANCE CORPORATION LIMITED; *Int'l*, pg. 5945
POWER FINANCIAL CORPORATION—See Power Corporation of Canada; *Int'l*, pg. 5943
POWER FINANCIAL EUROPE B.V.—See Power Corporation of Canada; *Int'l*, pg. 5944
POWER FLAME INC.—See Astec Industries, Inc.; *U.S. Public*, pg. 216
POWERFLEET GMBH—See PowerFleet, Inc.; *U.S. Public*, pg. 1706
POWERFLEET, INC.; *U.S. Public*, pg. 1706
POWERFLEET SYSTEMS LTD.—See PowerFleet, Inc.; *U.S. Public*, pg. 1706
POWER-FLO TECHNOLOGIES INC.; *U.S. Private*, pg. 3239
POWERFLOW, INC.—See Kinderhook Industries, LLC; *U.S. Private*, pg. 2306
POWER FLUIDTRONICS & INDUSTRIES SDN. BHD.—See Daikin Industries, Ltd.; *Int'l*, pg. 1936
POWERFLUTE INTERNATIONAL S.L.—See Mondi plc; *Int'l*, pg. 5027
POWERFORCE FIELD MARKETING & RETAIL SERVICES LTD—See Enero Group Limited; *Int'l*, pg. 2424

COMPANY NAME INDEX

POWERFORCE TOTAL MERCHANDISING PTY LIMITED—See Navis Capital Partners Limited; *Int'l*, pg. 5176

POWER FORD; *U.S. Private*, pg. 3238

POWERFUL TECHNOLOGIES LTD.; *Int'l*, pg. 5947

POWERGEM, LLC—See TA Associates, Inc.; *U.S. Private*, pg. 3917

POWER GENERATION ENGINEERING & SERVICES COMPANY; *Int'l*, pg. 5945

POWER GENERATION SERVICES, INC.—See Mitsubishi Heavy Industries, Ltd.; *Int'l*, pg. 4960

POWERGEN LIMITED—See E.ON SE; *Int'l*, pg. 2258

POWERGEN LUXEMBOURG HOLDINGS SARL—See E.ON SE; *Int'l*, pg. 2258

POWERGEN UK LIMITED—See E.ON SE; *Int'l*, pg. 2258

POWERGEN US HOLDINGS LIMITED—See E.ON SE; *Int'l*, pg. 2258

POWERGEN US INVESTMENTS—See E.ON SE; *Int'l*, pg. 2258

POWERGEN US SECURITIES LIMITED—See E.ON SE; *Int'l*, pg. 2258

POWERGRACE INDUSTRIES LIMITED—See Asian Granito India Limited; *Int'l*, pg. 617

POWER GREAT LAKES, INC—See Power Solutions International, Inc.; *U.S. Public*, pg. 1705

POWER GRID COMPANY OF BANGLADESH LTD.; *Int'l*, pg. 5945

POWER GRID CORPORATION OF INDIA LIMITED; *Int'l*, pg. 5945

POWER GRID ENGINEERING, LLC—See New Mountain Capital, LLC; *U.S. Private*, pg. 2903

POWERGRID INFRASTRUCTURE INVESTMENT TRUST; *Int'l*, pg. 5947

POWERGRID SOLUTIONS LLC—See AZZ, Inc.; *U.S. Public*, pg. 259

POWER GROUP COMPANY, LLC—See CRETCHER HEARTLAND LLC; *U.S. Private*, pg. 1099

POWER GROUP PROJECTS CORP.; *Int'l*, pg. 5945

POWER HAWK TECHNOLOGIES, INC.—See Snap-on Incorporated; *U.S. Public*, pg. 1898

POWER HF CO., LTD.; *Int'l*, pg. 5945

POWER HOLDING CORPORATION; *U.S. Public*, pg. 3238

POWER HOME REMODELING GROUP, INC.; *U.S. Private*, pg. 3238

POWER HOME TECHNOLOGIES INC.; *U.S. Private*, pg. 3238

POWERHOUSE DYNAMICS INC.—See The Middleby Corporation; *U.S. Public*, pg. 2115

POWERHOUSE ENERGY GROUP PLC; *Int'l*, pg. 5947

POWER HOUSE FOODS PTY LTD—See General Mills, Inc.; *U.S. Public*, pg. 922

THE POWER HOUSE, INC.; *U.S. Private*, pg. 4097

POWERHOUSE RETAIL SERVICES, LLC—See Lincolnshire Management, Inc.; *U.S. Private*, pg. 2459

POWERHOUSE VENTURES LIMITED; *Int'l*, pg. 5947

POWER INDIA PVT LTD.—See Langley Holdings Plc; *Int'l*, pg. 4410

POWER INDUSTRIES LTD.—See Stanley Black & Decker, Inc.; *U.S. Public*, pg. 1934

POWER INNOVATIONS INTERNATIONAL, INC.—See Lite-On Technology Corporation; *Int'l*, pg. 4526

POWER & INSTRUMENTATION (GUJARAT) LTD.; *Int'l*, pg. 5942

POWER INTEGRATIONS (EUROPE) LIMITED—See Power Integrations, Inc.; *U.S. Public*, pg. 1705

POWER INTEGRATIONS GMBH—See Power Integrations, Inc.; *U.S. Public*, pg. 1705

POWER INTEGRATIONS, INC.; *U.S. Public*, pg. 1705

POWER INTEGRATIONS, K.K.—See Power Integrations, Inc.; *U.S. Public*, pg. 1705

POWER INTEGRATIONS SINGAPORE PTE. LIMITED—See Power Integrations, Inc.; *U.S. Public*, pg. 1705

POWER INTEGRATIONS SWITZERLAND HOLDING GMBH—See Power Integrations, Inc.; *U.S. Public*, pg. 1705

POWER INTERNET LIMITED—See Horizon Capital LLP; *Int'l*, pg. 3479

POWERLAB INC.; *U.S. Private*, pg. 3239

POWERLAND COMPUTERS LTD.—See Xerox Holdings Corporation; *U.S. Public*, pg. 2386

POWERLASE TECHNOLOGIES LIMITED—See ANDRITZ AG; *Int'l*, pg. 456

POWERLEADER SCIENCE & TECHNOLOGY GROUP LTD.; *Int'l*, pg. 5947

POWERLEAGUE GROUP LIMITED—See Patron Capital Advisers LLP; *Int'l*, pg. 5759

POWER LEISURE BOOKMAKERS LTD.—See Flutter Entertainment plc; *Int'l*, pg. 2715

POWERLIFT MATERIAL HANDLING LTD.—See The Zuellig Group Inc.; *Int'l*, pg. 7705

POWER LINE ENGINEERING PUBLIC COMPANY LIMITED; *Int'l*, pg. 5945

POWER LINE SERVICES, INC.—See Primoris Services Corporation; *U.S. Public*, pg. 1718

POWERLINES PLUS PTY LTD.; *Int'l*, pg. 5947

POWER LINE SYSTEMS, INC.—See TA Associates, Inc.; *U.S. Private*, pg. 3917

POWERLINK LLC.; *U.S. Private*, pg. 3239

POWER LLC; *U.S. Private*, pg. 3238

POWERLOCK INTERNATIONAL CORP.; *U.S. Public*, pg. 1706

POWERLOGICS; *Int'l*, pg. 5947

POWERLONG COMMERCIAL MANAGEMENT HOLDINGS LIMITED; *Int'l*, pg. 5947

POWERLONG REAL ESTATE HOLDINGS LIMITED; *Int'l*, pg. 5947

POWERLONG REAL ESTATE (HONG KONG) HOLDINGS LIMITED—See Powerlong Real Estate Holdings Limited; *Int'l*, pg. 5947

POWERMACH IMP & EXP CO., LTD.—See Sichuan Dawn Precision Technology Co., Ltd.; *Int'l*, pg. 6878

POWER MACHINES REOSTAT PLANT LLC—See OOO Severgrupp; *Int'l*, pg. 5594

POWER MAINTENANCE & CONSTRUCTORS LLC; *U.S. Private*, pg. 3238

POWER MANAGEMENT, INC.—See Tetra Tech, Inc.; *U.S. Public*, pg. 2022

POWERMAN LTD—See Schneider Electric SE; *Int'l*, pg. 6628

POWERMATIC DATA SYSTEMS (HONG KONG) LIMITED—See Powermatic Data Systems Limited; *Int'l*, pg. 5947

POWERMATIC DATA SYSTEMS LIMITED; *Int'l*, pg. 5947

POWER/MATION; *U.S. Private*, pg. 3239

POWERMAT TECHNOLOGIES LTD.—See General Motors Company; *U.S. Public*, pg. 928

POWER MEASUREMENT LTD—See Schneider Electric SE; *Int'l*, pg. 6628

POWERMEC AB—See Addtech AB; *Int'l*, pg. 134

POWERMEC APS—See Addtech AB; *Int'l*, pg. 134

POWERMEC AS—See Addtech AB; *Int'l*, pg. 134

POWER MECH BSCPL CONSORTIUM PRIVATE LIMITED—See Power Mech Projects Ltd.; *Int'l*, pg. 5946

POWER MECH INDUSTRI PRIVATE LIMITED—See Power Mech Projects Ltd.; *Int'l*, pg. 5946

POWER MECH PROJECTS LIMITED LLC—See Power Mech Projects Ltd.; *Int'l*, pg. 5946

POWER MECH PROJECTS LTD.; *Int'l*, pg. 5946

POWER METAL RESOURCES PLC; *Int'l*, pg. 5946

POWER METALS CORP; *Int'l*, pg. 5946

POWERMETRIC METERING PTY. LTD.—See Shell plc; *Int'l*, pg. 6795

POWER MINERALS LIMITED; *Int'l*, pg. 5946

POWERMITE AFRICA (PTY) LTD. - AMPCO DIVISION—See Hudaco Industries Limited; *Int'l*, pg. 3521

POWERMITE AFRICA (PTY) LTD.—See Hudaco Industries Limited; *Int'l*, pg. 3521

POWER MOTIVE CORPORATION; *U.S. Private*, pg. 3238

POWER & MOTORYACHT—See TEN: The Enthusiast Network, Inc.; *U.S. Private*, pg. 3964

POWER MOUNTAIN COAL COMPANY—See Alpha Natural Resources, Inc.; *U.S. Private*, pg. 199

POWER MOUNTAIN CONTURA, LLC—See Alpha Metallurgical Resources, Inc.; *U.S. Public*, pg. 82

POWERNET CO., LTD.; *Int'l*, pg. 5948

POWERNET GLOBAL COMMUNICATIONS; *U.S. Private*, pg. 3239

POWER NICKEL INC.; *Int'l*, pg. 5946

POWERNOR AS—See Addtech AB; *Int'l*, pg. 134

POWER OF CLEAN ENERGY LLC—See Fidelity Engineering LLC; *U.S. Private*, pg. 1502

POWER OF THE DREAM VENTURES, INC.; *Int'l*, pg. 5946

POWER OF THREE LLC—See Casella Waste Systems, Inc.; *U.S. Public*, pg. 446

POWER-ONE INC.—See ABB Ltd.; *Int'l*, pg. 52

POWER-ONE ITALY S.P.A.—See ABB Ltd.; *Int'l*, pg. 52

POWERON SERVICES, INC.; *U.S. Private*, pg. 3239

POWER OPTICS CO., LTD.—See Sunny Optical Technology (Group) Company Limited; *Int'l*, pg. 7319

POWER PACKAGING, INC.—See HCI Equity Management, L.P.; *U.S. Private*, pg. 1889

POWER PACKER DO BRASIL LTDA.—See Enerpac Tool Group Corp.; *U.S. Public*, pg. 766

POWER PACKER EUROPA B.V.—See Enerpac Tool Group Corp.; *U.S. Public*, pg. 766

POWER-PACKER NORTH AMERICA, INC.—See Enerpac Tool Group Corp.; *U.S. Public*, pg. 766

POWER PARAGON—See L3Harris Technologies, Inc.; *U.S. Public*, pg. 1283

POWER PARTNERS MASTEC LLC—See MasTec, Inc.; *U.S. Public*, pg. 1393

POWER PARTNERS PTE. LTD.—See Air Water Inc.; *Int'l*, pg. 240

POWERPAY; *U.S. Private*, pg. 3239

POWERPLACE INC.—See Uchida Yoko Co., Ltd.; *Int'l*, pg. 8012

POWERPLAN, INC.—See Roper Technologies, Inc.; *U.S. Public*, pg. 1812

POWERPLAN OPERATIONS ANZ PTY. LTD.—See Roper Technologies, Inc.; *U.S. Public*, pg. 1812

POWERPLAN OPERATIONS LTD.—See Roper Technologies, Inc.; *U.S. Public*, pg. 1812

POWERPLANT MAINTENANCE SPECIALISTS INC.; *U.S. Private*, pg. 3239

POWERPLANT STAMFORD LTD—See Turner & Co. (Glasgow) Limited; *Int'l*, pg. 7978

POWER PLUMBING, INC.; *U.S. Private*, pg. 3238

POWER PLUS CABLE CO LLC—See Prysmian S.p.A.; *Int'l*, pg. 6012

POWER PLUS LIMITED—See Symphony Holdings Limited; *Int'l*, pg. 7379

POWERPOINT ELECTRICAL & MECHANICAL WORKS L.L.C.—See Al Shafar Group; *Int'l*, pg. 282

POWER PROCESS EQUIPMENT INC.; *U.S. Private*, pg. 3238

POWER PROCESS PIPING, INC.; *U.S. Private*, pg. 3238

POWER PRODUCT SERVICES, INC.—See High Road Capital Partners, LLC; *U.S. Private*, pg. 1936

POWER PRODUCTS, LLC—See Brunswick Corporation; *U.S. Public*, pg. 408

POWER PROJECT SANAYI INSAAT TICARET LIMITED SIRKETI—See Metlen Energy & Metals S.A.; *Int'l*, pg. 4855

POWER PROTECTION UNLIMITED—See Incline MGMT Corp.; *U.S. Private*, pg. 2054

POWER & PUMPS INC.; *U.S. Private*, pg. 3237

POWER QUALITY INTERNATIONAL, INC.; *U.S. Private*, pg. 3238

POWER QUOTIENT INTERNATIONAL CO., LTD.; *Int'l*, pg. 5946

POWER QUOTIENT INTERNATIONAL (H.K.) CO., LTD.—See Power Quotient International Co., Ltd.; *Int'l*, pg. 5946

POWER QUOTIENT INTERNATIONAL (SHENZHEN) CO., LTD.—See Power Quotient International Co., Ltd.; *Int'l*, pg. 5946

POWER REIT; *U.S. Public*, pg. 1705

POWER RENTAL & SALES, LLC—See The Stephens Group, LLC; *U.S. Private*, pg. 4121

POWER RESOURCE EXPLORATION, INC.; *Int'l*, pg. 5946

POWERREVIEWS, INC.—See Battery Ventures, L.P.; *U.S. Private*, pg. 488

POWER ROOT BERHAD; *Int'l*, pg. 5946

POWERSAFE ACUMULADORES INDUSTRIALIS UNIPESSOAL, LDA.—See EnerSys; *U.S. Public*, pg. 766

POWERS AGENCY; *U.S. Private*, pg. 3239

POWERS BRAND COMMUNICATIONS LLC—See 360 Public Relations LLC; *U.S. Private*, pg. 8

POWERSCHOOL GROUP LLC—See ONEX Corporation; *Int'l*, pg. 5579

POWERSCHOOL GROUP LLC—See Vista Equity Partners, LLC; *U.S. Private*, pg. 4399

POWERSCHOOL HOLDINGS, INC.—See Bain Capital, LP; *U.S. Private*, pg. 442

POWERS CONSTRUCTION CO., INC.; *U.S. Private*, pg. 3240

POWERSCOURT LIMITED—See TPG Capital, L.P.; *U.S. Public*, pg. 2177

POWERSCREEN INTERNATIONAL DISTRIBUTION LIMITED—See Terex Corporation; *U.S. Public*, pg. 2020

POWERSCREEN INTERNATIONAL LIMITED—See Terex Corporation; *U.S. Public*, pg. 2020

POWERSCREEN INTERNATIONAL (U.K.) LIMITED—See Terex Corporation; *U.S. Public*, pg. 2020

POWERSCREEN USA LLC—See Terex Corporation; *U.S. Public*, pg. 2020

POWER@SEA N.V.—See Ackermans & van Haaren NV; *Int'l*, pg. 105

POWERSECURE, INC.—See The Southern Company; *U.S. Public*, pg. 2131

POWERSECURE LIGHTING—See The Southern Company; *U.S. Public*, pg. 2131

POWERSECURE SERVICE, INC.—See The Southern Company; *U.S. Public*, pg. 2131

POWER SECURITIES COMPANY LIMITED—See Minerva Group Holding Limited; *Int'l*, pg. 4908

POWER SERVICE GMBH—See Ceconomy AG; *Int'l*, pg. 1385

POWER SERVICE, INC.—See DNOW Inc.; *U.S. Public*, pg. 671

POWER SERVICE PRODUCTS, INC.; *U.S. Private*, pg. 3238

POWERS FASTENERS AUSTRALASIA PTY LIMITED—See Stanley Black & Decker, Inc.; *U.S. Public*, pg. 1933

POWERS FASTENERS INC.—See Stanley Black & Decker, Inc.; *U.S. Public*, pg. 1933

POWERS FASTENERS (NZ) LIMITED & CO.—See Stanley Black & Decker, Inc.; *U.S. Public*, pg. 1933

POWERS HOLDINGS, INC.; *U.S. Private*, pg. 3240

POWERSOFT S.P.A.; *Int'l*, pg. 5948

POWER SOLUTIONS INTERNATIONAL, INC.; *U.S. Public*, pg. 1705

POWER SOLUTIONS LLC; *U.S. Private*, pg. 3238

POWER SOLUTIONS, LTD.; *Int'l*, pg. 5946

POWER SOLUTIONS; *U.S. Private*, pg. 3238

POWER SOLUTION TECHNOLOGIES PUBLIC COMPANY LIMITED; *Int'l*, pg. 5946

POWERSOLVE ELECTRONICS LIMITED—See XP Power Limited; *Int'l*, pg. 8537

POWER-SONIC CORPORATION

CORPORATE AFFILIATIONS

POWER-SONIC CORPORATION; *U.S. Private*, pg. 3239
POWER-SONIC EUROPE LTD.—See Power-Sonic Corporation; *U.S. Private*, pg. 3239
POWERSOUTH ENERGY COOPERATIVE; *U.S. Private*, pg. 3240
POWERSPEED ELECTRICAL LIMITED; *Int'l*, pg. 5948
POWERSPHYR INC.; *U.S. Private*, pg. 3240
POWERSPORTS EAST; *U.S. Private*, pg. 3240
POWERSPORTS NETWORK, INC.—See Irish Times; *U.S. Private*, pg. 2138
POWERS PROCESS CONTROLS—See Watts Water Technologies, Inc.; *U.S. Public*, pg. 2337
POWERS PRODUCTS CO.; *U.S. Private*, pg. 3240
POWERS & SONS CONSTRUCTION CO., INC.; *U.S. Private*, pg. 3239
POWERS & SONS, LLC - MONTPELIER—See Letts Industries, Inc.; *U.S. Private*, pg. 2433
POWERS & SONS, LLC—See Letts Industries, Inc.; *U.S. Private*, pg. 2433
POWERS & SULLIVAN, LLC—See CBIZ, Inc.; *U.S. Public*, pg. 457
POWERS-SWAIN CHEVROLET INC.; *U.S. Private*, pg. 3240
POWER STANDARDS LAB, INC.—See Power Survey & Equipment Ltd.; *Int'l*, pg. 5946
POWER STEEL & ELECTRO-PLATING WORKS SDN BHD—See Trifast plc; *Int'l*, pg. 7921
POWER STEP (CHILE) SPA—See Korvest Ltd.; *Int'l*, pg. 4289
POWERSTONE METALS CORP.; *Int'l*, pg. 5948
POWER STOP LLC; *U.S. Private*, pg. 3239
POWERSTORE LIMITED—See Smiths City Group Limited; *Int'l*, pg. 7009
POWERSTORM HOLDINGS, INC.; *U.S. Private*, pg. 3240
POWERSTREAM INC.; *Int'l*, pg. 5948
POWERSTRIDE BATTERY CO. INC.; *U.S. Private*, pg. 3240
POWERS TRUCK AND TRAILER SALES LLC—See American Securities LLC; *U.S. Private*, pg. 248
POWER SUPPLY COMPONENTS INC.; *U.S. Private*, pg. 3239
POWER SUPPLY TECHNOLOGY (THAILAND) CO., LTD.—See nms Holdings Corporation; *Int'l*, pg. 5393
POWER SURVEY & EQUIPMENT LTD.; *Int'l*, pg. 5946
POWERSYS 2000 S.L.—See Panasonic Holdings Corporation; *Int'l*, pg. 5725
POWER SYSTEMS, LLC—See Applied Industrial Technologies, Inc.; *U.S. Public*, pg. 171
POWER SYSTEMS MFG., LLC—See Hanwha Group; *Int'l*, pg. 3266
POWER SYSTEMS OPERATIONS, INC.—See Babcock & Wilcox Enterprises, Inc.; *U.S. Public*, pg. 263
POWER SYSTEMS TECHNOLOGIES FAR EAST LIMITED—See Flex Ltd.; *Int'l*, pg. 2704
POWERTAP HYDROGEN CAPITAL CORP.; *Int'l*, pg. 5948
POWERTEAM, INC.—See HCL Technologies Ltd.; *Int'l*, pg. 3298
POWERTECH CO., LTD.; *Int'l*, pg. 5948
POWERTECH INDUSTRIAL CO., LTD.; *Int'l*, pg. 5948
POWERTECH LABS, INC.—See B.C. Hydro; *Int'l*, pg. 789
POWER TECHNIC APS—See Addtech AB; *Int'l*, pg. 134
POWER TECHNIQUE NORTH AMERICA LLC—See Atlas Copco AB; *Int'l*, pg. 684
POWER TECHNO CO., LTD.—See Nitta Corporation; *Int'l*, pg. 5382
POWER TECHNOLOGIES (PROPRIETARY) LIMITED—See Altron Limited; *Int'l*, pg. 399
POWER TECHNOLOGY, INC.; *U.S. Private*, pg. 3239
POWER TECHNOLOGY LIMITED—See E.ON SE; *Int'l*, pg. 2256
POWERTECH SEMICONDUCTOR (XIAN) CO., LTD.—See Powertech Technology Inc.; *Int'l*, pg. 5948
POWERTECH SEMI SDN. BHD.—See PowerTECH Co., Ltd.; *Int'l*, pg. 5948
POWER TECH SYSTEMS PTY LTD—See Byte Power Group Limited; *Int'l*, pg. 1237
POWERTECH TECHNOLOGY INC. - PLANT 1—See Powertech Technology Inc.; *Int'l*, pg. 5948
POWERTECH TECHNOLOGY INC. - PLANT 2—See Powertech Technology Inc.; *Int'l*, pg. 5948
POWERTECH TECHNOLOGY INC.; *Int'l*, pg. 5948
POWERTECH TECHNOLOGY JAPAN LTD.—See Powertech Technology Inc.; *Int'l*, pg. 5948
POWERTECH TECHNOLOGY (SINGAPORE) PTE. LTD.—See Powertech Technology Inc.; *Int'l*, pg. 5948
POWERTECH TECHNOLOGY (SUZHOU) LTD.—See Shenzhen Longsys Electronics Company Limited; *Int'l*, pg. 6817
POWERTECH TECHNOLOGY USA INC.—See Powertech Technology Inc.; *Int'l*, pg. 5948
POWERTECH TECHNOLOGY (XIAN) LTD.—See Powertech Technology Inc.; *Int'l*, pg. 5948
POWERTECH (USA) INC.—See Azarga Uranium Corp.; *Int'l*, pg. 776
POWERTEC INDUSTRIAL MOTORS—See HBD Industries, Inc.; *U.S. Private*, pg. 1887
POWERTEC SUPPLIES INDIA PVT. LTD.—See P-Duke Technology Co., Ltd.; *Int'l*, pg. 5681
POWERTEK CORPORATION; *U.S. Private*, pg. 3240

POWERTEK ENERGY SDN BHD; *Int'l*, pg. 5948
POWERTEL COMMUNICATIONS (PVT) LTD.—See Zimbabwe Electricity Supply Authority; *Int'l*, pg. 8684
POWER & TELEPHONE SUPPLY COMPANY DO BRASIL—See Power & Telephone Supply Company; *U.S. Private*, pg. 3237
POWER & TELEPHONE SUPPLY COMPANY; *U.S. Private*, pg. 3237
POWER & TELEPHONE SUPPLY OF CANADA—See Power & Telephone Supply Company; *U.S. Private*, pg. 3237
POWER & TELEPHONE SUPPLY S.A. DE C.V.—See Power & Telephone Supply Company; *U.S. Private*, pg. 3237
POWER TEST, INC.; *U.S. Private*, pg. 3239
POWERTEST LTD.—See VINCI S.A.; *Int'l*, pg. 8225
POWERTHRU—See Phillips Service Industries, Inc. (PSI); *U.S. Private*, pg. 3171
POWERTIP IMAGE CORP.; *Int'l*, pg. 5948
POWERTIP TECH CORP.; *Int'l*, pg. 5948
POWERTON DIALYSIS, LLC—See DaVita Inc.; *U.S. Public*, pg. 642
POWER TOOLS DISTRIBUTION N.V.—See Atlas Copco AB; *Int'l*, pg. 684
POWER TOOL SPECIALISTS, INC.—See REXON Industrial Corp., Ltd.; *Int'l*, pg. 6317
POWER TOOLS & SUPPLY INC.; *U.S. Private*, pg. 3239
POWER TOWERS LIMITED—See Oshkosh Corporation; *U.S. Public*, pg. 1621
POWER TOWERS NETHERLANDS BV—See Oshkosh Corporation; *U.S. Public*, pg. 1621
POWER TO WHEELS S.A.—See s.a. D'Ieteren n.v.; *Int'l*, pg. 6448
POWERTRACK INTERNATIONAL, LLC—See Tecum Capital Partners, Inc.; *U.S. Private*, pg. 3957
POWERTRAIN INTEGRATION LLC—See Power Solutions International, Inc.; *U.S. Public*, pg. 1705
POWERTRAIN MEKANIK SANAYI VE TICARET ANONIOM SIRKETI—See Stellantis N.V.; *Int'l*, pg. 7203
POWERTRAIN PRODUCTS CORP.—See Sun Capital Partners, Inc.; *U.S. Private*, pg. 3860
POWER TRAIN SERVICES INC.—See Platinum Equity, LLC; *U.S. Private*, pg. 3209
POWER TRANSPORTATION, LLC—See DNOW Inc.; *U.S. Public*, pg. 671
POWERTRON GMBH—See Vishay Precision Group, Inc.; *U.S. Public*, pg. 2303
POWERUP ACQUISITION CORP.; *U.S. Public*, pg. 1706
POWER UTILITY PRODUCTS COMPANY—See WJ Partners, LLC; *U.S. Private*, pg. 4551
POWERVAR CANADA INC.—See AMETEK, Inc.; *U.S. Public*, pg. 118
POWERVAR DEUTSCHLAND GMBH—See AMETEK, Inc.; *U.S. Public*, pg. 118
POWERVAR INC.—See AMETEK, Inc.; *U.S. Public*, pg. 118
POWERVAR, LTD.—See AMETEK, Inc.; *U.S. Public*, pg. 118
POWERVISION, INC.—See Novartis AG; *Int'l*, pg. 5458
POWERWELL HOLDINGS BERHAD; *Int'l*, pg. 5948
POWERWELL INTERNATIONAL SDN. BHD.—See Powerwell Holdings Berhad; *Int'l*, pg. 5949
POWERWELL SDN. BHD.—See Powerwell Holdings Berhad; *Int'l*, pg. 5949
POWERWELL VIETNAM CO. LTD.—See Powerwell Holdings Berhad; *Int'l*, pg. 5949
POWER WIND HEALTH INDUSTRY, INC.; *Int'l*, pg. 5946
POWERWIN TECH GROUP LIMITED; *Int'l*, pg. 5949
POWEST OY—See Pohjolan Voima Oy; *Int'l*, pg. 5904
P&O WHARF MANAGEMENT PTY LTD—See Qube Holdings Limited; *Int'l*, pg. 6158
POWIN ENERGY CORPORATION; *U.S. Public*, pg. 1706
POWR-FLITE—See Tacony Corporation; *U.S. Private*, pg. 3921
POWR LITHIUM CORP.; *Int'l*, pg. 5949
POWRTEC INTERNATIONAL CORP.; *U.S. Private*, pg. 3240
POWSZECHNE TOWARZYSTWO EMERYTALNE BANKOWY S.A.—See PKO Bank Polski SA; *Int'l*, pg. 5887
POWSZECHNE TOWARZYSTWO INWESTYCYJNE S.A.; *Int'l*, pg. 5949
POWSZECHNY ZAKLAD UBEZPIECZEN S.A.; *Int'l*, pg. 5949
POXEL SA; *Int'l*, pg. 5949
POYA INTERNATIONAL CO., LTD.; *Int'l*, pg. 5949
POYRY (APPLETON) LLC—See AFRY AB; *Int'l*, pg. 195
POYRY CAPITAL LIMITED—See AFRY AB; *Int'l*, pg. 195
POYRY & COMPANY LLC—See AFRY AB; *Int'l*, pg. 195
POYRY CONSULTING AND ENGINEERING (INDIA) PRIVATE LIMITED—See AFRY AB; *Int'l*, pg. 195
POYRY DEUTSCHLAND GMBH—See AFRY AB; *Int'l*, pg. 195
POYRY DEUTSCHLAND GMBH—See AFRY AB; *Int'l*, pg. 195
POYRY ENERGY AG—See AFRY AB; *Int'l*, pg. 195
POYRY ENERGY CONSULTING GROUP AG—See AFRY AB; *Int'l*, pg. 195

POYRY ENERGY CONSULTING (ITALIA) S.R.L.—See AFRY AB; *Int'l*, pg. 195
POYRY ENERGY CONSULTING (SCHWEIZ) AG—See AFRY AB; *Int'l*, pg. 195
POYRY ENERGY GMBH—See AFRY AB; *Int'l*, pg. 195
POYRY ENERGY INC.—See AFRY AB; *Int'l*, pg. 195
POYRY ENERGY LIMITED—See AFRY AB; *Int'l*, pg. 195
POYRY ENERGY LTD.—See AFRY AB; *Int'l*, pg. 195
POYRY ENERGY LTD.—See AFRY AB; *Int'l*, pg. 195
POYRY ENERGY OY—See AFRY AB; *Int'l*, pg. 195
POYRY ENERGY SDN. BHD.—See AFRY AB; *Int'l*, pg. 195
POYRY ENERGY SRL—See AFRY AB; *Int'l*, pg. 195
POYRY EROTERV ZRT.—See AFRY AB; *Int'l*, pg. 195
POYRY FINLAND OY—See AFRY AB; *Int'l*, pg. 195
POYRY INFRA AG—See AFRY AB; *Int'l*, pg. 195
POYRY INFRA DE VENEZUELA S.A.—See AFRY AB; *Int'l*, pg. 195
POYRY INFRA GMBH—See AFRY AB; *Int'l*, pg. 195
POYRY INFRA GMBH—See AFRY AB; *Int'l*, pg. 195
POYRY INFRA LTD.—See AFRY AB; *Int'l*, pg. 195
POYRY INFRA S.A.—See AFRY AB; *Int'l*, pg. 195
POYRY INFRA SP. Z O.O.—See AFRY AB; *Int'l*, pg. 195
POYRY MANAGEMENT CONSULTING (AUSTRALIA) PTY. LTD.—See AFRY AB; *Int'l*, pg. 196
POYRY MANAGEMENT CONSULTING (DEUTSCHLAND) GMBH—See AFRY AB; *Int'l*, pg. 196
POYRY MANAGEMENT CONSULTING (DUSSELDORF) GMBH—See AFRY AB; *Int'l*, pg. 196
POYRY MANAGEMENT CONSULTING (ITALIA) S.R.L.—See AFRY AB; *Int'l*, pg. 196
POYRY MANAGEMENT CONSULTING (NORWAY) AS—See AFRY AB; *Int'l*, pg. 196
POYRY MANAGEMENT CONSULTING (NZ) LIMITED—See AFRY AB; *Int'l*, pg. 196
POYRY MANAGEMENT CONSULTING OY—See AFRY AB; *Int'l*, pg. 195
POYRY MANAGEMENT CONSULTING (SCHWEIZ) AG—See AFRY AB; *Int'l*, pg. 196
POYRY MANAGEMENT CONSULTING (SINGAPORE) PTE. LTD.—See AFRY AB; *Int'l*, pg. 196
POYRY MANAGEMENT CONSULTING (SWEDEN) AB—See AFRY AB; *Int'l*, pg. 196
POYRY MANAGEMENT CONSULTING (UK) LIMITED—See AFRY AB; *Int'l*, pg. 196
POYRY MANAGEMENT CONSULTING (USA) INC.—See AFRY AB; *Int'l*, pg. 196
POYRY (MEXICO) S.A. DE C.V.—See AFRY AB; *Int'l*, pg. 195
POYRY (MONTREAL) INC.—See AFRY AB; *Int'l*, pg. 195
POYRY NORWAY AS—See AFRY AB; *Int'l*, pg. 196
POYRY (PERU) S.A.C.—See AFRY AB; *Int'l*, pg. 195
POYRY PLC—See AFRY AB; *Int'l*, pg. 194
POYRY POLAND SP. Z O.O.—See AFRY AB; *Int'l*, pg. 196
POYRY SAS—See AFRY AB; *Int'l*, pg. 196
POYRY SHANDONG ENGINEERING CONSULTING CO., LTD.—See AFRY AB; *Int'l*, pg. 196
POYRY SILVICONSULT ENGENHARIA LTDA.—See AFRY AB; *Int'l*, pg. 196
POYRY SWEDEN AB—See AFRY AB; *Int'l*, pg. 196
POYRY (VANCOUVER) INC.—See AFRY AB; *Int'l*, pg. 195
PO YUEN CULTURAL HOLDINGS (HONG KONG) CO., LTD.; *Int'l*, pg. 5901
POZAVAROVALNICA SAVA, D.D.; *Int'l*, pg. 5949
POZAVAROVALNICA TRIGLAV RE, D.D.—See Zavarovalnica Triglav, d.d.; *Int'l*, pg. 8626
POZNAK LAW FIRM LTD.—See Winick & Gallagher, PC; *U.S. Private*, pg. 4542
POZNAN ONION SP. Z O.O.—See Orkla ASA; *Int'l*, pg. 5639
POZNANSKA KORPORACJA BUDOWLANA PEKABEX SA; *Int'l*, pg. 5949
POZUELO, S.A.—See Ebro Foods S.A.; *Int'l*, pg. 2287
POZZI MILANO SPA; *Int'l*, pg. 5949
POZZONI S.P.A.; *Int'l*, pg. 5949
PP146 FOOD HOUSE PTE. LTD.—See Kimly Limited; *Int'l*, pg. 4163
PP 2000 BUSINESS INTEGRATION AG—See Bechtle AG; *Int'l*, pg. 938
P.P.A.C. (M) SDN. BHD.—See Teo Guan Lee Corporation Berhad; *Int'l*, pg. 7562
THE PPA GROUP, LLC; *U.S. Private*, pg. 4097
PPA INTERNATIONAL LIMITED—See HH Global Group Limited; *Int'l*, pg. 3379
P. PAPAS & CO. O.E. TRADING COMPANY—See BASF SE; *Int'l*, pg. 884
PPAP AUTOMOTIVE LIMITED; *Int'l*, pg. 5950
PPAP TECHNOLOGY LIMITED—See PPAP Automotive Limited; *Int'l*, pg. 5950
P-PARKING INTERNATIONAL PTE. LTD.—See Polaris Capital Group Co., Ltd.; *Int'l*, pg. 5907
PPB GROUP BERHAD—See Kuok Brothers Sdn. Bhd.; *Int'l*, pg. 4334
PPB HARTABINA SDN BHD—See Kuok Brothers Sdn. Bhd.; *Int'l*, pg. 4335
PP BUDUCNOST A.D.; *Int'l*, pg. 5949
PPC AGGREGATE QUARRIES (PTY) LTD.—See PPC Ltd.; *Int'l*, pg. 5950

COMPANY NAME INDEX

PPC BOTSWANA (PTY) LTD.—See PPC Ltd.; *Int'l*, pg. 5950
PPC BROADBAND, INC.—See Belden, Inc.; *U.S. Public*, pg. 294
PPC BULGARIA JSCO—See Public Power Corporation S.A.; *Int'l*, pg. 6095
P.P.C. BUZET D.O.O.—See Palladio Holding SpA; *Int'l*, pg. 5708
PPC B.V.—See H2APEX Group SCA; *Int'l*, pg. 3199
PPC CEMENT SA (PTY) LTD.—See PPC Ltd.; *Int'l*, pg. 5950
PPC ELEKTRIK TEDARIC VE TICARET A.S.—See Public Power Corporation S.A.; *Int'l*, pg. 6095
PPC EVENT SERVICES, LLC; *U.S. Private*, pg. 3240
PPC FLEXIBLE PACKAGING LLC—See GTCR LLC; *U.S. Private*, pg. 1806
PPC INDUSTRIES INC.—See Kohlberg & Company, LLC; *U.S. Private*, pg. 2338
PPC INSULATORS HOLDING GMBH—See Seves S.p.A.; *Int'l*, pg. 6736
PPC INVESTMENT PARTNERS LP—See The Pritzker Group - Chicago, LLC; *U.S. Private*, pg. 4098
PPC LLC—See SNF SAS; *Int'l*, pg. 7027
PPC LTD.; *Int'l*, pg. 5950
PPC LUBRICANTS, INC.—See AIP, LLC; *U.S. Private*, pg. 136
PPC OF ALABAMA, INC.—See JBS S.A.; *Int'l*, pg. 3919
PPC POTASSE ET PRODUITS CHIMIQUES S.A.S.—See International Chemical Investors S.E.; *Int'l*, pg. 3745
PPC RENEWABLES ROKAS, S.A.—See Iberdrola, S.A.; *Int'l*, pg. 3573
PPC RENEWABLES S.A.—See Public Power Corporation S.A.; *Int'l*, pg. 6095
P.P.C.; *U.S. Private*, pg. 3060
PPCS USA INC.—See Silver Fern Farms Limited; *Int'l*, pg. 6923
PPC TRANSPORTATION COMPANY—See JBS S.A.; *Int'l*, pg. 3919
PPC ZIMBABWE LTD.—See PPC Ltd.; *Int'l*, pg. 5950
PPD AUSTRALIA PTY. LTD.—See Thermo Fisher Scientific Inc.; *U.S. Public*, pg. 2150
PPD BULGARIA EOOD—See Thermo Fisher Scientific Inc.; *U.S. Public*, pg. 2150
PPD CZECH REPUBLIC S.R.O.—See Thermo Fisher Scientific Inc.; *U.S. Public*, pg. 2150
PPD DEVELOPMENT (HK) LIMITED—See Thermo Fisher Scientific Inc.; *U.S. Public*, pg. 2150
PPD DEVELOPMENT IRELAND LIMITED—See Thermo Fisher Scientific Inc.; *U.S. Public*, pg. 2150
PPD DEVELOPMENT (S) PTE. LTD.—See Thermo Fisher Scientific Inc.; *U.S. Public*, pg. 2150
PPD DEVELOPMENT (THAILAND) CO., LTD.—See Thermo Fisher Scientific Inc.; *U.S. Public*, pg. 2150
PPD DO BRASIL-SUPORTE A PESQUISA CLINICA LTDA.—See Thermo Fisher Scientific Inc.; *U.S. Public*, pg. 2150
PPD GERMANY GMBH & CO KG—See Thermo Fisher Scientific Inc.; *U.S. Public*, pg. 2150
PPD GERMANY GMBH—See Thermo Fisher Scientific Inc.; *U.S. Public*, pg. 2150
PPD GLOBAL CENTRAL LABS BVBA—See Thermo Fisher Scientific Inc.; *U.S. Public*, pg. 2150
PPD GLOBAL CENTRAL LABS, LLC—See Thermo Fisher Scientific Inc.; *U.S. Public*, pg. 2150
PPD GLOBAL CENTRAL LABS (S) PTE. LTD.—See Thermo Fisher Scientific Inc.; *U.S. Public*, pg. 2150
PPD GLOBAL LTD.—See Thermo Fisher Scientific Inc.; *U.S. Public*, pg. 2150
PPD HUNGARY RESEARCH & DEVELOPMENT LIMITED—See Thermo Fisher Scientific Inc.; *U.S. Public*, pg. 2150
PPD, INC.—See Thermo Fisher Scientific Inc.; *U.S. Public*, pg. 2150
P P D, INC.; *U.S. Private*, pg. 3058
PPD INTERNATIONAL HOLDINGS, INC.—See Thermo Fisher Scientific Inc.; *U.S. Public*, pg. 2150
PPD ITALY S.R.L.—See Thermo Fisher Scientific Inc.; *U.S. Public*, pg. 2150
PPD-LANARK—See Thermo Fisher Scientific Inc.; *U.S. Public*, pg. 2150
PPD PERU S.A.C.—See Thermo Fisher Scientific Inc.; *U.S. Public*, pg. 2150
PPD PHARMACEUTICAL DEVELOPMENT PHILIPPINES CORP.—See Thermo Fisher Scientific Inc.; *U.S. Public*, pg. 2150
PPD PHASE I CLINIC - AUSTIN—See Thermo Fisher Scientific Inc.; *U.S. Public*, pg. 2151
PPD POLAND SP. Z O.O.—See Thermo Fisher Scientific Inc.; *U.S. Public*, pg. 2150
PPD ROMANIA S.R.L.—See Thermo Fisher Scientific Inc.; *U.S. Public*, pg. 2150
PPD SCANDINAVIA AB—See Thermo Fisher Scientific Inc.; *U.S. Public*, pg. 2150
PPD SERVICES, INC.—See Thermo Fisher Scientific Inc.; *U.S. Public*, pg. 2150
PPD SLOVAK REPUBLIC S.R.O.—See Thermo Fisher Scientific Inc.; *U.S. Public*, pg. 2150
PPE, LLC—See IDEX Corp; *U.S. Public*, pg. 1091

PPES CONCRETE PRODUCT SDN. BHD.—See Cahya Mata Sarawak Berhad; *Int'l*, pg. 1251
PPESW BPSB JV SDN. BHD.—See Cahya Mata Sarawak Berhad; *Int'l*, pg. 1251
PPES WORKS (SARAWAK) SDN. BHD.—See Cahya Mata Sarawak Berhad; *Int'l*, pg. 1251
PPF A.S.—See PPF Group N.V.; *Int'l*, pg. 5951
PPF BANKA, A.S.—See PPF Group N.V.; *Int'l*, pg. 5950
PPF GROUP N.V.; *Int'l*, pg. 5950
PPF PARAMOUNT ONE MARKET PLAZA OWNER, L.P.—See Paramount Group Inc.; *U.S. Public*, pg. 1637
PPG AEROSPACE MATERIALS (SUZHOU) CO. LTD.—See PPG Industries, Inc.; *U.S. Public*, pg. 1708
PPG AEROSPACE—See PPG Industries, Inc.; *U.S. Public*, pg. 1707
PPG AP RESINAS, S.A. DE C.V.—See PPG Industries, Inc.; *U.S. Public*, pg. 1708
PPG ARCHITECTURAL COATINGS CANADA, INC.—See PPG Industries, Inc.; *U.S. Public*, pg. 1708
PPG ARCHITECTURAL COATINGS EMEA—See PPG Industries, Inc.; *U.S. Public*, pg. 1708
PPG ARCHITECTURAL COATINGS—See PPG Industries, Inc.; *U.S. Public*, pg. 1708
PPG ARCHITECTURAL COATINGS—See PPG Industries, Inc.; *U.S. Public*, pg. 1708
PPG ARCHITECTURAL COATINGS UK LIMITED—See PPG Industries, Inc.; *U.S. Public*, pg. 1708
PPG ARCHITECTURAL FINISHES, INC.—See PPG Industries, Inc.; *U.S. Public*, pg. 1708
PPG (AUSTRIA) HANDELS GMBH—See PPG Industries, Inc.; *U.S. Public*, pg. 1707
PPG CAMEROUN SA—See PPG Industries, Inc.; *U.S. Public*, pg. 1708
PPG CANADA INC.—See PPG Industries, Inc.; *U.S. Public*, pg. 1708
PPG CEE PREMAZI (D.O.O.)—See PPG Industries, Inc.; *U.S. Public*, pg. 1708
PPG CEE PREMAZI—See PPG Industries, Inc.; *U.S. Public*, pg. 1708
PPG COATINGS BELGIUM BV—See PPG Industries, Inc.; *U.S. Public*, pg. 1708
PPG COATINGS BELUX N.V.—See PPG Industries, Inc.; *U.S. Public*, pg. 1708
PPG COATINGS BV—See PPG Industries, Inc.; *U.S. Public*, pg. 1708
PPG COATINGS DANMARK AS—See PPG Industries, Inc.; *U.S. Public*, pg. 1708
PPG COATINGS DEUTSCHLAND GMBH—See PPG Industries, Inc.; *U.S. Public*, pg. 1708
PPG COATINGS EUROPE B.V.—See PPG Industries, Inc.; *U.S. Public*, pg. 1708
PPG COATINGS (HONG KONG) CO., LIMITED—See PPG Industries, Inc.; *U.S. Public*, pg. 1708
PPG COATINGS (KUNSHAN) CO., LTD.—See PPG Industries, Inc.; *U.S. Public*, pg. 1708
PPG COATINGS MANUFACTURING SARL—See PPG Industries, Inc.; *U.S. Public*, pg. 1708
PPG COATINGS NEDERLAND BV—See PPG Industries, Inc.; *U.S. Public*, pg. 1708
PPG COATINGS S.A.—See PPG Industries, Inc.; *U.S. Public*, pg. 1708
PPG COATINGS (SINGAPORE) PTE LTD—See PPG Industries, Inc.; *U.S. Public*, pg. 1708
PPG COATINGS SOUTH AFRICA (PTY) LTD.—See PPG Industries, Inc.; *U.S. Public*, pg. 1708
PPG COATINGS (SUZHOU) COMPANY LTD.—See PPG Industries, Inc.; *U.S. Public*, pg. 1708
PPG COATINGS (THAILAND) CO., LTD.—See PPG Industries, Inc.; *U.S. Public*, pg. 1708
PPG COATINGS (TIANJIN) CO., LTD.—See PPG Industries, Inc.; *U.S. Public*, pg. 1708
PPG DAIHAN PACKAGING COATINGS, LTD.—See PPG Industries, Inc.; *U.S. Public*, pg. 1708
PPG DECO CZECH A.S.—See PPG Industries, Inc.; *U.S. Public*, pg. 1708
PPG DECO POLSKA SP. Z O.O.—See PPG Industries, Inc.; *U.S. Public*, pg. 1709
PPG DECORATIVE COATINGS-CAROLINA—See PPG Industries, Inc.; *U.S. Public*, pg. 1710
PPG DECORATIVE COATINGS-CARROLLTON—See PPG Industries, Inc.; *U.S. Public*, pg. 1710
PPG DECORATIVE COATINGS-HURON—See PPG Industries, Inc.; *U.S. Public*, pg. 1710
PPG DECO SLOVAKIA, S.R.O.—See PPG Industries, Inc.; *U.S. Public*, pg. 1708
PPG DEUTSCHLAND BUSINESS SUPORT GMBH—See PPG Industries, Inc.; *U.S. Public*, pg. 1708
PPG DEUTSCHLAND SALES SERVICES GMBH—See PPG Industries, Inc.; *U.S. Public*, pg. 1708
PPG GUADELOUPE SAS—See PPG Industries, Inc.; *U.S. Public*, pg. 1708
PPG HELLAS S.A.—See PPG Industries, Inc.; *U.S. Public*, pg. 1708
PPG HEMMELRATH LACKFABRIK GMBH—See PPG Industries, Inc.; *U.S. Public*, pg. 1708
PPG IBERICA, S.A.—See PPG Industries, Inc.; *U.S. Public*, pg. 1708
PPG INDUSTRIAL COATINGS B.V.—See PPG Industries, Inc.; *U.S. Public*, pg. 1708

PPHE HOTEL GROUP LIMITED

PPG INDUSTRIES AUSTRALIA PTY. LIMITED—See PPG Industries, Inc.; *U.S. Public*, pg. 1708
PPG INDUSTRIES BELGIUM S.A./N.V.—See PPG Industries, Inc.; *U.S. Public*, pg. 1709
PPG INDUSTRIES CHEMICALS B.V.—See PPG Industries, Inc.; *U.S. Public*, pg. 1709
PPG INDUSTRIES COLOMBIA LTDA.—See PPG Industries, Inc.; *U.S. Public*, pg. 1709
PPG INDUSTRIES DE MEXICO, SA DE CV—See PPG Industries, Inc.; *U.S. Public*, pg. 1709
PPG INDUSTRIES EUROPE SARL—See PPG Industries, Inc.; *U.S. Public*, pg. 1709
PPG INDUSTRIES FRANCE SAS—See PPG Industries, Inc.; *U.S. Public*, pg. 1709
PPG INDUSTRIES, INC. - MONROEVILLE CHEMICAL CENTER—See PPG Industries, Inc.; *U.S. Public*, pg. 1709
PPG INDUSTRIES, INC.; *U.S. Public*, pg. 1706
PPG INDUSTRIES ITALIA S.P.A.—See PPG Industries, Inc.; *U.S. Public*, pg. 1709
PPG INDUSTRIES ITALIA SRL—See PPG Industries, Inc.; *U.S. Public*, pg. 1709
PPG INDUSTRIES KIMYA SANAYI VE TICARET ANONIM SIRKETI—See PPG Industries, Inc.; *U.S. Public*, pg. 1709
PPG INDUSTRIES (KOREA) LTD.—See PPG Industries, Inc.; *U.S. Public*, pg. 1708
PPG INDUSTRIES LACKFABRIK GMBH—See PPG Industries, Inc.; *U.S. Public*, pg. 1709
PPG INDUSTRIES LIPETSK LLC—See PPG Industries, Inc.; *U.S. Public*, pg. 1709
PPG INDUSTRIES LLC—See PPG Industries, Inc.; *U.S. Public*, pg. 1709
PPG INDUSTRIES NETHERLANDS B.V.—See PPG Industries, Inc.; *U.S. Public*, pg. 1709
PPG INDUSTRIES NEW ZEALAND LIMITED—See PPG Industries, Inc.; *U.S. Public*, pg. 1709
PPG INDUSTRIES OHIO, INC.—See PPG Industries, Inc.; *U.S. Public*, pg. 1709
PPG INDUSTRIES POLAND SP. Z O.O.—See PPG Industries, Inc.; *U.S. Public*, pg. 1709
PPG INDUSTRIES SECURITIES, INC.—See PPG Industries, Inc.; *U.S. Public*, pg. 1709
PPG INDUSTRIES (UK) LTD.—See PPG Industries, Inc.; *U.S. Public*, pg. 1708
PPG ITALIA BUSINESS SUPPORT S.R.L.—See PPG Industries, Inc.; *U.S. Public*, pg. 1709
PPG ITALIA SALES & SERVICES SRL—See PPG Industries, Inc.; *U.S. Public*, pg. 1709
PPG KANSAI AUTOMOTIVE FINISHES CANADA, LP—See PPG Industries, Inc.; *U.S. Public*, pg. 1709
PPG KOREA LTD.—See PPG Industries, Inc.; *U.S. Public*, pg. 1709
PPG LUXEMBOURG FINANCE S.AR.L.—See PPG Industries, Inc.; *U.S. Public*, pg. 1709
PPG MANAGEMENT (SHANGHAI) CO., LTD—See PPG Industries, Inc.; *U.S. Public*, pg. 1709
PPG MEXICO, S.A. DE C.V.—See PPG Industries, Inc.; *U.S. Public*, pg. 1709
PPG PACKAGING COATINGS (SUZHOU) CO., LTD.—See PPG Industries, Inc.; *U.S. Public*, pg. 1709
PPG PAINTS TRADING (SHANGHAI) CO., LTD.—See PPG Industries, Inc.; *U.S. Public*, pg. 1709
PPG PERFORMANCE COATINGS (MALAYSIA) SDN. BHD.—See PPG Industries, Inc.; *U.S. Public*, pg. 1709
PPG PMC JAPAN CO LTD—See PPG Industries, Inc.; *U.S. Public*, pg. 1709
PPG PREMAZI CEE (D.O.O.)—See PPG Industries, Inc.; *U.S. Public*, pg. 1709
PPG PROTECTIVE & MARINE COATINGS—See PPG Industries, Inc.; *U.S. Public*, pg. 1709
PPG RETAIL FRANCE SAS—See PPG Industries, Inc.; *U.S. Public*, pg. 1709
PPG REUNION SAS—See PPG Industries, Inc.; *U.S. Public*, pg. 1709
PPG ROMANIA S.A.—See PPG Industries, Inc.; *U.S. Public*, pg. 1709
PPG SSC CO., LTD.—See PPG Industries, Inc.; *U.S. Public*, pg. 1709
PPG SWITZERLAND GMBH—See PPG Industries, Inc.; *U.S. Public*, pg. 1709
PPG TRILAK KFT.—See PPG Industries, Inc.; *U.S. Public*, pg. 1709
PPG UNIVER S.P.A.—See PPG Industries, Inc.; *U.S. Public*, pg. 1709
PPG WORWAG COATINGS GMBH & CO. KG—See PPG Industries, Inc.; *U.S. Public*, pg. 1710
PPHE HOTEL GROUP LIMITED; *Int'l*, pg. 5951
PPH.FORDEX SP.Z.O.O.—See Goldwin, Inc.; *Int'l*, pg. 3035
PPH KUNSTSTOFFTECHNIK GMBH—See Ring International Holding AG; *Int'l*, pg. 6343
PPH PRINTING & PACKAGING (KULIM) SDN. BHD.—See Public Packages Holdings Berhad; *Int'l*, pg. 6095
PPH PRINTING & PACKAGING (PENANG) SDN. BHD.—See Public Packages Holdings Berhad; *Int'l*, pg. 6095
PPI AEROSPACE ACQUISITION LLC—See X-Ray Industries Inc.; *U.S. Private*, pg. 4579

PPHE HOTEL GROUP LIMITED
CORPORATE AFFILIATIONS

PPI BENEFITS SOLUTIONS—See Principal Financial Group, Inc.; *U.S. Public*, pg. 1721

PPI, INC.—See Bally's Corporation; *U.S. Public*, pg. 268

PPI INDUSTRIES SDN. BHD.—See Wah Seong Corporation Berhad; *Int'l*, pg. 8330

PPI MEDIA US, INC.—See Allianz SE; *Int'l*, pg. 356

PPI MULTITASK SISTEMAS E AUTOMACAO S.A—See WEG S.A.; *Int'l*, pg. 8367

PPI TECHNOLOGIES GLOBAL, LLC; *U.S. Private*, pg. 3240

PPI/TIME ZERO INC.—See Insight Equity Holdings LLC; *U.S. Private*, pg. 2086

PPI TRADING PRETZER & PILSL GMBH; *Int'l*, pg. 5951

PPJ BERKAT SDN. BHD.—See Pappajack Berhad; *Int'l*, pg. 5734

PPJ HEALTHCARE ENTERPRISES, INC.; *U.S. Public*, pg. 1711

PPJ LANDAS EMAS SDN. BHD.—See Pappajack Berhad; *Int'l*, pg. 5734

PPJ MAJU SDN. BHD.—See Pappajack Berhad; *Int'l*, pg. 5734

PPJ MAKMUR SDN. BHD.—See Pappajack Berhad; *Int'l*, pg. 5734

PPJ SINAR SDN. BHD.—See Pappajack Berhad; *Int'l*, pg. 5734

PPJ SUKSES SDN. BHD.—See Pappajack Berhad; *Int'l*, pg. 5734

PPK GROUP LIMITED; *Int'l*, pg. 5951

PPK MINING EQUIPMENT PTY LIMITED—See PPK Group Limited; *Int'l*, pg. 5951

PPK MINING REPAIRS ALTERNATORS PTY LTD—See PPK Group Limited; *Int'l*, pg. 5951

PP+K; *U.S. Private*, pg. 3240

PPLA PARTICIPATIONS LTD.—See BTG Pactual Holding S.A.; *Int'l*, pg. 1204

PPL CORPORATION; *U.S. Public*, pg. 1711

PPL CZ S. R. O.—See Deutsche Post AG; *Int'l*, pg. 2082

PPL DEVELOPMENT CORPORATION—See PPL Corporation; *U.S. Public*, pg. 1711

PPL ELECTRIC UTILITIES CORPORATION—See PPL Corporation; *U.S. Public*, pg. 1711

PPL ENERGY FUNDING CORPORATION—See PPL Corporation; *U.S. Public*, pg. 1711

PPL GENERATION, LLC—See PPL Corporation; *U.S. Public*, pg. 1711

PPL GLOBAL, LLC—See PPL Corporation; *U.S. Public*, pg. 1712

P&P LINK SAATCHI & SAATCHI—See Publicis Groupe S.A.; *Int'l*, pg. 6108

PPL MONTANA HOLDINGS, LLC—See PPL Corporation; *U.S. Public*, pg. 1712

PPL MONTANA, LLC—See PPL Corporation; *U.S. Public*, pg. 1712

PPL MONTOUR, LLC—See PPL Corporation; *U.S. Public*, pg. 1712

PPL SHIPYARD PTE LTD—See Sembcorp Industries Ltd.; *Int'l*, pg. 6703

PPL SUSQUEHANNA LLC—See PPL Corporation; *U.S. Public*, pg. 1712

PPL UK INVESTMENTS LIMITED—See PPL Corporation; *U.S. Public*, pg. 1712

PPL WW HOLDINGS LIMITED—See PPL Corporation; *U.S. Public*, pg. 1712

PPM AMERICA, INC.—See Jackson Financial Inc.; *U.S. Public*, pg. 1183

PP MANUFACTURING CORPORATION—See Virbac S.A.; *Int'l*, pg. 8246

PPM CONSULTANTS, INC.; *U.S. Private*, pg. 3240

PPM D.D.; *Int'l*, pg. 5951

PPM FROHLEN-REDDEMANN GMBH—See KPP Group Holdings Co., Ltd.; *Int'l*, pg. 4298

PPMG POTSDAMER PLATZ MANAGEMENT GMBH—See ECE Projektmanagement GmbH & Co KG; *Int'l*, pg. 2288

PPM INTERNATIONAL (AUSTRALIA) LTD.—See Jiangsu Phoenix Publishing & Media Corporation Ltd.; *Int'l*, pg. 3952

PPM—See EMCOR Group, Inc.; *U.S. Public*, pg. 738

PPM TECHNOLOGIES EMEA LTD.—See Warburg Pincus LLC; *U.S. Private*, pg. 4438

PPM TECHNOLOGIES, INC.—See Warburg Pincus LLC; *U.S. Private*, pg. 4438

PPM TECHNOLOGIES INDIA LTD.—See Warburg Pincus LLC; *U.S. Private*, pg. 4438

PP NEPREMICNINE D.O.O.—See MHP SE; *Int'l*, pg. 4873

PPO-ELEKTRONIIKKA OY—See A.A.G. STUCCHI s.r.l.; *Int'l*, pg. 23

PPOONE, INC.—See UnitedHealth Group Incorporated; *U.S. Public*, pg. 2253

PP PACK MAKING JOINT STOCK COMPANY; *Int'l*, pg. 5950

PPP BETRIEB SCHULEN EUPEN SA—See VINCI S.A.; *Int'l*, pg. 8225

PPP CAMPUS BEDNAR PARK ERRICHTUNGS- UND BETRIEBS GMBH—See PORR AG; *Int'l*, pg. 5923

PP PRIME PUBLIC COMPANY LIMITED; *Int'l*, pg. 5950

PP PROFESSIONAL PAINT A/S—See Flugger Group A/S; *Int'l*, pg. 2712

PPP SCHLOSS SONNENSTEIN GMBH—See Bilfinger SE; *Int'l*, pg. 1028

PPP SCHULEN HALLE GMBH—See Bilfinger SE; *Int'l*, pg. 1028

PPP SCHULEN LANDKREIS HOF GMBH—See Bilfinger SE; *Int'l*, pg. 1028

PPR REALTY INC.—See Everest Consulting Group LP; *U.S. Private*, pg. 1438

PPR WASHINGTON SQUARE LLC—See The Macerich Company; *U.S. Public*, pg. 2110

PPSC, INC.; *U.S. Private*, pg. 3240

PPSC INDUSTRIES SDN. BHD.—See Wah Seong Corporation Berhad; *Int'l*, pg. 8329

PPS DATA, LLC—See Zions Bancorporation, National Association; *U.S. Public*, pg. 2408

P.P.S. ELECTRICAL LTD.—See Renew Holdings plc; *Int'l*, pg. 6278

PPS HOLDINGS AUSTRALIA PTY. LTD.—See Penske Automotive Group, Inc.; *U.S. Public*, pg. 1665

PPS, INC.; *U.S. Private*, pg. 3240

PPS, INC.; *U.S. Private*, pg. 3240

PPS INNOVATION CO., LTD.—See Project Planning Service Public Company Limited; *Int'l*, pg. 5991

PPS INTERNATIONAL (HOLDINGS) LIMITED; *Int'l*, pg. 5951

PPS ONEWORKS CO., LTD.—See Project Planning Service Public Company Limited; *Int'l*, pg. 5991

PPT INDUSTRIAL MACHINES INC.—See Quality Products Inc.; *U.S. Private*, pg. 3320

PPT INZENJERING A.D. BEOGRAD; *Int'l*, pg. 5951

P&P VALLEY VIEW HOLDINGS, INC.—See Pete & Pete Container Service, Inc.; *U.S. Private*, pg. 3157

PPX HOSPITALITY BRANDS INC.; *U.S. Private*, pg. 3241

PPX MINING CORP.; *Int'l*, pg. 5951

PPZ BRONISLAW S.A.—See Przedsiebiorstwo Przemyslu Spozywczego PEPEES S.A.; *Int'l*, pg. 6014

PQ AUSTRALIA PTY. LTD.—See The Carlyle Group Inc.; *U.S. Public*, pg. 2052

PQ CHEMICALS (THAILAND) LTD.—See The Carlyle Group Inc.; *U.S. Public*, pg. 2052

PQ CORPORATION—See The Carlyle Group Inc.; *U.S. Public*, pg. 2052

PQ CORPORATION—See Ecovyst Inc.; *U.S. Public*, pg. 717

PQ CORPORATION—See The Carlyle Group Inc.; *U.S. Public*, pg. 2052

PQ EUROPE GMBH—See The Carlyle Group Inc.; *U.S. Public*, pg. 2052

PQ FINLAND OY—See The Carlyle Group Inc.; *U.S. Public*, pg. 2052

PQ FRANCE S.A.S.—See The Carlyle Group Inc.; *U.S. Public*, pg. 2052

PQ HOLDINGS AUSTRALIA PTY LIMITED—See Ecovyst Inc.; *U.S. Public*, pg. 717

PQ HOLDINGS INC.—See The Carlyle Group Inc.; *U.S. Public*, pg. 2052

PQI CORPORATION—See Power Quotient International Co., Ltd.; *Int'l*, pg. 5946

PQI JAPAN CO LTD—See Power Quotient International Co., Ltd.; *Int'l*, pg. 5946

PQ INTERNATIONAL COOPERATIE U.A.—See Ecovyst Inc.; *U.S. Public*, pg. 717

PQ ITALY S.R.L.—See The Carlyle Group Inc.; *U.S. Public*, pg. 2052

PQMS LTD.—See Hexatronic Group AB; *Int'l*, pg. 3371

PQ NEDERLAND B.V.—See The Carlyle Group Inc.; *U.S. Public*, pg. 2052

PQR B.V.—See Bechtle AG; *Int'l*, pg. 938

PQR HOLDING B.V.—See Bechtle AG; *Int'l*, pg. 938

PQ SILICAS HOLDINGS SOUTH AFRICA PTY LTD.—See Ecovyst Inc.; *U.S. Public*, pg. 717

PQ SILICAS SOUTH AFRICA PTY LTD.—See Ecovyst Inc.; *U.S. Public*, pg. 717

PQ SILICAS UK LIMITED—See Ecovyst Inc.; *U.S. Public*, pg. 717

PQ SILICATES LTD.—See The Carlyle Group Inc.; *U.S. Public*, pg. 2052

PQ SWEDEN AB—See The Carlyle Group Inc.; *U.S. Public*, pg. 2052

PQ (TIANJIN) SILICATES TECHNOLOGY CO. LTD.—See The Carlyle Group Inc.; *U.S. Public*, pg. 2052

P. QUINTAINE & SON LTD.; *Int'l*, pg. 5682

PRABHA ENERGY PRIVATE LIMITED—See Deep Energy Resources Ltd.; *Int'l*, pg. 2002

PRABHAT DAIRY LIMITED; *Int'l*, pg. 5952

PRABHAT TECHNOLOGIES (INDIA) LTD.; *Int'l*, pg. 5952

PRABHAV INDUSTRIES LIMITED; *Int'l*, pg. 5952

PRABHHANS INDUSTRIES LIMITED; *Int'l*, pg. 5952

PRABHU BANK LTD.; *Int'l*, pg. 5952

PRABHU INSURANCE LIMITED; *Int'l*, pg. 5952

PRABHU STEEL INDUSTRIES LIMITED; *Int'l*, pg. 5952

PRAB, INC.; *U.S. Private*, pg. 3241

PRACHINBURI GLASS INDUSTRY CO., LTD.—See BG Container Glass Public Company Limited; *Int'l*, pg. 1007

PRACHUAP PORT CO. LTD.—See Sahaviriya Steel Industries Public Company Limited; *Int'l*, pg. 6481

PRACTICAL AUTOMATION INC.—See Alinabal Holdings Corporation; *U.S. Private*, pg. 168

PRACTICAL COMPUTER APPLICATIONS, INC.; *U.S. Private*, pg. 3241

PRACTICAL CPD LIMITED—See Vimian Group AB; *Int'l*, pg. 8208

THE PRACTICAL SOLUTION PUBLIC COMPANY LIMITED; *Int'l*, pg. 7676

PRACTICAR SYSTEMS INC.—See Grandville Equities Corp.; *Int'l*, pg. 3058

PRACTICE BUILDERS—See Ascend Integrated Media, LLC; *U.S. Private*, pg. 346

PRACTICEFORCES; *U.S. Private*, pg. 3241

PRACTICE FUSION, INC.—See Veradigm Inc.; *U.S. Public*, pg. 2280

THE PRACTICE (GROUP) LIMITED—See Centene Corporation; *U.S. Public*, pg. 470

PRACTICE INSIGHT, LLC—See Canada Pension Plan Investment Board; *Int'l*, pg. 1282

PRACTICE INSIGHT, LLC—See EQT AB; *Int'l*, pg. 2481

PRACTICELINK, LTD; *U.S. Private*, pg. 3241

PRACTICE MANAGEMENT INFORMATION CORPORATION; *U.S. Private*, pg. 3241

PRACTICE PARTNERS IN HEALTHCARE, LLC—See UnitedHealth Group Incorporated; *U.S. Public*, pg. 2249

THE PRACTICE PORTER NOVELLI—See Omnicom Group Inc.; *U.S. Public*, pg. 1592

PRACTICE PROMOTIONS, LLC; *U.S. Private*, pg. 3241

PRACTICE TRACK LIMITED—See Wilmington plc; *Int'l*, pg. 8422

PRACTICE VELOCITY, LLC—See Warburg Pincus LLC; *U.S. Private*, pg. 4438

PRACTICUS LTD.—See Practicus Ltd.; *Int'l*, pg. 5952

PRACTICUS LTD.; *Int'l*, pg. 5952

PRACTICUS PTY. LTD.—See Practicus Ltd.; *Int'l*, pg. 5952

PRACTIS INC.—See 424 Capital, LLC; *U.S. Private*, pg. 15

PRACTIS INC.—See Eagle Private Capital, LLC; *U.S. Private*, pg. 1310

PRACTIS INC.—See Plexus Capital, LLC; *U.S. Private*, pg. 3214

PRACTITIONERS PUBLISHING CO.—See Thomson Reuters Corporation; *Int'l*, pg. 7716

PRAC TRANSPORT SDN. BHD.—See Insas Berhad; *Int'l*, pg. 3718

PRADA HAWAII CORP.—See Prada S.p.A.; *Int'l*, pg. 5952

PRADA S.P.A.; *Int'l*, pg. 5952

PRADA U.S.A. CORP.—See Prada S.p.A.; *Int'l*, pg. 5952

PRADEEP METALS LIMITED; *Int'l*, pg. 5952

PRADELLA CONSTRUCTIONS PTY LTD—See Pradella Developments Pty Ltd; *Int'l*, pg. 5952

PRADELLA DEVELOPMENTS PTY LTD; *Int'l*, pg. 5952

PRADELLA DEVELOPMENTS PTY LTD—See Pradella Developments Pty Ltd; *Int'l*, pg. 5952

PRADERLOSINGER SA—See Bouygues S.A.; *Int'l*, pg. 1122

PRA DEVELOPMENT CENTER KK—See ICON plc; *Int'l*, pg. 3585

PRADHIN LTD.; *Int'l*, pg. 5952

PRADIP OVERSEAS LIMITED; *Int'l*, pg. 5952

PRADON CONSTRUCTION & TRUCKING CO.; *U.S. Private*, pg. 3241

PRADOTEL SAS—See Accor S.A.; *Int'l*, pg. 92

PRAECIPIO CONSULTING LLC; *U.S. Private*, pg. 3241

THE PRAEDIUM GROUP LLC; *U.S. Private*, pg. 4097

PRAEMITTIAS GROUP INC.; *U.S. Private*, pg. 3241

PRAEMIUM INTERNATIONAL LIMITED—See Praemium Limited; *Int'l*, pg. 5953

PRAEMIUM LIMITED; *Int'l*, pg. 5953

PRAESEPE PLC; *Int'l*, pg. 5953

PRAESES, LLC; *U.S. Private*, pg. 3241

PRAESIDIAN CAPITAL CORP.; *U.S. Private*, pg. 3241

PRAETORIAN DIGITAL, INC.; *U.S. Private*, pg. 3241

PRAETORIAN FINANCIAL GROUP, INC.—See QBE Insurance Group Limited; *Int'l*, pg. 6136

PRAETORIAN INSURANCE COMPANY—See QBE Insurance Group Limited; *Int'l*, pg. 6136

PRAETORIAN PROPERTY, INC.; *U.S. Public*, pg. 1712

PRAEZISION LIFE S.R.L.—See Ardian SAS; *Int'l*, pg. 555

PRAGATI DEVELOPMENT CONSULTING SERVICES LTD.—See Moody's Corporation; *U.S. Public*, pg. 1469

PRAGATI INSURANCE LIMITED; *Int'l*, pg. 5953

PRAGATI LIFE INSURANCE LIMITED; *Int'l*, pg. 5953

PRAG BOSIMI SYNTHETICS LIMITED; *Int'l*, pg. 5953

PRAGER & CO., LLC; *U.S. Private*, pg. 3241

PRAGER INC.—See Zurn Elkay Water Solutions Corporation; *U.S. Public*, pg. 2413

PRAGER METIS CPAS, LLC; *U.S. Private*, pg. 3241

PRAGER METIS INTERNATIONAL LLC; *U.S. Private*, pg. 3241

PRAGER UNIVERSITY FOUNDATION; *U.S. Private*, pg. 3242

PRAGER WINERY & PORT WORKS, INC.; *U.S. Private*, pg. 3242

PRAGMA FAKTORING S.A.; *Int'l*, pg. 5953

PRAGMA INKASO S.A.; *Int'l*, pg. 5953

PRAGMA PROGETTI S.R.L.—See Sesa S.p.A.; *Int'l*, pg. 6729

PRAGMATIC DRILLING FLUIDS ADDITIVES LTD—See Newpark Resources, Inc.; *U.S. Public*, pg. 1518

COMPANY NAME INDEX

PRAGMATIC INSTITUTE, LLC.—See MidOcean Partners, LLP; *U.S. Private*, pg. 2717
PRAGMATIC PLAY LTD.; *Int'l*, pg. 5953
PRAGMATICS INC.; *U.S. Private*, pg. 3242
PRAGMATIC WORKS INC.—See Gryphon Investors, LLC; *U.S. Private*, pg. 1798
PRAGMATIX, INC.—See Anexio, Inc.; *U.S. Private*, pg. 281
PRAGMATIX SA—See G7 Entreprises; *Int'l*, pg. 2867
PRAGOEDUCA A.S.—See Demos S.A.; *Int'l*, pg. 2026
PRA GROUP CANADA INC.—See PRA Group, Inc.; *U.S. Public*, pg. 1712
PRA GROUP DEUTSCHLAND GMBH—See PRA Group, Inc.; *U.S. Public*, pg. 1712
PRA GROUP EUROPE AS—See PRA Group, Inc.; *U.S. Public*, pg. 1712
PRA GROUP EUROPE FINANCIAL SERVICES AS—See PRA Group, Inc.; *U.S. Public*, pg. 1712
PRA GROUP EUROPE PORTFOLIO AS—See PRA Group, Inc.; *U.S. Public*, pg. 1712
PRA GROUP, INC.; *U.S. Public*, pg. 1712
PRA GROUP NORGE AS—See PRA Group, Inc.; *U.S. Public*, pg. 1712
PRA GROUP NORGE AS—See PRA Group, Inc.; *U.S. Public*, pg. 1712
PRA GROUP NORGE AS—See PRA Group, Inc.; *U.S. Public*, pg. 1712
PRA GROUP NORGE AS—See PRA Group, Inc.; *U.S. Public*, pg. 1712
PRA GROUP OSTERREICH INKASSO GMBH—See PRA Group, Inc.; *U.S. Public*, pg. 1712
PRA GROUP OSTERREICH PORTFOLIO GMBH—See PRA Group, Inc.; *U.S. Public*, pg. 1712
PRA GROUP POLAND SP. Z OO—See PRA Group, Inc.; *U.S. Public*, pg. 1712
PRA GROUP SVERIGE AB—See PRA Group, Inc.; *U.S. Public*, pg. 1712
PRA GROUP (UK) LIMITED—See PRA Group, Inc.; *U.S. Public*, pg. 1712
PRA HEALTH SCIENCES, INC.—See ICON plc; *Int'l*, pg. 3585
PRA IBERIA SLU—See PRA Group, Inc.; *U.S. Public*, pg. 1712
PRAIMIT, S. A. DE C. V.—See ALFA, S.A.B. de C.V.; *Int'l*, pg. 313
PRA INTERNATIONAL INC.—See ICON plc; *Int'l*, pg. 3585
PRA INTERNATIONAL INC.—See ICON plc; *Int'l*, pg. 3585
PRA INTERNATIONAL OPERATIONS B.V.—See ICON plc; *Int'l*, pg. 3585
PRAIRIE AG COOPERATIVE; *U.S. Private*, pg. 3242
PRAIRIE BANCSHARES CORPORATION; *U.S. Private*, pg. 3242
PRAIRIE BAND, LLC—See Prairie Band Potawatomi Nation; *U.S. Private*, pg. 3242
PRAIRIE BAND POTAWATOMI NATION; *U.S. Private*, pg. 3242
PRAIRIE CABLE LLC.; *U.S. Private*, pg. 3242
PRAIRIE CAPITAL MANAGEMENT, LLC—See UMB Financial Corporation; *U.S. Public*, pg. 2224
PRAIRIE CENTER HEALTH SYSTEMS, INC.—See Centerstone of America, Inc.; *U.S. Private*, pg. 817
PRAIRIE CITY BAKERY, CO.—See McKee Foods Corporation; *U.S. Private*, pg. 2637
PRAIRIE CONTRACTORS, INC.; *U.S. Private*, pg. 3242
PRAIRIE DEVELOPMENT SDN. BHD.—See Gromutual Berhad; *Int'l*, pg. 3087
PRAIRIE DIALYSIS, LLC—See DaVita Inc.; *U.S. Public*, pg. 642
PRAIRIE DISPOSAL LLC—See Waste Connections, Inc.; *Int'l*, pg. 8354
PRAIRIE DOG/TCG—See Trozzolo Communications Group; *U.S. Private*, pg. 4244
PRAIRIE FARMERS ASSOCIATION, INC.; *U.S. Private*, pg. 3242
PRAIRIE FARMS DAIRY, INC.; *U.S. Private*, pg. 3242
PRAIRIE FARMS DAIRY SUPPLY CORP.—See Prairie Farms Dairy, Inc.; *U.S. Private*, pg. 3242
PRAIRIE GARDENS INC.; *U.S. Private*, pg. 3242
PRAIRIE GRAIN PARTNERS LLC; *U.S. Private*, pg. 3242
PRAIRIE INTERNATIONAL TRUCKS; *U.S. Private*, pg. 3242
PRAIRIE ISLAND INDIAN COMMUNITY; *U.S. Private*, pg. 3242
PRAIRIE LAKES COOP; *U.S. Private*, pg. 3242
PRAIRIE LAND COOPERATIVE; *U.S. Private*, pg. 3242
PRAIRIE MALT LIMITED—See Cargill, Inc.; *U.S. Private*, pg. 759
PRAIRIE MANAGEMENT & DEVELOPMENT; *U.S. Private*, pg. 3242
PRAIRIE MATERIAL; *U.S. Private*, pg. 3243
PRAIRIE MECHANICAL CORPORATION; *U.S. Private*, pg. 3243
PRAIRIE MINES & ROYALTY ULC—See Westmoreland Coal Company; *U.S. Private*, pg. 4499
PRAIRIE MOUNTAIN PUBLISHING COMPANY LLP—See Alden Global Capital LLC; *U.S. Private*, pg. 157
PRAIRIE NORTH CONST. LTD.; *Int'l*, pg. 5953
PRAIRIE OPERATING CO.; *U.S. Public*, pg. 1712

PRAIRIE PACKAGING, INC.—See Pactiv Evergreen Inc.; *U.S. Private*, pg. 1633
PRAIRIE PELLA INC.; *U.S. Private*, pg. 3243
PRAIRIE PETRO-CHEM LTD.—See Clariant AG; *Int'l*, pg. 1645
PRAIRIE POWER, INC.; *U.S. Private*, pg. 3243
PRAIRIE PRIDE COOPERATIVE; *U.S. Private*, pg. 3243
PRAIRIE PROVIDENT RESOURCES CANADA LTD.—See Prairie Provident Resources Inc.; *Int'l*, pg. 5953
PRAIRIE PROVIDENT RESOURCES INC.; *Int'l*, pg. 5953
PRAIRIE QUEST, INC.; *U.S. Private*, pg. 3243
PRAIRIE RONDE REALTY COMPANY, INC.—See National Tube Holding Company Inc.; *U.S. Private*, pg. 2864
PRAIRIESKY ROYALTY LTD.; *Int'l*, pg. 5953
PRAIRIE STATE BANK AND TRUST; *U.S. Private*, pg. 3243
PRAIRIE STATE/SELECT SIRES—See Select Sires Inc.; *U.S. Private*, pg. 3601
PRAIRIE SYSTEMS, LLC—See Dairy, LLC; *U.S. Private*, pg. 1146
PRAIRIE TECHNOLOGIES, INC.—See Bruker Corporation; *U.S. Public*, pg. 407
PRAISE INTERNATIONAL NORTH AMERICA, INC.; *U.S. Private*, pg. 3243
PR. A. I. SRL—See Illinois Tool Works Inc.; *U.S. Public*, pg. 1110
PRAJAY ENGINEERS SYNDICATE LIMITED; *Int'l*, pg. 5953
PRAJ FAR EAST CO., LIMITED—See Praj Industries Ltd.; *Int'l*, pg. 5953
PRAJIN 1 STOP DISTRIBUTORS; *U.S. Private*, pg. 3243
PRAJ INDUSTRIES LTD.; *Int'l*, pg. 5953
PRAJ JARAGUA BIOENERGIA S.A.—See Praj Industries Ltd.; *Int'l*, pg. 5953
PRAJ-MATRIX—See Praj Industries Ltd.; *Int'l*, pg. 5953
PRAJO & CO GMBH—See PORR AG; *Int'l*, pg. 5924
PRAJ SCHNEIDER INC—See Praj Industries Ltd.; *Int'l*, pg. 5953
PRAKASH CERAMICS LTD.; *Int'l*, pg. 5953
PRAKASH INDUSTRIES LIMITED - COAL MINING DIVISION—See Prakash Industries Limited; *Int'l*, pg. 5953
PRAKASH INDUSTRIES LIMITED - PVC PIPE DIVICION—See Prakash Industries Limited; *Int'l*, pg. 5954
PRAKASH INDUSTRIES LIMITED; *Int'l*, pg. 5953
PRAKASH INDUSTRIES LIMITED - WIND MILL DIVISION—See Prakash Industries Limited; *Int'l*, pg. 5954
PRAKASH PIPES LIMITED; *Int'l*, pg. 5954
PRAKASH STEELAGE LTD.; *Int'l*, pg. 5954
PRAKASH WOOLLEN & SYNTHETIC MILLS LTD.; *Int'l*, pg. 5954
PRAKIT ADVERTISING LIMITED—See Prakit Holdings Public Company Limited; *Int'l*, pg. 5954
PRAKIT & FCB VIETNAM—See The Interpublic Group of Companies, Inc.; *U.S. Public*, pg. 2093
PRAKIT HOLDINGS PUBLIC COMPANY LIMITED; *Int'l*, pg. 5954
PRAKLA BOHRTECHNIK GMBH.—See BAUER Aktiengesellschaft; *Int'l*, pg. 893
PRAKOLAR ROTULOS AUTOADESIVOS LTDA.—See SATO Holdings Corporation; *Int'l*, pg. 6585
PRAKTIKER AG; *Int'l*, pg. 5954
PRAKTIKER DEUTSCHLAND GMBH—See Praktiker AG; *Int'l*, pg. 5954
PRAKTIKER EOOD; *Int'l*, pg. 5954
PRAKTIKER HELLAS A.E.—See Praktiker AG; *Int'l*, pg. 5954
PRAKTIKER HUNGARY KFT.—See Praktiker AG; *Int'l*, pg. 5954
PRAKTIKER YAPI MERKETLERI A.S.—See Praktiker AG; *Int'l*, pg. 5954
PRAKTISKA SVERIGE AB—See FSN Capital Partners AS; *Int'l*, pg. 2799
PRAKTISKA SVERIGE AB—See FSN Capital Partners AS; *Int'l*, pg. 2799
PRAKTISKA SVERIGE AB—See FSN Capital Partners AS; *Int'l*, pg. 2799
PRAKTISKA SVERIGE AB—See FSN Capital Partners AS; *Int'l*, pg. 2799
PRALMED SP.Z.O.O.—See Hollywood SA; *Int'l*, pg. 3452
PRAL SERWIS WARSZAWA SP.Z.O.O.—See Hollywood SA; *Int'l*, pg. 3452
PRAMAC ASIA PTE LTD—See Generac Holdings Inc.; *U.S. Public*, pg. 912
PRAMAC CARIBE SRL—See Generac Holdings Inc.; *U.S. Public*, pg. 912
PRAMAC EUROPE SAS—See Generac Holdings Inc.; *U.S. Public*, pg. 912
PRAMAC FU LEE FOSHAN POWER EQUIPMENT LTD—See Generac Holdings Inc.; *U.S. Public*, pg. 912
PRAMAC GMBH—See Generac Holdings Inc.; *U.S. Public*, pg. 912
PRAMAC IBERICA S.A.U.—See Generac Holdings Inc.; *U.S. Public*, pg. 912
PRAMAC RUS LTD—See Generac Holdings Inc.; *U.S. Public*, pg. 912

PRAMAC SP. Z.O.O.—See Generac Holdings Inc.; *U.S. Public*, pg. 912
PRAMAC STORAGE SYSTEMS GMBH—See Generac Holdings Inc.; *U.S. Public*, pg. 912
PRAMAC UK LIMITED—See Generac Holdings Inc.; *U.S. Public*, pg. 913
PRAMA HIKVISION INDIAN PRIVATE LIMITED—See Hangzhou Hikvision Digital Technology Co., Ltd.; *Int'l*, pg. 3248
PRAMARA PROMOTIONS LIMITED; *Int'l*, pg. 5954
PRAMERICA ASIA FUND MANAGEMENT LIMITED—See Prudential Financial, Inc.; *U.S. Public*, pg. 1732
PRAMERICA FIXED INCOME (ASIA) LIMITED—See Prudential Financial, Inc.; *U.S. Public*, pg. 1732
PRAMERICA FOSUN LIFE INSURANCE CO., LTD.—See Prudential Financial, Inc.; *U.S. Public*, pg. 1731
PRAMERICA INVESTMENT MANAGEMENT LIMITED—See Prudential Financial, Inc.; *U.S. Public*, pg. 1732
PRAMERICA LIFE INSURANCE COMPANY LIMITED—See Prudential Financial, Inc.; *U.S. Public*, pg. 1731
PRAMERICA REAL ESTATE INVESTORS (ASIA) PTE. LTD.—See Prudential Financial, Inc.; *U.S. Public*, pg. 1733
PRAMERICA SGR S.P.A—See Prudential Financial, Inc.; *U.S. Public*, pg. 1732
PRAMERICA SYSTEMS IRELAND LIMITED—See Prudential Financial, Inc.; *U.S. Public*, pg. 1732
PRAMERICA ZYCIE TOWARZYSTWO UBEZPIECZEN I REASEKURACJI SPOLKA AKCYJNA—See Unum Group; *U.S. Public*, pg. 2263
PRAMO EKONOMI & DATA AB—See TowerBrook Capital Partners, L.P.; *U.S. Private*, pg. 4195
PRAMSUR SA—See Pernod Ricard S.A.; *Int'l*, pg. 5811
PRANA CONSULTING, INC.—See Kinaxis Inc.; *Int'l*, pg. 4165
PRANA LIVING, LLC—See Columbia Sportswear Company; *U.S. Public*, pg. 535
PRANATAL-MEDIZIN MUNCHEN FRAUENARZTE UND HUMANGENETIKER MVZ GMBH—See Eurofins Scientific S.E.; *Int'l*, pg. 2551
PRANAVADITYA SPINNING MILLS LIMITED—See Indo Count Industries Ltd.; *Int'l*, pg. 3656
PRANAV VIKAS (INDIA) LTD—See Sanden Corporation; *Int'l*, pg. 6524
PRANDA AND KROLL GMBH AND CO.KG—See Pranda Jewelry Public Company Limited; *Int'l*, pg. 5954
PRANDA JEWELRY PUBLIC COMPANY LIMITED; *Int'l*, pg. 5954
PRANDA NORTH AMERICA INC.—See Pranda Jewelry Public Company Limited; *Int'l*, pg. 5954
PRANDA U.K. LIMITED—See Pranda Jewelry Public Company Limited; *Int'l*, pg. 5954
PRANEAT CO., LTD.—See Thoresen Thai Agencies Public Company Limited; *Int'l*, pg. 7718
PRANTALAY MARKETING PUBLIC COMPANY LIMITED; *Int'l*, pg. 5954
PRAP CHINA PUBLIC RELATIONS CONSULTANTS, INC.—See PRAP Japan, Inc.; *Int'l*, pg. 5954
PRA PHARMACEUTICAL S A (PROPRIETARY) LIMITED—See ICON plc; *Int'l*, pg. 3585
PRAP JAPAN, INC.; *Int'l*, pg. 5954
PRARAM 9 HOSPITAL PCL; *Int'l*, pg. 5954
PRA RECEIVABLES MANAGEMENT, LLC—See PRA Group, Inc.; *U.S. Public*, pg. 1712
PRASAC MICROFINANCE INSTITUTION PLC—See KB Financial Group Inc.; *Int'l*, pg. 4104
PRASE ENGINEERING SPA—See Midwich Group Plc; *Int'l*, pg. 4887
PRASHKOVSKY INVESTMENTS & CONSTRUCTION LTD.; *Int'l*, pg. 5954
PRASIDHA ANEKA NIAGA TBK; *Int'l*, pg. 5954
PRAS KHAZAR COMPANY—See Pars Tousheh Investment Company; *Int'l*, pg. 5746
PRASSAS METAL PRODUCTS, INC.—See The Mill Steel Co., Inc.; *U.S. Private*, pg. 4079
PRA SUOMI OY—See PRA Group, Inc.; *U.S. Public*, pg. 1712
PRA SUOMI OY—See PRA Group, Inc.; *U.S. Public*, pg. 1712
PRA SUOMI OY—See PRA Group, Inc.; *U.S. Public*, pg. 1712
PRA SUOMI OY—See PRA Group, Inc.; *U.S. Public*, pg. 1712
PRATAAP SNACKS LIMITED; *Int'l*, pg. 5955
PRATERKRAFTWERK GMBH—See Stadtwerke Munchen GmbH; *Int'l*, pg. 7162
PRATE ROOFING & INSTALLATIONS, LLC; *U.S. Private*, pg. 3243
PRATERSTRASSE EINS HOTELBETRIEBS GMBH—See UNIQA Insurance Group AG; *Int'l*, pg. 8058
PRATESI LINENS INC.; *U.S. Private*, pg. 3243
PRATIA S.A.—See NEUCA S.A.; *Int'l*, pg. 5218
PRATIBHA INDUSTRIES LIMITED; *Int'l*, pg. 5955
PRATICA KLIMAQUIP INDUSTRIA E COMERCIO SA; *Int'l*, pg. 5955
PRATICA PARTICIPACOES S.A.; *Int'l*, pg. 5955
PRATIK PANELS LTD.; *Int'l*, pg. 5955

PRATIKSHA CHEMICALS LTD.; *Int'l*, pg. 5955
PRATRIVERO S.P.A.—See Radici Partecipazioni S.p.A.; *Int'l*, pg. 6175
PRATRIVERO U.S.A. INC.—See Radici Partecipazioni S.p.A.; *Int'l*, pg. 6175
PRATT BURNERD INTERNATIONAL LIMITED—See The 600 Group PLC; *Int'l*, pg. 7609
PRATT CONSTRUCTION INCORPORATED; *U.S. Private*, pg. 3243
PRATT CORPORATION—See Vomela Specialty Company; *U.S. Private*, pg. 4412
PRATT INDUSTRIES-CORRUGATING DIVISION—See Visy Industries Holdings Pty. Ltd.; *Int'l*, pg. 8256
PRATT INDUSTRIES-CORRUGATING DIVISION—See Visy Industries Holdings Pty. Ltd.; *Int'l*, pg. 8256
PRATT INDUSTRIES-HUMBOLDT—See Visy Industries Holdings Pty. Ltd.; *Int'l*, pg. 8256
PRATT INDUSTRIES-STATESVILLE—See Visy Industries Holdings Pty. Ltd.; *Int'l*, pg. 8256
PRATT INDUSTRIES (USA), INC.—See Visy Industries Holdings Pty. Ltd.; *Int'l*, pg. 8256
PRATT & LAMBERT PAINTS—See The Sherwin-Williams Company; *U.S. Public*, pg. 2128
PRATT MANAGEMENT COMPANY LLC; *U.S. Private*, pg. 3243
PRATT MEDICAL CENTER, LTD.—See Sentara Healthcare; *U.S. Private*, pg. 3608
PRATT & MILLER ENGINEERING & FABRICATION, INC.—See Oshkosh Corporation; *U.S. Public*, pg. 1621
PRATTVILLE MEDICAL EQUIPMENT, INC.—See AdaptHealth Corp.; *U.S. Public*, pg. 39
PRATT & WHITNEY AUTO-AIR COMPOSITES, INC.—See RTX Corporation; *U.S. Public*, pg. 1823
PRATT & WHITNEY CANADA CORP.—See RTX Corporation; *U.S. Public*, pg. 1823
PRATT & WHITNEY CANADA HOLDINGS CORP.—See RTX Corporation; *U.S. Public*, pg. 1823
PRATT & WHITNEY CANADA LEASING, LIMITED PARTNERSHIP—See RTX Corporation; *U.S. Public*, pg. 1823
PRATT & WHITNEY COMPONENT SOLUTIONS, INC.—See RTX Corporation; *U.S. Public*, pg. 1823
PRATT & WHITNEY ENGINE SERVICES, INC.—See RTX Corporation; *U.S. Public*, pg. 1823
PRATT & WHITNEY MILITARY AFTERMARKET SERVICES, INC.—See RTX Corporation; *U.S. Public*, pg. 1823
PRATT & WHITNEY POWER SYSTEMS CIS LLC—See Mitsubishi Heavy Industries, Ltd.; *Int'l*, pg. 4960
PRATT & WHITNEY PSD INC.—See RTX Corporation; *U.S. Public*, pg. 1823
PRATT & WHITNEY RZESZOW S.A.—See RTX Corporation; *U.S. Public*, pg. 1824
PRATT & WHITNEY SERVICES PTE LTD—See RTX Corporation; *U.S. Public*, pg. 1824
PRATT & WHITNEY—See RTX Corporation; *U.S. Public*, pg. 1823
PRA TURKEY SAGLIK ARASTIRMA VE GELISTIRME LIMITED SIRKETI—See ICON plc; *Int'l*, pg. 3586
PR AUSTRALIA PTY LTD—See Generac Holdings Inc.; *U.S. Public*, pg. 912
PRAVEG LIMITED; *Int'l*, pg. 5955
PRAXAIR ARGENTINA S.A.—See Linde plc; *Int'l*, pg. 4509
PRAXAIR ASIA INC.—See Linde plc; *Int'l*, pg. 4509
PRAXAIR CHEMAX SEMICONDUCTOR MATERIALS CO., LTD.—See China Petrochemical Development Corp.; *Int'l*, pg. 1540
PRAXAIR CHEMAX SEMICONDUCTOR MATERIALS CO., LTD.—See Linde plc; *Int'l*, pg. 4509
PRAXAIR CHILE LTDA—See Linde plc; *Int'l*, pg. 4509
PRAXAIR (CHINA) INVESTMENT CO., LTD.—See Linde plc; *Int'l*, pg. 4509
PRAXAIR CONSULTORIA Y ADMINISTRACION S DE RL DE CV—See Linde plc; *Int'l*, pg. 4509
PRAXAIR COSTA RICA, S.A.—See Linde plc; *Int'l*, pg. 4509
PRAXAIR DISTRIBUTION, INC. - GEORGIA—See Linde plc; *Int'l*, pg. 4508
PRAXAIR DISTRIBUTION, INC.—See Linde plc; *Int'l*, pg. 4508
PRAXAIR DISTRIBUTION MID-ATLANTIC, LLC—See Linde plc; *Int'l*, pg. 4508
PRAXAIR GASES INDUSTRIALES LTDA—See Linde plc; *Int'l*, pg. 4509
PRAXAIR GASES IRELAND LIMITED—See Mitsubishi Chemical Group Corporation; *Int'l*, pg. 4937
PRAXAIR GASES UK LTD—See Mitsubishi Chemical Group Corporation; *Int'l*, pg. 4937
PRAXAIR GULF INDUSTRIAL GASES LLC—See Linde plc; *Int'l*, pg. 4509
PRAXAIR, INC.—See Linde plc; *Int'l*, pg. 4508
PRAXAIR INDIA PVT. LTD.—See Linde plc; *Int'l*, pg. 4509
PRAXAIR KOREA CO., LTD.—See Linde plc; *Int'l*, pg. 4509
PRAXAIR MEXICO S. DE R.L. DE C.V.—See Linde plc; *Int'l*, pg. 4509
PRAXAIR PERU S.R.L.—See Linde plc; *Int'l*, pg. 4509
PRAXAIR PHP S.A.S.—See Mitsubishi Chemical Group Corporation; *Int'l*, pg. 4937

PRAXAIR PLAINFIELD, INC.—See Linde plc; *Int'l*, pg. 4509
PRAXAIR PORTUGAL GASES S.A.—See Mitsubishi Chemical Group Corporation; *Int'l*, pg. 4937
PRAXAIR PUERTO RICO B. V.—See Linde plc; *Int'l*, pg. 4509
PRAXAIR PUERTO RICO, INC.—See Linde plc; *Int'l*, pg. 4509
PRAXAIR QINGDAO CO., LTD.—See Linde plc; *Int'l*, pg. 4509
PRAXAIR REPUBLICA DOMINICANA, SRL—See Linde plc; *Int'l*, pg. 4509
PRAXAIR SERVICES, INC.—See Linde plc; *Int'l*, pg. 4509
PRAXAIR SERVICES (UK) LIMITED—See Linde plc; *Int'l*, pg. 4509
PRAXAIR (SHANGHAI) CO., LTD.—See Linde plc; *Int'l*, pg. 4509
PRAXAIR (SHANGHAI) SEMICONDUCTOR GASES CO., LTD.—See Linde plc; *Int'l*, pg. 4509
PRAXAIR S.R.L.—See Linde plc; *Int'l*, pg. 4509
PRAXAIR SURFACE TECHNOLOGIES CO., LTD.—See Linde plc; *Int'l*, pg. 4509
PRAXAIR SURFACE TECHNOLOGIES DO BRASIL LTDA.—See Linde plc; *Int'l*, pg. 4509
PRAXAIR SURFACE TECHNOLOGIES GMBH—See Linde plc; *Int'l*, pg. 4509
PRAXAIR SURFACE TECHNOLOGIES, INC.—See Linde plc; *Int'l*, pg. 4509
PRAXAIR SURFACE TECHNOLOGIES K.K.—See Linde plc; *Int'l*, pg. 4509
PRAXAIR SURFACE TECHNOLOGIES LIMITED—See Linde plc; *Int'l*, pg. 4509
PRAXAIR SURFACE TECHNOLOGIES S.A.S.—See Linde plc; *Int'l*, pg. 4509
PRAXAIR SURFACE TECHONOLOGIES, INC.—See Linde plc; *Int'l*, pg. 4509
PRAXAIR (THAILAND) COMPANY LTD.—See Linde plc; *Int'l*, pg. 4509
PRAXAIR URUGUAY LTDA.—See Linde plc; *Int'l*, pg. 4509
PRAXAIR (WUHAN), INC.—See Linde plc; *Int'l*, pg. 4509
PRAX EXPLORATION & PRODUCTION PLC—See State Oil Limited; *Int'l*, pg. 7184
THE PRAXIS COMPANIES, LLC—See Meridian Venture Partners; *U.S. Private*, pg. 2674
PRAXIS CONSULTING INC.—See Crawford & Company; *U.S. Public*, pg. 592
PRAXIS ENGINEERING; *U.S. Private*, pg. 3243
PRAXIS FUND SERVICES (JERSEY) LIMITED; *Int'l*, pg. 5955
PRAXIS HOME RETAIL LIMITED; *Int'l*, pg. 5955
PRAXIS PRECISION MEDICINES, INC.; *U.S. Public*, pg. 1712
PRAXIS—See KKR & Co. Inc.; *U.S. Public*, pg. 1261
PRAXIS TECHNOLOGY CO. LTD.—See Capgemini SE; *Int'l*, pg. 1304
PRAXSYN CORPORATION; *U.S. Private*, pg. 3243
PRAZISIONSTEILE DRESDEN GMBH & CO. KG—See KAP Beteiligungs-AG; *Int'l*, pg. 4076
PRAZSKA PLYNARENSKA DISTRIBUCE, A.S.—See E.ON SE; *Int'l*, pg. 2258
PRAZSKA PLYNARENSKA HOLDING A.S.—See E.ON SE; *Int'l*, pg. 2259
PRAZSKA PLYNARENSKA SERVIS DISTRIBUCE, A.S.—See E.ON SE; *Int'l*, pg. 2259
PRAZSKA PLYNARENSKA SPRAVA MAJETKU, S.R.O.—See E.ON SE; *Int'l*, pg. 2259
PRAZSKE SLUZBY A.S.; *Int'l*, pg. 5955
PRAZSKE VODOVODY A KANALIZACE A.S.—See Veolia Environnement S.A.; *Int'l*, pg. 8153
P & R CANVAS, LLC.—See Pipe Welders Inc.; *U.S. Private*, pg. 3189
PRC-DESOTO AUSTRALIA PTY LTD.—See PPG Industries, Inc.; *U.S. Public*, pg. 1710
PRC-DESOTO INTERNATIONAL, INC. - MOUNT LAUREL—See PPG Industries, Inc.; *U.S. Public*, pg. 1708
PRC-DESOTO INTERNATIONAL, INC.—See PPG Industries, Inc.; *U.S. Public*, pg. 1708
PRC INDUSTRIAL SUPPLY, INC.—See AEA Investors LP; *U.S. Private*, pg. 115
PRC LASER CORP.—See Coherent Corp.; *U.S. Public*, pg. 528
PRC LASER EUROPE N.V.—See Coherent Corp.; *U.S. Public*, pg. 528
PRCO AMERICA, INC.—See Puyang Refractories Group Co., Ltd.; *Int'l*, pg. 6124
PRCO FUNCTIONAL REFRACTORIES CO., LTD.—See Puyang Refractories Group Co., Ltd.; *Int'l*, pg. 6124
PR CONSULTING DENTSU INC.—See Dentsu Group Inc.; *Int'l*, pg. 2039
THE PR CONSULTING GROUP, INC.-LOS ANGELES—See The PR Consulting Group, Inc.; *U.S. Private*, pg. 4097
THE PR CONSULTING GROUP, INC.; *U.S. Private*, pg. 4097
THE PR CONSULTING GROUP, INC.-WASHINGTON—See The PR Consulting Group, Inc.; *U.S. Private*, pg. 4097

PRCO YINGKOU MAGNESIA REFRACTORIES CO., LTD.—See Puyang Refractories Group Co., Ltd.; *Int'l*, pg. 6124
PRC REIT; *Int'l*, pg. 5955
P&R DENTAL STRATEGIES, LLC—See The Beekman Group, LLC; *U.S. Private*, pg. 3993
PRD INC.—See Specialty Manufacturers, Inc.; *U.S. Private*, pg. 3750
PREAMED S.R.O.—See Centene Corporation; *U.S. Public*, pg. 470
PREANALYTIX GMBH—See Becton, Dickinson & Company; *U.S. Public*, pg. 288
PREANALYTIX GMBH—See QIAGEN N.V.; *Int'l*, pg. 6139
PREAT CORP.—See The Jordan Company, L.P.; *U.S. Private*, pg. 4063
PREATO CAPITAL AB; *Int'l*, pg. 5955
PREATO OY; *Int'l*, pg. 5955
PREAXIA HEALTH CARE PAYMENT SYSTEMS, INC.; *Int'l*, pg. 5955
PREBEN Z. JENSEN A/S—See Beijer Alma AB; *Int'l*, pg. 943
PREBET AIUD S.A.; *Int'l*, pg. 5955
PREBETONG GALICIA S.A.—See Camargo Correa S.A.; *Int'l*, pg. 1268
PREBETONG LUGO HORMIGONES S.A.—See Camargo Correa S.A.; *Int'l*, pg. 1268
PREBETONG LUGO S.A.—See Camargo Correa S.A.; *Int'l*, pg. 1268
PREBONA AB; *Int'l*, pg. 5955
PREBON ENERGY INC—See TP ICAP Finance PLC; *Int'l*, pg. 7882
PREBON FINANCIAL PRODUCTS INC—See TP ICAP Finance PLC; *Int'l*, pg. 7882
PREBON YAMANE (INDIA) LIMITED—See TP ICAP Finance PLC; *Int'l*, pg. 7881
PRE-BUILT PUBLIC COMPANY LIMITED; *Int'l*, pg. 5955
PRECASH INC.; *U.S. Private*, pg. 3243
PRECAST SERVICES INC.; *U.S. Private*, pg. 3243
PRECAST SOFTWARE ENGINEERING GMBH—See Nemetschek SE; *Int'l*, pg. 5195
PRECEDENT COMMUNICATIONS; *Int'l*, pg. 5956
PRECEPT ADVISORY GROUP LLC—See Truist Financial Corporation; *U.S. Public*, pg. 2199
THE PRECEPT GROUP INC.; *Int'l*, pg. 7676
PRECEPT MEDICAL COMMUNICATIONS—See WPP plc; *Int'l*, pg. 8492
PRECEPT MEDICAL PRODUCTS INC.—See Audax Group, Limited Partnership; *U.S. Private*, pg. 386
PRECEPT MINISTRIES OF REACH OUT, INC.; *U.S. Private*, pg. 3243
PRECHECK HEALTH SERVICES, INC.; *U.S. Private*, pg. 3243
PRECHECK HEALTH SERVICES, INC.; *U.S. Private*, pg. 3243
PRECHECK, INC.—See Cisive.; *U.S. Private*, pg. 901
PRECHEZA, A.S.—See Agrofert Holding, a.s.; *Int'l*, pg. 219
PRECIA MOLEN AUSTRALIA PTY LTD—See Precia SA; *Int'l*, pg. 5956
PRECIA MOLEN CZ S.R.O.—See Precia SA; *Int'l*, pg. 5956
PRECIA-MOLEN INDIA PVT. LIMITED—See Precia SA; *Int'l*, pg. 5956
PRECIA MOLEN IRELAND LIMITED—See Precia SA; *Int'l*, pg. 5956
PRECIA MOLEN NEDERLAND BV—See Precia SA; *Int'l*, pg. 5956
PRECIA MOLEN NZ LTD.—See Precia SA; *Int'l*, pg. 5956
PRECIA MOLEN SCANDINAVIA AS—See Precia SA; *Int'l*, pg. 5956
PRECIA-MOLEN UK LIMITED—See Precia SA; *Int'l*, pg. 5956
PRECIA POLSKA SP. Z O.O.—See Precia SA; *Int'l*, pg. 5956
PRECIA SA; *Int'l*, pg. 5956
PRECICION TRIM, INC.; *U.S. Public*, pg. 1713
PRECICO GROUP SDN BHD—See Frencken Group Limited; *Int'l*, pg. 2773
PRECICULTURE SAS—See Exel Industries SA; *Int'l*, pg. 2582
PRECIGEN, INC.; *U.S. Public*, pg. 1713
PRECIMETER CONTROL AB—See Lagercrantz Group AB; *Int'l*, pg. 4394
PRECIMETER GMBH—See Lagercrantz Group AB; *Int'l*, pg. 4394
PRECIMETER INC.—See Lagercrantz Group AB; *Int'l*, pg. 4395
PRECINCT HUB PTY. LIMITED—See Prosegur Cash SA; *Int'l*, pg. 5999
PRECINCT PROPERTIES NEW ZEALAND LIMITED; *Int'l*, pg. 5956
PRECINCT—See Enero Group Limited; *Int'l*, pg. 2424
PRECINMAC, LP—See Bain Capital, LP; *U.S. Private*, pg. 442
PRECINMAC, LP—See Compass Advisers Group LLC; *U.S. Private*, pg. 998
PRECINMAC, LP—See Pine Island Capital Partners LLC; *U.S. Private*, pg. 3182
PRECINTIA INTERNATIONAL, S.A.—See Bertram Capital Management, LLC; *U.S. Private*, pg. 540

COMPANY NAME INDEX

PRECINTIA INTERNATIONAL, S.A.—See Crimson Investment; *U.S. Private*, pg. 1100
PRECIO FISHBONE AB; *Int'l*, pg. 5956
PRECIOUS METAL PRODUCTS DIVISION—See Johnson Matthey PLC; *Int'l*, pg. 3993
PRECIOUS METAL REFINING SERVICES INC.; *U.S. Private*, pg. 3244
PRECIOUS METALS EXPLORATION CORP.; *Int'l*, pg. 5956
PRECIOUS METALS & MINING TRUST; *Int'l*, pg. 5956
PRECIOUS SHIPPING PUBLIC COMPANY LIMITED; *Int'l*, pg. 5956
PRECIOUS TRADING & INVESTMENTS LTD.; *Int'l*, pg. 5956
PRECIOUS WOODS EUROPE B.V.—See Precious Woods Holding AG; *Int'l*, pg. 5956
PRECIOUS WOODS HOLDING AG; *Int'l*, pg. 5956
PRECIPIO DIAGNOSTICS LLC—See Precipio, Inc.; *U.S. Public*, pg. 1713
PRECIPIO, INC.; *U.S. Public*, pg. 1713
PRECIPITATE GOLD CORP.; *Int'l*, pg. 5956
PRECISE BIOMETRICS AB; *Int'l*, pg. 5957
PRECISE BIOMETRICS INC.—See Precise Biometrics AB; *Int'l*, pg. 5957
PRECISE BIOMETRICS SOLUTIONS AB—See Precise Biometrics AB; *Int'l*, pg. 5957
PRECIS E-BUISNESS SYSTEMS—See PIN Business Network; *U.S. Private*, pg. 3181
PRECISE CIRCUITS INC.—See Daburn Electronics & Cable Corp.; *U.S. Private*, pg. 1144
PRECISE COMPUTER TOOLING CO. LIMITED—See Suga International Holdings Limited; *Int'l*, pg. 7253
PRECISE CONSTRUCTION INC.; *U.S. Private*, pg. 3244
PRECISE CORPORATION PUBLIC COMPANY LIMITED; *Int'l*, pg. 5957
PRECISE DENTAL INTERNACIONAL, S.A. DE C.V.—See Integra LifeSciences Holdings Corporation; *U.S. Public*, pg. 1136
PRECISELY, INC.—See Clearlake Capital Group, L.P.; *U.S. Private*, pg. 936
PRECISELY, INC.—See TA Associates, Inc.; *U.S. Private*, pg. 3917
PRECISE MACHINE COMPANY INC.—See George T. Schmidt, Inc.; *U.S. Private*, pg. 1683
PRECISE MEDIA AND FULL SERVICE; *U.S. Private*, pg. 3244
PRECISE METAL PRODUCTS COMPANY; *U.S. Private*, pg. 3244
PRECISE PACKAGING, INC.—See The Pritzker Group - Chicago, LLC; *U.S. Private*, pg. 4099
PRECISE SYSTEMS, INC.—See Tucson Embedded Systems, Inc.; *U.S. Private*, pg. 4256
PRECISE TECH ELECTRONICS LTD.—See ESPEC Corp.; *U.S. Private*, pg. 2505
PRECISE TIME & FREQUENCY, LLC—See The LGL Group, Inc.; *U.S. Public*, pg. 2109
PRECISION AEROSPACE CORP.—See Shorehill Capital LLC; *U.S. Private*, pg. 3641
PRECISION AEROSPACE CORP.; *U.S. Private*, pg. 3244
PRECISION AIRMOTIVE LLC—See Aeries Enterprises, LLC; *U.S. Private*, pg. 117
PRECISION ASSESSMENT TECHNOLOGY CORPORATION; *Int'l*, pg. 5957
PRECISION ASSOCIATES INC.; *U.S. Private*, pg. 3244
PRECISION AUTO CARE, INC.—See Icahn Enterprises L.P.; *U.S. Public*, pg. 1085
PRECISION AUTOMATION CO., INC.; *U.S. Private*, pg. 3244
PRECISION AVIATION GROUP, INC.—See GenNx360 Capital Partners, L.P.; *U.S. Private*, pg. 1672
PRECISION AVIATION SERVICES PTY. LTD.—See Leonardo S.p.A.; *Int'l*, pg. 4460
PRECISION AVIATION TRAINING ACADEMY PTY. LTD.—See Leonardo S.p.A.; *Int'l*, pg. 4460
PRECISION BIOSCIENCES, INC.; *U.S. Public*, pg. 1713
PRECISION BIOSENSOR, INC.; *Int'l*, pg. 5957
PRECISIONBIOTICS GROUP LTD.—See Novonesis A/S; *Int'l*, pg. 5469
PRECISION BOILERS, INC.—See Source Capital, LLC; *U.S. Private*, pg. 3718
PRECISION CAMERA LP; *U.S. Private*, pg. 3244
PRECISION CAMSHAFTS LIMITED; *Int'l*, pg. 5957
PRECISION CASTPARTS CORP.—See Berkshire Hathaway Inc.; *U.S. Public*, pg. 313
PRECISION CASTPARTS CZ S.R.O.—See Berkshire Hathaway Inc.; *U.S. Public*, pg. 315
PRECISION CHRYSLER JEEP DODGE RAM; *U.S. Private*, pg. 3244
PRECISION COATING CO., INC.—See Katahdin Industries, Inc.; *U.S. Private*, pg. 2264
PRECISION COATINGS INC.; *U.S. Private*, pg. 3244
PRECISION COIL AND ROTOR—See Jay Industrial Repair, Inc.; *U.S. Private*, pg. 2191
PRECISION COMMUNICATION SERVICES CORP.—See Jabil Inc.; *U.S. Public*, pg. 1182
PRECISION COMPONENT INDUSTRIES, LLC—See Ohio Gratings, Inc.; *U.S. Private*, pg. 3004
PRECISION COMPONENTS CORPORATION; *U.S. Private*, pg. 3244

PRECISION COMPONENTS, INC.; *U.S. Private*, pg. 3244
PRECISION COMPONENTS INTL. INC.—See RTX Corporation; *U.S. Public*, pg. 1824
PRECISION COMPUTER SERVICES, INC.; *U.S. Private*, pg. 3244
PRECISION CONCEPTS GROUP LLC—See Wasatch Advantage Group, LLC; *U.S. Private*, pg. 4445
PRECISION CONCEPTS INTERNATIONAL LLC—See ONEX Corporation; *Int'l*, pg. 5578
PRECISION CONCEPTS (MEBANE) LLC—See ONEX Corporation; *Int'l*, pg. 5578
PRECISION CONSTRUCTION COMPANY—See Hoffman Corporation; *U.S. Private*, pg. 1960
PRECISION CONSTRUCTION & ROOFING; *U.S. Private*, pg. 3244
PRECISION CONTAINEURS LIMITED; *Int'l*, pg. 5957
PRECISION CONTROL SDN BHD—See CHINO Corporation; *Int'l*, pg. 1571
PRECISION COPIER SERVICE, INC.—See Xerox Holdings Corporation; *U.S. Public*, pg. 2388
PRECISION COUNTERTOPS INC.; *U.S. Private*, pg. 3244
PRECISION DATA PRODUCTS, INC.; *U.S. Private*, pg. 3244
PRECISION DEVELOPMENT; *U.S. Private*, pg. 3244
PRECISION DEVICES INCORPORATED; *U.S. Private*, pg. 3244
PRECISION DIAGNOSTICS, INC.—See Bruker Corporation; *U.S. Public*, pg. 407
PRECISION DIALING SERVICES, INC.—See UBS Group AG; *Int'l*, pg. 8006
PRECISION DIALOGUE DIRECT, INC.—See Chatham Asset Management, LLC; *U.S. Private*, pg. 864
PRECISION DIALOGUE MARKETING, LLC—See Chatham Asset Management, LLC; *U.S. Private*, pg. 864
PRECISION DIVERSIFIED OILFIELD SERVICES CORP.—See Precision Drilling Corporation; *Int'l*, pg. 5957
PRECISION DOORS & HARDWARE - FREDERICKSBURG—See Platinum Equity, LLC; *U.S. Private*, pg. 3209
PRECISION DOORS & HARDWARE—See Platinum Equity, LLC; *U.S. Private*, pg. 3209
PRECISION DORMER CANADA—See Sandvik AB; *Int'l*, pg. 6534
PRECISION DRILLING COMPANY LP—See Precision Drilling Corporation; *Int'l*, pg. 5957
PRECISION DRILLING CORPORATION - MIDDLE EAST—See Precision Drilling Corporation; *Int'l*, pg. 5957
PRECISION DRILLING CORPORATION; *Int'l*, pg. 5957
PRECISION DRILLING CORPORATION—See Precision Drilling Corporation; *Int'l*, pg. 5957
PRECISION DRILLING SERVICES M.E. W.L.L.—See Weatherford International plc; *U.S. Public*, pg. 2339
PRECISION DYNAMICS CORPORATION—See Brady Corporation; *U.S. Public*, pg. 379
PRECISION DYNAMICS—See Brady Corporation; *U.S. Public*, pg. 379
PRECISION EDGE SURGICAL PRODUCTS COMPANY INC.—See Berkshire Hathaway Inc.; *U.S. Public*, pg. 308
PRECISION ELECTRIC MOTOR WORKS, INC.—See Odyssey Investment Partners, LLC; *U.S. Private*, pg. 2995
PRECISION ELECTRONIC COIL MFG. CO.; *U.S. Private*, pg. 3244
PRECISION ELECTRONICS LIMITED; *Int'l*, pg. 5957
PRECISION ELECTRONIQUE—See Agilent Technologies, Inc.; *U.S. Public*, pg. 62
PRECISION ENERGY SERVICES SAUDI ARABIA CO. LTD.—See Weatherford International plc; *U.S. Public*, pg. 2340
PRECISIONENERGY SERVICES—See Precision Drilling Corporation; *Int'l*, pg. 5957
PRECISION ENGINE CONTROLS CORPORATION—See Parker Hannifin Corporation; *U.S. Public*, pg. 1643
PRECISION ENGINEERED PRODUCTS LLC - GENERAL METAL FINISHING—See NN, Inc.; *U.S. Public*, pg. 1531
PRECISION ENGINEERED PRODUCTS LLC - MICROPEP—See NN, Inc.; *U.S. Public*, pg. 1531
PRECISION ENGINEERED PRODUCTS, LLC—See NN, Inc.; *U.S. Public*, pg. 1531
PRECISION ENGINEERED PRODUCTS LLC - WAUCONDA—See NN, Inc.; *U.S. Public*, pg. 1531
PRECISION ENGINEERING, INC—See The Heico Companies, L.L.C.; *U.S. Private*, pg. 4051
PRECISION ENGINES, LLC—See Aeries Enterprises, LLC; *U.S. Private*, pg. 117
PRECISION ENTERPRISES INC—See Precision Resources Inc.; *U.S. Private*, pg. 3246
PRECISION ENVIRONMENTAL CO.; *U.S. Private*, pg. 3244
PRECISION FABRICATING & CLEANING CO—See Precision Resources Inc.; *U.S. Private*, pg. 3246
PRECISION FABRICS GROUP INC.; *U.S. Private*, pg. 3244
PRECISION FIBER OPTICS LTD.—See Fujikura Ltd.; *Int'l*, pg. 2829

PRECISION FITTING & GAUGE CO; *U.S. Private*, pg. 3245
PRECISION FLAMECUTTING AND STEEL, INC.—See Reliance Steel & Aluminum Co.; *U.S. Public*, pg. 1781
PRECISION FLOW TECHNOLOGIES, INC.—See Francisco Partners Management, LP; *U.S. Private*, pg. 1590
PRECISION FOR MEDICINE, INC.—See Precision Medicine Group, Inc.; *U.S. Private*, pg. 3245
PRECISION FOR MEDICINE—See Precision Medicine Group, Inc.; *U.S. Private*, pg. 3245
PRECISION FORMED PLASTICS, INC.—See Nefab AB; *Int'l*, pg. 5191
PRECISION FOR VALUE - NEW JERSEY—See Precision Medicine Group, Inc.; *U.S. Private*, pg. 3245
PRECISION FOUNDATIONS, INC.—See The Goldfield Corporation; *U.S. Public*, pg. 2076
PRECISION FRANCHISING LLC—See Icahn Enterprises L.P.; *U.S. Public*, pg. 1085
PRECISION GEAR HOLDINGS LLC—See Zurn Elkay Water Solutions Corporation; *U.S. Public*, pg. 2413
PRECISION GEARS, INC.—See United Stars Inc.; *U.S. Private*, pg. 4298
PRECISION GEARS LTD.—See I.M.A. Industria Macchine Automatiche S.p.A.; *Int'l*, pg. 3566
PRECISION GRINDING & MANUFACTURING; *U.S. Private*, pg. 3245
PRECISION GROUND FLAT STOCK DIVISION—See MiddleGround Management, LP; *U.S. Private*, pg. 2713
PRECISION GROUP INC.; *U.S. Private*, pg. 3245
PRECISIONHAWK INC.; *U.S. Private*, pg. 3247
PRECISION-HAYES INTERNATIONAL—See Enerpac Tool Group Corp.; *U.S. Public*, pg. 766
PRECISION HEALTHCARE, INC.—See IVX Health, Inc.; *U.S. Private*, pg. 2151
PRECISION HEALTH CARE SERVICES LIMITED—See China Biotech Services Holdings Limited; *Int'l*, pg. 1487
PRECISION HYDRAULIC CYLINDERS INC.—See Leggett & Platt, Incorporated; *U.S. Public*, pg. 1303
PRECISION HYDRAULIC CYLINDERS (UK) LIMITED—See Leggett & Platt, Incorporated; *U.S. Public*, pg. 1303
PRECISION HYDRAULICS PRIVATE LIMITED—See Leggett & Platt, Incorporated; *U.S. Public*, pg. 1303
PRECISION IBC INC; *U.S. Private*, pg. 3245
PRECISION INC.; *U.S. Private*, pg. 3245
PRECISION, INC.—See TT Electronics plc; *Int'l*, pg. 7959
PRECISION INDUSTRIES INC.—See Live Ventures Incorporated; *U.S. Public*, pg. 1332
PRECISION INDUSTRIES, INC.; *U.S. Private*, pg. 3245
PRECISION INTERCONNECT CONVERSIONS CORP.; *U.S. Private*, pg. 3245
PRECISION INTERCONNECT LLC—See TE Connectivity Ltd.; *Int'l*, pg. 7497
PRECISION INVESTMENT GROUP LLC—See Precision Environmental Co.; *U.S. Private*, pg. 3245
PRECISION KIDD STEEL CO. INC.—See Jade Steel Group, Ltd.; *U.S. Private*, pg. 2181
PRECISION KIDD STEEL CO. INC.—See Standard Horse Nail Company, LLC; *U.S. Private*, pg. 3778
PRECISION LASER SERVICES, INC.; *U.S. Private*, pg. 3245
PRECISION LIFT SERVICES LIMITED—See Analogue Holdings Limited; *Int'l*, pg. 446
PRECISION LIMITED PARTNERSHIP—See Precision Drilling Corporation; *Int'l*, pg. 5957
PRECISION LITHO, INC.—See Chatham Asset Management, LLC; *U.S. Private*, pg. 863
PRECISION LTC PHARMACY; *U.S. Private*, pg. 3245
PRECISION MACHINED PRODUCTS—See Mistequay Group Ltd.; *U.S. Private*, pg. 2750
PRECISION MACHINE MANUFACTURING CO.; *U.S. Private*, pg. 3245
PRECISION MACHINE WORKS, INC.—See Arlington Capital Partners LLC; *U.S. Private*, pg. 327
PRECISION MANUFACTURING GROUP, LLC—See American Securities LLC; *U.S. Private*, pg. 250
PRECISION MARKETING INFORMATION LIMITED—See An Post LLC; *Int'l*, pg. 443
PRECISION MECHANICAL INC.—See Precision Resources Inc.; *U.S. Private*, pg. 3246
PRECISION MEDICAL SERVICES PTE. LTD.—See Livingstone Health Holdings Limited; *Int'l*, pg. 4532
PRECISION MEDICINE GROUP, INC.; *U.S. Private*, pg. 3245
PRECISIONMED, LLC—See BioIVT, LLC; *U.S. Private*, pg. 562
PRECISION METAL FABRICATING LTD.; *Int'l*, pg. 5957
PRECISION METAL FABRICATION, INC.; *U.S. Private*, pg. 3245
PRECISION METALIKS LIMITED; *Int'l*, pg. 5957
PRECISION METAL INDUSTRIES, INC.; *U.S. Private*, pg. 3245
PRECISION METAL PRODUCTS INC.; *U.S. Private*, pg. 3245
PRECISION METROLOGY, INC.—See Ontario Municipal Employees Retirement System; *Int'l*, pg. 5585
PRECISION MICROBLENDERS INC.—See Archer-Daniels-Midland Company; *U.S. Public*, pg. 185

PRECISION METAL PRODUCTS INC.   CORPORATE AFFILIATIONS

PRECISION MOTION CONTROL PTE LTD—See ISDN Holdings Limited; *Int'l*, pg. 3813
PRECISION MOTOR CARS INC.; *U.S. Private*, pg. 3245
PRECISION MOTORCARS, INC.—See Asbury Automotive Group, Inc.; *U.S. Public*, pg. 210
PRECISION-MOTORS-DEUTSCHE-MINEBEA GMBH—See Minebea Mitsumi Inc.; *Int'l*, pg. 4905
PRECISION MOULDS, LTD.—See Mattel, Inc.; *U.S. Public*, pg. 1399
PRECISION MULTIPLE CONTROLS INC; *U.S. Private*, pg. 3245
PRECISION NANOSYSTEMS ULC—See Danaher Corporation; *U.S. Public*, pg. 630
PRECISION OILFIELD SERVICES, LLP—See Weatherford International plc; *U.S. Public*, pg. 2339
PRECISION OPTICAL TECHNOLOGIES, INC.—See Belden, Inc.; *U.S. Public*, pg. 294
PRECISION OPTICS CORPORATION, INC.; *U.S. Public*, pg. 1713
PRECISION PACKAGING INC.—See Goddard Enterprises Limited; *Int'l*, pg. 3019
PRECISION PACKAGING MATERIALS CORP.—See Solar Applied Materials Technology Corporation; *Int'l*, pg. 7069
PRECISION PACKAGING—See CRH plc; *Int'l*, pg. 1843
PRECISION PAPER TUBE COMPANY; *U.S. Private*, pg. 3246
PRECISION PARTNERS HOLDING COMPANY—See Cleveland-Cliffs, Inc.; *U.S. Public*, pg. 514
PRECISION PET PRODUCTS, INC.—See Texas Farm Products Company; *U.S. Private*, pg. 3975
PRECISION PHOTONICS CORPORATION—See IDEX Corp; *U.S. Public*, pg. 1091
PRECISION PHYSICAL THERAPY, LIMITED PARTNERSHIP—See U.S. Physical Therapy, Inc.; *U.S. Public*, pg. 2215
PRECISION PIPELINE LLC—See MasTec, Inc.; *U.S. Public*, pg. 1393
PRECISION PIPELINE SOLUTIONS, LLC.; *U.S. Private*, pg. 3246
PRECISION PIPING AND MECHANICAL INC.; *U.S. Private*, pg. 3246
PRECISION PLANTING, LLC—See AGCO Corporation; *U.S. Public*, pg. 59
PRECISION PLASTICS, INC.; *U.S. Private*, pg. 3246
PRECISION PLATING COMPANY, INC.—See Aalberts N.V.; *Int'l*, pg. 35
PRECISION PLATING INC.—See Precision Shooting Equipment Inc.; *U.S. Private*, pg. 3246
PRECISION PLUS, INC.; *U.S. Private*, pg. 3246
PRECISIONPOINT INC.—See Surveying And Mapping, LLC; *U.S. Private*, pg. 3885
PRECISION POLYMER ENGINEERING INTERNATIONAL LIMITED—See IDEX Corp; *U.S. Public*, pg. 1091
PRECISION POLYMER ENGINEERING LIMITED—See IDEX Corp; *U.S. Public*, pg. 1091
PRECISION PRESS, INC.—See Taylor Corporation; *U.S. Private*, pg. 3939
PRECISION PRESS INDUSTRIES SDN BHD (PPISB)—See Ewein Berhad; *Int'l*, pg. 2576
PRECISION PRINT CO., LTD.—See The Siam Cement Public Company Limited; *Int'l*, pg. 7683
PRECISION PRINTING, INC.—See Icahn Enterprises L.P.; *U.S. Public*, pg. 1085
PRECISION PRODUCTS GROUP, INC.—See Auxo Investment Partners, LLC; *U.S. Private*, pg. 402
PRECISION PRODUCTS, INC.—See Gleason Corporation; *U.S. Private*, pg. 1708
PRECISION PRODUCTS LTD—See Indutrade AB; *Int'l*, pg. 3680
PRECISION PRODUCTS—See Auxo Investment Partners, LLC; *U.S. Private*, pg. 402
PRECISION PUBLIC RELATIONS, INC.—See Peopletomysite.com, LLC; *U.S. Private*, pg. 3143
PRECISION PUBLISHING PAPERS LTD—See KPP Group Holdings Co., Ltd.; *Int'l*, pg. 4298
PRECISION PUNCH CORPORATION; *U.S. Private*, pg. 3246
PRECISION REALTY, LLC—See Markel Group Inc.; *U.S. Public*, pg. 1368
PRECISION RENTALS LTD.—See Precision Drilling Corporation; *Int'l*, pg. 5957
PRECISION REPORTING, INC.; *U.S. Private*, pg. 3246
PRECISION RESOURCE - CALIFORNIA—See Precision Resource Inc.; *U.S. Private*, pg. 3246
PRECISION RESOURCE CANADA LTD.—See Precision Resource Inc.; *U.S. Private*, pg. 3246
PRECISION RESOURCE - ILLINOIS—See Precision Resource Inc.; *U.S. Private*, pg. 3246
PRECISION RESOURCE INC - CANADA - CAMBRIDGE PLANT—See Precision Resource Inc.; *U.S. Private*, pg. 3246
PRECISION RESOURCE INC. - CONNECTICUT DIVISION—See Precision Resource Inc.; *U.S. Private*, pg. 3246
PRECISION RESOURCE INC. - MEXICO DIVISION—See Precision Resource Inc.; *U.S. Private*, pg. 3246
PRECISION RESOURCE INC.; *U.S. Private*, pg. 3246

PRECISION RESOURCE - KENTUCKY—See Precision Resource Inc.; *U.S. Private*, pg. 3246
PRECISION RESOURCES INC.; *U.S. Private*, pg. 3246
PRECISION ROLL GRINDERS, INC.; *U.S. Private*, pg. 3246
PRECISION RUBBER SEALINGS S.R.L.—See Freudenberg SE; *Int'l*, pg. 2790
PRECISIONRX—See Elevance Health, Inc.; *U.S. Public*, pg. 730
PRECISION SALES & SERVICE, INC.; *U.S. Private*, pg. 3246
PRECISION SAMPLERS INC.—See Standard Laboratories Inc.; *U.S. Private*, pg. 3780
PRECISIONSCIENTIA, INC.—See Precision Medicine Group, Inc.; *U.S. Private*, pg. 3245
PRECISION SHAPES, INC.—See HC Private Investments LLC; *U.S. Private*, pg. 1888
PRECISION SHOOTING EQUIPMENT INC.; *U.S. Private*, pg. 3246
PRECISION SILICON JAPAN CO., LTD.—See Episil Precision Inc.; *Int'l*, pg. 2463
PRECISION SINTERED PRODUCTS (WUXI) CO., LTD.—See Fine Sinter Co., Ltd.; *Int'l*, pg. 2673
PRECISION SOFTWARE LIMITED—See Thoma Bravo, L.P.; *U.S. Private*, pg. 4151
PRECISION SOLAR CONTROLS INC.—See New Enterprise Stone & Lime Co., Inc.; *U.S. Private*, pg. 2895
PRECISION SOUTHEAST INC.—See Gladstone Management Corporation; *U.S. Private*, pg. 1705
PRECISION SPECIALTY METALS, INC.—See Worthington Industries, Inc.; *U.S. Public*, pg. 2382
PRECISION STAFFING INCORPORATED; *U.S. Private*, pg. 3246
PRECISION STEEL SERVICES INC.; *U.S. Private*, pg. 3246
PRECISION STEEL WAREHOUSE, INC.—See Berkshire Hathaway Inc.; *U.S. Public*, pg. 315
PRECISION STRIP INC.; *U.S. Private*, pg. 3246
PRECISION STRUCTURES INCORPORATED (PSI); *U.S. Private*, pg. 3247
PRECISION STRUCTURES INC.—See Precision Structures Incorporated (PSI); *U.S. Private*, pg. 3247
PRECISION SUBSEA AS—See TE Connectivity Ltd.; *Int'l*, pg. 7495
PRECISION SURGERY CENTER, LLC—See Community Health Systems, Inc.; *U.S. Public*, pg. 556
PRECISION SWISS PRODUCTS, INC.; *U.S. Private*, pg. 3247
PRECISION SYSTEM SCIENCE CO., LTD.; *Int'l*, pg. 5958
PRECISION SYSTEM SCIENCE EUROPE GMBH—See Precision System Science Co., Ltd.; *Int'l*, pg. 5958
PRECISION SYSTEM SCIENCE USA, INC.—See Precision System Science Co., Ltd.; *Int'l*, pg. 5958
PRECISION TANK & EQUIP CO.; *U.S. Private*, pg. 3247
PRECISION TECHNOLOGIES PTE LTD—See Danaher Corporation; *U.S. Public*, pg. 626
PRECISION TECHNOLOGY INC.—See Insight Equity Holdings LLC; *U.S. Private*, pg. 2086
PRECISION TECHNOLOGY SUPPLIES LTD.—See Trifast plc; *Int'l*, pg. 7921
PRECISION TEXTILES LLC—See Chargeurs SA; *Int'l*, pg. 1449
PRECISION THERAPEUTICS, INC.; *U.S. Private*, pg. 3247
PRECISION TRADING CORP.; *U.S. Private*, pg. 3247
PRECISION TSUGAMI (CHINA) CORPORATION—See TSUGAMI CORPORATION; *Int'l*, pg. 7955
PRECISION TUBE COMPANY—See Mueller Industries, Inc.; *U.S. Public*, pg. 1485
PRECISION TUBE TECHNOLOGY INC.—See Techint S.p.A.; *Int'l*, pg. 7504
PRECISION TUBING, HYDRO ALUMINIUM JAPAN KK—See Norsk Hydro ASA; *Int'l*, pg. 5435
PRECISION TUNE AUTO CARE, INC.—See Icahn Enterprises L.P.; *U.S. Public*, pg. 1085
PRECISION TURNED COMPONENTS—See Groov-Pin Corporation; *U.S. Private*, pg. 1792
PRECISION UK LTD.—See Indutrade AB; *Int'l*, pg. 3681
PRECISION VALLEY COMMUNICATIONS OF VERMONT, LLC—See Dycom Industries, Inc.; *U.S. Public*, pg. 699
PRECISION VALVE CORPORATION—See Peak Rock Capital LLC; *U.S. Private*, pg. 3124
PRECISION VASCULAR SYSTEMS, INC.—See Boston Scientific Corporation; *U.S. Public*, pg. 375
PRECISION WALLS, INC.; *U.S. Private*, pg. 3247
PRECISION WELL SERVICING—See Precision Drilling Corporation; *Int'l*, pg. 5957
PRECISION WIRELESS LLC—See Amphenol Corporation; *U.S. Public*, pg. 132
PRECISION WIRE PRODUCTS INC.; *U.S. Private*, pg. 3247
PRECISION WIRES INDIA LTD.; *Int'l*, pg. 5958
PRECIS MARKETING; *Int'l*, pg. 5956
PRECITECH, INC.—See AMETEK, Inc.; *U.S. Public*, pg. 118
PRECITOOL-FENWICK NV—See Fuji Corporation; *Int'l*, pg. 2810
PRECIX INC.; *U.S. Private*, pg. 3247
PRECLINOMICS, INC.—See JSR Corp.; *Int'l*, pg. 4013

PRECO ELECTRONICS, LLC—See Sensata Technologies Holding plc; *U.S. Public*, pg. 1865
PRECOMP SOLUTIONS AB; *Int'l*, pg. 5958
PRECOMP SOLUTIONS EAD—See Precomp Solutions AB; *Int'l*, pg. 5958
PRECON GOIAS INDUSTRIAL LTDA.—See Eternit S.A.; *Int'l*, pg. 2521
PRE CON INC.; *U.S. Private*, pg. 3243
PRECON POLSKA SP.Z.O.O.—See Heidelberg Materials AG; *Int'l*, pg. 3319
PRE-CON PRODUCTS; *U.S. Private*, pg. 3243
PRECOR, INC.—See Peloton Interactive, Inc.; *U.S. Public*, pg. 1661
PRECOT LTD.; *Int'l*, pg. 5958
PREDATOR OIL & GAS HOLDINGS PLC; *Int'l*, pg. 5958
PREDIANA - SOCIEDADE DE PRE-ESFORCADOS S.A.—See Camargo Correa S.A.; *Int'l*, pg. 1268
PREDICA BMC SP. Z O O—See SoftwareONE Holding AG; *Int'l*, pg. 7057
PREDICA BULGARIA EOOD—See SoftwareONE Holding AG; *Int'l*, pg. 7057
PREDICA FZ LLC—See SoftwareONE Holding AG; *Int'l*, pg. 7057
PREDICA MIDDLE EAST LLC—See SoftwareONE Holding AG; *Int'l*, pg. 7057
PREDICA SP Z O.O.—See SoftwareONE Holding AG; *Int'l*, pg. 7057
PREDICTA - ADNETWORK IAS LTDA.; *Int'l*, pg. 5958
PREDICTA A.E.; *Int'l*, pg. 5958
PREDICTIV AI, INC.; *Int'l*, pg. 5958
PREDICTIVE DISCOVERY LIMITED; *Int'l*, pg. 5958
THE PREDICTIVE INDEX LLC; *U.S. Private*, pg. 4097
PREDICTIVEINTENT LTD.—See Altor Equity Partners AB; *Int'l*, pg. 395
PREDICTIVE LABORATORIES, INC.—See Predictive Technology Group, Inc.; *U.S. Public*, pg. 1714
PREDICTIVE MAINTENANCE SERVICES GROUP—See SES, LLC; *U.S. Private*, pg. 3617
PREDICTIVE ONCOLOGY INC.; *U.S. Public*, pg. 1713
PREDICTIVE SAFETY LLC; *U.S. Private*, pg. 3247
PREDICTIVE SERVICE, LLC—See Align Capital Partners, LLC; *U.S. Private*, pg. 167
PREDICTIVE SOLUTIONS SP. Z O.O.; *Int'l*, pg. 5958
PREDICTIVE TECHNOLOGY GROUP, INC.; *U.S. Public*, pg. 1713
PREDICTIVE THERAPEUTICS, LLC—See Predictive Technology Group, Inc.; *U.S. Public*, pg. 1714
PREDICTMEDIX, INC.; *Int'l*, pg. 5958
PREDIKTOR AS—See TGS ASA; *Int'l*, pg. 7587
PREDILIFE SA; *Int'l*, pg. 5958
PREDILYTICS, INC.—See Welltok, Inc.; *U.S. Private*, pg. 4478
PREDIONICA KLANJEC D.O.O.—See Linz Textil Holding AG; *Int'l*, pg. 4517
PREDISTRIBUCE A.S.—See EnBW Energie Baden-Wurttemberg AG; *Int'l*, pg. 2399
PREDSTAVITELSTVO FIRMY ENSO—See Stora Enso Oyj; *Int'l*, pg. 7225
PREDSTAVNISTVO AAK POLAND SP. Z O.O.—See AAK AB; *Int'l*, pg. 32
PREDUZECE ZA PUTEVE VALJEVO A.D.; *Int'l*, pg. 5958
PREDUZECE ZA PUTEVE ZAJECAR A.D.—See STRABAG SE; *Int'l*, pg. 7231
PREECE, INC.; *U.S. Private*, pg. 3247
PREECHA GROUP PUBLIC COMPANY LIMITED; *Int'l*, pg. 5958
PREEM AB; *Int'l*, pg. 5958
PREEMPTIVE SOLUTIONS, LLC—See HGGC, LLC; *U.S. Private*, pg. 1929
PREFA ALUMINIUMPRODUKTE S.R.O.—See CAG Holding GmbH; *Int'l*, pg. 1250
PREFABRICACIONES Y CONTRATAS, S.A.U.—See Cementos Molins S.A.; *Int'l*, pg. 1397
PREFABRICADOS DELTA, S.A.—See Fomento de Construcciones y Contratas, S.A.; *Int'l*, pg. 2723
PREFABRICADOS Y TRANSPORTES, S.A. DE C.V.—See Empresas ICA S.A.B. de C.V.; *Int'l*, pg. 2391
PREFAB TECHNOLOGY 3 PTE LTD—See Hor Kew Corporation Limited; *Int'l*, pg. 3474
PREFAB TECHNOLOGY PTE LTD—See Hor Kew Corporation Limited; *Int'l*, pg. 3474
PREFACO N.V.—See CRH plc; *Int'l*, pg. 1848
PREFA FRANCE SARL—See CAG Holding GmbH; *Int'l*, pg. 1250
PREFA GMBH—See CAG Holding GmbH; *Int'l*, pg. 1250
PREFA GRYGOV A.S.—See Heidelberg Materials AG; *Int'l*, pg. 3318
PREFA HUNGARIA KFT.—See CAG Holding GmbH; *Int'l*, pg. 1250
PREFA ITALIA SRL—See CAG Holding GmbH; *Int'l*, pg. 1250
PREFA PRO A.S.—See VINCI S.A.; *Int'l*, pg. 8225
PREFA SCHWEIZ AG—See CAG Holding GmbH; *Int'l*, pg. 1250
PREFCO DISTRIBUTION, LLC—See Palladium Equity Partners, LLC; *U.S. Private*, pg. 3078
PREFCO, INC.—See J.T. Walker Industries, Inc.; *U.S. Private*, pg. 2171

COMPANY NAME INDEX

PREFERE RESINS HOLDING GMBH—See One Rock Capital Partners, LLC; *U.S. Private*, pg. 3022
PREFERRED APARTMENT COMMUNITIES, INC.—See Blackstone Inc.; *U.S. Public*, pg. 351
PREFERRED APARTMENT COMMUNITIES OPERATING PARTNERSHIP, L.P.—See Blackstone Inc.; *U.S. Public*, pg. 351
PREFERRED AUTO CREDIT INC.—See Preferred Auto Inc.; *U.S. Private*, pg. 3247
PREFERRED AUTO INC.; *U.S. Private*, pg. 3247
PREFERRED BANCSHARES, INC.; *U.S. Private*, pg. 3247
PREFERRED BANK; *U.S. Public*, pg. 1714
PREFERRED BANK—See Preferred Bancshares, Inc.; *U.S. Private*, pg. 3247
PREFERRED BEEF GROUP; *U.S. Private*, pg. 3247
PREFERRED BENEFITS GROUP, INC.—See Aon plc; *Int'l*, pg. 497
PREFERRED BRANDS INTERNATIONAL, INC.—See Mars, Incorporated; *U.S. Private*, pg. 2590
PREFERRED CARE NETWORK, INC.—See UnitedHealth Group Incorporated; *U.S. Public*, pg. 2249
PREFERRED CARE PARTNERS HOLDING, CORP.—See UnitedHealth Group Incorporated; *U.S. Public*, pg. 2249
PREFERRED CARE PARTNERS, INC.—See UnitedHealth Group Incorporated; *U.S. Public*, pg. 2251
PREFERRED CARE PARTNERS MEDICAL GROUP, INC.—See UnitedHealth Group Incorporated; *U.S. Public*, pg. 2249
PREFERRED CHOICE MANAGEMENT SYSTEMS INC.; *U.S. Private*, pg. 3247
PREFERRED COMMERCE, INC.; *U.S. Public*, pg. 1714
PREFERRED COMPOUNDING CORP.—See HEXPOL AB; *Int'l*, pg. 3372
PREFERRED COMPOUNDING CORP. - TALLAPOOSA—See HEXPOL AB; *Int'l*, pg. 3372
PREFERRED CONCEPTS, LLC—See Stone Point Capital LLC; *U.S. Private*, pg. 3819
PREFERRED CORPORATE HOUSING; *U.S. Private*, pg. 3247
PREFERRED DATA SYSTEMS LLC; *U.S. Private*, pg. 3247
PREFERRED DENTAL TECHNOLOGIES, INC.; *Int'l*, pg. 5958
PREFERRED DISABILITY MANAGEMENT, LLC—See Rising Medical Solutions, LLC; *U.S. Private*, pg. 3440
PREFERRED ELECTRIC CO. INC.; *U.S. Private*, pg. 3247
PREFERRED EMPLOYERS INSURANCE COMPANY—See W.R. Berkley Corporation; *U.S. Public*, pg. 2318
PREFERRED FINANCIAL CORPORATION—See Health Care Service Corporation; *U.S. Private*, pg. 1892
PREFERRED FREEZER SERVICES INC.—See Bay Grove Capital LLC; *U.S. Private*, pg. 493
PREFERRED FREEZER SERVICES MIAMI, INC.—See Bay Grove Capital LLC; *U.S. Private*, pg. 493
PREFERRED FREEZER SERVICES OF HO CHI MINH CITY—See Bay Grove Capital LLC; *U.S. Private*, pg. 493
PREFERRED FREEZER SERVICES OF LINGANG LOGISTICS PARK—See Bay Grove Capital LLC; *U.S. Private*, pg. 493
PREFERRED FREEZER SERVICES OF PERTH AMBOY, LLC—See Bay Grove Capital LLC; *U.S. Private*, pg. 493
PREFERRED FREEZER SERVICES OF WAI GAO QIAO—See Bay Grove Capital LLC; *U.S. Private*, pg. 493
PREFERRED FURNITURE COMPONENTS INC.; *U.S. Private*, pg. 3248
PREFERRED GOVERNMENTAL CLAIM SOLUTIONS, INC.—See Brown & Brown, Inc.; *U.S. Public*, pg. 402
PREFERRED GROUP INC.; *U.S. Private*, pg. 3248
PREFERRED GUARDIAN INSURANCE—See GTCR LLC; *U.S. Private*, pg. 1804
PREFERRED HEALTH CARE, INC.; *U.S. Private*, pg. 3248
PREFERRED HEALTH PROFESSIONALS, INC.—See Blue Cross & Blue Shield of Kansas City, Inc.; *U.S. Private*, pg. 587
PREFERRED HEALTH SYSTEMS INC.—See Blue Cross & Blue Shield of South Carolina; *U.S. Private*, pg. 587
PREFERRED HOME HEALTH, L.P.—See Encompass Health Corporation; *U.S. Public*, pg. 758
PREFERRED HOME SERVICES, LLC; *U.S. Private*, pg. 3248
PREFERRED HOTELS GROUP; *U.S. Private*, pg. 3248
PREFERRED IMAGING, INC.—See JLL Partners, LLC; *U.S. Private*, pg. 2213
PREFERRED IMAGING OF AMARILLO, LLC—See Akumin, Inc.; *U.S. Public*, pg. 70
PREFERRED IMAGING OF AUSTIN, LLC—See Akumin, Inc.; *U.S. Public*, pg. 70
PREFERRED IMAGING OF CORINTH, LLC—See Akumin, Inc.; *U.S. Public*, pg. 70
PREFERRED IMAGING OF DENTON, LLC—See Akumin, Inc.; *U.S. Public*, pg. 70
PREFERRED IMAGING OF FORT WORTH, LLC—See Akumin, Inc.; *U.S. Public*, pg. 70
PREFERRED IMAGING OF FRISCO, LLC—See Akumin, Inc.; *U.S. Public*, pg. 70
PREFERRED IMAGING OF GRAPEVINE/COLLEYVILLE, LLC—See Akumin, Inc.; *U.S. Public*, pg. 70
PREFERRED IMAGING OF IRVING, LLC—See Akumin, Inc.; *U.S. Public*, pg. 70
PREFERRED IMAGING OF MCKINNEY, LLC—See Akumin, Inc.; *U.S. Public*, pg. 70
PREFERRED IMAGING OF MESQUITE, LLC—See Akumin, Inc.; *U.S. Public*, pg. 70
PREFERRED IMAGING ON PLANO PARKWAY, LLC—See Akumin, Inc.; *U.S. Public*, pg. 70
PREFERRED LEASING INC.—See Taylor & Martin Enterprises Inc.; *U.S. Private*, pg. 3937
PREFERRED LENDING SERVICES, LLC—See Rithm Capital Corp.; *U.S. Public*, pg. 1800
PREFERRED MARKETING SOLUTIONS, INC.—See T Enterprises, Inc.; *U.S. Private*, pg. 3909
PREFERRED MATERIALS, INC.—See CRH plc; *Int'l*, pg. 1848
PREFERRED MEALS, INC.—See Charterhouse Capital Partners LLP; *Int'l*, pg. 1455
PREFERRED MEDICAL MARKETING CORPORATION; *U.S. Private*, pg. 3248
PREFERRED MEDICAL PLAN, INC.; *U.S. Private*, pg. 3248
PREFERRED MILLWORK ENTERPRISES INC.—See McDonough Corporation; *U.S. Private*, pg. 2632
PREFERRED MOTOR SPORTS RISK PURCHASING GROUP, LLC—See Wells Fargo & Company; *U.S. Public*, pg. 2345
PREFERRED MUTUAL INSURANCE CO. INC.; *U.S. Private*, pg. 3248
PREFERRED MUTUAL INSURANCE CO.—See Preferred Mutual Insurance Co. Inc.; *U.S. Private*, pg. 3248
PREFERRED PACKAGING & CRATING, INC.; *U.S. Private*, pg. 3248
PREFERRED POPCORN LLC; *U.S. Private*, pg. 3248
PREFERRED PRODUCT NETWORK, INC.—See Principal Financial Group, Inc.; *U.S. Public*, pg. 1720
PREFERRED PRODUCTS, INC.—See United Natural Foods, Inc.; *U.S. Public*, pg. 2232
PREFERRED PROPERTIES OF VENICE INC.; *U.S. Private*, pg. 3248
PREFERRED PUMP & EQUIPMENT LP; *U.S. Private*, pg. 3248
PREFERRED REAL ESTATE GROUP INC.; *U.S. Private*, pg. 3248
PREFERRED SANDS, INC.; *U.S. Private*, pg. 3248
PREFERRED SNACKS, LLC—See Performance Food Group Company; *U.S. Public*, pg. 1675
PREFERRED SOLUTIONS, INC.; *U.S. Private*, pg. 3248
PREFERRED SYSTEMS SOLUTIONS, INC.—See Carl Marks & Co., Inc.; *U.S. Private*, pg. 763
PREFERRED TECHNOLOGY SYSTEMS, LLC.—See Source Capital, LLC; *U.S. Private*, pg. 3718
PREFERRED TRAVEL OF NAPLES INC.; *U.S. Private*, pg. 3248
PREFERRED UTILITIES MANUFACTURING CORPORATION—See PUMC Holding Corporation; *U.S. Private*, pg. 3303
PREFERRED WARRANTIES, INC.—See OPENLANE, Inc.; *U.S. Public*, pg. 1607
PREFINISHED STAINING PRODUCTS INC.—See Louisiana-Pacific Corporation; *U.S. Public*, pg. 1343
PREFLEXIBEL NV—See Wienerberger AG; *Int'l*, pg. 8405
PREFLIGHT LLC—See InterPark LLC; *U.S. Private*, pg. 2122
PREFORMADOS DE MEXICO SA—See Preformed Line Products Company; *U.S. Public*, pg. 1714
PREFORMED LINE PRODUCTS (AUSTRALIA) PTY LTD.—See Preformed Line Products Company; *U.S. Public*, pg. 1714
PREFORMED LINE PRODUCTS CANADA LTD.—See Preformed Line Products Company; *U.S. Public*, pg. 1714
PREFORMED LINE PRODUCTS COMPANY; *U.S. Public*, pg. 1714
PREFORMED LINE PRODUCTS (FRANCE) SAS—See Preformed Line Products Company; *U.S. Public*, pg. 1714
PREFORMED LINE PRODUCTS (GREAT BRITAIN) LTD.—See Preformed Line Products Company; *U.S. Public*, pg. 1714
PREFORMED LINE PRODUCTS (MALAYSIA) SDN. BHD—See Preformed Line Products Company; *U.S. Public*, pg. 1714
PREFORMED LINE PRODUCTS (SOUTH AFRICA) PTY. LTD.—See Preformed Line Products Company; *U.S. Public*, pg. 1714
PREFORMED LINE PRODUCTS (VIETNAM) LTD.—See Preformed Line Products Company; *U.S. Public*, pg. 1714
PREFORMED MARKINGS LTD—See Solix Group AB; *Int'l*, pg. 7074
PREGEN INC.—See Orient Precision Industries Inc.; *Int'l*, pg. 5622

PREMIER ANTI-AGING CO., LTD.

PREGER & WERTENTEIL, INC.; *U.S. Private*, pg. 3248
PREGIS LLC—See Warburg Pincus LLC; *U.S. Private*, pg. 4439
PREGLEM SA—See Gedeon Richter Plc.; *Int'l*, pg. 2910
PREGO S.A.—See Computer Generated Solutions Inc.; *U.S. Private*, pg. 1005
PREH DE MEXICO, S.A. DE C.V.—See Ningbo Joyson Electronic Corp.; *Int'l*, pg. 5304
PREHEAT, INC.—See Gibson Energy Inc.; *Int'l*, pg. 2963
PREH GMBH—See Ningbo Joyson Electronic Corp.; *Int'l*, pg. 5304
PREHRANA-PROMET D.D.; *Int'l*, pg. 5958
PREH SWEDEN AB—See Ningbo Joyson Electronic Corp.; *Int'l*, pg. 5304
PREI INTERNATIONAL, INC.—See Prudential Financial, Inc.; *U.S. Public*, pg. 1732
PREISER SCIENTIFIC, INC.; *U.S. Private*, pg. 3248
PREIT ASSOCIATES, L.P.—See Pennsylvania Real Estate Investment Trust; *U.S. Public*, pg. 1664
PREIT GADSDEN MALL LLC—See Pennsylvania Real Estate Investment Trust; *U.S. Public*, pg. 1664
PREIT-RUBIN, INC.—See Pennsylvania Real Estate Investment Trust; *U.S. Public*, pg. 1664
PRELAST, S.A.—See Fluidra SA; *Int'l*, pg. 2714
PRELERT INC.—See Elastic N.V.; *U.S. Public*, pg. 723
PRELIOS S.P.A.; *Int'l*, pg. 5959
PRELOAD CONCRETE STRUCTURES; *U.S. Private*, pg. 3249
PRELOADED LIMITED—See Learning Technologies Group plc; *Int'l*, pg. 4435
PRELUDE FERTILITY, INC.; *U.S. Private*, pg. 3249
PRELUDE SYSTEMS, INC.; *U.S. Private*, pg. 3249
PRELUDE THERAPEUTICS INCORPORATED; *U.S. Public*, pg. 1714
PREMAC SPOL. S.R.O.—See CRH plc; *Int'l*, pg. 1848
PREMACURE AB—See Takeda Pharmaceutical Company Limited; *Int'l*, pg. 7437
PREMARC CORPORATION; *U.S. Private*, pg. 3249
PREMARC/MARSH PRODUCTS—See Premarc Corporation; *U.S. Private*, pg. 3249
PREMARC—See Premarc Corporation; *U.S. Private*, pg. 3249
PREMA SEMICONDUCTOR GMBH; *Int'l*, pg. 5959
PREMAY EQUIPMENT L.P.—See Mullen Group Ltd.; *Int'l*, pg. 5080
PREMAY PIPELINE HAULING L.P.—See Mullen Group Ltd.; *Int'l*, pg. 5080
PREMCO GLOBAL LTD.; *Int'l*, pg. 5959
PREMCO, INC.—See NN, Inc.; *U.S. Public*, pg. 1531
THE PREMCOR PIPELINE CO.—See Valero Energy Corporation; *U.S. Public*, pg. 2272
PREMDOR CROSBY LIMITED—See Owens Corning; *U.S. Public*, pg. 1627
PREMDOR U.K. HOLDINGS LIMITED—See Owens Corning; *U.S. Public*, pg. 1627
PREMEDIA GLOBAL, INC. - NEW YORK—See PreMedia Global Pvt. Ltd.; *Int'l*, pg. 5959
PREMEDIA GLOBAL, INC. - OHIO—See PreMedia Global Pvt. Ltd.; *Int'l*, pg. 5959
PREMEDIA GLOBAL, INC.—See PreMedia Global Pvt. Ltd.; *Int'l*, pg. 5959
PREMEDIA GLOBAL PVT. LTD.; *Int'l*, pg. 5959
PREMERA BLUE CROSS; *U.S. Private*, pg. 3249
PREMERENI A.S.—See EnBW Energie Baden-Wurttemberg AG; *Int'l*, pg. 2399
PREMETALCO INC.—See Amalgamated Metal Corporation PLC; *Int'l*, pg. 409
PREMFIN PTY. LTD.—See Premier Investments Limited; *Int'l*, pg. 5960
PREMIA FINANCE S.P.A.; *Int'l*, pg. 5959
PREMIAFIT FACILITY UND IT MANAGEMENT U. SERVICE GMBH—See UNIQA Insurance Group AG; *Int'l*, pg. 8058
PREMIAFIT GMBH—See UNIQA Insurance Group AG; *Int'l*, pg. 8058
PREMIAFLEX PLASTICS LTD.—See Advanced Chemical Industries Limited; *Int'l*, pg. 158
PREMIA HOLDINGS LTD—See Kelso & Company, L.P.; *U.S. Private*, pg. 2279
PREMIAIR AVIATION MAINTENANCE PTY LTD—See Textron Inc.; *U.S. Public*, pg. 2028
PREMIA REAL ESTATE INVESTMENT COMPANY SA; *Int'l*, pg. 5959
PREMIER1 LITHIUM LTD.; *Int'l*, pg. 5962
PREMIER ACO PHYSICIANS NETWORK, LLC—See Tenet Healthcare Corporation; *U.S. Public*, pg. 2006
PREMIER ADJUSTERS, INC.—See Location Services, LLC; *U.S. Private*, pg. 2478
PREMIER AFRICAN MINERALS LIMITED; *Int'l*, pg. 5959
PREMIER AGENDAS, INC.—See SDI Innovations, Inc.; *U.S. Private*, pg. 3581
PREMIER AID INC.—See Prestige International Inc.; *Int'l*, pg. 5966
PREMIER ALUMINUM, LLC; *U.S. Private*, pg. 3249
PREMIER AMERICA CREDIT UNION; *U.S. Private*, pg. 3249
PREMIER ANTI-AGING CO., LTD.; *Int'l*, pg. 5959
PREMIER ASIAN AUTO PUBLICATIONS (M) SDN BHD—See Delloyd Ventures Sdn Bhd; *Int'l*, pg. 2014

PREMIER ASSET FINANCE LIMITED—See Paragon Banking Group PLC; *Int'l*, pg. 5736
PREMIER ASSET MANAGEMENT LIMITED—See Premier Miton Group plc; *Int'l*, pg. 5961
PREMIER ASSETS CO., LTD.—See Premier Marketing Public Company Limited; *Int'l*, pg. 5961
PREMIER ASSIST INC.—See Prestige International Inc.; *Int'l*, pg. 5966
PREMIER ASSIST NETWORK INC.—See Prestige International Inc.; *Int'l*, pg. 5966
PREMIER AT EXTON SURGERY CENTER LLC—See Tenet Healthcare Corporation; *U.S. Public*, pg. 2006
PREMIER AUTO FINANCE INC.—See Aon plc; *Int'l*, pg. 495
PREMIER AUTO TRADE PTY LTD—See Bapcor Limited; *Int'l*, pg. 857
PREMIER AVIATION SERVICES (PVT.) LTD.—See Akbar Group; *Int'l*, pg. 261
PREMIER BANKCARD, LLC—See United National Corporation; *U.S. Public*, pg. 4295
PREMIER BANK, INC.—See Premier Financial Bancorp, Inc.; *U.S. Public*, pg. 1715
THE PREMIER BANK LIMITED; *Int'l*, pg. 7676
PREMIER BANK; *U.S. Private*, pg. 3249
PREMIER BEAUTY SUPPLY INC.; *U.S. Private*, pg. 3249
PREMIER BEVERAGE COMPANY, LLC—See Breakthru Beverage Group, LLC; *U.S. Private*, pg. 643
PREMIER BEVERAGE GROUP CORP.; *U.S. Private*, pg. 3249
PREMIER BEVERAGE INC.—See Glazer's Family of Companies; *U.S. Private*, pg. 1707
PREMIER BIOMEDICAL, INC.; *U.S. Public*, pg. 1714
PREMIER BRANDS GROUP HOLDINGS LLC; *U.S. Private*, pg. 3249
PREMIER BROKERAGE SERVICES INC.—See Arthur J. Gallagher & Co.; *U.S. Public*, pg. 207
PREMIER BUILDING SYSTEMS—See Carlisle Companies Incorporated; *U.S. Public*, pg. 436
PREMIER BUSINESS & PROJECTS CO. LTD.; *Int'l*, pg. 5959
PREMIER CANNING INDUSTRY CO., LTD.—See Premier Marketing Public Company Limited; *Int'l*, pg. 5961
PREMIERCARE OF NORTHWEST ARKANSAS, LLC—See Community Health Systems, Inc.; *U.S. Public*, pg. 556
PREMIER CEMENT LIMITED—See CRH plc; *Int'l*, pg. 1848
PREMIER CEMENT MILLS LIMITED; *Int'l*, pg. 5959
PREMIER CHENNAI PROPERTIES LIMITED; *Int'l*, pg. 5959
PREMIER CHOICE HEALTHCARE LIMITED—See Brown & Brown, Inc.; *U.S. Public*, pg. 402
PREMIER COAL LIMITED—See Yankuang Group Co., Limited; *Int'l*, pg. 8562
PREMIER COIL SOLUTIONS, INC.; *U.S. Private*, pg. 3249
PREMIER COMMERCIAL, INC.—See The Scottsdale Co.; *U.S. Private*, pg. 4115
PREMIER & COMPANIES INC; *U.S. Private*, pg. 3249
PREMIER COMPONENTS DISTRBUTION CORP.—See OptConnect; *U.S. Private*, pg. 3034
PREMIER COMPUTING, INC.; *U.S. Private*, pg. 3249
PREMIER CONCEPTS LLC—See Premium Retail Services Inc.; *U.S. Private*, pg. 3252
PREMIER CONCRETE PUMPING LIMITED—See Concrete Pumping Holdings, Inc.; *U.S. Public*, pg. 566
PREMIER CONTROL TECHNOLOGIES, LTD.—See Badger Meter, Inc.; *U.S. Public*, pg. 263
PREMIER COOPERATIVE, INC.; *U.S. Private*, pg. 3250
PREMIER COOPERATIVE; *U.S. Private*, pg. 3249
PREMIER COS.; *U.S. Private*, pg. 3250
PREMIER CROWN CORP.—See Sirchie Fingerprint Labs; *U.S. Private*, pg. 3672
PREMIER DESIGN HOMES INC.; *U.S. Private*, pg. 3250
PREMIER DIAGNOSTIC HEALTH SERVICES (VANCOUVER) INC—See Premier Diversified Holdings Inc.; *Int'l*, pg. 5959
PREMIER DISTRIBUTING COMPANY—See Hensley & Co.; *U.S. Private*, pg. 1920
PREMIER DIVERSIFIED HOLDINGS INC.; *Int'l*, pg. 5959
PREMIER DODGE-CHRYSLER-JEEP—See Wilson County Automotive Dealer Group; *U.S. Private*, pg. 4530
PREMIERE BOBINE INC.—See Television Francaise 1 S.A.; *Int'l*, pg. 7543
PREMIERE CHEVROLET, INC.; *U.S. Private*, pg. 3251
PREMIERE CLASSE HOTEL—See Starwood Capital Group Global I, LLC; *U.S. Public*, pg. 3789
PREMIERE CONFERENCING E.U.R.L.—See Siris Capital Group, LLC; *U.S. Private*, pg. 3674
PREMIERE CONFERENCING GMBH—See Siris Capital Group, LLC; *U.S. Private*, pg. 3674
PREMIERE CONFERENCING (JAPAN), INC.—See Siris Capital Group, LLC; *U.S. Private*, pg. 3674
PREMIERE CONFERENCING PTE. LTD.—See Siris Capital Group, LLC; *U.S. Private*, pg. 3674
PREMIERE CONFERENCING PTY LIMITED—See Siris Capital Group, LLC; *U.S. Private*, pg. 3674
PREMIERE CONFERENCING (UK) LIMITED—See Siris Capital Group, LLC; *U.S. Private*, pg. 3674

PREMIERE EASTERN ENERGY LIMITED; *Int'l*, pg. 5962
PREMIERE EVENTS; *U.S. Private*, pg. 3251
PREMIERE GLOBAL SERVICES DENMARK APS—See Siris Capital Group, LLC; *U.S. Private*, pg. 3674
PREMIERE GLOBAL SERVICES, INC. - COLORADO SPRINGS—See Siris Capital Group, LLC; *U.S. Private*, pg. 3674
PREMIERE GLOBAL SERVICES, INC.-KANSAS—See Siris Capital Group, LLC; *U.S. Private*, pg. 3674
PREMIERE GLOBAL SERVICES, INC.—See Siris Capital Group, LLC; *U.S. Private*, pg. 3673
PREMIERE GLOBAL SERVICES ITALY SRL—See Siris Capital Group, LLC; *U.S. Private*, pg. 3674
PREMIERE GLOBAL SERVICES KOREA LTD.—See Siris Capital Group, LLC; *U.S. Private*, pg. 3674
PREMIERE GLOBAL SERVICES SWEDEN AB—See Siris Capital Group, LLC; *U.S. Private*, pg. 3674
PREMIERE GLOBAL SERVICES SWITZERLAND GMBH—See Siris Capital Group, LLC; *U.S. Private*, pg. 3674
PREMIERE HORIZON ALLIANCE CORPORATION; *Int'l*, pg. 5962
PREMIERE ISLAND POWER REIT CORPORATION; *Int'l*, pg. 5962
PREMIER ELASTIC WEBBING & ACCESSORIES (VIETNAM) CO., LTD.—See PRG Holdings Berhad; *Int'l*, pg. 5968
PREMIER ELECTION SOLUTIONS, INC.—See Lee Enterprises, Incorporated; *U.S. Public*, pg. 1298
PREMIER ELECTION SOLUTIONS, INC.—See McCarthy Group, LLC; *U.S. Private*, pg. 2626
PREMIER ELECTRICAL CORPORATION; *U.S. Private*, pg. 3250
PREMIERE LOCK COMPANY; *U.S. Private*, pg. 3251
PREMIERE MANUFACTURING, INC.—See Tupperware Brands Corporation; *U.S. Public*, pg. 2204
PREMIER ENDOSCOPY ASC, LLC—See Tenet Healthcare Corporation; *U.S. Public*, pg. 2006
PREMIER ENERGY CORP.; *U.S. Private*, pg. 3250
PREMIERE NETWORKS, INC.—See iHeartMedia, Inc.; *U.S. Public*, pg. 1096
PREMIER ENGINEERING LTD.—See Daikin Industries, Ltd.; *Int'l*, pg. 1936
PREMIER ENTERPRISE PUBLIC COMPANY LIMITED; *Int'l*, pg. 5959
PREMIER ENTERTAINMENT BILOXI, LLC—See Bally's Corporation; *U.S. Public*, pg. 268
PREMIERE PACKAGING, INC.; *U.S. Private*, pg. 3251
PREMIERE PACKAGING INDUSTRIES, INC.—See Central National Gottesman Inc.; *U.S. Private*, pg. 823
PREMIERE POST LIMITED—See LOQUS; *Int'l*, pg. 4557
PREMIER EQUIPMENT CO. INC.—See Premier Machinery Inc.; *U.S. Private*, pg. 3250
PREMIERE TRUCK CENTERS, INC.; *U.S. Private*, pg. 3251
PREMIER EXHIBITIONS, INC.; *U.S. Public*, pg. 1714
PREMIER EXPLOSIVES LTD; *Int'l*, pg. 5959
PREMIER EXPO—See Providence Equity Partners L.L.C.; *U.S. Private*, pg. 3293
PREMIER EXPO—See Searchlight Capital Partners, L.P.; *U.S. Private*, pg. 3588
PREMIER EYE CARE LLC—See H.I.G. Capital, LLC; *U.S. Private*, pg. 1833
PREMIERE FAB, INC.—See Ameripipe Supply, Inc.; *U.S. Private*, pg. 260
PREMIER FARNELL CANADA LIMITED—See Avnet, Inc.; *U.S. Public*, pg. 254
PREMIER FARNELL CORP.—See Avnet, Inc.; *U.S. Public*, pg. 254
PREMIER FARNELL ELECTRONICS DE MEXICO SRL—See Avnet, Inc.; *U.S. Public*, pg. 254
PREMIER FARNELL LIMITED—See Avnet, Inc.; *U.S. Public*, pg. 253
PREMIER FARNELL (SCOTLAND) LIMITED—See Avnet, Inc.; *U.S. Public*, pg. 254
PREMIER FARNELL UK LTD—See Avnet, Inc.; *U.S. Public*, pg. 254
PREMIER FASTENERS PTY LIMITED—See DFL Holdings Pty Ltd; *Int'l*, pg. 2095
PREMIER FEED MILLS COMPANY LIMITED—See Flour Mills of Nigeria Plc.; *Int'l*, pg. 2709
PREMIER FINANCIAL BANCORP, INC.; *U.S. Public*, pg. 1715
PREMIER FINANCIAL CORP.; *U.S. Public*, pg. 1715
PREMIER FINANCIAL SERVICES (PVT) LIMITED—See Crescent Fibres Limited; *Int'l*, pg. 1839
PREMIER FISHING & BRANDS LTD.—See African Equity Empowerment Investmts Limited; *Int'l*, pg. 191
PREMIER FOOD INDUSTRIES LTD—See Aga Khan Development Network; *Int'l*, pg. 199
PREMIER FOODS PLC; *Int'l*, pg. 5959
PREMIER FORGE GROUP, LLC—See Wynnchurch Capital, L.P.; *U.S. Private*, pg. 4578
PREMIER FUND MANAGERS LIMITED—See Premier Miton Group plc; *Int'l*, pg. 5961
PREMIER FUND; *Int'l*, pg. 5960
PREMIER GALVANIZING LIMITED—See Hill & Smith PLC; *Int'l*, pg. 3392
PREMIER GMC LTD.; *U.S. Private*, pg. 3250

PREMIER GOLD MINES LIMITED—See Equinox Gold Corp.; *Int'l*, pg. 2485
PREMIER GRAPHICS, LLC; *U.S. Private*, pg. 3250
THE PREMIER GROUP, INC.; *U.S. Private*, pg. 4097
PREMIER HAZARD LTD.—See Ecco Safety Group; *U.S. Private*, pg. 1326
PREMIER HEALTHCARE ALLIANCE, L.P.—See Premier, Inc.; *U.S. Public*, pg. 1715
PREMIER HEALTH CARE SERVICES, LLC—See Blackstone Inc.; *U.S. Public*, pg. 359
PREMIER HEALTHCARE SOLUTIONS INC—See Premier, Inc.; *U.S. Public*, pg. 1715
PREMIER HEALTH OF AMERICA, INC.; *Int'l*, pg. 5960
PREMIER HEALTH PARTNERS—See Catholic Health Initiatives; *U.S. Private*, pg. 790
PREMIER HEDSORBOARD—See Premier Paper Group Limited; *Int'l*, pg. 5961
PREMIER HOLDING CORP.; *U.S. Public*, pg. 1715
PREMIER HORTICULTURE LTD.—See Premier Tech Ltd.; *Int'l*, pg. 5960
PREMIER HYDRAULICS, LLC—See JRH Industries LLC; *U.S. Private*, pg. 2240
PREMIER INCENTIVES LIMITED—See J Sainsbury plc; *Int'l*, pg. 3852
PREMIER, INC.; *U.S. Public*, pg. 1715
PREMIER INK SYSTEMS INC.; *U.S. Private*, pg. 3250
PREMIER INN ESSEN CITY HAUPTBAHNHOF GMBH—See Whitbread PLC; *Int'l*, pg. 8398
PREMIER INN FRANKFURT CITY OSTBAHNHOF GMBH—See Whitbread PLC; *Int'l*, pg. 8398
PREMIER INN GLASGOW LIMITED—See Whitbread PLC; *Int'l*, pg. 8398
PREMIER INN HAMBURG NORDANALSTRASSE GMBH—See Whitbread PLC; *Int'l*, pg. 8398
PREMIER INN HOLDING GMBH—See Whitbread PLC; *Int'l*, pg. 8398
PREMIER INN HOTELS LIMITED—See Whitbread PLC; *Int'l*, pg. 8398
PREMIER INN (ISLE OF MAN) LIMITED—See Whitbread PLC; *Int'l*, pg. 8398
PREMIER INN (JERSEY) LIMITED—See Whitbread PLC; *Int'l*, pg. 8398
PREMIER INN LIMITED—See Whitbread PLC; *Int'l*, pg. 8398
PREMIER INN MANCHESTER AIRPORT LIMITED—See Whitbread PLC; *Int'l*, pg. 8398
PREMIER INN MANCHESTER TRAFFORD LIMITED—See Whitbread PLC; *Int'l*, pg. 8398
PREMIER INN MUNCHEN FRANKFURTER RING GMBH—See Whitbread PLC; *Int'l*, pg. 8398
PREMIER INN MUNCHEN MESSE GMBH—See Whitbread PLC; *Int'l*, pg. 8398
PREMIER INN NURNBERG CITY NORDOST GMBH—See Whitbread PLC; *Int'l*, pg. 8398
PREMIER INN STUTTGART FEUERBACH GMBH—See Whitbread PLC; *Int'l*, pg. 8398
PREMIER INSURANCE COMPANY (NEPAL) LIMITED; *Int'l*, pg. 5960
PREMIER INSURANCE CORPORATION, INC.—See GTCR LLC; *U.S. Private*, pg. 1804
PREMIER INSURANCE LIMITED; *Int'l*, pg. 5960
PREMIER INSURANCE MANAGEMENT SERVICES, INC.—See Premier, Inc.; *U.S. Public*, pg. 1715
PREMIER INSURANCE PARTNERS INC.—See Prestige International Inc.; *Int'l*, pg. 5966
PREMIER INSURANCE SERVICES INC.—See Dowling Capital Management, LLC; *U.S. Private*, pg. 1268
PREMIER INSURANCE SERVICES INC.—See Keystone Group, L.P.; *U.S. Private*, pg. 2298
PREMIER INSURANCE SOLUTIONS INC.—See Prestige International Inc.; *Int'l*, pg. 5966
PREMIER INTEGRITY SOLUTIONS; *U.S. Private*, pg. 3250
PREMIER INVESTMENTS LIMITED; *Int'l*, pg. 5960
PREMIER IRRIGATION ADRITEC INDIA—See Adritec Group International, E.C.; *Int'l*, pg. 153
PREMIER IT & PROCESS MANAGEMENT INC.—See Prestige International Inc.; *Int'l*, pg. 5966
PREMIER LEASING & FINANCE LIMITED; *Int'l*, pg. 5960
PREMIER LEASING SECURITIES LIMITED—See Premier Leasing & Finance Limited; *Int'l*, pg. 5960
PREMIER LIFE INC.—See Prestige International Inc.; *Int'l*, pg. 5966
PREMIER LIFTS HOLDINGS, INC.—See Savaria Corporation; *Int'l*, pg. 6596
PREMIER LODGE SOUTH AFRICA—See Accor S.A.; *Int'l*, pg. 92
PREMIER LOGIC INDIA PRIVATE LTD.—See Alten S.A.; *Int'l*, pg. 390
PREMIER LOGIC, LLC—See Alten S.A.; *Int'l*, pg. 389
PREMIER LOTAS NETWORK INC.—See Prestige International Inc.; *Int'l*, pg. 5966
PREMIER LTD. - CHINCHWAD PLANT—See Premier Ltd.; *Int'l*, pg. 5960
PREMIER LTD.; *Int'l*, pg. 5960
PREMIER MACHINERY INC.; *U.S. Private*, pg. 3250
PREMIER MAGNESIA, LLC; *U.S. Private*, pg. 3250
PREMIER MANUFACTURING CORPORATION—See Trive Capital Inc.; *U.S. Private*, pg. 4240

COMPANY NAME INDEX

PREMIER MANUFACTURING, INC.; *U.S. Private*, pg. 3250
PREMIER MARKETING PUBLIC COMPANY LIMITED; *Int'l*, pg. 5960
PREMIER MEDICAL CORPORATION—See New Mountain Capital, LLC; *U.S. Private*, pg. 2903
PREMIER MEDICAL GROUP LIMITED—See Capita plc; *Int'l*, pg. 1309
PREMIER MEDICAL SPECIALISTS, L.L.C.—See Tenet Healthcare Corporation; *U.S. Public*, pg. 2003
PREMIER METAL PRODUCTS CO.—See Pepco Manufacturing Company; *U.S. Private*, pg. 3143
PREMIER METAL RECYCLERS LTD—See HL Thorne & Co., Ltd.; *Int'l*, pg. 3430
PREMIER MILL CORP.—See SPX Technologies, Inc.; *U.S. Public*, pg. 1921
PREMIER MITON GLOBAL RENEWABLES TRUST PLC; *Int'l*, pg. 5961
PREMIER MITON GROUP PLC; *Int'l*, pg. 5961
PREMIER MITON INVESTORS; *Int'l*, pg. 5961
PREMIER MODULAR LIMITED—See Cabot Square Capital LLP; *Int'l*, pg. 1246
PREMIER MOLASSES COMPANY LIMITED—See Greencore Group plc; *Int'l*, pg. 3074
PREMIER MORTGAGE SERVICE LIMITED—See Aviva plc; *Int'l*, pg. 746
PREMIER MUSHROOMS LP; *U.S. Private*, pg. 3250
PREMIER NEEDLE ARTS, INC.—See Blue Point Capital Partners, LLC; *U.S. Private*, pg. 590
PREMIER NEWSPAPERS LTD—See JPIMedia Holdings Limited; *Int'l*, pg. 4006
PREMIER NUTRITION COMPANY, LLC—See Post Holdings, Inc.; *U.S. Public*, pg. 1704
PREMIER OFFICE CENTERS, LLC; *U.S. Private*, pg. 3250
PREMIER OFFICE EQUIPMENT—See Xerox Holdings Corporation; *U.S. Public*, pg. 2388
PREMIER OIL DO BRASIL PETROLEO E GAS LTDA.—See Harbour Energy plc; *Int'l*, pg. 3271
PREMIER OIL EXPLORATION LTD—See Harbour Energy plc; *Int'l*, pg. 3271
PREMIER OIL FAR EAST LIMITED—See Harbour Energy plc; *Int'l*, pg. 3271
PREMIER OILFIELD LABORATORIES LLC; *U.S. Private*, pg. 3250
PREMIER OIL GROUP LTD—See Harbour Energy plc; *Int'l*, pg. 3271
PREMIER OIL HOLDINGS LTD—See Harbour Energy plc; *Int'l*, pg. 3271
PREMIER OIL INDUSTRIES SDN. BHD.—See Paos Holdings Berhad; *Int'l*, pg. 5733
PREMIER OIL NATUNA SEA BV—See Harbour Energy plc; *Int'l*, pg. 3271
PREMIER OIL UK LTD—See Harbour Energy plc; *Int'l*, pg. 3271
PREMIER OIL VIETNAM OFFSHORE BV—See Harbour Energy plc; *Int'l*, pg. 3271
PREMIER ORTHODONTIC SPECIALISTS, PLLC; *U.S. Private*, pg. 3250
PREMIER ORTHOPAEDIC SURGERY CENTER—See HCA Healthcare, Inc.; *U.S. Public*, pg. 1006
PREMIER PACIFIC CONSTRUCTION, INC.; *U.S. Private*, pg. 3250
PREMIER PACIFIC SEAFOODS, INC.—See Maruha Nichiro Corporation; *Int'l*, pg. 4711
PREMIER PACKAGING CORPORATION—See DSS, Inc.; *U.S. Public*, pg. 689
PREMIER PAINTS PLC; *Int'l*, pg. 5961
PREMIER PAPER GROUP LIMITED; *Int'l*, pg. 5961
PREMIER PARK ASSIST INC.—See Prestige International Inc.; *Int'l*, pg. 5966
PREMIER PARTNERS, LLC—See McCarthy Bush Corporation; *U.S. Private*, pg. 2626
PREMIER PERFORMANCE, LLC—See Heartwood Partners, LLC; *U.S. Private*, pg. 1901
PREMIER PERICLASE LIMITED—See RHI Magnesita N.V.; *Int'l*, pg. 6325
PREMIER PET PRODUCTS—See Radio Systems Corporation; *U.S. Private*, pg. 3344
PREMIER PHYSICAL HEALTHCARE LIMITED—See Totally Plc; *Int'l*, pg. 7844
PREMIER PHYSICIAN SERVICES, INC.—See Blackstone Inc.; *U.S. Public*, pg. 359
PREMIER PICT PETROLEUM LTD—See Harbour Energy plc; *Int'l*, pg. 3271
PREMIER PIPE LLC—See Sumitomo Corporation; *Int'l*, pg. 7273
PREMIER PIPES LIMITED; *Int'l*, pg. 5961
PREMIER PLACEMENT MEDIA, LTD; *U.S. Private*, pg. 3250
PREMIER PLASTICS, INC.; *U.S. Private*, pg. 3250
PREMIER PL PLC—See Synergon Holding PLC; *Int'l*, pg. 7384
PREMIER POLYFILM LTD.; *Int'l*, pg. 5961
PREMIER PORTFOLIO MANAGERS LIMITED—See Premier Miton Group plc; *Int'l*, pg. 5961
PREMIER POWER RENEWABLE ENERGY, INC.; *U.S. Public*, pg. 1715

PREMIER PRECISION GROUP LLC—See Spell Capital Partners, LLC; *U.S. Private*, pg. 3754
PREMIER PRECISION GROUP - RDS FACILITY—See Spell Capital Partners, LLC; *U.S. Private*, pg. 3754
PREMIER PRINTING GROUP LIMITED—See SING TAO NEWS CORPORATION LIMITED; *Int'l*, pg. 6939
PREMIER PRINT & SERVICES GROUP INCORPORATED; *U.S. Private*, pg. 3250
PREMIER PRODUCT GROUP, INC.; *U.S. Public*, pg. 1715
PREMIER PRODUCT SALES, INC.; *U.S. Private*, pg. 3250
PREMIER PRODUCTS CO.; *U.S. Private*, pg. 3251
PREMIER PRODUCTS PUBLIC COMPANY LIMITED; *Int'l*, pg. 5961
PREMIER PUMP & SUPPLY, INC.; *U.S. Private*, pg. 3251
PREMIER PUMP & TANK CO., LTD.; *Int'l*, pg. 5961
PREMIER PURCHASING AND MARKETING ALLIANCE LLC—See ProBility Media Corporation; *U.S. Public*, pg. 1723
PREMIER QUALITY STARCH PUBLIC COMPANY LIMITED; *Int'l*, pg. 5961
PREMIER RECRUITMENT (INTERNATIONAL) UNLIMITED COMPANY; *Int'l*, pg. 5961
PREMIER RESEARCH GROUP INTERNATIONAL LTD.—See Metalmark Capital Holdings LLC; *U.S. Private*, pg. 2681
PREMIER RESEARCH INSTITUTE, INC.—See Premier, Inc.; *U.S. Public*, pg. 1715
PREMIER RESEARCH INTERNATIONAL LLC—See Metalmark Capital Holdings LLC; *U.S. Private*, pg. 2681
PREMIER RESTORATION HAWAII—See Koa Capital Partners LLC; *U.S. Private*, pg. 2325
PREMIER REVERSE CLOSINGS—See First American Financial Corporation; *U.S. Public*, pg. 838
PREMIER SALES INC.; *U.S. Private*, pg. 3251
PREMIER SEA & LAND PTE. LTD.—See MTQ Corporation Limited; *Int'l*, pg. 5072
PREMIER SECURITY SOLUTIONS CORP—See Wind Point Advisors LLC; *U.S. Private*, pg. 4535
PREMIER SERVICES, LLC—See Premier, Inc.; *U.S. Public*, pg. 1715
PREMIER SILICA LLC—See Pioneer Natural Resources Company; *U.S. Public*, pg. 1693
PREMIER SOLUTION CO., LTD.—See Chow Steel Industries Public Company Limited; *Int'l*, pg. 1584
PREMIER SOTHEBY'S INTERNATIONAL REALTY; *U.S. Private*, pg. 3251
PREMIER SPORTS & ENTERTAINMENT, INC.—See Zealot Networks, Inc.; *U.S. Private*, pg. 4599
PREMIER STAFFING, INC.—See Elwood Staffing Services, Inc.; *U.S. Private*, pg. 1377
PREMIER STATIONERY LIMITED—See Asia File Corporation Bhd.; *Int'l*, pg. 612
PREMIER STEEL DOORS & FRAMES—See ASSA ABLOY AB; *Int'l*, pg. 640
PREMIER STEEL INC.; *U.S. Private*, pg. 3251
PREMIER STRUCTURE PTE., LTD.—See NICHIREKI Co., Ltd.; *Int'l*, pg. 5270
THE PREMIER SUGAR MILLS & DISTILLERY CO., LTD.; *Int'l*, pg. 7676
PREMIER SUPPLY CHAIN IMPROVEMENT, INC.—See Premier, Inc.; *U.S. Public*, pg. 1715
PREMIER SYNTHETICS LIMITED; *Int'l*, pg. 5961
PREMIER SYSTEM ENGINEERING CO., LTD.—See Sri Trang Agro-Industry Public Company Limited; *Int'l*, pg. 7150
PREMIER TANK CORPORATION PUBLIC COMPANY LIMITED; *Int'l*, pg. 5961
PREMIER TECH BIOTECHNOLOGIES—See Premier Tech Ltd.; *Int'l*, pg. 5962
PREMIER TECH CHRONOS B.V.—See Premier Tech Ltd.; *Int'l*, pg. 5962
PREMIER TECH CHRONOS LIMITED—See Premier Tech Ltd.; *Int'l*, pg. 5962
PREMIER TECH CHRONOS S.A.—See Premier Tech Ltd.; *Int'l*, pg. 5962
PREMIER TECH CHRONOS S.R.L.—See Premier Tech Ltd.; *Int'l*, pg. 5962
PREMIER TECH ENVIRONMENT—See Premier Tech Ltd.; *Int'l*, pg. 5962
PREMIER TECH HOME & GARDEN, INC.—See Premier Tech Ltd.; *Int'l*, pg. 5962
PREMIER TECH IBEROTO, UNIPESSOAL LDA.—See Premier Tech Ltd.; *Int'l*, pg. 5962
PREMIER TECH LTD.; *Int'l*, pg. 5961
PREMIER TECHNICAL SERVICES GROUP PLC—See Macquarie Group Limited; *Int'l*, pg. 4630
PREMIER TECHNOLOGY INC.; *U.S. Private*, pg. 3251
PREMIER TECHNOLOGY PUBLIC COMPANY LIMITED; *Int'l*, pg. 5962
PREMIER TECH PRAIRIE, INC.—See Premier Tech Ltd.; *Int'l*, pg. 5962
PREMIER TECH—See Premier Tech Ltd.; *Int'l*, pg. 5962
PREMIER TECH SYSTEMS—See Premier Tech Ltd.; *Int'l*, pg. 5962
PREMIER TECH WATER FRANCE—See Premier Tech Ltd.; *Int'l*, pg. 5962

PREMIER THERMAL SOLUTIONS LLC—See Aalberts N.V.; *Int'l*, pg. 35
PREMIER TISSUES INDIA LIMITED—See Rubfila International Ltd.; *Int'l*, pg. 6422
PREMIER TRADE FRAMES LTD.—See Masco Corporation; *U.S. Public*, pg. 1391
PREMIER TRADING AG; *Int'l*, pg. 5962
PREMIER TRAILER LEASING, INC.—See Redwood Capital Investments, LLC; *U.S. Public*, pg. 3380
PREMIER TRANSPORTATION & WAREHOUSES; *U.S. Private*, pg. 3251
PREMIER TRAVELS, INC.—See Diplomat Hotel Corporation; *U.S. Private*, pg. 1234
PREMIER TRUCK GROUP OF OSHAWA—See Penske Automotive Group, Inc.; *U.S. Public*, pg. 1666
PREMIER TRUCK GROUP—See Penske Automotive Group, Inc.; *U.S. Public*, pg. 1666
PREMIER TRUST, INC.—See Reverence Capital Partners LLC; *U.S. Private*, pg. 3414
PREMIER VALLEY BANK—See Heartland Financial USA, Inc.; *U.S. Public*, pg. 1018
PREMIER VENTURES, INC.; *U.S. Private*, pg. 3251
PREMIER VISION, LLC—See Premier Exhibitions, Inc.; *U.S. Public*, pg. 1714
PREMIER WINE & SPIRITS INC.—See Cosco Capital, Inc.; *Int'l*, pg. 1809
PREMIER WIRE PRODUCTS LIMITED—See Premier Explosives Ltd; *Int'l*, pg. 5959
PREMIER WOODPROFILE SDN. BHD.—See Dominant Enterprise Berhad; *Int'l*, pg. 2161
PREMIER WORKCOMP MANAGEMENT, L.L.C.—See Blue Cross & Blue Shield of Kansas City, Inc.; *U.S. Private*, pg. 586
PREMIER X-VALUE INC.—See Prestige International Inc.; *Int'l*, pg. 5966
PREMIER YARN DYERS, INC.—See Tai Ping Carpets International Limited; *Int'l*, pg. 7408
PREMINET OY—See Elisa Corporation; *Int'l*, pg. 2361
PREMINGO GMBH—See Mountain Alliance AG; *Int'l*, pg. 5057
PREMIO COFFEE CO., LTD.—See S. ISHIMITSU & Co., LTD.; *Int'l*, pg. 6446
PREMIO FOODS, INC.; *U.S. Private*, pg. 3251
PREMIO INCORPORATED; *U.S. Private*, pg. 3251
PREMIQAMED HOLDING GMBH—See UNIQA Insurance Group AG; *Int'l*, pg. 8058
PREMIQAMED MANAGEMENT GMBH—See UNIQA Insurance Group AG; *Int'l*, pg. 8058
PREMISA—See Pristop d.o.o.; *Int'l*, pg. 5983
PREMIS CAPITAL PARTNERS, INC.—See Groupe BPCE; *Int'l*, pg. 3096
PREMISE HEALTH EMPLOYER SOLUTIONS, LLC—See Ontario Municipal Employees Retirement System; *Int'l*, pg. 5584
PREMISE IMMERSIVE MARKETING; *U.S. Private*, pg. 3251
PREMISTAR, LLC—See Partners Group Holding AG; *Int'l*, pg. 5750
PREMIUM 2000+ WARRANTIES; *U.S. Private*, pg. 3251
PREMIUM AEROTEC GMBH - AUGSBURG PLANT—See Airbus SE; *Int'l*, pg. 243
PREMIUM AEROTEC GMBH - BREMEN PLANT—See Airbus SE; *Int'l*, pg. 243
PREMIUM AEROTEC GMBH - NORDENHAM PLANT—See Airbus SE; *Int'l*, pg. 243
PREMIUM AEROTEC GMBH—See Airbus SE; *Int'l*, pg. 243
PREMIUM AEROTEC GMBH - VAREL PLANT—See Airbus SE; *Int'l*, pg. 243
PREMIUM AEROTEC SRL - BRASOV PLANT—See Airbus SE; *Int'l*, pg. 243
PREMIUM AEROTEC SRL—See Airbus SE; *Int'l*, pg. 243
PREMIUM AGENCY INC.—See Digital Hearts Holdings Co., Ltd.; *Int'l*, pg. 2122
PREMIUM ALLIED TOOL INC.—See The Hines Group, Inc.; *U.S. Private*, pg. 4053
PREMIUM ASSET CO., LTD.—See Jasmine International Public Company Limited; *Int'l*, pg. 3912
PREMIUM ASSIGNMENT CORPORATION—See IPFS Corporation; *U.S. Private*, pg. 2136
PREMIUM AUDIENCE NETWORK, SL.—See AdUX SA; *Int'l*, pg. 155
PREMIUM AUTO GLASS INC.—See s.a. D'Ieteren n.v.; *Int'l*, pg. 6448
THE PREMIUM BEER COMPANY—See Moosehead Breweries Limited; *Int'l*, pg. 5039
PREMIUM BEERS OKLAHOMA LLC; *U.S. Private*, pg. 3251
PREMIUM BEVERAGES LIMITED—See Coopers Brewery Limited; *Int'l*, pg. 1792
PREMIUM BRANDS HOLDINGS CORPORATION; *Int'l*, pg. 5962
PREMIUM BRANDS OF NORTHWEST ARKANSAS, INC.—See Franklin L. Haney Company; *U.S. Private*, pg. 1597
PREMIUM CAPITAL MARKET & INVESTMENTS LIMITED; *Int'l*, pg. 5963
PREMIUM CATERING (HOLDINGS) LIMITED; *Int'l*, pg. 5963

PREMIUM CREDIT LIMITED—See Cinven Limited; *Int'l*, pg. 1613
PREMIUM DESTINATIONS, INC.; *U.S. Private*, pg. 3251
PREMIUM DINING RESTAURANTS & PUBS LIMITED—See CK Asset Holdings Limited; *Int'l*, pg. 1635
PREMIUM DISTRIBUTORS OF MARYLAND, LLC—See Reyes Holdings, LLC; *U.S. Private*, pg. 3418
PREMIUM DISTRIBUTORS OF VIRGINIA, LLC—See Reyes Holdings, LLC; *U.S. Private*, pg. 3418
PREMIUM EDIBLE OIL PRODUCTS LIMITED—See Flour Mills of Nigeria Plc.; *Int'l*, pg. 2709
PREMIUM ENTERPRISES INC.—See Premium Transportation Staffing, Inc.; *U.S. Private*, pg. 3252
PREMIUM EXPLORATION INC.; *Int'l*, pg. 5963
PREMIUM FINANCE COMPANY (E.C.) LTD.—See Lockhart Companies Inc.; *U.S. Private*, pg. 2478
PREMIUM FINANCE CO. OF THE VIRGIN ISLANDS—See Lockhart Companies Inc.; *U.S. Private*, pg. 2478
PREMIUM FINANCIAL SERVICES CO., LTD.—See Premium Group Co., Ltd.; *Int'l*, pg. 5963
PREMIUM FLEXIBLE PACKAGING CO., LTD.—See Porn Prom Metal Public Company Limited; *Int'l*, pg. 5922
PREMIUM FLOORS AUSTRALIA PTY LIMITED—See Mohawk Industries, Inc.; *U.S. Public*, pg. 1458
PREMIUM FLOWERS CORP.; *U.S. Private*, pg. 3251
PREMIUM FOODS CO., LTD.—See R&B Food Supply Public Company Limited; *Int'l*, pg. 6168
PREMIUM GRINDING, S DE R.L. DE C.V.—See OSG Corporation; *Int'l*, pg. 5649
PREMIUM GROUP CO., LTD.; *Int'l*, pg. 5963
PREMIUM INCOME CORPORATION; *Int'l*, pg. 5963
PREMIUM INC.; *U.S. Private*, pg. 3251
PREMIUM INSPECTION & TESTING, INC.; *U.S. Private*, pg. 3252
PREMIUM LEISURE CORP.—See Belle Corporation; *Int'l*, pg. 966
PREMIUM MERIDIAN SDN. BHD.—See Perak Corporation Berhad; *Int'l*, pg. 5796
PREMIUM MORTGAGE CORPORATION; *U.S. Private*, pg. 3252
PREMIUM MOTOR CARS LLC.; *U.S. Private*, pg. 3252
PREMIUM NICKEL RESOURCES LTD.; *Int'l*, pg. 5963
PREMIUM OF NORTH CAROLINA INC.—See Premium Transportation Staffing, Inc.; *U.S. Private*, pg. 3252
PREMIUM OF TENNESSEE INC.—See Premium Transportation Staffing, Inc.; *U.S. Private*, pg. 3252
PREMIUM OILFIELD TECHNOLOGIES LLC; *U.S. Private*, pg. 3252
PREMIUM OILS & FATS SDN. BHD.—See Carson Cumberbatch PLC; *Int'l*, pg. 1347
PREMIUM PARKING SERVICE, LLC; *U.S. Private*, pg. 3252
PREMIUM PIPE SERVICES PTY LTD.—See Wangle Technologies Limited; *Int'l*, pg. 8341
PREMIUM PLASTIC SOLUTIONS LLC—See Wembly Enterprises LLC; *U.S. Private*, pg. 4480
PREMIUM.PL SP. Z O.O.—See United Internet AG; *Int'l*, pg. 8069
PREMIUM PROTEIN PRODUCTS, LLC.; *U.S. Private*, pg. 3252
PREMIUM RETAIL SERVICES INC.; *U.S. Private*, pg. 3252
PREMIUM SERVICE BRANDS LLC—See Susquehanna International Group, LLP; *U.S. Private*, pg. 3885
PREMIUM TEXTILE MILLS LIMITED; *Int'l*, pg. 5963
PREMIUM TRANSPORTATION SERVICES, INC.—See Saybrook Corporate Opportunity Fund LP; *U.S. Private*, pg. 3558
PREMIUM TRANSPORTATION STAFFING, INC.; *U.S. Private*, pg. 3252
PREMIUM TRUCK & TRAILER INC.—See Velocity Vehicle Group; *U.S. Private*, pg. 4355
PREMIUM TURF-CARE LTD.—See Iseki & Co., Ltd.; *Int'l*, pg. 3814
PREMIUM VALVE SERVICES, LLC—See Diefenthal Holdings, LLC; *U.S. Private*, pg. 1228
PREMIUM VEGITABLE OILS SDN. BHD.—See Carson Cumberbatch PLC; *Int'l*, pg. 1347
PREMIUM WATER HOLDINGS, INC.—See Hikari Tsushin, Inc.; *Int'l*, pg. 3390
PREMIX, INC.; *U.S. Private*, pg. 3252
PRE-MIX MARBLE TITE MANUFACTURING COMPANY; *U.S. Private*, pg. 3243
PREMIX-MARBLETITE MFG. CO.—See Q.E.P. Co., Inc.; *U.S. Public*, pg. 1741
PREMIX & PRECAST CONCRETE INCORPORATED—See CEMEX, S.A.B. de C.V.; *Int'l*, pg. 1400
PREMOULE INC - PORTES ET MOULURES OUELLET PLANT—See Premoule Inc; *Int'l*, pg. 5963
PREMOULE INC - PORTES EVOLUTION PLANT—See Premoule Inc; *Int'l*, pg. 5963
PREMOULE INC - PREMOULE COMPTOIRS PLANT—See Premoule Inc; *Int'l*, pg. 5963
PREMOULE INC - PREMOULE PORTES THERMO PLANT—See Premoule Inc; *Int'l*, pg. 5963
PREMOULE INC; *Int'l*, pg. 5963

PREMTEK INTERNATIONAL INC.—See Hanmi Semiconductor Co., Ltd.; *Int'l*, pg. 3256
PREMUDA (MONACO) SAM—See KKR & Co. Inc.; *U.S. Public*, pg. 1263
PREMUDA S.P.A.—See KKR & Co. Inc.; *U.S. Public*, pg. 1263
PRENATAL MOEDER EN KIND BV—See Mutares SE & Co. KGaA; *Int'l*, pg. 5105
PRENATAL RETAIL GROUP S.P.A.—See BI-Invest Advisors S.A.; *Int'l*, pg. 1016
PRENCO PROGRESS AND ENGINEERING CORPORATION LIMITED; *Int'l*, pg. 5963
PRENEED REINSURANCE COMPANY OF AMERICA—See National Guardian Life Insurance Company; *U.S. Private*, pg. 2855
PRENETCOM A.S.—See EnBW Energie Baden-Wurttemberg AG; *Int'l*, pg. 2399
PRENETICS GLOBAL LIMITED; *Int'l*, pg. 5963
PRENGER FOODS INC.; *U.S. Private*, pg. 3252
PRENGER'S INC.; *U.S. Private*, pg. 3252
PR ENGINEERING LTD.; *Int'l*, pg. 5951
PRENGLER PRODUCTS CORPORATION; *U.S. Private*, pg. 3252
PRENSAS SCHULER S.A.—See ANDRITZ AG; *Int'l*, pg. 456
PRENT CORPORATION; *U.S. Private*, pg. 3252
P&R ENTERPRISES INC.; *U.S. Private*, pg. 3059
PRENTICE CAPITAL MANAGEMENT, LP; *U.S. Private*, pg. 3252
PRENTIUM PACKAGING LLC—See Harbison Corporation; *U.S. Private*, pg. 1858
PRENTKE ROMICH COMPANY; *U.S. Private*, pg. 3252
PREOBRAZHENSKAYA BASE OF TRAWLING FLEET OAO; *Int'l*, pg. 5963
PREOL, A.S.—See Agrofert Holding, a.s.; *Int'l*, pg. 219
PREOPTIX CO., LTD.—See Delta Electronics, Inc.; *Int'l*, pg. 2018
PREOPTIX (JIANG SU) CO., LTD.—See Delta Electronics, Inc.; *Int'l*, pg. 2018
PREPACK THAILAND CO., LTD.—See Rengo Co., Ltd.; *Int'l*, pg. 5963
PRE-PAID LEGAL SERVICES, INC.—See Stone Point Capital LLC; *U.S. Private*, pg. 3825
PREPAID SERVICES PTY LIMITED—See Temasek Holdings (Private) Limited; *Int'l*, pg. 7553
PRE PAIN B.V.—See ARYZTA AG; *Int'l*, pg. 589
PREPARED INSURANCE COMPANY—See Lighthouse Property Insurance Corp.; *U.S. Private*, pg. 2453
PREPAR-VIE SA—See Groupe BPCE; *Int'l*, pg. 3099
PREPAYD, INC.; *U.S. Private*, pg. 3252
PREPERSA, PERITACION Y PREVENCION DE SEGUROS AIE—See Grupo Catalana Occidente, S.A.; *Int'l*, pg. 3124
PREPMATTERS; *U.S. Private*, pg. 3252
PREPNET; *U.S. Private*, pg. 3253
PREP SPORTSWEAR; *U.S. Private*, pg. 3252
PREPWORLD LTD—See Argent Group Europe Limited; *Int'l*, pg. 560
PREQAS AB—See MEKO AB; *Int'l*, pg. 4807
PREQAS AS—See MEKO AB; *Int'l*, pg. 4807
PRERNA INFRABUILD LTD.; *Int'l*, pg. 5964
PRESAGIS EUROPE (S.A.)—See CAE Inc.; *Int'l*, pg. 1249
PRESAGIS—See CAE Inc.; *Int'l*, pg. 1249
PRESAGIS USA INC.—See CAE Inc.; *Int'l*, pg. 1249
PRESBIA DEUTCHLAND GMBH—See Presbia PLC; *Int'l*, pg. 5964
PRESBIA PLC; *Int'l*, pg. 5964
PRESBY ENVIRONMENTAL, INC.—See Advanced Drainage Systems, Inc.; *U.S. Public*, pg. 46
PRESBYTERIAN COMMUNITY HOSPITAL INC; *U.S. Private*, pg. 3253
PRESBYTERIAN HEALTHCARE FOUNDATION; *U.S. Private*, pg. 3253
PRESBYTERIAN HEALTHCARE SERVICES; *U.S. Private*, pg. 3253
PRESBYTERIAN HOMES INC.; *U.S. Private*, pg. 3253
PRESBYTERIAN HOMES OF GEORGIA; *U.S. Private*, pg. 3253
PRESBYTERIAN HOMES OF TENNESSEE, INC.; *U.S. Private*, pg. 3253
PRESBYTERIAN HOMES & SERVICES OF KENTUCKY, INC.; *U.S. Private*, pg. 3253
PRESBYTERIAN HOMES; *U.S. Private*, pg. 3253
PRESBYTERIAN INTERCOMMUNITY HOSPITAL, INC.; *U.S. Private*, pg. 3253
PRESBYTERIAN MANORS OF MID-AMERICA INC.; *U.S. Private*, pg. 3253
PRESBYTERIAN PUBLISHING CORPORATION; *U.S. Private*, pg. 3253
PRESBYTERIAN RETIREMENT COMMUNITIES NORTHWEST; *U.S. Private*, pg. 3253
PRESBYTERIAN SENIORCARE; *U.S. Private*, pg. 3253
PRESBYTERIAN/ST. LUKE'S MEDICAL CENTER—See HCA Healthcare, Inc.; *U.S. Public*, pg. 998
PRESCIENT APPLIED INTELLIGENCE, INC.—See Repositrak Inc; *U.S. Public*, pg. 1785
PRESCIENT, INC.; *U.S. Private*, pg. 3253
PRESCIENT LIMITED—See Sithega Holdings (Pty) Ltd.; *Int'l*, pg. 6965

PRESCIENT MEDICAL, INC.; *U.S. Private*, pg. 3253
PRESCIENT MEDICINE HOLDINGS LLC; *U.S. Private*, pg. 3253
PRESCIENT THERAPEUTICS LIMITED; *Int'l*, pg. 5964
P.R.E.S.C.O. GROUP S.A.; *Int'l*, pg. 5682
PRESCOLITE INC.—See Hubbell Incorporated; *U.S. Public*, pg. 1067
PRESCOR PRODUCAO DE ESCORIAS MOIDAS, LDA.—See SODIM, SGPS, SA; *Int'l*, pg. 7049
PRESCOTT AEROSPACE, INC.; *U.S. Private*, pg. 3254
THE PRESCOTT AND NORTHWESTERN RAILROAD COMPANY—See Brookfield Infrastructure Partners L.P.; *Int'l*, pg. 1193
THE PRESCOTT AND NORTHWESTERN RAILROAD COMPANY—See GIC Pte. Ltd.; *Int'l*, pg. 2967
PRESCOTT BROTHERS, INC.; *U.S. Private*, pg. 3254
PRESCOTT HOLDINGS, INC.; *U.S. Private*, pg. 3254
PRESCOTT JONES LIMITED—See Brown & Brown, Inc.; *U.S. Public*, pg. 402
PRESCOTT NEWSPAPERS INC.—See Western Newspapers, Inc.; *U.S. Private*, pg. 4495
THE PRESCOTT & NORTHWESTERN RAILROAD CO.—See PotlatchDeltic Corporation; *U.S. Public*, pg. 1704
PRESCOTT NURSING HOME, INC.—See Welltower Inc.; *U.S. Public*, pg. 2349
PRESCOTT PRODUCTS INC.—See Melling Tool Company Inc.; *U.S. Private*, pg. 2662
PRESCOTT RESORT & CONVENTION CENTER L.P.—See W.M. Grace Development Company; *U.S. Private*, pg. 4422
PRESCOTT SECURITIES LIMITED—See Financial Index Australia Pty Ltd.; *Int'l*, pg. 2665
PRESCOTT'S, INC.—See Atlantic Street Capital Management LLC; *U.S. Private*, pg. 374
PRESCOT VETS4PETS LIMITED—See Pets at Home Group Plc; *Int'l*, pg. 5834
PRESCRIBEWELLNESS—See BlackRock, Inc.; *U.S. Public*, pg. 347
PRESCRIPTIVES INC.—See The Estee Lauder Companies Inc.; *U.S. Public*, pg. 2073
PRESCRYPTIVE HEALTH, INC.; *U.S. Private*, pg. 3254
PRESENCE FROM INNOVATION, LLC; *U.S. Private*, pg. 3254
PRESENCE HEALTH—See Ascension Health Alliance; *U.S. Private*, pg. 347
PRESENCELEARNING, INC.—See Genstar Capital, LLC; *U.S. Private*, pg. 1679
PRESENCE VERTE SA—See Groupama SA; *Int'l*, pg. 3091
PRESENTATION MINISTRIES; *U.S. Private*, pg. 3254
PRESENTATION PACKAGING—See Liberty Diversified International Inc.; *U.S. Private*, pg. 2443
PRESENTATION SERVICES, INC.—See Phase 3 Media, LLC; *U.S. Private*, pg. 3166
PRESERVATION CAPITAL PARTNERS LTD.; *Int'l*, pg. 5964
PRESERVATION NON-PROFIT HOUSING CORPORATION; *U.S. Private*, pg. 3254
PRESERVATION OF AFFORDABLE HOUSING, INC.; *U.S. Private*, pg. 3254
PRESERVATION RESOURCES—See Online Computer Library Center, Inc; *U.S. Private*, pg. 3027
PRESERVATION TECHNOLOGIES L.P.; *U.S. Private*, pg. 3254
PRESERVE, INC.—See Neogen Corporation; *U.S. Public*, pg. 1505
PRESERVE INTERNATIONAL—See Neogen Corporation; *U.S. Public*, pg. 1505
PRESERVISNF S.R.O.—See EnBW Energie Baden-Wurttemberg AG; *Int'l*, pg. 2399
PRESICARRE CORP.—See Uni-President Enterprises Corporation; *Int'l*, pg. 8028
PRESIDENT AND FELLOWS OF HARVARD COLLEGE; *U.S. Private*, pg. 3254
PRESIDENT ASSET GROUP LLC; *U.S. Private*, pg. 3254
PRESIDENT AUTOMOBILE INDUSTRIES PUBLIC COMPANY LIMITED; *Int'l*, pg. 5964
PRESIDENT BAKERY PUBLIC COMPANY LIMITED - BANGCHAN FACTORY—See Thai President Foods Public Company Limited; *Int'l*, pg. 7594
PRESIDENT BAKERY PUBLIC COMPANY LIMITED - LARDKRABANG FACTORY—See Thai President Foods Public Company Limited; *Int'l*, pg. 7594
PRESIDENT BAKERY PUBLIC COMPANY LIMITED—See Thai President Foods Public Company Limited; *Int'l*, pg. 7594
PRESIDENT CHAIN STORE CORP.—See Uni-President Enterprises Corporation; *Int'l*, pg. 8028
PRESIDENT COLLECT SERVICES CO. LTD.—See Uni-President Enterprises Corporation; *Int'l*, pg. 8028
PRESIDENT CONTAINER GROUP, INC.; *U.S. Private*, pg. 3254
PRESIDENT CONTAINER INC.—See President Container Group, Inc.; *U.S. Private*, pg. 3254
THE PRESIDENT COUNTRY CLUB INC.; *U.S. Private*, pg. 4098
PRESIDENT GLOBAL CORPORATION—See Uni-President Enterprises Corporation; *Int'l*, pg. 8029

COMPANY NAME INDEX

PRESIDENT HOTEL; *Int'l*, pg. 5964
PRESIDENT HOTEL & TOWER CO LTD.—See InterContinental Hotels Group PLC; *Int'l*, pg. 3739
PRESIDENTIAL BANK FSB - MORTGAGE DIVISION—See Presidential Bank, FSB; *U.S. Private*, pg. 3254
PRESIDENTIAL BANK, FSB; *U.S. Private*, pg. 3254
PRESIDENTIAL CENTER—See Formation Capital, LLC; *U.S. Private*, pg. 1571
PRESIDENTIAL FINANCIAL CORPORATION—See Midland Financial Co.; *U.S. Private*, pg. 2715
PRESIDENTIAL HEATING & AIR CONDITIONING, INC.—See Gryphon Investors, LLC; *U.S. Private*, pg. 1799
PRESIDENTIAL MORTGAGE CORP—See Presidential Bank, FSB; *U.S. Private*, pg. 3254
PRESIDENTIAL REALTY CORPORATION; *U.S. Public*, pg. 1715
PRESIDENT INDUSTRIAL PRODUCTS—See President Container Group, Inc.; *U.S. Private*, pg. 3254
PRESIDENT INTERNATIONAL DEVELOPMENT CORP—See Uni-President Enterprises Corporation; *Int'l*, pg. 8029
PRESIDENT KIKKOMAN, INC.—See Kikkoman Corporation; *Int'l*, pg. 4161
PRESIDENT KOURAKUEN CO., LTD.—See Thai President Foods Public Company Limited; *Int'l*, pg. 7594
PRESIDENT MUSASHINO CORP.—See Uni-President Enterprises Corporation; *Int'l*, pg. 8028
PRESIDENT NATURAL INDUSTRIAL CORP.—See Uni-President Enterprises Corporation; *Int'l*, pg. 8029
PRESIDENT NISSHIN CORP.—See The Nisshin OilliO Group, Ltd.; *Int'l*, pg. 7671
PRESIDENT PACKAGING INDUSTRIAL CORP.—See Uni-President Enterprises Corporation; *Int'l*, pg. 8029
PRESIDENT PHARMACEUTICAL CORP.—See Uni-President Enterprises Corporation; *Int'l*, pg. 8028
PRESIDENT'S CHOICE BANK—See George Weston Limited; *Int'l*, pg. 2938
PRESIDENT TOKYO CORP.—See Uni-President Enterprises Corporation; *Int'l*, pg. 8029
PRESIDENT TRANSNET CORP.—See Uni-President Enterprises Corporation; *Int'l*, pg. 8028
PRESIDENT YILAN ART AND CULTURE CORP.—See Uni-President Enterprises Corporation; *Int'l*, pg. 8028
PRESIDIO BENEFITS GROUP, INC.—See Marsh & McLennan Companies, Inc.; *U.S. Public*, pg. 1382
PRESIDIO - CALEDONIA—See BC Partners LLP; *Int'l*, pg. 925
THE PRESIDIO GROUP, INC.—See Arthur J. Gallagher & Co.; *U.S. Public*, pg. 203
THE PRESIDIO GROUP LLC; *U.S. Private*, pg. 4098
PRESIDIO HEALTH ASSOCIATES LLC—See The Ensign Group, Inc.; *U.S. Public*, pg. 2072
PRESIDIO, INC.—See BC Partners LLP; *Int'l*, pg. 925
PRESIDIO INVESTORS LLC; *U.S. Private*, pg. 3254
PRESIDIO - LEWISVILLE—See BC Partners LLP; *Int'l*, pg. 925
PRESIDIO - NORCROSS—See BC Partners LLP; *Int'l*, pg. 925
PRESIDIO PARTNERS; *U.S. Private*, pg. 3255
PRESIDIO PHARMACEUTICALS, INC.—See Panorama Capital Corp.; *U.S. Private*, pg. 1636
PRESIDIO PROPERTY TRUST, INC.; *U.S. Public*, pg. 1716
PRESILIENT, LLC; *U.S. Private*, pg. 3255
PRESLEY GROUP LTD; *U.S. Private*, pg. 3255
PRESONA AB; *Int'l*, pg. 5964
PRESONA DEUTSCHLAND GMBH—See Presona AB; *Int'l*, pg. 5964
PRESONA SERVICE GMBH—See Presona AB; *Int'l*, pg. 5964
PRESONA UK LTD—See Presona AB; *Int'l*, pg. 5964
PRESONUS AUDIO ELECTRONICS, INC.; *U.S. Private*, pg. 3255
PRESORT SOLUTIONS; *U.S. Private*, pg. 3255
PRESPERSE, INC.—See Sumitomo Corporation; *Int'l*, pg. 7273
PRESQUE ISLE DOWNS, INC.—See Churchill Downs, Inc.; *U.S. Public*, pg. 494
PRESQUE ISLE ELECTRIC & GAS CO-OP; *U.S. Private*, pg. 3255
PRESQU'ILE ENVIRONNEMENT SAS—See VINCI S.A.; *Int'l*, pg. 8225
PRESRAY CORP.—See Pawling Corporation; *U.S. Private*, pg. 3115
PRESRITE CORPORATION; *U.S. Private*, pg. 3255
PRESSANCE CORPORATION—See Open House Group Co., Ltd.; *Int'l*, pg. 5596
PRESS AND SINTER TECHNICS DE MEXICO, S.A. DE C.V.—See BC Partners LLP; *Int'l*, pg. 923
PRESSAN MADENI ESYA SAN. VE TICARET A.S.—See Brose Fahrzeugteile GmbH & Co. KG; *Int'l*, pg. 1196
PRESS AUTOMATION TECHNOLOGY PTE LTD—See Patec Precision Industry Co., Ltd.; *Int'l*, pg. 5755
PRESSBURG, LLC—See Citizen Energy Operating LLC; *U.S. Private*, pg. 902
PRESSCANE LIMITED—See Press Corporation Limited; *Int'l*, pg. 5964

PRESS-CITIZEN COMPANY INC.—See Gannett Co., Inc.; *U.S. Public*, pg. 899
PRESS COMMUNICATIONS, LLC; *U.S. Private*, pg. 3255
PRESS CORPORATION LIMITED; *Int'l*, pg. 5964
PRESS CORPORATION PLC; *Int'l*, pg. 5964
PRESSCO TECHNOLOGY INC.; *U.S. Private*, pg. 3255
PRESSCRETE ENGINEERING PTE LTD—See LIM WEN HENG CONSTRUCTION PTE LTD; *Int'l*, pg. 4498
THE PRESS DEMOCRAT—See Gannett Co., Inc.; *U.S. Public*, pg. 905
PRESSED PAPERBOARD TECHNOLOGIES, LLC—See May River Capital, LLC; *U.S. Private*, pg. 2620
PRESSE-DRUCK- UND VERLAGS-GMBH; *Int'l*, pg. 5965
PRESSE IMPORT SA—See Vivendi SE; *Int'l*, pg. 8276
PRESSEL POST B.V.B.A.—See Sycamore Partners Management, LP; *U.S. Private*, pg. 3897
PRESSEL SP.Z.O.O.—See Sycamore Partners Management, LP; *U.S. Private*, pg. 3897
PRESSEL VERSAND GMBH—See Sycamore Partners Management, LP; *U.S. Private*, pg. 3897
PRESSEL VERSAND INTERNATIONAL GMBH—See Sycamore Partners Management, LP; *U.S. Private*, pg. 3897
PRESSENGE MAQUINAS LTDA.—See Sintokogio Ltd.; *Int'l*, pg. 6958
PRESSENSYSTEME SCHULER-MEXICO, S.A. DE C.V.—See ANDRITZ AG; *Int'l*, pg. 456
PRESS-ENTERPRISE INC.; *U.S. Private*, pg. 3255
THE PRESS-ENTERPRISE—See Alden Global Capital LLC; *U.S. Private*, pg. 158
PRESSERVICE LJUNGBY AB—See Smalandsstenars Mekaniska Verkstad - SMV Industrier AB; *Int'l*, pg. 6999
PRESSE-SERVICE GULL GMBH—See Deutsche Post AG; *Int'l*, pg. 2082
PRESSE-VERTRIEB HERMANN TRUNK GMBH & CO. KG; *Int'l*, pg. 5965
PRESS GANEY ASSOCIATES, INC.—See Ares Management Corporation; *U.S. Public*, pg. 190
PRESS GANEY ASSOCIATES, INC.—See Leonard Green & Partners, L.P.; *U.S. Private*, pg. 2427
PRESS GANEY HOLDINGS, INC.—See Ares Management Corporation; *U.S. Public*, pg. 190
PRESS GANEY HOLDINGS, INC.—See Leonard Green & Partners, L.P.; *U.S. Private*, pg. 2427
PRESS & GUIDE—See Alden Global Capital LLC; *U.S. Private*, pg. 157
PRESS KOGYO CO., LTD. - ONOMICHI PLANT—See Press Kogyo Co., Ltd.; *Int'l*, pg. 5964
PRESS KOGYO CO., LTD. - SAITAMA PLANT—See Press Kogyo Co., Ltd.; *Int'l*, pg. 5964
PRESS KOGYO CO., LTD.; *Int'l*, pg. 5964
PRESS KOGYO CO., LTD. - UTSUNOMIYA PLANT—See Press Kogyo Co., Ltd.; *Int'l*, pg. 5964
PRESS KOGYO MINI CABIN (SUZHOU) CO., LTD.—See Press Kogyo Co., Ltd.; *Int'l*, pg. 5964
PRESS KOGYO SWEDEN AB—See Press Kogyo Co., Ltd.; *Int'l*, pg. 5965
PRESSLITE LTD—See Sertec Group Holdings Ltd.; *Int'l*, pg. 6724
PRESSL, SPOL. S R.O.—See FERMAT Group, a.s.; *Int'l*, pg. 2639
PRESSMAN ADVERTISING LIMITED—See Signpost India Limited; *Int'l*, pg. 6912
PRESSMAN-GUTMAN CO. INC.; *U.S. Private*, pg. 3255
PRESSMAN TOY CORPORATION; *U.S. Private*, pg. 3255
PRESSMART MEDIA LTD.; *Int'l*, pg. 5965
PRESSMASTER GMBH—See Investment AB Latour; *Int'l*, pg. 3782
PRESSMASTERS INC.; *U.S. Private*, pg. 3255
PRESS METAL ALUMINIUM HOLDINGS BHD; *Int'l*, pg. 5965
PRESS METAL BERHAD—See Press Metal Aluminium Holdings Bhd; *Int'l*, pg. 5965
PRESS METAL BINTULU SDN BHD—See Press Metal Aluminium Holdings Bhd; *Int'l*, pg. 5965
PRESS METAL INTERNATIONAL (HUBEI) LTD.—See Press Metal Aluminium Holdings Bhd; *Int'l*, pg. 5965
PRESSMETALL GUNZENHAUSEN GMBH & CO. KG—See CMP Capital Management-Partners GmbH; *Int'l*, pg. 1671
PRESS METAL SARAWAK SDN. BHD.—See Press Metal Aluminium Holdings Bhd; *Int'l*, pg. 5965
PRESS METAL UK LIMITED—See Press Metal Aluminium Holdings Bhd; *Int'l*, pg. 5965
PRESSOR; *Int'l*, pg. 5965
PRESSPART MANUFACTURING LTD.—See Heitkamp & Thumann KG; *Int'l*, pg. 3326
PRESSPART MANUFACTURING S.A.—See Heitkamp & Thumann KG; *Int'l*, pg. 3326
PRESS PARTS OUTLET GMBH—See Heidelberger Druckmaschinen AG; *Int'l*, pg. 3322
PRESS POINT INTERNATIONAL—See Vivendi SE; *Int'l*, pg. 8276
PRESS PROPERTIES LIMITED—See Press Corporation Plc; *Int'l*, pg. 5964
PRESS-REPUBLICAN—See The Retirement Systems of Alabama; *U.S. Private*, pg. 4105
PRESS SHOP ALG SA—See Vivendi SE; *Int'l*, pg. 8276

PRESS & SUN-BULLETIN—See Gannett Co., Inc.; *U.S. Public*, pg. 899
PRESSTEK EUROPE LTD.—See Mark Andy, Inc.; *U.S. Private*, pg. 2577
PRESSTEK LLC—See Mark Andy, Inc.; *U.S. Private*, pg. 2577
PRESSTONIC ENGINEERING LIMITED; *Int'l*, pg. 5965
THE PRESS-TRIBUNE—See Brehm Communications Inc.; *U.S. Private*, pg. 644
THE PRESS TRUST OF INDIA LIMITED; *Int'l*, pg. 7676
PRESSURE BIOSCIENCES, INC.; *U.S. Public*, pg. 1716
PRESSURE CHEMICAL CO.—See Minafin Sarl; *Int'l*, pg. 4899
PRESSURE COMPRESSORES LTDA.—See Atlas Copco AB; *Int'l*, pg. 684
PRESSURE ENGINEERING INTERNATIONAL LTD—See Langley Holdings Plc; *Int'l*, pg. 4410
PRESSURE PRODUCTS SDN. BHD.—See HupSteel Limited; *Int'l*, pg. 3538
PRESSURE-PRO, INC.—See NKT A/S; *Int'l*, pg. 5391
PRESSURE SYSTEMS INTERNATIONAL, INC.—See Genstar Capital, LLC; *U.S. Private*, pg. 1676
PRESSURE TECHNOLOGIES PLC; *Int'l*, pg. 5965
PRESSURE THERMAL DYNAMICS B.V.—See BENCIS Capital Partners B.V.; *Int'l*, pg. 970
PRESSWERK KREFELD GMBH & CO. KG—See HANNOVER Finanz GmbH; *Int'l*, pg. 3257
PRESTA CONTRACTORS SUPPLY, INC.—See Leonard Green & Partners, L.P.; *U.S. Private*, pg. 2429
PRESTADORA DE SERVICIOS INDUSTRIALES DE PERSONAL, S.A. DE R.L. DE C.V.—See Avient Corporation; *U.S. Public*, pg. 248
PRESTADORA DE SERVICIOS RELOJEROS SA DE CV—See The Swatch Group Ltd.; *Int'l*, pg. 7692
PRESTAGON LLC; *U.S. Private*, pg. 3255
PRESTAR ENGINEERING SDN. BHD.—See Prestar Resources Berhad; *Int'l*, pg. 5965
PRESTAR GALVANISING SDN. BHD.—See Prestar Resources Berhad; *Int'l*, pg. 5965
PRESTAR MANUFACTURING SDN. BHD.—See Prestar Resources Berhad; *Int'l*, pg. 5965
PRESTAR MARKETING SDN. BHD.—See Prestar Resources Berhad; *Int'l*, pg. 5965
PRESTAR PRECISION TUBE SDN. BHD.—See Prestar Resources Berhad; *Int'l*, pg. 5966
PRESTAR RESOURCES BERHAD; *Int'l*, pg. 5965
PRESTAR STEEL PIPES SDN. BHD.—See Prestar Resources Berhad; *Int'l*, pg. 5966
PRESTAR STORAGE SYSTEM SDN. BHD.—See Prestar Resources Berhad; *Int'l*, pg. 5966
PRES-T-CON LIMITED—See Massy Holdings Ltd.; *Int'l*, pg. 4724
PRESTEEL OY—See SSAB AB; *Int'l*, pg. 7153
PRESTEIGNE CHARTER LIMITED—See Presteigne Limited; *Int'l*, pg. 5966
PRESTEIGNE LIMITED; *Int'l*, pg. 5966
PRESTEL PUBLISHING LIMITED—See Bertelsmann SE & Co. KGaA; *Int'l*, pg. 993
PRESTERA CENTER; *U.S. Private*, pg. 3255
PRESTEVE FOODS LIMITED.; *Int'l*, pg. 5966
PRESTICINQUE S.P.A.—See BPER BANCA S.p.A.; *Int'l*, pg. 1132
PRESTIGE ASSURANCE PLC—See The New India Assurance Company Limited; *Int'l*, pg. 7670
PRESTIGE AUTO TRADERS AUSTRALIA PTY LTD—See Autosports Group Limited; *Int'l*, pg. 732
PRESTIGE BIOLOGICS CO. LTD.; *Int'l*, pg. 5966
PRESTIGE BOX CORPORATION; *U.S. Private*, pg. 3255
PRESTIGE BUILDING COMPANY—See The Michael's Development Company Inc.; *U.S. Private*, pg. 4079
PRESTIGE CAPITAL CORPORATION; *U.S. Private*, pg. 3255
PRESTIGE CAPITAL CORP.—See Forest Investments, Inc.; *U.S. Private*, pg. 1567
PRESTIGE CARS INTERNATIONAL, INC.; *U.S. Public*, pg. 1716
PRESTIGE CHRYSLER DODGE INC.; *U.S. Private*, pg. 3255
PRESTIGE & COLLECTIONS INTERNATIONAL SNC—See L'Oreal S.A.; *Int'l*, pg. 4381
PRESTIGE COMMUNICATIONS PVT. LTD.—See WPP plc; *Int'l*, pg. 8472
PRESTIGE CONSUMER HEALTHCARE INC.; *U.S. Public*, pg. 1716
PRESTIGE CORP.; *U.S. Private*, pg. 3255
PRESTIGE COSMETICS CORP.; *U.S. Private*, pg. 3256
PRESTIGE CRUISE HOLDINGS, INC—See Norwegian Cruise Line Holdings Ltd.; *U.S. Public*, pg. 1543
PRESTIGE CRUISES INTERNATIONAL, INC.—See Norwegian Cruise Line Holdings Ltd.; *U.S. Public*, pg. 1543
PRESTIGE DELIVERY SYSTEMS INC.; *U.S. Private*, pg. 3256
PRESTIGE EMBROIDERY CO., LTD.—See TPCS Public Company Limited; *Int'l*, pg. 7883
PRESTIGE EMPLOYEE ADMINISTRATORS, LLC—See TriSpan LLP; *Int'l*, pg. 7927
PRESTIGE ENTERPRISE INTERNATIONAL, INC.; *U.S. Private*, pg. 3256
PRESTIGE ESTATES PROJECTS LTD.; *Int'l*, pg. 5966

PRESTIGE ESTATES PROJECTS LTD.   CORPORATE AFFILIATIONS

PRESTIGE ET COLLECTIONS INTER. & CIE.—See L'Oreal S.A.; *Int'l*, pg. 4381
PRESTIGE FABRICATORS INC.—See Monomoy Capital Partners LLC; *U.S. Private*, pg. 2772
PRESTIGE FARMS INC.; *U.S. Private*, pg. 3256
PRESTIGE FINANCE LIMITED—See OneSavings Bank plc; *Int'l*, pg. 5577
PRESTIGE FORTUNE SDN. BHD.—See Leong Hup International Berhad; *Int'l*, pg. 4461
PRESTIGE HEALTH CHOICE LLC—See GuideWell Mutual Holding Corporation; *U.S. Private*, pg. 1814
PRESTIGE HOME CENTERS, INC.—See Nobility Homes, Inc.; *U.S. Public*, pg. 1531
PRESTIGE HUMANSOLUTION INC.—See Prestige International Inc.; *Int'l*, pg. 5966
PRESTIGE INTERNACIONAL DO BRASIL LTDA.—See Prestige International Inc.; *Int'l*, pg. 5966
PRESTIGE INTERNACIONAL MEXICO LTDA.—See Prestige International Inc.; *Int'l*, pg. 5966
PRESTIGE INTERNATIONAL AUSTRALIA PTY. LTD.—See Prestige International Inc.; *Int'l*, pg. 5967
PRESTIGE INTERNATIONAL CHINA CO., LTD.—See Prestige International Inc.; *Int'l*, pg. 5967
PRESTIGE INTERNATIONAL (HK) CO., LTD.—See Prestige International Inc.; *Int'l*, pg. 5966
PRESTIGE INTERNATIONAL INC.; *Int'l*, pg. 5966
PRESTIGE INTERNATIONAL MANAGEMENT PTE. LTD.—See Advancer Global Limited; *Int'l*, pg. 163
PRESTIGE INTERNATIONAL (M) SDN. BHD.—See Prestige International Inc.; *Int'l*, pg. 5966
PRESTIGE INTERNATIONAL (S) PTE. LTD.—See Prestige International Inc.; *Int'l*, pg. 5966
PRESTIGE INTERNATIONAL (TAIWAN) CO., LIMITED—See Prestige International Inc.; *Int'l*, pg. 5966
PRESTIGE INTERNATIONAL (THAILAND) CO., LTD.—See Prestige International Inc.; *Int'l*, pg. 5966
PRESTIGE INTERNATIONAL U.K. LTD.—See Prestige International Inc.; *Int'l*, pg. 5967
PRESTIGE INTERNATIONAL USA, INC.—See Prestige International Inc.; *Int'l*, pg. 5967
PRESTIGE INTERNATIONAL VIETNAM CO., LTD.—See Prestige International Inc.; *Int'l*, pg. 5967
PRESTIGE MEDICAL IMAGING LLC—See Atlantic Street Capital Management LLC; *U.S. Private*, pg. 374
PRESTIGE MEDICAL LIMITED—See National Industries Group Holding S.A.K.; *Int'l*, pg. 5159
PRESTIGE MOTORS, INC.; *U.S. Private*, pg. 3256
PRESTIGE MOTORS, INC.—See Prestige Motors, Inc.; *U.S. Private*, pg. 3256
PRESTIGE MOTORWORKS INC.; *U.S. Private*, pg. 3256
PRESTIGE OF BERGEN INC.; *U.S. Private*, pg. 3256
PRESTIGE PET PRODUCTS, INC.—See For The Earth Corp.; *U.S. Public*, pg. 864
PRESTIGE PHYSICAL THERAPY, LIMITED PARTNERSHIP—See U.S. Physical Therapy, Inc.; *U.S. Public*, pg. 2215
PRESTIGE PONTIAC BUICK GMC; *U.S. Private*, pg. 3256
PRESTIGE SERVICES CORP.—See Prestige Consumer Healthcare Inc.; *U.S. Public*, pg. 1716
PRESTIGE SERVICES INC.; *U.S. Private*, pg. 3256
PRESTIGE STAFFING; *U.S. Private*, pg. 3256
PRESTIGE STAMPING, INC.—See Auxo Investment Partners, LLC; *U.S. Private*, pg. 402
PRESTIGE TOY CORP; *U.S. Private*, pg. 3256
PRESTIGE TRAVEL, INC.; *U.S. Private*, pg. 3256
PRESTIGE TRAVEL, INC.; *U.S. Private*, pg. 3256
PRESTIGE TRAVEL SYSTEMS, INC.; *U.S. Private*, pg. 3256
PRESTIGE VOLKSWAGEN; *U.S. Private*, pg. 3256
PRESTIGE WEALTH INC.; *Int'l*, pg. 5967
PRESTIGE WHOLESALE INC.; *U.S. Private*, pg. 3256
PRESTIGE WINES DISTRIBUTORS, LLC—See Breakthru Beverage Group, LLC; *U.S. Private*, pg. 643
PRESTIGE YACHT SALES INC.; *U.S. Private*, pg. 3256
PRESTIGIO EUROPE SPOL. S.R.O.—See ASBISc Enterprises Plc; *Int'l*, pg. 600
PRESTIGIO PLAZA LTD.—See ASBISc Enterprises Plc; *Int'l*, pg. 600
PRESTINTER—See Groupe Crit, S.A.; *Int'l*, pg. 3101
PRESTITALIA S.P.A.—See Intesa Sanpaolo S.p.A.; *Int'l*, pg. 3766
PRESTIUM PHARMA, INC.—See Viatris Inc.; *U.S. Public*, pg. 2294
PREST, LLC—See Danaher Corporation; *U.S. Public*, pg. 630
PRESTO ABSORBENT PRODUCTS, INC.—See Drylock Technologies NV; *Int'l*, pg. 2207
PRESTO AUTOMATION, INC; *U.S. Public*, pg. 1716
PRESTO FOOD STORES, INC.; *U.S. Private*, pg. 3256
PRESTO LIFTS INC.—See Allied Systems Company; *U.S. Private*, pg. 188
PRESTOLITE ELECTRIC INCORPORATED—See Zhongshan Broad-Ocean Motor Co., Ltd.; *Int'l*, pg. 8674
PRESTON BENNETT LIMITED—See The Skipton Building Society; *Int'l*, pg. 7687
PRESTON CHEVROLET BUICK GMC CADILLAC LTD.; *Int'l*, pg. 5967

PRESTON CHEVROLET CADILLAC KIA INC.; *U.S. Private*, pg. 3256
PRESTONE PRODUCTS CORP.—See Centerbridge Partners, L.P.; *U.S. Private*, pg. 815
PRESTON FORD INC.; *U.S. Private*, pg. 3256
PRESTON HOLLOW COMMUNITY CAPITAL, INC.; *U.S. Public*, pg. 1716
PRESTON HOTEL (BMG) PTY LTD—See Woolworths Group Limited; *Int'l*, pg. 8451
PRESTON KELLY, INC.; *U.S. Private*, pg. 3256
PRESTON KINETIC—See DynamicSignals LLC; *U.S. Private*, pg. 1299
PRESTON LAKE REALTY—See Presidential Realty Corporation; *U.S. Public*, pg. 1716
PRESTON MEATS INC; *U.S. Private*, pg. 3256
PRESTON MEMORIAL HOMECARE, LLC—See UnitedHealth Group Incorporated; *U.S. Public*, pg. 2246
PRESTON MEMORIAL HOSPITAL; *U.S. Private*, pg. 3256
PRESTON NORTH END FOOTBALL CLUB LIMITED—See Preston North End plc; *Int'l*, pg. 5967
PRESTON NORTH END PLC; *Int'l*, pg. 5967
THE PRESTON PARTNERSHIP, LLC; *U.S. Private*, pg. 4098
PRESTON REFRIGERATION COMPANY INC.; *U.S. Private*, pg. 3257
PRESTON REFRIGERATION LIMITED—See Johnson Controls International plc; *Int'l*, pg. 3986
PRESTON VINEYARDS, INC.; *U.S. Private*, pg. 3257
PRESTONWOOD GOLF CLUB LLC—See Apollo Global Management, Inc.; *U.S. Public*, pg. 150
PRESTO PRESSE-VERTRIEBS AG—See Die Schweizerische Post AG; *Int'l*, pg. 2113
PRESTORAC SAS—See Aalberts N.V.; *Int'l*, pg. 35
PRESTOSIM, INC.—See CAE Inc.; *Int'l*, pg. 1249
PRESTOSIM, INC.—See Directional Capital LLC; *U.S. Private*, pg. 1236
PRESTOSPORTS, INC.—See Clubessential Holdings, LLC; *U.S. Private*, pg. 949
PRESTRESS SERVICES INDUSTRIES LLC; *U.S. Private*, pg. 3257
PRESUSCUBE CORPORATION—See Medipal Holdings Corporation; *Int'l*, pg. 4779
PRET A MANGER (EUROPE) LTD—See JAB Holding Company S.a.r.l.; *Int'l*, pg. 3863
PRET A MANGER (HONG KONG) LTD—See JAB Holding Company S.a.r.l.; *Int'l*, pg. 3864
PRET A MANGER—See JAB Holding Company S.a.r.l.; *Int'l*, pg. 3864
PRETEC CO., LTD.—See Tazmo Co., Ltd.; *Int'l*, pg. 7479
PRE-TECH CO., LTD.; *Int'l*, pg. 5955
PRETECT AS—See Gentian Diagnostics AS; *Int'l*, pg. 2928
PRETERSA-PRENAVISA ESTRUCTURAS DE HORMIGON S.L.—See Magnum Industrial Partners, S.L.; *Int'l*, pg. 4642
THE PRETESTING COMPANY, INC.; *U.S. Private*, pg. 4098
PRETEX TEXTILHANDELS GMBH—See French Connection Group plc; *Int'l*, pg. 2772
PRETIUM PACKAGING CORPORATION—See Clearlake Capital Group, L.P.; *U.S. Private*, pg. 937
PRETIUM PACKAGING - MANCHESTER—See Clearlake Capital Group, L.P.; *U.S. Private*, pg. 937
PRETIUM PACKAGING - PHILMONT—See Clearlake Capital Group, L.P.; *U.S. Private*, pg. 937
PRETIUM PARTNERS, LLC; *U.S. Private*, pg. 3257
PRETIUM RESOURCES INC.—See Newmont Corporation; *U.S. Public*, pg. 1517
PRETORIA PORTLAND CEMENT CO. LTD.—See Barloworld Ltd.; *Int'l*, pg. 866
PRETTYPORTERS CO., LTD.—See Senko Group Holdings Co., Ltd.; *Int'l*, pg. 6710
PRETTYWORK CREATIVE LLC—See CCL Industries Inc.; *Int'l*, pg. 1368
PRETZELS, INC.—See J&J Snack Foods Corporation; *U.S. Public*, pg. 1180
PRETZELS, INC.—See Peak Rock Capital LLC; *U.S. Private*, pg. 3124
PREUSSENELEKTRA GMBH—See E.ON SE; *Int'l*, pg. 2259
PREUSS GMBH—See CBRE Group, Inc.; *U.S. Public*, pg. 460
PREVACUS, INC.; *U.S. Private*, pg. 3257
PREVAIL THERAPEUTICS INC.—See Eli Lilly & Company; *U.S. Public*, pg. 734
PREVALENT POWER, INC—See Ontario Teachers' Pension Plan; *U.S. Private*, pg. 5586
PREVAS AB; *Int'l*, pg. 5967
PREVECEUTICAL MEDICAL, INC.; *Int'l*, pg. 5967
PREVENT APPAREL GMBH—See Prevent DEV GmbH; *Int'l*, pg. 5967
PREVENT AUSTRIA GMBH—See Prevent DEV GmbH; *Int'l*, pg. 5967
PREVENT AUTOMOTIVE ROMANIA S.R.L.—See Prevent DEV GmbH; *Int'l*, pg. 5967
PREVENT AVTO RUS OOO—See Prevent DEV GmbH; *Int'l*, pg. 5967
PREVENT BH D.O.O.—See Prevent DEV GmbH; *Int'l*, pg. 5967

PREVENT BRANDBEVEILIGING B.V.—See London Security PLC; *Int'l*, pg. 4547
PREVENT COMPONENTS D.O.O—See Prevent DEV GmbH; *Int'l*, pg. 5967
PREVENT DEV GMBH; *Int'l*, pg. 5967
PREVENT DIREKT D.O.O.—See Prevent DEV GmbH; *Int'l*, pg. 5967
PREVENT FABRICS D.O.O.—See Prevent DEV GmbH; *Int'l*, pg. 5968
PREVENT FAD DD—See Prevent DEV GmbH; *Int'l*, pg. 5968
PREVENT GORAZDE D.O.O.—See Prevent DEV GmbH; *Int'l*, pg. 5967
PREVENT HALOG, D.O.O.—See Prevent DEV GmbH; *Int'l*, pg. 5967
PREVENT HOME D.O.O.—See Prevent DEV GmbH; *Int'l*, pg. 5968
PR EVENT I BASTAD AB—See Vivendi SE; *Int'l*, pg. 8277
PREVENTICE, INC; *U.S. Private*, pg. 3257
PREVENT INTERIOR D.O.O.—See Prevent DEV GmbH; *Int'l*, pg. 5968
PREVENTIONGENETICS LLC—See Exact Sciences Corporation; *U.S. Public*, pg. 805
PREVENTION INSURANCE COM INC; *Int'l*, pg. 5968
PREVENTIVE DIAGNOSTICS, INC.; *U.S. Private*, pg. 3257
PREVENTIVE MAINTENANCE MEDICAL INC.—See Atlantic Street Capital Management LLC; *U.S. Private*, pg. 374
PREVENTIVI SRL—See Brookfield Corporation; *Int'l*, pg. 1188
PREVENT LAMITEX, D.O.O.—See Prevent DEV GmbH; *Int'l*, pg. 5967
PREVENT LEATHER D.O.O.—See Prevent DEV GmbH; *Int'l*, pg. 5967
PREVENT MEZICA, D.O.O.—See Prevent DEV GmbH; *Int'l*, pg. 5967
PREVENT MISLINJA, D.O.O.—See Prevent DEV GmbH; *Int'l*, pg. 5967
PREVENT MOLDOVA, D.O.O.—See Prevent DEV GmbH; *Int'l*, pg. 5968
PREVENT PREMIUM & INTERIOR KFT.—See Prevent DEV GmbH; *Int'l*, pg. 5968
PREVENT ROM S.A.R.L.—See Prevent DEV GmbH; *Int'l*, pg. 5968
PREVENT SAFETY D.O.O.—See Prevent DEV GmbH; *Int'l*, pg. 5967
PREVENT SARAJEVO, D.O.O.—See Prevent DEV GmbH; *Int'l*, pg. 5968
PREVENT SG, D.O.O.—See Prevent DEV GmbH; *Int'l*, pg. 5967
PREVENT SPARE PARTS D.O.O.—See Prevent DEV GmbH; *Int'l*, pg. 5968
PREVENT SREBRENICA D.O.O.—See Prevent DEV GmbH; *Int'l*, pg. 5968
PREVENT STEP D.O.O.—See Prevent DEV GmbH; *Int'l*, pg. 5968
PREVENT THIERRY BRASIL LTDA—See Prevent DEV GmbH; *Int'l*, pg. 5968
PREVENT TRAVNIK D.O.O.—See Prevent DEV GmbH; *Int'l*, pg. 5968
PREVENT TRO, D.O.O.—See Prevent DEV GmbH; *Int'l*, pg. 5967
PREVENT TURKEY OTOMOTIVE LIMITED SIRKETI—See Prevent DEV GmbH; *Int'l*, pg. 5967
PREVENT TWB DO BRASIL INDUSTRIA E COMERCIO LTDA.—See Prevent DEV GmbH; *Int'l*, pg. 5968
PREVENT TWB GMBH & CO. KG—See Prevent DEV GmbH; *Int'l*, pg. 5968
PREVENTURE, LLC—See Marlin Equity Partners, LLC; *U.S. Private*, pg. 2585
PREVENT VIGO SA—See Prevent DEV GmbH; *Int'l*, pg. 5968
PREVENT VISOKO D.O.O.—See Prevent DEV GmbH; *Int'l*, pg. 5968
PREVENT ZENICA D.O.O.—See Prevent DEV GmbH; *Int'l*, pg. 5968
PREVENT ZLATAR, D.O.O.—See Prevent DEV GmbH; *Int'l*, pg. 5968
PREVEST DENPRO LIMITED; *Int'l*, pg. 5968
PREVIEW GM SYSTEM SAS—See Videlio SA; *Int'l*, pg. 8190
PREVILAB ANALISES CLINICAS LTDA—See Diagnosticos da America S.A.; *Int'l*, pg. 2103
PREVISER CORPORATION—See Delta Dental Plan of New Hampshire, Inc.; *U.S. Private*, pg. 1199
PREVISTAR PRIVATE LIMITED—See Thoma Bravo, L.P.; *U.S. Private*, pg. 4147
PREVOST CAR, INC.—See AB Volvo; *Int'l*, pg. 43
PREVO SYSTEM AG—See msg group GmbH; *Int'l*, pg. 5067
PREVOZ RADNIKA KREKA D.D.; *Int'l*, pg. 5968
PREV PEPSICO SOCIEDADE PREVIDENCIARIA—See PepsiCo, Inc.; *U.S. Public*, pg. 1671
PR EXTON SQUARE PROPERTY L.P.—See Pennsylvania Real Estate Investment Trust; *U.S. Public*, pg. 1663
PREZAKAZNICKA A.S.—See EnBW Energie Baden-Wurttemberg AG; *Int'l*, pg. 2399

COMPANY NAME INDEX

PREZERO STIFTUNG & CO. KG—See Schwarz Unternehmenstreuhand KG; *Int'l*, pg. 6645
PREZISS DIAMANT S.L.—See Sandvik AB; *Int'l*, pg. 6530
PREZZO LIMITED—See TPG Capital, L.P.; *U.S. Public*, pg. 2175
PREZZYBOX.COM LTD—See Gift Universe Group Limited; *Int'l*, pg. 2970
P&R FASTENERS INC.; *U.S. Private*, pg. 3059
PRFOODS AS; *Int'l*, pg. 5968
PR FRANCIS SCOTT KEY LLC—See Pennsylvania Real Estate Investment Trust; *U.S. Public*, pg. 1663
PR GAINESVILLE LLC—See Pennsylvania Real Estate Investment Trust; *U.S. Public*, pg. 1663
PR GAZ HAUS HOLDINGS, INC.—See PR Gaz, Inc.; *Int'l*, pg. 5952
PR GAZ, INC.; *Int'l*, pg. 5951
PR GAZ INDUSTRIAL SOLUTIONS, INC.—See PR Gaz, Inc.; *Int'l*, pg. 5952
PRG CORPORATION PUBLIC COMPANY LIMITED; *Int'l*, pg. 5968
PRG DALLAS—See The Jordan Company, L.P.; *U.S. Private*, pg. 4061
PRG EML PRODUCTIONS—See The Jordan Company, L.P.; *U.S. Private*, pg. 4061
PRG GRANARY CO., LTD.—See PRG Corporation Public Company Limited; *Int'l*, pg. 5968
PRG HOLDINGS BERHAD; *Int'l*, pg. 5968
PRG HOLDINGS, LLC—See The Jordan Company, L.P.; *U.S. Private*, pg. 4061
PRG K.K.—See The Jordan Company, L.P.; *U.S. Private*, pg. 4061
P.R.G. METRO SP. Z.O.O.—See PBG S.A.; *Int'l*, pg. 5765
PRG NOCTURNE—See The Jordan Company, L.P.; *U.S. Private*, pg. 4061
PRG PACKING CORP.; *U.S. Private*, pg. 3257
PRG PARKING CENTURY, LLC—See Green Courte Partners, LLC; *U.S. Private*, pg. 1772
PRG PARKING MANAGEMENT, LLC - ATLANTA—See Green Courte Partners, LLC; *U.S. Private*, pg. 1772
PRG PARKING MANAGEMENT, LLC - DALLAS-CEDAR SPRINGS—See Green Courte Partners, LLC; *U.S. Private*, pg. 1772
PRG PARKING MANAGEMENT, LLC - DALLAS-PLAZA DRIVE—See Green Courte Partners, LLC; *U.S. Private*, pg. 1772
PRG PARKING MANAGEMENT, LLC - DALLAS-VALLEY VIEW—See Green Courte Partners, LLC; *U.S. Private*, pg. 1772
PRG PARKING MANAGEMENT, LLC - ORLANDO—See Green Courte Partners, LLC; *U.S. Private*, pg. 1772
PRG PASKAL LIGHTING—See The Jordan Company, L.P.; *U.S. Private*, pg. 4061
PRGR CO., LTD.—See The Yokohama Rubber Co., Ltd.; *Int'l*, pg. 7702
THE PR GROUP, INC.; *U.S. Private*, pg. 4097
PRGX ASIA, INC. - THAILAND—See PRGX Global, Inc.; *U.S. Private*, pg. 3257
PRGX AUSTRALIA, INC.—See PRGX Global, Inc.; *U.S. Private*, pg. 3257
PRGX BELGIUM, INC.—See PRGX Global, Inc.; *U.S. Private*, pg. 3257
PRGX BRASIL LTDA.—See PRGX Global, Inc.; *U.S. Private*, pg. 3257
PRGX CANADA CORP.—See PRGX Global, Inc.; *U.S. Private*, pg. 3257
PRGX COLOMBIA LTDA.—See PRGX Global, Inc.; *U.S. Private*, pg. 3257
PRGX DEUTSCHLAND GMBH—See PRGX Global, Inc.; *U.S. Private*, pg. 3257
PRGX FRANCE, INC.—See PRGX Global, Inc.; *U.S. Private*, pg. 3257
PRGX GLOBAL, INC.; *U.S. Private*, pg. 3257
PRGX INDIA PRIVATE LIMITED—See PRGX Global, Inc.; *U.S. Private*, pg. 3257
PRGX INTERNATIONAL PTE. LTD. - HONG KONG—See PRGX Global, Inc.; *U.S. Private*, pg. 3257
PRGX INTERNATIONAL PTE. LTD.—See PRGX Global, Inc.; *U.S. Private*, pg. 3257
PRGX MEXICO S DE RL DE CV—See PRGX Global, Inc.; *U.S. Private*, pg. 3257
PRGX PORTUGAL, INC.—See PRGX Global, Inc.; *U.S. Private*, pg. 3257
PRGX SPAIN, INC.—See PRGX Global, Inc.; *U.S. Private*, pg. 3257
PRGX SUZHOU CO., LTD.—See PRGX Global, Inc.; *U.S. Private*, pg. 3257
PRGX SVENSKA AB—See PRGX Global, Inc.; *U.S. Private*, pg. 3257
PRGX UK HOLDINGS LTD—See PRGX Global, Inc.; *U.S. Private*, pg. 3257
PRGX UK LTD.—See PRGX Global, Inc.; *U.S. Private*, pg. 3257
PRHC-ALABAMA, LLC—See Apollo Global Management, Inc.; *U.S. Public*, pg. 158
P.R. HOFFMAN MACHINE PRODUCTS, INC.—See Amtech Systems, Inc.; *U.S. Public*, pg. 134
P&R HOLDING; *Int'l*, pg. 5681
PR HOME OF SCANDINAVIA AB—See Storskogen Group AB; *Int'l*, pg. 7228

PRIAM PROPERTIES INC.; *U.S. Private*, pg. 3258
PRIAMUS SYSTEM TECHNOLOGIES AG—See Barnes Group Inc.; *U.S. Public*, pg. 277
PRIAMUS SYSTEM TECHNOLOGIES GMBH—See Barnes Group Inc.; *U.S. Public*, pg. 277
PRI ASPHALT TECHNOLOGIES, INC.—See OceanSound Partners, LP; *U.S. Private*, pg. 2991
PRIBUSS ENGINEERING, INC.; *U.S. Private*, pg. 3258
PRICE AND PIERCE INTERNATIONAL INC.—See Metsaliitto Osuuskunta; *Int'l*, pg. 4864
PRICE & ASSOCIATES CPAS, LLC; *U.S. Private*, pg. 3258
PRICE BAILEY FINANCIAL SERVICES LIMITED—See Tavistock Investments PLC; *Int'l*, pg. 7477
PRICE BROS EQUIPMENT CO; *U.S. Private*, pg. 3258
PRICE CARS LLC; *U.S. Private*, pg. 3258
PRICECHECK TOILETRIES LIMITED; *Int'l*, pg. 5969
PRICE CHEVROLET CO.—See Malloy Automotive of Winchester LLC; *U.S. Private*, pg. 2558
PRICE CHOPPER GOLUB CORPORATION—See Golub Corporation; *U.S. Private*, pg. 1736
PRICE CHOPPER, INC.; *U.S. Private*, pg. 3258
PRICE CHOPPER OPERATING CO., INC.—See Golub Corporation; *U.S. Private*, pg. 1737
PRICE CHOPPER OPERATING CO. OF MASSACHUSETTS, INC.—See Golub Corporation; *U.S. Private*, pg. 1737
PRICE CHOPPER SUPERMARKET—See Golub Corporation; *U.S. Private*, pg. 1737
THE PRICE COMPANIES, INC.; *U.S. Private*, pg. 4098
PRICE CONSTRUCTION INC.; *U.S. Private*, pg. 3258
PRICE CONTAINER & PACKAGING CORPORATION—See Ares Management Corporation; *U.S. Public*, pg. 191
PRICE CONTAINER & PACKAGING CORPORATION—See Ontario Teachers' Pension Plan; *Int'l*, pg. 5590
PRICE COSTCO CANADA HOLDINGS INC.—See Costco Wholesale Corporation; *U.S. Public*, pg. 587
PRICE-DAVIS, INC.; *U.S. Private*, pg. 3258
PRICE ENGINEERING COMPANY INC.; *U.S. Private*, pg. 3258
PRICE FORD LINCOLN; *U.S. Private*, pg. 3258
PRICE FOR PROFIT; *U.S. Private*, pg. 3258
PRICEGRABBER.COM INC.—See Symphony Technology Group, LLC; *U.S. Private*, pg. 3900
PRICE GREGORY INTERNATIONAL, INC.; *U.S. Private*, pg. 3258
PRICE GREGORY INTERNATIONAL, INC.—See Quanta Services, Inc.; *U.S. Public*, pg. 1752
THE PRICE GROUP, INC.; *U.S. Private*, pg. 4098
PRICE HEALTHCARE, INC.—See The Ensign Group, Inc.; *U.S. Public*, pg. 2072
PRICE INDUSTRIES INC.; *U.S. Private*, pg. 3258
PRICE KING WHOLESALE INC.; *U.S. Private*, pg. 3258
PRICE LEBLANC; *U.S. Private*, pg. 3258
PRICE-LESS DRUG STORES INC.; *U.S. Private*, pg. 3258
PRICELESS PARENTING, LLC; *U.S. Private*, pg. 3259
PRICE MART INC.; *U.S. Private*, pg. 3258
PRICE MASTER CORPORATION; *U.S. Private*, pg. 3258
PRICE MODERN LLC; *U.S. Private*, pg. 3258
PRICE PFISTER, INC.—See Spectrum Brands Holdings, Inc.; *U.S. Public*, pg. 1917
PRICE & PIERCE OY—See Japan Pulp and Paper Company Limited; *Int'l*, pg. 3904
PRICER AB; *Int'l*, pg. 5969
PRICER E.S.L. ISRAEL LTD.—See Pricer AB; *Int'l*, pg. 5969
PRICER INC.—See Pricer AB; *Int'l*, pg. 5969
PRICER SAS—See Pricer AB; *Int'l*, pg. 5969
PRICE RUBBER CORP.; *U.S. Private*, pg. 3258
PRICERUNNER.COM—See Publicis Groupe S.A.; *Int'l*, pg. 6099
PRICESMART COLOMBIA SAS—See PriceSmart Inc.; *U.S. Public*, pg. 1716
PRICESMART DOMINICANA, S.A.—See PriceSmart Inc.; *U.S. Public*, pg. 1716
PRICESMART EL SALVADOR, S.A. DE C.V.—See PriceSmart Inc.; *U.S. Public*, pg. 1716
PRICESMART (GUATELMALA), S.A.—See PriceSmart Inc.; *U.S. Public*, pg. 1716
PRICESMART (GUATEMALA), S.A.—See PriceSmart Inc.; *U.S. Public*, pg. 1716
PRICESMART HONDURAS, S.A. DE C.V.—See PriceSmart Inc.; *U.S. Public*, pg. 1716
PRICESMART INC.; *U.S. Public*, pg. 1716
PRICESMART (JAMAICA) LIMITED—See PriceSmart Inc.; *U.S. Public*, pg. 1716
PRICESMART PANAMA, S.A.—See PriceSmart Inc.; *U.S. Public*, pg. 1716
PRICESMART (TRINIDAD) LTD.—See PriceSmart Inc.; *U.S. Public*, pg. 1716
PRICE'S PATENT CANDLE LTD.—See Cereria Sgarbi S.p.A.; *Int'l*, pg. 1422
PRICESPECTIVE LLC—See ICON plc; *Int'l*, pg. 3586
PRICE STEEL LTD.; *Int'l*, pg. 5969
PRICE SYSTEMS DEUTSCHLAND GMBH—See The Carlyle Group Inc.; *U.S. Public*, pg. 2056

PRICE SYSTEMS, LLC—See The Carlyle Group Inc.; *U.S. Public*, pg. 2056
PRICE SYSTEMS LTD.—See The Carlyle Group Inc.; *U.S. Public*, pg. 2056
PRICE TRANSFER INC.; *U.S. Private*, pg. 3258
PRICE TRUCK LINES INC.; *U.S. Private*, pg. 3258
PRICEWATERHOUSECOOPERS AARATA LLC—See PricewaterhouseCoopers Co., Ltd.; *Int'l*, pg. 5970
PRICEWATERHOUSECOOPERS ADVISORY LLC—See PricewaterhouseCoopers Audit LLC; *Int'l*, pg. 5969
PRICEWATERHOUSECOOPERS ADVISORY SPA—See PricewaterhouseCoopers S.p.A.; *Int'l*, pg. 5972
PRICEWATERHOUSECOOPERS AG; *Int'l*, pg. 5969
PRICEWATERHOUSECOOPERS AG WIRTSCHAFTSPRUFUNGSGESELLSCHAFT; *Int'l*, pg. 5969
PRICEWATERHOUSECOOPERS ASESORES DE NEGOCIOS S.L.—See PricewaterhouseCoopers, S.L.; *Int'l*, pg. 5973
PRICEWATERHOUSECOOPERS & ASSOCIADOS - SOCIEDADE DE REVISORES OFICIAIS DE CONTAS, LDA. - PRAIA BRANCH—See PricewaterhouseCoopers & Associados - Sociedade de Revisores Oficiais de Contas, Lda.; *Int'l*, pg. 5969
PRICEWATERHOUSECOOPERS & ASSOCIADOS - SOCIEDADE DE REVISORES OFICIAIS DE CONTAS, LDA.; *Int'l*, pg. 5969
PRICEWATERHOUSECOOPERS AUDIT AZERBAIJAN LLC; *Int'l*, pg. 5969
PRICEWATERHOUSECOOPERS AUDIT CALEDONIE SELARL; *Int'l*, pg. 5969
PRICEWATERHOUSECOOPERS AUDITING COMPANY S.A.—See PricewaterhouseCoopers S.A.; *Int'l*, pg. 5972
PRICEWATERHOUSECOOPERS AUDITING LIMITED LIABILITY COMPANY—See PricewaterhouseCoopers Hungary Limited Liability Company; *Int'l*, pg. 5971
PRICEWATERHOUSECOOPERS AUDIT LLC; *Int'l*, pg. 5969
PRICEWATERHOUSECOOPERS AUDIT OOD—See PricewaterhouseCoopers Bulgaria EOOD; *Int'l*, pg. 5969
PRICEWATERHOUSECOOPERS AUDIT SAS—See PricewaterhouseCoopers France Sarl; *Int'l*, pg. 5970
PRICEWATERHOUSECOOPERS AUDIT SH.P.K.; *Int'l*, pg. 5969
PRICEWATERHOUSECOOPERS AUDIT S.R.L.; *Int'l*, pg. 5969
PRICEWATERHOUSECOOPERS AUDIT, S.R.O.—See PricewaterhouseCoo; *Int'l*, pg. 5970
PRICEWATERHOUSECOOPERS AUSTRALIA (INTERNATIONAL) PTY. LTD.; *Int'l*, pg. 5969
PRICEWATERHOUSECOOPERS BULGARIA EOOD; *Int'l*, pg. 5969
PRICEWATERHOUSECOOPERS BUSINESS CONSULTING (SHANGHAI) CO., LIMITED—See PricewaterhouseCoopers Consultants (Shenzhen) Limited; *Int'l*, pg. 5970
PRICEWATERHOUSECOOPERS (CAMBODIA) LTD.; *Int'l*, pg. 5969
PRICEWATERHOUSECOOPERS CESKA REPUBLIKA, S.R.O.; *Int'l*, pg. 5969
PRICEWATERHOUSECOOPERS CO., LTD.; *Int'l*, pg. 5970
PRICEWATERHOUSECOOPERS CONSEIL SA—See PricewaterhouseCoopers SARL; *Int'l*, pg. 5972
PRICEWATERHOUSECOOPERS CONSULTANTS CO., LTD.—See PricewaterhouseCoopers Co., Ltd.; *Int'l*, pg. 5970
PRICEWATERHOUSECOOPERS CONSULTANTS (SHENZHEN) LIMITED; *Int'l*, pg. 5970
PRICEWATERHOUSECOOPERS CONSULTING HONG KONG LTD.—See PricewaterhouseCoopers Limited; *Int'l*, pg. 5971
PRICEWATERHOUSECOOPERS CONSULTORES, S.A.—See PricewaterhouseCoopers InterAmericas; *Int'l*, pg. 5971
PRICEWATERHOUSECOOPERS CORPORATE FINANCE SAS—See PricewaterhouseCoopers France Sarl; *Int'l*, pg. 5970
PRICEWATERHOUSECOOPERS CORPORATE FINANCE, S.L.—See PricewaterhouseCoopers, S.L.; *Int'l*, pg. 5973
PRICEWATERHOUSECOOPERS DEL ECUADOR CIA. LTDA.—See PwC Asesores Empresariales Cia. Ltda.; *Int'l*, pg. 6126
PRICEWATERHOUSECOOPERS; *Int'l*, pg. 5973
PRICEWATERHOUSECOOPERS D.O.O.E.L; *Int'l*, pg. 5970
PRICEWATERHOUSECOOPERS D.O.O.; *Int'l*, pg. 5970
PRICEWATERHOUSECOOPERS D.O.O.; *Int'l*, pg. 5970
PRICEWATERHOUSECOOPERS DOO; *Int'l*, pg. 5970
PRICEWATERHOUSECOOPERS D.O.O.; *Int'l*, pg. 5970
PRICEWATERHOUSECOOPERS EHF; *Int'l*, pg. 5970
PRICEWATERHOUSECOOPERS ENTREPRISES SARL—See PricewaterhouseCoopers France Sarl; *Int'l*, pg. 5971
PRICEWATERHOUSECOOPERS FAS LTD.; *Int'l*, pg. 5970

2163

PRICEWATERHOUSECOOPERS FRANCE SARL · CORPORATE AFFILIATIONS

PRICEWATERHOUSECOOPERS FRANCE SARL; *Int'l*, pg. 5970
PRICEWATERHOUSECOOPERS (GHANA) LIMITED - FREETOWN BRANCH—See PricewaterhouseCoopers (Ghana) Limited; *Int'l*, pg. 5969
PRICEWATERHOUSECOOPERS (GHANA) LIMITED; *Int'l*, pg. 5969
PRICEWATERHOUSECOOPERS HUNGARY LIMITED LIABILITY COMPANY; *Int'l*, pg. 5971
PRICEWATERHOUSECOOPERS IAC—See PricewaterhouseCoopers Co., Ltd.; *Int'l*, pg. 5970
PRICEWATERHOUSECOOPERS INFORMATION TECHNOLOGIES (SHANGHAI) CO., LTD.—See PricewaterhouseCoopers Consultants (Shenzhen) Limited; *Int'l*, pg. 5970
PRICEWATERHOUSECOOPERS INTERAMERICA, S. DE R.L.; *Int'l*, pg. 5971
PRICEWATERHOUSECOOPERS INTERAMERICAS; *Int'l*, pg. 5971
PRICEWATERHOUSECOOPERS INTERNATIONAL ASSIGNMENT SERVICES (SHANGHAI) LIMITED—See PricewaterhouseCoopers Consultants (Shenzhen) Limited; *Int'l*, pg. 5970
PRICEWATERHOUSECOOPERS INTERNATIONAL LIMITED; *Int'l*, pg. 5971
PRICEWATERHOUSECOOPERSISLA LIPANA & CO.; *Int'l*, pg. 5973
PRICEWATERHOUSECOOPERS KYOTO—See PricewaterhouseCoopers Co., Ltd.; *Int'l*, pg. 5970
PRICEWATERHOUSECOOPERS LANKA (PRIVATE) LIMITED—See Deloitte Touche Tohmatsu Limited; *Int'l*, pg. 2015
PRICEWATERHOUSECOOPERS LEGAL CIS B.V.—See PricewaterhouseCoopers Russia B.V.; *Int'l*, pg. 5972
PRICEWATERHOUSECOOPERS LEGAL LLP—See PricewaterhouseCoopers LLP (UK); *Int'l*, pg. 5971
PRICEWATERHOUSECOOPERS LEGAL, S.R.O.—See PricewaterhouseCoopers Slovensko, s.r.o.; *Int'l*, pg. 5972
PRICEWATERHOUSECOOPERS LEGAL S.R.Q.—See PricewaterhouseCoo; *Int'l*, pg. 5970
PRICEWATERHOUSECOOPERS LEGAL & TAX CONSULTANTS LTD.—See PricewaterhouseCoopers FAS Ltd.; *Int'l*, pg. 5970
PRICEWATERHOUSECOOPERS LEGAL VIETNAM CO., LTD.—See PricewaterhouseCoopers (Vietnam) Ltd.; *Int'l*, pg. 5969
PRICEWATERHOUSECOOPERS LIMITED; *Int'l*, pg. 5971
PRICEWATERHOUSECOOPERS LIMITED; *Int'l*, pg. 5971
PRICEWATERHOUSECOOPERS LIMITED; *Int'l*, pg. 5971
PRICEWATERHOUSECOOPERS LIMITED; *Int'l*, pg. 5971
PRICEWATERHOUSECOOPERS LLP (CANADA); *Int'l*, pg. 5971
PRICEWATERHOUSECOOPERS LLP; *Int'l*, pg. 5971
PRICEWATERHOUSECOOPERS LLP (UK); *Int'l*, pg. 5971
PRICEWATERHOUSECOOPERS LLP (USA); *U.S. Private*, pg. 3259
PRICEWATERHOUSECOOPERS LTD.; *Int'l*, pg. 5971
PRICEWATERHOUSECOOPERS LTD.; *Int'l*, pg. 5971
PRICEWATERHOUSECOOPERS MANAGEMENT CONSULTING (SHANGHAI) LIMITED—See PricewaterhouseCoopers Consultants (Shenzhen) Limited; *Int'l*, pg. 5970
PRICEWATERHOUSECOOPERS ME LIMITED; *Int'l*, pg. 5971
PRICEWATERHOUSECOOPERS MYANMAR CO., LTD; *Int'l*, pg. 5972
PRICEWATERHOUSECOOPERS PRTM MANAGEMENT CONSULTANTS JAPAN LLC—See PricewaterhouseCoopers Co., Ltd.; *Int'l*, pg. 5970
PRICEWATERHOUSECOOPERS PVT. LTD.; *Int'l*, pg. 5972
PRICEWATERHOUSECOOPERS RUSSIA B.V.; *Int'l*, pg. 5972
PRICEWATERHOUSECOOPERS SALZBURG WIRTSCHAFTSPRUFUNG UND STEUERBERATUNG GMBH—See PwC Osterreich GmbH Wirtschaftsprufungsgesellschaft; *Int'l*, pg. 6126
PRICEWATERHOUSECOOPERS SARL; *Int'l*, pg. 5972
PRICEWATERHOUSECOOPERS SARL; *Int'l*, pg. 5972
PRICEWATERHOUSECOOPERS, S.A.; *Int'l*, pg. 5972
PRICEWATERHOUSECOOPERS S.A.; *Int'l*, pg. 5972
PRICEWATERHOUSECOOPERS SA; *Int'l*, pg. 5972
PRICEWATERHOUSECOOPERS SA; *Int'l*, pg. 5972
PRICEWATERHOUSECOOPERS SERVICE DELIVERY CENTER (BANGALORE) PVT. LTD.—See PricewaterhouseCoopers Pvt. Ltd.; *Int'l*, pg. 5972
PRICEWATERHOUSECOOPERS SERVICE DELIVERY CENTER (KOLKATA) PVT. LTD.—See PricewaterhouseCoopers Pvt. Ltd.; *Int'l*, pg. 5972
PRICEWATERHOUSECOOPERS SLOVENSKO, S.R.O.; *Int'l*, pg. 5972
PRICEWATERHOUSECOOPERS, S.L.; *Int'l*, pg. 5973
PRICEWATERHOUSECOOPERS S.P.A.; *Int'l*, pg. 5972
PRICEWATERHOUSECOOPERS S.R.L.; *Int'l*, pg. 5972
PRICEWATERHOUSECOOPERS TAX & ADVISORY LLP—See PricewaterhouseCoopers LLP; *Int'l*, pg. 5971
PRICEWATERHOUSECOOPERS TAX & LEGAL SA; *Int'l*, pg. 5972

PRICEWATERHOUSECOOPERS TAX & LEGAL SA—See PricewaterhouseCoopers SA; *Int'l*, pg. 5972
PRICEWATERHOUSECOOPERS TIROL WIRTSCHAFTSPRUFUNGSGESELLSCHAFT MBH—See PwC Osterreich GmbH Wirtschaftsprufungsgesellschaft; *Int'l*, pg. 6126
PRICEWATERHOUSECOOPERS (VIETNAM) LTD.; *Int'l*, pg. 5969
PRICEWATERHOUSECOOPERS VORARLBERG WIRTSCHAFTSPRUFUNGS GMBH—See PwC Osterreich GmbH Wirtschaftsprufungsgesellschaft; *Int'l*, pg. 6126
PRICEWATERHOUSECOOPERS WMS (SHANGHAI) CO., LTD—See PricewaterhouseCoopers Consultants (Shenzhen) Limited; *Int'l*, pg. 5970
PRICEWATERHOUSECOOPERS Y CIA, S.A.; *Int'l*, pg. 5972
PRICE WATERHOUSE Y COMPANIA DE EL SALVADOR—See PricewaterhouseCoopers InterAmericas; *Int'l*, pg. 5971
PRICEWEBER MARKETING COMMUNICATIONS, INC.; *U.S. Private*, pg. 3259
PRICEWORTH INTERNATIONAL BERHAD; *Int'l*, pg. 5973
PRICING SOLUTIONS LTD.—See Samsung BioLogics Co., Ltd.; *Int'l*, pg. 6510
PRICKETTS DISTRIBUTING INC.; *U.S. Private*, pg. 3259
PRICOA CAPITAL MANAGEMENT LIMITED—See Prudential Financial, Inc.; *U.S. Public*, pg. 1731
PRICOA CONSULTING (SHANGHAI) CO., LTD.—See Prudential Financial, Inc.; *U.S. Public*, pg. 1731
PRICOA RELOCATION ASIA PTE. LTD.—See Prudential Financial, Inc.; *U.S. Public*, pg. 1731
PRICOA RELOCATION FRANCE SAS—See Prudential Financial, Inc.; *U.S. Public*, pg. 1731
PRICOL CORPORATE SERVICES LTD—See Pricol Limited; *Int'l*, pg. 5973
PRICOL LIMITED - PLANT II—See Pricol Limited; *Int'l*, pg. 5973
PRICOL LIMITED - PLANT I—See Pricol Limited; *Int'l*, pg. 5973
PRICOL LIMITED; *Int'l*, pg. 5973
PRICOL PACKING LIMITED—See Pricol Limited; *Int'l*, pg. 5973
PRICOL PROPERTIES LIMITED—See Pricol Limited; *Int'l*, pg. 5973
PRICOL TRAVEL LIMITED—See Pricol Limited; *Int'l*, pg. 5973
PRIDA GUIDA & COMPANY, P.A.; *U.S. Private*, pg. 3259
PRIDAY DIALYSIS, LLC—See DaVita Inc.; *U.S. Public*, pg. 642
PRIDE ADVICE PTY, LTD.—See Azimut Holding SpA; *Int'l*, pg. 779
PRIDE AND JOYS INC.; *U.S. Private*, pg. 3259
PRIDE BODIES LTD—See Westinghouse Air Brake Technologies Corporation; *U.S. Public*, pg. 2359
PRIDE-CHEM INDUSTRIES PTE LTD; *Int'l*, pg. 5973
PRIDE CHEM INDUSTRIES SDN BHD—See Coogee Chemicals Pty Ltd.; *Int'l*, pg. 1788
PRIDE CHEM INDUSTRIES SDN BHD—See Pride-Chem Industries Pte Ltd; *Int'l*, pg. 5973
PRIDE CLEANERS INC.—See MJV Holdings, LLC; *U.S. Private*, pg. 2753
PRIDE CONVENIENCE INC.; *U.S. Private*, pg. 3259
PRIDE ELECTRIC, INC.—See MDU Resources Group, Inc.; *U.S. Public*, pg. 1410
PRIDE ENGINEERING, LLC—See Arcline Investment Management LP; *U.S. Private*, pg. 315
PRIDE FORASOL-FORAMER S.A.—See Valaris Limited; *Int'l*, pg. 8110
PRIDE FORASOL S.A.S.—See Valaris Limited; *Int'l*, pg. 8110
THE PRIDE GROUP (QLD) PTY. LTD.—See VISION ENERGY CORPORATION; *U.S. Public*, pg. 2304
PRIDE HYUNDAI OF SEEKONK; *U.S. Private*, pg. 3259
PRIDE INDUSTRIES INC.; *U.S. Private*, pg. 3259
PRIDE INSTITUTE, INC.—See Universal Health Services, Inc.; *U.S. Public*, pg. 2259
PRIDE INTERNATIONAL, INC.—See Valaris Limited; *Int'l*, pg. 8110
PRIDE INTERNATIONAL (SHANGHAI)CO., LTD.—See Bright Sheland International Co., Ltd.; *Int'l*, pg. 1162
PRIDE MANUFACTURING COMPANY, LLC—See Centre Partners Management LLC; *U.S. Private*, pg. 828
PRIDE MEDIA INC.—See Equal Entertainment LLC; *U.S. Private*, pg. 1415
PRIDE METAL POLISHING, INC.—See Sky Island Capital LLC; *U.S. Private*, pg. 3684
PRIDE MOBILITY PRODUCTS AUSTRALIA PTY. LTD.—See Pride Mobility Products Corp.; *U.S. Private*, pg. 3259
PRIDE MOBILITY PRODUCTS COMPANY—See Pride Mobility Products Corp.; *U.S. Private*, pg. 3259
PRIDE MOBILITY PRODUCTS CORP. - QUANTUM REHAB DIVISION—See Pride Mobility Products Corp.; *U.S. Private*, pg. 3259
PRIDE MOBILITY PRODUCTS CORP.; *U.S. Private*, pg. 3259
PRIDE MOBILITY PRODUCTS EUROPE BV—See Pride Mobility Products Corp.; *U.S. Private*, pg. 3259

PRIDE MOBILITY PRODUCTS ITALIA S.R.L.—See Pride Mobility Products Corp.; *U.S. Private*, pg. 3259
PRIDE MOBILITY PRODUCTS LTD.—See Pride Mobility Products Corp.; *U.S. Private*, pg. 3259
PRIDE MOBILITY PRODUCTS NEW ZEALAND LTD.—See Pride Mobility Products Corp.; *U.S. Private*, pg. 3259
PRIDE MOBILITY PRODUCTS SARL—See Pride Mobility Products Corp.; *U.S. Private*, pg. 3259
PRIDE OUTLET SDN BHD—See KPJ Healthcare Berhad; *Int'l*, pg. 4297
PRIDE PRODUCTS CORP; *U.S. Private*, pg. 3259
PRIDE PRODUCTS, INC., *U.S. Private*, pg. 3260
PRIDE SHIPPING COMPANY LTD.—See Regional Container Lines Public Company Limited; *Int'l*, pg. 6254
PRIDE SOLUTIONS, LLC—See Daggett Ventures, LLC; *U.S. Private*, pg. 1144
PRIDE SOLVENTS & CHEMICAL COMPANY; *U.S. Private*, pg. 3260
PRIDE SOLVENTS & CHEMICAL CO. OF NEW JERSEY, INC.—See Pride Solvents & Chemical Company; *U.S. Private*, pg. 3260
PRIDESTAFF, INC.; *U.S. Private*, pg. 3260
PRIDE TREE HOLDINGS, INC.; *U.S. Private*, pg. 3260
PRIDGEON & CLAY, INC.; *U.S. Private*, pg. 3260
PRIDGEON & CLAY, KFT—See Pridgeon & Clay, Inc.; *U.S. Private*, pg. 3260
PRIDGEON & CLAY, S.DE R.L. DE C.V.—See Pridgeon & Clay, Inc.; *U.S. Private*, pg. 3260
PRIEMA CETRA BV—See Priema Metaalwarenfabriek BV; *Int'l*, pg. 5973
PRIEMA METAALWARENFABRIEK BV; *Int'l*, pg. 5973
PRIESTER PECAN CO., INC.; *U.S. Private*, pg. 3260
PRI FOODS CO., LTD.—See Mitsui & Co., Ltd.; *Int'l*, pg. 4979
PRIJEDORCANKA A.D.; *Int'l*, pg. 5973
PRIJEDORPUTEVI A.D. PRIJEDOR—See Grupa Fortis d.o.o. Banja Luka; *Int'l*, pg. 3116
PRILAM S.A.S.; *Int'l*, pg. 5973
PRILEPSKA PIVARNICA AD; *Int'l*, pg. 5973
PRILLA 2000 (PTY) LTD—See Industrial Development Corporation of South Africa, Ltd.; *Int'l*, pg. 3672
PRIMA 200 LIMITED—See HICL Infrastructure PLC; *Int'l*, pg. 3383
PRIMA AFP; *Int'l*, pg. 5973
PRIMA AGRO LIMITED; *Int'l*, pg. 5973
PRIMA ANJUNG SDN. BHD.—See Emivest Berhad; *Int'l*, pg. 2383
PRIMABAGUZ SDN. BHD.—See Johnsonville, LLC; *U.S. Private*, pg. 2229
PRIMA BANKA SLOVENSKO AS; *Int'l*, pg. 5974
PRIMACH TECHNOLOGY PTE LTD—See D&G TECHNOLOGY HOLDING CO., LTD.; *Int'l*, pg. 1899
PRIMACOM BERLIN GMBH—See Morgan Stanley; *U.S. Public*, pg. 1473
PRIMA COMMUNICATIONS, INC.; *U.S. Private*, pg. 3260
PRIMA CONSTRUCT S.A.; *Int'l*, pg. 5974
PRIMAC PTY. LTD.—See Elders Limited; *Int'l*, pg. 2346
PRIMACY; *U.S. Private*, pg. 3260
PRIMACY UNDERWRITING MANAGEMENT PTY LIMITED—See Allianz SE; *Int'l*, pg. 347
PRIMA DENTAL GROUP—See Darby Group Companies, Inc.; *U.S. Private*, pg. 1158
PRIMA ELECTRONIC SERVICES LIMITED—See OSI Systems, Inc.; *U.S. Public*, pg. 1622
PRIMA ELECTRONICS S.P.A.—See Prima Industrie SpA; *Int'l*, pg. 5974
PRIMA ELECTRO SUZHOU CO. LTD.—See Prima Industrie SpA; *Int'l*, pg. 5974
PRIMA FINN-POWER CANADA LTD.—See Prima Industrie SpA; *Int'l*, pg. 5974
PRIMA FINN-POWER CENTRAL EUROPE SPZOO—See Prima Industrie SpA; *Int'l*, pg. 5974
PRIMA FINN-POWER FRANCE S.A.R.L.—See Prima Industrie SpA; *Int'l*, pg. 5974
PRIMA FINN-POWER GMBH—See Prima Industrie SpA; *Int'l*, pg. 5974
PRIMA FINN-POWER IBERICA S.L.—See Prima Industrie SpA; *Int'l*, pg. 5974
PRIMA FINN-POWER NV—See Prima Industrie SpA; *Int'l*, pg. 5974
PRIMA FINN-POWER SWEDEN AB—See Prima Industrie SpA; *Int'l*, pg. 5974
PRIMA FINN-POWER UK LTD—See Prima Industrie SpA; *Int'l*, pg. 5974
PRIMAFLOW LIMITED—See Travis Perkins plc; *Int'l*, pg. 7908
PRIMAFRUIT LTD—See Fresca Group Limited; *Int'l*, pg. 2774
PRIMAG AG; *Int'l*, pg. 5975
PRIMA GAMES—See Asteri Holdings; *U.S. Private*, pg. 360
PRIMA GARNET COMM LTD.—See WPP plc; *Int'l*, pg. 8488
PRIMAGAS AD—See Hera S.p.A.; *Int'l*, pg. 3356
PRIMAGAS GMBH—See SHV Holdings N.V.; *Int'l*, pg. 6873
PRIMAGAZ BELGIUM N.V.—See SHV Holdings N.V.; *Int'l*, pg. 6873

COMPANY NAME INDEX

PRIMAGAZ CENTRAL EUROPE GMBH—See SHV Holdings N.V.; *Int'l*, pg. 6873
PRIMAGAZ DANMARK A/S—See SHV Holdings N.V.; *Int'l*, pg. 6873
PRIMAGAZ DISTRIBUCION S.A.—See SHV Holdings N.V.; *Int'l*, pg. 6873
PRIMAGAZ GMBH—See SHV Holdings N.V.; *Int'l*, pg. 6873
PRIMAGAZ HUNGARIA RT.—See SHV Holdings N.V.; *Int'l*, pg. 6873
PRIMAGAZ NEDERLAND B.V.—See SHV Holdings N.V.; *Int'l*, pg. 6873
PRIMAGAZ NORGE AS—See SHV Holdings N.V.; *Int'l*, pg. 6873
PRIMAGAZ SVERIGE AB—See SHV Holdings N.V.; *Int'l*, pg. 6873
PRIMAGOLD INTERNATIONAL CO. LTD.—See Pranda Jewelry Public Company Limited; *Int'l*, pg. 5954
PRIMAGRA, A.S.—See Agrofert Holding, a.s.; *Int'l*, pg. 219
PRIMAHAM FOODS (THAILAND) CO., LTD.—See Prima Meat Packers Ltd.; *Int'l*, pg. 5975
PRIMAHAM (THAILAND) CO., LTD.—See Prima Meat Packers Ltd.; *Int'l*, pg. 5975
PRIMA INDUSTRIE (BEIJING) CO. LTD.—See Prima Industrie SpA; *Int'l*, pg. 5974
PRIMA INDUSTRIES LIMITED; *Int'l*, pg. 5974
PRIMA INDUSTRIE SPA; *Int'l*, pg. 5974
PRIMA INDUSTRIE UK LTD.—See Prima Industrie SpA; *Int'l*, pg. 5974
PRIMALAB D.O.O.—See Metrohm AG; *Int'l*, pg. 4862
PRIMALAB D.O.O.—See Metrohm AG; *Int'l*, pg. 4862
PRIMALAB D.O.O.—See Metrohm AG; *Int'l*, pg. 4862
PRIMALEX A.S.—See PPG Industries, Inc.; *U.S. Public*, pg. 1710
PRIMA LIGHTING CORPORATION; *U.S. Private*, pg. 3260
PRIMAL LIFE ORGANICS, LLC—See Society Brands, Inc.; *U.S. Private*, pg. 3703
PRIMAL MEDIA LIMITED—See STV Group plc; *Int'l*, pg. 7245
PRIMAL NUTRITION, LLC—See Berkshire Hathaway Inc.; *U.S. Public*, pg. 315
PRIMAL PET FOODS INC.; *U.S. Private*, pg. 3260
PRIMA MANAGEMENT SERVICE CO., LTD.—See Prima Meat Packers Ltd.; *Int'l*, pg. 5975
PRIMA MARINE PCL; *Int'l*, pg. 5974
PRIMA MEAT PACKERS LTD.; *Int'l*, pg. 5975
PRIMA MODA S.A.; *Int'l*, pg. 5975
PRIMA NORTH AMERICA INC.—See Prima Industrie SpA; *Int'l*, pg. 5974
PRIMA PACKAGING SDN. BHD.—See Pintaras Jaya Berhad; *Int'l*, pg. 5870
PRIMAPAC SDN. BHD.—See Pintaras Jaya Berhad; *Int'l*, pg. 5870
PRIMAPHOT SPRL—See Activa Capital S.A.S.; *Int'l*, pg. 119
PRIMA PLASTICS LTD.; *Int'l*, pg. 5975
PRIMAPLYN SPOL. S.R.O.—See SHV Holdings N.V.; *Int'l*, pg. 6873
PRIMAPOL-METAL-SPOT S.R.O.—See Scope Metals Group Ltd.; *Int'l*, pg. 6650
PRIMA POWER CENTRAL EUROPE SP. Z O.O.—See Prima Industrie SpA; *Int'l*, pg. 5974
PRIMA POWER CHINA CO. LTD.—See Prima Industrie SpA; *Int'l*, pg. 5974
PRIMA POWER FRANCE SARL—See Prima Industrie SpA; *Int'l*, pg. 5974
PRIMA POWER GMBH—See Prima Industrie SpA; *Int'l*, pg. 5974
PRIMA POWER IBERICA S.L.—See Prima Industrie SpA; *Int'l*, pg. 5974
PRIMA POWER INDIA PVT. LTD.—See Prima Industrie SpA; *Int'l*, pg. 5974
PRIMA POWER LASERDYNE LLC—See Prima Industrie SpA; *Int'l*, pg. 5974
PRIMA POWER MAKINA TICARET LIMITED SIRKETI—See Prima Industrie SpA; *Int'l*, pg. 5974
PRIMA POWER MEXICO S DE R.L. DE C.V.—See Prima Industrie SpA; *Int'l*, pg. 5974
PRIMA POWER SOUTH AMERICA LTDA—See Prima Industrie SpA; *Int'l*, pg. 5974
PRIMA POWER SUZHOU CO. LTD.—See Prima Industrie SpA; *Int'l*, pg. 5974
PRIMA POWER UK LTD.—See Prima Industrie SpA; *Int'l*, pg. 5974
PRIMA PUBLIC RELATIONS, LTD.; *U.S. Private*, pg. 3260
PRIMARIES OF WA PTY. LTD.—See Nutrien Ltd.; *Int'l*, pg. 5493
PRIMARILY CARE, INC.; *U.S. Private*, pg. 3260
PRIMARINDO ASIA INFRASTRUKTUR TBK; *Int'l*, pg. 5975
PRIMARK DEUTSCHLAND GMBH—See The Garfield Weston Foundation; *Int'l*, pg. 7649
PRIMARK STORES LIMITED—See The Garfield Weston Foundation; *Int'l*, pg. 7649
PRI MAR PETROLEUM INC.; *U.S. Private*, pg. 3258
PRIMARY AIM, LLC; *U.S. Private*, pg. 3260
PRIMARY BANK; *U.S. Public*, pg. 1716
PRIMARY CAPITAL LIMITED; *Int'l*, pg. 5975

PRIMARY CAPITAL PARTNERS LLP—See Primary Capital Limited; *Int'l*, pg. 5975
PRIMARY CARE AT HOME OF LOUISIANA II, LLC—See UnitedHealth Group Incorporated; *U.S. Public*, pg. 2246
PRIMARY CARE AT HOME OF MARYLAND, LLC—See UnitedHealth Group Incorporated; *U.S. Public*, pg. 2246
PRIMARY CARE AT HOME OF WEST VIRGINIA, LLC—See UnitedHealth Group Incorporated; *U.S. Public*, pg. 2246
PRIMARY CARE HEALTH SERVICES, INC.; *U.S. Private*, pg. 3260
PRIMARY CARE OF WEST END, LLC—See HCA Healthcare, Inc.; *U.S. Public*, pg. 1006
PRIMARY CARE PHYSICIANS CENTER, LLC—See Tenet Healthcare Corporation; *U.S. Public*, pg. 2014
PRIMARY COLOR SYSTEMS CORP; *U.S. Private*, pg. 3260
PRIMARY DESIGN INC.—See Cloud Mellow Consulting Ltd. Co.; *U.S. Private*, pg. 946
PRIMARY ENERGY RECYCLING CORPORATION—See SDCL Energy Efficiency Income Trust Plc; *Int'l*, pg. 6657
PRIMARY ENERGY VENTURES LLC—See EPCOR Utilities, Inc.; *Int'l*, pg. 2459
PRIMARY FLOW SIGNAL INC.; *U.S. Private*, pg. 3260
PRIMARY FREIGHT SERVICES INC.; *U.S. Private*, pg. 3260
THE PRIMARY GROUP, INC.; *U.S. Private*, pg. 4098
PRIMARY HEALTH CARE INC.; *U.S. Private*, pg. 3260
PRIMARY HEALTH GROUP, INC.—See HCA Healthcare, Inc.; *U.S. Public*, pg. 1006
PRIMARY HEALTH, INC.—See HCA Healthcare, Inc.; *U.S. Public*, pg. 1006
PRIMARY HEALTH PROPERTIES PLC; *Int'l*, pg. 5975
PRIMARY INDUSTRIES PTE. LTD.—See Temasek Holdings (Private) Limited; *Int'l*, pg. 7550
PRIMARY INDUSTRIES (QLD) PTY. LTD.—See Temasek Holdings (Private) Limited; *Int'l*, pg. 7550
PRIMARY INTELLIGENCE INC.—See The Riverside Company; *U.S. Private*, pg. 4108
PRIMARY OPINION LIMITED; *Int'l*, pg. 5976
PRIMARY PACKAGING INCORPORATED; *U.S. Private*, pg. 0260
PRIMARY PROVIDER MANAGEMENT COMPANY—See Clayton, Dubilier & Rice, LLC; *U.S. Private*, pg. 926
PRIMARY RESIDENTIAL MORTGAGE, INC.; *U.S. Private*, pg. 3261
PRIMARY SAATCHI & SAATCHI—See Publicis Groupe S.A.; *Int'l*, pg. 6108
PRIMARY SERVICES LP; *U.S. Private*, pg. 3261
PRIMARY SOURCING CORPORATION—See Sanmina Corporation; *U.S. Public*, pg. 1840
PRIMARY SUPPLY INC.; *U.S. Private*, pg. 3261
PRIMARY SYSTEMS, INC.; *U.S. Private*, pg. 3261
PRIMA-SARA LEE COFFEE & TEA POLAND SP. Z O.O.—See JAB Holding Company S.a.r.l.; *Int'l*, pg. 3863
PRIMAS FREEMAN FISHER LIMITED; *Int'l*, pg. 5976
PRIMA SIXTEEN SDN. BHD.—See GLOMAC Berhad; *Int'l*, pg. 3008
PRIMA SOLUTIONS BELGIUM SA—See Simulations Plus, Inc.; *U.S. Public*, pg. 1885
PRIMASSURE (AUSTRALIA) PTY. LTD.—See Steadfast Group Limited; *Int'l*, pg. 7187
PRIMA SYSTEM DEVELOPMENT CO., LTD.—See Prima Meat Packers Ltd.; *Int'l*, pg. 5975
PRI-MA-TECH VERWALTUNGS GMBH—See Brother Industries, Ltd.; *Int'l*, pg. 1198
PRIMATICS FINANCIAL LLC—See SS&C Technologies Holdings, Inc.; *U.S. Public*, pg. 1923
PRIMA TOY & LEISURE GROUP (PTY) LTD.—See E Media Holdings Limited; *Int'l*, pg. 2246
PRIMAT RD D.O.O.—See Honkarakenne Oyj; *Int'l*, pg. 3471
PRIMAT RECRUITMENT LIMITED—See John Wood Group PLC; *Int'l*, pg. 3983
PRIMAVERA CAPITAL ACQUISITION CORPORATION—See Fosun International Limited; *Int'l*, pg. 2751
PRIMAVERA CAPITAL GROUP LTD.; *Int'l*, pg. 5976
PRIMAVISTA GROUP—See Activa Capital S.A.S.; *Int'l*, pg. 119
PRIMA WOHNBAUTEN PRIVATISIERUNGS-MANAGEMENT GMBH—See Vonovia SE; *Int'l*, pg. 8305
PRIMAX ELECTRONICS LTD.; *Int'l*, pg. 5976
PRIMAX ELECTRONICS (THAILAND) CO., LTD.—See Primax Electronics Ltd.; *Int'l*, pg. 5976
PRIMAX INDUSTRIES (HONG KONG) LTD.—See Primax Electronics Ltd.; *Int'l*, pg. 5976
PRIMAX S.A.—See Grupo Romero; *Int'l*, pg. 3135
PRIMCO MANAGEMENT INC.; *U.S. Private*, pg. 3261
PRIME ABA, LP—See Godspeed Capital Management LP; *U.S. Private*, pg. 1725
PRIME ACCESS, INC.—See Global Advertising Strategies, Inc.; *U.S. Private*, pg. 1712
PRIME ACQUISITION CORP.; *Int'l*, pg. 5976

PRIMEDIA LIMITED

PRIME ADVERTISING; *Int'l*, pg. 5976
PRIME ADVISORS, INC.—See Sun Life Financial Inc.; *Int'l*, pg. 7305
PRIME AE GROUP, INC.—See NewHold Enterprises LLC; *U.S. Private*, pg. 2915
PRIME AIR EUROPE LIMITED—See HEICO Corporation; *U.S. Public*, pg. 1020
PRIME AIR, LLC—See HEICO Corporation; *U.S. Public*, pg. 1020
PRIME AIRPORT SERVICES INC.—See LATAM Airlines Group S.A.; *Int'l*, pg. 4422
PRIME ASIA LEATHER CORPORATION—See Yue Yuen Industrial Holdings Limited; *Int'l*, pg. 8610
PRIME ASSET VENTURES, INC.; *Int'l*, pg. 5976
PRIME ASSISTANCE INC.—See Sompo Holdings, Inc.; *Int'l*, pg. 7086
PRIME ASSOCIATES, INC.—See Fidelity National Infor; *U.S. Public*, pg. 833
PRIME ATLANTIC CEGELEC NIGERIA LTD—See VINCI S.A.; *Int'l*, pg. 8215
PRIME ATLANTIC GLOBAL INSTRUMENTS LIMITED—See Endress+Hauser (International) Holding AG; *Int'l*, pg. 2409
PRIME AURTOMOTIVE PARTS CO., INC.—See Hahn Automotive Warehouse, Inc.; *U.S. Private*, pg. 1840
PRIME AUTO CARE INC.—See Kingsway Financial Services Inc.; *U.S. Public*, pg. 1235
PRIME AUTO RESOURCES, INC.—See AutoNation, Inc.; *U.S. Public*, pg. 237
PRIME BANK INVESTMENT LIMITED—See Prime Bank PLC.; *Int'l*, pg. 5976
PRIME BANK PLC.; *Int'l*, pg. 5976
PRIME BANK SECURITIES LIMITED—See Prime Bank PLC.; *Int'l*, pg. 5976
PRIME BIOLOGICS PTE LTD—See NuSep Holdings Ltd.; *Int'l*, pg. 5491
PRIMEBRIDGE HOLDINGS, INC—See SM Investments Corporation; *Int'l*, pg. 6998
PRIME CAPITAL INVESTMENT ADVISORS, LLC; *U.S. Private*, pg. 3261
PRIME CAPITAL MARKET LIMITED; *Int'l*, pg. 5976
PRIME CARCARE GROUP, INC.; *Int'l*, pg. 5976
PRIMECARE, INC.; *U.S. Private*, pg. 3262
PRIMECARE MEDICAL NETWORK, INC.—See UnitedHealth Group Incorporated; *U.S. Public*, pg. 2249
PRIMECARE OF CITRUS VALLEY, INC.—See UnitedHealth Group Incorporated; *U.S. Public*, pg. 2249
PRIMECARE OF CORONA, INC.—See UnitedHealth Group Incorporated; *U.S. Public*, pg. 2249
PRIMECARE OF HEMET VALLEY, INC.—See UnitedHealth Group Incorporated; *U.S. Public*, pg. 2249
PRIMECARE OF INLAND VALLEY, INC.—See UnitedHealth Group Incorporated; *U.S. Public*, pg. 2249
PRIMECARE OF MORENO VALLEY, INC.—See UnitedHealth Group Incorporated; *U.S. Public*, pg. 2249
PRIMECARE OF REDLANDS, INC.—See UnitedHealth Group Incorporated; *U.S. Public*, pg. 2249
PRIMECARE OF RIVERSIDE, INC.—See UnitedHealth Group Incorporated; *U.S. Public*, pg. 2249
PRIMECARE OF SAN BERNARDINO, INC.—See UnitedHealth Group Incorporated; *U.S. Public*, pg. 2249
PRIMECARE OF SUN CITY, INC.—See UnitedHealth Group Incorporated; *U.S. Public*, pg. 2249
PRIMECARE OF TEMECULA, INC.—See UnitedHealth Group Incorporated; *U.S. Public*, pg. 2249
PRIME CARE PHARMACY SERVICES, INC.—See Precision LTC Pharmacy; *U.S. Private*, pg. 3245
PRIMECARE SYSTEMS, INC.; *U.S. Private*, pg. 1717
PRIME CARGO (H.K.), LTD.—See Mitsui-Soko Holdings Co., Ltd.; *Int'l*, pg. 4993
PRIME CARGO POLAND SP. Z O.O.—See Mitsui-Soko Holdings Co., Ltd.; *Int'l*, pg. 4993
PRIME CARGO SHANGHAI LTD.—See Mitsui-Soko Holdings Co., Ltd.; *Int'l*, pg. 4993
PRIME CAR MANAGEMENT S.A.; *Int'l*, pg. 5976
PRIMECH HOLDINGS LTD.; *Int'l*, pg. 5978
PRIME CHOICE FOODS, INC.; *U.S. Private*, pg. 3261
PRIMECITY INVESTMENT PLC; *Int'l*, pg. 5978
PRIME CITY ONE CAPITAL CORP.; *Int'l*, pg. 5976
PRIME COMMERCIAL BANK LTD.; *Int'l*, pg. 5976
PRIME COMMUNICATIONS LP; *U.S. Private*, pg. 3261
PRIME CONDUIT, INC.—See Mitsubishi Materials Corporation; *Int'l*, pg. 4965
PRIME CONDUIT, INC.—See Mitsubishi Materials Corporation; *Int'l*, pg. 4965
PRIME CONTRACTORS INC.; *U.S. Private*, pg. 3261
PRIME CONTROLS, LP; *U.S. Private*, pg. 3261
PRIME CREDIT LEASING BERHAD—See Berjaya Corporation Berhad; *Int'l*, pg. 984
PRIME DELICA CO., LTD.—See Prima Meat Packers Ltd.; *Int'l*, pg. 5975
PRIMED FYSIO OCH REHAB AB—See Indutrade AB; *Int'l*, pg. 3681
PRIMEDIA BROADCASTING—See Primedia Limited; *Int'l*, pg. 5979
PRIMEDIA, INC.; *U.S. Private*, pg. 3263
PRIMEDIA LIMITED; *Int'l*, pg. 5978
PRIMEDIA LIMITED - SPECTRUM DIVISION—See Primedia Limited; *Int'l*, pg. 5979

2165

PRIMEDIA LIMITED — CORPORATE AFFILIATIONS

PRIMEDIA ONLINE (PTY) LTD—See Primedia Limited; *Int'l*, pg. 5979
PRIMEDIA OUTDOOR (PTY) LIMITED—See Primedia Limited; *Int'l*, pg. 5979
PRIMEDIA UNLIMITED—See Primedia Limited; *Int'l*, pg. 5979
PRIME DIGITALWORKS PTY LIMITED—See Seven West Media Limited; *Int'l*, pg. 6734
PRIMEDISC INTERNATIONAL LIMITED—See Shinvest Holding Limited; *Int'l*, pg. 6849
PRIME DISTRIBUTION SERVICES, INC.—See C.H. Robinson Worldwide, Inc.; *U.S. Public*, pg. 415
PRIME DIVIDEND CORP.—See Quadravest Capital Management Inc.; *Int'l*, pg. 6150
PRIMED MANAGEMENT CONSULTING SERVICES INC.; *U.S. Private*, pg. 3262
PRIME DRINK GROUP CORP.; *Int'l*, pg. 5976
PRIME EDUCATION, LLC—See Ziff Davis, Inc.; *U.S. Public*, pg. 2403
PRIME ELECTRIC, INC.—See WestView Capital Partners, L.P.; *U.S. Private*, pg. 4501
PRIME ELECTRONICS & SATELLITICS INC.; *Int'l*, pg. 5976
PRIME ENERGY CORP.—See United Renewable Energy Co., Ltd.; *Int'l*, pg. 8073
PRIME ENERGY P.E. LTD.; *Int'l*, pg. 5976
PRIMEENERGY RESOURCES CORPORATION; *U.S. Public*, pg. 1717
PRIME EQUIPMENT GROUP, INC.—See John Bean Technologies Corporation; *U.S. Public*, pg. 1192
PRIME E-TECH INTERNATIONAL PTE. LTD.—See Hanmi Semiconductor Co., Ltd.; *Int'l*, pg. 3256
PRIME EVOLVE SINGAPORE PTE. LTD.—See Mitsui Chemicals, Inc.; *Int'l*, pg. 4983
PRIME EXCHANGE CO. PTE LTD—See Prime Bank PLC.; *Int'l*, pg. 5976
PRIME FINANCE CAPITAL MANAGEMENT LIMITED—See Prime Finance & Investment Limited; *Int'l*, pg. 5977
PRIME FINANCE & INVESTMENT LIMITED; *Int'l*, pg. 5977
PRIME FINANCIAL ASIA LTD.—See China United Insurance Service, Inc.; *U.S. Private*, pg. 1561
PRIME FINANCIAL GROUP LIMITED; *Int'l*, pg. 5977
PRIMEFLIGHT AVIATION SERVICES, INC.—See The Carlyle Group Inc.; *U.S. Public*, pg. 2052
PRIME FLOORING LLC—See Lynx Equity Limited; *Int'l*, pg. 4606
PRIME FOCUS ACADEMY OF MEDIA AND ENTERTAINMENT STUDIES PRIVATE LIMITED—See Prime Focus Limited; *Int'l*, pg. 5977
PRIME FOCUS LIMITED; *Int'l*, pg. 5977
PRIME FOCUS LONDON PLC—See Prime Focus Limited; *Int'l*, pg. 5977
PRIME FOCUS NORTH AMERICA INC.—See Prime Focus Limited; *Int'l*, pg. 5977
PRIME FOCUS VFX PACIFIC INC—See Prime Focus Limited; *Int'l*, pg. 5977
PRIME FOCUS VISUAL ENTERTAINMENT SERVICES LTD.—See Prime Focus Limited; *Int'l*, pg. 5977
PRIME FOOD PROCESSING CORP.; *U.S. Private*, pg. 3261
PRIME FOODS CO., LTD.—See Prima Meat Packers Ltd.; *Int'l*, pg. 5975
PRIME FOUNDATION INC.—See FIC Global, INC; *Int'l*, pg. 2653
PRIME FRESH LTD.; *Int'l*, pg. 5977
PRIME FUELS CORP.—See Uravan Minerals Inc.; *Int'l*, pg. 8094
PRIME GLOBAL CAPITAL GROUP INCORPORATED; *Int'l*, pg. 5977
PRIMEGROUP INSURANCE, INC.; *U.S. Private*, pg. 3263
PRIME HEALTHCARE FOUNDATION-COSHOCTON, LLC—See Prime Healthcare Services, Inc.; *U.S. Private*, pg. 3261
PRIME HEALTHCARE SERVICES, INC.; *U.S. Private*, pg. 3261
PRIME HEALTH FOR MEDICAL SERVICES SAE—See Mediterranean & Gulf Insurance & Reinsurance Company S.J.S.C.; *Int'l*, pg. 4781
PRIME HOLDING; *Int'l*, pg. 5977
PRIME HOME CARE, INC.—See TPG Capital, L.P.; *U.S. Public*, pg. 2168
PRIME/HOME IMPRESSIONS, LLC—See Craftmade International, Inc.; *U.S. Private*, pg. 1082
PRIME INCORPORACOES E CONSTRUCOES S.A.—See MRV Engenharia e Participacoes S.A.; *Int'l*, pg. 5064
PRIME, INC.; *U.S. Private*, pg. 3262
PRIME INDUSTRIES LIMITED; *Int'l*, pg. 5977
PRIME INDUSTRIES PRE-CAST PTE. LTD.—See TA Corporation Ltd.; *Int'l*, pg. 7399
PRIME INNOVATIONS FOR TRADE S.A.E.—See ADES International Holding PLC; *Int'l*, pg. 144
PRIME INSURANCE COMPANY LIMITED; *Int'l*, pg. 5977
PRIME INTELLIGENCE SOLUTIONS GROUP LIMITED; *Int'l*, pg. 5977
PRIME ISLAMI LIFE INSURANCE LIMITED; *Int'l*, pg. 5977

PRIME KI SOFTWARE SOLUTIONS PVT LTD.—See Frontenac Company LLC; *U.S. Private*, pg. 1614
PRIME LABEL & PACKAGING, LLC—See Kollman Label Group, LLC; *U.S. Private*, pg. 2341
PRIMELENDING, A PLAINSCAPITAL COMPANY—See Hilltop Holdings Inc.; *U.S. Public*, pg. 1039
PRIMELENDING VENTURES, LLC—See Hilltop Holdings Inc.; *U.S. Public*, pg. 1039
PRIME LIFE INSURANCE COMPANY LTD.; *Int'l*, pg. 5977
PRIMELINE ENERGY CHINA LIMITED—See Primeline Energy Holdings Inc.; *Int'l*, pg. 5979
PRIMELINE ENERGY HOLDINGS INC.; *Int'l*, pg. 5979
PRIME-LINE, INC.; *U.S. Private*, pg. 3262
PRIME-LINE PRODUCTS COMPANY; *U.S. Private*, pg. 3262
PRIMELINE UTILITY SERVICES LLC—See VINCI S.A.; *Int'l*, pg. 8225
PRIMELUX INSURANCE S.A.—See Deutsche Bank Aktiengesellschaft; *Int'l*, pg. 2061
PRIME MANAGEMENT LIMITED—See SS&C Technologies Holdings, Inc.; *U.S. Public*, pg. 1923
PRIME MANPOWER RESOURCES DEVELOPMENT INC.—See ManpowerGroup Inc.; *U.S. Public*, pg. 1361
PRIME MASONRY MATERIALS; *U.S. Private*, pg. 3262
PRIME MATERIAL HANDLING EQUIPMENT LIMITED; *Int'l*, pg. 5978
PRIME MEDIA HOLDINGS INC—See RYM Business Management Corporation; *Int'l*, pg. 6439
PRIMEMEDICAL SUPPLY COMPANY; *U.S. Private*, pg. 3263
PRIME MEDICINE, INC.; *U.S. Public*, pg. 1716
PRIME MEIDEN LIMITED—See Meidensha Corporation; *Int'l*, pg. 4798
PRIME MERIDIAN BANK—See Prime Meridian Holding Company; *U.S. Public*, pg. 1717
PRIME MERIDIAN HOLDING COMPANY; *U.S. Public*, pg. 1717
PRIME MERIDIAN RESOURCES CORP.; *Int'l*, pg. 5978
PRIME METALS & ALLOYS, INC.—See Amerinac Holding Corp.; *U.S. Private*, pg. 260
PRIME MINING CORP.; *Int'l*, pg. 5978
PRIME MORTGAGE USA INC.; *U.S. Private*, pg. 3262
PRIME MOTOR GROUP—See GPB Capital Holdings, LLC; *U.S. Private*, pg. 1748
PRIMEMOVERS EQUITY (S) PTE. LTD.; *Int'l*, pg. 5979
PRIMENET DIRECT MARKETING SOLUTIONS, LLC; *U.S. Private*, pg. 3263
PRIME - NGOI VIET JOINT STOCK COMPANY—See The Siam Cement Public Company Limited; *Int'l*, pg. 7683
PRIME OFFICE A/S; *Int'l*, pg. 5978
PRIME OFFSHORE L.L.C.—See PrimeEnergy Resources Corporation; *U.S. Public*, pg. 1717
PRIME OIL CHEMICAL SERVICE CORPORATION; *Int'l*, pg. 5978
PRIME OPERATING COMPANY—See PrimeEnergy Resources Corporation; *U.S. Public*, pg. 1717
PRIMEPAK COMPANY; *U.S. Private*, pg. 3263
PRIMEPAY, LLC; *U.S. Private*, pg. 3263
PRIME PENSIONS, INC.—See Lightyear Capital LLC; *U.S. Private*, pg. 2454
PRIME PEOPLE PLC; *Int'l*, pg. 5978
PRIME PERFORMANCE, INC.—See Lincoln Property Company; *U.S. Private*, pg. 2458
PRIME PHONG DIEN JOINT STOCK COMPANY—See The Siam Cement Public Company Limited; *Int'l*, pg. 7683
PRIME PLACE CO., LTD.—See Tokyo Tatemono Co. Ltd.; *Int'l*, pg. 7796
PRIME PLASTIC PRODUCTS, INC.; *U.S. Private*, pg. 3262
PRIME PLATING INC—See Cyton Industries Inc.; *U.S. Private*, pg. 1136
PRIME POLICY GROUP—See WPP plc; *Int'l*, pg. 8468
PRIME POLICY GROUP—See WPP plc; *Int'l*, pg. 8468
PRIME POLYMER CO., LTD.—See Idemitsu Kosan Co., Ltd.; *Int'l*, pg. 3592
PRIME POLYMER CO., LTD.—See Mitsui Chemicals, Inc.; *Int'l*, pg. 4983
PRIMEPOWER QUEENSLAND PTY LTD—See Babylon Pump & Power Limited; *Int'l*, pg. 793
PRIME PROPERTY BG REIT; *Int'l*, pg. 5978
PRIME PROPERTY CONSULTANTS LIMITED—See Jones Lang LaSalle Incorporated; *U.S. Public*, pg. 1205
PRIME PROPERTY DEVELOPMENT CORPORATION LTD.; *Int'l*, pg. 5978
PRIME PROPERTY INVESTORS, LTD.; *U.S. Private*, pg. 3262
PRIMEPULSE SE; *Int'l*, pg. 5979
PRIME PURCHASE LIMITED—See Savills plc; *Int'l*, pg. 6598
PRIMERAIL GMBH—See DFDS A/S; *Int'l*, pg. 2095
PRIMERA RED INTERACTIVA DE MEDIOS ARGENTINOS (PRIMA) S.A.—See Grupo Clarin S.A.; *Int'l*, pg. 3125
PRIME RATE PREMIUM FINANCE CORPORATION, INC.—See Truist Financial Corporation; *U.S. Public*, pg. 2201
PRIMERDESIGN LTD.—See Novacyt SA; *Int'l*, pg. 5454
PRIME REALTY INCOME TRUST, INC.; *U.S. Private*, pg. 3262

PRIME RESEARCH & ADVIOSRY LIMITED—See Prime Securities Limited; *Int'l*, pg. 5978
PRIME RESINS, INC.—See RPM International Inc.; *U.S. Public*, pg. 1820
PRIME RESTAURANTS INC.—See Fairfax Financial Holdings Limited; *Int'l*, pg. 2608
PRIMEREVENUE, INC; *U.S. Private*, pg. 3263
PRIMERICA FINANCIAL SERVICES (CANADA) LTD.—See Primerica, Inc.; *U.S. Public*, pg. 1717
PRIMERICA FINANCIAL SERVICES, INC.—See Primerica, Inc.; *U.S. Public*, pg. 1717
PRIMERICA, INC.; *U.S. Public*, pg. 1717
PRIMERICA LIFE INSURANCE COMPANY OF CANADA—See Primerica, Inc.; *U.S. Public*, pg. 1717
PRIMERICA LIFE INSURANCE COMPANY OF CANADA—See Primerica, Inc.; *U.S. Public*, pg. 1717
PRIMERICA LIFE INSURANCE COMPANY OF CANADA—See Primerica, Inc.; *U.S. Public*, pg. 1717
PRIMERICA LIFE INSURANCE COMPANY OF CANADA—See Primerica, Inc.; *U.S. Public*, pg. 1717
PRIMERICA LIFE INSURANCE COMPANY OF CANADA—See Primerica, Inc.; *U.S. Public*, pg. 1717
PRIMERICA LIFE INSURANCE COMPANY—See Primerica, Inc.; *U.S. Public*, pg. 1717
PRIME RISK PARTNERS INC.—See Keystone Group, L.P.; *U.S. Private*, pg. 2299
PRIMERITUS FINANCIAL SERVICES, INC—See Kinderhook Industries, LLC; *U.S. Private*, pg. 2307
PRIME ROAD POWER PUBLIC COMPANY LIMITED; *Int'l*, pg. 5978
PRIMERO GROUP LIMITED—See NRW Holdings Limited; *Int'l*, pg. 5475
PRIMEROSALUD, S.L.—See Centene Corporation; *U.S. Public*, pg. 470
PRIMERO SEGUROS, S.A. DE C.V.—See Stone Point Capital LLC; *U.S. Private*, pg. 3821
PRIMESCAPE SOLUTIONS, INC.—See HighPoint Global, LLC; *U.S. Private*, pg. 1941
PRIME SECURITIES LIMITED; *Int'l*, pg. 5978
PRIMESERV ABC RECRUITMENT (PROPRIETARY) LIMITED—See Primeserv Group Limited; *Int'l*, pg. 5979
PRIMESERV DENVERDRAFT (PROPRIETARY) LIMITED—See Primeserv Group Limited; *Int'l*, pg. 5980
PRIMESERV GROUP LIMITED; *Int'l*, pg. 5979
PRIME SERVICES GROUP INC.; *U.S. Private*, pg. 3262
PRIMESERV STAFF DYNAMIX (PROPRIETARY) LIMITED—See Primeserv Group Limited; *Int'l*, pg. 5980
PRIMESIGHT LTD.—See GMT Communications Partners LLP; *Int'l*, pg. 3015
PRIMESKILL STAFFING SERVICES; *U.S. Private*, pg. 3263
PRIME SOLAR LLC—See Tess Holdings Co., Ltd.; *Int'l*, pg. 7573
PRIME SOLUTIONS LLC—See Altamira Technologies Corporation; *U.S. Private*, pg. 204
PRIMESOURCE BUILDING PRODUCTS, INC.—See Clearlake Capital Group, L.P.; *U.S. Private*, pg. 937
PRIMESOURCE FOODSERVICE EQUIPMENT; *U.S. Private*, pg. 3263
PRIME SOURCE, LLC—See Bunzl plc; *Int'l*, pg. 1219
PRIMESOURCING INTERNATIONAL SDN BHD—See Petroliam Nasional Berhad; *Int'l*, pg. 5831
PRIMESOUTH BANCSHARES, INC.—See CB&S Bank, Inc.; *U.S. Private*, pg. 796
PRIMESOUTH BANCSHARES, INC.; *U.S. Private*, pg. 3263
PRIMESOUTH BANK—See PrimeSouth Bancshares, Inc.; *U.S. Private*, pg. 3263
PRIME STAFFING INC.; *U.S. Private*, pg. 3262
PRIMESTAFF, LLC—See Health Advocates Network, Inc.; *U.S. Private*, pg. 1892
PRIMESTAR SOLAR, INC.—See General Electric Company; *U.S. Public*, pg. 919
PRIME STEELKIT PTE LTD—See Keppel Corporation Limited; *Int'l*, pg. 4132
PRIMESTOCK SECURITIES LTD—See Prime Financial Group Limited; *Int'l*, pg. 5977
PRIMESTOR JORDAN DOWNS, LLC—See Federal Realty Investment Trust; *U.S. Public*, pg. 825
PRIME STRATEGY CO., LTD.; *Int'l*, pg. 5978
PRIME SURFACTANTS LIMITED I.L.—See BRENNTAG SE; *Int'l*, pg. 1149
PRIME SYSTEM KZ LTD.; *Int'l*, pg. 5978
PRIME SYSTEMS, INC.; *U.S. Private*, pg. 3262
PRIMETALS PTY LIMITED—See Primedia Limited; *Int'l*, pg. 5979
PRIMETALS INTERNATIONAL TRADING (SHANGHAI) LTD. INC.—See Mitsubishi Heavy Industries, Ltd.; *Int'l*, pg. 4960
PRIMETALS TECHNOLOGIES AUSTRIA GMBH—See Mitsubishi Heavy Industries, Ltd.; *Int'l*, pg. 4960
PRIMETALS TECHNOLOGIES BELGIUM S.A./N.V.—See Mitsubishi Heavy Industries, Ltd.; *Int'l*, pg. 4960
PRIMETALS TECHNOLOGIES BRAZIL LTDA.—See Mitsubishi Heavy Industries, Ltd.; *Int'l*, pg. 4960
PRIMETALS TECHNOLOGIES CZECH REPUBLIC S.R.O.—See Mitsubishi Heavy Industries, Ltd.; *Int'l*, pg. 4960
PRIMETALS TECHNOLOGIES FRANCE S.A.S.—See Mitsubishi Heavy Industries, Ltd.; *Int'l*, pg. 4960

COMPANY NAME INDEX

PRIMETALS TECHNOLOGIES GERMANY GMBH—See Mitsubishi Heavy Industries, Ltd.; *Int'l*, pg. 4960
PRIMETALS TECHNOLOGIES INDIA PRIVATE LTD.—See Mitsubishi Heavy Industries, Ltd.; *Int'l*, pg. 4961
PRIMETALS TECHNOLOGIES ITALY S.R.L.—See Mitsubishi Heavy Industries, Ltd.; *Int'l*, pg. 4961
PRIMETALS TECHNOLOGIES JAPAN, LTD.—See Mitsubishi Heavy Industries, Ltd.; *Int'l*, pg. 4961
PRIMETALS TECHNOLOGIES KOREA LIMITED—See Mitsubishi Heavy Industries, Ltd.; *Int'l*, pg. 4961
PRIMETALS TECHNOLOGIES, LIMITED—See Mitsubishi Heavy Industries, Ltd.; *Int'l*, pg. 4961
PRIMETALS TECHNOLOGIES MEXICO, S.R.L. DE C.V.—See Mitsubishi Heavy Industries, Ltd.; *Int'l*, pg. 4961
PRIMETALS TECHNOLOGIES POLAND SP. Z O.O.—See Mitsubishi Heavy Industries, Ltd.; *Int'l*, pg. 4961
PRIMETALS TECHNOLOGIES RUSSIA LLC—See Mitsubishi Heavy Industries, Ltd.; *Int'l*, pg. 4961
PRIMETALS TECHNOLOGIES (SHANHAI), INC.—See Mitsubishi Heavy Industries, Ltd.; *Int'l*, pg. 4960
PRIMETALS TECHNOLOGIES UKRAINE LLC—See Mitsubishi Heavy Industries, Ltd.; *Int'l*, pg. 4961
PRIMETALS TECHNOLOGIES USA INC—See Mitsubishi Heavy Industries, Ltd.; *Int'l*, pg. 4961
PRIMETALS TEKNOLOJI SANAYI VE TICARET A.S.—See Mitsubishi Heavy Industries, Ltd.; *Int'l*, pg. 4961
PRIMETECH COMMUNICATIONS INC.—See Warren Equity Partners, LLC; *U.S. Private*, pg. 4443
PRIMETECH CORPORATION—See Prima Meat Packers Ltd.; *Int'l*, pg. 5975
PRIME TECHNICAL SERVICES INC.; *U.S. Private*, pg. 3262
PRIME TECHNOLOGICAL SERVICES, LLC; *U.S. Private*, pg. 3262
PRIME TECHNOLOGY GROUP, INC.—See Frontenac Company LLC; *U.S. Private*, pg. 1614
PRIME TECHNOLOGY (GUANGZHOU) INC.—See FIC Global, INC; *Int'l*, pg. 2653
PRIME TELEVISION (HOLDINGS) PTY LIMITED—See Seven West Media Limited; *Int'l*, pg. 6734
PRIME TELEVISION (INVESTMENTS) PTY LIMITED—See Seven West Media Limited; *Int'l*, pg. 6734
PRIME TELEVISION (NORTHERN) PTY LIMITED—See Seven West Media Limited; *Int'l*, pg. 6734
PRIME TELEVISION (SOUTHERN) PTY LIMITED—See Seven West Media Limited; *Int'l*, pg. 6734
PRIME TELEVISION (VICTORIA) PTY LIMITED—See Seven West Media Limited; *Int'l*, pg. 6734
PRIMETEL PLC—See Signal Capital Partners Limited; *Int'l*, pg. 6910
PRIMET FLUID POWER COMPANY, INC.—See Frontenac Company LLC; *U.S. Private*, pg. 1614
PRIME THERAPEUTICS, LLC—See GuideWell Mutual Holding Corporation; *U.S. Private*, pg. 1814
PRIMETIME 24 JOINT VENTURE—See Great Universal Incorporated; *U.S. Private*, pg. 1768
PRIMETIME AMUSEMENTS OF SOUTH FLORIDA LLC; *U.S. Private*, pg. 3263
PRIME TIME HEALTHCARE LLC—See OEP Capital Advisors, L.P.; *U.S. Private*, pg. 2999
PRIME TIMES NEWSPAPER—See Aegon N.V.; *Int'l*, pg. 175
PRIME TIME—See The Interpublic Group of Companies, Inc.; *U.S. Public*, pg. 2105
PRIME TITLE SERVICES, INC.—See Hometown Financial Group, Inc.; *U.S. Private*, pg. 1975
PRIMETON INFORMATION TECHNOLOGIES, INC.; *Int'l*, pg. 5980
PRIMETOWN PROPERTY GROUP INC; *Int'l*, pg. 5980
PRIME - TRUONG XUAN JOINT STOCK COMPANY—See The Siam Cement Public Company Limited; *Int'l*, pg. 7683
PRIME TRUSS CO., LTD.—See Tomoku Co., Ltd.; *Int'l*, pg. 7801
PRIME TURBINES LLC—See PTB Group Limited; *Int'l*, pg. 6090
PRIME URBAN DEVELOPMENT INDIA LIMITED; *Int'l*, pg. 5978
PRIME US REIT; *Int'l*, pg. 5978
PRIMEVIGILANCE LIMITED—See Permira Advisers LLP; *Int'l*, pg. 5804
PRIMEVIGILANCE S.R.O.—See Permira Advisers LLP; *Int'l*, pg. 5804
PRIME WELLNESS OF CONNECTICUT, LLC—See Acreage Holdings, Inc.; *U.S. Public*, pg. 36
PRIME WELLNESS OF PENNSYLVANIA, LLC—See Acreage Holdings, Inc.; *U.S. Public*, pg. 36
PRIMEWEST AGRICHAIN MANAGEMENT PTY LTD—See Primewest Pty. Ltd.; *Int'l*, pg. 5980
PRIMEWEST MORTGAGE CORPORATION—See Heartland Financial USA, Inc.; *U.S. Public*, pg. 1018
PRIMEWEST MORTGAGE INVESTMENT CORPORATION; *Int'l*, pg. 5980
PRIMEWEST (NORTHLANDS) PTY LTD—See Centuria Capital Limited; *Int'l*, pg. 1416
PRIMEWEST PTY. LTD.; *Int'l*, pg. 5980
PRIME WHEEL CORPORATION; *U.S. Private*, pg. 3262

PRIMEWORKS STUDIOS SDN BHD—See Media Prima Berhad; *Int'l*, pg. 4771
PRIME X CO., LTD.—See Nomura Real Estate Holdings, Inc.; *Int'l*, pg. 5412
PRIMEX CORPORATION; *Int'l*, pg. 5980
PRIMEX LTDA.—See Aiphone Co., Ltd.; *Int'l*, pg. 235
PRIMEX PLASTICS CORP.—See ICC Industries, Inc.; *U.S. Private*, pg. 2030
PRIMEX PLASTICS CORP.—See ICC Industries, Inc.; *U.S. Private*, pg. 2030
PRIMEX PLASTICS LIMITED—See ICC Industries, Inc.; *U.S. Private*, pg. 2030
PRIMEXPO—See Providence Equity Partners L.L.C.; *U.S. Private*, pg. 3293
PRIMEXPO—See Searchlight Capital Partners, L.P.; *U.S. Private*, pg. 3588
PRIMINTER (HKG) LTD.—See Pochet S.A.; *Int'l*, pg. 5902
PRIMINTER—See Pochet S.A.; *Int'l*, pg. 5901
PRIMION TECHNOLOGY AG—See AZKOYEN S.A.; *Int'l*, pg. 780
PRIMIS BANK—See Primis Financial Corp.; *U.S. Public*, pg. 1717
PRIMIS FINANCIAL CORP.; *U.S. Public*, pg. 1717
PRIMITIVES BY KATHY INC.; *U.S. Private*, pg. 3263
PRIMITY BIO, INC.—See Arsenal Capital Management LP; *U.S. Private*, pg. 337
PRIMIX B.V.; *Int'l*, pg. 5980
PRIMKOP AIRPORT MANAGEMENT (PTY) LTD.—See ABB Ltd.; *Int'l*, pg. 55
PRIMMS LP; *U.S. Private*, pg. 3263
PRIMMUNE INC.—See Trans Genic Inc.; *Int'l*, pg. 7894
PRIMM VALLEY CASINO RESORTS—See Z Capital Group, LLC; *U.S. Private*, pg. 4595
PRIMOCO UAV SE; *Int'l*, pg. 5980
PRIMO FOODS INC.—See Sun-Brite Foods Inc.; *Int'l*, pg. 7309
PRIMO MECHANICAL INC.; *Int'l*, pg. 5980
PRIMO NUTRACEUTICALS, INC.; *Int'l*, pg. 5980
PRIMO PIATTO, INC.—See Post Holdings, Inc.; *U.S. Public*, pg. 1704
PRIMORDIAL, INC.—See Polaris, Inc.; *U.S. Public*, pg. 1701
PRIMORIGEN BIOSCIENCES.—See Nucleus Biologics LLC; *U.S. Private*, pg. 2972
PRIMORIS AEVENIA, INC.—See Primoris Services Corporation; *U.S. Public*, pg. 1719
PRIMORIS DESIGN & CONSTRUCTION, INC.—See Primoris Services Corporation; *U.S. Public*, pg. 1719
PRIMORIS DISTRIBUTION SERVICES, INC.—See Primoris Services Corporation; *U.S. Public*, pg. 1719
PRIMORIS ELECTRIC, INC.—See Primoris Services Corporation; *U.S. Public*, pg. 1719
PRIMORIS ENERGY SERVICES CORPORATION—See Primoris Services Corporation; *U.S. Public*, pg. 1719
PRIMORIS SERVICES CORPORATION; *U.S. Public*, pg. 1718
PRIMORIS T&D SERVICES, LLC—See Primoris Services Corporation; *U.S. Public*, pg. 1719
PRIMORSKO CLUB PLC; *Int'l*, pg. 5980
PRIMORUS INVESTMENTS PLC; *Int'l*, pg. 5980
PRIMO SCHINCARIOL INDUSTRIA DE CERVEJAS E REFRIGERANTES DO NORDESTE S.A.—See Kirin Holdings Company, Limited; *Int'l*, pg. 4187
PRIMO SCHINCARIOL INDUSTRIA DE CERVEJAS E REFRIGERANTES DO NORTE-NORDESTE S.A.—See Kirin Holdings Company, Limited; *Int'l*, pg. 4187
PRIMO SCHINCARIOL INDUSTRIA DE CERVEJAS E REFRIGERANTES S.A.—See Kirin Holdings Company, Limited; *Int'l*, pg. 4187
PRIMO SERVICE SOLUTION COMPANY LIMITED—See Origin Property Public Company Limited; *Int'l*, pg. 5630
PRIMO SERVICE SOLUTIONS COMPANY LIMITED—See Origin Property Public Company Limited; *Int'l*, pg. 5630
PRIMOS HUNTING—See Vista Outdoor Inc.; *U.S. Public*, pg. 2304
PRIMOSUD SAS—See Nexity SA; *Int'l*, pg. 5244
PRIMOTECS S. P. A.—See Mutares SE & Co. KGaA; *Int'l*, pg. 5105
PRIMOTEQ B.V.—See Kis Partners AS; *Int'l*, pg. 4192
PRIMO WATER CORPORATION; *U.S. Public*, pg. 1717
PRIMO ZRT.—See Fotex Holding SE; *Int'l*, pg. 2752
PRIMROSE CANDY CO.; *U.S. Private*, pg. 3263
PRIMROSE, LLC—See PepsiCo, Inc.; *U.S. Public*, pg. 1671
PRIMROSE SCHOOL FRANCHISING COMPANY—See Roark Capital Group Inc.; *U.S. Private*, pg. 3455
PRIMROSE WELLNESS GROUP, LLC—See Clearday, Inc.; *U.S. Public*, pg. 512
PRIM S.A.; *Int'l*, pg. 5973
PRIMSOTSBANK PJS SCBP; *Int'l*, pg. 5980
PRIMULATOR AS—See Storskogen Group AB; *Int'l*, pg. 7228
PRIMUS AB—See Verdane Capital Advisors AS; *Int'l*, pg. 8165
PRIMUS AEROSPACE, INC.—See Angeles Equity Partners, LLC; *U.S. Private*, pg. 282
PRIMUS AUTOMOTIVE FINANCIAL SERVICES, INC.—See Ford Motor Company; *U.S. Public*, pg. 866

PRINCE RESOURCE CORP.

PRIMUS AUTOMOTIVE FINANCIAL SERVICES LIMITED—See Ford Motor Company; *U.S. Public*, pg. 866
PRIMUS BUILDERS, INC.; *U.S. Private*, pg. 3263
PRIMUS CAPITAL PARTNERS, INC.; *U.S. Private*, pg. 3263
PRIMUS CORP.—See Trinity Biotech Plc; *Int'l*, pg. 7924
PRIMUS DESIGN SERVICES—See Primus Builders, Inc.; *U.S. Private*, pg. 3263
PRIMUS EESTI OU—See Verdane Capital Advisors AS; *Int'l*, pg. 8165
PRIMUS FINANCIAL HOLDINGS LTD.; *Int'l*, pg. 5980
PRIMUS GLOBAL SERVICES INC.; *U.S. Private*, pg. 3263
PRIMUS GREEN ENERGY INC.—See Israel Corporation Ltd.; *Int'l*, pg. 3822
PRIMUS LIMITED—See UGI Corporation; *U.S. Public*, pg. 2222
PRIMUS PHARMACEUTICALS, INC.; *U.S. Private*, pg. 3263
PRIMUS PIPE & TUBE, INC.—See Ta Chen Stainless Pipe, Ltd.; *Int'l*, pg. 7399
PRIMUS PROCESSAMENTO DE TUBOS S.A.—See IHI Corporation; *Int'l*, pg. 3606
PRIMUS STERILIZER COMPANY, LLC—See Chalmers Group of Companies; *Int'l*, pg. 1439
PRIMUS TECHNOLOGIES CORP.—See OEP Capital Advisors, L.P.; *U.S. Private*, pg. 3000
PRIMUSTECH PTE. LTD.—See Japan Display Inc.; *Int'l*, pg. 3887
PRIMUS TELECOMMUNICATIONS (AUSTRALIA) PTY. LTD.—See Aware Super Pty Ltd; *Int'l*, pg. 752
PRIMUS TELECOMMUNICATIONS (AUSTRALIA) PTY. LTD.—See Macquarie Group Limited; *Int'l*, pg. 4629
PRIMUS TELECOMMUNICATIONS CANADA INC.—See Distributel Communications Limited; *Int'l*, pg. 2136
PRIMUS TELECOM PTY. LTD.—See Aware Super Pty Ltd; *Int'l*, pg. 752
PRIMUS TELECOM PTY. LTD.—See Macquarie Group Limited; *Int'l*, pg. 4629
PRIMUS THERAPEUTICS, INC.; *U.S. Private*, pg. 3263
PRIM Z IMMOBILIEN LEASING GESELLSCHAFT M.B.H.—See UniCredit S.p.A.; *Int'l*, pg. 8037
PRINCE AGRI PRODUCTS, INC.—See Phibro Animal Health Corporation; *U.S. Public*, pg. 1685
PRINCE ARTHUR ADVERTISING INC.—See The Caldwell Partners International Inc.; *Int'l*, pg. 7630
PRINCE AUTOMOTIVE GROUP INC.; *U.S. Private*, pg. 3264
PRINCE-BUSH INVESTMENTS; *U.S. Private*, pg. 3264
PRINCE CASTLE, INC.—See Berkshire Hathaway Inc.; *U.S. Public*, pg. 310
PRINCE CONTRACTING, LLC—See ACS, Actividades de Construccion y Servicios, S.A.; *Int'l*, pg. 111
PRINCE CORPORATION; *U.S. Private*, pg. 3264
PRINCECRAFT BOATS, INC.—See Brunswick Corporation; *U.S. Public*, pg. 407
PRINCE FREDERICK SURGERY CENTER, LLC—See Tenet Healthcare Corporation; *U.S. Public*, pg. 2006
THE PRINCE GEORGE CITIZEN—See Glacier Media Inc.; *Int'l*, pg. 2987
PRINCE GEORGE MOTORS LTD; *Int'l*, pg. 5980
PRINCE GEORGE'S COUNTY MEMORIAL LIBRARY SYSTEM; *U.S. Private*, pg. 3264
PRINCE GEORGE'S RACING VENTURES, LLC—See The Stronach Group Inc.; *Int'l*, pg. 7689
PRINCE GOLF; *U.S. Private*, pg. 3264
THE PRINCE HOTEL LIMITED—See Wheelock & Company Limited; *Int'l*, pg. 8397
PRINCE HOTELS, INC.—See Seibu Holdings Inc.; *Int'l*, pg. 6685
PRINCE HOUSING & DEVELOPMENT CORP.; *Int'l*, pg. 5980
PRINCE INDUSTRIES, LLC—See HC Private Investments LLC; *U.S. Private*, pg. 1888
PRINCE INTERNATIONAL CORPORATION—See American Securities LLC; *U.S. Private*, pg. 253
PRINCE & IZANT COMPANY; *U.S. Private*, pg. 3264
PRINCE KUHIO PLAZA—See Brookfield Corporation; *Int'l*, pg. 1185
PRINCE MANUFACTURING CORPORATION; *U.S. Private*, pg. 3264
PRINCE MINERALS, GMBH—See American Securities LLC; *U.S. Private*, pg. 253
PRINCE MINERALS ITALY S.R.L.—See American Securities LLC; *U.S. Private*, pg. 253
PRINCE MINERALS, LTD.—See American Securities LLC; *U.S. Private*, pg. 253
PRINCE MINERALS, S.A.—See American Securities LLC; *U.S. Private*, pg. 253
PRINCE OCALA, LTD.—See Best Western International, Inc.; *U.S. Private*, pg. 544
PRINCE OF PEACE ENTERPRISES; *U.S. Private*, pg. 3264
PRINCE OF WALES COUNTRY CLUB S.A.; *Int'l*, pg. 5980
PRINCE-PARKER & ASSOCIATES INC—See Complete Recovery Corporation; *U.S. Private*, pg. 1001
PRINCE RESOURCE CORP.; *Int'l*, pg. 5980

PRINCE RUBBER & PLASTICS CO., INC. CORPORATE AFFILIATIONS

PRINCE RUBBER & PLASTICS CO., INC.; *U.S. Private*, pg. 3264
PRINCE RUPERT GRAIN LIMITED—See Prince Rupert Port Authority; *Int'l*, pg. 5980
PRINCE RUPERT PORT AUTHORITY; *Int'l*, pg. 5980
PRINCES LIMITED—See Mitsubishi Corporation; *Int'l*, pg. 4943
PRINCESS ALEXENDRA RETIREMENT VILLAGE—See Ryman Healthcare Ltd.; *Int'l*, pg. 6439
PRINCESS AUTO LTD; *Int'l*, pg. 5980
PRINCESS CRUISES—See Carnival Corporation; *U.S. Public*, pg. 438
PRINCESS GRACE HOSPITAL—See HCA Healthcare, Inc.; *U.S. Public*, pg. 1006
PRINCESS PRIVATE EQUITY HOLDING LIMITED; *Int'l*, pg. 5980
PRINCESS TOURS—See Carnival Corporation; *U.S. Public*, pg. 438
PRINCE TELECOM LLC—See Dycom Industries, Inc.; *U.S. Public*, pg. 699
PRINCETON AREA COMMUNITY FOUNDATION; *U.S. Private*, pg. 3264
PRINCETON BANCORP, INC.; *U.S. Public*, pg. 1719
PRINCETON BIOMEDITECH CORP.; *U.S. Private*, pg. 3264
PRINCETON BMW; *U.S. Private*, pg. 3264
PRINCETON CAPITAL CORPORATION; *U.S. Public*, pg. 1719
PRINCETON CHEVROLET, INC.—See General Motors Company; *U.S. Public*, pg. 928
PRINCETON CHEVROLET, INC.—See General Motors Company; *U.S. Public*, pg. 928
PRINCETON CLUB OF NEW YORK; *U.S. Private*, pg. 3264
PRINCETON COMMUNITY HOMECARE, LLC—See UnitedHealth Group Incorporated; *U.S. Public*, pg. 2246
PRINCETON COMMUNITY HOSPITAL; *U.S. Private*, pg. 3264
THE PRINCETON EXCESS AND SURPLUS LINES INSURANCE COMPANY LTD.—See Munchener Ruckversicherungs AG; *Int'l*, pg. 5092
PRINCETON FINANCIAL SYSTEMS, LLC—See State Street Corporation; *U.S. Public*, pg. 1940
PRINCETON HOLDINGS LIMITED; *Int'l*, pg. 5980
PRINCETON INFORMATION LTD.—See Digital Intelligence Systems, LLC; *U.S. Private*, pg. 1230
PRINCETON INSTRUMENTS INC.—See Teledyne Technologies Incorporated; *U.S. Public*, pg. 1992
PRINCETON INSURANCE COMPANY—See Berkshire Hathaway Inc.; *U.S. Public*, pg. 302
PRINCETON LAND ROVER; *U.S. Private*, pg. 3264
PRINCETON LTD.—See Minato Holdings Inc.; *Int'l*, pg. 4899
PRINCETONONE ASIA—See My Job Matcher, Inc.; *U.S. Private*, pg. 2823
PRINCETONONE LLC—See My Job Matcher, Inc.; *U.S. Private*, pg. 2823
PRINCETON OPTICS, INC.—See TE Connectivity Ltd.; *Int'l*, pg. 7497
PRINCETON PACKET INC.; *U.S. Private*, pg. 3264
PRINCETON PARTNERS, INC.; *U.S. Private*, pg. 3264
PRINCETON PROPERTY MANAGEMENT; *U.S. Private*, pg. 3264
PRINCETON PUBLIC AFFAIRS GROUP, INC.—See Winning Strategies Public Relations, LLC; *U.S. Private*, pg. 4543
PRINCETON PUBLISHING INC.—See Brehm Communications Inc.; *U.S. Private*, pg. 644
PRINCETON RESIDENCE (HK) LIMITED—See Legend Upstar Holdings Limited; *Int'l*, pg. 4444
THE PRINCETON REVIEW, INC.—See Charlesbank Capital Partners, LLC; *U.S. Private*, pg. 856
PRINCETON RISK PROTECTION, INC.—See Berkshire Hathaway Inc.; *U.S. Public*, pg. 302
PRINCETON TECHNOLOGY CORP.—See Intervala, LLC; *U.S. Private*, pg. 2127
PRINCETON TRAVELS (PVT) LTD.—See Lakson Group of Companies; *Int'l*, pg. 4398
PRINCETON UNIVERSITY PRESS; *U.S. Private*, pg. 3264
PRINCE WILLIAM AMBULATORY SURGERY CENTER, LLC—See Tenet Healthcare Corporation; *U.S. Public*, pg. 2006
PRINCE WILLIAM HEALTH SYSTEMS INC.—See Novant Health, Inc.; *U.S. Private*, pg. 2967
PRINCIPA DECISIONS PROPRIETARY LIMITED—See Transaction Capital Limited; *Int'l*, pg. 7894
PRINCIPAL ASSET MANAGEMENT BERHAD—See Principal Financial Group, Inc.; *U.S. Public*, pg. 1720
PRINCIPAL ASSET MANAGEMENT COMPANY ASIA, LTD.—See Principal Financial Group, Inc.; *U.S. Public*, pg. 1721
PRINCIPAL ASSET MANAGEMENT COMPANY PRIVATE LIMITED—See Principal Financial Group, Inc.; *U.S. Public*, pg. 1720
PRINCIPAL BANK—See Principal Financial Group, Inc.; *U.S. Public*, pg. 1720
PRINCIPAL BUILDING SERVICES, INC.; *U.S. Private*, pg. 3264
PRINCIPAL CAPITAL COMPANY PUBLIC COMPANY LIMITED; *Int'l*, pg. 5980

PRINCIPAL CHILE LIMITADA—See Principal Financial Group, Inc.; *U.S. Public*, pg. 1720
PRINCIPAL COMMERCIAL FUNDING, LLC—See Principal Financial Group, Inc.; *U.S. Public*, pg. 1720
PRINCIPAL COMPANIA DE SEGUROS DE VIDA CHILE S.A.—See Principal Financial Group, Inc.; *U.S. Public*, pg. 1720
PRINCIPAL CREDITOS HIPOTECARIOS, S.A.—See Compania de Seguros de Vida Cruz del Sur S.A; *Int'l*, pg. 1749
PRINCIPAL DEVELOPMENT INVESTORS, LLC—See Principal Financial Group, Inc.; *U.S. Public*, pg. 1720
PRINCIPAL ENTERPRISE CAPITAL, LLC—See Principal Financial Group, Inc.; *U.S. Public*, pg. 1720
PRINCIPAL FINANCIAL ADVISORS, INC.—See Principal Financial Group, Inc.; *U.S. Public*, pg. 1720
PRINCIPAL FINANCIAL GROUP (AUSTRALIA) PTY. LTD.—See Principal Financial Group, Inc.; *U.S. Public*, pg. 1720
PRINCIPAL FINANCIAL GROUP, INC. - APPLETON—See Principal Financial Group, Inc.; *U.S. Public*, pg. 1720
PRINCIPAL FINANCIAL GROUP, INC. - INDIANAPOLIS—See Principal Financial Group, Inc.; *U.S. Public*, pg. 1720
PRINCIPAL FINANCIAL GROUP, INC. - RALEIGH—See Principal Financial Group, Inc.; *U.S. Public*, pg. 1721
PRINCIPAL FINANCIAL GROUP, INC.; *U.S. Public*, pg. 1719
PRINCIPAL FINANCIAL SERVICES, INC.—See Principal Financial Group, Inc.; *U.S. Public*, pg. 1721
PRINCIPAL GENERA S.A. DE C.V.—See Principal Financial Group, Inc.; *U.S. Public*, pg. 1721
PRINCIPAL GLOBAL COLUMBUS CIRCLE, LLC—See Principal Financial Group, Inc.; *U.S. Public*, pg. 1721
PRINCIPAL GLOBAL INVESTORS (ASIA) LIMITED—See Principal Financial Group, Inc.; *U.S. Public*, pg. 1721
PRINCIPAL GLOBAL INVESTORS (AUSTRALIA) LIMITED—See Principal Financial Group, Inc.; *U.S. Public*, pg. 1721
PRINCIPAL GLOBAL INVESTORS (AUSTRALIA) SERVICE COMPANY PTY LIMITED—See Principal Financial Group, Inc.; *U.S. Public*, pg. 1721
PRINCIPAL GLOBAL INVESTORS (EUROPE) LIMITED—See Principal Financial Group, Inc.; *U.S. Public*, pg. 1721
PRINCIPAL GLOBAL INVESTORS, LLC—See Principal Financial Group, Inc.; *U.S. Public*, pg. 1721
PRINCIPAL GLOBAL INVESTORS (SINGAPORE), LTD—See Principal Financial Group, Inc.; *U.S. Public*, pg. 1721
PRINCIPAL GLOBAL INVESTORS—See Principal Financial Group, Inc.; *U.S. Public*, pg. 1721
PRINCIPAL GLOBAL SERVICES PRIVATE LIMITED—See Principal Financial Group, Inc.; *U.S. Public*, pg. 1721
PRINCIPAL HEALTHCARE CO., LTD.—See Principal Capital Company Public Company Limited; *Int'l*, pg. 5981
PRINCIPAL INSURANCE COMPANY (HONG KONG) LIMITED—See Principal Financial Group, Inc.; *U.S. Public*, pg. 1721
PRINCIPAL INTERNATIONAL ARGENTINA, S.A.—See Principal Financial Group, Inc.; *U.S. Public*, pg. 1721
PRINCIPAL INTERNATIONAL (ASIA) LIMITED—See Principal Financial Group, Inc.; *U.S. Public*, pg. 1721
PRINCIPAL INTERNATIONAL, INC.—See Principal Financial Group, Inc.; *U.S. Public*, pg. 1721
PRINCIPAL INVESTMENT & RETIREMENT SERVICES LIMITED—See Principal Financial Group, Inc.; *U.S. Public*, pg. 1721
PRINCIPAL ISLAMIC ASSET MANAGEMENT SDN. BHD.—See CIMB Group Holdings Berhad; *Int'l*, pg. 1608
PRINCIPAL ISLAMIC ASSET MANAGEMENT SDN. BHD.—See Principal Financial Group, Inc.; *U.S. Public*, pg. 1721
PRINCIPAL LIFE INSURANCE COMPANY—See Principal Financial Group, Inc.; *U.S. Public*, pg. 1721
PRINCIPAL MANUFACTURING CORP.; *U.S. Private*, pg. 3264
PRINCIPAL MARITIME TANKERS CORPORATION; *U.S. Private*, pg. 3264
PRINCIPAL MEXICO COMPANIA DE SEGUROS S.A. DE C.V.—See Principal Financial Group, Inc.; *U.S. Public*, pg. 1721
PRINCIPAL PENSIONES, S.A. DE C.V.—See Principal Financial Group, Inc.; *U.S. Public*, pg. 1721
PRINCIPAL REAL ESTATE B.V.—See Principal Financial Group, Inc.; *U.S. Public*, pg. 1722
PRINCIPAL REAL ESTATE EUROPE LIMITED—See Principal Financial Group, Inc.; *U.S. Public*, pg. 1722
PRINCIPAL REAL ESTATE GMBH—See Principal Financial Group, Inc.; *U.S. Public*, pg. 1722
PRINCIPAL REAL ESTATE INVESTORS, LLC—See Principal Financial Group, Inc.; *U.S. Public*, pg. 1721
PRINCIPAL REAL ESTATE KAPITALVERWALTUNGSGESELLSCHAFT MBH—See Principal Financial Group, Inc.; *U.S. Public*, pg. 1722
PRINCIPAL REAL ESTATE S.A.R.L.—See Principal Financial Group, Inc.; *U.S. Public*, pg. 1722

PRINCIPAL REAL ESTATE SAS—See Principal Financial Group, Inc.; *U.S. Public*, pg. 1722
PRINCIPAL REAL ESTATE S.L.—See Principal Financial Group, Inc.; *U.S. Public*, pg. 1722
PRINCIPAL RETIREMENT ADVISORS PRIVATE LIMITED—See Principal Financial Group, Inc.; *U.S. Public*, pg. 1722
PRINCIPAL SOLAR, INC.; *U.S. Public*, pg. 1722
PRINCIPAL TECHNOLOGIES INC.; *Int'l*, pg. 5981
PRINCIPAL TRUST COMPANY (ASIA) LIMITED—See Principal Financial Group, Inc.; *U.S. Public*, pg. 1721
PRINCIP A.S.—See W.A.G Payment Solutions Plc; *Int'l*, pg. 8321
PRINCIPIA BIOPHARMA INC.—See Sanofi; *Int'l*, pg. 6548
PRINCIPIA LAW LIMITED—See ZIGUP plc; *Int'l*, pg. 8682
PRINCIPLE CONSTRUCTION CORP.; *U.S. Private*, pg. 3265
PRINCIPLE INSURANCE COMPANY LIMITED—See R&Q Insurance Holdings Ltd.; *Int'l*, pg. 6168
PRINCIPLE MCD, INC.—See M&C Saatchi plc; *Int'l*, pg. 4611
PRINCIPLE POWER, INC.; *U.S. Private*, pg. 3265
PRINCIPLES GROUP LLC; *U.S. Private*, pg. 3265
PRINCIPLE SOLUTIONS GROUP, LLC—See Stone Point Capital LLC; *U.S. Private*, pg. 3823
PRINCIPLE VALUATION, LLC—See Prism Health Care Services, Inc.; *U.S. Private*, pg. 3267
PRINCI UK LIMITED—See Starbucks Corporation; *U.S. Public*, pg. 1938
PR INDUSTRIAL S.R.L.—See Generac Holdings Inc.; *U.S. Public*, pg. 912
P&R INDUSTRIES INC.; *U.S. Private*, pg. 3059
PRINEVILLE BANCORPORATION; *U.S. Public*, pg. 1722
PRINEVILLE SPE LLC—See National Storage Affiliates Trust; *U.S. Public*, pg. 1498
PRINGLE OF SCOTLAND LTD.—See Fang Brothers Knitting Ltd.; *Int'l*, pg. 2613
PRINGLES MANUFACTURING COMPANY—See Kellanova; *U.S. Public*, pg. 1218
PRINOTH FRANCE; *Int'l*, pg. 5981
PRINOVA GIDA VE KIMYA TICARETI LIMITED—See Nagase & Co., Ltd.; *Int'l*, pg. 5128
PRINOVA GROUP LLC—See Nagase & Co., Ltd.; *Int'l*, pg. 5128
PRINOVIS GMBH & CO. KG—See Bertelsmann SE & Co. KGaA; *Int'l*, pg. 995
PRINOVIS GMBH & CO. KG—See Bertelsmann SE & Co. KGaA; *Int'l*, pg. 995
PRINOVIS UK LIMITED—See Bertelsmann SE & Co. KGaA; *Int'l*, pg. 995
PRINSAMED - PROJECTOS INTERNACIONAIS DE SAUDE UNIPESSOAL LDA.—See Fresenius SE & Co. KGaA; *Int'l*, pg. 2780
PRINSBURG FARMERS CO-OP; *U.S. Private*, pg. 3265
PRINSCO INC.; *U.S. Private*, pg. 3265
PRINSIRI PUBLIC COMPANY LIMITED; *Int'l*, pg. 5981
PRINTALL AS—See AS Ekspress Grupp; *Int'l*, pg. 590
PRINT APPEAL, INC.—See Thomas H. Lee Partners, L.P.; *U.S. Private*, pg. 4156
PRINT ASSIST AG—See Koenig & Bauer AG; *Int'l*, pg. 4227
PRINTCENTER OY—See Sanoma Oyj; *Int'l*, pg. 6553
PRINTCONCEPT UV-SYSTEME GMBH—See Dr. Honle AG; *Int'l*, pg. 2192
PRINT CRAFT, INC.—See Taylor Corporation; *U.S. Private*, pg. 3939
PRINTEC CO., LTD.—See Air Water Inc.; *Int'l*, pg. 240
PRINTED CIRCUITS INTERNATIONAL INCORPORATED—See Platinum Equity, LLC; *U.S. Private*, pg. 3206
THE PRINTED GROUP LIMITED—See Silver Lake Group, LLC; *U.S. Private*, pg. 3661
PRINTEGRA CORPORATION—See Ennis, Inc.; *U.S. Public*, pg. 769
PRINTEK INC.; *U.S. Private*, pg. 3265
PRINTELECTRIC, INC.; *U.S. Private*, pg. 3265
PRINTELLECTUAL—See Jenkins Group, Inc.; *U.S. Private*, pg. 2199
PRINTER COMPONENTS INC.—See Flotum Inc.; *U.S. Private*, pg. 1551
PRINTERON CORPORATION—See HP Inc.; *U.S. Public*, pg. 1065
PRINTERS MERCHANDISING CORP.—See Printers' Service, Inc.; *U.S. Private*, pg. 3265
PRINTERS' SERVICE, INC.; *U.S. Private*, pg. 3265
PRINTERS SERVICE OF FLORIDA, INC.—See Printers' Service, Inc.; *U.S. Private*, pg. 3265
PRINTERS SQUARE, INC.; *U.S. Private*, pg. 3265
THE PRINTER WORKS INC.; *U.S. Private*, pg. 4098
PRINT FINANCE VERMITTLUNG GMBH—See Heidelberger Druckmaschinen AG; *Int'l*, pg. 3322
PRINTFLEX GRAPHICS, INC.; *U.S. Private*, pg. 3266
PRINTFLY CORP.; *U.S. Private*, pg. 3266
PRINTFUL, INC.; *U.S. Private*, pg. 3266
PRINTGLOBE, INC.; *U.S. Private*, pg. 3266
PRINTGRAPHICS, LLC—See Ennis, Inc.; *U.S. Public*, pg. 769
PRINTHOUSESERVICE GMBH—See Koenig & Bauer AG; *Int'l*, pg. 4227

COMPANY NAME INDEX

PRINT, INC.—See Pitney Bowes Inc.; *U.S. Public*, pg. 1695
PRINTING.COM EUROPE LIMITED—See Software Circle plc.; *Int'l*, pg. 7057
PRINTING.COM (UK FRANCHISE) LIMITED—See Software Circle plc.; *Int'l*, pg. 7057
PRINTING CONTROL GRAPHICS—See Chatham Asset Management, LLC; *U.S. Private*, pg. 863
PRINTINGFORLESS.COM, INC.; *U.S. Private*, pg. 3266
PRINTING MANAGEMENT ASSOCIATES; *U.S. Private*, pg. 3266
PRINT-IQ SINGAPORE PTE. LTD.—See Serial System Ltd.; *Int'l*, pg. 6722
PRINT IT 4 LESS; *U.S. Private*, pg. 3265
PRINT LAB PTE. LTD.—See Thai Beverage Public Company Limited; *Int'l*, pg. 7590
PRINT MAIL LOGISTICS LIMITED; *Int'l*, pg. 5981
PRINT MARKETING CONCEPTS INC.—See Cowles Company; *U.S. Private*, pg. 1074
PRINT N ETCH PTE. LTD.; *Int'l*, pg. 5981
PRINTNET, INC.; *Int'l*, pg. 5981
PRINT NW LLC; *U.S. Private*, pg. 3265
PRINT-O-STAT, INC.—See Pace Resources, Inc.; *U.S. Private*, pg. 3064
PRINT-O-TAPE, INC.; *U.S. Private*, pg. 3265
PRINTPACK INC.; *U.S. Private*, pg. 3266
PRINTPACK INC.—See Printpack Inc.; *U.S. Private*, pg. 3266
PRINTPLACE.COM, LLC; *U.S. Private*, pg. 3266
PRINT PLANNER (BEIJING) CO., LTD.—See A-Smart Holdings Ltd.; *Int'l*, pg. 20
PRINTPLUS LIMITED—See Prosperous Printing Company Limited; *Int'l*, pg. 6002
PRINTPOST LIMITED—See An Post LLC; *Int'l*, pg. 443
PRINT REACH, INC.; *U.S. Private*, pg. 3265
PRINT RESOURCES, INC.; *U.S. Private*, pg. 3265
PRINTRON ENGRAVERS INC.; *U.S. Private*, pg. 3266
PRINTRONIX, INC.—See Acacia Research Corporation; *U.S. Public*, pg. 27
PRINTRUNNER, INC.; *U.S. Private*, pg. 3266
PRINT SOUTH CORPORATION; *U.S. Private*, pg. 3265
PRINTSOUTH CORPORATION; *U.S. Private*, pg. 3266
PRINTSTOCK PRODUCTS LIMITED—See The Marygold Companies, Inc.; *U.S. Public*, pg. 2112
PRINT SYSTEMS, INC.—See HH Global Group Limited; *Int'l*, pg. 3379
PRINT TIME INC.; *U.S. Private*, pg. 3265
PRINTUS FACHVERTRIEB FUR BUROBEDARF GMBH; *Int'l*, pg. 5981
PRINTVISION, INC.; *U.S. Private*, pg. 3266
PRINTWEST COMMUNICATIONS LTD.—See GVIC Communications Corp.; *Int'l*, pg. 3189
PRINTWORKS LTD.; *Int'l*, pg. 5981
PRINTXCEL—See Ennis, Inc.; *U.S. Public*, pg. 769
PRINTXCEL - VISALIA PLANT—See Ennis, Inc.; *U.S. Public*, pg. 769
PRINUR, S.A.U.—See Sacyr, S.A.; *Int'l*, pg. 6466
PRINX CHENGSHAN HOLDINGS LTD.; *Int'l*, pg. 5981
PRINZ GRAIN & FEED INC.; *U.S. Private*, pg. 3266
PRINZING GEBAUDETECHNIK GMBH—See STRABAG SE; *Int'l*, pg. 7231
PRINZ VON PREUSSEN CAPITAL LTD. AD; *Int'l*, pg. 5981
PRIO BIOCOMBUSTIBIL SRL—See Bunge Limited; *U.S. Public*, pg. 412
PRIOR AVIATION SERVICE, INC.—See OnCore Aviation LLC; *U.S. Private*, pg. 3019
PRIORBANK JSC—See Raiffeisen Bank International AG; *Int'l*, pg. 6183
PRIORIA ROBOTICS, INC.; *U.S. Private*, pg. 3266
PRIORITY-1 INC—See Priority Wire & Cable Inc.; *U.S. Private*, pg. 3267
PRIORITY AIR EXPRESS, LLC—See Thermo Fisher Scientific Inc.; *U.S. Public*, pg. 2151
PRIORITY AMERICA, INC.; *U.S. Private*, pg. 3266
PRIORITY AVIATION, INC.; *U.S. Private*, pg. 3266
PRIORITY DISPATCH INC.; *U.S. Private*, pg. 3266
PRIORITY EXPRESS COURIER INC.—See H.I.G. Capital, LLC; *U.S. Private*, pg. 1827
PRIORITY HEALTH MANAGED BENEFITS, INC.—See Spectrum Health Continuing Care Group, Inc.; *U.S. Private*, pg. 3752
PRIORITY HOME HEALTH CARE, INC.—See Addus HomeCare Corporation; *U.S. Public*, pg. 40
PRIORITY LEASING, INC.; *U.S. Private*, pg. 3266
PRIORITY MARKETING; *U.S. Private*, pg. 3266
PRIORITYONE BANK—See PriorityOne Capital Corporation; *U.S. Private*, pg. 3267
PRIORITYONE CAPITAL CORPORATION; *U.S. Private*, pg. 3267
PRIORITY ONE FINANCIAL SERVICES INC.; *U.S. Private*, pg. 3266
PRIORITY ONE FINANCIAL SERVICES LIMITED—See AMP Limited; *Int'l*, pg. 433
PRIORITY ONE SERVICES INC.; *U.S. Private*, pg. 3266
PRIORITY PAPERS, INC.—See Aaron Group of Companies; *U.S. Private*, pg. 32
PRIORITY PASS LIMITED—See The Collinson Group Limited; *Int'l*, pg. 7634
PRIORITY PAYMENT SYSTEMS CALIFORNIA—See Priority Payment Systems, LLC; *U.S. Private*, pg. 3267
PRIORITY PAYMENT SYSTEMS, LLC; *U.S. Private*, pg. 3267
PRIORITY PAYMENT SYSTEMS RSM—See Priority Payment Systems, LLC; *U.S. Private*, pg. 3267
PRIORITY PAYMENT SYSTEMS WEST—See Priority Payment Systems, LLC; *U.S. Private*, pg. 3267
PRIORITY PERSONNEL, INC.—See Hamilton-Ryker Company; *U.S. Private*, pg. 1848
PRIORITY PLASTICS, INC.; *U.S. Private*, pg. 3267
PRIORITY POWER MANAGEMENT, LLC—See I Squared Capital Advisors (US) LLC; *U.S. Private*, pg. 2026
PRIORITY PROPERTY HOLDINGS, LLC—See First Busey Corporation; *U.S. Public*, pg. 840
PRIORITY PUBLIC RELATIONS; *U.S. Private*, pg. 3267
PRIORITY PUBLIC RELATIONS—See Priority Public Relations; *U.S. Private*, pg. 3267
PRIORITY SOFTWARE LTD—See Fortissimo Capital Management LLP; *Int'l*, pg. 2740
PRIORITY SOLUTIONS INTERNATIONAL, INC.—See Thermo Fisher Scientific Inc.; *U.S. Public*, pg. 2151
PRIORITY STAFFING SOLUTIONS, INC.; *U.S. Private*, pg. 3267
PRIORITY TECHNOLOGY HOLDINGS, INC.; *U.S. Public*, pg. 1722
PRIORITY TRAVEL GROUP (HOLDINGS) LIMITED—See The Collinson Group Limited; *Int'l*, pg. 7634
PRIORITY WASTE LLC; *U.S. Private*, pg. 3267
PRIORITY WIRE & CABLE INC.; *U.S. Private*, pg. 3267
PRIOR REMANUFACTURING, INC.—See The Brenlin Group, LLC; *U.S. Private*, pg. 4000
PRIORS HALL PARK MANAGEMENT COMPANY—See The Wellcome Trust Ltd; *Int'l*, pg. 7701
PRIORTECH LTD.; *Int'l*, pg. 5981
THE PRIORY GROUP LIMITED—See Acadia Healthcare Company, Inc.; *U.S. Public*, pg. 31
PRIO-VNESHTORGBANK PAO; *Int'l*, pg. 5981
PRIPPS RINGNES AB—See Carlsberg A/S; *Int'l*, pg. 1340
PRISA BRAND SOLUTIONS USA, INC.—See Promotora de Informaciones S.A.; *Int'l*, pg. 5995
PRISA MEDIA MEXICO, S.A. DE C.V.—See Promotora de Informaciones S.A.; *Int'l*, pg. 5995
PRISA MEDIA USA, INC.—See Promotora de Informaciones S.A.; *Int'l*, pg. 5995
PRISA RADIO, S.A.—See Promotora de Informaciones S.A.; *Int'l*, pg. 5995
PRISCILLA HOLLIDAY OF TEXAS, INC.—See InterContinental Hotels Group PLC; *Int'l*, pg. 3738
PRISCO DIGITAL, LLC—See Printers' Service, Inc.; *U.S. Private*, pg. 3265
PRISCO EUROPE BVBA—See Printers' Service, Inc.; *U.S. Private*, pg. 3265
PRISCO EUROPE LTD.—See Printers' Service, Inc.; *U.S. Private*, pg. 3265
PRISCO GRAPHICS OF CANADA, INC.—See Printers' Service, Inc.; *U.S. Private*, pg. 3266
PRISCO/PACIFIC, INC.—See Printers' Service, Inc.; *U.S. Private*, pg. 3266
PRISCO (SINGAPORE) PTE. LTD.—See JSC Primorsk Shipping Corporation; *Int'l*, pg. 4010
PRISJAKT SVERIGE AB—See Schibsted ASA; *Int'l*, pg. 6617
PRISKE-JONES COMPANY; *U.S. Private*, pg. 3267
PRISKE JONES SOUTHEAST—See Priske-Jones Company; *U.S. Private*, pg. 3267
PRISMA CAPITAL LTDA.; *Int'l*, pg. 5982
PRISMA CAPITAL MANAGEMENT INTERNATIONAL LLP—See PAAMCO Prisma Holdings, LLC; *U.S. Private*, pg. 3062
PRISMA CAPITAL PARTNERS LP—See PAAMCO Prisma Holdings, LLC; *U.S. Private*, pg. 3062
PRISMADE LABS GMBH—See Edding AG; *Int'l*, pg. 2304
PRISMA EXPLORATION INC.; *Int'l*, pg. 5982
PRISMAFLEX AB—See Prismaflex International SA; *Int'l*, pg. 5982
PRISMAFLEX CANADA INC.—See Prismaflex International SA; *Int'l*, pg. 5982
PRISMAFLEX IBERICA SA—See Prismaflex International SA; *Int'l*, pg. 5982
PRISMAFLEX INTERNATIONAL SA; *Int'l*, pg. 5982
PRISMAFLEX RSA (PTY) LTD.—See Prismaflex International SA; *Int'l*, pg. 5982
PRISMAFLEX UK LTD—See Prismaflex International SA; *Int'l*, pg. 5982
PRISMAFLEX USA, INC.—See Prismaflex International SA; *Int'l*, pg. 5982
PRISMA GRAPHIC CORPORATION; *U.S. Private*, pg. 3267
PRISMA KREDITVERSICHERUNGS-AKTIENGESELL—See Oesterreichische Kontrollbank AG; *Int'l*, pg. 5529
PRISMA PRESSE & CIE—See Bertelsmann SE & Co. KGaA; *Int'l*, pg. 993
PRISMA PUBLIC RELATIONS—See Omnicom Group Inc.; *U.S. Public*, pg. 1578
PRISMAR DE COSTA RICA, S.A.—See PriceSmart Inc.; *U.S. Public*, pg. 1716
PRISMA RENEWABLE COMPOSITES, LLC—See PT Sinar Mas Group; *Int'l*, pg. 6073
PRISMASTAR LIMITED; *Int'l*, pg. 5982
PRISMA TECHNOLOGIES PTE LTD—See Forise International Ltd.; *Int'l*, pg. 2733
PRISMATIBRO AB—See Addtech AB; *Int'l*, pg. 134
PRISMATIC LTD.—See BAE Systems plc; *Int'l*, pg. 798
PRISMA TRAINING SOLUTIONS PROPRIETARY LIMITED—See Workforce Holdings Ltd.; *Int'l*, pg. 8455
PRISMA VERLAG GMBH & CO. KG—See Bertelsmann SE & Co. KGaA; *Int'l*, pg. 993
PRISM CHEMICALS—See Banner Chemicals Limited; *Int'l*, pg. 851
PRISM CONSTRUCTION LTD.; *Int'l*, pg. 5982
PRISM ENGINEERING LLC—See Court Square Capital Partners, L.P.; *U.S. Private*, pg. 1069
PRISM FINANCE LTD.; *Int'l*, pg. 5982
PRISM GAS SYSTEMS I, LP; *U.S. Private*, pg. 3267
PRISM GROUP, INC.—See Sabre Corporation; *U.S. Public*, pg. 1833
PRISM HEALTH CARE SERVICES, INC.; *U.S. Private*, pg. 3267
PRISM HOSPITALITY, LP—See Advent International Corporation; *U.S. Private*, pg. 97
PRISM HOTEL COMPANY, INC.—See Advent International Corporation; *U.S. Private*, pg. 97
PRISM HYDRAULICS PVT LTD—See Yuken India Ltd.; *Int'l*, pg. 8612
PRISMIC PHARMACEUTICALS, INC.—See FSD Pharma Inc.; *Int'l*, pg. 2798
PRISM INTEGRATED SDN. BHD.—See Iron Mountain Incorporated; *U.S. Public*, pg. 1174
PRISM INTERGRATED SDN BHD—See Iron Mountain Incorporated; *U.S. Public*, pg. 1174
PRISMI S.P.A.; *Int'l*, pg. 5982
PRISM JOHNSON LIMITED; *Int'l*, pg. 5982
PRISM MEDIA PRODUCTS INC—See Prism Sound Limited; *Int'l*, pg. 5982
PRISM MEDICAL INC.—See Savaria Corporation; *Int'l*, pg. 6596
PRISM MEDICAL LTD.—See Savaria Corporation; *Int'l*, pg. 6596
PRISM MEDICAL MANUFACTURING CENTRE—See Limerston Capital LLP; *Int'l*, pg. 4499
PRISM MEDICAL PRODUCTS, L.L.C.—See Henry Schein, Inc.; *U.S. Public*, pg. 1027
PRISM MEDICAL UK - APLS DIVISION—See Limerston Capital LLP; *Int'l*, pg. 4499
PRISM MEDICAL UK - CAREFREE DIVISION—See Limerston Capital LLP; *Int'l*, pg. 4499
PRISM MEDICAL UK - HEALTHCARE DIVISION—See Limerston Capital LLP; *Int'l*, pg. 4499
PRISM MEDICAL UK - LIFTECH & TEST VALLEY DIVISION—See Limerston Capital LLP; *Int'l*, pg. 4499
PRISM MEDICAL UK - SALUSS DIVISION—See Limerston Capital LLP; *Int'l*, pg. 4499
PRISM MEDICAL UK - WESTHOLME DIVISION—See Limerston Capital LLP; *Int'l*, pg. 4499
PRISM MEDICO & PHARMACY LIMITED; *Int'l*, pg. 5982
PRISMO METALS, INC.; *Int'l*, pg. 5982
PRISMONE GROUP, INC.; *U.S. Public*, pg. 1722
PRISM PAYMENT TECHNOLOGIES (PTY) LIMITED—See Lesaka Technologies, Inc.; *Int'l*, pg. 4469
PRISM PLASTICS, INC. - HARLINGEN PLANT—See Berkshire Hathaway Inc.; *U.S. Public*, pg. 311
PRISM PLASTICS, INC. - MEADVILLE PLANT—See Berkshire Hathaway Inc.; *U.S. Public*, pg. 311
PRISM PLASTICS, INC.—See Berkshire Hathaway Inc.; *U.S. Public*, pg. 311
PRISM PLASTICS PRODUCTS, INC.—See BlackBern Partners LLC; *U.S. Private*, pg. 573
PRISM PLASTICS PRODUCTS, INC.—See Lee Equity Partners LLC; *U.S. Private*, pg. 2412
PRISM PROTECTION SERVICES SDN. BHD.—See Tradewinds Corporation Berhad; *Int'l*, pg. 7888
PRISMRBS, LLC—See Collegiate Retail Alliance; *U.S. Private*, pg. 968
PRISMRBS, LLC—See Concise Capital Management LP; *U.S. Private*, pg. 1009
PRISM RESOURCES, INC.; *Int'l*, pg. 5982
PRISM SECURITY MANAGEMENT SDN. BHD.—See Tradewinds Corporation Berhad; *Int'l*, pg. 7888
PRISM SEISMIC, INC.—See Symphony Technology Group, LLC; *U.S. Private*, pg. 3901
PRISM SOLAR TECHNOLOGIES INCORPORATED—See Genie Energy Ltd.; *U.S. Public*, pg. 931
PRISM SOUND LIMITED; *Int'l*, pg. 5982
PRISM SPECTRUM HOLDINGS LLC—See The White Oak Group, Inc.; *U.S. Private*, pg. 4135
PRISM TECHNOLOGIES GROUP, INC.; *U.S. Public*, pg. 1722
PRISM TECHNOLOGIES, LLC—See Prism Technologies Group, Inc.; *U.S. Public*, pg. 1722
PRISM UK MEDICAL LTD.—See Limerston Capital LLP; *Int'l*, pg. 4499
PRISM VENTURE MANAGEMENT, LLC; *U.S. Private*, pg. 3267
PRISMVIEW, LLC—See Samsung Group; *Int'l*, pg. 6512
PRISMX GLOBAL VENTURES LTD.; *Int'l*, pg. 5983

PRISON REHABILITATIVE INDUSTRIES, INC.

PRISON REHABILITATIVE INDUSTRIES, INC.; *U.S. Private,* pg. 3267
PRISTA OIL AD BEOGRAD—See Prista Oil Holding EAD; *Int'l,* pg. 5983
PRISMA TECHNOLOGIES CZECH REPUBLIC S.R.O.—See Prista Oil Holding EAD; *Int'l,* pg. 5983
PRISTA OIL HOLDING EAD; *Int'l,* pg. 5983
PRISTA OIL-HUNGARY KFT.—See Prista Oil Holding EAD; *Int'l,* pg. 5983
PRISTA OIL LLC—See Prista Oil Holding EAD; *Int'l,* pg. 5983
PRISTA OIL ROMANIA SA—See Prista Oil Holding EAD; *Int'l,* pg. 5983
PRISTA OIL YAG SANAYI VE TICARET LIMITED SIRKETI - LUBRICANT BLENDING PLANT—See Prista Oil Holding EAD; *Int'l,* pg. 5983
PRISTA OIL YAG SANAYI VE TICARET LIMITED SIRKETI—See Prista Oil Holding EAD; *Int'l,* pg. 5983
PRISTINE CAPITAL HOLDINGS, INC.—See T3 Live LLC; *U.S. Private,* pg. 3913
PRISTINE CAPITAL PLC; *Int'l,* pg. 5983
PRISTINE WATER SOLUTIONS INC.—See CECO Environmental Corp.; *U.S. Public,* pg. 464
PRISTOP BG—See Pristop d.o.o.; *Int'l,* pg. 5983
PRISTOP D.O.O.; *Int'l,* pg. 5983
PRISXTRA AB—See Axel Johnson Gruppen AB; *Int'l,* pg. 764
PRITCHARD AUTO CO; *U.S. Private,* pg. 3267
PRITCHARD BROADCASTING CORP.; *U.S. Private,* pg. 3267
PRITCHARD BROWN, LLC.; *U.S. Private,* pg. 3268
PRITCHARD ELECTRIC COMPANY, INC.; *U.S. Private,* pg. 3268
PRITCHARD EQUITY LIMITED—See Bendigo & Adelaide Bank Ltd.; *Int'l,* pg. 971
PRITCHARD INDUSTRIES, INC.—See Littlejohn & Co., LLC; *U.S. Private,* pg. 2471
PRITCHARD INDUSTRIES, INC. - VIENNA OFFICE—See Littlejohn & Co., LLC; *U.S. Private,* pg. 2471
PRITCHARD INDUSTRIES SOUTHWEST INC.—See Littlejohn & Co., LLC; *U.S. Private,* pg. 2471
PRITCHARD INSURANCE INC.—See Lovell Minnick Partners LLC; *U.S. Private,* pg. 2503
PRITCHETT-MOORE, INC.—See Galiot Insurance Services, Inc.; *U.S. Private,* pg. 1638
PRITCHETT TRUCKING INC.; *U.S. Private,* pg. 3268
PRITCHITTS—See Lakeland Dairies Co-Operative Society Ltd.; *Int'l,* pg. 4397
PRITEC CO., LTD.—See Rhythm Co., Ltd.; *Int'l,* pg. 6328
PRITEX LIMITED—See Compagnie de Saint-Gobain SA; *Int'l,* pg. 1725
PRITHVI EXCHANGE (INDIA) LIMITED; *Int'l,* pg. 5983
PRITHVI SOLUTIONS LIMITED; *Int'l,* pg. 5983
PRITI INTERNATIONAL LTD.; *Int'l,* pg. 5983
PRITIKA AUTOCAST LTD.; *Int'l,* pg. 5983
PRITIKA AUTO INDUSTRIES LIMITED; *Int'l,* pg. 5983
PRITIKIN LONGEVITY CENTER & SPA; *U.S. Private,* pg. 3268
PRITISH NANDY COMMUNICATIONS LIMITED; *Int'l,* pg. 5983
PRITT PRODUKTIONSGESELLSCHAFT GMBH—See Henkel AG & Co. KGaA; *Int'l,* pg. 3354
THE PRITZKER GROUP - CHICAGO, LLC; *U.S. Private,* pg. 4098
THE PRITZKER GROUP - LA, LLC—See The Pritzker Group - Chicago, LLC; *U.S. Private,* pg. 4098
THE PRITZKER ORGANIZATION, LLC; *U.S. Private,* pg. 4100
PRITZLAFF WHOLESALE MEATS INC.; *U.S. Private,* pg. 3268
PRIVACY ANALYTICS INC.—See IQVIA Holdings Inc.; *U.S. Public,* pg. 1170
PRIVACYLAB S.R.L.—See Tinexta S.p.A.; *Int'l,* pg. 7753
PRIVACY & VALUE INC.; *U.S. Private,* pg. 3268
PRIVA INC.—See Fiberlinks Textiles Inc.; *Int'l,* pg. 2652
PRIVAS DISTRIBUTION; *Int'l,* pg. 5983
PRIVASIA TECHNOLOGY BERHAD; *Int'l,* pg. 5983
PRIVATAIR GMBH—See SilverArrow Capital Holding Ltd.; *Int'l,* pg. 6925
PRIVATAIR SA—See SilverArrow Capital Holding Ltd.; *Int'l,* pg. 6925
PRIVATAIR SAUDI ARABIA—See SilverArrow Capital Holding Ltd.; *Int'l,* pg. 6925
PRIVATASSISTENZA S.A.—See Zambon Company S.p.A.; *Int'l,* pg. 8622
PRIVAT BANK AG DER RAIFFEISENLANDESBANK OBEROSTERREICH—See Raiffeisenlandesbank Oberosterreich Aktiengesellschaft; *Int'l,* pg. 6187
PRIVATBANK DEGROOF, S.A.U.—See Banque Degroof S.A.; *Int'l,* pg. 853
PRIVATBRAUEREI ERDINGER WEISSBRAU WERNER BROMBACH GMBH; *Int'l,* pg. 5983
PRIVAT-BRAUEREI HEINRICH REISSDORF GMBH & CO. KG; *Int'l,* pg. 5983
PRIVATBRAUEREI HOEPFNER GMBH—See L'Arche Green N.V.; *Int'l,* pg. 4377
PRIVATBRAUEREI HOEPFNER GMBH—See Schorghuber Stiftung & Co. Holding KG; *Int'l,* pg. 6639

PRIVAT-BRAUEREI SCHMUCKER GMBH & CO. KG—See L'Arche Green N.V.; *Int'l,* pg. 4376
PRIVAT-BRAUEREI SCHMUCKER GMBH & CO. KG—See Schorghuber Stiftung & Co. Holding KG; *Int'l,* pg. 6639
PRIVATE AND COMMERCIAL FINANCE COMPANY LIMITED—See PCF Group plc; *Int'l,* pg. 5768
PRIVATE ASSET MANAGEMENT, INC.—See Genstar Capital, LLC; *U.S. Private,* pg. 1677
PRIVATE ASSET MANAGEMENT, INC.—See Keystone Group, L.P.; *U.S. Private,* pg. 2298
PRIVATE BALLOON FLIGHTS LLC—See Rainbow Ryders Inc.; *U.S. Private,* pg. 3347
PRIVATE BANCORP OF AMERICA, INC.; *U.S. Public,* pg. 1722
PRIVATE CAPITAL INCORPORATED; *U.S. Private,* pg. 3268
PRIVATE CAPITAL MANAGEMENT, INC.—See Independent Bank Group, Inc.; *U.S. Public,* pg. 1116
PRIVATE CAPITAL MANAGEMENT, LLC; *U.S. Private,* pg. 3268
PRIVATE CLIENT SERVICES BY MERCER CHINA LIMITED—See Marsh & McLennan Companies, Inc.; *U.S. Public,* pg. 1388
PRIVATE CLIENT SERVICES BY MERCER LIMITED—See Marsh & McLennan Companies, Inc.; *U.S. Public,* pg. 1388
PRIVATE CLIENT SERVICES BY MERCER PTE. LTD.—See Marsh & McLennan Companies, Inc.; *U.S. Public,* pg. 1388
PRIVATE CLIENT SERVICES BY MERCER SA—See Marsh & McLennan Companies, Inc.; *U.S. Public,* pg. 1388
PRIVATE COMPANY KAUNAS HEAT AND POWER PLANT UAB—See PJSC Gazprom; *Int'l,* pg. 5880
PRIVATE ENERGY SYSTEMS, INC.; *U.S. Private,* pg. 3268
PRIVATE EQUITY CAPITAL CORPORATION; *U.S. Private,* pg. 3268
PRIVATE EQUITY GROUP, LLC; *U.S. Private,* pg. 3268
PRIVATE EQUITY HOLDING AG; *Int'l,* pg. 5983
PRIVATE EQUITY INTERNATIONAL S.A.—See Intesa Sanpaolo S.p.A.; *Int'l,* pg. 3766
PRIVATE EQUITY MANAGERS S.A.; *Int'l,* pg. 5983
PRIVATEERIT, LLC; *U.S. Private,* pg. 3268
PRIVATE EYES, INC.; *U.S. Private,* pg. 3268
THE PRIVATE HEALTH PARTNERSHIP LTD—See Punter Southall Group Limited; *Int'l,* pg. 6120
PRIVATE JOINT STOCK COMPANY—See Mayr-Melnhof Karton AG; *Int'l,* pg. 4747
PRIVATE LABEL BY G INC.; *U.S. Private,* pg. 3268
PRIVATE LABEL NUTRACEUTICALS, LLC.; *U.S. Private,* pg. 3268
PRIVATE MARKET CONNECT LLC—See S&P Global Inc.; *U.S. Public,* pg. 1831
PRIVATE MINI STORAGE REALTY LP; *U.S. Private,* pg. 3268
PRIVATE MORTGAGE ADVISORS, LLC—See Wells Fargo & Company; *U.S. Public,* pg. 2345
PRIVATE OCEAN LLC—See Aon plc; *Int'l,* pg. 498
PRIVATE SAFARIS (EAST AFRICA) LTD.—See Fairfax Financial Holdings Limited; *Int'l,* pg. 2608
PRIVATE SAFARIS NAMIBIA (PTY) LTD.—See Fairfax Financial Holdings Limited; *Int'l,* pg. 2608
PRIVATE SAFARIS (PTY) LTD.—See Fairfax Financial Holdings Limited; *Int'l,* pg. 2608
PRIVATE SALE GMBH—See Regent, L.P.; *U.S. Private,* pg. 3388
PRIVATES INSTITUT FUR QUANTITATIVE KAPITALMARKTFORSCHUNG DER DEKABANK GMBH—See DekaBank; *Int'l,* pg. 2005
THE PRIVATE TRUST COMPANY, N.A.—See LPL Financial Holdings Inc.; *U.S. Public,* pg. 1343
PRIVATE VISTA LLC; *U.S. Private,* pg. 3268
PRIVATINVESTOR VERMOGENSMANAGEMENT GMBH; *Int'l,* pg. 5983
PRIVATIZATION HOLDING COMPANY K.S.C.C.; *Int'l,* pg. 5984
PRIVATKLINIK DOBLING GMBH—See UNIQA Insurance Group AG; *Int'l,* pg. 8058
PRIVATKLINIK DR. ROBERT SCHINDLBECK GMBH & CO. KG—See Starnberger Kliniken GmbH; *Int'l,* pg. 7178
PRIVATKLINIK GRAZ RAGNITZ GMBH—See UNIQA Insurance Group AG; *Int'l,* pg. 8058
PRIVATKLINIK JOSEFSTADT GMBH—See UNIQA Insurance Group AG; *Int'l,* pg. 8058
PRIVATKLINIK WEHRLE GMBH—See UNIQA Insurance Group AG; *Int'l,* pg. 8058
PRIVATMEGLEREN AS—See Nordea Bank Abp; *Int'l,* pg. 5418
PRIVATPATH DIAGNOSTICS, INC.; *U.S. Private,* pg. 3268
PRIVATUM N.V.—See Alan Allman Associates SA; *Int'l,* pg. 290
PRIVCO MEDIA LLC; *U.S. Private,* pg. 3268
PRIVECO INC.; *U.S. Private,* pg. 3268
PRIVE JETS, LLC; *U.S. Private,* pg. 3268
PRIVEQ ADVISORY AB; *Int'l,* pg. 5984
PRIVERA AG—See PHM Group Holding Oyj; *Int'l,* pg. 5848

CORPORATE AFFILIATIONS

PRIVETERRA ACQUISITION CORP. II; *U.S. Public,* pg. 1722
PRIVET FUND MANAGEMENT, LLC; *U.S. Private,* pg. 3268
PRIVIA HEALTH GROUP, INC.; *U.S. Public,* pg. 1722
PRIVIA LLC—See Xait AS; *Int'l,* pg. 8519
PRIVILEGE INSURANCE COMPANY LIMITED—See NatWest Group plc; *Int'l,* pg. 5171
PRIVILEGE SAS; *Int'l,* pg. 5984
PRIVILEGE UNDERWRITERS, INC.—See Tokio Marine Holdings, Inc.; *Int'l,* pg. 7784
PRIVI ORGANICS INDIA LIMITED—See Privi Speciality Chemicals Limited; *Int'l,* pg. 5984
PRIVI ORGANICS USA CORPORATION—See Privi Speciality Chemicals Limited; *Int'l,* pg. 5984
PRIVI SPECIALITY CHEMICALS LIMITED; *Int'l,* pg. 5984
PRIVOWNY FRANCE SAS—See Assurant, Inc.; *U.S. Public,* pg. 215
PRIVOZ; *Int'l,* pg. 5984
PRIVREDNA BANKA SARAJEVO D.D. SARAJEVO; *Int'l,* pg. 5984
PRIVREDNA BANKA ZAGREB D.D.—See Intesa Sanpaolo S.p.A.; *Int'l,* pg. 3766
PRIVY, INC.; *U.S. Private,* pg. 3269
PRIXCAR SERVICES PTY. LTD.—See Japan Post Holdings Co., Ltd.; *Int'l,* pg. 3901
PRIXCAR SERVICES PTY. LTD.—See Kawasaki Kisen Kaisha, Ltd.; *Int'l,* pg. 4099
PRIXCAR SERVICES PTY. LTD.—See Qube Holdings Limited; *Int'l,* pg. 6158
PRIXCAR TRANSPORT SERVICES PTY. LTD.—See Japan Post Holdings Co., Ltd.; *Int'l,* pg. 3901
PRIXCAR TRANSPORT SERVICES PTY. LTD.—See Kawasaki Kisen Kaisha, Ltd.; *Int'l,* pg. 4099
PRIXCAR TRANSPORT SERVICES PTY. LTD.—See Qube Holdings Limited; *Int'l,* pg. 6158
PRIYADARSINI LTD.; *Int'l,* pg. 5984
PRIYA INTERNATIONAL LIMITED—See Priya Limited; *Int'l,* pg. 5984
PRIYA LIMITED; *Int'l,* pg. 5984
PRIZELOGIC, LLC—See Marlin Equity Partners, LLC; *U.S. Private,* pg. 2584
PRIZE PETROLEUM COMPANY LTD.—See Oil & Natural Gas Corporation Limited; *Int'l,* pg. 5534
PRIZMA PRES MATBAACILIK YAYINCILIK SANAYI VE TICARET AS; *Int'l,* pg. 5984
PRIZM LLC—See GIC Pte. Ltd.; *Int'l,* pg. 2964
PRIZM LLC—See Leonard Green & Partners, L.P.; *U.S. Private,* pg. 2425
PR JACKSONVILLE LIMITED PARTNERSHIP—See Pennsylvania Real Estate Investment Trust; *U.S. Public,* pg. 1663
PRJSC AGROFORT—See OJSC Myronivsky Hliboproduct; *Int'l,* pg. 5540
PRJSC MYRONIVSKA POULTRY FARM—See OJSC Myronivsky Hliboproduct; *Int'l,* pg. 5540
PRJSC ORIL LEADER—See OJSC Myronivsky Hliboproduct; *Int'l,* pg. 5540
PRJSC PHILIP MORRIS UKRAINE—See Philip Morris International Inc.; *U.S. Public,* pg. 1687
PRJSC PHILIP MORRIS UKRAINE—See Philip Morris International Inc.; *U.S. Public,* pg. 1687
PRJSC UKRAINIAN BACON—See OJSC Myronivsky Hliboproduct; *Int'l,* pg. 5541
PRJSC UROZHAI—See OJSC Myronivsky Hliboproduct; *Int'l,* pg. 5540
PRJSC ZERNOPRODUCT MHP—See OJSC Myronivsky Hliboproduct; *Int'l,* pg. 5540
PRK 7 NIERUCHOMOSCI SP. Z O.O.—See Trakcja PRKiI S.A.; *Int'l,* pg. 7891
P&R LIFTCARS PTY. LTD.—See Dewhurst Group plc; *Int'l,* pg. 2091
PRL INC.; *U.S. Private,* pg. 3269
PR LOGAN VALLEY LLC—See Pennsylvania Real Estate Investment Trust; *U.S. Public,* pg. 1663
PRL PORTUGAL, UNIPESSOAL LDA—See Ralph Lauren Corporation; *U.S. Public,* pg. 1761
P&R METALS, INC.; *U.S. Private,* pg. 3059
PRM GREEN TECHNOLOGIES LIMITED—See Restore plc; *Int'l,* pg. 6304
PR MIDDLE EAST FZE—See Generac Holdings Inc.; *U.S. Public,* pg. 912
PR MORTGAGE INVESTMENT MANAGEMENT, LLC—See Merchants Bancorp; *U.S. Public,* pg. 1415
PRN AMBULANCE, LLC—See ProTransport-1; *U.S. Private,* pg. 3290
PR NEWSCHANNEL—See Selig Multimedia Inc.; *U.S. Private,* pg. 3602
PR NEWSWIRE ASIA LTD—See Platinum Equity, LLC; *U.S. Private,* pg. 3202
PR NEWSWIRE ASSOCIATION LLC—See Platinum Equity, LLC; *U.S. Private,* pg. 3202
PRN HEALTH SERVICES, INC.—See McLarty Capital Partners UK LLP; *U.S. Private,* pg. 2640
PRNJAVOR EKSPRES A.D.; *Int'l,* pg. 5984
PR NORTH DARTMOUTH LLC—See Pennsylvania Real Estate Investment Trust; *U.S. Public,* pg. 1663
PRN PHARMACAL INC—See PBI/Gordon Corporation; *U.S. Private,* pg. 3118

PRN PHYSICIAN RECOMMENDED NUTRICEUTICALS LLC—See ALPHAEON Corporation; *U.S. Private*, pg. 200
PRN RECRUITMENT LTD.—See HFBG Holding B.V.; *Int'l*, pg. 3375
PRO 2000 CO., LTD.; *Int'l*, pg. 5984
PRO2 ANLAGENTECHNIK GMBH; *Int'l*, pg. 5985
PROA CAPITAL DE INVERSIONES SGEIC, S.A.; *Int'l*, pg. 5985
PROACT BELGIUM B.V.B.A.—See Proact IT Group AB; *Int'l*, pg. 5985
PROACT CZECH REPUBLIC,S.R.O.—See Proact IT Group AB; *Int'l*, pg. 5985
PROACT ESTONIA AS—See Proact IT Group AB; *Int'l*, pg. 5985
PROACT FINANCE AB—See Proact IT Group AB; *Int'l*, pg. 5986
PROACT FINLAND OY—See Proact IT Group AB; *Int'l*, pg. 5986
PRO ACTION OF STEUBEN & YATES, INC.; *U.S. Private*, pg. 3269
PROACTIS GROUP LIMITED—See Pollen Street Limited; *Int'l*, pg. 5910
PROACTIS HOLDINGS PLC—See DBAY Advisors Limited; *Int'l*, pg. 1987
PROACTIS HOLDINGS PLC—See Pollen Street Limited; *Int'l*, pg. 5910
PROACT IT GROUP AB; *Int'l*, pg. 5985
PROACT IT LATVIA SIA—See Proact IT Group AB; *Int'l*, pg. 5986
PROACT IT NORGE AS—See Proact IT Group AB; *Int'l*, pg. 5986
PROACT IT SWEDEN AB—See Proact IT Group AB; *Int'l*, pg. 5986
PROACT IT UK LTD.—See Proact IT Group AB; *Int'l*, pg. 5986
PROACTIVA MEDIO AMBIENTE ARGENTINA—See Veolia Environnement S.A.; *Int'l*, pg. 8154
PROACTIVA MEDIO AMBIENTE BRASIL—See Veolia Environnement S.A.; *Int'l*, pg. 8154
PROACTIVA MEDIO AMBIENTE CHILE—See Veolia Environnement S.A.; *Int'l*, pg. 8154
PROACTIVA MEDIO AMBIENTE COLOMBIA—See Veolia Environnement S.A.; *Int'l*, pg. 8154
PROACTIVA MEDIO AMBIENTE MEXICO—See Veolia Environnement S.A.; *Int'l*, pg. 8154
PROACTIVA MEDIO AMBIENTE PERU—See Veolia Environnement S.A.; *Int'l*, pg. 8154
PROACTIVA MEDIO AMBIENTE S.A.—See Veolia Environnement S.A.; *Int'l*, pg. 8154
PROACTIVA MEDIO AMBIENTE VENEZUELA—See Veolia Environnement S.A.; *Int'l*, pg. 8154
PROACTIVE CAPITAL GROUP, LLC; *U.S. Private*, pg. 3271
PRO-ACTIVE ENGINEERING, INC.—See Tide Rock Holdings, LLC; *U.S. Private*, pg. 4168
PROACTIVE PACKAGING AND DISPLAY, INC.—See Schwarz Partners, LP; *U.S. Private*, pg. 3572
PROACTIVE PACKAGING AND DISPLAY, INC.—See The Kraft Group LLC; *U.S. Private*, pg. 4066
PROACTIVE PHYSICAL THERAPY, LIMITED PARTNERSHIP—See U.S. Physical Therapy, Inc.; *U.S. Public*, pg. 2215
PRO-ACTIVE PROJECTS LIMITED—See Content Ventures Limited; *Int'l*, pg. 1779
PROACTIVE SALES & MARKETING INC.—See Alliance Foods Inc.; *U.S. Private*, pg. 182
PROACTIVE SPORTS INC.—See Kinzie Capital Partners LP; *U.S. Private*, pg. 2313
PROACTIVE TECHNOLOGIES, LLC—See WestView Capital Partners, L.P.; *U.S. Private*, pg. 4501
PRO ACTIVE THERAPY OF NORTH CAROLINA, INC.—See Select Medical Holdings Corporation; *U.S. Public*, pg. 1858
PRO ACTIVE THERAPY OF SOUTH CAROLINA, INC.—See Select Medical Holdings Corporation; *U.S. Public*, pg. 1858
PRO ACTIVE THERAPY OF VIRGINIA, INC.—See Select Medical Holdings Corporation; *U.S. Public*, pg. 1858
PROACT LIETUVA UAB—See Proact IT Group AB; *Int'l*, pg. 5986
PROACT NETHERLANDS B.V.—See Proact IT Group AB; *Int'l*, pg. 5986
PROACT SYSTEMS A/S—See Proact IT Group AB; *Int'l*, pg. 5986
PROADEC BRASIL LTDA.—See Surteco Group SE; *Int'l*, pg. 7345
PROADEC PORTUGAL, S.A.—See Surteco Group SE; *Int'l*, pg. 7345
PROADEC UK LTD.—See Surteco Group SE; *Int'l*, pg. 7345
PRO ADVANTAGE SERVICES, INC.—See Pharmacists Mutual Companies; *U.S. Private*, pg. 3165
PRO ADVANTAGE; *U.S. Private*, pg. 3269
PRO-AG FARMERS COOPERATIVE; *U.S. Private*, pg. 3270
PROAGRIA MILJO A/S—See Lagercrantz Group AB; *Int'l*, pg. 4395

PROAIR AVIATION MAINTENANCE, LLC—See Macquarie Group Limited; *Int'l*, pg. 4630
PROAIR, LLC—See KODA Enterprises Group, LLC; *U.S. Private*, pg. 2335
PRO-AIR SERVICES; *U.S. Private*, pg. 3270
PROALLIANCE CORPORATION; *U.S. Private*, pg. 3271
PROALPHA FRANCE—See COFRA Holding AG; *Int'l*, pg. 1694
PROALPHA SOFTWARE CORPORATION—See COFRA Holding AG; *Int'l*, pg. 1694
PROALPHA SOFTWARE GMBH—See COFRA Holding AG; *Int'l*, pg. 1694
PROAMERICAS; *U.S. Private*, pg. 3271
PROAM EXPLORATIONS CORPORATION; *Int'l*, pg. 5986
PROAMPAC LLC—See The Pritzker Group - Chicago, LLC; *U.S. Private*, pg. 4099
PRO-AM SAFETY, INC.; *U.S. Private*, pg. 3270
PRO A PRO DISTRIBUTION EXPORT SAS—See Metro AG; *Int'l*, pg. 4859
PRO A PRO DISTRIBUTION—See Colruyt Group N.V.; *Int'l*, pg. 1705
PROARCH IT SOLUTIONS, INC.; *U.S. Private*, pg. 3271
PROASIA SEMICONDUCTOR CORPORATION LTD.—See Star Asia Vision Corporation; *Int'l*, pg. 7173
PROASSURANCE - BIRMINGHAM—See ProAssurance Corporation; *U.S. Public*, pg. 1723
PROASSURANCE CASUALTY COMPANY—See ProAssurance Corporation; *U.S. Public*, pg. 1723
PROASSURANCE CORPORATION - MOBILE—See ProAssurance Corporation; *U.S. Public*, pg. 1723
PROASSURANCE CORPORATION—See ProAssurance Corporation; *U.S. Public*, pg. 1723
PROASSURANCE CORPORATION—See ProAssurance Corporation; *U.S. Public*, pg. 1723
PROASSURANCE CORPORATION—See ProAssurance Corporation; *U.S. Public*, pg. 1723
PROASSURANCE CORPORATION; *U.S. Public*, pg. 1722
PROASSURANCE INDEMNITY COMPANY INC—See ProAssurance Corporation; *U.S. Public*, pg. 1723
PROASSURANCE INDEMNITY COMPANY—See ProAssurance Corporation; *U.S. Public*, pg. 1723
PROASSURANCE INDEMNITY LLC—See ProAssurance Corporation; *U.S. Public*, pg. 1723
PROASSURANCE MID-CONTINENT UNDERWRITERS, INC.—See ProAssurance Corporation; *U.S. Public*, pg. 1723
PROASSURANCE—See ProAssurance Corporation; *U.S. Public*, pg. 1723
PROASSURANCE WISCONSIN INSURANCE COMPANY—See ProAssurance Corporation; *U.S. Public*, pg. 1723
PROAVANCE CORPORATION—See Marubeni Corporation; *Int'l*, pg. 4709
PROAXSIS LTD.—See NetScientific plc; *Int'l*, pg. 5215
PROAX TECHNOLOGIES LTD.; *Int'l*, pg. 5986
PROBANKA, D.D.; *Int'l*, pg. 5986
PROBANKA LEASING D.O.O.—See Probanka, d.d.; *Int'l*, pg. 5986
PROBANKA UPRAVLJANJE PREMOZENJA D.O.O.—See Probanka, d.d.; *Int'l*, pg. 5986
PROBAT BAHNHOF LINZ PROJEKTENTWICKLUNGS-GMBH—See OBB-Holding AG; *Int'l*, pg. 5509
PRO-BEAM AG & CO. KGAA; *Int'l*, pg. 5985
PRO-BEAM ELECTRON BEAM TECHNOLOGY SUZHOU CO. LTD—See pro-beam AG & Co. KGaA; *Int'l*, pg. 5985
PROBE INFORMATION SERVICES, LLC—See Trinity Hunt Management, L.P.; *U.S. Private*, pg. 4235
PROBE METALS INC.; *Int'l*, pg. 5986
PROBEMEX SA DE CV—See Tupperware Brands Corporation; *U.S. Public*, pg. 2204
PROBEMO DUBBELE BEDIENINGEN NV—See KBC Group NV; *Int'l*, pg. 4106
PROBE SPECIALISTS INC.—See Boston Semi Equipment LLC; *U.S. Private*, pg. 622
PROBI AB—See Symrise AG; *Int'l*, pg. 7380
PROBI ASIA-PACIFIC PTE LTD.—See Symrise AG; *Int'l*, pg. 7380
PROBI FOOD AB—See Symrise AG; *Int'l*, pg. 7380
PROBIGALP - LIGANTES BETUMINOSOS , S.A.—See Galp Energia SGPS, S.A.; *Int'l*, pg. 2875
PROBILITY MEDIA CORPORATION; *U.S. Public*, pg. 1723
PROBINVEST SAS—See LVMH Moet Hennessy Louis Vuitton SE; *Int'l*, pg. 4600
PROBIOTEC LIMITED—See Pyridam Farma Tbk; *Int'l*, pg. 6127
PROBIOTEC NUTRITIONALS PTY. LTD.—See Pyridam Farma Tbk; *Int'l*, pg. 6128
PROBIOTEC PHARMA PTY. LTD.—See Pyridam Farma Tbk; *Int'l*, pg. 6128
PROBIOTEC (QLD) PTY. LTD.—See Pyridam Farma Tbk; *Int'l*, pg. 6128
PROBIOTICA LABORATORIES LTDA.—See Bausch Health Companies Inc.; *Int'l*, pg. 897
PROBIOTICA LABORATORIOS LTDA.—See Bausch Health Companies Inc.; *Int'l*, pg. 897
PROBISA S.A.—See VINCI S.A.; *Int'l*, pg. 8237

PROBISA TECNOLOGIA Y CONSTRUCCION SA—See VINCI S.A.; *Int'l*, pg. 8220
PROBITY INTERNATIONAL CORPORATION; *U.S. Private*, pg. 3271
PROBI US, INC.—See Symrise AG; *Int'l*, pg. 7380
PROBLANC S.A.S.—See McBride plc; *Int'l*, pg. 4756
PROBLEM SOLVERS, INC.—See Elser & Aucone, Inc.; *U.S. Private*, pg. 1377
PROBLEM SOLVING COMPANY LLC—See PROSOCO, Inc.; *U.S. Private*, pg. 3287
PROBLEND-EUROGERM LLC—See Eurogerm SA; *Int'l*, pg. 2552
PROBO MEDICAL, LLC—See Avista Capital Partners, L.P.; *U.S. Private*, pg. 408
PRO BRAND INTERNATIONAL, INC.—See Sandmartin International Holdings Limited; *Int'l*, pg. 6526
PROBRAND LIMITED; *Int'l*, pg. 5986
PRO BRAND TECHNOLOGY, INC.—See Sandmartin International Holdings Limited; *Int'l*, pg. 6526
PROBST ELECTRIC INC.; *U.S. Private*, pg. 3271
PROBUGAS A.S.—See SHV Holdings N.V.; *Int'l*, pg. 6873
PROBUILD CONSTRUCTIONS (AUSTRALIA) PTY. LTD.—See Wilson Bayly Holmes-Ovcon Limited; *Int'l*, pg. 8422
PROBUS INSURANCE COMPANY EUROPE DAC—See Hertz Global Holdings, Inc.; *U.S. Public*, pg. 1029
PROBYN LOG, LTD.—See E.R. Probyn Ltd.; *Int'l*, pg. 2260
THE PROCACCIANTI GROUP; *U.S. Private*, pg. 4100
PROCACCIANTI HOTEL REIT, INC.; *U.S. Private*, pg. 3271
PROCACCI BROTHERS SALES CORPORATION—See Procacci Holdings LLC; *U.S. Private*, pg. 3271
PROCACCI HOLDINGS LLC; *U.S. Private*, pg. 3271
PROCAD S.A.; *Int'l*, pg. 5986
PROCAL GMBH—See Freudenberg SE; *Int'l*, pg. 2790
PROCALY SAS—See Amphenol Corporation; *U.S. Public*, pg. 132
PROCAM INTERNATIONAL INC.; *Int'l*, pg. 5986
PROCAM TELEVISION LTD.; *Int'l*, pg. 5986
PROCANAR—See LDC SA; *Int'l*, pg. 4431
PROCAP DUNA IPARI ZRT.—See Procap Holdings S.A.; *Int'l*, pg. 5986
PROCAP HOBOKEN NV—See Procap Holdings S.A.; *Int'l*, pg. 5986
PROCAP HOLDINGS S.A.; *Int'l*, pg. 5986
PROCAP LLAGOSTERA SAU—See Procap Holdings S.A.; *Int'l*, pg. 5986
PROCAP MESSIA S.A.S.—See Procap Holdings S.A.; *Int'l*, pg. 5986
PROCAP SCHWERIN GMBH—See Procap Holdings S.A.; *Int'l*, pg. 5986
PROCAPS GROUP, S.A.; *Int'l*, pg. 5986
PROCAP WICKLOW PLASTICS LTD.—See Procap Holdings S.A.; *Int'l*, pg. 5986
PROCARE CO., LTD.—See Senko Group Holdings Co., Ltd.; *Int'l*, pg. 6710
PROCARE HOME HEALTH SERVICES, INC.—See Progressive Health Systems Inc.; *U.S. Private*, pg. 3283
PROCARE LTC HOLDING LLC; *U.S. Private*, pg. 3271
PROCARENT—See Interlock Industries, Inc.; *U.S. Private*, pg. 2112
PROCARE ONE NURSES LLC—See ShiftMed, LLC; *U.S. Private*, pg. 3636
PROCARE PHYSIOTHERAPY & REHABILITATION CENTRE LIMITED—See UMP Healthcare Holdings Ltd.; *Int'l*, pg. 8026
PROCARSA, S.A. DE C.V.—See Industrias CH, S.A.B. de C.V.; *Int'l*, pg. 3674
PROCAT TESTING LLC—See BASF SE; *Int'l*, pg. 876
PROCCO FINANCIAL SERVICES W.L.L—See The International Investor Company K.S.C.C.; *Int'l*, pg. 7656
PROCEDA MODELLBAU GMBH—See Mercedes-Benz Group AG; *Int'l*, pg. 4829
PROCEDES HALLIER SAS—See Lucibel SA; *Int'l*, pg. 4573
PROCEDURELINK, LLC—See The Rudolph/Libbe Companies; *U.S. Private*, pg. 4113
PROCEED PORTFOLIO SERVICES GMBH—See Loancos GmbH; *Int'l*, pg. 4539
PROCE INC.; *U.S. Private*, pg. 3271
PROCENT INC.—See Sumitomo Mitsui Financial Group, Inc.; *Int'l*, pg. 7293
PROCEPT BIOROBOTICS CORPORATION; *U.S. Public*, pg. 1723
PROCERA NETWORKS AB—See Francisco Partners Management, LP; *U.S. Private*, pg. 1591
PROCERA NETWORKS, INC.—See Francisco Partners Management, LP; *U.S. Private*, pg. 1591
PROCESADORA DEL SUR S.A.—See ED&F Man Holdings Limited; *Int'l*, pg. 2303
PROCESADORA UNITAB, S.A.—See Universal Corporation; *U.S. Public*, pg. 2254
PROCESOS PLASTICOS S.R.L. DE C.V.—See PepsiCo, Inc.; *U.S. Public*, pg. 1671
PROCESOS Y DISENOS ENERGETICOS S.A.S.—See John Wood Group PLC; *Int'l*, pg. 3983
PROCESSA PHARMACEUTICALS, INC.; *U.S. Public*, pg. 1723

PROCESSA PHARMACEUTICALS, INC.   CORPORATE AFFILIATIONS

PROCESSA, S.A.S—See EVERTEC, Inc.; *U.S. Public*, pg. 802
PROCESS AUTOMATION (CHINA) LIMITED—See Asia Tele-Net & Technology Corporation Limited; *Int'l*, pg. 615
PROCESS AUTOMATION (EUROPE) LIMITED—See Asia Tele-Net & Technology Corporation Limited; *Int'l*, pg. 615
PROCESS AUTOMATION LTD.—See Endress+Hauser (International) Holding AG; *Int'l*, pg. 2409
PROCESS AUTOMATION (SHENZHEN) LIMITED—See Asia Tele-Net & Technology Corporation Limited; *Int'l*, pg. 615
PROCESS AUTOMATION SOLUTIONS GMBH—See ATS Corporation; *Int'l*, pg. 695
PROCESS AUTOMATION TAIWAN CO. LTD—See Asia Tele-Net & Technology Corporation Limited; *Int'l*, pg. 616
PROCESS CONCEPTION INGENIERIE S.A—See Tong-Tai Machine Tool Co., Ltd.; *Int'l*, pg. 7806
PROCESS CONTROL SERVICES, INC.—See Applied Industrial Technologies, Inc.; *U.S. Public*, pg. 171
PROCESS CONTROL SYSTEMS INTERNATIONAL; *U.S. Private*, pg. 3271
PROCESS & DATA AUTOMATION, LLC—See Krones AG; *Int'l*, pg. 4305
PROCESS DISPLAYS CO; *U.S. Private*, pg. 3271
PROCESSED FRUIT INGREDIENTS, BVBA—See Banco Safra S.A.; *Int'l*, pg. 824
PROCESSED FRUIT INGREDIENTS, BVBA—See Sucocitrico Cutrale Ltda.; *Int'l*, pg. 7251
PROCESS & ENERGY SOLUTIONS, S.A—See Endress+Hauser (International) Holding AG; *Int'l*, pg. 2409
PROCESS EQUIPMENT COMPANY OF TIPP CITY INC.; *U.S. Private*, pg. 3271
PROCESS EQUIPMENT INC.—See Carousel Capital Partners; *U.S. Public*, pg. 769
PROCESS ESSENTIALS PTY LTD—See Verbrec Limited; *Int'l*, pg. 8165
PROCESSIA SOLUTIONS INC.—See Atos SE; *Int'l*, pg. 692
PROCESS INNOVATION TECHNOLOGY PTE LTD—See Sinjia Land Limited; *Int'l*, pg. 6945
PROCESS INNOVATION TECHNOLOGY (SUZHOU) CO., LTD.—See Sinjia Land Limited; *Int'l*, pg. 6945
PROCESS INSIGHTS HOLDINGS LLC—See IGP Industries, LLC; *U.S. Private*, pg. 2040
PROCESS LAB. MICRON CO., LTD.—See Takeda iP Holdings Co.,Ltd.; *Int'l*, pg. 7437
PROCESS LAB. MICRON (SUZHOU) CO., LTD.—See Takeda iP Holdings Co.,Ltd.; *Int'l*, pg. 7437
PROCESS LABORATORIES NETHERLANDS (PROLAB NL) B.V.—See Sulzer Ltd.; *Int'l*, pg. 7256
PROCESS MACHINERY INC.; *U.S. Private*, pg. 3272
PROCESS METRIX, LLC—See Vesuvius plc; *Int'l*, pg. 8179
PROCESS PINK, LLC—See Mullen Automotive, Inc.; *U.S. Public*, pg. 1486
PROCESS PLUS LLC; *U.S. Private*, pg. 3272
PROCESSPUMPARAB I MOTALA AB—See Indutrade AB; *Int'l*, pg. 3681
PROCESSPUMPAR AB—See Indutrade AB; *Int'l*, pg. 3681
PROCESS PUMPS & EQUIPMENT INC.—See John H. Carter Company Incorporated; *U.S. Private*, pg. 2222
PROCESS SENSING TECHNOLOGIES LTD.—See Battery Ventures, L.P.; *U.S. Private*, pg. 489
PROCESS SOFTWARE, LLC—See Halo Technology Holdings, Inc.; *U.S. Private*, pg. 1845
PROCESS SOLUTIONS, INC.—See New Mountain Capital, LLC; *U.S. Private*, pg. 2900
PROCESS SOLUTIONS—See One Rock Capital Partners, LLC; *U.S. Private*, pg. 3023
PROCESS SYSTEMS, INC.—See Horizon Systems, Inc.; *U.S. Private*, pg. 1982
PROCESS TECHNOLOGIES AND PACKAGING, INC.—See Korea Kolmar Co., Ltd.; *Int'l*, pg. 4285
PROCETEL SA—See ELECTROMAGNETICA S.A.; *Int'l*, pg. 2353
PROCHEM S.A.; *Int'l*, pg. 5986
PROCHEM SERWIS SP. Z O.O.—See PROCHEM S.A.; *Int'l*, pg. 5987
PROCHIMIR INC.—See Arkema S.A.; *Int'l*, pg. 571
PROCHIMIR SAS—See Arkema S.A.; *Int'l*, pg. 571
PROCHOICE CHRIMATISTIRIAKI LTD—See A.L. Prochoice Group Public Ltd.; *Int'l*, pg. 25
PROCHON BIOTECH, LTD.—See Ocugen, Inc.; *U.S. Public*, pg. 1563
PRO CHRYSLER JEEP INC.; *U.S. Private*, pg. 3269
PROCINSA ENERGIAS RENOVABLES, S.L.—See Indra Sistemas, S.A.; *Int'l*, pg. 3661
PROCITIUS RESEARCH—See Sanmar Holdings Ltd.; *Int'l*, pg. 6546
PROCIUS LIMITED—See MITIE Group Plc; *Int'l*, pg. 4927
PROCIVITAS PRIVATA GYMNASIUM AB—See AcadeMedia AB; *Int'l*, pg. 77
PRO CLB GLOBAL LIMITED; *Int'l*, pg. 5984
PROCLICK VENTURES, INC.; *U.S. Private*, pg. 3272
PRO CNC, INC.—See Trulife Limited; *Int'l*, pg. 7942

PROCOATINGS B.V.—See PPG Industries, Inc.; *U.S. Public*, pg. 1710
PROCOIL COMPANY, LLC—See United States Steel Corporation; *U.S. Public*, pg. 2237
PROCOIL COMPANY, LLC—See Worthington Industries, Inc.; *U.S. Public*, pg. 2383
PROCOIN GMBH—See Giesecke & Devrient GmbH; *Int'l*, pg. 2970
PROCOMAC ENGENHARIA LTDA.—See GEA Group Aktiengesellschaft; *Int'l*, pg. 2903
PROCOM ANTENNAS AB—See Amphenol Corporation; *U.S. Public*, pg. 132
PROCOM A/S—See Amphenol Corporation; *U.S. Public*, pg. 132
PROCOM CONSULTANTS GROUP LTD; *Int'l*, pg. 5987
PROCOM DEUTSCHLAND GMBH—See Amphenol Corporation; *U.S. Public*, pg. 132
PROCOM FRANCE SARL—See Amphenol Corporation; *U.S. Public*, pg. 132
PROCOMMERCEBANK LTD.; *Int'l*, pg. 5987
PROCOMM, INC.; *U.S. Private*, pg. 3272
PROCOMP INDUSTRIA ELETRONICA LTDA—See Diebold Nixdorf, Inc.; *U.S. Public*, pg. 660
PROCOM PROFESSIONAL COMMUNICATION & SERVICE GMBH—See Zech Group SE; *Int'l*, pg. 8628
PRO COMPUTER SERVICE, LLC; *U.S. Private*, pg. 3269
PROCON AND ASSOCIATES, INC; *U.S. Private*, pg. 3272
PROCONCEPT MARKETING GROUP, INC.; *U.S. Private*, pg. 3272
PRO CONCRETE GROUP PTY LIMITED—See Seven Group Holdings Limited; *Int'l*, pg. 6732
PROCON ENGINEERING LTD.—See NOV, Inc.; *U.S. Public*, pg. 1546
PROCONEX INC.—See Proconex Management Group Inc.; *U.S. Private*, pg. 3272
PROCONEX MANAGEMENT GROUP INC.; *U.S. Private*, pg. 3272
PROCONFIANZA S.A. DE C.V—See ProCredit Holding AG & Co, KGaA; *Int'l*, pg. 5987
PROCONNECT SAUDI LLC—See Redington (India) Limited; *Int'l*, pg. 6247
PROCONNECT SUPPLY CHAIN LOGISTICS LLC—See Redington (India) Limited; *Int'l*, pg. 6247
PROCONNECT SUPPLY CHAIN SOLUTIONS LIMITED—See Redington (India) Limited; *Int'l*, pg. 6247
PROCONNEX GMBH—See AWS Achslagerwerk Stassfurt GmbH; *Int'l*, pg. 753
PROCON PRODUCTS—See Investindustrial Advisors Ltd.; *Int'l*, pg. 3779
PRO-CON PROGRESSIVE CONVERTING, INC.; *U.S. Private*, pg. 3270
PROCONSTRUCTION LLC—See FirstService Corporation; *Int'l*, pg. 2691
PRO CONSULT MANAGEMENT- UND SYSTEMBERATUNG GMBH—See EWE Aktiengesellschaft; *Int'l*, pg. 2575
PROCONTROL AG—See Moog Inc.; *U.S. Public*, pg. 1471
PROCON WIND ENERGY A/S—See Integrated Wind Solutions ASA; *Int'l*, pg. 3732
PROCON WIND ENERGY LTD.—See Integrated Wind Solutions ASA; *Int'l*, pg. 3732
PROCOOK GROUP PLC; *Int'l*, pg. 5987
PRO COOPERATIVE INC.; *U.S. Private*, pg. 3269
PROCOPLAST S.A.—See Methode Electronics, Inc.; *U.S. Public*, pg. 1429
PROCO PRODUCTS INC.; *U.S. Private*, pg. 3272
PRO-COPY TECHNOLOGIES, INC.; *U.S. Private*, pg. 3270
PROCORDIA FOOD AB - FAGELMARA PLANT—See Orkla ASA; *Int'l*, pg. 5639
PROCORDIA FOOD AB - TOLLARP PLANT—See Orkla ASA; *Int'l*, pg. 5639
PROCORDIA FOOD AB - VANSBRO PLANT—See Orkla ASA; *Int'l*, pg. 5639
PROCORE TECHNOLOGIES, INC.; *U.S. Public*, pg. 1724
PROCOR LIMITED—See Berkshire Hathaway Inc.; *U.S. Public*, pg. 311
PROCORNEA NEDERLAND B.V.—See The Cooper Companies, Inc.; *U.S. Public*, pg. 2066
PRO CORPORATE MANAGEMENT SERVICES SDN BHD—See Johor Corporation; *Int'l*, pg. 3994
PROCORP SAB DE CV; *Int'l*, pg. 5987
PROCOS ENGINEERS & CONSULTANTS B.V.—See La Cooperative WELCOOP SA; *Int'l*, pg. 4387
PROCOS S.P.A.—See CBC Co., Ltd.; *Int'l*, pg. 1365
PROCOUNTOR INTERNATIONAL OY—See Dovre Group Plc; *Int'l*, pg. 2182
PROCOVER UNDERWRITING AGENCY PTY LTD—See Steadfast Group Limited; *Int'l*, pg. 7187
PROCRANE ENGINEERING—See Berkshire Hathaway Inc.; *U.S. Public*, pg. 309
PROCRANE SALES INC.—See Berkshire Hathaway Inc.; *U.S. Public*, pg. 309
PRO CRANE SERVICES PROPRIETARY LIMITED—See ARGENT INDUSTRIAL LIMITED; *Int'l*, pg. 561
PROCREDIT ACADEMY GMBH—See ProCredit Holding AG & Co. KGaA; *Int'l*, pg. 5987

PROCREDIT BANK AD—See ProCredit Holding AG & Co. KGaA; *Int'l*, pg. 5987
PROCREDIT BANK A.D.—See ProCredit Holding AG & Co. KGaA; *Int'l*, pg. 5987
PROCREDIT BANK (BULGARIA) E.A.D.—See ProCredit Holding AG & Co. KGaA; *Int'l*, pg. 5987
PROCREDIT BANK CJSC—See ProCredit Holding AG & Co. KGaA; *Int'l*, pg. 5987
PROCREDIT BANK CONGO S.A.R.L.—See ProCredit Holding AG & Co. KGaA; *Int'l*, pg. 5987
PROCREDIT BANK D.D. SARAJEVO—See ProCredit Holding AG & Co. KGaA; *Int'l*, pg. 5987
PROCREDIT BANK S.A.—See ProCredit Holding AG & Co. KGaA; *Int'l*, pg. 5987
PROCREDIT BANK S.A.—See ProCredit Holding AG & Co. KGaA; *Int'l*, pg. 5987
PROCREDIT BANK SH.A—See ProCredit Holding AG & Co. KGaA; *Int'l*, pg. 5987
PROCREDIT BANK SH.A—See ProCredit Holding AG & Co. KGaA; *Int'l*, pg. 5987
PROCREDIT HOLDING AG & CO. KGAA; *Int'l*, pg. 5987
PROCS, S.R.O.—See VINCI S.A.; *Int'l*, pg. 8237
PROCTER & GAMBLE AMIENS S.A.S.—See The Procter & Gamble Company; *U.S. Public*, pg. 2121
PROCTER & GAMBLE ARGENTINA SRL—See The Procter & Gamble Company; *U.S. Public*, pg. 2121
PROCTER & GAMBLE ASIA HOLDING B.V.—See The Procter & Gamble Company; *U.S. Public*, pg. 2121
PROCTER & GAMBLE AUSTRALIA PROPRIETARY LIMITED—See The Procter & Gamble Company; *U.S. Public*, pg. 2121
PROCTER & GAMBLE AUSTRIA GMBH—See The Procter & Gamble Company; *U.S. Public*, pg. 2121
PROCTER & GAMBLE BLOIS S.A.S.—See The Procter & Gamble Company; *U.S. Public*, pg. 2121
PROCTER & GAMBLE BRAZIL HOLDINGS B.V.—See The Procter & Gamble Company; *U.S. Public*, pg. 2121
PROCTER & GAMBLE BULGARIA EOOD—See The Procter & Gamble Company; *U.S. Public*, pg. 2121
PROCTER & GAMBLE BUSINESS SERVICES CANADA COMPANY—See The Procter & Gamble Company; *U.S. Public*, pg. 2121
PROCTER & GAMBLE CANADA HOLDING B.V.—See The Procter & Gamble Company; *U.S. Public*, pg. 2121
PROCTER & GAMBLE CHILE LIMITADA—See The Procter & Gamble Company; *U.S. Public*, pg. 2121
PROCTER & GAMBLE (CHINA) LTD.—See The Procter & Gamble Company; *U.S. Public*, pg. 2121
PROCTER & GAMBLE COMMERCIAL COMPANY—See The Procter & Gamble Company; *U.S. Public*, pg. 2121
PROCTER & GAMBLE COMMERCIAL COMPANY—See The Procter & Gamble Company; *U.S. Public*, pg. 2121
THE PROCTER & GAMBLE COMPANY; *U.S. Public*, pg. 2120
PROCTER & GAMBLE CZECH REPUBLIC S.R.O.—See The Procter & Gamble Company; *U.S. Public*, pg. 2121
PROCTER & GAMBLE DANMARK APS—See The Procter & Gamble Company; *U.S. Public*, pg. 2121
PROCTER & GAMBLE DETERGENT (BEIJING) LTD.—See The Procter & Gamble Company; *U.S. Public*, pg. 2121
PROCTER & GAMBLE DISTRIBUTING COMPANY—See The Procter & Gamble Company; *U.S. Public*, pg. 2121
PROCTER & GAMBLE DISTRIBUTING NEW ZEALAND—See The Procter & Gamble Company; *U.S. Public*, pg. 2121
PROCTER & GAMBLE DISTRIBUTING (PHILIPPINES) INC.—See The Procter & Gamble Company; *U.S. Public*, pg. 2121
PROCTER & GAMBLE DISTRIBUTION COMPANY (EUROPE) BVBA—See The Procter & Gamble Company; *U.S. Public*, pg. 2122
PROCTER & GAMBLE DISTRIBUTION S.R.L.—See The Procter & Gamble Company; *U.S. Public*, pg. 2121
PROCTER & GAMBLE DO BRASIL S/A—See The Procter & Gamble Company; *U.S. Public*, pg. 2123
PROCTER & GAMBLE DO BRAZIL, LLC—See The Procter & Gamble Company; *U.S. Public*, pg. 2123
PROCTER & GAMBLE D.O.O.—See The Procter & Gamble Company; *U.S. Public*, pg. 2123
PROCTER & GAMBLE (EGYPT) MANUFACTURING COMPANY—See The Procter & Gamble Company; *U.S. Public*, pg. 2121
PROCTER & GAMBLE EGYPT—See The Procter & Gamble Company; *U.S. Public*, pg. 2121
PROCTER & GAMBLE ESPANA, S.A.—See The Procter & Gamble Company; *U.S. Public*, pg. 2121
PROCTER & GAMBLE FINLAND OY—See The Procter & Gamble Company; *U.S. Public*, pg. 2121
PROCTER & GAMBLE FRANCE S.A.S.—See The Procter & Gamble Company; *U.S. Public*, pg. 2121
PROCTER & GAMBLE GERMANY GMBH & CO. OPERATIONS OHG—See The Procter & Gamble Company; *U.S. Public*, pg. 2121
PROCTER & GAMBLE GERMANY GMBH—See The Procter & Gamble Company; *U.S. Public*, pg. 2121
PROCTER & GAMBLE GMBH—See The Procter & Gamble Company; *U.S. Public*, pg. 2121

COMPANY NAME INDEX

PROCTER & GAMBLE GRUNDSTUCKS-UND VERMO-GENSVERWALTUNGS GMBH & CO. KG—See The Procter & Gamble Company; *U.S. Public*, pg. 2122
PROCTER & GAMBLE GULF FZE—See The Procter & Gamble Company; *U.S. Public*, pg. 2122
PROCTER & GAMBLE HEALTH & BEAUTY CARE BELGIUM—See The Procter & Gamble Company; *U.S. Public*, pg. 2122
PROCTER & GAMBLE HEALTH & BEAUTY CARE LIMITED—See The Procter & Gamble Company; *U.S. Public*, pg. 2122
PROCTER & GAMBLE HEALTH LTD.—See The Procter & Gamble Company; *U.S. Public*, pg. 2123
PROCTER & GAMBLE HEALTH PRODUCTS—See The Procter & Gamble Company; *U.S. Public*, pg. 2122
PROCTER & GAMBLE HELLAS SINGLE MEMBER LTD.—See The Procter & Gamble Company; *U.S. Public*, pg. 2122
PROCTER & GAMBLE HOLDING FRANCE S.A.S.—See The Procter & Gamble Company; *U.S. Public*, pg. 2122
PROCTER & GAMBLE HOLDING GMBH—See The Procter & Gamble Company; *U.S. Public*, pg. 2122
PROCTER & GAMBLE HOLDING (HK) LIMITED—See The Procter & Gamble Company; *U.S. Public*, pg. 2122
PROCTER & GAMBLE HOLDING S.R.L.—See The Procter & Gamble Company; *U.S. Public*, pg. 2122
PROCTER & GAMBLE HOLDING (THAILAND) LIMITED—See The Procter & Gamble Company; *U.S. Public*, pg. 2122
PROCTER & GAMBLE HOME PRODUCTS LIMITED—See The Procter & Gamble Company; *U.S. Public*, pg. 2122
PROCTER & GAMBLE HONG KONG LIMITED—See The Procter & Gamble Company; *U.S. Public*, pg. 2122
PROCTER & GAMBLE HYGIENE AND HEALTH CARE LIMITED—See The Procter & Gamble Company; *U.S. Public*, pg. 2122
PROCTER & GAMBLE INC.—See The Procter & Gamble Company; *U.S. Public*, pg. 2122
PROCTER & GAMBLE INDUSTRIAL E COMERCIAL LTDA.—See The Procter & Gamble Company; *U.S. Public*, pg. 2122
PROCTER & GAMBLE INTERNATIONAL FUNDING SCA—See The Procter & Gamble Company; *U.S. Public*, pg. 2122
PROCTER & GAMBLE INTERNATIONAL OPERATIONS PTE. LTD.—See The Procter & Gamble Company; *U.S. Public*, pg. 2122
PROCTER & GAMBLE INTERNATIONAL OPERATIONS SA-ROHQ—See The Procter & Gamble Company; *U.S. Public*, pg. 2122
PROCTER & GAMBLE (IRELAND) LIMITED—See The Procter & Gamble Company; *U.S. Public*, pg. 2121
PROCTER & GAMBLE ITALIA, S.P.A.—See The Procter & Gamble Company; *U.S. Public*, pg. 2122
PROCTER & GAMBLE JAPAN K.K.—See The Procter & Gamble Company; *U.S. Public*, pg. 2122
PROCTER & GAMBLE LLC—See The Procter & Gamble Company; *U.S. Public*, pg. 2122
PROCTER & GAMBLE (MALAYSIA) SDN. BHD.—See The Procter & Gamble Company; *U.S. Public*, pg. 2121
PROCTER & GAMBLE MANUFACTURING BELGIUM N.V.—See The Procter & Gamble Company; *U.S. Public*, pg. 2122
PROCTER & GAMBLE MANUFACTURING BERLIN GMBH—See The Procter & Gamble Company; *U.S. Public*, pg. 2121
PROCTER & GAMBLE MANUFACTURING COLOGNE GMBH—See The Procter & Gamble Company; *U.S. Public*, pg. 2121
PROCTER & GAMBLE MANUFACTURING COMPANY—See The Procter & Gamble Company; *U.S. Public*, pg. 2122
PROCTER & GAMBLE MANUFACTURING MEXICO S. DE R.L. DE C.V.—See The Procter & Gamble Company; *U.S. Public*, pg. 2122
PROCTER & GAMBLE MANUFACTURING (THAILAND) LTD.—See The Procter & Gamble Company; *U.S. Public*, pg. 2122
PROCTER & GAMBLE MARKETING AND SERVICES DOO—See The Procter & Gamble Company; *U.S. Public*, pg. 2122
PROCTER & GAMBLE MARKETING ROMANIA SRL—See The Procter & Gamble Company; *U.S. Public*, pg. 2122
PROCTER & GAMBLE NEDERLAND B.V.—See The Procter & Gamble Company; *U.S. Public*, pg. 2122
PROCTER & GAMBLE NETHERLANDS SERVICES B.V.—See The Procter & Gamble Company; *U.S. Public*, pg. 2122
PROCTER & GAMBLE NEUILLY S.A.S.—See The Procter & Gamble Company; *U.S. Public*, pg. 2121
PROCTER & GAMBLE NIGERIA LIMITED—See The Procter & Gamble Company; *U.S. Public*, pg. 2122
PROCTER & GAMBLE NORDIC LLC—See The Procter & Gamble Company; *U.S. Public*, pg. 2122
PROCTER & GAMBLE NORGE AS—See The Procter & Gamble Company; *U.S. Public*, pg. 2122
PROCTER & GAMBLE OPERATIONS POLSKA-SPOLKA Z O.O.—See The Procter & Gamble Company; *U.S. Public*, pg. 2122
PROCTER & GAMBLE OVERSEAS INDIA B.V.—See The Procter & Gamble Company; *U.S. Public*, pg. 2123
PROCTER & GAMBLE PAKISTAN (PRIVATE) LIMITED—See The Procter & Gamble Company; *U.S. Public*, pg. 2123
PROCTER & GAMBLE PAPER PRODUCTS COMPANY—See The Procter & Gamble Company; *U.S. Public*, pg. 2123
PROCTER & GAMBLE PERU S.R.L.—See The Procter & Gamble Company; *U.S. Public*, pg. 2123
PROCTER & GAMBLE POLSKA-SPOLKA Z O.O—See The Procter & Gamble Company; *U.S. Public*, pg. 2123
PROCTER & GAMBLE PORTO - FABRICACAO DE PRODUTOS DE CONSUMO, SOCIEDADE UNIPES-SOAL LDA—See The Procter & Gamble Company; *U.S. Public*, pg. 2123
PROCTER & GAMBLE PORTUGAL - PRODUTOS DE CONSUMO, HIGIENE E SAUDE S.A.—See The Procter & Gamble Company; *U.S. Public*, pg. 2123
PROCTER & GAMBLE PRODUCT SUPPLY (U.K.) LIMITED—See The Procter & Gamble Company; *U.S. Public*, pg. 2123
PROCTER & GAMBLE-RAKONA, S.R.O.—See The Procter & Gamble Company; *U.S. Public*, pg. 2123
PROCTER & GAMBLE - RESEARCH & DEVELOPMENT—See The Procter & Gamble Company; *U.S. Public*, pg. 2122
PROCTER & GAMBLE SA (PTY) LTD.—See The Procter & Gamble Company; *U.S. Public*, pg. 2123
PROCTER & GAMBLE SATIS VE DAGITIM LTD. STI.—See The Procter & Gamble Company; *U.S. Public*, pg. 2123
PROCTER & GAMBLE SERVICE GMBH—See The Procter & Gamble Company; *U.S. Public*, pg. 2121
PROCTER & GAMBLE SERVICES COMPANY N.V.—See The Procter & Gamble Company; *U.S. Public*, pg. 2122
PROCTER & GAMBLE SERVICES GMBH—See The Procter & Gamble Company; *U.S. Public*, pg. 2123
PROCTER & GAMBLE SERVICES LT—See The Procter & Gamble Company; *U.S. Public*, pg. 2123
PROCTER & GAMBLE SERVICES (SWITZERLAND) SA—See The Procter & Gamble Company; *U.S. Public*, pg. 2123
PROCTER & GAMBLE SERVICSE EESTI OU—See The Procter & Gamble Company; *U.S. Public*, pg. 2123
PROCTER & GAMBLE SINGAPORE PTE. LTD.—See The Procter & Gamble Company; *U.S. Public*, pg. 2123
PROCTER & GAMBLE SOUTH AMERICA HOLDING B.V.—See The Procter & Gamble Company; *U.S. Public*, pg. 2123
PROCTER & GAMBLE S.R.L.—See The Procter & Gamble Company; *U.S. Public*, pg. 2123
PROCTER & GAMBLE SVERIGE AB—See The Procter & Gamble Company; *U.S. Public*, pg. 2123
PROCTER & GAMBLE SWEDEN—See The Procter & Gamble Company; *U.S. Public*, pg. 2123
PROCTER & GAMBLE SWITZERLAND SARL—See The Procter & Gamble Company; *U.S. Public*, pg. 2123
PROCTER & GAMBLE TAIWAN LIMITED—See The Procter & Gamble Company; *U.S. Public*, pg. 2123
PROCTER & GAMBLE TECHNICAL CENTRES LIMITED—See The Procter & Gamble Company; *U.S. Public*, pg. 2123
PROCTER & GAMBLE TECHNOLOGY (BEIJING) CO., LTD.—See The Procter & Gamble Company; *U.S. Public*, pg. 2123
PROCTER & GAMBLE TRADING (THAILAND) LIMITED—See The Procter & Gamble Company; *U.S. Public*, pg. 2123
PROCTER & GAMBLE TUKETIM MALLARI SANAYII A.S.—See The Procter & Gamble Company; *U.S. Public*, pg. 2123
PROCTER & GAMBLE UK LTD.—See The Procter & Gamble Company; *U.S. Public*, pg. 2123
PROCTER & GAMBLE UK PARENT COMPANY LTD.—See The Procter & Gamble Company; *U.S. Public*, pg. 2123
PROCTER & GAMBLE UKRAINE—See The Procter & Gamble Company; *U.S. Public*, pg. 2123
PROCTER & GAMBLE U.K.—See The Procter & Gamble Company; *U.S. Public*, pg. 2123
THE PROCTER & GAMBLE U.S. BUSINESS SERVICES COMPANY—See The Procter & Gamble Company; *U.S. Public*, pg. 2124
PROCTOR ACE HARDWARE NEPTUNE BEACH—See Ace Hardware Corporation; *U.S. Private*, pg. 56
PROCTOR CONSTRUCTION COMPANY INC.; *U.S. Private*, pg. 3272
PROCTOR FINANCIAL, INC.—See Brown & Brown, Inc.; *U.S. Public*, pg. 402
PROCTOR SALES INC.; *U.S. Private*, pg. 3272
PROCUDAN A/S; *Int'l*, pg. 5987
PROCUEBYNET CORPORATION—See Yamazen Corporation; *Int'l*, pg. 8558
PROCURA MANAGEMENT, INC.—See UnitedHealth Group Incorporated; *U.S. Public*, pg. 2247

PRODPI INC.

PROCUREABILITY, INC.—See Jabil Inc.; *U.S. Public*, pg. 1182
PROCURE IT RIGHT AB—See Tele2 AB; *Int'l*, pg. 7529
PROCUREMENT INTERNATIONAL (PTY) LIMITED—See Marriott International, Inc.; *U.S. Public*, pg. 1371
PROCURIAN INDIA PRIVATE LIMITED—See Accenture plc; *Int'l*, pg. 87
PROCURIAN LLC—See Accenture plc; *Int'l*, pg. 87
PROCURITAS PARTNERS AB; *Int'l*, pg. 5987
PROCURITAS PARTNERS GMBH—See Procuritas Partners AB; *Int'l*, pg. 5988
PROCURRI CORPORATION LIMITED—See EXEO Group Inc.; *Int'l*, pg. 2583
PROCURRI GMBH—See EXEO Group Inc.; *Int'l*, pg. 2583
PROCURRI INDIA PRIVATE LIMITED—See EXEO Group Inc.; *Int'l*, pg. 2583
PROCURRI LLC—See EXEO Group Inc.; *Int'l*, pg. 2583
PROCURRI MALAYSIA SDN. BHD.—See EXEO Group Inc.; *Int'l*, pg. 2583
PROCURRI S. DE R.L. DE C.V.—See EXEO Group Inc.; *Int'l*, pg. 2583
PROCURRI UK LIMITED—See EXEO Group Inc.; *Int'l*, pg. 2583
PRO-CUT INTERNATIONAL LLC—See Snap-on Incorporated; *U.S. Public*, pg. 1898
PRO-CUTS, INC.—See Regis Corporation; *U.S. Public*, pg. 1777
PROCYON CORP.; *U.S. Public*, pg. 1724
PRODAIR ET CIE S.C.S.—See Air Products & Chemicals, Inc.; *U.S. Public*, pg. 67
PRODALAM SA—See NV Bekaert SA; *Int'l*, pg. 5496
PRODAPT SOLUTIONS PRIVATE LIMITED; *Int'l*, pg. 5988
PRO-DATA INC.; *Int'l*, pg. 5985
PRODATA LDA.—See Brithol Michcoma Mozambique Limited; *Int'l*, pg. 1165
PRODEA SYSTEMS, INC.; *U.S. Private*, pg. 3272
PRODECO, A.S.—See CEZ, a.s.; *Int'l*, pg. 1428
PRODECO GROUP—See Glencore plc; *Int'l*, pg. 2991
PRODEGE, LLC—See Great Hill Partners, L.P.; *U.S. Private*, pg. 1763
PRODELCON SDN. BHD.—See Globaltec Formation Berhad; *Int'l*, pg. 3004
PRODEMO SASU—See Societe Anonyme d'Explosifs et de Produits Chimiques; *Int'l*, pg. 7035
PRODEON MEDICAL, INC.—See Medeon Biodesign, Inc.; *Int'l*, pg. 4769
PRO DESIGNS—See Berkshire Hathaway Inc.; *U.S. Public*, pg. 305
PRODEX D.O.O.—See Violeta d.o.o.; *Int'l*, pg. 8244
PRO-DEX, INC.; *U.S. Public*, pg. 1722
PRODFROID SA—See Ackermans & van Haaren NV; *Int'l*, pg. 105
PRODIA AB—See Indutrade AB; *Int'l*, pg. 3681
PRODIA - CUISEAUX PLANT—See Prodia SAS; *Int'l*, pg. 5988
PRODIALOG 2000 MARKETING & COMMUNICATION GMBH; *Int'l*, pg. 5988
PRODIA - SAINTE FLORENCE PLANT—See Prodia SAS; *Int'l*, pg. 5988
PRODIA SAS; *Int'l*, pg. 5988
PRODIGAL MEDIA COMPANY; *U.S. Private*, pg. 3272
PRODIGY HEALTH GROUP, INC.—See CVS Health Corporation; *U.S. Public*, pg. 615
PRODIGY PUBLIC COMPANY LIMITED; *Int'l*, pg. 5988
PRODIGY RESOURCES LLC; *U.S. Private*, pg. 3272
PRODIGY VENTURES, INC.; *Int'l*, pg. 5988
PRODIM SAS—See Carrefour SA; *Int'l*, pg. 1346
PRODINSA SA—See NV Bekaert SA; *Int'l*, pg. 5496
PRODIPACT SAS—See Schneider Electric SE; *Int'l*, pg. 6628
PRODIRECTIONAL; *U.S. Private*, pg. 3272
PRODITEC AG—See Pema Holding AG; *Int'l*, pg. 5784
PRODITION S.A.—See Demant A/S; *Int'l*, pg. 2023
PRODLIB OY—See Byggfakta Group Nordic HoldCo AB; *Int'l*, pg. 1235
PRO DOC LTEE—See Metro Inc.; *Int'l*, pg. 4860
PRODOMAX AUTOMATION LTD.—See Jenoptik AG; *Int'l*, pg. 3929
PRODOR A.D.; *Int'l*, pg. 5988
PRODOS CAPITAL MANAGEMENT LLC; *U.S. Private*, pg. 3272
PRODOTTI BAUMANN SPA—See Baumann Federn AG; *Int'l*, pg. 895
PRODPI INC.; *U.S. Private*, pg. 3272
PRODSERV SDN. BHD.—See TFP Solutions Berhad; *Int'l*, pg. 7587
PRODUAL A/S—See Investment AB Latour; *Int'l*, pg. 3782
PRODUAL OY—See Investment AB Latour; *Int'l*, pg. 3782
PRODUAL S.A.S.—See Investment AB Latour; *Int'l*, pg. 3782
PRODUAL SP. Z O.O.—See Investment AB Latour; *Int'l*, pg. 3784
PRODUAL S.R.L.—See Investment AB Latour; *Int'l*, pg. 3784
PRODUAL SVERIGE AB—See Investment AB Latour; *Int'l*, pg. 3782
PRODUCCION RHI MEXICO, S. DE R.L. DE C.V.—See RHI Magnesita N.V.; *Int'l*, pg. 6325

PRODUCCIONS DE GASTRONOMIA, S.L.U.—See Vocento, S.A.; *Int'l*, pg. 8284
PRODUCED WATER ABSORBENTS, INC.—See AQUANEX, Servicio Domiciliario del Agua de EXTREMADURA SA; *Int'l*, pg. 527
PRODUCE EXCHANGE CO INC.; *U.S. Private*, pg. 3272
THE PRODUCE EXCHANGE INCORPORATED; *U.S. Private*, pg. 4100
THE PRODUCE EXCHANGE, INC.—See Lipman & Lipman, Inc.; *U.S. Private*, pg. 2465
PRODUCE INVESTMENTS LIMITED—See Promethean Investments LLP; *Int'l*, pg. 5993
PRODUCEMBAL-PRODUCAO DE EMBALAGENS, LTDA—See Sealed Air Corporation; *U.S. Public*, pg. 1854
PRODUCER AG, LLC—See CHS INC.; *U.S. Public*, pg. 492
PRODUCERS AG INSURANCE GROUP, INC.—See Tokio Marine Holdings, Inc.; *Int'l*, pg. 7784
PRODUCERS AG MARKETING ASSOCIATION; *U.S. Private*, pg. 3272
PRODUCERS AGRICULTURE INSURANCE COMPANY—See Tokio Marine Holdings, Inc.; *Int'l*, pg. 7784
PRODUCERS ASSISTANCE CORPORATION—See John Wood Group PLC; *Int'l*, pg. 3984
PRODUCERS AT WORK GMBH—See ProSiebenSat.1 Media SE; *Int'l*, pg. 6000
THE PRODUCERS CHOICE LLC—See Raymond James Financial, Inc.; *U.S. Public*, pg. 1765
PRODUCERS CO-OP ASSOCIATION, INC.; *U.S. Private*, pg. 3272
PRODUCERS COOP OIL MILL; *U.S. Private*, pg. 3272
PRODUCERS CREDIT CORPORATION—See United Producers, Inc.; *U.S. Private*, pg. 4296
PRODUCERS DAIRY FOODS, INC.; *U.S. Private*, pg. 3272
PRODUCERS GAS SALES, INC.—See The Energy Cooperative, Inc.; *U.S. Private*, pg. 4026
PRODUCERS GRAIN CO. INC.; *U.S. Private*, pg. 3273
PRODUCERS HYBRIDS; *U.S. Private*, pg. 3273
PRODUCERS LIVESTOCK MARKETING ASSOCIATION; *U.S. Private*, pg. 3273
PRODUCERS RICE MILL, INC.; *U.S. Private*, pg. 3273
PRODUCT CLUB, INC.—See Burmax Company Inc.; *U.S. Private*, pg. 689
PRODUCT CONCEPTS RESIDENTIAL LLC—See Milliken & Company; *U.S. Private*, pg. 2737
PRODUCT DEVELOPMENT CORPORATION AUSTRALIA PTY LTD—See Product Development Corporation; *U.S. Private*, pg. 3273
PRODUCT DEVELOPMENT CORPORATION; *U.S. Private*, pg. 3273
PRODUCT DEVELOPMENT TECHNOLOGIES, INC.—See TZ LIMITED; *Int'l*, pg. 7996
PRODUCT DISTRIBUTION COMPANY—See General Electric Company; *U.S. Public*, pg. 920
PRODUCT HANDLING DESIGN INC.; *U.S. Private*, pg. 3273
PRODUCT INFORMATION NETWORK—See Access Television Network; *U.S. Private*, pg. 53
PRODUCTION CASTINGS INC.; *U.S. Private*, pg. 3273
PRODUCTION COMPONENTS, INC.; *U.S. Private*, pg. 3273
PRODUCTION CONTROL UNITS, INC.; *U.S. Private*, pg. 3273
PRODUCTION DESIGN SERVICES; *U.S. Private*, pg. 3273
PRODUCTIONHUB INC.; *U.S. Private*, pg. 3273
PRODUCTION INDUSTRIES INC.—See Frost Inc.; *U.S. Private*, pg. 1616
PRODUCTION MANAGEMENT INDUSTRIES, INC.—See Superior Energy Services, Inc.; *U.S. Private*, pg. 3877
PRODUCTION MANAGEMENT INSTITUTE OF SOUTH AFRICA (PTY) LIMITED—See Adcorp Holdings Limited; *Int'l*, pg. 127
PRODUCTION PRODUCTS, INC.—See Midway Products Group, Inc.; *U.S. Private*, pg. 2719
PRODUCTION PUMP SYSTEMS, INC.—See DXP Enterprises, Inc.; *U.S. Public*, pg. 697
PRODUCTIONQUEST—See Baker Hughes Company; *U.S. Public*, pg. 265
PRODUCTION RESOURCE GROUP AG—See The Jordan Company, L.P.; *U.S. Private*, pg. 4061
PRODUCTION RESOURCE GROUP (AUSTRALIA) PTY LTD.—See The Jordan Company, L.P.; *U.S. Private*, pg. 4061
PRODUCTION RESOURCE GROUP LLC—See The Jordan Company, L.P.; *U.S. Private*, pg. 4061
PRODUCTION RESOURCE GROUP—See The Jordan Company, L.P.; *U.S. Private*, pg. 4061
PRODUCTION ROBOTICS, INC.; *U.S. Private*, pg. 3273
PRODUCTION SEEDS PLUS, INC.—See S&W Seed Co.; *U.S. Public*, pg. 1832
PRODUCTION SERVICE COMPANY; *U.S. Private*, pg. 3273
PRODUCTION SERVICES NETWORK HOLDINGS CORP.—See John Wood Group PLC; *Int'l*, pg. 3983

PRODUCTION SERVICES NETWORK (UK) LIMITED—See John Wood Group PLC; *Int'l*, pg. 3983
PRODUCTION SERVICE SWITZERLAND AG—See CTS Eventim AG & Co. KGAA; *Int'l*, pg. 1873
PRODUCTIONS GRAPHICS AGENCEMENT ET VOLUME—See HH Global Group Limited; *Int'l*, pg. 3379
PRODUCTION SOLUTIONS, INC.—See LA Associates, Inc.; *U.S. Private*, pg. 2367
PRODUCTION SUPPORT SERVICES INCORPORATED (PSS)—See Energy Services Group International Inc. (ESG); *U.S. Private*, pg. 1396
PRODUCTION TECHNOLOGY—See Fuji Corporation; *Int'l*, pg. 2810
PRODUCTION TOOL CORPORATION; *U.S. Private*, pg. 3273
PRODUCTION TOOL SUPPLY COMPANY, LLC; *U.S. Private*, pg. 3273
PRODUCTIVE BUSINESS INTERIORS—See Indiana Records Managers, Inc.; *U.S. Private*, pg. 2062
PRODUCTIVE DATA SOLUTIONS INC.; *U.S. Private*, pg. 3273
PRODUCTIVE DENTIST ACADEMY; *U.S. Private*, pg. 3274
PRODUCTIVE HEAT TREATMENT CO. LTD.—See Chen Hsong Holdings Ltd.; *Int'l*, pg. 1464
PRODUCTIVE RESOURCES, LLC—See H.I.G. Capital, LLC; *U.S. Private*, pg. 1830
PRODUCTIVE SOLUTIONS, INC.—See River Associates Investments, LLC; *U.S. Private*, pg. 3443
PRODUCTIVE TECHNOLOGIES COMPANY LIMITED; *Int'l*, pg. 5988
PRODUCTIVITY ASSOCIATES, INC.; *U.S. Private*, pg. 3274
PRODUCTIVITY INC.; *U.S. Private*, pg. 3274
PRODUCTIVITY LEAP OY—See Digia Plc; *Int'l*, pg. 2118
PRODUCTIVITY QUALITY SYSTEMS, INC.—See Advantive LLC; *U.S. Private*, pg. 95
PRODUCT MARKETING MAYBORN LTD—See Ping An Insurance (Group) Company of China, Ltd.; *Int'l*, pg. 5870
PRODUCT MOVERS, LLC; *U.S. Private*, pg. 3273
PRODUCTO/DIECO—See PMT Group Inc; *U.S. Private*, pg. 3219
PRODUCTO DIEMAKERS SUPPLIES LTD.—See PMT Group Inc; *U.S. Private*, pg. 3219
THE PRODUCTO MACHINE CO.—See PMT Group Inc; *U.S. Private*, pg. 3219
PRODUCTORA DE ABRASIVOS LTDA.—See Compagnie de Saint-Gobain SA; *Int'l*, pg. 1725
PRODUCTORA DE ABRASIVOS PABSA LTDA—See Compagnie de Saint-Gobain SA; *Int'l*, pg. 1725
PRODUCTORA DE TEREFT DE ALTAMIRA, S.A. DE C.V.—See ALFA, S.A.B. de C.V.; *Int'l*, pg. 313
PRODUCTORA EXTREMENA DE TELEVISION, S.A.—See Promotora de Informaciones S.A.; *Int'l*, pg. 5995
PRODUCTORES DE ALCOHOL DE MELAZA S.A.—See Ledesma S.A.A.I.; *Int'l*, pg. 4439
PRODUCTORES AEREOS, S.A. DE C.V.—See Teleflex Incorporated; *U.S. Public*, pg. 1995
PRODUCTOS ALIMENTICIOS LA MODERNA S.A. DE C.V.—See Grupo La Moderna, S.A.B. de C.V.; *Int'l*, pg. 3131
PRODUCTOS ALIMENTICIOS DORIA S.A.S.—See Grupo Nutresa S.A.; *Int'l*, pg. 3133
PRODUCTOS ALIMENTICIOS LA MODERNA, S.A. DE C.V.—See Grupo La Moderna, S.A.B. de C.V.; *Int'l*, pg. 3131
PRODUCTOS ALIMENTICIOS PASCUAL, S.A.; *Int'l*, pg. 5988
PRODUCTOS AVON DE GUATEMALA S.A.—See Natura & Co Holding S.A.; *Int'l*, pg. 5167
PRODUCTOS AVON, S.A. DE C.V.—See Natura & Co Holding S.A.; *Int'l*, pg. 5167
PRODUCTOS AVON, S.A.—See Natura & Co Holding S.A.; *Int'l*, pg. 5167
PRODUCTOS AVON, S.A.—See Natura & Co Holding S.A.; *Int'l*, pg. 5167
PRODUCTOS BARD DE MEXICO S.A. DE C.V.—See Becton, Dickinson & Company; *U.S. Public*, pg. 291
PRODUCTOS BITUMINOSOS SA—See VINCI S.A.; *Int'l*, pg. 8219
PRODUCTOS CAPILARES L'OREAL S.A.—See L'Oreal S.A.; *Int'l*, pg. 4381
PRODUCTOS COLEMAN S.A.—See Newell Brands Inc.; *U.S. Public*, pg. 1515
PRODUCTOS COSMETICOS, S.L.U.—See The Procter & Gamble Company; *U.S. Public*, pg. 2123
PRODUCTOS DAMEL, S.L. - NUTS & SNACKS DIVISION—See Productos Damel, S.L.; *Int'l*, pg. 5988
PRODUCTOS DAMEL, S.L.; *Int'l*, pg. 5988
PRODUCTOS DAMEL, S.L. - VALLADOLID PLANT—See Productos Damel, S.L.; *Int'l*, pg. 5988
PRODUCTOS DE ACERO CASSADO SA—See NV Bekaert SA; *Int'l*, pg. 5496
PRODUCTOS DE CONCRETO S.A.; *Int'l*, pg. 5988
PRODUCTOS DEL CAFE S.A.—See Nestle S.A.; *Int'l*, pg. 5205

PRODUCTOS DE MAIZ S.A.—See Ingredion Incorporated; *U.S. Public*, pg. 1124
PRODUCTOS DE MAIZ URUGUAY S.A.—See Ingredion Incorporated; *U.S. Public*, pg. 1124
PRODUCTOS ELECTRICOS APLICADOS, S. DE R.L. DE C.V.—See Regal Rexnord Corporation; *U.S. Public*, pg. 1773
PRODUCTOS ESPECIALIZADOS DE MEXICO S. DE R.L. DE C.V.—See DuPont de Nemours, Inc.; *U.S. Public*, pg. 694
PRODUCTOS FAMILIA S.A.—See Essity Aktiebolag; *Int'l*, pg. 2517
PRODUCTOS FARMACEUTICOS HEEL CHILE LTDA.—See Delton AG; *Int'l*, pg. 2021
PRODUCTOS GILLETTE CHILE LIMITADA—See The Procter & Gamble Company; *U.S. Public*, pg. 2124
PRODUCTOS INDUSTRIALIZADOS SALTILLO, S. DE R.L. DE C.V.—See PepsiCo, Inc.; *U.S. Public*, pg. 1671
PRODUCTOS KRAFT S. DE R.L. DE C.V.—See Mondelez International, Inc.; *U.S. Public*, pg. 1462
PRODUCTOS MARINE DE MEXICO, S.A. DE C.V.—See Brunswick Corporation; *U.S. Public*, pg. 408
PRODUCTOS MEDICINALES MEDELA, S.L.—See Medela Holding AG; *Int'l*, pg. 4769
PRODUCTOS METALICOS DE SEGURIDAD, S.A. DE C.V.—See ASSA ABLOY AB; *Int'l*, pg. 640
PRODUCTOS MOCAP S. DE R.L. DE C.V.—See MOCAP Inc.; *U.S. Private*, pg. 2759
PRODUCTOS NATURELA S.A.S.—See Grupo Nutresa S.A.; *Int'l*, pg. 3133
PRODUCTOS NESTLE (NICARAGUA) S.A.—See Nestle S.A.; *Int'l*, pg. 5211
PRODUCTOS QUIMICOS MAGIAR S.A.—See Neogen Corporation; *U.S. Public*, pg. 1505
PRODUCTOS QUIMICOS NATURALES, S.A. DE C.V.—See Bayer Aktiengesellschaft; *Int'l*, pg. 910
PRODUCTOS RICH S.A. DE C.V. - OCOYOACAC MANUFACTURING FACILITY—See Rich Holdings, Inc.; *U.S. Private*, pg. 3426
PRODUCTOS RICH S.A. DE C.V.—See Rich Holdings, Inc.; *U.S. Private*, pg. 3426
PRODUCTOS ROCHE (EL SALVADOR) S.A.—See Roche Holding AG; *Int'l*, pg. 6373
PRODUCTOS ROCHE (GUATEMALA) S.A.—See Roche Holding AG; *Int'l*, pg. 6373
PRODUCTOS ROCHE GUATEMALA, SA—See Roche Holding AG; *Int'l*, pg. 6373
PRODUCTOS ROCHE LTDA.—See Roche Holding AG; *Int'l*, pg. 6373
PRODUCTOS ROCHE PANAMA S.A.—See Roche Holding AG; *Int'l*, pg. 6373
PRODUCTOS ROCHE QUIMICA FARMACEUTICA S.A.—See Roche Holding AG; *Int'l*, pg. 6373
PRODUCTOS ROCHE QUIMICOS E FARMACEUTICOS S.A.—See Roche Holding AG; *Int'l*, pg. 6373
PRODUCTOS ROCHE S.A. QUIMICA E INDUSTRIAL—See Roche Holding AG; *Int'l*, pg. 6373
PRODUCTOS ROCHE S.A.—See Roche Holding AG; *Int'l*, pg. 6373
PRODUCTOS ROCHE S.A.—See Roche Holding AG; *Int'l*, pg. 6373
PRODUCTOS TISSUE DEL ECUADOR S.A.—See Empresas CMPC S.A.; *Int'l*, pg. 2390
PRODUCTOS TOLEDANO, S.A.; *Int'l*, pg. 5988
PRODUCTOS TUBULARES, S.A.—See Tubos Reunidos, S.A.; *Int'l*, pg. 7963
PRODUCTOS Y DISTRIBUIDORA AZTECA, S.A. DE C.V.—See Gruma, S.A.B. de C.V.; *Int'l*, pg. 3114
PRODUCT PERCEPTIONS LIMITED—See Eurofins Scientific S.E.; *Int'l*, pg. 2551
PRODUCT QUEST MANUFACTURING, LLC.; *U.S. Private*, pg. 3273
PRODUCT SAFETY ENGINEERING INC.—See TUV SUD AG; *Int'l*, pg. 7984
PRODUCTS ENGINEERING CORP; *U.S. Private*, pg. 3274
PRODUCT SHIPPING LIMITED; *Int'l*, pg. 5988
PRODUCTS MANUFACTURING SDN BHD—See Kuok Brothers Sdn. Bhd.; *Int'l*, pg. 4335
PRODUCTS SUPPORT INC.; *U.S. Private*, pg. 3274
PRODUCT TRANSPORT (S) PTE. LTD—See B+H Ocean Carriers Ltd.; *Int'l*, pg. 784
PRODUCT TRANSPORT (US) INC—See B+H Ocean Carriers Ltd.; *Int'l*, pg. 784
PRODUCT VENTURES, LTD; *U.S. Private*, pg. 3274
PRODUITS CHIMIQUES AUXILIAIRES ET DE SYNTHESE SA - USINE DE BOURGOIN PLANT—See Eurazeo SE; *Int'l*, pg. 2530
PRODUITS CHIMIQUES AUXILIAIRES ET DE SYNTHESE SA - USINE DE COUTERNE PLANT—See Eurazeo SE; *Int'l*, pg. 2530
PRODUITS CHIMIQUES AUXILIAIRES ET DE SYNTHESE SA - USINE DE LIMAY PLANT—See Eurazeo SE; *Int'l*, pg. 2530
PRODUITS CHIMIQUES DE LOOS S.A.S.—See Tessenderlo Group NV; *Int'l*, pg. 7574
PRODUITS CHIMIQUES DE LUCETTE S.A.S.—See AMG Critical Materials N.V.; *Int'l*, pg. 426

COMPANY NAME INDEX

PRODUITS PHOENICIA INC.; *Int'l*, pg. 5988
PRODUITS PLASTIQUES PERFORMANTS - 3P—See Burelle S.A.; *Int'l*, pg. 1223
PRODUKT INVEST D.O.O.—See Inles d.d.; *Int'l*, pg. 3705
PRO-DUO DEUTSCHLAND GMBH—See Sally Beauty Holdings, Inc.; *U.S. Public*, pg. 1838
PRO-DUO NV—See Sally Beauty Holdings, Inc.; *U.S. Public*, pg. 1838
PRO-DUO SPAIN SL—See Sally Beauty Holdings, Inc.; *U.S. Public*, pg. 1838
PRODUR SAS—See Jacquet Metal Service SA; *Int'l*, pg. 3866
PRODUTORES ENERGETICOS DE MANSO S.A.; *Int'l*, pg. 5988
PRO DV AG; *Int'l*, pg. 5984
PRODVINALCO SA; *Int'l*, pg. 5988
PRODVINALCO S.A.; *Int'l*, pg. 5988
PRODWARE BELGIUM SA—See Prodware SA; *Int'l*, pg. 5989
PRODWARE BELUX—See Prodware SA; *Int'l*, pg. 5989
PRODWARE CZECH REPUBLIC, SRO—See Prodware SA; *Int'l*, pg. 5989
PRODWARE DEUTSCHLAND AG—See Prodware SA; *Int'l*, pg. 5989
PRODWARE ISRAEL LTD.—See Prodware SA; *Int'l*, pg. 5989
PRODWARE LUXEMBOURG SARL—See Prodware SA; *Int'l*, pg. 5989
PRODWARE MAROC S.A.R.L—See Prodware SA; *Int'l*, pg. 5989
PRODWARE NETHERLANDS B.V.—See Prodware SA; *Int'l*, pg. 5989
PRODWARE SA; *Int'l*, pg. 5988
PRODWARE SPAIN, S.A.—See Prodware SA; *Int'l*, pg. 5989
PRODWARE TUNISIE—See Prodware SA; *Int'l*, pg. 5989
PRODWARE (UK) LIMITED—See Prodware SA; *Int'l*, pg. 5989
PRODWAYS GROUP SA—See Groupe Gorge S.A.; *Int'l*, pg. 3103
PROEFBEDRIJF GEWASBESCHERMING DE BREDELAAR BV—See Eurofins Scientific S.E.; *Int'l*, pg. 2551
PROEKT STROY LLC—See Onexim Group Limited; *Int'l*, pg. 5581
PROEL A.D.; *Int'l*, pg. 5989
PRO ELEVATOR SERVICES INC—See Champion Elevator Corp.; *U.S. Private*, pg. 846
PROELT ENGENHARIA ELETRICA LTDA.—See Sonepar S.A.; *Int'l*, pg. 7093
PROEMION HOLDING GMBH—See Battery Ventures, L.P.; *U.S. Private*, pg. 489
PRO EM OPERATIONS, LLC; *U.S. Private*, pg. 3269
PROEN SCAFFOLD PTE. LTD.—See Hiap Seng Engineering Limited; *Int'l*, pg. 3382
PROEPTA, S.A. DE C.V—See Bunzl plc; *Int'l*, pg. 1219
PRO EQUINE PRODUCTS INC.; *U.S. Private*, pg. 3269
PROEQUITIES, INC.; *U.S. Private*, pg. 3274
PROEQUITY ASSET MANAGEMENT CORPORATION; *U.S. Private*, pg. 3274
PROEXCAR S.A.S.—See Kerry Group plc; *Int'l*, pg. 4139
PRO-FAC COOPERATIVE, INC.; *U.S. Private*, pg. 3270
PRO-FACE AMERICA, INC.—See Schneider Electric SE; *Int'l*, pg. 6632
PRO-FACE CHINA INTERNATIONAL TRADING CO., LTD.—See Schneider Electric SE; *Int'l*, pg. 6628
PROFACE CHINA INTERNATIONAL TRADING (SHANGHAI) CO. LTD—See Schneider Electric SE; *Int'l*, pg. 6629
PRO-FACE DEUTSCHLAND GMBH—See Schneider Electric SE; *Int'l*, pg. 6628
PRO-FACE ESPANA SL—See Schneider Electric SE; *Int'l*, pg. 6628
PRO-FACE EUROPE B.V.—See Schneider Electric SE; *Int'l*, pg. 6628
PRO-FACE FRANCE S.A.S.—See Schneider Electric SE; *Int'l*, pg. 6628
PRO-FACE ITALIA SPA—See Schneider Electric SE; *Int'l*, pg. 6632
PRO-FACE KOREA CO., LTD.—See Schneider Electric SE; *Int'l*, pg. 6628
PRO-FACE NORTHERN EUROPE APS—See Schneider Electric SE; *Int'l*, pg. 6628
PRO-FACE SCHWEIZ GMBH—See Schneider Electric SE; *Int'l*, pg. 6628
PRO-FACE SINGAPORE—See Schneider Electric SE; *Int'l*, pg. 6628
PRO-FACE SOUTH-EAST ASIA PACIFIC CO., LTD.—See Schneider Electric SE; *Int'l*, pg. 6632
PRO-FACE SWEDEN AB—See Schneider Electric SE; *Int'l*, pg. 6628
PRO-FACE TAIWAN CO., LTD.—See Schneider Electric SE; *Int'l*, pg. 6628
PRO-FACE (UK) LTD.—See Schneider Electric SE; *Int'l*, pg. 6632
PROFANT LUFTTECHNIK HANDELS GMBH—See SIG plc; *Int'l*, pg. 6906
PROFARMA DISTRIBUIDORA DE PRODUTOS FARMACEUTICOS S.A.; *Int'l*, pg. 5989
PRO FARM GROUP, INC.—See Bioceres S.A.; *Int'l*, pg. 1036
PRO FARM OU—See Bioceres S.A.; *Int'l*, pg. 1036
PRO FARM TECHNOGIES COMERCIO DE INSUMOS AGRICOLAS DO BRAISIL LTDA—See Bioceres S.A.; *Int'l*, pg. 1036
PRO FARM TECHNOLOGIES OY—See Bioceres S.A.; *Int'l*, pg. 1036
PRO FASTENING SYSTEMS INC.; *U.S. Private*, pg. 3269
PRO F&B GASTRONOMISCHE DIENSTLEISTUNGSGESELLSCHAFT MBH—See MK-Kliniken AG; *Int'l*, pg. 5001
PROFCORE BUSINESS SERVICES—See Randstad N.V.; *Int'l*, pg. 6202
PROFDOC ASA—See CompuGroup Medical SE & Co. KGaA; *Int'l*, pg. 1757
PROFDOC SDN BHD—See CompuGroup Medical SE & Co. KGaA; *Int'l*, pg. 1757
PROFECTUS, LLC; *U.S. Private*, pg. 3274
PRO FEET INC.; *U.S. Private*, pg. 3269
PROFEN MANUFACTURING SDN. BHD.—See Tracoma Holdings Berhad; *Int'l*, pg. 7887
PROFEN SDN. BHD.—See Tracoma Holdings Berhad; *Int'l*, pg. 7887
PROFERTIL S.A.—See Nutrien Ltd.; *Int'l*, pg. 5492
PROFERTIL S.A.—See YPF S.A.; *Int'l*, pg. 8605
PROFESSIONAL AIRCRAFT ACCESSORIES, INC.—See Greenwich AeroGroup, Inc.; *U.S. Private*, pg. 1781
PROFESSIONAL ALUMINIUM SMELTING SDN. BHD.—See P.A. Resources Berhad; *Int'l*, pg. 5682
PROFESSIONAL ASSOCIATION FOR CHILDHOOD EDUCATION; *U.S. Private*, pg. 3274
PROFESSIONAL AVIATION ASSOCIATES, INC.—See Greenwich AeroGroup, Inc.; *U.S. Private*, pg. 1781
PROFESSIONAL BAKEWARE CO., INC.—See Tablecraft Products Co., Inc.; *U.S. Private*, pg. 3920
PROFESSIONAL BANKERS CORP—See Continental Holding Company; *U.S. Private*, pg. 1029
PROFESSIONAL BANK—See Professional Holding Corp.; *U.S. Public*, pg. 1724
THE PROFESSIONAL BASKETBALL CLUB, LLC; *U.S. Private*, pg. 4100
PROFESSIONAL BENEFIT SERVICES, INC.—See IMA Financial Group, Inc.; *U.S. Private*, pg. 2043
PROFESSIONAL BENEFITS SOLUTIONS, INC.—See Aon plc; *Int'l*, pg. 497
PROFESSIONAL BIOLOGICAL COMPANY—See Colorado Serum Co.; *U.S. Private*, pg. 974
PROFESSIONAL BUILDERS SUPPLY, LLC; *U.S. Private*, pg. 3274
PROFESSIONAL BULL RIDERS, LLC—See Silver Lake Group, LLC; *U.S. Private*, pg. 3654
PROFESSIONAL CABINET SOLUTIONS—See American Woodmark Corporation; *U.S. Public*, pg. 113
PROFESSIONAL CARE LOGISTICS, S.L.U—See The Procter & Gamble Company; *U.S. Public*, pg. 2123
PROFESSIONAL COMMUNITY MANAGEMENT; *U.S. Private*, pg. 3274
PROFESSIONAL COMPUTER CENTER INC.; *U.S. Private*, pg. 3274
PROFESSIONAL COMPUTER SERVICES S.A.—See Marfin Investment Group Holdings S.A.; *Int'l*, pg. 4692
PROFESSIONAL COMPUTER TECHNOLOGY LIMITED; *Int'l*, pg. 5989
PROFESSIONAL COMPUTING RESOURCES, INC.—See Valsef Group; *Int'l*, pg. 8123
PROFESSIONAL CONCESSIONS, INC.; *U.S. Private*, pg. 3274
PROFESSIONAL CONSTRUCTION SERVICES INC.; *U.S. Private*, pg. 3274
PROFESSIONAL CONSTRUCTION STRATEGIES GROUP LIMITED—See Bentley Systems, Inc.; *U.S. Public*, pg. 297
PROFESSIONAL CONTROL CORPORATION; *U.S. Private*, pg. 3274
PROFESSIONAL CONVENTION MANAGEMENT ASSOCIATION; *U.S. Private*, pg. 3274
PROFESSIONAL COURSE MANAGEMENT, INC.; *U.S. Private*, pg. 3274
PROFESSIONAL DATA DIMENSIONS; *U.S. Private*, pg. 3275
PROFESSIONAL DATA SERVICES, INC.—See Audax Group, Limited Partnership; *U.S. Private*, pg. 390
PROFESSIONAL DATASOLUTIONS, INC.—See TA Associates, Inc.; *U.S. Private*, pg. 3917
PROFESSIONAL DENTAL REVIEWERS—See Aon plc; *Int'l*, pg. 489
PROFESSIONAL DISABILITY ASSOCIATES, PA—See Brown & Brown, Inc.; *U.S. Public*, pg. 397
PROFESSIONAL DISPOSABLES INTERNATIONAL, INC.—See Nice-Pak Products, Inc.; *U.S. Private*, pg. 2925
PROFESSIONAL DIVERSITY NETWORK, INC.; *U.S. Public*, pg. 1724
PROFESSIONAL EDUCATION INSTITUTE; *U.S. Private*, pg. 3275
PROFESSIONAL ELECTRIC PRODUCTS COMPANY, INC.; *U.S. Private*, pg. 3275
PROFESSIONAL ELECTRONICS MANUFACTURING SOLUTIONS (GUANGZHOU) LIMITED—See Trio Industrial Electronics Group Limited; *Int'l*, pg. 7925
PROFESSIONAL ELECTRONICS MANUFACTURING SOLUTIONS LIMITED—See Trio Industrial Electronics Group Limited; *Int'l*, pg. 7925
PROFESSIONAL EMERGENCY CARE PC; *U.S. Private*, pg. 3275
PROFESSIONAL EMPLOYMENT SOLUTIONS, INC.; *U.S. Private*, pg. 3275
PROFESSIONAL ENGINEERING CONSULTANTS, P.A.; *U.S. Private*, pg. 3275
PROFESSIONAL EQUIPMENT—See W.W. Grainger, Inc.; *U.S. Public*, pg. 2320
PROFESSIONAL EXAMINATION SERVICE; *U.S. Private*, pg. 3275
PROFESSIONAL FITNESS CONCEPTS, INC.; *U.S. Private*, pg. 3275
PROFESSIONAL FOAM INSULATORS LTD.—See Quad-C Management, Inc.; *U.S. Private*, pg. 3315
THE PROFESSIONAL GOLFERS ASSOCIATION OF AMERICA; *U.S. Private*, pg. 4100
PROFESSIONAL GROUNDS MANAGEMENT; *U.S. Private*, pg. 3275
PROFESSIONAL HAIR LABS, INC.; *U.S. Private*, pg. 3275
PROFESSIONAL HEALTHCARE RESOURCES, INC.; *U.S. Private*, pg. 3275
PROFESSIONAL HOLDING CORP.; *U.S. Public*, pg. 1724
PROFESSIONAL HOME CARE SERVICES, INC.—See Option Care Health, Inc.; *U.S. Public*, pg. 1610
PROFESSIONAL HOSPITAL SUPPLY, INC.—See Medline Industries, LP; *U.S. Private*, pg. 2658
PROFESSIONAL IMO PARTNERS S.A.; *Int'l*, pg. 5989
PROFESSIONAL IMPLEMENTATION CONSULTING SERVICES, INC.; *U.S. Private*, pg. 3275
PROFESSIONAL INDEMNITY AGENCY, INC.—See Tokio Marine Holdings, Inc.; *Int'l*, pg. 7784
PROFESSIONAL INSURANCE ASSOCIATES; *U.S. Private*, pg. 3275
PROFESSIONAL INVESTMENT ADVISORY SERVICES PTE. LTD.—See Aviva plc; *Int'l*, pg. 746
THE PROFESSIONAL LANDLORDS, LLC; *U.S. Private*, pg. 4100
PROFESSIONAL LIABILITY INSURANCE COMPANY OF AMERICA—See Berkshire Hathaway Inc.; *U.S. Public*, pg. 312
PROFESSIONAL LIFE ASSURANCE LTD.—See Livforsakringsaktiebolaget Skandia; *Int'l*, pg. 4531
PROFESSIONAL LIFE INTERLINK SECURITIES—See Comerica Incorporated; *U.S. Public*, pg. 542
PROFESSIONAL LIFE UNDERWRITERS SERVICES, LLC—See The Albrecht Companies, Inc.; *U.S. Private*, pg. 3983
PROFESSIONAL LINES UNDERWRITING SPECIALISTS, INC.—See IMA Financial Group, Inc.; *U.S. Private*, pg. 2044
PROFESSIONAL MEDIA MANAGEMENT; *U.S. Private*, pg. 3275
PROFESSIONAL MEDICAL EXPERTISE COMPANY; *Int'l*, pg. 5989
PROFESSIONAL & MEDICAL INSURANCE SOLUTIONS LIMITED—See Brown & Brown, Inc.; *U.S. Public*, pg. 402
PROFESSIONAL MEDICAL TRANSPORT, INC.—See KKR & Co. Inc.; *U.S. Public*, pg. 1252
PROFESSIONAL METAL CORPORATION; *U.S. Private*, pg. 3275
PROFESSIONAL NATIONAL TITLE NETWORK, INC.; *U.S. Private*, pg. 3275
PROFESSIONAL OFFICE ENVIRONMENTS; *U.S. Private*, pg. 3275
PROFESSIONAL OFFICE SERVICES INC.; *U.S. Private*, pg. 3275
PROFESSIONAL OFFICE SERVICES—See Professional Office Services Inc.; *U.S. Private*, pg. 3275
PROFESSIONAL OPHTHALMIC LABORATORIES, INC.—See EssilorLuxottica SA; *Int'l*, pg. 2514
PROFESSIONAL OUTSOURCING SOLUTIONS LIMITED—See Humanica Public Company Limited; *Int'l*, pg. 3530
PROFESSIONAL PACKAGE COMPANY; *U.S. Private*, pg. 3275
PROFESSIONAL PACKAGING SERVICES LIMITED—See HH Global Group Limited; *Int'l*, pg. 3379
PROFESSIONAL PACKAGING SYSTEMS INC.; *U.S. Private*, pg. 3275
PROFESSIONAL PARTS SWEDEN AB—See Indutrade AB; *Int'l*, pg. 3681
PROFESSIONAL PAVEMENT PRODUCTS, INC.; *U.S. Private*, pg. 3275
PROFESSIONAL PENSIONS, INC.—See Principal Financial Group, Inc.; *U.S. Public*, pg. 1722
PROFESSIONAL PHOTOGRAPHERS OF AMERICA; *U.S. Private*, pg. 3275
PROFESSIONAL PLACEMENT RESOURCES, LLC—See TPG Capital, L.P.; *U.S. Public*, pg. 2176
PROFESSIONAL PLASTICS CO. LTD.—See Professional Plastics, Inc.; *U.S. Private*, pg. 3276

PROFESSIONAL PLASTICS, INC.
CORPORATE AFFILIATIONS

PROFESSIONAL PLASTICS, INC.; *U.S. Private*, pg. 3276
PROFESSIONAL PLASTICS PTE LTD.—See Professional Plastics, Inc.; *U.S. Private*, pg. 3276
PROFESSIONAL PLAYGROUND—See Hesscor, Inc.; *U.S. Private*, pg. 1928
PROFESSIONAL PLUMBERS GROUP, INC.—See Sterling Infrastructure, Inc.; *U.S. Public*, pg. 1947
PROFESSIONAL PLUMBING GROUP, INC.—See Dunes Point Capital, LLC; *U.S. Private*, pg. 1289
PROFESSIONAL POWER PRODUCTS, INC.—See Power Solutions International, Inc.; *U.S. Public*, pg. 1705
PROFESSIONAL PROBATION SERVICES, INC.—See Universal Health Services, Inc.; *U.S. Public*, pg. 2259
PROFESSIONAL PRODUCE; *U.S. Private*, pg. 3276
PROFESSIONAL PRODUCTION PRODUCTS, INC.; *U.S. Private*, pg. 3276
PROFESSIONAL PRODUCTS, INC.; *U.S. Private*, pg. 3276
PROFESSIONAL PROJECT SERVICES, INC.; *U.S. Private*, pg. 3276
PROFESSIONAL PROTECTION SYSTEMS LTD.—See Kingswood Capital Management LLC; *U.S. Private*, pg. 2312
PROFESSIONAL PUBLICATIONS, INC.—See Graham Holdings Company; *U.S. Public*, pg. 956
THE PROFESSIONAL PUTTERS ASSOCIATION—See Putt-Putt, LLC; *U.S. Private*, pg. 3308
PROFESSIONAL REBUILD & OPTIMAL SERVICE LLC; *U.S. Private*, pg. 3276
PROFESSIONAL RECOVERY CONSULTANTS, INC.—See Longshore Capital Partners; *U.S. Private*, pg. 2493
PROFESSIONAL RECREATION ORGANIZATION INC.—See KKR & Co. Inc.; *U.S. Public*, pg. 1264
PROFESSIONAL RECYCLING, S.A. DE C.V.—See Promotora Ambiental S.A.B de C.V.; *Int'l*, pg. 5994
PROFESSIONAL REHABILITATION HOSPITAL, LLC—See SentryCare, Inc.; *U.S. Private*, pg. 3611
PROFESSIONAL RELIABLE NURSING SERVICE INC.—See Addus HomeCare Corporation; *U.S. Public*, pg. 40
PROFESSIONAL RESOURCES IN INFORMATION SYSTEMS MANAGEMENT, INC.; *U.S. Private*, pg. 3276
PROFESSIONAL RISK, AN ALERA GROUP AGENCY, LLC—See Genstar Capital, LLC; *U.S. Private*, pg. 1674
PROFESSIONAL RISK ASSOCIATES, INC.—See Kelso & Company, L.P.; *U.S. Private*, pg. 2280
PROFESSIONAL RISK MANAGEMENT SERVICES, INC.—See Berkshire Hathaway Inc.; *U.S. Public*, pg. 299
PROFESSIONAL RODEO COWBOYS ASSOCIATION; *U.S. Private*, pg. 3276
PROFESSIONAL ROOFING & EXTERIORS; *U.S. Private*, pg. 3276
THE PROFESSIONAL SEARCH GROUP—See The Reserves Network Inc.; *U.S. Private*, pg. 4105
PROFESSIONAL SECURITY TECHNOLOGIES LLC; *U.S. Private*, pg. 3276
PROFESSIONAL SERVICE INDUSTRIES, INC. - FLORIDA—See Intertek Group plc; *Int'l*, pg. 3764
PROFESSIONAL SERVICE INDUSTRIES, INC.—See Intertek Group plc; *Int'l*, pg. 3764
PROFESSIONAL SERVICE INDUSTRIES, INC. - WASHINGTON—See Intertek Group plc; *Int'l*, pg. 3764
PROFESSIONAL SOFTWARE ENGINEERING INC.; *U.S. Private*, pg. 3276
PROFESSIONAL SOLUTIONS; *U.S. Private*, pg. 3276
PROFESSIONAL STAFFING A BTS INC.; *U.S. Private*, pg. 3276
PROFESSIONAL STAFFING CORPORATION; *U.S. Private*, pg. 3276
PROFESSIONAL STAFF MANAGEMENT, INC.—See Paychex, Inc.; *U.S. Public*, pg. 1655
PROFESSIONAL SUPPORT INC.; *U.S. Private*, pg. 3276
PROFESSIONAL SYSTEMS (PVT) LTD; *Int'l*, pg. 5989
PROFESSIONAL TELECONCEPTS, INC.—See Dycom Industries, Inc.; *U.S. Public*, pg. 699
PROFESSIONAL TRADING SOLUTIONS, INC.; *U.S. Private*, pg. 3276
PROFESSIONAL TRAVEL INC.—See ABRY Partners, LLC; *U.S. Private*, pg. 41
PROFESSIONAL UNDERWRITERS LIABILITY INSURANCE COMPANY—See The Doctors Company; *U.S. Private*, pg. 4021
PROFESSIONAL VALUATION SERVICES, LLC—See Hilton Grand Vacations Inc.; *U.S. Public*, pg. 1039
PROFESSIONAL WARRANTY SERVICE CORPORATION—See PCF Insurance Services of The West, LLC; *U.S. Private*, pg. 3120
PROFESSIONAL WASTE CONSULTING, LLC—See O2 Investment Partners, LLC; *U.S. Private*, pg. 2982
PROFESSIONAL WASTE TECHNOLOGY (1999) PUBLIC COMPANY LIMITED; *Int'l*, pg. 5989
PROFEX S.A.S.—See OpenGate Capital Management, LLC; *U.S. Private*, pg. 3031
PROFF AB—See Enento Group Plc; *Int'l*, pg. 2415
PROFF APS—See Enento Group Plc; *Int'l*, pg. 2415
PROFF AS—See Enento Group Plc; *Int'l*, pg. 2415
PROFIALIS CLERVAL S.A.S.—See OpenGate Capital Management, LLC; *U.S. Private*, pg. 3031
PROFIALIS N.V.—See OpenGate Capital Management, LLC; *U.S. Private*, pg. 3031
PROFIALIS POLSKA SP.Z.O.O.—See OpenGate Capital Management, LLC; *U.S. Private*, pg. 3031
PROFI AUDIO SP. Z O.O—See Transition Evergreen; *Int'l*, pg. 7901
PROFIBRIX B.V.—See Novartis AG; *Int'l*, pg. 5460
PROFIBRIX, INC.—See Novartis AG; *Int'l*, pg. 5460
PROFICIENT ALPHA ACQUISITION CORP.; *U.S. Public*, pg. 1724
PROFICIENT AUTO LOGISTICS, INC.; *U.S. Public*, pg. 1724
PROFICIO, INC.; *U.S. Private*, pg. 3276
PROFIDATA AG—See Profidata Group AG; *Int'l*, pg. 5989
PROFIDATA GROUP AG; *Int'l*, pg. 5989
PROFIDATA SERVICES AG—See Profidata Group AG; *Int'l*, pg. 5989
PROFIDIS—See Carrefour SA; *Int'l*, pg. 1346
PROFIGEN DO BRAZIL LDTA—See Altria Group, Inc.; *U.S. Public*, pg. 89
PROFI GESUNDHEITS - SERVICE GMBH—See SOL S.p.A.; *Int'l*, pg. 7067
PROFILAGE OUEST; *Int'l*, pg. 5989
PROFIL-BAU INDUSTRIAL OY—See AFRY AB; *Int'l*, pg. 196
PROFILE CABINET & DESIGN; *U.S. Private*, pg. 3276
PROFILECOMP GMBH—See Albany International Corp.; *U.S. Public*, pg. 72
PROFILE CUSTOM EXTRUSION, LLC—See Highlander Partners, LP; *U.S. Private*, pg. 1939
PROFILE DEVELOPMENT, LLC; *U.S. Private*, pg. 3277
PROFILE DIGITAL SERVICES S.A.—See PROFILE SYSTEMS & SOFTWARE S.R.L.; *Int'l*, pg. 5989
PROFILE EXTRUSION COMPANY INC.; *U.S. Private*, pg. 3277
PROFILE FOOD INGREDIENTS, LLC—See RPM International, Inc.; *U.S. Public*, pg. 1817
THE PROFILE GROUP (UK) LIMITED—See Centaur Media plc; *Int'l*, pg. 1402
PROFILE METAL FORMING INC.; *U.S. Private*, pg. 3277
PROFILE PACKAGING INC—See PPi Technologies Global, LLC; *U.S. Private*, pg. 3240
PROFILE PHARMA LIMITED—See Koninklijke Philips N.V.; *Int'l*, pg. 4271
PROFILE PLUS (UK) LTD.—See Freshwater UK PLC; *Int'l*, pg. 2782
PROFILE PRECISION EXTRUSIONS—See Profile Extrusion Company Inc.; *U.S. Private*, pg. 3277
PROFILE PRODUCTS LLC—See Platte River Ventures, LLC; *U.S. Private*, pg. 3211
PROFILES IN HISTORY; *U.S. Private*, pg. 3277
PROFILE SOFTWARE (UK) LTD.—See PROFILE SYSTEMS & SOFTWARE S.R.L.; *Int'l*, pg. 5989
PROFILE STEEL & WIRE—See Whitesell Corporation; *U.S. Private*, pg. 4512
PROFILE SYSTEMS, INC.; *U.S. Private*, pg. 3277
PROFILE SYSTEMS & SOFTWARE (CYPRUS) LTD.—See PROFILE SYSTEMS & SOFTWARE S.R.L.; *Int'l*, pg. 5989
PROFILE SYSTEMS & SOFTWARE S.R.L.; *Int'l*, pg. 5989
PROFILGRUPPEN AB; *Int'l*, pg. 5989
PROFILGRUPPEN EXTRUSIONS AB—See ProfilGruppen AB; *Int'l*, pg. 5990
PROFILGRUPPEN LTD—See ProfilGruppen AB; *Int'l*, pg. 5990
PROFILGRUPPEN MANUFACTURING AB—See ProfilGruppen AB; *Int'l*, pg. 5990
PROFILGRUPPEN NORGE AS—See ProfilGruppen AB; *Int'l*, pg. 5990
PROFIL OPTIK A/S—See Synsam AB; *Int'l*, pg. 7386
PROFILTECH STUFENBANDPROFILE GMBH—See Gebr. Kemper GmbH & Co. KG; *Int'l*, pg. 2906
PROFIMEDIA.CZ A.S.; *Int'l*, pg. 5990
PRO FINANCIAL SERVICES, LLC—See Aon plc; *Int'l*, pg. 497
PRO FIN CAPITAL SERVICES LIMITED; *Int'l*, pg. 5984
PROF-IN D.O.O.—See Zavarovalnica Triglav, d.d.; *Int'l*, pg. 8626
PROFINE AUSTRIA GMBH—See Arcapita Group Holdings Limited; *Int'l*, pg. 542
PROFINE BELUX BVBA—See Arcapita Group Holdings Limited; *Int'l*, pg. 542
PROFINE BH D.O.O.—See Arcapita Group Holdings Limited; *Int'l*, pg. 542
PROFINE CROATIA DOO—See Arcapita Group Holdings Limited; *Int'l*, pg. 542
PROFINE FRANCE SAS—See Arcapita Group Holdings Limited; *Int'l*, pg. 542
PROFINE GMBH—See Arcapita Group Holdings Limited; *Int'l*, pg. 542
PROFINE IBERIA S.A.—See Arcapita Group Holdings Limited; *Int'l*, pg. 542
PROFINE ITALIA SRL—See Arcapita Group Holdings Limited; *Int'l*, pg. 542
PROFINE NEDERLAND B.V.—See Arcapita Group Holdings Limited; *Int'l*, pg. 543
PROFINE POLSKA SP. Z O.O.—See Arcapita Group Holdings Limited; *Int'l*, pg. 543
PROFINE ROMANIA SRL—See Arcapita Group Holdings Limited; *Int'l*, pg. 543
PROFINE SCHWEIZ AG—See Arcapita Group Holdings Limited; *Int'l*, pg. 543
PROFINE UK LTD.—See Arcapita Group Holdings Limited; *Int'l*, pg. 543
PROFINE UKRAINE—See Arcapita Group Holdings Limited; *Int'l*, pg. 543
PROFIRE COMBUSTION, INC.—See Profire Energy, Inc.; *U.S. Public*, pg. 1724
PROFIRE ENERGY, INC.; *U.S. Public*, pg. 1724
PROFIRENT GEPKOLCSONZO KFT.—See Oriens; *Int'l*, pg. 5621
PROFIT BUILDING INDUSTRIES LTD.; *Int'l*, pg. 5990
PROFIT CONSTRUCT SRL—See ELLAKTOR S.A.; *Int'l*, pg. 2365
PROFIT CULTURAL & CREATIVE GROUP CO., LTD.; *Int'l*, pg. 5990
PROFITECT, INC.—See Zebra Technologies Corporation; *U.S. Public*, pg. 2401
PROFITKEY INTERNATIONAL, INC.—See Apax Partners LLP; *Int'l*, pg. 503
PROFIT MANAGEMENT CORP.—See Family Inns of America, Inc.; *U.S. Private*, pg. 1470
PROFITMASTER CANADA INC.—See Constellation Software Inc.; *Int'l*, pg. 1773
PROFIT PLANNERS MANAGEMENT, INC.; *U.S. Public*, pg. 1724
PROFIT POINT MANUFACTURING SDN. BHD.—See Southern Capital Group Pte. Ltd.; *Int'l*, pg. 7118
PROFIT RANK, INC.; *U.S. Private*, pg. 3277
PROFIT RECOVERY BRASIL LTDA.—See PRGX Global, Inc.; *U.S. Private*, pg. 3258
PROFIT SENSE INNOVATIONS; *U.S. Private*, pg. 3277
PROFITSTARS/ALOGENT—See Jack Henry & Associates, Inc.; *U.S. Public*, pg. 1182
PROFITSTARS - DATATRADE DIVISION—See Jack Henry & Associates, Inc.; *U.S. Public*, pg. 1182
PROFITSTARS—See Jack Henry & Associates, Inc.; *U.S. Public*, pg. 1182
PROFITSTARS—See Jack Henry & Associates, Inc.; *U.S. Public*, pg. 1182
PRO-FLEX AS—See Indutrade AB; *Int'l*, pg. 3681
PROFLINE B.V.—See Novra Technologies Inc.; *Int'l*, pg. 5471
PROFLOORS, LLC; *U.S. Private*, pg. 3277
PROFLOWERS.COM—See Tenth Avenue Holdings LLC; *U.S. Private*, pg. 3968
PROFLUTE AB—See Munters Group AB; *Int'l*, pg. 5095
PROFMEDIA HOLDING COMPANY—See Interros Holding Company; *Int'l*, pg. 3759
PRO FOOD SYSTEMS, INC.; *U.S. Private*, pg. 3269
PRO FOOTBALL WEEKLY, LLC; *U.S. Private*, pg. 3269
PROFORMA ALBRECHT & COMPANY; *U.S. Private*, pg. 3277
PROFORMA BRAND PROFORMANCE; *U.S. Private*, pg. 3277
PROFORMA GPS GLOBAL PROMOTIONAL SOURCING; *U.S. Private*, pg. 3277
PROFORMA GRAPHIC SERVICES; *U.S. Private*, pg. 3277
PROFORMA POWERHOUSE SOLUTIONS; *U.S. Private*, pg. 3277
PROFORMA PRINT & PROMOTIONS; *U.S. Private*, pg. 3277
PROFORMA PROGRESSIVE MARKETING; *U.S. Private*, pg. 3277
PROFORMA PROMOTIONALLY YOURS; *U.S. Private*, pg. 3277
PROFORMA PROMOTION CONSULTANTS; *U.S. Private*, pg. 3277
PROFORMA SIGNATURE SOLUTIONS; *U.S. Private*, pg. 3277
PROFORMA STEWART & ASSOCIATES; *U.S. Private*, pg. 3277
PROFORM FINISHING PRODUCTS, LLC—See Spangler Companies, Inc.; *U.S. Private*, pg. 3745
PROFORM SA; *Int'l*, pg. 5990
PROFOTO AB—See Profoto Holding AB; *Int'l*, pg. 5990
PROFOTO B.V.—See Profoto Holding AB; *Int'l*, pg. 5990
PROFOTO DIGITAL SERVICES PTE LTD—See Teckwah Industrial Corporation Ltd; *Int'l*, pg. 7515
PROFOTO HOLDING AB; *Int'l*, pg. 5990
PROFOTO KK—See Profoto Holding AB; *Int'l*, pg. 5990
PROFOTO US INC.—See Profoto Holding AB; *Int'l*, pg. 5990
PROFOUND MEDICAL CORP.; *Int'l*, pg. 5990
PROFOUND MEDICAL GMBH—See Profound Medical Corp.; *Int'l*, pg. 5990
PROFRAC HOLDING CORP.; *U.S. Public*, pg. 1724
PROFRAC SERVICES LLC; *U.S. Private*, pg. 3277
PROFRMGO INTERNET MARKETING, LLC; *U.S. Private*, pg. 3277
PROFSAFE AB—See Lagercrantz Group AB; *Int'l*, pg. 4395
PROFUMA SPEZIALFUTTERWERKE GMBH & CO. KG—See AGRAVIS Raiffeisen AG; *Int'l*, pg. 215
PROFUMERIE DOUGLAS S.P.A.—See CVC Capital Partners SICAV-FIS S.A.; *Int'l*, pg. 1883

PROFUND SOLUTIONS LIMITED—See Marsh & McLennan Companies, Inc.; *U.S. Public*, pg. 1377
PROFUSION SARL—See LVMH Moet Hennessy Louis Vuitton SE; *Int'l*, pg. 4600
PROFUSS GMBH—See Asklepios Kliniken GmbH & Co. KGaA; *Int'l*, pg. 624
PROFUTURO A.F.P.—See The Bank of Nova Scotia; *Int'l*, pg. 7618
PROFUTURO GNP—See Grupo BAL; *Int'l*, pg. 3122
PROGALIM—See Groupe Limagrain Holding SA; *Int'l*, pg. 3108
PRO GALVANO MIKROMETAL A.D.; *Int'l*, pg. 5984
PROGEA DEUTSCHLAND GMBH—See Emerson Electric Co.; *U.S. Public*, pg. 751
PROGEA INTERNATIONAL, S.A.—See Emerson Electric Co.; *U.S. Public*, pg. 751
PROGEA NORTH AMERICA, CORP.—See Emerson Electric Co.; *U.S. Public*, pg. 751
PROGEA S.R.L.—See Emerson Electric Co.; *U.S. Public*, pg. 751
PROGECO—See CMA CGM S.A.; *Int'l*, pg. 1668
PROGEMA S.R.L.—See Piovan SpA; *Int'l*, pg. 5873
PROGEN BIOTECHNIK GESELLSCHAFT MIT BESCHRANKTER HAFTUNG—See R-Biopharm AG; *Int'l*, pg. 6169
PROGENE MOLECULAR DIAGNOSTIC CENTER LIMITED—See China Biotech Services Holdings Limited; *Int'l*, pg. 1487
PROGENET INNOVATIONS SDN. BHD.—See Key Alliance Group Berhad; *Int'l*, pg. 4144
PROGEN HOLDINGS LIMITED; *Int'l*, pg. 5990
PROGENICS PHARMACEUTICALS, INC.—See Avista Capital Partners, L.P.; *U.S. Private*, pg. 408
PROGENIKA BIOPHARMA, S.A.—See Level Biotechnology, Inc.; *Int'l*, pg. 4470
PROGENITOR METALS CORP.—See Val-d'Or Mining Corporation; *Int'l*, pg. 8110
PROGEN SYSTEMS AND TECHNOLOGIES LIMITED—See BGR Energy Systems Limited; *Int'l*, pg. 1009
PROGENY BIOVENTURES LIMITED—See ANGLE plc; *Int'l*, pg. 461
PROGENY SYSTEMS CORPORATION; *U.S. Private*, pg. 3277
PROGER S.P.A.; *Int'l*, pg. 5990
PRO.GES. SOCIETA COOPERATIVA SOCIALE—See Pro.Ges. Societa Cooperativa; *Int'l*, pg. 5985
PRO.GES. SOCIETA COOPERATIVA; *Int'l*, pg. 5985
PROGEX—See Immobel SA; *Int'l*, pg. 3627
PROG HOLDINGS, INC.; *U.S. Public*, pg. 1724
PROGILITY PLC; *Int'l*, pg. 5990
PROGINET LLC—See Vista Equity Partners, LLC; *U.S. Private*, pg. 4402
PROGISTIX-SOLUTIONS INC.—See Canada Post Corporation; *Int'l*, pg. 1282
PRO-GLASS LTD—See Bronsstadet AB; *Int'l*, pg. 1174
PROGNOS AG—See Verlagsgruppe Georg von Holtzbrinck GmbH; *Int'l*, pg. 8171
PROGNOS AG—See Verlagsgruppe Georg von Holtzbrinck GmbH; *Int'l*, pg. 8171
PROGNOSCENTRET AB—See Byggfakta Group Nordic HoldCo AB; *Int'l*, pg. 1235
PROGNOSESENTERET AS—See Byggfakta Group Nordic HoldCo AB; *Int'l*, pg. 1235
PROGNOST MACHINERY DIAGNOSTICS EQUIPMENT & SERVICES LLC—See Burckhardt Compression Holding AG; *Int'l*, pg. 1221
PROGNOST SYSTEMS GMBH—See Burckhardt Compression Holding AG; *Int'l*, pg. 1221
PROGNOST SYSTEMS INC.—See Burckhardt Compression Holding AG; *Int'l*, pg. 1221
PROGOLD LLC—See American Crystal Sugar Company; *U.S. Public*, pg. 98
PROGRAM LIGHTING LTD.—See SAS International; *Int'l*, pg. 6581
PROGRAMMED ELECTRICAL TECHNOLOGIES LTD—See Persol Holdings Co., Ltd.; *Int'l*, pg. 5820
PROGRAMMED FACILITY MANAGEMENT PTY. LTD.—See Persol Holdings Co., Ltd.; *Int'l*, pg. 5820
PROGRAMMED INDUSTRIAL MAINTENANCE PTY. LTD.—See Persol Holdings Co., Ltd.; *Int'l*, pg. 5820
PROGRAMMED INDUSTRIAL MAINTENANCE SERVICES PTY. LTD.—See Persol Holdings Co., Ltd.; *Int'l*, pg. 5820
PROGRAMMED INTEGRATED WORKFORCE LIMITED—See Persol Holdings Co., Ltd.; *Int'l*, pg. 5820
PROGRAMMED INTEGRATED WORKFORCE—See Persol Holdings Co., Ltd.; *Int'l*, pg. 5820
PROGRAMMED MAINTENANCE SERVICES LIMITED—See Persol Holdings Co., Ltd.; *Int'l*, pg. 5820
PROGRAMMED MAINTENANCE SERVICES (N.Z.) LTD.—See Persol Holdings Co., Ltd.; *Int'l*, pg. 5820
PROGRAMMED PROCESS OUTSOURCING PROPRIETARY LIMITED—See Workforce Holdings Ltd.; *Int'l*, pg. 8455
PROGRAMMER'S PARADISE, INC.—See Climb Global Solutions, Inc.; *U.S. Public*, pg. 515
PROGRAMMING RESEARCH INSTITUTE CO., LTD.—See Sprix Inc.; *Int'l*, pg. 7145

PROGRAM PARTNERS, INC.; *U.S. Private*, pg. 3278
PROGRAM PLANNING PROFESSIONALS; *U.S. Private*, pg. 3278
PROGRAM PRODUCTIONS, INC.; *U.S. Private*, pg. 3278
PROGRAM WATER TECHNOLOGIES—See Sloan Valve Company; *U.S. Private*, pg. 3689
PROGREEN US, INC.; *U.S. Private*, pg. 3278
PROGRES A.D.; *Int'l*, pg. 5990
PROGRES A.D.; *Int'l*, pg. 5990
PROGRESS ACQUISITION CORP.; *U.S. Public*, pg. 1724
PROGRESS ADULT SERVICES LIMITED—See Acadia Healthcare Company, Inc.; *U.S. Public*, pg. 29
PROGRESS APPARELS BANGLADESH LIMITED—See PDS Limited; *Int'l*, pg. 5771
PROGRESS APPRAISAL CO., LTD.—See Kasikornbank Public Company Limited; *Int'l*, pg. 4088
PROGRESS AUSSENWERBUNG GMBH—See JCDecaux S.A.; *Int'l*, pg. 3923
PROGRESS BANK & TRUST—See Oportun, Inc.; *U.S. Private*, pg. 3032
PROGRESS ENERGY CANADA LTD—See Petroliam Nasional Berhad; *Int'l*, pg. 5831
PROGRESS ENERGY, INC.—See Duke Energy Corporation; *U.S. Public*, pg. 691
PROGRESS ENGINEERING & TRADING ENTERPRISE—See TCS TurControlSysteme AG; *Int'l*, pg. 7485
PROGRESS EQUITY PARTNERS, LLC; *U.S. Private*, pg. 3278
PROGRESS FACILITIES MANAGEMENT CO., LTD.—See Kasikornbank Public Company Limited; *Int'l*, pg. 4088
PROGRESS-GARANT INSURANCE COMPANY OJSC—See Allianz SE; *Int'l*, pg. 355
PROGRESS GLASS CO. INC.; *U.S. Private*, pg. 3278
PROGRESS HR CO., LTD—See Kasikornbank Public Company Limited; *Int'l*, pg. 4088
THE PROGRESS-INDEX—See Gannett Co., Inc.; *U.S. Public*, pg. 905
PROGRESS INDUSTRIES; *U.S. Private*, pg. 3278
PROGRESSIO SGR S.P.A.; *Int'l*, pg. 5990
PROGRESSIVE ACUTE CARE LLC; *U.S. Private*, pg. 3278
PROGRESSIVE ADVANCED INSURANCE COMPANY—See The Progressive Corporation; *U.S. Public*, pg. 2125
PROGRESSIVE ALLOY STEELS UNLIMITED, LLC; *U.S. Private*, pg. 3278
PROGRESSIVE AMERICAN INSURANCE COMPANY—See The Progressive Corporation; *U.S. Public*, pg. 2125
PROGRESSIVE ARCHITECTURE ENGINEERING PLANNING, INC.; *U.S. Private*, pg. 3278
PROGRESSIVE AUTO STEREO INC.; *U.S. Private*, pg. 3278
PROGRESSIVE BUILDING SOCIETY; *Int'l*, pg. 5990
PROGRESSIVE BUSINESS PUBLICATIONS; *U.S. Private*, pg. 3278
PROGRESSIVE CAPITAL MANAGEMENT CORP.—See The Progressive Corporation; *U.S. Public*, pg. 2125
PROGRESSIVE CARE, INC.—See NextPlat Corp.; *U.S. Public*, pg. 1526
PROGRESSIVE CASUALTY INSURANCE COMPANY—See The Progressive Corporation; *U.S. Public*, pg. 2125
PROGRESSIVE COMMUNICATIONS INTERNATIONAL—See Taylor Corporation; *U.S. Private*, pg. 3939
PROGRESSIVE COMPONENTS INTERNATIONAL CORPORATION; *U.S. Private*, pg. 3278
PROGRESSIVE COMPUTER SYSTEMS, INC.—See Alpine Investors; *U.S. Private*, pg. 201
PROGRESSIVE CONSUMER INSURANCE—See The Progressive Corporation; *U.S. Public*, pg. 2125
PROGRESSIVE CONTRACTING CO; *U.S. Private*, pg. 3278
PROGRESSIVE CONTRACTING INCORPORATED; *U.S. Private*, pg. 3278
PROGRESSIVE CONTRACTORS INC.; *U.S. Private*, pg. 3278
PROGRESSIVE CORP. - AGENCY GROUP—See The Progressive Corporation; *U.S. Public*, pg. 2125
THE PROGRESSIVE CORPORATION; *U.S. Public*, pg. 2124
PROGRESSIVE COUNTY MUTUAL INSURANCE CO.—See The Progressive Corporation; *U.S. Public*, pg. 2125
PROGRESSIVE DIGITAL MEDIA LIMITED—See GlobalData Plc; *Int'l*, pg. 3003
PROGRESSIVE DISTRIBUTION SERVICES, INC.; *U.S. Private*, pg. 3278
PROGRESSIVE DRIVER SERVICES, INC.; *U.S. Private*, pg. 3279
PROGRESSIVE DYNAMICS, INC.; *U.S. Private*, pg. 3279
PROGRESSIVE ELDERCARE SERVICES - DREW INC.; *U.S. Private*, pg. 3279
PROGRESSIVE ELDERCARE SERVICES MORRILTON INC.; *U.S. Private*, pg. 3279
PROGRESSIVE ENERGY INC.; *U.S. Private*, pg. 3279

PROGRESSIVE ENGINEERING & CONSTRUCTION, INC.; *U.S. Private*, pg. 3279
PROGRESSIVE FARMS—See Arable Capital Partners LLC; *U.S. Private*, pg. 307
PROGRESSIVE FINANCE HOLDINGS, LLC—See Aaron's Company, Inc.; *U.S. Public*, pg. 13
PROGRESSIVE FINANCE LIMITED; *Int'l*, pg. 5990
PROGRESSIVE FOAM TECHNOLOGIES, INC.; *U.S. Private*, pg. 3279
PROGRESSIVE FURNITURE INC.; *U.S. Private*, pg. 3279
PROGRESSIVE GREEN SOLUTIONS, INC.; *U.S. Public*, pg. 1726
PROGRESSIVE GULF INSURANCE COMPANY—See The Progressive Corporation; *U.S. Public*, pg. 2125
PROGRESSIVE HALCYON INSURANCE CO.—See The Progressive Corporation; *U.S. Public*, pg. 2125
PROGRESSIVE HAWAII INSURANCE CORP.—See The Progressive Corporation; *U.S. Public*, pg. 2124
PROGRESSIVEHEALTH COMPANIES, LLC—See U.S. Physical Therapy, Inc.; *U.S. Public*, pg. 2215
PROGRESSIVE HEALTH GROUP, LLC; *U.S. Private*, pg. 3279
PROGRESSIVE HEALTH SYSTEMS INC.; *U.S. Private*, pg. 3279
PROGRESSIVE HYDRAULICS, INC.; *U.S. Private*, pg. 3279
PROGRESSIVE IMPACT CORPORATION BERHAD; *Int'l*, pg. 5990
PROGRESSIVE IMPRESSIONS INTERNATIONAL—See Taylor Corporation; *U.S. Private*, pg. 3939
PROGRESSIVE INCORPORATED—See Berkshire Hathaway Inc.; *U.S. Public*, pg. 314
PROGRESSIVE INSURANCE AGENCY, INC.—See The Progressive Corporation; *U.S. Public*, pg. 2125
PROGRESSIVE INSURANCE COMPANY LIMITED; *Int'l*, pg. 5991
PROGRESSIVE INTERNATIONAL CORP.—See Kainos Capital, LLC; *U.S. Private*, pg. 2255
PROGRESSIVE INVESTMENT COMPANY, INC.—See The Progressive Corporation; *U.S. Public*, pg. 2125
PROGRESSIVE LIFE CENTER; *U.S. Private*, pg. 3279
PROGRESSIVE LIFE INSURANCE COMPANY LIMITED; *Int'l*, pg. 5991
PROGRESSIVE LIGHTING, INC. (NORTH CAROLINA)—See Hubbell Incorporated; *U.S. Public*, pg. 1067
PROGRESSIVE LIGHTING INC.; *U.S. Private*, pg. 3279
PROGRESSIVE LOGISTICS INC.; *U.S. Private*, pg. 3279
PROGRESSIVE MANUFACTURING LTD.—See ASKO Holding A.S.; *Int'l*, pg. 625
PROGRESSIVE MARKETING PRODUCTS, INC.—See Main Street Capital Corporation; *U.S. Public*, pg. 1355
PROGRESSIVE MEDICAL ASSOCIATES, PLLC—See American Physician Partners, LLC; *U.S. Private*, pg. 243
PROGRESSIVE NORTHERN INSURANCE COMPANY—See The Progressive Corporation; *U.S. Public*, pg. 2125
PROGRESSIVE NURSING STAFFERS INC.—See Flexibility & Co., LLC; *U.S. Private*, pg. 1544
PROGRESSIVE NUTRITION, LLC—See Cargill, Inc.; *U.S. Private*, pg. 760
PROGRESSIVE PATH GROUP HOLDINGS LIMITED; *Int'l*, pg. 5991
PROGRESSIVE PLANET SOLUTIONS INC.; *Int'l*, pg. 5991
PROGRESSIVE PLUMBING INC.; *U.S. Private*, pg. 3279
PROGRESSIVE PLUMBING SUPPLY, CO.; *U.S. Private*, pg. 3279
PROGRESSIVE PREFERRED INSURANCE COMPANY—See The Progressive Corporation; *U.S. Public*, pg. 2125
PROGRESSIVE PREMIER INSURANCE COMPANY OF ILLINOIS—See The Progressive Corporation; *U.S. Public*, pg. 2125
PROGRESSIVE PROCESSING, LLC—See Hormel Foods Corporation; *U.S. Public*, pg. 1054
PROGRESSIVE PRODUCE LLC—See Arable Capital Partners LLC; *U.S. Private*, pg. 307
PROGRESSIVE PROMOTIONS, INC.—See Consolidated Marketing Services, Inc. of MA; *U.S. Private*, pg. 1021
PROGRESSIVE SAVINGS BANK; *U.S. Private*, pg. 3279
PROGRESSIVE SERVICES INC.; *U.S. Private*, pg. 3279
PROGRESSIVE SOUTHEASTERN INSURANCE COMPANY—See The Progressive Corporation; *U.S. Public*, pg. 2125
PROGRESSIVE SPECIALTY INSURANCE COMPANY—See The Progressive Corporation; *U.S. Public*, pg. 2125
PROGRESSIVE STAMPING, INC.—See Midway Products Group, Inc.; *U.S. Private*, pg. 2719
PROGRESSIVE STAR FINANCE PRIVATE LIMITED; *Int'l*, pg. 5991
PROGRESSIVE TECHNOLOGIES, INC.—See Universal Power Group, Inc.; *U.S. Public*, pg. 4306
PROGRESSIVE TRACTOR & IMPLEMENT COMPANY; *U.S. Private*, pg. 3279
PROGRESSIVE TRADERS LIMITED—See Steamships Trading Company Limited; *Int'l*, pg. 7189

PROGRESSIVE WATER TREATMENT, INC.—See Origin-Clear, Inc.; *U.S. Public*, pg. 1617
PROGRESSIVE WEST INSURANCE COMPANY—See The Progressive Corporation; *U.S. Public*, pg. 2125
PROGRESS JAPAN KK—See Progress Software Corporation; *U.S. Public*, pg. 1725
PROGRESS LIGHTING INC.—See Hubbell Incorporated; *U.S. Public*, pg. 1067
PROGRESS LIGHTING—See Hubbell Incorporated; *U.S. Public*, pg. 1066
PROGRESS MANAGEMENT CO., LTD.—See Kasikornbank Public Company Limited; *Int'l*, pg. 4088
PROGRESS MEDICAL A.S.—See Centene Corporation; *U.S. Public*, pg. 470
PROGRESS METAL RECLAMATION COMPANY—See Caterpillar, Inc.; *U.S. Public*, pg. 453
PROGRESS MULTI INSURANCE BROKER CO., LTD.—See Kasikornbank Public Company Limited; *Int'l*, pg. 4088
PROGRESS OPENEDGE—See Progress Software Corporation; *U.S. Public*, pg. 1725
PROGRESS PARTNERS, INC.; *U.S. Private*, pg. 3278
PROGRESS PHARMACY LTD—See AlerisLife Inc.; *U.S. Private*, pg. 162
PROGRESS PLASTIC PRODUCTS INC.; *U.S. Private*, pg. 3278
PROGRESS PRINTING COMPANY; *U.S. Private*, pg. 3278
PROGRESS RAIL - BEARING PLANT—See Caterpillar, Inc.; *U.S. Public*, pg. 453
PROGRESS RAIL - BEARING PLANT—See Caterpillar, Inc.; *U.S. Public*, pg. 453
PROGRESS RAIL CANADA CORPORATION—See Caterpillar, Inc.; *U.S. Public*, pg. 453
PROGRESS RAIL EQUIPMENT LEASING CORPORATION—See Paceline Equity Partners LLC; *U.S. Private*, pg. 3064
PROGRESS RAIL MANUFACTURING CORPORATION—See Caterpillar, Inc.; *U.S. Public*, pg. 453
PROGRESS RAIL RACELAND CORPORATION—See Caterpillar, Inc.; *U.S. Public*, pg. 453
PROGRESS RAIL SERVICES CORPORATION—See Caterpillar, Inc.; *U.S. Public*, pg. 453
PROGRESS RAIL SERVICES DE MEXICO S.A. DE C.V.—See Caterpillar, Inc.; *U.S. Public*, pg. 453
PROGRESS RAIL SERVICES UK LIMITED—See Caterpillar, Inc.; *U.S. Public*, pg. 453
PROGRESS RAIL SIGNALING S.P.A.—See Caterpillar, Inc.; *U.S. Public*, pg. 453
PROGRESS RAIL SWITCHING SERVICES LLC—See Caterpillar, Inc.; *U.S. Public*, pg. 453
PROGRESS SECURITY CORPORATION—See Progress Software Corporation; *U.S. Public*, pg. 1725
PROGRESS SERVICES CO., LTD—See Kasikornbank Public Company Limited; *Int'l*, pg. 4088
PROGRESS SOFTWARE AG—See Progress Software Corporation; *U.S. Public*, pg. 1725
PROGRESS SOFTWARE A/S—See Progress Software Corporation; *U.S. Public*, pg. 1725
PROGRESS SOFTWARE AS—See Progress Software Corporation; *U.S. Public*, pg. 1725
PROGRESS SOFTWARE B.V.—See Progress Software Corporation; *U.S. Public*, pg. 1725
PROGRESS SOFTWARE CO. LTD.—See Kasikornbank Public Company Limited; *Int'l*, pg. 4088
PROGRESS SOFTWARE CORPORATION LIMITED—See Progress Software Corporation; *U.S. Public*, pg. 1726
PROGRESS SOFTWARE CORPORATION OF CANADA LTD.—See Progress Software Corporation; *U.S. Public*, pg. 1725
PROGRESS SOFTWARE CORPORATION; *U.S. Public*, pg. 1724
PROGRESS SOFTWARE CORPORATION (S) PTE. LTD.—See Progress Software Corporation; *U.S. Public*, pg. 1726
PROGRESS SOFTWARE DEVELOPMENT PRIVATE LIMITED—See Progress Software Corporation; *U.S. Public*, pg. 1726
PROGRESS SOFTWARE DO BRASIL LTDA.—See Progress Software Corporation; *U.S. Public*, pg. 1726
PROGRESS SOFTWARE EAD—See Progress Software Corporation; *U.S. Public*, pg. 1725
PROGRESS SOFTWARE EUROPE B.V.—See Progress Software Corporation; *U.S. Public*, pg. 1725
PROGRESS SOFTWARE GESMBH—See Progress Software Corporation; *U.S. Public*, pg. 1725
PROGRESS SOFTWARE GMBH—See Progress Software Corporation; *U.S. Public*, pg. 1725
PROGRESS SOFTWARE GMBH—See Progress Software Corporation; *U.S. Public*, pg. 1725
PROGRESS SOFTWARE ITALY S.R.L.—See Progress Software Corporation; *U.S. Public*, pg. 1725
PROGRESS SOFTWARE JAPAN KK—See Progress Software Corporation; *U.S. Public*, pg. 1725
PROGRESS SOFTWARE LIMITED—See Progress Software Corporation; *U.S. Public*, pg. 1725
PROGRESS SOFTWARE NV—See Progress Software Corporation; *U.S. Public*, pg. 1725

PROGRESS SOFTWARE OY—See Progress Software Corporation; *U.S. Public*, pg. 1725
PROGRESS SOFTWARE PTY. LTD.—See Progress Software Corporation; *U.S. Public*, pg. 1725
PROGRESS SOFTWARE S.A.S.—See Progress Software Corporation; *U.S. Public*, pg. 1725
PROGRESS SOFTWARE S.L.—See Progress Software Corporation; *U.S. Public*, pg. 1725
PROGRESS SOFTWARE S.L.U.—See Progress Software Corporation; *U.S. Public*, pg. 1725
PROGRESS SOFTWARE—See Progress Software Corporation; *U.S. Public*, pg. 1725
PROGRESS SOFTWARE SP. Z O.O.—See Progress Software Corporation; *U.S. Public*, pg. 1725
PROGRESS SOFTWARE SVENSKA AB—See Progress Software Corporation; *U.S. Public*, pg. 1725
PROGRESS SOLUTIONS INDIA PRIVATE LIMITED—See Progress Software Corporation; *U.S. Public*, pg. 1726
PROGRESSUS THERAPY, INC.—See Golden Gate Capital Management II, LLC; *U.S. Private*, pg. 1731
PROGRESS VENTURES, INC.—See Progress Partners, Inc.; *U.S. Private*, pg. 3278
PROGRESS VULFIX LIMITED; *Int'l*, pg. 5990
PROGRESS WERBELAND WERBE. GMBH—See JCDecaux S.A.; *Int'l*, pg. 3923
PROGREXION HOLDINGS INC.; *U.S. Private*, pg. 3279
PROGREX VENTURES LTD.; *Int'l*, pg. 5991
PROGRIT INC.—See Vector Inc.; *Int'l*, pg. 8144
PRO GROUP, INC. - FARM MART DIVISION—See PRO Group, Inc.; *U.S. Private*, pg. 3270
PRO GROUP, INC.; *U.S. Private*, pg. 3269
PROGROUP NETWORK INC.—See BrandPoint Services, Inc.; *U.S. Private*, pg. 638
PROGUARD ACQUISITION CORP.; *U.S. Private*, pg. 3279
PROGYNY, INC.; *U.S. Public*, pg. 1726
PROHA OY—See Dovre Group Plc; *Int'l*, pg. 2182
PRO-HAWK CORPORATION; *Int'l*, pg. 5985
PROHEALTH CARE, INC.; *U.S. Private*, pg. 3280
PROHEALTH/CAREMOUNT DENTAL MANAGEMENT, LLC—See UnitedHealth Group Incorporated; *U.S. Public*, pg. 2249
PROHEALTH FITNESS OF LAKE SUCCESS, LLC—See UnitedHealth Group Incorporated; *U.S. Public*, pg. 2249
PROHEALTH INC.—See Progressive Health Systems Inc.; *U.S. Private*, pg. 3279
PROHEALTH MEDICAL GROUP—See Progressive Health Systems Inc.; *U.S. Private*, pg. 3279
PROHEALTH PHYSICIANS; *U.S. Private*, pg. 3280
PROHEAT, INC.—See Gryphon Investors, LLC; *U.S. Private*, pg. 1799
PROIECT BUCOVINA SA; *Int'l*, pg. 5991
PRO IMAGEM LTDA.—See Centro de Imagem Diagnosticos S.A.; *Int'l*, pg. 1413
PROINOVA AB—See Arthur J. Gallagher & Co.; *U.S. Public*, pg. 207
PROINSA LTDA.—See Sociedad Quimica y Minera de Chile S.A.; *Int'l*, pg. 7032
PROIN S.A.—See Banco Macro S.A.; *Int'l*, pg. 823
PRO INSURANCE SOLUTIONS LIMITED—See Financiere Pinault SCA; *Int'l*, pg. 2668
PROINTEC EXTREMADURA S.L.—See Indra Sistemas, S.A.; *Int'l*, pg. 3661
PROINTEC PANAMA, S.A.—See Indra Sistemas, S.A.; *Int'l*, pg. 3661
PROINTEC S.A.—See Indra Sistemas, S.A.; *Int'l*, pg. 3661
PROINTEC USA LLC—See Indra Sistemas, S.A.; *Int'l*, pg. 3661
PROIV TECHNOLOGY INC—See Alight, Inc.; *U.S. Public*, pg. 77
PROIZVODNJA MK D.O.O.—See Dalekovod d.d.; *Int'l*, pg. 1951
PROJECT/029 MEDIA & COMMUNICATIONS KFT.; *Int'l*, pg. 5991
PROJECT 2000 S.R.L.—See LCI Industries; *U.S. Public*, pg. 1296
PROJECT 321, INC.—See North Arc Capital Partners; *Int'l*, pg. 5439
PROJECT A VENTURES GMBH & CO. KG—See Otto GmbH & Co. KG; *Int'l*, pg. 5663
PROJECT CONTROL GROUP INC.—See Stantec Inc.; *Int'l*, pg. 7171
PROJECT COORDINATION (AUSTRALIA) PTY LTD; *Int'l*, pg. 5991
PROJECT DEVELOPERS, INC.; *U.S. Private*, pg. 3280
PROJECT DEVELOPMENT INTERNATIONAL, INC.; *U.S. Private*, pg. 3280
PROJECT DEVELOPMENT INTERNATIONAL LIMITED; *Int'l*, pg. 5991
PROJECT DEVELOPMENT INTERNATIONAL LIMITED—See Project Development International Limited; *Int'l*, pg. 5991
PROJECT DEVELOPMENT INTERNATIONAL LIMITED—See Project Development International Limited; *Int'l*, pg. 5991
PROJECT DEVELOPMENT SERVICES, INC.; *U.S. Private*, pg. 3280
PROJECT ENERGY REIMAGINED ACQUISITION CORP.; *U.S. Public*, pg. 1726

PROJECT ENHANCEMENT CORPORATION; *U.S. Private*, pg. 3280
PROJECT FOR PRIDE IN LIVING, INC.; *U.S. Private*, pg. 3280
PROJECT FROG, INC.; *U.S. Private*, pg. 3280
PROJECT HOLLYWOOD LLC; *U.S. Private*, pg. 3280
PROJECT HOPE; *U.S. Private*, pg. 3280
PROJECT HOSPITALITY, INC.; *U.S. Private*, pg. 3280
PROJECTINA AG—See Advent International Corporation; *U.S. Private*, pg. 100
PROJECT INFORMATICA SRL—See H.I.G. Capital, LLC; *U.S. Private*, pg. 1831
PROJECTION PRESENTATION TECHNOLOGY; *U.S. Private*, pg. 3281
PROJECTIONS, INC.; *U.S. Private*, pg. 3281
PROJECTIONS UNLIMITED INC.; *U.S. Private*, pg. 3281
PROJECT LEADERSHIP ASSOCIATES, INC.; *U.S. Private*, pg. 3280
PROJECT LEADERSHIP ASSOCIATES, INC.—See Project Leadership Associates, Inc.; *U.S. Private*, pg. 3280
PROJECT LIGHTING CO. INC.; *U.S. Private*, pg. 3280
PROJECTLINE SERVICES, INC.; *U.S. Private*, pg. 3281
PROJECT LOGISTICS INTERNATIONAL—See Emo-Trans Inc.; *U.S. Private*, pg. 1383
PROJECT MANAGEMENT GROUP, LLC—See Ashford Inc.; *U.S. Public*, pg. 211
PROJECT MANAGEMENT PARTNERS PTY. LTD.—See Bain Capital, LP; *U.S. Private*, pg. 435
PROJECTMANAGER.COM, INC.; *U.S. Private*, pg. 3281
PROJECTMATRIX CORP.—See Configura Sverige AB; *Int'l*, pg. 1768
PROJECT NOW, INC.; *U.S. Private*, pg. 3280
PROJECT ONE INC.—See Stone Point Capital LLC; *U.S. Private*, pg. 3823
PROJECT ONE INTEGRATED SERVICES LLC—See Cumming Construction Management, Inc.; *U.S. Private*, pg. 1123
PROJECTONTWIKKELINGSMAATSCHAPPIJ IMMO—See Immobel SA; *Int'l*, pg. 3627
PROJECTOR PSA, INC.—See Vista Equity Partners, LLC; *U.S. Private*, pg. 4895
PROJECT PARTNERS CORPORATION PTY LTD—See PeopleIn Limited; *Int'l*, pg. 5794
PROJECT PLANNING SERVICE PUBLIC COMPANY LIMITED; *Int'l*, pg. 5991
PROJECT RENDEZVOUS HOLDING CORPORATION—See Star Equity Holdings, Inc.; *U.S. Public*, pg. 1937
PROJECT RENEWAL; *U.S. Private*, pg. 3280
PROJECT SHOP LAND SPA—See H.I.G. Capital, LLC; *U.S. Private*, pg. 1831
PROJECT SLOANE LTD.—See Onward Holdings Co., Ltd.; *Int'l*, pg. 5593
PROJECT SOLUTIONS S.A.—See ManpowerGroup Inc.; *U.S. Public*, pg. 1361
PROJECTS UNLIMITED, INC.; *U.S. Private*, pg. 3281
PROJECT: WORLDWIDE, INC. - LOS ANGELES—See Project: Worldwide, Inc.; *U.S. Private*, pg. 3281
PROJECT: WORLDWIDE, INC.; *U.S. Private*, pg. 3280
PROJEK BANDAR SAMARIANG SDN. BHD.—See Cahya Mata Sarawak Berhad; *Int'l*, pg. 1251
PROJEK JAYA SDN BHD—See Lion Industries Corporation Berhad; *Int'l*, pg. 4519
PROJEK LEBUHRAYA UTARA-SELATAN BERHAD—See Khazanah Nasional Berhad; *Int'l*, pg. 4153
PROJEK LINTASAN KOTA HOLDINGS SDN BHD—See Permodalan Nasional Berhad; *Int'l*, pg. 5809
PROJEKT202 LLC—See Amdocs Limited; *Int'l*, pg. 420
PROJEKT A.D.; *Int'l*, pg. 5991
PROJEKTBAU GESMBH—See Vienna Insurance Group AG Wiener Versicherung Gruppe; *Int'l*, pg. 8195
PROJEKTBIRO A.D.; *Int'l*, pg. 5991
PROJEKT ELBPARK GMBH & CO. KG—See STRABAG SE; *Int'l*, pg. 7231
PROJEKTENGAGEMANG SWEDEN AB; *Int'l*, pg. 5991
PROJEKTENTWICKLUNGSGESELLSCHAFT GARTENSTADT WILDAU ROTHEGRUND II.MBH—See Erste Abwicklungsanstalt AoR; *Int'l*, pg. 2497
PROJEKTENTWICKLUNGSGES.M.B.H.—See PORR AG; *Int'l*, pg. 5924
PROJEKTENTWICKLUNGS-GMBH FRIESENHEIMER INSEL—See BASF SE; *Int'l*, pg. 884
PROJEKTGESELLSCHAFT JUSTIZVOLLZUG BURG GMBH & CO. KG—See Bilfinger SE; *Int'l*, pg. 1028
PROJEKTIERUNGSTEAM MUNCHEN GMBH—See PORR AG; *Int'l*, pg. 5924
PROJEKTINVEST A.D.; *Int'l*, pg. 5991
PROJEKTKONTOR AG—See Mobimo Holding AG; *Int'l*, pg. 5012
PROJEKTNI BIRO PALMOTICEVA 45 D.O.O.—See INSTITUT IGH d.d.; *Int'l*, pg. 3723
PROJEKTOMONTAZA AD BELGRADE; *Int'l*, pg. 5991
PROJEKT OST - IBC BUSINESS CENTER ENTWICKLUNGS- UND ERRICHTUNGS-GMBH AND CO KG—See PORR AG; *Int'l*, pg. 5924
PROJEKT-PARTNER-ONLINE GMBH—See Bilfinger SE; *Int'l*, pg. 1029

PROJEKT- UND BETRIEBSGESLLSCHAFT JUSTIZZENTRUM CHEMNITZ GMBH—See Bilfinger SE; *Int'l*, pg. 1028
PROJEKT WASSERTURM BAU GMBH & CO. KG.—See PATRIZIA SE; *Int'l*, pg. 5759
PROJEKT WASSERTURM VERWALTUNGS GMBH.—See PATRIZIA SE; *Int'l*, pg. 5759
PROJEKT WEST - IBC BUSINESS CENTER ENTWICKLUNGS- UND ERRICHTUNGS-GMBH AND CO KG—See PORR AG; *Int'l*, pg. 5924
PROJET AVIATION; *U.S. Private*, pg. 3281
PROJILITY; *U.S. Private*, pg. 3282
PROJOB WORKWEAR AB—See New Wave Group AB; *Int'l*, pg. 5230
PRO KAPITAL EESTI AS—See Pro Kapital Grupp AS; *Int'l*, pg. 5984
PRO KAPITAL GRUPP AS; *Int'l*, pg. 5984
PRO KAPITAL LATVIA JSC—See Pro Kapital Grupp AS; *Int'l*, pg. 5984
PRO KAPITAL VILNIUS REAL ESTATE UAB—See Pro Kapital Grupp AS; *Int'l*, pg. 5984
PROKAR, INC.—See Aurora Capital Group, LLC; *U.S. Private*, pg. 394
PROKAR, INC.—See The Jordan Company, L.P.; *U.S. Private*, pg. 4061
PROKARMA INC.—See Concentrix Corporation; *U.S. Public*, pg. 565
PROKARMA INC. - WASHINGTON—See Concentrix Corporation; *U.S. Public*, pg. 565
PROKIDNEY CORP.; *U.S. Public*, pg. 1726
PRO-KLIMA D.O.O.—See CENTROTEC SE; *Int'l*, pg. 1414
PRODODIS S.N.C.—See KONE Oyj; *Int'l*, pg. 4250
PROKOL D.O.O.—See Kolektor Group d.o.o.; *Int'l*, pg. 4233
PROKOM SP. Z.O.O.—See Koninklijke HaskoningDHV Groep B.V.; *Int'l*, pg. 4266
PROKUPAC A.D.; *Int'l*, pg. 5991
PROLAB NUTRITION INC.—See Aurobindo Pharma Ltd.; *Int'l*, pg. 712
PROLABO SARL—See Investis Holding SA; *Int'l*, pg. 3780
PROLAB TECHNOLOGIES INC.; *Int'l*, pg. 5991
PROLAB TECHNOLUB INC—See Prolab Technologies Inc.; *Int'l*, pg. 5991
PROLACOM SA; *Int'l*, pg. 5992
PROLAMINA CORPORATION—See The Pritzker Group - Chicago, LLC; *U.S. Private*, pg. 4099
PROLATAMEX, S.A. DE C.V.—See Crown Holdings, Inc.; *U.S. Public*, pg. 598
PROLAW LTD.—See Randstad N.V.; *Int'l*, pg. 6205
PROLEASING D.O.O.—See Probanka, d.d.; *Int'l*, pg. 5986
PROLEC LTD.—See Carl Bennet AB; *Int'l*, pg. 1332
PROLECTRIC SERVICES LIMITED—See Hill & Smith PLC; *Int'l*, pg. 3392
PROLERIDE TRANSPORT SYSTEMS, INC.—See Radius Recycling, Inc.; *U.S. Public*, pg. 1760
PROLERIZED NEW ENGLAND COMPANY LLC—See Radius Recycling, Inc.; *U.S. Public*, pg. 1760
PROLER STEEL INTERNATIONAL, LLC; *U.S. Private*, pg. 3282
PROLETER A.D. - ARILJE; *Int'l*, pg. 5992
PROLETER A.D.; *Int'l*, pg. 5992
PROLETER BEACEJ A.D.; *Int'l*, pg. 5992
PROLEXIC TECHNOLOGIES INC.—See Akamai Technologies, Inc.; *U.S. Public*, pg. 69
PROLIANCE HOLDINGS, LLC—See CenterPoint Energy, Inc.; *U.S. Public*, pg. 472
PROLIANCE INTERNATIONAL, INC.; *U.S. Public*, pg. 1726
PROLIANT INC.—See Lauridsen Group Inc.; *U.S. Private*, pg. 2400
PROLIANT; *U.S. Private*, pg. 3282
PROLIFE INDUSTRIES LIMITED; *Int'l*, pg. 5992
PROLIFIC TECHNOLOGY CO., LTD.—See Prolific Technology Inc.; *Int'l*, pg. 5992
PROLIFIC TECHNOLOGY INC.; *Int'l*, pg. 5992
PROLIFT INDUSTRIAL EQUIPMENT CO., LLC; *U.S. Private*, pg. 3282
PROLIGHT DIAGNOSTICS AB; *Int'l*, pg. 5992
PROLIGHT OPTO TECHNOLOGY CORP.; *Int'l*, pg. 5992
PROLIM PLM; *U.S. Private*, pg. 3282
PRO-LINE BOATS—See American Marine Holdings, LLC; *U.S. Private*, pg. 240
PROLINE GROUP AB—See Carl Bennet AB; *Int'l*, pg. 1332
PROLINE QUALITY FINISHING PTY. LTD.—See Oceania Capital Partners Limited; *Int'l*, pg. 5518
PRO LINGUIS—See Graham Holdings Company; *U.S. Public*, pg. 955
PROLINK MICROSYSTEMS CORP.; *Int'l*, pg. 5992
PROLINK STAFFING LLC; *U.S. Private*, pg. 3282
PROLIPHIX, INC.—See Yardi Systems, Inc.; *U.S. Private*, pg. 4586
PROLOGIC PLC; *Int'l*, pg. 5992
PROLOGIS B.V.—See Prologis, Inc.; *U.S. Public*, pg. 1727
PROLOGIS CANADA INCORPORATED—See Prologis, Inc.; *U.S. Public*, pg. 1727
PROLOGIS, INC.; *U.S. Public*, pg. 1726
PROLOGIS JAPAN INCORPORATED—See Prologis, Inc.; *U.S. Public*, pg. 1727

PROLOGIS, L.P.—See Prologis, Inc.; *U.S. Public*, pg. 1727
PROLOGIS PROPERTY FRANCE S.A.R.L.—See Prologis, Inc.; *U.S. Public*, pg. 1727
PRO-LOGISTIK-TEAM INTERNATIONALE SPEDITIONS GMBH; *Int'l*, pg. 5985
PROLOGIS UK HOLDINGS S.A.—See Prologis, Inc.; *U.S. Public*, pg. 1727
PROLOGIS UK LIMITED—See Prologis, Inc.; *U.S. Public*, pg. 1727
PRO-LOG IV GMBH—See DEKRA e.V.; *Int'l*, pg. 2009
PRO-LOG NIEDERRHEIN GMBH—See DEKRA e.V.; *Int'l*, pg. 2009
PRO-LOG ROSENHEIM GMBH—See DEKRA e.V.; *Int'l*, pg. 2009
PRO-LOG RUHR GMBH—See DEKRA e.V.; *Int'l*, pg. 2009
PROLOG SERVICES; *U.S. Private*, pg. 3282
PROLOGUE S.A.; *Int'l*, pg. 5992
PROLUXE PROPERTIES; *U.S. Private*, pg. 3282
PROLUX SOLUTIONS AG—See Arbonia AG; *Int'l*, pg. 538
PRO MACH GROUP, INC.—See Leonard Green & Partners, L.P.; *U.S. Private*, pg. 2427
PROMACH, INC.—See Leonard Green & Partners, L.P.; *U.S. Private*, pg. 2427
PROMAC, INC.; *U.S. Private*, pg. 3282
PROMAC ITALIA SRL—See Ali Holding S.r.l; *Int'l*, pg. 321
PROMACT IMPEX LIMITED; *Int'l*, pg. 5992
PRO MAGNET, S.R.O—See Centene Corporation; *U.S. Public*, pg. 470
PROMAK PRES OTOMASYON MAK. SAN. VE TIC. LTD.—See P/A Industries, Inc.; *U.S. Private*, pg. 3061
PROMAKS YAZILIM SANAYI VE TICARET A.S.—See Vontier Corporation; *U.S. Public*, pg. 2309
PROMAN SAS; *Int'l*, pg. 5992
PROMAN STAFFING LLC—See Proman SAS; *Int'l*, pg. 5992
PRO-MANUFACTURED PRODUCTS, INC.—See Pine Grove Holdings, LLC; *U.S. Private*, pg. 3182
PROMAR INSTITUCION CULTURAL MARITIMA MEXICANA, A.C.—See Grupo TMM, S.A.B.; *Int'l*, pg. 3137
PROMAR INTERNATIONAL LIMITED—See Genus Plc; *Int'l*, pg. 2931
PROMARK DIRECT INC.; *U.S. Private*, pg. 3282
PRO MARKETING SALES INC.; *U.S. Private*, pg. 3270
PROMARK INTERNATIONAL INC.; *U.S. Private*, pg. 3282
PRO MARK, LLC—See Platinum Equity, LLC; *U.S. Private*, pg. 3207
PROMARK TECHNOLOGY, INC.—See Hainan Traffic Administration Holding Co., Ltd.; *Int'l*, pg. 3215
PROMARKT HANDDELS GMBH—See Kingfisher plc; *Int'l*, pg. 4173
PRO-MART INDUSTRIAL PRODUCTS LTD.; *Int'l*, pg. 5985
PROMASIDOR HOLDINGS LIMITED—See Ajinomoto Company, Inc.; *Int'l*, pg. 257
PROMAS S.A—See ELLAKTOR S.A.; *Int'l*, pg. 2365
PROMAT AG—See Etex SA/NV; *Int'l*, pg. 2522
PROMAT AUSTRALIA PTY LTD.—See Etex SA/NV; *Int'l*, pg. 2522
PROMAT BUILDING SYSTEM PTE LTD.—See Etex SA/NV; *Int'l*, pg. 2522
PROMAT B.V.—See Etex SA/NV; *Int'l*, pg. 2522
PROMAT CHINA LTD.—See Etex SA/NV; *Int'l*, pg. 2522
PROMATE ELECTRONIC CO., LTD.; *Int'l*, pg. 5992
PROMATE ELECTRONICS COMPANY—See Promate Electronic Co., Ltd.; *Int'l*, pg. 5992
PROMATE ELECTRONIC (SHANGHAI) CO., LTD.—See Promate Electronic Co., Ltd.; *Int'l*, pg. 5992
PROMATE ELECTRONIC (SHENZHEN) CO., LTD.—See Promate Electronic Co., Ltd.; *Int'l*, pg. 5993
PROMATE JAPAN CO., LTD.—See Promate Solutions Corporation; *Int'l*, pg. 5993
PROMATERIS S.A.; *Int'l*, pg. 5993
PROMATE SOLUTIONS CORPORATION; *Int'l*, pg. 5993
PROMAT GLASGOW LTD.—See Etex SA/NV; *Int'l*, pg. 2522
PROMAT GMBH—See Etex SA/NV; *Int'l*, pg. 2522
PROMAT GMBH—See Etex SA/NV; *Int'l*, pg. 2522
PROMAT IBERICA S.A.—See Etex SA/NV; *Int'l*, pg. 2522
PROMATIK EMAS SDN. BHD.—See UOL Group Limited; *Int'l*, pg. 8086
PROMAT (MALAYSIA) SDN. BHD.—See Etex SA/NV; *Int'l*, pg. 2522
PRO-MATRIX PTE. LTD.—See Nippon Telegraph & Telephone Corporation; *Int'l*, pg. 5355
PROMAT S.A.S.—See Etex SA/NV; *Int'l*, pg. 2522
PROMAT SHANGAI LTD.—See Etex SA/NV; *Int'l*, pg. 2522
PROMAT S.P.A.—See Etex SA/NV; *Int'l*, pg. 2522
PROMAT S.R.O.—See Etex SA/NV; *Int'l*, pg. 2522
PROMAT TOP SP. Z O.O.—See Etex SA/NV; *Int'l*, pg. 2522
PROMAT UK LTD.—See Etex SA/NV; *Int'l*, pg. 2522
PROMAXBDA; *U.S. Private*, pg. 3282
PROMAXIMA MANUFACTURING LTD; *U.S. Private*, pg. 3282
PROMAX POWER LIMITED; *Int'l*, pg. 5993
PROMAX S.R.L.; *Int'l*, pg. 5993
PROMAX TOOLS L.P.—See PLANSEE Holding AG; *Int'l*, pg. 5890
PROMEC SP. Z O.O.—See E.ON SE; *Int'l*, pg. 2259

PROMED A.S.—See CompuGroup Medical SE & Co. KGaA; *Int'l*, pg. 1757
PROMEDEV, LLC; *U.S. Private*, pg. 3282
PROMEDIA A/S—See WPP plc; *Int'l*, pg. 8466
PROMEDIA DIRECTORIES PTE LTD—See Internet Technology Group Ltd.; *Int'l*, pg. 3754
PRO MEDIA GMBH—See DEAG Deutsche Entertainment AG; *Int'l*, pg. 1998
PROMEDIA TECHNOLOGY SERVICES INC.—See Advanced AV, LLC; *U.S. Private*, pg. 88
PROMEDICA ENDOSCOPY CENTER—See American Healthcare Systems Corp., Inc.; *U.S. Private*, pg. 236
PROMEDICA HEALTH SYSTEM, INC.—See American Healthcare Systems Corp., Inc.; *U.S. Private*, pg. 236
PROMEDICA INC.—See Arsenal Capital Management LP; *U.S. Private*, pg. 338
PROMEDICAL PERSONNEL LTD.; *Int'l*, pg. 5993
PROMEDICA RETTUNGSDIENST WALBECK-FRANKENBERG GMBH & CO. KG—See Lundbeckfonden; *Int'l*, pg. 4583
PROMEDICA SENIOR CARE—See American Healthcare Systems Corp., Inc.; *U.S. Private*, pg. 236
PRO MEDICUS LIMITED; *Int'l*, pg. 5984
PROMEDIOR, INC.—See Roche Holding AG; *Int'l*, pg. 6376
PROMED MOLDED PRODUCTS, INC.; *U.S. Private*, pg. 3282
PROMED WASTE SOLUTIONS LLC; *U.S. Private*, pg. 3282
PROMEGA CORPORATION; *U.S. Private*, pg. 3282
THE PROMENADE D'IBERVILLE, LLC—See CBL & Associates Properties, Inc.; *U.S. Public*, pg. 459
PROMENADE PLACE, LLC—See Veritex Holdings, Inc.; *U.S. Public*, pg. 2283
PROMENA ELEKTRONIK TICARET AS—See Koc Holding A.S.; *Int'l*, pg. 4223
PROMENERGOLAB LLC; *Int'l*, pg. 5993
PROMENS AS—See Berry Global Group, Inc; *U.S. Public*, pg. 323
PROMENS AS—See Berry Global Group, Inc; *U.S. Public*, pg. 323
PROMENS DEVENTER B.V.—See Berry Global Group, Inc; *U.S. Public*, pg. 323
PROMENS FIRENZE S.R.L.—See Berry Global Group, Inc; *U.S. Public*, pg. 323
PROMENS HOCKENHEIM GMBH—See Berry Global Group, Inc; *U.S. Public*, pg. 323
PROMENS MONASTIR SARL—See Berry Global Group, Inc; *U.S. Public*, pg. 323
PROMENS MUNCHEN GMBH—See Berry Global Group, Inc; *U.S. Public*, pg. 323
PROMENS NITRA S.R.O.—See Berry Global Group, Inc; *U.S. Public*, pg. 323
PROMENS OY—See Berry Global Group, Inc; *U.S. Public*, pg. 323
PROMENS PACKAGING GMBH - ETTLINGEN—See Berry Global Group, Inc; *U.S. Public*, pg. 323
PROMENS PACKAGING GMBH - NEUMUNSTER—See Berry Global Group, Inc; *U.S. Public*, pg. 323
PROMENS PACKAGING GMBH—See Berry Global Group, Inc; *U.S. Public*, pg. 323
PROMENS PACKAGING LTD.—See Berry Global Group, Inc; *U.S. Public*, pg. 323
PROMENS PACKAGING SAU—See Berry Global Group, Inc; *U.S. Public*, pg. 323
PROMENS RIJEN B.V.—See Berry Global Group, Inc; *U.S. Public*, pg. 323
PROMENS SA - GEOVREISSET—See Berry Global Group, Inc; *U.S. Public*, pg. 323
PROMENS SARL—See Berry Global Group, Inc; *U.S. Public*, pg. 323
PROMENS SA—See Berry Global Group, Inc; *U.S. Public*, pg. 323
PROMENS ZEVENAAR B.V.—See Berry Global Group, Inc; *U.S. Public*, pg. 323
PROMERIC TECHNOLOGIES INC.—See First American Financial Corporation; *U.S. Public*, pg. 838
PROMERUS, LLC—See Sumitomo Bakelite Co., Ltd.; *Int'l*, pg. 7263
PROMESSA—See Messe Munchen GmbH; *Int'l*, pg. 4842
PRO METALURGIA SA; *Int'l*, pg. 5985
PRO METCO INC.; *U.S. Private*, pg. 3270
PROMET CZECH S.R.O.—See Promet Froup a.s.; *Int'l*, pg. 5993
PROMETEON TYRE GROUP S.R.L.—See China National Chemical Corporation; *Int'l*, pg. 1529
PROMET FOUNDRY A.S.—See Promet Froup a.s.; *Int'l*, pg. 5993
PROMET FROUP A.S.; *Int'l*, pg. 5993
PROMETHEAN INC.—See NetDragon Websoft Holdings Limited; *Int'l*, pg. 5214
PROMETHEAN INVESTMENTS LLP; *Int'l*, pg. 5993
PROMETHEAN LIMITED—See NetDragon Websoft Holdings Limited; *Int'l*, pg. 5214
PROMETHEAN WORLD LIMITED—See NetDragon Websoft Holdings Limited; *Int'l*, pg. 5213
PROMETHERA BIOSCIENCES S.A./N.V.; *Int'l*, pg. 5993
PROMETHEUM, INC.; *U.S. Private*, pg. 3282

PROMETHEUM, INC.   CORPORATE AFFILIATIONS

PROMETHEUS BIOSCIENCES, INC.—See Merck & Co., Inc.; *U.S. Public*, pg. 1421
PROMETHEUS GLOBAL MEDIA LLC—See Valence Media Group; *U.S. Private*, pg. 4330
PROMETHEUS GROUP ENTERPRISES, LLC—See Genstar Capital, LLC; *U.S. Private*, pg. 1678
PROMETHEUS IMMOBILIENERRICHTUNGS-UND-BETEILIGUNGS GMBH—See UniCredit S.p.A.; *Int'l*, pg. 8040
PROMETHEUS LABORATORIES, INC.—See Merck & Co., Inc.; *U.S. Public*, pg. 1421
PROMETHEUS PARTNERS, L.P.; *U.S. Private*, pg. 3283
PROMETHEUS REAL ESTATE GROUP, INC.; *U.S. Private*, pg. 3283
PROMETHEUS RESEARCH, LLC; *U.S. Private*, pg. 3283
PROMETHEUS—See Omnicom Group Inc.; *U.S. Public*, pg. 1589
PROMETIC BIOSCIENCES INC.—See Thomvest Ventures LLC; *U.S. Private*, pg. 4162
PROMETIC BIOSCIENCES LTD - ENABLING TECHNOLOGY—See Thomvest Ventures LLC; *U.S. Private*, pg. 4162
PROMETIC BIOSCIENCES LTD—See Thomvest Ventures LLC; *U.S. Private*, pg. 4162
PROMETIC BIOSCIENCES (USA), INC.—See Thomvest Ventures LLC; *U.S. Private*, pg. 4162
PROMETIC BIOTHERAPEUTICS, INC.—See Thomvest Ventures LLC; *U.S. Private*, pg. 4162
PROMET LOGISTICS A.S.—See Promet Froup a.s.; *Int'l*, pg. 5993
PROMET METALS TESTING LABORATORY LIMITED—See Lee Kee Holdings Limited; *Int'l*, pg. 4440
PROMETNI INSTITUT LJUBLJANA D. O. O.—See Slovenske zeleznice, d.o.o.; *Int'l*, pg. 6997
PROMETRIC LLC—See Educational Testing Service Inc.; *U.S. Private*, pg. 1340
PROMET SLOVAKIA S.R.O.—See Promet Froup a.s.; *Int'l*, pg. 5993
PROMET TP A.D.; *Int'l*, pg. 5993
PROMGAZ—See PJSC Gazprom; *Int'l*, pg. 5880
PROMGIRL, LLC; *U.S. Private*, pg. 3283
PRO-MICRON GMBH—See Sandvik AB; *Int'l*, pg. 6530
PROMIGAS S.A. E.S.P.; *Int'l*, pg. 5993
PROMIMIC AB; *Int'l*, pg. 5993
PROMIM PTY LTD.—See Luminus Systems Limited; *Int'l*, pg. 4579
PROMINENCE ENERGY LTD.; *Int'l*, pg. 5993
PROMINENT ALGERIA—See Verder International B.V.; *Int'l*, pg. 8166
PROMINENT ARGENTINA S.A.—See Verder International B.V.; *Int'l*, pg. 8166
PROMINENT BELGIUM S.A.—See Verder International B.V.; *Int'l*, pg. 8166
PROMINENT BRASIL LTDA.—See Verder International B.V.; *Int'l*, pg. 8166
PROMINENT CHILE S.A.—See Verder International B.V.; *Int'l*, pg. 8166
PROMINENT COLOMBIA S.A.S—See Verder International B.V.; *Int'l*, pg. 8166
PROMINENT CONSTRUCTION, LLC; *U.S. Private*, pg. 3283
PROMINENT DEUTSCHLAND GMBH—See Verder International B.V.; *Int'l*, pg. 8166
PROMINENT DOSERTEKNIK AB—See Verder International B.V.; *Int'l*, pg. 8166
PROMINENT DOSIERTECHNIK AG—See Verder International B.V.; *Int'l*, pg. 8166
PROMINENT DOSIERTECHNIK CS S.R.O.—See Verder International B.V.; *Int'l*, pg. 8166
PROMINENT DOSIERTECHNIK GES.M.B.H—See ProMinent Dosiertechnik GmbH; *Int'l*, pg. 5994
PROMINENT DOSIERTECHNIK GMBH; *Int'l*, pg. 5994
PROMINENT DOSIERTECHNIK VIETNAM CO., LTD—See Verder International B.V.; *Int'l*, pg. 8166
PROMINENT DOSIRUYUSHAYA TECHNIKA LLC—See Verder International B.V.; *Int'l*, pg. 8166
PROMINENT DOZAJ TEKNIKLERI LTD.—See Verder International B.V.; *Int'l*, pg. 8166
PROMINENT DOZOTECHNIKA SP.Z.O.O.—See Verder International B.V.; *Int'l*, pg. 8166
PROMINENT (EUROPE) LIMITED—See ITOCHU Corporation; *Int'l*, pg. 3841
PROMINENT EXCEL SDN. BHD.—See GLOMAC Berhad; *Int'l*, pg. 3008
PROMINENT FINLAND OY—See Verder International B.V.; *Int'l*, pg. 8166
PROMINENT FLUID CONTROLS BG LTD.—See Verder International B.V.; *Int'l*, pg. 8167
PROMINENT FLUID CONTROLS (DALIAN) CO., LTD—See Verder International B.V.; *Int'l*, pg. 8166
PROMINENT FLUID CONTROLS DE MEXICO S.A. DE C.V.—See Verder International B.V.; *Int'l*, pg. 8167
PROMINENT FLUID CONTROLS (FE) PTE. LTD.—See Verder International B.V.; *Int'l*, pg. 8167
PROMINENT FLUID CONTROLS INC.—See Verder International B.V.; *Int'l*, pg. 8167
PROMINENT FLUID CONTROLS LTD.—See ProMinent Dosiertechnik GmbH; *Int'l*, pg. 5994
PROMINENT FLUID CONTROLS LTD.—See ProMinent Dosiertechnik GmbH; *Int'l*, pg. 5994
PROMINENT FLUID CONTROLS LTD.—See Verder International B.V.; *Int'l*, pg. 8167
PROMINENT FLUID CONTROLS (M) SDN. BHD.—See Verder International B.V.; *Int'l*, pg. 8167
PROMINENT FLUID CONTROLS PTY LTD.—See Verder International B.V.; *Int'l*, pg. 8167
PROMINENT FLUID CONTROLS (TAIWAN) LTD.—See Verder International B.V.; *Int'l*, pg. 8167
PROMINENT FLUID CONTROLS (THAILAND) CO. LTD.—See Verder International B.V.; *Int'l*, pg. 8167
PROMINENT FLUID CONTROLS (UK) LTD.—See Verder International B.V.; *Int'l*, pg. 8167
PROMINENT FRANCE S.A.S—See Verder International B.V.; *Int'l*, pg. 8167
PROMINENT GMBH—See Verder International B.V.; *Int'l*, pg. 8166
PROMINENT HELLAS LTD.—See Verder International B.V.; *Int'l*, pg. 8167
PROMINENT IBERIA, SA—See ProMinent Dosiertechnik GmbH; *Int'l*, pg. 5994
PROMINENT IBERIA, SA—See Verder International B.V.; *Int'l*, pg. 8167
PROMINENT ITALIANA S.R.L.—See Verder International B.V.; *Int'l*, pg. 8167
PROMINENT JAPAN LTD.—See Verder International B.V.; *Int'l*, pg. 8167
PROMINENT JUFFALI FZC—See ProMinent Dosiertechnik GmbH; *Int'l*, pg. 5994
PROMINENT KOREA CO., LTD.—See Verder International B.V.; *Int'l*, pg. 8167
PROMINENT MAGYARORSZ G KFT.—See Verder International B.V.; *Int'l*, pg. 8167
PROMINENT NORGE AS—See Verder International B.V.; *Int'l*, pg. 8167
PROMINENT SCOTLAND LTD.—See Verder International B.V.; *Int'l*, pg. 8167
PROMINENT SLOVENSKO, S.R.O.—See Verder International B.V.; *Int'l*, pg. 8167
PROMINENT SYSTEMS SPOL. S.R.O.—See Verder International B.V.; *Int'l*, pg. 8167
PROMINENT TITLE LLC; *U.S. Private*, pg. 3283
PROMINENT TRADING (DALIAN) CO., LTD—See ProMinent Dosiertechnik GmbH; *Int'l*, pg. 5994
PROMINENT USA LLC—See ITOCHU Corporation; *Int'l*, pg. 3838
PROMINENT VERDER B.V.—See ProMinent Dosiertechnik GmbH; *Int'l*, pg. 5994
PROMINENT VERDER SRL—See Verder International B.V.; *Int'l*, pg. 8167
PROMINEX RESOURCE CORP.; *Int'l*, pg. 5994
PROMINIC.NET; *U.S. Private*, pg. 3283
PROMINT DIENSTLEISTUNGSGRUPPE NEURUPPIN GMBH—See MK-Kliniken AG; *Int'l*, pg. 5001
PROMINUS VASTGOED BV; *Int'l*, pg. 5994
PROMORIENTE S.A. E.S.P—See Grupo Aval Acciones y Valores S.A.; *Int'l*, pg. 3121
PROMIS AS—See Itera ASA; *Int'l*, pg. 3833
PROMISE HOLDINGS, LLC; *U.S. Private*, pg. 3283
PROMISE (HONG KONG) CO., LTD.—See Sumitomo Mitsui Financial Group, Inc.; *Int'l*, pg. 7294
PROMISE HOSPITAL OF EAST LOS ANGELES, L.P.—See Apollo Global Management, Inc.; *U.S. Public*, pg. 157
PROMISE HOUSE, INC.—See Jonathan's Place; *U.S. Private*, pg. 2231
PROMISE MEDICAL, INC.—See AdaptHealth Corp.; *U.S. Public*, pg. 39
PROMISE NETWORK PRINTING LIMITED—See eprint Group Limited; *Int'l*, pg. 2465
PROMISE (SHENYANG) CO., LTD.—See Sumitomo Mitsui Financial Group, Inc.; *Int'l*, pg. 7294
PROMISE TECHNOLOGY, INC.; *Int'l*, pg. 5994
PROMISE (THAILAND) CO., LTD.—See Sumitomo Mitsui Financial Group, Inc.; *Int'l*, pg. 7294
PROMISIA HEALTHCARE LIMITED; *Int'l*, pg. 5994
PROMIS NEUROSCIENCES, INC.; *Int'l*, pg. 5994
PROMIS SP. Z O.O.—See PROCHEM S.A.; *Int'l*, pg. 5987
PROMIUS PHARMA LLC—See Dr. Reddy's Laboratories Limited; *Int'l*, pg. 2195
PROM KROG ALTSTIEL INC.; *U.S. Private*, pg. 3282
PROM MANAGEMENT GROUP, INC.—See Compass Group PLC; *Int'l*, pg. 1751
PROMMIS SOLUTIONS HOLDING CORP.; *U.S. Private*, pg. 3283
PROMOCEAN SPAIN SL—See Li & Fung Limited; *Int'l*, pg. 4480
PROMOCIONES MARRIOTT, S.A. DE C.V.—See Marriott Vacations Worldwide Corporation; *U.S. Public*, pg. 1374
PROMOCIONES MUNICH, C.A.—See Doppelmayr Group; *Int'l*, pg. 2175
PROMOCIONES UNIBAIL-RODAMCO GENERALES SLU—See Unibail-Rodamco-Westfield SE; *Int'l*, pg. 8029
PROMOCION Y OPERACION S.A. DE C.V.; *Int'l*, pg. 5994
PROMODEL CORPORATION—See AE Industrial Partners, LP; *U.S. Private*, pg. 112
PROMOFARMA ECOM, S.L.—See Zur Rose Group AG; *Int'l*, pg. 8697
PROMOHYPERMARKT AG—See Carrefour SA; *Int'l*, pg. 1346
PROMO METAL D.O.O.—See Metalac a.d.; *Int'l*, pg. 4845
PROMOMIDI—See Caisse des Depots et Consignations; *Int'l*, pg. 1258
PROMONITORING BV—See Eurofins Scientific S.E.; *Int'l*, pg. 2551
PROMONTORIA MMB SAS—See Cerberus Capital Management, L.P.; *U.S. Private*, pg. 839
PROMONTORY FINANCIAL GROUP AUSTRALASIA, LLP—See International Business Machines Corporation; *U.S. Public*, pg. 1149
PROMONTORY FINANCIAL GROUP GLOBAL SERVICES - JAPAN, LLC—See International Business Machines Corporation; *U.S. Public*, pg. 1149
PROMONTORY FINANCIAL GROUP LLC—See International Business Machines Corporation; *U.S. Public*, pg. 1149
PROMONTORY FINANCIAL GROUP (UK) LIMITED—See International Business Machines Corporation; *U.S. Public*, pg. 1149
PROMONTORY INTERFINANCIAL NETWORK, LLC—See The Bank of New York Mellon Corporation; *U.S. Public*, pg. 2038
PROMOPEDDLER.COM; *U.S. Private*, pg. 3283
PROMOPHARMA S.A.—See Toyota Tsusho Corporation; *Int'l*, pg. 7876
PROMORE PHARMA AB; *Int'l*, pg. 5994
PROMO SACHETS PROPRIETARY LIMITED—See The Bidvest Group Limited; *Int'l*, pg. 7626
PROMOSERVE BUSINESS SYSTEMS LIMITED—See Altitude Group plc; *Int'l*, pg. 393
PROMOSEVEN-MOROCCO—See The Interpublic Group of Companies, Inc.; *U.S. Public*, pg. 2100
PROMOS TECHNOLOGIES INC.; *Int'l*, pg. 5994
PROMOSUITE—See Banyan Software, Inc.; *U.S. Private*, pg. 470
PROMOTEC CORPORATION—See Hitachi Zosen Corporation; *Int'l*, pg. 3412
PROMOTE FOR LESS—See Metro Printed Products, Inc.; *U.S. Private*, pg. 2686
PROMOTE, INC.—See Nihon Enterprise Co., Ltd.; *Int'l*, pg. 5284
PROMOTER HYDRAULICS PTE. LTD.—See 9R Limited; *Int'l*, pg. 17
PROMOTER.IO INC.—See Thoma Bravo, L.P.; *U.S. Private*, pg. 4149
PROMOTICA S.P.A.; *Int'l*, pg. 5994
PROMOTIC BELGIUM SA/NV—See Aubay SA; *Int'l*, pg. 698
PROMOTIONAL PRODUCTS ASSOCIATION INTERNATIONAL; *U.S. Private*, pg. 3283
PROMOTIONAL SLIDEGUIDE CORP.; *U.S. Private*, pg. 3283
PROMOTION & DEVELOPMENT LIMITED; *Int'l*, pg. 5994
PROMOTION ET SPECTACLES D'EUROPE 1—See Vivendi SE; *Int'l*, pg. 8275
PRO MOTION, INC.; *U.S. Private*, pg. 3270
PROMOTION IN MOTION, INC.; *U.S. Private*, pg. 3283
PROMOTION LECCO S.R.L.—See Netweek S.p.A.; *Int'l*, pg. 5217
PROMOTIONS DISTRIBUTOR SERVICE CORPORATION—See eBay Inc.; *U.S. Public*, pg. 709
PROMOTORA AMBIENTAL DE LA LAGUNA, S.A. DE C.V.—See Promotora Ambiental S.A.B de C.V.; *Int'l*, pg. 5994
PROMOTORA AMBIENTAL S.A.B DE C.V.; *Int'l*, pg. 5994
PROMOTORA AUDIOVISUAL DE COLOMBIA PACSA, S.A.—See Promotora de Informaciones S.A.; *Int'l*, pg. 5995
PROMOTORA DE ACTIVIDADES AUDIOVISUALES DE COLOMBIA, LTDA.—See Promotora de Informaciones S.A.; *Int'l*, pg. 5995
PROMOTORA DE INFORMACIONES S.A.; *Int'l*, pg. 5995
PROMOTORA E INVERSORA ADISA, S.A. DE C.V.—See Empresas ICA S.A.B. de C.V.; *Int'l*, pg. 2391
PROMOTORA FUCHS S.A. DE C.V.—See FUCHS SE; *Int'l*, pg. 2804
PROMOTORA GENERAL DE REVISTAS, S.A.—See Promotora de Informaciones S.A.; *Int'l*, pg. 5995
PROMOTOR AKERSBERGA AB—See MEKO AB; *Int'l*, pg. 4807
PROMOTORA MEDITERRANEA-2, S.A.—See Cementos Molins S.A.; *Int'l*, pg. 1397
PROMOTORA Y DESARROLLADORA DE CENTROS COMERCIALES, S. A. DE C. V.—See Consorcio ARA, S.A.B. de C.V.; *Int'l*, pg. 1771
PROMOTORA Y OPERADORA DE INFRAESTRUCTURA, S.A.B. DE C.V.; *Int'l*, pg. 5996
PROMOVE CORRETORA DE SEGUROS LTDA.—See Alper Consultoria e Corretora de Seguros S.A.; *Int'l*, pg. 366
PROMOVERSITY LLC—See Barnes & Noble Education, Inc.; *U.S. Public*, pg. 276
PROMOWEST PRODUCTIONS, INC.—See The Anschutz Corporation; *U.S. Private*, pg. 3986

COMPANY NAME INDEX

PROMO WORKS, LLC—See Acosta, Inc.; *U.S. Private*, pg. 64
PROMPRYLAD. RENOVATION; *Int'l*, pg. 5996
THE PROMPTCARE COMPANIES, INC.—See The Halifax Group LLC; *U.S. Private*, pg. 4042
PROMPTNOW CO., LTD.—See TIS Inc.; *Int'l*, pg. 7758
PROMPT PARTICIPACOES S.A.; *Int'l*, pg. 5996
PROMPTWORKS LLC—See Modus Create, LLC; *U.S. Private*, pg. 2764
PROMSA—See Cementos Molins S.A.; *Int'l*, pg. 1397
PRO - M S.R.O.—See DEKRA e.V.; *Int'l*, pg. 2009
PROMSVYAZCAPITAL B.V; *Int'l*, pg. 5996
PROMSVYAZ CAPITAL B.V; *Int'l*, pg. 5996
PROMTRACTOR SERVICE JSC—See Promtraktor OAO; *Int'l*, pg. 5996
PROMTRAKTOR OAO; *Int'l*, pg. 5996
PRO MUJER INC.; *U.S. Private*, pg. 3270
PROMUS CAPITAL, LLC—See Promus Holdings, LLC; *U.S. Private*, pg. 3283
PROMUS EQUITY PARTNERS, LLC—See Promus Holdings, LLC; *U.S. Private*, pg. 3283
PROMUS HOLDINGS, LLC; *U.S. Private*, pg. 3283
PRO MUSIC RIGHTS INC.—See Nuvus Gro Corp.; *U.S. Private*, pg. 2975
PRONAL ASIA MANUFACTURING SDN BHD—See Pronal S.A.S.; *Int'l*, pg. 5996
PRONAL S.A.S.; *Int'l*, pg. 5996
PRONAL-USA, INC.—See Pronal S.A.S.; *Int'l*, pg. 5996
PRONATIONAL INSURANCE COMPANY—See ProAssurance Corporation; *U.S. Public*, pg. 1723
PRONATIONAL INSURANCE COMPANY—See ProAssurance Corporation; *U.S. Public*, pg. 1723
PRONAT STEINBRUCH PREG GMBH—See PORR AG; *Int'l*, pg. 5924
PRO NATURA B.V.—See Abattis Bioceuticals Corporation; *Int'l*, pg. 48
PRONDIL S.A.—See Merck & Co., Inc.; *U.S. Public*, pg. 1421
PRONDIL SOCIEDAD ANONIMA—See Merck & Co., Inc.; *U.S. Public*, pg. 1421
PRONET CO., LTD—See Core Corporation; *Int'l*, pg. 1797
PRONEXUS INC.; *Int'l*, pg. 5996
PRONGHORN CONTROLS LTD.; *Int'l*, pg. 5996
PRONK IMPORT B.V.—See Oettinger IMEX AG; *Int'l*, pg. 5530
PRONOMIC AB—See Amplex AB; *Int'l*, pg. 434
PRONORM EINBAUKUCHEN GMBH—See Nobia AB; *Int'l*, pg. 5396
PRONOVA BIOPHARMA ASA—See BASF SE; *Int'l*, pg. 872
PRONOVA BIOPHARMA NORGE AS—See BASF SE; *Int'l*, pg. 872
PRONOVIAS SL—See BC Partners LLP; *Int'l*, pg. 925
PRONOVIAS U.S.A., INC.—See BC Partners LLP; *Int'l*, pg. 925
PRONTODENTE ODONTOLOGIA INTEGRAL LTDA—See Odontoprev S.A.; *Int'l*, pg. 5527
PRONTO EUROPE S.A.R.L.; *Int'l*, pg. 5996
PRONTO GENERAL AGENCY , LTD.—See Arthur J. Gallagher & Co.; *U.S. Public*, pg. 207
PRONTO, LLC—See IAC Inc.; *U.S. Public*, pg. 1082
PRONTOPHOT AUSTRIA GMBH—See ME Group International plc; *Int'l*, pg. 4763
PRONTOPHOT HOLLAND BV—See ME Group International plc; *Int'l*, pg. 4763
PRONTOPHOT SA—See ME Group International plc; *Int'l*, pg. 4763
PRONTOPHOT (SCHWEIZ) AG—See ME Group International plc; *Int'l*, pg. 4763
PRONTOR GMBH—See VTC Partners GmbH; *Int'l*, pg. 8316
PRONTOSEAT SRL—See VEON Ltd.; *Int'l*, pg. 8164
PRONTOTV AS—See ZetaDisplay AB; *Int'l*, pg. 8639
PRONTO WATCH S.A.—See Stelux Holdings International Limited; *Int'l*, pg. 7204
PROOCEANO—See Collecte Localisation Satellites; *Int'l*, pg. 1699
PROODEFTIKH TECHNICAL COMPANY S.A.; *Int'l*, pg. 5996
PROOF ADVERTISING; *U.S. Private*, pg. 3284
PROOF AUTHENTICATION CORPORATION; *U.S. Private*, pg. 3284
PROOFFICE S.R.O.—See Ring International Holding AG; *Int'l*, pg. 6343
PROOFID LTD.; *Int'l*, pg. 5997
PROOF OF THE PUDDING—See Bruin Capital Holdings, LLC; *U.S. Private*, pg. 671
PROOFPOINT CANADA INC.—See Thoma Bravo, L.P.; *U.S. Private*, pg. 4151
PROOFPOINT EMAIL SOLUTIONS GMBH—See Thoma Bravo, L.P.; *U.S. Private*, pg. 4151
PROOFPOINT GMBH—See Thoma Bravo, L.P.; *U.S. Private*, pg. 4151
PROOFPOINT, INC.—See Thoma Bravo, L.P.; *U.S. Private*, pg. 4150
PROOFPOINT JAPAN KK—See Thoma Bravo, L.P.; *U.S. Private*, pg. 4151
PROOFPOINT LIMITED—See Thoma Bravo, L.P.; *U.S. Private*, pg. 4151

PROOFPOINT NETHERLANDS B.V.—See Thoma Bravo, L.P.; *U.S. Private*, pg. 4151
PROOFPOINT NI LTD.—See Thoma Bravo, L.P.; *U.S. Private*, pg. 4151
PROOFPOINT SINGAPORE PTE. LTD.—See Thoma Bravo, L.P.; *U.S. Private*, pg. 4151
PROOF RESEARCH, INC.; *U.S. Private*, pg. 3284
PRO OIL INC.; *U.S. Private*, pg. 3270
PRO OPTIC CANADA INC.—See EssilorLuxottica SA; *Int'l*, pg. 2516
PRO-OPTIK AG—See Fielmann Group AG; *Int'l*, pg. 2659
PRO-ORGANIKA S.A.—See PROCHEM S.A.; *Int'l*, pg. 5987
PROOST EN BRANDT BV—See KPP Group Holdings Co., Ltd.; *Int'l*, pg. 4298
PROPAC INTERNATIONAL AB—See Bong AB; *Int'l*, pg. 1107
PRO-PAC INTERNATIONAL, INC.—See Olympus Partners; *U.S. Private*, pg. 3013
PRO PAC LABS, INC.—See MeriCal LLC; *U.S. Private*, pg. 2672
PRO-PAC PACKAGING (AUST) PTY. LTD.—See Pro-Pac Packaging Limited; *Int'l*, pg. 5985
PRO-PAC PACKAGING LIMITED; *Int'l*, pg. 5985
PRO-PAC PACKAGING MANUFACTURING (MELB) PTY. LTD.—See Pro-Pac Packaging Limited; *Int'l*, pg. 5985
PROPAGANDA GEM LTD.—See Wanda Movie Co., Ltd.; *Int'l*, pg. 8340
PROPAK HESSIAN (PRIVATE) LIMITED—See TSL Limited; *Int'l*, pg. 7952
PRO-PAK INDUSTRIES; *U.S. Private*, pg. 3271
PROPAK OIL & GAS EQUIPMENT (SHENZHEN) CO., LTD.—See Propak Systems Ltd.; *Int'l*, pg. 5997
PROPAK SYSTEMS ARGENTINA S.A.—See Propak Systems Ltd.; *Int'l*, pg. 5997
PROPAK SYSTEMS LTD.; *Int'l*, pg. 5997
PROPAMSA, S.A.U.—See Cementos Molins S.A.; *Int'l*, pg. 1397
PROPANC BIOPHARMA, INC.; *Int'l*, pg. 5997
PROPANE EDUCATION & RESEARCH COUNCIL, INC.; *U.S. Private*, pg. 3284
PROPANE ENERGIES—See UGI Corporation; *U.S. Public*, pg. 2222
PROPANE PLUS INC.—See Southwestern Electric Co-Operativo Ino.; *U.S. Private*, pg. 3741
PROPAPER INDUSTRIA E COMERCIO DE PAPEIS LTDA.—See Illinois Tool Works Inc.; *U.S. Public*, pg. 1110
PROPARK, INC.; *U.S. Private*, pg. 3284
PRO-PARTNER INC.—See Grape King Bio Ltd.; *Int'l*, pg. 3060
PROPARTNER ZEITARBEIT + HANDELSAGENTUR GMBH—See Groupe Crit, S.A.; *Int'l*, pg. 3101
PROPATH SERVICES, LLC—See Sonic Healthcare Limited; *Int'l*, pg. 7098
PROPAY INC.—See Global Payments Inc.; *U.S. Public*, pg. 944
PROPEL CHEMICALS SDN. BHD.—See Propel Global Berhad; *Int'l*, pg. 5997
PROPEL EQUITY PARTNERS, LLC; *U.S. Private*, pg. 3284
PROPEL FINANCIAL SERVICES, LLC—See Encore Capital Group, Inc.; *U.S. Public*, pg. 760
PROPEL FUELS, INC.; *U.S. Private*, pg. 3285
PROPEL FUNERAL PARTNERS LIMITED; *Int'l*, pg. 5997
PROPEL GLOBAL BERHAD; *Int'l*, pg. 5997
PROPEL HOLDINGS INC.; *Int'l*, pg. 5997
PROPEL INC.; *U.S. Private*, pg. 3285
PROPEL INSURANCE AGENCY, LLC—See Edwards Capital, LLC; *U.S. Private*, pg. 1342
PROPEL INSURANCE-SEATTLE—See Edwards Capital, LLC; *U.S. Private*, pg. 1342
PROPELLER, INC.; *U.S. Private*, pg. 3285
PROPELLER MEDIA WORKS, LLC; *U.S. Private*, pg. 3285
PROPELL HOLDINGS LIMITED; *Int'l*, pg. 5997
PROPELL SERVICES PTY. LTD.—See Propell Holdings Limited; *Int'l*, pg. 5998
PROPEL MEDIA, INC.; *U.S. Public*, pg. 1727
PROPEL NETWORK SDN. BHD.—See KYOCERA Corporation; *Int'l*, pg. 4360
PROPEL-PRODUTOS DE PETROLEO, L.D.A.—See Mubadala Investment Company PJSC; *Int'l*, pg. 5074
PROPER FOODS, INC.; *U.S. Private*, pg. 3285
PROPER GROUP INTERNATIONAL; *U.S. Private*, pg. 3285
PROPER POLYMERS OF ANDERSON—See Proper Group International; *U.S. Private*, pg. 3285
PROPERST CO., LTD.; *U.S. Private*, pg. 5998
@PROPERTIES; *U.S. Private*, pg. 17
PROPER TOOLING—See Proper Group International; *U.S. Private*, pg. 3285
PROPERTUNITIES IMMOBILIEN CONSULTING GMBH—See BKW AG; *Int'l*, pg. 1056
PROPERTY ACQUISITION & MANAGEMENT LIMITED; *Int'l*, pg. 5998
PROPERTY AGENT INC.; *Int'l*, pg. 5998
PROPERTY AND BUILDING CORP. LTD.—See IDB Development Corporation Ltd.; *Int'l*, pg. 3588

PROPERTY & BUILDINGS COMMERCIAL CENTERS, LTD.—See IDB Development Corporation Ltd.; *Int'l*, pg. 3588
PROPERTY CARE SERVICES (THAILAND) LIMITED—See OCS Group Limited; *Int'l*, pg. 5521
PROPERTY CARE SPECIALISTS INC.; *U.S. Private*, pg. 3285
PROPERTY CONNECT HOLDINGS LIMITED; *Int'l*, pg. 5998
PROPERTY DAMAGE APPRAISERS, INC.—See Alacrity Solutions Group, Inc.; *U.S. Private*, pg. 148
PROPERTY DATA BANK, INC.; *Int'l*, pg. 5998
PROPERTY DEVELOPMENT LTD—See Bank of Ceylon; *Int'l*, pg. 841
THE PROPERTY DIRECTORY LIMITED—See Coventry Building Society; *Int'l*, pg. 1821
PROPERTY EXCHANGE AUSTRALIA LTD.—See PEXA Group Limited; *Int'l*, pg. 5835
PROPERTY FOR INDUSTRY; *Int'l*, pg. 5998
THE PROPERTY FRANCHISE GROUP PLC; *Int'l*, pg. 7676
PROPERTYGURU GROUP LIMITED; *Int'l*, pg. 5998
PROPERTY INDEX TRACKER MANAGERS (PTY) LTD.—See Resilient REIT Limited; *Int'l*, pg. 6296
PROPERTYINFO CORPORATION—See Stewart Information Services Corporation; *U.S. Public*, pg. 1948
PROPERTY INTERLINK, LLC—See Starrex International Ltd.; *Int'l*, pg. 7179
PROPERTYLINK (HOLDINGS) LIMITED; *Int'l*, pg. 5998
PROPERTY LINK INTERNATIONAL; *U.S. Private*, pg. 3285
PROPERTY MASTERS INC; *U.S. Private*, pg. 3285
PROPERTY-OWNERS INSURANCE CO.—See Auto-Owners Insurance Group; *U.S. Private*, pg. 398
PROPERTY PARTNERS HOUSING MANAGEMENT (UK) LIMITED—See Sanctuary Housing Association; *Int'l*, pg. 6523
PROPERTY PAVING INC.—See Harbor Beach Capital, LLC; *U.S. Private*, pg. 1858
PROPERTY PERFECT PUBLIC COMPANY LIMITED; *Int'l*, pg. 5998
PROPERTYPHOTOS.COM LLC—See Thoma Bravo, L.P.; *U.S. Private*, pg. 4153
PROPERTY RESOURCES CORP.; *U.S. Private*, pg. 3285
PROPERTY RESOURCES CORP.; *U.S. Private*, pg. 3285
PROPERTYROOM.COM INC.; *U.S. Private*, pg. 3285
PROPERTY SOLUTIONS INDIA PVT. LTD.—See Kalpataru Ltd.; *Int'l*, pg. 4058
PROPERTY SOLUTIONS INTERNATIONAL, INC.; *U.S. Private*, pg. 3285
PROPERTY TAX DIRECT, INC—See Fidelity National Financial, Inc.; *U.S. Public*, pg. 831
PROPERTY TECHNOLOGIES INC.; *Int'l*, pg. 5998
PROPERTY VILLAGE BERHAD—See IOI Corporation Berhad; *Int'l*, pg. 3792
PROPERTYWARE, INC.—See Thoma Bravo, L.P.; *U.S. Private*, pg. 4153
PRO-PET, LLC - KANSAS CITY—See Cargill, Inc.; *U.S. Private*, pg. 755
PRO-PET, LLC—See Cargill, Inc.; *U.S. Private*, pg. 755
PROPETRO HOLDING CORP.; *U.S. Public*, pg. 1727
PRO PETROLEUM, INC.—See BP plc; *Int'l*, pg. 1127
PROPETRO SERVICES, INC.; *U.S. Private*, pg. 3285
PROPEX CONCRETE SYSTEMS CORPORATION—See Sika AG; *Int'l*, pg. 6915
PROPEX GEOSOLUTIONS CORPORATION—See Wayzata Investment Partners LLC; *U.S. Private*, pg. 4461
PROPEX OPERATING COMPANY, LLC—See Wayzata Investment Partners LLC; *U.S. Private*, pg. 4461
PROPHARMA SALES LLC; *U.S. Private*, pg. 3285
PROPHARM LTD.—See McKesson Corporation; *U.S. Public*, pg. 1408
PROPHASE DIAGNOSTICS, INC.—See ProPhase Labs, Inc.; *U.S. Public*, pg. 1727
PROPHASE DIGITAL MEDIA, INC.—See ProPhase Labs, Inc.; *U.S. Public*, pg. 1727
PROPHASE LABS, INC.; *U.S. Public*, pg. 1727
PROPHECY AMERICAS INC—See Prophecy International Holdings Limited; *Int'l*, pg. 5998
PROPHECY DEFI INC.; *Int'l*, pg. 5998
PROPHECY EUROPE LIMITED—See Prophecy International Holdings Limited; *Int'l*, pg. 5998
PROPHECY INTERNATIONAL HOLDINGS LIMITED; *Int'l*, pg. 5998
PROPHECY INTERNATIONAL PTY LTD—See Prophecy International Holdings Limited; *Int'l*, pg. 5998
PROPHESY TRANSPORTATION SOLUTIONS, INC.—See Accellos, Inc.; *U.S. Private*, pg. 50
PROPHET BRAND STRATEGY, INC.; *U.S. Private*, pg. 3285
PROPHET CORP.; *U.S. Private*, pg. 3286
PROPHET EQUITY L.P.; *U.S. Private*, pg. 3286
PROPHETSTOWN EQUIPMENT INC.; *U.S. Private*, pg. 3286
PROPHOENIX INC.; *U.S. Private*, pg. 3286
PROPHOTONIX LIMITED—See Union Park Capital; *U.S. Private*, pg. 4284

PROPHOENIX INC.   CORPORATE AFFILIATIONS

PROPHOTONIX—See Union Park Capital; *U.S. Private*, pg. 4285
PROPHOTONIX—See Union Park Capital; *U.S. Private*, pg. 4285
PROPIO LANGUAGE SERVICES, LLC.—See Leonard Green & Partners, L.P.; *U.S. Private*, pg. 2428
PROPIO LANGUAGE SERVICES, LLC.—See TTCP Management Services, LLC.; *U.S. Private*, pg. 4254
PROPIPE TECHNOLOGIES, INC.—See Mueller Industries, Inc.; *U.S. Public*, pg. 1485
PROPLANNER, INC—See Advantive LLC; *U.S. Private*, pg. 95
PROPLAN PLANT PROTECTION COMPANY S.L.—See Kulczyk Investments S.A.; *Int'l*, pg. 4328
PRO PLASTICS INC.; *U.S. Private*, pg. 3270
PROPMART TECHNOLOGIES LIMITED—See Puravankara Ltd.; *Int'l*, pg. 6121
PROPNEX LIMITED; *Int'l*, pg. 5998
PROPNEX PROPERTY MANAGEMENT CONSULTANTS PTE. LTD.—See PropNex Limited; *Int'l*, pg. 5998
PROPNEX REALTY (VIETNAM) COMPANY LIMITED—See PropNex Limited; *Int'l*, pg. 5998
PROPOLY (M) SDN. BHD.—See Tracoma Holdings Berhad; *Int'l*, pg. 7887
PROPOSAL SOFTWARE, INC.—See Camden Partners Holdings, LLC; *U.S. Private*, pg. 728
PROP PARK SENDIRIAN BERHAD—See Hua Yang Berhad; *Int'l*, pg. 3510
PROPPER INTERNATIONAL, INC.; *U.S. Private*, pg. 3286
PROPPER MANUFACTURING COMPANY, INC.; *U.S. Private*, pg. 3286
PROPRIETARY CAPITAL LLC; *U.S. Private*, pg. 3286
PROPRIETARY CONTROL SYSTEMS CORP.—See TTIK Inc.; *U.S. Private*, pg. 4255
PROPRIETORS OF UNION WHARF; *U.S. Private*, pg. 3286
PRO PRINT, INC.; *U.S. Private*, pg. 3270
PROPRIUM CAPITAL PARTNERS, L.P.; *U.S. Private*, pg. 3286
PRO PRODUCTS, INC.—See AFM Capital Partners, Inc.; *U.S. Private*, pg. 123
PROPST BROTHERS DISTRIBUTORS; *U.S. Private*, pg. 3286
PROPST PROPERTIES, LLC; *U.S. Private*, pg. 3286
PROPTECH GROUP LIMITED—See GI Manager L.P.; *U.S. Private*, pg. 1693
PRO PUBLICA INC.; *U.S. Private*, pg. 3270
PROPULSION CONTROLS COMPANY—See NFS Holdings Inc.; *U.S. Private*, pg. 2923
PROPULSION CONTROLS ENGINEERING; *U.S. Private*, pg. 3286
PROQR THERAPEUTICS N.V.; *Int'l*, pg. 5998
PRO-QUAL INDUSTRIES, LLC.—See Sperber Landscape Cos. LLC; *U.S. Private*, pg. 3756
PROQUEST, LLC—See Clarivate PLC; *Int'l*, pg. 1649
PROQUIMIO PRODUTOS QUIMICOS OPOTERAPICOS LTDA.—See Akzo Nobel N.V.; *Int'l*, pg. 274
PRORA S.R.L.—See Garofalo Health Care SpA; *Int'l*, pg. 2886
PRO REAL ESTATE INVESTMENT TRUST; *Int'l*, pg. 5985
PRO REAL ESTATE INVESTMENT TRUST; *Int'l*, pg. 5985
PRORED PARTNERS CO., LTD.; *Int'l*, pg. 5986
PROREKA (M) SDN. BHD.—See Globaltec Formation Berhad; *Int'l*, pg. 3004
PROREKLAM-EUROPLAKAT D.O.O.—See APG/SGA SA; *Int'l*, pg. 513
PROREMAN PTY LTD.—See Epiroc AB; *Int'l*, pg. 2463
PRORENDITA EINS VERWALTUNGSGESELLSCHAFT MBH—See Munchener Ruckversicherungs AG; *Int'l*, pg. 5091
PRORENDITA VIER VERWALTUNGSGESELLSCHAFT MBH—See Munchener Ruckversicherungs AG; *Int'l*, pg. 5091
PRO RESOURCES INC.; *U.S. Private*, pg. 3270
PRORETA SP. Z O.O.—See Figene Capital SA; *Int'l*, pg. 2661
PRORISK S.A.S.—See Bunzl plc; *Int'l*, pg. 1219
PRORIT CORPORATION—See RITEK CORPORATION; *Int'l*, pg. 6351
PRO-ROD INC.—See Dover Corporation; *U.S. Public*, pg. 682
PRO ROOF STEEL MERCHANTS PROPRIETARY LIMITED—See Andulela Investment Holdings Limited; *Int'l*, pg. 457
PRO ROOF STEEL MERCHANTS (PTA) PROPRIETARY LIMITED—See Andulela Investment Holdings Limited; *Int'l*, pg. 457
PROROUTE MARUMITSU CO., LTD.; *Int'l*, pg. 5999
PRO RTG S.R.O.—See Centene Corporation; *U.S. Public*, pg. 470
PROSAAR MEDIENPRODUKTION GMBH—See Bavaria Film GmbH; *Int'l*, pg. 899
PRO-SAFE, INCORPORATED; *U.S. Private*, pg. 3271
PROSAFE OFFSHORE AS—See Prosafe SE; *Int'l*, pg. 5999
PROSAFE OFFSHORE B.V.—See Prosafe SE; *Int'l*, pg. 5999
PROSAFE OFFSHORE EMPLOYMENT COMPANY PTE LTD—See Prosafe SE; *Int'l*, pg. 5999

PROSAFE OFFSHORE LTD.—See Prosafe SE; *Int'l*, pg. 5999
PROSAFE OFFSHORE NORGE AS—See Prosafe SE; *Int'l*, pg. 5999
PROSAFE OFFSHORE PTE LTD—See Prosafe SE; *Int'l*, pg. 5999
PROSAFE PRODUCTION NIGERIA LIMITED—See BW Offshore Limited; *Int'l*, pg. 1232
PROSAFE RIGS PTE. LTD.—See Prosafe SE; *Int'l*, pg. 5999
PROSAFE SERVICES MARITIMOS LTDA.—See Prosafe SE; *Int'l*, pg. 5999
PROSAFE SE; *Int'l*, pg. 5999
PRO SAFETY SERVICES, LLC—See Kelso & Company, L.P.; *U.S. Private*, pg. 2280
PROSAGE SUSTAINABILITY DEVELOPMENT LIMITED—See Retech Technology Co., Limited; *Int'l*, pg. 6306
PROSAL TUBES S.A.—See Viohalco SA/NV; *Int'l*, pg. 8243
PROS BULGARIA EOOD—See PROS Holdings, Inc.; *U.S. Public*, pg. 1728
PROSCAPE LANDSCAPE MANAGEMENT CORPORATION; *U.S. Private*, pg. 3286
PROSEAL AMERICA, INC.—See John Bean Technologies Corporation; *U.S. Public*, pg. 1192
PROSEAL AUSTRALIA PTY. LTD.—See John Bean Technologies Corporation; *U.S. Public*, pg. 1192
PROSEAL UK LIMITED—See John Bean Technologies Corporation; *U.S. Public*, pg. 1192
PROSEARCH STRATEGIES, INC.—See Consello Management LP; *U.S. Private*, pg. 1019
PROSEAT GMBH & CO. KG—See Sekisui Kasei Co., Ltd.; *Int'l*, pg. 6698
PROSEAT MLADA BOLESLAV S.R.O.—See Sekisui Kasei Co., Ltd.; *Int'l*, pg. 6698
PROSEAT S.A.S.—See Recticel S.A.; *Int'l*, pg. 6241
PROSEAT SAS—See Sekisui Kasei Co., Ltd.; *Int'l*, pg. 6698
PROSEAT SP. Z O.O.—See Sekisui Kasei Co., Ltd.; *Int'l*, pg. 6698
PRO SECURITIES, LLC—See Beyond, Inc.; *U.S. Public*, pg. 327
PROSEGUR BRASIL SA TRANSPORTADORA DE VALORES E SEGURANCA—See Prosegur Compania de Seguridad S.A.; *Int'l*, pg. 5999
PROSEGUR CASH SA; *Int'l*, pg. 5999
PROSEGUR COMPANIA DE SEGURIDAD S.A.; *Int'l*, pg. 5999
PROSEGUR, S.A.—See Prosegur Compania de Seguridad S.A.; *Int'l*, pg. 5999
PROSEGUR SERVICES GROUP, INC.—See Prosegur Compania de Seguridad S.A.; *Int'l*, pg. 5999
PROSEGUR SINGAPORE PTE. LTD.—See Prosegur Compania de Seguridad S.A.; *Int'l*, pg. 5999
PROSEK PARTNERS; *U.S. Private*, pg. 3286
PROSEK PARTNERS—See Prosek Partners; *U.S. Private*, pg. 3286
PROSEK PARTNERS—See Prosek Partners; *U.S. Private*, pg. 3286
PROSEMEDIC S.A.C.—See UnitedHealth Group Incorporated; *U.S. Public*, pg. 2249
PROSERVE VERTRIEBS- UND BERATUNGS GMBH—See SFS Group AG; *Int'l*, pg. 6739
PROSERV HOLDINGS LIMITED—See Riverstone Holdings LLC; *U.S. Private*, pg. 3447
PROSERVIA GMBH—See ManpowerGroup Inc.; *U.S. Public*, pg. 1361
PROSERVIA SA—See ManpowerGroup Inc.; *U.S. Public*, pg. 1360
PROSERVICE HAWAII; *U.S. Private*, pg. 3287
PRO SERV SANDERS INC.; *U.S. Private*, pg. 3270
PROS FRANCE SAS—See PROS Holdings, Inc.; *U.S. Public*, pg. 1728
PROSHARES TRUST II; *U.S. Private*, pg. 3287
PRO-SHIP INCORPORATED; *Int'l*, pg. 5985
PROSHIP INC.—See Quadient SA; *Int'l*, pg. 6149
PROSHIP INFORMATION SYSTEM (DALIAN) CO., LTD.—See Pro-Ship Incorporated; *Int'l*, pg. 5985
PROS HOLDINGS, INC.; *U.S. Public*, pg. 1727
PROSHRED FRANCHISING CORP.—See Redishred Capital Corp.; *Int'l*, pg. 6248
PROSIEBENSAT.1 ACCELERATOR GMBH—See ProSiebenSat.1 Media SE; *Int'l*, pg. 6000
PROSIEBENSAT.1 ADVERTISING PLATFORM SOLUTIONS GMBH—See ProSiebenSat.1 Media SE; *Int'l*, pg. 6000
PROSIEBENSAT.1 DIGITAL DATA GMBH—See ProSiebenSat.1 Media SE; *Int'l*, pg. 6000
PROSIEBENSAT.1 GAMES GMBH—See ProSiebenSat.1 Media SE; *Int'l*, pg. 6000
PROSIEBENSAT.1 LICENSING GMBH—See ProSiebenSat.1 Media SE; *Int'l*, pg. 6000
PROSIEBENSAT.1 MEDIA SE; *Int'l*, pg. 5999
PROSIEBENSAT.1 PRODUKTION GMBH—See ProSiebenSat.1 Media SE; *Int'l*, pg. 6000
PROSIEBENSAT.1PULS 4 GMBH—See ProSiebenSat.1 Media SE; *Int'l*, pg. 6000

PROSIEBENSAT.1 WELT GMBH—See ProSiebenSat.1 Media SE; *Int'l*, pg. 6000
PROSIEBEN (SCHWEIZ) AG—See ProSiebenSat.1 Media SE; *Int'l*, pg. 6000
PROSIEBEN TELEVISION GMBH—See ProSiebenSat.1 Media SE; *Int'l*, pg. 6000
PROSIGHT GLOBAL, INC.—See Further Global Capital Management, L.P.; *U.S. Private*, pg. 1625
PROSIGHT GLOBAL, INC.—See TowerBrook Capital Partners, L.P.; *U.S. Private*, pg. 4195
PROSIGHT SPECIALTY INSURANCE GROUP, INC.—See TPG Capital, L.P.; *U.S. Private*, pg. 2175
PROSILIA SOFTWARE AB—See Addnode Group AB; *Int'l*, pg. 130
PROSIM KIMYA SANAYI VE TICARET LTD. STI.—See Bischof + Klein GmbH & Co. KG; *Int'l*, pg. 1048
PROSINTEX INDUSTRIE CHIMICHE ITALIANE SRL—See Teva Pharmaceutical Industries, Ltd.; *Int'l*, pg. 7580
PROSITES, INC.—See RockBridge Growth Equity, LLC; *U.S. Private*, pg. 3465
PROSKAUER ROSE LLP; *U.S. Private*, pg. 3287
PROSKIN LLC—See Bausch Health Companies Inc.; *Int'l*, pg. 897
PROSLIDE TECHNOLOGY INC.; *Int'l*, pg. 6001
PROSMART ENTERPRISES INC.; *Int'l*, pg. 6001
PROSNACK NATURAL FOODS INC.—See Naturally Splendid Enterprises Ltd.; *Int'l*, pg. 5168
PROSOCO, INC.; *U.S. Private*, pg. 3287
PROSODIE FRANCE S.A.—See Capgemini SE; *Int'l*, pg. 1307
PROSODIE IBERICA S.L.U.—See Capgemini SE; *Int'l*, pg. 1307
PROSOFT TECHNOLOGY (ASIA PACIFIC) SDN BHD—See Belden, Inc.; *U.S. Public*, pg. 294
PROSOFT TECHNOLOGY GROUP INC.; *U.S. Private*, pg. 3287
PROSOFT TECHNOLOGY, INC.—See Belden, Inc.; *U.S. Public*, pg. 294
PROSOFT TECHNOLOGY SAS—See Belden, Inc.; *U.S. Public*, pg. 294
PRO SOL INC.—See Frit Incorporated; *U.S. Private*, pg. 1612
PROSOL LACKE + FARBEN GMBH - OLDENBURG—See PROSOL Lacke + Farben GmbH; *Int'l*, pg. 6001
PROSOL LACKE + FARBEN GMBH; *Int'l*, pg. 6001
PROSOMNUS, INC.; *U.S. Public*, pg. 1728
PRO SOUND INC.; *U.S. Private*, pg. 3270
PRO SOURCE INC.; *U.S. Private*, pg. 3270
PROSOURCE.IT DMCC—See Prosource.it (UK) Ltd.; *Int'l*, pg. 6001
PROSOURCE.IT (UK) LTD.; *Int'l*, pg. 6001
PROSOURCE LLC—See Blue Sea Capital Management LLC; *U.S. Private*, pg. 592
PROSOUTH FASTENER—See Birmingham Fastener & Supply Inc.; *U.S. Private*, pg. 564
PROSPA GROUP LIMITED—See Salter Brothers Emerging Companies Limited; *Int'l*, pg. 6494
PROSPA NZ LIMITED—See Salter Brothers Emerging Companies Limited; *Int'l*, pg. 6494
PROSPECH LIMITED; *Int'l*, pg. 6001
PRO-SPEC INC.; *U.S. Private*, pg. 3271
PROSPEC PTE LTD—See Samson Paper Holdings Limited; *Int'l*, pg. 6509
PROSPECT AGGREGATES, INC.—See CRH plc; *Int'l*, pg. 1847
PROSPECT AIRPORT SERVICES INC.; *U.S. Private*, pg. 3287
PROSPECT BANK; *U.S. Private*, pg. 3287
PROSPECT CAPITAL CORPORATION; *U.S. Public*, pg. 1728
PROSPECT COMMODITIES LIMITED; *Int'l*, pg. 6001
PROSPECT DEVELOPMENT CO., LTD.—See Bangkok Bank Public Company Limited; *Int'l*, pg. 833
PROSPECT EDUCATION LLC; *U.S. Private*, pg. 3287
PROSPECT ENTERPRISES INC.; *U.S. Private*, pg. 3287
PROSPECT FOUNDRY, LLC—See TMB Industries Inc.; *U.S. Private*, pg. 4179
PROSPECT GLOBAL RESOURCES INC.; *U.S. Private*, pg. 3287
PROSPECT HILL GROWTH PARTNERS, L.P.; *U.S. Private*, pg. 3288
PROSPECT IMPLEMENT, INC.—See Ron's Equipment Co Inc.; *U.S. Private*, pg. 3477
PROSPECTIUNI S.A.; *Int'l*, pg. 6002
PROSPECTIVE PAYMENT SPECIALISTS, INC.—See Cognizant Technology Solutions Corporation; *U.S. Public*, pg. 523
PROSPECT MEDIA GROUP LTD.—See Ciscom Corp.; *Int'l*, pg. 1618
PROSPECT MEDICAL GROUP, INC.—See Leonard Green & Partners, L.P.; *U.S. Private*, pg. 2428
PROSPECT MEDICAL HOLDINGS, INC.—See Leonard Green & Partners, L.P.; *U.S. Private*, pg. 2428
PROSPECTOR CAPITAL CORP.—See LeddarTech Holdings Inc.; *Int'l*, pg. 4439
PROSPECTOR EQUITY CAPITAL, L.P.—See Kuwait Projects Company (Holding) K.S.C.P.; *Int'l*, pg. 4346
PROSPECTOR METALS CORP.; *Int'l*, pg. 6002
PROSPECT PARK CAPITAL CORP.; *Int'l*, pg. 6001

COMPANY NAME INDEX

PROSPECT PARK CRA-B1, LLC—See Independence Realty Trust, Inc.; *U.S. Public*, pg. 1116
PROSPECT PARTNERS, LLC; *U.S. Private*, pg. 3288
PROSPECT PICTURES LIMITED—See DCD Media plc; *Int'l*, pg. 1991
PROSPECT PROPERTY GROUP; *U.S. Private*, pg. 3288
PROSPECT RESEARCH & DEVELOPMENT STRATEGIES; *U.S. Private*, pg. 3288
PROSPECT RESOURCES LIMITED; *Int'l*, pg. 6002
PROSPECT RIDGE RESOURCES CORPORATION; *Int'l*, pg. 6002
PROSPECTSPLUS!, INC.; *U.S. Private*, pg. 3288
PROSPECT TRANSPORTATION INC.; *U.S. Private*, pg. 3288
PROSPECTUS BERCO; *U.S. Private*, pg. 3288
PROSPEKTERINGSTEKNIK I NORRLAND AB—See Nordisk Bergteknik AB; *Int'l*, pg. 5424
PROSPERA ENERGY INC.; *Int'l*, pg. 6002
PROSPERA FINANCIAL SERVICES; *U.S. Private*, pg. 3288
PROSPERA PLUS D.O.O.—See Nova Ljubljanska banka d.d.; *Int'l*, pg. 5451
PROSPER BUSINESS DEVELOPMENT CORP.; *U.S. Private*, pg. 3288
PROSPER CONSTRUCTION HOLDINGS LTD.—See Qingdao West Coast Development (Group) Co., Ltd.; *Int'l*, pg. 6145
PROSPER FUNDING LLC—See Prosper Marketplace, Inc.; *U.S. Private*, pg. 3288
PROSPER GOLD CORP.; *Int'l*, pg. 6002
THE PROSPER GROUP CORPORATION; *U.S. Private*, pg. 4101
PROSPER INSURANCE GROUP, LLC—See Integrum Holdings LP; *Int'l*, pg. 3732
PROSPERITY BANCSHARES, INC.; *U.S. Public*, pg. 1728
PROSPERITY BANK - CENTRAL OKLAHOMA REGIONAL OFFICE—See Prosperity Bancshares, Inc.; *U.S. Public*, pg. 1728
PROSPERITY BANK - EAST TEXAS/TYLER REGIONAL OFFICE—See Prosperity Bancshares, Inc.; *U.S. Public*, pg. 1728
PROSPERITY BANK—See Prosperity Bancshares, Inc.; *U.S. Public*, pg. 1728
PROSPERITY BANK - SOUTH TEXAS/VICTORIA REGIONAL OFFICE—See Prosperity Bancshares, Inc.; *U.S. Public*, pg. 1729
PROSPERITY BANK - WEST TEXAS REGIONAL OFFICE—See Prosperity Bancshares, Inc.; *U.S. Public*, pg. 1729
PROSPERITY CEMENT (ASIA) LIMITED—See Prosperity International Holdings (H.K.) Limited; *Int'l*, pg. 6002
PROSPERITY DIELECTRICS CO., LTD.; *Int'l*, pg. 6002
PROSPERITY GROUP HOLDINGS, LP; *U.S. Private*, pg. 3289
PROSPERITY INTERNATIONAL HOLDINGS (H.K.) LIMITED; *Int'l*, pg. 6002
PROSPERITY INVESTMENT HOLDINGS LIMITED; *Int'l*, pg. 6002
PROSPERITY LAND CLEANING SERVICE LIMITED—See Asia Orient Holdings Limited; *Int'l*, pg. 613
PROSPERITY LAND ESTATE MANAGEMENT LIMITED—See Asia Orient Holdings Limited; *Int'l*, pg. 613
PROSPERITY RESOURCES LIMITED; *Int'l*, pg. 6002
PROSPERITY WEAVING MILLS LIMITED—See Nagina Group; *Int'l*, pg. 5129
PROSPERITY WELLNESS CENTER—See Discovery Behavioral Health, Inc.; *U.S. Private*, pg. 1238
PROSPERLINK (MACAO COMMERCIAL OFFSHORE) LIMITED—See Fountain Set (Holdings) Limited; *Int'l*, pg. 2754
PROSPERLINK (MACAU COMMERCIAL OFFSHORE) LIMITED—See Fountain Set (Holdings) Limited; *Int'l*, pg. 2754
PROSPER MARKETPLACE, INC.; *U.S. Private*, pg. 3288
PROSPER ONE INTERNATIONAL HOLDINGS COMPANY LIMITED; *Int'l*, pg. 6002
PROSPEROUS FUTURE HOLDINGS LIMITED; *Int'l*, pg. 6002
PROSPEROUS INDUSTRIAL (HOLDINGS) LIMITED; *Int'l*, pg. 6002
PROSPEROUS PRINTING COMPANY LIMITED; *Int'l*, pg. 6002
PROSPEROUS PRINTING (SHENZHEN) CO., LTD.—See Prosperous Printing Company Limited; *Int'l*, pg. 6002
PROSPER PRODUCTIONS PTY. LTD.—See ITV plc; *Int'l*, pg. 3845
PROSPEX ENERGY PLC; *Int'l*, pg. 6002
PROSPEX RESOURCES LTD.—See Paramount Resources Ltd.; *Int'l*, pg. 5738
PRO-SPHERE TEK, INC.—See Planned Systems International, Inc.; *U.S. Private*, pg. 3196
PROSPORT AUTO LTD.—See WEDS CO., LTD.; *Int'l*, pg. 8367
PRO SPORT BV—See Macintosh Retail Group NV; *Int'l*, pg. 4622
PRO SPORTS MEMORABILIA, INC.—See Kynetic LLC; *U.S. Private*, pg. 2360

PROS REVENUE MANAGEMENT, L.P.—See PROS Holdings, Inc.; *U.S. Public*, pg. 1728
PROSTALUND AB; *Int'l*, pg. 6003
PROSTAR CAPITAL (AUSTRALIA) PTY LTD; *Int'l*, pg. 6003
PROSTAR COMPUTER, INC.; *U.S. Private*, pg. 3289
PROSTAR HOLDINGS INC.; *Int'l*, pg. 6003
PROSTAR PACKAGING INC.—See South Atlantic Packaging Corp.; *U.S. Private*, pg. 3719
PROSTART INVESTMENTS 93 (PTY) LIMITED—See Kansai Paint Co., Ltd.; *Int'l*, pg. 4072
THE PROSTATE CENTRE LIMITED—See HCA Healthcare, Inc.; *U.S. Public*, pg. 1012
PROSTATYPE GENOMICS AB; *Int'l*, pg. 6003
PROST BUILDERS INC.; *U.S. Private*, pg. 3289
PRO STEEL CO., LTD.—See Nippon Steel Corporation; *Int'l*, pg. 5336
PROSTEEL CO., LTD.—See Toyota Tsusho Corporation; *Int'l*, pg. 7877
PROSTEEL SECURITY PRODUCTS, INC.—See Promus Holdings, LLC; *U.S. Private*, pg. 3284
PROSTEN TECHNOLOGY COMPANY LIMITED—See China Brilliant Global Limited; *Int'l*, pg. 1487
PROSTEP AG—See General Motors Company; *U.S. Public*, pg. 927
PROSTHETIC LABORATORIES OF ROCHESTER, INC.—See Patient Square Capital, L.P.; *U.S. Private*, pg. 3107
PROSTICKS.COM LIMITED—See Shenzhen Sunline Tech Co., Ltd.; *Int'l*, pg. 6821
PRO STOP TRUCK SERVICE INC.—See Dart Transit Company; *U.S. Private*, pg. 1160
PROSTRAKAN AB—See Kirin Holdings Company, Limited; *Int'l*, pg. 4189
PROSTRAKAN FARMACEUTICA SLU—See Kirin Holdings Company, Limited; *Int'l*, pg. 4189
PROSTRAKAN GROUP PLC—See Kirin Holdings Company, Limited; *Int'l*, pg. 4189
PROSTRAKAN INC—See Kirin Holdings Company, Limited; *Int'l*, pg. 4189
PROSTRAKAN LTD—See Kirin Holdings Company, Limited; *Int'l*, pg. 4189
PROSTRAKAN PHARMA BV—See Kirin Holdings Company, Limited; *Int'l*, pg. 4189
PROSTRAKAN PHARMA GMBH—See Kirin Holdings Company, Limited; *Int'l*, pg. 4189
PROSTROLLO ALL-AMERICAN AUTO MALL; *U.S. Private*, pg. 3289
PROSTROLLO MOTOR SALES, INC.; *U.S. Private*, pg. 3289
PROSUM, INC.; *U.S. Private*, pg. 3289
PROSURANCE GROUP, INC.—See One80 Intermediaries LLC; *U.S. Private*, pg. 3024
PROSURANCE/REDEKER GROUP LTD.—See Kelso & Company, L.P.; *U.S. Private*, pg. 2280
PROSUS N.V.; *Int'l*, pg. 6003
PROSVETA A.D.; *Int'l*, pg. 6003
PROSYNC TECHNOLOGY GROUP LLC; *U.S. Private*, pg. 3289
PROSYS INFORMATION SYSTEMS INC—See TD Synnex Corp; *U.S. Public*, pg. 1985
PROSYS INNOVATIVE PACKAGING EQUIPMENT INC.—See Wynnchurch Capital, L.P.; *U.S. Private*, pg. 4578
PROSYS—See Bridgepoint Group Plc; *Int'l*, pg. 1155
PROSYSTAS CO., LTD.—See Warabeya Nichiyo Holdings Co., Ltd.; *Int'l*, pg. 8344
PRO SYSTEMS CORP; *U.S. Private*, pg. 3270
PROSYSTEMS IT GMBH—See Diebold Nixdorf, Inc.; *U.S. Public*, pg. 661
PRO SYSTEMS, LLC—See Lincoln Electric Holdings, Inc.; *U.S. Public*, pg. 1318
PROTAGENIC THERAPEUTICS, INC.; *U.S. Public*, pg. 1729
PROTAGENIC THERAPEUTICS, INC.—See Protagenic Therapeutics, Inc.; *U.S. Public*, pg. 1729
PROTAGONIST THERAPEUTICS, INC.; *U.S. Public*, pg. 1729
PROTAG SHOE SUPPLY B.V.—See Investment AB Latour; *Int'l*, pg. 3784
PRO (TAIWAN) PROCUREMENT CO., LTD.—See Shimano, Inc.; *Int'l*, pg. 6833
PROTAK SYSTEMS AB—See AFRY AB; *Int'l*, pg. 196
PROTALIX BIOTHERAPEUTICS, INC.; *U.S. Public*, pg. 1729
PROTAMEEN CHEMICALS INC.; *U.S. Private*, pg. 3289
PROTANG AB—See Etteplan Oyj; *Int'l*, pg. 2525
PROTANG TEKNIKINFORMATION AB—See Etteplan Oyj; *Int'l*, pg. 2525
PROTAN SA; *Int'l*, pg. 6003
PROTARA THERAPEUTICS, INC.; *U.S. Public*, pg. 1729
PROTASCO BERHAD; *Int'l*, pg. 6003
PROTASCO DEVELOPMENT SDN BHD—See Protasco Berhad; *Int'l*, pg. 6003
PROTASCO TRADING SDN BHD—See Protasco Berhad; *Int'l*, pg. 6003
PROTATEK INTERNATIONAL, INC.—See Jinhe Biotechnology Co., Ltd.; *Int'l*, pg. 3968

PROTECTIVE CAPITAL STRUCTURES CORP.

PROTEA BIOSCIENCES GROUP, INC.; *U.S. Private*, pg. 3289
PROTEAK UNO SAB DE CV; *Int'l*, pg. 6003
PROTEAM, INC.—See Emerson Electric Co.; *U.S. Public*, pg. 751
PROTEAN ENERGY LTD.; *Int'l*, pg. 6003
PROTEAN WAVE ENERGY INC.—See Protean Energy Ltd.; *Int'l*, pg. 6003
PROTEC ARISAWA AMERICA, INC.—See Arisawa Manufacturing Co., Ltd.; *Int'l*, pg. 566
PRO-TEC COATING COMPANY, INC.—See Kobe Steel, Ltd.; *Int'l*, pg. 4220
PRO-TEC COATING COMPANY, INC.—See United States Steel Corporation; *U.S. Public*, pg. 2236
PROTEC CO., LTD.; *Int'l*, pg. 6003
PROTEC DIRECT—See Bunzl plc; *Int'l*, pg. 1217
PROTEC-FEU S.A.—See VINCI S.A.; *Int'l*, pg. 8237
PRO-TECH AIR CONDITIONING & HEATING SERVICE, INC.; *U.S. Private*, pg. 3271
PROTECH ARMORED PRODUCTS—See BAE Systems plc; *Int'l*, pg. 796
PROTECH BIOSYSTEMS PVT. LTD.; *Int'l*, pg. 6004
PROTECH CHEMICALS LTD. - GULF POWDER POLYESTER & EPOXY COATING FACTORY—See Protech Chemicals Ltd.; *Int'l*, pg. 6004
PROTECH CHEMICALS LTD.; *Int'l*, pg. 6004
PRO TECH CONSTRUCTION, INC.—See Enterprise Group, Inc.; *Int'l*, pg. 2451
PROTECH ENGINEERING LTD—See J. Murphy & Sons Limited; *Int'l*, pg. 3856
PRO-TECH INDUSTRIES INC.; *U.S. Private*, pg. 3271
PROTECH MEXICANA S.A. DE C.V.—See Protech Chemicals Ltd.; *Int'l*, pg. 6004
PROTECH OXYPLAST CZ, S.R.O.—See Protech Chemicals Ltd.; *Int'l*, pg. 6004
PROTECH OXYPLAST POLAND SP. Z O.O.—See Protech Chemicals Ltd.; *Int'l*, pg. 6004
PROTECH PERFORMANCE PLASTICS LTD—See Madison Dearborn Partners, LLC; *U.S. Private*, pg. 2541
PROTECH POWDER COATINGS INC.—See Protech Chemicals Ltd.; *Int'l*, pg. 6004
PROTECH PROPERTY MANAGEMENT LIMITED—See Allied Group Limited; *Int'l*, pg. 357
PROTECH SOLUTIONS, INC.; *U.S. Private*, pg. 3289
PRO-TECH VALVE SALES, INC.—See Forum Energy Technologies, Inc.; *U.S. Public*, pg. 874
PRO-TECH VALVE SALES—See Forum Energy Technologies, Inc.; *U.S. Public*, pg. 874
PROTEC, INC.—See Apollo Global Management, Inc.; *U.S. Public*, pg. 146
PRO-TEC INDUSTRIES—See V. F. Corporation; *U.S. Public*, pg. 2269
PRO TECK EARNS INC.; *U.S. Private*, pg. 3270
PRO-TECK SERVICES LTD.—See Stewart Information Services Corporation; *U.S. Public*, pg. 1948
PROTECMA S.R.L.—See Maire Tecnimont S.p.A.; *Int'l*, pg. 4652
PROTEC MEMS TECHNOLOGY INC; *Int'l*, pg. 6003
PROTEC PTY. LTD.—See PPG Industries, Inc.; *U.S. Public*, pg. 1709
PRO-TEC ROOFING, INC.—See Altas Partners LP; *Int'l*, pg. 386
PROTECS A & A CMS SDN. BHD.—See Digistar Corporation Berhad; *Int'l*, pg. 2120
PROTEC S.R.L.—See Manutencoop Societa Cooperativa; *Int'l*, pg. 4680
PROTECTA GESELLSCHAFT FUR OBERFLACHENSCHUTZSCHICHTEN MIT BESCHRANKTER HAFTUNG—See STRABAG SE; *Int'l*, pg. 7231
PROTECTAGROUP ACQUISITIONS LTD.—See CCV Risk Solutions Limited; *Int'l*, pg. 1370
PROTECTA INSURANCE NEW ZEALAND LTD.—See Assurant, Inc.; *U.S. Public*, pg. 215
PROTECT ALARMS—See Pye-Barker Fire & Safety, LLC; *U.S. Private*, pg. 3309
PROTECT AMERICA, INC.—See ONEX Corporation; *Int'l*, pg. 5578
PROTECT AMERICA, INC.—See RockBridge Growth Equity, LLC; *U.S. Private*, pg. 3465
PROTECTA SA; *Int'l*, pg. 6004
PROTECTAS SA—See Securitas AB; *Int'l*, pg. 6675
PROTECTION 24 SACA—See BNP Paribas SA; *Int'l*, pg. 1092
PROTECTION ONE SERVICE GMBH—See Merca Leasing GmbH & Co. KG; *Int'l*, pg. 4819
PROTECTIVE APPAREL CORPORATION OF AMERICA—See JLL Partners, LLC; *U.S. Private*, pg. 2213
PROTECTIVE BUSINESS & HEALTH SYSTEMS, INC.—See Marlin Equity Partners, LLC; *U.S. Private*, pg. 2585
PROTECTIVE CAPITAL STRUCTURES CORP.; *U.S. Public*, pg. 1729
PROTECTIVE COATINGS INC.—See Berkshire Hathaway Inc.; *U.S. Public*, pg. 314
PROTECTIVE DOOR INDUSTRIES—See L B Industries, Inc.; *U.S. Private*, pg. 2361
PROTECTIVE INDUSTRIAL PRODUCTS, INC.—See Odyssey Investment Partners, LLC; *U.S. Private*, pg. 2995

2183

PROTECTIVE INDUSTRIES, INC.—See Windjammer Capital Investors, LLC; *U.S. Private*, pg. 4538
PROTECTIVE INSURANCE COMPANY—See The Progressive Corporation; *U.S. Public*, pg. 2125
PROTECTIVE INSURANCE CORPORATION—See The Progressive Corporation; *U.S. Public*, pg. 2125
PROTECTIVE LIFE & ANNUITY INSURANCE COMPANY—See Dai-ichi Life Holdings, Inc.; *Int'l*, pg. 1917
PROTECTIVE LIFE CORPORATION—See Dai-ichi Life Holdings, Inc.; *Int'l*, pg. 1917
PROTECTIVE LIFE INSURANCE COMPANY—See Dai-ichi Life Holdings, Inc.; *Int'l*, pg. 1917
PROTECTIVE LINING CORP.—See Ringmetall AG; *Int'l*, pg. 6344
PROTECTIVE MARKETING ENTERPRISES—See Aon plc; *Int'l*, pg. 495
PROTECTIVE PRODUCTS ENTERPRISES, INC.—See Sun Capital Partners, Inc.; *U.S. Private*, pg. 3860
PROTECTIVE SPECIALTY INSURANCE COMPANY—See The Progressive Corporation; *U.S. Public*, pg. 2125
PROTECTIVE TECHNOLOGY COMPANY LIMITED—See Riverstone Holdings Limited; *Int'l*, pg. 6353
PROTECTOR ALSAFE—See Wesfarmers Limited; *Int'l*, pg. 8382
PROTECTOR AS—See AF Gruppen ASA; *Int'l*, pg. 184
PROTECTOR FORSIKRING ASA; *Int'l*, pg. 6004
PROTECTOR HOLDINGS LLC—See Dowling Capital Management, LLC; *U.S. Private*, pg. 1268
PROTECTOR HOLDINGS LLC—See Keystone Group, L.P.; *U.S. Private*, pg. 2298
PROTECTOR KKS GMBH—See AF Gruppen ASA; *Int'l*, pg. 184
PROTECTOR TECHNOLOGIES BV—See Johnson Controls International plc; *Int'l*, pg. 3987
THE PROTECTOSEAL COMPANY; *U.S. Private*, pg. 4101
PROTECT PHARMACEUTICAL CORPORATION; *U.S. Public*, pg. 1729
PROTECT PLUS AIR, LLC—See Freudenberg SE; *Int'l*, pg. 2786
PRO TEC VINDUER A/S—See Ratos AB; *Int'l*, pg. 6220
PRO TEC WINDOWS UK LTD—See Ratos AB; *Int'l*, pg. 6220
PROTEDYNE CORPORATION—See Laboratory Corporation of America Holdings; *U.S. Public*, pg. 1287
PROTEGIS, LLC—See Align Capital Partners, LLC; *U.S. Private*, pg. 167
PROTEGRA INC.; *Int'l*, pg. 6004
PROTEGRITY CORPORATION—See Xcelera Inc.; *Int'l*, pg. 8520
PROTEGRITY HOLDINGS, INC; *U.S. Private*, pg. 3289
PROTEIN CONTOUR COMPANY LTD.—See Protek OAO; *Int'l*, pg. 6004
PROTEIN HOLDINGS INC.; *U.S. Private*, pg. 3289
PROTEINOIL OY - RAISIO FACTORY—See Raisio PLC; *Int'l*, pg. 6191
PROTEINONE; *U.S. Private*, pg. 3289
THE PROTEIN PARTNERS LTD.; *Int'l*, pg. 7677
PROTEIN POLYMER TECHNOLOGIES, INC.; *U.S. Private*, pg. 3289
PROTEIN PRODUCTS INTERNATIONAL LLC—See Omar Zawawi Establishment LLC; *Int'l*, pg. 5561
PROTEIN REACTOR COMBINED FUELS, INC.; *U.S. Public*, pg. 1729
PROTEIN SCIENCES CORP.—See Sanofi; *U.S. Public*, pg. 6548
PROTEINSIMPLE LTD.—See Bio-Techne Corporation; *U.S. Public*, pg. 334
PROTEINSIMPLE—See Bio-Techne Corporation; *U.S. Public*, pg. 334
PROTEIN SOLUTIONS, LLC; *U.S. Private*, pg. 3289
PROTEIN SOURCES, LLP.; *U.S. Private*, pg. 3289
PROTEINTECH GROUP, INC.; *U.S. Private*, pg. 3289
PROTEINTECH JAPAN CO., LTD.—See COSMO BIO Co., Ltd.; *Int'l*, pg. 1811
PROTEIN TECHNOLOGY VICTORIA PTY LTD—See Saputo Inc.; *Int'l*, pg. 6575
PROTEK CAPITAL, INC.; *U.S. Public*, pg. 1729
PROTEK MEDICAL PRODUCTS, INC.—See Audax Group, Limited Partnership; *U.S. Private*, pg. 386
PRO TEKO A.D.; *Int'l*, pg. 5985
PROTEK OAO; *Int'l*, pg. 6004
PROTEKON—See Transnet Ltd.; *Int'l*, pg. 7902
PROTEKTOR S.A.; *Int'l*, pg. 6004
PRO-TEK VAULTS—See LAC Group; *U.S. Private*, pg. 2371
PROTEL COMMUNICATIONS, INC.; *U.S. Private*, pg. 3290
PROTELCO SAS—See Iliad S.A.; *Int'l*, pg. 3614
PROTEL GESELLSCHAFT FUR KOMMUNIKATION MBH—See TUI AG; *Int'l*, pg. 7966
PROTEL INC.—See Warburg Pincus LLC; *U.S. Private*, pg. 4438
PROTELINDO TOWERS B.V.—See PT Sarana Menara Nusantara Tbk; *Int'l*, pg. 6070
PRO-TELLIGENT, LLC—See Tetra Tech, Inc.; *U.S. Public*, pg. 2023
PROTENERGY NATURAL FOODS CORPORATION—See TreeHouse Foods, Inc.; *U.S. Public*, pg. 2187

PROTENERGY NATURAL FOODS, INC.—See TreeHouse Foods, Inc.; *U.S. Public*, pg. 2187
PROTEO BIOTECH AG—See Proteo, Inc.; *U.S. Public*, pg. 1729
PROTEO, INC.; *U.S. Public*, pg. 1729
PROTEOME SCIENCES PLC; *Int'l*, pg. 6004
PROTEOME SCIENCES R&D GMBH & CO. KG—See Proteome Sciences plc; *Int'l*, pg. 6004
PROTEOMETECH, INC.; *Int'l*, pg. 6004
PROTEOMICS INTERNATIONAL LABORATORIES LTD.; *Int'l*, pg. 6004
PROTEOR SAS; *Int'l*, pg. 6004
PROTEOR USA, LLC—See Proteor SAS; *Int'l*, pg. 6004
PROTEOS BIOTECH, S.L.—See PMC Capital Partners, LLC; *U.S. Public*, pg. 3217
PROTEQ LEVENSVERZEKERINGEN N.V.—See Apollo Global Management, Inc.; *U.S. Public*, pg. 147
PROTEQ PTY LTD.—See Altus Renewables Limited; *Int'l*, pg. 399
PROTERIAL, LTD.; *Int'l*, pg. 6005
PROTERRA ADVERTISING; *U.S. Private*, pg. 3290
PROTERRA, INC.—See Proterra, Inc.; *U.S. Public*, pg. 1729
PROTERRA, INC.; *U.S. Public*, pg. 1729
PROTERRA INVESTMENT PARTNERS LP; *U.S. Private*, pg. 3290
PROTERTIA FM—See Electricite de France S.A.; *Int'l*, pg. 2352
PROTESA S.P.A.—See Sacmi Imola S.C.A.R.L.; *Int'l*, pg. 6464
PROTEUS B2B; *U.S. Private*, pg. 3290
PROTEUS DIGITAL HEALTH, INC.—See Otsuka Holdings Co., Ltd.; *Int'l*, pg. 5660
PROTEUS ENGINEERS PTY LTD.—See Tetra Tech, Inc.; *U.S. Public*, pg. 2023
PROTEUS FUND; *U.S. Private*, pg. 3290
PROTEXA INDUSTRIAS S.A. DE C.V.—See Grupo Protexa S.A. de C.V.; *Int'l*, pg. 3134
PROTEXA S.A. DE C.V.—See Grupo Protexa S.A. de C.V.; *Int'l*, pg. 3134
PROTEX CANADA INC.—See XPEL, Inc.; *U.S. Public*, pg. 2391
PROTEXIC—See Sonoco Products Company; *U.S. Public*, pg. 1905
PROTEXT MOBILITY, INC.; *U.S. Private*, pg. 3290
PROTEXX TECHNOLOGY CORPORATION—See WidePoint Corporation; *U.S. Public*, pg. 2370
PROTHENA BIOSCIENCES INC.—See Prothena Corporation plc; *Int'l*, pg. 6006
PROTHENA BIOSCIENCES LIMITED—See Prothena Corporation plc; *Int'l*, pg. 6006
PROTHENA CORPORATION PLC; *Int'l*, pg. 6006
PROTHENA SWITZERLAND GMBH—See Prothena Corporation plc; *Int'l*, pg. 6006
PROTHENA THERAPEUTICS LIMITED—See Prothena Corporation plc; *Int'l*, pg. 6006
PROTHERA, INC.—See Soho Flordis International Pty Ltd.; *Int'l*, pg. 7059
PRO THERAPY SUPPLIES; *U.S. Private*, pg. 3270
PROTHERICS UK LIMITED—See Boston Scientific Corporation; *U.S. Public*, pg. 374
PROTHERICS UTAH INC.—See Boston Scientific Corporation; *U.S. Public*, pg. 374
PROTHERMIC; *Int'l*, pg. 6006
PROTHERM SERVICES GROUP, LLC—See Brand Industrial Services, Inc.; *U.S. Private*, pg. 636
PROTHRO CHEVROLET BUICK GMC; *U.S. Private*, pg. 3290
PROTIDE PHARMACEUTICALS, INC.; *U.S. Public*, pg. 1729
PROTIM LTD.—See Koppers Holdings Inc.; *U.S. Public*, pg. 1272
PROTIM SOLIGNUM LTD.—See Koppers Holdings Inc.; *U.S. Public*, pg. 1272
PROTISA COLOMBIA S.A.—See Empresas CMPC S.A.; *Int'l*, pg. 2390
PROTISHABDA COMMUNICATIONS—See Publicis Groupe S.A.; *Int'l*, pg. 6104
PROTIVA BIOTHERAPEUTICS (USA), INC.—See Arbutus Biopharma Corporation; *U.S. Public*, pg. 178
PROTIVITI BVBA—See Robert Half Inc.; *U.S. Public*, pg. 1803
PROTIVITI B.V.—See Robert Half Inc.; *U.S. Public*, pg. 1803
PROTIVITI CONSULTING PRIVATE LIMITED—See Robert Half Inc.; *U.S. Public*, pg. 1803
PROTIVITI GMBH—See Robert Half Inc.; *U.S. Public*, pg. 1803
PROTIVITI GOVERNMENT SERVICES, INC.—See Robert Half Inc.; *U.S. Public*, pg. 1803
PROTIVITI HONG KONG CO. LTD.—See Robert Half Inc.; *U.S. Public*, pg. 1803
PROTIVITI INC.—See Robert Half Inc.; *U.S. Public*, pg. 1803
PROTIVITI PTE. LTD.—See Robert Half Inc.; *U.S. Public*, pg. 1803
PROTIVITI PTY. LIMITED—See Robert Half Inc.; *U.S. Public*, pg. 1803

PROTIVITI SAS—See Robert Half Inc.; *U.S. Public*, pg. 1803
PROTIVITI SHANGHAI CO., LTD.—See Robert Half Inc.; *U.S. Public*, pg. 1803
PROTIVITI S.R.L.—See Robert Half Inc.; *U.S. Public*, pg. 1803
PROTIVITI SWITZERLAND GMBH—See Robert Half Inc.; *U.S. Public*, pg. 1803
PROTOCALL NJ INC.; *U.S. Private*, pg. 3290
PROTOCOL GLOBAL SOLUTIONS—See Protocol Inc.; *U.S. Private*, pg. 3290
PROTOCOL INC.; *U.S. Private*, pg. 3290
PROTO CORPORATION; *Int'l*, pg. 6006
PROTOCUBE REPLY S.R.L.—See Reply S.p.A.; *Int'l*, pg. 6291
PROTO DEVELOPERS & TECHNOLOGIES LIMITED; *Int'l*, pg. 6006
PROTOGENIC, INC.—See CORE Industrial Partners, LLC; *U.S. Private*, pg. 1048
PROTOKINETIX, INC.; *U.S. Public*, pg. 1730
PROTO LABS ESCHENLOHE GMBH—See Proto Labs, Inc.; *U.S. Public*, pg. 1730
PROTO LABS, G.K.—See Proto Labs, Inc.; *U.S. Public*, pg. 1730
PROTO LABS GMBH—See Proto Labs, Inc.; *U.S. Public*, pg. 1730
PROTO LABS, INC.; *U.S. Public*, pg. 1729
PROTO LABS, INC.; *U.S. Public*, pg. 1729
PROTO LABS, LTD.—See Proto Labs, Inc.; *U.S. Public*, pg. 1730
PROTO LABS TOOLING GMBH—See Proto Labs, Inc.; *U.S. Public*, pg. 1730
PROTO MALAYSIA SDN. BHD.—See PROTO CORPORATION; *Int'l*, pg. 6006
PROTOMASTER RIEDEL & CO. GMBH—See Gesco AG; *Int'l*, pg. 2945
PROTO MEDICAL CARE CO., LTD.—See PROTO CORPORATION; *Int'l*, pg. 6006
PROTOM INTERNATIONAL, INC.; *U.S. Private*, pg. 3290
PROTON CARS AUSTRALIA PTY LIMITED—See DRB-HICOM Berhad; *Int'l*, pg. 2202
PROTON CARS (UK) LTD—See DRB-HICOM Berhad; *Int'l*, pg. 2202
PROTON CITY DEVELOPMENT CORPORATION SDN. BHD.—See DRB-HICOM Berhad; *Int'l*, pg. 2202
PROTON EDAR SDN. BHD.—See DRB-HICOM Berhad; *Int'l*, pg. 2202
PROTON ENERGY SYSTEMS, INC.; *U.S. Private*, pg. 3290
PROTON HOLDINGS BERHAD—See DRB-HICOM Berhad; *Int'l*, pg. 2202
PROTON MOTOR FUEL CELL GMBH—See Proton Motor Power Systems Plc; *Int'l*, pg. 6006
PROTON MOTOR POWER SYSTEMS PLC; *Int'l*, pg. 6006
PROTON MOTORS (THAILAND) LIMITED—See DRB-HICOM Berhad; *Int'l*, pg. 2202
PROTON PARTS CENTRE SDN BHD—See DRB-HICOM Berhad; *Int'l*, pg. 2202
PROTON SINGAPORE PTE LTD—See DRB-HICOM Berhad; *Int'l*, pg. 2202
PROTON TANJUNG MALIM SDN. BHD.—See DRB-HICOM Berhad; *Int'l*, pg. 2202
PROTON THERAPY PTE. LTD.—See Berjaya Corporation Berhad; *Int'l*, pg. 984
PROTON WORLD INTERNATIONAL N.V.—See STMicroelectronics N.V.; *Int'l*, pg. 7217
PROTOPHARMA GESELLSCHAFT FUR ENGINEERING UND CONSULTING MBH—See Bain Capital, LP; *U.S. Private*, pg. 443
PROTOPHARMA GESELLSCHAFT FUR ENGINEERING UND CONSULTING MBH—See Cinven Limited; *Int'l*, pg. 1613
PROTOPIA GLOBAL HOLDINGS INC.; *Int'l*, pg. 6006
PROTO PLASTICS INC.—See Thogus Products Company; *U.S. Private*, pg. 4145
PROTO RESOURCES & INVESTMENTS LTD.; *Int'l*, pg. 6006
PROTO RIOS INC.—See PROTO CORPORATION; *Int'l*, pg. 6006
PROTO SCRIPT PHARMACEUTICAL CORP.; *U.S. Public*, pg. 1730
PROTOSERA INC.—See Ushio, Inc.; *Int'l*, pg. 8097
PROTOSOURCE CORP.; *U.S. Public*, pg. 1730
PROTO TECHNOLOGIES, INC.—See Sea Lion Corporation; *U.S. Private*, pg. 3582
PROTOTEK HOLDINGS LLC—See TruArc Partners, L.P.; *U.S. Private*, pg. 4245
PROTOTEK SHEETMETAL FABRICATION, LLC—See CORE Industrial Partners, LLC; *U.S. Private*, pg. 1049
PROTOTYPE INDUSTRIES, INC.; *U.S. Private*, pg. 3290
PROTOTYPE MACHINE CO. INC.; *U.S. Private*, pg. 3290
PROTOTYPE PLASTICS, LLC; *U.S. Private*, pg. 3290
PROTOTYPE SOLUTIONS GROUP—See TruArc Partners, L.P.; *U.S. Private*, pg. 4245
PROTOTYPES; *U.S. Private*, pg. 3290
PROTOTYP-WERKE GMBH—See Sandvik AB; *Int'l*, pg. 6530
PRO TOUR MEMORABILIA; *U.S. Private*, pg. 3270
PROTOX CO., LTD.—See DSK Co., Ltd.; *Int'l*, pg. 2210

COMPANY NAME INDEX

PROTRACE ENGINEERING, INC.—See Spirax-Sarco Engineering plc; *Int'l*, pg. 7137
PROTRAK INTERNATIONAL, INC.—See Backstop Solutions Group, LLC; *U.S. Private*, pg. 423
PROTRANS BC OPERATIONS LTD.—See AtkinsRealis Group Inc.; *Int'l*, pg. 671
PROTRANS INTERNATIONAL INC.; *U.S. Private*, pg. 3290
PROTRANSLATING, INC.—See MSouth Equity Partners, LLC; *U.S. Private*, pg. 2808
PROTRANSPORT-1; *U.S. Private*, pg. 3290
PROTRAN TECHNOLOGIES PTY. LTD.—See Rectifier Technologies Limited; *Int'l*, pg. 6243
PROTRAVEL/AUSTIN—See Travel Leaders Group, LLC; *U.S. Private*, pg. 4213
PROTRAVEL INTERNATIONAL INC.—See Travel Leaders Group, LLC; *U.S. Private*, pg. 4213
PROTRAVEL—See Travel Leaders Group, LLC; *U.S. Private*, pg. 4213
PROTREADZ LTD; *Int'l*, pg. 6006
PROTREND LIMITED; *U.S. Private*, pg. 3291
PROTRIALS RESEARCH, INC.; *U.S. Private*, pg. 3291
THE PROUD COMPANY; *U.S. Private*, pg. 4101
PROUDFOOT CONSULTING GMBH—See Management Consulting Group PLC; *Int'l*, pg. 4666
PROUDFOOT CONSULTING SA—See Management Consulting Group PLC; *Int'l*, pg. 4666
PROUDFOOT CONSULTING SPAIN—See Management Consulting Group PLC; *Int'l*, pg. 4666
PROUDFOOT JAPAN LTD.—See Management Consulting Group PLC; *Int'l*, pg. 4666
PROUD REAL ESTATE PUBLIC COMPANY LIMITED; *Int'l*, pg. 6006
PROUDS JEWELLERS PTY. LTD.; *Int'l*, pg. 6006
PRO UNLIMITED GLOBAL JAPAN (YK) LTD.—See Harvest Partners L.P.; *U.S. Private*, pg. 1876
PRO UNLIMITED, INC.—See Harvest Partners L.P.; *U.S. Private*, pg. 1876
PRO-VAC, LLC—See Gallant Capital Partners, LLC; *U.S. Private*, pg. 1639
PROVADE, INC.—See Pinnacle Technical Resources, Inc.; *U.S. Private*, pg. 3185
PROVALLIANCE, SAS—See Core Equity Holdings SA; *Int'l*, pg. 1798
PROVANA LLC; *U.S. Private*, pg. 3291
PROVARIS ENERGY LTD; *Int'l*, pg. 6006
PROVATI INSURANCE COMPANY LIMITED; *Int'l*, pg. 6007
PROVATION MEDICAL, INC.—See Fortive Corporation; *U.S. Public*, pg. 871
PROVECTUS BIOPHARMACEUTICALS, INC.; *U.S. Public*, pg. 1730
PROVECTUS ROBOTICS SOLUTIONS INC.—See Rheinmetall AG; *Int'l*, pg. 6323
PROVEEDORA DE SEGURIDAD INDUSTRIAL DEL GOLFO S.A. DE C.V.—See Nautic Partners, LLC; *U.S. Private*, pg. 2872
PROVEEDORES DE INGENIERIA ALIMENTARIA, S.A. DE C.V.—See International Flavors & Fragrances Inc.; *U.S. Public*, pg. 1154
PROVELEC SUD SAS—See VINCI S.A.; *Int'l*, pg. 8225
PROVELOCITY LLC—See The Riverside Company; *U.S. Private*, pg. 4110
PROVEL, S.R.L.—See 3D Systems Corporation; *U.S. Public*, pg. 4
PROVENA FOODS INC.—See Hormel Foods Corporation; *U.S. Public*, pg. 1054
PROVENANCE CONSULTING LLC—See Keystone Group, L.P.; *U.S. Private*, pg. 2299
PROVENANCE GOLD CORP.; *Int'l*, pg. 6007
PROVENCE ALPES COTE D—See Smurfit Kappa Group plc; *Int'l*, pg. 7022
PROVENCE DISTRIBUTION SERVICES S.A.R.L.—See CNH Industrial N.V.; *Int'l*, pg. 1192
PROVENCE HUILES S.A.S.—See ITOCHU Corporation; *Int'l*, pg. 3841
PROVEN GROWTH & INCOME VCT PLC; *Int'l*, pg. 6007
PROVEN INC.; *U.S. Private*, pg. 3291
THE PROVEN METHOD INC.—See Marathon TS, Inc.; *U.S. Private*, pg. 2570
PROVEN ORAPI—See Orapi S.A.; *Int'l*, pg. 5612
PROVEN PROCESS MEDICAL DEVICES, INC.—See Kidd & Company LLC; *U.S. Private*, pg. 2302
PROVENTIA EMISSION CONTROL OY—See Head Invest Oy; *Int'l*, pg. 3301
PROVENTIA GMBH—See Head Invest Oy; *Int'l*, pg. 3301
PROVENTIA GROUP OY—See Head Invest Oy; *Int'l*, pg. 3301
PROVENTION BIO, INC.—See Sanofi; *Int'l*, pg. 6548
PROVENTURE CAPITAL INC.; *Int'l*, pg. 6007
PROVENTUS AB; *Int'l*, pg. 6007
PROVENTUS AGROCOM LIMITED; *Int'l*, pg. 6007
PROVENTUS AKADEMIE- UND VERTRIEBS GMBH—See Swiss Life Holding; *Int'l*, pg. 7370
PROVENTUS BINA SDN. BHD.—See Central Global Berhad; *Int'l*, pg. 1407
PROVEN VCT PLC; *Int'l*, pg. 6007
PROVEST LLC; *U.S. Private*, pg. 3291

PROVET HOLDINGS LIMITED—See Clayton, Dubilier & Rice, LLC; *U.S. Private*, pg. 921
PROVET HOLDINGS LIMITED—See TPG Capital, L.P.; *U.S. Public*, pg. 2170
PROVET (NSW) PTY LTD.—See Clayton, Dubilier & Rice, LLC; *U.S. Private*, pg. 922
PROVET (NSW) PTY LTD.—See TPG Capital, L.P.; *U.S. Public*, pg. 2170
PROVET NZ PTY LIMITED—See Clayton, Dubilier & Rice, LLC; *U.S. Private*, pg. 922
PROVET NZ PTY LIMITED—See TPG Capital, L.P.; *U.S. Public*, pg. 2170
PROVET QLD PTY LTD.—See Clayton, Dubilier & Rice, LLC; *U.S. Private*, pg. 922
PROVET QLD PTY LTD.—See TPG Capital, L.P.; *U.S. Public*, pg. 2170
PROVET SA PTY LTD.—See Clayton, Dubilier & Rice, LLC; *U.S. Private*, pg. 922
PROVET SA PTY LTD.—See TPG Capital, L.P.; *U.S. Public*, pg. 2170
PROVET VETERINER URUNLERI SAN. VE TIC. A.S.—See SeQuent Scientific Limited; *Int'l*, pg. 6719
PROVET VICTORIA PTY LTD.—See Clayton, Dubilier & Rice, LLC; *U.S. Private*, pg. 922
PROVET VICTORIA PTY LTD.—See TPG Capital, L.P.; *U.S. Public*, pg. 2170
PROVET VMS PTY LTD.—See Clayton, Dubilier & Rice, LLC; *U.S. Private*, pg. 922
PROVET VMS PTY LTD.—See TPG Capital, L.P.; *U.S. Public*, pg. 2170
PROVET WA PTY LTD.—See Clayton, Dubilier & Rice, LLC; *U.S. Private*, pg. 922
PROVET WA PTY LTD.—See TPG Capital, L.P.; *U.S. Public*, pg. 2170
PROVEXIS PLC; *Int'l*, pg. 6007
PROV FOODS PRIVATE LIMITED—See Proventus Agrocom Limited; *Int'l*, pg. 6007
PROVIA DOOR, INC.; *U.S. Private*, pg. 3291
PROVIAS CONSTRUCTION, L.L.C.; *U.S. Private*, pg. 3291
PROVICTOR IMMOBILIEN GMBH—See Munchener Ruckversicherungs AG; *Int'l*, pg. 5091
PROVIDACARE, LLC—See KKR & Co. Inc.; *U.S. Public*, pg. 1250
PROVIDE COMMERCE, INC.—See Tenth Avenue Holdings LLC; *U.S. Private*, pg. 3968
PROVIDENCE BANK—See PB Financial Corporation; *U.S. Public*, pg. 1657
PROVIDENCE BANK—See PB Financial Corporation; *U.S. Public*, pg. 1657
PROVIDENCE BANK—See PB Financial Corporation; *U.S. Public*, pg. 1657
PROVIDENCE BANK—See PB Financial Corporation; *U.S. Public*, pg. 1657
PROVIDENCE BANK & TRUST—See Providence Financial Corporation; *U.S. Private*, pg. 3294
PROVIDENCE BUSINESS NEWS INC.—See Woodward Communications, Inc.; *U.S. Private*, pg. 4561
PROVIDENCE CAPITAL FUNDING, INC.; *U.S. Private*, pg. 3291
PROVIDENCE EQUITY ADVISORS INDIA PRIVATE LIMITED—See Providence Equity Partners L.L.C.; *U.S. Private*, pg. 3293
PROVIDENCE EQUITY ASIA LIMITED—See Providence Equity Partners L.L.C.; *U.S. Private*, pg. 3293
PROVIDENCE EQUITY INVESTMENT CONSULTING (BEIJING) CO., LTD.—See Providence Equity Partners L.L.C.; *U.S. Private*, pg. 3293
PROVIDENCE EQUITY LLC—See Providence Equity Partners L.L.C.; *U.S. Private*, pg. 3293
PROVIDENCE EQUITY LLP—See Providence Equity Partners L.L.C.; *U.S. Private*, pg. 3293
PROVIDENCE EQUITY PARTNERS L.L.C.; *U.S. Private*, pg. 3291
PROVIDENCE FINANCIAL CORPORATION; *U.S. Private*, pg. 3294
PROVIDENCE GOLD MINES INC.; *Int'l*, pg. 6007
PROVIDENCE GOLD MINES (US) INC.—See Providence Gold Mines Inc.; *Int'l*, pg. 6007
THE PROVIDENCE GROUP OF GEORGIA, L.L.C.—See Green Brick Partners, Inc.; *U.S. Public*, pg. 963
PROVIDENCE HEALTH & SERVICES—See Providence St. Joseph Health; *U.S. Private*, pg. 3294
PROVIDENCE HOSPITAL, LLC—See Apollo Global Management, Inc.; *U.S. Public*, pg. 158
PROVIDENCE HOSPITAL, LLC; *U.S. Private*, pg. 3294
PROVIDENCE IMAGING CENTER, LLC—See Apollo Global Management, Inc.; *U.S. Public*, pg. 158
THE PROVIDENCE INSURANCE GROUP, INC.—See New Mountain Capital, LLC; *U.S. Private*, pg. 2901
THE PROVIDENCE JOURNAL COMPANY—See Gannett Co., Inc.; *U.S. Public*, pg. 905
PROVIDENCE LEASING LLC—See Kimberly-Clark Corporation; *U.S. Public*, pg. 1231
PROVIDENCE LIFE ASSURANCE COMPANY LTD.—See Alpha Growth PLC; *Int'l*, pg. 368
PROVIDENCE LIFE SERVICES; *U.S. Private*, pg. 3294
PROVIDENCE LUXURY HOMES, L.L.C.—See Green Brick Partners, Inc.; *U.S. Public*, pg. 963

PROVIDENCE MANAGEMENT COMPANY, LLC; *U.S. Private*, pg. 3294
PROVIDENCE MEDICAL CENTER; *U.S. Private*, pg. 3294
PROVIDENCE PERFORMING ARTS CENTER; *U.S. Private*, pg. 3294
PROVIDENCE RESOURCES, INC.; *U.S. Public*, pg. 1730
PROVIDENCE RESOURCES UK LIMITED—See Barryroe Offshore Energy plc; *Int'l*, pg. 870
PROVIDENCE REST; *U.S. Private*, pg. 3294
PROVIDENCE ST. JOSEPH HEALTH; *U.S. Private*, pg. 3294
PROVIDENCE TARZANA MEDICAL CENTER—See Providence St. Joseph Health; *U.S. Private*, pg. 3295
PROVIDENCE & WORCESTER RAILROAD COMPANY—See Brookfield Infrastructure Partners L.P.; *Int'l*, pg. 1192
PROVIDENCE & WORCESTER RAILROAD COMPANY—See GIC Pte. Ltd.; *Int'l*, pg. 2967
THE PROVIDENT BANK—See BankProv; *U.S. Public*, pg. 274
THE PROVIDENT BANK—See Provident Financial Services, Inc.; *U.S. Public*, pg. 1730
PROVIDENT FINANCIAL CORP—See Provident Financial Holdings, Inc.; *U.S. Public*, pg. 1730
PROVIDENT FINANCIAL HOLDINGS, INC.; *U.S. Public*, pg. 1730
PROVIDENT FINANCIAL MANAGEMENT, INC.; *U.S. Private*, pg. 3295
PROVIDENT FINANCIAL ROMANIA IFN S.A.—See International Personal Finance plc; *Int'l*, pg. 3751
PROVIDENT FINANCIAL SERVICES, INC.; *U.S. Public*, pg. 1730
PROVIDENT FINANCIAL S.R.O.—See International Personal Finance plc; *Int'l*, pg. 3751
PROVIDENT FINANCIAL S.R.O.—See Vanquis Banking Group plc; *Int'l*, pg. 8130
PROVIDENT FINANCIAL ZRT.—See International Personal Finance plc; *Int'l*, pg. 3751
PROVIDENT FUNDING; *U.S. Private*, pg. 3295
THE PROVIDENT GROUP—See Anderson & Vreeland, Inc.; *U.S. Private*, pg. 276
PROVIDENT HOUSING LIMITED—See Puravankara Ltd.; *Int'l*, pg. 6121
PROVIDENT JEWELRY & LOAN, INC.; *U.S. Private*, pg. 3295
PROVIDENT METALS CORP.—See A-Mark Precious Metals, Inc.; *U.S. Public*, pg. 10
PROVIDENT MEXICO S.A. DE C.V.—See International Personal Finance plc; *Int'l*, pg. 3751
PROVIDENT MORTGAGE CAPITAL ASSOCIATES, INC.; *U.S. Private*, pg. 3295
PROVIDENT MUSIC GROUP—See Sony Group Corporation; *Int'l*, pg. 7103
PROVIDENT PERSONAL CREDIT LIMITED—See Vanquis Banking Group plc; *Int'l*, pg. 8130
PROVIDENT POLSKA S.A.—See Vanquis Banking Group plc; *Int'l*, pg. 8130
PROVIDENT SAVINGS BANK, F.S.B.—See Provident Financial Holdings, Inc.; *U.S. Public*, pg. 1730
PROVIDENT SERVICIOS DE AGENCIA S.A DE C.V.—See International Personal Finance plc; *Int'l*, pg. 3751
PROVIDENT SERVICIOS S.A DE C.V.—See International Personal Finance plc; *Int'l*, pg. 3751
PROVIDENT TRUST GROUP, LLC—See Aquiline Capital Partners LLC; *U.S. Private*, pg. 304
PROVIDENT TRUST GROUP, LLC—See Genstar Capital, LLC; *U.S. Private*, pg. 1675
PROVIDEO MANAGEMENT, INC.; *U.S. Private*, pg. 3295
PROVIDER POWER LLC—See Via Renewables, Inc.; *U.S. Public*, pg. 2290
PROVIDGE CONSULTING, LLC; *U.S. Private*, pg. 3295
PROVIDIGM, LLC—See HealthStream, Inc.; *U.S. Public*, pg. 1017
PROVIDOM SAS—See PAUL HARTMANN AG; *Int'l*, pg. 5761
PROVIDOR LIMITED—See Cap10 Partners LLP; *Int'l*, pg. 1301
PROVIDOR LOGISTICS OY—See Revenio Group Oyj; *Int'l*, pg. 6312
PROVIDUS GROUP; *U.S. Private*, pg. 3295
PROVIDYN INC.—See Frontenac Company LLC; *U.S. Private*, pg. 1614
PROVIGO DISTRIBUTION—See George Weston Limited; *Int'l*, pg. 2939
PROVIGO INC.—See George Weston Limited; *Int'l*, pg. 2939
PROVIMI B.V.—See Cargill, Inc.; *U.S. Private*, pg. 760
PROVIMI FOODS INC; *U.S. Private*, pg. 3295
PROVIMI FRANCE—See Cargill, Inc.; *U.S. Private*, pg. 760
PROVIMI HOLDING B.V.—See Cargill, Inc.; *U.S. Private*, pg. 759
PROVIMI NORTH AMERICA, INC.—See Cargill, Inc.; *U.S. Private*, pg. 760
PROVIMI S.A.—See Cargill, Inc.; *U.S. Private*, pg. 759
THE PROVINCE—See Chatham Asset Management, LLC; *U.S. Private*, pg. 861
PROVINCIA BURSATIL S.A.—See Banco de la Provincia de Buenos Aires; *Int'l*, pg. 821

PROVIMI FOODS INC / CORPORATE AFFILIATIONS

PROVINCIAL AEROSPACE LTD.—See Exchange Income Corporation; *Int'l*, pg. 2579
PROVINCIAL MEDICAL SUPPLIES LTD.; *Int'l*, pg. 6007
PROVINCIAL WALLCOVERINGS LTD.—See Brewster Wallpaper Corp.; *U.S. Private*, pg. 647
PROVINCIA MICROEMPRESAS S.A.—See Banco de la Provincia de Buenos Aires; *Int'l*, pg. 821
PROVINCIA SEGUROS S.A.—See Banco de la Provincia de Buenos Aires; *Int'l*, pg. 821
PROVINCO ITALIA S.P.A.—See Italian Wine Brands S.p.A.; *Int'l*, pg. 3828
PROVING GROUND MEDIA, INC.; *U.S. Private*, pg. 3295
PROVIN LTD—See Grand Vin Ltd.; *U.S. Private*, pg. 1753
PROVINSURE, INC.; *U.S. Private*, pg. 3295
PROV INTERNATIONAL, INC.; *U.S. Private*, pg. 3291
PROVIRON AMERICA, INC.—See Proviron Holding N.V.; *Int'l*, pg. 6007
PROVIRON FINE CHEMICALS N.V.—See Proviron Holding N.V.; *Int'l*, pg. 6007
PROVIRON HOLDING N.V.; *Int'l*, pg. 6007
PROVIRON INDUSTRIES N.V.—See Proviron Holding N.V.; *Int'l*, pg. 6007
PROVISE MANAGEMENT GROUP, LLC—See Aon plc; *Int'l*, pg. 497
PROVISION CO., LTD.—See Systena Corporation; *Int'l*, pg. 7393
PROVISIONES LEGRAND INC.—See TraFon Group; *U.S. Private*, pg. 4203
PROVISION HOLDING, INC.; *U.S. Public*, pg. 1730
PRO-VISION INC.—See JMC Capital Partners LLC; *U.S. Private*, pg. 2215
PROVISION OPERATION SYSTEMS, INC.; *U.S. Public*, pg. 1731
PROVISION PTE LTD—See The Quarto Group, Inc.; *Int'l*, pg. 7677
PROVISIONS—See Carlson Companies Inc.; *U.S. Private*, pg. 764
PROVISIS GASE & SERVICE GMBH—See Linde plc; *Int'l*, pg. 4508
PROVIS MEDIA GROUP; *U.S. Private*, pg. 3295
PROVISTA, LLC—See Vizient, Inc.; *U.S. Private*, pg. 4407
PROVISUR TECHNOLOGIES, INC.—See Henry Crown & Company; *U.S. Private*, pg. 1917
PROVITAL SOLUTIONS A/S—See LiqTech International, Inc.; *Int'l*, pg. 4522
PROVIVERE GMBH—See Asklepios Kliniken GmbH & Co. KGaA; *Int'l*, pg. 624
PROVO CANYON SCHOOL, INC.—See Universal Health Services, Inc.; *U.S. Public*, pg. 2259
PROVODINSKE PISKY A.S.—See Quarzwerke GmbH; *Int'l*, pg. 6156
PROVUS SRL—See Wirecard AG; *Int'l*, pg. 8434
PROWEBCE SA—See Edenred S.A.; *Int'l*, pg. 2308
PROWERB GESELLSCHAFT FUR PRODUKTIVE WERBUNG GMBH—See Osterreichische Post AG; *Int'l*, pg. 5654
PRO-WESTERN PLASTICS LTD.—See Berry Global Group, Inc; *U.S. Public*, pg. 322
PROWINKO BELGIE B.V.—See Prowinko Nederland B.V.; *Int'l*, pg. 6007
PROWINKO CANADA LTD.—See Prowinko Nederland B.V.; *Int'l*, pg. 6007
PROWINKO NEDERLAND B.V.; *Int'l*, pg. 6007
PROWINKO PORTUGAL SA—See Prowinko Nederland B.V.; *Int'l*, pg. 6007
PROXAN DICHTSTOFFE GMBH—See Dortmunder Gussasphalt GmbH & Co. KG; *Int'l*, pg. 2180
PROXEON BIOSYSTEMS A/S—See Thermo Fisher Scientific Inc.; *U.S. Public*, pg. 2149
PROXES GMBH—See Capvis AG; *Int'l*, pg. 1318
PROXESS GMBH—See SPARTA AG; *Int'l*, pg. 7127
PROXES TECHNOLOGY GMBH—See Capvis AG; *Int'l*, pg. 1318
PROXIDIS EXPRESS—See Transalliance; *Int'l*, pg. 7895
PROXI-LINE S.A.R.L.—See ThyssenKrupp AG; *Int'l*, pg. 7725
PROXIMANIA S.A.; *Int'l*, pg. 6007
PROXIMAR LTD.—See Proximar Seafood AS; *Int'l*, pg. 6007
PROXIMAR SEAFOOD AS; *Int'l*, pg. 6007
PROXIMA SCANDINAVIA AS—See BKW AG; *Int'l*, pg. 1056
PROXIMA SOLUTIONS GMBH—See BKW AG; *Int'l*, pg. 1056
PROXIMEDIA SA—See Publicis Groupe S.A.; *Int'l*, pg. 6104
PROXIMEX CORPORATION—See Johnson Controls International plc; *Int'l*, pg. 3987
PROXIMIC, INC.—See comScore, Inc.; *U.S. Public*, pg. 561
PROXIMION AB—See Hexatronic Group AB; *Int'l*, pg. 3371
PROXIMITY BBDO—See Omnicom Group Inc.; *U.S. Public*, pg. 1575
PROXIMITY CONTROLS CORP.—See Arcline Investment Management LP; *U.S. Private*, pg. 313
PROXIMITY DESIGN; *U.S. Private*, pg. 3295
PROXIMO SPIRITS, INC.; *U.S. Private*, pg. 3295
PROXIMUS PLC; *Int'l*, pg. 6007

PROXIM WIRELESS CORPORATION; *U.S. Public*, pg. 1731
THE PROXY ADVISORY GROUP, LLC—See Alliance Advisors LLC; *U.S. Private*, pg. 181
PROXY BIOMEDICAL LTD.—See Sealed Air Corporation; *U.S. Public*, pg. 1854
PROXY PERSONNEL, LLC; *U.S. Private*, pg. 3295
PROYA COSMETICS CO., LTD.; *Int'l*, pg. 6008
PROYECTOS DE ENERGIA S.A. DE C.V.—See Siemens Aktiengesellschaft; *Int'l*, pg. 6887
PROYECTOS DE INFRAESTRUCTURA S.A.—See Grupo Aval Acciones y Valores S.A.; *Int'l*, pg. 3121
PROYECTOS DE INGENIERIA CORPORATIVA, S.A. DE C.V.—See Empresas Publicas de Medellin ESP; *Int'l*, pg. 2392
PROYECTOS EOLICOS VALENCIANOS SA—See Enel S.p.A.; *Int'l*, pg. 2414
PROYECTOS ESPECIALES PACIFICO S.A.—See AECOM; *U.S. Public*, pg. 51
PROYESO, S.A. DE C.V.—See Grupo Lamosa S.A. de C.V.; *Int'l*, pg. 3132
PROZAP SP. Z O.O.—See Grupa Azoty S.A.; *Int'l*, pg. 3116
PROZESS UND MASCHINEN AUTOMATION GMBH—See Danaher Corporation; *U.S. Public*, pg. 630
PROZNA PROPERTIES SP.Z.O.O.—See Warimpex Finanz- und Beteiligungs AG; *Int'l*, pg. 8345
PROZONE REALTY LTD.; *Int'l*, pg. 6008
PR PALMER PARK MALL LIMITED PARTNERSHIP—See Pennsylvania Real Estate Investment Trust; *U.S. Public*, pg. 1663
PRP-GP LLC—See The Mosaic Company; *U.S. Public*, pg. 2116
PRP HOLDINGS, LLC—See Bloomin' Brands, Inc.; *U.S. Public*, pg. 363
PRPI CONSULTING LIMITED—See PricewaterhouseCoopers LLP (UK); *Int'l*, pg. 5971
PR POMEROY RESTORATION & CONSTRUCTION LTD.; *Int'l*, pg. 5952
PRP-PLASTIC OY—See Indutrade AB; *Int'l*, pg. 3680
PRP-PUBLIC RELATIONS & PROMOTION GROUP—See The Interpublic Group of Companies, Inc.; *U.S. Public*, pg. 2105
PR PUNDIT PORTER NOVELLI—See Omnicom Group Inc.; *U.S. Public*, pg. 1591
PRP WINE INTERNATIONAL INC.; *U.S. Private*, pg. 3295
PRS, INC.—See PepsiCo, Inc.; *U.S. Public*, pg. 1669
PRS INTERNATIONAL CONSULTING INC—See EFG International AG; *Int'l*, pg. 2321
PR SPRINGFIELD TOWN CENTER LLC—See Pennsylvania Real Estate Investment Trust; *U.S. Public*, pg. 1663
THE PRS REIT PLC; *Int'l*, pg. 7677
PRT COMPANY LIMITED—See Seven West Media Limited; *Int'l*, pg. 6734
PRT GROWING SERVICES LTD.—See Mill Road Capital Management LLC; *U.S. Private*, pg. 2730
PR TIMES INC.—See Vector Inc.; *Int'l*, pg. 8144
PRTM MANAGEMENT CONSULTANTS (INDIA) PRIVATE LIMITED—See PricewaterhouseCoopers Pvt. Ltd.; *Int'l*, pg. 5972
PRT RADOMSKO SP. Z O.O.—See Alpla-Werke Alwin Lehner GmbH & Co. KG; *Int'l*, pg. 374
PRUCKNER REHATECHNIK GMBH—See KIRCHHOFF Gruppe; *Int'l*, pg. 4185
PRUCO LIFE INSURANCE COMPANY—See Prudential Financial, Inc.; *U.S. Public*, pg. 1733
PRUCO SECURITIES, LLC—See Prudential Financial, Inc.; *U.S. Public*, pg. 1732
PRUDENCE CRANDALL FUND III, LLC—See Wells Fargo & Company; *U.S. Public*, pg. 2345
PRUDENCE CREOLE S.A.—See Assicurazioni Generali S.p.A.; *Int'l*, pg. 645
PRUDENT BROKING SERVICES PRIVATE LIMITED—See Prudent Corporate Advisory Services Limited; *Int'l*, pg. 6008
PRUDENT CORPORATE ADVISORY SERVICES LIMITED; *Int'l*, pg. 6008
PRUDENTIAL AGRICULTURAL CREDIT, INC.—See Prudential Financial, Inc.; *U.S. Public*, pg. 1732
PRUDENTIAL AGRICULTURAL INVESTMENTS, INC.—See Prudential Financial, Inc.; *U.S. Public*, pg. 1732
PRUDENTIAL AGRICULTURAL PROPERTY HOLDING COMPANY, LLC—See Prudential Financial, Inc.; *U.S. Public*, pg. 1732
PRUDENTIAL AMERICANA GROUP REALTORS; *U.S. Private*, pg. 3295
PRUDENTIAL ANNUITIES LIFE ASSURANCE CORPORATION—See T&D Holdings, Inc.; *Int'l*, pg. 7395
PRUDENTIAL ANNUITIES LIFE ASSURANCE CORPORATION—See The Carlyle Group Inc.; *U.S. Public*, pg. 2047
PRUDENTIAL ANNUITIES—See Prudential Financial, Inc.; *U.S. Public*, pg. 1732
PRUDENTIAL ASSET RESOURCES, INC.—See Prudential Financial, Inc.; *U.S. Public*, pg. 1732
THE PRUDENTIAL ASSURANCE COMPANY LIMITED—See Prudential plc; *Int'l*, pg. 6009

PRUDENTIAL ASSURANCE COMPANY SINGAPORE (PTE) LIMITED—See Prudential plc; *Int'l*, pg. 6009
PRUDENTIAL ASSURANCE MALAYSIA BERHAD—See Prudential plc; *Int'l*, pg. 6009
PRUDENTIAL ASSURANCE UGANDA LIMITED—See Prudential plc; *Int'l*, pg. 6009
PRUDENTIAL BANCORP, INC.—See Fulton Financial Corporation; *U.S. Public*, pg. 892
PRUDENTIAL BANK—See Fulton Financial Corporation; *U.S. Public*, pg. 892
PRUDENTIAL BANK & TRUST, FSB—See Prudential Financial, Inc.; *U.S. Public*, pg. 1732
PRUDENTIAL BELIFE INSURANCE S.A.—See Prudential plc; *Int'l*, pg. 6009
PRUDENTIAL BENEFICIAL GENERAL INSURANCE CAMEROON S.A.—See Prudential plc; *Int'l*, pg. 6009
PRUDENTIAL BENEFICIAL LIFE INSURANCE TOGO S.A.—See Prudential plc; *Int'l*, pg. 6009
PRUDENTIAL CALIFORNIA REALTY—See Berkshire Hathaway Inc.; *U.S. Public*, pg. 307
PRUDENTIAL CALIFORNIA REALTY—See Berkshire Hathaway Inc.; *U.S. Public*, pg. 315
PRUDENTIAL (CAMBODIA) LIFE ASSURANCE PLC—See Prudential plc; *Int'l*, pg. 6009
PRUDENTIAL CAPITAL GROUP, L.P.—See Prudential Financial, Inc.; *U.S. Public*, pg. 1732
PRUDENTIAL CAPITAL & INVESTMENT SERVICES, LLC—See Prudential Financial, Inc.; *U.S. Public*, pg. 1732
PRUDENTIAL CAPITAL PLC—See Prudential plc; *Int'l*, pg. 6009
PRUDENTIAL CORPORATION ASIA—See Prudential plc; *Int'l*, pg. 6009
PRUDENTIAL CORPORATION HOLDINGS LIMITED—See Prudential plc; *Int'l*, pg. 6009
PRUDENTIAL DEFINED CONTRIBUTION SERVICES—See Prudential Financial, Inc.; *U.S. Public*, pg. 1732
PRUDENTIAL DISCOUNT & GUARANTEE HOUSE LTD.; *Int'l*, pg. 6008
PRUDENTIAL DO BRASIL SEGUROS DE VIDA S.A.—See Prudential Financial, Inc.; *U.S. Public*, pg. 1733
PRUDENTIAL EQUITY GROUP, LLC—See Prudential Financial, Inc.; *U.S. Public*, pg. 1732
PRUDENTIAL FINANCIAL ADVISERS SINGAPORE PTE. LTD.—See Prudential plc; *Int'l*, pg. 6009
PRUDENTIAL FINANCIAL, INC.; *U.S. Public*, pg. 1731
PRUDENTIAL FINANCIAL—See Prudential Financial, Inc.; *U.S. Public*, pg. 1732
PRUDENTIAL FINANCIAL—See Prudential Financial, Inc.; *U.S. Public*, pg. 1732
PRUDENTIAL FLORIDA WCI REALTY—See Prudential Financial, Inc.; *U.S. Public*, pg. 1732
PRUDENTIAL FUNDING LLC—See Prudential Financial, Inc.; *U.S. Public*, pg. 1732
PRUDENTIAL GENERAL SERVICES OF JAPAN Y.K.—See Prudential Financial, Inc.; *U.S. Public*, pg. 1734
PRUDENTIAL GIBRALTAR AGENCY CO., LTD.—See Prudential Financial, Inc.; *U.S. Public*, pg. 1732
THE PRUDENTIAL GIBRALTAR FINANCIAL LIFE INSURANCE CO., LTD.—See Prudential Financial, Inc.; *U.S. Public*, pg. 1733
PRUDENTIAL GLOBAL FUNDING, LLC—See Prudential Financial, Inc.; *U.S. Public*, pg. 1732
PRUDENTIAL GUARANTEE & ASSURANCE INC.; *Int'l*, pg. 6008
PRUDENTIAL HEALTH HOLDINGS LIMITED—See Discovery Limited; *Int'l*, pg. 2134
PRUDENTIAL HEALTH INSURANCE LTD—See Discovery Limited; *Int'l*, pg. 2134
PRUDENTIAL HUNTOON PAIGE ASSOCIATES, LTD.—See Prudential Financial, Inc.; *U.S. Public*, pg. 1732
THE PRUDENTIAL INSURANCE COMPANY OF AMERICA—See Prudential Financial, Inc.; *U.S. Public*, pg. 1733
PRUDENTIAL INSURANCE—See Prudential Financial, Inc.; *U.S. Public*, pg. 1732
PRUDENTIAL INTERNATIONAL ASSURANCE PLC—See Prudential plc; *Int'l*, pg. 6009
PRUDENTIAL INTERNATIONAL INSURANCE HOLDINGS, LTD.—See Prudential Financial, Inc.; *U.S. Public*, pg. 1732
PRUDENTIAL INTERNATIONAL INVESTMENTS CORPORATION—See Prudential Financial, Inc.; *U.S. Public*, pg. 1732
PRUDENTIAL INVESTMENT BANK LIMITED; *Int'l*, pg. 6008
PRUDENTIAL INVESTMENT MANAGEMENT, INC.—See Prudential Financial, Inc.; *U.S. Public*, pg. 1732
PRUDENTIAL INVESTMENTS, INC—See Bank of the Philippine Islands; *Int'l*, pg. 849
PRUDENTIAL INVESTMENTS LLC—See Prudential Financial, Inc.; *U.S. Public*, pg. 1733
PRUDENTIAL LIFE ASSURANCE KENYA LIMITED—See Prudential plc; *Int'l*, pg. 6009
PRUDENTIAL LIFE ASSURANCE (LAO) COMPANY LIMITED—See Prudential plc; *Int'l*, pg. 6009

COMPANY NAME INDEX

PRUDENTIAL LIFE ASSURANCE (THAILAND) PUBLIC COMPANY LIMITED—See Prudential plc; *Int'l*, pg. 6009
PRUDENTIAL LIFE ASSURANCE ZAMBIA LIMITED—See Prudential plc; *Int'l*, pg. 6009
THE PRUDENTIAL LIFE INSURANCE CO. LTD.—See Prudential Financial, Inc.; *U.S. Public*, pg. 1733
PRUDENTIAL LIFE INSURANCE COMPANY OF TAIWAN INC.—See Taishin Financial Holding Co., Ltd.; *Int'l*, pg. 7416
PRUDENTIAL LIFE INSURANCE GHANA LIMITED—See Prudential plc; *Int'l*, pg. 6009
THE PRUDENTIAL LIFE REALTY GROUP—See Prudential Financial, Inc.; *U.S. Public*, pg. 1734
PRUDENTIAL LIGHTING CORP; *U.S. Private*, pg. 3296
PRUDENTIAL MORTGAGE CAPITAL COMPANY II, LLC—See Prudential Financial, Inc.; *U.S. Public*, pg. 1733
PRUDENTIAL MORTGAGE CAPITAL COMPANY, LLC—See Prudential Financial, Inc.; *U.S. Public*, pg. 1733
PRUDENTIAL MUTUAL FUND SERVICES LLC—See Prudential Financial, Inc.; *U.S. Public*, pg. 1733
PRUDENTIAL MYANMAR LIFE INSURANCE LIMITED—See Prudential plc; *Int'l*, pg. 6009
PRUDENTIAL NEW JERSEY PROPERTIES; *U.S. Private*, pg. 3296
PRUDENTIAL NORTHWEST REALTY ASSOCIATES, LLC—See Berkshire Hathaway Inc.; *U.S. Public*, pg. 307
PRUDENTIAL OVERALL SUPPLY INC.; *U.S. Private*, pg. 3296
PRUDENTIAL PLC; *Int'l*, pg. 6008
PRUDENTIAL POLSKA SP. Z O.O—See M&G Plc; *Int'l*, pg. 4612
PRUDENTIAL PRIVATE PLACEMENT INVESTORS L.P.—See Prudential Financial, Inc.; *U.S. Public*, pg. 1733
PRUDENTIAL PROPERTY INVESTMENT MANAGERS LIMITED—See Prudential plc; *Int'l*, pg. 6009
PRUDENTIAL REAL ESTATE AFFILIATES, INC.—See Prudential Financial, Inc.; *U.S. Public*, pg. 1733
PRUDENTIAL REAL ESTATE INVESTORS INVESTIMENTOS IMOBILIARIOS LTDA.—See Prudential Financial, Inc.; *U.S. Public*, pg. 1733
PRUDENTIAL REAL ESTATE INVESTORS (JAPAN) K.K.—See Prudential Financial, Inc.; *U.S. Public*, pg. 1733
PRUDENTIAL REAL ESTATE INVESTORS, SOCIEDAD RESPONSABILIDAD LIMITADA DE CAPITAL VARIABLE—See Prudential Financial, Inc.; *U.S. Public*, pg. 1733
PRUDENTIAL REALTY COMPANY; *U.S. Private*, pg. 3296
PRUDENTIAL RELOCATION LTD.—See Prudential Financial, Inc.; *U.S. Public*, pg. 1733
PRUDENTIAL RETIREMENT INSURANCE AND ANNUITY COMPANY—See Prudential Financial, Inc.; *U.S. Public*, pg. 1733
PRUDENTIAL SEGUROS MEXICO, S.A.—See Prudential Financial, Inc.; *U.S. Public*, pg. 1732
PRUDENTIAL SEGUROS, S.A.—See Prudential Financial, Inc.; *U.S. Public*, pg. 1733
PRUDENTIAL SERVICIOS, S. DE R.L. DE C.V.—See Prudential Financial, Inc.; *U.S. Public*, pg. 1732
PRUDENTIAL STAFF PENSIONS LIMITED—See M&G Plc; *Int'l*, pg. 4612
PRUDENTIAL SUGAR CORPORATION LIMITED; *Int'l*, pg. 6009
PRUDENTIAL TRUST COMPANY—See Prudential Financial, Inc.; *U.S. Public*, pg. 1733
PRUDENTIAL UTAH REAL ESTATE; *U.S. Private*, pg. 3296
PRUDENTIAL VIETNAM ASSURANCE PRIVATE LIMITED—See Prudential plc; *Int'l*, pg. 6009
PRUDENTIAL WOODMONT REALTY INC; *U.S. Private*, pg. 3296
PRUDENT PUBLISHING COMPANY, INC.; *U.S. Private*, pg. 3295
PRUDENT TECHNOLOGIES INC.; *U.S. Private*, pg. 3295
PRUDEO PARTNERS L.L.C.—See Perigon Wealth Management LLC; *U.S. Private*, pg. 3150
PRUDSYS AG—See Fujitsu Limited; *Int'l*, pg. 2837
PRUEFINSTITUT HANSECONTROL GMBH—See Otto GmbH & Co. KG; *Int'l*, pg. 5663
PRUESLER & ASSOCIATES INC.; *U.S. Private*, pg. 3296
PRUETT FOREST PRODUCTS INC.; *U.S. Private*, pg. 3296
PRUFTECHNIK DIETER BUSCH GMBH—See Fortive Corporation; *U.S. Public*, pg. 871
PRUFZENTRUM BOXBERG GMBH—See Robert Bosch GmbH; *Int'l*, pg. 6361
PRUGEN, INC.; *U.S. Private*, pg. 3296
PRUITTS FOOD INC.; *U.S. Private*, pg. 3296
PRUKSA HOLDING PUBLIC COMPANY LIMITED; *Int'l*, pg. 6009
PRUKSA INDIA HOUSING PRIVATE LIMITED—See Pruksa Real Estate Public Company Limited; *Int'l*, pg. 6010

PRUKSA OVERSEAS COMPANY LIMITED—See Pruksa Holding Public Company Limited; *Int'l*, pg. 6010
PRUKSA REAL ESTATE PUBLIC COMPANY LIMITED - PS PRECAST FACTORY—See Pruksa Real Estate Public Company Limited; *Int'l*, pg. 6010
PRUKSA REAL ESTATE PUBLIC COMPANY LIMITED; *Int'l*, pg. 6010
PRUMER REISEBURO TUCKS INH. M.A.T. GMBH—See Metropolitan European Transport Limited; *Int'l*, pg. 4864
PRUMO LOGISTICA S.A.—See EIG Global Energy Partners, LLC; *U.S. Private*, pg. 1347
PRUMSTAV A.S.—See VINCI S.A.; *Int'l*, pg. 8231
PRUM-TURENWERK GMBH—See ACS, Actividades de Construccion y Servicios, S.A.; *Int'l*, pg. 114
PRU-ONE INC.; *U.S. Private*, pg. 3295
PRUSS ARMATUREN AG—See Certina Holding AG; *Int'l*, pg. 1423
PRUTEX NYLON CO., LTD.—See Zhe Jiang Taihua New Material Co., Ltd.; *Int'l*, pg. 8648
PRVA GROUP PLC; *Int'l*, pg. 6010
PR VALLEY VIEW LLC—See Pennsylvania Real Estate Investment Trust; *U.S. Public*, pg. 1663
PRVA STAMBENA STEDIONICA DD—See UniCredit S.p.A.; *Int'l*, pg. 8040
PRVA STRATEGICKA AS; *Int'l*, pg. 6010
PR VIEWMONT LLC—See Pennsylvania Real Estate Investment Trust; *U.S. Public*, pg. 1663
PRVI PARTIZAN EMO A.D.; *Int'l*, pg. 6010
PRVNI MOSTECKA A.S.—See Energeticky a Prumyslovy Holding, a.s.; *Int'l*, pg. 2420
PR WASHINGTON CROWN LIMITED PARTNERSHIP—See Pennsylvania Real Estate Investment Trust; *U.S. Public*, pg. 1663
PRW ASSOCIATES INSURANCE AGENCY, INC.—See Aon plc; *Int'l*, pg. 497
PR WIREGRASS COMMONS LLC—See Pennsylvania Real Estate Investment Trust; *U.S. Public*, pg. 1664
PRWT SERVICES, INC.; *U.S. Private*, pg. 3296
PR WYOMING VALLEY LIMITED PARTNERSHIP—See Pennsylvania Real Estate Investment Trust; *U.S. Public*, pg. 1664
PRXDIGITAL; *U.S. Private*, pg. 3296
PRYCE CORPORATION; *Int'l*, pg. 6010
PRYDA AUSTRALIA—See Illinois Tool Works Inc.; *U.S. Public*, pg. 1110
PRYKARPATTYAOBLENERGO PJSC; *Int'l*, pg. 6010
PRYM CONSUMER CANADA INC.—See William Prym GmbH & Co. KG; *Int'l*, pg. 8413
PRYM CONSUMER FINLAND OY—See William Prym GmbH & Co. KG; *Int'l*, pg. 8413
PRYM CONSUMER GMBH & CO. KG—See William Prym GmbH & Co. KG; *Int'l*, pg. 8413
PRYM CONSUMER MALAYSIA SDN. BHD.—See William Prym GmbH & Co. KG; *Int'l*, pg. 8413
PRYM CONSUMER USA—See William Prym GmbH & Co. KG; *Int'l*, pg. 8413
PRYM FASHION AMERICAS, LLC—See William Prym GmbH & Co. KG; *Int'l*, pg. 8413
PRYM FASHION ASIA PACIFIC & CO.—See William Prym GmbH & Co. KG; *Int'l*, pg. 8413
PRYM FASHION GMBH & CO. KG—See William Prym GmbH & Co. KG; *Int'l*, pg. 8413
PRYM FASHION INC.—See William Prym GmbH & Co. KG; *Int'l*, pg. 8413
PRYM INOVAN GMBH & CO. KG—See William Prym GmbH & Co. KG; *Int'l*, pg. 8413
PRYM INTIMATES EUROPE LTD.—See William Prym GmbH & Co. KG; *Int'l*, pg. 8413
PRYM MODA GMBH—See William Prym GmbH & Co. KG; *Int'l*, pg. 8414
PRYM NEWEY (HK) LTD—See William Prym GmbH & Co. KG; *Int'l*, pg. 8414
PRYMUS S.A.; *Int'l*, pg. 6010
PRYOR CHEMICAL COMPANY—See LSB Industries, Inc.; *U.S. Public*, pg. 1344
PRYOR GIGGEY CO., INC.; *U.S. Private*, pg. 3296
PRYSM GENERAL INSURANCE INC.—See iA Financial Corporation Inc.; *Int'l*, pg. 3567
PRYSMIAN AUSTRALIA PTY. LTD.—See Prysmian S.p.A.; *Int'l*, pg. 6012
PRYSMIAN CABLE HOLDING B.V.—See Prysmian S.p.A.; *Int'l*, pg. 6012
PRYSMIAN CABLES AND SYSTEMS INTERNATIONAL LTD.—See Prysmian S.p.A.; *Int'l*, pg. 6012
PRYSMIAN CABLES ASIA-PACIFIC PTE LTD.—See Prysmian S.p.A.; *Int'l*, pg. 6012
PRYSMIAN CABLES ET SYSTEMES FRANCE S.A.S—See Prysmian S.p.A.; *Int'l*, pg. 6012
PRYSMIAN CABLES ET SYSTEMES FRANCE S.A.S.—See Prysmian S.p.A.; *Int'l*, pg. 6012
PRYSMIAN CABLE (SHANGHAI) CO., LTD.—See Prysmian S.p.A.; *Int'l*, pg. 6012
PRYSMIAN CABLES LIMITED—See Prysmian S.p.A.; *Int'l*, pg. 6012
PRYSMIAN CABLES & SYSTEMS B.V.—See Prysmian S.p.A.; *Int'l*, pg. 6012
PRYSMIAN CABLES & SYSTEMS LIMITED—See Prysmian S.p.A.; *Int'l*, pg. 6012

PRYSTUP PACKAGING PRODUCTS

PRYSMIAN CABLES & SYSTEMS OY—See Prysmian S.p.A.; *Int'l*, pg. 6012
PRYSMIAN CABLES & SYSTEMS S.A.—See Prysmian S.p.A.; *Int'l*, pg. 6012
PRYSMIAN CABLES Y SISTEMAS S.A.—See Prysmian S.p.A.; *Int'l*, pg. 6012
PRYSMIAN CABLE SYSTEMS PTE. LTD.—See Prysmian S.p.A.; *Int'l*, pg. 6012
PRYSMIAN CABLE SYSTEMS PTE LTD.—See Prysmian S.p.A.; *Int'l*, pg. 6012
PRYSMIAN CABLURI SI SISTEME S.A.—See Prysmian S.p.A.; *Int'l*, pg. 6012
PRYSMIAN CAVI E SISTEMI ENERGIA S.R.L.—See Prysmian S.p.A.; *Int'l*, pg. 6012
PRYSMIAN CAVI E SISTEMI ITALIA S.R.L.—See Prysmian S.p.A.; *Int'l*, pg. 6012
PRYSMIAN CAVI E SISTEMI TELECOM S.R.L.—See Prysmian S.p.A.; *Int'l*, pg. 6013
PRYSMIAN COMMUNICATIONS CABLES & SYSTEMS USA, LLC—See Prysmian S.p.A.; *Int'l*, pg. 6013
PRYSMIAN (DUTCH) HOLDINGS B.V.—See Prysmian S.p.A.; *Int'l*, pg. 6012
PRYSMIAN ELECTRONICS S.R.L.—See Prysmian S.p.A.; *Int'l*, pg. 6013
PRYSMIAN ENERGIA CABLES Y SISTEMAS DE ARGENTINA S. A.—See Prysmian S.p.A.; *Int'l*, pg. 6012
PRYSMIAN ENERGIA CABOS E SISTEMAS DO BRASIL S.A.—See Prysmian S.p.A.; *Int'l*, pg. 6013
PRYSMIAN ENERGIE CABLES ET SYSTEMES FRANCE S.A.—See Prysmian S.p.A.; *Int'l*, pg. 6012
PRYSMIAN GROUP BALTICS AS—See Prysmian S.p.A.; *Int'l*, pg. 6012
PRYSMIAN GROUP DENMARK A/S—See Prysmian S.p.A.; *Int'l*, pg. 6013
PRYSMIAN GROUP FINLAND OY—See Prysmian S.p.A.; *Int'l*, pg. 6013
PRYSMIAN GROUP NORGE AS—See Prysmian S.p.A.; *Int'l*, pg. 6013
PRYSMIAN GROUP SVERIGE AB—See Prysmian S.p.A.; *Int'l*, pg. 6013
PRYSMIAN HONG KONG HOLDING LTD.—See Prysmian S.p.A.; *Int'l*, pg. 6013
PRYSMIAN KABEL UND SYSTEME GMBH—See Prysmian S.p.A.; *Int'l*, pg. 6013
PRYSMIAN KABELY S.R.O.—See Prysmian S.p.A.; *Int'l*, pg. 6013
PRYSMIAN KABLER OG SYSTMER AS—See Prysmian S.p.A.; *Int'l*, pg. 6013
PRYSMIAN KABLO S.R.O—See Prysmian S.p.A.; *Int'l*, pg. 6013
PRYSMIAN METALS LIMITED—See Prysmian S.p.A.; *Int'l*, pg. 6012
PRYSMIAN MKM MAGYAR KABEL MUVEK KFT—See Prysmian S.p.A.; *Int'l*, pg. 6013
PRYSMIAN OEKW GMBH—See Prysmian S.p.A.; *Int'l*, pg. 6013
PRYSMIAN POWER CABLES & SYSTEMS AUSTRALIA PTY. LIMITED—See Prysmian S.p.A.; *Int'l*, pg. 6013
PRYSMIAN POWER CABLES & SYSTEMS-HIGH VOLTAGE SYSTEMS & INSTALLATION DIVISION—See Prysmian S.p.A.; *Int'l*, pg. 6013
PRYSMIAN POWER CABLES & SYSTEMS NEW ZEALAND LTD.—See Prysmian S.p.A.; *Int'l*, pg. 6013
PRYSMIAN POWER CABLES & SYSTEMS - NORTH AMERICA—See Prysmian S.p.A.; *Int'l*, pg. 6013
PRYSMIAN POWER CABLES & SYSTEMS USA, LLC—See Prysmian S.p.A.; *Int'l*, pg. 6013
PRYSMIAN POWER CABLES & SYSTEMS USA, LLC—See Prysmian S.p.A.; *Int'l*, pg. 6013
PRYSMIAN POWERLINK S.R.L.—See Prysmian S.p.A.; *Int'l*, pg. 6013
PRYSMIAN S.P.A.; *Int'l*, pg. 6010
PRYSMIAN TELECOM CABLES AND SYSTEMS UK LTD.—See Prysmian S.p.A.; *Int'l*, pg. 6012
PRYSMIAN TELECOM CABLES & SYSTEMS AUSTRALIA PTY LTD.—See Prysmian S.p.A.; *Int'l*, pg. 6013
PRYSMIAN TIANJIN CABLES CO. LTD.—See Prysmian S.p.A.; *Int'l*, pg. 6013
PRYSMIAN TREASURY S.R.L.—See Prysmian S.p.A.; *Int'l*, pg. 6013
PRYSMIAN WUXI CABLE CO. LTD.—See Prysmian S.p.A.; *Int'l*, pg. 6013
PRYSM, INC.; *U.S. Private*, pg. 3296
PRYSTUP PACKAGING PRODUCTS; *U.S. Private*, pg. 3296
PRZEDSIEBIORSTWO BUDOWNICTWA OGOLNEGO I USLUG TECHNICZNYCH SLASK SP. Z O.O—See STRABAG SE; *Int'l*, pg. 7231
PRZEDSIEBIORSTWO BUDOWY KOPALN PEBEKA S.A.—See KGHM Polska Miedz S.A.; *Int'l*, pg. 4149
PRZEDSIEBIORSTWO BUDOWY SZYBOW S.A.—See Jastrzebska Spolka Weglowa S.A.; *Int'l*, pg. 3913
PRZEDSIEBIORSTWO EKSPLOATACJI ULIC I MOSTOW SP. Z O.O.—See Trakcja PRKii S.A.; *Int'l*, pg. 7891
PRZEDSIEBIORSTWO ENERGETYKI CIEPLNEJ - GOZDNICA SP. Z O.O.—See ENEA S.A.; *Int'l*, pg. 2410
PRZEDSIEBIORSTWO ENERGETYKI CIEPLNEJ SP. Z O.O.—See Polskie Gornictwo Naftowe i Gazownictwo S.A.; *Int'l*, pg. 5912

PRZEDSIEBIORSTWO ENERGETYKI CIEPLNEJ W BAR-LINKU SP. Z O.O.—See E.ON SE; *Int'l*, pg. 2259
PRZEDSIEBIORSTWO FARMACEUTYCZNE JELFA SA—See Bausch Health Companies Inc.; *Int'l*, pg. 898
PRZEDSIEBIORSTWO GORNICZE SILESIA SP. Z O.O.—See Energeticky a Prumyslovy Holding, a.s.; *Int'l*, pg. 2420
PRZEDSIEBIORSTWO GOSPODARKI WODNEJ I REKULTYWACJI S.A.—See Jastrzebska Spolka Weglowa S.A.; *Int'l*, pg. 3913
PRZEDSIEBIORSTWO HANDLU ZAGRANICZNEGO BALTONA S.A.; *Int'l*, pg. 6013
PRZEDSIEBIORSTWO HYDRAULIKI SILOWEJ HYDROTOR S.A.; *Int'l*, pg. 6013
PRZEDSIEBIORSTWO INWESTYCYJNO REMONTOWE REMWIL SP. Z O.O.—See Orlen S.A.; *Int'l*, pg. 5641
PRZEDSIEBIORSTWO INZYNIERSKIE CWIERTNIA SP. Z O.O.—See Tesgas S.A.; *Int'l*, pg. 7572
PRZEDSIEBIORSTWO PRODUKCYJNO HANDLOWE CONTO SP. Z O.O.—See Darling Ingredients Inc.; *U.S. Public*, pg. 634
PRZEDSIEBIORSTWO PRODUKCYJNO HANDLOWE KOMPAP S.A.; *Int'l*, pg. 6013
PRZEDSIEBIORSTWO PRODUKCYJNO-HANDLOWE "TOR-PAL" SPOLKA Z OGRANICZONA ODPOWIEDZIALNOSCIA—See International Paper Company; *U.S. Public*, pg. 1158
PRZEDSIEBIORSTWO PRODUKCYJNO-USLUGOWE ELEKTRO SP. Z O.O.—See Poludniowy Koncern Energetyczny S.A.; *Int'l*, pg. 5913
PRZEDSIEBIORSTWO PRZEMYSLU SPOZYWCZEGO PEPEES S.A.; *Int'l*, pg. 6014
PRZEDSIEBIORSTWO REMONTOWE PAK SERWIS SP. Z O.O.—See Zespol Elektrowni Patnow-Adamow-Konin S.A.; *Int'l*, pg. 8639
PRZEDSIEBIORSTWO ROBOT INZYNIERYJNYCH POLAQUA S.A.—See ACS, Actividades de Construccion y Servicios, S.A.; *Int'l*, pg. 111
PRZEDSIEBIORSTWO SWIADCZEN ZDROWOTNYCH I PROMOCJI ZDROWIA ELVITA-JAWORZNO III SP. Z O.O.—See Poludniowy Koncern Energetyczny S.A.; *Int'l*, pg. 5913
PRZEDSIEBIORSTWO USLUG REMONTOWYCH ENERGETYKI - JAWORZNO III SP. Z O.O.—See Poludniowy Koncern Energetyczny S.A.; *Int'l*, pg. 5913
PRZEDSIEBIORSTWO USLUG SPECJALISTYCZNYCH I PROJEKTOWYCH CHEMEKO SP. Z O.O.—See Orlen S.A.; *Int'l*, pg. 5641
PRZEDSTAWICIELSTWO METSO—See Valmet Oyj; *Int'l*, pg. 8119
PSA AIRLINES, INC.—See American Airlines Group Inc.; *U.S. Public*, pg. 96
PSA AVTEC POWERTRAIN PRIVATE LTD.—See Stellantis N.V.; *Int'l*, pg. 7202
PSA BANK DEUTSCHLAND GMBH—See Banco Santander, S.A.; *Int'l*, pg. 826
PSA BANQUE FRANCE SA—See Banco Santander, S.A.; *Int'l*, pg. 826
PSA CORPORATION PTE LTD.; *Int'l*, pg. 6014
PSA DEWBERRY—See Dewberry LLC; *U.S. Private*, pg. 1219
PSA FINANCE ARGENTINA COMPANIA FINANCIERA SA—See Banco Bilbao Vizcaya Argentaria, S.A.; *Int'l*, pg. 818
PSA FINANCE BELUX S.A—See Stellantis N.V.; *Int'l*, pg. 7201
PSA FINANCE CESKA REPUBLIKA S.R.O.—See Stellantis N.V.; *Int'l*, pg. 7201
PSA FINANCE NEDERLAND B.V.—See Stellantis N.V.; *Int'l*, pg. 7201
PSA FINANCE POLSKA SP. Z O.O.—See Banco Santander, S.A.; *Int'l*, pg. 826
PSA FINANCE SUISSE S.A.—See Stellantis N.V.; *Int'l*, pg. 7201
PSA FINANCE UK LIMITED—See Banco Santander, S.A.; *Int'l*, pg. 826
P.S.A. FINANCIAL ADVISORS, INC.—See PSA Holdings, Inc.; *U.S. Private*, pg. 3296
P.S.A. FINANCIAL CENTER, INC.—See PSA Holdings, Inc.; *U.S. Private*, pg. 3297
PSA FINANCIAL D.O.O.—See Stellantis N.V.; *Int'l*, pg. 7201
PSA FINANCIAL HOLDING B.V.—See Stellantis N.V.; *Int'l*, pg. 7201
P.S.A. FINANCIAL, INC.—See PSA Holdings, Inc.; *U.S. Private*, pg. 3296
PSAGOT OFEK INVESTMENT HOUSE LTD.—See Apax Partners LLP; *Int'l*, pg. 505
PSA HOLDINGS, INC.; *U.S. Private*, pg. 3296
P.S.A. INSURANCE, INC.—See PSA Holdings, Inc.; *U.S. Private*, pg. 3297
PSA INSURANCE SOLUTIONS LTD.—See Stellantis N.V.; *Int'l*, pg. 7202
PSA INTERNATIONAL PTE LTD.—See Temasek Holdings (Private) Limited; *Int'l*, pg. 7549
PSA INTERNATIONAL S.A.—See Stellantis N.V.; *Int'l*, pg. 7202
PSA MARINE (PTE) LTD—See PSA Corporation Pte Ltd.; *Int'l*, pg. 6014

PSA MASCHINENBAU GMBH—See William Prym GmbH & Co. KG; *Int'l*, pg. 8413
PSA PEUGEOT CITROEN AUTOMOBILES ESPANA—See Stellantis N.V.; *Int'l*, pg. 7203
PSA PEUGEOT CITROEN—See Stellantis N.V.; *Int'l*, pg. 7202
PSA PEUGEOT CITROEN—See Stellantis N.V.; *Int'l*, pg. 7203
PSA PEUGEOT CITROEN—See Stellantis N.V.; *Int'l*, pg. 7203
PSA PEUGEOT CITROEN—See Stellantis N.V.; *Int'l*, pg. 7202
PSA RETAIL AUSTRIA GMBH—See Stellantis N.V.; *Int'l*, pg. 7202
PSA RETAIL GMBH—See Stellantis N.V.; *Int'l*, pg. 7202
PSA RETAIL RENT POLAND SP. Z O.O.—See Stellantis N.V.; *Int'l*, pg. 7202
PSA TRANSPORT LTD.—See OT Logistics S.A.; *Int'l*, pg. 5656
PSA WHOLESALE LTD—See Stellantis N.V.; *Int'l*, pg. 7201
PSA WORLDWIDE CORP.—See Dry Fly Capital LLC; *U.S. Private*, pg. 1280
PSB CO.—See White Castle System, Inc.; *U.S. Private*, pg. 4508
PS BEVERAGE LTD.—See Sapporo Holdings Limited; *Int'l*, pg. 6573
PSB GMBH—See Bechtle AG; *Int'l*, pg. 938
PSB HOLDING CORP.—See Summit Financial Group, Inc.; *U.S. Public*, pg. 1959
PSB HOLDINGS, INC.; *U.S. Public*, pg. 1734
PSB INDUSTRIES SA; *Int'l*, pg. 6014
PSB MANAGEMENT CONSULTING (SHANGHAI) CO. LTD.—See TUV SUD AG; *Int'l*, pg. 7984
PSB TECHNOLOGIES PTE LTD—See Doerfer Corporation; *U.S. Private*, pg. 1253
PS BUSINESS PARKS, INC.—See Blackstone Inc.; *U.S. Public*, pg. 356
PSC COASTWIDE NEWCASTLE PTY LTD—See PSC Insurance Group Limited; *Int'l*, pg. 6016
PSC COMMUNITY SERVICES INC; *U.S. Private*, pg. 3297
PSC CONNECT LIFE NZ LTD.—See PSC Insurance Group Limited; *Int'l*, pg. 6016
PSC CONNECT NZ LTD—See PSC Insurance Group Limited; *Int'l*, pg. 6016
PSC CORPORATION LTD.; *Int'l*, pg. 6015
PSC ENVIRONMENTAL SERVICES, LLC—See Waste Management, Inc.; *U.S. Public*, pg. 2332
PSC FABRICATING, INC—See PMC Capital Partners, LLC; *U.S. Private*, pg. 3218
PSC FINANCIAL, LLC—See Emergent Capital, Inc.; *U.S. Private*, pg. 1381
PSC FREYSSINET (S) PTE LTD—See VINCI S.A.; *Int'l*, pg. 8233
PSC GROUP, LLC—See Netrix LLC; *U.S. Private*, pg. 2888
PSC GROUP LLC.—See Aurora Capital Group, LLC; *U.S. Private*, pg. 394
PSC GROUP LLC.—See The Jordan Company, L.P.; *U.S. Private*, pg. 4061
PSC GROUP S.A.L.—See WAMGROUP S.p.A.; *Int'l*, pg. 8338
PSCH, INC.; *U.S. Private*, pg. 3297
P. SCHOENFELD ASSET MANAGEMENT LLC; *U.S. Private*, pg. 3060
PSC INDUSTRIAL SERVICES, INC.—See Littlejohn & Co., LLC; *U.S. Private*, pg. 2471
PSC INDUSTRIES, INC. - GLASRITE DIVISION—See PMC Capital Partners, LLC; *U.S. Private*, pg. 3218
PSC INDUSTRIES, INC. - GRAHAM HYDRAULICS DIVISION—See PMC Capital Partners, LLC; *U.S. Private*, pg. 3218
PSC INDUSTRIES, INC.—See PMC Capital Partners, LLC; *U.S. Private*, pg. 3218
PSC INSURANCE BROKERS ADELAIDE PTY LTD—See PSC Insurance Group Limited; *Int'l*, pg. 6016
PSC INSURANCE BROKERS (BRISBANE) PTY LTD—See PSC Insurance Group Limited; *Int'l*, pg. 6016
PSC INSURANCE BROKERS (DARWIN) PTY LTD—See PSC Insurance Group Limited; *Int'l*, pg. 6016
PSC INSURANCE BROKERS (WAGGA) PTY LTD—See PSC Insurance Group Limited; *Int'l*, pg. 6016
PSC INSURANCE GROUP LIMITED; *Int'l*, pg. 6015
PSC INVESTMENT PTE LTD—See PSC Corporation Ltd.; *Int'l*, pg. 6015
PSC, LLC—See Littlejohn & Co., LLC; *U.S. Private*, pg. 2471
PSC MCKENNA HAMPTON INSURANCE BROKERS PTY LTD—See PSC Insurance Group Limited; *Int'l*, pg. 6016
PSC METALS - AKRON, LLC—See Icahn Enterprises L.P.; *U.S. Public*, pg. 1084
PSC METALS - ALIQUIPPA, LLC—See Icahn Enterprises L.P.; *U.S. Public*, pg. 1084
PSC METALS - ALLIANCE, LLC—See Icahn Enterprises L.P.; *U.S. Public*, pg. 1084
PSC METALS - CAW, LLC—See Icahn Enterprises L.P.; *U.S. Public*, pg. 1085

PSC METALS - ELYRIA, LLC—See Icahn Enterprises L.P.; *U.S. Public*, pg. 1085
PSC METALS - GARN, LLC—See Icahn Enterprises L.P.; *U.S. Public*, pg. 1085
PSC METALS INC.—See Icahn Enterprises L.P.; *U.S. Public*, pg. 1084
PSC METALS INC.—See Icahn Enterprises L.P.; *U.S. Public*, pg. 1085
PSC METALS - JOYCE, LLC—See Icahn Enterprises L.P.; *U.S. Public*, pg. 1085
PSC METALS - KNOXVILLE, LLC—See Icahn Enterprises L.P.; *U.S. Public*, pg. 1085
PSC METALS MASSILLON, LLC—See Icahn Enterprises L.P.; *U.S. Public*, pg. 1085
PSC METALS - METALLICS, LLC—See Icahn Enterprises L.P.; *U.S. Public*, pg. 1085
PSC METALS - MITCO, LLC—See Icahn Enterprises L.P.; *U.S. Public*, pg. 1085
PSC METALS—See Icahn Enterprises L.P.; *U.S. Public*, pg. 1084
PSC METALS—See Icahn Enterprises L.P.; *U.S. Public*, pg. 1084
PSC METALS - WOOSTER, LLC—See Icahn Enterprises L.P.; *U.S. Public*, pg. 1085
PSC NATIONAL FRANCHISE INSURANCE BROKERS PTY LTD—See PSC Insurance Group Limited; *Int'l*, pg. 6016
PS CONSTRUCTION CO.,LTD.—See Mitsubishi Corporation; *Int'l*, pg. 4942
PSC PRINT SERVICE CENTER GMBH—See Bertelsmann SE & Co. KGaA; *Int'l*, pg. 995
PSC "PROMINVESTBANK"—See VEB.RF; *Int'l*, pg. 8143
PSC "VEROPHARM"—See Abbott Laboratories; *U.S. Public*, pg. 20
PSC RELIANCE FRANCHISE PARTNERS PTY LTD—See PSC Insurance Group Limited; *Int'l*, pg. 6016
PSC TAIF; *Int'l*, pg. 6016
PSCU FINANCIAL SERVICES, INC.; *U.S. Private*, pg. 3297
PSD CODAX LIMITED—See Dover Corporation; *U.S. Public*, pg. 682
PS DEVICE & MATERIAL INC.—See Sato shoji Corporation; *Int'l*, pg. 6586
PSD GROUP GMBH—See PSD Group plc; *Int'l*, pg. 6016
PSD GROUP LIMITED—See PSD Group plc; *Int'l*, pg. 6016
PSD GROUP PLC; *Int'l*, pg. 6016
PSD GROUP SA—See PSD Group plc; *Int'l*, pg. 6016
PSE-CENTRUM SP. Z O.O.—See PGE Polska Grupa Energetyczna S.A.; *Int'l*, pg. 5837
PSE-ELECTRA S.A.—See PGE Polska Grupa Energetyczna S.A.; *Int'l*, pg. 5837
PSEG ENERGY HOLDINGS LLC—See Public Service Enterprise Group Incorporated; *U.S. Public*, pg. 1735
PSEG ENERGY RESOURCES & TRADE LLC—See Public Service Enterprise Group Incorporated; *U.S. Public*, pg. 1736
PSEG GLOBAL LLC—See Public Service Enterprise Group Incorporated; *U.S. Public*, pg. 1736
PSEG POWER FOSSIL LLC—See Public Service Enterprise Group Incorporated; *U.S. Public*, pg. 1736
PSEG POWER LLC—See Public Service Enterprise Group Incorporated; *U.S. Public*, pg. 1736
PSEG RESOURCES LLC—See Public Service Enterprise Group Incorporated; *U.S. Public*, pg. 1736
PSEG SERVICES CORP.—See Public Service Enterprise Group Incorporated; *U.S. Public*, pg. 1736
PSE-INFO SP. Z O.O.—See PGE Polska Grupa Energetyczna S.A.; *Int'l*, pg. 5837
PSE-OPERATOR SA—See PGE Polska Grupa Energetyczna S.A.; *Int'l*, pg. 5837
PSE-POLNOC SP. Z O.O.—See PGE Polska Grupa Energetyczna S.A.; *Int'l*, pg. 5837
PSE-POLUDNIE SP. Z O.O.—See PGE Polska Grupa Energetyczna S.A.; *Int'l*, pg. 5837
P-SERV PTE. LTD.—See Kelly Services, Inc.; *U.S. Public*, pg. 1274
PSE-SERWIS SP. Z.O.O.—See PGE Polska Grupa Energetyczna S.A.; *Int'l*, pg. 5837
PS EVENT GMBH—See ProSiebenSat.1 Media SE; *Int'l*, pg. 6000
PSE-WSCHOD SP. Z.O.O.—See PGE Polska Grupa Energetyczna S.A.; *Int'l*, pg. 5837
PSE-ZACHOD SP. Z.O.O.—See PGE Polska Grupa Energetyczna S.A.; *Int'l*, pg. 5837
PSF INDUSTRIES INC.; *U.S. Private*, pg. 3297
PSFINTERACTIVE S.R.L.—See Poligrafica S. Faustino S.p.A.; *Int'l*, pg. 5909
PSFK LLC; *U.S. Private*, pg. 3297
PSF MOSTINZHENERING JSC—See Trace Group Hold PLC; *Int'l*, pg. 7886
PSG CALIFORNIA LLC—See Dover Corporation; *U.S. Public*, pg. 682
PSG CO., LTD.—See Honda Motor Co., Ltd.; *Int'l*, pg. 3464
PSG CORPORATE SERVICES (PTY) LTD—See PSG Group Limited; *Int'l*, pg. 6017
PSG ENERGY LIMITED—See Security Research Group plc; *Int'l*, pg. 6677

COMPANY NAME INDEX

PSG EQUITY L.L.C.; *U.S. Private*, pg. 3297
PSG FINANCIAL SERVICES LIMITED—See PSG Group Limited; *Int'l*, pg. 6016
PSG FRANCHISING LTD.—See Security Research Group plc; *Int'l*, pg. 6677
PSG GERMANY GMBH—See Dover Corporation; *U.S. Public*, pg. 682
PSG GROUP LIMITED; *Int'l*, pg. 6016
PSG KONSULT LIMITED—See PSG Group Limited; *Int'l*, pg. 6017
PS GROUP HOLDINGS LTD; *Int'l*, pg. 6014
PSH EXPRESS SDN. BHD.—See Pos Malaysia Berhad; *Int'l*, pg. 5936
PSH GROUP HOLDINGS, INC.; *U.S. Public*, pg. 1734
PS HOLDCO LLC—See OEP Capital Advisors, L.P.; *U.S. Private*, pg. 2999
P & S HOLDINGS CORPORATION—See PHINMA Corporation; *Int'l*, pg. 5848
PSHS ALPHA PARTNERS, LTD.—See Bain Capital, LP; *U.S. Private*, pg. 446
PSHS BETA PARTNERS, LTD.—See Bain Capital, LP; *U.S. Private*, pg. 446
PSIAG SCANDINAVIA AB—See PSI Software SE; *Int'l*, pg. 6017
PSI AG SCHWEIZ—See PSI Software SE; *Int'l*, pg. 6017
PSI AG—See PSI Software SE; *Int'l*, pg. 6017
PSI AUTOMOTIVE & INDUSTRY AUSTRIA GMBH—See PSI Software SE; *Int'l*, pg. 6017
PSI BUSING UND BUCHWALD GMBH—See PSI Software SE; *Int'l*, pg. 6017
PSICONTROL NV—See Tessenderlo Group NV; *Int'l*, pg. 7574
PSICONTROL SRL—See Tessenderlo Group NV; *Int'l*, pg. 7574
PSI ENERGY MARKETS GMBH—See PSI Software SE; *Int'l*, pg. 6017
PSI ENVIRONMENTAL SERVICES, INC.—See Waste Connections, Inc.; *Int'l*, pg. 8353
PSI ENVIRONMENTAL SYSTEMS, INC.—See Waste Connections, Inc.; *Int'l*, pg. 8353
PSI FLS FUZZY LOGIK & NEURO SYSTEME GMBH—See PSI Software SE; *Int'l*, pg. 6017
PSIGEN SOFTWARE, INC.—See Clearlake Capital Group, L.P.; *U.S. Private*, pg. 936
PSIGEN SOFTWARE, INC.—See TA Associates, Inc.; *U.S. Private*, pg. 3916
PSIGMA INVESTMENT MANAGEMENT LIMITED—See Punter Southall Group Limited; *Int'l*, pg. 6120
PSI GUYANA INC.—See Seaboard Corporation; *U.S. Public*, pg. 1850
PSI HEALTH SOLUTIONS, INC.; *U.S. Private*, pg. 3297
PSI HOLDING GROUP INC.—See RPG Group; *Int'l*, pg. 6415
PSI INCONTROL SDN. BHD.—See PSI Software SE; *Int'l*, pg. 6017
PSI INFORMATION TECHNOLOGY CO., LTD.—See PSI Software SE; *Int'l*, pg. 6017
PSI INTERNATIONAL, INC.; *U.S. Private*, pg. 3297
PSI JSC—See Trace Group Hold PLC; *Int'l*, pg. 7886
PSI LOGISTICS GMBH—See PSI Software SE; *Int'l*, pg. 6017
PSILOS GROUP MANAGERS, LLC; *U.S. Private*, pg. 3297
PSI METALS AUSTRIA GMBH—See PSI Software SE; *Int'l*, pg. 6017
PSI METALS BELGIUM NV—See PSI Software SE; *Int'l*, pg. 6017
PSI METALS BRAZIL LTDA.—See PSI Software SE; *Int'l*, pg. 6017
PSI METALS GMBH—See PSI Software SE; *Int'l*, pg. 6017
PSI METALS NON FERROUS GMBH—See PSI Software SE; *Int'l*, pg. 6017
PSI METALS NORTH AMERICA INC.—See PSI Software SE; *Int'l*, pg. 6017
PSI METALS UK LTD.—See PSI Software SE; *Int'l*, pg. 6017
PSI MINES & ROADS GMBH—See PSI Software SE; *Int'l*, pg. 6017
PSI MOLDED PLASTICS NEW HAMPSHIRE, INC.—See Gladstone Management Corporation; *U.S. Private*, pg. 1705
PSINAPSE TECHNOLOGY LTD.; *U.S. Private*, pg. 3297
PSINAPTIC INC.; *Int'l*, pg. 6017
PS INDEPENDENT TRUSTEES LIMITED—See Punter Southall Group Limited; *Int'l*, pg. 6120
PSI NEPLAN AG—See PSI Software SE; *Int'l*, pg. 6017
PS INTERNATIONAL GROUP LTD.; *Int'l*, pg. 6014
P.S. INTERNATIONAL INC; *U.S. Private*, pg. 3061
PS INTERNATIONAL, LLC—See Seaboard Corporation; *U.S. Public*, pg. 1850
P&S INVESTMENT COMPANY INC.; *U.S. Private*, pg. 3059
PSION EUROPE S.A.S.—See Zebra Technologies Corporation; *U.S. Public*, pg. 2401
PSION MOBILE GROUP, S.L.—See Zebra Technologies Corporation; *U.S. Public*, pg. 2401
PSION N.V.—See Zebra Technologies Corporation; *U.S. Public*, pg. 2401

PSION SYSTEMS INC.—See Zebra Technologies Corporation; *U.S. Public*, pg. 2401
PSION SYSTEMS INDIA PRIVATE LIMITED—See Zebra Technologies Corporation; *U.S. Public*, pg. 2401
PSION TEKLOGIX DO BRASIL LTDA—See Zebra Technologies Corporation; *U.S. Public*, pg. 2401
PSION TEKLOGIX, S.A. DE C.V.—See Zebra Technologies Corporation; *U.S. Public*, pg. 2401
PSIPENTA SOFTWARE SYSTEMS GMBH—See PSI Software SE; *Int'l*, pg. 6017
PSI POLSKA SP. Z O.O.—See PSI Software SE; *Int'l*, pg. 6017
PSI PREMIER SPECIALTIES, INC.; *U.S. Private*, pg. 3297
PSI PRODUCTION GMBH—See PSI Software SE; *Int'l*, pg. 6017
PSI PRODUCTS GMBH—See Enpro Inc.; *U.S. Public*, pg. 775
PSI PROFESSIONAL SERVICE INDUSTRIES INC; *U.S. Private*, pg. 3297
PSI REPAIR SERVICES, INC.—See Phillips Service Industries, Inc. (PSI); *U.S. Private*, pg. 3171
PSI SEMICON SERVICES—See Phillips Service Industries, Inc. (PSI); *U.S. Private*, pg. 3171
PSI SERVICES LLC—See Educational Testing Service Inc.; *U.S. Private*, pg. 1339
PSI SOFTWARE SE; *Int'l*, pg. 6017
PSI SYSTEMS, INC.—See Thoma Bravo, L.P.; *U.S. Private*, pg. 4154
PSI TECHNOLOGIES HOLDINGS, INC.—See Ayala Corporation; *Int'l*, pg. 774
PS IT INFRASTRUCTURE & SERVICES LTD.; *Int'l*, pg. 6014
PSI TRANSCOM GMBH—See PSI Software SE; *Int'l*, pg. 6017
PSI-USA INC—See United Internet AG; *Int'l*, pg. 8069
PSIVIDA SECURITIES CORPORATION—See EyePoint Pharmaceuticals, Inc.; *U.S. Public*, pg. 817
PSJ ACQUISITION, LLC—See Universal Health Services, Inc.; *U.S. Public*, pg. 2258
PS JAPAN CORP.—See Asahi Kasei Corporation; *Int'l*, pg. 596
PSJ FABRICATIONS LTD.—See John Wood Group PLC; *Int'l*, pg. 3983
PSK, INC.; *Int'l*, pg. 6017
PSK INC—See PSK, Inc.; *Int'l*, pg. 6017
PSKOVNEFTEPRODUKT LTD—See Surgutneftegas OAO; *Int'l*, pg. 7344
PSK SUPERMARKETS INC.; *U.S. Private*, pg. 3297
PSK TECH AMERICA INC—See PSK, Inc.; *Int'l*, pg. 6017
PSKW, LLC—See Genstar Capital, LLC; *U.S. Private*, pg. 1678
PSL A.S.—See ThyssenKrupp AG; *Int'l*, pg. 7725
PSL ENGINEERING PTE. LTD.—See Kridhan Infra Limited; *Int'l*, pg. 4301
PSL ENGINEERING PVT. LTD.—See Fedders Electric and Engineering Limited; *Int'l*, pg. 2630
PSL HOLDINGS LIMITED; *Int'l*, pg. 6017
PSL OF AMERICA INC.—See ThyssenKrupp AG; *Int'l*, pg. 7731
PSL WALZLAGER GMBH—See ThyssenKrupp AG; *Int'l*, pg. 7725
P & S MACAO COMMERCIAL OFFSHORE LTD.—See Suga International Holdings Limited; *Int'l*, pg. 7253
P & S MASONRY, INC.; *U.S. Private*, pg. 3058
PSM CELADA FASTENERS S.R.L.—See Bulten AB; *Int'l*, pg. 1214
PSM FASTENER CORPORATION—See Bulten AB; *Int'l*, pg. 1215
PSM FASTENERS AB—See Bulten AB; *Int'l*, pg. 1214
PSM FASTENERS (HONG KONG) LTD.—See Bulten AB; *Int'l*, pg. 1214
PSM FINANCIAL SERVICES, LLC—See Paychex, Inc.; *U.S. Public*, pg. 1655
PSM INSTRUMENTATION LTD.—See Alfa Laval AB; *Int'l*, pg. 312
PSM INTERNATIONAL FASTENERS LIMITED—See Bulten AB; *Int'l*, pg. 1215
PSM INTERNATIONAL HOLDINGS LTD.—See Bulten AB; *Int'l*, pg. 1214
PSM INTERNATIONAL LTD.—See Bulten AB; *Int'l*, pg. 1215
PSM, LLC—See Toyota Industries Corporation; *Int'l*, pg. 7869
PSM PERKAPALAN SDN BHD—See Malaysian Bulk Carriers Berhad; *Int'l*, pg. 4662
PSM S.P.A.—See Trevi Finanziaria Industriale SpA.; *Int'l*, pg. 7916
PSMT (JAMAICA), LTD.—See PriceSmart Inc.; *U.S. Public*, pg. 1716
PSN OVERSEAS HOLDING COMPANY LIMITED—See John Wood Group PLC; *Int'l*, pg. 3983
PSN PRODUCTION SERVICES NETWORK PHILIPPINES CORP.—See John Wood Group PLC; *Int'l*, pg. 3983
PSOMAGEN, INC.—See Macrogen Inc.; *Int'l*, pg. 4632
PSOMASFMG, LLC.—See Psomas; *U.S. Private*, pg. 3297
PSOMAS; *U.S. Private*, pg. 3297
PS ORANGECO, INC.—See Public Storage; *U.S. Public*, pg. 1736
PSP BRASIL—See ESPEC Corp.; *Int'l*, pg. 2505

PSP CAPITAL PARTNERS, LLC; *U.S. Private*, pg. 3297
P+S PFLASTER- UND STRASSENBAU GMBH—See L. Possehl & Co. mbH; *Int'l*, pg. 4384
PSP GROUP, LLC—See B. Riley Financial, Inc.; *U.S. Public*, pg. 261
PSP GROUP, LLC—See Irradiant Partners, LP; *U.S. Private*, pg. 2141
PSP GROUP SERVICES LTD.—See PSP Swiss Property Ltd.; *Int'l*, pg. 6018
PSP INDUSTRIES INC.—See The Herrick Corporation; *U.S. Private*, pg. 4052
PS PLUS PORTFOLIO SOFTWARE + CONSULTING GMBH—See Deutsche Bank Aktiengesellschaft; *Int'l*, pg. 2061
PSP MANAGEMENT LTD.—See PSP Swiss Property Ltd.; *Int'l*, pg. 6018
PS POSTSERVICEGESELLSCHAFT M.B.H.—See Osterreichische Post AG; *Int'l*, pg. 5654
PSP PROJECTS LIMITED; *Int'l*, pg. 6017
PSP PROPERTIES LTD.—See PSP Swiss Property Ltd.; *Int'l*, pg. 6018
PSP REAL ESTATE LTD.—See PSP Swiss Property Ltd.; *Int'l*, pg. 6018
PSPRINT LLC; *U.S. Private*, pg. 3297
P.S.P. SPECIALTIES PUBLIC COMPANY LIMITED; *Int'l*, pg. 5682
PSP STORES LLC—See B. Riley Financial, Inc.; *U.S. Public*, pg. 261
PSP STORES LLC—See Irradiant Partners, LP; *U.S. Private*, pg. 2141
PSP SWISS PROPERTY LTD.; *Int'l*, pg. 6018
PSQ-SOCIEDADE DE INVESTIMENTOS MOBILIARIOS E IMOBILIARIOS, LDA.—See Jeronimo Martins SGPS SA; *Int'l*, pg. 3931
P SQUARED RENEWABLES, INC.; *Int'l*, pg. 5681
PSR COMPANY INC.; *U.S. Private*, pg. 3298
PSR ENGINEERING SOLUTIONS D.O.O.—See RCM Technologies, Inc.; *U.S. Public*, pg. 1767
PSS BELGIUM NV—See Value Enhancement Partners B.V.; *Int'l*, pg. 8124
PSS COMMODITIES, S. DE R.L. DE C.V.—See Seaboard Corporation; *U.S. Public*, pg. 1850
PS&S INTEGRATED SERVICES; *U.S. Private*, pg. 3296
PSSI STADIUM CORPORATION—See Pittsburgh Steelers Sports Inc.; *U.S. Private*, pg. 3191
PSSST FILM GMBH—See Highlight Event & Entertainment AG; *Int'l*, pg. 3388
PSS WEST, INC.—See W.W. Grainger, Inc.; *U.S. Public*, pg. 2320
PST CLC, A.S.—See Mitsui-Soko Holdings Co., Ltd.; *Int'l*, pg. 4993
PS TEC CO., LTD.; *Int'l*, pg. 6014
PS TECHNOLOGIES, LLC—See Black Box Limited; *Int'l*, pg. 1058
P.S. TELEFONIJA A.D. BEOGRAD; *Int'l*, pg. 5682
PST HUANAN ELECTRONICS CO., LTD.—See nms Holdings Corporation; *Int'l*, pg. 5393
PST HUNGARY KFT.—See Mitsui-Soko Holdings Co., Ltd.; *Int'l*, pg. 4993
PST PRESS + SINTERTECHNIK SP.Z.O.O.—See BC Partners LLP; *Int'l*, pg. 923
PST PRESS SINTERTECNICA BRASIL LTDA—See BC Partners LLP; *Int'l*, pg. 923
P&S TRANSPORTATION, INC.; *U.S. Private*, pg. 3059
PST STOMIL SP Z O.O. W RYMANOWIE ZDROJU—See Sanockie Zaklady Przemyslu Gumowego Stomil Sanok S.A.; *Int'l*, pg. 6547
PSV CLAIMS BUREAU LTD.—See Stagecoach Group plc; *Int'l*, pg. 7163
PSV COMPANY S.A.; *Int'l*, pg. 6018
PSV HOLDINGS LIMITED; *Int'l*, pg. 6018
PSV SERVICES (PTY) LIMITED—See WPIL Limited; *Int'l*, pg. 8462
PSV ZAMBIA LIMITED—See WPIL Limited; *Int'l*, pg. 8462
PS YANDEX.MONEY LLC—See Yandex N.V.; *Int'l*, pg. 8559
PSYC CORPORATION; *U.S. Public*, pg. 1734
PSYCH ASSOCIATES OF MARYLAND, LLC—See Comprehensive Behavioral Health; *U.S. Public*, pg. 1002
PSYCHED WELLNESS LTD.; *Int'l*, pg. 6018
PSYCHEMEDICS CORPORATION; *U.S. Public*, pg. 1734
PSYCHIATRIC CENTERS AT SAN DIEGO, INC.—See MindPath Care Centers PLLC; *U.S. Private*, pg. 2740
PSYCHIATRY SERVICES OF OSCEOLA, LLC—See HCA Healthcare, Inc.; *U.S. Public*, pg. 1006
PSYCHOLOGICAL ASSESSMENT RESOURCES, INC.; *U.S. Private*, pg. 3298
PSYCHOLOGICAL SERVICES, INC.—See ABRY Partners, LLC; *U.S. Private*, pg. 43
PSYCHOLOGICAL SOFTWARE SOLUTIONS, INC.; *U.S. Private*, pg. 3298
PSYCHOLOGY PRESS—See Informa plc; *Int'l*, pg. 3693
PSYCHOLOGY TODAY—See Sussex Publishers, LLC; *U.S. Public*, pg. 3886
PSYCHOSOMATISCHE FACHKLINIK GENGENBACH GMBH—See MK-Kliniken AG; *Int'l*, pg. 5001
PSYCHOSOMATISCHE KLINIK—See Asklepios Kliniken GmbH & Co. KGaA; *Int'l*, pg. 624

PSYCHOLOGICAL SOFTWARE SOLUTIONS, INC.　　　　　　　　　　　　　　　　　　　　　　　　　　　CORPORATE AFFILIATIONS

PSYCHOTHERAPY.NET LLC—See Moelis Asset Management LP; *U.S. Private*, pg. 2764
PSYCHSOFT; *U.S. Private*, pg. 3298
PSYENCE BIOMEDICAL LTD.; *Int'l*, pg. 6018
PSYKEY, INC.; *Int'l*, pg. 6018
PT. 3M INDONESIA—See 3M Company; *U.S. Public*, pg. 8
PT. ABADI TAMBAH MULIA INTERNASIONAL—See Seven Bank Ltd.; *Int'l*, pg. 6731
PT. ABBOTT INDONESIA—See Abbott Laboratories; *U.S. Public*, pg. 20
PT. ABBOTT INDONESIA—See Abbott Laboratories; *U.S. Public*, pg. 20
PT. ABBOTT PRODUCTS INDONESIA—See Abbott Laboratories; *U.S. Public*, pg. 20
PT ABB SAKTI INDUSTRI—See ABB Ltd.; *Int'l*, pg. 56
PT ABERDEEN STANDARD INVESTMENT—See abrdn PLC; *Int'l*, pg. 69
PT ABHIMATA CITRA ABADI—See PT. Elang Mahkota Teknologi Tbk.; *Int'l*, pg. 6086
PT ABM INVESTAMA TBK.; *Int'l*, pg. 6018
PT ABN AMRO MANAJEMEN INVESTASI—See BNP Paribas SA; *Int'l*, pg. 1082
PT AB SINAR MAS MULTIFINANCE—See PT Sinar Mas Multiartha Tbk; *Int'l*, pg. 6074
PTAC 4 LESS INC.—See Mollenhour Gross LLC; *U.S. Private*, pg. 2767
P.T. ACCENTURE—See Accenture plc; *Int'l*, pg. 86
PT ACCRETECH INDONESIA—See Tokyo Seimitsu Co., Ltd.; *Int'l*, pg. 7795
PT ACE HARDWARE INDONESIA TBK.; *Int'l*, pg. 6018
PT ACE OLDFIELDS TBK; *Int'l*, pg. 6018
PT ACER INDONESIA—See Acer Incorporated; *Int'l*, pg. 99
PT ACEZ INSTRUMENTS INDONESIA—See Acez Instruments Pte. Ltd.; *Int'l*, pg. 102
PTA CORPORATION; *U.S. Private*, pg. 3298
P.T. ACRYL TEXTILE MILLS—See Toray Industries, Inc.; *Int'l*, pg. 7823
PT ACSET INDONUSA TBK.—See PT United Tractors Tbk; *Int'l*, pg. 6080
PT ACUATICO AIR INDONESIA—See Moya Holdings Asia Limited; *Int'l*, pg. 5060
PT ADANI GLOBAL—See Adani Enterprises Limited; *Int'l*, pg. 125
PT ADARO ENERGY INDONESIA TBK; *Int'l*, pg. 6019
PT ADARO INDONESIA—See PT Adaro Energy Indonesia Tbk; *Int'l*, pg. 6019
PT ADARO MINERALS INDONESIA TBK; *Int'l*, pg. 6019
PT ADHI KARYA (PERSERO) TBK - EPC DIVISION—See PT Adhi Karya (Persero) Tbk; *Int'l*, pg. 6019
PT ADHI KARYA (PERSERO) TBK - INTERNATIONAL DIVISION—See PT Adhi Karya (Persero) Tbk; *Int'l*, pg. 6019
PT ADHI KARYA (PERSERO) TBK; *Int'l*, pg. 6019
PT ADHI PERSADA REALTI—See PT Adhi Karya (Persero) Tbk; *Int'l*, pg. 6019
P.T. ADHYA TIRTA BATAM—See Sembcorp Industries Ltd.; *Int'l*, pg. 6702
PT ADIB COLD LOGISTIC—See PT Samudera Indonesia Tbk; *Int'l*, pg. 6069
P.T. ADIDAS INDONESIA LTD.—See adidas AG; *Int'l*, pg. 146
PT. ADIKARSA ALAM RESOURCES—See PT SMR UTAMA Tbk; *Int'l*, pg. 6075
PT ADIMITRA BARATAMA NUSANTARA—See PT TBS Energi Utama Tbk; *Int'l*, pg. 6077
PT ADIRA DINAMIKA MULTI FINANCE TBK—See Mitsubishi UFJ Financial Group, Inc.; *Int'l*, pg. 4970
PT ADI SARANA ARMADA TBK; *Int'l*, pg. 6019
PT ADI SARANA INVESTINDO—See PT Adi Sarana Armada Tbk; *Int'l*, pg. 6019
PT ADI SARANA LOGISTIK—See PT Adi Sarana Armada Tbk; *Int'l*, pg. 6019
PT ADMINISTRASI MEDIKA—See Perusahaan Perseroan Indonesia Tbk; *Int'l*, pg. 5821
P.T. ADSTARS MEDIA PARIWARA—See Geniee, Inc.; *Int'l*, pg. 2923
P.T. ADVANCED AGRI INDONESIA—See Advanced Holdings Ltd.; *Int'l*, pg. 159
P.T. ADVANEX PRECISION INDONESIA—See Advanex Inc.; *Int'l*, pg. 163
PT ADVANTECH INTERNATIONAL—See Advantech Co., Ltd.; *Int'l*, pg. 165
P.T. ADVICS INDONESIA—See AISIN Corporation; *Int'l*, pg. 251
PT. ADWAYS INDONESIA—See Adways Inc.; *Int'l*, pg. 169
PT. ADYA TOURS - INDONESIA—See Ebix Inc.; *U.S. Public*, pg. 710
PT AEROJASA CARGO—See PT Garuda Indonesia (Persero) Tbk; *Int'l*, pg. 6040
PT AERO SYSTEMS INDONESIA—See PT Garuda Indonesia (Persero) Tbk; *Int'l*, pg. 6040
PT AEROTRANS SERVICES INDONESIA—See PT Garuda Indonesia (Persero) Tbk; *Int'l*, pg. 6040
PT. AEROWISATA INTERNATIONAL—See PT Garuda Indonesia (Persero) Tbk; *Int'l*, pg. 6040
P.T. AERO WISATA—See PT Garuda Indonesia (Persero) Tbk; *Int'l*, pg. 6040
PT AESLER GRUP LNTERNASIONAL; *Int'l*, pg. 6019

PT. AETNA GLOBAL BENEFITS INDONESIA—See CVS Health Corporation; *U.S. Public*, pg. 616
PT. AETRA AIR JAKARTA—See Moya Holdings Asia Limited; *Int'l*, pg. 5060
PT. AETRA AIR TANGERANG—See Moya Holdings Asia Limited; *Int'l*, pg. 5060
PT. AFFINITY EQUITY PARTNERS INDONESIA—See Affinity Equity Partners (HK) Ltd.; *Int'l*, pg. 186
PT. AFP DWILESTARI—See Sinarmas Land Limited; *Int'l*, pg. 6936
P.T. AFRY INDONESIA—See AFRY AB; *Int'l*, pg. 194
PT AGRINUSA JAYA SANTOSA—See PT Japfa Comfeed Indonesia Tbk; *Int'l*, pg. 6049
PT AGRO BAHARI NUSANTARA TBK; *Int'l*, pg. 6019
P.T. AGRO DYNAMICS INDO—See PT Mark Dynamics Indonesia Tbk; *Int'l*, pg. 6054
PT AGRO HARAPAN LESTARI—See Carson Cumberbatch PLC; *Int'l*, pg. 1347
PT AGRO INDOMAS—See Carson Cumberbatch PLC; *Int'l*, pg. 1347
P.T. AGROVETA HUSADA DHARMA—See PT Kalbe Farma Tbk.; *Int'l*, pg. 6050
PT AGROWIYANA—See PT Bakrie Sumatera Plantations Tbk; *Int'l*, pg. 6025
PT AGRO YASA LESTARI; *Int'l*, pg. 6020
PT AGUS NUSA PENIDA—See PT Metropolitan Land Tbk; *Int'l*, pg. 6056
PT AHLSTROM INDONESIA—See Ahlstrom Capital Oy; *Int'l*, pg. 223
PT. AHLSTROM INDONESIA—See Bain Capital, LP; *U.S. Private*, pg. 429
P.T. AIA FINANCIAL—See AIA Group Limited; *Int'l*, pg. 227
P.T. AICA INDONESIA—See AICA Kogyo Company, Limited; *Int'l*, pg. 229
PT.AICA INDRIA—See AICA Kogyo Company, Limited; *Int'l*, pg. 229
PT. AICHI FORGING INDONESIA—See Aichi Steel Corporation; *Int'l*, pg. 230
PT. AIDA INDONESIA—See AIDA Engineering, Ltd.; *Int'l*, pg. 231
PT. AIDA RATTAN INDUSTRY—See PT Gema Grahasarana Tbk; *Int'l*, pg. 6040
PT. AIDA STAMPING TECHNOLOGY INDONESIA—See AIDA Engineering, Ltd.; *Int'l*, pg. 231
PT AIG INSURANCE INDONESIA—See American International Group, Inc.; *U.S. Public*, pg. 105
P.T. AIK MOH CHEMICALS INDONESIA—See BRENNTAG SE; *Int'l*, pg. 1149
PT AINO INDONESIA—See TIS Inc.; *Int'l*, pg. 7757
PT AIRASIA INDONESIA TBK; *Int'l*, pg. 6020
PT. AIR LIQUIDE INDONESIA - CILEGON FACTORY—See L'Air Liquide S.A.; *Int'l*, pg. 4375
P.T. AIR LIQUIDE INDONESIA—See L'Air Liquide S.A.; *Int'l*, pg. 4375
PT. AIR PASIFIK UTAMA—See PT Multipolar Tbk; *Int'l*, pg. 6060
PT AIR PRODUCTS INDONESIA—See Air Products & Chemicals, Inc.; *U.S. Public*, pg. 67
P.T. AIRSPAN NETWORKS INDONESIA—See Airspan Networks Holdings Inc.; *U.S. Public*, pg. 68
P.T. AISAN NASMOCO INDUSTRI—See Aisan Industry Co., Ltd.; *Int'l*, pg. 251
P.T. AISIN INDONESIA—See AISIN Corporation; *Int'l*, pg. 253
P.T. AJINOMOTO INDONESIA—See Ajinomoto Company, Inc.; *Int'l*, pg. 257
PT AKASHA WIRA INTERNATIONAL TBK; *Int'l*, pg. 6020
PT. AKEBONO BRAKE ASTRA INDONESIA—See Akebono Brake Industry Co., Ltd.; *Int'l*, pg. 262
PT AKR CORPORINDO TBK; *Int'l*, pg. 6020
PT AKR NIAGA INDONESIA—See PT AKR Corporindo Tbk; *Int'l*, pg. 6020
PT AKR SEA TRANSPORT—See PT AKR Corporindo Tbk; *Int'l*, pg. 6020
PT AKSARA GLOBAL DEVELOPMENT TBK; *Int'l*, pg. 6020
PT. AKS PRECISION BALL INDONESIA—See NSK Ltd.; *Int'l*, pg. 5480
PT. AKTIO EQUIPMENT INDONESIA—See Aktio Holdings Corporation; *Int'l*, pg. 267
P.T. AKURABENITAMA—See Kurabo Industries Ltd.; *Int'l*, pg. 4336
PT AKZO NOBEL CAR REFINISHES INDONESIA—See Akzo Nobel N.V.; *Int'l*, pg. 274
PT. ALAKASA EXTRUSINDO—See PT. Alakasa Industrindo, Tbk; *Int'l*, pg. 6084
PT. ALAKASA INDUSTRINDO, TBK; *Int'l*, pg. 6084
PT ALAM HIJAU LESTARI—See NV Multi Asia Sdn. Bhd.; *Int'l*, pg. 5497
PT ALAM SUBUR TIRTA KENCANA—See IMCD N.V.; *Int'l*, pg. 3622
PT ALAM SUTERA REALTY TBK; *Int'l*, pg. 6084
PT. ALAM TRI ABADI—See PT Adaro Energy Indonesia Tbk; *Int'l*, pg. 6019
PT ALERE HEALTH—See Abbott Laboratories; *U.S. Public*, pg. 19
PT ALFA ENERGI INVESTAMA TBK; *Int'l*, pg. 6020
PT. ALFA KURNIA FISH ENTERPRISE—See Maruha Nichiro Corporation; *Int'l*, pg. 4711

PT. ALFA LAVAL INDONESIA—See Alfa Laval AB; *Int'l*, pg. 312
PT. ALFA POLIMER INDONESIA—See PT Alkindo Naratama Tbk; *Int'l*, pg. 6020
PT. ALFA RETAILINDO TBK—See Carrefour SA; *Int'l*, pg. 1346
PT ALFA TRANS RAYA—See PT ABM Investama Tbk.; *Int'l*, pg. 6018
PT ALKINDO NARATAMA TBK; *Int'l*, pg. 6020
PT ALL COSMOS INDONESIA—See All Cosmos Bio-Tech Holding Corporation; *Int'l*, pg. 332
PT ALLIGHTSYKES—See Seven Group Holdings Limited; *Int'l*, pg. 6733
PT ALLO BANK INDONESIA TBK; *Int'l*, pg. 6020
PT ALMARON PERKASA—See PT. Lippo Karawaci Tbk; *Int'l*, pg. 6053
P.T. ALPEN AGUNG RAYA—See PT Mitra Keluarga Karyasehat Tbk; *Int'l*, pg. 6057
P.T. ALPHA AUSTENITE—See PT. Tira Austenite Tbk; *Int'l*, pg. 6089
PT. ALSOK BASS INDONESIA SECURITY SERVICES—See Sohgo Security Services Co., Ltd.; *Int'l*, pg. 7059
PT. ALSTOM TRANSPORT INDONESIA—See Alstom S.A.; *Int'l*, pg. 383
PT. ALTAVINDO INDONESIA; *Int'l*, pg. 6084
PT. ALTECH ASIA PACIFIC INDONESIA—See Altech Co., Ltd.; *Int'l*, pg. 388
PT. ALTECH—See Altech Co., Ltd.; *Int'l*, pg. 388
PT. ALUCOBOND FAR EAST INDONESIA—See Schweiter Technologies AG; *Int'l*, pg. 6645
PT ALUMINDO LIGHT METAL INDUSTRY TBK - GEDANGAN FACTORY—See PT Alumindo Light Metal Industry Tbk; *Int'l*, pg. 6020
PT ALUMINDO LIGHT METAL INDUSTRY TBK; *Int'l*, pg. 6020
PT ALVINY INDONESIA—See NIPPON CARBIDE INDUSTRIES CO., INC.; *Int'l*, pg. 5311
PT AMADEUS TECHNOLOGY INDONESIA—See Amadeus IT Group, S.A.; *Int'l*, pg. 407
PT AMALGAMATED TRICOR—See The Bank of East Asia, Limited; *Int'l*, pg. 7615
P.T. AMANO INDONESIA—See Amano Corporation; *Int'l*, pg. 411
P.T. AMANRESORTS INDONESIA—See DLF Limited; *Int'l*, pg. 2141
PT AMEC BERCA INDONESIA—See John Wood Group PLC; *Int'l*, pg. 3983
PT. AMEC FOSTER WHEELER INDONESIA—See John Wood Group PLC; *Int'l*, pg. 3983
PT AMERICAN STANDARD INDONESIA—See LIXIL Group Corporation; *Int'l*, pg. 4535
PT AMERTA INDAH OTSUKA—See Otsuka Holdings Co., Ltd.; *Int'l*, pg. 5661
PT AMMAN MINERAL INTERNASIONAL TBK; *Int'l*, pg. 6020
PT AMMAN MINERAL NUSA TENGGARA—See PT Medco Energi Internasional Tbk; *Int'l*, pg. 6055
PT AMOS UTAMA INDONESIA—See AMOS Group Limited; *Int'l*, pg. 430
PT AMTEK ENGINEERING BATAM—See Blackstone Inc.; *U.S. Public*, pg. 355
PT AMTEK PLASTIC BATAM—See Blackstone Inc.; *U.S. Public*, pg. 355
PT AMTEK PRECISION COMPONENTS BATAM—See Blackstone Inc.; *U.S. Public*, pg. 355
PT ANABATIC TECHNOLOGIES TBK; *Int'l*, pg. 6020
PT ANCORA INDONESIA RESOURCES TBK.; *Int'l*, pg. 6021
PT ANDALAN PERKASA ABADI TBK; *Int'l*, pg. 6021
PT ANDALAN SAKTI PRIMAINDO TBK; *Int'l*, pg. 6021
PT ANDIRA AGRO TBK; *Int'l*, pg. 6021
PT. ANDRITZ HYDRO—See ANDRITZ AG; *Int'l*, pg. 453
PT. ANDRITZ—See ANDRITZ AG; *Int'l*, pg. 456
PT. ANEKA BOGA NUSANTARA—See Daesang Corporation; *Int'l*, pg. 1909
PT ANEKA BUMI KENCANA—See Prasidha Aneka Niaga Tbk; *Int'l*, pg. 5955
P.T. ANEKA BUMI PRATAMA—See ITOCHU Corporation; *Int'l*, pg. 3841
PT. ANEKA COFFEE INDUSTRY—See Prasidha Aneka Niaga Tbk; *Int'l*, pg. 5955
P.T. ANEKA DHARMA PERSADA—See PT Adhi Karya (Persero) Tbk; *Int'l*, pg. 6019
PT ANEKA GARMENTAMA INDAH—See Carry Wealth Holdings Limited; *Int'l*, pg. 1346
PT ANEKA GAS INDUSTRI TBK; *Int'l*, pg. 6021
PT ANEKAGRIYA BUMINUSA CO., LTD.—See Land & Houses Public Company Limited; *Int'l*, pg. 4403
PT ANEKA JARINGAN INDONESIA—See Aneka Jaringan Holdings Berhad; *Int'l*, pg. 457
PT ANEKA RAYA KONSTRUKSI MESINDO—See PT United Tractors Tbk; *Int'l*, pg. 6081
PT ANEKA TAMBANG (PERSERO) TBK; *Int'l*, pg. 6022
PT. ANEKA TUNA INDONESIA—See Hagoromo Foods Corporation; *Int'l*, pg. 3207
PT. ANEST IWATA INDONESIA—See ANEST IWATA Corporation; *Int'l*, pg. 458

COMPANY NAME INDEX

P.T. ANGLER BIOCHEM LAB LTD.—See Eurofins Scientific S.E.; *Int'l*, pg. 2551
P.T. ANGLO-EASTERN PLANTATIONS MANAGEMENT INDONESIA—See Anglo Eastern Plantations PLC; *Int'l*, pg. 463
PT. ANIXTER INDONESIA—See WESCO International, Inc.; *U.S. Public*, pg. 2351
PT. ANPARIO BIOTECH INDONESIA—See Anpario plc; *Int'l*, pg. 475
PT ANTAM (PERSERO) TBK; *Int'l*, pg. 6022
PT ANTAM RESOURCINDO—See PT Antam (Persero) Tbk; *Int'l*, pg. 6022
PT ANUGERAH KAGUM KARYA UTAMA TBK; *Int'l*, pg. 6022
P.T. ANUGERAH KIMIA INDONESIA—See PT AKR Corporindo Tbk; *Int'l*, pg. 6020
P.T. ANUGERAH KRIDA RETAILINDO—See PT AKR Corporindo Tbk; *Int'l*, pg. 6020
P.T. ANUGERAH LUBRINDO RAYA—See PT AKR Corporindo Tbk; *Int'l*, pg. 6020
P.T. ANUGERAH PHARMINDO LESTARI—See The Zuellig Group Inc.; *Int'l*, pg. 7705
P.T. ANUGERAH PUPUK LESTARI—See PT Saraswanti Anugerah Makmur Tbk; *Int'l*, pg. 6070
P.T. ANUGERAH PUPUK MAKMUR—See PT Saraswanti Anugerah Makmur Tbk; *Int'l*, pg. 6070
PT ANUGERAH SPAREPARTS SEJAHTERA TBK; *Int'l*, pg. 6022
PT ANUGRAH KARYA RAYA—See PT AKR Corporindo Tbk; *Int'l*, pg. 6020
P.T. ANZ PANIN BANK—See Australia & New Zealand Banking Group Limited; *Int'l*, pg. 720
PT AON INDONESIA—See Aon plc; *Int'l*, pg. 495
PT APEXINDO PRATAMA DUTA TBK—See PT Mitra International Resources Tbk.; *Int'l*, pg. 6057
PT APLIKASI KARYA ANAK BANGSA—See Mitsubishi Corporation; *Int'l*, pg. 4942
PT APL LOGISTICS INDONESIA—See Kintetsu Group Holdings Co.,Ltd.; *Int'l*, pg. 4183
P.T. APM ARMADA SUSPENSION—See APM Automotive Holdings Berhad; *Int'l*, pg. 516
PT APM AUTO COMPONENTS INDONESIA—See APM Automotive Holdings Berhad; *Int'l*, pg. 516
PT APPLE FLAVOR & FRAGRANCE INDONESIA—See Apple Flavor & Fragrance Group Co., Ltd.; *Int'l*, pg. 520
PT. APTAR B&H INDONESIA—See AptarGroup, Inc.; *U.S. Public*, pg. 174
P.T. APT MEDICAL INDONESIA—See APT Medical, Inc.; *Int'l*, pg. 523
PT ARBURG—See Arburg GmbH & Co.; *Int'l*, pg. 539
PT ARCHI INDONESIA TBK; *Int'l*, pg. 6022
PT ARDENDI JAYA SENTOSA—See PT Astra Otoparts Tbk; *Int'l*, pg. 6024
PT ARIAL NIAGA NUSANTARA—See PT Wintermar Offshore Marine Tbk; *Int'l*, pg. 6083
P.T. ARIANTO DARMAWAN—See Max Weishaupt GmbH; *Int'l*, pg. 4735
PT ARISTI JASADATA—See PT Anabatic Technologies Tbk; *Int'l*, pg. 6021
P.T. ARISTON THERMO INDONESIA—See Ariston Holding N.V.; *Int'l*, pg. 567
PT. ARISU GRAPHIC PRIMA—See Kyodo Printing Co. Ltd.; *Int'l*, pg. 4361
PT. ARITA PRIMA INDONESIA TBK.—See UNIMECH Group Berhad; *Int'l*, pg. 8048
PT. ARITA PRIMA TEKNINDO—See UNIMECH Group Berhad; *Int'l*, pg. 8049
PT ARJUNA UTAMA KIMIA—See PT AKR Corporindo Tbk; *Int'l*, pg. 6020
PT ARKADIA DIGITAL MEDIA; *Int'l*, pg. 6022
PT ARKHA JAYANTI PERSADA TBK; *Int'l*, pg. 6022
PT ARKORA HYDRO—See Nippon Koei Co., Ltd.; *Int'l*, pg. 5321
PT. ARKRAY—See ARKRAY, Inc.; *Int'l*, pg. 572
PT ARMADA BERJAYA TRANS; *Int'l*, pg. 6022
PT ARMOXINDO FARMA—See Bausch Health Companies Inc.; *Int'l*, pg. 897
PT ARPENI PRATAMA OCEAN LINE TBK; *Int'l*, pg. 6022
PT ARSY BUANA TRAVELINDO TBK.; *Int'l*, pg. 6022
PT. ARTHAASIA FINANCE—See Mitsubishi HC Capital Inc.; *Int'l*, pg. 4952
P.T. ARTHA BINA USAHA—See PT Sinar Mas Multiartha Tbk; *Int'l*, pg. 6074
P.T. ARTHA MAHIYA INVESTAMA TBK; *Int'l*, pg. 6084
P.T. ARTHAMAS INFORMATIKA—See PT Sinar Mas Multiartha Tbk; *Int'l*, pg. 6074
P.T. ARTHAMAS SOLUSINDO—See PT Sinar Mas Multiartha Tbk; *Int'l*, pg. 6074
P.T. ARTHA MULIA NUSANTAR—See UNIMECH Group Berhad; *Int'l*, pg. 8049
P.T. ARTHA PRIMA ENERGY—See PT Rukun Raharja Tbk; *Int'l*, pg. 6069
P.T. ARTHA TELEKOMINDO—See PT JAKARTA INTERNATIONAL HOTELS & DEVELOPMENT Tbk; *Int'l*, pg. 6048
PT ARTHAVEST TBK; *Int'l*, pg. 6022
P.T. ARTIFISIAL TEKNOLOGI PERSADA—See PT Rukun Raharja Tbk; *Int'l*, pg. 6069

PT ARTISAN WAHYU—See PT. PAKUWON JATI Tbk; *Int'l*, pg. 6088
PT. ART PISTON INDONESIA—See TPR Co., Ltd.; *Int'l*, pg. 7884
PT. ARUTMIN INDONESIA—See PT Bumi Resources Tbk; *Int'l*, pg. 6031
PT ARWANA CITRAMULIA TBK; *Int'l*, pg. 6022
P.T. ASAHI DIAMOND INDUSTRIAL INDONESIA—See Asahi Diamond Industrial Co. Ltd.; *Int'l*, pg. 592
PT. ASAHIMAS CHEMICAL - CILEGON FACTORY—See AGC Inc.; *Int'l*, pg. 204
PT. ASAHIMAS CHEMICAL—See AGC Inc.; *Int'l*, pg. 204
P.T. ASAHIMAS FLAT GLASS TBK; *Int'l*, pg. 5683
PT ASAHI SOLDER TECHNOLOGY INDONESIA—See Singapore Asahi Chemical & Solder Industries Pte. Ltd.; *Int'l*, pg. 6940
P.T. ASAHI SYNCHROTECH INDONESIA—See Chubu Electric Power Co., Inc.; *Int'l*, pg. 1593
PT ASHAPURA RESOURCES—See Ashapura Minechem Limited; *Int'l*, pg. 606
PT ASIA COCOA INDONESIA—See Guan Chong Berhad; *Int'l*, pg. 3152
PT ASIAN PAINTS INDONESIA—See Asian Paints Limited; *Int'l*, pg. 619
PT ASIA PACIFIC FIBERS TBK; *Int'l*, pg. 6022
PT ASIA PACIFIC INVESTAMA TBK; *Int'l*, pg. 6022
PT ASIAPLAST INDUSTRIES TBK; *Int'l*, pg. 6023
PT ASIA SEJAHTERA MINA TBK; *Int'l*, pg. 6023
PT. ASIASOFT—See Asphere Innovations Public Company Limited; *Int'l*, pg. 630
PT. ASL SHIPYARD INDONESIA—See ASL Marine Holdings Ltd; *Int'l*, pg. 625
PT. ASRI KENCANA GEMILANG—See PT. Bhuwanatala Indah Permai Tbk; *Int'l*, pg. 6085
PT. ASSAB STEELS INDONESIA—See voestalpine AG; *Int'l*, pg. 8289
PT. ASSOCIATED BRITISH BUDI—See PT Budi Starch & Sweetener Tbk; *Int'l*, pg. 6031
PT. ASTELLAS PHARMA INDONESIA—See Astellas Pharma Inc.; *Int'l*, pg. 653
P.T. AST INDONESIA—See Sumitomo Forestry Co., Ltd.; *Int'l*, pg. 7285
PT ASTRA AGRO LESTARI TBK; *Int'l*, pg. 6023
PT. ASTRA DAIDO STEEL INDONESIA—See PT Astra Otoparts Tbk; *Int'l*, pg. 6024
PT. ASTRA DAIHATSU MOTOR—See Toyota Motor Corporation; *Int'l*, pg. 7870
PT. ASTRA DIGITAL ARTA—See PT Astra International Tbk; *Int'l*, pg. 6023
PT. ASTRA DIGITAL INTERNATIONAL—See PT Astra International Tbk; *Int'l*, pg. 6023
PT. ASTRA GRAPHIA TBK.; *Int'l*, pg. 6084
PT ASTRAGRAPHIA XPRINS INDONESIA—See PT. Astra Graphia Tbk.; *Int'l*, pg. 6084
PT. ASTRA INTERNATIONAL TBK; *Int'l*, pg. 6023
P.T. ASTRA ISUZU CASTING COMPANY—See PT Astra International Tbk; *Int'l*, pg. 6023
PT. ASTRA JUOKU INDONESIA—See PT Astra International Tbk; *Int'l*, pg. 6023
PT. ASTRA KOMPONEN INDONESIA—See PT Astra Otoparts Tbk; *Int'l*, pg. 6024
PT. ASTRA LAND INDONESIA—See PT Astra International Tbk; *Int'l*, pg. 6023
PT. ASTRA NIPPON GASKET INDONESIA—See PT Astra International Tbk; *Int'l*, pg. 6023
PT. ASTRA NISSAN DIESEL INDONESIA—See PT Astra International Tbk; *Int'l*, pg. 6023
PT. ASTRA NUSA PERDANA—See PT Astra International Tbk; *Int'l*, pg. 6023
PT ASTRA OTOPARTS TBK; *Int'l*, pg. 6024
PT. ASTRA SEDAYA FINANCE—See PT Astra International Tbk; *Int'l*, pg. 6023
PT. ASTRATEL NUSANTARA—See PT Astra International Tbk; *Int'l*, pg. 6023
PT. ASTRA TOL NUSANTARA—See PT Astra International Tbk; *Int'l*, pg. 6023
PT ASTRAZENECA INDONESIA—See AstraZeneca PLC; *Int'l*, pg. 661
PT ASTRINDO NUSANTARA INFRASTRUKTUR TBK; *Int'l*, pg. 6024
PT. ASURANSI ADIRA DINAMIKA—See Zurich Insurance Group Limited; *Int'l*, pg. 8697
P.T. ASURANSI ALLIANZ LIFE INDONESIA—See Allianz SE; *Int'l*, pg. 355
P.T. ASURANSI ALLIANZ UTAMA INDONESIA—See Allianz SE; *Int'l*, pg. 355
PT ASURANSI ASTRA BUANA—See PT Astra International Tbk; *Int'l*, pg. 6023
PT. ASURANSI BINTANG TBK; *Int'l*, pg. 6084
PT ASURANSI CHUBB SYARIAH INDONESIA—See Chubb Limited; *Int'l*, pg. 1592
PT ASURANSI CIGNA—See Chubb Limited; *Int'l*, pg. 1592
PT ASURANSI ETIQA INTERNASIONAL INDONESIA—See Malayan Banking Berhad; *Int'l*, pg. 4661
PT. ASURANSI FPG INDONESIA—See The Zuellig Group Inc.; *Int'l*, pg. 7705
PT. ASURANSI HARTA AMAN PRATAMA TBK.; *Int'l*, pg. 6084

PT AVIANA SINAR ABADI TBK

PT ASURANSI JASA TANIA TBK; *Int'l*, pg. 6024
PT. ASURANSI JIWA ASIH GREAT EASTERN—See Oversea-Chinese Banking Corporation Limited; *Int'l*, pg. 5671
PT. ASURANSI JIWA ASTRA—See PT Astra International Tbk; *Int'l*, pg. 6023
PT. ASURANSI JIWA GENERALI INDONESIA—See Assicurazioni Generali S.p.A.; *Int'l*, pg. 647
PT. ASURANSI JIWA INHEALTH INDONESIA—See PT Bank Mandiri (Persero) Tbk.; *Int'l*, pg. 6027
P.T. ASURANSI JIWA MANULIFE INDONESIA—See Manulife Financial Corporation; *Int'l*, pg. 4679
PT. ASURANSI JIWA NASIONAL—See PT Bhakti Multi Artha Tbk; *Int'l*, pg. 6029
PT ASURANSI JIWA SYARIAH JASA MITRA ABADI TBK; *Int'l*, pg. 6024
PT ASURANSI MAXIMUS GRAHA PERSADA TBK; *Int'l*, pg. 6024
PT. ASURANSI MITRA PELINDUNG MUSTIKA—See PT Mitra Pinasthika Mustika Tbk; *Int'l*, pg. 6058
PT. ASURANSI MSIG INDONESIA—See MS&AD Insurance Group Holdings, Inc.; *Int'l*, pg. 5067
PT ASURANSI PAROLAMAS—See Tokio Marine Holdings, Inc.; *Int'l*, pg. 7784
PT. ASURANSI QBE POOL INDONESIA—See Oversea-Chinese Banking Corporation Limited; *Int'l*, pg. 5671
PT ASURANSI RAMAYANA TBK; *Int'l*, pg. 6024
PT. ASURANSI SIMAS INSURTECH—See PT Sinar Mas Multiartha Tbk; *Int'l*, pg. 6074
PT. ASURANSI SIMAS JIWA—See PT Sinar Mas Multiartha Tbk; *Int'l*, pg. 6074
PT. ASURANSI SINAR MAS—See PT Sinar Mas Multiartha Tbk; *Int'l*, pg. 6074
PT. ASURANSI SOMPO JAPAN NIPPONKOA INDONESIA—See Sompo Holdings, Inc.; *Int'l*, pg. 7087
PT. ASURANSI STACO MANDIRI—See PT Pertamina (Persero); *Int'l*, pg. 6064
PT. ASURANSI SUMIT OTO—See PT Sinar Mas Multiartha Tbk; *Int'l*, pg. 6074
PT. ASURANSI TOKIO MARINE INDONESIA—See Tokio Marine Holdings, Inc.; *Int'l*, pg. 7782
PT. ASURANSI TOKIO MARINE INDONESIA—See Tokio Marine Holdings, Inc.; *Int'l*, pg. 7784
PT ASURANSI TUGU PRATAMA INDONESIA TBK; *Int'l*, pg. 6024
PT ATELIERS MECANIDUQES D'INDONESIE TBK; *Int'l*,
PT. ATIKOM MEGA PRATAMA—See SUTL Enterprise Limited; *Int'l*, pg. 7347
PT ATLAS COPCO FLUIDCON—See Atlas Copco AB; *Int'l*, pg. 684
PT ATLAS COPCO INDONESIA—See Atlas Copco AB; *Int'l*, pg. 684
PT ATLAS RESOURCES TBK; *Int'l*, pg. 6024
PT ATMC PUMP SERVICES—See PT United Tractors Tbk; *Int'l*, pg. 6081
P.T. ATMINDO; *Int'l*, pg. 5683
PT AT OCEANIC OFFSHORE—See KS Energy Limited; *Int'l*, pg. 4310
PT. ATRI DISTRIBUSINDO—See Mitsubishi Corporation; *Int'l*, pg. 4942
PT ATTACHMENT SOLUTIONS, LLC—See Duke Energy Corporation; *U.S. Public*, pg. 691
PT AUDEX INDONESIA—See PEC Ltd.; *Int'l*, pg. 5778
PT. AURUM DIGITAL INTERNUSA—See PT Hartadinata Abadi Tbk; *Int'l*, pg. 6042
PT AUSTINDO NUSANTARA JAYA TBK.; *Int'l*, pg. 6025
PT AUSTIN ENGINEERING INDONESIA—See Austin Engineering Ltd.; *Int'l*, pg. 718
PT AUSTRALIAN SKILLS TRAINING—See John Wood Group PLC; *Int'l*, pg. 3983
PT. AUTOCOMP SYSTEMS INDONESIA—See Yazaki Corporation; *Int'l*, pg. 8572
PT. AUTO GLASS INDONESIA—See P.T. Asahimas Flat Glass Tbk; *Int'l*, pg. 5683
P.T. AUTOLIV INDONESIA—See Autoliv, Inc.; *Int'l*, pg. 730
P.T. AUTOPEDIA SUKSES GADAI—See PT Adi Sarana Armada Tbk; *Int'l*, pg. 6019
P.T. AUTOPEDIA SUKSES LESTARI TBK—See PT Adi Sarana Armada Tbk; *Int'l*, pg. 6019
P.T. AUTOPLASTIK INDONESIA—See PT Astra Otoparts Tbk; *Int'l*, pg. 6024
P.T. AUTOTECH INDONESIA—See JTEKT Corporation; *Int'l*, pg. 4017
P.T. AVATEC SERVICES INDONESIA—See United Overseas Bank Limited; *Int'l*, pg. 8071
PT. AVENTIS PHARMA—See Sanofi; *Int'l*, pg. 6550
PT AVERY DENNISON INDONESIA—See Avery Dennison Corporation; *U.S. Public*, pg. 244
P.T. AVESTA CONTINENTAL PACK—See PT Champion Pacific Indonesia Tbk; *Int'l*, pg. 6033
PT AVIA AVIAN TBK; *Int'l*, pg. 6025
PT AVIANA SINAR ABADI TBK; *Int'l*, pg. 6025
P.T. AVIENT COLORANTS INDONESIA—See Avient Corporation; *U.S. Public*, pg. 248
PT. AWAN TEKNOLOGI GLOBAL—See Amiya Corporation; *Int'l*, pg. 428
PT AXA MANDIRI FINANCIAL SERVICES—See AXA S.A.; *Int'l*, pg. 759

PT AVIANA SINAR ABADI TBK

CORPORATE AFFILIATIONS

PT AXA MANDIRI FINANCIAL SERVICES—See PT Bank Mandiri (Persero) Tbk.; *Int'l*, pg. 6027
PT AXIATA DIGITAL LABS INDONESIA—See Axiata Group Berhad; *Int'l*, pg. 768
P.T. AZBIL BERCA INDONESIA—See Azbil Corporation; *Int'l*, pg. 777
P.T. AZUREUS SIMULATOR ASIA—See PT Wintermar Offshore Marine Tbk; *Int'l*, pg. 6083
PT BAGASASI INTI PRATAMA—See PT Modernland Realty Tbk; *Int'l*, pg. 6059
PT BAHARI CAKRAWALA SEBUKU—See PTT Public Company Limited; *Int'l*, pg. 6092
PT BAHTERA LISTRINDO JAYA—See PT Cikarang Listrindo Tbk; *Int'l*, pg. 6034
PT BAJAJ AUTO INDONESIA—See Bajaj Auto Ltd.; *Int'l*, pg. 804
PT BAKRIE AUTOPARTS—See PT Bakrie & Brothers Tbk; *Int'l*, pg. 6025
PT BAKRIE & BROTHERS TBK; *Int'l*, pg. 6025
PT BAKRIE BUILDING INDUSTRIES—See PT Bakrie & Brothers Tbk; *Int'l*, pg. 6025
PT BAKRIE COMMUNICATIONS—See PT Bakrie & Brothers Tbk; *Int'l*, pg. 6025
PT BAKRIE CONSTRUCTION—See PT Bakrie & Brothers Tbk; *Int'l*, pg. 6025
PT BAKRIE INDO INFRASTRUCTURE—See PT Bakrie & Brothers Tbk; *Int'l*, pg. 6025
PT. BAKRIELAND DEVELOPMENT, TBK.; *Int'l*, pg. 6084
PT BAKRIE METAL INDUSTRIES—See PT Bakrie & Brothers Tbk; *Int'l*, pg. 6025
PT BAKRIE OIL & GAS INFRASTRUCTURE—See PT Bakrie & Brothers Tbk; *Int'l*, pg. 6025
PT BAKRIE PASAMAN PLANTATIONS—See PT Bakrie Sumatera Plantations Tbk; *Int'l*, pg. 6025
PT BAKRIE PIPE INDUSTRIES—See PT Bakrie & Brothers Tbk; *Int'l*, pg. 6025
PT BAKRIE POWER—See PT Bakrie & Brothers Tbk; *Int'l*, pg. 6025
PT BAKRIE STEEL INDUSTRIES—See PT Bakrie & Brothers Tbk; *Int'l*, pg. 6025
PT BAKRIE SUMATERA PLANTATIONS TBK; *Int'l*, pg. 6025
PT BAKRIE TOSANJAYA—See PT Bakrie & Brothers Tbk; *Int'l*, pg. 6025
P.T. BAKTI TANI NUSANTARA; *Int'l*, pg. 6084
PT BALAI LELANG CAREADY—See PT Blue Bird Tbk; *Int'l*, pg. 6030
P.T. BALAI LELANG SINARMAS—See PT Sinar Mas Multiartha Tbk; *Int'l*, pg. 6074
PT BALAI PUSTAKA—See PT Wijaya Karya (Persero) Tbk.; *Int'l*, pg. 6082
PT BALEBAT DEDIKASI PRIMA—See Perusahaan Perseroan Indonesia Tbk; *Int'l*, pg. 5821
PT BALI BINTANG SEJAHTERA TBK; *Int'l*, pg. 6025
P.T. BALI ENVIRONMENTAL PERSADA—See Koh Brothers Eco Engineering Ltd.; *Int'l*, pg. 4228
PT BALI GIRIKENCANA—See Hotel Properties Limited; *Int'l*, pg. 3488
PT BALI TOWERINDO SENTRA TBK; *Int'l*, pg. 6025
P.T. BANDO INDONESIA—See Bando Chemical Industries, Ltd.; *Int'l*, pg. 830
PT BANGUN PERSADA JAMBI ENERGI—See PT PLN (Persero); *Int'l*, pg. 6065
PT BANGUN PRIMA SEMESTA—See PT. Voksel Electric Tbk; *Int'l*, pg. 6090
PT BANK AGRIS TBK—See Industrial Bank of Korea; *Int'l*, pg. 3671
PT BANK ALADIN SYARIAH TBK; *Int'l*, pg. 6025
PT BANK AMAR INDONESIA TBK; *Int'l*, pg. 6026
PT BANK ANZ INDONESIA—See Australia & New Zealand Banking Group Limited; *Int'l*, pg. 720
PT BANK ARTHA GRAHA INTERNASIONAL TBK; *Int'l*, pg. 6026
PT BANK BNP PARIBAS INDONESIA—See BNP Paribas SA; *Int'l*, pg. 1081
PT BANK BTPN SYARIAH TBK.; *Int'l*, pg. 6026
PT BANK BTPN TBK—See Sumitomo Mitsui Financial Group, Inc.; *Int'l*, pg. 7293
P.T. BANK BUMI ARTA TBK; *Int'l*, pg. 5683
PT BANK CAPITAL INDONESIA TBK; *Int'l*, pg. 6026
PT BANK CHINA CONSTRUCTION BANK INDONESIA TBK—See China Construction Bank Corporation; *Int'l*, pg. 1491
PT BANK CIMB NIAGA TBK—See CIMB Group Holdings Berhad; *Int'l*, pg. 1608
PT BANK CIMB NIAGA TBK—See CIMB Group Holdings Berhad; *Int'l*, pg. 1608
PT. BANK COMMONWEALTH—See Oversea-Chinese Banking Corporation Limited; *Int'l*, pg. 5672
PT. BANK CTBC INDONESIA—See CTBC Financial Holding Co., Ltd.; *Int'l*, pg. 1869
PT BANK DANAMON INDONESIA TBK—See Mitsubishi UFJ Financial Group, Inc.; *Int'l*, pg. 4970
PT. BANK DBS INDONESIA—See DBS Group Holdings Ltd.; *Int'l*, pg. 1989
PT BANK GANESHA TBK; *Int'l*, pg. 6026
PT BANK HSBC INDONESIA—See HSBC Holdings plc; *Int'l*, pg. 3507

PT BANK IBK INDONESIA TBK—See Industrial Bank of Korea; *Int'l*, pg. 3671
PT. BANK ICBC INDONESIA—See Industrial & Commercial Bank of China Limited; *Int'l*, pg. 3670
PT BANK INA PERDANA TBK.; *Int'l*, pg. 6026
PT BANK JAGO TBK; *Int'l*, pg. 6026
PT BANK JTRUST INDONESIA TBK.; *Int'l*, pg. 6026
PT BANK KB BUKOPIN TBK; *Int'l*, pg. 6026
PT BANK KEB HANA INDONESIA—See Hana Financial Group, Inc.; *Int'l*, pg. 3241
PT. BANK KEB HANA—See Hana Financial Group, Inc.; *Int'l*, pg. 3241
PT BANK MANDIRI (PERSERO) TBK.; *Int'l*, pg. 6026
PT BANK MANDIRI TASPEN—See PT Bank Mandiri (Persero) Tbk; *Int'l*, pg. 6027
PT BANK MASPION INDONESIA TBK; *Int'l*, pg. 6027
PT BANK MAYAPADA INTERNASIONAL TBK.; *Int'l*, pg. 6027
PT BANK MAYBANK INDOCORP—See Malayan Banking Berhad; *Int'l*, pg. 4661
PT. BANK MAYBANK INDONESIA FINANCE—See PT. Wahana Ottomitra Multiartha Tbk.; *Int'l*, pg. 6090
PT BANK MAYBANK INDONESIA TBK.—See Malayan Banking Berhad; *Int'l*, pg. 4661
P.T. BANK MAYORA—See PT Bank Negara Indonesia (Persero) Tbk; *Int'l*, pg. 6027
PT BANK MEGA TBK; *Int'l*, pg. 6027
PT BANK MESTIKA DHARMA TBK; *Int'l*, pg. 6027
PT BANK MITRANIAGA TBK; *Int'l*, pg. 6027
P.T. BANK MIZUHO INTERNATIONAL INDONESIA—See Mizuho Financial Group, Inc.; *Int'l*, pg. 4998
PT BANK MNC INTERNASIONAL TBK; *Int'l*, pg. 6027
PT BANK MULTIARTA SENTOSA TBK; *Int'l*, pg. 6027
PT BANK NATIONALNOBU TBK; *Int'l*, pg. 6027
PT BANK NEGARA INDONESIA (PERSERO) TBK; *Int'l*, pg. 6027
PT BANK NEO COMMERCE TBK; *Int'l*, pg. 6027
PT BANK NOBUNALNOBU TBK—See PT. Lippo Securities, Tbk; *Int'l*, pg. 6087
PT BANK OCBC INDONESIA—See Oversea-Chinese Banking Corporation Limited; *Int'l*, pg. 5672
PT BANK OCBC NISP TBK—See Oversea-Chinese Banking Corporation Limited; *Int'l*, pg. 5672
PT BANK OF INDIA INDONESIA, TBK.—See Bank of India; *Int'l*, pg. 843
PT BANK OKE INDONESIA TBK; *Int'l*, pg. 6028
PT. BANK PAN INDONESIA TBK; *Int'l*, pg. 6028
PT BANK PANIN DUBAI SYARIAH TBK.—See PT. Bank Pan Indonesia Tbk; *Int'l*, pg. 6084
PT BANK PEMBANGUNAN DAERAH BANTEN TBK; *Int'l*, pg. 6028
PT. BANK PEMBANGUNAN DAERAH JAWA BARAT & BANTEN, TBK.; *Int'l*, pg. 6084
PT BANK PEMBANGUNAN DAERAH JAWA TIMUR TBK; *Int'l*, pg. 6028
PT BANK PERMATA TBK—See Bangkok Bank Public Company Limited; *Int'l*, pg. 833
PT BANK QNB INDONESIA TBK—See Qatar National Bank S.A.Q.; *Int'l*, pg. 6135
PT. BANK RABOBANK INTERNATIONAL INDONESIA—See Cooperatieve Centrale Raiffeisen-Boerenleenbank B.A.; *Int'l*, pg. 1791
PT BANK RAKYAT INDONESIA (PERSERO) TBK; *Int'l*, pg. 6028
PT BANK RAYA INDONESIA TBK—See PT Bank Rakyat Indonesia (Persero) Tbk; *Int'l*, pg. 6028
P.T. BANK RESONA PERDANIA—See Resona Holdings, Inc.; *Int'l*, pg. 6297
PT. BANK SBI INDONESIA—See State Bank of India; *Int'l*, pg. 7181
PT BANK SHINHAN INDONESIA—See Shinhan Financial Group Co., Ltd.; *Int'l*, pg. 6844
PT BANK SINARMAS TBK.; *Int'l*, pg. 6028
PT BANK SUMITOMO MITSUI INDONESIA—See Sumitomo Mitsui Financial Group, Inc.; *Int'l*, pg. 7293
PT BANK SWADESI TBK—See Bank of India; *Int'l*, pg. 843
PT BANK SYARIAH BUKOPIN—See PT Bank KB Bukopin Tbk; *Int'l*, pg. 6026
PT BANK SYARIAH INDONESIA TBK.—See PT Bank Rakyat Indonesia (Persero) Tbk; *Int'l*, pg. 6028
PT BANK SYARIAH MANDIRI—See PT Bank Mandiri (Persero) Tbk; *Int'l*, pg. 6027
PT BANK TABUNGAN NEGARA (PERSERO) TBK; *Int'l*, pg. 6028
PT BANK UOB INDONESIA—See United Overseas Bank Limited; *Int'l*, pg. 8071
PT BANK UOB INDONESIA—See United Overseas Bank Limited; *Int'l*, pg. 8071
PT BANK VICTORIA INTERNATIONAL TBK; *Int'l*, pg. 6028
PT BANK VICTORIA SYARIAH—See PT Bank Victoria International Tbk; *Int'l*, pg. 6028
PT BANK WOORI SAUDARA INDONESIA 1906 TBK; *Int'l*, pg. 6028
PT. BARADINAMIKA MUDASUKSES—See PT Mitrabara Adiperdana Tbk; *Int'l*, pg. 6058
PT BARA ENERGI LESTARI—See PT ABM Investama Tbk.; *Int'l*, pg. 6018

PT BARA JAYA INTERNASIONAL TBK.; *Int'l*, pg. 6028
PT BARAMULTI SUKSESSARANA TBK; *Int'l*, pg. 6028
PT BARENTZ—See Cinven Limited; *Int'l*, pg. 1611
PT BARITO PACIFIC TBK; *Int'l*, pg. 6028
PT BARITO RENEWABLES ENERGY TBK; *Int'l*, pg. 6029
PT BARUNA DIRGA DHARMA—See PT ABM Investama Tbk.; *Int'l*, pg. 6018
P.T. BASF CARE CHEMICALS INDONESIA—See BASF SE; *Int'l*, pg. 884
P.T. BASF INDONESIA—See BASF SE; *Int'l*, pg. 884
PT BATAMINDO EXECUTIVE VILLAGE—See Gallant Venture Ltd.; *Int'l*, pg. 2874
PT BATAMINDO INVESTMENT CAKRAWALA—See Gallant Venture Ltd.; *Int'l*, pg. 2874
PT BATAVIA PROSPERINDO ASET MANAJEMEN—See PT Batavia Prosperindo Internasional Tbk; *Int'l*, pg. 6029
PT BATAVIA PROSPERINDO INTERNASIONAL TBK; *Int'l*, pg. 6029
PT BATAVIA PROSPERINDO TRANS TBK—See PT Batavia Prosperindo Internasional Tbk; *Int'l*, pg. 6029
PT BATIQA HOTEL MANAJEMEN—See PT Surya Semesta Internusa Tbk; *Int'l*, pg. 6077
PT BATULICIN NUSANTARA MARITIM TBK; *Int'l*, pg. 6029
P.T. BATURAJA MULTI USAHA—See PT. Semen Indonesia (Persero) Tbk; *Int'l*, pg. 6088
P.T. BATUTUA TEMBAGA RAYA—See Finders Resources Limited; *Int'l*, pg. 2672
P.T. BAUER EQUIPMENT INDONESIA—See BAUER Aktiengesellschaft; *Int'l*, pg. 892
P.T. BAUER PRATAMA INDONESIA—See BAUER Aktiengesellschaft; *Int'l*, pg. 893
PT BAUSCH & LOMB INDONESIA—See Bausch Health Companies Inc.; *Int'l*, pg. 897
PT. BAYAN RESOURCES TBK.; *Int'l*, pg. 6084
P.T. BAYER INDONESIA—See Bayer Aktiengesellschaft; *Int'l*, pg. 909
PT BAYU BUANA TBK; *Int'l*, pg. 6029
PT. BAYU MARITIM BERKAH—See Falcon Energy Group Limited; *Int'l*, pg. 2611
PT. B.BRAUN MEDICAL INDONESIA—See B. Braun Melsungen AG; *Int'l*, pg. 788
P.T. BCI ASIA—See Byggfakta Group Nordic HoldCo AB; *Int'l*, pg. 1235
P.T. BDRC ASIA—See The BDRC Group; *Int'l*, pg. 7620
PT BECKERS INDONESIA—See Lindengruppen AB; *Int'l*, pg. 4511
PT BECTON DICKINSON INDONESIA—See Becton, Dickinson & Company; *U.S. Public*, pg. 292
P.T. BEIERSDORF INDONESIA—See maxingvest ag; *Int'l*, pg. 4740
PT BEKAERT ADVANCED FILTRATION—See NV Bekaert SA; *Int'l*, pg. 5496
PT BEKAERT INDONESIA—See NV Bekaert SA; *Int'l*, pg. 5496
PT BEKAERT TRADE INDONESIA—See NV Bekaert SA; *Int'l*, pg. 5496
PT BEKASI DEVELOPMENT—See PT Modernland Realty Tbk; *Int'l*, pg. 6059
PT. BEKASI FAJAR INDUSTRIAL ESTATE TBK.; *Int'l*, pg. 6084
PT BELFOODS INDONESIA—See PT Sreeya Sewu Indonesia Tbk; *Int'l*, pg. 6075
PT BELLANOVA COUNTRY MALL—See PT Lippo Karawaci Tbk; *Int'l*, pg. 6053
PT. BENEFIT ONE INDONESIA—See Pasona Group Inc.; *Int'l*, pg. 5753
PT. BENGAWAN SOLO GARMENT INDONESIA—See Nippon Steel Corporation; *Int'l*, pg. 5338
PT BENTELER DISTRIBUTION INDONESIA—See Benteler International AG; *Int'l*, pg. 977
PT BENTOEL INTERNASIONAL INVESTAMA TBK—See British American Tobacco plc; *Int'l*, pg. 1167
PT BERAU COAL ENERGY TBK; *Int'l*, pg. 6029
PT BERCA CARRIER INDONESIA—See Carrier Global Corporation; *U.S. Public*, pg. 444
P.T. BERCA HARDAYAPERKASA; *Int'l*, pg. 5683
PT BERCA SCHINDLER LIFTS—See Schindler Holding AG; *Int'l*, pg. 6619
PT BERDIKARI PONDASI PERKASA TBK; *Int'l*, pg. 6029
PT. BERDIRI MATAHARI LOGISTIK—See Hitachi, Ltd.; *Int'l*, pg. 3423
PT BERGER BATAM—See Beng Kuang Marine Limited; *Int'l*, pg. 973
PT BERJAYA COSWAY INDONESIA—See Berjaya Corporation Berhad; *Int'l*, pg. 984
P.T. BERJAYA DYNAMICS INDONESIA—See PT Mark Dynamics Indonesia Tbk; *Int'l*, pg. 6054
PT BERKAH BETON SADAYA TBK; *Int'l*, pg. 6029
PT BERKAH DAYA MANDIRI—See PT. Transcoal Pacific Tbk; *Int'l*, pg. 6079
PT BERKAH KAWASAN MANYAR SEJAHTERA—See PT AKR Corporindo Tbk; *Int'l*, pg. 6020
PT BERKAH PRIMA PERKASA TBK; *Int'l*, pg. 6029
PT BERKALA MAJU BERSAMA—See CB Industrial Product Holding Berhad; *Int'l*, pg. 1364
PT BERLIAN LAJU TANKER TBK; *Int'l*, pg. 6029

COMPANY NAME INDEX

PT. BERLICO MULIA FARMA—See PT Industri Jamu dan Farmasi Sido Muncul Tbk; *Int'l*, pg. 6047
PT. BERLINA TBK; *Int'l*, pg. 6085
PT BERSATU INTERNATIONAL FOOD INDUSTRIES—See EKA Noodles Berhad; *Int'l*, pg. 2338
PT. BESHA ANALITIKA—See HORIBA Ltd; *Int'l*, pg. 3478
PT BEST WORLD INDONESIA—See Best World International Ltd.; *Int'l*, pg. 1000
PT BETONJAYA MANUNGGAL TBK; *Int'l*, pg. 6029
PT BEYONICS MANUFACTURING—See ShawKwei & Partners Ltd.; *Int'l*, pg. 6792
PT. BFI FINANCE INDONESIA TBK.; *Int'l*, pg. 6085
PTB GROUP LIMITED; *Int'l*, pg. 6090
PT BHAKTI AGUNG PROPERTINDO TBK; *Int'l*, pg. 6029
PT BHAKTI CAHAYA UTAMA—See PT Bhakti Multi Artha Tbk; *Int'l*, pg. 6029
PT BHAKTI ENERGI PERSADA—See PT Adaro Energy Indonesia Tbk; *Int'l*, pg. 6019
PT BHAKTI FINTEK INDONESIA—See PT Bhakti Multi Artha Tbk; *Int'l*, pg. 6029
PT BHAKTI MULTI ARTHA TBK; *Int'l*, pg. 6029
PT. BHARINTO EKATAMA—See Banpu Public Company Limited; *Int'l*, pg. 852
PT BHIMASENA POWER INDONESIA—See PT Adaro Energy Indonesia Tbk; *Int'l*, pg. 6019
P.T. BHP INDONESIA—See BHP Group Limited; *Int'l*, pg. 1016
P.T. BHUMI JATI POWER—See PT Astra International Tbk; *Int'l*, pg. 6023
PT. BHUWANATALA INDAH PERMAI TBK; *Int'l*, pg. 6085
PT BIFARMA ADILUHUNG—See PT Kalbe Farma Tbk.; *Int'l*, pg. 6050
PT BIG BIRD PUSAKA—See PT Blue Bird Tbk; *Int'l*, pg. 6030
P.T. BILFINGER BERGER INDONESIA—See Bilfinger SE; *Int'l*, pg. 1028
P.T. BIMA BISALLOY—See Bisalloy Steel Group Ltd.; *Int'l*, pg. 1048
PT BIMA MULTI FINANCE—See PT Sinar Mas Multiartha Tbk; *Int'l*, pg. 6074
PT BIMA SAKTI PERTIWI TBK; *Int'l*, pg. 6029
PT BIMA SEPAJA ABADI—See PT. Semen Indonesia (Persero) Tbk; *Int'l*, pg. 6088
PT BIMATEKNO KAHYATAMA KONSULTAN—See Deca Group Limited; *Int'l*, pg. 936
P.T. BINA CITRA SENTO S.A.—See PT Trisula International Tbk; *Int'l*, pg. 6080
PT BINA GUNA KIMIA—See FMC Corporation; *U.S. Public*, pg. 862
P.T. BINA HUSADA GEMILANG—See PT Mitra Keluarga Karyasehat Tbk; *Int'l*, pg. 6057
PT BINA ILMA HUSADA—See PT Mitra Keluarga Karyasehat Tbk; *Int'l*, pg. 6057
PT. BINAKARYA JAYA ABADI TBK; *Int'l*, pg. 6030
PT BINA PERTIWI ENERGI—See PT United Tractors Tbk; *Int'l*, pg. 6081
PT BINARY VENTURA INDONESIA—See PT. Elang Mahkota Teknologi Tbk.; *Int'l*, pg. 6086
PT. BINATEK REKA KRUH—See PT Bintang Mitra Semestaraya Tbk; *Int'l*, pg. 6030
PT BINA UNGGUL KENCANA—See Bukalapak.com PT Tbk; *Int'l*, pg. 1213
PT. BINA USAHA MANDIRI MIZUSAWA—See PT Bakrie & Brothers Tbk; *Int'l*, pg. 6025
PT BINTAI KINDENKO ENGINEERING INDONESIA—See PT United Tractors Tbk; *Int'l*, pg. 6081
P.T. BINTANG LANGIT—See PT Metro Healthcare Indonesia Tbk; *Int'l*, pg. 6056
PT BINTANG MITRA SEMESTARAYA TBK; *Int'l*, pg. 6030
PT BINTANG OTO GLOBAL TBK; *Int'l*, pg. 6030
PT BINTANG SAMUDERA MANDIRI LINES TBK; *Int'l*, pg. 6030
PT BINTANG SMELTER INDONESIA—See PT Ifishdeco Tbk; *Int'l*, pg. 6044
PT BINTANG TOEDJOE—See PT Kalbe Farma Tbk.; *Int'l*, pg. 6050
PT BINTAN INTI INDUSTRIAL ESTATE—See Gallant Venture Ltd.; *Int'l*, pg. 2874
PT BINTAN RESORT CAKRAWALA—See Gallant Venture Ltd.; *Int'l*, pg. 2874
PT. BINTIKA BANGUNUSA—See Regional Container Lines Public Company Limited; *Int'l*, pg. 6254
PT BINTRACO DHARMA TBK; *Int'l*, pg. 6030
PT. BIOFOREST INDONESIA—See Samko Timber Limited; *Int'l*, pg. 6506
PT BIP SENTOSA—See PT. Bhuwanatala Indah Permai Tbk; *Int'l*, pg. 6085
P.T. BIROTIKA SEMESTA/DHL—See Deutsche Post AG; *Int'l*, pg. 2078
PT BISI INTERNATIONAL TBK; *Int'l*, pg. 6030
PT. BITNET KOMUNIKASINDO—See PT. Elang Mahkota Teknologi Tbk.; *Int'l*, pg. 6085
PT. BITRATEX INDUSTRIES—See PT. Sri Rejeki Isman Tbk; *Int'l*, pg. 6089
PT. BIT TEKNOLOGI NUSANTARA—See PT Sarana Menara Nusantara Tbk; *Int'l*, pg. 6070
PT. BITZER COMPRESSORS INDONESIA—See BITZER SE; *Int'l*, pg. 1052

P.T. BJB SEKURITAS—See PT. Bank Pembangunan Daerah Jawa Barat & Banten, Tbk.; *Int'l*, pg. 6084
PT BLISS PROPERTI INDONESIA, TBK; *Int'l*, pg. 6030
PT. BLOM NUSANTARA—See NRC Group ASA; *Int'l*, pg. 5473
PT. BLUE BIRD PUSAKA—See PT Blue Bird Tbk; *Int'l*, pg. 6030
PT BLUE BIRD TBK; *Int'l*, pg. 6030
PT. BLUE GAS INDONESIA—See PT Tigaraksa Satria Tbk; *Int'l*, pg. 6078
PT BLUE POWER TECHNOLOGY—See PT Anabatic Technologies Tbk; *Int'l*, pg. 6021
PT BLUESCOPE LYSAGHT INDONESIA—See BlueScope Steel Limited; *Int'l*, pg. 1074
PT BMW INDONESIA—See Bayerische Motoren Werke Aktiengesellschaft; *Int'l*, pg. 913
PT BNI LIFE INSURANCE—See PT Bank Negara Indonesia (Persero) Tbk; *Int'l*, pg. 6027
PT BNI MULTIFINANCE—See PT Bank Negara Indonesia (Persero) Tbk; *Int'l*, pg. 6027
PT BNI SECURITIES—See PT Bank Negara Indonesia (Persero) Tbk; *Int'l*, pg. 6027
PT BNI SYARIAH—See PT Bank Negara Indonesia (Persero) Tbk; *Int'l*, pg. 6027
PT BNP PARIBAS INVESTMENT PARTNERS—See BNP Paribas SA; *Int'l*, pg. 1082
PT BNP PARIBAS SECURITIES INDONESIA—See BNP Paribas SA; *Int'l*, pg. 1092
P.T. BOART LONGYEAR—See Boart Longyear Ltd.; *Int'l*, pg. 1095
PT BOBST GROUP INDONESIA—See Bobst Group S.A.; *Int'l*, pg. 1096
PT. BOBST JAKARTA—See Bobst Group S.A.; *Int'l*, pg. 1096
PT BOEHRINGER INGELHEIM INDONESIA—See C.H. Boehringer Sohn AG & Co. KG; *Int'l*, pg. 1243
P.T. BOGORINDO CEMERLANG—See PT Cahayasakti Investindo Sukses Tbk; *Int'l*, pg. 6032
PT BOHLER WELDING GROUP SOUTH EAST ASIA—See voestalpine AG; *Int'l*, pg. 8288
PT BOILERMECH MANUFACTURING INDONESIA—See BM GreenTech Bhd; *Int'l*, pg. 1075
PT BOLLORE LOGISTICS INDONESIA—See Financiere de L'Odet; *Int'l*, pg. 2668
P.T. BONANZA PRATAMA ABADI—See GCK Consolidated Holdings Berhad; *Int'l*, pg. 1367
PT BON CAFE INDONESIA—See Massimo Zanetti Beverage Group SpA; *Int'l*, pg. 4723
P.T. BONNA INDONESIA—See Bain Capital, LP; *U.S. Private*, pg. 438
P.T. BONNA INDONESIA—See P.T. Duta Sarana Perkasa; *Int'l*, pg. 5683
P.T. BONT TECHNOLOGIES NUSANTARA—See UNIMECH Group Berhad; *Int'l*, pg. 8049
PT BORMINDO NUSANTARA—See PT Ancora Indonesia Resources Tbk.; *Int'l*, pg. 6021
PT BORNEO EDO INTERNATIONAL—See PT Antam (Persero) Tbk; *Int'l*, pg. 6022
PT BORNEO LUMBUNG ENERGI & METAL TBK.; *Int'l*, pg. 6030
PT BORNEO OLAH SARANA SUKSES TBK; *Int'l*, pg. 6030
P.T. BOSCH REXROTH—See Robert Bosch GmbH; *Int'l*, pg. 6366
P.T. BOSKALIS INTERNATIONAL INDONESIA—See HAL Trust N.V.; *Int'l*, pg. 3226
P.T.BOSNET DISTRIBUTION INDONESIA—See Perusahaan Perseroan Indonesia Tbk; *Int'l*, pg. 5821
PT. BOSTIK INDONESIA—See Arkema S.A.; *Int'l*, pg. 571
PT BOSTON FURNITURE INDUSTRIES TBK; *Int'l*, pg. 6030
PT BOSTON SCIENTIFIC INDONESIA—See Boston Scientific Corporation; *U.S. Public*, pg. 375
PT BOUSTEAD MAXITHERM INDUSTRIES—See Boustead Singapore Limited; *Int'l*, pg. 1121
PT. BOXON NIKKON JAYAINDO—See Success Transformer Corporation Berhad; *Int'l*, pg. 7250
PT BOYAA INTERACTIVE INDONESIA—See Boyaa Interactive International Ltd; *Int'l*, pg. 1124
P.T. BOZZETTO INDONESIA—See Aimia Inc.; *Int'l*, pg. 234
P.T. BPR CAHAYA WIRAPUTRA—See PT Allo Bank Indonesia Tbk; *Int'l*, pg. 6020
P.T. BRAEMAR TECHNICAL SERVICES OFFSHORE—See Braemar PLC; *Int'l*, pg. 1136
PT. BRAHMAYASA BAHTERA—See PT Astra International Tbk; *Int'l*, pg. 6023
PT. BRATACO CHEMICA—See Brataco, PT; *Int'l*, pg. 1141
PT. BRAVO DELTA PERSADA—See PT Rukun Raharja Tbk; *Int'l*, pg. 6069
PT. BREDERO SHAW INDONESIA—See ShawCor Ltd.; *Int'l*, pg. 6791
PT BRENNTAG INDONESIA—See BRENNTAG SE; *Int'l*, pg. 1149
P.T. BRI DANAREKSA SEKURITAS—See PT Bank Rakyat Indonesia (Persero) Tbk; *Int'l*, pg. 6028
PT. BRIDGESTONE ENGINEERED PRODUCTS INDONESIA—See Bridgestone Corporation; *Int'l*, pg. 1160

PT BUYUNG POETRA SEMBADA TBK

PT. BRIDGESTONE TIRE INDONESIA - BEKASI PLANT—See Bridgestone Corporation; *Int'l*, pg. 1160
PT. BRIDGESTONE TIRE INDONESIA - KARAWANG PLANT—See Bridgestone Corporation; *Int'l*, pg. 1160
P.T. BRIDGESTONE TIRE INDONESIA—See Bridgestone Corporation; *Int'l*, pg. 1160
PT BRIDON—See Ontario Teachers' Pension Plan; *Int'l*, pg. 5587
PT BRI MULTIFINANCE INDONESIA—See Mitsubishi UFJ Financial Group, Inc.; *Int'l*, pg. 4970
PT BRI MULTIFINANCE INDONESIA—See PT Bank Rakyat Indonesia (Persero) Tbk; *Int'l*, pg. 6028
PT BRINKS SOLUTIONS INDONESIA—See The Brink's Company; *U.S. Public*, pg. 2043
PT BRI VENTURA INVESTAMA—See PT Bank Rakyat Indonesia (Persero) Tbk; *Int'l*, pg. 6028
PT BROADBAND WAHANA ASIA—See PT Sarana Menara Nusantara Tbk; *Int'l*, pg. 6070
PT BROTHER INTERNATIONAL SALES INDONESIA—See Brother Industries, Ltd.; *Int'l*, pg. 1198
PT BSH HOME APPLIANCES—See Robert Bosch GmbH; *Int'l*, pg. 6361
PT BSI GROUP INDONESIA—See The British Standards Institution; *Int'l*, pg. 7629
PT. BSM CREW SERVICE CENTRE INDONESIA—See Bernhard Schulte Shipmanagement (Cyprus) Ltd.; *Int'l*, pg. 989
P.T. BTPN SYARIAH VENTURA—See PT Bank BTPN Syariah Tbk.; *Int'l*, pg. 6026
PT BUANA ARTHA ANUGERAH TBK; *Int'l*, pg. 6030
PT BUANA DISTRINDO—See PT Indofood CBP Sukses Makmur Tbk; *Int'l*, pg. 6045
PT BUANA FINANCE TBK.; *Int'l*, pg. 6030
PT BUANA LINTAS LAUTAN TBK—See PT Berlian Laju Tanker Tbk; *Int'l*, pg. 6029
PT BUANA MEGAWISATAMA—See Gallant Venture Ltd.; *Int'l*, pg. 2874
PT BUAYA TRAVEL INDONESIA—See PT Destinasi Tirta Nusantara Tbk; *Int'l*, pg. 6036
PT BUDI LUMBUNG CIPTATANI—See PT Budi Starch & Sweetener Tbk; *Int'l*, pg. 6031
PT BUDI STARCH & SWEETENER TBK; *Int'l*, pg. 6031
PT BUKAKA TEKNIK UTAMA TBK; *Int'l*, pg. 6031
PT BUKA PENGADAAN INDONESIA—See Bukalapak.com PT Tbk; *Int'l*, pg. 1213
PT BUKIT ASAM (PERSERO) TBK - BRIQUETTE—See PT Bukit Asam (Persero) Tbk; *Int'l*, pg. 6031
PT BUKIT ASAM (PERSERO) TBK - GRESIK—See PT Bukit Asam (Persero) Tbk; *Int'l*, pg. 6031
PT BUKIT ASAM (PERSERO) TBK - LAMPUNG—See PT Bukit Asam (Persero) Tbk; *Int'l*, pg. 6031
PT BUKIT ASAM (PERSERO) TBK - SEMARANG—See PT Bukit Asam (Persero) Tbk; *Int'l*, pg. 6031
PT BUKIT ASAM (PERSERO) TBK; *Int'l*, pg. 6031
P.T. BUKIT ASAM PRIMA—See PT Bukit Asam (Persero) Tbk; *Int'l*, pg. 6031
PT. BUKIT DARMO PROPERTY TBK; *Int'l*, pg. 6085
P.T. BUKIT ENERGI SERVIS TERPADU—See PT Bukit Asam (Persero) Tbk; *Int'l*, pg. 6031
P.T. BUKIT LAGOI VILLA—See PT Bukit Uluwatu Villa Tbk; *Int'l*, pg. 6031
P.T. BUKIT LENTERA SEJAHTERA—See PT Bukit Uluwatu Villa Tbk; *Int'l*, pg. 6031
PT BUKIT MAKMUR MANDIRI UTAMA—See PT Delta Dunia Makmur Tbk; *Int'l*, pg. 6035
PT BUKIT PEMBANGKIT INNOVATIVE—See PT Bukit Asam (Persero) Tbk; *Int'l*, pg. 6031
PT BUKIT ULUWATU VILLA TBK; *Int'l*, pg. 6031
PT BUKOPIN FINANCE—See PT Bank KB Bukopin Tbk; *Int'l*, pg. 1000
PT BUMI BENOWO SUKSES SEJAHTERA TBK; *Int'l*, pg. 6031
PT BUMI CITRA PERMAI TBK; *Int'l*, pg. 6031
PT BUMI RESOURCES MINERALS TBK—See PT Bumi Resources Tbk; *Int'l*, pg. 6031
PT BUMI RESOURCES TBK; *Int'l*, pg. 6031
PT BUMI SERPONG DAMAI TBK—See PT Sinar Mas Group; *Int'l*, pg. 6072
PT BUMI SUKSESINDO—See PT Merdeka Copper Gold Tbk; *Int'l*, pg. 6056
PT BUMI TEKNOKULTURA UNGGUL TBK; *Int'l*, pg. 6031
PT BUNDA GLOBAL PHARMA—See PT Bundamedik Tbk; *Int'l*, pg. 6032
PT BUNDAMEDIK TBK; *Int'l*, pg. 6031
P.T. BUNDA MULIA MEDIKA—See PT Metro Healthcare Indonesia Tbk; *Int'l*, pg. 6056
PT BURSA AKSELERASI INDONESIA—See PT Surya Fajar Capital Tbk; *Int'l*, pg. 6077
PT BURSA EFEK INDONESIA; *Int'l*, pg. 6032
PT. BUSSAN AUTO FINANCE—See Mitsui & Co., Ltd.; *Int'l*, pg. 4979
PT BUYUNG POETRA SEMBADA TBK; *Int'l*, pg. 6032
PT BWL INDONESIA—See Best World International Ltd.; *Int'l*, pg. 1000
P.T. BYD MOTOR INDONESIA—See BYD Company Limited; *Int'l*, pg. 1234
P.T. CABLE SOLUTIONS INDONESIA—See KVC Industrial Supplies Sdn. Bhd.; *Int'l*, pg. 4349

PT BUYUNG POETRA SEMBADA TBK

CORPORATE AFFILIATIONS

PT CAHAYA BATU RAJA BLOK—See PT Capitalinc Investment Tbk; *Int'l*, pg. 6032
PT CAHAYA BINTANG MEDAN FURNITURE TBK; *Int'l*, pg. 6032
PT CAHAYAPUTRA ASA KERAMIK TBK; *Int'l*, pg. 6032
PT CAHAYASAKTI INVESTINDO SUKSES TBK; *Int'l*, pg. 6032
P.T. CAHAYA USAHA BERSAMA—See PT Metro Healthcare Indonesia Tbk; *Int'l*, pg. 6056
PT CAKRA BUANA RESOURCES ENERGI TBK; *Int'l*, pg. 6032
PT CAKRA COMPACT ALUMINIUM INDUSTRIES—See Compact Metal Industries Ltd.; *Int'l*, pg. 1721
P.T. CAKRA KENCANA—See PT Trisula International Tbk; *Int'l*, pg. 6080
PT CAKRA MINERAL, TBK.; *Int'l*, pg. 6032
PT CAKRA RADHA MUSTIKA—See PT Kalbe Farma Tbk.; *Int'l*, pg. 6050
PT CAKRAWALA ANDALAS TELEVISI—See PT Visi Media Asia Tbk; *Int'l*, pg. 6081
PTC ALLIANCE CORP.—See Black Diamond Capital Holdings, LLC; *U.S. Private*, pg. 570
PT CALPIS INDONESIA—See Asahi Group Holdings Ltd.; *Int'l*, pg. 593
PT CAMPINA ICE CREAM INDUSTRY TBK; *Int'l*, pg. 6032
PT CAPITAL ASSET MANAGEMENT—See PT Capital Financial Indonesia Tbk; *Int'l*, pg. 6032
PT CAPITAL FINANCIAL INDONESIA TBK; *Int'l*, pg. 6032
PT CAPITALINC INVESTMENT TBK; *Int'l*, pg. 6032
PT CAPITAL LIFE INDONESIA—See PT Capital Financial Indonesia Tbk; *Int'l*, pg. 6032
PT CAPITAL LIFE SYARIAH—See PT Capital Financial Indonesia Tbk; *Int'l*, pg. 6032
PT CAPITOL NUSANTARA INDONESIA TBK.; *Int'l*, pg. 6032
PT CAPRI NUSA SATU PROPERTI TBK; *Int'l*, pg. 6032
P.T. CAPSUGEL INDONESIA—See Pfizer Inc.; *U.S. Public*, pg. 1680
PT. CARDIG AERO SERVICES TBK; *Int'l*, pg. 6085
PT CARDIG ANUGRAH SARANA CATERING—See PT. Cardig Aero Services Tbk; *Int'l*, pg. 6085
PT CARDIG ANUGRA SARANA BERSAMA—See PT. Cardig Aero Services Tbk; *Int'l*, pg. 6085
PT CARGILL INDONESIA GUNUNG PUTRI—See Cargill, Inc.; *U.S. Private*, pg. 759
PT CARGILL INDONESIA—See Cargill, Inc.; *U.S. Private*, pg. 759
P.T. CAROLINE KARYA TEKNOLOGI—See PT Adi Sarana Armada Tbk; *Int'l*, pg. 6019
PT CARSURIN TBK; *Int'l*, pg. 6032
PT. CARTRACK TECHNOLOGIES INDONESIA—See Karooooo Ltd.; *Int'l*, pg. 4084
PT CASCO PERSADA—See Akzo Nobel N.V.; *Int'l*, pg. 273
PT CASHLEZ WORLDWIDE INDONESIA TBK; *Int'l*, pg. 6033
PT CAST LABORATORIES INDONESIA—See Tai Sin Electric Limited; *Int'l*, pg. 7409
PT. CASTROL INDONESIA—See BP plc; *Int'l*, pg. 1131
PT CATERINDO GARMENT INDUSTRI—See Carry Wealth Holdings Limited; *Int'l*, pg. 1346
P.T. CATERPILLAR FINANCE INDONESIA—See Caterpillar, Inc.; *U.S. Public*, pg. 453
P.T. CATERPILLAR INDONESIA—See Caterpillar, Inc.; *U.S. Public*, pg. 453
PT CATURADITYA SENTOSA—See PT Catur Sentosa Adiprana Tbk; *Int'l*, pg. 6033
PT CATUR AGRODAYA MANDIRI—See UPL Limited; *Int'l*, pg. 8089
PT CATUR HASIL SENTOSA—See PT Catur Sentosa Adiprana Tbk; *Int'l*, pg. 6033
PT CATURKARDA DEPO BANGUNAN TBK; *Int'l*, pg. 6033
PT CATUR KARDA SENTOSA—See PT Catur Sentosa Adiprana Tbk; *Int'l*, pg. 6033
PT CATUR LOGAMINDO SENTOSA—See PT Catur Sentosa Adiprana Tbk; *Int'l*, pg. 6033
PT CATUR MITRA SEJATI SENTOSA—See PT Catur Sentosa Adiprana Tbk; *Int'l*, pg. 6033
PT CATUR SENTOSA ADIPRANA TBK; *Int'l*, pg. 6033
PT CATUR SENTOSA ANUGERAH—See PT Catur Sentosa Adiprana Tbk; *Int'l*, pg. 6033
PT CATUR SENTOSA BERHASIL—See PT Catur Sentosa Adiprana Tbk; *Int'l*, pg. 6033
PT. CBC PRIMA—See CBC Co., Ltd.; *Int'l*, pg. 1365
PTC (CANADA) INC.—See PTC Inc.; *U.S. Public*, pg. 1734
PTC-CHIEN LI TRANSPORTATION PTE LTD—See Tower Capital Asia Pte. Ltd.; *Int'l*, pg. 7850
PT CCM INDONESIA—See Batu Kawan Berhad; *Int'l*, pg. 891
PTC CONSTRUCTION LTD.—See Paterson GlobalFoods Inc.; *Int'l*, pg. 5756
PTC EASTERN EUROPE LIMITED S.R.L.—See PTC Inc.; *U.S. Public*, pg. 1734
PT CEDEFINDO—See PT Martina Berto Tbk; *Int'l*, pg. 6055

P.T. CELLA MANAGEMENT LOGISTIK—See PT City Retail Developments Tbk; *Int'l*, pg. 6035
PT CELLMARK INTERINDO TRADE—See CellMark AB; *Int'l*, pg. 1394
PT. CEMANI TOKA—See T&K TOKA Corporation; *Int'l*, pg. 7395
PT CEMINDO GEMILANG TBK; *Int'l*, pg. 6033
PT CENDIKIA GLOBAL SOLUSI—See PT. Voksel Electric Tbk; *Int'l*, pg. 6090
PT CENTRAL DATA TECHNOLOGY—See PT Anabatic Technologies Tbk; *Int'l*, pg. 6021
PT CENTRAL OMEGA RESOURCES TBK; *Int'l*, pg. 6033
PT CENTRAL PROTEINAPRIMA TBK; *Int'l*, pg. 6033
PT CENTRAL SOLE AGENCY—See PT Indomobil Sukses Internasional Tbk; *Int'l*, pg. 6046
PT CENTRAM—See Mitsubishi Corporation; *Int'l*, pg. 4941
P.T. CENTRATAMA MENARA INDONESIA—See PT Centratama Telekomunikasi Indonesia Tbk; *Int'l*, pg. 6033
PT CENTRATAMA TELEKOMUNIKASI INDONESIA TBK; *Int'l*, pg. 6033
P.T. CENTURY ABADI PERKASA—See Rohas Tecnic Berhad; *Int'l*, pg. 6384
PT CENTURY BATTERIES INDONESIA—See PT Astra Otoparts Tbk; *Int'l*, pg. 6024
PT CENTURY DINAMIK DRILLING—See MB Holding Company LLC; *Int'l*, pg. 4750
PT. CENTURY TEXTILE INDUSTRY—See Toray Industries, Inc.; *Int'l*, pg. 7823
PT CENTURY TOKYO LEASING INDONESIA—See PT Sinar Mas Multiartha Tbk; *Int'l*, pg. 6074
PTC ERS SA DE CV—See FAYAT SAS; *Int'l*, pg. 2626
P.T. CETCO OILFIELD SERVICES INDONESIA—See Minerals Technologies, Inc.; *U.S. Public*, pg. 1449
PTC EXPRESS PTE LTD—See Tower Capital Asia Pte. Ltd.; *Int'l*, pg. 7850
PT CGG SERVICES INDONESIA—See CGG; *Int'l*, pg. 1432
PT CHAILEASE INDONESIA FINANCE—See Chailease Holding Company Limited; *Int'l*, pg. 1437
P.T. CHAMPION KURNIA DJAJA TECHNOLOGIES—See Ecolab Inc.; *U.S. Public*, pg. 716
PT CHAMPION PACIFIC INDONESIA TBK; *Int'l*, pg. 6033
PT CHANDRA ASRI PACIFIC TBK—See PT Barito Pacific Tbk; *Int'l*, pg. 6028
PT CHANDRA ASRI PACIFIC TBK—See The Siam Cement Public Company Limited; *Int'l*, pg. 7683
PT. CHANG CHUN DPN CHEMICAL INDUSTRY—See ChangChun Group; *Int'l*, pg. 1442
PT CHARLIE HOSPITAL SEMARANG TBK; *Int'l*, pg. 6033
PT CHAROEN POKPHAND INDONESIA TBK; *Int'l*, pg. 6033
PT CHC MEDIKA INDONESIA—See CHC Healthcare Group; *Int'l*, pg. 1458
PT CHEETHAM GARAM INDONESIA—See CK Hutchison Holdings Limited; *Int'l*, pg. 1637
PT. CHEILJEDANG INDONESIA (PASURUAN)—See CJ Corporation; *Int'l*, pg. 1631
PT.CHEIL JEDANG INDONESIA—See CJ Corporation; *Int'l*, pg. 1634
PT. CHEILJEDANG SUPERFEED—See CJ Corporation; *Int'l*, pg. 1631
P.T. CHEMCO HARAPAN NUSANTARA—See Honda Motor Co., Ltd.; *Int'l*, pg. 3463
PT. CHEMTRONICS INDONESIA—See Chemtronics Co., Ltd.; *Int'l*, pg. 1464
PT CHERNG TAY INDONESIA—See Cherng Tay Technology Co., Ltd.; *Int'l*, pg. 1471
PT CHEVRON PACIFIC INDONESIA—See Chevron Corporation; *U.S. Public*, pg. 487
P.T. CHICAGO BRIDGE & IRON—See McDermott International, Inc.; *U.S. Public*, pg. 1405
PT. CHINA GLAZE INDONESIA—See China Glaze Co., Ltd.; *Int'l*, pg. 1504
PT CHINA TAIPING INSURANCE INDONESIA—See China Taiping Insurance Holdings Company Limited; *Int'l*, pg. 1557
PT CHINA TELECOM INDONESIA—See China Telecommunications Corporation; *Int'l*, pg. 1558
PT CHITA INDONESIA—See KYB Corporation; *Int'l*, pg. 4354
PT CHITOSE C-ENGINEERING INDONESIA—See PT Chitose Internasional Tbk; *Int'l*, pg. 6034
PT CHITOSE INTERNASIONAL TBK; *Int'l*, pg. 6034
PT. CHIYODA INTEGRE INDONESIA—See Chiyoda Integre Co., Ltd.; *Int'l*, pg. 1575
PT. CHIYODA INTERNATIONAL INDONESIA—See Chiyoda Corporation; *Int'l*, pg. 1575
PT CHORI INDONESIA—See Chori Co., Ltd.; *Int'l*, pg. 1583
PT CHUBB GENERAL INSURANCE INDONESIA—See Chubb Limited; *Int'l*, pg. 1592
PT CHUBB GENERAL INSURANCE INDONESIA—See Chubb Limited; *Int'l*, pg. 1593
PT CHUBB LIFE INSURANCE INDONESIA—See Chubb Limited; *Int'l*, pg. 1593
PT. CHUGAI RO INDONESIA—See Chugai Ro Co., Ltd.; *Int'l*, pg. 1594

P.T. CHUGOKU PAINTS INDONESIA—See Chugoku Marine Paints, Ltd.; *Int'l*, pg. 1595
P.T. CHUHATSU INDONESIA—See Chuo Spring Co., Ltd.; *Int'l*, pg. 1599
P.T. CHU KONG STEEL INDONESIA—See Chu Kong Petroleum and Natural Gas Steel Pipe Holdings Limited; *Int'l*, pg. 1589
P.T. CHUO SENKO INDONESIA—See Chuo Senko Advertising Co., Ltd.; *Int'l*, pg. 1599
P.T. CIBA VISION BATAM—See Novartis AG; *Int'l*, pg. 5457
PT CIBOODLE INDONESIA—See Verint Systems Inc.; *U.S. Public*, pg. 2281
PT CIBUBUR UTAMA—See Lippo Malls Indonesia Retail Trust; *Int'l*, pg. 4522
PT CICOR PANATEC—See Cicor Technologies Ltd.; *Int'l*, pg. 1603
PT CIGWELD INDONESIA—See Enovis Corporation; *U.S. Public*, pg. 771
PT CIKARANG LISTRINDO TBK; *Int'l*, pg. 6034
PT CILEGON FABRICATORS—See IHI Corporation; *Int'l*, pg. 3606
PT CIMANGGIS CIBITUNG TOLLWAYS—See Khazanah Nasional Berhad; *Int'l*, pg. 4153
PT CIMB SECURITIES INDONESIA—See CIMB Group Holdings Berhad; *Int'l*, pg. 1608
PTC INC. - FAIRFAX—See PTC Inc.; *U.S. Public*, pg. 1734
PTC INC. - FORT COLLINS—See PTC Inc.; *U.S. Public*, pg. 1734
PTC INC. - NEEDHAM—See PTC Inc.; *U.S. Public*, pg. 1734
PTC, INC.; *U.S. Public*, pg. 1734
PTC INDIA FINANCIAL SERVICES LIMITED—See PTC India Limited; *Int'l*, pg. 6090
PTC INDIA LIMITED; *Int'l*, pg. 6090
PTC INDUSTRIES LIMITED; *Int'l*, pg. 6090
PT CINERE SERPONG JAYA—See PT. Jasa Marga (Persero) Tbk; *Int'l*, pg. 6086
PTC INTERNATIONAL LIMITED LIABILITY COMPANY—See PTC Inc.; *U.S. Public*, pg. 1734
PT CIOMAS ADISATWA—See PT Japfa Comfeed Indonesia Tbk; *Int'l*, pg. 6049
PT CIPTA KARYA TEKNIK—See PT. Voksel Electric Tbk; *Int'l*, pg. 6090
PT CIPTA KRIDA BAHARI—See PT ABM Investama Tbk.; *Int'l*, pg. 6018
PT CIPTA KRIDATAMA—See PT ABM Investama Tbk.; *Int'l*, pg. 6018
PT CIPTA MAPAN LOGISTIK—See PT. Lautan Luas Tbk; *Int'l*, pg. 6050
PT CIPTA SELERA MURNI TBK; *Int'l*, pg. 6034
PT CIPUTRA DEVELOPMENT TBK; *Int'l*, pg. 6034
PT CIPUTRA GRAHA MITRA—See PT Ciputra Development Tbk; *Int'l*, pg. 6034
PT CIPUTRA PROPERTY TBK—See PT Ciputra Development Tbk; *Int'l*, pg. 6034
PT CIREBON ELECTRIC POWER—See Samchully Co., Ltd.; *Int'l*, pg. 6503
P.T. CIRIAJASA E C—See PT Adhi Karya (Persero) Tbk; *Int'l*, pg. 6019
PT CISADANE SAWIT RAYA TBK; *Int'l*, pg. 6034
PT CISARUA MOUNTAIN DAIRY TBK; *Int'l*, pg. 6034
PT CISCO SYSTEMS INDONESIA—See Cisco Systems, Inc.; *U.S. Public*, pg. 500
PT. CITATAH TBK; *Int'l*, pg. 6085
PT CITILINK INDONESIA—See PT Garuda Indonesia (Persero) Tbk; *Int'l*, pg. 6040
PT CITRA BUANA PRASIDA TBK; *Int'l*, pg. 6085
PT CITRA LAUTAN TEDUH—See PT Wijaya Karya (Persero) Tbk; *Int'l*, pg. 6082
PT CITRA MAKMUR RITAILINDO—See Multi Indocitra Tbk; *Int'l*, pg. 5082
PT CITRA MANDIRI PRIMA—See PT Mitra Keluarga Karyasehat Tbk; *Int'l*, pg. 6057
P.T. CITRA MARGA LINTAS JABAR—See PT Citra Marga Nusaphala Persada Tbk.; *Int'l*, pg. 6034
PT CITRA MARGA NUSAPHALA PERSADA TBK.; *Int'l*, pg. 6034
P.T. CITRA MARGATAMA SURABAYA—See PT Citra Marga Nusaphala Persada Tbk.; *Int'l*, pg. 6034
P.T. CITRA PERSADA INFRASTRUKTUR—See PT Citra Marga Nusaphala Persada Tbk.; *Int'l*, pg. 6034
PT CITRA PUTRA REALTY TBK; *Int'l*, pg. 6034
PT. CITRA SARI MAKMUR—See Perusahaan Perseroan Indonesia Tbk; *Int'l*, pg. 5821
PT CITRA TUBINDO TBK.—See Vallourec SA; *Int'l*, pg. 8117
PT CITY RETAIL DEVELOPMENTS TBK; *Int'l*, pg. 6034
PTC JAPAN KK—See PTC Inc.; *U.S. Public*, pg. 1734
PT CJ FEED & CARE INDONESIA—See CJ Corporation; *Int'l*, pg. 1634
PT. CJ FEED JOMBANG—See CJ Corporation; *Int'l*, pg. 1631
PT CJ GLS INDONESIA—See CJ Corporation; *Int'l*, pg. 1633
PT CJ LOGISTICS INDONESIA—See CJ Corporation; *Int'l*, pg. 1634
PT CKD TRADING INDONESIA—See CKD Corporation; *Int'l*, pg. 1639

COMPANY NAME INDEX

PT. CLARIANT ADSORBENTS INDONESIA—See Clariant AG; *Int'l*, pg. 1648
P.T. CLARIANT INDONESIA—See Clariant AG; *Int'l*, pg. 1648
PT CLARIS LIFESCIENCES INDONESIA—See Claris Lifesciences Ltd.; *Int'l*, pg. 1649
PT CLASSIC FINE FOODS INDONESIA—See Metro AG; *Int'l*, pg. 4859
PT CLIPAN FINANCE INDONESIA TBK—See PT. Bank Pan Indonesia Tbk; *Int'l*, pg. 6084
PT CLIPSAL MANUFACTURING JAKARTA—See Schneider Electric SE; *Int'l*, pg. 6628
PT CLS ARGOS INDONESIA—See Collecte Localisation Satellites; *Int'l*, pg. 1699
P.T. CLS SYSTEM—See Advance Information Marketing Berhad; *Int'l*, pg. 156
PT. CLYDE BERGEMANN INDONESIA—See Clyde Blowers Capital IM LLP; *Int'l*, pg. 1665
PTC MARINE PRIVATE LIMITED—See Tower Capital Asia Pte. Ltd.; *Int'l*, pg. 7850
PT. CNBM INTERNATIONAL INDONESIA—See China National Building Material Group Co., Ltd.; *Int'l*, pg. 1526
PT COATS REJO INDONESIA—See Coats Group plc; *Int'l*, pg. 1682
PT. COCA-COLA DISTRIBUTION INDONESIA—See COCA-COLA EUROPACIFIC PARTNERS PLC; *Int'l*, pg. 1684
PTC OCEAN INDIEN—See FAYAT SAS; *Int'l*, pg. 2626
PT COGINDO DAYABERSAMA—See PT Indonesia Power; *Int'l*, pg. 6046
P.T. COGNIS INDONESIA—See BASF SE; *Int'l*, pg. 883
PT COKAL—See Cokal Limited; *Int'l*, pg. 1696
P.T. COLLEGA INTI PRATAMA—See Perusahaan Perseroan Indonesia Tbk; *Int'l*, pg. 5821
P.T. COLORANTS SOLUTIONS INDONESIA—See Clariant AG; *Int'l*, pg. 1648
P.T. COMBA TELECOM NETWORK INDONESIA—See Comba Telecom Systems Holdings Limited; *Int'l*, pg. 1708
PT COMETA INTERNATIONAL; *Int'l*, pg. 6035
PT.COMINIX INDONESIA—See Cominix Co., Ltd.; *Int'l*, pg. 1714
PT COMMUNICATION CABLE SYSTEMS INDONESIA TBK; *Int'l*, pg. 6035
P.T. COMMUNICATIONS & SECURITY—See C3E Global Ltd.; *Int'l*, pg. 1864
PT CONCH NORTH SULAWESI CEMENT—See Anhui Conch Cement Company Limited; *Int'l*, pg. 467
PT CONCH SOUTH KALIMANTAN CEMENT—See Anhui Conch Cement Company Limited; *Int'l*, pg. 467
PT CONSOLIDATED WATER BALI—See Consolidated Water Co. Ltd.; *Int'l*, pg. 1771
PT CONTACT - TELEMARKETING E SERVICOS DE INFORMACAO, S.A.—See Altice Europe N.V.; *Int'l*, pg. 392
PT. CONWOOD INDONESIA—See Siam City Cement Public Company Limited; *Int'l*, pg. 6874
PT CORDLIFE PERSADA—See Cordlife Group Limited; *Int'l*, pg. 1796
PT CORELAB INDONESIA—See Core Laboratories N.V.; *Int'l*, pg. 1798
PT. COSL INDO—See China National Offshore Oil Corp.; *Int'l*, pg. 1533
P.T. COSMO POLYURETHANE INDONESIA—See Mitsui Chemicals, Inc.; *Int'l*, pg. 4983
PT COTTONINDO ARIESTA TBK; *Int'l*, pg. 6035
P-T COUPLING COMPANY—See Parrish Enterprises, Ltd.; *U.S. Private*, pg. 3100
PT COVESTRO POLYMERS INDONESIA—See Bayer Aktiengesellschaft; *Int'l*, pg. 907
PT COWELL DEVELOPMENT TBK.; *Int'l*, pg. 6035
PTC PILING EQUIPMENT (FAR EAST) PTE LTD—See FAYAT SAS; *Int'l*, pg. 2626
P.T. CRANE INDONESIA—See Crane NXT, Co.; *U.S. Public*, pg. 591
P.T. CRANIUM ROYAL ADITAMA—See KT Corporation; *Int'l*, pg. 4315
PT CREADOR INDONESIA—See Creador Sdn. Bhd.; *Int'l*, pg. 1831
PT CREATIVE SOFTHOUSE—See PT Maha Properti Indonesia Tbk; *Int'l*, pg. 6054
PT CREATIVE VISIONS INDONESIA—See XTech Co., Ltd.; *Int'l*, pg. 8539
PT CREDIT SUISSE SECURITIES INDONESIA—See UBS Group AG; *Int'l*, pg. 8007
PT CRESTEC INDONESIA—See Crestec Inc.; *Int'l*, pg. 1841
PT CRIF—See CRIF S.p.A.; *Int'l*, pg. 1849
PT CRODA CIKARANG—See Croda International plc; *Int'l*, pg. 1853
PT CRODA INDONESIA LTD—See Croda International plc; *Int'l*, pg. 1853
PT CROMWELL TOOLS—See W.W. Grainger, Inc.; *U.S. Public*, pg. 2320
PTC SOFTWARE (INDIA) PRIVATE LIMITED—See PTC Inc.; *U.S. Public*, pg. 1734
PTC—See FAYAT SAS; *Int'l*, pg. 2626
PTC—See Nestle S.A.; *Int'l*, pg. 5210
PTC SRL—See Emak S.p.A.; *Int'l*, pg. 2373

PTC (SSI) LIMITED—See PTC Inc.; *U.S. Public*, pg. 1734
PT. CTCI INTERNATIONAL INDONESIA—See CTCI Corporation; *Int'l*, pg. 1870
PT CT CORPORA; *Int'l*, pg. 6035
PTC TECHNOLOGY COMPANY LIMITED—See TPV Technology Co., Ltd.; *Int'l*, pg. 7885
PTC THERAPEUTICS, INC.; *U.S. Public*, pg. 1735
PTC THERAPEUTICS INTERNATIONAL LIMITED—See PTC Therapeutics, Inc.; *U.S. Public*, pg. 1735
PT. CULINA GLOBAL UTAMA—See PT Bukit Uluwatu Villa Tbk; *Int'l*, pg. 6031
PT CUMAWIS—See PT Samudera Indonesia Tbk; *Int'l*, pg. 6069
PTC USA—See FAYAT SAS; *Int'l*, pg. 2626
PT CUSCAPI INDONESIA—See Cuscapi Berhad; *Int'l*, pg. 1880
PTC-XIN HUA TRANSPORTATION PTE LTD—See Tower Capital Asia Pte. Ltd.; *Int'l*, pg. 7850
PT. CYBERQUOTE INDONESIA—See Phillip Capital Pte. Ltd.; *Int'l*, pg. 5846
PT. CYTEC INDONESIA—See Solvay S.A.; *Int'l*, pg. 7078
P.T. DAEKYO INDONESIA—See Daekyo Co Ltd; *Int'l*, pg. 1907
PT. DAELIM INDONESIA—See DAELIM TRADING Co., Ltd.; *Int'l*, pg. 1908
PT. DAELIM UTAMA CONSTRUCTION—See Daelim Industrial Co., Ltd.; *Int'l*, pg. 1908
PT. DAEWOONG PHARMACEUTICAL COMPANY—See Daewoong Pharmaceutical Co., Ltd.; *Int'l*, pg. 1911
PT DAFAM PROPERTY INDONESIA TBK; *Int'l*, pg. 6035
PT DAGANG NET INDONESIA—See Dagang NeXchange Berhad; *Int'l*, pg. 1912
PT. DAIDO DMS INDONESIA—See Daido Steel Co., Ltd.; *Int'l*, pg. 1923
P.T. DAIDO INDONESIA MANUFACTURING—See Daido Kogyo Co., Ltd.; *Int'l*, pg. 1921
PT. DAIDO METAL INDONESIA—See Daido Metal Corporation; *Int'l*, pg. 1922
PT. DAIFUKU INDONESIA—See Daifuku Co., Ltd.; *Int'l*, pg. 1926
PT. DAIKI ALUMINIUM INDUSTRY INDONESIA—See Daiki Aluminium Industry Co., Ltd.; *Int'l*, pg. 1931
PT. DAIKI AXIS INDONESIA—See Daiki Axis Co., Ltd.; *Int'l*, pg. 1932
PT. DAIKIN AIRCONDITIONING INDONESIA—See Daikin Industries, Ltd.; *Int'l*, pg. 1936
PT. DAIKIN APPLIED SOLUTIONS INDONESIA—See Daikin Industries, Ltd.; *Int'l*, pg. 1936
PT. DAIKIN MANUFACTURING INDONESIA—See Daikin Industries, Ltd.; *Int'l*, pg. 1936
PT.DAIKI TRADING INDONESIA—See Daiki Aluminium Industry Co., Ltd.; *Int'l*, pg. 1932
PT. DAIMARU KOGYO—See J. Front Retailing Co., Ltd.; *Int'l*, pg. 3855
P.T. DAIMLERCHRYSLER INDONESIA—See Mercedes-Benz Group AG; *Int'l*, pg. 4828
PT. DAI NIPPON PRINTING INDONESIA—See Dai Nippon Printing Co., Inc.; *Int'l*, pg. 1916
PT DAIWABO INDUSTRIAL FABRICS INDONESIA—See Daiwabo Holdings Co., Ltd.; *Int'l*, pg. 1950
PT. DAIWABO NONWOVEN INDONESIA—See Daiwabo Holdings Co., Ltd.; *Int'l*, pg. 1950
PT DAIWABO SHEETEC INDONESIA—See Daiwabo Holdings Co., Ltd.; *Int'l*, pg. 1950
PT. DAIWA HOUSE INDONESIA—See Daiwa House Industry Co., Ltd.; *Int'l*, pg. 1947
PT. DAIWA LIFE NEXT INDONESIA—See Daiwa House Industry Co., Ltd.; *Int'l*, pg. 1947
PT DAMAI SEJAHTERA ABADI TBK; *Int'l*, pg. 6035
PT DAMI MAS SEJAHTERA—See Golden Agri-Resources Ltd.; *Int'l*, pg. 3028
PT. DAM KORPORINDO DIGITAL—See PT M Cash Integrasi Tbk; *Int'l*, pg. 6053
PT DANA BRATA LUHUR TBK; *Int'l*, pg. 6035
PT DANA PINJAMAN INKLUSIF—See PT Sinar Mas Multiartha Tbk; *Int'l*, pg. 6074
P.T. DANAREKSA INVESTMENT MANAGEMENT—See PT Bank Rakyat Indonesia (Persero) Tbk; *Int'l*, pg. 6028
PT DANAREKSA SEKURITAS—See PT Bank Rakyat Indonesia (Persero) Tbk; *Int'l*, pg. 6028
PT DANA SAHAM BERSAMA—See PT Sinar Mas Multiartha Tbk; *Int'l*, pg. 6074
PT DANASUPRA ERAPACIFIC TBK; *Int'l*, pg. 6035
PT DANAYASA ARTHATAMA TBK—See PT JAKARTA INTERNATIONAL HOTELS & DEVELOPMENT Tbk; *Int'l*, pg. 6048
PT. DANFOSS INDONESIA—See Danfoss A/S; *Int'l*, pg. 1961
PT DANKOS FARMA—See PT Kalbe Farma Tbk.; *Int'l*, pg. 6050
PT DANTOOL KARYA TEKNIK UTAMA—See PT HK Metals Utama; *Int'l*, pg. 6043
PT DANZAS SARANA PERKASA—See Deutsche Post AG; *Int'l*, pg. 2082
PT DAPO AGRO MAKMUR—See Oriental Holdings Berhad; *Int'l*, pg. 5624
PT DARMA HENWA TBK; *Int'l*, pg. 6035
PT DARMI BERSAUDARA TBK; *Int'l*, pg. 6035

PT DIGITAL MEDIATAMA MAXIMA TBK

PT DARYA-VARIA LABORATORIA TBK—See First Pacific Company Limited; *Int'l*, pg. 2686
PT DATA ARTS XPERIENCE—See PT Indomobil Sukses Internasional Tbk; *Int'l*, pg. 6046
P.T. DATA OPAL TERPADU—See PT Sinar Mas Multiartha Tbk; *Int'l*, pg. 6074
PT DATA SINERGITAMA JAYA TBK; *Int'l*, pg. 6035
PT. DAYA KOBELCO CONSTRUCTION MACHINERY INDONESIA—See Kobe Steel, Ltd.; *Int'l*, pg. 4220
PT DAYAMITRA TELEKOMUNIKASI TBK; *Int'l*, pg. 6035
PT DAYANI GARMENT INDONESIA (DGI)—See Daiwabo Holdings Co., Ltd.; *Int'l*, pg. 1950
PT DAYA SECADYME INDONESIA—See Propel Global Berhad; *Int'l*, pg. 5997
PT DAYTONA AZIA—See DAYTONA CORPORATION; *Int'l*, pg. 1985
P.T. DAY TRANS—See PT WEHA Transportasi Indonesia Tbk; *Int'l*, pg. 6082
P.T. DBS VICKERS SEKURITAS INDONESIA—See DBS Group Holdings Ltd.; *Int'l*, pg. 1988
PT DCI INDONESIA TBK; *Int'l*, pg. 6035
PT DEBINDO MITRA TAMA—See PT Dyandra Media Internasional Tbk; *Int'l*, pg. 6037
PT DEFENDER NUSA SEMESTA—See PT Anabatic Technologies Tbk; *Int'l*, pg. 6021
P.T. DEIN PRIMA GENERATOR—See Denyo Co., Ltd.; *Int'l*, pg. 2040
PT DELTA DUNIA MAKMUR TBK; *Int'l*, pg. 6035
PT DELTA FURINDOTAMA—See PT Chitose Internasional Tbk; *Int'l*, pg. 6034
PT. DENTSU CONSULTANTS INDONESIA—See Dentsu Group Inc.; *Int'l*, pg. 2037
PT. DENTSU MEDIA INDONESIA—See Dentsu Group Inc.; *Int'l*, pg. 2037
PT. DENTSU STRAT—See Dentsu Group Inc.; *Int'l*, pg. 2037
P.T. DESSIN JUNN INDONESIA—See Tokai Senko K.K.; *Int'l*, pg. 7781
PT DESTINASI GARUDA WISATA—See PT Destinasi Tirta Nusantara Tbk; *Int'l*, pg. 6036
PT DESTINASI TIRTA NUSANTARA TBK; *Int'l*, pg. 6036
PT DESTINATION ASIA—See The Emirates Group; *Int'l*, pg. 7639
PT DEUTSCHE SECURITIES INDONESIA—See Deutsche Bank Aktiengesellschaft; *Int'l*, pg. 2061
PT DEWATA FREIGHT INTERNATIONAL TBK; *Int'l*, pg. 6036
PT DGIT INDONESIA—See CSG Systems International, Inc.; *U.S. Public*, pg. 601
P.T. DHARMA AGUNG—See M.P. Evans Group PLC; *Int'l*, pg. 4616
PT DHARMA ANUGERAH—See PT Tunas Alfin Tbk; *Int'l*, pg. 6080
PT DHARMA POLIMETAL TBK; *Int'l*, pg. 6036
PT DHARMA SAMUDERA FISHING INDUSTRIES, TBK; *Int'l*, pg. 6085
PT DHARMA SATYA NUSANTARA TBK; *Int'l*, pg. 6036
PT DHL GLOBAL FORWARDING INDONESIA—See Deutsche Post AG; *Int'l*, pg. 2078
P.T. DIACHEM RESINS INDONESIA—See Mitsubishi Chemical Group Corporation; *Int'l*, pg. 4934
PT DIAGNOS LABORATORIUM UTAMA TBK; *Int'l*, pg. 6036
P.T. DIA-JAYA FORWARDING INDONESIA—See Mitsubishi Logistics Corporation; *Int'l*, pg. 4963
PT DIAMOND CITRA PROPERTINDO TBK; *Int'l*, pg. 6036
P.T. DIAMONDFAIR RITEL INDONESIA—See PT Diamond Food Indonesia Tbk; *Int'l*, pg. 6036
PT DIAMOND FOOD INDONESIA TBK; *Int'l*, pg. 6036
PT DIAN SEMESTA SENTOSA—See PT DIAN SWASTATIKA SENTOSA Tbk; *Int'l*, pg. 6036
PT DIAN SWASTATIKA SENTOSA TBK; *Int'l*, pg. 6036
PT DIANTA DAYA EMBARA—See PT ABM Investama Tbk.; *Int'l*, pg. 6018
PT DIC ASTRA CHEMICALS—See DIC Corporation; *Int'l*, pg. 2109
PT. DIC GRAPHICS—See DIC Corporation; *Int'l*, pg. 2109
PT. DIC TRADING INDONESIA—See DIC Corporation; *Int'l*, pg. 2109
PT. DIEBOLD NIXDORF INDONESIA—See Diebold Nixdorf, Inc.; *U.S. Public*, pg. 661
PT. DIGITAL APLIKASI SOLUSI—See Perusahaan Perseroan Indonesia Tbk; *Int'l*, pg. 5821
P.T. DIGITAL DAYA TEKNOLOGI—See PT Multipolar Tbk; *Int'l*, pg. 6060
PT DIGITAL MEDIATAMA MAXIMA TBK; *Int'l*, pg. 6036
PT DIGITAL NIAGA INDONESIA—See Multi Indocitra Tbk; *Int'l*, pg. 5082
P.T. DIGITAL SOLUSINDO NUSANTARA—See PT Sinar Mas Multiartha Tbk; *Int'l*, pg. 6074
PT DIMENSION DATA INDONESIA—See Nippon Telegraph & Telephone Corporation; *Int'l*, pg. 5341
P.T. DIPO ANGKASA MOTOR—See PT Putra Mandiri Jembar Tbk; *Int'l*, pg. 6067
PT. DIPO INTERNASIONAL PAHALA OTOMOTIF—See PT Putra Mandiri Jembar Tbk; *Int'l*, pg. 6067
PT DIRECT NICKEL PTE—See Direct Nickel Limited; *Int'l*, pg. 2130

Company Index

PT DISTRIBUSI VOUCHER NUSANTARA TBK; *Int'l*, pg. 6036
PT DISTRIVERSA BUANAMAS—See Brataco, PT; *Int'l*, pg. 1141
PT DIVERSEY INDONESIA—See Sealed Air Corporation; *U.S. Public*, pg. 1854
P.T. DIWANGKARA HOLIDAY VILLA BAL—See Advance Synergy Berhad; *Int'l*, pg. 156
PT DJASA UBERSAKTI TBK; *Int'l*, pg. 6036
P.T. DJK INDONESIA—See Daiichi Jitsugyo Co. Ltd.; *Int'l*, pg. 1927
PT DJUANDASAWIT LESTARI—See Golden Agri-Resources Ltd.; *Int'l*, pg. 3028
PT DKSH INDONESIA—See Diethelm Keller Holding Limited; *Int'l*, pg. 2117
P.T. DMG MORI INDONESIA—See DMG MORI Co., Ltd.; *Int'l*, pg. 2145
P.T. DMG MORI SEIKI INDONESIA—See DMG MORI Co., Ltd.; *Int'l*, pg. 2145
PT DMS PROPERTINDO TBK; *Int'l*, pg. 6037
PT DMT EXPLORATION ENGINEERING CONSULTING INDONESIA—See TUV NORD AG; *Int'l*, pg. 7980
PT DNT INDONESIA—See Dai Nippon Toryo Co., Ltd.; *Int'l*, pg. 1916
PT DNX INDONESIA—See Incitec Pivot Limited; *Int'l*, pg. 3648
P.T. DOEHLER INDONESIA—See Dohler GmbH; *Int'l*, pg. 2156
PT DOEKU PEDULI INDONESIA—See PT Hensel Davest Indonesia Tbk; *Int'l*, pg. 6043
P.T. DOELLKEN BINTAN EDGINGS & PROFILES—See Surteco Group SE; *Int'l*, pg. 7345
P.T. DONALDSON FILTRATION INDONESIA—See Donaldson Company, Inc.; *U.S. Public*, pg. 676
PT DONGIL METAL INDONESIA—See Dongil Metal Co., Ltd.; *Int'l*, pg. 2168
PT DONGIL RUBBER BELT INDONESIA—See DRB Holding Co., Ltd.; *Int'l*, pg. 2201
PT DONGJIN INDONESIA—See Dongjin Semichem Co., Ltd.; *Int'l*, pg. 2168
P.T. DONGSUNG JAKARTA—See Dongsung Chemical Co., Ltd.; *Int'l*, pg. 2170
PT DOULTON—See Fiskars Oyj Abp; *Int'l*, pg. 2694
PT DOWA THERMOTECH FURNACES—See Dowa Holdings Co., Ltd.; *Int'l*, pg. 2184
P.T. DOWA THERMOTECH INDONESIA—See Dowa Holdings Co., Ltd.; *Int'l*, pg. 2184
PT DOW INDONESIA—See Dow Inc.; *U.S. Public*, pg. 684
PT DRAEGERINDO JAYA—See Draegerwerk AG & Co. KGaA; *Int'l*, pg. 2198
PT DRAEGER MEDICAL INDONESIA—See Draegerwerk AG & Co. KGaA; *Int'l*, pg. 2198
PT DREAM FOOD—See PT Marga Abhinaya Abadi Tbk; *Int'l*, pg. 6054
PT DSG SURYA MAS INDONESIA—See DSG International Limited; *Int'l*, pg. 2210
P.T. DSI INDONESIA—See Sandvik AB; *Int'l*, pg. 6530
P.T. DSI UNDERGROUND—See Sandvik AB; *Int'l*, pg. 6530
P.T. DSM NUTRITIONAL PRODUCTS INDONESIA—See Koninklijke DSM N.V.; *Int'l*, pg. 4265
PT DST GLOBAL SOLUTIONS INDONESIA—See SS&C Technologies Holdings, Inc.; *U.S. Public*, pg. 1923
PT DSV TRANSPORT INDONESIA—See DSV A/S; *Int'l*, pg. 2214
PT DUA KUDA INDONESIA—See Zanyu Technology Group Co., Ltd.; *Int'l*, pg. 8625
PT DUA PUTRA UTAMA MAKMUR TBK.; *Int'l*, pg. 6037
P.T. DUMAI TIRTA PERSADA—See PT Adhi Karya (Persero) Tbk; *Int'l*, pg. 6019
PT DUNIA EXPRESS TRANSINDO—See Kanematsu Corporation; *Int'l*, pg. 4069
PT DUNIA KIMIA JAYA—See PT. Lautan Luas Tbk; *Int'l*, pg. 6087
PT DUNIA KIMIA UTAMA—See PT. Lautan Luas Tbk; *Int'l*, pg. 6087
PT DUNIA VISITAMA—See Bertelsmann SE & Co. KGaA; *Int'l*, pg. 995
P.T. DUPAN ANUGERAH LESTARI—See PT Saraswanti Anugerah Makmur Tbk; *Int'l*, pg. 6070
PT DURO FELGUERA INDONESIA—See Duro Felguera, S.A.; *Int'l*, pg. 2229
PT DURR SYSTEMS INDONESIA—See Durr AG; *Int'l*, pg. 2233
PT DUTA ANGGADA REALTY TBK; *Int'l*, pg. 6037
P.T. DUTA BUANA EXPRESS—See PT Bayu Buana Tbk; *Int'l*, pg. 6029
PT DUTAGRIYA SARANA—See Pasona Group Inc.; *Int'l*, pg. 5753
PT DUTA INTIDAYA TBK; *Int'l*, pg. 6037
PT DUTA MITRA SOLUSINDO—See PT Adi Sarana Armada Tbk; *Int'l*, pg. 6019
PT DUTA PERTIWI NUSANTARA TBK; *Int'l*, pg. 6037
PT DUTA PERTIWI TBK—See PT Sinar Mas Group; *Int'l*, pg. 6072
P.T. DUTA SARANA PERKASA; *Int'l*, pg. 5683
PT DWI GUNA LAKSANA TBK; *Int'l*, pg. 6037
PT DWIJAYA MANUNGGAL—See PT. PAKUWON JATI Tbk; *Int'l*, pg. 6088

PT DWIKARYA SEJATI UTAMA—See PT DIAN SWASTATIKA SENTOSA Tbk; *Int'l*, pg. 6036
PT DWIMITRA GRAHA MANDIRI—See Roda Vivatex Tbk; *Int'l*, pg. 6382
PT DWINAD NUSA SEJAHTERA—See Sumatra Copper & Gold plc; *Int'l*, pg. 7260
PT DWIPA MINA NUSANTARA—See PT Sreeya Sewu Indonesia Tbk; *Int'l*, pg. 6075
PT DYANDRA COMMUNICATION—See PT Dyandra Media International Tbk; *Int'l*, pg. 6037
PT DYANDRA GLOBAL EDUTAINMENT—See PT Dyandra Media International Tbk; *Int'l*, pg. 6037
PT DYANDRA MEDIA INTERNATIONAL TBK; *Int'l*, pg. 6037
PT DYANDRA PROMOSINDO—See PT Dyandra Media International Tbk; *Int'l*, pg. 6037
PT DYNAPLAST TBK.; *Int'l*, pg. 6037
P.T. DYSON ZEDMARK INDONESIA LIMITED—See Dyson Group plc; *Int'l*, pg. 2243
PT DYSTAR COLOURS INDONESIA—See Kiri Industries Ltd.; *Int'l*, pg. 4186
PT EAC INDONESIA—See BRENNTAG SE; *Int'l*, pg. 1149
P.T. EAGLEBURGMANN INDONESIA—See Eagle Industry Co., Ltd.; *Int'l*, pg. 2266
P.T. EAGLEBURGMANN INDONESIA—See Freudenberg SE; *Int'l*, pg. 2784
PT EAGLE HIGH PLANTATIONS TBK; *Int'l*, pg. 6037
P.T. EAGLE INDUSTRY INDONESIA—See Eagle Industry Co., Ltd.; *Int'l*, pg. 2266
PTE ALLIANZ POLSKA S.A.—See Allianz SE; *Int'l*, pg. 356
PTE ALLIANZ POLSKA SA—See Allianz SE; *Int'l*, pg. 355
PT EASPARC HOTEL TBK; *Int'l*, pg. 6037
PT EAST ASIA MINERALS INDONESIA—See Queen's Road Capital Investment Ltd.; *Int'l*, pg. 6159
PT EASTERN JASON—See PT Sillo Maritime Perdana Tbk; *Int'l*, pg. 6072
PT EASTERN LOGISTICS—See Rotary Engineering Pte. Ltd.; *Int'l*, pg. 6402
P.T. EASTERNTEX—See Toray Industries, Inc.; *Int'l*, pg. 7823
P.T. EAST JAKARTA INDUSTRIAL PARK—See Sumitomo Corporation; *Int'l*, pg. 7269
P.T. EBARA INDONESIA—See Ebara Corporation; *Int'l*, pg. 2284
P.T. EBARA INDONESIA—See Ebara Corporation; *Int'l*, pg. 2284
PT EBARA TURBOMACHINERY SERVICES INDONESIA—See Ebara Corporation; *Int'l*, pg. 2284
P.T. ECCO INDONESIA—See Ecco Sko A/S; *Int'l*, pg. 2288
P.T. ECLAT TEXTILE INTERNATIONAL—See Eclat Textile Co., Ltd.; *Int'l*, pg. 2291
P.T. ECOLAB INDONESIA—See Ecolab Inc.; *U.S. Public*, pg. 716
P.T. ECOLAB INTERNATIONAL INDONESIA—See Ecolab Inc.; *U.S. Public*, pg. 716
PTE COMPOUNDING DE MEXICO S.A. DE C.V.—See Woco Industrietechnik GmbH; *Int'l*, pg. 8442
PT ECO PAPER INDONESIA—See PT Alkindo Naratama Tbk; *Int'l*, pg. 6020
PTEC PRESSURE TECHNOLOGY GMBH—See Worthington Industries, Inc.; *U.S. Public*, pg. 2382
PT ECS INDO JAYA—See VSTECS Holdings Limited; *Int'l*, pg. 8314
PT ECU WORLDWIDE INDONESIA—See Allcargo Logistics Limited; *Int'l*, pg. 334
P. E D & F MAN INDONESIA—See ED&F Man Holdings Limited; *Int'l*, pg. 2303
PT. EDMI INDONESIA—See Osaki Electric Co., Ltd.; *Int'l*, pg. 5647
PT. EDS MANUFACTURING INDONESIA—See Yazaki Corporation; *Int'l*, pg. 8572
P.T. EDUKASI ATLIT INTERNET DIGITAL—See PT M Cash Integrasi Tbk; *Int'l*, pg. 6054
PTE ENGINEERING LIMITED—See King Fook Holdings Limited; *Int'l*, pg. 4168
P.T. EGEROO INOVASI TEKNOLOGI—See PT Anabatic Technologies Tbk; *Int'l*, pg. 6021
PT EGIS INDONESIA—See Caisse des Depots et Consignations; *Int'l*, pg. 1258
PT EGON ZEHNDER INTERNATIONAL—See Egon Zehnder International Inc.; *U.S. Private*, pg. 1345
PT. EIDAI INDUSTRIES INDONESIA—See Eidai Co., Ltd.; *Int'l*, pg. 2328
PT EISAI INDONESIA - BOGOR FACTORY—See Eisai Co., Ltd.; *Int'l*, pg. 2335
P.T. EISAI INDONESIA—See Eisai Co., Ltd.; *Int'l*, pg. 2335
PT EKA CHEMICALS INDONESIA—See Akzo Nobel N.V.; *Int'l*, pg. 274
PT EKADHARMA INTERNATIONAL TBK; *Int'l*, pg. 6037
PT EKA DHARMA JAYA SAKTI—See PT Indomobil Sukses Internasional Tbk; *Int'l*, pg. 6046
PT EKAGRATA DATA GEMILANG—See PT Indointernet Tbk; *Int'l*, pg. 6045
PT EKA MAS REPUBLIK—See PT DIAN SWASTATIKA SENTOSA Tbk; *Int'l*, pg. 6036
PT EKAMITA ARAHTEGAR—See PT Mitra Keluarga Karyasehat Tbk; *Int'l*, pg. 6057
PT EKA SARI LORENA TRANSPORT TBK.; *Int'l*, pg. 6085

PT. ELANG MAHKOTA TEKNOLOGI TBK.; *Int'l*, pg. 6085
PT. ELASTOMIX INDONESIA—See JSR Corp.; *Int'l*, pg. 4014
PT ELDERS INDONESIA; *Int'l*, pg. 6037
P.T. ELECTRA DISTRIBUSI INDONESIA—See PT. Indika Energy Tbk; *Int'l*, pg. 6044
PT. ELECTRONIC CITY INDONESIA TBK; *Int'l*, pg. 6086
PT ELEGANT TEXTILE INDUSTRY—See The Aditya Birla Group; *Int'l*, pg. 7612
PT ELGI EQUIPMENTS INDONESIA—See ELGI Equipments Limited; *Int'l*, pg. 2360
PT ELITE PRIMA HUTAMA—See PT. PAKUWON JATI Tbk; *Int'l*, pg. 6088
PT ELNUSA FABRIKASI KONSTRUKSI—See PT Elnusa Tbk; *Int'l*, pg. 6037
PT ELNUSA GEOSAINS INDONESIA—See PT Elnusa Tbk; *Int'l*, pg. 6038
PT ELNUSA OILFIELD SERVICES—See PT Elnusa Tbk; *Int'l*, pg. 6038
PT ELNUSA PETROFIN—See PT Elnusa Tbk; *Int'l*, pg. 6038
PT ELNUSA TBK; *Int'l*, pg. 6037
PT ELNUSA TRANS SAMUDERA—See PT Elnusa Tbk; *Int'l*, pg. 6038
P.T. ELO KARSA UTAMA—See BioLASCO Taiwan Co., Ltd.; *Int'l*, pg. 1038
P.T. EMAS ANTAM INDONESIA—See PT Aneka Tambang (Persero) Tbk; *Int'l*, pg. 6022
PT. EMBLEM ASIA—See Unitika Ltd.; *Int'l*, pg. 8074
PT EMDEKI UTAMA TBK; *Int'l*, pg. 6038
PT. EMERIO INDONESIA—See Nippon Telegraph & Telephone Corporation; *Int'l*, pg. 5344
PT. EMERSON INDONESIA—See Emerson Electric Co.; *U.S. Public*, pg. 751
PT EMERSON SOLUTIONS INDONESIA—See Emerson Electric Co.; *U.S. Public*, pg. 750
PT EMINA CHEESE INDONESIA—See Mitsubishi Corporation; *Int'l*, pg. 4942
PT EMITAMA WAHANA MANDIRI—See PT Quantum Clovera Investama Tbk; *Int'l*, pg. 6067
PT EMORI INDONESIA—See Kowa Co., Ltd.; *Int'l*, pg. 4294
P.T. EMOS GLOBAL DIGITAL—See PT Kalbe Farma Tbk.; *Int'l*, pg. 6050
PT EMPHI PHARMA SEJAHTERA—See PT Bundamedik Tbk; *Int'l*, pg. 6032
PT EMPOSH SINERGI ASIA—See PT Hensel Davest Indonesia Tbk; *Int'l*, pg. 6043
P.T.ENBLEM ASIA—See Unitika Ltd.; *Int'l*, pg. 8074
PT. ENDRESS+HAUSER INDONESIA—See Endress+Hauser (International) Holding AG; *Int'l*, pg. 2409
PT ENERGASINDO HEKSA KARYA—See PT Rukun Raharja Tbk; *Int'l*, pg. 6069
PT ENERGIA PRIMA NUSANTARA—See PT United Tractors Tbk; *Int'l*, pg. 6081
PT. ENERGI MAS ANUGERAH SEMESTA—See PT. DIAN SWASTATIKA SENTOSA Tbk; *Int'l*, pg. 6036
PT ENERGI MEGA PERSADA TBK; *Int'l*, pg. 6038
PT. ENPLAS INDONESIA—See ENPLAS CORPORATION; *Int'l*, pg. 2445
P.T. ENSCO SARIDA OFFSHORE—See Valaris Limited; *Int'l*, pg. 8110
PT ENSEVAL MEDIKA PRIMA—See PT Kalbe Farma Tbk.; *Int'l*, pg. 6050
PT ENSEVAL PUTERA MEGATRADING TBK.—See PT Kalbe Farma Tbk.; *Int'l*, pg. 6050
PT. ENSHU INDONESIA—See Enshu Limited; *Int'l*, pg. 2446
PT ENVY TECHNOLOGIES INDONESIA TBK; *Int'l*, pg. 6038
PT EPAC FLEXIBLES INDONESIA—See PT Megalestari Epack Sentosaraya Tbk; *Int'l*, pg. 6056
P.T. EPID MENARA ASSETCO—See PT Centratama Telekomunikasi Indonesia Tbk; *Int'l*, pg. 6033
PT EPIROC SOUTHERN ASIA—See Epiroc AB; *Int'l*, pg. 2463
P.T.EPSON BATAM—See Seiko Epson Corporation; *Int'l*, pg. 6687
PT. EPSON INDONESIA—See Seiko Epson Corporation; *Int'l*, pg. 6687
P.T. EQUINE GLOBAL—See PT Anabatic Technologies Tbk; *Int'l*, pg. 6021
PT EQUITY DEVELOPMENT INVESTMENT TBK; *Int'l*, pg. 6038
PT EQUITY FINANCE INDONESIA—See PT Equity Development Investment Tbk; *Int'l*, pg. 6038
PT EQUITY LIFE INDONESIA—See PT Equity Development Investment Tbk; *Int'l*, pg. 6038
P.T. ERA BLU ELEKTRONIK—See PT Erajaya Swasembada Tbk; *Int'l*, pg. 6038
PT ERA DIGITAL MEDIA TBK.; *Int'l*, pg. 6038
PT ERA GRAHAREALTY TBK—See Morgan Stanley; *U.S. Public*, pg. 1471
PT ERAJAYA SWASEMBADA TBK; *Int'l*, pg. 6038
PT ERA MANDIRI CEMERLANG TBK; *Int'l*, pg. 6038
PT ERA MEDIA SEJAHTERA TBK.; *Int'l*, pg. 6038
PT ERATEX DJAJA TBK; *Int'l*, pg. 6038

COMPANY NAME INDEX

P.T. ERICSSON INDONESIA—See Telefonaktiebolaget LM Ericsson; *Int'l*, pg. 7534
PTERIS GLOBAL (BEIJING) LTD.—See CIMC-TianDa Holdings Company Limited; *Int'l*, pg. 1609
PTERIS GLOBAL LIMITED—See CIMC-TianDa Holdings Company Limited; *Int'l*, pg. 1608
PTERIS GLOBAL SDN BHD—See CIMC-TianDa Holdings Company Limited; *Int'l*, pg. 1609
P.T. ESERVGLOBAL INDONESIA—See Seamless Distribution Systems AB; *Int'l*, pg. 6665
PT ESG PANATEC—See Cicor Technologies Ltd.; *Int'l*, pg. 1603
PT ESRI INDONESIA—See Boustead Singapore Limited; *Int'l*, pg. 1121
PT ESSA INDUSTRIES INDONESIA TBK.; *Int'l*, pg. 6038
PT ESSAR INDONESIA—See Essar Global Limited; *Int'l*, pg. 2508
PT ESSENTRA—See Essentra plc; *Int'l*, pg. 2511
PT ESTA MULTI USAHA TBK; *Int'l*, pg. 6039
PT ESTIKA TATA TIARA TBK; *Int'l*, pg. 6039
PT. ESTOP INDONESIA—See Denki Company Limited; *Int'l*, pg. 2027
PT. ETEC INDONESIA—See SGC eTEC E&C Co., Ltd.; *Int'l*, pg. 6741
PT ETERINDO NUSA GRAHA—See PT Tridomain Performance Materials Tbk; *Int'l*, pg. 6079
PT ETERINDO WAHANATAMA TBK; *Int'l*, pg. 6039
PT ETERNA KARYA SEJAHTERA—See Daikin Industries, Ltd.; *Int'l*, pg. 1936
PT ETERNAL BUANA CHEMICAL INDUSTRIES—See PT Tridomain Performance Materials Tbk; *Int'l*, pg. 6079
P.T. ETERNAL MATERIALS INDONESIA—See Eternal Materials Co., Ltd.; *Int'l*, pg. 2521
P.T. ETERNIT GRESIK—See PT. Semen Indonesia (Persero) Tbk; *Int'l*, pg. 6089
PT. EUROTRUK TRANSINDO—See PT. Kobexindo Tractors Tbk; *Int'l*, pg. 6087
PT. EUSU LOGISTICS INDONESIA—See Eusu Holdings Co., Ltd.; *Int'l*, pg. 2559
P.T. EVERGREEN SHIPPING AGENCY INDONESIA—See Evergreen Marine Corporation (Taiwan) Ltd.; *Int'l*, pg. 2566
PT EVER SHINE TEX TBK; *Int'l*, pg. 6039
PT. EXCELITAS TECHNOLOGIES BATAM—See AEA Investors LP; *U.S. Private*, pg. 113
PT. EXCLUSIVE NETWORKS INDONESIA—See Permira Advisers LLP; *Int'l*, pg. 5804
PT. EXEDY MANUFACTURING INDONESIA—See Exedy Corporation; *Int'l*, pg. 2581
P.T. EXEDY MOTORCYCLE INDONESIA—See Exedy Corporation; *Int'l*, pg. 2581
P.T. EXEDY PRIMA INDONESIA—See Exedy Corporation; *Int'l*, pg. 2581
P.T. EXPEDITORS INDONESIA—See Expeditors International of Washington, Inc.; *U.S. Public*, pg. 812
PT. EXPERIAN DECISION ANALYTICS INDONESIA—See Experian plc; *Int'l*, pg. 2588
PT EXPLOITASI ENERGI INDONESIA TBK; *Int'l*, pg. 6039
PT EXPRESS TRANSINDO UTAMA TBK—See PT Rajawali Corporation; *Int'l*, pg. 6067
PT EXSPAN PETROGAS INTRANUSA—See PT Medco Energi Internasional Tbk; *Int'l*, pg. 6055
PT. EXTERRAN INDONESIA—See Enerflex Ltd.; *Int'l*, pg. 2419
PT. EYE GRAPHIC INDONESIA—See Texchem Resources Bhd.; *Int'l*, pg. 7583
P.T. FABER-CASTELL INTERNATIONAL INDONESIA—See Faber-Castell AG; *Int'l*, pg. 2599
PT FAJAR BUMI SAKTI—See PT Bumi Resources Tbk; *Int'l*, pg. 6031
PT FAJARPUTERA DINASTI—See PT Metropolitan Land Tbk; *Int'l*, pg. 6056
PT FAJAR SURYA WISESA TBK - FACTORY - PABRIK—See The Siam Cement Public Company Limited; *Int'l*, pg. 7685
PT FAJAR SURYA WISESA TBK—See The Siam Cement Public Company Limited; *Int'l*, pg. 7685
PT FANAH JAYA MAINDO—See Sonepar S.A.; *Int'l*, pg. 7091
PT. FANUC INDONESIA—See FANUC Corporation; *Int'l*, pg. 2615
PT FAP AGRI TBK; *Int'l*, pg. 6039
PT. FAR EAST REFRIGERATION INDONESIA—See Far East Group Limited; *Int'l*, pg. 2616
PT FASEN CREATIVE QUALITY—See PT Dyandra Media International Tbk; *Int'l*, pg. 6037
PT FASTEL SARANA INDONESIA—See PT Centratama Telekomunikasi Indonesia Tbk; *Int'l*, pg. 6033
PT FAST FOOD INDONESIA TBK; *Int'l*, pg. 6039
PT. FAST OFFSHORE INDONESIA—See PT Wintermar Offshore Marine Tbk; *Int'l*, pg. 6083
PTFC REDEVELOPMENT CORPORATION; *Int'l*, pg. 6090
PT FDK INDONESIA—See Fujitsu Limited; *Int'l*, pg. 2833
PTFE COMPOUNDS GERMANY GMBH—See Freudenberg SE; *Int'l*, pg. 2790
PT FEDERAL INTERNATIONAL FINANCE—See PT Astra International Tbk; *Int'l*, pg. 6023
PT FEDERAL INTERNATIONAL—See Federal International (2000) Ltd; *Int'l*, pg. 2630

PT FEDERAL IZUMI MANUFACTURING—See PT Astra Otoparts Tbk; *Int'l*, pg. 6024
PT FEDERAL KARYATAMA—See Exxon Mobil Corporation; *U.S. Public*, pg. 817
PT. FEDERAL NITTAN INDUSTRIES—See NITTAN Corporation; *Int'l*, pg. 5383
PT FEDSIN REKAYASA PRATAMA—See Federal International (2000) Ltd; *Int'l*, pg. 2630
P.T. FENG TAY INDONESIA ENTERPRISES—See Feng Tay Enterprises Co., Ltd.; *Int'l*, pg. 2634
PT FENI HALTIM—See PT Aneka Tambang (Persero) Tbk; *Int'l*, pg. 6022
PTFE POLAR PACKAGING MFG./SEALS APS—See Parker Hannifin Corporation; *U.S. Public*, pg. 1648
PT FERRO CERAMIC COLORS INDONESIA—See American Securities LLC; *U.S. Private*, pg. 252
P.T. FERRO CONSTRUCTION CO.; *U.S. Private*, pg. 3061
PT FERRO MAS DINAMIKA—See American Securities LLC; *U.S. Private*, pg. 252
PT FERRO MATERIALS UTAMA—See American Securities LLC; *U.S. Private*, pg. 252
PT. FESTO—See Festo AG & Co. KG; *Int'l*, pg. 2648
PT FILEMON INTI MACHINERY—See Nicolas Correa S.A.; *Int'l*, pg. 5273
PT FIMPERKASA UTAMA TBK; *Int'l*, pg. 6039
PT FINACCEL TEKNOLOGI INDONESIA—See FinAccel Pte Ltd.; *Int'l*, pg. 2664
PT. FINE SINTER INDONESIA—See Fine Sinter Co., Ltd.; *Int'l*, pg. 2673
PT FINNET INDONESIA—See Perusahaan Perseroan Indonesia Tbk; *Int'l*, pg. 5821
PT FINUSOLPRIMA FARMA INTERNASIONAL—See PT Kalbe Farma Tbk.; *Int'l*, pg. 6050
PT FIRCROFT INDONESIA—See AEA Investors LP; *U.S. Private*, pg. 115
PT. FIRMENICH AROMATICS INDONESIA—See Firmenich International SA; *Int'l*, pg. 2681
PT. FIRMENICH INDONESIA—See Firmenich International SA; *Int'l*, pg. 2681
PT. FIRST ASIA INDONESIA—See First Asia Holdings Limited; *Int'l*, pg. 2682
PT FIRST INDO AMERICAM LEASING TBK; *Int'l*, pg. 6039
PT FIRST MEDIA TBK; *Int'l*, pg. 6039
P.T. FITAJA DIGITAL NUSANTARA—See PT Bank Mandiri (Persero) Tbk.; *Int'l*, pg. 6026
PT FKS FOOD SEJAHTERA TBK; *Int'l*, pg. 6039
PT FKS MULTI AGRO TBK; *Int'l*, pg. 6039
PT. FLASH MOBILE—See PT MNC Investama Tbk; *Int'l*, pg. 6058
PT FLEISHMAN-HILLIARD—See Omnicom Group Inc.; *U.S. Public*, pg. 1585
PT. FLEXINDOMAS—See THK CO., LTD.; *Int'l*, pg. 7712
PT FLEXLINK SYSTEMS—See Coesia S.p.A.; *Int'l*, pg. 1689
PT FLEXTRONICS TECHNOLOGY INDONESIA—See Flex Ltd.; *Int'l*, pg. 2704
PT. FLO-BEND INDONESIA—See Berkshire Hathaway Inc.; *U.S. Public*, pg. 314
PT FLORA SAWITA CHEMINDO—See PT Bakrie Sumatera Plantations Tbk; *Int'l*, pg. 6025
PT FLOWSERVE—See Flowserve Corporation; *U.S. Public*, pg. 857
PT FLSMIDTH INDONESIA—See FLSmidth & Co. A/S; *Int'l*, pg. 2710
PTF MANUFACTURING INC.—See Mission Ready Solutions Inc.; *Int'l*, pg. 4921
PT FMC INDONESIA—See Fresenius Medical Care AG; *Int'l*, pg. 2777
P.T. FMC SANTANA PETROLEUM EQUIPMENT INDONESIA—See TechnipFMC plc; *U.S. Public*, pg. 7507
PT. FM GLOBAL LOGISTICS—See FM Global Logistics Holdings Berhad; *Int'l*, pg. 2717
PT FORMOSA INGREDIENT FACTORY TBK; *Int'l*, pg. 6039
PT. FORSTA KALMEDIC GLOBAL—See PT Kalbe Farma Tbk.; *Int'l*, pg. 6050
PT FORTINET INDONESIA SECURITY—See Fortinet, Inc.; *U.S. Public*, pg. 869
PT FORTUNE MATE INDONESIA TBK; *Int'l*, pg. 6039
PT FORZA LAND INDONESIA TBK; *Int'l*, pg. 6039
PT. FOSECO INDONESIA—See Vesuvius plc; *Int'l*, pg. 8179
P.T. FOSTER ELECTRIC INDONESIA—See Foster Electric Co., Ltd.; *Int'l*, pg. 2750
PT FOSTER WHEELER O&G INDONESIA—See John Wood Group PLC; *Int'l*, pg. 3983
P.T. FPT SOFTWARE INDONESIA—See FPT Corporation; *Int'l*, pg. 2758
PT FRANKS INDONESIA—See Expro Group Holdings N.V.; *Int'l*, pg. 2591
PT FREAKOUT DEWINA INDONESIA—See FreakOut Holdings, Inc.; *Int'l*, pg. 2767
PT FREEPORT INDONESIA—See Freeport-McMoRan Inc.; *U.S. Public*, pg. 884
PT FREYABADI INDOTAMA—See Fuji Oil Holdings Inc.; *Int'l*, pg. 2815
PT FREYSSINET TOTAL TECHNOLOGY—See VINCI S.A.; *Int'l*, pg. 8225

P.T. FRIEDRICH KLUMPP WOODCOATINGS—See The Sherwin-Williams Company; *U.S. Public*, pg. 2128
PT FRIGOGLASS INDONESIA—See Frigoglass S.A.I.C.; *Int'l*, pg. 2792
PT FRISIAN FLAG INDONESIA—See Zuivelcooperatie FrieslandCampina U.A.; *Int'l*, pg. 8694
PT FRISTINDO JAYA PUMP—See FRISTAM Pumpen F. Stamp GmbH & Co. KG; *Int'l*, pg. 2793
P.T. FRONTIER INTERNATIONAL INDONESIA—See Frontier International, Inc.; *Int'l*, pg. 2795
PT FRONTKEN INDONESIA—See Frontken Corporation Berhad; *Int'l*, pg. 2796
PT. F.TECH INDONESIA—See F-Tech Inc.; *Int'l*, pg. 2595
PT. FTI CONSULTING INDONESIA—See FTI Consulting, Inc.; *U.S. Public*, pg. 891
PTF TRAINING LIMITED—See Wesfarmers Limited; *Int'l*, pg. 8381
PT FUCHS INDONESIA—See FUCHS SE; *Int'l*, pg. 2803
PT. FUGRO INDONESIA—See Fugro N.V.; *Int'l*, pg. 2808
PT FUJIBOLT INDONESIA - BOGOR FACTORY—See Okabe Co., Ltd.; *Int'l*, pg. 5544
P.T. FUJI DHARMA ELECTRIC—See Fuji Electric Co., Ltd.; *Int'l*, pg. 2812
PT. FUJIFILM INDONESIA—See FUJIFILM Holdings Corporation; *Int'l*, pg. 2823
PT FUJI FINANCE INDONESIA TBK; *Int'l*, pg. 6039
PT. FUJI FURUKAWA E&C INDONESIA—See Fuji Furukawa Engineering & Construction Co., Ltd.; *Int'l*, pg. 2813
PT FUJIKURA INDONESIA—See Fujikura Ltd.; *Int'l*, pg. 2829
PT. FUJIKURA KASEI INDONESIA—See Fujikura Kasei Co., Ltd.; *Int'l*, pg. 2827
PT. FUJILLOY INDONESIA—See Fuji Die Co., Ltd.; *Int'l*, pg. 2810
PT. FUJI METEC SEMARANG—See Fuji Electric Co., Ltd.; *Int'l*, pg. 2812
PT. FUJI OOZX INDONESIA—See Daido Steel Co., Ltd.; *Int'l*, pg. 1923
PT. FUJI SEAL INDONESIA—See Fuji Seal International, Inc.; *Int'l*, pg. 2816
PT.FUJI SEAL PACKAGING INDONESIA—See Fuji Seal International, Inc.; *Int'l*, pg. 2817
PT. FUJI SEIKI INDONESIA—See Fuji Seiki Co., Ltd.; *Int'l*, pg. 2817
PT FUJITA KANKO INDONESIA—See Fujita Kanko Inc.; *Int'l*, pg. 2831
PT FUJI TECHNICA INDONESIA—See PT Astra International Tbk; *Int'l*, pg. 6023
PT. FUJITEC INDONESIA—See Fujitec Co., Ltd.; *Int'l*, pg. 2831
PT. FUKOKU TOKAI RUBBER INDONESIA - FACTORY 1—See Fukoku Co., Ltd.; *Int'l*, pg. 2839
PT. FUKOKU TOKAI RUBBER INDONESIA - FACTORY 3—See Fukoku Co., Ltd.; *Int'l*, pg. 2839
PT. FUKOKU TOKAI RUBBER INDONESIA—See Fukoku Co., Ltd.; *Int'l*, pg. 2839
PT. FUKUDA TECHNOLOGY—See Nagano Keiki Co., Ltd.; *Int'l*, pg. 5125
PT. FUKUSHIMA INTERNATIONAL INDONESIA—See Fukushima Galilei Co. Ltd.; *Int'l*, pg. 2841
P.T. FUMAKILLA INDONESIA—See Fumakilla Limited; *Int'l*, pg. 2844
P.T. FURUKAWA AUTOMOTIVE SYSTEMS INDONESIA—See The Furukawa Electric Co., Ltd.; *Int'l*, pg. 7646
P.T. FURUKAWA ELECTRIC INDONESIA—See The Furukawa Electric Co., Ltd.; *Int'l*, pg. 7646
PT. FURUKAWA INDAL ALUMINUM—See UACJ Corporation; *Int'l*, pg. 7999
PT FURUKAWA INDOMOBIL BATTERY SALES—See PT Indomobil Sukses Internasional Tbk; *Int'l*, pg. 6046
P.T. FURUKAWA OPTICAL SOLUTIONS INDONESIA—See The Furukawa Electric Co., Ltd.; *Int'l*, pg. 7646
P.T. FURUKAWA PERMINTEX AUTOPARTS INDONESIA—See The Furukawa Electric Co., Ltd.; *Int'l*, pg. 7646
PT.FURUNO ELECTRIC INDONESIA—See Furuno Electric Co., Ltd.; *Int'l*, pg. 2848
PT FUSION TECHNOLOGIES INDONESIA—See AVK Holding A/S; *Int'l*, pg. 747
PT.FUTABA INDUSTRIAL INDONESIA—See Futaba Industrial Co., Ltd.; *Int'l*, pg. 2851
PT FUTURE PIPE INDUSTRIES—See Future Pipe Industries Group Ltd.; *Int'l*, pg. 2857
PT FYFE FIBRWRAP INDONESIA—See New Mountain Capital, LLC; *U.S. Private*, pg. 2900
P.T. GADAI CAHAYA ABADI MULIA—See PT Hartadinata Abadi Tbk; *Int'l*, pg. 6042
P.T. GADAI CAHAYA DANA ABADI—See PT Hartadinata Abadi Tbk; *Int'l*, pg. 6042
P.T. GADAI CAHAYA TERANG ABADI—See PT Hartadinata Abadi Tbk; *Int'l*, pg. 6042
P.T. GADAI HARTADINATA TERANG SEJATI—See PT Hartadinata Abadi Tbk; *Int'l*, pg. 6042
P.T. GADAI TERANG ABADI MULIA—See PT Hartadinata Abadi Tbk; *Int'l*, pg. 6042

PT FUJI FINANCE INDONESIA TBK   **CORPORATE AFFILIATIONS**

PT. GAGAS ENERGI INDONESIA—See PT Perusahaan Gas Negara (Persero) Tbk; *Int'l*, pg. 6064
PT. GAJAH TUNGGAL TBK - PLANT 1—See Giti Tire Pte. Ltd.; *Int'l*, pg. 2979
PT. GAJAH TUNGGAL TBK - PLANT 2—See Giti Tire Pte. Ltd.; *Int'l*, pg. 2979
PT. GAJAH TUNGGAL TBK—See Giti Tire Pte. Ltd.; *Int'l*, pg. 2979
PT GALVA TECHNOLOGIES TBK; *Int'l*, pg. 6039
P.T. GAMATA UTAMA—See Bioxyne Limited; *Int'l*, pg. 1045
PT. GANDARIA PERMAI—See PT Intiland Development Tbk.; *Int'l*, pg. 6048
PT. GAPURA ANGKASA—See PT Garuda Indonesia (Persero) Tbk; *Int'l*, pg. 6040
PT GARDA TUJUH BUANA TBK; *Int'l*, pg. 6040
PT. GARENA INDONESIA—See Sea Limited; *Int'l*, pg. 6660
PT GARUDA INDONESIA (PERSERO) TBK; *Int'l*, pg. 6040
PT. GARUDA MAINTENANCE FACILITY AEROASIA—See PT Garuda Indonesia (Persero) Tbk; *Int'l*, pg. 6040
PT GARUDA MAINTENANCE FACILITY AERO ASIA TBK; *Int'l*, pg. 6040
PT GARUDA METALINDO TBK; *Int'l*, pg. 6040
PT. GARUDA METAL UTAMA—See PT Garuda Metalindo Tbk; *Int'l*, pg. 6040
PT GAYA ABADI SEMPURNA TBK; *Int'l*, pg. 6040
PT. GAYLIN—See AMOS Group Limited; *Int'l*, pg. 430
PT. GDC TECHNOLOGY INDONESIA—See Huayi Brothers Media Corp.; *Int'l*, pg. 3516
PTG DEUTSCHLAND GMBH—See Chongqing Machinery & Electronics Holding (Group) Co., Ltd.; *Int'l*, pg. 1580
PT. GEA GRASSO INDONESIA—See GEA Group Aktiengesellschaft; *Int'l*, pg. 2903
PT. GEA WESTFALIA SEPARATOR INDONESIA—See GEA Group Aktiengesellschaft; *Int'l*, pg. 2901
P.T. GED LINTAS INDONESIA—See Trimuda Nuansa Citra PT; *Int'l*, pg. 7923
PT. GEELY MOBIL INDONESIA—See Zhejiang Geely Holding Group Co., Ltd.; *Int'l*, pg. 8652
PT. GEMA DWIMITRA PERSADA—See PT Sarana Menara Nusantara Tbk; *Int'l*, pg. 6070
PT GEMA GRAHASARANA TBK; *Int'l*, pg. 6040
PT. GEMALTO INDONESIA—See Thales S.A.; *Int'l*, pg. 7600
PT. GEMA TEKNOLOGI CAHAYA GEMILANG—See Freak-Out Holdings, Inc.; *Int'l*, pg. 2767
P.T. GEMILANG HARTADINATA ABADI—See PT Hartadinata Abadi Tbk; *Int'l*, pg. 6042
PTG ENERGY PUBLIC COMPANY LIMITED; *Int'l*, pg. 6090
P.T. GENTA LARAS SEMESTA—See PT. Tira Austenite Tbk; *Int'l*, pg. 6089
PT. GENTING PLANTATIONS NUSANTARA—See Genting Berhad; *Int'l*, pg. 2929
PT. GEO ENERGY COALINDO—See Geo Energy Resources Limited; *Int'l*, pg. 2932
PT. GEO LINK NUSANTARA—See Federal International (2000) Ltd; *Int'l*, pg. 2630
PT GEOPRIMA SOLUSI TBK; *Int'l*, pg. 6040
P.T. GEOTHERMAL ENERGI SEULAWAH—See PT Pertamina Geothermal Energy Tbk; *Int'l*, pg. 6064
PT. GERMANISCHER LLOYD NUSANTARA—See DNV GL Group AS; *Int'l*, pg. 2150
PT GEVAERT-AGFA HEALTHCARE INDONESIA—See Agfa-Gevaert N.V.; *Int'l*, pg. 209
PTG HEAVY INDUSTRIES LIMITED—See Chongqing Machinery & Electronics Holding (Group) Co., Ltd.; *Int'l*, pg. 1580
PT. GIESECKE & DEVRIENT INDONESIA—See Giesecke & Devrient GmbH; *Int'l*, pg. 2970
PTGI EUROPE, B.V.—See INNOVATE Corp.; *U.S. Public*, pg. 1126
P.T. GIFTEE INTERNATIONAL INDONESIA—See Giftee, Inc.; *Int'l*, pg. 2970
PT. GIH INDONESIA—See PT Garuda Indonesia (Persero) Tbk; *Int'l*, pg. 6040
PT GIHON TELEKOMUNIKASI INDONESIA TBK—See PT Tower Bersama Infrastructure Tbk; *Int'l*, pg. 6079
PTGI INTERNATIONAL CARRIER SERVICES LTD.—See INNOVATE Corp.; *U.S. Public*, pg. 1126
PT GINTING JAYA ENERGI TBK; *Int'l*, pg. 6040
PT. GIORDANO INDONESIA—See Giordano International Limited; *Int'l*, pg. 2978
P.T. GIRDER INDONESIA—See PT Citra Marga Nusaphala Persada Tbk.; *Int'l*, pg. 6034
P.T. GISTEX NISSHINBO INDONESIA—See Nisshinbo Holdings Inc.; *Int'l*, pg. 5375
PT. GIVAUDAN INDONESIA - DEPOK—See Givaudan S.A.; *Int'l*, pg. 2981
PT. GIVAUDAN INDONESIA—See Givaudan S.A.; *Int'l*, pg. 2981
PT. GLAXOSMITHKLINE INDONESIA—See GSK plc; *Int'l*, pg. 3149
PT. GLAXO WELLCOME INDONESIA—See GSK plc; *Int'l*, pg. 3149
PT. GLICO INDONESIA—See Ezaki Glico Co., Ltd.; *Int'l*, pg. 2593

P.T. GL- INDONESIA - STATION BATAM—See DNV GL Group AS; *Int'l*, pg. 2150
PT. GLOBAL CHEMINDO MEGATRADING—See PT. Kalbe Farma Tbk.; *Int'l*, pg. 6050
PT. GLOBAL INFORMASI BERMUTU—See PT MNC Investama Tbk; *Int'l*, pg. 6058
PT. GLOBAL JASA SEJAHTERA—See PT MNC Land Tbk; *Int'l*, pg. 6059
PT. GLOBAL KARSA MEDIKA—See PT Kalbe Farma Tbk.; *Int'l*, pg. 6051
PT. GLOBAL LOYALTY INDONESIA—See PT Sumber Alfaria Trijaya Tbk; *Int'l*, pg. 6076
PT GLOBAL MEDIACOM TBK; *Int'l*, pg. 6041
PT. GLOBAL ONKOLAB FARMA—See PT Kalbe Farma Tbk.; *Int'l*, pg. 6050
PT. GLOBAL PAHALA RENTAL—See PT Putra Mandiri Jembar Tbk; *Int'l*, pg. 6067
PT. GLOBAL PARAMA MEDIKA—See PT Kalbe Farma Tbk.; *Int'l*, pg. 6050
PT. GLOBAL PUTRA INTERNATIONAL GROUP; *Int'l*, pg. 6086
PT GLOBAL SUKSES SOLUSI TBK; *Int'l*, pg. 6041
P.T. GLOBAL TEKNINDO BERKATAMA—See Suzuki Co., Ltd.; *Int'l*, pg. 7354
PT GLOBAL TELESHOP TBK—See PT. Trikomsel Oke Tbk.; *Int'l*, pg. 6090
PT. GLOBAL USADHA ARANA—See PT Kalbe Farma Tbk.; *Int'l*, pg. 6050
P.T. GLOBE KITA TERANG TBK—See PT. Trikomsel Oke Tbk.; *Int'l*, pg. 6090
PT. GLORY GLOBAL SOLUTIONS INDONESIA—See GLORY Ltd.; *Int'l*, pg. 3010
PT GOLD COIN INDONESIA—See Gold Coin Holdings Sdn Bhd; *Int'l*, pg. 3024
PT GOLD COIN SPECIALITIES—See Gold Coin Holdings Sdn. Bhd; *Int'l*, pg. 3024
PT GOLDEN EAGLE ENERGY TBK; *Int'l*, pg. 6041
PT GOLDEN ENERGY MINES TBK—See PT DIAN SWASTATIKA SENTOSA Tbk; *Int'l*, pg. 6036
PT GOLDEN FLOWER TBK; *Int'l*, pg. 6041
PT GOLDEN HARVEST COCOA INDONESIA—See PT Bumi Teknokultura Unggul Tbk; *Int'l*, pg. 6031
PT GOLDEN PLANTATION TBK; *Int'l*, pg. 6041
PT. GOLDEN SURYA MAKMUR—See PT Modernland Realty Tbk; *Int'l*, pg. 6059
P.T. GOODYEAR INDONESIA TBK—See The Goodyear Tire & Rubber Company; *U.S. Public*, pg. 2084
PT GOTO GOJEK TOKOPEDIA TBK; *Int'l*, pg. 6041
PT GOWA MAKASSAR TOURISM DEVELOPMENT TBK; *Int'l*, pg. 6041
PT GOZCO PLANTATIONS TBK; *Int'l*, pg. 6041
PT. GRAHA ANDRASENTRA PROPERTINDO—See PT. Bakrieland Development, Tbk.; *Int'l*, pg. 6084
PT. GRAHA BARU RAYA—See Lippo Malls Indonesia Retail Trust; *Int'l*, pg. 4522
PT. GRAHA BUANA CIKARANG—See PT Jababeka Tbk; *Int'l*, pg. 6048
PT. GRAHA DESTINASI—See PT Destinasi Tirta Nusantara Tbk; *Int'l*, pg. 6036
PT GRAHA LAYAR PRIMA TBK; *Int'l*, pg. 6041
PT. GRAHA LESTARI INTERNUSA—See PT Rockfields Properti Indonesia Tbk; *Int'l*, pg. 6068
PT GRAHAMAS CITRAWISATA TBK; *Int'l*, pg. 6041
PT GRAHA MITRA ASIA TBK; *Int'l*, pg. 6041
PT. GRAHAMITRA LESTARIJAY—See PT Mitra Pinasthika Mustika Tbk; *Int'l*, pg. 6058
PT. GRAHA MULTIMEDIA NUSANTARA—See PT Bakrie & Brothers Tbk; *Int'l*, pg. 6025
P.T. GRAHA PANCA KARSA—See PT Indo Tambangraya Megah Tbk.; *Int'l*, pg. 6045
PT. GRAHA PLANET NUSANTARA—See PT Mitra Komunikasi Nusantara Tbk; *Int'l*, pg. 6057
PT GRAHA PRIMA MENTARI TBK; *Int'l*, pg. 6041
PT GRAHAPRIMA SUKSESMANDIRI TBK; *Int'l*, pg. 6041
PT. GRAHA SARANA DUTA—See Perusahaan Perseroan Indonesia Tbk; *Int'l*, pg. 5822
PT. GRAHA TEKNOLOGI NUSANTARA—See PT Multipolar Tbk; *Int'l*, pg. 6060
P.T. GRAHA TELKOMSIGMA—See Perusahaan Perseroan Indonesia Tbk; *Int'l*, pg. 5821
PT. GRAHA YASA SELARAS—See Perusahaan Perseroan Indonesia Tbk; *Int'l*, pg. 5821
PT GRAMA PRAMESI SIDDHI—See PT. PAKUWON JATI Tbk; *Int'l*, pg. 6088
P.T. GRAMEDIA DIGITAL NUSANTARA—See PT Tigaraksa Satria Tbk; *Int'l*, pg. 6078
PT. GRANDE FAMILY VIEW—See PT Intiland Development Tbk.; *Int'l*, pg. 6048
PT GRAND HOUSE MULIA TBK; *Int'l*, pg. 6041
PT GRAND KARTECH TBK; *Int'l*, pg. 6042
P.T. GRANIF KONSULTAN—See PT United Tractors Tbk; *Int'l*, pg. 6080
PT. GREEN ASIA FOOD INDONESIA—See Inner Mongolia Yili Industrial Group Co., Ltd.; *Int'l*, pg. 3708
PT. GREENLAM INDO PACIFIC—See Greenlam Industries Limited; *Int'l*, pg. 3075
PT GREENWOOD SEJAHTERA TBK; *Int'l*, pg. 6042

PTG REIFENDRUCKREGELSYSTEME GMBH—See Compagnie Generale des Etablissements Michelin SCA; *Int'l*, pg. 1745
PT.GRENTECH INDONESIA—See China GrenTech Corporation Limited; *Int'l*, pg. 1506
P.T. GRESIK POWER INDONESIA—See Linde plc; *Int'l*, pg. 4508
PT GRHA 165 TBK; *Int'l*, pg. 6042
PT GRIYATON INDONESIA—See PT PP (Persero) Tbk; *Int'l*, pg. 6066
PT GROZ-BECKERT INDONESIA—See Groz-Beckert KG; *Int'l*, pg. 3113
PT GRUNDFOS POMPA—See The Poul Due Jensen Foundation; *Int'l*, pg. 7676
PT. GS BATTERY INC.—See GS Yuasa Corporation; *Int'l*, pg. 3143
PT. GSI CREOS INDONESIA—See GSI Creos Corporation; *Int'l*, pg. 3145
PT. GSK CONSUMER HEALTHCARE INDONESIA—See GSK plc; *Int'l*, pg. 3149
PT GTSI TBK; *Int'l*, pg. 6042
PT GUARDIAN PHARMATAMA; *Int'l*, pg. 6042
PT GUDANG GARAM TBK; *Int'l*, pg. 6042
PT GUNA TIMUR RAYA TBK; *Int'l*, pg. 6042
PT GUNAWAN DIANJAYA STEEL; *Int'l*, pg. 6042
PT. GUNUNGGEULIS ELOK ABADI—See PT Sentul City Tbk.; *Int'l*, pg. 6072
PT GUNUNG MARAS LESTARI—See Oriental Holdings Berhad; *Int'l*, pg. 5625
PT GUNUNG RAJA PAKSI TBK; *Int'l*, pg. 6042
PT GUNUNGSAWIT BINALESTARI—See Oriental Holdings Berhad; *Int'l*, pg. 5625
PT GUNUNG SAWIT SALATAN LESTARI—See Oriental Holdings Berhad; *Int'l*, pg. 5625
P.T. GUNZE SOCKS INDONESIA—See Gunze Limited; *Int'l*, pg. 3186
PT GUTHRIE JAYA INDAH ISLAND RESORT—See Guthrie GTS Limited; *Int'l*, pg. 3189
PT. HAGIHARA WESTJAVA INDUSTRIES—See Hagihara Industries Inc.; *Int'l*, pg. 3207
PT. HAIDA AGRICULTURE INDONESIA—See Guangdong Haid Group Co., Ltd.; *Int'l*, pg. 3155
PT. HAI-O INDONESIA—See Hai-O Enterprise Berhad; *Int'l*, pg. 3209
PT HAKARU METALINDO PERKASA—See PT HK Metals Utama; *Int'l*, pg. 6043
PT HALE INTERNATIONAL—See PT Kalbe Farma Tbk.; *Int'l*, pg. 6050
PT HALEYORA POWER—See PT PLN (Persero); *Int'l*, pg. 6065
PT HALONI JANE TBK; *Int'l*, pg. 6042
PT. HALTRACO SARANA MULIA—See Huettenes-Albertus Chemische Werke GmbH; *Int'l*, pg. 3523
PT. HAMADEN INDONESIA MANUFACTURING—See Denso Corporation; *Int'l*, pg. 2032
P.T. HAMMAR MARINE OFFSHORE—See PT Wintermar Offshore Marine Tbk; *Int'l*, pg. 6083
PT HANDAL ALUMINIUM SUKSES—See PT HK Metals Utama; *Int'l*, pg. 6043
PT. HANEAGLE HEAVYPARTS INDONESIA—See Invicta Holdings Limited; *Int'l*, pg. 3788
PT HANJAYA MANDALA SAMPOERNA TBK.—See Philip Morris International Inc.; *U.S. Public*, pg. 1685
PT HANKEN INDONESIA—See Komatsu Ltd.; *Int'l*, pg. 4239
PT. HANKOOK TIRE SALES INDONESIA—See Hankook Tire & Technology Co.,Ltd.; *Int'l*, pg. 3254
PT HANSON INTERNATIONAL TBK; *Int'l*, pg. 6042
PT. HANS R. JOST—See Doppelmayr Group; *Int'l*, pg. 2175
PT HANTONG PRECISION MANUFACTURING BATAM—See CFM Holdings Limited; *Int'l*, pg. 1430
PT. HANWA INDONESIA—See Hanwa Co., Ltd.; *Int'l*, pg. 3263
PT. HANWA ROYAL METALS—See Hanwa Co., Ltd.; *Int'l*, pg. 3263
PT HANWA STEEL SERVICE INDONESIA—See Hanwa Co., Ltd.; *Int'l*, pg. 3263
PT. HANWHA LIFE INSURANCE—See Hanwha Group; *Int'l*, pg. 3266
PT. HANWHA MINING SERVICES—See Hanwha Group; *Int'l*, pg. 3266
PT HARAPAN DUTA PERTIWI TBK; *Int'l*, pg. 6042
PT. HARAPAN GLOBAL NIAGA—See Keppel Corporation Limited; *Int'l*, pg. 4132
PT. HARAPAN SAWIT LESTARI—See Cargill, Inc.; *U.S. Private*, pg. 759
PT. HARAPAN UTAMA PRIMA—See OCK Group Berhad; *Int'l*, pg. 5520
PT. HARBISON-WALKER REFRACTORIES—See Platinum Equity, LLC; *U.S. Private*, pg. 3203
PT HARTADINATA ABADI TBK; *Int'l*, pg. 6042
PT HARUM ENERGY TBK; *Int'l*, pg. 6042
PT HASNUR INTERNASIONAL SHIPPING TBK; *Int'l*, pg. 6043

PT HASSANA BOGA SEJAHTERA TBK; *Int'l*, pg. 6043
PT HATTEN BALI TBK; *Int'l*, pg. 6043
PT. HAZAMA ANDO MURINDA—See Hazama Ando Corporation; *Int'l*, pg. 3295

COMPANY NAME INDEX

P.T. HEIDELBERG INDONESIA—See Heidelberger Druckmaschinen AG; *Int'l*, pg. 3322
P.T. HEKSA ENERGI MITRANIAGA—See PT Rukun Raharja Tbk; *Int'l*, pg. 6069
PT. HELIOS INFORMATIKA NUSANTARA—See PT Anabatic Technologies Tbk; *Int'l*, pg. 6021
PT HELUKABEL INDONESIA—See HELUKABEL GmbH; *Int'l*, pg. 3339
PT HENKEL INDONESIEN—See Henkel AG & Co. KGaA; *Int'l*, pg. 3349
PT HENSEL DAVEST INDONESIA TBK; *Int'l*, pg. 6043
PT HERO SUPERMARKET TBK—See Jardine Matheson Holdings Limited; *Int'l*, pg. 3909
PT HEWLETT-PACKARD INDONESIA—See HP Inc.; *U.S. Public*, pg. 1064
PT HEXINDO ADIPERKASA TBK; *Int'l*, pg. 6043
PT HEXPHARM JAYA LABORATORIES—See PT Kalbe Farma Tbk.; *Int'l*, pg. 6050
PT HG METAL DISTRIBUTION INDONESIA—See HG Metal Manufacturing Limited; *Int'l*, pg. 3375
P.T. HICLEARANCE MEDICAL INDONESIA—See Hi-Clearance, Inc.; *Int'l*, pg. 3380
PT. HIGASHIFUJI INDONESIA—See Nidec Corporation; *Int'l*, pg. 5278
PT. HIJAU LESTARI RAYA FIBREBOARD—See Evergreen Fibreboard Berhad; *Int'l*, pg. 2565
PT. HIKVISION TECHNOLOGY INDONESIA—See Hangzhou Hikvision Digital Technology Co., Ltd.; *Int'l*, pg. 3248
PT. HI-LEX CIREBON—See Hi-Lex Corporation; *Int'l*, pg. 3381
PT. HI-LEX INDONESIA CIKARANG FACTORY—See Hi-Lex Corporation; *Int'l*, pg. 3381
PT.HI-LEX INDONESIA—See Hi-Lex Corporation; *Int'l*, pg. 3381
PT.HI-LEX PARTS INDONESIA—See Hi-Lex Corporation; *Int'l*, pg. 3381
PT HILLCON TBK; *Int'l*, pg. 6043
P.T. HILTI NUSANTARA—See Hilti AG; *Int'l*, pg. 3395
PT HIMALAYA ENERGI PERKASA TBK; *Int'l*, pg. 6043
PT. HIMALAYA EVEREST JAYA—See Miki Pulley Co., Ltd.; *Int'l*, pg. 4891
PT HINDOLI—See Cargill, Inc.; *U.S. Private*, pg. 759
P.T. HINO FINANCE INDONESIA—See PT Indomobil Multi Jasa Tbk; *Int'l*, pg. 6046
PT. HINO MOTORS MANUFACTURING—See Toyota Motor Corporation; *Int'l*, pg. 7871
PT. HIOKI ELECTRIC INSTRUMENT—See HIOKI E.E. Corporation; *Int'l*, pg. 3401
PT HIPERNET INDODATA—See Axiata Group Berhad; *Int'l*, pg. 768
PT HIROSE ELECTRIC INDONESIA—See Hirose Electric Co., Ltd.; *Int'l*, pg. 3405
PT. HISAKA WORKS INDONESIA—See Hisaka Works, Ltd.; *Int'l*, pg. 3406
PT. HISAMITSU PHARMA INDONESIA—See Hisamitsu Pharmaceutical Co., Inc.; *Int'l*, pg. 3406
PT. HITACHI ASIA INDONESIA—See Hitachi, Ltd.; *Int'l*, pg. 3423
PT. HITACHI CONSTRUCTION MACHINERY INDONESIA—See Hitachi, Ltd.; *Int'l*, pg. 3416
PT. HITACHI EBWORX INDONESIA—See Hitachi, Ltd.; *Int'l*, pg. 3422
PT. HITACHI HIGH-TECH INDONESIA—See Hitachi, Ltd.; *Int'l*, pg. 3424
PT. HITACHI HIGH-TECHNOLOGIES INDONESIA—See Hitachi, Ltd.; *Int'l*, pg. 3419
PT. HITACHI METALS INDONESIA—See Hitachi, Ltd.; *Int'l*, pg. 3424
PT. HITACHI MODERN SALES INDONESIA—See Hitachi, Ltd.; *Int'l*, pg. 3424
PT. HITACHI PLANT TECHNOLOGIES INDONESIA—See Hitachi, Ltd.; *Int'l*, pg. 3424
PT. HITACHI PLANT TECHNOLOGIES INDONESIA—See Hitachi, Ltd.; *Int'l*, pg. 3423
PT. HITACHI POWER SYSTEMS INDONESIA—See Hitachi, Ltd.; *Int'l*, pg. 3424
PT. HITACHI SUNWAY INFORMATION SYSTEMS INDONESIA—See Hitachi, Ltd.; *Int'l*, pg. 3424
PT. HITACHI TERMINAL SOLUTIONS INDONESIA—See Hitachi, Ltd.; *Int'l*, pg. 3424
P.T. HI-TECH INK INDONESIA—See Dainichiseika Color & Chemicals Mfg. Co., Ltd.; *Int'l*, pg. 1939
PT HITEK NUSANTARA OFFSHORE DRILLING—See Transocean Ltd.; *Int'l*, pg. 7903
PT. HITZ INDONESIA—See Hitachi Zosen Corporation; *Int'l*, pg. 3412
PT HK METALS UTAMA; *Int'l*, pg. 6043
P.T. HL DISPLAY INDONESIA—See Ratos AB; *Int'l*, pg. 6219
PT. HLN BATAM—See HLN Rubber Products Pte. Ltd.; *Int'l*, pg. 3431
PT. HMS BERGBAU INDONESIA—See HMS Bergbau AG; *Int'l*, pg. 3432
PT HOFFMEN CLEANINDO TBK; *Int'l*, pg. 6043
PT.HOKKAN DELTAPACK INDUSTRI—See Hokkan Holdings Limited; *Int'l*, pg. 3443
PT.HOKKAN INDONESIA—See Hokkan Holdings Limited; *Int'l*, pg. 3443

PT HOKURIKU UNITED FORGING INDUSTRY—See Komatsu Ltd.; *Int'l*, pg. 4239
PT HOLDING COMPANY, LLC—See Duke Energy Corporation; *U.S. Public*, pg. 691
PT HOLDING INVESTMENT B.V.—See Energeticky a Prumyslovy Holding, a.s.; *Int'l*, pg. 2420
PT HOLDINGS, LLC—See Berkshire Partners LLC; *U.S. Private*, pg. 535
PT HOLLAND COLOURS ASIA—See Holland Colours NV; *Int'l*, pg. 3451
PT. HONDA POWER PRODUCTS INDONESIA—See Honda Motor Co., Ltd.; *Int'l*, pg. 3464
P.T. HONDA PRECISION PARTS MANUFACTURING—See Honda Motor Co., Ltd.; *Int'l*, pg. 3464
P.T. HONDA PROSPECT MOTOR—See Honda Motor Co., Ltd.; *Int'l*, pg. 3464
P.T. HONDA TRADING INDONESIA—See Honda Motor Co., Ltd.; *Int'l*, pg. 3463
PT.H-ONE GOHI PRIMA AUTO TECHNOLOGIES INDONESIA—See H-One Co., Ltd.; *Int'l*, pg. 3194
PT HONFOONG PLASTIC INDUSTRIES—See Accrelist Ltd.; *Int'l*, pg. 93
PT HONGKONG LAND CONSULTANCY & MANAGEMENT—See Hong Kong Land Holdings Ltd.; *Int'l*, pg. 3467
PT HONGXIN ALGAE INTERNATIONA—See Green Future Food Hydrocolloid Marine Science Company Limited; *Int'l*, pg. 3071
PT HOPE OF INDONESIA—See New Hope Group Co., Ltd.; *Int'l*, pg. 5224
PT HORIBA INDONESIA—See HORIBA Ltd; *Int'l*, pg. 3478
PT HOTEL CIKINI REALTY—See PT Jakarta Setiabudi In; *Int'l*, pg. 6049
PT HOTEL ELTY TENGGARONG—See PT. Bakrieland Development, Tbk.; *Int'l*, pg. 6084
P.T. HOTEL INDONESIA PROPERTIY—See PT Wijaya Karya (Persero) Tbk.; *Int'l*, pg. 6082
PT HOTEL MANDARINE REGENCY TBK; *Int'l*, pg. 6043
PT HOTEL PROPERTI INTERNASIONAL—See PT Intikeramik Alamasri Industri Tbk; *Int'l*, pg. 6048
PT HOTEL SAHID JAYA INTERNATIONAL TBK; *Int'l*, pg. 6043
PT HOUSE & VOX INDONESIA—See House Foods Group Inc.; *Int'l*, pg. 3490
PT. HO WAH GENTING—See Ho Wah Genting Berhad; *Int'l*, pg. 3435
PT. HOWASKA MESIN INDONESIA—See Howa Machinery, Ltd.; *Int'l*, pg. 3493
PT HOWDEN INSURANCE BROKERS INDONESIA—See Howden Group Holdings Limited; *Int'l*, pg. 3494
PT HOYA LENS INDONESIA—See Hoya Corporation; *Int'l*, pg. 3498
PT H-TECH OILFIELD EQUIPMENT—See NOV, Inc.; *U.S. Public*, pg. 1546
PT HTECH TOOLS INDONESIA—See Halcyon Technology Public Company Limited; *Int'l*, pg. 3227
PT HUMPUSS INTERMODA TRANSPORTASI TBK; *Int'l*, pg. 6043
P.T. HUMPUSS MARITIM INTERNASIONAL—See PT Humpuss Intermoda Transportasi Tbk; *Int'l*, pg. 6043
PT HUMPUSS TRANSPORTASI KIMIA—See PT Humpuss Intermoda Transportasi Tbk; *Int'l*, pg. 6043
PT HUNTER DOUGLAS INDONESIA—See 3G Capital Partners L.P.; *U.S. Private*, pg. 13
PT HUNTING ENERGY ASIA—See Hunting Plc; *Int'l*, pg. 3537
PT HUNTSMAN INDONESIA—See Huntsman Corporation; *U.S. Public*, pg. 1075
PT HUR SALES INDONESIA—See H&R KGaA; *Int'l*, pg. 3193
P.T. HUTAMA KARYA—See PT Adhi Karya (Persero) Tbk; *Int'l*, pg. 6019
PT HUTAN KETAPANG INDUSTRI—See PT SAMPOERNA AGRO Tbk.; *Int'l*, pg. 6069
P.T. HUTCHINS CO., LTD.—See EQT AB; *Int'l*, pg. 2469
PT. HYDAC TECHNOLOGY INDONESIA—See Hydac International GmbH; *Int'l*, pg. 3545
PT. HYDRAXLE PERKASA—See PT Selamat Sempurna Tbk; *Int'l*, pg. 6071
PT HYUNDAI INTI DEVELOP—See Hyundai Corporation; *Int'l*, pg. 3555
PT IBM INDONESIA—See International Business Machines Corporation; *U.S. Public*, pg. 1149
PT IBS INSURANCE BROKING SERVICE—See Arthur J. Gallagher & Co.; *U.S. Public*, pg. 206
PT ICAP INDONESIA—See CME Group, Inc.; *U.S. Public*, pg. 517
PT. ICHIKOH INDONESIA—See Valeo S.A.; *Int'l*, pg. 8113
PTI COMMUNICATIONS OF KETCHIKAN, INC.—See Lumen Technologies, Inc.; *U.S. Public*, pg. 1347
PT ICON INTERNATIONAL COMMUNICATIONS INDONESIA—See ICON International Communications Pty. Ltd.; *Int'l*, pg. 3583
PT ICRA INDONESIA—See Moody's Corporation; *U.S. Public*, pg. 1469
PT ICTSI JASA PRIMA TBK; *Int'l*, pg. 6044
PT. ICT WORLDWIDE INDONESIA—See Dentium Co., Ltd; *Int'l*, pg. 2034

PT INDOINTERNET TBK

PT IDEA INDONESIA AKADEMI TBK; *Int'l*, pg. 6044
PT. IDEMITSU ENERGY INDONESIA—See Idemitsu Kosan Co., Ltd.; *Int'l*, pg. 3592
P.T. IDEMITSU LUBE INDONESIA—See Idemitsu Kosan Co., Ltd.; *Int'l*, pg. 3592
P.T. IDEMITSU LUBE TECHNO INDONESIA—See Idemitsu Kosan Co., Ltd.; *Int'l*, pg. 3592
PTI ENGINEERED PLASTICS INC.; *U.S. Private*, pg. 3298
PT IEV GAS—See Medi Lifestyle Limited; *Int'l*, pg. 4769
PT IEV INDONESIA—See Medi Lifestyle Limited; *Int'l*, pg. 4770
PT IFCA PROPERTY365 INDONESIA—See IFCA MSC Berhad; *Int'l*, pg. 3599
PT IFCA PROPERTY365 INDONESIA—See IFCA MSC Berhad; *Int'l*, pg. 3599
PT IFISHDECO TBK; *Int'l*, pg. 6044
PT. IFS CAPITAL INDONESIA—See IFS Capital Limited; *Int'l*, pg. 3600
PT. IHI TRANSPORT MACHINERY INDONESIA—See IHI Corporation; *Int'l*, pg. 3606
PT. IHI TRANSPORT MACHINERY INDONESIA—See IHI Corporation; *Int'l*, pg. 3606
PTI IMMOBILIENVERMITTLUNG GMBH—See Osterreichische Post AG; *Int'l*, pg. 5654
PTI INDUSTRIES, INC—See Wynnchurch Capital, L.P.; *U.S. Private*, pg. 4577
PT. IINO INDONESIA—See Daido Metal Corporation; *Int'l*, pg. 1922
PT IKAFOOD PUTRAMAS—See Brataco, PT; *Int'l*, pg. 1141
PT IKAPHARMINDO PUTRAMAS—See Brataco, PT; *Int'l*, pg. 1141
P.T. IKI INDAH KABEL—See Sumitomo Electric Industries, Ltd.; *Int'l*, pg. 7279
PT IKI KARUNIA INDONESIA—See PT Anabatic Technologies Tbk; *Int'l*, pg. 6021
PT IKM INDONESIA—See IKM Gruppen AS; *Int'l*, pg. 3612
PT. IK PRECISION INDONESIA—See Inabata & Co. Ltd.; *Int'l*, pg. 3644
PT. ILTHABI HANBELL INDONESIA—See Shanghai Hanbell Precise Machinery Co., Ltd.; *Int'l*, pg. 6769
PT IMAGO MULIA PERSADA TBK; *Int'l*, pg. 6044
PTI MARKETING TECHNOLOGIES, INC.—See Ricoh Company, Ltd.; *Int'l*, pg. 6336
PT. IMCD INDONESIA—See IMCD N.V.; *Int'l*, pg. 3622
PT IMPACK PRATAMA INDUSTRI TBK; *Int'l*, pg. 6044
PT. INABATA CREATION INDONESIA—See Inabata & Co. Ltd.; *Int'l*, pg. 3644
PT. INABATA INDONESIA—See Inabata & Co. Ltd.; *Int'l*, pg. 3644
PT. INA NUSANTARA ABADI—See ANEST IWATA Corporation; *Int'l*, pg. 458
PT INDAH KIAT PULP & PAPER TBK.—See PT Sinar Mas Group; *Int'l*, pg. 6072
PT INDAH PESONA BOGOR—See Lippo Malls Indonesia Retail Trust; *Int'l*, pg. 4522
PT INDAH PRAKASA SENTOSA TBK; *Int'l*, pg. 6044
PT INDAL ALUMINIUM INDUSTRY TBK - EAST JAVA FACTORY—See PT Indal Aluminium Industry Tbk; *Int'l*, pg. 6044
PT INDAL ALUMINIUM INDUSTRY TBK; *Int'l*, pg. 6044
PT INDALEX—See PT Indal Aluminium Industry Tbk; *Int'l*, pg. 6044
PT INDIKA ENERGY TBK; *Int'l*, pg. 6044
PT INDO ACIDATAMA TBK; *Int'l*, pg. 6044
PT INDOBAJA PRIMA MURNI—See PT Indospring Tbk; *Int'l*, pg. 6047
PT INDO CAFCO (ROBUSTAS)—See Ecom Agroindustrial Corporation Ltd.; *Int'l*, pg. 2296
PT INDOCEMENT TUNGGAL PRAKARSA TBK; *Int'l*, pg. 6045
PT INDOCORR PACKAGING CIKARANG—See The Siam Cement Public Company Limited; *Int'l*, pg. 7683
PT INDOFARMA GLOBAL MEDIKA—See PT Indofarma (Persero) Tbk; *Int'l*, pg. 6045
PT INDOFARMA (PERSERO) TBK; *Int'l*, pg. 6045
PT INDOFOOD CBP SUKSES MAKMUR TBK.; *Int'l*, pg. 6045
P.T. INDOFOOD COMSA SUKSES MAKMU—See PT Indofood CBP Sukses Makmur Tbk.; *Int'l*, pg. 6045
PT INDOFOOD SUKSES MAKMUR TBK.—See First Pacific Company Limited; *Int'l*, pg. 2686
PT INDOGAS KRIYA DWIGUNA—See PT Capitalinc Investment Tbk; *Int'l*, pg. 6032
PT INDO GENESIS MEDIKA—See Clearbridge Health Limited; *Int'l*, pg. 1656
PT INDOINTERNET TBK; *Int'l*, pg. 6045
PT. INDOJAPAN STEEL CENTER—See Nippon Steel Corporation; *Int'l*, pg. 5338
PT. INDOJAPAN WIRE PRODUCTS—See Nippon Steel Corporation; *Int'l*, pg. 5338
PT INDOKARLO PERKASA—See PT Astra Otoparts Tbk; *Int'l*, pg. 6024
PT. INDO KIDA PLATING—See PT Garuda Metalindo Tbk; *Int'l*, pg. 6040
PT. INDOKOEI INTERNATIONAL—See Nippon Koei Co., Ltd.; *Int'l*, pg. 5322

PT INDOINTERNET TBK

CORPORATE AFFILIATIONS

PT INDOKOMAS BUANA PERKASA—See VINCI S.A.; *Int'l,* pg. 8215
PT INDO KOMODITI KORPORA TBK; *Int'l,* pg. 6044
PT INDO KORDSA TBK; *Int'l,* pg. 6045
PT INDOKUAT SUKSES MAKMUR—See PT Indofood CBP Sukses Makmur Tbk.; *Int'l,* pg. 6045
PT INDOLAKTO—See PT Indofood CBP Sukses Makmur Tbk.; *Int'l,* pg. 6045
PT. INDO LOG—See Mitsui & Co., Ltd.; *Int'l,* pg. 4980
PT INDQMINING—See PT TBS Energi Utama Tbk; *Int'l,* pg. 6078
P.T. INDOMOBIL BUSSAN TRUCKING—See PT Indomobil Multi Jasa Tbk; *Int'l,* pg. 6046
PT INDOMOBIL FINANCE INDONESIA—See PT Indomobil Sukses Internasional Tbk; *Int'l,* pg. 6046
PT INDOMOBIL MULTI JASA TBK; *Int'l,* pg. 6045
PT INDOMOBIL MULTI TRADA—See Gallant Venture Ltd.; *Int'l,* pg. 2874
PT INDOMOBIL PRIMA NIAGA—See Gallant Venture Ltd.; *Int'l,* pg. 2874
PT INDOMOBIL SUKSES INTERNASIONAL TBK; *Int'l,* pg. 6046
PT INDOMOBIL WAHANA TRADA—See PT Indomobil Sukses Internasional Tbk; *Int'l,* pg. 6046
PT INDO MURO KENCANA—See Aeris Resources Limited; *Int'l,* pg. 180
PT INDONAKANO—See Nakano Corporation; *Int'l,* pg. 5133
PT INDO NAN PAO RESINS CHEMICAL CO., LTD.,—See Nan Pao Resins Chemical Co., Ltd.; *Int'l,* pg. 5138
P.T. INDONESIA AIR TRANSPORT—See PT MNC Energy Investments Tbk; *Int'l,* pg. 6058
PT. INDONESIA AIR WATER—See Air Water Inc.; *Int'l,* pg. 240
PT. INDONESIA APPLICAD CO., LTD.—See Applicad Public Company Limited; *Int'l,* pg. 521
PT INDONESIA ASAHAN ALUMINIUM (PERSERO); *Int'l,* pg. 6046
PT INDONESIA BULK TERMINAL—See PT Adaro Energy Indonesia Tbk; *Int'l,* pg. 6019
PT INDONESIA CHEMICAL ALUMINA—See Resonac Holdings Corporation; *Int'l,* pg. 6298
P.T. INDONESIA CHEMI-CON—See Nippon Chemi-Con Corporation; *Int'l,* pg. 5312
PT INDONESIA COAL RESOURCES—See PT Antam (Persero) Tbk; *Int'l,* pg. 6022
PT INDONESIA FIBREBOARD INDUSTRY; *Int'l,* pg. 6046
PT INDONESIA KENDARAAN TERMINAL—See PT Pelabuhan Indonesia II; *Int'l,* pg. 6062
PT. INDONESIA KOITO—See Koito Manufacturing Co., Ltd.; *Int'l,* pg. 4230
PT. INDONESIA KOSE—See KOSE Corporation; *Int'l,* pg. 4290
PT. INDONESIAN ACIDS INDUSTRY LIMITED—See PT. Lautan Luas Tbk; *Int'l,* pg. 6087
PT. INDONESIA NIKKA CHEMICALS—See Nicca Chemical Co., Ltd.; *Int'l,* pg. 5264
PT. INDONESIA NIPPON SEIKI—See Nippon Seiki Co., Ltd.; *Int'l,* pg. 5330
PT INDONESIA NITTO SEIKO TRADING—See Nitto Seiko Co., Ltd.; *Int'l,* pg. 5388
PT INDONESIAN PARADISE PROPERTY TBK; *Int'l,* pg. 6046
PT INDONESIAN TOBACCO TBK; *Int'l,* pg. 6046
PT INDO NESIAN TOOLING TECHNOLOGY—See PT Garuda Metalindo Tbk; *Int'l,* pg. 6040
PT INDONESIA PERSADA GEMILANG—See PT Quantum Clovera Investama Tbk; *Int'l,* pg. 6067
PT INDONESIA PONDASI RAYA TBK.; *Int'l,* pg. 6046
PT INDONESIA POWER; *Int'l,* pg. 6046
PT INDONESIA PRIMA PROPERTY TBK; *Int'l,* pg. 6046
PT INDONESIA PRIMA SPRING—See PT Indospring Tbk; *Int'l,* pg. 6047
P.T. INDONESIA STANLEY ELECTRIC—See Stanley Electric Co., Ltd.; *Int'l,* pg. 7170
PT INDONESIA STEEL TUBE WORKS—See Maruichi Steel Tube Ltd; *Int'l,* pg. 4714
P.T. INDONESIA SYNTHETIC TEXTILE MILLS—See Toray Industries, Inc.; *Int'l,* pg. 7823
P.T. INDONESIA TAROKO CORPORATION—See Taroko Co., Ltd.; *Int'l,* pg. 7464
P.T. INDONESIA TORAY SYNTHETICS—See Toray Industries, Inc.; *Int'l,* pg. 7823
P.T. INDONESIA TOYOBO FILM SOLUTIONS—See Toyobo Co., Ltd.; *Int'l,* pg. 7860
P.T. INDONESIA TRI SEMBILAM—See Pyxus International, Inc.; *U.S. Public,* pg. 1741
P.T. INDONESIA TRI SEMBILAN—See Pyxus International, Inc.; *U.S. Public,* pg. 1741
PT INDONUSA MINING SERVICES—See Cyprium Metals Limited; *Int'l,* pg. 1897
PT INDO OIL PERKASA; *Int'l,* pg. 6045
PT. INDO OJI SUKSES PRATAMA—See Oji Holdings Corporation; *Int'l,* pg. 5538
P.T. INDOPAY MERCHANT SERVICES—See PT. Elang Mahkota Teknologi Tbk.; *Int'l,* pg. 6085
PT. INDOPELITA AIRCRAFT SERVICE—See PT Pertamina (Persero); *Int'l,* pg. 6063

PT INDOPELL RAYA—See PT Japfa Comfeed Indonesia Tbk; *Int'l,* pg. 6049
P.T. INDOPHERIN JAYA—See Sumitomo Bakelite Co., Ltd.; *Int'l,* pg. 7263
PT INDOPOLY SWAKARSA INDUSTRY TBK; *Int'l,* pg. 6046
PT. INDORAMA PETROCHEMICALS—See Indorama Ventures Public Company Limited; *Int'l,* pg. 3659
PT. INDORAMA POLYCHEM INDONESIA—See Indorama Ventures Public Company Limited; *Int'l,* pg. 3659
PT. INDORAMA POLYESTER INDUSTRIES INDONESIA—See Indorama Ventures Public Company Limited; *Int'l,* pg. 3659
PT. INDORAMA POLYPET INDONESIA—See Indorama Ventures Public Company Limited; *Int'l,* pg. 3659
PT. INDORAMA SYNTHETICS - BANDUNG PLANT—See Indorama Corporation Pte. Ltd.; *Int'l,* pg. 3658
PT. INDORAMA SYNTHETICS - PURWAKARTA PLANT—See Indorama Corporation Pte. Ltd.; *Int'l,* pg. 3658
PT. INDO-RAMA SYNTHETICS TBK—See Indorama Corporation Pte. Ltd.; *Int'l,* pg. 3658
PT.INDORAMA VENTURES INDONESIA—See Indorama Ventures Public Company Limited; *Int'l,* pg. 3659
PT INDO RAYA TENAGA—See PT PLN (Persero); *Int'l,* pg. 6065
PT INDORIS PRINTINGDO—See The Siam Cement Public Company Limited; *Int'l,* pg. 7683
PT INDORITEL MAKMUR INTERNASIONAL TBK; *Int'l,* pg. 6047
PT INDORITEL PERSADA NUSANTARA—See PT Indoritel Makmur Internasional Tbk; *Int'l,* pg. 6047
P.T. INDOSARI NIAGA NUSANTARA—See PT Nippon Indosari Corpindo Tbk; *Int'l,* pg. 6060
PT. INDOSAT MEGA MEDIA—See Ooredoo Q.S.C.; *Int'l,* pg. 5594
PT. INDOSAT TBK—See Ooredoo Q.S.C.; *Int'l,* pg. 5594
PT. INDOSPED MAJU SEJAHTERA—See Sacmi Imola S.C.A.R.L.; *Int'l,* pg. 6464
PT INDOSPRING TBK; *Int'l,* pg. 6047
PT INDOSTERLING TECHNOMEDIA TBK; *Int'l,* pg. 6047
PT INDO STRAITS TBK.; *Int'l,* pg. 6045
P.T. INDOTAISEI INDAH DEVELOPMENT—See Taisei Corporation; *Int'l,* pg. 7416
PT INDO TAMBANGRAYA MEGAH TBK.; *Int'l,* pg. 6045
PT. INDOTAMBANGRAYA MEGAH TBK—See Banpu Public Company Limited; *Int'l,* pg. 852
PT. INDOTECH METAL NUSANTARA—See Jotech Metal Fabrication Industries Sdn. Bhd.; *Int'l,* pg. 4001
PT INDO TENAGA HIJAU—See PT PLN (Persero); *Int'l,* pg. 6065
PT. INDO TRAKTOR UTAMA—See PT Indomobil Sukses Internasional Tbk; *Int'l,* pg. 6046
PT. INDOTRUCK UTAMA—See PT Indomobil Sukses Internasional Tbk; *Int'l,* pg. 6046
PT INDRA INDONESIA—See Indra Sistemas, S.A.; *Int'l,* pg. 3661
PT INDUSTRI JAMU DAN FARMASI SIDO MUNCUL TBK.; *Int'l,* pg. 6047
PT. INDUSTRI KEMASAN SEMEN GRESIK—See PT. Semen Indonesia (Persero) Tbk; *Int'l,* pg. 6089
PT. INFINITT INDONESIA; *Int'l,* pg. 6086
PT. INFOKOM ELEKTRINDO—See PT MNC Investama Tbk; *Int'l,* pg. 6058
PT INFOMEDIA NUSANTARA—See Perusahaan Perseroan Indonesia Tbk; *Int'l,* pg. 5821
PT INFORMASI TEKNOLOGI INDONESIA TBK.; *Int'l,* pg. 6047
P.T. INFORMATICS OASE; *Int'l,* pg. 5683
PT INFRA SOLUSI INDONESIA—See PT Link Net Tbk.; *Int'l,* pg. 6053
PT. INFRASTRUKTUR TELEKOMUNIKASI INDONESIA—See Perusahaan Perseroan Indonesia Tbk; *Int'l,* pg. 5821
P.T. INFRASTUKTUR CAKRAWALA TELEKOMUNIKASI—See PT Jababeka Tbk; *Int'l,* pg. 6048
PT INFRATECH INDONESIA; *Int'l,* pg. 6047
PT. INGERSOLL-RAND INDONESIA—See Ingersoll Rand Inc.; *U.S. Public,* pg. 1122
PT. INGREDION INDONESIA—See Ingredion Incorporated; *U.S. Public,* pg. 1124
PT. INGRESS MALINDO VENTURES—See Ingress Corporation Berhad; *Int'l,* pg. 3703
PT. INGRESS TECHNOLOGIES INDONESIA—See Ingress Industrial (Thailand) Public Company Limited; *Int'l,* pg. 3703
PT INGRIA PRATAMA CAPITALINDO TBK; *Int'l,* pg. 6047
PT. INNOTECH SYSTEMS—See PT United Tractors Tbk; *Int'l,* pg. 6081
PT INOCYCLE TECHNOLOGY GROUP TBK; *Int'l,* pg. 6047
PT INOVACAO - ALTICE LABS—See Altice Europe N.V.; *Int'l,* pg. 392
PT INOVACAO BRASIL LTDA.—See Oi S.A.; *Int'l,* pg. 5533
PT INOVASI INFORMATIKA INDONESIA—See PT Anabatic Technologies Tbk; *Int'l,* pg. 6021

PT INOVATIF SINERGI INTERNATIONAL—See I Synergy Group Limited; *Int'l,* pg. 3562
PT. INPHOSOFT INDONESIA—See GINSMS Inc.; *Int'l,* pg. 2977
PT. INPOLA MITRA ELEKTRINDO—See Kinergy Advancement Berhad; *Int'l,* pg. 4166
PT. INTAGE INDONESIA—See Nippon Telegraph & Telephone Corporation; *Int'l,* pg. 5350
PT. INTAN BARU PRANA TBK—See PT INTRACO PENTA Tbk; *Int'l,* pg. 6048
PT. INTAN KENKOMAYO INDONESIA—See Kenko Mayonnaise Co., Ltd.; *Int'l,* pg. 4127
PT INTANWIJAYA INTERNASIONAL TBK; *Int'l,* pg. 6047
P.T. INTA SARANA INFRASTRUKTUR—See PT INTRACO PENTA Tbk; *Int'l,* pg. 6048
PT INTEGRA INDOCABINET TBK; *Int'l,* pg. 6047
PT. INTEGRASI JARINGAN EKOSISTEM—See PT Solusi Sinergi Digital Tbk; *Int'l,* pg. 6075
PT. INTEGRASI LOGISTIK CIPTA SOLUSI—See PT Pelabuhan Indonesia II; *Int'l,* pg. 6062
P.T. INTERA INDONESIA—See PT Integra Indocabinet Tbk; *Int'l,* pg. 6047
P.T. INTERCIPTA KIMIA PRATAMA—See Raisio PLC; *Int'l,* pg. 6191
PT. INTERKRAFT—See PT Integra Indocabinet Tbk; *Int'l,* pg. 6047
PT. INTERMEDIA CAPITAL TBK.; *Int'l,* pg. 6086
PT. INTERNASIONAL ASIA PASIFIK SINERGI—See UNI-MECH Group Berhad; *Int'l,* pg. 8049
PT. INTERNASIONAL ASIA PRIMA SUKSES—See UNI-MECH Group Berhad; *Int'l,* pg. 8049
PT INTERNATIONAL ALLIANCE FOOD INDONESIA—See Alliance Select Foods International, Inc.; *Int'l,* pg. 341
PT INTERNATIONAL DEVELOPMENT CORPORATION LTD.; *Int'l,* pg. 6047
P.T. INTERNATIONAL GREEN ENERGY—See Tess Holdings Co., Ltd.; *Int'l,* pg. 7573
PT. INTERNATIONAL KANSHA KANDOU INDONESIA—See IKK Holdings Inc; *Int'l,* pg. 3611
PT INTERNATIONAL PAPER PACKAGING INDONESIA BATAM—See International Paper Company; *U.S. Public,* pg. 1157
PT INTERPORT MANDIRI UTAMA—See PT Indika Energy Tbk; *Int'l,* pg. 6044
PT. INTERSKALA MANDIRI INDONESIA—See Zhonghang Electronic Measuring Instruments Co., Ltd.; *Int'l,* pg. 8673
PT. INTERSPACE INDONESIA—See Interspace Co., Ltd.; *Int'l,* pg. 3761
P.T. INTERTREND UTAMA—See PT Integra Indocabinet Tbk; *Int'l,* pg. 6047
PT INTI BANGUN SEJAHTERA TBK; *Int'l,* pg. 6047
PT INTI DINAMIKA ID LOGITAMA INDONESIA—See ID Logistics SAS; *Int'l,* pg. 3588
PT INTI FAJAR PRATAMA MENARD—See VINCI S.A.; *Int'l,* pg. 8233
PT. INTI GANDA PERDANA—See PT Astra International Tbk; *Int'l,* pg. 6023
PT. INTI KARYA PERSADA TEHNIK—See Toyo Engineering Corporation; *Int'l,* pg. 7853
PT INTIKERAMIK ALAMASRI INDUSTRI TBK; *Int'l,* pg. 6047
PT INTILAND DEVELOPMENT TBK.; *Int'l,* pg. 6048
PT INTINUSA SELAREKSA TBK; *Int'l,* pg. 6048
PT. INTI PROPERTINDO JAYA—See PT TOTAL BANGUN PERSADA Tbk; *Int'l,* pg. 6078
PT. INTI TULLETT PREBON INDONESIA—See TP ICAP Finance PLC; *Int'l,* pg. 7881
PT INTRACO PENTA TBK; *Int'l,* pg. 6048
PT INTRASARI RAYA—See Godrej & Boyce Mfg. Co. Ltd.; *Int'l,* pg. 3021
PT. INVE INDONESIA—See Benchmark Holdings Plc; *Int'l,* pg. 970
PT. ION EXCHANGE INDONESIA—See Ion Exchange India Ltd; *Int'l,* pg. 3793
P.T. I-POP INDONESIA—See InternetQ plc; *Int'l,* pg. 3754
PT. IPSOS MARKET RESEARCH—See Ipsos S.A.; *Int'l,* pg. 3802
PTI ROYSTON, LLC; *U.S. Private,* pg. 3298
P.T. ISEKI INDONESIA—See Iseki & Co., Ltd.; *Int'l,* pg. 3814
PT ISENTIA JAKARTA—See Pulsar Group; *Int'l,* pg. 6116
PT ISENTRIC TECHNOLOGY INDONESIA—See IOUpay Limited; *Int'l,* pg. 3795
PT. ISEWAN INDONESIA—See Isewan Terminal Service Co., Ltd.; *Int'l,* pg. 3816
PT.IS JAYA LOGISTIK—See Isewan Terminal Service Co., Ltd.; *Int'l,* pg. 3816
PT ISLAND CONCEPTS INDONESIA TBK; *Int'l,* pg. 6048
PT ISP CHEMICALS INDONESIA—See Ashland Inc.; *U.S. Public,* pg. 213
PT ISTANA KARANG LAUT—See VINCI S.A.; *Int'l,* pg. 8218
P.T. ISUZU ASTRA MOTOR INDONESIA—See Isuzu Motors Limited; *Int'l,* pg. 3826
PT ITAMA RANORAYA TBK; *Int'l,* pg. 6048
PTI TECHNOLOGIES INC.—See ESCO Technologies, Inc.; *U.S. Public,* pg. 794

COMPANY NAME INDEX

P.T. ITM BHINNEKA POWER—See PT Indo Tambangraya Megah Tbk.; *Int'l*, pg. 6045
PT. ITOCHU INDONESIA—See ITOCHU Corporation; *Int'l*, pg. 3841
PT. ITOCHU LOGISTICS INDONESIA—See ITOCHU Corporation; *Int'l*, pg. 3839
PT ITO EN ULTRAJAYA WHOLESALE—See ITO EN Ltd; *Int'l*, pg. 3834
PT ITOKI SOLUTIONS INDONESIA—See Itoki Corporation; *Int'l*, pg. 3844
PT ITSEC ASIA TBK; *Int'l*, pg. 6048
PT ITT FLUID TECHNOLOGY INDONESIA—See ITT Inc.; *U.S. Public*, pg. 1178
PTI USA MANUFACTURING L.L.C.—See Oil States International, Inc.; *U.S. Public*, pg. 1565
PT IZENO TEKNOLOGI INDONESIA—See Datatec Limited; *Int'l*, pg. 1981
PT JABABEKA INFRASTRUKTUR—See PT Jababeka Tbk; *Int'l*, pg. 6048
PT JABABEKA TBK; *Int'l*, pg. 6048
P.T. JABATO INTERNATIONAL TOUR & TRAVEL—See West Japan Railway Company; *Int'l*, pg. 8385
PT JACCS MITRA PINASTHIKA MUSTIKA FINANCE INDONESIA—See JACCS Co., Ltd.; *Int'l*, pg. 3864
PT JACOBS GROUP INDONESIA—See Jacobs Engineering Group, Inc.; *U.S. Public*, pg. 1186
PT JAFRA COSMETICS INDONESIA—See Vorwerk & Co. KG; *Int'l*, pg. 8307
PT JAGA NUSANTARA SATU—See PT Anabatic Technologies Tbk; *Int'l*, pg. 6021
PT JAGAT PERTALA NUSANTARA—See PT Lippo Karawaci Tbk; *Int'l*, pg. 6053
PT. JAIC INDONESIA—See Japan Asia Investment Co., Ltd.; *Int'l*, pg. 3886
PT JAKARTA AVIATION TRAINING CENTRE—See PT. Cardig Aero Services Tbk; *Int'l*, pg. 6085
PT JAKARTA GLOBE MEDIA—See PT First Media Tbk; *Int'l*, pg. 6039
PT JAKARTA INTERNATIONAL HOTELS & DEVELOPMENT TBK; *Int'l*, pg. 6048
P.T. JAKARTA KYOAI MEDICAL CENTER—See Prudential Financial, Inc.; *U.S. Public*, pg. 1733
PT JAKARTA KYOEI STEEL WORKS TBK; *Int'l*, pg. 6048
PT JAKARTA SETIADUDI INTERNASIONAL TBK; *Int'l*, pg. 6048
PT JAKARTA TANK TERMINAL—See PT AKR Corporindo Tbk; *Int'l*, pg. 6020
PT JAKARTA TEKNOLOGI UTAMA—See PT Sinar Mas Multiartha Tbk; *Int'l*, pg. 6074
PT JALANTOL LINGKARLUAR JAKARTA—See PT. Jasa Marga (Persero) Tbk; *Int'l*, pg. 6086
PT JALCO ELECTRONICS INDONESIA—See JALCO Holdings Inc.; *Int'l*, pg. 3874
P.T. JALINTIM ADHI ABIPRAYA—See PT Adhi Karya (Persero) Tbk; *Int'l*, pg. 6019
PT JANU PUTRA SEJAHTERA TBK.; *Int'l*, pg. 6049
P.T. JAPAN AE POWER SYSTEMS INDONESIA—See Hitachi, Ltd.; *Int'l*, pg. 3424
P.T. JAPAN DRILLING INDONESIA—See Japan Drilling Co., Ltd.; *Int'l*, pg. 3888
PT.JAPAN ENGINEERING TECHNOLOGY—See Fair Friend Group; *Int'l*, pg. 2605
PT JAPFA COMFEED INDONESIA TBK; *Int'l*, pg. 6049
PT JAPFA COMFEED INDONESIA TBK - WISMA JCI DIVISION—See PT Japfa Comfeed Indonesia Tbk; *Int'l*, pg. 6049
PT JAPFAFOOD NUSANTARA—See PT Japfa Comfeed Indonesia Tbk; *Int'l*, pg. 6049
PT JASA ANGKASA SEMESTA TBK—See PT. Cardig Aero Services Tbk; *Int'l*, pg. 6085
PT JASA ARMADA INDONESIA TBK; *Int'l*, pg. 6049
PT JASA BERDIKARI LOGISTICS TBK; *Int'l*, pg. 6049
PT JASA BOGA RAYA—See PT. Bakrieland Development, Tbk.; *Int'l*, pg. 6084
PT. JASA CENTINA SENTOSA—See Regional Container Lines Public Company Limited; *Int'l*, pg. 6254
PT JAS AERO ENGINEERING SERVICES—See PT. Cardig Aero Services Tbk; *Int'l*, pg. 6085
PT JASA LOGISTIK UTAMA—See PT Indomobil Sukses Internasional Tbk; *Int'l*, pg. 6046
PT JASAMARGA BALIKPAPAN SAMARINDA—See PT. Jasa Marga (Persero) Tbk; *Int'l*, pg. 6086
PT JASAMARGA BALI TOL—See PT. Jasa Marga (Persero) Tbk; *Int'l*, pg. 6086
PT JASAMARGA GEMPOL PASURUAN—See PT. Jasa Marga (Persero) Tbk; *Int'l*, pg. 6086
PT JASAMARGA JALANLAYANG CIKAMPEK—See PT. Jasa Marga (Persero) Tbk; *Int'l*, pg. 6086
PT JASAMARGA JAPEK SELATAN—See PT. Jasa Marga (Persero) Tbk; *Int'l*, pg. 6086
PT JASAMARGA KUALANAMU TOL—See PT. Jasa Marga (Persero) Tbk; *Int'l*, pg. 6086
PT JASAMARGA KUNCIRAN CENGKARENG—See PT. Jasa Marga (Persero) Tbk; *Int'l*, pg. 6086
PT JASAMARGA MANADO BITUNG—See PT. Jasa Marga (Persero) Tbk; *Int'l*, pg. 6086
PT JASAMARGA PANDAAN MALANG—See PT. Jasa Marga (Persero) Tbk; *Int'l*, pg. 6086

PT JASAMARGA PANDAAN TOL—See PT. Jasa Marga (Persero) Tbk; *Int'l*, pg. 6086
PT. JASA MARGA (PERSERO) TBK; *Int'l*, pg. 6086
PT JASAMARGA PROBOLINGGO BANYUWANGI—See PT. Jasa Marga (Persero) Tbk; *Int'l*, pg. 6086
PT JASAMARGA PROPERTI—See PT. Jasa Marga (Persero) Tbk; *Int'l*, pg. 6086
P.T. JASAMARGA RELATED BUSINESS—See PT. Jasa Marga (Persero) Tbk; *Int'l*, pg. 6086
PT JASAMARGA SURABAYA MOJOKERTO—See PT. Jasa Marga (Persero) Tbk; *Int'l*, pg. 6086
PT JASAMARGA TOLLROAD MAINTENANCE—See PT. Jasa Marga (Persero) Tbk; *Int'l*, pg. 6086
PT JASAMARGA TOLLROAD OPERATOR—See PT. Jasa Marga (Persero) Tbk; *Int'l*, pg. 6086
PT JASAMARGA TRANSJAWA TOL—See PT. Jasa Marga (Persero) Tbk; *Int'l*, pg. 6086
PT JASNITA TELEKOMINDO TBK; *Int'l*, pg. 6049
PT. JASON ELEKTRONIKA—See Jason Marine Group Limited; *Int'l*, pg. 3912
P.T. JATIM TAMAN STEEL MFG.—See Mitsubishi Steel Mfg. Co., Ltd.; *Int'l*, pg. 4968
PT. JAVA EGG SPECIALITIES—See PT Cisarua Mountain Dairy Tbk; *Int'l*, pg. 6034
P.T. JAVA PACIFIC—See Singamas Container Holdings Limited; *Int'l*, pg. 6939
PT JAYA AGRA WATTIE TBK; *Int'l*, pg. 6049
PT JAYA BERSAMA INDO TBK; *Int'l*, pg. 6049
PT JAYA BETON INDONESIA—See Jaya Konstruksi Manggala Pratama Tbk; *Int'l*, pg. 3914
PT. JAYA CELCON PRIMA—See Jaya Konstruksi Manggala Pratama Tbk; *Int'l*, pg. 3914
PT. JAYA DAIDO CONCRETE—See Jaya Konstruksi Manggala Pratama Tbk; *Int'l*, pg. 3914
PT JAYA GARDENPOLIS—See Jaya Real Property Tbk; *Int'l*, pg. 3914
PT. JAYA INDAH CASTING—See Panasonic Holdings Corporation; *Int'l*, pg. 5717
PT. JAYA MANDARIN AGUNG—See Jardine Matheson Holdings Limited; *Int'l*, pg. 3910
PT. JAYAMANDIRI GEMASEJATI; *Int'l*, pg. 6086
PT. JAYA MULTI SARANA INDONESIA—See Jaya Konstruksi Manggala Pratama Tbk; *Int'l*, pg. 3914
P.T. JAYA OBAYASHI—See Obayashi Corporation; *Int'l*, pg. 5509
PT JAYA PARI STEEL TBK; *Int'l*, pg. 6049
PT. JAYA PESONA ABADI—See Metis Energy Limited; *Int'l*, pg. 4854
PT JAYA SUKSES MAKMUR SENTOSA TBK; *Int'l*, pg. 6049
PT JAYA SWARASA AGUNG TBK; *Int'l*, pg. 6049
PT JAYA TEKNIK INDONESIA—See Jaya Konstruksi Manggala Pratama Tbk; *Int'l*, pg. 3914
PT. JAYA TRADE INDONESIA—See Jaya Konstruksi Manggala Pratama Tbk; *Int'l*, pg. 3914
PT JAYA TRISHINDO TBK; *Int'l*, pg. 6049
PT JBA INDONESIA—See PT Adi Sarana Armada Tbk; *Int'l*, pg. 6019
PT. JCB INTERNATIONAL INDONESIA—See JCB Co., Ltd.; *Int'l*, pg. 3920
PT. JCU INDONESIA—See JCU Corporation; *Int'l*, pg. 3924
PT. JEBE TRADING INDONESIA—See JB Foods Limited; *Int'l*, pg. 3917
PT JEBSEN & JESSEN BUSINESS SERVICES (I)—See Jebsen & Jessen (SEA) Pte Ltd; *Int'l*, pg. 3926
PT JEBSEN & JESSEN CHEMICALS INDONESIA—See Jebsen & Jessen (SEA) Pte Ltd; *Int'l*, pg. 3926
PT JEDI GLOBAL TEKNOLOGI—See PT Anabatic Technologies Tbk; *Int'l*, pg. 6021
P.T. JEMBO CABLE COMPANY—See Fujikura Ltd.; *Int'l*, pg. 2829
PT. JETEC INDONESIA - ACTEMIUM INDONESIA—See VINCI S.A.; *Int'l*, pg. 8237
PT. JFE ENGINEERING INDONESIA—See JFE Holdings, Inc.; *Int'l*, pg. 3935
PT. JFE SHOJI STEEL INDONESIA—See JFE Holdings, Inc.; *Int'l*, pg. 3937
PT. JF HILLEBRAND INDONESIA—See Deutsche Post AG; *Int'l*, pg. 2081
PT. JGC INDONESIA—See JGC Holdings Corporation; *Int'l*, pg. 3940
PT. JIBUHIN BAKRIE INDONESIA—See SPARX Group Co., Ltd.; *Int'l*, pg. 7128
PT. JICO AGUNG—See Daesang Corporation; *Int'l*, pg. 1909
PT JIMBARAN GREENHILL—See Kajima Corporation; *Int'l*, pg. 4055
PT. JMS BATAM—See JMS Co., Ltd.; *Int'l*, pg. 3975
PT. JOBSTREET INDONESIA—See SEEK Limited; *Int'l*, pg. 6679
PT JOBUBU JARUM MINAHASA TBK; *Int'l*, pg. 6050
PT. JOHN CRANE INDONESIA—See Smiths Group plc; *Int'l*, pg. 7011
P.T. JOHNSON & JOHNSON INDONESIA—See Kenvue Inc.; *U.S. Public*, pg. 1224
PT JORONG BARUTAMA GRESTON—See PT Indo Tambangraya Megah Tbk.; *Int'l*, pg. 6045

P.T. JOTUN POWDER COATINGS INDONESIA—See Jotun A/S; *Int'l*, pg. 4003
PT J RESOURCES ASIA PASIFIK TBK—See J&Partners L.P.; *Int'l*, pg. 3853
PT J RESOURCES BOLAANG MONGONDOW—See J&Partners L.P.; *Int'l*, pg. 3853
PT J RESOURCES NUSANTARA—See J&Partners L.P.; *Int'l*, pg. 3853
PT. JSW PLASTICS MACHINERY INDONESIA—See The Japan Steel Works, Ltd.; *Int'l*, pg. 7659
PT. JTB INDONESIA—See JTB Corp.; *Int'l*, pg. 4016
PT. JTEKT INDONESIA—See JTEKT Corporation; *Int'l*, pg. 4019
PT JTRUST INVESTMENTS INDONESIA—See PT Bank JTrust Indonesia Tbk.; *Int'l*, pg. 6026
PT JT UNIVERSAL INDONESIA—See Shenzhen JT Automation Equipment Company Limited; *Int'l*, pg. 6815
PT JUARA BIKE—See PT Gaya Abadi Sempurna Tbk; *Int'l*, pg. 6040
PT JUKEN TECHNOLOGY INDONESIA—See Frencken Group Limited; *Int'l*, pg. 2773
P.T. JVC ELECTRONICS INDONESIA—See JVCKENWOOD Corporation; *Int'l*, pg. 4034
PT. JVCKENWOOD INDONESIA—See JVCKENWOOD Corporation; *Int'l*, pg. 4034
PT JWC INDONESIA ENERGI—See C&G SYSTEMS INC.; *Int'l*, pg. 1238
PT KABELINDO MURNI TBK.; *Int'l*, pg. 6050
PTK ACQUISITION CORP.; *U.S. Public*, pg. 1735
PT KAI COMMUTER JABODETABEK—See PT. Kereta Api Indonesia; *Int'l*, pg. 6087
P.T. KAJIMA INDONESIA—See Kajima Corporation; *Int'l*, pg. 4055
PT KALBE FARMA TBK. - BEKASI FACTORY—See PT Kalbe Farma Tbk.; *Int'l*, pg. 6050
PT KALBE FARMA TBK.; *Int'l*, pg. 6050
PT KALBE GENEXINE BIOLOGICS—See PT Kalbe Farma Tbk.; *Int'l*, pg. 6050
PT KALBE MILKO INDONESIA—See PT Kalbe Farma Tbk.; *Int'l*, pg. 6050
P.T. KALBE MORINAGA INDONESIA—See PT Kalbe Farma Tbk.; *Int'l*, pg. 6050
PT KALBIO GLOBAL MEDIKA—See PT Kalbe Farma Tbk.; *Int'l*, pg. 6050
PT KALGEN DNA—See PT Kalbe Farma Tbk.; *Int'l*, pg. 6050
PT KALIMANTAN JAWA GAS—See PT Perusahaan Gas Negara (Persero) Tbk; *Int'l*, pg. 6064
PT KALIMANTAN PRIMA PERSADA—See PT United Tractors Tbk; *Int'l*, pg. 6081
PT KA LOGISTIK—See PT. Kereta Api Indonesia; *Int'l*, pg. 6086
PT. KALTIM METHANOL INDUSTRI—See Sojitz Corporation; *Int'l*, pg. 7063
PT KALTIM PRIMA COAL—See PT Bumi Resources Tbk; *Int'l*, pg. 6031
PT. KAMIGUMI INDONESIA—See Kamigumi Co., Ltd.; *Int'l*, pg. 4062
PT. KAMIGUMI LOGISTICS INDONESIA—See Kamigumi Co., Ltd.; *Int'l*, pg. 4063
PT. KANAKA GRAHAASRI CO., LTD.—See Land & Houses Public Company Limited; *Int'l*, pg. 4403
PT KANAMOTO INDONESIA—See Kanamoto Co., Ltd.; *Int'l*, pg. 4064
P.T. KANEFUSA INDONESIA—See KANEFUSA CORPORATION; *Int'l*, pg. 4066
P.T. KANEMATSU TRADING INDONESIA—See Kanematsu Corporation; *Int'l*, pg. 4069
PT. KANEMORY FOOD SERVICE—See Kanematsu Corporation; *Int'l*, pg. 4069
PT KANGAR CONSOLIDATED INDUSTRIES—See O-I Glass, Inc.; *U.S. Public*, pg. 1560
P.T. KANSAI PAINT INDONESIA—See Kansai Paint Co., Ltd.; *Int'l*, pg. 4073
PT KANSAI PRAKARSA COATINGS—See Kansai Paint Co., Ltd.; *Int'l*, pg. 4073
P.T. KAO INDONESIA CHEMICALS—See Kao Corporation; *Int'l*, pg. 4075
P.T. KAO INDONESIA—See Kao Corporation; *Int'l*, pg. 4075
PT KA PROPERTI MANAJEMEN—See PT. Kereta Api Indonesia; *Int'l*, pg. 6086
PT KAPUAS PRIMA COAL TBK; *Int'l*, pg. 6051
P.T. KARGO BERSAMA TEKNOLOGI—See PT Adi Sarana Armada Tbk; *Int'l*, pg. 6019
PT. KARSA LINTAS BUWANA—See PT Kalbe Farma Tbk.; *Int'l*, pg. 6050
PT KARTIKA PARAMA MEDIKA—See PT Mitra Keluarga Karyasehat Tbk; *Int'l*, pg. 6057
PT KARUNIA BUNDA SETIA—See PT Mitra Keluarga Karyasehat Tbk; *Int'l*, pg. 6057
P.T. KARYA ABDI LUHUR—See PT Mitra Investindo Tbk; *Int'l*, pg. 6057
PT KARYA BERSAMA ANUGERAH TBK; *Int'l*, pg. 6051
PT. KARYA BUMI BARATAMA—See SK Networks Co., Ltd.; *Int'l*, pg. 6974
PT KARYA CIPTANYATA WISESA—See PT Japfa Comfeed Indonesia Tbk; *Int'l*, pg. 6049

PT KARYA HASTA DINAMIKA—See PT Kalbe Farma Tbk.; *Int'l*, pg. 6051

PT KARYAPUTRA SURYAGEMILANG—See PT Anabatic Technologies Tbk; *Int'l*, pg. 6021

P.T. KARYA SUMIDEN INDONESIA—See Sumitomo Electric Industries, Ltd.; *Int'l*, pg. 7279

P.T. KARYATAMA INTI LESTARI—See PT Mitra Investindo Tbk; *Int'l*, pg. 6057

PT KARYA USAHA PERTIWI—See PT Harum Energy Tbk.; *Int'l*, pg. 6042

P.T. KASAI TECK SEE INDONESIA - KARAWANG 2ND PLANT—See Kasai Kogyo Co., Ltd.; *Int'l*, pg. 4086

KASAI TECK SEE INDONESIA—See Kasai Kogyo Co., Ltd.; *Int'l*, pg. 4086

P.T. KASIH ABDI DHARMA—See PT Mitra Keluarga Karyasehat Tbk; *Int'l*, pg. 6057

P.T. KATOLEC INDONESIA—See Katolec Corporation; *Int'l*, pg. 4092

PT KATSUSHIRO INDONESIA—See Komatsu Ltd.; *Int'l*, pg. 4239

PT KAWAI INDONESIA—See Kawai Musical Instruments Mfg. Co., Ltd.; *Int'l*, pg. 4094

PT. KAWAI MUSIC SCHOOL INDONESIA—See Kawai Musical Instruments Mfg. Co., Ltd.; *Int'l*, pg. 4094

P.T. KAWASAKI MOTOR INDONESIA—See Kawasaki Heavy Industries, Ltd.; *Int'l*, pg. 4098

PT KAWASAN INDUSTRI GRESIK—See PT. Semen Indonesia (Persero) Tbk; *Int'l*, pg. 6089

P.T. KAWATA INDONESIA—See KAWATA MFG.CO., LTD.; *Int'l*, pg. 4101

P.T. KAYABA INDONESIA—See KYB Corporation; *Int'l*, pg. 4354

P.T. KB BUKOPIN FINANCE—See PT Bank KB Bukopin Tbk; *Int'l*, pg. 6026

P.T. KB DATA SYSTEMS INDONESIA—See KB Financial Group Inc.; *Int'l*, pg. 4104

PT KB INSURANCE INDONESIA—See PT Sinar Mas Multiartha Tbk; *Int'l*, pg. 6074

P.T. KB VALBURY SEKURITAS—See KB Financial Group Inc.; *Int'l*, pg. 4104

PT KDB TIFA FINANCE TBK—See Korea Development Bank; *Int'l*, pg. 4282

PT. KDDI INDONESIA—See KDDI Corporation; *Int'l*, pg. 4112

PT. KDK INDONESIA—See Panasonic Holdings Corporation; *Int'l*, pg. 5717

PT. KDS INDONESIA—See Daishinku Corp.; *Int'l*, pg. 1942

PT KEDAWUNGSETIA CORRUGATED CARTON BOX INDUSTRIAL—See PT Kedawung Setia Industrial Tbk; *Int'l*, pg. 6051

PT KEDAWUNG SETIA INDUSTRIAL TBK; *Int'l*, pg. 6051

PT KEDOYA ADYARAYA TBK; *Int'l*, pg. 6051

P.T. KEIHIN INDONESIA—See Hitachi Astemo, Ltd.; *Int'l*, pg. 3409

PT. KELLER FRANKI INDONESIA—See Keller Group plc; *Int'l*, pg. 4121

PT KEMANG FOOD INDUSTRIES—See PT Sentra Food Indonesia Tbk; *Int'l*, pg. 6071

PT. KEMANG VILLAGE—See PT Lippo Karawaci Tbk; *Int'l*, pg. 6053

PT. KEMBANG GRIYA CAHAYA—See PT Metropolitan Land Tbk; *Int'l*, pg. 6056

PT KEMIRA INDONESIA—See Kemira Oyj; *Int'l*, pg. 4124

PT KENCANA ENERGI LESTARI TBK; *Int'l*, pg. 6051

PT KENCANA INTERNUSA ARTHA FINANCE—See CIMB Group Holdings Berhad; *Int'l*, pg. 1608

P.T. KENCANA SR BUILD—See SY Co., Ltd.; *Int'l*, pg. 7377

PT KENCANA UNGGUL SUKSES—See Agung Podomoro Land Tbk; *Int'l*, pg. 222

PT KENROPE SARANA PRATAMA—See Jaya Konstruksi Manggala Pratama Tbk; *Int'l*, pg. 3914

PT KENROPE UTAMA SENTUL—See Jaya Konstruksi Manggala Pratama Tbk; *Int'l*, pg. 3914

PT KEPLAND INVESTAMA—See Keppel Corporation Limited; *Int'l*, pg. 4131

PT KEPPEL LAND—See Keppel Corporation Limited; *Int'l*, pg. 4131

PT. KERAMIKA INDONESIA ASSOSIASI—See The Siam Cement Public Company Limited; *Int'l*, pg. 7684

PT. KERETA API INDONESIA; *Int'l*, pg. 6086

PT KERRY LOGISTICS (INDONESIA)—See Kerry Logistics Network Limited; *Int'l*, pg. 4140

PT KERTAS BASUKI RACHMAT INDONESIA TBK; *Int'l*, pg. 6051

P.T. KHATULISTIWA PRIMA SEJAHTERA—See PT. Kobexindo Tractors Tbk; *Int'l*, pg. 6087

PT. KHIND ENVIRONMENTAL SOLUTIONS—See Khind Holdings Berhad; *Int'l*, pg. 4155

PT KHI PIPE INDUSTRIES—See PT Krakatau Steel (Persero) Tbk; *Int'l*, pg. 6052

PT KHS PACKAGING MACHINERY INDONESIA—See Salzgitter AG; *Int'l*, pg. 6497

PT KIAN SANTANG MULIATAMA TBK.; *Int'l*, pg. 6051

PT. KIDECO JAYA AGUNG—See PT Indika Energy Tbk; *Int'l*, pg. 6044

PT. KIEVIT INDONESIA—See Zuivelcooperatie FrieslandCampina U.A.; *Int'l*, pg. 8694

PT KILLARA RESOURCES—See Eco Systems Ltd.; *Int'l*, pg. 2292

PT. KIM ENG SECURITIES—See Malayan Banking Berhad; *Int'l*, pg. 4660

PT KIMIA FARMA APOTEK—See PT. Kimia Farma (Persero) Tbk.; *Int'l*, pg. 6087

PT KIMIA FARMA DIAGNOSTIKA—See PT. Kimia Farma (Persero) Tbk.; *Int'l*, pg. 6087

PT. KIMIA FARMA (PERSERO) TBK.; *Int'l*, pg. 6087

PT. KIMIA FARMA SUNGWUN PHARMACOPIA—See PT. Kimia Farma (Persero) Tbk.; *Int'l*, pg. 6087

PT. KIMIA FARMA TRADING & DISTRIBUTION—See PT. Kimia Farma (Persero) Tbk.; *Int'l*, pg. 6087

PT KIM SEAH SHIPYARD INDONESIA—See Dymon Asia Capital (Singapore) Pte. Ltd; *Int'l*, pg. 2238

P.T. KINARYA LOKA BUANA—See PT Mitra Keluarga Karyasehat Tbk; *Int'l*, pg. 6057

PT. KINDEN INDONESIA—See Kinden Corporation; *Int'l*, pg. 4166

PT. KING JIM INDONESIA—See KING JIM CO., LTD.; *Int'l*, pg. 4169

PT KINGSMEN INDONESIA—See Kingsmen Creatives Ltd; *Int'l*, pg. 4175

PT KING TIRE INDONESIA TBK.; *Int'l*, pg. 6051

PT. KIN LONG HARDWARE INDONESIA—See Guangdong Kinlong Hardware Prdcts Co., Ltd.; *Int'l*, pg. 3157

PT. KINO FOOD INDONESIA—See PT Kino Indonesia Tbk.; *Int'l*, pg. 6051

PT KINO INDONESIA TBK.; *Int'l*, pg. 6051

PT KIOSON KOMERSIAL INDONESIA TBK; *Int'l*, pg. 6051

PT. KIRANA ANINDITA—See Schwan-STABILO Cosmetics GmbH & Co. KG; *Int'l*, pg. 6644

PT KIRANA MEGATARA TBK; *Int'l*, pg. 6051

PT KIRANA PERMATA—See PT Kirana Megatara Tbk; *Int'l*, pg. 6051

PT KIRANA PRIMA—See PT Kirana Megatara Tbk; *Int'l*, pg. 6051

PT KIRANA TRIPUTRA PERSADA—See PT Kirana Megatara Tbk; *Int'l*, pg. 6051

PT. KIRIU INDONESIA—See Sumitomo Corporation; *Int'l*, pg. 7269

PT. KITADIN—See PT Indo Tambangraya Megah Tbk; *Int'l*, pg. 6045

PT. KIWOOM SECURITIES INDONESIA—See Daou Data Corp.; *Int'l*, pg. 1970

PT KLIK EAT INDONESIA; *Int'l*, pg. 6051

PT K LINE INDONESIA—See Kawasaki Kisen Kaisha, Ltd.; *Int'l*, pg. 4101

P.T. KMI ELECTRIC SOLUTION—See PT KMI Wire & Cable Tbk.; *Int'l*, pg. 6051

PT KMI WIRE & CABLE TBK.; *Int'l*, pg. 6051

P.T. KML ICHIMASA FOODS—See Ichimasa Kamaboko Co., Ltd.; *Int'l*, pg. 3580

PT. KMW INDONESIA—See PT Astra Otoparts Tbk; *Int'l*, pg. 6024

PT. KNAUF GYPSUM INDONESIA—See Gebr. Knauf KG; *Int'l*, pg. 2908

P.T. KNET INDONESIA—See Hexatronic Group AB; *Int'l*, pg. 3371

PT. KOBAYASHI PHARMACEUTICAL INDONESIA—See Kobayashi Pharmaceutical Co., Ltd.; *Int'l*, pg. 4216

PT. KOBELINDO COMPRESSORS—See Kobe Steel, Ltd.; *Int'l*, pg. 4220

PT KOBEXINDO EQUIPMENT—See PT. Kobexindo Tractors Tbk; *Int'l*, pg. 6087

PT. KOBEXINDO KONSTRUKSI INDONESIA—See PT. Kobexindo Tractors Tbk; *Int'l*, pg. 6087

PT. KOBEXINDO TRACTORS TBK; *Int'l*, pg. 6087

PT KOEXIM MANDIRI FINANCE—See The Export-Import Bank of Korea; *Int'l*, pg. 7641

PT. KOH BROTHERS INDONESIA—See Koh Brothers Group Limited; *Int'l*, pg. 4228

PT KOKA INDONESIA TBK; *Int'l*, pg. 6051

PT. KOKOH INTI AREBAMA TBK—See The Siam Cement Public Company Limited; *Int'l*, pg. 7684

PT. KOKUSAI ENGINEERING INDONESIA—See KOKUSAI CO., LTD; *Int'l*, pg. 4231

PT. KOKUYO FURNITURE INDONESIA—See Kokuyo Co., Ltd.; *Int'l*, pg. 4232

P.T. KOLON INA—See Kolon Industries, Inc.; *Int'l*, pg. 4234

P.T. KOMALA INDONESIA—See PT Jaya Trishindo Tbk; *Int'l*, pg. 6050

P.T. KOMARITIM—See Stolt-Nielsen Limited; *Int'l*, pg. 7221

PT KOMARK LABELS & LABELLING INDONESIA—See Komarkcorp Berhad; *Int'l*, pg. 4234

PT. KOMATSU ASTRA FINANCE—See Komatsu Ltd.; *Int'l*, pg. 4239

PT KOMATSU INDONESIA TBK—See Komatsu Ltd.; *Int'l*, pg. 4239

PT KOMATSU MARKETING & SUPPORT INDONESIA—See Komatsu Ltd.; *Int'l*, pg. 4239

PT KOMATSU REMAN INDONESIA—See Komatsu Ltd.; *Int'l*, pg. 4239

PT KOMATSU REMANUFACTURING ASIA—See PT United Tractors Tbk; *Int'l*, pg. 6081

PT KOMATSU UNDERCARRIAGE INDONESIA—See Komatsu Ltd.; *Int'l*, pg. 4239

PT KONECRANES—See Konecranes Plc; *Int'l*, pg. 4252

PT KONE INDO ELEVATOR—See KONE Oyj; *Int'l*, pg. 4250

PT.KONOIKE TRANSPORT INDONESIA—See Konoike Transport Co.; *Int'l*, pg. 4275

PT KONUTARA SEJATI—See China Hanking Holdings Limited; *Int'l*, pg. 1506

PT KOREA INVESTMENT & SEKURITAS INDONESIA—See Korea Investment Holdings Co., Ltd.; *Int'l*, pg. 4285

PT KORINDO HEAVY INDUSTRY—See Korindo Group; *Int'l*, pg. 4289

PT. KORINTIGA HUTANI—See Oji Holdings Corporation; *Int'l*, pg. 5538

PT KORN/FERRY INTERNATIONAL—See Korn Ferry; *U.S. Public*, pg. 1275

PT KOTA SATU PROPERTI TBK; *Int'l*, pg. 6051

PTK PANONONIJA A.D.; *Int'l*, pg. 6090

PT. KRAFT ULTRAJAYA INDONESIA—See Mondelez International, Inc.; *U.S. Public*, pg. 1462

PT. KRAKATAU NIPPON STEEL SYNERGY—See Nippon Steel Corporation; *Int'l*, pg. 5339

P.T. KRAKATAU ARGO LOGISTICS—See PT Krakatau Steel (Persero) Tbk; *Int'l*, pg. 6052

P.T. KRAKATAU BANDAR SAMUDERA—See PT Krakatau Steel (Persero) Tbk; *Int'l*, pg. 6052

P.T. KRAKATAU DAYA LISTRIK—See PT Krakatau Steel (Persero) Tbk; *Int'l*, pg. 6052

P.T. KRAKATAU ENGINEERING—See PT Krakatau Steel (Persero) Tbk; *Int'l*, pg. 6052

P.T. KRAKATAU INDUSTRIAL ESTATE CILEGON—See PT Krakatau Steel (Persero) Tbk; *Int'l*, pg. 6052

P.T. KRAKATAU INFORMATION TECHNOLOGY—See PT Krakatau Steel (Persero) Tbk; *Int'l*, pg. 6052

P.T. KRAKATAU JASA INDUSTRI—See PT Krakatau Steel (Persero) Tbk; *Int'l*, pg. 6052

P.T. KRAKATAU JASA LOGISTICS—See PT Krakatau Steel (Persero) Tbk; *Int'l*, pg. 6052

P.T. KRAKATAU JASA SAMUDERA—See PT Krakatau Steel (Persero) Tbk; *Int'l*, pg. 6052

P.T. KRAKATAU KONSULTAN—See PT Krakatau Steel (Persero) Tbk; *Int'l*, pg. 6052

P.T. KRAKATAU MEDIKA—See PT Krakatau Steel (Persero) Tbk; *Int'l*, pg. 6052

P.T. KRAKATAU NIAGA INDONESIA—See PT Krakatau Steel (Persero) Tbk; *Int'l*, pg. 6052

P.T. KRAKATAU PERBENGKELAN DAN PERAWATAN—See PT Krakatau Steel (Persero) Tbk; *Int'l*, pg. 6052

P.T. KRAKATAU PIPE INDUSTRIES—See PT Krakatau Steel (Persero) Tbk; *Int'l*, pg. 6052

P.T. KRAKATAU SARANA PROPERTI—See PT Krakatau Steel (Persero) Tbk; *Int'l*, pg. 6052

P.T. KRAKATAU SEMEN INDONESIA—See PT. Semen Indonesia (Persero) Tbk; *Int'l*, pg. 6089

PT KRAKATAU STEEL (PERSERO) TBK; *Int'l*, pg. 6052

P.T. KRAKATAU TIRTA OPERASI DAN PEMELIHARAAN—See PT Krakatau Steel (Persero) Tbk; *Int'l*, pg. 6052

PT. KRAKATAU WAJATAMA—See PT Krakatau Steel (Persero) Tbk; *Int'l*, pg. 6052

PT. KRAMA YUDHA TIGA BERLIAN MOTORS—See Mitsubishi Corporation; *Int'l*, pg. 4942

P.T. KRAYON KONSULTAN INDONESIA—See Crayon Group Holding ASA; *Int'l*, pg. 1829

P.T. KREASI MANDIRI WINTOR INDONESIA—See PT Astra International Tbk; *Int'l*, pg. 6023

PT. KREASI MAS INDAH—See Golden Agri-Resources Ltd.; *Int'l*, pg. 3028

PT KREATIF MEDIA KARYA—See PT. Elang Mahkota Teknologi Tbk.; *Int'l*, pg. 6086

PT KRESNA ASSET MANAGEMENT—See PT Quantum Clovera Investama Tbk.; *Int'l*, pg. 6067

PT KRESNA DUTA AGROINDO—See Golden Agri-Resources Ltd.; *Int'l*, pg. 3028

PT KRESNA SEKURITAS—See PT Quantum Clovera Investama Tbk.; *Int'l*, pg. 6067

P.T. KRIDA GAWAI ABADI—See PT Adi Sarana Armada Tbk; *Int'l*, pg. 6019

PT KRIDA JARINGAN NUSANTARA TBK; *Int'l*, pg. 6052

PT. KROHNE INDONESIA—See Krohne International, Inc.; *Int'l*, pg. 4304

PT KROM BANK INDONESIA TBK—See FinAccel Pte Ltd.; *Int'l*, pg. 2664

P.T. KROMTEKINDO UTAMA—See Waters Corporation; *U.S. Public*, pg. 2335

PT. KRONE INDONESIA—See TE Connectivity Ltd.; *Int'l*, pg. 7479

PT. KRONES MACHINERY INDONESIA—See Krones AG; *Int'l*, pg. 4306

PT. KSB INDONESIA—See KSB SE & Co. KGaA; *Int'l*, pg. 4313

PT. KSB SALES INDONESIA—See KSB SE & Co. KGaA; *Int'l*, pg. 4313

PT. KSD INDONESIA—See KS Energy Limited; *Int'l*, pg. 4310

P.T. KSO ELNUSA - RAGA—See PT Elnusa Tbk; *Int'l*, pg. 6037

COMPANY NAME INDEX

PT KT&G INDONESIA—See KT&G Corporation; *Int'l*, pg. 4316
PT. KUBOTA INDONESIA—See Kubota Corporation; *Int'l*, pg. 4322
P.T. KUBU MULIA FORESTRY—See Sumitomo Forestry Co., Ltd.; *Int'l*, pg. 7286
P.T. KUEI MENG CHIAN INDONESIA—See KMC (Kuei Meng) International Inc.; *Int'l*, pg. 4204
P.T. KUEN LING INDONESIA—See Kuen Ling Refrigerating Machinery Co., Ltd.; *Int'l*, pg. 4326
P.T. KUKDONG INTERNATIONAL—See Kukdong Corporation; *Int'l*, pg. 4327
P.T. KUMKANG KIND INDONESIA—See Kumkang Kind; *Int'l*, pg. 4331
P.T. KURABO MANUNGGAL TEXTILE INDUSTRIES—See Kurabo Industries Ltd.; *Int'l*, pg. 4336
P.T. KURITA INDONESIA—See Kurita Water Industries Ltd.; *Int'l*, pg. 4341
PT KURNIAMITRA DUTA SENTOSA TBK; *Int'l*, pg. 6052
P.T. KURNIA REALTY JAYA—See PT Wijaya Karya (Persero) Tbk.; *Int'l*, pg. 6082
P.T. KUSTODIAN SENTRAL EFEK INDONESIA—See PT Bank Rakyat Indonesia (Persero) Tbk; *Int'l*, pg. 6028
PT KUSUMA KEMINDO SENTOSA—See PT Catur Sentosa Adiprana Tbk; *Int'l*, pg. 6033
P.T. KUTAI TIMBER INDONESIA - PROBOLINGGO FACTORY—See Sumitomo Forestry Co., Ltd.; *Int'l*, pg. 7285
P.T. KUTAI TIMBER INDONESIA—See Sumitomo Forestry Co., Ltd.; *Int'l*, pg. 7285
P.T. KYB HYDRAULICS MANUFACTURING INDONESIA—See KYB Corporation; *Int'l*, pg. 4354
P.T. KYOKUTO INDOMOBIL DISTRIBUTOR INDONESIA—See Kyokuto Kaihatsu Kogyo Co. Ltd.; *Int'l*, pg. 4363
P.T. KYOKUTO INDOMOBIL MANUFACTURING INDONESIA—See Kyokuto Kaihatsu Kogyo Co. Ltd.; *Int'l*, pg. 4363
P.T. KYORITSU ELECTRIC INDONESIA—See Kyoritsu Electric Corporation; *Int'l*, pg. 4365
P.T. KYOSHA INDONESIA—See KYOSHA CO., LTD.; *Int'l*, pg. 4365
PT LADANG BAJA MURNI TBK; *Int'l*, pg. 6052
PT LAMICITRA NUSANTARA TBK; *Int'l*, pg. 6052
P.T. LAMINATECH KREASI SARANA—See PT Gema Grahasarana Tbk; *Int'l*, pg. 6040
P.T. LAMIPAK PRIMULA INDONESIA—See PT. Berlina Tbk; *Int'l*, pg. 6085
P.T. LANCARJAYA MANDIRI ABADI—See PT PP (Persero) Tbk; *Int'l*, pg. 6066
PT LANCARTAMA SEJATI TBK; *Int'l*, pg. 6052
P.T. LANGGENG BAJAPRATAMA—See PT KMI Wire & Cable Tbk.; *Int'l*, pg. 6051
PT LANGGENG MAKMUR INDUSTRI TBK; *Int'l*, pg. 6052
PT LANGGENG MAKMUR INDUSTRI TBK - TROSOBO FACTORY—See PT Langgeng Makmur Industri Tbk; *Int'l*, pg. 6052
PT. LANNA MINING SERVICES—See Lanna Resources pcl; *Int'l*, pg. 4413
PT LANTRO TECHNOLOGIES INDONESIA—See MIRAIT ONE Corporation; *Int'l*, pg. 4917
PT LATIVI MEDIAKARYA—See PT Visi Media Asia Tbk; *Int'l*, pg. 6081
PT. LAUTAN JASAINDO—See PT. Lautan Luas Tbk; *Int'l*, pg. 6087
PT. LAUTAN LUAS TBK; *Int'l*, pg. 6087
P.T. LAUTAN MITRA KREASI—See PT. Lautan Luas Tbk; *Int'l*, pg. 6087
PT. LAUTAN ORGANO WATER—See Organo Corporation; *Int'l*, pg. 5618
P.T. LAUTAN OTSUKA CHEMICAL—See Otsuka Holdings Co., Ltd.; *Int'l*, pg. 5661
P.T. LAUTAN SULFAMAT LESTARI—See PT. Lautan Luas Tbk; *Int'l*, pg. 6087
PT LAVENDER BINA CENDIKIA TBK; *Int'l*, pg. 6052
PT. LAYANAN PUSAKA PRIMA—See PT Blue Bird Tbk; *Int'l*, pg. 6030
PT LAYAR LINTAS JAYA—See PT Harum Energy Tbk; *Int'l*, pg. 6042
PT LCK GLOBAL KEDATON TBK; *Int'l*, pg. 6052
PT. LEARNING RESOURCES—See Empresaria Group Plc; *Int'l*, pg. 2389
PT. LEEPORT INDONESIA—See Leeport (Holdings) Limited; *Int'l*, pg. 4442
PT. LEEPORT MACHINE TOOL INDONESIA—See Leeport (Holdings) Limited; *Int'l*, pg. 4442
PTL ENTERPRISES LTD.; *Int'l*, pg. 6091
PT. LEON TESTING & CONSULTANCY—See China Leon Inspection Holding Limited; *Int'l*, pg. 1514
PT. LES ENPHANTS INDONESIA CO., LTD.—See Les Enphants Group; *Int'l*, pg. 4467
PT LEYAND INTERNATIONAL TBK; *Int'l*, pg. 6053
PT. LG CNS INDONESIA—See LG Corp.; *Int'l*, pg. 4475
PT. LG ELECTRONICS INDONESIA—See LG Corp.; *Int'l*, pg. 4476
PT. LIEBHERR-INDONESIA PERKASA—See Liebherr-International AG; *Int'l*, pg. 4491
P.T. LIFUNG INDONESIA—See Li & Fung Limited; *Int'l*, pg. 4480

PT LIMA DUA LIMA TIGA TBK; *Int'l*, pg. 6053
PT LIMAS INDONESIA MAKMUR TBK; *Int'l*, pg. 6053
PT. LINCOLN ELECTRIC INDONESIA—See Lincoln Electric Holdings, Inc.; *U.S. Public*, pg. 1318
PT. LINCOLN INDOWELD—See Lincoln Electric Holdings, Inc.; *U.S. Public*, pg. 1318
PT. LINDE INDONESIA—See Linde plc; *Int'l*, pg. 4508
PTL INFORMATION TECHNOLOGY SERVICES CORP.—See Plexus Corp.; *U.S. Public*, pg. 1698
PT LINK NET TBK.; *Int'l*, pg. 6053
P.T. LINTAS MARGA SEDAYA—See PT Astra International Tbk; *Int'l*, pg. 6023
PT LINTAS SAMUDRA MARITIM—See PT Soechi Lines Tbk; *Int'l*, pg. 6075
PT LINTEC INDONESIA—See LINTEC Corporation; *Int'l*, pg. 4516
PT. LINTEC JAKARTA—See LINTEC Corporation; *Int'l*, pg. 4516
PT LION MENTARI AIRLINES; *Int'l*, pg. 6053
P.T. LION SUPER INDO—See Koninklijke Ahold Delhaize N.V.; *Int'l*, pg. 4261
PT. LION WINGS—See Lion Corporation; *Int'l*, pg. 4518
PT LIPPO CIKARANG TBK; *Int'l*, pg. 6053
PT LIPPO GENERAL INSURANCE TBK; *Int'l*, pg. 6053
PT LIPPO KARAWACI TBK; *Int'l*, pg. 6053
PT LIPPO LIFE INSURANCE—See PT Lippo General Insurance Tbk; *Int'l*, pg. 6053
PT. LIPPO SECURITIES, TBK; *Int'l*, pg. 6087
PT LOCK&LOCK INDONESIA—See Lock&Lock Co., Ltd.; *Int'l*, pg. 4540
PT LOGINDO SAMUDRAMAKMUR TBK; *Int'l*, pg. 6053
PT LOGISTICSPLUS INTERNATIONAL TBK; *Int'l*, pg. 6053
PT. LOGITAK DIGITAL NUSANTARA—See PT Telefast Indonesia Tbk; *Int'l*, pg. 6078
PT. LOGITEK DIGITAL NUSANTARA—See PT Telefast Indonesia Tbk; *Int'l*, pg. 6078
PT. LOHMANN ANIMAL HEALTH INDONESIA—See Eli Lilly & Company; *U.S. Public*, pg. 734
PT. LOMBOK TAKSI UTAMA—See PT Blue Bird Tbk; *Int'l*, pg. 6030
P.T. L'OREAL INDONESIA—See L'Oreal S.A.; *Int'l*, pg. 4381
P.T. LOSCAM INDONESIA—See China Merchants Group Limited; *Int'l*, pg. 1521
PT. LOTTE CHEMICAL TITAN NUSANTARA; *Int'l*, pg. 6053
PT LOUIS VUITTON INDONESIA LLC—See LVMH Moet Hennessy Louis Vuitton SE; *Int'l*, pg. 4596
PT LOVINA BEACH BREWERY TBK; *Int'l*, pg. 6053
PT. LUHAI INDUSTRIAL—See Lu Hai Holding Corp.; *Int'l*, pg. 4571
PT LUMBUNG SARI—See PT Equity Development Investment Tbk; *Int'l*, pg. 6038
PT LUPROMAX PELUMAS INDONESIA TBK; *Int'l*, pg. 6053
PT LUXCHEM INDONESIA—See Luxchem Corporation Berhad; *Int'l*, pg. 4588
PT. LUXINDO RAYA—See Vorwerk & Co. KG; *Int'l*, pg. 8307
PT. LX PANTOS INDONESIA—See LX Holdings Corp.; *Int'l*, pg. 4604
PT. LYRA AKRELUX—See F.I.L.A. - Fabbrica Italiana Lapis ed Affini S.p.A.; *Int'l*, pg. 2597
PT MACGREGOR PLIMSOLL INDONESIA—See Cargotec Corporation; *Int'l*, pg. 1329
PT. MACQUARIE CAPITAL SECURITIES INDONESIA—See Macquarie Group Limited; *Int'l*, pg. 4630
PT. MACROCHEMA PRATAMA; *Int'l*, pg. 6087
PT MACROLINK OMEGA ADIPERKASA—See PT Central Omega Resources Tbk; *Int'l*, pg. 6033
PT MAC SARANA DJAYA—See PT Centratama Telekomunikasi Indonesia Tbk; *Int'l*, pg. 6033
PT MADHUCON INDONESIA—See Madhucon Projects Limited; *Int'l*, pg. 4633
PT MADUSARI MURNI INDAH; *Int'l*, pg. 6054
P.T. MAGNA INVESTAMA MANDIRI TBK—See PT. Bhuwanatala Indah Permai Tbk; *Int'l*, pg. 6085
PT MAHACITTA TEKNOLOGI—See PT Anabatic Technologies Tbk; *Int'l*, pg. 6021
PT MAHAKA MEDIA TBK; *Int'l*, pg. 6054
PT MAHAKAM SUMBER JAYA—See PT Harum Energy Tbk.; *Int'l*, pg. 6043
PT MAHAKA RADIO INTEGRA TBK; *Int'l*, pg. 6054
PT MAHA PROPERTI INDONESIA TBK; *Int'l*, pg. 6054
PT MAHARAKSA BIRU ENERGI TBK; *Int'l*, pg. 6054
PT MAHKOTA GROUP TBK; *Int'l*, pg. 6054
PT. MAH SING INDONESIA—See Mah Sing Group Berhad; *Int'l*, pg. 4643
PT. MAJUKO UTAMA INDONESIA—See PT Rukun Raharja Tbk; *Int'l*, pg. 6069
P.T. MAKASSAR TERMINAL SERVICES INC.—See International Container Terminal Services, Inc.; *Int'l*, pg. 3746
PT MAKINO INDONESIA—See Makino Milling Machine Co., Ltd.; *Int'l*, pg. 4656
P.T. MAKMUR ABADI VALVE—See UNIMECH Group Berhad; *Int'l*, pg. 8049

PT MAS MURNI INDONESIA TBK

PT MAKMUR BERKAH AMANDA TBK; *Int'l*, pg. 6054
PT MAKMUR SEJAHTERA WISESA—See PT Adaro Energy Indonesia Tbk; *Int'l*, pg. 6019
PT MAKNA PRAKARSA UTAMA; *Int'l*, pg. 6054
PT MAKRO INDONESIA—See Lotte Co., Ltd.; *Int'l*, pg. 4560
PT MALINDO FEEDMILL TBK—See Emerging Glory Sdn Bhd; *Int'l*, pg. 2379
PT MALINDO FOOD DELIGHT—See Leong Hup International Berhad; *Int'l*, pg. 4461
PT MAMING ENAM SEMBILAN MINERAL TBK.; *Int'l*, pg. 6054
PT. MANDALA MULTIFINANCE TBK—See PT. Jayamandiri Gemasejati; *Int'l*, pg. 6086
PT MANDARA SPA INDONESIA—See OneSpaWorld Holdings Limited; *U.S. Public*, pg. 1604
PT MANDIRI AXA GENERAL INSURANCE—See PT Bank Mandiri (Persero) Tbk.; *Int'l*, pg. 6027
PT MANDIRI CAHAYA ABADI—See PT Dharma Satya Nusantara Tbk; *Int'l*, pg. 6036
P.T. MANDIRI CAPITAL INDONESIA—See PT Bank Mandiri (Persero) Tbk.; *Int'l*, pg. 6026
PT MANDIRI HERINDO ADIPERKASA TBK; *Int'l*, pg. 6054
PT MANDIRI MANAJEMEN INVESTASI—See PT Bank Mandiri (Persero) Tbk.; *Int'l*, pg. 6027
PT MANDIRI SEJAHTERA SENTRA—See PT Indocement Tunggal Prakarsa Tbk; *Int'l*, pg. 6045
PT MANDIRI SEKURITAS—See PT Bank Mandiri (Persero) Tbk.; *Int'l*, pg. 6027
PT MANDIRI TUNAS FINANCE—See PT Bank Mandiri (Persero) Tbk.; *Int'l*, pg. 6027
PT MANDIRI UTAMA FINANCE—See PT Bank Mandiri (Persero) Tbk.; *Int'l*, pg. 6027
PT. MANDOM INDONESIA TBK.—See Mandom Corporation; *Int'l*, pg. 4668
PT. MANE INDONESIA—See V. Mane Fils SA; *Int'l*, pg. 8106
PT MANGGALA KIAT ANANDA—See Kewpie Corporation; *Int'l*, pg. 4144
P.T. MANPOWER BUSINESS SOLUTIONS INDONESIA—See ManpowerGroup Inc.; *U.S. Public*, pg. 1361
PT MANROLAND INDONESIA—See Allianz SE; *Int'l*, pg. 355
PT MANUNGGAL WIRATAMA—See Lippo Malls Indonesia Retail Trust; *Int'l*, pg. 4522
PT MAP AKTIF ADIPERKASA TBK—See PT. Mitra Adiperkasa Tbk; *Int'l*, pg. 6088
PT MAPALUS MAKAWANUA CHARCOAL INDUSTRY—See Hayleys PLC; *Int'l*, pg. 3292
PT MAP BOGA ADIPERKASA TBK—See PT. Mitra Adiperkasa Tbk; *Int'l*, pg. 6088
PT MAPEI INDONESIA CONSTRUCTION SOLUTION—See Mapei SpA; *Int'l*, pg. 4683
PT. MARCOPOLO SHIPYARD—See Marco Polo Marine Ltd.; *Int'l*, pg. 4690
PT MARECO PRIMA MANDIRI—See PT Surya Fajar Capital Tbk; *Int'l*, pg. 6077
PT MARGA ABHINAYA ABADI TBK; *Int'l*, pg. 6054
PT MARGA LINGKAR JAKARTA—See PT. Jasa Marga (Persero) Tbk; *Int'l*, pg. 6086
PT MARGA MANDALASAKTI—See PT Astra International Tbk; *Int'l*, pg. 6023
PT MARGA SARANA JABAR—See PT. Jasa Marga (Persero) Tbk; *Int'l*, pg. 6086
PT MARGA TRANS NUSANTARA—See PT. Jasa Marga (Persero) Tbk; *Int'l*, pg. 6086
PT MARINE ENGINEERING SERVICES—See Pacific Radiance Ltd.; *Int'l*, pg. 5691
PT MARK DYNAMICS INDONESIA TBK; *Int'l*, pg. 6054
PT MARKETECH INTERNATIONAL INDONESIA—See Marketech International Corp.; *Int'l*, pg. 4696
PT MARSH INDONESIA—See Marsh & McLennan Companies, Inc.; *U.S. Public*, pg. 1383
PT MARSH REINSURANCE BROKERS INDONESIA—See Marsh & McLennan Companies, Inc.; *U.S. Public*, pg. 1388
PT MARSOL ABADI INDONESIA—See Rengo Co., Ltd.; *Int'l*, pg. 6280
PT MARTINA BERTO TBK; *Int'l*, pg. 6054
P.T. MARUBENI INDONESIA—See Marubeni Corporation; *Int'l*, pg. 4709
PT MARUBUN ARROW INDONESIA—See Arrow Electronics, Inc.; *U.S. Public*, pg. 199
PT. MARUKA INDONESIA—See Maruka Furusato Corporation; *Int'l*, pg. 4714
PT. MARUZEN SAMUDERA TAIHEIYO—See Maruzen Showa Unyu Co., Ltd.; *Int'l*, pg. 4716
PT MASAJI KARGOSENTRA TAMA—See PT Samudera Indonesia Tbk; *Int'l*, pg. 6069
PT MASAJI PRAYASA CARGO—See PT Samudera Indonesia Tbk; *Int'l*, pg. 6069
PT MASKAPAI REASURANSI INDONESIA TBK; *Int'l*, pg. 6055
PT MAS MURNI INDONESIA TBK; *Int'l*, pg. 6055
PT MASTER INDONESIA—See Beng Kuang Marine Limited; *Int'l*, pg. 973

P.T. MASTER PRINT—See PT Mitra Pack Tbk; *Int'l*, pg. 6057
PT MASTERSYSTEM INFOTAMA TBK; *Int'l*, pg. 6055
PT MATAHARI DEPARTMENT STORE TBK; *Int'l*, pg. 6055
PT MATAHARI PUTRA PRIMA TBK; *Int'l*, pg. 6055
P.T. MATAIR RUMAH KREATIF—See Tempo Inti Media Tbk; *Int'l*, pg. 7556
P&T MATERIAL SUPPLY JSC—See Vietnam Posts & Telecommunications Corporation; *Int'l*, pg. 8203
P.T. MATLAMAT CAKERA CANGGIH—See Marubeni Corporation; *Int'l*, pg. 4709
PT MAXINDO KARYA ANUGERAH TBK; *Int'l*, pg. 6055
PT MAXXTEC TEKNOLOGI INDONESIA—See Maxxtec AG; *Int'l*, pg. 4743
P.T. MAYANGSARI—See Pyxus International, Inc.; *U.S. Public*, pg. 1741
PT MAYBANK ASSET MANAGEMENT—See Malayan Banking Berhad; *Int'l*, pg. 4661
PT MAYBANK INDONESIA FINANCE—See Malayan Banking Berhad; *Int'l*, pg. 4661
P.T. MAYEKAWA INDONEISA—See Mayekawa Mfg. Co. Ltd.; *Int'l*, pg. 4744
PT. MAYORA INDAH TBK; *Int'l*, pg. 6087
P.T. MAZDA MOTOR INDONESIA—See Mazda Motor Corporation; *Int'l*, pg. 4749
PT M CASH INTEGRASI TBK; *Int'l*, pg. 6053
P.T. MCCONNELL DOWELL INDONESIA—See Aveng Limited; *Int'l*, pg. 738
P.T. MCLOGI-ARK INDONESIA—See Mitsubishi Corporation; *Int'l*, pg. 4942
P.T. MCNS POLYURETHANES INDONESIA—See Mitsui Chemicals, Inc.; *Int'l*, pg. 4983
PTM CORPORATION; *U.S. Private*, pg. 3298
PT MC PET FILM INDONESIA—See Mitsubishi Chemical Group Corporation; *Int'l*, pg. 4934
PT. MC TECHNOS INDONESIA—See Mitsubishi Corporation; *Int'l*, pg. 4941
PT MD PICTURES TBK; *Int'l*, pg. 6055
PT MECOINDO—See Itron, Inc.; *U.S. Public*, pg. 1176
PT MEDCO ENERGI INTERNASIONAL TBK; *Int'l*, pg. 6055
PT MEDCO E&P INDONESIA—See PT Medco Energi Internasional Tbk; *Int'l*, pg. 6055
PT MEDCO POWER INDONESIA—See PT Medco Energi Internasional Tbk; *Int'l*, pg. 6055
PT MEDIACOM PRIMA—See PT Equity Development Investment Tbk; *Int'l*, pg. 6038
PT. MEDIA INNITY—See Innity Corporation Berhad; *Int'l*, pg. 3708
PT. MEDIA NUSANTARA CITRA TBK; *Int'l*, pg. 6087
PT MEDIATAMA ANUGRAH CITRA—See PT. Elang Mahkota Teknologi Tbk.; *Int'l*, pg. 6086
PT. MEDIATE INDONESIA—See PT. MEDIA NUSANTARA CITRA TBK; *Int'l*, pg. 6088
PT MEDIKALOKA HERMINA TBK; *Int'l*, pg. 6055
PT MEDIKALOKA HUSADA—See PT Medikaloka Hermina Tbk; *Int'l*, pg. 6055
P.T. MEDIKALOKA PASTEUR—See PT Medikaloka Hermina Tbk; *Int'l*, pg. 6055
PT. MEDISAFE TECHNOLOGIES—See Indorama Corporation Pte. Ltd.; *Int'l*, pg. 3658
PT MEGA AGUNG NUSANTARA—See PT Modernland Realty Tbk; *Int'l*, pg. 6059
PT MEGA AKSES PERSADA—See PT Indoritel Makmur Internasional Tbk; *Int'l*, pg. 6047
PT MEGA ARTHA PERSADA—See K. S. Oils Limited; *Int'l*, pg. 4043
PT MEGA ASSET MANAGEMENT—See PT CT Corpora; *Int'l*, pg. 6035
P.T. MEGA AUTO FINANCE—See Marubeni Corporation; *Int'l*, pg. 4709
PT MEGA BUANA TEKNOLOG—See PT Anabatic Technologies Tbk; *Int'l*, pg. 6021
PT MEGA CAPITAL INVESTAMA—See PT CT Corpora; *Int'l*, pg. 6035
PT MEGA DUTA PERSADA—See PT Multipolar Tbk; *Int'l*, pg. 6060
PT MEGA FEDERAL ENERGY—See Federal International (2000) Ltd; *Int'l*, pg. 2630
PT MEGAH SEMESTA ABADI—See Lippo Malls Indonesia Retail Trust; *Int'l*, pg. 4522
PT MEGAH SUMBER SEJAHTERA—See PT Panca Anugrah Wisesa Tbk; *Int'l*, pg. 6061
PT MEGA INTI MANDIRI—See PT Chitose Internasional Tbk; *Int'l*, pg. 6034
P.T. MEGA KEMIRAYA—See Megachem Limited; *Int'l*, pg. 4793
PT MEGALESTARI EPACK SENTOSARAYA TBK; *Int'l*, pg. 6055
P.T. MEGALOPOLIS MANUNGGAL INDUSTRIAL DEVELOPMENT—See Marubeni Corporation; *Int'l*, pg. 4709
PT MEGA MANUNGGAL PROPERTY TBK; *Int'l*, pg. 6055
PT MEGA PERINTIS TBK; *Int'l*, pg. 6055
PT MEGAPOLITAN DEVELOPMENTS, TBK; *Int'l*, pg. 6056
PT MEGAPOWER MAKMUR TBK; *Int'l*, pg. 6056

PT MEGA PRATAMA FERINDO—See PT Garuda Metalindo Tbk; *Int'l*, pg. 6040
PT MEGA RAYA KUSUMA—See PT Golden Eagle Energy Tbk; *Int'l*, pg. 6041
PT MEGARON SEMESTA—See Wah Seong Corporation Berhad; *Int'l*, pg. 8330
PT MEGMILK SNOW BRAND INDONESIA—See MEGMILK SNOW BRAND Co., Ltd.; *Int'l*, pg. 4796
PT MEIDEN ENGINEERING INDONESIA—See Meidensha Corporation; *Int'l*, pg. 4798
P.T. MEIJI INDONESIAN PHARMACEUTICAL INDUSTRIES—See Meiji Holdings Co., Ltd.; *Int'l*, pg. 4801
P.T. MEISEI INDONESIA—See Meisei Industrial Co., Ltd.; *Int'l*, pg. 4804
PT. MEIWA TRADING INDONESIA—See Meiwa Corporation; *Int'l*, pg. 4805
PT MEKA ADIPRATAMA—See PT Bintraco Dharma Tbk; *Int'l*, pg. 6030
PT MEKANUSA CIPTA CO., LTD.—See Land & Houses Public Company Limited; *Int'l*, pg. 4403
PT MELON INDONESIA—See Perusahaan Perseroan Indonesia Tbk; *Int'l*, pg. 5821
PT MEMIONTEC INDONESIA—See Memiontec Holdings Ltd.; *Int'l*, pg. 4814
PT MENARA ASTRA—See PT Astra International Tbk; *Int'l*, pg. 6023
PT MENARA TERUS MAKMUR—See PT Astra Otoparts Tbk; *Int'l*, pg. 6024
PTM ENGINEERING PLASTICS (NANTONG) CO., LTD.—See Mitsubishi Gas Chemical Company, Inc.; *Int'l*, pg. 4950
PT MENN TEKNOLOGI INDONESIA; *Int'l*, pg. 6056
PT MENTENG HERITAGE REALTY TBK; *Int'l*, pg. 6056
P.T. MERAPI UTAMA PHARMA—See Otsuka Holdings Co., Ltd.; *Int'l*, pg. 5661
PT. MERATUS JAYA IRON & STEEL—See PT Krakatau Steel (Persero) Tbk; *Int'l*, pg. 6052
P.T. MERCEDES-BENZ INDONESIA—See Mercedes-Benz Group AG; *Int'l*, pg. 4828
PT MERCER INDONESIA—See Marsh & McLennan Companies, Inc.; *U.S. Public*, pg. 1388
P.T. MERCK SHARP & DOHME INDONESIA—See Merck & Co., Inc.; *U.S. Public*, pg. 1420
P.T. MERCK SHARP & DOHME INDONESIA—See Merck & Co., Inc.; *U.S. Public*, pg. 1420
PT MERCK SHARP DOHME PHARMA TBK—See Merck & Co., Inc.; *U.S. Public*, pg. 1420
PT MERDEKA BATTERY MATERIALS TBK; *Int'l*, pg. 6056
PT MERDEKA COPPER GOLD TBK; *Int'l*, pg. 6056
PT. MERDIS INTERNATIONAL—See Bain Capital, LP; *U.S. Private*, pg. 449
PT MERIMEN TECHNOLOGIES INDONESIA—See Silverlake Axis Ltd.; *Int'l*, pg. 6926
PT.MERITZ KORINDO INSURANCE—See Meritz Financial Group Inc.; *Int'l*, pg. 4836
P.T. MERMAID TEXTILE INDUSTRY INDONESIA—See Shikibo Ltd.; *Int'l*, pg. 6829
P. T. MESIN ISUZU INDONESIA—See Isuzu Motors Limited; *Int'l*, pg. 3826
PT MES MACHINERY INDONESIA—See Mitsui E&S Holdings Co., Ltd.; *Int'l*, pg. 4986
PT METABISULPHITE NUSANTARA—See PT. Lautan Luas Tbk; *Int'l*, pg. 6087
PT META EPSI TBK; *Int'l*, pg. 6056
PT METALUTAMA PERKASA JAYA—See PT HK Metals Utama; *Int'l*, pg. 6043
PT. METBELOSA—See Osaki Electric Co., Ltd.; *Int'l*, pg. 5647
PT METITO INDONESIA—See Metito Holdings Ltd.; *Int'l*, pg. 4854
PT METRA DIGITAL MEDIA—See Perusahaan Perseroan Indonesia Tbk; *Int'l*, pg. 5821
PT METRA-NET—See Perusahaan Perseroan Indonesia Tbk; *Int'l*, pg. 5821
P.T. METRA TV—See Perusahaan Perseroan Indonesia Tbk; *Int'l*, pg. 5821
PT METRODATA E BISNIS—See PT. Metrodata Electronics, Tbk.; *Int'l*, pg. 6088
PT. METRODATA ELECTRONICS, TBK.; *Int'l*, pg. 6088
PT METRO HEALTHCARE INDONESIA TBK; *Int'l*, pg. 6056
PT. METROHM INDONESIA—See Metrohm AG; *Int'l*, pg. 4862
PT METRO HOSPITALS INDONESIA—See PT Metro Healthcare Indonesia Tbk; *Int'l*, pg. 6056
PT METROPARK CONDOMINIUM INDAH—See PT. Jababeka Tbk; *Int'l*, pg. 6048
PT METROPOLITAN DETA GRAHA—See PT Metropolitan Land Tbk; *Int'l*, pg. 6056
PT METROPOLITAN GRAHA MANAGEMENT—See PT Metropolitan Land Tbk; *Int'l*, pg. 6056
PT METROPOLITAN KARYADEKA ASCENDAS—See PT Metropolitan Land Tbk; *Int'l*, pg. 6056
PT METROPOLITAN KARYADEKA DEVELOPMENT—See PT Metropolitan Land Tbk; *Int'l*, pg. 6056
PT METROPOLITAN KENTJANA TBK; *Int'l*, pg. 6056
PT METROPOLITAN LAND TBK; *Int'l*, pg. 6056

PT METROPOLITAN PERMATA DEVELOPMENT—See PT Metropolitan Land Tbk; *Int'l*, pg. 6056
PT METRO REALTY TBK; *Int'l*, pg. 6056
P.T. METROTECH JAYA KOMUNIKA INDONESIA—See Digilife Technologies Limited; *Int'l*, pg. 2119
PT. METSO MINERALS INDONESIA—See Metso Oyj; *Int'l*, pg. 4867
PT METTLER-TOLEDO INDONESIA—See Mettler-Toledo International, Inc.; *U.S. Public*, pg. 1433
PT. MHI ENGINE SYSTEM INDONESIA—See Mitsubishi Heavy Industries, Ltd.; *Int'l*, pg. 4960
PT MICHAEL PAGE INTERNASIONAL INDONESIA—See PageGroup plc; *Int'l*, pg. 5698
PT MICHELIN INDONESIA—See Compagnie Generale des Etablissements Michelin SCA; *Int'l*, pg. 1745
PT. MICROLINK INDONESIA—See Omesti Berhad; *Int'l*, pg. 5562
PT MIDI UTAMA INDONESIA TBK; *Int'l*, pg. 6057
P.T. MIDO INDONESIA—See PT Trisula International Tbk; *Int'l*, pg. 6080
P.T. MIDTRANS—See PT GoTo Gojek Tokopedia Tbk; *Int'l*, pg. 6041
PT MIFA BERSAUDARA—See PT ABM Investama Tbk.; *Int'l*, pg. 6018
PT MILLENIA DHARMA INSANI—See PT Kalbe Farma Tbk.; *Int'l*, pg. 6050
PT MILLENNIUM PHARMACON INTERNATIONAL TBK—See Lembaga Tabung Angkatan Tentera; *Int'l*, pg. 4448
PT MI MAGAZINES—See Singapore Press Holdings Ltd.; *Int'l*, pg. 6942
PT. MIMAKI INDONESIA—See MIMAKI ENGINEERING CO., LTD.; *Int'l*, pg. 4898
PT MINDA AUTOMOTIVE, INDONESIA—See Minda Corporation Limited; *Int'l*, pg. 4900
PT MINDRAY MEDICAL INDONESIA—See Mindray Medical International Ltd.; *Int'l*, pg. 4901
PT MINERAL INDUSTRI SUKABUMI—See PT Indocement Tunggal Prakarsa Tbk; *Int'l*, pg. 6045
PT MINNA PADI INVESTAMA SEKURITAS TBK; *Int'l*, pg. 6057
PT MISI HUTAMA INTERNATIONAL—See PT Humpuss Intermoda Transportasi Tbk; *Int'l*, pg. 6044
PT. MISUMI INDONESIA—See MISUMI Group Inc.; *Int'l*, pg. 4922
PT MISYS INTERNATIONAL FINANCIAL SYSTEMS—See Vista Equity Partners, LLC; *U.S. Private*, pg. 4397
PT. MITACHI INDONESIA—See MITACHI Co., LTD.; *Int'l*, pg. 4924
PT. MITRA ADIPERKASA; *Int'l*, pg. 6088
P.T. MITRA ALAM BAHARI SENTOSA—See PT Mitrabara Adiperdana Tbk; *Int'l*, pg. 6058
PT MITRABAHTERA SEGARA SEJATI TBK; *Int'l*, pg. 6058
PT MITRA BALI INDAH—See PT Catur Sentosa Adiprana Tbk; *Int'l*, pg. 6033
PT MITRABARA ADIPERDANA TBK; *Int'l*, pg. 6058
P.T. MITRA BRAYAN INDONESIA—See PT Mitra Keluarga Karyasehat Tbk; *Int'l*, pg. 6057
PT MITRACON GRAHA SOLUSINDO—See Kelington Group Berhad; *Int'l*, pg. 4119
P.T. MITRADELTA BAHARI PRATAMA—See PT Mitrabara Adiperdana Tbk; *Int'l*, pg. 6058
PT MITRA ENERGI PERSADA TBK; *Int'l*, pg. 6057
PT MITRA INTEGRASI INFORMATIKA—See PT. Metrodata Electronics, Tbk.; *Int'l*, pg. 6088
PT MITRA INTERNATIONAL RESOURCES TBK.; *Int'l*, pg. 6057
PT MITRA INVESTINDO TBK; *Int'l*, pg. 6057
PT MITRAIS INDOSERVICES - JAKARTA—See PT Mitrais Indoservices; *Int'l*, pg. 6058
PT MITRAIS INDOSERVICES; *Int'l*, pg. 6058
PT MITRA KARYA PRIMA—See PT PLN (Persero); *Int'l*, pg. 6065
PT MITRA KELUARGA KARYASEHAT TBK; *Int'l*, pg. 6057
PT MITRA KOMUNIKASI NUSANTARA TBK; *Int'l*, pg. 6057
PT MITRA LANGGENG SEJAHTERA—See PT. Bakrieland Development, Tbk.; *Int'l*, pg. 6084
PT MITRA LINGKUNGAN DUTACONSULT—See Koninklijke HaskoningDHV Groep B.V.; *Int'l*, pg. 4266
PT MITRA MUTIARA MAKMUR—See PT Modernland Realty Tbk; *Int'l*, pg. 6059
P.T. MITRA NEW GRAIN—See PT Nippon Indosari Corpindo Tbk; *Int'l*, pg. 6060
PT. MITRA OTO PRIMA—See PT Bintraco Dharma Tbk; *Int'l*, pg. 6030
PT MITRA PACK TBK; *Int'l*, pg. 6057
PT MITRA PEMUDA TBK.; *Int'l*, pg. 6057
P.T. MITRA PENGEMBANG KAWASAN—See PT. Jababeka Tbk; *Int'l*, pg. 6048
PT. MITRA PINASTHIKA MULIA—See PT Mitra Pinasthika Mustika Tbk; *Int'l*, pg. 6058
PT. MITRA PINASTHIKA MUSTIKA AUTO—See PT Mitra Pinasthika Mustika Tbk; *Int'l*, pg. 6058
PT. MITRA PINASTHIKA MUSTIKA FINANCE—See PT Mitra Pinasthika Mustika Tbk; *Int'l*, pg. 6058

COMPANY NAME INDEX

PT MITRA PINASTHIKA MUSTIKA RENT—See PT Mitra Pinasthika Mustika Tbk; *Int'l*, pg. 6058
PT MITRA PINASTHIKA MUSTIKA TBK; *Int'l*, pg. 6058
PT MITRA SINDO MAKMUR—See PT Modernland Realty Tbk; *Int'l*, pg. 6059
PT MITRA SINDO SUKSES—See PT Modernland Realty Tbk; *Int'l*, pg. 6059
PT MITRA TIRTA BUWANA TBK—See PT Makna Prakarsa Utama; *Int'l*, pg. 6054
PT MITRA TOUR & TRAVEL—See PT Pertamina (Persero); *Int'l*, pg. 6063
PT MITRA TRANSAKSI INDONESIA KEPEMILIKA—See PT Bank Mandiri (Persero) Tbk.; *Int'l*, pg. 6027
P.T. MITSUBA AUTOMOTIVE PARTS INDONESIA—See MITSUBA Corporation; *Int'l*, pg. 4929
P.T. MITSUBA INDONESIA—See MITSUBA Corporation; *Int'l*, pg. 4929
P.T. MITSUBISHI CHEMICAL INDONESIA—See Mitsubishi Chemical Group Corporation; *Int'l*, pg. 4934
P.T. MITSUBISHI HC CAPITAL AND FINANCE INDONESIA—See Mitsubishi HC Capital Inc.; *Int'l*, pg. 4952
P.T. MITSUBISHI HEAVY INDUSTRIES INDONESIA—See Mitsubishi Heavy Industries, Ltd.; *Int'l*, pg. 4960
P.T. MITSUBISHI JAYA ELEVATOR AND ESCALATOR—See Mitsubishi Electric Corporation; *Int'l*, pg. 4946
P.T. MITSUBISHI KRAMA YUDHA MOTORS & MANUFACTURING—See Mitsubishi Motors Corporation; *Int'l*, pg. 4967
P.T. MITSUBISHI LOGISTICS INDONESIA—See Mitsubishi Logistics Corporation; *Int'l*, pg. 4963
P.T. MITSUBISHI MOTORS KRAMA YUDHA SALES INDONESIA—See Mitsubishi Corporation; *Int'l*, pg. 4942
P.T. MITSUBISHI POWER INDONESIA—See Mitsubishi Heavy Industries, Ltd.; *Int'l*, pg. 4960
P.T. MITSUBISHI UFJ LEASE & FINANCE INDONESIA—See Mitsubishi HC Capital Inc.; *Int'l*, pg. 4952
P.T. MITSUBOSHI BELTING INDONESIA—See Mitsuboshi Belting Ltd.; *Int'l*, pg. 4972
P.T. MITSUBOSHI BELTING SALES INDONESIA—See Mitsuboshi Belting Ltd.; *Int'l*, pg. 4972
P.T. MITSUI INDONESIA—See Mitsui & Co., Ltd.; *Int'l*, pg. 4979
P.T. MITSUI-SOKO INDONESIA—See Mitsui-Soko Holdings Co., Ltd.; *Int'l*, pg. 4993
P.T. MIURA INDONESIA—See Miura Co., Ltd.; *Int'l*, pg. 4995
PT MIWON INDONESIA - GRESIK FACTORY—See Daesang Corporation; *Int'l*, pg. 1909
PT MIWON INDONESIA—See Daesang Corporation; *Int'l*, pg. 1909
PT MIZUHO LEASING INDONESIA TBK; *Int'l*, pg. 6058
PT. MK PRIMA INDONESIA—See PT Indospring Tbk; *Int'l*, pg. 6047
PT. MMC METAL FABRICATION—See Mitsubishi Materials Corporation; *Int'l*, pg. 4965
PT. MNC ASSET MANAGEMENT—See PT MNC Investama Tbk; *Int'l*, pg. 6058
PT. MNC ASURANSI INDONESIA—See PT MNC Investama Tbk; *Int'l*, pg. 6058
PT MNC DIGITAL ENTERTAINMENT TBK; *Int'l*, pg. 6058
PT MNC ENERGY INVESTMENTS TBK; *Int'l*, pg. 6058
PT. MNC FINANCE—See PT MNC Investama Tbk; *Int'l*, pg. 6058
PT MNC INVESTAMA TBK; *Int'l*, pg. 6058
P.T. MNC KABEL MEDIACOM—See PT MNC Vision Networks Tbk; *Int'l*, pg. 6059
PT MNC KAPITAL INDONESIA TBK—See PT MNC Investama Tbk; *Int'l*, pg. 6058
PT MNC LAND TBK; *Int'l*, pg. 6059
PT. MNC LIFE ASSURANCE—See PT MNC Investama Tbk; *Int'l*, pg. 6059
PT. MNC NETWORKS—See PT MNC Investama Tbk; *Int'l*, pg. 6059
PT. MNC SEKURITAS—See PT MNC Investama Tbk; *Int'l*, pg. 6059
PT. MNC SKY VISION TBK—See PT Global Mediacom Tbk.; *Int'l*, pg. 6041
PT. MNC TELEVISI NETWORK—See PT MNC Investama Tbk; *Int'l*, pg. 6059
PT MNC VISION NETWORKS TBK; *Int'l*, pg. 6059
P.T. MOBILE INNOVATION INDONESIA—See Nippon Telegraph & Telephone Corporation; *Int'l*, pg. 5355
PT. MODERN DATA SOLUSI—See PT Modern Internasional Tbk; *Int'l*, pg. 6059
PT MODERN INDUSTRIAL ESTAT—See PT Modernland Realty Tbk; *Int'l*, pg. 6059
PT MODERN INTERNASIONAL TBK; *Int'l*, pg. 6059
PT MODERNLAND REALTY TBK; *Int'l*, pg. 6059
PT. MODERN PANEL INDONESIA—See PT Modernland Realty Tbk; *Int'l*, pg. 6059
PT. MODULAR MINING INDONESIA—See Komatsu Ltd.; *Int'l*, pg. 4239
PT. MOLDS & DIES INDONESIA—See Sacmi Imola S.C.A.R.L.; *Int'l*, pg. 6464

P.T. MOLINDO INTI GAS—See PT Madusari Murni Indah; *Int'l*, pg. 6054
PT. MOLINDO RAYA INDUSTRIAL—See PT Madusari Murni Indah; *Int'l*, pg. 6054
PT. MOLITEC STEEL INDONESIA—See Molitec Steel Co., Ltd.; *Int'l*, pg. 5022
PT. MOL LOGISTICS WAREHOUSE—See Mitsui O.S.K. Lines, Ltd.; *Int'l*, pg. 4991
PT. MOLTEN ALUMINIUM PRODUCER INDONESIA—See Honda Motor Co., Ltd.; *Int'l*, pg. 3463
PT. MONAGRO KIMIA—See Bayer Aktiengesellschaft; *Int'l*, pg. 909
PT. MONDELEZ INDONESIA MANUFACTURING—See Mondelez International, Inc.; *U.S. Public*, pg. 1462
PT. MONDELEZ INDONESIA—See Mondelez International, Inc.; *U.S. Public*, pg. 1462
PT. MONOTARO INDONESIA—See Sumitomo Corporation; *Int'l*, pg. 7269
PT. MONOTARO INDONESIA—See W.W. Grainger, Inc.; *U.S. Public*, pg. 2320
PT. MONO TECHNOLOGY INDONESIA—See Mono Next Public Company Limited; *Int'l*, pg. 5034
PT. MONTIGO SEMINYAK—See KOP Limited; *Int'l*, pg. 4279
PT. MOONLION INDUSTRIES INDONESIA—See Chun Yu Works & Co., Ltd.; *Int'l*, pg. 1596
PT MORENZO ABADI PERKASA TBK; *Int'l*, pg. 6059
PT. MORESCO INDONESIA—See MORESCO Corporation; *Int'l*, pg. 5040
PT. MORESCO MACRO ADHESIVE—See MORESCO Corporation; *Int'l*, pg. 5040
PT. MORESCO MACRO ADHESIVE—See PT. Macrochema Pratama; *Int'l*, pg. 6087
PT. MORIROKU CHEMICALS INDONESIA—See Moriroku Holdings Company, Ltd.; *Int'l*, pg. 5047
PT. MORIROKU TECHNOLOGY INDONESIA—See Moriroku Holdings Company, Ltd.; *Int'l*, pg. 5047
PT MORULA INDONESIA—See PT Bundamedik Tbk; *Int'l*, pg. 6032
PT MORULA IVF PADANG—See PT Bundamedik Tbk; *Int'l*, pg. 6032
P.T. MOSTRANS GLOBAL DIGILOG—See PT Kalbe Farma Tbk.; *Int'l*, pg. 6050
PT MOTRANSFER OTORITAS INTERNASIONAL—See PT Hensel Davest Indonesia Tbk; *Int'l*, pg. 6043
PT. MOTT MACDONALD INDONESIA—See Mott MacDonald Group Ltd.; *Int'l*, pg. 5056
PT. MOYA INDONESIA—See Moya Holdings Asia Limited; *Int'l*, pg. 5060
PT. MPM INDONESIA—See Macquarie Group Limited; *Int'l*, pg. 4630
PT. MPS INDONESIA—See Mitsubishi Heavy Industries, Ltd.; *Int'l*, pg. 4960
PT MPX LOGISTICS INTERNATIONAL TBK; *Int'l*, pg. 6059
PT. MRC GLOBAL INDONESIA—See MRC Global Inc.; *U.S. Public*, pg. 1481
PT. MSA INDONESIA LTD—See MSA Safety Incorporated; *U.S. Public*, pg. 1482
PT. MSH NIAGA TELECOM INDONESIA—See PT First Media Tbk; *Int'l*, pg. 6039
PT MSIG LIFE INSURANCE INDONESIA TBK; *Int'l*, pg. 6059
PT. MSM INDONESIA—See Mitsubishi Steel Mfg. Co., Ltd.; *Int'l*, pg. 4968
P.T.M. S.R.L. S.U.—See Kingspan Group PLC; *Int'l*, pg. 4179
PTM STEEL INDUSTRY SDN BHD—See K. Seng Seng Corporation Bhd; *Int'l*, pg. 4043
PT. M.TECH PRODUCTS—See Multi-Chem Limited; *Int'l*, pg. 5082
PT. MTU INDONESIA—See Rolls-Royce Holdings plc; *Int'l*, pg. 6393
PT. MUKOMUKO BARATAMA SAJAHTERA—See Indus Coal Limited; *Int'l*, pg. 3662
PT MULIA BOGA RAYA TBK; *Int'l*, pg. 6059
PT MULIA INDUSTRINDO TBK; *Int'l*, pg. 6059
PT MULTI AGRO GEMILANG PLANTATION TBK; *Int'l*, pg. 6059
PT. MULTI BANGUN GALAXY—See Heidelberg Materials AG; *Int'l*, pg. 3318
P.T. MULTI BINA PURA INTERNATIONAL—See Evergreen Marine Corporation (Taiwan) Ltd.; *Int'l*, pg. 2566
P.T. MULTI BINA TRANSPORT—See Evergreen Marine Corporation (Taiwan) Ltd.; *Int'l*, pg. 2566
PT. MULTI BINTANG INDONESIA TBK—See L'Arche Green N.V.; *Int'l*, pg. 4377
PT MULTIBREEDER ADIRAMA INDONESIA TBK—See PT Japfa Comfeed Indonesia Tbk; *Int'l*, pg. 6049
PT. MULTIELOK COSMETIC—See Multi Indocitra Tbk; *Int'l*, pg. 5082
PT MULTIFILING MITRA INDONESIA TBK; *Int'l*, pg. 6060
PT MULTI GARAM UTAMA TBK; *Int'l*, pg. 6060
PT. MULTI HARAPAN UTAMA—See PT ABM Investama Tbk.; *Int'l*, pg. 6018
PT. MULTI KONTROL NUSANTARA—See PT Bakrie & Brothers Tbk; *Int'l*, pg. 6025
PT MULTI MAKMUR LEMINDO TBK.; *Int'l*, pg. 6060

PT NATURA CITY DEVELOPMENTS TBK

PT MULTIMEDIA NUSANTARA—See Perusahaan Perseroan Indonesia Tbk; *Int'l*, pg. 5821
PT. MULTI NITROTAMA KIMIA - PLANT—See PT Ancora Indonesia Resources Tbk.; *Int'l*, pg. 6021
PT. MULTI NITROTAMA KIMIA—See PT Ancora Indonesia Resources Tbk.; *Int'l*, pg. 6021
PT MULTIPOLAR TBK; *Int'l*, pg. 6060
PT MULTIPOLAR TECHNOLOGY TBK—See PT Multipolar Tbk; *Int'l*, pg. 6060
PT MULTI PRIMA SEJAHTERA TBK; *Int'l*, pg. 6060
PT MULTISARANA INTAN EDUKA TBK; *Int'l*, pg. 6060
PT MULTISTRADA ARAH SARANA TBK.—See Compagnie Generale des Etablissements Michelin SCA; *Int'l*, pg. 1745
P.T. MULTITRANS NUSANTARA LOGISTIK—See Multi Indocitra Tbk; *Int'l*, pg. 5082
PT MURAKAMI DELLOYD INDONESIA—See Murakami Corporation; *Int'l*, pg. 5095
PT. MURAMOTO ELECTRONIKA INDONESIA—See Muramoto Electron (Thailand) PCL; *Int'l*, pg. 5096
PT. MURATA MACHINERY INDONESIA—See Murata Machinery, Ltd.; *Int'l*, pg. 5096
PT. MU RESEARCH AND CONSULTING INDONESIA—See Mitsubishi UFJ Financial Group, Inc.; *Int'l*, pg. 4971
PT MURINIWOOD INDAH INDUSTRY—See First Resources Limited; *Int'l*, pg. 2687
PT MURNI SADAR TBK; *Int'l*, pg. 6060
PT. MUROTECH INDONESIA—See MURO CORPORATION; *Int'l*, pg. 5099
PT. MUSASHI AUTO PARTS INDONESIA—See Musashi Seimitsu Industry Co., Ltd.; *Int'l*, pg. 5102
PT. MUSIM MAS-FUJI—See Fuji Oil Holdings Inc.; *Int'l*, pg. 2815
PT MUSTIKA ALAM LESTARI—See PT Nusantara Pelabuhan Handal Tbk; *Int'l*, pg. 6061
PT. MUTIARA RAGA INDAH—See PT Intiland Development Tbk.; *Int'l*, pg. 6048
PT MUTUAGUNG LESTARI TBK; *Int'l*, pg. 6060
PTMW INC.; *U.S. Private*, pg. 3298
PT MY ICON TECHNOLOGY—See Synnex Technology International Corporation; *Int'l*, pg. 7385
PT. NACHI INDONESIA—See Nachi-Fujikoshi Corp.; *Int'l*, pg. 5122
P.T. NADESCO ENGINEERING INDONESIA—See NADEX CO., LTD.; *Int'l*, pg. 5124
P.T. NADESCO INDONESIA—See NADEX CO., LTD.; *Int'l*, pg. 5124
PT.NADITAMA-TRANCY LOGISTICS INDONESIA—See Japan Transcity Corporation; *Int'l*, pg. 3907
P.T. NAGASE IMPOR-EKSPOR INDONESIA—See Nagase & Co., Ltd.; *Int'l*, pg. 5128
P.T. NAIGAI SHIRTS INDONESIA—See Nisshinbo Holdings Inc.; *Int'l*, pg. 5375
PT NAKANO S BATAM—See Nakano Corporation; *Int'l*, pg. 5133
P.T. NALCO INDONESIA—See Ecolab Inc.; *U.S. Public*, pg. 716
PT NANOTECH INDONESIA GLOBAL TBK; *Int'l*, pg. 6060
PT.NARA SUMMIT INDUSTRY—See NARA Mold & Die Co., Ltd.; *Int'l*, pg. 5147
P.T. NARUMI INDONESIA—See Ishizuka Glass Co., Ltd.; *Int'l*, pg. 3818
P T NASARAL KEKAL MEDAL—See Bucher Industries AG; *Int'l*, pg. 1208
PT. NAS FITNESS INDONESIA—See Daiwa House Industry Co., Ltd.; *Int'l*, pg. 1947
PT NASIONAL INVESTINDO PERKASA—See PT Bhakti Multi Artha Tbk; *Int'l*, pg. 6029
PT NATARANG MINING—See ElringKlinger AG; *Int'l*, pg. 2370
PT NATIONAL INDUSTRIAL GASES—See Mitsubishi Chemical Group Corporation; *Int'l*, pg. 4936
PT. NATIONAL INSTRUMENTS INDONESIA—See National Instruments Corporation; *U.S. Private*, pg. 2858
PT NATIONAL STARCH & CHEMICAL INDONESIA—See Ingredion Incorporated; *U.S. Public*, pg. 1124
P.T. NATRA RAYA—See Caterpillar, Inc.; *U.S. Public*, pg. 451
PT NATURA CITY DEVELOPMENTS TBK; *Int'l*, pg. 6060
PT NATURA PLASTINDO—See PT. Berlina Tbk; *Int'l*, pg. 6085
P.T. NAVA BHARAT INDONESIA—See Nava Limited; *Int'l*, pg. 5173
P.T. NAVIGATE ENERGY—See PT Wijaya Karya (Persero) Tbk.; *Int'l*, pg. 6082
P.T. NBC INDONESIA—See Nisshin Seifun Group, Inc.; *Int'l*, pg. 5372
PT NDS GLOBAL TEKNOLOGI—See Nexgram Holdings Berhad; *Int'l*, pg. 5244
P.T. NEC INDONESIA—See NEC Corporation; *Int'l*, pg. 5186
PT. NERA INDONESIA—See Ennoconn Corporation; *Int'l*, pg. 2443
PT. NESIC BUKAKA—See NEC Corporation; *Int'l*, pg. 5185
P.T. NESTLE BEVERAGES INDONESIA—See Nestle S.A.; *Int'l*, pg. 5211

PT NATURA CITY DEVELOPMENTS TBK

CORPORATE AFFILIATIONS

P.T. NESTLE CONFECTIONERY INDONESIA—See Nestle S.A.; *Int'l*, pg. 5211
P.T. NESTLE INDONESIA—See Nestle S.A.; *Int'l*, pg. 5211
PT NETWORK, LLC—See CI Capital Partners LLC; *U.S. Private*, pg. 895
PT NETWORK QUALITY INDONESIA—See PT Centratama Telekomunikasi Indonesia Tbk; *Int'l*, pg. 6033
PT. NETZSCH INDONESIA—See Erich Netzsch GmbH & Co. Holding KG; *Int'l*, pg. 2493
PT. NEW HOPE FARM INDONISIA—See New Hope Group Co., Ltd.; *Int'l*, pg. 5224
PT. NEW HOPE JAWA TIMUR—See New Hope Group Co., Ltd.; *Int'l*, pg. 5225
PT. NEW HOPE MEDAN—See New Hope Group Co., Ltd.; *Int'l*, pg. 5224
PT NEW KALBAR PROCESSORS—See PT Kirana Megatara Tbk; *Int'l*, pg. 6051
PT. NEXANS INDONESIA—See Nexans S.A.; *Int'l*, pg. 5242
PT. NEXELITE CP INDONESIA—See Beng Kuang Marine Limited; *Int'l*, pg. 973
PT. NEX LOGISTICS INDONESIA—See Nippon Express Holdings, Inc.; *Int'l*, pg. 5317
PT. NEXUS ENGINEERING INDONESIA—See Beng Kuang Marine Limited; *Int'l*, pg. 973
PT NFC INDONESIA TBK; *Int'l*, pg. 6060
PT NGK BUSI INDONESIA—See Niterra Co., Ltd.; *Int'l*, pg. 5381
P.T. NGK CERAMICS INDONESIA—See NGK Insulators, Ltd.; *Int'l*, pg. 5255
PT NHF AUTO SUPPLIES INDONESIA—See New Hoong Fatt Holdings Berhad; *Int'l*, pg. 5224
PT. NIAGAPRIMA PARAMITRA—See PT Anabatic Technologies Tbk; *Int'l*, pg. 6021
P.T. NICHIAS METALWORKS INDONESIA—See Nichias Corporation; *Int'l*, pg. 5267
PT. NICHIAS ROCKWOOL INDONESIA—See Nichias Corporation; *Int'l*, pg. 5267
P.T. NICHIAS SUNIJAYA—See Nichias Corporation; *Int'l*, pg. 5267
PT. NICHIRIN INDONESIA—See Nichirin Co., Ltd.; *Int'l*, pg. 5271
P.T. NIDEC INDONESIA—See Nidec Corporation; *Int'l*, pg. 5280
P.T. NIDEC SANKYO PRECISION INDONESIA—See Nidec Corporation; *Int'l*, pg. 5278
PT. NIELSEN AUDIENCE MEASUREMENT—See Brookfield Corporation; *Int'l*, pg. 1180
PT. NIELSEN AUDIENCE MEASUREMENT—See Elliott Management Corporation; *U.S. Private*, pg. 1372
PT NIFCO INDONESIA—See Nifco Inc.; *Int'l*, pg. 5281
PT. NIHON DENKEI INDONESIA—See NIHON DENKEI CO., LTD.; *Int'l*, pg. 5284
P.T. NIHON PLAST INDONESIA P.T.—See Nihon Plast Co., Ltd.; *Int'l*, pg. 5287
P.T. NIKAWA TEXTILE INDUSTRY—See Nisshinbo Holdings Inc.; *Int'l*, pg. 5375
PT. NIKKEI TRADING INDONESIA—See Nippon Light Metal Holdings Company, Ltd.; *Int'l*, pg. 5324
PT NIKON INDONESIA—See Nikon Corporation; *Int'l*, pg. 5294
PT NIKOS INTERTRADE—See PT Ultra Jaya Milk Industry Tbk; *Int'l*, pg. 6080
PT. NINDYA KARYA—See PT Adhi Karya (Persero) Tbk; *Int'l*, pg. 6019
P.T. NIPPISUN INDONESIA—See NPK Co., Ltd.; *Int'l*, pg. 5473
PT. NIPPN FOODS INDONESIA—See NIPPN Corporation; *Int'l*, pg. 5310
PT. NIPPO MECHATRONICS INDONESIA—See NIPPO LTD.; *Int'l*, pg. 5310
P. T. NIPPON ELECTRIC GLASS INDONESIA—See Nippon Electric Glass Co., Ltd.; *Int'l*, pg. 5314
PT NIPPON INDOSARI CORPINDO TBK; *Int'l*, pg. 6060
PT. NIPPON SHOKUBAI INDONESIA—See Nippon Shokubai Co., Ltd.; *Int'l*, pg. 5333
PT. NIPPON STEEL TRADING INDONESIA—See Nippon Steel Corporation; *Int'l*, pg. 5338
P.T. NIPSEA PAINT AND CHEMICALS—See Nippon Paint Holdings Co., Ltd.; *Int'l*, pg. 5326
PT. NIRVANA MEMORIAL NUSANTARA—See Nirvana Asia Ltd.; *Int'l*, pg. 5363
PT. NISHIO RENT ALL INDONESIA—See Nishio Holdings Co., Ltd.; *Int'l*, pg. 5365
P.T. NISSAN MOTOR INDONESIA—See Nissan Motor Co., Ltd.; *Int'l*, pg. 5369
PT. NISSEI PLASTIC INDONESIA—See Nissei Plastic Industrial Co., Ltd.; *Int'l*, pg. 5371
P.T. NISSHIN KUWAHARA INDONESIA—See KKR & Co. Inc.; *U.S. Private*, pg. 1259
PT. NISSIN FOOD INDONESIA—See Mitsubishi Corporation; *Int'l*, pg. 4942
P.T. NISSIN JAYA INDONESIA—See Nissin Corporation; *Int'l*, pg. 5376
P.T. NISSINMAS—See Nissin Foods Holdings Co., Ltd.; *Int'l*, pg. 5377
PT. NISSIN TRANSPORT INDONESIA—See Nissin Corporation; *Int'l*, pg. 5376

PT NITTO ALAM INDONESIA - BEKASI FACTORY—See Nitto Seiko Co., Ltd.; *Int'l*, pg. 5388
PT. NITTO ALAM INDONESIA—See Nitto Seiko Co., Ltd.; *Int'l*, pg. 5388
PT. NITTO MATERIALS INDONESIA—See Nitto Denko Corporation; *Int'l*, pg. 5387
PT. NITTSU LEMO INDONESIA LOGISTIK—See Nippon Express Holdings, Inc.; *Int'l*, pg. 5317
PT NMS CONSULTING INDONESIA—See nms Holdings Corporation; *Int'l*, pg. 5393
PT. NOF MAS CHEMICAL INDUSTRIES—See NOF Corporation; *Int'l*, pg. 5400
PT. NOKIA INDONESIA—See Nokia Corporation; *Int'l*, pg. 5406
PT. NOKIA SOLUTIONS & NETWORKS—See Nokia Corporation; *Int'l*, pg. 5406
P.T. NOK INDONESIA—See NOK Corporation; *Int'l*, pg. 5402
PT. NOK PRECISION COMPONENT BATAM—See NOK Corporation; *Int'l*, pg. 5403
P.T. NOMURA INDONESIA—See Nomura Holdings, Inc.; *Int'l*, pg. 5410
PT. NOMURA RESEARCH INSTITUTE INDONESIA—See Nomura Research Institute, Ltd.; *Int'l*, pg. 5413
P.T. NOMURA SEKURITAS INDONESIA—See Nomura Holdings, Inc.; *Int'l*, pg. 5412
PT. NONGSA POINT MARINA—See Keppel Corporation Limited; *Int'l*, pg. 4132
PT. NORITAKE INDONESIA—See Noritake Co., Limited; *Int'l*, pg. 5429
PT NORTHCLIFF CITRANUSA INDONESIA TBK; *Int'l*, pg. 6061
PT NORTHSTAR PACIFIC CAPITAL; *Int'l*, pg. 6061
PT. NOVALUX INDONESIA—See Shinko Shoji Co., Ltd.; *Int'l*, pg. 6846
PT. NOVAMEX INDONESIA—See Acter Co., Ltd.; *Int'l*, pg. 117
PT NOVARTIS INDONESIA—See Novartis AG; *Int'l*, pg. 5460
PT. NSK BEARINGS MANUFACTURING INDONESIA - JAKARTA PLANT—See NSK Ltd.; *Int'l*, pg. 5480
PT. NSK BEARINGS MANUFACTURING INDONESIA—See NSK Ltd.; *Int'l*, pg. 5480
PT. NSK INDONESIA—See NSK Ltd.; *Int'l*, pg. 5480
P.T. NSK PRECISION BALL INDONESIA—See NSK Ltd.; *Int'l*, pg. 5480
PT. NSSOL SYSTEMS INDONESIA—See Nippon Steel Corporation; *Int'l*, pg. 5335
PT. NTL NAIGAI TRANS LINE INDONESIA—See Naigai Trans Line Ltd.; *Int'l*, pg. 5130
PT. NTN BEARING INDONESIA—See NTN Corporation; *Int'l*, pg. 5483
P.T. NTT DATA BUSINESS SOLUTIONS—See Nippon Telegraph & Telephone Corporation; *Int'l*, pg. 5355
P.T. NTT DATA INDONESIA—See Nippon Telegraph & Telephone Corporation; *Int'l*, pg. 5355
PT.NTT INDONESIA—See Nippon Telegraph & Telephone Corporation; *Int'l*, pg. 5345
PT NUFARINDO—See Insud Pharma, S.L.; *Int'l*, pg. 3725
PT. NUFARM INDONESIA—See Nufarm Limited; *Int'l*, pg. 5487
PT. NUNUKAN JAYA LESTARI—See Fima Corporation Berhad; *Int'l*, pg. 2664
P.T. NUON DIGITAL INDONESIA—See Perusahaan Perseroan Indonesia Tbk; *Int'l*, pg. 5821
PT. NUSA HALMAHERA MINERALS—See Newmont Corporation; *U.S. Public*, pg. 1517
PT. NUSA KEIHIN INDONESIA—See PT Astra Otoparts Tbk; *Int'l*, pg. 6024
PT NUSA KONSTRUKSI ENJINIRING TBK; *Int'l*, pg. 6061
PT. NUSA MARITIM JAYA—See PT Wintermar Offshore Marine Tbk; *Int'l*, pg. 6083
PT NUSANTARA ALMAZIA TBK; *Int'l*, pg. 6061
PT. NUSANTARA INFRASTRUCTURE TBK—See Metro Pacific Investments Corporation; *Int'l*, pg. 4861
PT NUSANTARA INTI CORPORA TBK; *Int'l*, pg. 6061
PT. NUSANTARA PARKERIZING—See Nihon Parkerizing Co., Ltd.; *Int'l*, pg. 5286
PT NUSANTARA PELABUHAN HANDAL TBK; *Int'l*, pg. 6061
PT NUSANTARA POLYMER SOLUTIONS—See The Siam Cement Public Company Limited; *Int'l*, pg. 7683
PT NUSANTARA SAWIT SEJAHTERA TBK; *Int'l*, pg. 6061
PT. NUSANTARA SECOM INFOTECH—See SECOM Co., Ltd.; *Int'l*, pg. 6671
PT NUSANTARA SEJAHTERA RAYA TBK; *Int'l*, pg. 6061
PT NUSA PALAPA GEMILANG TBK; *Int'l*, pg. 6061
PT. NUSAPANGAN SUKSES MAKMUR—See Multi Indocitra Tbk; *Int'l*, pg. 5082
PT. NUSA RAYA CIPTA TBK—See PT Surya Semesta Internusa Tbk; *Int'l*, pg. 6077
PT. NUSA TOYOTETSU ENGINEERING—See Toyoda Iron Works Co., Ltd.; *Int'l*, pg. 7863
PT. NUSA TOYOTETSU—See Toyoda Iron Works Co., Ltd.; *Int'l*, pg. 7863
PT. NUTECH INTEGRASI—See Perusahaan Perseroan Indonesia Tbk; *Int'l*, pg. 5822

PT NUTRICIA INDONESIA SEJAHTERA—See Danone; *Int'l*, pg. 1967
PTNW EQUITY, INC.—See Pike Street Capital, LP; *U.S. Private*, pg. 3179
PT. NX INDONESIA—See Proterial, Ltd.; *Int'l*, pg. 6006
P.T. NYK NEW WAVE LOGISTICS INDONESIA—See Nippon Yusen Kabushiki Kaisha; *Int'l*, pg. 5359
P.T. NYK NEW WAVE WAREHOUSING (INDONESIA)—See Nippon Yusen Kabushiki Kaisha; *Int'l*, pg. 5359
PT. NYK PUNINAR LOGISTICS INDONESIA—See Nippon Yusen Kabushiki Kaisha; *Int'l*, pg. 5359
PT. NYK-SPIL INDORORO—See Nippon Yusen Kabushiki Kaisha; *Int'l*, pg. 5359
PT NYLEX INDONESIA—See Nylex (Malaysia) Berhad; *Int'l*, pg. 5500
PT. OAT MITOKU AGRIO—See OAT Agrio Co., Ltd.; *Int'l*, pg. 5507
PT OBM DRILCHEM; *Int'l*, pg. 6061
PT OCEAN GLOBAL SHIPPING—See China COSCO Shipping Corporation Limited; *Int'l*, pg. 1496
PT. OCEAN GLOBAL SHIPPING—See PT. Global Putra International Group; *Int'l*, pg. 6086
P.T. ODG INDONESIA; *Int'l*, pg. 5683
PT. OILFIELD SERVICES & SUPPLIES—See Oilfield Services & Supplies Pte. Ltd.; *Int'l*, pg. 5535
PT OIL SPILL RESPONSE INDONESIA—See Oil Spill Response Limited; *Int'l*, pg. 5535
PT OILTANKING MERAK—See Marquard & Bahls AG; *Int'l*, pg. 4700
PT OJS KOMPLEX—See Offshore Joint Services, Inc.; *U.S. Private*, pg. 3003
PT. OKAYA INDONESIA—See Okaya & Co., Ltd.; *Int'l*, pg. 5547
PT. OKK INDONESIA—See OKK Corporation; *Int'l*, pg. 5550
PT. OKUMA INDONESIA—See Okuma Corporation; *Int'l*, pg. 5551
PT. OMNI INTIVISION—See PT. Elang Mahkota Teknologi Tbk.; *Int'l*, pg. 6086
P.T. OMNI PLUS SYSTEM—See Omni-Plus System Limited; *Int'l*, pg. 5563
PT. OMRON ELECTRONICS—See OMRON Corporation; *Int'l*, pg. 5567
PT. OMRON HEALTHCARE INDONESIA—See OMRON Corporation; *Int'l*, pg. 5567
PT OMRON MANUFACTURING OF INDONESIA—See OMRON Corporation; *Int'l*, pg. 5567
PT OMYA INDONESIA - EAST JAVA PLANT—See Omya (Schweiz) AG; *Int'l*, pg. 5572
PT OMYA INDONESIA - PACIRAN PLANT—See Omya (Schweiz) AG; *Int'l*, pg. 5572
PT OMYA INDONESIA—See Omya (Schweiz) AG; *Int'l*, pg. 5572
PT. ONAMBA INDONESIA—See Onamba Co., Ltd.; *Int'l*, pg. 5573
PT ONIX CAPITAL TBK; *Int'l*, pg. 6061
PT ONIX SEKURITAS—See PT Onix Capital Tbk; *Int'l*, pg. 6061
PT. ONMOBILE INDONESIA—See OnMobile Global Limited; *Int'l*, pg. 5582
PT. OOCL LOGISTICS INDONESIA—See China COSCO Shipping Corporation Limited; *Int'l*, pg. 1496
PT OPTIMA DATA INTERNATIONAL—See PT Anabatic Technologies Tbk; *Int'l*, pg. 6021
PT OPTIMA PRIMA METAL SINERGI TBK; *Int'l*, pg. 6061
P.T. ORACLE INDONESIA—See Oracle Corporation; *U.S. Public*, pg. 1612
PT ORICA MINING SERVICES—See Orica Limited; *Int'l*, pg. 5620
PT ORIENTAL ASAHI JP CARTON BOX—See Japan Pulp and Paper Company Limited; *Int'l*, pg. 3904
PT. ORIGIN DURACHEM INDONESIA—See Origin Co., Ltd.; *Int'l*, pg. 5629
PT ORIQN INDONESIA GROUP—See Orion Engineering Services Limited; *Int'l*, pg. 5632
P.T. ORIX INDONESIA FINANCE—See ORIX Corporation; *Int'l*, pg. 5636
PT ORPHEUS ENERGY—See SenSen Networks Limited; *Int'l*, pg. 6713
P.T. OSAKA GAS INDONESIA—See Osaka Gas Co., Ltd.; *Int'l*, pg. 5646
P.T. OSG INDONESIA—See OSG Corporation; *Int'l*, pg. 5649
PT. OSIM (OSIM SELARAS INDOESIA MAKMUR)—See OSIM International Ltd.; *Int'l*, pg. 5650
P.T. OSRAM INDONESIA—See ams AG; *Int'l*, pg. 440
P.T. OS SELNAJAYA INDONESIA—See Bain Capital, LP; *U.S. Private*, pg. 435
P.T. OSSTEM IMPLANT—See MBK Partners Ltd.; *Int'l*, pg. 4753
PT. OSSTEM IMPLANT—See Unison Capital, Inc.; *Int'l*, pg. 8061
P.T. OST FIBRE INDUSTRIES—See Toray Industries, Inc.; *Int'l*, pg. 7823
P.T. OTC DAIHEN INDONESIA—See Daihen Corporation; *Int'l*, pg. 1926
PT OTO MULTIARTHA—See PT Sinar Mas Multiartha Tbk; *Int'l*, pg. 6074

2206

COMPANY NAME INDEX

PT OTRACO INDONESIA—See Downer EDI Limited; *Int'l*, pg. 2186
P.T. OTSUKA INDONESIA—See Otsuka Holdings Co., Ltd.; *Int'l*, pg. 5661
P.T. OTSUKA JAYA INDAH—See Otsuka Holdings Co., Ltd.; *Int'l*, pg. 5661
P.T. OTTOBOCK HEALTHCARE INDONESIA—See Nader Holding GmbH & Co. KG; *Int'l*, pg. 5123
P.T. O WELL INDONESIA—See O-Well Corporation; *Int'l*, pg. 5503
PT OXYPLAST INDONESIA—See Protech Chemicals Ltd.; *Int'l*, pg. 6004
PT PACIFIC CAPITAL INVESTMENT—See PACIFIC STRATEGIC FINANCIAL Tbk; *Int'l*, pg. 5692
P.T. PACIFIC LABEL INCORPORATED—See Avery Dennison Corporation; *U.S. Public*, pg. 244
PT PACIFIC LUBRITAMA INDONESIA—See United Global Limited; *Int'l*, pg. 8067
PT PACIFIC PALMINDO INDUSTRY—See Hayel Saeed Anam Group of Companies; *Int'l*, pg. 3291
P.T. PACIFIC PLACE JAKARTA—See PT JAKARTA INTERNATIONAL HOTELS & DEVELOPMENT Tbk; *Int'l*, pg. 6048
PT PACIFIC SEKURITAS INDONESIA—See PACIFIC STRATEGIC FINANCIAL Tbk; *Int'l*, pg. 5692
PT PACIFIC WORLD NUSANTARA—See TUI AG; *Int'l*, pg. 7966
PT PACINESIA CHEMICAL INDUSTRY—See PT. Lautan Luas Tbk; *Int'l*, pg. 6087
PT PACKET SYSTEMS INDONESIA—See Datatec Limited; *Int'l*, pg. 1981
PT PACTO HOLIDAY TOURS—See Qantas Airways Limited; *Int'l*, pg. 6132
PT. PADANG GOLF CIKARANG—See PT Jababeka Tbk; *Int'l*, pg. 6048
PT PAGUNTAKAN CAHAYA NUSANTARA BALIKPAPAN—See PT PLN (Persero); *Int'l*, pg. 6065
PT PAITON ENERGY—See ENGIE SA; *Int'l*, pg. 2434
PT PAKOAKUINA—See PT Astra Otoparts Tbk; *Int'l*, pg. 6024
PT PAKUAN TBK; *Int'l*, pg. 6061
PT. PAKUWON JATI TBK; *Int'l*, pg. 6088
PT PAKUWON PERMAI—See PT. PAKUWON JATI Tbk; *Int'l*, pg. 6088
PT PAKUWON SENTOSA ABADI—See PT. PAKUWON JATI Tbk; *Int'l*, pg. 6088
PT PAKUWON SENTRA WISATA—See PT. PAKUWON JATI Tbk; *Int'l*, pg. 6088
PT PALINGDA NASIONAL—See PT Astra Otoparts Tbk; *Int'l*, pg. 6024
PT. PALL FILTRATION INDONESIA—See Danaher Corporation; *U.S. Public*, pg. 629
PT PALMA SERASIH TBK; *Int'l*, pg. 6061
PT PAMAPERSADA NUSANTARA—See PT United Tractors Tbk; *Int'l*, pg. 6081
P.T. PAMERAN MASA KINI—See PT Panorama Sentrawisata Tbk; *Int'l*, pg. 6062
PT PAMERINDO INDONESIA—See Informa plc; *Int'l*, pg. 3693
PT. PANAH JAYA SEJAHTERA—See Annica Holdings Limited; *Int'l*, pg. 474
P.T. PANALPINA NUSAJAYA TRANSPORT—See DSV A/S; *Int'l*, pg. 2214
PT PANASIA INDO RESOURCES TBK; *Int'l*, pg. 6061
P.T. PANASONIC ELECTRIC WORKS GOBEL SALES INDONESIA—See Panasonic Holdings Corporation; *Int'l*, pg. 5717
P.T. PANASONIC GOBEL ECO SOLUTIONS MANUFACTURING INDONESIA—See Panasonic Holdings Corporation; *Int'l*, pg. 5718
P.T. PANASONIC GOBEL ECO SOLUTIONS SALES INDONESIA—See Panasonic Holdings Corporation; *Int'l*, pg. 5718
P.T. PANASONIC GOBEL ENERGY INDONESIA—See Panasonic Holdings Corporation; *Int'l*, pg. 5718
P.T. PANASONIC GOBEL INDONESIA—See Panasonic Holdings Corporation; *Int'l*, pg. 5717
P.T. PANASONIC HEALTHCARE INDONESIA—See PHC Holdings Corporation; *Int'l*, pg. 5843
P.T. PANASONIC SHIKOKU ELECTRONICS BATAM—See Panasonic Holdings Corporation; *Int'l*, pg. 5717
P.T. PANATA JAYA MANDIRI—See Donaldson Company, Inc.; *U.S. Public*, pg. 676
PT. PAN BROTHERS TBK.; *Int'l*, pg. 6088
PT PANCA ANUGRAH WISESA TBK; *Int'l*, pg. 6061
PT PANCA BUDI IDAMAN; *Int'l*, pg. 6062
PT PANCA GLOBAL KAPITAL TBK; *Int'l*, pg. 6062
PT PANCA MITRA MULTIPERDANA TBK; *Int'l*, pg. 6062
PT PANCA PERMATA PEJATEN—See PT Lippo Karawaci Tbk; *Int'l*, pg. 6053
PT. PANCAPRIMA EKABROTHERS—See PT. Pan Brothers Tbk.; *Int'l*, pg. 6088
PT PANDROL INDONESIA—See CVC Capital Partners SICAV-FIS S.A.; *Int'l*, pg. 1887
PT. PANDU SATA UTAMA—See Universal Corporation; *U.S. Public*, pg. 2254
PT PANGAN LESTARI—See Sekar Laut Tbk; *Int'l*, pg. 6693

PT PANIN ASSET MANAGEMENT—See pt. panin sekuritas tbk; *Int'l*, pg. 6088
PT PANIN DAI-ICHI LIFE—See PT Paninvest Tbk; *Int'l*, pg. 6062
PT PANIN FINANCIAL TBK—See PT Paninvest Tbk; *Int'l*, pg. 6062
PT. PANIN SEKURITAS TBK; *Int'l*, pg. 6088
PT PANINVEST TBK; *Int'l*, pg. 6062
P.T. PANORAMA APLIKASI NUSANTARA—See PT Panorama Sentrawisata Tbk; *Int'l*, pg. 6062
PT PANORAMA SENTRAWISATA TBK; *Int'l*, pg. 6062
PT PANTAI INDAH KAPUK DUA TBK; *Int'l*, pg. 6062
P.T. PANTJA MOTOR—See PT Astra International Tbk; *Int'l*, pg. 6023
PT PANTJA SURYA—See PT Kirana Megatara Tbk; *Int'l*, pg. 6051
PT. PAN-UNITED CONCRETE—See Pan-United Corporation Ltd.; *Int'l*, pg. 5716
PT PAPEROCKS INDONESIA TBK; *Int'l*, pg. 6062
PT PARAMITA BANGUN SARANA TBK; *Int'l*, pg. 6062
P.T. PARAM MITRA COAL RESOURCES—See SINDHU TRADE LINKS LIMITED; *Int'l*, pg. 6938
P.T. PARDIC JAYA CHEMICALS—See DIC Corporation; *Int'l*, pg. 2109
P.T. PAREXEL INTERNATIONAL INDONESIA—See Pamplona Capital Management LLP; *Int'l*, pg. 5713
P.T. PARKER ENGINEERING INDONESIA—See Nihon Parkerizing Co., Ltd.; *Int'l*, pg. 5286
P.T. PARKER HANNIFIN INDONESIA—See Parker Hannifin Corporation; *U.S. Public*, pg. 1643
P.T. PARKER METAL TREATMENT INDONESIA—See Nihon Parkerizing Co., Ltd.; *Int'l*, pg. 5286
PT PARVI INDAH PERSADA—See PT Nusantara Pelabuhan Handal Tbk; *Int'l*, pg. 6061
PT. PASAR GADAI DIGITAL—See PT Sinar Mas Multiartha Tbk; *Int'l*, pg. 6074
PT PASONA HR INDONESIA—See Pasona Group Inc.; *Int'l*, pg. 5753
P.T. PATEC PRESISI ENGINEERING—See Patec Precision Industry Co., Ltd.; *Int'l*, pg. 5755
PT.PATLITE INDONESIA—See Inaba Denki Sangyo Co., Ltd.; *Int'l*, pg. 3643
PT PATRA DRILLING CONTRACTOR—See PT Pertamina (Persero); *Int'l*, pg. 6063
PT. PATRA NUSA DATA—See PT Elnusa Tbk; *Int'l*, pg. 6038
PT PATRA TEKNIK—See PT Pertamina (Persero); *Int'l*, pg. 6063
PT PATRIA MARITIME INDUSTRY—See PT United Tractors Tbk; *Int'l*, pg. 6081
PT PATRIA MARITIME LINES—See PT United Tractors Tbk; *Int'l*, pg. 6081
PT PATRIA MARITIM PERKASA—See PT United Tractors Tbk; *Int'l*, pg. 6081
PT PATRIA PERIKANAN LESTARI INDONESIA—See PT United Tractors Tbk; *Int'l*, pg. 6081
PT PAYASIA KONSULTANSI INDONESIA—See Deel, Inc.; *U.S. Private*, pg. 1189
PTPC PHYSICAL THERAPY & PERFORMANCE CENTER—See Confluent Health, LLC; *U.S. Private*, pg. 1013
PT. PDF PRESISI ENGINEERING—See Patec Precision Industry Co., Ltd.; *Int'l*, pg. 5755
P.T. PEGADAIAN—See PT Bank Rakyat Indonesia (Persero) Tbk; *Int'l*, pg. 6028
P.T. PEKANBARU PERMAI PROPERTINDO—See PT PP (Persero) Tbk; *Int'l*, pg. 6066
P.T. PELABUHAN BUANA REJA—See PT ABM Investama Tbk.; *Int'l*, pg. 6018
P.T. PELABUHAN BUKIT PRIMA—See PT Bukit Asam (Persero) Tbk; *Int'l*, pg. 6031
PT PELABUHAN INDONESIA II; *Int'l*, pg. 6062
PT PELANGI ARJUNA; *Int'l*, pg. 6062
PT PELAT TIMAH NUSANTARA TBK.; *Int'l*, pg. 6062
PT PELAYANAN LISTRIK NASIONAL BATAM—See PT PLN (Persero); *Int'l*, pg. 6065
PT PELAYANAN LISTRIK NASIONAL TARAKAN—See PT PLN (Persero); *Int'l*, pg. 6065
PT PELAYARAN ANTARBUWANA PERTALA—See PT Saratoga Investama Sedaya Tbk.; *Int'l*, pg. 6070
P.T. PELAYARAN KARANA LINE—See PT Mitra Investindo Tbk; *Int'l*, pg. 6057
PT PELAYARAN KURNIA LAUTAN SEMESTA TBK; *Int'l*, pg. 6062
PT PELAYARAN NASIONAL BINA BUANA RAYA TBK; *Int'l*, pg. 6062
PT PELAYARAN NELLY DWI PUTRI TBK; *Int'l*, pg. 6062
PT PELAYARAN STRAITS PERDANA—See PT Indo Straits Tbk.; *Int'l*, pg. 6045
PT PELAYARAN TAMARIN SAMUDRA TBK; *Int'l*, pg. 6062
PT. PELITA SAMUDERA SHIPPING—See IMC Pan Asia Alliance Pte. Ltd.; *Int'l*, pg. 3621
PT PELITA TEKNOLOGI GLOBAL TBK; *Int'l*, pg. 6062
PT. PEMALANG BATANG TOLL ROAD—See PT Waskita Karya (Persero) Tbk; *Int'l*, pg. 6082
PT PEMBANGKITAN JAWA BALI—See PT PLN (Persero); *Int'l*, pg. 6065

PT. PEMBANGUNAN GRAHA LESTARI INDAH, TBK.; *Int'l*, pg. 6088
PT. PEMBANGUNAN JAYA ANCOL .TBK; *Int'l*, pg. 6063
P.T. PENERBITAN PELANGI INDONESIA—See Pelangi Publishing Group Bhd; *Int'l*, pg. 5781
PT PENGERUKAN INDONESIA—See PT Pelabuhan Indonesia II; *Int'l*, pg. 6062
PT PENILAI HARGA EFEK INDONESIA—See PT Bursa Efek Indonesia; *Int'l*, pg. 6032
PT PENTAIR EURAPIPE INDONESIA—See Pentair plc; *Int'l*, pg. 5789
PT. PENTA OCEAN CONSTRUCTION—See Penta-Ocean Construction Co., Ltd.; *Int'l*, pg. 5788
PT PENTA VALENT TBK; *Int'l*, pg. 6063
PT PERDANA BANGUN PUSAKA TBK; *Int'l*, pg. 6063
PT PERDANA GAPURA PRIMA TBK; *Int'l*, pg. 6063
PT PERDANA KARYA PERKASA TBK; *Int'l*, pg. 6063
PT PERFETTI INDONESIA—See Perfetti Van Melle Holding B.V.; *Int'l*, pg. 5800
PT PERINTIS TRINITI PROPERTI TBK; *Int'l*, pg. 6063
P.T. PERKASALESTARI PERMAI—See PT Intiland Development Tbk.; *Int'l*, pg. 6048
P.T. PERKEBUNAN DAN INDUSTRI SEGAJUNG—See PT Intiland Development Tbk.; *Int'l*, pg. 6048
PT PERKEBUNAN KALTIM UTAMA I—See PT TBS Energi Utama Tbk; *Int'l*, pg. 6078
PT PERMA PLASINDO TBK; *Int'l*, pg. 6063
PT PERMATA BERLIAN REALTY—See PT. PAKUWON JATI Tbk; *Int'l*, pg. 6088
P.T. PERMATA BUSANA MAS—See PT Trisula International Tbk; *Int'l*, pg. 6080
PT PERMATA CIPTA REJEKI—See Macro Kiosk Berhad; *Int'l*, pg. 4631
PT PERMATA GRAHA NUSANTARA—See PT Perusahaan Gas Negara (Persero) Tbk; *Int'l*, pg. 6064
PT PERMATA KARYA JASA—See PT Perusahaan Gas Negara (Persero) Tbk; *Int'l*, pg. 6064
PT PERMATA KARYA PERDANA—See PT Tower Bersama Infrastructure Tbk; *Int'l*, pg. 6079
PT. PERMATA PRIMA SAKTI TBK; *Int'l*, pg. 6088
PT PEROKSIDA INDONESIA PRATAMA—See Mitsubishi Gas Chemical Company, Inc.; *Int'l*, pg. 4950
PT PERTA ARUN GAS—See PT Perusahaan Gas Negara (Persero) Tbk; *Int'l*, pg. 6064
PT PERTA DAYA GAS—See PT Perusahaan Gas Negara (Persero) Tbk; *Int'l*, pg. 6064
P.T. PERTAFENIKKI ENGINEERING—See JGC Holdings Corporation; *Int'l*, pg. 3940
PT PERTAGAS NIAGA—See PT Perusahaan Gas Negara (Persero) Tbk; *Int'l*, pg. 6064
PT PERTA KALIMANTAN GAS—See PT Perusahaan Gas Negara (Persero) Tbk; *Int'l*, pg. 6064
PT. PERTAMA PRECISION BINTAN—See I-PEX Inc.; *Int'l*, pg. 3564
PT PERTAMINA DANA VENTURA—See PT Pertamina (Persero); *Int'l*, pg. 6063
PT PERTAMINA DRILLING SERVICES INDONESIA—See PT Pertamina (Persero); *Int'l*, pg. 6063
PT PERTAMINA EP CEPU—See PT Pertamina (Persero); *Int'l*, pg. 6063
PT PERTAMINA EP—See PT Pertamina (Persero); *Int'l*, pg. 6063
PT PERTAMINA GAS—See PT Perusahaan Gas Negara (Persero) Tbk; *Int'l*, pg. 6064
P.T. PERTAMINA GEOTHERMAL ENERGY KOTAMOBAGU—See PT Pertamina Geothermal Energy Tbk; *Int'l*, pg. 6064
PT PERTAMINA GEOTHERMAL ENERGY TBK; *Int'l*, pg. 6064
PT PERTAMINA HULU ENERGI JAMBI MERANG—See PT Pertamina (Persero); *Int'l*, pg. 6063
P.T. PERTAMINA HULU ENERGI OGAN KOMERING—See PT Pertamina Geothermal Energy Tbk; *Int'l*, pg. 6064
PT PERTAMINA HULU ENERGI WEST MADURA OFFSHORE—See PT Pertamina (Persero); *Int'l*, pg. 6063
PT PERTAMINA (PERSERO); *Int'l*, pg. 6063
PT PERTAMINA (PERSERO) - UNIT II—See PT Pertamina (Persero); *Int'l*, pg. 6063
PT PERTAMINA (PERSERO) - UNIT V—See PT Pertamina (Persero); *Int'l*, pg. 6063
PT PERTAMINA RETAIL INDONESIA—See PT Pertamina (Persero); *Int'l*, pg. 6063
PT PERTAMINA TRANS KONTINENTAL—See PT Pertamina (Persero); *Int'l*, pg. 6063
PT. PERTA-SAMTAN GAS—See Samchully Co., Ltd.; *Int'l*, pg. 6503
P.T. PERUSAHAAN BONGKAR MUAT BERKAH SARANA INTI—See PT Mitra Investindo Tbk; *Int'l*, pg. 6057
P.T. PERUSAHAAN BONGKAR MUAT OLAH JASA ANDAL—See International Container Terminal Services, Inc.; *Int'l*, pg. 3746
PT PERUSAHAAN DAGANG TEMPO—See Tempo Scan Pacific Tbk; *Int'l*, pg. 7556
PT PERUSAHAAN GAS NEGARA (PERSERO) TBK; *Int'l*, pg. 6064
PT PERUSAHAAN GAS NEGARA (PERSERO) TBK - STRATEGIC BUSINESS UNIT REGION II—See PT Perusahaan Gas Negara (Persero) Tbk; *Int'l*, pg. 6064

PT PERUSAHAAN GAS NEGARA (PERSERO) TBK

CORPORATE AFFILIATIONS

PT PERUSAHAAN GAS NEGARA (PERSERO) TBK - STRATEGIC BUSINESS UNIT REGION I—See PT Perusahaan Gas Negara (Persero) Tbk; *Int'l,* pg. 6064
PT PERUSAHAAN GAS NEGARA (PERSERO) TBK - STRATEGIC BUSINESS UNIT SUMATERA-JAVA TRANSMISSION—See PT Perusahaan Gas Negara (Persero) Tbk; *Int'l,* pg. 6064
PT PETEKA KARYA GAPURA—See PT Pertamina (Persero); *Int'l,* pg. 6063
PT PETEKA KARYA JALA—See PT Pertamina (Persero); *Int'l,* pg. 6063
PT PETEKA KARYA SAMUDERA—See PT Pertamina (Persero); *Int'l,* pg. 6063
PT PETEKA KARYA TIRTA—See PT Pertamina (Persero); *Int'l,* pg. 6064
P.T. PETNESIA RESINDO—See Mitsui & Co., Ltd.; *Int'l,* pg. 4979
P.T. PETNESIA RESINDO—See Mitsui Chemicals, Inc.; *Int'l,* pg. 4983
P.T. PETNESIA RESINDO—See Toray Industries, Inc.; *Int'l,* pg. 7823
PT PETRINDO JAYA KREASI TBK; *Int'l,* pg. 6065
PT PETROCENTRAL—See PT Unggul Indah Cahaya Tbk; *Int'l,* pg. 6080
P.T. PETROLITE INDONESIA PRATAMA—See Baker Hughes Company; *U.S. Public,* pg. 265
PT PETRONIKA—See PT Tridomain Performance Materials Tbk; *Int'l,* pg. 6079
PT. PETRO PAPUA ENERGI—See KS Energy Limited; *Int'l,* pg. 4310
PT PETROPRIMA GEO-SERVIS NUSANTARA—See PGS ASA; *Int'l,* pg. 5839
PT PETROSEA TBK—See PT Indika Energy Tbk; *Int'l,* pg. 6044
P.T. PETROTECH PENTA NUSA—See PT Rukun Raharja Tbk; *Int'l,* pg. 6069
PT PFI MEGA LIFE INSURANCE—See Prudential Financial, Inc.; *U.S. Public,* pg. 1731
P.T. PFIZER INDONESIA—See Pfizer Inc.; *U.S. Public,* pg. 1680
PT PGAS SOLUTION—See PT Perusahaan Gas Negara (Persero) Tbk; *Int'l,* pg. 6064
PT PGAS TELEKOMUNIKASI NUSANTARA—See PT Perusahaan Gas Negara (Persero) Tbk; *Int'l,* pg. 6064
PT PGN LNG INDONESIA—See PT Perusahaan Gas Negara (Persero) Tbk; *Int'l,* pg. 6064
PT PGS NUSANTARA—See PGS ASA; *Int'l,* pg. 5839
PT PHAPROS TBK; *Int'l,* pg. 6065
PT PHARMA METRIC LABORATORIES—See PT Kalbe Farma Tbk.; *Int'l,* pg. 6050
PT PHILIP MORRIS INDONESIA—See Philip Morris International Inc.; *U.S. Public,* pg. 1685
PT. PHILIPS INDONESIA—See Koninklijke Philips N.V.; *Int'l,* pg. 4268
PT PHILLIP COMMODITIES INDONESIA—See Phillip Capital Pte. Ltd.; *Int'l,* pg. 5846
PT PHILLIP FUTURES—See Phillip Capital Pte. Ltd.; *Int'l,* pg. 5846
PT PHILLIP SECURITIES INDONESIA—See Phillip Capital Pte. Ltd.; *Int'l,* pg. 5846
PT PHOCEENNE INDONESIE—See Groupe BPCE; *Int'l,* pg. 3095
PT. PIALANG JEPANG BERJANGKA—See TRADERS HOLDINGS CO., LTD.; *Int'l,* pg. 7888
PT PICANOL INDONESIA—See Tessenderlo Group NV; *Int'l,* pg. 7573
PT PICO TBA—See Pico Far East Holdings Limited; *Int'l,* pg. 5861
PT PIKKO LAND DEVELOPMENT TBK; *Int'l,* pg. 6065
PT PINAGO UTAMA TBK; *Int'l,* pg. 6065
PT PINNACLE APPARELS—See Pearl Global Industries Limited; *Int'l,* pg. 5774
PT PINS INDONESIA—See Perusahaan Perseroan Indonesia Tbk; *Int'l,* pg. 5822
PT PIOLAX INDONESIA—See Piolax Inc.; *Int'l,* pg. 5871
PT PIONEERINDO GOURMET INTERNATIONAL TBK; *Int'l,* pg. 6065
PT PIONIRBETON INDUSTRI—See Heidelberg Materials AG; *Int'l,* pg. 3318
PT PJB INVESTASI—See PT PLN (Persero); *Int'l,* pg. 6065
PT PJB SERVICES—See PT PLN (Persero); *Int'l,* pg. 6065
PT PKG LAUTAN INDONESIA—See Nylex (Malaysia) Berhad; *Int'l,* pg. 5500
PT. PK MANUFACTURING INDONESIA—See Press Kogyo Co., Ltd.; *Int'l,* pg. 5964
PT PLANET PROPERINDO JAYA TBK; *Int'l,* pg. 6065
PT PLASMOTECH BATAM—See Amphenol Corporation; *U.S. Public,* pg. 132
PT PLATINUM TEKNOLOGI—See PT Sarana Menara Nusantara Tbk; *Int'l,* pg. 6070
PT PLATINUM WAHAB NUSANTARA TBK; *Int'l,* pg. 6065
PT PLAZA INDONESIA REALTY TBK; *Int'l,* pg. 6065
PT. PLN BATUBARA—See PT PLN (Persero); *Int'l,* pg. 6065
PT PLN GAS DAN GEOTHERMAL—See PT PLN (Persero); *Int'l,* pg. 6065
PT PLN (PERSERO); *Int'l,* pg. 6065

PT PLN SUKU CADANG—See PT PLN (Persero); *Int'l,* pg. 6065
PTP. MANAGEMENT INC.—See Cook Inlet Region, Inc.; *U.S. Private,* pg. 1038
PT PMT INDUSTRI—See Wah Seong Corporation Berhad; *Int'l,* pg. 8329
P.T. POJOK CELEBES MANDIRI—See Perusahaan Perseroan Indonesia Tbk; *Int'l,* pg. 5821
PT. POLARIS INDONESIA—See PT Polaris Investama Tbk; *Int'l,* pg. 6066
PT POLARIS INVESTAMA TBK; *Int'l,* pg. 6065
PT POLLUX HOTELS GROUP TBK; *Int'l,* pg. 6066
PT POLLUX PROPERTI INDONESIA TBK; *Int'l,* pg. 6066
PT POLYCHEM INDONESIA TBK; *Int'l,* pg. 6066
PT PONDOK KARYA MEDIKA—See PT Mitra Keluarga Karyasehat Tbk; *Int'l,* pg. 6057
PT PONTIL INDONESIA—See Major Drilling Group International Inc.; *Int'l,* pg. 4655
PT POOL ADVISTA FINANCE TBK; *Int'l,* pg. 6066
PT POOL ADVISTA INDONESIA TBK; *Int'l,* pg. 6066
PT. PORTEK INDONESIA—See Mitsui & Co., Ltd.; *Int'l,* pg. 4980
PT PORTUGAL, SGPS, S.A.—See Altice Europe N.V.; *Int'l,* pg. 392
PT POSB REKSABUMI INDONESIA—See PT Indika Energy Tbk; *Int'l,* pg. 6044
PT POSCO INDONESIA JAKARTA PROCESSING CENTER—See PT Selamat Sempurna Tbk; *Int'l,* pg. 6071
PT. POWERWELL LISTRIK INDONESIA—See Powerwell Holdings Berhad; *Int'l,* pg. 5949
PT. POYRY INDONESIA—See AFRY AB; *Int'l,* pg. 195
PT PP ENERGI—See PT PP (Persero) Tbk; *Int'l,* pg. 6066
PT. PPG COATINGS INDONESIA—See PPG Industries, Inc.; *U.S. Public,* pg. 1710
PT PP INFRASTRUKTUR—See PT PP (Persero) Tbk; *Int'l,* pg. 6066
P.T. PP KRAKATAU TIRTA—See PT PP (Persero) Tbk; *Int'l,* pg. 6066
PT PP LONDON SUMATRA INDONESIA TBK; *Int'l,* pg. 6066
PT PP (PERSERO) TBK; *Int'l,* pg. 6066
PT PP PRESISI TBK—See PT PP (Persero) Tbk; *Int'l,* pg. 6066
PT PP PROPERTI TBK; *Int'l,* pg. 6066
PT PPRO BIJB AEROCITY DEVELOPMENT—See PT PP (Persero) Tbk; *Int'l,* pg. 6066
P.T. P.P. TAISEI INDONESIA CONSTRUCTION—See Taisei Corporation; *Int'l,* pg. 7416
PT PP URBAN—See PT PP (Persero) Tbk; *Int'l,* pg. 6066
PT PRAISINDO TEKNOLOGI—See Censof Holdings Berhad; *Int'l,* pg. 1402
PT PRAMINDO IKAT NUSANTARA—See Perusahaan Perseroan Indonesia Tbk; *Int'l,* pg. 5822
PT PRAPAT TUNGGAL CIPTA—See PT Selamat Sempurna Tbk; *Int'l,* pg. 6071
P.T. PRASADHA PAMUNAH LIMBAH INDUSTRI—See Dowa Holdings Co., Ltd.; *Int'l,* pg. 2183
P.T. PRASETYA GEMAMULIA—See PT Gema Grahasarana Tbk; *Int'l,* pg. 6040
P.T. PRATAMA BETON NUSANTARA—See PT Pratama Widya Tbk; *Int'l,* pg. 6066
P.T. PRATAMA MITRA SEJATI—See PT Pertamina (Persero); *Int'l,* pg. 6064
PT PRATAMA PALM ABADI—See Oriental Holdings Berhad; *Int'l,* pg. 5625
P.T. PRATAMA UNGGUL LESTARI—See PT Sillo Maritime Perdana Tbk; *Int'l,* pg. 6072
P.T. PRATAMA WANA MOTOR—See PT INTRACO PENTA Tbk; *Int'l,* pg. 6048
PT PRATAMA WIDYA TBK; *Int'l,* pg. 6066
PT PREFORMED LINE PRODUCTS INDONESIA—See Preformed Line Products Company; *U.S. Public,* pg. 1714
P.T. PRESISI SUMBER ANUGERAH—See PT PP (Persero) Tbk; *Int'l,* pg. 6066
PT. PRESTIGE INDONESIA—See SEEK Limited; *Int'l,* pg. 6678
PT PRIMA ALLOY STEEL UNIVERSAL TBK; *Int'l,* pg. 6066
PT PRIMA ANDALAN MANDIRI; *Int'l,* pg. 6066
PT. PRIMA BUANA KARUNIA—See PT Golden Eagle Energy Tbk; *Int'l,* pg. 6041
PT PRIMA CAKRAWALA ABADI TBK; *Int'l,* pg. 6067
PT PRIMACORR MANDIRI—See The Siam Cement Public Company Limited; *Int'l,* pg. 7683
PT PRIMA GLOBALINDO LOGISTIK; *Int'l,* pg. 6067
PT PRIMAGRAHA KERAMINDO—See PT Arwana Citramulia Tbk; *Int'l,* pg. 6022
PT PRIMA INFOSARANA MEDIA—See China Oceanwide Holdings Group Co.; *Int'l,* pg. 1538
PT PRIMA INFOSARANA MEDIA—See IDG Capital; *Int'l,* pg. 3594
PT PRIMA LAYANAN NASIONAL ENJINIRING—See PT PLN (Persero); *Int'l,* pg. 6065
PT PRIMA MITRA ELEKTRINDO—See PT. Voksel Electric Tbk; *Int'l,* pg. 6090
PT PRIMA NUR PANURJWAN—See PT Samudera Indonesia Tbk; *Int'l,* pg. 6069

PT PRIMA POWER NUSANTARA—See PT PLN (Persero); *Int'l,* pg. 6065
PT. PRIMARAJULI SUKSES—See PT Ever Shine Tex Tbk; *Int'l,* pg. 6039
PT. PRIMA REZEKI PERTIWI—See Compagnie de Saint-Gobain SA; *Int'l,* pg. 1724
PT. PRIMA SENTRA MEGAH—See Giti Tire Pte. Ltd.; *Int'l,* pg. 2979
PT. PRIMA SHEATI CO., LTD.—See Land & Houses Public Company Limited; *Int'l,* pg. 4403
PT. PRIMATAMA NUSA INDAH—See Lippo Malls Indonesia Retail Trust; *Int'l,* pg. 4522
P.T. PRIMATEXCO INDONESIA—See Daiwabo Holdings Co., Ltd.; *Int'l,* pg. 1950
PT. PRIMA TOP BOGA—See PT Nippon Indosari Corpindo Tbk; *Int'l,* pg. 6060
PT. PRIMA VISTA SOLUSI—See Wirecard AG; *Int'l,* pg. 8434
PT. PRIMA WIGUNA PARAMA—See PT ABM Investama Tbk.; *Int'l,* pg. 6018
PT. PRIMAYUDHA MANDIRIJAYA—See PT. Sri Rejeki Isman Tbk; *Int'l,* pg. 6089
PT PRINCIPAL ASSET MANAGEMENT—See CIMB Group Holdings Berhad; *Int'l,* pg. 1608
PT PRINCIPAL ASSET MANAGEMENT—See Principal Financial Group, Inc.; *U.S. Public,* pg. 1720
P.T. PRODIA DIGITAL INDONESIA—See PT Prodia Widyahusada Tbk; *Int'l,* pg. 6067
PT PRODIA WIDYAHUSADA TBK; *Int'l,* pg. 6067
P.T. PROMATRIX FACILITIES MANAGEMENT—See Nippon Telegraph & Telephone Corporation; *Int'l,* pg. 5355
PT PROTEINDO KARYASEHAT—See PT Mitra Keluarga Karyasehat Tbk; *Int'l,* pg. 6057
PT PROTON EDAR INDONESIA—See DRB-HICOM Berhad; *Int'l,* pg. 2202
PT PROVIDENT INVESTASI BERSAMA TBK; *Int'l,* pg. 6067
P.T. PRUDENTIAL LIFE ASSURANCE—See Prudential plc; *Int'l,* pg. 6009
P.T.PRYSMIAN CABLES INDONESIA—See Prysmian S.p.A.; *Int'l,* pg. 6012
P.T. PSV INDONESIA—See PT Wintermar Offshore Marine Tbk; *Int'l,* pg. 6083
PT PUDJIADI PRESTIGE TBK; *Int'l,* pg. 6067
PT PUDJIADI & SONS TBK; *Int'l,* pg. 6067
PT PULAU KENCANA RAYA—See PT Mitra International Resources Tbk.; *Int'l,* pg. 6057
P.T. PUMA SPORTS INDONESIA—See Puma SE; *Int'l,* pg. 6117
PT PUNCH INDUSTRY INDONESIA—See Punch Industry Co., Ltd.; *Int'l,* pg. 6118
PT. PUNINAR MSE INDONESIA—See Mitsui-Soko Holdings Co., Ltd.; *Int'l,* pg. 4993
PT PUNJ LLOYD INDONESIA—See Punj Lloyd Ltd.; *Int'l,* pg. 6119
PT PURANTIA MITRA ANGKASA DUA—See PT. Cardig Aero Services Tbk; *Int'l,* pg. 6085
PT PURI GLOBAL SUKSES TBK; *Int'l,* pg. 6067
PT PURI LAND DEVELOPMENT—See Keppel Corporation Limited; *Int'l,* pg. 4132
PT PURIMAS SASMITA—See Golden Agri-Resources Ltd.; *Int'l,* pg. 3028
PT PURI PRIMA DEVELOPMENT—See PT Jakarta Setiabudi In; *Int'l,* pg. 6049
P.T. PURI-TRINITI BATAM—See PT Perintis Triniti Properti Tbk; *Int'l,* pg. 6063
PT PUTRA MANDIRI JEMBAR TBK; *Int'l,* pg. 6067
PT. PUTRA MUSTIKA PRIMA—See PT Mitra Pinasthika Mustika Tbk; *Int'l,* pg. 6058
PT PUTRA PRABUKARYA CO., LTD.—See Land & Houses Public Company Limited; *Int'l,* pg. 4403
PT PUTRA RAJAWALI KENCANA TBK; *Int'l,* pg. 6067
PT. PYROTEK INDONESIA—See Pyrotek Incorporated; *U.S. Private,* pg. 3311
PT PZ CUSSONS INDONESIA—See PZ Cussons Plc; *Int'l,* pg. 6128
PT Q2 TECHNOLOGIES—See PT Anabatic Technologies Tbk; *Int'l,* pg. 6021
PT QAD ASIA INDONESIA—See Thoma Bravo, L.P.; *U.S. Private,* pg. 4151
PT QBE GENERAL INSURANCE INDONESIA—See Oversea-Chinese Banking Corporation Limited; *Int'l,* pg. 5671
P.T. QIAN HU JOE AQUATIC INDONESIA—See Qian Hu Corporation Limited; *Int'l,* pg. 6140
PT QUANTEX—See PT. Berlina Tbk; *Int'l,* pg. 6085
PT QUANTUM CLOVERA INVESTAMA TBK; *Int'l,* pg. 6067
PT. QUIKSILVER INDONESIA—See Leonard Green & Partners, L.P.; *U.S. Private,* pg. 2424
PT. QUIKSILVER INDONESIA—See Leonard Green & Partners, L.P.; *U.S. Private,* pg. 2424
PT RADANA BHASKARA FINANCE TBK; *Int'l,* pg. 6067
PT RADHIA NITYA PRATAMA—See Sanurhasta Mitra Tbk; *Int'l,* pg. 6070
PT RADIANT UTAMA INTERISCO TBK.; *Int'l,* pg. 6067
PT. RADIO SUARA MONALISA—See PT MNC Investama Tbk; *Int'l,* pg. 6059

COMPANY NAME INDEX

PT RADITA HUTAMA INTERNUSA—See Lovell Minnick Partners LLC; *U.S. Private*, pg. 2502
PT RAFFLES DESIGN INSTITUTE—See Raffles Education Corporation Limited; *Int'l*, pg. 6177
PT RAFFLES MEDIKA INDONESIA—See Raffles Medical Group Ltd; *Int'l*, pg. 6177
PT RAGAMSEHAT MULTIFITA—See PT Mitra Keluarga Karyasehat Tbk; *Int'l*, pg. 6057
P.T. RAHARJA ENERGI CEPU—See PT Rukun Raharja Tbk; *Int'l*, pg. 6069
PT RAILINK—See PT. Kereta Api Indonesia; *Int'l*, pg. 6087
PT RAJAMANDALA ELECTRIC POWER—See PT Indonesia Power; *Int'l*, pg. 6046
PT. RAJAWALI CITRA TELEVISI INDONESIA—See PT MNC Investama Tbk; *Int'l*, pg. 6059
PT RAJAWALI CORPORATION; *Int'l*, pg. 6067
PT RAJAWALI RESOURCES—See PT Golden Eagle Energy Tbk; *Int'l*, pg. 6041
P.T. RAKINTAM ELECTRICAL CONTRACTORS—See Kinden Corporation; *Int'l*, pg. 4166
PT RAMAYANA LESTARI SENTOSA TBK; *Int'l*, pg. 6068
PT RAPALA INDONESIA—See Rapala VMC Oyj; *Int'l*, pg. 6209
PT RAPALA VMC BATAM—See Rapala VMC Oyj; *Int'l*, pg. 6209
PT RASA LANGGENG WIRA—See PT HK Metals Utama; *Int'l*, pg. 6043
PT RATU PRABU ENERGI TBK; *Int'l*, pg. 6068
PTR BALER & COMPACTOR COMPANY—See Komar Industries, LLC; *U.S. Private*, pg. 2342
PTR BALER & COMPACTOR SERVICE INC.—See Komar Industries, LLC; *U.S. Private*, pg. 2342
PTRC, INC.—See People's Jewelry Company, Inc.; *U.S. Private*, pg. 3141
PT. RECKITT BENCKISER INDONESIA—See Reckitt Benckiser Group plc; *Int'l*, pg. 6236
PT. RED HAT INDONESIA—See International Business Machines Corporation; *U.S. Public*, pg. 1150
P.T REDPATH INDONESIA—See ATON GmbH; *Int'l*, pg. 688
PT RED PLANET HOTEL BEKASI—See PT Red Planet Indonesia Tbk; *Int'l*, pg. 6068
PT RED PLANET HOTEL MAKASSAR—See PT Red Planet Indonesia Tbk; *Int'l*, pg. 6068
PT RED PLANET HOTEL PALEMBANG—See PT Red Planet Indonesia Tbk; *Int'l*, pg. 6068
PT RED PLANET HOTEL PEKANBARU—See PT Red Planet Indonesia Tbk; *Int'l*, pg. 6068
PT RED PLANET HOTELS SOLO—See PT Red Planet Indonesia Tbk; *Int'l*, pg. 6068
PT RED PLANET HOTEL SURABAYA—See PT Red Planet Indonesia Tbk; *Int'l*, pg. 6068
PT RED PLANET INDONESIA TBK; *Int'l*, pg. 6068
PT REKADAYA ELEKTRIKA CONSULT—See PT PLN (Persero); *Int'l*, pg. 6065
PT REKADAYA ELEKTRIKA—See PT PLN (Persero); *Int'l*, pg. 6065
PT REKAGUNATEK PERSADA—See PT Indonesia Pondasi Raya Tbk.; *Int'l*, pg. 6046
PT REKAJASA AKSES—See PT Sarana Menara Nusantara Tbk; *Int'l*, pg. 6070
PT RELIANCE ASSET MANAGEMENT—See PT Reliance Capital Management; *Int'l*, pg. 6068
PT RELIANCE CAPITAL MANAGEMENT; *Int'l*, pg. 6068
PT RELIANCE SECURITIES TBK—See PT Reliance Capital Management; *Int'l*, pg. 6068
PT RENALMED TIARA UTAMA—See PT Kalbe Farma Tbk.; *Int'l*, pg. 6050
PT RENTOKIL INDONESIA—See Rentokil Initial plc; *Int'l*, pg. 6287
P.T. RENTRACKS COCREATION INDONESIA—See Rentracks Co., Ltd.; *Int'l*, pg. 6289
P.T. RENTRACKS CREATIVE WORKS—See Rentracks Co., Ltd.; *Int'l*, pg. 6289
PT REPOWER ASIA INDONESIA TBK; *Int'l*, pg. 6068
PT RESKA MULTI USAHA—See PT. Kereta Api Indonesia; *Int'l*, pg. 6087
PT RESOURCE ALAM INDONESIA TBK; *Int'l*, pg. 6068
PT RESWARA MINERGI HARTAMA—See PT ABM Investama Tbk.; *Int'l*, pg. 6018
THE PTR GROUP, LLC—See Huntington Ingalls Industries, Inc.; *U.S. Public*, pg. 1072
PTR HARTMANN GMBH—See Phoenix Mecano AG; *Int'l*, pg. 5852
PTR HARTMANN (SHAOGUAN) CO., LTD.—See Phoenix Mecano AG; *Int'l*, pg. 5852
PT. RHB ASSET MANAGEMENT INDONESIA—See RHB Bank Berhad; *Int'l*, pg. 6320
PT RHB OSK SECURITIES INDONESIA—See RHB Bank Berhad; *Int'l*, pg. 6320
P.T. RHIPE INTERNATIONAL INDONESIA—See Crayon Group Holding ASA; *Int'l*, pg. 1829
P.T. RHYTHM KYOSHIN INDONESIA—See Rhythm Co., Ltd.; *Int'l*, pg. 6328
P.T. RICKY ARTA JAYA—See PT Ricky Putra Globalindo Tbk; *Int'l*, pg. 6068
P.T. RICKY JAYA SAKTI—See PT Ricky Putra Globalindo Tbk; *Int'l*, pg. 6068

P.T. RICKY KOBAYASHI—See PT Ricky Putra Globalindo Tbk; *Int'l*, pg. 6068
P.T. RICKY MUMBUL DAYA—See PT Ricky Putra Globalindo Tbk; *Int'l*, pg. 6068
P.T. RICKY MUSI WIJAYA—See PT Ricky Putra Globalindo Tbk; *Int'l*, pg. 6068
PT RICKY PUTRA GLOBALINDO TBK; *Int'l*, pg. 6068
PT. RICOBANA ABADI—See PT SMR UTAMA Tbk; *Int'l*, pg. 6075
PT. RICOBANA—See PT SMR UTAMA Tbk; *Int'l*, pg. 6075
PT. RIG TENDERS INDONESIA TBK.—See Scomi Group Berhad; *Int'l*, pg. 6650
PT. RIKEN INDONESIA—See Riken Technos Corporation; *Int'l*, pg. 6341
PT. RIMBA PLAMA SEJAHTERA—See ELL Environmental Holdings Limited; *Int'l*, pg. 2364
PT. RIMBA SUNKYONG—See SK Networks Co., Ltd.; *Int'l*, pg. 6974
PT. RIMEX INTERNATIONAL INDONESIA—See Rimex Supply Ltd.; *Int'l*, pg. 6342
PT RIMO INTERNATIONAL LESTARI TBK; *Int'l*, pg. 6068
P.T. RINNAI INDONESIA—See Rinnai Corporation; *Int'l*, pg. 6344
PT RISE ELECTRONIC INDONESIA—See NVC International Holdings Limited; *Int'l*, pg. 5498
PT. RISMAR DAEWOO APPAREL—See POSCO Holdings Inc.; *Int'l*, pg. 5938
PT RIZKY LANCAR SENTOSA—See PT Sinar Mas Multiartha Tbk; *Int'l*, pg. 6074
PTR MESSTECHNIK VERWALTUNGS-GMBH—See Phoenix Mecano AG; *Int'l*, pg. 5852
PT RMK ENERGY TBK; *Int'l*, pg. 6068
P.T. ROBERT BOSCH—See Robert Bosch GmbH; *Int'l*, pg. 6361
PT ROBERTET GROUP INDONESIA—See Robertet S.A.; *Int'l*, pg. 6369
PT. ROBERT WALTERS INDONESIA—See Robert Walters plc; *Int'l*, pg. 6368
PT. ROCHE INDONESIA DIAGNOSTICS—See Roche Holding AG; *Int'l*, pg. 6373
P.T. ROCHE INDONESIA—See Roche Holding AG; *Int'l*, pg. 6373
PT ROCKFIELDS PROPERTI INDONESIA TBK; *Int'l*, pg. 6068
P.T. ROCK PAINT INDONESIA—See Rock Paint Co., Ltd.; *Int'l*, pg. 6378
PT ROCKWELL AUTOMATION INDONESIA—See Rockwell Automation, Inc.; *U.S. Public*, pg. 1805
PT. ROHDE & SCHWARZ INDONESIA—See Rohde & Schwarz GmbH & Co. KG; *Int'l*, pg. 6384
PT ROHM AND HAAS INDONESIA—See Dow Inc.; *U.S. Public*, pg. 685
PT. ROLAND BERGER STRATEGY CONSULTANTS—See Roland Berger Strategy Consultants GmbH; *Int'l*, pg. 6389
PT ROLIMEX KIMIA NUSAMAS—See PT DIAN SWASTATIKA SENTOSA Tbk; *Int'l*, pg. 6036
PT. ROLLS-ROYCE—See Rolls-Royce Holdings plc; *Int'l*, pg. 6392
PT ROTHSCHILDCO ADVISORY INDONESIA—See Rothschild & Co SCA; *Int'l*, pg. 6403
PT ROTHSCHILD INDONESIA—See Rothschild & Co SCA; *Int'l*, pg. 6403
PT. ROXCEL INDONESIA—See Roxcel Handelsges.m.b.H.; *Int'l*, pg. 6408
PT ROYAL PRIMA JAMBI—See Royal Prima Tbk; *Int'l*, pg. 6068
PT ROYAL PRIMA TBK; *Int'l*, pg. 6068
PTR-PRECISION TECHNOLOGIES, INC.—See Rupf Industries GmbH; *Int'l*, pg. 6428
PT. R SYSTEMS IBIZCS INTERNATIONAL—See Blackstone Inc.; *U.S. Public*, pg. 357
PT RUKUN RAHARJA TBK; *Int'l*, pg. 6068
PT RUMAH SAKIT BUNDA SEJAHTERA—See PT Metro Healthcare Indonesia Tbk; *Int'l*, pg. 6056
PT. RUMAH SAKIT IBU DAN ANAK ROSIVA—See PT Murni Sadar Tbk; *Int'l*, pg. 6060
PT. RYOKO SANGYO INDONESIA—See Mitsubishi Materials Corporation; *Int'l*, pg. 4965
P.T. SAAT KEUANGAN INDONESIA—See United Overseas Bank Limited; *Int'l*, pg. 8071
PT. SABRE TRAVEL NETWORK INDONESIA—See PT Garuda Indonesia (Persero) Tbk; *Int'l*, pg. 6040
PT. SACMI INDONESIA—See Sacmi Imola S.C.A.R.L.; *Int'l*, pg. 6464
PTS ADVANCE; *U.S. Private*, pg. 3298
PT SAF INDONESIA - SIDOARJO FACTORY—See Compagnie des Levures Lesaffre SA; *Int'l*, pg. 1739
PT SAF INDONESIA—See Compagnie des Levures Lesaffre SA; *Int'l*, pg. 1739
PT SAHABAT FINANSIAL KELUARGA—See Bangkok Bank Public Company Limited; *Int'l*, pg. 833
PT SAHID INTERNATIONAL HOTEL MANGEMENT & CONSULTANTS—See PT Hotel Sahid Jaya International Tbk; *Int'l*, pg. 6043
PT. SAI GLOBAL INDONESIA—See EQT AB; *Int'l*, pg. 2471
PT. SAINT-GOBAIN ABRASIVES INDONESIA—See Compagnie de Saint-Gobain SA; *Int'l*, pg. 1724

PT SANURHASTA MITRA TBK

PT SAINT-GOBAIN WINTER DIAMAS—See Compagnie de Saint-Gobain SA; *Int'l*, pg. 1724
PT SAKA ENERGI INDONESIA—See PT Perusahaan Gas Negara (Persero) Tbk; *Int'l*, pg. 6064
P.T. SAKA FARMA LABORATORIES—See PT Kalbe Farma Tbk.; *Int'l*, pg. 6050
PT. SAKAI INDONESIA—See Sakai Heavy Industries Ltd; *Int'l*, pg. 6487
PT. SAKALAGUNA SEMESTA—See PT. Elang Mahkota Teknologi Tbk.; *Int'l*, pg. 6085
PT. SAKATA INX INDONESIA—See Sakata INX Corporation; *Int'l*, pg. 6487
PT. SALIM IVOMAS PRATAMA TBK—See First Pacific Company Limited; *Int'l*, pg. 2686
PT SAMADISTA KARYA—See PT Astra International Tbk; *Int'l*, pg. 6023
PT SAMCHEM PRASANDHA—See Samchem Holdings Berhad; *Int'l*, pg. 6503
PT. SAMCON—See Samwha Capacitor Group; *Int'l*, pg. 6518
P.T. SAMICK INDONESIA—See Samick Musical Instrument Co., Ltd.; *Int'l*, pg. 6505
PT SAMINDO RESOURCES TBK; *Int'l*, pg. 6069
PT SAMPOERNA AGRO TBK.; *Int'l*, pg. 6069
PT. SAMSONITE INDONESIA—See Samsonite International S.A.; *Int'l*, pg. 6509
PT SAMUDERA AGENCIES INDONESIA—See PT Samudera Indonesia Tbk; *Int'l*, pg. 6069
PT. SAMUDERA DAYA MITRA—See PT Samudera Indonesia Tbk; *Int'l*, pg. 6069
PT SAMUDERA INDONESIA SHIP MANAGEMENT—See PT Samudera Indonesia Tbk; *Int'l*, pg. 6069
PT SAMUDERA INDONESIA TBK; *Int'l*, pg. 6069
PT. SAMUDERA INDONESIA, TBK.—See Albert Ballin KG; *Int'l*, pg. 296
PT. SAMUDERA PERDANA—See PT Samudera Indonesia Tbk; *Int'l*, pg. 6069
PT SAMUDERA PROPERTI INDONESIA—See PT Samudera Indonesia Tbk; *Int'l*, pg. 6069
PT SAMUDERA SARANA LOGISTIK—See PT Samudera Indonesia Tbk; *Int'l*, pg. 6069
PT SAMUDERA SARANA TERMINAL INDONESIA—See PT Samudera Indonesia Tbk; *Int'l*, pg. 6069
PT SAMUDERA SHIPPING SERVICES—See PT Samudera Indonesia Tbk; *Int'l*, pg. 6069
PT SAMUDERA TERMINAL INDONESIA—See PT Samudera Indonesia Tbk; *Int'l*, pg. 6069
PT SAMUDRA DYAN PRAGA—See PT Dyandra Media International Tbk; *Int'l*, pg. 6037
PT SAMURAI PAINT—See Samurai 2K Aerosol Limited; *Int'l*, pg. 6516
P.T. SANDANG MUTIARA CEMERLANG—See Fountain Set (Holdings) Limited; *Int'l*, pg. 2754
P.T. SANDEN INDONESIA—See Sanden Corporation; *Int'l*, pg. 6524
P.T. SANDVIK MINING AND CONSTRUCTION INDONESIA—See Sandvik AB; *Int'l*, pg. 6531
PT SANDVIK SMC—See Sandvik AB; *Int'l*, pg. 6530
PT SANGGAR SARANA BAJA—See PT ABM Investama Tbk.; *Int'l*, pg. 6018
PT SANGGRAHA PELITA SENTOSA—See PT. Bakrieland Development, Tbk.; *Int'l*, pg. 6084
PT SANGHIANG PERKASA—See PT Kalbe Farma Tbk.; *Int'l*, pg. 6050
PT. SANGO INDONESIA—See Sango Co., Ltd.; *Int'l*, pg. 6537
P.T. SANKEN INDONESIA—See Sanken Electric Co., Ltd.; *Int'l*, pg. 6541
PT. SANKEN TRANSFORMER INDONESIA—See Sanken Electric Co., Ltd.; *Int'l*, pg. 6541
PT. SANKO GOSEI TECHNOLOGY INDONESIA—See Sanko Gosei Ltd.; *Int'l*, pg. 6541
PT. SANKOSHA INDONESIA—See Sankosha Corporation; *Int'l*, pg. 6542
P.T. SANKYU INDONESIA INTERNATIONAL—See Sankyu, Inc.; *Int'l*, pg. 6544
PT. SANNENG BAKEWARE INDONESIA—See San Neng Group Holdings Co., Ltd.; *Int'l*, pg. 6521
P.T. SANOH INDONESIA—See Sanoh Industrial Co., Ltd.; *Int'l*, pg. 6552
PT SANPAK UNGGUL—See PT Dynaplast Tbk.; *Int'l*, pg. 6037
PT SANTA FE INDONUSA—See EAC Invest AS; *Int'l*, pg. 2262
PT SANTA FE PROPERTIES—See Iron Mountain Incorporated; *U.S. Public*, pg. 1174
PT. SANTAKU SHINWA INDONESIA—See Shinwa Co., Ltd.; *Int'l*, pg. 6849
PT SANTAN BATUBARA—See PT Harum Energy Tbk.; *Int'l*, pg. 6043
PT SANURHASTA MITRA TBK; *Int'l*, pg. 6069
PT. SANWAMAS METAL INDUSTRY—See Sanwa Holdings Corporation; *Int'l*, pg. 6561
PT. SANY INDONESIA MACHINERY—See Sany Group Co., Ltd.; *Int'l*, pg. 6562
PT. SANYO COMPRESSOR INDONESIA—See Panasonic Holdings Corporation; *Int'l*, pg. 5723
PT. SANYO ELECTRONICS INDONESIA—See Panasonic Holdings Corporation; *Int'l*, pg. 5723

PT. SANYO ENERGY (BATAM) CORPORATE—See Panasonic Holdings Corporation; *Int'l*, pg. 5723
PT. SANYO JAYA COMPONENTS INDONESIA—See Panasonic Holdings Corporation; *Int'l*, pg. 5723
PT. SANYO PRECISION BATAM—See Panasonic Holdings Corporation; *Int'l*, pg. 5723
P.T. SANYO SPECIAL STEEL INDONESIA—See Nippon Steel Corporation; *Int'l*, pg. 5340
PT. SANYO TRADING INDONESIA—See Sanyo Trading Co., Ltd.; *Int'l*, pg. 6565
PT SAP INDONESIA—See SAP SE; *Int'l*, pg. 6568
PT SAPTAUSAHA GEMILANGINDAH TBK; *Int'l*, pg. 6070
PT SARANA ACEH UTAMA—See Jaya Konstruksi Manggala Pratama Tbk; *Int'l*, pg. 3914
PT SARANACENTRAL BAJATAMA TBK; *Int'l*, pg. 6070
PT SARANA INTI PERSADA—See PT Sarana Menara Nusantara Tbk; *Int'l*, pg. 6070
PT SARANA JAMBI UTAMA—See Jaya Konstruksi Manggala Pratama Tbk; *Int'l*, pg. 3914
PT SARANA MBAY UTAMA—See Jaya Konstruksi Manggala Pratama Tbk; *Int'l*, pg. 3914
PT SARANA MEDITAMA METROPOLITAN TBK; *Int'l*, pg. 6070
PT SARANA MENARA NUSANTARA TBK; *Int'l*, pg. 6070
PT SARANA MITRA LUAS TBK; *Int'l*, pg. 6070
PT SARANA MULTIGRIYA FINANSIAL (PERSERO) TBK; *Int'l*, pg. 6070
PT SARANA SAMPIT MENTAYA UTAMA—See Jaya Konstruksi Manggala Pratama Tbk; *Int'l*, pg. 3914
PT SARANA TIRTA REJEKI; *Int'l*, pg. 6070
PT SARASWANTI ANUGERAH MAKMUR TBK; *Int'l*, pg. 6070
PT SARASWATI GRIYA LESTARI TBK; *Int'l*, pg. 6070
PT SARATOGA INVESTAMA SEDAYA TBK.; *Int'l*, pg. 6070
P.T. SARI CHICKEN INDONESIA—See Restaurant Brands Asia Ltd.; *Int'l*, pg. 6303
PT SARIGUNA PRIMATIRTA TBK; *Int'l*, pg. 6070
PT. SARI HUSADA TBK—See Danone; *Int'l*, pg. 1967
PT SARIMELATI KENCANA TBK; *Int'l*, pg. 6070
PT. SARTORIUS MECHATRONICS INDONESIA—See Sartorius AG; *Int'l*, pg. 6579
P.T. SASAKURA INDONESIA—See Sasakura Engineering Co., Ltd.; *Int'l*, pg. 6582
PT. SASANA ARTHA FINANCE—See PT Mitra Pinasthika Mustika Tbk; *Int'l*, pg. 6058
PT SATELIT PALAPA INDONESIA SATELINDO—See Deutsche Telekom AG; *Int'l*, pg. 2084
PT SAT NUSAPERSADA TBK; *Int'l*, pg. 6071
PT. SATO LABEL SOLUTIONS—See SATO Holdings Corporation; *Int'l*, pg. 6585
P.T. SATOMO INDOVYL POLYMER—See Sumitomo Corporation; *Int'l*, pg. 7269
P.T. SATOMO INDOVYL POLYMER—See Tosoh Corporation; *Int'l*, pg. 7832
PT.SATO-SHOJI INDONESIA—See Sato shoji Corporation; *Int'l*, pg. 6586
PT SATRIA ANTARAN PRIMA TBK; *Int'l*, pg. 6071
PT SATRIA MEGA KENCANA TBK; *Int'l*, pg. 6071
PT. SATU SEMBILAN DELAPAN—See Kuala Lumpur Kepong Berhad; *Int'l*, pg. 4318
PT. SATU SUMMARECON SUKSES—See PT Summarecon Agung Tbk; *Int'l*, pg. 6076
PT. SATYA GALANG KEMIKA—See PT Catur Sentosa Adiprana Tbk; *Int'l*, pg. 6033
PT SATYAMITRA KEMAS LESTARI TBK; *Int'l*, pg. 6071
P.T. SAVANA LESTARI—See PT Trisula International Tbk; *Int'l*, pg. 6080
PT SAVINO DEL BENE—See Savino Del Bene S.p.A.; *Int'l*, pg. 6600
PT SAWITMAS AGRO PERKASA—See PT Bakrie Sumatera Plantations Tbk; *Int'l*, pg. 6025
PT SAWIT SUMBERMAS SARANA TBK; *Int'l*, pg. 6071
P.T. SBP INDONESIA—See Sumitomo Bakelite Co., Ltd.; *Int'l*, pg. 7263
PT. SCG PIPE AND PRECAST INDONESIA—See The Siam Cement Public Company Limited; *Int'l*, pg. 7685
PT. SCG TRADING INDONESIA—See The Siam Cement Public Company Limited; *Int'l*, pg. 7683
PT. SCHENKER PETROLOG UTAMA—See Deutsche Bahn AG; *Int'l*, pg. 2053
PT. SCHERING INDONESIA—See Bayer Aktiengesellschaft; *Int'l*, pg. 904
P.T. SCHLEMMER AUTOMOTIVE INDONESIA—See Ningbo Huaxiang Electronic Co., Ltd.; *Int'l*, pg. 5302
PT. SCHNEIDER ELECTRIC INDONESIA—See Schneider Electric SE; *Int'l*, pg. 6628
PT. SCHNEIDER ELECTRIC IT INDONESIA—See Schneider Electric SE; *Int'l*, pg. 6628
PT. SCHNEIDER ELECTRIC MANUFACTURING BATAM—See Schneider Electric SE; *Int'l*, pg. 6628
PT. SCHOTT IGAR GLASS—See Carl-Zeiss-Stiftung; *Int'l*, pg. 1336
PT SCHRODER INVESTMENT MANAGEMENT INDONESIA—See Schroders plc; *Int'l*, pg. 6640
P.T. S.C. JOHNSON & SON (INDONESIA) LTD.—See S.C. Johnson & Son, Inc.; *U.S. Private*, pg. 3516
PTS CO., LTD.—See Powdertech Co., Ltd.; *Int'l*, pg. 5942

P.T. SCREENPLAY PRODUKSI—See PT. Elang Mahkota Teknologi Tbk.; *Int'l*, pg. 6085
PT. SCS ASTRAGRAPHIA TECHNOLOGIES—See Temasek Holdings (Private) Limited; *Int'l*, pg. 7553
PT. SEA BRIDGE SHIPPING—See Samchully Co., Ltd.; *Int'l*, pg. 6503
PT SEAMLESS PIPE INDONESIA JAYA—See Techint S.p.A.; *Int'l*, pg. 7504
PT SECUREMETRIC TECHNOLOGY—See Securemetric Berhad; *Int'l*, pg. 6674
PT SEDAYA PRATAMA—See PT Astra International Tbk; *Int'l*, pg. 6023
P.T. SEHAT DIGITAL NUSANTARA—See PT Mitra Keluarga Karyasehat Tbk; *Int'l*, pg. 6057
PT. SEI CONSULTING JAKARTA—See Sumitomo Electric Industries, Ltd.; *Int'l*, pg. 7279
PT. SEIREN INDONESIA—See Seiren Co., Ltd.; *Int'l*, pg. 6691
PT. SEIWA INDONESIA—See Mitsuboshi Belting Ltd.; *Int'l*, pg. 4972
PT SEJAHTERA BALI FURINDO—See PT Chitose Internasional Tbk; *Int'l*, pg. 6034
PT SEJAHTERA BINTANG ABADI TEXTILE TBK; *Int'l*, pg. 6071
PT SEJAHTERA PALEMBANG FURINDO—See PT Chitose Internasional Tbk; *Int'l*, pg. 6034
PT SEJAHTERARAYA ANUGRAHJAYA TBK; *Int'l*, pg. 6071
PT SEJAHTERA SAMARINDA FURINDO—See PT Chitose Internasional Tbk; *Int'l*, pg. 6034
PT. SEJAHTERA USAHA BERSAMA—See Samko Timber Limited; *Int'l*, pg. 6506
PT SEJAHTERA WAHANA GEMILANG—See PT Chitose Internasional Tbk; *Int'l*, pg. 6034
P.T. SEKARBUMI ALAMLESTARI—See Kuala Lumpur Kepong Berhad; *Int'l*, pg. 4318
PT SEKAR BUMI TBK; *Int'l*, pg. 6071
PT. SEKISUI POLYMATECH INDONESIA—See Sekisui Chemical Co., Ltd.; *Int'l*, pg. 6694
PT. SEKISUI POLYMATECH TRADING INDONESIA—See Sekisui Chemical Co., Ltd.; *Int'l*, pg. 6694
PT. SELAMAT SEMPANA PERKASA—See PT Selamat Sempurna Tbk; *Int'l*, pg. 6071
PT SELAMAT SEMPURNA TBK; *Int'l*, pg. 6071
PT SELARAS CITRA NUSANTARA PERKASA TBK; *Int'l*, pg. 6071
PT SELULAR GLOBAL NET—See Digilife Technologies Limited; *Int'l*, pg. 2119
PT. SEMARANG AUTOCOMP MANUFACTURING INDONESIA—See Yazaki Corporation; *Int'l*, pg. 8572
PT SEMARANG HERBAL INDO PLANT—See PT Industri Jamu dan Farmasi Sido Muncul Tbk; *Int'l*, pg. 6047
PT. SEMEN BATURAJA (PERSERO) TBK—See PT. Semen Indonesia (Persero) Tbk; *Int'l*, pg. 6089
P.T. SEMEN GROBOGAN—See Heidelberg Materials AG; *Int'l*, pg. 3318
PT. SEMEN INDONESIA BETON—See PT. Semen Indonesia (Persero) Tbk; *Int'l*, pg. 6089
PT. SEMEN INDONESIA DISTRIBUTOR—See PT. Semen Indonesia (Persero) Tbk; *Int'l*, pg. 6089
PT. SEMEN INDONESIA INTERNASIONAL—See PT. Semen Indonesia (Persero) Tbk; *Int'l*, pg. 6088
PT. SEMEN INDONESIA LOGISTIK—See PT. Semen Indonesia (Persero) Tbk; *Int'l*, pg. 6089
PT SEMEN INDONESIA (PERSERO) TBK; *Int'l*, pg. 6088
PT. SEMEN PADANG—See PT. Semen Indonesia (Persero) Tbk; *Int'l*, pg. 6089
PT. SEMEN TONASA—See PT. Semen Indonesia (Persero) Tbk; *Int'l*, pg. 6089
PT. SEMPEC INDONESIA—See Punj Lloyd Ltd.; *Int'l*, pg. 6119
PT SENANTIASA MAKMUR—See PT Astra Otoparts Tbk; *Int'l*, pg. 6024
PT. SENAYAN TRIKARYA SEMPANA—See Kajima Corporation; *Int'l*, pg. 4055
PT. SENTOSASEGARA MULIA SHIPPING—See PT Wintermar Offshore Marine Tbk; *Int'l*, pg. 6083
PT SENTRABOGA INTISELERA—See Asahi Group Holdings Ltd.; *Int'l*, pg. 593
PT SENTRA FOOD INDONESIA TBK; *Int'l*, pg. 6071
PT. SENTRAL KREASI INOVAS—See PT Sentral Mitra Informatika Tbk; *Int'l*, pg. 6071
PT SENTRAL MITRA INFORMATIKA TBK; *Int'l*, pg. 6071
PT. SENTRAL PEMBAYARAN INDONESIA—See PT. Arthavest Tbk; *Int'l*, pg. 6022
PT SENTRAL SUPEL PERKASA—See PT Pelangi Arjuna; *Int'l*, pg. 6062
PT SENTUL CITY TBK.; *Int'l*, pg. 6071
PT SEPATIM BATAMTAMA—See PT. Semen Indonesia (Persero) Tbk; *Int'l*, pg. 6089
PT SEPCHEM—See PT ESSA Industries Indonesia Tbk.; *Int'l*, pg. 6038
PT SEPEDA BERSAMA INDONESIA TBK; *Int'l*, pg. 6072
PT SERASI AUTORAYA—See PT Astra International Tbk; *Int'l*, pg. 6023
PT SERASI LOGISTICS INDONESIA—See PT Astra International Tbk; *Int'l*, pg. 6023
PT SERASI TRANSPORTASI NUSANTARA—See PT Astra International Tbk; *Int'l*, pg. 6023

PT SERTIFIKASI KOMPETENSI PEMBANGKITAN TENAGA LISTRIK—See PT PLN (Persero); *Int'l*, pg. 6065
PTS GMBH—See Team Internet Group plc; *Int'l*, pg. 7500
PT SGMW MULTIFINANCE INDONESIA—See PT Sinar Mas Multiartha Tbk; *Int'l*, pg. 6074
PT. SGS INDONESIA—See SGS SA; *Int'l*, pg. 6743
P.T. SHARP ELECTRONICS INDONESIA—See Hon Hai Precision Industry Co., Ltd.; *Int'l*, pg. 3457
PT. SHELL INDONESIA—See Shell plc; *Int'l*, pg. 6795
PT SHIELD-ON SERVICE TBK; *Int'l*, pg. 6072
P.T. SHIMANO BATAM—See Shimano, Inc.; *Int'l*, pg. 6833
PT. SHIMATAMA GRAHA—See PT Lippo Karawaci Tbk; *Int'l*, pg. 6053
P.T. SHIMIZU BANGUN CIPTA KONTRAKTOR—See Shimizu Corporation; *Int'l*, pg. 6835
PT. SHINAGAWA REFRACTORIES INDONESIA—See Shinagawa Refractories Co., Ltd.; *Int'l*, pg. 6841
PT. SHINDENGEN INDONESIA—See Shindengen Electric Manufacturing Co., Ltd.; *Int'l*, pg. 6842
P.T. SHIN-ETSU MAGNETICS INDONESIA—See Shin-Etsu Chemical Co. Ltd.; *Int'l*, pg. 6839
PT. SHIN-ETSU POLYMER INDONESIA—See Shin-Etsu Chemical Co. Ltd.; *Int'l*, pg. 6840
PT SHINHAN ASSET MANAGEMENT INDONESIA—See Shinhan Financial Group Co., Ltd.; *Int'l*, pg. 6844
PT. SHINHAN INDO FINANCE—See Shinhan Financial Group Co., Ltd.; *Int'l*, pg. 6844
P.T. SHINHAN SEKURITAS INDONESIA—See Shinhan Financial Group Co., Ltd.; *Int'l*, pg. 6843
PT. SHINKO PLANTECH—See RAIZNEXT Corporation; *Int'l*, pg. 6192
PT. SHINKO TOYOBO GISTEX GARMENT—See Toyobo Co., Ltd.; *Int'l*, pg. 7860
PT. SHINTA UTAMA—See PT Sinar Mas Multiartha Tbk; *Int'l*, pg. 6074
PT. SHINWON EBENEZER—See Shinwon Corporation; *Int'l*, pg. 6850
PT. SHI PLASTICS MACHINERY (INDONESIA)—See Sumitomo Heavy Industries, Ltd.; *Int'l*, pg. 7287
P.T. SH MACHINERY INDONESIA—See Sin Heng Heavy Machinery Limited; *Int'l*, pg. 6935
PT. SHOPEE INTERNATIONAL INDONESIA—See Sea Limited; *Int'l*, pg. 6660
PT. SHOWA AUTOPARTS INDONESIA—See Hitachi Astemo, Ltd.; *Int'l*, pg. 3409
PT. SHOWA ESTERINDO INDONESIA—See Resonac Holdings Corporation; *Int'l*, pg. 6298
P.T. SHOWA INDONESIA MANUFACTURING—See Hitachi Astemo, Ltd.; *Int'l*, pg. 3409
PT SIBELCO LAUTAN MINERALS—See SCR Sibelco SA; *Int'l*, pg. 6519
PT. SICPA PERURI SECURINK—See SICPA Holding SA; *Int'l*, pg. 6882
PT SIDOMULYO SELARAS TBK; *Int'l*, pg. 6072
PT. SIEGWERK INDONESIA—See Siegwerk Druckfarben AG & Co. KGaA; *Int'l*, pg. 6884
P.T. SIEMENS HEALTHINEERS INDONESIA—See Siemens Aktiengesellschaft; *Int'l*, pg. 6887
P.T. SIEMENS HEARING INSTRUMENTS—See Siemens Aktiengesellschaft; *Int'l*, pg. 6897
P.T. SIEMENS INDONESIA—See Siemens Aktiengesellschaft; *Int'l*, pg. 6887
PT. SIEMENS MOBILITY INDONESIA—See Siemens Aktiengesellschaft; *Int'l*, pg. 6887
PT SIERAD INDUSTRIES—See PT Sreeya Sewu Indonesia Tbk; *Int'l*, pg. 6075
PT SIGMA CIPTA CARAKA—See Perusahaan Perseroan Indonesia Tbk; *Int'l*, pg. 5821
PT SIGMA CIPTA UTAMA—See PT Elnusa Tbk; *Int'l*, pg. 6038
PT SIGMA ENERGY COMPRESSINDO TBK; *Int'l*, pg. 6072
PT. SIGMA METRASYS—See Perusahaan Perseroan Indonesia Tbk; *Int'l*, pg. 5822
P.T. SIGMA SOLUSI INTEGRASI—See Perusahaan Perseroan Indonesia Tbk; *Int'l*, pg. 5821
PT SIGNET PRATAMA—See Perusahaan Perseroan Indonesia Tbk; *Int'l*, pg. 5822
PT SIIX ELECTRONICS INDONESIA—See SIIX CORPORATION; *Int'l*, pg. 6913
PT. SIIX EMS INDONESIA—See SIIX CORPORATION; *Int'l*, pg. 6913
PT. SIIX TRADING INDONESIA—See SIIX CORPORATION; *Int'l*, pg. 6913
P.T. SIKA INDONESIA—See Sika AG; *Int'l*, pg. 6915
PT. S-IK INDONESIA—See Inabata & Co. Ltd.; *Int'l*, pg. 3644
PT SILKARGO INDONESIA—See PT Samudera Indonesia Tbk; *Int'l*, pg. 6069
PT SILLO MARITIME PERDANA TBK; *Int'l*, pg. 6072
PT SILOAM INTERNATIONAL HOSPITALS TBK—See PT Lippo Karawaci Tbk; *Int'l*, pg. 6053
PT. SILVER BIRD—See PT Blue Bird Tbk; *Int'l*, pg. 6030
PT. SIMAS MONEY CHANGER—See PT Sinar Mas Multiartha Tbk; *Int'l*, pg. 6074
PTS IMPRESSION SDN. BHD.—See Yong Tai Berhad; *Int'l*, pg. 8597

COMPANY NAME INDEX

P.T. SINAR ABADI CITRANUSA—See PT Trisula International Tbk; *Int'l*, pg. 6080
P.T. SINAR ARTHA INFORINDO—See PT Sinar Mas Multiartha Tbk; *Int'l*, pg. 6074
P.T. SINAR ARTHA SOLUSINDO—See PT Sinar Mas Multiartha Tbk; *Int'l*, pg. 6074
P.T. SINAR ARTHA TRADING—See PT Sinar Mas Multiartha Tbk; *Int'l*, pg. 6074
PT SINAR CEMERLANG GEMILANG—See PT Intiland Development Tbk.; *Int'l*, pg. 6048
PT SINAR DYANDRA ABADI—See PT Dyandra Media International Tbk; *Int'l*, pg. 6037
PT SINAR INDRA NUSA JAYA—See PT Indospring Tbk; *Int'l*, pg. 6047
PT SINAR KENCANA INTI PERKASA—See Golden Agri-Resources Ltd.; *Int'l*, pg. 3028
PT SINAR MAS AGRO RESOURCES & TECHNOLOGY TBK—See Golden Agri-Resources Ltd.; *Int'l*, pg. 3028
PT SINARMAS ASSET MANAGEMENT—See PT Sinar Mas Multiartha Tbk; *Int'l*, pg. 6074
PT SINARMAS DISTRIBUSI NUSANTARA—See Golden Agri-Resources Ltd.; *Int'l*, pg. 3028
PT SINAR MAS GROUP; *Int'l*, pg. 6072
PT SINAR MAS MULTIARTHA TBK; *Int'l*, pg. 6074
PT SINAR MAS MULTIFINANCE—See PT Sinar Mas Multiartha Tbk; *Int'l*, pg. 6074
PT SINARMAS SEKURITAS—See PT Sinar Mas Multiartha Tbk; *Int'l*, pg. 6074
PT SINAR MAS VENTURA—See PT Sinar Mas Multiartha Tbk; *Int'l*, pg. 6074
P.T. SINAR MITRA SEPADAN FINANCE—See ORIX Corporation; *Int'l*, pg. 5636
PT SINAR SEJAHTERA MANDIRI—See PT Chitose Internasional Tbk; *Int'l*, pg. 6034
PTS, INC.; *U.S. Public*, pg. 1735
P.T. SINEMART INDONESIA—See PT. Elang Mahkota Teknologi Tbk.; *Int'l*, pg. 6085
PT SINERGI INFORMATIKA SEMEN INDONESIA—See PT. Semen Indonesia (Persero) Tbk; *Int'l*, pg. 6089
PT SINERGI INTI ANDALAN PRIMA TBK; *Int'l*, pg. 6074
PT SINERGI INTI PLASTINDO TBK; *Int'l*, pg. 6075
PT SINERGI MEGAH INTERNUSA TBK; *Int'l*, pg. 6075
PT SINERGI MITRA INVESTAMA—See PT. Semen Indonesia (Persero) Tbk; *Int'l*, pg. 6089
P.T. SINERGI SEHASI PRIMA—See PT Metro Healthcare Indonesia Tbk; *Int'l*, pg. 6056
PT. SINFONIA TECHNOLOGY INDONESIA—See Sinfonia Technology Co., Ltd.; *Int'l*, pg. 6938
PT SINGARAJA PUTRA TBK; *Int'l*, pg. 6075
PT SINKONA INDONESIA LESTARI—See PT. Kimia Farma (Persero) Tbk.; *Int'l*, pg. 6087
PT. SINOMINE RESOURCE EXPLORATION INDONESIA—See Sinomine Resource Group Co., Ltd.; *Int'l*, pg. 6953
PT. SINOTRANS CSC INDONESIA—See China Merchants Group Limited; *Int'l*, pg. 1522
PT. SINTO INDONESIA—See Sintokogio Ltd.; *Int'l*, pg. 6958
PT. SIOEN INDONESIA—See Sioen Industries NV; pg. 6960
PT. SIOEN SEMARANG ASIA—See Sioen Industries NV; *Int'l*, pg. 6960
PT. SISTEM LOKA TRIPRIMA—See PT Sinar Mas Multiartha Tbk; *Int'l*, pg. 6074
PT. SITC INDONESIA—See SITC International Holdings Company Limited; *Int'l*, pg. 6964
PT SITIAGUNG MAKMUR—See PT Surya Semesta Internusa Tbk; *Int'l*, pg. 6077
P.T. SKEFINDO PRIMATAMA—See SKF AB; *Int'l*, pg. 6981
P.T. SKF INDONESIA—See SKF AB; *Int'l*, pg. 6981
P.T. SKF INDUSTRIAL INDONESIA—See SKF AB; *Int'l*, pg. 6981
P.T. SKYLINE BUILDING—See PT Jakarta Setiabudi In; *Int'l*, pg. 6049
P.T. SK NETWORKS INDONESIA—See SK Networks Co., Ltd.; *Int'l*, pg. 6974
PT. SK NETWORKS INNI JOA PLANTATION—See SK Networks Co., Ltd.; *Int'l*, pg. 6974
PT. SK NETWORKS—See SK Networks Co., Ltd.; *Int'l*, pg. 6974
PT SKY ENERGY INDONESIA TBK; *Int'l*, pg. 6075
PT SKYLINE BUILDING—See PT Jakarta Setiabudi In; *Int'l*, pg. 6049
PT. SKYWORTH INDUSTRY INDONESIA—See Skyworth Group Limited; *Int'l*, pg. 6995
PT. SLIONTEC EKADHARMA INDONESIA—See Hitachi, Ltd.; *Int'l*, pg. 3424
PT SLJ GLOBAL TBK.; *Int'l*, pg. 6075
PT. SLS BEARINDO—See THK CO., LTD.; *Int'l*, pg. 7712
PTSMA, INC.—See Select Medical Holdings Corporation; *U.S. Public*, pg. 1858
PT SMARTFREN TELECOM TBK; *Int'l*, pg. 6075
PT SMARTNET MAGNA GLOBAL—See PT Anabatic Technologies Tbk; *Int'l*, pg. 6021
P.T. SMB INDUSTRI—See Hunting Plc; *Int'l*, pg. 3537
PT SMC AUTOMATION INDONESIA—See SMC Corporation; *Int'l*, pg. 7004
PT SMC PNEUMATICS INDONESIA—See SMC Corporation; *Int'l*, pg. 7004

PT SM-CYCLO INDONESIA—See Sumitomo Heavy Industries, Ltd.; *Int'l*, pg. 7287
PT. SMELTING—See Mitsubishi Materials Corporation; *Int'l*, pg. 4965
PT. SMFL LEASING INDONESIA—See Sumitomo Corporation; *Int'l*, pg. 7274
PT. SMFL LEASING INDONESIA—See Sumitomo Mitsui Financial Group, Inc.; *Int'l*, pg. 7295
PT. SMOE INDONESIA—See Sembcorp Industries Ltd.; *Int'l*, pg. 6703
PT SMR UTAMA TBK; *Int'l*, pg. 6075
PT SMS SIEMAG METALLURGICAL SERVICES—See SMS Holding GmbH; *Int'l*, pg. 7015
PT. SNC-LAVALIN TPS—See AtkinsRealis Group Inc.; *Int'l*, pg. 671
PT. S NET INDONESIA—See SNet Systems Inc.; *Int'l*, pg. 7027
PT. SNF FLORINDO—See SNF SAS; *Int'l*, pg. 7027
PT. SNOWMAN MANDIRI INDONESIA—See Fujian Snowman Co., Ltd.; *Int'l*, pg. 2819
PT SOBUTE GLOBAL INDONESIA—See Sobute New Materials Co., Ltd.; *Int'l*, pg. 7030
PT SOCFIN INDONESIA—See Socfinasia S.A.; *Int'l*, pg. 7031
PT. SOCFIN—See Socfinaf SA; *Int'l*, pg. 7031
PT SOCIALWIRE INDONESIA—See Socialwire Co., Ltd.; *Int'l*, pg. 7031
PT. SOCI MAS—See Golden Agri-Resources Ltd.; *Int'l*, pg. 3028
PT. SODA NIKKA INDONESIA—See Soda Nikka Co., Ltd.; *Int'l*, pg. 7045
PT SODICK TECHNOLOGY INDONESIA—See Sodick Co., Ltd.; *Int'l*, pg. 7048
PT SOECHI LINES TBK; *Int'l*, pg. 6075
PT. SOFTEX INDONESIA—See Kimberly-Clark Corporation; *U.S. Public*, pg. 1231
PT. SOFTKEY INDONESIA—See Securemetric Berhad; *Int'l*, pg. 6674
PT SOFTORB TECHNOLOGY INDONESIA—See PT Cashlez Worldwide Indonesia Tbk; *Int'l*, pg. 6033
PT SOFTWARE AG INDONESIA OPERATIONS—See Silver Lake Group, LLC; *U.S. Private*, pg. 3658
PT SOFTWAREONE INDONESIA—See SoftwareONE Holding AG; *Int'l*, pg. 7057
PT SOFYAN HOTELS TBK; *Int'l*, pg. 6075
PT SOHO GLOBAL HEALTH TBK; *Int'l*, pg. 6075
PT. SOHO GLOBAL MEDIKA—See SOHO Group; *Int'l*, pg. 7059
PT. SOHO INDUSTRI PHARMASI—See SOHO Group; *Int'l*, pg. 7059
PT SOJITZ INDONESIA—See Sojitz Corporation; *Int'l*, pg. 7063
P.T. SOLAR SERVICES INDONESIA—See Caterpillar, Inc.; *U.S. Public*, pg. 453
PT SOLTIUS INDONESIA—See PT. Metrodata Electronics, Tbk.; *Int'l*, pg. 6088
PT SOLUSI BANGUN INDONESIA TBK—See PT. Semen Indonesia (Persero) Tbk; *Int'l*, pg. 6089
PT. SOLUSI ENERGI NUSANTARA—See PT Perusahaan Gas Negara (Persero) Tbk; *Int'l*, pg. 6064
PT. SOLUSI JAYA PERKASA—See PT Tunas Baru Lampung Tbk; *Int'l*, pg. 6080
PT SOLUSI KEMASAN DIGITAL TBK; *Int'l*, pg. 6075
PT SOLUSI SINERGI DIGITAL TBK; *Int'l*, pg. 6075
PT SOLUSI TUNAS PRATAMA TBK—See PT Sarana Menara Nusantara Tbk; *Int'l*, pg. 6070
P.T. SOLVAY PHARMA INDONESIA—See Abbott Laboratories; *U.S. Public*, pg. 20
PT.SOMAGEDE INDONESIA—See Punch Industry Co., Ltd.; *Int'l*, pg. 6118
PT SOMPO INSURANCE INDONESIA—See Sompo Holdings, Inc.; *Int'l*, pg. 7086
PT SONA TOPAS TOURISM INDUSTRY TBK; *Int'l*, pg. 6075
PT. SONOCO INDONESIA—See Sonoco Products Company; *U.S. Public*, pg. 1905
PT SORINI AGRO ASIA CORPORINDO TBK.—See Cargill, Inc.; *U.S. Private*, pg. 759
PT. SOUTHEAST ASIA PIPE INDUSTRIES—See PT Bakrie & Brothers Tbk; *Int'l*, pg. 6025
PT. SOUTHERN INDONESIA—See Nanfang Zhongjin Environment Co., Ltd.; *Int'l*, pg. 5139
PT SOUTH PACIFIC VISCOSE—See Lenzing Aktiengesellschaft; *Int'l*, pg. 4456
PT. SOUTH SULAWESI LNG—See Energy World Corporation Ltd; *Int'l*, pg. 2423
PT. SPIRAX SARCO INDONESIA—See Spirax-Sarco Engineering plc; *Int'l*, pg. 7137
PT SPIRE INDONESIA—See YAMADA Consulting Group Co., Ltd.; *Int'l*, pg. 8547
PTS PLAST-BOX S.A.; *Int'l*, pg. 6091
PTS PLUMBING TRADE SUPPLIES—See Travis Perkins plc; *Int'l*, pg. 7908
PT. SP MINING & ENGINEERING—See Tuan Sing Holdings Limited; *Int'l*, pg. 7962
PTS PROGRESSIVE ENGINEERING CO., LTD.—See Hanmi Semiconductor Co., Ltd.; *Int'l*, pg. 3256
P.T. SPRUSON FERGUSON INDONESIA—See IPH Limited; *Int'l*, pg. 3797

PT SUMBER TANI AGUNG RESOURCES TBK

PT SRC INDONESIA SEMBILAN—See Philip Morris International Inc.; *U.S. Public*, pg. 1685
PT SREEYA SEWU INDONESIA TBK; *Int'l*, pg. 6075
PT. SRI REJEKI ISMAN TBK; *Int'l*, pg. 6089
PT SRI TRANG LINGGA INDONESIA—See Sri Trang Agro-Industry Public Company Limited; *Int'l*, pg. 7150
PT SRIWAHANA ADITYAKARTA TBK; *Int'l*, pg. 6076
PTS S.A.—See Bridgestone Corporation; *Int'l*, pg. 1160
PTS STAFFING SOLUTIONS; *U.S. Private*, pg. 3298
PT. SSY KONSTRUKSI INDONESIA—See Investment Corporation of Dubai; *Int'l*, pg. 3785
PT. STACO ESTIKA SEDAYA FINANCE—See PT Astra International Tbk; *Int'l*, pg. 6023
PT STACOMITRA GRAHA—See PT Astra International Tbk; *Int'l*, pg. 6024
P.T. STAEDTLER INDONESIA—See STAEDTLER MARS GmbH & Co KG; *Int'l*, pg. 7162
PT STAMFORD TYRES DISTRIBUTOR INDONESIA—See Stamford Tyres Corporation Limited; *Int'l*, pg. 7165
PT STAMFORD TYRES INDONESIA—See Stamford Tyres Corporation Limited; *Int'l*, pg. 7165
P.T. STANDARD TOYO POLYMER—See Mitsui & Co., Ltd.; *Int'l*, pg. 4979
P.T. STANDARD TOYO POLYMER—See Tosoh Corporation; *Int'l*, pg. 7832
PT STARASIA DISTRIBUTIONS—See JAB Holding Company S.a.r.l.; *Int'l*, pg. 3861
P.T. STAR ENGINES INDONESIA—See Mercedes-Benz Group AG; *Int'l*, pg. 4828
PT. STARIS CHEMICALS—See BRENNTAG SE; *Int'l*, pg. 1149
PT. STARLINGER SEA—See Starlinger & Co. GmbH; *Int'l*, pg. 7178
PT. STARLINK SOLUSI—See PT Hensel Davest Indonesia Tbk; *Int'l*, pg. 6043
PT. STAR MEDIA NUSANTARA—See PT. MEDIA NUSANTARA CITRA Tbk; *Int'l*, pg. 6088
PT STAR PACIFIC TBK; *Int'l*, pg. 6076
PT. STAR RUBBER—See Sri Trang Agro-Industry Public Company Limited; *Int'l*, pg. 7150
PT. STARTS INTERNATIONAL INDONESIA—See Starts Corporation, Inc.; *Int'l*, pg. 7180
PT STEEL PIPE INDUSTRY OF INDONESIA TBK; *Int'l*, pg. 6076
PT STEP OILTOOLS—See Akastor ASA; *Int'l*, pg. 260
PTS-TEXAS TITLE, INC.—See Altisource Portfolio Solutions S.A.; *Int'l*, pg. 393
P.T. STIMEC ELCOM—See P.T. Subur Sakti Putera; *Int'l*, pg. 5683
PT STRATEGIC PARTNER SOLUTION—See PT. Lautan Luas Tbk; *Int'l*, pg. 6087
P.T. STS BALI—See Vaibhav Global Limited; *Int'l*, pg. 8108
PT STUDIO ONE—See PT. Bhuwanatala Indah Permai Tbk; *Int'l*, pg. 6085
PT. SUARA PUBLISINDO—See Universal Music Group N.V.; *Int'l*, pg. 8080
PT. SUASA BENUA SUKSES—See PT Sillo Maritime Perdana Tbk; *Int'l*, pg. 6072
PT SUBSEA OFFSHORE—See Pacific Radiance Ltd.; *Int'l*, pg. 5691
P.T. SUBUR SAKTI PUTERA; *Int'l*, pg. 5683
PT SUGIH ENERGY TBK; *Int'l*, pg. 6076
PT. SUKANDA DJAYA—See PT Diamond Food Indonesia Tbk; *Int'l*, pg. 6036
PT. SUKAPUTRA GRAHACEMERLANG—See PT Sentul City Tbk.; *Int'l*, pg. 6072
PT SUKSES MANIS INDONESIA—See Keppel Corporation Limited; *Int'l*, pg. 4131
PT SUKSES MANIS TANGGUH—See Keppel Corporation Limited; *Int'l*, pg. 4132
PT SULUH ARDHI ENGINEERING—See PT Astrindo Nusantara Infrastruktur Tbk; *Int'l*, pg. 6024
PT. SULZER INDONESIA—See Sulzer Ltd.; *Int'l*, pg. 7256
PT SULZER TURBO SERVICES INDONESIA—See Sulzer Ltd.; *Int'l*, pg. 7257
P.T. SUMA SARANA—See PT MNC Energy Investments Tbk; *Int'l*, pg. 6058
PT SUMBER ALFARIA TRIJAYA TBK; *Int'l*, pg. 6076
PT SUMBERDAYA SEWATAMA—See PT ABM Investama Tbk.; *Int'l*, pg. 6018
PT SUMBER ENERGI ANDALAN TBK; *Int'l*, pg. 6076
PT SUMBER GLOBAL ENERGY TBK; *Int'l*, pg. 6076
P.T. SUMBER GRAHA MALUKU—See Samko Timber Limited; *Int'l*, pg. 6506
PT SUMBER GRAHA SEJAHTERA—See Samko Timber Limited; *Int'l*, pg. 6506
PT SUMBER INDAHPERKASA—See Golden Agri-Resources Ltd.; *Int'l*, pg. 3028
PT SUMBER KASIH—See PT Mitra Keluarga Karyasehat Tbk; *Int'l*, pg. 6057
P.T. SUMBER KITA INDAH—See PT Madusari Murni Indah; *Int'l*, pg. 6054
PT SUMBER MAS KONSTRUKSI TBK; *Int'l*, pg. 6076
P.T. SUMBER SELERA INDONESIA—See PT Metropolitan Land Tbk; *Int'l*, pg. 6056
PT SUMBERTAMA NUSAPERTIWI—See PT Bakrie Sumatera Plantations Tbk; *Int'l*, pg. 6025
PT SUMBER TANI AGUNG RESOURCES TBK; *Int'l*, pg. 6076

PT. SUMCO INDONESIA—See SUMCO Corporation; *Int'l*, pg. 7260
PT. SUMIDEN HARDMETAL MANUFACTURING INDONESIA—See Sumitomo Electric Industries, Ltd.; *Int'l*, pg. 7279
P.T. SUMIDEN SERASI WIRE PRODUCTS—See Sumitomo Electric Industries, Ltd.; *Int'l*, pg. 7279
PT. SUMIDEN SINTERED COMPONENTS INDONESIA—See Sumitomo Electric Industries, Ltd.; *Int'l*, pg. 7279
P.T. SUMI INDO KABEL TBK—See Sumitomo Electric Industries, Ltd.; *Int'l*, pg. 7279
PT. SUMI INDO WIRING SYSTEMS—See Sumitomo Electric Industries, Ltd.; *Int'l*, pg. 7279
PT. SUMIKO LEADFRAME BINTAN—See Sumitomo Metal Mining Co., Ltd.; *Int'l*, pg. 7292
PT. SUMINOE SURYA TECHNO—See Suminoe Textile Co., Ltd.; *Int'l*, pg. 7262
PT. SUMI RUBBER INDONESIA—See Sumitomo Rubber Industries, Ltd.; *Int'l*, pg. 7299
PT SUMISHO GLOBAL LOGISTICS INDONESIA—See Sumitomo Corporation; *Int'l*, pg. 7269
PT. SUMISO LOGISTICS INDONESIA—See The Sumitomo Warehouse Co. Ltd.; *Int'l*, pg. 7690
PT. SUMITOMO ELECTRIC HARDMETAL INDONESIA—See Sumitomo Electric Industries, Ltd.; *Int'l*, pg. 7279
PT. SUMITOMO ELECTRIC WINTEC INDONESIA—See Sumitomo Electric Industries, Ltd.; *Int'l*, pg. 7279
PT. SUMITOMO FORESTRY INDONESIA—See Sumitomo Forestry Co., Ltd.; *Int'l*, pg. 7286
PT. SUMITOMO HEAVY INDUSTRIES INDONESIA—See Sumitomo Heavy Industries, Ltd.; *Int'l*, pg. 7287
PT. SUMITOMO INDONESIA—See Sumitomo Corporation; *Int'l*, pg. 7269
PT SUMITOMO S.H.I. CONSTRUCTION MACHINERY INDONESIA—See Sumitomo Heavy Industries, Ltd.; *Int'l*, pg. 7287
PT SUMITOMO S.H.I. CONSTRUCTION MACHINERY SOUTHEAST ASIA—See Sumitomo Heavy Industries, Ltd.; *Int'l*, pg. 7287
P.T. SUMITOMO WIRING SYSTEMS BATAM INDONESIA—See Sumitomo Electric Industries, Ltd.; *Int'l*, pg. 7284
PT. SUMITRONICS INDONESIA—See Sumitomo Corporation; *Int'l*, pg. 7269
PT SUMMARECON AGUNG TBK; *Int'l*, pg. 6076
PT SUNCALL INDONESIA—See Suncall Corporation; *Int'l*, pg. 7310
PT SUNCHIRIN INDUSTRIES INDONESIA—See Sunrise Industry Co., Ltd.; *Int'l*, pg. 7321
PT. SUNGIN TEX—See Sioen Industries NV; *Int'l*, pg. 6960
PT SUNINDO ADIPERSADA TBK; *Int'l*, pg. 6076
P.T. SUNINDO KOOKMIN BEST FINANCE—See KB Financial Group Inc.; *Int'l*, pg. 4104
PT SUNINDO PRATAMA TBK; *Int'l*, pg. 6076
PT SUN LIFE INDONESIA—See Sun Life Financial Inc.; *Int'l*, pg. 7305
PT SUNLINE MASTER INTERNATIONAL—See Shenzhen Sunline Tech Co., Ltd.; *Int'l*, pg. 6821
PT SUNNINGDALE TECH BATAM—See Sunningdale Tech Ltd; *Int'l*, pg. 7318
PT SUNRISE BUMI TEXTILES—See The Aditya Birla Group; *Int'l*, pg. 7612
PT SUNSON TEXTILE MANUFACTURER TBK; *Int'l*, pg. 6076
PT SUNSTAR ENGINEERING INDONESIA—See Sunstar Suisse S.A.; *Int'l*, pg. 7323
PT SUNTER LAKESIDE HOTEL TBK; *Int'l*, pg. 6076
PT. SUNWA TECHNOS INDONESIA—See Sun-Wa Technos Corporation; *Int'l*, pg. 7309
PT SUNWAY FLOWTECH—See Sunway Berhad; *Int'l*, pg. 7330
PT SUNWAY INDOQUIP—See Sunway Berhad; *Int'l*, pg. 7329
PT SUNWAY PACIFIC FLOW—See Sunway Berhad; *Int'l*, pg. 7328
PT SUNWAY TREK MASINDO—See Sunway Berhad; *Int'l*, pg. 7330
PT SUNWAY-YASA PMI PILE—See Sunway Berhad; *Int'l*, pg. 7329
PT SUPARMA TBK; *Int'l*, pg. 6076
PT SUPER ENERGY TBK; *Int'l*, pg. 6076
PT. SUPERHELINDO JAYA—See Hyundai Group; *Int'l*, pg. 3557
PT SUPERKRANE MITRA UTAMA TBK; *Int'l*, pg. 6076
P.T. SUPER STEEL KARAWANG—See Sumitomo Corporation; *Int'l*, pg. 7269
PT. SUPER UNGGAS JAYA—See CJ Corporation; *Int'l*, pg. 1634
PT. SUPER WAHANA TEHNO—See Nihon Trim Co., Ltd.; *Int'l*, pg. 5288
PT SUPRA BOGA LESTARI TBK; *Int'l*, pg. 6077
PT. SUPRA SUMBER CIPTA—See PT Japfa Comfeed Indonesia Tbk; *Int'l*, pg. 6049
PT SUPREME CABLE MANUFACTURING & COMMERCE—See The Furukawa Electric Co., Ltd.; *Int'l*, pg. 7646

PT SURI TANI PEMUKA—See PT Japfa Comfeed Indonesia Tbk; *Int'l*, pg. 6049
PT. SURPRISE INDONESIA—See PT Distribusi Voucher Nusantara Tbk; *Int'l*, pg. 6036
PT. SURYA AIR—See PT Gudang Garam Tbk; *Int'l*, pg. 6042
PT SURYA ARTHA NUSANTARA FINANCE—See PT Astra International Tbk; *Int'l*, pg. 6024
PT SURYA BIRU MURNI ACETYLENE TBK; *Int'l*, pg. 6077
P.T. SURYA CAKRA ANUGERAH NUSANTARA—See PT Astra International Tbk; *Int'l*, pg. 6023
PT. SURYACIPTA SWADAYA—See PT Surya Semesta Internusa Tbk; *Int'l*, pg. 6077
PT SURYA DUMAI INDUSTRI TBK; *Int'l*, pg. 6077
PT SURYA ENERGI PARAHITA—See PT Surya Semesta Internusa Tbk; *Int'l*, pg. 6077
PT SURYA FAJAR CAPITAL TBK; *Int'l*, pg. 6077
PT SURYA FAJAR EQUITY FUND—See PT Surya Fajar Capital Tbk; *Int'l*, pg. 6077
PT SURYA FAJAR SEKURITAS—See PT Surya Fajar Capital Tbk; *Int'l*, pg. 6077
PT SURYA GENTA PERKASA—See XOX Technology Bhd; *Int'l*, pg. 8537
PT SURYA GEO MINERALS—See Patel Engineering Ltd.; *Int'l*, pg. 5755
PT SURYA INTERNUSA HOTELS—See PT Surya Semesta Internusa Tbk; *Int'l*, pg. 6077
PT SURYAINTI PERMATA TBK; *Int'l*, pg. 6077
PT SURYA INTISARI RAYA—See First Resources Limited; *Int'l*, pg. 2687
PT SURYA INTRINDO MAKMUR TBK; *Int'l*, pg. 6077
PT. SURYALAYA ANINDITA INTERNATIONAL—See PT Surya Semesta Internusa Tbk; *Int'l*, pg. 6077
PT SURYAMAS DUTAMAKMUR TBK—See PT Sinar Mas Group; *Int'l*, pg. 6072
PT SURYANA ISTANA PASUNDAN—See Lippo Malls Indonesia Retail Trust; *Int'l*, pg. 4522
PT SURYA PAMENANG—See PT Gudang Garam Tbk; *Int'l*, pg. 6042
PT SURYA PANEN SUBUR—See Johor Corporation; *Int'l*, pg. 3994
PT SURYA PERMATA ANDALAN TBK; *Int'l*, pg. 6077
PT SURYA PERTIWI TBK; *Int'l*, pg. 6077
PT SURYARAYA PRAWIRA—See PT Astra International Tbk; *Int'l*, pg. 6024
P.T. SURYARAYA RUBBERINDO INDUSTRIES—See PT Astra International Tbk; *Int'l*, pg. 6023
PT SURYA RENGO CONTAINERS - KARAWANG FACTORY—See PT Indofood CBP Sukses Makmur Tbk.; *Int'l*, pg. 6045
PT SURYA RENGO CONTAINERS - SEMARANG FACTORY—See PT Indofood CBP Sukses Makmur Tbk.; *Int'l*, pg. 6045
P.T. SURYA RENGO CONTAINERS—See Rengo Co., Ltd.; *Int'l*, pg. 6280
PT SURYA RENGO CONTAINERS—See PT Indofood CBP Sukses Makmur Tbk.; *Int'l*, pg. 6045
PT SURYA RENGO CONTAINERS - SURABAYA FACTORY—See PT Indofood CBP Sukses Makmur Tbk.; *Int'l*, pg. 6045
PT SURYA SARANA DINAMIKA—See THK CO., LTD.; *Int'l*, pg. 7712
PT SURYASARANA HIDUP JAYA—See KS Energy Limited; *Int'l*, pg. 4310
PT SURYA SEMESTA INTERNUSA TBK; *Int'l*, pg. 6077
PT SURYA TEKNOLOGI BATAM—See AEM Holdings Ltd.; *Int'l*, pg. 175
P.T. SURYA TOTO INDONESIA—See Toto Ltd.; *Int'l*, pg. 7845
PT. SUZUKI FINANCE INDONESIA—See ITOCHU Corporation; *Int'l*, pg. 3841
PT SWADAYA GRAHA—See PT. Semen Indonesia (Persero) Tbk; *Int'l*, pg. 6089
PT SWADHARMA BHAKTI SEDAYA FINANCE—See PT Astra International Tbk; *Int'l*, pg. 6024
PT SWIBER BERJAYA—See Swiber Holdings Limited; *Int'l*, pg. 7366
PT SWIBER OFFSHORE—See Swiber Holdings Limited; *Int'l*, pg. 7366
PT SWISS NIAGA INTERNATIONAL—See The Aditya Birla Group; *Int'l*, pg. 7612
PT SYBASE 365 INDONESIA—See SAP SE; *Int'l*, pg. 6566
P.T. SYMRISE—See Symrise AG; *Int'l*, pg. 7380
PT. SYNERGY RISK MANAGEMENT CONSULTANTS—See PT Pertamina (Persero); *Int'l*, pg. 6064
PT. SYNERGY WORLDWIDE INDONESIA—See Nature's Sunshine Products, Inc.; *U.S. Public*, pg. 1499
PT. SYNNEX METRODATA INDONESIA—See Synnex Technology International Corporation; *Int'l*, pg. 7385
PT SYSARMY INDOCYBER SECURITY—See Systech Bhd; *Int'l*, pg. 7390
PT. SYS INDONESIA—See SYS Holdings Co., Ltd.; *Int'l*, pg. 7388
PT. SYS-MAC INDONESIA—See Zicom Group Limited; *Int'l*, pg. 8681

PT. SYSMEX INDONESIA—See Sysmex Corporation; *Int'l*, pg. 7388
PT. SYSTEM ENERGI NUSANTARA—See PT Bakrie & Brothers Tbk; *Int'l*, pg. 6025
PT. TACHIBANA SALES (INDONESIA)—See Tachibana Eletech Co., Ltd.; *Int'l*, pg. 7403
PT. TAI ELECTRONIC INDONESIA—See Ta-I Technology Co., Ltd.; *Int'l*, pg. 7400
PT. TAIHAN INDONESIA—See Taihan Textile Co., Ltd.; *Int'l*, pg. 7411
PT. TAIHO NUSANTARA—See Taiho Kogyo Co., Ltd; *Int'l*, pg. 7413
P.T. TAIKISHA INDONESIA ENGINEERING—See Taikisha Ltd.; *Int'l*, pg. 7413
P.T. TAIKISHA MANUFACTURING INDONESIA—See Taikisha Ltd.; *Int'l*, pg. 7413
PT. TAINAN ENTERPRISES INDONESIA—See Tainan Enterprises Co., Ltd.; *Int'l*, pg. 7415
PT. TAISEI PULAUINTAN CONSTRUCTION INTERNATIONAL—See Taisei Corporation; *Int'l*, pg. 7416
PT. TAISHO PHARMACEUTICAL INDONESIA TBK—See Taisho Pharmaceutical Holdings Co., Ltd.; *Int'l*, pg. 7417
PT.TAIYO KOGYO INDONESIA—See Taiyo Kogyo Corporation; *Int'l*, pg. 7425
P.T. TAIYO SINAR RAYA TEKNIK—See Sumitomo Densetsu Co., Ltd.; *Int'l*, pg. 7276
PT. TAJIMA GUNUNG MAS—See Tajima Industries Ltd.; *Int'l*, pg. 7428
PT. TAKAMAZ INDONESIA—See Takamatsu Machinery Co., Ltd.; *Int'l*, pg. 7430
P.T. TAKARI KOKOH SEJAHTERA—See Mitsubishi HC Capital Inc.; *Int'l*, pg. 4952
P.T. TAKASAGO INDONESIA—See Takasago International Corporation; *Int'l*, pg. 7433
PT. TAKASAGO INTERNATIONAL INDONESIA—See Takasago International Corporation; *Int'l*, pg. 7433
PT. TAKASAGO THERMAL ENGINEERING—See Takasago Thermal Engineering Co., Ltd.; *Int'l*, pg. 7434
P.T. TAKEDA INDONESIA—See Takeda Pharmaceutical Company Limited; *Int'l*, pg. 7439
P.T. TAKENAKA INDONESIA—See Takenaka Corporation; *Int'l*, pg. 7441
PT. TAKIRON INDONESIA—See ITOCHU Corporation; *Int'l*, pg. 3835
P.T. TALENTA BUMI—See PT Dana Brata Luhur Tbk; *Int'l*, pg. 6035
PT. TAMBANG BATUBARA HARUM—See PT Harum Energy Tbk.; *Int'l*, pg. 6043
PT. TAMBANG RAYA USAHA TAMA—See PT Indo Tambangraya Megah Tbk.; *Int'l*, pg. 6045
PT. TAMBANG TIMAH—See PT Timah Tbk.; *Int'l*, pg. 6078
PT. TAMCO INDONESIA—See Schneider Electric SE; *Int'l*, pg. 6635
P.T. TANABE INDONESIA—See Mitsubishi Chemical Group Corporation; *Int'l*, pg. 4935
PT TANAH LAUT TBK; *Int'l*, pg. 6077
P.T. TANGARA MITRAKOM—See PT. Elang Mahkota Teknologi Tbk.; *Int'l*, pg. 6086
PT. TANGGUH SAMUDERA JAYA—See PT Samudera Indonesia Tbk.; *Int'l*, pg. 6069
PT. TANGKUBAN PARAHU GEOTHERMAL POWER—See PT Indonesia Power; *Int'l*, pg. 6046
PT. TANINDO INTERTRACO—See PT BISI International Tbk; *Int'l*, pg. 6030
PT. TANJUNGENIM LESTARI PULP AND PAPER—See Marubeni Corporation; *Int'l*, pg. 4709
P.T. TANJUNG KREASI PARQUET INDUSTRY—See PT Dharma Satya Nusantara Tbk; *Int'l*, pg. 6036
PT. TAPIAN NADENGGAN—See Golden Agri-Resources Ltd.; *Int'l*, pg. 3028
PT. TARUNACIPTA KENCANA—See Golden Agri-Resources Ltd.; *Int'l*, pg. 3028
PTT ASAHI CHEMICAL CO., LTD.—See Asahi Kasei Corporation; *Int'l*, pg. 596
PT. TASLY INDONESIA—See Tasly Pharmaceutical Group Co., Ltd.; *Int'l*, pg. 7465
PT TATA CONSULTANCY SERVICES INDONESIA—See Tata Sons Limited; *Int'l*, pg. 7469
PT. TATA HAMPARAN EKA PERSAD—See Samchully Co., Ltd.; *Int'l*, pg. 6503
PT TATA MOTORS INDONESIA—See Tata Motors Limited; *Int'l*, pg. 7467
PT TATINDO HEAVYEQUIPMENT—See Affirma Capital Limited; *Int'l*, pg. 187
PT. TATSUMI INDONESIA—See MITSUBA Corporation; *Int'l*, pg. 4929
P.T. TAURINA TRAVEL JAYA—See Japan Airlines Co., Ltd.; *Int'l*, pg. 3884
PT TBS ENERGI UTAMA TBK; *Int'l*, pg. 6077
PTT (CAMBODIA) CO., LTD—See PTT Public Company Limited; *Int'l*, pg. 6092
PT. TCK TEXTILES INDONESIA—See Toray Industries, Inc.; *Int'l*, pg. 7824
PT TCP INTERNUSA—See PT Surya Semesta Internusa Tbk; *Int'l*, pg. 6077
PT TC SUBARU—See Tan Chong International Limited; *Int'l*, pg. 7453

COMPANY NAME INDEX

PT. TDATA INDONESIA—See Teradata Corporation; *U.S. Public*, pg. 2016
P.T. TD AUTOMOTIVE COMPRESSOR INDONESIA—See Toyota Industries Corporation; *Int'l*, pg. 7866
PT. TDK ELECTRONICS INDONESIA—See TDK Corporation; *Int'l*, pg. 7487
P.T. TEAC ELECTRONICS INDONESIA—See Evolution Capital Management LLC; *U.S. Private*, pg. 1443
PT. TEAMWORX INDONESIA; *Int'l*, pg. 6089
PT. TECH DATA ADVANCED SOLUTIONS INDONESIA—See TD Synnex Corp; *U.S. Public*, pg. 1986
PT. TECH DATA ADVANCED SOLUTIONS INDONESIA—See Avnet, Inc.; *U.S. Public*, pg. 253
PT TECH, LLC—See The Timken Company; *U.S. Public*, pg. 2133
PT TECHNETINDO UTAMA—See PT Anabatic Technologies Tbk; *Int'l*, pg. 6021
PT TECHNIC ENGINEERING SDN. BHD.—See APFT Berhad; *Int'l*, pg. 512
PT TECHNICS OFFSHORE JAYA—See Technics Oil & Gas Limited; *Int'l*, pg. 7506
PT TECHNIP INDONESIA—See TechnipFMC plc; *Int'l*, pg. 7508
PT TECHNOMEDIA MULTI SEJAHTERA—See PT Indosterling Technomedia Tbk; *Int'l*, pg. 6047
PT TECHNOPIA JAKARTA—See Fumakilla Limited; *Int'l*, pg. 2844
PT. TECHNO WOOD INDONESIA—See AICA Kogyo Company, Limited; *Int'l*, pg. 229
PT TECKWAH PAPER PRODUCTS INDONESIA—See Teckwah Industrial Corporation Ltd; *Int'l*, pg. 7515
PT TECKWAH TRADING INDONESIA—See Teckwah Industrial Corporation Ltd; *Int'l*, pg. 7515
P.T. TECO MULTIGUNA ELECTRO—See Teco Electric & Machinery Co., Ltd.; *Int'l*, pg. 7518
PT TECPROTEC—See Stone Point Capital LLC; *U.S. Private*, pg. 3821
PT TEKNOLOGI KARYA DIGITAL NUSA TBK; *Int'l*, pg. 6078
PT TELADAN PRIMA AGRO TBK; *Int'l*, pg. 6078
PT TELE ATLAS NAVINDO—See TomTom N.V.; *Int'l*, pg. 7804
PT TELEFAST INDONESIA TBK; *Int'l*, pg. 6078
PT TELEKOMUNIKASI INDONESIA INTERNATIONAL (HONG KONG) LTD—See Perusahaan Perseroan Indonesia Tbk; *Int'l*, pg. 5822
PT TELEKOMUNIKASI INDONESIA INTERNATIONAL PTE. LTD.—See Perusahaan Perseroan Indonesia Tbk; *Int'l*, pg. 5822
PT TELEKOMUNIKASI INDONESIA INTERNATIONAL—See Perusahaan Perseroan Indonesia Tbk; *Int'l*, pg. 5822
PT. TELEKOMUNIKASI SELULAR—See Perusahaan Perseroan Indonesia Tbk; *Int'l*, pg. 5822
P.T. TELEMARKETING INDONESIA—See Teleperformance SE; *Int'l*, pg. 7540
PT TELEMEDIA DINAMIKA SARANA—See PT Perusahaan Gas Negara (Persero) Tbk; *Int'l*, pg. 6064
PT TELEPORTASI BISNIS INDONESIA—See Capital A Bhd; *Int'l*, pg. 1309
PT TELKOM AKSES—See Perusahaan Perseroan Indonesia Tbk; *Int'l*, pg. 5822
PT TELKOM LANDMARK TOWER—See Perusahaan Perseroan Indonesia Tbk; *Int'l*, pg. 5822
PT TELKOM SATELIT INDONESIA—See Perusahaan Perseroan Indonesia Tbk; *Int'l*, pg. 5822
PT TEMAS BULKER—See PT Temas Tbk; *Int'l*, pg. 6078
PT TEMAS TBK; *Int'l*, pg. 6078
P.T. TEMBAGA MULIA SEMANAN—See The Furukawa Electric Co., Ltd.; *Int'l*, pg. 7646
P.T. TEMPRINT INTI NIAGA—See Tempo Inti Media Tbk; *Int'l*, pg. 7556
PTT ENERGY RESOURCES CO., LTD.—See PTT Public Company Limited; *Int'l*, pg. 6092
PT. TENMA CIKARANG INDONESIA—See Tenma Corporation; *Int'l*, pg. 7560
PT. TENMA INDONESIA—See Tenma Corporation; *Int'l*, pg. 7560
PTTEP AUSTRALIA PERTH PTY LIMITED—See PTT Public Company Limited; *Int'l*, pg. 6093
PTTEP INDONESIA COMPANY LIMITED—See PTT Public Company Limited; *Int'l*, pg. 6093
PT TERMINAL NILAM UTARA—See PT AKR Corporindo Tbk; *Int'l*, pg. 6020
PT. TERREGRA ASIA ENERGY TBK; *Int'l*, pg. 6089
P.T. TERUMO INDONESIA—See Terumo Corporation; *Int'l*, pg. 7569
PT TEXCHEM INDONESIA—See Texchem Resources Bhd.; *Int'l*, pg. 7583
PT TEXMACO PERKASA ENGINEERING TBK; *Int'l*, pg. 6078
PTT EXPLORATION & PRODUCTION PUBLIC CO., LTD.—See PTT Public Company Limited; *Int'l*, pg. 6092
P.T. TG INOAC INDONESIA—See Toyoda Gosei Co., Ltd.; *Int'l*, pg. 7861
PTT GLOBAL CHEMICAL PUBLIC COMPANY LIMITED; *Int'l*, pg. 6091

PT. THAI NDT INDONESIA—See Thai Nondestructive Testing Public Company Limited; *Int'l*, pg. 7593
PT. THAI UNION KHARISMA LESTARI—See Thai Union Group Public Company Limited; *Int'l*, pg. 7596
PT. THE NIELSEN COMPANY INDONESIA—See Brookfield Corporation; *Int'l*, pg. 1180
PT. THE NIELSEN COMPANY INDONESIA—See Elliott Management Corporation; *U.S. Private*, pg. 1372
PT. THERMAX INTERNATIONAL—See Thermax Limited; *Int'l*, pg. 7707
PT. THERMAX—See Chart Industries, Inc.; *U.S. Public*, pg. 482
PT. THYSSENKRUPP ELEVATOR INDONESIA—See ThyssenKrupp AG; *Int'l*, pg. 7725
PT. THYSSENKRUPP INDUSTRIAL SOLUTIONS INDONESIA—See ThyssenKrupp AG; *Int'l*, pg. 7725
PT. THYSSENKRUPP POLYSIUS INDONESIA—See ThyssenKrupp AG; *Int'l*, pg. 7725
P.T. TIGA MUTIARA NUSANTARA—See Jaycorp Berhad; *Int'l*, pg. 3915
PT TIGARAKSA SATRIA TBK; *Int'l*, pg. 6078
PT TIMAH INVESTASI MINERAL—See PT Timah Tbk.; *Int'l*, pg. 6078
PT TIMAH KARYA PERSADA PROPERTI—See PT Timah Tbk.; *Int'l*, pg. 6078
PT TIMAH TBK.; *Int'l*, pg. 6078
P.T. TI MATSUOKA WINNER INDUSTRY—See Toray Industries, Inc.; *Int'l*, pg. 7823
PTT INFRA SDN. BHD.—See PTT Synergy Group; *Int'l*, pg. 6093
PTT INTERNATIONAL COMPANY LIMITED—See PTT Public Company Limited; *Int'l*, pg. 6092
PTT INTERNATIONAL TRADING LONDON LIMITED—See PTT Public Company Limited; *Int'l*, pg. 6092
PTT INTERNATIONAL TRADING PTE. LTD.—See PTT Public Company Limited; *Int'l*, pg. 6092
PT TIPHONE MOBILE INDONESIA TBK; *Int'l*, pg. 6078
PT. TIRA AUSTENITE TBK - BANDUNG FILLING STATION & PLANT—See PT. Tira Austenite Tbk; *Int'l*, pg. 6089
PT. TIRA AUSTENITE TBK - BANYUWANGI FILLING STATION & PLANT—See PT. Tira Austenite Tbk; *Int'l*, pg. 6089
PT. TIRA AUSTENITE TBK - CIKARANG FILLING STATION & PLANT—See PT. Tira Austenite Tbk; *Int'l*, pg. 6089
PT. TIRA AUSTENITE TBK - GRESIK FILLING STATION & PLANT—See PT. Tira Austenite Tbk; *Int'l*, pg. 6089
PT. TIRA AUSTENITE TBK - MAKASSAR FILLING STATION & PLANT—See PT. Tira Austenite Tbk; *Int'l*, pg. 6089
PT. TIRA AUSTENITE TBK - SEMARANG FILLING STATION & PLANT—See PT. Tira Austenite Tbk; *Int'l*, pg. 6089
PT. TIRA AUSTENITE TBK; *Int'l*, pg. 6089
P.T. TIRA STAHLINDO INDONESIA—See PT. Tira Austenite Tbk; *Int'l*, pg. 6089
PT TIRTA MAHAKAM RESOURCES TBK; *Int'l*, pg. 6078
PT TIRTA SARI SURYA—See PT Kirana Megatara Tbk; *Int'l*, pg. 6051
PT. TIRTHA BRIDAL—See Tsukada Global Holdings Inc.; *Int'l*, pg. 7956
PT. TITAN WHEELS INDONESIA—See Titan International, Inc.; *U.S. Public*, pg. 2160
PT. TJAHJA SAKTI MOTOR—See PT Astra International Tbk; *Int'l*, pg. 6024
PT TJB POWER SERVICES—See PT Medco Energi Internasional Tbk; *Int'l*, pg. 6055
PTT LNG CO., LTD.—See PTT Public Company Limited; *Int'l*, pg. 6092
PTT MAINTENANCE AND ENGINEERING COMPANY LIMITED—See PTT Global Chemical Public Company Limited; *Int'l*, pg. 6091
PTT MEA LTD.—See PTT Public Company Limited; *Int'l*, pg. 6092
PTT NATURAL GAS DISTRIBUTION CO., LTD.—See ENGIE SA; *Int'l*, pg. 2433
PTT NATURAL GAS DISTRIBUTION CO., LTD.—See PTT Public Company Limited; *Int'l*, pg. 6092
P.T. TOA-GALVA INDUSTRIES—See TOA Corporation; *Int'l*, pg. 7768
P.T. TOA-GALVA PRIMA KARYA—See TOA Corporation; *Int'l*, pg. 7768
PT TOARCO JAYA—See Key Coffee Inc.; *Int'l*, pg. 4145
P.T. TODA GROUP INDONESIA—See Toda Corporation; *Int'l*, pg. 7772
PTT OIL & RETAIL BUSINESS PUBLIC COMPANY LIMITED; *Int'l*, pg. 6091
PT. TOKAI RIKA INDONESIA—See Tokai Rika Co., Ltd.; *Int'l*, pg. 7780
PT. TOKAI TEXPRINT INDONESIA (TTI)—See Daiwabo Holdings Co., Ltd.; *Int'l*, pg. 1950
P.T. TOKYO CENTURY INDONESIA—See Tokyo Century Corporation; *Int'l*, pg. 7789
P.T. TOKYO KEISO INDONESIA—See Tokyo Keiso Co., Ltd.; *Int'l*, pg. 7792
P.T. TOKYO SANGYO INDONESIA—See Tokyo Sangyo Co., Ltd.; *Int'l*, pg. 7795

PT. TOKYO ZAIRYO INDONESIA—See Zeon Corporation; *Int'l*, pg. 8635
PT. TOKYU CONSTRUCTION INDONESIA—See Tokyu Construction Co., Ltd.; *Int'l*, pg. 7797
PT. TOKYU LAND INDONESIA—See Tokyu Fudosan Holdings Corporation; *Int'l*, pg. 7798
PT TOLAN TIGA—See SIPEF NV; *Int'l*, pg. 6961
PT TOLL GLOBAL FORWARDING INDONESIA—See Japan Post Holdings Co., Ltd.; *Int'l*, pg. 3901
PT TOLL INDONESIA—See Japan Post Holdings Co., Ltd.; *Int'l*, pg. 3901
PT. TOMATEC INDONESIA—See Toyo Seikan Group Holdings, Ltd.; *Int'l*, pg. 7856
PT. TOMITA INDONESIA.—See TOMITA CO., LTD.; *Int'l*, pg. 7800
P.T. TOPPAN PRINTING INDONESIA—See TOPPAN Holdings Inc.; *Int'l*, pg. 7817
P.T. TOPPAN SAMPOERNA INDONESIA—See TOPPAN Holdings Inc.; *Int'l*, pg. 7817
P.T. TOPRE REFRIGERATOR INDONESIA—See Topre Corporation; *Int'l*, pg. 7820
P.T. TORAY INDUSTRIES INDONESIA—See Toray Industries, Inc.; *Int'l*, pg. 7823
P.T. TORAY INTERNATIONAL INDONESIA—See Toray Industries, Inc.; *Int'l*, pg. 7823
P.T. TORAY INTERNATIONAL MATSUOKA WINNER INDUSTRY—See MATSUOKA Corporation, Ltd.; *Int'l*, pg. 4730
P.T. TORAY POLYTECH JAKARTA—See Toray Industries, Inc.; *Int'l*, pg. 7823
PTTOR CHINA (SHANGHAI) CO., LTD.—See PTT Public Company Limited; *Int'l*, pg. 6093
PTTOR INTERNATIONAL HOLDINGS (SINGAPORE) PTE. LTD.—See PTT Public Company Limited; *Int'l*, pg. 6093
PTTOR SINGAPORE PTE. LTD.—See PTT Public Company Limited; *Int'l*, pg. 6093
PT TOSEI INDONESIA—See Tokyo Seimitsu Co., Ltd.; *Int'l*, pg. 7795
P.T. TOSHIBA DISPLAY DEVICES INDONESIA—See Japan Industrial Partners, Inc.; *Int'l*, pg. 3890
PT. TOSHIBA VISUAL MEDIA NETWORK INDONESIA—See Japan Industrial Partners, Inc.; *Int'l*, pg. 3890
PT. TOSHINDO ELEVATOR UTAMA—See Japan Industrial Partners, Inc.; *Int'l*, pg. 3894
P.T. TOSJAYA ABADI VENTURA—See Japan Industrial Partners, Inc.; *Int'l*, pg. 3890
PT TOTAL BANGUN PERSADA TBK; *Int'l*, pg. 6078
PT. TOTAL E&P INDONESIE—See TotalEnergies SE; *Int'l*, pg. 7840
PT TOTALINDO EKA PERSADA TBK; *Int'l*, pg. 6078
PT TOTAL OIL INDONESIA—See TotalEnergies SE; *Int'l*, pg. 7837
PT TOURINDO GUIDE INDONESIA TBK; *Int'l*, pg. 6078
PT TOWER BERSAMA INFRASTRUCTURE TBK; *Int'l*, pg. 6079
PT. TOWERS WATSON INDONESIA—See Willis Towers Watson Public Limited Company; *Int'l*, pg. 8415
PT TOWERS WATSON PURBAJAGA—See Willis Towers Watson Public Limited Company; *Int'l*, pg. 8415
P.T. TOWNSVILLE WELDING SUPPLIES—See Linde plc; *Int'l*, pg. 4508
PT. TOYOBO INDONESIA—See Toyobo Co., Ltd.; *Int'l*, pg. 7860
PT. TOYOBO MANUFACTURING INDONESIA—See Toyobo Co., Ltd.; *Int'l*, pg. 7860
PT. TOYOBO TRIAS ECOSYAR—See Toyobo Co., Ltd.; *Int'l*, pg. 7860
P.T. TOYOCOM INDONESIA—See Seiko Epson Corporation; *Int'l*, pg. 6687
P.T. TOYODA GOSEI SAFETY SYSTEMS INDONESIA—See Toyoda Gosei Co., Ltd.; *Int'l*, pg. 7861
P.T. TOYOFUJI LOGISTICS INDONESIA—See PT Astra International Tbk; *Int'l*, pg. 6023
P.T. TOYOFUJI SERASI INDONESIA—See PT Astra Internasional Tbk; *Int'l*, pg. 6023
P.T. TOYO INK INDONESIA—See Toyo Ink SC Holdings Co., Ltd.; *Int'l*, pg. 7853
P.T. TOYO INK TRADING INDONESIA—See Toyo Ink SC Holdings Co., Ltd.; *Int'l*, pg. 7853
P.T. TOYO KANETSU INDONESIA—See TOYO KANETSU K.K.; *Int'l*, pg. 7855
P.T. TOYO QUALITY ONE INDONESIA—See Nagase & Co., Ltd.; *Int'l*, pg. 5128
P.T. TOYOTA-ASTRA MOTOR—See Toyota Motor Corporation; *Int'l*, pg. 7872
P.T.TOYOTA AUTO BODY-TOKAI EXTRUSION—See Toyota Motor Corporation; *Int'l*, pg. 7872
P.T. TOYOTA BOSHOKU INDONESIA—See Toyota Boshoku Corporation; *Int'l*, pg. 7864
P.T. TOYOTA MOTOR MANUFACTURING INDONESIA—See Toyota Motor Corporation; *Int'l*, pg. 7872
P.T. TOYO TANSO INDONESIA—See Toyo Tanso Co., Ltd.; *Int'l*, pg. 7858
P.T. TOYOTA TSUSHO INDONESIA—See Toyota Tsusho Corporation; *Int'l*, pg. 7878

PT TOWER BERSAMA INFRASTRUCTURE TBK / CORPORATE AFFILIATIONS

P.T. TOYOTA TSUSHO LOGISTIC CENTER—See Toyota Tsusho Corporation; *Int'l*, pg. 7877
PT TOYS GAMES INDONESIA—See PT ACE Hardware Indonesia Tbk.; *Int'l*, pg. 6018
PT. TOZY SENTOSA—See Parkson Retail Asia Limited; *Int'l*, pg. 5744
PT TPC INDO PLASTIC & CHEMICALS—See The Siam Cement Public Company Limited; *Int'l*, pg. 7683
PTT PHENOL COMPANY LIMITED—See PTT Global Chemical Public Company Limited; *Int'l*, pg. 6091
PTT POLYETHYLENE CO., LTD.—See PTT Global Chemical Public Company Limited; *Int'l*, pg. 6091
PTT POLYMER LOGISTICS CO., LTD—See PTT Global Chemical Public Company Limited; *Int'l*, pg. 6091
PTT POLYMER LOGISTICS CO., LTD—See PTT Public Company Limited; *Int'l*, pg. 6092
PTT POLYMER MARKETING CO., LTD—See PTT Global Chemical Public Company Limited; *Int'l*, pg. 6091
PTT POLYMER MARKETING CO., LTD—See PTT Public Company Limited; *Int'l*, pg. 6093
PT. TPR ENPLA INDONESIA—See TPR Co., Ltd.; *Int'l*, pg. 7884
PT. TPR INDONESIA—See TPR Co., Ltd.; *Int'l*, pg. 7884
PTT PROPERTY SDN. BHD.—See PTT Synergy Group; *Int'l*, pg. 6093
PT TPR SALES INDONESIA—See TPR Co., Ltd.; *Int'l*, pg. 7884
PTT PUBLIC COMPANY LIMITED; *Int'l*, pg. 6091
PT. TRACKSPARE—See Hoe Leong Corporation Ltd.; *Int'l*, pg. 3439
PT TRADA ALAM MINERA TBK; *Int'l*, pg. 6079
PT. T.RAD INDONESIA—See T.RAD Co., Ltd.; *Int'l*, pg. 7397
PT TRANSCOAL PACIFIC TBK; *Int'l*, pg. 6079
PT. TRANSCOR INDONESIA—See Transcor Astra Group S.A.; *Int'l*, pg. 7897
PT. TRANSCOSMOS COMMERCE—See Transcosmos Inc.; *Int'l*, pg. 7898
PT. TRANSCOSMOS INDONESIA—See Transcosmos Inc.; *Int'l*, pg. 7898
PT TRANSKON JAYA TBK—See PT Samindo Resources Tbk; *Int'l*, pg. 6069
PT TRANS LOGISTIK PERKASA—See PT Trans Power Marine Tbk; *Int'l*, pg. 6079
PT. TRANS MARGA JATENG—See PT. Jasa Marga (Persero) Tbk; *Int'l*, pg. 6086
PT TRANSOCEAN INDONESIA—See Transocean Ltd.; *Int'l*, pg. 7903
PT TRANSPORTASI GAS INDONESIA—See PT Perusahaan Gas Negara (Persero) Tbk; *Int'l*, pg. 6064
PT TRANS POWER MARINE TBK; *Int'l*, pg. 6079
PT TRANS RETAIL INDONESIA—See PT CT Corpora; *Int'l*, pg. 6035
PT TRANSSHIP TEKNIK SOLUSI—See PT Mitrabahtera Segara Sejati Tbk; *Int'l*, pg. 6058
PT TRANSTEL ENGINEERING—See CSE Global Ltd.; *Int'l*, pg. 1864
PT. TRAYA TIRTA CISADANE—See Moya Holdings Asia Limited; *Int'l*, pg. 5060
PT. TRELLEBORG INDONESIA—See Trelleborg AB; *Int'l*, pg. 7911
PTT RETAIL MANAGEMENT COMPANY LIMITED—See PTT Public Company Limited; *Int'l*, pg. 6093
PT TRI ADI BERSAMA—See PT Adi Sarana Armada Tbk; *Int'l*, pg. 6019
PT TRIARYANI—See PT Golden Eagle Energy Tbk; *Int'l*, pg. 6041
P.T. TRIAS SENTOSA TBK. - CHINA PLANT—See P.T. Trias Sentosa, Tbk; *Int'l*, pg. 5683
P.T. TRIAS SENTOSA, TBK; *Int'l*, pg. 5683
P.T. TRIAS SENTOSA TBK. - WARU PLANT—See P.T. Trias Sentosa, Tbk; *Int'l*, pg. 5683
PT TRI BANYAN TIRTA TBK; *Int'l*, pg. 6079
P.T. TRI DHARMA WISESA—See Akebono Brake Industry Co., Ltd.; *Int'l*, pg. 262
PT TRIDOMAIN CHEMICALS—See PT Tridomain Performance Materials Tbk; *Int'l*, pg. 6079
PT TRIDOMAIN PERFORMANCE MATERIALS TBK; *Int'l*, pg. 6079
PT TRIJATI PRIMULA—See PT Chitose Internasional Tbk; *Int'l*, pg. 6034
PT. TRIKOMSEL OKE TBK; *Int'l*, pg. 6089
PT TRIMAS SARANA GARMENT INDUSTRY—See PT Trisula International Tbk; *Int'l*, pg. 6080
PT TRIMEGAH ASSET MANAGEMENT—See PT Trimegah Sekuritas Indonesia Tbk.; *Int'l*, pg. 6079
PT TRIMEGAH BANGUN PERSADA TBK; *Int'l*, pg. 6079
PT TRIMEGAH KARYA PRATAMA TBK; *Int'l*, pg. 6079
PT TRIMEGAH SEKURITAS INDONESIA TBK.; *Int'l*, pg. 6079
PT TRIMITRA PRAWARA GOLDLAND TBK; *Int'l*, pg. 6079
PT TRIMITRA PROPERTINDO TBK; *Int'l*, pg. 6079
PT TRIMITRA TEHNIK—See Chien Wei Precise Technology Co., Ltd.; *Int'l*, pg. 1477
PT.TRIM RUBBER CO., LTD.—See Fukoku Co., Ltd.; *Int'l*, pg. 2839
PT TRINITAN METALS & MINERALS TBK; *Int'l*, pg. 6079
PT TRIPAR MULTIVISION PLUS TBK.; *Int'l*, pg. 6079

PT TRIPATRA ENGINEERING INDONESIA—See PT Indika Energy Tbk; *Int'l*, pg. 6044
PT TRIPATRA ENGINEERS & CONSTRUCTORS INDONESIA—See PT Indika Energy Tbk; *Int'l*, pg. 6044
PT TRIPUTRA AGRO PERSADA TBK; *Int'l*, pg. 6080
PT TRI SAPTA JAYA—See PT Kalbe Farma Tbk.; *Int'l*, pg. 6050
PT TRISENSA MINERAL UTAMA—See PT TBS Energi Utama Tbk; *Int'l*, pg. 6078
PT TRISULA INTERNATIONAL TBK; *Int'l*, pg. 6080
PT TRITIRTA SARANADAMAI—See PT Trisula International Tbk; *Int'l*, pg. 6080
PT TRIUMPH MOTORCYCLES INDONESIA—See Triumph Motorcycles Limited; *Int'l*, pg. 7936
PT TRI-WALL INDONESIA—See Rengo Co., Ltd.; *Int'l*, pg. 6280
PT TRIWIRA INSANLESTARI TBK; *Int'l*, pg. 6080
PT TRIXINDO SELARAS—See PT Maha Properti Indonesia Tbk; *Int'l*, pg. 6054
PT. TROPOSFIR PANCAR SEJATI—See PT SMR UTAMA Tbk; *Int'l*, pg. 6075
PT TRUMPF INDONESIA—See TRUMPF SE + Co. KG; *Int'l*, pg. 7942
PT TRUSCO NAKAYAMA INDONESIA—See Trusco Nakayama Corporation; *Int'l*, pg. 7944
PT TRUST TECH ENGINEERING SERVICE INDONESIA LIMITED—See Open Up Group Inc; *Int'l*, pg. 5599
PT. TS TECH INDONESIA—See TS Tech Co Ltd; *Int'l*, pg. 7948
PT. TSUBACO INDONESIA—See Tsubakimoto Kogyo Co., Ltd.; *Int'l*, pg. 7955
PT. TSUBAKI INDONESIA MANUFACTURING—See Tsubakimoto Chain Co.; *Int'l*, pg. 7953
PT. TSUBAKI INDONESIA TRADING—See Tsubakimoto Chain Co.; *Int'l*, pg. 7953
PT. TSURUMI POMPA INDONESIA—See Tsurumi Manufacturing Co., Ltd.; *Int'l*, pg. 7958
P.T. TSUZUKI & ASAMA MANUFACTURING—See Sumitomo Corporation; *Int'l*, pg. 7268
PTT SYNERGY GROUP; *Int'l*, pg. 6093
PT. TT NETWORK INTEGRATION INDONESIA—See Toyota Tsusho Corporation; *Int'l*, pg. 7878
PT. TUGU PRATAMA INDONESIA—See PT Pertamina (Persero); *Int'l*, pg. 6064
PT TUGU PRATAMA INTERINDO—See PT Pertamina (Persero); *Int'l*, pg. 6064
PT TUGU REASURANSI INDONESIA—See PT Asuransi Tugu Pratama Indonesia Tbk; *Int'l*, pg. 6024
PT. TUNAP INDONESIA—See Wurth Verwaltungsgesellschaft mbH; *Int'l*, pg. 8506
PT TUNAS ALFIN TBK; *Int'l*, pg. 6080
PT TUNAS BARU LAMPUNG TBK; *Int'l*, pg. 6080
PT. TUNAS RIDEAN TBK—See Jardine Matheson Holdings Limited; *Int'l*, pg. 3908
PT TUPPERWARE INDONESIA SERVICES—See Tupperware Brands Corporation; *U.S. Public*, pg. 2204
P.T. TURNAROUND ASSET INDONESIA—See PT. Bank JTrust Indonesia Tbk.; *Int'l*, pg. 6026
PTT UTILITY COMPANY LIMITED—See PTT Global Chemical Public Company Limited; *Int'l*, pg. 6091
PT. TUV NORD INDONESIA—See TUV NORD AG; *Int'l*, pg. 7980
PT TUV RHEINLAND INDONESIA—See TuV Rheinland Berlin-Brandenburg Pfalz e.V.; *Int'l*, pg. 7982
PT. TVS MOTOR COMPANY—See Sundaram Clayton Ltd.; *Int'l*, pg. 7312
PT. TWC BINTAN—See Meitech Offshore Engineering Pte. Ltd.; *Int'l*, pg. 4804
PT. TWC INDONESIA—See Tiong Woon Corporation Holding Ltd.; *Int'l*, pg. 7755
PT. TYCO PRECISION ELECTRONICS—See TE Connectivity Ltd.; *Int'l*, pg. 7495
PT. TYSM INDONESIA—See Toyoshima & Co., Ltd.; *Int'l*, pg. 7863
PT UANGEL INDONESIA—See UANGEL Corporation; *Int'l*, pg. 8000
PT UBM PAMERAN NIAGA INDONESIA—See Informa plc; *Int'l*, pg. 3693
PT UBS SECURITIES INDONESIA—See UBS Group AG; *Int'l*, pg. 8009
PT. U FINANCE INDONESIA—See Mitsubishi UFJ Financial Group, Inc.; *Int'l*, pg. 4972
PTUJSKA KLET D.O.O.—See MHP SE; *Int'l*, pg. 4873
PT ULTICAR OTO GALERI—See PT Bintraco Dharma Tbk; *Int'l*, pg. 6030
PT ULTRA JAYA MILK INDUSTRY TBK; *Int'l*, pg. 6080
P.T. ULTRA MANDIRI TELEKOMUNIKASI—See PT PP (Persero) Tbk; *Int'l*, pg. 6066
PT UNGASAN SEMESTA RESORT—See PT Surya Semesta Internusa Tbk; *Int'l*, pg. 6077
PT UNGGUL INDAH CAHAYA TBK; *Int'l*, pg. 6080
PT UNI-CHARM INDONESIA—See Unicharm Corporation; *Int'l*, pg. 8032
P.T. UNILEVER INDONESIA TBK—See Unilever PLC; *Int'l*, pg. 8046
PT. UNIPRES INDONESIA—See Unipres Corporation; *Int'l*, pg. 8056

PT. UNIQUE LOGISTICS INTERNATIONAL INDONESIA—See Unique Logistics International Inc.; *U.S. Public*, pg. 2227
PT. UNIQUE SOLUTIONS INDONESIA—See Maruka Furusato Corporation; *Int'l*, pg. 4714
PT UNITED AIR PRODUCTS INDONESIA—See Air Products & Chemicals, Inc.; *U.S. Public*, pg. 67
PT UNITED CHEMICALS INTER ANEKA—See Omya (Schweiz) AG; *Int'l*, pg. 5572
PT UNITED TOWERINDO—See PT Tower Bersama Infrastructure Tbk; *Int'l*, pg. 6079
PT UNITED TRACTORS PANDU ENGINEERING—See PT United Tractors Tbk; *Int'l*, pg. 6081
PT UNITED TRACTORS SEMEN GRESIK—See PT. Semen Indonesia (Persero) Tbk; *Int'l*, pg. 6089
PT UNITED TRACTORS TBK; *Int'l*, pg. 6080
PT. UNITEX TBK—See Unitika Ltd.; *Int'l*, pg. 8074
PT. UNITIKA TRADING INDONESIA—See Unitika Ltd.; *Int'l*, pg. 8074
PT. UNIVANCE INDONESIA—See Univance Corporation; *Int'l*, pg. 8076
PT. UNIVERSAL HEALTH NETWORK—See SOHO Group; *Int'l*, pg. 7059
PT UNIVERSAL TEKNO REKSAJAYA—See PT United Tractors Tbk; *Int'l*, pg. 6081
PT. UNZA VITALIS—See Wipro Limited; *Int'l*, pg. 8432
P.T. UOB ASSET MANAGEMENT INDONESIA—See United Overseas Bank Limited; *Int'l*, pg. 8071
PT UOB KAY HIAN SECURITIES—See UOB-Kay Hian Holdings Limited; *Int'l*, pg. 8085
PT. UPM RAFLATAC INDONESIA—See UPM-Kymmene Corporation; *Int'l*, pg. 8091
PT URBAN JAKARTA PROPERTINDO TBK; *Int'l*, pg. 6081
PT UROGEN ADVANCED SOLUTIONS—See PT Erajaya Swasembada Tbk; *Int'l*, pg. 6038
PT USAHA ERA PRATAMA NUSANTARA—See PT AKR Corporindo Tbk; *Int'l*, pg. 6020
PT USAHA GEDUNG BANK DAGANG NEGARA—See PT Bank Mandiri (Persero) Tbk.; *Int'l*, pg. 6027
PT. USHA MARTIN INDONESIA—See Usha Martin Limited; *Int'l*, pg. 8097
PT. UTAC MANUFACTURING SERVICES INDONESIA—See UTAC Holdings Ltd.; *Int'l*, pg. 8100
P.T. UTAMA PRATAMA MEDIKA—See PT. Elang Mahkota Teknologi Tbk.; *Int'l*, pg. 6086
P.T. UWAY ENERGI PERDANA—See PT United Tractors Tbk; *Int'l*, pg. 6080
PT. UYEMURA INDONESIA—See C.Uyemura & Co., Ltd.; *Int'l*, pg. 1244
PT VADS INDONESIA—See Telekom Malaysia Berhad; *Int'l*, pg. 7537
P.T. VAKSINDO SATWA NUSANTARA—See PT Japfa Comfeed Indonesia Tbk; *Int'l*, pg. 6049
PT VALE EKSPLORASI INDONESIA—See Vale S.A.; *Int'l*, pg. 8111
PT VALMET AUTOMATION INDONESIA—See Valmet Oyj; *Int'l*, pg. 8119
PT. VALMET—See Valmet Oyj; *Int'l*, pg. 8120
P.T. VAN REES INDONESIA—See ACOMO N.V.; *Int'l*, pg. 108
PT. V-APPAREL SEMARANG—See Ford Glory International Limited; *Int'l*, pg. 2731
PT VARIA USAHA BAHARI—See PT. Semen Indonesia (Persero) Tbk; *Int'l*, pg. 6089
PT VARIA USAHA BETON—See PT. Semen Indonesia (Persero) Tbk; *Int'l*, pg. 6089
PT VARIA USAHA DHARMA SEGARA—See PT. Semen Indonesia (Persero) Tbk; *Int'l*, pg. 6089
PT VARIA USAHA LINTAS SEGARA—See PT. Semen Indonesia (Persero) Tbk; *Int'l*, pg. 6089
PT VASTLAND INDONESIA TBK; *Int'l*, pg. 6081
PTV AUSTRIA PLANUNG TRANSPORT VERKEHR GMBH—See Porsche Automobil Holding SE; *Int'l*, pg. 5926
PT. V-CUBE INDONESIA—See PT. Altavindo Indonesia; *Int'l*, pg. 6084
PTV DISTRIBUTION PLANNING SOFTWARE LTD.—See Porsche Automobil Holding SE; *Int'l*, pg. 5926
PT VEOLIA WATER TECHNOLOGIES INDONESIA—See Veolia Environnement S.A.; *Int'l*, pg. 8161
P.T. VICTORIA ALIFE INDONESIA—See PT Victoria Investama Tbk; *Int'l*, pg. 6081
PT VICTORIA CARE INDONESIA TBK; *Int'l*, pg. 6081
PT VICTORIA INSURANCE TBK—See PT Victoria Investama Tbk; *Int'l*, pg. 6081
PT VICTORIA INVESTAMA TBK; *Int'l*, pg. 6081
P.T. VICTORIA MANAJEMEN INVESTASI—See PT Victoria Investama Tbk; *Int'l*, pg. 6081
P.T. VICTORIA SEKURITAS INDONESIA—See PT Victoria Investama Tbk; *Int'l*, pg. 6081
PT VICTOR TEKNOLOGI INDONESIA—See Enovis Corporation; *U.S. Public*, pg. 771
PT VIKING OFFSHORE—See 9R Limited; *Int'l*, pg. 17
PT VIKING SEATECH INDONESIA—See Enerpac Tool Group Corp.; *U.S. Public*, pg. 766
P.T. VINOTINDO GRAHASARANA—See PT Gema Grahasarana Tbk; *Int'l*, pg. 6040

COMPANY NAME INDEX

P.T. VIRTUS TECHNOLOGY INDONESIA—See PT Anabatic Technologies Tbk; *Int'l*, pg. 6021
PT VISI MEDIA ASIA TBK; *Int'l*, pg. 6081
PT VISIONET DATA INTERNASIONAL—See PT Multipolar Tbk; *Int'l*, pg. 6060
PT VISI TELEKOMUNIKASI INFRASTRUKTUR TBK—See PT Tower Bersama Infrastructure Tbk; *Int'l*, pg. 6079
PT VISI TELEKOMUNIKASI INFRASTRUKTUR TBK; *Int'l*, pg. 6081
P.T. VIVERE MULTI KREASI—See PT Gema Grahasarana Tbk; *Int'l*, pg. 6040
P.T. VKTR TEKNOLOGI MOBILITAS TBK—See PT Bakrie & Brothers Tbk; *Int'l*, pg. 6025
PT VMC FISHING TACKLE INDONESIA—See Rapala VMC Oyj; *Int'l*, pg. 6209
PT VOITH TURBO—See Voith GmbH & Co. KGaA; *Int'l*, pg. 8299
PT. VOKSEL ELECTRIC TBK; *Int'l*, pg. 6090
PT VOLEX INDONESIA—See Volex plc; *Int'l*, pg. 8301
PT VOLKOPI INDONESIA—See ED&F Man Holdings Limited; *Int'l*, pg. 2303
P.T. VOLTA INDONESIA SEMESTA—See PT M Cash Integrasi Tbk; *Int'l*, pg. 6054
PT VOPAK TERMINAL MERAK—See Koninklijke Vopak N.V.; *Int'l*, pg. 4272
P.T. V.S. TECHNOLOGY INDONESIA—See V.S. Industry Berhad; *Int'l*, pg. 8106
PTV TRANSPORT CONSULT GMBH—See Porsche Automobil Holding SE; *Int'l*, pg. 5926
P.T. WAAGNER-BIRO, INDONESIA—See Waagner-Biro AG; *Int'l*, pg. 8323
P.T. WACKER CHEMICALS INDONESIA—See Wacker Chemie AG; *Int'l*, pg. 8323
PT WAHANA ALAM LESTARI—See PT DIAN SWASTATIKA SENTOSA Tbk; *Int'l*, pg. 6036
PT WAHANA INDO TRADA—See Gallant Venture Ltd.; *Int'l*, pg. 2874
PT WAHANA INTERFOOD NUSANTARA TBK; *Int'l*, pg. 6081
PT WAHANA INTI MAKMUR TBK; *Int'l*, pg. 6081
PT. WAHANA OTTOMITRA MULTIARTHA TBK.; *Int'l*, pg. 6090
PT WAHANA SUN MOTOR SEMARANG—See PT Indomobil Sukses Internasional Tbk; *Int'l*, pg. 6046
P.T. WAH HONG INDONESIA—See Wan Hong Industrial Corp.; *Int'l*, pg. 8328
P.T. WAHLEE INDONESIA—See Wah Lee Industrial Corp.; *Int'l*, pg. 8329
P.T. WAH TECH INDONESIA—See Wah Lee Industrial Corp.; *Int'l*, pg. 8329
PT WALSIN LIPPO INDUSTRIES—See Walsin Lihwa Corporation; *Int'l*, pg. 8335
PT. WAMGROUP INDONESIA TRADING—See WAMGROUP S.p.A.; *Int'l*, pg. 8338
PT. WAMGROUP TR. INDONESIA—See WAMGROUP S.p.A.; *Int'l*, pg. 8338
PT WANA BAKTI SUKSES MINERAL—See PT Saratoga Investama Sedaya Tbk; *Int'l*, pg. 6070
PT. WARTSILA INDONESIA - JAWA BARAT POWER PLANT—See Wartsila Corporation; *Int'l*, pg. 8347
P.T. WARTSILA INDONESIA—See Wartsila Corporation; *Int'l*, pg. 8347
P.T. WASESA LINE—See PT Mitra Investindo Tbk; *Int'l*, pg. 6057
PTW-ASIA PACIFIC LTD.—See PTW Freiburg GmbH; *Int'l*, pg. 6093
PT WASKITA BETON PRECAST TBK—See PT Waskita Karya (Persero) Tbk; *Int'l*, pg. 6082
PT WASKITA KARYA (PERSERO) TBK - PASURUAN PLANT—See PT Waskita Karya (Persero) Tbk; *Int'l*, pg. 6082
PT WASKITA KARYA (PERSERO) TBK - PUSRI PLANT—See PT Waskita Karya (Persero) Tbk; *Int'l*, pg. 6082
PT WASKITA KARYA (PERSERO) TBK; *Int'l*, pg. 6082
PT WASKITA TOLL ROAD—See PT Waskita Karya (Persero) Tbk; *Int'l*, pg. 6082
PT. WATABE BALI—See Kowa Co., Ltd.; *Int'l*, pg. 4294
PT WATERCO INDONESIA—See Waterco Limited; *Int'l*, pg. 8356
PTW-BEIJING LTD—See PTW Freiburg GmbH; *Int'l*, pg. 6093
PTW DOSIMETRIA IBERIA S. L. U.—See PTW Freiburg GmbH; *Int'l*, pg. 6093
PTW DOSIMETRY INDIA PVT. LTD.—See PTW Freiburg GmbH; *Int'l*, pg. 6093
PT. WEATHERFORD INDONESIA—See Weatherford International plc; *U.S. Public*, pg. 2339
PT WEDA BAY NICKEL—See Eramet SA; *Int'l*, pg. 2489
PT WEHA TRANSPORTASI INDONESIA TBK; *Int'l*, pg. 6082
PT WELL HARVEST WINNING ALUMINA REFINERY—See China Hongqiao Group Limited; *Int'l*, pg. 1508
PTW ENERGY SERVICES LTD.; *Int'l*, pg. 6093
PT WESTCON INTERNATIONAL INDONESIA—See Datatec Limited; *Int'l*, pg. 1981
PT WESTFALIA INDONESIA—See GEA Group Aktiengesellschaft; *Int'l*, pg. 2903

PTW-FRANCE SARL—See PTW Freiburg GmbH; *Int'l*, pg. 6093
PTW FREIBURG GMBH; *Int'l*, pg. 6093
P.T. WH CERAMIC INDONESIA—See White Horse Berhad; *Int'l*, pg. 8399
PT WHITE OIL NUSANTARA—See PT. Lautan Luas Tbk; *Int'l*, pg. 6087
PT WIDAR MANDRIPA NUSANTARA—See PT Perusahaan Gas Negara (Persero) Tbk.; *Int'l*, pg. 6064
P.T. WIDATRA BHAKTI—See Otsuka Holdings Co., Ltd.; *Int'l*, pg. 5661
PT WIDIANT JAYA KRENINDO TBK; *Int'l*, pg. 6082
PT WIDJAJATUNGGAL SEJAHTERA; *Int'l*, pg. 6082
PT WIDODO MAKMUR PERKASA TBK; *Int'l*, pg. 6082
PT WIDODO MAKMUR UNGGAS TBK; *Int'l*, pg. 6082
P.T. WIDYA BHAKTI—See PT Pollux Hotels Group Tbk; *Int'l*, pg. 6066
PT WIJAYA CAHAYA TIMBER TBK; *Int'l*, pg. 6082
PT WIJAYA KARYA BANGUNAN GEDUNG TBK; *Int'l*, pg. 6083
PT WIJAYA KARYA BETON TBK.—See PT Wijaya Karya (Persero) Tbk.; *Int'l*, pg. 6082
PT WIJAYA KARYA BITUMEN—See PT Wijaya Karya (Persero) Tbk.; *Int'l*, pg. 6082
PT WIJAYA KARYA GEDUNG PRACETAK—See PT Wijaya Karya (Persero) Tbk.; *Int'l*, pg. 6082
PT WIJAYA KARYA INDUSTRI DAN KONSTRUKSI—See PT Wijaya Karya (Persero) Tbk.; *Int'l*, pg. 6082
PT WIJAYA KARYA INDUSTRI ENERGI—See PT Wijaya Karya (Persero) Tbk.; *Int'l*, pg. 6082
PT. WIJAYA KARYA KOMPONEN BETON—See PT Wijaya Karya (Persero) Tbk.; *Int'l*, pg. 6082
PT. WIJAYA KARYA KRAKATAU BETON—See PT Wijaya Karya (Persero) Tbk.; *Int'l*, pg. 6082
PT WIJAYA KARYA (PERSERO) TBK.; *Int'l*, pg. 6082
PT WIJAYA KARYA REALTY TBK—See PT Wijaya Karya (Persero) Tbk.; *Int'l*, pg. 6082
PT WIJAYA KARYA REKAYASA KONSTRUKSI—See PT Wijaya Karya (Persero) Tbk.; *Int'l*, pg. 6082
PT WIJAYA KARYA SERANG PANIMBANG—See PT Wijaya Karya (Persero) Tbk.; *Int'l*, pg. 6083
PT WIKA INDUSTRI MANUFAKTUR—See PT Wijaya Karya (Persero) Tbk.; *Int'l*, pg. 6083
PT WILLIS INDONESIA—See Willis Towers Watson Public Limited Company; *Int'l*, pg. 8416
PT WILLOWGLEN INDONESIA—See Willowglen MSC Berhad; *Int'l*, pg. 8420
PT WILMAR CAHAYA INDONESIA TBK; *Int'l*, pg. 6083
PT WILTON MAKMUR INDONESIA TBK; *Int'l*, pg. 6083
P.T. WIN MARITIM—See PT Wintermar Offshore Marine Tbk; *Int'l*, pg. 6083
P.T. WIN OFFSHORE—See PT Wintermar Offshore Marine Tbk; *Int'l*, pg. 6083
P.T. WINPAN OFFSHORE—See PT Wintermar Offshore Marine Tbk; *Int'l*, pg. 6083
P.T. WINTERMAR ASIA—See PT Wintermar Offshore Marine Tbk; *Int'l*, pg. 6083
P.T. WINTERMAR GEO OFFSHORE—See PT Wintermar Offshore Marine Tbk; *Int'l*, pg. 6083
PT WINTERMAR OFFSHORE MARINE TBK; *Int'l*, pg. 6083
P.T. WINTERMAR—See PT Wintermar Offshore Marine Tbk; *Int'l*, pg. 6083
PTW INTERNATIONAL UK LIMITED—See Pole To Win Holdings, Inc.; *Int'l*, pg. 5908
PT WIRA GLOBAL SOLUSI TBK; *Int'l*, pg. 6083
PT WIRANUSA GRAHATAMA—See PT Unggul Indah Cahaya Tbk; *Int'l*, pg. 6080
PT WIR ASIA TBK; *Int'l*, pg. 6083
PT WIRATAPURA INDO PARAHYANGAN—See PT Indointernet Tbk; *Int'l*, pg. 6045
PT WIRECARD TECHNOLOGIES INDONESIA—See Wirecard AG; *Int'l*, pg. 8434
PT. WISMILAK INTI MAKMUR TBK.; *Int'l*, pg. 6090
P.T. WM OFFSHORE—See PT Wintermar Offshore Marine Tbk; *Int'l*, pg. 6083
PTW-NEW YORK CORPORATION—See PTW Freiburg GmbH; *Int'l*, pg. 6093
P.T. WOODONE INTEGRA INDONESIA—See WOOD ONE Co., Ltd.; *Int'l*, pg. 8449
PT WOORI FINANCE INDONESIA TBK—See Woori Financial Group Inc.; *Int'l*, pg. 8453
PTW (SINGAPORE) PTE. LTD—See Pole To Win Holdings, Inc.; *Int'l*, pg. 5908
PT. WT INDONESIA—See Wipro Limited; *Int'l*, pg. 8432
PTW-UK LTD.—See PTW Freiburg GmbH; *Int'l*, pg. 6093
PT WUSHAN HIJAU LESTARI—See PT PP London Sumatra Indonesia Tbk; *Int'l*, pg. 6066
PT XAPIENS TEKNOLOGI INDONESIA—See PT Indika Energy Tbk; *Int'l*, pg. 6044
PT XDCI INDONESIA—See PT Anabatic Technologies Tbk; *Int'l*, pg. 6021
PT. XDC INDONESIA—See PT Anabatic Technologies Tbk; *Int'l*, pg. 6021
PT XL AXIATA TBK—See Axiata Group Berhad; *Int'l*, pg. 768
PTX METALS INC.; *Int'l*, pg. 6093
PTX-PENTRONIX, INC.—See Gasbarre Products Inc.; *U.S. Private*, pg. 1648

PT ZEBRA NUSANTARA TBK.

PT XSIS MITRA UTAMA—See PT Anabatic Technologies Tbk; *Int'l*, pg. 6021
PT. YACHIYO TRIMITRA INDONESIA—See Honda Motor Co., Ltd.; *Int'l*, pg. 3464
P.T. YAKULT INDONESIA PERSAD—See Yakult Honsha Co., Ltd.; *Int'l*, pg. 8546
PT YAMAHA INDONESIA MOTOR MANUFACTURING—See Mitsui & Co., Ltd.; *Int'l*, pg. 4979
P.T. YAMAHA INDONESIA—See Yamaha Corporation; *Int'l*, pg. 8549
P.T. YAMAHA MUSICAL PRODUCTS INDONESIA—See Yamaha Corporation; *Int'l*, pg. 8549
P.T. YAMAHA MUSIC INDONESIA (DISTRIBUTOR)—See Yamaha Corporation; *Int'l*, pg. 8549
P.T. YAMAHA MUSIC MANUFACTURING ASIA—See Yamaha Corporation; *Int'l*, pg. 8549
P.T. YAMAHA MUSIC MANUFACTURING INDONESIA—See Yamaha Corporation; *Int'l*, pg. 8549
PT YAMAHA MUSIK INDONESIA DISTRIBUTOR—See Yamaha Corporation; *Int'l*, pg. 8549
PT YAMATO INDONESIA FORWARDING—See Yamato Holdings Co., Ltd.; *Int'l*, pg. 8554
PT YAMATO INDONESIA—See Yamato Holdings Co., Ltd.; *Int'l*, pg. 8554
PT YAMAZAKI INDONESIA—See Yamazaki Baking Co., Ltd.; *Int'l*, pg. 8556
P.T. YAMAZEN INDONESIA—See Yamazen Corporation; *Int'l*, pg. 8558
PT YANAPRIMA HASTAPERSADA TBK; *Int'l*, pg. 6083
P.T. YAN JIN INDONESIA—See UACJ Corporation; *Int'l*, pg. 7999
P.T. YANMAR AGRICULTURAL MACHINERY MANUFACTURING INDONESIA—See Yanmar Co., Ltd.; *Int'l*, pg. 8563
P.T. YANMAR DIESEL INDONESIA—See Yanmar Co., Ltd.; *Int'l*, pg. 8563
PT. YANMAR INDONESIA—See Yanmar Co., Ltd.; *Int'l*, pg. 8563
PT YARA INDONESIA—See Yara International ASA; *Int'l*, pg. 8566
PT. YASKAWA ELECTRIC INDONESIA—See Yaskawa Electric Corporation; *Int'l*, pg. 8569
P.T. YASULOR INDONESIA—See L'Oreal S.A.; *Int'l*, pg. 4381
PT YELOOO INTEGRA DATANET TBK; *Int'l*, pg. 6083
PT. YES LOGISTICS INDONESIA—See Yang Ming Marine Transport Corporation; *Int'l*, pg. 8560
PT YHI INDONESIA—See YHI International Limited; *Int'l*, pg. 8580
PT YKK AP INDONESIA—See YKK Corporation; *Int'l*, pg. 8588
PT. YKK ZIPCO INDONESIA - FACTORY I—See YKK Corporation; *Int'l*, pg. 8588
P.T. YKK ZIPPER INDONESIA - FACTORY II—See YKK Corporation; *Int'l*, pg. 8588
P.T. YKK ZIPPER INDONESIA - FACTORY I—See YKK Corporation; *Int'l*, pg. 8588
P.T. YKK ZIPPER INDONESIA—See YKK Corporation; *Int'l*, pg. 8588
P.T. YKT GEAR INDONESIA—See Yanmar Co., Ltd.; *Int'l*, pg. 8563
PT. YOKOGAWA INDONESIA—See Yokogawa Electric Corporation; *Int'l*, pg. 8592
PT YOKOGAWA MANUFACTURING BATAM—See Yokogawa Electric Corporation; *Int'l*, pg. 8592
PT YOKOHAMA INDUSTRIAL PRODUCTS MANUFACTURING INDONESIA—See The Yokohama Rubber Co., Ltd.; *Int'l*, pg. 7702
PT YONTOMO SUKSES ABADI—See Nicolas Correa S.A.; *Int'l*, pg. 5273
PT. YOROZU AUTOMOTIVE INDONESIA—See Yorozu Corporation; *Int'l*, pg. 8599
PT YUANTA ASSET MANAGEMENT—See Yuanta Financial Holding Co., Ltd.; *Int'l*, pg. 8608
PT YUANTA SECURITIES INDONESIA CO., LTD.—See Yuanta Financial Holding Co., Ltd.; *Int'l*, pg. 8608
P.T. YUANTA SEKURITAS INDONESIA—See Yuanta Financial Holding Co., Ltd.; *Int'l*, pg. 8608
P.T. YUASA BATTERY INDONESIA—See GS Yuasa Corporation; *Int'l*, pg. 3143
PT. YUASA SHOJI INDONESIA—See Yuasa Trading Co., Ltd.; *Int'l*, pg. 8609
PT YULIE SEKURITAS INDONESIA TBK; *Int'l*, pg. 6083
PT YUNG SHIN PHARMACEUTICAL INDONESIA—See Y.S.P. Southeast Asia Holding Berhad; *Int'l*, pg. 8543
PT YUSEN LOGISTICS SOLUTIONS INDONESIA—See Nippon Yusen Kabushiki Kaisha; *Int'l*, pg. 5359
P.T. ZAGRO INDONESIA—See Zagro Asia Ltd; *Int'l*, pg. 8620
P.T. ZAMBON INDONESIA—See Zambon Company S.p.A.; *Int'l*, pg. 8622
PT ZEBRA NUSANTARA TBK.; *Int'l*, pg. 6083
PT. ZFAG AFTERMARKET JAKARTA—See ZF Friedrichshafen AG; *Int'l*, pg. 8641
PT. ZIMBA ONIX MUSTIKA—See PT Sinar Mas Multiartha Tbk; *Int'l*, pg. 6074
PTZ INSURANCE AGENCY, LTD.—See Fairfax Financial Holdings Limited; *Int'l*, pg. 2608

PT ZEBRA NUSANTARA TBK. CORPORATE AFFILIATIONS

PT ZI-TECHASIA—See The Zuellig Group Inc.; *Int'l*, pg. 7705
PT. ZKTECO BIOMETRICS INDONESIA—See Zkteco Co., Ltd.; *Int'l*, pg. 8687
PT ZOETIS ANIMALHEALTH INDONESIA—See Zoetis, Inc.; *U.S. Public*, pg. 2409
PT ZTT CABLE INDONESIA—See Jiangsu Zhongtian Technology Co., Ltd.; *Int'l*, pg. 3958
P.T. ZURICH ASURANSI INDONESIA TBK—See Zurich Insurance Group Limited; *Int'l*, pg. 8697
P.T. ZURICH INSURANCE INDONESIA—See Zurich Insurance Group Limited; *Int'l*, pg. 8697
PT ZYREXINDO MANDIRI BUANA TBK; *Int'l*, pg. 6083
PUBALI BANK PLC; *Int'l*, pg. 6093
PUBALI BANK SECURITIES LIMITED—See Pubali Bank PLC; *Int'l*, pg. 6093
PUBANG LANDSCAPE ARCHITECTURE CO., LTD.; *Int'l*, pg. 6093
PUBBLIBABY S.R.L—See RCS MediaGroup S.p.A.; *Int'l*, pg. 6229
PUBCO CORPORATION; *U.S. Private*, pg. 3298
PUBCO REPORTING SERVICES, INC.—See ProBility Media Corporation; *U.S. Public*, pg. 1723
PUBLIBIKE SA—See Die Schweizerische Post AG; *Int'l*, pg. 2113
PUBLICACIONES AQUARIO, S. DE R.L. DE C.V.—See Grupo Televisa, S.A.B.; *Int'l*, pg. 3136
THE PUBLIC AFFAIRS INC.; *Int'l*, pg. 7677
PUBLIC AFFAIRS JAPAN INC.—See Vector Inc.; *Int'l*, pg. 8144
PUBLICAFFAIRS, LLC—See Vivendi SE; *Int'l*, pg. 8273
PUBLIC ANALYST SCIENTIFIC SERVICES LTD—See Eurofins Scientific S.E.; *Int'l*, pg. 2551
PUBLIC ANALYST SCIENTIFIC SERVICES (NI) LTD—See Eurofins Scientific S.E.; *Int'l*, pg. 2551
PUBLIC AND INVESTOR RELATIONS PIR SVERIGE AB—See Platinum Equity, LLC; *U.S. Private*, pg. 3202
PUBLICATION FULFILLMENT SERVICES, INC.; *U.S. Private*, pg. 3300
PUBLICATIONS & COMMUNICATIONS, INC.; *U.S. Private*, pg. 3300
PUBLICATIONS GROUPE LOISIRS—See Vivendi SE; *Int'l*, pg. 8275
PUBLICATIONS INTERNATIONAL, LTD.; *U.S. Private*, pg. 3300
PUBLIC AUTOS LTD; *U.S. Private*, pg. 3298
PUBLIC BANK BERHAD; *Int'l*, pg. 6094
PUBLIC BANK LAO LIMITED—See Public Bank Berhad; *Int'l*, pg. 6094
PUBLIC BANK (L) LTD.—See Public Bank Berhad; *Int'l*, pg. 6094
PUBLIC BANK (NOMINEES) LIMITED—See Public Bank Berhad; *Int'l*, pg. 6094
PUBLIC BROADCASTING SERVICE; *U.S. Private*, pg. 3298
PUBLIC CLOTHING COMPANY INC.; *U.S. Private*, pg. 3298
PUBLIC COMMUNICATIONS SERVICES, INC.; *U.S. Private*, pg. 3298
PUBLIC COMPANY ACCOUNTING OVERSIGHT BOARD; *U.S. Private*, pg. 3298
PUBLIC COMPANY ERSTE BANK—See Erste Group Bank AG; *Int'l*, pg. 2499
PUBLIC COMPANY MANAGEMENT CORPORATION; *U.S. Public*, pg. 1735
PUBLIC CONSULTING GROUP, INC.; *U.S. Private*, pg. 3299
PUBLIC EDUCATION HEALTH TRUST; *U.S. Private*, pg. 3299
PUBLICENGINES INC.; *U.S. Private*, pg. 3300
PUBLICENTRO—See The Interpublic Group of Companies, Inc.; *U.S. Public*, pg. 2093
PUBLIC FINANCIAL HOLDINGS LIMITED—See Public Bank Berhad; *Int'l*, pg. 6094
PUBLIC FINANCIAL LIMITED—See Public Bank Berhad; *Int'l*, pg. 6094
PUBLIC FINANCIAL MANAGEMENT, INC.; *U.S. Private*, pg. 3299
PUBLIC FINANCIAL SECURITIES LIMITED—See Public Bank Berhad; *Int'l*, pg. 6094
PUBLIC HEALTH FOUNDATION ENTERPRISES; *U.S. Private*, pg. 3299
PUBLIC HEALTH MANAGEMENT CORPORATION; *U.S. Private*, pg. 3299
THE PUBLIC HEALTH MANAGEMENT SERVICES CORPORATION—See Public Health Management Corporation; *U.S. Private*, pg. 3299
PUBLIC HOLDINGS SDN. BHD.—See Public Bank Berhad; *Int'l*, pg. 6094
PUBLIC HOUSING DEVELOPMENT (CAMBODIA) LTD.—See Hong Lai Huat Group Limited; *Int'l*, pg. 3467
PUBLICIDAD COMERGIAL—See The Interpublic Group of Companies, Inc.; *U.S. Public*, pg. 2092
PUBLICIDAD FERRER Y ASOCIADOS, S.A. DE C.V.; *Int'l*, pg. 6097
PUBLICIDAD INTERAMERICANA, S.A.—See WPP plc; *Int'l*, pg. 8472

PUBLICIDAD INTERAMERICA—See The Interpublic Group of Companies, Inc.; *U.S. Public*, pg. 2092
PUBLICIDAD MCCANN ERICKSON CENTROAMERICANA (GUATEMALA) S.A.—See The Interpublic Group of Companies, Inc.; *U.S. Public*, pg. 2101
PUBLICIDAD VIRTUAL, S.A. DE C.V.—See Grupo Televisa, S.A.B.; *Int'l*, pg. 3136
PUBLICIDENTITY INC.; *U.S. Private*, pg. 3300
PUBLIC IMAGERY; *U.S. Private*, pg. 3299
PUBLIC INTELLIGENCE APS; *Int'l*, pg. 6094
PUBLIC INTEREST COMMUNICATION; *U.S. Private*, pg. 3299
PUBLIC INTEREST DATA, LLC—See Blackbaud, Inc.; *U.S. Public*, pg. 341
PUBLIC INTEREST REGISTRY; *U.S. Private*, pg. 3299
PUBLIC INVESTMENT BANK BERHAD—See Public Bank Berhad; *Int'l*, pg. 6094
PUBLIC INVESTMENT CORPORATION (SOC) LIMITED; *Int'l*, pg. 6094
PUBLIC INVESTMENT CORPORATION; *U.S. Private*, pg. 3299
PUBLIC INVEST NOMINEES (ASING) SDN. BHD.—See Public Bank Berhad; *Int'l*, pg. 6094
PUBLIC INVEST NOMINEES (TEMPATAN) SDN. BHD.—See Public Bank Berhad; *Int'l*, pg. 6094
PUBLICIS ACTIV ANNECY—See Publicis Groupe S.A.; *Int'l*, pg. 6104
PUBLICIS ACTIV LYON—See Publicis Groupe S.A.; *Int'l*, pg. 6104
PUBLICIS ARIELY—See Publicis Groupe S.A.; *Int'l*, pg. 6104
PUBLICIS ARREDONDO DE HARO—See Publicis Groupe S.A.; *Int'l*, pg. 6104
PUBLICIS ASIA/PACIFIC PTE. LTD.—See Publicis Groupe S.A.; *Int'l*, pg. 6104
PUBLICIS ASOCIADOS—See Publicis Groupe S.A.; *Int'l*, pg. 6104
PUBLICIS ATLANTIQUE—See Publicis Groupe S.A.; *Int'l*, pg. 6104
PUBLICIS (BEIJING)—See Publicis Groupe S.A.; *Int'l*, pg. 6104
PUBLICIS BRAND/DESIGN—See Publicis Groupe S.A.; *Int'l*, pg. 6104
PUBLICIS BRASIL COMMUNICAO—See Publicis Groupe S.A.; *Int'l*, pg. 6104
PUBLICIS BRASIL COMMUNICAO—See Publicis Groupe S.A.; *Int'l*, pg. 6104
PUBLICIS BRASIL COMMUNICAO—See Publicis Groupe S.A.; *Int'l*, pg. 6104
PUBLICIS CANADA INC.—See Publicis Groupe S.A.; *Int'l*, pg. 6104
PUBLICIS CARIBBEAN DOMINICANA—See Publicis Groupe S.A.; *Int'l*, pg. 6104
PUBLICIS CARIBBEAN—See Publicis Groupe S.A.; *Int'l*, pg. 6104
PUBLICIS CASADEVALL PEDRENO & PRG—See Publicis Groupe S.A.; *Int'l*, pg. 6104
PUBLICIS-CB—See Publicis Groupe S.A.; *Int'l*, pg. 6106
PUBLICIS CHILE SA—See Publicis Groupe S.A.; *Int'l*, pg. 6104
PUBLICIS COMMUNICATIONS SCHWEIZ AG—See Publicis Groupe S.A.; *Int'l*, pg. 6104
PUBLICIS CONSEIL—See Publicis Groupe S.A.; *Int'l*, pg. 6104
PUBLICIS CONSTELLATION—See Publicis Groupe S.A.; *Int'l*, pg. 6104
PUBLICIS CONSULTANTS—See Publicis Groupe S.A.; *Int'l*, pg. 6104
PUBLICIS CONSULTANTS—See Publicis Groupe S.A.; *Int'l*, pg. 6106
PUBLICIS CONSULTANTS—See Publicis Groupe S.A.; *Int'l*, pg. 6106
PUBLICIS DALLAS—See Publicis Groupe S.A.; *Int'l*, pg. 6106
PUBLICIS DIALOG BOISE—See Publicis Groupe S.A.; *Int'l*, pg. 6106
PUBLICIS DIALOG & INTERACTIVE-MONTREAL—See Publicis Groupe S.A.; *Int'l*, pg. 6105
PUBLICIS DIALOG MALAYSIA—See Publicis Groupe S.A.; *Int'l*, pg. 6103
PUBLICIS DIALOG—See Publicis Groupe S.A.; *Int'l*, pg. 6104
PUBLICIS DIALOG—See Publicis Groupe S.A.; *Int'l*, pg. 6105
PUBLICIS-DIALOG—See Publicis Groupe S.A.; *Int'l*, pg. 6106
PUBLICIS DIALOG—See Publicis Groupe S.A.; *Int'l*, pg. 6106
PUBLICIS DIRECT LTD.—See QMP Publicis; *Int'l*, pg. 6147
PUBLICIS D.O.O.—See Publicis Groupe S.A.; *Int'l*, pg. 6105
PUBLICIS DRUM PR—See Publicis Groupe S.A.; *Int'l*, pg. 6105
PUBLICIS ET NOUS—See Publicis Groupe S.A.; *Int'l*, pg. 6105
PUBLICIS FERGO, S.A.—See Publicis Groupe S.A.; *Int'l*, pg. 6105

PUBLICIS FULL PLAYER—See Publicis Groupe S.A.; *Int'l*, pg. 6105
PUBLICIS GRAFFITI S.A.—See Publicis Groupe S.A.; *Int'l*, pg. 6105
PUBLICIS GRAPHICS—See Publicis Groupe S.A.; *Int'l*, pg. 6105
PUBLICIS GRAPHICS—See Publicis Groupe S.A.; *Int'l*, pg. 6105
PUBLICIS GRAPHICS—See Publicis Groupe S.A.; *Int'l*, pg. 6105
PUBLICIS-GRAPHICS—See Publicis Groupe S.A.; *Int'l*, pg. 6106
PUBLICIS-GRAPHICS—See Publicis Groupe S.A.; *Int'l*, pg. 6106
PUBLICIS-GRAPHICS—See Publicis Groupe S.A.; *Int'l*, pg. 6106
PUBLICIS-GRAPHICS—See Publicis Groupe S.A.; *Int'l*, pg. 6106
PUBLICIS-GRAPHICS—See Publicis Groupe S.A.; *Int'l*, pg. 6106
PUBLICIS-GRAPHICS—See Publicis Groupe S.A.; *Int'l*, pg. 6106
PUBLICIS GROUPE S.A.; *Int'l*, pg. 6097
PUBLICIS GROUP MEDIA KAZAKHSTAN (METRO)—See Publicis Groupe S.A.; *Int'l*, pg. 6105
PUBLICIS GRUPO K—See Publicis Groupe S.A.; *Int'l*, pg. 6100
PUBLICIS GUANGZHOU—See Publicis Groupe S.A.; *Int'l*, pg. 6105
PUBLICIS & HAL RINEY—See Publicis Groupe S.A.; *Int'l*, pg. 6105
PUBLICIS HEALTHCARE COMMUNICATIONS GROUP, INC.—See Publicis Groupe S.A.; *Int'l*, pg. 6106
PUBLICIS HEALTHCARE COMMUNICATIONS GROUP LIMITED—See Publicis Groupe S.A.; *Int'l*, pg. 6106
PUBLICIS HEALTH LLC—See Publicis Groupe S.A.; *Int'l*, pg. 6105
PUBLICIS HELLAS—See Publicis Groupe S.A.; *Int'l*, pg. 6105
PUBLICIS HONG KONG—See Publicis Groupe S.A.; *Int'l*, pg. 6105
PUBLICIS HOURRA!—See Publicis Groupe S.A.; *Int'l*, pg. 6105
PUBLICIS IMPETU—See Publicis Groupe S.A.; *Int'l*, pg. 6105
PUBLICIS, INC.—See Publicis Groupe S.A.; *Int'l*, pg. 6105
PUBLICIS INDIA COMMUNICATIONS PVT. LTD.—See Publicis Groupe S.A.; *Int'l*, pg. 6105
PUBLICIS INDIA COMMUNICATIONS PVT. LTD.—See Publicis Groupe S.A.; *Int'l*, pg. 6105
PUBLICIS INDONESIA—See Publicis Groupe S.A.; *Int'l*, pg. 6105
PUBLICIS IN MID AMERICA—See Publicis Groupe S.A.; *Int'l*, pg. 6106
PUBLICIS JIMENEZBASIC—See Publicis Groupe S.A.; *Int'l*, pg. 6105
PUBLICIS KNUT—See Publicis Groupe S.A.; *Int'l*, pg. 6105
PUBLICIS KOUFRA—See Publicis Groupe S.A.; *Int'l*, pg. 6105
PUBLICIS KOUFRA—See Publicis Groupe S.A.; *Int'l*, pg. 6105
PUBLIC ISLAMIC BANK BERHAD—See Public Bank Berhad; *Int'l*, pg. 6094
PUBLICIS LIFE BRANDS CANADA—See Publicis Groupe S.A.; *Int'l*, pg. 6106
PUBLICIS LIFE BRANDS MADRID—See Publicis Groupe S.A.; *Int'l*, pg. 6106
PUBLICIS LIFE BRANDS OSAKA—See Publicis Groupe S.A.; *Int'l*, pg. 6106
PUBLICIS LIFE BRANDS PARIS—See Publicis Groupe S.A.; *Int'l*, pg. 6106
PUBLICIS LIFE BRANDS—See Publicis Groupe S.A.; *Int'l*, pg. 6106
PUBLICIS LIFE BRANDS—See Publicis Groupe S.A.; *Int'l*, pg. 6106
PUBLICIS (MALAYSIA) SDN. BHD.—See Publicis Groupe S.A.; *Int'l*, pg. 6104
PUBLICIS MANILA—See Publicis Groupe S.A.; *Int'l*, pg. 6105
PUBLICIS MEDIA GMBH—See Publicis Groupe S.A.; *Int'l*, pg. 6105
PUBLICIS MODEM & DIALOG, EAST—See Publicis Groupe S.A.; *Int'l*, pg. 6106
PUBLICIS MODEM & DIALOG—See Publicis Groupe S.A.; *Int'l*, pg. 6106
PUBLICIS MODEM FRANCE—See Publicis Groupe S.A.; *Int'l*, pg. 6106
PUBLICIS MODEM—See Publicis Groupe S.A.; *Int'l*, pg. 6106
PUBLICIS MODEM—See Publicis Groupe S.A.; *Int'l*, pg. 6106
PUBLICIS MODEM—See Publicis Groupe S.A.; *Int'l*, pg. 6106
PUBLICIS-MOJO GROUP—See Publicis Groupe S.A.; *Int'l*, pg. 6106
PUBLICIS-MOJOPARTNERS BRISBANE—See Publicis Groupe S.A.; *Int'l*, pg. 6106

COMPANY NAME INDEX

PUBLICIS-MOJOPARTNERS MELBOURNE—See Publicis Groupe S.A.; *Int'l*, pg. 6107
PUBLICIS-MOJOPARTNERS—See Publicis Groupe S.A.; *Int'l*, pg. 6106
PUBLICIS MONTREAL—See Publicis Groupe S.A., *Int'l*, pg. 6105
PUBLICIS.NET—See Publicis Groupe S.A.; *Int'l*, pg. 6107
PUBLICIS NETWORKS—See Publicis Groupe S.A.; *Int'l*, pg. 6105
PUBLICIS NEW YORK—See Publicis Groupe S.A.; *Int'l*, pg. 6106
PUBLICIS NURUN—See Publicis Groupe S.A.; *Int'l*, pg. 6104
PUBLICIS PIXELPARK GMBH—See Publicis Groupe S.A.; *Int'l*, pg. 6105
PUBLICIS SELLING SOLUTIONS—See Publicis Groupe S.A.; *Int'l*, pg. 6106
PUBLICIS SHANGHAI—See Publicis Groupe S.A.; *Int'l*, pg. 6105
PUBLICIS SINGAPORE—See Publicis Groupe S.A.; *Int'l*, pg. 6105
PUBLICIS SINGAPORE—See Publicis Groupe S.A.; *Int'l*, pg. 6105
PUBLICIS SOLEIL—See Publicis Groupe S.A.; *Int'l*, pg. 6105
PUBLICIS SOLEIL—See Publicis Groupe S.A.; *Int'l*, pg. 6105
PUBLICIS—See Publicis Groupe S.A.; *Int'l*, pg. 6100
PUBLICIS—See Publicis Groupe S.A.; *Int'l*, pg. 6104
PUBLICIS SP. Z.O.O.—See Publicis Groupe S.A.; *Int'l*, pg. 6105
PUBLICIS TAIWAN—See Publicis Groupe S.A.; *Int'l*, pg. 6105
PUBLICIS TECHNOLOGY—See Publicis Groupe S.A.; *Int'l*, pg. 6105
PUBLICIS (THAILAND) LTD.—See Publicis Groupe S.A.; *Int'l*, pg. 6104
PUBLICIS TORONTO—See Publicis Groupe S.A.; *Int'l*, pg. 6105
PUBLICIS TOUCHPOINT SOLUTIONS—See Publicis Groupe S.A.; *Int'l*, pg. 6106
PUBLICIS UNITED—See Publicis Groupe S.A.; *Int'l*, pg. 6105
PUBLICIS VENEZUELA—See Publicis Groupe S.A.; *Int'l*, pg. 6105
PUBLICIS WEBIMAGE—See Publicis Groupe S.A.; *Int'l*, pg. 6105
PUBLICIS WELLCARE—See Publicis Groupe S.A.; *Int'l*, pg. 6105
PUBLICIS WEST—See Publicis Groupe S.A.; *Int'l*, pg. 6106
PUBLICITARIA NASTA—See WPP plc; *Int'l*, pg. 8490
PUBLICITAS NAZCA SAATCHI & SAATCHI—See Publicis Groupe S.A.; *Int'l*, pg. 6108
THE PUBLICITY AGENCY—See Selig Multimedia Inc.; *U.S. Private*, pg. 3602
PUBLIC JOINT STOCK COMMERCIAL BANK—See Vietnam Oil and Gas Group; *Int'l*, pg. 8203
PUBLIC JOINT STOCK COMPANY ACRON; *Int'l*, pg. 6094
PUBLIC JOINT-STOCK COMPANY BANK OTKRITIE FINANCIAL CORPORATION—See Central Bank of the Russian Federation; *Int'l*, pg. 1405
PUBLIC JOINT STOCK COMPANY CHELINDBANK; *Int'l*, pg. 6095
PUBLIC JOINT STOCK COMPANY DEUTSCHE BANK DBU—See Deutsche Bank Aktiengesellschaft; *Int'l*, pg. 2061
PUBLIC JOINT STOCK COMPANY "BANK FORUM"—See Commerzbank AG; *Int'l*, pg. 1719
PUBLIC JOINT STOCK COMPANY ROSSETI CENTRE—See JSC ROSSETI; *Int'l*, pg. 4011
PUBLIC JOINT STOCK COMPANY ROSSETI VOLGA—See JSC ROSSETI; *Int'l*, pg. 4011
PUBLIC JOINT STOCK COMPANY UNICREDIT BANK—See UniCredit S.p.A.; *Int'l*, pg. 8035
PUBLIC JOINT STOCK INSURANCE COMPANY ENERGOGARANT; *Int'l*, pg. 6095
PUBLIC KNOWLEDGE, LLC—See Gaming Laboratories International LLC; *U.S. Private*, pg. 1640
PUBLIC MANAGEMENT CONSULTING CORPORATION—See FinTech Global Incorporated; *Int'l*, pg. 2677
PUBLIC MUTUAL BERHAD—See Public Bank Berhad; *Int'l*, pg. 6094
PUBLIC NOMINEES (TEMPATAN) SDN. BHD.—See Public Bank Berhad; *Int'l*, pg. 6094
PUBLICO - COMUNICACAO SOCIAL, S.A.—See Sonaecom SGPS SA; *Int'l*, pg. 7088
PUBLICO MCCANN—See The Interpublic Group of Companies, Inc.; *U.S. Public*, pg. 2102
PUBLICOM/HILL & KNOWLTON—See WPP plc; *Int'l*, pg. 8478
PUBLIC OPINION—See Gannett Co., Inc.; *U.S. Public*, pg. 900
PUBLIC OPINION STRATEGIES LLC; *U.S. Private*, pg. 3299
PUBLIC PACKAGES ASIA (S) PTE. LTD.—See Public Packages Holdings Berhad; *Int'l*, pg. 6095

PUBLIC PACKAGES HOLDINGS BERHAD; *Int'l*, pg. 6095
PUBLIC PACKAGES (NT) SDN. BHD.—See Public Packages Holdings Berhad; *Int'l*, pg. 6095
PUBLIC PACKAGES SDN. BHD.—See Public Packages Holdings Berhad; *Int'l*, pg. 6095
PUBLIC PACKAGES (SHAH ALAM) SDN. BHD.—See Public Packages Holdings Berhad; *Int'l*, pg. 6095
PUBLIC PENSION CAPITAL, LLC; *U.S. Private*, pg. 3300
PUBLICPLAN GMBH—See Allgeier SE; *Int'l*, pg. 338
PUBLIC POLICY HOLDING COMPANY; *U.S. Public*, pg. 1735
PUBLIC POWER CORPORATION S.A.; *Int'l*, pg. 6095
PUBLIC RISK UNDERWRITERS INSURANCE SERVICES OF TEXAS, LLC—See Brown & Brown, Inc.; *U.S. Public*, pg. 402
PUBLIC RISK UNDERWRITERS OF FLORIDA, INC.—See Brown & Brown, Inc.; *U.S. Public*, pg. 402
PUBLIC RISK UNDERWRITERS OF INDIANA, LLC—See Brown & Brown, Inc.; *U.S. Public*, pg. 402
PUBLIC RISK UNDERWRITERS OF THE NORTHWEST, INC.—See Brown & Brown, Inc.; *U.S. Public*, pg. 402
PUBLIC SAFETY EQUIPMENT (SUZHOU) CO., LTD.—See Ecco Safety Group; *U.S. Private*, pg. 1326
PUBLIC SECTOR PENSION INVESTMENT BOARD; *Int'l*, pg. 6095
PUBLIC SECURITIES LIMITED—See Public Bank Berhad; *Int'l*, pg. 6094
PUBLIC SECURITIES (NOMINEES) LIMITED—See Public Bank Berhad; *Int'l*, pg. 6094
PUBLIC SERVICE COMPANY OF NEW HAMPSHIRE—See Eversource Energy; *U.S. Public*, pg. 802
PUBLIC SERVICE COMPANY OF NEW MEXICO—See TXNM Energy, Inc.; *U.S. Public*, pg. 2208
PUBLIC SERVICE COMPANY OF NORTH CAROLINA, INCORPORATED—See Dominion Energy, Inc.; *U.S. Public*, pg. 674
PUBLIC SERVICE COMPANY OF OKLAHOMA—See American Electric Power Company, Inc.; *U.S. Public*, pg. 100
PUBLIC SERVICE CO OF NEW MEXICO; *U.S. Public*, pg. 1735
PUBLIC SERVICE ELECTRIC & GAS COMPANY—See Public Service Enterprise Group Incorporated; *U.S. Public*, pg. 1736
PUBLIC SERVICE ENTERPRISE GROUP INCORPORATED; *U.S. Public*, pg. 1735
PUBLIC SERVICE MORTGAGE, INC.; *U.S. Private*, pg. 3300
PUBLIC SERVICE PROPERTIES INVESTMENT LIMITED; *Int'l*, pg. 6097
PUBLIC SERVICE TELEPHONE CO; *U.S. Private*, pg. 3300
PUBLIC SPIRIT-AYER—See Alden Global Capital LLC; *U.S. Private*, pg. 157
PUBLICSQ. INC.; *U.S. Public*, pg. 1736
PUBLIC STORAGE OP, LP—See Public Storage; *U.S. Public*, pg. 1736
PUBLIC STORAGE PROPERTIES—See Public Storage; *U.S. Public*, pg. 1736
PUBLIC STORAGE; *U.S. Public*, pg. 1736
PUBLIC STRATEGIES, INC.—See WPP plc; *Int'l*, pg. 8483
PUBLICSTUFF, LLC—See Accela Inc.; *U.S. Private*, pg. 49
PUBLIC SUPPLY COMPANY; *U.S. Private*, pg. 3300
THE PUBLIC THEATER; *U.S. Private*, pg. 4101
PUBLIC UTILITIES REPORTS, INC.; *U.S. Private*, pg. 3300
PUBLIC UTILITY DISTRICT 1 LEWIS COUNTY; *U.S. Private*, pg. 3300
PUBLIC UTILITY DISTRICT 1 OF BENTON COUNTY; *U.S. Private*, pg. 3300
PUBLIC UTILITY DISTRICT 1 OF DOUGLAS COUNTY; *U.S. Private*, pg. 3300
PUBLIC UTILITY DISTRICT 1 OKANOGAN; *U.S. Private*, pg. 3300
PUBLIC UTILITY DISTRICT 2 PACIFIC COUNTY; *U.S. Private*, pg. 3300
PUBLIC UTILITY DISTRICT KLICKITAT COUNTY; *U.S. Private*, pg. 3300
PUBLIC UTILITY DISTRICT NO. 1 CHELAN COUNTY; *U.S. Private*, pg. 3300
PUBLIC UTILITY DISTRICT NO. 1 OF PEND OREILLE COUNTY; *U.S. Private*, pg. 3300
PUBLIC UTILITY DISTRICT NO. 2 OF GRANT COUNTY; *U.S. Private*, pg. 3300
PUBLIC WORKS COMMISSION; *U.S. Private*, pg. 3300
PUBLIC WORKS EQUIPMENT & SUPPLY, INC.—See Federal Signal Corporation; *U.S. Public*, pg. 826
PUBLIESPANA S.A.U.—See Mediaset S.p.A.; *Int'l*, pg. 4773
PUBLIEUROPE LTD.—See Mediaset S.p.A.; *Int'l*, pg. 4773
PUBLIFUTURA AFFICHAGE ITALIA SRL—See APG/SGA SA; *Int'l*, pg. 513
PUBLIGAS; *Int'l*, pg. 6114
PUBLIKOMPASS S.P.A.—See Stellantis N.V.; *Int'l*, pg. 7203
PUBLIMETRO S.A.—See Kinnevik AB; *Int'l*, pg. 4182
PUBLISETTE S.R.L.—See Netweek S.p.A.; *Int'l*, pg. 5217

PUEBLO BANCORPORATION

PUBLISHERS ADVERTISING ASSOCIATES; *U.S. Private*, pg. 3301
PUBLISHERS CIRCULATION FULFILLMENT INC.; *U.S. Private*, pg. 3301
PUBLISHERS CLEARING HOUSE, INC.; *U.S. Private*, pg. 3301
PUBLISHERS COMMUNICATION GROUP, INC. - OXFORD OFFICE—See Ingenta plc; *Int'l*, pg. 3701
PUBLISHERS COMMUNICATION GROUP, INC.—See Ingenta plc; *Int'l*, pg. 3701
PUBLISHER'S CREATIVE SYSTEMS; *U.S. Private*, pg. 3301
PUBLISHERS' GRAPHICS, LLC.; *U.S. Private*, pg. 3301
PUBLISHERS GROUP WEST—See Perseus Books, LLC; *U.S. Private*, pg. 3155
PUBLISHER'S INTERNATIONALE; *Int'l*, pg. 6115
PUBLISHERS PRESS, LLC—See Atlas Holdings, LLC; *U.S. Private*, pg. 377
PUBLISHERS WAREHOUSE—See EBSCO Industries, Inc.; *U.S. Private*, pg. 1325
PUBLISHING AND BROADCASTING INTERNATIONAL HOLDINGS LIMITED—See Nine Entertainment Co. Holdings Limited; *Int'l*, pg. 5299
PUBLISHING GROUP OF AMERICA; *U.S. Private*, pg. 3301
PUBLISHING TECHNOLOGY (EUROPE) LIMITED—See Ingenta plc; *Int'l*, pg. 3701
PUBLISHING TECHNOLOGY, INC.—See Ingenta plc; *Int'l*, pg. 3701
PUBLISUISSE SA—See SRG SSR Idee Suisse; *Int'l*, pg. 7149
PUBLITALIA '80 S.P.A.—See Mediaset S.p.A.; *Int'l*, pg. 4773
PUBLITEC B.V.—See Apax Partners LLP; *Int'l*, pg. 507
PUBLITEC B.V.—See Cinven Limited; *Int'l*, pg. 1615
PUBLITEK LIMITED—See Next 15 Group plc; *Int'l*, pg. 5246
PUBLITY AG; *Int'l*, pg. 6115
PUBLIVENOR BVBA—See Encres Dubuit SA; *Int'l*, pg. 2402
PUBLIX ALABAMA, LLC—See Publix Super Markets, Inc.; *U.S. Private*, pg. 3301
PUBLIX ASSET MANAGEMENT COMPANY—See Publix Super Markets, Inc.; *U.S. Private*, pg. 3301
PUBLIX SUPER MARKETS, INC. - GA, SC, TN & AL—See Publix Super Markets, Inc.; *U.S. Private*, pg. 3301
PUBLIX SUPER MARKETS, INC. - NORTH FLORIDA/SOUTHEAST GEORGIA—See Publix Super Markets, Inc.; *U.S. Private*, pg. 3301
PUBLIX SUPER MARKETS, INC.; *U.S. Private*, pg. 3301
PUBLIX SUPER MARKETS, INC. - SOUTH EAST FLORIDA—See Publix Super Markets, Inc.; *U.S. Private*, pg. 3301
PUBMATIC, INC.; *U.S. Public*, pg. 1736
PUBSQUARED LLC; *U.S. Private*, pg. 3301
PUCARA GOLD LTD.; *Int'l*, pg. 6115
PUCARA RESOURCES S.A.C.—See Pucara Gold Ltd.; *Int'l*, pg. 6115
PUCARO ELEKTRO-ISOLIERSTOFFE GMBH—See ABB Ltd.; *Int'l*, pg. 50
PUC BERHAD; *Int'l*, pg. 6115
PUCCINI HOLDING GMBH; *Int'l*, pg. 6115
PUCCINO'S WORLDWIDE LTD.—See Segafredo Zanetti S.p.A.; *Int'l*, pg. 6682
PUCHENG CHIA TAI BIOCHEMISTRY CO., LTD.—See Charoen Pokphand Foods Public Company Limited; *Int'l*, pg. 1452
PUCHENG CHIA TAI BIOCHEMISTRY LTD.—See Charoen Pokphand Foods Public Company Limited; *Int'l*, pg. 1453
PUCHENG YONGFANG FRAGRANCE TECHNOLOGY CO., LTD.—See International Flavors & Fragrances Inc.; *U.S. Public*, pg. 1154
PUCHLIK DESIGN ASSOCIATES, INC.—See Harley Ellis Devereaux Corporation; *U.S. Private*, pg. 1865
PUCKETT AMBULANCE SERVICE, INC.—See KKR & Co. Inc.; *U.S. Public*, pg. 1251
PUCKETT GROCERY CO. INC.; *U.S. Private*, pg. 3301
PUCKETT MACHINERY COMPANY INC.; *U.S. Private*, pg. 3301
PUCKETT RENTS INC—See Puckett Machinery Company Inc.; *U.S. Private*, pg. 3301
PUCKETT'S FLOORING COMPANY; *U.S. Private*, pg. 3301
PUCKRUP HALL HOTEL LIMITED—See Hilton Worldwide Holdings Inc.; *U.S. Public*, pg. 1041
PUDA COAL, INC.; *Int'l*, pg. 6115
PUDITEC CO., LTD.; *Int'l*, pg. 6115
PUDO INC.; *Int'l*, pg. 6115
PUDUMJEE PAPER PRODUCTS LTD.—See 3P Land Holdings Limited; *Int'l*, pg. 9
PUEBLA RESOURCES CORP.; *Int'l*, pg. 6115
PUEBLO BANCORPORATION; *Int'l*, pg. 6115
PUEBLO BANK & TRUST CO. INC.—See Pueblo Bancorporation; *U.S. Private*, pg. 3301
PUEBLO BONITO EMERALD BAY—See Pueblo Bonito Hotels & Resorts; *U.S. Private*, pg. 3301

2217

PUEBLO BONITO HOTELS & RESORTS

PUEBLO BONITO HOTELS & RESORTS; *U.S. Private*, pg. 3301
PUEBLO BONITO LOS CABOS—See Pueblo Bonito Hotels & Resorts; *U.S. Private*, pg. 3301
PUEBLO BONITO MAZATLAN—See Pueblo Bonito Hotels & Resorts; *U.S. Private*, pg. 3302
PUEBLO BONITO PACIFICA HOLISTIC RETREAT AND SPA—See Pueblo Bonito Hotels & Resorts; *U.S. Private*, pg. 3302
PUEBLO BONITO ROSE—See Pueblo Bonito Hotels & Resorts; *U.S. Private*, pg. 3302
PUEBLO BONITO SUNSET BEACH—See Pueblo Bonito Hotels & Resorts; *U.S. Private*, pg. 3302
PUEBLO MECHANICAL & CONTROLS, LLC—See Ontario Municipal Employees Retirement System; *Int'l*, pg. 5584
PUENTES BROTHERS INC.; *U.S. Private*, pg. 3302
PUEQU CO., LTD.; *Int'l*, pg. 6115
PUERTAS PUIG OLIVER, S.L.U.; *Int'l*, pg. 6115
PUERTO ANGAMOS—See Ultramar Ltda.; *Int'l*, pg. 8019
PUERTO DE CORONEL S.A.—See Ultramar Ltda.; *Int'l*, pg. 8019
PUERTO DE MEJILLONES S.A.—See Ultramar Ltda.; *Int'l*, pg. 8019
PUERTO LAS LOSAS S.A.—See CAP S.A.; *Int'l*, pg. 1301
PUERTO RICAN ACTION BOARD; *U.S. Private*, pg. 3302
PUERTO RICAN AMERICAN INSURANCE COMPANY—See MAPFRE S.A.; *Int'l*, pg. 4684
PUERTO RICAN FAMILY INSTITUTE, INC.; *U.S. Private*, pg. 3302
PUERTO RICAN INSURANCE AGENCY INC.—See MAPFRE S.A.; *Int'l*, pg. 4684
PUERTO RICO COFFEE ROASTERS, LLC—See CC 1 Limited Partnership; *U.S. Private*, pg. 797
PUERTO RICO CONSERVATION TRUST FUND; *U.S. Private*, pg. 3302
PUERTO RICO ELECTRIC POWER AUTHORITY; *U.S. Private*, pg. 3302
PUERTO RICO FARM CREDIT A C A; *U.S. Private*, pg. 3302
PUERTO RICO INDUSTRIAL DEVELOPMENT COMPANY; *U.S. Private*, pg. 3302
PUERTO RICO LEGAL SERVICES, INC.; *U.S. Private*, pg. 3302
PUERTO RICO PRECAST CONCRETE, INC.—See Atlantic Concrete Products, Inc.; *U.S. Private*, pg. 372
PUERTO RICO PUBLIC BROADCASTING CORP; *U.S. Private*, pg. 3302
PUERTO RICO SUPPLIES CO. INC.—See Puerto Rico Supply Group; *U.S. Private*, pg. 3302
PUERTO RICO SUPPLY GROUP; *U.S. Private*, pg. 3302
PUERTO RICO TOURISM COMPANY - NEW YORK—See Puerto Rico Tourism Company; *U.S. Private*, pg. 3302
PUERTO RICO TOURISM COMPANY; *U.S. Private*, pg. 3302
PUERTO RICO WIRE PRODUCTS INC.; *U.S. Private*, pg. 3302
PUERTO SECO SANTANDER-EBRO, S.A.—See ACS, Actividades de Construccion y Servicios, S.A.; *Int'l*, pg. 115
PUERTO VENTANAS S.A.; *Int'l*, pg. 6115
PUFFER SWEIVEN; *U.S. Private*, pg. 3302
PUFF N STUFF CATERING, LLC; *U.S. Private*, pg. 3302
PUFFS INC.—See TAAT Global Alternatives Inc.; *Int'l*, pg. 7401
PUF SECURITY CORPORATION—See eMemory Technology, Inc.; *Int'l*, pg. 2377
PUGET ENERGY, INC.—See Alberta Investment Management Corporation; *Int'l*, pg. 298
PUGET ENERGY, INC.—See British Columbia Investment Management Corp.; *Int'l*, pg. 1169
PUGET ENERGY, INC.—See Canada Pension Plan Investment Board; *Int'l*, pg. 1281
PUGET ENERGY, INC.—See Macquarie Group Limited; *Int'l*, pg. 4629
PUGET SOUND ALARM INC.—See Guardian Security Systems, Inc.; *U.S. Private*, pg. 1810
THE PUGET SOUND BUSINESS JOURNAL—See Advance Publications, Inc.; *U.S. Private*, pg. 85
PUGET SOUND ENERGY, INC.—See Alberta Investment Management Corporation; *Int'l*, pg. 298
PUGET SOUND ENERGY, INC.—See British Columbia Investment Management Corp.; *Int'l*, pg. 1169
PUGET SOUND ENERGY, INC.—See Canada Pension Plan Investment Board; *Int'l*, pg. 1281
PUGET SOUND ENERGY, INC.—See Macquarie Group Limited; *Int'l*, pg. 4629
PUGET SOUND INTERNATIONAL, INC.; *U.S. Private*, pg. 3302
PUGET SOUND & PACIFIC RAILROAD—See Brookfield Infrastructure Partners L.P.; *Int'l*, pg. 1192
PUGET SOUND & PACIFIC RAILROAD—See GIC Pte. Ltd.; *Int'l*, pg. 2967
PUGET SOUND PILOTS; *U.S. Private*, pg. 3302
PUGET SOUND PIPE & SUPPLY CO; *U.S. Private*, pg. 3302
PUGET TECHNOLOGIES, INC.; *U.S. Public*, pg. 1736
PUGET WESTERN, INC.—See Alberta Investment Management Corporation; *Int'l*, pg. 298
PUGET WESTERN, INC.—See British Columbia Investment Management Corp.; *Int'l*, pg. 1169
PUGET WESTERN, INC.—See Canada Pension Plan Investment Board; *Int'l*, pg. 1281
PUGET WESTERN, INC.—See Macquarie Group Limited; *Int'l*, pg. 4629
PUGH & COMPANY LIMITED—See Begbies Traynor Group plc; *Int'l*, pg. 941
PUGH MARINA—See Pugh Oil Company; *U.S. Private*, pg. 3303
PUGH OIL COMPANY INC.; *U.S. Private*, pg. 3303
PUGH OIL COMPANY; *U.S. Private*, pg. 3303
PUGLIA ENGINEERING INC.; *U.S. Private*, pg. 3303
PUGLIESE INTERIOR SYSTEMS INC.; *U.S. Private*, pg. 3303
PUGMIRE AUTOMOTIVE GROUP; *U.S. Private*, pg. 3303
PUHUI WEALTH INVESTMENT MANAGEMENT CO., LTD.; *Int'l*, pg. 6115
PUIG BRANDS S.A.; *Int'l*, pg. 6115
PUIG PRESTIGE BEAUTY—See Puig Brands S.A.; *Int'l*, pg. 6115
PUIG S.L.—See Puig Brands S.A.; *Int'l*, pg. 6115
PUILAETCO DEWAAY PRIVATE BANKERS S.A.—See KBL European Private Bankers S.A.; *Int'l*, pg. 4107
PUINPUL CO., LTD.—See Yamada Holdings Co., Ltd.; *Int'l*, pg. 8548
PUISSANT INDUSTRIES, INC.; *U.S. Public*, pg. 1736
PUJAAN PASIFIK SDN. BHD.—See M K Land Holdings Berhad; *Int'l*, pg. 4610
PUJEN LAND DEVELOPMENT CO., LTD.—See China Metal Products Co., Ltd.; *Int'l*, pg. 1523
PUJIANG INTERNATIONAL GROUP; *Int'l*, pg. 6116
PUJOL LDA.—See Somfy SA; *Int'l*, pg. 7085
PUKLICH CHEVROLET, INC.; *U.S. Private*, pg. 3303
PUK LTD.—See FLSmidth & Co. A/S; *Int'l*, pg. 2711
PULAI SPRINGS BERHAD; *Int'l*, pg. 6116
PULASKI COMMUNITY HOSPITAL, INC.—See HCA Healthcare, Inc.; *U.S. Public*, pg. 1006
PULASKI ELECTRIC SYSTEM, INC. (PES); *U.S. Private*, pg. 3303
PULASKI RUBBER CO.—See R.C.A. Rubber Company; *U.S. Private*, pg. 3335
PULASKI-WHITE RURAL TELEPHONE COOPERATIVE, INC.; *U.S. Private*, pg. 3303
PULAU CORPORATION; *U.S. Private*, pg. 3303
PULCRA CHEMICALS GMBH—See Kiri Industries Ltd.; *Int'l*, pg. 4186
PULDIN HOLDING SA; *Int'l*, pg. 6116
PULDIN PROPERTIES INVEST REIT; *Int'l*, pg. 6116
PULENG TECHNOLOGIES PROPRIETARY LIMITED—See AYO Technology Solutions Ltd.; *Int'l*, pg. 775
PULICE CONSTRUCTION, INC.—See ACS, Actividades de Construccion y Servicios, S.A.; *Int'l*, pg. 115
PULIC INSURANCE SERVICES, INC.—See The Doctors Company; *U.S. Private*, pg. 4021
PULIDO ASSOCIATES INC.; *U.S. Private*, pg. 3303
PULIKE BIOLOGICAL ENGINEERING INC.; *Int'l*, pg. 6116
PULITZER INC.—See Lee Enterprises, Incorporated; *U.S. Public*, pg. 1300
PULJONKI OY—See Nestle S.A.; *Int'l*, pg. 5211
PULL & BEAR BELGIQUE, S.A.—See Industria de Diseno Textil, S.A.; *Int'l*, pg. 3667
PULL & BEAR BULGARIA, LTD.—See Industria de Diseno Textil, S.A.; *Int'l*, pg. 3667
PULL & BEAR CESKA REPUBLIKA S.R.O.—See Industria de Diseno Textil, S.A.; *Int'l*, pg. 3667
PULL & BEAR DEUTSCHLAND BV & CO.—See Industria de Diseno Textil, S.A.; *Int'l*, pg. 3667
PULL & BEAR ESPANA, S.A.—See Industria de Diseno Textil, S.A.; *Int'l*, pg. 3667
PULL & BEAR FRANCE, S.A.R.L.—See Industria de Diseno Textil, S.A.; *Int'l*, pg. 3667
PULL & BEAR GIYIM ITH. IHRAC.VE TIC. LTD.—See Industria de Diseno Textil, S.A.; *Int'l*, pg. 3667
PULL & BEAR HELLAS, S.A.—See Industria de Diseno Textil, S.A.; *Int'l*, pg. 3667
PULL & BEAR HONG KONG LTD.—See Industria de Diseno Textil, S.A.; *Int'l*, pg. 3667
PULL & BEAR IRELAND, LTD.—See Industria de Diseno Textil, S.A.; *Int'l*, pg. 3667
PULL & BEAR ITALIA, S.R.L.—See Industria de Diseno Textil, S.A.; *Int'l*, pg. 3667
PULL & BEAR KOREA, LTD.—See Industria de Diseno Textil, S.A.; *Int'l*, pg. 3667
PULL & BEAR MAGYARORSZAG KFT.—See Industria de Diseno Textil, S.A.; *Int'l*, pg. 3667
PULL & BEAR MEXICO S.A. DE C.V.—See Industria de Diseno Textil, S.A.; *Int'l*, pg. 3667
PULL & BEAR NEDERLAND, B.V.—See Industria de Diseno Textil, S.A.; *Int'l*, pg. 3667
PULL & BEAR OSTERREICH CLOTHING, GMBH—See Industria de Diseno Textil, S.A.; *Int'l*, pg. 3667
PULL & BEAR POLSKA SP ZO.O—See Industria de Diseno Textil, S.A.; *Int'l*, pg. 3667
PULL & BEAR PORTUGAL CONF. LDA—See Industria de Diseno Textil, S.A.; *Int'l*, pg. 3667
PULL & BEAR RO, SRL—See Industria de Diseno Textil, S.A.; *Int'l*, pg. 3667
PULL & BEAR SLOVAKIA, S.R.O.—See Industria de Diseno Textil, S.A.; *Int'l*, pg. 3667
PULL & BEAR SUISSE, SARL—See Industria de Diseno Textil, S.A.; *Int'l*, pg. 3667
PULL & BEAR SVERIGE, AB—See Industria de Diseno Textil, S.A.; *Int'l*, pg. 3667
PULL & BEAR UK LIMITED—See Industria de Diseno Textil, S.A.; *Int'l*, pg. 3667
PULL & BEAR UKRAINE, LLC—See Industria de Diseno Textil, S.A.; *Int'l*, pg. 3667
PULLMAFLEX BENELUX N.V.—See Leggett & Platt, Incorporated; *U.S. Public*, pg. 1303
PULLMAFLEX U.K. LIMITED—See Leggett & Platt, Incorporated; *U.S. Public*, pg. 1303
THE PULLMAN COMPANY—See Apollo Global Management, Inc.; *U.S. Public*, pg. 163
PULLMAN INTERNATIONAL HOTELS—See Accor S.A.; *Int'l*, pg. 92
PULLMAN POWER, LLC—See Structural Group, Inc.; *U.S. Private*, pg. 3841
PULLMAN STT, INC.—See Structural Group, Inc.; *U.S. Private*, pg. 3841
PULLMANTUR SA—See Royal Caribbean Cruises Ltd.; *U.S. Public*, pg. 1815
PULLMANTUR SA—See Springwater Capital LLC; *Int'l*, pg. 7144
PULMATRIX, INC.; *U.S. Public*, pg. 1736
PULMATRIX OPERATING COMPANY—See Pulmatrix, Inc.; *U.S. Public*, pg. 1736
PULMETALL BODENMARKIERUNGEN GESELLSCHAFT MBH—See PORR AG; *Int'l*, pg. 5924
PULMONX AUSTRALIA PTY LTD—See Pulmonx Corporation; *U.S. Public*, pg. 1736
PULMONX CORPORATION; *U.S. Public*, pg. 1736
PULMONX INTERNATIONAL SARL—See Pulmonx Corporation; *U.S. Public*, pg. 1736
PULMOQUINE THERAPEUTICS, INC.—See Innoviva, Inc.; *U.S. Public*, pg. 1127
PULMUONE CO., LTD.; *Int'l*, pg. 6116
PULMUONE FOODS USA, INC.—See Pulmuone Co., Ltd.; *Int'l*, pg. 6116
PULMUONE WILDWOOD INC.—See Pulmuone Co., Ltd.; *Int'l*, pg. 6116
PULOON TECHNOLOGY INC. - CHUNGJU FACTORY—See Puloon Technology Inc.; *Int'l*, pg. 6116
PULOON TECHNOLOGY INC. - GASAN FACTORY—See Puloon Technology Inc.; *Int'l*, pg. 6116
PULOON TECHNOLOGY INC.; *Int'l*, pg. 6116
PULPO MEDIA, INC.—See Entravision Communications Corporation; *U.S. Public*, pg. 779
PULP TRADING GMBH—See Lenzing Aktiengesellschaft; *Int'l*, pg. 4456
PULS4 SHOPPING GMBH—See ProSiebenSat.1 Media SE; *Int'l*, pg. 6000
PULS 4 TV GMBH & CO KG—See ProSiebenSat.1 Media SE; *Int'l*, pg. 6000
PULSAFEEDER EUROPE B.V.—See IDEX Corp; *U.S. Public*, pg. 1091
PULSAFEEDER INC.—See IDEX Corp; *U.S. Public*, pg. 1091
PULSA MEDIA CONSULTING, S.L.—See The Walt Disney Company; *U.S. Public*, pg. 2140
PULSANT LIMITED—See Keystone Group, L.P.; *U.S. Private*, pg. 2299
PULSANT (SCOTLAND) LIMITED—See Keystone Group, L.P.; *U.S. Private*, pg. 2299
PULSAR ADVERTISING, INC.; *U.S. Private*, pg. 3303
PULSAR ADVERTISING, INC.—See Pulsar Advertising, Inc.; *U.S. Private*, pg. 3303
PULSAR ADVERTISING, INC.—See Pulsar Advertising, Inc.; *U.S. Private*, pg. 3303
PULSAR GROUP; *Int'l*, pg. 6116
PULSAR INTERNACIONAL S.A. DE C.V.; *Int'l*, pg. 6116
PULSAR INTERNATIONAL LIMITED; *Int'l*, pg. 6117
PULSAR SHIPPING AGENCIES (PRIVATE) LIMITED—See Expolanka Holdings PLC; *Int'l*, pg. 2589
PULSAR STATE PLANT JSC—See Russian Technologies State Corporation; *Int'l*, pg. 6432
PULSAR VASCULAR, INC.—See Johnson & Johnson; *U.S. Public*, pg. 1195
PULSE 360 INC.—See Seevast Corporation; *U.S. Private*, pg. 3598
PULSE8, LLC—See Veradigm Inc.; *U.S. Public*, pg. 2280
PULSE AEROSPACE, LLC—See AeroVironment, Inc.; *U.S. Public*, pg. 53
THE PULSE BEVERAGE CORPORATION; *U.S. Public*, pg. 2125
PULSE BIOSCIENCES, INC.; *U.S. Public*, pg. 1737
PULSE DESIGN DOO—See Pilot Corporation; *Int'l*, pg. 5867
PULSE ECOSYSTEMS PTE. LTD.—See Prudential plc; *Int'l*, pg. 6009
PULSE EFT ASSOCIATION—See Discover Financial Services; *U.S. Public*, pg. 668
PULSE ENERGY LIMITED—See Buller Electricity Ltd.; *Int'l*, pg. 1214
PULSE EVOLUTION CORPORATION; *U.S. Public*, pg. 1737

PULSE FILMS LIMITED—See Monroe Capital LLC; *U.S. Private*, pg. 2773
PULSE FILMS LIMITED—See SoftBank Group Corp.; *Int'l*, pg. 7054
PULSE FILMS LIMITED—See Soros Fund Management LLC; *U.S. Private*, pg. 3716
PULSE HEALTH LIMITED—See Luye Medical Group; *Int'l*, pg. 4589
PULSE INVESTMENTS LIMITED; *Int'l*, pg. 6117
PULSE LIVING APS—See Park Street Nordicom A/S; *Int'l*, pg. 5742
PULSE MARKETS PTY. LTD.—See BIR Financial Limited; *Int'l*, pg. 1046
PULSE MEDIATECH LIMITED—See Quali-Smart Holdings Ltd.; *Int'l*, pg. 6150
THE PULSE NETWORK, INC.; *U.S. Private*, pg. 4101
PULSE NETWORK LLC—See Discover Financial Services; *U.S. Public*, pg. 668
PULSENMORE LTD.; *Int'l*, pg. 6117
PULSE OFFICE DOO—See Pilot Corporation; *Int'l*, pg. 5867
PULSEPOINT GROUP, LLC—See ICF International, Inc.; *U.S. Public*, pg. 1086
PULSEPOINT INC.; *U.S. Private*, pg. 3303
PULSEPOINT LTD.—See PulsePoint Inc.; *U.S. Private*, pg. 3303
PULSE SEISMIC INC.; *Int'l*, pg. 6117
PULSE—See Myriad Restaurant Group; *U.S. Private*, pg. 2825
PULSE SYSTEMS, INC.—See Constellation Software Inc.; *Int'l*, pg. 1773
PULSE SYSTEMS, LLC—See United American Healthcare Corp.; *U.S. Public*, pg. 2229
PULSETECH PRODUCTS CORPORATION; *U.S. Private*, pg. 3303
PULSE TELESERVICE INC.—See Enghouse Systems Limited; *Int'l*, pg. 2427
PULSE TRADING, INC.—See State Street Corporation; *U.S. Public*, pg. 1940
PULSE VETERINARY TECHNOLOGIES, LLC—See Zomedica Corp.; *U.S. Private*, pg. 2410
PULSE VOICE INC—See Enghouse Systems Limited; *Int'l*, pg. 2427
PULSION BENELUX N.V.—See Getinge AB; *Int'l*, pg. 2952
PULSION FRANCE S.A.R.L.—See Getinge AB; *Int'l*, pg. 2952
PULSION MEDICAL SYSTEMS IBERICA S.L.—See Getinge AB; *Int'l*, pg. 2952
PULSION MEDICAL SYSTEMS SE—See Getinge AB; *Int'l*, pg. 2952
PULSION MEDICAL UK LTD.—See Getinge AB; *Int'l*, pg. 2952
PULSION SWITZERLAND GMBH—See Getinge AB; *Int'l*, pg. 2952
PULS MEDICAL DEVICES AS LC—See Becton, Dickinson & Company; *U.S. Public*, pg. 292
PULSO EUROPE BV—See Asklepios Kliniken GmbH & Co. KGaA; *Int'l*, pg. 624
PULSO EUROPE LDA—See Asklepios Kliniken GmbH & Co. KGaA; *Int'l*, pg. 624
PULSO INFORMATICA, S.L.U.—See Glintt - Global Intelligent Technologies, S.A.; *Int'l*, pg. 2992
PULSO SOUTH EAST EUROPE P.C.—See Asklepios Kliniken GmbH & Co. KGaA; *Int'l*, pg. 624
PULS RAZISKOVANJE D.O.O—See Ipsos S.A.; *Int'l*, pg. 3801
PULSTEC INDUSTRIAL CO LTD; *Int'l*, pg. 6117
PULSTEC USA INC.—See PULSTEC INDUSTRIAL Co Ltd; *Int'l*, pg. 6117
PULSTEKNIK AB—See Addtech AB; *Int'l*, pg. 134
PULTE ACQUISITION CORP.; *U.S. Private*, pg. 3303
PULTE ARIZONA SERVICES, INC.—See PulteGroup, Inc.; *U.S. Public*, pg. 1737
PULTE.COM, INC.—See PulteGroup, Inc.; *U.S. Public*, pg. 1738
PULTE GEORGIA—See PulteGroup, Inc.; *U.S. Public*, pg. 1737
PULTEGROUP, INC.; *U.S. Public*, pg. 1737
PULTE HOME COMPANY, LLC—See PulteGroup, Inc.; *U.S. Public*, pg. 1737
PULTE HOMES - CARY—See PulteGroup, Inc.; *U.S. Public*, pg. 1737
PULTE HOMES OF MICHIGAN, LLC—See PulteGroup, Inc.; *U.S. Public*, pg. 1737
PULTE HOMES OF NEW ENGLAND LLC—See PulteGroup, Inc.; *U.S. Public*, pg. 1737
PULTE HOMES OF PA, LIMITED PARTNERSHIP—See PulteGroup, Inc.; *U.S. Public*, pg. 1737
PULTE HOMES OF TEXAS, L.P. - DALLAS—See PulteGroup, Inc.; *U.S. Public*, pg. 1737
PULTE HOMES OF TEXAS, L.P. - HOUSTON—See PulteGroup, Inc.; *U.S. Public*, pg. 1737
PULTE HOMES OF TEXAS, L.P.—See PulteGroup, Inc.; *U.S. Public*, pg. 1737
PULTE HOMES - SOUTHWEST FLORIDA—See PulteGroup, Inc.; *U.S. Public*, pg. 1737
PULTE HOMES - ST. LOUIS—See PulteGroup, Inc.; *U.S. Public*, pg. 1737

PULTE HOMES - TAMPA—See PulteGroup, Inc.; *U.S. Public*, pg. 1737
PULTE HOMES TENNESSEE, INC.—See PulteGroup, Inc.; *U.S. Public*, pg. 1737
PULTE HOMES - WASHINGTON, DC—See PulteGroup, Inc.; *U.S. Public*, pg. 1737
PULTE INTERNATIONAL CORPORATION—See PulteGroup, Inc.; *U.S. Public*, pg. 1737
PULTE MORTGAGE LLC—See PulteGroup, Inc.; *U.S. Public*, pg. 1737
PULTE PAYROLL CORPORATION—See PulteGroup, Inc.; *U.S. Public*, pg. 1737
PULVERLACKEN I HILLERSTORP AB—See ITAB Shop Concept AB; *Int'l*, pg. 3828
PULVITEC DO BRASIL INDUSTRIA E COMERCIO DE COLAS E ADESIVOS LTDA—See SOPREMA SAS; *Int'l*, pg. 7111
PULZ ELECTRONICS LTD.; *Int'l*, pg. 6117
PUMA ALPHA VCT PLC; *Int'l*, pg. 6117
PUMA ASIA PACIFIC LTD—See Puma SE; *Int'l*, pg. 6117
PUMA AUSTRALIA PTY. LTD.—See Puma SE; *Int'l*, pg. 6117
PUMA BENELUX BV—See Puma SE; *Int'l*, pg. 6117
PUMA BIOTECHNOLOGY, INC.; *U.S. Public*, pg. 1738
PUMA CANADA, INC.—See Puma SE; *Int'l*, pg. 6117
PUMA CHILE S.P.A.—See Puma SE; *Int'l*, pg. 6117
PUMA CHINA LTD—See Puma SE; *Int'l*, pg. 6117
PUMACY TECHNOLOGIES AG; *Int'l*, pg. 6118
PUMA CZECH REPUBLIC S.R.O.—See Puma SE; *Int'l*, pg. 6117
PUMA DENMARK AS—See Puma SE; *Int'l*, pg. 6117
PUMA DOMINICANA, S.A.—See Sociedade Nacional de Combustiveis de Angola, E.P.; *Int'l*, pg. 7033
PUMA DOMINICANA, S.A.—See Trafigura Beheer B.V.; *Int'l*, pg. 7890
PUMA ENERGY BOTSWANA (PTY) LTD.—See Sociedade Nacional de Combustiveis de Angola, E.P.; *Int'l*, pg. 7033
PUMA ENERGY BOTSWANA (PTY) LTD.—See Trafigura Beheer B.V.; *Int'l*, pg. 7890
PUMA ENERGY COTE D'IVOIRE SA—See Sociedade Nacional de Combustiveis de Angola, E.P.; *Int'l*, pg. 7033
PUMA ENERGY COTE D'IVOIRE SA—See Trafigura Beheer B.V.; *Int'l*, pg. 7890
PUMA ENERGY GUATEMALA S.A.—See Sociedade Nacional de Combustiveis de Angola, E.P.; *Int'l*, pg. 7033
PUMA ENERGY GUATEMALA S.A.—See Trafigura Beheer B.V.; *Int'l*, pg. 7890
PUMA ENERGY HOLDINGS B.V.—See Sociedade Nacional de Combustiveis de Angola, E.P.; *Int'l*, pg. 7033
PUMA ENERGY HOLDINGS B.V.—See Trafigura Beheer B.V.; *Int'l*, pg. 7890
PUMA ENERGY INTERNATIONAL B.V.—See Sociedade Nacional de Combustiveis de Angola, E.P.; *Int'l*, pg. 7033
PUMA ENERGY INTERNATIONAL B.V.—See Trafigura Beheer B.V.; *Int'l*, pg. 7890
PUMA ENERGY NAMIBIA (PTY) LIMITED—See Sociedade Nacional de Combustiveis de Angola, E.P.; *Int'l*, pg. 7033
PUMA ENERGY NAMIBIA (PTY) LIMITED—See Trafigura Beheer B.V.; *Int'l*, pg. 7890
PUMA ENERGY PARAGUAY SA—See Sociedade Nacional de Combustiveis de Angola, E.P.; *Int'l*, pg. 7033
PUMA ENERGY PARAGUAY SA—See Trafigura Beheer B.V.; *Int'l*, pg. 7890
PUMA ENERGY PUERTO RICO, INC.—See Sociedade Nacional de Combustiveis de Angola, E.P.; *Int'l*, pg. 7033
PUMA ENERGY PUERTO RICO, INC.—See Trafigura Beheer B.V.; *Int'l*, pg. 7890
PUMA ENERGY SERVICES SOUTH AFRICA PTY LTD—See Sociedade Nacional de Combustiveis de Angola, E.P.; *Int'l*, pg. 7033
PUMA ENERGY SERVICES SOUTH AFRICA PTY LTD—See Trafigura Beheer B.V.; *Int'l*, pg. 7890
PUMA ENERGY ZAMBIA PLC—See Sociedade Nacional de Combustiveis de Angola, E.P.; *Int'l*, pg. 7033
PUMA ENERGY ZAMBIA PLC—See Trafigura Beheer B.V.; *Int'l*, pg. 7890
PUMA EXPLORATION INC.; *Int'l*, pg. 6117
PUMA FRANCE SAS—See Puma SE; *Int'l*, pg. 6117
PUMA INTERNATIONAL CONGO S.A.—See Sociedade Nacional de Combustiveis de Angola, E.P.; *Int'l*, pg. 7033
PUMA INTERNATIONAL CONGO S.A.—See Trafigura Beheer B.V.; *Int'l*, pg. 7890
PUMA ITALIA S.R.L.—See Puma SE; *Int'l*, pg. 6117
PUMA KOREA LTD—See Puma SE; *Int'l*, pg. 6117
PUMA NEW ZEALAND LIMITED—See Puma SE; *Int'l*, pg. 6117
PUMANGOL LDA—See Sociedade Nacional de Combustiveis de Angola, E.P.; *Int'l*, pg. 7033
PUMANGOL LDA—See Trafigura Beheer B.V.; *Int'l*, pg. 7890
PUMA NOMINEES LIMITED—See Shore Capital Group Plc; *Int'l*, pg. 6860
PUMA NORDIC AB—See Puma SE; *Int'l*, pg. 6117

PUMA NORTH AMERICA, INC.—See Puma SE; *Int'l*, pg. 6118
PUMA NORWAY AS—See Puma SE; *Int'l*, pg. 6117
PUMA POLSKA SP. Z O.O.—See Puma SE; *Int'l*, pg. 6118
PUMA PROPERTY ADVISORS LIMITED—See Shore Capital Group Plc; *Int'l*, pg. 6860
PUMA RETAIL AG—See Puma SE; *Int'l*, pg. 6118
PUMA-RUS O.O.O.—See Puma SE; *Int'l*, pg. 6117
PUMAS AUTOMATION & ROBOTICS PTE. LTD.—See Convum Ltd.; *Int'l*, pg. 1788
PUMA SE; *Int'l*, pg. 6117
PUMA SPORTS GOODS SDN BHD—See Puma SE; *Int'l*, pg. 6118
PUMA SPRINT GMBH—See Puma SE; *Int'l*, pg. 6117
PUMA TAIWAN SPORTS LTD—See Puma SE; *Int'l*, pg. 6117
PUMA UKRAINE LIMITED LIABILITY COMPANY—See Puma SE; *Int'l*, pg. 6117
PUMA UNITED KINGDOM LTD.—See Puma SE; *Int'l*, pg. 6118
PUMC HOLDING CORPORATION; *U.S. Private*, pg. 3303
PUMFORD CONSTRUCTION INC.; *U.S. Private*, pg. 3303
PUMPCO ENERGY SERVICES, INC.—See Superior Energy Services, Inc.; *U.S. Private*, pg. 3877
PUMPCO, INC.—See MasTec, Inc.; *U.S. Public*, pg. 1393
PUMPEN SERVICE BENTZ GMBH—See KSB SE & Co, KGaA; *Int'l*, pg. 4313
PUMPER PARTS LLC—See IDEX Corp; *U.S. Public*, pg. 1092
PUMPEX AB—See Sulzer Ltd.; *Int'l*, pg. 7258
PUMPEX AB—See Sulzer Ltd.; *Int'l*, pg. 7258
PUMPHUSET SVERIGE AB—See KSB SE & Co. KGaA; *Int'l*, pg. 4312
PUMPING SOLUTIONS, INC.—See DXP Enterprises, Inc.; *U.S. Public*, pg. 698
PUMPING SYSTEMS INC.; *U.S. Private*, pg. 3303
PUMPIRAN; *Int'l*, pg. 6118
PUMPJACK SOLAR I, LLC—See Duke Energy Corporation; *U.S. Public*, pg. 691
PUMPMAN HOLDINGS LLC—See Bain Capital, LP; *U.S. Private*, pg. 432
PUMPMAN, LLC—See Bain Capital, LP; *U.S. Private*, pg. 432
PUMP & METER SERVICE INC.; *U.S. Private*, pg. 3303
PUMPNSEAL AUSTRALIA PTY LIMITED—See Diploma PLC; *Int'l*, pg. 2129
PUMP & POWER EQUIPMENT, LLC—See DXP Enterprises, Inc.; *U.S. Public*, pg. 698
PUMP PRO'S, INC.—See Applied Industrial Technologies, Inc.; *U.S. Public*, pg. 171
PUMPS & MOTORS OF BELIZE LTD.—See Endress+Hauser (International) Holding AG; *Int'l*, pg. 2409
PUMPS PARTS & SERVICE INC.; *U.S. Private*, pg. 3304
PUMPTECH, LLC—See Pike Street Capital, LP; *U.S. Private*, pg. 3180
PUMPTRONICS EUROPE LTD—See Premier Pump & Tank Co.; *Int'l*, pg. 5961
PUMPTRON (PROPRIETARY) LIMITED—See The Gorman-Rupp Company; *U.S. Public*, pg. 2085
PUMTECH KOREA CO., LTD.; *Int'l*, pg. 6118
PUNA GEOTHERMAL VENTURE L.P.—See Ormat Technologies, Inc.; *U.S. Public*, pg. 1618
PUNAMUSTA MEDIA OYJ; *Int'l*, pg. 6118
PUNA PLANTATION HAWAII LTD.; *U.S. Private*, pg. 3304
PUNCAK KENCANA SDN BHD—See Nadayu Properties Berhad; *Int'l*, pg. 5123
PUNCAK LUYANG SDN. BHD.—See B.I.G. Industries Berhad; *Int'l*, pg. 790
PUNCAK NIAGA HOLDINGS BERHAD; *Int'l*, pg. 6118
PUNCAK NIAGA INFRASTRUCTURES & PROJECTS PRIVATE LIMITED—See Puncak Niaga Holdings Berhad; *Int'l*, pg. 6118
PUNCAK NIAGA (M) SDN. BHD.—See Puncak Niaga Holdings Berhad; *Int'l*, pg. 6118
PUNCAK OIL & GAS SDN. BHD.—See Puncak Niaga Holdings Berhad; *Int'l*, pg. 6118
THE PUNCH AGENCY—See WPP plc; *Int'l*, pg. 8462
PUNCHCRAFT MACHINING AND TOOLING, LLC—See American Axle & Manufacturing Holdings, Inc.; *U.S. Public*, pg. 97
PUNCH GRAPHIX UK LTD.—See Iep Invest SA; *Int'l*, pg. 3597
PUNCH INDUSTRY CO., LTD. - HYOGO PLANT—See Punch Industry Co., Ltd.; *Int'l*, pg. 6119
PUNCH INDUSTRY CO., LTD. - KITAKAMI PLANT—See Punch Industry Co., Ltd.; *Int'l*, pg. 6119
PUNCH INDUSTRY CO., LTD. - MIYAKO PLANT—See Punch Industry Co., Ltd.; *Int'l*, pg. 6119
PUNCH INDUSTRY CO., LTD.; *Int'l*, pg. 6118
PUNCH INDUSTRY (DALIAN) CO., LTD—See Punch Industry Co., Ltd.; *Int'l*, pg. 6118
PUNCH INDUSTRY (DONGGUAN) CO., LTD.—See Punch Industry Co., Ltd.; *Int'l*, pg. 6118
PUNCH INDUSTRY INDIA PVT. LTD.—See Punch Industry Co., Ltd.; *Int'l*, pg. 6118
PUNCH INDUSTRY MALAYSIA SDN. BHD.—See Punch Industry Co., Ltd.; *Int'l*, pg. 6119

PUNCH INDUSTRY CO., LTD. CORPORATE AFFILIATIONS

PUNCH INDUSTRY MANUFACTURING VIETNAM CO., LTD.—See Punch Industry Co., Ltd.; *Int'l*, pg. 6119
PUNCH INDUSTRY SINGAPORE PTE. LTD.—See Punch Industry Co., Ltd.; *Int'l*, pg. 6119
PUNCH INDUSTRY USA INC.—See Punch Industry Co., Ltd.; *Int'l*, pg. 6119
PUNCH INDUSTRY VIETNAM CO. LTD.—See Punch Industry Co., Ltd.; *Int'l*, pg. 6119
PUNCH INDUSTRY (WAFANGDIAN) CO., LTD.—See Punch Industry Co., Ltd.; *Int'l*, pg. 6119
PUNCH INDUSTRY (WUXI) CO., LTD.—See Punch Industry Co., Ltd.; *Int'l*, pg. 6119
PUNCH-LOK COMPANY—See Parrish Enterprises, Ltd.; *U.S. Private*, pg. 3100
PUNCH PARTNERSHIPS (PML) LIMITED—See Patron Capital Advisers LLP; *Int'l*, pg. 5759
PUNCH PARTNERSHIPS (PTL) LIMITED—See Patron Capital Advisers LLP; *Int'l*, pg. 5759
PUNCH PLASTX EVERGEM NV—See Iep Invest SA; *Int'l*, pg. 3597
PUNCH PLASTX SRO—See Iep Invest SA; *Int'l*, pg. 3597
PUNCH POWERGLIDE STRASBOURG SAS—See Iep Invest SA; *Int'l*, pg. 3597
PUNCH PRESS PRODUCTS, INC.; *U.S. Private*, pg. 3304
PUNCH PUNK SA; *Int'l*, pg. 6119
PUNCH SRO—See Iep Invest SA; *Int'l*, pg. 3597
PUNCH TAVERNS FINANCE PLC—See Patron Capital Advisers LLP; *Int'l*, pg. 5759
PUNCH TAVERNS LIMITED—See Patron Capital Advisers LLP; *Int'l*, pg. 5759
PUNCH TAVERNS (SERVICES) LIMITED—See Patron Capital Advisers LLP; *Int'l*, pg. 5759
PUNCH TECHNIX NV—See Iep Invest SA; *Int'l*, pg. 3597
PUNCH TELEMATIX FRANCE S.A.S—See Trimble, Inc.; *U.S. Public*, pg. 2191
PUNCH TELEMATIX IBERICA S.L—See Trimble, Inc.; *U.S. Public*, pg. 2191
PUNCTUAL TRADING LIMITED; *Int'l*, pg. 6119
PUNDMANN MOTOR CO. INC.; *U.S. Private*, pg. 3304
PUNE FOOTBALL CLUB LIMITED—See Ashok Piramal Group; *Int'l*, pg. 608
PUNE SHOLAPUR ROAD DEVELOPMENT COMPANY LIMITED—See Infrastructure Leasing & Financial Services Limited; *Int'l*, pg. 3698
PUNE STOCK EXCHANGE LIMITED; *Int'l*, pg. 6119
PUNGGUK ALCOHOL INDUSTRIAL CO., LTD; *Int'l*, pg. 6119
PUNGKANG CO., LTD; *Int'l*, pg. 6119
PUNG PEC, INC.—See Uni-President Enterprises Corporation; *Int'l*, pg. 8029
PUNICA GETRANKE GMBH—See PepsiCo, Inc.; *U.S. Public*, pg. 1671
PUNIT COMMERCIALS LIMITED; *Int'l*, pg. 6119
PUNJAB ALKALIES & CHEMICALS LIMITED.; *Int'l*, pg. 6120
PUNJAB CAPITAL SECURITIES (PRIVATE) LIMITED—See First Punjab Modaraba; *Int'l*, pg. 2687
PUNJAB CHEMICALS & CROP PROTECTION LIMITED - EXCEL PHOSPHO CHEM UNIT—See Punjab Chemicals & Crop Protection Limited; *Int'l*, pg. 6120
PUNJAB CHEMICALS & CROP PROTECTION LIMITED - PHARMA DIVISION—See Punjab Chemicals & Crop Protection Limited; *Int'l*, pg. 6120
PUNJAB CHEMICALS & CROP PROTECTION LIMITED; *Int'l*, pg. 6120
PUNJAB COMMUNICATIONS LIMITED; *Int'l*, pg. 6120
PUNJAB NATIONAL BANK; *Int'l*, pg. 6120
PUNJAB OIL MILLS LIMITED; *Int'l*, pg. 6120
PUNJAB & SIND BANK; *Int'l*, pg. 6120
PUNJ LLOYD CONSTRUCTION CONTRACTING COMPANY LIMITED—See Punj Lloyd Ltd.; *Int'l*, pg. 6119
PUNJ LLOYD DELTA RENEWABLES PVT LTD—See Punj Lloyd Ltd.; *Int'l*, pg. 6119
PUNJ LLOYD KAZAKHSTAN LLP—See Punj Lloyd Ltd.; *Int'l*, pg. 6119
PUNJ LLOYD LTD.; *Int'l*, pg. 6119
PUNJLLOYD OIL & GAS (MALAYSIA) SDN. BHD.—See Punj Lloyd Ltd.; *Int'l*, pg. 6119
PUNJ LLOYD PTE LTD—See Punj Lloyd Ltd.; *Int'l*, pg. 6119
PUNKTUM DK A/S—See Arbejdsmarkedets Tillaegspension; *Int'l*, pg. 537
PUNKTUM DK A/S—See Macquarie Group Limited; *Int'l*, pg. 4626
PUNKTUM DK A/S—See PFA Holding A/S; *Int'l*, pg. 5835
PUNKTUM DK A/S—See PKA A/S; *Int'l*, pg. 5887
PUNTA GORDA HMA, INC.—See Community Health Systems, Inc.; *U.S. Public*, pg. 556
PUNTA GORDA HMA PHYSICIAN MANAGEMENT, LLC—See Community Health Systems, Inc.; *U.S. Public*, pg. 556
PUNTER SOUTHALL FINANCIAL MANAGEMENT LTD—See Punter Southall Group Limited; *Int'l*, pg. 6120
PUNTER SOUTHALL GROUP LIMITED—See XPS Pensions Group; *Int'l*, pg. 8538
PUNTER SOUTHALL GROUP LIMITED; *Int'l*, pg. 6120

PUNTER SOUTHALL HEALTH & PROTECTION CONSULTING LIMITED—See Punter Southall Group Limited; *Int'l*, pg. 6120
PUNTERS PARADISE PTY LIMITED—See News Corporation; *U.S. Public*, pg. 1520
PUNTO APARTE; *Int'l*, pg. 6120
PUNTO OGILVY & MATHER—See WPP plc; *Int'l*, pg. 8488
PUNTO RADIO—See Vocento, S.A.; *Int'l*, pg. 8284
PUPIN TELECOM AD; *Int'l*, pg. 6120
PUPKIN FILM B.V.—See Television Francaise 1 S.A.; *Int'l*, pg. 7543
PUPPET LABS INC.; *U.S. Private*, pg. 3304
PUPPET WORKSHOP INC.; *U.S. Private*, pg. 3304
PURABI GENERAL INSURANCE COMPANY LIMITED; *Int'l*, pg. 6120
PURACAP CARIBE LLC—See PuraCap Pharmaceutical LLC; *U.S. Private*, pg. 3304
PURACAP LABORATORIES LLC—See PuraCap Pharmaceutical LLC; *U.S. Private*, pg. 3304
PURACAP PHARMACEUTICAL LLC; *U.S. Private*, pg. 3304
PURAC ASIA PACIFIC PTE. LTD.—See Corbion N.V.; *Int'l*, pg. 1795
PURAC BIOCHEM BV—See Corbion N.V.; *Int'l*, pg. 1795
PURAC BIOQUIMICA S.A.—See Corbion N.V.; *Int'l*, pg. 1795
PURAC CHINA—See Corbion N.V.; *Int'l*, pg. 1795
PURAC DEUTSCHLAND GMBH—See Corbion N.V.; *Int'l*, pg. 1795
PURAC INDIA PRIVATE LIMITED—See Corbion N.V.; *Int'l*, pg. 1795
PURAC JAPAN K.K.—See Corbion N.V.; *Int'l*, pg. 1795
PURAC KOREA—See Corbion N.V.; *Int'l*, pg. 1795
PURAC MEXICO S DE RL DE CV—See Corbion N.V.; *Int'l*, pg. 1795
PURAC POLSKA SP. Z O.O.—See Corbion N.V.; *Int'l*, pg. 1795
PURAC SINTESES—See Corbion N.V.; *Int'l*, pg. 1795
PURAC THAILAND LTD—See Corbion N.V.; *Int'l*, pg. 1795
PURAFIL, INC.—See Madison Industries Holdings LLC; *U.S. Private*, pg. 2543
PURAGRAFT, LLC—See The Jordan Company, L.P.; *U.S. Private*, pg. 4063
PURALUBE GMBH—See Allied Resource Corporation; *U.S. Private*, pg. 187
PURALUBE INC.—See Allied Resource Corporation; *U.S. Private*, pg. 187
PURAMED BIOSCIENCE INC.; *U.S. Private*, pg. 3304
PURA NATURALS, INC.; *U.S. Private*, pg. 3304
PURAPHARM AUSTRALIA PTY LTD—See PuraPharm Corporation Limited; *Int'l*, pg. 6121
PURAPHARM CANADA CORPORATION—See PuraPharm Corporation Limited; *Int'l*, pg. 6121
PURAPHARM CORPORATION LIMITED; *Int'l*, pg. 6121
PURAPHARM JAPAN CORPORATION—See PuraPharm Corporation Limited; *Int'l*, pg. 6121
PURATION, INC.—See American Cannabis Innovations Conglomerated; *U.S. Private*, pg. 226
PURAVANKARA LTD.; *Int'l*, pg. 6121
PURBOND AG—See Henkel AG & Co. KGaA; *Int'l*, pg. 3354
PURCARI WINERIES PUBLIC COMPANY LIMITED; *Int'l*, pg. 6121
PURCELL CO., INC.; *U.S. Private*, pg. 3304
PURCELL CONSTRUCTION CORP; *U.S. Private*, pg. 3304
PURCELL CONSTRUCTION INC.; *U.S. Private*, pg. 3304
PURCELL INTERNATIONAL INC.; *U.S. Private*, pg. 3304
PURCELL MURRAY COMPANY INC.; *U.S. Private*, pg. 3304
PURCELL SYSTEMS, INC.—See EnerSys; *U.S. Public*, pg. 767
PURCELL SYSTEMS INTERNATIONAL AB—See EnerSys; *U.S. Public*, pg. 767
PURCELL TIRE COMPANY OF KENTUCKY—See Purcell Tire & Rubber Company Inc.; *U.S. Private*, pg. 3305
PURCELL TIRE & RUBBER COMPANY INC.; *U.S. Private*, pg. 3304
PURCELL TIRE & RUBBER COMPANY—See Purcell Tire & Rubber Company Inc.; *U.S. Private*, pg. 3305
PURCHASE CLINIC, LLC—See HCA Healthcare, Inc.; *U.S. Public*, pg. 1006
PURCHASE FORD LINCOLN, INC.; *U.S. Private*, pg. 3305
PURCHASES SALES INC.; *U.S. Private*, pg. 3305
THE PURCHASING GROUP, LLC—See CHS INC.; *U.S. Public*, pg. 493
PURCHASING POWER, LLC—See Edwards Capital, LLC; *U.S. Private*, pg. 1342
PURCH GROUP, INC.; *U.S. Private*, pg. 3305
PURDEL, COOPERATIVE AGRO-ALIMENTAIRE; *Int'l*, pg. 6121
PURDICOM LIMITED; *Int'l*, pg. 6121
PURDIE ROGERS, INC.; *U.S. Private*, pg. 3305
PURDIE ROGERS, INC.—See Purdie Rogers, Inc.; *U.S. Private*, pg. 3305
PURDUE PHARMACEUTICALS L.P.—See Purdue Pharma LP; *U.S. Private*, pg. 3305
PURDUE PHARMA LP; *U.S. Private*, pg. 3305

PURDUE PRODUCTS L.P.—See Purdue Pharma LP; *U.S. Private*, pg. 3305
PURDUM GRAY INGLEDUE BECK, INC.—See First Mid Bancshares, Inc.; *U.S. Public*, pg. 846
PURDY BROTHERS TRUCKING COMPANY—See P&S Transportation, Inc.; *U.S. Private*, pg. 3059
PURDY ELECTRIC, INC.—See Kassel Equity Group, LLC; *U.S. Private*, pg. 2264
PURDY MOTOR S.A.; *Int'l*, pg. 6121
PURDYS CHOCOLATIER; *Int'l*, pg. 6121
PURE AIR CONTROL SERVICES, INC.—See RPM International Inc.; *U.S. Public*, pg. 1817
PUREAPPS LIMITED—See Accenture plc; *Int'l*, pg. 87
PUREAU FRESH WATER COMPANY PTY. LTD.—See The Bidvest Group Limited; *Int'l*, pg. 7626
PURE AUSTRALASIA PTY LTD—See Pure International Limited; *Int'l*, pg. 6121
PURE AUTO LLC—See Diversis Capital, LLC; *U.S. Private*, pg. 1244
PURE AUTO LLC—See Stage 1 Ventures, LLC; *U.S. Private*, pg. 3775
PUREBASE CORPORATION; *U.S. Public*, pg. 1738
PURE BIOLOGICS SA; *Int'l*, pg. 6121
PURE BIOSCIENCE, INC.; *U.S. Public*, pg. 1738
PURE BRAND COMMUNICATIONS, LLC; *U.S. Private*, pg. 3305
PURE BRAND COMMUNICATIONS—See Pure Brand Communications, LLC; *U.S. Private*, pg. 3305
PURE CAPITAL SOLUTIONS INC.; *U.S. Public*, pg. 1738
PURE CARBON COMPANY—See Morgan Advanced Materials plc; *Int'l*, pg. 5041
PURE CASTING COMPANY—See Lone Star Foundries, Inc.; *U.S. Private*, pg. 2484
PURE-CHEM PRODUCTS CO., INC.—See Alex C. Fergusson, Inc.; *U.S. Private*, pg. 162
PURECHEM VEOLIA ENVIRONMENTAL SERVICES—See Veolia Environnement S.A.; *Int'l*, pg. 8159
PURECHEM VEOLIA ES PTE. LTD.—See Veolia Environnement S.A.; *Int'l*, pg. 8159
PURECIRCLE AFRICA LIMITED—See Ingredion Incorporated; *U.S. Public*, pg. 1124
PURECIRCLE (JIANGXI) CO. LTD—See Ingredion Incorporated; *U.S. Public*, pg. 1124
PURECIRCLE LIMITED—See Ingredion Incorporated; *U.S. Public*, pg. 1124
PURECIRCLE NATURAL INGREDIENT INDIA PRIVATE LIMITED—See Ingredion Incorporated; *U.S. Public*, pg. 1124
PURECIRCLE SDN. BHD—See Ingredion Incorporated; *U.S. Public*, pg. 1124
PURECIRCLE SOUTH AMERICA SOCIEDAD ANONIMA—See Ingredion Incorporated; *U.S. Public*, pg. 1124
PURECIRCLE USA HOLDINGS INC—See Ingredion Incorporated; *U.S. Public*, pg. 1124
PURECOAT INTERNATIONAL, LLC; *U.S. Private*, pg. 3306
PURE COMMERCE KOREA YH—See Euronet Worldwide, Inc.; *U.S. Public*, pg. 798
PURE COMMERCE PTY LIMITED—See Euronet Worldwide, Inc.; *U.S. Public*, pg. 798
PURECOMMERCE; *U.S. Private*, pg. 3306
PURE COMMERCE (S) PTE. LTD.—See Euronet Worldwide, Inc.; *U.S. Public*, pg. 798
PURE CYCLE CORPORATION; *U.S. Public*, pg. 1738
PURECYCLE TECHNOLOGIES, INC.; *U.S. Public*, pg. 1738
PUREDEPTH, INC.—See Aptiv PLC; *Int'l*, pg. 524
PURE DIGITAL LIMITED—See Pure International Limited; *Int'l*, pg. 6121
PURE ENCAPSULATIONS, LLC—See Nestle S.A.; *Int'l*, pg. 5206
PURE ENERGIES GROUP INC.—See NRG Energy, Inc.; *U.S. Public*, pg. 1550
PURE ENERGY MINERALS LIMITED; *Int'l*, pg. 6121
PURE FINANCIAL ADVISORS, INC.; *U.S. Private*, pg. 3305
PURE FISHING ASIA CO., LTD.—See Sycamore Partners Management, LP; *U.S. Private*, pg. 3896
PURE FISHING DEUTSCHLAND GMBH—See Sycamore Partners Management, LP; *U.S. Private*, pg. 3896
PURE FISHING EUROPE S.A.S.—See Sycamore Partners Management, LP; *U.S. Private*, pg. 3896
PURE FISHING (GUANGZHOU) TRADING CO., LTD.—See Sycamore Partners Management, LP; *U.S. Private*, pg. 3896
PURE FISHING, INC.—See Sycamore Partners Management, LP; *U.S. Private*, pg. 3896
PURE FISHING MALAYSIA SDN. BHD.—See Sycamore Partners Management, LP; *U.S. Private*, pg. 3896
PURE FISHING NETHERLANDS B.V.—See Sycamore Partners Management, LP; *U.S. Private*, pg. 3896
PURE FISHING (THAILAND) CO., LTD.—See Sycamore Partners Management, LP; *U.S. Private*, pg. 3896
PURE FISHING (UK) LTD.—See Sycamore Partners Management, LP; *U.S. Private*, pg. 3896
THE PUREFOODS-HORMEL COMPANY, INC.—See Top Frontier Investment Holdings, Inc.; *Int'l*, pg. 7812
PUREFORMULAS.COM; *U.S. Private*, pg. 3306

PURE FRUIT TECHNOLOGIES, LLC; *U.S. Private*, pg. 3305
PUREFUN! INC.; *U.S. Private*, pg. 3306
PURE GLOBAL CANNABIS INC.; *Int'l*, pg. 6121
PUREGOLD JUNIOR SUPERMARKET, INC.—See Puregold Price Club, Inc.; *Int'l*, pg. 6122
PURE GOLD MINING INC.—See West Red Lake Gold Mines Ltd.; *Int'l*, pg. 8386
PUREGOLD PRICE CLUB, INC.; *Int'l*, pg. 6122
PUREGRAPHITE LLC—See NOVONIX Limited; *Int'l*, pg. 5469
PURE GYM LIMITED—See Leonard Green & Partners, L.P.; *U.S. Private*, pg. 2428
PURE H2O BIO-TECHNOLOGIES, INC.; *U.S. Private*, pg. 3305
PURE HARVEST CORPORATION GROUP, INC.; *U.S. Public*, pg. 1738
PURE HEALTH HOLDING LLC—See Alpha Dhabi Holding PJSC; *Int'l*, pg. 367
PURE HEALTH PRODUCTS, LLC—See Can B Corp.; *U.S. Public*, pg. 428
PURE HEALTH SOLUTIONS, INC.—See BDT Capital Partners, LLC; *U.S. Private*, pg. 502
PURE HELIUM GULF FZE—See L'Air Liquide S.A.; *Int'l*, pg. 4373
PURE HELIUM INDIA PVT. LTD.—See L'Air Liquide S.A.; *Int'l*, pg. 4372
PUREHM INC.—See Xylem Inc.; *U.S. Public*, pg. 2394
PUREHM U.S. INC.—See Xylem Inc.; *U.S. Public*, pg. 2394
PURE HYDROGEN CORPORATION LIMITED; *Int'l*, pg. 6121
PURE INDUSTRIAL REAL ESTATE TRUST—See Blackstone Inc.; *U.S. Public*, pg. 350
PURE INTEGRATION, LLC; *U.S. Private*, pg. 3305
PURE INTERNATIONAL LIMITED; *Int'l*, pg. 6121
PURE IRON PLANT OJSC; *Int'l*, pg. 6121
PURE LAB TECH LTD.—See HORIBA Ltd; *Int'l*, pg. 3478
PURELY ALASKAN WATER INC.; *U.S. Private*, pg. 3306
PURELY CREATIVE LTD—See DM plc; *Int'l*, pg. 2142
THE PURELY GROUP PTY LTD—See Vivendi SE; *Int'l*, pg. 8276
PURE MARKETING GROUP; *U.S. Private*, pg. 3305
PURE MEDIA LIMITED—See Providence Equity Partners L.L.C.; *U.S. Private*, pg. 3292
PURE METAL GALVANIZING, ULC—See Valmont Industries, Inc.; *U.S. Public*, pg. 2274
PURE MULTI-FAMILY REIT LP—See Cortland Partners, LLC; *U.S. Private*, pg. 1061
PURENA GMBH—See E.ON SE; *Int'l*, pg. 2259
PURE NERGY CO., LTD.—See Tongkah Harbour Public Company Limited; *Int'l*, pg. 7808
PURENERGY LLC—See ITOCHU Corporation; *Int'l*, pg. 3838
PURENERGY RENEWABLES, LTD—See Abengoa S.A.; *Int'l*, pg. 59
PURENERGY RENEWABLES, LTD—See Algonquin Power & Utilities Corp.; *Int'l*, pg. 319
PURE NETWORKS, INC.—See Hon Hai Precision Industry Co., Ltd.; *Int'l*, pg. 3456
PURE NORWEGIAN SEAFOOD AS—See Masoval AS; *Int'l*, pg. 4722
PUREN PHARMA GMBH & CO. KG—See Aurobindo Pharma Ltd.; *Int'l*, pg. 713
PUREOIL I/S—See Orkla ASA; *Int'l*, pg. 5639
PUREPAYMENTS LLC—See Rev19, LLC; *U.S. Private*, pg. 3413
PURE PETROLEUM CORP.—See Cosco Capital, Inc.; *Int'l*, pg. 1809
PUREPOINT URANIUM GROUP INC; *Int'l*, pg. 6122
PURE PORTFOLIOS HOLDINGS, LLC—See tru Independce LLC; *U.S. Private*, pg. 4244
PURE POWER TECHNOLOGIES, LLC; *U.S. Private*, pg. 3305
PUREPROFILE LIMITED; *Int'l*, pg. 6122
PUREPROMOTER LTD; *Int'l*, pg. 6122
PURE RATIOS INC.—See 4Front Ventures Corp.; *U.S. Public*, pg. 9
PURERAY CORPORATION; *U.S. Public*, pg. 1738
PURE RECRUITMENT GROUP LTD; *Int'l*, pg. 6121
PURE RED CREATIVE—See GA Communications Inc.; *U.S. Private*, pg. 1632
PURE RESOURCES LIMITED; *Int'l*, pg. 6122
PURERFID INC.—See SuperCom Ltd.; *Int'l*, pg. 7336
PURE ROMANCE PARTIES, INC.; *U.S. Private*, pg. 3306
PURE SEARCH INTERNATIONAL LIMITED—See Pure Recruitment Group Ltd.; *Int'l*, pg. 6122
PURE SEARCH INTERNATIONAL SINGAPORE PTE LTD—See Pure Recruitment Group Ltd.; *Int'l*, pg. 6122
PURE (SHANGHAI) TECHNOLOGIES CO., LTD.—See Xylem Inc.; *U.S. Public*, pg. 2394
PURESINO (GUANGHAN) WATER CO. LTD.—See Taliworks Corporation Berhad; *Int'l*, pg. 7447
PURESINSE INC.—See Pure Global Cannabis Inc.; *Int'l*, pg. 6121
PURE SOLAR POWER (IP) PTY. LTD.—See EnviroMission Limited; *Int'l*, pg. 2454
PURE SOLUTIONS NA, LLC—See Ashford Inc.; *U.S. Public*, pg. 211

PURE-STAT TECHNOLOGIES, INC.—See Huhtamaki Oyj; *Int'l*, pg. 3526
PURE STORAGE HK LTD.—See Pure Storage, Inc.; *U.S. Public*, pg. 1738
PURE STORAGE, INC.; *U.S. Public*, pg. 1738
PURE STORAGE LTD.—See Pure Storage, Inc.; *U.S. Public*, pg. 1738
PURE STORAGE NEW ZEALAND LIMITED—See Pure Storage, Inc.; *U.S. Public*, pg. 1738
PURE STORAGE (RUS) LIMITED LIABILITY COMPANY—See Pure Storage, Inc.; *U.S. Public*, pg. 1738
PURE SUNFARMS CORP.—See Village Farms International Inc.; *Int'l*, pg. 8206
PURE SURFACE TECHNOLOGY, LTD.—See ULVAC, Inc.; *Int'l*, pg. 8020
PURE-SYSTEMS GMBH—See PTC Inc.; *U.S. Public*, pg. 1735
PURETECH HEALTH PLC; *U.S. Public*, pg. 1738
PURE TECHNOLOGIES ABU DHABI—See Xylem Inc.; *U.S. Public*, pg. 2394
PURE TECHNOLOGIES (AUSTRALIA) PTY. LTD.—See Xylem Inc.; *U.S. Public*, pg. 2394
PURE TECHNOLOGIES CANADA LTD.—See Xylem Inc.; *U.S. Public*, pg. 2394
PURE TECHNOLOGIES LTD.—See Xylem Inc.; *U.S. Public*, pg. 2394
PURE TECHNOLOGIES (NANJING) LIMITED—See Xylem Inc.; *U.S. Public*, pg. 2394
PURETEK CORPORATION; *U.S. Private*, pg. 3306
PURE THAI ENERGY CO., LTD.—See RPCG Public Company Limited; *Int'l*, pg. 6414
PURE TO PURE BEAUTY INC.; *Int'l*, pg. 6122
PURE TOUCH BOTANICALS, LLC—See Vext Science, Inc.; *Int'l*, pg. 8182
PURE TRANSIT TECHNOLOGIES, INC.; *U.S. Private*, pg. 3306
PUREUN MUTUAL SAVINGS BANK; *Int'l*, pg. 6122
PURE WAFER INC.—See ZelnickMedia Corp.; *U.S. Private*, pg. 4600
PURE WATER SCANDINAVIA AB—See Sdiptech AB; *Int'l*, pg. 6659
PURE WATER SOLUTIONS, INC.—See Xylem Inc; *U.S. Public*, pg. 2394
PURE WATER TECH OF SAN DIEGO—See BDT Capital Partners, LLC; *U.S. Private*, pg. 503
PUREWICK CORPORATION—See Becton, Dickinson & Company; *U.S. Public*, pg. 292
PUREWORKS, INC.—See Underwriters Laboratories Inc.; *U.S. Private*, pg. 4280
PURE WORLD ENERGY LIMITED—See JLG Group PLC; *Int'l*, pg. 3973
PUREX INTERNATIONAL LIMITED—See Brother Industries, Ltd.; *Int'l*, pg. 1198
THE PUREY CUST NUFFIELD HOSPITAL—See Nuffield Health; *Int'l*, pg. 5488
PURFER SAS—See Derichebourg S.A.; *Int'l*, pg. 2041
PURFOODS, LLC—See Cressey & Company, LP; *U.S. Private*, pg. 1095
PURGATOIRE VALLEY CONSTRUCTION; *U.S. Private*, pg. 3306
PURIFICATION CELLUTIONS, LLC—See Ingevity Corporation; *U.S. Public*, pg. 1122
PURIFLOH LIMITED; *Int'l*, pg. 6122
PURINA ALIMENTOS LTDA.—See Nestle S.A.; *Int'l*, pg. 5209
PURINA GOLDEN SUN—See Land O'Lakes, Inc.; *U.S. Private*, pg. 2383
PURINA MILLS, LLC—See Land O'Lakes, Inc.; *U.S. Private*, pg. 2383
PURINA MILLS, LLC—See Nestle S.A.; *Int'l*, pg. 5209
PURINA PETCARE (MALAYSIA) SDN. BHD.—See Nestle S.A.; *Int'l*, pg. 5211
PURISMA, INC.—See Cannae Holdings, Inc.; *U.S. Public*, pg. 430
PURISMA, INC.—See CC Capital Partners, LLC; *U.S. Private*, pg. 798
PURISMA, INC.—See Intercontinental Exchange, Inc.; *U.S. Public*, pg. 1142
PURITAN BAKERY, INC.; *U.S. Private*, pg. 3306
PURITAN CHRYSLER-PLYMOUTH INC.; *U.S. Private*, pg. 3306
PURITAN CLEANERS; *U.S. Private*, pg. 3306
PURITAN CLOTHING COMPANY OF CAPE COD; *U.S. Private*, pg. 3306
PURITAN PRODUCTS, INC.—See Avantor, Inc.; *U.S. Public*, pg. 241
PURITAN'S PRIDE, INC.—See KKR & Co. Inc.; *U.S. Public*, pg. 1264
PURITAS (PVT) LTD.—See Hayleys PLC; *Int'l*, pg. 3292
PURIT CO., LTD.; *Int'l*, pg. 6122
PURITECH TECHNOLOGIES (S) PTE. LTD.—See Sunresin New Materials Co., Ltd.; *Int'l*, pg. 7320
PURITY BAKERIES—See Goddard Enterprises Limited; *Int'l*, pg. 3019
PURITY CYLINDER GASES INC.; *U.S. Private*, pg. 3306
PURITY DAIRIES - HOHENWALD PLANT—See Dean Foods Company; *U.S. Private*, pg. 1184

PURITY DAIRIES, LLC—See Dean Foods Company; *U.S. Private*, pg. 1184
PURITY FACTORIES LIMITED; *Int'l*, pg. 6122
PURITY FLEX PACK LTD.; *Int'l*, pg. 6122
PURITY IT AS—See Dustin Group AB; *Int'l*, pg. 2235
PURITY WHOLESALE GROCERS, INC.; *U.S. Private*, pg. 3306
PURKEY'S FLEET ELECTRIC, INC.—See Windjammer Capital Investors, LLC; *U.S. Private*, pg. 4538
PURMO GROUP BELGIUM N.V.—See Rettig Group Ltd.; *Int'l*, pg. 6310
PURMO GROUP DENMARK APS—See Rettig Group Ltd.; *Int'l*, pg. 6310
PURMO GROUP FINLAND OY AB—See Rettig Group Ltd.; *Int'l*, pg. 6310
PURMO GROUP FRANCE SAS—See Rettig Group Ltd.; *Int'l*, pg. 6310
PURMO GROUP LATVIA SIA—See Rettig Group Ltd.; *Int'l*, pg. 6310
PURMO GROUP POLAND SP.Z O.O.—See Rettig Group Ltd.; *Int'l*, pg. 6310
PURMO GROUP SWEDEN AB—See Rettig Group Ltd.; *Int'l*, pg. 6310
PURMORT & MARTIN INSURANCE AGENCY, LLC; *U.S. Private*, pg. 3306
PURNABINA SDN. BHD.—See Southern Capital Group Pte. Ltd.; *Int'l*, pg. 7118
PURNAVA LIMITED—See Renata Limited; *Int'l*, pg. 6273
PURNELL FURNITURE SERVICES, INC.—See Fidelitone, Inc.; *U.S. Private*, pg. 1502
PURNIMA BIKAS BANK LIMITED—See Shine Resunga Development Bank Limited; *Int'l*, pg. 6842
PURO.EARTH OY—See Nasdaq, Inc.; *U.S. Public*, pg. 1492
PUROHIT CONSTRUCTION LTD.; *Int'l*, pg. 6122
PUROHIT NAVIGATION, INC.; *U.S. Private*, pg. 3306
PUROLITE CORPORATION—See Ecolab Inc.; *U.S. Public*, pg. 716
PURONICS, INC.—See Franklin Electric Co., Inc.; *U.S. Public*, pg. 879
PUROSYSTEMS, INC.; *U.S. Private*, pg. 3306
PUR-O-ZONE, INC.; *U.S. Private*, pg. 3304
PURPLE BIOTECH LTD.; *Int'l*, pg. 6122
PURPLE COMMUNICATIONS, INC.—See Kinderhook Industries, LLC; *U.S. Private*, pg. 2306
PURPLE ENTERTAINMENT LIMITED; *Int'l*, pg. 6122
PURPLE FEET WINES, LLC—See The Winebow Group, LLC; *U.S. Private*, pg. 4137
PURPLE GROUP LIMITED; *Int'l*, pg. 6122
PURPLE INNOVATION, INC.; *U.S. Public*, pg. 1738
THE PURPLE PARTNERSHIP LIMITED—See Brown & Brown, Inc.; *U.S. Public*, pg. 397
PURPLEREAL.COM, CORP.; *U.S. Private*, pg. 3307
PURPLE SQUARE MANAGEMENT PARTNERS BV—See Ctac N.V.; *Int'l*, pg. 1869
PURPLE VENTURES CO., LTD.; *Int'l*, pg. 6122
PURPLE WAVE, INC; *U.S. Private*, pg. 3306
PURPLE WIFI LTD; *Int'l*, pg. 6122
PURPLE WINE COMPANY; *U.S. Private*, pg. 3306
PURPOSECARE HOMECARE LLC—See Lorient Capital Management LLC; *U.S. Private*, pg. 2495
PURPOSE ETHER STAKING CORP. ETF; *Int'l*, pg. 6123
PURPOSE FLOATING RATE INCOME FUND; *Int'l*, pg. 6123
PURPOSE GLOBAL FINANCIALS INCOME FUND—See Purpose Investments Inc.; *Int'l*, pg. 6123
PURPOSE INVESTMENTS INC.; *Int'l*, pg. 6123
PURPOSE SILVER BULLION FUND; *Int'l*, pg. 6123
PURSHOTTAM INVESTOFIN LTD.; *Int'l*, pg. 6123
PURSO GROUP OY; *Int'l*, pg. 6123
PURSO-TOOLS OY—See Purso Group Oy; *Int'l*, pg. 6123
THE PURSUANT GROUP, INC.—See Allegiance Fundraising LLC; *U.S. Private*, pg. 176
PURSUE ENERGY—See Petro-Hunt, L.L.C.; *U.S. Private*, pg. 3162
PURSUIT GOLD CORP.; *Int'l*, pg. 6123
PURSUIT MARINE DRIVE LIMITED—See Cellulac Limited; *Int'l*, pg. 1395
PURSUIT MINERALS LIMITED; *Int'l*, pg. 6123
PURSUIT OF EXCELLENCE, INC.; *U.S. Private*, pg. 3307
PURSUIT VASCULAR, INC.—See ICU Medical, Inc.; *U.S. Public*, pg. 1087
PUR-SYSTEMS GMBH—See Huntsman Corporation; *U.S. Public*, pg. 1073
PUR-SYSTEMS VERWANTUNGSGESELLSCHAFT MBH—See Huntsman Corporation; *U.S. Public*, pg. 1073
PURTHANOL RESOURCES LIMITED; *U.S. Public*, pg. 1738
PURTON CARBONS LTD.—See Kemira Oyj; *Int'l*, pg. 4124
PURVALAND PRIVATE LIMITED—See Puravankara Ltd.; *Int'l*, pg. 6121
PURVIS BEARING SERVICE LTD.; *U.S. Private*, pg. 3307
PURVIS BROTHERS INC.; *U.S. Private*, pg. 3307
PURVIS FORD, INC.; *U.S. Private*, pg. 3307
PURWANCHAL GRAMEEN BIKASH BANK LIMITED; *Int'l*, pg. 6123
PUSAN CAST IRON CO., LTD.; *Int'l*, pg. 6123

PUSAN CITY GAS CO., LTD.—See SK Inc.; *Int'l*, pg. 6972
PUSAT MEMBELI-BELAH KAMDAR (PENANG) SDN. BHD.—See Kamdar Group (M) Berhad; *Int'l*, pg. 4061
PUSAT MEMBELI-BELAH KAMDAR SDN. BHD.—See Kamdar Group (M) Berhad; *Int'l*, pg. 4061
PUSAT PAKAR KLUANG UTAMA SDN BHD—See KPJ Healthcare Berhad; *Int'l*, pg. 4297
PUSCH BAU GMBH & CO. KG—See H. Geiger GmbH; *Int'l*, pg. 3194
PUSH CREATIVE; *U.S. Private*, pg. 3307
PUSHFOR TECH INC.; *Int'l*, pg. 6123
PUSH INC.; *U.S. Private*, pg. 3307
PUSH, INC.; *U.S. Private*, pg. 3307
PUSH INTERACTIVE, LLC—See Logiq, Inc.; *U.S. Public*, pg. 1341
PUSHPANJALI REALMS & INFRATECH LTD.; *Int'l*, pg. 6123
PUSHPAY HOLDINGS LIMITED—See BGH Capital Pty Ltd; *Int'l*, pg. 1008
PUSHPAY HOLDINGS LIMITED—See Sixth Street Partners LLC; *U.S. Private*, pg. 3677
PUSH PAY, INC.—See OV Loop, Inc.; *U.S. Private*, pg. 3052
PUSH PEDAL PULL, INC.; *U.S. Private*, pg. 3307
PUSHPSONS INDUSTRIES LTD.; *Int'l*, pg. 6123
PUSH SEVEN, INC.—See Pipitone Group; *U.S. Private*, pg. 3190
PUSH; *U.S. Private*, pg. 3307
PUSPAKOM SDN. BHD.—See DRB-HICOM Berhad; *Int'l*, pg. 2202
PUSSIHUKKA OY—See Lassila & Tikanoja plc; *Int'l*, pg. 4421
PUSZTA KONZERV KFT.—See Avantha Group; *Int'l*, pg. 736
PUT A.D.; *Int'l*, pg. 6123
PUTEVI A.D.; *Int'l*, pg. 6123
PUTEVI A.D.; *Int'l*, pg. 6123
PUTEVI CACAK DOO—See STRABAG SE; *Int'l*, pg. 7232
PUTHEP CO., LTD.—See Padaeng Industry pcl; *Int'l*, pg. 5693
PUTIAN COMMUNICATION GROUP LTD.; *Int'l*, pg. 6123
PUTIAN DEXING ELECTRONIC CO., LTD—See Tak Shun Technology Group Limited; *Int'l*, pg. 7428
PUTINKI OY—See Karto Oy; *Int'l*, pg. 4085
PUTNALS PREMIUM PINESTRAW INC.; *U.S. Private*, pg. 3307
PUTNAM ADVISORY COMPANY, LLC—See Franklin Resources, Inc.; *U.S. Public*, pg. 883
PUTNAM ASSOCIATES, LLC—See Clayton, Dubilier & Rice, LLC; *U.S. Private*, pg. 928
PUTNAM BANK—See Centreville Bank; *U.S. Private*, pg. 829
PUTNAM CHEVROLET INC.—See Morse Operations Inc.; *U.S. Private*, pg. 2790
PUTNAM COMMUNITY MEDICAL CENTER, LLC—See Apollo Global Management, Inc.; *U.S. Public*, pg. 158
PUTNAM COMPANY; *U.S. Private*, pg. 3307
PUTNAM COUNTY BANK INC; *U.S. Private*, pg. 3307
PUTNAM COUNTY NATIONAL BANK; *U.S. Public*, pg. 1739
PUTNAM COUNTY SAVINGS BANK; *U.S. Private*, pg. 3307
PUTNAM-GREENE FINANCIAL CORPORATION; *U.S. Private*, pg. 3307
PUTNAM HOSPITAL, INC.—See HCA Healthcare, Inc.; *U.S. Public*, pg. 1006
PUTNAM INVESTMENTS, LLC—See Franklin Resources, Inc.; *U.S. Public*, pg. 883
PUTNAM LEXUS; *U.S. Private*, pg. 3307
PUTNAM MATERIALS CORP.—See Peckham Industries, Inc.; *U.S. Private*, pg. 3127
PUTNAM MECHANICAL, LLC—See White Wolf Capital LLC; *U.S. Private*, pg. 4510
PUTNAM MORTGAGE OPPORTUNITIES FUND—See Franklin Resources, Inc.; *U.S. Public*, pg. 883
PUTNAM PLASTICS COMPANY, LLC—See Foster Corporation; *U.S. Private*, pg. 1578
PUTNAM PLASTICS, INC.; *U.S. Private*, pg. 3307
PUTNAM RADIATION ONCOLOGY, LLC—See HCA Healthcare, Inc.; *U.S. Public*, pg. 1006
PUTNAM SOURCING GROUP; *U.S. Private*, pg. 3307
PUTNAM SURGICAL GROUP, LLC—See HCA Healthcare, Inc.; *U.S. Public*, pg. 1006
PUTNIK A.D.; *Int'l*, pg. 6123
PUTNIK A.D.—See METROPOL Group of Companies; *Int'l*, pg. 4863
PUTNIK A.D.; *Int'l*, pg. 6123
PUTPROP LIMITED; *Int'l*, pg. 6124
PUTRAJAYA PERDANA BERHAD; *Int'l*, pg. 6124
PUTSCH & COMPANY INC.—See Putsch GmbH & Co. KG; *Int'l*, pg. 6124
PUTSCH CST GMBH—See Putsch GmbH & Co. KG; *Int'l*, pg. 6124
PUTSCH GMBH & CO. KG; *Int'l*, pg. 6124
PUTSCH MENICONI S. P. A.—See Putsch GmbH & Co. KG; *Int'l*, pg. 6124
PUTSCH NERVA S.A.—See Putsch GmbH & Co. KG; *Int'l*, pg. 6124

PUTSCH STORD S.R.O.—See Putsch GmbH & Co. KG; *Int'l*, pg. 6124
PUTTHACHART ESTATE CO., LTD.—See Pruksa Real Estate Public Company Limited; *Int'l*, pg. 6010
PUTT-PUTT, LLC; *U.S. Private*, pg. 3308
PUTUMAYO WORLD MUSIC INC.; *U.S. Private*, pg. 3308
PUTZMEISTER AMERICA, INC.—See Sany Group Co., Ltd.; *Int'l*, pg. 6563
PUTZMEISTER CONCRETE PUMPS GMBH—See Sany Group Co., Ltd.; *Int'l*, pg. 6563
PUTZMEISTER FRANCE SARL—See Sany Group Co., Ltd.; *Int'l*, pg. 6563
PUTZMEISTER HOLDING GMBH—See Sany Group Co., Ltd.; *Int'l*, pg. 6562
PUTZMEISTER IBERICA S.A.—See Sany Group Co., Ltd.; *Int'l*, pg. 6563
PUTZMEISTER ITALIA S.R.L.—See Sany Group Co., Ltd.; *Int'l*, pg. 6563
PUTZMEISTER JAPAN LTD.—See Sany Group Co., Ltd.; *Int'l*, pg. 6563
PUTZMEISTER KOREA CO., LTD.—See Sany Group Co., Ltd.; *Int'l*, pg. 6563
PUTZMEISTER LTD.—See Sany Group Co., Ltd.; *Int'l*, pg. 6563
PUTZMEISTER MACHINERY (SHANGHAI) CO., LTD.—See Sany Group Co., Ltd.; *Int'l*, pg. 6563
PUTZMEISTER MORTELMASCHINEN GMBH—See Sany Group Co., Ltd.; *Int'l*, pg. 6563
PUTZMEISTER SHOTCRETE TECHNOLOGY, INC.—See Sany Group Co., Ltd.; *Int'l*, pg. 6563
PUTZMEISTER SOLID PUMPS GMBH—See Sany Group Co., Ltd.; *Int'l*, pg. 6563
PUTZMEISTER SOUTH AFRICA (PTY) LTD.—See Sany Group Co., Ltd.; *Int'l*, pg. 6563
PUUMERKKI AS—See Stora Enso Oyj; *Int'l*, pg. 7224
PUUMERKKI OY—See Mimir Invest AB; *Int'l*, pg. 4898
PUUR NV—See Colruyt Group N.V.; *Int'l*, pg. 1705
PUVAB AB—See Investment AB Latour; *Int'l*, pg. 3784
PUXING ENERGY LTD.; *Int'l*, pg. 6124
PUXIN LIMITED; *Int'l*, pg. 6124
THE PUYALLUP HERALD—See Chatham Asset Management, LLC; *U.S. Private*, pg. 867
PUYALLUP TRIBAL HEALTH AUTHORITY; *U.S. Private*, pg. 3308
PUYALLUP TRIBE OF INDIANS; *U.S. Private*, pg. 3308
PUYANG HUICHENG ELECTRONIC MATERIAL CO., LTD.; *Int'l*, pg. 6124
PUYANG REFRACTORIES GROUP CO., LTD.; *Int'l*, pg. 6124
PUY DU FOU RESTAURATION SAS—See Compass Group PLC; *Int'l*, pg. 1752
PUYLAERT DESIGNS OF THE TIME N.V.—See Dainichiseika Color & Chemicals Mfg. Co., Ltd.; *Int'l*, pg. 1939
PUZ MEIBES SP. Z.O.O.—See Aalberts N.V.; *Int'l*, pg. 35
PUZZLEPART AS—See Crayon Group Holding ASA; *Int'l*, pg. 1829
PUZZLER MEDIA LIMITED—See D.C. Thomson & Co. Ltd.; *Int'l*, pg. 1900
PV2 INVESTMENT JSC; *Int'l*, pg. 6125
PVA CONTROL GMBH—See PVA TePla AG; *Int'l*, pg. 6125
PVA CRYSTAL GROWING SYSTEMS GMBH—See PVA TePla AG; *Int'l*, pg. 6125
PVA INDUSTRIAL VACUUM SYSTEMS GMBH—See PVA TePla AG; *Int'l*, pg. 6125
PVA ITALY S.R.L.—See PVA TePla AG; *Int'l*, pg. 6125
PVA LOT- UND WERKSTOFFTECHNIK GMBH—See PVA TePla AG; *Int'l*, pg. 6125
P. VAN EERD BEHEERSMAATSCHAPPIJ B.V—See Gammon India Limited; *Int'l*, pg. 2879
P. VAN LEEUWEN JR'S BUIZENHANDEL B.V.—See Van Leeuwen Pipe & Tube Group B.V.; *Int'l*, pg. 8127
PVA SEMICONDUCTOR SYSTEMS XI'AN LTD.—See PVA TePla AG; *Int'l*, pg. 6125
PVA SPA SOFTWARE ENTWICKLUNGS GMBH—See PVA TePla AG; *Int'l*, pg. 6125
P&V ASSURANCES SCRL; *Int'l*, pg. 5681
PVA TEPLA AG; *Int'l*, pg. 6125
PVA TEPLA AMERICA INC.—See PVA TePla AG; *Int'l*, pg. 6125
PVA TEPLA ANALYTICAL SYSTEMS GMBH.—See PVA TePla AG; *Int'l*, pg. 6125
PVA TEPLA (CHINA) LTD.—See PVA TePla AG; *Int'l*, pg. 6125
PVA TEPLA SINGAPORE PTE. LTD.—See PVA TePla AG; *Int'l*, pg. 6125
PV AUTOMOTIVE GMBH—See Stahlgruber Otto Gruber GmbH & Co. KG; *Int'l*, pg. 7164
PVA VAKUUM ANLAGENBAU JENA GMBH.—See PVA TePla AG; *Int'l*, pg. 6125
P&V BBDO—See Omnicom Group Inc.; *U.S. Public*, pg. 1576
PVBJ INC.—See VISION ENERGY CORPORATION; *U.S. Public*, pg. 2304
PVCP CHINA REAL ESTATE BROKERAGE COMPANY LIMITED—See Pierre & Vacances SA; *Int'l*, pg. 5864
PV CRYSTALOX SOLAR GMBH—See PV Crystalox Solar plc; *Int'l*, pg. 6124
PV CRYSTALOX SOLAR KK—See PV Crystalox Solar plc; *Int'l*, pg. 6124

PV CRYSTALOX SOLAR PLC; *Int'l*, pg. 6124
PVD PRODUCTS—See High Temperature Superconductors, Inc.; *U.S. Private*, pg. 1937
PV ENGINEERING SA PTY LTD—See AVK Holding A/S; *Int'l*, pg. 748
PVE SHEFFLER, LLC; *U.S. Private*, pg. 3308
PVGASCITY JOIN STOCK COMPANY; *Int'l*, pg. 6125
PVH CORP.; *U.S. Public*, pg. 1739
PVH FINLAND OY—See PVH Corp.; *U.S. Public*, pg. 1739
PVH NECKWEAR, INC.—See PVH Corp.; *U.S. Public*, pg. 1739
PVH OSTERREICH GESMBH—See PVH Corp.; *U.S. Public*, pg. 1739
PVH SUPERBA/INSIGNIA NECKWEAR, INC.—See PVH Corp.; *U.S. Public*, pg. 1739
PVH WHOLESALE CORP.—See PVH Corp.; *U.S. Public*, pg. 1739
PVI ASSET MANAGEMENT JOINT STOCK COMPANY—See PVI Holdings; *Int'l*, pg. 6125
PVI HOLDINGS INC.—See MiddleGround Management, LP; *U.S. Private*, pg. 2712
PVI HOLDINGS; *Int'l*, pg. 6125
PVI INDUSTRIES LLC—See Watts Water Technologies, Inc.; *U.S. Public*, pg. 2337
PVI INSURANCE CORPORATION—See PVI Holdings; *Int'l*, pg. 6125
PVM FUTURES INC.—See TP ICAP Finance PLC; *Int'l*, pg. 7881
PVM OIL ASSOCIATES INC.—See TP ICAP Finance PLC; *Int'l*, pg. 7881
PVM OIL ASSOCIATES PTE. LTD.—See TP ICAP Finance PLC; *Int'l*, pg. 7881
PVM OIL FUTURES LIMITED—See TP ICAP Finance PLC; *Int'l*, pg. 7881
PV MORTGAGE COMPANY—See Platte Valley Financial Service Companies Inc.; *U.S. Private*, pg. 3211
PVM TAB TECH B.V.—See Perfetti Van Melle Holding B.V.; *Int'l*, pg. 5800
PVO-POOL OY—See Pohjolan Voima Oy; *Int'l*, pg. 5904
PVO-VESIVOIMA OY—See Pohjolan Voima Oy; *Int'l*, pg. 5904
PVP ADVANCED EO SYSTEMS, INC.—See Rafael Advanced Defense Systems Ltd.; *Int'l*, pg. 6177
PVPII - FNSS ACQUISITION, INC.; *U.S. Private*, pg. 3308
PV REPOWER INC.—See Abalance Corporation Ltd.; *Int'l*, pg. 48
PVR LIMITED; *Int'l*, pg. 6125
PVR TECHNOLOGIES INC.—See Alten S.A.; *Int'l*, pg. 390
PVS CHEMICALS BELGIUM N.V.—See PVS Chemicals, Inc.; *U.S. Private*, pg. 3308
PVS CHEMICALS, INC.; *U.S. Private*, pg. 3308
PVS CHEMICAL SOLUTIONS, INC.—See PVS Chemicals, Inc.; *U.S. Private*, pg. 3308
PVS CHEMICALS SOLUTIONS INC. - BUFFALO—See PVS Chemicals, Inc.; *U.S. Private*, pg. 3308
PVS CHEMICALS SOLUTIONS, INC. - CHICAGO—See PVS Chemicals, Inc.; *U.S. Private*, pg. 3308
PVS CHEMICALS SOLUTIONS INC. - COPLEY—See PVS Chemicals, Inc.; *U.S. Private*, pg. 3308
PVS-HUNGARY KFT.—See PVS-Kunststofftechnik GmbH & Co. KG; *Int'l*, pg. 6125
PV SILICON FORSCHUNGS UND PRODUKTIONS GMBH—See PV Crystalox Solar plc; *Int'l*, pg. 6125
PVS-KUNSTSTOFFTECHNIK GMBH & CO. KG; *Int'l*, pg. 6125
PVS-NOLWOOD CHEMICALS, INC.—See PVS Chemicals, Inc.; *U.S. Private*, pg. 3308
PVS PLASTICS TECHNOLOGY CORP.—See PVS-Kunststofftechnik GmbH & Co. KG; *Int'l*, pg. 6125
PVS PLASTICS TECHNOLOGY (SHANGHAI) CO., LTD.—See PVS-Kunststofftechnik GmbH & Co. KG; *Int'l*, pg. 6125
PVS TECHNOLOGIES, INC.—See PVS Chemicals, Inc.; *U.S. Private*, pg. 3308
PVS TRANSPORTATION, INC.—See PVS Chemicals, Inc.; *U.S. Private*, pg. 3308
PV SYSTEM AB—See Storskogen Group AB; *Int'l*, pg. 7228
PVTEC S.A.—See Quinenco S.A.; *Int'l*, pg. 6164
PV TOHUMCULUK VE TARIM URUNLERI SANAYIVE TICARET LIMITED SIRKETI—See KWS SAAT SE & Co. KGaA; *Int'l*, pg. 4353
PVT PORTAFOLIO DE VALORES S.A.; *Int'l*, pg. 6125
PVT SYSTEMS—See Cataract Steel Industries, Inc.; *U.S. Private*, pg. 788
PV VACUUM ENGINEERING PTE LTD—See Darco Water Technologies Limited; *Int'l*, pg. 1972
PVV INFRA LIMITED; *Int'l*, pg. 6125
PWA INSURANCE SERVICES, LLC—See Genstar Capital, LLC; *U.S. Private*, pg. 1674
PWA-PROSEP MALAYSIA—See AQUANEX, Servicio Domiciliario del Agua de EXTREMADURA SA; *Int'l*, pg. 527
PWB (M) SDN. BHD.—See OCS Group Limited; *Int'l*, pg. 5521
PWC ADVISORY CO., LTD.—See PricewaterhouseCoopers Co., Ltd.; *Int'l*, pg. 5970
PWC ASESORES EMPRESARIALES CIA. LTDA.; *Int'l*, pg. 6126

COMPANY NAME INDEX

PWC BURGENLAND WIRTSCHAFTSPRUFUNG UND STEUERBERATUNG GMBH—See PwC Osterreich GmbH Wirtschaftsprufungsgesellschaft; *Int'l*, pg. 6126
PWC INTERNATIONAL ASSIGNMENT SERVICES (HONG KONG) LTD.—See PricewaterhouseCoopers Limited; *Int'l*, pg. 5971
PWC KARNTEN WIRTSCHAFTSPRUFUNG UND STEUERBERATUNG GMBH—See PwC Osterreich GmbH Wirtschaftsprufungsgesellschaft; *Int'l*, pg. 6126
PWC OBEROSTERREICH WIRTSCHAFTSPRUFUNG UND STEUERBERATUNG GMBH—See PwC Osterreich GmbH Wirtschaftsprufungsgesellschaft; *Int'l*, pg. 6126
PWC OFFICE AUTOMATION (PTY) LIMITED—See Reunert Limited; *Int'l*, pg. 6312
PWC OSTERREICH GMBH WIRTSCHAFTSPRUFUNGSGESELLSCHAFT; *Int'l*, pg. 6126
PWC STEIERMARK WIRTSCHAFTSPRUFUNG UND STEUERBERATUNG GMBH—See PwC Osterreich GmbH Wirtschaftsprufungsgesellschaft; *Int'l*, pg. 6126
PWC STRATEGY& (AUSTRALIA) PTY. LTD.—See PricewaterhouseCoopers Australia (International) Pty. Ltd.; *Int'l*, pg. 5969
PWC STRATEGY& (CHINA) CO., LTD.—See PricewaterhouseCoopers Consultants (Shenzhen) Limited; *Int'l*, pg. 5970
PWC STRATEGY& FRANCE SAS—See PricewaterhouseCoopers France Sarl; *Int'l*, pg. 5971
PWC STRATEGY& (GERMANY) GMBH—See PricewaterhouseCoopers AG Wirtschaftsprufungsgesellschaft; *Int'l*, pg. 5969
PWC STRATEGY& INC.—See PricewaterhouseCoopers International Limited; *Int'l*, pg. 5971
PWC STRATEGY& (INDIA) PVT. LTD.—See PricewaterhouseCoopers Pvt. Ltd.; *Int'l*, pg. 5972
PWC STRATEGY& (ITALIA) S.R.L.—See PricewaterhouseCoopers S.p.A.; *Int'l*, pg. 5972
PWC STRATEGY& JAPAN, INC.—See PricewaterhouseCoopers Co., Ltd.; *Int'l*, pg. 5970
PWC STRATEGY& LLC—See PricewaterhouseCoopers Russia B.V.; *Int'l*, pg. 5972
PWC STRATEGY& (UK) LTD.—See PricewaterhouseCoopers LLP (UK); *Int'l*, pg. 5971
PWC STRATEGY& (US) INC.—See PricewaterhouseCoopers LLP (USA); *U.S. Private*, pg. 3259
PWC TRANSPORT COMPANY W.L.L.—See Agility; *Int'l*, pg. 210
PW&D INC.; *U.S. Private*, pg. 3308
PWE HOLDINGS PLC; *Int'l*, pg. 6126
P&W EXCAVATING INC.; *U.S. Private*, pg. 3059
PWF CORPORATION BHD.; *Int'l*, pg. 6126
PWF FEEDS SDN. BHD.—See PWF Corporation Bhd.; *Int'l*, pg. 6126
PWF FOODS SDN. BHD.—See PWF Corporation Bhd.; *Int'l*, pg. 6126
P&W FOREIGN CAR SERVICE INC.; *U.S. Private*, pg. 3059
PWG PROFILROLLEN-WERKZEUGBAU GMBH—See CAG Holding GmbH; *Int'l*, pg. 1250
PWH CO MFG, INC.; *U.S. Private*, pg. 3308
PWH FOUNDATION INC.—See Novant Health, Inc.; *U.S. Private*, pg. 2967
PWI CONSTRUCTION INC.; *U.S. Private*, pg. 3308
PW MEDTECH GROUP LIMITED; *Int'l*, pg. 6126
PWM ELECTRONIC PRICE SIGNS, INC.—See PWM GmbH & Co. KG; *Int'l*, pg. 6126
PWM GMBH & CO. KG; *Int'l*, pg. 6126
P.W. MINOR & SON, INC.; *U.S. Private*, pg. 3061
PWO AG; *Int'l*, pg. 6126
PWO CANADA INC.—See PWO AG; *Int'l*, pg. 6126
PWO CZECH REPUBLIC A.S.—See PWO AG; *Int'l*, pg. 6126
PWO DE MEXICO S.A. DE C.V.—See PWO AG; *Int'l*, pg. 6126
PWO HIGH-TECH METAL COMPONENTS (SUZHOU) CO., LTD.—See PWO AG; *Int'l*, pg. 6126
PWO HIGH-TECH TOOL TRADING (SUZHOU) CO., LTD.—See PWO AG; *Int'l*, pg. 6126
PWO UNITOOLS CZ A.S.—See PWO AG; *Int'l*, pg. 6126
PWP GROWTH EQUITY LLC—See Perella Weinberg Partners LP; *U.S. Public*, pg. 1674
PWP INDUSTRIES, INC.—See Pactiv Evergreen Inc.; *U.S. Public*, pg. 1633
PWP INZYNIERIA SP. Z O.O.—See Introl S.A.; *Int'l*, pg. 3769
PW POWER SYSTEMS, INC.—See Mitsubishi Heavy Industries, Ltd.; *Int'l*, pg. 4956
PWRCOR, INC.; *U.S. Public*, pg. 1739
PWR EUROPE LIMITED—See PWR Holdings Limited; *Int'l*, pg. 6126
PWR HOLDINGS LIMITED; *Int'l*, pg. 6126
PWR, LLC.; *U.S. Private*, pg. 3308
PWS DANMARK A/S—See Berry Global Group, Inc; *U.S. Public*, pg. 322
PWS EAST ASIA PTE LIMITED—See AmWINS Group, Inc.; *U.S. Private*, pg. 270
PWS FINLAND OY—See Berry Global Group, Inc; *U.S. Public*, pg. 322

PWS INC.—See BDT Capital Partners, LLC; *U.S. Private*, pg. 502
PWS INVESTMENTS, INC.; *U.S. Private*, pg. 3308
PWS NORDIC AB—See Berry Global Group, Inc; *U.S. Public*, pg. 322
PWS NORGE AS—See Berry Global Group, Inc; *U.S. Public*, pg. 322
PWS PRIVATE WEALTH SERVICES AG—See Mubadala Investment Company PJSC; *Int'l*, pg. 5074
PW STOELTING, L.L.C.—See The Vollrath Company LLC; *U.S. Private*, pg. 4132
PWW DEPONIJA D.O.O.—See PORR AG; *Int'l*, pg. 5923
PWW DEPONIJA DVA D.O.O.—See PORR AG; *Int'l*, pg. 5923
PWW D.O.O.—See PORR AG; *Int'l*, pg. 5923
PXP ENERGY CORPORATION—See Philex Mining Corporation; *Int'l*, pg. 5844
PXP OFFSHORE LLC—See Freeport-McMoRan Inc.; *U.S. Public*, pg. 884
PX SYSTEM COMPANY LIMITED—See Pico (Thailand) Public Company Limited; *Int'l*, pg. 5860
PYBAR HOLDINGS PTY. LTD.—See ACS, Actividades de Construccion y Servicios, S.A.; *Int'l*, pg. 113
PYBAR HOLDINGS PTY. LTD.—See Elliott Management Corporation; *U.S. Private*, pg. 1365
PYBAR MINING SERVICES PTY. LTD.—See ACS, Actividades de Construccion y Servicios, S.A.; *Int'l*, pg. 113
PYBAR MINING SERVICES PTY. LTD.—See Elliott Management Corporation; *U.S. Private*, pg. 1365
PYCO INDUSTRIES, INC.; *U.S. Private*, pg. 3308
PYC THERAPEUTICS LIMITED; *Int'l*, pg. 6126
PYE AUTOMOBILE SALES OF CHATTANOOGA; *U.S. Private*, pg. 3308
PYE-BARKER FIRE & SAFETY, LLC; *U.S. Private*, pg. 3308
PYE MOTORS LTD; *Int'l*, pg. 6126
PYEONG HWA AUTOMOTIVE BEIJING CO., LTD.—See Pyeong Hwa Automotive Co., Ltd; *Int'l*, pg. 6127
PYEONG HWA AUTOMOTIVE CO., LTD - ASAN PLANT—See Pyeong Hwa Automotive Co., Ltd; *Int'l*, pg. 6127
PYEONG HWA AUTOMOTIVE CO., LTD - IHYEON PLANT—See Pyeong Hwa Automotive Co., Ltd; *Int'l*, pg. 6127
PYEONG HWA AUTOMOTIVE CO., LTD - OEDONG PLANT—See Pyeong Hwa Automotive Co., Ltd; *Int'l*, pg. 6127
PYEONG HWA AUTOMOTIVE CO., LTD - SEONGSEO PLANT—See Pyeong Hwa Automotive Co., Ltd; *Int'l*, pg. 6127
PYEONG HWA AUTOMOTIVE CO., LTD; *Int'l*, pg. 6127
PYEONG HWA AUTOMOTIVE TAICANG CO., LTD.—See Pyeong Hwa Automotive Co., Ltd; *Int'l*, pg. 6127
PYEONG HWA AUTOMOTIVE YANGCHENG CO., LTD.—See Pyeong Hwa Automotive Co., Ltd; *Int'l*, pg. 6127
PYEONG SAN CO., LTD.; *Int'l*, pg. 6127
PYEONGTAEK DANGJIN CENTRAL PIER CO., LTD.—See Sebang Co., Ltd.; *Int'l*, pg. 6669
PYFA AUSTRALIA PTY LTD.—See Pyridam Farma Tbk; *Int'l*, pg. 6127
PYGOTT & CRONE LINCOLN LETTINGS LIMITED—See LSL Property Services plc; *Int'l*, pg. 4570
PYHASALMI MINE OY—See First Quantum Minerals Ltd.; *Int'l*, pg. 2687
PYI CORPORATION LIMITED; *Int'l*, pg. 6127
PYI MANAGEMENT LIMITED—See PYI Corporation Limited; *Int'l*, pg. 6127
PYLE TRANSPORT SERVICES INC.—See A. Duie Pyle Inc.; *U.S. Private*, pg. 23
PYLON MANUFACTURING CORPORATION—See Wellspring Capital Management LLC; *U.S. Private*, pg. 4477
PYLON PUBLIC COMPANY LIMITED; *Int'l*, pg. 6127
PYLON TECHNOLOGIES CO., LTD; *Int'l*, pg. 6127
PYMETRICS, INC.—See Rubicon Technology Partners, LLC; *U.S. Private*, pg. 3500
PYNE GOULD CORPORATION LIMITED; *Int'l*, pg. 6127
PYNG MEDICAL CORP.—See Teleflex Incorporated; *U.S. Public*, pg. 1996
PYNMAX TECHNOLOGY CO., LTD—See Pan Jit International Inc.; *Int'l*, pg. 5714
PYPE LLC—See Autodesk, Inc.; *U.S. Public*, pg. 229
PYPHA ENERGY, LLC.; *U.S. Private*, pg. 3309
PYRAMAX BANK—See 1895 Bancorp of Wisconsin, Inc.; *U.S. Public*, pg. 2
PYRAMID ADVISORS LLC; *U.S. Private*, pg. 3309
PYRAMID AG; *Int'l*, pg. 6127
PYRAMID AIRTECH PVT. LTD.—See AIRTECH JAPAN, LTD.; *Int'l*, pg. 249
PYRAMID BREWERIES INC—See Florida Ice and Farm Co. S.A.; *Int'l*, pg. 2707
PYRAMID BROKERAGE COMPANY INC.; *U.S. Private*, pg. 3310
PYRAMID BUILDING MAINTENANCE CORPORATION—See Ontario Teachers' Pension Plan; *Int'l*, pg. 5588

PYROPURE, INC.

PYRAMID BUILDING MAINTENANCE CORPORATION—See PAG Asia Capital Ltd.; *Int'l*, pg. 5695
PYRAMID BUILDING MAINTENANCE CORPORATION—See TPG Capital, L.P.; *U.S. Public*, pg. 2171
PYRAMID CONSULTING, INC.; *U.S. Private*, pg. 3310
PYRAMID CORPORATION—See PTW Energy Services Ltd.; *Int'l*, pg. 6093
PYRAMID DRILLING S.A.E.—See Gulf Petroleum Investment Co. S.A.K.C.; *Int'l*, pg. 3182
PYRAMID FLOOR COVERING, INC.; *U.S. Private*, pg. 3310
PYRAMID GILMAN STREET PROPERTY, LLC—See Florida Ice and Farm Co. S.A.; *Int'l*, pg. 2708
PYRAMID HEALTH CARE LP; *U.S. Private*, pg. 3310
PYRAMID HOTEL GROUP LLC—See Pyramid Advisors LLC; *U.S. Private*, pg. 3310
PYRAMID HOTELS & RESORTS, INC.; *U.S. Private*, pg. 3310
PYRAMID INDUSTRIES, INC.; *U.S. Private*, pg. 3310
PYRAMID MANAGEMENT GROUP, INC.; *U.S. Private*, pg. 3310
PYRAMID MANUFACTURING INDUSTRIES PTE. LTD.—See Turiya Berhad; *Int'l*, pg. 7974
PYRAMID MASONRY CONTRACTORS; *U.S. Private*, pg. 3310
PYRAMID MATERIALS—See Haines & Kibblehouse Inc.; *U.S. Private*, pg. 1841
PYRAMID MOLD & TOOL—See Crestview Partners, L.P.; *U.S. Private*, pg. 1099
PYRAMID MOULDINGS - GEORGIA PLANT—See Roller Die & Forming Company, Inc.; *U.S. Private*, pg. 3474
PYRAMID MOULDINGS, INC.—See Roller Die & Forming Company, Inc.; *U.S. Private*, pg. 3474
PYRAMID MOULDINGS - MEXICO PLANT—See Roller Die & Forming Company, Inc.; *U.S. Private*, pg. 3474
PYRAMID MOUNTAIN LUMBER; *U.S. Private*, pg. 3310
PYRAMID PLATFORM, LLC—See Radian Group, Inc.; *U.S. Public*, pg. 1759
PYRAMID PROJECT MANAGEMENT—See Pyramid Advisors LLC; *U.S. Private*, pg. 3310
PYRAMID RELO PVT. LTD.—See Relo Group, Inc.; *Int'l*, pg. 6265
PYRAMID RESORT GROUP—See Pyramid Advisors LLC; *U.S. Private*, pg. 3310
PYRAMID SEMICONDUCTOR CORP.—See HEICO Corporation; *U.S. Public*, pg. 1020
PYRAMID SERVICES, INC.; *U.S. Private*, pg. 3310
PYRAMID SOLUTIONS, INC.; *U.S. Private*, pg. 3310
PYRAMID SPECIALITIES PRODUCTS LTD.—See Compagnie de Saint-Gobain SA; *Int'l*, pg. 1730
PYRAMID SYSTEMS, INC.; *U.S. Private*, pg. 3310
PYRAMID TECHNOLOGIES INC.; *U.S. Private*, pg. 3310
PYRAMID TECHNOPLAST LIMITED; *Int'l*, pg. 6127
PYRAMISA HOTELS & RESORTS; *Int'l*, pg. 6127
PYRAMIS GLOBAL ADVISORS, LLC—See FMR LLC; *U.S. Private*, pg. 1555
PYRAMYD AIR LTD.—See Gen Cap America, Inc.; *U.S. Private*, pg. 1660
PYRENE CORPORATION—See Carrier Global Corporation; *U.S. Public*, pg. 441
PYRFORD INTERNATIONAL LIMITED—See Bank of Montreal; *Int'l*, pg. 846
PYRIDAM FARMA TBK; *Int'l*, pg. 6127
PYROALLIANCE—See Safran SA; *Int'l*, pg. 6473
PYROBAN BENELUX B.V.—See Caterpillar, Inc.; *U.S. Public*, pg. 453
PYROBAN ENVIROSAFE LIMITED—See Caterpillar, Inc.; *U.S. Public*, pg. 453
PYROBAN GROUP LIMITED—See Caterpillar, Inc.; *U.S. Public*, pg. 453
PYROBAN (SUZHOU) SAFETY SYSTEMS CO., LTD.—See Caterpillar, Inc.; *U.S. Public*, pg. 453
PYROBRAS COMERCIO E INDUSTRIA LTDA.—See Pyrotek Incorporated; *U.S. Private*, pg. 3311
PYROFUSE—See Sigmund Cohn Corp.; *U.S. Private*, pg. 3649
PYROGENESIS CANADA INC.; *Int'l*, pg. 6128
PYROLL GROUP OY; *Int'l*, pg. 6128
PYROMETER INSTRUMENT CO., INC.—See Makke LLC; *U.S. Public*, pg. 2556
PYRONIX LIMITED—See Hangzhou Hikvision Digital Technology Co., Ltd.; *Int'l*, pg. 3248
PYRON WIND FARM, LLC—See E.ON SE; *Int'l*, pg. 2259
PYROPAC AG—See Max Weishaupt GmbH; *Int'l*, pg. 4735
PYROPANEL DEVELOPMENTS PTY LTD—See ASSA ABLOY AB; *Int'l*, pg. 640
PYROPHYTE ACQUISITION CORP.; *U.S. Public*, pg. 1739
PYROPRESS ENGINEERING COMPANY LIMITED (THE)—See Caterpillar, Inc.; *U.S. Public*, pg. 453
PYROPURE, INC.; *U.S. Private*, pg. 3310
PYROSEQUENCING, INC.—See Biotage AB; *Int'l*, pg. 1042
PYROTEC FIRE PROTECTION LIMITED—See London Security PLC; *Int'l*, pg. 4547
PYROTECHNIC PROCESSING FACILITY—See Autoliv, Inc.; *Int'l*, pg. 729

PYROTEK (ASIA) LTD.—See Pyrotek Incorporated; *U.S. Private*, pg. 3311
PYROTEK BAHRAIN SPC—See Pyrotek Incorporated; *U.S. Private*, pg. 3311
PYROTEK CZ, S.R.O.—See Pyrotek Incorporated; *U.S. Private*, pg. 3311
PYROTEK DONGGUAN LIMITED—See Pyrotek Incorporated; *U.S. Private*, pg. 3311
PYROTEK ENGINEERING MATERIALS LTD.—See Pyrotek Incorporated; *U.S. Private*, pg. 3311
PYROTEK ENGINEERING MATERIALS (PTY) LTD.—See Pyrotek Incorporated; *U.S. Private*, pg. 3311
PYROTEK FZE—See Pyrotek Incorporated; *U.S. Private*, pg. 3311
PYROTEK (GUANGXI NANNING) HIGH TEMPERATURE MATERIALS CO., LTD.—See Pyrotek Incorporated; *U.S. Private*, pg. 3311
PYROTEK HIGH-TEMPERATURE INDUSTRIAL PRODUCTS INC.—See Pyrotek Incorporated; *U.S. Private*, pg. 3311
PYROTEK INCORPORATED; *U.S. Private*, pg. 3310
PYROTEK INC.—See Pyrotek Incorporated; *U.S. Private*, pg. 3311
PYROTEK INC.—See Pyrotek Incorporated; *U.S. Private*, pg. 3311
PYROTEK INDIA PVT. LTD.—See Pyrotek Incorporated; *U.S. Private*, pg. 3311
PYROTEK JAPAN CO., LTD.—See Pyrotek Incorporated; *U.S. Private*, pg. 3311
PYROTEK KOREA—See Pyrotek Incorporated; *U.S. Private*, pg. 3311
PYROTEK LTD.—See Pyrotek Incorporated; *U.S. Private*, pg. 3311
PYROTEK MEXICO, S. DE R. L. DE C. V.—See Pyrotek Incorporated; *U.S. Private*, pg. 3311
PYROTEK NETHERLANDS B.V.—See Pyrotek Incorporated; *U.S. Private*, pg. 3311
PYROTEK PRODUCTS LTD.—See Pyrotek Incorporated; *U.S. Private*, pg. 3311
PYROTEK PTY. LTD.—See Pyrotek Incorporated; *U.S. Private*, pg. 3311
PYROTEK REFRAKTER SANAYI VE TICARET LTD. STI.—See Pyrotek Incorporated; *U.S. Private*, pg. 3311
PYROTEK SA—See Pyrotek Incorporated; *U.S. Private*, pg. 3311
PYROTEK SCANDINAVIA AB—See Pyrotek Incorporated; *U.S. Private*, pg. 3311
PYROTEK THAILAND CO. LTD.—See Pyrotek Incorporated; *U.S. Private*, pg. 3311
PYROTEK (XI'AN) METALLURGICAL MATERIALS CO., LTD.—See Pyrotek Incorporated; *U.S. Private*, pg. 3311
PYROTEX SARL—See BNP Paribas SA; *Int'l*, pg. 1092
PYROVEN C.A.—See Pyrotek Incorporated; *U.S. Private*, pg. 3311
PYRRHA INVESTMENTS B.V.—See Caterpillar, Inc.; *U.S. Public*, pg. 453
PYRUM INNOVATIONS AG; *Int'l*, pg. 6128
PYSSLINGEN FORSKOLOR OCH SKOLOR AB—See AcadeMedia AB; *Int'l*, pg. 77
PYTON COMMUNICATION SERVICES B.V.—See Amadeus IT Group, S.A.; *Int'l*, pg. 407
PYTSA INDUSTRIAL DE MEXICO, S.A. DE C.V.—See Industrias CH, S.A.B. de C.V.; *Int'l*, pg. 3674
PYUNG HWA HOLDINGS CO., LTD.; *Int'l*, pg. 6128
PYUNG HWA INDUSTRIAL CO., LTD.—See Pyung Hwa Holdings Co., Ltd.; *Int'l*, pg. 6128
PYUNGHWA NOK DRIVE TRAIN CO., LTD.—See NOK Corporation; *Int'l*, pg. 5403
PYUNG HWA OIL SEAL INDUSTRY CO., LTD.—See NOK Corporation; *Int'l*, pg. 5403
PYURE BRANDS, LLC; *U.S. Private*, pg. 3311
PYXERA GLOBAL; *U.S. Private*, pg. 3311
PYXIS FINVEST LIMITED—See Centrum Capital Ltd.; *Int'l*, pg. 1415
PYXIS ONCOLOGY, INC; *U.S. Public*, pg. 1739
PYXIS SOLUTIONS, LLC—See Bain & Company, Inc.; *U.S. Private*, pg. 428
PYXIS TANKERS INC.; *Int'l*, pg. 6128
PYXIS TECHNOLOGIES, LLC; *U.S. Private*, pg. 3311
PYX RESOURCES LIMITED; *Int'l*, pg. 6128
PYXUS INTERNATIONAL, INC.; *U.S. Public*, pg. 1740
PZ COOLWORLD LIMITED—See PZ Cussons Plc; *Int'l*, pg. 6128
PZ CORMAY S.A.; *Int'l*, pg. 6128
PZC SPLIT D.D.—See STRABAG SE; *Int'l*, pg. 7231
PZ CUSSONS AUSTRALIA PTY LTD—See PZ Cussons Plc; *Int'l*, pg. 6128
PZ CUSSONS GHANA LIMITED—See PZ Cussons Plc; *Int'l*, pg. 6128
PZ CUSSONS (HOLDINGS) LTD.—See PZ Cussons Plc; *Int'l*, pg. 6128
PZ CUSSONS INDIA PVT. LTD.—See PZ Cussons Plc; *Int'l*, pg. 6128
PZ CUSSONS (INTERNATIONAL) LTD.—See PZ Cussons Plc; *Int'l*, pg. 6128
PZ CUSSONS MIDDLE EAST AND SOUTH ASIA FZE—See PZ Cussons Plc; *Int'l*, pg. 6128

PZ CUSSONS NIGERIA PLC.—See PZ Cussons Plc; *Int'l*, pg. 6128
PZ CUSSONS PLC; *Int'l*, pg. 6128
PZ CUSSONS POLSKA S.A.—See PZ Cussons Plc; *Int'l*, pg. 6128
PZ CUSSONS (THAILAND) LTD.—See PZ Cussons Plc; *Int'l*, pg. 6128
PZ CUSSONS UK LTD—See PZ Cussons Plc; *Int'l*, pg. 6128
PZENA FINANCIAL SERVICES, LLC—See Pzena Investment Management, Inc.; *U.S. Public*, pg. 1741
PZENA INVESTMENT MANAGEMENT, INC.; *U.S. Public*, pg. 1741
PZENA INVESTMENT MANAGEMENT, LTD—See Pzena Investment Management, Inc.; *U.S. Public*, pg. 1741
PZENA INVESTMENT MANAGEMENT PTY LTD—See Pzena Investment Management, Inc.; *U.S. Public*, pg. 1741
PZP HEATING A.S.—See Arbonia AG; *Int'l*, pg. 538
PZP ZAJECAR A.D.; *Int'l*, pg. 6129
PZU CENTRUM OPERACJI SA—See Powszechny Zaklad Ubezpieczen S.A.; *Int'l*, pg. 5949
PZU UKRAINA—See Powszechny Zaklad Ubezpieczen S.A.; *Int'l*, pg. 5949

Q

Q10 CAPITAL, L.L.C.; *U.S. Private*, pg. 3312
Q1 LABS INC.—See International Business Machines Corporation; *U.S. Public*, pg. 1149
Q1MEDIA; *U.S. Private*, pg. 3312
Q2 HOLDINGS, INC.; *U.S. Public*, pg. 1741
Q2 METALS CORP.; *Int'l*, pg. 6131
Q2 SOFTWARE, INC.—See Q2 Holdings, Inc.; *U.S. Public*, pg. 1741
Q2 TECHNOLOGIES, LLC—See Quaker Chemical Corporation; *U.S. Public*, pg. 1746
Q32 BIO INC.; *U.S. Public*, pg. 1741
Q3 CONTRACTING, INC.—See Primoris Services Corporation; *U.S. Public*, pg. 1719
Q3 INDUSTRIES—See Q3 Stamped Metal; *U.S. Private*, pg. 3312
Q3 STAMPED METAL; *U.S. Private*, pg. 3312
Q4 INC.—See Sumeru Equity Partners LLC; *U.S. Private*, pg. 3852
Q9 NETWORKS INC.—See BCE Inc.; *Int'l*, pg. 928
Q9 TECHNOLOGY COMPANY LIMITED—See Cloud Investment Holdings Limited; *Int'l*, pg. 1662
QA AMERICA, LLC—See Osaki Electric Co., Ltd.; *Int'l*, pg. 5647
QAAS CO., LTD.—See Pole To Win Holdings, Inc.; *Int'l*, pg. 5909
Q&A CORPORATION—See NEC Corporation; *Int'l*, pg. 5185
Q ACOUSTICS LIMITED; *Int'l*, pg. 6129
QAD AUSTRALIA PTY LTD.—See Thoma Bravo, L.P.; *U.S. Private*, pg. 4151
QAD BILGISAYER YAZILIM LTD.—See Thoma Bravo, L.P.; *U.S. Private*, pg. 4151
QAD BRASIL LTDA.—See Thoma Bravo, L.P.; *U.S. Private*, pg. 4151
QAD BRAZIL LTDA.—See Thoma Bravo, L.P.; *U.S. Private*, pg. 4151
QAD CHINA, INC.—See Thoma Bravo, L.P.; *U.S. Private*, pg. 4151
QAD CHINA LTD.—See Thoma Bravo, L.P.; *U.S. Private*, pg. 4151
QAD EUROPE GMBH—See Thoma Bravo, L.P.; *U.S. Private*, pg. 4151
QAD EUROPE (IRELAND) LIMITED—See Thoma Bravo, L.P.; *U.S. Private*, pg. 4151
QAD EUROPE LDA.—See Thoma Bravo, L.P.; *U.S. Private*, pg. 4151
QAD EUROPE LIMITED—See Thoma Bravo, L.P.; *U.S. Private*, pg. 4151
QAD EUROPE N.V./S.A.—See Thoma Bravo, L.P.; *U.S. Private*, pg. 4151
QAD EUROPE S.A.S.—See Thoma Bravo, L.P.; *U.S. Private*, pg. 4152
QAD EUROPE S.L.—See Thoma Bravo, L.P.; *U.S. Private*, pg. 4152
QAD INC.—See Thoma Bravo, L.P.; *U.S. Private*, pg. 4151
QAD INDIA PRIVATE LIMITED—See Thoma Bravo, L.P.; *U.S. Private*, pg. 4152
QAD IRELAND LIMITED—See Thoma Bravo, L.P.; *U.S. Private*, pg. 4152
QAD ITALY S.R.L.—See Thoma Bravo, L.P.; *U.S. Private*, pg. 4152
QAD JAPAN INC.—See Thoma Bravo, L.P.; *U.S. Private*, pg. 4152
QAD JAPAN, INC.—See Thoma Bravo, L.P.; *U.S. Private*, pg. 4152
QAD NETHERLANDS B.V.—See Thoma Bravo, L.P.; *U.S. Private*, pg. 4152
QADOS—See Checkit plc; *Int'l*, pg. 1459
QAD POLSKA SP. Z O.O.—See Thoma Bravo, L.P.; *U.S. Private*, pg. 4152
QAD SINGAPORE PTE LTD.—See Thoma Bravo, L.P.; *U.S. Private*, pg. 4152

QAD SISTEMAS INTEGRADOS CASA DE SOFTWARE, S.A. DE C.V.—See Thoma Bravo, L.P.; *U.S. Private*, pg. 4152
QAD SISTEMAS INTEGRADOS SERVICIOS DE CONSULTORIA, S.A. DE C.V.—See Thoma Bravo, L.P.; *U.S. Private*, pg. 4152
QAD (THAILAND) LTD.—See Thoma Bravo, L.P.; *U.S. Private*, pg. 4151
QAD UNITED KINGDOM—See Thoma Bravo, L.P.; *U.S. Private*, pg. 4152
QAF FRUITS COLD STORE PTE LTD.—See QAF Limited; *Int'l*, pg. 6132
QAF LIMITED; *Int'l*, pg. 6131
QAFQAZ KONSERV ZAVODU LLC—See International Sun Group FZCO; *Int'l*, pg. 3753
QAFQAZ METAL FABRIKASI LLC—See International Sun Group FZCO; *Int'l*, pg. 3753
QAFQAZ TRADE CO.—See International Sun Group FZCO; *Int'l*, pg. 3753
QAIGEN GMBH—See QIAGEN N.V.; *Int'l*, pg. 6139
QAISER BROTHERS (PVT) LTD—See THK CO., LTD.; *Int'l*, pg. 7712
QAIS OMANI ESTABLISHMENT LLC—See Muscat Overseas Co., L.L.C.; *Int'l*, pg. 5102
QA LTD.—See COFRA Holding AG; *Int'l*, pg. 1693
QA MANAGEMENT SERVICES PTY LTD—See I Squared Capital Advisors (US) LLC; *U.S. Private*, pg. 2023
QA MANAGEMENT SERVICES PTY LTD.—See TDR Capital LLP; *Int'l*, pg. 7493
Q ANALYSTS LLC—See Bridgepoint Group Plc; *Int'l*, pg. 1154
QANBAR DYWIDAG PRECAST CONCRETE CO. LTD.; *Int'l*, pg. 6132
QANTAS AIRWAYS LIMITED; *Int'l*, pg. 6132
QANTAS AIRWAYS - USA—See Qantas Airways Limited; *Int'l*, pg. 6132
QANTAS CATERING GROUP LIMITED—See Qantas Airways Limited; *Int'l*, pg. 6132
QANTAS COURIER LIMITED—See Qantas Airways Limited; *Int'l*, pg. 6132
QANTAS FLIGHT TRAINING—See Qantas Airways Limited; *Int'l*, pg. 6132
QANTAS FOUNDATION TRUSTEE LIMITED—See Qantas Airways Limited; *Int'l*, pg. 6132
QANTAS FREIGHT ENTERPRISES LIMITED—See Qantas Airways Limited; *Int'l*, pg. 6132
QANTAS INFORMATION TECHNOLOGY LTD.—See Qantas Airways Limited; *Int'l*, pg. 6132
QANTASLINK—See Qantas Airways Limited; *Int'l*, pg. 6132
QANTAS SUPERANNUATION LIMITED—See Qantas Airways Limited; *Int'l*, pg. 6132
Q.ANT GMBH—See TRUMPF SE + Co. KG; *Int'l*, pg. 7942
QANTM INTELLECTUAL PROPERTY LIMITED—See Adamantem Capital Management Pty Limited; *Int'l*, pg. 123
QANTOS GMBH—See senata GmbH; *Int'l*, pg. 6707
QANTUM COMMUNICATIONS CORPORATION—See Nautic Partners, LLC; *U.S. Private*, pg. 2871
QASSIM CEMENT CO.; *Int'l*, pg. 6133
Q ASSOCIATES LTD.; *Int'l*, pg. 6129
QA SYSTEMS INC.; *U.S. Private*, pg. 3312
QA SYSTEMS INTEGRATION (M.E.) LLC—See Osaki Electric Co., Ltd.; *Int'l*, pg. 5647
QA SYSTEMS INTEGRATION (M) SDN BHD—See Osaki Electric Co., Ltd.; *Int'l*, pg. 5647
QATALYS INCORPORATED; *U.S. Private*, pg. 3312
QATAR ACIDS COMPANY—See Qatar Industrial Manufacturing Company (S.A.Q.); *Int'l*, pg. 6133
QATAR AIRWAYS CARGO—See Qatar Investment Authority; *Int'l*, pg. 6134
QATAR AIRWAYS COMPANY—See Qatar Investment Authority; *Int'l*, pg. 6134
QATAR AVIATION SERVICES—See Qatar Investment Authority; *Int'l*, pg. 6134
QATAR BOOM ELECTRICAL ENGINEERING W.L.L.—See Aiphone Co., Ltd.; *Int'l*, pg. 235
QATAR CENTRAL BANK; *Int'l*, pg. 6133
QATAR CHEMICAL COMPANY LTD.—See Qatar Petroleum; *Int'l*, pg. 6135
QATAR CINEMA AND FILM DISTRIBUTION COMPANY QSC; *Int'l*, pg. 6133
QATAR CLAY BRICKS COMPANY—See Qatar Industrial Manufacturing Company (S.A.Q.); *Int'l*, pg. 6133
QATAR DATAMATION SYSTEMS—See Emirates Technology Company (EMITAC); *Int'l*, pg. 2382
QATAR ELECTRICITY & WATER COMPANY Q.S.C.; *Int'l*, pg. 6133
QATAR ENGINEERING & CONSTRUCTION COMPANY W.L.L.; *Int'l*, pg. 6133
QATAR EXCHANGE; *Int'l*, pg. 6133
QATAR EXECUTIVE—See Qatar Investment Authority; *Int'l*, pg. 6134
QATAR FERTILISER COMPANY (S.A.Q.)—See Qatar Petroleum; *Int'l*, pg. 6135
QATAR FLOUR MILLS COMPANY—See Zad Holding Company S.A.Q.; *Int'l*, pg. 8619
QATAR FOOD COMPANY—See Adeptio LLC; *Int'l*, pg. 143
QATAR FOODS INDUSTRIES—See Zad Holding Company S.A.Q.; *Int'l*, pg. 8619

COMPANY NAME INDEX

QATAR FUEL ADDITIVES COMPANY LTD.—See Qatar Petroleum; *Int'l*, pg. 6135
QATAR FUEL COMPANY Q.S.C.; *Int'l*, pg. 6133
QATAR GAS TRANSPORT COMPANY LIMITED (NAKILAT) Q.S.C.; *Int'l*, pg. 6133
QATAR GENERAL HOLDING COMPANY S.P.C.—See Qatar General Insurance and Reinsurance Company S.A.Q.; *Int'l*, pg. 6133
QATAR GENERAL INSURANCE AND REINSURANCE COMPANY S.A.Q.; *Int'l*, pg. 6133
QATAR DIAR REAL ESTATE INVESTMENT CO. MOROCO S.A.R.L—See Qatari Diar Real Estate Investment Company; *Int'l*, pg. 6136
QATARI DIAR REAL ESTATE INVESTMENT COMPANY; *Int'l*, pg. 6136
QATARI GERMAN COMPANY FOR MEDICAL DEVICES Q.S.C.; *Int'l*, pg. 6136
QATARI INVESTORS GROUP Q.S.C.; *Int'l*, pg. 6136
QATAR INDUSTRIAL GASES CO. W.L.L—See Taleb Group; *Int'l*, pg. 7446
QATAR INDUSTRIAL MANUFACTURING COMPANY (S.A.Q.); *Int'l*, pg. 6133
QATAR INSURANCE COMPANY - ABU DHABI—See Qatar Insurance Company S.A.Q.; *Int'l*, pg. 6134
QATAR INSURANCE COMPANY - AL KHOBAR—See Qatar Insurance Company S.A.Q.; *Int'l*, pg. 6134
QATAR INSURANCE COMPANY - DUBAI—See Qatar Insurance Company S.A.Q.; *Int'l*, pg. 6134
QATAR INSURANCE COMPANY S.A.Q.; *Int'l*, pg. 6133
QATAR INTERMEDIATE INDUSTRIES COMPANY LTD.—See Qatar Petroleum; *Int'l*, pg. 6135
QATAR INTERNATIONAL ISLAMIC BANK Q.S.C.; *Int'l*, pg. 6134
QATAR INVESTMENT AUTHORITY; *Int'l*, pg. 6134
QATARI SAUDI GYPSUM INDS. COMPANY—See Qatar Industrial Manufacturing Company (S.A.Q.); *Int'l*, pg. 6133
QATAR ISLAMIC BANK (S.A.Q.); *Int'l*, pg. 6134
QATAR ISLAMIC INSURANCE COMPANY Q.S.C.; *Int'l*, pg. 6134
QATAR JET FUEL COMPANY—See Qatar Industrial Manufacturing Company (S.A.Q.); *Int'l*, pg. 6133
QATAR JET FUEL COMPANY—See Qatar Petroleum; *Int'l*, pg. 6136
QATAR LIQUEFIED GAS COMPANY LTD.—See Qatar Petroleum; *Int'l*, pg. 6136
QATAR MARITIME & MERCANTILE INTL. CO.—See Albert Ballin KG; *Int'l*, pg. 296
QATAR METAL COATING COMPANY WLL—See Qatar Industrial Manufacturing Company (S.A.Q.); *Int'l*, pg. 6133
QATAR METAL COATING COMPANY WLL—See Qatar Steel Company; *Int'l*, pg. 6136
QATAR NATIONAL BANK ALAHLI—See Qatar National Bank S.A.Q.; *Int'l*, pg. 6135
QATAR NATIONAL BANK S.A.Q.; *Int'l*, pg. 6134
QATAR NATIONAL BANK-SYRIA—See Qatar National Bank S.A.Q.; *Int'l*, pg. 6135
QATAR NATIONAL CEMENT CO Q.S.C.; *Int'l*, pg. 6135
QATAR NAVIGATION (MILAHA) Q.P.S.C.; *Int'l*, pg. 6135
QATAR NITROGEN COMPANY—See Qatar Industrial Manufacturing Company (S.A.Q.); *Int'l*, pg. 6133
QATAR NITROGEN COMPANY—See Qatar Petroleum; *Int'l*, pg. 6136
QATAR OMAN INVESTMENT COMPANY Q.S.C.; *Int'l*, pg. 6135
QATAR PETROCHEMICAL COMPANY LTD.—See Qatar Petroleum; *Int'l*, pg. 6135
QATAR PETROCHEMICAL COMPANY LTD.—See TotalEnergies SE; *Int'l*, pg. 7842
QATAR PETROLEUM DEVELOPMENT CO., LTD.—See Cosmo Energy Holdings Co., Ltd.; *Int'l*, pg. 1812
QATAR PETROLEUM; *Int'l*, pg. 6135
QATAR PLASTIC PRODUCTS COMPANY W.L.L.—See Qatar Petroleum; *Int'l*, pg. 6135
QATAR PLASTIC PRODUCTS COMPANY W.L.L.—See TotalEnergies SE; *Int'l*, pg. 7842
QATAR PROJECT MANAGEMENT COMPANY Q.P.S.C.—See Barwa Real Estate Company Q.P.S.C.; *Int'l*, pg. 870
QATAR REAL ESTATE INVESTMENT COMPANY Q.P.S.C—See Barwa Real Estate Company Q.P.S.C.; *Int'l*, pg. 870
QATAR REINSURANCE COMPANY LIMITED—See Qatar Insurance Company S.A.Q.; *Int'l*, pg. 6134
QATAR REINSURANCE SERVICES LLC—See Qatar Insurance Company S.A.Q.; *Int'l*, pg. 6134
QATAR SHELL SERVICE COMPANY W.L.L.—See Shell plc; *Int'l*, pg. 6795
QATAR SHIPPING COMPANY S.P.C.—See Qatar Navigation (Milaha) Q.P.S.C.; *Int'l*, pg. 6135
QATAR STEEL COMPANY FZE—See Qatar Steel Company; *Int'l*, pg. 6136
QATAR STEEL COMPANY; *Int'l*, pg. 6136
QATAR TAKAFUL COMPANY S.O.C.—See Al Khaleej Takaful Insurance Company Q.P.S.C.; *Int'l*, pg. 280
QATAR TUNISIAN FOOD COMPANY—See Qatar Industrial Manufacturing Company (S.A.Q.); *Int'l*, pg. 6133
QATAR VINYL COMPANY LIMITED Q.S.C.—See Qatar Petroleum; *Int'l*, pg. 6136
QAYEN CEMENT COMPANY; *Int'l*, pg. 6136
QAZAQ BANKI JSC; *Int'l*, pg. 6136
QAZAQGAZ AIMAQ JSC; *Int'l*, pg. 6136
QAZAQSTAN INVESTMENT CORPORATION JOINT STOCK COMPANY—See National Managing Holding Baiterek JSC; *Int'l*, pg. 5161
QAZTECH VENTURES JOINT STOCK COMPANY—See National Managing Holding Baiterek JSC; *Int'l*, pg. 5161
QBE AGRI—See QBE Insurance Group Limited; *Int'l*, pg. 6137
QBE AMERICAS, INC.—See QBE Insurance Group Limited; *Int'l*, pg. 6136
QBE CORPORATE LIMITED—See QBE Insurance Group Limited; *Int'l*, pg. 6137
QBE EUROPEAN OPERATIONS—See QBE Insurance Group Limited; *Int'l*, pg. 6137
QBE EUROPEAN UNDERWRITING SERVICES (AUSTRALIA) PTY LIMITED—See QBE Insurance Group Limited; *Int'l*, pg. 6137
QBE FINANCIAL INSTITUTION RISK SERVICES, INC.—See QBE Insurance Group Limited; *Int'l*, pg. 6137
QBE HOLDINGS (EUROPE) LIMITED—See QBE Insurance Group Limited; *Int'l*, pg. 6137
QBE HOLDINGS (UK) LIMITED—See QBE Insurance Group Limited; *Int'l*, pg. 6137
QBE INSURANCE (AUSTRALIA) LIMITED—See QBE Insurance Group Limited; *Int'l*, pg. 6137
QBE INSURANCE (EUROPE) LIMITED—See QBE Insurance Group Limited; *Int'l*, pg. 6137
QBE INSURANCE (FIJI) LIMITED—See QBE Insurance Group Limited; *Int'l*, pg. 6138
QBE INSURANCE GROUP LIMITED; *Int'l*, pg. 6136
QBE INSURANCE (INTERNATIONAL) LIMITED—See QBE Insurance Group Limited; *Int'l*, pg. 6137
QBE INSURANCE (MALAYSIA) BERHAD—See QBE Insurance Group Limited; *Int'l*, pg. 6137
QBE INSURANCE (PNG) LIMITED—See QBE Insurance Group Limited; *Int'l*, pg. 6137
QBE INSURANCE (SINGAPORE) PTE. LTD.—See QBE Insurance Group Limited; *Int'l*, pg. 6137
QBE INSURANCE (VIETNAM) COMPANY LIMITED—See QBE Insurance Group Limited; *Int'l*, pg. 6137
QBE INTERNATIONAL (INVESTMENTS) PTY LIMITED—See QBE Insurance Group Limited; *Int'l*, pg. 6137
QBE INVESTMENTS (NORTH AMERICA) INC—See QBE Insurance Group Limited; *Int'l*, pg. 6137
QBE LENDERS MORTGAGE INSURANCE LIMITED—See QBE Insurance Group Limited; *Int'l*, pg. 6137
QBE MARINE AND ENERGY SERVICES PTE LIMITED—See QBE Insurance Group Limited; *Int'l*, pg. 6137
QBE MORTGAGE INSURANCE (ASIA) LIMITED—See QBE Insurance Group Limited; *Int'l*, pg. 6137
QBE NORDIC AVIATION INSURANCE A/S—See QBE Insurance Group Limited; *Int'l*, pg. 6137
QBE RE (EUROPE) LTD. - SECURA BRANCH—See QBE Insurance Group Limited; *Int'l*, pg. 6137
QBE REGIONAL INSURANCE—See QBE Insurance Group Limited; *Int'l*, pg. 6137
QBE REINSURANCE CORPORATION—See QBE Insurance Group Limited; *Int'l*, pg. 6137
QBE REINSURANCE (EUROPE) LIMITED—See QBE Insurance Group Limited; *Int'l*, pg. 6137
QBE REINSURANCE (UK) LIMITED—See QBE Insurance Group Limited; *Int'l*, pg. 6137
QBE SERVICES INC—See QBE Insurance Group Limited; *Int'l*, pg. 6137
QBE SPECIALTY INSURANCE COMPANY—See QBE Insurance Group Limited; *Int'l*, pg. 6137
QBE UNDERWRITING LIMITED—See QBE Insurance Group Limited; *Int'l*, pg. 6137
QBE UNDERWRITING SERVICES (IRELAND) LIMITED—See QBE Insurance Group Limited; *Int'l*, pg. 6137
QBE UNDERWRITING SERVICES LIMITED—See QBE Insurance Group Limited; *Int'l*, pg. 6137
QBE WORKERS COMPENSATION (NSW) LIMITED—See QBE Insurance Group Limited; *Int'l*, pg. 6137
QBE WORKERS COMPENSATION (SA) LIMITED—See QBE Insurance Group Limited; *Int'l*, pg. 6137
QBE WORKERS COMPENSATION (VIC) LIMITED—See QBE Insurance Group Limited; *Int'l*, pg. 6138
Q.BEYOND AG; *Int'l*, pg. 6131
Q.BEYOND DATA SOLUTIONS GMBH—See q.beyond AG; *Int'l*, pg. 6131
Q.BEYOND IBERICA SOCIEDAD LIMITADA—See q.beyond AG; *Int'l*, pg. 6131
Q.BEYOND LOGINEER GMBH—See q.beyond AG; *Int'l*, pg. 6131
Q&B FOODS, INC.—See Kewpie Corporation; *Int'l*, pg. 4144
QB HOUSE(HONG KONG) LTD.—See QB Net Holdings Co., Ltd.; *Int'l*, pg. 6136

QD SYSTEM AB

QBI ENTERPRISES, LTD.—See SBI Holdings, Inc.; *Int'l*, pg. 6604
QBIG GMBH—See EWE Aktiengesellschaft; *Int'l*, pg. 2576
Q.B. INDUSTRIAS, S.A. DE C.V.; *Int'l*, pg. 6131
Q BIOMED INC.; *U.S. Public*, pg. 1741
QBIQ B.V.—See Indutrade AB; *Int'l*, pg. 3681
Q BLACK, LLC; *U.S. Private*, pg. 3311
QB NET HOLDINGS CO., LTD.; *Int'l*, pg. 6136
QBR BRAKE, INC.; *U.S. Private*, pg. 3312
QBRICK AB; *Int'l*, pg. 6138
QBUZZ BV—See NV Nederlandse Spoorwegen; *Int'l*, pg. 5497
QC ALLY, LLC; *U.S. Private*, pg. 3312
QC AMERICAN, LLC—See Qinchuan Machine Tool & Tool Group Share Co., Ltd.; *Int'l*, pg. 6141
Q CAPITAL PARTNERS CO., LTD; *Int'l*, pg. 6129
Q-CARRIER (B) SENDIRIAN BERHAD—See Carrier Global Corporation; *U.S. Public*, pg. 444
Q CATERING CAIRNS PTY LIMITED—See Qantas Airways Limited; *Int'l*, pg. 6132
Q CATERING LIMITED—See Qantas Airways Limited; *Int'l*, pg. 6132
Q CATERING RIVERSIDE PTY LIMITED—See Qantas Airways Limited; *Int'l*, pg. 6132
QCC, LLC—See Promus Holdings, LLC; *U.S. Private*, pg. 3284
QC COPPER & GOLD, INC.; *Int'l*, pg. 6138
QC COPPER & GOLD INC.; *Int'l*, pg. 6138
QC CORP.—See AEA Investors LP; *U.S. Private*, pg. 116
QC DATA LLC—See General Atlantic Service Company, L.P.; *U.S. Private*, pg. 1662
QCE FINANCE LLC; *U.S. Private*, pg. 3312
QCE, LLC—See Quality Components Europe; *Int'l*, pg. 6152
Q-CELLS ASIA LTD.—See Hanwha Group; *Int'l*, pg. 3265
Q-CELLS NORTH AMERICA; *U.S. Private*, pg. 3312
QC ENERGY RESOURCES, LLC—See Apax Partners LLP; *Int'l*, pg. 505
QC FINANCIAL SERVICES, INC.—See QC Holdings, Inc.; *U.S. Public*, pg. 1742
QC FINANCIAL SERVICES OF TEXAS, INC.—See QC Holdings, Inc.; *U.S. Public*, pg. 1742
QCG COMPUTER GMBH—See Quanta Computer, Inc.; *Int'l*, pg. 6153
Q.C.& G. FINANCIAL, INC.—See JLL Partners, LLC; *U.S. Private*, pg. 2212
Q-CHECK SYSTEMS—See Synergis Technologies Group; *U.S. Private*, pg. 3903
QC HOLDINGS, INC.; *U.S. Public*, pg. 1741
QCI BRITANNIC—See ROW Inc.; *U.S. Private*, pg. 3490
QC, INC.—See Land O'Lakes, Inc.; *U.S. Private*, pg. 2383
QC INDUSTRIES INC.—See Guardian Fall Protection, Inc.; *U.S. Private*, pg. 1810
QCI TECHNOLOGY; *U.S. Private*, pg. 3312
QCITY TRANSIT PTY. LTD.—See ComfortDelGro Corporation Limited; *Int'l*, pg. 1713
Q-CON EASTERN CO., LTD.—See The Siam Cement Public Company Limited; *Int'l*, pg. 7684
QCP B.V.—See LyondellBasell Industries N.V.; *Int'l*, pg. 4608
QCP B.V.—See Veolia Environnement S.A.; *Int'l*, pg. 8158
QC PLZEN S.R.O.—See DEKRA e.V.; *Int'l*, pg. 2010
Q-CRETE PREMIX PTY LTD—See Seven Group Holdings Limited; *Int'l*, pg. 6732
QCR HOLDINGS, INC.; *U.S. Public*, pg. 1742
QC SOLAR (SUZHOU) CO., LTD.; *Int'l*, pg. 6138
QC SUPPLY LLC—See Charlesbank Capital Partners, LLC; *U.S. Private*, pg. 856
QC SUPPLY LLC—See Charlesbank Capital Partners, LLC; *U.S. Private*, pg. 856
QCT (BEIJING) CO., LTD.—See Quanta Computer, Inc.; *Int'l*, pg. 6153
QCT KOREA INC.—See Quanta Computer, Inc.; *Int'l*, pg. 6153
QCT LLC—See Quanta Computer, Inc.; *Int'l*, pg. 6153
QCUE, INC.; *U.S. Private*, pg. 3312
QC VENTURES LLC; *U.S. Private*, pg. 3312
QC VERIFY, LLC; *U.S. Private*, pg. 3312
QCX GOLD CORP.; *Int'l*, pg. 6138
Q & D CONSTRUCTION; *U.S. Private*, pg. 3311
QDIGI SERVICES LIMITED—See Onsite Electro Services Pvt. Ltd.; *Int'l*, pg. 5583
QDISCOVERY, LLC—See JLL Partners, LLC; *U.S. Private*, pg. 2213
QDI—See Arizona Wholesale Supply Company; *U.S. Private*, pg. 325
QD LASER, INC.; *Int'l*, pg. 6138
QDL LIMITED—See Sigma Healthcare Ltd.; *Int'l*, pg. 6907
QDM INTERNATIONAL INC.; *Int'l*, pg. 6138
QDOBA MEXICAN GRILL INC.—See Jack in the Box Inc.; *U.S. Public*, pg. 1183
QDOS EVENT HIRE LIMITED—See Newship Ltd; *Int'l*, pg. 5238
QD PHARMACEUTICALS ULC—See Viatris Inc.; *U.S. Public*, pg. 2294
Q-DSL HOME GMBH—See EnBW Energie Baden-Wurttemberg AG; *Int'l*, pg. 2399
QD SYSTEM AB; *Int'l*, pg. 6138

QD SYSTEM AB

CORPORATE AFFILIATIONS

QED ENVIRONMENTAL SYSTEMS, INC.—See Graco, Inc.; *U.S. Public*, pg. 954
Q.E.D. ENVIRONMENTAL SYSTEMS LIMITED—See Graco, Inc.; *U.S. Public*, pg. 954
QED, INC.—See Sonepar S.A.; *Int'l*, pg. 7093
QED NATIONAL; *U.S. Private*, pg. 3312
QED PUBLISHING LTD—See The Quarto Group, Inc.; *Int'l*, pg. 7677
QED SYSTEMS, INC. - HONOLULU OFFICE—See QED Systems, Inc.; *U.S. Private*, pg. 3312
QED SYSTEMS, INC. - PORT ORCHARD OFFICE—See QED Systems, Inc.; *U.S. Private*, pg. 3313
QED SYSTEMS, INC. - SAN DIEGO OFFICE—See QED Systems, Inc.; *U.S. Private*, pg. 3313
QED SYSTEMS, INC.; *U.S. Private*, pg. 3312
QED TECHNOLOGIES INTERNATIONAL, INC.—See Quad-C Management, Inc.; *U.S. Private*, pg. 3315
QED THERAPEUTICS, INC.—See BridgeBio Pharma, Inc.; *U.S. Public*, pg. 382
QEEKA HOME(CAYMAN), INC.; *Int'l*, pg. 6138
QEELIN CANADA LTD.—See Kering S.A.; *Int'l*, pg. 4136
QEELIN JAPAN LIMITED—See Kering S.A.; *Int'l*, pg. 4136
QEF (GLOBAL) IRELAND LIMITED—See Park-Ohio Holdings Corp.; *U.S. Public*, pg. 1640
QELL ACQUISITION CORP.; *U.S. Public*, pg. 1742
QELP B.V.—See Creadev SAS; *Int'l*, pg. 1831
QELP DO BRASIL SOFTWARE E CONTUEDO DIGITAL LTDA—See Creadev SAS; *Int'l*, pg. 1831
QEMETICA S.A.—See Kulczyk Investments S.A.; *Int'l*, pg. 4327
QEM LIMITED; *Int'l*, pg. 6138
Q-ENERGIE B.V.—See E.ON SE; *Int'l*, pg. 2259
QENEX COMMUNICATIONS, INC.; *U.S. Public*, pg. 1742
Q.E.P. AUSTRALIA PTY LIMITED—See Q.E.P. Co., Inc.; *U.S. Public*, pg. 1741
Q.E.P. CO., INC.; *U.S. Public*, pg. 1741
QEP RESOURCES, INC.—See Diamondback Energy, Inc.; *U.S. Public*, pg. 658
QES (ASIA-PACIFIC) SDN. BHD.—See QES Group Bhd; *Int'l*, pg. 6138
QES GROUP BHD; *Int'l*, pg. 6138
QESHM ZINC MELTING & REDUCTION COMPANY—See National Iranian Lead & Zinc Company; *Int'l*, pg. 5160
QEW ENGINEERED RUBBER BV—See Trelleborg AB; *Int'l*, pg. 7911
QEW ENGINEERED RUBBER B.V.—See Trelleborg AB; *Int'l*, pg. 7911
QEX LOGISTICS LTD.; *Int'l*, pg. 6138
Q-FLEX INDUSTRIES (M) SDN. BHD.—See UNIMECH Group Berhad; *Int'l*, pg. 8049
Q-FREE AMERICA INC.—See Guardian Capital Group Limited; *Int'l*, pg. 3170
Q-FREE AMERICA LATINA LTDA.—See Guardian Capital Group Limited; *Int'l*, pg. 3170
Q-FREE ASA—See Guardian Capital Group Limited; *Int'l*, pg. 3170
Q-FREE AUSTRALIA PTY. LTD.—See Guardian Capital Group Limited; *Int'l*, pg. 3170
Q-FREE (BRISTOL) UK LTD.—See Guardian Capital Group Limited; *Int'l*, pg. 3170
Q-FREE ESPANA S.L.U.—See Guardian Capital Group Limited; *Int'l*, pg. 3170
Q-FREE MALAYSIA SDN. BHD.—See Guardian Capital Group Limited; *Int'l*, pg. 3170
Q-FREE NETHERLANDS B.V.—See Guardian Capital Group Limited; *Int'l*, pg. 3170
Q-FREE PORTUGAL LDA.—See Guardian Capital Group Limited; *Int'l*, pg. 3170
Q-FREE SVERIGE AB—See Guardian Capital Group Limited; *Int'l*, pg. 3170
Q-FREE THAILAND CO LTD—See Guardian Capital Group Limited; *Int'l*, pg. 3170
Q-FREE TRAFFIC DESIGN D.O.O.—See Guardian Capital Group Limited; *Int'l*, pg. 3170
QGC PTY LIMITED—See Shell plc; *Int'l*, pg. 6795
QGENDA, LLC; *U.S. Private*, pg. 3313
Q/G HOLLAND B.V.—See Quad/Graphics, Inc.; *U.S. Public*, pg. 1744
QGIV, INC.—See Bloomerang, LLC; *U.S. Private*, pg. 584
QGLOBAL SMS, LLC—See IQSTEL Inc.; *U.S. Public*, pg. 1167
QGO FINANCE LIMITED; *Int'l*, pg. 6138
QGOG CONSTELLATION S.A.; *Int'l*, pg. 6138
QGOLD PTY. LTD.; *Int'l*, pg. 6138
Q-GOLD RESOURCES LTD.; *U.S. Public*, pg. 1741
Q. GRADY MINOR & ASSOCIATES, P.A.—See Palm Beach Capital Partners LLC; *U.S. Private*, pg. 3079
QG SAATCHI & SAATCHI—See Publicis Groupe S.A.; *Int'l*, pg. 6108
QGS DEVELOPMENT INC.; *U.S. Private*, pg. 3313
QH AUTO PARTS INDUSTRIES INC—See H-One Co., Ltd.; *Int'l*, pg. 3194
QHD GOLD LIMITED; *Int'l*, pg. 6138
QHG OF ENTERPRISE, INC.—See Community Health Systems, Inc.; *U.S. Public*, pg. 556
QHG OF FORT WAYNE COMPANY, LLC—See Community Health Systems, Inc.; *U.S. Public*, pg. 556
QHG OF HATTIESBURG, INC.—See Community Health Systems, Inc.; *U.S. Public*, pg. 556

QHG OF SOUTH CAROLINA, INC.—See Community Health Systems, Inc.; *U.S. Public*, pg. 556
QHG OF SPRINGDALE, INC.—See Community Health Systems, Inc.; *U.S. Public*, pg. 556
Q.H. INTERNATIONAL CO., LTD.—See Quality Houses Public Co., Ltd.; *Int'l*, pg. 6152
QHP CAPITAL, L.P.; *U.S. Private*, pg. 3313
QHR CORPORATION—See George Weston Limited; *Int'l*, pg. 2939
QHSLAB, INC.; *U.S. Public*, pg. 1742
QHY GROUP; *U.S. Public*, pg. 1742
QIAGEN AARHUS A/S—See QIAGEN N.V.; *Int'l*, pg. 6139
QIAGEN AB—See QIAGEN N.V.; *Int'l*, pg. 6139
QIAGEN AG—See QIAGEN N.V.; *Int'l*, pg. 6139
QIAGEN BIOTECNOLOGIA BRASIL LTDA—See QIAGEN N.V.; *Int'l*, pg. 6139
QIAGEN BUSINESS SERVICES S.P.Z.O.O.—See QIAGEN N.V.; *Int'l*, pg. 6139
QIAGEN CHINA (SHANGHAI) CO., LTD.—See QIAGEN N.V.; *Int'l*, pg. 6139
QIAGEN DEUTSCHLAND HOLDING GMBH—See QIAGEN N.V.; *Int'l*, pg. 6139
QIAGEN FRANCE S.A.S.—See QIAGEN N.V.; *Int'l*, pg. 6139
QIAGEN GMBH—See QIAGEN N.V.; *Int'l*, pg. 6139
QIAGEN IBERIA, S.L.—See QIAGEN N.V.; *Int'l*, pg. 6139
QIAGEN, INC.—See QIAGEN N.V.; *Int'l*, pg. 6140
QIAGEN INC.—See QIAGEN N.V.; *Int'l*, pg. 6139
QIAGEN INDIA PVT. LTD.—See QIAGEN N.V.; *Int'l*, pg. 6139
QIAGEN INSTRUMENTS AG—See QIAGEN N.V.; *Int'l*, pg. 6139
QIAGEN K.K.—See QIAGEN N.V.; *Int'l*, pg. 6139
QIAGEN KOREA LTD.—See QIAGEN N.V.; *Int'l*, pg. 6139
QIAGEN LAKE CONSTANCE GMBH—See QIAGEN N.V.; *Int'l*, pg. 6140
QIAGEN LTD.—See QIAGEN N.V.; *Int'l*, pg. 6139
QIAGEN MANCHESTER LTD.—See QIAGEN N.V.; *Int'l*, pg. 6140
QIAGEN MARSEILLE S.A.—See QIAGEN N.V.; *Int'l*, pg. 6140
QIAGEN NORDIC—See QIAGEN N.V.; *Int'l*, pg. 6139
QIAGEN NORTH AMERICAN HOLDINGS, INC.—See QIAGEN N.V.; *Int'l*, pg. 6139
QIAGEN N.V.; *Int'l*, pg. 6139
QIAGEN PTY. LTD.—See QIAGEN N.V.; *Int'l*, pg. 6139
QIAGEN REDWOOD CITY INC.—See QIAGEN N.V.; *Int'l*, pg. 6139
QIAGEN S.A.—See QIAGEN N.V.; *Int'l*, pg. 6139
QIAGEN S.A.S.—See QIAGEN N.V.; *Int'l*, pg. 6139
QIAGEN SHENZHEN CO. LTD.—See QIAGEN N.V.; *Int'l*, pg. 6140
QIAGEN SINGAPORE PTE. LTD.—See QIAGEN N.V.; *Int'l*, pg. 6140
QIAGEN S.P.A.—See QIAGEN N.V.; *Int'l*, pg. 6139
QIAGEN S.R.L.—See QIAGEN N.V.; *Int'l*, pg. 6139
QIAGEN TAIWAN CO LTD—See QIAGEN N.V.; *Int'l*, pg. 6140
QIAN CHE TECHNOLOGY SERVICE BEIJING CO., LTD.—See System Location Co., Ltd.; *Int'l*, pg. 7390
QIANHAI MERCANTILE EXCHANGE CO., LTD.—See Hong Kong Exchanges & Clearing Limited; *Int'l*, pg. 3466
QIANHE CONDIMENT AND FOOD CO., LTD.; *Int'l*, pg. 6140
QIAN HU AQUARIUM & PETS (M) SDN BHD—See Qian Hu Corporation Limited; *Int'l*, pg. 6140
QIAN HU CORPORATION LIMITED; *Int'l*, pg. 6140
QIAN HU MARKETING CO LTD—See Qian Hu Corporation Limited; *Int'l*, pg. 6140
QIAN HU TAT LENG PLASTIC PTE LTD—See Qian Hu Corporation Limited; *Int'l*, pg. 6140
QIAN HU THE PET FAMILY (M) SDN BHD—See Qian Hu Corporation Limited; *Int'l*, pg. 6140
QIANJIANG WATER RESOURCES DEVELOPMENT CO., LTD.; *Int'l*, pg. 6140
QIANJIANG YONGAN PHARMACEUTICAL CO., LTD.; *Int'l*, pg. 6140
QIANJIN PHARMACEUTICAL CO., LTD.; *Int'l*, pg. 6140
QIANLONG ASSET MANAGEMENT LIMITED—See China Financial Services Holdings Limited; *Int'l*, pg. 1503
QIAN LONG ASSETS MANAGEMENT COMPANY LIMITED—See China Financial Services Holdings Limited; *Int'l*, pg. 1503
QIANSUI INTERNATIONAL GROUP CO., LTD.; *U.S. Public*, pg. 1743
QI AN XIN TECHNOLOGY GROUP, INC.; *Int'l*, pg. 6138
QIAN YUAN BAIXING, INC.; *U.S. Public*, pg. 1743
QIAOTOU TBK CO., LTD.—See TBK Co. Ltd.; *Int'l*, pg. 7480
QIAO XING MOBILE COMMUNICATION CO., LTD.—See Qiao Xing Universal Resources, Inc.; *Int'l*, pg. 6140
QIAO XING UNIVERSAL RESOURCES, INC.; *Int'l*, pg. 6140
QIAOYIN CITY MANAGEMENT CO., LTD.; *Int'l*, pg. 6140
QIAQIA FOOD CO., LTD.; *Int'l*, pg. 6140
QIBU CO., LTD.; *Int'l*, pg. 6140
QIB (UK) PLC—See Qatar Islamic Bank (S.A.Q.); *Int'l*, pg. 6134

QIC ASIA PACIFIC PTE. LTD.—See RINA S.p.A.; *Int'l*, pg. 6342
QIC EUROPE LIMITED—See Qatar Insurance Company S.A.Q.; *Int'l*, pg. 6134
QIC INC.—See RINA S.p.A.; *Int'l*, pg. 6342
QIC INTERNATIONAL L.L.C.—See Qatar Insurance Company S.A.Q.; *Int'l*, pg. 6134
QIC LIMITED; *Int'l*, pg. 6140
QICOMM LIMITED; *Int'l*, pg. 6141
QIC UK LTD.—See RINA S.p.A.; *Int'l*, pg. 6342
QIDING TECHNOLOGY QINHUANGDAO CO., LTD.—See Zhen Ding Technology Holding Limited; *Int'l*, pg. 8669
QIDONG PACIFIC PORT CO., LTD.—See China COSCO Shipping Corporation Limited; *Int'l*, pg. 1493
QIDONG SINGAMAS ENERGY EQUIPMENT CO., LTD.—See China COSCO Shipping Corporation Limited; *Int'l*, pg. 1493
QIDONG SINGAMAS OFFSHORE EQUIPMENT CO., LTD.—See Singamas Container Holdings Limited; *Int'l*, pg. 6939
QIFENG NEW MATERIAL CO., LTD.; *Int'l*, pg. 6141
QIFU TECHNOLOGY, INC.; *Int'l*, pg. 6141
QIHOO 360 SECURITY TECHNOLOGY CO., LTD.—See SJEC Corporation; *Int'l*, pg. 6969
QI-HOUSE HOLDINGS LIMITED; *Int'l*, pg. 6139
QIIGO, INC.—See Listen360, Inc.; *U.S. Private*, pg. 2466
QIIWI GAMES AB; *Int'l*, pg. 6141
QIJIANG GEAR TRANSMISSION CO., LTD.—See Chongqing Machinery & Electronics Holding (Group) Co., Ltd.; *Int'l*, pg. 1580
QIJING MACHINERY CO., LTD; *Int'l*, pg. 6141
QILIAN INTERNATIONAL HOLDING GROUP LIMITED; *Int'l*, pg. 6141
QILINSOFT, LLC—See Innovation Technology Group; *U.S. Private*, pg. 2081
QI LTD.; *Int'l*, pg. 6138
QILU BANK CO., LTD.; *Int'l*, pg. 6141
QILU EASTMAN SPECIALTY CHEMICALS LTD.—See China Petrochemical Corporation; *Int'l*, pg. 1539
QILU EASTMAN SPECIALTY CHEMICALS LTD.—See Eastman Chemical Company; *U.S. Public*, pg. 705
QILU EXPRESSWAY COMPANY LIMITED; *Int'l*, pg. 6141
QIMING INFORMATION TECHNOLOGY CO., LTD.—See China FAW Group Corporation; *Int'l*, pg. 1502
QIMING VENTURE PARTNERS; *Int'l*, pg. 6141
QINCHUAN MACHINE TOOL GROUP BAOJI INSTRUMENT CO., LTD.—See Qinchuan Machine Tool & Tool Group Share Co., Ltd.; *Int'l*, pg. 6141
QINCHUAN MACHINE TOOL & TOOL GROUP SHARE CO., LTD.; *Int'l*, pg. 6141
QINCHUAN SEJONG AUTO PARTS.,LTD.—See SJG Sejong Co., Ltd.; *Int'l*, pg. 6969
Q, INC.—See DZ BANK AG Deutsche Zentral-Genossenschaftsbank; *Int'l*, pg. 2244
QINETIQ CONSULTING PTY LTD—See QinetiQ Group plc; *Int'l*, pg. 6142
QINETIQ GMBH—See QinetiQ Group plc; *Int'l*, pg. 6142
QINETIQ GROUP CANADA INC.—See QinetiQ Group plc; *Int'l*, pg. 6142
QINETIQ GROUP PLC; *Int'l*, pg. 6141
QINETIQ INC.—See QinetiQ Group plc; *Int'l*, pg. 6142
QINETIQ LIMITED—See QinetiQ Group plc; *Int'l*, pg. 6142
QINETIQ NANOMATERIALS LTD—See QinetiQ Group plc; *Int'l*, pg. 6142
QINETIQ NORTH AMERICA, INC.—See QinetiQ Group plc; *Int'l*, pg. 6142
QINETIQ NOVARE PTY. LTD.—See QinetiQ Group plc; *Int'l*, pg. 6142
QINETIQ PTY. LTD.—See QinetiQ Group plc; *Int'l*, pg. 6142
QINETIQ SOLUTIONS SDN. BHD.—See QinetiQ Group plc; *Int'l*, pg. 6142
QINETIQ SPACE NV—See Redwire Corporation; *U.S. Public*, pg. 1771
QINETIQ SWEDEN AB—See QinetiQ Group plc; *Int'l*, pg. 6142
QINETIQ TARGET SYSTEMS LIMITED—See QinetiQ Group plc; *Int'l*, pg. 6142
QINETIQ US HOLDINGS, INC.—See QinetiQ Group plc; *Int'l*, pg. 6142
QINGCI GAMES INC.; *Int'l*, pg. 6142
QINGCLOUD TECHNOLOGIES CORP.; *Int'l*, pg. 6142
QINGDACLARK MATERIAL HANDLING CO.—See Young An Hat Co., Ltd.; *Int'l*, pg. 8602
QINGDAO ADVANCED MARINE MATERIAL TECHNOLOGY CO., LTD.—See Zhejiang Yilida Ventilator Co., Ltd.; *Int'l*, pg. 8667
QINGDAO AEON DONGTAI CO., LTD.—See AEON Co., Ltd.; *Int'l*, pg. 178
QINGDAO AIKETE AUTOMATION INSTRUMENT CO., LTD.—See Endress+Hauser (International) Holding AG; *Int'l*, pg. 2409
QINGDAO AINNOVATION TECHNOLOGY GROUP CO., LTD.; *Int'l*, pg. 6142
QINGDAO ALMATIS CO. LTD.—See Ordu Yardimlasma Kurumu Genel Mudurlugu; *Int'l*, pg. 5616
QINGDAO AMERICAN STARBUCKS COFFEE COMPANY LIMITED—See Starbucks Corporation; *U.S. Public*, pg. 1938

COMPANY NAME INDEX

QINGDAO ANBANG PETROCHEMICAL CO LTD—See China National Chemical Corporation; *Int'l*, pg. 1526

QINGDAO ANODE KASEI CO., LTD.—See Mitsubishi Chemical Group Corporation; *Int'l*, pg. 4934

QINGDAO AOZE AUTOMOBILE SALES SERVICES CO., LTD.—See China ZhengTong Auto Services Holdings Limited; *Int'l*, pg. 1566

QINGDAO APPLE FOODS TECH CO., LTD.—See Apple Flavor & Fragrance Group Co., Ltd.; *Int'l*, pg. 520

QINGDAO ARIAKE FOODSTUFF CO., LTD.—See ARIAKE JAPAN Co., Ltd.; *Int'l*, pg. 564

QINGDAO BAHEAL MEDICAL INC.; *Int'l*, pg. 6142

QINGDAO BEIHAI SHIPBUILDING HEAVY INDUSTRY CO., LTD.—See China Shipbuilding Industry Company Limited; *Int'l*, pg. 1551

QINGDAO BONDED AREA LONGHAN INTERNATIONAL TRADE CO., LTD.—See Zhewen Interactive Group Co Ltd; *Int'l*, pg. 8671

QINGDAO BORTOME IMPORT & EXPORT CO., LTD—See Tongyu Heavy Industry Co., Ltd; *Int'l*, pg. 7809

QINGDAO CENTURY DONGYUAN HIGH TECH MECHANICAL AND ELECTRICAL CO., LTD.—See Shanghai Hanbell Precise Machinery Co., Ltd., *Int'l*, pg. 6769

QINGDAO CHANGHONG OPTOELECTRONICS LTD.—See Wah Hong Industrial Corp.; *Int'l*, pg. 8328

QINGDAO CHIA TAI AGRICULTURAL DEVELOPMENT CO., LTD.—See Charoen Pokphand Foods Public Company Limited; *Int'l*, pg. 1453

QINGDAO CHOHO INDUSTRIAL CO., LTD.; *Int'l*, pg. 6142

QINGDAO CHUNG LOONG PAPER CO., LTD.—See Cheng Loong Corp.; *Int'l*, pg. 1466

QINGDAO CHUN YUAN PRECISION MECHATRONIC CO., LTD.—See Chun Yuan Steel Industry Co., Ltd.; *Int'l*, pg. 1596

QINGDAO CIMC CONTAINER MANUFACTURE CO., LTD—See China International Marine Containers (Group) Co., Ltd.; *Int'l*, pg. 1512

QINGDAO CIMC ECO - EQUIPMENT CO., LTD.—See China International Marine Containers (Group) Co., Ltd.; *Int'l*, pg. 1512

QINGDAO CIMC REEFER CONTAINER MANUFACTURE CO., LTD.—See China International Marine Containers (Group) Co., Ltd.; *Int'l*, pg. 1512

QINGDAO CIMC REEFER TRAILER CO., LTD.—See CIMC Vehicle (Group) Co., Ltd.; *Int'l*, pg. 1608

QINGDAO CIMC SPECIAL REEFER CO., LTD.—See China International Marine Containers (Group) Co., Ltd.; *Int'l*, pg. 1512

QINGDAO CIMC SPECIAL VEHICLE CO., LTD.—See CIMC Vehicle (Group) Co., Ltd.; *Int'l*, pg. 1608

QINGDAO CITYMEDIA CO., LTD.; *Int'l*, pg. 6142

QINGDAO CJ GLS INC.—See CJ Corporation; *Int'l*, pg. 1633

QINGDAO COATS LIMITED—See Coats Group plc; *Int'l*, pg. 1682

QINGDAO COPTON TECHNOLOGY COMPANY LIMITED; *Int'l*, pg. 6142

QINGDAO COSCO KONOIKE LOGISTICS CO., LTD.—See Konoike Transport Co., Ltd.; *Int'l*, pg. 4275

QINGDAO DAEJOO ELECTRONIC MATERIALS CO., LTD.—See Daejoo Electronic Materials Co., Ltd.; *Int'l*, pg. 1907

QINGDAO DEREN ELECTRONIC CO., LTD.—See Shenzhen Deren Electronic Co., Ltd.; *Int'l*, pg. 6808

QINGDAO DIC FINECHEMICALS CO., LTD.—See DIC Corporation; *Int'l*, pg. 2109

QINGDAO DIC LIQUID CRYSTAL CO., LTD.—See DIC Corporation; *Int'l*, pg. 2109

QINGDAO DONGHWA CASTINGS CO., LTD—See Hands Corporation Ltd.; *Int'l*, pg. 3243

QINGDAO DONGJIANG ENVIRONMENTAL RECYCLED POWER LIMITED—See Dongjiang Environmental Company Limited; *Int'l*, pg. 2168

QINGDAO DOUBLESTAR CO., LTD.; *Int'l*, pg. 6142

QINGDAO DOUBLESTAR RUBBER & PLASTIC MACHINERY CO., LTD.—See Qingdao Doublestar Co., Ltd.; *Int'l*, pg. 6142

QINGDAO EASTSOFT COMMUNICATION TECHNOLOGY CO., LTD.; *Int'l*, pg. 6143

QINGDAO EAST STEEL TOWER STOCK CO., LTD.; *Int'l*, pg. 6142

QINGDAO EECON ELECTRONIC CONTROLS AND APPLIANCES CO., LTD.—See Nidec Corporation; *Int'l*, pg. 5280

QINGDAO FENGYUAN UNITE INTERNATIONAL TRADE CO., LTD.—See Shandong Fengyuan Chemical Co Ltd; *Int'l*, pg. 6753

QINGDAO FLOAT GLASS CO., LTD.—See Taiwan Glass Industry Corporation; *Int'l*, pg. 7420

QINGDAO FMG ASIA PACIFIC CO., LTD.—See ZF Friedrichshafen AG; *Int'l*, pg. 8641

QINGDAO FOODS CO., LTD; *Int'l*, pg. 6143

QINGDAO FOODWELL CORPORATION—See Foodwell Corporation; *Int'l*, pg. 2728

QINGDAO FUKOKU AUTO FITTINGS CO., LTD.—See Fukoku Co., Ltd.; *Int'l*, pg. 2839

QINGDAO FU QIANG ELECTRONICS CO., LTD.—See Fu Yu Corporation Limited; *Int'l*, pg. 2801

QINGDAO FUSHENG FOOD CO., LTD.—See Riken Vitamin Co., Ltd.; *Int'l*, pg. 6341

QINGDAO GAOCE TECHNOLOGY CO., LTD.; *Int'l*, pg. 6143

QINGDAO GLX LOGISTICS CO., LTD.—See China Master Logistics Co., Ltd.; *Int'l*, pg. 1517

QINGDAO GMB AUTOMOTIVE CO., LTD.—See GMB Corp.; *Int'l*, pg. 3012

QINGDAO GMB MACHINERY PRODUCT CO., LTD.—See GMB Corp.; *Int'l*, pg. 3012

QINGDAO GOERTEK TECHNOLOGY CO., LTD.—See GoerTek Inc.; *Int'l*, pg. 3021

QINGDAO GON TECHNOLOGY CO., LTD.; *Int'l*, pg. 6143

QINGDAO GRAND OCEAN MARITIME CO., LTD.—See China Master Logistics Co., Ltd.; *Int'l*, pg. 1517

QINGDAO GREENSUM ECOLOGY CO., LTD.; *Int'l*, pg. 6143

QINGDAO GUOLIN TECHNOLOGY GROUP CO., LTD.; *Int'l*, pg. 6143

QINGDAO HAIER BIOMEDICAL CO., LTD.; *Int'l*, pg. 6143

QINGDAO HAIER-CARRIER REFRIGERATION EQUIPMENT COMPANY LIMITED—See Carrier Global Corporation; *U.S. Public*, pg. 444

QINGDAO HAIER INTELLIGENT ELECTRONICS CO., LTD.—See Haier Smart Home Co., Ltd.; *Int'l*, pg. 3210

QINGDAO HANDSEN BIOTECHNOLOGY CO., LTD.—See Zhejiang Orient Gene Biotech Co., Ltd.; *Int'l*, pg. 8661

QINGDAO HANHE CABLE CO., LTD. - HANHE CABLE -AMERICAN BRANCH—See Qingdao Hanhe Cable Co., Ltd.; *Int'l*, pg. 6143

QINGDAO HANHE CABLE CO., LTD.; *Int'l*, pg. 6143

QINGDAO HANJIN LUHAI INTERNATIONAL LOGISTICS CO., LTD.—See Hanjin Transportation Co., Ltd.; *Int'l*, pg. 3253

QINGDAO HANSEN BIOLOGIC SCIENCE CO., LTD.—See Zhejiang Orient Gene Biotech Co., Ltd.; *Int'l*, pg. 8661

QINGDAO HBIS NEW MATERIAL TECHNOLOGY CO., LTD.—See HBIS Group Co., Ltd.; *Int'l*, pg. 3296

QINGDAO HIRON COMMERCIAL COLD CHAIN CO., LTD.; *Int'l*, pg. 6143

QINGDAO HI-TECH MODULDS & PLASTICS TECHNOLOGY CO., LTD.; *Int'l*, pg. 6143

QINGDAO HOLDINGS INTERNATIONAL LIMITED; *Int'l*, pg. 6143

QINGDAO HOME FASHION TEXTILE CO., LTD.—See Nippon Steel Corporation; *Int'l*, pg. 5338

QINGDAO HONGXING CHEMICAL GROUP CO., LTD.—See Guizhou Redstar Development Co., Ltd.; *Int'l*, pg. 3175

QINGDAO HONGXING CHEMICAL GROUP INORGANIC NEW MATERIAL TECHNOLOGY DEVELOPMENT CO., LTD.—See Guizhou Redstar Development Co., Ltd.; *Int'l*, pg. 3175

QINGDAO HOSIDEN ELECTRONICS CO., LTD.—See Hosiden Corporation; *Int'l*, pg. 3484

QINGDAO HUAZHONG PHARMACEUTICALS CO., LTD.—See China National Pharmaceuticals Group Corporation; *Int'l*, pg. 1534

QINGDAO HUAZHONG PHARMACEUTICALS CO., LTD.—See Hoyu Co., Ltd.; *Int'l*, pg. 3499

QINGDAO HUICHENG ENVIRONMENTAL TECHNOLOGY GROUP CO., LTD.; *Int'l*, pg. 6143

QINGDAO HUIJINTONG POWER EQUIPMENT CO., LTD.; *Int'l*, pg. 6143

QINGDAO HYUNDAI MACHINERY CO., LTD.—See Hyundai Steel Company; *Int'l*, pg. 3561

QINGDAO JIAONAN EBARA ELECTRIC POWER CO., LTD.—See Ebara Corporation; *Int'l*, pg. 2284

QINGDAO JINJING CO., LTD.—See Shandong Jinjing Science & Technology Co., Ltd.; *Int'l*, pg. 6755

QINGDAO JSD LOGISTICS CO., LTD.—See Sankyu, Inc.; *Int'l*, pg. 6544

QINGDAO JTB-ENSHU TRADING CO., LTD.—See The Sumitomo Warehouse Co., Ltd.; *Int'l*, pg. 7690

QINGDAO KAMAX BUFFER EQUIPMENT COMPANY LTD.—See ITT Inc.; *U.S. Public*, pg. 1178

QINGDAO KEDA REAL ESTATE CO., LTD.—See Zhewen Interactive Group Co Ltd; *Int'l*, pg. 8671

QINGDAO KEY FOODS CO LTD—See Temasek Holdings (Private) Limited; *Int'l*, pg. 7549

QINGDAO KINGKING APPLIED CHEMISTRY CO., LTD.; *Int'l*, pg. 6144

QINGDAO KISWIRE PRECISION METAL LTD.—See KISWIRE LTD.; *Int'l*, pg. 4194

QINGDAO KOMELON TOOL CORPORATION—See Komelon Corporation; *Int'l*, pg. 4242

QINGDAO KOOLL LOGISTICS CO., LTD.—See China International Marine Containers (Group) Co., Ltd.; *Int'l*, pg. 1512

QINGDAO KOWA SEIKO CO., LTD.—See Fujitsu COMPONENT LIMITED; *Int'l*, pg. 2832

QINGDAO KUTESMART CO., LTD.; *Int'l*, pg. 6144

QINGDAO KYOKUYO INTERNATIONAL CO., LTD.—See Kyokuyo Co. Ltd.; *Int'l*, pg. 4364

QINGDAO LARSEN & TOUBRO TRADING COMPANY LIMITED—See Larsen & Toubro Limited; *Int'l*, pg. 4419

QINGDAO LINGTONG TEXTILE CO., LTD.—See Mitsubishi Chemical Group Corporation; *Int'l*, pg. 4934

QINGDAO LONTEC ELECTRONIC TECHNOLOGY CO., LTD.—See Qingdao Guolin Technology Group Co., Ltd.; *Int'l*, pg. 6143

QINGDAO MATSUYA COMMERCIAL TRADE CO., LTD.—See Matsuya Foods Holdings Co., Ltd.; *Int'l*, pg. 4730

QINGDAO MITSUMI ELECTRONICS CO., LTD.—See Minebea Mitsumi Inc.; *Int'l*, pg. 4904

QINGDAO NATIONAL CONTAINER LINE CO., LTD.—See NCL International Logistics Public Company Limited; *Int'l*, pg. 5181

QINGDAO NATURAL PIGMENTS LIMITED—See Guizhou Redstar Development Co., Ltd.; *Int'l*, pg. 3175

QINGDAO NESCO MEDICAL CO., LTD.—See Alfresa Holdings Corporation; *Int'l*, pg. 317

QINGDAO NEW CENTURY TOOL CO., LTD.—See YG-1 Co., Ltd; *Int'l*, pg. 8579

QINGDAO NISSUI FOOD RESEARCH & DEVELOPMENT CO., LTD.—See Nissui Corporation; *Int'l*, pg. 5378

QINGDAO NONGSHIM FOODS CO., LTD.—See Nongshim Co., Ltd.; *Int'l*, pg. 5414

QINGDAO NOVELBEAM TECHNOLOGY CO., LTD.; *Int'l*, pg. 6144

QINGDAO NPA INDUSTRY CO., LTD.—See Gaona Aero Material Co., Ltd.; *Int'l*, pg. 2882

QINGDAO PACIFIC CONTAINER CO., LTD.—See China COSCO Shipping Corporation Limited; *Int'l*, pg. 1493

QINGDAO PACIFIC MILLENNIUM PACKAGING & PAPER INDUSTRIES CO., LTD.—See Pacific Millennium Packaging Group Corporation; *Int'l*, pg. 5691

QINGDAO POLY GRAND THEATRE MANAGEMENT CORPORATION LIMITED—See Poly Culture Group Corporation Limited; *Int'l*, pg. 5914

QINGDAO PORT DONGJIAKOU BULK LOGISTICS CENTER CO., LTD.—See China Master Logistics Co., Ltd.; *Int'l*, pg. 1518

QINGDAO PORT INTERNATIONAL CO., LTD.; *Int'l*, pg. 6144

QINGDAO PRESIDENT FEED & LIVESTOCK CO., LTD.—See Uni-President Enterprises Corporation; *Int'l*, pg. 8029

QINGDAO RED BUTTERFLY PRECISION MATERIALS CO., LTD.—See Chori Co., Ltd.; *Int'l*, pg. 1583

QINGDAO RENGO PACKAGING CO., LTD.—See Rengo Co., Ltd.; *Int'l*, pg. 6280

QINGDAO RICHEN FOOD CO., LTD.; *Int'l*, pg. 6144
QINGDAO RISO FOODS CO., LTD.; *Int'l*, pg. 6144

QINGDAO ROLLED GLASS CO., LTD.—See Taiwan Glass Industry Corporation; *Int'l*, pg. 7420

QINGDAO RUBBER SIX CONVEYOR BELT CO, LTD—See China National Chemical Corporation; *Int'l*, pg. 1529

QINGDAO RUNDE BIOTECHNOLOGY COMPANY LIMITED—See GLG LIFE TECH CORPORATION; *Int'l*, pg. 2992

QINGDAO RURAL COMMERCIAL BANK; *Int'l*, pg. 6144

QINGDAO SAMWHA ELECTRONICS CO., LTD.—See Samwha Capacitor Group; *Int'l*, pg. 6518

QINGDAO SAMYOUNG ELECTRONICS CO., LTD.—See Nippon Chemi-Con Corporation; *Int'l*, pg. 5312

QINGDAO SANKYU ASIA-PACIFIC LOGISTICS CO., LTD.—See Sankyu, Inc.; *Int'l*, pg. 6544

QINGDAO SEAH PRECISION METAL CO., LTD.—See SeAH Holdings Corp.; *Int'l*, pg. 6664

QINGDAO SECOM SECURITY CO., LTD.—See SECOM Co., Ltd.; *Int'l*, pg. 6671

QINGDAO SENKO LOGISTICS CO., LTD.—See Senko Group Holdings Co., Ltd.; *Int'l*, pg. 6710

QINGDAO SENTURY TIRE CO., LTD.; *Int'l*, pg. 6144

QINGDAO SEWOON MEDICAL CO., LTD.—See SEWOONMEDICAL Co. Ltd; *Int'l*, pg. 6737

QINGDAO SHINWON GARMENT CO., LTD.—See Shinwon Corporation; *Int'l*, pg. 6850

QINGDAO SIFANG KAWASAKI ROLLING STOCK TECHNOLOGY CO., LTD.—See Kawasaki Heavy Industries, Ltd.; *Int'l*, pg. 4098

QINGDAO SINOTRANS-AZUMA LOGISTICS CO., LTD.—See Azuma Shipping Co., Ltd.; *Int'l*, pg. 782

QINGDAO SINTO MACHINERY CO., LTD.—See Sintokogio Ltd.; *Int'l*, pg. 6958

QINGDAO SMITH ELECTRONIC MATERIALS CO., LTD.—See Shanghai Smith Adhesive New Material Co., Ltd.; *Int'l*, pg. 6779

QINGDAO SUNG MOON ELECTRONICS CO., LTD.—See Sungmoon Electronics Co., Ltd.; *Int'l*, pg. 7315

QINGDAO SUNJIN FEED CO., LTD.—See SUNJIN CO., LTD.; *Int'l*, pg. 7316

QINGDAO TAFCO FOOD CO., LTD.—See Maruha Nichiro Corporation; *Int'l*, pg. 4711

QINGDAO TAIHAN DYEING & PRINTING CO., LTD.—See Taihan Textile Co., Ltd.; *Int'l*, pg. 7411

QINGDAO TAYUAN TEXTILE LTD.—See Taihan Textile Co., Ltd.; *Int'l*, pg. 7411

QINGDAO TDK ELECTRONICS CO., LTD.—See TDK Corporation; *Int'l*, pg. 7487

QINGDAO TECO PRECISION MECHATRONICS CO., LTD.—See Teco Electric & Machinery Co., Ltd.; *Int'l*, pg. 7518
QINGDAO TGOOD ELECTRIC CO., LTD.; *Int'l*, pg. 6144
QINGDAO TIANDIHUI FOODSTUFFS CO., LTD.—See TDH Holdings, Inc.; *Int'l*, pg. 7486
QINGDAO TIANNENG HEAVY INDUSTRIES CO LTD; *Int'l*, pg. 6144
QINGDAO TOPSCOMM COMMUNICATION CO., LTD; *Int'l*, pg. 6144
QINGDAO TRACON ELECTRONIC CO., LTD.—See Chonbang Co., Ltd.; *Int'l*, pg. 1578
QINGDAO TSC OFFSHORE EQUIPMENT CO., LTD—See CM Energy Tech Co., Ltd.; *Int'l*, pg. 1666
QINGDAO TSINGTAO BEER & ASAHI BEVERAGE CO., LTD.—See Asahi Group Holdings Ltd.; *Int'l*, pg. 594
QINGDAO TSINGTAO BEER & ASAHI BEVERAGE CO., LTD.—See Tsingtao Brewery Group Company Ltd.; *Int'l*, pg. 7952
QINGDAO UNICK CO. LTD.—See Unick Corporation; *Int'l*, pg. 8032
QINGDAO VANKE REAL ESTATE COMPANY LIMITED—See China Vanke Co., Ltd.; *Int'l*, pg. 1562
QINGDAO VICTALL PRECISION MOULDS CO., LTD.—See Qingdao Victall Railway Co., Ltd.; *Int'l*, pg. 6144
QINGDAO VICTALL RAILWAY CO., LTD.; *Int'l*, pg. 6144
QINGDAO VICTORY PLASTIC CO., LTD—See Flex Ltd.; *Int'l*, pg. 2704
QINGDAO VLAND BIOTECH GROUP CO., LTD.—See Qingdao Vland Biotech, Inc.; *Int'l*, pg. 6145
QINGDAO VLAND BIOTECH, INC.; *Int'l*, pg. 6144
QINGDAO WEFLO VALVE CO., LTD.; *Int'l*, pg. 6145
QINGDAO WEST COAST DEVELOPMENT (GROUP) CO., LTD.; *Int'l*, pg. 6145
QINGDAO YG-1 TOOL CO., LTD.—See YG-1 Co., Ltd; *Int'l*, pg. 8579
QINGDAO YICAI FUND DISTRIBUTION CO. LTD.—See Intesa Sanpaolo S.p.A.; *Int'l*, pg. 3766
QINGDAO YONGTAI ALLY INTERNATIONAL LOGISTICS CO., LTD.—See Yongtaiyun Chemical Logistics Co., Ltd.; *Int'l*, pg. 8598
QINGDAO YTE SPECIAL PRODUCTS CO. LTD.—See TRF Ltd; *Int'l*, pg. 7917
QINGDAO YUYANG ELECTRONICS CO., LTD.—See Y2 Solution Co., Ltd.; *Int'l*, pg. 8544
QINGDAO ZHONGFU IN-LINE CONTAINER CO., LTD.—See Zhuhai Zhongfu Enterprise Co., Ltd.; *Int'l*, pg. 8679
QINGDAO ZHONGZI ZHONGCHENG GROUP CO., LTD.; *Int'l*, pg. 6145
QING DING PRECISION ELECTRONICS (HUAIAN) CO., LTD.—See Zhen Ding Technology Holding Limited; *Int'l*, pg. 8669
QINGHAI CONTEMPORARY AMPEREX TECHNOLOGY LIMITED—See Contemporary Amperex Technology Co., Ltd.; *Int'l*, pg. 1779
QINGHAI ELECTRIC POWER COMPANY—See State Grid Corporation of China; *Int'l*, pg. 7183
QINGHAI HUADING INDUSTRIAL CO., LTD.; *Int'l*, pg. 6145
QINGHAI HUZHU TIANYOUDE HIGHLAND BARLEY SPIRIT CO., LTD.; *Int'l*, pg. 6145
QINGHAI JINRUI MINERAL DEVELOPMENT CO., LTD.; *Int'l*, pg. 6145
QINGHAI SALT LAKE INDUSTRY CO., LTD.; *Int'l*, pg. 6145
QINGHAI SPRING MEDICINAL RESOURCES TECHNOLOGY CO., LTD.; *Int'l*, pg. 6145
QINGHAI TOPRAY SOLAR CO., LTD.—See Topray Solar Co., Ltd.; *Int'l*, pg. 7820
QINGHAI TUORI NEW ENERGY TECHNOLOGY CO., LTD.—See Topray Solar Co., Ltd.; *Int'l*, pg. 7820
QINGJIAN INTERNATIONAL (SOUTH PACIFIC) GROUP DEVELOPMENT CO., PTE. LTD.—See CNQC International Holdings Ltd.; *Int'l*, pg. 1678
QINGJIAN REALTY (SOUTH PACIFIC) GROUP PTE. LTD.—See CNQC International Holdings Ltd.; *Int'l*, pg. 1678
QINGLING ISUZU (CHONGQING) ENGINE CO., LTD.—See Isuzu Motors Limited; *Int'l*, pg. 3826
QINGLING MOTORS (GROUP) CO. LTD.; *Int'l*, pg. 6145
QINGMU DIGITAL TECHNOLOGY CO., LTD.; *Int'l*, pg. 6145
QINGQING ENVIRONMENTAL PROTECTION EQUIPMENT CO., LTD.—See Beijing Hanjian Heshan Pipeline Co.,LTD.; *Int'l*, pg. 951
QINGYAN ENVIRONMENTAL TECHNOLOGY CO., LTD.; *Int'l*, pg. 6145
QINGYANG DONGJIANG ENVIRONMENTAL TECHNOLOGIES COMPANY LIMITED—See Dongjiang Environmental Company Limited; *Int'l*, pg. 2168
QINGYUAN MEIDONG LEXUS AUTO SALES & SERVICES CO., LTD.—See China MeiDong Auto Holdings Limited; *Int'l*, pg. 1519
QINGYUAN WEILIBANG WOOD CO., LTD.—See Chengxin Lithium Group Co., Ltd.; *Int'l*, pg. 1470
QINHONG INTERNATIONAL GROUP; *Int'l*, pg. 6145

QINHUANGDAO ASANO CEMENT CO., LTD.; *Int'l*, pg. 6145
QINHUANGDAO GOLDENSEA FOODSTUFF INDUSTRIES CO., LTD—See Wilmar International Limited; *Int'l*, pg. 8421
QINHUANGDAO PORT CO., LTD.; *Int'l*, pg. 6145
QINHUANGDAO POWER GENERATION CO., LTD.—See State Grid Corporation of China; *Int'l*, pg. 7183
QINHUANGDAO TIANQIN EQUIPMENT MANUFACTURING CO., LTD.; *Int'l*, pg. 6145
QINIU LIMITED; *Int'l*, pg. 6145
QINQIN FOODSTUFFS GROUP (CAYMAN) COMPANY LIMITED; *Int'l*, pg. 6145
QINSTRUMENTS GMBH—See BICO Group AB; *Int'l*, pg. 1019
Q INTERNATIONAL COURIER, LLC; *U.S. Private*, pg. 3311
QINTERRA AS—See EQT AB; *Int'l*, pg. 2479
QINVEST LLC—See Qatar Islamic Bank (S.A.Q.); *Int'l*, pg. 6134
QINYANG ZHONGYU GAS CO., LTD.—See Zhongyu Energy Holdings Limited; *Int'l*, pg. 8676
QINZHOU SEMBCORP WATER CO LTD—See Sembcorp Industries Ltd.; *Int'l*, pg. 6702
QIOPTIQ LTD.—See AEA Investors LP; *U.S. Private*, pg. 114
QIOPTIQ PHOTONICS GMBH & CO. KG—See AEA Investors LP; *U.S. Private*, pg. 114
QIOPTIQ PHOTONICS LIMITED—See AEA Investors LP; *U.S. Private*, pg. 114
QI PHILIPPINES INC.—See QI Ltd.; *Int'l*, pg. 6139
QIPRO SOLUCIONES S.L.—See Banco Bilbao Vizcaya Argentaria, S.A.; *Int'l*, pg. 818
QIQIHAR RAILWAY ROLLING STOCK CO., LTD.—See CRRC Corporation Limited; *Int'l*, pg. 1859
QISDA CORPORATION; *Int'l*, pg. 6145
QISDA ELECTRONICS CORP.—See Qisda Corporation; *Int'l*, pg. 6146
QISDA ELECTRONICS (SUZHOU) CO. LTD.—See Qisda Corporation; *Int'l*, pg. 6146
QISDA JAPAN CO., LTD.—See Qisda Corporation; *Int'l*, pg. 6146
QISDA MEXICANA S.A. DE C.V.—See Qisda Corporation; *Int'l*, pg. 6146
QISDA (SHANGHAI) CO., LTD.—See Qisda Corporation; *Int'l*, pg. 6146
QISDA (SUZHOU) CO., LTD.—See PNE PCB Berhad; *Int'l*, pg. 5901
QISDA VIETNAM CO., LTD.—See Qisda Corporation; *Int'l*, pg. 6146
QI SERVICES (M) SDN BHD—See QI Ltd.; *Int'l*, pg. 6139
QI SERVICES (TH) LTD.—See QI Ltd.; *Int'l*, pg. 6139
QIS RESEARCH LABORATORY SDN. BHD.—See Hai-O Enterprise Berhad; *Int'l*, pg. 3209
QITIAN TECHNOLOGY GROUP CO., LTD.; *Int'l*, pg. 6146
QIT MADAGASCAR MINERALS SA—See Rio Tinto plc; *Int'l*, pg. 6346
QIVY SAS—See VINCI S.A.; *Int'l*, pg. 8225
QIVY TERTIAIRE SAS—See VINCI S.A.; *Int'l*, pg. 8225
QIWI PLC; *Int'l*, pg. 6146
QIXIAN HENGXING FRUIT JUICE CO., LTD.—See QAF Limited; *Int'l*, pg. 6132
QIZINI ALPHEN B.V.—See Parcom Capital Management B.V.; *Int'l*, pg. 5741
QIZINI GROUP B.V.—See Parcom Capital Management B.V.; *Int'l*, pg. 5741
QK HEALTHCARE, INC.—See Quality King Distributors Inc.; *U.S. Private*, pg. 3319
QK HONEYCOMB PRODUCTS LIMITED—See Tex Holdings Plc; *Int'l*, pg. 7582
QKL STORES, INC.; *Int'l*, pg. 6146
QL2 SOFTWARE, LLC—See DMEP Corporation; *U.S. Private*, pg. 1248
Q-LAB CORP.; *U.S. Private*, pg. 3312
QLARION, INC.—See Sagewind Capital LLC; *U.S. Private*, pg. 3527
QLEANAIR AB; *Int'l*, pg. 6146
QL ENDAU MARINE PRODUCTS SDN. BHD.—See QL Resources Berhad; *Int'l*, pg. 6146
QL FIGO (JOHOR) SDN. BHD.—See QL Resources Berhad; *Int'l*, pg. 6146
QL FISHMEAL SDN. BHD.—See QL Resources Berhad; *Int'l*, pg. 6146
QL FOODS SDN. BHD.—See QL Resources Berhad; *Int'l*, pg. 6146
QLIFE, INC.—See Sony Group Corporation; *Int'l*, pg. 7102
QLIKTECH INTERNATIONAL AB—See Thoma Bravo, L.P.; *U.S. Private*, pg. 4152
QLIKTECH INTERNATIONAL LTD.—See Hilan Ltd.; *Int'l*, pg. 3390
QLIKTECH ITALY S.R.L.—See Thoma Bravo, L.P.; *U.S. Private*, pg. 4152
QLIK TECHNOLOGIES INC.—See Thoma Bravo, L.P.; *U.S. Private*, pg. 4152
Q-LINEA AB; *Int'l*, pg. 6131
Q-LINE TRUCKING LTD.; *Int'l*, pg. 6131
QL LIAN HOE SDN. BHD.—See QL Resources Berhad; *Int'l*, pg. 6146
Q L LIGHT SOURCE COMPANY LIMITED; *Int'l*, pg. 6129

QL MARINE PRODUCTS SDN. BHD.—See QL Resources Berhad; *Int'l*, pg. 6146
QLM LIFE & MEDICAL INSURANCE W.L.L.—See Qatar Insurance Company S.A.Q.; *Int'l*, pg. 6134
QLOGIC INDIA PVT. LTD.—See Marvell Technology Group Ltd.; *Int'l*, pg. 4717
QLOSR GROUP AB; *Int'l*, pg. 6146
Q-LOUD GMBH—See q.beyond AG; *Int'l*, pg. 6131
QL POULTRY FARMS SDN. BHD.—See QL Resources Berhad; *Int'l*, pg. 6146
QL RESOURCES BERHAD; *Int'l*, pg. 6146
QLS HOLDINGS CO., LTD.; *Int'l*, pg. 6146
QLT INTERNATIONAL COMPANY LIMITED—See Qualitech Public Company Limited; *Int'l*, pg. 6152
QLUCORE AB; *Int'l*, pg. 6146
Q-MACHINE—See Questar Corporation; *U.S. Private*, pg. 3326
Q-MATION INC.; *U.S. Private*, pg. 3312
QMA WADHWANI LLP—See Prudential Financial, Inc.; *U.S. Public*, pg. 1733
QMAX COMMUNICATIONS PTE LTD.—See Creative Technology Ltd.; *Int'l*, pg. 1833
Q'MAX SOLUTIONS INC.—See Palladium Equity Partners, LLC; *U.S. Private*, pg. 3078
Q-MAX SYSTEMS LIMITED—See Netcall plc; *Int'l*, pg. 5213
QMC CO., LTD.; *Int'l*, pg. 6146
Q & M COLLEGE OF DENTISTRY PTE. LTD.—See Q&M Dental Group (Singapore) Limited; *Int'l*, pg. 6129
QM CORPORATION; *U.S. Private*, pg. 3313
QMC QUANTUM MINERALS CORP.; *Int'l*, pg. 6147
QMC SYSTEMS, INC.; *U.S. Private*, pg. 3313
Q & M DENTAL CENTRE (BALESTIER) PTE. LTD.—See Q&M Dental Group (Singapore) Limited; *Int'l*, pg. 6130
Q & M DENTAL CENTRE (KIM SENG) PTE. LTD.—See Q&M Dental Group (Singapore) Limited; *Int'l*, pg. 6130
Q & M DENTAL CENTRE (NORTH BRIDGE) PTE. LTD.—See Q&M Dental Group (Singapore) Limited; *Int'l*, pg. 6130
Q & M DENTAL CENTRE (ORCHARD) PTE. LTD.—See Q&M Dental Group (Singapore) Limited; *Int'l*, pg. 6130
Q & M DENTAL CENTRE (RAFFLES PLACE) PTE. LTD.—See Q&M Dental Group (Singapore) Limited; *Int'l*, pg. 6130
Q&M DENTAL GROUP (SINGAPORE) LIMITED; *Int'l*, pg. 6129
Q & M DENTAL SURGERY (ADMIRALTY) PTE. LTD.—See Q&M Dental Group (Singapore) Limited; *Int'l*, pg. 6130
Q & M DENTAL SURGERY (ALEXANDRA ROAD) PTE. LTD.—See Q&M Dental Group (Singapore) Limited; *Int'l*, pg. 6130
Q & M DENTAL SURGERY (ALJUNIED) PTE. LTD.—See Q&M Dental Group (Singapore) Limited; *Int'l*, pg. 6130
Q & M DENTAL SURGERY (ANG MO KIO CENTRAL) PTE. LTD.—See Q&M Dental Group (Singapore) Limited; *Int'l*, pg. 6130
Q & M DENTAL SURGERY (AUSTIN) SDN. BHD.—See Q&M Dental Group (Singapore) Limited; *Int'l*, pg. 6130
Q & M DENTAL SURGERY (BANDAR MELAKA) SDN. BHD.—See Q&M Dental Group (Singapore) Limited; *Int'l*, pg. 6130
Q & M DENTAL SURGERY (BANDAR PUTERI PUCHONG) SDN. BHD.—See Q&M Dental Group (Singapore) Limited; *Int'l*, pg. 6130
Q & M DENTAL SURGERY (BEDOK RESERVOIR) PTE. LTD.—See Q&M Dental Group (Singapore) Limited; *Int'l*, pg. 6130
Q & M DENTAL SURGERY (BOON LAY MRT) PTE. LTD.—See Q&M Dental Group (Singapore) Limited; *Int'l*, pg. 6130
Q & M DENTAL SURGERY (BRADDELL) PTE. LTD.—See Q&M Dental Group (Singapore) Limited; *Int'l*, pg. 6130
Q & M DENTAL SURGERY (BUKIT BATOK) PTE. LTD.—See Q&M Dental Group (Singapore) Limited; *Int'l*, pg. 6130
Q & M DENTAL SURGERY (BUKIT PANJANG) PTE. LTD.—See Q&M Dental Group (Singapore) Limited; *Int'l*, pg. 6130
Q & M DENTAL SURGERY (BUKIT TIMAH) PTE. LTD.—See Q&M Dental Group (Singapore) Limited; *Int'l*, pg. 6130
Q & M DENTAL SURGERY (CHOA CHU KANG) PTE. LTD.—See Q&M Dental Group (Singapore) Limited; *Int'l*, pg. 6130
Q & M DENTAL SURGERY (CLEMENTI CENTRAL) PTE. LTD.—See Q&M Dental Group (Singapore) Limited; *Int'l*, pg. 6130
Q & M DENTAL SURGERY (CLEMENTI) PTE. LTD.—See Q&M Dental Group (Singapore) Limited; *Int'l*, pg. 6130
Q & M DENTAL SURGERY (ELIAS MALL) PTE. LTD.—See Q&M Dental Group (Singapore) Limited; *Int'l*, pg. 6130
Q & M DENTAL SURGERY (GOMBAK MRT) PTE. LTD.—See Q&M Dental Group (Singapore) Limited; *Int'l*, pg. 6130
Q & M DENTAL SURGERY (GOMBAK) PTE. LTD.—See Q&M Dental Group (Singapore) Limited; *Int'l*, pg. 6130

COMPANY NAME INDEX

Q & M DENTAL SURGERY (HOUGANG CENTRAL) PTE. LTD.—See Q&M Dental Group (Singapore) Limited; *Int'l*, pg. 6130
Q & M DENTAL SURGERY (HOUGANG MALL) PTE. LTD.—See Q&M Dental Group (Singapore) Limited; *Int'l*, pg. 6130
Q & M DENTAL SURGERY (JELAPANG) PTE. LTD.—See Q&M Dental Group (Singapore) Limited; *Int'l*, pg. 6130
Q & M DENTAL SURGERY (JURONG EAST CENTRAL) PTE. LTD.—See Q&M Dental Group (Singapore) Limited; *Int'l*, pg. 6130
Q & M DENTAL SURGERY (KALLANG MRT) PTE. LTD.—See Q&M Dental Group (Singapore) Limited; *Int'l*, pg. 6130
Q & M DENTAL SURGERY (KHATIB) PTE. LTD.—See Q&M Dental Group (Singapore) Limited; *Int'l*, pg. 6130
Q & M DENTAL SURGERY (KIM TIAN) PTE. LTD.—See Q&M Dental Group (Singapore) Limited; *Int'l*, pg. 6130
Q & M DENTAL SURGERY (KOVAN) PTE. LTD.—See Q&M Dental Group (Singapore) Limited; *Int'l*, pg. 6130
Q & M DENTAL SURGERY (MARSILING) PTE. LTD.—See Q&M Dental Group (Singapore) Limited; *Int'l*, pg. 6130
Q & M DENTAL SURGERY (MOLEK) SDN. BHD.—See Q&M Dental Group (Singapore) Limited; *Int'l*, pg. 6130
Q & M DENTAL SURGERY (OLD AIRPORT RD) PTE. LTD.—See Q&M Dental Group (Singapore) Limited; *Int'l*, pg. 6130
Q & M DENTAL SURGERY (PASIR RIS) PTE. LTD.—See Q&M Dental Group (Singapore) Limited; *Int'l*, pg. 6130
Q & M DENTAL SURGERY (REDHILL MRT) PTE. LTD.—See Q&M Dental Group (Singapore) Limited; *Int'l*, pg. 6130
Q & M DENTAL SURGERY (SEMBAWANG MRT) PTE. LTD.—See Q&M Dental Group (Singapore) Limited; *Int'l*, pg. 6130
Q & M DENTAL SURGERY (SERANGOON CENTRAL) PTE. LTD.—See Q&M Dental Group (Singapore) Limited; *Int'l*, pg. 6130
Q & M DENTAL SURGERY (SERANGOON NORTH) PTE. LTD.—See Q&M Dental Group (Singapore) Limited; *Int'l*, pg. 6130
Q & M DENTAL SURGERY (SERANGOON) PTE. LTD.—See Q&M Dental Group (Singapore) Limited; *Int'l*, pg. 6130
Q & M DENTAL SURGERY (TAMAN MERDEKA) SDN. BHD.—See Q&M Dental Group (Singapore) Limited; *Int'l*, pg. 6130
Q & M DENTAL SURGERY (TANJONG KATONG) PTE. LTD.—See Q&M Dental Group (Singapore) Limited; *Int'l*, pg. 6130
Q & M DENTAL SURGERY (TOA PAYOH CENTRAL) PTE. LTD.—See Q&M Dental Group (Singapore) Limited; *Int'l*, pg. 6130
Q & M DENTAL SURGERY (TOA PAYOH) PTE. LTD.—See Q&M Dental Group (Singapore) Limited; *Int'l*, pg. 6130
Q & M DENTAL SURGERY (WOODLANDS) PTE. LTD.—See Q&M Dental Group (Singapore) Limited; *Int'l*, pg. 6130
Q & M DENTAL SURGERY (YISHUN CENTRAL) PTE. LTD.—See Q&M Dental Group (Singapore) Limited; *Int'l*, pg. 6130
Q-MED AB—See Abu Dhabi Investment Authority; *Int'l*, pg. 71
Q-MED AB—See EQT Corporation; *U.S. Public*, pg. 785
Q-MED AB—See Public Sector Pension Investment Board; *Int'l*, pg. 6096
Q-MED BRASIL COMERCIO E IMPORTACAO DE PRODUTOS MEDICOS LTDA—See Abu Dhabi Investment Authority; *Int'l*, pg. 71
Q-MED BRASIL COMERCIO E IMPORTACAO DE PRODUTOS MEDICOS LTDA—See EQT Corporation; *U.S. Public*, pg. 785
Q-MED BRASIL COMERCIO E IMPORTACAO DE PRODUTOS MEDICOS LTDA—See Public Sector Pension Investment Board; *Int'l*, pg. 6096
Q/MEDIA SOLUTIONS CORPORATION; *Int'l*, pg. 6131
Q-MEDIA SOLUTIONS—See Q/Media Solutions Corporation; *Int'l*, pg. 6131
Q-MED ICT S.R.L.—See Abu Dhabi Investment Authority; *Int'l*, pg. 71
Q-MED ICT S.R.L.—See EQT Corporation; *U.S. Public*, pg. 785
Q-MED ICT S.R.L.—See Public Sector Pension Investment Board; *Int'l*, pg. 6096
Q-MED INTERNATIONAL LTD—See Abu Dhabi Investment Authority; *Int'l*, pg. 71
Q-MED INTERNATIONAL LTD—See EQT Corporation; *U.S. Public*, pg. 785
Q-MED INTERNATIONAL LTD—See Public Sector Pension Investment Board; *Int'l*, pg. 6096
Q-MED INTERNATIONAL TRADING (SHANGHAI) LTD—See Abu Dhabi Investment Authority; *Int'l*, pg. 71
Q-MED INTERNATIONAL TRADING (SHANGHAI) LTD—See EQT Corporation; *U.S. Public*, pg. 785
Q-MED INTERNATIONAL TRADING (SHANGHAI) LTD—See Public Sector Pension Investment Board; *Int'l*, pg. 6096

Q-MED MEXICO S.A DE C.V.—See Abu Dhabi Investment Authority; *Int'l*, pg. 71
Q-MED MEXICO S.A DE C.V.—See EQT Corporation; *U.S. Public*, pg. 785
Q-MED MEXICO S.A DE C.V.—See Public Sector Pension Investment Board; *Int'l*, pg. 6096
Q-MED POLSKA SP. Z.O.O—See Abu Dhabi Investment Authority; *Int'l*, pg. 72
Q-MED POLSKA SP. Z.O.O—See EQT Corporation; *U.S. Public*, pg. 785
Q-MED POLSKA SP. Z.O.O—See Public Sector Pension Investment Board; *Int'l*, pg. 6096
Q-MED S.A.R.L.—See Abu Dhabi Investment Authority; *Int'l*, pg. 72
Q-MED S.A.R.L.—See EQT Corporation; *U.S. Public*, pg. 785
Q-MED S.A.R.L.—See Public Sector Pension Investment Board; *Int'l*, pg. 6096
Q-MED SPAIN S.L.—See Abu Dhabi Investment Authority; *Int'l*, pg. 72
Q-MED SPAIN S.L.—See EQT Corporation; *U.S. Public*, pg. 785
Q-MED SPAIN S.L.—See Public Sector Pension Investment Board; *Int'l*, pg. 6096
Q-MED (SWEDEN) AUSTRALIA PTY LTD—See Abu Dhabi Investment Authority; *Int'l*, pg. 71
Q-MED (SWEDEN) AUSTRALIA PTY LTD—See EQT Corporation; *U.S. Public*, pg. 785
Q-MED (SWEDEN) AUSTRALIA PTY LTD—See Public Sector Pension Investment Board; *Int'l*, pg. 6096
QMINES LIMITED; *Int'l*, pg. 6147
QMI - SAI CANADA LIMITED—See EQT AB; *Int'l*, pg. 2471
QMI SECURITY SOLUTIONS; *U.S. Private*, pg. 3313
Q MIX SUPPLY CO., LTD.—See The Siam Cement Public Company Limited; *Int'l*, pg. 7683
Q & M MEDICAL & AESTHETIC CLINIC (FARRER PARK) PTE. LTD.—See Q&M Dental Group (Singapore) Limited; *Int'l*, pg. 6130
Q & M MEDICAL & AESTHETIC CLINIC (TAMPINES CENTRAL) PTE. LTD.—See Q&M Dental Group (Singapore) Limited; *Int'l*, pg. 6131
Q & M MEDICAL CLINIC (BUANGKOK MRT) PTE. LTD.—See Q&M Dental Group (Singapore) Limited; *Int'l*, pg. 6131
Q & M MEDICAL CLINIC (BUKIT BATOK) PTE. LTD.—See Q&M Dental Group (Singapore) Limited; *Int'l*, pg. 6131
Q & M MEDICAL CLINIC (SERANGOON CENTRAL) PTE. LTD.—See Q&M Dental Group (Singapore) Limited; *Int'l*, pg. 6131
Q MODEL MANAGEMENT INC.; *U.S. Private*, pg. 3312
QMP METAL POWDERS (SUZHOU) CO., LTD—See Rio Tinto plc; *Int'l*, pg. 6346
QMP PUBLICIS; *Int'l*, pg. 6147
QMS CO., LTD.—See ENPLAS CORPORATION; *Int'l*, pg. 2445
QMSERVICE GMBH—See PAUL HARTMANN AG; *Int'l*, pg. 5761
QMS MEDIA LIMITED—See Quadrant Private Equity Pty. Ltd.; *Int'l*, pg. 6149
QM SYSTEMS LIMITED—See Pipehawk Plc; *Int'l*, pg. 5873
QMUSIC NEDERLAND B.V.—See DPG Media Group NV; *Int'l*, pg. 2188
QMX GOLD CORPORATION—See Eldorado Gold Corporation; *Int'l*, pg. 2347
QNARY LLC; *U.S. Private*, pg. 3313
QNB ALAHLI BANK S.A.E.—See Qatar National Bank S.A.Q.; *Int'l*, pg. 6135
QNB BANK—See QNB Corp.; *U.S. Public*, pg. 1743
QNB BANQUE PRIVEE (SUISSE) SA—See Qatar National Bank S.A.Q.; *Int'l*, pg. 6135
QNB CAPITAL LLC—See Qatar National Bank S.A.Q.; *Int'l*, pg. 6135
QNB CORP.; *U.S. Public*, pg. 1743
QNB EFINANS A.S.—See QNB Finans Faktoring A.S.; *Int'l*, pg. 6147
QNB FINANSBANK A.S.—See Qatar National Bank S.A.Q.; *Int'l*, pg. 6135
QNB FINANS FAKTORING A.S.; *Int'l*, pg. 6147
QNB FINANS FINANSAL KIRALAMA A.S.; *Int'l*, pg. 6147
QNB FINANSINVEST AS—See QNB Finans Faktoring A.S.; *Int'l*, pg. 6147
QNB FINANS LEASING A.S.—See QNB Finans Faktoring A.S.; *Int'l*, pg. 6147
QNB FINANSPORTFOY A.S.—See QNB Finans Faktoring A.S.; *Int'l*, pg. 6147
QNB FINANSVARLIK A.S.—See QNB Finans Faktoring A.S.; *Int'l*, pg. 6147
QNB FINANS VARLIK KIRALAMA A.S.; *Int'l*, pg. 6147
QNB (INDIA) PRIVATE LIMITED—See Qatar National Bank S.A.Q.; *Int'l*, pg. 6135
QNB SIGORTA A.S.—See QNB Finans Faktoring A.S.; *Int'l*, pg. 6147
QNB—See QNB Corp.; *U.S. Public*, pg. 1743
QNB SUISSE S.A.—See Qatar National Bank S.A.Q.; *Int'l*, pg. 6135
QNEXIS INC; *U.S. Private*, pg. 3313

QNTM GROUP AB—See Altor Equity Partners AB; *Int'l*, pg. 395
QOGNIFY, INC.—See Hexagon AB; *Int'l*, pg. 3369
QOL ASSIST CO., LTD.—See Qol Holdings Co., Ltd.; *Int'l*, pg. 6147
QOL CO., LTD.—See Qol Holdings Co., Ltd.; *Int'l*, pg. 6147
QOLEAD, LIMITED—See Dai-ichi Life Holdings, Inc.; *Int'l*, pg. 1918
QOL HOLDINGS CO., LTD.; *Int'l*, pg. 6147
QOL MEDS, LLC—See Genoa Healthcare LLC; *U.S. Private*, pg. 1673
QOMO HITEVISION, LLC.; *U.S. Private*, pg. 3313
QOMOLANGMA ACQUISITION CORP.; *U.S. Public*, pg. 1743
QOMPLX, INC.; *U.S. Private*, pg. 3313
QONIAC GMBH—See KLA Corporation; *U.S. Public*, pg. 1269
QONIAC JAPAN LTD.—See KLA Corporation; *U.S. Public*, pg. 1269
QONIAC KOREA LTD.—See KLA Corporation; *U.S. Public*, pg. 1269
QONTIGO GMBH—See Deutsche Borse AG; *Int'l*, pg. 2064
QONTIGO INDEX GMBH—See Deutsche Borse AG; *Int'l*, pg. 2064
QOO10 PTE. LTD; *Int'l*, pg. 6147
QORVAL, L.L.C.; *U.S. Private*, pg. 3313
QORVIS COMMUNICATIONS, LLC—See Publicis Groupe S.A.; *Int'l*, pg. 6103
QORVO (BEIJING) CO., LTD.—See Qorvo, Inc.; *U.S. Public*, pg. 1743
QORVO BELGIUM NV—See Qorvo, Inc.; *U.S. Public*, pg. 1743
QORVO CALIFORNIA, INC.—See Qorvo, Inc.; *U.S. Public*, pg. 1743
QORVO COSTA RICA S.R.L.—See Qorvo, Inc.; *U.S. Public*, pg. 1743
QORVO DENMARK APS—See Qorvo, Inc.; *U.S. Public*, pg. 1743
QORVO DEZHOU CO., LTD.—See Qorvo, Inc.; *U.S. Public*, pg. 1743
QORVO FLORIDA, INC.—See Qorvo, Inc.; *U.S. Public*, pg. 1743
QORVO GERMANY HOLDING GMBH—See Qorvo, Inc.; *U.S. Public*, pg. 1743
QORVO, INC.; *U.S. Public*, pg. 1743
QORVO INTERNATIONAL PTE. LTD.—See Qorvo, Inc.; *U.S. Public*, pg. 1743
QORVO JAPAN YK—See Qorvo, Inc.; *U.S. Public*, pg. 1743
QORVO KOREA LTD.—See Qorvo, Inc.; *U.S. Public*, pg. 1743
QORVO MUNICH GMBH—See Qorvo, Inc.; *U.S. Public*, pg. 1743
QORVO OREGON, INC.—See Qorvo, Inc.; *U.S. Public*, pg. 1743
QORVO SHANGHAI LTD.—See Qorvo, Inc.; *U.S. Public*, pg. 1743
QORVO TEXAS, LLC—See Qorvo, Inc.; *U.S. Public*, pg. 1743
QORVO UK LIMITED—See Qorvo, Inc.; *U.S. Public*, pg. 1743
QORVO US, INC.—See Qorvo, Inc.; *U.S. Public*, pg. 1743
QORVO UTRECHT, B.V.—See Qorvo, Inc.; *U.S. Public*, pg. 1743
QOSINA CORP.; *U.S. Private*, pg. 3313
QOSMOS SA—See Enea AB; *Int'l*, pg. 2410
QOS NETWORKS LLC—See DigitalBridge Group, Inc.; *U.S. Public*, pg. 665
QOS NETWORKS LLC—See EQT AB; *Int'l*, pg. 2481
Q-PACK (M) SDN BHD—See Citra Nusa Holdings Berhad; *Int'l*, pg. 1626
Q-PARTNERS CONSULTING & MANAGEMENT GMBH—See Devoteam SA; *Int'l*, pg. 2090
Q-PARTS24 GMBH & CO. KG—See LKQ Corporation; *U.S. Public*, pg. 1336
Q-PEAK—See Physical Sciences Inc.; *U.S. Private*, pg. 3175
QP ENERGY SERVICES, LLC—See Quanta Services, Inc.; *U.S. Public*, pg. 1752
Q_PERIOR AG; *Int'l*, pg. 6131
Q P GROUP HOLDINGS LIMITED; *Int'l*, pg. 6129
QPHARMA, INC.; *U.S. Private*, pg. 3313
QPI MULTIPRESS, INC.—See Quality Products Inc.; *U.S. Private*, pg. 3321
QPL INTERNATIONAL HOLDINGS LIMITED; *Int'l*, pg. 6147
QPL LIMITED - DONGGUAN CHANG AN QPL ELECTRONICS FACTORY—See QPL International Holdings Limited; *Int'l*, pg. 6147
QPL LIMITED—See QPL International Holdings Limited; *Int'l*, pg. 6147
QPL (PTE) LIMITED—See QPL International Holdings Limited; *Int'l*, pg. 6147
QPL (US) INC.—See QPL International Holdings Limited; *Int'l*, pg. 6147
QPM AEROSPACE INC.; *U.S. Private*, pg. 3313
QPR CIS OY—See QPR Software Plc; *Int'l*, pg. 6148
QPR SOFTWARE PLC; *Int'l*, pg. 6147

QPS AMERICA, INC.—See I Squared Capital Advisors (US) LLC; *U.S. Private*, pg. 2023
QPS AMERICA, INC.—See TDR Capital LLP; *Int'l*, pg. 7492
QPS AS—See Wienerberger AG; *Int'l*, pg. 8405
QPS COMPANIES INC.; *U.S. Private*, pg. 3313
QPS ENGINEERING, LLC—See Quanta Services, Inc.; *U.S. Public*, pg. 1752
QPS ENGINEERING LTD.—See Quanta Services, Inc.; *U.S. Public*, pg. 1752
QPS EUROPE B.V.—See I Squared Capital Advisors (US) LLC; *U.S. Private*, pg. 2023
QPS EUROPE B.V.—See TDR Capital LLP; *Int'l*, pg. 7492
QPS EVALUATION SERVICES INC.—See I Squared Capital Advisors (US) LLC; *U.S. Private*, pg. 2023
QPS EVALUATION SERVICES INC.—See TDR Capital LLP; *Int'l*, pg. 7492
QPSI / IPC—See Quality Packaging Specialists, Inc.; *U.S. Private*, pg. 3320
QQ SOLUTIONS, INC.—See Roper Technologies, Inc.; *U.S. Public*, pg. 1814
QR AGORACLOUD SDN. BHD.—See Silverlake Axis Ltd.; *Int'l*, pg. 6926
Q RESOURCES PLC; *Int'l*, pg. 6129
QRF COMM. VA; *Int'l*, pg. 6148
QRONS INC.; *U.S. Public*, pg. 1743
QRP, INC.—See Stanley Black & Decker, Inc.; *U.S. Public*, pg. 1934
QRSCIENCES SECURITY PTY. LTD.—See Q Technology Group Limited; *Int'l*, pg. 6129
QRS MUSIC TECHNOLOGY, INC.; *U.S. Public*, pg. 1744
QR S.R.L.—See Cefla S.c.; *Int'l*, pg. 1390
QRX MEDICAL MANAGEMENT, LLC—See KKR & Co. Inc.; *U.S. Public*, pg. 1250
QS/1 GOVERNMENTAL SOLUTIONS—See J.M. Smith Corporation; *U.S. Private*, pg. 2169
QS/1—See J.M. Smith Corporation; *U.S. Private*, pg. 2169
QSACK & ASSOCIATES, INC.; *U.S. Private*, pg. 3313
QSA GLOBAL INC.—See Illinois Tool Works Inc.; *U.S. Public*, pg. 1110
Q'SAI CO., LTD.—See Advantage Partners LLP; *Int'l*, pg. 164
Q'SAI CO., LTD.—See euglena Co., Ltd.; *Int'l*, pg. 2526
Q'SAI CO., LTD.—See Tokyo Century Corporation; *Int'l*, pg. 7789
Q SALES, LLC—See Lanco International Inc.; *U.S. Private*, pg. 2382
QSAM BIOSCIENCES, INC.; *U.S. Public*, pg. 1744
QSCH TERMELO ES KERESKEDELMI KFT—See Adval Tech Holding AG; *Int'l*, pg. 155
QSC, INC.; *U.S. Private*, pg. 3314
QSC, LLC; *U.S. Private*, pg. 3314
QSEARCH AB—See NGS Group AB; *Int'l*, pg. 5256
QS ENERGY, INC.; *U.S. Public*, pg. 1744
QSI CO., LTD.; *Int'l*, pg. 6148
QSI GROUP LTD.—See VINCI S.A.; *Int'l*, pg. 8225
QSI INC.; *U.S. Private*, pg. 3314
QSI INC.—See Pan Pacific International Holdings Corporation; *Int'l*, pg. 5715
QSI MANAGEMENT, LLC—See Thoma Bravo, L.P.; *U.S. Private*, pg. 4150
QS INVESTORS, LLC—See Franklin Resources, Inc.; *U.S. Public*, pg. 882
QSL OF AUSTINTOWN OHIO LLC—See BP plc; *Int'l*, pg. 1127
QSL QUEBEC INC.—See Mistras Group, Inc.; *U.S. Public*, pg. 1451
QS NEDERLAND B.V.—See Bunzl plc; *Int'l*, pg. 1219
Q SQUARED SOLUTIONS (BEIJING) CO. LTD.—See IQVIA Holdings Inc.; *U.S. Public*, pg. 1170
Q SQUARED SOLUTIONS EXPRESSION ANALYSIS LLC—See IQVIA Holdings Inc.; *U.S. Public*, pg. 1170
Q SQUARED SOLUTIONS K.K.—See IQVIA Holdings Inc.; *U.S. Public*, pg. 1170
Q SQUARED SOLUTIONS LIMITED—See IQVIA Holdings Inc.; *U.S. Public*, pg. 1170
Q SQUARED SOLUTIONS PTE. LTD.—See IQVIA Holdings Inc.; *U.S. Public*, pg. 1170
Q SQUARED SOLUTIONS (SHANGHAI) CO. LTD.—See IQVIA Holdings Inc.; *U.S. Public*, pg. 1170
QS QUARTERHOUSE SOFTWARE, INC.—See Sycamore Partners Management, LP; *U.S. Private*, pg. 3897
QSR BRANDS (M) HOLDINGS SDN. BHD.—See Johor Corporation; *Int'l*, pg. 3994
QSR STEEL CORPORATION, LLC; *U.S. Private*, pg. 3314
QSS INTERNATIONAL INC.; *U.S. Private*, pg. 3314
QSTAR FORSALJNING AB—See DCC plc; *Int'l*, pg. 1991
QST ASIA LTD. HONG KONG—See QST Industries, Inc.; *U.S. Private*, pg. 3314
QST DOMINICANA LLC—See QST Industries, Inc.; *U.S. Private*, pg. 3314
QST GROUP; *Int'l*, pg. 6148
QST INDUSTRIAS DE MEXICO, S.A. DE R.L. DE C.V.—See QST Industries, Inc.; *U.S. Private*, pg. 3314
QST INDUSTRIES ASIA (S) PTE. LTD.—See QST Industries, Inc.; *U.S. Private*, pg. 3314
QST INDUSTRIES, INC.; *U.S. Private*, pg. 3314
QST INDUSTRIES (SHANGHAI) CO., LTD.—See QST Industries, Inc.; *U.S. Private*, pg. 3314

QST TECHNOLOGIES (HK) CO. LTD.—See QST Group; *Int'l*, pg. 6148
QST TECHNOLOGIES PTE. LTD.—See QST Group; *Int'l*, pg. 6148
QST TRAVEL GROUP INC.; *U.S. Private*, pg. 3314
QST VIETNAM CO., LTD—See QST Industries, Inc.; *U.S. Private*, pg. 3314
QTC ENERGY PUBLIC COMPANY LIMITED; *Int'l*, pg. 6148
QTC MANAGEMENT, INC.—See Lockheed Martin Corporation; *U.S. Public*, pg. 1339
THE QT COMPANY AS—See Qt Group Plc; *Int'l*, pg. 6148
THE QT COMPANY GMBH—See Qt Group Plc; *Int'l*, pg. 6148
THE QT COMPANY LLC—See Qt Group Plc; *Int'l*, pg. 6148
THE QT COMPANY LTD.—See Qt Group Plc; *Int'l*, pg. 6148
Q-TECH CORPORATION; *U.S. Private*, pg. 3312
Q-TECH ENGINEERING LTD & CO.; *Int'l*, pg. 6131
Q TECHNOLOGY (GROUP) COMPANY LIMITED; *Int'l*, pg. 6129
Q TECHNOLOGY GROUP LIMITED; *Int'l*, pg. 6129
QTEC SOLUTIONS, INC.; *U.S. Private*, pg. 3314
QTERICS, INC.—See Lattice Semiconductor Corporation; *U.S. Public*, pg. 1294
QTEROS, INC.; *U.S. Private*, pg. 3314
QT GROUP PLC; *Int'l*, pg. 6148
Q THERAPEUTICS, INC.; *U.S. Private*, pg. 3312
QT HOTELS & RESORTS PTY LIMITED—See Event Hospitality & Entertainment Limited; *Int'l*, pg. 2562
QT IMAGING HOLDINGS, INC.; *U.S. Public*, pg. 1744
QT INDUSTRIES LLC; *U.S. Private*, pg. 3314
QTM, INC.; *U.S. Private*, pg. 3314
QTONE EDUCATION GROUP GUANGDONG LTD.; *Int'l*, pg. 6148
Q-TRONIC B.V.—See Addtech AB; *Int'l*, pg. 134
QTS FINANCE CORPORATION—See Blackstone Inc.; *U.S. Public*, pg. 351
QTS REALTY TRUST, INC.—See Blackstone Inc.; *U.S. Public*, pg. 351
QUABAUG CORPORATION; *U.S. Private*, pg. 3314
QUABBIN WIRE & CABLE CO. INC.; *U.S. Private*, pg. 3314
QUABIT INMOBILIARIA S.A.—See Neinor Homes SA; *Int'l*, pg. 5192
QUACKENBUSH CO., INC.; *U.S. Private*, pg. 3314
QUAD AREA COMMUNITY ACTION AGENCY INC.; *U.S. Private*, pg. 3314
QUAD, A SOLOMONEDWARDS COMPANY—See SolomonEdwardsGroup, LLC; *U.S. Private*, pg. 3710
QUADAX INC.; *U.S. Private*, pg. 3315
QUAD CITY BANK & TRUST COMPANY—See QCR Holdings, Inc.; *U.S. Public*, pg. 1742
QUAD-CITY PETERBILT INC.; *U.S. Private*, pg. 3315
QUAD CITY PHYSICAL THERAPY, LIMITED PARTNERSHIP—See U.S. Physical Therapy, Inc.; *U.S. Public*, pg. 2215
QUAD CITY TESTING LABORATORY—See Premium Inspection & Testing, Inc.; *U.S. Private*, pg. 3252
QUAD-CITY TIMES—See Lee Enterprises, Incorporated; *U.S. Public*, pg. 1300
QUAD-C MANAGEMENT, INC.; *U.S. Private*, pg. 3315
QUADCO INCORPORATED; *U.S. Private*, pg. 3315
QUADCO INC.—See Komatsu Ltd.; *Int'l*, pg. 4239
QUAD COUNTY CORN PROCESSORS COOPERATIVE; *U.S. Public*, pg. 1744
QUAD-COUNTY READY MIX CORP; *U.S. Private*, pg. 3315
QUADEC Z IMMOBILIEN LEASING GESELLSCHAFT M.B.H.—See UniCredit S.p.A.; *Int'l*, pg. 8037
QUADEL CONSULTING CORP.—See System One Holdings, LLC; *U.S. Private*, pg. 3906
QUADGEN WIRELESS SOLUTIONS INC.; *U.S. Private*, pg. 3315
QUAD/GRAPHICS EUROPE SP. Z O.O—See Quad/Graphics, Inc.; *U.S. Public*, pg. 1744
QUAD/GRAPHICS, INC. - ATGLEN—See Quad/Graphics, Inc.; *U.S. Public*, pg. 1744
QUAD/GRAPHICS, INC. - CHICAGO PREMEDIA—See Quad/Graphics, Inc.; *U.S. Public*, pg. 1744
QUAD/GRAPHICS, INC. - DICKSON—See Quad/Graphics, Inc.; *U.S. Public*, pg. 1744
QUAD/GRAPHICS, INC. - EFFINGHAM—See Quad/Graphics, Inc.; *U.S. Public*, pg. 1744
QUAD/GRAPHICS, INC. - ENFIELD—See Quad/Graphics, Inc.; *U.S. Public*, pg. 1744
QUAD/GRAPHICS, INC. - FAIRFIELD—See Quad/Graphics, Inc.; *U.S. Public*, pg. 1744
QUAD/GRAPHICS, INC. - FERNLEY—See Quad/Graphics, Inc.; *U.S. Public*, pg. 1745
QUAD/GRAPHICS, INC. - FRANKLIN—See Quad/Graphics, Inc.; *U.S. Public*, pg. 1745
QUAD/GRAPHICS, INC. - HAZLETON—See Quad/Graphics, Inc.; *U.S. Public*, pg. 1745
QUAD/GRAPHICS, INC. - LEOMINSTER—See Quad/Graphics, Inc.; *U.S. Public*, pg. 1745
QUAD/GRAPHICS, INC. - MIDLAND—See Quad/Graphics, Inc.; *U.S. Public*, pg. 1745

QUAD/GRAPHICS, INC. - PEWAUKEE—See Quad/Graphics, Inc.; *U.S. Public*, pg. 1745
QUAD/GRAPHICS, INC.; *U.S. Public*, pg. 1744
QUAD/GRAPHICS, INC. - ST. CLOUD—See Quad/Graphics, Inc.; *U.S. Public*, pg. 1745
QUAD/GRAPHICS, INC. - TAUNTON—See Quad/Graphics, Inc.; *U.S. Public*, pg. 1745
QUAD/GRAPHICS, INC. - VERSAILLES—See CJK Group, Inc.; *U.S. Private*, pg. 909
QUAD/GRAPHICS, INC. - WAUKEE—See Quad/Graphics, Inc.; *U.S. Public*, pg. 1745
QUAD/GRAPHICS, INC. - WOBURN—See Quad/Graphics, Inc.; *U.S. Public*, pg. 1745
QUAD/GRAPHICS QUERATARO S.A. DE C.V.—See Quad/Graphics, Inc.; *U.S. Public*, pg. 1744
QUADIENT AUSTRALIA PTY. LTD.—See Quadient SA; *Int'l*, pg. 6149
QUADIENT CHINA LTD.—See Quadient SA; *Int'l*, pg. 6149
QUADIENT DATA UK LTD.—See Quadient SA; *Int'l*, pg. 6149
QUADIENT DENMARK APS—See Quadient SA; *Int'l*, pg. 6149
QUADIENT FRANCE SAS—See Quadient SA; *Int'l*, pg. 6149
QUADIENT GERMANY GMBH—See Quadient SA; *Int'l*, pg. 6149
QUADIENT HUNGARY KFT.—See Quadient SA; *Int'l*, pg. 6149
QUADIENT POLAND SP. Z.O.O.—See Quadient SA; *Int'l*, pg. 6149
QUADIENT SA; *Int'l*, pg. 6148
QUADIENT SINGAPORE PTE. LTD.—See Quadient SA; *Int'l*, pg. 6149
QUADIENT SOFTWARE BRAZIL LTDA.—See Quadient SA; *Int'l*, pg. 6149
QUADIENT S.R.O—See Quadient SA; *Int'l*, pg. 6149
QUADIENT SWITZERLAND AG—See Quadient SA; *Int'l*, pg. 6149
QUADIGI UAB—See Draegerwerk AG & Co. KGaA; *Int'l*, pg. 2198
QUADION LLC - RIVER FALLS PLANT—See KKR & Co. Inc.; *U.S. Public*, pg. 1263
QUADION LLC—See KKR & Co. Inc.; *U.S. Public*, pg. 1263
QUADIX SAS—See VINCI S.A.; *Int'l*, pg. 8225
QUAD M SOLUTIONS, INC.; *U.S. Public*, pg. 1744
QUADNA INC.—See DXP Enterprises, Inc.; *U.S. Public*, pg. 698
QUADPACK INDUSTRIES SA—See PSB Industries SA; *Int'l*, pg. 6014
QUAD PARTNERS, LLC; *U.S. Private*, pg. 3314
QUAD PLUS LLC; *U.S. Private*, pg. 3315
QUADPRO ITES LIMITED; *Int'l*, pg. 6149
QUADRAD MANUFACTURING LTD.—See Linamar Corporation; *Int'l*, pg. 4502
QUADRALENE LTD.—See Getinge AB; *Int'l*, pg. 2952
QUADRAMED CORPORATION—See Constellation Software Inc.; *Int'l*, pg. 1774
QUADRANGLE ARCHITECTS LIMITED—See Nippon Koei Co., Ltd.; *Int'l*, pg. 5322
QUADRANGLE DEVELOPMENT CORPORATION; *U.S. Private*, pg. 3315
QUADRANGLE GROUP LLC; *U.S. Private*, pg. 3316
QUADRANGLE MANAGEMENT COMPANY—See Quadrangle Development Corporation; *U.S. Private*, pg. 3315
QUADRANT-AMROQ BEVERAGES S.R.L.—See PepsiCo, Inc.; *U.S. Public*, pg. 1671
QUADRANT B.V.—See Mitsubishi Chemical Group Corporation; *Int'l*, pg. 4930
QUADRANT CATERING LTD.—See International Distributions Services plc; *Int'l*, pg. 3748
QUADRANT CMS—See Mitsubishi Chemical Group Corporation; *Int'l*, pg. 4930
QUADRANT COMMUNICATIONS LTD.—See The Interpublic Group of Companies, Inc.; *U.S. Public*, pg. 2092
THE QUADRANT CORPORATION—See Tri Pointe Homes, Inc.; *U.S. Public*, pg. 2188
QUADRANT CREATIVE PTY LTD—See Adcorp Australia Limited; *Int'l*, pg. 127
QUADRANT EPP AG—See Mitsubishi Chemical Group Corporation; *Int'l*, pg. 4930
QUADRANT EPP FRANCE CESTIDUR DIVISION—See Mitsubishi Chemical Group Corporation; *Int'l*, pg. 4930
QUADRANT EPP GERMANY GMBH—See Mitsubishi Chemical Group Corporation; *Int'l*, pg. 4930
QUADRANT EPP S.A.—See Mitsubishi Chemical Group Corporation; *Int'l*, pg. 4930
QUADRANT EPP UK LTD.—See Mitsubishi Chemical Group Corporation; *Int'l*, pg. 4930
QUADRANT EPP USA, INC.—See Mitsubishi Chemical Group Corporation; *Int'l*, pg. 4930
QUADRANT EPP USA, INC.—See Mitsubishi Chemical Group Corporation; *Int'l*, pg. 4930
QUADRANT EPP USA, INC.—See Mitsubishi Chemical Group Corporation; *Int'l*, pg. 4930
QUADRANTE S.P.A—See Cassa Depositi e Prestiti S.p.A.; *Int'l*, pg. 1355

COMPANY NAME INDEX

QUADRANT KENKYO EPP LTD.—See Mitsubishi Chemical Group Corporation; *Int'l*, pg. 4930
QUADRANT MANAGEMENT, INC.; *U.S. Private*, pg. 3316
QUADRANT METALS TECHNOLOGIES, LLC—See ARC Group Worldwide, Inc.; *U.S. Public*, pg. 179
QUADRANT PACIFIC LIMITED—See John Swire & Sons Limited; *Int'l*, pg. 3980
QUADRANT PLASTIC COMPOSITES CANADA INC.—See Mitsubishi Chemical Group Corporation; *Int'l*, pg. 4930
QUADRANT POLYMER CHINA LTD.—See Mitsubishi Chemical Group Corporation; *Int'l*, pg. 4930
QUADRANT POLYPENCO JAPAN LTD.—See Mitsubishi Chemical Group Corporation; *Int'l*, pg. 4934
QUADRANT POLYPENCO LTD.—See Mitsubishi Chemical Group Corporation; *Int'l*, pg. 4930
QUADRANT PRIVATE EQUITY PTY. LTD.; *Int'l*, pg. 6149
QUADRANT SECURITY GROUP LIMITED—See Synectics plc; *Int'l*, pg. 7382
QUADRANT SECURITY GROUP PLC—See Synectics plc; *Int'l*, pg. 7382
QUADRANT SOFTWARE, INC.—See American Pacific Group, LLC; *U.S. Private*, pg. 242
QUADRANT S.R.L.—See Mitsubishi Chemical Group Corporation; *Int'l*, pg. 4930
QUADRANTS SCIENTIFIC, INC.—See Eurofins Scientific S.E.; *Int'l*, pg. 2550
QUADRANT SSS—See Synectics plc; *Int'l*, pg. 7382
QUADRANT TELEVENTURES LIMITED; *Int'l*, pg. 6149
QUADRAS, INC.; *U.S. Private*, pg. 3316
QUADRATEC INC.—See Stantec Inc.; *Int'l*, pg. 7172
QUADRATICA (UK) LIMITED—See OSI Systems, Inc.; *U.S. Public*, pg. 1622
QUADRAVEST CAPITAL MANAGEMENT INC.; *Int'l*, pg. 6149
QUADREL TRAVEL MANANGEMENT PROPRIETARY LIMITED—See The Bidvest Group Limited; *Int'l*, pg. 7626
QUADREP INCORPORATED; *U.S. Private*, pg. 3316
QUADRIA CAPITAL INVESTMENT MANAGEMENT PTE LTD; *Int'l*, pg. 6150
QUADRICA SARL—See TotalEnergies SE; *Int'l*, pg. 7837
QUADRIGA CAPITAL BETEILIGUNGSBERATUNG GMBH; *Int'l*, pg. 6150
QUADRIGA UK LTD.—See Exceptional Innovation BV; *Int'l*, pg. 2579
QUADRIGA WORLDWIDE LIMITED—See Exceptional Innovation BV; *Int'l*, pg. 2579
QUADRILATERO MARCHE-UMBRIA S.P.A.—See Ferrovie dello Stato Italiane S.p.A.; *Int'l*, pg. 2645
QUADRISE PLC; *Int'l*, pg. 6150
QUADRIS MEDICAL—See Taylor Corporation; *U.S. Private*, pg. 3939
QUADRIVIO SGR S.P.A.; *Int'l*, pg. 6150
QUADRIVIUS, INC.; *U.S. Private*, pg. 3316
QUADRO ACQUISITION ONE CORP.; *U.S. Public*, pg. 1745
QUADRO ENGINEERING CORP—See IDEX Corp; *U.S. Public*, pg. 1091
QUADRO RESOURCES LTD.; *Int'l*, pg. 6150
QUADSTONE PARAMICS LTD—See Pitney Bowes Inc.; *U.S. Public*, pg. 1695
QUAD/TECH EUROPE, INC.—See Quad/Graphics, Inc.; *U.S. Public*, pg. 1745
QUADTECH EUROPE—See Quad/Graphics, Inc.; *U.S. Public*, pg. 1745
QUADTECH IRELAND—See Quad/Graphics, Inc.; *U.S. Public*, pg. 1745
QUAD TECHNICAL SERVICES (PTY) LIMITED—See enX Group Limited; *Int'l*, pg. 2456
QUADTECH (SHANGHAI) TRADING COMPANY LIMITED—See Quad/Graphics, Inc.; *U.S. Public*, pg. 1745
QUAD VIDEO HALO, INC.—See Quad Video Holdings Corporation; *U.S. Private*, pg. 3315
QUAD VIDEO HOLDINGS CORPORATION; *U.S. Private*, pg. 3315
QUADWINKOWSKI—See Quad/Graphics, Inc.; *U.S. Public*, pg. 1745
QUAD/WINKOWSKI SP. ZOO—See Quad/Graphics, Inc.; *U.S. Public*, pg. 1745
QUAESTIO CAPITAL MANAGEMENT SGR S.P.A.—See Quaestio Holding S.A.; *Int'l*, pg. 6150
QUAESTIO HOLDING S.A.; *Int'l*, pg. 6150
QUAESTUS HOLDINGS, LLC; *U.S. Private*, pg. 3316
QUA GRANITE HAYAL YAPI VE URUNLERI SANAYI TICARET A.S.; *Int'l*, pg. 6148
QUAIL CREEK BANCSHARES INC.; *U.S. Private*, pg. 3316
QUAIL H FARMS, LLC.; *U.S. Private*, pg. 3316
QUAIL LODGE, INC.—See The Hongkong and Shanghai Hotels Limited; *Int'l*, pg. 7653
QUAIL MOUNTAIN INC.; *U.S. Private*, pg. 3316
QUAIL RUN SERVICES, LLC—See Republic Services, Inc.; *U.S. Public*, pg. 1788
QUAIL SPOL. S.R.O.—See Fomento de Construcciones y Contratas, S.A.; *Int'l*, pg. 2723
QUAIL SURGICAL AND PAIN MANAGEMENT CENTER, LLC—See Universal Health Services, Inc.; *U.S. Public*, pg. 2259

QUAIL TOOLS, L.P.—See Parker Wellbore Company; *U.S. Public*, pg. 1650
QUAIL TOOLS—See Parker Wellbore Company; *U.S. Public*, pg. 1650
QUAIL WEST LTD.—See SEGRO plc; *Int'l*, pg. 6683
QUAINTANCE-WEAVER INC.; *U.S. Private*, pg. 3316
QUAINT OAK BANCORP, INC.; *U.S. Public*, pg. 1745
QUAINT OAK BANK—See QUAINT OAK BANCORP, INC.; *U.S. Public*, pg. 1745
QUAKE GLOBAL, INC.; *U.S. Private*, pg. 3316
QUAKER AGENCY, INC.—See The Carlyle Group Inc.; *U.S. Public*, pg. 2047
QUAKER CHEMICAL (AUSTRALASIA) PTY. LTD.—See Quaker Chemical Corporation; *U.S. Public*, pg. 1746
QUAKER CHEMICAL B.V.—See Quaker Chemical Corporation; *U.S. Public*, pg. 1746
QUAKER CHEMICAL (CHINA) CO., LTD.—See Quaker Chemical Corporation; *U.S. Public*, pg. 1746
QUAKER CHEMICAL CORP. - MANUFACTURING & LOGISTICS - STEEL PRODUCTS—See Quaker Chemical Corporation; *U.S. Public*, pg. 1746
QUAKER CHEMICAL CORPORATION; *U.S. Public*, pg. 1745
QUAKER CHEMICAL EUROPE B.V.—See Quaker Chemical Corporation; *U.S. Public*, pg. 1746
QUAKER CHEMICAL INDIA LTD.—See Quaker Chemical Corporation; *U.S. Public*, pg. 1746
QUAKER CHEMICAL INDUSTRIA E COMERCIO LTDA.—See Quaker Chemical Corporation; *U.S. Public*, pg. 1746
QUAKER CHEMICAL LIMITED—See Quaker Chemical Corporation; *U.S. Public*, pg. 1746
QUAKER CHEMICAL MEA FZE—See Quaker Chemical Corporation; *U.S. Public*, pg. 1746
QUAKER CHEMICAL PARTICIPACOES, LTDA.—See Quaker Chemical Corporation; *U.S. Public*, pg. 1746
QUAKER CHEMICAL, S.A.—See Quaker Chemical Corporation; *U.S. Public*, pg. 1746
QUAKER CHEMICAL S.A.—See Quaker Chemical Corporation; *U.S. Public*, pg. 1746
QUAKER CHEMICAL, S.A.—See Quaker Chemical Corporation; *U.S. Public*, pg. 1746
QUAKER CHEMICAL SOUTH AFRICA (PTY.) LTD.—See Quaker Chemical Corporation; *U.S. Public*, pg. 1746
QUAKER CHEMICAL, S.R.L.—See Quaker Chemical Corporation; *U.S. Public*, pg. 1746
QUAKER CITY CHEMICALS INC.; *U.S. Private*, pg. 3316
QUAKER CITY MERCANTILE; *U.S. Private*, pg. 3316
QUAKER CITY STAMP & STENCIL—See American Marking Systems, Inc.; *U.S. Private*, pg. 241
QUAKER EQUITIES LTD., INC.; *U.S. Private*, pg. 3316
QUAKER HOLDINGS (UK) LTD.—See PepsiCo, Inc.; *U.S. Public*, pg. 1670
QUAKER LACE—See Lorraine Linens Inc.; *U.S. Private*, pg. 2496
QUAKER MAID MEATS INC.; *U.S. Private*, pg. 3317
QUAKER MANUFACTURING, LLC—See PepsiCo, Inc.; *U.S. Public*, pg. 1671
QUAKER MFG. CORP.; *U.S. Private*, pg. 3317
QUAKER OATS AUSTRALIA PTY LTD—See PepsiCo, Inc.; *U.S. Public*, pg. 1671
QUAKER OATS B.V.—See PepsiCo, Inc.; *U.S. Public*, pg. 1670
THE QUAKER OATS COMPANY—See PepsiCo, Inc.; *U.S. Public*, pg. 1670
QUAKER OATS EUROPE, INC.—See PepsiCo, Inc.; *U.S. Public*, pg. 1671
QUAKER OATS LIMITED—See PepsiCo, Inc.; *U.S. Public*, pg. 1670
QUAKER PARTNERS MANAGEMENT, L.P.—See Independence Capital Partners, LLC; *U.S. Private*, pg. 2057
QUAKER PERU S.R.L.—See PepsiCo, Inc.; *U.S. Public*, pg. 1671
QUAKER PLASTIC CORPORATION—See Wexco Incorporated; *U.S. Private*, pg. 4502
QUAKER PRODUCTS (MALAYSIA) SDN BHD—See PepsiCo, Inc.; *U.S. Public*, pg. 1670
QUAKER RUSSIA B.V.—See Quaker Chemical Corporation; *U.S. Public*, pg. 1746
QUAKER SECURITIES—See ACG Advisors (UK) LLP; *Int'l*, pg. 102
QUAKER STEAK & LUBE—See BP plc; *Int'l*, pg. 1127
QUAKER TRADING LIMITED—See PepsiCo, Inc.; *U.S. Public*, pg. 1671
QUAKER VALLEY FOODS INC.; *U.S. Private*, pg. 3317
QUAKESAFE TECHNOLOGIES CO., LTD.; *Int'l*, pg. 6150
QUALA-DIE, INC.—See Penn United Technologies, Inc.; *U.S. Private*, pg. 3135
QUALATEX BALLOON PTY. LTD.—See Continental American Corporation; *U.S. Public*, pg. 1028
QUALAWASH HOLDINGS, LLC—See KKR & Co. Inc.; *U.S. Public*, pg. 1241
QUALCARE ALLIANCE NETWORKS, INC.—See The Cigna Group; *U.S. Public*, pg. 2061
QUALCARE, INC.—See The Cigna Group; *U.S. Public*, pg. 2061
QUALCARE; *U.S. Private*, pg. 3317
QUALCHOICE OF ARKANSAS, INC.—See Centene Corporation; *U.S. Public*, pg. 470

QUALIFIED METAL FABRICATORS LTD

QUALCODUNA PROFICIENCY TESTING HUNGARY NONPROFIT KFT.—See Eurofins Scientific S.E.; *Int'l*, pg. 2551
QUALCOMM ATHEROS CANADA CORPORATION—See QUALCOMM Incorporated; *U.S. Public*, pg. 1747
QUALCOMM ATHEROS HONG KONG—See QUALCOMM Incorporated; *U.S. Public*, pg. 1747
QUALCOMM ATHEROS, INC.—See QUALCOMM Incorporated; *U.S. Public*, pg. 1747
QUALCOMM ATHEROS TAIWAN—See QUALCOMM Incorporated; *U.S. Public*, pg. 1747
QUALCOMM ATHEROS TECHNOLOGY (MACAO COMMERCIAL OFFSHORE) LIMITED—See QUALCOMM Incorporated; *U.S. Public*, pg. 1747
QUALCOMM CDMA TECHNOLOGIES ASIA-PACIFIC PTE. LTD.—See QUALCOMM Incorporated; *U.S. Public*, pg. 1747
QUALCOMM CDMA TECHNOLOGIES (KOREA) Y.H.—See QUALCOMM Incorporated; *U.S. Public*, pg. 1747
QUALCOMM CDMA TECHNOLOGIES—See QUALCOMM Incorporated; *U.S. Public*, pg. 1747
QUALCOMM COMMUNICATION TECHNOLOGIES LTD.—See QUALCOMM Incorporated; *U.S. Public*, pg. 1747
QUALCOMM CONNECTED EXPERIENCES SWITZERLAND AG—See PTC Inc.; *U.S. Public*, pg. 1735
QUALCOMM FIRETHORN HOLDINGS, LLC—See QUALCOMM Incorporated; *U.S. Public*, pg. 1747
QUALCOMM GLOBAL TRADING, INC.—See QUALCOMM Incorporated; *U.S. Public*, pg. 1747
QUALCOMM GOVERNMENT TECHNOLOGIES—See QUALCOMM Incorporated; *U.S. Public*, pg. 1747
QUALCOMM INCORPORATED; *U.S. Public*, pg. 1747
QUALCOMM INDIA PRIVATE LIMITED—See QUALCOMM Incorporated; *U.S. Public*, pg. 1747
QUALCOMM INNOVATION CENTER, INC.—See QUALCOMM Incorporated; *U.S. Public*, pg. 1747
QUALCOMM INTERNET SERVICES—See QUALCOMM Incorporated; *U.S. Public*, pg. 1747
QUALCOMM ISRAEL LTD—See QUALCOMM Incorporated; *U.S. Public*, pg. 1747
QUALCOMM JAPAN—See QUALCOMM Incorporated; *U.S. Public*, pg. 1747
QUALCOMM MEMS TECHNOLOGIES, INC.—See QUALCOMM Incorporated; *U.S. Public*, pg. 1748
QUALCOMM SERVICES LABS, INC.—See QUALCOMM Incorporated; *U.S. Public*, pg. 1748
QUALCOMM TECHNOLOGIES INTERNATIONAL, LTD.—See QUALCOMM Incorporated; *U.S. Public*, pg. 1748
QUALCOMM TECHNOLOGY LICENSING—See QUALCOMM Incorporated; *U.S. Public*, pg. 1748
QUALCOMM (UK) LIMITED—See QUALCOMM Incorporated; *U.S. Public*, pg. 1747
QUALCOMM VENTURES—See QUALCOMM Incorporated; *U.S. Public*, pg. 1748
QUALCOMM WIRELESS SEMI CONDUCTOR TECHNOLOGIES LIMITED—See QUALCOMM Incorporated; *U.S. Public*, pg. 1748
QUALEX CONSULTING GROUP, INC.—See Cumberland Technologies, Inc.; *U.S. Private*, pg. 1123
QUALFON GUYANA, INC.—See Qualfon SA de CV; *Int'l*, pg. 6150
QUALFON PHILIPPINES INC.—See Qualfon SA de CV; *Int'l*, pg. 6150
QUALFON SA DE CV; *Int'l*, pg. 6150
QUALIA DEVELOPMENT—See PKO Bank Polski SA; *Int'l*, pg. 5887
QUALIA, INC.; *U.S. Private*, pg. 3317
QUALICA ASIA PACIFIC PTE. LTD.—See TIS Inc.; *Int'l*, pg. 7758
QUALICA INC.—See TIS Inc.; *Int'l*, pg. 7758
QUALICAPS CO., LTD.—See Roquette Freres SA; *Int'l*, pg. 6398
QUALICAPS, INC.—See Roquette Freres SA; *Int'l*, pg. 6398
QUALICA(SHANGHAI) INC.—See TIS Inc.; *Int'l*, pg. 7758
QUALICA (THAILAND) CO., LTD.—See TIS Inc.; *Int'l*, pg. 7758
QUALICHEM, INC.—See Yushiro Chemical Industry Co. Ltd.; *Int'l*, pg. 8618
QUALICONTACT—See Omnicom Group Inc.; *U.S. Public*, pg. 1596
QUALICO PRECISION PRODUCTS, LLC—See Orscheln Group; *U.S. Private*, pg. 3045
QUALICORP CONSULTORIA E CORRETORA DE SEGUROS S.A.; *Int'l*, pg. 6150
QUALICO STEEL COMPANY INC.; *U.S. Private*, pg. 3317
QUALIFACTS SYSTEMS, INC.—See Warburg Pincus LLC; *U.S. Private*, pg. 4439
QUALIFIED INVESTORS FUND III, LLC—See SVB Financial Group; *U.S. Public*, pg. 1968
QUALIFIED METAL FABRICATORS LTD; *Int'l*, pg. 6151
QUALIFIED PLANS, LLC—See Aquiline Capital Partners LLC; *U.S. Private*, pg. 304
QUALIFIED PLANS, LLC—See Genstar Capital, LLC; *U.S. Private*, pg. 1675

QUALIGENICS MEDICAL LIMITED—See HKR International Limited; *Int'l*, pg. 3429
QUALIGEN THERAPEUTICS, INC.; *U.S. Public*, pg. 1748
QUALIPAC AMERICA—See Pochet S.A.; *Int'l*, pg. 5902
QUALIPAC S.A.—See Pochet S.A.; *Int'l*, pg. 5901
QUALIPOLY CHEMICAL CORPORATION; *Int'l*, pg. 6151
QUALI-PRO; *U.S. Private*, pg. 3317
QUALIS AUTOMOTIVE LLC—See Crowne Group LLC; *U.S. Private*, pg. 1112
QUALIS, CORPORATION; *U.S. Private*, pg. 3317
QUALISEAL TECHNOLOGY, LLC—See Enpro Inc.; *U.S. Public*, pg. 775
QUALIS HEALTH—See HealthInsight Management Corporation; *U.S. Private*, pg. 1896
QUALIS INNOVATIONS, INC.; *Int'l*, pg. 6151
QUALI-SMART HOLDINGS LTD.; *Int'l*, pg. 6150
QUALITA IN FARMACIA S.R.L.—See CompuGroup Medical SE & Co. KGaA; *Int'l*, pg. 1756
QUALITAIR AVIATION GROUP LIMITED—See Randstad N.V.; *Int'l*, pg. 6202
QUALITAIR AVIATION HOLLAND BV—See Randstad N.V.; *Int'l*, pg. 6202
QUALITAIR AVIATION SERVICES LIMITED—See Randstad N.V.; *Int'l*, pg. 6202
QUALITAS-AMS GMBH—See RWE AG; *Int'l*, pg. 6435
QUALITAS HEALTHCARE CORPORATION SDN. BHD.—See Qualitas Medical Group Limited; *Int'l*, pg. 6151
QUALITAS HEALTHCARE INTERNATIONAL SDN. BHD.—See Qualitas Medical Group Limited; *Int'l*, pg. 6151
QUALITAS LIMITED; *Int'l*, pg. 6151
QUALITAS MEDICAL GROUP LIMITED; *Int'l*, pg. 6151
QUALITAS PHARMA SDN. BHD.—See Qualitas Medical Group Limited; *Int'l*, pg. 6151
QUALITAS SEMICONDUCTOR CO., LTD.; *Int'l*, pg. 6151
QUALITAU, LTD.; *Int'l*, pg. 6151
QUALI TECH LLC—See MidOcean Partners, LLP; *U.S. Private*, pg. 2717
QUALITECH PHARMA CO., LTD.—See Rohto Pharmaceutical Co. Ltd.; *Int'l*, pg. 6387
QUALITECH PUBLIC COMPANY LIMITED; *Int'l*, pg. 6151
QUALITECH SOLUTION ENERGY COMPANY LIMITED—See Qualitech Public Company Limited; *Int'l*, pg. 6152
QUALITEK DELTA PHILIPPINES—See Qualitek International Inc.; *U.S. Private*, pg. 3317
QUALITEK ELECTRONIC SHENZHEN CHINA—See Qualitek International Inc.; *U.S. Private*, pg. 3317
QUALITEK EUROPE LTD.—See Qualitek International Inc.; *U.S. Private*, pg. 3317
QUALITEK INTERNATIONAL INC.; *U.S. Private*, pg. 3317
QUALITEK (SHANGHAI) TRADING CO., LTD.—See Qualitek International Inc.; *U.S. Private*, pg. 3317
QUALITEK SINGAPORE PTE. LTD—See Qualitek International Inc.; *U.S. Private*, pg. 3317
QUALITEK—See Westak, Inc.; *U.S. Private*, pg. 4488
QUALITEMPS INC.; *U.S. Private*, pg. 3317
QUALITE SPORTS LIGHTING, LLC—See Worth Investment Group, LLC; *U.S. Private*, pg. 4570
QUALITEST ALGERIE SPA—See SGS SA; *Int'l*, pg. 6743
QUALITEST GROUP; *U.S. Private*, pg. 3317
QUALITEST GROUP UK LTD.—See Bridgepoint Group Plc; *Int'l*, pg. 1154
QUALITEX SUPPLIES LTD.; *Int'l*, pg. 6152
QUALITI PRINTING & SOURCING LIMITED—See Realord Group Holdings Limited; *Int'l*, pg. 6234
QUALITOR, INC.—See Wellspring Capital Management LLC; *U.S. Private*, pg. 4477
QUALI TRADE INC.; *U.S. Private*, pg. 3317
QUALITROL COMPANY LLC—See Fortive Corporation; *U.S. Public*, pg. 871
QUALITRONIC ODD JUBAL-ANDERSEN & CO AS—See TCS TurControlSysteme AG; *Int'l*, pg. 7486
QUALITRON OY AB—See Helvar Merca Oy AB; *Int'l*, pg. 3339
QUALITY 1 AG—See Allianz SE; *Int'l*, pg. 355
QUALITY 1 PETROLEUM (PRIVATE) LIMITED—See Jahangir Siddiqui & Co. Ltd.; *Int'l*, pg. 3871
QUALITY ADDICTION MANAGEMENT INC.—See Acadia Healthcare Company, Inc.; *U.S. Public*, pg. 29
QUALITY ADVANTAGE HOME PRODUCTS, INC.—See West Shore Window & Door, Inc.; *U.S. Private*, pg. 4487
QUALITY AGGREGATES INC.; *U.S. Private*, pg. 3317
QUALITY AIRCRAFT ACCESSORIES, INC.—See BOK Financial Corporation; *U.S. Public*, pg. 367
QUALITY AIR FORWARDING, INC.—See Littlejohn & Co., LLC; *U.S. Private*, pg. 2470
QUALITY AIR HEATING AND COOLING, INC.—See Comfort Systems USA, Inc.; *U.S. Public*, pg. 544
QUALITY ALUMINUM FORGE, LLC—See SIFCO Industries, Inc.; *U.S. Public*, pg. 1877
QUALITY ALUMINUM PRODUCTS INC.—See Gibraltar Industries, Inc.; *U.S. Public*, pg. 936
QUALITY AMENITIES SUPPLY PTE. LTD—See Ming Fai International Holdings Limited; *Int'l*, pg. 4908
QUALITY ASSIST, INC.—See Summit Partners, L.P.; *U.S. Private*, pg. 3856

QUALITY ASSURED ENTERPRISES, INC.; *U.S. Private*, pg. 3317
QUALITY ASSURED LABEL, INC.—See Quality Assured Enterprises, Inc.; *U.S. Private*, pg. 3317
QUALITY BAKERS GROUP, INC.; *U.S. Private*, pg. 3317
QUALITY BAKERS OF AMERICA COOPERATIVE, INC.; *U.S. Private*, pg. 3317
THE QUALITY BAKERY CO., INC.—See Lancaster Colony Corporation; *U.S. Public*, pg. 1292
QUALITY BAKERY PRODUCTS, INC.; *U.S. Private*, pg. 3317
QUALITY BAKERY PRODUCTS, LLC—See Charlesbank Capital Partners, LLC; *U.S. Private*, pg. 855
QUALITY BAKERY PRODUCTS, LLC—See Partners Group Holding AG; *Int'l*, pg. 5749
QUALITY BEVERAGE LLC; *U.S. Private*, pg. 3317
QUALITY BEVERAGE LP; *U.S. Private*, pg. 3317
QUALITY BEVERAGES 2000 PROPRIETARY LTD—See Bowler Metcalf Limited; *Int'l*, pg. 1124
QUALITY BEVERAGE—See Quality Beverage LP; *U.S. Private*, pg. 3318
QUALITY BOLT & SCREW CORP.; *U.S. Private*, pg. 3318
QUALITY BONELESS BEEF INC.; *U.S. Private*, pg. 3318
QUALITY BUILDING CONTROLS, INC.—See Huron Capital Partners LLC; *U.S. Private*, pg. 2011
QUALITY BUILT, LLC—See Gallant Capital Partners, LLC; *U.S. Private*, pg. 1639
QUALITY BUSINESS SYSTEMS, INC.—See Xerox Holdings Corporation; *U.S. Public*, pg. 2388
QUALITY CARE FOR CHILDREN, INC.; *U.S. Private*, pg. 3318
QUALITY CARE SERVICES LIMITED—See Graphite Capital Management LLP; *Int'l*, pg. 3060
QUALITY CARE SITTER SERVICE, INC.; *U.S. Private*, pg. 3318
QUALITY CARRIERS, INC. - RIVER FALLS—See Apax Partners LLP; *Int'l*, pg. 505
QUALITY CARRIERS, INC.—See Apax Partners LLP; *Int'l*, pg. 505
QUALITY CARTON INC.; *U.S. Private*, pg. 3318
QUALITY CASTINGS COMPANY; *U.S. Private*, pg. 3318
QUALITY/CENTURY HOLDINGS CORPORATION—See Brookfield Corporation; *Int'l*, pg. 1176
QUALITY CERAMIC (ARKLOW) LIMITED—See Anchorage Capital Group, L.L.C.; *U.S. Private*, pg. 274
QUALITY CERAMIC (ARKLOW) LIMITED—See CVC Capital Partners SICAV-FIS S.A.; *Int'l*, pg. 1888
QUALITY CERAMICS (SALES) LIMITED—See Anchorage Capital Group, L.L.C.; *U.S. Private*, pg. 274
QUALITY CERAMICS (SALES) LIMITED—See CVC Capital Partners SICAV-FIS S.A.; *Int'l*, pg. 1888
QUALITY CHANNEL GMBH—See SPIEGEL-Verlag Rudolf Augstein GmbH & Co.; *Int'l*, pg. 7136
QUALITY CHEF FOODS—See 3G Capital Inc.; *U.S. Private*, pg. 10
QUALITY CHEF FOODS—See Berkshire Hathaway Inc.; *U.S. Public*, pg. 318
QUALITY CHEKD DAIRIES, INC.; *U.S. Private*, pg. 3318
QUALITY CHOICE TITLE LLC—See Anywhere Real Estate Inc.; *U.S. Public*, pg. 142
QUALITY CHRISTMAS TREE CO. INC.; *U.S. Private*, pg. 3318
QUALITY CIRCUITS INC.; *U.S. Private*, pg. 3318
QUALITY COFFEE PRODUCTS LTD.—See Nestle S.A.; *Int'l*, pg. 5204
QUALITY COILS INCORPORATED; *U.S. Private*, pg. 3318
QUALITY COLLISION GROUP, LLC—See Susquehanna International Group, LLP; *U.S. Private*, pg. 3885
QUALITY COMMUNICATIONS SYSTEMS INC.—See Kavveri Telecom Products Ltd; *Int'l*, pg. 4093
QUALITY COMPANIES USA, LLC.; *U.S. Private*, pg. 3318
QUALITY COMPONENTS EUROPE; *Int'l*, pg. 6152
QUALITY COMPONENTS, INC.—See Emerson Electric Co.; *U.S. Public*, pg. 751
QUALITY CONCRETE HOLDINGS BERHAD; *Int'l*, pg. 6152
QUALITY CONCRETE PRODUCTS, INC.—See CRH plc; *Int'l*, pg. 1846
QUALITY CONCRETE & RENTAL INC.; *U.S. Private*, pg. 3318
QUALITY CONSTRUCTION PRODUCTS PLC—See Land & Houses Public Company Limited; *Int'l*, pg. 4403
QUALITY CONSTRUCTION PRODUCTS PUBLIC CO .LTD—See The Siam Cement Public Company Limited; *Int'l*, pg. 7685
QUALITY CONTRACTORS INCORPORATED; *U.S. Private*, pg. 3318
QUALITY CONTROL CONSULTANTS LIMITED—See China Resources Building Materials Technology Holdings Limited; *Int'l*, pg. 1549
QUALITY CONTROLLED MANUFACTURING, INC; *U.S. Private*, pg. 3318
QUALITY CRAFT LTD—See Collins Co., Ltd.; *Int'l*, pg. 1702
QUALITY CUSTOM CABINETRY INC.; *U.S. Private*, pg. 3318
QUALITY CUSTOM DISTRIBUTION - SUFFOLK—See Golden State Foods Corp.; *U.S. Private*, pg. 1733

QUALITY CUSTOMS BROKER INC.; *U.S. Private*, pg. 3318
QUALITY CUTTING TOOLS, INC.—See Quaser Machine Tools, Inc.; *Int'l*, pg. 6157
QUALITY DAIRY COMPANY; *U.S. Private*, pg. 3318
QUALITY DIALYSIS CARE SDN. BHD.—See DaVita Inc.; *U.S. Public*, pg. 642
QUALITY DINING, INC.; *U.S. Private*, pg. 3318
QUALITY DISTRIBUTING COMPANY; *U.S. Private*, pg. 3318
QUALITY DISTRIBUTING UNION CITY—See Quality Distributing Company; *U.S. Private*, pg. 3318
QUALITY DISTRIBUTION, INC.—See Apax Partners LLP; *Int'l*, pg. 505
QUALITY DISTRIBUTORS, LLC; *U.S. Private*, pg. 3318
QUALITY ELASTICS LIMITED; *Int'l*, pg. 6152
QUALITY ELECTRODYNAMICS LLC—See Canon Inc.; *Int'l*, pg. 1298
QUALITY ENGINEERING SOLUTIONS, INC.; *U.S. Private*, pg. 3318
QUALITY ENVIRONMENTAL SERVICES, LLC—See Caymus Equity Partners LLC; *U.S. Private*, pg. 795
QUALITY EQUIPMENT DISTRIBUTORS INC.; *U.S. Private*, pg. 3318
QUALITY EXPERIENCE DESIGN CO., LTD.—See Arisawa Manufacturing Co., Ltd.; *Int'l*, pg. 566
QUALITY FABRICATING & SUPPLY LP—See Supreme Group; *Int'l*, pg. 7341
QUALITY FABRICATION, INC.—See Canrector Inc.; *Int'l*, pg. 1290
QUALITY FABRICATORS INC.; *U.S. Private*, pg. 3319
QUALITY FARM EQUIPMENT CO. INC.; *U.S. Private*, pg. 3319
QUALITY FASTENERS & SUPPLY CO.—See Kian Capital Partners, LLC; *U.S. Private*, pg. 2302
QUALITY FASTENERS & SUPPLY CO.—See Oakland Standard Co., LLC; *U.S. Private*, pg. 2985
QUALITY FINISHERS, INC.; *U.S. Private*, pg. 3319
QUALITY FLOAT WORKS, INC.; *U.S. Public*, pg. 3319
QUALITY FLOORING 4 LESS; *U.S. Private*, pg. 3319
QUALITY FOOD COMPANY, INC.; *U.S. Private*, pg. 3319
QUALITY FOODS CORPORATION; *U.S. Private*, pg. 3319
QUALITY FOODS INC.; *U.S. Private*, pg. 3319
QUALITY FORMING, LLC—See Arlington Capital Partners LLC; *U.S. Private*, pg. 327
QUALITY FROZEN FOODS INC.; *U.S. Private*, pg. 3319
QUALITY HARDWOODS LTD.—See Goodfellow Inc.; *Int'l*, pg. 3040
QUALITY HEALTHCARE MEDICAL CENTRE LIMITED—See The British United Provident Association Limited; *Int'l*, pg. 7630
QUALITY HEALTHCARE MEDICAL SERVICES LIMITED—See The British United Provident Association Limited; *Int'l*, pg. 7630
QUALITY HEALTHCARE NURSING AGENCY LIMITED—See The British United Provident Association Limited; *Int'l*, pg. 7630
QUALITY HEALTHCARE PHYSIOTHERAPY SERVICES LIMITED—See The British United Provident Association Limited; *Int'l*, pg. 7630
QUALITY HEALTH LIMITED—See IQVIA Holdings Inc.; *U.S. Public*, pg. 1170
QUALITY HERO CORPORATION SDN. BHD.—See Hengan International Group Co. Ltd.; *Int'l*, pg. 3346
QUALITY HOTEL & SUITES—See Northampton Group Inc.; *Int'l*, pg. 5442
QUALITY HOUSE PLC—See Land & Houses Public Company Limited; *Int'l*, pg. 4403
QUALITY HOUSES PUBLIC CO., LTD.; *Int'l*, pg. 6152
QUALITY HYDRAULICS & PNEUMATICS INC.; *U.S. Private*, pg. 3319
QUALITY IMPLEMENT COMPANY; *U.S. Private*, pg. 3319
QUALITY INDUSTRIAL CORP.—See Ilustrato Pictures International Inc.; *Int'l*, pg. 3617
QUALITY INDUSTRIES, INC.—See Anchor Fabrication Ltd.; *U.S. Private*, pg. 273
QUALITY INGREDIENTS CORPORATION; *U.S. Private*, pg. 3319
QUALITY INN AIRPORT WEST—See Northampton Group Inc.; *Int'l*, pg. 5442
QUALITY INNOVATIVE SOLUTIONS INC.; *U.S. Private*, pg. 3319
QUALITY INN & SUITES—See K2 Group; *Int'l*, pg. 4045
QUALITY IN REAL TIME—See TA Associates, Inc.; *U.S. Private*, pg. 3916
QUALITY INSPECTION SERVICES BVBA—See Team, Inc.; *U.S. Public*, pg. 1988
QUALITY INSPECTION SERVICES B.V.—See Team, Inc.; *U.S. Public*, pg. 1988
QUALITY INSPECTION SERVICES, INC.—See I Squared Capital Advisors (US) LLC; *U.S. Private*, pg. 2022
QUALITY INSPECTION SERVICES, INC.—See TDR Capital LLP; *Int'l*, pg. 7491
QUALITY INSULATION & ROOFING; *U.S. Private*, pg. 3319
QUALITY INVESTMENT PROPERTIES MIAMI, LLC—See Blackstone Inc.; *U.S. Public*, pg. 351
QUALITY INVESTMENT PROPERTIES RICHMOND, LLC—See Blackstone Inc.; *U.S. Public*, pg. 351

COMPANY NAME INDEX

QUALITY IS OUR RECIPE, LLC—See The Wendy's Company; *U.S. Public*, pg. 2141
QUALITY IT PARTNERS INC.; *U.S. Private*, pg. 3319
QUALITY JEEP-CHRYSLER, INC.; *U.S. Private*, pg. 3319
QUALITY KING DISTRIBUTORS INC.; *U.S. Private*, pg. 3319
QUALITY KING FRAGRANCE, INC.—See Perfumania Holdings, Inc.; *U.S. Private*, pg. 3150
QUALITYLABS BT GMBH—See Bio-Gate AG; *Int'l*, pg. 1035
QUALITY LEISURE MANAGEMENT LIMITED—See PHSC plc; *Int'l*, pg. 5857
QUALITY LIFE ENTERPRISE (INDIA) PVT. LTD.—See Hitachi, Ltd.; *Int'l*, pg. 3424
QUALITY LIGHT SOURCE LLC—See Q L Light Source Company Limited; *Int'l*, pg. 6129
QUALITY LIQUID FEEDS INC.; *U.S. Private*, pg. 3319
QUALITY LOGO PRODUCTS, INC.; *U.S. Private*, pg. 3319
QUALITY MANAGEMENT SOLUTIONS INC.; *U.S. Private*, pg. 3319
QUALITY MANUFACTURING CORP.; *U.S. Private*, pg. 3319
QUALITY MARBLE, INC.; *U.S. Private*, pg. 3319
QUALITY MEAT GROUP LTD.—See Sofina Foods Inc.; *Int'l*, pg. 7050
QUALITY MEAT PACKERS LIMITED; *Int'l*, pg. 6152
QUALITY METALCRAFT, INC.—See HMK Enterprises, Inc.; *U.S. Private*, pg. 1955
QUALITY METAL WORKS, INC.; *U.S. Private*, pg. 3319
QUALITYMETRIC INCORPORATED—See UnitedHealth Group Incorporated; *U.S. Public*, pg. 2250
QUALITY MILL SUPPLY CO. INC.; *U.S. Private*, pg. 3319
QUALITY MOBILE X RAY SERVICES, INC.—See Schryver Medical Sales; *U.S. Private*, pg. 3570
QUALITY MOLD INC.; *U.S. Private*, pg. 3320
QUALITY MORTGAGE SERVICES LLC; *U.S. Private*, pg. 3320
QUALITY MOTOR CARS STOCKTON; *U.S. Private*, pg. 3320
QUALITY MOTORS LIMITED—See Honda Motor Co., Ltd.; *Int'l*, pg. 3464
QUALITY NATURALLY FOODS, INC.—See Yum Yum Donut Shops, Inc.; *U.S. Private*, pg. 4595
QUALITY NATURALLY FOODS; *U.S. Private*, pg. 3320
QUALITY NISSAN, LTD.—See AutoNation, Inc.; *U.S. Public*, pg. 237
QUALITY OIL CO. INC.; *U.S. Private*, pg. 3320
QUALITY OIL COMPANY LLC; *U.S. Private*, pg. 3320
QUALITY ONLINE EDUCATION GROUP INC.; *Int'l*, pg. 6152
QUALITY PACKAGING, INC.; *U.S. Private*, pg. 3320
QUALITY PACKAGING SPECIALISTS, INC.; *U.S. Private*, pg. 3320
QUALITY PARTS SUPPLY, INC.; *U.S. Private*, pg. 3320
QUALITY PERFORATING, INC.; *U.S. Private*, pg. 3320
QUALITY PETROLEUM CORP.; *U.S. Private*, pg. 3320
QUALITY PETROLEUM INC.; *U.S. Private*, pg. 3320
QUALITY PETROLEUM OF ALABAMA, INC.—See Quality Petroleum Corp.; *U.S. Private*, pg. 3320
QUALITY PETROLEUM—See Quality Petroleum Inc.; *U.S. Private*, pg. 3320
QUALITY PLANNING CORPORATION—See Verisk Analytics, Inc.; *U.S. Public*, pg. 2283
QUALITY PLATES & PROFILES LIMITED. - SARNIA DIVISION—See Quality Plates & Profiles Limited.; *Int'l*, pg. 6152
QUALITY PLATES & PROFILES LIMITED.; *Int'l*, pg. 6152
QUALITY PLUS SERVICES INC.; *U.S. Private*, pg. 3320
QUALITY PLYWOOD SPECIALTIES, INC.; *U.S. Private*, pg. 3320
QUALITY PONTIAC GMC BUICK; *U.S. Private*, pg. 3320
QUALITY POOL SUPPLY CO.; *U.S. Private*, pg. 3320
QUALITY PORK PROCESSORS, INC.; *U.S. Private*, pg. 3320
QUALITY PRODUCTS INC.; *U.S. Private*, pg. 3320
QUALITY PROJECT MANAGEMENT LLC; *U.S. Private*, pg. 3321
QUALITY PROPERTIES ASSET MANAGEMENT COMPANY—See Bank of America Corporation; *U.S. Public*, pg. 272
QUALITY QUICKLY, INC.—See Docugraphics, LLC; *U.S. Private*, pg. 1252
QUALITY & RELIABILITY S.A.; *Int'l*, pg. 6152
QUALITY RELIABILITY TECHNOLOGY INC.; *Int'l*, pg. 6152
QUALITY RESTAURANT CONCEPTS; *U.S. Private*, pg. 3321
QUALITY RO INDUSTRIES LIMITED; *Int'l*, pg. 6152
QUALITY ROOFING CENTER OF SOUTHEAST MISSOURI; *U.S. Private*, pg. 3321
QUALITY ROOFING SUPPLY COMPANY INC.—See Beacon Sales Acquisition Inc.; *U.S. Private*, pg. 505
QUALITY SAFETY EDGE; *U.S. Private*, pg. 3321
QUALITY-SAFETY-ENGINEERING GMBH—See Christof Holding AG; *Int'l*, pg. 1587
QUALITY SAFETY SYSTEMS COMPANY—See Tokai Rika Co., Ltd.; *Int'l*, pg. 7780
QUALITY SAUSAGE COMPANY; *U.S. Private*, pg. 3321

QUALITY SCIENTIFIC PLASTICS, INC.—See Thermo Fisher Scientific Inc.; *U.S. Public*, pg. 2151
QUALITY SERVICES FOR THE AUTISM COMMUNITY; *U.S. Private*, pg. 3321
QUALITY SOFTWARE S.A.; *Int'l*, pg. 6152
QUALITY SOFTWARE SERVICES, INC.—See UnitedHealth Group Incorporated; *U.S. Public*, pg. 2250
QUALITY SOLUTIONS INC.—See Ontario Teachers' Pension Plan; *Int'l*, pg. 5589
QUALITY SOLUTIONS INC.—See PAG Asia Capital Ltd.; *Int'l*, pg. 5696
QUALITY SOLUTIONS INC.—See TPG Capital, L.P.; *U.S. Public*, pg. 2173
QUALITY STANDBY SERVICES, LLC—See High Road Capital Partners, LLC; *U.S. Private*, pg. 1936
QUALITY STATE OIL CO. INC.; *U.S. Private*, pg. 3321
QUALITY STEEL FABRICATION; *U.S. Private*, pg. 3321
QUALITY STEELS CORPORATION—See Miller Consolidated Industries Inc.; *U.S. Private*, pg. 2733
QUALITY STEEL WORKS LIMITED; *Int'l*, pg. 6152
QUALITY SYNTHETIC RUBBER INCORPORATED; *U.S. Private*, pg. 3321
QUALITYTECH, LP—See Blackstone Inc.; *U.S. Public*, pg. 351
QUALITY TECHNICAL SUPPLIES COMPANY—See Kharafi National; *Int'l*, pg. 4151
QUALITY TECHNICAL SUPPLIES CO. W.L.L.—See Kharafi National; *Int'l*, pg. 4151
QUALITY TECHNOLOGY INTERNATIONAL, INC.—See ITOCHU Corporation; *Int'l*, pg. 3839
QUALITY TEMPORARY SERVICES; *U.S. Private*, pg. 3321
QUALITY TERMINAL SERVICES, L.L.C.—See The Broe Companies, Inc.; *U.S. Private*, pg. 4001
QUALITY THERMISTOR, INC.—See CTS Corporation; *U.S. Public*, pg. 603
QUALITY TOOL INC.; *U.S. Private*, pg. 3321
QUALITY TRAILER SALES CORP.—See Great Western Leasing & Sales, LLC; *U.S. Private*, pg. 1768
QUALITY TRUCK CARE CENTER INC.; *U.S. Private*, pg. 3321
QUALITY TRUSS INC.; *U.S. Private*, pg. 3321
QUALITY TURNING INC.; *U.S. Private*, pg. 3321
QUALITY UPTIME SERVICES, LLC—See ABM Industries, Inc.; *U.S. Public*, pg. 26
QUALITY VISION INTERNATIONAL INC. - CERTIFIED COMPARATOR PRODUCTS DIVISION—See Quality Vision International Inc.; *U.S. Private*, pg. 3321
QUALITY VISION INTERNATIONAL INC.; *U.S. Private*, pg. 3321
QUALITY WHOLESALE BUILDING PRODUCTS INC.; *U.S. Private*, pg. 3321
QUALITY WINE COMPANY INC.—See Old Peoria Company Inc.; *U.S. Private*, pg. 3009
QUALITY WINE & SPIRITS, INC.—See The Winebow Group, LLC; *U.S. Private*, pg. 4137
QUALITY & WINNER MOTORS IMP EXP EIRELI—See Bridgestone Corporation; *Int'l*, pg. 1160
QUALITY WIRELINE & CABLE INC.—See Forum Energy Technologies, Inc.; *U.S. Public*, pg. 874
QUALITY WOODS INC.; *U.S. Private*, pg. 3321
QUALIUM INVESTISSEMENT; *Int'l*, pg. 6152
QUALIZORG B.V.—See CompuGroup Medical SE & Co. KGaA; *Int'l*, pg. 1757
QUALLION, LLC—See EnerSys; *U.S. Public*, pg. 767
QUALLY & COMPANY, INC.; *U.S. Private*, pg. 3322
QUALMARK CORPORATION—See ESPEC Corp.; *Int'l*, pg. 2505
QUALMETRIX INC.; *U.S. Private*, pg. 3322
QUAL-PRO CORPORATION; *U.S. Private*, pg. 3317
QUALSAT, LLC—See QualTek Services Inc.; *U.S. Public*, pg. 1748
QUALSERV SOLUTIONS LLC—See The Middleby Corporation; *U.S. Public*, pg. 2115
QUALSPEC, INC.—See Team, Inc.; *U.S. Public*, pg. 1988
QUALSTAR CORPORATION; *U.S. Public*, pg. 1748
QUALSTAR CREDIT UNION; *U.S. Private*, pg. 3322
QUALSTAR SALES AND SERVICE CORPORATION—See Qualstar Corporation; *U.S. Public*, pg. 1748
QUALTEC CO., LTD.; *Int'l*, pg. 6152
QUALTEK, LLC—See QualTek Services Inc.; *U.S. Public*, pg. 1748
QUALTEK MOLECULAR LABORATORIES—See Discovery Life Sciences, LLC; *U.S. Private*, pg. 1238
QUALTEK SERVICES INC.; *U.S. Public*, pg. 1748
QUALTER HALL & COMPANY LIMITED; *Int'l*, pg. 6152
QUALTEX LABORATORIES; *U.S. Private*, pg. 3322
QUALTRAX INC.—See HgCapital Trust plc; *Int'l*, pg. 3378
QUALTRICS INTERNATIONAL INC.—See Canada Pension Plan Investment Board; *Int'l*, pg. 1281
QUALTRICS INTERNATIONAL INC.—See Silver Lake Group, LLC; *Int'l*, pg. 3655
QUALTRICS JAPAN LLC—See SAP SE; *Int'l*, pg. 6566
QUALUS CORPORATION; *U.S. Private*, pg. 3322
QUALUS POWER SERVICES CORP.—See New Mountain Capital, LLC; *U.S. Private*, pg. 2903
QUALYS AUSTRALIA PTY LTD.—See Qualys, Inc.; *U.S. Public*, pg. 1748
QUALYS GMBH—See Qualys, Inc.; *U.S. Public*, pg. 1748

QUANTA, INC.

QUALYS HONG KONG LIMITED—See Qualys, Inc.; *U.S. Public*, pg. 1748
QUALYS, INC.; *U.S. Public*, pg. 1748
QUALYS INTERNATIONAL, INC.—See Qualys, Inc.; *U.S. Public*, pg. 1748
QUALYSITE TECHNOLOGIES INC.—See Canon Inc.; *Int'l*, pg. 1296
QUALYS JAPAN K.K.—See Qualys, Inc.; *U.S. Public*, pg. 1748
QUALYS LTD.—See Qualys, Inc.; *U.S. Public*, pg. 1748
QUALYS MIDDLE EAST FZE—See Qualys, Inc.; *U.S. Public*, pg. 1748
QUALYS SECURITY TECHSERVICES PRIVATE LTD.—See Qualys, Inc.; *U.S. Public*, pg. 1748
QUALYS TECHNOLOGIES, S.A.—See Qualys, Inc.; *U.S. Public*, pg. 1748
QUAM INVESTMENT ADVISORY (HANGZHOU) COMPANY LIMITED—See Quam Plus International Financial Limited; *Int'l*, pg. 6153
QUAM-NICHOLS COMPANY; *U.S. Private*, pg. 3322
QUAM PLUS INTERNATIONAL FINANCIAL LIMITED; *Int'l*, pg. 6153
THE QUANDEL CONSTRUCTION GROUP, INC.—See The Quandel Group Inc.; *U.S. Private*, pg. 4101
THE QUANDEL GROUP INC.; *U.S. Private*, pg. 4101
THE QUANDEL GROUP, MINERSVILLE—See The Quandel Group Inc.; *U.S. Private*, pg. 4101
QUANDEL VERPACKUNGS- UND FOERDERTECHNIK GMBH—See Illinois Tool Works Inc.; *U.S. Public*, pg. 1110
QUANERGY PERCEPTION TECHNOLOGIES, INC.—See Quanergy Systems, Inc.; *U.S. Public*, pg. 1749
QUANERGY SYSTEMS, INC.; *U.S. Public*, pg. 1749
QUANEX BUILDING PRODUCTS CORP.; *U.S. Public*, pg. 1749
QUANEX HOMESHIELD LLC - RICE LAKE SCREENS PLANT—See Quanex Building Products Corp.; *U.S. Public*, pg. 1749
QUANEX HOMESHIELD LLC - RICHMOND PLANT—See Quanex Building Products Corp.; *U.S. Public*, pg. 1749
QUANEX HOMESHIELD, LLC—See Quanex Building Products Corp.; *U.S. Public*, pg. 1749
QUANEX IG SYSTEMS, INC.—See Quanex Building Products Corp.; *U.S. Public*, pg. 1749
QUANEX SCREENS LLC—See Quanex Building Products Corp.; *U.S. Public*, pg. 1749
QUANG NAM MINERAL INDUSTRY CORPORATION; *Int'l*, pg. 6153
QUANGNAM POST-TELECOMS CONSTRUCTION AND SERVICES CORPORATION—See Vietnam Posts & Telecommunications Corporation; *Int'l*, pg. 8203
QUANG NAM RUBBER INVESTMENT JOINT STOCK COMPANY; *Int'l*, pg. 6153
QUANG NAM TRANSPORTATION CONSTRUCTION JSC; *Int'l*, pg. 6153
QUANG NGAI MINERAL INVESTMENT JOINT STOCK COMPANY—See 577 Investment Corporation; *Int'l*, pg. 13
QUANG NGAI PETROLIMEX COMPANY—See Vietnam National Petroleum Corporation; *Int'l*, pg. 8202
QUANG NINH BOOK & EDUCATIONAL EQUIPMENT JSC; *Int'l*, pg. 6153
QUANG NINH CONSTRUCTION & CEMENT COMPANY; *Int'l*, pg. 6153
QUANG VIET ENTERPRISE CO., LTD.; *Int'l*, pg. 6153
QUANMAX INC.—See Kontron AG; *Int'l*, pg. 4277
QUANMAX INC.—See Kontron AG; *Int'l*, pg. 4277
QUANMAX USA INC.—See Kontron AG; *Int'l*, pg. 4277
QUAN RUI (DONGGUAN) INDUSTRIAL CO., LTD.—See Chia Chang Co., Ltd.; *Int'l*, pg. 1475
QUANTA ADVERTISING; *U.S. Private*, pg. 3322
QUANTA CLOUD TECHNOLOGY GERMANY GMBH—See Quanta Computer, Inc.; *Int'l*, pg. 6153
QUANTA CLOUD TECHNOLOGY INC.—See Quanta Computer, Inc.; *Int'l*, pg. 6153
QUANTA CLOUD TECHNOLOGY JAPAN INC.—See Quanta Computer, Inc.; *Int'l*, pg. 6153
QUANTA CLOUD TECHNOLOGY USA LLC—See Quanta Computer, Inc.; *Int'l*, pg. 6153
QUANTA COMPUTER, INC.; *Int'l*, pg. 6153
QUANTA COMPUTER, INC.—See Quanta Computer, Inc.; *Int'l*, pg. 6153
QUANTA COMPUTER NASHVILLE LLC—See Quanta Computer, Inc.; *Int'l*, pg. 6153
QUANTA COMPUTER USA, INC—See Quanta Computer, Inc.; *Int'l*, pg. 6153
QUANTAFUEL ASA; *Int'l*, pg. 6154
QUANTA GOVERNMENT SOLUTIONS, INC.—See Quanta Services, Inc.; *U.S. Public*, pg. 1752
QUANTA, INC.; *U.S. Public*, pg. 1753
QUANTA INFRASTRUCTURE SOLUTIONS GROUP, LLC—See Quanta Services, Inc.; *U.S. Public*, pg. 1752
QUANTA INSURANCE GROUP PTY. LTD.—See Steadfast Group Limited; *Int'l*, pg. 7187
QUANTA LINES PTY. LTD.—See Quanta Services, Inc.; *U.S. Public*, pg. 1752
QUANTA MANUFACTURING INC.—See Quanta Computer, Inc.; *Int'l*, pg. 6153

QUANTA MARINE SERVICES, LLC—See Quanta Services, Inc.; *U.S. Public*, pg. 1752
QUANTAMATRIX INC.; *Int'l*, pg. 6154
QUANTA MICROSYSTEMS INC.—See Quanta Computer, Inc.; *Int'l*, pg. 6153
QUANTA SERVICES, INC.; *U.S. Public*, pg. 1750
QUANTA SHANGHAI MANUFACTURE CITY—See Quanta Computer, Inc.; *Int'l*, pg. 6153
QUANTASING GROUP LIMITED; *Int'l*, pg. 6154
QUANTA STORAGE, INC.; *Int'l*, pg. 6154
QUANTA SUBSURFACE, LLC—See Quanta Services, Inc.; *U.S. Public*, pg. 1752
QUANTASY, LLC; *U.S. Private*, pg. 3322
QUANTA SYSTEMS, LLC—See Black Box Limited; *Int'l*, pg. 1058
QUANTA SYSTEM S.P.A.—See El.En. S.p.A.; *Int'l*, pg. 2342
QUANTA TECHNOLOGY, LLC—See Quanta Services, Inc.; *U.S. Public*, pg. 1752
QUANTA TELECOM CANADA LTD.—See Quanta Services, Inc.; *U.S. Public*, pg. 1752
QUANTA TELECOMMUNICATION SERVICES, LLC—See Quanta Services, Inc.; *U.S. Public*, pg. 1752
QUANTA TELECOMMUNICATION SOLUTIONS, LLC—See Quanta Services, Inc.; *U.S. Public*, pg. 1752
QUANTA UTILITY ENGINEERING SERVICES, INC.—See Quanta Services, Inc.; *U.S. Public*, pg. 1752
QUANTCAST CORPORATION—See InMobi Pte Ltd.; *Int'l*, pg. 3706
QUANTEC GEOSCIENCE CHILE LTDA.—See Quantec Geoscience Ltd.; *Int'l*, pg. 6154
QUANTEC GEOSCIENCE LTD.; *Int'l*, pg. 6154
QUANTEC GEOSCIENCE (PERU) S.A.C.—See Quantec Geoscience Ltd.; *Int'l*, pg. 6154
QUANTECH SERVICES, INC.; *U.S. Private*, pg. 3322
QUANTEGY INC.; *U.S. Private*, pg. 3322
QUANTEL ASIA PACIFIC LTD.—See Lumibird Group; *Int'l*, pg. 4578
QUANTEL GMBH—See Lumibird Group; *Int'l*, pg. 4578
QUANTEL LASER DIODES—See Lumibird Group; *Int'l*, pg. 4578
QUANTEL MEDICAL, INC.—See Lumibird Group; *Int'l*, pg. 4578
QUANTEL MEDICAL SA—See Lumibird Group; *Int'l*, pg. 4578
QUANTEL PRIVATE LTD.—See Chroma ATE Inc.; *Int'l*, pg. 1588
QUANTEM AVIATION SERVICES; *U.S. Private*, pg. 3322
QUANTEM FBO GROUP LLC; *U.S. Private*, pg. 3322
QUANTERIX CORPORATION; *U.S. Public*, pg. 1753
QUANTGATE SYSTEMS INC.; *U.S. Public*, pg. 1753
QUANT HOUSE SAS—See IRESS Limited; *Int'l*, pg. 3808
QUANTICA—See The Kellan Group Plc; *Int'l*, pg. 7662
QUANTIC DIGITAL GMBH—See Nippon Telegraph & Telephone Corporation; *Int'l*, pg. 5355
QUANTIC SA—See Aubay SA; *Int'l*, pg. 698
QUANTIFI, INC.; *U.S. Private*, pg. 3322
QUANTILE TECHNOLOGIES LIMITED—See London Stock Exchange Group plc; *Int'l*, pg. 4548
QUANTIPARTS B.V.—See Wartsila Corporation; *Int'l*, pg. 8347
QUANTITATIVE BROKERS LLC—See Deutsche Borse AG; *Int'l*, pg. 2064
QUANTITATIVE BROKERS UK LIMITED—See Deutsche Borse AG; *Int'l*, pg. 2064
QUANTITATIVE MANAGEMENT ASSOCIATES LLC—See Prudential Financial, Inc.; *U.S. Public*, pg. 1733
QUANTITATIVE MEDICAL SYSTEMS, INC.—See Constellation Software Inc.; *Int'l*, pg. 1772
QUANTITECH LLC—See Millennium Engineering & Integration Company; *U.S. Private*, pg. 2731
QUANTIUM SOLUTIONS (AUSTRALIA) PTY. LTD.—See Singapore Post Limited; *Int'l*, pg. 6942
QUANTIUM SOLUTIONS (HONG KONG) LIMITED—See Singapore Post Limited; *Int'l*, pg. 6942
QUANTIUM SOLUTIONS (SINGAPORE) PTE. LTD.—See Singapore Post Limited; *Int'l*, pg. 6942
QUANTIX, INC.; *U.S. Private*, pg. 3322
QUANTIX SCS, INC.—See Wind Point Advisors LLC; *U.S. Private*, pg. 4535
QUANTRILL CHEVROLET BUICK GMC CADILLAC; *Int'l*, pg. 6154
QUANTRONIX, INC.; *U.S. Private*, pg. 3322
QUANTROS, INC.; *U.S. Private*, pg. 3322
QUANTRX BIOMEDICAL CORP.; *U.S. Public*, pg. 1753
QUANT SECURITIES PRIVATE LIMITED—See Reliance - ADA Group Limited; *Int'l*, pg. 6261
QUANTS INC.; *Int'l*, pg. 6154
QUANT SYSTEMS, INC.; *U.S. Private*, pg. 3322
QUANTUM3D INC.—See Havelsan Hava Elektronik Sanayi ve Ticaret AS; *Int'l*, pg. 3287
QUANTUMA ADVISORY LIMITED; *Int'l*, pg. 6155
QUANTUM ASIA PVT LTD—See NBA Quantum PLC; *Int'l*, pg. 5179
QUANTUM AUTOMATION PTE. LTD.—See Osaki Electric Co., Ltd.; *Int'l*, pg. 5647
QUANTUM AUTOMATION SYSTEMS (SHANGHAI) CO., LTD.—See Osaki Electric Co., Ltd.; *Int'l*, pg. 5647
QUANTUM BATTERY METALS CORP.; *Int'l*, pg. 6154

QUANTUM BLOCKCHAIN TECHNOLOGIES LTD.; *Int'l*, pg. 6154
QUANTUM BLOCKCHAIN TECHNOLOGIES PLC; *Int'l*, pg. 6154
QUANTUM BUILD-TECH LIMITED; *Int'l*, pg. 6154
QUANTUM BUSINESS STRATEGIES, INC.; *U.S. Private*, pg. 3322
QUANTUM CAPITAL GROUP LLC; *U.S. Private*, pg. 3322
QUANTUM CAPITAL, INC.; *U.S. Public*, pg. 6154
QUANTUM CAPITAL PARTNERS AG; *Int'l*, pg. 6154
QUANTUM CARE (UK) LIMITED—See Acadia Healthcare Company, Inc.; *U.S. Public*, pg. 29
QUANTUM CHEMICAL TECHNOLOGIES (S) PTE. LTD.—See Singapore Asahi Chemical & Solder Industries Pte. Ltd.; *Int'l*, pg. 6940
QUANTUM COLOR GRAPHICS LLC; *U.S. Private*, pg. 3322
QUANTUM COMMUNICATIONS; *U.S. Private*, pg. 3322
QUANTUM COMPLIANCE SYSTEMS, INC.—See Logic Solutions, Inc.; *U.S. Private*, pg. 2481
QUANTUM COMPOSITES INC.—See Premix, Inc.; *U.S. Private*, pg. 3252
QUANTUM COMPUTING INC.; *U.S. Public*, pg. 1753
QUANTUM CONSULTING AUSTRALIA PTY LTD.—See NBA Quantum PLC; *Int'l*, pg. 5179
QUANTUM CORP. - IRVINE—See Quantum Corporation; *U.S. Public*, pg. 1754
QUANTUM CORPORATION; *U.S. Public*, pg. 1753
QUANTUM CORP. - PIKES PEAK OPERATIONS—See Quantum Corporation; *U.S. Public*, pg. 1754
QUANTUM CORP. - SANTA MARIA—See Quantum Corporation; *U.S. Public*, pg. 1754
QUANTUMCORRUGATED S.R.L.—See Guangdong Dongfang Science & Technology Co., Ltd.; *Int'l*, pg. 3153
QUANTUMCTEK CO., LTD.; *Int'l*, pg. 6155
QUANTUMCTEK (SHANGAI) CO., LTD.—See QuantumCTek Co., Ltd.; *Int'l*, pg. 6155
QUANTUM DATA INC.—See Teledyne Technologies Incorporated; *U.S. Public*, pg. 1994
QUANTUM DESIGN INC.; *U.S. Private*, pg. 3323
QUANTUM DEVELOPMENTS REIT; *Int'l*, pg. 6154
QUANTUM DIAGNOSTICOS LTDA—See Abbott Laboratories; *U.S. Public*, pg. 18
QUANTUMDIGITAL, INC.; *U.S. Private*, pg. 3323
QUANTUM DIGITAL VISION (INDIA) LIMITED; *Int'l*, pg. 6154
QUANTUM EMOTION INC.; *Int'l*, pg. 6154
QUANTUM ENERGY, INC.; *U.S. Public*, pg. 1754
QUANTUM ENERGY, LLC; *U.S. Private*, pg. 3323
QUANTUM ENERGY PARTNERS, LLC; *U.S. Private*, pg. 3323
QUANTUM ENERGY TECHNOLOGIES (SUZHOU) CO., LTD.—See Paragon Care Limited; *Int'l*, pg. 5736
QUANTUM ENVIRONMENTAL SERVICES PTY LTD.—See Cleanaway Waste Management Limited; *Int'l*, pg. 1655
QUANTUM EXPLOSIVES—See ACS, Actividades de Construccion y Servicios, S.A.; *Int'l*, pg. 113
QUANTUM EXPLOSIVES—See Elliott Management Corporation; *U.S. Public*, pg. 1365
QUANTUM FERTILISERS LIMITED—See Incitec Pivot Limited; *Int'l*, pg. 3648
QUANTUM FINTECH ACQUISITION CORPORATION; *U.S. Public*, pg. 1754
QUANTUM FOODS HOLDINGS LTD.; *Int'l*, pg. 6154
QUANTUM FUEL SYSTEMS TECHNOLOGIES WORLDWIDE, INC.; *U.S. Public*, pg. 1754
QUANTUM GENOMICS SA; *Int'l*, pg. 6154
QUANTUM GRAPHITE LIMITED; *Int'l*, pg. 6155
QUANTUM GROUP, INC.; *U.S. Private*, pg. 3323
QUANTUM HEALTHCARE LIMITED; *Int'l*, pg. 6155
QUANTUM HEALTH GROUP LIMITED—See Paragon Care Limited; *Int'l*, pg. 5736
QUANTUM HEALTH, LLC—See Warburg Pincus LLC; *U.S. Private*, pg. 4439
QUANTUM HI-TECH (CHINA) BIOLOGICAL CO., LTD.; *Int'l*, pg. 6155
QUANTUM, INC.; *U.S. Private*, pg. 3323
QUANTUM INK COMPANY; *U.S. Private*, pg. 3323
QUANTUM INTERNATIONAL CORP.; *U.S. Public*, pg. 1754
QUANTUM INTERNATIONAL GROUP, INC.—See Terra Millenium Corporation; *U.S. Private*, pg. 3970
QUANTUMKORE INC.; *U.S. Public*, pg. 1754
QUANTUMLEAP HEALTHCARE PTE. LTD.—See Q&M Dental Group (Singapore) Limited; *Int'l*, pg. 6131
QUANTUM LUBRICANTS (E.A) LIMITED—See Maximus International Limited; *Int'l*, pg. 4738
QUANTUM MANAGEMENT GROUP, INC.—See The British Standards Institution; *Int'l*, pg. 7629
QUANTUM MANAGEMENT SERVICES, INC.—See Hoban & Associates, Llc; *U.S. Private*, pg. 1958
QUANTUM MARKET RESEARCH, INC.; *U.S. Private*, pg. 3323
QUANTUM MATERIALS CORP.; *U.S. Private*, pg. 3323
QUANTUM MEDICAL IMAGING, LLC—See Koninklijke Philips N.V.; *Int'l*, pg. 4271

QUANTUM MEDICAL TRANSPORT, INC.; *U.S. Public*, pg. 1754
QUANTUM NETWORKS, LLC—See Advantage Sales & Marketing, LLC; *U.S. Private*, pg. 95
QUANTUM OFFSHORE LIMITED—See Serba Dinamik Holdings Berhad; *Int'l*, pg. 6721
QUANTUM OPS, INC.—See Enovis Corporation; *U.S. Public*, pg. 773
QUANTUM ORTHOPAEDICS PTE. LTD.—See Livingstone Health Holdings Limited; *Int'l*, pg. 4532
QUANTUM PLASTICS, INC.; *U.S. Private*, pg. 3323
QUANTUM PUBLISHING LTD—See The Quarto Group, Inc.; *Int'l*, pg. 7677
QUANTUM PUMP SYSTEMS LIMITED—See Serba Dinamik Holdings Berhad; *Int'l*, pg. 6721
QUANTUM QGUAR SP. Z O.O.—See Quantum Software S.A.; *Int'l*, pg. 6155
QUANTUM RENEWABLE ENERGY SDN. BHD.—See AME Elite Consortium Berhad; *Int'l*, pg. 420
QUANTUM RESEARCH INTERNATIONAL, INC.; *U.S. Private*, pg. 3323
QUANTUM RESEARCH SERVICES, INC.; *U.S. Private*, pg. 3323
QUANTUM RHYTHM SDN. BHD.—See Ornapaper Berhad; *Int'l*, pg. 5641
QUANTUM SARL—See Quantum Corporation; *U.S. Public*, pg. 1754
QUANTUMSCAPE CORPORATION; *U.S. Public*, pg. 1754
QUANTUM SCREENING AND CRUSHING (PROPRIETARY) LIMITED—See Canaf Investments Inc.; *Int'l*, pg. 1287
QUANTUM SECURE, INC.—See ASSA ABLOY AB; *Int'l*, pg. 637
QUANTUM SERVICING CORPORATION—See Covius Holdings, Inc.; *U.S. Private*, pg. 1073
QUANTUM SIGNAL AI, LLC—See Ford Motor Company; *U.S. Public*, pg. 867
QUANTUM-SI INCORPORATED; *U.S. Public*, pg. 1754
QUANTUM SILICONES, INC.—See Akoya Capital LLC; *U.S. Private*, pg. 146
QUANTUM SILICONES, INC.—See Century Park Capital Partners, LLC; *U.S. Private*, pg. 834
QUANTUM SOFTWARE S.A.; *Int'l*, pg. 6155
QUANTUM SOLAR POWER CORP.; *Int'l*, pg. 6155
QUANTUM SOLUTIONS CO., LTD.; *Int'l*, pg. 6155
QUANTUM SPATIAL, INC.—See Arlington Capital Partners LLC; *U.S. Private*, pg. 328
QUANTUMSPHERE, INC.; *U.S. Public*, pg. 1754
QUANTUM STORAGE AUSTRALIA PTY, LTD.—See Quantum Corporation; *U.S. Public*, pg. 1754
QUANTUM STORAGE (HONG KONG) LIMITED—See Kronologi Asia Berhad; *Int'l*, pg. 4306
QUANTUM STORAGE JAPAN CORPORATION—See Quantum Corporation; *U.S. Public*, pg. 1754
QUANTUM STORAGE SINGAPORE PTE. LTD.—See Quantum Corporation; *U.S. Public*, pg. 1754
QUANTUM STORAGE SOUTH ASIA SDN. BHD.—See Kronologi Asia Berhad; *Int'l*, pg. 4306
QUANTUM STORAGE UK, LTD.—See Quantum Corporation; *U.S. Public*, pg. 1754
QUANTUM STRUCTURES & DESIGN—See Clear Channel Outdoor Holdings, Inc.; *U.S. Public*, pg. 512
QUANTUM TAIWAN LIMITED—See Kronologi Asia Berhad; *Int'l*, pg. 4306
QUANTUM TECHNICAL SERVICES, LLC—See Ecolab Inc.; *U.S. Public*, pg. 716
QUANTUM TECHNOLOGY SCIENCES, INC.—See GEOSPACE TECHNOLOGIES CORPORATION; *U.S. Public*, pg. 934
QUANTUMTEK INNOVATIVES CORPORATION—See GigaLane Co., Ltd.; *Int'l*, pg. 2971
QUANTUM THINKING LIMITED; *Int'l*, pg. 6155
QUANTUM TOTAL PACKAGES SDN. BHD.—See Muda Holdings Berhad; *Int'l*, pg. 5077
QUANTUM UTILITY GENERATION, LLC—See Quantum Energy Partners, LLC; *U.S. Private*, pg. 3323
QUANTUM VENTURES OF MICHIGAN, LLC; *U.S. Private*, pg. 3323
QUANTUM WINDOWS & DOORS, INC.—See Swiftsure Capital LLC; *U.S. Private*, pg. 3893
QUANTUMWORK ADVISORY—See Allegis Group, Inc.; *U.S. Private*, pg. 177
QUANTURN LIMITED—See Galaxy Entertainment Group Limited; *Int'l*, pg. 2871
QUANZHOU DALI FOODS CO., LTD.—See Dali Foods Group Co. Ltd.; *Int'l*, pg. 1951
QUANZHOU FENGZE NICE MECHANICAL & ELECTRICAL EQUIPMENT CO., LTD.—See Endress+Hauser (International) Holding AG; *Int'l*, pg. 2409
QUANZHOU FENSUN AUTOMOBILE PARTS CO., LTD.—See China Automobile Parts Holdings Limited; *Int'l*, pg. 1484
QUANZHOU GRAND PACIFIC CHEMICAL CO., LTD.—See Grand Pacific Petrochemical Corporation; *Int'l*, pg. 3055
QUANZHOU GRUENLUFT MOLDING ENGINEERING CO.,LTD.—See Xiamen Voke Mold & Plastic Engineering Co., Ltd.; *Int'l*, pg. 8526

COMPANY NAME INDEX

QUANZHOU HUIXIN MICRO-CREDIT CO., LTD.; *Int'l*, pg. 6155
QUANZHOU ITG MOTOR SALES & SERVICE CO., LTD.—See Xiamen ITG Group Corp., Ltd.; *Int'l*, pg. 8524
QUANZHOU LAKE COMMUNICATION CO., LTD.—See China GrenTech Corporation Limited; *Int'l*, pg. 1506
QUANZHOU MEIDONG TOYOTA AUTO SALES & SERVICES CO., LTD.—See China MeiDong Auto Holdings Limited; *Int'l*, pg. 1519
QUANZHOU RAYNEN AUTOMATION TECHNOLOGY CO., LTD.—See Fujian Raynen Technology Co., Ltd.; *Int'l*, pg. 2819
THE QUAPAW COMPANY—See Dolese Bros. Co.; *U.S. Private*, pg. 1254
QUARAS INC.—See Fuji Media Holdings, Inc.; *Int'l*, pg. 2814
QUARDEV, INC.; *U.S. Private*, pg. 3323
QUARK EXPEDITIONS, INC.—See TUI AG; *Int'l*, pg. 7966
QUARK PHARMACEUTICALS, INC.—See SBI Holdings, Inc.; *Int'l*, pg. 6604
QUARK SECURITY INC.—See Parsons Corporation; *U.S. Public*, pg. 1651
QUARK SOFTWARE, INC.—See Parallax Capital Partners, LLC; *U.S. Private*, pg. 3092
QUARK TECHNOLOGY GLOBAL INC.; *Int'l*, pg. 6155
QUARKXPRESS PUBLISHING R&D (INDIA) PVT. LTD.—See Parallax Capital Partners, LLC; *U.S. Private*, pg. 3092
QUARLES & BRADY LLP; *U.S. Private*, pg. 3324
QUARLES PETROLEUM INCORPORATED; *U.S. Private*, pg. 3324
QUARLES TRUCK STOP INC.—See Quarles Petroleum Incorporated; *U.S. Private*, pg. 3324
QUARRIES DIRECT INTERNATIONAL LLC; *U.S. Private*, pg. 3324
QUARRY CAPITAL MANAGEMENT LLC; *U.S. Private*, pg. 3324
QUARRY CITY SAVINGS AND LOAN ASSOCIATION INC.—See Community National Bank & Trust; *U.S. Private*, pg. 996
QUARRY INTEGRATED COMMUNICATIONS; *Int'l*, pg. 6155
QUARRY & MINING MANUFACTURE PTY. LTD.—See E&A Limited; *Int'l*, pg. 2247
QUARRY & MINING MANUFACTURE (QLD) PTY. LTD.—See E&A Limited; *Int'l*, pg. 2247
QUARRYVILLE PRESBYTERIAN RETIREMENT COMMUNITY; *U.S. Private*, pg. 3324
QUARTA-RAD, INC.; *U.S. Public*, pg. 1754
QUARTERHILL INC.; *Int'l*, pg. 6155
QUARTER HORSE RACING INC.; *U.S. Private*, pg. 3324
QUARTERLINE CONSULTING SERVICES, LLC—See Planned Systems International, Inc.; *U.S. Private*, pg. 3196
QUARTERMASTER, LLC—See Charlesbank Capital Partners, LLC; *U.S. Private*, pg. 855
QUARTER MOON INC.—See Full Moon Holdings Limited; *Int'l*, pg. 2842
QUARTERS AT DES PERES, LLC—See National HealthCare Corporation; *U.S. Public*, pg. 1496
QUARTERWAY GIN, INC.; *U.S. Private*, pg. 3324
QUARTIERS PROPERTIES AB; *Int'l*, pg. 6156
QUARTIX INC.—See Quartix Technologies plc; *Int'l*, pg. 6156
QUARTIX TECHNOLOGIES PLC; *Int'l*, pg. 6156
QUARTO CHILDREN'S BOOKS LTD—See The Quarto Group, Inc.; *Int'l*, pg. 7677
THE QUARTO GROUP, INC.; *Int'l*, pg. 7677
QUARTON INTERNATIONAL AG—See The Toronto-Dominion Bank; *Int'l*, pg. 7695
QUARTON INTERNATIONAL AG—See The Toronto-Dominion Bank; *Int'l*, pg. 7695
QUARTO PUBLISHING PLC—See The Quarto Group, Inc.; *Int'l*, pg. 7677
QUARTZDYNE INC.—See Dover Corporation; *U.S. Public*, pg. 679
QUARTZELEC LTD.; *Int'l*, pg. 6156
QUARTZELEC LTD—See Quartzelec Ltd.; *Int'l*, pg. 6156
QUART Z IMMOBILIEN LEASING GESELLSCHAFT M.B.H.—See UniCredit S.p.A.; *Int'l*, pg. 8037
QUARTZ LEAD CO., LTD.—See Screen Holdings Co., Ltd.; *Int'l*, pg. 6655
QUARTZ MEDIA, INC.—See Great Hill Partners, L.P.; *U.S. Private*, pg. 1763
QUARTZ MOUNTAIN ANIMAL HOSPITAL, INC.—See JAB Holding Company S.a.r.l.; *Int'l*, pg. 3862
QUARTZ MOUNTAIN RESOURCES LTD.; *Int'l*, pg. 6156
QUARTZTEQ GMBH—See Quartzelec Ltd.; *Int'l*, pg. 6156
QUARZSANDE GMBH—See Zementwerk LEUBE GmbH; *Int'l*, pg. 8632
QUARZWERKE GMBH HALTERN PLANT—See Quarzwerke GmbH; *Int'l*, pg. 6156
QUARZWERKE GMBH; *Int'l*, pg. 6156
QUARZWERKE GMBH ST. GEORGEN PLANT—See Quarzwerke GmbH; *Int'l*, pg. 6156
QUARZWERKE OSTERREICH GMBH—See Quarzwerke GmbH; *Int'l*, pg. 6156
QUASAR BIO TECH LLC; *U.S. Private*, pg. 3324

QUASAR COMUNICACIONES PORTER NOVELLI—See Omnicom Group Inc.; *U.S. Public*, pg. 1591
QUASAR INDIA LIMITED; *Int'l*, pg. 6156
QUASAR INDUSTRIES INC.; *U.S. Private*, pg. 3324
QUASAR MEDIA—See WPP plc; *Int'l*, pg. 8483
QUASAR SOFTWARE DEVELOPMENT PROPRIETARY LIMITED—See OneLogix Group Limited; *Int'l*, pg. 5576
QUASEM INDUSTRIES LIMITED; *Int'l*, pg. 6156
QUASER AMERICA MACHINE TOOLS INC.—See Quaser Machine Tools, Inc.; *Int'l*, pg. 6157
QUASER MACHINE TOOLS, INC.; *Int'l*, pg. 6156
QUASFAR M&F S.A.—See Eurofins Scientific S.E.; *Int'l*, pg. 2551
QUASH PRODUCTS PLC; *Int'l*, pg. 6157
QUASIUS INVESTMENT CORP.; *U.S. Private*, pg. 3324
QUAT-CHEM LTD.—See Neogen Corporation; *U.S. Public*, pg. 1505
QUATEC AG—See Droege Group AG; *Int'l*, pg. 2205
QUATECH, LLC—See B&B Electronics Manufacturing Company; *U.S. Private*, pg. 417
QUATRINE FURNITURE INC.; *U.S. Private*, pg. 3324
QUATRIS HEALTH LLC; *U.S. Private*, pg. 3324
QUATRO AIR TECHNOLOGIES INC.—See Absolent Air Care Group AB; *Int'l*, pg. 70
QUATRO COMPOSITES, LLC—See Sekisui Chemical Co., Ltd.; *Int'l*, pg. 6693
QUATRO RAIL TECH SOLUTIONS PVT. LTD.—See EMC Limited; *Int'l*, pg. 2376
QUATRO RESOURCES INC.—See NGP Energy Capital Management, LLC; *U.S. Private*, pg. 2924
QUATRRO BUSINESS SUPPORT SERVICES, INC.—See Trivest Partners, LP; *U.S. Private*, pg. 4241
QUATRX PHARMACEUTICALS CO.; *U.S. Private*, pg. 3324
QUATTOR PETROQUIMICA SA—See Novonor S.A.; *Int'l*, pg. 5470
QUATTRO DIRECT LLC; *U.S. Private*, pg. 3324
QUATTRO ENZYME SOLUTIONS B.V.—See Orkla ASA; *Int'l*, pg. 5639
QUATTRO EXPLORATION & PRODUCTION LTD.; *Int'l*, pg. 6157
QUATTROR SGR S.P.A.; *Int'l*, pg. 6157
QUATUOR S.A.—See Thermo Fisher Scientific Inc.; *U.S. Public*, pg. 2154
QUAY APPOINTMENTS PTY LTD—See Will Group, Inc.; *Int'l*, pg. 8412
QUAY BATHROOMS LIMITED—See Anchorage Capital Group, L.L.C.; *U.S. Private*, pg. 274
QUAY BATHROOMS LIMITED—See CVC Capital Partners SICAV-FIS S.A.; *Int'l*, pg. 1888
QUAY CARGO SERVICES LTD.—See Albert Ballin KG; *Int'l*, pg. 296
THE QUAY CORPORATION,INC.; *U.S. Private*, pg. 4101
QUAY COUNTY SUN—See Clovis Media, Inc.; *U.S. Private*, pg. 948
QUAYLE MUNRO HOLDINGS LIMITED; *Int'l*, pg. 6157
QUAY MARINAS LTD.; *Int'l*, pg. 6157
QUAYSIDE ASSOCIATES LTD.; *U.S. Private*, pg. 3325
QUAZEL TECHNOLOGIES INC.—See Ubisoft Entertainment S.A.; *Int'l*, pg. 8003
QUBA NEW MEDIA; *Int'l*, pg. 6157
QUBED DERIVATIVES LLP—See BGC Group, Inc.; *U.S. Public*, pg. 330
QUBEGB LTD.; *Int'l*, pg. 6158
QUBE GLOBAL SOFTWARE LTD.—See GI Manager L.P.; *U.S. Private*, pg. 1693
QUBE HOLDINGS LIMITED; *Int'l*, pg. 6157
QUBE LOGISTICS (AUST) PTY LTD—See Qube Holdings Limited; *Int'l*, pg. 6158
QUBE LOGISTICS (H&S) PTY LTD—See Qube Holdings Limited; *Int'l*, pg. 6158
QUBE LOGISTICS (QLD) PTY LTD—See Qube Holdings Limited; *Int'l*, pg. 6158
QUBE LOGISTICS (SA) PTY LTD—See Qube Holdings Limited; *Int'l*, pg. 6158
QUBE LOGISTICS (WA1) PTY LTD—See Qube Holdings Limited; *Int'l*, pg. 6158
QUBE PORTS & BULK—See Qube Holdings Limited; *Int'l*, pg. 6158
QUBICAAMF WORLDWIDE, LLC—See Bowlero Corp; *U.S. Public*, pg. 376
QUBIQA ESBJERG A/S—See BWB Partners P/S; *Int'l*, pg. 1232
QUBITIA SOLUTIONS S.L.—See Solventis A.V. SA; *Int'l*, pg. 7082
QUBIX S.P.A.—See Zech Group SE; *Int'l*, pg. 8628
QUBOLE INC.—See HGGC, LLC; *U.S. Private*, pg. 1929
QUDIAN INC.; *Int'l*, pg. 6158
QUDOTECH SDN. BHD.—See AWC Berhad; *Int'l*, pg. 752
QUEBEC CARTIER MINING CO.—See ArcelorMittal S.A.; *Int'l*, pg. 544
QUEBEC GATINEAU RAILWAY—See Brookfield Infrastructure Partners L.P.; *Int'l*, pg. 1191
QUEBEC GATINEAU RAILWAY—See GIC Pte. Ltd.; *Int'l*, pg. 2966
QUEBEC METAL POWDERS LTD—See Rio Tinto plc; *Int'l*, pg. 6346
QUEBEC NICKEL CORP.; *Int'l*, pg. 6158

QUEENS LANE CAPITAL PTY LTD

QUEBEC NORTH SHORE & LABRADOR RAILWAY COMPANY—See Rio Tinto plc; *Int'l*, pg. 6346
QUEBECOR INC.; *Int'l*, pg. 6158
QUEBECOR MEDIA INC.—See Quebecor Inc.; *Int'l*, pg. 6158
QUEBEC PRECIOUS METALS CORPORATION; *Int'l*, pg. 6158
QUEBEC RARE EARTH ELEMENTS CORP; *Int'l*, pg. 6158
QUEBEDEAUX BUICK GMC; *U.S. Private*, pg. 3325
QUEBIT CONSULTING, LLC; *U.S. Private*, pg. 3325
QUECHEN SILICON CHEMICAL CO., LTD.; *Int'l*, pg. 6159
QUECLINK WIRELESS SOLUTIONS CO., LTD.; *Int'l*, pg. 6159
QUECTEL WIRELESS SOLUTIONS CO., LTD.; *Int'l*, pg. 6159
QUEENCH, INC.; *U.S. Public*, pg. 1755
QUEEN CITY BROADCASTING OF NEW YORK, INC.—See The E.W. Scripps Company; *U.S. Public*, pg. 2068
QUEEN CITY FIRE EQUIPMENT, INC.—See TruArc Partners, L.P.; *U.S. Private*, pg. 4244
QUEEN CITY HOSPICE, LLC—See Addus HomeCare Corporation; *U.S. Public*, pg. 40
QUEEN CITY INVESTMENTS, INC.; *U.S. Public*, pg. 1754
QUEEN CITY MOTORS CO.; *U.S. Private*, pg. 3325
QUEEN CITY PLASTICS, INC.—See Clayton, Dubilier & Rice, LLC; *U.S. Private*, pg. 920
QUEEN CITY TELEVISION SERVICE CO. INC.; *U.S. Private*, pg. 3325
QUEEN CITY TERMINALS, INC.—See Kinder Morgan, Inc.; *U.S. Public*, pg. 1233
QUEEN CITY TERMINALS LLC—See Kinder Morgan, Inc.; *U.S. Public*, pg. 1234
QUEEN CITY TRANSPORTATION, LLC—See Mobico Group PLC; *Int'l*, pg. 5009
QUEENCO LEISURE INTERNATIONAL LTD.; *Int'l*, pg. 6159
QUEENSBORO FARM PRODUCTS INC.; *U.S. Private*, pg. 3325
THE QUEENSBORO SHIRT COMPANY; *U.S. Private*, pg. 4101
QUEENS CENTER REIT LLC—See The Macerich Company; *U.S. Public*, pg. 2110
QUEEN'S ENTERPRISES LTD. INC.—See HTH Corporation; *U.S. Private*, pg. 1999
QUEEN'S FINANCE LIMITED—See Prosperous Future Holdings Limited; *Int'l*, pg. 6002
QUEEN'S GAMBIT GROWTH CAPITAL; *U.S. Public*, pg. 1755
QUEENS HARBOUR YACHT & COUNTRY CLUB, LTD.—See Apollo Global Management, Inc.; *U.S. Public*, pg. 150
THE QUEEN'S HEALTH SYSTEMS; *U.S. Private*, pg. 4101
QUEEN'S ISETAN CO., LTD.—See Isetan Mitsukoshi Holdings Ltd.; *Int'l*, pg. 3815
QUEENSLAND ACCOMMODATION CORPORATION PTY. LTD.—See Minor International PCL; *Int'l*, pg. 4913
QUEENSLAND BREWERIES PTY LTD—See Anheuser-Busch InBev SA/NV; *Int'l*, pg. 464
QUEENSLAND COMMODITY SERVICE PTY LTD.—See Nordzucker AG; *Int'l*, pg. 5427
QUEENSLAND COMMUNITY NEWSPAPERS PTY LIMITED—See Nine Entertainment Co. Holdings Limited; *Int'l*, pg. 5299
QUEENSLAND DIAGNOSTIC IMAGING PTY LTD—See Healius Limited; *Int'l*, pg. 3302
QUEENSLAND ENVIRONMENT PTY LTD—See Enviro-Suite Limited; *Int'l*, pg. 2455
QUEENSLAND FERTILITY GROUP PTY. LTD.—See Virtus Health Limited; *Int'l*, pg. 8249
QUEENSLAND INSTITUTE OF BUSINESS AND TECHNOLOGY PTY LTD.—See Navitas Limited; *Int'l*, pg. 5177
QUEENSLAND NITRATES MANAGEMENT PTY LTD—See Incitec Pivot Limited; *Int'l*, pg. 3648
QUEENSLAND NITRATES MANAGEMENT PTY LTD—See Wesfarmers Limited; *Int'l*, pg. 8381
QUEENSLAND NITRATES PTY LTD.—See Incitec Pivot Limited; *Int'l*, pg. 3648
QUEENSLAND NITRATES PTY LTD.—See Wesfarmers Limited; *Int'l*, pg. 8381
QUEENSLAND POTASH PTY LIMITED—See Anglo American PLC; *Int'l*, pg. 461
QUEENSLAND RAIL LIMITED; *Int'l*, pg. 6159
QUEENSLAND RURAL PTY. LTD.—See Nutrien Ltd.; *Int'l*, pg. 5493
QUEENSLAND SHALE OIL PTY. LTD.—See Blue Ensign Technologies Limited; *Int'l*, pg. 1068
QUEENSLAND TELEVISION LTD.—See Nine Entertainment Co. Holdings Limited; *Int'l*, pg. 5299
QUEENSLAND TREASURY CORPORATION; *Int'l*, pg. 6159
QUEENSLAND URBAN PROJECTS PTY LTD—See Finasucre S.A.; *Int'l*, pg. 2670
QUEENSLAND X-RAY PTY LIMITED—See Sonic Healthcare Limited; *Int'l*, pg. 7098
QUEENS LANE CAPITAL PTY LTD; *Int'l*, pg. 6159

QUEEN SOUTH TEXTILE MILLS LTD.; Int'l, pg. 6159
QUEEN'S ROAD CAPITAL INVESTMENT LTD.; Int'l, pg. 6159
QUEEN'S ROAD CAPITAL INVESTMENT LTD.; Int'l, pg. 6159
QUEENS SYMPHONY ORCHESTRA; U.S. Private, pg. 3325
QUEENSTOWN BANK OF MARYLAND; U.S. Private, pg. 3325
QUEENSTOWN QUARRY (PTY) LIMITED—See Raubex Group Limited; Int'l, pg. 6221
QUEENSWAY GOLF INTERNATIONAL LIMITED—See China Fortune Investments (Holding) Limited; Int'l, pg. 1503
QUEENSWAY GROUP LIMITED; Int'l, pg. 6159
QUEIROZ GALVAO OLEO E GAS S.A.—See QGOG Constellation S.A.; Int'l, pg. 6138
QUELL CORP.—See HEICO Corporation; U.S. Public, pg. 1020
QUELL INDUSTRIAL SERVICES; U.S. Private, pg. 3325
QUELL THERAPEUTICS LIMITED—See Syncona Ltd.; Int'l, pg. 7382
QUELOZ SA—See Diethelm Keller Holding Limited; Int'l, pg. 2117
QUEMCHI SA; Int'l, pg. 6160
QUEMETCO, INC.—See Quexco Incorporated; U.S. Private, pg. 3326
QUEMETCO METALS LIMITED, INC.—See Quexco Incorporated; U.S. Private, pg. 3326
QUEMETCO REALTY, INC.—See Quexco Incorporated; U.S. Private, pg. 3326
QUENCH USA, INC.—See BDT Capital Partners, LLC; U.S. Private, pg. 502
QUENCHY CRUSTA SALES PTY LTD—See COCA-COLA EUROPACIFIC PARTNERS PLC; Int'l, pg. 1684
QUENDALE CAPITAL CORP.; Int'l, pg. 6160
QUENETS PROPRIETARY LIMITED—See Dis-Chem Pharmacies Ltd.; Int'l, pg. 2131
QUERCIA SOFTWARE SPA—See UniCredit S.p.A.; Int'l, pg. 8035
QUERCUS EDITIONS LTD.—See Vivendi SE; Int'l, pg. 8278
QUERCUS TOWARZYSTWO FUNDUSZY IN-WESTYCYJNYCH S.A.; Int'l, pg. 6160
QUERCY—See Carrefour SA; Int'l, pg. 1346
QUERETARO S DE RL DE CV—See Parker Hannifin Corporation; U.S. Public, pg. 1642
QUERY CO. LTD.—See TOKAI Corp.; Int'l, pg. 7779
QUERYO ADVANCE S.R.L.—See Tinexta S.p.A.; Int'l, pg. 7753
QUESADA KAPITALFORVALTNING AB—See EFG International AG; Int'l, pg. 2321
QUESCO SYSTEMS LIMITED—See ITE (Holdings) Limited; Int'l, pg. 3832
QUES INDUSTRIES, INC.; U.S. Private, pg. 3325
QUESS CORP LANKA (PRIVATE) LIMITED—See Quess Corp Limited; Int'l, pg. 6160
QUESS CORP LIMITED; Int'l, pg. 6160
QUESSCORP MANAGEMENT CONSULTANCIES—See Quess Corp Limited; Int'l, pg. 6160
QUESS CORP NA LLC—See Quess Corp Limited; Int'l, pg. 6160
QUESSGLOBAL (MALAYSIA) SDN. BHD.—See Quess Corp Limited; Int'l, pg. 6160
QUEST AIRCRAFT COMPANY, LLC—See DAHER Group; Int'l, pg. 1913
QUEST ANALYTICS LLC—See Vestar Capital Partners, LLC; U.S. Private, pg. 4372
QUESTAR AGENCY INC.—See Allianz SE; Int'l, pg. 355
QUESTAR ASSESSMENT, INC.—See Educational Testing Service, Inc.; U.S. Private, pg. 1340
QUESTAR CAPITAL CORPORATION—See Allianz SE; Int'l, pg. 347
QUESTAR CORPORATION; U.S. Private, pg. 3326
QUESTAR ENERGY SERVICES, INC.—See Dominion Energy, Inc.; U.S. Public, pg. 674
QUESTAR GAS COMPANY—See Enbridge Inc.; Int'l, pg. 2397
QUESTATE SDN. BHD.—See Ta Ann Holdings Berhad; Int'l, pg. 7398
QUESTAWEB, INC.—See The Descartes Systems Group Inc.; Int'l, pg. 7636
QUESTBACK GROUP AS; Int'l, pg. 6161
QUEST BUILDING PRODUCTS INC.—See Incline MGMT Corp.; U.S. Private, pg. 2053
THE QUEST BUSINESS AGENCY, INC.; U.S. Private, pg. 4101
QUEST CAPITAL MANAGEMENT INC—See Genstar Capital, LLC; U.S. Private, pg. 1677
QUEST CAPITAL MANAGEMENT INC—See Keystone Group, L.P.; U.S. Private, pg. 2298
QUEST CAPITAL MARKETS LTD.; Int'l, pg. 6160
QUEST CE; U.S. Private, pg. 3325
QUEST CO., LTD.; Int'l, pg. 6160
QUEST COMMERCIAL CAPITAL CORP.—See Pohlad Companies; U.S. Private, pg. 3220
QUEST CONTROLS, INC.; U.S. Private, pg. 3325
QUEST CORING INC.—See ALS Limited; Int'l, pg. 378

QUEST CORPORATION OF AMERICA, INC.; U.S. Private, pg. 3325
QUEST CREDIT UNION; U.S. Private, pg. 3325
QUEST DIAGNOSTICS CLINICAL LABORATORIES, INC.—See Quest Diagnostics, Inc.; U.S. Public, pg. 1755
QUEST DIAGNOSTICS - HOUSTON—See Quest Diagnostics, Inc.; U.S. Public, pg. 1755
QUEST DIAGNOSTICS INCORPORATED—See Quest Diagnostics, Inc.; U.S. Public, pg. 1755
QUEST DIAGNOSTICS INCORPORATED—See Quest Diagnostics, Inc.; U.S. Public, pg. 1756
QUEST DIAGNOSTICS INCORPORATED—See Quest Diagnostics, Inc.; U.S. Public, pg. 1756
QUEST DIAGNOSTICS, INC.; U.S. Public, pg. 1755
QUEST DIAGNOSTICS IRELAND LIMITED—See Quest Diagnostics, Inc.; U.S. Public, pg. 1756
QUEST DIAGNOSTICS - LENEXA—See Quest Diagnostics, Inc.; U.S. Public, pg. 1755
QUEST DIAGNOSTICS LIMITED—See Quest Diagnostics, Inc.; U.S. Public, pg. 1756
QUEST DIAGNOSTICS - NASHVILLE—See Quest Diagnostics, Inc.; U.S. Public, pg. 1755
QUEST DIAGNOSTICS NICHOLS INSTITUTE, INC.—See Quest Diagnostics, Inc.; U.S. Public, pg. 1756
QUEST DIAGNOSTICS NICHOLS INSTITUTE—See Quest Diagnostics, Inc.; U.S. Public, pg. 1756
QUEST DIAGNOSTICS - SAN ANTONIO—See Quest Diagnostics, Inc.; U.S. Public, pg. 1755
QUEST DIAGNOSTICS - SCHAUMBERG—See Quest Diagnostics, Inc.; U.S. Public, pg. 1755
QUEST DIAGNOSTICS - SEATTLE—See Quest Diagnostics, Inc.; U.S. Public, pg. 1755
QUEST DIAGNOSTICS - SYOSSET—See Quest Diagnostics, Inc.; U.S. Public, pg. 1755
QUEST DIAGNOSTICS - WEST HILLS—See Quest Diagnostics, Inc.; U.S. Public, pg. 1755
QUESTE CAPITAL; U.S. Private, pg. 3326
QUESTE COMMUNICATIONS LIMITED; Int'l, pg. 6161
QUESTEL SAS; Int'l, pg. 6161
QUEST ENGINEERING, INC.; U.S. Private, pg. 3325
QUEST ENVIRONMENTAL & SAFETY PRODUCTS, INC.; U.S. Private, pg. 3325
QUESTER BAUSTOFFHANDEL GMBH—See CRH plc; Int'l, pg. 1848
QUESTERRE ENERGY CORPORATION; Int'l, pg. 6161
QUESTERS BULGARIA EOOD—See TPXimpact Holdings PLC; Int'l, pg. 7885
QUESTERS GLOBAL GROUP LIMITED—See Nortal AS; Int'l, pg. 5438
QUEST EVENTS, LLC; U.S. Private, pg. 3325
QUESTEX GOLD & COPPER LTD.—See Skeena Resources Limited; Int'l, pg. 6980
QUESTEX MEDIA GROUP LLC—See MidOcean Partners, LLP; U.S. Private, pg. 2717
QUESTFIRE ENERGY CORP.; Int'l, pg. 6161
QUEST FLEXIBLE STAFFING SOLUTIONS (PTY) LIMITED—See Adcorp Holdings Limited; Int'l, pg. 127
QUEST FOR GROWTH NV; Int'l, pg. 6160
THE QUEST GROUP, INC.; U.S. Private, pg. 4101
QUEST HOLDINGS S.A.; Int'l, pg. 6160
QUEST INFORMATION SYSTEMS INC.—See Clearview Capital, LLC; U.S. Private, pg. 939
QUEST INSPAR, LLC—See Quest Integrated, LLC; U.S. Private, pg. 3325
QUEST INTEGRATED, LLC; U.S. Private, pg. 3325
QUEST INTEGRITY CAN LTD.—See Team, Inc.; U.S. Public, pg. 1988
QUEST INTEGRITY DEUTSCHLAND GMBH—See Team, Inc.; U.S. Public, pg. 1988
QUEST INTEGRITY GROUP, LLC—See Baker Hughes Company; U.S. Public, pg. 265
QUEST INTEGRITY MIDDLE EAST FZ-LLC—See Team, Inc.; U.S. Public, pg. 1988
QUEST INTEGRITY MYS SDN BHD—See Baker Hughes Company; U.S. Public, pg. 265
QUEST INTEGRITY NLD B.V.—See Team, Inc.; U.S. Public, pg. 1988
QUEST INTEGRITY NZL LIMITED—See Baker Hughes Company; U.S. Public, pg. 265
QUEST INTEGRITY USA, LLC—See Baker Hughes Company; U.S. Public, pg. 265
QUESTIONMARK CORPORATION—See Learnosity Ltd.; U.S. Private, pg. 2408
QUESTIONS & SOLUTIONS ENGINEERING, INC.; U.S. Private, pg. 3326
QUEST LABORATORIES PTE. LTD.—See Brookfield Corporation; Int'l, pg. 1176
QUESTLINE, INC.—See Constellation Software Inc.; Int'l, pg. 1774
QUEST LINER INC.; U.S. Private, pg. 3326
QUEST MANAGEMENT CONSULTANTS, INC—See Career Management Partners; U.S. Private, pg. 752
QUEST MARKETING, INC.—See OMNIQ Corp.; U.S. Public, pg. 1600
QUEST MEDIA & SUPPLIES INC—See Brown Brothers Harriman & Co.; U.S. Private, pg. 667
QUEST MEDICAL, INC.—See Nordson Corporation; U.S. Public, pg. 1532

QUEST NATIONAL SERVICES LLC; U.S. Private, pg. 3326
QUEST NUTRITION, LLC—See The Simply Good Foods Company; U.S. Public, pg. 2130
QUEST OIL CORP.; U.S. Private, pg. 3326
QUESTOR MANAGEMENT COMPANY, LLC; U.S. Private, pg. 3326
QUESTOR SOLUTIONS & TECHNOLOGY INC.—See Questor Technology Inc.; Int'l, pg. 6161
QUESTOR TECHNOLOGY INC.; Int'l, pg. 6161
QUEST PATENT RESEARCH CORPORATION; U.S. Public, pg. 1756
QUEST PHARMATECH INC.; Int'l, pg. 6160
QUEST PRODUCTS, INC.—See Promus Holdings, LLC; U.S. Private, pg. 3284
QUEST RAIL LLC—See Orscheln Group; U.S. Private, pg. 3045
QUEST RARE MINERALS LTD.; Int'l, pg. 6160
QUEST RECYCLING SERVICES LLC; U.S. Private, pg. 3326
QUEST RESOURCE HOLDING CORPORATION; U.S. Public, pg. 1756
QUEST RESOURCE MANAGEMENT GROUP, LLC—See Quest Resource Holding Corporation; U.S. Public, pg. 1756
QUESTRON TECHNOLOGIES CORP.—See HORIBA Ltd; Int'l, pg. 3478
QUEST SOFTWARE INC.—See Francisco Partners Management, LP; U.S. Private, pg. 1591
QUEST STOCKBROKERS (HK) LIMITED—See Murchison Holdings Limited; Int'l, pg. 5099
QUEST TECHNOLOGY INTERNATIONAL, INC.; U.S. Private, pg. 3326
QUEST TECHNOLOGY SDN. BHD.—See Straits Energy Resources Berhad; Int'l, pg. 7234
QUESTUS CAPITAL SOLUTIONS PTY. LTD.—See QUESTUS LIMITED; Int'l, pg. 6161
QUESTUS FUNDS MANAGEMENT LIMITED—See QUESTUS LIMITED; Int'l, pg. 6161
QUESTUS LIMITED; Int'l, pg. 6161
QUEST WATER GLOBAL, INC.; Int'l, pg. 6161
QUEST WINDOW SYSTEMS INC.—See Exchange Income Corporation; Int'l, pg. 2579
QUETTA ACQUISITION CORPORATION; U.S. Public, pg. 1756
QUETTA GROUP OF COMPANIES LLC; Int'l, pg. 6161
QUETTA POWER GENERATION LIMITED—See Quetta Group of Companies LLC; Int'l, pg. 6161
QUETTA TEXTILE MILLS LIMITED—See Quetta Group of Companies LLC; Int'l, pg. 6161
QUEUE CREATIVE; U.S. Private, pg. 3326
QUEXCO INCORPORATED; U.S. Private, pg. 3326
QUEZON MANAGEMENT SERVICE INC.—See Electricity Generating Public Co., Ltd.; Int'l, pg. 2352
QUEZON POWER (PHILIPPINES) LIMITED CO.—See Electricity Generating Public Co., Ltd.; Int'l, pg. 2352
QUFU SHENGREN PHARMACEUTICAL CO., LTD.—See Sunwin Stevia International, Inc.; Int'l, pg. 7331
QUFU SHENGWANG STEVIA BIOLOGY AND SCIENCE CO., LTD.—See Sunwin Stevia International, Inc.; Int'l, pg. 7331
QUHUO LIMITED; Int'l, pg. 6161
QUIAPEG PHARMACEUTICALS HOLDING AB; Int'l, pg. 6161
QUIBIDS, LLC; U.S. Private, pg. 3326
QUICE FOOD INDUSTRIES LIMITED; Int'l, pg. 6161
QUICK AMERICA CORPORATION—See Nikkei Inc.; Int'l, pg. 5290
QUICKASH MALAYSIA SDN. BHD.—See ManagePay Systems Berhad; Int'l, pg. 4667
QUICK BOX, LLC; U.S. Private, pg. 3326
QUICK BRIDGE FUNDING, LLC—See National Funding Inc.; U.S. Private, pg. 2855
QUICK CABLE CANADA LIMITED—See Tonka Bay Equity Partners LLC; U.S. Private, pg. 4185
QUICK CABLE CORPORATION—See Tonka Bay Equity Partners LLC; U.S. Private, pg. 4185
QUICK CHANGE INC.—See Floco Unlimited Inc.; U.S. Private, pg. 1546
QUICK CHECK LIMITED—See Beijing Shiji Information Technology Co., Ltd.; Int'l, pg. 956
QUICK CHEK CORPORATION—See Murphy USA Inc.; U.S. Public, pg. 1487
QUICK CHEK FOOD STORES INC.; U.S. Private, pg. 3326
QUICK CO., LTD.; Int'l, pg. 6161
QUICK CONNECTORS, INC.—See Intervale Capital, LLC; U.S. Private, pg. 2127
QUICK CORP.—See Nikkei Inc.; Int'l, pg. 5290
QUICK COURIER SERVICES, INC.—See Dropoff, Inc.; U.S. Private, pg. 1279
QUICK DELIVERY SERVICE, INC.—See Peoples Services Inc.; U.S. Private, pg. 3142
QUICKEN LOANS, INC.—See RockBridge Growth Equity, LLC; U.S. Private, pg. 3465
QUICKFEE GROUP LLC—See QuickFee Limited; Int'l, pg. 6162
QUICKFEE LIMITED; Int'l, pg. 6162

COMPANY NAME INDEX

QUICK FLASH OIL CO.—See Pugh Oil Company; *U.S. Private*, pg. 3303
QUICK FUEL FLEET SERVICES, LLC—See Jacobus Energy, Inc.; *U.S. Private*, pg. 2180
QUICKGEM OPTOELECTRONIC MATERIAL SCIENCE & TECHNOLOGY CO., LTD.—See Tianjin Futong Xinmao Science & Technology Co., Ltd.; *Int'l*, pg. 7739
QUICK HEAL JAPAN KK.—See Quick Heal Technologies (P) Ltd.; *Int'l*, pg. 6162
QUICK HEAL TECHNOLOGIES AFRICA LTD.—See Quick Heal Technologies (P) Ltd.; *Int'l*, pg. 6162
QUICK HEAL TECHNOLOGIES AMERICA INC—See Quick Heal Technologies (P) Ltd.; *Int'l*, pg. 6162
QUICK HEAL TECHNOLOGIES (MENA) FZE—See Quick Heal Technologies (P) Ltd.; *Int'l*, pg. 6162
QUICK HEAL TECHNOLOGIES (P) LTD.; *Int'l*, pg. 6162
QUICKIE DE MEXICO, S. DE R.L. DE C.V.—See Newell Brands Inc.; *U.S. Public*, pg. 1514
QUICKIE MANUFACTURING CORPORATION—See Newell Brands Inc.; *U.S. Public*, pg. 1514
QUICK INTELLIGENT EQUIPMENT CO., LTD.; *Int'l*, pg. 6162
QUICK INTERNATIONAL COURIER UK LIMITED—See Q International Courier, LLC; *U.S. Private*, pg. 3311
QUICKLINE COMMUNICATIONS LIMITED—See Bigblu Broadband Group PLC; *Int'l*, pg. 1022
QUICKLIZARD LTD.; *Int'l*, pg. 6162
QUICKLOGIC CORPORATION; *U.S. Public*, pg. 1756
QUICKLOGIC INTERNATIONAL INC.—See QuickLogic Corporation; *U.S. Public*, pg. 1756
QUICKLOGIC SOFTWARE (INDIA) PRIVATE LTD.—See QuickLogic Corporation; *U.S. Public*, pg. 1756
QUICK-MED TECHNOLOGIES, INC.; *U.S. Public*, pg. 1756
QUICKMILL INC.—See Batliboi Ltd.; *Int'l*, pg. 890
QUICKOFFICE, INC.—See Alphabet Inc.; *U.S. Public*, pg. 84
QUICKPARTS.COM, INC.—See Trilantic Capital Management L.P.; *U.S. Private*, pg. 4231
QUICKPIVOT CORPORATION—See MacAndrews & Forbes Incorporated; *U.S. Private*, pg. 2532
QUICKPLAY MEDIA INC.—See Highview Capital, LLC; *U.S. Private*, pg. 1942
QUICK POINT INCORPORATED; *U.S. Private*, pg. 3326
QUICK QUALITY RESTAURANT INC.; *U.S. Private*, pg. 3326
QUICK RELEASE AUTOMOTIVE LTD.—See Alten S.A.; *Int'l*, pg. 390
QUICK RESTAURANTS S.A.; *Int'l*, pg. 6162
QUICK SERVICE RESTAURANT HOLDINGS PTY LTD.—See PAG Asia Capital Ltd.; *Int'l*, pg. 5697
QUICK SERVICE TEXTILE GUATEMALA S.R.L—See QST Industries, Inc.; *U.S. Private*, pg. 3314
QUICK SERVICE TEXTILE MAROC—See QST Industries, Inc.; *U.S. Private*, pg. 3314
QUICK SIGN LLC—See Al Shafar Group; *Int'l*, pg. 282
QUICKSILVER EXPRESS COURIER INC.; *U.S. Private*, pg. 3326
QUICKSILVER EXPRESS COURIER OF COLORADO, INC.—See Quicksilver Express Courier Inc.; *U.S. Private*, pg. 3326
QUICKSILVER EXPRESS COURIER OF MINNESOTA INC.—See Quicksilver Express Courier Inc.; *U.S. Private*, pg. 3327
QUICKSILVER EXPRESS COURIER OF MISSOURI INC.—See Quicksilver Express Courier Inc.; *U.S. Private*, pg. 3327
QUICKSILVER EXPRESS COURIER OF WISCONSIN, INC.—See Quicksilver Express Courier Inc.; *U.S. Private*, pg. 3327
QUICKSILVER TRANSLATE; *Int'l*, pg. 6162
QUICK SOLUTIONS INC.; *U.S. Private*, pg. 3326
QUICKSTART INTELLIGENCE, CORP.—See 360training.com, Inc.; *U.S. Private*, pg. 8
QUICKSTEP HOLDINGS LIMITED; *Int'l*, pg. 6162
QUICKSTEP TECHNOLOGIES PTY. LTD.—See QUICKSTEP HOLDINGS LIMITED; *Int'l*, pg. 6162
QUICK TANKS INC.; *U.S. Private*, pg. 3326
QUICK-TECH MACHINERY CO., LTD.—See Tong-Tai Machine Tool Co., Ltd.; *Int'l*, pg. 7806
QUICK TEST/HEAKIN—See MVL Group, Inc.; *U.S. Private*, pg. 2821
QUICKTOUCH TECHNOLOGIES LIMITED; *Int'l*, pg. 6162
QUICK USA, INC.—See QUICK CO., LTD.; *Int'l*, pg. 6161
QUICK VIETNAM CO., LTD.—See QUICK CO., LTD.; *Int'l*, pg. 6162
QUICKWAY CARRIERS INC.—See Quickway Distribution Services LLC; *U.S. Private*, pg. 3327
QUICKWAY DISTRIBUTION SERVICES LLC; *U.S. Private*, pg. 3327
QUICKWAY EXPRESS INC.; *U.S. Private*, pg. 3327
QUICKWORK DIV.—See Beatty Machine & Mfg. Company; *U.S. Private*, pg. 507
QUIDEL CORPORATION - SANTA CLARA—See QuidelOrtho Corporation; *U.S. Public*, pg. 1757
QUIDEL CORPORATION—See QuidelOrtho Corporation; *U.S. Public*, pg. 1757
QUIDEL IRELAND LIMITED—See QuidelOrtho Corporation; *U.S. Public*, pg. 1757

QUIDELORTHO CORPORATION; *U.S. Public*, pg. 1756
QUID PRO QUO ALQUILER SEGURO SOCIMI SA—See Ktesios Real Estate SOCIMI, S.A.; *Int'l*, pg. 4316
QUIET ANGEL FOUNDATION; *U.S. Private*, pg. 3327
QUIETKAT, INC.—See Vista Outdoor Inc.; *U.S. Public*, pg. 2305
QUIET LIGHT COMMUNICATIONS INC.; *U.S. Private*, pg. 3327
QUIETUDE PROMOTION; *Int'l*, pg. 6162
QUIETUS MANAGEMENT LIMITED—See Live Nation Entertainment, Inc.; *U.S. Public*, pg. 1330
QUIEVRAIN RETAIL ASSOCIATE NV—See Carrefour SA; *Int'l*, pg. 1344
QUIGLEY COMPANY, INC.—See Pfizer Inc.; *U.S. Public*, pg. 1683
QUIGLEY CONTRACTING—See Petrowest Corp.; *U.S. Private*, pg. 5833
QUIGLEY MANUFACTURING INC.; *U.S. Private*, pg. 3327
QUI! GROUP S.P.A.; *Int'l*, pg. 6161
QUIJUL PTE. LTD.—See Platinum Equity, LLC; *U.S. Private*, pg. 3206
QUIKEY MANUFACTURING CO. INC.; *U.S. Private*, pg. 3327
QUIK-MART STORES INC.; *U.S. Private*, pg. 3327
QUIKORDER, LLC—See Yum! Brands, Inc.; *U.S. Public*, pg. 2400
QUIK PIX, INC.—See Dalrada Financial Corporation; *U.S. Public*, pg. 621
QUIK PRINT; *U.S. Private*, pg. 3327
THE QUIKRETE COMPANIES, LLC; *U.S. Private*, pg. 4101
QUIKRETE HOLDINGS, INC.—See The Quikrete Companies, LLC; *U.S. Private*, pg. 4101
QUIKRETE OF VIRGINIA—See The Quikrete Companies, LLC; *U.S. Private*, pg. 4101
QUIKRETE—See The Quikrete Companies, LLC; *U.S. Private*, pg. 4101
QUIKR INDIA PVT LTD.; *Int'l*, pg. 6162
QUIK-RUN COURIER LTD; *Int'l*, pg. 6162
QUIKSERV CORP.—See River Associates Investments, LLC; *U.S. Private*, pg. 3443
QUIKSILVER ASIA SOURCING LTD.—See Leonard Green & Partners, L.P.; *U.S. Public*, pg. 2424
QUIKSILVER AUSTRALIA PTY LTD.—See Leonard Green & Partners, L.P.; *U.S. Public*, pg. 2424
QUIKSILVER EUROPE—See Leonard Green & Partners, L.P.; *U.S. Public*, pg. 2424
QUIKSILVER EYEWEAR, USA—See Leonard Green & Partners, L.P.; *U.S. Public*, pg. 2424
QUIKSOL INTERNATIONAL HK PTE LIMITED—See Smart-Core Holdings Limited; *Int'l*, pg. 7001
QUIK STOP MARKETS, INC.—See TDR Capital LLP; *Int'l*, pg. 7494
QUIK STOP QUIK WASH; *U.S. Private*, pg. 3327
QUIK THRIFT FOOD STORES, INC.; *U.S. Private*, pg. 3327
QUIKTRAK INC.—See Bureau Veritas S.A.; *Int'l*, pg. 1222
QUIKTRIP CORPORATION; *U.S. Private*, pg. 3327
QUIK TRIP DISTRIBUTION—See QuikTrip Corporation; *U.S. Private*, pg. 3327
QUIKTRIP WEST, INC.—See QuikTrip Corporation; *U.S. Private*, pg. 3327
QUIKTRON, INC. - EAST PRODUCTION FACILITY—See Legrand S.A.; *Int'l*, pg. 4445
QUIKTRON, INC.—See Legrand S.A.; *Int'l*, pg. 4445
QUIK-WAY FOODS OF DALLAS INC.; *U.S. Private*, pg. 3327
QUILICURA S.A.; *Int'l*, pg. 6162
QUILIGOTTI CONTRACTS LTD.—See Pilkington's Tiles Group Plc; *Int'l*, pg. 5866
QUILIGOTTI TERRAZZO LTD.—See Pilkington's Tiles Group Plc; *Int'l*, pg. 5866
QUILL/AWA ENTERPRISES; *U.S. Private*, pg. 3327
QUILLEN BROTHERS, INC.—See Leaf Home, LLC; *U.S. Private*, pg. 2407
QUILLEN REHABILITATION HOSPITAL OF JOHNSON CITY, LLC—See Encompass Health Corporation; *U.S. Public*, pg. 758
QUILLER & BLAKE; *Int'l*, pg. 6162
QUILLER & BLAKE—See Quiller & Blake; *Int'l*, pg. 6162
QUILLE SA—See Bouygues S.A.; *Int'l*, pg. 1123
QUILLIN'S INC.; *U.S. Private*, pg. 3327
QUILL LINCOLNSHIRE, INC.—See Sycamore Partners Management, LP; *U.S. Private*, pg. 3897
QUILL LINCOLNSHIRE, INC.—See Sycamore Partners Management, LP; *U.S. Private*, pg. 3897
QUILL LLC—See Sycamore Partners Management, LP; *U.S. Private*, pg. 3897
QUILL LLC—See Sycamore Partners Management, LP; *U.S. Private*, pg. 3897
QUILL LLC—See Sycamore Partners Management, LP; *U.S. Private*, pg. 3897
QUILL LLC—See Sycamore Partners Management, LP; *U.S. Private*, pg. 3897
QUILL & QUIRE—See St. Joseph Communications Inc.; *Int'l*, pg. 7159
QUILTER CHEVIOT EUROPE LIMITED—See Quilter plc; *Int'l*, pg. 6163

QUILTER CHEVIOT LIMITED—See OM Residual UK Limited; *Int'l*, pg. 5559
QUILTER INTERNATIONAL ISLE OF MAN LIMITED—See Quilter plc; *Int'l*, pg. 6163
QUILTER INTERNATIONAL MIDDLE EAST LIMITED—See Quilter plc; *Int'l*, pg. 6163
QUILTER INTERNATIONAL TRUST COMPANY LIMITED—See Quilter plc; *Int'l*, pg. 6163
QUILTER INVESTORS LIMITED—See Quilter plc; *Int'l*, pg. 6163
QUILTER PLC; *Int'l*, pg. 6162
QUILTER PRIVATE CLIENT ADVISERS LIMITED—See Quilter plc; *Int'l*, pg. 6163
QUILVEST BANQUE PRIVEE S.A.—See Quilvest S.A.; *Int'l*, pg. 6163
QUILVEST DUBAI LTD.—See Quilvest S.A.; *Int'l*, pg. 6163
QUILVEST FRANCE S.A.S.—See Quilvest S.A.; *Int'l*, pg. 6163
QUILVEST HONG KONG LTD.—See Quilvest S.A.; *Int'l*, pg. 6163
QUILVEST S.A.; *Int'l*, pg. 6163
QUILVEST (SWITZERLAND) LTD.—See Quilvest S.A.; *Int'l*, pg. 6163
QUILVEST UK LTD.—See Quilvest S.A.; *Int'l*, pg. 6163
QUILVEST USA, INC.—See Quilvest S.A.; *Int'l*, pg. 6163
QUIMBAYA GOLD INC.; *Int'l*, pg. 6163
QUIMICA DEL REY S.A. DE C.V.—See Grupo BAL; *Int'l*, pg. 3121
QUIMICA EMPRESARIAL DE MEXICO, SA DE CV—See Cydsa S.A.B. de C.V.; *Int'l*, pg. 1895
QUIMICA FARMACEUTICA BAYER, S.A.—See Bayer Aktiengesellschaft; *Int'l*, pg. 905
QUIMICA HERCULES, S.A. DE C.V.—See Ashland Inc.; *U.S. Public*, pg. 212
QUIMICA INDUSTRIAL MEDITERRANEO, S.L.—See Illinois Tool Works Inc.; *U.S. Public*, pg. 1110
QUIMICA PUBLICIDAD—See Vivendi SE; *Int'l*, pg. 8269
QUIMICA REAL LTDA.—See Phibro Animal Health Corporation; *U.S. Public*, pg. 1685
QUIMICAS STOLLER DE CENTROAMERICA, S.A.—See Corteva, Inc.; *U.S. Public*, pg. 584
QUIMICAS UNIDAS S.A.—See Bayer Aktiengesellschaft; *Int'l*, pg. 910
QUIMICA Y FARMACIA S.A. DE C.V.—See Perrigo Company plc; *Int'l*, pg. 5813
QUIMICER POLSKA SP. Z O.O.—See American Securities LLC; *U.S. Private*, pg. 252
QUIMICER PORTUGAL S.A.—See American Securities LLC; *U.S. Private*, pg. 252
QUIMICER, S.A.—See American Securities LLC; *U.S. Private*, pg. 252
QUIMICOS HOLANDA COSTA RICA S.A.—See BRENNTAG SE; *Int'l*, pg. 1149
QUIMIGEST - SOC. QUIMICA DE PRESTACAO DE SERVICOS, S.A.—See Jose de Mello, SGPS, S.A.; *Int'l*, pg. 4001
QUIMIKAO S.A. DE C.V.—See Kao Corporation; *Int'l*, pg. 4075
QUIMILOG TRANSPORTES E LOGISTICA LTDA.—See BRENNTAG SE; *Int'l*, pg. 1149
QUIMIPEDRA - SECIL BRITAS, CALCARIOS E DERIADOS, LDA.—See SODIM, SGPS, SA; *Int'l*, pg. 7049
QUIMIPRODUCTOS, S. DE R.L. DE C.V.—See Ecolab Inc.; *U.S. Public*, pg. 716
QUIMOBASICOS, S.A. DE C.V.—See Cydsa S.A.B. de C.V.; *Int'l*, pg. 1895
QUIMPAC S.A.; *Int'l*, pg. 6163
QUINARY S.P.A.; *Int'l*, pg. 6163
QUINCAILLERIE LORRAINE—See Compagnie de Saint-Gobain SA; *Int'l*, pg. 1725
QUINCAILLERIE TERRASSIER; *Int'l*, pg. 6163
QUINCANNON ASSOCIATES, INC.; *U.S. Private*, pg. 3327
QUINCE CAPITAL (PTY) LIMITED—See Reunert Limited; *Int'l*, pg. 6312
QUINCE HOLDINGS, LLC—See Apollo Global Management, Inc.; *U.S. Public*, pg. 157
QUINCE THERAPEUTICS, INC.; *U.S. Public*, pg. 1757
QUINCY BIOSCIENCE; *U.S. Private*, pg. 3327
QUINCY COMMUNITY ACTION PROGRAMS, INC.; *U.S. Private*, pg. 3327
QUINCY COMPRESSOR INC.—See Atlas Copco AB; *Int'l*, pg. 680
QUINCY MEDIA, INC.—See Gray Television, Inc.; *U.S. Public*, pg. 961
QUINCY MUTUAL FIRE INSURANCE COMPANY; *U.S. Private*, pg. 3327
QUINCY PEPSI-COLA BOTTLING CO.; *U.S. Private*, pg. 3328
QUINCY SYMPHONY ORCHESTRA ASSOCIATION; *U.S. Private*, pg. 3328
QUINDELL BUSINESS PROCESS SERVICES LIMITED—See Watchstone Group plc; *Int'l*, pg. 8356
QUINDELL ENTERPRISE TECHNOLOGY SOLUTIONS LIMITED—See Watchstone Group plc; *Int'l*, pg. 8356
QUINDELL LIMITED—See Watchstone Group plc; *Int'l*, pg. 8356
QUINENCO S.A.; *Int'l*, pg. 6163

QUINLAN MARKETING COMMUNICATIONS

QUINLAN MARKETING COMMUNICATIONS; *U.S. Private*, pg. 3328
QUINLAN MOTORS, INC.—See AutoNation, Inc.; *U.S. Public*, pg. 237
QUINN APPAREL INC.; *U.S. Private*, pg. 3328
QUINN/BREIN PUBLIC RELATIONS; *U.S. Private*, pg. 3328
QUINN COMPANY INC.; *U.S. Private*, pg. 3328
QUINN CO.; *U.S. Private*, pg. 3328
QUINN EMANUEL URQUHART & SULLIVAN, LLP.; *U.S. Private*, pg. 3328
QUINN EVANS ARCHITECTS INC.; *U.S. Private*, pg. 3328
QUINN FABLE ADVERTISING; *U.S. Private*, pg. 3328
QUINN FUNERAL SERVICES PTY LTD—See Propel Funeral Partners Limited; *Int'l*, pg. 5997
QUINN MEDICAL, INC.—See Thuasne SA; *Int'l*, pg. 7721
QUINNOVA PHARMACEUTICALS, INC.—See Insud Pharma, S.L.; *Int'l*, pg. 3725
QUINNOX, INC.; *U.S. Private*, pg. 3328
QUINN PUMPS (CALIFORNIA) INC.—See KPS Capital Partners, LP; *U.S. Private*, pg. 2348
QUINN PUMPS CANADA LTD.—See KPS Capital Partners, LP; *U.S. Private*, pg. 2348
QUINN PUMPS INC.—See KPS Capital Partners, LP; *U.S. Private*, pg. 2348
QUINN RADIATORS LIMITED; *Int'l*, pg. 6164
QUINN RADIATORS NV—See Quinn Radiators Limited; *Int'l*, pg. 6164
QUINN USED PARTS INC—See Quinn Company Inc.; *U.S. Private*, pg. 3328
QUINSAM CAPITAL CORPORATION; *Int'l*, pg. 6164
QUINSERVIZI S.P.A.—See Gruppo MutuiOnline S.p.A; *Int'l*, pg. 3141
QUINSO B.V.—See Orbis SE; *Int'l*, pg. 5614
QUINSTREET EUROPE LTD.—See QuinStreet, Inc.; *U.S. Public*, pg. 1757
QUINSTREET, INC.; *U.S. Public*, pg. 1757
QUINSTREET INSURANCE AGENCY, INC.—See QuinStreet, Inc.; *U.S. Public*, pg. 1757
QUINTA DA PEDRA - SOCIEDADE VINICOLA DE MONCAO LDA.—See Unicer - Bebidas de Portugal, SGPS, SA; *Int'l*, pg. 8032
QUINTA DE CRAVEL, S.A.—See Teixeira Duarte SA; *Int'l*, pg. 7525
QUINTAIN LIMITED—See Lone Star Global Acquisitions, LLC; *U.S. Private*, pg. 2489
QUINTAIN STEEL CO., LTD. - KUAN-TIEN PLANT—See Quintain Steel Co., Ltd.; *Int'l*, pg. 6164
QUINTAIN STEEL CO., LTD. - MA-TOU PLANT—See Quintain Steel Co., Ltd.; *Int'l*, pg. 6164
QUINTAIN STEEL CO., LTD.; *Int'l*, pg. 6164
QUINTAIN STEEL CO., LTD. - YUNG-KUNG PLANT—See Quintain Steel Co., Ltd.; *Int'l*, pg. 6164
QUINTANA ASSOCIATES, INC.—See Thomas Scientific, LLC; *U.S. Private*, pg. 4157
QUINTANA CAPITAL GROUP, L.P.; *U.S. Private*, pg. 3328
QUINTANA ROO BICYCLES INC.—See The American Bicycle Group LLC; *U.S. Private*, pg. 3985
QUINTANA ROO WETSUITS INC.—See The American Bicycle Group LLC; *U.S. Private*, pg. 3986
QUINTANA SHIPPING LTD.; *Int'l*, pg. 6164
QUINTANO FOODS LIMITED—See Simonds Farsons Cisk plc; *Int'l*, pg. 6932
QUINTA SYSTEMS PVT. LTD.—See Posiflex Technology Inc.; *Int'l*, pg. 5938
QUINT DIGITAL MEDIA LIMITED; *Int'l*, pg. 6164
QUINTECH ELECTRONICS & COMMUNICATIONS, INC.—See Evertz Microsystems Limited; *Int'l*, pg. 2569
QUINTEGRA SOLUTIONS GMBH—See Quintegra Solutions Ltd.; *Int'l*, pg. 6165
QUINTEGRA SOLUTIONS LTD.; *Int'l*, pg. 6165
QUINTEL TECHNOLOGY LTD.—See Cirtek Holdings Philippines Corp.; *Int'l*, pg. 1618
QUINTESSENCE EDITIONS LTD—See The Quarto Group, Inc.; *Int'l*, pg. 7677
QUINTESSENTIALLY (UK) LTD; *Int'l*, pg. 6165
QUINTET PUBLISHING LTD—See The Quarto Group, Inc.; *Int'l*, pg. 7677
QUINTEVENTS LLC—See Liberty Media Corporation; *U.S. Public*, pg. 1311
QUINT GROUP LTD; *Int'l*, pg. 6164
QUINTICA GROUP FZ LLC—See Watchstone Group plc; *Int'l*, pg. 8356
QUINTICA SA (PTY) LIMITED—See Watchstone Group plc; *Int'l*, pg. 8356
QUINTILES B.V.—See IQVIA Holdings Inc.; *U.S. Public*, pg. 1170
QUINTILES ENTERPRISE MANAGEMENT (SHANGHAI) CO. LTD.—See IQVIA Holdings Inc.; *U.S. Public*, pg. 1170
QUINTILES HONG KONG LIMITED—See IQVIA Holdings Inc.; *U.S. Public*, pg. 1170
QUINTILES IMS INC. - PARSIPPANY—See IQVIA Holdings Inc.; *U.S. Public*, pg. 1169
QUINTILES ISRAEL LTD.—See IQVIA Holdings Inc.; *U.S. Public*, pg. 1170
QUINTILES LITHUANIA—See IQVIA Holdings Inc.; *U.S. Public*, pg. 1170
QUINTILES RUSSIA LLC—See IQVIA Holdings Inc.; *U.S. Public*, pg. 1170
QUINTILES TRANSNATIONAL CORP.—See IQVIA Holdings Inc.; *U.S. Public*, pg. 1170
QUINTILLION LIMITED—See U.S. Bancorp; *U.S. Public*, pg. 2212
QUINTILLION SERVICES LIMITED—See U.S. Bancorp; *U.S. Public*, pg. 2212
QUINTIS LIMITED; *Int'l*, pg. 6165
QUINTON & KAINES (HOLDINGS) LTD.—See Tex Holdings Plc; *Int'l*, pg. 7582
QUINTO REAL CAPITAL CORPORATION; *Int'l*, pg. 6165
QUINTRON SYSTEMS, INC.—See Godspeed Capital Management LP; *U.S. Private*, pg. 1725
QUINTUS TECHNOLOGIES AB—See John Bean Technologies Corporation; *U.S. Public*, pg. 1191
QUINTUS TECHNOLOGIES CO., LTD.—See Kobe Steel, Ltd.; *Int'l*, pg. 4220
QUINT Z IMMOBILIEN LEASING GESELLSCHAFT M.B.H.—See UniCredit S.p.A.; *Int'l*, pg. 8037
QUINVIR INVESTMENT INC.; *Int'l*, pg. 6165
QUIN WORKFORCE LIMITED—See AWF Madison Group Limited; *Int'l*, pg. 753
QUINYX AB; *Int'l*, pg. 6165
QUINZEL ACQUISITION COMPANY; *U.S. Private*, pg. 3328
QUIPT HOME MEDICAL CORP.; *U.S. Public*, pg. 1757
QUIPU GMBH—See ProCredit Holding AG & Co. KGaA; *Int'l*, pg. 5987
QUIRCH FOODS, LLC—See Palladium Equity Partners, LLC; *U.S. Private*, pg. 3078
QUIRINDI FEEDLOT SERVICES PTY. LTD.—See Apiam Animal Health Limited; *Int'l*, pg. 515
QUIRINDI VETERINARY CLINIC PTY. LTD.—See Apiam Animal Health Limited; *Int'l*, pg. 515
QUIRIN PRIVATBANK AG; *Int'l*, pg. 6165
QUIRK AUTO PARK; *U.S. Private*, pg. 3328
QUIRK CHEVROLET PORTLAND; *U.S. Private*, pg. 3328
QUIRKS AUSTRALIA PTY LTD—See COCA-COLA EUROPACIFIC PARTNERS PLC; *Int'l*, pg. 1684
QUIRKY INC.; *U.S. Private*, pg. 3329
QUIROGA LAW OFFICE, PLLC; *U.S. Private*, pg. 3329
QUIRUMED, S.L.U.—See Bunzl plc; *Int'l*, pg. 1219
QUISITIVE TECHNOLOGY SOLUTIONS, INC.; *U.S. Private*, pg. 3329
QUISITIVE TECHNOLOGY SOLUTIONS, INC.; *Int'l*, pg. 6165
QUISMA GMBH—See WPP plc; *Int'l*, pg. 8466
QUISS QUALITATS-LNSPEKTIONSSYSTEMEUND SERVICE AG—See Atlas Copco AB; *Int'l*, pg. 684
QUIVIRA INTERNAL MEDICINE, INC.—See HCA Healthcare, Inc.; *U.S. Public*, pg. 1007
QUIVIRA INTERNAL MEDICINE, INC.—See HCA Healthcare, Inc.; *U.S. Public*, pg. 1006
QUIXANT DEUTSCHLAND GMBH—See Quixant PLC; *Int'l*, pg. 6165
QUIXANT ITALIA SRL—See Quixant PLC; *Int'l*, pg. 6165
QUIXANT PLC; *Int'l*, pg. 6165
QUIXANT USA INC—See Quixant PLC; *Int'l*, pg. 6165
QUIXOTE ENTERPRISE INC.; *U.S. Private*, pg. 3329
QUIXOTE RESEARCH, MARKETING & PUBLIC RELATIONS; *U.S. Private*, pg. 3329
QUIXOTE STUDIOS, LLC—See Hudson Pacific Properties, Inc.; *U.S. Public*, pg. 1068
QUIZAM ENTERTAINMENT LLC—See Quizam Media Corporation; *Int'l*, pg. 6165
QUIZAM MEDIA CORPORATION; *Int'l*, pg. 6165
THE QUIZNO'S OPERATING COMPANY LLC—See QCE Finance LLC; *U.S. Private*, pg. 3312
QUIZ PLC; *Int'l*, pg. 6165
QUIZZ SPORTSWEAR INC.; *U.S. Private*, pg. 3329
QUJING GAS GROUP CO., LTD.—See Zhongyu Energy Holdings Limited; *Int'l*, pg. 8676
QUMAK S.A.; *Int'l*, pg. 6166
QUMEI HOME FURNISHINGS GROUP CO., LTD.; *Int'l*, pg. 6166
QUMU CORPORATION—See Enghouse Systems Limited; *Int'l*, pg. 2427
QUMU, INC.—See Enghouse Systems Limited; *Int'l*, pg. 2427
QUMU JAPAN CO., LTD.—See Enghouse Systems Limited; *Int'l*, pg. 2427
QUMU LTD.—See Enghouse Systems Limited; *Int'l*, pg. 2427
QUMU (SINGAPORE) PTE. LTD—See Enghouse Systems Limited; *Int'l*, pg. 2427
QUNAR CAYMAN ISLANDS LIMITED—See Baidu, Inc.; *Int'l*, pg. 801
QUNAR CAYMAN ISLANDS LIMITED—See Trip.com Group Ltd.; *Int'l*, pg. 7926
QUNDIS GMBH—See KALORIMETA GmbH; *Int'l*, pg. 4058
QUNIE CORPORATION—See Nippon Telegraph & Telephone Corporation; *Int'l*, pg. 5348
QUNXING PAPER HOLDINGS COMPANY LIMITED; *Int'l*, pg. 6166
QUO CARD CO., LTD.—See T-Gaia Corp.; *Int'l*, pg. 7396
QUOC CUONG GIA LAI JOINT STOCK COMPANY; *Int'l*, pg. 6166

CORPORATE AFFILIATIONS

QUODD FINANCIAL INFORMATION SERVICES, INC—See NewSpring Capital LLC; *U.S. Private*, pg. 2917
QUOIN INC.; *U.S. Private*, pg. 3329
QUOIZEL INC.—See Sycamore Partners Management, LP; *U.S. Private*, pg. 3896
QUONIAM ASSET MANAGEMENT GMBH—See Union Asset Management Holding AG; *Int'l*, pg. 8051
QUONIA SOCIMI SA; *Int'l*, pg. 6166
QUOPRRO GLOBAL SERVICES PVT. LTD.—See Cox & Kings Limited; *Int'l*, pg. 1823
QUORUM ARCHITECTS, INC.; *U.S. Private*, pg. 3329
QUORUM BUSINESS SOLUTIONS, INC. - DALLAS—See Thoma Bravo, L.P.; *U.S. Private*, pg. 4152
QUORUM BUSINESS SOLUTIONS, INC.—See Thoma Bravo, L.P.; *U.S. Private*, pg. 4152
QUORUM HEALTH CORPORATION; *U.S. Private*, pg. 3329
QUORUM HEALTH RESOURCES, LLC—See Grant Avenue Capital, LLC; *U.S. Private*, pg. 1756
QUORUM HOTELS & RESORTS, LTD.—See Somera Capital Management, LLC; *U.S. Private*, pg. 3711
QUORUM INFORMATION SYSTEMS—See Quorum Information Technologies Inc.; *Int'l*, pg. 6166
QUORUM INFORMATION TECHNOLOGIES INC.; *Int'l*, pg. 6166
QUORUM INTEGRATED, INC.; *U.S. Private*, pg. 3331
QUORUM NAZCA SAATCHI & SAATCHI—See Publicis Groupe S.A.; *Int'l*, pg. 6108
QUORUM SERVICES, INC.—See The Ensign Group, Inc.; *U.S. Public*, pg. 2072
QUORUM SOLUTIONS, LLC—See Quorum Health Corporation; *U.S. Private*, pg. 3330
QUOTABLE VALUE LIMITED; *Int'l*, pg. 6166
QUOTE COMPONENTS B.V.—See TD Synnex Corp; *U.S. Public*, pg. 1986
QUOTE.COM—See Osceola Capital Management, LLC; *U.S. Public*, pg. 3047
QUOTEMEDIA, INC.; *U.S. Public*, pg. 1757
QUOTEWIZARD.COM LLC—See LendingTree, Inc.; *U.S. Public*, pg. 1305
QUOTIENT INC.—See Jacmel Growth Partners Management LLC; *U.S. Private*, pg. 2179
QUOTIENT LIMITED; *Int'l*, pg. 6166
QUOTIENT TECHNOLOGY INC.—See Charlesbank Capital Partners, LLC; *U.S. Private*, pg. 855
QUOTIT CORPORATION—See The Allstate Corporation; *U.S. Public*, pg. 2034
QUOTIUM CORPORATION—See Quotium Technologies S.A; *Int'l*, pg. 6166
QUOTIUM TECHNOLOGIES LTD—See Quotium Technologies S.A.; *Int'l*, pg. 6166
QUOTIUM TECHNOLOGIES S.A; *Int'l*, pg. 6166
QUOTZ PTE. LTD.—See Singapore Press Holdings Ltd.; *Int'l*, pg. 6942
QUPACO INC.; *U.S. Private*, pg. 3331
QURAIN PETROCHEMICAL INDUSTRIES COMPANY K.S.C.P.—See Kuwait Projects Company (Holding) K.S.C.P.; *Int'l*, pg. 4347
QURATE RETAIL GROUP, INC.—See Qurate Retail, Inc.; *U.S. Public*, pg. 1758
QURATE RETAIL, INC.; *U.S. Public*, pg. 1757
QURATIS INC.; *Int'l*, pg. 6166
QUREO, INC.—See Sprix Inc.; *Int'l*, pg. 7145
QURIENT CO., LTD.; *Int'l*, pg. 6167
QURI-MAYU DEVELOPMENTS LTD.; *Int'l*, pg. 6167
QURUM BUSINESS GROUP GEOJIT SECURITIES LLC—See Geojit Financial Services Limited; *Int'l*, pg. 2933
QUSQU INTELLIGENCE GMBH—See Axxiome AG; *Int'l*, pg. 773
QUTOUTIAO INC.; *Int'l*, pg. 6167
QUVA NV; *Int'l*, pg. 6167
QUY NHON PLANTATION FOREST COMPANY OF VIETNAM LTD.—See Oji Holdings Corporation; *Int'l*, pg. 5538
QUYN PAYROLL & HR SERVICES PROPRIETARY LIMITED—See Workforce Holdings Ltd.; *Int'l*, pg. 8455
QUZHOU HUAYOU COBALT NEW MATERIAL CO., LTD.—See Huayou Cobalt Co., Ltd.; *Int'l*, pg. 3516
QUZHOU JISHAN REAL ESTATE DEVELOPMENT CO., LTD.—See China Jishan Holdings Limited; *Int'l*, pg. 1513
QUZHOU SUNLORD ELECTRONICS CO., LTD.—See Shenzhen Sunlord Electronics Co., Ltd.; *Int'l*, pg. 6822
QUZHOU XIN'AN DEVELOPMENT CO., LTD; *Int'l*, pg. 6167
QVALENT PTY LIMITED—See Westpac Banking Corporation; *Int'l*, pg. 8391
QVALITAS ARSTIKESKUS AS—See Mehiläinen Oy; *Int'l*, pg. 4796
QVC CHESAPEAKE, INC.—See Qurate Retail, Inc.; *U.S. Public*, pg. 1758
QVC DELAWARE, INC.—See Qurate Retail, Inc.; *U.S. Public*, pg. 1758
QVC DEUTSCHLAND INC. & CO. KG—See Qurate Retail, Inc.; *U.S. Public*, pg. 1758
QVC ESERVICE LLC & CO. KG—See Qurate Retail, Inc.; *U.S. Public*, pg. 1758

COMPANY NAME INDEX

QVC GRUNDSTUCKSVERWALTUNGS GMBH—See Qurate Retail, Inc.; *U.S. Public*, pg. 1758
QVC HANDEL S.A R.L. & CO. KG—See Qurate Retail, Inc.; *U.S. Public*, pg. 1758
QVC, INC.—See Qurate Retail, Inc.; *U.S. Public*, pg. 1758
QV EQUITIES LIMITED; *Int'l*, pg. 6167
QVF ENGINEERING GMBH—See De Dietrich Process Systems S.A.; *Int'l*, pg. 1995
QVF PROCESS SYSTEMS LTD.—See De Dietrich Process Systems S.A.; *Int'l*, pg. 1995
QV (HOLDINGS) LTD.—See WISeKey International Holding Ltd; *Int'l*, pg. 8436
QVIDIAN CORP.—See Upland Software, Inc.; *U.S. Public*, pg. 2264
QVIDIAN—See Upland Software, Inc.; *U.S. Public*, pg. 2264
QVINE LLC—See Godspeed Capital Management LP; *U.S. Private*, pg. 1725
QVISION AS—See Tomra Systems ASA; *Int'l*, pg. 7802
QVS HOLDING INC.; *U.S. Private*, pg. 3331
QVT FINANCIAL, LP; *U.S. Private*, pg. 3331
QWAMPLIFY S.A; *Int'l*, pg. 6167
Q-WARE SYSTEMS & SERVICES CORP.—See Uni-President Enterprises Corporation; *Int'l*, pg. 8029
Q/W COIN SERVICES LTD.; *U.S. Private*, pg. 3312
QWEST AIR PARTS, INC.—See Leonard Green & Partners, L.P.; *U.S. Private*, pg. 2424
QWEST BROADBAND SERVICES, INC.—See Lumen Technologies, Inc.; *U.S. Public*, pg. 1347
QWEST COMMUNICATIONS INTERNATIONAL INC.—See Lumen Technologies, Inc.; *U.S. Public*, pg. 1347
QWEST CORPORATION—See Lumen Technologies, Inc.; *U.S. Public*, pg. 1347
QWEST SERVICES CORPORATION—See Lumen Technologies, Inc.; *U.S. Public*, pg. 1347
QWICK MEDIA INC.; *Int'l*, pg. 6167
QWI INVESTMENT LIMITED—See Jamaican Teas Ltd.; *Int'l*, pg. 3874
QWINIX TECHNOLOGIES, INC.; *U.S. Private*, pg. 3331
QWINT B.V.—See UGI Corporation; *U.S. Public*, pg. 2222
QWIP TECHNOLOGIES, INC.—See Cantronic Systems Inc.; *Int'l*, pg. 1300
QWIZDOM—See Boxlight Corporation; *U.S. Public*, pg. 377
QWK INTEGRATED SOLUTIONS, LLC—See Veritas Capital Fund Management, LLC; *U.S. Private*, pg. 4364
QX LTD.—See Aecon Group Inc.; *Int'l*, pg. 172
QX NETWORKING & DESIGN, INC.—See Trive Capital Inc.; *U.S. Private*, pg. 4239
QXO, INC.; *U.S. Public*, pg. 1758
QYH BIOTECH CO., LTD.—See China Animal Husbandry Industry Co., Ltd.; *Int'l*, pg. 1482
QYOU MEDIA, INC.; *Int'l*, pg. 6167
QZINA SPECIALTY FOODS, INC.—See The Chefs' Warehouse, Inc.; *U.S. Public*, pg. 2059

R

R12 KAPITAL FUND I AB; *Int'l*, pg. 6171
R1 AIRLINES LTD.—See Avmax Group Inc.; *Int'l*, pg. 748
R1 RCM HOLDCO INC.—See R1 RCM Inc.; *U.S. Public*, pg. 1758
R1 RCM INC.; *U.S. Public*, pg. 1758
R1SOFT—See BBS Technologies, Inc.; *U.S. Private*, pg. 498
R2C GROUP, INC.; *U.S. Private*, pg. 3340
R2C ONLINE LIMITED—See Corpay, Inc.; *U.S. Public*, pg. 580
R2D AUTOMATION SAS—See Amtech Systems, Inc.; *U.S. Public*, pg. 134
R2 DERMATOLOGY INCORPORATED—See INNOVATE Corp.; *U.S. Public*, pg. 1126
R2 INNOVATIVE TECHNOLOGIES INC; *U.S. Private*, pg. 3340
R2INTEGRATED—See Robert Half Inc.; *U.S. Public*, pg. 1803
R2 LOGISTICS, INC.; *U.S. Private*, pg. 3340
R2 QUALITY CASTINGS, LLC; *U.S. Private*, pg. 3340
R2 UNIFIED TECHNOLOGIES; *U.S. Private*, pg. 3340
R360 ENVIRONMENTAL SOLUTIONS, LLC—See Waste Connections, Inc.; *Int'l*, pg. 8354
R360 PERMIAN BASIN, LLC—See Waste Connections, Inc.; *Int'l*, pg. 8354
R3 AWM—See Bunzl plc; *Int'l*, pg. 1217
R3D GLOBAL LIMITED; *Int'l*, pg. 6171
R3EI SAS—See VINCI S.A.; *Int'l*, pg. 8225
R3 ENERGY MANAGEMENT AUDIT & REVIEW LLC—See David Energy Systems, Inc.; *U.S. Private*, pg. 1170
R3, LLC—See Bunzl plc; *Int'l*, pg. 1217
R3 METRO SOUTH TEC—See Bunzl plc; *Int'l*, pg. 1217
R3 SAFETY—See Bunzl plc; *Int'l*, pg. 1217
R3 STRATEGIC SUPPORT GROUP, INC.; *U.S. Private*, pg. 3340
R4 CAPITAL INC.—See Regis Group PLC; *Int'l*, pg. 6255
R4, LLC—See Thoma Bravo, L.P.; *U.S. Private*, pg. 4148
R7 REAL ESTATE INC.—See Avison Young (Canada) Inc.; *Int'l*, pg. 745
R82 A/S—See Nordstjernan AB; *Int'l*, pg. 5425

R8 CAPITAL INVESTMENTS PLC; *Int'l*, pg. 6171
RAABE BULGARIEN EOOD—See Ernst Klett AG; *Int'l*, pg. 2495
RAABE TANACSADO ES KIADO KFT.—See Ernst Klett AG; *Int'l*, pg. 2495
RAAB KARCHER BAUSTOFFE GMBH—See Compagnie de Saint-Gobain SA; *Int'l*, pg. 1733
RAAB KARCHER BOUWSTOFFEN B.V.—See Compagnie de Saint-Gobain SA; *Int'l*, pg. 1733
RAAB KARCHER BOUWSTOFFEN—See Compagnie de Saint-Gobain SA; *Int'l*, pg. 1733
RAAB KARCHER FRANCE S.A.—See Compagnie de Saint-Gobain SA; *Int'l*, pg. 1733
RAAB KARCHER HAMM—See Compagnie de Saint-Gobain SA; *Int'l*, pg. 1733
RAAB KARCHER NEDERLAND B.V.—See Compagnie de Saint-Gobain SA; *Int'l*, pg. 1733
RAAB KARCHER SANITAR HEIZUNG FLIESEN GMBH—See Compagnie de Saint-Gobain SA; *Int'l*, pg. 1733
RAADR, INC.; *U.S. Private*, pg. 3340
RAAEN ENTREPRENOR AS—See Peab AB; *Int'l*, pg. 5773
RAA INSURANCE LIMITED; *Int'l*, pg. 6171
RAAJ MEDISAFE INDIA LIMITED; *Int'l*, pg. 6171
RAAMCO INTERNATIONAL INCORPORATED; *U.S. Private*, pg. 3341
RAASI REFRACTORIES LTD.; *Int'l*, pg. 6171
RABA AUTOMOTIVE HOLDING PLC; *Int'l*, pg. 6171
RAB AGGREGATOR, LLC—See Gemspring Capital Management, LLC; *U.S. Private*, pg. 1659
R&A BAILEY & CO.—See Diageo plc; *Int'l*, pg. 2102
RABALAIS CONSTRUCTORS, LLC—See EMCOR Group, Inc.; *U.S. Public*, pg. 738
RABANCO COMPANIES—See Republic Services, Inc.; *U.S. Public*, pg. 1787
RABASKA INC.—See Enbridge Inc.; *Int'l*, pg. 2397
RABAUD; *Int'l*, pg. 6171
RABBIT CAR NETWORK CO., LTD.—See USS Co., Ltd.; *Int'l*, pg. 8099
RABBIT COPIERS, INC.—See Xerox Holdings Corporation; *U.S. Public*, pg. 2387
RABBIT DIGITAL GROUP CO., LTD.—See AOI TYO Holdings Inc.; *Int'l*, pg. 488
RABBIT EVEN EMPREENDIMENTOS IMOBILIARIOS LTDA.—See Even Construtora e Incorporadora S.A.; *Int'l*, pg. 2562
RABBIT INTERNET CO., LTD.—See BTS Group Holdings Public Company Limited; *Int'l*, pg. 1205
RABBIT PROTOTYPE CO., LTD.—See Applicad Public Company Limited; *Int'l*, pg. 521
RABBIT REWARDS CO., LTD.—See BTS Group Holdings Public Company Limited; *Int'l*, pg. 1206
RAB CAPITAL LIMITED; *Int'l*, pg. 6171
RABEN EESTI OU—See Raben Management Services Sp. z o.o.; *Int'l*, pg. 6171
RABENHORST FUNERAL HOME INC.; *U.S. Private*, pg. 3341
RABENHORST LIFE INSURANCE COMPANY—See Service Corporation International; *U.S. Public*, pg. 1870
RABEN LATVIA SIA—See Raben Management Services Sp. z o.o.; *Int'l*, pg. 6171
RABEN LIETUVA UAB—See Raben Management Services Sp. z o.o.; *Int'l*, pg. 6171
RABEN LOGISTICS CZECH S.R.O.—See Raben Management Services Sp. z o.o.; *Int'l*, pg. 6171
RABEN LOGISTICS POLSKA SP. Z O.O.—See Raben Management Services Sp. z o.o.; *Int'l*, pg. 6171
RABEN LOGISTICS SLOVAKIA S.R.O.—See Raben Management Services Sp. z o.o.; *Int'l*, pg. 6171
RABEN MANAGEMENT SERVICES SP. Z O.O.; *Int'l*, pg. 6171
RABEN NETHERLANDS B.V.—See Raben Management Services Sp. z o.o.; *Int'l*, pg. 6171
RABEN TIRE CO. INC.—See The Goodyear Tire & Rubber Company; *U.S. Public*, pg. 2084
RABEN TRANS EUROPEAN GERMANY GMBH—See Raben Management Services Sp. z o.o.; *Int'l*, pg. 6171
RABEN TRANSPORT SP. Z O.O.—See Raben Management Services Sp. z o.o.; *Int'l*, pg. 6171
RABEN UKRAINE—See Raben Management Services Sp. z o.o.; *Int'l*, pg. 6171
RABERN RENTALS, LP—See Manitex International, Inc.; *U.S. Public*, pg. 1356
RABER PACKING CO.; *U.S. Private*, pg. 3341
RAB FOUNDATION REPAIR LLC; *U.S. Private*, pg. 3341
R.A.B. HOLDINGS, INC.; *U.S. Private*, pg. 3334
RABIDEAU GRAIN & LUMBER, INC.; *U.S. Private*, pg. 3341
RABIGH PETROCHEMICAL LOGISTICS LLC—See The Sumitomo Warehouse Co. Ltd.; *Int'l*, pg. 7690
RABIGH REFINING AND PETROCHEMICAL COMPANY; *Int'l*, pg. 6171
RABINE PAVING AMERICA, LLC; *U.S. Private*, pg. 3341
RABIN WORLDWIDE, INC.; *U.S. Private*, pg. 3341
RABITEBANK OJSC; *Int'l*, pg. 6171
RABLOCK CO., LTD.—See Transcosmos Inc.; *Int'l*, pg. 7898

RACHEL ALLAN, LLC

RABO AGRIFINANCE, INC.—See Cooperatieve Centrale Raiffeisen-Boerenleenbank B.A.; *Int'l*, pg. 1791
RABO AGRIINSURANCE SERVICES, INC.—See Cooperatieve Centrale Raiffeisen-Boerenleenbank B.A.; *Int'l*, pg. 1791
RABO AUSTRALIA LIMITED—See Cooperatieve Centrale Raiffeisen-Boerenleenbank B.A.; *Int'l*, pg. 1792
RABOBANK AUSTRALIA LIMITED—See Cooperatieve Centrale Raiffeisen-Boerenleenbank B.A.; *Int'l*, pg. 1792
RABOBANK AUSTRALIA & NEW ZEALAND GROUP—See Cooperatieve Centrale Raiffeisen-Boerenleenbank B.A.; *Int'l*, pg. 1792
RABOBANK CHILE S.A.—See Cooperatieve Centrale Raiffeisen-Boerenleenbank B.A.; *Int'l*, pg. 1792
RABOBANK CURACAO NV—See Cooperatieve Centrale Raiffeisen-Boerenleenbank B.A.; *Int'l*, pg. 1792
RABOBANK FRANCE—See Cooperatieve Centrale Raiffeisen-Boerenleenbank B.A.; *Int'l*, pg. 1792
RABOBANK IRELAND PLC—See Cooperatieve Centrale Raiffeisen-Boerenleenbank B.A.; *Int'l*, pg. 1792
RABOBANK NEW ZEALAND LIMITED—See Cooperatieve Centrale Raiffeisen-Boerenleenbank B.A.; *Int'l*, pg. 1792
RABOBANK SINGAPORE—See Cooperatieve Centrale Raiffeisen-Boerenleenbank B.A.; *Int'l*, pg. 1792
RABO CAPITAL SERVICES, INC.—See Cooperatieve Centrale Raiffeisen-Boerenleenbank B.A.; *Int'l*, pg. 1791
RABO INDIA FINANCE PVT LTD—See Cooperatieve Centrale Raiffeisen-Boerenleenbank B.A.; *Int'l*, pg. 1791
RABO PRIVATE EQUITY—See Cooperatieve Centrale Raiffeisen-Boerenleenbank B.A.; *Int'l*, pg. 1792
RABOUD ENERGIE SA—See BKW AG; *Int'l*, pg. 1056
RABO VASTGOEDGROEP HOLDING N.V.—See Cooperatieve Centrale Raiffeisen-Boerenleenbank B.A.; *Int'l*, pg. 1791
R.A. BROWNRIGG INVESTMENTS, INC.—See Waste Connections, Inc.; *Int'l*, pg. 8353
RABUCK STRANGER; *U.S. Private*, pg. 3341
RABYA TRADING AND AGRICULTURE COMPANY LTD.—See The Al Fadl Group of Companies; *Int'l*, pg. 7613
RAC ACCEPTANCE EAST, LLC—See Upbound Group, Inc.; *U.S. Public*, pg. 2263
RACAL ACOUSTICS INC.—See INVISIO A/S; *Int'l*, pg. 3789
RACAL ACOUSTICS LTD.—See INVISIO A/S; *Int'l*, pg. 3789
RACCOON HOLDINGS, INC.; *Int'l*, pg. 6171
RACCOON RENT, INC.—See RACCOON HOLDINGS, Inc.; *Int'l*, pg. 6171
RACEBETS INTERNATIONAL GAMING LTD.—See Betsson AB; *Int'l*, pg. 1003
RACEBROOK CAPITAL ADVISORS, LLC; *U.S. Private*, pg. 3341
RACE COMPLETIONS LTD—See Causeway Aero Group Ltd.; *Int'l*, pg. 1361
RACECOURSE HOTEL (BMG) PTY LTD—See Woolworths Group Limited; *Int'l*, pg. 8451
RACE ECO CHAIN LTD.; *Int'l*, pg. 6171
RACELAND RAW SUGAR CORP.—See M.A. Patout & Son Limited; *U.S. Private*, pg. 2528
RACEMARK INDUSTRIES, SA—See Racemark International, LP; *U.S. Private*, pg. 3341
RACEMARK INTERNATIONAL, LLC—See Racemark International, LP; *U.S. Private*, pg. 3341
RACEMARK INTERNATIONAL, LP; *U.S. Private*, pg. 3341
RAC ENTERPRISES INC.; *U.S. Private*, pg. 3341
RACEPAK, LLC—See Z Capital Group, LLC; *U.S. Private*, pg. 4595
RACE ROCK GP, L.L.C.; *U.S. Private*, pg. 3341
RACER TECHNOLOGY PTE LTD—See Trek 2000 International Ltd; *Int'l*, pg. 7910
RACE STREET FOODS INC.; *U.S. Private*, pg. 3341
RACE TIRES AMERICA INC.—See Polymer Enterprises Inc.; *U.S. Private*, pg. 3226
RACETRAC PETROLEUM, INC.; *U.S. Private*, pg. 3341
RACEWAY ASSOCIATES, LLC—See National Association for Stock Car Auto Racing, Inc.; *U.S. Private*, pg. 2846
RACEWAY PARK, INC.—See PENN Entertainment, Inc.; *U.S. Public*, pg. 1662
RACEWAY PETROLEUM INC.; *U.S. Private*, pg. 3341
RACE WINNING BRANDS, INC.—See MiddleGround Management, LP; *U.S. Private*, pg. 2712
RACEWIRE LLC—See Genstar Capital, LLC; *U.S. Private*, pg. 1678
R.A.C. GROUP INC.—See Mistras Group, Inc.; *U.S. Public*, pg. 1451
RACHAEL'S FOOD CORPORATION; *U.S. Private*, pg. 3341
RACHAS INC.; *U.S. Private*, pg. 3341
RACHEL ALLAN, LLC; *U.S. Private*, pg. 3341
RACHEL KAY PUBLIC RELATIONS LLC—See Finn Partners, Inc.; *U.S. Private*, pg. 1510
RACHELLI ITALIA S.R.L.—See Emmi AG; *Int'l*, pg. 2385
RACINE BROADCASTING LLC—See Adams Publishing Group, LLC; *U.S. Private*, pg. 74

RACINE INDUSTRIES INC. — CORPORATE AFFILIATIONS

RACINE INDUSTRIES INC.; *U.S. Private*, pg. 3342
RACINE SYMPHONY ORCHESTRA ASSOCIATION INC.; *U.S. Private*, pg. 3342
RACING AND SPORTS PTY. LTD.—See RAS Technology Holdings Limited; *Int'l*, pg. 6212
RACING ASSOCIATION OF CENTRAL IOWA; *U.S. Private*, pg. 3342
RACING FORCE S.P.A.; *Int'l*, pg. 6172
RACINGONE MULTIMEDIA, LLC—See National Association for Stock Car Auto Racing, Inc.; *U.S. Private*, pg. 2846
RACING TECHNOLOGY NORFOLK LTD.—See Porsche Automobil Holding SE; *Int'l*, pg. 5926
RACING VICTORIA LIMITED; *Int'l*, pg. 6172
RAC INSURANCE PARTNERS, LLC—See The Allstate Corporation; *U.S. Public*, pg. 2034
RACKEMANN, SAWYER & BREWSTER PROFESSIONAL CORPORATION—See Verrill Dana LLP; *U.S. Private*, pg. 4368
RACKHAMS LIMITED—See Headlam Group plc; *Int'l*, pg. 3301
RACKLA METALS INC.; *Int'l*, pg. 6172
RACKMOUNT SOLUTIONS, INC.; *U.S. Private*, pg. 3342
RACK PROCESSING COMPANY, INC.; *U.S. Private*, pg. 3342
RACK ROOM SHOES INC.—See Deichmann SE; *Int'l*, pg. 2005
RACKSPACE HOSTING, INC.—See Apollo Global Management, Inc.; *U.S. Public*, pg. 154
RACKSPACE LTD.—See Apollo Global Management, Inc.; *U.S. Public*, pg. 154
RACKSPACE TECHNOLOGY, INC.; *U.S. Public*, pg. 1759
RACKWISE, INC.; *U.S. Private*, pg. 3342
RACL GEARTECH LTD.; *Int'l*, pg. 6172
RAC LTD.—See The Carlyle Group Inc.; *U.S. Public*, pg. 2052
RAC MEXICO OPERACIONES, S. DE R.L. DE C.V.—See Upbound Group, Inc.; *U.S. Public*, pg. 2263
RAC NATIONAL PRODUCT SERVICE, LLC—See Upbound Group, Inc.; *U.S. Public*, pg. 2263
RAC NORWAY AS—See Avis Budget Group, Inc.; *U.S. Public*, pg. 249
RACO-ELEKTRO-MASCHINEN GMBH; *Int'l*, pg. 6172
RACO GENERAL CONTRACTORS INC.; *U.S. Private*, pg. 3342
RACO HOLDINGS, LLC—See The Graham Group, Inc.; *U.S. Private*, pg. 4037
RACO INCORPORATED; *U.S. Private*, pg. 3342
RACO INDUSTRIES, INC.; *U.S. Private*, pg. 3342
RACO INTERIOR PRODUCTS, INC.—See UMC Acquisition Corp.; *U.S. Private*, pg. 4278
RACOM CORPORATION; *U.S. Private*, pg. 3342
RA COMPUTER S.P.A.—See Cassa Depositi e Prestiti S.p.A.; *Int'l*, pg. 1354
RACON INC.; *U.S. Private*, pg. 3342
RACON SOFTWARE GMBH—See Raiffeisenlandesbank Oberosterreich Aktiengesellschaft; *Int'l*, pg. 6187
RACONTEUR GLOBAL RESOURCES LIMITED; *Int'l*, pg. 6172
RACONTROLS SP. Z O.O.—See Introl S.A.; *Int'l*, pg. 3769
RACON WEST SOFTWARE GMBH—See Raiffeisen-Landesbank Tirol AG; *Int'l*, pg. 6186
RACOO, INC.—See Hubbell Incorporated; *U.S. Public*, pg. 1067
RACO WIRELESS LLC—See The Graham Group, Inc.; *U.S. Private*, pg. 4037
RAC TRANSPORT COMPANY INC.; *U.S. Private*, pg. 3341
RADAAN MEDIAWORKS INDIA LIMITED; *Int'l*, pg. 6173
RAD A.D.; *Int'l*, pg. 6172
RAD A.D.; *Int'l*, pg. 6172
RAD A.D. TESLIC; *Int'l*, pg. 6172
RADA ELECTRONIC INDUSTRIES LTD.; *Int'l*, pg. 6173
RAD AMERICA LATINA S.A.—See RAD Group; *Int'l*, pg. 6172
RADAR AUTOMATION NV—See VINCI S.A.; *Int'l*, pg. 8225
RADAR AUTOMATION SARL—See VINCI S.A.; *Int'l*, pg. 8225
RADAR, INC.; *U.S. Private*, pg. 3342
RADARLUX RADAR SYSTEMS GMBH—See Jenoptik AG; *Int'l*, pg. 3929
RADAR SERVICIOUS CELAYA S. DE R.L. DE C.V.—See Shiloh Industries, Inc.; *U.S. Private*, pg. 3636
RADAR STAMPING TECHNOLOGIES S. DE R.L. DE C.V.—See Shiloh Industries, Inc.; *U.S. Private*, pg. 3636
RADARWORKS, INC.; *U.S. Private*, pg. 3342
RADARWORKS, INC.—See Radarworks, Inc.; *U.S. Private*, pg. 3342
RADASAND AB—See Peab AB; *Int'l*, pg. 5773
RADA SENSORS INC.—See RADA Electronic Industries Ltd.; *Int'l*, pg. 6173
RADATA, INC.—See RockBridge Growth Equity, LLC; *U.S. Private*, pg. 3465
RADA TECHNOLOGIES LLC—See RADA Electronic Industries Ltd.; *Int'l*, pg. 6173
RADCAL CORP.—See Ion Beam Applications, S.A.; *Int'l*, pg. 3793

RADCHROM ANALITICA LTDA.—See HORIBA Ltd; *Int'l*, pg. 3478
RADCLIFF-ECONOMY MARINE SERVICES; *U.S. Private*, pg. 3342
RADCO INDUSTRIES, INC.; *U.S. Private*, pg. 3342
RADCOM EQUIPMENT, INC.—See RAD Group; *Int'l*, pg. 6173
RADCOM LTD.—See RAD Group; *Int'l*, pg. 6172
RAD DATA AUSTRALIA PTY. LTD.—See RAD Group; *Int'l*, pg. 6172
RAD DATA COMMUNICATIONS GMBH—See RAD Group; *Int'l*, pg. 6172
RAD DATA COMMUNICATIONS IBERIA, SL—See RAD Group; *Int'l*, pg. 6172
RAD DATA COMMUNICATIONS, INC.—See RAD Group; *Int'l*, pg. 6172
RAD DATA COMMUNICATIONS INC.—See RAD Group; *Int'l*, pg. 6172
RAD DATA COMMUNICATIONS LTD. (UK)—See RAD Group; *Int'l*, pg. 6172
RAD DO BRASIL LTDA.—See RAD Group; *Int'l*, pg. 6172
RADDON FINANCIAL GROUP—See Fiserv, Inc.; *U.S. Public*, pg. 851
RADEBERGER GRUPPE AG—See Dr. August Oetker KG; *Int'l*, pg. 2190
RADE KONCAR A.D.; *Int'l*, pg. 6173
RADE KONCAR-APARATNA TEHNIKA AD; *Int'l*, pg. 6173
RADEMACHER HOLDING GMBH—See NQRD Holding Unternehmensbeteiligungsgesellschaft mbH; *Int'l*, pg. 5416
RADEMAKERS GIETERIJ B.V.—See Triacta BV; *Int'l*, pg. 7918
RADER FARMS, INC.—See Oregon Potato Company; *U.S. Private*, pg. 3040
RADER GMBH—See Bastei Lubbe AG; *Int'l*, pg. 888
RADEX VERTRIEBSGESELLSCHAFT MBH—See RHI Magnesita N.V.; *Int'l*, pg. 6326
RAD FAR EAST LTD.—See RAD Group; *Int'l*, pg. 6172
RADFORD AUTO AUCTION; *U.S. Private*, pg. 3342
RADFORD FAMILY MEDICINE, LLC—See HCA Healthcare, Inc.; *U.S. Public*, pg. 1007
RADFORD—See Aon plc; *Int'l*, pg. 491
RADFORD STUDIO CENTER INC.—See National Amusements, Inc.; *U.S. Private*, pg. 2843
RAD FRANCE—See RAD Group; *Int'l*, pg. 6172
RAD GAME TOOLS, INC.—See Epic Games Inc.; *U.S. Private*, pg. 1412
RAD GROUP; *Int'l*, pg. 6172
RADHAGOBIND COMMERCIAL LIMITED; *Int'l*, pg. 6173
RADHA MADHAV CORPORATION LIMITED; *Int'l*, pg. 6173
RADHAZ CONSULTING PTY LTD.—See Service Stream Limited; *Int'l*, pg. 6725
RADHI BIDHYUT CO., LTD.; *Int'l*, pg. 6173
RADHIKA JEWELTECH LIMITED; *Int'l*, pg. 6173
RADIAC ABRASIVES, INC.—See Swarovski & Co.; *Int'l*, pg. 7362
RADIADORES NISSEN, S.A.—See Standard Motor Products, Inc.; *U.S. Public*, pg. 1929
RADIADORES VISCONDE S/A—See Modine Manufacturing Company; *U.S. Public*, pg. 1455
RADIADYNE, LLC—See AngioDynamics, Inc.; *U.S. Public*, pg. 137
RADIAL BEARING CORP.—See Torque Capital Group, LLC; *U.S. Private*, pg. 4189
RADIAL CAPITAL PARTNERS GMBH & CO. KG; *Int'l*, pg. 6173
RADIAL DRILLING SERVICES INC.; *U.S. Private*, pg. 3342
RADIAL EQUITY PARTNERS LP; *U.S. Private*, pg. 3342
RADIAL, INC.—See bpost NV/SA; *Int'l*, pg. 1133
RADIAL ITALY SRL—See bpost NV/SA; *Int'l*, pg. 1133
RADIALL AB—See Radiall S.A.; *Int'l*, pg. 6174
RADIALL DO BRASIL COMPONENTES ELECTRONICOS LTDA—See Radiall S.A.; *Int'l*, pg. 6174
RADIALL ELECTRONICS (ASIA) LTD.—See Radiall S.A.; *Int'l*, pg. 6174
RADIALL ELETTRONICA SRL—See Radiall S.A.; *Int'l*, pg. 6174
RADIALL GMBH—See Radiall S.A.; *Int'l*, pg. 6174
RADIALL INDIA PVT. LTD.—See Radiall S.A.; *Int'l*, pg. 6174
RADIALL LTD.—See Radiall S.A.; *Int'l*, pg. 6174
RADIALL NEDERLAND B.V.—See Radiall S.A.; *Int'l*, pg. 6174
RADIALL S.A.; *Int'l*, pg. 6173
RADIALL SF—See Radiall S.A.; *Int'l*, pg. 6174
RADIALL SYSTEMS SA—See Radiall S.A.; *Int'l*, pg. 6174
RADIALL USA INC. - NEW HAVEN—See Radiall S.A.; *Int'l*, pg. 6174
RADIALL USA, INC.—See Radiall S.A.; *Int'l*, pg. 6174
RADIALL USA, INC.—See Radiall S.A.; *Int'l*, pg. 6174
RADIALL VENTURES CAPITAL SA—See Radiall S.A.; *Int'l*, pg. 6174
RADIAL RESEARCH CORP.; *Int'l*, pg. 6173
RADIANCE HOLDINGS GROUP COMPANY LIMITED; *Int'l*, pg. 6173
RADIANCE SAS—See Kadant Inc.; *U.S. Public*, pg. 1212

RADIANCE TECHNOLOGIES, INC.; *U.S. Private*, pg. 3343
RADIANCY, INC.—See Gadsden Properties, Inc.; *U.S. Public*, pg. 894
RADIAN GROUP, INC.; *U.S. Public*, pg. 1759
RADIAN GROUP LIMITED; *Int'l*, pg. 6174
RADIAN GUARANTY INC.—See Radian Group, Inc.; *U.S. Public*, pg. 1759
RADIAN INVESTOR SURETY INC.—See Radian Group, Inc.; *U.S. Public*, pg. 1759
RADIANS CAROLINA—See Radians, Inc.; *U.S. Private*, pg. 3343
RADIAN SERVICES LLC—See Radian Group, Inc.; *U.S. Public*, pg. 1759
RADIANS, INC.; *U.S. Private*, pg. 3343
RADIAN SUPPORT LIMITED—See Radian Group Limited; *Int'l*, pg. 6174
RADIANT CASH MANAGEMENT SERVICES LIMITED; *Int'l*, pg. 6174
RADIANT COLOR N.V.—See RPM International Inc.; *U.S. Public*, pg. 1820
RADIANT COMMUNICATIONS CORP.; *U.S. Private*, pg. 3343
RADIANT COMMUNICATIONS CORP.—See Comwave Networks, Inc.; *Int'l*, pg. 1763
RADIANT CUSTOMS SERVICES, INC.—See Radiant Logistics, Inc.; *U.S. Public*, pg. 1759
RADIANT ELITE INVESTMENTS LIMITED—See General Interface Solution (GIS) Holding Ltd.; *Int'l*, pg. 2918
RADIANT GEMS INTERNATIONAL PLC; *Int'l*, pg. 6174
RADIANT GLOBAL LOGISTICS (CA), INC.—See Radiant Logistics, Inc.; *U.S. Public*, pg. 1760
RADIANT GLOBAL LOGISTICS (HK) LIMITED—See Radiant Logistics, Inc.; *U.S. Public*, pg. 1759
RADIANT GLOBAL LOGISTICS, INC.—See Radiant Logistics, Inc.; *U.S. Public*, pg. 1759
RADIANT GLOBAL LOGISTICS LTD.—See Radiant Logistics, Inc.; *U.S. Public*, pg. 1759
RADIANT GLOBAL LOGISTICS (SHANGHAI) LTD.—See Radiant Logistics, Inc.; *U.S. Public*, pg. 1759
RADIANT GLOBALTECH BERHAD; *Int'l*, pg. 6174
RADIANT GROUP LLC; *U.S. Private*, pg. 3343
THE RADIANT GROUP, LLC—See Advent International Corporation; *U.S. Private*, pg. 103
RADIANT GROUP (PROPRIETARY) LIMITED—See South Ocean Holdings Limited; *Int'l*, pg. 7116
RADIANT GROWTH INVESTMENTS LIMITED; *Int'l*, pg. 6174
RADIANT HILLS HEALTH ASSOCIATES LLC—See The Ensign Group, Inc.; *U.S. Public*, pg. 2072
RADIANT HOLDINGS INC.; *U.S. Private*, pg. 3343
RADIANT HOSPITALITY SERVICES PVT. LIMITED—See OCS Group Limited; *Int'l*, pg. 5521
RADIANT INNOVATION, INC.; *Int'l*, pg. 6174
RADIAN TITLE INSURANCE INC.—See Radian Group, Inc.; *U.S. Public*, pg. 1759
RADIANT LOGIC, INC.; *U.S. Private*, pg. 3343
RADIANT LOGISTICS, INC.; *U.S. Public*, pg. 1759
RADIANT LOGISTICS PARTNERS LLC—See Radiant Logistics, Inc.; *U.S. Public*, pg. 1759
RADIANT MISSION SOLUTIONS INC.—See Advent International Corporation; *U.S. Private*, pg. 103
RADIANT NUTRACEUTICALS LIMITED—See Unjha Formulations Limited; *Int'l*, pg. 8084
RADIANT OIL & GAS, INC.; *U.S. Private*, pg. 3343
RADIANT OPTO-ELECTRONICS CORPORATION - GUANGZHOU FACTORY—See Radiant Opto-Electronics Corporation; *Int'l*, pg. 6175
RADIANT OPTO-ELECTRONICS CORPORATION - NANJING FACTORY—See Radiant Opto-Electronics Corporation; *Int'l*, pg. 6175
RADIANT OPTO-ELECTRONICS CORPORATION; *Int'l*, pg. 6174
RADIANT OPTO-ELECTRONICS CORPORATION - WUJIANG FACTORY—See Radiant Opto-Electronics Corporation; *Int'l*, pg. 6175
RADIANT OVERSEAS PTE. LTD.—See Legion Consortium Limited; *Int'l*, pg. 4444
RADIANT POOLS—See Latham Group, Inc.; *U.S. Public*, pg. 1294
RADIANT POWER CORP.—See HEICO Corporation; *U.S. Public*, pg. 1020
RADIANT RESEARCH INC.—See Kinderhook Industries, LLC; *U.S. Private*, pg. 2307
RADIANT RFID; *U.S. Private*, pg. 3343
RADIANT ROAD & RAIL, INC.—See Radiant Logistics, Inc.; *U.S. Public*, pg. 1760
RADIANT SYSTEMS, INC.—See NCR Voyix Corporation.; *U.S. Public*, pg. 1503
RADIANT TELECOM INC.—See Radiant Holdings Inc.; *U.S. Private*, pg. 3343
RADIANT VISION SYSTEMS, LLC—See Konica Minolta, Inc.; *Int'l*, pg. 4260
RADIATEC AG—See Zehnder Group AG; *Int'l*, pg. 8630
RADIATE GROUP—See Omnicom Group Inc.; *U.S. Public*, pg. 1593
RADIATE GROUP—See Omnicom Group Inc.; *U.S. Public*, pg. 1593

COMPANY NAME INDEX

RADIATION BILLING SOLUTIONS, INC.; *U.S. Private*, pg. 3343
RADIATION MONITORING DEVICES, INC.—See Dynasil Corporation of America; *U.S. Private*, pg. 1300
RADIATION ONCOLOGY SERVICES, INC.; *U.S. Private*, pg. 3343
RADIATION PHYSICS, INC.—See Preventive Diagnostics, Inc.; *U.S. Private*, pg. 3257
RADIATION SAFETY & CONTROL SERVICES, INC.—See Bernhard Capital Partners Management, LP; *U.S. Private*, pg. 536
RADIATION TECHNICAL SERVICES CO.; *U.S. Private*, pg. 3343
RADIATION TEST SOLUTIONS, INC.; *U.S. Private*, pg. 3343
RADIATORS AUSTRALIA (2000) PTY. LTD.—See APM Automotive Holdings Berhad; *Int'l*, pg. 516
RADIATORSONLINE.COM LTD.—See Brickability Group plc; *Int'l*, pg. 1151
RADIATOR SPECIALTY COMPANY - RSC CHEMICAL SOLUTIONS DIVISION—See Radiator Specialty Company; *U.S. Private*, pg. 3343
RADIATOR SPECIALTY COMPANY; *U.S. Private*, pg. 3343
RADICAL COSMETICS, LLC; *U.S. Private*, pg. 3343
THE RADICAL FRUIT COMPANY OF NEW YORK—See PepsiCo, Inc.; *U.S. Public*, pg. 1672
@RADICAL MEDIA; *U.S. Private*, pg. 17
RADICI CHEMIEFASER GMBH—See Radici Partecipazioni S.p.A.; *Int'l*, pg. 6175
RADICI CHEM (SHANGHAI) CO., LTD.—See Radici Partecipazioni S.p.A.; *Int'l*, pg. 6175
RADICI CHIMICA DEUTSCHLAND GMBH—See Radici Partecipazioni S.p.A.; *Int'l*, pg. 6175
RADICI CHIMICA S.P.A. - MENDRISIO BRANCH—See Radici Partecipazioni S.p.A.; *Int'l*, pg. 6175
RADICI CHIMICA S.P.A.—See Radici Partecipazioni S.p.A.; *Int'l*, pg. 6175
RADICI ENERGIE SRL—See Radici Partecipazioni S.p.A.; *Int'l*, pg. 6175
RADICIFIBRAS INDUSTRIA E COMERCIO LTDA—See Radici Partecipazioni S.p.A.; *Int'l*, pg. 6175
RADICIFIBRAS INDUSTRIA E COMERCIO LTDA—See Radici Partecipazioni S.p.A.; *Int'l*, pg. 6175
RADICI FIL S.P.A.—See Radici Partecipazioni S.p.A.; *Int'l*, pg. 6175
RADICIFIN S.P.A.—See Radici Partecipazioni S.p.A.; *Int'l*, pg. 6175
RADICI HOLDING MECCANOTESSILE S.P.A.—See Radici Partecipazioni S.p.A.; *Int'l*, pg. 6175
RADICI IMMOBILIARE S.P.A.—See Radici Partecipazioni S.p.A.; *Int'l*, pg. 6175
RADICI NOVACIPS S.P.A.—See Radici Partecipazioni S.p.A.; *Int'l*, pg. 6175
RADICI PARTECIPAZIONI S.P.A.; *Int'l*, pg. 6175
RADICI PIETRO INDUSTRIES & BRANDS S.P.A.; *Int'l*, pg. 6176
RADICI PLASTICS FRANCE SA—See Radici Partecipazioni S.p.A.; *Int'l*, pg. 6175
RADICI PLASTICS GMBH & CO. KG—See Radici Partecipazioni S.p.A.; *Int'l*, pg. 6175
RADICI PLASTICS IBERICA SL—See Radici Partecipazioni S.p.A.; *Int'l*, pg. 6175
RADICI PLASTICS INDIA PVT. LTD.—See Radici Partecipazioni S.p.A.; *Int'l*, pg. 6175
RADICI PLASTICS LTDA.—See Radici Partecipazioni S.p.A.; *Int'l*, pg. 6175
RADICI PLASTICS MEXICO S. DE R.L. DE C.V.—See Radici Partecipazioni S.p.A.; *Int'l*, pg. 6175
RADICI PLASTICS (SUZHOU) CO., LTD.—See Radici Partecipazioni S.p.A.; *Int'l*, pg. 6175
RADICI PLASTICS UK LTD.—See Radici Partecipazioni S.p.A.; *Int'l*, pg. 6175
RADICI PLASTICS USA, LLC—See Radici Partecipazioni S.p.A.; *Int'l*, pg. 6175
RADICI SPANDEX CORP.—See Radici Partecipazioni S.p.A.; *Int'l*, pg. 6175
RADICI YARN S.P.A.—See Radici Partecipazioni S.p.A.; *Int'l*, pg. 6175
RADICO KHAITAN LIMITED - PLANT 1—See Radico Khaitan Limited; *Int'l*, pg. 6176
RADICO KHAITAN LIMITED; *Int'l*, pg. 6176
RADICON TRANSMISSION UK LIMITED—See Elecon Engineering Company Ltd.; *Int'l*, pg. 2348
RADIENT TECHNOLOGIES INC.; *Int'l*, pg. 6176
RADIFLOW LTD.—See RAD Group; *Int'l*, pg. 6173
RADIKAL LTD.—See Transition Evergreen; *Int'l*, pg. 7901
RADIKO HOLDINGS CORP.; *Int'l*, pg. 6176
RADINE B.V.—See INA-Holding Schaeffler GmbH & Co. KG; *Int'l*, pg. 3640
RAD-INFO, INC.; *U.S. Private*, pg. 3342
RAD INFORMATICA S.R.L.—See Zucchetti Group S.p.A.; *Int'l*, pg. 8692
R.A. DINKEL & ASSOCIATES, INC.; *U.S. Private*, pg. 3334
RADIO 106.9 MHZ NUREMBERG GMBH—See NRJ Group SA; *Int'l*, pg. 5474
RADIO 1278 MELBOURNE PTY LIMITED—See Nine Entertainment Co. Holdings Limited; *Int'l*, pg. 5299
RADIO 2000 GESELLSCHAFT MBH—See NRJ Group SA; *Int'l*, pg. 5474
RADIO 24 AG—See BT Holding AG; *Int'l*, pg. 1204
RADIO 2CH PTY LIMITED—See Oceania Capital Partners Limited; *Int'l*, pg. 5518
RADIO 2GB SYDNEY PTY LTD—See Nine Entertainment Co. Holdings Limited; *Int'l*, pg. 5299
RADIO 2UE SYDNEY PTY LTD—See Nine Entertainment Co. Holdings Limited; *Int'l*, pg. 5299
RADIO 30, S.A.—See Promotora de Informaciones S.A.; *Int'l*, pg. 5995
RADIO 32 AG—See BT Holding AG; *Int'l*, pg. 1204
RADIO 3AW MELBOURNE PTY LIMITED—See Nine Entertainment Co. Holdings Limited; *Int'l*, pg. 5300
RADIO 4BC BRISBANE PTY LIMITED—See Nine Entertainment Co. Holdings Limited; *Int'l*, pg. 5300
RADIO 4BH BRISBANE PTY LIMITED—See Nine Entertainment Co. Holdings Limited; *Int'l*, pg. 5299
RADIO 6PR PERTH PTY LIMITED—See Nine Entertainment Co. Holdings Limited; *Int'l*, pg. 5299
RADIO 780 INC—See Salem Media Group, Inc.; *U.S. Public*, pg. 1836
RADIO 93.3 MHZ MUNCHEN GMBH PRODUKTION UND VERBREITUNG VON RUNDFUNKPROGRAMMEN—See NRJ Group SA; *Int'l*, pg. 5474
RADIO 96FM PERTH PTY. LIMITED—See ARN Media Limited; *Int'l*, pg. 576
RADIO 97.1 MHZ HAMBURG GMBH—See NRJ Group SA; *Int'l*, pg. 5474
RADIO ACTIVITY S.R.L.—See JVCKENWOOD Corporation; *Int'l*, pg. 4034
RADIO AIRE LTD—See Heinrich Bauer Verlag KG; *Int'l*, pg. 3324
RADIO CANADA INTERNATIONAL—See The Canadian Broadcasting Corporation; *Int'l*, pg. 7630
RADIO CITY 93.7 FM—See Bertelsmann SE & Co. KGaA; *Int'l*, pg. 995
RADIO CITY LTD.—See Heinrich Bauer Verlag KG; *Int'l*, pg. 3324
RADIO CITY PRODUCTIONS LLC—See Madison Square Garden Entertainment Corp.; *U.S. Public*, pg. 1353
RADIO CLASSIQUE SAS—See LVMH Moet Hennessy Louis Vuitton SE; *Int'l*, pg. 4592
RADIO COMPUTING SERVICES (AFRICA) PTY LTD.—See iHeartMedia, Inc.; *U.S. Public*, pg. 1095
RADIO COMPUTING SERVICES CANADA LTD.—See iHeartMedia, Inc.; *U.S. Public*, pg. 1096
RADIO COMPUTING SERVICES, INC.—See iHeartMedia, Inc.; *U.S. Public*, pg. 1096
RADIO COMPUTING SERVICES (INDIA) PVT. LTD.—See iHeartMedia, Inc.; *U.S. Public*, pg. 1095
RADIO COMPUTING SERVICES (SEA) PTE LTD.—See iHeartMedia, Inc.; *U.S. Public*, pg. 1095
RADIO COMPUTING SERVICES (UK) LTD.—See iHeartMedia, Inc.; *U.S. Public*, pg. 1096
RADIO CONTACT—See Bertelsmann SE & Co. KGaA; *Int'l*, pg. 995
RADIO COUNTY SOUND LIMITED—See News Corporation; *U.S. Public*, pg. 1520
RADIOCRAFTS AS—See LumenRadio AB; *Int'l*, pg. 4577
RADIO DATA TECHNOLOGY LTD.—See CML Microsystems Plc; *Int'l*, pg. 1671
RADIODETECTION B.V.—See SPX Technologies, Inc.; *U.S. Public*, pg. 1921
RADIODETECTION CANADA LTD.—See SPX Technologies, Inc.; *U.S. Public*, pg. 1921
RADIODETECTION CORP.—See SPX Technologies, Inc.; *U.S. Public*, pg. 1921
RADIO DIRECT RESPONSE; *U.S. Private*, pg. 3343
RADIO DISTRIBUTING CO.; *U.S. Private*, pg. 3343
RADIO ENGINEERING INDUSTRIES; *U.S. Private*, pg. 3343
RADIO FLYER INC.; *U.S. Private*, pg. 3343
RADIO FRANCE; *Int'l*, pg. 6176
RADIO FREE ASIA; *U.S. Private*, pg. 3344
RADIO FREQUENCY SIMULATION SYSTEMS, INC.—See Vadatech, Inc.; *U.S. Private*, pg. 4329
RADIO FREQUENCY SYSTEMS GMBH—See Radio Frequency Systems, Inc.; *U.S. Private*, pg. 3344
RADIO FREQUENCY SYSTEMS, INC.; *U.S. Private*, pg. 3344
RADIO FREQUENCY SYSTEMS PTY. LTD.—See Radio Frequency Systems, Inc.; *U.S. Private*, pg. 3344
RADIO FREQUENCY SYSTEMS SINGAPORE PTE LTD—See Radio Frequency Systems, Inc.; *U.S. Private*, pg. 3344
RADIO HAMBURG GMBH & CO KG—See Bertelsmann SE & Co. KGaA; *Int'l*, pg. 995
RADIOHIO, INC.—See TEGNA Inc.; *U.S. Public*, pg. 1990
RADIO-HOLLAND CURACAO—See Pon Holdings B.V.; *Int'l*, pg. 5919
RADIO HOLLAND EGYPT—See Pon Holdings B.V.; *Int'l*, pg. 5919
RADIO HOLLAND HONG KONG—See Pon Holdings B.V.; *Int'l*, pg. 5919
RADIO HOLLAND MIDDLE EAST—See Pon Holdings B.V.; *Int'l*, pg. 5919

RADIOMETRICS CORPORATION

RADIO HOLLAND NETHERLANDS B.V.—See Pon Holdings B.V.; *Int'l*, pg. 5919
RADIO HOLLAND NETHERLANDS—See Pon Holdings B.V.; *Int'l*, pg. 5919
RADIO HOLLAND NORWAY AS—See Pon Holdings B.V.; *Int'l*, pg. 5919
RADIO-HOLLAND SINGAPORE PTE. LTD.—See Pon Holdings B.V.; *Int'l*, pg. 5919
RADIO HOLLAND SOUTH AFRICA—See Pon Holdings B.V.; *Int'l*, pg. 5919
RADIO HOLLAND SOUTH AFRICA—See Pon Holdings B.V.; *Int'l*, pg. 5919
RADIOIO, INC.; *U.S. Public*, pg. 1760
RADIO JAMAICA LIMITED; *Int'l*, pg. 6176
RADIOLITE TRADING CO., LTD.—See Showa Chemical Industry Co., Ltd.; *Int'l*, pg. 6861
RADIOLOGY ALLIANCE DELIVERY SYSTEM, LLC—See RadNet, Inc.; *U.S. Public*, pg. 1761
RADIOLOGY ASSOCIATES OF HOLLYWOOD, INC.—See KKR & Co. Inc.; *U.S. Public*, pg. 1250
RADIOLOGY CONSULTANTS PTE LTD—See Khazanah Nasional Berhad; *Int'l*, pg. 4152
RADIOLOGY REGIONAL CENTER, P.A.; *U.S. Private*, pg. 3344
RADIOLOGY SERVICES OF JUPITER MEDICAL SPECIALISTS, LLC—See KKR & Co. Inc.; *U.S. Public*, pg. 1246
RADIOLOGY VICTORIA PTY LIMITED—See Sonic Healthcare Limited; *Int'l*, pg. 7098
RADIO MACKAY PTY LTD—See Seven West Media Limited; *Int'l*, pg. 6734
RADIO MELODI NORGE AS—See NRJ Group SA; *Int'l*, pg. 5474
RADIOMETER AMERICA INC.—See Danaher Corporation; *U.S. Public*, pg. 630
RADIOMETER A/S—See Danaher Corporation; *U.S. Public*, pg. 630
RADIOMETER BASEL AG—See Danaher Corporation; *U.S. Public*, pg. 630
RADIOMETER DANMARK A/S—See Danaher Corporation; *U.S. Public*, pg. 630
RADIOMETER GMBH—See Danaher Corporation; *U.S. Public*, pg. 630
RADIOMETER IBERICA S.L.—See Danaher Corporation; *U.S. Public*, pg. 630
RADIOMETER K.K.—See Danaher Corporation; *U.S. Public*, pg. 630
RADIOMETER K.K.—See Danaher Corporation; *U.S. Public*, pg. 631
RADIOMETER LIMITED—See Danaher Corporation; *U.S. Public*, pg. 630
RADIOMETER MEDICAL APS—See Danaher Corporation; *U.S. Public*, pg. 631
RADIOMETER MEDICAL A/S—See Danaher Corporation; *U.S. Public*, pg. 630
RADIOMETER MEDICAL EQUIPMENT (SHANGHAI) CO. LTD.—See Danaher Corporation; *U.S. Public*, pg. 631
RADIOMETER NEDERLAND B.V.—See Danaher Corporation; *U.S. Public*, pg. 631
RADIOMETER PACIFIC LTD.—See Danaher Corporation; *U.S. Public*, pg. 631
RADIOMETER PACIFIC PTY. LTD.—See Danaher Corporation; *U.S. Public*, pg. 631
RADIOMETER RSCH GMBH—See Danaher Corporation; *U.S. Public*, pg. 631
RADIOMETER S.A.—See Danaher Corporation; *U.S. Public*, pg. 631
RADIOMETER SOUTH AFRICA—See Danaher Corporation; *U.S. Public*, pg. 631
RADIOMETER TURKU OY—See Danaher Corporation; *U.S. Public*, pg. 631
RADIOMETER (UK) LTD.—See Danaher Corporation; *U.S. Public*, pg. 630
RADIOMETRICS CORPORATION; *U.S. Private*, pg. 3344
RADIO MITRE S.A.—See Grupo Clarin S.A.; *Int'l*, pg. 3125
RADIO MUSIC RRM SRL—See Czech Media Invest as; *Int'l*, pg. 1898
RADIO NACIONAL DE ESPANA, S.A.—See Sociedad Estatal de Participaciones Industriales; *Int'l*, pg. 7031
RADIO NETWORKS, LLC - DALLAS OFFICE—See Cumulus Media Inc.; *U.S. Public*, pg. 610
RADIO NETWORKS, LLC—See Cumulus Media Inc.; *U.S. Public*, pg. 610
RADIONICS LTD.—See RS Group plc; *Int'l*, pg. 6418
RADIO NOSTALGIE SAS—See NRJ Group SA; *Int'l*, pg. 5474
RADIO NRJ BERLIN UND BRANDENBURG GMBH—See NRJ Group SA; *Int'l*, pg. 5474
RADIO NRW—See Bertelsmann SE & Co. KGaA; *Int'l*, pg. 995
RADIO ONE LICENSES, LLC—See Urban One, Inc.; *U.S. Public*, pg. 2265
RADIO ONE OF ATLANTA, LLC—See Urban One, Inc.; *U.S. Public*, pg. 2265
RADIO ONE OF CHARLOTTE, LLC—See Urban One, Inc.; *U.S. Public*, pg. 2265
RADIO ONE OF DETROIT, LLC—See Urban One, Inc.; *U.S. Public*, pg. 2265

RADIOMETRICS CORPORATION

RADIO ONE OF INDIANA, L.P.—See Urban One, Inc.; *U.S. Public*, pg. 2265
RADIO PARTS COMPANY INC; *U.S. Private*, pg. 3344
RADIOPHARM THERANOSTICS LIMITED; *Int'l*, pg. 6176
RADIO PLUS POLSKA SP. Z O.O.—See Czech Media Invest as; *Int'l*, pg. 1898
RADIOPULSE, INC.—See Littelfuse, Inc.; *U.S. Public*, pg. 1327
RADIO RELOJ, S.A.S.—See Promotora de Informaciones S.A.; *Int'l*, pg. 5995
RADIO RESEARCH INSTRUMENT CO.; *U.S. Private*, pg. 3344
RADIO SALU - EURO-RADIO SAAR GMBH—See Vivendi SE; *Int'l*, pg. 8278
RADIOSHACK DE MEXICO S.A. DE C.V.—See Grupo Gigante, S.A.B. de C.V.; *Int'l*, pg. 3130
RADIOSHACK DISTRIBUTION CENTER—See RS Legacy Corporation; *U.S. Private*, pg. 3496
RADIOSHACK (HK) LTD—See RS Legacy Corporation; *U.S. Private*, pg. 3496
RADIOSHACK PACKAGING—See RS Legacy Corporation; *U.S. Private*, pg. 3496
RADIOSHACK STORE FIXTURES—See RS Legacy Corporation; *U.S. Private*, pg. 3496
RADIO STUDIO 105 S.P.A.—See Mediaset S.p.A.; *Int'l*, pg. 4773
RADIO SYSTEMS CORPORATION; *U.S. Private*, pg. 3344
RADIO SYSTEMS PETSAFE EUROPE LTD.—See Radio Systems Corporation; *U.S. Private*, pg. 3344
RADIO TV PODRINJE A.D.; *Int'l*, pg. 6176
RADIO VINCI AUTOROUTES SA—See VINCI S.A.; *Int'l*, pg. 8225
RADIOWAVE (BLACKPOOL) LIMITED—See News Corporation; *U.S. Public*, pg. 1520
RADIOWE DORADZTWO REKLAMOWE SP. Z.O.O.—See Agora S.A.; *Int'l*, pg. 213
RADISHBO-YA CO., LTD.—See Oisix ra daichi Inc.; *Int'l*, pg. 5536
RADISSON HOSPITALITY AB—See Carlson Companies Inc.; *U.S. Private*, pg. 764
RADISSON HOTELS & RESORTS—See Carlson Companies Inc.; *U.S. Private*, pg. 764
RADISSON MINING RESOURCES INC.; *Int'l*, pg. 6176
RADISSON PLAZA HOTEL ADMIRAL—See Northampton Group Inc.; *Int'l*, pg. 5442
R.A.D.I SVERIGE AB/ABVAC—See Borr Company; *Int'l*, pg. 1114
RADISYS CANADA ULC—See Reliance - ADA Group Limited; *Int'l*, pg. 6262
RADISYS CORPORATION—See Reliance - ADA Group Limited; *Int'l*, pg. 6262
RADISYS INDIA PRIVATE LIMITED—See Reliance - ADA Group Limited; *Int'l*, pg. 6262
RADIUM DEVELOPMENT BERHAD; *Int'l*, pg. 6176
RADIUM JSC—See Russian Technologies State Corporation; *Int'l*, pg. 6431
RADIUM LAMPENWERK GESELLSCHAFT MBH—See Siemens Aktiengesellschaft; *Int'l*, pg. 6887
RADIUM LIFE TECH CO., LTD.; *Int'l*, pg. 6176
RADIUMONE, INC.; *U.S. Private*, pg. 3344
RADIUM RESOURCES CORP.; *U.S. Public*, pg. 1760
RADIUS AEROSPACE, INC. - SHELBYVILLE—See Arlington Capital Partners LLC; *U.S. Private*, pg. 328
RADIUS AEROSPACE, INC.—See Arlington Capital Partners LLC; *U.S. Private*, pg. 328
RADIUS AEROSPACE UK LTD.—See Arlington Capital Partners LLC; *U.S. Private*, pg. 328
RADIUS BANCORP INC.—See LendingClub Corporation; *U.S. Public*, pg. 1305
RADIUS BANK—See LendingClub Corporation; *U.S. Public*, pg. 1305
RADIUS EMEA—See Radius Global Market Research; *U.S. Private*, pg. 3344
RADIUS FINANCIAL GROUP, INC.; *U.S. Private*, pg. 3344
RADIUS GLOBAL INFRASTRUCTURE, INC.—See EQT AB; *Int'l*, pg. 2479
RADIUS GLOBAL INFRASTRUCTURE, INC.—See Public Sector Pension Investment Board; *Int'l*, pg. 6096
RADIUS GLOBAL MARKET RESEARCH; *U.S. Private*, pg. 3344
RADIUS GLOBAL MARKET RESEARCH—See Radius Global Market Research; *U.S. Private*, pg. 3344
RADIUS GLOBAL MARKET RESEARCH—See Radius Global Market Research; *U.S. Private*, pg. 3344
RADIUS GLOBAL MARKET RESEARCH—See Radius Global Market Research; *U.S. Private*, pg. 3344
RADIUS GLOBAL MARKET RESEARCH—See Radius Global Market Research; *U.S. Private*, pg. 3344
RADIUS GLOBAL MARKET RESEARCH—See Radius Global Market Research; *U.S. Private*, pg. 3344
RADIUS GLOBAL MARKET RESEARCH—See Radius Global Market Research; *U.S. Private*, pg. 3344
RADIUS GLOBAL SOLUTIONS LLC; *U.S. Private*, pg. 3344
RADIUS GOLD INC.; *Int'l*, pg. 6176
RADIUS HEALTH, INC.—See Gurnet Point Capital LLC; *U.S. Private*, pg. 1819

RADIUS HEALTH, INC.—See Patient Square Capital, L.P.; *U.S. Private*, pg. 3107
RADIUS HONG KONG LTD—See Jabil Inc.; *U.S. Public*, pg. 1182
RADIUS LEO BURNETT—See Publicis Groupe S.A.; *Int'l*, pg. 6102
RADIUS POWER INC.—See Tinicum Enterprises, Inc.; *U.S. Private*, pg. 4174
RADIUS RECYCLING, INC.; *U.S. Public*, pg. 1760
RADIX COMMUNICATIONS, INC.; *U.S. Private*, pg. 3345
RADIX DEVELOPMENT COMPANY LIMITED—See Fullsun International Holdings Group Co., Limited; *Int'l*, pg. 2843
RADIX GROUP INTERNATIONAL, INC.—See Deutsche Post AG; *Int'l*, pg. 2082
RADIX INDUSTRIES (INDIA) LIMITED; *Int'l*, pg. 6176
RADIXWEB; *Int'l*, pg. 6176
RADIX WIRE COMPANY; *U.S. Private*, pg. 3345
RADIXX SOLUTIONS INTERNATIONAL, INC.—See Sabre Corporation; *U.S. Public*, pg. 1833
RAD LABUD A.D.; *Int'l*, pg. 6173
RADLER ENTERPRISES INC.; *U.S. Private*, pg. 3345
RADLER FINANCIAL INC.—See Radler Enterprises Inc.; *U.S. Private*, pg. 3345
RADLEY ACURA; *U.S. Private*, pg. 3345
RADLEY YELDAR; *Int'l*, pg. 6176
RADLINK PTY. LTD.—See Epiroc AB; *Int'l*, pg. 2463
RADMACHER BROTHERS EXCAVATING CO, INC.; *U.S. Private*, pg. 3345
RADMD INC.—See IK Investment Partners Limited; *Int'l*, pg. 3609
RADMER KIES GMBH & CO. KG—See PORR AG; *Int'l*, pg. 5924
RADMER KIESVERTRIEB VERWALTUNGS GMBH—See PORR AG; *Int'l*, pg. 5924
RADNET, INC.; *U.S. Public*, pg. 1760
RADNET MANAGED IMAGING SERVICES, INC.—See RadNet, Inc.; *U.S. Public*, pg. 1761
RADNET MANAGEMENT INC.—See RadNet, Inc.; *U.S. Public*, pg. 1761
RADNIK A.D.; *Int'l*, pg. 6176
RADO INTERNATIONAL LIMITED—See Oshidori International Holdings Limited; *Int'l*, pg. 5650
RADON MEDICAL IMAGING CORP.; *U.S. Private*, pg. 3345
RADONOVA, INC.—See Lagercrantz Group AB; *Int'l*, pg. 4395
RADONOVA LABORATORIES AB—See Lagercrantz Group AB; *Int'l*, pg. 4395
THE RADOS COMPANIES; *U.S. Private*, pg. 4102
RADOS EQUIPMENT CORPORATION—See The Rados Companies; *U.S. Private*, pg. 4102
RADO TRAVEL SERVICE CO., LTD.—See Adventure Inc.; *Int'l*, pg. 167
RADO UHREN AG—See The Swatch Group Ltd.; *Int'l*, pg. 7692
RADPOL S.A.; *Int'l*, pg. 6177
RAD POWER BIKES LLC; *U.S. Private*, pg. 3342
RADSATZFABRIK ILSENBURG GMBH—See Georgsmarienhutte Holding GmbH; *Int'l*, pg. 2941
RADSITE LLC—See RadNet, Inc.; *U.S. Public*, pg. 1761
RADSOURCE, LLC—See Tenet Healthcare Corporation; *U.S. Public*, pg. 2006
RAD SOURCE TECHNOLOGIES, INC.—See Shandong Weigao Group Medical Polymer Company Limited; *Int'l*, pg. 6759
RADTKE PHYSICAL THERAPY, LIMITED PARTNERSHIP—See U.S. Physical Therapy, Inc.; *U.S. Public*, pg. 2215
RADVA CORPORATION—See Wynnchurch Capital, L.P.; *U.S. Private*, pg. 4577
RADVIEW SOFTWARE INC.—See RadView Software Ltd.; *Int'l*, pg. 6177
RADVIEW SOFTWARE LTD.; *Int'l*, pg. 6177
RADVISION COMMUNICATION DEVELOPMENT (BEIJING) CO. LTD.—See Silver Lake Group, LLC; *U.S. Private*, pg. 3656
RADVISION COMMUNICATION DEVELOPMENT (BEIJING) CO. LTD.—See TPG Capital, L.P.; *U.S. Public*, pg. 2169
RADVISION FRANCE S.A.R.L.—See Silver Lake Group, LLC; *U.S. Private*, pg. 3656
RADVISION FRANCE S.A.R.L.—See TPG Capital, L.P.; *U.S. Public*, pg. 2169
RADVISION (HK) LTD.—See Silver Lake Group, LLC; *U.S. Private*, pg. 3656
RADVISION (HK) LTD.—See TPG Capital, L.P.; *U.S. Public*, pg. 2169
RADVISION JAPAN KK—See Silver Lake Group, LLC; *U.S. Private*, pg. 3656
RADVISION JAPAN KK—See TPG Capital, L.P.; *U.S. Public*, pg. 2169
RADVISION LTD.—See Silver Lake Group, LLC; *U.S. Private*, pg. 3656
RADVISION LTD.—See TPG Capital, L.P.; *U.S. Public*, pg. 2169
RADVISION (UK) LTD.—See Silver Lake Group, LLC; *U.S. Private*, pg. 3656

CORPORATE AFFILIATIONS

RADVISION (UK) LTD.—See TPG Capital, L.P.; *U.S. Public*, pg. 2169
RADWARE INC.—See RAD Group; *Int'l*, pg. 6173
RADWARE LTD.—See RAD Group; *Int'l*, pg. 6173
RADWELL INTERNATIONAL, INC.—See CVC Capital Partners SICAV-FIS S.A.; *Int'l*, pg. 1885
RAD WEST AFRICA LIMITED—See RAD Group; *Int'l*, pg. 6172
RADWIN LTD.—See RAD Group; *Int'l*, pg. 6173
RADYNE CORPORATION—See Indel, Inc.; *U.S. Private*, pg. 2055
RA ELECTRIC, INC.—See Hull Street Energy, LLC; *U.S. Private*, pg. 2005
RAE & LIPSKIE INVESTMENT COUNSEL INC.—See Guardian Capital Group Limited; *Int'l*, pg. 3170
RAEMONGRAEIN CO., LTD.; *Int'l*, pg. 6177
RAE REGIONALANTENNE ERMATINGEN AG—See Liberty Global plc; *Int'l*, pg. 4485
RAESCH QUARZ (GERMANY) GMBH—See Dr. Honle AG; *Int'l*, pg. 2192
RAESCH QUARZ (MALTA) LTD.—See Dr. Honle AG; *Int'l*, pg. 2192
RAET B.V.—See HgCapital Trust plc; *Int'l*, pg. 3377
RAFAEL ADVANCED DEFENSE SYSTEMS LTD.; *Int'l*, pg. 6177
RAFAEL BENITEZ CARRILLO, INC.—See Applied Industrial Technologies, Inc.; *U.S. Public*, pg. 171
RAFAEL HOLDINGS, INC.; *U.S. Public*, pg. 1761
RAFAELLA APPAREL GROUP, INC.—See Perry Ellis International, Inc.; *U.S. Private*, pg. 3154
RAFAELLA RESOURCES LTD.; *Int'l*, pg. 6177
RAFAEL LUMBER & SUPPLY COMPANY; *U.S. Private*, pg. 3345
RAFAEL MICROELECTRONICS, INC.; *Int'l*, pg. 6177
RAFAEL USA, INC.—See Rafael Advanced Defense Systems Ltd.; *Int'l*, pg. 6177
RAFAKO S.A.—See PBG S.A.; *Int'l*, pg. 5765
RAFAMET S.A.; *Int'l*, pg. 6177
RAFAUT SA—See HLD Associes SA; *Int'l*, pg. 3431
RAFFAELE CARUSO S.P.A.—See Fosun International Limited; *Int'l*, pg. 2751
RAFFAELLO CAPITAL LIMITED; *Int'l*, pg. 6177
RAFFAELLO CHICAGO HOTEL—See Menin Hotels, Inc.; *U.S. Private*, pg. 2666
RAFFERTY CAPITAL MARKETS, LLC—See Tradeweb Markets Inc.; *U.S. Public*, pg. 2178
RAFFERTY HOLDINGS, LLC; *U.S. Private*, pg. 3345
RAFFERTY PONTIAC GMC, SUBARU; *U.S. Private*, pg. 3345
RAFFERTY'S INC.; *U.S. Private*, pg. 3345
RAFFINERIE TIRLEMONTOISE S.A.—See Suddeutsche Zuckerruben-Verwertungs-Genossenschaft eG; *Int'l*, pg. 7252
RAFFLES CHINESE MEDICINE PTE LTD—See Raffles Medical Group Ltd; *Int'l*, pg. 6177
RAFFLES COLLEGE OF HIGHER EDUCATION SDN. BHD.—See Raffles Education Corporation Limited; *Int'l*, pg. 6177
RAFFLES CONCRETE PTE LTD—See Pan-United Corporation Ltd.; *Int'l*, pg. 5716
RAFFLES DESIGN INSTITUTE PTE LTD—See Raffles Education Corporation Limited; *Int'l*, pg. 6177
RAFFLES DESIGN INTERNATIONAL (THAILAND) LIMITED—See Raffles Education Corporation Limited; *Int'l*, pg. 6177
RAFFLES DIAGNOSTICA PTE LTD—See Raffles Medical Group Ltd; *Int'l*, pg. 6177
RAFFLES EDUCATION CORPORATION LIMITED; *Int'l*, pg. 6177
RAFFLES FINANCIAL GROUP LIMITED; *Int'l*, pg. 6177
RAFFLES HEALTH INSURANCE PTE. LTD.—See Raffles Medical Group Ltd; *Int'l*, pg. 6178
RAFFLES HEALTH PTE LTD—See Raffles Medical Group Ltd; *Int'l*, pg. 6178
RAFFLES HOLDINGS LIMITED—See CapitaLand Investment Limited; *Int'l*, pg. 1314
RAFFLES HOSPITAL BEIJING CO., LTD.—See Raffles Medical Group Ltd; *Int'l*, pg. 6178
RAFFLES HOSPITAL PTE LTD—See Raffles Medical Group Ltd; *Int'l*, pg. 6178
RAFFLES HOSPITAL SHANGHAI CO. LTD.—See Raffles Medical Group Ltd; *Int'l*, pg. 6178
RAFFLES INTERIOR LIMITED; *Int'l*, pg. 6177
RAFFLES INTERNATIONAL COLLEGE (HK) LTD—See Raffles Education Corporation Limited; *Int'l*, pg. 6177
RAFFLES INTERNATIONAL LTD—See Accor S.A.; *Int'l*, pg. 91
RAFFLES JAPANESE CLINIC PTE LTD—See Raffles Medical Group Ltd; *Int'l*, pg. 6178
RAFFLES MARINA LTD—See YTL Corporation Berhad; *Int'l*, pg. 8606
RAFFLES MEDICAL GROUP (HONG KONG) LIMITED—See Raffles Medical Group Ltd; *Int'l*, pg. 6178
RAFFLES MEDICAL GROUP LTD; *Int'l*, pg. 6177
RAFFLES SHIP MANAGEMENT SERVICES PTE LTD—See Wilmar International Limited; *Int'l*, pg. 8421
RAFFLES SHIPPING INTERNATIONAL PTE. LTD.—See Wilmar International Limited; *Int'l*, pg. 8421

RAFFLES SURGICENTRE PTE. LTD.—See Raffles Medical Group Ltd; *Int'l*, pg. 6178
RAFFLES UNITED HOLDINGS LTD.; *Int'l*, pg. 6178
RAF FLUID POWER, INC.—See Electro-Matic Ventures, Inc.; *U.S. Private*, pg. 1354
RAFHAN MAIZE PRODUCTS CO. LTD—See Ingredion Incorporated; *U.S. Public*, pg. 1124
RAFHAN MAIZE PRODUCTS CO. LTD.—See Ingredion Incorporated; *U.S. Public*, pg. 1124
RAFI GMBH & CO. KG—See Brookfield Corporation; *Int'l*, pg. 1182
RAFINA INNOVATIONS INC.; *Int'l*, pg. 6178
RAFINARIA ASTRA ROMANA S.A.; *Int'l*, pg. 6178
RAF INDUSTRIES, INC.; *U.S. Private*, pg. 3345
RAFINERIA TRZEBINIA S.A.—See Orlen S.A.; *Int'l*, pg. 5641
RAFINERIJA NAFTE A.D; *Int'l*, pg. 6178
RAFLATAC CANADA, INC.—See UPM-Kymmene Corporation; *Int'l*, pg. 8091
RAFRA JAPAN K.K.—See Unilever PLC; *Int'l*, pg. 8044
RAF TECHNOLOGY INC.—See Constellation Software Inc.; *Int'l*, pg. 1775
RAFTELIS FINANCIAL CONSULTANTS, INC.; *U.S. Private*, pg. 3345
THE RAFT MARKETING LIMITED; *Int'l*, pg. 7677
RAFT RIVER RURAL ELECTRIC COOPERATIVE, INC.; *U.S. Private*, pg. 3345
RAGAINS ENTERPRISES LLC—See Cineworld Group plc; *Int'l*, pg. 1611
RAG AKTIENGESELLSCHAFT—See RAG-Stiftung; *Int'l*, pg. 6179
RAGAMO SDN. BHD.—See Keck Seng (Malaysia) Berhad; *Int'l*, pg. 4114
RAG AUSTRIA AG—See EVN AG; *Int'l*, pg. 2571
RAG-BETEILIGUNGS-AKTIEN—See EVN AG; *Int'l*, pg. 2571
RAG DEUTSCHE STEINKOHLE AG—See RAG-Stiftung; *Int'l*, pg. 6179
RAGDOLL PRODUCTIONS LIMITED; *Int'l*, pg. 6181
RAGE ADMINISTRATIVE & MARKETING SERVICES, INC.; *U.S. Private*, pg. 3345
RAGE FRAMEWORKS, INC.—See Genpact Limited; *Int'l*, pg. 2927
RAGE FRAMEWORKS INDIA PVT. LTD.—See Genpact Limited; *Int'l*, pg. 2927
RAGEOT EDITEUR, S.N.C.—See Vivendi SE; *Int'l*, pg. 8278
RAGER MOUNTAIN STORAGE COMPANY, LLC—See EQT Corporation; *U.S. Public*, pg. 785
RAGHAVA ESTATES & PROPERTIES LIMITED; *Int'l*, pg. 6181
RAGHAV PRODUCTIVITY ENHANCERS LTD.; *Int'l*, pg. 6181
RAGHUNATH INTERNATIONAL LIMITED; *Int'l*, pg. 6181
RAG HUNGARY KFT.—See EVN AG; *Int'l*, pg. 2571
RAGHUVANSH AGROFARMS LTD.; *Int'l*, pg. 6181
RAGHUVIR SYNTHETICS LIMITED - AHMEDABAD FACTORY—See Raghuvir Synthetics Limited; *Int'l*, pg. 6181
RAGHUVIR SYNTHETICS LIMITED; *Int'l*, pg. 6181
RAGINGBULL.COM, LLC; *U.S. Private*, pg. 3345
RAGING WATERS—See Newgate Private Equity LLP; *Int'l*, pg. 5234
RAGING WATERS—See Newgate Private Equity LLP; *Int'l*, pg. 5234
RAGINGWIRE ENTERPRISE SOLUTIONS INC—See Nippon Telegraph & Telephone Corporation; *Int'l*, pg. 5345
RAGIS KARTOFFELZUCHT- UND HANDELSGESELLSCHAFT MBH—See KWS SAAT SE & Co. KGaA; *Int'l*, pg. 4353
RAGLAND BROS. RETAIL COMPANIES INC.; *U.S. Private*, pg. 3346
RAGLAND MILLS, INC.; *U.S. Private*, pg. 3346
RAGLAN RESOURCES LIMITED—See Dickson Concepts (International) Limited; *Int'l*, pg. 2112
RAGLE INC.; *U.S. Private*, pg. 3346
RA GLOBAL SERVICES, INC.; *U.S. Public*, pg. 1758
RAGNAR BENSON, INC.—See MasTec, Inc.; *U.S. Public*, pg. 1393
RAGNAROK VERMOGENSVERWALTUNG AG & CO. KG—See Hypo Real Estate Holding AG; *Int'l*, pg. 3554
RAGNAR SANDBERG & SONER AB—See Volati AB; *Int'l*, pg. 8301
RAGNI SAS; *Int'l*, pg. 6181
RAGOLD, INC.—See Ragolds Susswaren GmbH & Co.; *Int'l*, pg. 6181
RAGOLDS SUSSWAREN GMBH & CO.; *Int'l*, pg. 6181
RAGO & SON, INC.; *U.S. Private*, pg. 3346
RAGOZZINO FOODS INC.; *U.S. Private*, pg. 3346
RAGSDALE HEATING & AIR CONDITIONING, INC.—See Leonard Green & Partners, L.P.; *U.S. Private*, pg. 2430
RAG-STIFTUNG; *Int'l*, pg. 6178
RAGTAI CENTER CO., LTD.—See Vichitbhan Palmoil Public Company Limited; *Int'l*, pg. 8187
RAGUSA MINERALS LTD.; *Int'l*, pg. 6181
RAGUSE GESELLSCHAFT FUR MEDIZINISCHE PRODUKTE MBH—See INDUS Holding AG; *Int'l*, pg. 3664
RAGUS MEDIA, LLC; *U.S. Private*, pg. 3346

RAG VERKAUF GMBH—See RAG-Stiftung; *Int'l*, pg. 6179
RAHE INC.; *U.S. Private*, pg. 3346
RAHEJA DEVELOPERS PVT. LTD.; *Int'l*, pg. 6182
RAHEJA QBE GENERAL INSURANCE COMPANY LIMITED—See Prism Johnson Limited; *Int'l*, pg. 5982
RAHEJA QBE GENERAL INSURANCE COMPANY LIMITED—See QBE Insurance Group Limited; *Int'l*, pg. 6138
RAHEJA UNIVERSAL LIMITED; *Int'l*, pg. 6182
RAHI BILGI SISTEMLERI DIS TICARET LIMITED SIRKETI—See WESCO International, Inc.; *U.S. Public*, pg. 2351
RAHIMA FOOD CORPORATION LIMITED; *Int'l*, pg. 6182
RAHIM TEXTILE MILLS LIMITED; *Int'l*, pg. 6182
RAH INDUSTRIES; *U.S. Private*, pg. 3346
RAHI SHIPPING PTE. LTD—See Adani Enterprises Limited; *Int'l*, pg. 125
RAHI SYSTEMS AUSTRALIA PTY. LTD.—See WESCO International, Inc.; *U.S. Public*, pg. 2351
RAHI SYSTEMS EUROPE B.V.—See WESCO International, Inc.; *U.S. Public*, pg. 2351
RAHI SYSTEMS GMBH—See WESCO International, Inc.; *U.S. Public*, pg. 2351
RAHI SYSTEMS INC.—See WESCO International, Inc.; *U.S. Public*, pg. 2351
RAHI SYSTEMS JAPAN LLC—See WESCO International, Inc.; *U.S. Public*, pg. 2351
RAHI SYSTEMS LIMITED—See WESCO International, Inc.; *U.S. Public*, pg. 2351
RAHI SYSTEMS PTE. LTD.—See WESCO International, Inc.; *U.S. Public*, pg. 2351
RAHI TECHNOLOGIES LIMITED—See WESCO International, Inc.; *U.S. Public*, pg. 2351
RAHN BAHIA MAR, LLC—See Hilton Worldwide Holdings Inc.; *U.S. Public*, pg. 1041
RAHN CONTRACTING, LLC; *U.S. Private*, pg. 3346
RAHNS CONSTRUCTION MATERIAL CO.—See Haines & Kibblehouse Inc.; *U.S. Private*, pg. 1841
RA HOWARTH ENGINEERING LTD.—See Indutrade AB; *Int'l*, pg. 3681
RAHR CORPORATION; *U.S. Private*, pg. 3346
RAHR MALTING CANADA LTD—See Rahr Malting Co. Inc.; *U.S. Private*, pg. 3346
RAHR MALTING CO. INC.; *U.S. Private*, pg. 3346
RAHR MALTING CO—See Rahr Corporation; *U.S. Private*, pg. 3346
RAHUL MERCHANDISING LIMITED; *Int'l*, pg. 6182
THE RAHWAY SAVINGS INSTITUTION; *U.S. Private*, pg. 4102
RAHWAY STEEL DRUM COMPANY, INC.—See Kelso & Company, L.P.; *U.S. Private*, pg. 2278
RAIA DROGASIL S.A.; *Int'l*, pg. 6182
RAICHLE BOOTS AG—See Kneissl Tirol GmbH; *Int'l*, pg. 4206
RAICO BAUTECHNIK GMBH; *Int'l*, pg. 6182
RAICO EAST—See RAICO Bautechnik GmbH; *Int'l*, pg. 6182
RAICO FRANCE S.A.R.L.—See RAICO Bautechnik GmbH; *Int'l*, pg. 6182
RAI CORPORATION—See RAI Radiotelevisione Italiana S.p.A.; *Int'l*, pg. 6182
RAICO SWISS GMBH—See RAICO Bautechnik GmbH; *Int'l*, pg. 6182
RAICO UK—See RAICO Bautechnik GmbH; *Int'l*, pg. 6182
RAIDEEP INDUSTRIES LIMITED; *Int'l*, pg. 6182
RAIDEN RESOURCES LTD.; *Int'l*, pg. 6182
RAIFEISEN LEASING D.O.O.—See UniCredit S.p.A.; *Int'l*, pg. 8033
RAIFFEISEN AGRO D.O.O.—See BayWa AG; *Int'l*, pg. 918
RAIFFEISEN AGRO MAGYARORSZAG KFT.—See BayWa AG; *Int'l*, pg. 918
RAIFFEISEN APART GMBH—See Raiffeisen Bank International AG; *Int'l*, pg. 6183
RAIFFEISEN ASSET MANAGEMENT (BULGARIA) EAD—See KBC Group NV; *Int'l*, pg. 4106
RAIFFEISEN BANKA A.D.—See Raiffeisen Bank International AG; *Int'l*, pg. 6184
RAIFFEISENBANK A.S.—See Raiffeisen Bank International AG; *Int'l*, pg. 6184
RAIFFEISENBANK AUSTRIA D.D.—See Raiffeisen Bank International AG; *Int'l*, pg. 6184
RAIFFEISEN BANK AVAL, JSC—See Raiffeisen Bank International AG; *Int'l*, pg. 6183
RAIFFEISENBANK (BULGARIA) EAD—See KBC Group NV; *Int'l*, pg. 4106
RAIFFEISEN BANK D.D. BOSNA I HERCEGOVINA—See Raiffeisen Bank International AG; *Int'l*, pg. 6183
RAIFFEISENBANK-IMMOBILIEN GMBH—See Raiffeisen Bank Wesermarsch-Sud eG; *Int'l*, pg. 6184
RAIFFEISEN BANK INTERNATIONAL AG; *Int'l*, pg. 6182
RAIFFEISENBANK JSC; *Int'l*, pg. 6186
RAIFFEISEN BANK KOSOVO J.S.C—See Raiffeisen Bank International AG; *Int'l*, pg. 6183
RAIFFEISEN BANK (LIECHTENSTEIN) AG—See Walser Privatbank AG; *Int'l*, pg. 8334
RAIFFEISEN BANK POLSKA S.A.—See Raiffeisen Bank International AG; *Int'l*, pg. 6183
RAIFFEISENBANK REUTTE REG. GEN.M.B.H.; *Int'l*, pg. 6186

RAIFFEISEN BANK S.A.—See Raiffeisen Bank International AG; *Int'l*, pg. 6183
RAIFFEISEN BANK SH.A.—See Raiffeisen Bank International AG; *Int'l*, pg. 6183
RAIFFEISEN BANK WESERMARSCH-SUD EG; *Int'l*, pg. 6184
RAIFFEISEN BANK ZRT.—See Raiffeisen Bank International AG; *Int'l*, pg. 6183
RAIFFEISEN BAUSPARKASSE GESELLSCHAFT M.B.H.—See Raiffeisen Bank International AG; *Int'l*, pg. 6183
RAIFFEISEN BAU TIROL GMBH—See Raiffeisen-Landesbank Tirol AG; *Int'l*, pg. 6186
RAIFFEISEN CAPITAL A.D. BANJA LUKA—See Raiffeisen Bank International AG; *Int'l*, pg. 6183
RAIFFEISEN CENTROBANK AG—See Raiffeisen Bank International AG; *Int'l*, pg. 6183
RAIFFEISEN CORPORATE LIZING ZRT.—See UniCredit S.p.A.; *Int'l*, pg. 8033
RAIFFEISEN DIGITAL BANK AG—See Raiffeisen Bank International AG; *Int'l*, pg. 6183
RAIFFEISEN GROUP IT GMBH—See Raiffeisen Bank International AG; *Int'l*, pg. 6183
RAIFFEISEN-HOLDING NIEDEROSTERREICH-WIEN REG. GEN.M.B.H.; *Int'l*, pg. 6185
RAIFFEISEN IMMOBILIEN GESELLSCHAFT M.B.H.—See Raiffeisenlandesbank Vorarlberg Waren- und Revisionsverband reg. Gen.m.b.H.; *Int'l*, pg. 6188
RAIFFEISEN IMMOBILIEN GMBH, RENDSBURG—See VR-Immobilien Norddeutschland; *Int'l*, pg. 8313
RAIFFEISEN-IMPULS-LEASING GESELLSCHAFT M.B.H.—See Raiffeisenlandesbank Oberosterreich Aktiengesellschaft; *Int'l*, pg. 6187
RAIFFEISEN-IMPULS-LEASING GMBH & CO. KG—See Raiffeisenlandesbank Oberosterreich Aktiengesellschaft; *Int'l*, pg. 6187
RAIFFEISEN INFORMATIK GMBH—See Raiffeisen Bank International AG; *Int'l*, pg. 6183
RAIFFEISEN INFORMATIK GMBH—See Raiffeisen-Holding Niederosterreich-Wien reg. Gen.m.b.H.; *Int'l*, pg. 6185
RAIFFEISEN INVESTMENT POLSKA SP. Z O.O.—See Raiffeisen Bank International AG; *Int'l*, pg. 6183
RAIFFEISEN INVEST SH.A.—See Raiffeisen Bank International AG; *Int'l*, pg. 6183
RAIFFEISEN-LAGERHAUS GMBH—See BayWa AG; *Int'l*, pg. 918
RAIFFEISEN-LAGERHAUS INVESTITIONSHOLDING GMBH—See BayWa AG; *Int'l*, pg. 918
RAIFFEISENLANDESBANK BURGENLAND UND REVISIONSVERBAND REG. GEN.M.B.H.; *Int'l*, pg. 6186
RAIFFEISENLANDESBANK KARNTEN-RECHENZENTRUM UND REVISIONSVERBAND, REG. GEN.M.B.H.; *Int'l*, pg. 6187
RAIFFEISENLANDESBANK NIEDEROSTERREICH-WIEN AG—See Raiffeisen-Holding Niederosterreich-Wien reg. Gen.m.b.H.; *Int'l*, pg. 6185
RAIFFEISENLANDESBANK OBEROSTERREICH AKTIENGESELLSCHAFT; *Int'l*, pg. 6187
RAIFFEISEN-LANDESBANK STEIERMARK AG; *Int'l*, pg. 6186
RAIFFEISEN-LANDESBANK TIROL AG; *Int'l*, pg. 6186
RAIFFEISENLANDESBANK VORARLBERG WAREN- UND REVISIONSVERBAND REG. GEN.M.B.H.; *Int'l*, pg. 6188
RAIFFEISEN LEASING BULGARIA OOD—See KBC Group NV; *Int'l*, pg. 4106
RAIFFEISEN LEASING D.O.O.—See UniCredit S.p.A.; *Int'l*, pg. 8034
RAIFFEISEN LEASING D.O.O.—See Raiffeisen Bank International AG; *Int'l*, pg. 6184
RAIFFEISEN LEASING D.O.O.—See Raiffeisen Bank International AG; *Int'l*, pg. 6184
RAIFFEISEN-LEASING GMBH—See UniCredit S.p.A.; *Int'l*, pg. 8034
RAIFFEISEN LEASING IFN S.A.—See UniCredit S.p.A.; *Int'l*, pg. 8034
RAIFFEISEN LEASING KAZAKHSTAN LLP—See UniCredit S.p.A.; *Int'l*, pg. 8034
RAIFFEISEN-LEASING REAL ESTATE, S.R.O.—See Raiffeisen Bank International AG; *Int'l*, pg. 6184
RAIFFEISEN LEASING SH.A.—See UniCredit S.p.A.; *Int'l*, pg. 8034
RAIFFEISEN LIENEN-LENGERICH GMBH—See AGRAVIS Raiffeisen AG; *Int'l*, pg. 215
RAIFFEISEN LIFE INSURANCE COMPANY LLC—See UNIQA Insurance Group AG; *Int'l*, pg. 8058
RAIFFEISEN PROPERTY INTERNATIONAL GMBH—See Raiffeisen Bank International AG; *Int'l*, pg. 6184
RAIFFEISEN RECHENZENTRUM HOLDING GMBH—See Raiffeisen-Landesbank Steiermark AG; *Int'l*, pg. 6186
RAIFFEISEN REISEBURO GES.M.B.H.—See Raiffeisen- und Volksbanken Touristik GmbH; *Int'l*, pg. 6185
RAIFFEISEN SALZBURG INVEST KAPITALANLAGE GMBH—See Raiffeisen Bank International AG; *Int'l*, pg. 6184
RAIFFEISEN SCHWEIZ GENOSSENSCHAFT; *Int'l*, pg. 6185

RAIFFEISEN SCHWEIZ GENOSSENSCHAFT

RAIFFEISEN STAMBENA STEDIONICA D.D.—See Raiffeisen Bank International AG; *Int'l*, pg. 6184
RAIFFEISEN TECH GMBH—See Raiffeisen Bank International AG; *Int'l*, pg. 6184
RAIFFEISEN TOURISTIK GROUP GMBH; *Int'l*, pg. 6185
RAIFFEISEN TRGOVINA D.O.O.—See BayWa AG; *Int'l*, pg. 918
RAIFFEISEN- UND VOLKSBANKEN TOURISTIK GMBH; *Int'l*, pg. 6185
RAIFFEISENVERBAND SALZBURG REG. GEN.M.B.H.; *Int'l*, pg. 6188
RAIFFEISEN VERSICHERUNG AG—See UNIQA Insurance Group AG; *Int'l*, pg. 8058
RAIFFEISEN WAREN GMBH—See BayWa AG; *Int'l*, pg. 918
RAIFFEISEN-WARENVERBAND TIROL REG. GENOSSENSCHAFT M.B.H.; *Int'l*, pg. 6186
RAIFF PARTNERS, INC.; *U.S. Private*, pg. 3346
RAIGAM MARKETING SERVICES (PVT) LTD.; *Int'l*, pg. 6188
RAIGAM WAYAMBA SALTERNS (PVT.) LIMITED.—See Raigam Marketing Services (Pvt) Ltd; *Int'l*, pg. 6188
RAILAMERICA, INC.—See Brookfield Infrastructure Partners L.P.; *Int'l*, pg. 1192
RAILAMERICA, INC.—See GIC Pte. Ltd.; *Int'l*, pg. 2967
RAILAMERICA TRANSPORTATION CORP.—See Brookfield Infrastructure Partners L.P.; *Int'l*, pg. 1192
RAILAMERICA TRANSPORTATION CORP.—See GIC Pte. Ltd.; *Int'l*, pg. 2967
RAILAWAY AG—See Schweizerische Bundesbahnen SBB AG; *Int'l*, pg. 6646
RAIL BEARING SERVICE CORP.—See The Timken Company; *U.S. Public*, pg. 2133
THE RAIL-BRIDGE TERMINALS (NEW JERSEY) CORPORATION—See Kawasaki Kisen Kaisha, Ltd.; *Int'l*, pg. 4099
RAILCARE AG—See Coop-Gruppe Genossenschaft; *Int'l*, pg. 1790
RAILCARE GROUP AB; *Int'l*, pg. 6188
RAILCARE INC.—See Brookfield Infrastructure Partners L.P.; *Int'l*, pg. 1192
RAILCARE INC.—See GIC Pte. Ltd.; *Int'l*, pg. 2967
RAIL CARGO AUSTRIA AKTIENGESELLSCHAFT—See OBB-Holding AG; *Int'l*, pg. 5509
RAIL CARGO ITALIA S.R.L.—See OBB-Holding AG; *Int'l*, pg. 5510
RAIL CARGO LOGISTICS - CZECH REPUBLIC S.R.O.—See OBB-Holding AG; *Int'l*, pg. 5510
RAIL CARGO OPERATOR - HUNGARIA KFT.—See OBB-Holding AG; *Int'l*, pg. 5510
RAIL CARGO ROMANIA S.R.L.—See OBB-Holding AG; *Int'l*, pg. 5510
RAIL CARGO TERMINAL - BILK ZRT.—See OBB-Holding AG; *Int'l*, pg. 5510
RAILCAR MANAGEMENT, LLC—See General Electric Company; *U.S. Public*, pg. 920
RAILCERT B.V.—See TUV SUD AG; *Int'l*, pg. 7986
RAIL CITY CASINO—See Truckee Gaming LLC; *U.S. Private*, pg. 4246
RAILCOMM LLC—See Tracsis Plc; *Int'l*, pg. 7887
RAIL DELIVERY SERVICES, INC.; *U.S. Private*, pg. 3346
RAIL ELECTRIFICATION LTD.—See Renew Holdings plc; *Int'l*, pg. 6278
RAIL ENGINEERING SP. Z O.O.—See Alstom S.A.; *Int'l*, pg. 383
RAIL EQUIPMENT GMBH & CO KG—See OBB-Holding AG; *Int'l*, pg. 5509
RAIL EQUIPMENT GMBH—See OBB-Holding AG; *Int'l*, pg. 5509
RAIL EUROPE ESPANA—See SNCF; *Int'l*, pg. 7026
RAIL EUROPE INC.—See SNCF; *Int'l*, pg. 7026
RAILINC CORP.—See Association of American Railroads; *U.S. Private*, pg. 358
RAIL INTERMODEL SPECIALISTS—See TSL Companies; *U.S. Private*, pg. 4254
RAIL LINE COMPONENTS, S.L.U.—See Construcciones y Auxiliar de Ferrocarriles S.A.; *Int'l*, pg. 1777
RAIL LINK, INC.—See Brookfield Infrastructure Partners L.P.; *Int'l*, pg. 1192
RAIL LINK, INC.—See GIC Pte. Ltd.; *Int'l*, pg. 2967
RAIL & LOGISTIK CENTER WUSTERMARK GMBH & CO. KG—See Havellandische Eisenbahn AG; *Int'l*, pg. 3286
RAILMAINT GMBH—See Iberia Industry Capital Group SARL; *Int'l*, pg. 3574
RAILMARK HOLDINGS INC.; *U.S. Private*, pg. 3346
RAIL PRODUCTION AS—See Inin Group AS; *Int'l*, pg. 3703
RAIL PRODUCT SOLUTIONS LLC—See Caterpillar, Inc.; *U.S. Public*, pg. 453
RAILPROS, INC.—See Court Square Capital Partners, L.P.; *U.S. Private*, pg. 1070
RAILREST S.A.—See Cremonini S.p.A.; *Int'l*, pg. 1838
RAILROAD CONSTRUCTION COMPANY, INC.; *U.S. Private*, pg. 3346
RAILROAD CONTROLS, LP—See Westinghouse Air Brake Technologies Corporation; *U.S. Public*, pg. 2359
RAILROAD DEVELOPMENT CORP.; *U.S. Private*, pg. 3346
RAILROAD DISTRIBUTION SERVICES, INC.—See Pinsly Railroad Co. Inc.; *U.S. Private*, pg. 3186
RAILROAD DISTRIBUTION SERVICES, INC.—See Brookfield Infrastructure Partners L.P.; *Int'l*, pg. 1192
RAILROAD DISTRIBUTION SERVICES, INC.—See GIC Pte. Ltd.; *Int'l*, pg. 2967
RAILROAD DISTRIBUTION SERVICES, INC.—See Pinsly Railroad Co. Inc.; *U.S. Private*, pg. 3186
RAILROAD FRICTION PRODUCTS CORPORATION—See Westinghouse Air Brake Technologies Corporation; *U.S. Public*, pg. 2359
RAILROAD PASS INVESTMENT GROUP—See MGM Resorts International; *U.S. Public*, pg. 1435
RAILSBANK TECHNOLOGY LIMITED; *Int'l*, pg. 6188
RAILS COMPANY; *U.S. Private*, pg. 3346
RAILSERVE INC.—See Berkshire Hathaway Inc.; *U.S. Public*, pg. 311
RAIL SERVICE CENTER ROTTERDAM B. V.—See Deutsche Bahn AG; *Int'l*, pg. 2051
RAIL SERVICE HUNGARIA KFT.—See OBB-Holding AG; *Int'l*, pg. 5509
RAILTECH ALU SINGEN SAS—See CVC Capital Partners SICAV-FIS S.A.; *Int'l*, pg. 1887
RAILTECH AUSTRALIA LTD.—See CVC Capital Partners SICAV-FIS S.A.; *Int'l*, pg. 1887
RAILTECH BOUTET INC.—See CVC Capital Partners SICAV-FIS S.A.; *Int'l*, pg. 1887
RAILTECH CALOMEX S. DE R. L. DE C. V.—See CVC Capital Partners SICAV-FIS S.A.; *Int'l*, pg. 1887
RAILTECH DEUTSCHLAND GMBH—See CVC Capital Partners SICAV-FIS S.A.; *Int'l*, pg. 1887
RAILTECH INTERNATIONAL—See CVC Capital Partners SICAV-FIS S.A.; *Int'l*, pg. 1887
RAILTECH PANDROL CHINA LTD.—See CVC Capital Partners SICAV-FIS S.A.; *Int'l*, pg. 1887
RAILTECH PANDROL ITALIA SRL—See CVC Capital Partners SICAV-FIS S.A.; *Int'l*, pg. 1887
RAILTECH PORSOL LDA.—See CVC Capital Partners SICAV-FIS S.A.; *Int'l*, pg. 1887
RAILTECH SCHLATTER SYSTEMS, S.A.S.—See CVC Capital Partners SICAV-FIS S.A.; *Int'l*, pg. 1887
RAILTECH STEDEF LTD—See CVC Capital Partners SICAV-FIS S.A.; *Int'l*, pg. 1887
RAILTECH UK LTD—See CVC Capital Partners SICAV-FIS S.A.; *Int'l*, pg. 1887
RAILTEL CORPORATION OF INDIA LIMITED; *Int'l*, pg. 6188
RAILTEL ENTERPRISES LIMITED—See Railtel Corporation of India Limited; *Int'l*, pg. 6188
RAIL TO ROAD, INC.—See MDU Resources Group, Inc.; *U.S. Public*, pg. 1411
RAILTOUR SUISSE SA—See REWE-Zentral-Aktiengesellschaft; *Int'l*, pg. 6314
RAIL VIKAS NIGAM LTD.; *Int'l*, pg. 6188
RAIL VISION LTD.; *Int'l*, pg. 6188
RAILWAY APPROVALS GERMANY GMBH—See Deutsche Bahn AG; *Int'l*, pg. 2052
RAILWAY APPROVALS LTD—See Deutsche Bahn AG; *Int'l*, pg. 2052
RAILWAY CLAIM SERVICES INC.; *U.S. Private*, pg. 3346
RAILWAY DISTRIBUTING INC.; *U.S. Private*, pg. 3346
RAILWAY EDUCATIONAL BUREAU—See Simmons-Boardman Publishing Corp.; *U.S. Private*, pg. 3665
THE RAILWAY ENGINEERING COMPANY LIMITED—See Hitachi, Ltd.; *Int'l*, pg. 3417
RAILWAY GFT POLSKA SP. Z O.O.—See ZUE S.A.; *Int'l*, pg. 8692
RAILWAY TRACK AND STRUCTURES TECHNOLOGY CO., LTD.—See West Japan Railway Company; *Int'l*, pg. 8385
RAILWAY TRANSIT EQUIPMENT CO., LTD.—See Taiyuan Heavy Industry Co., Ltd.; *Int'l*, pg. 7427
RAILWORKS CORP.—See Wind Point Advisors LLC; *U.S. Private*, pg. 4535
RAILWORKS SIGNALS & COMMUNICATIONS, INC.—See Wind Point Advisors LLC; *U.S. Private*, pg. 4535
RAILWORKS TRACK SYSTEMS, INC.—See Wind Point Advisors LLC; *U.S. Private*, pg. 4535
RAILWORKS TRANSIT, INC.—See Wind Point Advisors LLC; *U.S. Private*, pg. 4535
RAILY AESTHETIC MEDICINE INTERNATIONAL HOLDINGS LIMITED; *Int'l*, pg. 6188
RAIMANN HOLZOPTIMIERUNG GMBH & CO. KG—See Michael Weinig AG; *Int'l*, pg. 4875
RAIMON LAND PUBLIC COMPANY LIMITED; *Int'l*, pg. 6188
RAI MOST S.R.O.—See Recticel S.A.; *Int'l*, pg. 6241
RAIN AND HAIL INSURANCE SERVICE, INC.—See Chubb Limited; *Int'l*, pg. 1592
RAIN AND HAIL INSURANCE SERVICE, LTD.—See Chubb Limited; *Int'l*, pg. 1592
RAIN ASSOCIATES; *U.S. Private*, pg. 3347
RAINBERGSTRASSE - IMMOBILIENPROJEKTENTWICKLUNGS GMBH—See PORR AG; *Int'l*, pg. 5925
RAIN BIRD CORPORATION - RAIN BIRD GOLF DIVISION—See Rain Bird Corporation; *U.S. Private*, pg. 3347

CORPORATE AFFILIATIONS

RAIN BIRD CORPORATION - RESIDENTIAL PRODUCTS DIVISION—See Rain Bird Corporation; *U.S. Private*, pg. 3347
RAIN BIRD CORPORATION; *U.S. Private*, pg. 3347
RAINBO OIL COMPANY; *U.S. Private*, pg. 3347
RAINBO RECORD MANUFACTURING CORP; *U.S. Private*, pg. 3347
RAINBOW APPAREL COMPANIES INC.—See AIJJ Enterprises Inc.; *U.S. Private*, pg. 132
RAINBOW AUTOMOTIVE LLC; *U.S. Private*, pg. 3347
RAINBOW CASINO-VICKSBURG PARTNERSHIP, L.P.—See Bally's Corporation; *U.S. Public*, pg. 268
RAINBOW CHILDREN'S HOSPITAL PRIVATE LIMITED—See Rainbow Children's Medicare Limited; *Int'l*, pg. 6189
RAINBOW CHILDREN'S MEDICARE LIMITED; *Int'l*, pg. 6189
RAINBOW CORAL CORP.; *U.S. Private*, pg. 3347
RAINBOW DENIM LTD; *Int'l*, pg. 6189
RAINBOW DESIGN BUILDERS, INC.; *U.S. Private*, pg. 3347
RAINBOW DIGITAL COMMERCIAL CO., LTD.; *Int'l*, pg. 6189
RAINBOW ENTITY SDN. BHD.—See Gromutual Berhad; *Int'l*, pg. 3087
RAINBOW ENVIRONMENTAL SERVICES, LLC—See Republic Services, Inc.; *U.S. Public*, pg. 1787
RAINBOW FORD SALES INC; *Int'l*, pg. 6189
RAINBOW FOUNDATIONS LTD.; *Int'l*, pg. 6190
RAINBOW GRAPHICS INC.; *U.S. Private*, pg. 3347
RAINBOW HOLDCO LIMITED; *Int'l*, pg. 6190
RAINBOW INC.; *U.S. Private*, pg. 3347
RAINBOW INTERNATIONAL LLC—See Harvest Partners L.P.; *U.S. Private*, pg. 1877
RAINBOW LIGHT NUTRITIONAL SYSTEMS, INC.; *U.S. Private*, pg. 3347
RAINBOW MARBLE & TILING SDN. BHD.—See Stone Master Corporation Berhad; *Int'l*, pg. 7222
RAINBOW MOTOR SCHOOL CO., LTD.—See Honda Motor Co., Ltd.; *Int'l*, pg. 3464
RAINBOW MOVERS INC.; *U.S. Private*, pg. 3347
RAINBOW PAPERS LTD - COATING DIVISION—See Rainbow Papers Ltd; *Int'l*, pg. 6190
RAINBOW PAPERS LTD - PAPER & CREPE UNITS—See Rainbow Papers Ltd; *Int'l*, pg. 6190
RAINBOW PAPERS LTD; *Int'l*, pg. 6190
RAINBOW PROPERTIES SDN BHD—See GSH Corporation Limited; *Int'l*, pg. 3144
RAINBOW RARE EARTHS LTD.; *Int'l*, pg. 6190
RAINBOW RASCALS LEARNING CENTER, INC.; *U.S. Private*, pg. 3347
RAINBOW ROBOTICS CO., LTD.; *Int'l*, pg. 6190
RAINBOW RYDERS INC.; *U.S. Private*, pg. 3347
RAINBOW SHOKUHIN CO., LTD.—See Aohata Corporation; *Int'l*, pg. 487
RAINBOW STATION INC.; *U.S. Private*, pg. 3347
RAINBOW TECH INFORMATION (HK) LTD.—See SYSTEX Corporation; *Int'l*, pg. 7393
RAINBOW TECHNOLOGY CORPORATION; *U.S. Private*, pg. 3347
RAINBOW TOURISM GROUP LIMITED; *Int'l*, pg. 6190
RAINBOW TOURS S.A.; *Int'l*, pg. 6190
RAINBOW TRANSFER/RECYCLING, INC.—See Republic Services, Inc.; *U.S. Public*, pg. 1787
RAINBOW WEST APPAREL, INC.—See Platinum Equity, LLC; *U.S. Private*, pg. 3203
RAIN CARBON B.V.—See Rain Industries Limited; *Int'l*, pg. 6189
RAIN CARBON CANADA INC.—See Rain Industries Limited; *Int'l*, pg. 6189
RAIN CARBON GERMANY GMBH—See Rain Industries Limited; *Int'l*, pg. 6189
RAIN CARBON INC.—See Rain Industries Limited; *Int'l*, pg. 6189
RAIN CARBON (SHANGHAI) TRADING CO. LTD.—See Rain Industries Limited; *Int'l*, pg. 6189
RAIN CII CARBON (INDIA) LIMITED—See Rain Industries Limited; *Int'l*, pg. 6189
RAIN CII CARBON (INDIA) LIMITED - VISAKHAPATNAM—See Rain Industries Limited; *Int'l*, pg. 6189
RAIN CII CARBON LLC - CHALMETTE—See Rain Industries Limited; *Int'l*, pg. 6189
RAIN CII CARBON LLC - GRAMERCY—See Rain Industries Limited; *Int'l*, pg. 6189
RAIN CII CARBON LLC - LAKE CHARLES—See Rain Industries Limited; *Int'l*, pg. 6189
RAIN CII CARBON LLC - NORCO—See Rain Industries Limited; *Int'l*, pg. 6189
RAIN CII CARBON LLC - PURVIS—See Rain Industries Limited; *Int'l*, pg. 6189
RAIN CII CARBON LLC - ROBINSON—See Rain Industries Limited; *Int'l*, pg. 6189
RAIN CII CARBON LLC—See Rain Industries Limited; *Int'l*, pg. 6189
RAIN CITY RESOURCES, INC.; *Int'l*, pg. 6189
RAINDANCE TECHNOLOGIES, INC.—See Bio-Rad Laboratories, Inc.; *U.S. Public*, pg. 334

COMPANY NAME INDEX

RAINDROP HEARING CLINICI INC.—See Amplifon S.p.A.; *Int'l*, pg. 436
RAINERI BUILDING MATERIALS, INC.—See Breedon Group plc; *Int'l*, pg. 1144
RAINER KIEL KANALSANIERUNG GMBH; *Int'l*, pg. 6190
RAINES IMPORTS, INC.; *U.S. Private*, pg. 3347
RAINEY KELLY CAMPBELL ROALFE/Y&R—See WPP plc; *Int'l*, pg. 8492
RAINEY ROAD HOLDINGS, INC.; *U.S. Private*, pg. 3347
RAINEY ROAD LLC—See Rainey Road Holdings, Inc.; *U.S. Private*, pg. 3347
RAINFOREST ALLIANCE; *U.S. Private*, pg. 3348
RAINFOREST CAFE, INC.—See Fertitta Entertainment, Inc.; *U.S. Private*, pg. 1499
RAINFOREST DISTRIBUTION CORP; *U.S. Private*, pg. 3348
RAINFOREST INC.; *U.S. Private*, pg. 3348
RAIN FOREST INTERNATIONAL, INC.; *Int'l*, pg. 6189
RAINFOREST RESOURCES, INC.; *U.S. Public*, pg. 1761
RAIN GLOBAL SERVICES LLC—See Rain Industries Limited; *Int'l*, pg. 6189
RAIN GUARD; *U.S. Private*, pg. 3347
RAIN & HAIL LLC—See Chubb Limited; *Int'l*, pg. 1592
RAIN HOLDING LIMITED—See Rain Industries Limited; *Int'l*, pg. 6189
RAIN HOME ATTENDANT SERVICES INC; *U.S. Private*, pg. 3347
RAINIER INDUSTRIES, LTD.; *U.S. Private*, pg. 3348
RAINIER INVESTMENT MANAGEMENT, INC.—See Callodine Acquisition Corporation; *U.S. Public*, pg. 424
RAINIER PARTNERS LP; *U.S. Private*, pg. 3348
RAINIER SEED INC.; *U.S. Private*, pg. 3348
RAINIER SYMPHONY; *U.S. Private*, pg. 3348
RAINIER VIEW WATER CO, INC.—See California Water Service Group; *U.S. Public*, pg. 424
RAINIER WELDING, INC.—See Ranch Creek Partners, LLC; *U.S. Private*, pg. 3352
RAIN INDUSTRIES LIMITED; *Int'l*, pg. 6189
RAINING ROSE, INC.; *U.S. Private*, pg. 3348
RAININ INSTRUMENT LLC—See Mettler-Toledo International, Inc.; *U.S. Public*, pg. 1433
RAIN KING SOFTWARE, INC.—See TA Associates, Inc.; *U.S. Private*, pg. 3915
RAINMAKER BLUE LIMITED—See Optic Security Group Limited; *Int'l*, pg. 5602
RAINMAKER CAPITAL, LLC; *U.S. Private*, pg. 3348
RAINMAKER DOCUMENT TECHNOLOGIES, INC.—See Sentinel Capital Partners, L.L.C.; *U.S. Private*, pg. 3609
THE RAINMAKER GROUP VENTURES, LLC.; *U.S. Private*, pg. 4102
RAINMAKER SYSTEMS, INC.; *U.S. Public*, pg. 1761
RAINMAKER WORLDWIDE, INC.; *Int'l*, pg. 6190
RAIN MASTER IRRIGATION SYSTEMS, INC.—See The Toro Company; *U.S. Public*, pg. 2135
RAINMED MEDICAL LTD.; *Int'l*, pg. 6190
RAIN ONCOLOGY INC.—See Pathos AI, Inc.; *U.S. Private*, pg. 3106
RAINSBERGER WEALTH ADVISORS, INC.—See Affiliated Managers Group, Inc.; *U.S. Public*, pg. 56
RAINSBERGER WEALTH ADVISORS, LLC—See HGGC, LLC; *U.S. Private*, pg. 1930
RAINS BIRCHARD INC.; *U.S. Private*, pg. 3348
RAINSOFT WATER TREATMENT SYSTEMS—See Aquion Partners L.P.; *U.S. Private*, pg. 305
RAIN; *U.S. Private*, pg. 3346
RAIN; *U.S. Private*, pg. 3346
RAINSVILLE TECHNOLOGY, INC.—See Moriroku Holdings Company, Ltd.; *Int'l*, pg. 5047
RA INTERNATIONAL GROUP PLC; *Int'l*, pg. 6171
RAINTON GARDENS (CHILTON MOOR) MANAGEMENT COMPANY LIMITED—See Persimmon plc; *Int'l*, pg. 5817
RAINTREE COVE PTE. LTD.—See Top Global Limited; *Int'l*, pg. 7812
RAINTREE LUMBER SPECIALTIES LTD—See E.R. Probyn Ltd.; *Int'l*, pg. 2260
RAINTREE SYSTEMS, INC.; *U.S. Private*, pg. 3348
RAINTREE VILLAGE, L.L.C.—See Lennar Corporation; *U.S. Public*, pg. 1307
RAINY MOUNTAIN ROYALTY CORP.; *Int'l*, pg. 6190
RAI RADIOTELEVISIONE ITALIANA S.P.A.; *Int'l*, pg. 6182
RAIRANG HYDROPOWER DEVELOPMENT CO., LTD.—See Ridi Power Company Limited; *Int'l*, pg. 6338
RAISBECK ENGINEERING, INC.—See Acorn Growth Companies, LC; *U.S. Private*, pg. 63
RAISECOM TECHNOLOGY CO., LTD.; *Int'l*, pg. 6190
RAISER SENIOR SERVICES LLC; *U.S. Private*, pg. 3348
RAISING CANE'S USA, LLC; *U.S. Private*, pg. 3348
RAISIOAGRO LTD - KOUVOLA FACTORY—See Raisio PLC; *Int'l*, pg. 6191
RAISIOAGRO LTD - RAISIO FACTORY—See Raisio PLC; *Int'l*, pg. 6191
RAISIOAGRO LTD - YLIVIESKA FACTORY—See Raisio PLC; *Int'l*, pg. 6191
RAISIO BENECOL LTD.—See Raisio PLC; *Int'l*, pg. 6191
RAISIO ECHEVESTE S.A.—See Raisio PLC; *Int'l*, pg. 6191
RAISIO EESTI AS—See Raisio PLC; *Int'l*, pg. 6191
RAISIO FEED LTD.—See Raisio PLC; *Int'l*, pg. 6191

RAISIO GRAIN STARCH LTD.—See Raisio PLC; *Int'l*, pg. 6191
RAISIO GROUP, ST. PETERSBURG—See Raisio PLC; *Int'l*, pg. 6191
RAISIO MALT—See Raisio PLC; *Int'l*, pg. 6191
RAISION KONSERNIPALVELUT OY—See Raisio PLC; *Int'l*, pg. 6191
RAISIO NORDIC, LITHUANIA—See Raisio PLC; *Int'l*, pg. 6191
RAISIO NUTRITION LTD - NOKIA FACTORY—See Raisio PLC; *Int'l*, pg. 6191
RAISIO NUTRITION LTD - RAISIO FACTORY—See Raisio PLC; *Int'l*, pg. 6191
RAISIO NUTRITION LTD—See Raisio PLC; *Int'l*, pg. 6191
RAISIO PLC; *Int'l*, pg. 6190
RAISIO PORTUGAL-PRODUTOS QUIMICOS, LDA.—See Raisio PLC; *Int'l*, pg. 6191
RAISIO SP. Z.O.O.—See Raisio PLC; *Int'l*, pg. 6191
RAISON D'ETRE SPAS SWEDEN AB—See InterContinental Hotels Group PLC; *Int'l*, pg. 3739
RAIT FINANCIAL TRUST; *U.S. Private*, pg. 3348
RAIT-MELODY 2016 HOLDINGS TRUST—See RAIT Financial Trust; *U.S. Private*, pg. 3349
RAITO, INC.—See RAITO KOGYO Co., Ltd.; *Int'l*, pg. 6191
RAITO KOGYO CO., LTD.; *Int'l*, pg. 6191
RAITO SINGAPORE PTE. LTD.—See RAITO KOGYO Co., Ltd.; *Int'l*, pg. 6191
RAIT PARTNERSHIP, L.P.—See RAIT Financial Trust; *U.S. Private*, pg. 3349
RAI WAY S.P.A.; *Int'l*, pg. 6182
RAIZEN ENERGIA S.A.—See Raizen S.A.; *Int'l*, pg. 6191
RAIZEN S.A.; *Int'l*, pg. 6191
RAIZEN TRADING LLP—See Raizen S.A.; *Int'l*, pg. 6192
RAIZ INVEST LIMITED; *Int'l*, pg. 6191
RAIZNEXT CORPORATION; *Int'l*, pg. 6192
RAJA BAHADUR INTERNATIONAL LIMITED; *Int'l*, pg. 6192
RAJA FERRY PORT PCL; *Int'l*, pg. 6192
THE RAJA GROUP; *Int'l*, pg. 7677
RAJANG PLYWOOD (SABAH) SDN. BHD.—See Eksons Corporation Berhad; *Int'l*, pg. 2339
RAJANG PLYWOOD SAWMILL SDN. BHD.—See Eksons Corporation Berhad; *Int'l*, pg. 2339
RAJANI, SINGHANIA & PARTNERS; *Int'l*, pg. 6192
RAJANI, SINGHANIA & PARTNERS—See Rajani, Singhania & Partners; *Int'l*, pg. 6193
RAJAPALAYAM MILLS LTD; *Int'l*, pg. 6193
RAJA SA—See The RAJA Group; *Int'l*, pg. 7678
RAJASTHAN CYLINDERS & CONTAINERS LTD.; *Int'l*, pg. 6193
RAJASTHAN GASES LTD.; *Int'l*, pg. 6193
RAJASTHAN PETRO SYNTHETICS LTD.; *Int'l*, pg. 6193
RAJASTHAN TUBE MANUFACTURING COMPANY LTD.; *Int'l*, pg. 6193
RAJATH FINANCE LIMITED; *Int'l*, pg. 6193
RAJA UCHINO CO., LTD.—See Saha Pathanapibul Public Company Limited; *Int'l*, pg. 6479
RAJA UCHINO CO., LTD. - SRIRACHA FACTORY—See Saha Pathanapibul Public Company Limited; *Int'l*, pg. 6479
RAJA UCHINO CO., LTD. - SUKSAWAD FACTORY—See Saha Pathanapibul Public Company Limited; *Int'l*, pg. 6479
RAJBURI FOODS CO., LTD.—See Charoen Pokphand Foods Public Company Limited; *Int'l*, pg. 1453
RAJCHAPLUEK ENGINEERING COMPANY LIMITED—See Takuni Group Public Company Limited; *Int'l*, pg. 7443
RAJDARSHAN INDUSTRIES LIMITED; *Int'l*, pg. 6193
R.A. JEFFREYS DISTRIBUTING CO.; *U.S. Private*, pg. 3334
RAJESH EXPORTS LTD; *Int'l*, pg. 6193
RAJESHWARI CANS LIMITED; *Int'l*, pg. 6193
RAJESWARI INFRASTRUCTURE LTD.; *Int'l*, pg. 6193
RAJKAMAL SYNTHETICS LIMITED; *Int'l*, pg. 6193
RAJKOT INVESTMENT TRUST LIMITED; *Int'l*, pg. 6193
RAJKUMAR FORGE LIMITED; *Int'l*, pg. 6193
RAJ MANUFACTURING LLC—See Swander Pace Capital, LLC; *U.S. Private*, pg. 3890
RAJNANDINI METAL LTD.; *Int'l*, pg. 6193
RAJNI INTERNATIONAL—See Max Weishaupt GmbH; *Int'l*, pg. 4735
RAJNISH WELLNESS LIMITED; *Int'l*, pg. 6193
R.A. JOHNSON INC.; *U.S. Private*, pg. 3334
RAJ OIL MILLS LTD.; *Int'l*, pg. 6192
R.A. JONES & CO. INC.—See Coesia S.p.A.; *Int'l*, pg. 1690
R.A. JONES & CO.—See Coesia S.p.A.; *Int'l*, pg. 1690
R.A JONES GROUP LTD—See Coesia S.p.A.; *Int'l*, pg. 1690
RAJOO ENGINEERS LIMITED; *Int'l*, pg. 6193
RAJ PACKAGING INDUSTRIES LTD.; *Int'l*, pg. 6192
RAJ PATEL, MD LLC; *U.S. Private*, pg. 3349
RAJ PETRO SPECIALITIES PRIVATE LIMITED—See BRENNTAG SE; *Int'l*, pg. 1149
RAJ PETRO SPECIALITIES DMCC—See BRENNTAG SE; *Int'l*, pg. 1149

RAJPUTANA INVESTMENT & FINANCE LTD.; *Int'l*, pg. 6193
RAJRATAN GLOBAL WIRE LIMITED; *Int'l*, pg. 6193
RAJRATAN THAI WIRE CO. LIMITED—See Rajratan Global Wire Limited; *Int'l*, pg. 6194
RAJ RAYON INDUSTRIES LIMITED; *Int'l*, pg. 6192
RAJSANKET REALTY LIMITED; *Int'l*, pg. 6194
RAJSHREE POLYPACK LTD.; *Int'l*, pg. 6194
RAJSHREE SUGARS & CHEMICALS LIMITED; *Int'l*, pg. 6194
RAJ TELEVISION NETWORK LIMITED; *Int'l*, pg. 6192
RAJTHANEE HOSPITAL PCL; *Int'l*, pg. 6194
RAJTHANEE REALTY CO., LTD.—See Thonburi Healthcare Group PCL; *Int'l*, pg. 7716
RAJTHANEE ROJANA HOSPITAL CO., LTD.—See Rajthanee Hospital PCL; *Int'l*, pg. 6194
RAJVI LOGITRADE LIMITED; *Int'l*, pg. 6194
RAJVIR INDUSTRIES LIMITED; *Int'l*, pg. 6194
RAK CERAMICS AUSTRALIA PTY LIMITED—See Ras Al Khaimah Ceramics PJSC; *Int'l*, pg. 6211
RAK CERAMICS (BANGLADESH) LTD.—See Ras Al Khaimah Ceramics PJSC; *Int'l*, pg. 6211
RAK CERAMICS GMBH—See Ras Al Khaimah Ceramics PJSC; *Int'l*, pg. 6211
RAK CERAMICS INDIA PRIVATE LIMITED—See Ras Al Khaimah Ceramics PJSC; *Int'l*, pg. 6211
RAK CERAMICS SAUDI LLC—See Ras Al Khaimah Ceramics PJSC; *Int'l*, pg. 6211
RAK DEVELOPMENT COMPANY; *U.S. Private*, pg. 3349
RAK DISTRIBUTION EUROPE SARL—See Ras Al Khaimah Ceramics PJSC; *Int'l*, pg. 6211
RAKENNUSHANKE H. LUMIVIRTA OY—See Sweco AB; *Int'l*, pg. 7363
RAKENNUSLIIKE A. TASKINEN OY—See YIT Corporation; *Int'l*, pg. 8586
RAKENNUSLIIKE PURMONEN OY—See SRV Group Plc; *Int'l*, pg. 7153
RAKENNUSTOIMISTO PALMBERG OY—See YIT Corporation; *Int'l*, pg. 8586
RAKER GOLDSTEIN & CO., INC.—See CHR Group LLC; *U.S. Private*, pg. 889
RAK FREE ZONE BUSINESS PROMOTION CENTRE—See Ras Al Khaimah Free Trade Zone; *Int'l*, pg. 6211
RAK FREE ZONE BUSINESS PROMOTION CENTRE—See Ras Al Khaimah Free Trade Zone; *Int'l*, pg. 6212
RAK FREE ZONE PROMOTION CENTRE—See Ras Al Khaimah Free Trade Zone; *Int'l*, pg. 6212
RAK FTZ BUSINESS CENTER L.L.C—See Ras Al Khaimah Free Trade Zone; *Int'l*, pg. 6211
RAK GHANI GLASS LLC—See Ghani Glass Limited; *Int'l*, pg. 2958
RAKHAT-TALDYKORGAN LTD.—See Lotte Co., Ltd.; *Int'l*, pg. 4560
RAK INDUSTRIES INC.; *U.S. Private*, pg. 3349
RAKISA HOLDING CO.; *Int'l*, pg. 6194
RAKO ETIKETTEN GMBH & CO. KG—See Triton Advisers Limited; *Int'l*, pg. 7929
RAKON AMERICA LLC—See Rakon Limited; *Int'l*, pg. 6194
RAKON FRANCE SAS—See Rakon Limited; *Int'l*, pg. 6194
RAKON LIMITED; *Int'l*, pg. 6194
RAKON TEMEX SA—See Rakon Limited; *Int'l*, pg. 6194
RAKON UK LIMITED—See Rakon Limited; *Int'l*, pg. 6194
RAKOVINA THERAPEUTICS INC.; *Int'l*, pg. 6194
RAK PAINTS LLC—See Ras Al Khaimah Ceramics PJSC; *Int'l*, pg. 6211
RAK PETROLEUM PLC; *Int'l*, pg. 6194
RAK PORCELAIN USA INC.—See Ras Al Khaimah Ceramics PJSC; *Int'l*, pg. 6211
RAK PROPERTIES P.J.S.C; *Int'l*, pg. 6194
RAKS BUILDING SUPPLY INC; *U.S. Private*, pg. 3349
RAK SECURITIES & SERVICES PRIVATE LTD.—See Ras Al Khaimah Ceramics PJSC; *Int'l*, pg. 6211
RAKS PHARMA PVT. LTD.—See Amneal Pharmaceuticals, Inc.; *U.S. Public*, pg. 125
RAKSUL, INC.; *Int'l*, pg. 6194
RAKSYSTEMS INSINOORITOIMISTO OY—See MB Rahastot Oy; *Int'l*, pg. 4750
RAKU CO., LTD.; *Int'l*, pg. 6194
RAKUHOKU LANDSCAPE, INC.—See Nissha Co., Ltd.; *Int'l*, pg. 5372
RAKUMO COMPANY LIMITED—See Rakumo, Inc.; *Int'l*, pg. 6195
RAKUMO, INC.; *Int'l*, pg. 6195
RAK UNITY PETROLEUM COMPANY PLC.; *Int'l*, pg. 6194
RAK UNIVERSAL PLASTICS INDUSTRIES LLC—See Ras Al Khaimah Ceramics PJSC; *Int'l*, pg. 6211
RAKUS CO., LTD.; *Int'l*, pg. 6195
RAKUS PARTNERS CO., LTD.—See RAKUS Co., Ltd.; *Int'l*, pg. 6195
RAKUS VIETNAM CO., LTD.—See RAKUS Co., Ltd.; *Int'l*, pg. 6195
RAKUTEN AUCTION, INC.—See Rakuten Group, Inc.; *Int'l*, pg. 6195
RAKUTEN BANK, LTD.; *Int'l*, pg. 6195

RAKUTEN BANK, LTD.   CORPORATE AFFILIATIONS

RAKUTEN BANK SYSTEMS, LTD.—See Rakuten Bank, Ltd.; *Int'l*, pg. 6195
RAKUTEN BASEBALL, INC.—See Rakuten Group, Inc.; *Int'l*, pg. 6195
RAKUTEN CARD CO., LTD.—See Rakuten Group, Inc.; *Int'l*, pg. 6195
RAKUTEN COMMUNICATIONS CORP.—See Rakuten Group, Inc.; *Int'l*, pg. 6195
RAKUTEN DEUTSCHLAND GMBH—See Rakuten Group, Inc.; *Int'l*, pg. 6195
RAKUTEN DIRECT, INC.—See Rakuten Group, Inc.; *Int'l*, pg. 6195
RAKUTEN GENERAL INSURANCE CO., LTD.—See Rakuten Group, Inc.; *Int'l*, pg. 6195
RAKUTEN GROUP, INC.; *Int'l*, pg. 6195
RAKUTEN INSURANCE PLANNING CO., LTD.—See Rakuten Group, Inc.; *Int'l*, pg. 6195
RAKUTEN INTELLIGENCE, INC.—See Advent International Corporation; *U.S. Private*, pg. 105
RAKUTEN KC CO., LTD.—See J Trust Co., Ltd.; *Int'l*, pg. 3853
RAKUTEN LIFE INSURANCE CO., LTD.—See Rakuten Group, Inc.; *Int'l*, pg. 6195
RAKUTEN LINKSHARE CORPORATION—See Rakuten Group, Inc.; *Int'l*, pg. 6195
RAKUTEN READY, INC.—See Rakuten Group, Inc.; *Int'l*, pg. 6195
RAKUTEN REALTY MANAGEMENT CO., LTD.—See Rakuten Group, Inc.; *Int'l*, pg. 6195
RAKUTEN RESEARCH, INC.—See Rakuten Group, Inc.; *Int'l*, pg. 6195
RAKUTEN SECURITIES AUSTRALIA PTY. LTD.—See AT Global Markets (UK) Limited; *Int'l*, pg. 664
RAKUTEN SECURITIES, INC.—See Rakuten Group, Inc.; *Int'l*, pg. 6195
RAKUTEN SS INSURANCE CO., LTD.—See Rakuten Group, Inc.; *Int'l*, pg. 6195
RAKUTEN TRAVEL, INC.—See Rakuten Group, Inc.; *Int'l*, pg. 6195
RAKUTEN USA, INC.—See Rakuten Group, Inc.; *Int'l*, pg. 6195
RAKUTEN VISSEL KOBE, INC.—See Rakuten Group, Inc.; *Int'l*, pg. 6195
RAKYAT HARTANAH SDN BHD—See Bank Kerjasama Rakyat Malaysia Berhad; *Int'l*, pg. 838
RAKYAT HOLDINGS SDN BHD—See Bank Kerjasama Rakyat Malaysia Berhad; *Int'l*, pg. 838
RAKYAT MANAGEMENT SERVICES SDN BHD—See Bank Kerjasama Rakyat Malaysia Berhad; *Int'l*, pg. 838
RAKYAT NIAGA SDN BHD—See Bank Kerjasama Rakyat Malaysia Berhad; *Int'l*, pg. 838
RAKYAT TRAVEL SDN BHD—See Bank Kerjasama Rakyat Malaysia Berhad; *Int'l*, pg. 838
RALAND TECHNOLOGIES LLC; *U.S. Private*, pg. 3349
RALAWISE LIMITED; *Int'l*, pg. 6196
RALCO AGENCIES LTD.; *Int'l*, pg. 6196
RALCO CORPORATION BERHAD; *Int'l*, pg. 6196
RALCO INDUSTRIES, INC.; *U.S. Private*, pg. 3349
RALCO NUTRITION, INC.; *U.S. Private*, pg. 3349
RALCORP FROZEN BAKERY PRODUCTS—See Grupo Bimbo, S.A.B. de C.V.; *Int'l*, pg. 3122
RALCORP RECEIVABLES, LLC—See Conagra Brands, Inc.; *U.S. Public*, pg. 564
RAL DIAGNOSTICS SAS—See CellaVision AB; *Int'l*, pg. 1392
RALEC ELECTRONIC CORPORATION - CHINA KUNSHAN FACTORY—See Ralec Electronic Corporation; *Int'l*, pg. 6196
RALEC ELECTRONIC CORPORATION; *Int'l*, pg. 6196
RALEC ELECTRONIC CORPORATION - TAIWAN KAOHSIUNG FACTORY—See Ralec Electronic Corporation; *Int'l*, pg. 6196
RALEIGH ADHESIVE COATINGS LIMITED—See Advanced Medical Solutions Group plc; *Int'l*, pg. 161
RALEIGH CYCLE CO. LTD—See Accell Group N.V.; *Int'l*, pg. 81
RALEIGH ENTERPRISES; *U.S. Private*, pg. 3349
RALEIGH GENERAL HOSPITAL, LLC—See Apollo Global Management, Inc.; *U.S. Public*, pg. 158
THE RALEIGH HOTEL—See SBEEG Holdings, LLC; *U.S. Private*, pg. 3559
RALEIGH MINE & INDUSTRIAL SUPPLY, INC.; *U.S. Private*, pg. 3349
THE RALEIGH NC ENDOSCOPY ASC, LLC—See KKR & Co. Inc.; *U.S. Public*, pg. 1248
RALEIGH STUDIOS, INC.—See Raleigh Enterprises; *U.S. Private*, pg. 3349
RALEIGH TRACTOR & TRUCK COMPANY; *U.S. Private*, pg. 3350
RALEIGH UK LTD—See Accell Group N.V.; *Int'l*, pg. 81
RALEY'S INC.; *U.S. Private*, pg. 3350
RALF TEICHMANN GMBH; *Int'l*, pg. 6196
RALINK TECHNOLOGY CORP.—See MediaTek Inc.; *Int'l*, pg. 4774
RALINK TECHNOLOGY (SAMOA) CORPORATION (CHINA)—See MediaTek Inc.; *Int'l*, pg. 4774
R ALKAN & CIE; *Int'l*, pg. 6167
R ALLIANCE CO., LTD.—See RS Public Company Limited; *Int'l*, pg. 6418

RALLING AB—See Peab AB; *Int'l*, pg. 5772
RALLIS INDIA LIMITED; *Int'l*, pg. 6196
RALLY4, INC.—See GRYYT, LLC; *U.S. Private*, pg. 1800
RALLY AUTO GROUP, INC.; *U.S. Private*, pg. 3350
RALLYBIO CORPORATION; *U.S. Public*, pg. 1761
RALLYE MOTORS LLC; *U.S. Private*, pg. 3350
RALLY ENERGY LIMITED—See Citadel Capital S.A.E.; *Int'l*, pg. 1619
RALLYE S.A.—See Finatis SA; *Int'l*, pg. 2670
RALLY GM SUPERSTORE—See Rally Auto Group, Inc.; *U.S. Private*, pg. 3350
RALLY MANUFACTURING, INC.; *U.S. Private*, pg. 3350
RALLY POINT MANAGEMENT, LLC; *U.S. Private*, pg. 3350
RALLYSPORT DIRECT, LLC—See Heartwood Partners, LLC; *U.S. Private*, pg. 1901
RALMANA PTY. LTD.; *Int'l*, pg. 6196
R&A LOGISTICS INC.—See Raymond Limited; *Int'l*, pg. 6224
RALOID CORPORATION—See Angeles Equity Partners, LLC; *U.S. Private*, pg. 282
RALOS NEW ENERGIES AG; *Int'l*, pg. 6196
RALPH A. HILLER COMPANY INC—See Rotork Plc; *Int'l*, pg. 6406
RALPH CLAYTON & SONS; *U.S. Private*, pg. 3350
RALPH C WILSON AGENCY, INC.—See Kelso & Company, L.P.; *U.S. Private*, pg. 2280
RALPH E. DAVIS ASSOCIATES LP—See Opportune LLP; *U.S. Private*, pg. 3033
RALPH HONDA; *U.S. Private*, pg. 3350
THE RALPH J. STOLLE COMPANY; *U.S. Private*, pg. 4102
RALPH LAUREN BELGIUM S.P.R.L.—See Ralph Lauren Corporation; *U.S. Public*, pg. 1761
RALPH LAUREN CORPORATION; *U.S. Public*, pg. 1761
RALPH LAUREN FRANCE S.A.S.—See Ralph Lauren Corporation; *U.S. Public*, pg. 1761
RALPH LAUREN GERMANY GMBH—See Ralph Lauren Corporation; *U.S. Public*, pg. 1761
RALPH LAUREN LONDON LTD.—See Ralph Lauren Corporation; *U.S. Public*, pg. 1761
RALPH LAUREN NETHERLANDS BV—See Ralph Lauren Corporation; *U.S. Public*, pg. 1762
RALPH LAUREN SCANDINAVIA AB—See Ralph Lauren Corporation; *U.S. Public*, pg. 1762
THE RALPH LAUREN WOMENSWEAR COMPANY, L.P.—See Ralph Lauren Corporation; *U.S. Public*, pg. 1762
RALPH L. WADSWORTH CONSTRUCTION COMPANY, INC.; *U.S. Private*, pg. 3350
RALPH MCELROY & ASSOCIATES, LTD.—See TranslateMedia Ltd.; *Int'l*, pg. 7901
RALPH & PAUL ADAMS, INC.—See Jones Dairy Farm; *U.S. Private*, pg. 2232
RALPH SELLERS CHEVROLET—See Ralph Sellers Motor Co.; *U.S. Private*, pg. 3350
RALPH SELLERS MOTOR CO.; *U.S. Private*, pg. 3350
RALPHS GROCERY COMPANY—See The Kroger Co.; *U.S. Public*, pg. 2107
RALPH'S MIRROR AND GLASS (PTY) LIMITED—See AG Industries Limited; *Int'l*, pg. 198
RALPH'S OF LAFAYETTE INC.; *U.S. Private*, pg. 3350
RALPH THAYER CHEVROLET-TOYOTA INC.; *U.S. Private*, pg. 3350
RALPH W. EARL CO., INC.; *U.S. Private*, pg. 3350
RALSEY GROUP LIMITED—See Li & Fung Limited; *Int'l*, pg. 4480
RALSTON FOODS, INC.—See Conagra Brands, Inc.; *U.S. Public*, pg. 564
RALSTON FOODS, INC.—See Conagra Brands, Inc.; *U.S. Public*, pg. 564
RALSTON FOODS, INC.—See Conagra Brands, Inc.; *U.S. Public*, pg. 564
RALSTON FOODS, INC.—See Conagra Brands, Inc.; *U.S. Public*, pg. 564
RALSTON FOODS—See Conagra Brands, Inc.; *U.S. Public*, pg. 564
RALSTON PURINA OVERSEAS FINANCE N.V.—See Nestle S.A.; *Int'l*, pg. 5209
RAL SUPPLY GROUP INC.; *U.S. Private*, pg. 3350
RALTRON ELECTRONICS CORP.—See Rami Technology Group; *U.S. Private*, pg. 3351
RALTRON ISRAEL LTD.—See Rami Technology Group; *U.S. Private*, pg. 3351
RALTRON KOREA CO., LTD.—See Rami Technology Group; *U.S. Private*, pg. 3351
RAL YATIRIM HOLDING A.S.; *Int'l*, pg. 6196
RAMA 9 SQUARE CO., LTD.—See Central Pattana Public Company Limited; *Int'l*, pg. 1409
RAMACO RESOURCES, INC.; *U.S. Public*, pg. 1762
RAM ACTIVE INVESTMENTS (EUROPE) SA—See Mediobanca S.P.A.; *Int'l*, pg. 4778
RAM ACTIVE INVESTMENTS S.A.—See Mediobanca-Banca de Credito Finanziario S.p.A.; *Int'l*, pg. 4778
RAMADA WAIKIKI—See China Airlines Ltd.; *Int'l*, pg. 1481
RAMADA WORLDWIDE INC.—See Travel & Leisure Co.; *U.S. Public*, pg. 2185
RAMAKRISHNA ELECTRO COMPONENTS HK PVT LTD.—See STMicroelectronics N.V.; *Int'l*, pg. 7217

RAMAKRISHNA ELECTRO COMPONENTS PVT LTD.—See STMicroelectronics N.V.; *Int'l*, pg. 7217
RAMALAND DEVELOPMENT CO., LTD.—See Kajima Corporation; *Int'l*, pg. 4055
RAMALHO ROSA COBETAR SOCIEDADE DE CONSTRUCOES, S.A.—See Fomento de Construcciones y Contratas, S.A.; *Int'l*, pg. 2723
RAMALLAH SUMMER RESORTS COMPANY; *Int'l*, pg. 6197
RAMA PAPER MILLS LIMITED; *Int'l*, pg. 6196
RAMA PETROCHEMICALS LTD; *Int'l*, pg. 6196
RAMA PHOSPHATES LTD.; *Int'l*, pg. 6196
RAMAR FOODS INTERNATIONAL CORPORATION; *U.S. Private*, pg. 3351
RAMASIGNS INDUSTRIES LIMITED; *Int'l*, pg. 6197
RAMA STEEL TUBES LIMITED; *Int'l*, pg. 6197
RAMA VISION LIMITED; *Int'l*, pg. 6197
RAMBLER-AFISHA—See Interros Holding Company; *Int'l*, pg. 3759
RAMBLER FABRICATION INC.—See Trotter & Morton Ltd.; *Int'l*, pg. 7939
RAMBLER METALS & MINING PLC; *Int'l*, pg. 6197
RAMBOLL DANMARK A/S—See Ramboll Gruppen A/S; *Int'l*, pg. 6197
RAMBOLL EESTI AS—See Ramboll Gruppen A/S; *Int'l*, pg. 6197
RAMBOLL ENVIRON GERMANY GMBH—See Ramboll Gruppen A/S; *Int'l*, pg. 6197
RAMBOLL ENVIRON, INC.—See Ramboll Gruppen A/S; *Int'l*, pg. 6197
RAMBOLL FINLAND OY—See Ramboll Gruppen A/S; *Int'l*, pg. 6197
RAMBOLL FUTURE AS—See Ramboll Gruppen A/S; *Int'l*, pg. 6197
RAMBOLL GRUPPEN A/S; *Int'l*, pg. 6197
RAMBOLL HANNEMANN OG HOJLUND INGENIORTUT SIUNNERSUISARFIK A/S—See Ramboll Gruppen A/S; *Int'l*, pg. 6197
RAMBOLL HANNEMANN OG HOJLUND INGENIORTUT SIUNNERSUISARFIK A/S—See Ramboll Gruppen A/S; *Int'l*, pg. 6197
RAMBOLL IMS INGENIEURGESELLSCHAFT MBH—See Ramboll Gruppen A/S; *Int'l*, pg. 6197
RAMBOLL INFORMATIK A/S—See Ramboll Gruppen A/S; *Int'l*, pg. 6197
RAMBOLL MANAGEMENT A/S—See Ramboll Gruppen A/S; *Int'l*, pg. 6197
RAMBOLL MANAGEMENT CONSULTING GMBH—See Ramboll Gruppen A/S; *Int'l*, pg. 6197
RAMBOLL NORGE AS—See Ramboll Gruppen A/S; *Int'l*, pg. 6197
RAMBOLL NYVIG LDT.—See Ramboll Gruppen A/S; *Int'l*, pg. 6197
RAMBOLL POLAND SP. Z OO—See Ramboll Gruppen A/S; *Int'l*, pg. 6197
RAMBOLL ROMANIA S.R.L.—See Ramboll Gruppen A/S; *Int'l*, pg. 6197
RAMBOLL SVERIGE AB—See Ramboll Gruppen A/S; *Int'l*, pg. 6197
RAMBOLL (THAILAND) CO., LTD.—See Ramboll Gruppen A/S; *Int'l*, pg. 6197
RAMBOLL TOWERS SP. Z O.O.—See Ramboll Gruppen A/S; *Int'l*, pg. 6197
RAMBOLL TRANSPORT GERMANY RAMBOLL IMS INGENIEURGESELLSCHAFT MBH—See Ramboll Gruppen A/S; *Int'l*, pg. 6197
RAMBOLL UK HOLDING LTD.—See Ramboll Gruppen A/S; *Int'l*, pg. 6197
RAMBOLL UK LIMITED—See Ramboll Gruppen A/S; *Int'l*, pg. 6197
RAMBO MARINE, INC.—See OneWater Marine Holdings LLC; *U.S. Private*, pg. 3026
RAMBOR PTY LTD—See PPK Group Limited; *Int'l*, pg. 5951
RAMB SP. Z O.O.—See PGE Polska Grupa Energetyczna S.A.; *Int'l*, pg. 5837
RAM-BUL LLC—See Bulten AB; *Int'l*, pg. 1215
RAMBUS CANADA INC.—See Rambus Inc.; *U.S. Public*, pg. 1762
RAMBUS DELAWARE LLC—See Rambus Inc.; *U.S. Public*, pg. 1762
RAMBUS INC.; *U.S. Public*, pg. 1762
RAMBUS K.K.—See Rambus Inc.; *U.S. Public*, pg. 1762
RAMBUS KOREA, INC.—See Rambus Inc.; *U.S. Public*, pg. 1762
RAMCAST ORNAMENTAL SUPPLY CO.; *U.S. Private*, pg. 3351
RAMCHANDRA LEASING & FINANCING LIMITED; *Int'l*, pg. 6197
THE RAMCO CEMENTS LIMITED; *Int'l*, pg. 7678
RAMCO INDUSTRIES LIMITED - ARAKONAM FACTORY—See Ramco Industries Limited; *Int'l*, pg. 6198
RAMCO INDUSTRIES LIMITED - GANGAIKONDAN FACTORY—See Ramco Industries Limited; *Int'l*, pg. 6198
RAMCO INDUSTRIES LIMITED - KHARAGPUR FACTORY—See Ramco Industries Limited; *Int'l*, pg. 6198

COMPANY NAME INDEX

RAMCO INDUSTRIES LIMITED - MAKSI FACTORY—See Ramco Industries Limited; *Int'l*, pg. 6198
RAMCO INDUSTRIES LIMITED - RANE BENNUR FACTORY—See Ramco Industries Limited; *Int'l*, pg. 6198
RAMCO INDUSTRIES LIMITED - SILVASSA FACTORY—See Ramco Industries Limited; *Int'l*, pg. 6198
RAMCO INDUSTRIES LIMITED; *Int'l*, pg. 6198
RAMCO INNOVATIONS, INC.—See Sukup Manufacturing Co; *U.S. Private*, pg. 3850
RAMCO/LION VENTURE LP—See Kimco Realty Corporation; *U.S. Public*, pg. 1232
RAMCOM INTERNATIONAL CORP.; *U.S. Private*, pg. 3351
RAM CONSOLIDATED INDUSTRIES, INC.; *U.S. Private*, pg. 3350
RAM CONSTRUCTION INC.; *Int'l*, pg. 6196
RAM CONSTRUCTION SERVICES OF MICHIGAN, INC.; *U.S. Private*, pg. 3350
RAM CONSULTING—See Intertek Group plc; *Int'l*, pg. 3764
RAMCO - RELIABLE ARCHITECTURAL METALS CO.; *U.S. Private*, pg. 3351
RAMCO SYSTEM INC.—See Ramco Systems Limited; *Int'l*, pg. 6198
RAMCO SYSTEMS AUSTRALIA PTY LTD—See Ramco Systems Limited; *Int'l*, pg. 6198
RAMCO SYSTEMS CORPORATION—See Ramco Systems Limited; *Int'l*, pg. 6198
RAMCO SYSTEMS FZ-LLC—See Ramco Systems Limited; *Int'l*, pg. 6198
RAMCO SYSTEMS LIMITED; *Int'l*, pg. 6198
RAMCO SYSTEMS PTE. LTD.—See Ramco Systems Limited; *Int'l*, pg. 6198
RAMCO SYSTEMS SDN. BHD.—See Ramco Systems Limited; *Int'l*, pg. 6198
RAM COUNTRY CHRYSLER DODGE INC.; *U.S. Private*, pg. 3350
RAMDEV CHEMICAL PRIVATE LIMITED—See Ipca Laboratories Ltd.; *Int'l*, pg. 3796
RAM DEVELOPMENT COMPANY, INC.; *U.S. Private*, pg. 3350
RAM DIS TICARET AS—See Koc Holding A.S.; *Int'l*, pg. 4224
RAM DO BRASIL, LTDA—See Schneider Electric SE; *Int'l*, pg. 6629
RAMEDER ANHANGERKUPPLUNGEN UND AUTOTEILE GMBH—See FSN Capital Partners AS; *Int'l*, pg. 2799
RAMELIUS MILLING SERVICES PTY. LTD.—See Ramelius Resources Limited; *Int'l*, pg. 6198
RAMELIUS RESOURCES LIMITED; *Int'l*, pg. 6198
RAMEN PLAY PTE. LTD.—See BreadTalk Group Pte Ltd.; *Int'l*, pg. 1143
RAMERICA INTERNATIONAL INC—See Koc Holding A.S.; *Int'l*, pg. 4224
RAMESHWARAM STEEL & POWER PVT. LTD.—See Apollo Global Management, Inc.; *U.S. Public*, pg. 153
RAMESHWARAM STEEL & POWER PVT. LTD.—See JSW Steel Ltd.; *Int'l*, pg. 4015
RAMEX, INC.; *U.S. Private*, pg. 3351
THE RAMEY AGENCY LLC; *U.S. Private*, pg. 4102
THE RAMEY AGENCY—See The Ramey Agency LLC; *U.S. Private*, pg. 4102
THE RAMEY AGENCY—See The Ramey Agency LLC; *U.S. Private*, pg. 4102
THE RAMEY AGENCY—See The Ramey Agency LLC; *U.S. Private*, pg. 4102
RAMEY AUTOMOTIVE INC.; *U.S. Private*, pg. 3351
RAMEY ENVIRONMENTAL COMPLIANCE INC.—See Consolidated Water Co. Ltd.; *Int'l*, pg. 1771
RAMEY MOTORS INC.; *U.S. Private*, pg. 3351
RAM FASTENERS (PTY) LIMITED—See The Bidvest Group Limited; *Int'l*, pg. 7626
RAM FUNDING SERVICES CORP.; *U.S. Private*, pg. 3351
RAMGOPAL POLYTEX LIMITED; *Int'l*, pg. 6198
RAM GRAPHICS, INC.; *U.S. Private*, pg. 3351
RAMI LEVI CHAIN STORES HASHIKMA MARKETING 2006 LTD.; *Int'l*, pg. 6198
RAM INC.; *U.S. Private*, pg. 3351
RAM INFO LTD.; *Int'l*, pg. 6198
RAM INTERNATIONAL INC.; *U.S. Private*, pg. 3351
RAM INTERNATIONAL LTD.; *U.S. Private*, pg. 3351
RAMIRENT AB—See Loxam SAS; *Int'l*, pg. 4566
RAMIRENT A/S—See Access Capital Partners SA; *Int'l*, pg. 88
RAMIRENT A/S—See Catacap Management AS; *Int'l*, pg. 1358
RAMIRENT AS—See Loxam SAS; *Int'l*, pg. 4566
RAMIRENT BALTIC AS—See Loxam SAS; *Int'l*, pg. 4566
RAMIRENT FINLAND OY—See Loxam SAS; *Int'l*, pg. 4566
RAMIRENT MACHINERY LLC—See Loxam SAS; *Int'l*, pg. 4566
RAMIRENT PLC—See Loxam SAS; *Int'l*, pg. 4566
RAMIRENT S.R.O.—See Loxam SAS; *Int'l*, pg. 4566
RAMIRENT UKRAINE LLC—See Loxam SAS; *Int'l*, pg. 4566
RAMI TECHNOLOGY GROUP; *U.S. Private*, pg. 3351

RAMI TECHNOLOGY (S) PTE LTD—See Rami Technology Group; *U.S. Private*, pg. 3351
RAMIUS LLC—See The Toronto-Dominion Bank; *Int'l*, pg. 7695
RAMIUS TRADING STRATEGIES LLC—See The Toronto-Dominion Bank; *Int'l*, pg. 7695
RAMIVO MANUFACTURING HUNGARY KFT.—See SKion GmbH; *Int'l*, pg. 6990
RAMKHAMHAENG HOSPITAL PUBLIC COMPANY LIMITED; *Int'l*, pg. 6198
RAMKRISHNA FORGINGS LIMITED - PLANT III & IV—See Ramkrishna Forgings Limited; *Int'l*, pg. 6198
RAMKRISHNA FORGINGS LIMITED - PLANT II—See Ramkrishna Forgings Limited; *Int'l*, pg. 6198
RAMKRISHNA FORGINGS LIMITED - PLANT I—See Ramkrishna Forgings Limited; *Int'l*, pg. 6198
RAMKRISHNA FORGINGS LIMITED; *Int'l*, pg. 6198
RAMKY CLEANTECH SERVICES PTE. LTD.—See KKR & Co. Inc.; *U.S. Public*, pg. 1263
RAMKY ENCLAVE LIMITED—See Ramky Group; *Int'l*, pg. 6199
RAMKY ENVIRO ENGINEERS MIDDLE EAST FZLLC—See KKR & Co. Inc.; *U.S. Public*, pg. 1263
RAMKY ESTATES AND FARMS LIMITED—See Ramky Group; *Int'l*, pg. 6198
RAMKY GROUP; *Int'l*, pg. 6198
RAMKY INFRASTRUCTURE LIMITED—See Ramky Group; *Int'l*, pg. 6198
RAMKY PHARMA CITY (INDIA) LIMITED—See Ramky Group; *Int'l*, pg. 6199
RAM MINERALS AND CHEMICALS LIMITED—See Intellivate Capital Ventures Limited; *Int'l*, pg. 3734
RAMMKERR, INC.; *U.S. Private*, pg. 3351
RAMM PHARMA CORP.; *Int'l*, pg. 6199
RAMONA AUTO SERVICES INC.; *U.S. Private*, pg. 3351
RAMONA MUNICIPAL WATER DISTRICT; *U.S. Private*, pg. 3351
RAMONA RESEARCH, INC.—See HEICO Corporation; *U.S. Public*, pg. 1020
RAMONA'S MEXICAN FOOD PRODUCTS; *U.S. Private*, pg. 3351
RAMONA—See Stagwell, Inc.; *U.S. Public*, pg. 1928
RAMON SABATER, S.A.U.—See Portobello Capital Advisors SL; *Int'l*, pg. 5935
RAM OPTICAL INSTRUMENTATION INC.—See Quality Vision International Inc.; *U.S. Private*, pg. 3321
RAMOS OIL CO. INC.; *U.S. Private*, pg. 3351
RAM PACIFIC LTD.—See Koc Holding A.S.; *Int'l*, pg. 4224
RAM-PAC INTERNATIONAL INC.—See Hader Industries Inc.; *U.S. Private*, pg. 1839
RAMPAGE CLOTHING COMPANY; *U.S. Private*, pg. 3351
RAMPAI-NIAGA SDN BHD—See Aurelius Equity Opportunities SE & Co. KGaA; *Int'l*, pg. 710
RAMPART CAPITAL CORPORATION; *U.S. Private*, pg. 3352
RAMPART DETECTION SYSTEMS, LTD.; *Int'l*, pg. 6199
RAMPART GROUP; *U.S. Private*, pg. 3352
RAMPART PLUMBING & HEATING SUPPLY INC.; *U.S. Private*, pg. 3352
RAMPART STUDIOS INC.—See Rampart Capital Corporation; *U.S. Private*, pg. 3352
RAMPF FORMEN GMBH—See Nimbus B.V.; *Int'l*, pg. 5296
RAMPF FORMEN KFT.—See Nimbus B.V.; *Int'l*, pg. 5296
RAMPF FORMEN POLSKA SP. Z O.O.—See Nimbus B.V.; *Int'l*, pg. 5296
RAMPF FORMEN (TAICANG) CO., LTD.—See Nimbus B.V.; *Int'l*, pg. 5296
RAMPF MOLDS INC.—See Nimbus B.V.; *Int'l*, pg. 5296
RAMPF MOLDS INDUSTRIES INC.—See Nimbus B.V.; *Int'l*, pg. 5296
RAMPHASTOS INVESTMENTS MANAGEMENT BV; *Int'l*, pg. 6199
RAMP HOLDINGS INC.—See VBrick Systems Inc.; *U.S. Private*, pg. 4348
RAMP TECHNOLOGY GROUP, LLC; *U.S. Private*, pg. 3351
RAM QUEST SOFTWARE, INC.—See Tyler Technologies, Inc.; *U.S. Public*, pg. 2209
RAMQUEST SOFTWARE, INC.—See Old Republic International Corporation; *U.S. Public*, pg. 1569
RAM RATNA WIRES LIMITED; *Int'l*, pg. 6196
RAM REINSURANCE COMPANY LTD.—See American Overseas Group Limited; *Int'l*, pg. 422
RAMROD INDUSTRIES LLC—See Ligon Industries LLC; *U.S. Private*, pg. 2455
RAMSAY AGED CARE HOLDINGS PTY LIMITED—See Ramsay Health Care Limited; *Int'l*, pg. 6199
RAMSAY AGED CARE PROPERTIES PTY LIMITED—See Ramsay Health Care Limited; *Int'l*, pg. 6199
RAMSAY CENTAURI PTY LIMITED—See Ramsay Health Care Limited; *Int'l*, pg. 6199
RAMSAY GENERALE DE SANTE SA—See Ramsay Health Care Limited; *Int'l*, pg. 6199
RAMSAY HEALTH CARE (ASIA PACIFIC) PTY LIMITED—See Ramsay Health Care Limited; *Int'l*, pg. 6200
RAMSAY HEALTH CARE AUSTRALIA PTY LIMITED—See Ramsay Health Care Limited; *Int'l*, pg. 6200

RAMSAY HEALTH CARE HOLDINGS UK LIMITED—See Ramsay Health Care Limited; *Int'l*, pg. 6200
RAMSAY HEALTH CARE INVESTMENTS PTY LIMITED—See Ramsay Health Care Limited; *Int'l*, pg. 6200
RAMSAY HEALTH CARE LIMITED; *Int'l*, pg. 6199
RAMSAY HEALTH CARE—See Ramsay Health Care Limited; *Int'l*, pg. 6200
RAMSAY HEALTH CARE (SOUTH AUSTRALIA) PTY LIMITED—See Ramsay Health Care Limited; *Int'l*, pg. 6200
RAMSAY HEALTH CARE UK OPERATIONS LIMITED—See Ramsay Health Care Limited; *Int'l*, pg. 6200
RAMSAY HEALTH CARE UK—See Ramsay Health Care Limited; *Int'l*, pg. 6200
RAMSAY HEALTH CARE (VICTORIA) PTY LIMITED—See Ramsay Health Care Limited; *Int'l*, pg. 6200
RAMSAY HOSPITAL HOLDINGS PTY LIMITED—See Ramsay Health Care Limited; *Int'l*, pg. 6200
RAMSAY HOSPITAL HOLDINGS (QUEENSLAND) PTY LIMITED—See Ramsay Health Care Limited; *Int'l*, pg. 6200
RAMSAY PROFESSIONAL SERVICES PTY LIMITED—See Ramsay Health Care Limited; *Int'l*, pg. 6200
RAMSAY REALTY; *U.S. Private*, pg. 3352
RAMSAY YOUTH SERVICES OF GEORGIA, INC.—See Universal Health Services, Inc.; *U.S. Public*, pg. 2259
THE RAMS CLUB; *U.S. Private*, pg. 4102
RAMSDENS FINANCIAL LIMITED; *Int'l*, pg. 6200
RAMSDENS HOLDINGS PLC; *Int'l*, pg. 6200
RAM SERVICES INC.—See AEMS Service Company; *U.S. Private*, pg. 117
RAMSES-IMMOBILIENHOLDING GMBH—See UniCredit S.p.A.; *Int'l*, pg. 8040
RAMSES IMMOBILIEN LEASING GESELLSCHAFT MBH & CO OG—See UniCredit S.p.A.; *Int'l*, pg. 8040
RAMSEY ADVERTISING; *U.S. Private*, pg. 3352
RAMSEY AUTO GROUP; *U.S. Private*, pg. 3352
RAMSEY FINANCIAL CORPORATION; *U.S. Private*, pg. 3352
RAMSEY GREIG & CO. LTD.—See Blue Wolf Capital Partners LLC; *U.S. Private*, pg. 595
RAMSEY INDUSTRIES INC.—See Gridiron Capital, LLC; *U.S. Private*, pg. 1786
RAMSEY INSURANCE AGENCY, INC.—See GTCR LLC; *U.S. Private*, pg. 1804
RAMSEY NATIONAL BANK—See Ramsey Financial Corporation; *U.S. Private*, pg. 3352
RAMSEY OUTDOOR STORE INC.; *U.S. Private*, pg. 3352
RAMSEY VOLVO; *U.S. Private*, pg. 3352
RAMSEY & WALKER, LLC; *U.S. Private*, pg. 3352
RAMSEY WINCH COMPANY INC.—See Gridiron Capital, LLC; *U.S. Private*, pg. 1786
RAMS FINANCIAL GROUP PTY LIMITED—See Westpac Banking Corporation; *Int'l*, pg. 8391
THE RAMS FOOTBALL COMPANY, LLC—See The Los Angeles Rams, LLC; *U.S. Private*, pg. 4072
R.A.M. SHIPPING SERVICES LIMITED—See PanJam Investment Limited; *Int'l*, pg. 5728
RAMSHYAM TEXTILE INDUSTRIES LTD.—See First Winner Industries Limited; *Int'l*, pg. 2688
RAM SOFTWARE SYSTEMS INC.—See ComTec Solutions; *U.S. Private*, pg. 1006
RAMSONS PROJECTS LIMITED; *Int'l*, pg. 6200
RAMSTROM TRANSMISSION AB—See Addtech AB; *Int'l*, pg. 135
RAMTA DIVISION COMMERCIAL AIRCRAFT GROUP—See Israel Aerospace Industries Ltd.; *Int'l*, pg. 3822
RAMTECH ELECTRONICS LIMITED—See Halma plc; *Int'l*, pg. 3232
RAM TECH MANUFACTURING DE MEXICO S DE R.L. DE C.V.—See Schneider Electric SE; *Int'l*, pg. 6629
RAM TECHNOLOGIES, INC.; *U.S. Private*, pg. 3351
RAM TECHNOLOGY CO., LTD.; *Int'l*, pg. 6196
RAM TECH SERVICES DE MEXICO S DE R.L. DE C.V.—See Schneider Electric SE; *Int'l*, pg. 6629
RAMTECH SOFTWARE SOLUTIONS PVT. LTD.; *Int'l*, pg. 6200
RAM TECH SYSTEMS, INC.; *U.S. Private*, pg. 3351
RAM TOOL & SUPPLY CO. INC.; *U.S. Private*, pg. 3351
R.A. MUELLER, INC.—See DXP Enterprises, Inc.; *U.S. Public*, pg. 698
RAMUNELES VAISTINE UAB—See Walgreens Boots Alliance, Inc.; *U.S. Public*, pg. 2322
RAMUSA ENGINEERING SDN. BHD.—See Ingress Corporation Berhad; *Int'l*, pg. 3703
RAM WARE, LLC—See Guggenheim Partners, LLC; *U.S. Private*, pg. 1812
RANADIVE GROUP; *U.S. Private*, pg. 3352
RANA GRUBER AS; *Int'l*, pg. 6200
RANA-LIEGENSCHAFTSVERWERTUNG GMBH—See UniCredit S.p.A.; *Int'l*, pg. 8040
RANAS BILFJADRAR AB—See Axel Johnson Gruppen AB; *Int'l*, pg. 765
RANA SUGARS LIMITED; *Int'l*, pg. 6200

RANA SUGARS LIMITED / CORPORATE AFFILIATIONS

RANBAXY AUSTRALIA PTY LTD—See Sun Pharmaceutical Industries Ltd.; *Int'l*, pg. 7307
RANBAXY EGYPT COMPANY L.L.C.—See Sun Pharmaceutical Industries Ltd.; *Int'l*, pg. 7307
RANBAXY FARMACEUTICA LTDA.—See Sun Pharmaceutical Industries Ltd.; *Int'l*, pg. 7307
RANBAXY, INC.—See Sun Pharmaceutical Industries Ltd.; *Int'l*, pg. 7307
RANBAXY ITALIA SPA—See Sun Pharmaceutical Industries Ltd.; *Int'l*, pg. 7307
RANBAXY (MALAYSIA) SDN. BHD.—See Sun Pharmaceutical Industries Ltd.; *Int'l*, pg. 7307
RANBAXY (NETHERLANDS) B.V.—See Sun Pharmaceutical Industries Ltd.; *Int'l*, pg. 7307
RANBAXY NIGERIA LIMITED—See Sun Pharmaceutical Industries Ltd.; *Int'l*, pg. 7307
RANBAXY PHARMACEUTICALS CANADA INC.—See Sun Pharmaceutical Industries Ltd.; *Int'l*, pg. 7307
RANBAXY PHARMACEUTICALS, INC.—See Sun Pharmaceutical Industries Ltd.; *Int'l*, pg. 7307
RANBAXY PHARMACEUTICALS (PTY) LTD—See Sun Pharmaceutical Industries Ltd.; *Int'l*, pg. 7307
RANBAXY PHARMACEUTICALS UKRAINE LLC—See Sun Pharmaceutical Industries Ltd.; *Int'l*, pg. 7307
RANBAXY (POLAND) SP. Z O.O.—See Sun Pharmaceutical Industries Ltd.; *Int'l*, pg. 7307
RANBAXY- PRP (PERU) S.A.C.—See Sun Pharmaceutical Industries Ltd.; *Int'l*, pg. 7307
RANBAXY SOUTH AFRICA PROPRIETARY LIMITED—See Sun Pharmaceutical Industries Ltd.; *Int'l*, pg. 7307
RANBAXY (THAILAND) CO., LTD.—See Sun Pharmaceutical Industries Ltd.; *Int'l*, pg. 7307
RANBAXY (U.K.) LTD.—See Sun Pharmaceutical Industries Ltd.; *Int'l*, pg. 7307
THE RANCH AT DOVE TREE LLC—See FFL Partners, LLC; *U.S. Private*, pg. 1500
THE RANCH AT DOVE TREE LLC—See Lee Equity Partners LLC; *U.S. Private*, pg. 2412
RANCH CREEK PARTNERS, LLC; *U.S. Private*, pg. 3352
THE RANCHER INC.—See White Construction Company Inc.; *U.S. Private*, pg. 4508
RANCHERO GOLD CORP.; *Int'l*, pg. 6200
RANCHERS SUPPLY COMPANY, INC.; *U.S. Private*, pg. 3352
RANCH HAND, INC.—See The Kaspar Companies; *U.S. Private*, pg. 4064
RANCH & HOME SUPPLY LLC; *U.S. Private*, pg. 3352
RANCHO CADIZ MUTUAL WATER COMPANY—See Cadiz Inc.; *U.S. Public*, pg. 419
RANCHO DIALYSIS, LLC—See DaVita Inc.; *U.S. Public*, pg. 642
RANCHO DISPOSAL SERVICE, INC.—See Burrtec Waste Industries, Inc.; *U.S. Private*, pg. 692
RANCHO FORD, INC.; *U.S. Private*, pg. 3352
RANCHO MOTOR COMPANY INC.; *U.S. Private*, pg. 3352
RANCHO SANTA FE FOUNDATION; *U.S. Private*, pg. 3352
RANCHO SANTA FE MINING, INC.; *U.S. Private*, pg. 3352
RANCHO SIMI RECREATION PARK DISTRICT; *U.S. Private*, pg. 3352
RANCHO VIEJO PROPERTIES—See Pinnacle West Capital Corporation; *U.S. Public*, pg. 1692
THE RANCH WINERY—See E. & J. Gallo Winery; *U.S. Private*, pg. 1303
RANCHWOOD HOMES CORPORATION; *U.S. Private*, pg. 3353
RANCILIO GROUP DEUTSCHLAND GMBH—See Ali Holding S.r.l; *Int'l*, pg. 321
RANCILIO GROUP ESPANA S.A.—See Ali Holding S.r.l; *Int'l*, pg. 321
RANCILIO GROUP NORTH AMERICA INC.—See Ali Holding S.r.l; *Int'l*, pg. 321
RANCILIO GROUP PORTUGAL LDA—See Ali Holding S.r.l; *Int'l*, pg. 321
RANCILIO GROUP S.P.A.—See Ali Holding S.r.l; *Int'l*, pg. 321
RANCON REAL ESTATE CORPORATION; *U.S. Private*, pg. 3353
RANDA ACCESSORIES LEATHER GOODS LLC—See Randa Corp.; *U.S. Private*, pg. 3353
RANDA CORP.; *U.S. Private*, pg. 3353
RAND AIR & GAS INSTALLATIONS (PTY) LIMITED—See PSV Holdings Limited; *Int'l*, pg. 6018
RAND AIR SOUTH AFRICA PTY LTD—See Atlas Copco AB; *Int'l*, pg. 684
RANDALL/BAYLON ARCHITECTS, INC.—See JCJ Architecture; *U.S. Private*, pg. 2195
RANDALL BEARINGS, INC.—See Wieland-Werke AG; *Int'l*, pg. 8403
RANDALL BROTHERS INC.; *U.S. Private*, pg. 3353
RANDALL COUNTY FEED YARD—See Friona Industries, LP; *U.S. Private*, pg. 1612
RANDALL FOODS, INC.—See Highview Capital, LLC; *U.S. Private*, pg. 1942
THE RANDALL GROUP INC.; *U.S. Private*, pg. 4102

RANDALL MANUFACTURING, LLC—See The Sterling Group, L.P.; *U.S. Private*, pg. 4123
RANDALL METALS CORPORATION; *U.S. Private*, pg. 3353
RANDALL MOTORS INC.; *U.S. Private*, pg. 3353
RANDALL NOE AUTO GROUP; *U.S. Private*, pg. 3353
RANDALL PR, LLC; *U.S. Private*, pg. 3353
RANDALL & QUILTER UNDERWRITING MANAGEMENT HOLDINGS LIMITED—See R&Q Insurance Holdings Ltd.; *Int'l*, pg. 6168
RANDALL REED'S PRESTIGE LINCOLN MERCURY; *U.S. Private*, pg. 3353
RANDALL-REILLY, LLC—See Aurora Capital Group, LLC; *U.S. Private*, pg. 394
RANDALLS FOOD & DRUGS, LP—See Cerberus Capital Management, L.P.; *U.S. Private*, pg. 836
RANDALLS PROPERTIES, INC.—See Cerberus Capital Management, L.P.; *U.S. Private*, pg. 836
RANDA LUGGAGE—See Randa Corp.; *U.S. Private*, pg. 3353
RANDA NECKWEAR CORP.—See Randa Corp.; *U.S. Private*, pg. 3353
RANDASH INVESTMENT LIMITED—See CK Asset Holdings Limited; *Int'l*, pg. 1635
RANDA SOLUTIONS; *U.S. Private*, pg. 3353
RAND A TECHNOLOGY CORPORATION—See Ampersand Management LLC; *U.S. Private*, pg. 265
RAND CAPITAL CORPORATION; *U.S. Public*, pg. 1762
RAND CAPITAL SBIC, INC.—See Rand Capital Corporation; *U.S. Public*, pg. 1762
RAND CONSTRUCTION CORPORATION; *U.S. Private*, pg. 3353
THE RAND CORPORATION; *U.S. Private*, pg. 4102
RAND ENGINEERING & ARCHITECTURE, PC; *U.S. Private*, pg. 3353
RANDFONTEIN ESTATES LIMITED—See Harmony Gold Mining Company Limited; *Int'l*, pg. 3278
RANDGOLD & EXPLORATION COMPANY LIMITED; *Int'l*, pg. 6200
RANDGOLD RESOURCES BURKINA FASO SARL—See Barrick Gold Corporation; *Int'l*, pg. 870
RANDGOLD RESOURCES (COTE D'IVOIRE) LTD.—See Barrick Gold Corporation; *Int'l*, pg. 869
RANDGOLD RESOURCES COTE D'IVOIRE SARL—See Barrick Gold Corporation; *Int'l*, pg. 869
RANDGOLD RESOURCES LIMITED—See Barrick Gold Corporation; *Int'l*, pg. 869
RANDGOLD RESOURCES (MALI) LTD—See Barrick Gold Corporation; *Int'l*, pg. 869
RANDGOLD RESOURCES MALI SARL—See Barrick Gold Corporation; *Int'l*, pg. 869
RANDGOLD RESOURCES (SENEGAL) LTD—See Barrick Gold Corporation; *Int'l*, pg. 869
RANDGOLD RESOURCES TANZANIA LTD—See Barrick Gold Corporation; *Int'l*, pg. 870
RANDGOLD RESOURCES (UK) LTD—See Barrick Gold Corporation; *Int'l*, pg. 870
RAND GRAPHICS INC.; *U.S. Private*, pg. 3353
RANDI A/S—See Allegion Public Limited Company; *Int'l*, pg. 335
RAND INTERNATIONAL LEISURE PRODUCTS; *U.S. Private*, pg. 3353
RAND LOGISTICS, INC.—See AIP, LLC; *U.S. Private*, pg. 135
RAND MATERIALS HANDLING EQUIPMENT—See W.W. Grainger, Inc.; *U.S. Public*, pg. 2320
RAND MCNALLY & COMPANY—See Patriarch Partners, LLC; *U.S. Private*, pg. 3109
RAND MERCHANT BANK—See FirstRand Limited; *Int'l*, pg. 2690
RAND MINING LIMITED; *Int'l*, pg. 6200
RANDOLPH ACQUISITIONS, INC.; *U.S. Private*, pg. 3354
RANDOLPH BANCORP, INC.—See Hometown Financial Group, Inc.; *U.S. Private*, pg. 1975
RANDOLPH COMPANY; *U.S. Private*, pg. 3354
RANDOLPH ELECTRIC MEMBERSHIP CORPORATION; *U.S. Private*, pg. 3354
RANDOLPH GROUP, INC.; *U.S. Private*, pg. 3354
RANDOLPH PACKING COMPANY; *U.S. Private*, pg. 3354
RANDOLPH PACKING CO.; *U.S. Private*, pg. 3354
RANDOLPH SAVINGS BANK—See Hometown Financial Group, Inc.; *U.S. Private*, pg. 1975
RANDOM HOUSE ADULT TRADE GROUP—See Bertelsmann SE & Co. KGaA; *Int'l*, pg. 991
RANDOM HOUSE CHILDREN'S BOOKS—See Bertelsmann SE & Co. KGaA; *Int'l*, pg. 991
RANDOM HOUSE LLC—See Bertelsmann SE & Co. KGaA; *Int'l*, pg. 990
RANDOM HOUSE TRADE PUBLISHING GROUP—See Bertelsmann SE & Co. KGaA; *Int'l*, pg. 991
RANDOM LENGTHS PUBLICATIONS, INC.—See Astorg Partners S.A.S.; *Int'l*, pg. 656
RANDOM LENGTHS PUBLICATIONS, INC.—See Epiris Managers LLP; *Int'l*, pg. 2461
RANDON ARGENTINA S.A.—See Randon S.A. Implementos e. Participacoes.; *Int'l*, pg. 6201
RANDON PERU S.A.C.—See Randon S.A. Implementos e. Participacoes.; *Int'l*, pg. 6201

RANDON S.A. IMPLEMENTOS E. PARTICIPACOES.; *Int'l*, pg. 6200
RAND REALTY LLC; *U.S. Private*, pg. 3353
RANDSTAD AB—See Randstad N.V.; *Int'l*, pg. 6202
RANDSTAD AE—See Randstad N.V.; *Int'l*, pg. 6202
RANDSTAD ARGENTINA S.A.—See Randstad N.V.; *Int'l*, pg. 6202
RANDSTAD A/S—See Randstad N.V.; *Int'l*, pg. 6202
RANDSTAD AUSTRIA GMBH—See Randstad N.V.; *Int'l*, pg. 6202
RANDSTAD BELGIUM—See Randstad N.V.; *Int'l*, pg. 6202
RANDSTAD BOUW—See Randstad N.V.; *Int'l*, pg. 6202
RANDSTAD BRASIL RECURSOS HUMANOS LTDA—See Randstad N.V.; *Int'l*, pg. 6202
RANDSTAD CALLFLEX—See Randstad N.V.; *Int'l*, pg. 6203
RANDSTAD CANADA—See Randstad N.V.; *Int'l*, pg. 6203
RANDSTAD CARE - BELFAST—See Randstad N.V.; *Int'l*, pg. 6205
RANDSTAD CARE LTD.—See Randstad N.V.; *Int'l*, pg. 6205
RANDSTAD CHILE S.A.—See Randstad N.V.; *Int'l*, pg. 6203
RANDSTAD CPE LIMITED—See Randstad N.V.; *Int'l*, pg. 6205
RANDSTAD DEUTSCHLAND—See Randstad N.V.; *Int'l*, pg. 6203
RANDSTAD EDUCATION LTD.—See Randstad N.V.; *Int'l*, pg. 6205
RANDSTAD EDUCATION—See Randstad N.V.; *Int'l*, pg. 6204
RANDSTAD EDUCATION—See Randstad N.V.; *Int'l*, pg. 6205
RANDSTAD EMPLEO E.T.T.—See Randstad N.V.; *Int'l*, pg. 6203
RANDSTAD ENGINEERING USA—See Randstad N.V.; *Int'l*, pg. 6203
RANDSTAD ENGINNERING—See Randstad N.V.; *Int'l*, pg. 6203
RANDSTAD ESPANA S.L.—See Randstad N.V.; *Int'l*, pg. 6202
RANDSTAD FINANCE & ACCOUNTING—See Randstad N.V.; *Int'l*, pg. 6203
RANDSTAD FINANCIAL & PROFESSIONAL LTD.—See Randstad N.V.; *Int'l*, pg. 6205
RANDSTAD GEZONDHEIDSZORG—See Randstad N.V.; *Int'l*, pg. 6203
RANDSTAD GROEP NEDERLAND BV—See Randstad N.V.; *Int'l*, pg. 6203
RANDSTAD GROUP BELGIUM N.V.—See Randstad N.V.; *Int'l*, pg. 6203
RANDSTAD HEALTHCARE—See Randstad N.V.; *Int'l*, pg. 6203
RANDSTAD HELLAS S.A.—See Randstad N.V.; *Int'l*, pg. 6202
RANDSTAD HONG KONG LIMITED—See Randstad N.V.; *Int'l*, pg. 6203
RANDSTAD HR SOLUTIONS BV—See Randstad N.V.; *Int'l*, pg. 6203
RANDSTAD HR SOLUTIONS BV—See Randstad N.V.; *Int'l*, pg. 6203
RANDSTAD HR SOLUTIONS LIMITED—See Randstad N.V.; *Int'l*, pg. 6203
RANDSTAD HR SOLUTIONS S.R.O.—See Randstad N.V.; *Int'l*, pg. 6203
RANDSTAD HUMAN RESOURCES UNITED STATES—See Randstad N.V.; *Int'l*, pg. 6203
RANDSTAD INDIA PRIVATE LIMITED—See Randstad N.V.; *Int'l*, pg. 6203
RANDSTAD INHOUSE SERVICES LTD—See Randstad N.V.; *Int'l*, pg. 6203
RANDSTAD INHOUSE SERVICES S.A.—See Randstad N.V.; *Int'l*, pg. 6203
RANDSTAD INHOUSE SERVICES—See Randstad N.V.; *Int'l*, pg. 6203
RANDSTAD INTERIM EXECUTIVES LTD.—See Randstad N.V.; *Int'l*, pg. 6205
RANDSTAD INTERIM INC.—See Randstad N.V.; *Int'l*, pg. 6203
RANDSTAD INTERIM—See Randstad N.V.; *Int'l*, pg. 6203
RANDSTAD IRELAND OPERATIONS LIMITED—See Randstad N.V.; *Int'l*, pg. 6203
RANDSTAD ITALIA SPA—See Randstad N.V.; *Int'l*, pg. 6203
RANDSTAD-IT DIVISION—See Randstad N.V.; *Int'l*, pg. 6204
RANDSTAD-IT DIVISION—See Randstad N.V.; *Int'l*, pg. 6204
RANDSTAD KK—See Randstad N.V.; *Int'l*, pg. 6203
RANDSTAD LEGAL—See Randstad N.V.; *Int'l*, pg. 6204
RANDSTAD MANAGED SERVICES NV—See Randstad N.V.; *Int'l*, pg. 6203
RANDSTAD MANAGED SOLUTIONS SDN BHD—See Randstad N.V.; *Int'l*, pg. 6203
RANDSTAD MIDDLE EAST LIMITED—See Randstad N.V.; *Int'l*, pg. 6203
RANDSTAD MOBILITEITSDIENSTEN—See Randstad N.V.; *Int'l*, pg. 6203

COMPANY NAME INDEX

RANDSTAD NEDERLAND BV—See Randstad N.V.; *Int'l*, pg. 6203
RANDSTAD NORWAY AS—See Randstad N.V.; *Int'l*, pg. 6203
RANDSTAD N.V.; *Int'l*, pg. 6201
RANDSTAD OUTSOURCING GMBH—See Randstad N.V.; *Int'l*, pg. 6203
RANDSTAD OUTSOURCING & PROJECT SERVICES—See Randstad N.V.; *Int'l*, pg. 6203
RANDSTAD PHARMA, INC.—See Randstad N.V.; *Int'l*, pg. 6203
RANDSTAD POLSKA SP. Z O.O.—See Randstad N.V.; *Int'l*, pg. 6203
RANDSTAD PROFESSIONALS SA—See Randstad N.V.; *Int'l*, pg. 6203
RANDSTAD PROFESSIONALS SA.—See Randstad N.V.; *Int'l*, pg. 6204
RANDSTAD PROFESSIONALS—See Randstad N.V.; *Int'l*, pg. 6202
RANDSTAD PROFESSIONALS US L.P.—See Randstad N.V.; *Int'l*, pg. 6203
RANDSTAD PTE LTD.—See Randstad N.V.; *Int'l*, pg. 6204
RANDSTAD PTY LIMITED - MELBOURNE—See Randstad N.V.; *Int'l*, pg. 6204
RANDSTAD PTY LIMITED—See Randstad N.V.; *Int'l*, pg. 6204
RANDSTAD RECURSOS HUMANOS, EMPRESA DE TRABALHO TEMPORARIO S.A.—See Randstad N.V.; *Int'l*, pg. 6204
RANDSTAD RECURSOS HUMANOS S.A.—See Randstad N.V.; *Int'l*, pg. 6204
RANDSTAD RISESMART AB—See Randstad N.V.; *Int'l*, pg. 6204
RANDSTAD ROMANIA SRL—See Randstad N.V.; *Int'l*, pg. 6204
RANDSTAD SA DE CV—See Randstad N.V.; *Int'l*, pg. 6202
RANDSTAD SA—See Randstad N.V.; *Int'l*, pg. 6202
RANDSTAD S.A.—See Randstad N.V.; *Int'l*, pg. 6202
RANDSTAD SA—See Randstad N.V.; *Int'l*, pg. 6204
RANDSTAD S.A.—See Randstad N.V.; *Int'l*, pg. 6204
RANDSTAD SCHWEIZ AG—See Randstad N.V.; *Int'l*, pg. 6204
RANDSTAD SEARCH & SELECTION PERSONEL SECME VE YERLESTIRME LIMITED SIRKETI—See Randstad N.V.; *Int'l*, pg. 6204
RANDSTAD SEARCH & SELECTION—See Randstad N.V.; *Int'l*, pg. 6204
RANDSTAD—See Randstad N.V.; *Int'l*, pg. 6204
RANDSTAD SOURCERIGHT B.V.—See Randstad N.V.; *Int'l*, pg. 6204
RANDSTAD SOURCERIGHT CANADA—See Randstad N.V.; *Int'l*, pg. 6204
RANDSTAD SOURCERIGHT GMBH—See Randstad N.V.; *Int'l*, pg. 6204
RANDSTAD SOURCERIGHT SDN. BHD.—See Randstad N.V.; *Int'l*, pg. 6204
RANDSTAD SOURCERIGHT UK—See Randstad N.V.; *Int'l*, pg. 6204
RANDSTAD SOURCERIGHT US—See Randstad N.V.; *Int'l*, pg. 6204
RANDSTAD SP. Z O.O.—See Randstad N.V.; *Int'l*, pg. 6204
RANDSTAD SRI LANKA (PVT) LTD.—See Randstad N.V.; *Int'l*, pg. 6204
RANDSTAD S.R.O.—See Randstad N.V.; *Int'l*, pg. 6205
RANDSTAD, S.R.O.—See Randstad N.V.; *Int'l*, pg. 6205
RANDSTAD STAFFING—See Randstad N.V.; *Int'l*, pg. 6204
RANDSTAD TECHNIEK—See Randstad N.V.; *Int'l*, pg. 6204
RANDSTAD TECHNOLOGIES INC.—See Randstad N.V.; *Int'l*, pg. 6204
RANDSTAD TECHNOLOGIES, LDA.—See Randstad N.V.; *Int'l*, pg. 6204
RANDSTAD TECHNOLOGIES LTD.—See Randstad N.V.; *Int'l*, pg. 6205
RANDSTAD TECHNOLOGIES U.S.—See Randstad N.V.; *Int'l*, pg. 6204
RANDSTAD TRANSPORTDIENSTEN—See Randstad N.V.; *Int'l*, pg. 6204
RANDSTAD UK HOLDING LTD.—See Randstad N.V.; *Int'l*, pg. 6205
RANDSTAD UK LIMITED—See Randstad N.V.; *Int'l*, pg. 6204
RANDSTAD URUGUAY S.A.—See Randstad N.V.; *Int'l*, pg. 6205
RANDSTAD USA—See Randstad N.V.; *Int'l*, pg. 6204
RANDSTAD VIKAR—See Randstad N.V.; *Int'l*, pg. 6205
RAND TECHNOLOGY INC.; *U.S. Private*, pg. 3353
RAND-TEC INSURANCE AGENCY, INC.—See GTCR LLC; *U.S. Private*, pg. 1804
RAND TRANSPORT (1986) PTY LTD—See Eagers Automotive Limited; *Int'l*, pg. 2263
RAND TRANSPORT PTY LTD—See Eagers Automotive Limited; *Int'l*, pg. 2263

RAND TRUST FINANCIERS PROPRIETARY LIMITED—See Transaction Capital Limited; *Int'l*, pg. 7894
RAND WEALTH, LLC—See Stifel Financial Corp.; *U.S. Public*, pg. 1949
RAND-WHITNEY GROUP, LLC—See The Kraft Group LLC; *U.S. Private*, pg. 4066
RAND WORLDWIDE, INC.; *U.S. Public*, pg. 1762
RANDY MARION CHEVROLET-PONTIAC-BUICK, LLC—See Randy Marion Incorporated; *U.S. Private*, pg. 3354
RANDY MARION INCORPORATED; *U.S. Private*, pg. 3354
RANDY MERREN AUTO SALES INC.; *U.S. Private*, pg. 3354
RANDY'S SANITATION, INC.; *U.S. Private*, pg. 3354
RANE BRAKE LINING LIMITED—See Rane Holdings Limited; *Int'l*, pg. 6206
RANE ENGINE VALVE LIMITED—See Rane Holdings Limited; *Int'l*, pg. 6206
RANE HOLDINGS AMERICA INC.—See Rane Holdings Limited; *Int'l*, pg. 6206
RANE HOLDINGS LIMITED; *Int'l*, pg. 6206
RANE (MADRAS) LIMITED—See Rane Holdings Limited; *Int'l*, pg. 6206
RANE NASTECH LIMITED—See NSK Ltd.; *Int'l*, pg. 5480
RANE STEERING SYSTEMS PVT LTD—See Rane Holdings Limited; *Int'l*, pg. 6206
THE RANEW INSURANCE AGENCY, INC.—See GTCR LLC; *U.S. Private*, pg. 1804
RANEW'S TRUCK & EQUIPMENT CO. LLC—See ALJ Regional Holdings, Inc.; *U.S. Public*, pg. 78
RANEY'S TRUCK CENTER, INC.—See American Securities LLC; *U.S. Private*, pg. 248
RANFURLY MANOR LIMITED—See Promisia Healthcare Limited; *Int'l*, pg. 5994
RANGAIRE MANUFACTURING COMPANY, LP; *U.S. Private*, pg. 3354
RANGAM CONSULTANTS INC.; *U.S. Private*, pg. 3354
RANG DONG LIGHT SOURCE & VACUUM FLASK JOINT STOCK COMPANY; *Int'l*, pg. 6206
RANGE CYLINDERS LIMITED—See Kingspan Group PLC; *Int'l*, pg. 4179
RANGEFORD RESOURCES, INC.; *U.S. Private*, pg. 3354
RANGE GENERATION NEXT, LLC—See RTX Corporation; *U.S. Public*, pg. 1824
RANGE GOLD CORP.; *Int'l*, pg. 6206
RANGE IMPACT, INC.; *U.S. Public*, pg. 1762
RANGE INTELLIGENT COMPUTING TECHNOLOGY GROUP COMPANY LIMITED; *Int'l*, pg. 6206
RANGE INTERNATIONAL LIMITED; *Int'l*, pg. 6206
RANGE KLEEN MFG., INC.; *U.S. Private*, pg. 3354
RANGELAND COOPERATIVES INC.; *U.S. Private*, pg. 3354
RANGELAND ENERGY—See EnCap Investments L.P.; *U.S. Private*, pg. 1390
RANGE LIGHT LLC; *U.S. Private*, pg. 3354
RANGEN AQUACULTURE RESEARCH—See Wilbur-Ellis Company; *U.S. Private*, pg. 4518
RANGEN, INC. - AQUACULTURE DIVISION—See Wilbur-Ellis Company; *U.S. Private*, pg. 4518
RANGEN, INC. - COMMODITIES DIVISION—See Wilbur-Ellis Company; *U.S. Private*, pg. 4518
RANGEN, INC. - RANGEN LOGISTICS DIVISION—See Wilbur-Ellis Company; *U.S. Private*, pg. 4518
RANGEN, INC.—See Wilbur-Ellis Company; *U.S. Private*, pg. 4518
RANGER AEROSPACE LLC; *U.S. Private*, pg. 3354
RANGER AIR AVIATION LTD.—See JLL Partners, LLC; *U.S. Private*, pg. 2212
RANGER ENERGY EQUIPMENT, LLC—See Ranger Energy Services, Inc.; *U.S. Public*, pg. 1762
RANGER ENERGY SERVICES, INC.; *U.S. Public*, pg. 1762
RANGER ENERGY SERVICES, LLC—See Ranger Energy Services, Inc.; *U.S. Public*, pg. 1762
RANGE RESOURCES-APPALACHIA, LLC—See Range Resources Corporation; *U.S. Public*, pg. 1762
RANGE RESOURCES CORPORATION; *U.S. Public*, pg. 1762
RANGE RESOURCES-LOUISIANA, INC.—See Range Resources Corporation; *U.S. Public*, pg. 1762
RANGER GOLD CORP.; *U.S. Private*, pg. 3354
RANGER INSURANCE INC.; *Int'l*, pg. 6206
RANGER JOE'S COLUMBUS ARMY SURPLUS CO.; *U.S. Private*, pg. 3355
RANGER LIFT TRUCKS; *U.S. Private*, pg. 3355
RANGER METAL PRODUCTS LTD.; *Int'l*, pg. 6206
RANGER OIL CORPORATION—See Baytex Energy Corp.; *Int'l*, pg. 915
RANGERS BASEBALL EXPRESS LLC; *U.S. Private*, pg. 3355
RANGERS BASEBALL LLC—See Rangers Baseball Express LLC; *U.S. Private*, pg. 3355
THE RANGERS FOOTBALL CLUB LIMITED—See Rangers International Football Club plc; *Int'l*, pg. 6207
RANGERS INTERNATIONAL FOOTBALL CLUB PLC; *Int'l*, pg. 6207

RANGER SPECIALIZED GLASS INC.; *U.S. Private*, pg. 3355
RANGERS VALLEY CATTLE STATION PYT LTD—See Marubeni Corporation; *Int'l*, pg. 4707
RANGE TELEPHONE COOPERATIVE INC.; *U.S. Private*, pg. 3354
RANGE VALLEY EXTRUSIONS LTD—See Deceuninck NV; *Int'l*, pg. 2000
RANGOONEERS COMPANY LIMITED—See Endress+Hauser (International) Holding AG; *Int'l*, pg. 2409
RANGPUR DAIRY & FOOD PRODUCTS LIMITED; *Int'l*, pg. 6207
RANGPUR FOUNDRY LIMITED; *Int'l*, pg. 6207
RANHILL BERSEKUTU SDN BHD—See Ranhill Utilities Berhad; *Int'l*, pg. 6207
RANHILL ENERGY SDN BHD—See Ranhill Utilities Berhad; *Int'l*, pg. 6207
RANHILL ENGINEERS AND CONSTRUCTORS SDN BHD—See Ranhill Utilities Berhad; *Int'l*, pg. 6207
RANHILL POWER BERHAD—See Ranhill Utilities Berhad; *Int'l*, pg. 6207
RANHILL POWERTRON SDN BHD—See Ranhill Utilities Berhad; *Int'l*, pg. 6207
RANHILL SAJ SDN BHD—See Ranhill Utilities Berhad; *Int'l*, pg. 6207
RANHILL UTILITIES BERHAD—See YTL Corporation Berhad; *Int'l*, pg. 8606
RANHILL UTILITIES BERHAD; *Int'l*, pg. 6207
RANHILL UTILITIES BERHAD—See Ranhill Utilities Berhad; *Int'l*, pg. 6207
RANHILL WATER SERVICES SDN BHD—See Ranhill Utilities Berhad; *Int'l*, pg. 6207
RANHILL WATER TECHNOLOGIES (THAI) LTD.—See YTL Corporation Berhad; *Int'l*, pg. 8606
RANHILL WORLEYPARSONS SDN BHD—See Ranhill Utilities Berhad; *Int'l*, pg. 6207
RANI FOODS, INC.; *U.S. Private*, pg. 3355
RANIR GMBH - SCHONAU IM SCHWARZWALD—See Perrigo Company plc; *Int'l*, pg. 5814
RANIR GMBH—See Perrigo Company plc; *Int'l*, pg. 5814
RANIR, LLC—See Perrigo Company plc; *Int'l*, pg. 5813
RANI SOFT DRINKS PRIVATE LTD.—See Aujan Industries Co., L.L.C.; *Int'l*, pg. 704
RANI THERAPEUTICS HOLDINGS, INC.; *U.S. Public*, pg. 1762
RANIX, INC.; *Int'l*, pg. 6207
RANI ZIM SHOPPING CENTERS LTD.; *Int'l*, pg. 6207
RANJEET MECHATRONICS LTD.; *Int'l*, pg. 6207
RANJIT SECURITIES LIMITED; *Int'l*, pg. 6207
RANK CHEMICAL SDN. BERHAD—See Brite-Tech Berhad; *Int'l*, pg. 1165
RANK GROUP GAMING DIVISION LIMITED—See The Rank Group Plc; *Int'l*, pg. 7678
RANK GROUP INVESTMENTS LTD.—See Rank Group Ltd.; *Int'l*, pg. 6207
RANK GROUP LTD.; *Int'l*, pg. 6207
THE RANK GROUP PLC; *Int'l*, pg. 7678
RANKINGS.IO, LLC; *U.S. Private*, pg. 3355
RANKIN INDUSTRIES, INC.—See Broco, Inc.; *U.S. Private*, pg. 661
RANK INTERACTIVE (GIBRALTAR) LIMITED—See The Rank Group Plc; *Int'l*, pg. 7678
RANK METAL SDN. BHD.—See LB Aluminium Berhad; *Int'l*, pg. 4428
RANK PROGRESS S.A.; *Int'l*, pg. 6208
RANK + RALLY, LLC—See Compass Group PLC; *Int'l*, pg. 1752
RAN-MAR INC.; *U.S. Private*, pg. 3352
RANMARINE TECHNOLOGY B.V.; *Int'l*, pg. 6208
RANNIE PUBLICATIONS INC.—See Chatham Asset Management, LLC; *U.S. Private*, pg. 861
RANON & PARTNERS INC.; *U.S. Private*, pg. 3355
RANOR, INC.—See TechPrecision Corporation; *U.S. Public*, pg. 1988
RANPAK BV—See Ranpak Holdings Corp.; *U.S. Public*, pg. 1763
RANPAK CORP. - RENO—See Ranpak Holdings Corp.; *U.S. Public*, pg. 1763
RANPAK CORP.—See Ranpak Holdings Corp.; *U.S. Public*, pg. 1763
RANPAK HOLDINGS CORP.; *U.S. Public*, pg. 1763
RANPAK PTE. LTD.—See Ranpak Holdings Corp.; *U.S. Public*, pg. 1763
RANPLAN GROUP AB; *Int'l*, pg. 6208
RANSA COMERCIAL S.A.—See Grupo Romero; *Int'l*, pg. 3135
RANSBURG INDUSTRIAL FINISHING K.K.—See Carlisle Companies Incorporated; *U.S. Public*, pg. 436
RANSOHOFF—See Alpha Capital Partners, Ltd.; *U.S. Private*, pg. 197
RANSOM CONSULTING, LLC—See Pinchin Ltd; *Int'l*, pg. 5867
RANSOME ENGINE—See Giles & Ransome, Inc.; *U.S. Private*, pg. 1699
RANSOME RENTS—See Giles & Ransome, Inc.; *U.S. Private*, pg. 1699
RANSOMES JACOBSEN FRANCE S.A.S.—See Textron Inc.; *U.S. Public*, pg. 2028

RANPLAN GROUP AB — CORPORATE AFFILIATIONS

RANSOM PUMP & SUPPLY INC.—See Bain Capital, LP; *U.S. Private*, pg. 432
RANSOM & RANDOLPH COMPANY—See PMC Capital Partners, LLC; *U.S. Private*, pg. 3218
RANSON PTE LTD—See Thirumalai Chemicals Ltd; *Int'l*, pg. 7710
RANTEC MICROWAVE SYSTEMS, INC.; *U.S. Private*, pg. 3355
RANTRONICS INTERNATIONAL LTD.; *U.S. Private*, pg. 3355
RANUAN MEIJERI OY—See Arla Foods amba; *Int'l*, pg. 572
RAO DESIGN INTERNATIONAL, INC.; *U.S. Private*, pg. 3355
RAO NORDIC OY—See JSC INTER RAO UES; *Int'l*, pg. 4009
RAONSECURE CO. LTD; *Int'l*, pg. 6208
RAONTEC INC; *Int'l*, pg. 6209
RAOOM TRADING CO.; *Int'l*, pg. 6209
RAPAC COMMUNICATION & INFRASTRUCTURE LTD.—See Inter-Gamma Investment Company Ltd.; *Int'l*, pg. 3735
RAPAC INC.—See MSD Capital, L.P.; *U.S. Private*, pg. 2807
RAPAK AD—See Sealed Air Corporation; *U.S. Public*, pg. 1853
RAPAK ASIA PACIFIC LIMITED—See Sealed Air Corporation; *U.S. Public*, pg. 1853
RAPAK, LLC - INDIANAPOLIS PLANT—See Sealed Air Corporation; *U.S. Public*, pg. 1853
RAPAK, LLC—See Sealed Air Corporation; *U.S. Public*, pg. 1853
RAPAK, LLC - UNION CITY PLANT—See Sealed Air Corporation; *U.S. Public*, pg. 1853
RAPALA B.V.—See Rapala VMC Oyj; *Int'l*, pg. 6209
RAPALA EESTI AS—See Rapala VMC Oyj; *Int'l*, pg. 6209
RAPALA FINANCE N.V.—See Rapala VMC Oyj; *Int'l*, pg. 6209
RAPALA-FISHCO AG—See Rapala VMC Oyj; *Int'l*, pg. 6210
RAPALA FRANCE SAS—See Rapala VMC Oyj; *Int'l*, pg. 6209
RAPALA FREETIME AUSTRALIA PTY. LTD.—See Rapala VMC Oyj; *Int'l*, pg. 6209
RAPALA JAPAN K.K.—See Rapala VMC Oyj; *Int'l*, pg. 6209
RAPALA MAIL ORDER INC.—See Rapala VMC Oyj; *Int'l*, pg. 6209
RAPALA VMC (ASIA PACIFIC) SDN. BHD.—See Rapala VMC Oyj; *Int'l*, pg. 6209
RAPALA VMC AUSTRALIA PTY LTD.—See Rapala VMC Oyj; *Int'l*, pg. 6209
RAPALA VMC CHINA CO.—See Rapala VMC Oyj; *Int'l*, pg. 6209
RAPALA VMC CORPORATION—See Rapala VMC Oyj; *Int'l*, pg. 6210
RAPALA VMC ICELAND EHF—See Rapala VMC Oyj; *Int'l*, pg. 6210
RAPALA VMC KOREA CO., LTD—See Rapala VMC Oyj; *Int'l*, pg. 6210
RAPALA VMC MEXICO S. DE R.L. DE C.V—See Rapala VMC Oyj; *Int'l*, pg. 6210
RAPALA VMC OYJ; *Int'l*, pg. 6209
RAPALA VMC (SHENZHEN) LTD.—See Rapala VMC Oyj; *Int'l*, pg. 6209
RAPALA VMC SINGAPORE PTE. LTD.—See Rapala VMC Oyj; *Int'l*, pg. 6210
RAPALA VMC SOUTH AFRICA DISTRIBUTORS PTY. LTD.—See Rapala VMC Oyj; *Int'l*, pg. 6210
RAPALA VMC (THAILAND) CO., LTD.—See Rapala VMC Oyj; *Int'l*, pg. 6210
RAPELLI SA—See Orior AG; *Int'l*, pg. 5633
RAPER, TOM, INC.; *U.S. Private*, pg. 3355
RAPHAEL HOTEL GROUP; *U.S. Private*, pg. 3355
THE RAPHAEL HOTEL—See Blue Beacon International, Inc.; *U.S. Private*, pg. 585
RAPHAEL MICHEL SA; *Int'l*, pg. 6210
RAPHAELS PARTY RENTALS INC.; *U.S. Private*, pg. 3355
RAPHAEL S.R.L.—See YaGuang Technology Group Company Limited; *Int'l*, pg. 8545
RAPHAEL VALVES INDUSTRIES LTD.—See Triton Advisers Limited; *Int'l*, pg. 7934
RA PHARMACEUTICALS, INC.—See UCB S.A.; *Int'l*, pg. 8011
RAPHAS CHINA CO., LTD.—See Raphas Co., Ltd.; *Int'l*, pg. 6210
RAPHAS CO., LTD.; *Int'l*, pg. 6210
RAPICUT CARBIDES LIMITED; *Int'l*, pg. 6210
RAPID7 CANADA, INC.—See Rapid7, Inc.; *U.S. Public*, pg. 1763
RAPID7, INC.; *U.S. Public*, pg. 1763
RAPID7 SINGAPORE PTE. LTD.—See Rapid7, Inc.; *U.S. Public*, pg. 1763
RAPID ACCESS LLC—See Loxam SAS; *Int'l*, pg. 4566
RAPID ACTION PACKAGING LTD.—See The Pritzker Group - Chicago, LLC; *U.S. Private*, pg. 4099
RAPID A.D.; *Int'l*, pg. 6210
RAPID A.D.; *Int'l*, pg. 6210

RAPID ARMORED CORPORATION—See Founders Equity, Inc.; *U.S. Private*, pg. 1581
RAPID BIOSENSOR SYSTEMS LIMIT—See Xylem Inc.; *U.S. Public*, pg. 2394
RAPID BRIDGE LLC—See QUALCOMM Incorporated; *U.S. Public*, pg. 1747
RAPID CHEVROLET CO. INC.; *U.S. Private*, pg. 3355
RAPID CITY JOURNAL—See Lee Enterprises, Incorporated; *U.S. Public*, pg. 1300
RAPID CITY, PIERRE & EASTERN RAILROAD, INC.—See Brookfield Infrastructure Partners L.P.; *Int'l*, pg. 1192
RAPID CITY, PIERRE & EASTERN RAILROAD, INC.—See GIC Pte. Ltd.; *Int'l*, pg. 2967
RAPID CONN INC.—See Waja Konsortium Berhad; *Int'l*, pg. 8331
RAPID CONN (SHENZHEN) CO., LTD.—See Waja Konsortium Berhad; *Int'l*, pg. 8331
RAPID CONN (S) PTE. LTD.—See Waja Konsortium Berhad; *Int'l*, pg. 8331
RAPID DIAGNOSTICS, INC.—See Bausch Health Companies Inc.; *Int'l*, pg. 898
RAPID DIE & MOLDING CO.; *U.S. Private*, pg. 3355
RAPID DISPLAYS, INC.—See Gemspring Capital Management, LLC; *U.S. Public*, pg. 1659
RAPID DISPLAYS - UNION CITY—See Gemspring Capital Management, LLC; *U.S. Private*, pg. 1659
RAPID DOSE THERAPEUTICS, INC.; *Int'l*, pg. 6210
RAPID ELECTRONICS LIMITED; *Int'l*, pg. 6210
RAPID ENGINEERING INC.; *U.S. Private*, pg. 3355
RAPIDES AFTER HOURS CLINIC, L.L.C.—See HCA Healthcare, Inc.; *U.S. Public*, pg. 1007
RAPIDES REGIONAL MEDICAL CENTER—See HCA Healthcare, Inc.; *U.S. Public*, pg. 1007
RAPIDES REGIONAL PHYSICIAN GROUP, LLC—See HCA Healthcare, Inc.; *U.S. Public*, pg. 1007
RAPIDES REGIONAL PHYSICIAN GROUP, LLC—See HCA Healthcare, Inc.; *U.S. Public*, pg. 1007
RAPIDES REGIONAL PHYSICIAN GROUP PRIMARY CARE, LLC—See HCA Healthcare, Inc.; *U.S. Public*, pg. 1007
RAPIDES REGIONAL PHYSICIAN GROUP SPECIALTY CARE, LLC—See HCA Healthcare, Inc.; *U.S. Public*, pg. 1007
RAPID FINANCIAL SOLUTIONS, LLC—See Tyler Technologies, Inc.; *U.S. Public*, pg. 2209
RAPID FIRE MARKETING, INC.; *U.S. Private*, pg. 3355
RAPID FIRE PROTECTION, INC.—See Pye-Barker Fire & Safety, LLC; *U.S. Private*, pg. 3309
RAPID FIRE SAFETY & SEQURITY LLC—See Financial Investments Corporation; *U.S. Private*, pg. 1507
RAPIDFIT N.V.—See Materialise NV; *Int'l*, pg. 4727
RAPIDFORMS, INC.—See Deluxe Corporation; *U.S. Public*, pg. 652
RAPID GLOBAL BUSINESS SOLUTIONS, INC.; *U.S. Private*, pg. 3355
RAPID GROWTH TECHNOLOGY SDN. BHD.—See RGT Berhad; *Int'l*, pg. 6319
RAPID INDUSTRIES, INC.; *U.S. Private*, pg. 3356
RAPID INVESTMENTS LIMITED; *Int'l*, pg. 6210
RAPIDLD; *U.S. Private*, pg. 3356
RAPID LEARNING DEPLOYMENT, LLC—See Tier 1 Performance Solutions, LLC; *U.S. Private*, pg. 4169
RAPID LEASING, INC.—See CRST International, Inc.; *U.S. Private*, pg. 1113
RAPID MACHINING TECHNOLOGIES PRIVATE LIMITED—See Menon Pistons Ltd.; *Int'l*, pg. 4816
RAPID MANUFACTURING, LCR; *U.S. Private*, pg. 3356
RAPID METAL DEVELOPMENTS (AUSTRALIA) PTY LTD.—See Interserve Plc; *Int'l*, pg. 3759
RAPID METAL DEVELOPMENTS NZ LTD.—See Interserve Plc; *Int'l*, pg. 3759
RAPID MICRO BIOSYSTEMS, INC.; *U.S. Public*, pg. 1763
RAPID NUTRITION PLC; *Int'l*, pg. 6210
RAPIDO PRET SA; *Int'l*, pg. 6210
RAPIDO SAS; *Int'l*, pg. 6210
RAPIDPARTS, INC.—See Caterpillar, Inc.; *U.S. Public*, pg. 453
RAPID PATHOGEN SCREENING, INC.; *U.S. Private*, pg. 3356
RAPID PRINT—See Bidwell Industrial Group, Inc.; *U.S. Private*, pg. 551
RAPID RACK INDUSTRIES INC.; *U.S. Private*, pg. 3356
RAPID RACKING LTD—See Manutan International SA; *Int'l*, pg. 4680
RAPID REALTY FRANCHISE LLC; *U.S. Private*, pg. 3356
RAPID RESPONSE DELIVERY INC.—See H.I.G. Capital, LLC; *U.S. Private*, pg. 1827
RAPID RESPONSE MARKETING LLC; *U.S. Private*, pg. 3356
RAPID ROBERTS INC.; *U.S. Private*, pg. 3356
RAPID SECURITY SOLUTIONS, LLC; *U.S. Private*, pg. 3356
RAPID SHEET METAL LLC—See Proto Labs, Inc.; *U.S. Public*, pg. 1730
RAPID SYNERGY BERHAD; *Int'l*, pg. 6210
RAPID SYSTEMS LTD.—See Arjun Infrastructure Partners Limited; *Int'l*, pg. 568

RAPID TECHNOLOGIES INC.—See Sverica Capital Management LP; *U.S. Public*, pg. 3889
RAPID THERAPEUTIC SCIENCE LABORATORIES, INC.; *U.S. Public*, pg. 1763
RAPIDTRON, INC.; *U.S. Private*, pg. 3356
RAPIDVISA INC.—See Boundless Immigration Inc.; *U.S. Private*, pg. 623
RAPIDWERKS LLC—See Emerson Electric Co.; *U.S. Public*, pg. 752
RAPIDX LTD.—See TechnoPlus Ventures Ltd.; *Int'l*, pg. 7511
RAPIER COMMUNICATIONS LIMITED—See CHI & Partners Limited; *Int'l*, pg. 1474
RAPIER SOLUTIONS, INC.; *U.S. Private*, pg. 3356
RAPISCAN SECURITY PRODUCTS (USA), INC.—See OSI Systems, Inc.; *U.S. Public*, pg. 1622
RAPISCAN SYSTEMS AUSTRALIA PTY LTD—See OSI Systems, Inc.; *U.S. Public*, pg. 1622
RAPISCAN SYSTEMS HONG KONG LIMITED—See OSI Systems, Inc.; *U.S. Public*, pg. 1622
RAPISCAN SYSTEMS, INC.—See OSI Systems, Inc.; *U.S. Public*, pg. 1622
RAPISCAN SYSTEMS LTD.—See OSI Systems, Inc.; *U.S. Public*, pg. 1622
RAPISCAN SYSTEMS OY—See OSI Systems, Inc.; *U.S. Public*, pg. 1622
RAPISCAN SYSTEMS PTE. LTD.—See OSI Systems, Inc.; *U.S. Public*, pg. 1622
RAPITHELA CORPORATION—See JSR Corp.; *Int'l*, pg. 4014
RAPLEX SDN. BHD.—See Ta Ann Holdings Berhad; *Int'l*, pg. 7398
RAPLEY WILKINSON PROPERTY PTY LTD.—See Onterran Limited; *Int'l*, pg. 5591
RAPLEY WILKINSON PTY LTD.—See Onterran Limited; *Int'l*, pg. 5591
RAPMAN (DONGGUAN) LIMITED—See Leeport (Holdings) Limited; *Int'l*, pg. 4442
RAPMAN LIMITED—See Leeport (Holdings) Limited; *Int'l*, pg. 4442
RAP MEDIA LTD.; *Int'l*, pg. 6209
RAPOCA ENERGY CO. LP; *U.S. Private*, pg. 3356
RAPPAHANNOCK ELECTRIC COOP; *U.S. Private*, pg. 3356
RAPPAHANNOCK WESTMINSTER-CANTERBURY, INC.; *U.S. Private*, pg. 3356
RAPP ARGENTINA—See Omnicom Group Inc.; *U.S. Public*, pg. 1592
RAPP BARCELONA—See Omnicom Group Inc.; *U.S. Public*, pg. 1592
RAPP BRAZIL—See Omnicom Group Inc.; *U.S. Public*, pg. 1592
RAPP BUDAPEST—See Omnicom Group Inc.; *U.S. Public*, pg. 1592
RAPP CENTRO AMERICA—See Omnicom Group Inc.; *U.S. Public*, pg. 1592
RAPP DALLAS—See Omnicom Group Inc.; *U.S. Public*, pg. 1592
RAPPDATA COMPANY—See Omnicom Group Inc.; *U.S. Public*, pg. 1592
RAPPDIGITAL BRAZIL—See Omnicom Group Inc.; *U.S. Public*, pg. 1592
RAPP HEALTHCARE—See Omnicom Group Inc.; *U.S. Public*, pg. 1592
RAPP HONG KONG—See Omnicom Group Inc.; *U.S. Public*, pg. 1592
RAPP LONDON—See Omnicom Group Inc.; *U.S. Public*, pg. 1592
RAPP LOS ANGELES—See Omnicom Group Inc.; *U.S. Public*, pg. 1592
RAPP MALAYSIA—See Omnicom Group Inc.; *U.S. Public*, pg. 1592
RAPPMEDIA—See Omnicom Group Inc.; *U.S. Public*, pg. 1592
RAPP MEXICO—See Omnicom Group Inc.; *U.S. Public*, pg. 1592
RAPP NEW YORK—See Omnicom Group Inc.; *U.S. Public*, pg. 1592
RAPPOLD, HERMANN & CO. GMBH—See E.ON SE; *Int'l*, pg. 2259
RAPPOLD WINTERTHUR TECHNOLOGIE GMBH—See 3M Company; *U.S. Public*, pg. 8
RAPPORT, INC.; *U.S. Private*, pg. 3356
RAPP PARIS—See Omnicom Group Inc.; *U.S. Public*, pg. 1592
RAPP—See Omnicom Group Inc.; *U.S. Public*, pg. 1592
RAPP TOKYO—See Omnicom Group Inc.; *U.S. Public*, pg. 1592
RAPP/TRIBAL—See Omnicom Group Inc.; *U.S. Public*, pg. 1582
RAPP UK—See Omnicom Group Inc.; *U.S. Public*, pg. 1592
RAPP UK—See Omnicom Group Inc.; *U.S. Public*, pg. 1592
RAPP WORLDWIDE—See Omnicom Group Inc.; *U.S. Public*, pg. 1592
RAPSONA AB—See AAK AB; *Int'l*, pg. 32
RAPTIM INTERNATIONAL TRAVEL—See Key Travel Limited; *Int'l*, pg. 4145

COMPANY NAME INDEX

RAPTIS GROUP LIMITED; *Int'l*, pg. 6210
RAPTOR MATERIALS LLC—See Eagle Materials Inc.; *U.S. Public*, pg. 702
RAPTOR MINING LLC—See T-REX Acquisition Corp.; *U.S. Public*, pg. 1978
RAPTOR RIG LTD.; *Int'l*, pg. 6211
RAPTOR SCIENTIFIC LLC—See L Squared Capital Management LP; *U.S. Private*, pg. 2362
RAPTOR TECHNOLOGIES, INC; *U.S. Private*, pg. 3356
RAPT THERAPEUTICS, INC.; *U.S. Public*, pg. 1763
RAQUALIA PHARMA INC.; *Int'l*, pg. 6211
RARE CONSTRUCTION ZAMBIA—See Rare Holdings Limited; *Int'l*, pg. 6211
RARE EARTH MAGNESIUM TECHNOLOGY GROUP HOLDINGS LIMITED—See Century Sunshine Group Holdings Limited; *Int'l*, pg. 1419
RARE ELEMENT RESOURCES, INC—See Rare Element Resources Ltd.; *U.S. Public*, pg. 1763
RARE ELEMENT RESOURCES LTD.; *U.S. Public*, pg. 1763
RARE ENTERPRISES LTD.; *Int'l*, pg. 6211
RARE FOODS AUSTRALIA LTD.; *Int'l*, pg. 6211
RARE HOLDINGS LIMITED; *Int'l*, pg. 6211
RAREJOB INC.; *Int'l*, pg. 6211
RAREJOB PHILIPPINES, INC.—See RareJob Inc.; *Int'l*, pg. 6211
RARE SYSTEMS INC.; *U.S. Private*, pg. 3356
RAREX LIMITED; *Int'l*, pg. 6211
RARITAN ADVERTISING AGENCY; *U.S. Private*, pg. 3356
RARITAN AUSTRALIA PTY LTD—See Legrand S.A.; *Int'l*, pg. 4446
RARITAN AUSTRALIA PTY LTD - SYDNEY—See Legrand S.A.; *Int'l*, pg. 4446
RARITAN COMPUTER FRANCE—See Legrand S.A.; *Int'l*, pg. 4446
RARITAN EUROPE BV—See Legrand S.A.; *Int'l*, pg. 4446
RARITAN GERMANY GMBH—See Legrand S.A.; *Int'l*, pg. 4446
RARITAN INC. - INDIA—See Legrand S.A.; *Int'l*, pg. 4446
RARITAN INC. - SINGAPORE—See Legrand S.A.; *Int'l*, pg. 4446
RARITAN, INC.—See Legrand S.A.; *Int'l*, pg. 4446
RARITAN INC. - TAIWAN—See Legrand S.A.; *Int'l*, pg. 4446
RARITAN INC. - UK—See Legrand S.A.; *Int'l*, pg. 4446
RARITAN JAPAN, INC.—See Legrand S.A.; *Int'l*, pg. 4446
RA RODRIGUEZ INC.; *U.S. Private*, pg. 3340
RA ROSSBOROUGH (INSURANCE BROKERS) LTD—See Arthur J. Gallagher & Co.; *U.S. Public*, pg. 207
RARTEL S.A.—See Leonardo S.p.A.; *Int'l*, pg. 4460
RASA CORPORATION; *Int'l*, pg. 6212
RASADNIK A.D.; *Int'l*, pg. 6212
RASA FLOORS & CARPET CLEANING, LLC; *U.S. Private*, pg. 3356
RASA INDUSTRIES, LTD. - HAINUZUKA FACTORY—See Rasa Industries, Ltd.; *Int'l*, pg. 6212
RASA INDUSTRIES, LTD. - ISESAKI FACTORY—See Rasa Industries, Ltd.; *Int'l*, pg. 6212
RASA INDUSTRIES, LTD. - MIYAKO FACTORY—See Rasa Industries, Ltd.; *Int'l*, pg. 6212
RASA INDUSTRIES, LTD. - NODA FACTORY—See Rasa Industries, Ltd.; *Int'l*, pg. 6212
RASA INDUSTRIES, LTD. - OSAKA FACTORY—See Rasa Industries, Ltd.; *Int'l*, pg. 6212
RASA INDUSTRIES, LTD. - SANBONGI FACTORY—See Rasa Industries, Ltd.; *Int'l*, pg. 6212
RASA INDUSTRIES, LTD.; *Int'l*, pg. 6212
RASA LAND COMPANY LIMITED; *Int'l*, pg. 6212
RAS AL KHAIMAH CEMENT COMPANY PSC; *Int'l*, pg. 6211
RAS AL KHAIMAH CERAMICS PJSC; *Int'l*, pg. 6211
RAS AL KHAIMAH COMPANY FOR WHITE CEMENT & CONSTRUCTION MATERIALS PSC—See The Aditya Birla Group; *Int'l*, pg. 7611
RAS AL KHAIMAH FREE TRADE ZONE; *Int'l*, pg. 6211
RAS AL KHAIMAH NATIONAL INSURANCE COMPANY P.S.C.—See The National Bank of Ras Al-Khaimah PSC; *Int'l*, pg. 7670
RAS AL KHAIMAH POULTRY & FEEDING CO.; *Int'l*, pg. 6212
RASAMAS HOLDING SDN BHD—See Johor Corporation; *Int'l*, pg. 3994
RASAMNY-YOUNIS MOTOR CO., S.A.L.; *Int'l*, pg. 6212
RASANDIK ENGINEERING INDUSTRIES INDIA LIMITED; *Int'l*, pg. 6212
RASANT-ALCOTEC BESCHICHTUNGSTECHNIK GMBH—See Coherent Corp.; *U.S. Public*, pg. 528
RASA SAYANG VILLAGE PTE. LTD.—See GS Holdings Limited; *Int'l*, pg. 3143
RA S.A.—See Bridgestone Corporation; *Int'l*, pg. 1160
RAS ASSET MANAGEMENT SGR S.P.A.—See Allianz SE; *Int'l*, pg. 350
RAS ASSOCIATES LLC—See EQT AB; *Int'l*, pg. 2483
RASCHE HOLDING GMBH—See Mutares SE & Co. KGaA; *Int'l*, pg. 5105
RASCHETNYI SERVISNYI CENTER LLP—See Kazakhstan Utility Systems LLP; *Int'l*, pg. 4102
RASCHE UMFORMTECHNIK GMBH&CO.KG—See Mutares SE & Co. KGaA; *Int'l*, pg. 5105
RASCHIG GMBH - ESPENHAIN—See PMC Capital Partners, LLC; *U.S. Private*, pg. 3217
RASCHIG GMBH—See PMC Capital Partners, LLC; *U.S. Private*, pg. 3217
RASCHIG UK LTD.—See PMC Capital Partners, LLC; *U.S. Private*, pg. 3217
RASCHKA ENGINEERING LTD.—See Suzhou Hailu Heavy Industry Co., Ltd.; *Int'l*, pg. 7350
RASCHKA GUANGZHOU ENGINEERING & CONSULTING CO., LTD.—See Suzhou Hailu Heavy Industry Co., Ltd.; *Int'l*, pg. 7350
RASCO GMBH—See Cohu, Inc.; *U.S. Public*, pg. 529
RAS CO., LTD—See ULVAC, Inc.; *Int'l*, pg. 8020
RA SCOTTSDALE CORP.—See TPG Capital, L.P.; *U.S. Public*, pg. 2167
RASHED AL-RASHED & SONS-DONALDSON COMPANY LTD.—See Donaldson Company, Inc.; *U.S. Public*, pg. 676
RASHTRIYA CHEMICALS & FERTILIZERS LTD.; *Int'l*, pg. 6212
THE R.A. SIEGEL COMPANY; *U.S. Private*, pg. 4101
RASI ELECTRODES LIMITED; *Int'l*, pg. 6212
RASIRC, INC.—See Mitsubishi Chemical Group Corporation; *Int'l*, pg. 4937
RAS LAFFAN LIQUEFIED NATURAL GAS COMPANY LTD.—See Qatar Petroleum; *Int'l*, pg. 6136
RAS LAFFAN OPERATING COMPANY W.L.L.—See Qatar Electricity & Water Company Q.S.C.; *Int'l*, pg. 6133
RASMALA PLC; *Int'l*, pg. 6212
RASMUSSEN COLLEGE, LLC—See Renovus Capital Partners; *U.S. Private*, pg. 3399
RASMUSSEN EQUIPMENT COMPANY; *U.S. Private*, pg. 3356
RASMUSSEN EQUIPMENT CO.—See RC Rasmussen Corporation; *U.S. Private*, pg. 3361
RASMUSSEN GROUP INC.; *U.S. Private*, pg. 3356
RASMUSSEN WIRE ROPE RIGGING CO—See RC Rasmussen Corporation; *U.S. Private*, pg. 3361
RASOI LIMITED; *Int'l*, pg. 6212
RASOI MAGIC FOODS PVT. LIMITED—See Orkla ASA; *Int'l*, pg. 5639
RASOYA PROTEINS LTD.; *Int'l*, pg. 6212
RASPUTIN RECORDS INC.; *U.S. Private*, pg. 3357
RAS RESORTS & APART HOTELS LTD.; *Int'l*, pg. 6212
RASSINI S.A.B. DE C.V.; *Int'l*, pg. 6212
RASSINI SAB DE CV; *Int'l*, pg. 6213
RASTACLAT, LLC; *U.S. Private*, pg. 3357
RASTAR ENVIRONMENTAL PROTECTION MATERIALS CO., LTD.; *Int'l*, pg. 6213
RASTAR GROUP; *Int'l*, pg. 6213
RASTAR (HK) INDUSTRIAL CO., LTD.—See Rastar Group; *Int'l*, pg. 6213
RAS TECHNOLOGY HOLDINGS LIMITED; *Int'l*, pg. 6212
RAST ELEKTRO AG—See Burkhalter Holding AG; *Int'l*, pg. 1225
RASTELLI BROTHERS INC.; *U.S. Private*, pg. 3357
RASTERPUNKT-DRUCKVORSTUFEFURVERPAKUNGEN GMBH—See Matthews International Corporation; *U.S. Public*, pg. 1400
RASTRAC; *U.S. Private*, pg. 3357
RASTREATOR.COM LIMITED—See Admiral Group plc; *Int'l*, pg. 151
RASTRIYA BEEMA COMPANY LIMITED; *Int'l*, pg. 6213
RASTRIYA BEEMA SANSTHAN; *Int'l*, pg. 6213
RAS TUTELA GIUDIZIARIA S.P.A.—See Allianz SE; *Int'l*, pg. 350
RA SUSHI ATLANTA MIDTOWN CORP.—See TPG Capital, L.P.; *U.S. Public*, pg. 2167
RA SUSHI BALTIMORE CORP.—See TPG Capital, L.P.; *U.S. Public*, pg. 2167
RA SUSHI CHICAGO CORP.—See TPG Capital, L.P.; *U.S. Public*, pg. 2167
RA SUSHI CHINO HILLS CORP.—See TPG Capital, L.P.; *U.S. Public*, pg. 2167
RA SUSHI CITY CENTER CORP.—See TPG Capital, L.P.; *U.S. Public*, pg. 2167
RA SUSHI CORONA CORP.—See TPG Capital, L.P.; *U.S. Public*, pg. 2167
RA SUSHI FORT WORTH CORP.—See TPG Capital, L.P.; *U.S. Public*, pg. 2167
RA SUSHI GLENVIEW CORP.—See TPG Capital, L.P.; *U.S. Public*, pg. 2167
RA SUSHI HOLDING CORP.—See TPG Capital, L.P.; *U.S. Public*, pg. 2167
RA SUSHI HUNTINGTON BEACH CORP.—See TPG Capital, L.P.; *U.S. Public*, pg. 2167
RA SUSHI LAS VEGAS CORP.—See TPG Capital, L.P.; *U.S. Public*, pg. 2167
RA SUSHI LEAWOOD CORP.—See TPG Capital, L.P.; *U.S. Public*, pg. 2167
RA SUSHI LOMBARD CORP.—See TPG Capital, L.P.; *U.S. Public*, pg. 2167
RA SUSHI MESA CORP.—See TPG Capital, L.P.; *U.S. Public*, pg. 2167
RA SUSHI PALM BEACH GARDENS CORP.—See TPG Capital, L.P.; *U.S. Public*, pg. 2167
RA SUSHI PEMBROKE PINES CORP.—See TPG Capital, L.P.; *U.S. Public*, pg. 2167
RA SUSHI PLANO CORP.—See TPG Capital, L.P.; *U.S. Public*, pg. 2167
RA SUSHI SAN DIEGO CORP.—See TPG Capital, L.P.; *U.S. Public*, pg. 2167
RA SUSHI SOUTH MIAMI CORP.—See TPG Capital, L.P.; *U.S. Public*, pg. 2168
RA SUSHI TORRANCE CORP.—See TPG Capital, L.P.; *U.S. Public*, pg. 2168
RA SUSHI TUCSON CORP.—See TPG Capital, L.P.; *U.S. Public*, pg. 2168
RA SUSHI TUSTIN CORP.—See TPG Capital, L.P.; *U.S. Public*, pg. 2168
RASUWAGADHI HYDROPOWER COMPANY LIMITED—See Chilime Hydropower Company Limited; *Int'l*, pg. 1478
RASWA COMPANY LTD.—See SWARCO AG; *Int'l*, pg. 7360
RATANPUR STEEL RE-ROLLING MILLS LTD.; *Int'l*, pg. 6213
RATAR A.D.; *Int'l*, pg. 6213
RATCHABURI ALLIANCES COMPANY LIMITED—See RATCH Group Public Company Limited; *Int'l*, pg. 6213
RATCHABURI ELECTRICITY GENERATING CO., LTD.—See RATCH Group Public Company Limited; *Int'l*, pg. 6213
RATCHABURI ENERGY CO., LTD.—See RATCH Group Public Company Limited; *Int'l*, pg. 6213
RATCHABURI GAS COMPANY LIMITED—See RATCH Group Public Company Limited; *Int'l*, pg. 6213
RATCHABURI GLASS INDUSTRY CO., LTD.—See BG Container Glass Public Company Limited; *Int'l*, pg. 1007
RATCHAPHRUEK HOSPITAL PCL; *Int'l*, pg. 6213
RATCHASIMA RICE CO., LTD.—See PRG Corporation Public Company Limited; *Int'l*, pg. 5968
RATCH-AUSTRALIA CORPORATION PTY. LTD.—See RATCH Group Public Company Limited; *Int'l*, pg. 6213
RATCH COGENERATION CO., LTD.—See RATCH Group Public Company Limited; *Int'l*, pg. 6213
RATCH GROUP PUBLIC COMPANY LIMITED; *Int'l*, pg. 6213
RATCH-LAO SERVICES CO., LTD.—See RATCH Group Public Company Limited; *Int'l*, pg. 6213
RATCHSIMA RICE COMPANY LIMITED—See MBK Public Company Limited; *Int'l*, pg. 4754
RATCHTHANI LEASING PUBLIC COMPANY LIMITED—See TMBThanachart Bank Public Company Limited; *Int'l*, pg. 7766
RATCH UDOM POWER COMPANY LIMITED—See RATCH Group Public Company Limited; *Int'l*, pg. 6213
RATCLIFF PALFINGER LTD.—See Palfinger AG; *Int'l*, pg. 5708
RATEGAIN TECHNOLOGIES INC.; *U.S. Private*, pg. 3357
RATEGAIN TRAVEL TECHNOLOGIES LIMITED; *Int'l*, pg. 6213
R&A TELECOMMUNICATION GROUP BERHAD; *Int'l*, pg. 6168
RATEMYPROFESSORS.COM, LLC—See Altice USA, Inc.; *U.S. Public*, pg. 88
RATEPAY GMBH—See Advent International Corporation; *U.S. Private*, pg. 105
RATEPAY GMBH—See Bain Capital, LP; *U.S. Private*, pg. 442
RATERMANN MANUFACTURING, INC.; *U.S. Private*, pg. 3357
RATESPECIAL INTERACTIVE; *U.S. Private*, pg. 3357
RATEX BUSINESS SOLUTIONS, INC.—See Collegiate Retail Alliance; *U.S. Private*, pg. 968
RATH AG; *Int'l*, pg. 6213
RATH AUTO RESOURCES; *U.S. Private*, pg. 3357
RATHBONE GREENBANK INVESTMENTS—See Rathbones Group Plc; *Int'l*, pg. 6214
RATHBONE INVESTMENT MANAGEMENT INTERNATIONAL LIMITED—See Rathbones Group Plc; *Int'l*, pg. 6214
RATHBONE INVESTMENT MANAGEMENT LTD.—See Rathbones Group Plc; *Int'l*, pg. 6214
RATHBONE, KING & SEELEY INSURANCE SERVICES—See H.W. Kaufman Financial Group, Inc.; *U.S. Private*, pg. 1836
RATHBONE PENSION & ADVISORY SERVICES LIMITED—See Rathbones Group Plc; *Int'l*, pg. 6214
RATHBONE PRECISION METALS, INC.—See Calvi Holding S.r.l.; *Int'l*, pg. 1266
RATHBONES GROUP PLC; *Int'l*, pg. 6214
RATHBONE TRUST COMPANY (BVI) LIMITED—See Rathbones Group Plc; *Int'l*, pg. 6214
RATHBONE TRUST COMPANY LTD.—See Rathbones Group Plc; *Int'l*, pg. 6214
RATHBONE UNIT TRUST MANAGEMENT LIMITED—See Rathbones Group Plc; *Int'l*, pg. 6214
RATHBUN REGIONAL WATER ASSOCIATION, INC.; *U.S. Private*, pg. 3357
RATHDOWNEY RESOURCES LTD.; *Int'l*, pg. 6214
RATHENOWER OPTIK GMBH—See Fielmann Group AG; *Int'l*, pg. 2659

RATHENOWER OPTISCHE WERKE GMBH—See Fielmann Group AG; *Int'l*, pg. 2659
RATHGIBSON JANESVILLE LLC—See Berkshire Hathaway Inc.; *U.S. Public*, pg. 314
RATHGIBSON NORTH BRANCH LLC—See Berkshire Hathaway Inc.; *U.S. Public*, pg. 314
RATH GMBH—See Rath AG; *Int'l*, pg. 6214
RATH HUNGARIA KFT.—See Rath AG; *Int'l*, pg. 6214
RATHI BARS LTD.; *Int'l*, pg. 6214
RATH INC.—See Rath AG; *Int'l*, pg. 6214
RATHI STEEL & POWER LTD.; *Int'l*, pg. 6214
RATHJE ENTERPRISES INC.; *U.S. Private*, pg. 3357
RATH POLSKA SP. Z O.O.—See Rath AG; *Int'l*, pg. 6214
RATHSCHECK SCHIEFER UND DACH-SYSTEME KG—See Wilh. Werhahn KG; *Int'l*, pg. 8410
RATH UKRAJINA TOW—See Rath AG; *Int'l*, pg. 6214
RATH ZAROTECHNIKA SPOL. S R.O.—See Rath AG; *Int'l*, pg. 6214
RATIER-FIGEAC SA—See RTX Corporation; *U.S. Public*, pg. 1821
RATING AND INVESTMENT INFORMATION, INC.—See Nikkei Inc.; *Int'l*, pg. 5290
RATINJAT SAUDIA CO. LTD.—See Jotun A/S; *Int'l*, pg. 4003
RATIO ARCHITECTS, INC.; *U.S. Private*, pg. 3357
RATIONAL AG; *Int'l*, pg. 6214
RATIONAL AUSTRALIA PTY LTD.—See RATIONAL AG; *Int'l*, pg. 6214
RATIONAL AUSTRIA GMBH—See RATIONAL AG; *Int'l*, pg. 6215
RATIONAL CANADA INC.—See RATIONAL AG; *Int'l*, pg. 6215
RATIONAL COLOMBIA - AMERICA CENTRAL SAS—See RATIONAL AG; *Int'l*, pg. 6215
RATIONAL COOKING SYSTEMS, INC.—See RATIONAL AG; *Int'l*, pg. 6215
RATIONAL CZECH REPUBLIC S.R.O.—See RATIONAL AG; *Int'l*, pg. 6214
RATIONAL DEUTSCHLAND GMBH—See RATIONAL AG; *Int'l*, pg. 6214
RATIONAL ENDUSTRIYEL MUTFAK EKIPMANLARI TICARET LIMITED SIRKETI—See RATIONAL AG; *Int'l*, pg. 6215
RATIONAL ENDUSTRIYEL MUTFAK—See RATIONAL AG; *Int'l*, pg. 6215
RATIONAL ENTERTAINMENT ENTERPRISES LIMITED—See Flutter Entertainment plc; *Int'l*, pg. 2715
RATIONAL FRANCE S.A.S.—See RATIONAL AG; *Int'l*, pg. 6215
RATIONAL GROUP LIMITED—See Flutter Entertainment plc; *Int'l*, pg. 2715
RATIONAL IBERICA COOKING SYSTEMS S.L.—See RATIONAL AG; *Int'l*, pg. 6215
RATIONAL INTERACTION, INC.—See Wipro Limited; *Int'l*, pg. 8432
RATIONAL INTERNATIONAL AG—See RATIONAL AG; *Int'l*, pg. 6215
RATIONAL INTERNATIONAL INDIA PRIVATE LIMITED—See RATIONAL AG; *Int'l*, pg. 6215
RATIONAL ITALIA S.R.L.—See RATIONAL AG; *Int'l*, pg. 6215
RATIONAL KITCHEN & CATERING EQUIPMENT TRADING FZCO—See RATIONAL AG; *Int'l*, pg. 6215
RATIONAL MEXICO, S.A. DE C.V.—See RATIONAL AG; *Int'l*, pg. 6215
RATIONAL MOTION GMBH—See Dana Incorporated; *U.S. Public*, pg. 623
RATIONAL NZ LTD.—See RATIONAL AG; *Int'l*, pg. 6215
RATIONAL SCANDINAVIA AB—See RATIONAL AG; *Int'l*, pg. 6215
RATIONAL SCHWEIZ AG—See RATIONAL AG; *Int'l*, pg. 6215
RATIONAL SLOVENIJA SLORATIONAL D.O.O.—See RATIONAL AG; *Int'l*, pg. 6215
RATIONAL SP.Z.O.O.—See RATIONAL AG; *Int'l*, pg. 6215
RATIONAL UK LTD.—See RATIONAL AG; *Int'l*, pg. 6215
RATIONAL WITTENHEIM S.A.S.—See RATIONAL AG; *Int'l*, pg. 6215
RATIONEL VINDUER A/S—See VKR Holding A/S; *Int'l*, pg. 8281
RATIONEL VINDUER LTD.—See VKR Holding A/S; *Int'l*, pg. 8281
RATIONEL WINDOWS (UK) LTD.—See VKR Holding A/S; *Int'l*, pg. 8281
RATIO OIL EXPLORATION 1992 LP; *Int'l*, pg. 6214
RATIO OIL EXPLORATIONS (FINANCE) LTD.; *Int'l*, pg. 6214
RATIO PETROLEUM ENERGY LP; *Int'l*, pg. 6214
RATIOPHARM ARZNEIMITTEL VERTRIEBS-GMBH—See Teva Pharmaceutical Industries, Ltd.; *Int'l*, pg. 7581
RATIOPHARM A/S—See Teva Pharmaceutical Industries, Ltd.; *Int'l*, pg. 7581
RATIOPHARM CZ S.R.O.—See Teva Pharmaceutical Industries, Ltd.; *Int'l*, pg. 7581
RATIOPHARM GMBH—See Teva Pharmaceutical Industries, Ltd.; *Int'l*, pg. 7581
RATIOPHARM INC.—See Teva Pharmaceutical Industries, Ltd.; *Int'l*, pg. 7581

RATIOPHARM KAZAKHSTAN LLP—See Teva Pharmaceutical Industries, Ltd.; *Int'l*, pg. 7579
RATIOPHARM OY—See Teva Pharmaceutical Industries, Ltd.; *Int'l*, pg. 7581
RATKO MITROVIC COMPANY; *Int'l*, pg. 6215
RATNABALI CAPITAL MARKETS LTD.; *Int'l*, pg. 6215
RATNABHUMI DEVELOPERS LIMITED; *Int'l*, pg. 6215
RATNAMANI INC.—See Ratnamani Metals & Tubes Ltd; *Int'l*, pg. 6215
RATNAMANI METALS & TUBES LTD - KUTCH DIVISION—See Ratnamani Metals & Tubes Ltd; *Int'l*, pg. 6215
RATNAMANI METALS & TUBES LTD - SAW PIPES DIVISION—See Ratnamani Metals & Tubes Ltd; *Int'l*, pg. 6215
RATNAMANI METALS & TUBES LTD; *Int'l*, pg. 6215
RATNAMANI METALS & TUBES LTD - STAINLESS STEEL TUBE & PIPES (SSTP) DIVISION—See Ratnamani Metals & Tubes Ltd; *Int'l*, pg. 6215
RATNAMANI TECHNO CASTS LTD—See Ratnamani Metals & Tubes Ltd; *Int'l*, pg. 6215
THE RATNER COMPANIES - COLORWORKS DIVISION—See The Ratner Companies; *U.S. Private*, pg. 4102
THE RATNER COMPANIES; *U.S. Private*, pg. 4102
RATNER & PRESTIA PC—See Buchanan Ingersoll & Rooney PC; *U.S. Private*, pg. 676
RATOS AB; *Int'l*, pg. 6215
RATOS FASTIGHETS AB—See Ratos AB; *Int'l*, pg. 6220
R.A. TOWNSEND COMPANY; *U.S. Private*, pg. 3334
RAT PACK FILMPRODUKTION GMBH—See Highlight Communications AG; *Int'l*, pg. 3388
RATP DEV AMERICA—See Regie Autonome des Transports Parisiens; *Int'l*, pg. 6253
RATP DEV RHONE-ALPES—See Regie Autonome des Transports Parisiens; *Int'l*, pg. 6253
RATP DEV—See Regie Autonome des Transports Parisiens; *Int'l*, pg. 6253
RATP YELLOW BUSES—See Regie Autonome des Transports Parisiens; *Int'l*, pg. 6253
RA TRAVEL, INC.—See Corporate Travel Management Limited; *Int'l*, pg. 1805
RATTANINDIA ENTERPRISES LIMITED—See RattanIndia Group; *Int'l*, pg. 6220
RATTANINDIA GROUP; *Int'l*, pg. 6220
RATTANINDIA POWER LIMITED—See RattanIndia Group; *Int'l*, pg. 6221
RATT INTERNET KAPACITET I SVERIGE AB—See Telia Company AB; *Int'l*, pg. 7543
RATTI S.P.A.; *Int'l*, pg. 6221
RATTLE ADVERTISING; *U.S. Private*, pg. 3357
RATTLER MIDSTREAM LP—See Diamondback Energy, Inc.; *U.S. Public*, pg. 658
RAUBEX CONSTRUCTION (PTY) LTD.—See Raubex Group Limited; *Int'l*, pg. 6221
RAUBEX CONSTRUCTION ZAMBIA LTD.—See Raubex Group Limited; *Int'l*, pg. 6221
RAUBEX GROUP LIMITED; *Int'l*, pg. 6221
RAUBEX INFRA (PTY) LTD.—See Raubex Group Limited; *Int'l*, pg. 6221
RAUBEX KZN (PTY) LTD.—See Raubex Group Limited; *Int'l*, pg. 6221
RAUBEX (PTY) LIMITED—See Raubex Group Limited; *Int'l*, pg. 6221
RAUBLING PAPIER GMBH—See Heinzel Holding GmbH; *Int'l*, pg. 3325
RAUCH INDUSTRIES, INC.—See Blackstreet Capital Management, LLC; *U.S. Private*, pg. 577
RAUDEV (PTY) LTD.—See Raubex Group Limited; *Int'l*, pg. 6221
RAUEN INCORPORATED; *U.S. Private*, pg. 3357
RAUFOSS METALL GMBH—See Aalberts N.V.; *Int'l*, pg. 35
RAUFOSS WATER & GAS AS—See Aalberts N.V.; *Int'l*, pg. 35
RAUHEAT OY—See OEM International AB; *Int'l*, pg. 5528
RAUKAESKO—See Kesko Corporation; *Int'l*, pg. 4142
RAULAND-BORG CORPORATION OF FLORIDA—See AMETEK, Inc.; *U.S. Public*, pg. 119
RAULAND-BORG CORPORATION—See AMETEK, Inc.; *U.S. Public*, pg. 118
RAULERSON GYN, LLC—See HCA Healthcare, Inc.; *U.S. Public*, pg. 1007
RAULERSON HOSPITAL—See HCA Healthcare, Inc.; *U.S. Public*, pg. 1007
RAULLI & SONS INC.; *U.S. Private*, pg. 3357
RAULT GRANIT SAS—See VINCI S.A.; *Int'l*, pg. 8225
RAUL WALTERS PROPERTIES, LLC; *U.S. Private*, pg. 3357
RAUMAN BIOVOIMA OY—See Pohjolan Voima Oy; *Int'l*, pg. 5904
RAUMA TERMINAL SERVICES OY—See Aspo Oyj; *Int'l*, pg. 631
RAUMIX AGGREGATES (PTY) LTD.—See Raubex Group Limited; *Int'l*, pg. 6221
RAUMIX (PTY) LIMITED—See Raubex Group Limited; *Int'l*, pg. 6221

RAUMTECHNIK MESSEBAU & EVENT SERVICES GMBH—See Project: Worldwide, Inc.; *U.S. Private*, pg. 3281
RAUNAQ EPC INTERNATIONAL LIMITED; *Int'l*, pg. 6221
RAUSCHBERGBAHN GESELLSCHAFT MIT BESCHRANKTER HAFTUNG—See E.ON SE; *Int'l*, pg. 2259
RAUSCH NETZWERKTECHNIK GMBH—See Avnet, Inc.; *U.S. Public*, pg. 254
RAU SERTA HYDRAULIK GMBH—See Hydrokit; *Int'l*, pg. 3548
RAUTAKESKO A/S—See Kesko Corporation; *Int'l*, pg. 4142
RAUTAKESKO LTD.—See Kesko Corporation; *Int'l*, pg. 4142
RAUTAKIRJA ESTONIA AS—See Reitangruppen AS; *Int'l*, pg. 6258
RAUTARUUKKI OYJ—See SSAB AB; *Int'l*, pg. 7153
RAUTARUUKKI STALSERVIS SPBL—See SSAB AB; *Int'l*, pg. 7153
RAUTARUUKKI STEEL - KANKAANPAA WORKS—See SSAB AB; *Int'l*, pg. 7153
RAUTARUUKKI STEEL—See SSAB AB; *Int'l*, pg. 7153
RAUTARUUKKI STEEL STRUCTURE—See SSAB AB; *Int'l*, pg. 7154
RAUTE OYJ; *Int'l*, pg. 6221
RAUXA DIRECT LLC—See Publicis Groupe S.A.; *Int'l*, pg. 6107
RAVAD LTD.; *Int'l*, pg. 6222
RAVAGLIOLI DEUTSCHLAND GMBH—See Dover Corporation; *U.S. Public*, pg. 682
RAVAGLIOLI S.P.A.—See Dover Corporation; *U.S. Public*, pg. 682
RAVAGO AMERICAS LLC—See Ravago Holding S.A.; *Int'l*, pg. 6222
RAVAGO HOLDING S.A.; *Int'l*, pg. 6222
RAV AGRO LLC—See PPF Group N.V.; *Int'l*, pg. 5951
RAVAL ACS LTD.; *Int'l*, pg. 6222
RAVAL AUTOMOTIVE SHANGHAI LTD.—See RAVAL ACS Ltd.; *Int'l*, pg. 6222
RAVAL EUROPE S.A.—See RAVAL ACS Ltd.; *Int'l*, pg. 6222
RAVALGAON SUGAR FARM LTD.; *Int'l*, pg. 6222
RAVAL LACE DIVISION—See Fab Industries Corp.; *U.S. Private*, pg. 1458
RAVALLI REPUBLIC—See Lee Enterprises, Incorporated; *U.S. Public*, pg. 1300
RAVAL USA INC.—See RAVAL ACS Ltd.; *Int'l*, pg. 6222
RAVASQUEIRA S.A.—See Jose de Mello, SGPS, S.A.; *Int'l*, pg. 4001
RAV BARIACH 08 INDUSTRIES LTD.; *Int'l*, pg. 6221
RAVE LLC—See Bruker Corporation; *U.S. Public*, pg. 407
RAVE MOBILE SAFETY, INC.—See Motorola Solutions, Inc.; *U.S. Public*, pg. 1479
RAVEN ANTENNA SYSTEMS, INC.—See Global Invacom Group Limited; *Int'l*, pg. 2998
RAVEN APPLIED TECHNOLOGIES, LLC—See CNH Industrial N.V.; *Int'l*, pg. 1676
THE RAVEN AT THREE PEAKS—See Escalante Golf, Inc.; *U.S. Private*, pg. 1424
RAVEN CAPITAL MANAGEMENT LLC—See MetLife, Inc.; *U.S. Public*, pg. 1430
RAVEN DO BRASIL PARTICIPACOES E SERVICOS TECHNICOS LTDA—See CNH Industrial N.V.; *Int'l*, pg. 1676
RAVEN EUROPE, B.V.—See CNH Industrial N.V.; *Int'l*, pg. 1676
RAVEN GOLD CORP.; *Int'l*, pg. 6222
RAVEN INDUSTRIES AUSTRALIA PTY LTD—See CNH Industrial N.V.; *Int'l*, pg. 1676
RAVEN INDUSTRIES CANADA, INC.—See CNH Industrial N.V.; *Int'l*, pg. 1676
RAVEN INDUSTRIES, INC. - ELECTRONIC SYSTEMS DIVISION—See CNH Industrial N.V.; *Int'l*, pg. 1676
RAVEN INDUSTRIES, INC. - ENGINEERED FILMS DIVISION—See CNH Industrial N.V.; *Int'l*, pg. 1676
RAVEN INDUSTRIES, INC. - FLOW CONTROL DIVISION—See CNH Industrial N.V.; *Int'l*, pg. 1676
RAVEN INDUSTRIES, INC. - MADISON—See CNH Industrial N.V.; *Int'l*, pg. 1676
RAVEN INDUSTRIES, INC.—See CNH Industrial N.V.; *Int'l*, pg. 1676
RAVEN LINING SYSTEMS, INC.—See Cohesant, Inc.; *U.S. Private*, pg. 963
RAVEN MOUNT GROUP PLC—See Raven Property Group Limited; *Int'l*, pg. 6222
RAVENNA CASTING CENTER, INC.—See Metal Technologies, Inc.; *U.S. Private*, pg. 2680
RAVENNA DESIGN; *U.S. Private*, pg. 3357
RAVENNA KRAKOW SP. Z.O.O.—See Commerzbank AG; *Int'l*, pg. 1719
RAVENNA MOTORS INC.; *U.S. Private*, pg. 3357
RAVENNA OIL CO.—See Croton Holding Company; *U.S. Private*, pg. 1108
RAVENNA TERMINALI PASSEGERI SRL—See Global Yatirim Holding A.S.; *Int'l*, pg. 3003
RAVEN PROPERTY GROUP LIMITED; *Int'l*, pg. 6222
RAVENQUEST BIOMED INC.; *Int'l*, pg. 6222

RAVEN ROCK STRATEGIC INCOME FUND; *Int'l*, pg. 6222
RAVENSBERGER MATRATZEN GMBH—See The Social Chain AG; *Int'l*, pg. 7687
RAVENSBERGER SCHMIERSTOFFVERTRIEB GMBH—See FUCHS SE; *Int'l*, pg. 2804
RAVENSBURGER AG; *Int'l*, pg. 6222
RAVENSCROFT HOLDINGS LTD.—See Southern Cross Capital Management SA; *Int'l*, pg. 7118
RAVENSCROFT JERSEY LIMITED—See Ravenscroft Limited; *Int'l*, pg. 6223
RAVENSCROFT LIMITED; *Int'l*, pg. 6222
RAVENSCROFT SHIP MANAGEMENT INC.—See Southern Cross Capital Management SA; *Int'l*, pg. 7118
RAVENSDOWN AERO WORK—See Ravensdown Limited; *Int'l*, pg. 6223
RAVENSDOWN GROWING MEDIA LIMITED—See Ravensdown Limited; *Int'l*, pg. 6223
RAVENSDOWN LIMITED; *Int'l*, pg. 6223
RAVENSEFT INDUSTRIAL ESTATES LIMITED—See Land Securities Group Plc; *Int'l*, pg. 4404
RAVENSEFT PROPERTIES LIMITED—See Land Securities Group Plc; *Int'l*, pg. 4404
RAVENSIDE INVESTMENTS LIMITED—See Land Securities Group Plc; *Int'l*, pg. 4404
RAVENSTHORPE NICKEL OPERATIONS PTY. LTD.—See First Quantum Minerals Ltd.; *Int'l*, pg. 2687
RAVENSWOOD INGREDIENTS PTY. LTD.—See BRENNTAG SE; *Int'l*, pg. 1149
RAVENSWOOD WINERY, INC.—See Constellation Brands, Inc.; *U.S. Public*, pg. 570
RAVENSWORTH OPERATIONS PTY LIMITED—See Glencore plc; *Int'l*, pg. 2990
RAVEN TRANSPORT COMPANY INC.—See Raven Transport Holding, Inc.; *U.S. Private*, pg. 3357
RAVEN TRANSPORT HOLDING, INC.; *U.S. Private*, pg. 3357
RAVEON TECHNOLOGIES CORPORATION; *U.S. Private*, pg. 3357
RAV EQUIPOS ESPANA, S.L.—See Dover Corporation; *U.S. Public*, pg. 682
RAVE RESTAURANT GROUP, INC.; *U.S. Public*, pg. 1763
RAV FRANCE—See Dover Corporation; *U.S. Public*, pg. 682
RAVI INDUSTRIES LTD.—See Hayleys PLC; *Int'l*, pg. 3292
RAVIKUMAR DISTILLERIES LTD; *Int'l*, pg. 6223
RAVILEELA GRANITES LIMITED; *Int'l*, pg. 6223
RAVIN CABLES LIMITED—See Prysmian S.p.A.; *Int'l*, pg. 6012
RAVINDER HEIGHTS LTD.; *Int'l*, pg. 6223
RAVINDRA ENERGY LIMITED; *Int'l*, pg. 6223
RAVING BRANDS, INC.; *U.S. Private*, pg. 3357
RAVINIA GREEN COUNTRY CLUB—See Apollo Global Management, Inc.; *U.S. Public*, pg. 150
RAV INVESTIGATIVE & SECURITIES SERVICES LTD; *U.S. Private*, pg. 3357
RAVISA DISTRIBUTION CENTER LLC.; *U.S. Private*, pg. 3358
RAVI TECHNOFORGE PRIVATE LIMITED—See Ratnamani Metals & Tubes Ltd; *Int'l*, pg. 6215
RAVIX FINANCIAL, INC.—See Kingsway Financial Services Inc.; *U.S. Public*, pg. 1235
RAVNAJA U RESTRUKTURIRANJU A.D.; *Int'l*, pg. 6223
RAVNICA A.D.; *Int'l*, pg. 6223
RAVNISTE A.D.; *Int'l*, pg. 6223
RAVO B.V.—See Federal Signal Corporation; *U.S. Public*, pg. 826
RAVVA OIL (SINGAPORE) PTE. LTD.—See Marubeni Corporation; *Int'l*, pg. 4709
RAWANG SPECIALIST HOSPITAL SDN BHD—See KPJ Healthcare Berhad; *Int'l*, pg. 4297
RAW ARTISTS, INC.; *U.S. Private*, pg. 3358
RAW EDGE INDUSTRIAL SOLUTIONS LIMITED; *Int'l*, pg. 6223
RAWICKA FABRYKA WYPOSAZENIA WAGONOW SP.Z.O.O.—See The Carlyle Group Inc.; *U.S. Public*, pg. 2053
RAWL AUSTRALASIA PTY. LTD.—See Stanley Black & Decker, Inc.; *U.S. Public*, pg. 1934
RAWLE MURDY ASSOCIATES, INC.—See Troon Golf L.L.C.; *U.S. Private*, pg. 4242
RAWLINGS CANADA INC.—See Major League Baseball; *U.S. Private*, pg. 2555
RAWLINGS CANADA INC.—See The Seidler Company, LLC; *U.S. Private*, pg. 4116
RAWLINGS MECHANICAL CORP.; *U.S. Private*, pg. 3358
RAWLINGS SPORTING GOODS CO., INC.—See Major League Baseball; *U.S. Private*, pg. 2555
RAWLINGS SPORTING GOODS CO.—See The Seidler Company, LLC; *U.S. Private*, pg. 4116
RAWLINSON & BROWN PTY LTD—See Nutrien Ltd.; *Int'l*, pg. 5493
RAWLINSON RENAULT; *Int'l*, pg. 6223
RAWLPLUG IRELAND LTD.—See Rawlplug S.A.; *Int'l*, pg. 6223
RAWLPLUG LTD.—See Rawlplug S.A.; *Int'l*, pg. 6223
RAWLPLUG S.A.; *Int'l*, pg. 6223

RAWL SALES & PROCESSING CO.—See Alpha Natural Resources, Inc.; *U.S. Private*, pg. 199
RAW MATERIALS CORPORATION; *U.S. Private*, pg. 3358
RAWNET LIMITED—See Castelnau Group Limited; *Int'l*, pg. 1356
RAWSOFT INC.; *U.S. Private*, pg. 3358
RAWSON, INC.—See SHV Holdings N.V.; *Int'l*, pg. 6871
RAWSON-KOENIG, INC.; *U.S. Private*, pg. 3358
RAWSON OIL & GAS LIMITED—See Lakes Blue Energy NL; *Int'l*, pg. 4397
RAWTENSTALL VETS4PETS LIMITED—See Pets at Home Group Plc; *Int'l*, pg. 5834
RAW TV LTD.—See Liberty Global plc; *Int'l*, pg. 4484
RAW TV LTD.—See Warner Bros. Discovery, Inc.; *U.S. Public*, pg. 2326
RAXA SECURITY SERVICES LIMITED—See GMR Airports Infrastructure Limited; *Int'l*, pg. 3015
RAXCO SOFTWARE, INC.; *U.S. Private*, pg. 3358
RAYA ACADEMY—See Raya Holding Company; *Int'l*, pg. 6224
RAYA CONTACT CENTER—See Raya Holding Company; *Int'l*, pg. 6224
RAYA FOR DATA CENTRES COMPANY—See Raya Holding Company; *Int'l*, pg. 6224
RAYA FOR INFORMATION TECHNOLOGY & MANAGEMENT COMPANY—See Raya Holding Company; *Int'l*, pg. 6224
RAYA GULF FZ-LLC—See Raya Holding Company; *Int'l*, pg. 6224
RAYA HOLDING COMPANY; *Int'l*, pg. 6223
RAYA INTEGRATION—See Raya Holding Company; *Int'l*, pg. 6224
RAY ALDERMAN & SONS INC.; *U.S. Private*, pg. 3358
RAYA NETWORKS SERVICES—See Raya Holding Company; *Int'l*, pg. 6224
RAY ANGELINI, INC.; *U.S. Private*, pg. 3358
RAYA SAUDI LTD.—See Raya Holding Company; *Int'l*, pg. 6224
RAYBAN SUN OPTICS INDIA LIMITED—See EssilorLuxottica SA; *Int'l*, pg. 2515
RAY BELL CONSTRUCTION COMPANY INC.; *U.S. Private*, pg. 3358
RAYBERN COMPANY, INC.—See Richelieu Hardware Ltd.; *Int'l*, pg. 6331
RAYBERN FOODS, LLC—See Premium Brands Holdings Corporation; *Int'l*, pg. 5963
RAYBESTOS POWERTRAIN, LLC—See Sun Capital Partners, Inc.; *U.S. Private*, pg. 3860
RAY BRANDT CHRYSLER DODGE JEEP—See Ray Brandt Nissan Inc.; *U.S. Private*, pg. 3358
RAY BRANDT NISSAN INC.; *U.S. Private*, pg. 3358
RAY BRANDT TOYOTA OF METAIRIE; *U.S. Private*, pg. 3358
RAYBRO ELECTRIC SUPPLIES—See Blackfriars Corp.; *U.S. Private*, pg. 574
RAYBROS DARKSIDE SUBARU SPORT SERVICE—See RAYS Co., Ltd.; *Int'l*, pg. 6225
RAYBROS S.T.W—See RAYS Co., Ltd.; *Int'l*, pg. 6225
RAYBURNS MARINE WORLD LTD; *Int'l*, pg. 6224
RAYCAP CORPORATION; *Int'l*, pg. 6224
RAYCAP, INC.—See Raycap Corporation; *Int'l*, pg. 6224
RAY-CARROLL COUNTY GRAIN GROWERS, INC.; *U.S. Private*, pg. 3359
RAY-CARROLL FUELS, L.L.C.—See Ray-Carroll County Grain Growers, Inc.; *U.S. Private*, pg. 3359
RAY CATENA MOTOR CAR; *U.S. Private*, pg. 3358
RAYCHEM ELECTRONICS (SHANGHAI) LTD.—See TE Connectivity Ltd.; *Int'l*, pg. 7495
RAYCHEM JUAREZ, S.A. DE C.V.—See TE Connectivity Ltd.; *Int'l*, pg. 7495
RAYCHEM LIMITED—See TE Connectivity Ltd.; *Int'l*, pg. 7495
RAYCHEM SHANGHAI CABLE ACCESSORIES LTD—See TE Connectivity Ltd.; *Int'l*, pg. 7495
RAYCLIFF CAPITAL; *U.S. Private*, pg. 3359
RAYCO MANUFACTURING, INC.—See Alamo Group Inc.; *U.S. Public*, pg. 71
RAYCOM ELECTRONICS, INC.—See Electro Technik Industries; *U.S. Private*, pg. 2237
RAYCONG INDUSTRIAL (H.K.) LTD.—See Wah Lee Industrial Corp.; *Int'l*, pg. 8329
RAY CORPORATION; *Int'l*, pg. 6223
RAYCO TECHNOLOGIES PTE. LTD.—See Parker Hannifin Corporation; *U.S. Public*, pg. 1649
RAYDIENT LLC—See Rayonier Inc.; *U.S. Public*, pg. 1765
RAYDIUS GMBH—See IG Group Holdings plc; *Int'l*, pg. 3601
RAYENCE CO., LTD.; *Int'l*, pg. 6224
RAYENCE INC.—See Rayence Co., Ltd.; *Int'l*, pg. 6224
RAYEN CURA, S.A.I.C.—See Compagnie de Saint-Gobain SA; *Int'l*, pg. 1725
RAYENERGO—See TE Connectivity Ltd.; *Int'l*, pg. 7495
RAY FOGG BUILDING METHODS INC.; *U.S. Private*, pg. 3358
RAYGEN CO., LTD.; *Int'l*, pg. 6224
RAYHOO MOTOR DIES CO., LTD.; *Int'l*, pg. 6224
RAY HUFFINES CHEVROLET PLANO; *U.S. Private*, pg. 3358

RAY INDUSTRIES, INC.—See Joshua Partners, LLC; *U.S. Private*, pg. 3358
RAY LAETHEM BUICK-GMC, INC.—See Ray Laethem, Inc.; *U.S. Private*, pg. 3358
RAY LAETHEM CHRYSLER DODGE JEEP RAM—See Ray Laethem, Inc.; *U.S. Private*, pg. 3358
RAY LAETHEM, INC.; *U.S. Private*, pg. 3358
RAY LEE EQUIPMENT COMPANY—See Western Equipment LLC; *U.S. Private*, pg. 4493
RAYLE ELECTRIC MEMBERSHIP; *U.S. Private*, pg. 3359
RAY LEWIS & CO.—See AEA Investors LP; *U.S. Private*, pg. 115
RAY L HELLWIG PLUMBING & HEATING CO, INC.—See M+W Group GmbH; *Int'l*, pg. 4614
RAYLIFE SRL—See El.En. S.p.A.; *Int'l*, pg. 2342
RAYLIGHT ALUMINIUM LIMITED—See Fletcher Building Limited; *Int'l*, pg. 2701
RAYLOC—See Genuine Parts Company; *U.S. Public*, pg. 932
RAYMARINE INC.—See Teledyne Technologies Incorporated; *U.S. Public*, pg. 1993
RAYMARINE UK LTD.—See Teledyne Technologies Incorporated; *U.S. Public*, pg. 1993
RAYMARK ASIA LIMITED—See Mi9 Retail, Inc.; *U.S. Private*, pg. 2696
RAYMARK EUROPE—See Mi9 Retail, Inc.; *U.S. Private*, pg. 2696
RAYMARK XPERT BUSINESS SYSTEMS INC.—See Mi9 Retail, Inc.; *U.S. Private*, pg. 2696
RAYMED LABS LIMITED; *Int'l*, pg. 6224
RAYMOND BUILDING SUPPLY LLC—See Bain Capital, LP; *U.S. Private*, pg. 451
RAYMOND CHEVROLET; *U.S. Private*, pg. 3359
RAYMOND CONSTRUCTION COMPANY INCORPORATED; *U.S. Private*, pg. 3359
THE RAYMOND CORPORATION—See Toyota Industries Corporation; *Int'l*, pg. 7869
RAYMOND DE STEIGER INC.; *U.S. Private*, pg. 3359
RAYMOND DISTRIBUTION-MEXICO, S.A. DE C.V.—See OEP Capital Advisors, L.P.; *U.S. Private*, pg. 2998
RAYMOND EXPRESS INTERNATIONAL CORPORATION; *U.S. Private*, pg. 3359
RAYMOND GRANITE CO.—See Cold Spring Granite Company; *U.S. Private*, pg. 966
RAYMOND GUBBAY LTD—See Sony Group Corporation; *Int'l*, pg. 7104
RAYMOND HANDLING CONCEPTS CORPORATION; *U.S. Private*, pg. 3359
RAYMOND INDUSTRIAL LIMITED; *Int'l*, pg. 6224
RAYMOND JAMES AFFORDABLE HOUSING INVESTMENTS—See Raymond James Financial, Inc.; *U.S. Public*, pg. 1764
RAYMOND JAMES ARGENTINA SOCIEDAD DE BOLSA, S.A.—See Raymond James Financial, Inc.; *U.S. Public*, pg. 1765
RAYMOND JAMES & ASSOCIATES, INC.—See Raymond James Financial, Inc.; *U.S. Public*, pg. 1764
RAYMOND JAMES BANK, NATIONAL ASSOCIATION—See Raymond James Financial, Inc.; *U.S. Public*, pg. 1764
RAYMOND JAMES CAPITAL, INC.—See Raymond James Financial, Inc.; *U.S. Public*, pg. 1764
RAYMOND JAMES CORPORATE FINANCE GMBH—See Raymond James Financial, Inc.; *U.S. Public*, pg. 1764
RAYMOND JAMES FINANCIAL, INC.; *U.S. Public*, pg. 1763
RAYMOND JAMES FINANCIAL INTERNATIONAL, LTD. (U.K.)—See Raymond James Financial, Inc.; *U.S. Public*, pg. 1764
RAYMOND JAMES FINANCIAL PLANNING LTD.—See Raymond James Financial, Inc.; *U.S. Public*, pg. 1764
RAYMOND JAMES FINANCIAL SERVICES ADVISORS, INC.—See Raymond James Financial, Inc.; *U.S. Public*, pg. 1764
RAYMOND JAMES GENEVA S.A.—See Raymond James Financial, Inc.; *U.S. Public*, pg. 1764
RAYMOND JAMES INSURANCE GROUP, INC.—See Raymond James Financial, Inc.; *U.S. Public*, pg. 1764
RAYMOND JAMES INVESTMENT COUNSEL LTD.—See Raymond James Financial, Inc.; *U.S. Public*, pg. 1765
RAYMOND JAMES INVESTMENT SERVICES LIMITED—See Raymond James Financial, Inc.; *U.S. Public*, pg. 1764
RAYMOND JAMES LATIN ADVISORS LIMITED—See Raymond James Financial, Inc.; *U.S. Public*, pg. 1764
RAYMOND JAMES LTD.—See Raymond James Financial, Inc.; *U.S. Public*, pg. 1764
RAYMOND JAMES MORTGAGE COMPANY, INC.—See Raymond James Financial, Inc.; *U.S. Public*, pg. 1764
RAYMOND JAMES SOUTH AMERICAN HOLDINGS, INC.—See Raymond James Financial, Inc.; *U.S. Public*, pg. 1765
RAYMOND JAMES URUGUAY, S.A.—See Raymond James Financial, Inc.; *U.S. Public*, pg. 1765
RAYMOND & LAE ENGINEERING, INC.—See May River Capital, LLC; *U.S. Private*, pg. 2620
RAYMOND LIMITED; *Int'l*, pg. 6224
RAYMOND MOTORS (1989) CO. LTD.; *Int'l*, pg. 6224

RAYMOND-MUSCATINE INC.—See Toyota Industries Corporation; *Int'l*, pg. 7869
RAYMOND (PANYU NANSHA) ELECTRICAL APPLIANCES DEVELOPMENT COMPANY LIMITED—See Raymond Industrial Limited; *Int'l*, pg. 6224
RAYMOND SAUDI ARABIA LIMITED—See A.H. Algosaibi & Bros.; *Int'l*, pg. 24
RAYMONDS SUPPLY CO., LTD.—See KS Energy Limited; *Int'l*, pg. 4310
RAYMONDS SUPPLY (SHANGHAI) CO., LTD.—See KS Energy Limited; *Int'l*, pg. 4310
RAYMONDS SUPPLY (SHENZHEN) CO., LTD.—See KS Energy Limited; *Int'l*, pg. 4310
RAYMOND T. JOHNSON INC.; *U.S. Private*, pg. 3359
RAYMOND V. DAMADIAN M.D. MR SCANNING CENTER MANAGEMENT COMPANY—See FONAR Corporation; *U.S. Public*, pg. 863
RAYMOND WEIL DEUTSCHLAND GMBH—See Raymond Weil S.A.; *Int'l*, pg. 6224
RAYMOND WEIL S.A.; *Int'l*, pg. 6224
RAYMORE MEDICAL GROUP, LLC—See HCA Healthcare, Inc.; *U.S. Public*, pg. 1007
RAYMOR INDUSTRIES INC.; *Int'l*, pg. 6224
RAYMOUR & FLANIGAN FURNITURE CO.; *U.S. Private*, pg. 3359
RAY MURRAY INC.; *U.S. Private*, pg. 3358
RAY M. WRIGHT INC.; *U.S. Private*, pg. 3358
RAYNAL & CIE SAS—See William Grant & Sons Ltd.; *Int'l*, pg. 8413
RAYNER & RINN-SCOTT INC.; *U.S. Private*, pg. 3359
RAYNE STATE BANK & TRUST COMPANY—See Financial Corporation of Louisiana; *U.S. Private*, pg. 1506
RAYNET OGILVY—See WPP plc; *Int'l*, pg. 8488
RAYNERI MARCHETTI S.A.; *Int'l*, pg. 6224
RAYNOR DISTRIBUTION CENTER—See Neisewander Enterprises Inc.; *U.S. Private*, pg. 2882
RAYNOR DISTRIBUTION CENTER—See Neisewander Enterprises Inc.; *U.S. Private*, pg. 2882
RAYNOR GARAGE DOORS—See Neisewander Enterprises Inc.; *U.S. Private*, pg. 2882
RAYNOR MANUFACTURING. CO., INC.—See Neisewander Enterprises Inc.; *U.S. Private*, pg. 2882
RAYONESE TEXTILES, INC.—See Culp, Inc.; *U.S. Public*, pg. 604
RAYONG ELECTRICITY GENERATING CO., LTD.—See Electricity Generating Public Co., Ltd.; *Int'l*, pg. 2352
RAYONG ELECTRICITY GENERATING CO., LTD.—See EGAT Public Company Limited; *Int'l*, pg. 2322
RAYONG ENGINEERING & PLANT SERVICE CO., LTD.—See The Siam Cement Public Company Limited; *Int'l*, pg. 7683
RAYONG FERTILIZER TRADING CO., LTD.—See UBE Corporation; *Int'l*, pg. 8001
RAYONG OLEFINS CO., LTD.—See The Siam Cement Public Company Limited; *Int'l*, pg. 7683
RAYONG PURIFIER PUBLIC COMPANY LIMITED - RAYONG FACTORY—See RPCG Public Company Limited; *Int'l*, pg. 6414
RAYONG WIRE INDUSTRIES PUBLIC COMPANY LIMITED - MUANG FACTORY—See Rayong Wire Industries Public Company Limited; *Int'l*, pg. 6225
RAYONG WIRE INDUSTRIES PUBLIC COMPANY LIMITED; *Int'l*, pg. 6225
RAYONIER ADVANCED MATERIALS INC.; *U.S. Public*, pg. 1765
RAYONIER INC.; *U.S. Public*, pg. 1765
RAYONIER MISSISSIPPI TIMBERLANDS COMPANY—See Rayonier Inc.; *U.S. Public*, pg. 1765
RAYONIER NEW ZEALAND LTD.—See Rayonier Inc.; *U.S. Public*, pg. 1765
RAYONIER PERFORMANCE FIBERS, LLC—See Rayonier Advanced Materials Inc.; *U.S. Public*, pg. 1765
RAYONIER TIMBERLANDS, L.P.—See Rayonier Inc.; *U.S. Public*, pg. 1765
RAYONIER TRS FOREST OPERATIONS, LLC—See Rayonier Inc.; *U.S. Public*, pg. 1765
RAYONT INC.; *Int'l*, pg. 6225
RAYOTEK SCIENTIFIC, INC.—See Artemis Capital Partners Management Co., LLC; *U.S. Public*, pg. 341
RAYOVAC ARGENTINA SRL—See Energizer Holdings, Inc.; *U.S. Public*, pg. 761
RAYOVAC CHILE SOCIEDAD COMERCIAL LTDA—See Energizer Holdings, Inc.; *U.S. Public*, pg. 761
RAYOVAC COSTA RICA, SA—See Energizer Holdings, Inc.; *U.S. Public*, pg. 761
RAY-O-VAC DE MEXICO, S.A. DE C.V.—See Energizer Holdings, Inc.; *U.S. Public*, pg. 761
RAYOVAC DOMINICAN REPUBLIC, SA—See Energizer Holdings, Inc.; *U.S. Public*, pg. 761
RAYOVAC EL SALVADOR SA DE CV—See Energizer Holdings, Inc.; *U.S. Public*, pg. 761
RAYOVAC EUROPE LIMITED—See Spectrum Brands Holdings, Inc.; *U.S. Public*, pg. 1915
RAYOVAC HONDURAS, SA—See Energizer Holdings, Inc.; *U.S. Public*, pg. 761
RAYOVAC (UK) LIMITED—See Energizer Holdings, Inc.; *U.S. Public*, pg. 761
RAYO WHOLESALE INC.; *U.S. Private*, pg. 3359

RAYPAK, INC.—See Paloma Industries Limited; *Int'l*, pg. 5709
RAY PEARMAN LINCOLN, INC.; *U.S. Private*, pg. 3358
RAYPRESS CORP.—See Ares Management Corporation; *U.S. Public*, pg. 191
RAYSAT ANTENNA SYSTEMS LLC—See Gilat Satellite Networks Ltd.; *Int'l*, pg. 2973
RAYS CHEVROLET OLDS INC.; *U.S. Private*, pg. 3359
RAYS CO., LTD.; *Int'l*, pg. 6225
RAYS CREATIVE CO., LTD.—See RAYS Co., Ltd.; *Int'l*, pg. 6225
RAYSEARCH AUSTRALIA PYD. LTD.—See RaySearch Laboratories AB; *Int'l*, pg. 6225
RAYSEARCH BELGIUM SPRL—See RaySearch Laboratories AB; *Int'l*, pg. 6225
RAYSEARCH FRANCE SAS—See RaySearch Laboratories AB; *Int'l*, pg. 6225
RAYSEARCH GERMANY GMBH—See RaySearch Laboratories AB; *Int'l*, pg. 6225
RAYSEARCH JAPAN K.K.—See RaySearch Laboratories AB; *Int'l*, pg. 6225
RAYSEARCH KOREA LLC—See RaySearch Laboratories AB; *Int'l*, pg. 6225
RAYSEARCH LABORATORIES AB; *Int'l*, pg. 6225
RAYSEARCH (SHANGHAI) MEDICAL DEVICE CO., LTD.—See RaySearch Laboratories AB; *Int'l*, pg. 6225
RAYSEARCH SINGAPORE PTE. LTD.—See RaySearch Laboratories AB; *Int'l*, pg. 6225
RAYS ENGINEERING CO., LTD.—See RAYS Co., Ltd.; *Int'l*, pg. 6225
RAY SERAPHIN FORD, INC.; *U.S. Private*, pg. 3358
RAY'S FLOORING SPECIALIST, INC.; *U.S. Private*, pg. 3359
RAY'S FOOD PLACE; *U.S. Private*, pg. 3359
RAYSIDE TRUCK & TRAILER INC.—See J.B. Poindexter & Co., Inc.; *U.S. Private*, pg. 2159
RAY SIGORTA A.S.—See Vienna Insurance Group AG Wiener Versicherung Gruppe; *Int'l*, pg. 8195
RAYSON RTK PTY LTD.—See Scholz Industries Pty Ltd.; *Int'l*, pg. 6638
RAYSPEC LTD.—See Nippon Kayaku Co., Ltd.; *Int'l*, pg. 5321
RAYS R & D CO., LTD.—See RAYS Co., Ltd.; *Int'l*, pg. 6225
RAYS TAKAMATSU CO., LTD.—See RAYS Co., Ltd.; *Int'l*, pg. 6225
RAY STONE INCORPORATED; *U.S. Private*, pg. 3359
RAYSTOWN DEVELOPMENTAL SERVICES, INC.—See ATAR LLC; *U.S. Private*, pg. 364
RAY'S TRASH SERVICE, INC.—See Waste Management, Inc.; *U.S. Public*, pg. 2331
RAYSUM CO., LTD.—See Hulic Co., Ltd.; *Int'l*, pg. 3528
RAYSUT CEMENT COMPANY SAOG; *Int'l*, pg. 6225
RAYS WHOLESALE MEAT, INC.; *U.S. Private*, pg. 3359
RAY TECH ACOT SINGAPORE PTE. LTD.—See Acma Ltd.; *Int'l*, pg. 107
RAYTECH INDUSTRIES DIVISION—See Lyman Products Corporation; *U.S. Private*, pg. 2520
RAYTEC LIMITED—See Optex Group Co., Ltd.; *Int'l*, pg. 5602
RAYTEC SYSTEMS INC.—See Optex Group Co., Ltd.; *Int'l*, pg. 5602
RAYTEC VISION S.P.A.—See ATS Corporation; *Int'l*, pg. 695
RAYTEK CHINA COMPANY—See Fortive Corporation; *U.S. Public*, pg. 870
RAYTEK CORPORATION—See Fortive Corporation; *U.S. Public*, pg. 870
RAYTEL CARDIAC SERVICES, INC.—See Koninklijke Philips N.V.; *Int'l*, pg. 4270
RAYTELLIGENCE AB; *Int'l*, pg. 6225
RAYTEX FABRICS INC.; *U.S. Private*, pg. 3359
RAYTHEON ANALYSIS & TEST LABORATORY—See RTX Corporation; *U.S. Public*, pg. 1825
RAYTHEON ANSCHUETZ GMBH SHANGHAI—See DMB Dr. Dieter Murmann Beteiligungsgesellschaft mbH; *Int'l*, pg. 2142
RAYTHEON APPLIED SIGNAL TECHNOLOGY, INC.—See RTX Corporation; *U.S. Public*, pg. 1825
RAYTHEON AUSTRALIA AIR WARFARE DESTROYER—See RTX Corporation; *U.S. Public*, pg. 1824
RAYTHEON AUSTRALIA INTEGRATED SOLUTIONS—See RTX Corporation; *U.S. Public*, pg. 1824
RAYTHEON AUSTRALIA MISSION SUPPORT—See RTX Corporation; *U.S. Public*, pg. 1824
RAYTHEON AUSTRALIA PTY LTD—See RTX Corporation; *U.S. Public*, pg. 1824
RAYTHEON AUSTRALIA SECURITY SOLUTIONS—See RTX Corporation; *U.S. Public*, pg. 1824
RAYTHEON BBN TECHNOLOGIES—See RTX Corporation; *U.S. Public*, pg. 1824
RAYTHEON CANADA LIMITED—See RTX Corporation; *U.S. Public*, pg. 1824
RAYTHEON CANADA LIMITED SUPPORT SERVICES DIVISION—See RTX Corporation; *U.S. Public*, pg. 1824

RAYTHEON CANADA LIMITED - WATERLOO—See RTX Corporation; *U.S. Public*, pg. 1824
RAYTHEON CIVIL COMMUNICATIONS SOLUTIONS—See RTX Corporation; *U.S. Public*, pg. 1824
RAYTHEON COMBAT SYSTEMS—See RTX Corporation; *U.S. Public*, pg. 1824
RAYTHEON COMPANY—See RTX Corporation; *U.S. Public*, pg. 1824
RAYTHEON COMPANY—See RTX Corporation; *U.S. Public*, pg. 1824
RAYTHEON DEUTSCHLAND GMBH—See RTX Corporation; *U.S. Public*, pg. 1824
RAYTHEON ELCAN OPTICAL TECHNOLOGIES—See RTX Corporation; *U.S. Public*, pg. 1824
RAYTHEON INTEGRATED COMMUNICATIONS SYSTEMS—See RTX Corporation; *U.S. Public*, pg. 1824
RAYTHEON INTEGRATED DEFENSE SYSTEMS—See RTX Corporation; *U.S. Public*, pg. 1824
RAYTHEON INTELLIGENCE, INFORMATION & SERVICES—See RTX Corporation; *U.S. Public*, pg. 1824
RAYTHEON INTELLIGENCE & SPACE—See RTX Corporation; *U.S. Public*, pg. 1825
RAYTHEON INTERNATIONAL, INC.—See RTX Corporation; *U.S. Public*, pg. 1824
RAYTHEON KTECH—See RTX Corporation; *U.S. Public*, pg. 1824
RAYTHEON MISSILE SYSTEMS—See RTX Corporation; *U.S. Public*, pg. 1824
RAYTHEON PIKEWERKS CORPORATION—See RTX Corporation; *U.S. Public*, pg. 1824
RAYTHEON PROFESSIONAL SERVICES LLC—See RTX Corporation; *U.S. Public*, pg. 1825
RAYTHEON SI GOVERNMENT SOLUTIONS—See RTX Corporation; *U.S. Public*, pg. 1824
RAYTHEON SOLIPSYS—See RTX Corporation; *U.S. Public*, pg. 1824
RAYTHEON SPACE & AIRBORNE SYSTEMS—See RTX Corporation; *U.S. Public*, pg. 1825
RAYTHEON SPAIN—See RTX Corporation; *U.S. Public*, pg. 1825
RAYTHEON SYSTEMS LIMITED—See RTX Corporation; *U.S. Public*, pg. 1825
RAYTHEON TECHNICAL SERVICES COMPANY LLC - MISSION SUPPORT OPERATIONS—See RTX Corporation; *U.S. Public*, pg. 1825
RAYTHEON TECHNICAL SERVICES COMPANY LLC—See RTX Corporation; *U.S. Public*, pg. 1825
RAYTHEON UNITED KINGDOM—See RTX Corporation; *U.S. Public*, pg. 1825
RAYTHEON VISION SYSTEMS—See RTX Corporation; *U.S. Public*, pg. 1825
RAY TLV GROUP LTD; *Int'l*, pg. 6223
RAYVAG VAGON SANAYI VE TICARET A.S.—See The Greenbrier Companies, Inc.; *U.S. Public*, pg. 2086
RAY VARNER FORD, LLC; *U.S. Private*, pg. 3359
RAYVEN, INC.—See OpenGate Capital Management, LLC; *U.S. Private*, pg. 3030
RAYZEBIO, INC.—See Bristol-Myers Squibb Company; *U.S. Public*, pg. 387
RAYZOR RANCH, LP—See Forestar Group Inc.; *U.S. Public*, pg. 867
RAZAK LABORATORY CO.; *Int'l*, pg. 6225
RAZEL ALGERIE SARL—See FAYAT SAS; *Int'l*, pg. 2626
RAZEL ANGOLA—See FAYAT SAS; *Int'l*, pg. 2626
RAZEL-BEC COTE-D'AZUR—See FAYAT SAS; *Int'l*, pg. 2626
RAZEL-BEC SAS—See FAYAT SAS; *Int'l*, pg. 2626
RAZEL CAMEROUN—See FAYAT SAS; *Int'l*, pg. 2626
RAZEL CATALYSTS CORPORATION—See Shenghe Resources Holding Co., Ltd.; *Int'l*, pg. 6801
RAZEL GUINEE EQUATORIALE—See FAYAT SAS; *Int'l*, pg. 2626
RAZEL MALAISIE—See FAYAT SAS; *Int'l*, pg. 2626
RAZEL MAURITANIE—See FAYAT SAS; *Int'l*, pg. 2626
RAZEL NIGER—See FAYAT SAS; *Int'l*, pg. 2626
RAZER INC.; *U.S. Private*, pg. 3359
RAZER USA LTD.—See Razer Inc.; *U.S. Private*, pg. 3359
RAZES HYBRIDES S.A.R.L.—See KWS SAAT SE & Co. KGaA; *Int'l*, pg. 4352
RAZ IMPORTS INC.; *U.S. Private*, pg. 3359
RAZIOL ZIBULLA & SOHN GMBH; *Int'l*, pg. 6225
RAZI PHARMACEUTICAL GLASS; *Int'l*, pg. 6225
RAZI PHARMACUTICAL GLASS; *Int'l*, pg. 6225
RAZMATAZ; *U.S. Private*, pg. 3359
RAZORBACK CONCRETE CO.; *U.S. Private*, pg. 3360
RAZORBACK FOUNDATION; *U.S. Private*, pg. 3360
RAZOR ENERGY CORP.; *Int'l*, pg. 6225
RAZORFISH ATLANTA—See Publicis Groupe S.A.; *Int'l*, pg. 6107
RAZORFISH CHICAGO—See Publicis Groupe S.A.; *Int'l*, pg. 6107
RAZORFISH NEW YORK—See Publicis Groupe S.A.; *Int'l*, pg. 6107
RAZORFISH PHILADELPHIA—See Publicis Groupe S.A.; *Int'l*, pg. 6107

COMPANY NAME INDEX

RAZORFISH SAN FRANCISCO—See Publicis Groupe S.A.; *Int'l*, pg. 6107
RAZORFISH—See Publicis Groupe S.A.; *Int'l*, pg. 6107
RAZORFISH TECHNOLOGY PLATFORMS—See Publicis Groupe S.A.; *Int'l*, pg. 6107
RAZORFISH UK—See Publicis Groupe S.A.; *Int'l*, pg. 6107
RAZORGATOR, INC.; *U.S. Private*, pg. 3360
RAZOR GENOMICS, INC.—See OncoCyte Corporation; *U.S. Public*, pg. 1601
RAZOR LABS LTD.; *Int'l*, pg. 6225
RAZORLEAF CORPORATION; *U.S. Private*, pg. 3360
RAZOR RESOURCES INC.; *Int'l*, pg. 6225
RAZOR RISK TECHNOLOGIES LIMITED—See Parabellum Limited; *Int'l*, pg. 5734
RAZOR RISK TECHNOLOGIES PTY. LIMITED—See Parabellum Limited; *Int'l*, pg. 5734
RAZORSIGHT INC.; *U.S. Private*, pg. 3360
RAZORSYNC, LLC—See Independence Capital Partners, LLC; *U.S. Private*, pg. 2056
RAZOR TECHNICAL STAFFING; *U.S. Private*, pg. 3360
RAZPISI D.O.O.—See Ratos AB; *Int'l*, pg. 6217
RAZ TRANSPORTATION INC.—See Variant Equity Advisors, LLC; *U.S. Private*, pg. 4346
RAZVITAK A.D.; *Int'l*, pg. 6225
RAZVOJNA BANKA VOJVODINE A.D. NOVI SAD; *Int'l*, pg. 6226
RAZZARI DODGE CHRYSLER JEEP; *U.S. Private*, pg. 3360
RAZZOOS INC.; *U.S. Private*, pg. 3360
RB2 ENERGY SERVICES INC.—See Vertex Resource Group Ltd.; *Int'l*, pg. 8174
RBAB, INC.—See Riverstone Logistics, LLC; *U.S. Private*, pg. 3448
RBA FRANCE—See RBA Holding Editorial S.A.; *Int'l*, pg. 6227
RBA GOLF CLUB SDN. BHD.—See Royal Brunei Airlines Sdn. Bhd.; *Int'l*, pg. 6411
RBA HOLDING EDITORIAL S.A.; *Int'l*, pg. 6227
RBA, INC.; *U.S. Private*, pg. 3360
RBA ITALIA SRL—See RBA Holding Editorial S.A.; *Int'l*, pg. 6227
RBAJ HOLDING, INC.—See Robert Bosch GmbH; *Int'l*, pg. 6367
R. BAKER & SON ALL INDUSTRIAL SERVICES; *U.S. Private*, pg. 3333
RBA LIBROS, S.A.—See RBA Holding Editorial S.A.; *Int'l*, pg. 6227
RBA MADRID—See RBA Holding Editorial S.A.; *Int'l*, pg. 6227
R BANK—See R Corp Financial; *U.S. Private*, pg. 3331
RBA POLAND SP. Z OO—See RBA Holding Editorial S.A.; *Int'l*, pg. 6227
RBA PORTUGAL—See RBA Holding Editorial S.A.; *Int'l*, pg. 6227
RBA PUBLICACOES—See RBA Holding Editorial S.A.; *Int'l*, pg. 6227
RBAZ BANCORP, INC.; *U.S. Public*, pg. 1765
R.B. BAKER CONSTRUCTION INC.—See Reeves Construction Company; *U.S. Private*, pg. 3384
RBB BANCORP; *U.S. Public*, pg. 1766
RBB PUBLIC RELATIONS, LLC; *U.S. Private*, pg. 3360
RBC AEROSTRUCTURES LLC—See RBC Bearings Incorporated; *U.S. Public*, pg. 1766
RBC AIRCRAFT PRODUCTS, INC.—See RBC Bearings Incorporated; *U.S. Public*, pg. 1766
RB CAPITAL COMPANHIA DE SECURITIZACAO S.A.; *Int'l*, pg. 6226
RB CAPITAL S.A.—See ORIX Corporation; *Int'l*, pg. 5636
RB CAPITAL SECURITIZADORA S.A.; *Int'l*, pg. 6226
RB CAR COMPANY; *U.S. Private*, pg. 3360
RBC BANK, (GEORGIA) N.A.—See Royal Bank of Canada; *Int'l*, pg. 6409
RBC BEARINGS INC. - LINEAR PRECISION PRODUCTS DIVISION—See RBC Bearings Incorporated; *U.S. Public*, pg. 1766
RBC BEARINGS INCORPORATED; *U.S. Public*, pg. 1766
RBC BEARINGS POLSKA SP. Z O.O.—See RBC Bearings Incorporated; *U.S. Public*, pg. 1766
RBC CAPITAL MARKETS CORPORATION—See Royal Bank of Canada; *Int'l*, pg. 6410
RBC CAPITAL MARKETS (QUEBEC) INC.—See Royal Bank of Canada; *Int'l*, pg. 6410
RBC CAPITAL MARKETS REAL ESTATE GROUP INC.—See Royal Bank of Canada; *Int'l*, pg. 6410
RBC CAPITAL MARKETS—See Royal Bank of Canada; *Int'l*, pg. 6410
RBC CORRESPONDENT SERVICES—See Royal Bank of Canada; *Int'l*, pg. 6410
RBC DANIELS L.P.—See Royal Bank of Canada; *Int'l*, pg. 6410
RBC DE MEXICO S DE RL DE CV—See RBC Bearings Incorporated; *U.S. Public*, pg. 1766
RBC DEVELOPMENT, LLC—See Ampersand Management LLC; *U.S. Private*, pg. 266
RBC DEXIA INVESTOR SERVICES ESPANA, S.A.—See Royal Bank of Canada; *Int'l*, pg. 6410
RBC DEXIA INVESTOR SERVICES (MALAYSIA) SDN. BHD.—See Royal Bank of Canada; *Int'l*, pg. 6410

RBC DIRECT INVESTING INC.—See Royal Bank of Canada; *Int'l*, pg. 6410
RBC DOMINION SECURITIES INC.—See Royal Bank of Canada; *Int'l*, pg. 6410
RBC FINANCE B.V.—See Royal Bank of Canada; *Int'l*, pg. 6410
RBC GLOBAL ASSET MANAGEMENT INC.—See Royal Bank of Canada; *Int'l*, pg. 6410
RBC HOLDINGS (CHANNEL ISLANDS) LIMITED—See Royal Bank of Canada; *Int'l*, pg. 6410
RBC HOLDINGS (LUXEMBOURG) S.A.R.L.—See Royal Bank of Canada; *Int'l*, pg. 6410
RBC, INC.; *U.S. Private*, pg. 3360
RBC INSURANCE COMPANY OF CANADA—See Royal Bank of Canada; *Int'l*, pg. 6410
RBC INSURANCE HOLDING INC.—See Royal Bank of Canada; *Int'l*, pg. 6410
RBC INSURANCE SERVICES INC.—See Royal Bank of Canada; *Int'l*, pg. 6410
RBC INVESTOR SERVICES CANADA—See Royal Bank of Canada; *Int'l*, pg. 6410
RBC INVESTOR SERVICES LIMITED—See Royal Bank of Canada; *Int'l*, pg. 6410
RBC INVESTOR & TREASURY SERVICES—See Royal Bank of Canada; *Int'l*, pg. 6410
RBC LIFE INSURANCE COMPANY—See Royal Bank of Canada; *Int'l*, pg. 6410
RBC LIFE SCIENCES, INC.; *U.S. Public*, pg. 1766
RBC MANUFACTURING CORPORATION—See Regal Rexnord Corporation; *U.S. Public*, pg. 1773
RBC NICE BEARINGS, INC.—See RBC Bearings Incorporated; *U.S. Public*, pg. 1766
R&B COMPANY—See Core & Main, Inc.; *U.S. Public*, pg. 576
RB CONTROLS CO., LTD.—See Rinnai Corporation; *Int'l*, pg. 6344
RBC PJSC; *Int'l*, pg. 6227
RBC PRECISION PRODUCTS-BREMEN, INC.—See RBC Bearings Incorporated; *U.S. Public*, pg. 1766
RBC PRECISION PRODUCTS-PLYMOUTH, INC.—See RBC Bearings Incorporated; *U.S. Public*, pg. 1766
RBC PRECISION PRODUCTS - PLYMOUTH—See RBC Bearings Incorporated; *U.S. Public*, pg. 1766
RBC ROYAL BANK (ARUBA) N.V.—See Royal Bank of Canada; *Int'l*, pg. 6410
RBC ROYAL BANK (BARBADOS) LIMITED—See Royal Bank of Canada; *Int'l*, pg. 6410
RBC ROYAL BANK N.V.—See Royal Bank of Canada; *Int'l*, pg. 6411
RBC ROYAL BANK (TRINIDAD & TOBAGO) LIMITED—See Royal Bank of Canada; *Int'l*, pg. 6411
RBC SOUTHWEST PRODUCTS, INC.—See RBC Bearings Incorporated; *U.S. Public*, pg. 1766
RBC TRANSPORT DYNAMICS CORPORATION—See RBC Bearings Incorporated; *U.S. Public*, pg. 1766
RBC WEALTH MANAGEMENT—See Royal Bank of Canada; *Int'l*, pg. 6410
RBC WEALTH MANAGEMENT - USA—See Royal Bank of Canada; *Int'l*, pg. 6410
RBC WEALTH MANAGEMENT - USA—See Royal Bank of Canada; *Int'l*, pg. 6410
RBC WEALTH MANAGEMENT—See Royal Bank of Canada; *Int'l*, pg. 6410
RBC WEALTH MANAGEMENT - USA—See Royal Bank of Canada; *Int'l*, pg. 6410
R&B DENIMS LTD; *Int'l*, pg. 6168
RBDS BROADCASTING AB—See NRJ Group SA; *Int'l*, pg. 5474
R. BEE CRUSHING LTD—See Petrowest Corp.; *Int'l*, pg. 5833
R.B. EVERETT & COMPANY; *U.S. Private*, pg. 3334
RB FACTORING LLC—See Societe Generale S.A.; *Int'l*, pg. 7040
R&B FALCON (A) PTY LTD—See Transocean Ltd.; *Int'l*, pg. 7903
R&B FALCON B.V.—See Transocean Ltd.; *Int'l*, pg. 7903
R&B FALCON DRILLING (INTERNATIONAL & DEEPWATER) INC. LLC—See Transocean Ltd.; *Int'l*, pg. 7903
R&B FALCON INTERNATIONAL ENERGY SERVICES B.V.—See Transocean Ltd.; *Int'l*, pg. 7903
RB FIDUCIARIA S.P.A—See Allianz SE; *Int'l*, pg. 355
R&B FOOD SUPPLY PUBLIC COMPANY LIMITED; *Int'l*, pg. 6168
RBG BROADCASTING AB—See NRJ Group SA; *Int'l*, pg. 5474
RBG HOLDINGS PLC; *Int'l*, pg. 6227
RB GLOBAL, INC.; *Int'l*, pg. 6226
R&B GRINDING CO. INC.; *U.S. Private*, pg. 3331
R B HILTON SAUDI ARABIA LIMITED—See Altrad Investment Authority SAS; *Int'l*, pg. 398
R.B. HINKLE CONSTRUCTION, INC.—See Primoris Services Corporation; *U.S. Public*, pg. 1719
RBH LOGISTICS GMBH—See Deutsche Bahn AG; *Int'l*, pg. 2051
RBI BEARING CANADA - CALGARY—See R.B. International Inc.; *U.S. Private*, pg. 3334

RBI BEARING CANADA - TORONTO—See R.B. International Inc.; *U.S. Private*, pg. 3334
RBI CORPORATION; *U.S. Private*, pg. 3360
RBID.COM, INC.; *U.S. Public*, pg. 1767
RB INDUSTRIES LTD.—See R&B Denims Ltd; *Int'l*, pg. 6168
RB INTERIOR TRIM; *U.S. Private*, pg. 3360
RB INTERNATIONAL FINANCE (USA) LLC—See Raiffeisen Bank International AG; *Int'l*, pg. 6183
R.B. INTERNATIONAL INC.; *U.S. Private*, pg. 3334
R-BIOPHARM AG; *Int'l*, pg. 6169
R-BIOPHARM ANALYSIS SYSTEMS TRADING (BEIJING) CO. LTD.—See R-Biopharm AG; *Int'l*, pg. 6169
R-BIOPHARM AUSTRALIA—See R-Biopharm AG; *Int'l*, pg. 6169
R-BIOPHARM BRASIL LTDA—See R-Biopharm AG; *Int'l*, pg. 6169
R-BIOPHARM ESPANA S.A.—See R-Biopharm AG; *Int'l*, pg. 6169
R-BIOPHARM FRANCE—See R-Biopharm AG; *Int'l*, pg. 6169
R-BIOPHARM INC.—See R-Biopharm AG; *Int'l*, pg. 6169
R-BIOPHARM ITALIA SRL—See R-Biopharm AG; *Int'l*, pg. 6169
R-BIOPHARM LATINOAMERICA S.A.—See R-Biopharm AG; *Int'l*, pg. 6169
R-BIOPHARM NEUGEN PVT. LTD.—See R-Biopharm AG; *Int'l*, pg. 6169
R-BIOPHARM RHONE LTD.—See R-Biopharm AG; *Int'l*, pg. 6169
RBI SOLAR BRAZIL LTDA—See Gibraltar Industries, Inc.; *U.S. Public*, pg. 936
RBI SOLAR, INC.—See Gibraltar Industries, Inc.; *U.S. Public*, pg. 936
RBI SOLAR KK—See Gibraltar Industries, Inc.; *U.S. Public*, pg. 936
RBJ & ASSOCIATES LLC—See Berkshire Hathaway Inc.; *U.S. Public*, pg. 313
RB JERGENS CONTRACTORS INC.; *U.S. Private*, pg. 3360
RB KOREA LTD.—See Rinnai Corporation; *Int'l*, pg. 6344
RBKR BROADCASTING AB—See NRJ Group SA; *Int'l*, pg. 5474
RBK THAILAND, INC.—See Leonard Green & Partners, L.P.; *U.S. Private*, pg. 2424
R. BLACKETT CHARLTON—See Redhall Group plc; *Int'l*, pg. 6247
RB LEASING LLC—See Societe Generale S.A.; *Int'l*, pg. 7040
RB LLC—See TopBuild Corp.; *U.S. Public*, pg. 2163
RBL LEASING CORP.—See Bergeys Inc.; *U.S. Private*, pg. 531
RBL PRODUCTS, INC.—See MPE Partners, LLC; *U.S. Private*, pg. 2803
R.B. MATHESON TRUCKING INC.; *U.S. Private*, pg. 3334
RBMM—See The Richards Group, Inc.; *U.S. Private*, pg. 4107
RBM PRECISION METAL PRODUCTS INC.—See 13i Capital Corporation; *U.S. Private*, pg. 3
R.B.N. CO., LTD.—See Takuma Co., Ltd.; *Int'l*, pg. 7442
RB NL BRANDS B.V.—See Reckitt Benckiser Group plc; *Int'l*, pg. 6236
RBN ROMANIAN BILLBOARD NETWORK SRL—See APG/SGA SA; *Int'l*, pg. 513
R. BONNETERRE SAS—See PAI Partners S.A.S.; *Int'l*, pg. 5700
RB OPPENHEIM ASSOCIATES, INC.; *U.S. Private*, pg. 3360
RBO PRINTLOGISTIX, INC.; *U.S. Private*, pg. 3360
RBO REGIONALBUS OSTBAYERN GMBH—See Deutsche Bahn AG; *Int'l*, pg. 2052
R. BOURGEOIS JFE SHOJI MAGNETIC LAMINATION, INC.—See JFE Holdings, Inc.; *Int'l*, pg. 3937
R.B. PAMPLIN CORPORATION; *U.S. Private*, pg. 3334
RB PATEL GROUP LIMITED—See Fijian Holdings Limited; *Int'l*, pg. 2662
RBP CHEMICAL TECHNOLOGY, INC.; *U.S. Private*, pg. 3360
R & B PLASTICS MACHINERY, LLC—See Talon LLC; *U.S. Private*, pg. 3927
R&B RECEIVABLES MANAGEMENT; *U.S. Private*, pg. 3331
R-B RECYCLING INC.—See Carlisle Companies Incorporated; *U.S. Public*, pg. 436
RBR GROUP LIMITED; *Int'l*, pg. 6227
R. BROOKS ASSOCIATES, INC.—See Rolls-Royce Holdings plc; *Int'l*, pg. 6393
R. BROOKS MECHANICAL, INC.—See LP First Capital; *U.S. Private*, pg. 2507
R. BROOKS MECHANICAL, INC.—See The RLJ Companies, LLC; *U.S. Private*, pg. 4111
RBS ASIA CORPORATE FINANCE LIMITED—See NatWest Group plc; *Int'l*, pg. 5171
RBS ASIA LIMITED—See NatWest Group plc; *Int'l*, pg. 5171
RBS BANK (ROMANIA) SA—See NatWest Group plc; *Int'l*, pg. 5171
RBS BUSINESS SERVICES PRIVATE LIMITED—See NatWest Group plc; *Int'l*, pg. 5171

RBR GROUP LIMITED

RBS CAPITAL MARKETS (CANADA) LIMITED—See NatWest Group plc; *Int'l*, pg. 5171
RBS CAPITAL MARKETS (CANADA) LTD.-MONTREAL—See NatWest Group plc; *Int'l*, pg. 5171
RBS CITIZENS INSURANCE AGENCY, INC.—See Citizens Financial Group, Inc.; *U.S. Public*, pg. 506
RBS CORPORATE FINANCE (AUSTRALIA) LIMITED—See NatWest Group plc; *Int'l*, pg. 5171
RBS EQUITY CAPITAL MARKETS (AUSTRALIA) LIMITED—See NatWest Group plc; *Int'l*, pg. 5171
RBS FINANCE NV (NORTH AMERICA), INC.—See NatWest Group plc; *Int'l*, pg. 5171
RBS FINANCIAL SERVICES (INDIA) PRIVATE LIMITED—See NatWest Group plc; *Int'l*, pg. 5171
RBS GLOBAL BANKING (LUXEMBOURG) S.A.—See NatWest Group plc; *Int'l*, pg. 5171
RBS GROUP (AUSTRALIA) PTY. LIMITED—See NatWest Group plc; *Int'l*, pg. 5171
RBS HOLDINGS (AUSTRALIA) PTY LIMITED—See NatWest Group plc; *Int'l*, pg. 5171
RBS HOLDINGS N.V.—See NatWest Group plc; *Int'l*, pg. 5171
RBS HOLDINGS USA INC.—See NatWest Group plc; *Int'l*, pg. 5171
RBS HOLLANDSCHE N.V.—See NatWest Group plc; *Int'l*, pg. 5171
RBS INVOICE FINANCE LIMITED—See NatWest Group plc; *Int'l*, pg. 5172
RBS (NEW ZEALAND) LIMITED—See NatWest Group plc; *Int'l*, pg. 5171
RB SPECIALIZED DEPOSITARY LLC—See Societe Generale S.A.; *Int'l*, pg. 7040
RBS ROHRBAU-SCHWEISSTECHNIK GESELLSCHAFT M.B.H—See STRABAG SE; *Int'l*, pg. 7232
RBS ROHRBAU SCHWEISTECHNIK GMBH—See STRABAG SE; *Int'l*, pg. 7232
RBS SECURITIES INC.—See NatWest Group plc; *Int'l*, pg. 5171
RBS SECURITIES JAPAN LIMITED—See NatWest Group plc; *Int'l*, pg. 5171
RBS WAVE GMBH—See EnBW Energie Baden-Wurttemberg AG; *Int'l*, pg. 2399
RB TECHNICS NV—See VINCI S.A.; *Int'l*, pg. 8225
R & B TELEPHONE LLC—See EQT AB; *Int'l*, pg. 2480
RBTT BANK CARIBBEAN LIMITED—See Royal Bank of Canada; *Int'l*, pg. 6411
RBTT BANK CARIBBEAN LTD.-ANTIGUA—See Royal Bank of Canada; *Int'l*, pg. 6411
RBTT BANK CARIBBEAN LTD.-SAINT LUCIA—See Royal Bank of Canada; *Int'l*, pg. 6411
RBTT BANK GRENADA LIMITED—See Royal Bank of Canada; *Int'l*, pg. 6411
RBTT BANK (SKN) LIMITED—See Royal Bank of Canada; *Int'l*, pg. 6411
RBTT FINANCIAL HOLDINGS LIMITED—See Royal Bank of Canada; *Int'l*, pg. 6410
RBTT INSURANCE AGENCY LIMITED—See Royal Bank of Canada; *Int'l*, pg. 6411
RBTT MERCHANT BANK LIMITED—See Royal Bank of Canada; *Int'l*, pg. 6411
RBTT TRUST LIMITED—See Royal Bank of Canada; *Int'l*, pg. 6411
RBV LEAF BELGIUM N.V.—See Cloetta AB; *Int'l*, pg. 1661
R&B WAGNER CO. INC.; *U.S. Private*, pg. 3331
RB&W CORPORATION OF CANADA—See Park-Ohio Holdings Corp.; *U.S. Public*, pg. 1640
R&B WHOLESALE DISTRIBUTORS; *U.S. Private*, pg. 3331
RBW INC.; *Int'l*, pg. 6227
RBW LOGISTICS CORPORATION; *U.S. Private*, pg. 3361
RB&W-MANUFACTURING LLC—See Park-Ohio Holdings Corp.; *U.S. Public*, pg. 1640
RBZ JEWELLERS LIMITED; *Int'l*, pg. 6227
RC-1, INC.; *U.S. Private*, pg. 3361
RC365 HOLDING PLC; *Int'l*, pg. 6227
RCA HOLDINGS LTD.—See Vantiva SA; *Int'l*, pg. 8131
RCA MUSIC GROUP—See Sony Group Corporation; *Int'l*, pg. 7103
RCAP HOLDINGS, LLC; *U.S. Private*, pg. 3361
RCAPITAL PARTNERS LLP; *Int'l*, pg. 6227
RCAP SECURITIES, INC.—See Annaly Capital Management, Inc.; *U.S. Public*, pg. 138
R.C.A. RUBBER COMPANY; *U.S. Private*, pg. 3335
R.C. AULETTA & CO. LLC; *U.S. Private*, pg. 3334
RCB BANK LTD.; *Int'l*, pg. 6227
RCB BANK—See RCB Holding Company, Inc.; *U.S. Private*, pg. 3361
RCBC BANKARD SERVICES CORPORATION—See Yuchengco Group of Companies; *Int'l*, pg. 8610
RCBC FOREX BROKERS CORPORATION—See Yuchengco Group of Companies; *Int'l*, pg. 8610
RCBC-JPL HOLDING COMPANY, INC.—See Yuchengco Group of Companies; *Int'l*, pg. 8610
RCBC LEASING AND FINANCE CORPORATION—See Yuchengco Group of Companies; *Int'l*, pg. 8610
RCBC NORTH AMERICA, INC.—See Yuchengco Group of Companies; *Int'l*, pg. 8610
RCBC SAVINGS BANK, INC.—See Yuchengco Group of Companies; *Int'l*, pg. 8610
RCBC SECURITIES, INC.—See Yuchengco Group of Companies; *Int'l*, pg. 8610
RCBC TELEMONEY EUROPE, SPA—See Yuchengco Group of Companies; *Int'l*, pg. 8610
RC BETON A/S—See CRH plc; *Int'l*, pg. 1848
RCB HOLDING COMPANY, INC.; *U.S. Private*, pg. 3361
R.C. BIGELOW, INC.; *U.S. Private*, pg. 3334
RCB INVESTIMENTOS S.A.—See Banco Bradesco S.A.; *Int'l*, pg. 819
RCB PLANEJAMENTO FINANCEIRO LTDA.—See PRA Group, Inc.; *U.S. Public*, pg. 1712
RCB PORTFOLIOS LTDA.—See PRA Group, Inc.; *U.S. Public*, pg. 1712
RC BRAZIL LTDA—See KMD Brands Limited; *Int'l*, pg. 4204
RCC ASSOCIATES, INC.; *U.S. Private*, pg. 3361
RCC BUILDERS & DEVELOPERS, INC.—See Railroad Construction Company, Inc.; *U.S. Private*, pg. 3346
RCC BUSINESS MORTGAGE BROKERS LTD.—See Christie Group plc; *Int'l*, pg. 1587
RCC CEMENTS LIMITED; *Int'l*, pg. 6227
RCC FABRICATORS, INC.—See Railroad Construction Company, Inc.; *U.S. Private*, pg. 3346
RCC INSURANCE BROKERS PLC—See Christie Group plc; *Int'l*, pg. 1587
RC&C MANUFACTURING COMPANY (PTY) LIMITED—See Reunert Limited; *Int'l*, pg. 6312
R.C.COBB, INC.—See Cineworld Group plc; *Int'l*, pg. 1611
R.C.CORE CO., LTD.; *Int'l*, pg. 6170
RCCT TECHNOLOGY CO., LTD.—See ChangChun Group; *Int'l*, pg. 1442
RCC WESTERN STORES, INC.—See Boot Barn Holdings, Inc.; *U.S. Public*, pg. 368
RCD COMPONENTS INC.—See The Jordan Company, L.P.; *U.S. Private*, pg. 4063
RCD GENERAL CONTRACTORS; *U.S. Private*, pg. 3361
RC DOLNER LLC; *U.S. Private*, pg. 3361
RC+E AG—See Knill Holding GmbH; *Int'l*, pg. 4208
RCE CAPITAL BERHAD; *Int'l*, pg. 6227
RC&E, LLC—See Southfield Capital Advisors, LLC; *U.S. Private*, pg. 3736
RC ENERGO INSTALL SRL—See ROMCARBON S.A.; *Int'l*, pg. 6395
RCF ACQUISITION CORP.; *U.S. Public*, pg. 1767
RCF GROUP SPA; *Int'l*, pg. 6227
RCF MANAGEMENT LLC; *U.S. Private*, pg. 3361
RCG GLOBAL SERVICES, INC.—See Frontenac Company LLC; *U.S. Private*, pg. 1614
RCG LOGISTICS LLC—See Tailwind Capital Group, LLC; *U.S. Private*, pg. 3924
RCG PRODUCTIONS; *U.S. Private*, pg. 3362
RC GROUP S.P.A—See Mitsubishi Electric Corporation; *Int'l*, pg. 4943
RCH COMPANY, INC.; *U.S. Private*, pg. 3362
RCH DISTRIBUTORS INC.—See Riechman Crosby Hays Company, Inc.; *U.S. Private*, pg. 3434
RCH RECYCLING CENTER HIMBERG GMBH—See PORR AG; *Int'l*, pg. 5924
RCI BANK AG—See Renault S.A.; *Int'l*, pg. 6274
RCI BANK POLSKA—See Renault S.A.; *Int'l*, pg. 6274
RCI BANQUE—See Renault S.A.; *Int'l*, pg. 6274
RCI CONSULTANTS, INC.—See TUV SUD AG; *Int'l*, pg. 7985
RCI DINING SERVICES (16328 I-35), INC.—See RCI Hospitality Holdings, Inc.; *U.S. Public*, pg. 1767
RCI DINING SERVICES (37TH STREET), INC.—See RCI Hospitality Holdings, Inc.; *U.S. Public*, pg. 1767
RCI DINING SERVICES (AIRPORT FREEWAY), INC.—See RCI Hospitality Holdings, Inc.; *U.S. Public*, pg. 1767
RCI DINING SERVICES (GLENWOOD), INC.—See RCI Hospitality Holdings, Inc.; *U.S. Public*, pg. 1767
RCI DINING SERVICES (NEW YORK), INC.—See RCI Hospitality Holdings, Inc.; *U.S. Public*, pg. 1767
RCI DINING SERVICES (ROUND ROCK), INC.—See RCI Hospitality Holdings, Inc.; *U.S. Public*, pg. 1767
RCI DINING SERVICES (SULPHUR), INC.—See RCI Hospitality Holdings, Inc.; *U.S. Public*, pg. 1767
RCI ENTERTAINMENT (FORT WORTH), INC.—See RCI Hospitality Holdings, Inc.; *U.S. Public*, pg. 1767
RCI ENTERTAINMENT (MINNESOTA), INC.—See RCI Hospitality Holdings, Inc.; *U.S. Public*, pg. 1767
RCI ENTERTAINMENT (SAN ANTONIO), INC.—See RCI Hospitality Holdings, Inc.; *U.S. Public*, pg. 1767
RCI FINANCE MAROC—See Renault S.A.; *Int'l*, pg. 6274
RCI FINANCE SA—See Renault S.A.; *Int'l*, pg. 6274
RCI FINANCIAL SERVICES BV—See Renault S.A.; *Int'l*, pg. 6274
RCI FINANCIAL SERVICES LTD—See Renault S.A.; *Int'l*, pg. 6274
RCI HOSPITALITY HOLDINGS, INC.; *U.S. Public*, pg. 1767
RCI INDUSTRIES & TECHNOLOGIES LTD; *Int'l*, pg. 6228
RC II S.A.R.L.—See DZ BANK AG Deutsche Zentral-Genossenschaftsbank; *Int'l*, pg. 2244
R.C.I. JAPAN CO., LTD.—See RESORT TRUST INC.; *Int'l*, pg. 6301
RCI KOREA—See Renault S.A.; *Int'l*, pg. 6274

CORPORATE AFFILIATIONS

RCI LEASING ROMANIA IFN S.A.—See Renault S.A.; *Int'l*, pg. 6274
RCI LIME SDN. BHD.—See Mega First Corporation Berhad; *Int'l*, pg. 4792
RCI, LLC—See Travel & Leisure Co.; *U.S. Public*, pg. 2185
RCI MARKETING SDN. BHD.—See Mega First Corporation Berhad; *Int'l*, pg. 4792
RCI (MICHIGAN), INC.—See Select Medical Holdings Corporation; *U.S. Public*, pg. 1858
RCI MID-AMERICAN OFFICE—See Travel & Leisure Co.; *U.S. Public*, pg. 2185
RCI SERVICES LTD—See Renault S.A.; *Int'l*, pg. 6274
RCI SP. Z.O.O.—See OT Logistics S.A.; *Int'l*, pg. 5656
RCI TRAVEL—See Travel & Leisure Co.; *U.S. Public*, pg. 2185
RCI VERSICHERUNGS SERVICE GMBH—See Renault S.A.; *Int'l*, pg. 6274
RCI (WRS), INC.—See Select Medical Holdings Corporation; *U.S. Public*, pg. 1858
RCKT GMBH & CO. KG—See Rocket Internet SE; *Int'l*, pg. 6379
R. C. LACY, INC.; *U.S. Private*, pg. 3333
RCL AGENCIES (M) SDN. BHD.—See Regional Container Lines Public Company Limited; *Int'l*, pg. 6254
R. CLAIR PHYSICAL THERAPY, LIMITED PARTNERSHIP—See U.S. Physical Therapy, Inc.; *U.S. Public*, pg. 2215
RCL AUSTRALIA PTY. LTD.—See Regional Container Lines Public Company Limited; *Int'l*, pg. 6254
RCL CRUISES LTD.—See Royal Caribbean Cruises Ltd.; *U.S. Public*, pg. 1815
RCL FEEDER PTE. LTD.—See Regional Container Lines Public Company Limited; *Int'l*, pg. 6254
RCL FEEDERS PHILS., INC.—See Regional Container Lines Public Company Limited; *Int'l*, pg. 6254
RCL FOODS LIMITED—See Remgro Limited; *Int'l*, pg. 6270
RCL HOLDINGS LTD.—See Regional Container Lines Public Company Limited; *Int'l*, pg. 6254
RCL INVESTMENT PTE. LTD.—See Regional Container Lines Public Company Limited; *Int'l*, pg. 6254
RCL (KOREA) LTD.—See Regional Container Lines Public Company Limited; *Int'l*, pg. 6254
RCL LOGISTICS CO., LTD.—See Regional Container Lines Public Company Limited; *Int'l*, pg. 6254
RCL (MYANMAR) COMPANY LIMITED—See Regional Container Lines Public Company Limited; *Int'l*, pg. 6254
RCL SERVICES S.A.—See Regional Container Lines Public Company Limited; *Int'l*, pg. 6254
RCL SHIPMANAGEMENT PTE. LTD.—See Regional Container Lines Public Company Limited; *Int'l*, pg. 6254
RCL (UK) LTD.—See Royal Caribbean Cruises Ltd.; *U.S. Public*, pg. 1815
RCL (VIETNAM) CO., LTD.—See Regional Container Lines Public Company Limited; *Int'l*, pg. 6254
RCMA AMERICAS INC.—See Tong Teik Pte Ltd; *Int'l*, pg. 7806
RCM BETEILIGUNGS AG; *Int'l*, pg. 6228
RCM CAPITAL MANAGEMENT PTY LTD—See Allianz SE; *Int'l*, pg. 346
RCM DESIGN—See S. Rothschild & Co., Inc.; *U.S. Private*, pg. 3515
RCM INDUSTRIES, INC.; *U.S. Private*, pg. 3362
RCM MANUFACTURING CORP.—See S. Rothschild & Co., Inc.; *U.S. Private*, pg. 3515
RCM MANUFACTURING, INC.—See Koninklijke Philips N.V.; *Int'l*, pg. 4271
RCM SOLUTIONS, INC.; *U.S. Private*, pg. 3362
RCM TECHNOLOGIES, INC.; *U.S. Public*, pg. 1767
RCM TECHNOLOGIES (USA), INC.—See RCM Technologies, Inc.; *U.S. Public*, pg. 1767
RCM (UK) LTD.—See Allianz SE; *Int'l*, pg. 355
R.C. MULTIBOND DURAL S.R.L.—See CFS Group, Inc.; *Int'l*, pg. 1430
RCN COMMUNICATIONS LLC—See Renodis, Inc.; *U.S. Private*, pg. 3399
RCN TELECOM SERVICES, LLC—See Stonepeak Partners L.P.; *U.S. Private*, pg. 3829
RCO ENGINEERING INC.; *U.S. Private*, pg. 3362
R.C. OLMSTEAD, INC.—See Nymbus, Inc.; *U.S. Private*, pg. 2976
R.C. OLSEN CADILLAC; *U.S. Private*, pg. 3334
R-CONTROL DESINFECTIONS SA—See Rentokil Initial plc; *Int'l*, pg. 6287
R CORP FINANCIAL; *U.S. Private*, pg. 3331
R.C. OWEN COMPANY OF TENNESSEE—See R.C. Owen Holding Company; *U.S. Private*, pg. 3335
R.C. OWEN HOLDING COMPANY; *U.S. Private*, pg. 3335
RCPAY LTD.—See RC365 Holding Plc; *Int'l*, pg. 6227
RCP BLOCK & BRICK, INC.; *U.S. Private*, pg. 3362
RCP DEVELOPMENT INC.—See Rock Creek Pharmaceuticals, Inc.; *U.S. Public*, pg. 1804
RCP RANSTADT GMBH—See Nimbus B.V.; *Int'l*, pg. 5296
RCP SARL—See AmRest Holdings SE; *Int'l*, pg. 437
RCP TECHNOLOGIES SDN. BHD.—See Greenyield Berhad; *Int'l*, pg. 3078
RC RASMUSSEN CORPORATION; *U.S. Private*, pg. 3361

COMPANY NAME INDEX

RCR BUILDING PRODUCTS (HOLDINGS) PTY LTD—See RCR Tomlinson Ltd.; *Int'l*, pg. 6228
RCR CONSTRUCTION & MAINTENANCE PTY LTD.—See RCR Tomlinson Ltd.; *Int'l*, pg. 6228
RCR CORPORATE PTY LTD—See RCR Tomlinson Ltd.; *Int'l*, pg. 6228
RCR ENERGY LIMITED—See Max Weishaupt GmbH; *Int'l*, pg. 4735
RCR ENERGY PTY LTD—See RCR Tomlinson Ltd.; *Int'l*, pg. 6228
RCR ENERGY SERVICE P/L—See Max Weishaupt GmbH; *Int'l*, pg. 4735
RCR ENERGY SERVICES PTY LTD.—See The Environmental Group Limited; *Int'l*, pg. 7640
RCR ENERGY—See RCR Tomlinson Ltd.; *Int'l*, pg. 6228
RCR ENERGY (STELFORM) PTY LTD—See RCR Tomlinson Ltd.; *Int'l*, pg. 6228
RCR ENERGY (STELFORM VRBT) PTY LTD—See RCR Tomlinson Ltd.; *Int'l*, pg. 6228
RCR ENGINEERING PTY LTD.—See RCR Tomlinson Ltd.; *Int'l*, pg. 6228
RC RESOURCES, INC.—See Hecla Mining Company; *U.S. Public*, pg. 1019
RCR HADEN (HOLDINGS) PTY LTD—See RCR Tomlinson Ltd.; *Int'l*, pg. 6228
RCR HADEN PTY LTD—See RCR Tomlinson Ltd.; *Int'l*, pg. 6228
RCR HEAT TREATMENT—See NRW Holdings Limited; *Int'l*, pg. 5475
RCR INFRASTRUCTURE GROUP (XNFK) LTD.—See RCR Tomlinson Ltd.; *Int'l*, pg. 6228
RCR INFRASTRUCTURE (NEW ZEALAND) LIMITED—See RCR Tomlinson Ltd.; *Int'l*, pg. 6228
RCR INFRASTRUCTURE (NEW ZEALAND) LIMITED—See RCR Tomlinson Ltd.; *Int'l*, pg. 6228
RCR LASER PTY LTD—See RCR Tomlinson Ltd.; *Int'l*, pg. 6228
RCR LASER TOOWOOMBA—See RCR Tomlinson Ltd.; *Int'l*, pg. 6228
RCR LASER WELSHPOOL—See RCR Tomlinson Ltd.; *Int'l*, pg. 6228
RCR MAINTENANCE NEWMAN—See RCR Tomlinson Ltd.; *Int'l*, pg. 6228
RCR MAINTENANCE TOM PRICE—See RCR Tomlinson Ltd.; *Int'l*, pg. 6228
RCR METALBILT DOORS—See RCR Tomlinson Ltd.; *Int'l*, pg. 6228
RCR MINING (SPLICELINE) PTY LTD—See NRW Holdings Limited; *Int'l*, pg. 5475
RCR MINING TECHNOLOGIES PTY LTD—See NRW Holdings Limited; *Int'l*, pg. 5475
RCR MINING TECHNOLOGIES—See NRW Holdings Limited; *Int'l*, pg. 5475
RCR MINNG OSR—See RCR Tomlinson Ltd.; *Int'l*, pg. 6228
RCR O'DONNELL GRIFFIN (HOLDINGS) PTY LIMITED—See RCR Tomlinson Ltd.; *Int'l*, pg. 6228
RCR O'DONNELL GRIFFIN PTY LIMITED—See RCR Tomlinson Ltd.; *Int'l*, pg. 6228
RCR POWER PTY LTD—See RCR Tomlinson Ltd.; *Int'l*, pg. 6228
RCR RESOLVE FM PTY LIMITED—See RCR Tomlinson Ltd.; *Int'l*, pg. 6228
RCR RESOURCES (HEAT TREATMENT) PTY LTD—See RCR Tomlinson Ltd.; *Int'l*, pg. 6228
RCR RESOURCES PTY LTD—See RCR Tomlinson Ltd.; *Int'l*, pg. 6229
RCR RESOURCES (TRIPOWER) PTY LTD—See RCR Tomlinson Ltd.; *Int'l*, pg. 6228
RCR TOMLINSON BUNBURY—See RCR Tomlinson Ltd.; *Int'l*, pg. 6229
RCR TOMLINSON (CUSTODIAN) PTY LTD—See RCR Tomlinson Ltd.; *Int'l*, pg. 6229
RCR TOMLINSON LTD.; *Int'l*, pg. 6228
RCS BROADCAST S.P.A.—See RCS MediaGroup S.p.A.; *Int'l*, pg. 6229
RCS COMPANY OF TAMPA; *U.S. Private*, pg. 3362
RCS DIRECT S.R.L.—See RCS MediaGroup S.p.A.; *Int'l*, pg. 6229
RCS ENGINEERING PTE LTD—See Sim Lian Group Limited; *Int'l*, pg. 6927
R&C SERVICES INC.; *U.S. Private*, pg. 3332
RCS ETM SICUREZZA S.P.A.—See CY4Gate S.p.A.; *Int'l*, pg. 1891
RCS GMBH RAIL COMPONENTS AND SYSTEMS—See senata GmbH; *Int'l*, pg. 6707
RCS GMBH; *Int'l*, pg. 6229
RCSH OPERATIONS, LLC—See Darden Restaurants, Inc.; *U.S. Public*, pg. 633
RCS INVESTIMENTI S.P.A.—See RCS MediaGroup S.p.A.; *Int'l*, pg. 6229
RCS LTD—See Afarak Group SE; *Int'l*, pg. 185
RCS MEDIAGROUP S.P.A.; *Int'l*, pg. 6229
R. C. SMITH COMPANIES, LLC—See Vulcan Materials Company; *U.S. Public*, pg. 2313
R-C SPAIN, S.L.—See Marriott International, Inc.; *U.S. Public*, pg. 1371
RCS PERIODICI S.P.A.—See RCS MediaGroup S.p.A.; *Int'l*, pg. 6229

RCSPL SHARE BROKING PRIVATE LIMITED—See Riddhi Corporate Services Limited; *Int'l*, pg. 6337
RCS PRODUZIONI S.P.A.—See RCS MediaGroup S.p.A.; *Int'l*, pg. 6229
RCS PUBBLICITA S.P.A.—See RCS MediaGroup S.p.A.; *Int'l*, pg. 6229
RCS QUOTIDIANI S.P.A.—See RCS MediaGroup S.p.A.; *Int'l*, pg. 6229
RCS & RDS S.A.—See Digi Communications N.V; *Int'l*, pg. 2118
RCS SPORT S.P.A.—See RCS MediaGroup S.p.A.; *Int'l*, pg. 6229
RCS TELECOMMUNICATIONS PTY LTD—See CSE Global Ltd.; *Int'l*, pg. 1864
RC STEVENS CONSTRUCTION COMPANY—See Cianbro Corporation; *U.S. Private*, pg. 896
RCT GLOBAL SPA—See Epiroc AB; *Int'l*, pg. 2463
RCT HYDRAULIC-TOOLING AG—See Accu Holding AG; *Int'l*, pg. 94
R & C TOURS GUAM INC—See R & C Tours Japan Inc.; *Int'l*, pg. 6167
R & C TOURS JAPAN INC.; *Int'l*, pg. 6167
R & C TRADING L.L.C.—See HF Foods Group Inc.; *U.S. Public*, pg. 1033
R C TREATT & CO LTD—See Treatt Plc; *Int'l*, pg. 7909
RCT SACHSEN GMBH—See Accu Holding AG; *Int'l*, pg. 94
RCTS AUTOWORX INC.—See HKS CO., LTD.; *Int'l*, pg. 3429
R. C. TWAY COMPANY, LLC—See Berkshire Hathaway Inc.; *U.S. Public*, pg. 298
R. CUSHMAN & ASSOCIATES, INC.—See Stone River Capital Partners, LLC; *U.S. Private*, pg. 3826
R. CUSHMAN & ASSOCIATES, INC.—See Wynnchurch Capital, L.P.; *U.S. Private*, pg. 4577
RC VAS DIRECT PROPRIETARY LIMITED—See Transaction Capital Limited; *Int'l*, pg. 7894
R.C. WILLEY HOME FURNISHINGS—See Berkshire Hathaway Inc.; *U.S. Public*, pg. 315
R. C. WILLEY HOME FURNISHINGS—See Berkshire Hathaway Inc.; *U.S. Public*, pg. 316
RDA CORPORATION; *U.S. Private*, pg. 3363
RDA HOLDING CO.; *U.S. Private*, pg. 3363
RDA INTERNATIONAL; *U.S. Private*, pg. 3364
R&D ALTANOVA, INC.—See Advantest Corporation; *Int'l*, pg. 166
RDA MICROELECTRONICS, INC.—See Tsinghua Holdings Co., Ltd.; *Int'l*, pg. 7951
R.D. BANKS CHEVROLET, INC.; *U.S. Private*, pg. 3335
RDB GROUP—See NTC Industries Ltd.; *Int'l*, pg. 5481
R.D. BITZER CO. INC.; *U.S. Private*, pg. 3335
RDB PLASTICS GMBH—See Alba SE; *Int'l*, pg. 293
RDB RASAYANS LIMITED; *Int'l*, pg. 6230
RDB REALTY & INFRASTRUCTURE LIMITED—See NTC Industries Ltd.; *Int'l*, pg. 5481
R&D BUSINESS FACTORY CO., LTD.—See Fukuoka Financial Group, Inc.; *Int'l*, pg. 2840
R&D CARY ENTERPRISES; *U.S. Private*, pg. 3332
RDC CONCRETE (INDIA) PVT. LIMITED—See India Value Fund Advisors Pvt Ltd.; *Int'l*, pg. 3652
RDC CONCRETE (INDIA) PVT LTD AHMEDABAD PLANT—See India Value Fund Advisors Pvt Ltd.; *Int'l*, pg. 3652
RDC CONCRETE (INDIA) PVT LTD BENGALURU PLANT—See India Value Fund Advisors Pvt Ltd.; *Int'l*, pg. 3652
RDC CONCRETE (INDIA) PVT LTD CHENNAI PLANT—See India Value Fund Advisors Pvt Ltd.; *Int'l*, pg. 3653
RDC CONCRETE (INDIA) PVT LTD COIMBATORE PLANT—See India Value Fund Advisors Pvt Ltd.; *Int'l*, pg. 3653
RDC CONCRETE (INDIA) PVT LTD GURGAON PLANT—See India Value Fund Advisors Pvt Ltd.; *Int'l*, pg. 3653
RDC CONCRETE (INDIA) PVT LTD HYDERABAD PLANT—See India Value Fund Advisors Pvt Ltd.; *Int'l*, pg. 3653
RDC CONCRETE (INDIA) PVT LTD JAIPUR PLANT—See India Value Fund Advisors Pvt Ltd.; *Int'l*, pg. 3653
RDC CONCRETE (INDIA) PVT LTD KERALA PLANT—See India Value Fund Advisors Pvt Ltd.; *Int'l*, pg. 3653
RDC CONCRETE (INDIA) PVT LTD KERALA PLANT—See India Value Fund Advisors Pvt Ltd.; *Int'l*, pg. 3653
RDC CONCRETE (INDIA) PVT LTD KOLKATA PLANT—See India Value Fund Advisors Pvt Ltd.; *Int'l*, pg. 3653
RDC CONCRETE (INDIA) PVT LTD MANGALORE PLANT—See India Value Fund Advisors Pvt Ltd.; *Int'l*, pg. 3653
RDC CONCRETE (INDIA) PVT LTD MUMBAI PLANT—See India Value Fund Advisors Pvt Ltd.; *Int'l*, pg. 3653
RDC CONCRETE (INDIA) PVT LTD PUNE PLANT—See India Value Fund Advisors Pvt Ltd.; *Int'l*, pg. 3653

RDR PROPERTIES INC.

RDC CONCRETE (INDIA) PVT LTD VISAKAPATTANAM PLANT—See India Value Fund Advisors Pvt Ltd.; *Int'l*, pg. 3653
RD CHERRY, INC.—See EssilorLuxottica SA; *Int'l*, pg. 2514
RDC HOLDINGS LUXEMBOURG S.A R.L.—See Valaris Limited; *Int'l*, pg. 8110
RDC INC.; *U.S. Private*, pg. 3364
R & D CIRCUITS, INC.—See Guardian Capital Partners, LLC; *U.S. Private*, pg. 1810
RDC MACHINE INC.; *U.S. Private*, pg. 3364
RDCM, S. DE R.L. DE C.V—See Ryobi Limited; *Int'l*, pg. 6440
R&D COMPUTER CO., LTD.; *Int'l*, pg. 6168
RDC RAFAEL DEVELOPMENT CORPORATION LTD.—See Elron Ventures Ltd; *Int'l*, pg. 2370
RDC SEMICONDUCTOR CO., LTD.; *Int'l*, pg. 6230
RDDS AVIONICS LIMITED—See Croma Security Solutions Group Plc; *Int'l*, pg. 1853
RDDT PTY, LTD.—See Vyant Bio, Inc.; *U.S. Public*, pg. 2315
RDE, INC.; *U.S. Public*, pg. 1767
RD ENGINEERING & CONSTRUCTION INC.; *U.S. Private*, pg. 3362
R & D ENTERPRISES, INC.—See Resilience Capital Partners, LLC; *U.S. Private*, pg. 3405
R&D ENTERPRISES, INC.; *U.S. Private*, pg. 3332
RDE REGIONALE DIENSTLEISTUNGEN ENERGIE GMBH & CO. KG—See E.ON SE; *Int'l*, pg. 2259
RDE VERWALTUNGS-GMBH—See E.ON SE; *Int'l*, pg. 2259
RD&F ADVERTISING, INC.—See Quad/Graphics, Inc.; *U.S. Public*, pg. 1744
RDF CONSULTING LIMITED—See RDF Group plc; *Int'l*, pg. 6230
RDF GROUP PLC; *Int'l*, pg. 6230
RDF RESOURCES LIMITED—See RDF Group plc; *Int'l*, pg. 6230
RDF TELEVISION—See De Agostini S.p.A.; *Int'l*, pg. 1995
RDF TELEVISION WEST—See De Agostini S.p.A.; *Int'l*, pg. 1995
RD&G HOLDINGS CORPORATION; *U.S. Private*, pg. 3362
RDG OUTPATIENT COUNSELING, L.L.C.—See Universal Health Services, Inc.; *U.S. Public*, pg. 2259
RDH MINING EQUIPMENT LTD—See Yankuang Group Co., Limited; *Int'l*, pg. 8562
RDI DIAMONDS, INC.; *U.S. Private*, pg. 3364
THE RDI GROUP—See Ardian SAS; *Int'l*, pg. 556
RDI, INC.; *U.S. Private*, pg. 3364
RDI, LLC—See Regent Contracting Corp.; *U.S. Private*, pg. 3387
RD INTERNATIONAL SERVICES PTE LTD.—See Valaris Limited; *Int'l*, pg. 8110
RDI REIT P.L.C.—See Starwood Capital Group Global I, LLC; *U.S. Private*, pg. 3789
RDI TECHNOLOGIES, INC.—See SFW Capital Partners LLC; *U.S. Private*, pg. 3622
R.D. JOHNSON EXCAVATING COMPANY, LLC—See Summit Materials, Inc.; *U.S. Public*, pg. 1959
RDK TRANSPORTATION CO. INC.—See Mullen Group Ltd.; *Int'l*, pg. 5080
RDK TRUCK SALES; *U.S. Private*, pg. 3364
RDL CORPORATION LIMITED; *Int'l*, pg. 6230
RDL LL, LTD.—See Platinum Equity, LLC; *U.S. Private*, pg. 3209
R&D MAINTENANCE SERVICES, INC.; *U.S. Private*, pg. 3332
R.D. MANUFACTURING CORPORATION—See RDA Holding Co.; *U.S. Private*, pg. 3363
R.D.M ARNSBERG GMBH—See Cascades Inc.; *Int'l*, pg. 1351
R.D.M BARCELONA CARTONBOARD S.A.—See Cascades Inc.; *Int'l*, pg. 1351
RDM CORPORATION—See Deluxe Corporation; *U.S. Public*, pg. 653
RD MERRILL COMPANY; *U.S. Private*, pg. 3362
R.D.M LA ROCHETTE S.A.S.—See Cascades Inc.; *Int'l*, pg. 1351
R&D MOLDERS, INC.—See Lomont Molding LLC; *U.S. Private*, pg. 2483
R.D.M. OVARO—See Apollo Global Management, Inc.; *U.S. Private*, pg. 159
R&D NICKERSON FISH PRODUCTS LTD.; *Int'l*, pg. 6168
R.D. NIVEN & ASSOCIATES LTD.; *U.S. Private*, pg. 3335
RDNS HOMECARE LIMITED—See Royal District Nursing Service; *Int'l*, pg. 6412
RDO EQUIPMENT CO.—See R.D. Offutt Company; *U.S. Private*, pg. 3335
R.D. OFFUTT COMPANY; *U.S. Private*, pg. 3335
R.D. OLSON CONSTRUCTION; *U.S. Private*, pg. 3335
RDO VERMEER, LLC—See R.D. Offutt Company; *U.S. Private*, pg. 3335
RD PLASTICS COMPANY, INC.; *U.S. Private*, pg. 3362
RD PUBLICATIONS, INC.—See RDA Holding Co.; *U.S. Private*, pg. 3363
RDR INC; *U.S. Private*, pg. 3364
RDR PROPERTIES INC.; *U.S. Private*, pg. 3364

RDR PROPERTIES INC.
CORPORATE AFFILIATIONS

RDS IT-SUPPORT—See La Cooperative WELCOOP SA; *Int'l*, pg. 4387

RDSK, INC.; *U.S. Private*, pg. 3364

RDS MANAGEMENT, INC.—See LaFontaine Automotive Group, LLC; *U.S. Private*, pg. 2373

R.D.S REPROTECH LTD.—See Yen Sun Technology Corp.; *Int'l*, pg. 8577

RDS SOLUTIONS LLC—See UPSTACK, Inc.; *U.S. Private*, pg. 4313

R&D SYSTEMS CHINA CO., LTD.—See Bio-Techne Corporation; *U.S. Public*, pg. 334

R&D SYSTEMS EUROPE, LTD.—See Bio-Techne Corporation; *U.S. Public*, pg. 334

R&D SYSTEMS GMBH—See Bio-Techne Corporation; *U.S. Public*, pg. 334

R.D. TAYLOR & COMPANY LIMITED—See Platinum Equity, LLC; *U.S. Private*, pg. 3210

R&D THIEL INC.-CARPENTER CONTRACTORS OF AMERICA; *U.S. Private*, pg. 3332

RD TRADING LIMITED—See Computacenter plc; *Int'l*, pg. 1758

RDV CORPORATION; *U.S. Private*, pg. 3364

RDV SPORTS, INC.—See RDV Corporation; *U.S. Private*, pg. 3364

RDV SPORTSPLEX—See RDV Corporation; *U.S. Private*, pg. 3364

R. D. WING CO., INC.; *U.S. Private*, pg. 3333

RE2, INC.—See Palladyne AI Corp.; *U.S. Public*, pg. 1634

REAAL SCHADEVERZEKERINGEN N.V.—See Apollo Global Management, Inc.; *U.S. Public*, pg. 147

REA & ASSOCIATES, INC.; *U.S. Private*, pg. 3365

REA AUSTIN PTY LTD.—See News Corporation; *U.S. Public*, pg. 1521

REABOLD RESOURCES PLC; *Int'l*, pg. 6230

REAC AB—See Investment AB Latour; *Int'l*, pg. 3782

REACAP FINANCIAL INVESTMENTS; *Int'l*, pg. 6230

REACC CO., LTD.—See PTT Public Company Limited; *Int'l*, pg. 6093

REAC GROUP, INC.; *U.S. Private*, pg. 3365

REACH4ENTERTAINMENT ENTERPRISES PLC; *Int'l*, pg. 6232

REACH AIR MEDICAL SERVICES, LLC—See KKR & Co. Inc.; *U.S. Public*, pg. 1252

REACHBIRD SOLUTIONS GMBH—See adesso SE; *Int'l*, pg. 144

REACH COMMUNITY DEVELOPMENT, INC.; *U.S. Private*, pg. 3365

REACH EAP, LLC—See Highmark Health; *U.S. Private*, pg. 1940

REACH ENERGY BERHAD; *Int'l*, pg. 6230

REACH GENETICS, INC.; *U.S. Private*, pg. 3365

REACH GLOBAL SERVICES S.A.; *Int'l*, pg. 6230

REACH GMBH—See Reach; *Int'l*, pg. 6230

REACHLOCAL AUSTRALIA PTY LTD—See Gannett Co., Inc.; *U.S. Public*, pg. 899

REACHLOCAL EUROPE BV—See Gannett Co., Inc.; *U.S. Public*, pg. 899

REACHLOCAL GMBH—See Gannett Co., Inc.; *U.S. Public*, pg. 899

REACHLOCAL, INC.—See Gannett Co., Inc.; *U.S. Public*, pg. 899

REACHLOCAL JAPAN SERVICES G.K.—See Gannett Co., Inc.; *U.S. Public*, pg. 899

REACHLOCAL SERVICES PVT. LTD.—See Gannett Co., Inc.; *U.S. Public*, pg. 899

REACH MARKETING LLC; *U.S. Private*, pg. 3365

REACH MEDIA, INC.—See Urban One, Inc.; *U.S. Public*, pg. 2265

REACH MEDIA NEW ZEALAND LIMITED—See IVE Group Limited; *Int'l*, pg. 3847

REACH MESSAGING HOLDINGS, INC.; *U.S. Private*, pg. 3365

REACH NEW HOLDINGS LIMITED; *Int'l*, pg. 6230

REACH NOW INTERNATIONAL INC.; *U.S. Private*, pg. 3365

REACH PLC; *Int'l*, pg. 6231

REACH PRINTING SERVICES (OLDHAM) LIMITED—See Reach PLC; *Int'l*, pg. 6231

REACH PRINTING SERVICES (TEESSIDE) LIMITED—See Reach PLC; *Int'l*, pg. 6231

REACH PRINTING SERVICES (WATFORD) LIMITED—See Reach PLC; *Int'l*, pg. 6231

REACH PUBLISHING SERVICES LIMITED—See Reach PLC; *Int'l*, pg. 6231

REACH SATELLITE NETWORK INC.—See Salem Media Group, Inc.; *U.S. Public*, pg. 1836

REACH; *Int'l*, pg. 6230

REACH SPORTS MARKETING GROUP; *U.S. Private*, pg. 3365

REACH SUBSEA ASA—See Caiano AS; *Int'l*, pg. 1252

REACH TECHNOLOGY, INC.—See Novanta Inc.; *U.S. Public*, pg. 1548

REACHTEL PTY LTD—See Equifax Inc.; *U.S. Public*, pg. 787

REACT2MEDIA, LLC.; *U.S. Private*, pg. 3366

REACT GROUP PLC; *Int'l*, pg. 6232

REACTION AUDIO VISUAL LLC; *U.S. Private*, pg. 3366

REACTION BIOLOGY CORPORATION; *U.S. Private*, pg. 3366

REACTION DESIGN, INC.—See ANSYS, Inc.; *U.S. Public*, pg. 139

REACTION PHYSICAL THERAPY, LLC—See U.S. Physical Therapy, Inc.; *U.S. Public*, pg. 2215

REACTION TECHNOLOGY EPI, LLC—See Littelfuse, Inc.; *U.S. Public*, pg. 1327

REACTIVE GROUP; *Int'l*, pg. 6232

READABOO, INC.; *U.S. Private*, pg. 3366

REA DALMINE S.P.A.—See Green Holding S.p.A.; *Int'l*, pg. 3071

READBOY EDUCATION HOLDING COMPANY LIMITED; *Int'l*, pg. 6232

READCLOUD LIMITED; *Int'l*, pg. 6232

READCO KURIMOTO, LLC—See Kurimoto Ltd; *Int'l*, pg. 4339

READCREST CAPITAL AG; *Int'l*, pg. 6232

READE COMMUNICATIONS GROUP; *U.S. Private*, pg. 3366

READE COMMUNICATIONS GROUP—See Reade Communications Group; *U.S. Private*, pg. 3366

READE MANUFACTURING COMPANY—See Luxfer Holdings PLC; *Int'l*, pg. 4588

READEN HOLDING CORP.; *Int'l*, pg. 6232

READER CEMENT PRODUCTS LIMITED—See Langley Holdings Plc; *Int'l*, pg. 4410

READEREST; *U.S. Private*, pg. 3366

READER GROUT & EQUIPMENT LTD—See Langley Holdings Plc; *Int'l*, pg. 4410

READER'S DIGEST AB—See CIL Group SL; *Int'l*, pg. 1607

READER'S DIGEST ASSOCIATION FAR EAST LTD.—See RDA Holding Co.; *U.S. Private*, pg. 3363

THE READER'S DIGEST ASSOCIATION, INC.—See RDA Holding Co.; *U.S. Private*, pg. 3363

THE READER'S DIGEST ASSOCIATION PTY LIMITED—See RDA Holding Co.; *U.S. Private*, pg. 3364

THE READER'S DIGEST ASSOCIATION (RUSSIA) INC.—See RDA Holding Co.; *U.S. Private*, pg. 3363

READER'S DIGEST (AUSTRALIA) PTY LTD.—See RDA Holding Co.; *U.S. Private*, pg. 3363

READER'S DIGEST CHILDREN'S PUBLISHING, INC.—See RDA Holding Co.; *U.S. Private*, pg. 3363

READER'S DIGEST CHILDREN'S PUBLISHING LIMITED—See RDA Holding Co.; *U.S. Private*, pg. 3363

READER'S DIGEST COLOMBIA, LTDA.—See RDA Holding Co.; *U.S. Private*, pg. 3363

READER'S DIGEST CONSUMER SERVICES, INC.—See RDA Holding Co.; *U.S. Private*, pg. 3363

READER'S DIGEST ENTERTAINMENT, INC.—See RDA Holding Co.; *U.S. Private*, pg. 3363

READER'S DIGEST EUROPE LIMITED—See RDA Holding Co.; *U.S. Private*, pg. 3363

READER'S DIGEST KIADO KFT—See RDA Holding Co.; *U.S. Private*, pg. 3363

READER'S DIGEST (MALAYSIA) SDN. BHD—See RDA Holding Co.; *U.S. Private*, pg. 3363

READER'S DIGEST MEXICO S.A. DE C.V.—See RDA Holding Co.; *U.S. Private*, pg. 3363

THE READER'S DIGEST (NEW ZEALAND) LIMITED—See RDA Holding Co.; *U.S. Private*, pg. 3363

READER'S DIGEST N.V. S.A.—See RDA Holding Co.; *U.S. Private*, pg. 3363

READER'S DIGEST (PHILIPPINES) INC.—See RDA Holding Co.; *U.S. Private*, pg. 3363

READER'S DIGEST PRZEGLAD SP.Z.O.O.—See RDA Holding Co.; *U.S. Private*, pg. 3363

READER'S DIGEST SALES & SERVICES, INC.—See RDA Holding Co.; *U.S. Private*, pg. 3363

READER'S DIGEST SALES & SERVICES, INC.—See RDA Holding Co.; *U.S. Private*, pg. 3363

READER'S DIGEST S.A.—See RDA Holding Co.; *U.S. Private*, pg. 3363

READER'S DIGEST SELECCIONES S.A.—See RDA Holding Co.; *U.S. Private*, pg. 3363

READER'S DIGEST (THAILAND) LIMITED—See RDA Holding Co.; *U.S. Private*, pg. 3363

READER'S DIGEST VYBER S.R.O.—See RDA Holding Co.; *U.S. Private*, pg. 3363

READER'S DIGEST WORLD SERVICES, S.A.—See RDA Holding Co.; *U.S. Private*, pg. 3363

READER'S WHOLESALE DISTRIBUTORS INC.; *U.S. Private*, pg. 3366

READEX—See NewsBank, Inc.; *U.S. Private*, pg. 2917

READFIELD MEATS INC.—See Dominion Equity LLC; *U.S. Private*, pg. 1256

READ-GENE SA; *Int'l*, pg. 6232

THE READING ADVOCATE—See Gannett Co., Inc.; *U.S. Public*, pg. 905

READING ALLOYS, INC.—See Palladium Equity Partners, LLC; *U.S. Private*, pg. 3078

READING ANTHRACITE COMPANY; *U.S. Private*, pg. 3366

READING BAKERY SYSTEMS, INC.—See Markel Group Inc.; *U.S. Public*, pg. 1369

READING EAGLE COMPANY; *U.S. Private*, pg. 3366

READING EQUIPMENT & DISTRIBUTION, INC.; *U.S. Private*, pg. 3366

READING FOUNDRY & SUPPLY CO.; *U.S. Private*, pg. 3366

THE READING GROUP, LLC—See J.B. Poindexter & Co., Inc.; *U.S. Private*, pg. 2159

READING HOSPITAL—See Tower Health; *U.S. Private*, pg. 4193

READING INTERNATIONAL, INC.; *U.S. Public*, pg. 1768

READING IS FUNDAMENTAL, INC.; *U.S. Private*, pg. 3366

READING PARTNERS; *U.S. Private*, pg. 3366

READING PRETZEL MACHINERY CORPORATION—See Markel Group Inc.; *U.S. Public*, pg. 1369

READING ROCK INCORPORATED; *U.S. Private*, pg. 3367

READING ROOM, LTD.—See Fat Media Ltd.; *Int'l*, pg. 2622

READING ROUSE HILL PTY LTD—See Reading International, Inc.; *U.S. Public*, pg. 1768

READING SCIENTIFIC SERVICES LTD.—See Mondelez International, Inc.; *U.S. Public*, pg. 1461

READING SITE CONTRACTORS—See Haines & Kibblehouse, Inc.; *U.S. Private*, pg. 1841

READING STOVE COMPANY—See Reading Anthracite Company; *U.S. Private*, pg. 3366

READING TRUCK BODY, INC.—See J.B. Poindexter & Co., Inc.; *U.S. Private*, pg. 2159

READING TUBE DIVISION—See Cambridge-Lee Industries, Inc.; *U.S. Private*, pg. 727

READ JONES CHRISTOFFERSEN LTD.; *Int'l*, pg. 6232

READLY INTERNATIONAL AB; *Int'l*, pg. 6232

RE-AD MARKETING INC.; *U.S. Private*, pg. 3364

READ WINDOW PRODUCTS, LLC—See Culp, Inc.; *U.S. Public*, pg. 604

READY AT DAWN STUDIOS, LLC—See Meta Platforms, Inc.; *U.S. Public*, pg. 1427

READY BAKE FOODS INC.—See George Weston Limited; *Int'l*, pg. 2939

READY CAPITAL CORPORATION—See Waterfall Asset Management LLC; *U.S. Private*, pg. 4452

READYCONNECT CONCIERGE—See News Corporation; *U.S. Public*, pg. 1521

READY CREDIT CORP.; *U.S. Public*, pg. 1768

READY FINANCIAL GROUP, INC.—See Green Dot Corporation; *U.S. Public*, pg. 963

READY FIT PHYSIOTHERAPY PRIVATE LIMITED—See Singapore Paincare Holdings Limited; *Int'l*, pg. 6941

READY GARMENT TECHNOLOGY ITALIA SRL.—See Dr. Bock Industries AG; *Int'l*, pg. 2190

READY GARMENT TECHNOLOGY ROMANIA SRL—See Dr. Bock Industries AG; *Int'l*, pg. 2190

READY GARMENT TECHNOLOGY UKRAINE LTD.—See Dr. Bock Industries AG; *Int'l*, pg. 2190

READY KOREA CO., LTD.—See WiseTech Global Limited; *Int'l*, pg. 8437

READYLIFT SUSPENSION, INC.—See Clearlake Capital Group, L.P.; *U.S. Private*, pg. 938

READY MADE CLOTHES CO.; *Int'l*, pg. 6232

READYMADE MAGAZINE—See Meredith Corporation; *U.S. Public*, pg. 1423

READYMADE STEEL SINGAPORE PTE LTD—See Kridhan Infra Limited; *Int'l*, pg. 4301

READY METAL MANUFACTURING COMPANY; *U.S. Private*, pg. 3367

READY MIX CONCRETE & CONSTRUCTION SUPPLIES P.L.C; *Int'l*, pg. 6232

READY MIX CONCRETE, INC.—See CEMEX, S.A.B. de C.V.; *Int'l*, pg. 1399

READYMIX CONCRETE PRODUCTS (ISRAEL) LTD—See CEMEX, S.A.B. de C.V.; *Int'l*, pg. 1398

READY MIX CONCRETE SOMERSET INC.; *U.S. Private*, pg. 3367

READY MIX CONCRETE; *U.S. Private*, pg. 3367

READY MIXED CONCRETE CO.—See Brannan Sand & Gravel Co.; *U.S. Private*, pg. 639

READYMIX INDUSTRIES (ISRAEL) LIMITED—See CEMEX, S.A.B. de C.V.; *Int'l*, pg. 1398

READYMIX LIMITED—See CEMEX, S.A.B. de C.V.; *Int'l*, pg. 1400

READYMIX (ROI) LTD—See CEMEX, S.A.B. de C.V.; *Int'l*, pg. 1400

READYMIX—See CEMEX, S.A.B. de C.V.; *Int'l*, pg. 1400

READY MIX USA - EAST TENNESSEE—See CEMEX, S.A.B. de C.V.; *Int'l*, pg. 1399

READY MIX USA, INC.; *U.S. Private*, pg. 3367

READY MIX USA - TRI-STATES DIV—See Ready Mix USA, Inc.; *U.S. Private*, pg. 3367

READYMIX (WEST INDIES) LIMITED—See CEMEX, S.A.B. de C.V.; *Int'l*, pg. 1400

READYNURSE STAFFING SERVICES—See ShiftMed, LLC; *U.S. Private*, pg. 3636

READYOP COMMUNICATIONS, INC.—See Cleartronic, Inc.; *U.S. Public*, pg. 513

READY PAC FOODS, INC.—See Bonduelle SAS; *Int'l*, pg. 1106

READYPLANET PUBLIC COMPANY LIMITED; *Int'l*, pg. 6232

READY SEAFOOD CO.—See Premium Brands Holdings Corporation; *Int'l*, pg. 5963
READYTALK; *U.S. Private*, pg. 3367
READY WELDER CORPORATION—See Broco, Inc.; *U.S. Private*, pg. 661
READY WIRELESS LLC; *U.S. Private*, pg. 3367
READY WORKFORCE (A DIVISION OF CHANDLER MACLEOD) PTY LTD—See Recruit Holdings Co., Ltd.; *Int'l*, pg. 6240
READY WORKFORCE AUSTRALIA PTY LTD—See Recruit Holdings Co., Ltd.; *Int'l*, pg. 6240
REA ENERGY CO-OPERATIVE CORP.; *U.S. Private*, pg. 3365
REAGAN ASSET MANAGEMENT, LLC; *U.S. Private*, pg. 3367
REAGAN STREET SURGERY CENTER, L.L.C.—See Tenet Healthcare Corporation; *U.S. Public*, pg. 2006
REAGAN-UDALL FOUNDATION; *U.S. Private*, pg. 3367
REAGENS DEUTSCHLAND GMBH—See Reagens S.p.A.; *Int'l*, pg. 6232
REAGENS IBERICA S.L.—See Reagens S.p.A.; *Int'l*, pg. 6232
REAGENS S.P.A.; *Int'l*, pg. 6232
REAGENS (UK) LIMITED—See Reagens S.p.A.; *Int'l*, pg. 6232
REAGENS U.S.A. INC.—See Reagens S.p.A.; *Int'l*, pg. 6232
REAGENT AND TECHNOLOGY SERVICES—See HBM Holdings Company; *U.S. Private*, pg. 1887
REAGENT CHEMICAL & RESEARCH INC.—See Wynnchurch Capital, L.P.; *U.S. Private*, pg. 4578
REAGRA SA—See Belfius Bank SA/NV; *Int'l*, pg. 963
REA GROUP LIMITED—See News Corporation; *U.S. Public*, pg. 1521
R.E.A HOLDINGS PLC; *Int'l*, pg. 6170
REA INDIA PTE. LTD.—See News Corporation; *U.S. Public*, pg. 1521
REA INTERNATIONAL INC—See Martinrea International, Inc.; *Int'l*, pg. 4704
REAKTOR AB—See Know IT AB; *Int'l*, pg. 4214
REAKTOR AS—See Know IT AB; *Int'l*, pg. 4214
REAKTOR EMERGE AS—See Know IT AB; *Int'l*, pg. 4214
REAKTORTEST SRO—See Enel S.p.A.; *Int'l*, pg. 2414
REAL ADVISORS, LLC; *U.S. Private*, pg. 3367
REALAGE, INC.—See Altaris Capital Partners, LLC; *U.S. Private*, pg. 206
REAL AI PIC SECURITIZADORA DE CREDITOS IMOBILIARIOS S.A.; *Int'l*, pg. 6232
REAL ALLOY CANADA LTD.—See Elah Holdings, Inc.; *U.S. Public*, pg. 722
REAL ALLOY GERMANY GMBH—See Norsk Hydro ASA; *Int'l*, pg. 5437
REAL ALLOY HOLDING, INC.—See Elah Holdings, Inc.; *U.S. Public*, pg. 722
REAL ALLOY RECYCLING (GERMAN WORKS) GMBH - TOGING FACILITY—See Norsk Hydro ASA; *Int'l*, pg. 5437
REAL ALLOY RECYCLING, INC. - MORGANTOWN—See Elah Holdings, Inc.; *U.S. Public*, pg. 722
REAL ALLOY RECYCLING, INC. - SAPULPA—See Elah Holdings, Inc.; *U.S. Public*, pg. 722
REAL ALLOY SPECIFICATION, INC.—See Elah Holdings, Inc.; *U.S. Public*, pg. 722
REAL AMERICAN CAPITAL CORPORATION; *U.S. Public*, pg. 1768
REAL APPEAL, INC.—See UnitedHealth Group Incorporated; *U.S. Public*, pg. 2250
REAL ASSET MANAGEMENT, INC.—See GI Manager L.P.; *U.S. Private*, pg. 1693
REAL ASSET MANAGEMENT LTD—See GI Manager L.P.; *U.S. Private*, pg. 1693
REAL AUTO DYNAMICS INC.—See HKS CO., LTD.; *Int'l*, pg. 3429
REALBASE PTY. LTD.—See Nine Entertainment Co. Holdings Limited; *Int'l*, pg. 5300
REALBEEF S.R.L.—See Cremonini S.p.A.; *Int'l*, pg. 1838
REAL BRANDS, INC.; *U.S. Public*, pg. 1768
THE REAL BROKERAGE INC.; *U.S. Public*, pg. 7678
REAL BULLAND JSC; *Int'l*, pg. 6232
REALCAN PHARMACEUTICAL CO.,LTD.; *Int'l*, pg. 6233
REAL CAPITAL ANALYTICS, INC.—See MSCI Inc.; *U.S. Public*, pg. 1483
REALCAPITALMARKETS.COM, LLC; *U.S. Private*, pg. 3368
REAL CAPITAL SOLUTIONS INC.; *U.S. Private*, pg. 3367
REALCARE INSURANCE MARKETING, INC.—See Aon plc; *Int'l*, pg. 497
REAL CLUB DE GOLF LA HERRERIA S.A.—See Imperial Brands PLC; *Int'l*, pg. 3634
REALCOLD NEW ZEALAND LTD.—See Beijer Ref AB; *Int'l*, pg. 945
REALCOM SOLUTIONS—See Charlesbank Capital Partners, LLC; *U.S. Private*, pg. 854
REALCOM TECHNOLOGY INDIA PVT LTD.—See Abalance Corporation Ltd.; *Int'l*, pg. 48
REALCO SA; *Int'l*, pg. 6233
REAL DATA, INC.; *U.S. Private*, pg. 3367
REAL DATA MANAGEMENT INC.—See Building Engines, Inc.; *U.S. Private*, pg. 682

REALDEFENSE LLC; *U.S. Private*, pg. 3368
REALD EUROPE LIMITED—See Rizvi Traverse Management LLC; *U.S. Private*, pg. 3449
REAL DIGITAL MEDIA LLC—See Stratacache Inc.; *U.S. Private*, pg. 3834
REAL,- DIGITAL SERVICES GMBH—See Metro AG; *Int'l*, pg. 4860
REALD INC.—See Rizvi Traverse Management LLC; *U.S. Private*, pg. 3449
REALDOLMEN NV—See Mannai Corporation QPSC; *Int'l*, pg. 4674
REALEC TECHNOLOGIES, INC.—See Fidelity National Financial, Inc.; *U.S. Public*, pg. 831
R.E.A.L. EDUCATION GROUP SDN. BHD.—See Paramount Corporation Berhad; *Int'l*, pg. 5738
REALEFLOW, LLC; *U.S. Private*, pg. 3368
REAL ENERGY CORPORATION LIMITED—See Pure Hydrogen Corporation Limited; *Int'l*, pg. 6121
REALEN PROPERTIES; *U.S. Private*, pg. 3368
REALE SEGUROS GENERALES, S.A.—See Societa Reale Mutua di Assicurazioni; *Int'l*, pg. 7034
REAL ESTATE 11 JOINT STOCK COMPANY; *Int'l*, pg. 6232
REAL ESTATE AGENT PERFORMANCE PTY LTD—See Vection Technologies Ltd.; *Int'l*, pg. 8143
REAL ESTATE BUSINESS SERVICES, INC.—See California Association of Realtors; *U.S. Private*, pg. 718
REALESTATE.COM.AU PTY LTD—See News Corporation; *U.S. Public*, pg. 1521
REAL ESTATE CREDIT INVESTMENTS LTD.; *Int'l*, pg. 6232
REAL ESTATE DELIVERY, INC.—See BNP Paribas SA; *Int'l*, pg. 1088
REAL ESTATE DEVELOPMENT CO.; *Int'l*, pg. 6233
REAL ESTATE ECONOMICS—See MidOcean Partners, LLP; *U.S. Private*, pg. 2717
REAL ESTATE GROUP INC.; *U.S. Private*, pg. 3367
THE REAL ESTATE GROUP, LLC; *U.S. Private*, pg. 4102
REAL ESTATE III INC.; *U.S. Private*, pg. 3367
REAL ESTATE INSYNC; *U.S. Private*, pg. 3367
REAL ESTATE & INVESTMENT PORTFOLIO COMPANY; *Int'l*, pg. 6232
REAL ESTATE INVESTMENTS ZAMBIA PLC.; *Int'l*, pg. 6233
REAL ESTATE INVESTORS PLC; *Int'l*, pg. 6233
REAL ESTATE LENDERS—See Wells Fargo & Company; *U.S. Public*, pg. 2345
REAL ESTATE MANAGEMENT POLAND SP. Z O.O.—See UniCredit S.p.A.; *Int'l*, pg. 8036
REAL ESTATE REFERRALS LLC—See Anywhere Real Estate Inc.; *U.S. Public*, pg. 142
REAL ESTATE RESEARCH CONSULTANTS, INC.—See Comvest Group Holdings LLC; *U.S. Private*, pg. 1007
REAL ESTATE SECURITY AGENCY, LLC—See Towne Bank; *U.S. Public*, pg. 2166
REAL ESTATES INVESTMENT FUND; *Int'l*, pg. 6233
REAL ESTATE SOFIA REIT; *Int'l*, pg. 6233
REAL ESTATE SOLUTION & TECHNOLOGY SRL—See Covivio; *Int'l*, pg. 1821
REAL ESTATE TRADE CENTERS COMPANY (K.S.C.C.); *Int'l*, pg. 6233
REAL FF PTY LTD—See Ampol Limited; *Int'l*, pg. 436
REALFICTION HOLDING AB; *Int'l*, pg. 6234
REAL FINANCE ASSET MANAGEMENT JSC—See Holding Varna AD-Varna; *Int'l*, pg. 3450
REALFLEET CO., LTD.—See BALS CORPORATION; *Int'l*, pg. 811
REAL FOUNDATIONS, INC.; *U.S. Private*, pg. 3367
REAL FREEDOM INC.; *U.S. Private*, pg. 3367
REAL GOLD MINING LIMITED; *Int'l*, pg. 6233
REAL GOOD FOOD COMPANY, INC.; *U.S. Public*, pg. 1768
REAL GOOD FOOD PLC; *Int'l*, pg. 6233
REAL GRANDY VALLEY PIZZA HUT, LLC; *U.S. Private*, pg. 3367
REAL GROWTH COMMERCIAL ENTERPRISES LIMITED; *Int'l*, pg. 6233
REALGY, LLC; *U.S. Private*, pg. 3368
THE REAL HIP-HOP NETWORK, INC.; *U.S. Private*, pg. 4103
REAL,- HOLDING GMBH—See Metro AG; *Int'l*, pg. 4860
REAL HOLDING MANAGEMENT CORP.; *U.S. Private*, pg. 3367
REALHOME.COM INC.; *U.S. Private*, pg. 3368
REAL HUOT INC.—See Groupe Deschenes Inc.; *Int'l*, pg. 3102
REAL,- HYPERMARKET ROMANIA S.R.L.—See Metro AG; *Int'l*, pg. 4860
REALIA BUSINESS S.A.; *Int'l*, pg. 6234
REALIA GROUP OY—See Altor Equity Partners AB; *Int'l*, pg. 396
REALIA, INC.—See Broadcom Inc.; *U.S. Public*, pg. 390
REALIA INTERNATIONAL BV—See Kungsleden AB; *Int'l*, pg. 4332
REALIA MANAGEMENT OY—See Altor Equity Partners AB; *Int'l*, pg. 396
REALIA PROPERTIES INC.; *Int'l*, pg. 6234
REALIGN CAPITAL STRATEGIES; *U.S. Private*, pg. 3368
REALI, INC.; *U.S. Private*, pg. 3368

REALINFO, L.L.C.—See Fidelity National Financial, Inc.; *U.S. Public*, pg. 831
REAL INVEST IMMOBILIEN GMBH—See UniCredit S.p.A.; *Int'l*, pg. 8035
REAL I.S. AG GESELLSCHAFT FUR IMMOBILIEN ASSETMANAGEMENT—See BayernLB Holding AG; *Int'l*, pg. 914
REALISE TECH-SERVICE CO., LTD.—See Action Electronics Co., Ltd.; *Int'l*, pg. 119
REAL I.S. MANAGEMENT HAMBURG GMBH—See BayernLB Holding AG; *Int'l*, pg. 914
REAL I.S. MANAGEMENT SA—See BayernLB Holding AG; *Int'l*, pg. 914
REALITES SA; *Int'l*, pg. 6234
REALITY BY DESIGN INC.—See Advanced Interactive Systems; *U.S. Private*, pg. 90
REALIZE CO., LTD. - KITSUKI PLANT—See Future Innovation Group, Inc.; *Int'l*, pg. 2856
REALIZE CO., LTD.—See Future Innovation Group, Inc.; *Int'l*, pg. 2856
REALIZE CORPORATION—See Nippon Telegraph & Telephone Corporation; *Int'l*, pg. 5348
REALIZE INFORMATION TECHNOLOGY LLC—See Tonka Bay Equity Partners LLC; *U.S. Private*, pg. 4185
REALIZE MOBILE COMMUNICATIONS CORP.—See SoftBank Group Corp.; *Int'l*, pg. 7051
REALIZZA S.R.L.—See Duna House Holding Public Company Limited; *Int'l*, pg. 2225
REALKREDIT DANMARK A/S—See Danske Bank A/S; *Int'l*, pg. 1969
REAL-LEASE GRUNDSTUCKSVERWALTUNGSGESELLSCHAFT M.B.H.—See UniCredit S.p.A.; *Int'l*, pg. 8037
REAL LIVING CYPRESS REALTY, INC.; *U.S. Private*, pg. 3367
REAL LIVING, INC.; *U.S. Private*, pg. 3368
REAL LIVING PITTMAN PROPERTIES; *U.S. Private*, pg. 3367
REAL LOGIC TECHNOLOGY COMPANY LIMITED—See Novacon Technology Group Limited; *Int'l*, pg. 5454
REALLY GOOD COPY CO.; *U.S. Private*, pg. 3368
REALLY GOOD STUFF, LLC—See Brentwood Associates; *U.S. Private*, pg. 646
REALLY RAW HONEY; *U.S. Private*, pg. 3368
REALLY STRATEGIES, INC.; *U.S. Private*, pg. 3368
REALLY USEFUL COMPANY ASIA PACIFIC PTY LTD—See Really Useful Holdings Limited; *Int'l*, pg. 6234
THE REALLY USEFUL COMPANY (AUSTRALIA) PTY. LTD.—See Really Useful Holdings Limited; *Int'l*, pg. 6234
THE REALLY USEFUL COMPANY, INC.—See Really Useful Holdings Limited; *Int'l*, pg. 6234
THE REALLY USEFUL GROUP LIMITED—See Really Useful Holdings Limited; *Int'l*, pg. 6234
REALLY USEFUL HOLDINGS LIMITED; *Int'l*, pg. 6234
THE REALLY USEFUL PICTURE COMPANY—See Really Useful Holdings Limited; *Int'l*, pg. 6234
THE REALLY USEFUL THEATER COMPANY LIMITED—See Really Useful Holdings Limited; *Int'l*, pg. 6234
REALMAD MEDIA, LLC; *U.S. Private*, pg. 3368
REAL MAGNET, LLC—See Higher Logic, LLC; *U.S. Private*, pg. 1937
REALMARK DEVELOPMENT, LLC; *U.S. Private*, pg. 3368
REAL MATTERS, INC.; *Int'l*, pg. 6233
REAL MAX CO., LTD.—See TV TOKYO Holdings Corporation; *Int'l*, pg. 7987
REALM COMMUNICATIONS GROUP, INC.—See Reichle & De-Massari AG; *Int'l*, pg. 6256
REAL MEAT COMPANY LTD.—See Amatheon Agri Holding N.V.; *Int'l*, pg. 413
REAL MECHANICAL INC.—See GEMCO Constructors, LLC; *U.S. Private*, pg. 1657
REAL MEDIA SCANDINAVIA—See WPP plc; *Int'l*, pg. 8491
REAL MEDIA SPAIN S.A.—See WPP plc; *Int'l*, pg. 8491
REALM ENERGY OPERATIONS CORPORATION—See San Leon Energy plc; *Int'l*, pg. 6521
REALNET SOLUTIONS, INC.—See Zillow Group, Inc.; *U.S. Public*, pg. 2405
REALNETWORKS ASIA PACIFIC CO., LTD.—See RealNetworks, Inc.; *U.S. Private*, pg. 3369
REALNETWORKS GMBH—See RealNetworks, Inc.; *U.S. Private*, pg. 3369
REALNETWORKS, INC. - RESTON—See RealNetworks, Inc.; *U.S. Private*, pg. 3369
REALNETWORKS, INC.; *U.S. Private*, pg. 3368
REALNETWORKS, LTD.—See RealNetworks, Inc.; *U.S. Private*, pg. 3369
REAL NEWS & VIEWS LIMITED; *Int'l*, pg. 6233
REAL NUTRICEUTICAL GROUP LIMITED; *Int'l*, pg. 6233
REALOGY BROKERAGE GROUP LLC—See Anywhere Real Estate Inc.; *U.S. Public*, pg. 143
REALOGY FRANCHISE GROUP LLC—See Anywhere Real Estate Inc.; *U.S. Public*, pg. 142
REALOGY TITLE GROUP LLC—See Anywhere Real Estate Inc.; *U.S. Public*, pg. 143

REAL NUTRICEUTICAL GROUP LIMITED

REALORD ASIA PACIFIC SECURITIES LIMITED—See Realord Group Holdings Limited; *Int'l*, pg. 6234
REALORD ENVIRONMENTAL PROTECTION JAPAN CO., LTD.—See Realord Group Holdings Limited; *Int'l*, pg. 6234
REALORD GROUP HOLDINGS LIMITED; *Int'l*, pg. 6234
REALORD MANUREEN SECURITIES LIMITED—See Realord Group Holdings Limited; *Int'l*, pg. 6234
REALORD, SHENZHEN TECHNOLOGY CO., LTD.—See Realord Group Holdings Limited; *Int'l*, pg. 6234
REALPAGE, INC.—See Thoma Bravo, L.P.; *U.S. Private*, pg. 4152
REALPAGE PAYMENTS SERVICES LLC—See Thoma Bravo, L.P.; *U.S. Private*, pg. 4153
REALPHA TECH CORP.; *U.S. Public*, pg. 1768
REAL PROPERTY MANAGEMENT—See Harvest Partners L.P.; *U.S. Private*, pg. 1876
REAL PROPERTY SERVICES CORP; *U.S. Private*, pg. 3368
REAL PROPERTY TAX ADVISORS; *U.S. Private*, pg. 3368
THE REALREAL, INC.; *U.S. Public*, pg. 2125
REAL SALT LAKE—See SCP Worldwide; *U.S. Private*, pg. 3579
REALSELF INC.; *U.S. Private*, pg. 3369
REAL SERVICES, INC.—See Anywhere Real Estate Inc.; *U.S. Public*, pg. 141
REALSIL MICROELECTRONICS (SUZHOU) CO., LTD.—See Realtek Semiconductor Corp.; *Int'l*, pg. 6235
REAL SOCIAL DYNAMICS, INC.; *U.S. Private*, pg. 3368
REAL SOFTWARE SYSTEMS, LLC—See Klass Capital Corp.; *Int'l*, pg. 4199
REAL SOLUTIONS SA—See Mannai Corporation QPSC; *Int'l*, pg. 4675
REAL,- SP. Z O.O. I SPOLKA SPOLKA KOMANDYTOWA—See Metro AG; *Int'l*, pg. 4860
REAL STAFFING GROUP LIMITED—See SThree Plc.; *Int'l*, pg. 7214
REAL STRIPS LTD; *Int'l*, pg. 6233
REAL SUB, LLC—See Publix Super Markets, Inc.; *U.S. Private*, pg. 3301
REAL SYSTEM RESEARCH CO., LTD.—See Valtes Co., Ltd.; *Int'l*, pg. 8123
REALTA' INFORMATCA SRL—See Capgemini SE; *Int'l*, pg. 1307
REALTECH AG; *Int'l*, pg. 6234
REALTECH CONSULTING GMBH—See REALTECH AG; *Int'l*, pg. 6234
REALTECH, INC.; *U.S. Private*, pg. 3369
REALTECH JAPAN CO., LTD.; *Int'l*, pg. 6234
REALTECH LTD.—See REALTECH AG; *Int'l*, pg. 6234
REALTECH PORTUGAL SYSTEM CONSULTING SOCIEDADE UNIPESSOL LDA.—See REALTECH AG; *Int'l*, pg. 6234
REALTECH SERVICE GMBH—See REALTECH AG; *Int'l*, pg. 6234
REALTECH SYSTEM CONSULTING SL; *Int'l*, pg. 6234
REALTECH TITLE LLC—See Anywhere Real Estate Inc.; *U.S. Public*, pg. 143
REALTECH VERWALTUNGS GMBH—See REALTECH AG; *Int'l*, pg. 6234
REALTEK SEMICONDUCTOR CORP.—See Realtek Semiconductor Corp.; *Int'l*, pg. 6235
REALTEK SEMICONDUCTOR CORP.; *Int'l*, pg. 6234
REALTEK SEMICONDUCTOR (JAPAN) CORP.—See Realtek Semiconductor Corp.; *Int'l*, pg. 6235
REALTEX CONSTRUCTION, LLC—See Realtex Development Corporation; *U.S. Private*, pg. 3369
REALTEX DEVELOPMENT CORPORATION; *U.S. Private*, pg. 3369
REALTEX HOUSING MANAGEMENT, LLC—See Realtex Development Corporation; *U.S. Private*, pg. 3369
REAL TIME COMPANIES, LLC.; *U.S. Private*, pg. 3368
REAL TIME CONSULTANTS, INC.—See Netsurit (Pty) Ltd; *Int'l*, pg. 5215
REAL TIME ENTERPRISES, INC.—See Elbit Systems Limited; *Int'l*, pg. 2344
REAL TIME FORWARDING PTE. LTD.—See Legion Consortium Limited; *Int'l*, pg. 4444
REAL-TIME LABORATORIES, LLC—See Elbit Systems Limited; *Int'l*, pg. 2344
REAL TIME LOGIC, INC.—See Kratos Defense & Security Solutions, Inc.; *U.S. Public*, pg. 1276
REALTIME LOGIC, INC.—See Kratos Defense & Security Solutions, Inc.; *U.S. Public*, pg. 1276
REAL TIME MEASUREMENTS, INC.; *Int'l*, pg. 6233
REALTIME MOBILE PTY. LIMITED—See TPC Consolidated Limited; *Int'l*, pg. 7882
REALTIME NORTH AMERICA, INC.; *U.S. Private*, pg. 3369
REALTIME UTILITY ENGINEERS, INC.—See Quanta Services, Inc.; *U.S. Public*, pg. 1752
REAL-T INC.—See Memory-Tech Corporation; *Int'l*, pg. 4814
RE.ALTO-ENERGY B.V./S.R.L.—See Elia Group SA; *Int'l*, pg. 2360

REALTOR.COM.AU PTY LTD—See Insight Venture Management, LLC; *U.S. Private*, pg. 2089
REALTOR.COM.AU PTY LTD—See Stone Point Capital LLC; *U.S. Private*, pg. 3823
REAL TOUCH FINANCE LTD.; *Int'l*, pg. 6233
REAL TRAVEL LTD—See TUI AG; *Int'l*, pg. 7966
REAL TREASURE INVESTMENT LIMITED—See OCI International Holdings Limited; *Int'l*, pg. 5519
REAL TRENDS, INC.—See HW Media, LLC; *U.S. Private*, pg. 2015
REAL-TREUHAND IMMOBILIEN BAYERN GMBH—See Raiffeisenlandesbank Oberosterreich Aktiengesellschaft; *Int'l*, pg. 6187
REAL-TREUHAND IMMOBILIEN VERTRIEBS GMBH—See Raiffeisenlandesbank Oberosterreich Aktiengesellschaft; *Int'l*, pg. 6187
REAL-TREUHAND MANAGEMENT GMBH—See Raiffeisenlandesbank Oberosterreich Aktiengesellschaft; *Int'l*, pg. 6187
REALTRUCK, INC.; *U.S. Private*, pg. 3369
REALTUR, S. A.—See Melia Hotels International, S.A.; *Int'l*, pg. 4809
REALTY AUSTIN, LLC—See Compass, Inc.; *U.S. Public*, pg. 561
REALTY EXECUTIVES ASSOCIATES INC.; *U.S. Private*, pg. 3369
REALTY EXECUTIVES OF TUCSON, INC.; *U.S. Private*, pg. 3369
REALTY EXECUTIVES, RIVERSIDE; *U.S. Private*, pg. 3369
REALTY HOME MORTGAGE CO. LLC—See Presidential Bank, FSB; *U.S. Private*, pg. 3254
REALTY INCOME CORPORATION; *U.S. Public*, pg. 1768
REALTY INTERNATIONAL ASSOCIATES PTE. LTD.—See Morgan Stanley; *U.S. Public*, pg. 1471
REALTY MANAGEMENT SERVICE INC.—See Morgan Stanley; *U.S. Public*, pg. 1475
REALTY ONE GROUP, INC.; *U.S. Private*, pg. 3369
REALTY PARTNERS LLC; *U.S. Private*, pg. 3369
REALTY RESOURCES CHARTERED; *U.S. Private*, pg. 3369
REALTYSOUTH—See Berkshire Hathaway Inc.; *U.S. Public*, pg. 307
REALTY SUPPORT SERVICES, INC.—See Stone Point Capital LLC; *U.S. Private*, pg. 3819
REALTY SYSTEMS, INC.—See Equity LifeStyle Properties, Inc.; *U.S. Public*, pg. 790
REALTY USA CAPITAL, INC.—See Realty USA LLC; *U.S. Private*, pg. 3369
REALTY USA CNY, INC. - SARATOGA SPRINGS-BROADWAY OFFICE—See Realty USA LLC; *U.S. Private*, pg. 3369
REALTY USA CNY, INC.—See Realty USA LLC; *U.S. Private*, pg. 3369
REALTY USA LLC; *U.S. Private*, pg. 3369
REALTY USA WNY, INC. - PITTSFORD OFFICE—See Realty USA LLC; *U.S. Private*, pg. 3369
REALTY USA WNY, INC.—See Realty USA LLC; *U.S. Private*, pg. 3369
REALTYWORKS INC.; *U.S. Private*, pg. 3369
REALUS INC—See Sega Sammy Holdings, Inc.; *Int'l*, pg. 6681
REAL VALUE, INC.; *U.S. Private*, pg. 3368
REAL VERSICHERUNGS-MAKLER GMBH—See UNIQA Insurance Group AG; *Int'l*, pg. 8058
REAL VERWALTUNGSGESELLSCHAFT MBH—See Advent International Corporation; *U.S. Private*, pg. 97
REAL VERWALTUNGSGESELLSCHAFT MBH—See Centerbridge Partners, L.P.; *U.S. Private*, pg. 813
REALVIEW TV, LLC—See ITC Holding Company, LLC; *U.S. Public*, pg. 2149
REAL & VIRTUAL TECHNOLOGIES SDN BHD—See Digilife Technologies Limited; *Int'l*, pg. 2120
REALVOICE LLC; *U.S. Public*, pg. 3369
REALVOLVE, INC.; *U.S. Private*, pg. 3369
REALWINWIN, INC.; *U.S. Private*, pg. 3369
REALXDATA GMBH—See Moody's Corporation; *U.S. Public*, pg. 1469
REALZYME LLC—See Realco SA; *Int'l*, pg. 6234
REA MAGNET WIRE COMPANY, INC. - AR PLANT—See REA Magnet Wire Company, Inc.; *U.S. Private*, pg. 3365
REA MAGNET WIRE COMPANY, INC. - ASHLAND—See REA Magnet Wire Company, Inc.; *U.S. Private*, pg. 3365
REA MAGNET WIRE COMPANY, INC. - INDIANA PLANT—See REA Magnet Wire Company, Inc.; *U.S. Private*, pg. 3365
REA MAGNET WIRE COMPANY, INC. - NEW HAVEN AVENUE PLANT—See REA Magnet Wire Company, Inc.; *U.S. Private*, pg. 3365
REA MAGNET WIRE COMPANY, INC.; *U.S. Private*, pg. 3365
REAMCO, INC.—See Drilling Tools International Corp.; *U.S. Public*, pg. 688
REAMES & SON CONSTRUCTION CO.; *U.S. Private*, pg. 3370
REAM REAL ESTATE COMPANY KPSC; *Int'l*, pg. 6235
REAM'S FOOD STORES; *U.S. Private*, pg. 3370

CORPORATE AFFILIATIONS

REAMS SPRINKLER SUPPLY COMPANY; *U.S. Private*, pg. 3370
REAPIT LTD—See Accel Partners L.P.; *U.S. Private*, pg. 48
REAPIT LTD—See KKR & Co. Inc.; *U.S. Public*, pg. 1238
REARDEN MINERALS, LLC—See Sitio Royalties Corp.; *U.S. Public*, pg. 1890
REARDON ASSOCIATES INC.; *U.S. Private*, pg. 3370
REARDON OFFICE EQUIPMENT, INC.—See Loffler Companies, Inc.; *U.S. Private*, pg. 2480
R.E.A. SERVICES LIMITED—See R.E.A Holdings plc; *Int'l*, pg. 6170
REASORS INC.; *U.S. Private*, pg. 3370
REASSURE GROUP PLC—See Phoenix Group Holdings PLC; *Int'l*, pg. 5851
REASSURE LIFE LIMITED—See Phoenix Group Holdings PLC; *Int'l*, pg. 5851
REASSURE LIMITED—See Phoenix Group Holdings PLC; *Int'l*, pg. 5851
REASSURE, LLC—See PT Sinar Mas Group; *Int'l*, pg. 6073
REATA PHARMACEUTICALS, INC.—See Biogen Inc.; *U.S. Public*, pg. 337
REATILE TIMRITE (PTY) LTD—See Thebe Investment Corporation; *Int'l*, pg. 7706
THE REAVES AGENCY, LLC—See New Mountain Capital, LLC; *U.S. Private*, pg. 2901
REA VIPINGO PLANTATIONS LIMITED; *Int'l*, pg. 6230
REBA ORGANIZACJA ODZYSKU S.A.—See Edgewell Personal Care Company; *U.S. Public*, pg. 718
REBASE CONSULTING OY—See Gofore PLC; *Int'l*, pg. 3022
REBBEC MOTOR CO.; *U.S. Private*, pg. 3370
REBBIZ CO LTD—See Frontier Digital Ventures Limited; *Int'l*, pg. 2795
REBBL INC.; *U.S. Private*, pg. 3370
REBECCA MINKOFF LLC; *U.S. Private*, pg. 3370
REBEKAH CHILDREN'S SERVICES.; *U.S. Private*, pg. 3370
REBEKAH REHAB & EXTENDED CARE CENTER; *U.S. Private*, pg. 3370
REBELLION PHOTONICS, INC.—See Honeywell International Inc.; *U.S. Public*, pg. 1051
REBEL METAL FABRICATORS LTD—See McCoy Global Inc.; *Int'l*, pg. 4757
REBELMOUSE, INC.; *U.S. Private*, pg. 3370
REBEL OIL COMPANY, INC.; *U.S. Private*, pg. 3370
REBEL SPORT LIMITED—See Briscoe Group Limited; *Int'l*, pg. 1164
REBEL WINE CO. LLC—See Trinchero Family Estates; *U.S. Private*, pg. 4232
REBER SCHINDLER HEIS A/S—See Schindler Holding AG; *Int'l*, pg. 6619
REBFOAM S.R.L.—See Recticel S.A.; *Int'l*, pg. 6241
REBHAN FPS KUNSTSTOFF-VERPACKUNGEN GMBH—See Certina Holding AG; *Int'l*, pg. 1423
REBITA INC.—See Keio Corporation; *Int'l*, pg. 4118
REBO INC.; *U.S. Private*, pg. 3370
REBOLUCION, LLC; *U.S. Private*, pg. 3370
REBOOT MARKETING LLC; *U.S. Private*, pg. 3370
REBOOT NETWORKS LLC—See Trinity Hunt Management, L.P.; *U.S. Private*, pg. 4234
REBOOT TECHNOLOGY SERVICES AND CAPITECH LIMITED—See NEC Capital Solutions Limited; *Int'l*, pg. 5183
REBOPLASTIC GMBH & CO. KG—See INDUS Holding AG; *Int'l*, pg. 3664
REBORN CABINETS, INC.—See Audax Group, Limited Partnership; *U.S. Private*, pg. 389
REBORN COFFEE, INC.; *U.S. Public*, pg. 1769
REBORN PRODUCTS CO., INC.—See Kinderhook Industries, LLC; *U.S. Private*, pg. 2307
REBOSIS PROPERTY FUND LTD.; *Int'l*, pg. 6235
REBOUL SAS—See AptarGroup, Inc.; *U.S. Public*, pg. 175
REBOUND THERAPEUTICS CORPORATION—See Integra LifeSciences Holdings Corporation; *U.S. Public*, pg. 1136
REBRISA SA; *Int'l*, pg. 6235
REBUD OCCUPATIONAL & PHYSICAL THERAPY, LIMITED PARTNERSHIP—See U.S. Physical Therapy, Inc.; *U.S. Public*, pg. 2215
REBUILDERS AUTOMOTIVE SUPPLY CO. INC.; *U.S. Private*, pg. 3370
REBUILD NORTHWEST FLORIDA, INC.; *U.S. Private*, pg. 3370
REBUILD RECRUITMENT SERVICES LTD—See The Rethink Group Limited; *Int'l*, pg. 7678
R.E. BULLOCK & COMPANY; *U.S. Private*, pg. 3335
REBUS HOLDINGS INC.; *U.S. Public*, pg. 1769
RECA AG—See Wurth Verwaltungsgesellschaft mbH; *Int'l*, pg. 8507
RECAB AB—See Addtech AB; *Int'l*, pg. 135
RECA BELUX S.A./N.V.—See Wurth Verwaltungsgesellschaft mbH; *Int'l*, pg. 8507
RECA BUCURESTI S.R.L.—See Wurth Verwaltungsgesellschaft mbH; *Int'l*, pg. 8507
RECAB UK LTD.—See Addtech AB; *Int'l*, pg. 135
RECA BULGARIA E.O.O.D.—See Wurth Verwaltungsgesellschaft mbH; *Int'l*, pg. 8507

COMPANY NAME INDEX

RECA D.O.O., BEOGRAD—See Wurth Verwaltungsgesellschaft mbH; *Int'l*, pg. 8507
RECA D.O.O., SARAJEVO—See Wurth Verwaltungsgesellschaft mbH; *Int'l*, pg. 8507
RECA D.O.O.—See Wurth Verwaltungsgesellschaft mbH; *Int'l*, pg. 8507
RECA D.O.O.—See Wurth Verwaltungsgesellschaft mbH; *Int'l*, pg. 8507
REC ADVANCED SILICON MATERIALS LLC—See REC Silicon ASA; *Int'l*, pg. 6235
RECA FRANCE SAS—See Wurth Verwaltungsgesellschaft mbH; *Int'l*, pg. 8507
RECA HISPANIA, S.A.U.—See Wurth Verwaltungsgesellschaft mbH; *Int'l*, pg. 8507
RECAIR B.V.—See Zehnder Group AG; *Int'l*, pg. 8630
RECA KFT.—See Wurth Verwaltungsgesellschaft mbH; *Int'l*, pg. 8507
RECAMBIA—See Berge y Cia SA; *Int'l*, pg. 979
REC AMERICAS, LLC—See China National Chemical Corporation; *Int'l*, pg. 1527
RECAN D.O.O.—See Ball Corporation; *U.S. Public*, pg. 267
RECAN ORGANIZACJA ODZYSKU S.A.—See Ball Corporation; *U.S. Public*, pg. 268
RECA NORM GMBH & CO. KG—See Wurth Verwaltungsgesellschaft mbH; *Int'l*, pg. 8507
RECA POLSKA SPOLKA Z O.O.—See Wurth Verwaltungsgesellschaft mbH; *Int'l*, pg. 8507
RECARO AIRCRAFT SEATING GMBH & CO.—See Putsch GmbH & Co. KG; *Int'l*, pg. 6124
RECARO AIRCRAFT SEATING INC.—See Putsch GmbH & Co. KG; *Int'l*, pg. 6124
RECARO AUTOMOTIVE SEATING GMBH—See Adient plc; *Int'l*, pg. 148
RECARO GMBH & CO.—See Putsch GmbH & Co. KG; *Int'l*, pg. 6124
RECARO NORTH AMERICA, INC.—See Adient plc; *Int'l*, pg. 148
R.E. CARROLL INC.; *U.S. Private*, pg. 3335
RECA (SHANGHAI) INTERNATIONAL TRADING CO., LTD.—See Wurth Verwaltungsgesellschaft mbH; *Int'l*, pg. 8507
RECA SLOVENSKO S.R.O.—See Wurth Verwaltungsgesellschaft mbH; *Int'l*, pg. 8507
RECA SPOL. S R. O.—See Wurth Verwaltungsgesellschaft mbH; *Int'l*, pg. 8507
RECAST SOFTWARE INC.; *U.S. Private*, pg. 3370
RECAT GMBH—See Elemental Holding S.A.; *Int'l*, pg. 2358
RECA-UK LTD.—See Wurth Verwaltungsgesellschaft mbH; *Int'l*, pg. 8507
RECA UNION FRANCE SARL—See Wurth Verwaltungsgesellschaft mbH; *Int'l*, pg. 8507
RECA VERWALTUNGSGESELLSCHAFT GMBH—See Wurth Verwaltungsgesellschaft mbH; *Int'l*, pg. 8506
REC BOAT HOLDINGS, LLC—See Beneteau S.A; *Int'l*, pg. 972
RECCE PHARMACEUTICALS LTD; *Int'l*, pg. 6235
RECEIVABLES MANAGEMENT (NZ) LIMITED—See Collection House Limited; *Int'l*, pg. 1699
RECEIVABLES MANAGEMENT PARTNERS, LLC—See Thompson Street Capital Manager LLC; *U.S. Private*, pg. 4161
RECEIVABLE SOLUTIONS SPECIALIST, INC.—See Kriya Capital, LLC; *U.S. Private*, pg. 2352
RECEIVABLES OUTSOURCING, LLC—See Cognizant Technology Solutions Corporation; *U.S. Public*, pg. 523
RECELLULAR INCORPORATED; *U.S. Private*, pg. 3370
RECEM S.A.—See Heidelberg Materials AG; *Int'l*, pg. 3319
REC ENGINEERING COMPANY LIMITED—See Yau Lee Holdings Limited; *Int'l*, pg. 8572
REC ENGINEERING CONTRACTING COMPANY LIMITED—See Yau Lee Holdings Limited; *Int'l*, pg. 8572
RECEPTEL NV—See Recruit Holdings Co., Ltd.; *Int'l*, pg. 6240
RECEPTOR BIOLOGIX, INC.—See Les Laboratoires Servier SAS; *Int'l*, pg. 4468
RECEPTOS SERVICES LLC—See Bristol-Myers Squibb Company; *U.S. Public*, pg. 386
REC EQUIPMENT CORP.—See The Rados Companies; *U.S. Private*, pg. 4102
REC GREEN ENERGY SOLUTIONS COMPANY LIMITED—See Yau Lee Holdings Limited; *Int'l*, pg. 8572
R.E. CHAIX & ASSOCIATES INSURANCE BROKERS, INC.; *U.S. Private*, pg. 3335
RECHARGE ACQUISITION CORP.; *U.S. Public*, pg. 1769
RECHARGE METALS LIMITED; *Int'l*, pg. 6235
RECHARGE RESOURCES LTD.; *Int'l*, pg. 6235
RECHEIO CASH & CARRY S.A.—See Jeronimo Martins SGPS SA; *Int'l*, pg. 3931
RECHEIO-DISTRIBUICAO, LDA.—See Jeronimo Martins SGPS SA; *Int'l*, pg. 3931
RECHI PRECISION CO., LTD.; *Int'l*, pg. 6235
RECHI PRECISION(JIUJIANG) ELECTRIC MACHINERY CO., LTD.—See Rechi Precision Co., Ltd.; *Int'l*, pg. 6235
RECHI PRECISION MECHANISM (HUIZHOU) CO., LTD.—See Rechi Precision Co., Ltd.; *Int'l*, pg. 6235
RECHI PRECISION (QINGDAO) ELECTRIC MACHINERY CO., LTD.—See Rechi Precision Co., Ltd.; *Int'l*, pg. 6235
RECHI REFRIGERATION (DONGGUAN) CO., LTD.—See China Steel Corporation; *Int'l*, pg. 1556
RECHTIEN INTERNATIONAL TRUCKS; *U.S. Private*, pg. 3370
RECHTSSCHUTZ UNION VERSICHERUNGS-AG—See Alte Leipziger Versicherung AG; *Int'l*, pg. 388
RECICLAJES ECOLOGICOS MARITIMOS, S.A. DE C.V.—See Promotora Ambiental S.A.B de C.V.; *Int'l*, pg. 5994
RE-CICLAR S.A.—See Embotelladora Andina S.A.; *Int'l*, pg. 2375
RECIPE UNLIMITED CORPORATION—See Fairfax Financial Holdings Limited; *Int'l*, pg. 2608
RECIPHARM AB; *Int'l*, pg. 6235
RECIPHARM FONTAINE S.A.S.—See Recipharm AB; *Int'l*, pg. 6236
RECIPHARM HOGANAS AB—See Blue Wolf Capital Partners LLC; *U.S. Private*, pg. 595
RECIPHARM HOLDINGS LIMITED—See Recipharm AB; *Int'l*, pg. 6236
RECIPHARM ISRAEL LTD.—See Recipharm AB; *Int'l*, pg. 6236
RECIPHARM KARLSKOGA AB—See Blue Wolf Capital Partners LLC; *U.S. Private*, pg. 595
RECIPHARM LABORATORIES, INC.—See Recipharm AB; *Int'l*, pg. 6236
RECIPHARM LEGANES S.L.U.—See Recipharm AB; *Int'l*, pg. 6236
RECIPHARM LTD.—See Recipharm AB; *Int'l*, pg. 6236
RECIPHARM OT CHEMISTRY AB—See Blue Wolf Capital Partners LLC; *U.S. Private*, pg. 595
RECIPHARM PARETS SL—See Blue Wolf Capital Partners LLC; *U.S. Private*, pg. 595
RECIPHARM PESSAC S.A.S.—See Blue Wolf Capital Partners LLC; *U.S. Private*, pg. 595
RECIPHARM PHARMACEUTICAL DEVELOPMENT AB—See Blue Wolf Capital Partners LLC; *U.S. Private*, pg. 595
RECIPHARM PHARMASERVICES PVT. LTD.—See Recipharm AB; *Int'l*, pg. 6236
RECIPHARM STOCKHOLM AB—See Recipharm AB; *Int'l*, pg. 6236
RECIPHARM STRANGNAS AB—See Blue Wolf Capital Partners LLC; *U.S. Private*, pg. 595
RECIPHARM UPPSALA AB—See Clinical Trial Consultants AB; *Int'l*, pg. 1660
RECIPHARM VENTURE FUND AB—See Recipharm AB; *Int'l*, pg. 6236
RECIPROCAL LABS CORPORATION—See ResMed Inc.; *U.S. Public*, pg. 1790
RECIPROCAL RESULTS; *U.S. Private*, pg. 3370
RECKER & BOERGER INC.; *U.S. Private*, pg. 3370
RECKITT BENCKISER ARABIA FZE—See Reckitt Benckiser Group plc; *Int'l*, pg. 6237
RECKITT BENCKISER ARGENTINA SA—See Reckitt Benckiser Group plc; *Int'l*, pg. 6237
RECKITT BENCKISER (AUSTRALIA) PTY. LTD.—See Reckitt Benckiser Group plc; *Int'l*, pg. 6236
RECKITT BENCKISER AUSTRIA GMBH—See Reckitt Benckiser Group plc; *Int'l*, pg. 6237
RECKITT BENCKISER (BELGIUM) SA/NV—See Reckitt Benckiser Group plc; *Int'l*, pg. 6236
RECKITT BENCKISER (BRAZIL) LTDA.—See Reckitt Benckiser Group plc; *Int'l*, pg. 6236
RECKITT BENCKISER BULGARIA EOOD—See Reckitt Benckiser Group plc; *Int'l*, pg. 6236
RECKITT BENCKISER (CANADA) INC.—See Reckitt Benckiser Group plc; *Int'l*, pg. 6237
RECKITT BENCKISER (CENTROAMERICA) SA—See Reckitt Benckiser Group plc; *Int'l*, pg. 6236
RECKITT BENCKISER CHILE SA—See Reckitt Benckiser Group plc; *Int'l*, pg. 6237
RECKITT BENCKISER COLOMBIA SA—See Reckitt Benckiser Group plc; *Int'l*, pg. 6237
RECKITT BENCKISER (CZECH REPUBLIC) SPOL S. R. O.—See Reckitt Benckiser Group plc; *Int'l*, pg. 6236
RECKITT BENCKISER DEUTSCHLAND GMBH—See Reckitt Benckiser Group plc; *Int'l*, pg. 6237
RECKITT BENCKISER D.O.O—See Reckitt Benckiser Group plc; *Int'l*, pg. 6237
RECKITT BENCKISER (EGYPT) LIMITED—See Reckitt Benckiser Group plc; *Int'l*, pg. 6236
RECKITT BENCKISER ESPANA SL—See Reckitt Benckiser Group plc; *Int'l*, pg. 6237
RECKITT BENCKISER FRANCE—See Reckitt Benckiser Group plc; *Int'l*, pg. 6237
RECKITT BENCKISER GROUP PLC; *Int'l*, pg. 6236
RECKITT BENCKISER HEALTHCARE (ITALIA) SPA—See Reckitt Benckiser Group plc; *Int'l*, pg. 6237
RECKITT BENCKISER HEALTHCARE (UK) LTD.—See Reckitt Benckiser Group plc; *Int'l*, pg. 6237
RECKITT BENCKISER HELLAS CHEMICALS SA—See Reckitt Benckiser Group plc; *Int'l*, pg. 6237
RECKITT BENCKISER HONG KONG LIMITED—See Reckitt Benckiser Group plc; *Int'l*, pg. 6237
RECKITT BENCKISER HOUSEHOLD & HEALTHCARE UKRAINE LLC—See Reckitt Benckiser Group plc; *Int'l*, pg. 6237
RECKITT BENCKISER HOUSEHOLD PRODUCTS (CHINA) COMPANY LIMITED—See Reckitt Benckiser Group plc; *Int'l*, pg. 6237
RECKITT BENCKISER (HUNGARY) KFT.—See Reckitt Benckiser Group plc; *Int'l*, pg. 6236
RECKITT BENCKISER INC.—See Reckitt Benckiser Group plc; *Int'l*, pg. 6237
RECKITT BENCKISER (INDIA) LTD.—See Reckitt Benckiser Group plc; *Int'l*, pg. 6236
RECKITT BENCKISER IRELAND LIMITED—See Reckitt Benckiser Group plc; *Int'l*, pg. 6237
RECKITT BENCKISER ITALIA SPA—See Reckitt Benckiser Group plc; *Int'l*, pg. 6237
RECKITT BENCKISER JAPAN LIMITED—See Reckitt Benckiser Group plc; *Int'l*, pg. 6237
RECKITT BENCKISER (LANKA) LIMITED—See Reckitt Benckiser Group plc; *Int'l*, pg. 6236
RECKITT BENCKISER (LATVIA) SIA—See Reckitt Benckiser Group plc; *Int'l*, pg. 6236
RECKITT BENCKISER (MALAYSIA) SDN BHD—See Reckitt Benckiser Group plc; *Int'l*, pg. 6236
RECKITT BENCKISER MEXICO, SA DE CV—See Reckitt Benckiser Group plc; *Int'l*, pg. 6237
RECKITT BENCKISER (NEAR EAST) LIMITED—See Reckitt Benckiser Group plc; *Int'l*, pg. 6236
RECKITT BENCKISER (NEW ZEALAND) LIMITED—See Reckitt Benckiser Group plc; *Int'l*, pg. 6236
RECKITT BENCKISER NIGERIA LIMITED—See Reckitt Benckiser Group plc; *Int'l*, pg. 6237
RECKITT BENCKISER NORDIC A/S—See Reckitt Benckiser Group plc; *Int'l*, pg. 6237
RECKITT BENCKISER PAKISTAN LIMITED—See Reckitt Benckiser Group plc; *Int'l*, pg. 6236
RECKITT BENCKISER (PLANET D.O.O)—See Reckitt Benckiser Group plc; *Int'l*, pg. 6236
RECKITT BENCKISER PLC—See Reckitt Benckiser Group plc; *Int'l*, pg. 6237
RECKITT BENCKISER POLAND SA—See Reckitt Benckiser Group plc; *Int'l*, pg. 6237
RECKITT BENCKISER (PORTUGAL) SA—See Reckitt Benckiser Group plc; *Int'l*, pg. 6236
RECKITT BENCKISER (ROMANIA) SRL—See Reckitt Benckiser Group plc; *Int'l*, pg. 6236
RECKITT BENCKISER SERVICES (KENYA) LIMITED—See Reckitt Benckiser Group plc; *Int'l*, pg. 6237
RECKITT BENCKISER (SINGAPORE) PTE LIMITED—See Reckitt Benckiser Group plc; *Int'l*, pg. 6236
RECKITT BENCKISER (SLOVAK REPUBLIC) SPOL. S. R. O.—See Reckitt Benckiser Group plc; *Int'l*, pg. 6236
RECKITT BENCKISER SOUTH AFRICA (PTY) LIMITED—See Reckitt Benckiser Group plc; *Int'l*, pg. 6237
RECKITT BENCKISER (SWITZERLAND) AG—See Reckitt Benckiser Group plc; *Int'l*, pg. 6236
RECKITT BENCKISER TAIWAN LIMITED—See Reckitt Benckiser Group plc; *Int'l*, pg. 6237
RECKITT BENCKISER (TURKEY) A.S.—See Reckitt Benckiser Group plc; *Int'l*, pg. 6237
RECKITT BENCKISER VENEZUELA SA—See Reckitt Benckiser Group plc; *Int'l*, pg. 6237
RECKITT BENCKISER (ZAMBIA) LTD.—See Reckitt Benckiser Group plc; *Int'l*, pg. 6237
RECKITT BENCKISER (ZIMBABWE) PVT. LTD.—See Reckitt Benckiser Group plc; *Int'l*, pg. 6237
RECKON; *Int'l*, pg. 6237
RECKON NEW ZEALAND PTY LIMITED—See Reckon Limited; *Int'l*, pg. 6237
RECKSON OPERATING PARTNERSHIP, L.P.—See SL Green Realty Corp.; *U.S. Public*, pg. 1894
RECLAIMS GLOBAL LIMITED; *Int'l*, pg. 6237
RECLAMATION, LLC—See Peckham Industries, Inc.; *U.S. Private*, pg. 3127
RECLAMATION TECHNOLOGIES, INC.—See A-Gas Limited; *Int'l*, pg. 19
RECLAMATION TECHNOLOGIES, INC.—See BC Partners LLP; *Int'l*, pg. 923
RECLAMATION TECHNOLOGIES, INC.—See EQT AB; *Int'l*, pg. 2482
RECLAMATION TECHNOLOGIES USA, LLC—See BC Partners LLP; *Int'l*, pg. 923
RECLAMATION TECHNOLOGIES USA, LLC—See EQT AB; *Int'l*, pg. 2482
RECLAY CESKA REPUBLIKA S.R.O.—See Reclay Holding GmbH; *Int'l*, pg. 6238
RECLAY GMBH—See Reclay Holding GmbH; *Int'l*, pg. 6238
RECLAY HOLDING GMBH; *Int'l*, pg. 6237
RECLAY OSTERREICH GMBH—See Reclay Holding GmbH; *Int'l*, pg. 6238
RECLAY SLOVAKIA, S.R.O.—See Reclay Holding GmbH; *Int'l*, pg. 6238
RECLAY STEWARDEDGE INC.—See Reclay Holding GmbH; *Int'l*, pg. 6238

RECLAY HOLDING GMBH

RECLAY UFH GMBH—See Reclay Holding GmbH; *Int'l*, pg. 6238
RECLAY VFW GMBH—See Reclay Holding GmbH; *Int'l*, pg. 6238
REC LIMITED—See Power Finance Corporation Limited; *Int'l*, pg. 5945
REC NARODA A.D.; *Int'l*, pg. 6235
RECO BIOTEK CO., LTD.—See General Interface Solution (GIS) Holding Ltd.; *Int'l*, pg. 2918
RECOCHEM (B.C.) INC.—See Recochem Inc.; *Int'l*, pg. 6238
RECOCHEM CENTRAL DISTRICT CONSUMER DIVISION—See Recochem Inc.; *Int'l*, pg. 6238
RECOCHEM ENGINE COOLANTS (TIANJIN) CO., LTD.—See Recochem Inc.; *Int'l*, pg. 6238
RECOCHEM GROUP, INC.—See CapVest Limited; *Int'l*, pg. 1318
RECOCHEM INC.; *Int'l*, pg. 6238
RECOCHEM (INDIA) PRIVATE LIMITED—See Recochem Inc.; *Int'l*, pg. 6238
RECOCHEM WESTERN DISTRICT CONSUMER DIVISION—See Recochem Inc.; *Int'l*, pg. 6238
RECOCHEM WESTERN DISTRICT CONSUMER DIVISION—See Recochem Inc.; *Int'l*, pg. 6238
RECO CONSTRUCTORS, INC.; *U.S. Private*, pg. 3371
RECO DECORATION GROUP INC.—See Reco International Group Inc.; *Int'l*, pg. 6238
RECO EQUIPMENT INC.; *U.S. Private*, pg. 3371
RECOFARMA ILAC VE HAMMADDELERI SANAYI VE TICARET L.S.—See Recordati S.p.A.; *Int'l*, pg. 6239
RECOF CORPORATION—See M&A Capital Partners Co., Ltd.; *Int'l*, pg. 4610
RECOGIDA DE ACEITES Y GRASAS MARESME, S.L.U.—See Cie Automotive S.A.; *Int'l*, pg. 1605
RECOGNISE BANK LIMITED—See City of London Group PLC; *Int'l*, pg. 1627
RECOGNITION PUBLIC RELATIONS—See Omnicom Group Inc.; *U.S. Public*, pg. 1578
RECOGNITION SYSTEMS INC.; *U.S. Private*, pg. 3371
RECO INTERNATIONAL GROUP INC.; *Int'l*, pg. 6238
RECOLIFT SA—See KONE Oyj; *Int'l*, pg. 4250
RECO, LLC—See WESCO International, Inc.; *U.S. Public*, pg. 2352
RECOLOGY ASHLAND—See Arakelian Enterprises, Inc.; *U.S. Private*, pg. 307
RECOLOGY CLEANSCAPES, INC.—See Arakelian Enterprises, Inc.; *U.S. Private*, pg. 307
RECOLOGY DEL NORTE, INC.—See Arakelian Enterprises, Inc.; *U.S. Private*, pg. 307
RECOLOGY ENVIRONMENTAL SOLUTIONS INC.—See Arakelian Enterprises, Inc.; *U.S. Private*, pg. 307
RECOLOGY HAY ROAD—See Arakelian Enterprises, Inc.; *U.S. Private*, pg. 307
RECOLOGY INC.—See Arakelian Enterprises, Inc.; *U.S. Private*, pg. 307
RECOLOGY MOUNTAIN VIEW—See Arakelian Enterprises, Inc.; *U.S. Private*, pg. 307
RECOLOGY OSTROM ROAD—See Arakelian Enterprises, Inc.; *U.S. Private*, pg. 307
RECOLOGY PORTLAND INC.—See Arakelian Enterprises, Inc.; *U.S. Private*, pg. 307
RECOLOGY SAN FRANCISCO—See Arakelian Enterprises, Inc.; *U.S. Private*, pg. 307
RECOLOGY VACAVILLE SOLANO—See Arakelian Enterprises, Inc.; *U.S. Private*, pg. 307
RECOLOGY YUBA-SUTTER—See Arakelian Enterprises, Inc.; *U.S. Private*, pg. 307
RECOLTE, S.A.U.—See Teixeira Duarte SA; *Int'l*, pg. 7525
RECOMM CO. LTD.; *Int'l*, pg. 6238
RECOMMERCE HOLDINGS, LLC; *U.S. Private*, pg. 3371
RECOMMIND GMBH—See Open Text Corporation; *Int'l*, pg. 5598
RECOMMIND, INC.—See Open Text Corporation; *Int'l*, pg. 5598
RE COMMUNITY HOLDINGS II, INC.; *U.S. Private*, pg. 3364
RECONCRAFT; *U.S. Private*, pg. 3371
RECONDITIONED SYSTEMS, INC.; *U.S. Public*, pg. 1769
RECONDO TECHNOLOGY, INC.—See Canada Pension Plan Investment Board; *Int'l*, pg. 1282
RECONDO TECHNOLOGY, INC.—See EQT AB; *Int'l*, pg. 2481
RECON DRILLING S.A.C.—See Geodrill Limited; *Int'l*, pg. 2933
RECON ENGINEERING & CONSTRUCTION, INC.; *U.S. Private*, pg. 3371
RECON ENVIRONMENTAL, INC.; *U.S. Private*, pg. 3371
RECONFIGURATION BV—See BNP Paribas SA; *Int'l*, pg. 1092
RECON LOGISTICS; *U.S. Private*, pg. 3371
RECONNAISSANCE ENERGY AFRICA LTD.; *Int'l*, pg. 6238
RECONOMY (UK) LTD; *Int'l*, pg. 6238
RECON PROPELLER & ENGINEERING PTE. LTD.—See Mencast Holdings Ltd.; *Int'l*, pg. 4815
RECON REFRACTORY & CONSTRUCTION INC.; *U.S. Private*, pg. 3371
RECONSERVE, INC.—See ReConserve, Inc.; *U.S. Private*, pg. 3371

RECONSERVE, INC.—See ReConserve, Inc.; *U.S. Private*, pg. 3371
RECONSERVE, INC.; *U.S. Private*, pg. 3371
RECONSERVE, INC.—See ReConserve, Inc.; *U.S. Private*, pg. 3371
RECONSERVE, INC.—See ReConserve, Inc.; *U.S. Private*, pg. 3371
RECONSERVE OF CALIFORNIA-LOS ANGELES, INC.—See ReConserve, Inc.; *U.S. Private*, pg. 3371
RECONSERVE OF CALIFORNIA-STOCKTON, INC.—See ReConserve, Inc.; *U.S. Private*, pg. 3371
RECONSERVE OF MARYLAND—See ReConserve, Inc.; *U.S. Private*, pg. 3371
RECONSTRUCTION EXPERTS INC.—See Johns Lyng Group Limited; *Int'l*, pg. 3984
RECON TECHNOLOGY, LTD.; *Int'l*, pg. 6238
RECON TRUST COMPANY, N.A.—See Bank of America Corporation; *U.S. Public*, pg. 271
RECON UTILITY SEARCH L.P.—See Mullen Group Ltd.; *Int'l*, pg. 5080
RECOOP TOUR A.S.—See Warimpex Finanz- und Beteiligungs AG; *Int'l*, pg. 8345
RECOPART AB—See LKQ Corporation; *U.S. Public*, pg. 1336
RECOPRINT DOS HERMANAS S.L.U.—See RCS MediaGroup S.p.A.; *Int'l*, pg. 6229
RECOPRINT RABADE S.L.U.—See RCS MediaGroup S.p.A.; *Int'l*, pg. 6229
RECOPRINT SAGUNTO S.L.U.—See RCS MediaGroup S.p.A.; *Int'l*, pg. 6229
RECORD AJTO KFT—See ASSA ABLOY AB; *Int'l*, pg. 638
RECORDATI AB—See Recordati S.p.A.; *Int'l*, pg. 6239
RECORDATI AG—See Recordati S.p.A.; *Int'l*, pg. 6239
RECORDATI BULGARIA LTD.—See Recordati S.p.A.; *Int'l*, pg. 6239
RECORDATI B.V.—See Recordati S.p.A.; *Int'l*, pg. 6239
RECORDATI ESPANA S.L.—See Recordati S.p.A.; *Int'l*, pg. 6239
RECORDATI HELLAS PHARMACEUTICALS S.A.—See Recordati S.p.A.; *Int'l*, pg. 6239
RECORDATI ILAC SANAYI VE TICARET A.S.—See Recordati S.p.A.; *Int'l*, pg. 6239
RECORDATI IRELAND LTD.—See Recordati S.p.A.; *Int'l*, pg. 6239
RECORDATI PHARMACEUTICAL CHEMICALS DIVISION—See Recordati S.p.A.; *Int'l*, pg. 6239
RECORDATI PHARMACEUTICAL CHEMICALS PRODUCTIONS—See Recordati S.p.A.; *Int'l*, pg. 6239
RECORDATI PHARMACEUTICALS LTD.—See Recordati S.p.A.; *Int'l*, pg. 6239
RECORDATI PHARMA GMBH—See Recordati S.p.A.; *Int'l*, pg. 6239
RECORDATI POLSKA SP. Z O.O.—See Recordati S.p.A.; *Int'l*, pg. 6239
RECORDATI RARE DISEASES AUSTRALIA PTY. LTD.—See Recordati S.p.A.; *Int'l*, pg. 6239
RECORDATI RARE DISEASES CANADA INC.—See Recordati S.p.A.; *Int'l*, pg. 6239
RECORDATI RARE DISEASES COLOMBIA S.A.S—See Recordati S.p.A.; *Int'l*, pg. 6239
RECORDATI RARE DISEASES COMERCIO DE MEDICAMENTOS LTDA.—See Recordati S.p.A.; *Int'l*, pg. 6239
RECORDATI RARE DISEASES FZCO—See Recordati S.p.A.; *Int'l*, pg. 6239
RECORDATI RARE DISEASES INC.—See Recordati S.p.A.; *Int'l*, pg. 6239
RECORDATI RARE DISEASES ITALY S.R.L.—See Recordati S.p.A.; *Int'l*, pg. 6239
RECORDATI RARE DISEASES JAPAN K.K.—See Recordati S.p.A.; *Int'l*, pg. 6239
RECORDATI RARE DISEASES MIDDLE EAST FZ-LLC—See Recordati S.p.A.; *Int'l*, pg. 6239
RECORDATI RARE DISEASES S.A DE C.V.—See Recordati S.p.A.; *Int'l*, pg. 6239
RECORDATI RARE DISEASES S.A.R.L.—See Recordati S.p.A.; *Int'l*, pg. 6239
RECORDATI RARE DISEASES SPAIN S.L.—See Recordati S.p.A.; *Int'l*, pg. 6239
RECORDATI RARE DISEASES UK LIMITED—See Recordati S.p.A.; *Int'l*, pg. 6239
RECORDATI ROMANIA S.R.L.—See Recordati S.p.A.; *Int'l*, pg. 6240
RECORDATI S.P.A.; *Int'l*, pg. 6238
RECORDATI UKRAINE LLC—See Recordati S.p.A.; *Int'l*, pg. 6240
RECORD AUSTRIA GMBH—See ASSA ABLOY AB; *Int'l*, pg. 638
RECORD AUTOMATIC DOORS (AUSTRALIA) PTY. LTD.—See ASSA ABLOY AB; *Int'l*, pg. 638
RECORD AUTOMATIC DOORS (CANADA), INC.—See ASSA ABLOY AB; *Int'l*, pg. 638
RECORD AUTOMATIC DOOR (SHANGHAI) CO., LTD.—See ASSA ABLOY AB; *Int'l*, pg. 638
RECORD AUTOMATIC DOORS (M) SDN BHD—See ASSA ABLOY AB; *Int'l*, pg. 638
RECORD AUTOMATISCHE DEUREN B.V.—See ASSA ABLOY AB; *Int'l*, pg. 638
RECORD AVTOMATSKA VRATA D.O.O.—See ASSA ABLOY AB; *Int'l*, pg. 638

CORPORATE AFFILIATIONS

RECORD BANK N.V.—See ING Groep N.V.; *Int'l*, pg. 3700
RECORD BMT AS—See ASSA ABLOY AB; *Int'l*, pg. 638
RECORD BRANDBEVEILIGING B.V.—See London Security PLC; *Int'l*, pg. 4547
RECORD CONFECCIONES IMPORTACIONES LTDA.—See Lectra SA; *Int'l*, pg. 4438
RECORD CURRENCY MANAGEMENT LIMITED—See Record plc; *Int'l*, pg. 6238
RECORD DORRAUTOMATIK SWEDEN AB—See ASSA ABLOY AB; *Int'l*, pg. 638
RECORD DRZWI AUTOMATYCZNE SP.ZO.O—See ASSA ABLOY AB; *Int'l*, pg. 638
RECORDED BOOKS, INC.—See Shamrock Holdings, Inc.; *U.S. Private*, pg. 3624
RECORD ELEMAT, S.A.—See ASSA ABLOY AB; *Int'l*, pg. 638
RECORDER PUBLISHING CO.; *U.S. Private*, pg. 3371
RECORD GROUP SERVICES LIMITED—See Record plc; *Int'l*, pg. 6238
RECORD HOLDING NEDERLAND B.V.—See ASSA ABLOY AB; *Int'l*, pg. 638
RECORD INDIANA—See ASSA ABLOY AB; *Int'l*, pg. 638
RECORD INDUSTRY—See ASSA ABLOY AB; *Int'l*, pg. 638
RECORD INTERNATIONAL LTD.—See ASSA ABLOY AB; *Int'l*, pg. 638
THE RECORD-JOURNAL PUBLISHING COMPANY; *U.S. Private*, pg. 4103
RECORDKEEPER RECORDS MANAGEMENT SYSTEMS LTD.—See GRM Information Management Services; *U.S. Private*, pg. 1791
RECORD NORTH AMERICA INC.—See ASSA ABLOY AB; *Int'l*, pg. 638
RECORD PLC; *Int'l*, pg. 6238
RECORD PORTES AUTOMATIQUES S.A—See ASSA ABLOY AB; *Int'l*, pg. 638
RECORD PUBLISHING COMPANY—See Gannett Co., Inc.; *U.S. Public*, pg. 904
RECORD PUERTAS AUTOMATICAS SA—See ASSA ABLOY AB; *Int'l*, pg. 638
RECORD S.A.; *Int'l*, pg. 6238
THE RECORD—See Gannett Co., Inc.; *U.S. Public*, pg. 904
THE RECORD—See Torstar Corporation; *Int'l*, pg. 7831
RECORD STREET BREWING COMPANY—See UPD Holding Corp.; *U.S. Public*, pg. 2264
RECORD SVERIGE AB—See ASSA ABLOY AB; *Int'l*, pg. 638
RECORDTRAK INC.; *U.S. Private*, pg. 3371
RECORD TURAUTOMATION AG—See ASSA ABLOY AB; *Int'l*, pg. 638
RECORD TURAUTOMATION GMBH—See ASSA ABLOY AB; *Int'l*, pg. 638
RECORD UK LTD—See ASSA ABLOY AB; *Int'l*, pg. 638
RECORD - USA INC—See ASSA ABLOY AB; *Int'l*, pg. 638
RECO SRL—See Videndum plc; *Int'l*, pg. 8191
RECO TECHNOLOGY (BVI) LIMITED—See General Interface Solution (GIS) Holding Ltd.; *Int'l*, pg. 2919
RECO TECHNOLOGY (CHENGDU) CO., LTD.—See General Interface Solution (GIS) Holding Ltd.; *Int'l*, pg. 2919
RECO TECHNOLOGY HONG KONG LIMITED—See General Interface Solution (GIS) Holding Ltd.; *Int'l*, pg. 2919
RECOURSE COMMUNICATIONS, INC.; *U.S. Private*, pg. 3371
RECOVERCARE LLC—See Joerns Healthcare, LLC; *U.S. Private*, pg. 2219
RECOVERED CLOTHING LIMITED—See PDS Limited; *Int'l*, pg. 5771
RECOVER GEAR, LLC; *U.S. Private*, pg. 3371
RECOVER HEALTH, INC.; *U.S. Private*, pg. 3372
RECOVERIES CORPORATION PROPRIETARY LIMITED—See Transaction Capital Limited; *Int'l*, pg. 7895
RECOVERY CENTERS OF AMERICA OPERATIONS, LLC; *U.S. Private*, pg. 3372
RECOVERY DATABASE NETWORK, INC.—See OPENLANE, Inc.; *U.S. Public*, pg. 1607
RECOVERY FIRST OF FLORIDA, LLC—See AAC Holdings, Inc.; *U.S. Private*, pg. 30
RECOVERY HEALTH SERVICES; *U.S. Private*, pg. 3372
RECOVERY ONE, LLC—See WSFS Financial Corporation; *U.S. Public*, pg. 2383
RECOVERY PHYSICIANS GROUP OF GEORGIA, LLC—See Universal Health Services, Inc.; *U.S. Public*, pg. 2259
RECOVERY PHYSICIANS GROUP OF TENNESSEE, LLC—See Universal Health Services, Inc.; *U.S. Public*, pg. 2259
RECOVERY SERVICES INTERNATIONAL, INC.—See Chubb Limited; *Int'l*, pg. 1593
RECOVERY SERVICES OF NEW JERSEY, INC.—See Recovery Centers of America Operations, LLC; *U.S. Private*, pg. 3372
RECOVIA AB—See Kinnevik AB; *Int'l*, pg. 4182
THE RECOVRE GROUP PTY LIMITED—See Marsh & McLennan Companies, Inc.; *U.S. Public*, pg. 1377
REC POWER DEVELOPMENT & CONSULTANCY LTD.—See Power Finance Corporation Limited; *Int'l*, pg. 5945

COMPANY NAME INDEX

REC POWER DISTRIBUTION COMPANY LIMITED—See Power Finance Corporation Limited; *Int'l*, pg. 5945
R.E. CRAWFORD CONSTRUCTION LLC; *U.S. Private*, pg. 3335
RECREA LIFE AGENT CO., LTD.—See Relo Group, Inc.; *Int'l*, pg. 6265
RECREATE ASA; *Int'l*, pg. 6240
RECREATIEPROJECTEN ZEELAND B.V.—See Novomatic AG; *Int'l*, pg. 5467
RECREATIONAL EQUIPMENT, INC.; *U.S. Private*, pg. 3372
THE RECREATIONAL GROUP LLC—See Sentinel Capital Partners, L.L.C.; *U.S. Private*, pg. 3609
RECREATIONAL PRODUCTS DIV.—See Bell Industries, Inc.; *U.S. Public*, pg. 295
RECREATIONAL PRODUCTS DIV.—See Bell Industries, Inc.; *U.S. Public*, pg. 295
RECREATIONAL PRODUCTS DIV.—See Bell Industries, Inc.; *U.S. Public*, pg. 295
RECREATIONAL SPORTS & IMPORTS INC.; *U.S. Private*, pg. 3372
RECREATION CENTERS OF SUN CITY WEST, INC.; *U.S. Private*, pg. 3372
RECREATION CREATIONS, LLC—See Worth Investment Group, LLC; *U.S. Private*, pg. 4570
RECREATION WORLD INC.; *U.S. Private*, pg. 3372
RECRO GAINESVILLE LLC—See NovaQuest Capital Management, LLC; *U.S. Private*, pg. 2967
RECRUIT CAREER CO., LTD.—See Recruit Holdings Co., Ltd.; *Int'l*, pg. 6241
RECRUIT COMMUNICATIONS CO., LTD.—See Recruit Holdings Co., Ltd.; *Int'l*, pg. 6241
RECRUITCO PROPRIETARY LIMITED—See Workforce Holdings Ltd.; *Int'l*, pg. 8455
RECRUITER.COM GROUP, INC.—See Chicken Soup for the Soul Entertainment, Inc.; *U.S. Public*, pg. 488
RECRUIT EXPRESS PTE. LTD.—See HRnetGroup Limited; *Int'l*, pg. 3502
RECRUITFIRST LIMITED—See HRnetGroup Limited; *Int'l*, pg. 3502
RECRUITFIRST PTE. LTD.—See HRnetGroup Limited; *Int'l*, pg. 3502
RECRUIT HOLDINGS CO., LTD.; *Int'l*, pg. 6240
RECRUITICS, LLC; *U.S. Private*, pg. 3372
RECRUITING FORCE LLC; *U.S. Private*, pg. 3372
RECRUIT JOBS CO., LTD.—See Recruit Holdings Co., Ltd.; *Int'l*, pg. 6241
RECRUIT LIFESTYLE CO., LTD.—See Recruit Holdings Co., Ltd.; *Int'l*, pg. 6241
RECRUIT MANAGEMENT SOLUTIONS CO., LTD.—See Recruit Holdings Co., Ltd.; *Int'l*, pg. 6241
RECRUIT MARKETING PARTNERS CO., LTD.—See Recruit Holdings Co., Ltd.; *Int'l*, pg. 6241
THE RECRUITMENT BUSINESS LIMITED—See Empresaria Group Plc; *Int'l*, pg. 2389
THE RECRUITMENT COMPANY PTY LTD—See Viel & Compagnie SA; *Int'l*, pg. 8193
RECRUIT STAFFING CO., LTD.—See Recruit Holdings Co., Ltd.; *Int'l*, pg. 6241
RECRUIT SUMAI COMPANY LTD.—See Recruit Holdings Co., Ltd.; *Int'l*, pg. 6241
RECRUITWISE; *U.S. Private*, pg. 3372
RECRUSUL S.A.; *Int'l*, pg. 6241
REC SILICON ASA; *Int'l*, pg. 6235
REC SILICON INC.—See REC Silicon ASA; *Int'l*, pg. 6235
REC SITE SERVICES PTE LTD—See China National Chemical Corporation; *Int'l*, pg. 1527
REC SOLAR COMMERCIAL CORPORATION—See Duke Energy Corporation; *U.S. Public*, pg. 691
REC SOLAR EMEA GMBH—See China National Chemical Corporation; *Int'l*, pg. 1527
REC SOLAR GRADE SILICON LLC—See REC Silicon ASA; *Int'l*, pg. 6235
REC SOLAR HOLDINGS AS—See China National Chemical Corporation; *Int'l*, pg. 1527
REC SOLAR, INC.—See Duke Energy Corporation; *U.S. Public*, pg. 691
REC SOLAR PTE. LTD.—See China National Chemical Corporation; *Int'l*, pg. 1527
REC TECHNOLOGY US INC.—See REC Silicon ASA; *Int'l*, pg. 6235
RECTEC TECHNOLOGY & COMMUNICATION—See Northeast Oklahoma Electric Cooperative Inc.; *U.S. Private*, pg. 2951
RECTICEL AB—See Recticel S.A.; *Int'l*, pg. 6241
RECTICEL AS—See Recticel S.A.; *Int'l*, pg. 6241
RECTICEL AUTOMOBILSYSTEME GMBH—See Recticel S.A.; *Int'l*, pg. 6242
RECTICEL BEDDING ROMANIA S.R.L.—See Recticel S.A.; *Int'l*, pg. 6242
RECTICEL BEDDING (SCHWEIZ) GMBH—See Recticel S.A.; *Int'l*, pg. 6242
RECTICEL BETEILIGUNGSMANAGEMENT GMBH—See Recticel S.A.; *Int'l*, pg. 6242
RECTICEL B.V.—See Recticel S.A.; *Int'l*, pg. 6242
RECTICEL B.V.—See Recticel S.A.; *Int'l*, pg. 6242
RECTICEL CORBY LTD—See Recticel S.A.; *Int'l*, pg. 6242
RECTICEL CZECH AUTOMOTIVE S.R.O.—See Recticel S.A.; *Int'l*, pg. 6242
RECTICEL DAMMSYSTEME GMBH—See Recticel S.A.; *Int'l*, pg. 6242
RECTICEL FOAM CORPORATION INC.—See Recticel S.A.; *Int'l*, pg. 6242
RECTICEL FOAMS (SHANGHAI) CO LTD—See Recticel S.A.; *Int'l*, pg. 6242
RECTICEL GRUNDSTUCKSVERWALTUNG GMBH & CO. KG—See Recticel S.A.; *Int'l*, pg. 6242
RECTICEL HANDEL GMBH—See Recticel S.A.; *Int'l*, pg. 6242
RECTICEL IBERICA S.L.—See Recticel S.A.; *Int'l*, pg. 6242
RECTICEL INDIA PRIVATE LIMITED—See Recticel S.A.; *Int'l*, pg. 6242
RECTICEL INSULATION B.V.—See Recticel S.A.; *Int'l*, pg. 6242
RECTICEL INSULATION OY—See Recticel S.A.; *Int'l*, pg. 6242
RECTICEL INSULATION PRODUCTS—See Recticel S.A.; *Int'l*, pg. 6241
RECTICEL INSULATION S.A.S.—See Recticel S.A.; *Int'l*, pg. 6242
RECTICEL INTERIORS CZ S.R.O.—See Recticel S.A.; *Int'l*, pg. 6242
RECTICEL INTERNATIONAL B.V.—See Recticel S.A.; *Int'l*, pg. 6242
RECTICEL LIMITED—See Recticel S.A.; *Int'l*, pg. 6242
RECTICEL N.V.—See Recticel S.A.; *Int'l*, pg. 6242
RECTICEL OU—See Recticel S.A.; *Int'l*, pg. 6242
RECTICEL OY—See Recticel S.A.; *Int'l*, pg. 6242
RECTICEL S.A.; *Int'l*, pg. 6241
RECTICEL S.A.S.—See Recticel S.A.; *Int'l*, pg. 6242
RECTICEL SCHLAFKOMFORT GMBH—See Recticel S.A.; *Int'l*, pg. 6242
RECTICEL TEKNIK SUNGER IZOLASYON SANAYI VE TICARET A.S.—See Recticel S.A.; *Int'l*, pg. 6242
RECTICEL (UK) LIMITED—See Recticel S.A.; *Int'l*, pg. 6241
RECTICEL VERWALTUNG GMBH & CO. KG—See Recticel S.A.; *Int'l*, pg. 6242
RECTIFIER TECHNOLOGIES LIMITED; *Int'l*, pg. 6242
RECTIFIER TECHNOLOGIES SINGAPORE PTE. LTD.—See Rectifier Technologies Limited; *Int'l*, pg. 6243
RECTIGRO BV—See Recticel S.A.; *Int'l*, pg. 6242
RECTIPHASE SAS—See Schneider Electric SE; *Int'l*, pg. 6629
RECTOR-HAYDEN REALTORS—See Berkshire Hathaway Inc.; *U.S. Public*, pg. 307
RECTOR MOTOR CAR CO.; *U.S. Private*, pg. 3372
RECTORSEAL AUSTRALIA PROPRIETARY LIMITED—See CSW Industrials, Inc.; *U.S. Public*, pg. 601
RECTORSEAL LLC—See CSW Industrials, Inc.; *U.S. Public*, pg. 601
REC TRANSMISSION PROJECTS COMPANY LIMITED—See Power Finance Corporation Limited; *Int'l*, pg. 5945
RECTRIX AVIATION, INC.; *U.S. Private*, pg. 3372
RECTRON EUROPE LIMITED—See RECTRON LTD.; *Int'l*, pg. 6243
RECTRON HOLDINGS LIMITED—See Mustek Limited; *Int'l*, pg. 5103
RECTRON LTD.; *Int'l*, pg. 6243
RECTRON SEMICONDUCTOR INC.—See RECTRON LTD.; *Int'l*, pg. 6243
RECTUS AG—See Parker Hannifin Corporation; *U.S. Public*, pg. 1646
RECUBRIMIENTOS INTERCERAMIC, S.A. DE C.V.—See Internacional de Ceramica, S.A.B. de C.V.; *Int'l*, pg. 3743
RECUPERACION DE RODAS E MADEIRA, S.L.—See ACS, Actividades de Construccion y Servicios, S.A.; *Int'l*, pg. 115
RECUPERATOR S.P.A.—See Carel Industries S.p.A.; *Int'l*, pg. 1324
RECUPERO ETICO SOSTENIBILE S.P.A.; *Int'l*, pg. 6243
RECUP-OIL B.V.B.A.—See Avista Oil AG; *Int'l*, pg. 745
RECURLY, INC.; *U.S. Private*, pg. 3372
RECURRENT ENERGY, LLC—See Canadian Solar Inc.; *Int'l*, pg. 1286
RECURSION PHARMACEUTICALS, INC.; *U.S. Public*, pg. 1769
RECURSION SOFTWARE, INC.; *U.S. Private*, pg. 3372
RECURSOS CORPORATIVOS ALAMEDA, S.C.—See Grupo Televisa, S.A.B.; *Int'l*, pg. 3136
RECURSOS MILLROCK S DE R.L. DE C.V.—See Grupo Mexico, S.A.B. de C.V.; *Int'l*, pg. 3132
RECURSOS QUELIZ, INC.; *Int'l*, pg. 6243
RECUTECH S.R.O.—See Systemair AB; *Int'l*, pg. 7391
RECYCLABLE-FUEL STORAGE COMPANY—See Tokyo Electric Power Company Holdings, Incorporated; pg. 7790
RECYCLA S.P.A.—See Hera S.p.A.; *Int'l*, pg. 3356
RECYCLE AMERICA CO., L.L.C.—See Waste Management, Inc.; *U.S. Public*, pg. 2331
RECYCLEBANK LLC—See Recycle Track Systems, Inc.; *U.S. Private*, pg. 3372
RECYCLED AGGREGATE MATERIALS COMPANY, INC.—See Arcosa, Inc.; *U.S. Public*, pg. 186
RECYCLED POLYMERIC MATERIALS, INC.—See Diversified Chemical Technologies Inc.; *U.S. Private*, pg. 1241
RECYCLE METAL & COMMODITIES PRIVATE LTD—See European Metal Recycling Limited; *Int'l*, pg. 2556
RECYCLE MIDLAND—See M. Lipsitz & Co., Ltd.; *U.S. Private*, pg. 2527
RECYCLEN PLASTIC PROCESSING LTD.—See PannErgy Nyrt.; *Int'l*, pg. 5729
RECYCLE TO CONSERVE, TX, INC.—See ReConserve, Inc.; *U.S. Private*, pg. 3371
RECYCLE TRACK SYSTEMS, INC.; *U.S. Private*, pg. 3372
RECYCLICO BATTERY MATERIALS INC.; *Int'l*, pg. 6243
RECYCLING ASSET HOLDINGS, INC.—See Nucor Corporation; *U.S. Public*, pg. 1554
RECYCLING MANAGEMENT JAPAN, INC.—See JFE Holdings, Inc.; *Int'l*, pg. 3939
RECYCLING SERVICES, INC.—See Waste Management, Inc.; *U.S. Public*, pg. 2331
RECYCLING SERVICES INTERNATIONAL—See IMS Recycling Service Inc.; *U.S. Private*, pg. 2051
RECYCLING & WASTE SOLUTIONS, LLC—See ATAR Capital, LLC; *U.S. Private*, pg. 365
RECYCOMB S.A.U.—See Loma Negra Compania Industrial Argentina Sociedad Anonima; *Int'l*, pg. 4545
RECYDEL S.A.—See Renewi plc; *Int'l*, pg. 6278
RECYDE, S.A.U.—See Cie Automotive S.A.; *Int'l*, pg. 1605
RECYDIA AS—See Cimentas Izmir Cimento Fabrikasi Turk A.S.; *Int'l*, pg. 1609
RECYLEX S.A. - ADMINISTRATIVE OFFICE—See Recylex S.A.; *Int'l*, pg. 6243
RECYLEX S.A.; *Int'l*, pg. 6243
RECYPET AG—See Veolia Environnement S.A.; *Int'l*, pg. 8154
RECYTECH S.A.; *Int'l*, pg. 6243
RECYTE THERAPEUTICS, INC.—See Lineage Cell Therapeutics, Inc.; *U.S. Public*, pg. 1320
RED 212; *U.S. Private*, pg. 3372
RED212; *U.S. Private*, pg. 3376
RED24 CRM (PTY) LIMITED—See iJET International, Inc.; *U.S. Private*, pg. 2040
RED24 LIMITED—See iJET International, Inc.; *U.S. Private*, pg. 2040
RED 5 LIMITED; *Int'l*, pg. 6243
RED 5 STUDIOS, INC.—See The9 Limited; *Int'l*, pg. 7706
RED7E; *U.S. Private*, pg. 3377
RED 7 MEDIA, LLC; *U.S. Private*, pg. 3372
R.E. DAFFAN, INC.—See The Branch Group, Inc.; *U.S. Private*, pg. 3999
REDA INTERNATIONAL, INC.—See Data Recognition Corporation; *U.S. Private*, pg. 1163
REDAKTORERNA I STOCKHOLM AB—See Modern Times Group MTG AB; *Int'l*, pg. 5015
REDAL SA—See Veolia Environnement S.A.; *Int'l*, pg. 8154
RED AND YELLOW CO., LTD—See Idemitsu Kosan Co., Ltd.; *Int'l*, pg. 3592
REDAN S.A.; *Int'l*, pg. 6245
RED APPLE GROUP, INC.; *U.S. Private*, pg. 3372
RED APPOINTMENTS PTY LTD—See Bain Capital, LP; *U.S. Private*, pg. 435
REDAPT ENGINEERING COMPANY LIMITED—See Eaton Corporation plc; *Int'l*, pg. 2279
REDAPTIVE, INC.; *U.S. Private*, pg. 3377
RED ARC ASSURED LIMITED—See The Skipton Building Society; *Int'l*, pg. 7687
REDARHCS INC.; *U.S. Private*, pg. 3377
RED ARROW ENTERTAINMENT LIMITED—See ProSiebenSat.1 Media SE; *Int'l*, pg. 6000
RED ARROW EQUIPMENT COMPANY, INC.—See Kerry Group plc; *Int'l*, pg. 4139
RED ARROW HANDELS-GMBH—See Kerry Group plc; *Int'l*, pg. 4139
RED ARROW INTERNATIONAL LLC—See Kerry Group plc; *Int'l*, pg. 4139
RED ARROW LOGISTICS INC.; *U.S. Private*, pg. 3373
RED ARROW PRODUCTS COMPANY LLC—See Kerry Group plc; *Int'l*, pg. 4139
RED ARTS CAPITAL, LLC; *U.S. Private*, pg. 3373
RED AVENUE NEW MATERIALS GROUP CO., LTD.; *Int'l*, pg. 6243
REDBACK DRILLING TOOLS LTD—See SGS SA; *Int'l*, pg. 6742
REDBACK NETWORKS INC.—See Telefonaktiebolaget LM Ericsson; *Int'l*, pg. 7532
REDBALL ACQUISITION CORP.; *U.S. Public*, pg. 1770
RED BALL OXYGEN CO. INC.; *U.S. Private*, pg. 3373
RED BALL TIGER; *U.S. Private*, pg. 3373
REDBANK COPPER LIMITED; *Int'l*, pg. 6245
REDBANK ENERGY LIMITED; *Int'l*, pg. 6245
REDBANK MANUFACTURING COMPANY LIMITED—See Heidelberg Materials AG; *Int'l*, pg. 3319
RED BANK TITLE AGENCY INC.—See Foundation Title, LLC; *U.S. Private*, pg. 1580
REDBEAT ACADEMY SDN. BHD.—See Capital A Bhd; *Int'l*, pg. 1309

REDBANK ENERGY LIMITED
CORPORATE AFFILIATIONS

RED BEE MEDIA LIMITED—See Telefonaktiebolaget LM Ericsson; *Int'l*, pg. 7534
RED BELL REAL ESTATE, LLC—See Radian Group, Inc.; *U.S. Public*, pg. 1759
RED BEND SOFTWARE, INC.; *U.S. Private*, pg. 3373
REDBERRY AMBIENT SDN. BHD.—See Ancom Nylex Berhad; *Int'l*, pg. 449
REDBERRY CONTACT CENTER SDN. BHD.—See Ancom Nylex Berhad; *Int'l*, pg. 449
REDBERRY OUTDOORS SDN. BHD.—See Ancom Nylex Berhad; *Int'l*, pg. 449
REDBERRY SDN. BHD.—See Ancom Nylex Berhad; *Int'l*, pg. 449
REDBIRD CAPITAL PARTNERS L.P.; *U.S. Private*, pg. 3377
REDBIRD SQUARE ENDOSCOPY CENTER, LLC—See KKR & Co. Inc.; *U.S. Public*, pg. 1246
REDBLACK SOFTWARE, LLC—See Invesco Ltd.; *U.S. Public*, pg. 1163
REDBLACK SOFTWARE PRIVATE LIMITED—See Invesco Ltd.; *U.S. Public*, pg. 1163
RED BLUFF DAILY NEWS—See Alden Global Capital LLC; *U.S. Private*, pg. 156
RED BOOK AUTOMOTIVE DATA SERVICES (BEIJING) LIMITED—See carsales.com Limited; *Int'l*, pg. 1347
RED BOOK AUTOMOTIVE SERVICES (M) SDN. BHD.—See carsales.com Limited; *Int'l*, pg. 1347
RED BOOK CONNECT, LLC—See Marlin Equity Partners, LLC; *U.S. Private*, pg. 2585
REDBOOK—See The Hearst Corporation; *U.S. Private*, pg. 4046
REDBOURNE WEALTH MANAGEMENT LTD.—See Schroders plc; *Int'l*, pg. 6640
REDBOX AUTOMATED RETAIL, LLC—See Apollo Global Management, Inc.; *U.S. Public*, pg. 150
REDBOX CONSULTING SERVICES LIMITED—See Datatec Limited; *Int'l*, pg. 1981
REDBOX ENTERTAINMENT INC.—See Chicken Soup for the Soul Entertainment, Inc.; *U.S. Public*, pg. 488
REDBRICK INVESTMENTS S.A R.L.; *Int'l*, pg. 6245
RED BRICK PIZZA LLC—See BRIX Holdings, LLC; *U.S. Private*, pg. 657
REDBRICK SURVEY AND VALUATION LIMITED—See Paragon Banking Group PLC; *Int'l*, pg. 5736
REDBRICK TECHNOLOGIES INC.; *Int'l*, pg. 6245
REDBROOK BLENTECH LIMITED—See International Flavors & Fragrances Inc.; *U.S. Public*, pg. 1154
REDBROOK INGREDIENT SERVICES LIMITED—See International Flavors & Fragrances Inc.; *U.S. Public*, pg. 1154
RED BROWN KLE; *U.S. Private*, pg. 3373
REDBUBBLE EUROPE GMBH—See Redbubble Limited; *Int'l*, pg. 6245
REDBUBBLE LIMITED; *Int'l*, pg. 6245
RED BUD CLINIC CORP.—See Quorum Health Corporation; *U.S. Private*, pg. 3330
RED BUD HOME CARE SERVICES, LLC—See Community Health Systems, Inc.; *U.S. Public*, pg. 556
RED BUD ILLINOIS HOSPITAL COMPANY, LLC—See Quorum Health Corporation; *U.S. Private*, pg. 3330
RED BUD REGIONAL CLINIC COMPANY, LLC—See Quorum Health Corporation; *U.S. Private*, pg. 3330
REDBUILT LLC—See Atlas Holdings, LLC; *U.S. Private*, pg. 378
RED BULL ADRIA D.O.O.—See Red Bull GmbH; *Int'l*, pg. 6243
RED BULL AG—See Red Bull GmbH; *Int'l*, pg. 6243
RED BULL AUSTRALIA PTY LTD.—See Red Bull GmbH; *Int'l*, pg. 6243
RED BULL COMPANY LIMITED—See Red Bull GmbH; *Int'l*, pg. 6243
RED BULL DENMARK APS—See Red Bull GmbH; *Int'l*, pg. 6243
RED BULL DEUTSCHLAND GMBH—See Red Bull GmbH; *Int'l*, pg. 6243
RED BULL FINLAND OY—See Red Bull GmbH; *Int'l*, pg. 6243
RED BULL FRANCE SASU—See Red Bull GmbH; *Int'l*, pg. 6243
RED BULL FZE—See Red Bull GmbH; *Int'l*, pg. 6243
RED BULL GMBH; *Int'l*, pg. 6243
RED BULL HELLAS—See Red Bull GmbH; *Int'l*, pg. 6243
RED BULL HUNGARIA KFT.—See Red Bull GmbH; *Int'l*, pg. 6243
RED BULL MEDIA HOUSE GMBH—See Red Bull GmbH; *Int'l*, pg. 6243
RED BULL NEDERLAND B.V.—See Red Bull GmbH; *Int'l*, pg. 6243
RED BULL NEW ZEALAND LIMITED—See Red Bull GmbH; *Int'l*, pg. 6243
RED BULL NORTH AMERICA, INC.—See Red Bull GmbH; *Int'l*, pg. 6243
RED BULL NORWAY AS—See Red Bull GmbH; *Int'l*, pg. 6243
RED BULL SINGAPORE PTE LTD.—See Red Bull GmbH; *Int'l*, pg. 6244
RED BULL SP. Z O.O.—See Red Bull GmbH; *Int'l*, pg. 6244
RED BULL S.R.L.—See Red Bull GmbH; *Int'l*, pg. 6243

REDBURN (EUROPE) LIMITED—See Rothschild & Co SCA; *Int'l*, pg. 6403
REDBURN TIRE COMPANY; *U.S. Private*, pg. 3377
THE REDBURY HOTEL—See SBEEG Holdings, LLC; *U.S. Private*, pg. 3559
RED BUS LTD—See Christchurch City Holdings Ltd.; *Int'l*, pg. 1586
RED BUTTERFLY STRONTIUM INDUSTRY CO., LTD.—See Chori Co., Ltd.; *Int'l*, pg. 1583
RED CANOE CREDIT UNION; *U.S. Private*, pg. 3373
RED CANYON AT PALOMINO PARK L.L.C.—See Moody's Corporation; *U.S. Public*, pg. 1469
RED CANYON RESOURCES LTD.; *Int'l*, pg. 6244
REDCAPE HOTEL GROUP PTY LTD—See MA Financial Group Limited; *Int'l*, pg. 4618
RED CAPITAL GROUP, LLC—See ORIX Corporation; *Int'l*, pg. 5636
RED CAPITAL MARKETS, LLC—See ORIX Corporation; *Int'l*, pg. 5636
RED CAPITAL PARTNERS, LLC—See ORIX Corporation; *Int'l*, pg. 5636
RED CAPITAL PLC; *Int'l*, pg. 6244
REDCAPTOUR CO LTD; *Int'l*, pg. 6246
REDCARE S.R.L.—See Shop Apotheke Europe N.V.; *Int'l*, pg. 6859
RED CARPET LANDFILL, INC.—See Waste Connections, Inc.; *Int'l*, pg. 8354
RED CARPET TICKETS INC.; *U.S. Private*, pg. 3373
RED CARTEL PTY. LTD.—See xReality Group Ltd; *Int'l*, pg. 8538
RED CAT HOLDINGS, INC.; *U.S. Public*, pg. 1769
REDCATS ITALY S.R.L.—See Galeries Lafayette SA; *Int'l*, pg. 2872
RED CEDAR ARBORISTS & LANDSCAPERS, INC.—See Apax Partners LLP; *Int'l*, pg. 506
RED CEDAR GATHERING COMPANY—See Kinder Morgan, Inc.; *U.S. Public*, pg. 1234
RED CEDAR INSURANCE COMPANY—See Conifer Holdings, Inc.; *U.S. Public*, pg. 567
RED CEDAR SURGERY CENTER, LLC—See Tenet Healthcare Corporation; *U.S. Public*, pg. 2006
RED CELL DRM ACQUISITION CORP.; *U.S. Public*, pg. 1769
REDCENTRIC MS LIMITED—See Redcentric plc; *Int'l*, pg. 6246
REDCENTRIC PLC; *Int'l*, pg. 6246
RED CHAMBER CO.; *U.S. Private*, pg. 3373
REDCHIP CHINA—See RedChip Companies, Inc.; *U.S. Private*, pg. 3377
REDCHIP COMPANIES, INC.; *U.S. Private*, pg. 3377
REDCHIP KOREA—See RedChip Companies, Inc.; *U.S. Private*, pg. 3377
RED CHRIS DEVELOPMENT COMPANY LTD.—See Imperial Metals Corporation; *Int'l*, pg. 3635
RED CHRIS DEVELOPMENT COMPANY LTD.—See Newmont Corporation; *U.S. Public*, pg. 1517
RED CIRCLE TECHNOLOGIES LIMITED—See Zamano plc; *Int'l*, pg. 8622
RED CLAY INDUSTRIES INC.; *U.S. Private*, pg. 3373
RED CLAY INTERACTIVE; *U.S. Private*, pg. 3373
REDCLIFF DIALYSIS, LLC—See DaVita Inc.; *U.S. Public*, pg. 642
REDCLIFFE PENINSULA MEDICAL SERVICES PTY LIMITED—See Sonic Healthcare Limited; *Int'l*, pg. 7098
REDCLIFFE PROJECT PTY LTD—See Genesis Minerals Limited; *Int'l*, pg. 2921
RED CLIFFS HEALTHCARE, INC.—See The Ensign Group, Inc.; *U.S. Public*, pg. 2072
REDCLOUD CONSULTING INC.; *U.S. Private*, pg. 3377
RED CLOUD PROMOTIONS; *U.S. Private*, pg. 3373
RED COATS INC. - NORTH CAROLINA DIVISION—See Red Coats Inc.; *U.S. Private*, pg. 3374
RED COATS INC. - NORTH FLORIDA DIVISION—See Red Coats Inc.; *U.S. Private*, pg. 3374
RED COATS INC.; *U.S. Private*, pg. 3373
RED COATS INC.—See Red Coats Inc.; *U.S. Private*, pg. 3374
RED COATS INC. - SOUTH FLORIDA DIVISION—See Red Coats Inc.; *U.S. Private*, pg. 3374
RED COATS INC. - VIRGINIA SOUTHERN DIVISION—See Red Coats Inc.; *U.S. Private*, pg. 3374
REDCO FOODS, INC.—See Teekanne GmbH; *Int'l*, pg. 7520
THE REDCO GROUP, INC.—See ATAR Capital, LLC; *U.S. Private*, pg. 365
RED COLLAR PET FOODS, INC.; *U.S. Private*, pg. 3374
RED COMMA MEDIA, INC.; *U.S. Private*, pg. 3374
THE RED CONSULTANCY—See Clayton, Dubilier & Rice, LLC; *U.S. Private*, pg. 925
THE RED CONSULTANCY—See Clayton, Dubilier & Rice, LLC; *U.S. Private*, pg. 925
THE RED CONSULTANCY—See Clayton, Dubilier & Rice, LLC; *U.S. Private*, pg. 925
REDCOON BENELUX BV—See redcoon GmbH; *Int'l*, pg. 6246
REDCOON ELECTRONIC TRADE S.L.—See redcoon GmbH; *Int'l*, pg. 6246
REDCOON ELECTRONIC TRADE S.L.U.—See redcoon GmbH; *Int'l*, pg. 6246

REDCOON GMBH; *Int'l*, pg. 6246
REDCOON GMBH—See redcoon GmbH; *Int'l*, pg. 6246
REDCOON ITALIA S.R.L.—See redcoon GmbH; *Int'l*, pg. 6246
REDCOON LOGISTICS GMBH—See Ceconomy AG; *Int'l*, pg. 1388
REDCOON POLSKA SP. Z O.O.—See redcoon GmbH; *Int'l*, pg. 6246
REDCO PROPERTIES GROUP LIMITED; *Int'l*, pg. 6246
REDCORE (INDIA) PRIVATE LIMITED—See Accenture plc; *Int'l*, pg. 87
REDCO TEXTILES LIMITED; *Int'l*, pg. 6246
RED CRESCENT RESOURCES LIMITED; *Int'l*, pg. 6244
RED-D-ARC B.V.—See L'Air Liquide S.A.; *Int'l*, pg. 4372
RED-D-ARC (FR) SAS—See L'Air Liquide S.A.; *Int'l*, pg. 4372
RED-D-ARC, INC.—See L'Air Liquide S.A.; *Int'l*, pg. 4372
RED-D-ARC LIMITED—See L'Air Liquide S.A.; *Int'l*, pg. 4372
RED-D-ARC LTD.—See L'Air Liquide S.A.; *Int'l*, pg. 4372
RED-D-ARC (NETHERLANDS) B.V.—See L'Air Liquide S.A.; *Int'l*, pg. 4372
RED-D-ARC, S.A. DE C.V.—See L'Air Liquide S.A.; *Int'l*, pg. 4372
REDDELL HONDA; *U.S. Private*, pg. 3377
REDDE LTD.—See ZIGUP plc; *Int'l*, pg. 8682
RED DELUXE BRAND DEVELOPMENT; *U.S. Private*, pg. 3374
REDDEN MARINE SUPPLY INC.; *U.S. Private*, pg. 3377
RED DEVIL, INC.; *U.S. Private*, pg. 3374
REDDI INDUSTRIES, INC.; *U.S. Private*, pg. 3377
REDDING BANK OF COMMERCE—See Bank of Commerce Holdings; *U.S. Public*, pg. 272
REDDING FREIGHTLINER LLC; *U.S. Private*, pg. 3377
REDDING LUMBER TRANSPORT, INC.; *U.S. Private*, pg. 3378
REDDING OIL CO. INC.; *U.S. Private*, pg. 3378
REDDING RECORD SEARCHLIGHT, LLC—See Gannett Co., Inc.; *U.S. Public*, pg. 898
REDDING ROOFING SUPPLY INC.; *U.S. Private*, pg. 3378
REDDION B.V.—See WPP plc; *Int'l*, pg. 8477
RED DIRT METALS LIMITED; *Int'l*, pg. 6244
REDDI SERVICES, INC.; *U.S. Private*, pg. 3377
RED DISTRIBUTION—See Sony Group Corporation; *Int'l*, pg. 7103
REDDIT INC.—See Advance Publications, Inc.; *U.S. Private*, pg. 87
RED DOG EQUITY LLC; *U.S. Private*, pg. 3374
RED DOG HOLDINGS, LLC—See EZCORP, Inc.; *U.S. Public*, pg. 818
RED DOOR CHINA PTY LIMITED—See Pearl River Holdings Limited; *Int'l*, pg. 5775
RED DOOR INTERACTIVE, INC.; *U.S. Private*, pg. 3374
RED DOT CORPORATION; *U.S. Private*, pg. 3374
RED DOT PAYMENT PRIVATE LIMITED—See Prosus N.V.; *Int'l*, pg. 6003
REDD PAPER COMPANY; *U.S. Private*, pg. 3377
REDDY CLINIC SDN. BHD.—See Qualitas Medical Group Limited; *Int'l*, pg. 6151
REDDY HOLDING GMBH—See Dr. Reddy's Laboratories Limited; *Int'l*, pg. 2195
REDDY ICE CORPORATION—See Centerbridge Partners, L.P.; *U.S. Private*, pg. 815
REDDY ICE HOLDINGS, INC.—See Centerbridge Partners, L.P.; *U.S. Private*, pg. 815
REDDY ICE—See Centerbridge Partners, L.P.; *U.S. Private*, pg. 815
REDDY PHARMA IBERIA SA—See Dr. Reddy's Laboratories Limited; *Int'l*, pg. 2195
REDDY RAW, INC.; *U.S. Private*, pg. 3378
RED EAGLE EXPLORATION LIMITED—See Red Eagle Mining Corporation; *Int'l*, pg. 6244
RED EAGLE MINING CORPORATION; *Int'l*, pg. 6244
REDECARD S.A.—See Itau Unibanco Holding S.A.; *Int'l*, pg. 3830
REDE DENTAL—See Odontoprev S.A.; *Int'l*, pg. 5527
REDE D'OR SAO LUIZ SA; *Int'l*, pg. 6246
RED EDUCATION PTY. LTD.—See Arrow Electronics, Inc.; *U.S. Public*, pg. 199
REDEFINE PROPERTIES INTERNATIONAL LIMITED—See Redefine Properties Limited; *Int'l*, pg. 6246
REDEFINE PROPERTIES LIMITED; *Int'l*, pg. 6246
REDEFY CORPORATION; *U.S. Public*, pg. 1770
REDEFY, INC.—See Redefy Corporation; *U.S. Public*, pg. 1770
REDEIA CORPORATION, S.A.; *Int'l*, pg. 6246
RED ELECTRICA DEL SUR S.A—See Redeia Corporation, S.A.; *Int'l*, pg. 6246
RED ELECTRICA INTERNATIONAL S.A.U.—See Redeia Corporation, S.A.; *Int'l*, pg. 6246
REDELFI S.P.A.; *Int'l*, pg. 6246
REDEMPTION PLUS, LLC.; *U.S. Private*, pg. 3378
RED ENERGY PTY. LIMITED—See Snowy Hydro Limited; *Int'l*, pg. 7028
REDEN SOLAR SAS—See British Columbia Investment Management Corp.; *Int'l*, pg. 1169

COMPANY NAME INDEX

REDEN SOLAR SAS—See Macquarie Group Limited; *Int'l*, pg. 4630
REDEN SOLAR SAS—See Munchener Ruckversicherungs AG; *Int'l*, pg. 5091
REDEN SRL—See CogenInfra SpA; *Int'l*, pg. 1694
REDERI AB NORDO-LINK—See Grimaldi Group SpA; *Int'l*, pg. 3085
REDERIAKSJESELSKAPET TORVALD KLAVENESS; *Int'l*, pg. 6246
REDERIET A.P. MOLLER A/S—See A.P. Moller-Maersk A/S; *Int'l*, pg. 27
REDERIJ CEMENT-TANKVAART B.V.—See Heidelberg Materials AG; *Int'l*, pg. 3319
RED ESPANOLA DE SERVICIOS S.A.U—See Mubadala Investment Company PJSC; *Int'l*, pg. 5074
REDEVCO B.V.—See COFRA Holding AG; *Int'l*, pg. 1694
REDEVCO FRANCE S.A.—See COFRA Holding AG; *Int'l*, pg. 1694
REDEVCO NETHERLANDS—See COFRA Holding AG; *Int'l*, pg. 1694
REDEVCO RETAIL ESPANA S.L.U.—See COFRA Holding AG; *Int'l*, pg. 1694
REDEVCO SERVICES DEUTSCHLAND GMBH—See COFRA Holding AG; *Int'l*, pg. 1694
REDEVCO (SUISSE) AG—See COFRA Holding AG; *Int'l*, pg. 1694
REDEVCO UK—See COFRA Holding AG; *Int'l*, pg. 1694
REDEYE COFFEE ROASTING, LLC; *U.S. Private*, pg. 3378
REDFERN INTEGRATED OPTICS, INC.—See QinetiQ Group plc; *Int'l*, pg. 6141
REDFIELD & COMPANY INC.; *U.S. Private*, pg. 3378
REDFIELD ENERGY, LLC; *U.S. Private*, pg. 3378
REDFIN CORPORATION; *U.S. Public*, pg. 1770
REDFIN MORTGAGE, LLC—See Redfin Corporation; *U.S. Public*, pg. 1770
REDFIN NETWORK, INC.; *U.S. Private*, pg. 3378
REDFISH HOLDINGS, INC.; *U.S. Private*, pg. 3378
REDFISH LONGTERM CAPITAL S.P.A.; *Int'l*, pg. 6246
REDFLEX HOLDINGS LIMITED—See Verra Mobility Corporation; *U.S. Public*, pg. 2286
REDFLEX TRAFFIC SYSTEMS (CALIFORNIA) INC.—See Verra Mobility Corporation; *U.S. Public*, pg. 2286
REDFLEX TRAFFIC SYSTEMS INC—See Verra Mobility Corporation; *U.S. Public*, pg. 2286
REDFLEX TRAFFIC SYSTEMS INDIA PRIVATE LIMITED—See Verra Mobility Corporation; *U.S. Public*, pg. 2287
REDFLEX TRAFFIC SYSTEMS LIMITED—See Verra Mobility Corporation; *U.S. Public*, pg. 2287
REDFLEX TRAFFIC SYSTEMS MALAYSIA SDN. BHD.—See Verra Mobility Corporation; *U.S. Public*, pg. 2287
REDFLEX TRAFFIC SYSTEMS PTY LTD—See Verra Mobility Corporation; *U.S. Public*, pg. 2287
REDFLOW INTERNATIONAL PTY LTD—See RedFlow Limited; *Int'l*, pg. 6247
REDFLOW LIMITED; *Int'l*, pg. 6247
RED FOOTBALL LIMITED—See Manchester United plc; *Int'l*, pg. 4667
RED FROG EVENTS, LLC; *U.S. Private*, pg. 3374
RED FROG MARKETING—See Highland Productions, LLC; *U.S. Private*, pg. 1939
REDF; *U.S. Private*, pg. 3378
REDGATE MEDIA GROUP; *Int'l*, pg. 6247
RED GIANT OIL COMPANY—See HF Sinclair Corporation; *U.S. Public*, pg. 1034
RED GOAT DISPOSERS - UNITED SERVICE EQUIPMENT—See Standex International; *U.S. Public*, pg. 1930
RED GOLD INC. - ELWOOD FACILITY—See Red Gold Inc.; *U.S. Private*, pg. 3374
RED GOLD INC. - GENEVA FACILITY—See Red Gold Inc.; *U.S. Private*, pg. 3374
RED GOLD INC. - ORESTES FACILITY—See Red Gold Inc.; *U.S. Private*, pg. 3374
RED GOLD INC.; *U.S. Private*, pg. 3374
RED GOLD—See Red Gold Inc.; *U.S. Private*, pg. 3374
R.E.D. GRANITI BRASIL LTDA.—See R.E.D. Graniti S.p.A.; *Int'l*, pg. 6170
R.E.D. GRANITI DEUTSCHLAND GMBH—See R.E.D. Graniti S.p.A.; *Int'l*, pg. 6170
R.E.D. GRANITI ESPANA SL—See R.E.D. Graniti S.p.A.; *Int'l*, pg. 6170
R.E.D. GRANITI MADAGASCAR SARL—See R.E.D. Graniti S.p.A.; *Int'l*, pg. 6170
R.E.D. GRANITI MINERACAO LTDA—See R.E.D. Graniti S.p.A.; *Int'l*, pg. 6170
RED GRANITI POLAND SP. Z O.O.—See R.E.D. Graniti S.p.A.; *Int'l*, pg. 6170
R.E.D. GRANITI QUARRIES & BLOCKS INDIA PVT LTD—See R.E.D. Graniti S.p.A.; *Int'l*, pg. 6170
R.E.D. GRANITI SA SOUTH AFRICA PTY LTD—See R.E.D. Graniti S.p.A.; *Int'l*, pg. 6170
R.E.D. GRANITI S.P.A.; *Int'l*, pg. 6170
R.E.D GRANITI XIAMEN CO., LTD—See R.E.D. Graniti S.p.A.; *Int'l*, pg. 6170
REDGRAVE PARTNERS LLP; *Int'l*, pg. 6247

RED GROUP (M) SDN. BHD.—See NV5 Global, Inc.; *U.S. Public*, pg. 1557
REDGROUP SP. Z O.O.—See Cyber_Folks S.A.; *Int'l*, pg. 1892
REDHALL ENGINEERING—See Redhall Group plc; *Int'l*, pg. 6247
REDHALL GROUP PLC; *Int'l*, pg. 6247
REDHALL NUCLEAR LTD.—See Redhall Group plc; *Int'l*, pg. 6247
RED HALL PHARMACY LIMITED—See Bestway (Holdings) Limited; *Int'l*, pg. 1001
RED HAND MEDIA, LLC—See The Pilot LLC; *U.S. Private*, pg. 4095
RED HAT AB—See International Business Machines Corporation; *U.S. Public*, pg. 1150
RED HAT ASIA PACIFIC PTE LTD.—See International Business Machines Corporation; *U.S. Public*, pg. 1150
RED HAT ASIA PACIFIC PTY LTD—See International Business Machines Corporation; *U.S. Public*, pg. 1150
RED HAT ASIA PACIFIC PTY. LTD.—See International Business Machines Corporation; *U.S. Public*, pg. 1150
RED HAT BRASIL LIMITADA—See International Business Machines Corporation; *U.S. Public*, pg. 1150
RED HAT, BVBA—See International Business Machines Corporation; *U.S. Public*, pg. 1150
RED HAT BV—See International Business Machines Corporation; *U.S. Public*, pg. 1150
RED HAT CHILE LIMITADA—See International Business Machines Corporation; *U.S. Public*, pg. 1150
RED HAT COLOMBIA S.A.S—See International Business Machines Corporation; *U.S. Public*, pg. 1150
RED HAT CZECH, S.R.O.—See International Business Machines Corporation; *U.S. Public*, pg. 1150
RED HAT FRANCE SARL—See International Business Machines Corporation; *U.S. Public*, pg. 1150
RED HAT FZ LLC—See International Business Machines Corporation; *U.S. Public*, pg. 1150
RED HAT GMBH—See International Business Machines Corporation; *U.S. Public*, pg. 1150
RED HAT GMBH—See International Business Machines Corporation; *U.S. Public*, pg. 1150
RED HAT, INC.—See International Business Machines Corporation; *U.S. Public*, pg. 1149
RED HAT INDIA PVT. LTD.—See International Business Machines Corporation; *U.S. Public*, pg. 1150
RED HAT ISRAEL LTD.—See International Business Machines Corporation; *U.S. Public*, pg. 1150
RED HAT KK—See International Business Machines Corporation; *U.S. Public*, pg. 1150
RED HAT LIMITED—See International Business Machines Corporation; *U.S. Public*, pg. 1150
RED HAT MALAYSIA SDN. BHD.—See International Business Machines Corporation; *U.S. Public*, pg. 1150
RED HAT PHILIPPINES SOFTWARE SOLUTIONS CORP.—See International Business Machines Corporation; *U.S. Public*, pg. 1150
RED HAT POLAND SP.Z.O.O—See International Business Machines Corporation; *U.S. Public*, pg. 1150
RED HAT, S.L.—See International Business Machines Corporation; *U.S. Public*, pg. 1150
RED HAT SOFTWARE SERVICES (INDIA) PVT. LTD.—See International Business Machines Corporation; *U.S. Public*, pg. 1150
RED HAT SOUTH AFRICA (PTY) LTD—See International Business Machines Corporation; *U.S. Public*, pg. 1150
RED HAT S.R.L.—See International Business Machines Corporation; *U.S. Public*, pg. 1150
RED HAT (THAILAND) LIMITED—See International Business Machines Corporation; *U.S. Public*, pg. 1150
RED HAT UK LTD.—See International Business Machines Corporation; *U.S. Public*, pg. 1150
RED HAT YAZILIM SERVISLERI A.S.—See International Business Machines Corporation; *U.S. Public*, pg. 1150
RED HAWK FIRE & SECURITY (NY) LLC—See GTCR LLC; *U.S. Private*, pg. 1802
REDHAWK GLOBAL, LLC; *U.S. Private*, pg. 3378
REDHAWK HOLDINGS CORP.; *U.S. Public*, pg. 1770
REDHAWK MEDICAL PRODUCTS UK LTD.—See Redhawk Holdings Corp.; *U.S. Public*, pg. 1770
RED HAWK NETWORK ESSENTIALS, INC.—See Belden, Inc.; *U.S. Public*, pg. 294
REDHEAD COMPANIES; *U.S. Private*, pg. 3378
REDHEAD EQUIPMENT LTD; *Int'l*, pg. 6247
RED HERRING, INC.; *U.S. Private*, pg. 3374
REDHILL BIOPHARMA LTD.; *Int'l*, pg. 6247
REDHILL EDUCATION LIMITED—See iCollege Limited; *Int'l*, pg. 3582
RED HILL MINERALS LIMITED; *Int'l*, pg. 6244
RED HILL MONGOLIA LLC—See Silver Elephant Mining Corp.; *Int'l*, pg. 6923
RED HILLS FINANCE, LLC—See Acciona, S.A.; *Int'l*, pg. 90
RED HOAGLAND HYUNDAI; *U.S. Private*, pg. 3374
RED HOLDINGS GROUP INC.; *U.S. Private*, pg. 3374
REDHORSE CORPORATION; *U.S. Private*, pg. 3378
RED HORSE OIL COMPANY INCORPORATED; *U.S. Private*, pg. 3375
RED HOT & BLUE RESTAURANTS, INC.; *U.S. Private*, pg. 3375

RED HOUSE MANAGEMENT COMPANY (NORFOLK) LIMITED—See Barclays PLC; *Int'l*, pg. 862
RED HOUSE NORTH AMERICA, INC.; *U.S. Private*, pg. 3375
REDI2 TECHNOLOGIES, INC.—See Bain Capital, LP; *U.S. Private*, pg. 439
REDI-BAG, INC.—See Ardian SAS; *Int'l*, pg. 554
REDI-CARPET, INC.—See The Home Depot, Inc.; *U.S. Public*, pg. 2089
REDI-CARPET SALES OF DALLAS; *U.S. Private*, pg. 3378
REDICLINIC LLC—See New Rite Aid, LLC; *U.S. Private*, pg. 2905
REDI-DIRECT MARKETING, INC.; *U.S. Private*, pg. 3378
REDIFF.COM INDIA LIMITED; *Int'l*, pg. 6247
REDIFF.COM INDIA LTD.; *Int'l*, pg. 6247
REDIFFUSION DY&R—See WPP plc; *Int'l*, pg. 8492
REDIFFUSION WUNDERMAN—See WPP plc; *Int'l*, pg. 8481
REDIFFUSION Y&R PVT. LTD.-CORPORATE OFFICE—See WPP plc; *Int'l*, pg. 8492
REDIFFUSION Y&R PVT. LTD.—See WPP plc; *Int'l*, pg. 8492
REDIFFUSION Y&R PVT. LTD.—See WPP plc; *Int'l*, pg. 8492
REDIFFUSION Y&R PVT. LTD.—See WPP plc; *Int'l*, pg. 8492
REDIFFUSION Y&R PVT. LTD.—See WPP plc; *Int'l*, pg. 8492
REDIFFUSION Y&R PVT. LTD.—See WPP plc; *Int'l*, pg. 8492
REDIFY GROUP INC.; *U.S. Private*, pg. 3378
REDI-MIX CONCRETE, LP—See Vulcan Materials Company; *U.S. Public*, pg. 2314
RED INC.; *U.S. Private*, pg. 3375
REDING GRAVEL & EXCAVATING CO., INC.; *U.S. Private*, pg. 3378
REDINGTON AFRICA DISTRIBUTION FZE—See Redington (India) Limited; *Int'l*, pg. 6247
REDINGTON BAHRAIN SPC—See Redington (India) Limited; *Int'l*, pg. 6247
REDINGTON BANGLADESH LIMITED—See Redington (India) Limited; *Int'l*, pg. 6247
REDINGTON DISTRIBUTION COMPANY—See Redington (India) Limited; *Int'l*, pg. 6247
REDINGTON DISTRIBUTION PTE LTD—See Redington (India) Limited; *Int'l*, pg. 6247
REDINGTON-FAIRVIEW GENERAL HOSPITAL; *U.S. Private*, pg. 3379
REDINGTON GULF & CO. LLC—See Redington (India) Limited; *Int'l*, pg. 6247
REDINGTON GULF FZE—See Redington (India) Limited; *Int'l*, pg. 6247
REDINGTON (INDIA) INVESTMENTS PRIVATE LIMITED—See Redington (India) Limited; *Int'l*, pg. 6247
REDINGTON (INDIA) LIMITED; *Int'l*, pg. 6247
REDINGTON INTERNATIONAL MAURITIUS LIMITED—See Redington (India) Limited; *Int'l*, pg. 6247
REDINGTON KAZAKHSTAN LLP—See Redington (India) Limited; *Int'l*, pg. 6248
REDINGTON KENYA LIMITED—See Redington (India) Limited; *Int'l*, pg. 6248
REDINGTON MIDDLE EAST LLC—See Redington (India) Limited; *Int'l*, pg. 6248
REDINGTON NIGERIA LTD—See Redington (India) Limited; *Int'l*, pg. 6248
REDINGTON QATAR DISTRIBUTION WLL—See Redington (India) Limited; *Int'l*, pg. 6248
REDINGTON QATAR WLL—See Redington (India) Limited; *Int'l*, pg. 6248
REDINGTON SAUDI ARABIA DISTRIBUTION COMPANY—See Redington (India) Limited; *Int'l*, pg. 6248
REDINGTON SENEGAL LIMITED S.A.R.L—See Redington (India) Limited; *Int'l*, pg. 6248
REDINGTON SL PRIVATE LIMITED—See Redington (India) Limited; *Int'l*, pg. 6248
REDINGTON SOUTH AFRICA DISTRIBUTION (PTY.) LTD.—See Redington (India) Limited; *Int'l*, pg. 6248
REDINGTON SOUTH AFRICA (PTY.) LTD.—See Redington (India) Limited; *Int'l*, pg. 6248
REDINGTON UGANDA LIMITED—See Redington (India) Limited; *Int'l*, pg. 6248
REDISCOVER; *U.S. Private*, pg. 3379
REDI-SERVE FOODS—See On-Cor Frozen Foods LLC; *U.S. Private*, pg. 3018
REDISHRED CAPITAL CORP.; *Int'l*, pg. 6248
REDI S.P.A.—See Aliaxis S.A./N.V.; *Int'l*, pg. 325
REDI-TAG CORP.—See Tops Products; *U.S. Private*, pg. 4188
REDITUS II TELECOMUNICACOES, S.A.—See Reditus SGPS S.A.; *Int'l*, pg. 6248
REDITUS SGPS S.A.; *Int'l*, pg. 6248
REDKEN FRANCE—See L'Oreal S.A.; *Int'l*, pg. 4381
REDKEN LABORATORIES LLC—See L'Oreal S.A.; *Int'l*, pg. 4380

REDKNEE (AUSTRALIA) PTY LIMITED—See Optiva, Inc.; *Int'l*, pg. 5605
REDKNEE INC—See Optiva, Inc.; *Int'l*, pg. 5605
REDKNEE (INDIA) TECHNOLOGIES PVT. LIMITED—See Optiva, Inc.; *Int'l*, pg. 5605
REDKNEE SOLUTIONS (UK) LIMITED—See Optiva, Inc.; *Int'l*, pg. 5605
REDKNEE SPAIN, S.L.—See Optiva, Inc.; *Int'l*, pg. 5605
REDKNEE (UK) LIMITED—See Optiva, Inc.; *Int'l*, pg. 5605
RED LAKE GAMING INC.; *U.S. Private*, pg. 3375
RED LAKE GOLD, INC.; *Int'l*, pg. 6244
REDLAKE INC.—See Roper Technologies, Inc.; *U.S. Public*, pg. 1813
REDLAND BRICK INC.—See The Belden Brick Company Inc.; *U.S. Private*, pg. 3993
REDLANDS DAILY FACTS—See Alden Global Capital LLC; *U.S. Private*, pg. 158
REDLATTICE, INC.—See AE Industrial Partners, LP; *U.S. Private*, pg. 112
RED LEDGE LTD.—See L. Possehl & Co. mbH; *Int'l*, pg. 4385
RED LEOPARD HOLDINGS PLC; *Int'l*, pg. 6244
RED LEVEL NETWORKS; *U.S. Private*, pg. 3375
REDLEVER, INC.—See Adconion Media Group Ltd.; *Int'l*, pg. 127
RED LIGHT HOLLAND CORP.; *Int'l*, pg. 6244
REDLINE CAPITAL MANAGEMENT SA; *Int'l*, pg. 6248
REDLINE COMMUNICATIONS GROUP INC.—See Aviat Networks, Inc.; *U.S. Public*, pg. 246
REDLINE COMMUNICATIONS ROMANIA LTD.—See Aviat Networks, Inc.; *U.S. Public*, pg. 246
REDLINE DESIGN GROUP, P.A.; *U.S. Private*, pg. 3379
REDLINE ENGINEERING SERVICES LTD—See Active Energy Group plc; *Int'l*, pg. 120
REDLINE ENTERTAINMENT, INC.—See Best Buy Co., Inc.; *U.S. Public*, pg. 326
REDLINE PERFORMANCE AUTOMOTIVE LTD; *Int'l*, pg. 6248
REDLINE—See The Interpublic Group of Companies, Inc.; *U.S. Public*, pg. 2093
RED LION ANAHEIM, LLC—See The RMR Group Inc.; *U.S. Public*, pg. 2126
RED LION CONTROLS INC.—See HMS Networks AB; *Int'l*, pg. 3433
RED LION HOTELS CORP.—See The RMR Group Inc.; *U.S. Public*, pg. 2126
RED LOBSTER HOSPITALITY LLC—See Golden Gate Capital Management II, LLC; *U.S. Private*, pg. 1731
REDLOCK, INC.—See Palo Alto Networks, Inc.; *U.S. Public*, pg. 1635
RED LOTUS PROPERTIES LIMITED—See Sansiri pcl; *Int'l*, pg. 6556
REDLYNX OY—See Ubisoft Entertainment S.A.; *Int'l*, pg. 8003
REDMAN EQUIPMENT & MANUFACTURING CO.—See EMCOR Group, Inc.; *U.S. Public*, pg. 738
REDMAN FISHER ENGINEERING LTD—See Hill & Smith PLC; *Int'l*, pg. 3392
REDMAN FITTINGS LIMITED—See Tricorn Group plc; *Int'l*, pg. 7920
RED MANGO, LLC—See BRIX Holdings, LLC; *U.S. Private*, pg. 657
REDMAN HEENAN PROPERTIES LIMITED—See Blackstone Inc.; *U.S. Public*, pg. 358
REDMAS ARGENTINA, S.A.—See Entravision Communications Corporation; *U.S. Public*, pg. 779
REDMAS COLUMBIA, S.A.S.—See Entravision Communications Corporation; *U.S. Public*, pg. 779
REDMAS PERU, S.A.C.—See Entravision Communications Corporation; *U.S. Public*, pg. 779
REDMAS—See The Cisneros Group of Companies; *Int'l*, pg. 7633
RED MCCOMBS SUPERIOR HYUNDAI—See McCombs Enterprises; *U.S. Private*, pg. 2629
RED METAL LIMITED; *Int'l*, pg. 6244
RED METAL RESOURCES LTD.; *Int'l*, pg. 6244
RED MILE ENTERTAINMENT, INC.; *U.S. Public*, pg. 1769
REDMILE GROUP LLC; *U.S. Private*, pg. 3379
REDMOND ANESTHESIA SERVICES, LLC—See HCA Healthcare, Inc.; *U.S. Public*, pg. 1007
REDMOND CARE & REHABILITATION CENTER—See The Ensign Group, Inc.; *U.S. Public*, pg. 2072
REDMOND GENERAL INSURANCE AGENCY, INC.—See GTCR LLC; *U.S. Private*, pg. 1804
REDMOND HEIGHTS SENIOR LIVING—See The Ensign Group, Inc.; *U.S. Public*, pg. 2072
REDMOND INTEGRATORS GMBH—See Bechtle AG; *Int'l*, pg. 938
REDMOND REGIONAL MEDICAL CENTER—See HCA Healthcare, Inc.; *U.S. Public*, pg. 1007
REDMOND RIDGE MANAGEMENT, LLC—See U.S. Physical Therapy, Inc.; *U.S. Public*, pg. 2216
REDMOND SPOKESMAN—See Western Communications Inc.; *U.S. Private*, pg. 4491
RED MONKEY FOODS, INC.—See Wells Fargo & Company; *U.S. Public*, pg. 2344
RED MOON MARKETING LLC; *U.S. Private*, pg. 3375
RED MORTGAGE CAPITAL, LLC—See ORIX Corporation; *Int'l*, pg. 5636

RED MOUNTAIN CAPITAL PARTNERS LLC; *U.S. Private*, pg. 3375
RED MOUNTAIN COLLISION—See Boyd Group Services Inc.; *Int'l*, pg. 1124
RED MOUNTAIN ENTERTAINMENT, LLC—See Live Nation Entertainment, Inc.; *U.S. Public*, pg. 1330
RED MOUNTAIN MINING LTD.; *Int'l*, pg. 6244
REDNECK INC.—See Brookfield Corporation; *Int'l*, pg. 1176
REDNER'S MARKETS INC.; *U.S. Private*, pg. 3379
REDNISS & MEAD, INC.; *U.S. Private*, pg. 3379
RED NOLAND CADILLAC; *U.S. Private*, pg. 3375
RED OAK MINING CORP.; *Int'l*, pg. 6244
RED OAK REALTY; *U.S. Private*, pg. 3375
RED OAK SOURCING, LLC—See CVS Health Corporation; *U.S. Public*, pg. 615
REDOCTANE, INC.—See Microsoft Corporation; *U.S. Public*, pg. 1438
THE REDONDO BEACH EDUCATIONAL FOUNDATION; *U.S. Private*, pg. 4103
REDONDO'S INC.—See NH Foods Ltd.; *Int'l*, pg. 5257
RED OPTICS SOLUTIONS (M) SDN. BHD.—See Wuhan Raycus Fiber Laser Technologies Co., Ltd.; *Int'l*, pg. 8501
REDO SP.Z.O.O.—See Marie Brizard Wine & Spirits S.A.; *Int'l*, pg. 4693
REDOX CHEMICALS SDN BHD—See Redox Pty. Ltd.; *Int'l*, pg. 6248
REDOX PTY. LTD.; *Int'l*, pg. 6248
REDOX SRL—See Waters Corporation; *U.S. Public*, pg. 2335
REDOZE HOLDING N.V.—See Assicurazioni Generali S.p.A.; *Int'l*, pg. 647
REDPATH ARGENTINA CONSTRUCCIONES S.A.—See ATON GmbH; *Int'l*, pg. 688
REDPATH AUSTRALIA PTY LIMITED—See ATON GmbH; *Int'l*, pg. 688
REDPATH CANADA LIMITED—See ATON GmbH; *Int'l*, pg. 688
REDPATH CHILENA CONSTRUCCIONES Y CIA. LIMITADA—See ATON GmbH; *Int'l*, pg. 688
THE REDPATH GROUP—See ATON GmbH; *Int'l*, pg. 688
REDPATH MINING AUSTRALIA PTY. LTD.—See ATON GmbH; *Int'l*, pg. 688
REDPATH MINING INC.—See ATON GmbH; *Int'l*, pg. 689
REDPATH MINING (S.A.) (PTY.) LTD.—See ATON GmbH; *Int'l*, pg. 688
REDPATH MINING ZAMBIA LIMITED—See ATON GmbH; *Int'l*, pg. 688
REDPATH MONGOLIA LLC—See ATON GmbH; *Int'l*, pg. 688
REDPATH SUGAR LTD.—See Florida Crystals Corporation; *U.S. Private*, pg. 1548
RED PEACOCK INTERNATIONAL, INC.; *U.S. Private*, pg. 3375
THE RED PEAK GROUP LLC—See Hakuhodo DY Holdings Incorporated; *Int'l*, pg. 3222
REDPEG MARKETING, INC.; *U.S. Private*, pg. 3379
RED PEPPER INC.; *U.S. Private*, pg. 3375
RED PEPPER, INC—See Red Pepper Inc.; *U.S. Private*, pg. 3375
RED PHASE INC.; *Int'l*, pg. 6244
RED PINE CAPITAL GROUP, INC.; *Int'l*, pg. 6244
RED PINE EXPLORATION INC.; *Int'l*, pg. 6244
RED PLANET JAPAN, INC.—See Evolution Capital Management LLC; *U.S. Private*, pg. 1443
REDPOINT BIO CORPORATION; *U.S. Private*, pg. 3379
REDPOINT GLOBAL INC.; *U.S. Private*, pg. 3379
RED POINT SECURITY SP. Z O.O.; *Int'l*, pg. 6244
REDPOINT VENTURES—See Brentwood Venture Management, LLC; *U.S. Private*, pg. 646
REDPOINT VENTURES—See Brentwood Venture Management, LLC; *U.S. Private*, pg. 646
RED RABBIT LEO BURNETT—See Publicis Groupe S.A.; *Int'l*, pg. 6102
REDRA CONSTRUCT GROUP S.A—See Edrasis - C. Psallidas S.A.; *Int'l*, pg. 2315
RED RIBBON ADVISORY SERVICES PVT. LTD.—See Red Ribbon Asset Management PLC; *Int'l*, pg. 6245
RED RIBBON ASSET MANAGEMENT PLC; *Int'l*, pg. 6244
RED RIBBON BAKESHOP (USA), INC.—See Jollibee Foods Corporation; *Int'l*, pg. 3996
RED RIBBON IMPACT INVESTMENTS LIMITED—See Red Ribbon Asset Management PLC; *Int'l*, pg. 6245
REDRIDGE FINANCE GROUP, LLC; *U.S. Private*, pg. 3379
RED RIVER BANCSHARES, INC.; *U.S. Public*, pg. 1769
RED RIVER BANK—See Red River Bancshares, Inc.; *U.S. Public*, pg. 1769
RED RIVER CAPITAL CORP.; *Int'l*, pg. 6245
RED RIVER COMMODITIES INC—See ACOMO N.V.; *Int'l*, pg. 108
RED RIVER COMPUTER CO., INC.; *U.S. Private*, pg. 3375
RED RIVER COOPERATIVE LTD.; *Int'l*, pg. 6245
RED RIVER ENTERTAINMENT OF SHREVEPORT, LLC—See Boyd Gaming Corporation; *U.S. Public*, pg. 378

RED RIVER GRAIN COMPANY; *U.S. Private*, pg. 3375
RED RIVER HOLDING COMPANY, LLC—See Acadia Healthcare Company, Inc.; *U.S. Public*, pg. 29
RED RIVER HOSPITAL, LLC—See Acadia Healthcare Company, Inc.; *U.S. Public*, pg. 29
RED RIVER HUMAN SERVICES FOUNDATION; *U.S. Private*, pg. 3375
RED RIVER INTERMODAL INC.; *U.S. Private*, pg. 3375
RED RIVER MACHINERY INC.; *U.S. Private*, pg. 3375
RED RIVER MOTOR COMPANY; *U.S. Private*, pg. 3375
RED RIVER SOFTWARE—See Constellation Software Inc.; *Int'l*, pg. 1775
RED RIVER SOLUTIONS; *U.S. Private*, pg. 3375
RED RIVER SPECIALTIES INC.; *U.S. Private*, pg. 3375
RED RIVER TECHNOLOGY LLC—See Cerberus Capital Management, L.P.; *U.S. Private*, pg. 839
RED RIVER TERMINALS, L.L.C.—See Genesis Energy, L.P.; *U.S. Public*, pg. 930
RED RIVER TITLE SERVICES, INC.—See Stewart Information Services Corporation; *U.S. Public*, pg. 1948
RED RIVER VALLEY PHYSICAL THERAPY, LIMITED PARTNERSHIP—See U.S. Physical Therapy, Inc.; *U.S. Public*, pg. 2215
RED RIVER VALLEY RURAL ELECTRIC ASSOCIATION; *U.S. Private*, pg. 3375
RED RIVER VAN ECK B.V.—See ACOMO N.V.; *Int'l*, pg. 108
RED ROBIN FREDERICK COUNTY, LLC—See Red Robin Gourmet Burgers, Inc.; *U.S. Public*, pg. 1769
RED ROBIN GOURMET BURGERS, INC.; *U.S. Public*, pg. 1769
RED ROBIN INTERNATIONAL, INC.—See Red Robin Gourmet Burgers, Inc.; *U.S. Public*, pg. 1769
RED ROBIN OF BALTIMORE COUNTY, INC.—See Red Robin Gourmet Burgers, Inc.; *U.S. Public*, pg. 1769
RED ROBIN OF CHARLES COUNTY, INC.—See Red Robin Gourmet Burgers, Inc.; *U.S. Public*, pg. 1769
RED ROBIN WEST, INC.—See Red Robin Gourmet Burgers, Inc.; *U.S. Public*, pg. 1769
RED ROCK AT SMOKE RANCH, LLC—See HCA Healthcare, Inc.; *U.S. Public*, pg. 1007
RED ROCK AUSTRALASIA PTY LTD—See Red Rock Resources plc; *Int'l*, pg. 6245
RED ROCK CAPITAL CORP.; *Int'l*, pg. 6245
RED ROCK CONSULTING PTY LTD—See DXC Technology Company; *U.S. Public*, pg. 695
RED ROCK DISPOSAL LLC—See BC Partners LLP; *Int'l*, pg. 924
RED ROCK HEALTHCARE, INC.—See The Ensign Group, Inc.; *U.S. Public*, pg. 2072
RED ROCK INSULATION LLC—See Installed Building Products, Inc.; *U.S. Public*, pg. 1133
REDROCK LEADERSHIP; *U.S. Private*, pg. 3379
RED ROCK POWER LIMITED—See SDIC Power Holdings Co., Ltd.; *Int'l*, pg. 6658
RED ROCK RESORTS, INC.; *U.S. Public*, pg. 1769
RED ROCK RESORT—See Red Rock Resorts, Inc.; *U.S. Public*, pg. 1770
RED ROCK RESOURCES PLC; *Int'l*, pg. 6245
RED ROCKS RADIATION & ONCOLOGY, LLC—See HCA Healthcare, Inc.; *U.S. Public*, pg. 1007
RED ROCKS SURGERY CENTER, LLC—See HCA Healthcare, Inc.; *U.S. Public*, pg. 1007
RED ROCK WEALTH MANAGEMENT—See Lightyear Capital LLC; *U.S. Private*, pg. 2454
RED ROCK WEALTH MANAGEMENT—See Ontario Teachers' Pension Plan; *Int'l*, pg. 5586
RED ROOF INNS, INC.; *U.S. Private*, pg. 3375
RED ROOSTER WINERY LTD.—See Andrew Peller Limited; *Int'l*, pg. 451
RED ROSE COMMONS ASSOCIATES, L.P.—See Pennsylvania Real Estate Investment Trust; *U.S. Public*, pg. 1664
REDROVER CO. LTD.; *Int'l*, pg. 6248
RED ROVER LTD.—See Kajeet, Inc.; *U.S. Private*, pg. 2256
REDROW HOMES (EASTERN) LIMITED—See Barratt Developments PLC; *Int'l*, pg. 868
REDROW HOMES (LANCASHIRE) LIMITED—See Barratt Developments PLC; *Int'l*, pg. 868
REDROW HOMES (MIDLANDS) LIMITED—See Barratt Developments PLC; *Int'l*, pg. 868
REDROW HOMES (NORTHWEST) LTD.—See Barratt Developments PLC; *Int'l*, pg. 868
REDROW HOMES (SOUTHERN) LIMITED—See Barratt Developments PLC; *Int'l*, pg. 868
REDROW HOMES (SOUTH MIDLANDS) LIMITED—See Barratt Developments PLC; *Int'l*, pg. 868
REDROW HOMES SOUTH WALES LIMITED—See Barratt Developments PLC; *Int'l*, pg. 868
REDROW HOMES SOUTH WEST LTD—See Barratt Developments PLC; *Int'l*, pg. 868
REDROW HOMES (YORKSHIRE) LIMITED—See Barratt Developments PLC; *Int'l*, pg. 868
REDROW PLC—See Barratt Developments PLC; *Int'l*, pg. 868
REDSALSA TECHNOLOGIES INC.; *U.S. Private*, pg. 3379

COMPANY NAME INDEX

REDS BASEBALL PARTNERS, LLC; *U.S. Private*, pg. 3379
REDSCOUT LLC - SAN FRANCISCO—See Stagwell, Inc.; *U.S. Public*, pg. 1927
REDSCOUT LLC—See Stagwell, Inc.; *U.S. Public*, pg. 1927
RED SEA GATEWAY TERMINAL COMPANY LIMITED—See Sustained Infrastructure Holding Company SJSC; *Int'l*, pg. 7347
RED SEA HOUSING SERVICES COMPANY (PAPUA NEW GUINEA) LIMITED—See Dabbagh Group Holding Company Ltd.; *Int'l*, pg. 1902
RED SEA HOUSING SERVICES COMPANY—See Dabbagh Group Holding Company Ltd.; *Int'l*, pg. 1902
RED SEA HOUSING SERVICES (GHANA) LIMITED—See Dabbagh Group Holding Company Ltd.; *Int'l*, pg. 1903
RED SEA HOUSING SERVICES LLC—See Dabbagh Group Holding Company Ltd.; *Int'l*, pg. 1903
RED SEA HOUSING SERVICES (MOZAMBIQUE), LDA—See Dabbagh Group Holding Company Ltd.; *Int'l*, pg. 1903
RED SEA HOUSING SERVICES PTY LTD—See Dabbagh Group Holding Company Ltd.; *Int'l*, pg. 1903
RED SEA INTERNATIONAL COMPANY—See Dabbagh Group Holding Company Ltd.; *Int'l*, pg. 1902
RED SEA PAINTS CO. LTD.—See Jotun A/S; *Int'l*, pg. 4003
RED SENA BERHAD; *Int'l*, pg. 6245
REDSENSE MEDICAL AB; *Int'l*, pg. 6248
RED SENTRY PTE. LTD.—See Secura Group Limited; *Int'l*, pg. 6673
REDSEVEN ENTERTAINMENT GMBH—See ProSiebenSat.1 Media SE; *Int'l*, pg. 6001
RED SIX MEDIA, LLC; *U.S. Private*, pg. 3376
RED SKY BLUE WATER, LLC; *U.S. Private*, pg. 3376
RED SKY ENERGY LIMITED; *Int'l*, pg. 6245
REDSLAND CORPORATION—See Mitsubishi Heavy Industries, Ltd.; *Int'l*, pg. 4961
REDSPEED INTERNATIONAL LTD.—See Sdiptech AB; *Int'l*, pg. 6659
REDSPIN—See Altaris Capital Partners, LLC; *U.S. Private*, pg. 206
RED SPOT INTERACTIVE; *U.S. Private*, pg. 3376
RED SPOT PAINT & VARNISH CO., INC.—See Fujikura Ltd.; *Int'l*, pg. 2829
RED SPOT WESTLAND INC.—See Fujikura Ltd.; *Int'l*, pg. 2829
RED SPRINGS FUEL OIL COMPANY; *U.S. Private*, pg. 3376
RED SQUARE; *U.S. Private*, pg. 3376
REDS S.A.; *Int'l*, pg. 6248
RED'S SHOE BARN INC.; *U.S. Private*, pg. 3376
REDSTACK PTY. LTD.—See Schneider Electric SE; *Int'l*, pg. 6625
RED STAR DAQING LVYOU NATURAL PIGMENT CO., LTD.—See Guizhou Redstar Development Co., Ltd.; *Int'l*, pg. 3175
RED STAR EXPRESS PLC; *Int'l*, pg. 6245
REDSTAR GOLD USA INC.—See Heliostar Metals Ltd.; *Int'l*, pg. 3331
RED STAR MACALLINE GROUP CORPORATION LTD.; *Int'l*, pg. 6245
RED STAR OIL CO. INC.; *U.S. Private*, pg. 3376
RED STAR OUTDOOR LLC—See Shamrock Capital Advisors, LLC; *U.S. Private*, pg. 3624
REDSTAR PRECISION ELECTORN (FUQING) CO., LTD.—See Shin Zu Shing Co., Ltd.; *Int'l*, pg. 6838
REDSTONE AEROSPACE CORPORATION—See Coherent Corp.; *U.S. Public*, pg. 529
REDSTONE COMMUNICATIONS INC.; *U.S. Private*, pg. 3380
REDSTONE COMMUNICATIONS LTD—See GI Manager L.P.; *U.S. Private*, pg. 1693
REDSTONE COMPANIES HOSPITALITY, LLC—See The Redstone Companies, L.P.; *U.S. Private*, pg. 4103
THE REDSTONE COMPANIES, L.P.; *U.S. Private*, pg. 4103
REDSTONE GROUP HOLDINGS LTD—See GI Manager L.P.; *U.S. Private*, pg. 1693
REDSTONE INVESTMENTS; *U.S. Private*, pg. 3380
REDSTONE MORTGAGES LIMITED—See UniCredit S.p.A.; *Int'l*, pg. 8039
REDSTONE PRESBYTERIAN SENIORCARE; *U.S. Private*, pg. 3380
REDSTONE RESOURCES LIMITED; *Int'l*, pg. 6248
REDSTONE STRATEGY GROUP, LLC—See Arabella Advisors, LLC; *U.S. Private*, pg. 307
RED STONE TAX EXEMPT PARTNERS LP; *U.S. Private*, pg. 3376
RED STORM ENTERTAINMENT INC.—See Ubisoft Entertainment S.A.; *Int'l*, pg. 8003
REDSUN PROPERTIES GROUP LTD.; *Int'l*, pg. 6248
REDSUN SERVICES GROUP LIMITED; *Int'l*, pg. 6248
REDTAIL SOLUTIONS INC—See Accellos, Inc.; *U.S. Private*, pg. 50
REDTAIL TECHNOLOGY, INC.—See Orion Advisor Solutions, LLC; *U.S. Private*, pg. 3042
RED TECHNOLOGIES (S) PTE, LTD.—See NV5 Global, Inc.; *U.S. Public*, pg. 1557

RED THE UNIFORM TAILOR INC.—See Unisync Corp.; *Int'l*, pg. 8062
RED THREAD SPACES LLC; *U.S. Private*, pg. 3376
REDTONE ASIA, INC.; *Int'l*, pg. 6248
REDTONE DIGITAL BERHAD—See Berjaya Corporation Berhad; *Int'l*, pg. 984
RED TOP WIND POWER, LLC.—See ACS, Actividades de Construccion y Servicios, S.A.; *Int'l*, pg. 115
RED TRAIL ENERGY, LLC; *U.S. Public*, pg. 1770
REDUCTORES DE MEXICO S.A.—See Berkshire Hathaway Inc.; *U.S. Public*, pg. 311
RED URBAN—See Omnicom Group Inc.; *U.S. Public*, pg. 1593
REDUR GMBH + CO. KG—See Phoenix Mecano AG; *Int'l*, pg. 5853
REDUS CHARLOTTE HOUSING, LLC—See Wells Fargo & Company; *U.S. Public*, pg. 2345
REDUS FLORIDA COMMERCIAL, LLC—See Wells Fargo & Company; *U.S. Public*, pg. 2345
REDUS FL PROPERTIES, LLC—See Wells Fargo & Company; *U.S. Public*, pg. 2345
REDUS FREDERICA CLUB, LLC—See Wells Fargo & Company; *U.S. Public*, pg. 2345
REDU SPACE SERVICES S.A.—See SES S.A.; *Int'l*, pg. 6727
RED VALVE CO., INC.—See Granite Equity Partners LLC; *U.S. Private*, pg. 1755
REDVECTOR.COM, LLC—See Genstar Capital, LLC; *U.S. Private*, pg. 1679
REDVECTOR.COM, LLC—See Providence Equity Partners L.L.C.; *U.S. Private*, pg. 3294
RED VENTURES, LLC; *U.S. Private*, pg. 3376
REDVIKING GROUP, LLC—See Lincoln Electric Holdings, Inc.; *U.S. Public*, pg. 1318
REDVIKING - RESEARCH TRIANGLE ENGINEERING CENTER—See Lincoln Electric Holdings, Inc.; *U.S. Public*, pg. 1318
RED VIOLET, INC.; *U.S. Public*, pg. 1770
REDVISION SYSTEMS INC.; *U.S. Private*, pg. 3380
REDVISION SYSTEMS, INC; *U.S. Private*, pg. 3380
RED WAGON ADVERTISING & DESIGN; *U.S. Private*, pg. 3376
REDWARE SISTEMAS DE INFORMACAO, S.A.—See Reditus SGPS S.A.; *Int'l*, pg. 6248
REDWAVE BV—See Cooperatieve Centrale Raiffeisen-Boerenleenbank B.A.; *Int'l*, pg. 1792
RED WHITE & BLOOM BRANDS INC.; *Int'l*, pg. 6245
RED WILLOW DIALYSIS, LLC—See DaVita Inc.; *U.S. Public*, pg. 642
REDWING ECOLOGICAL SERVICE INC.—See KKR & Co. Inc.; *U.S. Public*, pg. 1263
RED WING PROPERTIES, INC.; *U.S. Private*, pg. 3376
REDWING REPUBLICAN EAGLE—See Forum Communications Company; *U.S. Private*, pg. 1577
RED WING SHOE COMPANY, INC.; *U.S. Private*, pg. 3376
RED WING SHOE VASQUE DIV.—See Red Wing Shoe Company, Inc.; *U.S. Private*, pg. 3376
REDWIRE CORPORATION; *U.S. Public*, pg. 1770
REDWIRE,LLC—See Redwire Corporation; *U.S. Public*, pg. 1771
REDWIRE LLC; *U.S. Private*, pg. 3380
RED WOLF COMPANY, LLC—See Broadwind, Inc.; *U.S. Public*, pg. 392
REDWOOD BIOSCIENCE INC.—See Catalent, Inc.; *U.S. Public*, pg. 449
REDWOOD CAPITAL BANK; *U.S. Public*, pg. 1771
REDWOOD CAPITAL GROUP, LLC; *U.S. Private*, pg. 3380
REDWOOD CAPITAL INVESTMENTS, LLC; *U.S. Private*, pg. 3380
REDWOOD COAST DEVELOPMENTAL SERVICES CORPORATION; *U.S. Private*, pg. 3380
REDWOOD CREDIT UNION; *U.S. Private*, pg. 3381
REDWOOD DISTRIBUTION LTD.; *Int'l*, pg. 6249
THE REDWOOD EMPIRE FOOD BANK; *U.S. Private*, pg. 4103
REDWOOD FINANCIAL, INC.; *U.S. Public*, pg. 1771
THE REDWOOD GROUP, LLC; *U.S. Private*, pg. 4103
REDWOOD HILL FARM & CREAMERY, INC.—See Emmi AG; *Int'l*, pg. 2385
REDWOOD INDUSTRIES INC.; *U.S. Private*, pg. 3381
REDWOOD INVESTMENTS LLC; *U.S. Private*, pg. 3381
REDWOOD LANDFILL, INC.—See Waste Management, Inc.; *U.S. Public*, pg. 2331
REDWOOD LOGISTICS LLC—See AEA Investors LP; *U.S. Private*, pg. 115
REDWOOD MORTGAGE INVESTORS IX, LLC; *U.S. Private*, pg. 3381
REDWOOD OIL COMPANY; *U.S. Private*, pg. 3381
REDWOOD PAINTING CO, INC.—See Arctic Slope Regional Corporation; *U.S. Public*, pg. 316
REDWOODS ACQUISITION CORP.; *U.S. Public*, pg. 1771
REDWOOD SCIENTIFIC TECHNOLOGIES, INC.; *U.S. Private*, pg. 3381
REDWOODS CO., LTD.; *Int'l*, pg. 6249
REDWOOD SHORES OWNERS ASSOCIATION—See Equity Residential; *U.S. Public*, pg. 792
REDWOOD SOFTWARE, INC.; *U.S. Private*, pg. 3381

REDWOOD TELECOMMUNICATIONS LIMITED—See Horizon Capital LLP; *Int'l*, pg. 3479
REDWOOD TIMES—See Alden Global Capital LLC; *U.S. Private*, pg. 157
REDWOOD TOXICOLOGY LABORATORY, INC.—See Abbott Laboratories; *U.S. Public*, pg. 19
REDWOOD TRUST, INC.; *U.S. Public*, pg. 1771
RED WORKS—See WPP plc; *Int'l*, pg. 8488
REDWORKS—See WPP plc; *Int'l*, pg. 8488
REDW STANLEY FINANCIAL ADVISORS LLC; *U.S. Private*, pg. 3380
REDX ANTI-INFECTIVES LTD—See Redmile Group LLC; *U.S. Private*, pg. 3379
REDX PHARMA PLC—See Redmile Group LLC; *U.S. Private*, pg. 3379
RED & YELLOW SCHOOL—See WPP plc; *Int'l*, pg. 8488
REDYREF INTERACTIVE KIOSKS; *U.S. Private*, pg. 3381
REDZONE COIL TUBING, LLC—See Nine Energy Service, Inc.; *U.S. Public*, pg. 1529
RED ZONE LLC; *U.S. Private*, pg. 3376
REEBLE INC.; *U.S. Private*, pg. 3381
REEBOK-CCM HOCKEY AB—See adidas AG; *Int'l*, pg. 147
REEBOK-CCM HOCKEY AS—See adidas AG; *Int'l*, pg. 147
REEBOK-CCM HOCKEY GMBH—See Leonard Green & Partners, L.P.; *U.S. Private*, pg. 2425
REEBOK-CCM HOCKEY, INC.—See Leonard Green & Partners, L.P.; *U.S. Private*, pg. 2425
REEBOK-CCM HOCKEY OY—See Leonard Green & Partners, L.P.; *U.S. Private*, pg. 2425
REEBOK DE MEXICO, S.A. DE C.V.—See Leonard Green & Partners, L.P.; *U.S. Private*, pg. 2425
REEBOK INDIA COMPANY—See Leonard Green & Partners, L.P.; *U.S. Private*, pg. 2424
REEBOK INTERNATIONAL LTD.—See Leonard Green & Partners, L.P.; *U.S. Private*, pg. 2424
REEBOK IRELAND LIMITED—See adidas AG; *Int'l*, pg. 146
REEBOK JOFA AB—See Leonard Green & Partners, L.P.; *U.S. Private*, pg. 2424
REEBOK JOFA AS—See Leonard Green & Partners, L.P.; *U.S. Private*, pg. 2424
REEBOK PRODUTOS ESPORTIVOS BRASIL LTDA.—See Leonard Green & Partners, L.P.; *U.S. Private*, pg. 2424
REEBONZ HOLDING LIMITED; *Int'l*, pg. 6249
REECE ALBERT INC.; *U.S. Private*, pg. 3381
REECE AUSTRALIA PTY LTD.—See Reece Limited; *Int'l*, pg. 6249
REECE-CAMPBELL, INC.; *U.S. Private*, pg. 3381
REECE GROUP LTD.; *Int'l*, pg. 6249
REECE-HOPPER SALES, LLC - HOUSTON—See Reece-Hopper Sales, LLC; *U.S. Private*, pg. 3381
REECE-HOPPER SALES, LLC; *U.S. Private*, pg. 3381
REECE LIMITED; *Int'l*, pg. 6249
REECE NEW ZEALAND LIMITED—See Reece Limited; *Int'l*, pg. 6249
REECE & NICHOLS REALTORS—See Berkshire Hathaway Inc.; *U.S. Public*, pg. 307
REECES FANTASIES INC.—See Wind Point Advisors LLC; *U.S. Private*, pg. 4535
REECE SUPPLY COMPANY OF DALLAS; *U.S. Private*, pg. 3381
REECE SUPPLY COMPANY OF HOUSTON—See Reece Supply Company of Dallas; *U.S. Private*, pg. 3381
REECE SUPPLY COMPANY OF SAN ANTONIO—See Reece Supply Company of Dallas; *U.S. Private*, pg. 3381
REED BEVERAGE, INC.; *U.S. Private*, pg. 3382
REED BRENNAN MEDIA ASSOCIATES, INC.—See The Hearst Corporation; *U.S. Private*, pg. 4046
REED BROTHERS INC.—See Reed Grain & Bean Company, Inc.; *U.S. Private*, pg. 3382
REED CITY POWER LINE SUPPLY CO., INC.; *U.S. Private*, pg. 3382
REED CONTRACTING SERVICES, INC.; *U.S. Private*, pg. 3382
REED ELSEVIER SHARED SERVICES (PHILIPPINES) INC. - ILOILO OFFICE—See RELX plc; *Int'l*, pg. 6268
REED ELSEVIER SHARED SERVICES (PHILIPPINES) INC.—See RELX plc; *Int'l*, pg. 6268
REEDER CHEVROLET COMPANY; *U.S. Private*, pg. 3383
REEDEREI HIDDENSEE GMBH—See FRS GmbH & Co. KG; *Int'l*, pg. 2797
REEDEREI NORD B.V.—See Reederei NORD Klaus E. Oldendorff Limited; *Int'l*, pg. 6249
REEDEREI NORD KLAUS E. OLDENDORFF GMBH—See Reederei NORD Klaus E. Oldendorff Limited; *Int'l*, pg. 6249
REEDEREI NORD KLAUS E. OLDENDORFF LIMITED; *Int'l*, pg. 6249
REEDEREI PETER DEILMANN GMBH—See Callista Private Equity GmbH & Co. KG; *Int'l*, pg. 1265
REEDER-TRAUSCH MARINE; *U.S. Private*, pg. 3383
REED EXHIBITIONS ALCANTARA MACHADO LTDA.—See RELX plc; *Int'l*, pg. 6266
REED EXHIBITIONS - AMERICAS—See RELX plc; *Int'l*, pg. 6266

REED EXHIBITIONS AUSTRALIA PTY. LTD.—See RELX plc; *Int'l*, pg. 6267
REED EXHIBITIONS (CHINA) CO., LTD.—See RELX plc; *Int'l*, pg. 6266
REED EXHIBITIONS LIMITED—See RELX plc; *Int'l*, pg. 6266
REED EXPOSITIONS FRANCE SAS—See RELX plc; *Int'l*, pg. 6267
REED FOOD TECHNOLOGY; *U.S. Private*, pg. 3382
REED & GRAHAM, INC. - GEOSYNTHETICS DIVISION-SAN JOSE—See Reed & Graham Inc.; *U.S. Private*, pg. 3381
REED & GRAHAM, INC. - GEOSYNTHETICS DIVISION—See Reed & Graham Inc.; *U.S. Private*, pg. 3381
REED & GRAHAM INC.; *U.S. Private*, pg. 3381
REED GRAIN & BEAN COMPANY, INC.; *U.S. Private*, pg. 3382
REED GROUP MANAGEMENT LLC—See Alight, Inc.; *U.S. Public*, pg. 77
REEDHYCALOG CIS, LLC—See NOV, Inc.; *U.S. Public*, pg. 1546
REED-HYCALOG DE MEXICO, S DE R.L. DE C.V.—See NOV, Inc.; *U.S. Public*, pg. 1546
REEDHYCALOG, L.P.—See NOV, Inc.; *U.S. Public*, pg. 1546
REEDHYCALOG UK LTD—See NOV, Inc.; *U.S. Public*, pg. 1546
REED INC.; *U.S. Private*, pg. 3382
REED LALLIER CHEVROLET, INC.; *U.S. Private*, pg. 3382
REEDLEY HIGH SCHOOL; *U.S. Private*, pg. 3383
REED LIMITED; *Int'l*, pg. 6249
REED MACHINERY, INC.; *U.S. Private*, pg. 3382
REED MANAGEMENT LLC—See NACCO Industries, Inc.; *U.S. Public*, pg. 1489
REEDMAN TOLL AUTO WORLD; *U.S. Private*, pg. 3383
REED MANUFACTURING COMPANY INC.; *U.S. Private*, pg. 3382
REED MANUFACTURING COMPANY—See J.F. Shea Co., Inc.; *U.S. Private*, pg. 2164
REED MIDEM SAS—See RELX plc; *Int'l*, pg. 6267
REED MINERALS, INC.—See NACCO Industries, Inc.; *U.S. Public*, pg. 1490
REED NATIONAL COMPANY—See Mestek, Inc.; *U.S. Public*, pg. 1426
REED NISSAN; *U.S. Private*, pg. 3382
REED OIL COMPANY; *U.S. Private*, pg. 3382
REED & PERRINE SALES, INC.; *U.S. Private*, pg. 3382
REEDPOP—See RELX plc; *Int'l*, pg. 6266
REED SENDECKE KREBSBACH; *U.S. Private*, pg. 3382
REED'S, INC.; *U.S. Public*, pg. 1771
REED SINOPHARM EXHIBITIONS CO., LTD.—See China National Pharmaceutical Group Corporation; *Int'l*, pg. 1534
REED SINOPHARM EXHIBITIONS CO., LTD.—See RELX plc; *Int'l*, pg. 6266
REEDS JEWELERS, INC.; *U.S. Private*, pg. 3383
REED'S METALS, INC.—See Clayton, Dubilier & Rice, LLC; *U.S. Private*, pg. 921
REED SMITH LLP; *U.S. Private*, pg. 3382
REEDS NAUTICAL ALMANAC—See Bloomsbury Publishing Plc; *Int'l*, pg. 1065
REEDS RAINS CLECKHEATON LIMITED—See LSL Property Services plc; *Int'l*, pg. 4571
REEDS & SON FURNITURE INC.; *U.S. Private*, pg. 3383
REED TECH IP SERVICES—See RELX plc; *U.S. Public*, pg. 6268
REED TECHNOLOGY & INFORMATION SERVICES INC.—See RELX plc; *Int'l*, pg. 6268
REED TECHNOLOGY & INFORMATION SERVICES INC. - VIRGINIA—See RELX plc; *Int'l*, pg. 6268
REEDY CREEK ENERGY SERVICES—See The Walt Disney Company; *U.S. Public*, pg. 2139
REEDY LAGOON CORPORATION LTD; *Int'l*, pg. 6249
R.E.E ELECTRIC APPLIANCES JOINT STOCK COMPANY—See Refrigeration Electrical Engineering Corporation; *Int'l*, pg. 6250
REE ENTERPRISES, INC.—See Rusty Eck Ford, Inc.; *U.S. Private*, pg. 3507
REEFCO, LLC—See Carrier Global Corporation; *U.S. Public*, pg. 444
REEF DIALYSIS, LLC—See DaVita Inc.; *U.S. Public*, pg. 642
REEFERTEC PTE LTD—See Eng Kong Holdings Pte Ltd.; *Int'l*, pg. 2426
REEF INDUSTRIES INCORPORATED; *U.S. Private*, pg. 3383
REEF MAGIC CRUISES PTY. LTD.—See Experience Co Limited; *Int'l*, pg. 2588
REEHER LLC—See Blackbaud, Inc.; *U.S. Public*, pg. 341
REE INC.; *U.S. Private*, pg. 3381
R.E.E LAND CORPORATION—See Refrigeration Electrical Engineering Corporation; *Int'l*, pg. 6250
REELAN INDUSTRIES INC.; *U.S. Private*, pg. 3383
REELCRAFT INDUSTRIES INC.—See Madison Industries, Inc.; *U.S. Private*, pg. 2543
REELEX CO., LTD.—See Chuo Spring Co., Ltd.; *Int'l*, pg. 1599

REEL GROUP INC—See Global Energy (Holdings) Ltd.; *Int'l*, pg. 2995
REELL PRECISION MANUFACTURING CORP.; *U.S. Private*, pg. 3383
REEL LUMBER SERVICE; *U.S. Private*, pg. 3383
REEL-O-MATIC, INC.; *U.S. Private*, pg. 3383
REEL ONE ENTERTAINMENT, INC.—See Television Francaise 1 S.A.; *Int'l*, pg. 7543
REEL ONE ENTERTAINMENT—See Television Francaise 1 S.A.; *Int'l*, pg. 7543
REEL ONE INTERNATIONAL LIMITED—See Television Francaise 1 S.A.; *Int'l*, pg. 7543
REEL SERVICE LIMITED—See ASTI Holdings Limited; *Int'l*, pg. 655
REEL SERVICE (PHILIPPINES), INC.—See ASTI Holdings Limited; *Int'l*, pg. 655
REEL S.R.L.—See KSB SE & Co. KGaA; *Int'l*, pg. 4313
REEL TELECOMMUNICATION SERVICES, LLC—See Guggenheim Partners, LLC; *Int'l*, pg. 1812
REELTIME RENTALS, INC.; *U.S. Public*, pg. 1771
REEM BATTERIES & POWER APPLIANCES COMPANY SAOC—See Omar Zawawi Establishment LLC; *Int'l*, pg. 5561
R.E.E MECHANICAL & ELECTRICAL ENGINEERING JOINT STOCK COMPANY—See Refrigeration Electrical Engineering Corporation; *Int'l*, pg. 6250
REEM EMIRATES ALUMINUM LLC—See Alpha Dhabi Holding PJSC; *Int'l*, pg. 367
REEM READY MIX LLC—See Alpha Dhabi Holding PJSC; *Int'l*, pg. 368
REEM RICE MILLS (PRIVATE) LIMITED—See A.K. Al-Muhaidib & Sons Group of Companies; *Int'l*, pg. 24
REEMTSMA CIGARETTENFABRIKEN GMBH—See Imperial Brands PLC; *Int'l*, pg. 3634
REEMTSMA INTERNATIONAL CHINA LTD.—See Imperial Brands PLC; *Int'l*, pg. 3634
REEMTSMA KIEV TYUTYUNOVA FABRIKA—See Imperial Brands PLC; *Int'l*, pg. 3634
REENGINEERING CONSULTANTS, LLC—See Konica Minolta, Inc.; *Int'l*, pg. 4259
REENGUS WIRES PRIVATE LIMITED—See RTS Power Corporation Limited; *Int'l*, pg. 6420
REENOVA INVESTMENT HOLDING LIMITED; *Int'l*, pg. 6249
R.E.E REAL ESTATE COMPANY LIMITED—See Refrigeration Electrical Engineering Corporation; *Int'l*, pg. 6250
REES CONTRACT SERVICE INC.; *U.S. Private*, pg. 3383
REESE ENTERPRISES, INC. - ASTRO PLASTICS DIVISION—See Reese Enterprises, Inc.; *U.S. Private*, pg. 3383
REESE ENTERPRISES, INC.; *U.S. Private*, pg. 3383
REESE ENTERPRISES, INC. - WEATHER STRIP DIVISION—See Reese Enterprises, Inc.; *U.S. Private*, pg. 3383
REESE INTEGRATED MARKETING; *U.S. Private*, pg. 3383
REESE, TOMASES & ELLICK, INC. (RT&E); *U.S. Private*, pg. 3383
REES-JONES FAMILY HOLDINGS LP; *U.S. Private*, pg. 3383
REESMANS EXCAVATING & GRADING, INC.; *U.S. Private*, pg. 3383
REETECH INTERNATIONAL CARGO & COURIER LIMITED; *Int'l*, pg. 6249
REEVE (DERBY) LIMITED—See General Motors Company; *U.S. Public*, pg. 928
REEVES CONSTRUCTION COMPANY; *U.S. Private*, pg. 3384
REEVES FLORAL PRODUCTS, INC.; *U.S. Private*, pg. 3384
REEVES HARDWARE COMPANY; *U.S. Private*, pg. 3384
REEVES IMPORT MOTORCARS INC.; *U.S. Private*, pg. 3384
REEVES INTERNATIONAL, INC.; *U.S. Private*, pg. 3384
REEVES INTERNATIONAL, INC.—See Reeves International, Inc.; *U.S. Private*, pg. 3384
REEVES LAVERDURE PUBLIC RELATIONS; *U.S. Private*, pg. 3384
REEVES OILFIELD SERVICES LTD.—See Weatherford International plc; *U.S. Public*, pg. 2339
REEVES-SAIN DRUG STORE, INC.—See Fred's Inc.; *U.S. Public*, pg. 884
REEVE STORE EQUIPMENT COMPANY; *U.S. Private*, pg. 3383
REEVES-WIEDEMAN COMPANY; *U.S. Private*, pg. 3384
REEVE TRUCKING CO.; *U.S. Private*, pg. 3384
REEVOO; *Int'l*, pg. 6249
REEVO S.P.A.; *Int'l*, pg. 6249
REF-CHEM, L.P. - BROWNFIELD—See Ref-Chem, L.P.; *U.S. Private*, pg. 3384
REF-CHEM, L.P.; *U.S. Private*, pg. 3384
REFCO EMPLOYEE SERVICES LLC—See VINCI S.A.; *Int'l*, pg. 8232
REFCO HOLDINGS INC.—See VINCI S.A.; *Int'l*, pg. 8233
REFCOMP ITALY S.R.L.—See Fujian Snowman Co., Ltd.; *Int'l*, pg. 2819
REFEL S.P.A.—See RHI Magnesita N.V.; *Int'l*, pg. 6326

REFERENCE DATA FACTORY LLC—See FD Technologies PLC; *Int'l*, pg. 2628
REFERRAL NETWORK PLUS, INC.—See Anywhere Real Estate Inc.; *U.S. Public*, pg. 142
REFEX GREEN MOBILITY LIMITED—See Refex Industries Limited; *Int'l*, pg. 6250
REFEX INDUSTRIES LIMITED; *Int'l*, pg. 6250
REFEX RENEWABLES & INFRASTRUCTURE LIMITED; *Int'l*, pg. 6250
REF HOLDINGS LIMITED; *Int'l*, pg. 6249
REFICOR S.R.O.—See Assicurazioni Generali S.p.A.; *Int'l*, pg. 647
REFINAL INDUSTRIES SAS—See Derichebourg S.A.; *Int'l*, pg. 2042
REFINANCIA S.A.—See Encore Capital Group, Inc.; *U.S. Public*, pg. 760
REFINARIA DE PETROLEO RIOGRANDENSE S.A.—See Ultrapar Participacoes S.A.; *Int'l*, pg. 8019
REFINARIA DE PETROLEOS DE MANGUINHOS S.A.; *Int'l*, pg. 6250
REFINE CO., LTD.; *Int'l*, pg. 6250
REFINED ENERGY CORP.; *Int'l*, pg. 6250
REFINED OIL PRODUCTS (PTY.) LTD.—See Sefalana Holdings Company Limited; *Int'l*, pg. 6679
REFINERIA DE CARTAGENA S.A.S.—See Ecopetrol S.A.; *Int'l*, pg. 2299
REFINERIA ISLA (CURAZAO), S.A.—See Petroleos de Venezuela S.A.; *Int'l*, pg. 5828
REFINERIA LA PAMPILLA SA—See Repsol, S.A.; *Int'l*, pg. 6292
REFINERY 29, INC.—See Monroe Capital LLC; *U.S. Private*, pg. 2773
REFINERY 29, INC.—See SoftBank Group Corp.; *Int'l*, pg. 7054
REFINERY 29, INC.—See Soros Fund Management LLC; *U.S. Private*, pg. 3716
REFINERY TERMINAL FIRE COMPANY; *U.S. Private*, pg. 3384
REFINING & MANUFACTURING RESEARCH INSTITUTE—See CPC Corporation; *Int'l*, pg. 1824
REFINING & TRADING HOLLAND N.V.—See Avista Oil AG; *Int'l*, pg. 745
REFINITIV IRELAND LIMITED—See London Stock Exchange Group plc; *Int'l*, pg. 4548
REFINITIV NORGE AS—See London Stock Exchange Group plc; *Int'l*, pg. 4548
REFINITIV US HOLDINGS INC.—See London Stock Exchange Group plc; *Int'l*, pg. 4548
REFINVERSE, INC.; *Int'l*, pg. 6250
REFLECTANCE MEDICAL, INC.—See Sotera Wireless, Inc.; *U.S. Private*, pg. 3716
REFLECTION POINTE CEMETERY, INC.—See Traditional Service Corporation; *U.S. Private*, pg. 4203
REFLECTIONS WINDOW AND PRESSURE WASHING.—See ACON Investments, LLC; *U.S. Private*, pg. 62
REFLECTIX, INC.—See Sealed Air Corporation; *U.S. Public*, pg. 1854
REFLECTOR ENTERTAINMENT LTD.—See BANDAI NAMCO Holdings Inc.; *Int'l*, pg. 829
REFLECT SCIENTIFIC, INC.; *U.S. Public*, pg. 1771
REFLECT SYSTEMS, INC.—See Creative Realities, Inc.; *U.S. Public*, pg. 593
REFLECTX SERVICES—See Maxim Healthcare Services, Inc.; *U.S. Private*, pg. 2618
REFLEX ADVANCED MATERIALS CORP.; *Int'l*, pg. 6250
REFLEX HR LIMITED—See Empresaria Group Plc; *Int'l*, pg. 2389
REFLEX INSTRUMENT NORTH AMERICA LTD.—See Imdex Limited; *Int'l*, pg. 3623
REFLEX INSTRUMENTS ASIA PACIFIC PTY LTD—See Imdex Limited; *Int'l*, pg. 3623
REFLEX INSTRUMENTS EUROPE LTD—See Imdex Limited; *Int'l*, pg. 3623
REFLEXION NETWORKS, INC.—See Apax Partners LLP; *Int'l*, pg. 506
REFLEXIS SYSTEMS GMBH—See Zebra Technologies Corporation; *U.S. Public*, pg. 2401
REFLEXIS SYSTEMS, INC.—See Zebra Technologies Corporation; *U.S. Public*, pg. 2401
REFLEXIS SYSTEMS INDIA PRIVATE LIMITED—See Zebra Technologies Corporation; *U.S. Public*, pg. 2401
REFLEXIS SYSTEMS (UK) LIMITED—See Zebra Technologies Corporation; *U.S. Public*, pg. 2401
REFLEX KFT—See Gedeon Richter Plc.; *Int'l*, pg. 2910
REFLEX PACKAGING, INC.—See Nefab AB; *Int'l*, pg. 5191
REFLEX SYSTEMS, LLC; *U.S. Private*, pg. 3384
REFNOL RESINS & CHEMICALS LIMITED; *Int'l*, pg. 6250
REFOBAR AUSTRALIA PTY LTD—See SRG Global Limited; *Int'l*, pg. 7149
REFOCUS GROUP, INC.; *U.S. Public*, pg. 1771
REFOJOULE CO., LTD.—See Fukuvi Chemical Industry Co., Ltd.; *Int'l*, pg. 2841
REFORESTATION SERVICES, INC.—See Sterling Partners; *U.S. Private*, pg. 3806
REFORMKONTOR GMBH & CO. KG; *Int'l*, pg. 6250
REFORM MASCHINENFABRIK ADOLF RABENSEIFNER GMBH & CO. KG—See ATON GmbH; *Int'l*, pg. 689

RE FORMSNET, LLC—See Lone Wolf Real Estate Technologies Inc.; *Int'l*, pg. 4548
REFORM STUDIO CO., LTD.—See AEON Co., Ltd.; *Int'l*, pg. 178
REFPLUS INC.—See Madison Industries Holdings LLC; *U.S. Private*, pg. 2543
REFRACTARIA, S.A.—See Krosaki Harima Corporation; *Int'l*, pg. 4307
REFRACTARIOS NACIONALES S.A.—See Morgan Advanced Materials plc; *Int'l*, pg. 5043
REFRACTORY INTELLECTUAL PROPERTY GMBH & CO KG—See RHI Magnesita N.V.; *Int'l*, pg. 6326
REFRACTORY SALES & SERVICE CO., INCORPORATED—See CFS Group, Inc.; *Int'l*, pg. 1430
REFRESCO BEVERAGES US INC. - SAN ANTONIO—See KKR & Co. Inc.; *U.S. Public*, pg. 1263
REFRESCO BEVERAGES US INC. - SIKESTON—See KKR & Co. Inc.; *U.S. Public*, pg. 1263
REFRESCO BEVERAGES US INC.—See KKR & Co. Inc.; *U.S. Public*, pg. 1263
REFRESCO B.V.—See KKR & Co. Inc.; *U.S. Public*, pg. 1263
REFRESCO DRINKS UK LTD.—See KKR & Co. Inc.; *U.S. Public*, pg. 1263
REFRESCO GROUP N.V.—See KKR & Co. Inc.; *U.S. Public*, pg. 1263
REFRESCO (NELSON) LIMITED—See KKR & Co. Inc.; *U.S. Public*, pg. 1263
REFRESHMENT PRODUCT SERVICES, INC.—See The Coca-Cola Company; *U.S. Public*, pg. 2065
REFRESHMENT SERVICES INC.; *U.S. Private*, pg. 3384
REFRESH PLASTICS PTY LTD—See Eneco Refresh Limited; *Int'l*, pg. 2411
REFRESH WATERS PTY LTD. - OZ WATER FILTERS—See Eneco Refresh Limited; *Int'l*, pg. 2411
REFRESH WATERS PTY LTD.—See Eneco Refresh Limited; *Int'l*, pg. 2411
REFRESH WATERS QUEENSLAND PTY LTD—See Eneco Refresh Limited; *Int'l*, pg. 2411
REFRICENTER OF MIAMI INC.—See Refricentro Inc.; *U.S. Private*, pg. 3384
REFRICENTRO INC.; *U.S. Private*, pg. 3384
REFRIGERATED FOOD EXPRESS INC.; *U.S. Private*, pg. 3384
REFRIGERATION ELECTRICAL ENGINEERING CORPORATION; *Int'l*, pg. 6250
REFRIGERATION & ELECTRIC SUPPLY CO.; *U.S. Private*, pg. 3384
REFRIGERATION INDUSTRIES CO. S.A.K.; *Int'l*, pg. 6250
REFRIGERATION SALES CORPORATION—See Novacap Management Inc.; *Int'l*, pg. 5454
REFRIGERATION SUPPLIES DISTRIBUTORS; *U.S. Private*, pg. 3384
REFRIGERATION SUPPLIES DISTRIBUTORS—See Refrigeration Supplies Distributors; *U.S. Private*, pg. 3384
REFRIGERATION SUPPLIES INC.; *U.S. Private*, pg. 3385
REFRIGIWEAR, INC.; *U.S. Private*, pg. 3385
REFTRANS, S.A.—See Trane Technologies Plc; *Int'l*, pg. 7892
REFUEL, LLC—See First Reserve Management, L.P.; *U.S. Private*, pg. 1526
REFUEL OPERATING COMPANY, LLC—See First Reserve Management, L.P.; *U.S. Private*, pg. 1526
REFUELS N.V.; *Int'l*, pg. 6250
THE REFUGE, A HEALING PLACE, LLC—See Acadia Healthcare Company, Inc.; *U.S. Public*, pg. 31
THE REFUGE-THE NEST, LLC—See Acadia Healthcare Company, Inc.; *U.S. Public*, pg. 31
REFURBISHED OFFICE FURNITURE, INC.; *U.S. Private*, pg. 3385
REFUSE, INC.—See Waste Management, Inc.; *U.S. Public*, pg. 2332
REFUSE SERVICES, INC.—See Waste Management, Inc.; *U.S. Public*, pg. 2331
REGA FARMA-PROMOCAO DE PRODUTOS FARMACEUTICOS, S.A—See Angelini ACRAF S.p.A.; *Int'l*, pg. 460
REGALA INVEST AD; *Int'l*, pg. 6251
REGAL AMUSEMENT MACHINE SALES LTD.—See Light & Wonder, Inc.; *U.S. Public*, pg. 1314
REGAL ASIAN INVESTMENTS LIMITED—See VGI Partners Global Investments Limited; *Int'l*, pg. 8182
REGAL ASSETS, LLC; *U.S. Private*, pg. 3385
REGAL AUSTRALIA PTY LTD.—See Regal Rexnord Corporation; *U.S. Public*, pg. 1773
REGAL AUTOMOTIVE GROUP; *U.S. Private*, pg. 3385
REGAL AVIATION INSURANCE—See GTCR LLC; *U.S. Private*, pg. 1804
REGAL BANK; *U.S. Private*, pg. 3385
REGAL BELOIT AMERICA, INC.—See Regal Rexnord Corporation; *U.S. Public*, pg. 1773
REGAL BELOIT CANADA, AN ALBERTA LIMITED PARTNERSHIP—See Regal Rexnord Corporation; *U.S. Public*, pg. 1773
REGAL BELOIT FZE—See Regal Rexnord Corporation; *U.S. Public*, pg. 1773
REGAL BELOIT ISRAEL—See CMG Pty. Ltd.; *Int'l*, pg. 1670
REGAL BELOIT NEW ZEALAND LTD.—See Regal Rexnord Corporation; *U.S. Public*, pg. 1773
REGAL BELOIT SPAIN, S.A.—See Regal Rexnord Corporation; *U.S. Public*, pg. 1773
REGAL BELOIT SPAIN SA—See Regal Rexnord Corporation; *U.S. Public*, pg. 1773
REGAL BELOIT (WUXI) CO., LTD.—See Regal Rexnord Corporation; *U.S. Public*, pg. 1773
REG ALBERT LEA, LLC—See Chevron Corporation; *U.S. Public*, pg. 487
REGAL BUILDING MATERIALS LTD.; *Int'l*, pg. 6250
REGAL CAST INC—See PRL Inc.; *U.S. Private*, pg. 3269
REGAL CERAMICS LIMITED; *Int'l*, pg. 6250
REGAL CHEMICAL COMPANY—See SiteOne Landscape Supply, Inc.; *U.S. Public*, pg. 1889
REGAL CINEMAS CORPORATION—See Cineworld Group plc; *Int'l*, pg. 1611
REGAL CINEMAS, INC.—See Cineworld Group plc; *Int'l*, pg. 1611
REGAL CORPORATION; *Int'l*, pg. 6250
REGAL CORPORATION; *U.S. Private*, pg. 3385
REGAL CROWN TECHNOLOGY LIMITED—See RC365 Holding Plc; *Int'l*, pg. 6227
REGAL CUTTING TOOLS. INC—See YG-1 Co., Ltd; *Int'l*, pg. 8579
REGAL DIVING AND TOURS LIMITED—See Cox & Kings Limited; *Int'l*, pg. 1823
REGALE INTERNATIONAL TRAVEL COMPANY LTD.—See EQT AB; *Int'l*, pg. 2478
REGAL ELECTRIC, INC.; *U.S. Private*, pg. 3385
REGAL ELECTRONICS, INC.; *U.S. Private*, pg. 3385
REGAL ENTERTAINMENT & CONSULTANTS LTD.; *Int'l*, pg. 6251
REGAL ESTATE MANAGEMENT LIMITED—See Century City International Holdings Ltd; *Int'l*, pg. 1418
REGALETTE—See LDC SA; *Int'l*, pg. 4431
REGAL GIFTS CORPORATION—See York Management Services, Inc.; *U.S. Private*, pg. 4591
REGAL GROUP SERVICES LIMITED—See Enwell Energy plc; *Int'l*, pg. 2456
REGAL HOTELS INTERNATIONAL HOLDINGS LIMITED—See Century City International Holdings Ltd; *Int'l*, pg. 1418
REGAL HOTELS INVESTMENT & MANAGEMENT (SHANGHAI) LTD—See Century City International Holdings Ltd; *Int'l*, pg. 1418
REGALIAA REALTY LTD.—See Karvy Financial Services Limited; *Int'l*, pg. 4086
REGAL INDUSTRIES LLC—See Salem Tools, Inc.; *U.S. Private*, pg. 3531
REGAL INTERNATIONAL GROUP LTD.; *Int'l*, pg. 6251
REGALLIA HOLDINGS & INVESTMENTS PUBLIC LTD.; *Int'l*, pg. 6251
REGAL LAGER, INC.; *U.S. Private*, pg. 3385
REGAL LOGISTICS; *U.S. Private*, pg. 3385
REGAL MARINE INDUSTRIES, INC.; *U.S. Private*, pg. 3385
REGAL MARKETING, INC.; *U.S. Private*, pg. 3385
REGAL METAL PRODUCTS CO.; *U.S. Private*, pg. 3385
REGALMONT (SABAH) SDN. BHD.—See Ireka Corporation Berhad; *Int'l*, pg. 3806
REGAL MOTORS INC.; *U.S. Private*, pg. 3385
REGAL NISSAN, INC.; *U.S. Private*, pg. 3385
REGAL OIL INC.; *U.S. Private*, pg. 3385
REGAL PAINTS UGANDA LIMITED—See Crown Paints Kenya Plc; *Int'l*, pg. 1858
REGAL PARTNERS LIMITED; *Int'l*, pg. 6251
REGAL-PIEDMONT PLASTICS, LLC—See Piedmont Plastics, Inc.; *U.S. Private*, pg. 3178
REGAL-PIEDMONT PLASTICS, LLC—See Regal Plastic Supply Co.; *U.S. Private*, pg. 3385
REGAL PLASTIC SUPPLY COMPANY, INC.; *U.S. Private*, pg. 3385
REGAL PLASTIC SUPPLY CO.; *U.S. Private*, pg. 3385
REGAL POWER TRANSMISSION SOLUTIONS—See Regal Rexnord Corporation; *U.S. Public*, pg. 1773
REGAL PRESS INC.; *U.S. Private*, pg. 3385
REGAL REXNORD CORPORATION; *U.S. Public*, pg. 1771
REGAL RIVERSIDE HOTEL LIMITED—See Century City International Holdings Ltd; *Int'l*, pg. 1418
REGAL & ROYAL WINE CO.—See Jackson Family Wines, Inc.; *U.S. Private*, pg. 2176
REGAL STEEL CO.; *U.S. Private*, pg. 3385
THE REGAL SUNDERLAND STADIUM LIMITED—See William Hill Plc; *Int'l*, pg. 8413
REGAL SUPPLY COMPANY INC.; *U.S. Private*, pg. 3385
REGAL TECHNOLOGIES LLC—See e-Complish LLC; *U.S. Private*, pg. 1302
REGAL TEMPORARY SERVICES INC.; *U.S. Private*, pg. 3386
REGAL TRANSPORT GROUP PTY. LTD.—See K&S Corporation Limited; *Int'l*, pg. 4039
REGAL TRAVEL, INC.—See International Management Services Group, Inc.; *U.S. Private*, pg. 2118
REGAL WARE, INC.; *U.S. Private*, pg. 3386
REGAL WARE, INC.—See Regal Ware, Inc.; *U.S. Private*, pg. 3386
REGAL WINGS, INC.; *U.S. Private*, pg. 3386
REGAN CAMPBELL WARD MCCANN—See The Interpublic Group of Companies, Inc.; *U.S. Public*, pg. 2101
REGAN CAMPBELL WARD WEST—See The Interpublic Group of Companies, Inc.; *U.S. Public*, pg. 2101
REGAN COMMUNICATIONS GROUP, INC. - FLORIDA—See Regan Communications Group, Inc.; *U.S. Private*, pg. 3386
REGAN COMMUNICATIONS GROUP, INC. - PROVIDENCE—See Regan Communications Group, Inc.; *U.S. Private*, pg. 3386
REGAN COMMUNICATIONS GROUP, INC.; *U.S. Private*, pg. 3386
REGAN HOLDING CORPORATION; *U.S. Private*, pg. 3386
REGAN TECHNOLOGIES CORPORATION; *U.S. Private*, pg. 3386
R. E. GARRISON TRUCKING INC.; *U.S. Private*, pg. 3333
REGATE TECHNOLOGY, INC.—See AWC Frac Valves Inc.; *U.S. Private*, pg. 410
REG ATLANTA, LLC—See Chevron Corporation; *U.S. Public*, pg. 487
REGATTA AS—See Regatta Ltd.; *Int'l*, pg. 6251
REGATTA BENELUX BV—See Regatta Ltd.; *Int'l*, pg. 6251
REGATTA GMBH—See Regatta Ltd.; *Int'l*, pg. 6251
REGATTA ISRAEL LTD.—See Regatta Ltd.; *Int'l*, pg. 6251
REGATTA ITALIA S.R.L.—See Regatta Ltd.; *Int'l*, pg. 6251
REGATTA LTD.; *Int'l*, pg. 6251
REGATTA MEDICAL HOLDINGS LLC—See GTCR LLC; *U.S. Private*, pg. 1806
REGATTA NEDERLAND—See Regatta Ltd.; *Int'l*, pg. 6251
REGATTA PACIFIC ALLIANCE USA INC.—See Li & Fung Limited; *Int'l*, pg. 4480
REGATTA POLSKA SP. Z O.O.—See Regatta Ltd.; *Int'l*, pg. 6251
REGATTA SAS—See Regatta Ltd.; *Int'l*, pg. 6251
REGATTA SERVICE FINLAND OY—See Regatta Ltd.; *Int'l*, pg. 6251
REGATTA S.R.O.—See Regatta Ltd.; *Int'l*, pg. 6251
REGATTA SWEDEN AB—See Regatta Ltd.; *Int'l*, pg. 6251
REGATTA USA, LLC—See Regatta Ltd.; *Int'l*, pg. 6251
REGBERG & ASSOCIATES, INC.; *U.S. Private*, pg. 3386
REG DANVILLE, LLC—See Chevron Corporation; *U.S. Public*, pg. 487
REGED, INC.—See Gryphon Investors, LLC; *U.S. Private*, pg. 1799
REGEN BIOPHARMA, INC.—See Bio-Matrix Scientific Group, Inc.; *U.S. Public*, pg. 332
REGENBOGEN AG; *Int'l*, pg. 6251
REGENCE BLUECROSS BLUESHIELD OF OREGON—See Cambia Health Solutions, Inc.; *U.S. Private*, pg. 726
REGENCE BLUECROSS BLUESHIELD OF UTAH—See Cambia Health Solutions, Inc.; *U.S. Private*, pg. 726
REGENCE HEALTH NETWORK, INC.; *U.S. Private*, pg. 3386
REGENCE HMO OREGON, INC.—See Cambia Health Solutions, Inc.; *U.S. Private*, pg. 726
REGENCE LIFE & HEALTH INSURANCE CO.—See Cambia Health Solutions, Inc.; *U.S. Private*, pg. 726
REGENCELL BIOSCIENCE HOLDINGS LIMITED; *Int'l*, pg. 6251
REGENCY AFFILIATES, INC.; *U.S. Public*, pg. 1774
REGENCY ALLIANCE INSURANCE PLC.; *Int'l*, pg. 6251
REGENCY AT DOMINION VALLEY LLC—See Apollo Global Management, Inc.; *U.S. Public*, pg. 150
REGENCY AUTO INVESTMENTS INC; *Int'l*, pg. 6252
REGENCY-BRENTANO, INC.—See Odyssey Investment Partners, LLC; *U.S. Private*, pg. 2995
REGENCY CENTERS CORPORATION; *U.S. Public*, pg. 1774
REGENCY CENTERS, L.P.—See Regency Centers Corporation; *U.S. Public*, pg. 1774
REGENCY CERAMICS LIMITED; *Int'l*, pg. 6252
REGENCY COMMERCIAL ASSOCIATES LLC—See Regency Management Service LLC; *U.S. Private*, pg. 3386
REGENCY DESOTO-HESCO SERVICES LLC—See Energy Transfer LP; *U.S. Public*, pg. 764
REGENCY ENERGY PARTNERS LP—See Energy Transfer LP; *U.S. Public*, pg. 763
REGENCY ENTERPRISES INC.; *U.S. Private*, pg. 3386
REGENCY ESCROW CORPORATION—See First American Financial Corporation; *U.S. Public*, pg. 838
REGENCY FIELD SERVICES LLC—See Energy Transfer LP; *U.S. Public*, pg. 763
REGENCY FINCORP LTD.; *Int'l*, pg. 6252
REGENCY FRANCHISE GROUP, LLC—See The ODP Corporation; *U.S. Public*, pg. 2118
REGENCY GAS SERVICES LP—See Energy Transfer LP; *U.S. Public*, pg. 763
REGENCY HOSPITAL COMPANY OF MACON, LLC—See Select Medical Holdings Corporation; *U.S. Public*, pg. 1858
REGENCY HOSPITAL COMPANY OF MERIDIAN, L.L.C.—See Select Medical Holdings Corporation; *U.S. Public*, pg. 1858

REGENCY FINCORP LTD.
CORPORATE AFFILIATIONS

REGENCY HOSPITAL COMPANY OF SOUTH ATLANTA, L.L.C.—See Select Medical Holdings Corporation; *U.S. Public*, pg. 1858
REGENCY HOSPITAL COMPANY OF SOUTH CAROLINA, L.L.C.—See Select Medical Holdings Corporation; *U.S. Public*, pg. 1858
REGENCY HOSPITAL LIMITED; *Int'l*, pg. 6252
REGENCY HOSPITAL OF CINCINNATI, LLC—See Select Medical Holdings Corporation; *U.S. Public*, pg. 1858
REGENCY HOSPITAL OF COLUMBUS, LLC—See Select Medical Holdings Corporation; *U.S. Public*, pg. 1858
REGENCY HOSPITAL OF COVINGTON, LLC—See Select Medical Holdings Corporation; *U.S. Public*, pg. 1858
REGENCY HOSPITAL OF FORT WORTH, LLLP—See Select Medical Holdings Corporation; *U.S. Public*, pg. 1859
REGENCY HOSPITAL OF GREENVILLE, LLC—See Select Medical Holdings Corporation; *U.S. Public*, pg. 1859
REGENCY HOSPITAL OF JACKSON, LLC—See Select Medical Holdings Corporation; *U.S. Public*, pg. 1859
REGENCY HOSPITAL OF MINNEAPOLIS, LLC—See Select Medical Holdings Corporation; *U.S. Public*, pg. 1859
REGENCY HOSPITAL OF NORTH CENTRAL OHIO, LLC—See Select Medical Holdings Corporation; *U.S. Public*, pg. 1859
REGENCY HOSPITAL OF NORTHWEST ARKANSAS, LLC—See Select Medical Holdings Corporation; *U.S. Public*, pg. 1859
REGENCY HOSPITAL OF NORTHWEST INDIANA, LLC—See Select Medical Holdings Corporation; *U.S. Public*, pg. 1859
REGENCY HOSPITAL OF SOUTHERN MISSISSIPPI, LLC—See Select Medical Holdings Corporation; *U.S. Public*, pg. 1859
THE REGENCY HOTEL—See Loews Corporation; *U.S. Public*, pg. 1340
REGENCY INSURANCE BROKERAGE SERVICES, INC.—See Caisse de Depot et Placement du Quebec; *Int'l*, pg. 1257
REGENCY INSURANCE BROKERAGE SERVICES, INC.—See KKR & Co, Inc.; *U.S. Public*, pg. 1265
REGENCY-KLEBAN PROPERTIES, LLC—See Regency Centers Corporation; *U.S. Public*, pg. 1774
REGENCY LAND SDN. BHD.—See GLOMAC Berhad; *Int'l*, pg. 3008
REGENCY MANAGEMENT SERVICE LLC; *U.S. Private*, pg. 3386
REGENCY MEDIA PTY. LTD.; *Int'l*, pg. 6252
REGENCY NEM INSURANCE GHANA LIMITED—See Regency Alliance Insurance Plc.; *Int'l*, pg. 6251
REGENCY OFFICE PRODUCTS, LLC—See The ODP Corporation; *U.S. Public*, pg. 2118
REGENCY PARK SENIOR LIVING, INC.—See Fish Construction Company; *U.S. Private*, pg. 1533
REGENCY PIPELINE LLC—See Energy Transfer LP; *U.S. Public*, pg. 764
REGENCY PLASTICS COMPANY LTD.; *Int'l*, pg. 6252
REGENCY PLASTICS - UBLY INC.; *U.S. Private*, pg. 3386
REGENCY SPECIALIST HOSPITAL SDN.BHD.—See EQT AB; *Int'l*, pg. 2475
REGENCY STEEL ASIA PTE LTD.—See Mitsui & Co., Ltd.; *Int'l*, pg. 4980
REGENCY STEEL JAPAN LTD.—See Keppel Corporation Limited; *Int'l*, pg. 4132
REGENCY TECHNOLOGIES, INC.; *U.S. Private*, pg. 3386
REGENCY THERMOGRAPHERS—See Taylor Corporation; *U.S. Private*, pg. 3939
REGENCY TRANSPORTATION INC.; *U.S. Private*, pg. 3386
REGENCY TRAVEL INC.; *U.S. Private*, pg. 3386
REGENCY TRUST LIMITED; *Int'l*, pg. 6252
REGENCY UTICA GAS GATHERING LLC—See Energy Transfer LP; *U.S. Public*, pg. 764
REGENER8 RESOURCES NL; *Int'l*, pg. 6252
REGENERATIVE MEDICINE SOLUTIONS LLC; *U.S. Private*, pg. 3386
REGENERON CANADA COMPANY—See Regeneron Pharmaceuticals, Inc.; *U.S. Public*, pg. 1775
REGENERON FRANCE SAS—See Regeneron Pharmaceuticals, Inc.; *U.S. Public*, pg. 1775
REGENERON IRELAND DESIGNATED ACTIVITY COMPANY—See Regeneron Pharmaceuticals, Inc.; *U.S. Public*, pg. 1775
REGENERON IRELAND—See Regeneron Pharmaceuticals, Inc.; *U.S. Public*, pg. 1775
REGENERON ITALY S.R.L.—See Regeneron Pharmaceuticals, Inc.; *U.S. Public*, pg. 1775
REGENERON JAPAN KK—See Regeneron Pharmaceuticals, Inc.; *U.S. Public*, pg. 1775
REGENERON NL B.V.—See Regeneron Pharmaceuticals, Inc.; *U.S. Public*, pg. 1775
REGENERON PHARMACEUTICALS, INC.; *U.S. Public*, pg. 1774
REGENERON—See Regeneron Pharmaceuticals, Inc.; *U.S. Public*, pg. 1775

REGENERSIS (BUCHAREST) SRL—See Francisco Partners Management, LP; *U.S. Private*, pg. 1588
REGENERSIS (CZECH) S.R.O—See Francisco Partners Management, LP; *U.S. Private*, pg. 1588
REGENERSIS (DEUTSCHLAND) GMBH—See Francisco Partners Management, LP; *U.S. Private*, pg. 1588
REGENERSIS DIGITAL CARE AB—See Francisco Partners Management, LP; *U.S. Private*, pg. 1588
REGENERSIS (GLENROTHES) LTD.—See Francisco Partners Management, LP; *U.S. Private*, pg. 1588
REGENERSIS (HUNTINGDON) LTD.—See Francisco Partners Management, LP; *U.S. Private*, pg. 1588
REGENERSIS INC.—See Francisco Partners Management, LP; *U.S. Private*, pg. 1588
REGENERSIS ISTANBUL TEKNOLOJI DANISMANLIGI LIMITED SIRKETI—See Francisco Partners Management, LP; *U.S. Private*, pg. 1588
REGENERSIS MEXICO S.A,DE C.V.—See Francisco Partners Management, LP; *U.S. Private*, pg. 1588
REGENERSIS (NEDERLAND) BV—See Francisco Partners Management, LP; *U.S. Private*, pg. 1588
REGENERSIS (PORTUGAL) LTD.—See Francisco Partners Management, LP; *U.S. Private*, pg. 1588
REGENERSIS RUS O.O.O.—See Francisco Partners Management, LP; *U.S. Private*, pg. 1588
REGENERSIS (SOMMERDA) GMBH—See Francisco Partners Management, LP; *U.S. Private*, pg. 1588
REGENERSIS (SOUTH AFRICA) (PTY) LTD—See Francisco Partners Management, LP; *U.S. Private*, pg. 1588
REGENERSIS (SPAIN) COMANDITARIA SIMPLE—See Francisco Partners Management, LP; *U.S. Private*, pg. 1588
REGENERSIS (WARSAW) SP.Z.O.O.—See Francisco Partners Management, LP; *U.S. Private*, pg. 1588
REGENERX BIOPHARMACEUTICALS INC.; *U.S. Public*, pg. 1775
REGENERYS LTD; *Int'l*, pg. 6252
REGENERYS LTD—See Regenerys Ltd; *Int'l*, pg. 6252
REGENESIS BIOMEDICAL, INC; *U.S. Private*, pg. 3387
REGENESYS BVBA—See Healios K.K.; *Int'l*, pg. 3302
REGENEUS ANIMAL HEALTH PTY LTD—See Cambium Bio Limited; *Int'l*, pg. 1269
REGENICIN, INC.; *U.S. Public*, pg. 1775
REGEN III CORP.; *Int'l*, pg. 6251
REGENSBURGER FRISCHMÖRTEL GMBH & CO.KG—See BERGER Holding GmbH; *Int'l*, pg. 979
REGENT AEROSPACE CORPORATION; *U.S. Private*, pg. 3387
REGENT BANK NA—See Regent Capital Corporation; *U.S. Private*, pg. 3387
REGENT BERLIN GMBH—See Formosa International Hotels Corp.; *Int'l*, pg. 2734
REGENT CAPITAL CORPORATION; *U.S. Private*, pg. 3387
REGENT CONTRACTING CORP.; *U.S. Private*, pg. 3387
REGENT DRUGS LIMITED—See Teva Pharmaceutical Industries, Ltd.; *Int'l*, pg. 7579
REGENT ELECTRON (CHONG QING) CO., LTD.—See Taiwan Surface Mounting Technology Corp.; *Int'l*, pg. 7424
REGENT ELECTRON (DONGGUAN) CO., LTD.—See Taiwan Surface Mounting Technology Corp.; *Int'l*, pg. 7424
REGENT ELECTRON (HE FEI) CO., LTD.—See Taiwan Surface Mounting Technology Corp.; *Int'l*, pg. 7424
REGENT ELECTRON (NINGBO) CO., LTD.—See Taiwan Surface Mounting Technology Corp.; *Int'l*, pg. 7424
REGENT ELECTRON (SUZHOU) CO., LTD.—See Taiwan Surface Mounting Technology Corp.; *Int'l*, pg. 7424
REGENT ELECTRON (XIAMEN) CO., LTD.—See Taiwan Surface Mounting Technology Corp.; *Int'l*, pg. 7424
REGENT ELECTRON (XIAN YANG) CO., LTD.—See Taiwan Surface Mounting Technology Corp.; *Int'l*, pg. 7424
REGENT ENTERPRISES LIMITED; *Int'l*, pg. 6252
REGENT ENTERTAINMENT, INC.—See Regent Entertainment Partnership, L.P.; *U.S. Private*, pg. 3387
REGENT ENTERTAINMENT PARTNERSHIP, L.P.; *U.S. Private*, pg. 3387
REGENT FINANCIAL SERVICES LIMITED—See Regent Pacific Group Limited; *Int'l*, pg. 6252
REGENT GAS HOLDINGS LIMITED; *Int'l*, pg. 6252
REGEN THERAPEUTICS LIMITED; *Int'l*, pg. 6251
REGENT HOSE & HYDRAULICS LIMITED—See Illinois Tool Works Inc.; *U.S. Public*, pg. 1110
REGENT INSURANCE COMPANY—See QBE Insurance Group Limited; *Int'l*, pg. 6137
REGENT INTERNATIONAL; *U.S. Private*, pg. 3387
REGENT, L.P.; *U.S. Private*, pg. 3387
REGENT MOTORS LIMITED—See Sime Darby Berhad; *Int'l*, pg. 6929
REGENT PACIFIC GROUP LIMITED; *Int'l*, pg. 6252
REGENT PACIFIC PROPERTIES INC.; *Int'l*, pg. 6252
REGENT PUBLISHING SERVICES LIMITED—See Lion Rock Group Ltd; *Int'l*, pg. 4519
REGENT SEVEN SEAS CRUISES UK LTD—See Norwegian Cruise Line Holdings Ltd.; *U.S. Public*, pg. 1543
REGENT SPORTS CORPORATION; *U.S. Private*, pg. 3387
REGENT SQUARE CAPITAL, LLC; *U.S. Private*, pg. 3387

REGENT'S SCHOOL OF FASHION & DESIGN—See Regent's University London; *Int'l*, pg. 6253
REGENT'S UNIVERSITY LONDON; *Int'l*, pg. 6253
REGENT SYSTEMS, INC.; *U.S. Private*, pg. 3387
REGENT TAIPEI CO., LTD.—See Formosa International Hotels Corp.; *Int'l*, pg. 2734
REGENT TECHNOLOGIES, INC.; *U.S. Private*, pg. 3387
REGENT VENTURES LTD.; *Int'l*, pg. 6253
REGENTYS CORPORATION—See Generex Biotechnology Corporation; *U.S. Public*, pg. 930
REGENXBIO INC.; *U.S. Public*, pg. 1775
REGENX TECH CORP.; *Int'l*, pg. 6253
REG GEISMAR, LLC—See Chevron Corporation; *U.S. Public*, pg. 487
REG GERMANY GMBH—See Chevron Corporation; *U.S. Public*, pg. 487
REGGIANA RIDUTTORI S.R.L.—See Interpump Group S.p.A.; *Int'l*, pg. 3757
REGGIANA RIDUTTORI (SUZHOU) CO./LTD.—See Interpump Group S.p.A.; *Int'l*, pg. 3757
REGGIANI MACCHINE S.P.A.—See Siris Capital Group, LLC; *U.S. Private*, pg. 3673
REG GRAYS HARBOR, LLC—See Chevron Corporation; *U.S. Public*, pg. 488
REG HOUSTON, LLC—See Chevron Corporation; *U.S. Public*, pg. 488
REGIE 1 S.C.S.—See Vivendi SE; *Int'l*, pg. 8275
REGIE AUTONOME DES TRANSPORTS PARISIENS; *Int'l*, pg. 6253
REGIE NETWORKS BELGIUM SA—See NRJ Group SA; *Int'l*, pg. 5474
REGIE NETWORKS LEMAN SAS—See NRJ Group SA; *Int'l*, pg. 5474
REGIE NETWORKS SAS—See NRJ Group SA; *Int'l*, pg. 5474
REGIER CARR & MONROE LLP; *U.S. Private*, pg. 3388
REGIMEN EQUITY PARTNERS INC.; *Int'l*, pg. 6253
REGINA COMMUNITY NURSING CENTER; *U.S. Private*, pg. 3388
REGINA HEALTH LTD—See Vitamins Direct (UK) Limited; *Int'l*, pg. 8258
REGINA MIRACLE INTERNATIONAL HOLDINGS LTD.; *Int'l*, pg. 6253
REGINA MIRACLE INTERNATIONAL (VIETNAM) LIMITED CO., LTD.—See Regina Miracle International Holdings Ltd.; *Int'l*, pg. 6254
REGINA MIRACLE INTERNATIONAL (VIETNAM) LIMITED—See Regina Miracle International Holdings Ltd.; *Int'l*, pg. 6253
R.E. GINNA NUCLEAR POWER PLANT, LLC—See Constellation Energy Corporation; *U.S. Public*, pg. 571
REGINOVA GMBH.—See MVV Energie AG; *Int'l*, pg. 5110
REGIOHELDEN GMBH—See Stroer SE & Co. KGaA; *Int'l*, pg. 7242
REGIO MOLKEREI BEIDER BASEL AG—See Emmi AG; *Int'l*, pg. 2385
REGION 13 EDUCATION SERVICE CENTER; *U.S. Private*, pg. 3388
REGIONAL ACCEPTANCE CORPORATION—See Truist Financial Corporation; *U.S. Public*, pg. 2199
REGIONAL AIRPORT AUTHORITY; *U.S. Private*, pg. 3388
REGIONAL AIR SERVICES—See AirKenya Aviation Ltd.; *Int'l*, pg. 248
REGIONAL BRANDS INC.; *U.S. Private*, pg. 1775
REGIONALBUS BRAUNSCHWEIG GMBH—See Deutsche Bahn AG; *Int'l*, pg. 2052
REGIONAL BUSINESS SYSTEMS INC.—See Kensington Court Limited; *Int'l*, pg. 4128
REGIONAL BUS STUTTGART GMBH—See Deutsche Bahn AG; *Int'l*, pg. 2052
REGIONAL CANCER TREATMENT CENTER, LTD.—See Community Health Systems, Inc.; *U.S. Public*, pg. 556
REGIONALCARE HOSPITAL PARTNERS, INC.—See Apollo Global Management, Inc.; *U.S. Public*, pg. 154
REGIONAL CENTER OF THE EAST BAY; *U.S. Private*, pg. 3388
REGIONAL & CITY AIRPORTS LIMITED—See Rigby Group (RG) PLC; *Int'l*, pg. 6340
REGIONAL COMPAGNIE AERIENNE EUROPEENNE—See Air France-KLM S.A.; *Int'l*, pg. 238
REGIONAL CONSTRUCTION CORP.—See National Realty & Development Corp.; *U.S. Private*, pg. 2861
REGIONAL CONTAINER LINE (HK) CO., LTD.—See Regional Container Lines Public Company Limited; *Int'l*, pg. 6254
REGIONAL CONTAINER LINES PTE. LTD.—See Regional Container Lines Public Company Limited; *Int'l*, pg. 6254
REGIONAL CONTAINER LINES PUBLIC COMPANY LIMITED; *Int'l*, pg. 6254
REGIONAL CONTAINER LINES SHIPPING CO., LTD.—See Regional Container Lines Public Company Limited; *Int'l*, pg. 6254
REGIONAL DIALYSIS CENTER OF LANCASTER LLC—See Nautic Partners, LLC; *U.S. Private*, pg. 2870
REGIONAL DIALYSIS CENTER OF MESQUITE LLC—See Nautic Partners, LLC; *U.S. Private*, pg. 2870
REGIONAL DOORS & HARDWARE; *Int'l*, pg. 6254

REGIONAL ECONOMY VITALIZATION CORPORATION OF JAPAN—See Deposit Insurance Corporation of Japan; *Int'l*, pg. 2041
REGIONAL EMERGENCY MEDICAL SERVICES AUTHORITY; *U.S. Private*, pg. 3388
REGIONAL EMPLOYEE ASSISTANCE PROGRAM—See Community Health Systems, Inc.; *U.S. Public*, pg. 556
REGIONAL ENERGY HOLDINGS, INC.; *U.S. Private*, pg. 3388
REGIONAL EXPLORATION MANAGEMENT PTY LTD—See Diatreme Resources Limited; *Int'l*, pg. 2107
REGIONAL EXPRESS HOLDINGS LIMITED; *Int'l*, pg. 6254
REGIONAL EXPRESS PTY LIMITED—See REGIONAL EXPRESS HOLDINGS LIMITED; *Int'l*, pg. 6254
REGIONAL FINANCE COMPANY OF NEW MEXICO, LLC—See Regional Management Corp.; *U.S. Public*, pg. 1776
REGIONAL FINANCE COMPANY OF OKLAHOMA, LLC—See Regional Management Corp.; *U.S. Public*, pg. 1776
REGIONAL FINANCE CORPORATION OF ALABAMA—See Regional Management Corp.; *U.S. Public*, pg. 1776
REGIONAL FINANCE CORPORATION OF GEORGIA—See Regional Management Corp.; *U.S. Public*, pg. 1776
REGIONAL FINANCE CORPORATION OF NORTH CAROLINA—See Regional Management Corp.; *U.S. Public*, pg. 1776
REGIONAL FINANCE CORPORATION OF SOUTH CAROLINA—See Regional Management Corp.; *U.S. Public*, pg. 1776
REGIONAL FINANCE CORPORATION OF TENNESSEE—See Regional Management Corp.; *U.S. Public*, pg. 1776
REGIONAL FINANCE CORPORATION OF TEXAS—See Regional Management Corp.; *U.S. Public*, pg. 1776
REGIONAL FOOD BANK OF OKLAHOMA; *U.S. Private*, pg. 3388
REGIONAL GROUP AUSTRALIA PTY. LIMITED—See MAAS Group Holdings Limited; *Int'l*, pg. 4618
REGIONAL HEALTH PROPERTIES, INC.; *U.S. Public*, pg. 1775
REGIONALHELPWANTED.COM, INC.—See Ziff Davis, Inc.; *U.S. Public*, pg. 2404
REGIONAL INDUSTRIAL DEVELOPMENT CORPORATION OF SOUTHWESTERN PENNSYLVANIA INC.; *U.S. Private*, pg. 3388
REGIONAL INTERNATIONAL CORP.; *U.S. Private*, pg. 3388
REGIONAL JET CENTER BV—See Air France-KLM S.A.; *Int'l*, pg. 238
REGIONAL MANAGEMENT CORP.; *U.S. Public*, pg. 1776
REGIONAL MANAGEMENT, INC.; *U.S. Private*, pg. 3388
REGIONAL MANAGEMENT RECEIVABLES, LLC—See Regional Management Corp.; *U.S. Public*, pg. 1776
REGIONAL MEDICAL CENTER BAYONET POINT—See HCA Healthcare, Inc.; *U.S. Public*, pg. 1007
REGIONAL MEDICAL CENTER OF SAN JOSE—See HCA Healthcare, Inc.; *U.S. Public*, pg. 1007
REGIONAL MERCHANTS MARITIME LTD.—See Regional Container Lines Public Company Limited; *Int'l*, pg. 6254
REGIONAL MISSOURI BANK—See RMB Bancshares, Inc.; *U.S. Private*, pg. 3451
REGIONALNOE AGROPROIZVODSTVENNOE OBJEDINENIE LLC—See AFI Development PLC; *Int'l*, pg. 189
REGIONALNY PARK PRZEMYSLOWY SWIDNIK SP. Z O.O.—See Leonardo S.p.A.; *Int'l*, pg. 4460
REGIONAL ONE HEALTH; *U.S. Private*, pg. 3388
REGIONAL ONE, INC.—See Exchange Income Corporation; *Int'l*, pg. 2579
REGIONAL PHYSICAL THERAPY CENTER, LIMITED PARTNERSHIP—See U.S. Physical Therapy, Inc.; *U.S. Public*, pg. 2216
REGIONAL POWER, INC.—See Connor, Clark & Lunn Financial Group; *Int'l*, pg. 1769
REGIONAL POWER, INC.—See Mouvement des caisses Desjardins; *Int'l*, pg. 5058
REGIONAL PRINTERS PTY LIMITED—See Nine Entertainment Co. Holdings Limited; *Int'l*, pg. 5299
REGIONALPS SA—See Schweizerische Bundesbahnen SBB AG; *Int'l*, pg. 6646
REGIONAL PUBLISHERS PTY LTD—See Nine Entertainment Co. Holdings Limited; *Int'l*, pg. 5299
REGIONAL PUBLISHERS (WESTERN VICTORIA) PTY LIMITED—See Nine Entertainment Co. Holdings Limited; *Int'l*, pg. 5299
REGIONAL RAIL, LLC—See 3i Group plc; *Int'l*, pg. 9
REGIONAL REIT LIMITED; *Int'l*, pg. 6254
REGIONAL REPORTING INC.; *U.S. Private*, pg. 3389
REGIONAL, S.A.B. DE C.V.; *Int'l*, pg. 6254
REGIONAL SUPPLY, LLC—See Platte River Ventures, LLC; *U.S. Private*, pg. 3211
REGIONAL TOXICOLOGY SERVICES, LLC—See Waud Capital Partners LLC; *U.S. Private*, pg. 4457
REGIONAL TRANSIT AUTHORITY; *U.S. Private*, pg. 3389
REGIONAL TRANSPORTATION AUTHORITY; *U.S. Private*, pg. 3389

REGIONAL TRANSPORTATION DISTRICT INC.; *U.S. Private*, pg. 3389
REGIONAL UTILITY SERVICES, INC.; *U.S. Private*, pg. 3389
REGIONALVERKEHR ALLGAU GMBH—See Deutsche Bahn AG; *Int'l*, pg. 2052
REGIONALVERKEHR DRESDEN GMBH—See OVPS - Oberelbische Verkehrsgesellschaft Pirna-Sebnitz mbH; *Int'l*, pg. 5673
REGIONALVERKEHRE START DEUTSCHLAND GMBH—See Deutsche Bahn AG; *Int'l*, pg. 2052
REGIONALVERKEHR KURHESSEN GMBH—See Deutsche Bahn AG; *Int'l*, pg. 2052
REGIONDO GMBH—See ProSiebenSat.1 Media SE; *Int'l*, pg. 6001
REGIONDO SOFTWARE S.R.L.—See ProSiebenSat.1 Media SE; *Int'l*, pg. 6001
REGION GROUP; *Int'l*, pg. 6254
REGION II COMMISSION ON SERVICES TO THE AGING; *U.S. Private*, pg. 3388
REGIONOIL PLUMBING, HEATING & COOLING CO., INC.—See Star Group, L.P.; *U.S. Public*, pg. 1938
REGIONS ASSET COMPANY—See Regions Financial Corporation; *U.S. Public*, pg. 1776
REGIONS BANK—See Regions Financial Corporation; *U.S. Public*, pg. 1776
REGIONS BUSINESS CAPITAL CORPORATION—See Regions Financial Corporation; *U.S. Public*, pg. 1776
REGIONS COMMERCIAL EQUIPMENT FINANCE, LLC—See Regions Financial Corporation; *U.S. Public*, pg. 1776
REGIONS FACILITY SERVICES INC.; *U.S. Private*, pg. 3389
REGIONS FINANCIAL CORPORATION; *U.S. Public*, pg. 1776
REGIONS INVESTMENT MANAGEMENT, INC.—See Regions Financial Corporation; *U.S. Public*, pg. 1776
REGIONS MORTGAGE, INC.—See Regions Financial Corporation; *U.S. Public*, pg. 1776
REGION SUPPLIERS PTE LTD—See GRP Limited; *Int'l*, pg. 3114
REGION VII AREA AGENCY ON AGING; *U.S. Private*, pg. 3388
REGIOPLAN INGENIEURE SALZBURG GMBH—See MVV Energie AG; *Int'l*, pg. 5109
REGIO VERKEHRSVERBUND LORRACH GMBH—See Deutsche Bahn AG; *Int'l*, pg. 2052
REGIS CORPORATION; *U.S. Public*, pg. 1776
REGIS GROUP FRANCE—See Regis Group PLC; *Int'l*, pg. 6255
REGIS GROUP PLC; *Int'l*, pg. 6255
REGIS HEALTHCARE LIMITED; *Int'l*, pg. 6255
REGIS MANAGEMENT COMPANY LLC—See Genstar Capital, LLC; *U.S. Private*, pg. 1677
REGIS MANAGEMENT COMPANY LLC—See Keystone Group, L.P.; *U.S. Private*, pg. 2299
REGIS RESOURCES LIMITED; *Int'l*, pg. 6255
THE REGISTER CITIZEN—See Alden Global Capital LLC; *U.S. Private*, pg. 159
REGISTER.COM, INC.—See Siris Capital Group, LLC; *U.S. Private*, pg. 3675
REGISTERED AGENT SOLUTIONS, INC.—See Apax Partners LLP; *Int'l*, pg. 503
THE REGISTER MAIL—See Gannett Co., Inc.; *U.S. Public*, pg. 905
REGISTER S.P.A—See HgCapital Trust plc; *Int'l*, pg. 3377
THE REGISTER STAR—See Johnson Newspaper Corporation; *U.S. Public*, pg. 2228
REGISTRAR CORP—See Paine Schwartz Partners, LLC; *U.S. Private*, pg. 3076
REGISTRAR & TRANSFER COMPANY; *U.S. Private*, pg. 3389
REGISTRO DE PRESTACIONES INFORMATICAS, S.A.—See Lone Star Funds; *U.S. Private*, pg. 2485
REGISTRYGATE GMBH—See Team Internet Group plc; *Int'l*, pg. 7500
REGISTRY MONITORING INSURANCE SERVICES, INC.—See Internet Truckstop Group, LLC; *U.S. Private*, pg. 2122
REGISTRY NETWORK, INC.; *U.S. Private*, pg. 3389
REGITAR U.S.A., INC.; *U.S. Private*, pg. 3389
REGI U.S., INC.—See New World Solutions Inc.; *Int'l*, pg. 5231
REGIUTTI S.P.A.—See Quanex Building Products Corp.; *U.S. Public*, pg. 1749
REG LENNA CENTER FOR THE ARTS; *U.S. Private*, pg. 3385
REG LIFE SCIENCES, LLC—See Chevron Corporation; *U.S. Public*, pg. 488
REG MADISON, LLC—See Chevron Corporation; *U.S. Public*, pg. 488
REG MARKETING & LOGISTICS GROUP, LLC—See Chevron Corporation; *U.S. Public*, pg. 488
REG MASON CITY, LLC—See Chevron Corporation; *U.S. Public*, pg. 488
REGNERY PUBLISHING, INC.—See Skyhorse Publishing Co., Inc.; *U.S. Private*, pg. 3684
REG NEW BOSTON, LLC—See Chevron Corporation; *U.S. Public*, pg. 488

REG NEWTON, LLC—See Chevron Corporation; *U.S. Public*, pg. 488
REGNIS (LANKA) PLC; *Int'l*, pg. 6255
REGNON S.A.; *Int'l*, pg. 6255
REGNUM CORP.; *U.S. Public*, pg. 1777
REGO EUROPE GMBH—See Windjammer Capital Investors, LLC; *U.S. Private*, pg. 4537
REGO INTERACTIVE CO., LTD.; *Int'l*, pg. 6255
REGOLA S.R.L.—See Frequentis AG; *Int'l*, pg. 2773
REGO PAYMENT ARCHITECTURES, INC.; *U.S. Public*, pg. 1777
REGO S. DE R.L. DE C.V.—See Windjammer Capital Investors, LLC; *U.S. Private*, pg. 4537
REGOS S.R.O.—See Minerals Technologies, Inc.; *U.S. Public*, pg. 1449
REG RALSTON, LLC—See Chevron Corporation; *U.S. Public*, pg. 488
R.E. GRIESEMER INC.; *U.S. Private*, pg. 3335
RE-GRIP INC.—See Chicago Aerosol, LLC; *U.S. Private*, pg. 877
RE:GROUP, INC.; *U.S. Private*, pg. 3365
REGROUP THERAPY, INC.—See Harbour Point Management LLC; *U.S. Private*, pg. 1861
REG SENECA, LLC—See Chevron Corporation; *U.S. Public*, pg. 488
REGSTAER-SP LLC—See Avolta AG; *Int'l*, pg. 749
REG SYNTHETIC FUELS, LLC—See Chevron Corporation; *U.S. Public*, pg. 488
REG-UB PROPERTIES, LLC—See Regency Centers Corporation; *U.S. Public*, pg. 1774
REGULATORY ASSISTANCE PROJECT; *U.S. Private*, pg. 3389
REGULATORY CONSULTANTS, INC.—See DEKRA e.V.; *Int'l*, pg. 2010
REGULATORY DATACORP, INC.—See Moody's Corporation; *U.S. Public*, pg. 1469
REGULUS RESOURCES INC.; *Int'l*, pg. 6255
REGULUS THERAPEUTICS, INC.; *U.S. Public*, pg. 1777
REGUM GMBH—See Bermuller & Co. GmbH; *Int'l*, pg. 986
REGUS ADVISORS, INC.; *U.S. Private*, pg. 3389
REGUS BRASIL LIMITADA—See IWG Plc; *Int'l*, pg. 3850
REGUSCI S.A.—See CRH plc; *Int'l*, pg. 1848
REGUS FRANKFURT HERRIOT'S GMBH & CO., KG—See IWG Plc; *Int'l*, pg. 3850
REHABABILITIES, INC.; *U.S. Private*, pg. 3389
REHAB ASSOCIATES OF JACKSON HOSPITAL, LLC—See Select Medical Holdings Corporation; *U.S. Public*, pg. 1859
REHAB ASSOCIATES; *U.S. Private*, pg. 3389
REHABCARE GROUP, INC.—See Select Rehabilitation, LLC; *U.S. Private*, pg. 3601
THE REHAB CENTER—See Select Medical Holdings Corporation; *U.S. Public*, pg. 1861
REHABCLINICS (SPT), INC.—See Select Medical Holdings Corporation; *U.S. Public*, pg. 1859
REHABILITATION ASSOCIATES OF CENTRAL VIRGINIA, LIMITED PARTNERSHIP—See U.S. Physical Therapy, Inc.; *U.S. Public*, pg. 2216
REHABILITATION CENTER OF WASHINGTON, D.C., INC.—See Select Medical Holdings Corporation; *U.S. Public*, pg. 1859
REHABILITATION CENTERS, INC.—See Acadia Healthcare Company, Inc.; *U.S. Public*, pg. 30
REHABILITATION HOSPITAL CORPORATION OF AMERICA, LLC—See Encompass Health Corporation; *U.S. Public*, pg. 758
REHABILITATION HOSPITAL OF BRISTOL, LLC—See Encompass Health Corporation; *U.S. Public*, pg. 758
REHABILITATION HOSPITAL OF COLORADO SPRINGS, INC.—See Encompass Health Corporation; *U.S. Public*, pg. 758
REHABILITATION HOSPITAL OF NEVADA-LAS VEGAS, L.P.—See Encompass Health Corporation; *U.S. Public*, pg. 758
REHABILITATION HOSPITAL OF NORTH ALABAMA, LLC—See Encompass Health Corporation; *U.S. Public*, pg. 758
REHABILITATION HOSPITAL OF PHENIX CITY, L.L.C.—See Encompass Health Corporation; *U.S. Public*, pg. 758
REHABILITATION HOSPITAL OF THE CAPE AND ISLANDS—See Partners HealthCare System, Inc.; *U.S. Private*, pg. 3101
REHABILITATION INSTITUTE OF DENTON, LLC—See Select Medical Holdings Corporation; *U.S. Public*, pg. 1859
REHABILITATIONSKLINIK BARBY BESITZGESELLSCHAFT MBH—See Advent International Corporation; *U.S. Private*, pg. 97
REHABILITATIONSKLINIK BARBY BESITZGESELLSCHAFT MBH—See Centerbridge Partners, L.P.; *U.S. Private*, pg. 813
REHABILITATIONSKLINIK IM MONTAFON BETRIEBSGMBH—See Fresenius SE & Co. KGaA; *Int'l*, pg. 2780
REHABILITATION SUPPORT SERVICES, INC.; *U.S. Private*, pg. 3389

REHABILITATION SUPPORT SERVICES, INC. — CORPORATE AFFILIATIONS

REHABILITATIONSZENTRUM GERNSBACH/SCHWARZWALD GMBH & CO. KG—See Asklepios Kliniken GmbH & Co. KGaA; *Int'l*, pg. 623
REHABILITATIONSZENTRUM KITZBUHEL BETRIEBS-GMBH—See Fresenius SE & Co. KGaA; *Int'l*, pg. 2780
REHABILITATIONSZENTRUM OBERNDORF BETRIEBS-GMBH & CO KG—See Fresenius SE & Co. KGaA; *Int'l*, pg. 2780
REHABILITATIONSZENTRUM ST. VEIT IM PONGAU BETRIEBS-GMBH—See Fresenius SE & Co. KGaA; *Int'l*, pg. 2780
REHAB PROVIDER NETWORK-EAST I, INC.—See Select Medical Holdings Corporation; *U.S. Public*, pg. 1859
REHAB PROVIDER NETWORK-MICHIGAN, INC.—See Select Medical Holdings Corporation; *U.S. Public*, pg. 1859
REHAB PROVIDER NETWORK-PENNSYLVANIA, INC.—See Select Medical Holdings Corporation; *U.S. Public*, pg. 1859
REHAB-ROBOTICS COMPANY LIMITED—See Vincent Medical Holdings Limited; *Int'l*, pg. 8211
REHABWORKS LTD.; *Int'l*, pg. 6255
REHAB XCEL, LLC—See Select Medical Holdings Corporation; *U.S. Public*, pg. 1859
REHACARE GMBH—See Allianz SE; *Int'l*, pg. 356
REHAKLINIK DUSSNANG AG—See Fresenius SE & Co. KGaA; *Int'l*, pg. 2780
REHA-KLINIK GMBH & CO. KG—See Asklepios Kliniken GmbH & Co. KGaA; *Int'l*, pg. 623
REHA-KLINIK SIGMUND WEIL GMBH—See MK-Kliniken AG; *Int'l*, pg. 5001
REHAKLINIK WIEN BAUMGARTEN BETRIEBS-GMBH—See Fresenius SE & Co. KGaA; *Int'l*, pg. 2780
REHAKLINIK ZIHLSCHLACHT AG—See Fresenius SE & Co. KGaA; *Int'l*, pg. 2781
R.E. HANA II ENTERPRISES INC.; *U.S. Private*, pg. 3335
THE REHANCEMENT GROUP, INC.; *U.S. Private*, pg. 4103
RE HARRINGTON UNEMPLOYMENT TAX SERVICE—See PlanVista Corporation; *U.S. Private*, pg. 3198
REHA SEEWIS AG—See Fresenius SE & Co. KGaA; *Int'l*, pg. 2780
REHA-SERVICE LOOSE GMBH—See PAUL HARTMANN AG; *Int'l*, pg. 5761
REHAU VERWALTUNGSZENTRALE AG; *Int'l*, pg. 6255
REHAZENTRUM HARBURG GMBH—See Fresenius SE & Co. KGaA; *Int'l*, pg. 2781
REHAZENTRUM LUBECK GMBH—See Fresenius SE & Co. KGaA; *Int'l*, pg. 2781
REHAZENTRUM NORDERSTEDT GMBH—See Fresenius SE & Co. KGaA; *Int'l*, pg. 2781
R.E. HEIDT CONSTRUCTION CO.; *U.S. Private*, pg. 3335
REH HOLDINGS INC.; *U.S. Private*, pg. 3389
REH HOLDINGS INC—See REH Holdings Inc.; *U.S. Private*, pg. 3389
REHMANN ROBSON PC; *U.S. Private*, pg. 3389
REHM GMBH U. CO. KG SCHWEISSTECHNIK; *Int'l*, pg. 6256
REHM HEGESZTESTECHNIKA KFT—See REHM GmbH u. Co. KG Schweisstechnik; *Int'l*, pg. 6256
REHM NEDERLAND B.V.—See REHM GmbH u. Co. KG Schweisstechnik; *Int'l*, pg. 6256
REHM SCHWEISSTECHNIK GMBH—See REHM GmbH u. Co. KG Schweisstechnik; *Int'l*, pg. 6256
REHOBOTH MCKINLEY CHRISTIAN HEALTH CARE SERVICES; *U.S. Private*, pg. 3389
REHRIG PACIFIC COMPANY - ATLANTA PLANT—See Rehrig Pacific Company; *U.S. Private*, pg. 3390
REHRIG PACIFIC COMPANY - DALLAS PLANT—See Rehrig Pacific Company; *U.S. Private*, pg. 3390
REHRIG PACIFIC COMPANY DE MEXICO S.A. DE C.V.—See Rehrig Pacific Company; *U.S. Private*, pg. 3390
REHRIG PACIFIC COMPANY - ERIE PLANT—See Rehrig Pacific Company; *U.S. Private*, pg. 3390
REHRIG PACIFIC COMPANY - KANSAS PLANT—See Rehrig Pacific Company; *U.S. Private*, pg. 3390
REHRIG PACIFIC COMPANY - KENOSHA PLANT—See Rehrig Pacific Company; *U.S. Private*, pg. 3390
REHRIG PACIFIC COMPANY - ORLANDO PLANT—See Rehrig Pacific Company; *U.S. Private*, pg. 3390
REHRIG PACIFIC COMPANY; *U.S. Private*, pg. 3389
REHT (ANHUI) PERMANENT MAGNET TECHNOLOGY CO., LTD.—See Earth-Panda Advance Magnetic Material Co., Ltd.; *Int'l*, pg. 2268
REI AUTOMATION, INC.—See HAHN Group GmbH; *Int'l*, pg. 3208
REIBEL N.V.; *Int'l*, pg. 6256
REI-BIWATER CONSORTIUM SDN BHD—See Biwater Holdings Limited; *Int'l*, pg. 1052
REICHARD STAFFING, INC.; *U.S. Private*, pg. 3390
REICHERT CHEVROLET BUICK OF WOODSTOCK; *U.S. Private*, pg. 3390
REICHERT, INC.—See AMETEK, Inc.; *U.S. Public*, pg. 116
REICHERT MICROSCOPE SERVICES—See AMETEK, Inc.; *U.S. Public*, pg. 116

REICHHOLD AS—See Reichhold, Inc.; *U.S. Private*, pg. 3391
REICHHOLD CZ S.R.O—See Reichhold, Inc.; *U.S. Private*, pg. 3391
REICHHOLD FINANCE BV—See Reichhold, Inc.; *U.S. Private*, pg. 3391
REICHHOLD GMBH—See Reichhold, Inc.; *U.S. Private*, pg. 3391
REICHHOLD, INC.; *U.S. Private*, pg. 3390
REICHHOLD INDIA PRIVATE LIMITED—See Reichhold, Inc.; *U.S. Private*, pg. 3391
REICHHOLD KIMYA SANAYI VE TICARET AS—See Reichhold, Inc.; *U.S. Private*, pg. 3391
REICHHOLD LIMITED—See Reichhold, Inc.; *U.S. Private*, pg. 3391
REICHHOLD OY AB—See Reichhold, Inc.; *U.S. Private*, pg. 3391
REICHHOLD POLYMERS (TIANJIN) LTD.—See Reichhold, Inc.; *U.S. Private*, pg. 3391
REICHHOLD SAS—See Reichhold, Inc.; *U.S. Private*, pg. 3391
REICHHOLD SRL—See Reichhold, Inc.; *U.S. Private*, pg. 3391
REICHHOLD TRADING (BEIJING) LTD.—See Reichhold, Inc.; *U.S. Private*, pg. 3391
REICHHOLD UK LIMITED—See Reichhold, Inc.; *U.S. Private*, pg. 3391
REICHLE & DE-MASSARI AG; *Int'l*, pg. 6256
REICHLE & DE-MASSARI AUSTRALIA PTY LTD—See Reichle & De-Massari AG; *Int'l*, pg. 6256
REICHLE & DE-MASSARI AUSTRIA GMBH—See Reichle & De-Massari AG; *Int'l*, pg. 6256
REICHLE & DE-MASSARI FAR EAST (PTE) LTD—See Reichle & De-Massari AG; *Int'l*, pg. 6256
REICHLE & DE-MASSARI FRANCE—See Reichle & De-Massari AG; *Int'l*, pg. 6256
REICHLE & DE-MASSARI GMBH—See Reichle & De-Massari AG; *Int'l*, pg. 6256
REICHLE & DE-MASSARI IBERIA S.L.U.—See Reichle & De-Massari AG; *Int'l*, pg. 6256
REICHLE & DE-MASSARI ITALIA S.R.L.—See Reichle & De-Massari AG; *Int'l*, pg. 6256
REICHLE & DE-MASSARI KFT.—See Reichle & De-Massari AG; *Int'l*, pg. 6256
REICHLE & DE-MASSARI KSA—See Reichle & De-Massari AG; *Int'l*, pg. 6256
REICHLE & DE-MASSARI - META—See Reichle & De-Massari AG; *Int'l*, pg. 6256
REICHLE & DE-MASSARI NETHERLANDS B.V.—See Reichle & De-Massari AG; *Int'l*, pg. 6256
REICHLE & DE-MASSARI POLSKA SP.Z O.O.—See Reichle & De-Massari AG; *Int'l*, pg. 6256
REICHLE & DE-MASSARI UK LTD—See Reichle & De-Massari AG; *Int'l*, pg. 6256
REICH LOGISTICS SERVICES INC.—See Best Logistics Group, Inc.; *U.S. Private*, pg. 543
REICHL UND PARTNER WERBEAGENTUR GMBH; *Int'l*, pg. 6256
REICHMANNHAUER CAPITAL PARTNERS INC.; *Int'l*, pg. 6256
REICHMANSCAPITAL—See Investec Limited; *Int'l*, pg. 3778
REICHMANS HOLDINGS LIMITED—See Investec Limited; *Int'l*, pg. 3778
REICH ONLINE SERVICES GMBH—See Calida Holding AG; *Int'l*, pg. 1264
REICH & TANG DEPOSIT NETWORKS, LLC—See Reich & Tang, Inc.; *U.S. Private*, pg. 3390
REICH & TANG, INC.; *U.S. Private*, pg. 3390
REICO, INC.; *U.S. Private*, pg. 3391
REICO INVESTICNI SPOLECNOST CESKE SPORITELNY, A.S.—See Erste Group Bank AG; *Int'l*, pg. 2499
REID, JONES, MCRORIE & WILLIAMS, INC.—See Aquiline Capital Partners LLC; *U.S. Private*, pg. 305
REID MIDDLETON INC.; *U.S. Private*, pg. 3391
REID & MITCHELL (PTY.) LTD.—See ACTOM (Pty) Ltd.; *Int'l*, pg. 120
REID/O'DONAHUE & ASSOCIATES INC.; *U.S. Private*, pg. 3391
REID PETROLEUM CORP.; *U.S. Private*, pg. 3391
REID'S PALACE HOTEL—See LVMH Moet Hennessy Louis Vuitton SE; *Int'l*, pg. 4591
REIDSVILLE GROCERY CO. INC.; *U.S. Private*, pg. 3391
THE REIDSVILLE REVIEW—See Lee Enterprises, Incorporated; *U.S. Public*, pg. 1299
REID & TAYLOR (INDIA) LIMITED—See S. Kumars Nationwide Limited; *Int'l*, pg. 6447
REID-WORLD WIDE CORPORATION; *Int'l*, pg. 6256
REIF 2000 KFT.—See Duna House Holding Public Company Limited; *Int'l*, pg. 2225
REIFEN BAIERLACHER GMBH—See The Goodyear Tire & Rubber Company; *U.S. Public*, pg. 2084
REIFENCOM GMBH—See Apollo Tyres Ltd.; *Int'l*, pg. 519
REIFENHAUSER GMBH & CO. KG MASCHINENFABRIK; *Int'l*, pg. 6256
REIFENHAUSER INC.—See Reifenhauser GmbH & Co. KG Maschinenfabrik; *Int'l*, pg. 6257

REIFENHAUSER (INDIA) MARKETING LTD.—See Reifenhauser GmbH & Co. KG Maschinenfabrik; *Int'l*, pg. 6257
REIFENHAUSER KIEFEL EXTRUSION GMBH—See Reifenhauser GmbH & Co. KG Maschinenfabrik; *Int'l*, pg. 6257
REIFENHAUSER KIEFEL S.A.—See Reifenhauser GmbH & Co. KG Maschinenfabrik; *Int'l*, pg. 6257
REIFENHAUSER LTD.—See Reifenhauser GmbH & Co. KG Maschinenfabrik; *Int'l*, pg. 6257
REIFENHAUSER MASKINER A/S—See Reifenhauser GmbH & Co. KG Maschinenfabrik; *Int'l*, pg. 6257
REIFENHAUSER PRIVATE LTD.—See Reifenhauser GmbH & Co. KG Maschinenfabrik; *Int'l*, pg. 6257
REIFEN KRUPP GMBH & CO. KG; *Int'l*, pg. 6256
REIFF & ASSOCIATES, LLC—See Kelso & Company, L.P.; *U.S. Private*, pg. 2280
REIFF GRAIN & FEED INC.; *U.S. Private*, pg. 3391
REIFF TECHNISCHE PRODUKTE GMBH—See THK CO., LTD.; *Int'l*, pg. 7712
REIG JOFRE GROUP; *Int'l*, pg. 6257
REIGN BEVERAGE COMPANY LLC—See Monster Beverage Corporation; *U.S. Public*, pg. 1465
REIGNCOM TECH LTD.—See STMicroelectronics N.V.; *Int'l*, pg. 7217
REIGN PRINT SOLUTIONS, INC.—See RBO PrintLogistix, Inc.; *U.S. Private*, pg. 3360
REIGNWOOD GROUP; *Int'l*, pg. 6257
REI HI-TECH SDN BHD—See Chasen Holdings Limited; *Int'l*, pg. 1457
REIKEN (THAILAND) CO., LTD—See KAWATA MFG CO., LTD.; *Int'l*, pg. 4101
REIL ELECTRICALS INDIA LIMITED; *Int'l*, pg. 6257
REILEY REALTY, INC.; *U.S. Private*, pg. 3391
REILING GLAS RECYCLING GMBH & CO. KG; *Int'l*, pg. 6257
REILLY CONSTRUCTION CO. INC.; *U.S. Private*, pg. 3391
REILLY ELECTRICAL CONTRACTORS; *U.S. Private*, pg. 3391
REILLY WINDOWS & DOORS—See Westny Building Products Co.; *U.S. Private*, pg. 4500
REILOY WESTLAND CORPORATION—See Reifenhauser GmbH & Co. KG Maschinenfabrik; *Int'l*, pg. 6257
REILY FOODS COMPANY; *U.S. Private*, pg. 3391
REIMA DANMARK APS—See Intertek Group plc; *Int'l*, pg. 3762
REIMA GMBH—See Intertek Group plc; *Int'l*, pg. 3762
REIMAN MEDIA GROUP, INC.—See RDA Holding Co.; *U.S. Private*, pg. 3363
REIMA OY—See The Riverside Company; *U.S. Private*, pg. 4110
REIMBURSEMENT SERVICES GROUP, INC.—See Veritas Capital Fund Management, LLC; *U.S. Private*, pg. 4362
REIMBURSEMENT TECHNOLOGIES, INC.—See KKR & Co. Inc.; *U.S. Public*, pg. 1249
REIMED, SCR—See Bracco S.p.A.; *Int'l*, pg. 1134
REIMER HARDWOODS LTD.; *Int'l*, pg. 6257
REIMOTEC MASCHINEN- UND ANLAGENBAU GMBH—See Reifenhauser GmbH & Co. KG Maschinenfabrik; *Int'l*, pg. 6257
REIMOTEC WINDING TECHNOLOGY SRL—See Reifenhauser GmbH & Co. KG Maschinenfabrik; *Int'l*, pg. 6257
THE REINALT-THOMAS CORPORATION; *U.S. Private*, pg. 4103
REINARDA MINERACAO LTDA.—See Troy Resources Limited; *Int'l*, pg. 7940
REINAUER TRANSPORTATION COMPANIES; *U.S. Private*, pg. 3391
REINDEER AUTO RELOCATION; *U.S. Private*, pg. 3392
REINDERS INCORPORATED; *U.S. Private*, pg. 3392
REINDL PRINTING INC.; *U.S. Private*, pg. 3392
REINEKE FAMILY DEALERSHIPS; *U.S. Private*, pg. 3392
REINEKE FORD, INC.—See Reineke Family Dealerships; *U.S. Private*, pg. 3392
REINEKE LINCOLN MERCURY MAZDA INC.—See Reineke Family Dealerships; *U.S. Private*, pg. 3392
REINEKE MOTORS, INC.—See Reineke Family Dealerships; *U.S. Private*, pg. 3392
REINER APPELRATH CUEPPER NACHF. GMBH—See OpCapita LLP; *Int'l*, pg. 5595
REINER COMMUNITIES L.P.—See Sun Life Financial Inc.; *Int'l*, pg. 7305
REINET INVESTMENTS S.C.A.; *Int'l*, pg. 6257
REINFORCED EARTH CNY LTD.—See VINCI S.A.; *Int'l*, pg. 8225
REINFORCED EARTH COMPANY LTD—See VINCI S.A.; *Int'l*, pg. 8232
THE REINFORCED EARTH COMPANY; *U.S. Private*, pg. 4103
THE REINFORCED EARTH COMPANY—See The Reinforced Earth Company; *U.S. Private*, pg. 4103
REINFORCED EARTH INDIA PVT. LTD—See VINCI S.A.; *Int'l*, pg. 8232
REINFORCED EARTH INSAAT PROJE VE TICARET A.S.—See VINCI S.A.; *Int'l*, pg. 8232

COMPANY NAME INDEX

REINFORCED EARTH MALAYSIA SDN BHD—See VINCI S.A.; *Int'l*, pg. 8225
REINFORCED EARTH PACIFIC LTD—See VINCI S.A.; *Int'l*, pg. 8232
REINFORCED EARTH (PTY) LTD—See VINCI S.A.; *Int'l*, pg. 8232
REINFORCED EARTH PTY LTD—See VINCI S.A.; *Int'l*, pg. 8232
REINFORCED EARTH PVT. LTD—See VINCI S.A.; *Int'l*, pg. 8232
REINFORCED EARTH SEA (SINGAPORE) PTE. LTD.—See VINCI S.A.; *Int'l*, pg. 8225
REINFORCED EARTH THAILAND—See VINCI S.A.; *Int'l*, pg. 8232
REINFORCING SERVICES, INC.—See AZZ, Inc.; *U.S. Public*, pg. 260
REINFORCING STEEL CONTRACTORS (PTY) LTD.; *Int'l*, pg. 6257
REINFURT-CR, K.S.—See Arcline Investment Management LP; *U.S. Private*, pg. 314
REINGOLD LINK, LLC; *U.S. Private*, pg. 3392
REINHARD DI LENA GMBH—See Mauna Kea Technologies SA; *Int'l*, pg. 4732
REINHARDT CORP.; *U.S. Private*, pg. 3392
REINHARDT MICROTECH GMBH—See Cicor Technologies Ltd.; *Int'l*, pg. 1603
REINHARDT MOTORS INC.; *U.S. Private*, pg. 3392
REINHARDT TRANSPORT GROUP (PTY) LTD.—See Labat Africa Ltd; *Int'l*, pg. 4389
REINHART FOODSERVICE, LLC - ATLANTA DIVISION—See Performance Food Group Company; *U.S. Public*, pg. 1675
REINHART FOODSERVICE, LLC - BURLINGTON DIVISION—See Performance Food Group Company; *U.S. Public*, pg. 1675
REINHART FOODSERVICE, LLC - CEDAR RAPIDS DIVISION—See Performance Food Group Company; *U.S. Public*, pg. 1675
REINHART FOODSERVICE, LLC - CHICAGO DIVISION—See Performance Food Group Company; *U.S. Public*, pg. 1675
REINHART FOODSERVICE, LLC - CINCINNATI DIVISION—See Performance Food Group Company; *U.S. Public*, pg. 1675
REINHART FOODSERVICE, LLC - CLEVELAND DIVISION—See Performance Food Group Company; *U.S. Public*, pg. 1675
REINHART FOODSERVICE, LLC - DETROIT DIVISION—See Performance Food Group Company; *U.S. Public*, pg. 1675
REINHART FOODSERVICE, LLC - EASTERN PENNSYLVANIA DIVISION—See Performance Food Group Company; *U.S. Public*, pg. 1675
REINHART FOODSERVICE, LLC - JACKSONVILLE DIVISION—See Performance Food Group Company; *U.S. Public*, pg. 1675
REINHART FOODSERVICE, LLC - JOHNSON CITY DIVISION—See Performance Food Group Company; *U.S. Public*, pg. 1675
REINHART FOODSERVICE, LLC - KANSAS CITY DIVISION—See Performance Food Group Company; *U.S. Public*, pg. 1675
REINHART FOODSERVICE, LLC - KNOXVILLE DIVISION—See Performance Food Group Company; *U.S. Public*, pg. 1675
REINHART FOODSERVICE, LLC - LA CROSSE DIVISION—See Performance Food Group Company; *U.S. Public*, pg. 1675
REINHART FOODSERVICE, LLC - LAFAYETTE DIVISION—See Performance Food Group Company; *U.S. Public*, pg. 1675
REINHART FOODSERVICE, LLC - LOUISVILLE DIVISION—See Performance Food Group Company; *U.S. Public*, pg. 1675
REINHART FOODSERVICE, LLC - MARQUETTE DIVISION—See Performance Food Group Company; *U.S. Public*, pg. 1675
REINHART FOODSERVICE, LLC - MILWAUKEE DIVISION—See Performance Food Group Company; *U.S. Public*, pg. 1675
REINHART FOODSERVICE, LLC - NEW BEDFORD DIVISION—See Performance Food Group Company; *U.S. Public*, pg. 1675
REINHART FOODSERVICE, LLC - NEW ORLEANS DIVISION—See Performance Food Group Company; *U.S. Public*, pg. 1675
REINHART FOODSERVICE, LLC - PITTSBURGH DIVISION—See Performance Food Group Company; *U.S. Public*, pg. 1675
REINHART FOODSERVICE, LLC - RICHMOND DIVISION—See Performance Food Group Company; *U.S. Public*, pg. 1675
REINHART FOODSERVICE, LLC - SHAWANO DIVISION—See Performance Food Group Company; *U.S. Public*, pg. 1675
REINHART FOODSERVICE, LLC - SHREVEPORT DIVISION—See Performance Food Group Company; *U.S. Public*, pg. 1676

REINHART FOODSERVICE, LLC—See Performance Food Group Company; *U.S. Public*, pg. 1675
REINHART FOODSERVICE, LLC - SPRINGFIELD DIVISION—See Performance Food Group Company; *U.S. Public*, pg. 1676
REINHART FOODSERVICE, LLC - TIDEWATER DIVISION—See Performance Food Group Company; *U.S. Public*, pg. 1676
REINHART FOODSERVICE, LLC - TWIN CITIES DIVISION—See Performance Food Group Company; *U.S. Public*, pg. 1676
REINHART FOODSERVICE, LLC - VALDOSTA DIVISION—See Performance Food Group Company; *U.S. Public*, pg. 1676
REINHART INDUSTRIES INC.; *U.S. Private*, pg. 3392
REINHOLD CORP.; *U.S. Private*, pg. 3392
REINHOLD EUROPE AB; *Int'l*, pg. 6257
REINHOLD GONDROM GMBH & CO. KG—See Thalia Bucher GmbH; *Int'l*, pg. 7607
REINHOLD HANDELS AG—See Wurth Verwaltungsgesellschaft mbH; *Int'l*, pg. 8507
REINHOLD HOLDINGS, INC.—See HEICO Corporation; *U.S. Public*, pg. 1021
REINHOLD INDUSTRIES INC.—See HEICO Corporation; *U.S. Public*, pg. 1021
REINHOLD KELLER GMBH; *Int'l*, pg. 6257
REINHOLD WURTH MUSIKSTIFTUNG GEMEINNIJTZIGE GMBH—See Wurth Verwaltungsgesellschaft mbH; *Int'l*, pg. 8507
REININ LIHA OY—See Kesko Corporation; *Int'l*, pg. 4143
REINKE MANUFACTURING COMPANY, INC.; *U.S. Private*, pg. 3392
REIN MEDICAL GMBH—See JVCKENWOOD Corporation; *Int'l*, pg. 4034
REINO CAPITAL SA; *Int'l*, pg. 6257
REINO LINEN SERVICES INC.—See York Capital Management Global Advisors, LLC; *U.S. Private*, pg. 4590
REINS INTERNATIONAL (SINGAPORE) PTE. LTD.—See Colowide Co., Ltd.; *Int'l*, pg. 1705
REINSURANCE FINANCE CONSULTANTS LTD.—See Swiss Re Ltd.; *Int'l*, pg. 7371
REINSURANCE GROUP OF AMERICA, INC.; *U.S. Public*, pg. 1777
REINSURANCE SOLUTIONS INTERNATIONAL, L.L.C.—See Marsh & McLennan Companies, Inc.; *U.S. Public*, pg. 1376
REINSURANCE SOLUTIONS LIMITED—See R&Q Insurance Holdings Ltd.; *Int'l*, pg. 6168
RE:INTERACTION; *U.S. Private*, pg. 3365
REINTJES SERVICES INC.—See George P. Reintjes Co., Inc.; *U.S. Private*, pg. 1683
REINZ-DICHTUNGS-GMBH & CO KG—See Dana Incorporated; *U.S. Public*, pg. 623
REI PROMAX TECHNOLOGIES PTE LTD—See Chasen Holdings Limited; *Int'l*, pg. 1457
REI REAL ESTATE SERVICES LLC; *U.S. Private*, pg. 3390
REISCHLING PRESS, INC.; *U.S. Private*, pg. 3392
REISEBURO DR. TIGGES GMBH—See ThyssenKrupp AG; *Int'l*, pg. 7725
REISEBURO KUONI GES.M.B.H.—See EQT AB; *Int'l*, pg. 2478
REISELAND GMBH & CO. KG—See Otto GmbH & Co. KG; *Int'l*, pg. 5663
REISEN ENERGY CO., LTD.—See AJ Advance Technology Public Company Limited; *Int'l*, pg. 255
REIS ENVIRONMENTAL INC.—See Wise El Santo Company Inc.; *U.S. Private*, pg. 4549
THE REISER GROUP; *U.S. Private*, pg. 4103
REISER SIMULATION & TRAINING GMBH; *Int'l*, pg. 6257
REISEWELT GMBH—See Raiffeisenlandesbank Oberosterreich Aktiengesellschaft; *Int'l*, pg. 6187
REISGIES SCHAUMSTOFF E GMBH—See Bystronic AG; *Int'l*, pg. 1236
REIS, INC.—See Moody's Corporation; *U.S. Public*, pg. 1469
REIS & IRVY'S, INC.—See Generation NEXT Franchise Brands, Inc.; *U.S. Public*, pg. 1668
REISS CORPORATION INC.; *U.S. Private*, pg. 3392
REISSER CSAVAR KFT—See Wurth Verwaltungsgesellschaft mbH; *Int'l*, pg. 8507
REISSER SCHRAUBENTECHNIK GMBH—See Wurth Verwaltungsgesellschaft mbH; *Int'l*, pg. 8507
REISSER TEHNIC S.R.L.—See Wurth Verwaltungsgesellschaft mbH; *Int'l*, pg. 8507
REIS SERVICE GMBH—See GLORY Ltd.; *Int'l*, pg. 3010
REISSWOLF AG—See REISSWOLF International AG; *Int'l*, pg. 6258
REISSWOLF AKTEN- U DATENVERNICHTUNG GMBH—See REISSWOLF International AG; *Int'l*, pg. 6258
REISSWOLF ALBANIA SH.P.K.—See REISSWOLF International AG; *Int'l*, pg. 6257
REISSWOLF AZERBAIJAN LIVING DATA LLC—See REISSWOLF International AG; *Int'l*, pg. 6258
REISSWOLF BALEARES S.L.—See REISSWOLF International AG; *Int'l*, pg. 6257
REISSWOLF BALTIC SIA—See REISSWOLF International AG; *Int'l*, pg. 6257

REIT-SYD EQUIPMENT LTD.

REISSWOLF BUDAPEST ADAT- ES DOKUMENTUMKEZELO KFT—See REISSWOLF International AG; *Int'l*, pg. 6258
REISSWOLF BULGARIA JSC—See REISSWOLF International AG; *Int'l*, pg. 6258
REISSWOLF CENTRE EST SERVICES (SARL)—See REISSWOLF International AG; *Int'l*, pg. 6258
REISSWOLF CYPRUS LTD.—See REISSWOLF International AG; *Int'l*, pg. 6258
REISSWOLF DEUTSCHLAND GMBH—See REISSWOLF International AG; *Int'l*, pg. 6258
REISSWOLF DOKUMAN YONETIMI HIZ. A.S.—See REISSWOLF International AG; *Int'l*, pg. 6258
REISSWOLF D.O.O.—See REISSWOLF International AG; *Int'l*, pg. 6258
REISSWOLF D.O.O.—See REISSWOLF International AG; *Int'l*, pg. 6258
REISSWOLF D.O.O.—See REISSWOLF International AG; *Int'l*, pg. 6258
REISSWOLF INTERNATIONAL AG; *Int'l*, pg. 6257
REISSWOLF KAZAKHSTAN LLP—See REISSWOLF International AG; *Int'l*, pg. 6258
REISSWOLF LDA.—See REISSWOLF International AG; *Int'l*, pg. 6258
REISSWOLF LIKVIDACE DOKUMENTU A DAT S.R.O.—See REISSWOLF International AG; *Int'l*, pg. 6258
REISSWOLF LLC—See REISSWOLF International AG; *Int'l*, pg. 6258
REISSWOLF MACEDONIA—See REISSWOLF International AG; *Int'l*, pg. 6258
REISSWOLF OSTERREICH GMBH—See REISSWOLF International AG; *Int'l*, pg. 6258
REISSWOLF POLSKA SP. Z O.O.—See REISSWOLF International AG; *Int'l*, pg. 6258
REISSWOLF RANDSTAD I B.V.—See REISSWOLF International AG; *Int'l*, pg. 6258
REISSWOLF S.A.—See REISSWOLF International AG; *Int'l*, pg. 6258
REISSWOLF SERBIA D.O.O.—See REISSWOLF International AG; *Int'l*, pg. 6258
REISSWOLF SLOVAKIA S.R.O.—See REISSWOLF International AG; *Int'l*, pg. 6258
REISSWOLF SUROESTE S.L.L.—See REISSWOLF International AG; *Int'l*, pg. 6258
REISSWOLF SUR, S.L.U.—See REISSWOLF International AG; *Int'l*, pg. 6258
REISSWOLF TURKEY—See REISSWOLF International AG; *Int'l*, pg. 6258
REISSWOLF UKRAINE LLC—See REISSWOLF International AG; *Int'l*, pg. 6258
REISTERSTOWN AUTO PARTS, INC.—See Genuine Parts Company; *U.S. Public*, pg. 933
REISTERSTOWN PLAZA ASSOCIATES, LLC—See Kite Realty Group Trust; *U.S. Public*, pg. 1237
REI SYSTEMS, INC.; *U.S. Private*, pg. 3390
REIT 1 LTD.; *Int'l*, pg. 6258
REITAN CONVENIENCE AS—See Reitangruppen AS; *Int'l*, pg. 6258
REITAN CONVENIENCE NORWAY AS—See Reitangruppen AS; *Int'l*, pg. 6258
REITAN CONVENIENCE SWEDEN AB—See Reitangruppen AS; *Int'l*, pg. 6259
REITAN EIENDOM AS—See Reitangruppen AS; *Int'l*, pg. 6259
REITANGRUPPEN AS; *Int'l*, pg. 6258
REITAN SERVICEHANDEL DANMARK AS—See Reitangruppen AS; *Int'l*, pg. 6259
REIT ASSET MANAGEMENT LIMITED—See Bank of Montreal; *Int'l*, pg. 847
REIT AZORIM HF LIVING LTD.; *Int'l*, pg. 6258
REI TECHNOLOGIES PTE LTD—See Chasen Holdings Limited; *Int'l*, pg. 1457
REITEN & CO AS; *Int'l*, pg. 6259
REITER DAIRY, LLC—See Dean Foods Company; *U.S. Private*, pg. 1184
REITER DAIRY, LLC—See Dean Foods Company; *U.S. Private*, pg. 1184
REITIR FASTEIGNAFELAG HF; *Int'l*, pg. 6259
REITMANS (CANADA) LIMITED; *Int'l*, pg. 6259
REIT-SYD EQUIPMENT LTD.; *Int'l*, pg. 6258
REITZ COAL COMPANY LLC—See Berwind Corporation; *U.S. Private*, pg. 540
REITZ DO BRASIL LTDA.—See Konrad REITZ Ventilatoren GmbH & Co. KG; *Int'l*, pg. 4275
REITZ FANS (SUZHOU) LTD.—See Konrad REITZ Ventilatoren GmbH & Co. KG; *Int'l*, pg. 4275
REITZ INDIA LIMITED—See Konrad REITZ Ventilatoren GmbH & Co. KG; *Int'l*, pg. 4275
REITZ MIDDLE EAST FZE—See Konrad REITZ Ventilatoren GmbH & Co. KG; *Int'l*, pg. 4275
REITZ SOUTH EAST ASIA PTE. LTD.—See Konrad REITZ Ventilatoren GmbH & Co. KG; *Int'l*, pg. 4275
REITZ UMWELTTECHNIK + VENTILATOREN GMBH & CO. KG—See Konrad REITZ Ventilatoren GmbH & Co. KG; *Int'l*, pg. 4275
REITZ WENTYLATORY POLSKA SP. Z O.O.—See Konrad REITZ Ventilatoren GmbH & Co. KG; *Int'l*, pg. 4275

REIWA SPECIALTY STEEL CORPORATION—See UEX, Ltd.; *Int'l*, pg. 8015
REJ CO., LTD.—See AIDA Engineering, Ltd.; *Int'l*, pg. 231
THE REJECT SHOP LIMITED; *Int'l*, pg. 7678
REJESTR DLUZNIKOW ERIF BIG S.A.—See Kruk S.A.; *Int'l*, pg. 4308
REJLERS AB; *Int'l*, pg. 6259
REJLERS AS—See Rejlers AB; *Int'l*, pg. 6259
REJLERS ELSIKKERHET AS—See Rejlers AB; *Int'l*, pg. 6259
REJLERS EMBRIQ AS—See Rejlers AB; *Int'l*, pg. 6259
REJLERS INGENJOER AB—See Rejlers AB; *Int'l*, pg. 6259
REJLERS OY—See Rejlers AB; *Int'l*, pg. 6259
REJOICE CONTAINER SERVICES (PTE) LTD.—See Legion Consortium Limited; *Int'l*, pg. 4444
REJUVEL BIO-SCIENCES, INC.; *U.S. Private*, pg. 1778
REJUVENATION INC.—See Williams-Sonoma, Inc.; *U.S. Public*, pg. 2371
REJUVENATION LABS—See Crocker Ventures LLC; *U.S. Private*, pg. 1102
REKAB ENTREPRENAD AB; *Int'l*, pg. 6259
REKAH PHARMACEUTICAL INDUSTRY LTD.; *Int'l*, pg. 6259
REKA INDUSTRIAL PLC; *Int'l*, pg. 6259
REKA KAAPELI OY—See Nexans S.A.; *Int'l*, pg. 5242
REKA KABEL AB—See Reka Industrial Plc; *Int'l*, pg. 6259
REKA KABEL AS—See Reka Industrial Plc; *Int'l*, pg. 6259
REKA KABEL A/S—See Reka Industrial Plc; *Int'l*, pg. 6259
REKATECH CAPITAL BERHAD; *Int'l*, pg. 6259
REKCUT PHOTOGRAPHIC INC.; *U.S. Private*, pg. 3392
REKISEI KAGAKU K.K.—See Idemitsu Kosan Co., Ltd.; *Int'l*, pg. 3592
REKLAIM LTD.; *Int'l*, pg. 6260
REKLAMEPARTNER GRAPHICS AS—See ITAB Shop Concept AB; *Int'l*, pg. 3828
REKLUSE MOTOR SPORTS, INC.—See MiddleGround Management, LP; *U.S. Private*, pg. 2712
REKO AUTOMATION GROUP INC—See Reko International Group Inc.; *Int'l*, pg. 6260
REKO INTERNATIONAL GROUP INC.; *Int'l*, pg. 6260
REKO MACHINE BUILDERS INC.—See Reko International Group Inc.; *Int'l*, pg. 6260
REKO MANUFACTURING GROUP INC.—See Reko International Group Inc.; *Int'l*, pg. 6260
REKORD VERSICHERUNGVERMITTLUNGS-UND BETREUUNGSGESELLSCHAFT FUR SELBSTANDIGE MBH & CO. KG—See Dexia SA; *Int'l*, pg. 2092
REKOR GIDA PAZARLAMA A.S.—See Yildiz Holding AS; *Int'l*, pg. 8583
REKOR RECOGNITION SYSTEMS—See Rekor Systems, Inc.; *U.S. Public*, pg. 1778
REKOR SYSTEMS, INC.; *U.S. Public*, pg. 1778
RE KRAMIG & CO. INC.; *U.S. Private*, pg. 3364
REKREACIJSKO TURISTICNI CENTER KRVAVEC, D.D.—See Unior Kovaska Idemitrija d.d.; *Int'l*, pg. 8055
REKREATURS A.D.; *Int'l*, pg. 6260
THE R.E. KRUG CORPORATION; *U.S. Private*, pg. 4101
REKTGLOBAL, INC.—See Infinite Realty; *U.S. Private*, pg. 2071
REKVINA LABORATORIES LIMITED; *Int'l*, pg. 6260
RELACOM AB—See Altor Equity Partners AB; *Int'l*, pg. 396
RELADYNE LLC—See AIP, LLC; *U.S. Private*, pg. 135
RELA-HIEROJAT OY—See Terveystalo PLC; *Int'l*, pg. 7571
RELAIS DE CHAMPAGNE SA; *Int'l*, pg. 6260
RELAIS GROUP PLC; *Int'l*, pg. 6260
RELAIS VERT; *Int'l*, pg. 6260
RELAKS AD; *Int'l*, pg. 6260
RELATECH S.P.A.; *Int'l*, pg. 6260
RELATED BEAL, LLC—See The Related Companies, L.P.; *U.S. Private*, pg. 4103
RELATED CALIFORNIA, LLC—See The Related Companies, L.P.; *U.S. Private*, pg. 4103
RELATED CHINA LIMITED—See The Related Companies, L.P.; *U.S. Private*, pg. 4103
THE RELATED COMPANIES, L.P.; *U.S. Private*, pg. 4103
RELATED FLORIDA, INC.; *U.S. Private*, pg. 3392
RELATED FUND MANAGEMENT LLC—See The Related Companies, L.P.; *U.S. Private*, pg. 4103
RELATED GROUP—See The Related Companies, L.P.; *U.S. Private*, pg. 4104
RELATED MANAGEMENT COMPANY, L.P.—See The Related Companies, L.P.; *U.S. Private*, pg. 4104
RELATED RETAIL, L.P.—See The Related Companies, L.P.; *U.S. Private*, pg. 4104
RELATED SALES LLC—See The Related Companies, L.P.; *U.S. Private*, pg. 4104
RELATED URBAN DEVELOPMENT, L.P.—See The Related Companies, L.P.; *U.S. Private*, pg. 4104
RELATIONAL LLC—See Relational LLC; *U.S. Private*, pg. 3392
RELATIONAL LLC; *U.S. Private*, pg. 3392
RELATIONAL NETWORKS, INC.—See Silver Lake Group, LLC; *U.S. Private*, pg. 3660
RELATIONAL TECHNOLOGY SERVICES—See Relational LLC; *U.S. Private*, pg. 3392
RELATIONAL TECHNOLOGY SOLUTIONS—See Relational LLC; *U.S. Private*, pg. 3392

RELATION INSURANCE, INC.—See Aquiline Capital Partners LLC; *U.S. Private*, pg. 305
RELATION INSURANCE SERVICES INC.—See Aquiline Capital Partners LLC; *U.S. Private*, pg. 305
RELATIONSHIP TRAVEL & EVENT SOLUTIONS—See Aimia Inc.; *Int'l*, pg. 233
RELATIVE VALUE INVESTMENTS UK LIMITED LIABILITY PARTNERSHIP—See Barclays PLC; *Int'l*, pg. 862
RELATIVITY ACQUISITION CORP.; *U.S. Private*, pg. 3392
RELATIVITY, INC.; *U.S. Private*, pg. 3393
RELATIVITY MEDIA, LLC; *U.S. Private*, pg. 3392
RELATRA AG—See Die Schweizerische Post AG; *Int'l*, pg. 2113
RELAU ESTATES SDN BHD—See Mechmar Corporation (Malaysia) Berhad; *Int'l*, pg. 4766
RELAXNEWS SA—See Publicis Groupe S.A.; *Int'l*, pg. 6107
RELAXO FOOTWEARS LIMITED; *Int'l*, pg. 6260
RELAX THE BACK CORPORATION—See CI Capital Partners LLC; *U.S. Private*, pg. 895
RELAY ENGINEERING LIMITED—See J&J Denholm Ltd.; *Int'l*, pg. 3853
RELAY EXPRESS; *U.S. Private*, pg. 3393
RELAY FRANCE—See Vivendi SE; *Int'l*, pg. 8276
RELAYHEALTH—See McKesson Corporation; *U.S. Public*, pg. 1408
RELAYHEALTH—See McKesson Corporation; *U.S. Public*, pg. 1408
RELAY & POWER SYSTEMS—See Rumsey Electric Company; *U.S. Private*, pg. 3504
RELAY RESOURCES; *U.S. Private*, pg. 3393
RELAYR GMBH; *Int'l*, pg. 6260
RELAY—See Publicis Groupe S.A.; *Int'l*, pg. 6111
RELAY THERAPEUTICS, INC.; *U.S. Public*, pg. 1778
RELAY WORLDWIDE—See Publicis Groupe S.A.; *Int'l*, pg. 6107
RELAY WORLDWIDE—See Publicis Groupe S.A.; *Int'l*, pg. 6107
RELCO PRODUCTS INC.; *U.S. Private*, pg. 3393
RELCO SYSTEMS INC.; *U.S. Private*, pg. 3393
RELEASE AFRICA B.V.—See Scatec ASA; *Int'l*, pg. 6613
RELEASE S.P.A.—See Banco BPM S.p.A.; *Int'l*, pg. 819
RELEC ELECTRONICS LTD.—See Ault Alliance, Inc.; *U.S. Public*, pg. 227
RELECTRIC, INC; *U.S. Private*, pg. 3393
RELEKTA AS—See Indutrade AB; *Int'l*, pg. 3681
RE'LEM PUBLIC BENEFIT COMPANY—See Energizer Holdings, Inc.; *U.S. Public*, pg. 761
RELEPLEX AS—See Kendrion N.V.; *Int'l*, pg. 4127
RELESYS A/S; *Int'l*, pg. 6260
RELEVANCE INC.; *U.S. Private*, pg. 3393
RELEVANT ADS, INC.; *U.S. Private*, pg. 3393
RELEVANT CONSULTING (INDIA) PRIVATE LIMITED—See Relevante, Inc.; *U.S. Private*, pg. 3393
RELEVANTE, INC.; *U.S. Private*, pg. 3393
RELEVANT INDUSTRIAL LLC; *U.S. Private*, pg. 3393
RELEVANT INFORMATION SVERIGE AB—See Ratos AB; *Int'l*, pg. 6217
RELEVANT MARKETING (HK) LIMITED—See Great Wall Terroir Holdings Limited; *Int'l*, pg. 3066
RELEVANT TRAFFIC SPAIN S.L.—See Kinnevik AB; *Int'l*, pg. 4182
RELEVANT TRAFFIC SWEDEN AB—See Kinnevik AB; *Int'l*, pg. 4182
RELEVATE HEALTH, LLC—See Mountaingate Capital Management, L.P.; *U.S. Private*, pg. 2801
RELEVENT PARTNERS LLC—See Stagwell, Inc.; *U.S. Public*, pg. 1927
RELEVIUM TECHNOLOGIES, INC.; *Int'l*, pg. 6260
RELIABILITY INCORPORATED; *U.S. Public*, pg. 1778
RELIABLE ANALYSIS (SHANGHAI) INC.—See I Squared Capital Advisors (US) LLC; *U.S. Private*, pg. 2023
RELIABLE ANALYSIS (SHANGHAI) INC.—See TDR Capital LLP; *Int'l*, pg. 7492
RELIABLE AUTOMATIC SPRINKLER CO., INC.; *U.S. Private*, pg. 3393
RELIABLE BEARING CO. LTD.—See FICODIS Inc.; *Int'l*, pg. 2653
RELIABLE BIOPHARMACEUTICAL LLC—See Avantor, Inc.; *U.S. Public*, pg. 241
RELIABLE CARRIERS INC.; *U.S. Private*, pg. 3393
RELIABLE CASTINGS CORPORATION - SIDNEY PLANT—See Reliable Castings Corporation; *U.S. Private*, pg. 3393
RELIABLE CASTINGS CORPORATION; *U.S. Private*, pg. 3393
RELIABLE CHEVROLET; *U.S. Private*, pg. 3393
RELIABLE CHURCHILL, LLP—See Breakthru Beverage Group, LLC; *U.S. Private*, pg. 643
RELIABLE CONTAINER CORPORATION—See Koch Industries, Inc.; *U.S. Private*, pg. 2329
RELIABLE CONTRACTING COMPANY INC.; *U.S. Private*, pg. 3393
RELIABLE DATA SERVICES LTD.; *Int'l*, pg. 6260
RELIABLE ENVIRONMENTAL TRANSPORT, INC.—See Waste Management, Inc.; *U.S. Public*, pg. 2332
RELIABLE FASTENERS—See Richelieu Hardware Ltd.; *Int'l*, pg. 6331
RELIABLE FIRE EQUIPMENT CO.; *U.S. Private*, pg. 3394

RELIABLE FIRE SPRINKLER AUSTRALIA PTY. LTD.—See Reliable Automatic Sprinkler Co., Inc.; *U.S. Private*, pg. 3393
RELIABLE FIRE SPRINKLER LTD.—See Reliable Automatic Sprinkler Co., Inc.; *U.S. Private*, pg. 3393
RELIABLE GOVERNMENT SOLUTIONS INC.; *U.S. Private*, pg. 3394
RELIABLE GROUP, LLC—See Reliable Contracting Company Inc.; *U.S. Private*, pg. 3393
RELIABLE INDUSTRIES INC.; *U.S. Private*, pg. 3394
RELIABLE INSURANCE SERVICES CORP.—See Wells Fargo & Company; *U.S. Public*, pg. 2345
RELIABLE IT, LLC—See Vitruvian Partners LLP; *Int'l*, pg. 8263
RELIABLE JET MAINTENANCE LLC; *U.S. Private*, pg. 3394
RELIABLE KNITTING WORKS, INC.; *U.S. Private*, pg. 3394
RELIABLE LANDFILL, LLC—See Waste Management, Inc.; *U.S. Public*, pg. 2332
THE RELIABLE LIFE INSURANCE COMPANY—See Kemper Corporation; *U.S. Public*, pg. 1221
RELIABLE LIFE INSURANCE COMPANY—See Old Republic International Corporation; *U.S. Public*, pg. 1569
RELIABLE MEDICAL EQUIPMENT LLC—See AdaptHealth Corp.; *U.S. Public*, pg. 39
RELIABLE MEDICAL OF CONWAY, LLC—See AdaptHealth Corp.; *U.S. Public*, pg. 39
RELIABLE OIL EQUIPMENT INC.; *U.S. Private*, pg. 3394
RELIABLE PARTS LTD.; *Int'l*, pg. 6261
RELIABLE POLICY MANAGEMENT, LLC—See Truist Financial Corporation; *U.S. Public*, pg. 2201
RELIABLE PRODUCTION SERVICE, INC.; *U.S. Private*, pg. 3394
RELIABLE PROPANE, INC.—See Ferrellgas Partners, L.P.; *U.S. Public*, pg. 829
RELIABLE SILVER, INC.; *U.S. Private*, pg. 3394
RELIABLE SOFTWARE RESOURCES, INC; *U.S. Private*, pg. 3394
RELIABLE TANK LINE, LLC—See Quality Oil Company LLC; *U.S. Private*, pg. 3320
RELIABLE TIRE DISTRIBUTORS INC.; *U.S. Private*, pg. 3394
RELIABLE TOOL & MACHINE CO.; *U.S. Private*, pg. 3394
RELIABLE TOY CORPORATION—See Allied Plastic Skylight; *Int'l*, pg. 358
RELIABLE TRUCKING INC.; *U.S. Private*, pg. 3394
RELIABLE TURBINE SERVICES LLC—See Fuji Electric Co., Ltd.; *Int'l*, pg. 2812
RELIABLE VAN & STORAGE CO., INC.; *U.S. Private*, pg. 3394
RELIABLE VENTURES INDIA LIMITED; *Int'l*, pg. 6261
RELIABLE WHOLESALE LUMBER INC.; *U.S. Private*, pg. 3394
RELIA DIGITAL INC.—See Relia, Inc.; *Int'l*, pg. 6260
RELIA, INC.; *Int'l*, pg. 6260
RELIANCE - ADA GROUP LIMITED; *Int'l*, pg. 6261
RELIANCE AEROTECH INC.; *U.S. Private*, pg. 3394
RELIANCE ASSET RECONSTRUCTION COMPANY LIMITED—See Reliance Insurance Limited; *Int'l*, pg. 6264
RELIANCE BANCORP, INC.; *U.S. Private*, pg. 3394
RELIANCE BANCSHARES, INC.—See Simmons First National Corporation; *U.S. Public*, pg. 1881
RELIANCE BANK—See Simmons First National Corporation; *U.S. Public*, pg. 1881
RELIANCE BIG TV LIMITED—See Pantel Technologies Pvt. Ltd.; *Int'l*, pg. 5730
RELIANCE BROADCAST NETWORK LIMITED; *Int'l*, pg. 6263
RELIANCE CAPITAL LIMITED—See Reliance - ADA Group Limited; *Int'l*, pg. 6261
RELIANCE CAPITAL MARKETS II, LLC - RCM ALTERNATIVES DIVISION—See Reliance Capital Markets II, LLC; *U.S. Private*, pg. 3394
RELIANCE CAPITAL MARKETS II, LLC; *U.S. Private*, pg. 3394
RELIANCE CAPITAL TRUSTEE CO. LIMITED—See Reliance - ADA Group Limited; *Int'l*, pg. 6261
RELIANCE CHEMOTEX INDUSTRIES LTD.; *Int'l*, pg. 6263
RELIANCE COMFORT LIMITED PARTNERSHIP—See CK Asset Holdings Limited; *Int'l*, pg. 1635
RELIANCE COMMODITIES LIMITED—See Reliance - ADA Group Limited; *Int'l*, pg. 6261
RELIANCE COMMUNICATIONS (AUSTRALIA) PTY LIMITED—See Reliance - ADA Group Limited; *Int'l*, pg. 6261
RELIANCE COMMUNICATIONS INC.—See Reliance - ADA Group Limited; *Int'l*, pg. 6261
RELIANCE COMMUNICATIONS INTERNATIONAL INC.—See Reliance - ADA Group Limited; *Int'l*, pg. 6261
RELIANCE COMMUNICATIONS LIMITED—See Reliance - ADA Group Limited; *Int'l*, pg. 6261
RELIANCE COMPOSITE INSURANCE BROKING LIMITED—See Reliance - ADA Group Limited; *Int'l*, pg. 6261

COMPANY NAME INDEX

RELIANCE COTTON SPINNING MILLS LTD.; *Int'l*, pg. 6263
RELIANCE DOORS PTY LTD.; *Int'l*, pg. 6263
RELIANCE ENERGY TRADING LIMITED—See Reliance - ADA Group Limited; *Int'l*, pg. 6263
RELIANCE ENTERTAINMENT PVT. LTD.—See Reliance - ADA Group Limited; *Int'l*, pg. 6262
RELIANCE EQUITY ADVISORS (INDIA) LIMITED—See Reliance - ADA Group Limited; *Int'l*, pg. 6261
RELIANCE FINANCIAL CORPORATION—See Fidelity National Infor; *U.S. Public*, pg. 832
RELIANCE FIRE PROTECTION, INC.—See APi Group Corporation; *Int'l*, pg. 514
RELIANCE FIRST CAPITAL, LLC—See Tiptree Inc.; *U.S. Public*, pg. 2159
RELIANCE GEAR LTD.—See First Israel Mezzanine Investors Ltd.; *Int'l*, pg. 2685
RELIANCE GENERAL INSURANCE COMPANY LIMITED—See Reliance - ADA Group Limited; *Int'l*, pg. 6261
RELIANCE GLOBALCOM - BELGIUM—See Reliance - ADA Group Limited; *Int'l*, pg. 6261
RELIANCE GLOBALCOM B.V.—See Reliance - ADA Group Limited; *Int'l*, pg. 6262
RELIANCE GLOBALCOM - FRANCE—See Reliance - ADA Group Limited; *Int'l*, pg. 6262
RELIANCE GLOBALCOM - ITALY—See Reliance - ADA Group Limited; *Int'l*, pg. 6262
RELIANCE GLOBALCOM LIMITED—See Reliance - ADA Group Limited; *Int'l*, pg. 6262
RELIANCE GLOBALCOM - POLAND—See Reliance - ADA Group Limited; *Int'l*, pg. 6262
RELIANCE GLOBALCOM SERVICES, INC.—See Reliance - ADA Group Limited; *Int'l*, pg. 6262
RELIANCE GLOBALCOM (UK) LIMITED—See Reliance - ADA Group Limited; *Int'l*, pg. 6261
RELIANCE GLOBAL GROUP, INC.; *U.S. Public*, pg. 1778
RELIANCE GLOBAL HOLDINGS LIMITED; *Int'l*, pg. 6263
RELIANCE HEATING & AIR CONDITIONING COMPANY; *U.S. Private*, pg. 3394
RELIANCE HIGH-TECH LTD.; *Int'l*, pg. 6263
RELIANCE HOME FINANCE LIMITED - RELIANCE PROPERTY DIVISION—See Reliance - ADA Group Limited; *Int'l*, pg. 6261
RELIANCE HOME FINANCE LIMITED—See Reliance - ADA Group Limited; *Int'l*, pg. 6261
RELIANCE HOUSE INC.; *U.S. Private*, pg. 3394
RELIANCE INC.; *U.S. Private*, pg. 3394
RELIANCE INDUSTRIAL INFRASTRUCTURE LTD.—See Reliance - ADA Group Limited; *Int'l*, pg. 6262
RELIANCE INDUSTRIAL INVESTMENTS AND HOLDINGS LTD—See Reliance - ADA Group Limited; *Int'l*, pg. 6262
RELIANCE INDUSTRIAL PRODUCTS USA, LTD.—See Applied Industrial Technologies, Inc.; *U.S. Public*, pg. 171
RELIANCE INDUSTRIES LIMITED—See Reliance - ADA Group Limited; *Int'l*, pg. 6262
RELIANCE INFORMATION TECHNOLOGY LLC—See NMC Health PLC; *Int'l*, pg. 5392
RELIANCE INFOTECH—See NMC Health PLC; *Int'l*, pg. 5392
RELIANCE INFRASTRUCTURE LIMITED—See Reliance - ADA Group Limited; *Int'l*, pg. 6263
RELIANCE INFRATEL LTD—See Reliance - ADA Group Limited; *Int'l*, pg. 6262
RELIANCE INSURANCE COMPANY LIMITED; *Int'l*, pg. 6263
RELIANCE INSURANCE LIMITED; *Int'l*, pg. 6264
RELIANCE INTEGRATED SOLUTIONS LLC—See Fidelity National Infor; *U.S. Public*, pg. 832
RELIANCE JIO INFOCOMM LTD—See Reliance - ADA Group Limited; *Int'l*, pg. 6262
RELIANCE MEDIAWORKS LIMITED—See Reliance - ADA Group Limited; *Int'l*, pg. 6263
RELIANCE MEDIAWORKS (USA), INC. - BURBANK—See Reliance - ADA Group Limited; *Int'l*, pg. 6263
RELIANCE MEDICAL GROUP, LLC—See Four Corners Property Trust, Inc.; *U.S. Public*, pg. 875
RELIANCE METALCENTER ASIA PACIFIC PTE. LTD.—See Reliance Steel & Aluminum Co.; *U.S. Public*, pg. 1781
RELIANCE METALS CANADA LIMITED—See Reliance Steel & Aluminum Co.; *U.S. Public*, pg. 1781
RELIANCE METALS (SHANGHAI) CO., LTD.—See Reliance Steel & Aluminum Co.; *U.S. Public*, pg. 1781
RELIANCE MONEY EXPRESS LIMITED—See Reliance - ADA Group Limited; *Int'l*, pg. 6261
RELIANCE MONEY PRECIOUS METALS PRIVATE LIMITED—See Reliance - ADA Group Limited; *Int'l*, pg. 6261
RELIANCE NAVAL AND ENGINEERING LTD.; *Int'l*, pg. 6264
RELIANCE NIPPON LIFE INSURANCE COMPANY LIMITED—See Nippon Life Insurance Company; *Int'l*, pg. 5323
RELIANCE NIPPON LIFE INSURANCE COMPANY LIMITED—See Reliance - ADA Group Limited; *Int'l*, pg. 6261

RELIANCE OPERATIONS SERVICES LLC—See Fidelity National Infor; *U.S. Public*, pg. 832
RELIANCE PETROLEUM COMPANY INC.—See Donnini Enterprises Inc.; *U.S. Private*, pg. 1261
RELIANCE POWER LIMITED—See Reliance - ADA Group Limited; *Int'l*, pg. 6263
RELIANCE PRODUCTS, LTD.—See Greif Inc.; *U.S. Public*, pg. 968
RELIANCE PROPERTY LOANS LIMITED—See J.C. Flowers & Co. LLC; *U.S. Private*, pg. 2160
RELIANCE PROPERTY RESOURCES CO.—See LandPark Advisors, LLC; *U.S. Private*, pg. 2386
RELIANCE RETAIL VENTURES LTD.—See Reliance - ADA Group Limited; *Int'l*, pg. 6262
RELIANCE SAVINGS BANK—See Reliance Bancorp, Inc.; *U.S. Private*, pg. 3394
RELIANCE SECURITIES LIMITED—See Reliance - ADA Group Limited; *Int'l*, pg. 6261
RELIANCE STANDARD LIFE INSURANCE COMPANY—See Tokio Marine Holdings, Inc.; *Int'l*, pg. 7782
RELIANCE STAR PAYMENT SERVICES INC.; *U.S. Private*, pg. 3394
RELIANCE STATE BANK—See Ames National Corporation; *U.S. Public*, pg. 115
RELIANCE STEEL & ALUMINUM CO.; *U.S. Public*, pg. 1779
RELIANCE TRUST COMPANY—See Fidelity National Infor; *U.S. Public*, pg. 832
RELIANCE UTILITIES & POWER PVT. LTD.—See Reliance - ADA Group Limited; *Int'l*, pg. 6262
RELIANCE VANCO GROUP LIMITED—See Reliance - ADA Group Limited; *Int'l*, pg. 6262
RELIANCE WEALTH MANAGEMENT LIMITED—See Reliance - ADA Group Limited; *Int'l*, pg. 6261
RELIANCE WEAVING MILLS LIMITED; *Int'l*, pg. 6264
RELIANCE WORKPLACE SOLUTIONS PTY LTD—See PSC Insurance Group Limited; *Int'l*, pg. 6016
RELIANCE WORLDWIDE CORPORATION (AUST.) PTY. LTD.—See Reliance Worldwide Corporation Limited; *Int'l*, pg. 6264
RELIANCE WORLDWIDE CORPORATION LIMITED; *Int'l*, pg. 6264
RELIANCE WORLDWIDE CORPORATION (UK) LIMITED—See Reliance Worldwide Corporation Limited; *Int'l*, pg. 6264
RELIANT ASSET MANAGEMENT LLC; *U.S. Private*, pg. 3395
RELIANT BANCORP, INC.—See United Community Banks, Inc.; *U.S. Public*, pg. 2230
RELIANT BANK—See United Community Banks, Inc.; *U.S. Public*, pg. 2230
RELIANT ENERGY RETAIL HOLDINGS, LLC—See NRG Energy, Inc.; *U.S. Public*, pg. 1551
RELIANT ENERGY RETAIL HOLDINGS, LLC—See NRG Energy, Inc.; *U.S. Public*, pg. 1550
RELIANT ENERGY RETAIL SERVICES, LLC—See NRG Energy, Inc.; *U.S. Public*, pg. 1551
RELIANT FINANCIAL SERVICES INC.; *U.S. Private*, pg. 3395
RELIANT FOODSERVICE; *U.S. Private*, pg. 3395
RELIANT HOLDINGS, INC.; *U.S. Public*, pg. 1782
RELIANT HOME HEALTH, INC.—See Merit Capital Partners; *U.S. Private*, pg. 2674
RELIANT INVENTORY SERVICES, INC.—See Reliant Inventory Services; *U.S. Private*, pg. 3395
RELIANT INVENTORY SERVICES; *U.S. Private*, pg. 3395
RELIANT MEDICAL SYSTEMS, INC.—See Radon Medical Imaging Corp.; *U.S. Private*, pg. 3345
RELIANT MISSION, INC.; *U.S. Private*, pg. 3395
RELIANT POOLS, INC.—See Reliant Holdings, Inc.; *U.S. Public*, pg. 1782
RELIANT REALTY, LLC; *U.S. Private*, pg. 3395
RELIANT REHABILITATION HOLDINGS, INC.—See H.I.G. Capital, LLC; *U.S. Private*, pg. 1831
RELIANT SERVICE, INC.; *Int'l*, pg. 6264
RELIANT TRANSPORTATION, INC.; *U.S. Private*, pg. 3395
RELIAQUEST LLC; *U.S. Private*, pg. 3395
RELIAQUOTE, INC.—See Fiserv, Inc.; *U.S. Public*, pg. 851
RELIAS LEARNING LLC—See Bertelsmann SE & Co. KGaA; *Int'l*, pg. 991
RELIAS LLC—See Bertelsmann SE & Co. KGaA; *Int'l*, pg. 996
RELIASTAR LIFE INSURANCE COMPANY OF NEW YORK—See Voya Financial, Inc.; *U.S. Public*, pg. 2311
RELIASTAR LIFE INSURANCE COMPANY—See Voya Financial, Inc.; *U.S. Public*, pg. 2311
RELIA VIETNAM JOINT STOCK COMPANY—See Relia, Inc.; *Int'l*, pg. 6260
RELICAB CABLE MANUFACTURING LIMITED; *Int'l*, pg. 6264
RELIC TECHNOLOGIES LIMITED; *Int'l*, pg. 6264
RELIEF INTERNATIONAL; *U.S. Private*, pg. 3395
RELIEF THERAPEUTICS HOLDING SA; *Int'l*, pg. 6264
RELIEF THERAPEUTICS SA—See Sonnet BioTherapeutics Holdings, Inc.; *U.S. Public*, pg. 1904
RELIEVANT MEDSYSTEMS INC.—See Boston Scientific Corporation; *U.S. Public*, pg. 375

RELPOL S.A.

RELIGARE ARTS INITIATIVE LIMITED—See Religare Enterprises Limited; *Int'l*, pg. 6264
RELIGARE CAPITAL MARKETS CORPORATE FINANCE PTE LIMITED—See Religare Enterprises Limited; *Int'l*, pg. 6264
RELIGARE CAPITAL MARKETS (HONG KONG) LIMITED—See Religare Enterprises Limited; *Int'l*, pg. 6264
RELIGARE CAPITAL MARKETS LIMITED—See Religare Enterprises Limited; *Int'l*, pg. 6264
RELIGARE CAPITAL MARKETS (SINGAPORE) PTE LIMITED—See Religare Enterprises Limited; *Int'l*, pg. 6264
RELIGARE ENTERPRISES LIMITED; *Int'l*, pg. 6264
RELIGARE GLOBAL ASSET MANAGEMENT INC.—See Religare Enterprises Limited; *Int'l*, pg. 6264
RELIGARE HOUSING DEVELOPMENT FINANCE CORPORATION LIMITED—See Religare Enterprises Limited; *Int'l*, pg. 6264
RELIGARE SECURITIES LIMITED—See Religare Enterprises Limited; *Int'l*, pg. 6264
RELIGION NEWS LLC; *U.S. Private*, pg. 3395
RELIGION NEWS SERVICE—See Religion News LLC; *U.S. Private*, pg. 3395
RELINE CO., LTD.—See Persol Holdings Co., Ltd.; *Int'l*, pg. 5820
RELIQ HEALTH TECHNOLOGIES INC.; *Int'l*, pg. 6264
RELISH LABS LLC—See The Kroger Co.; *U.S. Public*, pg. 2109
RELIUS PHARMACEUTICALS LTDA.—See Remus Pharmaceuticals Limited; *Int'l*, pg. 6272
RELIUS PHARMA S.R.L.—See Remus Pharmaceuticals Limited; *Int'l*, pg. 6272
RELIV AUSTRALIA PTY, LIMITED—See Reliv International, Inc.; *U.S. Public*, pg. 1782
RELIV EUROPE LIMITED—See Reliv International, Inc.; *U.S. Public*, pg. 1782
RELIV, INC.—See Reliv International, Inc.; *U.S. Public*, pg. 1782
RELIV INTERNATIONAL, INC.; *U.S. Public*, pg. 1782
RELJIN SLAVKO A.D.; *Int'l*, pg. 6264
RELLOK CUTTING SOLUTIONS GMBH—See MB Holding Company LLC; *Int'l*, pg. 4750
RELMADA THERAPEUTICS, INC.; *U.S. Public*, pg. 1782
RELMEC MECHANICAL LLC; *U.S. Private*, pg. 3395
RELM HOLDINGS, INC.; *U.S. Public*, pg. 1782
THE RELOCATION FREIGHT CORPORATION OF AMERICA—See Prudential Financial, Inc.; *U.S. Public*, pg. 1734
RELOCATION INTERNATIONAL, INC.—See Relo Group, Inc.; *Int'l*, pg. 6265
RELOCATION JAPAN, LIMITED—See Relo Group, Inc.; *Int'l*, pg. 6265
RELOCATION MANAGEMENT RESOURCES, INC. - BUSINESS SOLUTIONS—See Relocation Management Resources, Inc.; *U.S. Private*, pg. 3395
RELOCATION MANAGEMENT RESOURCES, INC.; *U.S. Private*, pg. 3395
RELOCATION PROPERTIES MANAGEMENT LLC—See Valvoline Inc.; *U.S. Public*, pg. 2274
RELOCATION SERVICES INTERNATIONAL; *U.S. Private*, pg. 3395
RELOCATION TAXES, LLC—See Orion Mobility; *U.S. Private*, pg. 3043
RELO CLUB, LIMITED—See Relo Group, Inc.; *Int'l*, pg. 6265
RELO CREATE, LIMITED—See Relo Group, Inc.; *Int'l*, pg. 6265
RELO ESTATE, LIMITED—See Relo Group, Inc.; *Int'l*, pg. 6265
RELOEXCEL, INC.—See Relo Group, Inc.; *Int'l*, pg. 6265
RELO EXCEL INTERNATIONAL, INC.—See Relo Group, Inc.; *Int'l*, pg. 6265
RELO FINANCIAL SOLUTIONS, LIMITED—See Relo Group, Inc.; *Int'l*, pg. 6265
RELO GROUP, INC.; *Int'l*, pg. 6265
RELONCHEM LIMITED—See Marksans Pharma Ltd; *Int'l*, pg. 4697
RELO PANASONIC EXCEL INTERNATIONAL CO., LTD.—See Relo Group, Inc.; *Int'l*, pg. 6265
RELO PARTNERS, LIMITED—See Relo Group, Inc.; *Int'l*, pg. 6265
RELO PARTNERS PROPERTY, INC.—See Relo Group, Inc.; *Int'l*, pg. 6265
RELO REDAC, INC.—See Relo Group, Inc.; *Int'l*, pg. 6265
RELO REDAC STRATTONS LIMITED—See Relo Group, Inc.; *Int'l*, pg. 6265
RELO TRANSEURO, LTD.—See Relo Group, Inc.; *Int'l*, pg. 6265
RELO VACATIONS, LIMITED—See Relo Group, Inc.; *Int'l*, pg. 6265
RELPOL BG—See Relpol S.A.; *Int'l*, pg. 6265
RELPOL FRANCE SARL—See Relpol S.A.; *Int'l*, pg. 6265
RELPOL HUNGARY KFT—See Relpol S.A.; *Int'l*, pg. 6265
RELPOL M LTD.—See Relpol S.A.; *Int'l*, pg. 6265
RELPOL S.A.; *Int'l*, pg. 6265
RELS, LLC—See Insight Venture Management, LLC; *U.S. Private*, pg. 2089

RELPOL S.A.

CORPORATE AFFILIATIONS

RELS, LLC—See Stone Point Capital LLC; *U.S. Private*, pg. 3823
RELSTRUCT BUILDCON LIMITED; *Int'l*, pg. 6265
RELTCO, INC.—See Live Oak Bancshares, Inc.; *U.S. Public*, pg. 1331
REL-TECH ELECTRONICS, INC.—See RF Industries, Ltd.; *U.S. Public*, pg. 1796
RELUME TECHNOLOGIES, INC.—See Revolution Lighting Technologies, Inc.; *U.S. Public*, pg. 1793
RELWARE; *U.S. Private*, pg. 3395
RELX CAPITAL NV—See RELX plc; *Int'l*, pg. 6268
RELX GROUP PLC—See RELX plc; *Int'l*, pg. 6266
RELX INC. - CHICAGO OFFICE—See RELX plc; *Int'l*, pg. 6268
RELX INC. - COLORADO SPRINGS OFFICE—See RELX plc; *Int'l*, pg. 6268
RELX INC. - D.C. OFFICE—See RELX plc; *Int'l*, pg. 6268
RELX INC. - RALEIGH OFFICE—See RELX plc; *Int'l*, pg. 6268
RELX INC.—See RELX plc; *Int'l*, pg. 6267
RELX INFORMATION ANALYTICS (THAILAND) CO., LTD.—See RELX plc; *Int'l*, pg. 6268
RELX NEDERLAND B.V.—See RELX plc; *Int'l*, pg. 6268
RELX PLC; *Int'l*, pg. 6265
RELX (SINGAPORE) PTE. LTD.—See RELX plc; *Int'l*, pg. 6266
RELX (UK) LIMITED—See RELX plc; *Int'l*, pg. 6266
RELYANCE BANK, N.A.; *U.S. Private*, pg. 3395
RELYCO SALES, INC.; *U.S. Private*, pg. 3395
RELY INTRACAST PRECISION CASTINGS (PTY) LTD—See Pamodzi Investment Holdings; *Int'l*, pg. 5711
RELYON GROUP LIMITED—See Steinhoff International Holdings N.V.; *Int'l*, pg. 7195
RELYON LIMITED—See Steinhoff International Holdings N.V.; *Int'l*, pg. 7195
REMA 1000 AS—See Reitangruppen AS; *Int'l*, pg. 6258
REMA 1000 NORGE AS—See Reitangruppen AS; *Int'l*, pg. 6258
REMACLE NV/SA.—See CRH plc; *Int'l*, pg. 1848
REMACOM NV—See Ackermans & van Haaren NV; *Int'l*, pg. 105
REMACONTROL SWEDEN AB—See Image Systems AB; *Int'l*, pg. 3618
RE.MAC.UT. S.R.L.—See NOV, Inc.; *U.S. Public*, pg. 1546
REMAK ENERGOMONTAZ SA; *Int'l*, pg. 6269
REMAKO PAPER & BOARD B.V.—See Nimbus B.V.; *Int'l*, pg. 5296
REMAR, INC.—See Fidelitone, Inc.; *U.S. Private*, pg. 1502
REMARK ENTERTAINMENT (SHANGHAI) CO. LTD.—See Remark Holdings, Inc.; *U.S. Public*, pg. 1782
REMARK GROUP BV—See SCOR SE; *Int'l*, pg. 6650
REMARK HOLDINGS, INC.; *U.S. Public*, pg. 1782
REMARK HONG KONG—See SCOR SE; *Int'l*, pg. 6650
REMARK INTERNATIONAL BV—See SCOR SE; *Int'l*, pg. 6650
REMARK PAPER COMPANY INC.; *U.S. Private*, pg. 3396
REMARO GROUP CORP.; *Int'l*, pg. 6269
REM ARROWHEAD, INC.—See Centerbridge Partners, L.P.; *U.S. Private*, pg. 814
REMARUL 16 FEBRUARIE SA; *Int'l*, pg. 6269
REMASAWCO AB—See Image Systems AB; *Int'l*, pg. 3618
REMASAWCO AS—See Image Systems AB; *Int'l*, pg. 3618
RE-MATCH A/S—See Verdane Capital Advisors AS; *Int'l*, pg. 8165
RE-MATCH HOLDING A/S—See Verdane Capital Advisors AS; *Int'l*, pg. 8165
REMATCH INC—See CME Group, Inc.; *U.S. Public*, pg. 517
RE-MATCH NETHERLANDS B.V.—See Verdane Capital Advisors AS; *Int'l*, pg. 8165
REMATE LINCE, S.A.P.I. DE C.V.—See BGC Group, Inc.; *U.S. Public*, pg. 330
REMATE USA INC.—See BGC Group, Inc.; *U.S. Public*, pg. 330
REMAT HULLADEKHASZNOSITO ZRT.—See MOL Magyar Olaj- es Gazipari Nyrt.; *Int'l*, pg. 5021
REMA TIP TOP/NORTH AMERICA, INC.—See Stahlgruber Otto Gruber GmbH & Co. KG; *Int'l*, pg. 7164
REMAT MARAMURES SA; *Int'l*, pg. 6269
RE MAT S.R.L.—See Iren S.p.A.; *Int'l*, pg. 3808
RE/MAX ACCORD; *U.S. Private*, pg. 3364
RE/MAX ALLEGIANCE; *U.S. Private*, pg. 3364
RE/MAX ALLEGIANCE - VIRGINIA BEACH—See RE/MAX Allegiance; *U.S. Private*, pg. 3364
RE/MAX ALLIANCE GROUP; *U.S. Private*, pg. 3364
RE/MAX BENCH REALTY GROUP—See RE/MAX Holdings, Inc.; *U.S. Public*, pg. 1768
RE/MAX CHOICE PROPERTIES; *U.S. Private*, pg. 3365
RE/MAX HEARTLAND; *U.S. Private*, pg. 3365
RE/MAX HOLDINGS, INC.; *U.S. Public*, pg. 1768
RE/MAX, LLC—See RE/MAX Holdings, Inc.; *U.S. Public*, pg. 1768
RE/MAX OF NAPERVILLE INC.; *U.S. Private*, pg. 3365
RE/MAX ONTARIO-ATLANTIC CANADA, INC.—See RE/MAX Holdings, Inc.; *U.S. Public*, pg. 1768
RE/MAX PROPERTIES EAST, INC.; *U.S. Private*, pg. 3365
RE/MAX REALTORS INC.; *U.S. Private*, pg. 3365
RE/MAX VILLA REALTORS; *U.S. Private*, pg. 3365

THE REMBAR COMPANY, LLC; *U.S. Private*, pg. 4104
REMBRANDT ENTERPRISES, INC.; *U.S. Private*, pg. 3396
REMBRANDTIN FARBEXPERTE GMBH—See Ring International Holding AG; *Int'l*, pg. 6343
REMBRANDTIN LACK GMBH NFG KG; *Int'l*, pg. 6269
REMBRANDTIN OBEROSTERREICH GMBH & CO KG—See Kansai Paint Co., Ltd.; *Int'l*, pg. 4071
REMBRANDTIN S.R.O.—See Kansai Paint Co., Ltd.; *Int'l*, pg. 4072
REM CENTRAL LAKES, INC.—See Centerbridge Partners, L.P.; *U.S. Private*, pg. 814
REMC LIMITED—See RITES Ltd; *Int'l*, pg. 6352
REM COMMUNITY OPTIONS, LLC—See Centerbridge Partners, L.P.; *U.S. Private*, pg. 814
REM CONNECTICUT COMMUNITY SERVICES, INC.—See Centerbridge Partners, L.P.; *U.S. Private*, pg. 814
REMCON PLASTICS INCORPORATED; *U.S. Private*, pg. 3396
REMCO SUPPLY INC.; *U.S. Private*, pg. 3396
REM DEVELOPMENTAL SERVICES, INC.—See Centerbridge Partners, L.P.; *U.S. Private*, pg. 814
REMEA SAS—See VINCI S.A.; *Int'l*, pg. 8225
REM EAST, LLC—See Centerbridge Partners, L.P.; *U.S. Private*, pg. 814
REMEC DEFENSE & SPACE, INC—See Advent International Corporation; *U.S. Private*, pg. 99
REMECH SP. Z O.O.—See Zaklady Chemiczne POLICE S.A.; *Int'l*, pg. 8621
REMECH SYSTEMTECHNIK GMBH—See Siemens Aktiengesellschaft; *Int'l*, pg. 6887
REMED CO., LTD.; *Int'l*, pg. 6269
REMEDENT, INC.; *Int'l*, pg. 6269
REMEDENT N.V.—See Remedent, Inc.; *Int'l*, pg. 6269
REMEDIAL CONSTRUCTION SERVICES, L.P.—See Keller Group plc; *Int'l*, pg. 4121
REMEDIATION SERVICES, INC.—See Koninklijke Philips N.V.; *Int'l*, pg. 4271
REMEDICA LTD.—See Ascendis Health Limited; *Int'l*, pg. 601
REMEDI SENIORCARE HOLDING CORPORATION; *U.S. Private*, pg. 3396
REMEDI SENIORCARE OF OHIO - NORTHEAST, LLC—See Remedi SeniorCare Holding Corporation; *U.S. Private*, pg. 3396
REMEDIUM LIFECARE LTD.; *Int'l*, pg. 6269
REMEDY EMPLOYER SERVICES, LLC—See Aquiline Capital Partners LLC; *U.S. Private*, pg. 304
REMEDY ENTERTAINMENT PLC; *Int'l*, pg. 6269
REMEDY HEALTHCARE GROUP PTY LTD—See Australian Unity Limited; *Int'l*, pg. 723
REMEDY HEALTH MEDIA, LLC—See Topspin Partners, L.P.; *U.S. Private*, pg. 4188
REMEDY INFORMATICS; *U.S. Private*, pg. 3396
REMEDY INTELLIGENT STAFFING, INC.—See Affiliated Managers Group, Inc.; *U.S. Public*, pg. 54
REMEDY INTELLIGENT STAFFING, INC.—See Anchorage Capital Group, L.L.C.; *U.S. Private*, pg. 274
REMEDY INTERACTIVE, INC.—See Thoma Bravo, L.P.; *U.S. Private*, pg. 4146
REMEDY ROOFING, INC.; *U.S. Private*, pg. 3396
REMEDY THERAPY STAFFING PLLC—See InHome Therapy Inc.; *U.S. Private*, pg. 2077
REMEGEN BIOSCIENCES, INC.—See RemeGen Company Limited; *Int'l*, pg. 6269
REMEGEN COMPANY LIMITED; *Int'l*, pg. 6269
REMEGENIX, INC.; *U.S. Private*, pg. 3396
REMEHA B.V.—See BDR Thermea Group B.V.; *Int'l*, pg. 931
REMEHA SRL—See BDR Thermea Group B.V.; *Int'l*, pg. 931
REMEJE PHARMACEUTICALS (CHINA) CO., LTD.—See ITOCHU Corporation; *Int'l*, pg. 3841
REM ELECTRONICS SUPPLY CO. INC.; *U.S. Private*, pg. 3395
REMEL EUROPE LIMITED—See Thermo Fisher Scientific Inc.; *U.S. Public*, pg. 2151
REMEL INC.—See Thermo Fisher Scientific Inc.; *U.S. Public*, pg. 2151
REMEN SLUKFABRIKK AS—See Rapala VMC Oyj; *Int'l*, pg. 6210
REMEO DEUTSCHLAND GMBH—See Linde plc; *Int'l*, pg. 4508
REMER INC, CREATIVE MARKETING; *U.S. Private*, pg. 3396
REMESAS QUISQUEYANA INC.—See Palladium Equity Partners, LLC; *U.S. Private*, pg. 3078
THE REMET COMPANY LTD.; *Int'l*, pg. 7678
REMET CORPORATION—See BP plc; *Int'l*, pg. 1131
REMEX MINERALSTOFF GMBH—See RETHMANN AG & Co. KG; *Int'l*, pg. 6306
REM GLOBAL, INC.; *U.S. Private*, pg. 3395
REMGRO LIMITED; *Int'l*, pg. 6269
REMGRO MANAGEMENT SERVICES LIMITED—See Remgro Limited; *Int'l*, pg. 6270
REM GROUP (HOLDINGS) LTD.; *Int'l*, pg. 6269
REM HEARTLAND, INC.—See Centerbridge Partners, L.P.; *U.S. Private*, pg. 814

REM HENNEPIN, INC.—See Centerbridge Partners, L.P.; *U.S. Private*, pg. 814
R.E. MICHEL COMPANY INC.; *U.S. Private*, pg. 3335
REMICON JOINT STOCK COMPANY; *Int'l*, pg. 6271
REMI EDELSTAHL TUBULARS LIMITED—See Remi Group; *Int'l*, pg. 6271
REMI ELEKTROTECHNIK LIMITED—See Remi Group; *Int'l*, pg. 6271
THE REMI GROUP, LLC; *U.S. Private*, pg. 4104
REMI GROUP; *Int'l*, pg. 6271
REM INDIANA COMMUNITY SERVICES, INC.—See Centerbridge Partners, L.P.; *U.S. Private*, pg. 814
REM INDIANA, INC.—See Centerbridge Partners, L.P.; *U.S. Private*, pg. 814
REMINGTON ARMS COMPANY, INC. - AMMUNITION & COMPONENTS PLANT—See Cerberus Capital Management, L.P.; *U.S. Private*, pg. 839
REMINGTON ARMS COMPANY, INC. - MAYFIELD FIREARMS PLANT—See Cerberus Capital Management, L.P.; *U.S. Private*, pg. 839
REMINGTON ARMS COMPANY, INC.—See Cerberus Capital Management, L.P.; *U.S. Private*, pg. 839
REMINGTON ASSOCIATES LTD.; *U.S. Private*, pg. 3396
REMINGTON CONSUMER PRODUCTS (IRELAND) LTD.—See Spectrum Brands Holdings, Inc.; *U.S. Public*, pg. 1916
REMINGTON CONSUMER PRODUCTS—See Spectrum Brands Holdings, Inc.; *U.S. Public*, pg. 1916
REMINGTON DEVELOPMENT CORPORATION; *Int'l*, pg. 6271
THE REMINGTON GROUP INC—See Avison Young (Canada) Inc.; *Int'l*, pg. 745
REMINGTON LICENSING CORPORATION—See Spectrum Brands Holdings, Inc.; *U.S. Public*, pg. 1916
REMINGTON OUTDOOR COMPANY INC.—See Cerberus Capital Management, L.P.; *U.S. Private*, pg. 839
REMINGTON PRODUCTS COMPANY; *U.S. Private*, pg. 3396
REMINGTON PRODUCTS NEW ZEALAND LTD.—See Spectrum Brands Holdings, Inc.; *U.S. Public*, pg. 1916
REMINGTON RESOURCES INC; *Int'l*, pg. 6271
REMINGTON SHIPPING INC.—See Sealift Holdings Inc.; *U.S. Private*, pg. 3585
REMINGTON STEEL, INC.—See Westfield Steel Inc.; *U.S. Private*, pg. 4498
REM IOWA COMMUNITY SERVICES, INC.—See Centerbridge Partners, L.P.; *U.S. Private*, pg. 814
REM IOWA, INC.—See Centerbridge Partners, L.P.; *U.S. Private*, pg. 814
REMI PROCESS PLANT & MACHINERY LIMITED; *Int'l*, pg. 6271
REMI SALES & ENGINEERING LIMITED—See Remi Group; *Int'l*, pg. 6271
REMI SECURITIES LIMITED—See Remi Group; *Int'l*, pg. 6271
REMITDATA, INC.; *U.S. Private*, pg. 3396
REMITLY GLOBAL, INC.; *U.S. Public*, pg. 1782
REMITLY U.K., LTD.—See Remitly Global, Inc.; *U.S. Public*, pg. 1782
REMITTANCE PROCESSING SERVICES, LLC—See The AES Corporation; *U.S. Public*, pg. 2032
REMIXPOINT INC.; *Int'l*, pg. 6271
REM, JSC—See OAO AK Transneft; *Int'l*, pg. 5505
REMKE MARKETS INCORPORATED—See Fresh Encounter Inc.; *U.S. Private*, pg. 1609
REMKO GMBH & CO. KG KLIMA- UND WARMETECHNIK—See INDUS Holding AG; *Int'l*, pg. 3664
REMKO GMBH & CO. KG—See INDUS Holding AG; *Int'l*, pg. 3664
REM MARKET LLC; *U.S. Private*, pg. 3396
REM MARYLAND, INC.—See Centerbridge Partners, L.P.; *U.S. Private*, pg. 814
REMMERT HOLLAND B.V.—See Akzo Nobel N.V.; *Int'l*, pg. 274
REM MINNESOTA COMMUNITY SERVICES, INC.—See Centerbridge Partners, L.P.; *U.S. Private*, pg. 814
REM MINNESOTA, INC.—See Centerbridge Partners, L.P.; *U.S. Private*, pg. 814
REM NEVADA, INC.—See Centerbridge Partners, L.P.; *U.S. Private*, pg. 814
REM NORTH DAKOTA, INC.—See Centerbridge Partners, L.P.; *U.S. Private*, pg. 814
REM NORTH STAR, INC.—See Centerbridge Partners, L.P.; *U.S. Private*, pg. 814
REM OCCAZIO, INC.—See Centerbridge Partners, L.P.; *U.S. Private*, pg. 814
REMODELERS SUPPLY CENTER—See Logan Square Aluminum Supply, Inc.; *U.S. Private*, pg. 2481
THE REMODELING COMPANY; *U.S. Private*, pg. 4104
REM OHIO II, LLC—See Centerbridge Partners, L.P.; *U.S. Private*, pg. 814
REM OHIO, INC.—See Centerbridge Partners, L.P.; *U.S. Private*, pg. 814
REM OHIO WAIVERED SERVICES, INC.—See Centerbridge Partners, L.P.; *U.S. Private*, pg. 814
REMO INC.; *U.S. Private*, pg. 3396
REMOLCADORES DE PUERTO Y ALTURA, S.A.—See Dubai World Corporation; *Int'l*, pg. 2222

COMPANY NAME INDEX

REMONDIS AG & CO. KG—See RETHMANN AG & Co. KG; *Int'l*, pg. 6306
REMONDIS ALVA GMBH—See RETHMANN AG & Co. KG; *Int'l*, pg. 6307
REMONDIS AQUA B.V.—See RETHMANN AG & Co. KG; *Int'l*, pg. 6307
REMONDIS AQUA GMBH & CO. KG—See RETHMANN AG & Co. KG; *Int'l*, pg. 6306
REMONDIS AQUA (INDIA) PRIVATE LTD.—See RETHMANN AG & Co. KG; *Int'l*, pg. 6307
REMONDIS AQUA TRZEMESZNO SP. Z O.O.—See RETHMANN AG & Co. KG; *Int'l*, pg. 6307
REMONDIS ARGENTIA B.V.—See RETHMANN AG & Co. KG; *Int'l*, pg. 6307
REMONDIS ATIK YONETIMLERI LTD. STI—See RETHMANN AG & Co. KG; *Int'l*, pg. 6307
REMONDIS AUSTRIA GMBH—See RETHMANN AG & Co. KG; *Int'l*, pg. 6307
REMONDIS BELGIEN S.P.R.L.—See RETHMANN AG & Co. KG; *Int'l*, pg. 6307
REMONDIS BRANDENBURG GMBH—See RETHMANN AG & Co. KG; *Int'l*, pg. 6307
REMONDIS BURCU ATIK YONETIMLERI GERI DONUSUM VE TEMIZLIK HIZMETLERI TICARET A.S.—See RETHMANN AG & Co. KG; *Int'l*, pg. 6307
REMONDIS BYDGOSZCZ SP. Z O.O.—See RETHMANN AG & Co. KG; *Int'l*, pg. 6307
REMONDIS CHIEMGAU GMBH—See RETHMANN AG & Co. KG; *Int'l*, pg. 6307
REMONDIS CHINA LTD.—See RETHMANN AG & Co. KG; *Int'l*, pg. 6307
REMONDIS DROBIN KOMUNALNA SP. Z O.O.—See RETHMANN AG & Co. KG; *Int'l*, pg. 6307
REMONDIS EILENBURG GMBH—See RETHMANN AG & Co. KG; *Int'l*, pg. 6307
REMONDIS ELBE-RODER GMBH—See RETHMANN AG & Co. KG; *Int'l*, pg. 6307
REMONDIS ELECTRORECYCLING S.A.S.—See RETHMANN AG & Co. KG; *Int'l*, pg. 6307
REMONDIS ELECTRORECYCLING SP. Z O.O.—See RETHMANN AG & Co. KG; *Int'l*, pg. 6306
REMONDIS ENVIRONMENTAL SERVICES CO., LTD.—See RETHMANN AG & Co. KG; *Int'l*, pg. 6307
REMONDIS EURAWASSER GMBH—See RETHMANN AG & Co. KG; *Int'l*, pg. 6307
REMONDIS FRANCE S.A.S.—See RETHMANN AG & Co. KG; *Int'l*, pg. 6307
REMONDIS GLIWICE SP. Z O.O.—See RETHMANN AG & Co. KG; *Int'l*, pg. 6307
REMONDIS GMBH & CO. KG—See RETHMANN AG & Co. KG; *Int'l*, pg. 6307
REMONDIS GMBH—See RETHMANN AG & Co. KG; *Int'l*, pg. 6307
REMONDIS HOLZAUFBEREITUNG GMBH—See RETHMANN AG & Co. KG; *Int'l*, pg. 6307
REMONDIS INDUSTRIAL SERVICE S.A./N.V.—See RETHMANN AG & Co. KG; *Int'l*, pg. 6307
REMONDIS INDUSTRIE SERVICE GMBH—See RETHMANN AG & Co. KG; *Int'l*, pg. 6307
REMONDIS INDUSTRIE SERVICE SUD GMBH & CO. KG—See RETHMANN AG & Co. KG; *Int'l*, pg. 6307
REMONDIS INTERNATIONAL GMBH—See RETHMANN AG & Co. KG; *Int'l*, pg. 6307
REMONDIS ITALIA S.R.L.—See RETHMANN AG & Co. KG; *Int'l*, pg. 6307
REMONDIS KIEL GMBH—See RETHMANN AG & Co. KG; *Int'l*, pg. 6307
REMONDIS KOMMUNALE DIENSTE SUD GMBH—See RETHMANN AG & Co. KG; *Int'l*, pg. 6307
REMONDIS KROEKO SP. Z O.O.—See RETHMANN AG & Co. KG; *Int'l*, pg. 6307
REMONDIS KYFFHAUSER GMBH—See RETHMANN AG & Co. KG; *Int'l*, pg. 6307
REMONDIS LIQUID WASTE PTY LTD—See RETHMANN AG & Co. KG; *Int'l*, pg. 6307
REMONDIS MAINTENANCE & SERVICES GMBH—See RETHMANN AG & Co. KG; *Int'l*, pg. 6307
REMONDIS MECKLENBURG GMBH—See RETHMANN AG & Co. KG; *Int'l*, pg. 6307
REMONDIS MEDISON D.O.O.—See RETHMANN AG & Co. KG; *Int'l*, pg. 6307
REMONDIS MEDISON SP. Z O.O.—See RETHMANN AG & Co. KG; *Int'l*, pg. 6307
REMONDIS MITTELRHEIN GMBH—See RETHMANN AG & Co. KG; *Int'l*, pg. 6308
REMONDIS MRAGOWO SP. Z O.O.—See RETHMANN AG & Co. KG; *Int'l*, pg. 6308
REMONDIS MUNSTERLAND GMBH & CO. KG—See RETHMANN AG & Co. KG; *Int'l*, pg. 6308
REMONDIS NEDERLAND B.V.—See RETHMANN AG & Co. KG; *Int'l*, pg. 6308
REMONDIS OLPE GMBH—See RETHMANN AG & Co. KG; *Int'l*, pg. 6308
REMONDIS OLSZTYN SPOLKA OGRANICZONA ODPOWIEDZIALNOSCIA S.K.A—See RETHMANN AG & Co. KG; *Int'l*, pg. 6308
REMONDIS OPOLE SP. Z O.O.—See RETHMANN AG & Co. KG; *Int'l*, pg. 6308
REMONDIS OTWOCK SP. Z O.O.—See RETHMANN AG & Co. KG; *Int'l*, pg. 6308
REMONDIS OUEST FRANCE S.A.S—See RETHMANN AG & Co. KG; *Int'l*, pg. 6308
REMONDIS PAPIER B. V.—See RETHMANN AG & Co. KG; *Int'l*, pg. 6308
REMONDIS PLETTENBERG GMBH—See RETHMANN AG & Co. KG; *Int'l*, pg. 6308
REMONDIS PTY. LTD.—See RETHMANN AG & Co. KG; *Int'l*, pg. 6308
REMONDIS RECYCLING TAIWAN CO. LTD.—See RETHMANN AG & Co. KG; *Int'l*, pg. 6308
REMONDIS RHEIN-WUPPER GMBH & CO. KG—See RETHMANN AG & Co. KG; *Int'l*, pg. 6308
REMONDIS ROS S.L.—See RETHMANN AG & Co. KG; *Int'l*, pg. 6308
REMONDIS SAAR ENTSORGUNG GMBH—See RETHMANN AG & Co. KG; *Int'l*, pg. 6308
REMONDIS SACHSEN-ANHALT GMBH—See RETHMANN AG & Co. KG; *Int'l*, pg. 6308
REMONDIS SANITECH POZNAN SP. Z O.O.—See RETHMANN AG & Co. KG; *Int'l*, pg. 6308
REMONDIS SCHWEIZ AG—See RETHMANN AG & Co. KG; *Int'l*, pg. 6308
REMONDIS SE & CO. KG—See RETHMANN AG & Co. KG; *Int'l*, pg. 6308
REMONDIS SP. Z O.O.—See RETHMANN AG & Co. KG; *Int'l*, pg. 6308
REMONDIS SUD FRANCE S.A.S.—See RETHMANN AG & Co. KG; *Int'l*, pg. 6308
REMONDIS SUD GMBH—See RETHMANN AG & Co. KG; *Int'l*, pg. 6308
REMONDIS SU VE ATIKSU TEKNOLOJILERI SANAYI VE TICARET A.S.—See RETHMANN AG & Co. KG; *Int'l*, pg. 6308
REMONDIS SWIDNIK SP. Z O.O.—See RETHMANN AG & Co. KG; *Int'l*, pg. 6308
REMONDIS SZCZECIN SP. Z O.O.—See RETHMANN AG & Co. KG; *Int'l*, pg. 6308
REMONDIS TARNOWSKIE GORY SP. Z O.O.—See RETHMANN AG & Co. KG; *Int'l*, pg. 6308
REMONDIS THERMISCHE ABFALLVERWERTUNG GMBH—See RETHMANN AG & Co. KG; *Int'l*, pg. 6308
REMONDIS TRADE AND SALES GMBH—See RETHMANN AG & Co. KG; *Int'l*, pg. 6308
REMONDIS UK LTD.—See RETHMANN AG & Co. KG; *Int'l*, pg. 6308
REMONDIS VORPOMMERN GMBH—See RETHMANN AG & Co. KG; *Int'l*, pg. 6308
R.E. MONKS CONSTRUCTION COMPANY LLC; *U.S. Private*, pg. 3335
RE MONKS CONSTRUCTION COMPANY; *U.S. Private*, pg. 3364
REMONTEES MECANIQUES CRANS MONTANA AMINONA (CMA) SA—See Vail Resorts, Inc.; *U.S. Public*, pg. 2271
REMONTMONTAZA D.D. TUZLA; *Int'l*, pg. 6271
REMORA ROYALTIES, INC.; *U.S. Private*, pg. 3396
REMOSA S.R.L.—See IMI plc; *Int'l*, pg. 3626
REMOTE ACCESS TECHNOLOGY INTERNATIONAL—See Rockwood Holdings Limited Partnership; *U.S. Private*, pg. 3468
REMOTE BACKUP SYSTEMS INC.; *U.S. Private*, pg. 3396
REMOTEC, INC.—See Northrop Grumman Corporation; *U.S. Public*, pg. 1540
REMOTE CONTROL TECHNOLOGIES PTY LTD.—See Epiroc AB; *Int'l*, pg. 2463
REMOTE IT.COM, INC.—See Hergo Ergonomic Support Systems, Inc.; *U.S. Private*, pg. 1921
REMOTE-LEARNER.NET, INC—See Marlin Equity Partners, LLC; *U.S. Private*, pg. 2584
REMOTE MARINE SYSTEMS LIMITED—See James Fisher & Sons Public Limited Company; *Int'l*, pg. 3876
REMOTE MEDICAL INTERNATIONAL, INC.; *U.S. Private*, pg. 3396
REMOTE TIGER; *U.S. Private*, pg. 3396
REMO ZAANDAM B.V.—See Metro AG; *Int'l*, pg. 4859
REMPEL BROS. CONCRETE LTD.—See Heidelberg Materials AG; *Int'l*, pg. 3319
REMPEX PHARMACEUTICALS, INC.—See Novartis AG; *Int'l*, pg. 5460
REMPLOY LIMITED—See MAXIMUS, Inc.; *U.S. Public*, pg. 1402
REM RAMSEY, INC.—See Centerbridge Partners, L.P.; *U.S. Private*, pg. 814
REM RIVER BLUFFS, INC.—See Centerbridge Partners, L.P.; *U.S. Private*, pg. 814
REM SALES, LLC—See Morris Group, Inc.; *U.S. Private*, pg. 2787
REMSAN A.S.—See Ozkoseoglu Isi Sanayi ve Ticaret A.S.; *Int'l*, pg. 5679
REMSDAQ LIMITED; *Int'l*, pg. 6271
REMSENSE TECHNOLOGIES LIMITED; *Int'l*, pg. 6271
REMSLEEP HOLDINGS, INC.; *U.S. Public*, pg. 1782
REMSONS INDUSTRIES LIMITED; *Int'l*, pg. 6271
REM SOUTH CENTRAL SERVICES, INC.—See Centerbridge Partners, L.P.; *U.S. Private*, pg. 814
REM SOUTHWEST SERVICES, INC.—See Centerbridge Partners, L.P.; *U.S. Private*, pg. 814
REMSTAR CORPORATION; *Int'l*, pg. 6271
REMSTAR FILMS—See Remstar Corporation; *Int'l*, pg. 6271
REMTEC AUTOMATION LLC—See The C. M. Paula Company; *U.S. Private*, pg. 4003
R.E.M. TRANSPORT LTD.—See SeaFort Capital, Inc.; *Int'l*, pg. 6663
REMUS PHARMACEUTICALS LIMITED; *Int'l*, pg. 6271
REM WEST VIRGINIA, LLC—See Centerbridge Partners, L.P.; *U.S. Private*, pg. 814
REM WISCONSIN III, INC.—See Centerbridge Partners, L.P.; *U.S. Private*, pg. 814
REM WISCONSIN, INC.—See Centerbridge Partners, L.P.; *U.S. Private*, pg. 814
REM WOODVALE, INC.—See Centerbridge Partners, L.P.; *U.S. Private*, pg. 814
REMY COINTREAU S.A.; *Int'l*, pg. 6272
REMY COINTREAU USA INC.—See Remy Cointreau S.A.; *Int'l*, pg. 6272
REMY & GEISER GMBH—See Triton Advisers Limited; *Int'l*, pg. 7934
REMY POWER PRODUCTS, LLC—See Torque Capital Group, LLC; *U.S. Private*, pg. 4189
REMZAP SP. Z O.O.—See Grupa Azoty S.A.; *Int'l*, pg. 3116
RENACON PHARMA LIMITED—See Treet Corporation Limited; *Int'l*, pg. 7910
RENAGEN INC.—See EnviTec Biogas AG; *Int'l*, pg. 2456
RENAISSANCE ASIA SILK ROAD GROUP LIMITED; *Int'l*, pg. 6272
RENAISSANCE ASSET FINANCE LIMITED—See Arbuthnot Banking Group plc; *Int'l*, pg. 539
RENAISSANCE ASSOCIATES INC.—See Rev19, LLC; *U.S. Private*, pg. 3413
RENAISSANCE AUSTRALIA PTY LTD—See International Equities Corporation Limited; *Int'l*, pg. 3748
RENAISSANCE BENEFIT ADVISORS, INC.—See Aon plc; *Int'l*, pg. 497
RENAISSANCE CAPITAL HOLDINGS LIMITED—See Onexim Group Limited; *Int'l*, pg. 5581
RENAISSANCE DO BRASIL HOTELERIA LTDA.—See Marriott International, Inc.; *U.S. Public*, pg. 1371
RENAISSANCE DOORS & WINDOWS INC.; *U.S. Private*, pg. 3397
RENAISSANCE DUSSELDORF HOTEMMANAGMENT GMBH—See Marriott International, Inc.; *U.S. Public*, pg. 1371
RENAISSANCE ENTERTAINMENT CORP.—See Renaissance Entertainment Productions; *U.S. Private*, pg. 3397
RENAISSANCE ENTERTAINMENT PRODUCTIONS; *U.S. Private*, pg. 3397
RENAISSANCE FOOD GROUP, LLC.—See Calavo Growers, Inc.; *U.S. Public*, pg. 422
RENAISSANCE FOUNDATION—See Renaissance Management SA; *Int'l*, pg. 6272
RENAISSANCE GLOBAL LIMITED; *Int'l*, pg. 6272
THE RENAISSANCE GROUP LLC—See Affiliated Managers Group, Inc.; *U.S. Public*, pg. 56
THE RENAISSANCE GROUP LLC; *U.S. Private*, pg. 4104
RENAISSANCE GROUP; *Int'l*, pg. 6272
RENAISSANCE HAMBURG HOTELMANAGEMENT GMBH—See Marriott International, Inc.; *U.S. Public*, pg. 1371
RENAISSANCE HOTEL GROUP N.V.—See Marriott International, Inc.; *U.S. Public*, pg. 1371
RENAISSANCE, INC.; *Int'l*, pg. 6273
RENAISSANCE INDUSTRIES SAS; *Int'l*, pg. 6272
RENAISSANCE JEWELRY NEW YORK INC.—See Renaissance Global Limited; *Int'l*, pg. 6272
RENAISSANCE KNITWEAR INC.; *U.S. Private*, pg. 3397
RENAISSANCE LEARNING, INC.—See Francisco Partners Management, LP; *U.S. Private*, pg. 1591
RENAISSANCE LEARNING UK LIMITED—See Francisco Partners Management, LP; *U.S. Private*, pg. 1591
RENAISSANCE MANAGEMENT SA; *Int'l*, pg. 6272
RENAISSANCE MARINE GROUP, INC.; *U.S. Private*, pg. 3397
RENAISSANCE MORTGAGE GROUP INC.; *U.S. Private*, pg. 3397
RENAISSANCE PHARMA INC.—See RoundTable Healthcare Management, Inc.; *U.S. Private*, pg. 3489
RENAISSANCE POWER SYSTEMS, LLC—See Mill City Capital, L.P.; *U.S. Private*, pg. 2730
RENAISSANCERE HOLDINGS LTD.; *Int'l*, pg. 6273
RENAISSANCE REINSURANCE LTD.—See RenaissanceRe Holdings Ltd.; *Int'l*, pg. 6273
RENAISSANCERE OF EUROPE—See RenaissanceRe Holdings Ltd.; *Int'l*, pg. 6273
RENAISSANCERE SPECIALTY RISKS LTD.—See RenaissanceRe Holdings Ltd.; *Int'l*, pg. 6273
RENAISSANCERE SYNDICATE 1458—See RenaissanceRe Holdings Ltd.; *Int'l*, pg. 6273
RENAISSANCE SCIENCES CORPORATION; *U.S. Private*, pg. 3397
RENAISSANCE SERVICES SAOG; *Int'l*, pg. 6272

RENAISSANCE SPORTS & ENTERTAINMENT, LLC
CORPORATE AFFILIATIONS

RENAISSANCE SPORTS & ENTERTAINMENT, LLC; *U.S. Private*, pg. 3397
RENAISSANCE SURGERY CENTER, LLC—See Tenet Healthcare Corporation; *U.S. Public*, pg. 2006
RENAISSANCE SYSTEMS, INC.; *U.S. Private*, pg. 3397
RENAISSANCE TECHNOLOGIES, LLC; *U.S. Private*, pg. 3397
RENAISSANCE TERRACE CARE & REHABILITATION CENTER—See Formation Capital, LLC; *U.S. Private*, pg. 1571
RENAISSANCE UNITED LIMITED; *Int'l*, pg. 6272
RENAISSANCE URANIUM LIMITED; *Int'l*, pg. 6273
THE RENAISSANCE WAILEA BEACH RESORT—See Marriott International, Inc.; *U.S. Public*, pg. 1373
RENAL CENTER OF FLOWER MOUND, LLC—See DaVita Inc.; *U.S. Public*, pg. 642
RENAL CENTER OF FRISCO, LLC—See DaVita Inc.; *U.S. Public*, pg. 642
RENAL CENTER OF LEWISVILLE, LLC—See DaVita Inc.; *U.S. Public*, pg. 642
RENAL CENTER OF NEDERLAND, LLC—See DaVita Inc.; *U.S. Public*, pg. 642
RENAL CENTER OF NORTH DENTON, L.L.L.P.—See DaVita Inc.; *U.S. Public*, pg. 642
RENAL CENTER OF PORT ARTHUR, LLC—See DaVita Inc.; *U.S. Public*, pg. 642
RENAL CENTER OF STORM LAKE, LLC—See DaVita Inc.; *U.S. Public*, pg. 642
RENAL LIFE LINK, INC.—See DaVita Inc.; *U.S. Public*, pg. 642
RENAL TREATMENT CENTERS-CALIFORNIA, INC.—See DaVita Inc.; *U.S. Public*, pg. 642
RENAL TREATMENT CENTERS - HAWAII, INC.—See DaVita Inc.; *U.S. Public*, pg. 642
RENAL TREATMENT CENTERS-ILLINOIS, INC.—See DaVita Inc.; *U.S. Public*, pg. 642
RENAL TREATMENT CENTERS-MID-ATLANTIC, INC.—See DaVita Inc.; *U.S. Public*, pg. 642
RENAL TREATMENT CENTERS-WEST, INC.—See DaVita Inc.; *U.S. Public*, pg. 642
RENALYSIS MEDICAL CARE CO. LTD.—See Hi-Clearance, Inc.; *Int'l*, pg. 3380
RENALYTIX PLC; *Int'l*, pg. 6273
RENAPHARMA-VIFOR AB—See CSL Limited; *Int'l*, pg. 1866
RENARD MANUFACTURING CO. INC.—See Wetherill Associates Inc.; *U.S. Private*, pg. 4502
RENARD PAPER COMPANY, INC.—See HP Products Corporation; *U.S. Private*, pg. 1996
RENASANT BANK - ALABAMA REGION HEADQUARTERS—See Renasant Corporation; *U.S. Public*, pg. 1783
RENASANT BANK - GEORGIA REGION HEADQUARTERS—See Renasant Corporation; *U.S. Public*, pg. 1783
RENASANT BANK—See Renasant Corporation; *U.S. Public*, pg. 1783
RENASANT BANK - TENNESSEE REGION HEADQUARTERS—See Renasant Corporation; *U.S. Public*, pg. 1783
RENASANT CORPORATION; *U.S. Public*, pg. 1782
RENASANT FINANCIAL PARTNERS LTD.; *Int'l*, pg. 6273
RENASCOR RESOURCES LIMITED; *Int'l*, pg. 6273
RENA—See Mars, Incorporated; *U.S. Private*, pg. 2589
RENATA LIMITED; *Int'l*, pg. 6273
RENATA S.A.—See The Swatch Group Ltd.; *Int'l*, pg. 7692
RENA TECHNICAL SERVICES CO.—See Saipa Diesel Company; *Int'l*, pg. 6484
RENA THERAPEUTICS INC.—See Nippon Shokubai Co., Ltd.; *Int'l*, pg. 5333
REN ATLANTICO, TERMINAL DE GNL S.A.—See REN - Redes Energeticas Nacionais SGPS, S.A.; *Int'l*, pg. 6272
RENAUDAT CENTRE CONSTRUCTIONS; *Int'l*, pg. 6273
RENAULT ALGERIE S.P.A.—See Renault S.A.; *Int'l*, pg. 6274
RENAULT ARGENTINA S.A.—See Renault S.A.; *Int'l*, pg. 6274
RENAULT BELGIQUE LUXEMBOURG SA—See Renault S.A.; *Int'l*, pg. 6274
RENAULT CREDIT POLSKA—See Renault S.A.; *Int'l*, pg. 6274
RENAULT DEUTSCHLAND GMBH—See Renault S.A.; *Int'l*, pg. 6274
RENAULT DO BRASIL SA—See Renault S.A.; *Int'l*, pg. 6274
RENAULT ESPANA SA—See Renault S.A.; *Int'l*, pg. 6274
RENAULT IRLANDE—See Renault S.A.; *Int'l*, pg. 6274
RENAULT ITALIA SPA—See Renault S.A.; *Int'l*, pg. 6274
RENAULT JAPON CO., LTD.—See Nissan Motor Co., Ltd.; *Int'l*, pg. 5369
RENAULT LEASING CZ, S.R.O.—See UniCredit S.p.A.; *Int'l*, pg. 8038
RENAULT NORDIC—See Renault S.A.; *Int'l*, pg. 6274
RENAULT OSTERREICH—See Renault S.A.; *Int'l*, pg. 6274
RENAULT POLSKA—See Renault S.A.; *Int'l*, pg. 6274
RENAULT PORTUGUESA—See Renault S.A.; *Int'l*, pg. 6274
RENAULT PRIVATE LTD—See Renault S.A.; *Int'l*, pg. 6274
RENAULT RETAIL GROUP SA—See Renault S.A.; *Int'l*, pg. 6274
RENAULT RETAIL GROUP UK LIMITED—See Renault S.A.; *Int'l*, pg. 6274
RENAULT S.A.; *Int'l*, pg. 6273
RENAULT S.A.S—See Renault S.A.; *Int'l*, pg. 6274
RENAULT SOUTH AFRICA (PTY) LTD—See Motus Holdings Limited; *Int'l*, pg. 5056
RENAULT SUISSE SA—See Renault S.A.; *Int'l*, pg. 6274
RENAULT TRUCKS ITALIA SPA—See AB Volvo; *Int'l*, pg. 45
RENAULT TRUCKS S.A.S.—See AB Volvo; *Int'l*, pg. 45
RENAULT TRUCKS UK LTD.—See AB Volvo; *Int'l*, pg. 45
RENAULT U.K. LTD.—See Renault S.A.; *Int'l*, pg. 6274
RENAULT UKRAINE—See Renault S.A.; *Int'l*, pg. 6274
RENAULT USA, INC.—See Renault S.A.; *Int'l*, pg. 6274
RENAVATIO HEALTHCARE COMMUNICATIONS LLC; *U.S. Private*, pg. 3397
RENAVOTIO, INC.; *U.S. Public*, pg. 1783
RENA WARE DE CHILE, S.A.I.C.—See Rena-Ware Distributors Inc.; *U.S. Private*, pg. 3397
RENA WARE DE COSTA RICA, S.A.—See Rena-Ware Distributors Inc.; *U.S. Private*, pg. 3397
RENA WARE DEL PERU, S.A.—See Rena-Ware Distributors Inc.; *U.S. Private*, pg. 3397
RENA WARE DISTRIBUTORS, C.A.—See Rena-Ware Distributors Inc.; *U.S. Private*, pg. 3397
RENA-WARE DISTRIBUTORS INC.; *U.S. Private*, pg. 3397
RENA WARE (THAILAND) LIMITED—See Rena-Ware Distributors Inc.; *U.S. Private*, pg. 3397
RENBENXINDONG TECHNOLOGY LTD.—See NSD CO., LTD.; *Int'l*, pg. 5477
RENCO ELECTRONICS INC.—See Standex International; *U.S. Public*, pg. 1930
THE RENCO GROUP INC.; *U.S. Private*, pg. 4104
RENCO HOLDINGS GROUP LIMITED; *Int'l*, pg. 6274
RENCOL TOLERANCE RINGS LTD.—See Compagnie de Saint-Gobain SA; *Int'l*, pg. 1725
RENCOR DEVELOPMENTS INC.; *Int'l*, pg. 6275
RENDAC BVBA—See Darling Ingredients Inc.; *U.S. Public*, pg. 634
RENDAC B.V.—See Darling Ingredients Inc.; *U.S. Public*, pg. 634
RENDAC ICKER GMBH & CO. KG—See Darling Ingredients Inc.; *U.S. Public*, pg. 634
RENDALL & RITTNER LTD.; *Int'l*, pg. 6275
RENDELL SALES COMPANY LIMITED—See I-PEX Inc.; *Int'l*, pg. 3564
RENDER CUBE SA; *Int'l*, pg. 6275
RENDERSPACE D.O.O.—See TX Group AG; *Int'l*, pg. 7992
RENDEZVOUS TOURS, INC.—See International Management Services Group, Inc.; *U.S. Private*, pg. 2118
RENDONG HOLDINGS CO., LTD.; *Int'l*, pg. 6275
RENEE CLAIRE, BEDHEAD PAJAMAS, INC.—See Charles Komar & Sons, Inc.; *U.S. Private*, pg. 852
RENE EGLI, S.L.U.—See Melia Hotels International, S.A.; *Int'l*, pg. 4810
RENEE'S GOURMET FOODS, INC.—See 3G Capital Inc.; *U.S. Private*, pg. 9
RENEE'S GOURMET FOODS, INC.—See Berkshire Hathaway Inc.; *U.S. Public*, pg. 317
RENEGADE EXPLORATION LIMITED; *Int'l*, pg. 6275
RENEGADE GOLD INC.; *Int'l*, pg. 6275
RENEGADE MATERIALS CORPORATION—See Teijin Limited; *Int'l*, pg. 7523
RENEGADE; *U.S. Private*, pg. 3397
RENEGADE VENTURES, INC.; *U.S. Private*, pg. 3397
RENEGY HOLDINGS, INC.; *U.S. Private*, pg. 3397
RENEGY, LLC—See Renegy Holdings, Inc.; *U.S. Private*, pg. 3397
RENE LAURENT, A SOCIETE PAR ACTIONS SIMPLIFIEE—See International Flavors & Fragrances Inc.; *U.S. Public*, pg. 1154
RENEL SAS; *Int'l*, pg. 6275
RENE' OF PARIS—See Aderans Co., Ltd.; *Int'l*, pg. 144
RENE PRINSEN SPOORWEGMATERIALEN B.V.—See voestalpine AG; *Int'l*, pg. 8294
RENERCO GEM 2 GMBH—See BayWa AG; *Int'l*, pg. 918
RENERCO PLAN CONSULT GMBH—See BayWa AG; *Int'l*, pg. 918
RENERCO RENEWABLE ENERGY CONCEPTS AG—See BayWa AG; *Int'l*, pg. 918
RENERGEN LTD.; *Int'l*, pg. 6275
RENERGETICA S.P.A.; *Int'l*, pg. 6275
R ENERGY 1 S.A.; *Int'l*, pg. 6167
RENERGY ELECTRIC TIANJIN LTD.—See China Ming Yang Wind Power Group Limited; *Int'l*, pg. 1524
RENESAN SOFTWARE; *U.S. Private*, pg. 3397
RENESAS DESIGN CORP.—See Renesas Electronics Corporation; *Int'l*, pg. 6276
RENESAS DESIGN FRANCE S.A.S.—See Renesas Electronics Corporation; *Int'l*, pg. 6276
RENESAS DESIGN VIETNAM CO., LTD.—See Renesas Electronics Corporation; *Int'l*, pg. 6276
RENESAS EASTERN JAPAN SEMICONDUCTOR, INC.—See Renesas Electronics Corporation; *Int'l*, pg. 6276
RENESAS EASTON AMERICA INC.—See Macnica Holdings, Inc.; *Int'l*, pg. 4624
RENESAS EASTON (HONG KONG) LTD.—See Macnica Holdings, Inc.; *Int'l*, pg. 4624
RENESAS EASTON (SHANGHAI) TRADING CO., LTD.—See Macnica Holdings, Inc.; *Int'l*, pg. 4624
RENESAS EASTON (SINGAPORE) PTE. LTD.—See Macnica Holdings, Inc.; *Int'l*, pg. 4624
RENESAS EASTON (TAIWAN) CO., LTD.—See Macnica Holdings, Inc.; *Int'l*, pg. 4624
RENESAS EASTON (THAILAND) CO., LTD.—See Macnica Holdings, Inc.; *Int'l*, pg. 4624
RENESAS ELECTRONICS AMERICA INC.—See Renesas Electronics Corporation; *Int'l*, pg. 6276
RENESAS ELECTRONICS BRASIL-SERVICOS LTDA.—See Renesas Electronics Corporation; *Int'l*, pg. 6276
RENESAS ELECTRONICS CANADA LIMITED—See Renesas Electronics Corporation; *Int'l*, pg. 6276
RENESAS ELECTRONICS (CHINA) CO., LTD.—See Renesas Electronics Corporation; *Int'l*, pg. 6276
RENESAS ELECTRONICS CORPORATION - NISHIKI FACTORY—See Renesas Electronics Corporation; *Int'l*, pg. 6276
RENESAS ELECTRONICS CORPORATION - OITA FACTORY—See Renesas Electronics Corporation; *Int'l*, pg. 6276
RENESAS ELECTRONICS CORPORATION; *Int'l*, pg. 6275
RENESAS ELECTRONICS CORPORATION - YONEZAWA FACTORY—See Renesas Electronics Corporation; *Int'l*, pg. 6276
RENESAS ELECTRONICS EUROPE GMBH—See Renesas Electronics Corporation; *Int'l*, pg. 6276
RENESAS ELECTRONICS EUROPE LIMITED—See Renesas Electronics Corporation; *Int'l*, pg. 6276
RENESAS ELECTRONICS GERMANY GMBH—See Renesas Electronics Corporation; *Int'l*, pg. 6276
RENESAS ELECTRONICS HONG KONG LIMITED—See Renesas Electronics Corporation; *Int'l*, pg. 6276
RENESAS ELECTRONICS INDIA PVT. LTD.—See Renesas Electronics Corporation; *Int'l*, pg. 6276
RENESAS ELECTRONICS KOREA CO., LTD.—See Renesas Electronics Corporation; *Int'l*, pg. 6276
RENESAS ELECTRONICS MALAYSIA SDN. BHD.—See Renesas Electronics Corporation; *Int'l*, pg. 6276
RENESAS ELECTRONICS (PENANG) SDN. BHD.—See Renesas Electronics Corporation; *Int'l*, pg. 6276
RENESAS ELECTRONICS (SHANGHAI) CO., LTD.—See Renesas Electronics Corporation; *Int'l*, pg. 6276
RENESAS ELECTRONICS SINGAPORE PTE. LTD.—See Renesas Electronics Corporation; *Int'l*, pg. 6276
RENESAS ELECTRONICS TAIWAN CO., LTD.—See Renesas Electronics Corporation; *Int'l*, pg. 6277
RENESAS ENGINEERING SERVICES CO., LTD.—See Renesas Electronics Corporation; *Int'l*, pg. 6277
RENESAS KANSAI SEMICONDUCTOR CO., LTD.—See Renesas Electronics Corporation; *Int'l*, pg. 6277
RENESAS MICRO SYSTEMS CO., LTD.—See Renesas Electronics Corporation; *Int'l*, pg. 6277
RENESAS NAKA SEMICONDUCTOR CO., LTD.—See Renesas Electronics Corporation; *Int'l*, pg. 6277
RENESAS NORTHERN JAPAN SEMICONDUCTOR, INC.—See Renesas Electronics Corporation; *Int'l*, pg. 6277
RENESAS SEMICONDUCTOR (BEIJING) CO., LTD.—See Renesas Electronics Corporation; *Int'l*, pg. 6277
RENESAS SEMICONDUCTOR DESIGN (BEIJING) CO., LTD.—See Renesas Electronics Corporation; *Int'l*, pg. 6277
RENESAS SEMICONDUCTOR DESIGN (MALAYSIA) SDN. BHD—See Renesas Electronics Corporation; *Int'l*, pg. 6277
RENESAS SEMICONDUCTOR (KEDAH) SDN. BHD.—See Renesas Electronics Corporation; *Int'l*, pg. 6277
RENESAS SEMICONDUCTOR KL SDN. BHD.—See Renesas Electronics Corporation; *Int'l*, pg. 6277
RENESAS SEMICONDUCTOR KYUSHU YAMAGUCHI CO., LTD.—See Renesas Electronics Corporation; *Int'l*, pg. 6277
RENESAS SEMICONDUCTOR (MALAYSIA) SDN. BHD.—See Renesas Electronics Corporation; *Int'l*, pg. 6277
RENESAS SEMICONDUCTOR MANUFACTURING CO., LTD. - KAWASHIRI FACTORY—See Renesas Electronics Corporation; *Int'l*, pg. 6277
RENESAS SEMICONDUCTOR MANUFACTURING CO., LTD. - SAIJO FACTORY—See Renesas Electronics Corporation; *Int'l*, pg. 6277
RENESAS SEMICONDUCTOR MANUFACTURING CO., LTD. - SHIGA FACTORY—See Renesas Electronics Corporation; *Int'l*, pg. 6277
RENESAS SEMICONDUCTOR MANUFACTURING CO., LTD.—See Renesas Electronics Corporation; *Int'l*, pg. 6277

RENESAS SEMICONDUCTOR MANUFACTURING CO., LTD. - TAKASAKI FACTORY—See Renesas Electronics Corporation; *Int'l*, pg. 6277
RENESAS SEMICONDUCTOR MANUFACTURING CO., LTD. - YAMAGUCHI FACTORY—See Renesas Electronics Corporation; *Int'l*, pg. 6277
RENESAS SEMICONDUCTOR (SUZHOU) CO., LTD—See Renesas Electronics Corporation; *Int'l*, pg. 6277
RENESAS SEMICONDUCTOR TECHNOLOGY (M) SDN. BHD.—See Renesas Electronics Corporation; *Int'l*, pg. 6277
RENESAS SOLUTIONS CORP.—See Renesas Electronics Corporation; *Int'l*, pg. 6277
RENESAS SYSTEM SOLUTIONS KOREA CO., LTD.—See Renesas Electronics Corporation; *Int'l*, pg. 6277
RENESAS YAMAGATA SEMICONDUCTOR CO., LTD—See Renesas Electronics Corporation; *Int'l*, pg. 6277
RENESAS YANAI SEMICONDUCTOR, INC.—See Renesas Electronics Corporation; *Int'l*, pg. 6277
RENESOLA DEUTSCHLAND GMBH—See EMEREN GROUP LTD; *U.S. Public*, pg. 739
RENESOLA SINGAPORE PTE. LTD.—See EMEREN GROUP LTD; *U.S. Public*, pg. 739
RENET JAPAN GROUP, INC.; *Int'l*, pg. 6277
RENEUCO BERHAD; *Int'l*, pg. 6277
RENEURON GROUP PLC; *Int'l*, pg. 6277
RENEWABLE CHOICE ENERGY, INC.—See Schneider Electric SE; *Int'l*, pg. 6633
THE RENEWABLE CORPORATION; *U.S. Public*, pg. 2125
RENEWABLE ENERGY ACQUISITION CORP.; *U.S. Private*, pg. 3398
RENEWABLE ENERGY GROUP, INC.—See Chevron Corporation; *U.S. Public*, pg. 487
RENEWABLE ENERGY LOSS ADJUSTERS LIMITED—See Marsh & McLennan Companies, Inc.; *U.S. Public*, pg. 1388
RENEWABLE ENERGY & POWER, INC.; *U.S. Public*, pg. 1783
RENEWABLE ENERGY PRODUCTS GMBH—See Christof Holding AG; *Int'l*, pg. 1587
RENEWABLE ENERGY SOLUTION SYSTEMS, INC.; *U.S. Public*, pg. 1783
RENEWABLE ENERGY SYSTEMS LTD; *Int'l*, pg. 6278
RENEWABLE FUEL CORP.; *U.S. Private*, pg. 3398
RENEWABLE FUNDING GROUP, INC.; *U.S. Private*, pg. 3398
RENEWABLE HOLDING MANAGEMENT S.A.—See ELECTROARGES SA; *Int'l*, pg. 2353
RENEWABLE JAPAN CO., LTD.; *Int'l*, pg. 6278
RENEWABLE PROPERTIES, INC.—See Eversource Energy; *U.S. Public*, pg. 802
RENEWABLE RESOURCES GROUP INC.; *U.S. Private*, pg. 3398
THE RENEWABLES INFRASTRUCTURE GROUP LIMITED; *Int'l*, pg. 7678
RENEWABLE SOLUTIONS LIGHTING LIMITED—See eEnergy Group Plc; *Int'l*, pg. 2317
RENEWABLE VENTURES NORDIC AB; *Int'l*, pg. 6278
RENEWABLE WATER RESOURCES; *U.S. Private*, pg. 3398
RENEWAGY A/S—See 7C Solarparken AG; *Int'l*, pg. 15
RENEWAL BY ANDERSEN CORPORATION—See Andersen Corporation; *U.S. Private*, pg. 275
RENEWAL DESIGN-BUILD INC.; *U.S. Private*, pg. 3398
RENEWAL FUELS, INC.; *U.S. Public*, pg. 1783
RENEW DATA CORP.; *U.S. Private*, pg. 3398
RENEW FINANCIAL CORP. II—See Renewable Funding Group, Inc.; *U.S. Private*, pg. 3398
RENEW FINANCIAL II LLC—See Renewable Funding Group, Inc.; *U.S. Private*, pg. 3398
RENEW HOLDINGS PLC; *Int'l*, pg. 6277
RENEWI COMMERCIAL B.V.—See Renewi plc; *Int'l*, pg. 6278
RENEW INDIANAPOLIS, INC.; *U.S. Private*, pg. 3398
RENEWI PLC; *Int'l*, pg. 6278
RENEWI TISSELT N.V.—See Renewi plc; *Int'l*, pg. 6278
RENEWI UK SERVICES LIMITED—See Renewi plc; *Int'l*, pg. 6278
RENEWI WESTPOORT B.V.—See Renewi plc; *Int'l*, pg. 6279
RENEW LIFE CANADA INC.—See The Clorox Company; *U.S. Public*, pg. 2062
RENEW LIFE FORMULAS, LLC—See The Clorox Company; *U.S. Public*, pg. 2062
RENEWSTABLE BARBADOS—See Rubis SCA; *Int'l*, pg. 6423
RENFORTH RESOURCES INC.; *Int'l*, pg. 6279
THE RENFREW CENTERS INC.; *U.S. Private*, pg. 4104
RENFRO ASSOCIATES, INC.—See Rotork Plc; *Int'l*, pg. 6406
RENFRO BV—See The Renco Group Inc.; *U.S. Private*, pg. 4104
RENFRO CANADA INC.—See The Renco Group Inc.; *U.S. Private*, pg. 4104
RENFRO CORPORATION—See The Renco Group Inc.; *U.S. Private*, pg. 4104

RENFROE PECAN CO. INC.; *U.S. Private*, pg. 3398
RENFRO INDIA PVT LTD.—See The Renco Group Inc.; *U.S. Private*, pg. 4104
RENFRO JAPAN—See The Renco Group Inc.; *U.S. Private*, pg. 4104
RENFRO MEXICO, S.A. DE C.V.—See The Renco Group Inc.; *U.S. Private*, pg. 4104
RENGASLINJA OY—See Deutsche Bahn AG; *Int'l*, pg. 2052
REN GASODUTOS S.A.—See REN - Redes Energeticas Nacionais SGPS, S.A.; *Int'l*, pg. 6272
RENGO CO., LTD. - AMAGASAKI MILL—See Rengo Co., Ltd.; *Int'l*, pg. 6280
RENGO CO., LTD. - AOMORI PLANT—See Rengo Co., Ltd.; *Int'l*, pg. 6280
RENGO CO., LTD. - ASAHIKAWA PLANT—See Rengo Co., Ltd.; *Int'l*, pg. 6280
RENGO CO., LTD. - CHIBA PLANT—See Rengo Co., Ltd.; *Int'l*, pg. 6280
RENGO CO., LTD. - ENIWA PLANT—See Rengo Co., Ltd.; *Int'l*, pg. 6280
RENGO CO., LTD. - FUKUI PLANT—See Rengo Co., Ltd.; *Int'l*, pg. 6280
RENGO CO., LTD. - HIROSHIMA PLANT—See Rengo Co., Ltd.; *Int'l*, pg. 6280
RENGO CO., LTD. - HOFU PLANT—See Rengo Co., Ltd.; *Int'l*, pg. 6280
RENGO CO., LTD. - KANAZU CHEMICALS & BIOTECHNOLOGY PLANT—See Rengo Co., Ltd.; *Int'l*, pg. 6280
RENGO CO., LTD. - KATSUSHIKA PLANT—See Rengo Co., Ltd.; *Int'l*, pg. 6280
RENGO CO., LTD. - MAEBASHI PLANT—See Rengo Co., Ltd.; *Int'l*, pg. 6280
RENGO CO., LTD. - MATSUMOTO SUB-PLANT—See Rengo Co., Ltd.; *Int'l*, pg. 6280
RENGO CO., LTD. - MATSUYAMA PLANT—See Rengo Co., Ltd.; *Int'l*, pg. 6280
RENGO CO., LTD. - NAGANO PLANT—See Rengo Co., Ltd.; *Int'l*, pg. 6280
RENGO CO., LTD. - NAGOYA PLANT—See Rengo Co., Ltd.; *Int'l*, pg. 6281
RENGO CO., LTD. - NIIGATA PLANT—See Rengo Co., Ltd.; *Int'l*, pg. 6281
RENGO CO., LTD. - OKAYAMA PLANT—See Rengo Co., Ltd.; *Int'l*, pg. 6281
RENGO CO., LTD. - OYAMA PLANT—See Rengo Co., Ltd.; *Int'l*, pg. 6281
RENGO CO., LTD. - SANDA PLANT—See Rengo Co., Ltd.; *Int'l*, pg. 6281
RENGO CO., LTD. - SEMARANG FACTORY—See Rengo Co., Ltd.; *Int'l*, pg. 6281
RENGO CO., LTD. - SENDAI PLANT—See Rengo Co., Ltd.; *Int'l*, pg. 6281
RENGO CO., LTD. - SHIGA PLANT—See Rengo Co., Ltd.; *Int'l*, pg. 6281
RENGO CO., LTD. - SHIMIZU PLANT—See Rengo Co., Ltd.; *Int'l*, pg. 6281
RENGO CO., LTD. - SHIN-KYOTO PLANT—See Rengo Co., Ltd.; *Int'l*, pg. 6281
RENGO CO., LTD. - SHONAN PLANT—See Rengo Co., Ltd.; *Int'l*, pg. 6281
RENGO CO., LTD.; *Int'l*, pg. 6279
RENGO CO., LTD. - TAKEFU PLANT—See Rengo Co., Ltd.; *Int'l*, pg. 6281
RENGO CO., LTD. - TOKYO PLANT—See Rengo Co., Ltd.; *Int'l*, pg. 6281
RENGO CO., LTD. - TONEGAWA CARTON PLANT—See Rengo Co., Ltd.; *Int'l*, pg. 6281
RENGO CO., LTD. - TONEGAWA CONVERTING PLANT—See Rengo Co., Ltd.; *Int'l*, pg. 6281
RENGO CO., LTD. - TONEGAWA DIVISION—See Rengo Co., Ltd.; *Int'l*, pg. 6281
RENGO CO., LTD. - TOSU PLANT—See Rengo Co., Ltd.; *Int'l*, pg. 6281
RENGO CO., LTD. - TOYOHASHI PLANT—See Rengo Co., Ltd.; *Int'l*, pg. 6281
RENGO CO., LTD. - WAKAYAMA PLANT—See Rengo Co., Ltd.; *Int'l*, pg. 6281
RENGO CO., LTD. - YASHIO MILL—See Rengo Co., Ltd.; *Int'l*, pg. 6281
RENGO LOGISTICS CO., LTD.—See Rengo Co., Ltd.; *Int'l*, pg. 6281
RENGO NONWOVEN PRODUCTS CO., LTD.—See Rengo Co., Ltd.; *Int'l*, pg. 6281
RENGO PACKAGING MALAYSIA SDN. BHD.—See Rengo Co., Ltd.; *Int'l*, pg. 6281
RENGO PAPER BUSINESS CO., LTD.—See Rengo Co., Ltd.; *Int'l*, pg. 6281
RENGO RIVERWOOD PACKAGING, LTD.—See Graphic Packaging Holding Company; *U.S. Public*, pg. 959
RENGO TOPPAN CONTAINERS CO., LTD—See Rengo Co., Ltd.; *Int'l*, pg. 6281
RENG—See Set Point Group Limited; *Int'l*, pg. 6730
RENHENG ENTERPRISE HOLDINGS LIMITED; *Int'l*, pg. 6282
RENHE PHARMACY CO., LTD.; *Int'l*, pg. 6282
RENHE ZHONGFANG PHARMACEUTICAL CO., LTD.—See Renhe Pharmacy Co., Ltd.; *Int'l*, pg. 6282
RENHILL GROUP INC.; *U.S. Private*, pg. 3398

RENHOLMEN AB—See Carl Bennet AB; *Int'l*, pg. 1332
RENHOLMEN AB—See Carl Bennet AB; *Int'l*, pg. 1332
RENIN CANADA CORPORATION—See Hilton Grand Vacations Inc.; *U.S. Public*, pg. 1040
RENIN UK CORPORATION—See Hilton Grand Vacations Inc.; *U.S. Public*, pg. 1040
RENISHAW AB—See Renishaw plc; *Int'l*, pg. 6283
RENISHAW A.G.—See Renishaw plc; *Int'l*, pg. 6283
RENISHAW (AUSTRIA) GMBH—See Renishaw plc; *Int'l*, pg. 6283
RENISHAW BENELUX B.V.—See Renishaw plc; *Int'l*, pg. 6283
RENISHAW (CANADA) LIMITED—See Renishaw plc; *Int'l*, pg. 6283
RENISHAW DIAGNOSTICS LIMITED—See Renishaw plc; *Int'l*, pg. 6283
RENISHAW FIXTURING SOLUTIONS, LLC—See Renishaw plc; *Int'l*, pg. 6283
RENISHAW GMBH—See Renishaw plc; *Int'l*, pg. 6283
RENISHAW HEALTHCARE, INC.—See Renishaw plc; *Int'l*, pg. 6283
RENISHAW (HONG KONG) LTD.—See Renishaw plc; *Int'l*, pg. 6283
RENISHAW HUNGARY KFT—See Renishaw plc; *Int'l*, pg. 6283
RENISHAW IBERICA S.A.—See Renishaw plc; *Int'l*, pg. 6283
RENISHAW INC.—See Renishaw plc; *Int'l*, pg. 6283
RENISHAW INTERNATIONAL LTD—See Renishaw plc; *Int'l*, pg. 6283
RENISHAW (IRELAND) LIMITED—See Renishaw plc; *Int'l*, pg. 6283
RENISHAW (ISRAEL) LTD—See Renishaw plc; *Int'l*, pg. 6283
RENISHAW K.K.—See Renishaw plc; *Int'l*, pg. 6283
RENISHAW (KOREA) LTD—See Renishaw plc; *Int'l*, pg. 6283
RENISHAW LATINO AMERICANA LTD.—See Renishaw plc; *Int'l*, pg. 6283
RENISHAW (MALAYSIA) SDN. BHD.—See Renishaw plc; *Int'l*, pg. 6282
RENISHAW MAYFIELD SARL—See Renishaw plc; *Int'l*, pg. 6283
RENISHAW METROLOGY SYSTEMS PVT. LTD.—See Renishaw plc; *Int'l*, pg. 6283
RENISHAW MEXICO S. DE R.L. DE C.V.—See Renishaw plc; *Int'l*, pg. 6283
RENISHAW OCEANIA PTY LTD—See Renishaw plc; *Int'l*, pg. 6283
RENISHAW PLC - RICCARTON—See Renishaw plc; *Int'l*, pg. 6283
RENISHAW PLC; *Int'l*, pg. 6282
RENISHAW SAS—See Renishaw plc; *Int'l*, pg. 6283
RENISHAW (SHANGHAI) TRADING COMPANY LIMITED—See Renishaw plc; *Int'l*, pg. 6283
RENISHAW (SINGAPORE) PTE LIMITED—See Renishaw plc; *Int'l*, pg. 6283
RENISHAW S.P.A.—See Renishaw plc; *Int'l*, pg. 6283
RENISHAW SP. Z.O.O.—See Renishaw plc; *Int'l*, pg. 6283
RENISHAW S.R.O.—See Renishaw plc; *Int'l*, pg. 6283
RENISHAW (TAIWAN) INC—See Renishaw plc; *Int'l*, pg. 6283
RENISHAW TEKNOLOJI COZUMLERI LS—See Renishaw plc; *Int'l*, pg. 6283
RENISHAW UK SALES LIMITED—See Renishaw plc; *Int'l*, pg. 6283
RENIX CORP.; *U.S. Private*, pg. 3398
RENJIE OLDSICHUAN CATERING MANAGEMENT CONSULT; *Int'l*, pg. 6283
RENK AKTIENGESELLSCHAFT—See Triton Advisers Limited; *Int'l*, pg. 7935
RENKE GEBAUDETECHNIK GMBH—See Zech Group SE; *Int'l*, pg. 8629
RENKER-EICH-PARKS ARCHITECTS, INC.; *U.S. Private*, pg. 3398
RENK SEED COMPANY; *U.S. Private*, pg. 3398
RENK SYSTEMS CORPORATION—See Triton Advisers Limited; *Int'l*, pg. 7935
REN LIMITED—See Unilever PLC; *Int'l*, pg. 8047
RENNA COMMUNICATIONS; *U.S. Private*, pg. 3398
RENNCO LLC—See Leonard Green & Partners, L.P.; *U.S. Private*, pg. 2428
RENNEL LIMITED—See ENL Limited; *Int'l*, pg. 2441
RENNEN INTERNATIONAL; *U.S. Private*, pg. 3398
RENNER MOTORS, INC.; *U.S. Private*, pg. 3398
RENNERT TRAVEL—See Corporate Travel Management Limited; *Int'l*, pg. 1805
RENNET PTY. LTD.—See Metcash Limited; *Int'l*, pg. 4852
RENN FUND, INC.; *U.S. Public*, pg. 1783
RENNIE MURRAY AND COMPANY (PTY) LIMITED—See The Bidvest Group Limited; *Int'l*, pg. 7626
RENNIES DISTRIBUTION SERVICES (PTY) LIMITED—See The Bidvest Group Limited; *Int'l*, pg. 7626
RENNIES SHIPS AGENCY MOZAMBIQUE LIMITADA—See The Bidvest Group Limited; *Int'l*, pg. 7626
RENNIES SHIPS AGENCY (PTY) LIMITED—See The Bidvest Group Limited; *Int'l*, pg. 7626

RENNIES TRAVEL (NAMIBIA) (PTY) LIMITED—See The Bidvest Group Limited; *Int'l*, pg. 7626
RENNIES TRAVEL (PTY) LIMITED—See The Bidvest Group Limited; *Int'l*, pg. 7626
RENN KIRBY CHEVROLET BUICK, LLC.; *U.S. Private*, pg. 3398
RENN KIRBY MITSUBISHI INC.; *U.S. Private*, pg. 3398
RENNOVA HEALTH, INC.; *U.S. Public*, pg. 1783
RENN TRANSPORTATION, INC.; *U.S. Private*, pg. 3398
RENO A/S—See Atlas Copco AB; *Int'l*, pg. 684
RENO CONTRACTING, INC.; *U.S. Private*, pg. 3399
RENO CYBERKNIFE, LLC—See Akumin, Inc.; *U.S. Public*, pg. 70
RENO DE MEDICI ALMAZAN—See Apollo Global Management, Inc.; *U.S. Public*, pg. 159
RENO DE MEDICI ARNSBERG—See Apollo Global Management, Inc.; *U.S. Public*, pg. 159
RENO DE MEDICI BLENDECQUES—See Apollo Global Management, Inc.; *U.S. Public*, pg. 159
RENO DE MEDICI SANTA GIUSTINA—See Apollo Global Management, Inc.; *U.S. Public*, pg. 159
RENO DE MEDICI S.P.A.—See Apollo Global Management, Inc.; *U.S. Public*, pg. 159
RENO DE MEDICI VILLA SANTA LUCIA—See Apollo Global Management, Inc.; *U.S. Public*, pg. 159
RENO-DEPOT INC.—See Kingfisher plc; *Int'l*, pg. 4173
RENODIS, INC.; *U.S. Private*, pg. 3399
RENO DISPOSAL CO. - COMMERCIAL ROW FACILITY—See Waste Management, Inc.; *U.S. Public*, pg. 2332
RENO DISPOSAL CO.—See Waste Management, Inc.; *U.S. Public*, pg. 2332
RENOESTE - VALORIZACAO DE RECURSOS NATURAIS, S.A.—See Jose de Mello, SGPS, S.A.; *Int'l*, pg. 4001
RENO GAZETTE-JOURNAL—See Gannett Co., Inc.; *U.S. Public*, pg. 899
RENOGEN S.A.—See 2Valorise N.V.; *Int'l*, pg. 5
RENO GOLD CORP.; *Int'l*, pg. 6284
RENO HARDWARE & SUPPLY INC.—See Clayton, Dubilier & Rice, LLC; *U.S. Private*, pg. 930
RENOLAB SRL; *Int'l*, pg. 6284
RENOLD A/S—See Renold plc; *Int'l*, pg. 6284
RENOLD AUSTRALIA PROPRIETARY LIMITED—See Renold plc; *Int'l*, pg. 6284
RENOLD CANADA LIMITED—See Renold plc; *Int'l*, pg. 6284
RENOLD (CHINA) TRANSMISSION PRODUCTS CO. LTD.—See Renold plc; *Int'l*, pg. 6284
RENOLD CONTINENTAL LIMITED—See Renold plc; *Int'l*, pg. 6284
RENOLD CROFTS (PTY) LIMITED—See Renold plc; *Int'l*, pg. 6284
RENOLD GMBH—See Renold plc; *Int'l*, pg. 6284
RENOLD GMBH—See Renold plc; *Int'l*, pg. 6284
RENOLD (HANGZHOU) CO. LIMITED—See Renold plc; *Int'l*, pg. 6284
RENOLD HI-TEC COUPLINGS SA—See Renold plc; *Int'l*, pg. 6284
RENOLD, INC.—See Renold plc; *Int'l*, pg. 6284
RENOLD (MALAYSIA) SDN BHD—See Renold plc; *Int'l*, pg. 6284
RENOLD NEW ZEALAND LIMITED—See Renold plc; *Int'l*, pg. 6284
RENOLD PLC; *Int'l*, pg. 6284
RENOLD POLAND SP. Z O.O.—See Renold plc; *Int'l*, pg. 6284
RENOLD POLSKA SP.Z O.O.—See Renold plc; *Int'l*, pg. 6284
RENOLD RUSSIA OOO—See Renold plc; *Int'l*, pg. 6284
RENOLD (SWITZERLAND) GMBH—See Renold plc; *Int'l*, pg. 6284
RENOLD TECHNOLOGIES (SHANGHAI) COMPANY LIMITED—See Renold plc; *Int'l*, pg. 6284
RENOLD (THAILAND) LIMITED—See Renold plc; *Int'l*, pg. 6284
RENOLD TRANSMISSION LIMITED—See Renold plc; *Int'l*, pg. 6284
RENOLD TRANSMISSION (SHANGHAI) COMPANY LIMITED—See Renold plc; *Int'l*, pg. 6284
RENOLIT BEIJING MEDICAL—See RENOLIT SE; *Int'l*, pg. 6284
RENOLIT BELGIUM N.V.—See RENOLIT SE; *Int'l*, pg. 6284
RENOLIT BENELUX B.V.—See RENOLIT SE; *Int'l*, pg. 6284
RENOLIT CRAMLINGTON LIMITED—See RENOLIT SE; *Int'l*, pg. 6284
RENOLIT CZECH S.R.O.—See RENOLIT SE; *Int'l*, pg. 6284
RENOLIT FRANCE SASU—See RENOLIT SE; *Int'l*, pg. 6284
RENOLIT GOR S.P.A.—See RENOLIT SE; *Int'l*, pg. 6284
RENOLIT GUANGZHOU LTD.—See RENOLIT SE; *Int'l*, pg. 6284
RENOLIT HISPANIA, S.A.—See RENOLIT SE; *Int'l*, pg. 6285
RENOLIT HONG KONG LTD.—See RENOLIT SE; *Int'l*, pg. 6285

RENOLIT HUNGARY KFT.—See RENOLIT SE; *Int'l*, pg. 6285
RENOLIT IBERICA, S.A.—See RENOLIT SE; *Int'l*, pg. 6285
RENOLIT INDIA PRIVATE LIMITED—See RENOLIT SE; *Int'l*, pg. 6285
RENOLIT ISTANBUL PLASTIK SANAYI VE TICARET LIMITED SIRKETI—See RENOLIT SE; *Int'l*, pg. 6285
RENOLIT ITALIA SRL—See RENOLIT SE; *Int'l*, pg. 6285
RENOLIT MEXICO S.A. DE C.V.—See RENOLIT SE; *Int'l*, pg. 6285
RENOLIT MILANO S.R.L.—See RENOLIT SE; *Int'l*, pg. 6285
RENOLIT NEDERLAND B.V.—See RENOLIT SE; *Int'l*, pg. 6285
RENOLIT NORDIC K/S—See RENOLIT SE; *Int'l*, pg. 6285
RENOLIT ONDEX S.A.S.—See RENOLIT SE; *Int'l*, pg. 6285
RENOLIT POLSKA SP. Z O.O.—See RENOLIT SE; *Int'l*, pg. 6285
RENOLIT PORTUGAL LDA.—See RENOLIT SE; *Int'l*, pg. 6285
RENOLIT SE - FRANKENTHAL PLANT—See RENOLIT SE; *Int'l*, pg. 6285
RENOLIT SE; *Int'l*, pg. 6284
RENOLIT SE - THANSAU PLANT—See RENOLIT SE; *Int'l*, pg. 6285
RENOLIT SE - WALDKRAIBURG PLANT—See RENOLIT SE; *Int'l*, pg. 6285
RENOLIT SOUTH AFRICA PTY. LTD.—See RENOLIT SE; *Int'l*, pg. 6285
RENOLIT TABOR S.R.O.—See RENOLIT SE; *Int'l*, pg. 6285
RENO LUMBER; *U.S. Private*, pg. 3399
RENO NEWSPAPERS, INC.—See Gannett Co., Inc.; *U.S. Public*, pg. 899
RENOR AS—See Heidelberg Materials AG; *Int'l*, pg. 3319
RENO'S APPLIANCE INC.; *U.S. Private*, pg. 3399
RENOS HADJIOANNOU FARM PUBLIC COMPANY LTD.; *Int'l*, pg. 6285
RENOSOL CORPORATION; *U.S. Private*, pg. 3399
RENOSOL—See Veolia Environnement S.A.; *Int'l*, pg. 8159
RENOSUN INTERNATIONAL SDN. BHD.—See Annica Holdings Limited; *Int'l*, pg. 474
RENOSY ASSET MANAGEMENT CO., LTD.—See GAtechnologies Co., Ltd.; *Int'l*, pg. 2889
RENOSY FINANCE INC.—See GAtechnologies Co., Ltd.; *Int'l*, pg. 2889
RENOSY PLUS CO., LTD.—See GAtechnologies Co., Ltd.; *Int'l*, pg. 2889
RENOSY (THAILAND) CO., LTD.—See GAtechnologies Co., Ltd.; *Int'l*, pg. 2889
RENOSY X CO., LTD.—See GAtechnologies Co., Ltd.; *Int'l*, pg. 2889
RENOTEX GROUP LTD.; *Int'l*, pg. 6285
RENO TOYOTA INC.; *U.S. Private*, pg. 3399
RENOVACARE, INC.; *U.S. Public*, pg. 1783
RENOVA ENERGIA SA; *Int'l*, pg. 6285
RENOVA GROUP; *Int'l*, pg. 6285
RENOVA, INC.; *Int'l*, pg. 6285
RENOVALIA ENERGY, S.A.—See F2i - Fondi Italiani per le infrastrutture SGR S.p.A.; *Int'l*, pg. 2598
RENOVA LIGHTING SYSTEMS, INC.; *U.S. Private*, pg. 3399
RENOVALO S.P.A.; *Int'l*, pg. 6285
RENOVA MEDIA—See Renova Group; *Int'l*, pg. 6285
RENOVA PARTNERS, LLC—See Allstar Financial Group Inc.; *U.S. Private*, pg. 193
RENOVARE ENVIRONMENTAL, INC.; *U.S. Public*, pg. 1783
RENOVARO BIOSCIENCES INC.; *U.S. Public*, pg. 1783
RENOVA SURGICAL LIMITED—See STERIS plc; *Int'l*, pg. 7210
RENOVATE BY BERKOWITZ LLC—See J.E. Berkowitz, LP; *U.S. Private*, pg. 2161
RENOVATE NEIGHBORHOODS, INC.; *U.S. Public*, pg. 1783
THE RENOVATOR'S SUPPLY, INC.; *U.S. Private*, pg. 4104
RENOVERU CO., LTD.—See Vector Inc.; *Int'l*, pg. 8144
RENOVO CAPITAL, LLC; *U.S. Private*, pg. 3399
RENOVO EMPLOYMENT GROUP LIMITED—See Bain Capital, LP; *U.S. Private*, pg. 435
RENOVO HOME PARTNERS—See Audax Group, Limited Partnership; *U.S. Private*, pg. 389
RENOVRX, INC; *U.S. Public*, pg. 1784
RENOVUS CAPITAL PARTNERS; *U.S. Private*, pg. 3399
RENOWN CONSTRUCTION OF TEXAS LLC—See Restoration Builders Inc.; *U.S. Private*, pg. 3409
RENOWN HEALTH; *U.S. Private*, pg. 3399
RENOWN INX INCORPORATED—See Atsugi Co., Ltd.; *Int'l*, pg. 696
RENOWN NETWORK SERVICES; *U.S. Private*, pg. 3399
RENOWN STEEL—See Samuel, Son & Co., Limited; *Int'l*, pg. 6515
RENOWORKS SOFTWARE INC.; *Int'l*, pg. 6285
REN - REDES ENERGETICAS NACIONAIS SGPS, S.A.; *Int'l*, pg. 6272

RENRENLE COMMERCIAL GROUP CO., LTD.; *Int'l*, pg. 6286
RENRUI HUMAN RESOURCES TECHNOLOGY HOLDINGS LIMITED; *Int'l*, pg. 6286
RENSA FILTRATION, INC.—See Audax Group, Limited Partnership; *U.S. Private*, pg. 389
RENSBURG FUND MANAGEMENT LIMITED—See Franklin Resources, Inc.; *U.S. Public*, pg. 883
REN SCOTT CREATIVE MARKETING; *U.S. Private*, pg. 3396
RENSHAWNAPIER LIMITED—See Real Good Food plc; *Int'l*, pg. 6233
RENSOL CO., LTD.—See Tosoh Corporation; *Int'l*, pg. 7833
RENSON ENTERPRISES—See Benson Motors Corporation; *U.S. Private*, pg. 528
RENSSELAER HONDA; *U.S. Private*, pg. 3400
RENSUI KOREA CO., LTD.—See Mitsubishi Chemical Group Corporation; *Int'l*, pg. 4933
RENS-WERK; *Int'l*, pg. 6286
RENTA 4 BANCO, S.A.; *Int'l*, pg. 6286
RENTA 4 BURGOS, S.A.—See Renta 4 Banco, S.A.; *Int'l*, pg. 6286
RENTA 4 COLOMBIA SAS—See Renta 4 Banco, S.A.; *Int'l*, pg. 6286
RENTA 4 HUESCA, S.A.—See Renta 4 Banco, S.A.; *Int'l*, pg. 6286
RENTA 4 SOCIEDAD DE VALORES, S.A.; *Int'l*, pg. 6286
RENT-A-CENTER CORPORATE LEASING—See Upbound Group, Inc.; *U.S. Public*, pg. 2263
RENTACO ANGOLA - EQUIPAMENTOS E TRANSPORTES, (SU) LIMITADA.—See Mota-Engil SGPS, S.A.; *Int'l*, pg. 5052
RENTA CORPORACION REAL ESTATE ES, S.A.—See Renta Corporacion Real Estate, S.A.; *Int'l*, pg. 6286
RENTA CORPORACION REAL ESTATE, S.A.; *Int'l*, pg. 6286
RENTA GROUP OY; *Int'l*, pg. 6286
RENTAL CAR FINANCE LLC—See Hertz Global Holdings, Inc.; *U.S. Public*, pg. 1029
RENTAL EQUIPMENT INVESTMENT CORP.—See Kinderhook Industries, LLC; *U.S. Private*, pg. 2307
RENTAL EXPRESS GROUP LTD.; *Int'l*, pg. 6286
RENTAL HISTORY REPORTS—See GI Manager L.P.; *U.S. Private*, pg. 1693
RENTAL MAX LLC; *U.S. Private*, pg. 3400
RENTALS UNLIMITED INC.; *U.S. Private*, pg. 3400
RENTAL UNIFORM SERVICE OF FLORENCE; *U.S. Private*, pg. 3400
RENTALUTIONS, INC.—See News Corporation; *U.S. Public*, pg. 1519
RENT-A-PC, INC.—See Abcom Computer Rental, Inc.; *U.S. Private*, pg. 37
RENT-A-PORT GREEN ENERGY N.V.—See Ackermans & van Haaren NV; *Int'l*, pg. 106
RENTA PROPERTIES (UK) LIMITED—See Renta Corporacion Real Estate, S.A.; *Int'l*, pg. 6286
RENT-A-WRECK OF AMERICA, INC.—See JJF Management Services, Inc.; *U.S. Private*, pg. 2211
RENT-A-WRECK SYSTEMS INC—See Franchise Services of North America Inc.; *U.S. Private*, pg. 1587
RENTBITS.COM; *U.S. Private*, pg. 3400
RENTECH DEVELOPMENT CORPORATION—See Rentech, Inc.; *U.S. Private*, pg. 3400
RENTECH ENERGY MIDWEST CORPORATION—See Rentech, Inc.; *U.S. Private*, pg. 3400
RENTECH, INC.; *U.S. Private*, pg. 3400
RENTECH NITROGEN FINANCE CORPORATION—See Rentech, Inc.; *U.S. Private*, pg. 3400
RENTECH SERVICES CORPORATION—See Rentech, Inc.; *U.S. Private*, pg. 3400
RENTENBACH CONSTRUCTORS INCORPORATED—See The Christman Company Inc.; *U.S. Private*, pg. 4009
RENTENBACH CONSTRUCTORS INC.—See The Christman Company Inc.; *U.S. Private*, pg. 4009
RENTENBACH ENGINEERING COMPANY—See The Christman Company Inc.; *U.S. Private*, pg. 4009
RENTERS LEGAL LIABILITY LLC—See DOXA Insurance Holdings LLC; *U.S. Private*, pg. 1270
RENTERS WAREHOUSE—See Appreciate Holdings, Inc.; *U.S. Public*, pg. 173
RENTGUARD LIMITED—See Arthur J. Gallagher & Co.; *U.S. Public*, pg. 207
RENTIAN TECHNOLOGY HOLDINGS LIMITED; *Int'l*, pg. 6286
RENTING DEL PACIFICO S.A.C.—See Mercedes-Benz Group AG; *Int'l*, pg. 4828
RENTLYTICS, INC.—See Thoma Bravo, L.P.; *U.S. Private*, pg. 4153
RENTOKIL AB—See Rentokil Initial plc; *Int'l*, pg. 6287
RENTOKIL BAHAMAS LTD—See Rentokil Initial plc; *Int'l*, pg. 6287
RENTOKIL DING SHARN CO LTD—See Rentokil Initial plc; *Int'l*, pg. 6287
RENTOKIL ENGUARD LTD—See Rentokil Initial plc; *Int'l*, pg. 6287
RENTOKIL INDIA PTE LTD—See Rentokil Initial plc; *Int'l*, pg. 6287

COMPANY NAME INDEX

RENTOKIL INITIAL A/S—See Rentokil Initial plc; *Int'l*, pg. 6288
RENTOKIL INITIAL (AUSTRIA) GMBH—See Rentokil Initial plc; *Int'l*, pg. 6287
RENTOKIL INITIAL (BARBADOS) LTD.—See Rentokil Initial plc; *Int'l*, pg. 6288
RENTOKIL INITIAL (BARBADOS) LTD. - WASHROOM HYGIENE SERVICES—See Rentokil Initial plc; *Int'l*, pg. 6288
RENTOKIL INITIAL B.V.—See Rentokil Initial plc; *Int'l*, pg. 6288
RENTOKIL INITIAL ESPANA S.A.—See Rentokil Initial plc; *Int'l*, pg. 6288
RENTOKIL INITIAL (FIJI) LTD.—See Rentokil Initial plc; *Int'l*, pg. 6288
RENTOKIL INITIAL FIRE SERVICES LIMITED—See Rentokil Initial plc; *Int'l*, pg. 6288
RENTOKIL INITIAL GMBH—See Rentokil Initial plc; *Int'l*, pg. 6288
RENTOKIL INITIAL GUADELOUPE SARL—See Rentokil Initial plc; *Int'l*, pg. 6288
RENTOKIL INITIAL GUYANA LTD.—See Rentokil Initial plc; *Int'l*, pg. 6288
RENTOKIL INITIAL HELLAS EPE—See Rentokil Initial plc; *Int'l*, pg. 6288
RENTOKIL INITIAL HOLDINGS LTD—See Rentokil Initial plc; *Int'l*, pg. 6288
RENTOKIL INITIAL HONG KONG LTD.—See Rentokil Initial plc; *Int'l*, pg. 6288
RENTOKIL INITIAL ITALIA SPA—See Rentokil Initial plc; *Int'l*, pg. 6288
RENTOKIL INITIAL (JAMAICA) LTD.—See Rentokil Initial plc; *Int'l*, pg. 6288
RENTOKIL INITIAL KENYA LTD.—See Rentokil Initial plc; *Int'l*, pg. 6288
RENTOKIL INITIAL LTD—See Rentokil Initial plc; *Int'l*, pg. 6288
RENTOKIL INITIAL MARTINIQUE SARL—See Rentokil Initial plc; *Int'l*, pg. 6288
RENTOKIL INITIAL (M) SDN. BHD.—See Rentokil Initial plc; *Int'l*, pg. 6288
RENTOKIL INITIAL NEW ZEALAND—See Rentokil Initial plc; *Int'l*, pg. 6288
RENTOKIL INITIAL NORGE AS—See Rentokil Initial plc; *Int'l*, pg. 6288
RENTOKIL INITIAL (PHILIPPINES) INC.—See Rentokil Initial plc; *Int'l*, pg. 6288
RENTOKIL INITIAL PLC; *Int'l*, pg. 6286
RENTOKIL INITIAL PORTUGAL-SERVICOS DE PROTECAO AMBIENTAL LDA.—See Rentokil Initial plc; *Int'l*, pg. 6288
RENTOKIL INITIAL PTY. LTD.—See Rentokil Initial plc; *Int'l*, pg. 6288
RENTOKIL INITIAL SA—See Rentokil Initial plc; *Int'l*, pg. 6288
RENTOKIL INITIAL SINGAPORE PTE. LTD.—See Rentokil Initial plc; *Int'l*, pg. 6288
RENTOKIL INITIAL (THAILAND) LTD.—See Rentokil Initial plc; *Int'l*, pg. 6288
RENTOKIL INITIAL (TRINIDAD) LTD—See Rentokil Initial plc; *Int'l*, pg. 6288
RENTOKIL INITIAL UK LIMITED—See Rentokil Initial plc; *Int'l*, pg. 6288
RENTOKIL INSURANCE LTD—See Rentokil Initial plc; *Int'l*, pg. 6288
RENTOKIL LUXEMBOURG SARL—See Rentokil Initial plc; *Int'l*, pg. 6288
RENTOKIL NORTH AMERICA, INC.—See Rentokil Initial plc; *Int'l*, pg. 6288
RENTOKIL N.V.—See Rentokil Initial plc; *Int'l*, pg. 6288
RENTOKIL OU—See Rentokil Initial plc; *Int'l*, pg. 6288
RENTOKIL PEST CONTROL CANADA LIMITED—See Rentokil Initial plc; *Int'l*, pg. 6288
RENTOKIL SCHWEIZ AG—See Rentokil Initial plc; *Int'l*, pg. 6288
RENTOKIL SKADEDYRSKONTROL—See Rentokil Initial plc; *Int'l*, pg. 6288
RENTON CADILLAC PONTIAC GMC, INC.—See General Motors Company; *U.S. Public*, pg. 928
RENTON H IMPORTS, INC.—See AutoNation, Inc.; *U.S. Public*, pg. 237
RENTPATH, LLC—See Redfin Corporation; *U.S. Public*, pg. 1770
RENTRACKS CO., LTD.; *Int'l*, pg. 6289
RENTRACKS LANKA (PRIVATE) LIMITED—See Rentracks Co., Ltd.; *Int'l*, pg. 6289
RENTRACKS MALAYSIA SDN. BHD.—See Rentracks Co., Ltd.; *Int'l*, pg. 6289
RENTRACKS MONGOL LLC—See Rentracks Co., Ltd.; *Int'l*, pg. 6289
RENTRACKS TAIWAN CO., LIMITED—See Rentracks Co., Ltd.; *Int'l*, pg. 6289
RENTRACKS VIETNAM CO., LTD.—See Rentracks Co., Ltd.; *Int'l*, pg. 6289
REN TRADING S.A.—See REN - Redes Energeticas Nacionais SGPS, S.A.; *Int'l*, pg. 6272
RENTRANS CARGO SP. Z O.O.—See OT Logistics S.A.; *Int'l*, pg. 5656

RENTRANS INTERNATIONAL SPEDITION SP Z O.O.—See OT Logistics S.A.; *Int'l*, pg. 5656
RENT READY, LLC; *U.S. Private*, pg. 3400
RENT SOLUTIONS; *U.S. Private*, pg. 3400
RENTTECH SOUTH AFRICA PROPRIETARY LIMITED—See The Bidvest Group Limited; *Int'l*, pg. 7626
RENT THE RUNWAY, INC.; *U.S. Public*, pg. 1784
RENTUNDER HOLDING AB; *Int'l*, pg. 6289
RENTWERX, LLC; *U.S. Private*, pg. 3400
RENTWORKS AFRICA (PTY) LTD—See FirstRand Limited; *Int'l*, pg. 2690
RENTZEL PUMP MANUFACTURING, LP; *U.S. Private*, pg. 3400
RE NU BODY SHOP SUPPLY, INC.—See Investcorp Holdings B.S.C.; *Int'l*, pg. 3776
RENU ENERGY LIMITED; *Int'l*, pg. 6289
RENU ENERGY SOLUTIONS LLC—See Swell Energy Inc; *U.S. Private*, pg. 3892
RENUEVA COMERCIAL SAPI DE CV—See EZCORP, Inc.; *U.S. Public*, pg. 818
RENUKA AGRI FOODS LIMITED; *Int'l*, pg. 6289
RENUKA CITY HOTELS PLC; *Int'l*, pg. 6289
RENUKA DO BRASIL S/A—See Shree Renuka Sugars Limited; *Int'l*, pg. 6864
RENUKA HOTELS PLC; *Int'l*, pg. 6290
RENUKA VALE DO IVAI S/A - CAMBUI UNIT—See Shree Renuka Sugars Limited; *Int'l*, pg. 6864
RENUKA VALE DO IVAI S/A—See Shree Renuka Sugars Limited; *Int'l*, pg. 6864
RENUKOOT CHEMICAL WORKS DIVISION—See Kanoria Chemicals & Industries Ltd; *Int'l*, pg. 4071
RENU MEDICAL INC.—See Getinge AB; *Int'l*, pg. 2948
RENUSOL EUROPE GMBH—See Pari Capital GmbH; *Int'l*, pg. 5741
RENWICK JAJNESWAR & CO. (BD); *Int'l*, pg. 6290
RENWOOD REALTYTRAC, LLC; *U.S. Private*, pg. 3400
RENYCO INC.; *Int'l*, pg. 6290
RENZO PIANO BUILDING WORKSHOP; *Int'l*, pg. 6290
REO AMERICA, INC.; *U.S. Private*, pg. 3400
REOBIJN B.V.; *Int'l*, pg. 6290
REOPCO INC.; *U.S. Private*, pg. 3400
REO PLASTICS, INC.; *U.S. Public*, pg. 1784
REORG RESEARCH, INC.—See Warburg Pincus LLC; *U.S. Private*, pg. 1439
REORIENT FINANCIAL MARKETS (USA) LLC—See Yunfeng Financial Group Limited; *Int'l*, pg. 8613
REOSTAR ENERGY CORPORATION; *U.S. Public*, pg. 1784
REPACORP INC.; *U.S. Private*, pg. 3400
REPAIR CENTER, LLC; *U.S. Private*, pg. 3400
REPAIR & MAINTENANCE PLANS LIMITED—See Cambria Automobiles plc; *Int'l*, pg. 1269
REPAIRSMITH, INC.—See AutoNation, Inc.; *U.S. Public*, pg. 237
REPARALIA DIRECT SL—See Brookfield Corporation; *Int'l*, pg. 1188
REPARALIA S.A.—See Brookfield Corporation; *Int'l*, pg. 1188
REPARCO NEDERLAND B.V.—See H2 Equity Partners B.V.; *Int'l*, pg. 3199
REPARCO NIJMEGEN B.V.—See H2 Equity Partners B.V.; *Int'l*, pg. 3199
REPARCO RANDSTAD B.V.—See H2 Equity Partners B.V.; *Int'l*, pg. 3199
REPARCO RENKUM B.V.—See H2 Equity Partners B.V.; *Int'l*, pg. 3199
REPARCO TRADING B.V.—See H2 Equity Partners B.V.; *Int'l*, pg. 3199
REPARCO UK LTD.—See H2 Equity Partners B.V.; *Int'l*, pg. 3199
REPARE THERAPEUTICS INC.; *Int'l*, pg. 6290
REPARIO—See JLL Partners, LLC; *U.S. Private*, pg. 2213
REPARTIM S. A.S.—See Mutares SE & Co. KGaA; *Int'l*, pg. 5105
REPASACK GMBH—See Alba SE; *Int'l*, pg. 293
REPASS-SANIERUNGSTECHNIK GMBH KORROSIONSSCHUTZ UND BETONINSTANDSETZUNG—See STRABAG SE; *Int'l*, pg. 7232
REPASYS CO., LTD.—See Japan Pulp and Paper Company Limited; *Int'l*, pg. 3904
REPATRIATES CO-OPERATIVE FINANCE AND DEVELOPMENT BANK LIMITED; *Int'l*, pg. 6290
REPAY HOLDINGS CORPORATION; *U.S. Public*, pg. 1784
REPAY HOLDINGS LLC—See Repay Holdings Corporation; *U.S. Public*, pg. 1784
REPCO HOME FINANCE LIMITED—See Repatriates Co-operative Finance and Development Bank Limited; *Int'l*, pg. 6290
REPCON, INC.; *U.S. Private*, pg. 3400
REPCONSTRICKLAND, INC.—See EMCOR Group, Inc.; *U.S. Public*, pg. 738
REPEATER COMMUNICATIONS GROUP, LLC—See American Tower Corporation; *U.S. Public*, pg. 111
REPECHAGE INVESTMENTS LIMITED; *Int'l*, pg. 6290
REPEQUITY INC.—See Trinity Hunt Management, L.P.; *U.S. Private*, pg. 4235
REPEQUITY; *U.S. Private*, pg. 3400

REPERTOIRE GENESIS CO., LTD.—See Eurofins Scientific S.E.; *Int'l*, pg. 2551
REP GREY COLOMBIA—See WPP plc; *Int'l*, pg. 8472
REPICCI'S FRANCHISE GROUP, LLC—See Cardiff Lexington Corporation; *U.S. Public*, pg. 433
REPIPE-CALIFORNIA—See J.F. Lehman & Company, Inc.; *U.S. Private*, pg. 2163
REPIPE, INC.—See J.F. Lehman & Company, Inc.; *U.S. Private*, pg. 2163
REPIPE SPECIALISTS, INC.; *U.S. Private*, pg. 3400
REPLACEMENT PARTS INC.; *U.S. Private*, pg. 3401
REPLACEMENTS, LTD.; *U.S. Private*, pg. 3401
REPLA CYCLE GMBH—See Reclay Holding GmbH; *Int'l*, pg. 6238
REPLEK AD; *Int'l*, pg. 6290
REPLENEX INC.; *U.S. Private*, pg. 3401
REPLENISH NUTRIENTS HOLDING CORP.; *Int'l*, pg. 6290
REPLICEL LIFE SCIENCES INC.; *Int'l*, pg. 6290
REPLICO CORPORATION—See Bain Capital, LP; *U.S. Private*, pg. 438
REPLICON AUSTRALIA PTY LTD—See Roper Technologies, Inc.; *U.S. Public*, pg. 1811
REPLICON EUROPE LTD—See Roper Technologies, Inc.; *U.S. Public*, pg. 1811
REPLICON INC.—See Roper Technologies, Inc.; *U.S. Public*, pg. 1811
REPLIGEN CORPORATION; *U.S. Public*, pg. 1784
REPLIGEN ESTONIA OU—See Repligen Corporation; *U.S. Public*, pg. 1784
REPLIGEN GMBH—See Repligen Corporation; *U.S. Public*, pg. 1784
REPLIGEN INDIA PRIVATE LIMITED—See Repligen Corporation; *U.S. Public*, pg. 1784
REPLIGEN IRELAND LIMITED—See Repligen Corporation; *U.S. Public*, pg. 1784
REPLIGEN JAPAN LLC—See Repligen Corporation; *U.S. Public*, pg. 1784
REPLIGEN KOREA CO. LTD.—See Repligen Corporation; *U.S. Public*, pg. 1784
REPLIGEN (SHANGHAI) BIOTECHNOLOGY CO. LTD.—See Repligen Corporation; *U.S. Public*, pg. 1784
REPLIGEN SWEDEN AB—See Repligen Corporation; *U.S. Public*, pg. 1784
REPLIMUNE GROUP, INC.; *U.S. Public*, pg. 1785
REPLOGLE GLOBES PARTNERS LLC; *U.S. Private*, pg. 3401
REPLY CROATIA D.O.O.—See Reply S.p.A.; *Int'l*, pg. 6291
REPLY DO BRASIL SISTEMAS DE INFORMATICA LTDA.—See Reply S.p.A.; *Int'l*, pg. 6291
REPLY FRANCE SARL—See Reply S.p.A.; *Int'l*, pg. 6291
REPLY GMBH—See Reply S.p.A.; *Int'l*, pg. 6291
REPLY! INC.; *U.S. Private*, pg. 3401
REPLY—See Reply S.p.A.; *Int'l*, pg. 6291
REPLY S.P.A.; *Int'l*, pg. 6290
REP. OFFICE DECEUNINCK NV—See Deceuninck NV; *Int'l*, pg. 2000
THE REPORTER PUBLISHING CO.—See Alden Global Capital LLC; *U.S. Private*, pg. 159
THE REPORTER—See Alden Global Capital LLC; *U.S. Private*, pg. 155
THE REPORTER—See Gannett Co., Inc.; *U.S. Public*, pg. 900
REPORT INTERNATIONAL LIMITED—See Optimisa PLC; *Int'l*, pg. 5604
REPORT PORTER NOVELLI-ROME—See Omnicom Group Inc.; *U.S. Public*, pg. 1592
REPORT PORTER NOVELLI—See Omnicom Group Inc.; *U.S. Public*, pg. 1592
REPOSITRAK INC; *U.S. Public*, pg. 1785
REPOWER ENERGY DEVELOPMENT CORPORATION; *Int'l*, pg. 6291
REPOXIT AG; *Int'l*, pg. 6291
REPPE AB—See Lantmannen ek for; *Int'l*, pg. 4414
REPRESENTACIONES TECHLAB S.A.C—See HORIBA Ltd; *Int'l*, pg. 3478
REPRESENTACIONES ZIMMER INC., S. DE R.L. DE C.V.—See Zimmer Biomet Holdings, Inc.; *U.S. Public*, pg. 2406
REPREVE RENEWABLES, LLC—See Unifi, Inc.; *U.S. Public*, pg. 2226
REPRISE MEDIA ASIA—See The Interpublic Group of Companies, Inc.; *U.S. Public*, pg. 2104
REPRISE MEDIA AUSTRALIA—See The Interpublic Group of Companies, Inc.; *U.S. Public*, pg. 2104
REPRISE MEDIA, INC.—See The Interpublic Group of Companies, Inc.; *U.S. Public*, pg. 2104
REPRISE RECORDS, INC.—See Access Industries, Inc.; *U.S. Private*, pg. 52
REPRO BEBER GMBH & CO. KG—See EnviTec Biogas AG; *Int'l*, pg. 2456
REPRO BOOKS LIMITED—See Repro India Limited; *Int'l*, pg. 6292
REPRO BUSEK DRUCKVORSTUFENTECHNIK GMBH & CO. KG—See Matthews International Corporation; *U.S. Public*, pg. 1400
REPRO-BUSEK GMBH & CO. KG—See Matthews International Corporation; *U.S. Public*, pg. 1399

2281

REPROCELL INC.

CORPORATE AFFILIATIONS

REPROCELL INC.; *Int'l*, pg. 6292
REPROCELL USA, INC.—See ReproCELL Inc.; *Int'l*, pg. 6292
REPRODUCCIONES FOTOMECANICAS S.A. DE C.V.—See Quad/Graphics, Inc.; *U.S. Public*, pg. 1745
REPRODUCTIVE PARTNERS, INC.—See Power Corporation of Canada; *Int'l*, pg. 5944
REPROFLEX GMBH LEIPZIG—See Matthews International Corporation; *U.S. Public*, pg. 1399
REPROFLEX VIETNAM LIMITED COMPANY—See Matthews International Corporation; *U.S. Public*, pg. 1400
REPRO-FORM GMBH—See Janoschka GmbH; *Int'l*, pg. 3880
REPROGENETICS, LLC—See The Cooper Companies, Inc.; *U.S. Public*, pg. 2066
REPROGRAPHICS ONE INC.; *U.S. Private*, pg. 3401
REPRO INDIA LIMITED; *Int'l*, pg. 6292
REPROJET AG—See Implenia AG; *Int'l*, pg. 3636
REPRO-MS 03 D.O.O.—See Avtotehna, d.d.; *Int'l*, pg. 751
REPROSERVICE EURODIGITAL GMBH—See Matthews International Corporation; *U.S. Public*, pg. 1399
REPROSOURCE, INC.—See Quest Diagnostics, Inc.; *U.S. Public*, pg. 1756
REPROS THERAPEUTICS INC.—See AbbVie Inc.; *U.S. Public*, pg. 23
REPROTECH LIMITED; *U.S. Private*, pg. 3401
REPROWORLD CO., LTD.—See USS Co., Ltd.; *Int'l*, pg. 8099
REPSO E&P DE BOLIVIA, S.A.—See Repsol, S.A.; *Int'l*, pg. 6292
REPSOL BUTANO, S.A.—See Repsol, S.A.; *Int'l*, pg. 6292
REPSOL CAPITAL, S.L.—See Repsol, S.A.; *Int'l*, pg. 6292
REPSOL CENTRAL ALBERTA PARTNERSHIP—See Repsol, S.A.; *Int'l*, pg. 6293
REPSOL CHEMICAL (U.K.) LTD.—See Repsol, S.A.; *Int'l*, pg. 6292
REPSOL CHEMIE DEUTSCHLAND—See Repsol, S.A.; *Int'l*, pg. 6292
REPSOL COMERCIAL DE PRODUCTOS PETROLIFEROS, S.A.—See Repsol, S.A.; *Int'l*, pg. 6293
REPSOL COMERCIAL, S.A.C.—See Repsol, S.A.; *Int'l*, pg. 6292
REPSOL COMERCIAL, S.C.A.—See Repsol, S.A.; *Int'l*, pg. 6292
REPSOL DIRECTO LDA—See Repsol, S.A.; *Int'l*, pg. 6293
REPSOL DIRECTO, S.A.—See Repsol, S.A.; *Int'l*, pg. 6292
REPSOL ECUADOR, S.A.—See Repsol, S.A.; *Int'l*, pg. 6292
REPSOL ELECTRICA DE DISTRIBUCION, S.L.—See Repsol, S.A.; *Int'l*, pg. 6293
REPSOL ENERGY NORTH AMERICA CORP.—See Repsol, S.A.; *Int'l*, pg. 6292
REPSOL E&P USA, INC—See Repsol, S.A.; *Int'l*, pg. 6292
REPSOL EXPLORACAO BRASIL, LTDA.—See Repsol, S.A.; *Int'l*, pg. 6292
REPSOL EXPLORACION ALGERIE, S.A.—See Repsol, S.A.; *Int'l*, pg. 6292
REPSOL EXPLORACION COLOMBIA, S.A.—See Repsol, S.A.; *Int'l*, pg. 6292
REPSOL EXPLORACION KAZAKHSTAN, S.A.—See Repsol, S.A.; *Int'l*, pg. 6292
REPSOL EXPLORACION PERU, S.A.—See Repsol, S.A.; *Int'l*, pg. 6292
REPSOL EXPLORACION, S.A.—See Repsol, S.A.; *Int'l*, pg. 6292
REPSOL EXPLORACION SECURE, S.A.—See Repsol, S.A.; *Int'l*, pg. 6292
REPSOL EXPLORACION—See Repsol, S.A.; *Int'l*, pg. 6292
REPSOL EXPLORATION NORGE AS—See Repsol, S.A.; *Int'l*, pg. 6292
REPSOL FRANCE SA—See Repsol, S.A.; *Int'l*, pg. 6292
REPSOL GAS PORTUGAL, S.A.—See Repsol, S.A.; *Int'l*, pg. 6292
REPSOL GREECE IONIAN, S.L.—See Repsol, S.A.; *Int'l*, pg. 6292
REPSOL GROUNDBIRCH PARTNERSHIP—See Repsol, S.A.; *Int'l*, pg. 6293
REPSOL ITALIA S.P.A.—See Repsol, S.A.; *Int'l*, pg. 6292
REPSOL LUBRICANTES Y ESPECIALIDADES, S.A.—See Repsol, S.A.; *Int'l*, pg. 6293
REPSOL MARKETING, S.A.C.—See Repsol, S.A.; *Int'l*, pg. 6292
REPSOL MOROCCO—See Repsol, S.A.; *Int'l*, pg. 6293
REPSOL NUEVAS ENERGIAS, S.A.—See Repsol, S.A.; *Int'l*, pg. 6293
REPSOL OIL & GAS CANADA INC.—See Repsol, S.A.; *Int'l*, pg. 6293
REPSOL ORIENTE MEDIO, S.A.—See Repsol, S.A.; *Int'l*, pg. 6292
REPSOL PETROLEO, S.A.—See Repsol, S.A.; *Int'l*, pg. 6293
REPSOL POLIMEROS LDA—See Repsol, S.A.; *Int'l*, pg. 6293
REPSOL PORTUGAL PETROLEO E DENVADOS LDA.—See Repsol, S.A.; *Int'l*, pg. 6293
REPSOL PORTUGUESA, S.A.—See Repsol, S.A.; *Int'l*, pg. 6293

REPSOL QUIMICA S.A.—See Repsol, S.A.; *Int'l*, pg. 6293
REPSOL QUIMICA, S.A.—See Repsol, S.A.; *Int'l*, pg. 6293
REPSOL, S.A.; *Int'l*, pg. 6292
REPSOL SINOPEC BRASIL, S.A.—See Repsol, S.A.; *Int'l*, pg. 6293
REPSOL SINOPEC RESOURCES UK LTD.—See Repsol, S.A.; *Int'l*, pg. 6293
REPSOL TRADING PERU, S.A.C.—See Repsol, S.A.; *Int'l*, pg. 6293
REPSOL TRADING SINGAPORE PTE. LTD.—See Repsol, S.A.; *Int'l*, pg. 6293
REPSOL TRADING USA CORPORATION—See Repsol, S.A.; *Int'l*, pg. 6293
REPSOL U.K. LTD.—See Repsol, S.A.; *Int'l*, pg. 6293
REPSOL USA HOLDINGS CORP—See Repsol, S.A.; *Int'l*, pg. 6292
REPSOL VENEZUELA GAS, S.A.—See Repsol, S.A.; *Int'l*, pg. 6294
REPSOL VENEZUELA, S.A.—See Repsol, S.A.; *Int'l*, pg. 6294
REPTILE URANIUM NAMIBIA (PTY.) LTD.—See Deep Yellow Limited; *Int'l*, pg. 2002
REPUBLICA HAVAS, LLC—See Vivendi SE; *Int'l*, pg. 8270
REPUBLICA HOLDING AD; *Int'l*, pg. 6295
REPUBLIC AIRLINE INC.—See Republic Airways Holdings Inc.; *U.S. Private*, pg. 3401
REPUBLIC AIRWAYS HOLDINGS INC.; *U.S. Private*, pg. 3401
REPUBLICAN COLLEGE, INC.—See PHINMA Corporation; *Int'l*, pg. 5848
REPUBLICAN COMPANY INC.—See Advance Publications, Inc.; *U.S. Private*, pg. 87
REPUBLICAN COMPANY INC.—See Advance Publications, Inc.; *U.S. Private*, pg. 87
REPUBLICAN COMPANY INC.—See Advance Publications, Inc.; *U.S. Private*, pg. 87
REPUBLICAN & HERALD—See Alden Global Capital LLC; *U.S. Private*, pg. 157
REPUBLIC AUTO PTE LTD—See Jardine Matheson Holdings Limited; *Int'l*, pg. 3910
REPUBLIC BAG INC.—See Alpha Industries, Inc.; *U.S. Private*, pg. 198
REPUBLIC BANCORP CO.; *U.S. Private*, pg. 3401
REPUBLIC BANCORP, INC.; *U.S. Public*, pg. 1785
REPUBLIC BANCSHARES, INC.; *U.S. Private*, pg. 3401
REPUBLIC BANK (ANGUILLA) LIMITED—See Republic Financial Holdings Limited; *Int'l*, pg. 6294
REPUBLIC BANK (BARBADOS) LIMITED—See Republic Financial Holdings Limited; *Int'l*, pg. 6294
REPUBLIC BANK (BVI) LIMITED—See Republic Financial Holdings Limited; *Int'l*, pg. 6294
REPUBLIC BANK (CAYMAN) LIMITED—See Republic Financial Holdings Limited; *Int'l*, pg. 6294
REPUBLIC BANK (EC) LIMITED - DOMINICA—See Republic Financial Holdings Limited; *Int'l*, pg. 6294
REPUBLIC BANK (EC) LIMITED—See Republic Financial Holdings Limited; *Int'l*, pg. 6294
REPUBLIC BANK (EC) LIMITED - ST. KITTS & NEVIS—See Republic Financial Holdings Limited; *Int'l*, pg. 6294
REPUBLIC BANK (EC) LIMITED - ST. LUCIA—See Republic Financial Holdings Limited; *Int'l*, pg. 6294
REPUBLIC BANK (EC) LIMITED - ST. VINCENT & GRENADINES—See Republic Financial Holdings Limited; *Int'l*, pg. 6294
REPUBLIC BANK (GHANA) LIMITED; *Int'l*, pg. 6294
REPUBLIC BANK (GRENADA) LIMITED—See Republic Financial Holdings Limited; *Int'l*, pg. 6294
REPUBLIC BANK (GUYANA) LIMITED—See Republic Financial Holdings Limited; *Int'l*, pg. 6294
REPUBLIC BANK INC.—See Republic Bancshares, Inc.; *U.S. Private*, pg. 3401
REPUBLIC BANK OF ARIZONA—See RBAZ BANCORP, INC.; *U.S. Public*, pg. 1765
REPUBLIC BANK OF CHICAGO—See Republic Bancorp Co.; *U.S. Private*, pg. 3401
REPUBLIC BANK (ST. MAARTEN) N.V.—See Republic Financial Holdings Limited; *Int'l*, pg. 6294
REPUBLIC BANK (SURINAME) N.V.—See Republic Financial Holdings Limited; *Int'l*, pg. 6294
REPUBLIC BANK TRINIDAD & TOBAGO (BARBADOS) LIMITED—See Republic Financial Holdings Limited; *Int'l*, pg. 6294
REPUBLIC BANK & TRUST COMPANY—See Republic Bancorp, Inc.; *U.S. Public*, pg. 1785
REPUBLIC BUSINESS CREDIT, LLC; *U.S. Private*, pg. 3401
REPUBLIC CEMENT & BUILDING MATERIALS INC.—See Aboitiz Equity Ventures, Inc.; *Int'l*, pg. 66
REPUBLIC CEMENT & BUILDING MATERIALS INC.—See CRH plc; *Int'l*, pg. 1842
REPUBLIC CEMENT SERVICES, INC. - BATANGAS PLANT—See Aboitiz Equity Ventures, Inc.; *Int'l*, pg. 66
REPUBLIC CEMENT SERVICES, INC. - BATANGAS PLANT—See CRH plc; *Int'l*, pg. 1842
REPUBLIC CEMENT SERVICES, INC. - BULACAN CEMENT PLANT—See Aboitiz Equity Ventures, Inc.; *Int'l*, pg. 66

REPUBLIC CEMENT SERVICES, INC. - BULACAN CEMENT PLANT—See CRH plc; *Int'l*, pg. 1842
REPUBLIC CEMENT SERVICES, INC. - NORZAGARAY PLANT—See Aboitiz Equity Ventures, Inc.; *Int'l*, pg. 66
REPUBLIC CEMENT SERVICES, INC. - NORZAGARAY PLANT—See CRH plc; *Int'l*, pg. 1842
REPUBLIC CEMENT SERVICES, INC.—See Aboitiz Equity Ventures, Inc.; *Int'l*, pg. 66
REPUBLIC CEMENT SERVICES, INC.—See CRH plc; *Int'l*, pg. 1842
REPUBLIC CEMENT SERVICES, INC. - TERESA PLANT—See Aboitiz Equity Ventures, Inc.; *Int'l*, pg. 66
REPUBLIC CEMENT SERVICES, INC. - TERESA PLANT—See CRH plc; *Int'l*, pg. 1842
REPUBLIC CONDUIT INC.—See Nucor Corporation; *U.S. Public*, pg. 1554
REPUBLIC CONTRACTING CORP.; *U.S. Private*, pg. 3401
REPUBLIC CRANE & EQUIPMENT CO.; *U.S. Private*, pg. 3402
REPUBLIC/CSC DISPOSAL AND LANDFILL, INC.—See Republic Services, Inc.; *U.S. Public*, pg. 1787
REPUBLIC DOORS AND FRAMES, LLC—See Allegion Public Limited Company; *Int'l*, pg. 335
REPUBLIC ENVIRONMENTAL TECHNOLOGIES, INC.—See Republic Services, Inc.; *U.S. Public*, pg. 1787
REPUBLIC FASTENER PRODUCTS CORP.; *U.S. Private*, pg. 3402
REPUBLIC FINANCE LLC; *U.S. Private*, pg. 3402
REPUBLIC FINANCE & MERCHANT BANK LIMITED—See Republic Financial Holdings Limited; *Int'l*, pg. 6294
REPUBLIC FINANCE & TRUST (BARBADOS) CORPORATION—See Republic Financial Holdings Limited; *Int'l*, pg. 6294
REPUBLIC FINANCIAL CORPORATION; *U.S. Private*, pg. 3402
REPUBLIC FINANCIAL CORPORATION; *U.S. Private*, pg. 3402
REPUBLIC FINANCIAL HOLDINGS LIMITED; *Int'l*, pg. 6294
REPUBLIC FINANCIAL INDEMNITY GROUP, INC.—See Old Republic International Corporation; *U.S. Public*, pg. 1569
REPUBLIC FIRST BANCORP, INC.; *U.S. Public*, pg. 1785
REPUBLIC FIRST BANK—See Republic First Bancorp, Inc.; *U.S. Public*, pg. 1785
REPUBLIC FRANKLIN INSURANCE CO.—See Utica National Insurance Group; *U.S. Private*, pg. 4325
REPUBLIC GLASS HOLDINGS CORPORATION; *Int'l*, pg. 6294
THE REPUBLIC GROUP—See Delek Group Ltd.; *Int'l*, pg. 2011
REPUBLIC HEALTHCARE LTD.; *Int'l*, pg. 6294
REPUBLIC INDEMNITY COMPANY OF AMERICA—See American Financial Group, Inc.; *U.S. Public*, pg. 103
REPUBLIC INDEMNITY COMPANY OF CALIFORNIA—See American Financial Group, Inc.; *U.S. Public*, pg. 103
REPUBLIC INDUSTRIES INC.; *U.S. Private*, pg. 3402
REPUBLIC INDUSTRIES; *U.S. Private*, pg. 3402
REPUBLIC INSURANCE COMPANY LIMITED; *Int'l*, pg. 6295
REPUBLIC INTELLIGENT TRANSPORTATION SERVICES, INC.—See Siemens Aktiengesellschaft; *Int'l*, pg. 6895
REPUBLIC LEASING CORPORATION—See Luther Holding Company; *U.S. Private*, pg. 2517
REPUBLIC LIFE INSURANCE COMPANY LIMITED—See Republic Financial Holdings Limited; *Int'l*, pg. 6294
REPUBLIC MACHINE INC.—See Piovan SpA; *Int'l*, pg. 5873
REPUBLIC/MALOY LANDFILL & SANITATION—See Republic Services, Inc.; *U.S. Public*, pg. 1787
REPUBLIC METALS CORP.—See ARE Holdings, Inc.; *Int'l*, pg. 557
REPUBLIC MORTGAGE HOME LOAN LLC; *U.S. Private*, pg. 3402
REPUBLIC MORTGAGE INSURANCE COMPANY OF NORTH CAROLINA—See Old Republic International Corporation; *U.S. Public*, pg. 1569
REPUBLIC MORTGAGE INSURANCE COMPANY—See Arch Capital Group Ltd.; *Int'l*, pg. 546
REPUBLIC NATIONAL CABINET CORPORATION—See The Cypress Group LLC; *U.S. Private*, pg. 4017
REPUBLIC NATIONAL DISTRIBUTING COMPANY; *U.S. Private*, pg. 3402
REPUBLIC NATIONAL DISTRIBUTING COMPANY—See Republic National Distributing Company; *U.S. Private*, pg. 3402
REPUBLIC NATIONAL DISTRIBUTING COMPANY—See Republic National Distributing Company; *U.S. Private*, pg. 3402
REPUBLIC NATIONAL DISTRIBUTING COMPANY—See Republic National Distributing Company; *U.S. Private*, pg. 3402

COMPANY NAME INDEX

REPUBLIC NATIONAL DISTRIBUTING COMPANY—See Republic National Distributing Company; *U.S. Private*, pg. 3402
REPUBLIC NATIONAL DISTRIBUTING COMPANY—See Republic National Distributing Company; *U.S. Private*, pg. 3402
REPUBLIC NATIONAL DISTRIBUTING COMPANY - WASHINGTON—See Republic National Distributing Company; *U.S. Private*, pg. 3402
REPUBLIC PACKAGING CORP.; *U.S. Private*, pg. 3402
REPUBLIC PAPERBOARD COMPANY LLC—See Eagle Materials Inc.; *U.S. Public*, pg. 702
REPUBLIC PLUMBING SUPPLY COMPANY INC.; *U.S. Private*, pg. 3402
REPUBLIC POWDERED METALS, INC.—See RPM International Inc.; *U.S. Public*, pg. 1817
REPUBLIC SECURITIES LIMITED—See Republic Financial Holdings Limited; *Int'l*, pg. 6294
REPUBLIC SERVICES, INC. - GRANTS PASS—See Republic Services, Inc.; *U.S. Public*, pg. 1787
REPUBLIC SERVICES, INC.; *U.S. Public*, pg. 1785
REPUBLIC SERVICES OF CANADA, INC.—See Republic Services, Inc.; *U.S. Public*, pg. 1787
REPUBLIC SERVICES OF COLORADO HAULING, LLC—See Republic Services, Inc.; *U.S. Public*, pg. 1787
REPUBLIC SERVICES OF GEORGIA, LIMITED PARTNERSHIP—See Republic Services, Inc.; *U.S. Public*, pg. 1787
REPUBLIC SERVICES OF INDIANA TRANSPORTATION, LLC—See Republic Services, Inc.; *U.S. Public*, pg. 1787
REPUBLIC SERVICES OF IOWA, LLC—See Republic Services, Inc.; *U.S. Public*, pg. 1787
REPUBLIC SERVICES OF KENTUCKY, LLC—See Republic Services, Inc.; *U.S. Public*, pg. 1787
REPUBLIC SERVICES OF MURFREESBORO - ALLIED WASTE DIV—See Republic Services, Inc.; *U.S. Public*, pg. 1787
REPUBLIC SERVICES OF NEW JERSEY, LLC—See Republic Services, Inc.; *U.S. Public*, pg. 1787
REPUBLIC SERVICES OF NORTH CAROLINA, LLC—See Republic Services, Inc.; *U.S. Public*, pg. 1787
REPUBLIC SERVICES OF OHIO HAULING, LLC—See Republic Services, Inc.; *U.S. Public*, pg. 1787
REPUBLIC SERVICES OF PENNSYLVANIA, LLC—See Republic Services, Inc.; *U.S. Public*, pg. 1787
REPUBLIC SERVICES OF SOUTH CAROLINA, LLC—See Republic Services, Inc.; *U.S. Public*, pg. 1787
REPUBLIC SERVICES VASCO ROAD, LLC—See Republic Services, Inc.; *U.S. Public*, pg. 1787
THE REPUBLIC—See Home News Enterprises, LLC; *U.S. Private*, pg. 1971
REPUBLIC STATE MORTGAGE CO.; *U.S. Private*, pg. 3402
REPUBLIC STEEL; *U.S. Private*, pg. 3402
REPUBLIC STORAGE SYSTEMS, LLC—See Independence Capital Partners, LLC; *U.S. Private*, pg. 2057
REPUBLIC TECHNOLOGIES INTERNATIONAL LLC—See Republic Steel; *U.S. Private*, pg. 3402
REPUBLIC TITLE OF TEXAS, INC.—See First American Financial Corporation; *U.S. Public*, pg. 838
REPUBLIC TOBACCO LP; *U.S. Private*, pg. 3402
REPUBLIC WASTE SERVICES OF TEXAS LP, INC.—See Republic Services, Inc.; *U.S. Public*, pg. 1787
REPUBLIC WASTE SERVICES OF TEXAS, LTD.—See Republic Services, Inc.; *U.S. Public*, pg. 1787
REPUBLIC WIRE, INC.; *U.S. Private*, pg. 3402
REPUESTOS PARA EQUIPO PESADO F.M. S.A.; *Int'l*, pg. 6295
THE REPULSE BAY COMPANY, LIMITED—See The Hongkong and Shanghai Hotels Limited; *Int'l*, pg. 7653
R.E. PURCELL CONSTRUCTION COMPANY INCORPORATED; *U.S. Private*, pg. 3335
REPUTATION.COM, INC.; *U.S. Private*, pg. 3403
REPUTATION MANAGEMENT CONSULTANTS; *U.S. Private*, pg. 3403
REPUTATION PARTNERS, LLC; *U.S. Private*, pg. 3403
REPUTATION—See Publicis Groupe S.A.; *Int'l*, pg. 6107
REPWEST INSURANCE COMPANY—See U-Haul Holding Company; *U.S. Public*, pg. 2211
REQROUTE INC.; *U.S. Private*, pg. 3403
REQUEST FOODS INC.; *U.S. Private*, pg. 3403
REQUEST, INC.; *U.S. Private*, pg. 3403
REQUIRE LLC—See Covius Holdings, Inc.; *U.S. Private*, pg. 1073
REQUISIGHT, LLC—See Morningstar, Inc.; *U.S. Public*, pg. 1477
RERIYA CORPORATION—See SEMBA Corporation; *Int'l*, pg. 6702
REROOF AMERICA CORPORATION; *U.S. Private*, pg. 3403
RE ROYALTIES LTD.; *Int'l*, pg. 6230
R.E.R RADIO ELETTRICA ROMANA—See Sonepar S.A.; *Int'l*, pg. 7092
RESAAS SERVICES INC.; *Int'l*, pg. 6295
RESAG PROPERTY MANAGEMENT GMBH—See Vonovia SE; *Int'l*, pg. 8305

RESAPHENE DEUTSCHLAND GMBH—See Resaphene Suisse AG; *Int'l*, pg. 6295
RESAPHENE SUISSE AG; *Int'l*, pg. 6295
RESAPHENE UK LTD.—See Resaphene Suisse AG; *Int'l*, pg. 6295
RESAPHENE US LLC—See Resaphene Suisse AG; *Int'l*, pg. 6295
RESA POWER, LLC—See Blue Sea Capital Management LLC; *U.S. Private*, pg. 592
RESAPP HEALTH LIMITED—See Pfizer Inc.; *U.S. Public*, pg. 1680
RESBUD SE; *Int'l*, pg. 6295
RESCAN INTERNATIONAL PTY. LIMITED—See Compagnie Generale des Etablissements Michelin SCA; *Int'l*, pg. 1745
RESCAP LIQUIDATING TRUST; *U.S. Public*, pg. 1789
RES-CARE, INC.—See KKR & Co. Inc.; *U.S. Public*, pg. 1262
RESCAR INC.; *U.S. Private*, pg. 3403
RESCASET CONCEPT—See Groupe Guillin SA; *Int'l*, pg. 3104
RESCHOP CARRE HATTINGEN GMBH—See Aviva plc; *Int'l*, pg. 746
RESCHOP CARRE MARKETING GMBH—See Aviva plc; *Int'l*, pg. 746
RESCO PRODUCTS ENGINEERING DIVISION—See Balmoral Funds LLC; *U.S. Private*, pg. 461
RESCO PRODUCTS GREENSBORO—See Balmoral Funds LLC; *U.S. Private*, pg. 461
RESCO PRODUCTS INC—See Balmoral Funds LLC; *U.S. Private*, pg. 461
RESCO PRODUCTS, INC.—See Balmoral Funds LLC; *U.S. Private*, pg. 461
RESCO PRODUCTS UK—See Balmoral Funds LLC; *U.S. Private*, pg. 461
RESCUECOM CORPORATION; *U.S. Private*, pg. 3403
RESCUE MISSION MINISTRIES, INC.; *U.S. Private*, pg. 3403
RESCUE ONE FINANCIAL; *U.S. Private*, pg. 3403
RESCUE SOCIAL CHANGE GROUP, LLC.; *U.S. Private*, pg. 3403
RES DIRECT, LLC—See Insight Venture Management, LLC; *U.S. Private*, pg. 2089
RES DIRECT, LLC—See Stone Point Capital LLC; *U.S. Private*, pg. 3823
RESDOOR COMPANY, INC.—See R.E. Sweeney Company Inc.; *U.S. Private*, pg. 3335
RESEARCH AMERICA, INC.; *U.S. Private*, pg. 3403
RESEARCH ANALYSIS & MAINTENANCE, INC.; *U.S. Private*, pg. 3403
RESEARCH AND DIAGNOSTIC SYSTEMS, INC.—See Bio-Techne Corporation; *U.S. Public*, pg. 334
THE RESEARCH BOARD, INC.—See Gartner, Inc.; *U.S. Public*, pg. 907
RESEARCH BY DESIGN LLC; *U.S. Private*, pg. 3403
RESEARCH CORPORATION TECHNOLOGIES, INC.; *U.S. Private*, pg. 3403
RESEARCH DATA SERVICES, INC.; *U.S. Private*, pg. 3403
RESEARCH & DEVELOPMENT, INC.—See Cross Marketing Group Inc.; *Int'l*, pg. 1856
RESEARCH, DEVELOPMENT & MANUFACTURING CORPORATION—See Deluxe Corporation; *U.S. Public*, pg. 653
RESEARCH & DEVELOPMENT MARKETING LAB SL—See Vivendi SE; *Int'l*, pg. 8270
RESEARCH DEVELOPMENT & PROMOTIONS; *U.S. Private*, pg. 3404
RESEARCH & EDUCATION ASSOCIATION, INC.—See Atlas Holdings, LLC; *U.S. Private*, pg. 377
RESEARCH ELECTRONICS INTERNATIONAL, LLC—See HEICO Corporation; *U.S. Public*, pg. 1020
RESEARCH ELECTRO-OPTICS INC.—See AEA Investors LP; *U.S. Private*, pg. 114
RESEARCH ENGINEERS INTERNATIONAL—See Bentley Systems, Inc.; *U.S. Public*, pg. 297
RESEARCH FOUNDATION FOR MENTAL HYGIENE, INC.; *U.S. Private*, pg. 3404
RESEARCH FOUNDATION OF THE CITY UNIVERSITY OF NEW YORK; *U.S. Private*, pg. 3404
RESEARCH FRONTIERS INCORPORATED; *U.S. Public*, pg. 1789
RESEARCH INSTITUTE FOR QUALITY LIVING CO., LTD.—See AEON Co., Ltd.; *Int'l*, pg. 178
RESEARCH INSTRUMENTS SDN BHD—See Waters Corporation; *U.S. Public*, pg. 2335
RESEARCH INTERNATIONAL LIMITED—See Bain Capital, LP; *U.S. Private*, pg. 448
RESEARCH MEDICAL CENTER—See HCA Healthcare, Inc.; *U.S. Public*, pg. 1007
RESEARCH NOW PLC—See e-Rewards, Inc.; *U.S. Private*, pg. 1302
RESEARCH ORGANICS LLC—See Merck KGaA; *Int'l*, pg. 4832
RESEARCH PANEL, INC.—See Polaris Capital Group Co., Ltd.; *Int'l*, pg. 5906
RESEARCH PHARMACEUTICAL SERVICES, INC.—See ICON plc; *Int'l*, pg. 3585

RESEARCH PRODUCTS COMPANY—See McShares, Inc.; *U.S. Private*, pg. 2644
RESEARCH PRODUCTS CORPORATION - APRILAIRE DIVISION—See Research Products Corporation; *U.S. Private*, pg. 3404
RESEARCH PRODUCTS CORPORATION; *U.S. Private*, pg. 3404
RESEARCH PRODUCTS INTERNATIONAL CORPORATION; *U.S. Private*, pg. 3404
RESEARCH SITES RESTORATION LIMITED—See Babcock International Group PLC; *Int'l*, pg. 793
RESEARCH SOLUTIONS GROUP, INC.; *U.S. Private*, pg. 3404
RESEARCH SOLUTIONS, INC.; *U.S. Public*, pg. 1789
RESEARCH SQUARE AJE LLC—See MPS Limited; *Int'l*, pg. 5063
RESEARCH SQUARE; *U.S. Private*, pg. 3404
RESEARCH SUPPORT INSTRUMENTS, LANHAM OPERATIONS—See Physical Sciences Inc.; *U.S. Private*, pg. 3175
RESEARCH SUPPORT INSTRUMENTS, PRINCETON OPERATIONS—See Physical Sciences Inc.; *U.S. Private*, pg. 3175
RESEARCH SURGICAL CENTER, LLC—See UnitedHealth Group Incorporated; *U.S. Public*, pg. 2250
RESEARCH TRIANGLE INSTITUTE; *U.S. Private*, pg. 3404
RESEAU BOIS S.A.R.L.—See Owens Corning; *U.S. Public*, pg. 1627
RESEAU CHERIE FM—See NRJ Group SA; *Int'l*, pg. 5474
RESEAU ENERGIES SAS—See Brookfield Corporation; *Int'l*, pg. 1188
RESEAU NRJ—See NRJ Group SA; *Int'l*, pg. 5474
RESEAUX LUMIERE D'ALSACE SAS—See VINCI S.A.; *Int'l*, pg. 8226
RE-SENSE LIGHTING TECHNOLOGY (SHANGHAI) CO., LTD.—See Tecnon Electronics Co., Ltd.; *Int'l*, pg. 7517
R E & S ENTERPRISES (M) SDN. BHD.—See RE&S Holdings Limited; *Int'l*, pg. 6230
RESER'S FINE FOODS INC.; *U.S. Private*, pg. 3404
RESER'S FINE FOODS—See Reser's Fine Foods Inc.; *U.S. Private*, pg. 3404
RESERVAS DE RESTAURANTES, SL—See TripAdvisor, Inc.; *U.S. Public*, pg. 2195
RESERVATION DATA MAINTENANCE INDIA PRIVATE LTD.—See Deutsche Lufthansa AG; *Int'l*, pg. 2070
RESERVEAGE, LLC.; *U.S. Private*, pg. 3405
RESERVEAMERICA INC.—See IAC Inc.; *U.S. Public*, pg. 1082
THE RESERVE BANK OF AUSTRALIA; *Int'l*, pg. 7678
RESERVE BANK OF FIJI; *Int'l*, pg. 6295
RESERVE BANK OF INDIA; *Int'l*, pg. 6295
RESERVE BANK OF MALAWI; *Int'l*, pg. 6296
RESERVE BANK OF NEW ZEALAND; *Int'l*, pg. 6296
RESERVE BANK OF VANUATU; *Int'l*, pg. 6296
RESERVE BANK OF ZIMBABWE; *Int'l*, pg. 6296
RESERVE GROUP MANAGEMENT COMPANY; *U.S. Private*, pg. 3404
RESERVE LIFE NUTRITION, L.L.C.—See Twinlab Consolidated Holdings, Inc.; *U.S. Public*, pg. 2207
RESERVE LIFE ORGANICS, LLC—See Twinlab Consolidated Holdings, Inc.; *U.S. Public*, pg. 2207
RESERVE NATIONAL INSURANCE COMPANY—See Medical Mutual of Ohio; *U.S. Public*, pg. 2655
THE RESERVE PETROLEUM COMPANY; *U.S. Public*, pg. 2125
THE RESERVES NETWORK INC.; *U.S. Private*, pg. 4104
RESERVOIR CAPITAL GROUP, L.L.C.; *U.S. Private*, pg. 3405
RESERVOIR GROUP LIMITED—See ALS Limited; *Int'l*, pg. 378
RESERVOIR LINK ENERGY BERHAD; *Int'l*, pg. 6296
RESERVOIR LINK (LABUAN) LTD.—See Reservoir Link Energy Berhad; *Int'l*, pg. 6296
RESERVOIR LINK SDN. BHD.—See Reservoir Link Energy Berhad; *Int'l*, pg. 6296
RESERVOIR MEDIA, INC.; *U.S. Public*, pg. 1789
RESERVOIR OPERATIONS, L.P.—See Reservoir Capital Group, L.L.C.; *U.S. Private*, pg. 3405
RESERVOIR PROD SASU—See Vivendi SE; *Int'l*, pg. 8275
RESERVOIRS X. PAUCHARD—See FAYAT SAS; *Int'l*, pg. 2626
RESET MIND SCIENCES LTD.—See Little Green Pharma Ltd.; *Int'l*, pg. 4528
RESET PTE LIMITED—See CME Group, Inc.; *U.S. Public*, pg. 517
RESGEN LIMITED; *Int'l*, pg. 6296
RES GESTAE SOCIMI, S.A.; *Int'l*, pg. 6295
RESHAM TEXTILE INDUSTRIES LIMITED; *Int'l*, pg. 6296
RESHAPE LIFESCIENCES INC.; *U.S. Public*, pg. 1789
RESHAPE LIFESCIENCES INC.—See ReShape Lifesciences Inc.; *U.S. Public*, pg. 1789
RESH MARKETING CONSULTANTS, INC.; *U.S. Private*, pg. 3405
RE&S HOLDINGS LIMITED; *Int'l*, pg. 6230
RESIDENCE AU BON VIEUX TEMPS PLC—See Clariane SE; *Int'l*, pg. 1644

RE&S HOLDINGS LIMITED

RESIDENCE AUX DEUX PARCS SA—See Clariane SE; *Int'l*, pg. 1644
RESIDENCE BELGICKA, S.R.O.—See CPI Property Group, S.A.; *Int'l*, pg. 1825
RESIDENCE DU MARCHE INC.—See Ventas, Inc.; *U.S. Public*, pg. 2278
RESIDENCE INN BY MARRIOTT, LLC—See Marriott International, Inc.; *U.S. Public*, pg. 1371
RESIDENCE INN DALLAS RICHARDSON—See Marriott International, Inc.; *U.S. Public*, pg. 1371
RESIDENCE IZABELLA, ZRT.—See CPI Property Group, S.A.; *Int'l*, pg. 1825
RESIDENCE JOLI AUTOMNE SA—See Swiss Prime Site AG; *Int'l*, pg. 7370
RESIDENCE LA PASSERINETTE SA—See Clariane SE; *Int'l*, pg. 1644
RESIDENCE LE PACIFIC SA—See Swiss Prime Site AG; *Int'l*, pg. 7370
RESIDENCE LE PROGRES PLC—See Clariane SE; *Int'l*, pg. 1644
THE RESIDENCE MAURITIUS—See Bonvests Holdings Limited; *Int'l*, pg. 1110
RESIDENCE MELOPEE PLC—See Clariane SE; *Int'l*, pg. 1644
RESIDENCE REINE ASTRID SA—See Clariane SE; *Int'l*, pg. 1644
RESIDENCE RY DU CHEVREUIL SPRL—See Clariane SE; *Int'l*, pg. 1644
RESIDENCE SEIGNEURIE DU VAL SA—See Clariane SE; *Int'l*, pg. 1644
RESIDENCIAL MONTE CARMELO, S.A—See ACS, Actividades de Construccion y Servicios, S.A.; *Int'l*, pg. 115
RESIDENCIAS FAMILIARES PARA MAYORES SL—See Clariane SE; *Int'l*, pg. 1644
RESIDENSEA; *U.S. Private*, pg. 3405
RESIDENT FIRST CO., LTD.—See Mitsui Fudosan Co., Ltd.; *Int'l*, pg. 4988
RESIDENTIAL CONTROL SYSTEMS, INC.—See Universal Electronics, Inc.; *U.S. Public*, pg. 2255
RESIDENTIAL DESIGN SERVICES, LLC—See Sun Capital Partners, Inc.; *U.S. Private*, pg. 3861
RESIDENTIAL HOSPICE, LLC—See Graham Holdings Company; *U.S. Public*, pg. 956
RESIDENTIAL INSURANCE AGENCY, LLC—See Equity Residential; *U.S. Public*, pg. 792
RESIDENTIAL MANAGEMENT GROUP LIMITED—See Places for People Group Limited; *Int'l*, pg. 5888
RESIDENTIAL MANAGEMENT GROUP SCOTLAND LIMITED—See Places for People Group Limited; *Int'l*, pg. 5888
RESIDENTIAL MANAGEMENT SYSTEMS—See Starrez Inc.; *U.S. Private*, pg. 3788
RESIDENTIAL MORTGAGE, LLC; *U.S. Private*, pg. 3405
RESIDENTIAL MORTGAGE SERVICES, INC.—See American National Corporation; *U.S. Private*, pg. 241
RESIDENTIAL REALTY GROUP I INC.; *U.S. Private*, pg. 3405
RESIDENTIAL SECURE INCOME PLC; *Int'l*, pg. 6296
RESIDENTIAL SYSTEMS, INC.—See Presidio Investors LLC; *U.S. Private*, pg. 3255
RESIDENTIAL WARRANTY SERVICES, INC.—See Porch Group, Inc.; *U.S. Public*, pg. 1702
RESIDENTIE BONEPUT PLC—See Clariane SE; *Int'l*, pg. 1644
RESIDENTIE EDELWEIS PLC—See Clariane SE; *Int'l*, pg. 1644
RESIDENTIE PALOKE NV—See Clariane SE; *Int'l*, pg. 1644
RESIDENTIE PRINSENPARK NV—See Clariane SE; *Int'l*, pg. 1644
RESIDENZA VILLA CARLA SRL—See Clariane SE; *Int'l*, pg. 1644
RESIDENZ LOBBERICH GMBH—See Clariane SE; *Int'l*, pg. 1643
RESIDEO INTERNATIONAL (INDIA) PVT. LTD.—See Resideo Technologies, Inc.; *U.S. Public*, pg. 1789
RESIDEO KORLATOLT FELELOSSEGU TARSASAG—See Resideo Technologies, Inc.; *U.S. Public*, pg. 1789
RESIDEO LIFE CARE SOLUTIONS LLC—See Resideo Technologies, Inc.; *U.S. Public*, pg. 1789
RESIDEO SARL—See Resideo Technologies, Inc.; *U.S. Public*, pg. 1790
RESIDEO S.R.L.—See Resideo Technologies, Inc.; *U.S. Public*, pg. 1790
RESIDEO S.R.O.—See Resideo Technologies, Inc.; *U.S. Public*, pg. 1790
RESIDEO TECHNOLOGIES, INC.; *U.S. Public*, pg. 1789
RESIDE WORLDWIDE, INC.—See Westbridge Capital Ltd.; *Int'l*, pg. 8387
RESIDEX PTY. LTD.—See Onthehouse Holdings Limited; *Int'l*, pg. 5591
RESIDUOS INDUSTRIALES DE ZARAGOZA, S.A—See ACS, Actividades de Construccion y Servicios, S.A.; *Int'l*, pg. 116
RESIDUOS INDUSTRIALES MULTIQUIM, S.A. DE C.V - CHIHUAHUA TRANSFER STATION FACILITY—See Veolia Environnement S.A.; *Int'l*, pg. 8159

RESIDUOS INDUSTRIALES MULTIQUIM, S.A. DE C.V - CIUDAD JUAREZ TRANSFER STATION FACILITY—See Veolia Environnement S.A.; *Int'l*, pg. 8159
RESIDUOS INDUSTRIALES MULTIQUIM, S.A. DE C.V - COATZACOALCOS—See Veolia Environnement S.A.; *Int'l*, pg. 8159
RESIDUOS INDUSTRIALES MULTIQUIM, S.A. DE C.V - GUADALAJARA TREATMENT AND FINAL DISPOSAL FACILITY—See Veolia Environnement S.A.; *Int'l*, pg. 8159
RESIDUOS INDUSTRIALES MULTIQUIM, S.A. DE C.V - HEAT TREATMENT PLANT—See Veolia Environnement S.A.; *Int'l*, pg. 8159
RESIDUOS INDUSTRIALES MULTIQUIM, S.A. DE C.V - HERMOSILLO TRANSFER STATION FACILITY—See Veolia Environnement S.A.; *Int'l*, pg. 8159
RESIDUOS INDUSTRIALES MULTIQUIM, S.A. DE C.V - MEXICALI TRANSFER STATION FACILITY—See Veolia Environnement S.A.; *Int'l*, pg. 8159
RESIDUOS INDUSTRIALES MULTIQUIM, S.A. DE C.V - SILAO TRANSFER STATION FACILITY—See Veolia Environnement S.A.; *Int'l*, pg. 8159
RESIDUOS INDUSTRIALES MULTIQUIM, S.A. DE C.V—See Veolia Environnement S.A.; *Int'l*, pg. 8159
RESIDUOS INDUSTRIALES MULTIQUIM, S.A. DE C.V - TIJUANA TRANSFER STATION FACILITY—See Veolia Environnement S.A.; *Int'l*, pg. 8159
RESIDUOS INDUSTRIALES MULTIQUIM, S.A. DE C.V - TREATMENT AND FINAL DISPOSAL FACILITY—See Veolia Environnement S.A.; *Int'l*, pg. 8159
RESILIA S.R.L.—See OpenGate Capital Management, LLC; *U.S. Private*, pg. 3031
RESILIENCE CAPITAL PARTNERS, LLC; *U.S. Private*, pg. 3405
RESILIENCE TECHNOLOGY CORPORATION; *U.S. Private*, pg. 3405
RESILIENT ASSET MANAGEMENT BV; *Int'l*, pg. 6296
RESILIENT REIT LIMITED; *Int'l*, pg. 6296
RESILUX AMERICA, LLC—See Resilux NV; *Int'l*, pg. 6296
RESILUX CENTRAL EUROPE PACKAGING KFT.—See Resilux NV; *Int'l*, pg. 6296
RESILUX DISTRIBUTION LLC—See Resilux NV; *Int'l*, pg. 6296
RESILUX IBERICA PACKAGING S.A.U.—See Resilux NV; *Int'l*, pg. 6296
RESILUX NV; *Int'l*, pg. 6296
RESILUX PACKAGING SOUTH EAST EUROPE S.R.L.—See Resilux NV; *Int'l*, pg. 6296
RESILUX PACKAGING SOUTH EUROPE A.B.E.E—See Resilux NV; *Int'l*, pg. 6296
RESILUX SCHWEIZ AG—See Resilux NV; *Int'l*, pg. 6296
RESILUX SOUTH EAST EUROPE SRL—See Resilux NV; *Int'l*, pg. 6296
RESILUX UKRAINE LLC—See Resilux NV; *Int'l*, pg. 6296
RESILUX-VOLGA OOO—See Resilux NV; *Int'l*, pg. 6296
RESIMAC GROUP LIMITED; *Int'l*, pg. 6296
RESIMAC LIMITED—See Resimac Group Limited; *Int'l*, pg. 6296
RESI MEDIA LLC—See BGH Capital Pty Ltd; *Int'l*, pg. 1008
RESI MEDIA LLC—See Sixth Street Partners LLC; *U.S. Private*, pg. 3678
RESIMON, C.A.—See Corimon, C.A.; *Int'l*, pg. 1801
RESINALL CORP; *U.S. Private*, pg. 3406
RESIN DESIGNS, LLC—See KKR & Co. Inc.; *U.S. Public*, pg. 1243
RESINDION S.R.L.—See Mitsubishi Chemical Group Corporation; *Int'l*, pg. 4934
RESIN FORMULATORS—See Carl Marks & Co., Inc.; *U.S. Private*, pg. 763
RESINIT AB—See XANO Industri AB; *Int'l*, pg. 8519
RESINO COLOR INDUSTRY CO., LTD.—See Sakai Chemical Industry Co., Ltd.; *Int'l*, pg. 6486
RESINOID ENGINEERING CORP.; *U.S. Private*, pg. 3406
RESINOPLAST S.A.—See OpenGate Capital Management, LLC; *U.S. Private*, pg. 3031
RESINOVA CHEMIE LIMITED—See Astral Limited; *Int'l*, pg. 658
RESIN PARTNERS INC.; *U.S. Private*, pg. 3405
RESIN & PIGMENT TECHNOLOGIES PTE LTD—See En-Gro Corporation Limited; *Int'l*, pg. 2435
RESINS, INC.; *Int'l*, pg. 6296
RESINTECH BERHAD; *Int'l*, pg. 6297
RESINTECH INC.; *U.S. Private*, pg. 3406
RESIN TECHNOLOGY GROUP LLC—See Henkel AG & Co. KGaA; *Int'l*, pg. 3353
RESIN TECHNOLOGY LLC; *U.S. Private*, pg. 3405
RESINTECH PLASTICS (M) SDN. BHD.—See Resintech Berhad; *Int'l*, pg. 6297
RESINTEX INDUSTRIALE S.R.L.—See Hoftex Group AG; *Int'l*, pg. 3440
RESIP—See Cegedim S.A.; *Int'l*, pg. 1390
RESIRENE, S.A. DE C.V.—See Grupo Kuo, S.A.B. de C.V.; *Int'l*, pg. 3131
RESISTOTECH INDUSTRIES PVT LTD; *Int'l*, pg. 6297
RESITECH GERMANY GMBH—See OpenGate Capital Management, LLC; *U.S. Private*, pg. 3031

CORPORATE AFFILIATIONS

RE&S JAPAN CO., LTD.—See RE&S Holdings Limited; *Int'l*, pg. 6230
RES-KEM LLC—See Ecolab Inc.; *U.S. Public*, pg. 716
RES MANUFACTURING COMPANY; *U.S. Private*, pg. 3403
RESMED ASIA OPERATIONS PTY LTD—See ResMed Inc.; *U.S. Public*, pg. 1791
RESMED (BEIJING) MEDICAL DEVICE CO., LTD—See ResMed Inc.; *U.S. Public*, pg. 1791
RESMED (BEIJING) TRADING CO., LTD.—See ResMed Inc.; *U.S. Public*, pg. 1790
RESMED CZ S.R.O.—See ResMed Inc.; *U.S. Public*, pg. 1790
RESMED DEUTSCHLAND GMBH—See ResMed Inc.; *U.S. Public*, pg. 1791
RESMED FINLAND OY—See ResMed Inc.; *U.S. Public*, pg. 1791
RESMED GERMANY SAAS HOLDINGS GMBH—See ResMed Inc.; *U.S. Public*, pg. 1791
RESMED HOLDINGS LTD.—See ResMed Inc.; *U.S. Public*, pg. 1791
RESMED INC.; *U.S. Public*, pg. 1790
RESMED INDIA PRIVATE LTD—See ResMed Inc.; *U.S. Public*, pg. 1791
RESMED KK—See ResMed Inc.; *U.S. Public*, pg. 1791
RESMED LTD.—See ResMed Inc.; *U.S. Public*, pg. 1791
RESMED MARIBO A/S—See ResMed Inc.; *U.S. Public*, pg. 1791
RESMED NEW ZEALAND LIMITED—See ResMed Inc.; *U.S. Public*, pg. 1791
RESMED NORWAY AS—See ResMed Inc.; *U.S. Public*, pg. 1791
RESMED PARIS SAS—See ResMed Inc.; *U.S. Public*, pg. 1791
RESMED POLSKA SP ZOO—See ResMed Inc.; *U.S. Public*, pg. 1791
RESMED SAS—See ResMed Inc.; *U.S. Public*, pg. 1791
RESMED SCHWEIZ AG—See ResMed Inc.; *U.S. Public*, pg. 1791
RESMED SENSOR TECHNOLOGIES LTD.—See ResMed Inc.; *U.S. Public*, pg. 1791
RESMED SLEEP SOLUTIONS LIMITED—See ResMed Inc.; *U.S. Public*, pg. 1791
RESMED SWEDEN AB—See ResMed Inc.; *U.S. Public*, pg. 1791
RESMED TAIWAN CO., LTD—See ResMed Inc.; *U.S. Public*, pg. 1791
RESMED (UK) LIMITED—See ResMed Inc.; *U.S. Public*, pg. 1791
RESMI FINANCE & INVESTMENT HOUSE JSC; *Int'l*, pg. 6297
RESMI GROUP LTD.; *Int'l*, pg. 6297
RESO DETECT SAS—See VINCI S.A.; *Int'l*, pg. 8226
RESOL HOLDINGS GO., LTD.—See Nomura Holdings, Inc.; *Int'l*, pg. 5412
RESOL HOLDINGS CO., LTD.—See Toyota Motor Corporation; *Int'l*, pg. 7873
RESO LOGISTIQUE SAS—See VINCI S.A.; *Int'l*, pg. 8226
RESOLUTE ACQUISITION CORPORATION—See Acadia Healthcare Company, Inc.; *U.S. Public*, pg. 30
RESOLUTE ADMINISTRATION, INC.; *U.S. Private*, pg. 3406
RESOLUTE FOREST PRODUCTS INC.—See PT Sinar Mas Group; *Int'l*, pg. 6073
RESOLUTE FP AUGUSTA LLC—See PT Sinar Mas Group; *Int'l*, pg. 6073
RESOLUTE FP US INC. - COOSA PINES—See PT Sinar Mas Group; *Int'l*, pg. 6074
RESOLUTE FP US INC. - GRENADA—See PT Sinar Mas Group; *Int'l*, pg. 6074
RESOLUTE FP US INC.—See PT Sinar Mas Group; *Int'l*, pg. 6073
RESOLUTE HEALTH FAMILY URGENT CARE, INC.—See Tenet Healthcare Corporation; *U.S. Public*, pg. 2014
RESOLUTE HEALTH PHYSICIANS NETWORK, INC.—See Tenet Healthcare Corporation; *U.S. Public*, pg. 2014
RESOLUTE INVESTMENT MANAGERS, INC.—See Kelso & Company, L.P.; *U.S. Private*, pg. 2280
RESOLUTE MINING LIMITED; *Int'l*, pg. 6297
RESOLUTE NATURAL RESOURCES COMPANY, LLC—See Coterra Energy Inc.; *U.S. Public*, pg. 587
RESOLUTE PARTNERS LLC.; *U.S. Private*, pg. 3406
RESOLUTE REINSURANCE COMPANY—See Berkshire Hathaway Inc.; *U.S. Public*, pg. 305
RESOLUTE RESOURCES PTY LTD—See Resolute Mining Limited; *Int'l*, pg. 6297
RESOLUTE SOLUTIONS CORPORATION; *U.S. Private*, pg. 3406
RESOLUTE (TANZANIA) LIMITED—See Resolute Mining Limited; *Int'l*, pg. 6297
RESOLUTE TECHNOLOGIES LLC; *U.S. Private*, pg. 3406
RESOLUTION CAPITAL LIMITED; *Int'l*, pg. 6297
RESOLUTION CONSULTING, INC.—See Grant Avenue Capital, LLC; *U.S. Private*, pg. 1756
RESOLUTION ECONOMICS, LLC—See Levine Leichtman Capital Partners, LLC; *U.S. Private*, pg. 2436
RESOLUTION, INC.; *U.S. Private*, pg. 3406

COMPANY NAME INDEX

RESOLUTION LIFE GROUP HOLDINGS LP; *Int'l*, pg. 6297
RESOLUTION LIFE GROUP SERVICES LIMITED—See Resolution Life Group Holdings LP; *Int'l*, pg. 6297
RESOLUTION MEDIA—See Omnicom Group Inc.; *U.S. Public*, pg. 1593
RESOLUTION MINERALS LTD.; *Int'l*, pg. 6297
RESOLUTION OPERATIONS LLP—See Resolution Capital Limited; *Int'l*, pg. 6297
RESOLUTION PACKAGING—See The Westervelt Company; *U.S. Private*, pg. 4134
RESOLUTION SARL—See CVC Capital Partners SICAV-FIS S.A.; *Int'l*, pg. 1882
RESOLVE INTERIM SOLUTIONS LIMITED—See Empresaria Group Plc; *Int'l*, pg. 2389
RESOLVE MARINE SERVICES, INC.; *U.S. Private*, pg. 3406
RESOLVER INC.—See Permira Advisers LLP; *Int'l*, pg. 5807
RESOLVE SYSTEMS, LLC—See Insight Venture Management, LLC; *U.S. Private*, pg. 2091
RESOLVIT, LLC—See Aditi Consulting LLC; *U.S. Private*, pg. 79
RESOLVIT RESOURCES, LLC—See Aditi Consulting LLC; *U.S. Private*, pg. 79
RESOMATION LIMITED—See Co-operative Group Limited; *Int'l*, pg. 1679
RESONA ASSET MANAGEMENT CO., LTD.—See Resona Holdings, Inc.; *Int'l*, pg. 6297
RESONA BANK (CAPITAL MANAGEMENT) PLC—See Resona Holdings, Inc.; *Int'l*, pg. 6298
RESONA BANK, LIMITED—See Resona Holdings, Inc.; *Int'l*, pg. 6298
RESONA BANK, LTD. - SINGAPORE REPRESENTATIVE OFFICE—See Resona Holdings, Inc.; *Int'l*, pg. 6298
RESONA BUSINESS SERVICE CO., LTD.—See Resona Holdings, Inc.; *Int'l*, pg. 6298
RESONA CARD CO. LTD.—See Resona Holdings, Inc.; *Int'l*, pg. 6298
RESONAC CORPORATION—See Resonac Holdings Corporation; *Int'l*, pg. 6298
RESONAC HOLDINGS CORPORATION; *Int'l*, pg. 6298
RESONA HOLDINGS, INC.; *Int'l*, pg. 6297
RESONA INC.—See Core Corporation; *Int'l*, pg. 1797
RESONA KESSAI SERVICE CO., LTD.—See Resona Holdings, Inc.; *Int'l*, pg. 6298
RESONANCE EMERGING MARKETS MACRO TRUST; *U.S. Private*, pg. 3406
RESONANCE HEALTH ANALYSIS SERVICES PTY LTD—See Resonance Health Limited; *Int'l*, pg. 6301
RESONANCE HEALTH LIMITED; *Int'l*, pg. 6301
RESONANCE SPECIALTIES LTD.; *Int'l*, pg. 6301
RESONANT INC.—See Murata Manufacturing Co., Ltd.; *Int'l*, pg. 5097
RESONANT LLC—See Murata Manufacturing Co., Ltd.; *Int'l*, pg. 5097
RESONA RESEARCH INSTITUTE CO., LTD.—See Resona Holdings, Inc.; *Int'l*, pg. 6298
RESONATE BLENDS, INC.; *U.S. Public*, pg. 1791
RESONATE, INC.; *U.S. Private*, pg. 3406
RESONATE NETWORKS, INC.; *U.S. Private*, pg. 3406
RESONETICS, LLC—See GTCR LLC; *U.S. Private*, pg. 1806
RESOPAL GMBH—See Clayton, Dubilier & Rice, LLC; *U.S. Private*, pg. 930
RESORBA MEDICAL GMBH—See Advanced Medical Solutions Group plc; *Int'l*, pg. 161
RESORBA OOO—See Advanced Medical Solutions Group plc; *Int'l*, pg. 161
RESORBA S.R.O.—See Advanced Medical Solutions Group plc; *Int'l*, pg. 161
RESORT ASSOCIATION MANAGEMENT; *U.S. Private*, pg. 3406
THE RESORT AT LONGBOAT KEY CLUB—See Ocean Properties, Ltd.; *U.S. Private*, pg. 2989
THE RESORT COMPANY—See Tonka Bay Equity Partners LLC; *U.S. Private*, pg. 4185
RESORT COSTUMING SERVICE CO., LTD.—See Oriental Land Co., Ltd.; *Int'l*, pg. 5625
RESORT COSTUMING SERVICES CO., LTD.—See Oriental Land Co., Ltd.; *Int'l*, pg. 5625
RESORT DEVELOPERS LIMITED—See DEAP Capital Management & Trust plc; *Int'l*, pg. 1998
RESORTES ARGENTINA S.A.—See Barnes Group Inc.; *U.S. Public*, pg. 277
RESORTES Y PRODUCTOS METALICOS S.A.-QUERETARO PLANT—See MiddleGround Management, LP; *U.S. Private*, pg. 2712
RESORT FUNDING LLC—See Bank of America Corporation; *U.S. Public*, pg. 272
RESORT HOSPITALITY ENTERPRISES LTD.; *U.S. Private*, pg. 3406
RESORT INNS OF AMERICA INC.; *U.S. Private*, pg. 3406
RESORTQUEST INTERNATIONAL, INC.—See Jefferies Financial Group Inc.; *U.S. Public*, pg. 1189
RESORT SAVINGS & LOANS PLC; *Int'l*, pg. 6301
RESORT SERVICES INTERNATIONAL (CAYO LARGO), L.P., S.E.—See InterContinental Hotels Group PLC; *Int'l*, pg. 3738

RESORTS OF THE CANADIAN ROCKIES, INC.; *Int'l*, pg. 6301
RESORT SOLUTIONS LIMITED—See Marriott Vacations Worldwide Corporation; *U.S. Public*, pg. 1374
RESORTS WORLD AT SENTOSA PTE. LTD.—See Genting Berhad; *Int'l*, pg. 2929
RESORTS WORLD LAS VEGAS LLC—See Genting Berhad; *Int'l*, pg. 2929
RESORT TELEVISION CABLE COMPANY INCORPORATED—See Wehco Media, Inc.; *U.S. Private*, pg. 4469
RESORT TRUST INC.; *Int'l*, pg. 6301
RESORT VILLA DEVELOPMENT SDN BHD—See IOI Corporation Berhad; *Int'l*, pg. 3792
RESORT VILLA GOLF COURSE BERHAD—See IOI Properties Group Berhad; *Int'l*, pg. 3792
RESORT VILLA GOLF COURSE DEVELOPMENT SDN BHD—See IOI Corporation Berhad; *Int'l*, pg. 3792
RESOURCE ADVISORY SERVICES INC.—See The Mather Group, LLC; *U.S. Private*, pg. 4075
RESOURCE ALLIANCE LLC; *U.S. Private*, pg. 3406
RESOURCE AMERICA, INC.—See Island Capital Group LLC; *U.S. Private*, pg. 2144
RESOURCE/AMMIRATI—See International Business Machines Corporation; *U.S. Public*, pg. 1150
RESOURCE AUTOMOTIVE, INC.—See Assurant, Inc.; *U.S. Public*, pg. 215
RESOURCE BANK NATIONAL ASSOCIATION—See Resource Bank; *U.S. Private*, pg. 3406
RESOURCE BANK; *U.S. Private*, pg. 3406
RESOURCE BASE LIMITED; *Int'l*, pg. 6301
RESOURCE CAPITAL GOLD CORP.; *Int'l*, pg. 6302
RESOURCE CENTER FOR INDEPENDENT LIVING, INC.; *U.S. Private*, pg. 3406
RESOURCE CENTRIX HOLDINGS INC.; *Int'l*, pg. 6302
RE:SOURCE COLORADO, INC.—See ACON Investments, LLC; *U.S. Private*, pg. 62
RESOURCE CONSERVATION SYSTEMS, LLC—See Bonita Bay Properties, Inc.; *U.S. Private*, pg. 614
RESOURCE CONSULTING GROUP, INC.; *U.S. Private*, pg. 3406
RESOURCE DEVELOPMENT GROUP LIMITED; *Int'l*, pg. 6302
RESOURCE ENVIRONMENTAL GROUP SERVICES, LLC—See Strategic Environmental & Energy Resources, Inc.; *U.S. Public*, pg. 1954
RESOURCE ENVIRONMENTAL SOLUTIONS, LLC—See KKR & Co. Inc.; *U.S. Public*, pg. 1263
RESOURCE EXPERIENCE LIMITED—See Navis Capital Partners Limited; *Int'l*, pg. 5176
RESOURCEFUL HR LLC—See New Mountain Capital, LLC; *U.S. Private*, pg. 2901
RESOURCE GENERATION LIMITED; *Int'l*, pg. 6302
THE RESOURCE GROUP, INC.; *Int'l*, pg. 7678
THE RESOURCE GROUP INTERNATIONAL LTD.; *U.S. Private*, pg. 4105
RESOURCE GROUP INTERNATIONAL; *U.S. Private*, pg. 3407
RESOURCE HARDWARE AND TRADING PTE LTD—See PSL Holdings Limited; *Int'l*, pg. 6017
RESOURCE HOLDING MANAGEMENT LIMITED; *Int'l*, pg. 6302
RESOURCEHOUSE LIMITED; *Int'l*, pg. 6302
RESOURCE INNOVATION OFFICE REIT, INC.—See Island Capital Group LLC; *U.S. Private*, pg. 2144
RESOURCE INNOVATIONS, LLC—See BV Investment Partners, LLC; *U.S. Private*, pg. 699
RESOURCE LABEL GROUP, LLC—See Ares Management Corporation; *U.S. Public*, pg. 190
RESOURCE LENDERS INC.; *U.S. Private*, pg. 3407
RESOURCE MANAGEMENT ASSOCIATES, INC—See Global Infrastructure Solutions, Inc.; *U.S. Private*, pg. 1715
RESOURCE MANAGEMENT ENTERPRISES INC.; *U.S. Private*, pg. 3407
RESOURCE MANAGEMENT INC.—See Vensure Employer Services, Inc.; *U.S. Private*, pg. 4357
RESOURCE MANAGEMENT ROCKFORD LLC—See Resource Management Enterprises Inc.; *U.S. Private*, pg. 3407
RESOURCE MECHANICAL INSULATION LLC—See The Rudolph/Libbe Companies; *U.S. Private*, pg. 4113
RESOURCE MINING CORPORATION LIMITED; *Int'l*, pg. 6302
RESOURCE ONE CREDIT UNION; *U.S. Private*, pg. 3407
RESOURCE ONE, INC.; *U.S. Private*, pg. 3407
RESOURCE ONE—See Moore DM Group, LLC; *U.S. Private*, pg. 2780
RESOURCE OPTIMIZATION & INNOVATION, L.L.C.—See HCA Healthcare, Inc.; *U.S. Public*, pg. 1007
RESOURCE OPTIONS, INC.; *U.S. Private*, pg. 3407
RESOURCE PARTNERS ENTERPRISES, LLC—See Suarez Corporation Industries; *U.S. Private*, pg. 3847
RESOURCE PARTNERS GROUP, INC.; *U.S. Private*, pg. 3407
RESOURCE PILING PTE. LTD.—See Keller Group plc; *Int'l*, pg. 4121
RESOURCE PLANNING GROUP LTD.—See Genstar Capital, LLC; *U.S. Private*, pg. 1677

RESOURCE PLANNING GROUP LTD.—See Keystone Group, L.P.; *U.S. Private*, pg. 2298
RESOURCE PLUS OF NORTH FLORIDA, INC.—See SPAR Group, Inc.; *U.S. Public*, pg. 1914
RESOURCE PRO, LLC; *U.S. Private*, pg. 3407
RESOURCE PROPERTY MANAGEMENT, LLC—See Island Capital Group LLC; *U.S. Private*, pg. 2144
RESOURCE PROVIDERS, INC.; *U.S. Private*, pg. 3407
RESOURCE REAL ESTATE, INC.—See Island Capital Group LLC; *U.S. Private*, pg. 2144
RESOURCE REAL ESTATE OPPORTUNITY REIT, INC.—See Island Capital Group LLC; *U.S. Private*, pg. 2144
RESOURCE RECOVERY SYSTEMS, LLC—See Republic Services, Inc.; *U.S. Public*, pg. 1787
RESOURCE RECYCLING, INC.—See The Association of Plastic Recyclers; *U.S. Private*, pg. 3989
RESOURCE RECYCLING, LLC—See European Metal Recycling Limited; *Int'l*, pg. 2557
RESOURCE REIT, INC.—See Blackstone Inc.; *U.S. Public*, pg. 351
RESOURCE RIG SUPPLY INC.—See Transocean Ltd.; *Int'l*, pg. 7903
RESOURCES ACQUISITION CORP.; *Int'l*, pg. 6302
RESOURCES COMPANY FOR DEVELOPMENT & INVESTMENT PLC; *Int'l*, pg. 6302
RESOURCES CONNECTION, INC.; *U.S. Public*, pg. 1791
RESOURCES CONNECTION LLC—See Resources Connection, Inc.; *U.S. Public*, pg. 1791
RESOURCES CONNECTION MEXICO S DE RL DE CV—See Resources Connection, Inc.; *U.S. Public*, pg. 1791
RESOURCES & ENERGY GROUP LIMITED; *Int'l*, pg. 6302
RESOURCES ENGINEERING SERVICES INC.—See CTCI Corporation; *Int'l*, pg. 1870
RESOURCES FOR HUMAN DEVELOPMENT; *U.S. Private*, pg. 3407
RESOURCES GLOBAL DEVELOPMENT LIMITED; *Int'l*, pg. 6302
RESOURCES GLOBAL PROFESSIONALS (EUROPE) BV—See Resources Connection, Inc.; *U.S. Public*, pg. 1791
RESOURCES GLOBAL PROFESSIONALS (FRANCE) SAS—See Resources Connection, Inc.; *U.S. Public*, pg. 1791
RESOURCES GLOBAL PROFESSIONALS (GERMANY) GMBH—See Resources Connection, Inc.; *U.S. Public*, pg. 1791
RESOURCES GLOBAL PROFESSIONALS (HONG KONG) LIMITED—See Resources Connection, Inc.; *U.S. Public*, pg. 1791
RESOURCES GLOBAL PROFESSIONALS, INC.—See Resources Connection, Inc.; *U.S. Public*, pg. 1792
RESOURCES GLOBAL PROFESSIONALS (INDIA) PRIVATE LTD.—See Resources Connection, Inc.; *U.S. Public*, pg. 1791
RESOURCES GLOBAL PROFESSIONALS (IRELAND) LTD.—See Resources Connection, Inc.; *U.S. Public*, pg. 1792
RESOURCES GLOBAL PROFESSIONALS (JAPAN) K.K.—See Resources Connection, Inc.; *U.S. Public*, pg. 1792
RESOURCES GLOBAL PROFESSIONALS (KOREA) LTD.—See Resources Connection, Inc.; *U.S. Public*, pg. 1792
RESOURCES GLOBAL PROFESSIONALS (NORWAY) AS—See Resources Connection, Inc.; *U.S. Public*, pg. 1792
RESOURCES GLOBAL PROFESSIONALS (SINGAPORE) PTE. LTD.—See Resources Connection, Inc.; *U.S. Public*, pg. 1792
RESOURCES GLOBAL PROFESSIONALS; *U.S. Private*, pg. 3407
RESOURCES GLOBAL PROFESSIONALS SWEDEN AB—See Resources Connection, Inc.; *U.S. Public*, pg. 1792
RESOURCES GLOBAL PROFESSIONALS (TAIWAN) CO. LTD.—See Resources Connection, Inc.; *U.S. Public*, pg. 1792
RESOURCES HOLDINGS LIMITED; *Int'l*, pg. 6302
RESOURCES LEGACY FUND; *U.S. Private*, pg. 3407
RESOURCE SOLUTIONS GROUP, INC.; *U.S. Public*, pg. 1791
RESOURCE SOLUTIONS GROUP LLC—See TPG Capital, L.P.; *U.S. Public*, pg. 2176
RESOURCE SOLUTIONS INC.; *U.S. Private*, pg. 3407
RESOURCE SOLUTIONS LIMITED—See Robert Walters plc; *Int'l*, pg. 6368
RESOURCES PRIMA GROUP LIMITED; *Int'l*, pg. 6302
RESOURCES TRUCKING, INC.—See Pyramid Industries, Inc.; *U.S. Private*, pg. 3310
RE:SOURCES USA—See Publicis Groupe S.A.; *Int'l*, pg. 6106
RESOURCE SYSTEMS GROUP, INC.; *U.S. Private*, pg. 3407
RESOURCE SYSTEMS & SERVICES PTY LTD—See JCurve Solutions Limited; *Int'l*, pg. 3924

RESOURCE UNDERWRITING PACIFIC PTY LTD—See Arch Capital Group Ltd.; *Int'l*, pg. 547
RESOURCEWISE—See Battery Ventures, L.P.; *U.S. Private*, pg. 489
RESOURCIS INFORMATION SERVICES, INC.; *U.S. Private*, pg. 3407
RESPATEX INTERNATIONAL LTD.—See Norske Skog ASA; *Int'l*, pg. 5437
RESPEC INC.; *U.S. Private*, pg. 3407
RESPECT YOUR UNIVERSE, INC.—See RYU Apparel Inc.; *Int'l*, pg. 6441
RESPICARDIA, INC.—See Asahi Kasei Corporation; *Int'l*, pg. 597
RESPIRATORY CARE AFRICA (PTY) LTD—See Ascendis Health Limited; *Int'l*, pg. 601
RESPIRATORY DISTRIBUTORS INC.; *U.S. Private*, pg. 3407
RESPIRATORY HOME CARE OF BRISTOL, LLC—See AdaptHealth Corp.; *U.S. Public*, pg. 39
RESPIRATORY HOMECARE SOLUTIONS CANADA INC.—See L'Air Liquide S.A.; *Int'l*, pg. 4375
RESPIRATORY SERVICES OF WESTERN NEW YORK, INC.—See AdaptHealth Corp.; *U.S. Public*, pg. 39
RESPIRATORY SUPPORT PRODUCTS INC.—See ICU Medical, Inc.; *U.S. Public*, pg. 1087
RESPIRATORY TECHNOLOGIES, INC.—See Koninklijke Philips N.V.; *Int'l*, pg. 4271
RESPIRATORY THERAPY HOME CARE—See New Mountain Capital, LLC; *U.S. Private*, pg. 2903
RESPIRERX PHARMACEUTICALS INC.; *U.S. Public*, pg. 1792
RESPIRI LIMITED; *Int'l*, pg. 6302
RESPIRONICS DEUTSCHLAND GMBH & CO. KG—See Koninklijke Philips N.V.; *Int'l*, pg. 4271
RESPIRONICS DEUTSCHLAND VERWALTUNGSGE-SELLSCHAFT MBH—See Koninklijke Philips N.V.; *Int'l*, pg. 4271
RESPIRONICS, INC.—See Koninklijke Philips N.V.; *Int'l*, pg. 4270
RESPIRONICS INTERNATIONAL INC.—See Koninklijke Philips N.V.; *Int'l*, pg. 4270
RESPIRONICS LTD.—See Koninklijke Philips N.V.; *Int'l*, pg. 4271
RESPIRONICS RESPIRATORY DRUG DELIVERY (UK) LTD.—See Koninklijke Philips N.V.; *Int'l*, pg. 4271
RESPIRONICS SWEDEN AB—See Koninklijke Philips N.V.; *Int'l*, pg. 4271
RESPITEK AS—See SOL S.p.A.; *Int'l*, pg. 7067
RESPITEK MEDICAL SERVICES; *U.S. Private*, pg. 3407
RESPOND2 CMEDIA; *U.S. Private*, pg. 3407
RESPOND BEHEER B.V.—See Thoma Bravo, L.P.; *U.S. Private*, pg. 4147
RESPOND.COM—See TEOCO Corporation; *U.S. Private*, pg. 3969
RESPONDER SYSTEMS CORPORATION—See AMETEK, Inc.; *U.S. Public*, pg. 121
RESPONSABILITY AFRICA LTD.—See M&G Plc; *Int'l*, pg. 4612
RESPONSABILITY AMERICA LATINA S.A.C.—See M&G Plc; *Int'l*, pg. 4612
RESPONSABILITY FRANCE S.A.S.—See M&G Plc; *Int'l*, pg. 4612
RESPONSABILITY INDIA BUSINESS ADVISORS PVT. LTD.—See M&G Plc; *Int'l*, pg. 4612
RESPONSABILITY INVESTMENTS AG—See M&G Plc; *Int'l*, pg. 4612
RESPONSABILITY THAILAND LTD.—See M&G Plc; *Int'l*, pg. 4612
RESPONSE BIOMEDICAL CORP.—See OrbiMed Advisors LLC; *U.S. Private*, pg. 3038
RESPONSE ENVELOPE INC.; *U.S. Private*, pg. 3408
RESPONSE INFORMATICS INC.—See Response Informatics Limited; *Int'l*, pg. 6302
RESPONSE INFORMATICS LIMITED; *Int'l*, pg. 6302
RESPONSE INSURANCE COMPANY—See Kemper Corporation; *U.S. Public*, pg. 1221
RESPONSE, LLC; *U.S. Private*, pg. 3408
RESPONSE MAIL EXPRESS INC.; *U.S. Private*, pg. 3408
RESPONSE MARKETING GROUP LLC; *U.S. Private*, pg. 3408
RESPONSE MEDIA, INC.; *U.S. Private*, pg. 3408
RESPONSE PERSONNEL, INC.; *U.S. Private*, pg. 3408
THE RESPONSE SHOP, INC.; *U.S. Private*, pg. 4105
RESPONSESOURCE LTD.—See Pulsar Group; *Int'l*, pg. 6116
RESPONSE TEAM 1 LLC—See Franklin Resources, Inc.; *U.S. Public*, pg. 879
RESPONSIVE INDUSTRIES LLC—See Responsive Industries Ltd; *Int'l*, pg. 6302
RESPONSIVE INDUSTRIES LTD; *Int'l*, pg. 6302
RESPONSIVE INNOVATIONS, LLC—See Centre Lane Partners, LLC; *U.S. Private*, pg. 828
RESPONSIVE ORTHOPEDICS, LLC—See Medtronic plc; *Int'l*, pg. 4790
RESPONSYS, INC.—See Oracle Corporation; *U.S. Public*, pg. 1613
RES PUBLICA CONSULTING GROUP INC.; *Int'l*, pg. 6295

RES-Q HEALTHCARE SYSTEMS, INC.—See Clearlake Capital Group, L.P.; *U.S. Private*, pg. 937
RES-Q HEALTHCARE SYSTEMS, INC.—See SkyKnight Capital LLC; *U.S. Private*, pg. 3685
RESSLER MOTORS; *U.S. Private*, pg. 3408
RESSORTS SPEC, SAS—See Barnes Group Inc.; *U.S. Public*, pg. 277
RESSOURCES APPALACHES INC.; *Int'l*, pg. 6302
RESTALLIANCE; *Int'l*, pg. 6303
RESTAR HOLDINGS CORPORATION; *Int'l*, pg. 6303
RESTART SIIQ; *Int'l*, pg. 6303
RESTAURANGAKDEMIEN AB—See Sysco Corporation; *U.S. Public*, pg. 1975
RESTAURANT ASSOCIATES (AUSTRALIA) PTY LTD—See Compass Group PLC; *Int'l*, pg. 1752
RESTAURANT ASSOCIATES CORPORATION—See Compass Group PLC; *Int'l*, pg. 1751
RESTAURANT BRANDS ASIA LTD.; *Int'l*, pg. 6303
RESTAURANT BRANDS AUSTRALIA PTY LIMITED—See Grupo Finaccess S.A.P.I. de C.V.; *Int'l*, pg. 3129
RESTAURANT BRANDS INTERNATIONAL INC.; *Int'l*, pg. 6304
RESTAURANT BRANDS INTERNATIONAL LIMITED PARTNERSHIP—See Restaurant Brands International Inc.; *Int'l*, pg. 6304
RESTAURANT BRANDS LIMITED—See Grupo Finaccess S.A.P.I. de C.V.; *Int'l*, pg. 3129
RESTAURANT BRANDS NEW ZEALAND LIMITED—See Grupo Finaccess S.A.P.I. de C.V.; *Int'l*, pg. 3129
RESTAURANT BUSINESS INC.; *U.S. Private*, pg. 3408
RESTAURANT BUSINESS—See Schofield Media Ltd.; *U.S. Private*, pg. 3567
RESTAURANT CONCEPTS LLC—See Yum! Brands, Inc.; *U.S. Public*, pg. 2400
RESTAURANT COVERAGE ASSOCIATES, INC.—See Patriot National, Inc.; *U.S. Private*, pg. 3110
RESTAURANT DEPOT, LLC—See Jetro Cash & Carry Enterprises, LLC; *U.S. Private*, pg. 2204
RESTAURANT D'VIJFF VLIEGHEN, B.V.—See Minor International PCL; *Int'l*, pg. 4912
RESTAURANTES MCDONALD'S S.A—See McDonald's Corporation; *U.S. Public*, pg. 1406
THE RESTAURANT GROUP PLC—See Apollo Global Management, Inc.; *U.S. Public*, pg. 164
RESTAURANT MANAGEMENT CORP.; *U.S. Private*, pg. 3408
RESTAURANT MANAGEMENT INC.; *U.S. Private*, pg. 3408
RESTAURANT MANAGEMENT OF SOUTH CAROLINA INC.; *U.S. Private*, pg. 3408
RESTAURANT RECRUIT, INC.; *U.S. Private*, pg. 3408
RESTAURANT SERVICES, INC.; *U.S. Private*, pg. 3408
RESTAURANTS MANORA SA—See Maus Freres S.A.; *Int'l*, pg. 4732
RESTAURANTS NO LIMIT, INC.; *U.S. Private*, pg. 3408
RESTAURANTS OF AMERICA, INC.; *U.S. Private*, pg. 3408
RESTAURANTS OF AMERICA MANAGEMENT, INC.—See Restaurants of America, Inc.; *U.S. Private*, pg. 3408
THE RESTAURANT SOURCE—See Bargreen-Ellingson Inc.; *U.S. Private*, pg. 474
RESTAURANTS UNLIMITED, INC.—See Sun Capital Partners, Inc.; *U.S. Private*, pg. 3860
RESTAURANT SUNTORY USA INC.—See Suntory Holdings Limited; *Int'l*, pg. 7326
RESTAURANT SYSTEMS INC.; *U.S. Private*, pg. 3408
RESTAURANT TECHNOLOGIES, INC.—See The Goldman Sachs Group, Inc.; *U.S. Public*, pg. 2080
RESTAURANT TECHNOLOGY SERVICES UK LIMITED—See Xerox Holdings Corporation; *U.S. Public*, pg. 2388
RESTAXIL GMBH—See PharmaSGP Holding SE; *Int'l*, pg. 5841
REST EASY GROUP LTD.; *Int'l*, pg. 6303
RESTEC CONTRACTORS INC.—See Anson Industries, Inc.; *U.S. Private*, pg. 286
RESTECH—See Washington H. Soul Pattinson & Company Limited; *Int'l*, pg. 8351
RE STEEL SUPPLY COMPANY INC.; *U.S. Private*, pg. 3364
RESTEK CORPORATION; *U.S. Private*, pg. 3408
REST EZ, INC.; *U.S. Public*, pg. 1792
RESTHAVEN CARE COMMUNITY; *U.S. Private*, pg. 3408
REST HAVEN FUNERAL HOME, INC.—See Carriage Services, Inc.; *U.S. Public*, pg. 440
RESTILE CERAMICS LIMITED; *Int'l*, pg. 6304
RESTO BELLE EPINE SNC—See Eurazeo SE; *Int'l*, pg. 2529
RESTOCKIT.COM; *U.S. Private*, pg. 3409
RESTO CLERMONT-FERRAND SNC—See Eurazeo SE; *Int'l*, pg. 2529
RESTO LES HALLES SNC—See Eurazeo SE; *Int'l*, pg. 2529
RESTO L'ISLE ADAM SNC—See Eurazeo SE; *Int'l*, pg. 2529
RESTO MAREUIL SNC—See Eurazeo SE; *Int'l*, pg. 2529
RESTO MONTLHERY SNC—See Eurazeo SE; *Int'l*, pg. 2529
RESTON ASSOCIATION; *U.S. Private*, pg. 3409

RESTON HOSPITAL CENTER—See HCA Healthcare, Inc.; *U.S. Public*, pg. 1007
RESTONIC MATTRESS CORPORATION - RESTONIC BRITISH COLUMBIA FACTORY—See Restonic Mattress Corporation; *U.S. Private*, pg. 3409
RESTONIC MATTRESS CORPORATION - RESTONIC CARIBBEAN FACTORY—See Restonic Mattress Corporation; *U.S. Private*, pg. 3409
RESTONIC MATTRESS CORPORATION - RESTONIC DOMINICAN REPUBLIC FACTORY—See Restonic Mattress Corporation; *U.S. Private*, pg. 3409
RESTONIC MATTRESS CORPORATION - RESTONIC ECUADOR FACTORY—See Restonic Mattress Corporation; *U.S. Private*, pg. 3409
RESTONIC MATTRESS CORPORATION - RESTONIC MIDDLE EAST FACTORY—See Restonic Mattress Corporation; *U.S. Private*, pg. 3409
RESTONIC MATTRESS CORPORATION - RESTONIC OF INDIA FACTORY—See Restonic Mattress Corporation; *U.S. Private*, pg. 3409
RESTONIC MATTRESS CORPORATION - RESTONIC OF KOREA FACTORY—See Restonic Mattress Corporation; *U.S. Private*, pg. 3409
RESTONIC MATTRESS CORPORATION - RESTONIC QUEBEC FACTORY—See Restonic Mattress Corporation; *U.S. Private*, pg. 3409
RESTONIC MATTRESS CORPORATION; *U.S. Private*, pg. 3409
RESTON LIMOUSINE & TRAVEL SERVICE, INC.; *U.S. Private*, pg. 3409
RESTON SURGERY CENTER, L.P.—See HCA Healthcare, Inc.; *U.S. Public*, pg. 1007
RESTON SURGERY CENTER—See HCA Healthcare, Inc.; *U.S. Public*, pg. 1007
RESTO PESSAC SNC—See Eurazeo SE; *Int'l*, pg. 2529
RESTOQUE COMERCIO E CONFECCOES DE ROUPAS S.A.; *Int'l*, pg. 6304
RESTOR3D, INC.; *U.S. Private*, pg. 3409
RESTORAMA AG—See Compass Group PLC; *Int'l*, pg. 1750
RESTORAN PETROKEMIJA D.O.O.—See PETROKEMIJA d.d.; *Int'l*, pg. 5826
RESTORATION BUILDERS INC.; *U.S. Private*, pg. 3409
RESTORATION BUILDERS INC.; *U.S. Private*, pg. 3409
RESTORATION CLEANERS, LLC; *U.S. Private*, pg. 3410
RESTORATION DESIGN LLC—See NRG Energy, Inc.; *U.S. Public*, pg. 1551
RESTORATION HARDWARE CANADA, INC.—See RH; *U.S. Public*, pg. 1796
RESTORATION HARDWARE, INC.—See RH; *U.S. Public*, pg. 1796
RESTORATION INDUSTRIES, INC.; *U.S. Private*, pg. 3410
RESTORATION MEDIA; *U.S. Private*, pg. 3410
RESTORATION + RECOVERY SERVICES, LLC—See DFW Capital Partners; *U.S. Private*, pg. 1221
RESTORATIVE CARE OF AMERICA, INC.—See Restorative Care of America; *U.S. Private*, pg. 3410
RESTORATIVE CARE OF AMERICA; *U.S. Private*, pg. 3410
RESTORE DATASHRED LIMITED—See Restore plc; *Int'l*, pg. 6304
RESTORED DIGITAL SOLUTIONS, LLC; *U.S. Private*, pg. 3410
RESTORE DIGITAL LIMITED—See Restore plc; *Int'l*, pg. 6304
RESTORE FORCE INC.—See FOODFEST INTERNATIONAL 2000 INC.; *U.S. Public*, pg. 863
RESTORE INCORPORATED; *U.S. Private*, pg. 3410
RESTORE LTD—See Restore plc; *Int'l*, pg. 6304
RESTORE NEIGHBORHOODS LA, INC.; *U.S. Private*, pg. 3410
RESTORE ONE; *U.S. Private*, pg. 3410
RESTORE PLC; *Int'l*, pg. 6304
RESTORE REHAB SERVICES, LLC; *U.S. Private*, pg. 3410
RESTORE SCAN LIMITED—See Restore plc; *Int'l*, pg. 6304
RESTORE TECHNOLOGY LIMITED—See Restore plc; *Int'l*, pg. 6304
RESTORIA; *Int'l*, pg. 6305
RESTORIXHEALTH LLC—See Sverica Capital Management LP; *U.S. Private*, pg. 3888
RESTO ROSNY SNC—See Eurazeo SE; *Int'l*, pg. 2529
RESTORX OF TEXAS, LTD.—See Interstate Restoration Group, Inc.; *U.S. Private*, pg. 2126
RESTO SAINT-GERMAIN SNC—See Eurazeo SE; *Int'l*, pg. 2529
RESTO TOURS SNC—See Eurazeo SE; *Int'l*, pg. 2529
RESTO TRAPPES SNC—See Eurazeo SE; *Int'l*, pg. 2529
RESTO VELIZY SNC—See Eurazeo SE; *Int'l*, pg. 2529
RESTO VILLIERS SNC—See Eurazeo SE; *Int'l*, pg. 2529
RESTO WASQUEHAL SNC—See Eurazeo SE; *Int'l*, pg. 2529
RESTPLATZBORSE GES.M.B.H.—See EQT AB; *Int'l*, pg. 2478
RESTRONICS CO., INC—See Fuji Corporation; *Int'l*, pg. 2810
RESTRUCTURE INC.; *U.S. Private*, pg. 3410

COMPANY NAME INDEX

RESTRUCTURE PETRO MARKETING SERVICES—See Restructure Inc.; *U.S. Private*, pg. 3410
RESTU S.R.O.—See Metro AG; *Int'l*, pg. 4859
RESUL, EQUIPAMENTOS DE ENERGIA S.A.; *Int'l*, pg. 6305
RESUL, EQUIPAMENTOS DE ENERGIA S.A.; *Int'l*, pg. 6305
RESUL, EQUIPAMENTOS DE ENERGIA SA; *Int'l*, pg. 6305
RESULTANT, LLC—See Investcorp Holdings B.S.C.; *Int'l*, pg. 3776
THE RESULTS COMPANIES LLC—See OEP Capital Advisors, L.P.; *U.S. Private*, pg. 3000
RESULTSCX; *U.S. Private*, pg. 3410
RESULTS DIRECT MARKETING; *U.S. Private*, pg. 3410
RESULTS GENERATION; *U.S. Private*, pg. 3410
RESULTS SOFTWARE LLC—See Thomas H. Lee Partners, L.P.; *U.S. Private*, pg. 4155
RESULTS TECHNOLOGY; *U.S. Private*, pg. 3410
RESURGENCE FINANCIAL, LLC; *U.S. Private*, pg. 3410
RESURGENS EAST SURGERY CENTER, LLC—See Tenet Healthcare Corporation; *U.S. Public*, pg. 2006
RESURGENS FAYETTE SURGERY CENTER, LLC—See Tenet Healthcare Corporation; *U.S. Public*, pg. 2006
RESURGENS SPECIALTY UNDERWRITING, INC.—See Berkshire Hathaway Inc.; *U.S. Public*, pg. 299
RESURGENS SURGERY CENTER, LLC—See Tenet Healthcare Corporation; *U.S. Public*, pg. 2012
RESURGENS TECHNOLOGY PARTNERS, LLC; *U.S. Private*, pg. 3410
RESURGENT CAPITAL SERVICES, LP—See Sherman Financial Group LLC; *U.S. Private*, pg. 3634
RESURGERE MINES & MINERALS INDIA LIMITED; *Int'l*, pg. 6305
RESURS HOLDING AB; *Int'l*, pg. 6305
RE SUSTAINABILITY INTERNATIONAL (SINGAPORE) PTE. LTD.—See KKR & Co. Inc.; *U.S. Public*, pg. 1263
RE SUSTAINABILITY LIMITED—See KKR & Co. Inc.; *U.S. Public*, pg. 1263
RESVERLOGIX CORP.; *Int'l*, pg. 6305
RESVERLOGIX INC.—See Resverlogix Corp.; *Int'l*, pg. 6305
R.E. SWEENEY COMPANY INC.; *U.S. Private*, pg. 3335
RESY NETWORK, INC.—See American Express Company; *U.S. Public*, pg. 101
RETAIL 161 LIMITED—See Hallenstein Glasson Holdings Limited; *Int'l*, pg. 3230
RETAIL BUSINESS DEVELOPMENT, INC.; *U.S. Private*, pg. 3411
RETAIL BUSINESS SERVICES LLC—See Koninklijke Ahold Delhaize N.V.; *Int'l*, pg. 4260
THE RETAIL BUS TOUR, INC.; *U.S. Private*, pg. 4105
RETAIL CLOUD TECHNOLOGIES, LLC; *U.S. Private*, pg. 3411
RETAILCO, LLC—See TxEx Energy Investments, LLC; *U.S. Private*, pg. 4267
RETAIL CONCEPTS, INC.; *U.S. Private*, pg. 3411
RETAIL CONSTRUCTION SERVICES; *U.S. Private*, pg. 3411
RETAIL CREDIT PROPERTY TRUST, INC.—See AR Global Investments, LLC; *U.S. Private*, pg. 306
RETAIL DATA, LLC—See Markel Group Inc.; *U.S. Public*, pg. 1369
RETAIL ENGINEERING LTD.; *Int'l*, pg. 6305
THE RETAIL EQUATION INC.—See Appriss Holdings, Inc.; *U.S. Private*, pg. 300
RETAILER SHAKTI SUPPLY CHAIN PRIVATE LIMITED—See Sastasundar Ventures Limited; *Int'l*, pg. 6584
RETAILERS & MANUFACTURERS DISTRIBUTION MARKETING SERVICES INC.; *U.S. Private*, pg. 3411
RETAILERS SUPPLY CO INC.—See American Securities LLC; *U.S. Private*, pg. 247
RETAIL ESTATES N.V.; *Int'l*, pg. 6305
RETAIL FINANCIAL SERVICES—See New Heritage Capital LLC; *U.S. Private*, pg. 2897
RETAIL FIXTURE, LLC; *U.S. Private*, pg. 3411
RETAIL FOOD GROUP LIMITED; *Int'l*, pg. 6305
RETAIL HOLDINGS N.V.; *Int'l*, pg. 6305
RETAIL INDUSTRY LEADERS ASSOCIATION; *U.S. Private*, pg. 3411
RETAIL INFORMATION SYSTEMS, INC.; *U.S. Private*, pg. 3411
RETAIL IN MOTION LIMITED—See Deutsche Lufthansa AG; *Int'l*, pg. 2070
RETAIL IN MOTION MEXICO S. DE R.L. DE C.V.—See Deutsche Lufthansa AG; *Int'l*, pg. 2070
RETAIL INSIGHT LIMITED—See Navis Capital Partners Limited; *Int'l*, pg. 5176
RETAIL INVESTORS OF TEXAS, LTD.; *U.S. Private*, pg. 3411
RETAIL INVEST, S.L.—See Minor International PCL; *Int'l*, pg. 4913
RETAIL MAINTENANCE, INC.; *U.S. Private*, pg. 3411
RETAIL MEDIA GMBH—See Stroer SE & Co. KGaA; *Int'l*, pg. 7242
RETAIL MEETUP, LLC—See Providence Equity Partners L.L.C.; *U.S. Private*, pg. 3293

RETAIL MEETUP, LLC—See Searchlight Capital Partners, L.P.; *U.S. Private*, pg. 3588
RETAILMENOT, FRANCE, SAS—See MacAndrews & Forbes Incorporated; *U.S. Private*, pg. 2532
RETAILMENOT, INC.—See MacAndrews & Forbes Incorporated; *U.S. Private*, pg. 2532
RETAILMENOT UK LTD.—See MacAndrews & Forbes Incorporated; *U.S. Private*, pg. 2532
RETAIL NETWORK BV—See CVC Capital Partners SICAV-FIS S.A.; *Int'l*, pg. 1886
RETAIL NETWORKS CO. LTD.—See Oriental Land Co., Ltd.; *Int'l*, pg. 5626
RETAILNEXT, INC.; *U.S. Private*, pg. 3411
RETAILNEXT RP UK LTD.—See RetailNext, Inc.; *U.S. Private*, pg. 3411
RETAIL OPPORTUNITY INVESTMENTS CORP.; *U.S. Public*, pg. 1792
RETAIL OPPORTUNITY INVESTMENTS PARTNERSHIP, LP—See RETAIL OPPORTUNITY INVESTMENTS CORP.; *U.S. Public*, pg. 1792
RETAILORS LTD.; *Int'l*, pg. 6306
THE RETAIL OUTSOURCE; *U.S. Private*, pg. 4105
RETAIL PARTNERS COLRUYT GROUP NV—See Colruyt Group N.V.; *Int'l*, pg. 1705
RETAIL PARTNERS CO., LTD.; *Int'l*, pg. 6306
RETAIL PROFILE GMBH—See SpaceandPeople plc; *Int'l*, pg. 7123
RETAIL PRO INTERNATIONAL, LLC—See Nayax Ltd.; *Int'l*, pg. 5178
RETAIL PROPERTIES OF AMERICA, INC.—See Kite Realty Group Trust; *U.S. Public*, pg. 1236
RETAIL RADIO; *U.S. Private*, pg. 3411
RETAIL READY FOODS INC; *Int'l*, pg. 6306
RETAIL SALES, LLC—See NE Media Group, Inc.; *U.S. Private*, pg. 2877
RETAIL S.A.—See Cencosud S.A.; *Int'l*, pg. 1401
RETAIL SECURITY SERVICES, INC.; *U.S. Private*, pg. 3411
RETAIL SERVICE GROEP B.V.—See Sligro Food Group N.V.; *Int'l*, pg. 6997
RETAIL SOLUTIONS, INC.—See Hellman & Friedman LLC; *U.S. Private*, pg. 1910
RETAIL STORE OPERATIONS, INC.—See Bath & Body Works, Inc.; *U.S. Public*, pg. 279
RETAIL THERAPY LLC; *U.S. Private*, pg. 3411
RETAIL VALUE INC.; *U.S. Public*, pg. 1792
RETAIL VENTURES SERVICES, INC.—See Schottenstein Stores Corporation; *U.S. Private*, pg. 3569
RETAINING (UK) LIMITED—See SigmaRoc Plc; *Int'l*, pg. 6909
RETALIGENT SOLUTIONS, INC.—See Mi9 Retail, Inc.; *U.S. Private*, pg. 2696
RETALIX LTD.—See NCR Voyix Corporation.; *U.S. Public*, pg. 1502
RETEC DIGITAL PLC; *Int'l*, pg. 6306
RETECH TECHNOLOGY CO., LIMITED; *Int'l*, pg. 6306
RETE FERROVIARIA ITALIANA - RFI S.P.A.—See Ferrovie dello Stato Italiane S.p.A.; *Int'l*, pg. 2645
RETE GAS FIDENZA S.R.L.—See Gas Plus S.p.A.; *Int'l*, pg. 2887
RETELA CREA SECURITIES CO., LTD.—See Daiwa Securities Group Inc.; *Int'l*, pg. 1949
RETELE COMPANY; *U.S. Private*, pg. 3411
RETELIT S.P.A.; *Int'l*, pg. 6306
RETE RINNOVABILE S.R.L.—See Terra Firma Capital Partners Ltd.; *Int'l*, pg. 7566
RETERRA CO., LTD.—See F-Tech Inc.; *Int'l*, pg. 2595
RETE S.R.L.—See Terna S.p.A. - Rete Elettrica Nazionale; *Int'l*, pg. 7566
RETEVISION MOVIL, S.A.—See Orange S.A.; *Int'l*, pg. 5610
RETEZAT SA; *Int'l*, pg. 6306
THE RETHINK GROUP LIMITED; *Int'l*, pg. 7678
RE:THINK GROUP; *U.S. Private*, pg. 3365
RETHINK MEA FZCO—See The Rethink Group Limited; *Int'l*, pg. 7678
RETHINK RECRUITMENT SOLUTIONS LTD—See The Rethink Group Limited; *Int'l*, pg. 7678
RETHINK ROBOTICS, INC.; *U.S. Private*, pg. 3411
RETHMANN AG & CO. KG; *Int'l*, pg. 6306
RETIF OIL & FUEL, LLC; *U.S. Private*, pg. 3412
RETINA ASSOCIATES OF NEW JERSEY, P.A.—See Quad-C Management, Inc.; *U.S. Private*, pg. 3315
RETINA CONSULTANTS OF SOUTHWEST FLORIDA, INC.; *U.S. Private*, pg. 3412
RETINA CONSULTANTS OF WNY—See Ophthalmic Consultants of Long Island; *U.S. Private*, pg. 3032
RETINA HEALTH CENTER; *U.S. Private*, pg. 3412
RETINALGENIX TECHNOLOGIES INC.—See Sanovas, Inc.; *U.S. Private*, pg. 3546
RETINA PAINTS LIMITED; *Int'l*, pg. 6310
RETIREINVEST PTY LIMITED—See ING Groep N.V.; *Int'l*, pg. 3699
RETIREMENT ADVISORY GROUP—See TA Associates, Inc.; *U.S. Private*, pg. 3919
RETIREMENT COMMUNITY SPECIALISTS, INC.; *U.S. Private*, pg. 3412
RETIREMENT INVESTMENT ADVISORS, INC.—See Aon plc; *Int'l*, pg. 497

RETTEW ASSOCIATES INC.

RETIREMENT LIVING, INC.; *U.S. Private*, pg. 3412
RETIREMENT, LLC - SERIES TWO, OPERATIONS OFFICE—See Retirement, LLC - Series Two; *U.S. Private*, pg. 3412
RETIREMENT, LLC - SERIES TWO; *U.S. Private*, pg. 3412
RETIREMENT PLAN SERVICES, LLC—See NBT Bancorp Inc.; *U.S. Public*, pg. 1501
RETIREMENT STRATEGIES, INC.—See TA Associates, Inc.; *U.S. Private*, pg. 3919
THE RETIREMENT SYSTEMS OF ALABAMA; *U.S. Private*, pg. 4105
RETIRO BAIXO ENERGETICA S.A.—See Centrais Eletricas Brasileiras S.A.; *Int'l*, pg. 1403
RETI S.P.A.; *Int'l*, pg. 6310
RETO ECO-SOLUTIONS, INC.; *Int'l*, pg. 6310
RETORTE GMBH—See Aurubis AG; *Int'l*, pg. 715
RETOTUB S.A.S.; *Int'l*, pg. 6310
RET PARTICIPACOES S.A.—See Citigroup Inc.; *U.S. Public*, pg. 504
RETRACTABLE TECHNOLOGIES, INC.; *U.S. Public*, pg. 1792
RETRA ENGINEERING (THAILAND) CO., LTD.—See Maruka Furusato Corporation; *Int'l*, pg. 4714
RETRAGAS SRL—See A2A S.p.A.; *Int'l*, pg. 29
RETRA HOLDINGS LIMITED—See Warpaint London PLC; *Int'l*, pg. 8346
RETRAOIL, S.L.—See ACS, Actividades de Construccion y Servicios, S.A.; *Int'l*, pg. 116
THE RETREAT AT RIDGEGATE, LLC—See Century Communities, Inc.; *U.S. Public*, pg. 475
RETREAT CAPITAL MANAGEMENT, INC.—See Quess Corp Limited; *Int'l*, pg. 6160
RETREAT DOCTORS' HOSPITAL—See HCA Healthcare, Inc.; *U.S. Public*, pg. 997
RETREAT INTERNAL MEDICINE, LLC—See HCA Healthcare, Inc.; *U.S. Public*, pg. 1007
RETRIEVE MEDICAL HOLDINGS, INC.; *U.S. Public*, pg. 1792
RETRIEVER LIMITED—See Karooooo Ltd.; *Int'l*, pg. 4085
RETRIEVER MEDICAL/DENTAL PAYMENTS, LLC; *U.S. Private*, pg. 3412
RETRIEV TECHNOLOGIES, INC.—See Heritage Group; *U.S. Private*, pg. 1923
RETRO ELEVATOR CORP.; *U.S. Private*, pg. 3412
RETROFICIENCY, INC.—See ENGIE SA; *Int'l*, pg. 2431
RETRO GREEN REVOLUTION LIMITED; *Int'l*, pg. 6310
RETRONIC SDN. BHD.—See M2I Corporation; *Int'l*, pg. 4617
RETRONIX GLOBAL INC.—See Jabil Inc.; *U.S. Public*, pg. 1182
RETRONIX LTD.—See Jabil Inc.; *U.S. Public*, pg. 1182
RE-TRON TECHNOLOGIES—See WaveTech Global, Inc.; *U.S. Private*, pg. 4458
RETROSCREEN VIROLOGY LIMITED—See Open Orphan plc; *Int'l*, pg. 5596
RETROSENSE THERAPEUTICS, LLC—See AbbVie Inc.; *U.S. Public*, pg. 23
RETROSPECT, INC.—See StorCentric, Inc.; *U.S. Private*, pg. 3831
RETRO STUDIOS, INC.—See Nintendo Co., Ltd.; *Int'l*, pg. 5308
RETROTEC, INC.—See Wohler Technik GmbH; *Int'l*, pg. 8442
RETSCH FRANCE—See Verder International B.V.; *Int'l*, pg. 8167
RETSCH GMBH—See Verder International B.V.; *Int'l*, pg. 8167
RETSCH KOREA & CO. LTD.—See Verder International B.V.; *Int'l*, pg. 8167
RETSCH NORGE AS—See Verder International B.V.; *Int'l*, pg. 8167
RETSCH OSTERREICH VERDER GES.M.B.H.—See Verder International B.V.; *Int'l*, pg. 8167
RETS TIMBER OY LTD.—See Stora Enso Oyj; *Int'l*, pg. 7222
RETTENMAIER AUSTRIA GMBH & CO.KG—See J. Rettenmaier & Sohne GmbH & Co. KG; *Int'l*, pg. 3856
RETTENMAIER FRANCE SARL—See J. Rettenmaier & Sohne GmbH & Co. KG; *Int'l*, pg. 3856
RETTENMAIER IBERICA S.L. Y CIA. S. COM—See J. Rettenmaier & Sohne GmbH & Co. KG; *Int'l*, pg. 3856
RETTENMAIER INDIA PVT LTD.—See J. Rettenmaier & Sohne GmbH & Co. KG; *Int'l*, pg. 3856
RETTENMAIER ITALIA SRL & C. SAS—See J. Rettenmaier & Sohne GmbH & Co. KG; *Int'l*, pg. 3856
RETTENMAIER JAPAN CO., LTD.—See J. Rettenmaier & Sohne GmbH & Co. KG; *Int'l*, pg. 3856
RETTENMAIER MEXICANA S.A. DE C.V.—See J. Rettenmaier & Sohne GmbH & Co. KG; *Int'l*, pg. 3856
RETTENMAIER POLSKA SP. Z O.O.—See J. Rettenmaier & Sohne GmbH & Co. KG; *Int'l*, pg. 3856
RETTENMAIER (SHANGHAI) FIBER TRADING CO., LTD.—See J. Rettenmaier & Sohne GmbH & Co. KG; *Int'l*, pg. 3856
RETTENMAIER UK LTD.—See J. Rettenmaier & Sohne GmbH & Co. KG; *Int'l*, pg. 3857
RETTEW ASSOCIATES INC.; *U.S. Private*, pg. 3412

RETTIG AUSTRIA GMBH—See Rettig Group Ltd.; *Int'l*, pg. 6310
RETTIG BELGIUM N.V.—See Rettig Group Ltd.; *Int'l*, pg. 6310
RETTIG (CHINA) CO., LTD—See Rettig Group Ltd.; *Int'l*, pg. 6310
RETTIG GERMANY GMBH—See Rettig Group Ltd.; *Int'l*, pg. 6310
RETTIG GROUP CESKA S.R.O.—See Rettig Group Ltd.; *Int'l*, pg. 6310
RETTIG GROUP LTD.; *Int'l*, pg. 6310
RETTIG HEATING EQUIPMENT (JIANGSU) CO., LTD.—See Rettig Group Ltd.; *Int'l*, pg. 6310
RETTIG HEATING GROUP FRANCE SAS—See Rettig Group Ltd.; *Int'l*, pg. 6310
RETTIG HEATING SP.Z O.O.—See Rettig Group Ltd.; *Int'l*, pg. 6311
RETTIG HRVATSKA D.O.O.—See Rettig Group Ltd.; *Int'l*, pg. 6311
RETTIG HUNGARY KFT—See Rettig Group Ltd.; *Int'l*, pg. 6311
RETTIG ICC B.V.—See Rettig Group Ltd.; *Int'l*, pg. 6311
RETTIG INC.—See Rettig Group Ltd.; *Int'l*, pg. 6311
RETTIG IRELAND LIMITED—See Rettig Group Ltd.; *Int'l*, pg. 6311
RETTIG METAL TICARET VE SANAYI A.S.—See Rettig Group Ltd.; *Int'l*, pg. 6311
RETTIG SLOVENIJA D.O.O.—See Rettig Group Ltd.; *Int'l*, pg. 6311
RETTIG SRL.—See Rettig Group Ltd.; *Int'l*, pg. 6311
RETTIG SWEDEN AB—See Rettig Group Ltd.; *Int'l*, pg. 6311
RETTIG (UK) LTD—See Rettig Group Ltd.; *Int'l*, pg. 6310
RETTIG VARME AB—See Rettig Group Ltd.; *Int'l*, pg. 6311
RETTY, INC.; *Int'l*, pg. 6311
RETURNABLE SERVICES LLC—See Tomra Systems ASA; *Int'l*, pg. 7803
RETURN ON INNOVATION ADVISORS LTD.; *Int'l*, pg. 6311
RETURN PATH AUSTRALIA—See Silversmith Management, L.P.; *U.S. Private*, pg. 3664
RETURN PATH BRAZIL—See Silversmith Management, L.P.; *U.S. Private*, pg. 3664
RETURN PATH FRANCE—See Silversmith Management, L.P.; *U.S. Private*, pg. 3664
RETURN PATH GERMANY—See Silversmith Management, L.P.; *U.S. Private*, pg. 3664
RETURN PATH, INC.—See Silversmith Management, L.P.; *U.S. Private*, pg. 3664
RETURN PATH UK—See Silversmith Management, L.P.; *U.S. Private*, pg. 3664
RETURN POLYMERS, INC.—See The AZEK Company Inc.; *U.S. Public*, pg. 2035
RETVIEWS SA—See Lectra SA; *Int'l*, pg. 4438
RETZLAFF INCORPORATED; *U.S. Private*, pg. 3412
REUBEN BROTHERS LIMITED—See Reuben Brothers SA; *Int'l*, pg. 6311
REUBEN BROTHERS SA; *Int'l*, pg. 6311
REUDINK B.V.—See ForFarmers Group B.V; *Int'l*, pg. 2732
REUEL, INC.—See Hubbell Incorporated; *U.S. Public*, pg. 1067
REUKERS B.V.—See Heijmans N.V.; *Int'l*, pg. 3322
REUKERS B.V.—See Heijmans N.V.; *Int'l*, pg. 3323
REULAND ELECTRIC COMPANY - BRAKE DIVISION—See Reuland Electric Company; *U.S. Private*, pg. 3412
REULAND ELECTRIC COMPANY - ENGINEERING SERVICES DIVISION—See Reuland Electric Company; *U.S. Private*, pg. 3412
REULAND ELECTRIC COMPANY - FOUNDRY DIVISION—See Reuland Electric Company; *U.S. Private*, pg. 3412
REULAND ELECTRIC COMPANY; *U.S. Private*, pg. 3412
REU LIVING SDN. BHD.—See IGB Berhad; *Int'l*, pg. 3601
REUNERT LIMITED; *Int'l*, pg. 6311
REUNERT MANAGEMENT SERVICES LIMITED—See Reunert Limited; *Int'l*, pg. 6312
RE-UNION DIVISION—See Seattle Pacific Industries, Inc.; *U.S. Private*, pg. 3592
REUNION GOLD CORPORATION—See G Mining Ventures Corp.; *Int'l*, pg. 2861
REUNION HOSPITALITY TRUST, INC.; *U.S. Private*, pg. 3412
REUNION NEUROSCIENCE INC.; *Int'l*, pg. 6312
REUNION RECORDS—See Sony Group Corporation; *Int'l*, pg. 7103
REUNION TITLE, INC.; *U.S. Private*, pg. 3412
R. E. UPTEGRAFF MANUFACTURING CO.—See Shenda International Engineering Co. Ltd.; *Int'l*, pg. 6800
REUSCHEL & CO. KOMMANDITGESELLSCHAFT—See Commerzbank AG; *Int'l*, pg. 1718
REUSS MEATS INC.—See Ellenbee-Leggett Company Inc.; *U.S. Private*, pg. 1363
REUS S.R.O; *Int'l*, pg. 6312
REUSS-SEIFERT GMBH—See CRH plc; *Int'l*, pg. 1848
REUTECH COMMUNICATIONS (PTY) LIMITED—See Reunert Limited; *Int'l*, pg. 6312

REUTECH COMMUNICATIONS (PTY) LIMITED—See Reunert Limited; *Int'l*, pg. 6312
REUTECH LTD—See Reunert Limited; *Int'l*, pg. 6312
REUTECH RADAR SYSTEMS (PTY) LIMITED—See Reunert Limited; *Int'l*, pg. 6312
REUTECH SOLUTIONS (PTY) LIMITED—See Reunert Limited; *Int'l*, pg. 6312
REUTER EQUIPMENT COMPANY; *U.S. Private*, pg. 3412
REUTERS AMERICA INC—See Thomson Reuters Corporation; *Int'l*, pg. 7716
REUTERS AUSTRALIA PTY. LTD.—See Thomson Reuters Corporation; *Int'l*, pg. 7716
REUTERS HONG KONG LIMITED—See Thomson Reuters Corporation; *Int'l*, pg. 7716
REUTERS ITALIA SPA—See Thomson Reuters Corporation; *Int'l*, pg. 7716
REUTERS JAPAN LTD—See Thomson Reuters Corporation; *Int'l*, pg. 7716
REUTERS LIMITED—See Thomson Reuters Corporation; *Int'l*, pg. 7716
REUTERS RESEARCH—See Thomson Reuters Corporation; *Int'l*, pg. 7716
REUTERS SA—See Thomson Reuters Corporation; *Int'l*, pg. 7716
REUTERS SERVICES SARL—See Thomson Reuters Corporation; *Int'l*, pg. 7716
REUTERS SINGAPORE PTE LIMITED—See Thomson Reuters Corporation; *Int'l*, pg. 7716
REUTHER INVESTMENT CO. INC.; *U.S. Private*, pg. 3412
REUTHER JEEP CHRYSLER; *U.S. Private*, pg. 3412
REUTHER VERPACKUNG GMBH & CO. KG—See Sun Capital Partners, Inc.; *U.S. Private*, pg. 3862
THE REUTLINGER COMMUNITY FOR JEWISH LIVING; *U.S. Private*, pg. 4106
REV19, LLC; *U.S. Private*, pg. 3413
REV.1 ENGINEERING, INC.—See Asahi Intecc Co., Ltd.; *Int'l*, pg. 594
REVACOMM, INC—See Enlightenment Capital LLC; *U.S. Private*, pg. 1400
REVAI NYOMEDA—See Sun Capital Partners, Inc.; *U.S. Private*, pg. 3862
REVAL.COM, INC.—See ION Investment Group Ltd.; *Int'l*, pg. 3794
REVALEA S.P.A.—See Banca IFIS S.p.A.; *Int'l*, pg. 815
REVAL HOLDINGS, INC.; *U.S. Private*, pg. 3413
REVALIZE, INC.—See TA Associates, Inc.; *U.S. Private*, pg. 3918
REVALO SPA—See Covivio; *Int'l*, pg. 1821
RE VALUTA S.P.A.—See Tinexta S.p.A.; *Int'l*, pg. 7753
REV AMBULANCE GROUP ORLANDO, INC.—See AIP, LLC; *U.S. Private*, pg. 135
REVA MEDICAL, INC.; *U.S. Private*, pg. 3413
REVANCE THERAPEUTICS, INC.; *U.S. Public*, pg. 1792
REVA SA; *Int'l*, pg. 6312
REV-A-SHELF LLC—See Jones Plastic & Engineering Company, LLC; *U.S. Private*, pg. 2234
REVASUM, INC.; *U.S. Public*, pg. 1792
REVATI ORGANICS LTD.; *Int'l*, pg. 6312
REVATI S.A—See Shree Renuka Sugars Limited; *Int'l*, pg. 6864
REV CAR WASH, LLC—See WhiteWater Holding Company, LLC; *U.S. Private*, pg. 4512
REVCHAIN SOLUTIONS, LLC—See Windstream Holdings, Inc.; *U.S. Public*, pg. 2373
REVCO ELECTRICAL SUPPLY, INC.; *U.S. Private*, pg. 3413
REVCO INDUSTRIES, INC.—See Bunzl plc; *Int'l*, pg. 1219
REVCOM INC.; *U.S. Private*, pg. 3413
REVCON CONSTRUCTION CORP.; *U.S. Private*, pg. 3413
REVCOR, INC.; *U.S. Private*, pg. 3413
REVCO SOLUTIONS, INC.—See Longshore Capital Partners; *U.S. Private*, pg. 2493
REVEAL BIOSCIENCES, INC.—See Arsenal Capital Management LP; *U.S. Private*, pg. 337
REVEAL DATA CORPORATION—See K1 Investment Management, LLC; *U.S. Private*, pg. 2252
REVELATION BIOSCIENCES, INC.; *U.S. Public*, pg. 1792
REVELATION PHARMA CORPORATION LLC—See Osceola Capital Management, LLC; *U.S. Private*, pg. 3047
REVEL CONSULTING INC.—See ChrysCapital Investment Advisors (India) Private Limited; *U.S. Private*, pg. 1588
REVELL COMMUNICATIONS; *U.S. Private*, pg. 3413
REVELL GMBH—See Carrera Revell of Americas, Inc.; *U.S. Private*, pg. 771
REVELL, INC.—See Hobbico, Inc.; *U.S. Private*, pg. 1958
REVELO RESOURCES CORP.—See Austral Gold Limited; *Int'l*, pg. 719
REVELSTOKE CAPITAL PARTNERS LLC; *U.S. Private*, pg. 3413
REVELSTONE CAPITAL ACQUISITION CORP.; *U.S. Public*, pg. 1792
REVELS TRACTOR CO. INC.; *U.S. Private*, pg. 3413
REVEL SYSTEMS, INC.; *U.S. Private*, pg. 3413
REVELWOOD, INC.; *U.S. Private*, pg. 3413
REVENEER, INC.; *U.S. Private*, pg. 3413
REVENIO GROUP OYJ; *Int'l*, pg. 6312
REVENIO RESEARCH OY—See Revenio Group Oyj; *Int'l*, pg. 6312
REVENTURE GMBH—See WIIT SpA; *Int'l*, pg. 8408

REVENUEADS—See LeadVision Media, LLC; *U.S. Private*, pg. 2407
REVENUE.COM CORPORATION; *U.S. Private*, pg. 3414
REVENUE DISCOVERY SYSTEMS—See Guggenheim Partners, LLC; *U.S. Private*, pg. 1812
REVENUE ENTERPRISES LLC; *U.S. Private*, pg. 3413
REVENUE GROUP BHD; *Int'l*, pg. 6312
REVENUE HARVEST SDN—See Revenue Group Bhd; *Int'l*, pg. 6312
REVENUE MANAGEMENT SYSTEMS INC.—See Warburg Pincus LLC; *U.S. Private*, pg. 4439
REVENUE PROPERTIES (AMERICA) INC.—See Morguard Corporation; *Int'l*, pg. 5045
REVENUE—See mThink LLC; *U.S. Private*, pg. 2809
REVENUE WELL SYSTEMS, LLC—See Marlin Equity Partners, LLC; *U.S. Private*, pg. 2585
REVERA INCORPORATED—See Nova Ltd.; *Int'l*, pg. 5451
REVERA INC.—See Public Sector Pension Investment Board; *Int'l*, pg. 6096
REVERB-DBC—See Diccicco Battista Communications; *U.S. Private*, pg. 1225
REVERB, INC.—See Etsy, Inc.; *U.S. Public*, pg. 797
REVER CORPORATION—See Rever Holdings Corporation; *Int'l*, pg. 6313
REVERE COPPER PRODUCTS INC.; *U.S. Private*, pg. 3414
REVERE DATA, LLC—See FactSet Research Systems Inc.; *U.S. Public*, pg. 820
REVERE ELECTRIC SUPPLY COMPANY; *U.S. Private*, pg. 3414
REVERE GAS, INC.—See Quarles Petroleum Incorporated; *U.S. Private*, pg. 3324
THE REVERE GROUP, LTD.—See Nippon Telegraph & Telephone Corporation; *Int'l*, pg. 5348
REVERE INDUSTRIES, LLC; *U.S. Private*, pg. 3414
REVEREIT LLC; *U.S. Private*, pg. 3414
REVERE MILLS INTERNATIONAL GROUP; *U.S. Private*, pg. 3414
REVERENCE ACQUISITION CORP.; *U.S. Public*, pg. 1793
REVERENCE CAPITAL PARTNERS LLC; *U.S. Private*, pg. 3414
REVERE PACKAGING; *U.S. Private*, pg. 3414
REVERE PLASTICS SYSTEMS, LLC - POPLAR BLUFF—See Ardian SAS; *Int'l*, pg. 554
REVERE PLASTICS SYSTEMS, LLC—See Ardian SAS; *Int'l*, pg. 554
REVERE PRODUCTS—See Pioneer Manufacturing Company; *U.S. Private*, pg. 3187
REVER HOLDINGS CORPORATION; *Int'l*, pg. 6313
REVER OFFSHORE UK LIMITED—See HAL Trust N.V.; *Int'l*, pg. 3226
REVERSE CORP LIMITED; *Int'l*, pg. 6313
REVERSE LOGISTICS GMBH—See Monitor Clipper Partners, LLC; *U.S. Private*, pg. 2771
REVERSE MORTGAGE INVESTMENT TRUST INC.; *U.S. Private*, pg. 3416
REVERSE MORTGAGE SOLUTIONS, INC.—See Onity Group Inc.; *U.S. Public*, pg. 1605
REVERSO PUMPS, INC.—See Crawford United Corporation; *U.S. Public*, pg. 592
REVERTECH SOLUTIONS—See Leading Ridge Management, LLC; *U.S. Private*, pg. 2406
REVERTEX (MALAYSIA) SDN. BHD.—See Synthomer plc; *Int'l*, pg. 7387
REVERT RISK MANAGEMENT SOLUTIONS (PTY) LTD.—See CSG Holdings Limited; *Int'l*, pg. 1864
REV ES TARSAI NEMESACEL KERESKEDELMI KFT.—See Jacquet Metal Service SA; *Int'l*, pg. 3867
REVESTIMIENTOS ESPECIALES DE MEXICO S DE RL DE CV—See ZF Friedrichshafen AG; *Int'l*, pg. 8645
REVESTIMIENTOS PORCELANITE LAMOSA, S.A. DE C.V.—See Grupo Lamosa S.A. de C.V.; *Int'l*, pg. 3132
REVETT SILVER COMPANY—See Hecla Mining Company; *U.S. Public*, pg. 1019
REVGEN PARTNERS, INC.; *U.S. Private*, pg. 3416
REV GROUP, INC.—See AIP, LLC; *U.S. Public*, pg. 134
REVIEW AUSTRALIA PTY. LTD.—See Queens Lane Capital Pty Ltd; *Int'l*, pg. 6159
REVIEWPRO ASIA PACIFIC PTE LTD—See Beijing Shiji Information Technology Co., Ltd.; *Int'l*, pg. 956
REVIEWPRO, INC—See Beijing Shiji Information Technology Co., Ltd.; *Int'l*, pg. 956
REVIEW PUBLISHING COMPANY LIMITED—See News Corporation; *U.S. Public*, pg. 1518
REVIEW RANK S.A.—See Beijing Shiji Information Technology Co., Ltd.; *Int'l*, pg. 956
REVILLE TIRE CO.; *U.S. Private*, pg. 3416
REVIMA GROUP SAS—See Ardian SAS; *Int'l*, pg. 556
REVIMA SASU—See Ardian SAS; *Int'l*, pg. 556
REVIMPORT; *Int'l*, pg. 6313
REVINT SOLUTIONS—See New Mountain Capital, LLC; *U.S. Private*, pg. 2904
REV.IO, LLC; *U.S. Private*, pg. 3413
REVIORA, LLC; *U.S. Private*, pg. 3416
REVIOS SWEDEN REINSURANCE COMPANY—See SCOR SE; *Int'l*, pg. 6650
REVISIONES TECNICAS APPLUS DEL ECUADOR APPLUSITEUVE, S.A.—See I Squared Capital Advisors (US) LLC; *U.S. Private*, pg. 2023

COMPANY NAME INDEX — REX MOORE ELECTRICAL CONTRACTORS & ENGINEERS

REVISIONES TECNICAS APPLUS DEL ECUADOR APPLUSITEUVE, S.A.—See TDR Capital LLP; *Int'l*, pg. 7492
REVISION MILITARY LTD.—See ASGARD Partners & Co., LLC; *U.S. Private*, pg. 349
REVISION MILITARY LTD.—See Merit Capital Partners; *U.S. Private*, pg. 2674
REVISION; *U.S. Private*, pg. 3416
REVISIOS B.V.—See Kuros Biosciences AG; *Int'l*, pg. 4342
REVISTAS DEPORTIVAS S.A.—See AT&T Inc.; *U.S. Public*, pg. 220
REVITALISED LIMITED—See MAXIMUS, Inc.; *U.S. Public*, pg. 1402
REVITALIZATION PARTNERS, LLC—See Formula Brewing, LLC; *U.S. Private*, pg. 1572
REVITALIZE CAPITAL; *U.S. Private*, pg. 3416
REVITAL PROPERTY DEVELOPMENT INCORPORATED—See Warimpex Finanz- und Beteiligungs AG; *Int'l*, pg. 8345
REVITI LIMITED—See Philip Morris International Inc.; *U.S. Public*, pg. 1687
REV IT LOGISTICS LLC; *U.S. Private*, pg. 3412
REVITRANS, A.S.—See CEZ, a.s.; *Int'l*, pg. 1428
REVITUP ENTERPRISES LLC; *U.S. Private*, pg. 3416
REVIV3 PROCARE COMPANY; *U.S. Public*, pg. 1793
REVIVA INC.; *U.S. Private*, pg. 3416
REVIVA LABS, INC.—See SenDayCo, LLC; *U.S. Private*, pg. 3605
REVIVAL EVENT VENUE INC.—See Live Nation Entertainment, Inc.; *U.S. Public*, pg. 1330
REVIVAL EXPANSION SA—See Galloo n.v.; *Int'l*, pg. 2875
REVIVAL GOLD INC.; *Int'l*, pg. 6313
REVIVAL S.A.S.—See Derichebourg S.A.; *Int'l*, pg. 2041
REVIVA PHARMACEUTICALS HOLDINGS, INC.; *U.S. Public*, pg. 1793
REVIVE THERAPEUTICS LTD.; *Int'l*, pg. 6313
REVIVICOR, INC.—See United Therapeutics Corporation; *U.S. Public*, pg. 2238
REVLOCAL, LLC—See H.I.G. Capital, LLC; *U.S. Private*, pg. 1834
REVLON AUSTRALIA PTY LIMITED—See MacAndrews & Forbes Incorporated; *U.S. Private*, pg. 2533
REVLON CANADA INC.—See MacAndrews & Forbes Incorporated; *U.S. Private*, pg. 2533
REVLON CONSUMER PRODUCTS CORPORATION—See MacAndrews & Forbes Incorporated; *U.S. Private*, pg. 2533
REVLON DEVELOPMENT CORP.—See MacAndrews & Forbes Incorporated; *U.S. Private*, pg. 2533
REVLON GOVERNMENT SALES, INC.—See MacAndrews & Forbes Incorporated; *U.S. Private*, pg. 2533
REVLON GROUP LIMITED—See MacAndrews & Forbes Incorporated; *U.S. Private*, pg. 2533
REVLON, INC.—See MacAndrews & Forbes Incorporated; *U.S. Private*, pg. 2532
REVLON INTERNATIONAL CORPORATION—See MacAndrews & Forbes Incorporated; *U.S. Private*, pg. 2533
REVLON MANUFACTURING LTD.—See MacAndrews & Forbes Incorporated; *U.S. Private*, pg. 2533
REVLON NEW ZEALAND LIMITED—See MacAndrews & Forbes Incorporated; *U.S. Private*, pg. 2533
REVLON (PUERTO RICO), INC.—See MacAndrews & Forbes Incorporated; *U.S. Private*, pg. 2533
REVLON REAL ESTATE CORPORATION—See MacAndrews & Forbes Incorporated; *U.S. Private*, pg. 2533
REVLON, S.A. DE C.V.—See MacAndrews & Forbes Incorporated; *U.S. Private*, pg. 2533
REVLON, S.A.—See MacAndrews & Forbes Incorporated; *U.S. Private*, pg. 2533
REVLON SOUTH AFRICA (PROPRIETARY) LIMITED—See MacAndrews & Forbes Incorporated; *U.S. Private*, pg. 2533
REVLON S.P.A.—See MacAndrews & Forbes Incorporated; *U.S. Private*, pg. 2533
REVLON (SUISSE) S.A.—See MacAndrews & Forbes Incorporated; *U.S. Private*, pg. 2533
REV MEDIA GROUP SDN. BHD.—See Media Prima Berhad; *Int'l*, pg. 4771
REVNOST A.D.; *Int'l*, pg. 6313
REVO BIOLOGICS, INC.—See LFB S.A.; *Int'l*, pg. 4473
REVOCOAT FRANCE SAS—See PPG Industries, Inc.; *U.S. Public*, pg. 1710
REVOCOAT IBERICA SL—See PPG Industries, Inc.; *U.S. Public*, pg. 1710
REVOCOM LTD.; *Int'l*, pg. 6313
REVOIL S.A.; *Int'l*, pg. 6313
REVO INSURANCE S.P.A.; *Int'l*, pg. 6313
REVOLENT CAPITAL SOLUTIONS; *U.S. Private*, pg. 3416
REVOLUFIN INC.—See RevoluGROUP Canada, Inc.; *Int'l*, pg. 6313
REVOLUGROUP CANADA INC.; *Int'l*, pg. 6313
REVOLUGROUP CANADA, INC.; *Int'l*, pg. 6313
REVOLUPAY EP S.L.—See RevoluGROUP Canada Inc.; *Int'l*, pg. 6313
REVOLUPAY S.L.—See RevoluGROUP Canada, Inc.; *Int'l*, pg. 6313

REVOLUTIONARY CONCEPTS, INC.; *U.S. Private*, pg. 3417
REVOLUTION BARS GROUP PLC; *Int'l*, pg. 6313
REVOLUTION BEAUTY GROUP PLC; *Int'l*, pg. 6313
REVOLUTION CAPITAL GROUP, LLC; *U.S. Private*, pg. 3416
REVOLUTION CO., LTD.; *Int'l*, pg. 6313
REVOLUTION DANCEWEAR LLC—See Audax Group, Limited Partnership; *U.S. Private*, pg. 389
REVOLUTION ENVIRONMENTAL SOLUTIONS ACQUISITION GP INC.—See Birch Hill Equity Partners Management Inc.; *Int'l*, pg. 1046
REVOLUTION FOODS, INC.; *U.S. Private*, pg. 3416
REVOLUTION HEALTHCARE ACQUISITION CORP.; *U.S. Public*, pg. 1793
REVOLUTION II WI HOLDING COMPANY, LLC—See Mountain Capital Partners, LP; *U.S. Private*, pg. 2799
REVOLUTION LIGHTING TECHNOLOGIES, INC.; *U.S. Public*, pg. 1793
REVOLUTION, LLC; *U.S. Private*, pg. 3416
REVOLUTION MANUFACTURING, LLC; *U.S. Private*, pg. 3416
REVOLUTION MEDICINES, INC.; *U.S. Public*, pg. 1793
REVOLUTION MONEY INC.—See American Express Company; *U.S. Public*, pg. 102
REVOLUTION PARTNERS, LLC—See Regions Financial Corporation; *U.S. Public*, pg. 1776
REVOLUTION PREP, LLC; *U.S. Private*, pg. 3416
REVOLUTION PUBLIC RELATIONS; *U.S. Private*, pg. 3416
REVOLUTION RETAIL SYSTEMS, LLC—See GLORY Ltd.; *Int'l*, pg. 3010
REVOLUTIONS MEDICAL CORPORATION; *U.S. Private*, pg. 3417
REVOLUTION; *U.S. Private*, pg. 3416
REVOLUTION STUDIOS—See Content Partners LLC; *U.S. Private*, pg. 1027
REVOLUTION SUSTAINABLE SOLUTIONS, LLC—See Arsenal Capital Management LP; *U.S. Private*, pg. 339
REVOLUTION TECHNOLOGIES, LLC; *U.S. Private*, pg. 3416
REVOLUVIP INTERNATIONAL INC.—See RevoluGROUP Canada, Inc.; *Int'l*, pg. 6313
REVOLVE GROUP, INC.; *U.S. Public*, pg. 1793
REVOLVER BREWING, LLC—See Tilray Brands, Inc.; *Int'l*, pg. 7748
REVOLVE RENEWABLE POWER CORP.; *Int'l*, pg. 6314
REVOLVE TECHNOLOGIES LIMITED; *Int'l*, pg. 6314
REVONA PROPERTIES; *U.S. Private*, pg. 3417
REVOZ—See Renault S.A.; *Int'l*, pg. 6274
REV RECREATION GROUP, INC.—See AIP, LLC; *U.S. Private*, pg. 135
REV RENEWABLES, INC.; *U.S. Private*, pg. 3412
REV SOLUTIONS INC.—See GXO Logistics, Inc.; *U.S. Public*, pg. 975
REVSPRING, INC. - OAKS—See GTCR LLC; *U.S. Private*, pg. 1806
REVSPRING, INC. - PHOENIX—See GTCR LLC; *U.S. Private*, pg. 1806
REVSPRING, INC.—See GTCR LLC; *U.S. Private*, pg. 1806
REVSTREAM INC.; *U.S. Private*, pg. 3417
REVTECH SOLUTIONS INDIA PRIVATE LIMITED—See GXO Logistics, Inc.; *U.S. Public*, pg. 976
REV VENTURE PARTNERS LIMITED—See RELX plc; *Int'l*, pg. 6266
REVVITY, INC.; *U.S. Public*, pg. 1793
REV WORLDWIDE, INC.; *U.S. Public*, pg. 3412
R.E. WACKER ASSOCIATES, INC.—See U.S. Bancorp; *U.S. Public*, pg. 2212
REWALK ROBOTICS, INC.—See ReWalk Robotics Ltd.; *Int'l*, pg. 6314
REWALK ROBOTICS LTD.; *Int'l*, pg. 6314
REWALK ROBOTICS—See ReWalk Robotics Ltd.; *Int'l*, pg. 6314
REWARD GATEWAY (UK) LTD—See Edenred S.A.; *Int'l*, pg. 2308
REWARDED HOLDINGS LIMITED; *Int'l*, pg. 6314
REWARD MINERALS LTD; *Int'l*, pg. 6314
REWARDS ARVATO SERVICES GMBH—See Bertelsmann SE & Co. KGaA; *Int'l*, pg. 996
THE REWARDS FACTORY LIMITED; *Int'l*, pg. 7679
REWARDS NETWORK INC.—See TowerBrook Capital Partners, L.P.; *U.S. Private*, pg. 4195
REWARDSNOW, INC.; *U.S. Private*, pg. 3417
REWARD SUPPLY CO. PTY. LTD.—See Groupe BPCE; *Int'l*, pg. 3095
REWARD WOOL INDUSTRY CORPORATION - HSIN-WU MILL—See Reward Wool Industry Corporation; *Int'l*, pg. 6314
REWARD WOOL INDUSTRY CORPORATION - LIU-TU MILL—See Reward Wool Industry Corporation; *Int'l*, pg. 6314
REWARD WOOL INDUSTRY CORPORATION; *Int'l*, pg. 6314
REWAY GROUP S.P.A.; *Int'l*, pg. 6314
REWE MARKT GMBH—See REWE-Zentral-Aktiengesellschaft; *Int'l*, pg. 6315
R E W ENTERPRISES, INC.; *U.S. Private*, pg. 3331

R E WEST INC.; *U.S. Private*, pg. 3331
REWE-ZENTRAL-AKTIENGESELLSCHAFT; *Int'l*, pg. 6314
REWIND INC.—See Dentsu Group Inc.; *Int'l*, pg. 2039
REW INVESTMENTS INCORPORATED; *U.S. Private*, pg. 3417
REWITEC GMBH—See Croda International plc; *Int'l*, pg. 1853
REWORLD MEDIA SA; *Int'l*, pg. 6315
REXAIR, LLC—See Rhone Group, LLC; *U.S. Private*, pg. 3424
REXALL PHARMACY GROUP LTD.—See McKesson Corporation; *U.S. Public*, pg. 1408
REXALL SUNDOWN, INC.—See KKR & Co. Inc.; *U.S. Public*, pg. 1264
REX AMERICAN RESOURCES CORPORATION; *U.S. Public*, pg. 1795
REXAM LIMITED—See Ball Corporation; *U.S. Public*, pg. 267
REXAM PENSION TRUSTEES LIMITED—See Ball Corporation; *U.S. Public*, pg. 268
REX AUTOMATISIERUNGSTECHNIK GMBH—See Eckelmann AG; *Int'l*, pg. 2290
REXCAPITAL SECURITIES LIMITED—See REXLot Holdings Limited; *Int'l*, pg. 6317
REXCELL TISSUE & AIRLAID AB—See Duni AB; *Int'l*, pg. 2227
REXCO EQUIPMENT INC.; *U.S. Private*, pg. 3417
REX CO., LTD.—See Tokushu Tokai Paper Co., Ltd.; *Int'l*, pg. 7786
REXCON, INC.—See Astec Industries, Inc.; *U.S. Public*, pg. 216
REXCON, LLC—See Astec Industries, Inc.; *U.S. Public*, pg. 216
REX CONTRUCTION SERVICES—See REX Engineering Group, Inc.; *U.S. Private*, pg. 3417
REX DAIKOU, LIMITED—See Relo Group, Inc.; *Int'l*, pg. 6265
REX DIRECT NET, INC.; *U.S. Private*, pg. 3417
REXEL ARABIA ELECTRICAL SUPPLIES LLC—See Rexel, S.A.; *Int'l*, pg. 6316
REXEL AUSTRALIA LIMITED—See Rexel, S.A.; *Int'l*, pg. 6316
REXEL AUSTRIA GMBH—See Rexel, S.A.; *Int'l*, pg. 6316
REXEL BELGIUM NV/SA—See Rexel, S.A.; *Int'l*, pg. 6316
REXEL CANADA ELECTRICAL, INC.—See Rexel, S.A.; *Int'l*, pg. 6316
REXEL CHINA MANAGEMENT CO. LTD.—See Rexel, S.A.; *Int'l*, pg. 6316
REXEL DISTRIBUICAO DE MATERIAL ELECRICO S.A.—See Rexel, S.A.; *Int'l*, pg. 6316
REXEL FINLAND OY—See Rexel, S.A.; *Int'l*, pg. 6316
REXEL GMBH—See Rexel, S.A.; *Int'l*, pg. 6316
REXEL HOLDINGS USA CORP.—See Rexel, S.A.; *Int'l*, pg. 6316
REXEL, INC.—See Rexel, S.A.; *Int'l*, pg. 6316
REXEL INDIA PRIVATE LIMITED—See Rexel, S.A.; *Int'l*, pg. 6316
REXEL ITALIA SPA—See Rexel, S.A.; *Int'l*, pg. 6316
REXEL NCE B.V.—See Rexel, S.A.; *Int'l*, pg. 6317
REXEL NEDERLAND B.V.—See Rexel, S.A.; *Int'l*, pg. 6316
REXEL, S.A.; *Int'l*, pg. 6316
REXELSENATE—See Rexel, S.A.; *Int'l*, pg. 6317
REXEL SPAIN, SL—See Rexel, S.A.; *Int'l*, pg. 6317
REXEL SVERIGE AB—See Rexel, S.A.; *Int'l*, pg. 6317
REXEL UK LIMITED—See Rexel, S.A.; *Int'l*, pg. 6317
REXEL USA, INC.—See Rexel, S.A.; *Int'l*, pg. 6317
REX ENGINEERING GROUP, INC.; *U.S. Private*, pg. 3417
REX FEATURES LTD.—See Shutterstock, Inc.; *U.S. Public*, pg. 1876
REXFORD INDUSTRIAL REALTY, INC.; *U.S. Public*, pg. 1795
REXFORET INC.—See Investissement Quebec; *Int'l*, pg. 3780
REX GORELL GROUP; *Int'l*, pg. 6315
REX-HIDE INC.; *U.S. Private*, pg. 3417
REX INDUSTRY BERHAD; *Int'l*, pg. 6315
REX INTERNATIONAL HOLDING LTD; *Int'l*, pg. 6315
REXIT BERHAD; *Int'l*, pg. 6317
REXITE, S.A. DE C.V.—See Melling Tool Company Inc.; *U.S. Private*, pg. 2662
REXIT, INC.; *U.S. Private*, pg. 3417
REXIUS FOREST BY-PRODUCTS; *U.S. Private*, pg. 3417
REXLOT HOLDINGS LIMITED; *Int'l*, pg. 6317
REX LUMBER COMPANY; *U.S. Private*, pg. 3417
REX MARINE CENTER, INC.; *U.S. Private*, pg. 3417
REX MINERALS LIMITED; *Int'l*, pg. 6315
REX MINERALS (SA) PTY LTD—See REX MINERALS LIMITED; *Int'l*, pg. 6315
REX MOORE ELECTRICAL CONTRACTORS & ENGINEERS; *U.S. Private*, pg. 3417
REXNORD ASIA PACIFIC PTE. LTD.—See Zurn Elkay Water Solutions Corporation; *U.S. Public*, pg. 2413
REXNORD AUSTRALIA PTY LTD.—See Zurn Elkay Water Solutions Corporation; *U.S. Public*, pg. 2413
REXNORD CANADA LIMITED—See Zurn Elkay Water Solutions Corporation; *U.S. Public*, pg. 2413

REX MOORE ELECTRICAL CONTRACTORS & ENGINEERS

CORPORATE AFFILIATIONS

Company Index

REXNORD DO BRASIL INDUSTRIAL LTDA—See Zurn Elkay Water Solutions Corporation; *U.S. Public*, pg. 2413
REXNORD ELECTRONICS & CONTROLS LTD.; *Int'l*, pg. 6317
REXNORD ELECTRONICS & CONTROLS LTD. - THANE FACTORY—See Rexnord Electronics & Controls Ltd.; *Int'l*, pg. 6317
REXNORD FINANCE BV—See Zurn Elkay Water Solutions Corporation; *U.S. Public*, pg. 2413
REXNORD FLATTOP EUROPE BV—See Zurn Elkay Water Solutions Corporation; *U.S. Public*, pg. 2413
REXNORD FLATTOP EUROPE SRL—See Zurn Elkay Water Solutions Corporation; *U.S. Public*, pg. 2413
REXNORD FLAT TOP ITALY SRL—See Zurn Elkay Water Solutions Corporation; *U.S. Public*, pg. 2413
REXNORD FRANCE HOLDINGS SAS—See Zurn Elkay Water Solutions Corporation; *U.S. Public*, pg. 2413
REXNORD I.H. B.V.—See Zurn Elkay Water Solutions Corporation; *U.S. Public*, pg. 2413
REXNORD INDUSTRIES, LLC—See Zurn Elkay Water Solutions Corporation; *U.S. Public*, pg. 2413
REXNORD INTERNATIONAL INC.—See Zurn Elkay Water Solutions Corporation; *U.S. Public*, pg. 2413
REXNORD KETTE GMBH—See Zurn Elkay Water Solutions Corporation; *U.S. Public*, pg. 2413
REXNORD MARBETT SRL—See Zurn Elkay Water Solutions Corporation; *U.S. Public*, pg. 2413
REXNORD MIDDLE EAST FZE—See Zurn Elkay Water Solutions Corporation; *U.S. Public*, pg. 2413
REXNORD POWER TRANSMISSION PRODUCTS (TAICING) CO. LTD.—See Zurn Elkay Water Solutions Corporation; *U.S. Public*, pg. 2413
REXNORD S.A. DE C.V.—See Zurn Elkay Water Solutions Corporation; *U.S. Public*, pg. 2413
REXNORD TOLLOK SRL—See Zurn Elkay Water Solutions Corporation; *U.S. Public*, pg. 2413
REXNORD-ZURN HOLDINGS, INC.—See Zurn Elkay Water Solutions Corporation; *U.S. Public*, pg. 2413
REX OIL COMPANY INC.; *U.S. Private*, pg. 3417
REX OIL COMPANY—See PetroChoice LLC; *U.S. Private*, pg. 3162
REXON EUROPE GMBH—See REXON Industrial Corp., Ltd.; *Int'l*, pg. 6317
REXON INDUSTRIAL CORP., LTD.; *Int'l*, pg. 6317
REX PIPES & CABLES INDUSTRIES LIMITED; *Int'l*, pg. 6315
REX PIPE & SUPPLY CO.; *U.S. Private*, pg. 3417
REXPORT, INC.—See American Express Company; *U.S. Public*, pg. 102
REX POWER MAGNETICS; *Int'l*, pg. 6316
REX PRECAST SYSTEMS, INC.—See Superior Products Distributors Inc.; *U.S. Private*, pg. 3880
REX RADIO AND TELEVISION, INC.—See REX American Resources Corporation; *U.S. Public*, pg. 1795
REX-ROTARY SAS—See Ricoh Company, Ltd.; *Int'l*, pg. 6334
REXROTH INDRAMAT GMBH—See Robert Bosch GmbH; *Int'l*, pg. 6366
REXROTH PNEUMATICS AG—See Robert Bosch GmbH; *Int'l*, pg. 6366
REX SEALING & PACKING INDUSTRIES PVT. LTD.; *Int'l*, pg. 6316
REX SPENCER EQUIPMENT COMPANY INC.—See VLP Holding Co. Inc.; *U.S. Private*, pg. 4408
REX SUPPLY COMPANY—See Production Tool Supply Company, LLC; *U.S. Private*, pg. 3273
REXTON INC.—See Siemens Aktiengesellschaft; *Int'l*, pg. 6889
REXTON REALTY COMPANY; *U.S. Private*, pg. 3417
REX TRUEFORM GROUP LIMITED; *Int'l*, pg. 6316
REXX INDEX, LLC—See BGC Group, Inc.; *U.S. Public*, pg. 330
REYAL URBIS S.A.; *Int'l*, pg. 6317
REYDEL AUTOMOTIVE HOLDINGS B.V.—See Cerberus Capital Management, L.P.; *U.S. Private*, pg. 839
REYDEL AUTOMOTIVE SPAIN, S.L.U.—See Cerberus Capital Management, L.P.; *U.S. Private*, pg. 839
REYES BEVERAGE GROUP—See Reyes Holdings, LLC; *U.S. Private*, pg. 3417
REYES HOLDINGS, LLC; *U.S. Private*, pg. 3417
REY HOLDINGS CORPORATION—See Supermercados la Favorita C.A.; *Int'l*, pg. 7339
REYL & CIE (MALTA) LTD.—See Intesa Sanpaolo S.p.A.; *Int'l*, pg. 3766
REYL & CO (UK) LLP—See Intesa Sanpaolo S.p.A.; *Int'l*, pg. 3766
REYM B.V—See RETHMANN AG & Co. KG; *Int'l*, pg. 6308
REYNA CAPITAL CORPORATION—See The Reynolds & Reynolds Company; *U.S. Private*, pg. 4106
REYNALDOS MEXICAN FOOD COMPANY; *U.S. Private*, pg. 3418
REYNA SILVER CORP.; *Int'l*, pg. 6318
REYNEN & BARDIS COMMUNITIES, INC.; *U.S. Private*, pg. 3418
REYNOLDS AMERICAN INC.—See British American Tobacco plc; *Int'l*, pg. 1168
REYNOLDS AND REYNOLDS B.V.—See The Reynolds & Reynolds Company; *U.S. Private*, pg. 4106
REYNOLDS ASPHALT & CONSTRUCTION COMPANY; *U.S. Private*, pg. 3418
THE REYNOLDS COMPANY—See McNaughton-McKay Electric Company; *U.S. Private*, pg. 2643
REYNOLDS CONSTRUCTION, LLC; *U.S. Private*, pg. 3418
REYNOLDS CONSUMER PRODUCTS CANADA INC.—See Pactiv Evergreen Inc.; *U.S. Public*, pg. 1633
REYNOLDS CONSUMER PRODUCTS INC.—See Pactiv Evergreen Inc.; *U.S. Public*, pg. 1633
REYNOLDS CUIVRE S.A.—See Viohalco SA/NV; *Int'l*, pg. 8243
REYNOLDS CYCLING, LLC—See MacLean-Fogg Company; *U.S. Private*, pg. 2537
REYNOLDS ENTERPRISES OF BROOME, INC.; *U.S. Private*, pg. 3418
REYNOLDS EUROPEAN S.A.S.—See Klockner & Co. SE; *Int'l*, pg. 4202
REYNOLDS FLEXIBLE PACKAGING-BELLWOOD PRINTING PLANT—See Pactiv Evergreen Inc.; *U.S. Public*, pg. 1634
REYNOLDS FLEXIBLE PACKAGING-GROTTOES PLASTICS PLANT—See Pactiv Evergreen Inc.; *U.S. Public*, pg. 1634
REYNOLDS FLEXIBLE PACKAGING—See Pactiv Evergreen Inc.; *U.S. Public*, pg. 1634
REYNOLDS FOOD PACKAGING-CHICAGO—See Pactiv Evergreen Inc.; *U.S. Public*, pg. 1634
REYNOLDS FOOD PACKAGING LLC—See Pactiv Evergreen Inc.; *U.S. Public*, pg. 1634
REYNOLDS FOOD PACKAGING—See Pactiv Evergreen Inc.; *U.S. Public*, pg. 1634
REYNOLDS FOOD PACKAGING—See Pactiv Evergreen Inc.; *U.S. Public*, pg. 1634
REYNOLDS FOOD PACKAGING—See Pactiv Evergreen Inc.; *U.S. Public*, pg. 1634
REYNOLDS FORD INC.; *U.S. Private*, pg. 3418
REYNOLDS INDUSTRIAL CONTRACTORS, INC.—See Catamaran Solutions, LLC; *U.S. Private*, pg. 787
REYNOLDS MOTOR COMPANY; *U.S. Private*, pg. 3418
REYNOLDS OIL COMPANY INC.; *U.S. Private*, pg. 3418
REYNOLDS OUTDOOR MEDIA—See OUTFRONT Media Inc.; *U.S. Public*, pg. 1625
REYNOLDS PACKING CO. INC.; *U.S. Private*, pg. 3418
REYNOLDS PLANTATION, INC.—See MetLife, Inc.; *U.S. Public*, pg. 1431
REYNOLDS PRESTO PRODUCTS INC.—See Pactiv Evergreen Inc.; *U.S. Public*, pg. 1634
REYNOLDS READY MIX LLC; *U.S. Private*, pg. 3418
REYNOLDS & REYNOLDS (CANADA) LTD.—See The Reynolds & Reynolds Company; *U.S. Private*, pg. 4106
THE REYNOLDS & REYNOLDS COMPANY; *U.S. Private*, pg. 4106
THE REYNOLDS & REYNOLDS COMPANY; *U.S. Private*, pg. 4106
REYNOLDS S.A.S.—See Nordic Capital AB; *Int'l*, pg. 5420
REYNOLDS S.A.S.—See Trelleborg AB; *Int'l*, pg. 7911
REYNOLDS, SMITH & HILLS INC.; *U.S. Private*, pg. 3418
REYN SPOONER, INC.—See Wedbush Capital Partners; *U.S. Private*, pg. 4468
REYON PHARMACEUTICAL CO., LTD - JINCHEON FACTORY—See Reyon Pharmaceutical Co., Ltd; *Int'l*, pg. 6318
REYON PHARMACEUTICAL CO., LTD; *Int'l*, pg. 6318
REY RESOURCES LIMITED; *Int'l*, pg. 6317
REYSAS GAYRIMENKUL YATIRIM ORTAKLIGI A.S.—See Reysas Tasimacilik ve Lojistik Ticaret A.S.; *Int'l*, pg. 6318
REYSAS TASIMACILIK VE LOJISTIK TICARET A.S.; *Int'l*, pg. 6318
REYTEC CONSTRUCTION RESOURCES, INC.; *U.S. Private*, pg. 3418
REYTON METALS LTD.—See Nordic Capital AB; *Int'l*, pg. 5421
REYTON METALS LTD.—See Trelleborg AB; *Int'l*, pg. 7911
REYTON WIRE LTD—See Nordic Capital AB; *Int'l*, pg. 5421
REYTON WIRE LTD—See Trelleborg AB; *Int'l*, pg. 7911
REYUU JAPAN INC.; *Int'l*, pg. 6318
REZ 1, INC.—See Apollo Global Management, Inc.; *U.S. Public*, pg. 150
REZEK EQUIPMENT; *U.S. Private*, pg. 3419
REZMAN EXPRESS INC.—See Kismet International Limousine Service Inc.; *U.S. Private*, pg. 2315
REZN8 PRODUCTIONS, INC.; *U.S. Private*, pg. 3419
REZOLUTE, INC.; *U.S. Public*, pg. 1795
REZOPIA, INC.—See Sonata Software Limited; *Int'l*, pg. 7089
RF2M LTD.—See AEA Investors LP; *U.S. Private*, pg. 113
RF360 EUROPE GMBH—See QUALCOMM Incorporated; *U.S. Public*, pg. 1748
RFA CAPITAL HOLDINGS INC.; *Int'l*, pg. 6318
RF ACQUISITION CORP II; *Int'l*, pg. 6318
RF ACQUISITION CORP.; *Int'l*, pg. 6318
RFA-TECH LTD.—See Celsa Group; *Int'l*, pg. 1395
RF BINDER PARTNERS—See Ruder Finn Group, Inc.; *U.S. Private*, pg. 3501
RF BINDER PARTNERS—See Ruder Finn Group, Inc.; *U.S. Private*, pg. 3501
RF CABLE ASSEMBLIES DIVISION—See RF Industries, Ltd.; *U.S. Public*, pg. 1796
RFC AMBRIAN GROUP LIMITED; *Int'l*, pg. 6318
RF CAPITAL GROUP INC.; *Int'l*, pg. 6318
RF CAPITAL PTY LTD.; *Int'l*, pg. 6318
RFC CORPORATE FINANCE, INC.—See Peabody Energy Corporation; *U.S. Public*, pg. 1659
RFC FINANCIAL SERVICES HOLDING LLC—See Regions Financial Corporation; *U.S. Public*, pg. 1776
RFC, INC.—See Leonard Green & Partners, L.P.; *U.S. Private*, pg. 2424
RF CONNECTORS DIVISION—See RF Industries, Ltd.; *U.S. Public*, pg. 1796
RF CONTROLS CO., LTD.—See INZI Controls Co., Ltd; *Int'l*, pg. 3790
RFC RADIO-, FERNSEH- U. COMPUTERTECHNIK GMBH—See Morgan Stanley; *U.S. Public*, pg. 1473
RFC-SHARON LLC—See voestalpine AG; *Int'l*, pg. 8289
RFD NEW ZEALAND LIMITED—See ONEX Corporation; *Int'l*, pg. 5580
RF DUROPLAST GMBH—See RF Plast GmbH; *Int'l*, pg. 6318
RFE HOLDING (CANADA) CORP.—See Fox Factory Holding Corp.; *U.S. Public*, pg. 877
RFE INVESTMENT PARTNERS; *U.S. Private*, pg. 3419
RFEL LTD.—See Rheinmetall AG; *Int'l*, pg. 6323
RF ENCORE S.A.S.—See Encore Capital Group, Inc.; *U.S. Public*, pg. 760
R F ENERGY CO., LTD.—See Neturen Co., Ltd.; *Int'l*, pg. 5217
RF ENERGY INVESTMENTS LTD.—See Vitol Holding B.V.; *Int'l*, pg. 8260
RF ENGINES LIMITED—See Rheinmetall AG; *Int'l*, pg. 6323
RFE/RL INC.; *U.S. Private*, pg. 3420
R.F. FISHER ELECTRIC CO LLC; *U.S. Private*, pg. 3335
RFG DISTRIBUTING INC.; *U.S. Private*, pg. 3420
RFHIC CORPORATION; *Int'l*, pg. 6318
RFI BANK JSC; *Int'l*, pg. 6318
RFI CORPORATION—See Advent International Corporation; *U.S. Private*, pg. 100
RF IDEAS, INC.—See Roper Technologies, Inc.; *U.S. Public*, pg. 1812
RFID GLOBAL SOLUTION INC.; *U.S. Private*, pg. 3420
RFI ELECTRONICS, INC.—See Wind Point Advisors LLC; *U.S. Private*, pg. 4535
RFI ENTERPRISES INC.—See Wind Point Advisors LLC; *U.S. Private*, pg. 4535
R.F. INC.; *U.S. Private*, pg. 3336
R&F INDUSTRIES, INC.; *U.S. Private*, pg. 3332
RF INDUSTRIES, LTD.; *U.S. Public*, pg. 1795
RFIP INC.; *U.S. Private*, pg. 3420
R.F. KNOX COMPANY, INC.; *U.S. Private*, pg. 3336
RFK VALJCICI—See NN, Inc.; *U.S. Public*, pg. 1531
RFL ELECTRONICS, INC.—See Hubbell Incorporated; *U.S. Public*, pg. 1067
R.F. MACDONALD CO.; *U.S. Private*, pg. 3336
RF-MATERIALS CO., LTD.; *Int'l*, pg. 6318
RFM CORPORATION; *Int'l*, pg. 6319
RFM ENTREPRISES S.A.S.—See Vivendi SE; *Int'l*, pg. 8275
RFM INC.—See Mitsubishi Materials Corporation; *Int'l*, pg. 4965
RFM INTEGRATED DEVICE INC.—See Akoustis Technologies, Inc.; *U.S. Public*, pg. 69
RFM LOYALTY CO—See The International Investor Company K.S.C.C.; *Int'l*, pg. 7656
RF MORSE & SON INC.; *U.S. Private*, pg. 3419
RFM RESEAU NORD S.A.S.—See Vivendi SE; *Int'l*, pg. 8275
RFM RESEAU SUD—See Vivendi SE; *Int'l*, pg. 8275
RF MUSIC PUBLISHER INC.—See Nippon Television Holdings Inc.; *Int'l*, pg. 5356
RF NEULINK—See Raveon Technologies Corporation; *U.S. Private*, pg. 3357
R.F. PECK CO., INC.—See Ardian SAS; *Int'l*, pg. 554
RF PLAST GMBH; *Int'l*, pg. 6318
R & F PROPERTIES (CAMBODIA) CO., LTD.—See Guangzhou R&F Properties Co., Ltd.; *Int'l*, pg. 3167
R&F PROPERTY AUSTRALIA PTY LTD—See Guangzhou R&F Properties Co., Ltd.; *Int'l*, pg. 3167
R & F PROPERTY PTY LTD—See Guangzhou R&F Properties Co., Ltd.; *Int'l*, pg. 3167
RF RADIO NIPPON CO., LTD.—See Nippon Television Holdings Inc.; *Int'l*, pg. 5356
R. FRIEDRICH & SONS INC.; *U.S. Private*, pg. 3333
RF RUNDFUNK-FERNSEHEN ANTENNEN, MONTAGE UND HANDELS GMBH; *Int'l*, pg. 6318
RFS CATERING SUPPLIES (PTY) LIMITED—See The Bidvest Group Limited; *Int'l*, pg. 7626
R.F. SCURLOCK COMPANY INC.; *U.S. Private*, pg. 3336
RF SECURITIES CLEARING LP—See RF Capital Group Inc.; *Int'l*, pg. 6318
RFSEMI TECHNOLOGIES, INC. - SHENZHEN FACTORY—See RFsemi Technologies, Inc.; *Int'l*, pg. 6319
RFSEMI TECHNOLOGIES, INC.; *Int'l*, pg. 6319

RFSEMI TECHNOLOGIES, INC. - WANJU FACTORY—See RFsemi Technologies, Inc.; *Int'l*, pg. 6319
RFSEMI TECHNOLOGIES, INC. - WEIHAI FACTORY—See RFsemi Technologies, Inc.; *Int'l*, pg. 6319
R F STEARNS INC; *U.S. Private*, pg. 3331
RFS TECHNOLOGIES, INC.—See Amphenol Corporation; *U.S. Public*, pg. 132
RF SYSCON UMWELTSYSTEME GMBH; *Int'l*, pg. 6318
RFTECH CO., LTD.; *Int'l*, pg. 6319
RFT S.P.A.—See SKF AB; *Int'l*, pg. 6981
RFXCEL CORPORATION—See Antares Vision SpA; *Int'l*, pg. 482
RFX INCORPORATED; *U.S. Private*, pg. 3420
RGA CAPITAL LIMITED U.K.—See Reinsurance Group of America, Inc.; *U.S. Public*, pg. 1777
RGA GLOBAL REINSURANCE COMPANY, LTD.—See Reinsurance Group of America, Inc.; *U.S. Public*, pg. 1777
RGA INTERNATIONAL REINSURANCE COMPANY LIMITED—See Reinsurance Group of America, Inc.; *U.S. Public*, pg. 1777
RGA INTERNATIONAL REINSURANCE COMPANY—See Reinsurance Group of America, Inc.; *U.S. Public*, pg. 1777
RGA LIFE REINSURANCE COMPANY OF CANADA—See Reinsurance Group of America, Inc.; *U.S. Public*, pg. 1777
RGA LIFE REINSURANCE COMPANY OF CANADA—See Reinsurance Group of America, Inc.; *U.S. Public*, pg. 1777
R/GA LONDON—See The Interpublic Group of Companies, Inc.; *U.S. Public*, pg. 2104
R/GA LOS ANGELES—See The Interpublic Group of Companies, Inc.; *U.S. Public*, pg. 2104
R/GA MEDIA GROUP, INC.—See The Interpublic Group of Companies, Inc.; *U.S. Public*, pg. 2103
RGA REINSURANCE COMPANY MIDDLE EAST LIMITED—See Reinsurance Group of America, Inc.; *U.S. Public*, pg. 1777
RGA REINSURANCE COMPANY OF AUSTRALIA LIMITED—See Reinsurance Group of America, Inc.; *U.S. Public*, pg. 1777
RGA REINSURANCE COMPANY OF SOUTH AFRICA, LIMITED—See Reinsurance Group of America, Inc.; *U.S. Public*, pg. 1778
RGA REINSURANCE COMPANY—See Reinsurance Group of America, Inc.; *U.S. Public*, pg. 1777
RGA REINSURANCE UK LIMITED—See Reinsurance Group of America, Inc.; *U.S. Public*, pg. 1778
R/GA SAN FRANCISCO—See The Interpublic Group of Companies, Inc.; *U.S. Public*, pg. 2104
R/GA SAO PAULO—See The Interpublic Group of Companies, Inc.; *U.S. Public*, pg. 2104
RGA SERVICES INDIA PRIVATE LIMITED—See Reinsurance Group of America, Inc.; *U.S. Public*, pg. 1778
RGA SERVICES (SINGAPORE) PTE. LTD.—See Reinsurance Group of America, Inc.; *U.S. Public*, pg. 1778
RGA UK SERVICES LIMITED—See Reinsurance Group of America, Inc.; *U.S. Public*, pg. 1778
RGA UNDERWRITING LIMITED—See Arthur J. Gallagher & Co.; *U.S. Public*, pg. 207
R.G.AUTOMATION S.P.A.—See Trevisan Cometal SpA; *Int'l*, pg. 7917
R/GA VENTURES LLC—See The Interpublic Group of Companies, Inc.; *U.S. Public*, pg. 2104
RGAX LLC—See Reinsurance Group of America, Inc.; *U.S. Public*, pg. 1778
R.G. BARRY CORPORATION—See Mill Road Capital Management LLC; *U.S. Private*, pg. 2730
RGB INTERNATIONAL BHD.; *Int'l*, pg. 6319
RGB LTD.—See RGB International Bhd.; *Int'l*, pg. 6319
RGB (MACAU) LIMITED—See RGB International Bhd.; *Int'l*, pg. 6319
RGB MECHANICAL CONTRACTORS INC.; *U.S. Private*, pg. 3420
RG BOGDANKA SP. Z O.O.—See Lubelski Wegiel BOGDANKA Spolka Akcyjna; *Int'l*, pg. 4572
RG BROSE AUTOMOTIVE COMPONENTS (PTY.) LTD.—See Brose Fahrzeugteile GmbH & Co. KG; *Int'l*, pg. 1196
RGB SDN. BHD.—See RGB International Bhd.; *Int'l*, pg. 6319
RGB SYSTEMS INC.; *U.S. Private*, pg. 3420
RGB VENTURES LLC—See Blend Images, LLC; *U.S. Private*, pg. 580
R&G CONSTRUCTION COMPANY; *U.S. Private*, pg. 3332
RG COPPER CORP.—See Vizsla Copper Corp.; *Int'l*, pg. 8280
RGC RESOURCES, INC.; *U.S. Public*, pg. 1796
RGC VENTURES OF VIRGINIA, INC.—See RGC Resources, Inc.; *U.S. Public*, pg. 1796
RG ENGINEERING INC.; *U.S. Private*, pg. 3420
RGE RIO GRANDE ENERGIA S.A.—See State Grid Corporation of China; *Int'l*, pg. 7182
RGE STORM LAKE—See Reding Gravel & Excavating Co., Inc.; *U.S. Private*, pg. 3379

RGE SUL DISTRIBUIDORA DE ENERGIA S/A—See State Grid Corporation of China; *Int'l*, pg. 7182
RGF CAPITAL MARKETS LTD.; *Int'l*, pg. 6319
RGF ENVIRONMENTAL GROUP; *U.S. Private*, pg. 3420
RGF INDUSTRIES INCORPORATED; *U.S. Private*, pg. 3420
RGF INTERNATIONAL RECRUITMENT HOLDINGS LIMITED—See Recruit Holdings Co., Ltd.; *Int'l*, pg. 6240
RGF STAFFING APEJ PTY. LTD.—See Recruit Holdings Co., Ltd.; *Int'l*, pg. 6240
RGF STAFFING B.V.—See Recruit Holdings Co., Ltd.; *Int'l*, pg. 6240
RGF STAFFING GERMANY GMBH—See Recruit Holdings Co., Ltd.; *Int'l*, pg. 6241
RGF STAFFING UK LIMITED—See Recruit Holdings Co., Ltd.; *Int'l*, pg. 6241
RGH ENTERPRISES, INC.—See Cardinal Health, Inc.; *U.S. Public*, pg. 433
RG INDUSTRIES, INC.; *U.S. Private*, pg. 3420
RG INMOBILIARIA, S.A.; *Int'l*, pg. 6319
RGIS—See Blackstone Inc.; *U.S. Public*, pg. 357
RGL-FORENSIC ACCOUNTANTS & CONSULTANTS; *U.S. Private*, pg. 3420
RG MARKETING CO LTD—See TBS Holdings, Inc.; *Int'l*, pg. 7481
RG MARKETING CO., LTD.—See Senshukai Co., Ltd.; *Int'l*, pg. 6713
R.G. MCGRAW INSURANCE AGENCY, INC.—See Fifth Third Bancorp; *U.S. Public*, pg. 834
RG PARENT LLC—See Centric Brands Inc.; *U.S. Private*, pg. 829
R & G PHARMASTUDIES CO., LTD.; *Int'l*, pg. 6167
RGP HOLDING, INC.; *U.S. Private*, pg. 3420
RGP PROPERTIES LTD.; *Int'l*, pg. 6319
RGP VRDNIK A.D.; *Int'l*, pg. 6319
R.G. RAY CORPORATION; *U.S. Private*, pg. 3336
R.G.RAY CORPORATION—See NORMA Group SE; *Int'l*, pg. 5431
RGR CANADA INC.—See High Tide, Inc.; *Int'l*, pg. 3386
R. GRIGGS GROUP LIMITED—See Permira Advisers LLP; *Int'l*, pg. 5808
R.G. RILEY & SONS INC.; *U.S. Private*, pg. 3336
RGS ASSOCIATES, INC.—See Carl Marks & Co., Inc.; *U.S. Private*, pg. 763
R.G. SMITH CO. INC.; *U.S. Private*, pg. 3336
RGS NORDIC A/S—See Triton Advisers Limited; *Int'l*, pg. 7933
RG STEEL WARREN, INC.—See Hilco Trading, LLC; *U.S. Private*, pg. 1944
RG STEEL WHEELING, LLC—See Esmark Incorporated; *U.S. Private*, pg. 1426
RGT ADVERTISING AGENCY; *U.S. Private*, pg. 3420
RGT BERHAD; *Int'l*, pg. 6319
RGT INDUSTRIES SDN. BHD.—See RGT Berhad; *Int'l*, pg. 6319
RGT LOGISTICS, LLC.—See Red Gold Inc.; *U.S. Private*, pg. 3374
RGT WEALTH ADVISORS, LLC—See CI Financial Corporation; *Int'l*, pg. 1601
RGW CONSTRUCTION INC.; *U.S. Private*, pg. 3421
RHA HEALTH SERVICES INC.—See Blue Wolf Capital Partners LLC; *U.S. Private*, pg. 595
R.H. AMAR & CO. LTD.; *Int'l*, pg. 6170
R HANNAH & CO LIMITED—See Bapcor Limited; *Int'l*, pg. 857
RHA NORTH CAROLINA MR INC; *U.S. Private*, pg. 3421
RHAPSODY INTERNATIONAL, INC.—See Napster Group PLC; *Int'l*, pg. 5147
RHAPSODY LIMITED—See Walstead Investments Ltd.; *Int'l*, pg. 8336
R. HASLER AG—See Heliad AG; *Int'l*, pg. 3329
RHA SULLIVAN INC; *U.S. Private*, pg. 3421
R.H. BARRINGER DISTRIBUTING CO. INC.; *U.S. Private*, pg. 3336
RHB ASSET MANAGEMENT PTE. LTD.—See RHB Bank Berhad; *Int'l*, pg. 6320
RHB ASSET MANAGEMENT SDN. BHD.—See RHB Bank Berhad; *Int'l*, pg. 6320
RHB BANK BERHAD; *Int'l*, pg. 6319
RHB BANK LAO LIMITED—See RHB Bank Berhad; *Int'l*, pg. 6320
RHB BANK (L) LTD—See RHB Bank Berhad; *Int'l*, pg. 6320
RHB BANK NOMINEES PTE LTD—See RHB Bank Berhad; *Int'l*, pg. 6320
RHB HOLDINGS HONG KONG LIMITED—See RHB Bank Berhad; *Int'l*, pg. 6320
RHB INDOCHINA BANK LIMITED—See RHB Bank Berhad; *Int'l*, pg. 6320
RHB INSURANCE BERHAD—See RHB Bank Berhad; *Int'l*, pg. 6320
RHB INVESTMENT BANK BERHAD—See RHB Bank Berhad; *Int'l*, pg. 6320
RHB INVESTMENT MANAGEMENT SDN. BHD.—See RHB Bank Berhad; *Int'l*, pg. 6320
RHB ISLAMIC BANK BERHAD—See RHB Bank Berhad; *Int'l*, pg. 6320

RHB LEASING SDN BHD—See RHB Bank Berhad; *Int'l*, pg. 6320
RH BOPHELO LTD.—See Public Investment Corporation; *U.S. Private*, pg. 3299
RHB OSK CAPITAL HONG KONG LIMITED—See RHB Bank Berhad; *Int'l*, pg. 6320
RHB OSK FUTURES HONG KONG LIMITED—See RHB Bank Berhad; *Int'l*, pg. 6320
RHB OSK PRECIOUS METALS HONG KONG LIMITED—See RHB Bank Berhad; *Int'l*, pg. 6320
RHB OSK SECURITIES HONG KONG LIMITED—See RHB Bank Berhad; *Int'l*, pg. 6320
RHB OSK SECURITIES (THAILAND) PUBLIC COMPANY LIMITED—See RHB Bank Berhad; *Int'l*, pg. 6320
RHB RESEARCH INSTITUTE SDN. BHD.—See RHB Bank Berhad; *Int'l*, pg. 6320
RHB SECURITIES (CAMBODIA) PLC.—See RHB Bank Berhad; *Int'l*, pg. 6320
RHB SECURITIES HONG KONG LIMITED—See RHB Bank Berhad; *Int'l*, pg. 6320
RHB SECURITIES SINGAPORE PTE LTD—See RHB Bank Berhad; *Int'l*, pg. 6320
RHB SECURITIES (THAILAND) PUBLIC COMPANY LIMITED—See RHB Bank Berhad; *Int'l*, pg. 6320
RHB SECURITIES VIETNAM COMPANY LIMITED—See RHB Bank Berhad; *Int'l*, pg. 6320
RH BUILD & DESIGN, INC.—See RH; *U.S. Public*, pg. 1796
RHC HOLDING PRIVATE LIMITED; *Int'l*, pg. 6320
RHC, INC.; *U.S. Private*, pg. 3421
R&H CONSTRUCTION CO. - CENTRAL OREGON—See R&H Construction Co.; *U.S. Private*, pg. 3332
R&H CONSTRUCTION CO.; *U.S. Private*, pg. 3332
RHEA ELECTRONIQUE—See Hiolle Industries S.A.; *Int'l*, pg. 3401
RHEA GIRISIM SERMAYESI YATIRIM ORTAKLIGI A.S.; *Int'l*, pg. 6320
RHEA LANA'S, INC.; *U.S. Private*, pg. 3421
RHEA, S.A.—See Allianz SE; *Int'l*, pg. 355
RHEBAU RHEINISCHE BETON- UND BAUINDUSTRIE GMBH & CO. KG—See Buzzi SpA; *Int'l*, pg. 1230
RHEE BROS. INC.; *U.S. Private*, pg. 3421
RHEEM AUSTRALIA PTY LTD.—See Paloma Industries Limited; *Int'l*, pg. 5709
RHEEM AUSTRALIA—See Paloma Industries Limited; *Int'l*, pg. 5709
RHEEM CANADA LTD.—See Paloma Industries Limited; *Int'l*, pg. 5709
RHEEM MANUFACTURING - AIR CONDITIONING DIV—See Paloma Industries Limited; *Int'l*, pg. 5709
RHEEM MANUFACTURING COMPANY—See Paloma Industries Limited; *Int'l*, pg. 5709
RHEEM S.A. ARGENTINA—See Paloma Industries Limited; *Int'l*, pg. 5710
RHEEM WATER HEATER—See Paloma Industries Limited; *Int'l*, pg. 5710
RHE HANDEL ENGINEERING GMBH & CO. KG—See Josef Meissner GmbH & Co. KG; *Int'l*, pg. 4001
RHE HATCO, INC.—See Pro Equine Products Inc.; *U.S. Private*, pg. 3269
RHEIDOL 2008 TRUSTEES LTD.—See Statkraft AS; *Int'l*, pg. 7185
RHEINBRAUN BRENNSTOFF GMBH—See RWE AG; *Int'l*, pg. 6435
RHEIN CHEMIE CORPORATION—See LANXESS AG; *Int'l*, pg. 4416
RHEIN CHEMIE JAPAN LTD—See LANXESS AG; *Int'l*, pg. 4416
RHEIN CHEMIE (QINGDAO) LTD.—See LANXESS AG; *Int'l*, pg. 4416
RHEIN CHEMIE RHEINAU GMBH—See LANXESS AG; *Int'l*, pg. 4416
RHEINENERGIE WINDKRAFT GMBH—See Electricite de France S.A.; *Int'l*, pg. 2350
RHEINGOLD CAPITAL GMBH; *Int'l*, pg. 6320
RHEINGRUND IMMOBILIEN VERWALTUNGS-GMBH; *Int'l*, pg. 6320
RHEIN-INVEST GMBH—See Immofinanz AG; *Int'l*, pg. 3628
RHEINISCHE BAUSTOFFWERKE GMBH & CO. KG—See ACS, Actividades de Construccion y Servicios, S.A.; *Int'l*, pg. 114
RHEINISCHE-BERGISCHE VERLAGSGESELLSCHAFT MBH; *Int'l*, pg. 6320
RHEINISCHE COMPOUNDING GMBH—See Medios AG; *Int'l*, pg. 4778
RHEINISCHE LAGERHAUS GMBH—See Immofinanz AG; *Int'l*, pg. 3628
RHEINISCHE POST VERLAGSGESELLSCHAFT MBH—See Rheinische-Bergische Verlagsgesellschaft mbH; *Int'l*, pg. 6321
RHEINKALK GMBH & CO. KG—See Lhoist S.A.; *Int'l*, pg. 4478
RHEINKRAFT PRODUCTION GMBH—See Cliq Digital AG; *Int'l*, pg. 1660
RHEINKRAFTWERK IFFEZHEIM GMBH—See EnBW Energie Baden-Wurttemberg AG; *Int'l*, pg. 2400
RHEINLAND KRAFTSTOFF GMBH—See Shell plc; *Int'l*, pg. 6795

RHEINLAND-PFALZ BANK—See Landesbank Baden-Wurttemberg; *Int'l*, pg. 4405
RHEIN LIPPE WOHNEN GMBH—See RAG-Stiftung; *Int'l*, pg. 6179
RHEIN LOGISTICS GMBH—See Dubai Islamic Bank PSJ; *Int'l*, pg. 2220
RHEIN MAIN COMPOUNDING GMBH—See Medios AG; *Int'l*, pg. 4778
RHEIN-MAIN-DONAU AG—See Fortum Oyj; *Int'l*, pg. 2742
RHEIN-MAIN-VERKEHRSVERBUND GMBH; *Int'l*, pg. 6320
RHEIN MEDICAL, INC.—See Audax Group, Limited Partnership; *U.S. Private*, pg. 388
RHEINMETALL AG; *Int'l*, pg. 6321
RHEINMETALL AIR DEFENCE AG—See Rheinmetall AG; *Int'l*, pg. 6323
RHEINMETALL AUSTRALIA PTY LTD.—See Rheinmetall AG; *Int'l*, pg. 6323
RHEINMETALL AUTOMOTIVE AG—See Rheinmetall AG; *Int'l*, pg. 6323
RHEINMETALL BUROSYSTEME GMBH—See Rheinmetall AG; *Int'l*, pg. 6323
RHEINMETALL CANADA INC.—See Rheinmetall AG; *Int'l*, pg. 6323
RHEINMETALL CHEMPRO GMBH—See Rheinmetall AG; *Int'l*, pg. 6323
RHEINMETALL DEFENCE AUSTRALIA PTY. LTD.—See Rheinmetall AG; *Int'l*, pg. 6324
RHEINMETALL DEFENCE ELECTRONICS GMBH—See Rheinmetall AG; *Int'l*, pg. 6323
RHEINMETALL DEFENCE POLSKA SP. Z.O.O.—See Rheinmetall AG; *Int'l*, pg. 6324
RHEINMETALL DEFENCE—See Rheinmetall AG; *Int'l*, pg. 6323
RHEINMETALL DENEL MUNITION (PTY.) LTD.—See Denel SOC Ltd.; *Int'l*, pg. 2026
RHEINMETALL DENEL MUNITION (PTY.) LTD.—See Rheinmetall AG; *Int'l*, pg. 6324
RHEINMETALL DIENSTLEISTUNGSZENTRUM ALTMARK GMBH—See Rheinmetall AG; *Int'l*, pg. 6324
RHEINMETALL EASTERN MARKETS GMBH—See Rheinmetall AG; *Int'l*, pg. 6324
RHEINMETALL ELECTRONICS GMBH—See Rheinmetall AG; *Int'l*, pg. 6324
RHEINMETALL HELLAS S.A.—See Rheinmetall AG; *Int'l*, pg. 6323
RHEINMETALL IMMOBILIEN GMBH—See Rheinmetall AG; *Int'l*, pg. 6324
RHEINMETALL INDUSTRIETECHNIK GMBH—See Rheinmetall AG; *Int'l*, pg. 6324
RHEINMETALL INSURANCE SERVICES GMBH—See Rheinmetall AG; *Int'l*, pg. 6324
RHEINMETALL ITALIA S.P.A.—See Rheinmetall AG; *Int'l*, pg. 6324
RHEINMETALL LAINGSDALE (PTY) LTD.—See Rheinmetall AG; *Int'l*, pg. 6324
RHEINMETALL LANDSYSTEME GMBH—See Rheinmetall AG; *Int'l*, pg. 6323
RHEINMETALL MAN MILITARY VEHICLES AUSTRALIA PTY LTD.—See Rheinmetall AG; *Int'l*, pg. 6324
RHEINMETALL MAN MILITARY VEHICLES CANADA LTD.—See Rheinmetall AG; *Int'l*, pg. 6324
RHEINMETALL MAN MILITARY VEHICLES GMBH—See Rheinmetall AG; *Int'l*, pg. 6323
RHEINMETALL MAN MILITARY VEHICLES OSTERREICH GESMBH—See Rheinmetall AG; *Int'l*, pg. 6324
RHEINMETALL MAN MILITARY VEHICLES OSTERREICH HOLDING GESMBH—See Rheinmetall AG; *Int'l*, pg. 6324
RHEINMETALL MAN MILITARY VEHICLE SYSTEMS LTD.—See Rheinmetall AG; *Int'l*, pg. 6323
RHEINMETALL MASCHINENBAU GMBH—See Rheinmetall AG; *Int'l*, pg. 6324
RHEINMETALL NEDERLAND B.V.—See Rheinmetall AG; *Int'l*, pg. 6323
RHEINMETALL NIOA MUNITIONS PTY. LTD.—See Rheinmetall AG; *Int'l*, pg. 6324
RHEINMETALL NORDIC AS—See Rheinmetall AG; *Int'l*, pg. 6324
RHEINMETALL NORDIC AS—See Rheinmetall AG; *Int'l*, pg. 6324
RHEINMETALL NORTH AMERICA INC.—See Rheinmetall AG; *Int'l*, pg. 6324
RHEINMETALL PROTECTION SYSTEMS GMBH—See Rheinmetall AG; *Int'l*, pg. 6324
RHEINMETALL SCHWEIZ AG—See Rheinmetall AG; *Int'l*, pg. 6324
RHEINMETALL SIMULATION AUSTRALIA PTY. LTD.—See Rheinmetall AG; *Int'l*, pg. 6324
RHEINMETALL SINGAPORE PTE. LTD.—See Rheinmetall AG; *Int'l*, pg. 6324
RHEINMETALL SOLDIER ELECTRONICS GMBH—See Rheinmetall AG; *Int'l*, pg. 6323
RHEINMETALL TECHNICAL PUBLICATIONS GMBH—See Rheinmetall AG; *Int'l*, pg. 6324
RHEINMETALL TECHNICAL PUBLICATIONS SCHWEIZ AG—See Rheinmetall AG; *Int'l*, pg. 6324
RHEINMETALL VERSEIDAG BALLISTIC PROTECTION GMBH—See Rheinmetall AG; *Int'l*, pg. 6324

RHEINMETALL VERWALTUNGSGESELLSCHAFT MBH—See Rheinmetall AG; *Int'l*, pg. 6324
RHEINMETALL WAFFE MUNITION ARGES GMBH—See Rheinmetall AG; *Int'l*, pg. 6324
RHEINMETALL WAFFE MUNITION GMBH—See Rheinmetall AG; *Int'l*, pg. 6323
RHEINPFALZBUS GMBH—See Deutsche Bahn AG; *Int'l*, pg. 2052
RHEINTAL TIEFKUHLKOST ZWEIGNIEDERLASSUNG DER FROSTA AG—See FRoSTA AG; *Int'l*, pg. 2797
RHEIN-WESTERWALD NAHVERKEHR GMBH—See Deutsche Bahn AG; *Int'l*, pg. 2052
RHEINZINK AUSTRIA GMBH—See RHEINZINK GmbH & Co. KG; *Int'l*, pg. 6324
RHEINZINK BELUX S.A./N.V.—See RHEINZINK GmbH & Co. KG; *Int'l*, pg. 6324
RHEINZINK CANADA LTD—See RHEINZINK GmbH & Co. KG; *Int'l*, pg. 6324
RHEINZINK CR, S.R.O.—See RHEINZINK GmbH & Co. KG; *Int'l*, pg. 6324
RHEINZINK DANMARK A/S—See RHEINZINK GmbH & Co. KG; *Int'l*, pg. 6324
RHEINZINK FRANCE S.A.—See RHEINZINK GmbH & Co. KG; *Int'l*, pg. 6325
RHEINZINK GMBH & CO. KG; *Int'l*, pg. 6324
RHEINZINK HUNGARIA KFT.—See RHEINZINK GmbH & Co. KG; *Int'l*, pg. 6325
RHEINZINK (SCHWEIZ) AG—See RHEINZINK GmbH & Co. KG; *Int'l*, pg. 6324
RHEINZINK ZINC MANUFACTURING (SHANGHAI) CO., LTD.—See RHEINZINK GmbH & Co. KG; *Int'l*, pg. 6325
RHE MICROSYSTEMS GMBH—See Cicor Technologies Ltd.; *Int'l*, pg. 1603
RHENAG RHEINISCHE ENERGIE AKTIENGESELLSCHAFT—See RWE AG; *Int'l*, pg. 6436
RHENOY ONDERDELEN B.V.—See LKQ Corporation; *U.S. Public*, pg. 1336
RHENUM METALL LTD.—See Georg Fischer AG; *Int'l*, pg. 2937
RHENUS ALPINA AG—See RETHMANN AG & Co. KG; *Int'l*, pg. 6309
RHENUS AUTOMOTIVE SYSTEMS GMBH—See RETHMANN AG & Co. KG; *Int'l*, pg. 6309
RHENUS CONTRACT LOGISTICS AG—See RETHMANN AG & Co. KG; *Int'l*, pg. 6308
RHENUS CONTRACT LOGISTICS SA—See RETHMANN AG & Co. KG; *Int'l*, pg. 6308
RHENUS FREIGHT LOGISTICS AG—See RETHMANN AG & Co. KG; *Int'l*, pg. 6308
RHENUS INTERNATIONAL LIMITED—See RETHMANN AG & Co. KG; *Int'l*, pg. 6308
RHENUS KFT.—See RETHMANN AG & Co. KG; *Int'l*, pg. 6308
RHENUS LOGISTICS ALSACE S.A.—See RETHMANN AG & Co. KG; *Int'l*, pg. 6309
RHENUS LOGISTICS ASIA-PACIFIC LTD.—See RETHMANN AG & Co. KG; *Int'l*, pg. 6308
RHENUS LOGISTICS BULGARIA OOD—See RETHMANN AG & Co. KG; *Int'l*, pg. 6308
RHENUS LOGISTICS CHINA LTD.—See RETHMANN AG & Co. KG; *Int'l*, pg. 6308
RHENUS LOGISTICS CO., LTD.—See RETHMANN AG & Co. KG; *Int'l*, pg. 6308
RHENUS LOGISTIC SDN. BHD.—See RETHMANN AG & Co. KG; *Int'l*, pg. 6308
RHENUS LOGISTICS DO BRASIL LTDA—See RETHMANN AG & Co. KG; *Int'l*, pg. 6309
RHENUS LOGISTICS FRANCE S.A.S.—See RETHMANN AG & Co. KG; *Int'l*, pg. 6308
RHENUS LOGISTICS GMBH—See RETHMANN AG & Co. KG; *Int'l*, pg. 6308
RHENUS LOGISTICS, INC.—See RETHMANN AG & Co. KG; *Int'l*, pg. 6309
RHENUS LOGISTICS LTD.—See RETHMANN AG & Co. KG; *Int'l*, pg. 6308
RHENUS LOGISTICS LTD.—See RETHMANN AG & Co. KG; *Int'l*, pg. 6308
RHENUS LOGISTICS NV—See RETHMANN AG & Co. KG; *Int'l*, pg. 6308
RHENUS LOGISTICS OU—See RETHMANN AG & Co. KG; *Int'l*, pg. 6308
RHENUS LOGISTICS PTE. LTD.—See RETHMANN AG & Co. KG; *Int'l*, pg. 6309
RHENUS LOGISTICS S.A.—See RETHMANN AG & Co. KG; *Int'l*, pg. 6309
RHENUS LOGISTICS, S.A.U.—See RETHMANN AG & Co. KG; *Int'l*, pg. 6309
RHENUS LOGISTICS S.P.A.—See RETHMANN AG & Co. KG; *Int'l*, pg. 6309
RHENUS LOGISTICS SRL—See RETHMANN AG & Co. KG; *Int'l*, pg. 6309
RHENUS LOGISTICS, S.R.O.—See RETHMANN AG & Co. KG; *Int'l*, pg. 6309
RHENUS LOGISTICS S.R.O.—See RETHMANN AG & Co. KG; *Int'l*, pg. 6309
RHENUS LOGISTICS SVERIGE AB—See RETHMANN AG & Co. KG; *Int'l*, pg. 6309

RHENUS LOGISTICS TAIWAN LTD.—See RETHMANN AG & Co. KG; *Int'l*, pg. 6309
RHENUS LOGISTIKA D.O.O.—See RETHMANN AG & Co. KG; *Int'l*, pg. 6309
RHENUS MIDI DATA GMBH—See RETHMANN AG & Co. KG; *Int'l*, pg. 6309
RHENUS PORT LOGISTCS SP. Z O. O.—See RETHMANN AG & Co. KG; *Int'l*, pg. 6309
RHENUS PORT LOGISTICS B.V.—See RETHMANN AG & Co. KG; *Int'l*, pg. 6309
RHENUS SE & CO. KG—See RETHMANN AG & Co. KG; *Int'l*, pg. 6309
RHENUS TRANSITARIOS E LOGISTICA LDA.—See RETHMANN AG & Co. KG; *Int'l*, pg. 6309
RHEOCHEM INDIA PVT.—See Newpark Resources, Inc.; *U.S. Public*, pg. 1518
RHEOMINERALS INC.—See Lithium Americas Corp.; *Int'l*, pg. 4526
RHEON AUTOMATIC MACHINERY ASIA PACIFIC CO., LTD.—See Rheon Automatic Machinery Co., Ltd.; *Int'l*, pg. 6325
RHEON AUTOMATIC MACHINERY CO., LTD. - KAMIKAWACHI PLANT—See Rheon Automatic Machinery Co., Ltd.; *Int'l*, pg. 6325
RHEON AUTOMATIC MACHINERY CO., LTD.; *Int'l*, pg. 6325
RHEON AUTOMATIC MACHINERY GMBH—See Rheon Automatic Machinery Co., Ltd.; *Int'l*, pg. 6325
RHEON U.S.A. INC.—See Rheon Automatic Machinery Co., Ltd.; *Int'l*, pg. 6325
RHETAN ROLLING MILLS PRIVATE LIMITED—See Ashoka Metcast Limited; *Int'l*, pg. 608
RHETECH ENGINEERED PLASTICS LTD.—See HEXPOL AB; *Int'l*, pg. 3372
RHETECH, INC.—See HEXPOL AB; *Int'l*, pg. 3372
RHETECH LLC—See HEXPOL AB; *Int'l*, pg. 3372
RHETECH THERMOCOLOR LLC—See HEXPOL AB; *Int'l*, pg. 3372
RH F&B MINNESOTA, LLC—See RH; *U.S. Public*, pg. 1796
RH F&B OPERATIONS CANADA, INC.—See RH; *U.S. Public*, pg. 1796
RH FLORIDA, LLC—See Rosner Management Group, LLC; *U.S. Private*, pg. 3485
R.H. FOSTER ENERGY LLC; *U.S. Private*, pg. 3336
RHG GROUP, INC.; *U.S. Private*, pg. 3421
RHG HOME LOANS PTY. LTD.—See Resimac Group Limited; *Int'l*, pg. 6296
RHG MORTGAGE CORPORATION LIMITED—See Resimac Group Limited; *Int'l*, pg. 6296
R. & H. HALL LIMITED—See ARYZTA AG; *Int'l*, pg. 589
R & H HALL TRADING LIMITED—See ARYZTA AG; *Int'l*, pg. 589
RHHC LLC—See Robert Half Inc.; *U.S. Public*, pg. 1803
RHIAG GROUP LTD.—See LKQ Corporation; *U.S. Public*, pg. 1336
RHI CANADA INC.—See RHI Magnesita N.V.; *Int'l*, pg. 6325
RHI CHILE S.A.—See RHI Magnesita N.V.; *Int'l*, pg. 6325
RHI CLASIL LIMITED—See RHI Magnesita N.V.; *Int'l*, pg. 6325
RHI DINARIS GMBH—See RHI Magnesita N.V.; *Int'l*, pg. 6325
RHI GLAS GMBH—See RHI Magnesita N.V.; *Int'l*, pg. 6325
RHI HOLDING LLC—See NOV, Inc.; *U.S. Public*, pg. 1546
RHI MAGNESITA INDIA LIMITED—See RHI Magnesita N.V.; *Int'l*, pg. 6325
RHI MAGNESITA INDIA REFRACTORIES LIMITED—See RHI Magnesita N.V.; *Int'l*, pg. 6325
RHI MAGNESITA N.V.; *Int'l*, pg. 6325
RHI MAGNESITA SERVICES EUROPE GMBH—See RHI Magnesita N.V.; *Int'l*, pg. 6325
RHI MAGNESITA TURKEY REFRAKTER TICARET ANONIM SIRKETI—See RHI Magnesita N.V.; *Int'l*, pg. 6325
RHI MARVO S.R.L.—See RHI Magnesita N.V.; *Int'l*, pg. 6325
RHI MONOFRAX, LTD.—See RHI Magnesita N.V.; *Int'l*, pg. 6326
RHINEBECK BANCORP, INC.; *U.S. Public*, pg. 1796
RHINEBECK BANK; *U.S. Private*, pg. 3421
RHINE EQUIPMENT COMPANY; *U.S. Private*, pg. 3421
RHINEHART EQUIPMENT COMPANY; *U.S. Private*, pg. 3421
RHINEHART OIL CO. INC. - AMERICAN FORK—See Parkland Corporation; *Int'l*, pg. 5744
RHINEHART OIL CO. INC.—See Parkland Corporation; *Int'l*, pg. 5744
RHINE RUHR PUMPS & VALVES (PTY.) LTD.—See Aliaxis S.A./N.V.; *Int'l*, pg. 324
RHIN-NECKAR S.A.—See Landesbank Baden-Wurttemberg; *Int'l*, pg. 4405
RHINO 7 FRANCHISE DEVELOPMENT CORPORATION; *U.S. Private*, pg. 3421
RHINOAG, INC.—See Alamo Group Inc.; *U.S. Public*, pg. 71
RHINO COMMUNICATION RENTALS, LLC—See OwnersEdge Inc.; *U.S. Private*, pg. 3055

COMPANY NAME INDEX

RHINOCORPS LTD. CO.; *U.S. Private*, pg. 3421
RHINO EXPLORATION INC.; *Int'l*, pg. 6326
RHINO FOODS INC.; *U.S. Private*, pg. 3421
RHINO FOOTWEAR LTD.—See Alam Group of Companies; *Int'l*, pg. 289
RHINO LININGS CORPORATION; *U.S. Private*, pg. 3421
RHINOMED LIMITED; *Int'l*, pg. 6326
RHINO MINERALS PTY LTD—See Groupe Bruxelles Lambert SA; *Int'l*, pg. 3100
RHINO NOVI, INC.; *U.S. Public*, pg. 1796
RHINO RESEARCH INDUSTRIES, LLC—See New Pendulum Corporation; *U.S. Private*, pg. 2905
RHINO RESOURCE PARTNERS LP—See Royal Energy Resources, Inc.; *U.S. Public*, pg. 1815
RHI NORMAG AS—See RHI Magnesita N.V.; *Int'l*, pg. 6326
RHINO TOOL HOUSE—See Blue Sea Capital Management LLC; *U.S. Private*, pg. 592
RH INTERNACIONAL LIMITADA—See Randstad N.V.; *Int'l*, pg. 6202
RH INTERNATIONAL CORPORATION LTD.—See RATCH Group Public Company Limited; *Int'l*, pg. 6213
RHIPE JAPAN KK—See Crayon Group Holding ASA; *Int'l*, pg. 1829
RHIPE LANKA (PVT.) LIMITED—See Crayon Group Holding ASA; *Int'l*, pg. 1830
RHIPE MALAYSIA SDN. BHD.—See Crayon Group Holding ASA; *Int'l*, pg. 1830
RHIPE NEW ZEALAND LTD.—See Crayon Group Holding ASA; *Int'l*, pg. 1830
RHIPE PHILIPPINES, INC.—See Crayon Group Holding ASA; *Int'l*, pg. 1830
RHIPE SINGAPORE PTE. LTD.—See Crayon Group Holding ASA; *Int'l*, pg. 1830
RHIPE TECHNOLOGY PHILIPPINES, INC.—See Crayon Group Holding ASA; *Int'l*, pg. 1830
RHIPE TECHNOLOGY (THAILAND) CO., LTD.—See Crayon Group Holding ASA; *Int'l*, pg. 1830
RHI-REFMEX, S.A. DE C.V.—See RHI Magnesita N.V.; *Int'l*, pg. 6326
RHI REFRACTORIES AFRICA (PTY.) LTD.—See RHI Magnesita N.V.; *Int'l*, pg. 6326
RHI REFRACTORIES ANDINO C.A.—See RHI Magnesita N.V.; *Int'l*, pg. 6326
RHI REFRACTORIES ASIA LTD.—See RHI Magnesita N.V.; *Int'l*, pg. 6326
RHI REFRACTORIES ASIA PACIFIC PTE LTD—See RHI Magnesita N.V.; *Int'l*, pg. 6326
RHI REFRACTORIES ESPANA S.A.—See RHI Magnesita N.V.; *Int'l*, pg. 6326
RHI REFRACTORIES FRANCE S.A.—See RHI Magnesita N.V.; *Int'l*, pg. 6326
RHI REFRACTORIES HOLDING COMPANY—See RHI Magnesita N.V.; *Int'l*, pg. 6326
RHI REFRACTORIES ITALIANA S.R.L.—See RHI Magnesita N.V.; *Int'l*, pg. 6326
RHI REFRACTORIES NORD AB—See RHI Magnesita N.V.; *Int'l*, pg. 6326
RHI REFRACTORIES RAW MATERIAL GMBH—See RHI Magnesita N.V.; *Int'l*, pg. 6326
RHI REFRACTORIES SITE SERVICES GMBH—See RHI Magnesita N.V.; *Int'l*, pg. 6326
RHI REFRACTORIES (SITE SERVICES) LTD.—See RHI Magnesita N.V.; *Int'l*, pg. 6326
RHI REFRACTORIES—See RHI Magnesita N.V.; *Int'l*, pg. 6326
RHI REFRACTORIES UK LIMITED—See RHI Magnesita N.V.; *Int'l*, pg. 6326
R. HIRT JR. CO.; *U.S. Private*, pg. 3333
RHI TRADING (DALIAN) CO., LTD.—See RHI Magnesita N.V.; *Int'l*, pg. 6326
RHI US LTD.—See RHI Magnesita N.V.; *Int'l*, pg. 6326
R.H. KUHN COMPANY, INC.; *U.S. Private*, pg. 3336
R H LABORATORIES, INC.—See HEICO Corporation; *U.S. Public*, pg. 1021
RHL HAMBURGER LLOYD SHIPPING TRUST GMBH—See M.M. Warburg & Co. KGaA; *Int'l*, pg. 4616
RHLI INC.; *U.S. Private*, pg. 3421
RH MARINE GROUP B.V.—See Pon Holdings B.V.; *Int'l*, pg. 5919
RH MARINE NETHERLANDS B.V.—See Pon Holdings B.V.; *Int'l*, pg. 5919
RH MEXICO SIMULATION & TRAINING S.A. DE C.V.—See Rheinmetall AG; *Int'l*, pg. 6323
RHM FLUID POWER INC.; *U.S. Private*, pg. 3421
RHM KLINIK- UND ALTENHEIMBETRIEBE B.V. & CO. KG—See Waterland Private Equity Investments B.V.; *Int'l*, pg. 8357
R.H.MOORE COMPANY, INC.; *U.S. Private*, pg. 3336
R&H MOTOR CARS LTD; *U.S. Private*, pg. 3332
RHN CLARK MEMORIAL HOSPITAL, LLC—See Apollo Global Management, Inc.; *U.S. Public*, pg. 158
RHN CLARK MEMORIAL PHYSICIAN PRACTICES, LLC—See Apollo Global Management, Inc.; *U.S. Public*, pg. 158
RHN SCOTT PHYSICIAN PRACTICES, LLC—See Apollo Global Management, Inc.; *U.S. Public*, pg. 158

RHO ACCELERATION, L.P.—See Rho Capital Partners, Inc.; *U.S. Private*, pg. 3421
THE RHOADS GROUP—See The Interpublic Group of Companies, Inc.; *U.S. Public*, pg. 2105
RHOADS METAL FABRICATIONS INC.; *U.S. Private*, pg. 3421
RHO CAPITAL PARTNERS, INC.; *U.S. Private*, pg. 3421
RHODA LEE, INC.; *U.S. Private*, pg. 3421
RHODAR LTD.—See Lexia Solutions Group Ltd; *Int'l*, pg. 4472
RHODE INVESTMENTS LLC—See Goff Capital, Inc.; *U.S. Private*, pg. 1726
RHODE ISLAND AIRPORT CORP; *U.S. Private*, pg. 3422
RHODE ISLAND BLOOD CENTER; *U.S. Private*, pg. 3422
RHODE ISLAND COMMUNITY FOOD BANK; *U.S. Private*, pg. 3422
RHODE ISLAND CONVENTION CENTER AUTHORITY; *U.S. Private*, pg. 3422
RHODE ISLAND CREDIT UNION; *U.S. Private*, pg. 3422
THE RHODE ISLAND FOUNDATION; *U.S. Private*, pg. 4106
RHODE ISLAND MONTHLY COMMUNICATIONS, INC.—See Gannett Co., Inc.; *U.S. Public*, pg. 905
RHODE ISLAND MONTHLY COMMUNICATIONS, INC—See Gannett Co., Inc.; *U.S. Public*, pg. 905
RHODE ISLAND NOVELTY, INC.; *U.S. Private*, pg. 3422
RHODE ISLAND PBS FOUNDATION; *U.S. Private*, pg. 3422
RHODE ISLAND PHILHARMONIC ORCHESTRA INC.; *U.S. Private*, pg. 3422
THE RHODE ISLAND QUALITY INSTITUTE; *U.S. Private*, pg. 4106
RHODE ISLAND TEXTILE COMPANY, INC.; *U.S. Private*, pg. 3422
RHODEN AUTO CENTER INC.; *U.S. Private*, pg. 3422
RHODES ASSOCIATES; *U.S. Private*, pg. 3422
RHODE & SCHWARZ DVS GMBH—See Rohde & Schwarz GmbH & Co. KG; *Int'l*, pg. 6384
RHODE & SCHWARZ UK LTD.—See Rohde & Schwarz GmbH & Co. KG; *Int'l*, pg. 6384
RHODES FOOD GROUP (PTY) LTD.; *Int'l*, pg. 6326
RHODES GROCERY INC.; *U.S. Private*, pg. 3422
RHODES INC.; *U.S. Private*, pg. 3422
RHODES INTERNATIONAL, INC.; *U.S. Private*, pg. 3422
RHODES INTERNATIONAL—See Rhodes International, Inc.; *U.S. Private*, pg. 3422
RHODES OIL COMPANY INC.; *U.S. Private*, pg. 3422
RHODES TECHNOLOGIES L.P.—See Purdue Pharma LP; *U.S. Private*, pg. 3305
RHODIA ARGENTIA SA—See Solvay S.A.; *Int'l*, pg. 7081
RHODIA ASIA PACIFIC PTE LTD—See Solvay S.A.; *Int'l*, pg. 7081
RHODIA BELGIUM SA—See Solvay S.A.; *Int'l*, pg. 7081
RHODIA BRAZIL LTDA—See Solvay S.A.; *Int'l*, pg. 7081
RHODIA CHILE LTDA—See Solvay S.A.; *Int'l*, pg. 7081
RHODIA CHINA CO., LTD—See Solvay S.A.; *Int'l*, pg. 7081
RHODIA DE MEXICO SA DE CV—See Solvay S.A.; *Int'l*, pg. 7081
RHODIA ENERGY ASIA PACIFIC CO. LTD—See Solvay S.A.; *Int'l*, pg. 7081
RHODIA ENERGY BRAZIL LTDA—See Solvay S.A.; *Int'l*, pg. 7081
RHODIA ENERGY GHG S.A.S.—See Solvay S.A.; *Int'l*, pg. 7081
RHODIA ENERGY S.A.S.—See Solvay S.A.; *Int'l*, pg. 7081
RHODIA ESPECIALIDADES SA DE CV—See Solvay S.A.; *Int'l*, pg. 7081
RHODIA FEIXIANG SPECIALTY CHEMICALS CO., LTD—See Solvay S.A.; *Int'l*, pg. 7081
RHODIA GMBH—See Solvay S.A.; *Int'l*, pg. 7081
RHODIA HALIFAX—See Solvay S.A.; *Int'l*, pg. 7081
RHODIA HOLDING INC—See Solvay S.A.; *Int'l*, pg. 7081
RHODIA HOLDINGS LTD—See Solvay S.A.; *Int'l*, pg. 7081
RHODIA IBERIA S.L.—See Solvay S.A.; *Int'l*, pg. 7081
RHODIA ITALIA SPA—See Solvay S.A.; *Int'l*, pg. 7081
RHODIA JAPAN K.K.—See Solvay S.A.; *Int'l*, pg. 7081
RHODIA KOREA CO. LTD—See Solvay S.A.; *Int'l*, pg. 7081
RHODIA LABORATOIRE DU FUTUR S.A.S.—See Solvay S.A.; *Int'l*, pg. 7081
RHODIA LIMITED—See Solvay S.A.; *Int'l*, pg. 7081
RHODIANA CORP.; *U.S. Private*, pg. 3422
RHODIA NICCA LTD—See Solvay S.A.; *Int'l*, pg. 7081
RHODIA OPERATIONS S.A.S.—See Solvay S.A.; *Int'l*, pg. 7081
RHODIA POLIAMIDA BRASIL LTDA—See Solvay S.A.; *Int'l*, pg. 7081
RHODIA POLIAMIDA E ESPECIALIDADES LTDA—See Solvay S.A.; *Int'l*, pg. 7081
RHODIA POLYMERS & SPECIALTIES INDIA PRIVATE LIMITED—See Solvay S.A.; *Int'l*, pg. 7081
RHODIA REORGANISATION LTD—See Solvay S.A.; *Int'l*, pg. 7081
RHODIA SAS—See Solvay S.A.; *Int'l*, pg. 7081
RHODIA SILICA KOREA CO. LTD—See Solvay S.A.; *Int'l*, pg. 7081
RHODIA SILICA QINGDAO CO., LTD—See Solvay S.A.; *Int'l*, pg. 7081

RHODIUM ENTERPRISES, INC.; *U.S. Private*, pg. 3422
RHODIUS GMBH—See Equistone Partners Europe Limited; *Int'l*, pg. 2487
RHODIUS MAGYARORSZAG KFT.—See Equistone Partners Europe Limited; *Int'l*, pg. 2487
RHODIUS SAFETY AND ENVIRONMENTAL SOLUTIONS (KUNSHAN) CO., LTD—See Equistone Partners Europe Limited; *Int'l*, pg. 2487
RHOMBERG BAHNTECHNIK GMBH—See Rhomberg Sersa Rail Holding GmbH; *Int'l*, pg. 6327
RHOMBERG FAHRLEITUNGSBAU GMBH—See Rhomberg Sersa Rail Holding GmbH; *Int'l*, pg. 6327
RHOMBERG RAIL AUSTRALIA PTY LTD—See Rhomberg Sersa Rail Holding GmbH; *Int'l*, pg. 6327
RHOMBERG RAIL CONSULT GMBH—See Rhomberg Sersa Rail Holding GmbH; *Int'l*, pg. 6327
RHOMBERG SERSA RAIL HOLDING GMBH; *Int'l*, pg. 6326
RHOMBERG SERSA UK LIMITED—See Rhomberg Sersa Rail Holding GmbH; *Int'l*, pg. 6327
RHOM BHO PROPERTY PCL; *Int'l*, pg. 6326
RHOMBIC CORPORATION—See Mitsubishi Chemical Group Corporation; *Int'l*, pg. 4934
RHOMBUS ENERGY SOLUTIONS, INC. - HIGH POWER ENERGY GROUP—See BorgWarner Inc.; *U.S. Public*, pg. 371
RHOMBUS ENERGY SOLUTIONS, INC.—See BorgWarner Inc.; *U.S. Public*, pg. 371
RHOMOBILE, INC.; *U.S. Private*, pg. 3422
RHON-CATERINGGESELLSCHAFT MBH—See Asklepios Kliniken GmbH & Co. KGaA; *Int'l*, pg. 624
RHONE ALPES CREATION SA; *Int'l*, pg. 6327
RHONE CAPITAL LLC—See Rhone Group, LLC; *U.S. Private*, pg. 3422
RHONE GAZ—See UGI Corporation; *U.S. Public*, pg. 2222
RHONE GROUP ADVISORS LLC—See Rhone Group, LLC; *U.S. Private*, pg. 3424
RHONE GROUP, LLC; *U.S. Private*, pg. 3422
RHONE MA HOLDINGS BERHAD; *Int'l*, pg. 6327
RHONE SUD EST DECORATION S.A.—See Akzo Nobel N.V.; *Int'l*, pg. 274
RHONG KHEN INDUSTRIES SDN. BHD.—See Rhong Khen International Berhad; *Int'l*, pg. 6327
RHONG KHEN INTERNATIONAL BERHAD; *Int'l*, pg. 6327
RHON-INNOVATIONS GMBH—See Asklepios Kliniken GmbH & Co. KGaA; *Int'l*, pg. 624
RHON-KLINIKUM AKTIENGESELLSCHAFT—See Asklepios Kliniken GmbH & Co. KGaA; *Int'l*, pg. 624
RHOSS DEUTSCHLAND GMBH—See NIBE Industrier AB; *Int'l*, pg. 5262
RHOTERRA GESELLSCHAFT FUR IMMOBILIENVERWALTUNG MBH—See UniCredit S.p.A.; *Int'l*, pg. 8038
RHO VENTURES LLC—See Rho Capital Partners, Inc.; *U.S. Private*, pg. 3421
R.H. PETERSON CO.; *U.S. Private*, pg. 3336
RH PETROGAS LIMITED; *Int'l*, pg. 6319
RHP HOTEL PROPERTIES, LP—See Ryman Hospitality Properties, Inc.; *U.S. Public*, pg. 1829
RHP INVESTMENTS, INC.—See Ryman Hospitality Properties, Inc.; *U.S. Public*, pg. 1829
RHP (MUKAH) PTE. LTD.—See RH Petrogas Limited; *Int'l*, pg. 6319
RHP PARTNER, LLC—See Ryman Hospitality Properties, Inc.; *U.S. Public*, pg. 1829
RHP SALAWATI HOLDINGS BV—See RH Petrogas Limited; *Int'l*, pg. 6319
R.H. RENY INC.; *U.S. Private*, pg. 3336
RH RETAIL HOLDING GMBH—See Aurelius Equity Opportunities SE & Co. KGaA; *Int'l*, pg. 709
RH SAN FRANCISCO F&B, LLC—See RH; *U.S. Public*, pg. 1796
RH SCALES CO. INC.; *U.S. Private*, pg. 3421
R.H. SHEPPARD CO., INC.—See Balmoral Funds LLC; *U.S. Private*, pg. 461
R.H. SMITH DISTRIBUTING CO.; *U.S. Private*, pg. 3336
RH; *U.S. Public*, pg. 1796
RHT CAPITAL PTE.LTD.—See RHT Holdings Pte. Ltd.; *Int'l*, pg. 6327
RH TECHNOLOGIES LTD.; *Int'l*, pg. 6319
RHT HEALTH TRUST; *Int'l*, pg. 6327
RHT HOLDING LTD.; *Int'l*, pg. 6327
RHT HOLDINGS PTE. LTD.; *Int'l*, pg. 6327
R & H TRANSPORT SERVICES PTY LTD—See Japan Post Holdings Co., Ltd.; *Int'l*, pg. 3901
R.H. VERDUYN GRANITE CO. LTD.—See Family Memorials Inc.; *Int'l*, pg. 2612
RH WEALTH ADVISORS, INC.—See Larry Mathis Financial Planning, LLC; *U.S. Private*, pg. 2393
R.H. WHITE COMPANIES INC.; *U.S. Private*, pg. 3336
R.H. WHITE CONSTRUCTION COMPANY, INC.—See R.H. White Companies Inc.; *U.S. Private*, pg. 3336
R.H. WHITE CONSTRUCTION CO.—See R.H. White Companies Inc.; *U.S. Private*, pg. 3336
R.H. WYNER ASSOCIATES INC.; *U.S. Private*, pg. 3336
RHYMES AND COMPANY ADVERTISING; *U.S. Private*, pg. 3424
RHYOLITE RESOURCES LTD.; *Int'l*, pg. 6327

RH YOUNTVILLE F&B, LLC—See RH; *U.S. Public,* pg. 1796
RHYTHM AND HUES INC.; *U.S. Private,* pg. 3424
RHYTHM BIOSCIENCES LTD.; *Int'l,* pg. 6327
RHYTHM CO., LTD.; *Int'l,* pg. 6327
RHYTHM ENGINEERING; *U.S. Private,* pg. 3424
RHYTHM GUANGZHOU CORPORATION—See THK CO., LTD.; *Int'l,* pg. 7713
RHYTHM HOLDING COMPANY, INC.; *U.S. Private,* pg. 3424
RHYTHMIA MEDICAL, INC.—See Boston Scientific Corporation; *U.S. Public,* pg. 375
RHYTHM INDUSTRIAL (DONGGUAN) LTD.—See Rhythm Co., Ltd.; *Int'l,* pg. 6328
RHYTHM INDUSTRIAL (H.K.) CO., LTD—See Rhythm Co., Ltd.; *Int'l,* pg. 6328
RHYTHM KAIHATSU CO., LTD.—See Rhythm Co., Ltd.; *Int'l,* pg. 6328
RHYTHM KYOSHIN HANOI CO., LTD.—See Rhythm Co., Ltd.; *Int'l,* pg. 6328
RHYTHMLINK INTERNATIONAL, LLC—See The Graham Group, Inc.; *U.S. Private,* pg. 4037
RHYTHM NORTH AMERICA CORPORATION—See THK CO., LTD.; *Int'l,* pg. 7713
RHYTHMONE, LLC—See Nexxen International Ltd.; *Int'l,* pg. 5251
RHYTHM PHARMACEUTICALS, INC.; *U.S. Public,* pg. 1796
RHYTHM PRECISION VIETNAM CO., LTD.—See Rhythm Co., Ltd.; *Int'l,* pg. 6328
RHYTHM SERVICE CO., LTD.—See Rhythm Co., Ltd.; *Int'l,* pg. 6328
RHYTHM U.S.A. INC.—See Rhythm Co., Ltd.; *Int'l,* pg. 6328
RHYWACO (H.K.) CO., LTD—See Rhythm Co., Ltd.; *Int'l,* pg. 6328
RIA ADVISORY LLC—See Avance Investment Management, LLC; *U.S. Private,* pg. 403
RIACON SDN. BHD.—See Eupe Corporation Berhad; *Int'l,* pg. 2526
RIADA TRADING COMPANY INCORPORATED; *U.S. Private,* pg. 3424
RIA DE CENTROAMERICA, S.A. DE C.V.—See Euronet Worldwide, Inc.; *U.S. Public,* pg. 798
RIA DEUTSCHLAND GMBH—See Euronet Worldwide, Inc.; *U.S. Public,* pg. 798
RIA ENVIA, INC.—See Euronet Worldwide, Inc.; *U.S. Public,* pg. 798
RIA FINANCIAL SERVICES NORWAY AS—See Euronet Worldwide, Inc.; *U.S. Public,* pg. 798
RIA FINANCIAL SERVICES SWEDEN AB—See Euronet Worldwide, Inc.; *U.S. Public,* pg. 798
RIA FOOD CENTRE SDN. BHD.—See Eupe Corporation Berhad; *Int'l,* pg. 2526
RIAG OBERFLACHENTECHNIK AG—See Aalberts N.V.; *Int'l,* pg. 35
RIA IN A BOX LLC; *U.S. Private,* pg. 3424
RIALCA—See Corporacion Venezolana de Guayana; *Int'l,* pg. 1805
RIAL LEICHTMETALLFELGEN GMBH—See UNIWHEELS Management (Switzerland) AG; *Int'l,* pg. 8083
RIALTO CAPITAL MANAGEMENT, LLC—See Stone Point Capital LLC; *U.S. Private,* pg. 3825
RIALTO DISTRIBUTION LTD—See Reading International, Inc.; *U.S. Public,* pg. 1768
RIALTO HOLDINGS, LLC—See Lennar Corporation; *U.S. Public,* pg. 1307
RIALTO MANAGEMENT GROUP, LLC—See Lennar Corporation; *U.S. Public,* pg. 1307
RIANLON AMERICAS, INC.—See Rianlon Corporation; *Int'l,* pg. 6328
RIANLON CORPORATION; *Int'l,* pg. 6328
RIANTA PACKAGING SYSTEMS GMBH—See OPTIMA Packaging Group GmbH; *Int'l,* pg. 5603
RIANTICS A/S—See Korber AG; *Int'l,* pg. 4281
RIA PAYMENT INSTITUTION EP, S.A.—See Euronet Worldwide, Inc.; *U.S. Public,* pg. 798
RIA ROHR- UND INDUSTRIEANLAGENBAU GMBH—See Christof Holding AG; *Int'l,* pg. 1587
RIAS A/S; *Int'l,* pg. 6328
RIATA CAPITAL GROUP LLC; *U.S. Private,* pg. 3424
RIATA LIFE SCIENCES PVT. LTD.—See Novonesis A/S; *Int'l,* pg. 5469
RIA TELECOMMUNICATIONS OF NEW YORK, INC.—See Euronet Worldwide, Inc.; *U.S. Public,* pg. 798
RIAZZI RHYNE & SWAIM INVESTMENT GROUP OF WELLS FARGO ADVISORS—See Wells Fargo & Company; *U.S. Public,* pg. 2345
RIBAGRANDE ENERGIA, S.L.—See ACS, Actividades de Construccion y Servicios, S.A.; *Int'l,* pg. 116
RIBA MUNDO TECNOLOGIA SA; *Int'l,* pg. 6328
RIBA NERETVA D.D. KONJIC; *Int'l,* pg. 6328
RIBARSKO GAZDINSTVO AD; *Int'l,* pg. 6328
RIBARSTVO A.D.; *Int'l,* pg. 6328
RIB ASIA LTD.—See Schneider Electric SE; *Int'l,* pg. 6625
RIB A/S—See Schneider Electric SE; *Int'l,* pg. 6625
RIBA TEXTILES LIMITED; *Int'l,* pg. 6328
RI/BB ACQUISITION CORP.—See AutoNation, Inc.; *U.S. Public,* pg. 237

RIBBIT LEAP, LTD.; *U.S. Public,* pg. 1796
RIBBON COMMUNICATIONS CZECH REPUBLIC S.R.O.—See Ribbon Communications Inc.; *U.S. Public,* pg. 1797
RIBBON COMMUNICATIONS DO BRASIL LTDA—See Ribbon Communications Inc.; *U.S. Public,* pg. 1797
RIBBON COMMUNICATIONS FEDERAL INC.—See Ribbon Communications Inc.; *U.S. Public,* pg. 1797
RIBBON COMMUNICATIONS FRANCE EURL—See Ribbon Communications Inc.; *U.S. Public,* pg. 1797
RIBBON COMMUNICATIONS GERMANY GMBH—See Ribbon Communications Inc.; *U.S. Public,* pg. 1797
RIBBON COMMUNICATIONS HONG KONG LIMITED—See Ribbon Communications Inc.; *U.S. Public,* pg. 1797
RIBBON COMMUNICATIONS INC.; *U.S. Public,* pg. 1796
RIBBON COMMUNICATIONS ISRAEL LIMITED—See Ribbon Communications Inc.; *U.S. Public,* pg. 1797
RIBBON COMMUNICATIONS K.K.—See Ribbon Communications Inc.; *U.S. Public,* pg. 1797
RIBBON COMMUNICATIONS MALAYSIA SDN. BHD.—See Ribbon Communications Inc.; *U.S. Public,* pg. 1797
RIBBON COMMUNICATIONS OPERATING COMPANY, INC.—See Ribbon Communications Inc.; *U.S. Public,* pg. 1797
RIBBON COMMUNICATIONS RUS LIMITED LIABILITY COMPANY—See Ribbon Communications Inc.; *U.S. Public,* pg. 1797
RIBBON COMMUNICATIONS SINGAPORE PTE. LTD.—See Ribbon Communications Inc.; *U.S. Public,* pg. 1797
RIBBON COMMUNICATIONS SWITZERLAND GMBH—See Ribbon Communications Inc.; *U.S. Public,* pg. 1797
RIBBON NETWORKS LTD. CO.—See Ribbon Communications Inc.; *U.S. Public,* pg. 1797
RIBBONS EXPRESS, INC.; *U.S. Private,* pg. 3425
RIB CADX PTY LIMITED—See Schneider Electric SE; *Int'l,* pg. 6625
RIB CITY GRILL, INC.; *U.S. Private,* pg. 3424
RIB COSINUS AG—See Schneider Electric SE; *Int'l,* pg. 6625
RIB COSINUS GMBH—See Schneider Electric SE; *Int'l,* pg. 6625
RIB CRIB BBQ INC.; *U.S. Private,* pg. 3424
RIB DEUTSCHLAND GMBH—See Schneider Electric SE; *Int'l,* pg. 6625
RIBECK & CO.; *U.S. Private,* pg. 3425
RIBEKK AS—See Entra ASA; *Int'l,* pg. 2452
RIBELIN SALES INC.—See EQT AB; *Int'l,* pg. 2469
RIBERA LAB, S.L.U.—See Centene Corporation; *U.S. Public,* pg. 470
RIBER S.A.; *Int'l,* pg. 6328
RIB GROUP LIMITED—See Brown & Brown, Inc.; *U.S. Public,* pg. 402
RIB ITWO SOFTWARE, INC.—See Schneider Electric SE; *Int'l,* pg. 6625
RIB ITWO SOFTWARE PRIVATE LIMITED—See Schneider Electric SE; *Int'l,* pg. 6625
RIB LEIPZIG GMBH—See Schneider Electric SE; *Int'l,* pg. 6625
RIB MC2 INCORPORATED—See Schneider Electric SE; *Int'l,* pg. 6625
RIBNJAK SUTJESKA A.D.; *Int'l,* pg. 6328
RIBO FASHION GROUP CO., LTD.; *Int'l,* pg. 6328
RIBOMIC; *Int'l,* pg. 6328
RIBOTEKS D.O.O.—See Victoria Group a.d.; *Int'l,* pg. 8188
RIB PTE. LIMITED—See Schneider Electric SE; *Int'l,* pg. 6625
RIB SAA SOFTWARE ENGINEERING GMBH—See Schneider Electric SE; *Int'l,* pg. 6625
RIB SOFTWARE (AMERICAS) INC.—See Schneider Electric SE; *Int'l,* pg. 6625
RIB SOFTWARE DMCC—See Schneider Electric SE; *Int'l,* pg. 6625
RIB SOFTWARE GMBH—See Schneider Electric SE; *Int'l,* pg. 6624
RIB SOFTWARE NZ LIMITED—See Schneider Electric SE; *Int'l,* pg. 6625
RIB SOFTWARE PTY. LTD.—See Schneider Electric SE; *Int'l,* pg. 6625
RIB SOFTWARE (UK) LTD.—See Schneider Electric SE; *Int'l,* pg. 6625
RIB SPAIN SA—See Schneider Electric SE; *Int'l,* pg. 6625
RIB STAVEBNI SOFTWARE S.R.O.—See Schneider Electric SE; *Int'l,* pg. 6625
RIB U.S. COST INCORPORATED—See Schneider Electric SE; *Int'l,* pg. 6625
RICA AUTO PARTS CO LTD—See Tokai Rika Co., Ltd.; *Int'l,* pg. 7780
RICARDO-AEA LIMITED—See Ricardo plc; *Int'l,* pg. 6329
RICARDO AUSTRALIA PTY. LTD.—See Ricardo plc; *Int'l,* pg. 6328
RICARDO BEIJING COMPANY LIMITED—See Ricardo plc; *Int'l,* pg. 6328
RICARDO BEVERLY HILLS, INC.; *U.S. Private,* pg. 3425

RICARDO CERTIFICATION B.V.—See Ricardo plc; *Int'l,* pg. 6329
RICARDO CERTIFICATION DENMARK APS—See Ricardo plc; *Int'l,* pg. 6329
RICARDO.CH AG—See TX Group AG; *Int'l,* pg. 7992
RICARDO DEFENSE, INC.—See Ricardo plc; *Int'l,* pg. 6329
RICARDO DEUTSCHLAND GMBH—See Ricardo plc; *Int'l,* pg. 6329
RICARDO ENERGY ENVIRONMENT & PLANNING PTY. LTD.—See Ricardo plc; *Int'l,* pg. 6329
RICARDO HONG KONG LIMITED—See Ricardo plc; *Int'l,* pg. 6329
RICARDO, INC.—See Ricardo plc; *Int'l,* pg. 6329
RICARDO INDIA PRIVATE LIMITED—See Ricardo plc; *Int'l,* pg. 6329
RICARDO JAPAN K.K.—See Ricardo plc; *Int'l,* pg. 6329
RICARDO MOTORCYCLE ITALIA S.R.L.—See Ricardo plc; *Int'l,* pg. 6329
RICARDO NEDERLAND B.V.—See Ricardo plc; *Int'l,* pg. 6329
RICARDO PEREZ, S.A.—See ITOCHU Corporation; *Int'l,* pg. 3841
RICARDO PLC; *Int'l,* pg. 6328
RICARDO PRAGUE S.R.O.—See Ricardo plc; *Int'l,* pg. 6329
RICARDO RAIL AUSTRALIA PTY. LTD.—See Ricardo plc; *Int'l,* pg. 6329
RICARDO RAIL (TAIWAN) LTD.—See Ricardo plc; *Int'l,* pg. 6329
RICARDO SHANGHAI COMPANY LIMITED—See Ricardo plc; *Int'l,* pg. 6329
RICARDO SOUTH AFRICA (PTY) LTD.—See Ricardo plc; *Int'l,* pg. 6329
RICARDO STRATEGIC CONSULTING GMBH—See Ricardo plc; *Int'l,* pg. 6329
RICARDO UK LIMITED—See Ricardo plc; *Int'l,* pg. 6329
RICARD SA—See Pernod Ricard S.A.; *Int'l,* pg. 5811
RICART FORD INC.; *U.S. Private,* pg. 3425
RICAUTO S.P.A.—See s.a. D'Ieteren n.v.; *Int'l,* pg. 6448
RICCAR AMERICA, INC.—See Tacony Corporation; *U.S. Private,* pg. 3921
RICCHETTI CERAMIC INC.—See QuattroR SGR S.p.A.; *Int'l,* pg. 6157
RICCIARDI BROTHERS INC.; *U.S. Private,* pg. 3425
THE RICCIARDI GROUP CORP.; *U.S. Private,* pg. 4106
RICCIARELLI S.P.A.; *Int'l,* pg. 6329
RICE AUTOMOTIVE GROUP; *U.S. Private,* pg. 3425
RICEBRAN TECHNOLOGIES; *U.S. Private,* pg. 1797
RICE BUICK-GMC, INC.—See Rice Automotive Group; *U.S. Private,* pg. 3425
RICE CHRIST, INC.; *U.S. Private,* pg. 3425
RICE CHRYSLER DODGE, INC.—See Rice Automotive Group; *U.S. Private,* pg. 3425
RICECO INTERNATIONAL BANGLADESH LTD.—See UPL Limited; *Int'l,* pg. 8089
RICECO LLC—See UPL Limited; *Int'l,* pg. 8090
THE RICE COMPANY OF FIJI LIMITED—See Flour Mills of Fiji Limited; *Int'l,* pg. 2708
THE RICE COMPANY; *U.S. Private,* pg. 4106
RICE DAUBNEY PTY LTD—See HDR, Inc.; *U.S. Private,* pg. 1890
RICE EPICUREAN MARKET; *U.S. Private,* pg. 3425
RICE FIELD CORPORATION; *U.S. Private,* pg. 3425
RICE GARDEN INC.—See Arbor Private Investment Company, LLC; *U.S. Private,* pg. 309
RICEGROWERS LIMITED; *Int'l,* pg. 6329
RICE, HALL, JAMES & ASSOCIATES; *U.S. Private,* pg. 3425
RICE-KILROY CONSTRUCTION COMPANY INC.; *U.S. Private,* pg. 3425
RICE LAKE DE MEXICO—See Rice Lake Weighing Systems, Inc.; *U.S. Private,* pg. 3425
RICE LAKE WEIGHING SYSTEMS EUROPE B.V.—See Rice Lake Weighing Systems, Inc.; *U.S. Private,* pg. 3425
RICE LAKE WEIGHING SYSTEMS, INC.; *U.S. Private,* pg. 3425
RICELAND FOODS, INC.; *U.S. Private,* pg. 3425
RICELAND MAGYARORSZAG KFT—See Ebro Foods S.A.; *Int'l,* pg. 2287
RICELAND PETROLEUM COMPANY; *U.S. Private,* pg. 3425
RICE PACKAGING, INC.; *U.S. Private,* pg. 3425
RICEPOINT ADMINISTRATION INC.—See Computershare Limited; *Int'l,* pg. 1760
RICERCHE E STUDI R & S S.P.A.—See Mediobanca-Banca di Credito Finanziario S.p.A.; *Int'l,* pg. 4778
RICE REHABILITATION ASSOCIATES, LIMITED PARTNERSHIP—See U.S. Physical Therapy, Inc.; *U.S. Public,* pg. 2216
RICE RESEARCH AUSTRALIA PTY LTD—See Ricegrowers Limited; *Int'l,* pg. 6329
RICETEC, INC.; *U.S. Private,* pg. 3425
RICE TOYOTA SCION & COLLISION CENTER; *U.S. Private,* pg. 3425
RICHA INDUSTRIES LTD.; *Int'l,* pg. 6330
RICHA INFO SYSTEMS LIMITED; *Int'l,* pg. 6330

RICH ANDVORD GRAFISK AS—See Sycamore Partners Management, LP; *U.S. Private*, pg. 3897
RICHANN LLP; *U.S. Private*, pg. 3427
RICHARD-ALLAN SCIENTIFIC COMPANY—See Thermo Fisher Scientific Inc.; *U.S. Public*, pg. 2152
RICHARD BAUER & CO. INC.; *U.S. Private*, pg. 3427
RICHARD BITTNER AG—See Perrigo Company plc; *Int'l*, pg. 5814
RICHARD BRADY & ASSOCIATES, INC.; *U.S. Private*, pg. 3427
RICHARD CANTRELL; *U.S. Private*, pg. 3428
RICHARD COSTAIN LTD—See Costain Group PLC; *Int'l*, pg. 1815
RICHARD C. YOUNG & CO., LTD.; *U.S. Private*, pg. 3428
RICHARD DOLTON LIMITED—See The Skipton Building Society; *Int'l*, pg. 7687
THE RICHARD E. JACOBS GROUP, LLC; *U.S. Private*, pg. 4106
RICHARD E. PIERSON CONSTRUCTION COMPANY, INC. - ASPHALT PLANT—See Richard E. Pierson Construction Company, Inc.; *U.S. Private*, pg. 3428
RICHARD E. PIERSON CONSTRUCTION COMPANY, INC. - LOGAN PLANT—See Richard E. Pierson Construction Company, Inc.; *U.S. Private*, pg. 3428
RICHARD E. PIERSON CONSTRUCTION COMPANY, INC.; *U.S. Private*, pg. 3428
RICHARD FRITZ GMBH & CO. KG—See Turkiye Is Bankasi A.S.; *Int'l*, pg. 7976
RICHARD GINORI 1735 S.P.A.—See Kering S.A.; *Int'l*, pg. 4135
RICHARD G. JENNINGS III ENTERPRISES; *U.S. Private*, pg. 3428
RICHARD GOETTLE INC.; *U.S. Private*, pg. 3428
RICHARD HOGGS LINDLEY (HELLAS) GREECE LIMITED—See Lovell Minnick Partners LLC; *U.S. Private*, pg. 2502
RICHARD HOGGS LINDLEY (INDIA) LIMITED—See Lovell Minnick Partners LLC; *U.S. Private*, pg. 2502
RICHARD IRVIN & SONS LIMITED; *Int'l*, pg. 6330
RICHARD KARR CADILLAC BUICK PONTIAC GMC; *U.S. Private*, pg. 3428
RICHARD KAY AUTOMOTIVE; *U.S. Private*, pg. 3428
RICHARD LAYNE; *U.S. Private*, pg. 3428
RICHARD LEEDS INTERNATIONAL; *U.S. Private*, pg. 3420
RICHARD MEEK AIR CONDITIONING, INC.—See Wind Point Advisors LLC; *U.S. Private*, pg. 4536
RICHARD O'BRIEN COMPANIES, INC.; *U.S. Private*, pg. 3428
RICHARD OIL AND FUEL LLC—See AIP, LLC; *U.S. Private*, pg. 136
RICHARD OLIVER UNDERWRITING MANAGERS PTY LIMITED—See Willis Towers Watson Public Limited Company; *Int'l*, pg. 8416
RICHARD PETTY DRIVING EXPERIENCE, INC.—See BV Investment Partners, LLC; *U.S. Private*, pg. 699
RICHARD PETTY MOTORSPORTS LLC—See Booth Creek Management Corporation; *U.S. Private*, pg. 616
RICHARD PETTY MOTORSPORTS LLC—See BV Investment Partners, LLC; *U.S. Private*, pg. 699
RICHARD PIERIS & CO. LTD.; *Int'l*, pg. 6330
RICHARD PIERIS DISTRIBUTORS LTD.—See Richard Pieris & Co. Ltd.; *Int'l*, pg. 6330
RICHARD PIERIS EXPORTS LTD.—See Richard Pieris & Co. Ltd.; *Int'l*, pg. 6330
RICHARD PIERIS FINANCE LTD.—See Richard Pieris & Co. Ltd.; *Int'l*, pg. 6330
RICHARD PIERIS GROUP SERVICES (PVT) LTD.—See Richard Pieris & Co. Ltd.; *Int'l*, pg. 6330
RICHARD PIERIS NATURAL FOAMS LTD.—See Richard Pieris & Co. Ltd.; *Int'l*, pg. 6330
RICHARD PIERIS RUBBER COMPOUNDS LTD.—See Richard Pieris & Co. Ltd.; *Int'l*, pg. 6330
RICHARD PIERIS RUBBER PRODUCTS LTD—See Richard Pieris & Co. Ltd.; *Int'l*, pg. 6330
RICHARD PIERIS SECURITIES (PVT) LTD—See Richard Pieris & Co. Ltd.; *Int'l*, pg. 6330
RICHARD PIERIS TYRE CO. LTD.—See Richard Pieris & Co. Ltd.; *Int'l*, pg. 6330
RICHARD P. MORTENSON P. C.; *U.S. Private*, pg. 3428
RICHARD SANKEY & SON LTD.—See Fiskars Oyj Abp; *Int'l*, pg. 2694
RICHARDSAPEX INC.; *U.S. Private*, pg. 3428
RICHARD SAS—See Sioen Industries NV; *Int'l*, pg. 6960
RICHARDS BAY MINERALS PTY LTD.—See Rio Tinto plc; *Int'l*, pg. 6347
RICHARD'S BRICK CO.; *U.S. Private*, pg. 3428
RICHARDS BROTHERS OF MOUNTAIN GROVE; *U.S. Private*, pg. 3428
RICHARDS BUILDING SUPPLY COMPANY; *U.S. Private*, pg. 3428
RICHARD'S CAJUN FOODS CORP.—See Altamont Capital Partners; *U.S. Private*, pg. 205
RICHARDS/CARLBERG; *U.S. Private*, pg. 3429
RICHARD SCHERPE GMBH & CO.—See Aurelius Equity Opportunities SE & Co. KGaA; *Int'l*, pg. 709
RICHARD SCHULTZ DESIGN, LLC—See MillerKnoll, Inc.; *U.S. Public*, pg. 1447
RICHARDS CORPORATION; *U.S. Private*, pg. 3428

RICHARDS ELECTRIC MOTOR CO.; *U.S. Private*, pg. 3428
RICHARDS ELECTRIC SUPPLY CO., INC.; *U.S. Private*, pg. 3429
THE RICHARDS GROUP, INC.; *U.S. Private*, pg. 4106
THE RICHARDS GROUP, INC.—See The Richards Group, Inc.; *U.S. Private*, pg. 4107
THE RICHARDS HOGG LINDLEY GROUP LIMITED—See Lovell Minnick Partners LLC; *U.S. Private*, pg. 2502
RICHARDS HOGG LINDLEY (HELLAS) LTD.—See Lovell Minnick Partners LLC; *U.S. Private*, pg. 2502
RICHARDS HOGG LINDLEY (INDIA) LTD—See Lovell Minnick Partners LLC; *U.S. Private*, pg. 2502
RICHARDS, INCORPORATED; *U.S. Private*, pg. 3429
RICHARDS INDUSTRIES VALVE GROUP; *U.S. Private*, pg. 3429
RICHARDS/LERMA—See The Richards Group, Inc.; *U.S. Private*, pg. 4107
RICHARDS MARINE MARKETING, INC.—See West Coast Sales & Associates LLC; *U.S. Private*, pg. 4484
RICHARD SMYKAL INCORPORATED; *U.S. Private*, pg. 3428
RICHARDSON AVIATION—See Sid Richardson Carbon & Energy Ltd.; *U.S. Private*, pg. 3645
RICHARDSON BOTTLING COMPANY; *U.S. Private*, pg. 3429
RICHARDSON BRANDS COMPANY—See Founders Equity, Inc.; *U.S. Private*, pg. 1581
RICHARDSON CENTRE LIMITED—See James Richardson & Sons, Limited; *Int'l*, pg. 3878
RICHARDSON & EDWARDS PRINTING, INC.—See Wellspring Capital Management LLC; *U.S. Private*, pg. 4477
RICHARDSON ELECTRONICS BENELUX B.V.—See Richardson Electronics, Ltd.; *U.S. Public*, pg. 1797
RICHARDSON ELECTRONICS DO BRASIL LTDA.—See Richardson Electronics, Ltd.; *U.S. Public*, pg. 1798
RICHARDSON ELECTRONICS GMBH—See Richardson Electronics, Ltd.; *U.S. Public*, pg. 1797
RICHARDSON ELECTRONICS IBERICA S.A.—See Richardson Electronics, Ltd.; *U.S. Public*, pg. 1798
RICHARDSON ELECTRONICS INDIA PRIVATE LIMITED—See Richardson Electronics, Ltd.; *U.S. Public*, pg. 1798
RICHARDSON ELECTRONICS ITALY, S.R.L.—See Richardson Electronics, Ltd.; *U.S. Public*, pg. 1798
RICHARDSON ELECTRONICS JAPAN CO., LTD.—See Richardson Electronics, Ltd.; *U.S. Public*, pg. 1798
RICHARDSON ELECTRONICS LTD.-CENTRAL—See Richardson Electronics, Ltd.; *U.S. Public*, pg. 1798
RICHARDSON ELECTRONICS LTD.-NORTHEASTERN—See Richardson Electronics, Ltd.; *U.S. Public*, pg. 1798
RICHARDSON ELECTRONICS, LTD.; *U.S. Public*, pg. 1797
RICHARDSON ELECTRONICS, LTD.—See Richardson Electronics, Ltd.; *U.S. Public*, pg. 1798
RICHARDSON ELECTRONICS, LTD. - SPAIN—See Richardson Electronics, Ltd.; *U.S. Public*, pg. 1798
RICHARDSON ELECTRONICS S.R.L.—See Richardson Electronics, Ltd.; *U.S. Public*, pg. 1798
RICHARDSON ELECTRONIQUE SAS—See Richardson Electronics, Ltd.; *U.S. Public*, pg. 1798
RICHARDSON GROUP INC.; *U.S. Private*, pg. 3429
RICHARDSON HOUSING GROUP INC.; *U.S. Private*, pg. 3429
RICHARDSON INDUSTRIES, INC.; *U.S. Private*, pg. 3429
RICHARDSON INTERNATIONAL LIMITED—See James Richardson & Sons, Limited; *Int'l*, pg. 3878
RICHARDSON INVESTMENTS, INC.; *U.S. Private*, pg. 3429
RICHARDSON MEDICAL CENTER HOMECARE, LLC—See UnitedHealth Group Incorporated; *U.S. Public*, pg. 2246
RICHARDSON METALS, INC.; *U.S. Private*, pg. 3429
RICHARDSON MOLDING, INC.—See Owner Resource Group, LLC; *U.S. Private*, pg. 3055
RICHARDSON MOLDING, LLC; *U.S. Private*, pg. 3429
RICHARDSON OILSEED LIMITED—See James Richardson & Sons, Limited; *Int'l*, pg. 3878
RICHARDSON PIONEER LIMITED—See James Richardson & Sons, Limited; *Int'l*, pg. 3878
RICHARDSON REALTY AUCTION; *U.S. Private*, pg. 3429
RICHARDSON RFPD AUSTRALIA PTY. LTD.—See Arrow Electronics, Inc.; *U.S. Public*, pg. 200
RICHARDSON RFPD CANADA, INC.—See Arrow Electronics, Inc.; *U.S. Public*, pg. 196
RICHARDSON RFPD CANADA LTD.—See Arrow Electronics, Inc.; *U.S. Public*, pg. 200
RICHARDSON RFPD DO BRASIL LTDA—See Arrow Electronics, Inc.; *U.S. Public*, pg. 200
RICHARDSON RFPD FRANCE SAS—See Arrow Electronics, Inc.; *U.S. Public*, pg. 200
RICHARDSON RFPD GERMANY GMBH—See Arrow Electronics, Inc.; *U.S. Public*, pg. 200
RICHARDSON RFPD, INC.—See Arrow Electronics, Inc.; *U.S. Public*, pg. 200
RICHARDSON RFPD ISRAEL LTD.—See Arrow Electronics, Inc.; *U.S. Public*, pg. 200

RICHARDSON RFPD ITALY SRL—See Arrow Electronics, Inc.; *U.S. Public*, pg. 200
RICHARDSON RFPD JAPAN KK—See Arrow Electronics, Inc.; *U.S. Public*, pg. 200
RICHARDSON RFPD KOREA LTD.—See Arrow Electronics, Inc.; *U.S. Public*, pg. 200
RICHARDSON RFPD NETHERLANDS BV—See Arrow Electronics, Inc.; *U.S. Public*, pg. 200
RICHARDSON RFPD SINGAPORE—See Arrow Electronics, Inc.; *U.S. Public*, pg. 200
RICHARDSON RFPD SPAIN SL—See Arrow Electronics, Inc.; *U.S. Public*, pg. 200
RICHARDSON RFPD SWEDEN AB—See Arrow Electronics, Inc.; *U.S. Public*, pg. 200
RICHARDSON RFPD TAIWAN—See Arrow Electronics, Inc.; *U.S. Public*, pg. 200
RICHARDSON RFPD (THAILAND) LIMITED—See Arrow Electronics, Inc.; *U.S. Public*, pg. 200
RICHARDSON RFPD UK LTD.—See Arrow Electronics, Inc.; *U.S. Public*, pg. 200
RICHARDSON'S FURNITURE EMPORIUM—See Richardson Industries, Inc.; *U.S. Private*, pg. 3429
THE RICHARDSON TRIDENT COMPANY, L.L.C.—See Reliance Steel & Aluminum Co.; *U.S. Public*, pg. 1781
RICHARDSON-WAYLAND ELECTRIC COMPANY LLC—See Cadent Energy Partners, LLC; *U.S. Private*, pg. 713
RICHARDSON WEALTH LIMITED—See RF Capital Group Inc.; *Int'l*, pg. 6318
THE RICHARDS ORGANIZATION; *U.S. Private*, pg. 4107
RICHARDS PACKAGING INCOME FUND; *U.S. Private*, pg. 3429
RICHARD'S PAINT MANUFACTURING COMPANY, INC.; *U.S. Private*, pg. 3428
RICHARDS PARTNERS—See The Richards Group, Inc.; *U.S. Private*, pg. 4107
RICHARDS PLUMBING & HEATING SUPPLIES; *U.S. Private*, pg. 3429
RICHARDS QUALITY BEDDING, INC.; *U.S. Private*, pg. 3429
RICHARD'S RESTAURANTS INC.; *U.S. Private*, pg. 3428
RICHARDS SUPPLY COMPANY; *U.S. Private*, pg. 3429
RICHARDS TRACTORS & IMPLEMENTS; *U.S. Private*, pg. 3429
RICHARDS-WILCOX, INC.; *U.S. Private*, pg. 3429
RICH ASIA CORPORATION PUBLIC COMPANY LIMITED; *Int'l*, pg. 6329
RICH BAKERY PRODUCTS (TIANJIN) CO., LTD.—See Rich Holdings, Inc.; *U.S. Private*, pg. 3426
RICH BRANDS, LLC; *U.S. Private*, pg. 3426
RICH CAPITAL HOLDINGS LIMITED; *Int'l*, pg. 6329
RICH & CARTMILL, INC.; *U.S. Private*, pg. 3425
RICHCO, INC.—See Essentra plc; *Int'l*, pg. 2511
RICHCO INVESTORS INC.; *Int'l*, pg. 6330
RICHCO STRUCTURES—See Richardson Industries, Inc.; *U.S. Private*, pg. 3429
RICHCO STRUCTURES—See Richardson Industries, Inc.; *U.S. Private*, pg. 3429
RICH DAD EDUCATION, INC.; *U.S. Private*, pg. 3426
RICH DAD EDUCATION LTD.—See Legacy Education Alliance, Inc.; *U.S. Public*, pg. 1301
RICH DEALERS; *U.S. Private*, pg. 3426
RICH DE ARGENTINA S.A.—See Rich Holdings, Inc.; *U.S. Private*, pg. 3427
RICH DE COLOMBIA S.A.S.—See Rich Holdings, Inc.; *U.S. Private*, pg. 3427
RICH DEVELOPMENT CO., LTD.; *Int'l*, pg. 6329
RICH DO BRASIL LTDA. - MARINIQUE MANUFACTURING FACILITY—See Rich Holdings, Inc.; *U.S. Private*, pg. 3427
RICH DO BRASIL LTDA.—See Rich Holdings, Inc.; *U.S. Private*, pg. 3427
RICH DUNCAN CONSTRUCTION INC.; *U.S. Private*, pg. 3426
RICHE ET SEBASTIEN; *Int'l*, pg. 6330
RICHELIEU AMERICA LTD—See Richelieu Hardware Ltd.; *Int'l*, pg. 6331
RICHELIEU FOODS, INC.—See Suddeutsche Zuckerruben-Verwertungs-Genossenschaft eG; *Int'l*, pg. 7252
RICHELIEU GESTION—See Societe Generale de Banque au Liban s.a.l.; *Int'l*, pg. 7038
RICHELIEU GROUP, LLC—See Suddeutsche Zuckerruben-Verwertungs-Genossenschaft eG; *Int'l*, pg. 7252
RICHELIEU HARDWARE LTD. - BOISERIES LUSSIER, LONGUEUIL—See Richelieu Hardware Ltd.; *Int'l*, pg. 6331
RICHELIEU HARDWARE LTD. - BOISERIES LUSSIER—See Richelieu Hardware Ltd.; *Int'l*, pg. 6331
RICHELIEU HARDWARE LTD. - DAYVAN, TORONTO—See Richelieu Hardware Ltd.; *Int'l*, pg. 6331
RICHELIEU HARDWARE LTD. - HIALEAH—See Richelieu Hardware Ltd.; *Int'l*, pg. 6331
RICHELIEU HARDWARE LTD. - HIGH POINT—See Richelieu Hardware Ltd.; *Int'l*, pg. 6331

RICHE ET SEBASTIEN / CORPORATE AFFILIATIONS

RICHELIEU HARDWARE LTD. - LAKNORD, DRUMMONDVILLE—See Richelieu Hardware Ltd.; *Int'l*, pg. 6331
RICHELIEU HARDWARE LTD. - LAKNORD, LAVAL—See Richelieu Hardware Ltd.; *Int'l*, pg. 6331
RICHELIEU HARDWARE LTD. - MISSISSAUGA—See Richelieu Hardware Ltd.; *Int'l*, pg. 6331
RICHELIEU HARDWARE LTD. - NEOS PRODUCTS, SUDBURY—See Richelieu Hardware Ltd.; *Int'l*, pg. 6331
RICHELIEU HARDWARE LTD. - ONWARD, KITCHENER—See Richelieu Hardware Ltd.; *Int'l*, pg. 6331
RICHELIEU HARDWARE LTD. - RELIABLE FASTENERS, LONGUEUIL—See Richelieu Hardware Ltd.; *Int'l*, pg. 6331
RICHELIEU HARDWARE LTD. - RIVERIA BEACH—See Richelieu Hardware Ltd.; *Int'l*, pg. 6331
RICHELIEU HARDWARE LTD. - SIMTAB NEOS, LAVAL—See Richelieu Hardware Ltd.; *Int'l*, pg. 6331
RICHELIEU HARDWARE LTD.; *Int'l*, pg. 6330
RICHELIEU HARDWARE LTD. - SPECIALTY SUPPLIES, POMPANO BEACH—See Richelieu Hardware Ltd.; *Int'l*, pg. 6331
RICHELIEU LTD-BUILDING SPECIALTIES DIVISION-DISTRIBUTION CENTER—See Richelieu Hardware Ltd.; *Int'l*, pg. 6331
RICHELL CORPORATION; *Int'l*, pg. 6331
RICHELL KOREA CORPORATION—See Richell Corporation; *Int'l*, pg. 6331
RICHELL KUN SHAN PLASTIC SCIENCE AND TECHNOLGY CO., LTD.—See Richell Corporation; *Int'l*, pg. 6331
RICHELL (SHANGHAI) CO.—See Richell Corporation; *Int'l*, pg. 6331
RICHELL U.S.A—See Richell Corporation; *Int'l*, pg. 6331
RICHEL SERRES DE FRANCE SA; *Int'l*, pg. 6330
RI CHEMICAL CORP.—See Resins, Inc.; *Int'l*, pg. 6297
RICHEMONT ASIA PACIFIC LIMITED—See Compagnie Financiere Richemont S.A.; *Int'l*, pg. 1741
RICHEMONT AUSTRALIA PTY LIMITED—See Compagnie Financiere Richemont S.A.; *Int'l*, pg. 1741
RICHEMONT DE MEXICO SA DE CV—See Compagnie Financiere Richemont S.A.; *Int'l*, pg. 1741
RICHEMONT HOLDINGS (UK) LIMITED—See Compagnie Financiere Richemont S.A.; *Int'l*, pg. 1741
RICHEMONT IBERIA SL—See Compagnie Financiere Richemont S.A.; *Int'l*, pg. 1741
RICHEMONT INTERNATIONAL LTD.—See Reinet Investments S.C.A.; *Int'l*, pg. 6257
RICHEMONT INTERNATIONAL SA—See Compagnie Financiere Richemont S.A.; *Int'l*, pg. 1741
RICHEMONT NORTHERN EUROPE GMBH—See Compagnie Financiere Richemont S.A.; *Int'l*, pg. 1741
RICHEMONT SUISSE SA—See Compagnie Financiere Richemont S.A.; *Int'l*, pg. 1741
RICH ENTERTAINMENT GROUP, LLC—See Rich Holdings, Inc.; *U.S. Private*, pg. 3426
RICHER POORER, INC.—See TerraMar Capital LLC; *U.S. Private*, pg. 3971
RICHEY CAPACITOR INC.; *U.S. Private*, pg. 3429
RICH FARMS INC.; *U.S. Private*, pg. 3426
RICHFIELD FINANCIAL SERVICES LTD.; *Int'l*, pg. 6331
RICHFIELD HOSPITALITY, INC.; *U.S. Private*, pg. 3429
RICHFIELD INDUSTRIES, CORP; *U.S. Private*, pg. 3430
RICHFIELD INTERNATIONAL LIMITED; *Int'l*, pg. 6331
RICHFIELD MARINE AGENCIES (S) PTE LTD—See Richfield International Limited; *Int'l*, pg. 6331
RICHFIELD MIHO CO., LTD—See Tokyu Construction Co., Ltd.; *Int'l*, pg. 7797
THE RICHFIELD REAPER—See Brehm Communications Inc.; *U.S. Private*, pg. 644
RICH FIRE PROTECTION COMPANY, INC.—See APi Group Corporation; *Int'l*, pg. 514
RICH FULL INTERNATIONAL INDUSTRIES LIMITED—See CCT Fortis Holdings Limited; *Int'l*, pg. 1370
RICH GOLDMAN HOLDINGS LIMITED; *Int'l*, pg. 6329
RICH GRAVISS PRODUCTS PVT. LTD. - KALA AMB MANUFACTURING FACILITY—See Rich Holdings, Inc.; *U.S. Private*, pg. 3426
RICH HOLDINGS, INC.; *U.S. Private*, pg. 3426
RICH ICE CREAM CO.; *U.S. Private*, pg. 3427
RICHIE PHARMACAL COMPANY INC.; *U.S. Private*, pg. 3430
RICHIE'S SUPER PREMIUM ITALIAN ICE; *U.S. Private*, pg. 3430
RICHINFO TECHNOLOGY CO., LTD.; *Int'l*, pg. 6332
RICHIRICH INVENTURES LIMITED; *Int'l*, pg. 6332
RICH KRAMER CONSTRUCTION INC.; *U.S. Private*, pg. 3430
RICHLAND BANK—See Park National Corporation; *U.S. Public*, pg. 1638
RICHLAND CHEVROLET COMPANY; *U.S. Private*, pg. 3430
RICHLAND COUNTY LANDFILL, INC.—See Waste Management, Inc.; *U.S. Public*, pg. 2332
RICHLAND LIBRARY; *U.S. Private*, pg. 3430
RICHLAND, LLC; *U.S. Private*, pg. 3430

RICHLAND LOGISTICS SERVICES PTE. LTD.—See Eneco Energy Limited; *Int'l*, pg. 2411
RICHLAND PARTNERS LLC—See Star Group, L.P.; *U.S. Public*, pg. 1938
RICHLAND PROPERTIES INC.; *U.S. Private*, pg. 3430
RICHLAND RESEARCH CORPORATION; *U.S. Private*, pg. 3430
RICHLAND TOWERS INC.—See Richland Properties Inc.; *U.S. Private*, pg. 3430
RICHLAND TOWERS - KANSAS CITY, LLC—See American Tower Corporation; *U.S. Public*, pg. 111
RICHLAND TOWERS MANAGEMENT, LLC—See American Tower Corporation; *U.S. Public*, pg. 111
RICHLAND TOWERS - ORLANDO, LLC—See American Tower Corporation; *U.S. Public*, pg. 111
RICHLAND TOWERS - SAN ANTONIO, LLC—See American Tower Corporation; *U.S. Public*, pg. 111
RICHLAND VILLAGE DRUG INC.—See Portage Pharma Ltd.; *U.S. Private*, pg. 3231
RICHLEE SHOE COMPANY—See Alto Enterprises, Inc.; *U.S. Private*, pg. 210
RICHLEE VANS INC.—See Cook-Illinois Corp.; *U.S. Private*, pg. 1039
RICH LEGEND INTERNATIONAL LIMITED—See China Gas Holdings Limited; *Int'l*, pg. 1504
RICHLEY DENTAL CERAMICS LIMITED—See The British United Provident Association Limited; *Int'l*, pg. 7630
RICHLIFE (SHANGHAI) CO., LTD—See OSIM International Ltd.; *Int'l*, pg. 5650
RICHLIND METAL FABRICATORS, INC.—See CORE Industrial Partners, LLC; *U.S. Private*, pg. 1048
RICHLINE GROUP, INC.—See Berkshire Hathaway Inc.; *U.S. Public*, pg. 316
RICH LTD.—See San Francisco Equity Partners; *U.S. Private*, pg. 3540
RICHLY FIELD CHINA DEVELOPMENT LIMITED; *Int'l*, pg. 6332
THE RICHMAN GROUP DEVELOPMENT CORPORATION; *U.S. Private*, pg. 4107
THE RICHMAN GROUP OF FLORIDA, INC.—See The Richman Group Development Corporation; *U.S. Private*, pg. 4107
RICH MARK ENGINEERING LIMITED.—See Fujitec Co., Ltd.; *Int'l*, pg. 2831
RICHMOND ACURA; *Int'l*, pg. 6332
RICHMOND AMBULANCE AUTHORITY; *U.S. Private*, pg. 3430
RICHMOND AMERICAN HOMES OF ARIZONA, INC.—See Sekisui House, Ltd.; *Int'l*, pg. 6697
RICHMOND AMERICAN HOMES OF ARIZONA, INC.—See Sekisui House, Ltd.; *Int'l*, pg. 6697
RICHMOND AMERICAN HOMES OF CALIFORNIA, INC.—See Sekisui House, Ltd.; *Int'l*, pg. 6697
RICHMOND AMERICAN HOMES OF CALIFORNIA, INC. (SOUTH)—See Sekisui House, Ltd.; *Int'l*, pg. 6697
RICHMOND AMERICAN HOMES OF COLORADO, INC.—See Sekisui House, Ltd.; *Int'l*, pg. 6697
RICHMOND AMERICAN HOMES OF COLORADO, INC.—See Sekisui House, Ltd.; *Int'l*, pg. 6697
RICHMOND AMERICAN HOMES OF FLORIDA, LP—See Sekisui House, Ltd.; *Int'l*, pg. 6697
RICHMOND AMERICAN HOMES OF MARYLAND, INC.—See Sekisui House, Ltd.; *Int'l*, pg. 6697
RICHMOND AMERICAN HOMES OF NEVADA, INC.—See Sekisui House, Ltd.; *Int'l*, pg. 6697
RICHMOND AMERICAN HOMES OF VIRGINIA, INC.—See Sekisui House, Ltd.; *Int'l*, pg. 6697
RICHMOND AMERICAN HOMES OF WASHINGTON, INC.—See Sekisui House, Ltd.; *Int'l*, pg. 6697
RICHMOND AREA ASSOCIATION FOR RETARDED CITIZENS; *U.S. Private*, pg. 3430
RICHMOND BONDED WAREHOUSE CORP.; *U.S. Private*, pg. 3430
RICHMOND CHRYSLER DODGE JEEP LTD.—See The Go Auto Group; *Int'l*, pg. 7650
RICHMOND CORRUGATED BOX INC.; *U.S. Private*, pg. 3430
RICHMOND DENTAL—See Barnhardt Manufacturing Company; *U.S. Private*, pg. 478
RICHMOND EEI LTD—See Chemring Group PLC; *Int'l*, pg. 1463
RICHMOND ELECTRICAL SUPPLY, LLC—See Graybar Electric Company, Inc.; *U.S. Private*, pg. 1760
RICHMOND FORD; *U.S. Private*, pg. 3430
RICHMOND HILL-H, LP—See Lithia Motors, Inc.; *U.S. Public*, pg. 1326
RICHMOND HILL INVESTMENTS, LLC—See Essex Equity Management, LLC; *U.S. Private*, pg. 1428
RICHMOND HOME NEED SERVICES INC; *U.S. Private*, pg. 3430
RICHMOND HONAN MEDICAL PROPERTIES INC.; *U.S. Private*, pg. 3430
RICHMOND INTERNATIONAL FOREST PRODUCTS, LLC—See Forest City Trading Group, LLC; *U.S. Private*, pg. 1566
RICHMOND INTERNATIONAL RACEWAY, INC.—See National Association for Stock Car Auto Racing, Inc.; *U.S. Private*, pg. 2846

RICHMOND INTERNATIONAL TRAVEL & TOURS CO., LTD.; *Int'l*, pg. 6332
RICHMOND MASTER DISTRIBUTORS INC.—See AMCON Distributing Company; *U.S. Public*, pg. 93
RICHMOND METAL FINISHING—See DWA, Inc.; *U.S. Private*, pg. 1295
RICHMOND MINERALS INC.; *Int'l*, pg. 6332
RICHMOND PEDIATRIC SURGEONS, LLC—See HCA Healthcare, Inc.; *U.S. Public*, pg. 1007
RICHMOND PRESSED METAL WORKS, INC.—See DWA, Inc.; *U.S. Private*, pg. 1295
RICHMOND PUBLISHING, S.A. DE C.V.—See Promotora de Informaciones S.A.; *Int'l*, pg. 5995
RICHMOND RECRUITMENT LIMITED—See Bain Capital, LP; *U.S. Private*, pg. 434
RICHMOND REFRIGERATION SERVICE, INC.—See Ares Management Corporation; *U.S. Public*, pg. 189
RICHMOND REGIONAL DIALYSIS, LLC—See Nautic Partners, LLC; *U.S. Private*, pg. 2871
RICHMOND SANITARY SERVICE, INC.—See Republic Services, Inc.; *U.S. Public*, pg. 1787
RICHMOND SENIOR SERVICES, INC.—See The Ensign Group, Inc.; *U.S. Public*, pg. 2072
RICHMOND STEEL RECYCLING LIMITED—See Sims Limited; *U.S. Public*, pg. 1883
RICHMOND SUBARU; *Int'l*, pg. 6332
RICHMOND TECHNOLOGY SDN. BHD.—See D'nonce Technology Bhd.; *Int'l*, pg. 1900
RICHMOND TIMES-DISPATCH—See Lee Enterprises, Incorporated; *U.S. Public*, pg. 1299
RICHMOND TITLE SERVICES—See K.K. Birla Group; *Int'l*, pg. 4044
RICHMOND TOWN SQUARE MALL, LLC—See Washington Prime Group Inc.; *U.S. Private*, pg. 4448
RICHMOND TREATMENT CENTER, LLC—See Acadia Healthcare Company, Inc.; *U.S. Public*, pg. 30
RICHMOND VANADIUM TECHNOLOGY LIMITED; *Int'l*, pg. 6332
RICHMOR AVIATION INC.; *U.S. Private*, pg. 3430
RICH MORTONS GLEN BURNIE LINCOLN MERCURY; *U.S. Private*, pg. 3427
RICHNER COMMUNICATIONS, INC.; *U.S. Private*, pg. 3430
RICHNEX MICROELECTRONICS CORP.—See MediaTek Inc.; *Int'l*, pg. 4774
RICHOUX GROUP PLC; *Int'l*, pg. 6332
RICH PHARMACEUTICALS, INC.; *U.S. Private*, pg. 3427
RICHPORT PROPERTIES INC.; *U.S. Private*, pg. 3430
RICHPOWER ELECTRONIC DEVICES CO,, LTD.—See WPG Holdings Limited; *Int'l*, pg. 8461
RICHPOWER MICROELECTRONICS CORPORATION—See Richtek Technology Corporation; *Int'l*, pg. 6332
RICH PRODUCTS AUSTRALIA PTY LTD.—See Rich Holdings, Inc.; *U.S. Private*, pg. 3426
RICH PRODUCTS CORPORATION - ARLINGTON MANUFACTURING FACILITY—See Rich Holdings, Inc.; *U.S. Private*, pg. 3426
RICH PRODUCTS CORPORATION - BROWNSVILLE MANUFACTURING FACILITY—See Rich Holdings, Inc.; *U.S. Private*, pg. 3426
RICH PRODUCTS CORPORATION - BRUNSWICK MANUFACTURING FACILITY—See Rich Holdings, Inc.; *U.S. Private*, pg. 3426
RICH PRODUCTS CORPORATION - BURLINGTON MANUFACTURING FACILITY—See Rich Holdings, Inc.; *U.S. Private*, pg. 3426
RICH PRODUCTS CORPORATION - EAGAN MANUFACTURING FACILITY—See Rich Holdings, Inc.; *U.S. Private*, pg. 3426
RICH PRODUCTS CORPORATION - FOUNTAIN INN MANUFACTURING FACILITY—See Rich Holdings, Inc.; *U.S. Private*, pg. 3426
RICH PRODUCTS CORPORATION - FRESNO MANUFACTURING FACILITY—See Rich Holdings, Inc.; *U.S. Private*, pg. 3426
RICH PRODUCTS CORPORATION - GALLATIN MANUFACTURING FACILITY—See Rich Holdings, Inc.; *U.S. Private*, pg. 3426
RICH PRODUCTS CORPORATION - HILLIARD MANUFACTURING FACILITY—See Rich Holdings, Inc.; *U.S. Private*, pg. 3427
RICH PRODUCTS CORPORATION - MISSOURI CITY MANUFACTURING FACILITY—See Rich Holdings, Inc.; *U.S. Private*, pg. 3427
RICH PRODUCTS CORPORATION - MORRISTOWN MANUFACTURING FACILITY—See Rich Holdings, Inc.; *U.S. Private*, pg. 3427
RICH PRODUCTS CORPORATION - MURFREESBORO MANUFACTURING FACILITY—See Rich Holdings, Inc.; *U.S. Private*, pg. 3427
RICH PRODUCTS CORPORATION - NEW BRITAIN MANUFACTURING FACILITY—See Rich Holdings, Inc.; *U.S. Private*, pg. 3427
RICH PRODUCTS CORPORATION - NILES MANUFACTURING FACILITY—See Rich Holdings, Inc.; *U.S. Private*, pg. 3427

COMPANY NAME INDEX

RICH PRODUCTS CORPORATION - ROCHESTER MANUFACTURING FACILITY—See Rich Holdings, Inc.; *U.S. Private*, pg. 3427
RICH PRODUCTS CORPORATION - SANTA ANA MANUFACTURING FACILITY—See Rich Holdings, Inc.; *U.S. Private*, pg. 3427
RICH PRODUCTS CORPORATION - SANTA FE SPRINGS - ANN STREET MANUFACTURING FACILITY—See Rich Holdings, Inc.; *U.S. Private*, pg. 3427
RICH PRODUCTS CORPORATION - SANTA FE SPRINGS - BUSCH PLACE MANUFACTURING FACILITY—See Rich Holdings, Inc.; *U.S. Private*, pg. 3427
RICH PRODUCTS CORPORATION—See Rich Holdings, Inc.; *U.S. Private*, pg. 3426
RICH PRODUCTS CORPORATION - UNION CITY MANUFACTURING FACILITY—See Rich Holdings, Inc.; *U.S. Private*, pg. 3427
RICH PRODUCTS CORPORATION - VINELAND MANUFACTURING FACILITY—See Rich Holdings, Inc.; *U.S. Private*, pg. 3427
RICH PRODUCTS CORPORATION - WAYCROSS MANUFACTURING FACILITY—See Rich Holdings, Inc.; *U.S. Private*, pg. 3427
RICH PRODUCTS CORP. - SOUTH AFRICA—See Rich Holdings, Inc.; *U.S. Private*, pg. 3426
RICH PRODUCTS GIDA SANAYI VE TICARET LIMITED SIRKETI—See Rich Holdings, Inc.; *U.S. Private*, pg. 3427
RICH PRODUCTS LIMITED - KIDDERMINSTER MANUFACTURING FACILITY—See Rich Holdings, Inc.; *U.S. Private*, pg. 3427
RICH PRODUCTS LIMITED—See Rich Holdings, Inc.; *U.S. Private*, pg. 3427
RICH PRODUCTS LIMITED—See Rich Holdings, Inc.; *U.S. Private*, pg. 3427
RICH PRODUCTS MANUFACTURING (THAILAND) CO., LTD.—See Rich Holdings, Inc.; *U.S. Private*, pg. 3427
RICH PRODUCTS (M) SDN. BHD.—See Rich Holdings, Inc.; *U.S. Private*, pg. 3426
RICH PRODUCTS OF CANADA, LTD. - FORT ERIE MANUFACTURING FACILITY—See Rich Holdings, Inc.; *U.S. Private*, pg. 3427
RICH PRODUCTS OF CANADA, LTD.—See Rich Holdings, Inc.; *U.S. Private*, pg. 3427
RICH PRODUCTS (SUZHOU) CO., LTD.—See Rich Holdings, Inc.; *U.S. Private*, pg. 3426
RICH PRODUCTS (SUZHOU) CO., LTD. - SUZHOU PLANT MANUFACTURING FACILITY—See Rich Holdings, Inc.; *U.S. Private*, pg. 3426
RICHREACH CORPORATION PUBLIC LTD.; *Int'l*, pg. 6332
RICHRELEVANCE FRANCE—See RichRelevance, Inc.; *U.S. Private*, pg. 3430
RICHRELEVANCE, INC.; *U.S. Private*, pg. 3430
RICHRELEVANCE UK—See RichRelevance, Inc.; *U.S. Private*, pg. 3430
RICH SALES, INC.—See Fuji Corporation; *Int'l*, pg. 2810
RICH SHIPPING (USA) INC.; *U.S. Private*, pg. 3427
RICHSPACE ACQUISITION CORP.; *U.S. Public*, pg. 1798
RICH SPORT PUBLIC COMPANY LIMITED; *Int'l*, pg. 6329
RICHTEK TECHNOLOGY CORPORATION; *Int'l*, pg. 6332
RICHTER7; *U.S. Private*, pg. 3430
RICHTER & ASSOCIATES INC.—See Bowman Consulting Group Ltd.; *U.S. Public*, pg. 376
RICHTER-CHEMIE-TECHNIK GMBH—See IDEX Corp; *U.S. Public*, pg. 1091
RICHTER-HELM BIOLOGIC MANAGEMENT GMBH—See Gedeon Richter Plc.; *Int'l*, pg. 2910
RICHTER-HELM BIOLOGICS GMBH & CO KG—See Gedeon Richter Plc.; *Int'l*, pg. 2910
RICHTER-HELM BIOLOGICS MANAGE - MENT GMBH—See Chemical Works of Gedeon Richter Plc; *Int'l*, pg. 1462
RICHTER INTERNATIONAL CONSULTING, LLC—See Arthur J. Gallagher & Co.; *U.S. Public*, pg. 207
RICHTER PUMPS AND VALVES INC.—See IDEX Corp; *U.S. Public*, pg. 1091
RICHTER & RATNER CONTRACTING CORPORATION; *U.S. Private*, pg. 3430
RICHTER SZOLGALTATO KFT—See Gedeon Richter Plc.; *Int'l*, pg. 2910
RICHTER-THEMIS MEDICARE (INDIA) PRIVATE LTD.—See Gedeon Richter Plc.; *Int'l*, pg. 2910
RICHTREE MARKET RESTAURANTS, INC.; *Int'l*, pg. 6332
RICH UNIVERSE NETWORK LIMITED; *Int'l*, pg. 6330
RICHVALE YORK BLOCK INC.; *Int'l*, pg. 6332
RICHWAVE TECHNOLOGY CORPORATION; *Int'l*, pg. 6332
RICHWELL GLOBAL FORWARDING PTE. LTD.—See Legion Consortium Limited; *Int'l*, pg. 4444
RICHWOOD BANCSHARES, INC.; *U.S. Private*, pg. 3431
THE RICHWOOD BANKING COMPANY—See Richwood Bancshares, Inc.; *U.S. Private*, pg. 3431
RICHWOOD INDUSTRIES, INC.—See Argosy Capital Group, LLC; *U.S. Private*, pg. 321

RICHY PLACE 2002 PUBLIC COMPANY LIMITED; *Int'l*, pg. 6332
RICI HEALTHCARE HOLDINGS LIMITED; *Int'l*, pg. 6332
RIC INVESTMENTS, LLC—See Koninklijke Philips N.V.; *Int'l*, pg. 4271
RICK BALL GM SUPERSTORE INC; *U.S. Private*, pg. 3431
RICK BURNSTEAD CONSTRUCTION LLC—See Burnstead Construction Company; *U.S. Private*, pg. 691
RICK BUS COMPANY, INC.—See Caisse de Depot et Placement du Quebec; *Int'l*, pg. 1255
RICK BUS COMPANY, INC.—See Ullico Inc.; *U.S. Private*, pg. 4276
RICK CASE ACURA—See Rick Case Enterprises, Inc.; *U.S. Private*, pg. 3431
RICK CASE ENTERPRISES, INC.; *U.S. Private*, pg. 3431
RICK CASE HYUNDAI - FT. LAUDERDALE—See Rick Case Enterprises, Inc.; *U.S. Private*, pg. 3431
RICKENBACKER INTERNATIONAL CORPORATION; *U.S. Private*, pg. 3431
RICK ENGINEERING COMPANY; *U.S. Private*, pg. 3431
RICKER OIL COMPANY INC.—See Giant Eagle, Inc.; *U.S. Private*, pg. 1694
RICKETTS FARM SERVICE, INC.; *U.S. Private*, pg. 3431
RICKEY'S RESTAURANT & LOUNGE, INC.; *U.S. Private*, pg. 3431
RICK HILL IMPORTS INC—See Don Hill Automotive Associates Inc.; *U.S. Private*, pg. 1257
RICK JOHNSON & COMPANY, INC.; *U.S. Private*, pg. 3431
RICK KOCH OIL CO.; *U.S. Private*, pg. 3431
RICKMERS HOLDING AG; *Int'l*, pg. 6332
RICKMERS-LINE (BELGIUM) N.V.—See ZEABORN Ship Management GmbH & Cie. KG; *Int'l*, pg. 8627
RICKMERS-LINE GMBH & CO. KG—See ZEABORN Ship Management GmbH & Cie. KG; *Int'l*, pg. 8627
RICKMERS-LINE (JAPAN) INC.—See ZEABORN Ship Management GmbH & Cie. KG; *Int'l*, pg. 8627
RICKMERS-LINE (KOREA) INC.—See ZEABORN Ship Management GmbH & Cie. KG; *Int'l*, pg. 8627
RICKMERS-LINE (SINGAPORE) PTE. LTD.—See ZEABORN Ship Management GmbH & Cie. KG; *Int'l*, pg. 8627
RICKMERS-LINE (USA) INC.—See ZEABORN Ship Management GmbH & Cie. KG; *Int'l*, pg. 8628
RICKMERS MARINE AGENCY ROMANIA S.R.L.—See Rickmers Holding AG; *Int'l*, pg. 6333
RICKMERS REEDEREI GMBH & CIE. KG—See Rickmers Holding AG; *Int'l*, pg. 6333
RICKMERS REEDEREI (SINGAPORE) PTE. LTD.—See Rickmers Holding AG; *Int'l*, pg. 6333
RICKMERS SHIPPING (SHANGHAI) CO. LTD.—See Rickmers Holding AG; *Int'l*, pg. 6332
RICKMERS TRUST MANAGEMENT PTE. LTD.—See Rickmers Holding AG; *Int'l*, pg. 6333
RICK'S CUSTOM FENCING & DECKING; *U.S. Private*, pg. 3431
RICKSHAW BAGWORKS; *U.S. Private*, pg. 3431
RICKSOFT CO., LTD.; *Int'l*, pg. 6333
RICK'S RESTORATIONS; *U.S. Private*, pg. 3431
RICK WEAVER BUICK-PONTIAC-GMC; *U.S. Private*, pg. 3431
RICK YOUNG & ASSOCIATES, INC.—See Genstar Capital, LLC; *U.S. Private*, pg. 1674
RICKY'S OIL & ENVIRONMENTAL SERVICES, LLC—See Clean Harbors, Inc.; *U.S. Public*, pg. 510
RIC MICROFINANCE BANK LIMITED—See Regency Alliance Insurance Plc.; *Int'l*, pg. 6251
RICO AUTO INDUSTRIES INC.—See Rico Auto Industries Limited; *Int'l*, pg. 6333
RICO AUTO INDUSTRIES LIMITED; *Int'l*, pg. 6333
RICO AUTO INDUSTRIES (UK) LTD.—See Rico Auto Industries Limited; *Int'l*, pg. 6333
RICOCHET LIMITED—See Warner Bros. Discovery, Inc.; *U.S. Public*, pg. 2329
RICOCHET PARTNERS, INC.; *U.S. Private*, pg. 3431
RICO ELASTOMERE PROJECTING GMBH; *Int'l*, pg. 6333
RICO GROUP GMBH—See Semperit AG Holding; *Int'l*, pg. 6706
RICOH AMERICAS HOLDINGS, INC.—See Ricoh Company, Ltd.; *Int'l*, pg. 6336
RICOH ARGENTINA, S.A.—See Ricoh Company, Ltd.; *Int'l*, pg. 6333
RICOH ASIA INDUSTRY LTD.—See Ricoh Company, Ltd.; *Int'l*, pg. 6333
RICOH ASIA INDUSTRY (SHENZHEN) LTD.—See Ricoh Company, Ltd.; *Int'l*, pg. 6333
RICOH ASIA PACIFIC OPERATIONS LTD.—See Ricoh Company, Ltd.; *Int'l*, pg. 6333
RICOH ASIA PACIFIC PTE LTD.—See Ricoh Company, Ltd.; *Int'l*, pg. 6333
RICOH AUSTRALIA PTY, LTD.—See Ricoh Company, Ltd.; *Int'l*, pg. 6334
RICOH AUSTRIA GMBH—See Ricoh Company, Ltd.; *Int'l*, pg. 6334
RICOH BELGIUM NV—See Ricoh Company, Ltd.; *Int'l*, pg. 6334

RICOH COMPANY, LTD.

RICOH BRASIL, S.A.—See Ricoh Company, Ltd.; *Int'l*, pg. 6336
RICOH CANADA INC.—See Ricoh Company, Ltd.; *Int'l*, pg. 6336
RICOH CANADA INC. - TORONTO SALES OFFICE—See Ricoh Company, Ltd.; *Int'l*, pg. 6336
RICOH CAPITAL LIMITED—See Ricoh Company, Ltd.; *Int'l*, pg. 6334
RICOH CHILE, S.A.—See Ricoh Company, Ltd.; *Int'l*, pg. 6334
RICOH CHINA CO., LTD.—See Ricoh Company, Ltd.; *Int'l*, pg. 6334
RICOH COLOMBIA, S.A.—See Ricoh Company, Ltd.; *Int'l*, pg. 6334
RICOH COMPANY, LTD. - ATSUGI PLANT—See Ricoh Company, Ltd.; *Int'l*, pg. 6334
RICOH COMPANY, LTD. - FUKUI PLANT—See Ricoh Company, Ltd.; *Int'l*, pg. 6334
RICOH COMPANY, LTD. - GOTEMBA PLANT—See Ricoh Company, Ltd.; *Int'l*, pg. 6334
RICOH COMPANY, LTD. - IKEDA PLANT—See Ricoh Company, Ltd.; *Int'l*, pg. 6334
RICOH COMPANY, LTD. - NUMAZU PLANT—See Ricoh Company, Ltd.; *Int'l*, pg. 6334
RICOH COMPANY, LTD. - OHMORI PLANT—See Ricoh Company, Ltd.; *Int'l*, pg. 6334
RICOH COMPANY, LTD.; *Int'l*, pg. 6333
RICOH COMPANY, LTD. - YASHIRO PLANT—See Ricoh Company, Ltd.; *Int'l*, pg. 6334
RICOH COMPONENTS ASIA (HONG KONG) CO., LTD.—See Ricoh Company, Ltd.; *Int'l*, pg. 6334
RICOH COMPONENTS & PRODUCTS (SHENZHEN) CO., LTD.—See Ricoh Company, Ltd.; *Int'l*, pg. 6334
RICOH COSTA RICA, S.A.—See Ricoh Company, Ltd.; *Int'l*, pg. 6334
RICOH DANMARK A/S—See Ricoh Company, Ltd.; *Int'l*, pg. 6335
RICOH DEL PERU S.A.C.—See Ricoh Company, Ltd.; *Int'l*, pg. 6334
RICOH DENMARK A/S—See Ricoh Company, Ltd.; *Int'l*, pg. 6335
RICOH DEUTSCHLAND GMBH—See Ricoh Company, Ltd.; *Int'l*, pg. 6335
RICOH DEUTSCHLAND GMBH—See Ricoh Company, Ltd.; *Int'l*, pg. 6335
RICOH DEVELOPMENT OF CALIFORNIA, INC.—See Ricoh Company, Ltd.; *Int'l*, pg. 6336
RICOH ELECTRONIC DEVICES CO., LTD.—See Nisshinbo Holdings Inc.; *Int'l*, pg. 5375
RICOH ELECTRONIC DEVICES KOREA CO., LTD.—See Ricoh Company, Ltd.; *Int'l*, pg. 6334
RICOH ELECTRONIC DEVICES SHANGHAI CO., LTD.—See Ricoh Company, Ltd.; *Int'l*, pg. 6334
RICOH ELECTRONICS, INC. - GEORGIA PLANT—See Ricoh Company, Ltd.; *Int'l*, pg. 6336
RICOH ELECTRONICS, INC.—See Ricoh Company, Ltd.; *Int'l*, pg. 6336
RICOH ELECTRONIC TECHNOLOGY (CHINA) CO., LTD.—See Ricoh Company, Ltd.; *Int'l*, pg. 6334
RICOH ELEMEX AT CORPORATION—See Ricoh Company, Ltd.; *Int'l*, pg. 6334
RICOH ELEMEX CORPORATION—See Ricoh Company, Ltd.; *Int'l*, pg. 6334
RICOH ELEMEX HONG KONG LIMITED—See Ricoh Company, Ltd.; *Int'l*, pg. 6334
RICOH EL SALVADOR, S.A. DE C.V.—See Ricoh Company, Ltd.; *Int'l*, pg. 6334
RICOH ESPANA, S.A.—See Ricoh Company, Ltd.; *Int'l*, pg. 6335
RICOH EUROPE HOLDINGS B.V.—See Ricoh Company, Ltd.; *Int'l*, pg. 6335
RICOH EUROPE (NETHERLANDS) B.V.—See Ricoh Company, Ltd.; *Int'l*, pg. 6334
RICOH EUROPE PLC—See Ricoh Company, Ltd.; *Int'l*, pg. 6335
RICOH EUROPE SCM B.V.—See Ricoh Company, Ltd.; *Int'l*, pg. 6335
RICOH FINANCE NEDERLAND B.V.—See Ricoh Company, Ltd.; *Int'l*, pg. 6335
RICOH FINLAND OY—See Ricoh Company, Ltd.; *Int'l*, pg. 6335
RICOH FRANCE S.A.S.—See Ricoh Company, Ltd.; *Int'l*, pg. 6335
RICOH GESTETNER SOUTH AFRICA (PTY) LIMITED—See Ricoh Company, Ltd.; *Int'l*, pg. 6335
RICOH HONG KONG LTD.—See Ricoh Company, Ltd.; *Int'l*, pg. 6334
RICOH HUNGARY KFT.—See Ricoh Company, Ltd.; *Int'l*, pg. 6335
RICOH IMAGING AMERICAS CORPORATION—See Ricoh Company, Ltd.; *Int'l*, pg. 6335
RICOH IMAGING CO., LTD.—See Ricoh Company, Ltd.; *Int'l*, pg. 6335
RICOH IMAGING TECHNOLOGY (SHANGHAI) CO., LTD.—See Ricoh Company, Ltd.; *Int'l*, pg. 6335
RICOH INDUSTRIE FRANCE S.A.S.—See Ricoh Company, Ltd.; *Int'l*, pg. 6335
RICOH INNOVATIONS, INC.—See Ricoh Company, Ltd.; *Int'l*, pg. 6336

RICOH COMPANY, LTD.

CORPORATE AFFILIATIONS

RICOH INNOVATIONS PRIVATE LIMITED—See Ricoh Company, Ltd.; *Int'l*, pg. 6336
RICOH INTERNATIONAL B.V.—See Ricoh Company, Ltd.; *Int'l*, pg. 6335
RICOH INTERNATIONAL LOGISTICS (HK) LTD.—See SBS Holdings Inc.; *Int'l*, pg. 6607
RICOH INTERNATIONAL (SHANGHAI) CO., LTD.—See Ricoh Company, Ltd.; *Int'l*, pg. 6335
RICOH IRELAND LTD.—See Ricoh Company, Ltd.; *Int'l*, pg. 6335
RICOH ITALIA S.P.A.—See Ricoh Company, Ltd.; *Int'l*, pg. 6335
RICOH IT SOLUTIONS CO., LTD.—See Ricoh Company, Ltd.; *Int'l*, pg. 6335
RICOH JAPAN CORPORATION—See Ricoh Company, Ltd.; *Int'l*, pg. 6335
RICOH LATIN AMERICA, INC.—See Ricoh Company, Ltd.; *Int'l*, pg. 6336
RICOH LEASING COMPANY, LTD.—See Ricoh Company, Ltd.; *Int'l*, pg. 6335
RICOH LEGAL DOCUMENT SERVICES - TORONTO—See Ricoh Company, Ltd.; *Int'l*, pg. 6336
RICOH LUXEMBOURG PSF SARL—See Ricoh Company, Ltd.; *Int'l*, pg. 6335
RICOH (MALAYSIA) SDN. BHD.—See Ricoh Company, Ltd.; *Int'l*, pg. 6334
RICOH MANUFACTURING (THAILAND) LTD.—See Ricoh Company, Ltd.; *Int'l*, pg. 6335
RICOH MEXICANA, S.A. DE C.V.—See Ricoh Company, Ltd.; *Int'l*, pg. 6336
RICOH NEDERLAND B.V.—See Ricoh Company, Ltd.; *Int'l*, pg. 6335
RICOH NEW ZEALAND LTD.—See Ricoh Company, Ltd.; *Int'l*, pg. 6335
RICOH NORGE A.S.—See Ricoh Company, Ltd.; *Int'l*, pg. 6335
RICOH OPTICAL INDUSTRIES CO., LTD.—See Ricoh Company, Ltd.; *Int'l*, pg. 6335
RICOH PANAMA, S.A.—See Ricoh Company, Ltd.; *Int'l*, pg. 6335
RICOH POLSKA SP. Z.O.O.—See Ricoh Company, Ltd.; *Int'l*, pg. 6335
RICOH PORTUGAL, UNIPESSOAL, LDA—See Ricoh Company, Ltd.; *Int'l*, pg. 6335
RICOH PRINTING SYSTEMS AMERICA, INC.—See Ricoh Company, Ltd.; *Int'l*, pg. 6335
RICOH PRINTING SYSTEMS, LTD.—See Ricoh Company, Ltd.; *Int'l*, pg. 6335
RICOH PUERTO RICO, INC.—See Ricoh Company, Ltd.; *Int'l*, pg. 6336
RICOH RUS, LTD.—See Ricoh Company, Ltd.; *Int'l*, pg. 6336
RICOH SCHWEIZ AG—See Ricoh Company, Ltd.; *Int'l*, pg. 6336
RICOH SINGAPORE PTE. LTD.—See Ricoh Company, Ltd.; *Int'l*, pg. 6334
RICOH SOFTWARE RESEARCH CENTER (BEIJING) CO., LTD.—See Ricoh Company, Ltd.; *Int'l*, pg. 6336
RICOH SOUTH AFRICA (PTY) LIMITED—See Ricoh Company, Ltd.; *Int'l*, pg. 6335
RICOH SVERIGE AB—See Ricoh Company, Ltd.; *Int'l*, pg. 6336
RICOH SWEDEN AB—See Ricoh Company, Ltd.; *Int'l*, pg. 6335
RICOH TAIWAN CO., LTD—See Ricoh Company, Ltd.; *Int'l*, pg. 6336
RICOH TECHNOSYSTEMS CO., LTD.—See Ricoh Company, Ltd.; *Int'l*, pg. 6336
RICOH THERMAL MEDIA (BEIJING) CO., LTD.—See Ricoh Company, Ltd.; *Int'l*, pg. 6336
RICOH THERMAL MEDIA (WUXI) CO., LTD.—See Ricoh Company, Ltd.; *Int'l*, pg. 6336
RICOH UK LTD.—See Ricoh Company, Ltd.; *Int'l*, pg. 6335
RICOH UNITECHNO CO., LTD.—See Ricoh Company, Ltd.; *Int'l*, pg. 6336
RICOH USA, INC.—See Ricoh Company, Ltd.; *Int'l*, pg. 6336
RICOH VIETNAM COMPANY LIMITED—See Ricoh Company, Ltd.; *Int'l*, pg. 6336
RICO INDUSTRIES INC.; *U.S. Private*, pg. 3431
RICO INTERNATIONAL—See D'Addario & Company, Inc.; *U.S. Private*, pg. 1138
RICOLA AG; *Int'l*, pg. 6336
RICOLA (ASIA-PACIFIC) LTD—See Ricola AG; *Int'l*, pg. 6336
RICOLA ASIA PACIFIC PTE LTD.—See Ricola AG; *Int'l*, pg. 6336
RICOLA USA, INC.—See Ricola AG; *Int'l*, pg. 6336
RICOLA VERTRIEBS AG—See Ricola AG; *Int'l*, pg. 6337
RICO LOGISTICS LTD—See TVS Logistics Services Ltd.; *Int'l*, pg. 7989
RICO MOTOR COMPANY; *U.S. Private*, pg. 3431
RICOM PUBLISHING DOO—See Universal Music Group N.V.; *Int'l*, pg. 8080
RICOM-TRUST INVESTMENT COMPANY LIMITED; *Int'l*, pg. 6337
RICON CORP.—See Westinghouse Air Brake Technologies Corporation; *U.S. Public*, pg. 2359

RICON INTERNATIONAL FREIGHT AGENCY (SHENZHEN) CO., LTD.—See SBS Holdings Inc.; *Int'l*, pg. 6607
RICON PRIVATE LIMITED—See Kobe Steel, Ltd.; *Int'l*, pg. 4220
RICO'S PRODUCTS COMPANY INC.—See Liberto Specialty Company Inc.; *U.S. Private*, pg. 2443
RIC PROPERTIES & INVESTMENT LIMITED—See Regency Alliance Insurance Plc.; *Int'l*, pg. 6251
RICS SOFTWARE; *U.S. Private*, pg. 3431
RICSTON LIMITED—See EPAM Systems, Inc.; *U.S. Public*, pg. 783
RICSTON UK LIMITED—See EPAM Systems, Inc.; *U.S. Public*, pg. 783
RICWIL JAPAN LTD.—See Nippon Steel Corporation; *Int'l*, pg. 5338
RIDA DEVELOPMENT CORP.; *U.S. Private*, pg. 3431
RIDDARHYTTAN RESOURCES AB—See Agnico Eagle Mines Limited; *Int'l*, pg. 212
RIDDELL, INC.—See Fenway Partners, LLC; *U.S. Private*, pg. 1495
RIDDELL SPORTS GROUP, INC.—See Fenway Partners, LLC; *U.S. Private*, pg. 1495
RIDDERHEIMS AS—See Atria Plc; *Int'l*, pg. 694
RIDDHI CORPORATE SERVICES LIMITED; *Int'l*, pg. 6337
RIDDHI SIDDHI GLUCO BIOLS LTD - GOKAK UNIT—See Riddhi Siddhi Gluco Biols Ltd.; *Int'l*, pg. 6337
RIDDHI SIDDHI GLUCO BIOLS LTD - PONDICHERRY UNIT—See Riddhi Siddhi Gluco Biols Ltd.; *Int'l*, pg. 6337
RIDDHI SIDDHI GLUCO BIOLS LTD.; *Int'l*, pg. 6337
RIDDHI STEEL & TUBE LIMITED; *Int'l*, pg. 6337
RIDDLEBERGER BROS., INC.; *U.S. Private*, pg. 3431
RIDDLEBERGER BROTHERS, INC.—See Comfort Systems USA, Inc.; *U.S. Public*, pg. 544
RIDDLES GROUP, INC.; *U.S. Private*, pg. 3431
RIDDLE VILLAGE; *U.S. Private*, pg. 3431
RIDDOCK INTERNATIONAL LIMITED; *Int'l*, pg. 6337
RIDEAU INC.; *Int'l*, pg. 6337
RIDEAU PACKAGING, INC.; *U.S. Private*, pg. 3432
RIDE-AWAY HANDICAP EQUIPMENT; *U.S. Private*, pg. 3432
RIDE ENTERTAINMENT SYSTEMS, INC.; *U.S. Private*, pg. 3432
RIDEGEAR.COM; *U.S. Private*, pg. 3432
RIDE ON EXPRESS CO., LTD.; *Int'l*, pg. 6337
RIDER DICKERSON, INC.; *U.S. Private*, pg. 3432
RIDER HUNT INTERNATIONAL (ALBERTA) INC.—See Rider Hunt International Limited; *Int'l*, pg. 6337
RIDER HUNT INTERNATIONAL (AUSTRALIA) PTY. LTD.—See John Wood Group PLC; *Int'l*, pg. 3983
RIDER HUNT INTERNATIONAL BV—See Rider Hunt International Limited; *Int'l*, pg. 6337
RIDER HUNT INTERNATIONAL LIMITED; *Int'l*, pg. 6337
RIDER HUNT INTERNATIONAL (MALAYSIA) SDN. BHD.—See Rider Hunt International Limited; *Int'l*, pg. 6337
RIDER HUNT INTERNATIONAL (SINGAPORE) PTE LTD.—See Rider Hunt International Limited; *Int'l*, pg. 6337
RIDER HUNT INTERNATIONAL SOUTH AFRICA (PTY.) LTD—See John Wood Group PLC; *Int'l*, pg. 3983
RIDER HUNT INTERNATIONAL (USA) INC.—See Rider Hunt International Limited; *Int'l*, pg. 6337
RIDER HUNT INTERNATIONAL (WA) PTY LTD.—See Rider Hunt International Limited; *Int'l*, pg. 6337
RIDER PRODUCTIONS LLC—See Comcast Corporation; *U.S. Public*, pg. 541
RIDERS BIKE SHOP INC.; *U.S. Private*, pg. 3432
RIDESAFELY BULGARIA—See RideSafely.com, Inc.; *U.S. Private*, pg. 3432
RIDESAFELY CANADA, INC.—See RideSafely.com, Inc.; *U.S. Private*, pg. 3432
RIDESAFELY.COM, INC.; *U.S. Private*, pg. 3432
RIDESAFELY EUROPE GMBH—See RideSafely.com, Inc.; *U.S. Private*, pg. 3432
RIDESAFELY MIDDLE EAST—See RideSafely.com, Inc.; *U.S. Private*, pg. 3432
RIDESCOUT LLC—See Mercedes-Benz Group AG; *Int'l*, pg. 4829
RIDESHARE CAR RENTALS LLC—See EVmo, Inc.; *U.S. Public*, pg. 803
RIDE SPORTS ANZ PTY LTD—See Domino's Pizza Enterprises Ltd.; *Int'l*, pg. 2162
RIDGEBACK RESOURCES INC.; *Int'l*, pg. 6337
RIDGE (CHATHAM) HOLDINGS G.P. INC.—See Waste Connections, Inc.; *Int'l*, pg. 8352
THE RIDGE COMPANY; *U.S. Private*, pg. 4107
RIDGECREST HERBALS, INC.; *U.S. Private*, pg. 3432
RIDGECREST PLC; *Int'l*, pg. 6337
RIDGE DIAGNOSTICS, INC.; *U.S. Private*, pg. 3432
RIDGEFIELD ACQUISITION CORP.; *U.S. Public*, pg. 1798
RIDGE-FORT WAYNE COMPANY, INC.; *U.S. Private*, pg. 3432
RIDGEHILL FORD; *Int'l*, pg. 6337
RIDGE-I INC.; *Int'l*, pg. 6337
RIDGE LANDFILL CORPORATION LIMITED—See Waste Connections, Inc.; *Int'l*, pg. 8352

RIDGELINE ENDOSCOPY CENTER—See HCA Healthcare, Inc.; *U.S. Public*, pg. 1007
RIDGELINE ENERGY, LLC—See Veolia Environnement S.A.; *Int'l*, pg. 8153
RIDGELINE INTERNATIONAL INC.; *U.S. Private*, pg. 3432
RIDGELINE MANAGEMENT COMPANY; *U.S. Private*, pg. 3432
RIDGELINE MINERALS CORP.; *Int'l*, pg. 6337
RIDGELINK, LLC—See Blue Ridge Electric Membership Corporation; *U.S. Private*, pg. 591
RIDGEMONDE CHEMICALS & RESINS SDN BHD—See Jiankun International Berhad; *Int'l*, pg. 3961
RIDGEMONT PARTNERS MANAGEMENT LLC; *U.S. Private*, pg. 3432
RIDGE OUTPATIENT COUNSELING, L.L.C.—See Universal Health Services, Inc.; *U.S. Public*, pg. 2259
THE RIDGES AT MOUNTAIN HARBOUR, LLC—See Wells Fargo & Company; *U.S. Public*, pg. 2345
RIDGE SERVICES INC.; *U.S. Private*, pg. 3432
RIDGESTONE MINING, INC.; *Int'l*, pg. 6337
RIDGE TOOL AUSTRALIA PTY., LTD.—See Emerson Electric Co.; *U.S. Public*, pg. 751
RIDGE TOOL COMPANY—See Emerson Electric Co.; *U.S. Public*, pg. 749
RIDGE TOOL EUROPE N.V.—See Emerson Electric Co.; *U.S. Public*, pg. 749
RIDGE TOOL GMBH & CO. OHG—See Emerson Electric Co.; *U.S. Public*, pg. 749
RIDGE TOOL GMBH—See Emerson Electric Co.; *U.S. Public*, pg. 752
RIDGE TOOL N.V.—See Emerson Electric Co.; *U.S. Public*, pg. 752
RIDGETOP HOLDING CO., INC.; *U.S. Private*, pg. 3433
RIDGEVIEW INDUSTRIES; *U.S. Private*, pg. 3433
RIDGEVIEW INSTITUTE, INC.—See US Healthvest LLC; *U.S. Private*, pg. 4319
RIDGEVIEW MEDICAL CENTER; *U.S. Private*, pg. 3433
RIDGE VINEYARDS INC.—See Otsuka Holdings Co., Ltd.; *Int'l*, pg. 5660
RIDGEWAY CHEVROLET, INC.; *U.S. Private*, pg. 3433
RIDGEWAY FURNITURE COMPANY—See Howard Miller Company; *U.S. Private*, pg. 1995
RIDGEWAY GROUP; *Int'l*, pg. 6337
RIDGEWAY PHARMACY; *U.S. Private*, pg. 3433
RIDGEWOOD CEMETERY COMPANY, INC.—See Service Corporation International; *U.S. Public*, pg. 1870
RIDGEWOOD INFRASTRUCTURE LLC; *U.S. Private*, pg. 3433
RIDGEWOOD LAKES GOLF & COUNTRY CLUB, INC.; *U.S. Private*, pg. 3434
RIDGEWOOD REAL ESTATE PARTNERS, LLC; *U.S. Private*, pg. 3434
RIDGEWOOD SAVINGS BANK; *U.S. Private*, pg. 3434
RIDGEWOOD—See Dorel Industries, Inc.; *Int'l*, pg. 2176
RIDGID, INC.—See Emerson Electric Co.; *U.S. Public*, pg. 749
RIDGID PRODUCTS—See Emerson Electric Co.; *U.S. Public*, pg. 749
RIDGID SCANDINAVIA A/S—See Emerson Electric Co.; *U.S. Public*, pg. 749
RIDGID WERKZEUGE AG—See Emerson Electric Co.; *U.S. Public*, pg. 740
RIDG-U-RAK, INC.; *U.S. Private*, pg. 3432
RIDHI SYNTHETICS LIMITED; *Int'l*, pg. 6337
RIDINGS CONSULTING ENGINEERS INDIA LTD.; *Int'l*, pg. 6338
RIDI POWER COMPANY LIMITED; *Int'l*, pg. 6338
RIDLEY AGRIPRODUCTS PTY. LTD.—See Ridley Corporation Limited; *Int'l*, pg. 6338
RIDLEY BLOCK OPERATIONS, INC.—See Alltech, Inc.; *U.S. Private*, pg. 194
RIDLEY CORPORATION LIMITED; *Int'l*, pg. 6338
RIDLEY ELECTRIC CO. INC.; *U.S. Private*, pg. 3434
RIDLEYS FOOD CORP; *U.S. Private*, pg. 3434
RIDLEY TERMINALS INC.; *Int'l*, pg. 6338
RIDLEY USA INC.—See Alltech, Inc.; *U.S. Private*, pg. 194
RIDOUT BARRETT & CO PC—See Aprio, LLP; *U.S. Private*, pg. 301
RIDOUT LUMBER COMPANY OF BATESVILLE, LLC—See Bain Capital, LP; *U.S. Private*, pg. 451
RIDOUT LUMBER COMPANY OF JOPLIN, INC.—See Bain Capital, LP; *U.S. Private*, pg. 451
RIDOUT LUMBER CO. OF BRINKLEY, INC.—See Bain Capital, LP; *U.S. Private*, pg. 451
RIDOUT LUMBER CO. OF RUSSELLVILLE, INC.—See Bain Capital, LP; *U.S. Private*, pg. 451
RIDOUT LUMBER COS., INC.—See Bain Capital, LP; *U.S. Private*, pg. 451
RIDOUT & MAYBEE LLP—See IPH Limited; *Int'l*, pg. 3797
RIEBER & SON ASA—See Orkla ASA; *Int'l*, pg. 5639
RIEBER & SON AS; *Int'l*, pg. 6338
RIEBER & SON GERMANY GMBH—See Orkla ASA; *Int'l*, pg. 5639
RIEBER & SON PLC—See Orkla ASA; *Int'l*, pg. 5639
RIEBE'S AUTO PARTS; *U.S. Private*, pg. 3434
RIECHESBAIRD, INC.; *U.S. Private*, pg. 3434
RIECHMAN CROSBY HAYS COMPANY, INC.; *U.S. Private*, pg. 3434

COMPANY NAME INDEX

RIECHMANN BROS LLC; *U.S. Private*, pg. 3434
RIECHMANN TRANSPORT INC.—See OEP Capital Advisors, L.P.; *U.S. Private*, pg. 2999
RIECKERMANN (SINGAPORE) PTE. LTD.—See Quaser Machine Tools, Inc.; *Int'l*, pg. 6157
RIEDEL B.V.—See Standard Investment Management B.V.; *Int'l*, pg. 7169
RIEDEL CRYSTAL; *U.S. Private*, pg. 3434
RIEDEL RESOURCES LIMITED; *Int'l*, pg. 6338
RIEDEL TEXTIL GMBH; *Int'l*, pg. 6338
RIEDHAMMER GMBH—See Sacmi Imola S.C.A.R.L.; *Int'l*, pg. 6464
RIEDHAMMER JAPAN CO LTD.—See Sacmi Imola S.C.A.R.L.; *Int'l*, pg. 6464
RIEDL G.M.B.H.—See GPI S.p.A.; *Int'l*, pg. 3046
RIEDON, INC.; *U.S. Private*, pg. 3434
RIEGER BETEILIGUNGS-GMBH—See EnBW Energie Baden-Wurttemberg AG; *Int'l*, pg. 2400
RIEGER GMBH & CO. KG—See EnBW Energie Baden-Wurttemberg AG; *Int'l*, pg. 2400
RIEGLER & CO. KG—See Brd. Klee A/S; *Int'l*, pg. 1143
RIEGNER & ASSOCIATES, INC.; *U.S. Private*, pg. 3434
RIEKE CORPORATION—See TriMas Corporation; *U.S. Public*, pg. 2189
RIEKES EQUIPMENT COMPANY; *U.S. Private*, pg. 3434
RIELLO CANADA INC.—See Carrier Global Corporation; *U.S. Public*, pg. 444
RIELLO HUNGARY KERESKEDELMI ZARTKORUEN MUKODO RESZVENYTARSASAG—See Carrier Global Corporation; *U.S. Public*, pg. 444
RIELLO LTD.—See Carrier Global Corporation; *U.S. Public*, pg. 444
RIELLO MANDELLI MACHINE TOOLS UK LTD.—See Gruppo Riello Sistemi S.p.A.; *Int'l*, pg. 3141
RIELLO RO S.R.L.—See Carrier Global Corporation; *U.S. Public*, pg. 444
RIELLO S.A.—See Carrier Global Corporation; *U.S. Public*, pg. 444
RIELLO SISTEMI (SHANGHAI) TRADE CO., LTD—See Gruppo Riello Sistemi S.p.A.; *Int'l*, pg. 3141
RIELLO S.P.A.—See RTX Corporation; *U.S. Public*, pg. 1825
RIEMAN & ARSZMAN CUSTOM DISTRIBUTORS; *U.S. Private*, pg. 3434
RIEMSER PHARMA GMBH—See Ardian SAS; *Int'l*, pg. 556
RIENZI & SONS, INC.; *U.S. Private*, pg. 3434
RIESBECK FOOD MARKETS INC.; *U.S. Private*, pg. 3434
RIESE ELECTRONIC GMBH; *Int'l*, pg. 6338
THE RIESE ORGANIZATION; *U.S. Private*, pg. 4107
RIESS FORD SALES INC.; *U.S. Private*, pg. 3434
RIESTERER & SCHNELL INC.; *U.S. Private*, pg. 3434
RIESTER-ROBB—See Riester; *U.S. Private*, pg. 3434
RIESTER; *U.S. Private*, pg. 3434
RIETER AMERICA, LLC—See Rieter Holding Ltd.; *Int'l*, pg. 6338
RIETER ASIA (HONG KONG) LTD.—See Rieter Holding Ltd.; *Int'l*, pg. 6338
RIETER ASIA (TAIWAN) LTD.—See Rieter Holding Ltd.; *Int'l*, pg. 6338
RIETER AUTOMATIC WINDER GMBH—See Rieter Holding Ltd.; *Int'l*, pg. 6339
RIETER AUTOMOTIVE ARGENTINA S.A.—See Rieter Holding Ltd.; *Int'l*, pg. 6339
RIETER AUTOMOTIVE BRASIL-ARTEFATOS DE FIBRAS TEXTEIS LTDA.—See Rieter Holding Ltd.; *Int'l*, pg. 6339
RIETER AUTOMOTIVE (INTERNATIONAL) AG—See Autoneum Holding Ltd.; *Int'l*, pg. 731
RIETER AUTOMOTIVE NORTH AMERICA CARPET—See Rieter Holding Ltd.; *Int'l*, pg. 6339
RIETER CHANGZHOU TEXTILE INSTRUMENTS CO. LTD.—See Rieter Holding Ltd.; *Int'l*, pg. 6339
RIETER CHINA TEXTILE INSTRUMENTS CO. LTD.—See Rieter Holding Ltd.; *Int'l*, pg. 6339
RIETER CORP.—See Rieter Holding Ltd.; *Int'l*, pg. 6339
RIETER CZ S.R.O—See Rieter Holding Ltd.; *Int'l*, pg. 6339
RIETER HOLDING LTD.; *Int'l*, pg. 6338
RIETER IMMOBILIEN AG—See Rieter Holding Ltd.; *Int'l*, pg. 6339
RIETER INDIA PVT. LTD.—See Rieter Holding Ltd.; *Int'l*, pg. 6339
RIETER INGOLSTADT GMBH—See Rieter Holding Ltd.; *Int'l*, pg. 6339
RIETER INGOLSTADT SPINNERELMASCHINENBAU AG—See Rieter Holding Ltd.; *Int'l*, pg. 6339
RIETER MACHINE WORKS LTD.—See SKion GmbH; *Int'l*, pg. 6987
RIETER MANAGEMENT AG—See Rieter Holding Ltd.; *Int'l*, pg. 6339
RIETER SOUTH AMERICA LTDA.—See Rieter Holding Ltd.; *Int'l*, pg. 6339
RIETER TEXTILE MACHINERY TRADING & SERVICES LTD.—See Rieter Holding Ltd.; *Int'l*, pg. 6339
RIETER TEXTILE SYSTEMS (SHANGHAI) CO. LTD.—See Rieter Holding Ltd.; *Int'l*, pg. 6339
RIETER UZBEKISTAN FE LLC—See Rieter Holding Ltd.; *Int'l*, pg. 6339

RIETER VERTRIEBS GMBH—See Rieter Holding Ltd.; *Int'l*, pg. 6339
RIETH-RILEY CONSTRUCTION CO., INC. - BIG RAPIDS—See Rieth-Riley Construction Co., Inc.; *U.S. Private*, pg. 3435
RIETH-RILEY CONSTRUCTION CO., INC. - GRAND VALLEY—See Rieth-Riley Construction Co., Inc.; *U.S. Private*, pg. 3435
RIETH-RILEY CONSTRUCTION CO., INC. - LANSING—See Rieth-Riley Construction Co., Inc.; *U.S. Private*, pg. 3435
RIETH-RILEY CONSTRUCTION CO., INC.; *U.S. Private*, pg. 3434
RIETVELD SERIGRAFIE B.V.—See Avery Dennison Corporation; *U.S. Public*, pg. 245
RIFA ADVANCES MATERIALS CO., LTD.—See RIFA Co., Ltd.; *Int'l*, pg. 6339
RIFA CO., LTD.—See RIFA Co., Ltd.; *Int'l*, pg. 6339
RIFA CO., LTD.; *Int'l*, pg. 6339
RIFAS UAB—See Harju Elekter AS; *Int'l*, pg. 3277
RIFCO INC.—See Chesswood Group Limited; *Int'l*, pg. 1472
RIFE ENERGY OPERATING LLC—See East West Energy Ltd.; *U.S. Private*, pg. 1318
RIFENBURG CONSTRUCTION INC.; *U.S. Private*, pg. 3435
RIFENG QINGYUAN ELECTRONIC CO., LTD.—See Man Yue Technology Holdings Limited; *Int'l*, pg. 4665
RIFE RESOURCES LTD—See Freehold Royalties Ltd.; *Int'l*, pg. 2770
RIFFLE & ASSOCIATES INC.; *U.S. Private*, pg. 3435
RI FINANCE, INC.—See Koninklijke Philips N.V.; *Int'l*, pg. 4271
RIFLE AIR, LLC—See Macquarie Group Limited; *Int'l*, pg. 4627
RIFLED AIR CONDITIONING—See The Matthews Group Inc.; *U.S. Private*, pg. 4076
RIFLE JET CENTER, LLC—See Macquarie Group Limited; *Int'l*, pg. 4627
RIFLEX FILM AB—See KAP Beteiligungs-AG; *Int'l*, pg. 4076
RIFOX-HANS RICHTER GMBH—See Thermax Limited; *Int'l*, pg. 7707
RIFT OIL LIMITED—See Repsol, S.A.; *Int'l*, pg. 6293
RIFT VALLEY EQUITY PARTNERS, LLC; *U.S. Private*, pg. 3435
RIFT VALLEY RESOURCES CORP.; *Int'l*, pg. 6339
RIGA ANALYTICAL LAB INC.—See Covalent Metrology Services, Inc.; *U.S. Private*, pg. 1071
RIGAKU AMERICAS CORP—See Rigaku Corporation; *Int'l*, pg. 6339
RIGAKU ANALYTICAL DEVICES, INC.—See Rigaku Corporation; *Int'l*, pg. 6339
RIGAKU BEIJING CORPORATION—See Rigaku Corporation; *Int'l*, pg. 6339
RIGAKU CORPORATION; *Int'l*, pg. 6339
RIGAKU CORPORATION - VACUUM PRODUCTS DIVISION—See Rigaku Corporation; *Int'l*, pg. 6339
RIGAKU EUROPE SE—See Rigaku Corporation; *Int'l*, pg. 6339
RIGAKU INNOVATIVE TECHNOLOGIES EUROPE S.R.O.—See Rigaku Corporation; *Int'l*, pg. 6339
RIGAKU INNOVATIVE TECHNOLOGIES, INC.—See Rigaku Corporation; *Int'l*, pg. 6339
RIGAKU LATIN AMERICA CONSULTORIA LTDA.—See Rigaku Corporation; *Int'l*, pg. 6340
RIGAKU RAMAN TECHNOLOGIES, INC.—See Rigaku Corporation; *Int'l*, pg. 6340
RIG-A-LITE PARTNERSHIP, LTD.—See AZZ, Inc.; *U.S. Public*, pg. 260
RIGAL SAS—See AdVini S.A.; *Int'l*, pg. 168
RIGAMONTI SALUMIFICIO S.P.A.—See JBS S.A.; *Int'l*, pg. 3919
RIGAS ELEKTROMASINBUVES RUPNICA AS; *Int'l*, pg. 6340
RIGAS JUVELIERIZSTRADAJUMU RUPNICA; *Int'l*, pg. 6340
RIGAS KUGU BUVETAVA; *Int'l*, pg. 6340
RIGA SUGAR COMPANY LTD; *Int'l*, pg. 6339
RIGBY GROUP (RG) PLC; *Int'l*, pg. 6340
RIGCOOL AUSTRALIA PTY LTD—See James Fisher & Sons Public Limited Company; *Int'l*, pg. 3876
RIGCOOL LIMITED—See James Fisher & Sons Public Limited Company; *Int'l*, pg. 3876
RIGDATA—See Hellman & Friedman LLC; *U.S. Private*, pg. 1908
RIGEL PHARMACEUTICALS, INC.; *U.S. Public*, pg. 1798
RIGEL RESOURCE ACQUISITION CORP.; *U.S. Public*, pg. 1798
RIGEL SHIPPING CANADA INC.; *Int'l*, pg. 6340
RIGER ADVERTISING AGENCY, INC.; *U.S. Private*, pg. 3435
RIGESA, CELULOSE, PAPEL E EMBALAGENS LTDA.—See WestRock Company; *U.S. Public*, pg. 2362
RIGESA, LTDA.—See WestRock Company; *U.S. Public*, pg. 2362
RIGETTI COMPUTING, INC.; *U.S. Public*, pg. 1798

RIGFIT OFFSHORE LTD—See Global Energy (Holdings) Ltd.; *Int'l*, pg. 2995
RIGGINS, INC.; *U.S. Private*, pg. 3435
RIGGS, COUNSELMAN, MICHAELS & DOWNES, INC.—See JBO Holding Company; *U.S. Private*, pg. 2194
RIGGS DISTLER & COMPANY INC.; *U.S. Private*, pg. 3435
RIGGS DISTLER & COMPANY INC.—See Southwest Gas Holdings, Inc.; *U.S. Public*, pg. 1913
RIGGS DISTRIBUTING, INC.; *U.S. Private*, pg. 3435
RIGGS INDUSTRIES, INC.; *U.S. Private*, pg. 3435
RIGGS OIL COMPANY INC.; *U.S. Private*, pg. 3435
RIGGS PARTNERS; *U.S. Private*, pg. 3435
RIGGS RENTAL SERVICES INC.—See J.A. Riggs Tractor Co.; *U.S. Private*, pg. 2158
RIGHCAST LIMITED—See SigmaRoc Plc; *Int'l*, pg. 6909
RIGHT ANSWER INSURANCE AGENCY, LLC—See The Allstate Corporation; *U.S. Public*, pg. 2034
RIGHTANSWERS, INC.—See Upland Software, Inc.; *U.S. Public*, pg. 2264
RIGHT AT HOME, INC.; *U.S. Private*, pg. 3435
RIGHT AWAY DISPOSAL, L.L.C.—See Waste Connections, Inc.; *Int'l*, pg. 8352
RIGHT AWAY REDY MIX INCORPORATED—See Vulcan Materials Company; *U.S. Public*, pg. 2314
RIGHT CENTURY LIMITED—See E. Bon Holdings Ltd; *Int'l*, pg. 2250
RIGHTCHOICE BENEFIT ADMINISTRATORSSM—See Elevance Health, Inc.; *U.S. Public*, pg. 730
RIGHT COOPERATIVE ASSOCIATION; *U.S. Private*, pg. 3435
THE RIGHT CROWD TRUSTEES LIMITED; *Int'l*, pg. 7679
RIGHT CZECH REPUBLIC—See ManpowerGroup Inc.; *U.S. Public*, pg. 1361
RIGHT DO BRASIL LTDA—See ManpowerGroup Inc.; *U.S. Public*, pg. 1361
RIGHTEOUS CLOTHING AGENCY; *U.S. Private*, pg. 3436
THE RIGHTER COMPANY, INC.; *U.S. Private*, pg. 4107
THE RIGHT FUELCARD COMPANY LIMITED—See Edenred S.A.; *Int'l*, pg. 2308
RIGHT LANE ACQUISITION I, INC.; *U.S. Private*, pg. 3435
RIGHT LANE INDUSTRIES, INC.; *U.S. Private*, pg. 3435
RIGHT MANAGEMENT ARGENTINA S.A.—See ManpowerGroup Inc.; *U.S. Public*, pg. 1361
RIGHT MANAGEMENT CANADA—See ManpowerGroup Inc.; *U.S. Public*, pg. 1361
RIGHT MANAGEMENT CHINA—See ManpowerGroup Inc.; *U.S. Public*, pg. 1361
RIGHT MANAGEMENT CONSULTANTS, INC.—See ManpowerGroup Inc.; *U.S. Public*, pg. 1361
RIGHT MANAGEMENT CONSULTANTS INTERNATIONAL PTY LTD—See ManpowerGroup Inc.; *U.S. Public*, pg. 1361
RIGHT MANAGEMENT CONSULTANTS PTY LTD—See ManpowerGroup Inc.; *U.S. Public*, pg. 1361
RIGHT MANAGEMENT CONSULTING (SHANGHAI) CO., LTD—See ManpowerGroup Inc.; *U.S. Public*, pg. 1361
RIGHT MANAGEMENT DENMARK A/S—See ManpowerGroup Inc.; *U.S. Public*, pg. 1361
RIGHT MANAGEMENT KOREA CO. LTD.—See ManpowerGroup Inc.; *U.S. Public*, pg. 1361
RIGHT MANAGEMENT LIMITED—See ManpowerGroup Inc.; *U.S. Public*, pg. 1361
RIGHT MANAGEMENT LUXEMBOURG SA—See ManpowerGroup Inc.; *U.S. Public*, pg. 1361
RIGHT MANAGEMENT MEXICO, S.A. DE C.V.—See ManpowerGroup Inc.; *U.S. Public*, pg. 1361
RIGHT MANAGEMENT NEDERLAND B.V.—See ManpowerGroup Inc.; *U.S. Public*, pg. 1361
RIGHT MANAGEMENT NORDIC HOLDING A/S—See ManpowerGroup Inc.; *U.S. Public*, pg. 1361
RIGHT MANAGEMENT NORWAY A/S—See ManpowerGroup Inc.; *U.S. Public*, pg. 1361
RIGHT MANAGEMENT PERU S.A.C.—See ManpowerGroup Inc.; *U.S. Public*, pg. 1361
RIGHT MANAGEMENT S.A.—See ManpowerGroup Inc.; *U.S. Public*, pg. 1361
RIGHT MANAGEMENT SINGAPORE PTE. LTD.—See ManpowerGroup Inc.; *U.S. Public*, pg. 1361
RIGHT MANAGEMENT SPAIN, S.L.U.—See ManpowerGroup Inc.; *U.S. Public*, pg. 1361
RIGHT MANAGEMENT SPAIN, S.L.U.—See ManpowerGroup Inc.; *U.S. Public*, pg. 1361
RIGHT MANAGEMENT SWEDEN AB—See ManpowerGroup Inc.; *U.S. Public*, pg. 1361
RIGHT MANAGEMENT SWITZERLAND AG—See ManpowerGroup Inc.; *U.S. Public*, pg. 1361
RIGHT MANAGEMENT TAIWAN CO., LTD.—See ManpowerGroup Inc.; *U.S. Public*, pg. 1361
RIGHTMOVE GROUP LIMITED—See Rightmove plc; *Int'l*, pg. 6340
RIGHTMOVE PLC; *Int'l*, pg. 6340
RIGHT NETWORKS, LLC; *U.S. Private*, pg. 3435
RIGHT OF REPLY LTD; *Int'l*, pg. 6340
RIGHT ON BRANDS, INC.; *U.S. Public*, pg. 1798
RIGHT ON CO., LTD.; *Int'l*, pg. 6340
RIGHT ON INTERACTIVE, LLC; *U.S. Private*, pg. 3436

RIGHT PEOPLE TECHNOLOGIES; *Int'l*, pg. 6340
RIGHTPOINT COMPANY—See Genpact Limited; *Int'l*, pg. 2926
RIGHTPOINT CONSULTING LLC—See Genpact Limited; *Int'l*, pg. 2926
RIGHTPOINT INDIA DIGITAL PRIVATE LIMITED—See Genpact Limited; *Int'l*, pg. 2927
RIGHTSCALE ASIA PACIFIC—See Ontario Teachers' Pension Plan; *Int'l*, pg. 5589
RIGHTSCALE ASIA PACIFIC—See TA Associates, Inc.; *U.S. Private*, pg. 3915
RIGHTSCALE AUSTRALIA—See Ontario Teachers' Pension Plan; *Int'l*, pg. 5589
RIGHTSCALE AUSTRALIA—See TA Associates, Inc.; *U.S. Private*, pg. 3915
RIGHTSCALE, INC.—See Ontario Teachers' Pension Plan; *Int'l*, pg. 5589
RIGHTSCALE, INC.—See TA Associates, Inc.; *U.S. Private*, pg. 3915
RIGHTSCALE UK LTD—See Ontario Teachers' Pension Plan; *Int'l*, pg. 5589
RIGHTSCALE UK LTD—See TA Associates, Inc.; *U.S. Private*, pg. 3915
RIGHTSCORP, INC.; *U.S. Public*, pg. 1798
RIGHT SIDE CAPITAL MANAGEMENT, LLC; *U.S. Private*, pg. 3436
RIGHTSIDE GROUP, LTD.—See Ethos Capital, LLC; *U.S. Private*, pg. 1432
RIGHT SINOVA AB—See ManpowerGroup Inc.; *U.S. Public*, pg. 1361
RIGHTS & ISSUES INVESTMENT TRUST PLC; *Int'l*, pg. 6340
RIGHTSLINE SOFTWARE INC.—See Klass Capital Corp.; *Int'l*, pg. 4199
RIGHTSMILE, INC.; *U.S. Public*, pg. 1798
RIGHTSSCALE, INC.—See Faith, Inc.; *Int'l*, pg. 2609
RIGHTSTAFF, INC.; *U.S. Private*, pg. 3436
RIGHTSURE INSURANCE GROUP; *U.S. Private*, pg. 3436
RIGHT SYSTEMS INC.; *U.S. Private*, pg. 3436
RIGHT TIME GROUP INC.—See Gryphon Investors, LLC; *U.S. Private*, pg. 1799
RIGHT TUNNELLING PUBLIC COMPANY LIMITED; *Int'l*, pg. 6340
RIGHT WAY AUTO; *U.S. Private*, pg. 3436
RIGHTWAY GATE, INC.; *U.S. Private*, pg. 3436
RIGHTWAY HOLDINGS CO., LTD.; *Int'l*, pg. 6340
RIGHT WAY INDUSTRIAL CO., LTD.; *Int'l*, pg. 6340
RIGID CONTAINERS IRELAND PLANT—See VPK Packaging Group NV; *Int'l*, pg. 8312
RIGID GLOBAL BUILDINGS, LLC; *U.S. Private*, pg. 3436
RIGIDIZED METALS CORP.; *U.S. Private*, pg. 3436
RIGID—See VPK Packaging Group NV; *Int'l*, pg. 8312
RIGIFA CARE HOME PERTH—See Balhousie Holdings Limited; *Int'l*, pg. 808
RIGIPS AG—See Compagnie de Saint-Gobain SA; *Int'l*, pg. 1725
RIGIPS AUSTRIA GMBH—See Compagnie de Saint-Gobain SA; *Int'l*, pg. 1725
RIGIPS BOSNIA—See Compagnie de Saint-Gobain SA; *Int'l*, pg. 1725
RIGIPS BULGARIA E.O.O.D.—See Compagnie de Saint-Gobain SA; *Int'l*, pg. 1725
RIGIPS CROATIA—See Compagnie de Saint-Gobain SA; *Int'l*, pg. 1725
RIGIPS HUNGARIA GIPSZKARTON KFT—See Compagnie de Saint-Gobain SA; *Int'l*, pg. 1725
RIGIPS POLSKA-STAWIANY SP. Z O.O.—See Compagnie de Saint-Gobain SA; *Int'l*, pg. 1725
RIGIPS SLOVAKIA SRO—See Compagnie de Saint-Gobain SA; *Int'l*, pg. 1725
RIGIPS SLOVENIA—See Compagnie de Saint-Gobain SA; *Int'l*, pg. 1726
RIGIPS VERWALTUNGS GMBH—See Compagnie de Saint-Gobain SA; *Int'l*, pg. 1726
RIGK GMBH GESELLSCHAFT ZUR RUCKFUHRUNG INDUSTRIELLER & GEWERBLICHER KUNSTSTOFFVERPACKUNGEN MBH—See LyondellBasell Industries N.V.; *Int'l*, pg. 4608
RIGMANAGER INC.—See PHX Energy Services Corp.; *Int'l*, pg. 5858
RIGMAX H2O, LLC—See RigMax, LLC; *U.S. Private*, pg. 3436
RIGMAX, LLC; *U.S. Private*, pg. 3436
RIG METALS LLC—See Lamprell plc; *Int'l*, pg. 4402
RIGNET AS—See ViaSat, Inc.; *U.S. Public*, pg. 2292
RIGNET AUSTRALIA PTY LTD—See ViaSat, Inc.; *U.S. Public*, pg. 2292
RIGNET, INC.—See ViaSat, Inc.; *U.S. Public*, pg. 2292
RIGNET PTE LTD—See ViaSat, Inc.; *U.S. Public*, pg. 2292
RIGNET QATAR W.L.L.—See ViaSat, Inc.; *U.S. Public*, pg. 2292
RIGNET SERVICOS DE TELECOMUNICACOES BRASIL LTDA.—See ViaSat, Inc.; *U.S. Public*, pg. 2292
RIGONTEC GMBH—See Merck & Co., Inc.; *U.S. Public*, pg. 1421
RIGO OIL COMPANY TUNISIA LTD—See CYGAM Energy Inc.; *Int'l*, pg. 1895

RIGOR, INC.—See Cisco Systems, Inc.; *U.S. Public*, pg. 500
RIG TOOLS, INC.—See Gibson Energy Inc.; *Int'l*, pg. 2963
RIGUAN CLOSURE (CHANGSHU) CO., LTD.—See Toyo Seikan Group Holdings, Ltd.; *Int'l*, pg. 7856
RIGZONE.COM, INC.—See Westwood Global Energy Group; *Int'l*, pg. 8393
RIH ACQUISITIONS MS II, LLC—See PENN Entertainment, Inc.; *U.S. Public*, pg. 1662
RIHAM GENERAL TRADING & CONTR. CO. W.L.L—See Fouad Alghanim & Sons Group of Companies; *Int'l*, pg. 2753
RIH DING WATER ENTERPRISE CO., LTD.—See Radium Life Tech Co., Ltd.; *Int'l*, pg. 6176
RIHM MOTOR COMPANY; *U.S. Private*, pg. 3436
RI/HOLLYWOOD NISSAN ACQUISITION CORP.—See AutoNation, Inc.; *U.S. Public*, pg. 237
RI/HOLLYWOOD NISSAN ACQUISITION CORP.—See AutoNation, Inc.; *U.S. Public*, pg. 237
RI HONG STAINLESS (SHANGHAI) CO., LTD.—See Hanwa Co., Ltd.; *Int'l*, pg. 3263
RIHONG (YAAN) ELECTRONICS CO., LTD.—See Man Yue Technology Holdings Limited; *Int'l*, pg. 4665
RI.ISA D.O.O.—See Atlas Holdings, LLC; *U.S. Private*, pg. 378
RIISER OIL COMPANY INC.; *U.S. Private*, pg. 3436
RIISER TRANSPORTATION—See Riiser Oil Company Inc.; *U.S. Private*, pg. 3436
RIJNAARDE B.V.—See Dubai World Corporation; *Int'l*, pg. 2221
RIJNMOND DISTRIBUTIE SERVICES B.V.—See La Cooperative WELCOOP SA; *Int'l*, pg. 4387
RIKASEIKI CO., LTD.—See Tokai Rika Co., Ltd.; *Int'l*, pg. 7780
R.I.K. ASSISTANS AKTIEBOLAG—See Humana AB; *Int'l*, pg. 3530
RIKAZ DEVELOPMENT COMPANY—See HAK Algahtani Group of Companies; *Int'l*, pg. 3219
RIKCO INTERNATIONAL LLC—See Enovis Corporation; *U.S. Public*, pg. 772
RIKEI CORPORATION; *Int'l*, pg. 6340
RIKE, INC.; *U.S. Private*, pg. 3436
RIKELEKTRO AB—See Instalco AB; *Int'l*, pg. 3722
RIKEN CHEMICAL PRODUCTS CORPORATION—See Riken Technos Corporation; *Int'l*, pg. 6341
RIKEN CORUNDUM CO., LTD. - GUNMA NIIHARU FACTORY—See Okamoto Industries, Inc.; *Int'l*, pg. 5544
RIKEN CORUNDUM CO., LTD. - GUNMA NUMATA FACTORY—See Okamoto Industries, Inc.; *Int'l*, pg. 5544
RIKEN CORUNDUM CO., LTD.—See Okamoto Industries, Inc.; *Int'l*, pg. 5544
RIKEN ELASTOMERS CORPORATION—See Riken Technos Corporation; *Int'l*, pg. 6341
RIKEN ELECTRIC WIRE CO., LTD.—See The Furukawa Electric Co., Ltd.; *Int'l*, pg. 7646
RIKEN FABRO CORPORATION—See Riken Technos Corporation; *Int'l*, pg. 6341
RIKEN FOOD CO., LTD.—See Riken Vitamin Co., Ltd.; *Int'l*, pg. 6341
RIKEN FOOD (DALIAN) CO., LTD.—See Riken Vitamin Co., Ltd.; *Int'l*, pg. 6341
RIKEN FORGE CO., LTD.—See Toyota Motor Corporation; *Int'l*, pg. 7871
RIKEN GENESIS CO., LTD.—See Sysmex Corporation; *Int'l*, pg. 7388
RIKENGREEN CO., LTD.—See Kumiai Chemical Industry Co., Ltd.; *Int'l*, pg. 4331
RIKEN KEIKI CO., LTD.; *Int'l*, pg. 6340
RIKEN KEIKI COMMERCIAL (SHANGHAI) CO., LTD.—See Riken Keiki Co., Ltd.; *Int'l*, pg. 6341
RIKEN KEIKI GMBH—See Riken Keiki Co., Ltd.; *Int'l*, pg. 6341
RIKEN KEIKI KOREA CO., LTD.—See Riken Keiki Co., Ltd.; *Int'l*, pg. 6341
RIKEN KEIKI TAIWAN CO., LTD.—See Riken Keiki Co., Ltd.; *Int'l*, pg. 6341
RIKEN LIGHT METAL INDUSTRIAL CO., LTD.—See Nippon Light Metal Holdings Company, Ltd.; *Int'l*, pg. 5324
RIKEN LIGHT METAL INDUSTRY COMPANY LTD.—See Nippon Light Metal Holdings Company, Ltd.; *Int'l*, pg. 5324
RIKEN MOTOR SALES INC.—See HKS CO., LTD.; *Int'l*, pg. 3429
RIKEN SEIKO CO., LTD.—See Daido Steel Co., Ltd.; *Int'l*, pg. 1923
RIKEN SUURI CORPORATION—See Nippon Telegraph & Telephone Corporation; *Int'l*, pg. 5355
RIKEN TECHNOS CORPORATION - GUNMA PLANT—See Riken Technos Corporation; *Int'l*, pg. 6341
RIKEN TECHNOS CORPORATION - MIE PLANT—See Riken Technos Corporation; *Int'l*, pg. 6341
RIKEN TECHNOS CORPORATION - SAITAMA PLANT—See Riken Technos Corporation; *Int'l*, pg. 6341
RIKEN TECHNOS CORPORATION; *Int'l*, pg. 6341

RIKEN U.S.A. CORPORATION—See Riken Technos Corporation; *Int'l*, pg. 6341
RIKEN VITAMIN CO., LTD.; *Int'l*, pg. 6341
RIKEN VITAMIN EUROPE GMBH—See Riken Vitamin Co., Ltd.; *Int'l*, pg. 6341
RIKEN VITAMIN USA INC.—See Riken Vitamin Co., Ltd.; *Int'l*, pg. 6341
RIKER PRODUCTS, INC.; *U.S. Private*, pg. 3436
RIKEVITA ASIA CO., LTD.—See Riken Vitamin Co., Ltd.; *Int'l*, pg. 6341
RIKEVITA FINE CHEMICAL & FOOD INDUSTRY (SHANGHAI) CO., LTD.—See Riken Vitamin Co., Ltd.; *Int'l*, pg. 6341
RIKEVITA (INDIA) PRIVATE LIMITED—See Riken Vitamin Co., Ltd.; *Int'l*, pg. 6341
RIKEVITA (MALAYSIA) SDN. BHD.—See Riken Vitamin Co., Ltd.; *Int'l*, pg. 6341
RIKEVITA (SINGAPORE) PTE LTD—See Riken Vitamin Co., Ltd.; *Int'l*, pg. 6341
RIKEVITA TURKEY FOOD INDUSTRY LIMITED COMPANY—See Riken Vitamin Co., Ltd.; *Int'l*, pg. 6341
R.I.K. INDUSTRIES PTE. LTD.—See Japan Fawick Co., Ltd.; *Int'l*, pg. 3889
RIK INDUSTRIES—See Japan Fawick Co., Ltd.; *Int'l*, pg. 3889
RIKO, LTD.—See Kurimoto Ltd; *Int'l*, pg. 4340
THE RIKOON GROUP, LLC—See Lee Equity Partners LLC; *U.S. Private*, pg. 2412
RIK SILEKS AD; *Int'l*, pg. 6340
RIKSTEN FRILUFTSSTAD AB—See Peab AB; *Int'l*, pg. 5773
R.I.K. (THAILAND) CO., LTD.—See Japan Fawick Co., Ltd.; *Int'l*, pg. 3888
RI-KUAN METAL CORPORATION—See Casetek Holdings Limited; *Int'l*, pg. 1351
RIKUYOSHA CO., LTD.—See Nomura Co., Ltd.; *Int'l*, pg. 5409
RILEA GROUP INC.; *U.S. Private*, pg. 3436
RILEY BROTHERS, INC.—See ORIX Corporation; *Int'l*, pg. 5636
RILEY CONSTRUCTION COMPANY INC.; *U.S. Private*, pg. 3436
RILEY EXPLORATION GROUP, LLC; *U.S. Private*, pg. 3436
RILEY EXPLORATION PERMIAN, INC.; *U.S. Public*, pg. 1798
RILEY EXPLORATION - PERMIAN, LLC—See Riley Exploration Permian, Inc.; *U.S. Public*, pg. 1798
RILEY GEAR CORPORATION; *U.S. Private*, pg. 3437
RILEY GOLD CORP.; *Int'l*, pg. 6341
RILEY HAYES ADVERTISING; *U.S. Private*, pg. 3437
RILEY NATURAL GAS COMPANY—See Chevron Corporation; *U.S. Public*, pg. 487
RILEY NATURAL GAS—See Chevron Corporation; *U.S. Public*, pg. 487
RILEY PARK TIRE SERVICES—See Indy Tire Centers, Inc.; *U.S. Private*, pg. 2069
RILEY PAVING, INC.—See Construction Partners, Inc.; *U.S. Public*, pg. 572
RILEY PERMIAN OPERATING COMPANY, LLC—See Riley Exploration Permian, Inc.; *U.S. Public*, pg. 1798
RILEY POWER, INC.—See Babcock Power, Inc.; *U.S. Private*, pg. 422
RILEY SALES INC.; *U.S. Private*, pg. 3437
RILEY TECHNOLOGIES, LLC; *U.S. Private*, pg. 3437
RILEY WELDING & FABRICATING LLC—See Stewart & Tate, Inc.; *U.S. Private*, pg. 3811
RILKEN COSMETICS INDUSTRY S.A.—See Henkel AG & Co. KGaA; *Int'l*, pg. 3350
RI/LLC ACQUISITION CORP.—See AutoNation, Inc.; *U.S. Public*, pg. 237
RILLFUNG COMPANY LTD.—See Sinochem Corporation; *Int'l*, pg. 6950
RIL PROPERTY PLC; *Int'l*, pg. 6341
RILTA ENVIRONMENTAL LTD—See Exponent Private Equity LLP; *Int'l*, pg. 2589
RIMAGE CORPORATION—See Equus Holdings, Inc.; *U.S. Private*, pg. 1417
RIMAGE EUROPE GMBH—See Equus Holdings, Inc.; *U.S. Private*, pg. 1417
RIMAGE JAPAN CO., LTD.—See Equus Holdings, Inc.; *U.S. Private*, pg. 1417
RIMAL ENGINEERING PRODUCTS; *Int'l*, pg. 6342
RIMA MANUFACTURING COMPANY; *U.S. Private*, pg. 3437
RIMA - RESIDUOS INDUSTRIAIS E MEIO AMBIENTE, S.A.—See Mota-Engil SGPS, S.A.; *Int'l*, pg. 5052
RIMAS APS—See Mitsubishi Heavy Industries, Ltd.; *Int'l*, pg. 4961
RIMBACO GROUP GLOBAL LIMITED; *Int'l*, pg. 6342
RIMBO WARE AG—See Rena-Ware Distributors Inc.; *U.S. Private*, pg. 3397
RIMBUNAN HIJAU PLYWOOD SDN. BHD.—See Jaya Tiasa Holdings Berhad; *Int'l*, pg. 3915
RIMBUNAN MELATI SDN. BHD.—See Khazanah Nasional Berhad; *Int'l*, pg. 4153
RIMBUNAN SAWIT BERHAD; *Int'l*, pg. 6342
RIMCO INC.; *U.S. Private*, pg. 3437

COMPANY NAME INDEX

RIMES TECHNOLOGIES CORPORATION—See EQT AB; *Int'l*, pg. 2479
RIMEX A.D.; *Int'l*, pg. 6342
RIMEX ESPANA—See Rimex Metals (U.K.) Limited; *Int'l*, pg. 6342
RIMEX INC—See Rimex Supply Ltd.; *Int'l*, pg. 6342
RIMEX METALS (AUSTRALIA) PTY LTD—See Rimex Metals (U.K.) Limited; *Int'l*, pg. 6342
RIMEX METALS (DEUTSCHLAND) GMBH—See Rimex Metals (U.K.) Limited; *Int'l*, pg. 6342
RIMEX METALS (FRANCE) SA—See Rimex Metals (U.K.) Limited; *Int'l*, pg. 6342
RIMEX METALS (SOUTH AFRICA) PTY LTD—See Rimex Metals (U.K.) Limited; *Int'l*, pg. 6342
RIMEX METALS (U.K.) LIMITED; *Int'l*, pg. 6342
RIMEX METALS (USA) INC—See Rimex Metals (U.K.) Limited; *Int'l*, pg. 6342
RIMEX SUPPLY LTD DO BRASIL—See Rimex Supply Ltd.; *Int'l*, pg. 6342
RIMEX SUPPLY LTD.; *Int'l*, pg. 6342
RIMEX WHEEL PTY LTD—See Rimex Supply Ltd.; *Int'l*, pg. 6342
RIMFIRE PACIFIC MINING NL; *Int'l*, pg. 6342
RIM FOREST LUMBER, CO.; *U.S. Private*, pg. 3437
RIMHUB, INC.; *U.S. Private*, pg. 3437
RIMHUB INDIA PVT. LTD.—See Rimhub, Inc.; *U.S. Private*, pg. 3437
RIMILIA CANADA LTD.—See BlackLine, Inc.; *U.S. Public*, pg. 342
RIMILIA EUROPE LTD.—See BlackLine, Inc.; *U.S. Public*, pg. 342
RI MING (SHANGHAI) CO., LTD.—See Casetek Holdings Limited; *Int'l*, pg. 1351
RIMINI STREET AUSTRALIA PTY. LIMITED—See Rimini Street, Inc.; *U.S. Public*, pg. 1799
RIMINI STREET BRAZILS SERVICOS DE TECNOLOGIA LTDA.—See Rimini Street, Inc.; *U.S. Public*, pg. 1799
RIMINI STREET CANADA INC.—See Rimini Street, Inc.; *U.S. Public*, pg. 1799
RIMINI STREET FZ, LLC—See Rimini Street, Inc.; *U.S. Public*, pg. 1799
RIMINI STREET GMBH—See Rimini Street, Inc.; *U.S. Public*, pg. 1799
RIMINI STREET, INC.; *U.S. Public*, pg. 1798
RIMINI STREET, LTD.—See Rimini Street, Inc.; *U.S. Public*, pg. 1799
RIMKUS CONSULTING GROUP, INC.; *U.S. Private*, pg. 3437
RIM LOGISTICS LTD; *U.S. Private*, pg. 3437
RIMMA S.R.L.—See KONE Oyj; *Int'l*, pg. 4250
RIMMEL INC.—See JAB Holding Company S.a.r.l.; *Int'l*, pg. 3861
RIMOLDI DA AMAZONIA IND. E COM. LTDA.—See CF Italia srl; *Int'l*, pg. 1429
RIMOLDI OF AMERICA INC.—See CF Italia srl; *Int'l*, pg. 1429
RIMON COHEN-WEBER SHANDWICK—See The Interpublic Group of Companies, Inc.; *U.S. Public*, pg. 2105
RIMON GROUP; *Int'l*, pg. 6342
RIMONI INDUSTRIES LTD.; *Int'l*, pg. 6342
RIM OPERATING, INC.; *U.S. Private*, pg. 3437
RIMPLAS INDUSTRIES SDN BHD—See Vicplas International Ltd; *Int'l*, pg. 8187
R.I.M. PORTER NOVELLI—See Omnicom Group Inc.; *U.S. Public*, pg. 1591
RIMPORTS, LLC—See Compass Diversified Holdings; *U.S. Public*, pg. 560
RIMPULL CORPORATION; *U.S. Private*, pg. 3437
RIMROCK AUTO GROUP, INC.; *U.S. Private*, pg. 3437
RIMROCK CORPORATION—See Lincoln Electric Holdings, Inc.; *U.S. Public*, pg. 1318
RIMROCK GOLD CORP.; *U.S. Public*, pg. 1799
RIMROCK GROUP, INC.—See BCER Engineering, Inc.; *U.S. Private*, pg. 499
RIMROCK HOLDINGS CORPORATION—See Lincoln Electric Holdings, Inc.; *U.S. Public*, pg. 1318
RIMROCK SUBURU, INC.—See Rimrock Auto Group, Inc.; *U.S. Private*, pg. 3437
RIMSTORM, INC.; *U.S. Private*, pg. 3437
RINA CHECK SRL—See RINA S.p.A.; *Int'l*, pg. 6342
RINANI GROUP BERHAD; *Int'l*, pg. 6343
RINA S.P.A.; *Int'l*, pg. 6342
RINAT NEUROSCIENCE CORP.—See Pfizer Inc.; *U.S. Public*, pg. 1683
RINCHEM COMPANY INCORPORATED; *U.S. Private*, pg. 3437
RINCON BROADCASTING LLC—See Point Broadcasting Company; *U.S. Private*, pg. 3221
RINCON CENTER COMMERCIAL, LLC—See Hudson Pacific Properties, Inc.; *U.S. Public*, pg. 1068
RINCON CONSULTANTS, INC.; *U.S. Private*, pg. 3437
RINCON RESOURCES LIMITED—See Gunsynd plc; *Int'l*, pg. 3185
RINCO ULTRASONICS AG—See Crest Group Inc.; *U.S. Private*, pg. 1096
RINCO ULTRASONICS DANMARK A/S—See Crest Group Inc.; *U.S. Private*, pg. 1096
RINCO ULTRASONICS GMBH—See Crest Group Inc.; *U.S. Private*, pg. 1096

RINCO ULTRASONICS (INDIA) PRIVATE LIMITED—See Crest Group Inc.; *U.S. Private*, pg. 1096
RINCO ULTRASONICS ITALIA S.R.L.—See Crest Group Inc.; *U.S. Private*, pg. 1096
RINCO ULTRASONICS (SHANGHAI) CO., LTD.—See Crest Group Inc.; *U.S. Private*, pg. 1096
RINCO ULTRASONICS USA INC.—See Crest Group Inc.; *U.S. Private*, pg. 1096
RINDCHEN'S WEINKONTOR GMBH & CO. KG—See Schloss Wachenheim AG; *Int'l*, pg. 6622
RINDES Y CULTIVOS DAS S.A.—See Corteva, Inc.; *U.S. Public*, pg. 582
RINDIN ENTERPRISES PTY. LIMITED—See Johnson Controls International plc; *Int'l*, pg. 3987
RINECO CHEMICAL INDUSTRIES—See EQT AB; *Int'l*, pg. 2482
RINEHART MOTION SYSTEMS LLC—See BorgWarner Inc.; *U.S. Public*, pg. 371
RINEHART OIL, INC.; *U.S. Private*, pg. 3437
RING2 MEDIA—See Osceola Capital Management, LLC; *U.S. Private*, pg. 3047
RINGCENTRAL AUSTRALIA PTY LTD—See RingCentral, Inc.; *U.S. Public*, pg. 1799
RINGCENTRAL CH GMBH—See RingCentral, Inc.; *U.S. Public*, pg. 1799
RINGCENTRAL FRANCE—See RingCentral, Inc.; *U.S. Public*, pg. 1799
RINGCENTRAL GERMANY GMBH—See RingCentral, Inc.; *U.S. Public*, pg. 1799
RINGCENTRAL, INC.; *U.S. Public*, pg. 1799
RINGCENTRAL IRELAND LTD.—See RingCentral, Inc.; *U.S. Public*, pg. 1799
RING CONTAINER TECHNOLOGIES INC.—See MSD Capital, L.P.; *U.S. Private*, pg. 2807
RINGCUBE SOFTWARE TECH PVT LTD.—See Elliott Management Corporation; *U.S. Private*, pg. 1367
RINGCUBE SOFTWARE TECH PVT LTD.—See Vista Equity Partners, LLC; *U.S. Private*, pg. 4396
RINGDALE GMBH—See Network Technology PLC; *Int'l*, pg. 5218
RINGDALE, INC.—See Network Technology PLC; *Int'l*, pg. 5218
RINGDALE KK—See Network Technology PLC; *Int'l*, pg. 5218
RINGDALE (UK) LTD.—See Network Technology PLC; *Int'l*, pg. 5218
RING EIENDOMSMEGLING AS—See Storebrand ASA; *Int'l*, pg. 7226
RING ENERGY, INC.; *U.S. Public*, pg. 1799
RINGER HUT CO., LTD. - FUJI HILL FACTORY—See Ringer Hut Co., Ltd.; *Int'l*, pg. 6343
RINGER HUT CO., LTD. - SAGA FACTORY—See Ringer Hut Co., Ltd.; *Int'l*, pg. 6343
RINGER HUT CO., LTD.; *Int'l*, pg. 6343
RINGER HUT DEVELOPMENT CORPORATION—See Ringer Hut Co., Ltd.; *Int'l*, pg. 6343
RINGFEDER POWER TRANSMISSION GMBH—See VBG Group AB; *Int'l*, pg. 8138
RINGFEDER POWER TRANSMISSION S.R.O.—See VBG Group AB; *Int'l*, pg. 8138
RINGFEDER POWER TRANSMISSION USA CORPORATION—See VBG Group AB; *Int'l*, pg. 8138
RING GARAGE AG CHUR—See Mercedes-Benz Group AG; *Int'l*, pg. 4828
RINGGOLD TELEPHONE CO. INC.; *U.S. Private*, pg. 3438
RINGHALS AB—See Vattenfall AB; *Int'l*, pg. 8136
RINGIER AG—See Ringier Holding AG; *Int'l*, pg. 6343
RINGIER AXEL SPRINGER D.O.O.—See Ringier Holding AG; *Int'l*, pg. 6343
RINGIER AXEL SPRINGER MAGYARORSZAG KFT—See Axel Springer SE; *Int'l*, pg. 766
RINGIER AXEL SPRINGER MEDIA AG—See Ringier Holding AG; *Int'l*, pg. 6343
RINGIER AXEL SPRINGER POLSKA SP. Z OO—See Ringier Holding AG; *Int'l*, pg. 6343
RINGIER CR A.S.—See Ringier Holding AG; *Int'l*, pg. 6343
RINGIER DIGITAL AG—See Ringier Holding AG; *Int'l*, pg. 6343
RINGIER GHANA LTD.—See Ringier Holding AG; *Int'l*, pg. 6343
RINGIER HOLDING AG; *Int'l*, pg. 6343
RINGIER KENYA LTD.—See Ringier Holding AG; *Int'l*, pg. 6343
RINGIER KFT.—See Ringier Holding AG; *Int'l*, pg. 6343
RINGIER MEDIA NIGERIA LTD.—See Ringier Holding AG; *Int'l*, pg. 6343
RINGIER PRINT ADLIGENSWIL AG—See Ringier Holding AG; *Int'l*, pg. 6343
RINGIER PRINT BUDAPEST INC.—See Ringier Holding AG; *Int'l*, pg. 6343
RINGIER PRINT CZ A.S.—See Ringier Holding AG; *Int'l*, pg. 6344
RINGIER PRINT HOLDING AG—See Ringier Holding AG; *Int'l*, pg. 6343
RINGIER PUBLISHING GMBH—See Ringier Holding AG; *Int'l*, pg. 6344
RINGIER SA—See Ringier Holding AG; *Int'l*, pg. 6343

RINGIER SENEGAL S.A.—See Ringier Holding AG; *Int'l*, pg. 6344
RINGIER SLOVAKIA, A.S.—See Ringier Holding AG; *Int'l*, pg. 6344
RINGIER TRADE MEDIA LTD.; *Int'l*, pg. 6344
RINGIER TV—See Ringier Holding AG; *Int'l*, pg. 6344
RINGIER VIETNAM CO., LTD.—See Ringier Holding AG; *Int'l*, pg. 6344
RING INTERNATIONAL HOLDING AG; *Int'l*, pg. 6343
RINGKJOBING LANDBOBANK A/S; *Int'l*, pg. 6344
RINGLAND CONSTRUCTION INC.; *U.S. Private*, pg. 3438
RINGLAND-JOHNSON INC.; *U.S. Private*, pg. 3438
RINGLEAD, INC.—See ZoomInfo Technologies Inc.; *U.S. Public*, pg. 2411
RINGLER ASSOCIATES INC.; *U.S. Private*, pg. 3438
RING LIFT—See Ring Power Corporation; *U.S. Private*, pg. 3438
RINGLING BROS., BARNUM & BAILEY COMBINED SHOWS, INC.—See Feld Entertainment, Inc.; *U.S. Private*, pg. 1493
RINGLING COLLEGE LIFELONG LEARNING ACADEMY—See Ringling College of Art and Design, Inc.; *U.S. Private*, pg. 3438
RINGLING COLLEGE OF ART AND DESIGN, INC.; *U.S. Private*, pg. 3438
RINGMETALL AG; *Int'l*, pg. 6344
RINGNES A/S—See Carlsberg A/S; *Int'l*, pg. 1341
RING & PINION SERVICE INC.—See Linsalata Capital Partners, Inc.; *U.S. Private*, pg. 2463
RING PLUS AQUA LIMITED—See Raymond Limited; *Int'l*, pg. 6224
RING POWER CORPORATION; *U.S. Private*, pg. 3438
RING POWER CORPORATION—See Ring Power Corporation; *U.S. Private*, pg. 3438
RINGPOWER CORP—See Ring Power Corporation; *U.S. Private*, pg. 3438
RING PRECISON COMPONENTS—See PMT Group Inc; *U.S. Private*, pg. 3219
RINGPU (BAODING) BIOLOGICAL PHARMACEUTICAL CO.,LTD.—See Tianjin Ringpu Bio-Technology Co., Ltd.; *Int'l*, pg. 7740
RINGSAKER VEGG- OG TAKELEMENTER AS—See Kingspan Group PLC; *Int'l*, pg. 4178
RINGS END INC.; *U.S. Private*, pg. 3438
RING'S END OF BETHEL INC.—See Rings End Inc.; *U.S. Private*, pg. 3438
RINGSTED ENTREPRENORFORRETNING A.P.S.—See Hojgaard Holding A/S; *Int'l*, pg. 3442
RING TECHS CO., LTD.—See Topy Industries, Ltd.; *Int'l*, pg. 7822
RING-TECHS GUANGZHOU COMPANY LIMITED—See Topy Industries, Ltd.; *Int'l*, pg. 7822
RINGTURM KAPITALANLAGEGESELLSCHAFT M.B.H.—See Erste Group Bank AG; *Int'l*, pg. 2499
RINGWAY BABTIE LIMITED—See Jacobs Engineering Group, Inc.; *U.S. Public*, pg. 1186
RINGWAY GROUP LTD—See VINCI S.A.; *Int'l*, pg. 8220
RINGWAY HOUNSLOW HIGHWAYS LIMITED—See VINCI S.A.; *Int'l*, pg. 8226
RINGWAY INFRASTRUCTURE SERVICES LTD.—See VINCI S.A.; *Int'l*, pg. 8220
RINGWAY ISLAND ROADS LIMITED—See VINCI S.A.; *Int'l*, pg. 8226
RINGWAY JACOBS LIMITED—See Jacobs Engineering Group, Inc.; *U.S. Public*, pg. 1186
RINKAGAKU KOGYO CO., LTD.—See Tosoh Corporation; *Int'l*, pg. 7833
RINKER MATERIALS-CONCRETE PIPE & STORMWATER TREATMENT—See CEMEX, S.A.B. de C.V.; *Int'l*, pg. 1399
RINKER MATERIALS-ENVIRONMENTAL SERVICES—See CEMEX, S.A.B. de C.V.; *Int'l*, pg. 1399
RINKER MATERIALS-HARRISBURG—See CEMEX, S.A.B. de C.V.; *Int'l*, pg. 1399
RINKER MATERIALS-TWIN MOUNTAIN—See CEMEX, S.A.B. de C.V.; *Int'l*, pg. 1399
RINKER OIL CORPORATION; *U.S. Private*, pg. 3438
RINKO CORPORATION; *Int'l*, pg. 6344
RINNAI AMERICA CORP.—See Rinnai Corporation; *Int'l*, pg. 6345
RINNAI AUSTRAILIA W.A—See Rinnai Corporation; *Int'l*, pg. 6345
RINNAI AUSTRALIA PTY. LTD.—See Rinnai Corporation; *Int'l*, pg. 6345
RINNAI CHUBU—See Rinnai Corporation; *Int'l*, pg. 6345
RINNAI CORPORATION; *Int'l*, pg. 6344
RINNAI CORPORATION—See Rinnai Corporation; *Int'l*, pg. 6345
RINNAI CORPORATION—See Rinnai Corporation; *Int'l*, pg. 6345
RINNAI CORPORATION—See Rinnai Corporation; *Int'l*, pg. 6345
RINNAI ENTERPRISE CO., LTD.—See Rinnai Corporation; *Int'l*, pg. 6345
RINNAI HOLDINGS (PACIFIC) PTE LTD.—See Rinnai Corporation; *Int'l*, pg. 6345
RINNAI HONG KONG LTD.—See Rinnai Corporation; *Int'l*, pg. 6345

RINNAI CORPORATION

RINNAI HYOGO—See Rinnai Corporation; *Int'l*, pg. 6345
RINNAI ITALIA S.R.L.—See Rinnai Corporation; *Int'l*, pg. 6345
RINNAI KOREA CORPORATION—See Rinnai Corporation; *Int'l*, pg. 6345
RINNAI KYUSHU—See Rinnai Corporation; *Int'l*, pg. 6345
RINNAI MALAYSIA SDN. BHD.—See Rinnai Corporation; *Int'l*, pg. 6345
RINNAI NET CO., LTD.—See Rinnai Corporation; *Int'l*, pg. 6345
RINNAI NEW ZEALAND LTD.—See Rinnai Corporation; *Int'l*, pg. 6345
RINNAI OSAKA CO—See Rinnai Corporation; *Int'l*, pg. 6345
RINNAI PRECISION CO., LTD.—See Rinnai Corporation; *Int'l*, pg. 6345
RINNAI TAIWAN CORPORATION—See Rinnai Corporation; *Int'l*, pg. 6345
RINNAI TAKAMATSU—See Rinnai Corporation; *Int'l*, pg. 6345
RINNAI TECH HIROSHIMA CO., LTD.—See Rinnai Corporation; *Int'l*, pg. 6345
RINNAI TECH KINKI CO., LTD.—See Rinnai Corporation; *Int'l*, pg. 6345
RINNAI TECH SAPPORO CO., LTD.—See Rinnai Corporation; *Int'l*, pg. 6345
RINNAI THAILAND CO., LTD.—See Rinnai Corporation; *Int'l*, pg. 6345
RINNAI UK LTD.—See Rinnai Corporation; *Int'l*, pg. 6345
RINNAI VIETNAM CO., LTD.—See Rinnai Corporation; *Int'l*, pg. 6345
RINOCLOUD LIMITED—See Deepverge PLC; *Int'l*, pg. 2003
RINO MASTROTTO GROUP S.P.A. - AREA DESIGN DIVISION—See Rino Mastrotto Group S.p.A.; *Int'l*, pg. 6345
RINO MASTROTTO GROUP S.P.A. - BASMAR DIVISION—See Rino Mastrotto Group S.p.A.; *Int'l*, pg. 6345
RINO MASTROTTO GROUP S.P.A. - POMARI DIVISION—See Rino Mastrotto Group S.p.A.; *Int'l*, pg. 6345
RINO MASTROTTO GROUP S.P.A. - RMG CHINA DIVISION—See Rino Mastrotto Group S.p.A.; *Int'l*, pg. 6345
RINO MASTROTTO GROUP S.P.A. - RMG VIETNAM DIVISION—See Rino Mastrotto Group S.p.A.; *Int'l*, pg. 6345
RINO MASTROTTO GROUP S.P.A.; *Int'l*, pg. 6345
RINSOCO TRADING CO. LIMITED; *Int'l*, pg. 6345
RINSYOIYAKU INC.—See Sony Group Corporation; *Int'l*, pg. 7102
RINTEKNO OY—See Neste Oyj; *Int'l*, pg. 5202
RIO2 LIMITED; *Int'l*, pg. 6348
RIO ALGOM INC.—See BHP Group Limited; *Int'l*, pg. 1016
RIOBEL INC.—See Fortune Brands Innovations, Inc.; *U.S. Public*, pg. 873
RIO BRANDS, INC.—See Guardian Capital Partners, LLC; *U.S. Private*, pg. 1810
RIO BRAVO OIL, INC.; *U.S. Private*, pg. 3438
RIOCAN REAL ESTATE INVESTMENT TRUST; *Int'l*, pg. 6348
RIO DE JANEIRO REFRESCOS LTDA.—See Embotelladora Andina S.A.; *Int'l*, pg. 2375
RIOFISA S.A.—See Inmobiliaria Colonial SOCIMI SA; *Int'l*, pg. 3706
RIOFISA SEMA, S.L.—See Inmobiliaria Colonial SOCIMI SA; *Int'l*, pg. 3706
RIO FRESH, INC.; *U.S. Private*, pg. 3438
RIO GRANDE BEHAVIORAL HEALTH SERVICES, INC—See ModivCare, Inc.; *U.S. Public*, pg. 1456
RIO GRANDE CO.; *U.S. Private*, pg. 3438
RIO GRANDE DRYWALL SUPPLY CO LLC—See Eagle Materials Inc.; *U.S. Public*, pg. 702
RIO GRANDE ELECTRIC COOP; *U.S. Private*, pg. 3438
RIO GRANDE HOLDINGS—See General Atomics; *U.S. Private*, pg. 1663
RIO GRANDE INC.—See Berkshire Hathaway Inc.; *U.S. Public*, pg. 316
RIO GRANDE MANAGEMENT COMPANY, LLC—See ModivCare, Inc.; *U.S. Public*, pg. 1456
RIO GRANDE REGIONAL HOSPITAL, INC.—See HCA Healthcare, Inc.; *U.S. Public*, pg. 1007
RIO GRANDE RESOURCES CORPORATION—See General Atomics; *U.S. Private*, pg. 1663
RIO GRANDE SILVER, INC.—See Hecla Mining Company; *U.S. Public*, pg. 1019
RIO GRANDE STEEL, LTD.; *U.S. Private*, pg. 3438
RIO GRANDE TRAVEL CENTERS, INC.; *U.S. Private*, pg. 3438
RIO GRANDE VALLEY CARDIOLOGY, PLLC—See HCA Healthcare, Inc.; *U.S. Public*, pg. 1007
RIOJAS ENTERPRISES INC.; *U.S. Private*, pg. 3438
RIO LOPES TRANSPORTES LTD.—See Deutsche Post AG; *Int'l*, pg. 2082
RIOLOY LIMITED—See Hang Lung Group Limited; *Int'l*, pg. 3245
RIO MINAS ENERGIA PARTICIPACOES S.A.—See Companhia Energetica de Minas Gerais - CEMIG; *Int'l*, pg. 1747
RIO MOTOR CO.; *U.S. Private*, pg. 3438
RIO NARCEA GOLD MINES S.L—See Edgewater Exploration Ltd.; *Int'l*, pg. 2309
RION CO. LTD.; *Int'l*, pg. 6348
RIONIL COMPOSTOS VINILCOS LTDA—See Arkema S.A.; *Int'l*, pg. 571
RION SERVICE CENTER CO., LTD.—See RION Co. Ltd.; *Int'l*, pg. 6348
RION TECHNO CO., LTD.—See RION Co. Ltd.; *Int'l*, pg. 6348
RIOPAILA AGRICOLA SA; *Int'l*, pg. 6348
RIO PARANAPANEMA ENERGIA S.A.—See China Three Gorges Corporation; *Int'l*, pg. 1558
RIO PARANAPANEMA PARTICIPACOES S.A.—See China Three Gorges Corporation; *Int'l*, pg. 1558
RIO PCH I S.A.—See ContourGlobal Limited; *Int'l*, pg. 1785
RIO PRODUCTS INTL., INC.—See Joshua Green Corporation; *U.S. Private*, pg. 2237
RIO PROPERTIES, INC.—See Caesars Entertainment, Inc.; *U.S. Public*, pg. 420
RIO RANCHO PHYSICAL THERAPY—See Gryphon Investors, LLC; *U.S. Private*, pg. 1799
RIORDAN, LEWIS & HADEN, INC.; *U.S. Private*, pg. 3439
RIORDAN MATERIALS CORPORATION—See DXP Enterprises, Inc.; *U.S. Public*, pg. 698
RIO RICO PROPERTIES INC.—See Brookfield Corporation; *Int'l*, pg. 1183
RIO SEO, INC.—See Ares Management Corporation; *U.S. Public*, pg. 190
RIO SEO, INC.—See Leonard Green & Partners, L.P.; *U.S. Private*, pg. 2427
RIO SILVER INC.; *Int'l*, pg. 6346
RIO SUD; *Int'l*, pg. 6346
RIOT GAMES, INC.—See Tencent Holdings Limited; *Int'l*, pg. 7559
RIO TINTO ALCAN INC.—See Rio Tinto plc; *Int'l*, pg. 6346
RIO TINTO ALCAN PACKAGING GROUP—See Amcor plc; *Int'l*, pg. 417
RIO TINTO BORAX—See Rio Tinto plc; *Int'l*, pg. 6347
RIO TINTO BRASIL LIMITADA—See Rio Tinto plc; *Int'l*, pg. 6346
RIO TINTO CANADA INC—See Rio Tinto plc; *Int'l*, pg. 6346
RIO TINTO COAL AUSTRALIA PTY LIMITED—See Rio Tinto plc; *Int'l*, pg. 6347
RIO TINTO (COMMERCIAL PAPER) LIMITED—See Rio Tinto plc; *Int'l*, pg. 6346
RIO TINTO COPPER—See Rio Tinto plc; *Int'l*, pg. 6346
RIO TINTO DIAMONDS NV—See Rio Tinto plc; *Int'l*, pg. 6347
RIO TINTO DIAMONDS—See Rio Tinto plc; *Int'l*, pg. 6346
RIO TINTO EASTERN INVESTMENTS BV—See Rio Tinto plc; *Int'l*, pg. 6347
RIO TINTO ENERGY AMERICA INC.—See Rio Tinto plc; *Int'l*, pg. 6347
RIO TINTO ENERGY—See Rio Tinto plc; *Int'l*, pg. 6347
RIO TINTO EUROPEAN HOLDINGS LIMITED—See Rio Tinto plc; *Int'l*, pg. 6347
RIO TINTO EXPLORATION CANADA INC.—See Benton Resources Inc.; *Int'l*, pg. 977
RIO TINTO, FER ET TITANE—See Rio Tinto plc; *Int'l*, pg. 6348
RIO TINTO FINANCE LIMITED—See Rio Tinto plc; *Int'l*, pg. 6347
RIO TINTO FINANCE PLC—See Rio Tinto plc; *Int'l*, pg. 6347
RIO TINTO FINANCE (USA) LIMITED—See Rio Tinto plc; *Int'l*, pg. 6347
RIO TINTO (HONG KONG) LIMITED—See Rio Tinto plc; *Int'l*, pg. 6347
RIO TINTO ICELAND LTD.—See Rio Tinto plc; *Int'l*, pg. 6347
RIO TINTO INDIA PRIVATE LIMITED—See Rio Tinto plc; *Int'l*, pg. 6347
RIO TINTO INVESTMENTS ONE PTY LIMITED—See Rio Tinto plc; *Int'l*, pg. 6347
RIO TINTO INVESTMENTS TWO PTY LIMITED—See Rio Tinto plc; *Int'l*, pg. 6347
RIO TINTO IRON ORE—See Rio Tinto plc; *Int'l*, pg. 6347
RIO TINTO IRON & TITANIUM LIMITED—See Rio Tinto plc; *Int'l*, pg. 6347
RIO TINTO JAPAN LIMITED—See Rio Tinto plc; *Int'l*, pg. 6347
RIO TINTO KOREA LTD—See Rio Tinto plc; *Int'l*, pg. 6347
RIO TINTO LIMITED—See Rio Tinto plc; *Int'l*, pg. 6346
RIO TINTO LTD CHINA—See Rio Tinto plc; *Int'l*, pg. 6347
RIO TINTO MINERALS DEVELOPMENT LIMITED—See Rio Tinto plc; *Int'l*, pg. 6347
RIO TINTO MINERALS—See Rio Tinto plc; *Int'l*, pg. 6347
RIO TINTO MONGOLIA LLC—See Rio Tinto plc; *Int'l*, pg. 6347
RIO TINTO NAMIBIAN HOLDINGS LIMITED—See Rio Tinto plc; *Int'l*, pg. 6347
RIO TINTO OVERSEAS HOLDINGS LIMITED—See Rio Tinto plc; *Int'l*, pg. 6347
RIO TINTO PLC; *Int'l*, pg. 6346
RIO TINTO PROCUREMENT—See Rio Tinto plc; *Int'l*, pg. 6347
RIO TINTO SHIPPING (ASIA) PTE LTD—See Rio Tinto plc; *Int'l*, pg. 6347
RIO TINTO SHIPPING PTY. LIMITED.—See Rio Tinto plc; *Int'l*, pg. 6347
RIO TINTO SINGAPORE HOLDINGS PTE LTD—See Rio Tinto plc; *Int'l*, pg. 6347
RIO TINTO URANIUM LIMITED—See Rio Tinto plc; *Int'l*, pg. 6347
RIO TINTO WESTERN HOLDINGS LIMITED—See Rio Tinto plc; *Int'l*, pg. 6348
RIOT PLATFORMS, INC.; *U.S. Public*, pg. 1799
RIOT—See Ascent Capital Group, Inc.; *U.S. Private*, pg. 348
RIO TUBA NICKEL MINING CORPORATION—See Nickel Asia Corporation; *Int'l*, pg. 5271
RIOVIA S.A.—See HAL Trust N.V.; *Int'l*, pg. 3226
RIOZIM LIMITED; *Int'l*, pg. 6348
RIPA & ASSOCIATES, INC.; *U.S. Private*, pg. 3439
RIPARIUS COMMUNICATION SERVICES—See Riparius Corporation; *U.S. Private*, pg. 3439
RIPARIUS CONSTRUCTION INC.—See Riparius Corporation; *U.S. Private*, pg. 3439
RIPARIUS CORPORATION; *U.S. Private*, pg. 3439
RIPATTI OY—See Kingspan Group PLC; *Int'l*, pg. 4178
RIP CHILE S.A.—See KMD Brands Limited; *Int'l*, pg. 4204
RIP COMERCIO LTDA.—See ThyssenKrupp AG; *Int'l*, pg. 7725
RIP CURL CANADA INC.—See KMD Brands Limited; *Int'l*, pg. 4204
RIP CURL EUROPE—See KMD Brands Limited; *Int'l*, pg. 4204
RIP CURL GROUP PTY LTD.—See KMD Brands Limited; *Int'l*, pg. 4204
RIP CURL INDONESIA—See KMD Brands Limited; *Int'l*, pg. 4204
RIP CURL NEW ZEALAND—See KMD Brands Limited; *Int'l*, pg. 4204
RIP CURL (THAILAND) CO., LTD—See KMD Brands Limited; *Int'l*, pg. 4204
RIP CURL USA—See KMD Brands Limited; *Int'l*, pg. 4204
RIPERT FRERES S.A.S.; *Int'l*, pg. 6348
RIP GRIFFIN TRUCK SERVICE CENTER, INC.—See BP plc; *Int'l*, pg. 1127
RIPKEN BASEBALL, INC.; *U.S. Private*, pg. 3439
THE RIPLEY COMPANY—See CapitalWorks, LLC; *U.S. Private*, pg. 742
RIPLEY CORP S.A.; *Int'l*, pg. 6348
RIPLEY DIALYSIS, LLC—See DaVita Inc.; *U.S. Public*, pg. 642
RIPLEY ENTERTAINMENT INC.—See The Jim Pattison Group; *Int'l*, pg. 7660
RIPLEY EUROPE LIMITED—See Hubbell Incorporated; *U.S. Public*, pg. 1067
RIPOCHE INDUSTRIES; *Int'l*, pg. 6348
RIPON ATHLETIC, INC.; *U.S. Private*, pg. 3439
RIPON PRINTERS - MILWAUKEE—See Walsworth Publishing Company, Inc.; *U.S. Private*, pg. 4433
RIPPE & KINGSTON, LLC; *U.S. Private*, pg. 3439
RIPPE & KINGSTON SYSTEMS, INC.—See Rippe & Kingston, LLC; *U.S. Private*, pg. 3439
RIPPLE E-BUSINESS INTERNATIONAL, INC.; *Int'l*, pg. 6348
RIPPLEFFECT STUDIO LIMITED—See IDOX PLC; *Int'l*, pg. 3596
RIPPLE INDUSTRIES LLC; *U.S. Private*, pg. 3439
RIPPLE KIDS EDUCATIONAL SERVICES, INC.—See RareJob Inc.; *Int'l*, pg. 6211
RIPPLEWOOD HOLDINGS LLC; *U.S. Private*, pg. 3439
RIPPON HOMES LIMITED—See Artisan (UK) plc; *Int'l*, pg. 584
RIPPY CADILLAC, LLC; *U.S. Private*, pg. 3440
RIP'S COUNTRY INN; *U.S. Private*, pg. 3439
RIP SERVICOS INDUSTRIAIS LTDA.—See ThyssenKrupp AG; *Int'l*, pg. 7725
RIPS PROFESSIONAL LAWN CARE, INC.—See Juniper Landscaping, Inc.; *U.S. Private*, pg. 2244
RIPT APPAREL, LLC; *U.S. Private*, pg. 3440
RIRAKU CO., LTD.—See Advantage Partners LLP; *Int'l*, pg. 164
RIRBRO ESTATE MANAGEMENT S.R.L.—See Raiffeisen Bank International AG; *Int'l*, pg. 6183
RIRE ET CHANSONS SAS—See NRJ Group SA; *Int'l*, pg. 5474
RI/RMC ACQUISITION, LTD.—See AutoNation, Inc.; *U.S. Public*, pg. 237
RI/RMP ACQUISITION CORP.—See AutoNation, Inc.; *U.S. Public*, pg. 237
RI/RMT ACQUISITION, LTD.—See AutoNation, Inc.; *U.S. Public*, pg. 237
RI/RMT ACQUISITION, LTD.—See AutoNation, Inc.; *U.S. Public*, pg. 237
RISA FUNDS & ASSETS SOLUTIONS, INC.—See NEC Capital Solutions Limited; *Int'l*, pg. 5183
RISA INTERNATIONAL LIMITED; *Int'l*, pg. 6348
RISA LOAN SERVICES INC.—See NEC Capital Solutions Limited; *Int'l*, pg. 5183

COMPANY NAME INDEX

RISA LOAN SERVICING INC.—See NEC Capital Solutions Limited; *Int'l*, pg. 5183
RISANAMENTO S.P.A.—See Domus Fin S.A.; *Int'l*, pg. 2162
RISA PARTNERS ASIA PTE. LTD.—See NEC Capital Solutions Limited; *Int'l*, pg. 5183
RISA PARTNERS, INC.; *Int'l*, pg. 6348
RISA TECH, INC.—See Nemetschek SE; *Int'l*, pg. 5195
RISCO ENERGY PTE. LTD.; *Int'l*, pg. 6349
RISCO GROUP AUSTRALIA PTY. LTD.—See RISCO Ltd.; *Int'l*, pg. 6349
RISCO GROUP FRANCE SAS—See RISCO Ltd.; *Int'l*, pg. 6349
RISCO GROUP IBERIA S.L.—See RISCO Ltd.; *Int'l*, pg. 6349
RISCO GROUP, INC.—See RISCO Ltd.; *Int'l*, pg. 6349
RISCO GROUP UK LTD.—See RISCO Ltd.; *Int'l*, pg. 6349
RISCO INSURANCE SERVICES, INC.—See Inszone Insurance Services, LLC; *U.S. Private*, pg. 2096
RISCO LTD.; *Int'l*, pg. 6349
RISCONSULT GMBH—See MLP SE; *Int'l*, pg. 5004
RISDALL MARKETING GROUP, LLC; *U.S. Private*, pg. 3440
RISDALL PUBLIC RELATIONS—See Risdall Marketing Group, LLC; *U.S. Private*, pg. 3440
RISDON INTERNATIONAL, INC.; *U.S. Private*, pg. 3440
RISE AGAINST HUNGER; *U.S. Private*, pg. 3440
RISECOMM GROUP HOLDINGS LIMITED; *Int'l*, pg. 6349
RISECOMM MICROELECTRONICS (SHENZHEN) CO., LTD.—See Risecomm Group Holdings Limited; *Int'l*, pg. 6349
RISE CONSULTING GROUP, INC.; *Int'l*, pg. 6349
RISE CREDIT SERVICE OF TEXAS, LLC—See Park Cities Asset Management LLC; *U.S. Private*, pg. 3095
RISE ENGINEERING, INC.—See Thielsch Engineering, Inc.; *U.S. Private*, pg. 4144
THE RISE FUND—See TPG Capital, L.P.; *U.S. Public*, pg. 2177
RISE GOLD CORP.; *Int'l*, pg. 6349
RISE GROUP, INC.—See Thielsch Engineering, Inc.; *U.S. Private*, pg. 4144
RISE HEALTH, INC.—See Teladoc Health, Inc.; *U.S. Public*, pg. 1992
RISE INC.; *Int'l*, pg. 6349
RISE, INC.; *U.S. Private*, pg. 3440
RISE INTERACTIVE, INC.; *U.S. Private*, pg. 3440
RISE INTERACTIVE MEDIA & ANALYTICS, LLC—See Quad/Graphics, Inc.; *U.S. Public*, pg. 1745
RISE INTERACTIVE SRL—See Quad/Graphics, Inc.; *U.S. Public*, pg. 1745
RISE INTERNATIONAL L.L.C.—See ARCADIS N.V.; *Int'l*, pg. 541
RISE MEDICAL STAFFING, LLC—See AMN Healthcare Services, Inc.; *U.S. Public*, pg. 125
RISEN ENERGY CO., LTD.; *Int'l*, pg. 6349
RISEN ENERGY EUROPE & LATAM S.L.—See Risen Energy Co., Ltd.; *Int'l*, pg. 6349
RISEN ENERGY HONG KONG CO., LTD.—See Risen Energy Co., Ltd.; *Int'l*, pg. 6349
RISER FOODS COMPANY—See Giant Eagle, Inc.; *U.S. Private*, pg. 1694
RISERIA TAVERNE S.A.—See The Federation of Migros Cooperatives; *Int'l*, pg. 7643
RISER ID SERVICES GMBH—See Deutsche Post AG; *Int'l*, pg. 2082
RI SERVICES CO LTD—See Rentokil Initial plc; *Int'l*, pg. 6287
RISESUN REAL ESTATE DEVELOPMENT CO., LTD.; *Int'l*, pg. 6349
RISHAB FINANCIAL SERVICES LIMITED; *Int'l*, pg. 6349
RISHABH DIGHA STEEL & ALLIED PRODUCTS LTD. - INDUSTRIAL UNIT 2—See Rishabh Digha Steel & Allied Products Ltd.; *Int'l*, pg. 6349
RISHABH DIGHA STEEL & ALLIED PRODUCTS LTD.; *Int'l*, pg. 6349
RISHABH INSTRUMENTS LIMITED; *Int'l*, pg. 6349
RISHAB SPECIAL YARNS LTD.; *Int'l*, pg. 6349
RISH EQUIPMENT COMPANY—See Davis Mining & Manufacturing Inc.; *U.S. Private*, pg. 1174
RISHI LASER LTD.; *Int'l*, pg. 6349
RISHIROOP LTD.; *Int'l*, pg. 6350
RISHI TECHTEX LIMITED; *Int'l*, pg. 6350
RISICOM RUCKVERSICHERUNG AG—See Siemens Aktiengesellschaft; *Int'l*, pg. 6887
RISI, INC—See Astorg Partners S.A.S.; *Int'l*, pg. 656
RISI, INC—See Epiris Managers LLP; *Int'l*, pg. 2461
RISIKOMANAGEMENT UND SOFTWAREENTWICKLUNG GMBH—See Allianz SE; *Int'l*, pg. 355
RISIMA CONSULTING GMBH—See 3U Holding AG; *Int'l*, pg. 10
RISINGER BROS TRANSFER INC.; *U.S. Private*, pg. 3440
RISING INDIA, INC.; *U.S. Private*, pg. 3440
RISING INVESTMENT CO., LTD.—See Guangdong Rising Assets Management Co., Ltd.; *Int'l*, pg. 3159
RISING JAPAN EQUITY, INC.; *Int'l*, pg. 6350
RISING MEDICAL SOLUTIONS, LLC; *U.S. Private*, pg. 3440

RISING NONFERROUS METALS CO., LTD.—See Guangdong Rising Assets Management Co., Ltd.; *Int'l*, pg. 3159
RISINGNOVAS (HK) LIMITED—See Ingdan, Inc.; *Int'l*, pg. 3701
RISING PHARMACEUTICALS, LLC—See Suven Life Sciences Ltd.; *Int'l*, pg. 7348
RISING PHARMA HOLDINGS, INC.—See Suven Life Sciences Ltd.; *Int'l*, pg. 7348
RISING PHOENIX HOLDINGS CORPORATION; *U.S. Private*, pg. 3440
RISING STARS UK LTD.—See Vivendi SE; *Int'l*, pg. 8278
RISING SUN FARMS; *U.S. Private*, pg. 3440
RISING SUN SOLAR & ELECTRIC; *U.S. Private*, pg. 3440
RISION LIMITED; *Int'l*, pg. 6350
RISK-AKTIV VERSICHERUNGSSERVICE GMBH—See Assicurazioni Generali S.p.A.; *Int'l*, pg. 646
RISK ASSISTANCE NETWORK + EXCHANGE NETWORK, INC.; *U.S. Private*, pg. 3440
RISK BASED SECURITY, INC.—See EJ2 Communications, Inc.; *U.S. Private*, pg. 1348
RISK BROKING PTY. LTD.—See Steadfast Group Limited; *Int'l*, pg. 7187
RISK CAPITAL PARTNERS LTD.; *Int'l*, pg. 6350
RISK CONSULT SICHERHEITS- UND RISIKO- MANAGEMENTBERATUNG GESELLSCHAFT M.B.H.—See Vienna Insurance Group AG Wiener Versicherung Gruppe; *Int'l*, pg. 8195
RISK ENTERPRISE MANAGEMENT LIMITED; *U.S. Private*, pg. 3440
RISK.IDENT GMBH—See Otto GmbH & Co. KG; *Int'l*, pg. 5663
RISKIFIED LTD.; *Int'l*, pg. 6350
RISK & INSURANCE MANAGEMENT SOCIETY, INC.; *U.S. Private*, pg. 3440
RISK & INSURANCE S.A.—See Achmea B.V.; *Int'l*, pg. 103
RISK INSURANCE SERVICES OF INDIANA, INC—See US 1 Industries, Inc.; *U.S. Private*, pg. 4317
RISK & INSURANCE SERVICES S.A.—See Topdanmark A/S; *Int'l*, pg. 7816
RISK INTERNATIONAL SERVICES INC.—See Arthur J. Gallagher & Co.; *U.S. Public*, pg. 202
RISKLAB GMBH—See Allianz SE; *Int'l*, pg. 347
RISK MANAGEMENT ADVISORS, INC.—See Kelso & Company, L.P.; *U.S. Private*, pg. 2280
RISK MANAGEMENT CLAIM SERVICES—See Landstar System, Inc.; *U.S. Public*, pg. 1292
RISK MANAGEMENT PARTNERS LTD.—See Arthur J. Gallagher & Co.; *U.S. Public*, pg. 203
RISK MANAGEMENT SERVICES, LLC—See Hilton Grand Vacations Inc.; *U.S. Public*, pg. 1040
RISK MANAGEMENT SOLUTIONS - EAST COAST US—See Moody's Corporation; *U.S. Public*, pg. 1469
RISK MANAGEMENT SOLUTIONS, INC.—See Moody's Corporation; *U.S. Public*, pg. 1469
RISK MANAGEMENT SOLUTIONS - MIDWEST US—See Moody's Corporation; *U.S. Public*, pg. 1469
RISK MANAGEMENT S.P.A.—See Stellantis N.V.; *Int'l*, pg. 7203
RISKMETRICS GROUP, LLC—See MSCI Inc.; *U.S. Public*, pg. 1483
RISKMETRICS (SINGAPORE) PTE. LTD.—See MSCI Inc.; *U.S. Public*, pg. 1483
RISKMETRICS SOLUTIONS, LLC—See MSCI Inc.; *U.S. Public*, pg. 1483
RISKMETRICS (UK) LTD.—See MSCI Inc.; *U.S. Public*, pg. 1483
RISK MITIGATION CONSULTING INC.; *U.S. Private*, pg. 3441
RISKMONSTER.COM; *Int'l*, pg. 6350
RISKON INTERNATIONAL, INC.; *U.S. Public*, pg. 1799
RISKONNECT ACTIVE RISK GROUP LIMITED—See Sword Group SE; *Int'l*, pg. 7376
RISKONNECT CLEARSIGHT LLC—See TA Associates, Inc.; *U.S. Private*, pg. 3918
RISKONNECT, INC.—See TA Associates, Inc.; *U.S. Private*, pg. 3918
RISK PARTNERS PTY LTD—See Steadfast Group Limited; *Int'l*, pg. 7187
RISK PLACEMENT SERVICES, INC.—See Arthur J. Gallagher & Co.; *U.S. Public*, pg. 207
RISK PLANNERS, INC.—See Arthur J. Gallagher & Co.; *U.S. Public*, pg. 207
RISKPOINT INSURANCE ADVISORS, LLC—See IMA Financial Group, Inc.; *U.S. Private*, pg. 2043
RISKPRONET INTERNATIONAL INC.; *U.S. Private*, pg. 3441
RISKRIGHTER, LLC—See Truist Financial Corporation; *U.S. Public*, pg. 2200
RISK SCIENCES GROUP, INC.—See Crawford & Company; *U.S. Public*, pg. 592
RISKSENSE, INC.(1)—See Lumen Technologies, Inc.; *U.S. Public*, pg. 1347
RISK SERVICES, LLC—See Stone Point Capital LLC; *U.S. Private*, pg. 3821
RISK SERVICES-VERMONT, INC.—See Stone Point Capital LLC; *U.S. Private*, pg. 3821

RISKSOL CONSULTING LTD.—See Coller Capital Ltd.; *Int'l*, pg. 1699
RISK SPECIALISTS COMPANIES, INC.—See American International Group, Inc.; *U.S. Public*, pg. 107
RISK & STRATEGIC MANAGEMENT, CORP.—See Growth Catalyst Partners, LLC; *U.S. Private*, pg. 1796
RISKTEC SOLUTIONS CANADA LTD.—See TUV Rheinland Berlin-Brandenburg Pfalz e.V.; *Int'l*, pg. 7982
RISKTEC SOLUTIONS DMCC—See TUV Rheinland Berlin-Brandenburg Pfalz e.V.; *Int'l*, pg. 7982
RISKTEC SOLUTIONS, INC.—See TUV Rheinland Berlin-Brandenburg Pfalz e.V.; *Int'l*, pg. 7982
RISKTEC SOLUTIONS LTD. - ABERDEEN—See TUV Rheinland Berlin-Brandenburg Pfalz e.V.; *Int'l*, pg. 7982
RISKTEC SOLUTIONS LTD. - ALDERLEY EDGE—See TUV Rheinland Berlin-Brandenburg Pfalz e.V.; *Int'l*, pg. 7982
RISKTEC SOLUTIONS LTD. - ASHFORD—See TUV Rheinland Berlin-Brandenburg Pfalz e.V.; *Int'l*, pg. 7982
RISKTEC SOLUTIONS LTD. - CRAWLEY—See TUV Rheinland Berlin-Brandenburg Pfalz e.V.; *Int'l*, pg. 7982
RISKTEC SOLUTIONS LTD. - EDINBURGH—See TUV Rheinland Berlin-Brandenburg Pfalz e.V.; *Int'l*, pg. 7982
RISKTEC SOLUTIONS LTD. - GLASGOW—See TUV Rheinland Berlin-Brandenburg Pfalz e.V.; *Int'l*, pg. 7982
RISKTEC SOLUTIONS LTD. - LONDON—See TUV Rheinland Berlin-Brandenburg Pfalz e.V.; *Int'l*, pg. 7982
RISKTEC SOLUTIONS LTD.—See TUV Rheinland Berlin-Brandenburg Pfalz e.V.; *Int'l*, pg. 7982
RISKTEC SOLUTIONS LTD—See TUV Rheinland Berlin-Brandenburg Pfalz e.V.; *Int'l*, pg. 7982
RISKTEC SOLUTIONS LTD.—See TUV Rheinland Berlin-Brandenburg Pfalz e.V.; *Int'l*, pg. 7982
RISKTRAC INC.—See Liberty Mutual Holding Company Inc.; *U.S. Private*, pg. 2446
RISK TRANSFER UNDERWRITING INC—See R&Q Insurance Holdings Ltd.; *Int'l*, pg. 6168
RISLAND (THAILAND) CO., LTD.—See Country Garden Holdings Company Limited; *Int'l*, pg. 1818
RISMA SA; *Int'l*, pg. 6350
RISMA SYSTEMS A/S; *Int'l*, pg. 6350
RISMON MUSCLE DATA CO., LTD.—See RISKMONSTER.COM; *Int'l*, pg. 6350
RIS NEWS—See RFE Investment Partners; *U.S. Private*, pg. 3419
R.I.S.N. OPERATIONS INC.; *U.S. Private*, pg. 3336
RISO AFRICA (PTY) LTD.—See Riso Kagaku Corporation; *Int'l*, pg. 6350
RISO CANADA, INC.—See Riso Kagaku Corporation; *Int'l*, pg. 6350
RISO DE MEXICO, S.A. DE C.V.—See Riso Kagaku Corporation; *Int'l*, pg. 6351
RISO (DEUTSCHLAND) GMBH—See Riso Kagaku Corporation; *Int'l*, pg. 6350
RISO EURASIA KAZAKHSTAN LLC—See Riso Kagaku Corporation; *Int'l*, pg. 6350
RISO FRANCE S.A.—See Riso Kagaku Corporation; *Int'l*, pg. 6350
RISOGRAPH ITALIA—See Riso Kagaku Corporation; *Int'l*, pg. 6351
RISO HONG KONG LTD.—See Riso Kagaku Corporation; *Int'l*, pg. 6350
RISO IBERICA S.A.—See Riso Kagaku Corporation; *Int'l*, pg. 6350
RISO, INC.—See Riso Kagaku Corporation; *Int'l*, pg. 6351
RISO INDIA PRIVATE LTD.—See Riso Kagaku Corporation; *Int'l*, pg. 6350
RISO INDUSTRIES (H.K.) LTD.—See Riso Kagaku Corporation; *Int'l*, pg. 6350
RISO KAGAKU CORPORATION; *Int'l*, pg. 6350
RISO KOREA LTD.—See Riso Kagaku Corporation; *Int'l*, pg. 6350
RISO KYOIKU CO., LTD.—See Hulic Co., Ltd.; *Int'l*, pg. 3528
RISO LATIN AMERICA, INC.—See Riso Kagaku Corporation; *Int'l*, pg. 6350
RI-SOLUTION DATA GMBH—See BayWa AG; *Int'l*, pg. 918
RI-SOLUTION GMBH GESELLSCHAFT FUR RETAIL-INFORMATIONSSYSTEME, SERVICES UND LOSUNGEN MBH—See BayWa AG; *Int'l*, pg. 918
RI-SOLUTION GMBH—See BayWa AG; *Int'l*, pg. 918
RI-SOLUTION SERVICE GMBH—See BayWa AG; *Int'l*, pg. 918
RISO OKINAWA CORPORATION—See Riso Kagaku Corporation; *Int'l*, pg. 6350
RISO (SHANGHAI) INTERNATIONAL TRADING CO., LTD.—See Riso Kagaku Corporation; *Int'l*, pg. 6350
RISO TECHNOLOGY CHINA CO., LTD.—See Riso Kagaku Corporation; *Int'l*, pg. 6351
RISO (THAILAND) LIMITED—See Riso Kagaku Corporation; *Int'l*, pg. 6350
RISO (UK) LIMITED—See Riso Kagaku Corporation; *Int'l*, pg. 6350
RISOUL DOMINICANA S.R.L.—See RS Group plc; *Int'l*, pg. 6418
RISOUL IBERICA S.A.—See RS Group plc; *Int'l*, pg. 6418
RISQUE ET SERENITE S.A.—See Assicurazioni Generali S.p.A.; *Int'l*, pg. 645

RISSER OIL CORP.
CORPORATE AFFILIATIONS

RISSER OIL CORP.; *U.S. Private*, pg. 3441
RISSHIN ELECTRONICS CO., LTD.—See NGK Insulators, Ltd.; *Int'l*, pg. 5255
RISTAL INC.; *U.S. Private*, pg. 3441
RISTIA BINTANG MAHKOTASEJATI TBK; *Int'l*, pg. 6351
RISTKEN SOFTWARE SERVICES, L.P.; *U.S. Private*, pg. 3441
RIST TRANSPORT LTD.—See Wadhams Enterprises Inc.; *U.S. Private*, pg. 4425
RISUNTEK, INC.; *Int'l*, pg. 6351
RITA ANGUS RETIREMENT VILLAGE LIMITED—See Ryman Healthcare Ltd.; *Int'l*, pg. 6440
RITA-ANN DISTRIBUTORS—See Sun Capital Partners, Inc.; *U.S. Private*, pg. 3860
RITA BLANCA ELECTRIC COOPERATIVE, INC.; *U.S. Private*, pg. 3441
RITA CORPORATION; *U.S. Private*, pg. 3441
RITA FINANCE & LEASING LTD.; *Int'l*, pg. 6351
R.I.T.A INTERNATIONAL INC.—See RITA Corporation; *U.S. Private*, pg. 3441
RITAMIX GLOBAL LIMITED; *Int'l*, pg. 6351
RITAMIX SDN. BHD.—See Ritamix Global Limited; *Int'l*, pg. 6351
RITA RANCH DIALYSIS, LLC—See DaVita Inc.; *U.S. Public*, pg. 642
RITA RESTAURANT CORP.—See Food Management Partners, Inc.; *U.S. Private*, pg. 1561
RITA'S FRANCHISE COMPANY; *U.S. Private*, pg. 3441
RITA STAFFING INC.; *U.S. Private*, pg. 3441
RITASUE SIEGEL RESOURCES—See Aquent Inc.; *U.S. Private*, pg. 303
RIT CAPITAL PARTNERS ASSOCIATES LIMITED—See RIT Capital Partners plc; *Int'l*, pg. 6351
RIT CAPITAL PARTNERS PLC; *Int'l*, pg. 6351
RIT CAPITAL PARTNERS SECURITIES LIMITED—See RIT Capital Partners plc; *Int'l*, pg. 6351
RITCHEY LTD.—See Tru-Test Group; *Int'l*, pg. 7940
RITCHEY METALS COMPANY INC.; *U.S. Private*, pg. 3441
RITCHIE BROS. AUCTIONEERS (AMERICA) INC.—See RB Global, Inc.; *Int'l*, pg. 6226
RITCHIE BROS. AUCTIONEERS (CANADA) LTD.—See RB Global, Inc.; *Int'l*, pg. 6226
RITCHIE BROS. AUCTIONEERS FRANCE SAS—See RB Global, Inc.; *Int'l*, pg. 6226
RITCHIE BROS. AUCTIONEERS GMBH—See RB Global, Inc.; *Int'l*, pg. 6226
RITCHIE BROS. AUCTIONEERS (JAPAN) K.K.—See RB Global, Inc.; *Int'l*, pg. 6226
RITCHIE BROS. AUCTIONEERS (PANAMA) S.A.—See RB Global, Inc.; *Int'l*, pg. 6226
RITCHIE BROS. AUCTIONEERS (POLAND) SP.Z.O.O.—See RB Global, Inc.; *Int'l*, pg. 6226
RITCHIE BROS. AUCTIONEERS (SPAIN) S.L.U.—See RB Global, Inc.; *Int'l*, pg. 6226
RITCHIE BROS. AUCTIONEERS S.R.L.—See RB Global, Inc.; *Int'l*, pg. 6226
RITCHIE BROS. AUCTIONEERS (UK) LIMITED—See RB Global, Inc.; *Int'l*, pg. 6226
RITCHIE BROS. B.V.—See RB Global, Inc.; *Int'l*, pg. 6226
RITCHIE BROS. DEUTSCHLAND GMBH—See RB Global, Inc.; *Int'l*, pg. 6226
RITCHIE BROS. HOLDINGS B.V.—See RB Global, Inc.; *Int'l*, pg. 6226
RITCHIE BROS. HOLDINGS PTY LTD.—See RB Global, Inc.; *Int'l*, pg. 6226
RITCHIE BROS. ITALIA S.R.L.—See RB Global, Inc.; *Int'l*, pg. 6226
RITCHIE BROS. PROPERTIES LTD.—See RB Global, Inc.; *Int'l*, pg. 6226
RITCHIE CORPORATION; *U.S. Private*, pg. 3441
RITCHIE CRANE HIRE (PROPRIETARY) LIMITED—See Unicorn Capital Partners Limited; *Int'l*, pg. 8033
RITCHIE-CURBOW CONSTRUCTION CO.; *U.S. Private*, pg. 3441
RITCHIE ENGINEERING COMPANY; *U.S. Private*, pg. 3441
RITCHIE GROCER COMPANY; *U.S. Private*, pg. 3441
RITCHIE IMPLEMENT INC.; *U.S. Private*, pg. 3441
RITCHIE INDUSTRIES, INC.; *U.S. Private*, pg. 3441
RITCHIE TRACTOR COMPANY, LLC.; *U.S. Private*, pg. 3441
RITCO LOGISTICS LIMITED; *Int'l*, pg. 6351
RITCO TRAVELS & TOURS PVT. LTD.—See Transcorp International Limited; *Int'l*, pg. 7898
RITDISPLAY CORPORATION; *Int'l*, pg. 6351
RITE AID CORPORATION—See New Rite Aid, LLC; *U.S. Private*, pg. 2905
RITE AID DRUG PALACE, INC.—See New Rite Aid, LLC; *U.S. Private*, pg. 2905
RITE AID LEASE MANAGEMENT COMPANY—See New Rite Aid, LLC; *U.S. Private*, pg. 2905
RITE AID OF ALABAMA, INC.—See New Rite Aid, LLC; *U.S. Private*, pg. 2905
RITE AID OF CONNECTICUT, INC.—See New Rite Aid, LLC; *U.S. Private*, pg. 2905
RITE AID OF DELAWARE, INC.—See New Rite Aid, LLC; *U.S. Private*, pg. 2905

RITE AID OF ILLINOIS, INC.—See New Rite Aid, LLC; *U.S. Private*, pg. 2905
RITE AID OF MAINE, INC.—See New Rite Aid, LLC; *U.S. Private*, pg. 2906
RITE AID OF MARYLAND, INC.—See New Rite Aid, LLC; *U.S. Private*, pg. 2906
RITE AID OF NEW HAMPSHIRE, INC.—See New Rite Aid, LLC; *U.S. Private*, pg. 2906
RITE AID OF SOUTH CAROLINA, INC.—See New Rite Aid, LLC; *U.S. Private*, pg. 2906
RITE AID OF VIRGINIA, INC.—See New Rite Aid, LLC; *U.S. Private*, pg. 2906
RITE AID OF WASHINGTON, D.C., INC.—See New Rite Aid, LLC; *U.S. Private*, pg. 2906
RITE-HITE CORPORATION—See Rite-Hite Holding Corporation; *U.S. Private*, pg. 3442
RITE-HITE DOOR DIVISION—See Rite-Hite Holding Corporation; *U.S. Private*, pg. 3442
RITE-HITE FROMMELT DIVISION—See Rite-Hite Holding Corporation; *U.S. Private*, pg. 3442
RITE-HITE HOLDING CORPORATION; *U.S. Private*, pg. 3441
RITE-HITE MATERIAL HANDLING EQUIPMENT (KUNSHAN) CO., LTD.—See Rite-Hite Holding Corporation; *U.S. Private*, pg. 3442
RITE INTERNET VENTURES HOLDING AB; *Int'l*, pg. 6351
RITEK CORPORATION; *Int'l*, pg. 6351
RITEK FOUNDATION CO., LTD.—See RITEK CORPORATION; *Int'l*, pg. 6351
RITEK LATIN AMERICA, INC.—See RITEK CORPORATION; *Int'l*, pg. 6351
RITEK VIETNAM CO., LTD.—See RITEK CORPORATION; *Int'l*, pg. 6351
RITE-MADE PAPER CONVERTERS; *U.S. Private*, pg. 3442
RITENET CORPORATION; *U.S. Private*, pg. 3442
RI-TENG COMPUTER ACCESSORY (SHANGHAI) CO., LTD.—See Casetek Holdings Limited; *Int'l*, pg. 1351
RITEPRO CORPORATION—See Bray International, Inc.; *U.S. Private*, pg. 642
RITE PRODUCTS INCORPORATED—See BELIMO Holding AG; *Int'l*, pg. 965
RITE RUG CO.—See Rite Rug Co.; *U.S. Private*, pg. 3441
RITE RUG CO.; *U.S. Private*, pg. 3441
RITES (AFRIKA) (PTY.) LIMITED—See RITES Ltd; *Int'l*, pg. 6352
THE RITESCREEN COMPANY, LLC—See Seven Point Equity Partners, LLC; *U.S. Private*, pg. 3619
RITESCREEN—See Seven Point Equity Partners, LLC; *U.S. Private*, pg. 3619
RITESH INTERNATIONAL LIMITED; *Int'l*, pg. 6352
RITESH PROPERTIES & INDUSTRIES LTD.; *Int'l*, pg. 6352
RITES LTD; *Int'l*, pg. 6352
RITE STUFF FOODS, INC.—See EMERAM Capital Partners GmbH; *Int'l*, pg. 2378
RITE-STYLE OPTICAL CO; *U.S. Private*, pg. 3442
RITE TRACK EQUIPMENT SERVICES, LLC—See OEM Group, Inc.; *U.S. Private*, pg. 2997
RITE UGLJEVIK AD; *Int'l*, pg. 6351
RITEVE SYC, S.A.—See I Squared Capital Advisors (US) LLC; *U.S. Private*, pg. 2023
RITEVE SYC, S.A.—See TDR Capital LLP; *Int'l*, pg. 7492
RITEWAY BUS SERVICE, INC.; *U.S. Private*, pg. 3442
RITE WAY OIL & GAS CO., INC.; *U.S. Private*, pg. 3441
RITE WAY SERVICE INC.—See Diversified Maintenance Systems, LLC; *U.S. Private*, pg. 1243
RITEWOOD, INC.; *U.S. Private*, pg. 3442
RITHM CAPITAL CORP.; *U.S. Public*, pg. 1799
RITHWIK FACILITY MANAGEMENT SERVICES LIMITED; *Int'l*, pg. 6352
RITMAN & ASSOCIATES, INC.—See Caisse de Depot et Placement du Quebec; *Int'l*, pg. 1256
RITMAN & ASSOCIATES, INC.—See KKR & Co. Inc.; *U.S. Public*, pg. 1265
RITMA PREMIER PTE. LTD.—See Leong Hup International Berhad; *Int'l*, pg. 4461
RITMA PRESTASI SDN BHD—See Emerging Glory Sdn Bhd; *Int'l*, pg. 2379
RITOCH-POWELL & ASSOC RPA INC.—See Littlejohn & Co., LLC; *U.S. Private*, pg. 2469
RITO GROUP CORP.; *Int'l*, pg. 6352
RITTAL GMBH & CO. KG—See Friedhelm Loh Stiftung & Co. KG; *Int'l*, pg. 2791
RIT TECHNOLOGIES INC.—See STINS COMAN Incorporated; *Int'l*, pg. 7216
RIT TECHNOLOGIES LTD.—See STINS COMAN Incorporated; *Int'l*, pg. 7216
RITTENHOUSE MARKETING ASSOCIATES; *U.S. Private*, pg. 3442
RITTENHOUSE SCHOOL LP—See Edison International; *U.S. Public*, pg. 719
RITTENHOUSE SENIOR LIVING OF INDIANAPOLIS LLC—See Rittenhouse Senior Living; *U.S. Private*, pg. 3442
RITTENHOUSE SENIOR LIVING; *U.S. Private*, pg. 3442
RITTENHOUSE VENTURES, LLC; *U.S. Private*, pg. 3442

RITTER COURIVAUD LIMITED—See Musgrave Group plc; *Int'l*, pg. 5102
RITTER D.O.O.—See Avantor, Inc.; *U.S. Public*, pg. 242
RITTER HAFTETIKETTEN GMBH & CO. KG—See Triton Advisers Limited; *Int'l*, pg. 7929
RITTER INSURANCE MARKETING; *U.S. Private*, pg. 3442
RITTER LUMBER CO.; *U.S. Private*, pg. 3442
RITTER TRANSPORT, INC.—See EVO Transportation & Energy Services, Inc.; *U.S. Public*, pg. 804
RITTMAN MEAD CONSULTING PRIVATE LIMITED—See Huron Consulting Group Inc.; *U.S. Public*, pg. 1076
RITTOR MUSIC, INC.—See Impress Holdings Inc.; *Int'l*, pg. 3637
RITUS CORP.—See Blue Point Capital Partners, LLC; *U.S. Private*, pg. 590
RITWIN CORPORATION—See RITEK CORPORATION; *Int'l*, pg. 6352
RITZ ASSOCIATES; *U.S. Private*, pg. 3442
THE RITZ-CARLTON CHICAGO—See Cascade Investment LLC; *U.S. Private*, pg. 780
THE RITZ-CARLTON HOTEL COMPANY (BERLIN) GMBH—See W.P. Carey Inc.; *U.S. Public*, pg. 2316
THE RITZ-CARLTON HOTEL COMPANY LLC—See W.P. Carey Inc.; *U.S. Public*, pg. 2316
THE RITZ-CARLTON HOTEL COMPANY OF CANADA LIMITED—See W.P. Carey Inc.; *U.S. Public*, pg. 2316
THE RITZ-CARLTON HOTEL COMPANY OF JAMAICA LIMITED—See W.P. Carey Inc.; *U.S. Public*, pg. 2316
THE RITZ-CARLTON HOTEL COMPANY OF MEXICO, S.A. DE C.V.—See W.P. Carey Inc.; *U.S. Public*, pg. 2316
THE RITZ-CARLTON HOTEL COMPANY OF QATAR LIMITED—See Marriott International, Inc.; *U.S. Public*, pg. 1373
THE RITZ-CARLTON HOTEL COMPANY OF SINGAPORE PTE LTD.—See W.P. Carey Inc.; *U.S. Public*, pg. 2316
THE RITZ-CARLTON HOTEL MANAGEMENT GMBH—See W.P. Carey Inc.; *U.S. Public*, pg. 2316
RITZ-CRAFT CORP. OF PA; *U.S. Private*, pg. 3442
RITZ FORMULATIONS PRIVATE LIMITED—See Medico Intercontinental Limited; *Int'l*, pg. 4776
THE RITZ HOTEL (LONDON) LIMITED—See Ellerman Investments Ltd.; *Int'l*, pg. 2365
RITZ SAFETY, LLC; *U.S. Private*, pg. 3442
RITZVILLE WAREHOUSE CO. INC.; *U.S. Private*, pg. 3442
RIU HOTELS S.A.; *Int'l*, pg. 6352
RIUSA II S.A.—See TUI AG; *Int'l*, pg. 7966
RIUVERT S.A.—See Aliaxis S.A./N.V.; *Int'l*, pg. 325
RIVA ACCIAIO—See Riva Forni Elettrici; *Int'l*, pg. 6352
RIVA ACIER S.A.—See Riva Forni Elettrici; *Int'l*, pg. 6352
RIVA FINANCIAL INC.; *U.S. Private*, pg. 3442
RIVA FORNI ELETTRICI; *Int'l*, pg. 6352
RIVAGES DU MONDE; *Int'l*, pg. 6352
RIVAL DOWNHOLE TOOLS LC; *U.S. Private*, pg. 3442
RIVALHEALTH, LLC—See Global Behavioral Solutions LLC; *U.S. Private*, pg. 1712
RIVAL HOLDINGS, LLC; *U.S. Private*, pg. 3442
RIVAL LABS, INC.—See Live Nation Entertainment, Inc.; *U.S. Public*, pg. 1330
RIVALRY CORP.; *Int'l*, pg. 6352
RIVAL TECHNOLOGIES, INC.; *U.S. Public*, pg. 1800
RIVA ROAD SURGERY CENTER, LLC—See Tenet Healthcare Corporation; *U.S. Public*, pg. 2006
RIVA ROAD SURGICAL CENTER, L.L.C.—See Tenet Healthcare Corporation; *U.S. Public*, pg. 2006
RIV CAPITAL INC—See Cansortium, Inc.; *U.S. Public*, pg. 430
RIVEKA BVBA—See BayWa AG; *Int'l*, pg. 919
RIVENDELL GARDEN CENTRE LIMITED—See Notcutts Ltd.; *Int'l*, pg. 5449
RIVENDELL MEDIA INC.; *U.S. Private*, pg. 3443
RIVENROCK CAPITAL LLC; *U.S. Private*, pg. 3443
RIVERA FIGUEROA FRANCISCO INC.; *U.S. Private*, pg. 3444
RIVER AGGREGATES, LLC—See Sun Capital Partners, Inc.; *U.S. Private*, pg. 3861
RIVERA (HOLDINGS) LIMITED; *Int'l*, pg. 6352
RIVER ASSOCIATES INVESTMENTS, LLC; *U.S. Private*, pg. 3443
RIVER BANK HOLDING CO.; *U.S. Private*, pg. 3443
RIVER BANK—See River Bank Holding Co.; *U.S. Private*, pg. 3443
RIVERBED TECHNOLOGY AB—See Vector Capital Management, L.P.; *U.S. Private*, pg. 4352
RIVERBED TECHNOLOGY AG—See Vector Capital Management, L.P.; *U.S. Private*, pg. 4352
RIVERBED TECHNOLOGY (BEIJING) LIMITED—See Vector Capital Management, L.P.; *U.S. Private*, pg. 4352
RIVERBED TECHNOLOGY B.V.—See Vector Capital Management, L.P.; *U.S. Private*, pg. 4352
RIVERBED TECHNOLOGY FZ-LLC—See Vector Capital Management, L.P.; *U.S. Private*, pg. 4352
RIVERBED TECHNOLOGY GMBH—See Vector Capital Management, L.P.; *U.S. Private*, pg. 4352
RIVERBED TECHNOLOGY, INC.—See Vector Capital Management, L.P.; *U.S. Private*, pg. 4351

COMPANY NAME INDEX — RIVERSIDE SCRAP IRON & METAL CORPORATION

RIVERBED TECHNOLOGY INDIA PRIVATE LIMITED—See Vector Capital Management, L.P.; *U.S. Private*, pg. 4352
RIVERBED TECHNOLOGY K.K.—See Vector Capital Management, L.P.; *U.S. Private*, pg. 4352
RIVERBED TECHNOLOGY KOREA, INC.—See Vector Capital Management, L.P.; *U.S. Private*, pg. 4352
RIVERBED TECHNOLOGY LIMITED—See Vector Capital Management, L.P.; *U.S. Private*, pg. 4352
RIVERBED TECHNOLOGY LIMITED—See Vector Capital Management, L.P.; *U.S. Private*, pg. 4352
RIVERBED TECHNOLOGY LLC—See Vector Capital Management, L.P.; *U.S. Private*, pg. 4352
RIVERBED TECHNOLOGY LTD.—See Vector Capital Management, L.P.; *U.S. Private*, pg. 4352
RIVERBED TECHNOLOGY LTD.—See Vector Capital Management, L.P.; *U.S. Private*, pg. 4352
RIVERBED TECHNOLOGY PHILIPPINES—See Vector Capital Management, L.P.; *U.S. Private*, pg. 4352
RIVERBED TECHNOLOGY PTE LTD.—See Vector Capital Management, L.P.; *U.S. Private*, pg. 4352
RIVERBED TECHNOLOGY PTY LTD.—See Vector Capital Management, L.P.; *U.S. Private*, pg. 4352
RIVERBED TECHNOLOGY SARL—See Vector Capital Management, L.P.; *U.S. Private*, pg. 4352
RIVERBED TECHNOLOGY S. DE R.L. DE C.V.—See Vector Capital Management, L.P.; *U.S. Private*, pg. 4352
RIVERBED TECHNOLOGY SDN. BHD.—See Vector Capital Management, L.P.; *U.S. Private*, pg. 4352
RIVERBED TECHNOLOGY SHANGHAI—See Vector Capital Management, L.P.; *U.S. Private*, pg. 4352
RIVERBED TECHNOLOGY SL—See Vector Capital Management, L.P.; *U.S. Private*, pg. 4352
RIVERBED TECHNOLOGY SOUTH AFRICA (PROPRIETARY) LIMITED—See Vector Capital Management, L.P.; *U.S. Private*, pg. 4352
RIVERBED TECHNOLOGY S.R.L.—See Vector Capital Management, L.P.; *U.S. Private*, pg. 4352
RIVERBED TECHNOLOGY TAIWAN—See Vector Capital Management, L.P.; *U.S. Private*, pg. 4352
RIVERBED TECNOLOGIA DE INFORMACAO LTDA—See Vector Capital Management, L.P.; *U.S. Private*, pg. 4352
RIVERBEND CROSSING RETIREMENT COMMUNITY INC.—See Extendicare Inc.; *Int'l*, pg. 2591
RIVERBEND INDUSTRIES INC.—See Bee Street Holdings LLC; *U.S. Private*, pg. 513
RIVER BEND INDUSTRIES LLC; *U.S. Private*, pg. 3443
RIVER BEND INDUSTRIES-NORTH LIBERTY DIVISION—See River Bend Industries LLC; *U.S. Private*, pg. 3443
RIVER BEND INDUSTRIES-VICTOR DIVISION—See River Bend Industries LLC; *U.S. Private*, pg. 3443
RIVERBEND LANDFILL CO.—See Waste Management, Inc.; *U.S. Public*, pg. 2332
RIVER BEND MATERIALS INC.—See GMS Inc.; *U.S. Public*, pg. 948
RIVERBEND MEDICAL GROUP—See Trinity Health Corporation; *U.S. Private*, pg. 4234
RIVERBEND TIMBER FRAMING, LLC—See The Riverside Company; *U.S. Private*, pg. 4109
RIVERBEND TITLE, LLC—See Anywhere Real Estate Inc.; *U.S. Public*, pg. 142
RIVER BEND TRANSPORT COMPANY INC.—See ITOCHU Corporation; *Int'l*, pg. 3835
RIVER BEND TRANSPORT COMPANY INC.—See National Federation of Agricultural Co-Operative Associations; *Int'l*, pg. 5156
RIVER BIRCH HOMES INC.—See Berkshire Hathaway Inc.; *U.S. Public*, pg. 304
RIVERBOAT CORPORATION OF MISSISSIPPI—See Bally's Corporation; *U.S. Public*, pg. 268
RIVERBRIDGE PARTNERS, LLC—See Northill Capital LLP; *U.S. Private*, pg. 5445
RIVERCHASE DERMATOLOGY & COSMETIC SURGERY LLC—See GTCR LLC; *U.S. Private*, pg. 1806
RIVERCHASE DERMATOLOGY & COSMETIC SURGERY - PEMBROKE PINES—See GTCR LLC; *U.S. Private*, pg. 1806
RIVER CITIES CAPITAL FUNDS; *U.S. Private*, pg. 3443
RIVER CITIES PRINTING—See Champion Industries, Inc.; *U.S. Public*, pg. 478
RIVER CITY BANK INC.; *U.S. Public*, pg. 1800
RIVER CITY CONSTRUCTION L.L.C.; *U.S. Private*, pg. 3443
RIVER CITY CONSTRUCTION—See River City Construction L.L.C.; *U.S. Private*, pg. 3443
RIVER CITY FABRICATION, INC.—See EverArc Holdings Limited; *Int'l*, pg. 2563
RIVER CITY LANDSCAPE SUPPLY; *U.S. Private*, pg. 3443
RIVER CITY MILLWORK, INC.—See Hardwoods Distribution Inc.; *Int'l*, pg. 3273
RIVERCITY MOTORWAY PTY. LTD.; *Int'l*, pg. 6353
RIVER CITY PETROLEUM, INC.; *U.S. Private*, pg. 3443
RIVERCITY WHOLESALE INC.—See Leonard Green & Partners, L.P.; *U.S. Private*, pg. 2429
RIVER COMMUNICATIONS, INC.; *U.S. Private*, pg. 3443

RIVER CONCERTS GMBH—See DEAG Deutsche Entertainment AG; *Int'l*, pg. 1998
RIVER COUNTRY COOPERATIVE; *U.S. Private*, pg. 3443
RIVER COUNTRY CO-OP; *U.S. Private*, pg. 3443
RIVER CREST HOSPITAL—See Universal Health Services, Inc.; *U.S. Public*, pg. 2260
RIVERDALE GOLF & COUNTRY CLUB COMPANY LIMITED—See MBK Public Company Limited; *Int'l*, pg. 4754
RIVERDALE OIL & GAS CORP.; *U.S. Public*, pg. 1801
RIVERDALE PLACE CARE & REHABILITATION CENTER—See Formation Capital, LLC; *U.S. Private*, pg. 1571
RIVERDEEP, INC.—See Veritas Capital Fund Management, LLC; *U.S. Private*, pg. 4363
RIVER DRIVE SURGERY CENTER, LLC—See KKR & Co. Inc.; *U.S. Public*, pg. 1250
RIVEREDGE HOSPITAL, INC.—See Universal Health Services, Inc.; *U.S. Public*, pg. 2259
RIVER ELECTRONICS (IPOH) SDN. BHD.—See River Eletec Corporation; *Int'l*, pg. 6352
RIVER ELECTRONICS (SINGAPORE) PTE. LTD.—See River Eletec Corporation; *Int'l*, pg. 6352
RIVER ELETEC CORPORATION; *Int'l*, pg. 6352
RIVERENCE HOLDINGS LLC; *U.S. Private*, pg. 3444
RIVER FALLS MANUFACTURING CO. INC.—See S. Rothschild & Co., Inc.; *U.S. Private*, pg. 3515
RIVER FALLS MUTUAL INSURANCE COMPANY; *U.S. Private*, pg. 3444
RIVER FINANCIAL CORPORATION; *U.S. Public*, pg. 1801
RIVERFORT GLOBAL OPPORTUNITIES PLC; *Int'l*, pg. 6353
RIVERFRONT ACTIVITY CENTER, INC.; *U.S. Private*, pg. 3444
RIVERFRONT MUSIC PUBLISHING CO., INC.—See The Procter & Gamble Company; *U.S. Public*, pg. 2123
RIVERFRONT PACKING COMPANY, LLC; *U.S. Private*, pg. 3444
RIVERFRONT TIMES, LLC—See Village Voice Media Holdings, LLC; *U.S. Private*, pg. 4384
RIVERGATE MALL LIMITED PARTNERSHIP—See CBL & Associates Properties, Inc.; *U.S. Public*, pg. 459
RIVER/GULF GRAIN COMPANY—See Alter Companies; *U.S. Private*, pg. 206
RIVERHAWK FAST SEA FRAMES, LLC; *U.S. Private*, pg. 3444
RIVERHEAD BUILDING SUPPLY CORP.—See Riverhead Building Supply Corp.; *U.S. Private*, pg. 3444
RIVERHEAD BUILDING SUPPLY CORP.; *U.S. Private*, pg. 3444
RIVER HILL COAL COMPANY INC.; *U.S. Private*, pg. 3444
RIVERIA CITY SDN. BHD.—See Titijaya Land Berhad; *Int'l*, pg. 7761
RIVERINA (AUSTRALIA) PTY., LTD.—See Mitsubishi Corporation; *Int'l*, pg. 4943
RIVERINA FUNERAL SERVICES PTY LTD—See Propel Funeral Partners Limited; *Int'l*, pg. 5997
RIVERINA HOTEL PLC; *Int'l*, pg. 6353
RIVERINE CHINA HOLDINGS LIMITED; *Int'l*, pg. 6353
RIVER ISLAND CLOTHING CO. LTD.; *Int'l*, pg. 6352
RIVER KWAI INTERNATIONAL FOOD INDUSTRY COMPANY LIMITED—See Agripure Holdings Company Limited; *Int'l*, pg. 218
RIVERLAKE PARTNERS, LLC; *U.S. Private*, pg. 3444
RIVERLAND REPLY GMBH—See Reply S.p.A.; *Int'l*, pg. 6291
RIVERLAND RESOURCES INC.; *U.S. Private*, pg. 3444
RIVERMARK COMMUNITY CREDIT UNION; *U.S. Private*, pg. 3444
RIVER MEDICAL INCORPORATED—See KKR & Co. Inc.; *U.S. Public*, pg. 1249
RIVER & MERCANTILE GROUP PLC—See AssetCo plc; *Int'l*, pg. 643
RIVER & MERCANTILE LLC—See Agilis Holding Company LLC; *U.S. Private*, pg. 128
RIVER & MERCANTILE UK MICRO CAP INVESTMENT COMPANY LIMITED; *Int'l*, pg. 6352
RIVER METALS RECYCLING LLC—See Nucor Corporation; *U.S. Public*, pg. 1554
RIVERMORPH, LLC—See Stantec Inc.; *Int'l*, pg. 7172
RIVERNORTH/DOUBLELINE STRATEGIC OPPORTUNITY FUND, INC.; *U.S. Public*, pg. 1801
RIVERNORTH OPPORTUNITIES FUND, INC.; *U.S. Public*, pg. 1801
RIVER NORTH SAME DAY SURGERY, L.L.C.—See Tenet Healthcare Corporation; *U.S. Public*, pg. 2012
RIVER OAKS BANK BUILDING, INC.—See Banco Bilbao Vizcaya Argentaria, S.A.; *Int'l*, pg. 818
RIVER OAKS CENTER, LLC—See Washington Prime Group Inc.; *U.S. Public*, pg. 4448
RIVER OAKS HOSPITAL, INC.—See Community Health Systems, Inc.; *U.S. Public*, pg. 556
RIVER OAKS HOSPITAL—See Universal Health Services, Inc.; *U.S. Public*, pg. 2260
RIVER OAKS, INC.—See Universal Health Services, Inc.; *U.S. Public*, pg. 2259

RIVER OAKS—See Stonerise Healthcare LLC; *U.S. Private*, pg. 3830
RIVERO, GORDIMER & COMPANY, P.A.; *U.S. Private*, pg. 3445
RIVERON CONSULTING, LLC—See Kohlberg & Company, LLC; *U.S. Private*, pg. 2339
RIVER PARISHES HOSPITAL, LLC—See Apollo Global Management, Inc.; *U.S. Public*, pg. 158
RIVER PARISHES PHYSICIAN PRACTICES, LLC—See Apollo Global Management, Inc.; *U.S. Public*, pg. 158
RIVERPARK ASC, LLC—See Community Health Systems, Inc.; *U.S. Public*, pg. 556
RIVERPARK COMMUNITY CATH LAB, LLC—See Community Health Systems, Inc.; *U.S. Public*, pg. 556
RIVER PARK WEST APARTMENTS OWNER, LLC—See RAIT Financial Trust; *U.S. Public*, pg. 3349
RIVERPOINT CAPITAL MANAGEMENT, INC.—See Mariner Wealth Advisors, LLC; *U.S. Private*, pg. 2575
RIVER POINTE (DE), LLC—See Greystar Real Estate Partners, LLC; *U.S. Private*, pg. 1785
RIVERPOINT KANSAS, L.L.C.—See Lyon & Dittrich Holding Company; *U.S. Private*, pg. 2522
RIVERPOINT MEDICAL, LLC—See Arlington Capital Partners LLC; *U.S. Private*, pg. 328
RIVER PRODUCTS COMPANY, INC.; *U.S. Private*, pg. 3444
RIVER REGION COOPERATIVE; *U.S. Private*, pg. 3444
RIVER ROAD ASSET MANAGEMENT LLC—See Affiliated Managers Group, Inc.; *U.S. Public*, pg. 55
RIVERROCK EUROPEAN CAPITAL PARTNERS LLP; *Int'l*, pg. 6353
RIVER RUN COMPUTERS, INC.; *U.S. Private*, pg. 3444
RIVERSAND TECHNOLOGIES, INC.—See The Jordan Company, L.P.; *U.S. Private*, pg. 4062
THE RIVER'S EDGE OUTFITTERS, LLC—See Vista Outdoor Inc.; *U.S. Public*, pg. 2305
RIVER'S EDGE REHABILITATION & LIVING CENTER—See The Ensign Group, Inc.; *U.S. Public*, pg. 2072
RIVERSGOLD LIMITED; *Int'l*, pg. 6353
RIVERS GROUP LIMITED—See Marsh & McLennan Companies, Inc.; *U.S. Public*, pg. 1388
RIVERSIDE ACURA; *U.S. Private*, pg. 3445
RIVERSIDE AMBULATORY SURGERY CENTER, LLC—See Tenet Healthcare Corporation; *U.S. Public*, pg. 2012
RIVERSIDE AUTO SALES INC.; *U.S. Private*, pg. 3445
RIVERSIDE COMMUNITY CARE, INC.; *U.S. Private*, pg. 3445
RIVERSIDE COMMUNITY HOSPITAL—See HCA Healthcare, Inc.; *U.S. Public*, pg. 1007
THE RIVERSIDE COMPANY - CLEVELAND OFFICE—See The Riverside Company; *U.S. Private*, pg. 4110
THE RIVERSIDE COMPANY - DALLAS OFFICE—See The Riverside Company; *U.S. Private*, pg. 4110
THE RIVERSIDE COMPANY; *U.S. Private*, pg. 4107
RIVERSIDE DODGE CHRYSLER JEEP; *Int'l*, pg. 6353
RIVERSIDE ELECTRONICS LTD.; *U.S. Private*, pg. 3445
RIVERSIDE ENGINEERING, INC.—See FCF Partners, LP; *U.S. Private*, pg. 1485
RIVERSIDE FOODS, INC.; *U.S. Private*, pg. 3445
RIVERSIDE FORD INC.; *U.S. Private*, pg. 3445
RIVERSIDE FORD SALES LIMITED; *Int'l*, pg. 6353
RIVERSIDE FOREST PRODUCTS INC.; *U.S. Private*, pg. 3445
RIVERSIDE FURNITURE CORPORATION; *U.S. Private*, pg. 3445
RIVERSIDE GAS & OIL CO. INC.; *U.S. Private*, pg. 3445
RIVERSIDE GOLF COURSE—See OnCourse Strategies; *U.S. Private*, pg. 3020
RIVERSIDE HOSPITAL, INC.—See HCA Healthcare, Inc.; *U.S. Public*, pg. 1007
RIVERSIDE MANAGEMENT SERVICES INC.—See Health Quest Systems, Inc.; *U.S. Private*, pg. 1894
RIVERSIDE METRO AUTO GROUP LLC; *U.S. Private*, pg. 3445
RIVERSIDE MILLWORK GROUP; *Int'l*, pg. 6353
RIVERSIDE ORAL SURGERY; *U.S. Private*, pg. 3445
RIVERSIDE PAPER COMPANY INC.; *U.S. Private*, pg. 3445
RIVERSIDE PARTNERS, LLC; *U.S. Private*, pg. 3445
RIVERSIDE PAYMENTS, INC.; *U.S. Private*, pg. 3446
RIVERSIDE PROPERTY PTE LTD—See Frasers Property Limited; *Int'l*, pg. 2766
THE RIVERSIDE PUBLISHING CO.—See Veritas Capital Fund Management, LLC; *U.S. Private*, pg. 4363
RIVERSIDE REALTY GROUP, LLC; *U.S. Private*, pg. 3446
RIVERSIDE REFRACTORIES, INC.; *U.S. Private*, pg. 3446
RIVERSIDE RESOURCES INC.; *Int'l*, pg. 6353
RIVERSIDE RESOURCES MEXICO, S.A. DE C.V.—See Riverside Resources Inc.; *Int'l*, pg. 6353
RIVERSIDE-SAN BERNARDINO COUNTY INDIAN HEALTH, INC.; *U.S. Private*, pg. 3446
RIVERSIDE SCRAP IRON & METAL CORPORATION; *U.S. Private*, pg. 3446

RIVERSIDE SURGICAL CENTER OF MEADOWLANDS, LLC—See UnitedHealth Group Incorporated; *U.S. Public*, pg. 2250
RIVERSIDE TECHNOLOGY, INC.; *U.S. Private*, pg. 3446
RIVERSIDE TERRACE INC.—See Lanesborough Real Estate Investment Trust; *Int'l*, pg. 4408
RIVERSIDE TOOL CORP.—See Audax Group, Limited Partnership; *U.S. Private*, pg. 389
RIVERSIDE TOWER COMMERCIAL CENTER LTD.—See Kajima Corporation; *Int'l*, pg. 4055
RIVERSIDE TRANSPORT INC.; *U.S. Private*, pg. 3446
RIVERSIDE WEST CAR PARK LIMITED—See The Berkeley Group Holdings plc; *Int'l*, pg. 7620
RIVERSIDE WORLD PUBLISHING, INC.; *U.S. Private*, pg. 3446
RIVERSOURCE DISTRIBUTORS, INC.—See Ameriprise Financial, Inc.; *U.S. Public*, pg. 114
RIVERSOURCE LIFE INSURANCE COMPANY—See Ameriprise Financial, Inc.; *U.S. Public*, pg. 114
RIVERSOURCE LIFE INSURANCE CO. OF NEW YORK—See Ameriprise Financial, Inc.; *U.S. Public*, pg. 114
RIVER STATES TRUCK & TRAILER—See Penske Automotive Group, Inc.; *U.S. Public*, pg. 1664
RIVER STEEL CO., LTD.—See JFE Holdings, Inc.; *Int'l*, pg. 3939
RIVER STEEL, INC.; *U.S. Private*, pg. 3444
RIVERSTONE CREDIT OPPORTUNITIES INCOME PLC; *Int'l*, pg. 6353
RIVERSTONE ENERGY LIMITED; *Int'l*, pg. 6353
RIVERSTONE GROUP, INC.; *U.S. Private*, pg. 3446
THE RIVERSTONE GROUP, LLC; *U.S. Private*, pg. 4110
RIVERSTONE HOLDINGS LIMITED; *Int'l*, pg. 6353
RIVERSTONE HOLDINGS LLC - HOUSTON OFFICE—See Riverstone Holdings LLC; *U.S. Private*, pg. 3447
RIVERSTONE HOLDINGS LLC - LONDON OFFICE—See Riverstone Holdings LLC; *U.S. Private*, pg. 3447
RIVERSTONE HOLDINGS LLC; *U.S. Private*, pg. 3447
RIVERSTONE INSURANCE (UK) LIMITED—See CVC Capital Partners SICAV-FIS S.A.; *Int'l*, pg. 1884
RIVERSTONE LOGISTICS, LLC; *U.S. Private*, pg. 3448
RIVERSTONE MANAGING AGENCY LIMITED—See Fairfax Financial Holdings Limited; *Int'l*, pg. 2608
RIVERSTONE RESIDENTIAL GROUP, LLC—See Greystar Real Estate Partners, LLC; *U.S. Private*, pg. 1785
RIVERSTONE RESOURCES SDN BHD—See Riverstone Holdings Limited; *Int'l*, pg. 6353
RIVERSTONE RESOURCES (WUXI) COMPANY LIMITED—See Riverstone Holdings Limited; *Int'l*, pg. 6353
RIVER STREET ASSOCIATES—See Welltower Inc.; *U.S. Public*, pg. 2349
RIVER SURPLUS AND SUPPLY, LLC—See Fastenal Company; *U.S. Public*, pg. 824
RIVER TECH P.L.C.; *Int'l*, pg. 6352
RIVERTON MEMORIAL HOSPITAL LLC—See Apollo Global Management, Inc.; *U.S. Public*, pg. 158
RIVERTON MOTOR COMPANY, INC.; *U.S. Private*, pg. 3448
RIVERTON TRUCKERS, INC.—See Gohmann Asphalt & Construction Inc.; *U.S. Private*, pg. 1726
RIVER TO RIVER HEART GROUP, LLC—See Quorum Health Corporation; *U.S. Private*, pg. 3330
RIVERTY GROUP GMBH—See Bertelsmann SE & Co. KGaA; *Int'l*, pg. 996
RIVER VALLEY AG CREDIT; *U.S. Private*, pg. 3444
RIVER VALLEY APARTMENTS PTE LTD—See Frasers Property Limited; *Int'l*, pg. 2766
RIVER VALLEY ASC, LLC—See UnitedHealth Group Incorporated; *U.S. Public*, pg. 2250
RIVER VALLEY BANCORPORATION, INC.; *U.S. Private*, pg. 3444
RIVER VALLEY BANK—See River Valley Bancorporation, Inc.; *U.S. Private*, pg. 3444
RIVER VALLEY COMMUNITY BANK; *U.S. Public*, pg. 1801
RIVER VALLEY COOPERATIVE; *U.S. Private*, pg. 3444
RIVER VALLEY DIALYSIS, LLC—See DaVita Inc.; *U.S. Public*, pg. 642
RIVER VALLEY FOODS INC.; *U.S. Private*, pg. 3444
RIVER VALLEY HORTICULTURAL PRODUCTS, INC.—See SiteOne Landscape Supply, Inc.; *U.S. Public*, pg. 1889
RIVER VALLEY PAPER CO.; *U.S. Private*, pg. 3444
RIVER VALLEY SHOPPING CENTRE PTE LTD—See Frasers Property Limited; *Int'l*, pg. 2766
RIVER VALLEY TOWER PTE LTD—See Frasers Property Limited; *Int'l*, pg. 2766
RIVER VALLEY TRUCK CENTERS; *U.S. Private*, pg. 3444
RIVERVIEW ACQUISITION CORP.—See Westrock Coffee Company; *U.S. Public*, pg. 2361
RIVERVIEW ASSET MANAGEMENT CORP.—See Riverview Bancorp, Inc.; *U.S. Public*, pg. 1801
RIVERVIEW BANCORP, INC.; *U.S. Public*, pg. 1801
RIVERVIEW BANK—See Mid Penn Bancorp, Inc.; *U.S. Public*, pg. 1444

RIVERVIEW BEHAVIORAL HEALTH, LLC—See Acadia Healthcare Company, Inc.; *U.S. Public*, pg. 30
RIVERVIEW COMMUNITY BANK—See Riverview Bancorp, Inc.; *U.S. Public*, pg. 1801
RIVERVIEW FINANCIAL CORPORATION—See Mid Penn Bancorp, Inc.; *U.S. Public*, pg. 1444
RIVERVIEW HEALTH & REHAB CENTER INC.; *U.S. Private*, pg. 3448
RIVERVIEW HOTEL; *U.S. Private*, pg. 3448
RIVERVIEW INTERNATIONAL TRUCKS INC; *U.S. Private*, pg. 3448
RIVERVIEW MARINA INC.; *U.S. Private*, pg. 3448
RIVERVIEW MEDICAL CENTER, LLC—See Apollo Global Management, Inc.; *U.S. Public*, pg. 158
RIVERVIEW MEDICAL CENTER—See Hackensack Meridian Health, Inc.; *U.S. Private*, pg. 1838
RIVERVIEW PHYSICAL THERAPY, LIMITED PARTNERSHIP—See U.S. Physical Therapy, Inc.; *U.S. Public*, pg. 2216
RIVERVIEW REGIONAL MEDICAL CENTER, LLC—See Prime Healthcare Services, Inc.; *U.S. Private*, pg. 3261
RIVERVIEW RUBBER ESTATES BERHAD; *Int'l*, pg. 6353
RIVERVIEW TERMINAL COMPANY—See Peabody Energy Corporation; *U.S. Public*, pg. 1659
RIVERVIEW VILLAGE SENIOR LIVING, INC.—See The Ensign Group, Inc.; *U.S. Public*, pg. 2070
RIVERWALK ASC, LLC—See HCA Healthcare, Inc.; *U.S. Public*, pg. 1007
RIVERWALK G URBAN RENEWAL L.L.C.—See Veris Residential, Inc.; *U.S. Public*, pg. 2282
RIVERWALK HEALTHCARE, INC.—See The Ensign Group, Inc.; *U.S. Public*, pg. 2072
RIVERWALK HOLDINGS, LTD.—See Sunoco LP; *U.S. Public*, pg. 1964
RIVERWALK MARKETPLACE (NEW ORLEANS), LLC—See Howard Hughes Holdings Inc.; *U.S. Public*, pg. 1060
RIVERWALK SURGERY CENTER—See HCA Healthcare, Inc.; *U.S. Public*, pg. 1007
RIVERWOOD BANK—See Great River Holding Company; *U.S. Public*, pg. 1767
RIVERWOOD CAPITAL LP; *U.S. Private*, pg. 3448
RIVERWOOD GOLF CLUB—See Coral Hospitality, LLC; *U.S. Public*, pg. 1046
RIVERWOODS BEHAVIORAL HEALTH, LLC—See Acadia Healthcare Company, Inc.; *U.S. Public*, pg. 30
RIVERWOODS MILL, INC.; *U.S. Private*, pg. 3448
RIVERWOODS PRESERVATION, L.P.—See Apartment Investment and Management Company; *U.S. Public*, pg. 144
RIVER XEMEX CO., LTD.—See Zeon Corporation; *Int'l*, pg. 8635
RIVERY EXPLOITATION; *Int'l*, pg. 6353
RIVES E. WORRELL COMPANY, INC.; *U.S. Private*, pg. 3448
RIVES-MONTEIRO ENGINEERING, LLC—See InterCloud Systems, Inc.; *U.S. Public*, pg. 1141
RIVES & REYNOLDS LUMBER COMPANY, INC.; *U.S. Private*, pg. 3448
RIVE TECHNOLOGY INC—See Standard Industries Holdings Inc.; *U.S. Private*, pg. 3780
RIVET ENERGY AVIATION PTY. LIMITED—See Rivet Pty. Ltd.; *Int'l*, pg. 6353
RIVET ENERGY PTY. LTD.—See Rivet Pty. Ltd.; *Int'l*, pg. 6353
RIVET MARKCOM MIDWEST, INC. - CHICAGO OFFICE—See The Interpublic Group of Companies, Inc.; *U.S. Public*, pg. 2103
RIVET MINING SERVICES PTY. LTD.—See Rivet Pty. Ltd.; *Int'l*, pg. 6354
RIVET PTY. LTD.; *Int'l*, pg. 6353
THE RIVETT GROUP LLC; *U.S. Private*, pg. 4110
RIVEX TECHNOLOGY CORP.; *U.S. Public*, pg. 1801
RIVIANA FOODS CANADA CORPORATION—See Ebro Foods S.A.; *Int'l*, pg. 2287
RIVIANA FOODS INC.—See Ebro Foods S.A.; *Int'l*, pg. 2287
RIVIANA FOODS PTY LTD—See Ricegrowers Limited; *Int'l*, pg. 6329
RIVIANA INTERNATIONAL INC.—See Ebro Foods S.A.; *Int'l*, pg. 2287
RIVIAN AUTOMOTIVE CANADA, INC.—See Rivian Automotive, Inc.; *U.S. Public*, pg. 1801
RIVIAN AUTOMOTIVE, INC.; *U.S. Public*, pg. 1801
RIVIERA DUNES MARINA CONDOMINIUM ASSOCIATION, INC.; *U.S. Private*, pg. 3448
RIVIERA DUNES MARINA—See Riviera Dunes Marina Condominium Association, Inc.; *U.S. Private*, pg. 3448
RIVIERA FINANCE LLC; *U.S. Private*, pg. 3448
RIVIERA PARTNERS; *U.S. Private*, pg. 3448
RIVIERA POINT HOLDINGS, LLC; *U.S. Private*, pg. 3448
RIVIERA POINT LLC—See Keppel Corporation Limited; *Int'l*, pg. 4132
RIVIERA TRADING INC.; *U.S. Private*, pg. 3448
RIVIERA TRASPORTI LINEA S.P.A.—See Deutsche Bahn AG; *Int'l*, pg. 2052
RIVKIN RADLER LLP; *U.S. Private*, pg. 3448
RIVNOBUD LLC—See Dragon Ukrainian Properties & Development Plc; *Int'l*, pg. 2199

RIVOIRA GAS S.R.L.—See Mitsubishi Chemical Group Corporation; *Int'l*, pg. 4937
RIVOIRA REFRIGERANT GASES SRL—See Mitsubishi Chemical Group Corporation; *Int'l*, pg. 4937
RIVOLI GROUP L.L.C.—See The Swatch Group Ltd.; *Int'l*, pg. 7692
RIVULIS IRRIGATION, INC.—See Temasek Holdings (Private) Limited; *Int'l*, pg. 7550
RIVULIS IRRIGATION LTD.—See Temasek Holdings (Private) Limited; *Int'l*, pg. 7549
RIWI CORP.; *Int'l*, pg. 6354
RIWISA AG, KUNSTSTOFFWERKE HAGGLINGEN—See Flex Ltd.; *Int'l*, pg. 2704
RIX CORPORATION CO., LTD.—See RIX Corporation; *Int'l*, pg. 6354
RIX CORPORATION; *Int'l*, pg. 6354
RIX FM—See Modern Times Group MTG AB; *Int'l*, pg. 5015
RIX INDUSTRIES; *U.S. Private*, pg. 3448
RIXONA B.V.—See Royal Cosun U.A.; *Int'l*, pg. 6412
RIXONWAY KITCHENS LTD.—See Nobia AB; *Int'l*, pg. 5396
RIX TECHNOLOGY (THAILAND) CO., LTD.—See RIX Corporation; *Int'l*, pg. 6354
RIYAD BANK; *Int'l*, pg. 6354
RIYAD CAPITAL COMPANY—See Riyad Bank; *Int'l*, pg. 6354
RIYADH CABLES GROUP OF COMPANIES—See A.K. Al-Muhaidib & Sons Group of Companies; *Int'l*, pg. 24
RIYADH HOUSE COMPANY—See Jeraisy Group; *Int'l*, pg. 3931
RIYADH HOUSE ESTABLISHMENT—See Jeraisy Group; *Int'l*, pg. 3931
RIYAD REIT FUND; *Int'l*, pg. 6354
RIYAM COMPUTER SERVICES LLC—See Omar Zawawi Establishment LLC; *Int'l*, pg. 5561
RI YING HOLDINGS LIMITED; *Int'l*, pg. 6328
RIYUE HEAVY INDUSTRY CO., LTD.; *Int'l*, pg. 6354
RIZAL COLLEGE OF LAGUNA—See PHINMA Corporation; *Int'l*, pg. 5848
RIZAL COMMERCIAL BANKING CORPORATION—See Yuchengco Group of Companies; *Int'l*, pg. 8610
RIZAL RESOURCES CORPORATION; *Int'l*, pg. 6354
RIZAP GROUP, INC.; *Int'l*, pg. 6354
RIZHAO COSCO LOGISTICS LIMITED—See China COSCO Shipping Corporation Limited; *Int'l*, pg. 1493
RIZHAO LANDBRIDGE PORT SUPPLY CHAIN MANAGEMENT CO., LTD.—See China Master Logistics Co., Ltd.; *Int'l*, pg. 1518
RIZHAO NICHIRO & RONGSENSE FOODS CO., LTD.—See Maruha Nichiro Corporation; *Int'l*, pg. 4712
RIZHAO NITTAN VALVE CO., LTD.—See NITTAN Corporation; *Int'l*, pg. 5383
RIZHAO NPC PLASTIC CO., LTD.—See NPC Co., Ltd.; *Int'l*, pg. 5472
RIZHAO PARKER SURFACE TREATMENT CO., LTD.—See Nihon Parkerizing Co., Ltd.; *Int'l*, pg. 5287
RIZHAO PORT CO., LTD.; *Int'l*, pg. 6354
RIZHAO PORT JURONG CO., LTD.—See Rizhao Port Co., Ltd.; *Int'l*, pg. 6354
RIZHAO SP AUTOMOBILE PARTS CO., LTD.—See NITTAN Corporation; *Int'l*, pg. 5383
RIZHAO YUSHUN CASSAVA. CO., LTD.—See Asia Cassava Resources Holdings Limited; *Int'l*, pg. 611
RIZING GEOSPATIAL, LLC—See Wipro Limited; *Int'l*, pg. 8432
RIZING LANKA (PVT.) LTD.—See Wipro Limited; *Int'l*, pg. 8432
RIZING, LLC—See Wipro Limited; *Int'l*, pg. 8432
RIZING PHILIPPINES INC.—See Wipro Limited; *Int'l*, pg. 8432
RIZING SDN. BHD.—See Wipro Limited; *Int'l*, pg. 8432
RIZVI TRAVERSE MANAGEMENT LLC; *U.S. Private*, pg. 3449
RIZZETTA & COMPANY, INC.—See FirstService Corporation; *Int'l*, pg. 2691
RIZZICONI ENERGIA SPA—See Axpo Holding AG; *Int'l*, pg. 771
RIZZO ENVIRONMENTAL SERVICES, INC.—See BC Partners LLP; *Int'l*, pg. 924
RIZZO GROUP AB; *Int'l*, pg. 6355
RIZZOLI INTERNATIONAL PUBLICATIONS, INC.—See Fininvest S.p.A.; *Int'l*, pg. 2675
RIZZOLI LIBRI S.P.A.—See Fininvest S.p.A.; *Int'l*, pg. 2675
RIZZOLI PUBLISHING ITALIA S.R.L.—See RCS MediaGroup S.p.A.; *Int'l*, pg. 6229
RIZZON AUTOMOBILES; *Int'l*, pg. 6355
RIZZUTI/AUSTIN MARKETING GROUP; *U.S. Private*, pg. 3449
R&J ADVERTISING INC.—See Ron Jon Surf Shop; *U.S. Private*, pg. 3477
RJB DEVELOPMENT CO. INC.—See World Holdings Inc.; *U.S. Public*, pg. 4565
RJB ENGINEERING (UK) LIMITED—See Schlumberger Limited; *U.S. Public*, pg. 1844
R J BIO-TECH LIMITED; *Int'l*, pg. 6167
RJB MANAGEMENT CO.—See World Holdings Inc.; *U.S. Private*, pg. 4565
RJ BRANDS LLC; *U.S. Private*, pg. 3449

COMPANY NAME INDEX

R.J. BURNSIDE & ASSOCIATES LIMITED; *Int'l*, pg. 6170
R.J. CARROLL COMPANY INC.; *U.S. Private*, pg. 3337
RJ CONNECT S.A.—See M2I Corporation; *Int'l*, pg. 4617
R.J. CONSULTORES E INFORMATICA LTD.—See TOTVS S.A.; *Int'l*, pg. 7846
R.J. CORMAN RAILPOWER—See R.J. Corman Railroad Group LLC; *U.S. Private*, pg. 3337
R.J. CORMAN RAILROAD GROUP LLC; *U.S. Private*, pg. 3337
R.J. DALE ADVERTISING & PUBLIC RELATIONS; *U.S. Private*, pg. 3337
R.J. DAUM CONSTRUCTION COMPANY; *U.S. Private*, pg. 3337
RJ DELTA CAPITAL S.A.—See Raymond James Financial, Inc.; *U.S. Public*, pg. 1765
RJ DELTA FUND MANAGEMENT S.A.—See Raymond James Financial, Inc.; *U.S. Public*, pg. 1765
RJD GREEN, INC.; *U.S. Public*, pg. 1801
RJE BUSINESS INTERIORS INC.; *U.S. Private*, pg. 3449
RJ EQUITIES, INC.—See Raymond James Financial, Inc.; *U.S. Public*, pg. 1764
RJE TELECOM, LLC—See Dycom Industries, Inc.; *U.S. Public*, pg. 699
RJ FINANCE CORP. ONE—See Bombardier Inc.; *Int'l*, pg. 1104
RJF INTERNATIONAL CORPORATION; *U.S. Private*, pg. 3449
R.J. GRONDIN & SONS; *U.S. Private*, pg. 3337
RJ INVESTMENT CO.—See Renewable Japan Co., Ltd.; *Int'l*, pg. 6278
RJK EXPLORATIONS LTD.; *Int'l*, pg. 6355
R.J. KIELTY PLUMBING INC.; *U.S. Private*, pg. 3337
R.J. KILN & CO. LIMITED—See Tokio Marine Holdings, Inc.; *Int'l*, pg. 7784
RJ KING & ASSOCIATES; *U.S. Private*, pg. 3449
RJ LEE GROUP INC.; *U.S. Private*, pg. 3449
RJL HOLDING CO. LLC; *U.S. Private*, pg. 3449
THE R.J. MARSHALL COMPANY EUROPE BVBA—See The R.J. Marshall Company; *U.S. Private*, pg. 4102
THE R.J. MARSHALL COMPANY; *U.S. Private*, pg. 4101
RJM BUILDERS INCORPORATED; *U.S. Private*, pg. 3449
RJM CONSTRUCTION LLC; *U.S. Private*, pg. 3449
RJM EQUIPMENT SALES LLC—See Tym Corporation; *Int'l*, pg. 7995
RJMETRICS INC.; *U.S. Private*, pg. 3449
R.J. MILLER & ASSOCIATES INC.; *U.S. Private*, pg. 3337
RJMS CORPORATION; *U.S. Private*, pg. 3449
RJM SYSTEMS INC.—See Jenzabar, Inc.; *U.S. Private*, pg. 2201
R.J. NOBLE COMPANY; *U.S. Private*, pg. 3337
R.J. O'BRIEN & ASSOCIATES CANADA INC.—See R.J. O'Brien & Associates, LLC; *U.S. Private*, pg. 3337
R.J. O'BRIEN & ASSOCIATES, LLC; *U.S. Private*, pg. 3337
R.J. O'BRIEN (EUROPE) LIMITED—See R.J. O'Brien & Associates, LLC; *U.S. Private*, pg. 3337
R.J. O'BRIEN LIMITED—See R.J. O'Brien & Associates, LLC; *U.S. Private*, pg. 3337
R.J. O'BRIEN (UK) LIMITED—See R.J. O'Brien & Associates, LLC; *U.S. Private*, pg. 3337
R.J. REYNOLDS GLOBAL PRODUCTS, INC.—See British American Tobacco plc; *Int'l*, pg. 1168
R.J. REYNOLDS TOBACCO COMPANY—See British American Tobacco plc; *Int'l*, pg. 1168
R.J. REYNOLDS TOBACCO HOLDINGS, INC.—See British American Tobacco plc; *Int'l*, pg. 1168
R.J. REYNOLDS TOBACCO INTERNATIONAL, INC.—See British American Tobacco plc; *Int'l*, pg. 1168
R.J. ROBERTS, INC.—See PTS Advance; *U.S. Private*, pg. 3298
RJR POLYMERS INC.; *U.S. Private*, pg. 3449
RJR REALTY RELOCATION SERVICES, INC.—See British American Tobacco plc; *Int'l*, pg. 1168
R J SAFETY SUPPLY CO, INC.—See Mallory Safety & Supply LLC; *U.S. Private*, pg. 2558
R.J.S. & ASSOCIATES INC.; *U.S. Private*, pg. 3338
R.J. SCHINNER CO. INC.; *U.S. Private*, pg. 3337
RJS CONSTRUCTION GROUP, LLC; *U.S. Private*, pg. 3449
R.J. SHAH & COMPANY LIMITED; *Int'l*, pg. 6170
RJT COMPUQUEST, INC.; *U.S. Private*, pg. 3449
R.J. THROCKMORTON SALES CO.; *U.S. Private*, pg. 3337
RJ TORCHING, INC.; *U.S. Private*, pg. 3449
R & J TRUCKING INC.—See American Bulk Commodities Inc.; *U.S. Private*, pg. 225
R.J. VAN DRUNEN & SONS INC.; *U.S. Private*, pg. 3337
R.J. WALKER CO. INC.; *U.S. Private*, pg. 3337
RJW, INC.; *U.S. Private*, pg. 3449
RJW MEDIA; *U.S. Private*, pg. 3449
RJW & PARTNERS LTD.—See The Mission Group Public Limited Company; *Int'l*, pg. 7667
R.J. YOUNG CO., INC.; *U.S. Private*, pg. 3337
R.K. ALLEN OIL CO., INC.; *U.S. Private*, pg. 3338
RK ANTRIEBS- UND HANDHABUNGS-TECHNIK GMBH—See Phoenix Mecano AG; *Int'l*, pg. 5853
RKA PETROLEUM COMPANIES, LLC; *U.S. Private*, pg. 3450
R.K. AUTO GROUP, INC.; *U.S. Private*, pg. 3338

RKB AGRO INDUSTRIES LIMITED; *Int'l*, pg. 6355
RKB HANDYMAN SERVICES, INC.; *U.S. Private*, pg. 3450
R.K. BLACK INC.; *U.S. Private*, pg. 3338
RKB MAINICHI HOLDINGS CORP.; *Int'l*, pg. 6355
R&K BUILDING SUPPLIES—See Farnsworth Development Companies; *U.S. Private*, pg. 1480
RK CAPITAL PARTNERS, LLC; *U.S. Private*, pg. 3450
RKD AGRI & RETAIL LTD.; *Int'l*, pg. 6355
RKD GROUP, LLC—See Incline MGMT Corp.; *U.S. Private*, pg. 2054
RK DISTRIBUTING INC.; *U.S. Private*, pg. 3450
R&K DISTRIBUTORS INC.; *U.S. Private*, pg. 3332
R. K. DIXON COMPANY—See Xerox Holdings Corporation; *U.S. Public*, pg. 2389
RK DIXON—See Xerox Holdings Corporation; *U.S. Public*, pg. 2389
RKEC PROJECTS LTD.; *Int'l*, pg. 6355
R.K. ELECTRIC INC.; *U.S. Private*, pg. 3338
RK ENVIRONMENTAL SERVICES LLC; *U.S. Private*, pg. 3450
RKF GROUP CANADA REALTY—See Newmark Group, Inc.; *U.S. Public*, pg. 1516
RKF GROUP ILLINOIS LLC—See Newmark Group, Inc.; *U.S. Public*, pg. 1516
RKF GROUP NEW JERSEY LLC—See Newmark Group, Inc.; *U.S. Public*, pg. 1516
RK GROUP LIMITED—See The Kellan Group Plc; *Int'l*, pg. 7662
THE RK GROUP, LLC; *U.S. Private*, pg. 4110
THE RK GROUP WEST, LLC—See The RK Group, LLC; *U.S. Private*, pg. 4110
RKI, INC.; *U.S. Private*, pg. 3450
RKI INSTRUMENTS, INC.—See Riken Keiki Co., Ltd.; *Int'l*, pg. 6340
R-KIOSKI OY—See Reitangruppen AS; *Int'l*, pg. 6258
RKK COMPUTER SERVICE CO., INC.—See Kyushu Electric Power Co., Inc.; *Int'l*, pg. 4368
RK KLINIK BETRIEBS GMBH NR. 31—See Asklepios Kliniken GmbH & Co. KGaA; *Int'l*, pg. 624
R.K.L. BUILDING SPECIALTIES CO., INC.—See Berkshire Hathaway Inc.; *U.S. Public*, pg. 312
RKL ESOLUTIONS, LLC; *U.S. Private*, pg. 3450
THE RK LOGISTICS GROUP, INC.; *U.S. Private*, pg. 4110
RK MECHANICAL, INC.; *U.S. Private*, pg. 3450
R.K. MILES; *U.S. Private*, pg. 3338
RKN RHEINKRAFTWERK NEUHAUSEN AG—See EnBW Energie Baden-Wurttemberg AG; *Int'l*, pg. 2398
R-KOMA LTD.—See UBE Corporation; *Int'l*, pg. 8001
RKON, INC.; *U.S. Private*, pg. 3450
RKO STEEL LTD; *Int'l*, pg. 6355
RK PRECISION CO., LTD.—See Rinnai Corporation; *Int'l*, pg. 6344
RKR GEBLASE UND VERDICHTER GMBH; *Int'l*, pg. 6355
RKR HESS ASSOCIATES, INC.—See Universal Technical Resource Services, Inc.; *U.S. Private*, pg. 4306
RKR MOTORS, INC.—See AutoNation, Inc.; *U.S. Public*, pg. 237
RKR MOTORS, INC.—See AutoNation, Inc.; *U.S. Public*, pg. 237
RK ROSE + KRIEGER GMBH—See Phoenix Mecano AG; *Int'l*, pg. 5853
RK SCHMIDT SYSTEMTECHNIK GMBH—See Phoenix Mecano AG; *Int'l*, pg. 5853
RKS ELECTRIC CORP.; *U.S. Private*, pg. 3450
RK SLOVAKIA S.R.O.—See Beijer Ref AB; *Int'l*, pg. 945
RK SPECIALTIES, INC.—See RK Mechanical, Inc.; *U.S. Private*, pg. 3450
RKS S.A.-SKF SLEWING BEARINGS—See SKF AB; *Int'l*, pg. 6983
R.K. STRATMAN INCORPORATED; *U.S. Private*, pg. 3338
R.K. SWAMY BBDO—See Omnicom Group Inc.; *U.S. Public*, pg. 1576
R.K. SWAMY/BBDO—See Omnicom Group Inc.; *U.S. Public*, pg. 1576
R.K. SWAMY/BBDO—See Omnicom Group Inc.; *U.S. Public*, pg. 1576
R.K. SWAMY/BBDO—See Omnicom Group Inc.; *U.S. Public*, pg. 1576
R.K. SWAMY/BBDO—See Omnicom Group Inc.; *U.S. Public*, pg. 1577
R.K. SWAMY/BBDO—See Omnicom Group Inc.; *U.S. Public*, pg. 1577
R&K TECH AB—See Addtech AB; *Int'l*, pg. 134
RK TEKNIK I GUSUM AB—See Balco Group AB; *Int'l*, pg. 807
RKW ACE SA.—See Standard Investment Management B.V.; *Int'l*, pg. 7169
RKW AGRI GMBH & CO. KG—See RKW SE; *Int'l*, pg. 6355
RKW CASTELLETTA S.A.S—See RKW SE; *Int'l*, pg. 6355
RKW FINLAND LTD.—See RKW SE; *Int'l*, pg. 6355
RKW GUANGZHOU COMPANY LTD.—See RKW SE; *Int'l*, pg. 6355
RKW HYDROSPUN GMBH—See RKW SE; *Int'l*, pg. 6355
RKW HYPLAST NV—See RKW SE; *Int'l*, pg. 6355
RKW ITER S.A.U.—See RKW SE; *Int'l*, pg. 6355

RKW LOTUS LTD.—See RKW SE; *Int'l*, pg. 6355
RKW NORTH AMERICA, INC.—See RKW SE; *Int'l*, pg. 6355
RKW REMY S.A.S.—See RKW SE; *Int'l*, pg. 6355
RKW SAINT FRERES EMBALLAGE S.A.S.—See RKW SE; *Int'l*, pg. 6355
RKW SE; *Int'l*, pg. 6355
RKW SWEDEN AB—See RKW SE; *Int'l*, pg. 6355
RL360 INSURANCE CO. LTD.—See International Financial Group Ltd.; *Int'l*, pg. 3748
RLA GROUP LIMITED—See The Mission Group Public Limited Company; *Int'l*, pg. 7667
R.L. ALBERT & SON, INC.; *U.S. Private*, pg. 3338
THE R. LANG COMPANY; *U.S. Private*, pg. 3338
RLA NORTHERN IRELAND LIMITED—See The Mission Group Public Limited Company; *Int'l*, pg. 7667
RLA POLYMERS PTY. LTD.—See TPG Capital, L.P.; *U.S. Public*, pg. 2175
R.L. BRINK CORP.; *U.S. Private*, pg. 3338
R.L. BROOKDALE MOTORS INC.—See Luther Holding Company; *U.S. Private*, pg. 2517
R&L BROSAMER INC.—See The Walsh Group; *U.S. Private*, pg. 4133
THE R.L. BRYAN COMPANY; *U.S. Private*, pg. 4102
R.L. CAMPBELL ROOFING CO. INC.; *U.S. Private*, pg. 3338
R & L CARRIERS, INC.; *U.S. Private*, pg. 3331
RLC HOLDING CO. INC.; *U.S. Private*, pg. 3450
R & L CONSTRUCTION INC.; *U.S. Private*, pg. 3331
RLDATIX LIMITED—See Rothschild & Co SCA; *Int'l*, pg. 6403
RLDATIX LIMITED—See TA Associates, Inc.; *U.S. Private*, pg. 3917
RL DEPPMANN COMPANY; *U.S. Private*, pg. 3450
R&L DEVELOPMENT COMPANY; *U.S. Private*, pg. 3332
R. L. DRAKE HOLDINGS, LLC—See Blonder Tongue Laboratories, Inc.; *U.S. Public*, pg. 362
R. L. DRAKE HOLDINGS, LLC—See Blonder Tongue Laboratories, Inc.; *U.S. Public*, pg. 362
R.L.E. CORP.; *U.S. Private*, pg. 3338
RLE GLOBAL OPERATIONS (CHINA) INC.—See RLE International Produktentwicklungsgesellschaft mbH; *Int'l*, pg. 6355
RLE INDIA PRIVATE LIMITED—See RLE International Produktentwicklungsgesellschaft mbH; *Int'l*, pg. 6355
RLE INTERNATIONAL CHINA INC.—See RLE International Produktentwicklungsgesellschaft mbH; *Int'l*, pg. 6355
RLE INTERNATIONAL NORTH AMERICA INC.—See RLE International Produktentwicklungsgesellschaft mbH; *Int'l*, pg. 6355
RLE INTERNATIONAL PRODUKTENTWICKLUNGSGESELLSCHAFT MBH; *Int'l*, pg. 6355
RLF AGTECH LTD.; *Int'l*, pg. 6355
RLF LIMITED; *Int'l*, pg. 6355
R.L. FRENCH CORPORATION; *U.S. Private*, pg. 3338
R.L. FRIDLEY THEATRES INC.; *U.S. Private*, pg. 3338
RLG DO BRASIL VAREJO LTDA.—See Compagnie Financiere Richemont S.A.; *Int'l*, pg. 1741
RLG INTERNATIONAL INC.; *Int'l*, pg. 6355
RLG INVESTMENTS, INC. -U.S.A; *U.S. Private*, pg. 3450
RL HAINES CONSTRUCTION, LLC; *U.S. Private*, pg. 3450
R L H ENGINEERING, INC.—See Accenture plc; *Int'l*, pg. 86
RLH PROPERTIES SAB DE CV; *Int'l*, pg. 6356
R.L. HUDSON & COMPANY; *U.S. Private*, pg. 3338
R+L HYDRAULICS GMBH—See The Timken Company; *U.S. Public*, pg. 2133
RLI ATLANTA - P/C—See RLI Corp.; *U.S. Public*, pg. 1801
RLI CHICAGO REGIONAL OFFICE—See RLI Corp.; *U.S. Public*, pg. 1802
RLI CORP.; *U.S. Public*, pg. 1801
RLI & HAWAII PRODUCT LINES—See RLI Corp.; *U.S. Public*, pg. 1801
RLI INSURANCE COMPANY—See RLI Corp.; *U.S. Public*, pg. 1801
RLI LOS ANGELES REGIONAL OFFICE—See RLI Corp.; *U.S. Public*, pg. 1802
R.L. IMPORTS INC.—See Luther Holding Company; *U.S. Private*, pg. 2517
RLI NORTHERN CALIFORNIA REGIONAL OFFICE—See RLI Corp.; *U.S. Public*, pg. 1802
RLI SOUTHEAST REGIONAL OFFICE—See RLI Corp.; *U.S. Public*, pg. 1802
RLI SPECIAL RISK—See RLI Corp.; *U.S. Public*, pg. 1802
R.L. JAMES INC.; *U.S. Private*, pg. 3338
THE RLJ COMPANIES, LLC; *U.S. Private*, pg. 4110
RLJ ENTERTAINMENT, INC.—See AMC Networks Inc.; *U.S. Public*, pg. 92
RLJ EQUITY PARTNERS LLC—See The RLJ Companies, LLC; *U.S. Private*, pg. 4110
RLJ LODGING TRUST L.P.—See The RLJ Companies, LLC; *U.S. Private*, pg. 4111
RLJ LODGING TRUST—See The RLJ Companies, LLC; *U.S. Private*, pg. 4111
RLJ-MCLARTY-LANDERS AUTOMOTIVE HOLDINGS, LLC—See The RLJ Companies, LLC; *U.S. Private*, pg. 4111

R.L. JONES CUSTOMHOUSE BROKERS INC.

CORPORATE AFFILIATIONS

R.L. JONES CUSTOMHOUSE BROKERS INC.; *U.S. Private*, pg. 3338
R.L. JORDAN OIL CO; *U.S. Private*, pg. 3338
RLK & COMPANY; *U.S. Private*, pg. 3450
R.L. KISTLER INC.; *U.S. Private*, pg. 3338
R.L. LIPTON WHOLESALERS INC.—See Tri County Wholesale Distributors Inc.; *U.S. Private*, pg. 4220
R.L. MCCOY, INC.; *U.S. Private*, pg. 3338
RLM FINSBURY LIMITED—See WPP plc; *Int'l*, pg. 8466
R.L. MILSNER, INC. INSURANCE BROKERAGE—See Peter C. Foy & Associates Insurance Services, Inc.; *U.S. Private*, pg. 3158
R.L. MORGAN COMPANY INC.; *U.S. Private*, pg. 3338
RLM PUBLIC RELATIONS; *U.S. Private*, pg. 3450
RLM, S.A.—See Promotora de Informaciones S.A.; *Int'l*, pg. 5995
RLMS SALES LTD.—See Novomatic AG; *Int'l*, pg. 5467
RL-NEDVISHIMOSTI EOOD—See Raiffeisen Bank International AG; *Int'l*, pg. 6183
RL-NORDIC AB—See Raiffeisen Bank International AG; *Int'l*, pg. 6183
R-LOGIC INTERNATIONAL PTE. LTD.—See MCJ Co., Ltd.; *Int'l*, pg. 4759
RL PUBLIC RELATIONS + MARKETING—See RL Public Relations + Marketing; *U.S. Private*, pg. 3450
RL PUBLIC RELATIONS + MARKETING; *U.S. Private*, pg. 3450
RLR ADVERTISING INC.; *U.S. Private*, pg. 3450
RLR ADVERTISING; *U.S. Private*, pg. 3450
RL RETAIL FRANCE S.A.S.—See Ralph Lauren Corporation; *U.S. Public*, pg. 1761
RLR, INC.; *U.S. Private*, pg. 3450
RLR INDUSTRIES INC.; *U.S. Private*, pg. 3450
RLS MERILNA TEHNIKA D.O.O.—See Renishaw plc; *Int'l*, pg. 6283
R. L. STONE COMPANY, INC.—See Applied Industrial Technologies, Inc.; *U.S. Public*, pg. 171
R.L. VALLEE INC.; *U.S. Private*, pg. 3338
R.L. WILLIAMS COMPANY; *U.S. Private*, pg. 3338
RLX TECHNOLOGY INC.; *Int'l*, pg. 6356
R.L. ZEIGLER CO. INC.; *U.S. Private*, pg. 3338
RM2 INTERNATIONAL S.A.; *Int'l*, pg. 6356
RMA BROKERAGE LLC; *U.S. Private*, pg. 3451
RMA ENERGY LIMITED; *Int'l*, pg. 6356
RMA GLOBAL LIMITED; *Int'l*, pg. 6356
RMA GROUP, INC.—See OceanSound Partners, LP; *U.S. Private*, pg. 2991
RMA HOME SERVICES INC.; *U.S. Private*, pg. 3451
RMA LAND CONSTRUCTION, INC.; *U.S. Private*, pg. 3451
RM ASPHALT GMBH & CO. KG—See STRABAG SE; *Int'l*, pg. 7232
RMA TRANSPORTATION SERVICES INC.; *U.S. Private*, pg. 3451
R&M AUSBAU LEIPZIG GMBH—See Bilfinger SE; *Int'l*, pg. 1028
RMA WATANIYA—See Groupama SA; *Int'l*, pg. 3091
RMAX INC.; *U.S. Private*, pg. 3451
R.M. BARROWS, INC. ADVERTISING & PUBLIC RELATIONS; *U.S. Private*, pg. 3338
RMB ASSET MANAGEMENT (PTY) LIMITED—See FirstRand Limited; *Int'l*, pg. 2690
R&M BAUDIENSTLEISTUNGEN GMBH—See Bilfinger SE; *Int'l*, pg. 1028
RMB AUSTRALIA LTD.—See FirstRand Limited; *Int'l*, pg. 2690
RMB BANCSHARES, INC.; *U.S. Private*, pg. 3451
RMB CAPITAL MANAGEMENT, LLC—See Curi Holdings, Inc.; *U.S. Private*, pg. 1125
RMB CIS MANCO (PROPRIETARY) LIMITED—See Ashburton; *Int'l*, pg. 606
RMB CORVEST (PTY) LTD.—See FirstRand Limited; *Int'l*, pg. 2690
RMB FINANCIAL SERVICES LIMITED—See FirstRand Limited; *Int'l*, pg. 2690
RMB GROUP; *Int'l*, pg. 6356
RMB HOLDINGS LIMITED; *Int'l*, pg. 6356
RMBL MISSOURI, LLC—See RumbleON, Inc.; *U.S. Public*, pg. 1826
RMB PRIVATE EQUITY HOLDINGS (PTY) LTD—See FirstRand Limited; *Int'l*, pg. 2690
RMB STRUCTURED INSURANCE LIMITED PCC—See FirstRand Limited; *Int'l*, pg. 2690
RMB STRUCTURED INSURANCE LIMITED—See FirstRand Limited; *Int'l*, pg. 2690
R & M BULGARIA EOOD—See Reichle & De-Massari AG; *Int'l*, pg. 6256
R.M. BURRITT MOTORS - BUICK CHEVROLET OSWEGO—See R.M. Burritt Motors, Inc.; *U.S. Private*, pg. 3339
R.M. BURRITT MOTORS, INC.; *U.S. Private*, pg. 3338
RMC ADVANCED TECHNOLOGIES INC.—See NanoXplore Inc.; *Int'l*, pg. 5145
R. MCALLISTER SERVICE COMPANY; *U.S. Private*, pg. 3334
RMCA PROFESSIONALS MGMT, LLC—See HCA Healthcare, Inc.; *U.S. Public*, pg. 1007
R. MCCLOSKEY INSURANCE AGENCY; *U.S. Private*, pg. 3334

RMC DISTRIBUTING LLC; *U.S. Private*, pg. 3451
RMCN CREDIT SERVICES, INC.; *U.S. Private*, pg. 3451
RMC PROPERTY GROUP LLC; *U.S. Private*, pg. 3451
RMC REINSURANCE, LTD—See Regional Management Corp.; *U.S. Public*, pg. 1776
RM CROWE MANAGEMENT COMPANY; *U.S. Private*, pg. 3451
RMC SWITCHGEARS LIMITED; *Int'l*, pg. 6356
RMC VANGUARD MORTGAGE CORPORATION; *U.S. Private*, pg. 3451
RMC WATER & ENVIRONMENT—See Woodard & Curran Inc.; *U.S. Private*, pg. 4557
RMD-CONSULT GMBH WASSERBAU UND ENERGIE—See E.ON SE; *Int'l*, pg. 2259
RMD HOLDINGS, LTD.; *U.S. Private*, pg. 3451
RMD INSTRUMENTS CORPORATION—See Dynasil Corporation of America; *U.S. Private*, pg. 1300
RMD KWIKFORM AL MAHA QATAR WLL—See Interserve Plc; *Int'l*, pg. 3759
RMD KWIKFORM ALMOAYED BAHRAIN WLL—See Interserve Plc; *Int'l*, pg. 3759
RMD KWIKFORM HONG KONG LIMITED.—See Interserve Plc; *Int'l*, pg. 3759
RMD KWIKFORM IBERICA SA—See Interserve Plc; *Int'l*, pg. 3759
RMD KWIKFORM INDIA PRIVATE LTD.—See Interserve Plc; *Int'l*, pg. 3759
RMD KWIKFORM IRELAND LTD.—See Interserve Plc; *Int'l*, pg. 3759
RMD KWIKFORM LTD—See Interserve Plc; *Int'l*, pg. 3759
RMD KWIKFORM MIDDLE EAST HEAD LLC—See Interserve Plc; *Int'l*, pg. 3759
RMD KWIKFORM MIDDLE EAST LLC—See Interserve Plc; *Int'l*, pg. 3759
RMD KWIKFORM OMEN LLC—See Interserve Plc; *Int'l*, pg. 3759
RMD KWIKFORM PHILIPPINES INC.—See Interserve Plc; *Int'l*, pg. 3759
RMD KWIKFORM SAUDI ARABIA LLC—See Interserve Plc; *Int'l*, pg. 3759
RMD KWIKFORM (SOUTH AFRICA) (PROPRIETARY) LTD.—See Interserve Plc; *Int'l*, pg. 3759
RMD NEW ZEALAND PTY LTD—See Interserve Plc; *Int'l*, pg. 3759
R M DRIP & SPRINKLERS SYSTEMS LTD.; *Int'l*, pg. 6167
RMD TECHNOLOGIES, INC.; *U.S. Private*, pg. 3451
RMD WASSERSTRASSEN GMBH; *Int'l*, pg. 6356
RM EDUCATION PLC—See RM plc; *Int'l*, pg. 6356
RM EDUCATION SOLUTIONS INDIA PVT LTD—See RM plc; *Int'l*, pg. 6356
R. MEES & ZOONEN ASSURADEUREN B.V.—See Marsh & McLennan Companies, Inc.; *U.S. Public*, pg. 1388
RM EURO B.V.—See Rheinmetall AG; *Int'l*, pg. 6323
R&M FASSADENTECHNIK SUDWEST GMBH—See Bilfinger SE; *Int'l*, pg. 1028
RMG ACQUISITION CORP.; *U.S. Public*, pg. 1802
RMG AUSTRALIA PTY. LTD—See Rino Mastrotto Group S.p.A.; *Int'l*, pg. 6345
RMG HONG KONG—See Rino Mastrotto Group S.p.A.; *Int'l*, pg. 6345
RMG LIMITED; *Int'l*, pg. 6357
RMG MEDIA, LLC; *U.S. Private*, pg. 3451
RMG NETWORKS HOLDING CORPORATION; *U.S. Private*, pg. 3451
RMG NETWORKS, INC.—See RMG Networks Holding Corporation; *U.S. Private*, pg. 3451
RMG NETWORKS LIMITED—See RMG Networks Holding Corporation; *U.S. Private*, pg. 3452
RMH ACQUISITION, LLC; *U.S. Private*, pg. 3452
RMH FOODS LLC—See Sandridge Food Corporation; *U.S. Private*, pg. 3544
RMH FRANCHISE CORPORATION; *U.S. Private*, pg. 3452
RMH HOLDINGS LIMITED; *Int'l*, pg. 6357
RMH LACHISH INDUSTRIES LTD.; *Int'l*, pg. 6357
RMH SYSTEMS, INC.; *U.S. Private*, pg. 3452
RMIC COMPANIES, INC.—See Arch Capital Group Ltd.; *Int'l*, pg. 546
RMIC CORPORATION—See Old Republic International Corporation; *U.S. Public*, pg. 1569
RMIG AG—See RM Industrial Group A/S; *Int'l*, pg. 6356
RMIG AS—See RM Industrial Group A/S; *Int'l*, pg. 6356
RMIG BV—See RM Industrial Group A/S; *Int'l*, pg. 6356
RMIG GMBH—See RM Industrial Group A/S; *Int'l*, pg. 6356
RMIG LOCHBLECHE GMBH—See RM Industrial Group A/S; *Int'l*, pg. 6356
RMIG LTD.—See RM Industrial Group A/S; *Int'l*, pg. 6356
RMIG NOLD GMBH—See RM Industrial Group A/S; *Int'l*, pg. 6356
RMIG NV/SA—See RM Industrial Group A/S; *Int'l*, pg. 6356
RMIG PERFORACION, S.A.—See RM Industrial Group A/S; *Int'l*, pg. 6356
RMIG S.A.S.—See RM Industrial Group A/S; *Int'l*, pg. 6356
RMIG SP. Z O.O.—See RM Industrial Group A/S; *Int'l*, pg. 6356

RMIG SWEDEN AB—See RM Industrial Group A/S; *Int'l*, pg. 6356
RMI, LLC; *U.S. Private*, pg. 3452
RMI MARKETING & ADVERTISING; *U.S. Private*, pg. 3452
RM INDUSTRIAL GROUP A/S; *Int'l*, pg. 6356
R&M INDUSTRIES INC.; *U.S. Private*, pg. 3332
RM INFRASTRUCTURE INCOME PLC; *Int'l*, pg. 6356
RM INGENIERIE SAS—See Cegedim S.A.; *Int'l*, pg. 1390
R&M INTERNATIONAL GMBH; *Int'l*, pg. 6168
RMIS IMAGING SERVICES, INC.—See RadNet, Inc.; *U.S. Public*, pg. 1761
RMJM HILLIER GROUP, INC.—See Matthew Johnson Marshall Ltd.; *Int'l*, pg. 4731
RMJM HILLIER—See Matthew Johnson Marshall Ltd.; *Int'l*, pg. 4731
RMJM HONG KONG LIMITED—See Matthew Johnson Marshall Ltd.; *Int'l*, pg. 4731
RMJM LONDON LTD.—See Matthew Johnson Marshall Ltd.; *Int'l*, pg. 4731
RMJM LTD.—See Matthew Johnson Marshall Ltd.; *Int'l*, pg. 4731
RMJM MIDDLE EAST LIMITED—See Matthew Johnson Marshall Ltd.; *Int'l*, pg. 4731
RMJM SINGAPORE PTE. LTD.—See Matthew Johnson Marshall Ltd.; *Int'l*, pg. 4731
R.M. KERNER CO.; *U.S. Private*, pg. 3339
RMK HOLDINGS CORP.; *U.S. Private*, pg. 3452
RMK MARINE AS—See Koc Holding A.S.; *Int'l*, pg. 4224
RMK PROMET D.D. ZENICA; *Int'l*, pg. 6357
R&M KUHLLAGERBAU BIELEFELD GMBH—See Bilfinger SE; *Int'l*, pg. 1028
R&M KUHLLAGERBAU HOLDING GMBH—See Bilfinger SE; *Int'l*, pg. 1028
RML HEALTH PROVIDERS LIMITED PARTNERSHIP; *U.S. Private*, pg. 3452
RM LIFE SCIENCE CO., LTD.—See Solco Biomedical Co., Ltd.; *Int'l*, pg. 7071
RML - RESIDENCIA MEDICALIZADA DE LOURES, SGPS, S.A.—See Fosun International Limited; *Int'l*, pg. 2751
RM MART SDN. BHD.—See Bridgestone Corporation; *Int'l*, pg. 1160
R&M MATERIALS HANDLING INC.—See Konecranes Plc; *Int'l*, pg. 4252
RM MECHANICAL INC.; *U.S. Private*, pg. 3451
RMM GLOBAL, INC.—See MOLD-TEK Technologies Limited; *Int'l*, pg. 5021
RMO INC.; *U.S. Private*, pg. 3452
R. MONNET & CIE SA—See BKW AG; *Int'l*, pg. 1056
R.M. PALMER COMPANY; *U.S. Private*, pg. 3339
R.M. PARKS INCORPORATED; *U.S. Private*, pg. 3339
RM PERSONNEL INC.; *U.S. Private*, pg. 3451
RM PLC; *Int'l*, pg. 6356
R.M. PROPERTY CO., LTD.—See Industrial & Commercial Bank of China Limited; *Int'l*, pg. 3670
RMR ADVISORS LLC—See The RMR Group Inc.; *U.S. Public*, pg. 2126
RM RAILCARS LLC—See Interstate Commodities Inc.; *U.S. Private*, pg. 2124
RMR & ASSOCIATES, INC.; *U.S. Private*, pg. 3452
R&M REALTY INC.; *U.S. Private*, pg. 3332
THE RMR GROUP INC.; *U.S. Public*, pg. 2125
THE RMR GROUP LLC—See The RMR Group Inc.; *U.S. Public*, pg. 2126
R&M RICHARDS INC.; *U.S. Private*, pg. 3332
R&M ROMANIA—See R&M International GmbH; *Int'l*, pg. 6168
RMR PREFERRED INCOME FUND; *U.S. Private*, pg. 3452
RMR RADIOBETRIEBS UND BETEILIGUNGSGESELLSCHAFT MBH—See NRJ Group SA; *Int'l*, pg. 5474
RMR SCIENCE TECHNOLOGIES, INC.; *Int'l*, pg. 6357
RMS, A.S. KOSICE—See United States Steel Corporation; *U.S. Public*, pg. 2237
RMS CRANES INC.—See First Reserve Management, L.P.; *U.S. Private*, pg. 1526
RMS EQUIPMENT LLC—See The Heico Companies, L.L.C.; *U.S. Private*, pg. 4050
R&M SHIP INTERIOR AS—See Reichle & De-Massari AG; *Int'l*, pg. 6256
R&M SHIP TECHNOLOGIES GMBH—See R&M International GmbH; *Int'l*, pg. 6168
RMS HYDRAULIC SERVICES CO.—See Road Machinery & Supplies Company; *U.S. Private*, pg. 3453
RMS INTEGRATED SOLUTIONS LIMITED—See Westminster Group Plc; *Int'l*, pg. 8391
RMSI PRIVATE LIMITED—See Moody's Corporation; *U.S. Public*, pg. 1469
RMS LIFELINE, INC.—See DaVita Inc.; *U.S. Public*, pg. 642
RMS LTD.—See Moody's Corporation; *U.S. Public*, pg. 1469
RMS LTD.—See Mapal Communications Ltd.; *Int'l*, pg. 4681
RMS MEZZANINE, A.S.; *Int'l*, pg. 6357
RMS MORS SMITT—See Westinghouse Air Brake Technologies Corporation; *U.S. Public*, pg. 2359
RMS OMEGA TECHNOLOGIES GROUP, INC.; *U.S. Private*, pg. 3452

RM SOURCE, INC.—See Check Point Software Technologies Ltd.; *Int'l*, pg. 1459
RMSPUMPTOOLS LIMITED—See ChampionX Corporation; *U.S. Public*, pg. 478
RMS RENTALS COMPANY—See Road Machinery & Supplies Company; *U.S. Private*, pg. 3453
RMS SYSTEMS INC.—See PHX Energy Services Corp.; *Int'l*, pg. 5858
R.M. STARK & CO. INC.; *U.S. Private*, pg. 3339
RMS TITANIC INC—See Premier Exhibitions, Inc.; *U.S. Public*, pg. 1714
R.M. THORNTON, INC.—See Harris Companies; *U.S. Private*, pg. 1869
RMTS, LLC; *U.S. Private*, pg. 3452
RMU BANOVICI D.D.; *Int'l*, pg. 6357
RMU KAMENGRAD D.D. SANSKI MOST; *Int'l*, pg. 6357
RMV RHEIN-MOSEL VERKEHRSGESELLSCHAFT MBH—See Deutsche Bahn AG; *Int'l*, pg. 2052
R.M. WADE & CO.—See Arnold Machinery Company; *U.S. Private*, pg. 333
RMW ARCHITECTURE & INTERIORS; *U.S. Private*, pg. 3452
R&M WHOLESALE CO. INC.; *U.S. Private*, pg. 3332
R.M. WILLIAMS PTY. LTD.; *Int'l*, pg. 6170
RM WILSON CO. INC.; *U.S. Private*, pg. 3451
RN2 TECHNOLOGIES CO., LTD.; *Int'l*, pg. 6357
RNA-DAVITA DIALYSIS, LLC—See DaVita Inc.; *U.S. Public*, pg. 642
RNA, INC.; *U.S. Private*, pg. 3452
RN BETEILIGUNGS-GMBH I.L.—See Portigon AG; *Int'l*, pg. 5934
RNB INDUSTRIES LIMITED; *Int'l*, pg. 6357
RN-BURENIE LLC—See OJSC Rosneftegaz; *Int'l*, pg. 5541
RND AUTOMATION & ENGINEERING, LLC; *U.S. Private*, pg. 3452
RNDC ALLIANCE WEST AFRICA LIMITED—See Redington (India) Limited; *Int'l*, pg. 6247
R.N. EATON & COMPANY INC.; *U.S. Private*, pg. 3339
RN FIELD CONSTRUCTION INC.; *U.S. Private*, pg. 3452
RNI-DALBO—See Lincolnshire Management, Inc.; *U.S. Private*, pg. 2459
RN INDUSTRIES TRUCKING, INC.; *U.S. Private*, pg. 3452
RNI NEGOCIOS IMOBILIARIOS S.A.; *Int'l*, pg. 6357
RN-KAIGANNEFTEGAZ LLC—See OJSC Rosneftegaz; *Int'l*, pg. 5541
RNK GLOBAL DEVELOPMENT ACQUISITION CORP.; *Int'l*, pg. 6357
RNK INC.; *U.S. Private*, pg. 3452
R&N KNITTED; *U.S. Private*, pg. 3332
RNL & ASSOCIATES—See Berkshire Hills Bancorp, Inc.; *U.S. Public*, pg. 320
RNMC INC.; *U.S. Private*, pg. 3452
RNM DYNAMICS (PHILS) INC.—See Hanmi Semiconductor Co., Ltd.; *Int'l*, pg. 3256
RN-PURNEFTEGAZ LLC—See OJSC Rosneftegaz; *Int'l*, pg. 5541
RNR CONSULTING; *U.S. Private*, pg. 3453
RNR HOLIDAY RV INC.; *U.S. Private*, pg. 3453
R.N. ROUSE & CO. INC.—See Danis Building Construction Company Inc.; *U.S. Private*, pg. 1156
R. N. SPINNING MILLS LIMITED; *Int'l*, pg. 6169
RNY PROPERTY TRUST—See Aurora Funds Management Limited; *Int'l*, pg. 713
ROAD BUILDERS, LLC—See Sun Capital Partners, Inc.; *U.S. Private*, pg. 3861
ROAD BUILDERS MACHINERY & SUPPLY CO.; *U.S. Private*, pg. 3453
ROAD BUILDERS SINGAPORE PTE. LTD.—See Wei Yuan Holdings Limited; *Int'l*, pg. 8369
ROADCARE (M) SDN BHD—See Protasco Berhad; *Int'l*, pg. 6003
ROADCHEF MOTORWAYS LTD—See BNP Paribas SA; *Int'l*, pg. 1082
ROADCLIPPER ENTERPRISES INC.; *U.S. Private*, pg. 3453
ROADCRETE AFRICA (PTY) LIMITED—See Basil Read Holdings Limited; *Int'l*, pg. 887
ROAD ENVIRONMENT TECHNOLOGY CO., LTD.; *Int'l*, pg. 6357
ROAD & HIGHWAY BUILDERS LLC—See Sterling Infrastructure, Inc.; *U.S. Public*, pg. 1947
ROADHOUND ELECTRONICS PTY. LIMITED; *Int'l*, pg. 6357
ROADHOUSE GRILL ITALIA S.R.L.—See Cremonini S.p.A.; *Int'l*, pg. 1838
@ROAD, INC.—See Trimble, Inc.; *U.S. Public*, pg. 2192
ROAD INFRASTRUCTURE DEVELOPMENT COMPANY OF RAJASTHAN LIMITED—See Infrastructure Leasing & Financial Services Limited; *Int'l*, pg. 3698
ROAD INFRASTRUCTURE INVESTMENT HOLDINGS, INC.—See PPG Industries, Inc.; *U.S. Public*, pg. 1710
ROAD KING INFRASTRUCTURE LIMITED; *Int'l*, pg. 6357
ROAD LINK (A69) LIMITED—See Henry Boot PLC; *Int'l*, pg. 3355
ROAD MACHINERY COMPANY—See Mitsui & Co., Ltd.; *Int'l*, pg. 4975
ROAD MACHINERY & SUPPLIES COMPANY; *U.S. Private*, pg. 3453

ROADMAC (PTY) LIMITED—See Raubex Group Limited; *Int'l*, pg. 6221
ROADMAC SURFACING CAPE (PTY) LIMITED—See Raubex Group Limited; *Int'l*, pg. 6221
ROADMAC SURFACING (PTY) LTD.—See Raubex Group Limited; *Int'l*, pg. 6221
ROADMAINT CO., LTD.; *Int'l*, pg. 6357
ROADMAN INVESTMENTS CORP.; *Int'l*, pg. 6357
ROADMARK CORPORATION; *U.S. Private*, pg. 3453
ROAD MARSHALL, INC.; *Int'l*, pg. 6357
ROAD-MART INC.; *U.S. Private*, pg. 3453
ROADMASTER DRIVERS SCHOOL OF TAMPA, INC.—See Career Path Training Corp.; *U.S. Private*, pg. 752
ROADMASTER TRANSPORTATION, INC.—See Daseke, Inc.; *U.S. Private*, pg. 1161
ROADNET TECHNOLOGIES, INC.—See Vista Equity Partners, LLC; *U.S. Private*, pg. 4399
ROADPOST INC.; *Int'l*, pg. 6358
ROADPOST USA, INC.—See Roadpost Inc.; *Int'l*, pg. 6358
ROAD RESCUE USA, INC.—See AIP, LLC; *U.S. Private*, pg. 135
ROADRUNNER CARRIERS, LLC—See Roadrunner Transportation Systems, Inc.; *U.S. Public*, pg. 1802
ROADRUNNER INTERMODAL SERVICES, LLC—See Universal Logistics Holdings, Inc.; *U.S. Public*, pg. 2261
ROAD RUNNER MOVING & STORAGE INC.—See Wheaton Van Lines, Inc.; *U.S. Private*, pg. 4505
ROADRUNNER RECORDS INC.; *U.S. Private*, pg. 3453
ROADRUNNER STORAGE LLC—See Enel S.p.A.; *Int'l*, pg. 2414
ROADRUNNER SUNTOWER, LLC—See NRG Energy, Inc.; *U.S. Public*, pg. 1551
ROADRUNNER TRANSPORTATION SYSTEMS, INC.—See Roadrunner Transportation Systems, Inc.; *U.S. Public*, pg. 1802
ROADRUNNER TRANSPORTATION SYSTEMS, INC.; *U.S. Public*, pg. 1802
ROADSAFE TRAFFIC SYSTEMS, INC.—See Investcorp Holdings B.S.C.; *Int'l*, pg. 3776
ROADSAFE TRAFFIC SYSTEMS, INC.—See Trilantic Capital Management L.P.; *U.S. Private*, pg. 4231
ROAD SAFETY CONSULTING N.V.—See DEKRA e.V.; *Int'l*, pg. 2009
ROAD SAFETY OPERATIONS IRELAND LTD—See Groupe Egis S.A.; *Int'l*, pg. 3102
ROAD SCHOLAR TRANSPORT INC.; *U.S. Private*, pg. 3453
ROADSHOW BMW MINI; *U.S. Private*, pg. 3453
ROADSHOW CREATIONS LIMITED—See Xynomic Pharmaceuticals Holdings, Inc.; *Int'l*, pg. 8542
ROADSHOW FILMS PTY. LIMITED—See Village Roadshow Limited; *Int'l*, pg. 8206
ROADSHOW MEDIA HOLDINGS LTD.—See Xynomic Pharmaceuticals Holdings, Inc.; *Int'l*, pg. 8542
ROADSHOW MEDIA LTD.—See Xynomic Pharmaceuticals Holdings, Inc.; *Int'l*, pg. 8542
ROADSIDE REAL ESTATE PLC; *Int'l*, pg. 6358
ROADS NIGERIA PLC.; *Int'l*, pg. 6358
ROADSPAN SURFACES (PTY) LTD.—See Wilson Bayly Holmes-Ovcon Limited; *Int'l*, pg. 8423
ROADSTAR DEUTSCHLAND GMBH—See Harvard International Ltd.; *Int'l*, pg. 3280
ROADSTAR ITALIA SPA—See Harvard International Ltd.; *Int'l*, pg. 3280
ROADSTAR MANAGEMENT SA—See Harvard International Ltd.; *Int'l*, pg. 3280
ROADSTER AUTOMOTIVE BV—See ZF Friedrichshafen AG; *Int'l*, pg. 8645
ROADSTER, INC.—See Brookfield Corporation; *Int'l*, pg. 1175
THE ROADSTER SHOP; *U.S. Private*, pg. 4111
ROADSTONE LIMITED—See CRH plc; *Int'l*, pg. 1848
ROAD SURFACES GROUP PTY LTD—See Seven Group Holdings Limited; *Int'l*, pg. 6732
ROADTEC, INC.—See Astec Industries, Inc.; *U.S. Public*, pg. 216
ROAD & TRACK—See The Hearst Corporation; *U.S. Private*, pg. 4046
ROADVISION HOLDINGS (CHINA) LIMITED—See Xynomic Pharmaceuticals Holdings, Inc.; *Int'l*, pg. 8542
ROADWAY MANAGEMENT, INC.—See VINCI S.A.; *Int'l*, pg. 8220
ROADWAY REVERSE LOGISTICS, INC.—See Yellow Corporation; *U.S. Public*, pg. 2398
ROADWORKS MANUFACTURING, INC.—See CCMP Capital Advisors, LP; *U.S. Private*, pg. 801
ROADWORKS MANUFACTURING, INC.—See TA Associates, Inc.; *U.S. Private*, pg. 3919
ROADZEN ASSISTANCE INDIA PRIVATE LIMITED—See Roadzen Technologies Private Limited; *Int'l*, pg. 6358
ROADZEN, INC.; *U.S. Public*, pg. 1802
ROADZEN TECHNOLOGIES PRIVATE LIMITED; *Int'l*, pg. 6358
ROAM1 TELECOM LTD.—See Virtualsoft Systems Ltd.; *Int'l*, pg. 8248
ROANE HOMECARE, LLC—See UnitedHealth Group Incorporated; *U.S. Public*, pg. 2247
ROANE MEDICAL CENTER; *U.S. Private*, pg. 3453

ROAN HOLDINGS GROUP CO., LTD.; *Int'l*, pg. 6358
ROANKABIN MANUFACTURING LIMITED—See Siteserv Investments Limited; *Int'l*, pg. 6964
ROANKABIN SALES & MARKETING LIMITED—See Siteserv Investments Limited; *Int'l*, pg. 6965
THE ROANOKE COMPANIES INC.—See Munchener Ruckversicherungs AG; *Int'l*, pg. 5092
ROANOKE ELECTRIC MEMBERSHIP; *U.S. Private*, pg. 3453
ROANOKE GAS COMPANY—See RGC Resources, Inc.; *U.S. Public*, pg. 1796
ROANOKE INSURANCE GROUP CANADA INC.—See Munchener Ruckversicherungs AG; *Int'l*, pg. 5091
ROANOKE INSURANCE GROUP INC.—See Munchener Ruckversicherungs AG; *Int'l*, pg. 5091
ROANOKE INTERNATIONAL BROKERS LIMITED—See Munchener Ruckversicherungs AG; *Int'l*, pg. 5091
ROANOKE INTERNATIONAL INSURANCE AGENCY INC.—See Munchener Ruckversicherungs AG; *Int'l*, pg. 5091
ROANOKE RAPIDS SAVINGS BANK, SSB; *U.S. Private*, pg. 3453
ROANOKE SURGERY CENTER, L.P.—See HCA Healthcare, Inc.; *U.S. Public*, pg. 1007
ROANOKE TELEPHONE COMPANY, INC.—See Telephone Electronics Corporation; *U.S. Private*, pg. 3961
THE ROANOKE TIMES—See Irish Times; *U.S. Private*, pg. 2139
ROANOKE TRADE SERVICES INC.; *U.S. Private*, pg. 3453
ROANWELL CORP. - ABSOLUTE MANUFACTURING DIVISION—See Roanwell Corporation; *U.S. Private*, pg. 3454
ROANWELL CORPORATION; *U.S. Private*, pg. 3453
ROAR.COM PTY LIMITED—See Enero Group Limited; *Int'l*, pg. 2424
ROARING LLC—See Fitzpatrick Companies Inc.; *U.S. Private*, pg. 1536
ROARK CAPITAL GROUP INC.; *U.S. Private*, pg. 3454
ROARK CAPITAL MANAGEMENT, LLC—See Roark Capital Group Inc.; *U.S. Private*, pg. 3455
ROAR MEDIA LLC; *U.S. Private*, pg. 3454
ROASTERS ASIA PACIFIC (M) SDN BHD—See Berjaya Corporation Berhad; *Int'l*, pg. 984
ROBALLO ENGINEERING CO. LTD.—See ThyssenKrupp AG; *Int'l*, pg. 7731
ROBALLO FRANCE S.A.R.L.—See ThyssenKrupp AG; *Int'l*, pg. 7731
ROBAM APPLIANCES PVT. LTD.—See Hangzhou Robam Appliances Co., Ltd.; *Int'l*, pg. 3250
ROBAM MALAYSIA SDN BHD—See Hangzhou Robam Appliances Co., Ltd.; *Int'l*, pg. 3250
ROBANDA INTERNATIONAL, INC.; *U.S. Private*, pg. 3456
ROBAPHARM A.G.—See Pierre Fabre S.A.; *Int'l*, pg. 5864
ROBAR ENTERPRISES INC.; *U.S. Private*, pg. 3456
ROBASCIOTTI & ASSOCIATES, INC.—See Abacus Wealth Partners, LLC; *U.S. Private*, pg. 34
ROBATEL, INC.—See ROUSSELET Centrifugation SA; *Int'l*, pg. 6407
ROBATEL UK LTD.—See ROUSSELET Centrifugation SA; *Int'l*, pg. 6407
ROBBI DAVIS AGENCY INC.—See Arthur J. Gallagher & Co.; *U.S. Public*, pg. 207
ROBBIE D. WOOD INC.; *U.S. Private*, pg. 3456
ROBBINS 8TH & WALNUT; *U.S. Private*, pg. 3456
ROBBINS (ASIA PACIFIC), LTD.—See Northern Heavy Industries Group Co. Ltd.; *Int'l*, pg. 5443
ROBBINS ASIA PACIFIC PTE LTD—See Northern Heavy Industries Group Co. Ltd.; *Int'l*, pg. 5443
ROBBINS ASIA PACIFIC PTY LTD.—See Northern Heavy Industries Group Co. Ltd.; *Int'l*, pg. 5443
ROBBINS AUTO PARTS, INC.; *U.S. Private*, pg. 3456
ROBBINS BRICK & BLOCK INC.; *U.S. Private*, pg. 3456
ROBBINS BROTHERS; *U.S. Private*, pg. 3456
ROBBINS CHILE & ROBBINS BRAZIL—See Northern Heavy Industries Group Co. Ltd.; *Int'l*, pg. 5443
ROBBINS (CHINA) UNDERGROUND EQUIPMENT CO., LTD.—See Northern Heavy Industries Group Co. Ltd.; *Int'l*, pg. 5443
THE ROBBINS COMPANY—See Northern Heavy Industries Group Co. Ltd.; *Int'l*, pg. 5443
THE ROBBINS COMPANY - WASHINGTON FACILITY—See Northern Heavy Industries Group Co. Ltd.; *Int'l*, pg. 5443
ROBBINS DIAMONDS; *U.S. Private*, pg. 3456
ROBBINS EUROPE GMBH—See Northern Heavy Industries Group Co. Ltd.; *Int'l*, pg. 5443
ROBBINS-GIOIA INC.—See Informa plc; *Int'l*, pg. 3692
ROBBINS HISPANIA S.L.—See Northern Heavy Industries Group Co. Ltd.; *Int'l*, pg. 5443
ROBBINS, INC.—See L2 Capital Partners; *U.S. Private*, pg. 2367
ROBBINS LLC—See HEXPOL AB; *Int'l*, pg. 3372
ROBBINS MANUFACTURING COMPANY; *U.S. Private*, pg. 3457
ROBBINS MEXICO—See Northern Heavy Industries Group Co. Ltd.; *Int'l*, pg. 5443

ROBBINS MANUFACTURING COMPANY

ROBBINS NORWAY—See Northern Heavy Industries Group Co. Ltd.; *Int'l*, pg. 5443
ROBBINS PARKING SERVICE; *Int'l*, pg. 6358
ROBBINS PROPERTY ASSOCIATES, LLC—See Elco Limited; *Int'l*, pg. 2345
ROBBINS RESEARCH INTERNATIONAL; *U.S. Private*, pg. 3457
ROBBINS TBM KOREA—See Northern Heavy Industries Group Co. Ltd.; *Int'l*, pg. 5443
ROBBINS TUNNELING AND TRENCHLESS TECHNOLOGY (INDIA) PVT. LTD.—See Northern Heavy Industries Group Co. Ltd.; *Int'l*, pg. 5443
ROBB REPORT - NEW YORK—See RockBridge Growth Equity, LLC; *U.S. Private*, pg. 3465
ROBB & STUCKY INTERNATIONAL; *U.S. Private*, pg. 3456
ROBCO, INC.; *U.S. Private*, pg. 3457
ROBCO MADEIRAS LTDA.—See Robinson Lumber & Export Company; *U.S. Private*, pg. 3462
ROBECO INSTITUTIONAL ASSET MANAGEMENT B.V.—See ORIX Corporation; *Int'l*, pg. 5636
ROBECO INVESTMENT MANAGEMENT, INC. - BOSTON—See ORIX Corporation; *Int'l*, pg. 5634
ROBECO INVESTMENT MANAGEMENT, INC.—See ORIX Corporation; *Int'l*, pg. 5634
ROBECO NEDERLAND B.V.—See ORIX Corporation; *Int'l*, pg. 5635
ROBECOSAM AG—See ORIX Corporation; *Int'l*, pg. 5635
ROBECO SECURITIES, LLC—See ORIX Corporation; *Int'l*, pg. 5634
ROBEKS CORPORATION; *U.S. Private*, pg. 3457
ROBELLE INDUSTRIES INC.; *U.S. Private*, pg. 3457
ROBERINE B.V.—See Alamo Group Inc.; *U.S. Public*, pg. 71
ROBE RIVER MINING CO. PTY. LTD.—See Rio Tinto plc; *Int'l*, pg. 6347
ROBERN, INC.—See Kohler Company; *U.S. Private*, pg. 2340
ROBERSON MOTORS INC.; *U.S. Private*, pg. 3457
ROBERT ABBEY INC.; *U.S. Private*, pg. 3457
ROBERT AEBI AG—See SKion GmbH; *Int'l*, pg. 6987
ROBERT ALAN AGENCY, INC.—See Kelso & Company, L.P.; *U.S. Private*, pg. 2280
THE ROBERT ALLEN GROUP, INC.—See Decor Holdings, Inc.; *U.S. Private*, pg. 1187
ROBERT A. SHERMAN & ASSOCIATES, INC.; *U.S. Private*, pg. 3457
ROBERT B. AIKENS & ASSOCIATES, LLC; *U.S. Private*, pg. 3457
THE ROBERT BAKER COMPANIES; *U.S. Private*, pg. 4111
ROBERT BAKER, INC.—See The Robert Baker Companies; *U.S. Private*, pg. 4111
ROBERT BARE ASSOCIATES; *U.S. Private*, pg. 3457
ROBERT BELL INSURANCE BROKERS, INC.—See GCP Capital Partners Holdings LLC; *U.S. Private*, pg. 1654
ROBERT BERBER & SON INCORPORATED; *U.S. Private*, pg. 3457
ROBERT BERNARD PNEUS ET MECANIQUE; *Int'l*, pg. 6358
ROBERT BIGGAR (ESTD. 1830) LIMITED—See Lone Star Global Acquisitions, LLC; *U.S. Private*, pg. 2487
ROBERT BOSCH AB—See Robert Bosch GmbH; *Int'l*, pg. 6362
ROBERT BOSCH AG—See Robert Bosch GmbH; *Int'l*, pg. 6362
ROBERT BOSCH AG—See Robert Bosch GmbH; *Int'l*, pg. 6362
ROBERT BOSCH ARGENTINA INDUSTRIAL S.A.—See Robert Bosch GmbH; *Int'l*, pg. 6362
ROBERT BOSCH AS—See Robert Bosch GmbH; *Int'l*, pg. 6362
ROBERT BOSCH A/S—See Robert Bosch GmbH; *Int'l*, pg. 6362
ROBERT BOSCH (AUSTRALIA) PTY LTD.—See Robert Bosch GmbH; *Int'l*, pg. 6361
ROBERT BOSCH AUTOMOTIVE STEERING GMBH—See Robert Bosch GmbH; *Int'l*, pg. 6362
ROBERT BOSCH AUTOMOTIVE STEERING KFT.—See Robert Bosch GmbH; *Int'l*, pg. 6362
ROBERT BOSCH AUTOMOTIVE TECHNOLOGIES (THAILAND) CO., LTD.—See Robert Bosch GmbH; *Int'l*, pg. 6362
ROBERT BOSCH AUTOMOTIVE TECHNOLOGY GROUP—See Robert Bosch GmbH; *Int'l*, pg. 6362
ROBERT BOSCH BATTERY SOLUTIONS GMBH—See Robert Bosch GmbH; *Int'l*, pg. 6363
ROBERT BOSCH BATTERY SYSTEMS GMBH—See Robert Bosch GmbH; *Int'l*, pg. 6363
ROBERT BOSCH BATTERY SYSTEMS LLC—See Robert Bosch GmbH; *Int'l*, pg. 6367
ROBERT BOSCH B.V.—See Robert Bosch GmbH; *Int'l*, pg. 6363
ROBERT BOSCH (CAMBODIA) CO., LTD.—See Robert Bosch GmbH; *Int'l*, pg. 6361
ROBERT BOSCH CAR MULTIMEDIA GMBH—See Robert Bosch GmbH; *Int'l*, pg. 6363

ROBERT BOSCH CONSUMER GOODS & BUILDING TECHNOLOGY GROUP—See Robert Bosch GmbH; *Int'l*, pg. 6363
ROBERT BOSCH CZ S.R.O.—See Robert Bosch GmbH; *Int'l*, pg. 6363
ROBERT BOSCH DOO—See Robert Bosch GmbH; *Int'l*, pg. 6364
ROBERT BOSCH D.O.O.—See Robert Bosch GmbH; *Int'l*, pg. 6367
ROBERT BOSCH EAST AFRICA LTD.—See Robert Bosch GmbH; *Int'l*, pg. 6364
ROBERT BOSCH ELEKTRONIKA GYARTO KFT.—See Robert Bosch GmbH; *Int'l*, pg. 6365
ROBERT BOSCH ELEKTRONIK GMBH—See Robert Bosch GmbH; *Int'l*, pg. 6364
ROBERT BOSCH ELEKTRONIK THURINGEN GMBH—See Robert Bosch GmbH; *Int'l*, pg. 6365
ROBERT BOSCH ELEKTROWERKZEUGE GMBH—See Robert Bosch GmbH; *Int'l*, pg. 6362
ROBERT BOSCH ENERGY AND BODY SYSTEMS KFT.—See Robert Bosch GmbH; *Int'l*, pg. 6365
ROBERT BOSCH ENGINEERING AND BUSINESS SOLUTIONS LTD.—See Robert Bosch GmbH; *Int'l*, pg. 6365
ROBERT BOSCH ENGINEERING AND BUSINESS SOLUTIONS VIETNAM CO. LTD.—See Robert Bosch GmbH; *Int'l*, pg. 6365
ROBERT BOSCH EOOD—See Robert Bosch GmbH; *Int'l*, pg. 6364
ROBERT BOSCH ESPANA FABRICA MADRID S.A.—See Robert Bosch GmbH; *Int'l*, pg. 6361
ROBERT BOSCH ESPANA FABRICA TRETO S.A.—See Robert Bosch GmbH; *Int'l*, pg. 6361
ROBERT BOSCH (FRANCE) SAS—See Robert Bosch GmbH; *Int'l*, pg. 6362
ROBERT BOSCH FUEL SYSTEMS—See Robert Bosch GmbH; *Int'l*, pg. 6363
ROBERT BOSCH GHANA LTD.—See Robert Bosch GmbH; *Int'l*, pg. 6365
ROBERT BOSCH GMBH AUTOMOTIVE AFTERMARKET DIVISION—See Robert Bosch GmbH; *Int'l*, pg. 6363
ROBERT BOSCH GMBH; *Int'l*, pg. 6358
ROBERT BOSCH HAUSGERATE GMBH—See Robert Bosch GmbH; *Int'l*, pg. 6363
ROBERT BOSCH HEALTHCARE, INC.—See Robert Bosch GmbH; *Int'l*, pg. 6367
ROBERT BOSCH IMMOBILIENVERWALTUNGS GMBH & CO. KG—See Robert Bosch GmbH; *Int'l*, pg. 6365
ROBERT BOSCH INC.—See Robert Bosch GmbH; *Int'l*, pg. 6365
ROBERT BOSCH INC.—See Robert Bosch GmbH; *Int'l*, pg. 6365
ROBERT BOSCH INDUSTRIAL TECHNOLOGY GROUP—See Robert Bosch GmbH; *Int'l*, pg. 6365
ROBERT BOSCH INTERNATIONALE BETEILIGUNGEN AG—See Robert Bosch GmbH; *Int'l*, pg. 6366
ROBERT BOSCH KOREA LTD.—See Robert Bosch GmbH; *Int'l*, pg. 6366
ROBERT BOSCH LANKA (PVT.) LTD.—See Robert Bosch GmbH; *Int'l*, pg. 6367
ROBERT BOSCH, LIMITADA—See Robert Bosch GmbH; *Int'l*, pg. 6367
ROBERT BOSCH LIMITED—See Robert Bosch GmbH; *Int'l*, pg. 6367
ROBERT BOSCH LIZENZVERWALTUNGSGESELLSCHAFT MBH—See Robert Bosch GmbH; *Int'l*, pg. 6367
ROBERT BOSCH LLC - AUTOMOTIVE AFTERMARKET DIVISION—See Robert Bosch GmbH; *Int'l*, pg. 6363
ROBERT BOSCH LLC - AUTOMOTIVE DIVISION—See Robert Bosch GmbH; *Int'l*, pg. 6363
ROBERT BOSCH LLC RESEARCH AND TECHNOLOGY CENTER NORTH AMERICA—See Robert Bosch GmbH; *Int'l*, pg. 6363
ROBERT BOSCH LLC—See Robert Bosch GmbH; *Int'l*, pg. 6366
ROBERT BOSCH LOLLAR GUSS GMBH—See Robert Bosch GmbH; *Int'l*, pg. 6367
ROBERT BOSCH LTDA—See Robert Bosch GmbH; *Int'l*, pg. 6367
ROBERT BOSCH LTDA.—See Robert Bosch GmbH; *Int'l*, pg. 6367
ROBERT BOSCH LTD.—See Robert Bosch GmbH; *Int'l*, pg. 6367
ROBERT BOSCH LTD.—See Robert Bosch GmbH; *Int'l*, pg. 6367
ROBERT BOSCH LTD.—See Robert Bosch GmbH; *Int'l*, pg. 6367
ROBERT BOSCH (MALAYSIA) SDN. BHD.—See Robert Bosch GmbH; *Int'l*, pg. 6361
ROBERT BOSCH MEXICO SISTEMAS AUTOMOTRICES, S.A. DE C.V.—See Robert Bosch GmbH; *Int'l*, pg. 6367
ROBERT BOSCH MIDDLE EAST FZE—See Robert Bosch GmbH; *Int'l*, pg. 6367
ROBERT BOSCH MOTORLU ARACLAR YAN SANAYI VE TICARET AS—See Robert Bosch GmbH; *Int'l*, pg. 6367
ROBERT BOSCH N.V.—See Robert Bosch GmbH; *Int'l*, pg. 6367

CORPORATE AFFILIATIONS

ROBERT BOSCH OU—See Robert Bosch GmbH; *Int'l*, pg. 6367
ROBERT BOSCH OY—See Robert Bosch GmbH; *Int'l*, pg. 6367
ROBERT BOSCH PACKAGING TECHNOLOGY B.V.—See Robert Bosch GmbH; *Int'l*, pg. 6367
ROBERT BOSCH PANAMA S.A.—See Robert Bosch GmbH; *Int'l*, pg. 6367
ROBERT BOSCH POWER TOOLS DIVISION—See Robert Bosch GmbH; *Int'l*, pg. 6364
ROBERT BOSCH POWER TOOLS SDN. BHD.—See Robert Bosch GmbH; *Int'l*, pg. 6361
ROBERT BOSCH PRODUCTION N.V.—See Robert Bosch GmbH; *Int'l*, pg. 6367
ROBERT BOSCH (PTY) LTD.—See Robert Bosch GmbH; *Int'l*, pg. 6362
ROBERT BOSCH S.A.C.—See Robert Bosch GmbH; *Int'l*, pg. 6367
ROBERT BOSCH, S.A. DE C.V.—See Robert Bosch GmbH; *Int'l*, pg. 6368
ROBERT BOSCH S.A.—See Robert Bosch GmbH; *Int'l*, pg. 6367
ROBERT BOSCH S.A.—See Robert Bosch GmbH; *Int'l*, pg. 6367
ROBERT BOSCH S.A.—See Robert Bosch GmbH; *Int'l*, pg. 6367
ROBERT BOSCH S.A.—See Robert Bosch GmbH; *Int'l*, pg. 6367
ROBERT BOSCH SA—See Robert Bosch GmbH; *Int'l*, pg. 6367
ROBERT BOSCH, S. DE R.L. DE C.V.—See Robert Bosch GmbH; *Int'l*, pg. 6367
ROBERT BOSCH SDN. BHD.—See Robert Bosch GmbH; *Int'l*, pg. 6367
ROBERT BOSCH SEMICONDUCTOR LLC—See Robert Bosch GmbH; *Int'l*, pg. 6367
ROBERT BOSCH SERVICE SOLUTIONS - COSTA RICA, S.A.—See Robert Bosch GmbH; *Int'l*, pg. 6367
ROBERT BOSCH SIA—See Robert Bosch GmbH; *Int'l*, pg. 6367
ROBERT BOSCH SISTEMAS AUTOMOTRICES, S.A. DE C.V.—See Robert Bosch GmbH; *Int'l*, pg. 6367
ROBERT BOSCH (SOUTH EAST ASIA) PTE. LTD.—See Robert Bosch GmbH; *Int'l*, pg. 6362
ROBERT BOSCH S.P.A. SOCIETA UNIPERSONALE—See Robert Bosch GmbH; *Int'l*, pg. 6361
ROBERT BOSCH SPOL. S.R.O.—See Robert Bosch GmbH; *Int'l*, pg. 6367
ROBERT BOSCH, SPOL. S.R.O.—See Robert Bosch GmbH; *Int'l*, pg. 6368
ROBERT BOSCH SP. Z O.O.—See Robert Bosch GmbH; *Int'l*, pg. 6361
ROBERT BOSCH S.R.L.—See Robert Bosch GmbH; *Int'l*, pg. 6361
ROBERT BOSCH START-UP GMBH—See Robert Bosch GmbH; *Int'l*, pg. 6367
ROBERT BOSCH TAIWAN CO., LTD.—See Robert Bosch GmbH; *Int'l*, pg. 6367
ROBERT BOSCH TECNOLOGIA DE EMBALAGEM LTDA.—See CVC Capital Partners SICAV-FIS S.A.; *Int'l*, pg. 1884
ROBERT BOSCH TOOL CORPORATION - CANADA OFFICE—See Robert Bosch GmbH; *Int'l*, pg. 6364
ROBERT BOSCH TOOL CORPORATION-GREENVILLE—See Robert Bosch GmbH; *Int'l*, pg. 6364
ROBERT BOSCH TOOL CORPORATION-LINCOLNTON—See Robert Bosch GmbH; *Int'l*, pg. 6364
ROBERT BOSCH TOOL CORPORATION—See Robert Bosch GmbH; *Int'l*, pg. 6364
ROBERT BOSCH UNIPESSOAL, LDA.—See Robert Bosch GmbH; *Int'l*, pg. 6367
ROBERT BOSCH URUGUAY S.A.—See Robert Bosch GmbH; *Int'l*, pg. 6367
ROBERT BOWDEN INC.; *U.S. Private*, pg. 3457
ROBERT B. SOLOMON HOLDING COMPANY, INC.; *U.S. Private*, pg. 3457
ROBERT BUGATTO ENTERPRISES, INC.; *U.S. Private*, pg. 3457
ROBERT CARRIERES ET INDUSTRIES SAS—See VINCI S.A.; *Int'l*, pg. 8226
ROBERT COWEN INVESTMENT PROPRIETARY LIMITED—See Anchor Group Limited; *Int'l*, pg. 448
ROBERT C. RHEIN INTERESTS INC.; *U.S. Private*, pg. 3457
ROBERT DIETRICK CO. INC.; *U.S. Private*, pg. 3457
ROBERT E. LAMB, INC.; *U.S. Private*, pg. 3457
ROBERT E. LEE & ASSOCIATES, INC.; *U.S. Private*, pg. 3457
THE ROBERT E. MORRIS COMPANY—See Morris Group, Inc.; *U.S. Private*, pg. 2787
ROBERTET ANDINA SAS—See Robertet S.A.; *Int'l*, pg. 6369
ROBERTET ARGENTINA S.A.—See Robertet S.A.; *Int'l*, pg. 6369
ROBERTET ASIA PTE. LTD.—See Robertet S.A.; *Int'l*, pg. 6369

COMPANY NAME INDEX

ROBERTET DE MEXICO, S.A. DE C.V.—See Robertet S.A.; *Int'l*, pg. 6369
ROBERTET DO BRASIL IND. E COM. LTDA.—See Robertet S.A.; *Int'l*, pg. 6370
ROBERTET ESPANA SA—See Robertet S.A.; *Int'l*, pg. 6369
ROBERTET ET CIE SA—See Robertet S.A.; *Int'l*, pg. 6370
ROBERTET FLAVORS—See Robertet S.A.; *Int'l*, pg. 6370
ROBERTET FLAVOURS & FRAGRANCES INDIA PVT. LTD.—See Robertet S.A.; *Int'l*, pg. 6369
ROBERTET FRAGRANCE, INC.—See Robertet S.A.; *Int'l*, pg. 6369
ROBERTET FRAGRANCES AND INGREDIENTS—See Robertet S.A.; *Int'l*, pg. 6369
ROBERTET GMBH—See Robertet S.A.; *Int'l*, pg. 6369
ROBERTET HIYOKI LTD.—See Robertet S.A.; *Int'l*, pg. 6369
ROBERTET, INC.—See Robertet S.A.; *Int'l*, pg. 6370
ROBERTET INDIA PRIVATE LIMITED—See Robertet S.A.; *Int'l*, pg. 6369
ROBERTET ITALIA SRL—See Robertet S.A.; *Int'l*, pg. 6370
ROBERTET S.A.; *Int'l*, pg. 6369
ROBERTET S.A.—See Robertet S.A.; *Int'l*, pg. 6370
ROBERTET SOUTH AFRICA AROMATICS LTD.—See Robertet S.A.; *Int'l*, pg. 6370
ROBERTET UK LTD.—See Robertet S.A.; *Int'l*, pg. 6370
ROBERT FAWCETT & SON CO. INC.; *U.S. Private*, pg. 3457
ROBERT FERRILLI, LLC; *U.S. Private*, pg. 3457
ROBERT F. HENRY TILE COMPANY; *U.S. Private*, pg. 3457
ROBERT FINVARB COMPANIES, LLC; *U.S. Private*, pg. 3458
ROBERT F. KENNEDY CHILDREN'S ACTION CORPS; *U.S. Private*, pg. 3457
ROBERT F. KENNEDY MEDICAL CENTER—See Daughters of Charity Health System; *U.S. Private*, pg. 1167
ROBERT FLEEGE & PARTNERS; *U.S. Private*, pg. 3458
ROBERT FLEMING HOLDINGS LIMITED—See JPMorgan Chase & Co.; *U.S. Public*, pg. 1210
ROBERT FORBIS INC.; *U.S. Private*, pg. 3458
ROBERT FOX INC.; *U.S. Private*, pg. 3458
ROBERT GIBB & SONS, INC.; *U.S. Private*, pg. 3458
ROBERT GRAHAM DESIGNS LLC—See Tengram Capital Partners, Limited Partnership; *U.S. Private*, pg. 3967
ROBERT GREEN AUTO & TRUCK, INC.; *U.S. Private*, pg. 3458
ROBERT HALF ASSESSORIA EM RECURSOS HUMANOS LTDA.—See Robert Half Inc.; *U.S. Public*, pg. 1803
ROBERT HALF AUSTRALIA PTY. LTD.—See Robert Half Inc.; *U.S. Public*, pg. 1803
ROBERT HALF AUSTRIA GMBH—See Robert Half Inc.; *U.S. Public*, pg. 1803
ROBERT HALF BVBA—See Robert Half Inc.; *U.S. Public*, pg. 1803
ROBERT HALF CANADA INC.—See Robert Half Inc.; *U.S. Public*, pg. 1803
ROBERT HALF CONSULTING SERVICES BVBA—See Robert Half Inc.; *U.S. Public*, pg. 1803
ROBERT HALF CORPORATION - ACCOUNTEMPS DIVISION—See Robert Half Inc.; *U.S. Public*, pg. 1803
ROBERT HALF CORPORATION - FINANCE & ACCOUNTING DIVISION—See Robert Half Inc.; *U.S. Public*, pg. 1803
ROBERT HALF CORPORATION - LEGAL DIVISION—See Robert Half Inc.; *U.S. Public*, pg. 1803
ROBERT HALF CORPORATION - MANAGEMENT RESOURCES DIVISION—See Robert Half Inc.; *U.S. Public*, pg. 1803
ROBERT HALF CORPORATION - OFFICETEAM DIVISION—See Robert Half Inc.; *U.S. Public*, pg. 1803
ROBERT HALF CORPORATION—See Robert Half Inc.; *U.S. Public*, pg. 1803
ROBERT HALF CORPORATION - TECHNOLOGY DIVISION—See Robert Half Inc.; *U.S. Public*, pg. 1803
ROBERT HALF CORPORATION - THE CREATIVE GROUP DIVISION—See Robert Half Inc.; *U.S. Public*, pg. 1803
ROBERT HALF DEUTSCHLAND BETEILIGUNGSGESELLSCHAFT GMBH—See Robert Half Inc.; *U.S. Public*, pg. 1803
ROBERT HALF HONG KONG LIMITED—See Robert Half Inc.; *U.S. Public*, pg. 1803
ROBERT HALF HUMAN RESOURCES SHANGHAI COMPANY LIMITED—See Robert Half Inc.; *U.S. Public*, pg. 1804
ROBERT HALF INC.; *U.S. Public*, pg. 1802
ROBERT HALF INTERNATIONAL B.V.—See Robert Half Inc.; *U.S. Public*, pg. 1804
ROBERT HALF INTERNATIONAL (DUBAI) LTD.—See Robert Half Inc.; *U.S. Public*, pg. 1804
ROBERT HALF INTERNATIONAL IRELAND LIMITED—See Robert Half Inc.; *U.S. Public*, pg. 1804
ROBERT HALF INTERNATIONAL PTE. LTD.—See Robert Half Inc.; *U.S. Public*, pg. 1804
ROBERT HALF INTERNATIONAL S.A./N.V.—See Robert Half Inc.; *U.S. Public*, pg. 1804
ROBERT HALF JAPAN LTD.—See Robert Half Inc.; *U.S. Public*, pg. 1804
ROBERT HALF LIMITED—See Robert Half Inc.; *U.S. Public*, pg. 1804
ROBERT HALF NEDERLAND B.V.—See Robert Half Inc.; *U.S. Public*, pg. 1804
ROBERT HALF SARL—See Robert Half Inc.; *U.S. Public*, pg. 1804
ROBERT HALF S.R.L.—See Robert Half Inc.; *U.S. Public*, pg. 1804
ROBERT HORNE GROUP LIMITED—See KPP Group Holdings Co., Ltd.; *Int'l*, pg. 4298
ROBERT HORNE PAPER CO.—See KPP Group Holdings Co., Ltd.; *Int'l*, pg. 4298
ROBERT HORNE PAPER (IRELAND) LIMITED—See KPP Group Holdings Co., Ltd.; *Int'l*, pg. 4298
ROBERT HORNE PAPER (SCOTLAND) LIMITED—See KPP Group Holdings Co., Ltd.; *Int'l*, pg. 4298
ROBERT H. VOGEL ENGINEERING, INC.—See Timmons Group, Inc.; *U.S. Private*, pg. 4173
ROBERT JAMES SALES INC.; *U.S. Private*, pg. 3458
ROBERT J. BERNS ADVERTISING LTD.; *U.S. Private*, pg. 3458
ROBERT J. YOUNG COMPANY, LLC; *U.S. Private*, pg. 3458
ROBERT KARP CONTAINER CORP; *U.S. Private*, pg. 3458
ROBERT KAUFMAN CO. INC.; *U.S. Private*, pg. 3458
ROBERT KENNEDY PUBLISHING; *Int'l*, pg. 6368
ROBERT KRAEMER GMBH & CO. KG; *Int'l*, pg. 6368
ROBERT LARSON AUTOMOTIVE GROUP; *U.S. Private*, pg. 3458
ROBERT L. HANSON INC.; *U.S. Private*, pg. 3458
ROBERT L. HENDRICKS FUNERAL HOME, INC.—See Service Corporation International; *U.S. Public*, pg. 1870
ROBERT LIGHTON FURNITURE, INC.; *U.S. Private*, pg. 3458
ROBERT LLOYD SHEET METAL INC.; *U.S. Private*, pg. 3458
ROBERT MADDEN INDUSTRIES; *U.S. Private*, pg. 3458
ROBERT MANN PACKAGING, INC.; *U.S. Private*, pg. 3458
ROBERT MCBRIDE LIMITED—See McBride plc; *Int'l*, pg. 4756
ROBERT MCKEOWN CO. INC.; *U.S. Private*, pg. 3458
ROBERT M. GOFF & ASSOCIATES; *U.S. Private*, pg. 3458
ROBERT M. NEFF INC.; *U.S. Private*, pg. 3458
ROBERT MONDAVI WINERY—See Constellation Brands, Inc.; *U.S. Public*, pg. 570
ROBERT MORRIS EXPERIENTIAL COLLEGE—See Roosevelt University; *U.S. Private*, pg. 3480
ROBERT MOTORS; *Int'l*, pg. 6368
ROBERT M. SIDES INC.; *U.S. Private*, pg. 3458
ROBERT N. KARPP CO. INC.—See GMS Inc.; *U.S. Public*, pg. 948
ROBERTO CAVALLI S.P.A.—See DAMAC Group; *Int'l*, pg. 1955
ROBERTO COIN S.P.A.; *Int'l*, pg. 6370
ROBERTO DELFINO & CO.—See Windmoeller & Hoelscher KG; *Int'l*, pg. 8426
ROBERT ORR-SYSCO FOOD SERVICES, LLC—See Sysco Corporation; *U.S. Public*, pg. 1975
ROBERT PAUL PROPERTIES, INC.—See Berkshire Hathaway Inc.; *U.S. Public*, pg. 304
ROBERT REID WEDDING ARCHITECTS & PLANNERS, AIA, INC.; *U.S. Private*, pg. 3459
ROBERT REISER & COMPANY INC.; *U.S. Private*, pg. 3459
ROBERT R. MCCORMICK FOUNDATION; *U.S. Private*, pg. 3458
ROBERT ROBERTS LIMITED—See DCC plc; *Int'l*, pg. 1991
ROBERT ROHLINGER GMBH—See Hornbach Holding AG & Co. KGaA; *Int'l*, pg. 3482
ROBERT ROTHSCHILD FARM LLC—See Glencoe Capital LLC; *U.S. Private*, pg. 1709
ROBERTS AIRCRAFT COMPANY; *U.S. Private*, pg. 3459
ROBERTS CHEVROLET INC.; *U.S. Private*, pg. 3459
ROBERTS CIGAR & TOBACCO COMPANY; *U.S. Private*, pg. 3459
ROBERTS COMMUNICATIONS INC.; *U.S. Private*, pg. 3459
ROBERTS COMMUNICATIONS NETWORK; *U.S. Private*, pg. 3459
ROBERTS COMPANY CANADA LIMITED—See Q.E.P. Co., Inc.; *U.S. Public*, pg. 1741
THE ROBERTS COMPANY FABRICATION SERVICES, INC.—See Argan, Inc.; *U.S. Public*, pg. 191
THE ROBERTS COMPANY, INC.—See Argan, Inc.; *U.S. Public*, pg. 191
ROBERTS CONSOLIDATED INDUSTRIES INC.—See Q.E.P. Co., Inc.; *U.S. Public*, pg. 1741
ROBERTS CONSTRUCTION COMPANY INC.—See McCormick Incorporated; *U.S. Private*, pg. 2630
ROBERT SCOTT & SONS LTD.; *Int'l*, pg. 6368
ROBERTS DISTRIBUTORS INC.; *U.S. Private*, pg. 3459
ROBERTS DON MAC PTY. LTD.—See Nutrien Ltd.; *Int'l*, pg. 5493

ROBERTS TRADING CORPORATION

ROBERTS & DYBDAHL INC.—See Roberts Trading Corporation; *U.S. Private*, pg. 3460
ROBERTS-GIBSON INC.; *U.S. Private*, pg. 3460
THE ROBERTS GROUP, INC.; *U.S. Private*, pg. 4111
ROBERT'S HAWAII CRUISES INC.—See Robert's Hawaii Inc.; *U.S. Private*, pg. 3459
ROBERT'S HAWAII HOTELS INC.—See Robert's Hawaii Inc.; *U.S. Private*, pg. 3459
ROBERT'S HAWAII INC.; *U.S. Private*, pg. 3459
ROBERT'S HAWAII LEASING INC.—See Robert's Hawaii Inc.; *U.S. Private*, pg. 3459
ROBERT'S HAWAII TOURS AND TRANSPORTATION—See Robert's Hawaii Inc.; *U.S. Private*, pg. 3459
ROBERT'S HAWAII TOURS INC.—See Robert's Hawaii Inc.; *U.S. Private*, pg. 3459
ROBERTSHAW CONTROLS COMPANY—See One Rock Capital Partners, LLC; *U.S. Private*, pg. 3023
ROBERTS HAWKINS PTY. LTD.—See Nutrien Ltd.; *Int'l*, pg. 5493
ROBERTS, J. R. CORP.; *U.S. Private*, pg. 3460
ROBERT SKEELS & CO.; *U.S. Private*, pg. 3459
ROBERTS + LANGER DDB—See Omnicom Group Inc.; *U.S. Public*, pg. 1582
ROBERTS LIMITED—See Nutrien Ltd.; *Int'l*, pg. 5493
ROBERTS MANUFACTURING COMPANY LTD—See Barbados Shipping & Trading Co. Ltd.; *Int'l*, pg. 858
ROBERTS MARKEL WEINBERG BUTLER HAILEY PC; *U.S. Private*, pg. 3459
ROBERT S. MAXAM INC.—See American International Group, Inc.; *U.S. Public*, pg. 107
ROBERT SMYTH & SONS LIMITED—See Fane Valley Co-operative Society Ltd.; *Int'l*, pg. 2613
ROBERTS OIL CO., INC.; *U.S. Private*, pg. 3460
ROBERTSON BANKING COMPANY—See RBC, Inc.; *U.S. Private*, pg. 3360
ROBERTSON BOIS DICKSON ANDERSON LIMITED—See Camellia Plc; *Int'l*, pg. 1271
ROBERTSON BUILDING SYSTEMS LIMITED—See Clayton, Dubilier & Rice, LLC; *U.S. Private*, pg. 921
ROBERTSON CHOO OEHLERS LEE & LYE PTE. LTD.—See Pacific Healthcare Holdings Ltd.; *Int'l*, pg. 5689
ROBERTSON DEVELOPMENT INC.; *U.S. Private*, pg. 3460
ROBERTSON FUEL SYSTEMS, LLC—See HEICO Corporation; *U.S. Public*, pg. 1020
ROBERTSON GEOLOGGING (ASIA) INC.—See OYO Corporation; *Int'l*, pg. 5678
ROBERTSON GEOLOGGING LIMITED—See OYO Corporation; *Int'l*, pg. 5678
ROBERTSON GEOLOGGING (USA) INC.—See OYO Corporation; *Int'l*, pg. 5678
ROBERTSON GLOBAL HEALTH SOLUTIONS CORPORATION; *U.S. Private*, pg. 3460
THE ROBERTSON GROUP, INC.; *U.S. Private*, pg. 4111
ROBERTSON HEATING SUPPLY CO., INC.; *U.S. Private*, pg. 3460
ROBERTSON INC.—See Berkshire Hathaway Inc.; *U.S. Public*, pg. 311
ROBERTSON INDUSTRIES, INC.—See Court Square Capital Partners, L.P.; *U.S. Private*, pg. 1070
ROBERTS ONSITE INC.—See Black & McDonald Limited; *Int'l*, pg. 1056
ROBERTSON'S READY MIX, LTD.—See Mitsubishi Materials Corporation; *Int'l*, pg. 4965
ROBERTSON SUPPLY INC.; *U.S. Private*, pg. 3460
ROBERTSON TIRE CO. INC.—See Big Brand Tire & Service; *U.S. Private*, pg. 552
ROBERTSON (UK) LIMITED—See CGG; *Int'l*, pg. 1432
ROBERTSON (USA) INC.—See CGG; *Int'l*, pg. 1432
ROBERTSON WOOD ADVERTISING; *U.S. Private*, pg. 3460
ROBERTS OXYGEN COMPANY INC.; *U.S. Private*, pg. 3460
ROBERTS POLYPRO INC.—See Leonard Green & Partners, L.P.; *U.S. Private*, pg. 2428
ROBERTS PROPERTIES CONSTRUCTION, INC.—See Roberts Properties, Inc.; *U.S. Private*, pg. 3460
ROBERTS PROPERTIES, INC.; *U.S. Private*, pg. 3460
ROBERTS RADIO LIMITED—See The Glen Dimplex Group; *Int'l*, pg. 7650
ROBERTS & SCHAEFER COMPANY—See KBR, Inc.; *U.S. Public*, pg. 1216
ROBERTS & SCHAEFER COMPANY—See KBR, Inc.; *U.S. Public*, pg. 1216
ROBERTS SHEARWATER PTY. LTD.—See Nutrien Ltd.; *Int'l*, pg. 5493
ROBERTS SINTO DE MEXICO, S. DE R. L. DE C. V.—See Sintokogio Ltd.; *Int'l*, pg. 6958
ROBERT STEMMLER WINERY—See A. Racke GmbH; *Int'l*, pg. 21
ROBERT'S TOURS & TRANSPORTATION INC.—See Robert's Hawaii Inc.; *U.S. Private*, pg. 3459
ROBERTS TRADING CORPORATION; *U.S. Private*, pg. 3460
ROBERTS TRUCK CENTER, LTD. - ALBUQUERQUE—See Roberts Truck Center, Ltd.; *U.S. Private*, pg. 3460

2311

ROBERTS TRUCK CENTER, LTD.

ROBERTS TRUCK CENTER, LTD.; *U.S. Private*, pg. 3460
ROBERT'S TRUCKING—See Wavepoint 3PI Expedite LLC; *U.S. Private*, pg. 4458
ROBERT TALBOTT, INC.; *U.S. Private*, pg. 3459
ROBERT T. WINZINGER INC.; *U.S. Private*, pg. 3459
ROBERT V. JENSEN INC.; *U.S. Private*, pg. 3459
ROBERT W. AGEE OIL CO. INC.; *U.S. Private*, pg. 3459
ROBERT WALTERS ASSOCIATES INC.—See Robert Walters plc; *Int'l*, pg. 6368
ROBERT WALTERS BRAZIL LIMITADA—See Robert Walters plc; *Int'l*, pg. 6368
ROBERT WALTERS BUSINESS CONSULTING (SHANGHAI) LTD.—See Robert Walters plc; *Int'l*, pg. 6369
ROBERT WALTERS B.V.—See Robert Walters plc; *Int'l*, pg. 6368
ROBERT WALTERS CANADA INC.—See Robert Walters plc; *Int'l*, pg. 6369
ROBERT WALTERS CHILE SPA—See Robert Walters plc; *Int'l*, pg. 6369
ROBERT WALTERS COMPANY LIMITED—See Robert Walters plc; *Int'l*, pg. 6369
ROBERT WALTERS EASTERN SEABOARD LTD.—See Robert Walters plc; *Int'l*, pg. 6369
ROBERT WALTERS GERMANY GMBH—See Robert Walters plc; *Int'l*, pg. 6369
ROBERT WALTERS HOLDINGS LIMITED—See Robert Walters plc; *Int'l*, pg. 6369
ROBERT WALTERS HOLDINGS SAS—See Robert Walters plc; *Int'l*, pg. 6369
ROBERT WALTERS (HONG KONG) LIMITED—See Robert Walters plc; *Int'l*, pg. 6368
ROBERT WALTERS JAPAN KK—See Robert Walters plc; *Int'l*, pg. 6369
ROBERT WALTERS KOREA LIMITED—See Robert Walters plc; *Int'l*, pg. 6369
ROBERT WALTERS LIMITED—See Robert Walters plc; *Int'l*, pg. 6369
ROBERT WALTERS MIDDLE EAST LIMITED—See Robert Walters plc; *Int'l*, pg. 6369
ROBERT WALTERS NEW ZEALAND LIMITED—See Robert Walters plc; *Int'l*, pg. 6369
ROBERT WALTERS OPERATIONS LIMITED—See Robert Walters plc; *Int'l*, pg. 6369
ROBERT WALTERS PLC; *Int'l*, pg. 6368
ROBERT WALTERS PORTUGAL UNIPESSOAL LDA.—See Robert Walters plc; *Int'l*, pg. 6369
ROBERT WALTERS PTY LIMITED—See Robert Walters plc; *Int'l*, pg. 6369
ROBERT WALTERS RECRUITMENT (THAILAND) LTD—See Robert Walters plc; *Int'l*, pg. 6369
ROBERT WALTERS SARL—See Robert Walters plc; *Int'l*, pg. 6369
ROBERT WALTERS SA—See Robert Walters plc; *Int'l*, pg. 6369
ROBERT WALTERS SDN BHD—See Robert Walters plc; *Int'l*, pg. 6369
ROBERT WALTERS (SINGAPORE) PTE LIMITED—See Robert Walters plc; *Int'l*, pg. 6368
ROBERT WALTERS SOUTH AFRICA PROPRIETARY LIMITED—See Robert Walters plc; *Int'l*, pg. 6369
ROBERT WALTERS SWITZERLAND AG—See Robert Walters plc; *Int'l*, pg. 6369
ROBERT WALTERS TALENT CONSULTING (SHANGHAI) LTD—See Robert Walters plc; *Int'l*, pg. 6369
ROBERT WALTERS VIETNAM COMPANY LIMITED—See Robert Walters plc; *Int'l*, pg. 6369
ROBERT W. BAIRD & CO., INCORPORATED—See Baird Financial Group, Inc.; *U.S. Private*, pg. 453
ROBERT W. BAKER NURSERY INC.—See The Robert Baker Companies; *U.S. Private*, pg. 4111
ROBERT WHOLEY & CO.; *U.S. Private*, pg. 3459
ROBERT WIDMER AG—See Burkhalter Holding AG; *Int'l*, pg. 1225
ROBERT WINNER SONS INC.; *U.S. Private*, pg. 3459
ROBERT WOOD JOHNSON UNIVERSITY HOSPITAL RAHWAY—See Barnabas Health Medical Group; *U.S. Private*, pg. 476
ROBERT W. STANHOPE CO.; *U.S. Private*, pg. 3459
ROBERT YATES REAL ESTATE, INC.; *U.S. Private*, pg. 3459
ROBESON HEALTH CARE CORPORATION; *U.S. Private*, pg. 3460
ROBESONIA LOGISTICS LLC—See C&S Wholesale Grocers, Inc.; *U.S. Private*, pg. 704
THE ROBESONIAN—See Heartland Publications, LLC; *U.S. Private*, pg. 1900
ROB-EX A/S—See Novotek AB; *Int'l*, pg. 5471
ROBEX LLC—See Angeles Equity Partners, LLC; *U.S. Private*, pg. 282
ROBEX RESOURCES INC.; *Int'l*, pg. 6370
ROBFRANKEL.COM; *U.S. Private*, pg. 3460
ROBI AXIATA LIMITED—See Axiata Group Berhad; *Int'l*, pg. 768
ROBICHAUX AUTOMATION & CONTROL, INC.—See J.F. Lehman & Company, Inc.; *U.S. Private*, pg. 2164
ROBIC, LLP—See IPH Limited; *Int'l*, pg. 3797
ROBIDUS GROEP B.V.—See Aegon N.V.; *Int'l*, pg. 175
ROBIMATIC LTD.—See Genuit Group plc; *Int'l*, pg. 2930

ROBINA LAND CORPORATION PTY LTD—See Robin Holdings Pte Ltd; *Int'l*, pg. 6370
ROBINA MAZDA PTY. LIMITED—See Peter Warren Automotive Holdings Ltd.; *Int'l*, pg. 5824
ROBIN AMERICA INC.—See Subaru Corporation; *Int'l*, pg. 7247
ROBINETTE COMPANY; *U.S. Private*, pg. 3460
ROBIN EUROPE GMBH—See Subaru Corporation; *Int'l*, pg. 7247
ROBIN HOLDINGS PTE LTD; *Int'l*, pg. 6370
ROBINHOOD MARKETS, INC.; *U.S. Public*, pg. 1804
ROBIN HOOD SUPPLIES, INC.; *U.S. Private*, pg. 3460
ROBIN INDUSTRIES, INC.; *U.S. Private*, pg. 3460
ROBIN LEEDY & ASSOCIATES; *U.S. Private*, pg. 3460
ROBIN MANUFACTURING USA, INC.—See Subaru Corporation; *Int'l*, pg. 7247
ROBIN MARIETON; *Int'l*, pg. 6370
THE ROBINS AND MORTON GROUP; *U.S. Private*, pg. 4111
ROBINS & DAY LTD—See Stellantis N.V.; *Int'l*, pg. 7202
ROBINS DONUTS—See Chairman's Brands Corporation; *Int'l*, pg. 1437
ROBIN SHEPHERD STUDIOS, INC.; *U.S. Private*, pg. 3460
ROBIN SHEPHERD STUDIOS, INC.—See Robin Shepherd Studios, Inc.; *U.S. Private*, pg. 3460
ROBINS KAPLAN LLP - LOS ANGELES—See Robins, Kaplan, Miller & Ciresi L.L.P.; *U.S. Private*, pg. 3461
ROBINS, KAPLAN, MILLER & CIRESI L.L.P. - ATLANTA—See Robins, Kaplan, Miller & Ciresi L.L.P.; *U.S. Private*, pg. 3461
ROBINS, KAPLAN, MILLER & CIRESI L.L.P. - BOSTON—See Robins, Kaplan, Miller & Ciresi L.L.P.; *U.S. Private*, pg. 3461
ROBINS, KAPLAN, MILLER & CIRESI L.L.P. - NAPLES—See Robins, Kaplan, Miller & Ciresi L.L.P.; *U.S. Private*, pg. 3461
ROBINS, KAPLAN, MILLER & CIRESI L.L.P. - NEW YORK—See Robins, Kaplan, Miller & Ciresi L.L.P.; *U.S. Private*, pg. 3461
ROBINS, KAPLAN, MILLER & CIRESI L.L.P.; *U.S. Private*, pg. 3460
ROBIN'S NEST INTERIORS (MAURITIUS) LTD.—See ENL Limited; *Int'l*, pg. 2441
ROBINSON AUSTRIA CLUBHOTEL GMBH—See TUI AG; *Int'l*, pg. 7966
ROBINSON AVIATION (RVA) INC.; *U.S. Private*, pg. 3461
ROBINSON & BELEW INC.; *U.S. Private*, pg. 3461
ROBINSON BROTHERS CONSTRUCTION, LLC—See Quanta Services, Inc.; *U.S. Public*, pg. 1752
ROBINSON BUICK GMC; *Int'l*, pg. 6370
ROBINSON CAPITAL & INVESTMENTS INC.; *U.S. Private*, pg. 3461
ROBINSON CLUB GMBH—See TUI AG; *Int'l*, pg. 7966
ROBINSON CLUB ITALIA S.P.A.—See TUI AG; *Int'l*, pg. 7966
ROBINSON CLUB MALDIVES PRIVATE LIMITED—See TUI AG; *Int'l*, pg. 7966
ROBINSON CLUB (SCHWEIZ) AG—See TUI AG; *Int'l*, pg. 7966
ROBINSON & COLE LLP; *U.S. Private*, pg. 3461
ROBINSON & CO. (S) PTE. LTD.; *Int'l*, pg. 6370
ROBINSON CREATIVE INC.; *U.S. Private*, pg. 3461
ROBINSON DEPARTMENT STORE PCL—See Central Group Company Limited; *Int'l*, pg. 1407
ROBINSON DIALYSIS, LLC—See DaVita Inc.; *U.S. Public*, pg. 642
ROBINSON ELECTRIC SUPPLY CO.; *U.S. Private*, pg. 3461
ROBINSON ENTERPRISES INC.; *U.S. Private*, pg. 3461
ROBINSON ENTERPRISES INC.; *U.S. Private*, pg. 3461
ROBINSON EXCAVATING OF FLORIDA—See Ross Brothers Construction Co; *U.S. Private*, pg. 3485
ROBINSON EXPORT AND IMPORT CORPORATION; *U.S. Private*, pg. 3461
ROBINSON FANS, INC.; *U.S. Private*, pg. 3461
ROBINSON FRESH BV—See C.H. Robinson Worldwide, Inc.; *U.S. Public*, pg. 415
ROBINSON GAREISS LC; *U.S. Private*, pg. 3461
ROBINSON GRAY STEPP & LAFFITTE, LLC; *U.S. Private*, pg. 3461
ROBINSON HELICOPTER COMPANY; *U.S. Private*, pg. 3462
ROBINSON HOME PRODUCTS INC.; *U.S. Private*, pg. 3462
ROBINSON HOTELS PORTUGAL SA—See TUI AG; *Int'l*, pg. 7966
ROBINSON INDUSTRIES INC.; *U.S. Private*, pg. 3462
ROBINSON INDUSTRIES, INC.; *U.S. Private*, pg. 3462
ROBINSON LUMBER & EXPORT COMPANY; *U.S. Private*, pg. 3462
ROBINSON & MAITES, INC.; *U.S. Private*, pg. 3461
ROBINSON MANUFACTURING COMPANY INC.; *U.S. Private*, pg. 3462
ROBINSON MECHANICAL CONTRACTORS INC.; *U.S. Private*, pg. 3462
ROBINSON METAL, INC.; *U.S. Private*, pg. 3462
ROBINSON NEVADA MINING COMPANY—See KGHM Polska Miedz S.A.; *Int'l*, pg. 4149

CORPORATE AFFILIATIONS

ROBINSON NOBLE, INC.; *U.S. Private*, pg. 3462
ROBINSON OIL CORP.; *U.S. Private*, pg. 3462
ROBINSON OTELCILIK A.S.—See TUI AG; *Int'l*, pg. 7966
ROBINSON PACKAGING DANMARK A/S—See Robinson Plc; *Int'l*, pg. 6370
ROBINSON PACKAGING POLSKA SP. Z OO—See Robinson Plc; *Int'l*, pg. 6370
ROBINSON PAVING COMPANY—See Construction Partners, Inc.; *U.S. Public*, pg. 572
ROBINSON PHARMA INC.; *U.S. Private*, pg. 3462
ROBINSON PIPE CLEANING CO.—See Carylon Corporation; *U.S. Private*, pg. 777
ROBINSON PIPE SERVICES, INC.—See Carylon Corporation; *U.S. Private*, pg. 777
ROBINSON PLASTIC PACKAGING LTD.—See Robinson Plc; *Int'l*, pg. 6370
ROBINSON PLASTIC PACKAGING (STANTON HILL) LIMITED—See Robinson Plc; *Int'l*, pg. 6370
ROBINSON PLC; *Int'l*, pg. 6370
ROBINSON RADIO, INC.; *U.S. Private*, pg. 3462
ROBINSON-RANSBOTTOM POTTERY COMPANY—See Brittany Stamping, LLC; *U.S. Private*, pg. 657
ROBINSON'S AMBULANCE & OXYGEN SERVICE, INC.—See Lundbeckfonden; *Int'l*, pg. 4580
ROBINSONS APPLIANCES CORP.—See Robinsons Retail Holdings, Inc.; *Int'l*, pg. 6370
ROBINSONS BANK CORPORATION—See Bank of the Philippine Islands; *Int'l*, pg. 849
ROBINSON'S BEND OPERATING II, LLC—See Castleton Commodities International LLC; *U.S. Private*, pg. 785
ROBINSONS CARAVANS LIMITED—See MBH Corporation Plc; *Int'l*, pg. 4752
ROBINSONS HANDYMAN INC.—See Robinsons Retail Holdings, Inc.; *Int'l*, pg. 6370
ROBINSON'S INDUSTRIAL GAS & EQUIPMENT CORP.; *U.S. Private*, pg. 3462
ROBINSONS LAND CORPORATION—See JG Summit Holdings, Inc.; *Int'l*, pg. 3939
ROBINSONS MOTOR GROUP; *Int'l*, pg. 6370
ROBINSON SPORTS INC.; *U.S. Private*, pg. 3462
ROBINSONS RETAIL HOLDINGS, INC.; *Int'l*, pg. 6370
ROBINSON SUPPLY CO. INC.; *U.S. Private*, pg. 3462
ROBINSON TERMINAL WAREHOUSE LLC—See Nash Holdings LLC; *U.S. Private*, pg. 2835
ROBINSON WAY LIMITED; *Int'l*, pg. 6370
ROB INT S.R.L.—See Fincantieri S.p.A.; *Int'l*, pg. 2671
RQBION AG—See Stratec SE; *Int'l*, pg. 7235
ROBISON-NIERI-WHITE CONSTRUCTION; *U.S. Private*, pg. 3462
ROBISON & SMITH, INC.; *U.S. Private*, pg. 3462
ROBIT AUSTRALIA PTY LTD.—See Robit Plc; *Int'l*, pg. 6370
ROBIT PLC; *Int'l*, pg. 6370
ROBKE B.V.—See Leifheit AG; *Int'l*, pg. 4447
ROBLING MEDICAL, INC.—See SV Health Investors, LLP; *U.S. Private*, pg. 3888
ROBLIN INSURANCE AGENCY, INC.—See Keystone Group, L.P.; *U.S. Private*, pg. 2299
ROBLON A/S; *Int'l*, pg. 6371
ROBLON US INC.—See Roblon A/S; *Int'l*, pg. 6371
ROBLOX CORPORATION; *U.S. Public*, pg. 1804
ROBNA KUCA TUZLANKA D.D.; *Int'l*, pg. 6371
ROBNO TRANSPORNI CENTAR A.D. SABAC; *Int'l*, pg. 6371
ROBO3 CO LTD; *Int'l*, pg. 6371
ROBOCOM US, LLC; *U.S. Private*, pg. 3462
ROBOGROUP T.E.K. LTD.; *Int'l*, pg. 6371
ROBOLUTION GMBH—See Lincoln Electric Holdings, Inc.; *U.S. Public*, pg. 1318
ROBOPROJEKT SP. Z.O.O—See Air Products & Chemicals, Inc.; *U.S. Public*, pg. 67
ROBORE CUTS LIMITED—See Robore Holdings Ltd.; *Int'l*, pg. 6371
ROBORE HOLDINGS LTD.; *Int'l*, pg. 6371
ROBOREPS, INC.—See M2I Corporation; *Int'l*, pg. 4617
ROBORE SPECIAL PROJECTS—See Robore Holdings Ltd.; *Int'l*, pg. 6371
ROBORETEC—See Northern Heavy Industries Group Co. Ltd.; *Int'l*, pg. 5443
ROBOR INDUSTRIAL (PTY) LIMITED—See Barloworld Ltd.; *Int'l*, pg. 866
ROBOROBO CO., LTD.; *Int'l*, pg. 6371
ROBOROUGH HOUSE LIMITED—See Sheikh Holdings Group (Investments) Limited; *Int'l*, pg. 6794
ROBOSERVER SYSTEMS CORP.; *U.S. Public*, pg. 1804
ROBOSOFT NV—See Haco N.V.; *Int'l*, pg. 3205
ROBOSOFT TECHNOLOGIES PVT. LTD.; *Int'l*, pg. 6371
ROBOSTAR CO., LTD. - 2ND PLANT—See Robostar Co., Ltd.; *Int'l*, pg. 6371
ROBOSTAR CO., LTD.; *Int'l*, pg. 6371
ROBOSTAR (SHANGHAI) CO., LTD.—See Robostar Co., Ltd.; *Int'l*, pg. 6371
ROBOTA AB—See Indutrade AB; *Int'l*, pg. 3681
ROBOT COMMUNICATIONS INC.—See Imagica Group Inc.; *Int'l*, pg. 3619
ROBO TECHNIK INTELLIGENT TECHNOLOGY CO., LTD.; *Int'l*, pg. 6371
ROBOTEC SYSTEMS GMBH—See HELUKABEL GmbH; *Int'l*, pg. 3339

COMPANY NAME INDEX

ROBOTEQ, INC.—See Nidec Corporation; *Int'l*, pg. 5275
ROBOT FUND CO., LTD.—See Minkabu The Infonoid, Inc.; *Int'l*, pg. 4910
ROBOT HOME CO., LTD.—See Robot Home, Inc.; *Int'l*, pg. 6371
ROBOT HOME, INC.; *Int'l*, pg. 6371
ROBOTICS TECHNOLOGY CONSORTIUM; *U.S. Private*, pg. 3462
ROBOTIS CO., LTD.; *Int'l*, pg. 6371
ROBOT NEDERLAND B.V.—See Jenoptik AG; *Int'l*, pg. 3929
ROBOTNIK.COM INCORPORATED; *Int'l*, pg. 6371
ROBOT PAYMENT INC.—See Vector Inc.; *Int'l*, pg. 8144
THE ROBOT REPORT—See WTWH Media, LLC; *U.S. Private*, pg. 4574
ROBOTWORX—See JBS S.A.; *Int'l*, pg. 3918
ROBOX SPA—See EFORT Intelligent Equipment Co., Ltd.; *Int'l*, pg. 2321
ROBRADY, INC.; *U.S. Private*, pg. 3462
ROBRASA ROLAMENTOS ESPECIAIS ROTHE ERDE LTDA.—See ThyssenKrupp AG; *Int'l*, pg. 7731
ROBROY INDUSTRIES INC.; *U.S. Private*, pg. 3463
ROBROY INDUSTRIES TEXAS INC.—See Robroy Industries Inc.; *U.S. Private*, pg. 3463
ROB-SEE-CO; *U.S. Private*, pg. 3456
ROBSON COMMUNITIES, INC.; *U.S. Private*, pg. 3463
ROBSON DENTON DEVELOPMENT, LP.—See Robson Communities, Inc.; *U.S. Private*, pg. 3463
ROBTEC URUGUAY—See 3D Systems Corporation; *U.S. Public*, pg. 4
ROB'T J. BAGGETT INC.; *U.S. Private*, pg. 3456
ROB-TOM INC.—See Vollers, Inc.; *U.S. Private*, pg. 4411
ROBUCK HOMES; *U.S. Private*, pg. 3463
ROBUR INDUSTRY SERVICE GROUP GMBH—See Clayton, Dubilier & Rice, LLC; *U.S. Private*, pg. 926
ROBUR KAPITALFORVALTNING AB—See Swedbank AB; *Int'l*, pg. 7364
ROBUR PROTOTYPING & MATERIALS GMBH—See Clayton, Dubilier & Rice, LLC; *U.S. Private*, pg. 926
ROBUSCHI BENELUX BV—See Ingersoll Rand Inc.; *U.S. Public*, pg. 1119
ROBUSCHI DO BRASIL LTD.—See Ingersoll Rand Inc.; *U.S. Public*, pg. 1119
ROBUSCHI FLUID TECHNOLOGY (SHANGHAI) CO. LTD.—See Ingersoll Rand Inc.; *U.S. Public*, pg. 1119
ROBUSCHI FRANCE SARL—See Ingersoll Rand Inc.; *U.S. Public*, pg. 1119
ROBUS GROUP AS; *Int'l*, pg. 6371
ROBUST AB—See Sanwa Holdings Corporation; *Int'l*, pg. 6561
ROBUST HOTELS PRIVATE LIMITED—See Asian Hotels (East) Limited; *Int'l*, pg. 617
ROBUST UK LIMITED—See Sanwa Holdings Corporation; *Int'l*, pg. 6561
ROBUSTWEALTH, INC.—See Principal Financial Group, Inc.; *U.S. Public*, pg. 1722
ROBUTEC AG—See Halma plc; *Int'l*, pg. 3232
ROBYG S.A.—See The Goldman Sachs Group, Inc.; *U.S. Public*, pg. 2080
ROBYN, INC.; *U.S. Private*, pg. 3463
ROBYN MEREDITH, INC.; *U.S. Private*, pg. 3463
ROCAMAT S.A.—See TorQuest Partners Inc.; *Int'l*, pg. 7830
ROCA MINES INC.; *Int'l*, pg. 6372
ROCA SANITARIO, S.A.; *Int'l*, pg. 6372
ROCA TILES SPAIN, S.L.—See Grupo Lamosa S.A. de C.V.; *Int'l*, pg. 3132
ROCBOLT TECHNOLOGIES AFRICA PTY LTD.—See Sandvik AB; *Int'l*, pg. 6530
ROCBOLT TECHNOLOGIES PTY. LTD.—See Sandvik AB; *Int'l*, pg. 6530
ROCCA AL MARE KAUBANDUSKESKUSE AS—See Citycon Oyj; *Int'l*, pg. 1629
ROCCA INTERNATIONAL S.A.—See Damiani S.p.A.; *Int'l*, pg. 1957
ROCCA S.P.A.—See Damiani S.p.A.; *Int'l*, pg. 1957
ROCCO FORTE & FAMILY PLC.; *Int'l*, pg. 6372
ROCCOR LLC—See Redwire Corporation; *U.S. Public*, pg. 1771
ROCEDES APPAREL S.A.; *Int'l*, pg. 6372
ROCELL BATHWARE LTD.—See Royal Ceramics Lanka PLC; *Int'l*, pg. 6411
ROCH CAPITAL INC.; *U.S. Private*, pg. 3463
ROCHDALE CORPORATION; *U.S. Private*, pg. 3463
ROCHDALE INSURANCE COMPANY—See Stone Point Capital LLC; *U.S. Private*, pg. 3821
ROCHDALE INVESTMENT MANAGEMENT LLC—See Royal Bank of Canada; *Int'l*, pg. 6409
ROCHDALE SECURITIES LLC; *U.S. Private*, pg. 3463
ROCHDALE VILLAGE INC.; *U.S. Private*, pg. 3463
ROCHE AB—See Roche Holding AG; *Int'l*, pg. 6373
ROCHE APPLIED SCIENCE—See Roche Holding AG; *Int'l*, pg. 6374
ROCHE A/S—See Roche Holding AG; *Int'l*, pg. 6376
ROCHE AUSTRIA GMBH—See Roche Holding AG; *Int'l*, pg. 6373
ROCHE BAY PLC—See Borealis Exploration Limited; *Int'l*, pg. 1113
ROCHE BETEILIGUNGS GMBH—See Roche Holding AG; *Int'l*, pg. 6373
ROCHE BOBOIS SA; *Int'l*, pg. 6372
ROCHE BROS. SUPERMARKETS INC.; *U.S. Private*, pg. 3463
ROCHE BULGARIA EOOD—See Roche Holding AG; *Int'l*, pg. 6373
ROCHE CHILE LIMITADA—See Roche Holding AG; *Int'l*, pg. 6373
ROCHE CONSTRUCTION INC.—See Roche Ltd., Consulting Group; *Int'l*, pg. 6376
ROCHE CONSTRUCTORS INC. - LAS VEGAS—See Roche Constructors, Inc.; *U.S. Private*, pg. 3463
ROCHE CONSTRUCTORS, INC.; *U.S. Private*, pg. 3463
ROCHE CONSULTING GROUP—See Roche Ltd., Consulting Group; *Int'l*, pg. 6376
ROCHE CONTRACTORS PTY LTD—See Downer EDI Limited; *Int'l*, pg. 2186
ROCHE DEUTSCHLAND HOLDING GMBH—See Roche Holding AG; *Int'l*, pg. 6374
ROCHE DIABETES CARE AG—See Roche Holding AG; *Int'l*, pg. 6374
ROCHE DIAGNOSTICS AB—See Roche Holding AG; *Int'l*, pg. 6374
ROCHE DIAGNOSTICS ASIA PACIFIC PTE. LTD.—See Roche Holding AG; *Int'l*, pg. 6374
ROCHE DIAGNOSTICS A/S—See Roche Holding AG; *Int'l*, pg. 6375
ROCHE DIAGNOSTICS AUSTRALIA PTY. LIMITED—See Roche Holding AG; *Int'l*, pg. 6374
ROCHE DIAGNOSTICS BELGIUM S.A.—See Roche Holding AG; *Int'l*, pg. 6374
ROCHE DIAGNOSTICS CORANGE INTERNATIONAL LIMITED—See Roche Holding AG; *Int'l*, pg. 6374
ROCHE DIAGNOSTICS CORPORATION—See Roche Holding AG; *Int'l*, pg. 6374
ROCHE DIAGNOSTICS FRANCE S.A.S.—See Roche Holding AG; *Int'l*, pg. 6374
ROCHE DIAGNOSTICS GMBH—See Roche Holding AG; *Int'l*, pg. 6374
ROCHE DIAGNOSTICS GMBH—See Roche Holding AG; *Int'l*, pg. 6374
ROCHE DIAGNOSTICS GRAZ GMBH—See Roche Holding AG; *Int'l*, pg. 6374
ROCHE DIAGNOSTICS (HELLAS) S.A.—See Roche Holding AG; *Int'l*, pg. 6374
ROCHE DIAGNOSTICS (HONG KONG) LIMITED—See Roche Holding AG; *Int'l*, pg. 6374
ROCHE DIAGNOSTICS (INDIA) PVT. LTD.—See Roche Holding AG; *Int'l*, pg. 6374
ROCHE DIAGNOSTICS INTERNATIONAL LTD.—See Roche Holding AG; *Int'l*, pg. 6374
ROCHE DIAGNOSTICS K.K.—See Roche Holding AG; *Int'l*, pg. 6374
ROCHE DIAGNOSTICS KOREA CO., LTD.—See Roche Holding AG; *Int'l*, pg. 6374
ROCHE DIAGNOSTICS LTD.—See Roche Holding AG; *Int'l*, pg. 6374
ROCHE DIAGNOSTICS NEDERLAND B.V.—See Roche Holding AG; *Int'l*, pg. 6374
ROCHE DIAGNOSTICS NORGE A/S—See Roche Holding AG; *Int'l*, pg. 6374
ROCHE DIAGNOSTICS NZ LIMITED—See Roche Holding AG; *Int'l*, pg. 6374
ROCHE DIAGNOSTICS OPERATIONS, INC.—See Roche Holding AG; *Int'l*, pg. 6374
ROCHE DIAGNOSTICS OY—See Roche Holding AG; *Int'l*, pg. 6374
ROCHE DIAGNOSTICS POLSKA SP. Z.O.O.—See Roche Holding AG; *Int'l*, pg. 6374
ROCHE DIAGNOSTICS PUERTO RICO—See Roche Holding AG; *Int'l*, pg. 6374
ROCHE DIAGNOSTICS (SHANGHAI) LIMITED—See Roche Holding AG; *Int'l*, pg. 6374
ROCHE DIAGNOSTICS S.L.—See Roche Holding AG; *Int'l*, pg. 6374
ROCHE DIAGNOSTICS S.P.A.—See Roche Holding AG; *Int'l*, pg. 6374
ROCHE DIAGNOSTICS (THAILAND) LIMITED—See Roche Holding AG; *Int'l*, pg. 6374
ROCHE DIAGNOSTICS VIETNAM CO., LTD.—See Roche Holding AG; *Int'l*, pg. 6375
ROCHE DIAGNOSTIC SYSTEMS—See Roche Holding AG; *Int'l*, pg. 6374
ROCHE D.O.O. PHARMACEUTICAL COMPANY—See Roche Holding AG; *Int'l*, pg. 6376
ROCHE D.O.O.—See Roche Holding AG; *Int'l*, pg. 6376
ROCHE ECUADOR S.A.—See Roche Holding AG; *Int'l*, pg. 6375
ROCHE EESTI OU—See Roche Holding AG; *Int'l*, pg. 6375
ROCHE ENGINEERING, INC.—See Roche Ltd., Consulting Group; *Int'l*, pg. 6376
ROCHE FARMACEUTICA QUIMICA LDA.—See Roche Holding AG; *Int'l*, pg. 6375
ROCHE FARMA S.A.—See Roche Holding AG; *Int'l*, pg. 6375
ROCHE FARMA, S.A.—See Roche Holding AG; *Int'l*, pg. 6375
ROCHE GLYCART AG—See Roche Holding AG; *Int'l*, pg. 6375
ROCHE HEALTH SOLUTIONS INC.—See Roche Holding AG; *Int'l*, pg. 6374
ROCHE (HELLAS) S.A.—See Roche Holding AG; *Int'l*, pg. 6373
ROCHE HOLDING AG; *Int'l*, pg. 6372
ROCHE HOLDING (UK) LIMITED—See Roche Holding AG; *Int'l*, pg. 6375
ROCHE HONG KONG LIMITED—See Roche Holding AG; *Int'l*, pg. 6375
ROCHE (HUNGARY) LTD.—See Roche Holding AG; *Int'l*, pg. 6373
ROCHE INNOVATION CENTER COPENHAGEN A/S—See Roche Holding AG; *Int'l*, pg. 6375
ROCHE INTERNATIONAL LTD.—See Roche Holding AG; *Int'l*, pg. 6375
ROCHE INTERNATIONAL LTD.—See Roche Holding AG; *Int'l*, pg. 6375
ROCHE INTERTRADE LIMITED—See Roche Holding AG; *Int'l*, pg. 6375
ROCHE IRELAND LIMITED—See Roche Holding AG; *Int'l*, pg. 6375
ROCHE KOREA COMPANY LTD.—See Roche Holding AG; *Int'l*, pg. 6375
ROCHE LATVIJA SIA—See Roche Holding AG; *Int'l*, pg. 6375
ROCHELLE FOODS, INC.—See Hormel Foods Corporation; *U.S. Public*, pg. 1054
ROCHELLE FURNITURE—See The Lightning Group, Inc.; *U.S. Private*, pg. 4070
ROCHELLE HOLDING COMPANY; *U.S. Private*, pg. 3463
ROCHE LTD., CONSULTING GROUP; *Int'l*, pg. 6376
ROCHE MAGHREB—See Roche Ltd., Consulting Group; *Int'l*, pg. 6376
ROCHE MALAYSIA SDN. BHD.—See Roche Holding AG; *Int'l*, pg. 6375
ROCHE MINING (MT) INDIA PVT LTD.—See Downer EDI Limited; *Int'l*, pg. 2186
ROCHE MOLECULAR DIAGNOSTICS—See Roche Holding AG; *Int'l*, pg. 6374
ROCHE MOSCOW LTD.—See Roche Holding AG; *Int'l*, pg. 6375
ROCHE MTM LABORATORIES AG—See Roche Holding AG; *Int'l*, pg. 6376
ROCHE MUSTAHZARLARI A.S.—See Roche Holding AG; *Int'l*, pg. 6375
ROCHE NEDERLAND B.V.—See Roche Holding AG; *Int'l*, pg. 6375
ROCHE NORGE A/S—See Roche Holding AG; *Int'l*, pg. 6375
ROCHE N.V./S.A.—See Roche Holding AG; *Int'l*, pg. 6375
ROCHE OY—See Roche Holding AG; *Int'l*, pg. 6375
ROCHE PALO ALTO LLC—See Roche Holding AG; *Int'l*, pg. 6375
ROCHE PHARMA AG—See Roche Holding AG; *Int'l*, pg. 6375
ROCHE PHARMACEUTICALS (ISRAEL) LTD.—See Roche Holding AG; *Int'l*, pg. 6375
ROCHE PHARMA (SWITZERLAND) LTD.—See Roche Holding AG; *Int'l*, pg. 6375
ROCHE (PHILIPPINES), INC.—See Roche Holding AG; *Int'l*, pg. 6373
ROCHE POLSKA SP. Z O.O.—See Roche Holding AG; *Int'l*, pg. 6375
ROCHE PRODUCTS (INDIA) PVT. LTD.—See Roche Holding AG; *Int'l*, pg. 6375
ROCHE PRODUCTS (IRELAND) LIMITED—See Roche Holding AG; *Int'l*, pg. 6375
ROCHE PRODUCTS LTD.—See Roche Holding AG; *Int'l*, pg. 6375
ROCHE PRODUCTS LTD.—See Roche Holding AG; *Int'l*, pg. 6375
ROCHE PRODUCTS (NEW ZEALAND) LTD.—See Roche Holding AG; *Int'l*, pg. 6375
ROCHE PRODUCTS (PROPRIETARY) LIMITED—See Roche Holding AG; *Int'l*, pg. 6375
ROCHE PRODUCTS (PTY.) LTD.—See Roche Holding AG; *Int'l*, pg. 6375
ROCHE PROFESSIONAL SERVICE CENTERS, INC.—See Roche Holding AG; *Int'l*, pg. 6373
ROCHE R&D CENTER (CHINA) LTD.—See Roche Holding AG; *Int'l*, pg. 6375
ROCHE REGISTRATION LIMITED—See Roche Holding AG; *Int'l*, pg. 6375
ROCHER MANGANESE INC.—See RecycLiCo Battery Materials Inc.; *Int'l*, pg. 6243
ROCHE ROMANIA S.R.L.—See Roche Holding AG; *Int'l*, pg. 6375
ROCHE S.A.—See Roche Holding AG; *Int'l*, pg. 6375
ROCHE S.A.—See Roche Holding AG; *Int'l*, pg. 6375
ROCHE S.A.S.—See Roche Holding AG; *Int'l*, pg. 6375
ROCHE SCIENTIFIC COMPANY (INDIA) PRIVATE LTD.—See Roche Holding AG; *Int'l*, pg. 6375
ROCHE SERVICIOS S.A.—See Roche Holding AG; *Int'l*, pg. 6376
ROCHE SINGAPORE PTE. LTD.—See Roche Holding AG; *Int'l*, pg. 6376

ROCHE SINGAPORE TECHNICAL OPERATIONS, PTE. LTD.—See Roche Holding AG; *Int'l*, pg. 6376
ROCHE SISTEMAS DE DIAGNOSTICOS, LDA.—See Roche Holding AG; *Int'l*, pg. 6376
ROCHE S.P.A.—See Roche Holding AG; *Int'l*, pg. 6375
ROCHE S.R.O.—See Roche Holding AG; *Int'l*, pg. 6376
ROCHESTER COLONIAL MANUFACTURING; *U.S. Private*, pg. 3463
ROCHESTER COMMUNITY BASEBALL, INC.; *U.S. Public*, pg. 1804
ROCHESTER CORPORATION—See TE Connectivity Ltd.; *Int'l*, pg. 7497
ROCHESTER ELECTRONICS INC.; *U.S. Private*, pg. 3463
ROCHESTER GAS & ELECTRIC CORPORATION—See Iberdrola, S.A.; *Int'l*, pg. 3571
ROCHESTER GAUGES INTERNATIONAL—See Gas Equipment Company, Inc.; *U.S. Private*, pg. 1647
ROCHESTER GEAR, INC.—See Cie Automotive S.A.; *Int'l*, pg. 1604
ROCHESTER GIANT EAGLE; *U.S. Private*, pg. 3463
ROCHESTER INDUSTRIAL CONTROL, INC.—See Cerberus Capital Management, L.P.; *U.S. Private*, pg. 838
ROCHESTER METAL PRODUCTS CORP.; *U.S. Private*, pg. 3463
ROCHESTER MIDLAND CORPORATION; *U.S. Private*, pg. 3463
ROCHESTER PRIMARY CARE NETWORK, INC.; *U.S. Private*, pg. 3463
ROCHESTER PUBLIC LIBRARY; *U.S. Private*, pg. 3464
ROCHESTER RESORTS INC.; *U.S. Private*, pg. 3464
ROCHESTER RESOURCES LTD.; *Int'l*, pg. 6376
ROCHESTER RIVERSIDE CONVENTION CENTER; *U.S. Private*, pg. 3464
ROCHESTER SENSORS, LLC—See Renovo Capital, LLC; *U.S. Private*, pg. 3399
ROCHESTER SHOE TREE COMPANY, INC.; *U.S. Private*, pg. 3464
ROCHESTER SUPPLY CORPORATION—See First Supply LLC; *U.S. Private*, pg. 1529
ROCHESTER TV, LLC—See Entertainment Studios, Inc.; *U.S. Private*, pg. 1405
ROCHESTER WIRE & CABLE LLC—See Hexatronic Group AB; *Int'l*, pg. 3371
ROCHE THAILAND LTD.—See Roche Holding AG; *Int'l*, pg. 6376
ROCHE UKRAINE LLC—See Roche Holding AG; *Int'l*, pg. 6376
ROCHEUX INTERNATIONAL INC.; *U.S. Private*, pg. 3464
ROCHEUX INTERNATIONAL—See Rocheux International Inc.; *U.S. Private*, pg. 3464
ROCHE ZHONGYA (WUXI) CITRIC ACID LTD.—See Roche Holding AG; *Int'l*, pg. 6376
ROCHLING AUTOMOTIVE ARAIA S.L.U.—See Rochling SE & Co. KG; *Int'l*, pg. 6376
ROCHLING AUTOMOTIVE ASAN CO., LTD.—See Rochling SE & Co. KG; *Int'l*, pg. 6376
ROCHLING AUTOMOTIVE ASIA GMBH—See Rochling SE & Co. KG; *Int'l*, pg. 6376
ROCHLING AUTOMOTIVE DO BRASIL LTDA—See Rochling SE & Co. KG; *Int'l*, pg. 6377
ROCHLING AUTOMOTIVE FILTERS S.R.L.—See Rochling SE & Co. KG; *Int'l*, pg. 6376
ROCHLING AUTOMOTIVE GERMANY SE & CO. KG—See Rochling SE & Co. KG; *Int'l*, pg. 6376
ROCHLING AUTOMOTIVE GIJZEGEM N.V.—See Rochling SE & Co. KG; *Int'l*, pg. 6376
ROCHLING AUTOMOTIVE KOPRIVNICE S.R.O—See Rochling SE & Co. KG; *Int'l*, pg. 6377
ROCHLING AUTOMOTIVE MEXICO S. DE R.L. DE C.V.—See Rochling SE & Co. KG; *Int'l*, pg. 6377
ROCHLING AUTOMOTIVE MILZKALNE SIA—See Rochling SE & Co. KG; *Int'l*, pg. 6377
ROCHLING AUTOMOTIVE PARTS CHANGCHUN CO., LTD.—See Rochling SE & Co. KG; *Int'l*, pg. 6377
ROCHLING AUTOMOTIVE PARTS CHENGDU CO., LTD.—See Rochling SE & Co. KG; *Int'l*, pg. 6377
ROCHLING AUTOMOTIVE PARTS KUNSHAN CO., LTD.—See Rochling SE & Co. KG; *Int'l*, pg. 6377
ROCHLING AUTOMOTIVE PARTS SHENYANG CO., LTD.—See Rochling SE & Co. KG; *Int'l*, pg. 6377
ROCHLING AUTOMOTIVE PARTS SUZHOU CO., LTD.—See Rochling SE & Co. KG; *Int'l*, pg. 6377
ROCHLING AUTOMOTIVE PITESTI SRL.—See Rochling SE & Co. KG; *Int'l*, pg. 6377
ROCHLING AUTOMOTIVE SE & CO, KG—See Rochling SE & Co. KG; *Int'l*, pg. 6377
ROCHLING AUTOMOTIVE SLOVAKIA S.R.O—See Rochling SE & Co. KG; *Int'l*, pg. 6377
ROCHLING AUTOMOTIVE USA L.L.P.—See Rochling SE & Co. KG; *Int'l*, pg. 6377
ROCHLING ENGINEERED PLASTICS—See Rochling SE & Co. KG; *Int'l*, pg. 6377
ROCHLING ENGINEERING PLASTICS (INDIA) PVT. LTD.—See Rochling SE & Co. KG; *Int'l*, pg. 6377
ROCHLING ENGINEERING PLASTICS (INDIA) PVT. LTD. - VADODARA PLANT—See Rochling SE & Co. KG; *Int'l*, pg. 6377

ROCHLING ENGINEERING PLASTICS ITALIA S.R.L.—See Rochling SE & Co. KG; *Int'l*, pg. 6377
ROCHLING ENGINEERING PLASTICS JAPAN CO., LTD.—See Rochling SE & Co. KG; *Int'l*, pg. 6377
ROCHLING ENGINEERING PLASTICS KG—See Rochling SE & Co. KG; *Int'l*, pg. 6377
ROCHLING ENGINEERING PLASTICS LTD.—See Rochling SE & Co. KG; *Int'l*, pg. 6377
ROCHLING ENGINEERING PLASTICS (RUSSIA) LTD.—See Rochling SE & Co. KG; *Int'l*, pg. 6377
ROCHLING ENGINEERING PLASTICS, S.R.O.—See Rochling SE & Co. KG; *Int'l*, pg. 6377
ROCHLING ENGINEERING PLASTICS (UK) LTD—See Rochling SE & Co. KG; *Int'l*, pg. 6377
ROCHLING ENGINEERING PLASTIQUES S.A.S.—See Rochling SE & Co. KG; *Int'l*, pg. 6377
ROCHLING ENGINEERING S.A.R.L.—See Rochling SE & Co. KG; *Int'l*, pg. 6377
ROCHLING FIBRACON LTD.—See Rochling SE & Co. KG; *Int'l*, pg. 6377
ROCHLING FORMATERM AB—See Rochling SE & Co. KG; *Int'l*, pg. 6377
ROCHLING HYDROMA GMBH—See Rochling SE & Co. KG; *Int'l*, pg. 6377
ROCHLING INDUSTRIAL LAUPHEIM GMBH—See Rochling SE & Co. KG; *Int'l*, pg. 6377
ROCHLING INDUSTRIAL NOVE MESTO NM S.R.O.—See Rochling SE & Co. KG; *Int'l*, pg. 6377
ROCHLING INDUSTRIAL XANTEN GMBH—See Rochling SE & Co. KG; *Int'l*, pg. 6377
ROCHLING INSOLL LTD.—See Rochling SE & Co. KG; *Int'l*, pg. 6377
ROCHLING LERIPA PAPERTECH GMBH & CO. KG—See Rochling SE & Co. KG; *Int'l*, pg. 6377
ROCHLING LERIPA PAPERTECH LLC—See Rochling SE & Co. KG; *Int'l*, pg. 6377
ROCHLING LUTZEN SE & CO. KG—See Rochling SE & Co. KG; *Int'l*, pg. 6377
ROCHLING MACHINED COMPONENTS (KUNSHAN) CO., LTD.—See Rochling SE & Co. KG; *Int'l*, pg. 6377
ROCHLING MACHINED PLASTICS ITALIA S.R.L.—See Rochling SE & Co. KG; *Int'l*, pg. 6377
ROCHLING MEDICAL NEUHAUS GMBH & CO. KG—See Rochling SE & Co. KG; *Int'l*, pg. 6377
ROCHLING MEDICAL ROCHESTER, L.P.—See Rochling SE & Co. KG; *Int'l*, pg. 6377
ROCHLING MEDICAL WALDACHTAL AG—See Rochling SE & Co. KG; *Int'l*, pg. 6377
ROCHLING META-PLAST A/S—See Rochling SE & Co. KG; *Int'l*, pg. 6377
ROCHLING META-PLAST LSEZ SIA—See Rochling SE & Co. KG; *Int'l*, pg. 6378
ROCHLING OERTL KUNSTSTOFFTECHNIK GMBH—See Rochling SE & Co. KG; *Int'l*, pg. 6378
ROCHLING PERMALI COMPOSITES S.A.S.—See Rochling SE & Co. KG; *Int'l*, pg. 6378
ROCHLING PLASTICOS DE ENGENHARIA DO BRASIL LTDA.—See Rochling SE & Co. KG; *Int'l*, pg. 6378
ROCHLING PLASTICOS TECNICOS S.A.U.—See Rochling SE & Co. KG; *Int'l*, pg. 6378
ROCHLING PRECISION COMPONENTS KRASLICE SPOL. S R.O.—See Rochling SE & Co. KG; *Int'l*, pg. 6378
ROCHLING PRECISION COMPONENTS PITESTI S.R.L.—See Rochling SE & Co. KG; *Int'l*, pg. 6378
ROCHLING PRECISION COMPONENTS (SUZHOU) CO., LTD.—See Rochling SE & Co. KG; *Int'l*, pg. 6378
ROCHLING RIMITO PLAST OY—See Rochling SE & Co. KG; *Int'l*, pg. 6378
ROCHLING RODING GMBH—See Rochling SE & Co. KG; *Int'l*, pg. 6378
ROCHLING SE & CO. KG; *Int'l*, pg. 6376
ROCHLING SGT SPRITZGIESSTECHNIK GMBH—See Rochling SE & Co. KG; *Int'l*, pg. 6378
ROCHLING SUSTAPLAST SE & CO. KG—See Rochling SE & Co. KG; *Int'l*, pg. 6378
ROCHLING TECHNISCHE KUNSTSTOFFE KG—See Rochling SE & Co. KG; *Int'l*, pg. 6378
ROCHLING TECHNISCHE TEILE KG—See Rochling SE & Co. KG; *Int'l*, pg. 6378
ROCHON CORPORATION; *U.S. Private*, pg. 3464
ROCKALL TECHNOLOGIES LIMITED—See Broadridge Financial Solutions, Inc.; *U.S. Public*, pg. 392
ROCK & ALLUVIUM LIMITED—See Van Elle Holdings PLC; *Int'l*, pg. 8126
ROCK ARMOUR TRADING AB—See Per Aarsleff Holding A/S; *Int'l*, pg. 5796
ROCKAWAY CAPITAL SE; *Int'l*, pg. 6378
ROCKAWAY HOME ATTENDANT SERVICES INC.; *U.S. Private*, pg. 3465
ROCKAWAY SHOPRITE ASSOCIATES, INC.—See Glass Gardens Inc.; *U.S. Private*, pg. 1706
ROCKAWAY TOWN COURT, LLC—See Washington Prime Group Inc.; *U.S. Private*, pg. 4448
ROCKBESTOS-SUPRENANT CABLE CORP. OIL/PETROCHEMICAL DIVISION—See Berkshire Hathaway Inc.; *U.S. Public*, pg. 310

ROCKBESTOS-SUPRENANT CABLE CORP. TRANSPORTATION MARKET DIVISION—See Berkshire Hathaway Inc.; *U.S. Public*, pg. 310
ROCKBESTOS-SUPRENANT CABLE CORP. UTILITY/INDUSTRIAL MARKET DIVISION—See Berkshire Hathaway Inc.; *U.S. Public*, pg. 310
ROCKBESTOS-SUPRENANT CABLE CORP.—See Berkshire Hathaway Inc.; *U.S. Public*, pg. 310
ROCKBOCHS, INC.—See Sangoma Technologies Corporation; *Int'l*, pg. 6538
ROCKBOTTOMGOLF.COM; *U.S. Private*, pg. 3465
ROCKBOX LTD.—See iHeartMedia, Inc.; *U.S. Public*, pg. 1096
ROCKBRIDGE GROWTH EQUITY, LLC; *U.S. Private*, pg. 3465
ROCKBRIDGE MEMORIAL GARDENS LLC—See Axar Capital Management L.P.; *U.S. Private*, pg. 412
ROCK BRIDGE SURGICAL INSTITUTE, L.L.C.—See Tenet Healthcare Corporation; *U.S. Public*, pg. 2003
ROCKCASTLE GLOBAL REAL ESTATE COMPANY LIMITED—See NEPI Rockcastle N.V.; *Int'l*, pg. 5200
ROCKCASTLE POLAND SP. Z O.O.—See NEPI Rockcastle N.V.; *Int'l*, pg. 5200
ROCKCASTLE REGIONAL HOSPITAL AND RESPIRATORY CARE CENTER, INC.; *U.S. Private*, pg. 3465
ROCK CHEMICAL INDUSTRIES (MALAYSIA) SDN BERHAD—See Mega First Corporation Berhad; *Int'l*, pg. 4792
ROCK CITY MECHANICAL CO. LLC; *U.S. Private*, pg. 3464
ROCKCLIFF METALS CORPORATION—See HudBay Minerals Inc.; *Int'l*, pg. 3521
ROCK COMMUNICATIONS LTD.; *U.S. Private*, pg. 3464
ROCK CONTENT SERVICOS DE MIDIA LTDA.—See e.Bricks Ventures; *Int'l*, pg. 2251
ROCK CREEK ATHLETICS, INC.—See Neff Motivation Inc.; *U.S. Private*, pg. 2880
ROCK CREEK AUSTIN FUND, L.P.—See Wells Fargo & Company; *U.S. Public*, pg. 2345
ROCK CREEK FUND (E) LTD.—See Wells Fargo & Company; *U.S. Public*, pg. 2345
THE ROCK CREEK GROUP, LP; *U.S. Private*, pg. 4111
ROCK CREEK PHARMACEUTICALS, INC.; *U.S. Public*, pg. 1804
ROCK CREEK STRATEGIC MARKETING; *U.S. Private*, pg. 3464
ROCKDALE PIPELINE INC.; *U.S. Private*, pg. 3465
ROCKDALE, SANDOW & SOUTHERN RAILROAD COMPANY—See Brookfield Infrastructure Partners L.P.; *Int'l*, pg. 1192
ROCKDALE, SANDOW & SOUTHERN RAILROAD COMPANY—See GIC Pte. Ltd.; *Int'l*, pg. 2967
ROCKDELTA A/S—See ROCKWOOL A/S; *Int'l*, pg. 6380
ROCKE BROTHERS PTY. LTD.—See Silk Logistics Holdings Limited; *Int'l*, pg. 6921
ROCKEFELLER CAPITAL MANAGEMENT; *U.S. Private*, pg. 3466
ROCKEFELLER GROUP DEVELOPMENT CORPORATION—See Mitsubishi Estate Co., Ltd.; *Int'l*, pg. 4947
ROCKEFELLER GROUP, INC.—See Mitsubishi Estate Co., Ltd.; *Int'l*, pg. 4947
ROCKEFELLER GROUP INTERNATIONAL, INC.—See Mitsubishi Estate Co., Ltd.; *Int'l*, pg. 4947
ROCK EQUIPMENT INC.—See J.W. Jones Company, LLC; *U.S. Private*, pg. 2172
ROCKERHEADS—See Omnicom Group Inc.; *U.S. Public*, pg. 1585
ROCKET CLICKS—See BizLab, Inc.; *U.S. Private*, pg. 567
ROCKET COMMUNICATIONS INC.; *U.S. Private*, pg. 3466
ROCKET COMPANIES, INC.; *U.S. Public*, pg. 1804
THE ROCKET COMPANY; *U.S. Private*, pg. 4111
ROCKETCREATIVE; *U.S. Private*, pg. 3466
ROCKETDNA LTD.; *Int'l*, pg. 6379
ROCKET DOG BRANDS, LLC—See Circle Peak Capital LLC; *U.S. Private*, pg. 900
ROCKET DOG BRANDS, LLC—See Golden Gate Capital Management II, LLC; *U.S. Private*, pg. 1731
ROCKET ELECTRIC CO., LTD. - GWANGJU FACTORY—See Rocket Electric Co., Ltd.; *Int'l*, pg. 6378
ROCKET ELECTRIC CO., LTD. - OCHANG FACTORY—See Rocket Electric Co., Ltd.; *Int'l*, pg. 6378
ROCKET ELECTRIC CO., LTD. - ROCKET SUZHOU FACTORY—See Rocket Electric Co., Ltd.; *Int'l*, pg. 6378
ROCKET ELECTRIC CO., LTD.; *Int'l*, pg. 6378
ROCKET ELECTRIC CO., LTD.—See Rocket Electric Co., Ltd.; *Int'l*, pg. 6378
ROCKETFUEL BLOCKCHAIN, INC.; *U.S. Public*, pg. 1805
ROCKET FUEL LTD.—See Zeta Interactive Corporation; *U.S. Private*, pg. 4603
ROCKET GLOBAL ACQUISITION CORP.; *U.S. Private*, pg. 3466
ROCKET HARLEY-DAVIDSON—See Scott Fischer Enterprises LLC; *U.S. Private*, pg. 3577

ROCKET HOMES REAL ESTATE LLC; *U.S. Private*, pg. 3466
ROCKETICK, INC.—See Cadence Design Systems, Inc.; *U.S. Public*, pg. 419
ROCKETICK TECHNOLOGIES LTD.—See Cadence Design Systems, Inc.; *U.S. Public*, pg. 419
ROCKET INNOVATIONS, INC.—See Societe BIC S.A.; *Int'l*, pg. 7037
ROCKET INTERNET GROWTH OPPORTUNITIES CORP.; *Int'l*, pg. 6378
ROCKET INTERNET SE; *Int'l*, pg. 6378
ROCKET LAB USA, INC.; *U.S. Public*, pg. 1804
ROCKET LAWYER INCORPORATED; *U.S. Private*, pg. 3466
ROCKET MEDIA, INC.; *U.S. Private*, pg. 3466
ROCKET OSS—See Bain Capital, LP; *U.S. Private*, pg. 442
ROCKET PHARMACEUTICALS, INC.; *U.S. Public*, pg. 1805
ROCKET PHARMACEUTICALS, INC.; *U.S. Public*, pg. 1805
ROCKET POLAND CO., LTD—See Rocket Electric Co., Ltd.; *Int'l*, pg. 6378
ROCKET SCIENCE CONSULTING CORP.; *U.S. Private*, pg. 3466
THE ROCKET SCIENCE GROUP LLC—See Intuit Inc.; *U.S. Public*, pg. 1160
ROCKET SCIENCE; *U.S. Private*, pg. 3466
ROCKET SHARING COMPANY S.P.A.; *Int'l*, pg. 6379
ROCKET SOFTWARE, INC.—See Bain Capital, LP; *U.S. Private*, pg. 442
ROCKETS PARTNER LP; *U.S. Private*, pg. 3466
ROCKET SUPPLY CORP.—See Hicks Oil-Hicks Gas, Inc.; *U.S. Private*, pg. 1934
ROCKET SUPPLY—See Wulco Inc.; *U.S. Private*, pg. 4575
ROCKET SUPPORT SERVICES, LLC—See Kratos Defense & Security Solutions, Inc.; *U.S. Public*, pg. 1276
ROCKET THAI CO., LTD—See Rocket Electric Co., Ltd.; *Int'l*, pg. 6378
ROCKETT LUMBER & BUILDING SUPPLIES LTD.; *Int'l*, pg. 6379
ROCKEX MINING CORPORATION; *Int'l*, pg. 6379
ROCKEY HILL & KNOWLTON—See WPP plc; *Int'l*, pg. 8478
ROCKEY HILL & KNOWLTON—See WPP plc; *Int'l*, pg. 8478
ROCKEY & ROCKWELL ADVERTISING, INC.; *U.S. Private*, pg. 3466
ROCK FALL COMPANY LTD.—See HAL Trust N.V.; *Int'l*, pg. 3225
ROCKFARM SUPPLY CHAIN SOLUTIONS INC.—See AEA Investors LP; *U.S. Private*, pg. 115
ROCK FIELD CO., LTD.; *Int'l*, pg. 6378
ROCKFIRE RESOURCES PLC; *Int'l*, pg. 6379
ROCKFISH DIGITAL—See WPP plc; *Int'l*, pg. 8483
ROCKFON AB—See ROCKWOOL A/S; *Int'l*, pg. 6380
ROCKFON A/S—See ROCKWOOL A/S; *Int'l*, pg. 6380
ROCKFON B.V.—See ROCKWOOL A/S; *Int'l*, pg. 6380
ROCKFON LIMITED—See ROCKWOOL A/S; *Int'l*, pg. 6380
ROCKFON SP. Z O.O.—See ROCKWOOL A/S; *Int'l*, pg. 6380
ROCKFORD ACROMATIC PRODUCT CO.—See Aircraft Gear Corporation; *U.S. Private*, pg. 140
ROCKFORD BUSINESS INTERIORS INC.; *U.S. Private*, pg. 3466
ROCKFORD CONSTANT VELOCITY—See Aircraft Gear Corporation; *U.S. Private*, pg. 140
ROCKFORD CORPORATION; *U.S. Private*, pg. 3466
ROCKFORD CORPORATION—See Patrick Industries, Inc.; *U.S. Public*, pg. 1653
THE ROCKFORD GROUP; *U.S. Private*, pg. 4111
ROCKFORD MUTUAL INSURANCE COMPANY; *U.S. Private*, pg. 3466
ROCKFORD OIL CORP.; *U.S. Private*, pg. 3466
ROCKFORD PRODUCTS, LLC—See BlackEagle Partners, LLC; *U.S. Public*, pg. 573
ROCKFORD REGISTER STAR—See Gannett Co., Inc.; *U.S. Public*, pg. 904
ROCKFORD SPECIALTIES CO.—See Generation Growth Capital, Inc.; *U.S. Private*, pg. 1668
ROCKFORD TRUCK SALES INC—See William Charles, Ltd.; *U.S. Private*, pg. 4522
ROCKFORT MINERAL BATH COMPLEX LIMITED—See CEMEX, S.A.B. de C.V.; *Int'l*, pg. 1400
ROCK FUSCO & CONNELLY, LLC; *U.S. Private*, pg. 3464
ROCKGAS LTD.—See Gas Services NZ Ltd.; *Int'l*, pg. 2887
ROCK GATE PARTNERS LLC; *U.S. Private*, pg. 3464
ROCKHAVEN RESOURCES LTD.; *Int'l*, pg. 6379
ROCKHEDGE HERB FARMS; *U.S. Private*, pg. 3466
ROCK HILL CAPITAL GROUP, LLC; *U.S. Private*, pg. 3464
ROCK HILL CONCRETE; *U.S. Private*, pg. 3464
ROCK HILL HEALTHCARE—See The Ensign Group, Inc.; *U.S. Public*, pg. 2071
ROCKHILL HOLDING COMPANY—See State Automobile Mutual Insurance Company; *U.S. Private*, pg. 3791

ROCKHILL INSURANCE COMPANY—See State Automobile Mutual Insurance Company; *U.S. Private*, pg. 3791
ROCK HILL MECHANICAL CORP; *U.S. Private*, pg. 3464
ROCKHOPPER EXPLORATION PLC; *Int'l*, pg. 6379
ROCKHOUSE IMAGES, LLC—See Lions Gate Entertainment Corp.; *Int'l*, pg. 4521
ROCK HUNTER LIMITED—See NBA Quantum PLC; *Int'l*, pg. 5179
ROCKINGHAM CARS LTD; *Int'l*, pg. 6379
ROCKINGHAM CONSTRUCTION CO; *U.S. Private*, pg. 3466
ROCKINGHAM COOPERATIVE FARM BUREAU; *U.S. Private*, pg. 3466
ROCKINGHAM ELECTRICAL SUPPLY COMPANY, INC.; *U.S. Private*, pg. 3466
ROCKINGHAM MUTUAL INSURANCE COMPANY; *U.S. Private*, pg. 3467
ROCKINGHAM STEEL; *U.S. Private*, pg. 3467
ROCKINGHAM STEEL—See Rockingham Steel; *U.S. Private*, pg. 3467
ROCKIN' JUMP HOLDINGS LLC—See CircusTrix LLC; *U.S. Private*, pg. 900
ROCK IN RIO MADRID SA—See Live Nation Entertainment, Inc.; *U.S. Public*, pg. 1329
ROCK ISLAND CAPITAL LLC; *U.S. Private*, pg. 3464
ROCK ISLAND CORPORATION; *U.S. Private*, pg. 3465
ROCK ISLAND INTEGRATED SERVICES—See Fluor Corporation; *U.S. Public*, pg. 859
ROCK-IT AIR CHARTER, INC.—See ATL Partners, LLC; *U.S. Private*, pg. 369
ROCK-IT CARGO USA LLC - LOS ANGELES-RIC—See ATL Partners, LLC; *U.S. Private*, pg. 369
ROCK-IT CARGO USA LLC—See ATL Partners, LLC; *U.S. Private*, pg. 369
ROCKIT PTY. LTD.—See FirstRand Limited; *Int'l*, pg. 2690
ROCK-IT SAND & GRAVEL, INC.; *U.S. Private*, pg. 3465
ROCKIT SOLUTIONS, LLC—See Fitek, LLC; *U.S. Private*, pg. 1536
ROCKKLASSIKER SVERIGE AB—See Warner Bros. Discovery, Inc.; *U.S. Public*, pg. 2326
ROCKLABS LIMITED—See JBS S.A.; *Int'l*, pg. 3918
ROCKLAND AUTO PLAZA; *U.S. Private*, pg. 3467
ROCKLAND BAKERY; *U.S. Private*, pg. 3467
ROCKLAND CAPITAL, LLC; *U.S. Private*, pg. 3467
ROCKLAND ELECTRIC COMPANY—See Consolidated Edison, Inc.; *U.S. Public*, pg. 570
ROCKLAND INDUSTRIES, INC.; *U.S. Private*, pg. 3467
ROCKLAND TREE EXPERT CO, INC.—See The Davey Tree Expert Company; *U.S. Private*, pg. 4018
ROCKLAND TRUST COMPANY—See Independent Bank Corp.; *U.S. Public*, pg. 1116
THE ROCKLEDGE FL ENDOSCOPY ASC, LLC—See KKR & Co. Inc.; *U.S. Public*, pg. 1248
ROCKLER COMPANIES, INC.; *U.S. Private*, pg. 3467
ROCKLEY PHOTONICS HOLDINGS, LTD.; *Int'l*, pg. 6379
ROCKLIN PHYSICAL THERAPY, INC.—See Gryphon Investors, LLC; *U.S. Private*, pg. 1799
ROCKLOANS MARKETPLACE LLC—See Rocket Companies, Inc.; *U.S. Public*, pg. 1804
ROCKLYN MEDICAL SUPPLY, INC.—See Mi-Med Supply Co. Inc.; *U.S. Private*, pg. 2696
ROCKMAN COMPANY (U.S.A.), INC.; *U.S. Private*, pg. 3467
ROCKMONT CAPITAL PARTNERS LTD.; *U.S. Private*, pg. 3467
ROCKNEL FASTENER, INC.—See Meira, Inc.; *Int'l*, pg. 4804
ROCK (NOMINEES) LIMITED—See Raymond James Financial, Inc.; *U.S. Public*, pg. 1764
ROCK OF AGES CANADA, INC.—See TorQuest Partners Inc.; *Int'l*, pg. 7830
ROCK OF AGES CORPORATION—See TorQuest Partners Inc.; *Int'l*, pg. 7830
ROCK OLDSMOBILE CADILLAC—See Gurley-Leep Buick-GMC Truck, Inc; *U.S. Private*, pg. 1819
ROCKON ENTERPRISES LIMITED; *Int'l*, pg. 6379
ROCKONTROL TECHNOLOGY GROUP CO., LTD.; *Int'l*, pg. 6379
ROCK PAINT CO., LTD.; *Int'l*, pg. 6378
ROCKPANEL A/S—See ROCKWOOL A/S; *Int'l*, pg. 6380
ROCKPOINT EUROPE LIMITED—See Rockpoint Group, LLC; *U.S. Private*, pg. 3467
ROCKPOINT GAS STORAGE LP—See Brookfield Infrastructure Partners L.P.; *Int'l*, pg. 1190
ROCKPOINT GROUP, LLC - DALLAS OFFICE—See Rockpoint Group, LLC; *U.S. Private*, pg. 3467
ROCKPOINT GROUP, LLC - SAN FRANCISCO OFFICE—See Rockpoint Group, LLC; *U.S. Private*, pg. 3467
ROCKPOINT GROUP, LLC; *U.S. Private*, pg. 3467
ROCKPOOL ACQUISITIONS PLC; *Int'l*, pg. 6379
THE ROCKPORT COMPANY, LLC—See Charlesbank Capital Partners, LLC; *U.S. Private*, pg. 856
ROCKPORT HOLDING COMPANY INC.; *U.S. Private*, pg. 3467
ROCKPORT PUBLISHERS INC—See The Quarto Group, Inc.; *Int'l*, pg. 7677
ROCK & RAIL LLC—See Martin Marietta Materials, Inc.; *U.S. Public*, pg. 1389

ROCKRESORTS INTERNATIONAL, LLC—See Vail Resorts, Inc.; *U.S. Public*, pg. 2271
ROCK RIDGE RESOURCES, INC.; *U.S. Public*, pg. 1804
ROCKRIDGE RESOURCES LTD.; *Int'l*, pg. 6379
ROCK RIVER ENVIRONMENTAL SERVICES, INC.—See Waste Connections, Inc.; *Int'l*, pg. 8354
ROCK RIVER LUMBER & GRAIN CO; *U.S. Private*, pg. 3465
ROCKROSE ENERGY PLC—See Viaro Investment Ltd.; *Int'l*, pg. 8184
ROCKSAUCE STUDIOS, LLC—See Builder Homesite, Inc.; *U.S. Private*, pg. 681
ROCK SOLID AMUSEMENTS, LLC—See Boyd Gaming Corporation; *U.S. Public*, pg. 378
ROCK SOLID CONSTRUCTION GROUP, INC.; *U.S. Private*, pg. 3465
ROCK SOLID STABILIZATION & RECLAMATION, INC.; *U.S. Private*, pg. 3465
ROCK SOLID UK LTD.; *U.S. Private*, pg. 3465
ROCKSTAR INC.—See PepsiCo, Inc.; *U.S. Public*, pg. 1671
ROCKSTAR INTERNATIONAL LIMITED—See Take-Two Interactive Software, Inc.; *U.S. Public*, pg. 1979
ROCKSTAR LONDON, LTD.—See Take-Two Interactive Software, Inc.; *U.S. Public*, pg. 1979
ROCKSTAR NORTH LTD.—See Take-Two Interactive Software, Inc.; *U.S. Public*, pg. 1979
ROCKSTAR SAN DIEGO, INC.—See Take-Two Interactive Software, Inc.; *U.S. Public*, pg. 1979
ROCKSTONE CO., LTD.—See Prudential Financial, Inc.; *U.S. Public*, pg. 1733
ROCKTAPE, INC.—See Berkshire Partners LLC; *U.S. Private*, pg. 535
ROCK TECH LITHIUM INC.; *Int'l*, pg. 6378
ROCKTECH SYSTEMS, LLC—See Desktop Metal, Inc.; *U.S. Public*, pg. 656
ROCKTEK LIMITED—See Perenti Global Limited; *Int'l*, pg. 5798
ROCK TRANSPORT, INC.—See Vulcan Materials Company; *U.S. Public*, pg. 2314
ROCK VALLEY OIL & CHEMICAL COMPANY; *U.S. Private*, pg. 3465
ROCK VENTURES LLC; *U.S. Private*, pg. 3465
ROCKVIEW DAIRIES INC.; *U.S. Private*, pg. 3467
ROCKVILLE ENTERPRISES LLC—See Limoneira Company; *U.S. Public*, pg. 1316
THE ROCKVILLE/ESC-NORTH MD ENDOSCOPY ASC, LLC—See KKR & Co. Inc.; *U.S. Public*, pg. 1248
ROCKVILLE EYE SURGERY CENTER, LLC—See UnitedHealth Group Incorporated; *U.S. Public*, pg. 2250
ROCKVILLE FABRICS CORPORATION; *U.S. Private*, pg. 3467
ROCKVILLE FUEL & FEED COMPANY; *U.S. Private*, pg. 3467
ROCKVILLE LUXURY IMPORTS, LLC—See AutoNation, Inc.; *U.S. Public*, pg. 237
ROCKVILLE PIKE HOLDINGS, LLC—See Saul Centers, Inc.; *U.S. Public*, pg. 1842
ROCKVILLE SURGICAL SUITES, LLC—See Tenet Healthcare Corporation; *U.S. Public*, pg. 2006
ROCKWALL AMBULATORY SURGERY CENTER, L.L.P.—See Tenet Healthcare Corporation; *U.S. Public*, pg. 2012
ROCKWALL/HEATH SURGERY CENTER, L.L.P.—See Tenet Healthcare Corporation; *U.S. Public*, pg. 2012
ROCKWALL-H, INC.—See Lithia Motors, Inc.; *U.S. Public*, pg. 1326
ROCKWALL PROPERTY CORPORATION—See Columbia Ventures Corporation; *U.S. Private*, pg. 978
ROCKWATER ENERGY SOLUTIONS, INC. - MIDLAND—See Select Water Solutions, Inc.; *U.S. Public*, pg. 1862
ROCKWATER ENERGY SOLUTIONS, INC.—See Select Water Solutions, Inc.; *U.S. Public*, pg. 1862
ROCK & WATERSCAPE SYSTEMS INC.; *U.S. Private*, pg. 3464
ROCKWELL AMERICAN—See Questor Management Company, LLC; *U.S. Private*, pg. 3326
ROCKWELL AUTOMATION AB—See Rockwell Automation, Inc.; *U.S. Public*, pg. 1805
ROCKWELL AUTOMATION ARGENTINA S.A.—See Rockwell Automation, Inc.; *U.S. Public*, pg. 1805
ROCKWELL AUTOMATION ASIA PACIFIC LIMITED—See Rockwell Automation, Inc.; *U.S. Public*, pg. 1805
ROCKWELL AUTOMATION A/S—See Rockwell Automation, Inc.; *U.S. Public*, pg. 1805
ROCKWELL AUTOMATION AUSTRALIA LTD.—See Rockwell Automation, Inc.; *U.S. Public*, pg. 1805
ROCKWELL AUTOMATION B.V.—See Rockwell Automation, Inc.; *U.S. Public*, pg. 1805
ROCKWELL AUTOMATION CANADA LTD.—See Rockwell Automation, Inc.; *U.S. Public*, pg. 1805
ROCKWELL AUTOMATION CARIBBEAN LLP—See Rockwell Automation, Inc.; *U.S. Public*, pg. 1805
ROCKWELL AUTOMATION CHILE S.A.—See Rockwell Automation, Inc.; *U.S. Public*, pg. 1806
ROCKWELL AUTOMATION (CHINA) COMPANY LIMITED—See Rockwell Automation, Inc.; *U.S. Public*, pg. 1805

ROCKWELL AUTOMATION DE MEXICO, S.A. DE C.V.—See Rockwell Automation, Inc.; *U.S. Public*, pg. 1806
ROCKWELL AUTOMATION DE MEXICO, S.A. DE C.V.—See Rockwell Automation, Inc.; *U.S. Public*, pg. 1806
ROCKWELL AUTOMATION DO BRASIL LTDA.—See Rockwell Automation, Inc.; *U.S. Public*, pg. 1806
ROCKWELL AUTOMATION DRIVES SYSTEMS—See Rockwell Automation, Inc.; *U.S. Public*, pg. 1806
ROCKWELL AUTOMATION EUROPEAN HEADQUARTERS S.A./N.V.—See Rockwell Automation, Inc.; *U.S. Public*, pg. 1806
ROCKWELL AUTOMATION GERMANY G.M.B.H. & CO. KG—See Rockwell Automation, Inc.; *U.S. Public*, pg. 1806
ROCKWELL AUTOMATION GESMBH—See Rockwell Automation, Inc.; *U.S. Public*, pg. 1806
ROCKWELL AUTOMATION G.M.B.H.—See Rockwell Automation, Inc.; *U.S. Public*, pg. 1806
ROCKWELL AUTOMATION, INC.; *U.S. Public*, pg. 1805
ROCKWELL AUTOMATION INDIA LTD.—See Rockwell Automation, Inc.; *U.S. Public*, pg. 1806
ROCKWELL AUTOMATION JAPAN CO., LTD.—See Rockwell Automation, Inc.; *U.S. Public*, pg. 1806
ROCKWELL AUTOMATION KOREA LTD.—See Rockwell Automation, Inc.; *U.S. Public*, pg. 1806
ROCKWELL AUTOMATION LDA—See Rockwell Automation, Inc.; *U.S. Public*, pg. 1806
ROCKWELL AUTOMATION LIMITED—See Rockwell Automation, Inc.; *U.S. Public*, pg. 1806
ROCKWELL AUTOMATION L.L.C.—See Rockwell Automation, Inc.; *U.S. Public*, pg. 1806
ROCKWELL AUTOMATION LTD.—See Rockwell Automation, Inc.; *U.S. Public*, pg. 1806
ROCKWELL AUTOMATION (MALAYSIA) SDN. BHD.—See Rockwell Automation, Inc.; *U.S. Public*, pg. 1805
ROCKWELL AUTOMATION MIDDLE EAST—See Rockwell Automation, Inc.; *U.S. Public*, pg. 1806
ROCKWELL AUTOMATION (N.Z.) LTD.—See Rockwell Automation, Inc.; *U.S. Public*, pg. 1805
ROCKWELL AUTOMATION OF OHIO, INC.—See Rockwell Automation, Inc.; *U.S. Public*, pg. 1806
ROCKWELL AUTOMATION (PHILIPPINES) INC.—See Rockwell Automation, Inc.; *U.S. Public*, pg. 1805
ROCKWELL AUTOMATION PROPRIETARY LIMITED—See Rockwell Automation, Inc.; *U.S. Public*, pg. 1806
ROCKWELL AUTOMATION PUERTO RICO, INC.—See Rockwell Automation, Inc.; *U.S. Public*, pg. 1806
ROCKWELL AUTOMATION S.A./N.V.—See Rockwell Automation, Inc.; *U.S. Public*, pg. 1806
ROCKWELL AUTOMATION S.A.—See Rockwell Automation, Inc.; *U.S. Public*, pg. 1806
ROCKWELL AUTOMATION S.A.—See Rockwell Automation, Inc.; *U.S. Public*, pg. 1806
ROCKWELL AUTOMATION S.A.—See Rockwell Automation, Inc.; *U.S. Public*, pg. 1806
ROCKWELL AUTOMATION SAS—See Rockwell Automation, Inc.; *U.S. Public*, pg. 1806
ROCKWELL AUTOMATION SERVICES S.R.O.—See Rockwell Automation, Inc.; *U.S. Public*, pg. 1806
ROCKWELL AUTOMATION SOFT SWITCHING TECHNOLOGIES—See Rockwell Automation, Inc.; *U.S. Public*, pg. 1806
ROCKWELL AUTOMATION SOLUTIONS GMBH—See Rockwell Automation, Inc.; *U.S. Public*, pg. 1806
ROCKWELL AUTOMATION—See Rockwell Automation, Inc.; *U.S. Public*, pg. 1806
ROCKWELL AUTOMATION SOUTHEAST ASIA PTE. LTD.—See Rockwell Automation, Inc.; *U.S. Public*, pg. 1806
ROCKWELL AUTOMATION SP. Z.O.O.—See Rockwell Automation, Inc.; *U.S. Public*, pg. 1806
ROCKWELL AUTOMATION S.R.L.—See Rockwell Automation, Inc.; *U.S. Public*, pg. 1806
ROCKWELL AUTOMATION S.R.O.—See Rockwell Automation, Inc.; *U.S. Public*, pg. 1806
ROCKWELL AUTOMATION SWITZERLAND GMBH—See Rockwell Automation, Inc.; *U.S. Public*, pg. 1806
ROCKWELL AUTOMATION TAIWAN CO., LTD.—See Rockwell Automation, Inc.; *U.S. Public*, pg. 1806
ROCKWELL AUTOMATION THAI CO. LTD.—See Rockwell Automation, Inc.; *U.S. Public*, pg. 1806
ROCKWELL AUTOMATION (XIAMEN) LTD.—See Rockwell Automation, Inc.; *U.S. Public*, pg. 1805
ROCKWELL COLLINS AUSTRALIA PTY LIMITED—See RTX Corporation; *U.S. Public*, pg. 1823
ROCKWELL COLLINS CANADA INC.—See RTX Corporation; *U.S. Public*, pg. 1823
ROCKWELL COLLINS CHINA—See RTX Corporation; *U.S. Public*, pg. 1823
ROCKWELL COLLINS CONTROL TECHNOLOGIES, LLC—See RTX Corporation; *U.S. Public*, pg. 1823
ROCKWELL COLLINS DEUTSCHLAND GMBH—See RTX Corporation; *U.S. Public*, pg. 1823
ROCKWELL COLLINS DEUTSCHLAND HOLDINGS GMBH—See RTX Corporation; *U.S. Public*, pg. 1823

ROCKWELL COLLINS DO BRASIL LTDA.—See RTX Corporation; *U.S. Public*, pg. 1823
ROCKWELL COLLINS FRANCE, S.A.S.—See RTX Corporation; *U.S. Public*, pg. 1823
ROCKWELL COLLINS, INC.—See RTX Corporation; *U.S. Public*, pg. 1822
ROCKWELL COLLINS OPTRONICS, INC.—See RTX Corporation; *U.S. Public*, pg. 1823
ROCKWELL COLLINS SIMULATION & TRAINING SOLUTIONS LLC—See RTX Corporation; *U.S. Public*, pg. 1823
ROCKWELL COLLINS SOUTHEAST ASIA PTE. LTD.—See RTX Corporation; *U.S. Public*, pg. 1823
ROCKWELL COLLINS UK LIMITED—See RTX Corporation; *U.S. Public*, pg. 1823
ROCKWELL COLLINS UK LTD. - INFORMATION MANAGEMENT SERVICES—See RTX Corporation; *U.S. Public*, pg. 1823
ROCKWELL COLOMBIA S.A—See Rockwell Automation, Inc.; *U.S. Public*, pg. 1806
ROCKWELL COMMERCIAL HOLDINGS, LTD.—See Rockwell Automation, Inc.; *U.S. Public*, pg. 1806
ROCKWELL COMMUNITY DEVELOPMENT, INC.—See Bickerdike Redevelopment Corporation; *Int'l*, pg. 550
ROCKWELL DIAMONDS INC.; *Int'l*, pg. 6379
ROCKWELL LAND CORPORATION—See Manila Electric Company; *Int'l*, pg. 4671
ROCKWELL MEDICAL, INC.; *U.S. Public*, pg. 1807
ROCKWELL OTOMASYON TICARET A.S.—See Rockwell Automation, Inc.; *U.S. Public*, pg. 1807
ROCKWELL PETROLEUM INC.; *Int'l*, pg. 6379
ROCKWELL PRIMARIES DEVELOPMENT CORPORATION—See Lopez, Inc.; *Int'l*, pg. 4557
ROCKWELL PROPERTY CO.; *U.S. Private*, pg. 3467
ROCKWELL SERVICE—See Ensign Energy Services Inc.; *Int'l*, pg. 2447
ROCKWELL SERVICING, INC.—See Ensign Energy Services Inc.; *Int'l*, pg. 2447
ROCKWELL SOFTWARE, INC.—See Rockwell Automation, Inc.; *U.S. Public*, pg. 1807
ROCKWELL TRANSPORTATION, INC.—See Rockwell Medical, Inc.; *U.S. Public*, pg. 1807
ROCK WEST COMPOSITES, INC.; *U.S. Private*, pg. 3465
ROCKWEST TECHNOLOGY GROUP LLC—See Identiv, Inc.; *U.S. Public*, pg. 1089
ROCKWOOD BANCSHARES, INC.; *U.S. Private*, pg. 3467
ROCKWOOD BANK—See Rockwood Bancshares, Inc.; *U.S. Private*, pg. 3467
ROCKWOOD CAPITAL LLC; *U.S. Private*, pg. 3468
ROCKWOOD CASUALTY INSURANCE CO.—See Brookfield Reinsurance Ltd.; *Int'l*, pg. 1194
ROCKWOOD & CO. INC.—See Rockwood Holding Company Inc.; *U.S. Private*, pg. 3468
ROCKWOOD EQUITY PARTNERS, LLC; *U.S. Private*, pg. 3468
ROCKWOOD HOLDING COMPANY INC.; *U.S. Private*, pg. 3468
ROCKWOOD HOLDINGS LIMITED PARTNERSHIP; *U.S. Private*, pg. 3468
ROCKWOOD LITHIUM INDIA PVT. LTD.—See Albemarle Corporation; *U.S. Public*, pg. 73
ROCKWOOD LITHIUM KOREA LLC—See Albemarle Corporation; *U.S. Public*, pg. 73
ROCKWOOD LITHIUM SHANGHAI CO., LTD.—See Albemarle Corporation; *U.S. Public*, pg. 73
ROCKWOOD LITHIUM TAIWAN CO., LTD.—See Albemarle Corporation; *U.S. Public*, pg. 73
ROCKWOOD SERVICE CORPORATION—See Rockwood Holdings Limited Partnership; *U.S. Private*, pg. 3468
ROCKWOOL AB—See ROCKWOOL A/S; *Int'l*, pg. 6380
ROCKWOOL ADRIATIC D.O.O.—See ROCKWOOL A/S; *Int'l*, pg. 6380
ROCKWOOL A/S; *Int'l*, pg. 6379
ROCKWOOL A/S—See ROCKWOOL A/S; *Int'l*, pg. 6380
ROCKWOOL A.S.—See ROCKWOOL A/S; *Int'l*, pg. 6381
ROCKWOOL A.S.—See ROCKWOOL A/S; *Int'l*, pg. 6381
ROCKWOOL AUSTRALIA PTY. LTD.—See ROCKWOOL A/S; *Int'l*, pg. 6380
ROCKWOOL BELGIUM B.V.—See ROCKWOOL A/S; *Int'l*, pg. 6380
ROCKWOOL BENELUX B.V.—See ROCKWOOL A/S; *Int'l*, pg. 6380
ROCKWOOL BENELUX HOLDING B.V.—See ROCKWOOL A/S; *Int'l*, pg. 6381
ROCKWOOL BETEILIGUNGS GMBH—See ROCKWOOL A/S; *Int'l*, pg. 6380
ROCKWOOL BUILDING MATERIALS LTD.—See ROCKWOOL A/S; *Int'l*, pg. 6381
ROCKWOOL BUILDING MATERIALS (PHILIPPINES) LTD.—See ROCKWOOL A/S; *Int'l*, pg. 6381
ROCKWOOL BUILDING MATERIALS (SINGAPORE) PTE LTD.—See ROCKWOOL A/S; *Int'l*, pg. 6381
ROCKWOOL BULGARIA EOOD—See ROCKWOOL A/S; *Int'l*, pg. 6380
ROCKWOOL BULGARIA LTD.—See ROCKWOOL A/S; *Int'l*, pg. 6381
ROCKWOOL B.V.—See ROCKWOOL A/S; *Int'l*, pg. 6380

ROCKWOOL.COM GMBH—See ROCKWOOL A/S; *Int'l*, pg. 6380
ROCKWOOL DANMARK A/S—See ROCKWOOL A/S; *Int'l*, pg. 6380
ROCKWOOL EE OU—See ROCKWOOL A/S; *Int'l*, pg. 6381
ROCKWOOL FINLAND OY—See ROCKWOOL A/S; *Int'l*, pg. 6381
ROCKWOOL FIRESAFE INSULATION (GUANGZHOU) CO. LTD.—See ROCKWOOL A/S; *Int'l*, pg. 6381
ROCKWOOL FIRESAFE INSULATION (SHANGHAI) CO. LTD.—See ROCKWOOL A/S; *Int'l*, pg. 6381
ROCKWOOL FRANCE S.A.S—See ROCKWOOL A/S; *Int'l*, pg. 6381
ROCKWOOL GMBH—See ROCKWOOL A/S; *Int'l*, pg. 6380
ROCKWOOL HANDELSGESELLSCHAFT M.B.H—See ROCKWOOL A/S; *Int'l*, pg. 6381
ROCKWOOL HUNGARIA KFT.—See ROCKWOOL A/S; *Int'l*, pg. 6381
ROCKWOOL HUNGARY KFT.—See ROCKWOOL A/S; *Int'l*, pg. 6380
ROCKWOOL IBERICA S.A.—See ROCKWOOL A/S; *Int'l*, pg. 6381
ROCKWOOL INSAAT VE YALITIM SISTEMLERI SAN. VE TIC. LTD. STI.—See ROCKWOOL A/S; *Int'l*, pg. 6380
ROCKWOOL INVESTMENTS LTD.—See ROCKWOOL A/S; *Int'l*, pg. 6381
ROCKWOOL ISOLATION S.A.—See ROCKWOOL A/S; *Int'l*, pg. 6381
ROCKWOOL ITALIA S.R.L.—See ROCKWOOL A/S; *Int'l*, pg. 6381
ROCKWOOL LAPINUS N.V.—See ROCKWOOL A/S; *Int'l*, pg. 6381
ROCKWOOL LAPINUS PRODUCTIE B.V.—See ROCKWOOL A/S; *Int'l*, pg. 6381
ROCKWOOL LIMITED—See ROCKWOOL A/S; *Int'l*, pg. 6381
ROCKWOOL LIMITED—See ROCKWOOL A/S; *Int'l*, pg. 6381
ROCKWOOL LTD.—See ROCKWOOL A/S; *Int'l*, pg. 6381
ROCKWOOL MALAYSIA SDN. BHD.—See ROCKWOOL A/S; *Int'l*, pg. 6381
ROCKWOOL MINERALWOLLE GMBH—See ROCKWOOL A/S; *Int'l*, pg. 6380
ROCKWOOL N.V.—See ROCKWOOL A/S; *Int'l*, pg. 6381
ROCKWOOL PENINSULAR S.A.—See ROCKWOOL A/S; *Int'l*, pg. 6381
ROCKWOOL POLSKA SP. Z.O.O.—See ROCKWOOL A/S; *Int'l*, pg. 6381
ROCKWOOL ROCKFON GMBH—See ROCKWOOL A/S; *Int'l*, pg. 6380
ROCKWOOL ROCKPANEL B.V.—See ROCKWOOL A/S; *Int'l*, pg. 6381
ROCKWOOL ROMANIA S.R.L.—See ROCKWOOL A/S; *Int'l*, pg. 6380
ROCKWOOL SLOVENSKO S.R.O.—See ROCKWOOL A/S; *Int'l*, pg. 6381
ROCKWOOL TECHNICAL INSULATION INDIA PVT. LTD.—See ROCKWOOL A/S; *Int'l*, pg. 6380
ROCKWOOL TECHNICAL INSULATION - NORWAY—See ROCKWOOL A/S; *Int'l*, pg. 6379
ROCKWOOL (THAILAND) LIMITED—See ROCKWOOL A/S; *Int'l*, pg. 6380
ROCK WORLD LISBOA S.A.—See Live Nation Entertainment, Inc.; *U.S. Public*, pg. 1330
ROCKWORTH PUBLIC COMPANY LIMITED - AYUDHAYA FACILITY—See Rockworth Public Company Limited; *Int'l*, pg. 6381
ROCKWORTH PUBLIC COMPANY LIMITED; *Int'l*, pg. 6381
ROCKWORTH SYSTEMS FURNITURE INDIA PVT. LTD.—See Rockworth Public Company Limited; *Int'l*, pg. 6382
ROCK YARD INC.—See GLM Landscape Supply, LLC; *U.S. Private*, pg. 1711
ROCKY BRANDS CANADA, INC.—See Rocky Brands, Inc.; *U.S. Public*, pg. 1807
ROCKY BRANDS, INC.; *U.S. Public*, pg. 1807
ROCKY BRANDS US, LLC—See Rocky Brands, Inc.; *U.S. Public*, pg. 1807
ROCKY CANADA, INC.—See Rocky Brands, Inc.; *U.S. Public*, pg. 1807
ROCKY CREEK LUMBER COMPANY LLC; *U.S. Private*, pg. 3468
ROCKY GAP CASINO RESORT—See Golden Entertainment, Inc.; *U.S. Public*, pg. 950
ROCKY MOUNTAIN ADVISORY, LLC—See Marshall & Stevens Inc.; *U.S. Private*, pg. 2592
ROCKY MOUNTAIN AGRONOMICS INC.; *U.S. Private*, pg. 3468
ROCKY MOUNTAIN BANK—See Heartland Financial USA, Inc.; *U.S. Public*, pg. 1018
ROCKY MOUNTAIN CARE; *U.S. Private*, pg. 3468
ROCKY MOUNTAIN CHOCOLATE FACTORY, INC.—See Rocky Mountain Chocolate Factory, Inc.; *U.S. Public*, pg. 1807
ROCKY MOUNTAIN CHOCOLATE FACTORY, INC.; *U.S. Public*, pg. 1807

COMPANY NAME INDEX

ROCKY MOUNTAIN CLOTHING CO.—See Miller International, Inc.; *U.S. Private*, pg. 2734
ROCKY MOUNTAIN CONTRACTORS, INC.—See MDU Resources Group, Inc.; *U.S. Public*, pg. 1410
ROCKY MOUNTAIN DEVELOPMENT COUNCIL; *U.S. Private*, pg. 3468
ROCKY MOUNTAIN ELK FOUNDATION, INC.; *U.S. Private*, pg. 3468
ROCKY MOUNTAIN EQUIPMENT ALBERTA LTD.; *Int'l*, pg. 6382
ROCKY MOUNTAIN EQUIPMENT—See Rocky Mountain Equipment Alberta Ltd.; *Int'l*, pg. 6382
ROCKY MOUNTAIN EQUIPMENT—See Rocky Mountain Equipment Alberta Ltd.; *Int'l*, pg. 6382
ROCKY MOUNTAIN EXPRESS CORP; *U.S. Private*, pg. 3468
ROCKY MOUNTAIN FABRICATION INC.; *U.S. Private*, pg. 3468
ROCKY MOUNTAIN FIBER PLUS; *U.S. Private*, pg. 3468
ROCKY MOUNTAIN HARDWARE INC.; *U.S. Private*, pg. 3468
ROCKY MOUNTAIN HEALTH MAINTENANCE ORGANIZATION INCORPORATED; *U.S. Private*, pg. 3469
ROCKY MOUNTAIN HEALTH MAINTENANCE ORGANIZATION, INCORPORATED—See UnitedHealth Group Incorporated; *U.S. Public*, pg. 2250
ROCKY MOUNTAIN HIGH BRANDS, INC.; *U.S. Public*, pg. 1807
ROCKY MOUNTAIN HUMAN SERVICES; *U.S. Private*, pg. 3469
ROCKY MOUNTAIN HYDROSTATICS, LLC—See HEICO Corporation; *U.S. Public*, pg. 1021
ROCKY MOUNTAIN INDUSTRIAL SERVICES, LLC—See TorQuest Partners Inc.; *Int'l*, pg. 7830
ROCKY MOUNTAIN INDUSTRIALS, INC.; *U.S. Public*, pg. 1807
ROCKY MOUNTAIN INDUSTRIAL SUPPLY, INC—See Mallory Safety & Supply LLC; *U.S. Private*, pg. 2558
ROCKY MOUNTAIN INFRASTRUCTURE, LLC—See Civitas Resources, Inc.; *U.S. Public*, pg. 507
ROCKY MOUNTAIN INSTRUMENT, INC.; *U.S. Private*, pg. 3469
ROCKY MOUNTAIN LIQUOR INC.; *Int'l*, pg. 6382
ROCKY MOUNTAIN LOG HOMES-CANADA, LLC, *U.S. Private*, pg. 3469
ROCKY MOUNTAIN MATERIALS & ASPHALT, INC.; *U.S. Private*, pg. 3469
ROCKY MOUNTAIN MEDICAL, LLC—See Coloplast A/S; *Int'l*, pg. 1704
ROCKY MOUNTAIN NATURAL GAS LLC—See Black Hills Corporation; *U.S. Public*, pg. 340
ROCKY MOUNTAIN OILFIELD WAREHOUSE; *U.S. Private*, pg. 3469
ROCKY MOUNTAIN PEDIATRIC HEMATOLOGY ONCOLOGY, LLC—See HCA Healthcare, Inc.; *U.S. Public*, pg. 1007
ROCKY MOUNTAIN PIES, LLC.; *U.S. Private*, pg. 3469
ROCKY MOUNTAIN POWER—See Berkshire Hathaway Inc.; *U.S. Public*, pg. 301
ROCKY MOUNTAIN PRESTRESS, LLC—See Phelps Tointon Inc.; *U.S. Private*, pg. 3167
ROCKY MOUNTAIN PUBLIC BROADCASTING NETWORK, INC.; *U.S. Private*, pg. 3469
ROCKY MOUNTAIN SANITATION, LLC; *U.S. Private*, pg. 3469
ROCKY MOUNTAIN STRUCTURES INC.—See First Reserve Management, L.P.; *U.S. Private*, pg. 1526
ROCKY MOUNTAIN SUPPLY INC—See DXP Enterprises, Inc.; *U.S. Public*, pg. 698
ROCKY MOUNTAIN SUPPLY INC.; *U.S. Private*, pg. 3469
ROCKY MOUNTAIN SURGERY CENTER, LLC—See HCA Healthcare, Inc.; *U.S. Public*, pg. 1007
ROCKY MOUNTAIN SURGERY CENTER, LLC—See HCA Healthcare, Inc.; *U.S. Public*, pg. 1007
ROCKY MOUNTAIN TOURS—See Summit Sports, Inc.; *U.S. Private*, pg. 3857
THE ROCKY MOUNTAIN TRUCK CENTER—See Interstate Companies, Inc.; *U.S. Private*, pg. 2124
ROCKY MOUNT STOP & SHOP INC; *U.S. Private*, pg. 3468
ROCKYOU, INC.; *U.S. Private*, pg. 3469
ROCKY OUTDOOR GEAR—See Rocky Brands, Inc.; *U.S. Public*, pg. 1807
ROCKY OUTDOOR GEAR STORE, LLC—See Rocky Brands, Inc.; *U.S. Public*, pg. 1807
ROCKY RESEARCH—See Honeywell International Inc.; *U.S. Public*, pg. 1051
ROCKY RIDGE TRUCKS, INC.—See Fox Factory Holding Corp.; *U.S. Public*, pg. 877
THE ROCKY RIVER REALTY COMPANY—See Eversource Energy; *U.S. Public*, pg. 802
ROCKY ROCOCO CORPORATION; *U.S. Private*, pg. 3469
ROCKY'S HARDWARE INCORPORATED; *U.S. Private*, pg. 3469
ROCKY TOP MARKETS LLC; *U.S. Private*, pg. 3469
ROCKY TOP MATERIALS, INC.—See GMS Inc.; *U.S. Public*, pg. 948
ROCLA CONCRETE TIE, INC. - BEAR PLANT—See Vossloh AG; *Int'l*, pg. 8308
ROCLA CONCRETE TIE, INC.—See Vossloh AG; *Int'l*, pg. 8308
ROCLA OYJ—See Mitsubishi Heavy Industries, Ltd.; *Int'l*, pg. 4961
ROCLA (PROPRIETARY) LIMITED—See Murray & Roberts Holdings Ltd.; *Int'l*, pg. 5100
ROCLA PTY LIMITED—See Heidelberg Materials AG; *Int'l*, pg. 3314
ROC NORTH WEST LIMITED—See Sheikh Holdings Group (Investments) Limited; *Int'l*, pg. 6794
ROC-OFF PRODUCTIONS, INC.—See Mountain Productions, Inc.; *U.S. Private*, pg. 2799
ROC OIL (BOHAI) COMPANY—See Fosun International Limited; *Int'l*, pg. 2752
ROC OIL COMPANY LIMITED—See Fosun International Limited; *Int'l*, pg. 2752
ROC OIL MALAYSIA (HOLDING) SDN BHD—See Fosun International Limited; *Int'l*, pg. 2752
ROC OIL (WA) PTY LIMITED—See Fosun International Limited; *Int'l*, pg. 2752
ROCOMAMAS FRANCHISE CO (PTY). LTD.—See Spur Corporation; *Int'l*, pg. 7146
ROCOM ELECTRIC COMPANY LIMITED—See Legrand S.A.; *Int'l*, pg. 4446
ROCOM LTD.—See Nycomm Holdings Limited; *Int'l*, pg. 5500
R&O CONSTRUCTION COMPANY INC.; *U.S. Private*, pg. 3332
ROC PARTNERS PTY LTD; *Int'l*, pg. 6372
ROC SALES, INC.—See RPM International Inc.; *U.S. Public*, pg. 1817
ROC SEARCH GMBH—See Roc Search Ltd.; *Int'l*, pg. 6372
ROC SEARCH LTD.; *Int'l*, pg. 6372
ROC SERVICE COMPANY; *U.S. Private*, pg. 3463
ROCS, INC.; *U.S. Private*, pg. 3469
ROC SPICER, LTD.—See Dana Incorporated; *U.S. Public*, pg. 623
ROC SYSTEMS CONSULTING LTD.—See Zalaris ASA; *Int'l*, pg. 8621
ROCTEC GLOBAL PUBLIC COMPANY LIMITED—See BTS Group Holdings Public Company Limited; *Int'l*, pg. 1206
ROCTEC TECHNOLOGY LIMITED—See BTS Group Holdings Public Company Limited; *Int'l*, pg. 1206
ROCTEL MANUFACTURING, LTD.—See Linamar Corporation; *Int'l*, pg. 4502
ROCTEST INC.—See Nova Ventures Group Corp.; *U.S. Private*, pg. 2966
ROCTEST LTD.—See Nova Ventures Group Corp.; *U.S. Private*, pg. 2966
ROCTOOL JAPAN—See RocTool SA; *Int'l*, pg. 6382
ROCTOOL NORTH AMERICA—See RocTool SA; *Int'l*, pg. 6382
ROCTOOL SA; *Int'l*, pg. 6382
ROCTOOL TAIWAN—See RocTool SA; *Int'l*, pg. 6382
RODACENTER LTDA.—See THK CO., LTD.; *Int'l*, pg. 7712
RODACOM SARL—See Axel Springer SE; *Int'l*, pg. 766
RODA DEACO VALVE, INC.—See Roper Technologies, Inc.; *U.S. Public*, pg. 1813
RODAG PROPERTIES (PTY) LIMITED—See Afrimat Limited; *Int'l*, pg. 193
RODAMCO CESKA REPUBLIKA SRO—See Unibail-Rodamco-Westfield SE; *Int'l*, pg. 8029
RODAMCO ENEBY AB—See Unibail-Rodamco-Westfield SE; *Int'l*, pg. 8029
RODAMCO EUROPE N.V.—See Unibail-Rodamco-Westfield SE; *Int'l*, pg. 8030
RODAMCO NEDERLAND WINKELS BV—See Unibail-Rodamco-Westfield SE; *Int'l*, pg. 8030
RODAMCO TYRESO CENTRUM AB—See Unibail-Rodamco-Westfield SE; *Int'l*, pg. 8030
RODAMCO VASBY CENTRUM AB—See Unibail-Rodamco-Westfield SE; *Int'l*, pg. 8030
RODAMIENTOS FAG S.A. DE C.V—See INA-Holding Schaeffler GmbH & Co. KG; *Int'l*, pg. 3640
RODAMIENTOS Y ACCESORIOS SA DE CV; *Int'l*, pg. 6382
RODAN & FIELDS, LLC; *U.S. Private*, pg. 3469
RODATA INC.; *U.S. Private*, pg. 3469
RODA VIVATEX TBK; *Int'l*, pg. 6382
RODAX S.A.—See Metlen Energy & Metals S.A.; *Int'l*, pg. 4855
RODDA PAINT CO.—See Cloverdale Paint Inc.; *Int'l*, pg. 1663
RODDEY ENGINEERING SERVICES, INC.—See Martin Resource Management Corporation; *U.S. Private*, pg. 2596
RODEDAWG INTERNATIONAL INDUSTRIES, INC.; *U.S. Public*, pg. 1807
RODELLE INC.—See Archer-Daniels-Midland Company; *U.S. Public*, pg. 185
RODELTA PUMPS INTERNATIONAL B.V.—See Kirloskar Brothers Limited; *Int'l*, pg. 4191
RODE MICROPHONES; *Int'l*, pg. 6382
RODEM INC.; *U.S. Private*, pg. 3470

RODROCK & ASSOCIATES INC.

RODENHURST ESTATES LIMITED—See Highcroft Investments PLC; *Int'l*, pg. 3387
RODENSTOCK AUSTRALIA PTY. LTD.—See Compass Advisers Group LLC; *U.S. Private*, pg. 999
RODENSTOCK CANADA INC.—See Compass Advisers Group LLC; *U.S. Private*, pg. 999
RODENSTOCK GMBH—See Compass Advisers Group LLC; *U.S. Private*, pg. 999
RODENSTOCK OSTERREICH GMBH—See Compass Advisers Group LLC; *U.S. Private*, pg. 999
RODENS VARME & SANITET AB—See Instalco AB; *Int'l*, pg. 3722
RODEO CAPITAL II CORP.; *Int'l*, pg. 6382
RODEO CO., LTD—See Sega Sammy Holdings, Inc.; *Int'l*, pg. 6681
RODET SAS—See Fermob SA; *Int'l*, pg. 2639
RODEX FASTENERS CORP.; *Int'l*, pg. 6382
ROD FRASER ENTERPRISES INC.; *U.S. Private*, pg. 3469
RODGAS AD BACKA TOPOLA—See Petrol, Slovenska energetska druzba, d.d.; *Int'l*, pg. 5827
RODGERS BUILDERS, INC.; *U.S. Private*, pg. 3470
RODGERS CADILLAC, INC.; *U.S. Private*, pg. 3470
RODGERS FORGE CONDOMINIUMS, INC.—See UDR, Inc.; *U.S. Public*, pg. 2218
RODGERS INSTRUMENTS CORPORATION—See Roland Corporation; *Int'l*, pg. 6390
RODGERS METAL CRAFT, INC.; *U.S. Private*, pg. 3470
RODGERS TOWNSEND, LLC—See Omnicom Group Inc.; *U.S. Public*, pg. 1593
RODGERS TRUCKING CO.; *U.S. Private*, pg. 3470
RODHE SECURITY, S.A. DE C.V.—See Aiphone Co., Ltd.; *Int'l*, pg. 235
RODHES MARKET INCORPORATED; *U.S. Private*, pg. 3470
RODI AUTOMOTIVE INC.; *U.S. Private*, pg. 3470
RODINA-91 AD; *Int'l*, pg. 6382
RODINA; *Int'l*, pg. 6382
RODINGER INGENIEURBAU GMBH—See STRABAG SE; *Int'l*, pg. 7232
RODINIA LITHIUM INC.; *Int'l*, pg. 6382
RODIN INCOME TRUST, INC.; *U.S. Private*, pg. 3470
RODIO CIMENTACIONES ESPECIALES, S.A.—See Empresas ICA S.A.B. de C.V.; *Int'l*, pg. 2391
RODIO - KRONSA .S.A.—See VINCI S.A.; *Int'l*, pg. 8226
RODIO SWISSBORING COSTA RICA S.A.—See VINCI S.A.; *Int'l*, pg. 8226
RODIO SWISSBORING EL SALVADOR S.A.C.V.—See VINCI S.A.; *Int'l*, pg. 8226
RODIO SWISSBORING GUATEMALA S.A.—See VINCI S.A.; *Int'l*, pg. 8226
RODIO SWISSBORING HONDURAS S.A.—See VINCI S.A.; *Int'l*, pg. 8226
RODIO SWISSBORING NICARAGUA S.A.—See VINCI S.A.; *Int'l*, pg. 8226
RODIO SWISSBORING PANAMA SOCIEDAD ANONIMA—See VINCI S.A.; *Int'l*, pg. 8226
RODI SYSTEMS CORPORATION; *U.S. Private*, pg. 3470
RODIUM REALTY LIMITED; *Int'l*, pg. 6382
RODKAERSBRO DYREKLINIK APS—See Vimian Group AB; *Int'l*, pg. 8208
ROD-L ELECTRONICS INC.; *U.S. Private*, pg. 3469
RODMAN ENTERPRISES LIMITED—See Pearl River Holdings Limited; *Int'l*, pg. 5775
RODMAN FORD SALES INC.; *U.S. Private*, pg. 3470
RODMAN INSURANCE AGENCY, INC.—See Brown & Brown, Inc.; *U.S. Public*, pg. 399
RODMAN LINCOLN-MERCURY INC.—See Rodman Ford Sales Inc.; *U.S. Private*, pg. 3470
RODMAN RIDE FOR KIDS; *U.S. Private*, pg. 3470
ROD MCLELLAN COMPANY—See The Scotts Miracle-Gro Company; *U.S. Public*, pg. 2127
RODNA ZEMYA HOLDING AD; *Int'l*, pg. 6382
RODNEY D. YOUNG INSURANCE AGENCY, INC.; *U.S. Private*, pg. 3470
RODNEY HUNT COMPANY—See Zurn Elkay Water Solutions Corporation; *U.S. Public*, pg. 2414
RODNEY HUNT-FONTAINE, INC.—See Zurn Elkay Water Solutions Corporation; *U.S. Public*, pg. 2414
RODNEY HUNT-FONTAINE LTD.—See Zurn Elkay Water Solutions Corporation; *U.S. Public*, pg. 2414
RODNEY HUNT INC.—See Jash Engineering Limited; *Int'l*, pg. 3912
RODNIC LLC—See Benchmark Electronics, Inc.; *U.S. Public*, pg. 296
RODOBAN SEGURANCA E TRANPSORTE DE VALORES LTDA—See The Brink's Company; *U.S. Public*, pg. 2043
RODOBO INTERNATIONAL, INC.; *Int'l*, pg. 6382
RODOCANACHI CAPITAL INC.; *Int'l*, pg. 6382
RODON FOODS INC.; *U.S. Private*, pg. 3470
RODOPA TRACE LTD.—See Trace Group Hold PLC; *Int'l*, pg. 7886
RODOPSKA SLAVA AD; *Int'l*, pg. 6382
RODOVIAS DAS COLINAS S.A.; *Int'l*, pg. 6382
RODRIGO TEKSTIL SANAYI VE TICARET AS; *Int'l*, pg. 6382
RODROCK & ASSOCIATES INC.; *U.S. Private*, pg. 3470

RODROCK & ASSOCIATES INC.   CORPORATE AFFILIATIONS

RODWELLS & CO NSW PTY. LTD.—See Nutrien Ltd.; *Int'l*, pg. 5493
RODWELLS & CO PTY. LTD.—See Nutrien Ltd.; *Int'l*, pg. 5493
ROD WORKS INC.; *U.S. Private*, pg. 3469
RODYK & DAVIDSON LLP—See Dentons Group; *U.S. Private*, pg. 1207
RODY TRUCK CENTER OF MIAMI, INC.; *U.S. Private*, pg. 3470
ROEBLING MANAGEMENT COMPANY, LLC; *U.S. Private*, pg. 3470
ROEBUCK ASSET MANAGEMENT LLP—See GFH Financial Group B.S.C.; *Int'l*, pg. 2956
ROEBUCK FOOD GROUP PLC; *Int'l*, pg. 6382
ROECHLING AUTOMOTIVE CHONBURI CO., LTD.—See Rochling SE & Co. KG; *Int'l*, pg. 6378
ROECHLING ENGINEERING PLASTICS PTE LTD—See Rochling SE & Co. KG; *Int'l*, pg. 6378
ROECHLING ENGINEERING PLASTICS (SUZHOU) CO., LTD.—See Rochling SE & Co. KG; *Int'l*, pg. 6378
ROECHLING INTERNATIONAL (SHANGHAI) CO., LTD.—See Rochling SE & Co. KG; *Int'l*, pg. 6378
ROECHLING MEDICAL LANCASTER LLC—See Rochling SE & Co. KG; *Int'l*, pg. 6378
ROEDERER ESTATE INC.—See LVMH Moet Hennessy Louis Vuitton SE; *Int'l*, pg. 4604
ROEDER IMPLEMENT INC.; *U.S. Private*, pg. 3470
ROEDIGER GEBAUDETECHNIK GMBH—See Bilfinger SE; *Int'l*, pg. 1028
ROEDIGER GRUNDBESITZ GMBH—See Bilfinger SE; *Int'l*, pg. 1028
ROEDING GROUP COMPANIES, INC.; *U.S. Private*, pg. 3470
ROEHLEN ENGRAVING BF PERKINS—See Standex International; *U.S. Public*, pg. 1930
ROEHLEN INDUSTRIES PTY. LIMITED—See Standex International; *U.S. Public*, pg. 1930
ROEHL LOGISTICS, INC.—See Roehl Transport, Inc.; *U.S. Private*, pg. 3470
ROEHL TRANSPORT, INC.; *U.S. Private*, pg. 3470
ROEHRS & COMPANY, INC.—See GTCR LLC; *U.S. Private*, pg. 1804
ROEHRS POLAND SP. ZO.O.—See Rohrs AG; *Int'l*, pg. 6387
ROEMER INSURANCE, INC.—See GTCR LLC; *U.S. Private*, pg. 1804
ROEPKE PHYSICAL THERAPY, LIMITED PARTNERSHIP—See U.S. Physical Therapy, Inc.; *U.S. Public*, pg. 2216
ROERSMA & WURN BUILDERS; *U.S. Private*, pg. 3470
ROESCH INC.; *U.S. Private*, pg. 3470
ROESER HOUSING DEVELOPMENT CORPORATION; *U.S. Private*, pg. 3470
ROETO LTD.—See Gefen International A.I Ltd.; *Int'l*, pg. 2911
ROETTGERS COMPANY INC.; *U.S. Private*, pg. 3471
ROETZEL & ANDRESS; *U.S. Private*, pg. 3471
ROEVIN LIMITED—See Adecco Group AG; *Int'l*, pg. 138
ROEVIN MANAGEMENT SERVICES LTD.—See Adecco Group AG; *Int'l*, pg. 138
ROEVIN TECHNICAL PEOPLE LIMITED—See Adecco Group AG; *Int'l*, pg. 138
ROE VISUAL CO., LTD.—See Unilumin Group Co., Ltd.; *Int'l*, pg. 8048
ROEWEKAMP GMBH & CO KOMMANDITGESELLSCHAFT—See Heidelberg Materials AG; *Int'l*, pg. 3319
ROEWEKAMP GMBH—See Heidelberg Materials AG; *Int'l*, pg. 3319
ROFAN SERVICES LLC—See Dow Inc.; *U.S. Public*, pg. 685
ROFF GLOBAL—See Reditus SGPS S.A.; *Int'l*, pg. 6248
ROFF LOGISTICS INC.; *Int'l*, pg. 6383
ROFIN BAASEL BENELUX BV—See Coherent Corp.; *U.S. Public*, pg. 528
ROFIN-BAASEL CANADA LTD.—See Coherent Corp.; *U.S. Public*, pg. 527
ROFIN-BAASEL CHINA CO., LTD.—See Coherent Corp.; *U.S. Public*, pg. 528
ROFIN-BAASEL ESPANA SL—See Coherent Corp.; *U.S. Public*, pg. 528
ROFIN-BAASEL FRANCE SA—See Coherent Corp.; *U.S. Public*, pg. 528
ROFIN-BAASEL, INC.—See Coherent Corp.; *U.S. Public*, pg. 527
ROFIN-BAASEL JAPAN CORP.—See Coherent Corp.; *U.S. Public*, pg. 527
ROFIN-BAASEL KOREA CO., LTD.—See Coherent Corp.; *U.S. Public*, pg. 527
ROFIN-BAASEL LASERTECH GMBH & CO. KG—See Coherent Corp.; *U.S. Public*, pg. 528
ROFIN-BAASEL TAIWAN LTD.—See Coherent Corp.; *U.S. Public*, pg. 527
ROFIN-BAASEL UK LTD.—See Coherent Corp.; *U.S. Public*, pg. 528
ROFIN-SINAR, INC.—See Coherent Corp.; *U.S. Public*, pg. 527
ROFIN-SINAR LASER GMBH—See Coherent Corp.; *U.S. Public*, pg. 527

ROFIN-SINAR TECHNOLOGIES EUROPE S.L.—See Coherent Corp.; *U.S. Public*, pg. 528
ROFIN-SINAR TECHNOLOGIES, INC.—See Coherent Corp.; *U.S. Public*, pg. 527
ROFIN-SINAR UK LTD.—See CMR GmbH; *Int'l*, pg. 1672
ROFSON ASSOCIATES, INC.; *U.S. Private*, pg. 3471
ROGAMA INDUSTRIA COMERCIO LTDA.—See Neogen Corporation; *U.S. Public*, pg. 1505
ROGAN & ASSOCIATES, INC.; *U.S. Private*, pg. 3471
ROGAN CORPORATION; *U.S. Private*, pg. 3471
ROGAN SHOES INCORPORATED—See Shoe Carnival, Inc.; *U.S. Public*, pg. 1875
ROGENSI LTD—See TTEC Holdings, Inc.; *U.S. Public*, pg. 2203
ROGENSI PTY LTD.—See TTEC Holdings, Inc.; *U.S. Public*, pg. 2203
ROGENSI SERVICES PTY LTD.—See TTEC Holdings, Inc.; *U.S. Public*, pg. 2203
ROGER ARTZ; *U.S. Private*, pg. 3471
ROGER BEASLEY MAZDA INC.; *U.S. Private*, pg. 3471
ROGER B. KENNEDY, INC.; *U.S. Private*, pg. 3471
ROGER BOUCHARD INSURANCE, INC.—See Marsh & McLennan Companies, Inc.; *U.S. Public*, pg. 1382
ROGER BULLIVANT LTD.—See VINCI S.A.; *Int'l*, pg. 8226
ROGER BURDICK AUTO SALES INC.; *U.S. Private*, pg. 3471
ROGER CLEVELAND GOLF COMPANY, INC.—See Sumitomo Rubber Industries, Ltd.; *Int'l*, pg. 7300
ROGER DEAN CHEVROLET, INC.; *U.S. Private*, pg. 3471
ROGER ENTERPRISES INC.—See Rogers & Hollands Enterprises Inc.; *U.S. Private*, pg. 3471
ROGER FOWLER SALES & SERVICE, INC.—See Tym Corporation; *Int'l*, pg. 7995
ROGER MERTENS DISTRIBUTORS; *U.S. Private*, pg. 3471
THE ROGERS AR OPHTHALMOLOGY ASO, LLC—See KKR & Co. Inc.; *U.S. Public*, pg. 1248
ROGERS ASSET MANAGEMENT LIMITED—See Rogers & Company Limited; *Int'l*, pg. 6383
ROGERS BRIDGE COMPANY, INC.—See Shepherd Construction Co., Inc.; *U.S. Private*, pg. 3632
ROGERS & BROWN CUSTOM BROKERS, INC. - GREER—See Rogers & Brown Custom Brokers, Inc.; *U.S. Private*, pg. 3471
ROGERS & BROWN CUSTOM BROKERS, INC.; *U.S. Private*, pg. 3471
ROGERS B.V.B.A.—See Rogers Corporation; *U.S. Public*, pg. 1808
ROGERS CABLE INC.—See Rogers Communications Inc.; *Int'l*, pg. 6383
ROGERS CAPITAL LTD.—See ENL Limited; *Int'l*, pg. 2442
ROGERSCASEY, INC.—See The Segal Group, Inc.; *U.S. Private*, pg. 4116
ROGER SCHWEITZER & SONS, INC.—See Partners Group Holding AG; *Int'l*, pg. 5750
ROGERS COMMUNICATIONS INC.; *Int'l*, pg. 6383
ROGERS COMMUNICATIONS PARTNERSHIP—See Rogers Communications Inc.; *Int'l*, pg. 6383
ROGERS & COMPANY LIMITED; *Int'l*, pg. 6383
THE ROGERS COMPANY; *U.S. Private*, pg. 4111
ROGERS CONSTRUCTION INC.; *U.S. Private*, pg. 3471
ROGERS CORP. - ADVANCED CIRCUIT MATERIALS DIVISION - FLEXIBLE PRODUCTS—See Rogers Corporation; *U.S. Public*, pg. 1808
ROGERS CORP. - ADVANCED CIRCUIT MATERIALS DIVISION - HIGH FREQUENCY PRODUCTS—See Rogers Corporation; *U.S. Public*, pg. 1808
ROGERS CORP. - DUREL DIVISION—See Rogers Corporation; *U.S. Public*, pg. 1808
ROGERS CORP. - HIGH PERFORMANCE FOAMS DIVISION - BISCO SILICONES—See Rogers Corporation; *U.S. Public*, pg. 1808
ROGERS CORP. - HIGH PERFORMANCE FOAMS DIVISION - COMPOSITE MATERIALS—See Rogers Corporation; *U.S. Public*, pg. 1808
ROGERS CORP. - HIGH PERFORMANCE FOAMS DIVISION - PORON URETHANES—See Rogers Corporation; *U.S. Public*, pg. 1808
ROGERS CORPORATION - DELAWARE FACILITY—See Rogers Corporation; *U.S. Public*, pg. 1808
ROGERS CORPORATION; *U.S. Public*, pg. 1807
ROGERS & COWAN—See The Interpublic Group of Companies, Inc.; *U.S. Public*, pg. 2105
ROGERS & COWAN—See The Interpublic Group of Companies, Inc.; *U.S. Public*, pg. 2105
ROGERS-DABBS CHEVROLET, INC.; *U.S. Private*, pg. 3472
ROGERS FAMILY COMPANY; *U.S. Private*, pg. 3471
ROGERS FOAM CORPORATION; *U.S. Private*, pg. 3472
ROGERS FOODS LTD.—See Nisshin Seifun Group, Inc.; *Int'l*, pg. 5372
ROGERS FORD SALES INC.; *U.S. Private*, pg. 3472
ROGERS GERMANY GMBH—See Rogers Corporation; *U.S. Public*, pg. 1808
ROGERS GRAIN INC.; *U.S. Private*, pg. 3472
ROGERSGRAY INC.—See The Baldwin Insurance Group, Inc.; *U.S. Public*, pg. 2036
ROGERS GROUP INC.; *U.S. Private*, pg. 3472

THE ROGERS GROUP—See Ruder Finn Group, Inc.; *U.S. Private*, pg. 3501
ROGERS & HOLLANDS ENTERPRISES INC.; *U.S. Private*, pg. 3471
ROGERS INOAC CORPORATION—See INOAC Corporation; *Int'l*, pg. 3714
ROGERS INOAC CORPORATION—See Rogers Corporation; *U.S. Public*, pg. 1808
ROGERS INSURANCE LTD.; *Int'l*, pg. 6383
ROGERS INVESTMENTS INC.; *U.S. Private*, pg. 3472
ROGERS IRON & METAL CORP.—See Yaffe Iron & Metal Company Inc.; *U.S. Private*, pg. 4584
ROGERS JAPAN INC.—See Rogers Corporation; *U.S. Public*, pg. 1808
ROGERS JEWELRY COMPANY; *U.S. Private*, pg. 3472
ROGERS KOREA, INC.—See Rogers Corporation; *U.S. Public*, pg. 1808
ROGERS MANUFACTURING CORP; *U.S. Private*, pg. 3472
ROGERS MEDIA INC.—See Rogers Communications Inc.; *Int'l*, pg. 6383
ROGER SMITH HOTELS CORP.; *U.S. Private*, pg. 3471
ROGERS MORNING NEWS—See Wehco Media, Inc.; *U.S. Private*, pg. 4470
ROGERS MOTORS, INC.; *U.S. Private*, pg. 3472
ROGERS NORTHWEST INC.; *U.S. Private*, pg. 3472
ROGERS N.V.—See Rogers Corporation; *U.S. Public*, pg. 1808
ROGERS-O'BRIEN CONSTRUCTION COMPANY INC.; *U.S. Private*, pg. 3472
ROGERSON AIRCRAFT CONTROLS—See Rogerson Aircraft Corporation; *U.S. Private*, pg. 3472
ROGERSON AIRCRAFT CORPORATION; *U.S. Private*, pg. 3472
ROGERSON AIRCRAFT SYSTEMS—See Rogerson Aircraft Corporation; *U.S. Private*, pg. 3472
ROGERSON KRATOS—See Rogerson Aircraft Corporation; *U.S. Private*, pg. 3472
ROGER & SONS CONSTRUCTION INC.; *U.S. Private*, pg. 3471
ROGERS PETROLEUM INC.; *U.S. Private*, pg. 3472
ROGERS PETROLEUM SERVICES INCORPORATED; *U.S. Private*, pg. 3472
ROGERS READY MIX & MATERIALS; *U.S. Private*, pg. 3472
ROGERS & ROGERS, INC.; *U.S. Private*, pg. 3471
ROGERS (SHANGHAI) INTERNATIONAL TRADING CO. LTD.—See Rogers Corporation; *U.S. Public*, pg. 1808
ROGERS SHIPPING LTD.—See ENL Limited; *Int'l*, pg. 2442
ROGERS SOFTWARE DEVELOPMENT, INC.; *U.S. Private*, pg. 3472
ROGERS STEREO INC.; *U.S. Private*, pg. 3472
ROGERS SUGAR INC.; *Int'l*, pg. 6384
ROGERS SUPPLY COMPANY INC.; *U.S. Private*, pg. 3472
ROGERS TAIWAN, INC.—See Rogers Corporation; *U.S. Public*, pg. 1808
ROGERS TECHNOLOGIES SINGAPORE, INC.—See Rogers Corporation; *U.S. Public*, pg. 1808
ROGERS TECHNOLOGIES (SUZHOU) CO., LTD.—See Rogers Corporation; *U.S. Public*, pg. 1808
ROGERS TECHNOLOGY (SUZHOU) CO., LTD.—See Rogers Corporation; *U.S. Public*, pg. 1808
ROGERS TELECOMMUNICATIONS LIMITED—See Rogers Communications Inc.; *Int'l*, pg. 6383
ROGERS WIRELESS COMMUNICATIONS INC.—See Rogers Communications Inc.; *Int'l*, pg. 6383
ROGER TV; *U.S. Private*, pg. 3471
ROGER WARD INC.; *U.S. Private*, pg. 3471
ROGESA ROHEISENGESELLSCHAFT SAAR MBH—See Saarstahl AG; *Int'l*, pg. 6461
ROGGE GLOBAL PARTNERS LTD.—See Allianz SE; *Int'l*, pg. 346
ROGGEN FARMERS ELEVATOR ASSOCIATION INC.; *U.S. Private*, pg. 3472
ROGUE PRESSURE SERVICES LTD.—See Steel Partners Holdings L.P.; *U.S. Public*, pg. 1943
ROGUE STATION COMPANIES, INC.; *U.S. Public*, pg. 1808
ROGUE VALLEY TERMINAL RAILROAD CORPORATION—See CCT Rail System Corporation; *U.S. Private*, pg. 801
ROGUE WAVE SOFTWARE, INC.—See Clearlake Capital Group, L.P.; *U.S. Private*, pg. 936
ROGUE WAVE SOFTWARE, INC.—See Francisco Partners Management, LP; *U.S. Private*, pg. 1591
ROGUE WAVE SOFTWARE JAPAN K.K.—See Clearlake Capital Group, L.P.; *U.S. Private*, pg. 936
ROGUE WAVE SOFTWARE JAPAN K.K.—See Francisco Partners Management, LP; *U.S. Private*, pg. 1591
ROHA SOFTWARE SUPPORT GMBH—See VINCI S.A.; *Int'l*, pg. 8225
ROHA SOFTWARE SUPPORT GMBH—See VINCI S.A.; *Int'l*, pg. 8225
ROHAS TECNIC BERHAD; *Int'l*, pg. 6384
ROHASYS B.V.—See Porvair plc; *Int'l*, pg. 5935
ROHATEC S.A.R.L—See TCS TurControlSysteme AG; *Int'l*, pg. 7486

R.O.H. AUTO PRODUCTS PHILIPPINES, INC.—See Arrowcrest Group Pty. Ltd.; *Int'l*, pg. 580
ROHDE AND SCHWARZ SOUTH AFRICA (PTY) LTD.—See Rohde & Schwarz GmbH & Co. KG; *Int'l*, pg. 6385
ROHDE OTTMERS SIEGEL REALTY, INC.—See Island Capital Group LLC; *U.S. Private*, pg. 2144
ROHDE & SCHWARZ (AUSTRALIA) PTY LTD—See Rohde & Schwarz GmbH & Co. KG; *Int'l*, pg. 6384
ROHDE & SCHWARZ BELGIUM N.V.—See Rohde & Schwarz GmbH & Co. KG; *Int'l*, pg. 6384
ROHDE & SCHWARZ CANADA INC.—See Rohde & Schwarz GmbH & Co. KG; *Int'l*, pg. 6384
ROHDE & SCHWARZ COLOMBIA S.A.—See Rohde & Schwarz GmbH & Co. KG; *Int'l*, pg. 6384
ROHDE & SCHWARZ DANMARK A/S—See Rohde & Schwarz GmbH & Co. KG; *Int'l*, pg. 6384
ROHDE & SCHWARZ DE MEXICO S DE RL DE CV—See Rohde & Schwarz GmbH & Co. KG; *Int'l*, pg. 6385
ROHDE & SCHWARZ DO BRASIL LTDA—See Rohde & Schwarz GmbH & Co. KG; *Int'l*, pg. 6385
ROHDE & SCHWARZ EMIRATES LLC—See Rohde & Schwarz GmbH & Co. KG; *Int'l*, pg. 6385
ROHDE & SCHWARZ ENGINEERING & SALES GMBH—See Rohde & Schwarz GmbH & Co. KG; *Int'l*, pg. 6384
ROHDE & SCHWARZ ESPANA, S.A.—See Rohde & Schwarz GmbH & Co. KG; *Int'l*, pg. 6384
ROHDE & SCHWARZ FINLAND OY—See Rohde & Schwarz GmbH & Co. KG; *Int'l*, pg. 6384
ROHDE & SCHWARZ FRANCE SAS—See Rohde & Schwarz GmbH & Co. KG; *Int'l*, pg. 6384
ROHDE & SCHWARZ GMBH & CO. KG; *Int'l*, pg. 6384
ROHDE & SCHWARZ GMBH WERK KOLN—See Rohde & Schwarz GmbH & Co. KG; *Int'l*, pg. 6385
ROHDE & SCHWARZ HELLAS SA—See Rohde & Schwarz GmbH & Co. KG; *Int'l*, pg. 6384
ROHDE & SCHWARZ HONG KONG LTD.—See Rohde & Schwarz GmbH & Co. KG; *Int'l*, pg. 6384
ROHDE & SCHWARZ, INC.—See Rohde & Schwarz GmbH & Co. KG; *Int'l*, pg. 6385
ROHDE & SCHWARZ INDIA (PVT) LIMITED—See Rohde & Schwarz GmbH & Co. KG; *Int'l*, pg. 6384
ROHDE & SCHWARZ INTERNATIONAL GMBH—See Rohde & Schwarz GmbH & Co. KG; *Int'l*, pg. 6384
ROHDE & SCHWARZ JAPAN K.K.—See Rohde & Schwarz GmbH & Co. KG; *Int'l*, pg. 6384
ROHDE & SCHWARZ KOREA LIMITED—See Rohde & Schwarz GmbH & Co. KG; *Int'l*, pg. 6384
ROHDE & SCHWARZ MALAYSIA SDN BHD—See Rohde & Schwarz GmbH & Co. KG; *Int'l*, pg. 6384
ROHDE & SCHWARZ MESSGERAETEBAU GMBH—See Rohde & Schwarz GmbH & Co. KG; *Int'l*, pg. 6384
ROHDE & SCHWARZ MIDDLE EAST AND AFRICA FZ-LLC—See Rohde & Schwarz GmbH & Co. KG; *Int'l*, pg. 6384
ROHDE & SCHWARZ NEDERLAND B.V.—See Rohde & Schwarz GmbH & Co. KG; *Int'l*, pg. 6384
ROHDE & SCHWARZ NORGE AS—See Rohde & Schwarz GmbH & Co. KG; *Int'l*, pg. 6384
ROHDE & SCHWARZ OSTERREICH GES.M.B.H.—See Rohde & Schwarz GmbH & Co. KG; *Int'l*, pg. 6385
ROHDE & SCHWARZ OSTERREICH SP Z O.O.—See Rohde & Schwarz GmbH & Co. KG; *Int'l*, pg. 6385
ROHDE & SCHWARZ PAKISTAN (PRIVATE) LTD—See Rohde & Schwarz GmbH & Co. KG; *Int'l*, pg. 6385
ROHDE & SCHWARZ (PHILIPPINES), INC.—See Rohde & Schwarz GmbH & Co. KG; *Int'l*, pg. 6384
ROHDE & SCHWARZ PORTUGAL, LDA.—See Rohde & Schwarz GmbH & Co. KG; *Int'l*, pg. 6385
ROHDE & SCHWARZ - PRAHA, S.R.O.—See Rohde & Schwarz GmbH & Co. KG; *Int'l*, pg. 6384
ROHDE & SCHWARZ REGIONAL HEADQUARTERS SINGAPORE PTE. LTD.—See Rohde & Schwarz GmbH & Co. KG; *Int'l*, pg. 6385
ROHDE & SCHWARZ RUS OOO—See Rohde & Schwarz GmbH & Co. KG; *Int'l*, pg. 6384
ROHDE & SCHWARZ SAUDI ARABIA LTD.—See Rohde & Schwarz GmbH & Co. KG; *Int'l*, pg. 6385
ROHDE & SCHWARZ SIT GMBH—See Rohde & Schwarz GmbH & Co. KG; *Int'l*, pg. 6385
ROHDE & SCHWARZ SVERIGE AB—See Rohde & Schwarz GmbH & Co. KG; *Int'l*, pg. 6385
ROHDE & SCHWARZ TAIWAN LTD.—See Rohde & Schwarz GmbH & Co. KG; *Int'l*, pg. 6385
ROHDE & SCHWARZ (THAILAND) CO., LTD.—See Rohde & Schwarz GmbH & Co. KG; *Int'l*, pg. 6384
ROHDE & SCHWARZ VERTRIEBS GMBH—See Rohde & Schwarz GmbH & Co. KG; *Int'l*, pg. 6385
ROHDE & SCHWARZ VIETNAM CO., LTD.—See Rohde & Schwarz GmbH & Co. KG; *Int'l*, pg. 6385
ROH DEVELOPMENTS LIMITED—See The Royal Opera House Covent Garden Ltd; *Int'l*, pg. 7679
ROHER PUBLIC RELATIONS; *U.S. Private*, pg. 3473
ROHER PUBLIC RELATIONS—See Roher Public Relations; *U.S. Private*, pg. 3473
ROHE & WRIGHT BUILDERS, INC.; *U.S. Private*, pg. 3472

ROHINI INDUSTRIAL ELECTRICALS LIMITED—See Tata Sons Limited; *Int'l*, pg. 7473
ROHIT FERRO-TECH LIMITED—See Tata Sons Limited; *Int'l*, pg. 7471
ROHLAND FUNERAL HOME—See Service Corporation International; *U.S. Public*, pg. 1870
ROH, LLC—See Community Health Systems, Inc.; *U.S. Public*, pg. 556
ROHL LLC—See Fortune Brands Innovations, Inc.; *U.S. Public*, pg. 873
ROHM AMAGI CO., LTD.—See ROHM Co., Ltd.; *Int'l*, pg. 6386
ROHM AMERICA LLC—See RAG-Stiftung; *Int'l*, pg. 6179
ROHM AND HAAS CANADA LP—See Dow Inc.; *U.S. Public*, pg. 685
ROHM AND HAAS CHEMICALS LLC - BRISTOL PLANT—See Dow Inc.; *U.S. Public*, pg. 686
ROHM AND HAAS CHEMICALS LLC—See Dow Inc.; *U.S. Public*, pg. 685
ROHM AND HAAS CHEMICALS SINGAPORE PTE LTD.—See Dow Inc.; *U.S. Public*, pg. 686
ROHM AND HAAS CHEMICAL (THAILAND) LIMITED—See Dow Inc.; *U.S. Public*, pg. 686
ROHM AND HAAS CHILE LIMITADA—See Dow Inc.; *U.S. Public*, pg. 686
ROHM AND HAAS ELECTRONIC MATERIALS ASIA PACIFIC CO., LTD.—See DuPont de Nemours, Inc.; *U.S. Public*, pg. 694
ROHM AND HAAS ELECTRONIC MATERIALS CMP INC.—See DuPont de Nemours, Inc.; *U.S. Public*, pg. 694
ROHM AND HAAS ELECTRONIC MATERIALS KOREA, LTD.—See DuPont de Nemours, Inc.; *U.S. Public*, pg. 694
ROHM AND HAAS ELECTRONIC MATERIALS LLC—See DuPont de Nemours, Inc.; *U.S. Public*, pg. 694
ROHM AND HAAS ELECTRONIC MATERIALS TAIWAN LTD.—See DuPont de Nemours, Inc.; *U.S. Public*, pg. 694
ROHM AND HAAS ESPANA PRODUCTION HOLDING, S.L.—See Dow Inc.; *U.S. Public*, pg. 686
ROHM AND HAAS FINLAND OY—See Dow Inc.; *U.S. Public*, pg. 686
ROHM AND HAAS (FOSHAN) SPECIALTY MATERIALS CO., LTD.—See Dow Inc.; *U.S. Public*, pg. 686
ROHM AND HAAS INTERNATIONAL TRADING (SHANGHAI) CO., LTD.—See Dow Inc.; *U.S. Public*, pg. 686
ROHM AND HAAS ITALIA SRL—See Dow Inc.; *U.S. Public*, pg. 686
ROHM AND HAAS KIMYA SANAYI LIMITED SIRKETI—See Dow Inc.; *U.S. Public*, pg. 686
ROHM AND HAAS MALAYSIA SDN. BHD.—See Dow Inc.; *U.S. Public*, pg. 686
ROHM AND HAAS MEXICO, S. DE R.L. DE C.V.—See Dow Inc.; *U.S. Public*, pg. 686
ROHM AND HAAS SHANGHAI CHEMICAL INDUSTRY CO., LTD.—See DuPont de Nemours, Inc.; *U.S. Public*, pg. 694
ROHM AND HAAS SINGAPORE (PTE.) LTD.—See Dow Inc.; *U.S. Public*, pg. 686
ROHM AND HAAS TEXAS INCORPORATED—See Dow Inc.; *U.S. Public*, pg. 686
ROHM APOLLO CO. LTD.—See ROHM Co., Ltd.; *Int'l*, pg. 6386
ROHM APOLLO DEVICE CO., LTD.—See ROHM Co., Ltd.; *Int'l*, pg. 6386
ROHM CO., LTD.; *Int'l*, pg. 6385
ROHM ELECTRONICS ASIA PTE. LTD.—See ROHM Co., Ltd.; *Int'l*, pg. 6386
ROHM ELECTRONICS COMPONENTS (TIANJIN) CO., LTD.—See ROHM Co., Ltd.; *Int'l*, pg. 6386
ROHM ELECTRONICS (DALIAN) CO., LTD.—See ROHM Co., Ltd.; *Int'l*, pg. 6386
ROHM ELECTRONICS (H.K.) CO., LTD.—See ROHM Co., Ltd.; *Int'l*, pg. 6386
ROHM ELECTRONICS (MALAYSIA) SDN. BHD.—See ROHM Co., Ltd.; *Int'l*, pg. 6386
ROHM ELECTRONICS (PHILIPPINES), INC.—See ROHM Co., Ltd.; *Int'l*, pg. 6386
ROHM ELECTRONICS (PHILIPPINES) SALES CORPORATION—See ROHM Co., Ltd.; *Int'l*, pg. 6386
ROHM ELECTRONICS (TAIWAN) CO., LTD.—See ROHM Co., Ltd.; *Int'l*, pg. 6386
ROHM FUKUOKA CO., LTD.—See ROHM Co., Ltd.; *Int'l*, pg. 6386
ROHM & HAAS COMPANY—See Dow Inc.; *U.S. Public*, pg. 685
ROHM & HAAS ELECTRONIC MATERIALS CMP KOREA LTD.—See DuPont de Nemours, Inc.; *U.S. Public*, pg. 694
ROHM & HAAS ELECTRONIC MATERIALS K.K.—See DuPont de Nemours, Inc.; *U.S. Public*, pg. 694
ROHM & HAAS ELECTRONIC MATERIALS SINGAPORE PTE. LTD.—See DuPont de Nemours, Inc.; *U.S. Public*, pg. 694
ROHM HAMAMATSU CO., LTD.—See ROHM Co., Ltd.; *Int'l*, pg. 6386
ROHM INTEGRATED SEMICONDUCTOR (THAILAND) CO., LTD.—See ROHM Co., Ltd.; *Int'l*, pg. 6386

ROHM INTEGRATED SYSTEMS (THAILAND) CO., LTD.—See ROHM Co., Ltd.; *Int'l*, pg. 6386
ROHM ITALIA S.R.L.—See ThyssenKrupp AG; *Int'l*, pg. 7725
ROHM KOREA CORPORATION—See ROHM Co., Ltd.; *Int'l*, pg. 6386
ROHM LOGISTEC CO., LTD.—See ROHM Co., Ltd.; *Int'l*, pg. 6386
ROHM MECHATECH CO., LTD.—See ROHM Co., Ltd.; *Int'l*, pg. 6386
ROHM MECHATECH (PHILIPPINES), INC.—See ROHM Co., Ltd.; *Int'l*, pg. 6386
ROHM PRODUCTS OF AMERICA; *U.S. Private*, pg. 3473
ROHM SEMICONDUCTOR (CHINA) CO., LTD.—See ROHM Co., Ltd.; *Int'l*, pg. 6385
ROHM SEMICONDUCTOR GMBH—See ROHM Co., Ltd.; *Int'l*, pg. 6386
ROHM SEMICONDUCTOR GMBH—See ROHM Co., Ltd.; *Int'l*, pg. 6386
ROHM SEMICONDUCTOR HONG KONG CO., LTD.—See ROHM Co., Ltd.; *Int'l*, pg. 6385
ROHM SEMICONDUCTOR INDIA PVT. LTD.—See ROHM Co., Ltd.; *Int'l*, pg. 6385
ROHM SEMICONDUCTOR KOREA CORPORATION—See ROHM Co., Ltd.; *Int'l*, pg. 6385
ROHM SEMICONDUCTOR MALAYSIA SDN. BHD.—See ROHM Co., Ltd.; *Int'l*, pg. 6385
ROHM SEMICONDUCTOR PHILIPPINES CORPORATION—See ROHM Co., Ltd.; *Int'l*, pg. 6385
ROHM SEMICONDUCTOR (SHANGHAI) CO., LTD.—See ROHM Co., Ltd.; *Int'l*, pg. 6385
ROHM SEMICONDUCTOR SINGAPORE PTE. LTD.—See ROHM Co., Ltd.; *Int'l*, pg. 6385
ROHM SEMICONDUCTOR TAIWAN CO., LTD.—See ROHM Co., Ltd.; *Int'l*, pg. 6385
ROHM SEMICONDUCTOR (THAILAND) CO., LTD.—See ROHM Co., Ltd.; *Int'l*, pg. 6385
ROHM SEMICONDUCTOR (THAILAND) CO., LTD.—See ROHM Co., Ltd.; *Int'l*, pg. 6386
ROHM SEMICONDUCTOR TRADING (DALIAN) CO., LTD.—See ROHM Co., Ltd.; *Int'l*, pg. 6385
ROHM SEMICONDUCTOR U.S.A., LLC - ALPHARETTA—See ROHM Co., Ltd.; *Int'l*, pg. 6386
ROHM SEMICONDUCTOR U.S.A., LLC - DALLAS—See ROHM Co., Ltd.; *Int'l*, pg. 6386
ROHM SEMICONDUCTOR U.S.A., LLC—See ROHM Co., Ltd.; *Int'l*, pg. 6386
ROHM SERVICES, CORP.; *U.S. Private*, pg. 3473
ROHM TSUKUBA CO., LTD.—See ROHM Co., Ltd.; *Int'l*, pg. 6385
ROHM USA, INC.—See ROHM Co., Ltd.; *Int'l*, pg. 6386
ROHM WAKO CO., LTD.—See ROHM Co., Ltd.; *Int'l*, pg. 6386
ROHM WAKO DEVICE CO., LTD.—See ROHM Co., Ltd.; *Int'l*, pg. 6386
ROHM-WAKO ELECTRONICS (MALAYSIA) SDN. BHD.—See ROHM Co., Ltd.; *Int'l*, pg. 6386
ROHN ROGERS ASSOCIATES INC.; *U.S. Private*, pg. 3473
RO HO HO INC.; *U.S. Private*, pg. 3453
ROHO, INC.—See Investor AB; *Int'l*, pg. 3787
ROHOL-AUFSUCHUNGS AKTIENGESELLSCHAFT—See EVN AG; *Int'l*, pg. 2571
ROHRBACK COSASCO SYSTEMS, INC.—See Halma plc; *Int'l*, pg. 3232
ROHRBACK COSASCO SYSTEMS UK LTD.—See Halma plc; *Int'l*, pg. 3232
ROHR BAGGER GMBH—See Markel Group Inc.; *U.S. Public*, pg. 1369
ROHRDORFER GRUPPE; *Int'l*, pg. 6386
ROHR DREDGE NA, LLC—See Markel Group Inc.; *U.S. Public*, pg. 1368
ROHRER CORP. - BUFORD PLANT—See Wellspring Capital Management LLC; *U.S. Private*, pg. 4477
ROHRER CORP. - HUNTLEY PLANT—See Wellspring Capital Management LLC; *U.S. Private*, pg. 4477
ROHRER CORPORATION OF PENNSYLVANIA—See Wellspring Capital Management LLC; *U.S. Private*, pg. 4477
ROHRER CORPORATION—See Wellspring Capital Management LLC; *U.S. Private*, pg. 4477
ROHRER CORP. - PRINTING SERVICES—See Wellspring Capital Management LLC; *U.S. Private*, pg. 4477
ROHRER ENTERPRISES, INC.; *U.S. Private*, pg. 3473
ROHRERS QUARRY INC.; *U.S. Private*, pg. 3473
ROHRICH AUTOMOTIVE GROUP; *U.S. Private*, pg. 3473
ROHRICH CADILLAC INC.—See Rohrich Automotive Group; *U.S. Private*, pg. 3473
ROHR, INC.—See RTX Corporation; *U.S. Public*, pg. 1821
ROHR-INDY MOTORS INC.; *U.S. Private*, pg. 3473
ROHR-LEX MOTORS INC.; *U.S. Private*, pg. 3473
ROHRS AG; *Int'l*, pg. 6386
ROHR SA—See Derichebourg S.A.; *Int'l*, pg. 2041
ROHRS KRAFTWERKSTECHNIK GMBH—See Rohrs AG; *Int'l*, pg. 6387
ROHRS KRANVERLEIH GMBH—See Rohrs AG; *Int'l*, pg. 6387
ROHSTOFF RECYCLING DORTMUND GMBH—See Georgsmarienhutte Holding GmbH; *Int'l*, pg. 2941

ROHTO ADVANCED RESERCH HK LTD.—See Rohto Pharmaceutical Co. Ltd.; *Int'l*, pg. 6387
ROHTO MEDICAL CHINA CO., LTD.—See Rohto Pharmaceutical Co. Ltd.; *Int'l*, pg. 6387
ROHTO MENTHOLATUM (BANGLADESH) LIMITED—See Rohto Pharmaceutical Co. Ltd.; *Int'l*, pg. 6387
ROHTO-MENTHOLATUM (CAMBODIA) CO., LTD.—See Rohto Pharmaceutical Co. Ltd.; *Int'l*, pg. 6387
ROHTO-MENTHOLATUM DO BRASIL COMERCIO DE PRODUTOS PARA SAUDE LTDA.—See Rohto Pharmaceutical Co. Ltd.; *Int'l*, pg. 6387
ROHTO-MENTHOLATUM (KENYA) LIMITED—See Rohto Pharmaceutical Co. Ltd.; *Int'l*, pg. 6387
ROHTO-MENTHOLATUM (MALAYSIA) SDN. BHD.—See Rohto Pharmaceutical Co. Ltd.; *Int'l*, pg. 6387
ROHTO-MENTHOLATUM (MYANMAR) CO., LTD.—See Rohto Pharmaceutical Co. Ltd.; *Int'l*, pg. 6387
ROHTO-MENTHOLATUM (NEPAL) CO., LTD.—See Rohto Pharmaceutical Co. Ltd.; *Int'l*, pg. 6387
ROHTO MENTHOLATUM RU LLC—See Rohto Pharmaceutical Co. Ltd.; *Int'l*, pg. 6387
ROHTO-MENTHOLATUM (THAILAND) LIMITED—See Rohto Pharmaceutical Co. Ltd.; *Int'l*, pg. 6387
ROHTO-MENTHOLATUM (VIETNAM) CO., LTD.—See Rohto Pharmaceutical Co. Ltd.; *Int'l*, pg. 6387
ROHTO NITTEN CO., LTD.—See Rohto Pharmaceutical Co. Ltd.; *Int'l*, pg. 6387
ROHTO PHARMACEUTICAL CO. LTD.; *Int'l*, pg. 6387
ROHTO PHARMA (INDIA) PVT. LTD.—See Rohto Pharmaceutical Co. Ltd.; *Int'l*, pg. 6387
ROHWEDDER MACRO ASSEMBLY GMBH—See MAX Automation SE; *Int'l*, pg. 4733
ROH WHEELS AUSTRALIA—See Arrowcrest Group Pty. Ltd.; *Int'l*, pg. 580
ROI CANADIAN REAL ESTATE FUND—See Return On Innovation Advisors Ltd.; *Int'l*, pg. 6311
ROI COMMUNICATION; *U.S. Private*, pg. 3473
ROI-ET GREEN CO. LTD—See EGAT Public Company Limited; *Int'l*, pg. 2322
ROI INSTITUTE, INC.; *U.S. Private*, pg. 3473
ROI LAND INVESTMENTS LTD.; *Int'l*, pg. 6388
RO INNOVATION; *U.S. Private*, pg. 3453
ROINS FINANCIAL SERVICES LIMITED—See Intact Financial Corporation; *Int'l*, pg. 3727
ROINS FINANCIAL SERVICES LIMITED—See Tryg A/S; *Int'l*, pg. 7947
ROIRET ENERGIES SAS—See VINCI S.A.; *Int'l*, pg. 8226
ROIRET TRANSPORT SAS—See VINCI S.A.; *Int'l*, pg. 8226
ROISERV LIFESTYLE SERVICES COMPANY LIMITED; *Int'l*, pg. 6388
ROISUM ELITE SALES & MARKETING COMPANY INC.; *U.S. Private*, pg. 3473
ROIVANT SCIENCES LTD.; *Int'l*, pg. 6388
ROIZIN REFINING CO. INC.; *U.S. Private*, pg. 3473
ROJANA DISTRIBUTION CENTER CO., LTD.—See The Sumitomo Warehouse Co. Ltd.; *Int'l*, pg. 7690
ROJAN ADVANCED CERAMICS PTY LTD—See FLSmidth & Co. A/S; *Int'l*, pg. 2711
ROJANA INDUSTRIAL MANAGEMENT CO., LTD.—See Rojana Industrial Park Public Company Limited; *Int'l*, pg. 6388
ROJANA INDUSTRIAL PARK (CHANGZHOU) CO., LTD.—See Rojana Industrial Park Public Company Limited; *Int'l*, pg. 6388
ROJANA INDUSTRIAL PARK PUBLIC COMPANY LIMITED; *Int'l*, pg. 6388
ROJANA POWER CO., LTD—See Rojana Industrial Park Public Company Limited; *Int'l*, pg. 6388
ROJANA PROPERTY CO., LTD.—See Rojana Industrial Park Public Company Limited; *Int'l*, pg. 6388
RO JEWELS LIMITED; *Int'l*, pg. 6357
ROJNARUEMIT LIMITED—See Sansiri pcl; *Int'l*, pg. 6557
ROJO ARCHITECTURE, LLC; *U.S. Private*, pg. 3473
ROJUKISS INTERNATIONAL PUBLIC COMPANY LIMITED; *Int'l*, pg. 6388
ROKANA INDUSTRIES PLC.; *Int'l*, pg. 6388
ROKAS AEOLIKI EVIA, S.A.—See Iberdrola, S.A.; *Int'l*, pg. 3573
ROKAS AEOLIKI KOMITO, S.A.—See Iberdrola, S.A.; *Int'l*, pg. 3573
ROKAS AEOLIKI KRITI, S.A.—See Iberdrola, S.A.; *Int'l*, pg. 3573
ROKAS AEOLIKI, S.A.—See Iberdrola, S.A.; *Int'l*, pg. 3573
ROKAS AEOLIKI THRAKI III, S.A.—See Iberdrola, S.A.; *Int'l*, pg. 3573
ROKAS AEOLIKI THRAKI II, S.A.—See Iberdrola, S.A.; *Int'l*, pg. 3573
ROKAS AEOLIKI THRAKI, S.A.—See Iberdrola, S.A.; *Int'l*, pg. 3573
ROKAS AEOLIKI ZARAKES, S.A.—See Iberdrola, S.A.; *Int'l*, pg. 3573
ROKAS CONSTRUCTION, S.A.—See Iberdrola, S.A.; *Int'l*, pg. 3573
ROKEL COMMERCIAL BANK (SIERRA LEONE) LIMITED; *Int'l*, pg. 6388
ROKE MANOR RESEARCH LTD—See Chemring Group PLC; *Int'l*, pg. 1463

ROKICKI SP Z.O.O.—See Marie Brizard Wine & Spirits S.A.; *Int'l*, pg. 4694
ROKISKIO PIENAS UAB—See Rokiskio Suris AB; *Int'l*, pg. 6388
ROKISKIO PIENO GAMYBA UAB—See Rokiskio Suris AB; *Int'l*, pg. 6388
ROKISKIO SURIS AB; *Int'l*, pg. 6388
ROKK3R INC.; *U.S. Private*, pg. 3473
ROKKAN; *U.S. Private*, pg. 3473
ROKKASHO REPROCESSING PLANT MAINTENANCE SERVICE CO., LTD.—See Mitsubishi Heavy Industries, Ltd.; *Int'l*, pg. 4961
ROKKEDAHL FOOD APS—See Rokkedahl Holding A/S; *Int'l*, pg. 6388
ROKKEDAHL FOOD HOLDING A/S—See Rokkedahl Holding A/S; *Int'l*, pg. 6388
ROKKEDAHL HOLDING A/S; *Int'l*, pg. 6388
ROKKO BUTTER CO., LTD.; *Int'l*, pg. 6388
ROKKO HOLDINGS LTD.; *Int'l*, pg. 6388
ROKKO LEADFRAMES PTE LTD—See Rokko Holdings Ltd.; *Int'l*, pg. 6388
ROKKO MATERIALS PTE. LTD.—See Rokko Holdings Ltd.; *Int'l*, pg. 6388
ROKKO MECHATRONICS PTE. LTD.—See Rokko Holdings Ltd.; *Int'l*, pg. 6389
ROKKO STAMPING PTE. LTD.—See Rokko Holdings Ltd.; *Int'l*, pg. 6388
ROKKO SYSTEMS PTE. LTD.—See Rokko Holdings Ltd.; *Int'l*, pg. 6388
ROKKO TECHNOLOGY EUROPE LTD—See Rokko Holdings Ltd.; *Int'l*, pg. 6388
ROKKO TECHNOLOGY PTE. LTD.—See Rokko Holdings Ltd.; *Int'l*, pg. 6388
ROKKO VENTURES PTE. LTD.—See Rokko Holdings Ltd.; *Int'l*, pg. 6388
ROKKU DESIGNSTUDIO GMBH—See Fielmann Group AG; *Int'l*, pg. 2659
ROKMASTER RESOURCES CORP.; *Int'l*, pg. 6389
ROK RESOURCES INC.; *Int'l*, pg. 6388
ROK STARS PLC; *Int'l*, pg. 6388
ROKUGO ELEMEC CO., LTD.—See Okaya & Co., Ltd.; *Int'l*, pg. 5547
ROKUGO ELEMEC (THAILAND) CO., LTD.—See Okaya & Co., Ltd.; *Int'l*, pg. 5547
ROKUGO SERVICE TECHNO CO., LTD.—See Okaya & Co., Ltd.; *Int'l*, pg. 5547
ROKUGO SYSTEM ELECTRONICS IND. CO., LTD.—See Okaya & Co., Ltd.; *Int'l*, pg. 5547
ROKU, INC.; *U.S. Public*, pg. 1808
ROKUYON CO., LTD.—See Nippon Parking Development Co., Ltd.; *Int'l*, pg. 5328
ROLACO TRADING & CONTRACTING CO. - BUILDING MATERIAL DIVISION—See Rolaco Trading & Contracting Co.; *Int'l*, pg. 6389
ROLACO TRADING & CONTRACTING CO.; *Int'l*, pg. 6389
ROLAND ASIA PACIFIC SDN. BHD.—See Roland Corporation; *Int'l*, pg. 6390
ROLAND ASSISTANCE GMBH—See AXA S.A.; *Int'l*, pg. 759
ROLAND BERGER AG STRATEGY CONSULTANTS—See Roland Berger Strategy Consultants GmbH; *Int'l*, pg. 6389
ROLAND BERGER CONSULTORES DE ESTRATEGIA LDA.—See Roland Berger Strategy Consultants GmbH; *Int'l*, pg. 6389
ROLAND BERGER LTD.—See Roland Berger Strategy Consultants GmbH; *Int'l*, pg. 6389
ROLAND BERGER STRATEGY CONSULTANTS AB—See Roland Berger Strategy Consultants GmbH; *Int'l*, pg. 6389
ROLAND BERGER STRATEGY CONSULTANTS (BEIJING) LTD.—See Roland Berger Strategy Consultants GmbH; *Int'l*, pg. 6389
ROLAND BERGER STRATEGY CONSULTANTS B.V.—See Roland Berger Strategy Consultants GmbH; *Int'l*, pg. 6389
ROLAND BERGER STRATEGY CONSULTANTS CO., LTD.—See Roland Berger Strategy Consultants GmbH; *Int'l*, pg. 6389
ROLAND BERGER STRATEGY CONSULTANTS D.O.O.—See Roland Berger Strategy Consultants GmbH; *Int'l*, pg. 6390
ROLAND BERGER STRATEGY CONSULTANTS GMBH; *Int'l*, pg. 6389
ROLAND BERGER STRATEGY CONSULTANTS GMBH—See Roland Berger Strategy Consultants GmbH; *Int'l*, pg. 6389
ROLAND BERGER STRATEGY CONSULTANTS INC.—See Roland Berger Strategy Consultants GmbH; *Int'l*, pg. 6389
ROLAND BERGER STRATEGY CONSULTANTS KFT.—See Roland Berger Strategy Consultants GmbH; *Int'l*, pg. 6389
ROLAND BERGER STRATEGY CONSULTANTS LIMITED—See Roland Berger Strategy Consultants GmbH; *Int'l*, pg. 6389

ROLAND BERGER STRATEGY CONSULTANTS, LLC - DETROIT—See Roland Berger Strategy Consultants GmbH; *Int'l*, pg. 6389
ROLAND BERGER STRATEGY CONSULTANTS LLC—See Roland Berger Strategy Consultants GmbH; *Int'l*, pg. 6389
ROLAND BERGER STRATEGY CONSULTANTS LTD.—See Roland Berger Strategy Consultants GmbH; *Int'l*, pg. 6389
ROLAND BERGER STRATEGY CONSULTANTS, LTD.—See Roland Berger Strategy Consultants GmbH; *Int'l*, pg. 6390
ROLAND BERGER STRATEGY CONSULTANTS MIDDLE EAST—See Roland Berger Strategy Consultants GmbH; *Int'l*, pg. 6389
ROLAND BERGER STRATEGY CONSULTANTS MIDDLE EAST—See Roland Berger Strategy Consultants GmbH; *Int'l*, pg. 6389
ROLAND BERGER STRATEGY CONSULTANTS MIDDLE EAST—See Roland Berger Strategy Consultants GmbH; *Int'l*, pg. 6389
ROLAND BERGER STRATEGY CONSULTANTS - PARIS—See Roland Berger Strategy Consultants GmbH; *Int'l*, pg. 6389
ROLAND BERGER STRATEGY CONSULTANTS PTE LTD.—See Roland Berger Strategy Consultants GmbH; *Int'l*, pg. 6389
ROLAND BERGER STRATEGY CONSULTANTS PVT. LTD.—See Roland Berger Strategy Consultants GmbH; *Int'l*, pg. 6389
ROLAND BERGER STRATEGY CONSULTANTS S.A./N.V.—See Roland Berger Strategy Consultants GmbH; *Int'l*, pg. 6389
ROLAND BERGER STRATEGY CONSULTANTS SARL—See Roland Berger Strategy Consultants GmbH; *Int'l*, pg. 6389
ROLAND BERGER STRATEGY CONSULTANTS S.A.—See Roland Berger Strategy Consultants GmbH; *Int'l*, pg. 6389
ROLAND BERGER STRATEGY CONSULTANTS S/C LTDA.—See Roland Berger Strategy Consultants GmbH; *Int'l*, pg. 6389
ROLAND BERGER STRATEGY CONSULTANTS SDN BHD—See Roland Berger Strategy Consultants GmbH; *Int'l*, pg. 6390
ROLAND BERGER STRATEGY CONSULTANTS (SHANGHAI) LTD.—See Roland Berger Strategy Consultants GmbH; *Int'l*, pg. 6389
ROLAND BERGER STRATEGY CONSULTANTS SP.Z O.O.—See Roland Berger Strategy Consultants GmbH; *Int'l*, pg. 6390
ROLAND BERGER STRATEGY CONSULTANTS S.R.L.—See Roland Berger Strategy Consultants GmbH; *Int'l*, pg. 6389
ROLAND BERGER STRATEGY CONSULTANTS SRL—See Roland Berger Strategy Consultants GmbH; *Int'l*, pg. 6390
ROLAND BERGER STRATEGY CONSULTANTS TOV—See Roland Berger Strategy Consultants GmbH; *Int'l*, pg. 6390
ROLAND BERGER STRATEJI DANISMANLIK LTD. STI.—See Roland Berger Strategy Consultants GmbH; *Int'l*, pg. 6390
ROLAND BOULANGER & CIE LTEE; *Int'l*, pg. 6390
ROLAND BRASIL IMPORTACAO, EXPORTACAO, COMERCIO, REPRESENTACAO E SERVICOS LTDA.—See Roland Corporation; *Int'l*, pg. 6390
ROLAND CANADA MUSIC LTD.—See Roland Corporation; *Int'l*, pg. 6390
ROLAND CENTRAL EUROPE N.V.—See Roland Corporation; *Int'l*, pg. 6390
ROLAND CONSULT STASCHE & FINGER GMBH—See Gaush Meditech Ltd.; *Int'l*, pg. 2891
ROLAND CORPORATION AUSTRALIA PTY. LTD.—See Roland Corporation; *Int'l*, pg. 6390
ROLAND CORPORATION - MATSUMOTO FACTORY—See Roland Corporation; *Int'l*, pg. 6390
ROLAND CORPORATION - MIYAKODA FACTORY—See Roland Corporation; *Int'l*, pg. 6390
ROLAND CORPORATION; *Int'l*, pg. 6390
ROLAND CORPORATION U.S.—See Roland Corporation; *Int'l*, pg. 6390
ROLAND DGA CORPORATION—See Roland DG Corporation; *Int'l*, pg. 6391
ROLAND DG AUSTRALIA PTY. LTD.—See Roland DG Corporation; *Int'l*, pg. 6391
ROLAND DG BENELUX N.V.—See Roland DG Corporation; *Int'l*, pg. 6391
ROLAND DG BRASIL LTD.—See Roland DG Corporation; *Int'l*, pg. 6391
ROLAND DG (CHINA) CORPORATION—See Roland DG Corporation; *Int'l*, pg. 6391
ROLAND DG CORPORATION; *Int'l*, pg. 6390
ROLAND DG DEUTSCHLAND GMBH—See Roland DG Corporation; *Int'l*, pg. 6391
ROLAND DG EUROPE HOLDINGS B.V.—See Roland DG Corporation; *Int'l*, pg. 6391
ROLAND DG FRANCE SAS—See Roland DG Corporation; *Int'l*, pg. 6391

COMPANY NAME INDEX

ROLAND DG KOREA INC.—See Roland DG Corporation; *Int'l*, pg. 6391
ROLAND DG MID EUROPE S.R.L.—See Roland DG Corporation; *Int'l*, pg. 6391
ROLAND DG NORTH EUROPE A/S—See Roland DG Corporation; *Int'l*, pg. 6391
ROLAND DG RUS LLC—See Roland DG Corporation; *Int'l*, pg. 6391
ROLAND DG (U.K.) LTD.—See Roland DG Corporation; *Int'l*, pg. 6391
ROLAND DIGITAL GROUP IBERIA, S.L.—See Roland DG Corporation; *Int'l*, pg. 6391
ROLAND D. KELLY INFINITI INC.; *U.S. Private*, pg. 3473
ROLAND EAST EUROPE LTD.—See Roland Corporation; *Int'l*, pg. 6390
ROLAND ELEKTRONISCHE MUSIKINSTRUMENTE HANDELSGESELLSCHAFT MBH—See Roland Corporation; *Int'l*, pg. 6390
ROLAND EUROPE S.P.A.—See Roland Corporation; *Int'l*, pg. 6390
ROLAND FOODS, LLC—See Vestar Capital Partners, LLC; *U.S. Private*, pg. 4372
ROLAND IBERIA S.L.—See Roland Corporation; *Int'l*, pg. 6390
ROLAND ITALY S.P.A.—See Roland Corporation; *Int'l*, pg. 6390
ROLAND LAND INVESTMENT CO., INC.; *U.S. Private*, pg. 3473
ROLAND MACHINERY COMPANY INC.; *U.S. Private*, pg. 3474
ROLAND MURTEN AG—See Cornu S.A.; *Int'l*, pg. 1801
ROLAND MUSIC LLC—See Roland Corporation; *Int'l*, pg. 6390
ROLAND PARK-VICTOR'S MARKET INC.; *U.S. Private*, pg. 3474
ROLAND POLSKA SP. Z O.O.—See Roland Corporation; *Int'l*, pg. 6390
ROLAND PROZESSFINANZ AG—See IMF Bentham Limited; *Int'l*, pg. 3624
ROLAND REAL ESTATE SP. Z O.O.—See Sioen Industries NV; *Int'l*, pg. 6960
ROLAND RECHTSSCHUTZ BETEILIGUNGS GMBH—See Baloise Holding AG; *Int'l*, pg. 811
ROLAND RECHTSSCHUTZ-VERSICHERUNGS-AG - AMSTERDAM—See AXA S.A.; *Int'l*, pg. 759
ROLAND RECHTSSCHUTZ-VERSICHERUNGS-AG—See AXA S.A.; *Int'l*, pg. 759
ROLAND RECHTSSCHUTZ-VERSICHERUNGS-AG - VIENNA—See AXA S.A.; *Int'l*, pg. 759
ROLAND SCANDINAVIA A/S—See Roland Corporation; *Int'l*, pg. 6390
ROLAND SCHUTZBRIEF-VERSICHERUNG AG—See AXA S.A.; *Int'l*, pg. 759
ROLAND SHANGHAI ELECTRONICS CO., LTD.—See Roland Corporation; *Int'l*, pg. 6390
ROLAND'S TIRE SERVICE, INC.; *U.S. Private*, pg. 3474
ROLAND (SWITZERLAND) AG—See Roland Corporation; *Int'l*, pg. 6390
ROLAND SYSTEMS GROUP EMEA, S.L.—See Roland Corporation; *Int'l*, pg. 6390
ROLAND SYSTEMS GROUP FRANCE S.A.—See Roland Corporation; *Int'l*, pg. 6390
ROLAND SYSTEMS GROUP SCANDINAVIA—See Roland Corporation; *Int'l*, pg. 6390
ROLAND SYSTEMS GROUP U.S.—See Roland Corporation; *Int'l*, pg. 6390
ROLAND TAIWAN ENTERPRISE CO., LTD.—See Roland Corporation; *Int'l*, pg. 6390
ROLAND THIBAULT INC.—See TFI International Inc.; *Int'l*, pg. 7586
ROLAND TRANSPORT KG—See Dr. August Oetker KG; *Int'l*, pg. 2190
ROLAND (U.K.) LTD.—See Roland Corporation; *Int'l*, pg. 6390
ROLARK EDMONTON INC.—See Jacquet Metal Service SA; *Int'l*, pg. 3867
ROLA SECURITY SOLUTIONS GMBH—See Deutsche Telekom AG; *Int'l*, pg. 2085
ROL-AWAY TRUCK MANUFACTURING CO. INC.—See The Cutler Corporation; *U.S. Private*, pg. 4017
ROLCON ENGINEERING COMPANY LIMITED; *Int'l*, pg. 6391
ROLDAN S.A.—See Acerinox, S.A.; *Int'l*, pg. 101
ROLEC PROZESS - UND BRAUTECHNIK GMBH—See ATS Corporation; *Int'l*, pg. 695
ROLEC SERVICES LTD.—See Sdiptech AB; *Int'l*, pg. 6659
ROLEX RINGS LIMITED; *Int'l*, pg. 6391
ROLEX S.A.; *Int'l*, pg. 6391
ROLEX WATCH U.S.A., INC.—See Rolex S.A.; *Int'l*, pg. 6391
ROLF C. HAGEN (FRANCE) S.A.—See Rolf C. Hagen, Inc.; *Int'l*, pg. 6391
ROLF C. HAGEN, INC.; *Int'l*, pg. 6391
ROLF C. HAGEN (SEA) SDN. BHD.—See Rolf C. Hagen, Inc.; *Int'l*, pg. 6391
ROLF C. HAGEN (UK) LTD.—See Rolf C. Hagen, Inc.; *Int'l*, pg. 6391
ROLF C. HAGEN (USA) CORP.—See Rolf C. Hagen, Inc.; *Int'l*, pg. 6391

ROLFES HOLDINGS LIMITED—See Phatisa Group Limited; *Int'l*, pg. 5842
ROLF LLC—See Delance Limited; *Int'l*, pg. 2010
ROLF LOGISTIC LLC—See Nippon Yusen Kabushiki Kaisha; *Int'l*, pg. 5359
ROLF PLOTZ GMBH & CO. KG—See CVC Capital Partners SICAV-FIS S.A.; *Int'l*, pg. 1887
ROLF SCHMIDT INDUSTRI PLAST A/S—See CENTROTEC SE; *Int'l*, pg. 1414
ROLIC TECHNOLOGIES AG—See BASF SE; *Int'l*, pg. 884
ROLIC TECHNOLOGIES LTD.—See BASF SE; *Int'l*, pg. 884
ROLIC TECHNOLOGIES (SHANGHAI) CO., LTD.—See BASF SE; *Int'l*, pg. 884
ROLITE PLASTICS INC.—See Jordan Industries, Inc.; *U.S. Private*, pg. 2235
ROLITH, INC.—See Meta Materials Inc.; *Int'l*, pg. 4844
ROLKE PHARMA GMBH; *Int'l*, pg. 6391
ROLKO KOHLGRUBER GMBH—See INDUS Holding AG; *Int'l*, pg. 3664
ROLKO NEDERLAND BV—See INDUS Holding AG; *Int'l*, pg. 3664
ROLKO SCANDINAVIA APS—See INDUS Holding AG; *Int'l*, pg. 3664
ROLLAC SHUTTER OF TEXAS, INC.; *U.S. Private*, pg. 3474
ROLLADEN INC.; *U.S. Private*, pg. 3474
ROLLALONG LTD.—See Newship Ltd; *Int'l*, pg. 5238
ROLLAND ENTERPRISES INC.—See H.I.G. Capital, LLC; *U.S. Private*, pg. 1831
ROLL-A-SHADE; *U.S. Private*, pg. 3474
ROLLA SP PROPELLERS SA—See Twin Disc, Incorporated; *U.S. Public*, pg. 2206
ROLLATAINERS LIMITED; *Int'l*, pg. 6391
ROLL CALL INC.—See The Economist Group Limited; *Int'l*, pg. 7637
ROLLCAST ENERGY, INC.—See I Squared Capital Advisors (US) LLC; *U.S. Private*, pg. 2025
ROLLCO AB—See Addtech AB; *Int'l*, pg. 135
ROLLCO A/S—See Addtech AB; *Int'l*, pg. 135
ROLLCO NORGE AS—See Addtech AB; *Int'l*, pg. 135
ROLLCO OY—See Addtech AB; *Int'l*, pg. 135
ROLLCO TAIWAN CO., LTD.—See Addtech AB; *Int'l*, pg. 135
ROLLED ALLOYS, INC. - LOS ANGELES—See Rolled Alloys, Inc.; *U.S. Private*, pg. 3474
ROLLED ALLOYS, INC.; *U.S. Private*, pg. 3474
ROLLED ALLOYS LTD.—See Rolled Alloys, Inc.; *U.S. Private*, pg. 3474
ROLLED ALLOYS SINGAPORE, LTD.—See Rolled Alloys, Inc.; *U.S. Private*, pg. 3474
ROLLED ALLOYS—See Rolled Alloys, Inc.; *U.S. Private*, pg. 3474
ROLLED ALLOYS (SUZHOU) LTD.—See Rolled Alloys, Inc.; *U.S. Private*, pg. 3474
ROLLED EDGE, INC.—See WestRock Company; *U.S. Public*, pg. 2362
ROLLED STEEL PRODUCTS CORPORATION; *U.S. Private*, pg. 3474
ROLL ENG S.R.L.—See EUROLLS S.p.A.; *Int'l*, pg. 2553
ROLLER BEARING COMPANY OF AMERICA INC.—See RBC Bearings Incorporated; *U.S. Public*, pg. 1766
ROLLER DERBY SKATE CORP.; *U.S. Private*, pg. 3474
ROLLER DIE & FORMING COMPANY, INC.; *U.S. Private*, pg. 3474
ROLLESTON BUILDING SUPPLIES LIMITED—See Fletcher Building Limited; *Int'l*, pg. 2701
ROLLESTON MANOR MANAGEMENT COMPANY LIMITED—See Bellway plc; *Int'l*, pg. 968
ROLLETTE OIL CO. INC.; *U.S. Private*, pg. 3474
ROLLEX CORPORATION; *U.S. Private*, pg. 3474
ROLLEX (PTY) LIMITED—See Lonrho Limited; *Int'l*, pg. 4552
ROLLEX TRANSPORTATION INC—See Gestion Claude Robert Inc.; *Int'l*, pg. 2946
ROLLEX TRANSPORTATION INC—See Robert Bernard Pneus et Mecanique; *Int'l*, pg. 6358
ROLL FORMING CORPORATION - PENNSYLVANIA—See voestalpine AG; *Int'l*, pg. 8289
ROLL FORMING CORPORATION—See voestalpine AG; *Int'l*, pg. 8289
ROLL-GOM S.A.—See Aurea, S.A.; *Int'l*, pg. 707
ROLL & HILL, LLC; *U.S. Private*, pg. 3474
ROLLIN B. CHILD INCORPORATED; *U.S. Private*, pg. 3475
ROLLING GREEN MEMORIAL PARK LLC—See Axar Capital Management L.P.; *U.S. Private*, pg. 412
ROLLING GREENS, INC.—See Universal Engeisha Co., Ltd.; *Int'l*, pg. 8078
ROLLING HILLS AUTO PLAZA; *U.S. Private*, pg. 3475
ROLLING HILLS BANK & TRUST; *U.S. Private*, pg. 3475
ROLLING HILLS COUNTRY CLUB; *U.S. Private*, pg. 3475
ROLLING HILLS HOSPITAL, LLC—See Universal Health Services, Inc.; *U.S. Public*, pg. 2259
ROLLING HILLS HOSPITALS, INC.—See Acadia Healthcare Company, Inc.; *U.S. Public*, pg. 30
ROLLING HILLS MEMORIAL PARK—See Carriage Services, Inc.; *U.S. Public*, pg. 440

ROLLS-ROYCE HOLDINGS PLC

ROLLING OAKS MALL, LLC—See Washington Prime Group Inc.; *U.S. Public*, pg. 4449
ROLLING OAKS RADIOLOGY, INC.—See RadNet, Inc.; *U.S. Public*, pg. 1761
ROLLING ROCK CLUB; *U.S. Public*, pg. 3475
ROLLING SHIELD, INC.; *U.S. Private*, pg. 3475
ROLLING STONE MAGAZINE—See Penske Media Corporation; *U.S. Private*, pg. 3139
THE ROLLINS AGENCY, INC.—See Brown & Brown, Inc.; *U.S. Public*, pg. 399
ROLLINS, INC.; *U.S. Public*, pg. 1808
ROLLINS-PCI CONSTRUCTION COMPANY; *U.S. Private*, pg. 3475
ROLLINS SUPPLY, INC.—See Rollins, Inc.; *U.S. Public*, pg. 1809
ROLLKALL TECHNOLOGIES LLC; *U.S. Private*, pg. 3475
ROLL-KRAFT, INC.; *U.S. Private*, pg. 3474
ROLLMAN GROUP PLC; *Int'l*, pg. 6391
ROLLMANN TRADING COMPANY—See THK CO., LTD.; *Int'l*, pg. 7712
ROLL-N-LOCK CORP.—See CCMP Capital Advisors, LP; *U.S. Private*, pg. 801
ROLL-N-LOCK CORP.—See TA Associates, Inc.; *U.S. Private*, pg. 3919
ROLL N OILFIELD INDUSTRIES LTD.; *Int'l*, pg. 6391
ROLLOFFS USA INC.; *U.S. Private*, pg. 3475
ROLLON B.V.—See The Timken Company; *U.S. Public*, pg. 2133
ROLLON CORPORATION—See The Timken Company; *U.S. Public*, pg. 2133
ROLLON GMBH—See The Timken Company; *U.S. Public*, pg. 2133
ROLLON INDIA PVT. LTD.—See The Timken Company; *U.S. Public*, pg. 2133
ROLLON JAPAN KK—See The Timken Company; *U.S. Public*, pg. 2133
ROLLON LTD. UK LIMITED—See The Timken Company; *U.S. Public*, pg. 2133
ROLLON S.A.R.L.—See The Timken Company; *U.S. Public*, pg. 2133
ROLLON S.P.A.—See The Timken Company; *U.S. Public*, pg. 2133
ROLLPACK SASU—See Poincare Gestion SAS; *Int'l*, pg. 5904
ROLLPAK CORPORATION—See Berry Global Group, Inc; *U.S. Public*, pg. 321
ROLLPRINT PACKAGING PRODUCTS INC.; *U.S. Private*, pg. 3475
ROLL-RITE, LLC—See Genstar Capital, LLC; *U.S. Private*, pg. 1676
ROLLS-ROYCE AB—See Rolls-Royce Holdings plc; *Int'l*, pg. 6392
ROLLS-ROYCE AUSTRALIA SERVICES PTY LIMITED—See Rolls-Royce Holdings plc; *Int'l*, pg. 6392
ROLLS-ROYCE BRASIL LIMITAD—See Rolls-Royce Holdings plc; *Int'l*, pg. 6392
ROLLS-ROYCE CANADA LIMITED - NAVAL MARINE—See Rolls-Royce Holdings plc; *Int'l*, pg. 6392
ROLLS-ROYCE CANADA LIMITED - NAVAL MARINE—See Rolls-Royce Holdings plc; *Int'l*, pg. 6392
ROLLS-ROYCE CANADA LTD.—See Rolls-Royce Holdings plc; *Int'l*, pg. 6392
ROLLS-ROYCE CHINA HOLDING LIMITED—See Rolls-Royce Holdings plc; *Int'l*, pg. 6392
ROLLS-ROYCE CIVIL NUCLEAR SAS—See Rolls-Royce Holdings plc; *Int'l*, pg. 6392
ROLLS-ROYCE COMMERCIAL MARINE INC—See Kongsberg Gruppen ASA; *Int'l*, pg. 4256
ROLLS-ROYCE CONTROLS AND DATA SERVICES LIMITED—See Rolls-Royce Holdings plc; *Int'l*, pg. 6393
ROLLS-ROYCE CORPORATION—See Rolls-Royce Holdings plc; *Int'l*, pg. 6393
ROLLS-ROYCE CROSSPOINTE LLC - ROLLS-ROYCE OUTDOOR JET ENGINE TEST FACILITY—See Rolls-Royce Holdings plc; *Int'l*, pg. 6393
ROLLS-ROYCE CROSSPOINTE LLC—See Rolls-Royce Holdings plc; *Int'l*, pg. 6393
ROLLS-ROYCE DEFENSE SERVICES INC.—See Rolls-Royce Holdings plc; *Int'l*, pg. 6393
ROLLS-ROYCE DEUTSCHLAND LTD & CO. KG—See Rolls-Royce Holdings plc; *Int'l*, pg. 6392
ROLLS-ROYCE ENGINE SERVICES-OAKLAND INC.—See Rolls-Royce Holdings plc; *Int'l*, pg. 6393
ROLLS-ROYCE FUEL CELL SYSTEMS LIMITED—See Rolls-Royce Holdings plc; *Int'l*, pg. 6392
ROLLS-ROYCE HOLDINGS PLC; *Int'l*, pg. 6391
ROLLS-ROYCE INDIA LIMITED—See Rolls-Royce Holdings plc; *Int'l*, pg. 6392
ROLLS-ROYCE INDIA PRIVATE LIMITED—See Rolls-Royce Holdings plc; *Int'l*, pg. 6392
ROLLS-ROYCE INTERNATIONAL LIMITED—See Rolls-Royce Holdings plc; *Int'l*, pg. 6392
ROLLS-ROYCE INTERNATIONAL LIMITED—See Rolls-Royce Holdings plc; *Int'l*, pg. 6392
ROLLS-ROYCE INTERNATIONAL LIMITED—See Rolls-Royce Holdings plc; *Int'l*, pg. 6392
ROLLS-ROYCE INTERNATIONAL LIMITED—See Rolls-Royce Holdings plc; *Int'l*, pg. 6392

ROLLS-ROYCE HOLDINGS PLC

CORPORATE AFFILIATIONS

ROLLS-ROYCE INTERNATIONAL LIMITED—See Rolls-Royce Holdings plc; *Int'l*, pg. 6392
ROLLS-ROYCE INTERNATIONAL LIMITED—See Rolls-Royce Holdings plc; *Int'l*, pg. 6392
ROLLS-ROYCE INTERNATIONAL LLC—See Rolls-Royce Holdings plc; *Int'l*, pg. 6392
ROLLS-ROYCE INTERNATIONAL—See Rolls-Royce Holdings plc; *Int'l*, pg. 6392
ROLLS-ROYCE INTERNATIONAL—See Rolls-Royce Holdings plc; *Int'l*, pg. 6392
ROLLS-ROYCE INTERNATIONAL—See Rolls-Royce Holdings plc; *Int'l*, pg. 6392
ROLLS-ROYCE INTERNATIONAL—See Rolls-Royce Holdings plc; *Int'l*, pg. 6392
ROLLS-ROYCE INTERNATIONAL—See Rolls-Royce Holdings plc; *Int'l*, pg. 6392
ROLLS-ROYCE INTERNATIONAL—See Rolls-Royce Holdings plc; *Int'l*, pg. 6392
ROLLS-ROYCE INTERNATIONAL—See Rolls-Royce Holdings plc; *Int'l*, pg. 6392
ROLLS-ROYCE INTERNATIONAL—See Rolls-Royce Holdings plc; *Int'l*, pg. 6392
ROLLS-ROYCE INTERNATIONAL—See Rolls-Royce Holdings plc; *Int'l*, pg. 6392
ROLLS-ROYCE INTERNATIONAL—See Rolls-Royce Holdings plc; *Int'l*, pg. 6392
ROLLS-ROYCE INTERNATIONAL—See Rolls-Royce Holdings plc; *Int'l*, pg. 6392
ROLLS-ROYCE JAPAN CO. LTD—See Rolls-Royce Holdings plc; *Int'l*, pg. 6392
ROLLS-ROYCE MALAYSIA SDN BHD—See Rolls-Royce Holdings plc; *Int'l*, pg. 6392
ROLLS-ROYCE MARINE AS—See Rolls-Royce Holdings plc; *Int'l*, pg. 6393
ROLLS-ROYCE MARINE AS—See Rolls-Royce Holdings plc; *Int'l*, pg. 6392
ROLLS-ROYCE MARINE AS—See Rolls-Royce Holdings plc; *Int'l*, pg. 6392
ROLLS-ROYCE MARINE ELECTRICAL SYSTEMS LIMITED—See Rolls-Royce Holdings plc; *Int'l*, pg. 6393
ROLLS-ROYCE MARINE POWER OPERATIONS LIMITED—See Rolls-Royce Holdings plc; *Int'l*, pg. 6393
ROLLS-ROYCE MARINE (SHANGHAI) LIMITED—See Rolls-Royce Holdings plc; *Int'l*, pg. 6392
ROLLS-ROYCE MOTOR CARS LIMITED—See Bayerische Motoren Werke Aktiengesellschaft; *Int'l*, pg. 913
ROLLS-ROYCE MOTOR CARS NA LLC—See Bayerische Motoren Werke Aktiengesellschaft; *Int'l*, pg. 913
ROLLS-ROYCE NAVAL MARINE INC.—See Rolls-Royce Holdings plc; *Int'l*, pg. 6393
ROLLS-ROYCE NAVAL MARINE INC.—See Rolls-Royce Holdings plc; *Int'l*, pg. 6393
ROLLS-ROYCE NEW ZEALAND LIMITED—See Rolls-Royce Holdings plc; *Int'l*, pg. 6393
ROLLS-ROYCE NORTH AMERICA INC.—See Rolls-Royce Holdings plc; *Int'l*, pg. 6393
ROLLS-ROYCE OMAN LIMITED LIABILITY COMPANY—See Rolls-Royce Holdings plc; *Int'l*, pg. 6393
ROLLS-ROYCE OY AB—See Rolls-Royce Holdings plc; *Int'l*, pg. 6392
ROLLS-ROYCE POWER DEVELOPMENT LIMITED—See Rolls-Royce Holdings plc; *Int'l*, pg. 6393
ROLLS-ROYCE POWER ENGINEERING PLC—See Rolls-Royce Holdings plc; *Int'l*, pg. 6393
ROLLS-ROYCE POWER SYSTEMS AG—See Rolls-Royce Holdings plc; *Int'l*, pg. 6393
ROLLS-ROYCE SAUDI ARABIA LIMITED—See Rolls-Royce Holdings plc; *Int'l*, pg. 6394
ROLLS-ROYCE SINGAPORE PTE LIMITED—See Rolls-Royce Holdings plc; *Int'l*, pg. 6392
ROLLS-ROYCE—See Rolls-Royce Holdings plc; *Int'l*, pg. 6392
ROLLS-ROYCE SP Z.O.O.—See Rolls-Royce Holdings plc; *Int'l*, pg. 6394
ROLLS-ROYCE TECHNICAL SUPPORT SARL—See Rolls-Royce Holdings plc; *Int'l*, pg. 6394
ROLLS-ROYCE (THAILAND) LIMITED—See Rolls-Royce Holdings plc; *Int'l*, pg. 6392
ROLLS-ROYCE TURBOMECA LIMITED—See Safran SA; *Int'l*, pg. 6476
ROLLSTONE BANK & TRUST; *U.S. Private*, pg. 3475
ROLL-UP CAPITAL CORP.; *Int'l*, pg. 6391
ROLLWAY BEARING N.V.—See Emerson Electric Co.; *U.S. Public*, pg. 752
ROL MANUFACTURING OF AMERICA INC.; *U.S. Private*, pg. 3473
ROLMAN WORLD FZCO—See THK CO., LTD.; *Int'l*, pg. 7712
ROLMEX SA; *Int'l*, pg. 6394
ROL NORMANDIE SAS—See VINCI S.A.; *Int'l*, pg. 8226
ROLNYVIK SP. Z O.O.—See Kinnevik AB; *Int'l*, pg. 4182
ROLOTEC AG—See SIX Group AG; *Int'l*, pg. 6967
ROLOX INC.—See True Home Value, Inc.; *U.S. Private*, pg. 4247
ROL-RYZ SP. ZO.O.—See Marbour SAS; *Int'l*, pg. 4688
ROLTA AMERICAS—See Rolta Americas; *U.S. Private*, pg. 3475
ROLTA AMERICAS; *U.S. Private*, pg. 3475

ROLTA ASIA PACIFIC PTY LTD.—See Rolta India Ltd.; *Int'l*, pg. 6394
ROLTA BENELUX B.V.—See Rolta India Ltd.; *Int'l*, pg. 6394
ROLTA DEFENCE TECHNOLOGY SYSTEMS PVT. LTD.—See Rolta India Ltd.; *Int'l*, pg. 6394
ROLTA DEUTSCHLAND GMBH—See Rolta India Ltd.; *Int'l*, pg. 6394
ROLTA INDIA LTD.; *Int'l*, pg. 6394
ROLTA INTERNATIONAL INC—See Rolta India Ltd.; *Int'l*, pg. 6394
ROLTA MIDDLE EAST FZ - LLC—See Rolta India Ltd.; *Int'l*, pg. 6394
ROLTA MIDDLE EAST FZ LLC UAE—See Rolta India Ltd.; *Int'l*, pg. 6394
ROLTA UK LIMITED—See Rolta India Ltd.; *Int'l*, pg. 6394
ROL-TECH-FORT LORAMIE—See ROL Manufacturing of America Inc.; *U.S. Private*, pg. 3473
ROLTRANS TEGELEN BV—See Sioen Industries NV; *Int'l*, pg. 6960
ROLYN CONSTRUCTION CORPORATION; *U.S. Private*, pg. 3475
ROMA 2000 SRL—See UniCredit S.p.A.; *Int'l*, pg. 8034
ROMAC INDUSTRIAL PARTS, INC.—See Kinderhook Industries, LLC; *U.S. Private*, pg. 2306
ROMAC INDUSTRIAL PARTS, INC.—See Kinderhook Industries, LLC; *U.S. Private*, pg. 2307
ROMAC INDUSTRIES, INC. - ROMAC FOUNDRY DIVISION—See Romac Industries, Inc.; *U.S. Private*, pg. 3475
ROMAC INDUSTRIES, INC.; *U.S. Private*, pg. 3475
RO-MAC LUMBER & SUPPLY INC.; *U.S. Private*, pg. 3453
ROMACO DO BRASIL LTDA.—See Truking Technology Limited; *Int'l*, pg. 7941
ROMACO FRANCE S.A.S.—See Truking Technology Limited; *Int'l*, pg. 7941
ROMACO HOLDING GMBH—See Truking Technology Limited; *Int'l*, pg. 7941
ROMACO PHARMATECHNIK GMBH—See Truking Technology Limited; *Int'l*, pg. 7941
ROMACORP, INC.; *U.S. Private*, pg. 3475
ROMACO S.R.L.—See Truking Technology Limited; *Int'l*, pg. 7941
ROMAERO S.A.; *Int'l*, pg. 6394
ROMA FOOD ENTERPRISES INC.—See Performance Food Group Company; *U.S. Public*, pg. 1676
ROMAG LTD.—See Clayton Glass Ltd.; *Int'l*, pg. 1653
ROMAIN BUICK INC.; *U.S. Private*, pg. 3475
ROMA (META) GROUP LIMITED; *Int'l*, pg. 6394
ROMANA CHIMICI S.P.A.—See BRENNTAG SE; *Int'l*, pg. 1149
ROMANDE ENERGIE COMMERCE SA—See Romande Energie Holding S.A.; *Int'l*, pg. 6394
ROMANDE ENERGIE HOLDING S.A.; *Int'l*, pg. 6394
ROMANDE ENERGIE RENOUVELABLE SA—See Romande Energie Holding S.A.; *Int'l*, pg. 6394
ROMANDE ENERGIE S.A.—See Romande Energie Holding S.A.; *Int'l*, pg. 6394
ROMANDE ENERGIE SERVICES S.A.—See Romande Energie Holding S.A.; *Int'l*, pg. 6394
ROMAN DIETSCHE GMBH—See International Building Products Ltd.; *Int'l*, pg. 3744
ROMAN EAGLE REHABILITATION AND HEALTH CARE CENTER, INC.; *U.S. Private*, pg. 3475
ROMAN ELECTRIC COMPANY, INC.; *U.S. Private*, pg. 3475
ROMAN HOLDINGS CORPORATION; *U.S. Private*, pg. 3475
ROMANIA CURT GEORGI ROMANIA S.R.L.—See Curt Georgi GmbH & Co. KG; *Int'l*, pg. 1880
THE ROMANIAN PUBLISHING GROUP S.R.L.—See Vivendi SE; *Int'l*, pg. 8278
ROMANIJAPUTEVI A.D.; *Int'l*, pg. 6395
ROMAN, INC.; *U.S. Private*, pg. 3476
ROMAN MANUFACTURING INC.; *U.S. Private*, pg. 3476
ROMAN MEAL COMPANY; *U.S. Private*, pg. 3476
ROMANOFF FLOOR COVERING; *U.S. Private*, pg. 3476
ROMANOFF TECHNOLOGIES OHIO LLC; *U.S. Private*, pg. 3476
ROMANO FORD OF FAYETTEVILLE LTD.; *U.S. Private*, pg. 3476
ROMANO TOYOTA; *U.S. Private*, pg. 3476
ROMANOW INC.; *U.S. Private*, pg. 3476
ROMAN RESEARCH, INC.; *U.S. Private*, pg. 3476
ROMAN ROOFING, INC.; *U.S. Private*, pg. 3476
ROMANS AUTOMOBILES SA; *Int'l*, pg. 6395
ROMANTA ESTIVAL 2002 SA; *Int'l*, pg. 6395
ROMA PLASTIK A.S.—See Fritz Egger GmbH & Co.; *Int'l*, pg. 2794
ROMARCO NV—See Eiffage S.A.; *Int'l*, pg. 2331
ROMARIC AUTOMATION DESIGN, INC.—See Meyer Burger Technology AG; *Int'l*, pg. 4869
ROMARK LABORATORIES, L.C.; *U.S. Private*, pg. 3476
ROMARK LOGISTICS, INC.; *U.S. Private*, pg. 3476
RO-MAR TRANSPORTATION SYSTEMS INC.; *U.S. Private*, pg. 3453
ROMAR-VOSS B.V.—See ShawCor Ltd.; *Int'l*, pg. 6791

ROMBALDS RUN-OFF LIMITED—See Enstar Group Limited; *Int'l*, pg. 2449
ROMBAUER VINEYARDS, LLC—See E. & J. Gallo Winery; *U.S. Private*, pg. 1303
ROMBERGER FERTIGTEILE GMBH—See Swietelsky Baugesellschaft m.b.H.; *Int'l*, pg. 7367
ROMB S.A.—See Grupa Kety S.A.; *Int'l*, pg. 3116
ROMCARBON S.A.; *Int'l*, pg. 6395
ROMCIM S.A.—See CRH plc; *Int'l*, pg. 1848
ROMCO EQUIPMENT CO.—See SMT Belgium NV; *Int'l*, pg. 7017
ROM COMMUNICATIONS, INC.—See Total Telcom Inc.; *Int'l*, pg. 7835
ROME 2000 SRL—See UniCredit S.p.A.; *Int'l*, pg. 8035
ROME BUILDING PRODUCTS INC.—See Hendricks Holding Company, Inc.; *U.S. Private*, pg. 1915
ROMEC LIMITED—See International Distributions Services plc; *Int'l*, pg. 3748
ROME & COMPANY; *U.S. Private*, pg. 3476
ROMEDIC B.V.—See Advent International Corporation; *U.S. Private*, pg. 104
ROMELEBYGDENS KABEL-TV AB—See Telia Company AB; *Int'l*, pg. 7543
ROMELT-SAIL (INDIA) LTD—See Steel Authority of India Limited; *Int'l*, pg. 7189
ROMEO ENTERTAINMENT GROUP, INC.; *U.S. Private*, pg. 3476
ROMEO GAS S.P.A.—See Ascopiave S.p.A.; *Int'l*, pg. 603
ROMEO MUSIC; *U.S. Private*, pg. 3476
ROMEO POWER, INC.—See Nikola Corp.; *U.S. Public*, pg. 1529
ROMEO RIM, INC.—See Reserve Group Management Company; *U.S. Private*, pg. 3404
ROME RESOURCES PLC; *Int'l*, pg. 6395
ROMERIKE ELEKTRO AS—See Instalco AB; *Int'l*, pg. 3722
ROMERIKE SPAREBANK; *Int'l*, pg. 6395
ROMER LABS, INC.; *U.S. Private*, pg. 3476
ROMERO GENERAL CONSTRUCTION CORPORATION; *U.S. Private*, pg. 3476
ROMERO MOTORS CORPORATION; *U.S. Private*, pg. 3476
ROMERO'S FOOD PRODUCTS, INCORPORATED; *U.S. Private*, pg. 3476
ROME STRIP STEEL CO., INC.—See Worthington Industries, Inc.; *U.S. Public*, pg. 2382
ROMEX WORLD TRADE CO., L.L.C.—See Roy O. Martin Lumber Company, LLC; *U.S. Private*, pg. 3491
ROMFORD STADIUM LIMITED—See Entain PLC; *Int'l*, pg. 2450
ROMFOR SA; *Int'l*, pg. 6395
ROM GROUP LIMITED—See Celsa Group; *Int'l*, pg. 1395
ROMI EUROPA GMBH—See Industrias Romi S.A.; *Int'l*, pg. 3674
ROMI FRANCE SAS—See Industrias Romi S.A.; *Int'l*, pg. 3674
ROMI ITALIA S.R.L.—See Industrias Romi S.A.; *Int'l*, pg. 3674
ROMIKA AG—See Romika Shoes GmbH; *Int'l*, pg. 6395
ROMIKA SHOES GMBH; *Int'l*, pg. 6395
ROMIKA USA, INC.—See Romika Shoes GmbH; *Int'l*, pg. 6395
ROMI MACHINES UK LTD.—See Industrias Romi S.A.; *Int'l*, pg. 3674
ROMI MACHINE TOOLS, LTD.—See Industrias Romi S.A.; *Int'l*, pg. 3674
ROMI MAQUINAS ESPANA S.A.—See Industrias Romi S.A.; *Int'l*, pg. 3674
ROMIN SLOVAKIA, SPOL. S.R.O.—See Minerals Technologies, Inc.; *U.S. Public*, pg. 1449
ROMIOS GOLD NEVADA INC.—See Romios Gold Resources Inc.; *Int'l*, pg. 6395
ROMIOS GOLD RESOURCES INC.; *Int'l*, pg. 6395
ROMLIFT SERV S.R.L.—See Group Thermote & Vanhalst; *Int'l*, pg. 3089
ROMLOGIC TECHNOLOGY S.A.—See BRK Financial Group S.A.; *Int'l*, pg. 1171
ROMMEL HOLDINGS INC.; *U.S. Private*, pg. 3476
ROMNAV S.A.; *Int'l*, pg. 6395
ROMOLD LTD.—See Empteezy Ltd; *Int'l*, pg. 2392
ROMO-SYLT LINIE GMBH & CO. KG—See FRS GmbH & Co. KG; *Int'l*, pg. 2797
ROMPETROL DOWNSTREAM S.R.L.—See ROMPETROL RAFINARE S.A.; *Int'l*, pg. 6395
ROMPETROL RAFINARE S.A.; *Int'l*, pg. 6395
ROMPETROL WELL SERVICES S.A.; *Int'l*, pg. 6395
ROMPLUMB SA; *Int'l*, pg. 6395
ROMPO PRODUCTS CO. LTD.—See DCON Products Public Company Limited; *Int'l*, pg. 1993
ROMRADIATOARE SA; *Int'l*, pg. 6395
ROM RAIL S.R.L.—See Ferrovie dello Stato Italiane S.p.A.; *Int'l*, pg. 2645
ROMREAL LTD.; *Int'l*, pg. 6395
ROMRECYCLING SRL—See Derichebourg S.A.; *Int'l*, pg. 2042
ROMSAN INTERNATIONAL COMPANY S.R.L.—See OSG Corporation; *Int'l*, pg. 5649
ROMSDAL SPAREBANK; *Int'l*, pg. 6395

COMPANY NAME INDEX ROOSEVELT & CROSS INC.

Company Index

ROMSTAL LEASING IFN SA—See KBC Group NV; *Int'l*, pg. 4106
ROMSTRADE S.R.L.—See Salini Costruttori S.p.A.; *Int'l*, pg. 6493
ROMULUS INC.; *U.S. Private*, pg. 3477
THE ROMWEBER COMPANY; *U.S. Private*, pg. 4112
ROMY FOODS CORPORATION LTD.; *Int'l*, pg. 6395
RONA INC.—See Lowe's Companies, Inc.; *U.S. Public*, pg. 1343
RONAL AG; *Int'l*, pg. 6396
RONAL CR S.R.O.—See RONAL AG; *Int'l*, pg. 6396
RONALD MARK ASSOCIATES INC.; *U.S. Private*, pg. 3477
RONALD MCDONALD HOUSE CHARITIES, INC.—See McDonald's Corporation; *U.S. Public*, pg. 1406
RONALD R. WREN ADVERTISING, INC.; *U.S. Private*, pg. 3477
RONALD THOMPSON LIMITED—See Environ Group (Investments) plc; *Int'l*, pg. 2454
RONAL FRANCE S.A.S—See RONAL AG; *Int'l*, pg. 6396
RONAL GMBH—See RONAL AG; *Int'l*, pg. 6396
RONAL IBERICA S.A.U.—See RONAL AG; *Int'l*, pg. 6396
RONAL POLSKA SP.Z O.O.—See RONAL AG; *Int'l*, pg. 6396
RONAL QUERETARO S.A. DE C.V.—See RONAL AG; *Int'l*, pg. 6396
RON AND ANN ENTERPRISES INC.; *U.S. Private*, pg. 3477
RONANE INTERNATIONAL PTY LTD—See Grove International Pty Limited; *Int'l*, pg. 3112
RONAN ENGINEERING COMPANY, MEASUREMENTS DIVISION—See Ronan Engineering Company; *U.S. Private*, pg. 3477
RONAN ENGINEERING COMPANY; *U.S. Private*, pg. 3477
RONAN ENGINEERING LTD.—See Ronan Engineering Company; *U.S. Private*, pg. 3477
RONAUTICA MIDDLE EAST O.M.C.—See United Development Company PSC; *Int'l*, pg. 8066
RON BOUCHARD'S AUTO SALES, INC.; *U.S. Private*, pg. 3477
RON BOWERS, INC.; *U.S. Private*, pg. 3477
RON CARTER; *U.S. Private*, pg. 3477
RONCASA IMMOBILIEN-VERWALTUNGS GMBH—See UniCredit S.p.A.; *Int'l*, pg. 8035
RONCHETTI DISTRIBUTING CO; *U.S. Private*, pg. 3478
RONCO COMMUNICATIONS & ELECTRONICS INC.; *U.S. Private*, pg. 3478
RONCO CONSULTING CORPORATION—See Allied Universal Manager LLC; *U.S. Private*, pg. 189
RONCO INVENTIONS LLC; *U.S. Private*, pg. 3478
RONCO MACHINE AND RIGGING; *U.S. Private*, pg. 3478
RONCUZZI S.R.L—See WAMGROUP S.p.A.; *Int'l*, pg. 8338
RONDELLI ADVISERS S.R.L.—See Compass Advisers Group LLC; *U.S. Private*, pg. 999
RONDEX (THAILAND) CO., LTD—See Naigai Co., Ltd.; *Int'l*, pg. 5130
RONDO AG—See Korber AG; *Int'l*, pg. 4280
RONDO B.V.—See DPG Media Group NV; *Int'l*, pg. 2189
RONDO LEASING GMBH—See UniCredit S.p.A.; *Int'l*, pg. 8035
RONDO OBALY S.R.O.—See Korber AG; *Int'l*, pg. 4280
RONDO-PAK INC.—See Korber AG; *Int'l*, pg. 4280
RONDOR MUSIC INTERNATIONAL, INC.—See Universal Music Group N.V.; *Int'l*, pg. 8079
RONE ENGINEERING SERVICES, LLC—See Ocean-Sound Partners, LP; *U.S. Private*, pg. 2992
RONELL INDUSTRIES INC.; *U.S. Private*, pg. 3478
RONESANS HOLDING A.S.; *Int'l*, pg. 6396
RONETCO SUPERMARKETS INC.; *U.S. Private*, pg. 3478
RONEZ LIMITED—See SigmaRoc Plc; *Int'l*, pg. 6909
RONGAN PROPERTY CO., LTD.; *Int'l*, pg. 6397
RONGCHENG HAWTAI AUTOMOBILE CO., LTD.—See Hawtai Motor Group Limited; *Int'l*, pg. 3289
RONGCHENG SHIYUAN ELECTRIC EQUIPMENT CO., LTD—See YURATECH Co., Ltd.; *Int'l*, pg. 8617
RONGDE ASSET MANAGEMENT CO., LTD.—See China CITIC Financial Asset Management Co., Ltd.; *Int'l*, pg. 1489
RONGFENG HOLDING GROUP CO., LTD.; *Int'l*, pg. 6397
RONGFU AQUACULTURE, INC.; *Int'l*, pg. 6397
RONGSHENG PETRO CHEMICAL CO., LTD.; *Int'l*, pg. 6397
RONGTAI INDUSTRIAL DEVELOPMENT LEON S. DE R.L. DE C.V.—See Jiangsu Rongtai Industry Co., Ltd.; *Int'l*, pg. 3953
RONG VIET SECURITIES CORPORATION; *Int'l*, pg. 6397
RON HERMAN INC.; *U.S. Private*, pg. 3477
RON HODGSON PONTIAC BUICK GMC LTD.; *Int'l*, pg. 6395
RONI HOUSEHOLDS LTD.; *Int'l*, pg. 6397
RONI, INC.—See Amplex AB; *Int'l*, pg. 434
RONILE, INC.; *U.S. Private*, pg. 3478
RONIN ADVERTISING GROUP; *U.S. Private*, pg. 3478
RONIN RESOURCES LIMITED; *Int'l*, pg. 6397
RONIN STAFFING LLC; *U.S. Private*, pg. 3478
RONIS-DOM LTD.—See Groupe SFPI SA; *Int'l*, pg. 3111
RONIS S.A.S.—See Groupe SFPI SA; *Int'l*, pg. 3111
RON JON SURF SHOP; *U.S. Private*, pg. 3477
RON MACGILLIVRAY CHEV BUICK GMC LTD.; *Int'l*, pg. 6395
RON MARHOFER CHEVROLET INC.; *U.S. Private*, pg. 3477
RONNER VERWALTUNGSGESELLSCHAFT MBH; *Int'l*, pg. 6397
RONNIE WATKINS FORD INC.; *U.S. Private*, pg. 3478
RONNINGEN RESEARCH & DEVELOPMENT CO; *U.S. Private*, pg. 3478
RONNING ENTERPRISES; *U.S. Private*, pg. 3478
RONNI NICOLE II INC.; *U.S. Private*, pg. 3478
RONN MOTOR GROUP, INC.; *U.S. Private*, pg. 3478
RONNOCO COFFEE, LLC—See Huron Capital Partners LLC; *U.S. Private*, pg. 2012
RON NORRIS BUICK GMC; *U.S. Private*, pg. 3477
RONPAK INC.; *U.S. Private*, pg. 3478
RON ROSE PRODUCTIONS LTD; *U.S. Private*, pg. 3477
RON SANTATERESA C.A.; *Int'l*, pg. 6396
RON SAYER'S CHRYSLER JEEP DODGE; *U.S. Private*, pg. 3477
RONSEAL LIMITED—See The Sherwin-Williams Company; *U.S. Public*, pg. 2128
RON'S EQUIPMENT CO INC.; *U.S. Private*, pg. 3477
RONSHINE CHINA HOLDINGS LTD.; *Int'l*, pg. 6397
RON'S OIL COMPANY; *U.S. Private*, pg. 3477
RONSON CONSUMER PRODUCTS CORP.—See Zippo Manufacturing Company, Inc.; *U.S. Private*, pg. 4606
RONSON DEVELOPMENT SE; *Int'l*, pg. 6397
RONSONET BUICK-GMC TRUCK, INC.; *U.S. Private*, pg. 3478
RON-SON FOODS INC.; *U.S. Private*, pg. 3477
RON SONNTAG PUBLIC RELATIONS; *U.S. Private*, pg. 3477
RONTARCA WILLIS, C.A.—See Willis Towers Watson Public Limited Company; *Int'l*, pg. 8416
RONTEC CO., LTD.—See ITOCHU Corporation; *Int'l*, pg. 3835
RONTGEN TECHNISCHE DIENST B.V.—See I Squared Capital Advisors (US) LLC; *U.S. Private*, pg. 2023
RONTGEN TECHNISCHE DIENST B.V.—See TDR Capital LLP; *Int'l*, pg. 7492
RON TIRAPELLI FORD; *U.S. Private*, pg. 3477
RONTO GROUP, INC.; *U.S. Private*, pg. 3478
RON TONKIN CHEVROLET CO.; *U.S. Private*, pg. 3477
RON TONKIN TOYOTA INC.—See Ron Tonkin Chevrolet Co.; *U.S. Private*, pg. 3477
RON WESTPHAL CHEVROLET INC.; *U.S. Private*, pg. 3477
RON WILLIAMS CONSTRUCTION INC.; *U.S. Private*, pg. 3477
ROOCHI TRADERS (NY) INC.; *U.S. Private*, pg. 3478
ROODLANE MEDICAL LIMITED—See HCA Healthcare, Inc.; *U.S. Public*, pg. 1007
ROOD WIT BLAUW HOLDING B.V.—See METAWATER Co., Ltd.; *Int'l*, pg. 4851
ROOF CARE CO.—See Henkel AG & Co. KGaA; *Int'l*, pg. 3354
ROOFCLAD LTD.—See Alam Group of Companies; *Int'l*, pg. 289
ROOF DIAGNOSTICS SOLAR OF MASS., LLC—See NRG Energy, Inc.; *U.S. Public*, pg. 1551
ROOFED RIGHT AMERICA, LLC; *U.S. Private*, pg. 3478
ROOFERS MART, INC.; *U.S. Private*, pg. 3478
ROOFERS MART OF SOUTHERN CALIFORNIA, INC.—See Beacon Roofing Supply, Inc.; *U.S. Public*, pg. 286
ROOFERS SUPPLY INC.—See Leonard Green & Partners, L.P.; *U.S. Private*, pg. 2429
ROOFERS' SUPPLY OF GREENVILLE, INC.—See Beacon Roofing Supply, Inc.; *U.S. Public*, pg. 286
THE ROOFING CENTRE (TASMANIA) PTY LTD.—See BlueScope Steel Limited; *Int'l*, pg. 1074
ROOFING CORP OF AMERICA, LLC—See FirstService Corporation; *Int'l*, pg. 2691
ROOFING & INSULATION SUPPLY INC.—See Beacon Roofing Supply, Inc.; *U.S. Public*, pg. 286
ROOFING SUPPLY GROUP - ALABAMA, LLC—See Beacon Roofing Supply, Inc.; *U.S. Public*, pg. 286
ROOFING SUPPLY GROUP - AUSTIN—See Beacon Roofing Supply, Inc.; *U.S. Public*, pg. 286
ROOFING SUPPLY GROUP - BAY AREA, LLC—See Beacon Roofing Supply, Inc.; *U.S. Public*, pg. 286
ROOFING SUPPLY GROUP-CINCINNATI—See Beacon Roofing Supply, Inc.; *U.S. Public*, pg. 286
ROOFING SUPPLY GROUP - CORPUS CHRISTI—See Beacon Roofing Supply, Inc.; *U.S. Public*, pg. 286
ROOFING SUPPLY GROUP - KANSAS CITY—See Beacon Roofing Supply, Inc.; *U.S. Public*, pg. 286
ROOFING SUPPLY GROUP - KENTUCKY, LLC—See Beacon Roofing Supply, Inc.; *U.S. Public*, pg. 286
ROOFING SUPPLY GROUP, LLC—See Beacon Roofing Supply, Inc.; *U.S. Public*, pg. 286
ROOFING SUPPLY GROUP OF COLUMBUS, LLC—See Beacon Roofing Supply, Inc.; *U.S. Public*, pg. 286
ROOFING SUPPLY GROUP OF OKLAHOMA, LLC—See Beacon Roofing Supply, Inc.; *U.S. Public*, pg. 286
ROOFING SUPPLY GROUP OF VIRGINIA, LLC—See Beacon Roofing Supply, Inc.; *U.S. Public*, pg. 286
ROOFING SUPPLY GROUP-OMAHA—See Beacon Roofing Supply, Inc.; *U.S. Public*, pg. 286
ROOFING SUPPLY GROUP ORLANDO, LLC—See Beacon Roofing Supply, Inc.; *U.S. Public*, pg. 286
ROOFING SUPPLY GROUP - POLK COUNTY, LLC—See Beacon Roofing Supply, Inc.; *U.S. Public*, pg. 286
ROOFING SUPPLY GROUP - RALEIGH, LCC—See Beacon Roofing Supply, Inc.; *U.S. Public*, pg. 286
ROOFING SUPPLY GROUP SAN DIEGO, LLC—See Beacon Roofing Supply, Inc.; *U.S. Public*, pg. 286
ROOFING SUPPLY GROUP - TAMPA, LLC—See Beacon Roofing Supply, Inc.; *U.S. Public*, pg. 286
ROOFING SUPPLY GROUP - TUSCALOOSA, LLC—See Beacon Roofing Supply, Inc.; *U.S. Public*, pg. 286
ROOFING SUPPLY GROUP UTAH, LLC—See Beacon Roofing Supply, Inc.; *U.S. Public*, pg. 286
ROOFING SUPPLY, LLC - HOUSTON—See Beacon Roofing Supply, Inc.; *U.S. Public*, pg. 286
ROOFING SUPPLY OF ARIZONA-EAST VALLEY—See Beacon Roofing Supply, Inc.; *U.S. Public*, pg. 286
ROOFING SUPPLY OF ARIZONA, LLC—See Beacon Roofing Supply, Inc.; *U.S. Public*, pg. 287
ROOFING SUPPLY OF ARIZONA - TUCSON, LLC—See Beacon Roofing Supply, Inc.; *U.S. Public*, pg. 287
ROOFING SUPPLY OF ATLANTA, LLC—See Beacon Roofing Supply, Inc.; *U.S. Public*, pg. 287
ROOFING SUPPLY OF CHARLOTTE, LLC—See Beacon Roofing Supply, Inc.; *U.S. Public*, pg. 287
ROOFING SUPPLY OF NASHVILLE, LLC—See Beacon Roofing Supply, Inc.; *U.S. Public*, pg. 287
ROOFING SUPPLY OF NEW MEXICO, LLC—See Beacon Roofing Supply, Inc.; *U.S. Public*, pg. 287
ROOFING SUPPLY OF TENNESSEE, LLC—See Beacon Roofing Supply, Inc.; *U.S. Public*, pg. 287
ROOFING SUPPLY TRANSPORTATION, LLC—See Beacon Roofing Supply, Inc.; *U.S. Public*, pg. 286
ROOFING WHOLESALE CO., INC.; *U.S. Private*, pg. 3479
ROOFING WHOLESALE INC.; *U.S. Private*, pg. 3479
ROOFLINE SUPPLY & DELIVERY, INC.—See Leonard Green & Partners, L.P.; *U.S. Private*, pg. 2429
ROOFLINE SUPPLY—See Leonard Green & Partners, L.P.; *U.S. Private*, pg. 2429
ROOFLITE FRANCE S.A.R.L—See VKR Holding A/S; *Int'l*, pg. 8281
ROOF MART, LLC—See Trachte Building Systems Inc.; *U.S. Private*, pg. 4200
ROOF-PRO—See The Alumasc Group plc; *Int'l*, pg. 7613
ROOF SERVICES JGM CORPORATION—See Altas Partners LP; *Int'l*, pg. 386
ROOFSTOCK, INC.; *U.S. Private*, pg. 3479
ROOF SYSTEMS OF MAINE—See Altas Partners LP; *Int'l*, pg. 386
ROOF SYSTEMS OF VA INC.; *U.S. Private*, pg. 3478
ROOFTOP2 PRODUCTIONS INC.—See Vivendi SE; *Int'l*, pg. 8278
ROOFTOP COMMUNICATIONS; *U.S. Private*, pg. 3479
ROOFTOP SYSTEMS INC.—See Canada Pension Plan Investment Board; *Int'l*, pg. 1281
THE ROOF TRUSS COMPANY (NORTHERN) LIMITED; *Int'l*, pg. 7679
ROOF TRUSS SUPPLY INC.; *U.S. Private*, pg. 3478
ROO HSING CO., LTD.; *Int'l*, pg. 6397
ROOIERHEIDE NV—See Clariane SE; *Int'l*, pg. 1644
ROOK SECURITY, LLC—See Apax Partners LLP; *Int'l*, pg. 506
ROOLIFEGROUP LIMITED; *Int'l*, pg. 6397
ROOM 214 INC.; *U.S. Private*, pg. 3479
ROOM 77, INC.—See Lexyl Travel Technologies LLC; *U.S. Private*, pg. 2441
ROOM BANK INSURE., LTD.—See Good Com Asset Co., Ltd.; *Int'l*, pg. 3038
ROOM & BOARD, INC.; *U.S. Private*, pg. 3479
ROOMI ENTERPRISES PVT. LTD.—See Mahmood Group of Companies LLC; *Int'l*, pg. 4649
ROOMPLUS (SELF STORAGE) LIMITED—See Jardine Matheson Holdings Limited; *Int'l*, pg. 3909
ROOMS TO GO, INC.; *U.S. Private*, pg. 3479
ROOMSTORE, INC.; *U.S. Private*, pg. 3479
ROOMSTORES OF PHOENIX LLC; *U.S. Private*, pg. 3479
ROONEY ENGINEERING, INC.—See Tetra Tech, Inc.; *U.S. Public*, pg. 2023
ROONEY HOLDINGS, INC.; *U.S. Private*, pg. 3479
ROONEY HOLDINGS, INC.—See Rooney Holdings, Inc.; *U.S. Private*, pg. 3479
ROONEY INSURANCE AGENCY, INC.—See Rooney Holdings, Inc.; *U.S. Private*, pg. 3479
ROOPA INDUSTRIES LTD.; *Int'l*, pg. 6397
ROOP & CO.; *U.S. Private*, pg. 3479
ROOPSHRI RESORTS LIMITED; *Int'l*, pg. 6397
ROOSEVELT ASSOCIATES—See Republic Services, Inc.; *U.S. Public*, pg. 1787
ROOSEVELT COUNTY ELECTRIC COOPERATIVE, INC.; *U.S. Private*, pg. 3479
ROOSEVELT & CROSS INC.; *U.S. Private*, pg. 3479
THE ROOSEVELT INVESTMENT GROUP, INC.—See CI Financial Corporation; *Int'l*, pg. 1601
ROOSEVELT MANAGEMENT COMPANY, LLC—See Mr. Cooper Group Inc.; *U.S. Public*, pg. 1480

ROOSEVELT PAPER COMPANY

ROOSEVELT PAPER COMPANY; *U.S. Private,* pg. 3480
ROOSEVELT PAPER COMPANY—See Roosevelt Paper Company; *U.S. Private,* pg. 3480
ROOSEVELT PAPER COMPANY—See Roosevelt Paper Company; *U.S. Private,* pg. 3480
ROOSEVELT UNIVERSITY; *U.S. Private,* pg. 3480
ROOSHINE, INC.; *U.S. Public,* pg. 1810
ROOS - KCB HOLLAND BV—See Serafin Unternehmensgruppe GmbH; *Int'l,* pg. 6720
ROOS SPEDITION GMBH; *Int'l,* pg. 6397
ROOS SPEDITION S.A.—See Roos Spedition GmbH; *Int'l,* pg. 6397
ROOS SPEDITION SP.Z.O.O.—See Roos Spedition GmbH; *Int'l,* pg. 6397
ROOST 2007 LIMITED—See AMP Limited; *Int'l,* pg. 433
ROOSTER ENERGY LTD.; *U.S. Public,* pg. 1810
ROOSTER ESSENTIALS APP SPV, LLC—See APPLife Digital Solutions, Inc.; *U.S. Public,* pg. 173
ROOT9B HOLDINGS, INC.; *U.S. Public,* pg. 1810
ROOT DESIGN COMPANY; *U.S. Private,* pg. 3480
ROOTFRUIT SCANDINAVIA AB—See FMCG Business Partner AB; *Int'l,* pg. 2717
ROOT, INC.; *U.S. Public,* pg. 1810
ROOT LLC—See Accenture plc; *Int'l,* pg. 87
THE ROOTO CORPORATION; *U.S. Private,* pg. 4112
ROOTS CORPORATION; *Int'l,* pg. 6397
ROOTS EQUITY GROUP LLC; *U.S. Private,* pg. 3480
ROOTS OF OXFORD LIMITED—See Sysco Corporation; *U.S. Public,* pg. 1975
ROOTS OF PEACE; *U.S. Private,* pg. 3480
ROOTS SUSTAINABLE AGRICULTURAL TECHNOLOGIES LTD.; *Int'l,* pg. 6397
ROOT WIRELESS, INC.—See Ziff Davis, Inc.; *U.S. Public,* pg. 2403
ROPA SIETE LEGUAS SA DE CV; *Int'l,* pg. 6398
ROPE ACCESS CALGARY, INC.—See Mistras Group, Inc.; *U.S. Public,* pg. 1451
ROPEOK TECHNOLOGY GROUP CO., LTD.; *Int'l,* pg. 6398
ROPER BRASIL COMERCIO E PROMOCAO DE PRODUCTOS E SERVICOS LTDA—See Roper Technologies, Inc.; *U.S. Public,* pg. 1813
ROPER BROTHERS LUMBER CO., INC.; *U.S. Private,* pg. 3480
ROPER BUICK GMC, INC.; *U.S. Private,* pg. 3480
ROPER CORPORATION—See Haier Smart Home Co., Ltd.; *Int'l,* pg. 3210
ROPER ENGINEERING S.R.O.—See Roper Technologies, Inc.; *U.S. Public,* pg. 1813
ROPER INDUSTRIES LIMITED—See Roper Technologies, Inc.; *U.S. Public,* pg. 1813
ROPER MIDDLE EAST LTD.—See Roper Technologies, Inc.; *U.S. Public,* pg. 1813
ROPER PERSONNEL SERVICES INC.; *U.S. Private,* pg. 3480
ROPER PUMP COMPANY—See Roper Technologies, Inc.; *U.S. Public,* pg. 1813
ROPER SCIENTIFIC GMBH—See Roper Technologies, Inc.; *U.S. Public,* pg. 1813
ROPER SCIENTIFIC, INC.—See Teledyne Technologies Incorporated; *U.S. Public,* pg. 1992
ROPER SCIENTIFIC SAS—See Roper Technologies, Inc.; *U.S. Public,* pg. 1813
ROPER TECHNOLOGIES, INC.; *U.S. Public,* pg. 1810
ROPER WHITNEY OF ROCKFORD INC.; *U.S. Private,* pg. 3480
ROPES & GRAY LLP; *U.S. Private,* pg. 3480
ROPLAN AB—See IDEX Corp; *U.S. Public,* pg. 1091
ROPLAN INC.—See IDEX Corp; *U.S. Public,* pg. 1091
ROPLAN LTD.—See IDEX Corp; *U.S. Public,* pg. 1091
ROPLAN MACHINERY (NINGBO) CO., LTD.—See IDEX Corp; *U.S. Public,* pg. 1092
ROPOX A/S—See AddLife AB; *Int'l,* pg. 130
ROPPE CORPORATION; *U.S. Private,* pg. 3480
ROPPEL INDUSTRIES INC.; *U.S. Private,* pg. 3480
ROPPING LIFE CO., LTD.—See TV Asahi Holdings Corporation; *Int'l,* pg. 7987
ROQUEFORT THERAPEUTICS PLC; *Int'l,* pg. 6398
ROQUEMORE & ROQUEMORE INC.—See Kinderhook Industries, LLC; *U.S. Private,* pg. 2307
ROQUETTE AMERICA INC.—See Roquette Freres SA; *Int'l,* pg. 6398
ROQUETTE AMILINA, AB—See Roquette Freres SA; *Int'l,* pg. 6398
ROQUETTE APS—See Roquette Freres SA; *Int'l,* pg. 6398
ROQUETTE ASIA PACIFIC PTE. LTD.—See Roquette Freres SA; *Int'l,* pg. 6398
ROQUETTE BELGIUM S.A.—See Roquette Freres SA; *Int'l,* pg. 6398
ROQUETTE BIOTECH NUTRITIONALS (WUHAN) CO., LTD.—See Roquette Freres SA; *Int'l,* pg. 6398
ROQUETTE CANADA LTD.—See Roquette Freres SA; *Int'l,* pg. 6398
ROQUETTE CHINA CO., LTD.—See Roquette Freres SA; *Int'l,* pg. 6398
ROQUETTE CH SA—See Roquette Freres SA; *Int'l,* pg. 6398
ROQUETTE CZECH REPUBLIC S.R.O—See Roquette Freres SA; *Int'l,* pg. 6398

ROQUETTE FRERES SA; *Int'l,* pg. 6398
ROQUETTE GMBH—See Roquette Freres SA; *Int'l,* pg. 6398
ROQUETTE INDIA PRIVATE LIMITED—See Roquette Freres SA; *Int'l,* pg. 6398
ROQUETTE ITALIA S.P.A.—See Roquette Freres SA; *Int'l,* pg. 6398
ROQUETTE JAPAN INC.—See Roquette Freres SA; *Int'l,* pg. 6398
ROQUETTE JAPAN K.K.—See Roquette Freres SA; *Int'l,* pg. 6398
ROQUETTE KLOTZE GMBH & CO. KG—See Roquette Freres SA; *Int'l,* pg. 6398
ROQUETTE KOREA LTD.—See Roquette Freres SA; *Int'l,* pg. 6398
ROQUETTE LAISA SPAIN, S.A.—See Roquette Freres SA; *Int'l,* pg. 6398
ROQUETTE MALAYSIA SDN. BHD.—See Roquette Freres SA; *Int'l,* pg. 6398
ROQUETTE MANAGEMENT (SHANGHAI) CO., LTD.—See Roquette Freres SA; *Int'l,* pg. 6398
ROQUETTE MEXICO S.A. DE C.V.—See Roquette Freres SA; *Int'l,* pg. 6398
ROQUETTE NETHERLANDS B.V.—See Roquette Freres SA; *Int'l,* pg. 6398
ROQUETTE NORDICA OY—See Roquette Freres SA; *Int'l,* pg. 6398
ROQUETTE POLAND SP. Z O.O.—See Roquette Freres SA; *Int'l,* pg. 6398
ROQUETTE ROMANIA S.A.—See Roquette Freres SA; *Int'l,* pg. 6398
ROQUETTE SALES (SHANGHAI) CO., LTD.—See Roquette Freres SA; *Int'l,* pg. 6398
ROQUETTE SINGAPORE PTE. LTD.—See Roquette Freres SA; *Int'l,* pg. 6398
ROQUETTE TARIM VE GIDA SAN. VE TIC. LTD. STI.—See Roquette Freres SA; *Int'l,* pg. 6398
ROQUETTE UK LTD.—See Roquette Freres SA; *Int'l,* pg. 6398
RO RESTORATION SPECIALISTS—See Rogers-O'Brien Construction Company Inc.; *U.S. Private,* pg. 3472
RORGRUPPEN AB—See Instalco AB; *Int'l,* pg. 3722
RORINE INTERNATIONAL HOLDING CORPORATION; *U.S. Public,* pg. 1814
RORMAN INSTALLATION & SERVICE SVERIGE AB—See Peab AB; *Int'l,* pg. 5773
RORMAN I SVEDALA AB—See Instalco AB; *Int'l,* pg. 3722
RO-RO INTERNATIONAL TM AB—See Axel Johnson Gruppen AB; *Int'l,* pg. 764
ROROS FLYSERVICE AS—See Avia Solutions Group AB; *Int'l,* pg. 741
RORTEFT AS—See Instalco AB; *Int'l,* pg. 3722
RORTEMA I NYKOPING AB—See Instalco AB; *Int'l,* pg. 3722
RORZE AUTOMATION, INC.—See Rorze Corporation; *Int'l,* pg. 6399
RORZE CORPORATION; *Int'l,* pg. 6399
RORZE CREATECH CO., LTD.—See Rorze Corporation; *Int'l,* pg. 6399
RORZE ENGINEERING GMBH—See Rorze Corporation; *Int'l,* pg. 6399
RORZE ROBOTECH CO., LTD.—See Rorze Corporation; *Int'l,* pg. 6399
RORZE SYSTEMS CORPORATION; *Int'l,* pg. 6399
RORZE TECHNOLOGY, INC.—See Rorze Corporation; *Int'l,* pg. 6399
RORZE TECHNOLOGY SINGAPORE PTE. LTD.—See Rorze Corporation; *Int'l,* pg. 6399
RORZE TECHNOLOGY TRADING CO., LTD.—See Rorze Corporation; *Int'l,* pg. 6399
ROSABEL ADVERTISING LTD.—See Publicis Groupe S.A.; *Int'l,* pg. 6102
ROS AGRO PLC; *Int'l,* pg. 6399
ROSANA LTD.—See RUSNANO JSC; *Int'l,* pg. 6429
ROSAN RESOURCES HOLDINGS LIMITED; *Int'l,* pg. 6399
ROSAR SA; *Int'l,* pg. 6399
ROSATI WINDOWS; *U.S. Private,* pg. 3480
ROSATOM AFRICA (PTY) LTD—See State Atomic Energy Corporation ROSATOM; *Int'l,* pg. 7181
ROSATOM ASIA PTE. LTD—See State Atomic Energy Corporation ROSATOM; *Int'l,* pg. 7181
ROSATOM CENTRAL EUROPE S.R.O.—See State Atomic Energy Corporation ROSATOM; *Int'l,* pg. 7181
ROSATOM EASTERN EUROPE, LLC—See State Atomic Energy Corporation ROSATOM; *Int'l,* pg. 7181
ROSATOM FRANCE, SARL—See State Atomic Energy Corporation ROSATOM; *Int'l,* pg. 7181
ROSAUERS SUPERMARKETS, INC.—See URM Stores, Inc.; *U.S. Private,* pg. 4316
ROSBANK GROUP—See Societe Generale S.A.; *Int'l,* pg. 7040
ROSBERG FOZMAN ROLANDELLI ADVERTISING; *U.S. Private,* pg. 3481
ROSCAN GOLD CORP.; *Int'l,* pg. 6399
ROSCHI ROHDE & SCHWARZ AG—See Rohde & Schwarz GmbH & Co. KG; *Int'l,* pg. 6385
ROSCOE FINANCIAL CORPORATION; *U.S. Private,* pg. 3481

ROSCOE MEDICAL, INC.—See Tenex Capital Management, L.P.; *U.S. Private,* pg. 3966
ROSCOE MOSS COMPANY; *U.S. Private,* pg. 3481
THE ROSCOE STATE BANK—See Cornerstone Mortgage Co.; *U.S. Private,* pg. 1052
ROSCOE WIND FARM, LLC—See E.ON SE; *Int'l,* pg. 2259
ROSCO LABORATORIES, INC.; *U.S. Private,* pg. 3481
ROSCO PETROAVANCE LIMITED—See Agostini's Limited; *Int'l,* pg. 213
ROSCO PROCOM LIMITED—See Agostini's Limited; *Int'l,* pg. 213
ROSCOR CORPORATION; *U.S. Private,* pg. 3481
ROSDERRA IRISH MEATS GROUP LTD - EDENDERRY FACTORY—See Rosderra Irish Meats Group Ltd; *Int'l,* pg. 6399
ROSDERRA IRISH MEATS GROUP LTD; *Int'l,* pg. 6399
ROSDEV MANAGEMENT INC.; *Int'l,* pg. 6399
ROSDEV MANAGEMENT INC. - USA DIVISION—See Rosdev Management Inc.; *Int'l,* pg. 6399
ROSDORBANK OJSC; *Int'l,* pg. 6399
ROSE-AMERICA CORPORATION; *U.S. Private,* pg. 3482
ROSE & ASSOCIATES LLC; *U.S. Private,* pg. 3481
ROSEBAY INTERNATIONAL, INC.; *U.S. Private,* pg. 3482
ROSEBEL GOLD MINES N.V.—See IAMGOLD Corporation; *Int'l,* pg. 3568
ROSEBRAND WIPERS INC.; *U.S. Private,* pg. 3482
ROSE BROTHERS FURNITURE; *U.S. Private,* pg. 3481
ROSE BROTHERS PAVING, INC.; *U.S. Private,* pg. 3481
ROSEBUD CO., LTD.—See TSI Holdings Co., Ltd.; *Int'l,* pg. 7950
ROSEBUD MEDIA, LLC; *U.S. Private,* pg. 3482
ROSEBUD MINING COMPANY; *U.S. Private,* pg. 3482
ROSEBURG FOREST PRODUCTS CO.—See Roseburg Forest Products; *U.S. Private,* pg. 3482
ROSEBURG FOREST PRODUCTS; *U.S. Private,* pg. 3482
ROSEBURG MANUFACTURING DIVISION—See Caddock Electronics, Inc.; *U.S. Private,* pg. 712
ROSEBURG RESOURCES CO.—See Roseburg Forest Products; *U.S. Private,* pg. 3482
ROSECC CO., LTD.—See Kyokuto Sanki Co., Ltd.; *Int'l,* pg. 4363
ROSECLAIM LIMITED—See Live Nation Entertainment, Inc.; *U.S. Public,* pg. 1330
ROSECOMM, INC.; *U.S. Private,* pg. 3482
ROSE COMMUNITY FOUNDATION; *U.S. Private,* pg. 3481
ROSE CONSTRUCTION CO., INC.—See Rose Design Build, Inc.; *U.S. Private,* pg. 3481
ROSE CONSTRUCTION, INC.; *U.S. Private,* pg. 3481
ROSECRANCE, INC.; *U.S. Private,* pg. 3482
ROSEDALE AVIATION HOLDINGS LTD; *Int'l,* pg. 6399
ROSEDALE CEMETERY COMPANY—See Service Corporation International; *U.S. Public,* pg. 1870
ROSEDALE CHILDREN'S SERVICES LIMITED—See Sheikh Holdings Group (Investments) Limited; *Int'l,* pg. 6794
ROSEDALE FEDERAL SAVINGS & LOAN ASSOCIATION; *U.S. Private,* pg. 3482
ROSEDALE FINANCE & LEASING LIMITED—See Lookers plc; *Int'l,* pg. 4555
ROSEDALE GROUP INC.; *U.S. Private,* pg. 3482
ROSEDALE HOTEL GROUP LIMITED—See Greater Bay Area Dynamic Growth Holdings Limited; *Int'l,* pg. 3067
ROSEDALE HOTEL KOWLOON LIMITED—See Greater Bay Area Dynamic Growth Holdings Limited; *Int'l,* pg. 3067
ROSEDALE HOTEL SHENYANG COMPANY LIMITED—See Greater Bay Area Dynamic Growth Holdings Limited; *Int'l,* pg. 3067
ROSEDALE PARK LIMITED—See Greater Bay Area Dynamic Growth Holdings Limited; *Int'l,* pg. 3067
ROSEDALE PRODUCTS INC.; *U.S. Private,* pg. 3482
ROSE DESIGN BUILD, INC.; *U.S. Private,* pg. 3481
ROSE DRUCK GMBH; *Int'l,* pg. 6399
ROSE ELECTRONICS DISTRIBUTING CO, INC.—See Tropical Battery Company Limited; *U.S. Public,* pg. 2198
ROSE EXTERMINATOR CO.; *U.S. Private,* pg. 3481
ROSE HILL ACQUISITION CORPORATION; *U.S. Public,* pg. 1814
ROSE HILL BANK—See American State Bancshares, Inc.; *U.S. Private,* pg. 255
ROSE HILL MEMORIAL PARK; *U.S. Private,* pg. 3481
ROSEHILL RESOURCES INC.; *U.S. Private,* pg. 3482
ROSE HILLS COMPANY—See Service Corporation International; *U.S. Public,* pg. 1870
THE ROSE HILLS FOUNDATION; *U.S. Private,* pg. 4112
ROSE INTERNATIONAL INC.; *U.S. Private,* pg. 3481
ROSEKAMAL TEXTILES LTD.; *Int'l,* pg. 6399
ROSE & KIERNAN INC.—See Aon plc; *Int'l,* pg. 497
ROSE & KINDEL—See Clayton, Dubilier & Rice, LLC; *U.S. Private,* pg. 925
ROSE & KINDEL—See Clayton, Dubilier & Rice, LLC; *U.S. Private,* pg. 925
ROSELABS FINANCE LIMITED; *Int'l,* pg. 6399
ROSELAND COMMUNITY HOSPITAL; *U.S. Private,* pg. 3482

COMPANY NAME INDEX

ROSELAND MANAGEMENT CO., LLC—See Veris Residential, Inc.; *U.S. Public*, pg. 2282
ROSELAND MANAGEMENT SERVICES, L.P.—See Veris Residential, Inc.; *U.S. Public*, pg. 2282
ROSELAND PARTNERS LLC; *U.S. Private*, pg. 3482
ROSELAND RESIDENTIAL TRUST—See Veris Residential, Inc.; *U.S. Public*, pg. 2282
ROSELAND WORLD CORP.—See Symrise AG; *Int'l*, pg. 7380
ROSE LAWN CEMETERIES SUBSIDIARY, INCORPORATED—See Axar Capital Management L.P.; *U.S. Private*, pg. 412
ROSELAWN DEVELOPMENT LLC—See Axar Capital Management L.P.; *U.S. Private*, pg. 412
ROSELLE PAPER CO., INC.; *U.S. Private*, pg. 3482
ROSELLE SAVINGS BANK; *U.S. Private*, pg. 3483
ROSELON INDUSTRIES INC.; *U.S. Private*, pg. 3483
ROSE MART INC.; *U.S. Private*, pg. 3481
ROSE-MARY CENTER; *U.S. Private*, pg. 3482
ROSEMEAD OIL PRODUCTS, INC.—See Clean Harbors, Inc.; *U.S. Public*, pg. 510
ROSE MEDICAL CENTER INC.—See HCA Healthcare, Inc.; *U.S. Public*, pg. 1008
ROSE MERC LIMITED; *Int'l*, pg. 6399
ROSEMONT EXPOSITION SERVICES INC.; *U.S. Private*, pg. 3483
ROSEMONT PHARMACEUTICALS LTD.—See Inflexion Private Equity Partners LLP; *Int'l*, pg. 3689
ROSEMONT PROJECT MANAGEMENT, LLC—See Hyatt Hotels Corporation; *U.S. Public*, pg. 1078
ROSEMONT PROPERTY MANAGEMENT LLC; *U.S. Private*, pg. 3483
ROSEMONT PROPERTY MANAGEMENT OF TEXAS LLC—See Rosemont Property Management LLC; *U.S. Private*, pg. 3483
ROSE MOON INC.—See Mattel, Inc.; *U.S. Public*, pg. 1398
ROSEMOOR FOUNDATION, INC.; *U.S. Private*, pg. 3483
ROSEMORE HOLDINGS INC.—See Rosemore Inc.; *U.S. Private*, pg. 3483
ROSEMORE INC.; *U.S. Private*, pg. 3483
ROSEMOUNT AEROSPACE INC.—See RTX Corporation; *U.S. Public*, pg. 1821
ROSEMOUNT AEROSPACE INC. - UNION—See RTX Corporation; *U.S. Public*, pg. 1822
ROSEMOUNT AEROSPACE LIMITED—See RTX Corporation; *U.S. Public*, pg. 1822
ROSEMOUNT CHINA INC.—See Emerson Electric Co.; *U.S. Public*, pg. 747
ROSEMOUNT INC.—See Emerson Electric Co.; *U.S. Public*, pg. 747
ROSEMOUNT INC.—See Emerson Electric Co.; *U.S. Public*, pg. 747
ROSEMOUNT MEASUREMENT LIMITED—See Emerson Electric Co.; *U.S. Public*, pg. 752
ROSEMOUNT NUCLEAR INSTRUMENTS—See Emerson Electric Co.; *U.S. Public*, pg. 747
ROSEMOUNT OFFICE SYSTEMS LLC—See Hillcrest Capital Partners LP; *U.S. Private*, pg. 1946
ROSEMOUNT SPECIALTY PRODUCTS LLC—See Emerson Electric Co.; *U.S. Public*, pg. 747
ROSEMOUNT TANK GAUGING NORTH AMERICA, INC.—See Emerson Electric Co.; *U.S. Public*, pg. 747
ROSEMOUNT TANK RADAR AB—See Emerson Electric Co.; *U.S. Public*, pg. 748
ROSEMOUNT TANK RADAR PROPERTIES AB—See Emerson Electric Co.; *U.S. Public*, pg. 748
ROSE MOVING AND STORAGE CO.—See Corporate Installation Services; *U.S. Private*, pg. 1055
ROSEMUNDE APS—See Boozt AB; *Int'l*, pg. 1111
ROSEN ASSOCIATES MANAGEMENT CORP.; *U.S. Private*, pg. 3483
ROSENAU BECK INC.; *U.S. Private*, pg. 3483
ROSENAU TRANSPORT LTD.—See International Distributions Services plc; *Int'l*, pg. 3747
ROSENBAUER AMERICA, LLC—See Rosenbauer International AG; *Int'l*, pg. 6400
ROSENBAUER AUSTRALIA PTY. LTD.—See Rosenbauer International AG; *Int'l*, pg. 6400
ROSENBAUER BRANDSCHUTZ DEUTSCHLAND GMBH—See Rosenbauer International AG; *Int'l*, pg. 6400
ROSENBAUER DEUTSCHLAND GMBH—See Rosenbauer International AG; *Int'l*, pg. 6400
ROSENBAUER DEUTSCHLAND GMBH—See Rosenbauer International AG; *Int'l*, pg. 6400
ROSENBAUER D.O.O.—See Rosenbauer International AG; *Int'l*, pg. 6400
ROSENBAUER ESPANOLA SA—See Rosenbauer International AG; *Int'l*, pg. 6400
ROSENBAUER E-TECHNOLOGY DEVELOPMENT GMBH—See Rosenbauer International AG; *Int'l*, pg. 6400
ROSENBAUER FINANZIERUNG GMBH—See Rosenbauer International AG; *Int'l*, pg. 6400
ROSENBAUER FRANCE S.A.R.L.—See Rosenbauer International AG; *Int'l*, pg. 6400
ROSENBAUER HOLDINGS INC.—See Rosenbauer International AG; *Int'l*, pg. 6400

ROSENBAUER INTERNATIONAL AG; *Int'l*, pg. 6399
ROSENBAUER ITALIA S.R.L.—See Rosenbauer International AG; *Int'l*, pg. 6400
ROSENBAUER KARLSRUHE GMBH—See Rosenbauer International AG; *Int'l*, pg. 6400
ROSENBAUER MANAGEMENT SERVICES GMBH—See Rosenbauer International AG; *Int'l*, pg. 6400
ROSENBAUER MODE HANDELS GMBH—See Rosenbauer International AG; *Int'l*, pg. 6400
ROSENBAUER MOTORS LLC—See Rosenbauer International AG; *Int'l*, pg. 6400
ROSENBAUER OSTERREICH GMBH—See Rosenbauer International AG; *Int'l*, pg. 6400
ROSENBAUER POLSKA SP.Z. O.O.—See Rosenbauer International AG; *Int'l*, pg. 6400
ROSENBAUER ROVERETO SRL—See Rosenbauer International AG; *Int'l*, pg. 6400
ROSENBAUER SAUDI ARABIA LTD.—See Rosenbauer International AG; *Int'l*, pg. 6400
ROSENBAUER SCHWEIZ AG—See Rosenbauer International AG; *Int'l*, pg. 6400
ROSENBAUER SOUTH AFRICA (PTY.) LTD.—See Rosenbauer International AG; *Int'l*, pg. 6400
ROSENBAUER SOUTH DAKOTA, LLC—See Rosenbauer International AG; *Int'l*, pg. 6400
ROSENBAUER SWITZERLAND AG—See Rosenbauer International AG; *Int'l*, pg. 6400
ROSENBAUER UK PLC—See Rosenbauer International AG; *Int'l*, pg. 6400
ROSENBAUER YONGQIANG FIRE FIGHTING VEHICLES LTD.—See Rosenbauer International AG; *Int'l*, pg. 6400
ROSENBAUM FINANCIAL, INC.—See Hersman Serles Almond PLLC; *U.S. Private*, pg. 1927
ROSENBAUM FINANCIAL, INC.—See Seidman Insurance Consultants LLC; *U.S. Private*, pg. 3599
ROSENBERGERS DAIRIES, LLC—See Catamount Dairy Holdings L.P.; *U.S. Private*, pg. 787
ROSENBERG WORLEY AS—See Worley Limited; *Int'l*, pg. 8459
ROSENBERG WORLEYPARSONS AS—See Worley Limited; *Int'l*, pg. 8459
ROSENBLATT LIMITED—See RBG Holdings PLC; *Int'l*, pg. 6227
ROSENBLUM CELLARS—See Bronco Wine Company; *U.S. Private*, pg. 662
ROSEN & BRICHTA; *U.S. Private*, pg. 3483
ROSEN CENTRE HOTEL—See Rosen Hotels & Resorts, Inc.; *U.S. Private*, pg. 3483
ROSENDAHL INDUSTRIAL SERVICES S.R.L.—See Knill Holding GmbH; *Int'l*, pg. 4208
ROSENDAHL NEXTROM ELECTRICAL MACHINERY TRADING CO. LTD.—See Knill Holding GmbH; *Int'l*, pg. 4208
ROSENDAHL NEXTROM GMBH—See Knill Holding GmbH; *Int'l*, pg. 4208
ROSENDAHL NEXTROM OOO—See Knill Holding GmbH; *Int'l*, pg. 4208
ROSENDAHL NEXTROM OY—See Knill Holding GmbH; *Int'l*, pg. 4208
ROSENDAHL NEXTROM SA—See Knill Holding GmbH; *Int'l*, pg. 4208
ROSENDIN ELECTRIC, INC.; *U.S. Private*, pg. 3483
ROSEN EISKREM SUD GMBH - PRENZLAU—See DMK Deutsches Milchkontor GmbH; *Int'l*, pg. 2146
ROSENFELD CONCRETE CORP.—See Boston Sand & Gravel Company; *U.S. Public*, pg. 373
ROSENFELD EINSTEIN & ASSOCIATES, INC.—See Marsh & McLennan Companies, Inc.; *U.S. Public*, pg. 1382
THE ROSEN GROUP; *U.S. Private*, pg. 4112
ROSEN HOTELS & RESORTS, INC.; *U.S. Private*, pg. 3483
ROSEN MOTOR SALES; *U.S. Private*, pg. 3483
ROSENMUHLE GMBH—See Raiffeisen-Holding Niederosterreich-Wien reg. Gen.m.b.H.; *Int'l*, pg. 6185
ROSEN PLAZA HOTEL—See Rosen Hotels & Resorts, Inc.; *U.S. Private*, pg. 3483
ROSENQVISTS FOOD TECHNOLOGIES—See Warburg Pincus LLC; *U.S. Private*, pg. 4438
ROSENS DIVERSIFIED, INC.; *U.S. Private*, pg. 3483
ROSENS, INC.—See Rosens Diversified, Inc.; *U.S. Private*, pg. 3484
ROSEN SUPPLY COMPANY INC.—See Winsupply, Inc.; *U.S. Private*, pg. 4545
ROSENTHAL COLLINS GROUP, LLC—See JRJ Ventures LLP; *Int'l*, pg. 4008
ROSENTHAL CORPORATE SERVICES, INC.; *U.S. Private*, pg. 3484
ROSENTHAL GMBH—See Sambonet Paderno Industrie S.p.A.; *Int'l*, pg. 6502
ROSENTHAL LIFESTYLE TRADING SHANGHAI CO., LTD.—See Sambonet Paderno Industrie S.p.A.; *Int'l*, pg. 6502
ROSENTHAL & ROSENTHAL, INC.; *U.S. Private*, pg. 3484
ROSENTHAL U.S.A. LIMITED—See Sambonet Paderno Industrie S.p.A.; *Int'l*, pg. 6502
ROSENZWEIG INSURANCE AGENCY, INC.—See Arthur J. Gallagher & Co.; *U.S. Public*, pg. 207

THE ROSEWOOD CORPORATION

ROSE PACKING COMPANY, INC.—See OSI Group, LLC; *U.S. Private*, pg. 3047
ROSE PARK ADVISORS LLC; *U.S. Private*, pg. 3481
ROSE PARK HEALTHCARE ASSOCIATES, INC.—See The Ensign Group, Inc.; *U.S. Public*, pg. 2072
ROSE PARTNERS LP; *U.S. Private*, pg. 3481
ROSE PAVING CO.; *U.S. Private*, pg. 3481
ROSE PHARMACY, INC.—See Robinsons Retail Holdings, Inc.; *Int'l*, pg. 6370
ROSE PRINTING COMPANY, INC.; *U.S. Private*, pg. 3481
ROSE ROCK FINANCE CORPORATION—See Energy Transfer LP; *U.S. Public*, pg. 764
ROSE ROCK MIDSTREAM, L.P.—See Energy Transfer LP; *U.S. Public*, pg. 764
ROSE RYAN INC.—See RFE Investment Partners; *U.S. Private*, pg. 3420
ROSE SA—See PSB Industries SA; *Int'l*, pg. 6015
ROSE SAS—See PSB Industries SA; *Int'l*, pg. 6014
ROSE & SHORE; *U.S. Private*, pg. 3481
ROSE'S SOUTHWEST PAPERS, INC.; *U.S. Private*, pg. 3482
ROSE STANTON INSURANCE BROKERS PTY. LTD.—See Steadfast Group Limited; *Int'l*, pg. 7187
ROSE SURGICAL CENTER—See HCA Healthcare, Inc.; *U.S. Public*, pg. 1008
ROSE SURGICAL CENTER—See HCA Healthcare, Inc.; *U.S. Public*, pg. 1008
ROSE SYSTEMTECHNIK GMBH & CO. KG.—See Phoenix Mecano AG; *Int'l*, pg. 5853
ROSE SYSTEMTECHNIK GMBH—See Phoenix Mecano AG; *Int'l*, pg. 5853
ROSE SYSTEMTECHNIK MIDDLE EAST (FZE)—See Phoenix Mecano AG; *Int'l*, pg. 5853
ROSE TRUCKING CORP—See Rose Partners LP; *U.S. Private*, pg. 3481
ROSETTA CAPITAL LIMITED; *Int'l*, pg. 6400
ROSETTA GENOMICS INC.—See NeoGenomics, Inc.; *U.S. Public*, pg. 1506
ROSETTA GENOMICS LTD.—See NeoGenomics, Inc.; *U.S. Public*, pg. 1505
ROSETTA MARKETING GROUP, LLC—See Publicis Groupe S.A.; *Int'l*, pg. 6107
ROSETTA—See Publicis Groupe S.A.; *Int'l*, pg. 6107
ROSETTA—See Publicis Groupe S.A.; *Int'l*, pg. 6107
ROSETTA—See Publicis Groupe S.A.; *Int'l*, pg. 6107
ROSETTA—See Publicis Groupe S.A.; *Int'l*, pg. 6107
ROSETTA STONE INC.—See Veritas Capital Fund Management, LLC; *U.S. Private*, pg. 4361
ROSETTA STONE JAPAN CO., LTD.—See SOURCENEXT CORPORATION; *Int'l*, pg. 7115
ROSETTA STONE (UK) LTD.—See Veritas Capital Fund Management, LLC; *U.S. Private*, pg. 4361
ROSETTA TECHNOLOGIES CORP.; *U.S. Private*, pg. 3484
ROSETTI DOO—See Rosetti Marino S.p.A.; *Int'l*, pg. 6400
ROSETTI GENERAL CONTRACTING LDA—See Rosetti Marino S.p.A.; *Int'l*, pg. 6400
ROSETTI HANDBAGS AND ACCESSORIES, LTD.—See Li & Fung Limited; *Int'l*, pg. 4480
ROSETTI KAZAKHSTAN L.L.P.—See Rosetti Marino S.p.A.; *Int'l*, pg. 6400
ROSETTI MARINO PROJECT OOO—See Rosetti Marino S.p.A.; *Int'l*, pg. 6400
ROSETTI MARINO S.P.A.; *Int'l*, pg. 6400
ROSE VALLEY WATER COMPANY, INC.—See Northwest Natural Holding Company; *U.S. Public*, pg. 1542
ROSEVIEW CAPITAL PARTNERS LLC—See Madison Marquette Development Corporation; *U.S. Private*, pg. 2544
THE ROSEVIEW GROUP LLC—See Madison Marquette Development Corporation; *U.S. Private*, pg. 2544
ROSEVILLE CHRYSLER PLYMOUTH JEEP INC.; *U.S. Private*, pg. 3484
ROSEVILLE-C, INC.—See Lithia Motors, Inc.; *U.S. Public*, pg. 1326
ROSEVILLE MOTOR CORPORATION—See AutoNation, Inc.; *U.S. Public*, pg. 237
ROSEVILLE SURGERY CENTER, L.P.—See Tenet Healthcare Corporation; *U.S. Public*, pg. 2012
ROSEWOOD ACQUISITION CORPORATION—See The Rosewood Corporation; *U.S. Private*, pg. 4112
ROSEWOOD APARTMENTS CORPORATION—See Apartment Investment and Management Company; *U.S. Public*, pg. 144
THE ROSEWOOD CORPORATION; *U.S. Private*, pg. 4112
ROSEWOOD DEVELOPMENT CORPORATION—See Emerson Developments (Holdings) Limited; *Int'l*, pg. 2380
ROSEWOOD HOTELS & RESORTS LLC—See Chow Tai Fook Enterprises Limited; *Int'l*, pg. 1585
ROSEWOOD LAFAYETTE COMMONS, L.L.C.—See Veris Residential, Inc.; *U.S. Public*, pg. 2282
ROSEWOOD MANUFACTURING COMPANY (GATESHEAD) LIMITED—See Rengo Co., Ltd.; *Int'l*, pg. 6281
ROSEWOOD PACKAGING (MANCHESTER) LIMITED—See Rengo Co., Ltd.; *Int'l*, pg. 6281
ROSEWOOD PACKAGING (WOLVERHAMPTON) LIMITED—See Rengo Co., Ltd.; *Int'l*, pg. 6281

ROSGOSSTRAKH INSURANCE COMPANY PJSC

CORPORATE AFFILIATIONS

ROSGOSSTRAKH INSURANCE COMPANY PJSC; *Int'l*, pg. 6400
ROSHAN PACKAGES LIMITED; *Int'l*, pg. 6400
ROSHAN TRADING INC.; *U.S. Private*, pg. 3484
ROSHOW TECHNOLOGY CO., LTD.; *Int'l*, pg. 6400
ROSIA MONTANA GOLD CORPORATION S.A.—See Gabriel Resources Ltd.; *Int'l*, pg. 2867
ROSICA STRATEGIC PUBLIC RELATIONS; *U.S. Private*, pg. 3484
ROSIEK CONSTRUCTION CO. INC.; *U.S. Private*, pg. 3484
ROSIER FRANCE S.A.S.—See OMV Aktiengesellschaft; *Int'l*, pg. 5570
ROSIER NEDERLAND B.V.—See OMV Aktiengesellschaft; *Int'l*, pg. 5569
ROSIER S.A.—See OMV Aktiengesellschaft; *Int'l*, pg. 5569
ROSIGNANO ENERGIA SPA—See ENGIE SA; *Int'l*, pg. 2434
ROSINA FOOD PRODUCTS, INC.—See Rosina Holding, Inc.; *U.S. Private*, pg. 3484
ROSINA HOLDING, INC.; *U.S. Private*, pg. 3484
ROSINOX SAS—See Ali Holding S.r.l; *Int'l*, pg. 321
ROSKA DIRECT; *U.S. Private*, pg. 3484
ROSKAM BAKING COMPANY INC.; *U.S. Private*, pg. 3484
ROSKAMP CHAMPION—See Gilbert Global Equity Partners; *U.S. Private*, pg. 1699
ROSKAMP INSTITUTE; *U.S. Private*, pg. 3485
ROSLAGSGJUTERIET AB—See Storskogen Group AB; *Int'l*, pg. 7228
ROSLYN SUPPLY COMPANY INC.; *U.S. Private*, pg. 3485
ROSMAR LITHO, INC.—See Novacap Management Inc.; *Int'l*, pg. 5454
ROSMERTA ENGINEERING PVT. LTD.—See Rosmerta Technologies Limited; *Int'l*, pg. 6401
ROSMERTA TECHNOLOGIES LIMITED; *Int'l*, pg. 6401
ROSNEFT-TUAPSENEFTEPRODUKT OJSC—See OJSC Rosneftegaz; *Int'l*, pg. 5541
ROSNER MANAGEMENT GROUP, LLC; *U.S. Private*, pg. 3485
ROSNER MOTORS, INC.—See Rosner Management Group, LLC; *U.S. Private*, pg. 3485
ROSNO INSURANCE COMPANY OJSC—See Allianz SE; *Int'l*, pg. 355
ROSNO MS—See Sogaz JSC; *Int'l*, pg. 7058
ROSOKA SOFTWARE, INC.—See Constellation Software Inc.; *Int'l*, pg. 1774
ROSOLITE MORTGAGES LIMITED—See Computershare Limited; *Int'l*, pg. 1760
THE ROSS AGENCY; *U.S. Private*, pg. 4112
ROSS ALUMINUM CASTINGS, LLC—See Advanced Metals Group, LLC; *U.S. Private*, pg. 91
ROSSANO JOINT STOCK COMPANY; *Int'l*, pg. 6401
ROSSAREDS FASTIGHETS AB—See AB Volvo; *Int'l*, pg. 42
ROSSARI BIOTECH LIMITED; *Int'l*, pg. 6401
ROSS AVIATION INC—See Pierce Enterprises Inc.; *U.S. Private*, pg. 3178
ROSS & BARUZZINI, INC.; *U.S. Private*, pg. 3485
ROSSBOROUGH INSURANCE (IOM) LTD.—See Arthur J. Gallagher & Co.; *U.S. Public*, pg. 207
ROSS BREEDERS (BOTSWANA) (PTY) LIMITED—See Country Bird Holdings Limited; *Int'l*, pg. 1818
ROSS BROTHERS CONSTRUCTION CO; *U.S. Private*, pg. 3485
ROSS BROTHERS CONSTRUCTION INC.; *U.S. Private*, pg. 3485
ROSS CASTING & INNOVATION, LLC—See Revere Industries, LLC; *U.S. Private*, pg. 3414
ROSS CATHERALL AEROSPACE LIMITED—See Dubai Holding LLC; *Int'l*, pg. 2218
THE ROSS CENTER FOR ANXIETY & RELATED DISORDERS, LLC—See Thurston Group, LLC; *U.S. Private*, pg. 4166
ROSS CERAMICS LIMITED—See Dubai Holding LLC; *Int'l*, pg. 2218
ROSS CONSOLIDATED CORP.; *U.S. Private*, pg. 3485
ROSS DOWNING CHEVROLET, INC.; *U.S. Private*, pg. 3485
ROSS DRESS FOR LESS, INC.—See Ross Stores, Inc.; *U.S. Public*, pg. 1815
ROSSDRULISCUSENBERY ARCHITECTURE, INC.—See DLR Holding, LLC; *U.S. Private*, pg. 1247
ROSS EDUCATION, LLC—See JLL Partners, LLC; *U.S. Private*, pg. 2213
ROSSELL INDIA LTD.; *Int'l*, pg. 6401
ROSSELL TECHSYS INC.—See Rossell India Ltd.; *Int'l*, pg. 6401
ROSSELL TECHSYS LTD.—See Rossell India Ltd.; *Int'l*, pg. 6401
ROSSENDALE PET CREMATORIUM LIMITED—See CVS Group Plc; *Int'l*, pg. 1890
ROSSENDALE SCHOOL LIMITED—See Acadia Healthcare Company, Inc.; *U.S. Public*, pg. 30
ROSS ENVIRONMENTAL SERVICES, INC.—See Ross Consolidated Corp.; *U.S. Private*, pg. 3485
ROSS EQUIPMENT, INC.—See Ross Consolidated Corp.; *U.S. Private*, pg. 3485
ROSSER INTERNATIONAL, INC.; *U.S. Private*, pg. 3486

ROSSETI NORTHERN CAUCASUS, PJSC—See JSC ROSSETI; *Int'l*, pg. 4011
ROSSETI VOLGA PJSC—See JSC ROSSETI; *Int'l*, pg. 4011
ROSS GROUP PLC; *Int'l*, pg. 6401
ROSS HAMMOCK RANCH, INC.; *U.S. Private*, pg. 3485
ROSSI COMERCIAL IMP. EXP. LTDA.—See ICC Industries, Inc.; *U.S. Private*, pg. 2030
ROSSIGNOL GMBH—See Altor Equity Partners AB; *Int'l*, pg. 396
ROSSIGNOL LANGE SRL—See Altor Equity Partners AB; *Int'l*, pg. 396
ROSSIGNOL OSTERREICH GMBH—See Altor Equity Partners AB; *Int'l*, pg. 396
ROSSIGNOL SCI SARL—See Altor Equity Partners AB; *Int'l*, pg. 396
ROSSIGNOL SKI COMPANY, INC.—See Altor Equity Partners AB; *Int'l*, pg. 396
ROSSIGNOL SKI DEUTSCHLAND GMBH—See Altor Equity Partners AB; *Int'l*, pg. 396
THE ROSSI GROUP, LLC—See H.I.G. Capital, LLC; *U.S. Private*, pg. 1832
ROSSI LUMBER COMPANY—See H.I.G. Capital, LLC; *U.S. Private*, pg. 1832
ROSSIMODA SPA—See LVMH Moet Hennessy Louis Vuitton SE; *Int'l*, pg. 4596
ROSS INCINERATION SERVICES, INC.—See Ross Consolidated Corp.; *U.S. Private*, pg. 3485
ROSS INDUSTRIES INC.; *U.S. Private*, pg. 3485
ROSSING URANIUM LTD.—See China National Nuclear Corporation; *Int'l*, pg. 1532
ROSS INNOVATIVE EMPLOYMENT SOLUTIONS CORP.—See ModivCare, Inc.; *U.S. Public*, pg. 1456
ROSS INVESTMENT VENTURES; *U.S. Private*, pg. 3485
ROSSI RESIDENCIAL SA; *Int'l*, pg. 6401
ROSS ISLAND SAND & GRAVEL CO., INC.—See R.B. Pamplin Corporation; *U.S. Private*, pg. 3334
ROSSI'S TIRE & AUTO SERVICE; *U.S. Private*, pg. 3486
ROSSITTIS GMBH; *Int'l*, pg. 6401
ROSSIYA BANK JSC; *Int'l*, pg. 6401
ROSSLITOR BUCHER LTD.—See Orell Fussli Holding AG; *Int'l*, pg. 5616
ROSSLYN DATA TECHNOLOGIES PLC; *Int'l*, pg. 6401
ROSSMANN SAS; *Int'l*, pg. 6401
ROSSMAX INTERNATIONAL LTD.; *Int'l*, pg. 6401
ROSSMAX (SHANGHAI) INCORPORATION LTD.—See Rossmax International Ltd.; *Int'l*, pg. 6401
ROSSMAX SWISS GMBH—See Rossmax International Ltd.; *Int'l*, pg. 6401
ROSS MORTGAGE CORPORATION; *U.S. Private*, pg. 3485
ROSSMOYNE, INC.; *U.S. Private*, pg. 3486
ROSS NETWORK INC.; *U.S. Private*, pg. 3486
ROSSO AMARANTO S.R.L.—See High Fashion International Limited; *Int'l*, pg. 3385
ROSS OPTICAL INDUSTRIES, INC.—See Precision Optics Corporation, Inc.; *U.S. Public*, pg. 1713
ROSS ORGANIC SPECIALTY SALES, INC.—See EQT AB; *Int'l*, pg. 2469
ROSS PALLETS INC.; *U.S. Private*, pg. 3485
ROSS POULTRY BREEDERS (PTY) LTD.—See Astral Foods Limited; *Int'l*, pg. 658
ROSS PROMOTIONAL PRODUCTS LIMITED—See Altitude Group plc; *Int'l*, pg. 393
ROSS REAL ESTATE LTD.—See BGC Group, Inc.; *U.S. Public*, pg. 329
THE ROSS REALTY GROUP, INC.—See RMC Property Group LLC; *U.S. Private*, pg. 3451
ROSS REALTY INC.; *U.S. Private*, pg. 3485
ROSS RIVER MINERALS INC.; *Int'l*, pg. 6401
ROSS & ROBERTS LIMITED—See Capita plc; *Int'l*, pg. 1309
ROSS-SHIRE ENGINEERING LTD—See Global Energy (Holdings) Ltd.; *Int'l*, pg. 2995
ROSS-SIMONS INC.—See Nonantum Capital Partners LLC; *U.S. Private*, pg. 2934
ROSS SPORTSWEAR INC.; *U.S. Private*, pg. 3485
ROSSS SPA; *Int'l*, pg. 6401
ROSS STORES, INC.; *U.S. Public*, pg. 1814
ROSS SYSTEMS IBERICA S.L.—See TA Associates, Inc.; *U.S. Private*, pg. 3914
ROSS SYSTEMS (UK) LIMITED—See TA Associates, Inc.; *U.S. Private*, pg. 3914
ROSS TECHNOLOGY CORPORATION; *U.S. Private*, pg. 3485
ROSS TRANSPORTATION SERVICES, INC.—See Ross Consolidated Corp.; *U.S. Private*, pg. 3485
ROSS VIDEO LIMITED; *Int'l*, pg. 6401
ROSSWEINER ARMATUREN UND MESSGERATE GMBH & CO OHG—See Aalberts N.V.; *Int'l*, pg. 35
ROSTA AG—See Miki Pulley Co., Ltd.; *Int'l*, pg. 4891
ROSTEL INDUSTRIES LTD.—See Precision Drilling Corporation; *Int'l*, pg. 5957
ROSTER FINANCIAL LLC—See Allianz SE; *Int'l*, pg. 355
ROSTFRIA VA-SYSTEM I STORFORS AB—See Indutrade AB; *Int'l*, pg. 3681
ROSTFRIA VA-SYSTEM I STORFORS AB—See Indutrade AB; *Int'l*, pg. 3681
ROSTI A/S—See Nordstjernan AB; *Int'l*, pg. 5426

ROSTI GP AB—See Nordstjernan AB; *Int'l*, pg. 5426
ROSTI GP—See Nordstjernan AB; *Int'l*, pg. 5426
ROSTI GROUP AB—See Nordstjernan AB; *Int'l*, pg. 5426
ROSTI IMS SDN BHD—See Nordstjernan AB; *Int'l*, pg. 5426
ROSTI INTEGRATED MANUFACTURING SOLUTIONS (SUZHOU) CO.,LTD—See Nordstjernan AB; *Int'l*, pg. 5426
ROSTI MCKECHNIE LTD.- PICKERING—See Nordstjernan AB; *Int'l*, pg. 5426
ROSTI MCKECHNIE LTD.—See Nordstjernan AB; *Int'l*, pg. 5426
ROSTI POLAND SP. Z O.O.—See Nordstjernan AB; *Int'l*, pg. 5426
ROSTI (POLSKA) SP. Z O.O.—See Nordstjernan AB; *Int'l*, pg. 5426
ROSTI TEBPLAST PLASTIK SAN.TIC.A.S.—See Nordstjernan AB; *Int'l*, pg. 5426
ROSTI TECHNICAL PLASTICS (INDIA) PVT. LTD.—See Nordstjernan AB; *Int'l*, pg. 5426
ROSTI TECHNICAL PLASTICS UK LTD.—See Nordstjernan AB; *Int'l*, pg. 5426
ROSTI UK LTD.—See Nordstjernan AB; *Int'l*, pg. 5426
ROSTOCKER ZEMENTUMSCHLAGSGESELLSCHAFT MBH—See Heidelberg Materials AG; *Int'l*, pg. 3319
ROSTRA HOLDINGS PTE. LTD.; *Int'l*, pg. 6401
ROSTRA PRECISION CONTROLS, INC.—See Superior Capital Partners LLC; *U.S. Private*, pg. 3876
ROSTRVM SOLUTIONS LIMITED—See Cisco Systems, Inc.; *U.S. Public*, pg. 500
ROSULARIA VERMOGENSVERWALTUNGSGESELLSCHAFT MBH; *Int'l*, pg. 6401
ROSWELL BOOKBINDING CORP.—See Signet LLC; *U.S. Private*, pg. 3650
ROSWELL GEORGIA SURGERY CENTER, L.L.C.—See WellStar Health System, Inc.; *U.S. Private*, pg. 4478
ROSWELL HOSPITAL CORPORATION—See Community Health Systems, Inc.; *U.S. Public*, pg. 556
ROSWELL SURGERY CENTER, L.L.C.—See Tenet Healthcare Corporation; *U.S. Public*, pg. 2012
ROSWIL INC.; *U.S. Private*, pg. 3486
ROSYBLUE HONG KONG LTD.—See Rosy Blue Inc.; *U.S. Private*, pg. 3486
ROSY BLUE INC.; *U.S. Private*, pg. 3486
ROSY BLUE (INDIA) PVT. LTD.—See Rosy Blue Inc.; *U.S. Private*, pg. 3486
ROSY BLUE JEWELRY INC.—See Rosy Blue Inc.; *U.S. Private*, pg. 3486
ROSY BLUE LTD—See Rosy Blue Inc.; *U.S. Private*, pg. 3486
ROSY BLUE NV—See Rosy Blue Inc.; *U.S. Private*, pg. 3486
ROSYBLUE TRADING LLC—See Rosy Blue Inc.; *U.S. Private*, pg. 3486
ROSY BLUE TRADING (PTY) LTD—See Rosy Blue Inc.; *U.S. Private*, pg. 3486
RO SYSTEC GROUP SRL—See BOWE SYSTEC AG; *Int'l*, pg. 1123
ROSYTH ROYAL DOCKYARD LIMITED—See Babcock International Group PLC; *Int'l*, pg. 793
ROTADYNE—See Rotation Dynamics Corp.; *U.S. Private*, pg. 3486
ROTAIR S.P.A.—See ELGI Equipments Limited; *Int'l*, pg. 2360
ROTAK INSTRUMENTS (PVT) LTD; *Int'l*, pg. 6401
ROTALA GROUP LIMITED; *Int'l*, pg. 6401
ROTALA PLC—See Rotala Group Limited; *Int'l*, pg. 6402
ROTA LOGISTICS CENTER S.A.—See YALCO - SOCRATES D. CONSTANTINOU & SON S.A.; *Int'l*, pg. 8547
ROTAM AGROCHEMICAL CO., LTD.—See Rotam Global AgroSciences Ltd.; *Int'l*, pg. 6402
ROTAM AGROCHEMICAL EUROPE LIMITED—See Rotam Global AgroSciences Ltd.; *Int'l*, pg. 6402
ROTAM AGRO COLOMBIA S.A.S.—See Rotam Global AgroSciences Ltd.; *Int'l*, pg. 6402
ROTAM COSTA RICA CRI S.A.—See Rotam Global AgroSciences Ltd.; *Int'l*, pg. 6402
ROTAM DE ARGENTINA AGROQUIMICA SRL—See Rotam Global AgroSciences Ltd.; *Int'l*, pg. 6402
ROTAM DE CHILE AGROQUIMICA LTDA.—See Rotam Global AgroSciences Ltd.; *Int'l*, pg. 6402
ROTAM EUROPE LTD.—See Rotam Global AgroSciences Ltd.; *Int'l*, pg. 6402
ROTAM GLOBAL AGROSCIENCES LTD.; *Int'l*, pg. 6402
ROTAM MAGHREB LIMITED—See Rotam Global AgroSciences Ltd.; *Int'l*, pg. 6402
ROTAM MEXICO S.A. DE C.V.—See Rotam Global AgroSciences Ltd.; *Int'l*, pg. 6402
ROTAM NORTH AMERICA, INC.—See Rotam Global AgroSciences Ltd.; *Int'l*, pg. 6402
ROTAM TAIWAN LIMITED—See Rotam Global AgroSciences Ltd.; *Int'l*, pg. 6402
ROTANA HOTEL MANAGEMENT CORPORATION LTD; *Int'l*, pg. 6402
THE ROTARIAN MAGAZINE—See Rotary International; *U.S. Private*, pg. 3486
ROTARY COMPRESSOR SYSTEMS, INC.—See EQT AB; *Int'l*, pg. 2478

COMPANY NAME INDEX

ROTARY DIES, S.L.—See MPE Partners, LLC; *U.S. Private*, pg. 2803
ROTARY DRILLING COMPANY LIMITED—See INA-Industrija Nafte, d.d.; *Int'l*, pg. 3642
ROTARY DRILLING TOOLS USA, LLC—See Tubos Reunidos, S.A.; *Int'l*, pg. 7963
ROTARY ENGINEERING PTE. LTD.; *Int'l*, pg. 6402
ROTARY FORMS PRESS, INC.; *U.S. Private*, pg. 3486
ROTARY INTERNATIONAL; *U.S. Private*, pg. 3486
ROTARY LIFT—See Dover Corporation; *U.S. Public*, pg. 679
ROTARY MULTIFORMS, INC.; *U.S. Private*, pg. 3486
ROTARY OFFSET PRESS—See Blethen Corporation; *U.S. Private*, pg. 581
ROTARY OFFSET PRESS—See Chatham Asset Management, LLC; *U.S. Private*, pg. 867
ROTARY POWER LIMITED—See British Engines Ltd.; *Int'l*, pg. 1171
ROTARY VORTEX LIMITED—See WH Group Limited; *Int'l*, pg. 8394
ROTARY WATCHES LIMITED—See Citychamp Watch & Jewellery Group Limited; *Int'l*, pg. 1629
ROTAS A.D.; *Int'l*, pg. 6402
ROTASERVE B.V.—See Kirloskar Brothers Limited; *Int'l*, pg. 4191
ROTATE BLACK, INC.; *U.S. Public*, pg. 1815
ROTATING MACHINERY SERVICES, INC.—See Cortec Group Management Services, LLC; *U.S. Private*, pg. 1060
ROTATIONAL MOLDING, INC.—See Olympus Partners; *U.S. Private*, pg. 3013
ROTATION DYNAMICS CORP.; *U.S. Private*, pg. 3486
ROTATION MEDICAL, INC.—See Smith & Nephew plc; *Int'l*, pg. 7009
ROTA YOKOGAWA GMBH & CO.KG—See Yokogawa Electric Corporation; *Int'l*, pg. 8592
ROTEA D.O.O.—See August Rueggeberg GmbH & Co. KG PFERD-Werkzeuge; *Int'l*, pg. 703
ROTECH HEALTHCARE HOLDINGS INC.; *U.S. Public*, pg. 1815
ROTECH HEALTHCARE, INC.; *U.S. Private*, pg. 3486
ROTEC INDUSTRIES INC.; *U.S. Private*, pg. 3486
ROTEC TECHNOLOGY GMBH—See FORTEC Elektronik AG; *Int'l*, pg. 2738
ROTEK ENGINEERING (PTY) LTD.—See Eskom Holdings SOC Limited; *Int'l*, pg. 2504
ROTEK INCORPORATED—See ThyssenKrupp AG; *Int'l*, pg. 7731
ROTEK INCORPORATED—See ThyssenKrupp AG; *Int'l*, pg. 7731
ROTELEC SA—See Danieli & C. Officine Meccaniche S.p.A.; *Int'l*, pg. 1963
ROTELLAS ITALIAN BAKERY INCORPORATED; *U.S. Private*, pg. 3486
ROTELLI PIZZA & PASTA; *U.S. Private*, pg. 3486
ROTEM ENERGY MINERAL; *Int'l*, pg. 6402
ROTEM SHANI LTD.; *Int'l*, pg. 6402
ROTEM USA CORPORATION—See Hyundai Motor Company; *Int'l*, pg. 3560
ROTEX EUROPE LTD.—See Hillenbrand, Inc.; *U.S. Public*, pg. 1036
ROTEX GLOBAL, LLC—See Hillenbrand, Inc.; *U.S. Public*, pg. 1037
ROTEX HEATING SYSTEMS GMBH—See Daikin Industries, Ltd.; *Int'l*, pg. 1934
ROTEX INC.; *U.S. Private*, pg. 3486
ROTEX POLSKA SP. Z O.O.—See Daikin Industries, Ltd.; *Int'l*, pg. 1936
ROTH AGENCY INC.—See Seeman Holtz Property & Casualty, LLC; *U.S. Private*, pg. 3598
ROTH CAPITAL PARTNERS LLC; *U.S. Private*, pg. 3486
ROTH CH ACQUISITION CO.; *U.S. Public*, pg. 1815
ROTH DISTRIBUTING COMPANY; *U.S. Private*, pg. 3487
ROTHE ERDE GMBH—See ThyssenKrupp AG; *Int'l*, pg. 7731
ROTHE ERDE IBERICA S.A. - ROTEISA—See ThyssenKrupp AG; *Int'l*, pg. 7731
ROTHE ERDE INDIA PRIVATE LTD.—See ThyssenKrupp AG; *Int'l*, pg. 7731
ROTHE ERDE INDIA—See ThyssenKrupp AG; *Int'l*, pg. 7731
ROTHE ERDE METALLURGICA ROSSI S.P.A.—See ThyssenKrupp AG; *Int'l*, pg. 7731
ROTHENBERGER AG—See Dr. Helmut Rothenberger Holding GmbH; *Int'l*, pg. 2191
ROTHENBERGER AUSTRALIA PTY. LTD.—See Dr. Helmut Rothenberger Holding GmbH; *Int'l*, pg. 2191
ROTHENBERGER BENELUX BVBA—See Dr. Helmut Rothenberger Holding GmbH; *Int'l*, pg. 2191
ROTHENBERGER BULGARIA GMBH—See Dr. Helmut Rothenberger Holding GmbH; *Int'l*, pg. 2191
ROTHENBERGER DO BRASIL LTDA.—See Dr. Helmut Rothenberger Holding GmbH; *Int'l*, pg. 2192
ROTHENBERGER FRANCE S.A.—See Dr. Helmut Rothenberger Holding GmbH; *Int'l*, pg. 2191
ROTHENBERGER HELLAS S.A.—See Dr. Helmut Rothenberger Holding GmbH; *Int'l*, pg. 2191
ROTHENBERGER HUNGARY KFT.—See Dr. Helmut Rothenberger Holding GmbH; *Int'l*, pg. 2191
ROTHENBERGER ITALIANA S.R.L.—See Dr. Helmut Rothenberger Holding GmbH; *Int'l*, pg. 2191
ROTHENBERGER NARADI A STROJE, S.R.O.—See Dr. Helmut Rothenberger Holding GmbH; *Int'l*, pg. 2191
ROTHENBERGER NEDERLAND BV—See Dr. Helmut Rothenberger Holding GmbH; *Int'l*, pg. 2191
ROTHENBERGER PIPE TOOL (SHANGHAI) CO., LTD.—See Dr. Helmut Rothenberger Holding GmbH; *Int'l*, pg. 2191
ROTHENBERGER POLSKA SP. Z.O.O.—See Dr. Helmut Rothenberger Holding GmbH; *Int'l*, pg. 2191
ROTHENBERGER S.A.—See Dr. Helmut Rothenberger Holding GmbH; *Int'l*, pg. 2191
ROTHENBERGER SCANDINAVIA A/S—See Dr. Helmut Rothenberger Holding GmbH; *Int'l*, pg. 2191
ROTHENBERGER SCHWEIZ AG—See Dr. Helmut Rothenberger Holding GmbH; *Int'l*, pg. 2191
ROTHENBERGER SWEDEN AB—See Dr. Helmut Rothenberger Holding GmbH; *Int'l*, pg. 2191
ROTHENBERGER-TOOLS SA (PTY) LTD.—See Dr. Helmut Rothenberger Holding GmbH; *Int'l*, pg. 2192
ROTHENBERGER UK LIMITED—See Dr. Helmut Rothenberger Holding GmbH; *Int'l*, pg. 2191
ROTHENBERGER USA LLC—See Dr. Helmut Rothenberger Holding GmbH; *Int'l*, pg. 2191
ROTHENBERGER USA - WEST COAST OPERATIONS—See Dr. Helmut Rothenberger Holding GmbH; *Int'l*, pg. 2191
ROTHENBERGER WERKZEUGE GMBH—See Dr. Helmut Rothenberger Holding GmbH; *Int'l*, pg. 2191
ROTHENBERGER WERKZEUGE PRODUKTION GMBH—See Dr. Helmut Rothenberger Holding GmbH; *Int'l*, pg. 2192
ROTHENBERGER WERKZEUG UND MASCHINEN GMBH—See Dr. Helmut Rothenberger Holding GmbH; *Int'l*, pg. 2191
ROTH GERUSTE AG—See Altrad Investment Authority SAS; *Int'l*, pg. 397
ROTH HEIZOLE GMBH.—See MOL Magyar Olaj- es Gazipari Nyrt.; *Int'l*, pg. 5020
ROTH HILL ENGINEERING PARTNERS, LLC—See Stantec Inc.; *Int'l*, pg. 7172
ROTHIDI SA—See Carrefour SA; *Int'l*, pg. 1344
ROTH IGA FOODLINER INC.; *U.S. Private*, pg. 3487
ROTH KASE USA, LTD.; *U.S. Private*, pg. 3487
ROTHMAN FURNITURE STORES, INC.; *U.S. Private*, pg. 3487
ROTH & RAU AG—See Meyer Burger Technology AG; *Int'l*, pg. 4869
ROTH & RAU B.V.—See Meyer Burger Technology AG; *Int'l*, pg. 4869
ROTHROCK MOTOR SALES, INC.; *U.S. Private*, pg. 3487
ROTHSAY FARMERS CO-OP; *U.S. Private*, pg. 3487
ROTHSCHILD ASSET MANAGEMENT INC.—See Rothschild & Co SCA; *Int'l*, pg. 6404
ROTHSCHILD BANK AG—See Rothschild & Co SCA; *Int'l*, pg. 6404
ROTHSCHILD BANK INTERNATIONAL LIMITED—See Rothschild & Co SCA; *Int'l*, pg. 6404
ROTHSCHILD (CANADA) HOLDINGS LIMITED—See Rothschild & Co SCA; *Int'l*, pg. 6404
ROTHSCHILD (CANADA) INC.—See Rothschild & Co SCA; *Int'l*, pg. 6404
ROTHSCHILD & CIE BANQUE SCS—See Rothschild & Co SCA; *Int'l*, pg. 6403
ROTHSCHILD & CO ADVISORY (BEIJING) COMPANY LIMITED—See Rothschild & Co SCA; *Int'l*, pg. 6403
ROTHSCHILD & CO AUSTRALIA LIMITED—See Rothschild & Co SCA; *Int'l*, pg. 6403
ROTHSCHILD & CO BELGIUM SA NV—See Rothschild & Co SCA; *Int'l*, pg. 6403
ROTHSCHILD & CO BRASIL LTDA—See Rothschild & Co SCA; *Int'l*, pg. 6403
ROTHSCHILD & CO DEUTSCHLAND GMBH—See Rothschild & Co SCA; *Int'l*, pg. 6403
ROTHSCHILD & CO DOHA LLC—See Rothschild & Co SCA; *Int'l*, pg. 6403
ROTHSCHILD & CO ESPANA S.A.—See Rothschild & Co SCA; *Int'l*, pg. 6403
ROTHSCHILD & CO GREECE SMSA—See Rothschild & Co SCA; *Int'l*, pg. 6403
ROTHSCHILD & CO HONG KONG LIMITED—See Rothschild & Co SCA; *Int'l*, pg. 6403
ROTHSCHILD & CO INDIA PRIVATE LIMITED—See Rothschild & Co SCA; *Int'l*, pg. 6403
ROTHSCHILD & CO ISRAEL BV—See Rothschild & Co SCA; *Int'l*, pg. 6403
ROTHSCHILD & CO JAPAN LTD.—See Rothschild & Co SCA; *Int'l*, pg. 6403
ROTHSCHILD & CO KURUMSAL FINANSMAN HIZMETLERI LIMITED SIRKETI—See Rothschild & Co SCA; *Int'l*, pg. 6403
ROTHSCHILDCO MALAYSIA SDN. BHD.—See Rothschild & Co SCA; *Int'l*, pg. 6404
ROTHSCHILD & CO MEXICO, S.A. DE C.V—See Rothschild & Co SCA; *Int'l*, pg. 6403
ROTHSCHILD & CO MIDDLE EAST LIMITED—See Rothschild & Co SCA; *Int'l*, pg. 6403
ROTHSCHILD & CO NORDIC AB—See Rothschild & Co SCA; *Int'l*, pg. 6403
ROTHSCHILD & CO PORTUGAL LIMITADA—See Rothschild & Co SCA; *Int'l*, pg. 6403
ROTHSCHILD & CO SCA; *Int'l*, pg. 6402
ROTHSCHILD & CO SINGAPORE LIMITED—See Rothschild & Co SCA; *Int'l*, pg. 6403
ROTHSCHILD & CO WEALTH MANAGEMENT ITALY SIM SPA—See Rothschild & Co SCA; *Int'l*, pg. 6403
ROTHSCHILD & CO WEALTH MANAGEMENT SPAIN, A.V., S.A.—See Rothschild & Co SCA; *Int'l*, pg. 6403
ROTHSCHILD & CO WEALTH MANAGEMENT UK LIMITED—See Rothschild & Co SCA; *Int'l*, pg. 6404
ROTHSCHILD INC.—See Rothschild & Co SCA; *Int'l*, pg. 6404
ROTHSCHILD MALAYSIA SENDIRIAN BERHAD—See Rothschild & Co SCA; *Int'l*, pg. 6404
ROTHSCHILD MARTIN MAUREL—See Rothschild & Co SCA; *Int'l*, pg. 6404
ROTHSCHILD (MEXICO) SA DE CV—See Rothschild & Co SCA; *Int'l*, pg. 6404
ROTHSCHILD (MIDDLE EAST) LIMITED—See Rothschild & Co SCA; *Int'l*, pg. 6404
ROTHSCHILD NORDIC AB—See Rothschild & Co SCA; *Int'l*, pg. 6404
ROTHSCHILD POLSKA SP. Z O.O.—See Rothschild & Co SCA; *Int'l*, pg. 6404
ROTHSCHILD PORTUGAL LIMITADA—See Rothschild & Co SCA; *Int'l*, pg. 6404
ROTHSCHILD S.A. DE C.V.—See Rothschild & Co SCA; *Int'l*, pg. 6404
ROTHSCHILD S.A.—See Rothschild & Co SCA; *Int'l*, pg. 6404
ROTHSCHILD S.P.A—See Rothschild & Co SCA; *Int'l*, pg. 6404
ROTHSCHILD TRUST B.V.I. LIMITED—See Rothschild & Co SCA; *Int'l*, pg. 6404
ROTHSCHILD TRUST GUERNSEY LIMITED—See Rothschild & Co SCA; *Int'l*, pg. 6404
ROTHSCHILD TRUST (SCHWEIZ) AG—See Rothschild & Co SCA; *Int'l*, pg. 6404
ROTHSCHILD TRUST (SINGAPORE) LIMITED—See Rothschild & Co SCA; *Int'l*, pg. 6404
ROTHSCHILD VERMOGENSVERWALTUNGS GMBH—See Rothschild & Co SCA; *Int'l*, pg. 6404
ROTHSCHILD WEALTH MANAGEMENT (HONG KONG) LIMITED—See Rothschild & Co SCA; *Int'l*, pg. 6404
ROTHSCHILD WEALTH MANAGEMENT (SINGAPORE) LIMITED—See Rothschild & Co SCA; *Int'l*, pg. 6404
ROTHSCHILD WEALTH MANAGEMENT (UK) LIMITED—See Rothschild & Co SCA; *Int'l*, pg. 6404
ROTHSTEIN CORP.; *U.S. Private*, pg. 3487
ROTHTEC ENGRAVING CORP.; *U.S. Private*, pg. 3487
ROTHWELL INTERNATIONAL CO LTD; *Int'l*, pg. 6404
ROTH-ZACHRY HEATING INC.; *U.S. Private*, pg. 3487
ROTKAEPPCHEN-MUMM SEKTKELLEREIEN GMBH; *Int'l*, pg. 6404
ROTKAPPCHEN-MUMM SEKTKELLEREIEN GMBH; *Int'l*, pg. 6404
ROTOBLOCK CORPORATION; *U.S. Private*, pg. 3487
ROTOGRAPHICS INDIA LTD.; *Int'l*, pg. 6405
ROTO-GRO INTERNATIONAL LIMITED; *Int'l*, pg. 6405
ROTO HAMMER INDUSTRIES, INC.—See Rotork Plc; *Int'l*, pg. 6406
ROTOKAWA GEOTHERMAL LIMITED—See Mercury NZ Limited; *Int'l*, pg. 4834
ROTOLO CONSULTANTS, INC.; *U.S. Private*, pg. 3487
ROTOMADRID SL—See Vocento, S.A.; *Int'l*, pg. 8284
ROTOMETRICS AUSTRALIA PTY. LTD.—See MPE Partners, LLC; *U.S. Private*, pg. 2803
ROTOMETRICS CANADA INC.—See MPE Partners, LLC; *U.S. Private*, pg. 2803
ROTOMETRICS CHINA LTD.—See MPE Partners, LLC; *U.S. Private*, pg. 2803
ROTOMETRICS, INC.—See MPE Partners, LLC; *U.S. Private*, pg. 2803
ROTOMETRICS INTERNATIONAL A/S—See MPE Partners, LLC; *U.S. Private*, pg. 2803
ROTOMETRICS INTERNATIONAL LTD—See MPE Partners, LLC; *U.S. Private*, pg. 2803
ROTOMETRICS ITALIA SRL—See MPE Partners, LLC; *U.S. Private*, pg. 2803
ROTOMETRICS ROTATIONSWERKZEUGE GMBH—See MPE Partners, LLC; *U.S. Private*, pg. 2803
ROTOMETRICS (SE ASIA) CO., LTD.—See MPE Partners, LLC; *U.S. Private*, pg. 2803
ROTO MOULDERS LIMITED—See Flame Tree Group Holdings Ltd.; *Int'l*, pg. 2698
ROTONDA HOLDINGS INC.; *U.S. Private*, pg. 3487
ROTONDE—See Carrefour SA; *Int'l*, pg. 1346
ROTOPRECISION INC.; *Int'l*, pg. 6405
ROTO PUMPEN GMBH—See Roto Pumps Ltd.; *Int'l*, pg. 6404
ROTO PUMPS (AFRICA) PTY LTD—See Roto Pumps Ltd.; *Int'l*, pg. 6404
ROTO PUMPS GMBH—See Roto Pumps Ltd.; *Int'l*, pg. 6404
ROTO PUMPS LTD.; *Int'l*, pg. 6404

ROTO PUMPS (MALAYSIA) SDN. BHD.—See Roto Pumps Ltd.; *Int'l*, pg. 6404
ROTO PUMPS NORTH AMERICA, INC.—See Roto Pumps Ltd.; *Int'l*, pg. 6404
ROTO PUMPS NORTH AMERICAS INC.—See Roto Pumps Ltd.; *Int'l*, pg. 6405
ROTOR A.D.; *Int'l*, pg. 6405
ROTOR BLADES LIMITED—See Textron Inc.; *U.S. Public*, pg. 2028
ROTOR B.V.—See Regal Rexnord Corporation; *U.S. Public*, pg. 1773
ROTORCOMP VERDICHTER GMBH—See BAUER COMP Holding AG; *Int'l*, pg. 894
ROTORCRAFT LEASING COMPANY, L.L.C.—See H.I.G. Capital, LLC; *U.S. Private*, pg. 1831
ROTORCRAFT SERVICES GROUP, INC.—See Trinity Hunt Management, L.P.; *U.S. Private*, pg. 4235
ROTOR ELECTRIC LLC.—See Motor City Electric Co., Inc.; *U.S. Private*, pg. 2796
ROTOR JSC—See Russian Technologies State Corporation; *Int'l*, pg. 6432
ROTORK (ACTUATION) SDN BHD—See Rotork Plc; *Int'l*, pg. 6405
ROTORK AFRICA (PTY) LTD—See Rotork Plc; *Int'l*, pg. 6405
ROTORK AUSTRALIA PTY LTD—See Rotork Plc; *Int'l*, pg. 6405
ROTORK BV—See Rotork Plc; *Int'l*, pg. 6405
ROTORK CHILE SPA—See Rotork Plc; *Int'l*, pg. 6405
ROTORK CONTROLS BEIJING—See Rotork Plc; *Int'l*, pg. 6405
ROTORK CONTROLS (CANADA) LTD—See Rotork Plc; *Int'l*, pg. 6405
ROTORK CONTROLS COMERCIO DE ATUADORES LTD.—See Rotork Plc; *Int'l*, pg. 6405
ROTORK CONTROLS (DEUTSCHLAND) GMBH - RFS MELLE DIVISION—See Rotork Plc; *Int'l*, pg. 6405
ROTORK CONTROLS (DEUTSCHLAND) GMBH—See Rotork Plc; *Int'l*, pg. 6405
ROTORK CONTROLS DE VENEZUELA SA—See Rotork Plc; *Int'l*, pg. 6406
ROTORK CONTROLS (ESPANA) SL—See Rotork Plc; *Int'l*, pg. 6405
ROTORK CONTROLS INC.—See Rotork Plc; *Int'l*, pg. 6406
ROTORK CONTROLS (INDIA) PRIVATE LIMITED—See Rotork Plc; *Int'l*, pg. 6405
ROTORK CONTROLS (INDIA) PVT LTD-CHENNAI—See Rotork Plc; *Int'l*, pg. 6405
ROTORK CONTROLS (ITALIA) SRL—See Rotork Plc; *Int'l*, pg. 6405
ROTORK CONTROLS (KOREA) CO. LTD—See Rotork Plc; *Int'l*, pg. 6405
ROTORK CONTROLS LTD—See Rotork Plc; *Int'l*, pg. 6406
ROTORK CONTROLS (SHANGHAI) LTD—See Rotork Plc; *Int'l*, pg. 6405
ROTORK CONTROLS (SINGAPORE) PTE LTD—See Rotork Plc; *Int'l*, pg. 6405
ROTORK FLUID SYSTEM SRL—See Rotork Plc; *Int'l*, pg. 6406
ROTORK GEARS BV—See Rotork Plc; *Int'l*, pg. 6406
ROTORK GEARS (HOLDINGS) BV—See Rotork Plc; *Int'l*, pg. 6406
ROTORK GEARS SRL—See Rotork Plc; *Int'l*, pg. 6406
ROTORK GMBH—See Rotork Plc; *Int'l*, pg. 6406
ROTORK INC.—See Rotork Plc; *Int'l*, pg. 6406
ROTORK INSTRUMENTS ITALY SRL—See Rotork Plc; *Int'l*, pg. 6406
ROTORK JAPAN CO. LTD—See Rotork Plc; *Int'l*, pg. 6406
ROTORK LTD—See Rotork Plc; *Int'l*, pg. 6406
ROTORK (MALAYSIA) SDN BHD—See Rotork Plc; *Int'l*, pg. 6405
ROTORK MIDDLE EAST FZE JEBEL ALI—See Rotork Plc; *Int'l*, pg. 6406
ROTORK MIDDLE EAST FZE—See Rotork Plc; *Int'l*, pg. 6406
ROTORK MIDLAND LIMITED—See Rotork Plc; *Int'l*, pg. 6406
ROTORK MIDLAND LIMITED - WOLVERHAMPTON PLANT—See Rotork Plc; *Int'l*, pg. 6406
ROTORK MOTORISATION SAS—See Rotork Plc; *Int'l*, pg. 6406
ROTORK NORGE AS—See Rotork Plc; *Int'l*, pg. 6406
ROTORK NORWAY—See Rotork Plc; *Int'l*, pg. 6406
ROTORK PLC; *Int'l*, pg. 6405
ROTORK POLSKA SP. Z O.O.—See Rotork Plc; *Int'l*, pg. 6406
ROTORK PROCESS CONTROLS - USA—See Rotork Plc; *Int'l*, pg. 6406
ROTORK RUS LLC—See Rotork Plc; *Int'l*, pg. 6406
ROTORK SAUDI ARABIA LLC—See Rotork Plc; *Int'l*, pg. 6406
ROTORK SERVO CONTROLES DE MEXICO S.A DE C.V—See Rotork Plc; *Int'l*, pg. 6406
ROTORK SWEDEN AB—See Rotork Plc; *Int'l*, pg. 6406
ROTORK (THAILAND) LTD—See Rotork Plc; *Int'l*, pg. 6405

ROTORK TRADING (SHANGHAI) CO. LTD—See Rotork Plc; *Int'l*, pg. 6405
ROTORK TULSA INC.—See Rotork Plc; *Int'l*, pg. 6406
ROTORK TURKEY AKIS KONTROL SISTEMLERI TICARET LIMITED—See Rotork Plc; *Int'l*, pg. 6406
ROTORK YTC LIMITED—See Rotork Plc; *Int'l*, pg. 6406
ROTO-ROOTER CANADA, LTD.—See Chemed Corporation; *U.S. Public*, pg. 484
ROTO-ROOTER, CORP.—See Chemed Corporation; *U.S. Public*, pg. 484
ROTO-ROOTER GROUP, INC.—See Chemed Corporation; *U.S. Public*, pg. 484
ROTO-ROOTER SERVICES CO—See Chemed Corporation; *U.S. Public*, pg. 484
ROTORSIM S.R.L.—See CAE Inc.; *Int'l*, pg. 1249
ROTORSIM S.R.L.—See Leonardo S.p.A.; *Int'l*, pg. 4458
ROTOR SOURCE, INC.—See Munters AB; *Int'l*, pg. 5094
ROTOR U.K. LIMITED—See Regal Rexnord Corporation; *U.S. Public*, pg. 1773
ROTOS 360 LIMITED—See James Fisher & Sons Public Limited Company; *Int'l*, pg. 3876
ROTOSTAT SERVICES PRIVATE LIMITED—See ManpowerGroup Inc.; *U.S. Public*, pg. 1361
ROTO SUBARU MAZDA, INC.; *U.S. Private*, pg. 3487
ROTOTEC GEOTHERMAL ENERGY PLC; *Int'l*, pg. 6406
ROTOTECH ELECTRICAL COMPONENTS INC.; *U.S. Private*, pg. 3487
ROTOTEC OY—See Rototec Geothermal Energy PLC; *Int'l*, pg. 6406
ROTOTRON CORPORATION; *U.S. Private*, pg. 3487
ROTOVAC CORPORATION; *U.S. Private*, pg. 3487
ROTOVISION SA—See The Quarto Group, Inc.; *Int'l*, pg. 7677
ROTRADA HOLDING B.V.; *Int'l*, pg. 6406
ROTRA, LLC—See Delmar International, Inc.; *U.S. Private*, pg. 2014
R&O TRANSPORTATION LLC—See Castellini Company, Inc.; *U.S. Private*, pg. 784
ROTSHTEIN REALESTATE LTD.; *Int'l*, pg. 6406
ROTTENECKER-CAGGIATI GMBH—See Matthews International Corporation; *U.S. Public*, pg. 1400
ROTTERDAM AIRPORT B.V.—See Schiphol Group NV; *Int'l*, pg. 6621
ROTTERDAM FREIGHT STATION B.V.—See Allcargo Logistics Limited; *Int'l*, pg. 334
ROTTERDAM FRUIT WHARF B.V.—See SEA-invest Group; *Int'l*, pg. 6661
ROTTERDAM INDUSTRIAL PARK—See Galesi Group; *U.S. Private*, pg. 1637
ROTTERDAMSE ELEMENTEN FABRIEK B.V.—See NIBE Industrier AB; *Int'l*, pg. 5262
ROTTERDAM SQUARE, LLC—See The Macerich Company; *U.S. Public*, pg. 2110
ROTTERDAM VENTURES INC.—See Galesi Group; *U.S. Private*, pg. 1637
ROTTERDAM WORLD GATEWAY B.V.—See Mitsui O.S.K. Lines, Ltd.; *Int'l*, pg. 4991
ROTTER GROUP INC.; *U.S. Private*, pg. 3487
ROTTER GROUP INC.—See Rotter Group Inc.; *U.S. Private*, pg. 3487
ROTTINGHAUS CO. INC.; *U.S. Private*, pg. 3487
ROTTNEROS AB—See Arctic Paper S.A.; *Int'l*, pg. 552
ROTTNEROS BRUK AB—See Arctic Paper S.A.; *Int'l*, pg. 552
ROTTNEROS MIRANDA SA—See Arctic Paper S.A.; *Int'l*, pg. 552
ROTTNEROS PACKAGING AB—See Arctic Paper S.A.; *Int'l*, pg. 552
ROTUNDA CAPITAL PARTNERS LLC; *U.S. Private*, pg. 3487
ROTZINGER AG; *Int'l*, pg. 6407
ROUCHON INDUSTRIES, INC.; *U.S. Public*, pg. 1815
R.O.U CO., LTD.—See AEON Co., Ltd.; *Int'l*, pg. 178
ROUDIERE SA—See Chargeurs SA; *Int'l*, pg. 1449
ROUGH BROTHERS GREENHOUSE MANUFACTURING (SHANGHAI) CO., LTD—See Gibraltar Industries, Inc.; *U.S. Public*, pg. 936
ROUGH BROTHERS, INC.—See Gibraltar Industries, Inc.; *U.S. Public*, pg. 936
ROUGH BROTHERS MANUFACTURING, INC.—See Gibraltar Industries, Inc.; *U.S. Public*, pg. 936
ROUGH GUIDES INC—See Pearson plc; *Int'l*, pg. 5778
THE ROUGH NOTES COMPANY, INC.; *U.S. Private*, pg. 4112
ROUGHRIDER ELECTRIC COOPERATIVE, INC.; *U.S. Private*, pg. 3488
ROUGHRIDER EXPLORATION LIMITED; *Int'l*, pg. 6407
ROUGIER GABON S.A.—See Rougier S.A.; *Int'l*, pg. 6407
ROUGIER INTERNATIONAL SA—See Rougier S.A.; *Int'l*, pg. 6407
ROUGIER PANNEAUX S.A.S.—See Rougier S.A.; *Int'l*, pg. 6407
ROUGIER S.A.; *Int'l*, pg. 6407
ROULARTA MEDIA GROUP NV; *Int'l*, pg. 6407
ROUMANIE SRL—See ENGIE SA; *Int'l*, pg. 2434
ROUND2 COMMUNICATIONS, LLC; *U.S. Private*, pg. 3488
ROUND 2 CORP., LLC—See Praesidian Capital Corp.; *U.S. Private*, pg. 3241

ROUND2 INC.—See Avnet, Inc.; *U.S. Public*, pg. 254
ROUND2/SF—See Round2 Communications, LLC; *U.S. Private*, pg. 3488
ROUND2 TECHNOLOGIES, INC.—See Avnet, Inc.; *U.S. Public*, pg. 254
ROUNDBANK; *U.S. Private*, pg. 3488
ROUNDER RECORDS CORPORATION—See Massachusetts Mutual Life Insurance Company; *U.S. Private*, pg. 2605
ROUND HILL CLUB; *U.S. Private*, pg. 3488
ROUND HILL SECURITIES; *U.S. Private*, pg. 3488
ROUNDHOUSE MARKETING & PROMOTION, INC.; *U.S. Private*, pg. 3488
ROUND MOUNTAIN GOLD CORPORATION—See Barrick Gold Corporation; *Int'l*, pg. 869
ROUND MOUNTAIN GOLD CORPORATION—See Kinross Gold Corporation; *Int'l*, pg. 4182
ROUND ONE CORPORATION; *Int'l*, pg. 6407
ROUNDPEG; *U.S. Private*, pg. 3488
ROUNDPOINT MORTGAGE SERVICING LLC—See Two Harbors Investment Corp.; *U.S. Public*, pg. 2207
ROUND ROCK BASEBALL CLUB, L.P.—See Ryan Sanders Baseball, L.P.; *U.S. Private*, pg. 3510
ROUND ROCK COPIER, LLC—See Stargel Office Systems, Inc.; *U.S. Private*, pg. 3786
ROUND ROCK HOSPITAL, INC.—See HCA Healthcare, Inc.; *U.S. Public*, pg. 1008
ROUND ROCK MEDICAL CENTER—See HCA Healthcare, Inc.; *U.S. Public*, pg. 1008
ROUND ROCK SOLUTIONS, INC.—See ADVANTEX; *U.S. Private*, pg. 95
ROUND ROCK TRAUMA SURGEONS, PLLC—See HCA Healthcare, Inc.; *U.S. Public*, pg. 1008
ROUND ROOM LLC; *U.S. Private*, pg. 3488
ROUND SKY INC; *U.S. Private*, pg. 3488
ROUND TABLE CAPITAL MANAGEMENT, LP; *U.S. Private*, pg. 3488
ROUND TABLE GROUP, INC.—See Thomson Reuters Corporation; *Int'l*, pg. 7715
ROUNDTABLE HEALTHCARE MANAGEMENT, INC.; *U.S. Private*, pg. 3488
ROUND TABLE PIZZA—See Fog Cutter Capital Group Inc.; *U.S. Private*, pg. 1557
ROUNDTOP MACHINERY INDUSTRIES CO., LTD. - SHEN KANG FACTORY—See Roundtop Machinery Industries Co., Ltd.; *Int'l*, pg. 6407
ROUNDTOP MACHINERY INDUSTRIES CO., LTD.; *Int'l*, pg. 6407
ROUNDTOP MOUNTAIN RESORT—See Vail Resorts, Inc.; *U.S. Public*, pg. 2271
ROUNDTOWER TECHNOLOGIES, LLC; *U.S. Private*, pg. 3489
ROUNDTREE AUTOMOTIVE GROUP, LLC; *U.S. Private*, pg. 3489
ROUNDTREE I VAN NUYS, LLC—See Roundtree Automotive Group, LLC; *U.S. Private*, pg. 3489
ROUNDTREE MOBILE, LLC—See AutoNation, Inc.; *U.S. Public*, pg. 237
ROUNDTREE N VAN NUYS, LLC—See Roundtree Automotive Group, LLC; *U.S. Private*, pg. 3489
ROUNDWOOD ASSET MANAGEMENT LLC—See Berkshire Hathaway Inc.; *U.S. Public*, pg. 299
ROUNDY APPAREL; *U.S. Private*, pg. 3489
ROUNDYS, INC.—See The Kroger Co.; *U.S. Public*, pg. 2109
ROUNDY'S SUPERMARKETS INC.—See The Kroger Co.; *U.S. Public*, pg. 2109
ROUNTREE MOORE TOYOTA—See Morgan Auto Group, LLC; *U.S. Private*, pg. 2783
ROUNTREE MOTORS INC.; *U.S. Private*, pg. 3489
ROURA CEVASA, S.A—See ACS, Actividades de Construccion y Servicios, S.A.; *Int'l*, pg. 116
ROURA IRON WORKS, INC.; *U.S. Private*, pg. 3489
ROURA IRON WORKS, INC.—See Roura Iron Works, Inc.; *U.S. Private*, pg. 3489
ROUSCH PAKISTAN LIMITED—See Nimir Resins Limited; *Int'l*, pg. 5297
ROUSCH (PAKISTAN) POWER LIMITED—See Crescent Steel and Allied Products Limited; *Int'l*, pg. 1839
ROUSE ASSET SERVICES, INC.—See RB Global, Inc.; *Int'l*, pg. 6226
ROUSE KENT (CENTRAL) LIMITED—See Prologis, Inc.; *U.S. Public*, pg. 1727
ROUSE KENT (RESIDENTIAL) LIMITED—See Prologis, Inc.; *U.S. Public*, pg. 1727
ROUSE'S ENTERPRISES LLC; *U.S. Private*, pg. 3489
ROUSH CORPORATION—See Fenway Sports Group Holdings, LLC; *U.S. Private*, pg. 1496
ROUSH CORPORATION—See Roush Enterprises, Inc.; *U.S. Private*, pg. 3489
ROUSHE DIALYSIS, LLC—See DaVita Inc.; *U.S. Public*, pg. 642
ROUSH ENTERPRISES, INC.; *U.S. Private*, pg. 3489
ROUSH EQUIPMENT COMPANY INC.; *U.S. Private*, pg. 3489
ROUSH MANUFACTURING, INC.—See Roush Enterprises, Inc.; *U.S. Private*, pg. 3489
ROUSH PERFORMANCE PRODUCTS, INC.—See Roush Enterprises, Inc.; *U.S. Private*, pg. 3489

COMPANY NAME INDEX

ROUSSEAU METAL, INC.; *Int'l*, pg. 6407
ROUSSEAU SAS—See Alamo Group Inc.; *U.S. Public*, pg. 70
ROUSSELET CENTRIFUGATION SA—See ROUSSELET Centrifugation SA; *Int'l*, pg. 6407
ROUSSELET CENTRIFUGATION SA; *Int'l*, pg. 6407
ROUSSELOT ANGOULEME SAS—See Darling Ingredients Inc.; *U.S. Public*, pg. 634
ROUSSELOT ARGENTINA SA—See Darling Ingredients Inc.; *U.S. Public*, pg. 634
ROUSSELOT BVBA—See Darling Ingredients Inc.; *U.S. Public*, pg. 634
ROUSSELOT B.V.—See VION Holding N.V.; *Int'l*, pg. 8244
ROUSSELOT (DA'AN) GELATIN CO. LTD—See Darling Ingredients Inc.; *U.S. Public*, pg. 634
ROUSSELOT GELATIN SL—See Darling Ingredients Inc.; *U.S. Public*, pg. 634
ROUSSELOT (GUANGDONG) GELATIN CO. LTD—See Darling Ingredients Inc.; *U.S. Public*, pg. 634
ROUSSELOT INC.—See VION Holding N.V.; *Int'l*, pg. 8244
ROUSSELOT ISLE SUR LA SORGUE SAS—See Darling Ingredients Inc.; *U.S. Public*, pg. 634
ROUSSELOT JAPAN KK—See Darling Ingredients Inc.; *U.S. Public*, pg. 634
ROUSSELOT (M) SDN.BHD—See Darling Ingredients Inc.; *U.S. Public*, pg. 634
ROUSSELOT S.A.S.—See VION Holding N.V.; *Int'l*, pg. 8244
ROUSSELOT (WHENZOU) GELATIN CO. LTD—See Darling Ingredients Inc.; *U.S. Public*, pg. 634
ROUSSELOT (ZHEJIANG) GELATIN CO. LTD—See Darling Ingredients Inc.; *U.S. Public*, pg. 634
ROUSSEY SAS—See VINCI S.A.; *Int'l*, pg. 8226
ROUSSIN ENERGIES SAS—See Brookfield Corporation; *Int'l*, pg. 1188
ROUSSO APPAREL GROUP INC; *U.S. Private*, pg. 3489
ROUSSO/FISHER PUBLIC RELATIONS, INC.; *U.S. Private*, pg. 3489
ROUSTER WIRE ROPE & RIGGING INC.—See Mazzella Lifting Technologies; *U.S. Private*, pg. 2623
ROUST INC.—See CJSC Russian Standard Corporation; *Int'l*, pg. 1634
ROUTE 12 WASH 'N' GAS INC.; *U.S. Private*, pg. 3489
ROUTE1 INC.; *Int'l*, pg. 6407
ROUTE 22 HONDA; *U.S. Private*, pg. 3490
ROUTE 22 TOYOTA; *U.S. Private*, pg. 3490
ROUTE 23 AUTO MALL; *U.S. Private*, pg. 3490
ROUTE 2 CAPITAL PARTNERS; *U.S. Private*, pg. 3490
ROUTE 33 NISSAN—See Auto Mall 46, Inc.; *U.S. Private*, pg. 397
ROUTE 66 RACEWAY, LLC—See National Association for Stock Car Auto Racing, Inc.; *U.S. Private*, pg. 2846
ROUTE 9G INC.—See create restaurants holdings inc.; *Int'l*, pg. 1832
ROUTECO LIMITED—See Sonepar S.A.; *Int'l*, pg. 7091
ROUTEMATCH SOFTWARE, INC.—See Constellation Software Inc.; *Int'l*, pg. 1775
ROUTE MOBIEL—See Apollo Global Management, Inc.; *U.S. Public*, pg. 148
ROUTE MOBILE LTD.—See Proximus PLC; *Int'l*, pg. 6008
ROUTE MOBILE UK LIMITED—See Proximus PLC; *Int'l*, pg. 6008
ROUTIERE DE L'EST PARISIEN—See Veolia Environnement S.A.; *Int'l*, pg. 8154
ROUTIERE DES PYRENEES SAS—See VINCI S.A.; *Int'l*, pg. 8226
ROUTON ELECTRONIC CO., LTD.; *Int'l*, pg. 6407
ROUX AGENCY, INC.—See Aon plc; *Int'l*, pg. 497
ROUX COMBALUZIER SCHINDLER—See Schindler Holding AG; *Int'l*, pg. 6619
ROUXEL SECAMA; *Int'l*, pg. 6407
ROUX LABORATORIES, INC.—See MacAndrews & Forbes Incorporated; *U.S. Private*, pg. 2533
ROVACABIN LIMITED—See Enviri Corporation; *U.S. Public*, pg. 781
ROVALIN AB—See Nordisk Bergteknik AB; *Int'l*, pg. 5424
ROVALIN NORD AB—See Nordisk Bergteknik AB; *Int'l*, pg. 5424
ROVCAL, INC.—See Energizer Holdings, Inc.; *U.S. Public*, pg. 761
ROVEMA GMBH—See Franz Haniel & Cie. GmbH; *Int'l*, pg. 2763
ROVENSA SA; *Int'l*, pg. 6407
ROVER METALS CORP.; *Int'l*, pg. 6407
ROVERT PTY LTD; *Int'l*, pg. 6408
ROV GERMAN LIMITED GMBH—See Energizer Holdings, Inc.; *U.S. Public*, pg. 761
ROV HOLDING, INC.—See Energizer Holdings, Inc.; *U.S. Public*, pg. 761
ROVI CORPORATION—See Adeia Inc.; *U.S. Public*, pg. 41
ROVI EUROPE LIMITED—See Adeia Inc.; *U.S. Public*, pg. 41
ROVI KK—See Adeia Inc.; *U.S. Public*, pg. 41
ROVI NETHERLANDS BV—See Adeia Inc.; *U.S. Public*, pg. 41
ROVINJTURIST D.D.—See Adris Grupa d.d.; *Int'l*, pg. 153
ROV INTERNATIONAL HOLDINGS LLC—See Energizer Holdings, Inc.; *U.S. Public*, pg. 761

ROVIO ENTERTAINMENT OYJ—See Sega Sammy Holdings, Inc.; *Int'l*, pg. 6681
ROVION, LLC—See TEGNA Inc.; *U.S. Public*, pg. 1990
ROVIRA BISCUIT CORPORATION; *U.S. Private*, pg. 3490
ROVITA S.A.; *Int'l*, pg. 6408
ROVITHAI LTD.—See Koninklijke DSM N.V.; *Int'l*, pg. 4265
ROVSING A/S; *Int'l*, pg. 6408
R.O.V. TECHNOLOGIES INC.—See Rolls-Royce Holdings plc; *Int'l*, pg. 6393
ROW 44, INC.—See PAR Capital Management, Inc.; *U.S. Private*, pg. 3089
ROWAD TOURISM COMPANY; *Int'l*, pg. 6408
ROWAN COMPANIES PLC—See Valaris Limited; *Int'l*, pg. 8110
ROWAND MACHINERY COMPANY; *U.S. Private*, pg. 3490
ROWANDRILL, INC.—See Valaris Limited; *Int'l*, pg. 8111
ROWAN DRILLING MEXICO, S. DE R.L. DE C.V.—See Valaris Limited; *Int'l*, pg. 8111
ROWAN DRILLING (U.K.) LIMITED—See Valaris Limited; *Int'l*, pg. 8110
ROWAN INTERNATIONAL, INC.—See Valaris Limited; *Int'l*, pg. 8111
ROWAN NORWAY LIMITED—See Valaris Limited; *Int'l*, pg. 8111
ROWAN WILLIAMS DAVIES & IRWIN INC.; *Int'l*, pg. 6408
ROW-CARE LLC—See The Townsend Corporation; *U.S. Private*, pg. 4127
ROWE ENTERPRISES INC.; *U.S. Private*, pg. 3490
ROWE ENTERPRISES, INC.; *U.S. Private*, pg. 3490
ROWE FARMING LIMITED—See Promethean Investments LLP; *Int'l*, pg. 5993
ROWE FURNITURE—See Sun Capital Partners, Inc.; *U.S. Private*, pg. 3860
ROWELL CHEMICAL CORPORATION; *U.S. Private*, pg. 3490
ROWENA AG—See Hinduja Group Ltd.; *Int'l*, pg. 3399
ROWENA JACKSON RETIREMENT VILLAGE LIMITED—See Ryman Healthcare Ltd.; *Int'l*, pg. 6440
ROWE & NEWBERRY INC.; *U.S. Private*, pg. 3490
ROWEN STRUCTURES LIMITED—See Severfield Plc; *Int'l*, pg. 6735
ROWENTA FRANCE S.A.—See SEB S.A.; *Int'l*, pg. 6668
ROWENTA (USA), INC.—See SEB S.A.; *Int'l*, pg. 6668
ROWENTA WERKE GMBH—See SEB S.A.; *Int'l*, pg. 6668
ROWERDINK INC.; *U.S. Private*, pg. 3490
ROWE SUPPLY CO—See Leonard Green & Partners, L.P.; *U.S. Private*, pg. 2429
ROWE TRUCK EQUIPMENT INC.; *U.S. Private*, pg. 3490
R.O. WHITESELL & ASSOCIATES, INC.; *U.S. Private*, pg. 3339
R.O. WILLIAMS & CO., INC; *U.S. Private*, pg. 3339
ROW INC.; *U.S. Private*, pg. 3490
THE ROWING TEAM, LLC—See Waud Capital Partners LLC; *U.S. Private*, pg. 4457
ROWLAND COFFEE ROASTERS, INC.—See The J.M. Smucker Company; *U.S. Public*, pg. 2107
THE ROWLAND COMPANY—See Publicis Groupe S.A.; *Int'l*, pg. 6106
ROWLAND HEIGHTS HIGHLANDER—See Alden Global Capital LLC; *U.S. Private*, pg. 158
ROWLAND PUBLISHING, INC.; *U.S. Private*, pg. 3490
ROWLANDS & BARRANCA AGENCY, INC.—See Brown & Brown, Inc.; *U.S. Public*, pg. 402
ROWLANDS INTERNATIONAL S.A.—See Randstad N.V.; *Int'l*, pg. 6205
ROWLEY COMPANY, LLC; *U.S. Private*, pg. 3490
ROWL, INC.; *U.S. Private*, pg. 3490
ROWLINSON KNITWEAR LIMITED; *Int'l*, pg. 6408
ROWMAN & LITTLEFIELD PUBLISHERS, INC.—See The Rowman & Littlefield Publishing Group, Inc.; *U.S. Private*, pg. 4112
THE ROWMAN & LITTLEFIELD PUBLISHING GROUP, INC.; *U.S. Private*, pg. 4112
ROWMARK LLC—See Windjammer Capital Investors, LLC; *U.S. Private*, pg. 4538
ROWOHLT VERLAG GMBH—See Verlagsgruppe Georg von Holtzbrinck GmbH; *Int'l*, pg. 8171
ROWSLEY SPORTS PTE. LTD.—See Thomson Medical Group Limited; *Int'l*, pg. 7714
ROXACO LAND CORPORATION—See Roxas & Company, Inc.; *Int'l*, pg. 6408
ROXAR ASA—See Emerson Electric Co.; *U.S. Public*, pg. 752
ROXAR SOFTWARE SOLUTIONS AS—See Emerson Electric Co.; *U.S. Public*, pg. 752
ROXAS & COMPANY, INC.; *Int'l*, pg. 6408
ROXAS HOLDINGS, INC.; *Int'l*, pg. 6408
ROXBORO EXCAVATION, INC.; *Int'l*, pg. 6408
ROXBURY TECHNOLOGY CORP; *U.S. Private*, pg. 3490
ROXBURY TENANTS OF HARVARD; *U.S. Private*, pg. 3490
ROXCAL S.A.R.L.—See Roxcel Handelsges.m.b.H.; *Int'l*, pg. 6408
ROXCEL ARGENTINA—See Roxcel Handelsges.m.b.H.; *Int'l*, pg. 6408
ROXCEL AUSTRALASIA PTY LTD.—See Roxcel Handelsges.m.b.H.; *Int'l*, pg. 6408

ROX RESOURCES LIMITED

ROXCEL CORPORATION—See Roxcel Handelsges.m.b.H.; *Int'l*, pg. 6408
ROXCEL DO BRASIL—See Roxcel Handelsges.m.b.H.; *Int'l*, pg. 6408
ROXCEL HANDELSGES.M.B.H.; *Int'l*, pg. 6408
ROXCEL ISTANBUL - KAGIT PAZARLAMA VE TICARET LIMITED SIRKETI—See Roxcel Handelsges.m.b.H.; *Int'l*, pg. 6408
ROXCEL ITALIA S.R.L.—See Roxcel Handelsges.m.b.H.; *Int'l*, pg. 6408
ROXCEL MOSCOW JOINT STOCK CO.—See Roxcel Handelsges.m.b.H.; *Int'l*, pg. 6408
ROXCEL SOUTH AFRICA (PTY) LTD—See Roxcel Handelsges.m.b.H.; *Int'l*, pg. 6408
ROXCEL THAILAND LTD.—See Roxcel Handelsges.m.b.H.; *Int'l*, pg. 6408
ROXCEL TRADING CHINA LIMITED—See Roxcel Handelsges.m.b.H.; *Int'l*, pg. 6408
ROXCEL TRADING CORPORATION—See Roxcel Handelsges.m.b.H.; *Int'l*, pg. 6408
ROXCOAL, INC.—See Quintana Capital Group, L.P.; *U.S. Private*, pg. 3328
ROX EGYPT—See Mellby Gard Holding AB; *Int'l*, pg. 4811
ROXEL FRANCE—See Airbus SE; *Int'l*, pg. 247
ROXEL FRANCE—See BAE Systems plc; *Int'l*, pg. 798
ROXEL FRANCE—See Leonardo S.p.A.; *Int'l*, pg. 4460
ROXEL FRANCE—See Safran SA; *Int'l*, pg. 6473
ROXEL S.A.S.—See Airbus SE; *Int'l*, pg. 247
ROXEL S.A.S.—See BAE Systems plc; *Int'l*, pg. 798
ROXEL S.A.S.—See Leonardo S.p.A.; *Int'l*, pg. 4460
ROXEL S.A.S.—See Safran SA; *Int'l*, pg. 6473
ROX EQUITY PARTNERS LIMITED; *Int'l*, pg. 6408
ROXGOLD INC.—See Fortuna Mining Corp.; *Int'l*, pg. 2743
ROXGOLD SANGO S.A.—See Fortuna Mining Corp.; *Int'l*, pg. 2743
ROX HAMANN GMBH; *Int'l*, pg. 6408
ROXIO, INC.—See Vector Capital Management, L.P.; *U.S. Private*, pg. 4352
ROXIO UK LTD.—See Vector Capital Management, L.P.; *U.S. Private*, pg. 4352
ROXI PETROLEUM KAZAKHSTAN LLP—See Caspian Sunrise Plc; *Int'l*, pg. 1354
ROX RESOURCES LIMITED; *Int'l*, pg. 6408
ROXSPUR MEASUREMENT & CONTROL LTD.—See TT Electronics plc; *Int'l*, pg. 7959
ROXTEC AB—See Mellby Gard Holding AB; *Int'l*, pg. 4811
ROXTEC AFRICA (PTY) LTD—See Mellby Gard Holding AB; *Int'l*, pg. 4811
ROXTEC AS—See Mellby Gard Holding AB; *Int'l*, pg. 4811
ROXTEC AUSTRALIA PTY LTD—See Mellby Gard Holding AB; *Int'l*, pg. 4811
ROXTEC BVBA/SPRL—See Mellby Gard Holding AB; *Int'l*, pg. 4812
ROXTEC BV—See Mellby Gard Holding AB; *Int'l*, pg. 4811
ROXTEC CZ S.R.O—See Mellby Gard Holding AB; *Int'l*, pg. 4811
ROXTEC DELEGACION NORTE—See Mellby Gard Holding AB; *Int'l*, pg. 4811
ROXTEC DE MEXICO, S.A. DE C.V.—See Mellby Gard Holding AB; *Int'l*, pg. 4812
ROXTEC DENMARK APS—See Mellby Gard Holding AB; *Int'l*, pg. 4811
ROXTEC D.O.O.—See Mellby Gard Holding AB; *Int'l*, pg. 4812
ROXTEC FINLAND OY—See Mellby Gard Holding AB; *Int'l*, pg. 4811
ROXTEC FRANCE SAS—See Mellby Gard Holding AB; *Int'l*, pg. 4811
ROXTEC GMBH—See Mellby Gard Holding AB; *Int'l*, pg. 4811
ROXTEC INC—See Mellby Gard Holding AB; *Int'l*, pg. 4811
ROXTEC INDIA PVT LTD—See Mellby Gard Holding AB; *Int'l*, pg. 4811
ROXTEC ITALIA S.R.L.—See Mellby Gard Holding AB; *Int'l*, pg. 4811
ROXTEC JAPAN K.K.—See Mellby Gard Holding AB; *Int'l*, pg. 4811
ROXTEC LATIN AMERICA LTDA—See Mellby Gard Holding AB; *Int'l*, pg. 4811
ROXTEC LTD—See Mellby Gard Holding AB; *Int'l*, pg. 4811
ROXTEC MIDDLE EAST FZE—See Mellby Gard Holding AB; *Int'l*, pg. 4811
ROXTEC POLAND SP. Z O. O.—See Mellby Gard Holding AB; *Int'l*, pg. 4812
ROXTEC RO S.R.L.—See Mellby Gard Holding AB; *Int'l*, pg. 4812
ROXTEC SEALING SYSTEM(SHANGHAI)CO., LTD.—See Mellby Gard Holding AB; *Int'l*, pg. 4812
ROXTEC SINGAPORE PTE LTD—See Mellby Gard Holding AB; *Int'l*, pg. 4812
ROXTEC SISTEMAS PASAMUROS SL—See Mellby Gard Holding AB; *Int'l*, pg. 4812
ROXTEC YALITIM COZUMLERI SAN. VE TIC. LTD. STI.—See Mellby Gard Holding AB; *Int'l*, pg. 4812
ROXUL INC.—See ROCKWOOL A/S; *Int'l*, pg. 6381
ROXUL ROCKWOOL INSULATION INDIA LTD.—See ROCKWOOL A/S; *Int'l*, pg. 6381

ROX RESOURCES LIMITED

Company Index

ROXUL ROCKWOOL TECHNICAL INSULATION INDIA PVT LTD.—See ROCKWOOL A/S; *Int'l*, pg. 6381
ROXWOOD MEDICAL, INC.—See Boston Scientific Corporation; *U.S. Public*, pg. 374
ROXX INC.—See Vector Inc.; *Int'l*, pg. 8144
ROXY HOMES PTE LTD—See TKL & Family Pte. Ltd.; *Int'l*, pg. 7766
ROXY LAND PTE. LTD.—See TKL & Family Pte. Ltd.; *Int'l*, pg. 7766
ROXY LINK LIMITED—See Oshidori International Holdings Limited; *Int'l*, pg. 5650
ROXY-PACIFIC DEVELOPMENTS PTE LTD—See TKL & Family Pte. Ltd.; *Int'l*, pg. 7766
ROXY-PACIFIC HOLDINGS PTE. LTD.—See TKL & Family Pte. Ltd.; *Int'l*, pg. 7766
ROXY TRADING INC.; *U.S. Private*, pg. 3490
ROYAL ADHESIVES & SEALANTS, LLC—See H.B. Fuller Company; *U.S. Public*, pg. 978
ROYAL ADHESIVES & SEALANTS, LLC - WAYNE—See H.B. Fuller Company; *U.S. Public*, pg. 978
ROYALAIRE MECHANICAL SERVICES, LLC—See Comfort Systems USA, Inc.; *U.S. Public*, pg. 544
ROYAL AIR MAROC SA; *Int'l*, pg. 6409
ROYAL ALBION HOTEL (BROADSTAIRS) LIMITED—See Shepherd Neame Limited; *Int'l*, pg. 6826
ROYAL ALLIANCE ASSOCIATES, INC.—See Reverence Capital Partners LLC; *U.S. Private*, pg. 3415
ROYAL ALMA BOUTIQUE SAS—See Melia Hotels International, S.A.; *Int'l*, pg. 4809
ROYAL AMBULANCE; *U.S. Private*, pg. 3491
ROYAL AMERICAN CONSTRUCTION—See Peoples First Properties Inc.; *U.S. Private*, pg. 3142
ROYAL AMERICAN MANAGEMENT, INC.; *U.S. Private*, pg. 3491
ROYAL APPLIANCE INTERNATIONAL GMBH—See Techtronic Industries Co., Ltd.; *Int'l*, pg. 7513
ROYAL APPLIANCE MFG. CO.—See Techtronic Industries Co., Ltd.; *Int'l*, pg. 7513
ROYAL ARCTIC HAVNESERVICE—See Royal Arctic Line A/S; *Int'l*, pg. 6409
ROYAL ARCTIC LINE A/S; *Int'l*, pg. 6409
ROYAL ARCTIC LOGISTICS A/S—See Royal Arctic Line A/S; *Int'l*, pg. 6409
ROYAL ARCTIC SPEDITION A/S—See Royal Arctic Line A/S; *Int'l*, pg. 6409
ROYAL ATLANTIC ENERGY (CYPRUS) LIMITED—See Zoltav Resources Inc.; *Int'l*, pg. 8688
ROYAL AUPING B.V.; *Int'l*, pg. 6409
ROYAL AUTOMOTIVE COMPANY; *U.S. Private*, pg. 3491
ROYAL AUTOMOTIVE GROUP INC.; *U.S. Private*, pg. 3491
ROYAL AUTOMOTIVE GROUP LTD—See Martinrea International, Inc.; *Int'l*, pg. 4704
ROYAL AUTOMOTIVE; *U.S. Private*, pg. 3491
ROYAL BAFOKENG HOLDINGS (PTY) LIMITED; *Int'l*, pg. 6409
ROYAL BAFOKENG PLATINUM LIMITED—See Impala Platinum Holdings Limited; *Int'l*, pg. 3630
ROYAL BAM GROEP N.V.—See Koninklijke BAM Groep N.V.; *Int'l*, pg. 4261
ROYAL BANCSHARES, INC.; *U.S. Private*, pg. 3491
ROYAL BANCSHARES, INC.; *U.S. Private*, pg. 3491
ROYAL BANK EQUITY FINANCE—See NatWest Group plc; *Int'l*, pg. 5172
ROYAL BANK MORTGAGE CORPORATION—See Royal Bank of Canada; *Int'l*, pg. 6411
ROYAL BANK OF CANADA (ASIA) LIMITED—See Royal Bank of Canada; *Int'l*, pg. 6411
ROYAL BANK OF CANADA EUROPE LTD.—See Royal Bank of Canada; *Int'l*, pg. 6411
ROYAL BANK OF CANADA; *Int'l*, pg. 6409
THE ROYAL BANK OF SCOTLAND ASIA LIMITED—See NatWest Group plc; *Int'l*, pg. 5171
THE ROYAL BANK OF SCOTLAND (CHINA) CO. LIMITED—See NatWest Group plc; *Int'l*, pg. 5171
THE ROYAL BANK OF SCOTLAND - FRANCE—See NatWest Group plc; *Int'l*, pg. 5171
THE ROYAL BANK OF SCOTLAND (GIBRALTAR) LIMITED—See NatWest Group plc; *Int'l*, pg. 5172
THE ROYAL BANK OF SCOTLAND GROUP - INVESTOR RELATIONS—See NatWest Group plc; *Int'l*, pg. 5172
THE ROYAL BANK OF SCOTLAND (GUERNSEY) LIMITED—See NatWest Group plc; *Int'l*, pg. 5172
THE ROYAL BANK OF SCOTLAND INTERNATIONAL (HOLDINGS) LIMITED—See NatWest Group plc; *Int'l*, pg. 5172
THE ROYAL BANK OF SCOTLAND (I.O.M.) LIMITED—See NatWest Group plc; *Int'l*, pg. 5172
THE ROYAL BANK OF SCOTLAND (JERSEY) LTD.—See NatWest Group plc; *Int'l*, pg. 5172
THE ROYAL BANK OF SCOTLAND N.V. - ATHENS—See NatWest Group plc; *Int'l*, pg. 5171
THE ROYAL BANK OF SCOTLAND N.V. - BANGKOK—See NatWest Group plc; *Int'l*, pg. 5171
THE ROYAL BANK OF SCOTLAND N.V. - BRUSSELS—See NatWest Group plc; *Int'l*, pg. 5171
THE ROYAL BANK OF SCOTLAND N.V. - DOHA—See NatWest Group plc; *Int'l*, pg. 5171

THE ROYAL BANK OF SCOTLAND N.V. - ISTANBUL—See NatWest Group plc; *Int'l*, pg. 5171
THE ROYAL BANK OF SCOTLAND N.V. - MADRID—See NatWest Group plc; *Int'l*, pg. 5171
THE ROYAL BANK OF SCOTLAND N.V. - MUMBAI—See NatWest Group plc; *Int'l*, pg. 5171
THE ROYAL BANK OF SCOTLAND N.V. - PRAGUE—See NatWest Group plc; *Int'l*, pg. 5171
THE ROYAL BANK OF SCOTLAND N.V. - ROME—See NatWest Group plc; *Int'l*, pg. 5171
THE ROYAL BANK OF SCOTLAND N.V. - SINGAPORE—See NatWest Group plc; *Int'l*, pg. 5171
THE ROYAL BANK OF SCOTLAND N.V.—See NatWest Group plc; *Int'l*, pg. 5171
THE ROYAL BANK OF SCOTLAND N.V. - SYDNEY—See NatWest Group plc; *Int'l*, pg. 5171
THE ROYAL BANK OF SCOTLAND N.V. - TOKYO—See NatWest Group plc; *Int'l*, pg. 5172
THE ROYAL BANK OF SCOTLAND N.V. - VIENNA—See NatWest Group plc; *Int'l*, pg. 5172
THE ROYAL BANK OF SCOTLAND N.V. - ZURICH—See NatWest Group plc; *Int'l*, pg. 5172
THE ROYAL BANK OF SCOTLAND PLC—See NatWest Group plc; *Int'l*, pg. 5172
THE ROYAL BANK OF SCOTLAND TRUST COMPANY (GUERNSEY) LIMITED—See NatWest Group plc; *Int'l*, pg. 5172
THE ROYAL BANK OF SCOTLAND TRUST COMPANY (JERSEY) LIMITED—See NatWest Group plc; *Int'l*, pg. 5172
ROYAL BANKS OF MISSOURI—See Royal Bancshares, Inc.; *U.S. Private*, pg. 3491
ROYAL BANK—See Royal Bancshares, Inc.; *U.S. Private*, pg. 3491
ROYAL BATHS MANUFACTURING CO. LTD.—See Cotton Creek Capital Management LLC; *U.S. Private*, pg. 1063
ROYAL BEDDING COMPANY INC.; *U.S. Private*, pg. 3491
ROYAL BOSKALIS WESTMINSTER N.V.; *Int'l*, pg. 6411
ROYAL BOSKALIS WESTMINSTER N.V.—See HAL Trust N.V.; *Int'l*, pg. 3224
ROYAL BRASS INC.; *U.S. Private*, pg. 3491
ROYAL BRUNEI AIRLINES SDN. BHD.; *Int'l*, pg. 6411
ROYAL BRUNEI CATERING SDN BHD—See Royal Brunei Airlines Sdn. Bhd.; *Int'l*, pg. 6411
ROYAL BRUNEI TRADING SDN BHD—See Royal Brunei Airlines Sdn. Bhd.; *Int'l*, pg. 6411
ROYAL BUILDING PRODUCTS—See Westlake Corporation; *U.S. Public*, pg. 2360
ROYAL BUILDING PRODUCTS (USA) INC.—See Westlake Corporation; *U.S. Public*, pg. 2360
ROYAL BUSINESS BANK—See RBB Bancorp; *U.S. Public*, pg. 1766
ROYAL BUSINESS FORMS, INC.—See Ennis, Inc.; *U.S. Public*, pg. 769
ROYAL BUSINESS RESTAURANTS GMBH—See Compass Group PLC; *Int'l*, pg. 1752
ROYAL BUYING GROUP, INC.; *U.S. Private*, pg. 3491
ROYAL CANADIAN MINT; *Int'l*, pg. 6411
ROYAL CANIN S.A.—See Mars, Incorporated; *U.S. Private*, pg. 2590
ROYAL CANIN USA INC.—See Mars, Incorporated; *U.S. Private*, pg. 2590
ROYAL CAR CENTER; *U.S. Private*, pg. 3491
ROYAL CARIBBEAN CRUISE LINES AS—See Royal Caribbean Cruises Ltd.; *U.S. Public*, pg. 1815
ROYAL CARIBBEAN CRUISES (ASIA) PTE. LTD.—See Royal Caribbean Cruises Ltd.; *U.S. Public*, pg. 1815
ROYAL CARIBBEAN CRUISES (AUSTRALIA) PTY. LTD—See Royal Caribbean Cruises Ltd.; *U.S. Public*, pg. 1815
ROYAL CARIBBEAN CRUISES LTD.; *U.S. Public*, pg. 1815
ROYAL CASINO DGB GMBH—See Gauselmann AG; *Int'l*, pg. 2890
ROYAL CELEBRITY TOURS INC.—See Royal Caribbean Cruises Ltd.; *U.S. Public*, pg. 1815
ROYAL CENTURY RESOURCES HOLDINGS LIMITED; *Int'l*, pg. 6411
THE ROYAL CERAMIC INDUSTRY PUBLIC COMPANY LIMITED - NONGKHAE MILL—See The Royal Ceramic Industry Public Company Limited; *Int'l*, pg. 7679
THE ROYAL CERAMIC INDUSTRY PUBLIC COMPANY LIMITED; *Int'l*, pg. 7679
ROYAL CERAMICS LANKA PLC; *Int'l*, pg. 6411
ROYAL CHALLENGERS SPORTS PRIVATE LIMITED—See Diageo plc; *Int'l*, pg. 2103
ROYAL CHEMICAL COMPANY—See Paro Services Corp.; *U.S. Private*, pg. 3099
ROYAL CHEMICAL COMPANY—See Paro Services Corp.; *U.S. Private*, pg. 3099
THE ROYAL CHINA & PORCELAIN COMPANIES INC.—See Spode Limited; *Int'l*, pg. 7141
ROYAL CIRCUIT SOLUTIONS, INC.—See Summit Interconnect, Inc.; *U.S. Private*, pg. 3855
ROYAL CLARENCE YARD (MARINA) LIMITED—See The Berkeley Group Holdings plc; *Int'l*, pg. 7620
ROYAL COAL CORP.; *Int'l*, pg. 6411
ROYAL COFFEE INC.; *U.S. Private*, pg. 3491

CORPORATE AFFILIATIONS

ROYAL COMFORT BEDDING PTY LTD—See Steinhoff International Holdings N.V.; *Int'l*, pg. 7194
ROYAL COMMERCIAL REALTY INC—See Royal Seal Construction Inc.; *U.S. Private*, pg. 3493
ROYAL CONSUMER INFORMATION PRODUCTS INC.; *U.S. Private*, pg. 3491
ROYAL CONTINENTAL BOX COMPANY INC.; *U.S. Private*, pg. 3491
ROYAL CONTRACT SERVICE CORPORATION—See Royal Holdings Co., Ltd.; *Int'l*, pg. 6413
ROYAL COPENHAGEN A/S—See Fiskars Oyj Abp; *Int'l*, pg. 2694
ROYAL COPENHAGEN FLAGSHIP STORE—See Fiskars Oyj Abp; *Int'l*, pg. 2694
ROYAL COPENHAGEN KOREA LTD.—See Fiskars Oyj Abp; *Int'l*, pg. 2694
ROYALCO RESOURCES LIMITED—See Fitzroy River Corporation Ltd; *Int'l*, pg. 2695
ROYAL CORINTHIAN HOMES INC.; *U.S. Private*, pg. 3492
ROYAL COSUN U.A.; *Int'l*, pg. 6411
THE ROYAL COUNTRY CLUB AND RECREATION HOLDINGS, INC.; *Int'l*, pg. 7679
ROYAL CREDIT UNION; *U.S. Private*, pg. 3492
ROYAL CRESCENT VALLEY, INC.—See Royal Gold, Inc.; *U.S. Public*, pg. 1815
ROYAL CREST DAIRY INC.; *U.S. Private*, pg. 3492
ROYAL CROWN BOTTLING CO. OF WINCHESTER INC.; *U.S. Private*, pg. 3492
ROYAL CROWN LEASING INC.; *U.S. Private*, pg. 3492
ROYAL CUP INC.; *U.S. Private*, pg. 3492
ROYAL CUSHION VINYL PRODUCTS LIMITED; *Int'l*, pg. 6412
ROYAL DAIRY PRODUCTS LIMITED—See Sumaria Group; *Int'l*, pg. 7259
ROYAL DE BOER STALINRICHTINGEN B.V.—See Turntide Technologies Inc.; *U.S. Private*, pg. 4261
ROYAL DELUXE HOLDINGS LIMITED; *Int'l*, pg. 6412
ROYAL DIE & STAMPING CO., INC.—See Eaton Corporation plc; *Int'l*, pg. 2282
ROYAL DISTRICT NURSING SERVICE NEW ZEALAND LIMITED—See Royal District Nursing Service; *Int'l*, pg. 6412
ROYAL DISTRICT NURSING SERVICE; *Int'l*, pg. 6412
ROYAL DOCUMENT DESTRUCTION; *U.S. Private*, pg. 3492
ROYAL DOORS LIMITED—See Nabtesco Corporation; *Int'l*, pg. 5119
ROYALE COMFORT SEATING INC.; *U.S. Private*, pg. 3494
ROYALE ENERGY, INC.; *U.S. Public*, pg. 1816
ROYALE HOME HOLDINGS LTD.; *Int'l*, pg. 6414
ROYALE HOUSE INC.—See Seater Construction Co. Inc.; *U.S. Private*, pg. 3591
ROYALE INTERNATIONAL COURIERS INC.; *U.S. Private*, pg. 3494
ROYAL ELECTRIC CO., LTD.—See Odawara Engineering Co., Ltd.; *Int'l*, pg. 5524
ROYAL ELECTRIC TRADING (SHENZHEN) CO., LTD.—See Odawara Engineering Co., Ltd.; *Int'l*, pg. 5524
ROYALE MANOR HOTELS AND INDUSTRIES LIMITED; *Int'l*, pg. 6414
ROYAL ENERGY RESOURCES, INC.; *U.S. Public*, pg. 1815
ROYAL ENGINEERING FABRICATION COMPANY LLC—See Al Ghurair Group; *Int'l*, pg. 277
ROYAL ENVELOPE CORP.—See Supremex Inc.; *Int'l*, pg. 7341
ROYAL ENVIRONMENTAL INC.—See Municipal Enterprises Limited; *Int'l*, pg. 5093
ROYAL ESTATES TEA COMPANY—See Unilever PLC; *Int'l*, pg. 8048
ROYAL EUROPA LTD.; *Int'l*, pg. 6412
ROYAL EXCHANGE GENERAL INSURANCE COMPANY LIMITED—See Royal Exchange Plc.; *Int'l*, pg. 6412
ROYAL EXCHANGE PLC.; *Int'l*, pg. 6412
ROYAL FIBERGLASS POOLS, INC.—See Pamplona Capital Management LLP; *Int'l*, pg. 5711
ROYAL FINANCE CORP—See Gentry Finance Corporation; *U.S. Private*, pg. 1680
ROYAL FINANCIAL, INC.; *U.S. Public*, pg. 1815
ROYAL FORK RESTAURANT CORP; *U.S. Private*, pg. 3492
ROYAL FURNITURE COMPANY; *U.S. Private*, pg. 3492
ROYAL GATE INC.—See Daiwa House Industry Co., Ltd.; *Int'l*, pg. 1947
ROYAL GEA GRASSO HOLDING NV-REFRIGERATION DIVISION—See GEA Group Aktiengesellschaft; *Int'l*, pg. 2902
ROYAL GLOBAL EXPRESS INC.—See RPM Consolidated Services, Inc.; *U.S. Private*, pg. 3495
ROYAL GOLD, INC.; *U.S. Public*, pg. 1815
ROYAL GROUP CO., LTD.; *Int'l*, pg. 6412
ROYAL GROUP HOLDINGS INTERNATIONAL COMPANY LIMITED; *Int'l*, pg. 6412
ROYAL GROUP OF COMPANIES LTD.; *Int'l*, pg. 6412
ROYAL HALI IPLIK TEKSTIL MOBILYA SANAYI VE TICARET A.S.; *Int'l*, pg. 6413

COMPANY NAME INDEX

ROYAL HASKONINGDHV (PTY) LTD.—See Koninklijke HaskoningDHV Groep B.V.; *Int'l*, pg. 4266
ROYAL HAWAIIAN HERITAGE JEWELRY LTD.; *U.S. Private*, pg. 3492
ROYAL HAWAIIAN INSURANCE COMPANY LTD—See LVMH Moet Hennessy Louis Vuitton SE; *Int'l*, pg. 4600
ROYAL HAWAIIAN MOVERS, INC.; *U.S. Private*, pg. 3492
ROYAL HAWAIIAN RESOURCES, INC.—See Hawaiian Macadamia Nut Orchards, L.P.; *U.S. Private*, pg. 1882
ROYAL HEALTH CARE OF LONG ISLAND, LLC—See Independent Living Systems, LLC.; *U.S. Private*, pg. 2059
THE ROYAL HEALTH GROUP LLC; *U.S. Private*, pg. 4112
ROYAL HELIUM LTD.; *Int'l*, pg. 6413
ROYAL HILLS CO., LTD.—See Alpen Co., Ltd.; *Int'l*, pg. 366
ROYAL HOLDINGS CO., LTD.; *Int'l*, pg. 6413
ROYAL HOLDINGS, INC.—See Republic Services, Inc.; *U.S. Public*, pg. 1787
ROYAL HOME CENTER CO., LTD.—See Daiwa House Industry Co., Ltd.; *Int'l*, pg. 1947
ROYAL HOSPITALITY CORP.; *U.S. Private*, pg. 3492
THE ROYAL HOTEL LIMITED; *Int'l*, pg. 7679
ROYALHOUSE ISHIOKA CO., LTD.—See Zensho Holdings Co., Ltd.; *Int'l*, pg. 8634
ROYAL HYWAY TOURS, INC.—See Carnival Corporation; *U.S. Public*, pg. 438
ROYAL IMPERIAL GROUP INC.; *U.S. Private*, pg. 3492
ROYAL INDEMNITY CO.—See Arrowpoint Capital Corp.; *U.S. Private*, pg. 336
ROYAL INDIA CORPORATION LTD.; *Int'l*, pg. 6413
ROYAL INDUSTRIES, INC.; *U.S. Private*, pg. 3492
ROYAL INDUSTRIES, INC.; *U.S. Private*, pg. 3492
ROYAL INSURANCE AGENCY INC.—See Mutual Benefit Association Hawaii; *U.S. Private*, pg. 2819
ROYAL INTERNATIONAL CORPORATION; *Int'l*, pg. 6413
ROYAL INTER PACK CO., LTD.; *U.S. Private*, pg. 3492
ROYAL JORDANIAN AIRLINES; *Int'l*, pg. 6413
ROYAL LEPAGE REAL ESTATE SERVICES LTD.—See Brookfield Corporation; *Int'l*, pg. 1186
ROYAL LIVER ASSURANCE LIMITED—See The Royal London Mutual Insurance Society Limited; *Int'l*, pg. 7679
ROYAL LONDON 360—See The Royal London Mutual Insurance Society Limited; *Int'l*, pg. 7679
ROYAL LONDON ASSET MANAGEMENT LIMITED—See Ravenscroft Limited; *Int'l*, pg. 6223
THE ROYAL LONDON MUTUAL INSURANCE SOCIETY LIMITED; *Int'l*, pg. 7679
ROYAL LONDON SAVINGS LIMITED—See The Royal London Mutual Insurance Society Limited; *Int'l*, pg. 7679
ROYAL LONDON UNIT TRUST MANAGERS LIMITED—See The Royal London Mutual Insurance Society Limited; *Int'l*, pg. 7679
ROYAL MAIL INVESTMENTS LTD.—See International Distributions Services plc; *Int'l*, pg. 3748
ROYAL MAIL—See International Distributions Services plc; *Int'l*, pg. 3748
ROYAL MANUFACTURING CO. INC.; *U.S. Private*, pg. 3492
ROYAL MEDIA GROUP, INC.; *U.S. Private*, pg. 3492
ROYAL MEDIC (HOLDINGS) LIMITED—See Shunten International (Holdings) Limited; *Int'l*, pg. 6870
ROYAL MELROSE GRANITES—See Cold Spring Granite Company; *U.S. Private*, pg. 966
ROYAL MERCANTILE TRUST CORP. OF AMERICA; *U.S. Private*, pg. 3492
ROYAL METAL POWDERS INC.—See American Chemet Corporation; *U.S. Private*, pg. 227
ROYAL MINES & MINERALS CORP.; *U.S. Public*, pg. 1816
ROYALMNANDI—See The Bidvest Group Limited; *Int'l*, pg. 7625
ROYAL MONETARY AUTHORITY OF BHUTAN; *Int'l*, pg. 6413
ROYAL MOONLIGHT CORPORATION—See Moonlight Packing Corporation; *U.S. Private*, pg. 2779
ROYAL MOORE AUTO CENTER; *U.S. Private*, pg. 3492
ROYAL MOORE BUICK PONTIAC - GMC TRUCK—See Royal Moore Auto Center; *U.S. Private*, pg. 3492
ROYAL MOTOR SALES OF SAN FRANCISCO; *U.S. Private*, pg. 3492
ROYAL MOTORS OF MIDDLEBURY, INC.—See Heritage Financial Group, Inc.; *U.S. Private*, pg. 1923
ROYAL MOZAMBIQUE LTDA.—See The Bidvest Group Limited; *Int'l*, pg. 7626
ROYAL NATIONAL THEATRE; *Int'l*, pg. 6413
ROYAL NEIGHBORS OF AMERICA; *U.S. Private*, pg. 3493
ROYAL NIRMAN PVT LTD.; *Int'l*, pg. 6413
ROYAL OAK ENTERPRISES, INC.; *U.S. Private*, pg. 3493
ROYAL OAK FORD, INC.; *U.S. Private*, pg. 3493
ROYAL OAK HOMES, LLC—See Brookfield Corporation; *Int'l*, pg. 1183
ROYAL OAK INDUSTRIES INC.; *U.S. Private*, pg. 3493
ROYAL OAKS HOMES—See The Mattamy Corporation; *Int'l*, pg. 7665

ROYAL OAKS NISSAN, INC.; *U.S. Private*, pg. 3493
ROYAL OAK UNDERWRITERS, INC.—See AmWINS Group, Inc.; *U.S. Private*, pg. 270
ROYAL OAK VENTURES INC.—See Brookfield Corporation; *Int'l*, pg. 1189
ROYAL OLYMPIC CRUISE LINES, INC.; *Int'l*, pg. 6413
THE ROYAL OPERA HOUSE COVENT GARDEN LTD; *Int'l*, pg. 7679
ROYAL ORCHID HOTELS LIMITED; *Int'l*, pg. 6413
ROYAL ORCHID HOTEL (THAILAND) PUBLIC COMPANY LIMITED—See Grande Asset Hotels & Property Public Company Limited; *Int'l*, pg. 3057
ROYAL PACKING COMPANY—See Dole plc; *Int'l*, pg. 2157
ROYAL PALM CAPITAL, LLC—See Bimini Capital Management, Inc.; *U.S. Public*, pg. 332
ROYAL PALMS BEACH HOTELS PLC; *Int'l*, pg. 6413
ROYAL PALMS SENIOR RESIDENCE; *U.S. Private*, pg. 3493
ROYAL PAPER BOX OF CALIFORNIA; *U.S. Private*, pg. 3493
ROYAL PAPER CONVERTING INC.; *U.S. Private*, pg. 3493
ROYAL PAPER CORPORATION; *U.S. Private*, pg. 3493
ROYAL PAPERS INC.; *U.S. Private*, pg. 3493
ROYAL PAPER STOCK COMPANY INC.; *U.S. Private*, pg. 3493
ROYAL PARK HOTEL CO., LTD.—See Mitsubishi Estate Co., Ltd.; *Int'l*, pg. 4947
ROYAL PARK HOTEL MANAGEMENT CO., LTD.—See Mitsubishi Estate Co., Ltd.; *Int'l*, pg. 4947
ROYAL PARK HOTELS & RESORTS CO., LTD.—See Mitsubishi Estate Co., Ltd.; *Int'l*, pg. 4947
ROYAL PARK INN NAGOYA CO., LTD.—See Mitsubishi Estate Co., Ltd.; *Int'l*, pg. 4947
ROYAL PARK SHIODOME TOWER CO., LTD.—See Mitsubishi Estate Co., Ltd.; *Int'l*, pg. 4947
ROYAL PEST SOLUTIONS INC.—See Ecolab Inc.; *U.S. Public*, pg. 716
ROYAL PETROLEUM CORPORATION; *U.S. Private*, pg. 3493
ROYAL PET SUPPLIES INC.—See Quarry Capital Management LLC; *U.S. Private*, pg. 3324
ROYAL PLACE OWNER, LLC—See Hilton Worldwide Holdings Inc.; *U.S. Public*, pg. 1041
ROYAL PLUS ELECTRIC, INC.; *U.S. Private*, pg. 3493
ROYAL PLUS INC.; *U.S. Private*, pg. 3493
ROYAL PLUS PUBLIC COMPANY LIMITED; *Int'l*, pg. 6413
ROYAL POLSKA TU NA ZYCIE S.A.—See Vienna Insurance Group AG Wiener Versicherung Gruppe; *Int'l*, pg. 8194
ROYAL PORCELAIN (PVT) LTD—See Royal Ceramics Lanka PLC; *Int'l*, pg. 6411
ROYAL PREMIUM BUDGET, INC.—See H.W. Kaufman Financial Group, Inc.; *U.S. Private*, pg. 1836
ROYAL PRESTIGE OF NEW YORK—See Hy Cite Corporation; *U.S. Private*, pg. 2015
ROYAL PRODUCE SALES INC.—See S&H Packing & Sales Co. Inc.; *U.S. Private*, pg. 3513
ROYAL RAILWAY CO. LTD—See Royal Group of Companies Ltd.; *Int'l*, pg. 6413
ROYAL RAVINTOLAT OY—See NoHo Partners Plc; *Int'l*, pg. 5400
ROYAL REESINK B.V.—See Triton Advisers Limited; *Int'l*, pg. 7935
ROYAL RESOURCES PARTNERS LP; *U.S. Private*, pg. 3493
ROYAL RIDGE FRUIT & COLD STORAGE, LLC—See Arable Capital Partners LLC; *U.S. Private*, pg. 307
ROYAL ROAD MINERALS LIMITED; *Int'l*, pg. 6413
ROYAL ROBBINS, LLC—See Fenix Outdoor International AG; *Int'l*, pg. 2634
ROYAL ROOFING MATERIALS B.V.—See CRH plc; *Int'l*, pg. 1848
ROYAL SAVINGS BANK—See Royal Financial, Inc.; *U.S. Public*, pg. 1815
ROYAL SCANDINAVIA A/S—See Axcel Management A/S; *Int'l*, pg. 762
ROYALS COMMERCIAL SERVICES, INC.—See Installed Building Products, Inc.; *U.S. Public*, pg. 1133
ROYAL SCOTTISH ASSURANCE PLC—See NatWest Group plc; *Int'l*, pg. 5172
ROYAL SEA CLIFF KONA BY OUTRIGGER—See KSL Capital Partners, LLC; *U.S. Private*, pg. 2355
ROYAL SEAL CONSTRUCTION INC.; *U.S. Private*, pg. 3493
ROYAL SEAL INVESTMENTS INC—See Royal Seal Construction Inc.; *U.S. Private*, pg. 3493
ROYALSERVE CLEANING (PROPRIETARY) LIMITED—See The Bidvest Group Limited; *Int'l*, pg. 7625
ROYAL SHAKESPEARE COMPANY OF AMERICA, INC.—See Royal Shakespeare Company; *Int'l*, pg. 6413
ROYAL SHAKESPEARE COMPANY; *Int'l*, pg. 6413
ROYAL SKANDIA LIFE ASSURANCE LTD.—See Livforsakringsaktiebolaget Skandia; *Int'l*, pg. 4531

ROYAL WINE CORP.

ROYAL SOAP AND DETERGENT INDUSTRIES—See Mohammed Enterprises Tanzania Limited; *Int'l*, pg. 5018
ROYAL SONESTA NEW ORLEANS—See The RMR Group Inc.; *U.S. Public*, pg. 2126
ROYAL SPEEDWAY, INC.; *U.S. Private*, pg. 3493
ROYALS PRODUCTIONS, INC.—See Lions Gate Entertainment Corp.; *Int'l*, pg. 4521
ROYAL STANDARD MINERALS INC.; *Int'l*, pg. 6413
ROYAL STATE FINANCIAL CORP.—See MS&AD Insurance Group Holdings, Inc.; *Int'l*, pg. 5065
ROYAL STATE INSURANCE—See Mutual Benefit Association Hawaii; *U.S. Private*, pg. 2819
ROYAL STREET CORPORATION; *U.S. Private*, pg. 3493
ROYAL STREET LAND CO.—See Royal Street Corporation; *U.S. Private*, pg. 3493
ROYAL STREET OF UTAH INC.—See Royal Street Corporation; *U.S. Private*, pg. 3493
ROYAL & SUN ALLIANCE INSURANCE COMPANY OF CANADA—See Intact Financial Corporation; *Int'l*, pg. 3727
ROYAL & SUN ALLIANCE INSURANCE COMPANY OF CANADA—See Tryg A/S; *Int'l*, pg. 7947
ROYAL & SUN ALLIANCE INSURANCE PLC—See Intact Financial Corporation; *Int'l*, pg. 3727
ROYAL & SUN ALLIANCE INSURANCE PLC—See Tryg A/S; *Int'l*, pg. 7947
ROYAL SUNDARAM ALLIANCE INSURANCE COMPANY LIMITED—See Sundaram Finance Ltd; *Int'l*, pg. 7312
ROYAL SUPPLY CO.; *U.S. Private*, pg. 3493
ROYAL SUPPLY CO.; *U.S. Private*, pg. 3493
ROYAL SWAZI DISTILLER (PTY) LTD.—See Royal Swaziland Sugar Corporation Limited; *Int'l*, pg. 6414
ROYAL SWAZILAND SUGAR CORPORATION LIMITED; *Int'l*, pg. 6413
ROYAL TECHNOLOGIES CORPORATION; *U.S. Private*, pg. 3493
ROYALTEK CO., LTD.; *Int'l*, pg. 6414
ROYAL TIRE INC.; *U.S. Private*, pg. 3494
ROYALTON ANTIGUA RESORT & SPA—See Sunwing Travel Group, Inc.; *Int'l*, pg. 7332
ROYALTON BAVARO RESORT & SPA—See Sunwing Travel Group, Inc.; *Int'l*, pg. 7332
ROYALTON BLUE WATERS—See Sunwing Travel Group, Inc.; *Int'l*, pg. 7332
ROYALTON CAYO SANTA MARIA—See Sunwing Travel Group, Inc.; *Int'l*, pg. 7332
ROYALTON GRENADA RESORT & SPA—See Sunwing Travel Group, Inc.; *Int'l*, pg. 7332
ROYALTON HICACOS RESORT & SPA—See Sunwing Travel Group, Inc.; *Int'l*, pg. 7332
ROYALTON, LLC—See MCR Development LLC; *U.S. Private*, pg. 2644
ROYALTON NEGRIL—See Sunwing Travel Group, Inc.; *Int'l*, pg. 7332
ROYALTON PUNTA CANA RESORT & CASINO—See Sunwing Travel Group, Inc.; *Int'l*, pg. 7332
ROYALTON RESORTS & SPA—See Sunwing Travel Group, Inc.; *Int'l*, pg. 7332
ROYALTON RIVIERA CANCUN RESORT & SPA—See Sunwing Travel Group, Inc.; *Int'l*, pg. 7332
ROYALTON SAINT LUCIA RESORT & SPA—See Sunwing Travel Group, Inc.; *Int'l*, pg. 7332
ROYALTON SUITES CANCUN RESORT & SPA—See Sunwing Travel Group, Inc.; *Int'l*, pg. 7332
ROYALTON WHITE SANDS RESORT—See Sunwing Travel Group, Inc.; *Int'l*, pg. 7332
ROYAL TOTO METAL CO., LTD.—See Toto Ltd.; *Int'l*, pg. 7845
ROYAL TOURIST CO., LTD.—See Panasonic Holdings Corporation; *Int'l*, pg. 5723
ROYAL TRACTOR CO., INC.—See Greenbriar Equity Group, L.P.; *U.S. Private*, pg. 1776
ROYAL TRUCK & EQUIPMENT, LLC—See Alamo Group Inc.; *U.S. Public*, pg. 71
ROYAL TRUCKING COMPANY; *U.S. Private*, pg. 3494
ROYALTY CARPET MILLS INC.; *U.S. Private*, pg. 3494
ROYALTY FLOW INC.; *U.S. Private*, pg. 3494
ROYALTY MANAGEMENT HOLDING CORPORATION—See American Acquisition Opportunity, Inc.; *U.S. Public*, pg. 95
ROYALTY PHARMA PLC; *U.S. Public*, pg. 1816
ROYAL UNIBREW A/S; *Int'l*, pg. 6414
ROYAL UNIBREW CARIBBEAN INC.—See Royal Unibrew A/S; *Int'l*, pg. 6414
ROYAL UNIBREW EESTI OU—See Royal Unibrew A/S; *Int'l*, pg. 6414
ROYAL UNITED CORPORATION; *U.S. Private*, pg. 3494
ROYAL UNITED MINT BV—See Groep Heylen Business & Building BV; *Int'l*, pg. 3087
ROYAL UTILITIES PARTNERSHIP—See Sherritt International Corporation; *Int'l*, pg. 6826
ROYAL VACACIONES SA—See TUI AG; *Int'l*, pg. 7966
ROYAL VAN LENT SHIPYARD BV—See LVMH Moet Hennessy Louis Vuitton SE; *Int'l*, pg. 4602
ROYAL VENDORS, INC.; *U.S. Private*, pg. 3494
ROYAL WINDOW FILMS, INC.—See Solar Art Window Film, Inc.; *U.S. Public*, pg. 3707
ROYAL WINDOWS INC.; *U.S. Private*, pg. 3494
ROYAL WINE CORP.; *U.S. Private*, pg. 3494

ROYAL WINE CORP.

ROYAL WOLF HOLDINGS LIMITED—See United Rentals, Inc.; *U.S. Public*, pg. 2235
ROYAL WOLF TRADING AUSTRALIA PTY LIMITED—See United Rentals, Inc.; *U.S. Public*, pg. 2235
ROYAL WOLF TRADING NEW ZEALAND LIMITED—See United Rentals, Inc.; *U.S. Public*, pg. 2235
ROYAL WOODWORKING CO. LIMITED—See Specialty Building Products, LLC; *U.S. Private*, pg. 3749
ROYAL ZOUTE GOLF CLUB SA—See Compagnie Het Zoute NV; *Int'l*, pg. 1745
ROY ANDERSON CORP - RIDGELAND—See Tutor Perini Corporation; *U.S. Public*, pg. 2206
ROY ANDERSON CORP—See Tutor Perini Corporation; *U.S. Public*, pg. 2206
ROY ASSET HOLDING SE; *Int'l*, pg. 6408
ROYBALT INGREDIENTS S.A. DE C.V—See BayWa AG; *Int'l*, pg. 919
ROYCE APPAREL INC.; *U.S. Private*, pg. 3494
ROYCE & ASSOCIATES, LLC—See Franklin Resources, Inc.; *U.S. Public*, pg. 882
ROYCE & ASSOCIATES, LP—See Franklin Resources, Inc.; *U.S. Public*, pg. 882
ROYCE ASSOCIATES; *U.S. Private*, pg. 3494
ROYCE GLOBAL VALUE TRUST, INC.; *U.S. Public*, pg. 1816
ROYCE GROFF OIL COMPANY; *U.S. Private*, pg. 3494
ROYCE HILL REAL ESTATE; *U.S. Private*, pg. 3494
ROYCE IMAGING INDUSTRIES (PTY) LIMITED; *Int'l*, pg. 6414
ROYCE INSTRUMENTS, INC.—See V-Tek Incorporated; *U.S. Private*, pg. 4328
ROYCE MICRO-CAP TRUST, INC.; *U.S. Public*, pg. 1816
ROYCE TECHNOLOGIES—See Xylem Inc.; *U.S. Public*, pg. 2395
ROYCO INTERNATIONAL INC.; *U.S. Private*, pg. 3494
ROY D. GOODNER INC.; *U.S. Private*, pg. 3490
ROY E. HANSON JR. MANUFACTURING; *U.S. Private*, pg. 3490
ROY E. LADD INC.; *U.S. Private*, pg. 3490
ROYER & SCHUTTS INC.; *U.S. Private*, pg. 3494
ROY ET TREMBLAY INC.—See Avison Young (Canada) Inc.; *Int'l*, pg. 745
ROY FOSS MOTORS LTD.; *Int'l*, pg. 6409
ROY HANKINSON (HOLDINGS) LIMITED; *Int'l*, pg. 6409
ROY JORGENSEN ASSOCIATES, INC.; *U.S. Private*, pg. 3490
ROY LARSON CONSTRUCTION—See Petrowest Corp.; *Int'l*, pg. 5833
ROYLE CORPORATE PRINT LTD.—See Chevrillon Philippe Industrie; *Int'l*, pg. 1474
ROYLE EXTRUSION SYSTEMS PVT. LTD.—See Royle Systems Group; *U.S. Private*, pg. 3494
ROYLE FINANCIAL PRINT LTD—See Chevrillon Philippe Industrie; *Int'l*, pg. 1474
ROYLE PRINTING; *U.S. Private*, pg. 3494
ROYLE SYSTEMS GROUP; *U.S. Private*, pg. 3494
ROYMAR SHIP MANAGEMENT INC.—See TBS INTERNATIONAL PLC; *Int'l*, pg. 7481
ROY METAL FINISHING CO, INC.—See Aalberts N.V.; *Int'l*, pg. 35
ROY MILLER FREIGHT LINES LLC; *U.S. Private*, pg. 3490
ROYNAT CAPITAL INC.—See The Bank of Nova Scotia; *Int'l*, pg. 7617
ROYNAT INC.—See The Bank of Nova Scotia; *Int'l*, pg. 7617
ROYNE CO., LTD.—See ITOCHU Corporation; *Int'l*, pg. 3841
ROY NICHOLS MOTORS LTD.; *Int'l*, pg. 6409
ROY O'BRIEN INC.; *U.S. Private*, pg. 3491
ROY O. ELDER LUMBER COMPANY INC.; *U.S. Private*, pg. 3491
ROY O. MARTIN LUMBER COMPANY, LLC; *U.S. Private*, pg. 3491
ROY ROBINSON, INC.—See Camping World Holdings, Inc.; *U.S. Public*, pg. 428
ROYS & ASSOCIATES; *U.S. Private*, pg. 3494
ROYSCOT TRUST PLC—See NatWest Group plc; *Int'l*, pg. 5172
ROY'S GRAND DODGE, CHRYSLER, JEEP ON LOCUST, L.L.C.; *U.S. Private*, pg. 3491
ROY SMITH COMPANY; *U.S. Private*, pg. 3491
ROY'S OF BALTIMORE, LLC—See United Ohana, LLC; *U.S. Private*, pg. 4295
ROY STROM FAMILY OF COMPANIES—See Macquarie Group Limited; *Int'l*, pg. 4628
ROYTEX, INC.; *U.S. Private*, pg. 3494
ROYWELL SERVICES, INC.; *U.S. Private*, pg. 3494
ROZACHIM AD; *Int'l*, pg. 6414
ROZALADO & CO.; *U.S. Private*, pg. 3494
ROZALMA AGRISOLUTIONS, S.L.U.—See Ingersoll Tillage Group, Inc.; *Int'l*, pg. 3702
THE ROZIER MERCANTILE COMPANY; *U.S. Private*, pg. 4113
ROZINN ELECTRONICS, INC.—See Berkshire Hathaway Inc.; *U.S. Public*, pg. 300
ROZINVEST LLC—See Onexim Group Limited; *Int'l*, pg. 5581

RO ZKTI—See PJSC EnergoMashinostroitelny Alliance; *Int'l*, pg. 5878
ROZ MARKETING GROUP A CALIFORNIA CORPORATION; *U.S. Private*, pg. 3494
RPA CO-OP; *U.S. Private*, pg. 3495
R P ADAM LIMITED—See Ecolab Inc.; *U.S. Public*, pg. 716
R.P. ADAMS COMPANY, INC.—See SERFILCO, Ltd.; *U.S. Private*, pg. 3613
RPA ENGINEERING INC.—See OPEN Group, Inc.; *Int'l*, pg. 5596
RPAI CHICAGO BRICKYARD, L.L.C.—See Kite Realty Group Trust; *U.S. Public*, pg. 1237
RPAI PACIFIC PROPERTY SERVICES LLC—See Kite Realty Group Trust; *U.S. Public*, pg. 1237
RPAI SOUTHWEST MANAGEMENT LLC—See Kite Realty Group Trust; *U.S. Public*, pg. 1237
RPAI US MANAGEMENT LLC—See Kite Realty Group Trust; *U.S. Public*, pg. 1237
RPAI WILLISTON MAPLE TREE, L.L.C.—See Kite Realty Group Trust; *U.S. Public*, pg. 1237
RP BIO INC.; *Int'l*, pg. 6414
RPCA—See WPP plc; *Int'l*, pg. 8479
RPC ASTRAPAK PROPRIETARY LIMITED—See Berry Global Group, Inc; *U.S. Public*, pg. 322
RPC ASTRAPAK—See Berry Global Group, Inc; *U.S. Public*, pg. 323
RPC BEAUTE MAROLLES SAS—See Berry Global Group, Inc; *U.S. Public*, pg. 324
RPC BEBO FOOD PACKAGING GMBH—See Berry Global Group, Inc; *U.S. Public*, pg. 324
RPC BEBO FOOD PACKAGING - KRISTIANSAND—See Berry Global Group, Inc; *U.S. Public*, pg. 324
RPC BEBO NEDERLAND BV—See Berry Global Group, Inc; *U.S. Public*, pg. 324
RPC BEBO PLASTIK GMBH—See Berry Global Group, Inc; *U.S. Public*, pg. 324
RPC BEBO POLSKA SP. Z.O.O.—See Berry Global Group, Inc; *U.S. Public*, pg. 324
RPC BEBO PRINT PATENT GMBH—See Berry Global Group, Inc; *U.S. Public*, pg. 324
RPC BPI AGRICULTURE—See Berry Global Group, Inc; *U.S. Public*, pg. 322
RPC BRAMLAGE ANTWERPEN NV—See Berry Global Group, Inc; *U.S. Public*, pg. 324
RPC BRAMLAGE DIVISION GMBH & CO., KG—See Berry Global Group, Inc; *U.S. Public*, pg. 322
RPC BRAMLAGE FOOD GMBH—See Berry Global Group, Inc; *U.S. Public*, pg. 324
RPC BRAMLAGE GMBH—See Berry Global Group, Inc; *U.S. Public*, pg. 324
RPC BRAMLAGE - LAINATE—See Berry Global Group, Inc; *U.S. Public*, pg. 324
RPC BRAMLAGE VELKY MEDER S.R.O.—See Berry Global Group, Inc; *U.S. Public*, pg. 324
RPC BRAMLAGE WARSZAWA SP. Z.O.O.—See Berry Global Group, Inc; *U.S. Public*, pg. 324
RPC CONSTRUCTION (PVT) LTD.—See Richard Pieris & Co. Ltd.; *Int'l*, pg. 6330
RPC CONTAINERS LTD.—See Berry Global Group, Inc; *U.S. Public*, pg. 324
RPC DATA LIMITED; *Int'l*, pg. 6414
RPC DATA (ZAMBIA)—See RPC Data Limited; *Int'l*, pg. 6414
RPC EMBALLAGES MONTPONT SA—See Berry Global Group, Inc; *U.S. Public*, pg. 324
RPC ENERGY SERVICES OF CANADA, LTD—See RPC, Inc.; *U.S. Public*, pg. 1816
RPC ENVASES SA—See Berry Global Group, Inc; *U.S. Public*, pg. 324
RPC FORMATEC GMBH—See Berry Global Group, Inc; *U.S. Public*, pg. 324
RPCG PUBLIC COMPANY LIMITED; *Int'l*, pg. 6414
RPC GROUP PLC—See Berry Global Group, Inc; *U.S. Public*, pg. 322
RPC, INC.; *U.S. Public*, pg. 1816
RPC KOLDING A/S—See Berry Global Group, Inc; *U.S. Public*, pg. 325
RPC NEUTRAUBLING GMBH—See Berry Global Group, Inc; *U.S. Public*, pg. 324
RP CONSTRUCTION SERVICES, LLC—See Quanta Services, Inc.; *U.S. Public*, pg. 1752
RPC PACKAGING GENT NV—See Berry Global Group, Inc; *U.S. Public*, pg. 324
RPC PACKAGING HOLDINGS BV—See Berry Global Group, Inc; *U.S. Public*, pg. 324
RPC PACKAGING KERKRADE BV—See Berry Global Group, Inc; *U.S. Public*, pg. 324
RPC PHOTONICS, INC.—See Viavi Solutions Inc.; *U.S. Public*, pg. 2295
RPC PROMENS A/S—See Berry Global Group, Inc; *U.S. Public*, pg. 325
RPC PROMENS BJAEVERSKOV A/S—See Berry Global Group, Inc; *U.S. Public*, pg. 325
RPC PROMENS EKE NV—See Berry Global Group, Inc; *U.S. Public*, pg. 325
RPC PROMENS GROUP AS—See Berry Global Group, Inc; *U.S. Public*, pg. 325

CORPORATE AFFILIATIONS

RPC PROMENS INDUSTRIAL JAGTENBERG B.V—See Berry Global Group, Inc; *U.S. Public*, pg. 325
RPC SUPERFOS A/S—See Berry Global Group, Inc; *U.S. Public*, pg. 325
RPC SUPERFOS BALKAN D.O.O.—See Berry Global Group, Inc; *U.S. Public*, pg. 325
RPC SUPERFOS BESANCON SAS—See Berry Global Group, Inc; *U.S. Public*, pg. 325
RPC SUPERFOS - HAMBURG—See Berry Global Group, Inc; *U.S. Public*, pg. 325
RPC SUPERFOS ITALY S.R.L.—See Berry Global Group, Inc; *U.S. Public*, pg. 325
RPC SUPERFOS LA GENETE SAS—See Berry Global Group, Inc; *U.S. Public*, pg. 325
RPC SUPERFOS LIDKOPING AB—See Berry Global Group, Inc; *U.S. Public*, pg. 325
RPC SUPERFOS MULLSJO AB—See Berry Global Group, Inc; *U.S. Public*, pg. 325
RPC SUPERFOS PAMPLONA SA—See Berry Global Group, Inc; *U.S. Public*, pg. 325
RPC SUPERFOS POLAND SP. Z O.O.—See Berry Global Group, Inc; *U.S. Public*, pg. 325
RPC SUPERFOS PORI OY—See Berry Global Group, Inc; *U.S. Public*, pg. 325
RPC SUPERFOS STILLING A/S—See Berry Global Group, Inc; *U.S. Public*, pg. 325
RPC SUPERFOS US INC.—See Berry Global Group, Inc; *U.S. Public*, pg. 325
RPC SUPERFOS WETTEREN NV—See Berry Global Group, Inc; *U.S. Public*, pg. 325
RPC TEDECO-GIZEH GMBH—See Berry Global Group, Inc; *U.S. Public*, pg. 325
RPC TEDECO-GIZEH KFT—See Berry Global Group, Inc; *U.S. Public*, pg. 325
RPC TEDECO-GIZEH SAS—See Berry Global Group, Inc; *U.S. Public*, pg. 325
RPC TEDECO-GIZEH TROYES SASU—See Berry Global Group, Inc; *U.S. Public*, pg. 325
RPC TEDECO-GIZEH (UK) LIMITED—See Berry Global Group, Inc; *U.S. Public*, pg. 325
RPC VERPACKUNGEN KUTENHOLZ GMBH—See Berry Global Group, Inc; *U.S. Public*, pg. 325
RPC WIKO GMBH—See Berry Global Group, Inc; *U.S. Public*, pg. 324
RPC ZELLER PLASTIK LIBERTYVILLE INC.—See Berry Global Group, Inc; *U.S. Public*, pg. 325
RPDA; *Int'l*, pg. 6415
RP DATA LIMITED—See Insight Venture Management, LLC; *U.S. Private*, pg. 2089
RP DATA LIMITED—See Stone Point Capital LLC; *U.S. Private*, pg. 3823
RP DATA NEW ZEALAND LIMITED—See Insight Venture Management, LLC; *U.S. Private*, pg. 2089
RP DATA NEW ZEALAND LIMITED—See Stone Point Capital LLC; *U.S. Private*, pg. 3823
RP DATA VALUATION SERVICES PTY LTD—See Insight Venture Management, LLC; *U.S. Private*, pg. 2089
RP DATA VALUATION SERVICES PTY LTD—See Stone Point Capital LLC; *U.S. Private*, pg. 3823
RP FRUKT AB—See Martin Olsson Handels AB; *Int'l*, pg. 4704
RP FUNDING, INC.; *U.S. Private*, pg. 3494
RPG GROUP; *Int'l*, pg. 6415
RPG LIFE SCIENCES LIMITED—See RPG Group; *Int'l*, pg. 6415
R-PHARM CJSC; *Int'l*, pg. 6169
R-PHARM GERMANY GMBH—See R-Pharm CJSC; *Int'l*, pg. 6169
R-PHARM-US LLC—See R-Pharm CJSC; *Int'l*, pg. 6169
RPH FINANCIAL SERVICES INC.—See The Mather Group, LLC; *U.S. Private*, pg. 4075
RPH PHARMACEUTICALS AB—See Recipharm AB; *Int'l*, pg. 6236
RPI COMPONENTEN BV—See VDL Groep B.V.; *Int'l*, pg. 8140
RP INDUSTRIES INC.; *U.S. Private*, pg. 3495
RPI OF INDIANA INC.—See JMAC Inc.; *U.S. Private*, pg. 2214
R. PIPER & CO VERLAG GMBH—See Bonnier AB; *Int'l*, pg. 1108
RPI PROFESSIONAL ALTERNATIVES—See Response Personnel, Inc.; *U.S. Private*, pg. 3408
R.P. KINCHELOE COMPANY INC.; *U.S. Private*, pg. 3339
RP LUMBER CO, INC.; *U.S. Private*, pg. 3495
RPM ADVERTISING; *U.S. Private*, pg. 3495
RP MANAGEMENT, INC.; *U.S. Private*, pg. 3495
RP MANAGEMENT, LLC; *U.S. Private*, pg. 3495
RP MARTIN (AUSTRIA) AG—See R P Martin Holdings Limited; *Int'l*, pg. 6167
R P MARTIN HOLDINGS LIMITED; *Int'l*, pg. 6167
RP MARTIN HOLDINGS LIMITED; *Int'l*, pg. 6414
R P MARTIN LLC—See R P Martin Holdings Limited; *Int'l*, pg. 6167
RP MARTIN STOCKHOLM AB—See RP Martin Holdings Limited; *Int'l*, pg. 6414
RPM AUTOMOTIVE GROUP LIMITED; *Int'l*, pg. 6415
RPM/BELGIUM N.V.—See RPM International Inc.; *U.S. Public*, pg. 1819

COMPANY NAME INDEX

RPM CANADA—See RPM International Inc.; *U.S. Public*, pg. 1818
RPMC EUROPE LTD.—See RPMC, Inc.; *U.S. Private*, pg. 3496
RPMC, INC.; *U.S. Private*, pg. 3495
RPMC - NEW YORK—See RPMC, Inc.; *U.S. Private*, pg. 3496
RPM CO., LTD.—See Bain Capital, LP; *U.S. Private*, pg. 435
RPM CONNECT—See Ryan Partnership, LLC; *U.S. Private*, pg. 3510
RPM CONSOLIDATED SERVICES, INC.; *U.S. Private*, pg. 3495
RPM CONSUMER HOLDING COMPANY—See RPM International Inc.; *U.S. Public*, pg. 1817
RPM/DETROIT—See RPM Advertising; *U.S. Private*, pg. 3495
RPM DEVELOPMENT GROUP; *U.S. Private*, pg. 3495
RPM EQUIPMENT CO.; *U.S. Private*, pg. 3495
RPMGLOBAL AFRICA (PTY) LTD—See RPMGlobal Holdings Ltd.; *Int'l*, pg. 6415
RPMGLOBAL ASIA LIMITED—See RPMGlobal Holdings Ltd.; *Int'l*, pg. 6415
RPM GLOBAL CANADA LTD.—See RPMGlobal Holdings Ltd.; *Int'l*, pg. 6415
RPMGLOBAL CHILE LIMITADA—See RPMGlobal Holdings Ltd.; *Int'l*, pg. 6415
RPMGLOBAL CHINA LIMITED—See RPMGlobal Holdings Ltd.; *Int'l*, pg. 6415
RPMGLOBAL HOLDINGS LTD.; *Int'l*, pg. 6415
RPMGLOBAL KAZAKHSTAN LLP—See RPMGlobal Holdings Ltd.; *Int'l*, pg. 6415
RPMGLOBAL LLC—See RPMGlobal Holdings Ltd.; *Int'l*, pg. 6415
RPM GLOBAL TURKEY DANISMANLIK HIZMETLERI VE TICARET A.S.—See RPMGlobal Holdings Ltd.; *Int'l*, pg. 6415
RPM GLOBAL USA, INC.—See RPMGlobal Holdings Ltd.; *Int'l*, pg. 6415
RPM HARBOR SERVICES, INC.—See RPM Consolidated Services, Inc.; *U.S. Private*, pg. 3495
RPM, INC.—See RPM International Inc.; *U.S. Public*, pg. 1819
RPM INDUSTRIAL HOLDING CO.—See RPM International Inc.; *U.S. Public*, pg. 1817
RPM INTERNATIONAL INC.; *U.S. Public*, pg. 1816
RPM/LAS VEGAS—See RPM Advertising; *U.S. Private*, pg. 3495
RPM LUX ENTERPRISES S.AR.L.—See RPM International Inc.; *U.S. Public*, pg. 1818
RPM MACHINERY LLC; *U.S. Private*, pg. 3495
RPM MANAGEMENT INC.; *U.S. Private*, pg. 3495
RPM MORTGAGE, INC.; *U.S. Private*, pg. 3495
RPM PERFORMANCE COATINGS GROUP, INC.—See RPM International Inc.; *U.S. Public*, pg. 1818
RPM PIZZA INC.; *U.S. Private*, pg. 3495
RPM POJIST'OVACI MAKLERSTVI SPOL. S.R.O.—See Raiffeisenlandesbank Oberosterreich Aktiengesellschaft; *Int'l*, pg. 6187
RPM RADAR REKLAM PAZARLAMA MUSAVIRLIK A.S.—See Dentsu Group Inc.; *Int'l*, pg. 2037
RPM-RIGHT PLACE MEDIA; *U.S. Private*, pg. 3495
RPM STEEL INC.; *U.S. Private*, pg. 3495
R.P.M. TECH INC.—See Alamo Group Inc.; *U.S. Public*, pg. 71
RPM TRANSPORTATION INC.—See RPM Consolidated Services, Inc.; *U.S. Private*, pg. 3495
RPM WOOD FINISHES GROUP, INC.—See RPM International Inc.; *U.S. Public*, pg. 1819
RPP INFRA PROJECTS LTD; *Int'l*, pg. 6415
RPP, LLC—See Emerson Electric Co.; *U.S. Public*, pg. 751
RP PROPERTIES PTE. LTD.—See TKL & Family Pte. Ltd.; *Int'l*, pg. 7766
RPQ ASPHALT PTY. LTD.—See Downer EDI Limited; *Int'l*, pg. 2186
RPQ MACKAY PTY. LTD.—See Downer EDI Limited; *Int'l*, pg. 2186
RPQ NORTH COAST PTY. LTD.—See Downer EDI Limited; *Int'l*, pg. 2186
RPQ PTY. LTD.—See Downer EDI Limited; *Int'l*, pg. 2186
RPS ADVIES BV—See RPS Group plc; *Int'l*, pg. 6415
RPS ANALYSE BV—See RPS Group plc; *Int'l*, pg. 6415
RPS ASKLEP INC.—See Nippon Telegraph & Telephone Corporation; *Int'l*, pg. 5350
RPS AUSTRALIA EAST PTY LTD—See RPS Group plc; *Int'l*, pg. 6415
RPS BEIJING, INC—See ICON plc; *Int'l*, pg. 3585
RPS CHILE LTDA.—See ICON plc; *Int'l*, pg. 3585
RPS COLOMBIA LTDA.—See ICON plc; *Int'l*, pg. 3585
RPS COMPOSITES, INC.; *U.S. Private*, pg. 3496
RPS COMPOSITES ONTARIO INC.—See RPS Composites, Inc.; *U.S. Private*, pg. 3496
RPS CONSULTANTS NZ LIMITED—See RPS Group plc; *Int'l*, pg. 6415
RPS CONSULTANTS PTY LIMITED—See RPS Group plc; *Int'l*, pg. 6416
RPS CONSULTING ENGINEERS LIMITED—See RPS Group plc; *Int'l*, pg. 6416

RPS DO BRASIL SERVICOS DE PESQUISA LTDA.—See ICON plc; *Int'l*, pg. 3585
RPS ENERGY CANADA LIMITED—See RPS Group plc; *Int'l*, pg. 6416
RPS ENERGY LIMITED—See RPS Group plc; *Int'l*, pg. 6416
RPS ENERGY PTY LIMITED—See RPS Group plc; *Int'l*, pg. 6416
RPS ENGINEERING SERVICES LIMITED—See RPS Group plc; *Int'l*, pg. 6416
RPS ENVIRONMENT SUBIACO—See RPS Group plc; *Int'l*, pg. 6416
RPS ESPEY—See RPS Group plc; *Int'l*, pg. 6416
RPS EVANS-HAMILTON, INC.—See RPS Group plc; *Int'l*, pg. 6416
RPS EVANS-HAMILTON, INC.—See RPS Group plc; *Int'l*, pg. 6416
RPS EXCEL—See Arthur J. Gallagher & Co.; *U.S. Public*, pg. 207
RPS GROEP BV—See RPS Group plc; *Int'l*, pg. 6416
RPS GROUP LIMITED—See RPS Group plc; *Int'l*, pg. 6416
RPS GROUP PLC—See RPS Group plc; *Int'l*, pg. 6416
RPS GROUP PLC; *Int'l*, pg. 6415
RPSG VENTURES LIMITED; *Int'l*, pg. 6416
RPS HEALTH IN BUSINESS LIMITED—See RPS Group plc; *Int'l*, pg. 6416
RPS JD CONSULTING INC—See RPS Group plc; *Int'l*, pg. 6416
RPS KNOWLEDGE RESERVOIR, LP—See RPS Group plc; *Int'l*, pg. 6416
RPS KRAAN CONSULTING BV—See RPS Group plc; *Int'l*, pg. 6416
RPS LATVIA SIA—See ICON plc; *Int'l*, pg. 3586
RPS PRODUCTS, INC.; *U.S. Private*, pg. 3496
RPS RESEARCH FRANCE, S.A.S.—See ICON plc; *Int'l*, pg. 3585
RPS RESEARCH IBERICA, S.L.U.—See ICON plc; *Int'l*, pg. 3585
RPS RESEARCH S.A.—See ICON plc; *Int'l*, pg. 3585
RPS RESEARCH SERVICIOS, S. DE RL DE CV—See ICON plc; *Int'l*, pg. 3585
RPS RESEARCH (THAILAND) CO., LTD.—See ICON plc; *Int'l*, pg. 3586
RPS SPAIN S.L—See ICON plc; *Int'l*, pg. 3586
RPS WATER SERVICES LIMITED—See RPS Group plc; *Int'l*, pg. 6416
RPT BYGGFAKTA OY—See Byggfakta Group Nordic HoldCo AB; *Int'l*, pg. 1235
RPT REALTY—See Kimco Realty Corporation; *U.S. Public*, pg. 1232
R.P. WEDDELL & SONS CO.; *U.S. Private*, pg. 3339
R.P. WILLIAMS & SONS, INC.; *U.S. Private*, pg. 3339
RPX ASIA CORPORATION—See HGGC, LLC; *U.S. Private*, pg. 1930
RPX CORPORATION—See HGGC, LLC; *U.S. Private*, pg. 1930
RPX FREEDOM CORPORATION—See HGGC, LLC; *U.S. Private*, pg. 1930
RQAW CORP.—See White Wolf Capital LLC; *U.S. Private*, pg. 4510
R&Q CAPTIVE MANAGEMENT LLC—See R&Q Insurance Holdings Ltd.; *Int'l*, pg. 6168
R&Q CENTRAL SERVICES LIMITED—See R&Q Insurance Holdings Ltd.; *Int'l*, pg. 6168
R&Q INSURANCE HOLDINGS LTD.; *Int'l*, pg. 6168
R&Q INSURANCE MANAGEMENT (GIBRALTAR) LIMITED—See R&Q Insurance Holdings Ltd.; *Int'l*, pg. 6168
R&Q MGA LIMITED—See R&Q Insurance Holdings Ltd.; *Int'l*, pg. 6168
R&Q QUEST MANAGEMENT SERVICES LIMITED—See R&Q Insurance Holdings Ltd.; *Int'l*, pg. 6168
R&Q SOLUTIONS LLC—See R&Q Insurance Holdings Ltd.; *Int'l*, pg. 6168
R-RANCH MARKET INC.; *U.S. Private*, pg. 3333
RR APPLIANCE SERVICES, INC.; *U.S. Private*, pg. 3496
R&R ASSOCIATES LLC - CANADA—See R&R Associates LLC; *U.S. Private*, pg. 3332
R&R ASSOCIATES LLC - HEAVY PRODUCTION DIVISION—See R&R Associates LLC; *U.S. Private*, pg. 3332
R&R ASSOCIATES LLC - QUALITY ASSURANCE DIVISION—See R&R Associates LLC; *U.S. Private*, pg. 3332
R&R ASSOCIATES LLC; *U.S. Private*, pg. 3332
R & R AUTO GROUP; *U.S. Private*, pg. 3331
RRB BERATUNGSGESELLSCHAFT FUR ALTERSVERSORGUNG MBH—See Marsh & McLennan Companies, Inc.; *U.S. Public*, pg. 1388
R.R. BOWKER LLC—See Cambridge Information Group, Inc.; *U.S. Private*, pg. 727
R&R CABLE COMPANY INC.; *U.S. Private*, pg. 3333
RR CANADA INC.—See Fenix Outdoor International AG; *Int'l*, pg. 2634
R & R CO., LTD.—See Nishio Holdings Co., Ltd.; *Int'l*, pg. 5365
R.R. DAWSON BRIDGE COMPANY LLC; *U.S. Private*, pg. 3339

RRD DUTCH HOLDCO, INC.—See Chatham Asset Management, LLC; *U.S. Private*, pg. 865
RRD HOLDING COMPANY—See Waste Connections, Inc.; *Int'l*, pg. 8354
R & R DIRECT MAIL, INC.; *U.S. Private*, pg. 3331
RR DONNELLEY ASIA PRINTING SOLUTIONS LIMITED—See Chatham Asset Management, LLC; *U.S. Private*, pg. 865
R. R. DONNELLEY-ATLANTA WEST PLANT—See Chatham Asset Management, LLC; *U.S. Private*, pg. 864
RR DONNELLEY (AUSTRALIA) PTY LIMITED—See Chatham Asset Management, LLC; *U.S. Private*, pg. 865
RR DONNELLEY (CHENGDU) PRINTING CO., LTD.—See Chatham Asset Management, LLC; *U.S. Private*, pg. 865
RR DONNELLEY (CHINA) HOLDING CO., LTD.—See Chatham Asset Management, LLC; *U.S. Private*, pg. 865
R.R. DONNELLEY COMMERCIAL PRESS—See Chatham Asset Management, LLC; *U.S. Private*, pg. 865
R.R. DONNELLEY DE COSTA RICA S.A.—See Chatham Asset Management, LLC; *U.S. Private*, pg. 865
R. R. DONNELLEY DE EL SALVADOR, S.A. DE C.V.—See Chatham Asset Management, LLC; *U.S. Private*, pg. 864
R. R. DONNELLEY DE GUATEMALA, S.A.—See Chatham Asset Management, LLC; *U.S. Private*, pg. 864
R. R. DONNELLEY DEUTSCHLAND GMBH—See Chatham Asset Management, LLC; *U.S. Private*, pg. 864
R. R. DONNELLEY DOCUMENT SOLUTIONS (SWITZERLAND) GMBH—See Chatham Asset Management, LLC; *U.S. Private*, pg. 864
RR DONNELLEY EDITORA E GRAFICA LTDA.—See Chatham Asset Management, LLC; *U.S. Private*, pg. 865
RR DONNELLEY ELECTRONICS (SUZHOU) CO., LTD.—See Chatham Asset Management, LLC; *U.S. Private*, pg. 865
R. R. DONNELLEY EUROPE SP. Z O.O—See Chatham Asset Management, LLC; *U.S. Private*, pg. 864
RR DONNELLEY FINANCIAL COMUNICACAO CORPORATIVA LTDA.—See Chatham Asset Management, LLC; *U.S. Private*, pg. 865
RR DONNELLEY FINLAND OY—See Chatham Asset Management, LLC; *U.S. Private*, pg. 865
RR DONNELLEY GLOBAL TURNKEY SOLUTIONS MEXICO, S. DE R.L. DE C.V.—See Chatham Asset Management, LLC; *U.S. Private*, pg. 865
R.R. DONNELLEY GLOBAL TURNKEY SOLUTIONS—See Chatham Asset Management, LLC; *U.S. Private*, pg. 865
RR DONNELLEY INDIA OUTSOURCE PRIVATE LIMITED—See Chatham Asset Management, LLC; *U.S. Private*, pg. 865
RR DONNELLEY INTERNATIONAL DE MEXICO, S.A. DE C.V.—See Chatham Asset Management, LLC; *U.S. Private*, pg. 865
RR DONNELLEY ITALY S.R.L.—See Chatham Asset Management, LLC; *U.S. Private*, pg. 865
RR DONNELLEY JAPAN, INC.—See Chatham Asset Management, LLC; *U.S. Private*, pg. 865
RR DONNELLEY KOREA ELECTRONIC SOLUTION LLC—See Chatham Asset Management, LLC; *U.S. Private*, pg. 865
R. R. DONNELLEY LIMITED—See Chatham Asset Management, LLC; *U.S. Private*, pg. 864
R.R. DONNELLEY - LITHO PLANT—See Chatham Asset Management, LLC; *U.S. Private*, pg. 865
RR DONNELLEY LOGISTICS SERVICES WORLDWIDE, INC.—See Chatham Asset Management, LLC; *U.S. Private*, pg. 865
R.R. DONNELLEY LOGISTICS—See Chatham Asset Management, LLC; *U.S. Private*, pg. 865
R.R. DONNELLEY MANUFACTURING—See Chatham Asset Management, LLC; *U.S. Private*, pg. 865
R.R. DONNELLEY NORWEST INC.—See Chatham Asset Management, LLC; *U.S. Private*, pg. 865
R.R. DONNELLEY OF PUERTO RICO—See Chatham Asset Management, LLC; *U.S. Private*, pg. 865
R. R. DONNELLEY PRINTING COMPANY—See Chatham Asset Management, LLC; *U.S. Private*, pg. 864
R.R. DONNELLEY RECEIVABLES, INC.—See Chatham Asset Management, LLC; *U.S. Private*, pg. 865
R.R. DONNELLEY RESPONSE MARKETING SERVICES—See Chatham Asset Management, LLC; *U.S. Private*, pg. 865
R.R. DONNELLEY SEYMOUR INC.—See Chatham Asset Management, LLC; *U.S. Private*, pg. 865
RR DONNELLEY (SHANGHAI) INFORMATION TECHNOLOGY CO., LTD.—See Chatham Asset Management, LLC; *U.S. Private*, pg. 865
RR DONNELLEY SINGAPORE PTE LTD.—See Chatham Asset Management, LLC; *U.S. Private*, pg. 865
R.R. DONNELLEY & SONS CO. - CHICAGO (111 WACKER) OFFICE—See Chatham Asset Management, LLC; *U.S. Private*, pg. 865

R.R. DONNELLEY & SONS COMPANY—See Chatham Asset Management, LLC; *U.S. Private*, pg. 862
R.R. DONNELLEY & SONS CO. - NASHVILLE—See Chatham Asset Management, LLC; *U.S. Private*, pg. 865
R.R. DONNELLEY & SONS CO. - PINEVILLE—See Chatham Asset Management, LLC; *U.S. Private*, pg. 865
R.R. DONNELLEY & SONS CO.—See Chatham Asset Management, LLC; *U.S. Private*, pg. 864
R.R. DONNELLEY & SONS CO.—See Chatham Asset Management, LLC; *U.S. Private*, pg. 864
R.R. DONNELLEY & SONS CO.—See Chatham Asset Management, LLC; *U.S. Private*, pg. 864
R.R. DONNELLEY & SONS CO.—See Chatham Asset Management, LLC; *U.S. Private*, pg. 864
R.R. DONNELLEY & SONS CO.—See Chatham Asset Management, LLC; *U.S. Private*, pg. 864
R.R. DONNELLEY & SONS CO.—See Chatham Asset Management, LLC; *U.S. Private*, pg. 864
R.R. DONNELLEY & SONS CO.—See Chatham Asset Management, LLC; *U.S. Private*, pg. 865
R.R. DONNELLEY & SONS CO.—See Chatham Asset Management, LLC; *U.S. Private*, pg. 864
R.R. DONNELLEY & SONS CO.—See Chatham Asset Management, LLC; *U.S. Private*, pg. 864
R.R. DONNELLEY & SONS CO.—See Chatham Asset Management, LLC; *U.S. Private*, pg. 865
R.R. DONNELLEY & SONS CO.—See Chatham Asset Management, LLC; *U.S. Private*, pg. 865
R.R. DONNELLEY—See Chatham Asset Management, LLC; *U.S. Private*, pg. 864
R.R. DONNELLEY—See Chatham Asset Management, LLC; *U.S. Private*, pg. 864
R.R. DONNELLEY—See Chatham Asset Management, LLC; *U.S. Private*, pg. 864
R.R. DONNELLEY—See Chatham Asset Management, LLC; *U.S. Private*, pg. 864
R.R. DONNELLEY—See Chatham Asset Management, LLC; *U.S. Private*, pg. 864
R.R. DONNELLEY—See Chatham Asset Management, LLC; *U.S. Private*, pg. 864
R.R. DONNELLEY—See Chatham Asset Management, LLC; *U.S. Private*, pg. 864
R.R. DONNELLEY—See Chatham Asset Management, LLC; *U.S. Private*, pg. 864
R.R. DONNELLEY—See Chatham Asset Management, LLC; *U.S. Private*, pg. 864
R.R. DONNELLEY—See Chatham Asset Management, LLC; *U.S. Private*, pg. 864
R.R. DONNELLEY—See Chatham Asset Management, LLC; *U.S. Private*, pg. 864
R.R. DONNELLEY—See Chatham Asset Management, LLC; *U.S. Private*, pg. 864
R. R. DONNELLEY STARACHOWICE SP. Z O.O—See Chatham Asset Management, LLC; *U.S. Private*, pg. 864
R. R. DONNELLEY (U.K.) LIMITED—See Chatham Asset Management, LLC; *U.S. Private*, pg. 864
RRD PENDAFLEX DE MEXICO, S. DE R.L. DE C.V.—See Chatham Asset Management, LLC; *U.S. Private*, pg. 865
RRD SECAUCUS FINANCIAL, INC.—See Chatham Asset Management, LLC; *U.S. Private*, pg. 865
RRD STARACHOWICE SP. Z O.O.—See Chatham Asset Management, LLC; *U.S. Private*, pg. 865
RREAL TACOS SANDY SPRINGS LLC; *U.S. Private*, pg. 3496
RREEF CHINA COMMERCIAL TRUST; *Int'l*, pg. 6416
RREEF CHINA REIT MANAGEMENT LIMITED—See Deutsche Bank Aktiengesellschaft; *Int'l*, pg. 2057
RREEF INVESTMENT GMBH—See Deutsche Bank Aktiengesellschaft; *Int'l*, pg. 2061
RREEF MANAGEMENT GMBH—See Deutsche Bank Aktiengesellschaft; *Int'l*, pg. 2061
RREEF MANAGEMENT LLC—See Deutsche Bank Aktiengesellschaft; *Int'l*, pg. 2057
RREEF MANAGEMENT LLC—See Deutsche Bank Aktiengesellschaft; *Int'l*, pg. 2057
RREEF NORTH AMERICAN INFRASTRUCTURE ONSHORE FUND A, L.P.—See Deutsche Bank Aktiengesellschaft; *Int'l*, pg. 2058
RREEF PROPERTY TRUST, INC.—See Deutsche Bank Aktiengesellschaft; *Int'l*, pg. 2058
RREEF SPEZIAL INVEST GMBH—See Deutsche Bank Aktiengesellschaft; *Int'l*, pg. 2061
RR EQUITY BROKERS PRIVATE LIMITED—See RR Financial Consultants Ltd.; *Int'l*, pg. 6416
RR FINANCIAL CONSULTANTS LTD.; *Int'l*, pg. 6416

RRF LIMITED PARTNERSHIP—See InnSuites Hospitality Trust; *U.S. Public*, pg. 1128
R. R. FLOODY COMPANY, INC.—See Applied Industrial Technologies, Inc.; *U.S. Public*, pg. 171
RR FRANCE S.A.R.L.—See Interpump Group S.p.A.; *Int'l*, pg. 3757
R&R FUJIKURA LTD.—See Fujikura Composites Inc.; *Int'l*, pg. 2826
RRGP SERVICES, INC.; *U.S. Private*, pg. 3496
RR HOLLAND BV—See Interpump Group S.p.A.; *Int'l*, pg. 3757
R&R ICE CREAM DEUTSCHLAND GMBH—See PAI Partners S.A.S.; *Int'l*, pg. 5702
R&R ICE CREAM FRANCE S.A.S.—See PAI Partners S.A.S.; *Int'l*, pg. 5702
R&R ICE CREAM PLC—See PAI Partners S.A.S.; *Int'l*, pg. 5702
RRI ENERGY SERVICES, INC.—See NRG Energy, Inc.; *U.S. Public*, pg. 1550
RRIL LIMITED; *Int'l*, pg. 6416
R & R IMAGES, INC.—See Apollo Global Management, Inc.; *U.S. Public*, pg. 159
R&R INC.; *U.S. Private*, pg. 3333
RR INDIA PVT. LTD.—See Interpump Group S.p.A.; *Int'l*, pg. 3757
R & R INDUSTRIAL PRODUCTS (M) SDN. BHD.—See KVC Industrial Supplies Sdn. Bhd.; *Int'l*, pg. 4349
RR INFORMATION AND INVESTMET RESEARCH PRIVATE LIMITED—See RR Financial Consultants Ltd.; *Int'l*, pg. 6416
RR INSURANCE BROKERS PRIVATE LIMITED—See RR Financial Consultants Ltd.; *Int'l*, pg. 6416
R&R INSURANCE SERVICES, INC.; *U.S. Private*, pg. 3333
RR INVESTOR RETAIL SERVICES PRIVATE LIMITED—See RR Financial Consultants Ltd.; *Int'l*, pg. 6416
RRJ CAPITAL LTD.; *Int'l*, pg. 6416
RRJ MANAGEMENT (HK) LIMITED—See RRJ Capital Ltd.; *Int'l*, pg. 6416
R R KABEL LIMITED; *Int'l*, pg. 6167
RR LIFECARE PVT. LTD.—See RR Metalmakers India Limited; *Int'l*, pg. 6416
R&R MARKETING, LLC—See Breakthru Beverage Group, LLC; *U.S. Private*, pg. 643
RR METALMAKERS INDIA LIMITED; *Int'l*, pg. 6416
R. ROESE CONTRACTING CO., INC.; *U.S. Private*, pg. 3334
R & R OPTICAL LABORATORY LTD.—See EssilorLuxottica SA; *Int'l*, pg. 2516
RRO ROHSTOFF RECYCLING OSNABRUECK GMBH—See Georgsmarienhutte Holding GmbH; *Int'l*, pg. 2941
RR PACIFIC PTY. LTD.—See Interpump Group S.p.A.; *Int'l*, pg. 3757
R&R PARTNERS; *U.S. Private*, pg. 3333
R&R PARTNERS—See R&R Partners; *U.S. Private*, pg. 3333
R&R PARTNERS—See R&R Partners; *U.S. Private*, pg. 3333
R&R PARTNERS—See R&R Partners; *U.S. Private*, pg. 3333
R&R PARTNERS—See R&R Partners; *U.S. Private*, pg. 3333
R&R PLASTICS; *U.S. Private*, pg. 3333
R&R POOL & PATIO INC.; *U.S. Private*, pg. 3333
R & R PROPERTY MANAGERS—See Reading Anthracite Company; *U.S. Private*, pg. 3366
R&R PROVISION COMPANY; *U.S. Private*, pg. 3333
RR PUBLIC RELATIONS, INC.; *U.S. Private*, pg. 3496
R&R REAL ESTATE INVESTMENT TRUST; *Int'l*, pg. 6168
RRR INDUSTRIAL SALES, INC.—See Reece-Hopper Sales, LLC; *U.S. Private*, pg. 3381
R.R. SECURITIES LIMITED; *Int'l*, pg. 6170
R.R. SIMMONS CONSTRUCTION CORP.; *U.S. Private*, pg. 3339
RRS INC; *U.S. Private*, pg. 3496
RRS, INC.; *U.S. Private*, pg. 3496
RR SLOVAKIA A.S.—See Interpump Group S.p.A.; *Int'l*, pg. 3757
R-R (THAILAND) LIMITED—See Rolls-Royce Holdings plc; *Int'l*, pg. 6392
R&R TRANSPORTATION INC.; *U.S. Private*, pg. 3333
RRTS UNIPESSOAL LDA—See Elekta AB; *Int'l*, pg. 2356
RR USA INC.; *U.S. Private*, pg. 3496
RS2D S.A.S.—See Nanalysis Scientific Corp.; *Int'l*, pg. 5138
RS2 GERMANY GMBH—See RS2 Software PLC; *Int'l*, pg. 6419
RS2I—See Neurones S.A.; *Int'l*, pg. 5219
RS2 SMART PROCESSING LTD.—See RS2 Software PLC; *Int'l*, pg. 6419
RS2 SOFTWARE APAC INC.—See RS2 Software PLC; *Int'l*, pg. 6419
RS2 SOFTWARE INC.—See RS2 Software PLC; *Int'l*, pg. 6419
RS2 SOFTWARE PLC; *Int'l*, pg. 6419
RS2 TECHNOLOGIES, LLC—See ACRE, LLC; *U.S. Private*, pg. 65

RSA ACTUARIAL SERVICES (INDIA) PRIVATE LIMITED—See Intact Financial Corporation; *Int'l*, pg. 3727
RSA ACTUARIAL SERVICES (INDIA) PRIVATE LIMITED—See Tryg A/S; *Int'l*, pg. 7946
RS ADVANCED STRUCTURES INC.—See Melbye Skandinavia AS; *Int'l*, pg. 4807
RS ADVANCED STRUCTURES INC.—See Werklund Capital Corporation; *Int'l*, pg. 8379
RSA ENTGRAT- U. TRENN-SYSTEME VERWALTUNGS-GMBH—See BayernLB Holding AG; *Int'l*, pg. 914
RSA ENVIRONMENTAL HEALTH LTD.—See PHSC plc; *Int'l*, pg. 5857
RSA FILMS INC.; *U.S. Private*, pg. 3496
RSA FRATESOLE SRL—See Clariane SE; *Int'l*, pg. 1644
RSA INSURANCE GROUP PLC—See Intact Financial Corporation; *Int'l*, pg. 3726
RSA INSURANCE GROUP PLC—See Tryg A/S; *Int'l*, pg. 7946
RSA INSURANCE IRELAND LIMITED—See Intact Financial Corporation; *Int'l*, pg. 3727
RSA INSURANCE IRELAND LIMITED—See Tryg A/S; *Int'l*, pg. 7946
RSA LAW LIMITED—See Intact Financial Corporation; *Int'l*, pg. 3727
RSA LAW LIMITED—See Tryg A/S; *Int'l*, pg. 7947
RS ALPHA CO., LTD.—See RS Public Company Limited; *Int'l*, pg. 6418
RSAL STEEL PRIVATE LIMITED—See IMEC Services Limited; *Int'l*, pg. 3623
RSA MEDIA, INC.—See American Tower Corporation; *U.S. Public*, pg. 111
RS AMERICAS (CANADA), INC.—See RS Group plc; *Int'l*, pg. 6417
RS AMERICAS, INC.—See RS Group plc; *Int'l*, pg. 6417
R.S. ANDREWS ENTERPRISES INC.; *U.S. Private*, pg. 3339
R&S ANTIQUES, INC.; *U.S. Private*, pg. 3333
RSA SECURITY GMBH—See Ontario Teachers' Pension Plan; *Int'l*, pg. 5586
RSA SECURITY GMBH—See Symphony Technology Group, LLC; *U.S. Private*, pg. 3901
RSA SECURITY GMBH—See The Carlyle Group Inc.; *U.S. Public*, pg. 2044
RSA SECURITY LLC—See Ontario Teachers' Pension Plan; *Int'l*, pg. 5586
RSA SECURITY LLC—See Symphony Technology Group, LLC; *U.S. Private*, pg. 3901
RSA SECURITY LLC—See The Carlyle Group Inc.; *U.S. Public*, pg. 2044
RSA SECURITY UK LIMITED—See Ontario Teachers' Pension Plan; *Int'l*, pg. 5586
RSA SECURITY UK LIMITED—See Symphony Technology Group, LLC; *U.S. Private*, pg. 3901
RSA SECURITY UK LIMITED—See The Carlyle Group Inc.; *U.S. Public*, pg. 2045
RSA SYSTEMES EBAVURAGE ET TRONCONNAGE S.A.R.L.—See BayernLB Holding AG; *Int'l*, pg. 914
RS AUTOMATION CO., LTD.; *Int'l*, pg. 6417
RSB ANLAGENVERMIETUNG GESELLSCHAFT M.B.H.—See UniCredit S.p.A.; *Int'l*, pg. 8037
RSB BONDCO LLC—See Exelon Corporation; *U.S. Public*, pg. 807
RSBG SE—See RAG-Stiftung; *Int'l*, pg. 6179
R.S. BRASWELL COMPANY INC.; *U.S. Private*, pg. 3339
RSB RIGGING SOLUTIONS S.L.—See Windway Capital Corp.; *U.S. Private*, pg. 4540
RSB SOLUTIONS, LC; *U.S. Private*, pg. 3496
RSCC AEROSPACE & DEFENSE—See Berkshire Hathaway Inc.; *U.S. Public*, pg. 310
RSCC WIRE & CABLE LLC—See Berkshire Hathaway Inc.; *U.S. Public*, pg. 310
RS CESKA A SLOVENSKA REPUBLIKA, ORG. SLOZKA—See J. Rettenmaier & Sohne GmbH & Co. KG; *Int'l*, pg. 3856
RSC INSURANCE BROKERAGE, INC.—See Kelso & Company, L.P.; *U.S. Private*, pg. 2279
RSC INTERNATIONAL LTD.; *Int'l*, pg. 6419
RSC NEW HOMES LIMITED—See LSL Property Services plc; *Int'l*, pg. 4571
RS COMPONENTES ELECTRONICOS LIMITADA—See RS Group plc; *Int'l*, pg. 6417
RS COMPONENTS AB—See RS Group plc; *Int'l*, pg. 6418
RS COMPONENTS AMIDATA S.A.U.—See STMicroelectronics N.V.; *Int'l*, pg. 7217
RS COMPONENTS A/S—See RS Group plc; *Int'l*, pg. 6418
RS COMPONENTS AS—See RS Group plc; *Int'l*, pg. 6418
RS COMPONENTS B.V.—See RS Group plc; *Int'l*, pg. 6418
RS COMPONENTS B.V.—See RS Group plc; *Int'l*, pg. 6418
RS COMPONENTS CO., LTD.—See RS Group plc; *Int'l*, pg. 6418
RS COMPONENTS & CONTROLS (INDIA) LTD.—See Siemens Aktiengesellschaft; *Int'l*, pg. 6897
RS COMPONENTS GESMBH—See RS Group plc; *Int'l*, pg. 6418

RS COMPONENTS GMBH—See RS Group plc; *Int'l*, pg. 6418
RS COMPONENTS HANDELSGES.M.B.H.—See RS Group plc; *Int'l*, pg. 6418
RS COMPONENTS HOLDINGS LIMITED—See RS Group plc; *Int'l*, pg. 6418
RS COMPONENTS KK—See RS Group plc; *Int'l*, pg. 6418
RS COMPONENTS LTD—See RS Group plc; *Int'l*, pg. 6418
RS COMPONENTS LTD.—See RS Group plc; *Int'l*, pg. 6418
RS COMPONENTS LTD.—See RS Group plc; *Int'l*, pg. 6418
RS COMPONENTS LTD.—See RS Group plc; *Int'l*, pg. 6418
RS COMPONENTS PTE LTD—See RS Group plc; *Int'l*, pg. 6418
RS COMPONENTS PTY LTD—See RS Group plc; *Int'l*, pg. 6418
RS COMPONENTS SA—See RS Group plc; *Int'l*, pg. 6418
RS COMPONENTS SAS—See RS Group plc; *Int'l*, pg. 6418
RS COMPONENTS SDN BHD—See RS Group plc; *Int'l*, pg. 6418
RS COMPONENTS (SHANGHAI) COMPANY LIMITED—See RS Group plc; *Int'l*, pg. 6417
RS COMPONENTS SPA—See RS Group plc; *Int'l*, pg. 6418
RS COMPONENTS S.R.L.—See RS Group plc; *Int'l*, pg. 6418
RS CONNECT CO., LTD.—See RS Public Company Limited; *Int'l*, pg. 6418
RS CONSULTANTS CO., LTD.—See MITSUBA Corporation; *Int'l*, pg. 4929
RS CONSULTING LIMITED—See Arsenal Capital Management LP; *U.S. Private*, pg. 338
RSC RAIFFEISEN SERVICE CENTER GMBH—See Raiffeisen Bank International AG; *Int'l*, pg. 6183
RSC TRANSPORTATION INC.; *U.S. Private*, pg. 3496
R&S DAIRY QUEENS, INC.; *U.S. Private*, pg. 3333
R.S. DAVIS RECYCLING, INC.; *U.S. Private*, pg. 3339
RSD FINANCE LIMITED; *Int'l*, pg. 6419
RSD TRANSPORTATION INC.—See RS Group plc; *Int'l*, pg. 3496
RS EDEN; *U.S. Private*, pg. 3496
RSE GRUNDBESITZ UND BETEILIGUNGS-AKTIENGESELLSCHAFT—See Salzgitter AG; *Int'l*, pg. 6498
R&S ELECTRONICS SYSTEMS INDIA PRIVATE LIMITED—See Pulz Electronics Ltd.; *Int'l*, pg. 6117
RS ENTERPRISES; *U.S. Private*, pg. 3496
RSE PHOENIX HOLDING GMBH—See Salzgitter AG; *Int'l*, pg. 6498
RSE PROJEKTENTWICKLUNGS-GMBH—See Salzgitter AG; *Int'l*, pg. 6498
RSE PROJEKTMANAGEMENT GMBH—See Salzgitter AG; *Int'l*, pg. 6498
RSE PROJEKTMANAGEMENT HOLDING-VERWALTUNGS- GMBH—See Salzgitter AG; *Int'l*, pg. 6498
RSF REIT V SP, L.L.C.—See Welltower Inc.; *U.S. Public*, pg. 2349
RSG AVIATION—See Trinity Hunt Management, L.P.; *U.S. Private*, pg. 4235
RSG COLUMBIA—See Beacon Roofing Supply, Inc.; *U.S. Public*, pg. 286
RSG ELECTRONIC COMPONENTS GMBH—See discoverIE Group plc; *Int'l*, pg. 2133
RSG FOREST PRODUCTS INC.; *U.S. Private*, pg. 3496
RSG GROUP GMBH; *Int'l*, pg. 6419
RSG KAPITAL D.O.O.; *Int'l*, pg. 6419
RSG MEDIA SYSTEMS, LLC—See Klass Capital Corp.; *Int'l*, pg. 4199
R&S GOURMET EXPRESS VERTRIEBSGES.M.B.H.—See KROSWANG GmbH; *Int'l*, pg. 4307
RSG - RISIKO SERVICE UND SACHVERSTANDIGEN GMBH—See UNIQA Insurance Group AG; *Int'l*, pg. 8058
RS GROUP PLC; *Int'l*, pg. 6417
RSG SPOKANE INTERMOUNTAIN SUPPLY—See Beacon Roofing Supply, Inc.; *U.S. Public*, pg. 286
RSG UNDERWRITING MANAGERS, LLC—See Ryan Specialty Holdings, Inc.; *U.S. Public*, pg. 1828
R.S. HARRITAN & COMPANY, INC.—See EMCOR Group, Inc.; *U.S. Public*, pg. 737
RSHB ASSET MANAGEMENT LIMITED LIABILITY COMPANY—See Russian Agricultural Bank JSC; *Int'l*, pg. 6430
R-S-H ENGINEERING, INC.; *U.S. Private*, pg. 3333
RSH GMBH—See Punch Industry Co., Ltd.; *Int'l*, pg. 6119
R.S. HUGHES CO., INC.; *U.S. Private*, pg. 3339
R.S. HUGHES CO.—See R.S. Hughes Co., Inc.; *U.S. Private*, pg. 3339
RSI HOLDINGS INC.; *U.S. Private*, pg. 3496
RSI INC.; *U.S. Private*, pg. 3497
RSI LEASING INC.—See Trinity Industries, Inc.; *U.S. Public*, pg. 2193
RSI LOGISTICS INC.—See Trinity Industries, Inc.; *U.S. Public*, pg. 2193

RS INTEGRATED SUPPLY UK LIMITED—See RS Group plc; *Int'l*, pg. 6418
R. SISKIND & CO. INC.; *U.S. Private*, pg. 3334
RSK ABERDEEN—See RSK Group plc; *Int'l*, pg. 6419
RSK BENELUX BVBA—See RSK Group plc; *Int'l*, pg. 6419
RSK CEVRE HIZMETLERI AS—See RSK Group plc; *Int'l*, pg. 6419
RSK EMN BV—See RSK Group plc; *Int'l*, pg. 6419
RSK ENVIRONMENT LLC—See RSK Group plc; *Int'l*, pg. 6419
RSK ENVIRONNEMENT SAS—See RSK Group plc; *Int'l*, pg. 6419
RSK GERMANY GMBH—See RSK Group plc; *Int'l*, pg. 6419
RSK GROUP PLC; *Int'l*, pg. 6419
RSK HEMEL HEMPSTEAD—See RSK Group plc; *Int'l*, pg. 6419
RSK (IRELAND) LTD.—See RSK Group plc; *Int'l*, pg. 6419
R.S. KNAPP CO. INC.; *U.S. Private*, pg. 3339
RS KOREA LTD.—See Rinnai Corporation; *Int'l*, pg. 6345
RSK POLSKA SP. Z O.O.—See RSK Group plc; *Int'l*, pg. 6419
RSK ROMANIA SRL—See RSK Group plc; *Int'l*, pg. 6419
RSK TRANSPORT LLC; *U.S. Private*, pg. 3497
RS LEGACY CORPORATION; *U.S. Private*, pg. 3496
RSL ELECTRONICS LTD.; *Int'l*, pg. 6419
RSL ENTERPRISE SOLUTIONS (PTY) LTD—See Ramco Systems Limited; *Int'l*, pg. 6198
RSL FIBER SYSTEMS, LLC.; *U.S. Private*, pg. 3497
RS LINING SYSTEMS, LLC—See The Toro Company; *U.S. Public*, pg. 2135
R.S. LIPMAN BREWING COMPANY, LLC; *U.S. Private*, pg. 3339
RS LIVEWELL CO., LTD.—See RS Public Company Limited; *Int'l*, pg. 6418
RSL MICROELECTRONICS COMPANY LIMITED—See S.A.S. Dragon Holdings Limited; *Int'l*, pg. 6449
RSL N.V.—See Bio-Rad Laboratories, Inc.; *U.S. Public*, pg. 334
RSL REAL ESTATE DEVELOPMENT S.R.L.—See Ablon Group Limited; *Int'l*, pg. 63
RSL TELECOM PANAMA SA—See Enel S.p.A.; *Int'l*, pg. 2415
RSL WOODWORKING PRODUCTS CO.; *U.S. Private*, pg. 3497
RS MALL CO., LTD.—See RS Public Company Limited; *Int'l*, pg. 6419
R.S. MEANS COMPANY LLC—See Fortive Corporation; *U.S. Public*, pg. 872
R.S. MEANS COMPANY LLC—See Fortive Corporation; *U.S. Public*, pg. 871
RSM ELECTRON POWER INC.; *U.S. Private*, pg. 3497
RSM INTERNATIONAL LIMITED; *Int'l*, pg. 6419
RS MULTIMEDIA CO., LTD.—See RS Public Company Limited; *Int'l*, pg. 6419
RSM US LLP; *U.S. Private*, pg. 3497
RSNB BANCORP; *U.S. Private*, pg. 3497
RSNB BANK—See RSNB Bancorp; *U.S. Private*, pg. 3497
RSN SIHN GMBH—See Tyrol Equity AG; *Int'l*, pg. 7996
RS OCCUPATIONAL HEALTH LTD—See Audax Group, Limited Partnership; *U.S. Private*, pg. 387
RSOFT DESIGN GROUP, INC.—See Synopsys, Inc.; *U.S. Public*, pg. 1970
RSOFT, INC.—See Synopsys, Inc.; *U.S. Public*, pg. 1970
R.S. OWENS & COMPANY; *U.S. Private*, pg. 3339
RSP ARCHITECTS, LTD.; *U.S. Private*, pg. 3497
RS PET ALL CO., LTD.—See RS Public Company Limited; *Int'l*, pg. 6419
RSP INFORMATION SERVICE COMPANY LTD.—See SinoPac Financial Holdings Company Ltd.; *Int'l*, pg. 6954
RSP SYSTEMS PTE LTD—See Far East Group Limited; *Int'l*, pg. 2616
RS PUBLIC COMPANY LIMITED; *Int'l*, pg. 6418
R SQUARE, INC.; *U.S. Private*, pg. 3331
RSR CORPORATION—See Quexco Incorporated; *U.S. Private*, pg. 3326
RSR DEVELOPMENT CORP.; *U.S. Private*, pg. 3497
RS RESOURCE SOLUTIONS GERMANY GMBH—See Robert Walters plc; *Int'l*, pg. 6368
R & S RESTAURANT SERVICES GMBH—See Siemens Aktiengesellschaft; *Int'l*, pg. 6887
RSR GROUP INC.; *U.S. Private*, pg. 3497
RSR GROUP TEXAS INC—See RSR Group Inc.; *U.S. Private*, pg. 3497
RSR MANAGEMENT CORP.—See RSR Group Inc.; *U.S. Private*, pg. 3497
RSR POWER PRIVATE LIMITED—See Siemens Energy AG; *Int'l*, pg. 6902
RSR SINGULAR ASSETS EUROPE SOCIMI, S.A.; *Int'l*, pg. 6419
RSR WHOLESALE GUNS INC.—See RSR Group Inc.; *U.S. Private*, pg. 3497
RSR WHOLESALE GUNS WEST INC.—See RSR Group Inc.; *U.S. Private*, pg. 3497
RSR WHOLESALE SOUTH INC.—See RSR Group Inc.; *U.S. Private*, pg. 3497
R S SOFTWARE INDIA LTD; *Int'l*, pg. 6167
R + S STANZFORMEN GMBH—See Mayr-Melnhof Karton AG; *Int'l*, pg. 4747

R&S STEEL COMPANY INC.—See Triple-S Steel Holdings Inc.; *U.S. Private*, pg. 4237
R. STAHL AG; *Int'l*, pg. 6169
R. STAHL AUSTRALIA PTY. LTD.—See R. Stahl AG; *Int'l*, pg. 6169
R. STAHL CO. LTD.—See R. Stahl AG; *Int'l*, pg. 6169
R. STAHL DO BRASIL LTDA.—See R. Stahl AG; *Int'l*, pg. 6170
R. STAHL ENGINEERING & MANUFACTURING SDN. BHD.—See R. Stahl AG; *Int'l*, pg. 6169
R. STAHL EX-PROOF (SHANGHAI) CO., LTD.—See R. Stahl AG; *Int'l*, pg. 6169
R. STAHL FRANCE S.A.S.—See R. Stahl AG; *Int'l*, pg. 6169
R. STAHL GULF FZCO—See R. Stahl AG; *Int'l*, pg. 6169
R. STAHL HMI SYSTEMS GMBH—See R. Stahl AG; *Int'l*, pg. 6169
R STAHL, INC.—See R. Stahl AG; *Int'l*, pg. 6169
R. STAHL JAPAN KABUSHIKI KAISHA—See R. Stahl AG; *Int'l*, pg. 6169
R. STAHL KABUSHIKI KAISHA—See R. Stahl AG; *Int'l*, pg. 6169
R. STAHL LLP—See R. Stahl AG; *Int'l*, pg. 6169
R. STAHL LTD.—See R. Stahl AG; *Int'l*, pg. 6169
R. STAHL LTD.—See R. Stahl AG; *Int'l*, pg. 6170
R. STAHL MIDDLE EAST FZE—See R. Stahl AG; *Int'l*, pg. 6170
R. STAHL NORGE AS—See R. Stahl AG; *Int'l*, pg. 6170
R. STAHL (P) LIMITED—See R. Stahl AG; *Int'l*, pg. 6169
R. STAHL PRIVATE LIMITED—See R. Stahl AG; *Int'l*, pg. 6170
R. STAHL PTE. LTD.—See R. Stahl AG; *Int'l*, pg. 6170
R. STAHL SCHALTGERATE GMBH—See R. Stahl AG; *Int'l*, pg. 6170
R. STAHL SERVICES GMBH—See R. Stahl AG; *Int'l*, pg. 6170
R. STAHL SOUTH AFRICA (PTY) LTD.—See R. Stahl AG; *Int'l*, pg. 6170
R. STAHL S.R.L.—See R. Stahl AG; *Int'l*, pg. 6170
R. STAHL SVENSKA AB—See R. Stahl AG; *Int'l*, pg. 6170
R. STAHL SWITZERLAND AG—See R. Stahl AG; *Int'l*, pg. 6170
R. STAHL TRANBERG AS—See R. Stahl AG; *Int'l*, pg. 6170
RS TECHNICS BV—See Indutrade AB; *Int'l*, pg. 3681
R+S TECHNIK GMBH—See Matthews International Corporation; *U.S. Public*, pg. 1400
RS TECHNOLOGIES CO., LTD. - OSAKI FACTORY—See RS Technologies Co., Ltd.; *Int'l*, pg. 6419
RS TECHNOLOGIES CO., LTD.; *Int'l*, pg. 6419
RS TECHNOLOGIES INC.—See Melbye Skandinavia AS; *Int'l*, pg. 4807
RS TECHNOLOGIES INC.—See Werklund Capital Corporation; *Int'l*, pg. 8379
RSTEC SEMICONDUCTOR TAIWAN CO., LTD.—See RS Technologies Co., Ltd.; *Int'l*, pg. 6419
RST RALF SCHMIDT TIEFBAU, KABEL & KABEL-ROHRVERLEGUNG GMBH—See Heidelberg Materials AG; *Int'l*, pg. 3319
R STRATTON & CO LIMITED—See Penske Automotive Group, Inc.; *U.S. Public*, pg. 1666
R STREET INSTITUTE; *U.S. Private*, pg. 3331
RST ROSTOCK SYSTEM-TECHNIK GMBH—See Airbus SE; *Int'l*, pg. 243
RSUI GROUP, INC.—See Berkshire Hathaway Inc.; *U.S. Public*, pg. 299
RSUI INDEMNITY COMPANY—See Berkshire Hathaway Inc.; *U.S. Public*, pg. 299
RS-UNIX; *U.S. Private*, pg. 3496
RSUPPORT CO., LTD.; *Int'l*, pg. 6419
RSVP.COM.AU PTY LIMITED—See Nine Entertainment Co. Holdings Limited; *Int'l*, pg. 5299
RSVP—See King James Group Company; *Int'l*, pg. 4169
R & S WELL SERVICE, INC.—See Rock Hill Capital Group, LLC; *U.S. Private*, pg. 3464
RSWM LTD.; *Int'l*, pg. 6420
R.S. YOUNG EXCAVATING, INC.; *U.S. Private*, pg. 3339
RSYS TECHNOLOGIES LTD.—See Blackstone Inc.; *U.S. Public*, pg. 357
R SYSTEMS COMPUTARIS EUROPE SRL—See Blackstone Inc.; *U.S. Public*, pg. 357
R SYSTEMS COMPUTARIS MALAYSIA SDN. BHD.—See Blackstone Inc.; *U.S. Public*, pg. 357
R SYSTEMS COMPUTARIS PHILIPPINES PTE. LTD. INC.—See Blackstone Inc.; *U.S. Public*, pg. 357
R SYSTEMS COMPUTARIS POLAND SP Z O.O.—See Blackstone Inc.; *U.S. Public*, pg. 357
R SYSTEMS COMPUTARIS S.R.L.—See Blackstone Inc.; *U.S. Public*, pg. 357
R SYSTEMS CONSULTING SERVICES (SHANGHAI) CO., LTD.—See Blackstone Inc.; *U.S. Public*, pg. 357
R SYSTEMS EUROPE B.V.—See Blackstone Inc.; *U.S. Public*, pg. 357
R SYSTEMS IBIZCS SDN. BHD.—See Blackstone Inc.; *U.S. Public*, pg. 357
R SYSTEMS INC.—See Blackstone Inc.; *U.S. Public*, pg. 357

R SYSTEMS INTERNATIONAL LIMITED—See Blackstone Inc.; *U.S. Public*, pg. 357
R SYSTEMS S.A.S.—See Blackstone Inc.; *U.S. Public*, pg. 357
R SYSTEMS SINGAPORE LTD.—See Blackstone Inc.; *U.S. Public*, pg. 357
R SYSTEMS SOLUTIONS, INC.—See Blackstone Inc.; *U.S. Public*, pg. 357
RTA CABINET STORE; *U.S. Private*, pg. 3498
RTA FURNITURE DISTRIBUTORS; *U.S. Private*, pg. 3498
RTA LABORATUVARLARI BIYOLOJIK URUNLER ILAC VE MAKINE SANAYI TICARET A.S.; *Int'l*, pg. 6420
R. T. BRISCOE (NIGERIA) PLC; *Int'l*, pg. 6170
RTC GROUP PLC; *Int'l*, pg. 6420
RT-CHEMCOMPOSITE—See Russian Technologies State Corporation; *Int'l*, pg. 6432
RTC HOLDINGS, L.L.C.; *U.S. Private*, pg. 3498
RTC INC.—See Kajima Corporation; *Int'l*, pg. 4055
RTCL LIMITED; *Int'l*, pg. 6420
RTC LUKA LEGET A.D.; *Int'l*, pg. 6420
RTC NEVADA, LLC—See Rush Enterprises, Inc.; *U.S. Public*, pg. 1826
RT COMMUNICATIONS INC.—See Range Telephone Cooperative Inc.; *U.S. Private*, pg. 3354
RT CONTRACTING CORP.—See CVC Capital Partners SICAV-FIS S.A.; *Int'l*, pg. 1887
RTD CONSTRUCTION, INC.; *U.S. Private*, pg. 3498
RTD QUALITY SERVICES NIGERIA LTD.—See I Squared Capital Advisors (US) LLC; *U.S. Private*, pg. 2023
RTD QUALITY SERVICES NIGERIA LTD.—See TDR Capital LLP; *Int'l*, pg. 7492
RTDS TECHNOLOGIES INC.—See AMETEK, Inc.; *U.S. Public*, pg. 121
RTE GROUP; *Int'l*, pg. 6420
RT&E INTEGRATED COMMUNICATIONS—See Reese, Tomases & Ellick, Inc. (RT&E); *U.S. Private*, pg. 3383
RT ENGINEERING CO., LTD.—See Rinnai Corporation; *Int'l*, pg. 6345
R.T. EXPORTS LIMITED; *Int'l*, pg. 6171
RT FACILITY MANAGEMENT GMBH & CO. KG—See ADLER Group SA; *Int'l*, pg. 150
RTG MEDICAL; *U.S. Private*, pg. 3498
RTG MINING INC.; *Int'l*, pg. 6420
RTG RAMMTECHNIK GMBH.—See BAUER Aktiengesellschaft; *Int'l*, pg. 893
RTH MECHANICAL CONTRACTORS, INC.; *U.S. Private*, pg. 3498
RTI ADVANCED FORMING, LTD.—See Endless LLP; *Int'l*, pg. 2403
RTI AUSTRIA GMBH—See RTi Rohrtechnik international GmbH; *Int'l*, pg. 6420
RTI DONOR SERVICES, INC.—See Montagu Private Equity LLP; *Int'l*, pg. 5036
RTI GERMANY GMBH—See RTi Rohrtechnik international GmbH; *Int'l*, pg. 6420
RTI GLOBAL, INC.—See Hybrid Software Group PLC; *Int'l*, pg. 3544
RTI HEALTH SOLUTIONS—See Research Triangle Institute; *U.S. Private*, pg. 3404
RTI, INC.—See DRI Corporation; *U.S. Private*, pg. 1277
RTI JSC—See Sistema PJSFC; *Int'l*, pg. 6963
RTI LABORATORIES, INC.; *U.S. Private*, pg. 3498
RTI ROCKVILLE—See Research Triangle Institute; *U.S. Private*, pg. 3404
RTI ROHRTECHNIK INTERNATIONAL GMBH; *Int'l*, pg. 6420
RTI SERVICES, INC.—See Montagu Private Equity LLP; *Int'l*, pg. 5036
RTI—See Groupe BPCE; *Int'l*, pg. 3095
R.T.I. S.P.A.—See Mediaset S.p.A.; *Int'l*, pg. 4773
RTI SURGICAL-SINGAPORE PTE LTD—See Montagu Private Equity LLP; *Int'l*, pg. 5036
RTI SYSTEMS LTD.—See Sopra Steria Group S.A.; *Int'l*, pg. 7109
RTI TECHNOLOGY CHINA LIMITED—See Avnet, Inc.; *U.S. Public*, pg. 254
RTK.IO, INC.—See Magnite, Inc.; *U.S. Public*, pg. 1354
RTKL ASSOCIATES INC.—See ARCADIS N.V.; *Int'l*, pg. 541
RTKL INTERNATIONAL LTD.—See ARCADIS N.V.; *Int'l*, pg. 541
RTL4 HOLDING SA—See Bertelsmann SE & Co. KGaA; *Int'l*, pg. 995
RTL ADCONNECT INTERNATIONAL, S.A.—See Metropole Television SA; *Int'l*, pg. 4863
RTL ADCONNECT S.R.L.—See Bertelsmann SE & Co. KGaA; *Int'l*, pg. 993
RTL ADCONNECT UK LTD.—See Bertelsmann SE & Co. KGaA; *Int'l*, pg. 993
RTL AUDIO CENTER BERLIN GMBH—See Bertelsmann SE & Co. KGaA; *Int'l*, pg. 993
RTL AUDIO VERMARKTUNG GMBH—See Bertelsmann SE & Co. KGaA; *Int'l*, pg. 993
RTL DISNEY FERNSEHEN GMBH & CO. KG—See Bertelsmann SE & Co. KGaA; *Int'l*, pg. 995
RTL DISNEY FERNSEHEN GMBH & CO. KG—See The Walt Disney Company; *U.S. Public*, pg. 2139
RTL FRANCE RADIO SASU—See Metropole Television SA; *Int'l*, pg. 4863

RTL GROUP CABLE & SATELLITE GMBH—See Bertelsmann SE & Co. KGaA; *Int'l*, pg. 995
RTL GROUP S.A.—See Bertelsmann SE & Co. KGaA; *Int'l*, pg. 993
RTL HESSEN GMBH—See Bertelsmann SE & Co. KGaA; *Int'l*, pg. 995
RTL HESSEN PROGRAMMFENSTER GMBH—See Bertelsmann SE & Co. KGaA; *Int'l*, pg. 995
RTL HRVATSKA D.O.O.—See PPF Group N.V.; *Int'l*, pg. 5950
RTL JOURNALISTENSCHULE GMBH—See Bertelsmann SE & Co. KGaA; *Int'l*, pg. 995
RTL KLUB—See Bertelsmann SE & Co. KGaA; *Int'l*, pg. 995
RTL MUSIC PUBLISHING GMBH—See Bertelsmann SE & Co. KGaA; *Int'l*, pg. 996
RTL NEDERLAND BV—See Bertelsmann SE & Co. KGaA; *Int'l*, pg. 995
RTL NEDERLAND INTERACTIEF BV—See Bertelsmann SE & Co. KGaA; *Int'l*, pg. 995
RTL NEDERLAND PRODUCTIES BV—See Bertelsmann SE & Co. KGaA; *Int'l*, pg. 995
RTL NETWORKS, INC.; *U.S. Private*, pg. 3498
RTL NORD GMBH—See Bertelsmann SE & Co. KGaA; *Int'l*, pg. 995
RTL RADIO LETZEBURG—See Bertelsmann SE & Co. KGaA; *Int'l*, pg. 995
RTL RADIO—See Bertelsmann SE & Co. KGaA; *Int'l*, pg. 995
RTL RADIO—See Bertelsmann SE & Co. KGaA; *Int'l*, pg. 995
RTL STUDIOS GMBH—See Bertelsmann SE & Co. KGaA; *Int'l*, pg. 996
RTL TELE LETZEBURG—See Bertelsmann SE & Co. KGaA; *Int'l*, pg. 995
RTL TELEVISION GMBH—See Bertelsmann SE & Co. KGaA; *Int'l*, pg. 995
RTM & ASSOCIATES, INC.; *U.S. Private*, pg. 3498
RTM CONSULTING, INC.—See AE Industrial Partners, LP; *U.S. Private*, pg. 111
R.T. MILORD CO.; *U.S. Private*, pg. 3339
RT MINERALS CORP.; *Int'l*, pg. 6420
RTM REALTIME MONITORING GMBH—See Silver Lake Group, LLC; *U.S. Private*, pg. 3658
RT MYCOCK & SONS LIMITED—See Breedon Group plc; *Int'l*, pg. 1144
RT NEW DAY—See Ryan Specialty Holdings, Inc.; *U.S. Public*, pg. 1828
RTN INSURANCE BROKER CO., LTD.—See Thanachart Capital PCL; *Int'l*, pg. 7607
RTO ASSET MANAGEMENT INC.—See goeasy Ltd.; *Int'l*, pg. 3021
RTO DISTRIBUTION INC—See goeasy Ltd.; *Int'l*, pg. 3021
R TO FIFTH, INC.; *U.S. Private*, pg. 3331
RTO LIMITED; *Int'l*, pg. 6420
RTP COMPANY; *U.S. Private*, pg. 3498
RTP CORP.; *U.S. Private*, pg. 3498
RTP KOREA CO. LTD.—See RTP Corp.; *U.S. Private*, pg. 3498
R&T PLUMBING TECHNOLOGY CO.,LTD; *Int'l*, pg. 6168
RTP-UK LTD.—See Rheinmetall AG; *Int'l*, pg. 6323
RTS EMBALAJES DE ARGENTINA SA—See Sonoco Products Company; *U.S. Public*, pg. 1905
RTS EMBALAJES DE CHILE LIMITADA—See Sonoco Products Company; *U.S. Public*, pg. 1905
RTS EMPAQUES, S. DE R.L. DE CV—See Sonoco Products Company; *U.S. Public*, pg. 1905
RTS EXCELSIOR CO., LTD.—See Excelsior Medical Co., Ltd.; *Int'l*, pg. 2579
RTS GENEVA SA—See Rothschild & Co SCA; *Int'l*, pg. 6403
RTS HOLDINGS, LLC—See Ridgemont Partners Management LLC; *U.S. Private*, pg. 3433
RTS OIL HOLDINGS, INC.; *U.S. Public*, pg. 1820
RTS PACKAGING, LLC—See Sonoco Products Company; *U.S. Public*, pg. 1905
RTS PACKAGING - ORANGE—See Sonoco Products Company; *U.S. Public*, pg. 1905
R-T SPECIALTY, LLC—See Ryan Specialty Holdings, Inc.; *U.S. Public*, pg. 1828
RTS POWER CORPORATION LIMITED; *Int'l*, pg. 6420
RTS RAIL TRANSPORT SERVICE GERMANY GMBH—See Swietelsky Baugesellschaft m.b.H.; *Int'l*, pg. 7367
RTS RAIL TRANSPORT SERVICE GMBH—See Swietelsky Baugesellschaft m.b.H.; *Int'l*, pg. 7367
RTS RIEGER TEAM WERBEAGENTUR GMBH; *Int'l*, pg. 6420
RTS RIEGER TEAM WERBEAGENTUR GMBH—See RTS Rieger Team Werbeagentur GmbH; *Int'l*, pg. 6420
RTS UNIFIED COMMUNICATIONS; *U.S. Private*, pg. 3498
RT&T GROUP, INC.; *U.S. Private*, pg. 3497
RTT GROUP (PTY) LTD—See TRG Management LP; *U.S. Private*, pg. 4219
RTUNET (AUSTRALIA) PTY LTD.—See CSE Global Ltd.; *Int'l*, pg. 1864
R.T. VANDERBILT HOLDING COMPANY, INC.; *U.S. Private*, pg. 3339

RTV MEDIA GROUP GMBH—See Bertelsmann SE & Co. KGaA; *Int'l*, pg. 996
RTW BIOTECH OPPORTUNITIES LTD.—See RTW Investments, LP; *U.S. Private*, pg. 3498
R T WESTERN MISSOURI FRANCHISE LLC; *U.S. Private*, pg. 3331
RTW, INC.—See State Automobile Mutual Insurance Company; *U.S. Private*, pg. 3791
R. TWINING & CO. LTD.—See The Garfield Weston Foundation; *Int'l*, pg. 7649
RTW INVESTMENTS, LP; *U.S. Private*, pg. 3498
RTW RETAILWINDS, INC.; *U.S. Public*, pg. 1820
RTX AMERICA, INC—See RTX A/S; *Int'l*, pg. 6421
RTX A/S; *Int'l*, pg. 6420
RTX CORPORATION; *U.S. Public*, pg. 1820
RTX PRODUCTS HONG KONG LTD.—See RTX A/S; *Int'l*, pg. 6421
RUAG AEROSPACE SERVICES GMBH—See RUAG Holding AG; *Int'l*, pg. 6421
RUAG AMMOTEC AG—See RUAG Holding AG; *Int'l*, pg. 6421
RUAG AMMOTEC AUSTRIA GMBH—See RUAG Holding AG; *Int'l*, pg. 6421
RUAG AMMOTEC BENELUX B.V.B.A.—See RUAG Holding AG; *Int'l*, pg. 6421
RUAG AMMOTEC FRANCE S.A.S.—See RUAG Holding AG; *Int'l*, pg. 6421
RUAG AMMOTEC GMBH—See RUAG Holding AG; *Int'l*, pg. 6421
RUAG AMMOTEC UK LTD.—See RUAG Holding AG; *Int'l*, pg. 6421
RUAG AMMOTEC USA INC.—See RUAG Holding AG; *Int'l*, pg. 6421
RUAG AUSTRALIA PTY LTD—See RUAG Holding AG; *Int'l*, pg. 6421
RUAG AUSTRALIA—See RUAG Holding AG; *Int'l*, pg. 6421
RUAG AVIATION AG—See RUAG Holding AG; *Int'l*, pg. 6421
RUAG COMPONENTS AG—See RUAG Holding AG; *Int'l*, pg. 6421
RUAG DEFENCE DEUTSCHLAND GMBH—See RUAG Holding AG; *Int'l*, pg. 6421
RUAG ELECTRONICS AG—See RUAG Holding AG; *Int'l*, pg. 6421
RUAG HOLDING AG; *Int'l*, pg. 6421
RUAG HUNGARIAN AMMOTEC INC.—See RUAG Holding AG; *Int'l*, pg. 6421
RUAG LAND SYSTEMS AG—See RUAG Holding AG; *Int'l*, pg. 6421
RUA GOLD INC.; *Int'l*, pg. 6421
RUAG SCHWEIZ AG—See RUAG Holding AG; *Int'l*, pg. 6421
RUAG SPACE AB—See RUAG Holding AG; *Int'l*, pg. 6421
RUAG SPACE AG—See RUAG Holding AG; *Int'l*, pg. 6421
RUAG SPACE GMBH—See RUAG Holding AG; *Int'l*, pg. 6421
RUAG SPACE USA—See RUAG Holding AG; *Int'l*, pg. 6421
RUAHINE MOTORS LTD.—See The Colonial Motor Company Limited; *Int'l*, pg. 7635
RUA LIFE SCIENCES PLC; *Int'l*, pg. 6421
RUA MEDICAL DEVICES LIMITED—See RUA Life Sciences Plc; *Int'l*, pg. 6421
RUAN TRANSPORTATION MANAGEMENT SYSTEMS, INC.; *U.S. Private*, pg. 3498
RU&A PORTER NOVELLI—See Omnicom Group Inc.; *U.S. Public*, pg. 1591
RUASHI HOLDINGS (PTY) LIMITED—See Jinchuan Group Limited; *Int'l*, pg. 3966
RUASHI MINING SAS—See Jinchuan Group International Resources Co. Ltd.; *Int'l*, pg. 3965
RUBBENS NV—See Mutares SE & Co. KGaA; *Int'l*, pg. 5105
RUBBER & ACCESSORIES, INC.; *U.S. Private*, pg. 3499
RUBBER ASSOCIATES, INC.; *U.S. Private*, pg. 3499
RUBBERCARE PROTECTION PRODUCTS SDN BHD—See Careplus Group Berhad; *Int'l*, pg. 1325
RUBBER CITY ARCHES, LLC; *U.S. Private*, pg. 3499
RUBBER COMPOUNDING HOLLAND B.V.—See Elgi Rubber Company Limited; *Int'l*, pg. 2360
RUBBER ENTERPRISES INC.; *U.S. Private*, pg. 3499
RUBBER FLEX CORPORATION—See Tigers Polymer Corporation; *Int'l*, pg. 7746
RUBBERLAND PRODUCTS CO., LTD.—See Sri Trang Agro-Industry Public Company Limited; *Int'l*, pg. 7150
RUBBER LEAF INC.; *Int'l*, pg. 6421
RUBBERLINE PRODUCTS LTD.; *Int'l*, pg. 6422
RUBBERLITE INC.; *U.S. Private*, pg. 3499
RUBBERMAID COMMERCIAL PRODUCTS LLC—See Newell Brands Inc.; *U.S. Public*, pg. 1514
RUBBERMAID HOME PRODUCTS—See Newell Brands Inc.; *U.S. Public*, pg. 1514
RUBBER NANO PRODUCTS EUROPE SRL—See Esseco Group SRL; *Int'l*, pg. 2509
RUBBER & PLASTICS NEWS—See Crain Communications, Inc.; *U.S. Private*, pg. 1084
RUBBER RESOURCES B.V.—See Rubber Resources Holding N.V.; *Int'l*, pg. 6422

COMPANY NAME INDEX

RUBBER RESOURCES HOLDING N.V.; *Int'l*, pg. 6422
RUBBER RESOURCES S.A. (PTY) LTD.—See Rubber Resources Holding N.V.; *Int'l*, pg. 6422
RUBBER ROLLS INC.; *U.S. Private*, pg. 3499
RUBBER & SPECIALTIES INC.; *U.S. Private*, pg. 3499
RUBBER TECHNOLOGY INC.—See Polymer Enterprises Inc.; *U.S. Private*, pg. 3226
RUBEAN AG; *Int'l*, pg. 6422
RUBELLITE ENERGY CORP.; *Int'l*, pg. 6422
RUBEN-HOLLAND DEVELOPMENT, LLC; *U.S. Private*, pg. 3499
RUBENSTEIN ASSOCIATES, INC.; *U.S. Private*, pg. 3499
RUBENSTEIN PARTNERS, L.P.—See Independence Capital Partners, LLC; *U.S. Private*, pg. 2057
RUBENSTEIN PUBLIC RELATIONS, INC.—See Rubenstein Associates, Inc.; *U.S. Private*, pg. 3499
RUBENSTEIN'S CONTRACT CARPET, LLC; *U.S. Private*, pg. 3499
RUBENSTEIN & ZIFF, INC.; *U.S. Private*, pg. 3499
RUBEX, INC.—See Gladstone Management Corporation; *U.S. Private*, pg. 1705
RUBEX INTERNATIONAL FOR PLASTIC & ACRYLIC MANUFACTURING; *Int'l*, pg. 6422
RUBFILA INTERNATIONAL LTD.; *Int'l*, pg. 6422
RUBIA INDUSTRIES LIMITED—See Berli Jucker Public Co. Ltd.; *Int'l*, pg. 985
RUBIAN BAKERY LLC—See Trive Capital Inc.; *U.S. Private*, pg. 4240
RUBICON ESTATE WINERY; *U.S. Private*, pg. 3499
RUBICON FINANCIAL INCORPORATED; *U.S. Private*, pg. 3499
RUBICON GENOMICS, INC.—See Takara Holdings, Inc.; *Int'l*, pg. 7432
THE RUBICON GROUP, LLC—See Amadeus IT Group, S.A.; *Int'l*, pg. 407
RUBICON LLC—See Huntsman Corporation; *U.S. Public*, pg. 1075
RUBICON OILFIELD INTERNATIONAL LIMITED—See Intervale Capital, LLC; *U.S. Private*, pg. 2127
RUBICON ORGANICS, INC.; *Int'l*, pg. 6422
RUBICON PARTNERS INDUSTRIES LLP—See Rubicon Partners Limited; *Int'l*, pg. 6422
RUBICON PARTNERS LIMITED; *Int'l*, pg. 6422
RUBICON PARTNERS S.A.; *Int'l*, pg. 6422
RUBICON PROFESSIONAL SERVICES; *U.S. Private*, pg. 3499
RUBICON PROGRAMS; *U.S. Private*, pg. 3499
THE RUBICON PROJECT LTD.—See Magnite, Inc.; *U.S. Public*, pg. 1354
RUBICON PROJECT SERVICOS DE INTERNET LTDA.—See Magnite, Inc.; *U.S. Public*, pg. 1354
RUBICON RESOURCES, LLC—See High Liner Foods Incorporated; *Int'l*, pg. 3385
RUBICON—See Myriad Restaurant Group; *U.S. Private*, pg. 2825
RUBICON TECHNOLOGIES HOLDINGS, LLC—See Rubicon Technologies, Inc.; *U.S. Public*, pg. 1825
RUBICON TECHNOLOGIES, INC.; *U.S. Public*, pg. 1825
RUBICON TECHNOLOGY, INC.; *U.S. Public*, pg. 1825
RUBICON TECHNOLOGY PARTNERS, LLC; *U.S. Private*, pg. 3499
RUBICON TV AS—See LOV Group Invest SAS; *Int'l*, pg. 4565
RUBICON WORLDWIDE LLC—See Rubicon Technology, Inc.; *U.S. Public*, pg. 1825
RUBICOR GROUP LIMITED; *Int'l*, pg. 6422
RUBICOR SW PERSONNEL PTY LIMITED—See Rubicor Group Limited; *Int'l*, pg. 6423
RUBICOR (T1) PTY LIMITED—See Rubicor Group Limited; *Int'l*, pg. 6423
RUBIE'S COSTUME COMPANY INC.; *U.S. Private*, pg. 3500
RUBIE'S DEUTSCHLAND GMBH—See Rubie's Costume Company Inc.; *U.S. Private*, pg. 3500
RUBIE'S MASQUERADE LTD—See Rubie's Costume Company Inc.; *U.S. Private*, pg. 3500
RUBIK FINANCIAL TECHNOLOGY PTY LTD—See Temenos AG; *Int'l*, pg. 7554
RUBIN A.D.; *Int'l*, pg. 6423
RUBINBROWN LLP; *U.S. Private*, pg. 3500
RUBINETTERIE MARIANI S.P.A.—See Ostnor AB; *Int'l*, pg. 5655
RUBIN GMBH—See Bijou Brigitte modische Accessoires AG; *Int'l*, pg. 1022
THE RUBIN GROUP, INC.; *U.S. Private*, pg. 4113
RUBIN INDUSTRIAL CO. INC.—See GenNx360 Capital Partners, L.P.; *U.S. Private*, pg. 1672
RUBIN MEDICAL AB—See Indutrade AB; *Int'l*, pg. 3681
RUBIN POSTAER & ASSOCIATES - ATLANTA OFFICE—See Rubin Postaer & Associates; *U.S. Private*, pg. 3500
RUBIN POSTAER & ASSOCIATES - CHICAGO OFFICE—See Rubin Postaer & Associates; *U.S. Private*, pg. 3500
RUBIN POSTAER & ASSOCIATES - DALLAS OFFICE—See Rubin Postaer & Associates; *U.S. Private*, pg. 3500

RUBIN POSTAER & ASSOCIATES - DENVER OFFICE—See Rubin Postaer & Associates; *U.S. Private*, pg. 3500
RUBIN POSTAER & ASSOCIATES - MOORESTOWN OFFICE—See Rubin Postaer & Associates; *U.S. Private*, pg. 3500
RUBIN POSTAER & ASSOCIATES - PORTLAND OFFICE—See Rubin Postaer & Associates; *U.S. Private*, pg. 3500
RUBIN POSTAER & ASSOCIATES; *U.S. Private*, pg. 3500
RUBIO'S RESTAURANTS, INC.—See Mill Road Capital Management LLC; *U.S. Private*, pg. 2730
RUBIS ENERGY BERMUDA LTD.—See Rubis SCA; *Int'l*, pg. 6423
RUBIS ENERGY KENYA PLC—See Rubis SCA; *Int'l*, pg. 6423
RUBIS ENERGY RWANDA LTD.—See Rubis SCA; *Int'l*, pg. 6423
RUBIS ENERGY UGANDA LTD.—See Rubis SCA; *Int'l*, pg. 6423
RUBIS ENERGY ZAMBIA LTD.—See Rubis SCA; *Int'l*, pg. 6423
RUBIS SCA; *Int'l*, pg. 6423
RUBIS TERMINAL SA—See Rubis SCA; *Int'l*, pg. 6423
RUBIS TERMINAL—See Rubis SCA; *Int'l*, pg. 6423
RUBIUS THERAPEUTICS, INC.; *U.S. Public*, pg. 1825
RUBIX CZECH A.S.—See THK CO., LTD.; *Int'l*, pg. 7712
RUBIX GMBH—See Rubix Group International Limtied; *Int'l*, pg. 6423
RUBIX GROUP INTERNATIONAL LIMTIED; *Int'l*, pg. 6423
RUBIXIS INC.—See TransUnion; *U.S. Public*, pg. 2184
RUBIX RESOURCES LIMITED; *Int'l*, pg. 6423
RUBIX SLOVAKIA S.R.O.—See THK CO., LTD.; *Int'l*, pg. 7712
RUBLEVO ARCHANGELSKOE JSC—See OJSC Sberbank of Russia; *Int'l*, pg. 5542
RUBLOFF DEVELOPMENT GROUP, INC.; *U.S. Private*, pg. 3500
RUBLOFF JET EXPRESS, LLC—See Rubloff Development Group, Inc.; *U.S. Private*, pg. 3500
RUBSCHLAGER BAKING CORPORATION—See George Weston Limited; *Int'l*, pg. 2939
RUBSTEEL AB—See Huhtamaki Oyj; *Int'l*, pg. 3526
RUBUS HOLDINGS PTY LTD—See Cleanaway Waste Management Limited; *Int'l*, pg. 1655
RUBY ASSOCIATES, PC—See Degenkolb Engineers; *U.S. Private*, pg. 1191
RUBY CABLES LIMITED; *Int'l*, pg. 6424
RUBY COLLINS COMPANY INC.; *U.S. Private*, pg. 3500
RUBYCON AMERICA INC.—See Rubycon Corporation; *Int'l*, pg. 6424
RUBYCON CORPORATION; *Int'l*, pg. 6424
RUBYCON INTERNATIONAL (SHANGHAI) CO., LTD.—See Rubycon Corporation; *Int'l*, pg. 6424
RUBYCON INTERNATIONAL (THAILAND) CO., LTD.—See Rubycon Corporation; *Int'l*, pg. 6424
RUBYCON KOREA CO., LTD.—See Rubycon Corporation; *Int'l*, pg. 6424
RUBYCON SINGAPORE PTE., LTD.—See Rubycon Corporation; *Int'l*, pg. 6424
RUBY GOLD, INC.—See NORTH BAY RESOURCES INC.; *U.S. Public*, pg. 2942
RUBY GROUPE INC.—See Sony Group Corporation; *Int'l*, pg. 7107
THE RUBY GROUP; *U.S. Private*, pg. 4113
RUBY HILL MINE—See Barrick Gold Corporation; *Int'l*, pg. 869
THE RUBY MILLS LIMITED; *Int'l*, pg. 7679
RUBY RECEPTIONISTS—See Updata Partners; *U.S. Private*, pg. 4311
RUBY'S INN INC.; *U.S. Private*, pg. 3500
RUBY'S RESTAURANT GROUP; *U.S. Private*, pg. 3500
RUBYTECH CORP.; *Int'l*, pg. 6424
RUBY TEXTILE MILLS LIMITED; *Int'l*, pg. 6424
RUBY TUESDAY, INC.—See NRD Capital Management, LLC; *U.S. Private*, pg. 2969
RUBY TUESDAY LONG ISLAND; *U.S. Private*, pg. 3500
RUBY TUESDAY OF ANDERSON, INC.—See NRD Capital Management, LLC; *U.S. Private*, pg. 2969
RUBY TUESDAY OF ARVADA, INC.—See NRD Capital Management, LLC; *U.S. Private*, pg. 2969
RUBY TUESDAY OF COLUMBIA, INC.—See NRD Capital Management, LLC; *U.S. Private*, pg. 2969
RUBY TUESDAY OF DEERWOOD, INC.—See NRD Capital Management, LLC; *U.S. Private*, pg. 2969
RUBY TUESDAY OF FREDERICK, INC.—See NRD Capital Management, LLC; *U.S. Private*, pg. 2969
RUBY TUESDAY OF LINTHICUM, INC.—See NRD Capital Management, LLC; *U.S. Private*, pg. 2969
RUBY TUESDAY OF MARLEY STATION, INC.—See NRD Capital Management, LLC; *U.S. Private*, pg. 2969
RUBY TUESDAY OF POCOMOKE CITY, INC.—See NRD Capital Management, LLC; *U.S. Private*, pg. 2969
RUBY TUESDAY OF RUSSELLVILLE, INC.—See NRD Capital Management, LLC; *U.S. Private*, pg. 2969
RUBY TUESDAY OF SALISBURY, INC.—See NRD Capital Management, LLC; *U.S. Private*, pg. 2969
RUBY TUESDAY OF SOUTHCASE, INC.—See NRD Capital Management, LLC; *U.S. Private*, pg. 2969

RUDOLF WILD GMBH & CO. KG

RUBY TUESDAY TAMPA FRANCHISE LP; *U.S. Private*, pg. 3500
RUBY WAY LIMITED—See Far East Consortium International Limited; *Int'l*, pg. 2615
RUC CEMENTATION MINING CONTRACTORS (PROPRIETARY) LIMITED—See Murray & Roberts Holdings Ltd.; *Int'l*, pg. 5100
RUCHI INFRASTRUCTURE LTD; *Int'l*, pg. 6424
RUCHIRA PAPERS LTD.; *Int'l*, pg. 6424
RUCHSER FENSTERBAUMASCHINEN GMBH; *Int'l*, pg. 6424
RUCKER ITALIA S.R.L.—See ATON GmbH; *Int'l*, pg. 689
RUCKER & KOLLS INC—See Eico Inc.; *U.S. Private*, pg. 1346
RUCKER LYPSA S.L.U.—See ATON GmbH; *Int'l*, pg. 689
RUCKER & SILL LTD. INC.; *U.S. Private*, pg. 3500
RUCKER SR SPOL.S.R.O. I.L.—See ATON GmbH; *Int'l*, pg. 689
RUCKUS WIRELESS, INC.—See CommScope Holding Company, Inc.; *U.S. Public*, pg. 548
RUCKUS WIRELESS PRIVATE LTD.—See CommScope Holding Company, Inc.; *U.S. Public*, pg. 548
RUDCO PRODUCTS INC.; *U.S. Private*, pg. 3500
RUDD CONTAINER CORPORATION; *U.S. Private*, pg. 3500
RUDD EQUIPMENT COMPANY INC.—See Ferronordic AB; *Int'l*, pg. 2642
RUDDICK OPERATING COMPANY—See The Kroger Co.; *U.S. Public*, pg. 2108
RUDEN HOLDINGS CO., LTD.; *Int'l*, pg. 6424
RUDER FINN FRANCE, SARL—See Ruder Finn Group, Inc.; *U.S. Private*, pg. 3501
RUDER FINN GROUP, INC.; *U.S. Private*, pg. 3501
RUDER FINN HEALTHCARE—See Ruder Finn Group, Inc.; *U.S. Private*, pg. 3501
RUDER FINN, INC.—See Ruder Finn Group, Inc.; *U.S. Private*, pg. 3501
RUDER FINN, INC.—See Ruder Finn Group, Inc.; *U.S. Private*, pg. 3501
RUDER FINN—See Ruder Finn Group, Inc.; *U.S. Private*, pg. 3501
RUDER FINN UK, LTD.—See Ruder Finn Group, Inc.; *U.S. Private*, pg. 3501
RUDER FINN WEST—See Ruder Finn Group, Inc.; *U.S. Private*, pg. 3501
RUDIGOZ—See Vicat S.A.; *Int'l*, pg. 8186
RUDING A.D.; *Int'l*, pg. 6424
RUDISA AGENCIES N.V.—See Rudisa Holdingmaatschappij N.V.; *Int'l*, pg. 6424
RUDISA BEVERAGES & JUICES N.V.—See Rudisa Holdingmaatschappij N.V.; *Int'l*, pg. 6424
RUDISA BROADCASTING, COMMUNICATIONS & PUBLICATIONS N.V.—See Rudisa Holdingmaatschappij N.V.; *Int'l*, pg. 6424
RUDISA FURNITURE—See Rudisa Holdingmaatschappij N.V.; *Int'l*, pg. 6424
RUDISA HOLDINGMAATSCHAPPIJ N.V.; *Int'l*, pg. 6424
RUDISA JAMAICA LTD.—See Rudisa Holdingmaatschappij N.V.; *Int'l*, pg. 6424
RUDISA MOTOR COMPANY N.V.—See Rudisa Holdingmaatschappij N.V.; *Int'l*, pg. 6424
RUDISA SHIPPING COMPANY N.V.—See Rudisa Holdingmaatschappij N.V.; *Int'l*, pg. 6424
RUDISILL ENTERPRISES, INC.; *U.S. Private*, pg. 3502
RUDI'S ORGANIC BAKERY, INC.—See The Hain Celestial Group, Inc.; *U.S. Public*, pg. 2087
RUDNICI BANJANI; *Int'l*, pg. 6424
RUDNIK KAOLINA MOTAJICA A.D.; *Int'l*, pg. 6424
RUDNIK KOVIN U RESTRUKTURIRANJU A.D.; *Int'l*, pg. 6424
RUDNIK MANGANA D.D.; *Int'l*, pg. 6425
RUDNIK SOLI TUZLA D.D.; *Int'l*, pg. 6425
RUDNIK ZELJEZNE RUDE D.D. VARES; *Int'l*, pg. 6425
RUDO A.D.; *Int'l*, pg. 6425
RUDOLF ACHENBACH GMBH & CO KG; *Int'l*, pg. 6425
RUDOLF-ERICH MULLER GMBH & CO KG; *Int'l*, pg. 6425
RUDOLF FRITZ GMBH—See CEZ, a.s.; *Int'l*, pg. 1428
RUDOLF GROSSFURTNER GES.M.B.H. & CO; *Int'l*, pg. 6425
RUDOLF HAUFE VERLAG GMBH & CO. KG; *Int'l*, pg. 6425
RUDOLF REPROFLEX GMBH & CO. KG—See Matthews International Corporation; *U.S. Public*, pg. 1399
RUDOLF RIESTER GMBH—See Halma plc; *Int'l*, pg. 3232
RUDOLF ROST INTERIORS GMBH—See Rudolf Rost Sperrholz GmbH; *Int'l*, pg. 6425
RUDOLF ROST SPERRHOLZ GMBH; *Int'l*, pg. 6425
RUDOLF WILD (BEIJING) FOOD INGREDIENTS CO., LTD.—See Rudolf Wild GmbH & Co. KG; *Int'l*, pg. 6425
RUDOLF WILD GMBH & CO. KG—See Archer-Daniels-Midland Company; *U.S. Public*, pg. 184
RUDOLF WILD GMBH & CO. KG; *Int'l*, pg. 6425
RUDOLPH AND SLETTEN, INC.—See Tutor Perini Corporation; *U.S. Public*, pg. 2206
RUDOLPH FOODS COMPANY - DALLAS FACILITY—See Rudolph Foods Company; *U.S. Private*, pg. 3502

2337

RUDOLF WILD GMBH & CO. KG

CORPORATE AFFILIATIONS

RUDOLPH FOODS COMPANY - LAWRENCEVILLE FACILITY—See Rudolph Foods Company; *U.S. Private*, pg. 3502
RUDOLPH FOODS COMPANY - NEW HEBRON FACILITY—See Rudolph Foods Company; *U.S. Private*, pg. 3502
RUDOLPH FOODS COMPANY - SAN BERNARDINO FACILITY—See Rudolph Foods Company; *U.S. Private*, pg. 3502
RUDOLPH FOODS COMPANY; *U.S. Private*, pg. 3502
THE RUDOLPH/LIBBE COMPANIES; *U.S. Private*, pg. 4113
RUDOLPH/LIBBE, INC.—See The Rudolph/Libbe Companies; *U.S. Private*, pg. 4113
RUDOLPH/LIBBE PROPERTIES, INC.—See The Rudolph/Libbe Companies; *U.S. Private*, pg. 4113
RUDOLPH & SLETTEN, INC.—See Tutor Perini Corporation; *U.S. Public*, pg. 2206
RUDOLPH TECHNOLOGIES, INC. - INSPECTION SYSTEMS—See Onto Innovation Inc.; *U.S. Public*, pg. 1605
RUDOLPH TECHNOLOGIES, INC.—See Onto Innovation Inc.; *U.S. Public*, pg. 1605
RUDONG FUZHAN SCIENTIFIC CO., LTD.—See Taiflex Scientific Co., Ltd.; *Int'l*, pg. 7410
RUD. OTTO MEYER TECHNIK LTD. & CO. KG—See Zech Group SE; *Int'l*, pg. 8628
RUDRABHISHEK ENTERPRISES LIMITED; *Int'l*, pg. 6425
RUDRABHISHEK INFOSYSTEM PRIVATE LIMITED—See Rudrabhishek Enterprises Limited; *Int'l*, pg. 6425
RUDRA GLOBAL INFRA PRODUCTS LIMITED; *Int'l*, pg. 6425
RUDSTROJ D.D. KAKANJ; *Int'l*, pg. 6425
RUDUS OY AB—See CRH plc; *Int'l*, pg. 1848
RUDY INC.; *U.S. Private*, pg. 3502
RUDY LUTHERS HOPKINS HONDA—See Luther Holding Company; *U.S. Private*, pg. 2517
RUDY LUTHER TOYOTA SCION—See Luther Holding Company; *U.S. Private*, pg. 2517
RUDY'S FOOD PRODUCTS, INC.—See TruArc Partners, L.P.; *U.S. Private*, pg. 4246
RUDY'S MARKETS INC.; *U.S. Private*, pg. 3502
RUE21, INC.—See Apax Partners LLP; *Int'l*, pg. 507
RUECKERT ADVERTISING; *U.S. Private*, pg. 3502
RUE DE LA PAYE SAS—See Cegedim S.A.; *Int'l*, pg. 1390
RUE DU COMMERCE SAS—See Carrefour SA; *Int'l*, pg. 1346
RUEFER INGENIEURE AG—See BKW AG; *Int'l*, pg. 1056
RUELALA, INC.—See Kynetic LLC; *U.S. Private*, pg. 2360
RUELCO SERVICES INC.; *U.S. Private*, pg. 3502
RUEN HOLDING AD; *Int'l*, pg. 6425
RUENMONGKOL CO., LTD.—See Bumrungrad Hospital Public Company Limited; *Int'l*, pg. 1215
RUENTEX DEVELOPMENT CO., LTD.—See Ruentex Group; *Int'l*, pg. 6426
RUENTEX ENGINEERING & CONSTRUCTION CO., LTD.—See Ruentex Group; *Int'l*, pg. 6426
RUENTEX GROUP; *Int'l*, pg. 6425
RUENTEX INDUSTRIES LIMITED—See Ruentex Group; *Int'l*, pg. 6426
RUENTEX MATERIALS CO., LTD.—See Ruentex Group; *Int'l*, pg. 6426
RUETERS RED POWER; *U.S. Private*, pg. 3502
RUETGERS BELGIUM N.V.—See Rain Industries Limited; *Int'l*, pg. 6189
RUETGERS CANADA INC.—See Rain Industries Limited; *Int'l*, pg. 6189
RUETGERS HOLDING GERMANY GMBH—See Rain Industries Limited; *Int'l*, pg. 6189
RUETGERS NOVARES GMBH—See Rain Industries Limited; *Int'l*, pg. 6189
RUETGERS N.V.—See Rain Industries Limited; *Int'l*, pg. 6189
RUETTIGER, TONELLI & ASSOCIATES, INC.—See The Will Group, Inc.; *U.S. Private*, pg. 4136
RUF DEUTSCHLAND GMBH—See Ruf Gruppe; *Int'l*, pg. 6426
RUF DIFFUSION SA—See Ruf Gruppe; *Int'l*, pg. 6426
RUFFALO NOEL LEVITZ, LLC; *U.S. Private*, pg. 3502
RUFFER INVESTMENT CO., LTD.; *Int'l*, pg. 6426
RUFFIN COMPANIES; *U.S. Private*, pg. 3502
RUFFINO HILLS TRANSFER STATION, LP—See BC Partners LLP; *Int'l*, pg. 924
RUFFINO S.R.L.—See Constellation Brands, Inc.; *U.S. Public*, pg. 571
RUFFLEBUTTS, INC.; *U.S. Private*, pg. 3502
RUF GRUPPE; *Int'l*, pg. 6426
RUF TELEMATIK AG—See Toyota Industries Corporation; *Int'l*, pg. 7868
RUFUS LEONARD; *Int'l*, pg. 6426
RUGANI HOSPITAL S.R.L.—See Garofalo Health Care SpA; *Int'l*, pg. 2886
THE RUG BARN INC.—See The InterTech Group, Inc.; *U.S. Private*, pg. 4057
RUGBY FARMERS UNION ELEVATOR COMPANY; *U.S. Private*, pg. 3502
RUGBY HOLDINGS LLC—See Hardwoods Distribution Inc.; *Int'l*, pg. 3273

RUGBY IPD CORP.—See Hardwoods Distribution Inc.; *Int'l*, pg. 3273
RUGBY MANUFACTURING COMPANY—See Federal Signal Corporation; *U.S. Public*, pg. 826
RUGBY MINING LIMITED; *Int'l*, pg. 6426
RUGBY PREFABRYKATY SP. Z O.O.—See INPRO S.A.; *Int'l*, pg. 3717
THE RUG COMPANY LIMITED—See Palamon Capital Partners, LP; *Int'l*, pg. 5706
RUG DOCTOR, LLC—See Ares Management Corporation; *U.S. Public*, pg. 191
RUGELEY POWER LTD—See ENGIE SA; *Int'l*, pg. 2433
RUGEN FISCH AG—See Thai Union Group Public Company Limited; *Int'l*, pg. 7597
RUGER CHEMICAL COMPANY, INC.—See H.I.G. Capital, LLC; *U.S. Private*, pg. 1832
RUGE'S AUTOMOTIVE; *U.S. Private*, pg. 3502
RUGGED INFORMATION TECHNOLOGY EQUIPMENT CORP.—See AstroNova, Inc.; *U.S. Public*, pg. 218
RUGGED LINER INC.; *U.S. Private*, pg. 3502
RUGGED WEARHOUSE INC.; *U.S. Private*, pg. 3502
RUGG MANUFACTURING COMPANY; *U.S. Private*, pg. 3502
RUG RAIFFEISEN UMWELTGESELLSCHAFT M.B.H—See BayWa AG; *Int'l*, pg. 918
RUG RIELLO URZADZENIA GRZEWCZE SA—See Carrier Global Corporation; *U.S. Public*, pg. 444
RUGS AMERICA CORPORATION; *U.S. Private*, pg. 3502
RUGVISTA AB—See Rugvista Group AB; *Int'l*, pg. 6426
RUGVISTA GROUP AB; *Int'l*, pg. 6426
RUHLAND-KALLENBORN & CO. GMBH—See Hornbach Holding AG & Co. KGaA; *Int'l*, pg. 3482
RUHL AND RUHL REALTORS LLC; *U.S. Private*, pg. 3502
RUHLE COMPANIES, INC.; *U.S. Private*, pg. 3503
RUHLE GMBH; *Int'l*, pg. 6426
THE RUHLIN COMPANY; *U.S. Private*, pg. 4113
RUHL-PARR/MORAN ARCHITECTS LLC; *U.S. Private*, pg. 3502
RUHNN HOLDING LIMITED; *Int'l*, pg. 6426
RUHRGLAS RECYCLING GMBH & CO. KG—See Reiling Glas Recycling GmbH & Co. KG; *Int'l*, pg. 6257
RUHRPUMEN INDIA PRIVATE LIMITED—See Corporacion EG S.A.; *Int'l*, pg. 1803
RUHRPUMPEN DO BRASIL IND. E COM DE BOMBAS. HIDRAULICAS LTDA.—See Corporacion EG S.A.; *Int'l*, pg. 1803
RUHRPUMPEN GMBH—See Corporacion EG S.A.; *Int'l*, pg. 1803
RUHRPUMPEN, INC. - ORLAND PLANT—See Corporacion EG S.A.; *Int'l*, pg. 1803
RUHRPUMPEN INC.—See Corporacion EG S.A.; *Int'l*, pg. 1803
RUHRPUMPEN LIMITED—See Corporacion EG S.A.; *Int'l*, pg. 1803
RUHRPUMPEN METALS, S.A. DE C.V.—See Corporacion EG S.A.; *Int'l*, pg. 1803
RUIA GLOBAL FASTENERS AG—See Ruia Group; *Int'l*, pg. 6426
RUIA GROUP; *Int'l*, pg. 6426
RUI'AN YONGDA NANYANG LUJIE AUTOMOBILE SALES & SERVICES CO., LTD.—See China Yongda Automobiles Services Holdings Limited; *Int'l*, pg. 1564
RUICHENG CHINA MEDIA GROUP LIMITED; *Int'l*, pg. 6426
RUIDA FUTURES CO., LTD.; *Int'l*, pg. 6426
RUIDOSO DOWNS RACING INC.; *U.S. Private*, pg. 3503
RUIDOSO NEWS—See Gannett Co., Inc.; *U.S. Public*, pg. 900
RUI FENG GROUP HOLDINGS COMPANY LIMITED; *Int'l*, pg. 6426
RUIFENG POWER GROUP COMPANY LIMITED; *Int'l*, pg. 6426
RUIGENG GARMENTS (DALIAN) CO., LTD.—See Nippon Steel Corporation; *Int'l*, pg. 5338
RUIJIE NETWORKS CO., LTD.—See Fujian Star-net Communication Co.,Ltd; *Int'l*, pg. 2819
RUILI GROUP CO., LTD.; *Int'l*, pg. 6426
RUINART UK LTD.—See LVMH Moet Hennessy Louis Vuitton SE; *Int'l*, pg. 4599
RUISLIP AND NORTHWOOD AGED PEOPLE'S HOUSING COMPANY LIMITED—See Home Group Limited; *Int'l*, pg. 3454
RUITAI MATERIALS TECHNOLOGY CO., LTD.; *Int'l*, pg. 6427
RUITAI NEW MATERIAL TECHNOLOGY (DONGGUAN) CO., LTD.—See J.Pond Precision Technology Co., Ltd.; *Int'l*, pg. 3858
RUITING CONTEMPORARY AMPEREX TECHNOLOGY (SHANGHAI) LIMITED—See Contemporary Amperex Technology Co., Ltd.; *Int'l*, pg. 1779
RUIXIN INTERNATIONAL HOLDINGS LIMITED; *Int'l*, pg. 6427
RUIYUAN CAPITAL ASSET MANAGEMENT CO., LTD.—See GF Securities Co., Ltd.; *Int'l*, pg. 2955
RUIZ FOOD PRODUCTS, INC.; *U.S. Private*, pg. 3503
RUIZ MEXICAN FOODS INC.; *U.S. Private*, pg. 3503
RUIZ PROTECTIVE SERVICE, INC.; *U.S. Private*, pg. 3503

RUKERT TERMINALS CORPORATION; *U.S. Private*, pg. 3503
RUKO A/S—See ASSA ABLOY AB; *Int'l*, pg. 640
RUKO GMBH PRAZISIONSWERKZEUGE—See Dr. Helmut Rothenberger Holding GmbH; *Int'l*, pg. 2191
RULE DIVISION—See Xylem Inc.; *U.S. Public*, pg. 2396
RULLION LIMITED; *Int'l*, pg. 6427
RULMECA CORPORATION; *U.S. Private*, pg. 3503
RULMECA HOLDING SPA—See Rulmeca Corporation; *U.S. Private*, pg. 3503
RULMENTI S.A.—See Bera Holding A.S.; *Int'l*, pg. 978
RULO N.V.—See Aurea, S.A.; *Int'l*, pg. 707
RULQUIN DISTRIBUTION; *Int'l*, pg. 6427
RUMAH & CO. PTE. LTD.; *Int'l*, pg. 6427
RUMA INDUSTRIEVERPACKUNG LEIPZIG GMBH—See Silgan Holdings, Inc.; *U.S. Public*, pg. 1878
RUMAN S.R.L.—See KONE Oyj; *Int'l*, pg. 4250
RUMATRANS A.D.; *Int'l*, pg. 6427
RUMBERGER, KIRK & CALDWELL PROFESSIONAL ASSOCIATION; *U.S. Private*, pg. 3503
RUMBLE, INC.; *U.S. Public*, pg. 1825
RUMBLEON, INC.; *U.S. Public*, pg. 1825
RUMBLE RESOURCES INC.; *Int'l*, pg. 6427
RUMBLE RESOURCES LIMITED; *Int'l*, pg. 6427
RUMBLETREE, INC.; *U.S. Private*, pg. 3503
RUMBLING BRIDGE CARE HOME KINROSS—See Balhousie Holdings Limited; *Int'l*, pg. 808
RUM CREEK COAL SALES, INC.—See Alpha Natural Resources, Inc.; *U.S. Private*, pg. 199
RUMERE CO., LTD.; *Int'l*, pg. 6427
RUM GROUP FOR TRANSPORTATION & TOURISM INVESTMENT P.L.C.; *Int'l*, pg. 6427
RUMIANO CHEESE COMPANY; *U.S. Private*, pg. 3503
RUMMEL, KLEPPER & KAHL; *U.S. Private*, pg. 3503
RUMO MALHA NORTE SA; *Int'l*, pg. 6427
RUMORS SALON & SPA; *U.S. Private*, pg. 3503
RUMO S.A.—See Cosan S.A.; *Int'l*, pg. 1809
RUMOS S.A.—See Enka Insaat ve Sanayi A.S.; *Int'l*, pg. 2440
RUMPF CORPORATION; *U.S. Private*, pg. 3503
RUMPKE CONSOLIDATED COMPANIES, INC.; *U.S. Private*, pg. 3503
RUMPKE HYDRAULICS & MACHINING—See Rumpke Consolidated Companies, Inc.; *U.S. Private*, pg. 3503
RUMPKE OF INDIANA, INC.—See Rumpke Consolidated Companies, Inc.; *U.S. Private*, pg. 3503
RUMPKE OF KENTUCKY, INC.—See Rumpke Consolidated Companies, Inc.; *U.S. Private*, pg. 3503
RUMPKE OF OHIO, INC.—See Rumpke Consolidated Companies, Inc.; *U.S. Private*, pg. 3503
RUMPKE RECYCLING—See Rumpke Consolidated Companies, Inc.; *U.S. Private*, pg. 3503
RUMPKE SANITARY LANDFILL, INC.—See Rumpke Consolidated Companies, Inc.; *U.S. Private*, pg. 3503
RUMPKE TRANSPORTATION COMPANY, LLC—See Rumpke Consolidated Companies, Inc.; *U.S. Private*, pg. 3503
RUMPKE WASTE, INC.—See Rumpke Consolidated Companies, Inc.; *U.S. Private*, pg. 3503
RUMP & PRYM GMBH & CO. KG—See William Prym GmbH & Co. KG; *Int'l*, pg. 8414
RUMSEY ELECTRIC COMPANY; *U.S. Private*, pg. 3504
RUMS OF PUERTO RICO—See Puerto Rico Industrial Development Company; *U.S. Private*, pg. 3302
RUNABOUT, LLC—See Avis Budget Group, Inc.; *U.S. Public*, pg. 249
RUNACRES LIMITED—See AUB Group Limited; *Int'l*, pg. 698
RUNA SMART EQUIPMENT CO., LTD.; *Int'l*, pg. 6427
RUNCO INTERNATIONAL, LLC—See Leyard Optoelectronic Co., Ltd.; *Int'l*, pg. 4472
RUNCORN VETS4PETS LIMITED—See Pets at Home Group Plc; *U.S. Private*, pg. 5834
RUNDE CHEVROLET INC; *U.S. Private*, pg. 3504
RUNDLE & CO., LIMITED—See Bain Capital, LP; *U.S. Private*, pg. 435
RUNDLE-SPENCE MANUFACTURING CO; *U.S. Private*, pg. 3504
RUNELANDHS FORSALJNINGS AB—See Brady Corporation; *U.S. Public*, pg. 379
RUNESTONE ELECTRIC ASSOCIATION; *U.S. Private*, pg. 3504
RUNGE ASIA LIMITED—See Runge ICT Group Pty Limited; *Int'l*, pg. 6428
RUNGE ICT GROUP PTY LIMITED; *Int'l*, pg. 6427
RUNGE LATIN AMERICA LIMITADA—See Runge ICT Group Pty Limited; *Int'l*, pg. 6428
RUNGIS EXPRESS GMBH—See Metro AG; *Int'l*, pg. 4859
RUNGSIROJVANIT CO., LTD.—See BEC World Public Company Limited; *Int'l*, pg. 936
RUNGTA IRRIGATION LIMITED - PONDICHERRY UNIT—See Rungta Irrigation Limited; *Int'l*, pg. 6428
RUNGTA IRRIGATION LIMITED; *Int'l*, pg. 6428
RUNGTA IRRIGATION LIMITED - UTTARPRADESH UNIT—See Rungta Irrigation Limited; *Int'l*, pg. 6428
RUNHUA LIVING SERVICE GROUP HOLDINGS LTD.; *Int'l*, pg. 6428
RUNIC GAMES, INC.—See Perfect World Co., Ltd.; *Int'l*, pg. 5799

COMPANY NAME INDEX

RUNJIAN CO., LTD.; *Int'l*, pg. 6428
RUN LONG CONSTRUCTION CO., LTD.; *Int'l*, pg. 6427
RUNMART INC.—See Aucnet Inc.; *Int'l*, pg. 700
RUNNEBOHM CONSTRUCTION COMPANY INC.; *U.S. Private*, pg. 3504
RUNNERS POINT ADMINISTRATION GMBH—See Foot Locker, Inc.; *U.S. Public*, pg. 864
RUNNERS POINT WARENHANDELSGESELLSCHAFT MBH—See Foot Locker, Inc.; *U.S. Public*, pg. 863
RUNNER XIAMEN CORP.; *Int'l*, pg. 6428
RUNNING FOX RESOURCE CORP.; *U.S. Public*, pg. 1826
RUNNING PRESS—See Vivendi SE; *Int'l*, pg. 8273
THE RUNNING SPECIALTY GROUP, INC.—See CriticalPoint Capital, LLC; *U.S. Private*, pg. 1102
RUNNING SUPPLY INC.; *U.S. Private*, pg. 3504
RUNON CO., LTD.—See Suminoe Textile Co., Ltd.; *Int'l*, pg. 7262
RUNPATH REGULATED SERVICES LIMITED—See Experian plc; *Int'l*, pg. 2588
RUNSYSTEM CO., LTD.; *Int'l*, pg. 6428
RUNTAL ITALIA S.R.L.—See Zehnder Group AG; *Int'l*, pg. 8630
RUNTAL NORTH AMERICA, INC.—See Zehnder Group AG; *Int'l*, pg. 8630
RUNTAL RADIADORES S.A.—See Zehnder Group AG; *Int'l*, pg. 8630
RUNTEC CORPORATION—See Senko Group Holdings Co., Ltd.; *Int'l*, pg. 6710
RUNTECH SYSTEMS, INC.—See Ingersoll Rand Inc.; *U.S. Public*, pg. 1122
RUNTECH SYSTEMS OY—See Ingersoll Rand Inc.; *U.S. Public*, pg. 1122
RUNTIME COLLECTIVE LIMITED—See Platinum Equity, LLC; *U.S. Private*, pg. 3202
RUNTIME DESIGN AUTOMATION—See Altair Engineering, Inc.; *U.S. Public*, pg. 86
RUNTIME REVOLUTION LTD.; *Int'l*, pg. 6428
RUNWAY GROWTH FINANCE CORP.; *U.S. Public*, pg. 1826
RUNYON SALTZMAN & EINHORN; *U.S. Private*, pg. 3504
RUNZA DRIVE-INNS OF AMERICA INC.; *U.S. Private*, pg. 3504
RUNZA NATIONAL INC.—See Runza Drive-Inns of America Inc.; *U.S. Private*, pg. 3504
RUNZHEIMER INTERNATIONAL LLC—See Thoma Bravo, L.P.; *U.S. Private*, pg. 4150
RUOFF MORTGAGE COMPANY, INC.; *U.S. Private*, pg. 3504
RUOKAKESKO LTD—See Kesko Corporation; *Int'l*, pg. 4143
RUOTOLO ASSOCIATES, INC.—See Collegium Holdings, Inc.; *U.S. Private*, pg. 968
RUPA & CO LIMITED; *Int'l*, pg. 6428
RUPALI BANK PLC; *Int'l*, pg. 6428
RUPALI BANK SECURITIES LIMITED—See Rupali Bank PLC; *Int'l*, pg. 6428
RUPALI INSURANCE COMPANY LIMITED; *Int'l*, pg. 6428
RUPALI INVESTMENT LIMITED—See Rupali Bank PLC; *Int'l*, pg. 6428
RUPALI LIFE INSURANCE CO. LTD.; *Int'l*, pg. 6428
RUPALI POLYESTER LIMITED - POLYESTER PLANT—See Rupali Polyester Limited; *Int'l*, pg. 6428
RUPALI POLYESTER LIMITED; *Int'l*, pg. 6428
RUPE INVESTMENT CORPORATION; *U.S. Private*, pg. 3504
RUPERT FINLAND OY—See Rupert Resources Ltd.; *Int'l*, pg. 6428
RUPERT RESOURCES LTD.; *Int'l*, pg. 6428
RUPF INDUSTRIES GMBH; *Int'l*, pg. 6428
RUPP AG; *Int'l*, pg. 6429
RUPP CHEESE INNOVATION GMBH—See Rupp AG; *Int'l*, pg. 6429
RUPPERT LANDSCAPE, LLC; *U.S. Private*, pg. 3504
RUPPERT NURSERIES, INC.; *U.S. Private*, pg. 3504
RUPPERTSBERGER WINZERVEREIN HOHEBURG EG; *Int'l*, pg. 6429
RUPP & HUBRACH OPTIK GMBH—See EssilorLuxottica SA; *Int'l*, pg. 2516
RUPP KASEEXPORT GMBH—See Rupp AG; *Int'l*, pg. 6429
RURALAUS PLANTATION MANAGEMENT PTY LTD—See Kiland Ltd.; *Int'l*, pg. 4161
RURAL BANK LIMITED—See Bendigo & Adelaide Bank Ltd.; *Int'l*, pg. 971
RURAL BANK OF ANGELES, INC.—See Asia United Bank Corporation; *Int'l*, pg. 616
RURAL BUILDING COMPANY PTY LTD—See JWH Group Pty Ltd; *Int'l*, pg. 4035
RURAL CAPITAL AREA WORKFORCE DEVELOPMENT BOARD, INC.; *U.S. Private*, pg. 3504
RURALCO FINANCE PTY. LTD.—See Nutrien Ltd.; *Int'l*, pg. 5493
RURALCO HOLDINGS LIMITED—See Nutrien Ltd.; *Int'l*, pg. 5492
RURAL COMMUNITY INSURANCE COMPANY—See Zurich Insurance Group Limited; *Int'l*, pg. 8699
RURAL ELECTRIC COOPERATIVE, INC.; *U.S. Private*, pg. 3504

RURAL ELECTRIC SUPPLY COOPERATIVE INC.; *U.S. Private*, pg. 3504
RURAL FINANCE CORPORATION OF VICTORIA—See Bendigo & Adelaide Bank Ltd.; *Int'l*, pg. 971
RURAL FUNDS MANAGEMENT LTD.; *Int'l*, pg. 6429
RURAL/METRO CORPORATION—See KKR & Co. Inc.; *U.S. Public*, pg. 1249
RURAL METRO CORPORATION—See KKR & Co. Inc.; *U.S. Public*, pg. 1252
RURAL/METRO FIRE DEPT., INC.—See KKR & Co. Inc.; *U.S. Public*, pg. 1251
RURAL/METRO OF NORTHERN OHIO, INC.—See KKR & Co. Inc.; *U.S. Public*, pg. 1252
RURAL MUTUAL INSURANCE COMPANY INC.; *U.S. Private*, pg. 3504
RURAL PRESS PTY LIMITED; *Int'l*, pg. 6429
RURAL SOURCING, INC.—See Bain Capital, LP; *U.S. Private*, pg. 431
RURAL TELECOMMUNICATIONS OF AMERICA, INC.; *U.S. Public*, pg. 3504
RURAL TELEPHONE SERVICE CO; *U.S. Private*, pg. 3505
RURBANC DATA SERVICES, INC.—See SB Financial Group, Inc.; *U.S. Public*, pg. 1842
RURO INCORPORATED—See Azenta, Inc.; *U.S. Public*, pg. 258
RUSAGRO-INVEST—See Gruppa Kompaniy Rusagro OOO; *Int'l*, pg. 3140
RUSAL AMERICA CORP.—See United Company RUSAL Plc; *Int'l*, pg. 8066
RUSAL MARKETING GMBH—See United Company RUSAL Plc; *Int'l*, pg. 8066
THE RUSCA HOTEL; *Int'l*, pg. 7679
RUSCH AUSTRIA GMBH—See Teleflex Incorporated; *U.S. Public*, pg. 1995
RUSCH URUGUAY LTDA.—See Teleflex Incorporated; *U.S. Public*, pg. 1996
RUSCILLI CONSTRUCTION CO. INC.; *U.S. Private*, pg. 3505
THE RUSCOE COMPANY; *U.S. Private*, pg. 4113
RUSCON CORPORATION; *U.S. Private*, pg. 3505
RUSELECTRONICS JSC—See Russian Technologies State Corporation; *Int'l*, pg. 6432
RUSFIC LLC—See Recordati S.p.A.; *Int'l*, pg. 6240
RUSFOREST AB; *Int'l*, pg. 6429
RUSFOREST LLC—See RusForest AB; *Int'l*, pg. 6429
RUSH ACCESSORIES CORPORATION—See Rush Enterprises, Inc.; *U.S. Public*, pg. 1826
RUSH ADMINISTRATIVE SERVICES, INC.—See Rush Enterprises, Inc.; *U.S. Public*, pg. 1826
RUSHCO, INC.—See Rush Enterprises, Inc.; *U.S. Public*, pg. 1827
RUSH COMMUNICATIONS, INC.; *U.S. Private*, pg. 3505
RUSH COMPUTER RENTALS INC.—See Platinum Equity, LLC; *U.S. Private*, pg. 3203
RUSH-COPLEY MEDICAL CENTER—See Advent International Corporation; *U.S. Private*, pg. 96
RUSH ENTERPRISES, INC.; *U.S. Public*, pg. 1826
RUSHER OIL CO, INC.—See Sampson-Bladen Oil Co. Inc.; *U.S. Private*, pg. 3538
RUSHES POSTPRODUCTION LTD—See Deluxe Corporation; *U.S. Public*, pg. 653
RUSH GMC TRUCK CENTER OF EL PASO, INC.—See Rush Enterprises, Inc.; *U.S. Public*, pg. 1826
RUSH GMC TRUCK CENTER OF TUCSON, INC.—See Rush Enterprises, Inc.; *U.S. Public*, pg. 1826
RUSH HEALTH SYSTEMS INC.; *U.S. Private*, pg. 3505
RUSHIL DECOR LIMITED; *Int'l*, pg. 6429
RUSH INDUSTRIES INC.; *U.S. Private*, pg. 3505
RUSHLAKE HOTELS USA INC.; *U.S. Private*, pg. 3505
RUSHLIFT LTD.—See Doosan Corporation; *Int'l*, pg. 2174
RUSH LOGISTICS, INC.—See Rush Enterprises, Inc.; *U.S. Public*, pg. 1826
RUSH MEDIUM DUTY TRUCK CENTERS OF COLORADO, INC.—See Rush Enterprises, Inc.; *U.S. Public*, pg. 1826
RUSHMORE COMMUNICATIONS INC.—See Rushmore Electric Power Cooperative Inc.; *U.S. Private*, pg. 3505
RUSHMORE ELECTRIC POWER COOPERATIVE INC.; *U.S. Private*, pg. 3505
RUSHNET, INC.; *U.S. Public*, pg. 1827
RUSH OAK BROOK SURGERY CENTER, LLC—See UnitedHealth Group Incorporated; *U.S. Public*, pg. 2250
RUSH OAK PARK HOSPITAL—See Wheaton Franciscan Services Inc.; *U.S. Private*, pg. 4505
RUSH ONTARIO, LLC—See The Marcus Corporation; *U.S. Public*, pg. 2112
RUSH PETERBILT TRUCK CENTER—See Rush Enterprises, Inc.; *U.S. Public*, pg. 1826
RUSH PRESS—See Chatham Asset Management, LLC; *U.S. Private*, pg. 863
RUSH RARE METALS CORP.; *Int'l*, pg. 6429
RUSH SALES COMPANY—See Tenex Capital Management, L.P.; *U.S. Private*, pg. 3966
RUSH STREET INTERACTIVE, INC.; *U.S. Public*, pg. 1827
RUSH TRUCK CENTER OF ALBUQUERQUE, INC.—See Rush Enterprises, Inc.; *U.S. Public*, pg. 1826

RUSSCO INC.

RUSH TRUCK CENTERS - KANSAS CITY—See Rush Enterprises, Inc.; *U.S. Public*, pg. 1826
RUSH TRUCK CENTERS - LOWELL—See Rush Enterprises, Inc.; *U.S. Public*, pg. 1826
RUSH TRUCK CENTERS - MEMPHIS—See Rush Enterprises, Inc.; *U.S. Public*, pg. 1826
RUSH TRUCK CENTERS - NORTH LITTLE ROCK—See Rush Enterprises, Inc.; *U.S. Public*, pg. 1826
RUSH TRUCK CENTERS OF ARIZONA, INC.—See Rush Enterprises, Inc.; *U.S. Public*, pg. 1826
RUSH TRUCK CENTERS OF CALIFORNIA INC.—See Rush Enterprises, Inc.; *U.S. Public*, pg. 1826
RUSH TRUCK CENTERS OF COLORADO INC.—See Rush Enterprises, Inc.; *U.S. Public*, pg. 1826
RUSH TRUCK CENTERS OF FLORIDA, INC.—See Rush Enterprises, Inc.; *U.S. Public*, pg. 1826
RUSH TRUCK CENTERS OF GEORGIA, INC.—See Rush Enterprises, Inc.; *U.S. Public*, pg. 1826
RUSH TRUCK CENTERS OF IDAHO, INC.—See Rush Enterprises, Inc.; *U.S. Public*, pg. 1826
RUSH TRUCK CENTERS OF ILLINOIS, INC.—See Rush Enterprises, Inc.; *U.S. Public*, pg. 1826
RUSH TRUCK CENTERS OF INDIANA, INC.—See Rush Enterprises, Inc.; *U.S. Public*, pg. 1826
RUSH TRUCK CENTERS OF KANSAS, INC.—See Rush Enterprises, Inc.; *U.S. Public*, pg. 1826
RUSH TRUCK CENTERS OF KENTUCKY, INC.—See Rush Enterprises, Inc.; *U.S. Public*, pg. 1827
RUSH TRUCK CENTERS OF MISSOURI, INC.—See Rush Enterprises, Inc.; *U.S. Public*, pg. 1827
RUSH TRUCK CENTERS OF NEVADA, INC.—See Rush Enterprises, Inc.; *U.S. Public*, pg. 1827
RUSH TRUCK CENTERS OF NEW MEXICO, INC.—See Rush Enterprises, Inc.; *U.S. Public*, pg. 1827
RUSH TRUCK CENTERS OF OHIO, INC.—See Rush Enterprises, Inc.; *U.S. Public*, pg. 1827
RUSH TRUCK CENTERS OF OREGON, INC.—See Rush Enterprises, Inc.; *U.S. Public*, pg. 1827
RUSH TRUCK CENTERS OF TENNESSEE, INC.—See Rush Enterprises, Inc.; *U.S. Public*, pg. 1827
RUSH TRUCK CENTERS OF TEXAS, L.P.—See Rush Enterprises, Inc.; *U.S. Public*, pg. 1827
RUSH TRUCK CENTERS OF UTAH, INC.—See Rush Enterprises, Inc.; *U.S. Public*, pg. 1827
RUSH TRUCK CENTER; *U.S. Private*, pg. 3505
RUSH TRUCK CENTRES OF CANADA; *Int'l*, pg. 6429
RUSH TRUCKING CORPORATION; *U.S. Private*, pg. 3505
RUSH TRUCK LEASING, INC.—See Rush Enterprises, Inc.; *U.S. Public*, pg. 1827
RUSH TRUCK LEASING-JACKSONVILLE—See Rush Enterprises, Inc.; *U.S. Public*, pg. 1827
RUSHYDRO INTERNATIONAL AG—See PJSC RusHydro; *Int'l*, pg. 5884
RUS INC.—See Recticel S.A.; *Int'l*, pg. 6241
RUS INTERRA INC.—See JK Holdings Co., Ltd.; *Int'l*, pg. 3972
RUSK COUNTY ELECTRIC COOP; *U.S. Private*, pg. 3505
RUSKEN PACKAGING INC.; *U.S. Private*, pg. 3505
RUSKIN AIR MANAGEMENT LIMITED—See Investment AB Latour; *Int'l*, pg. 3783
RUSKIN COMPANY—See Canada Pension Plan Investment Board; *Int'l*, pg. 1281
RUSK, INC.—See American Securities LLC; *U.S. Private*, pg. 248
RUSK REHABILITATION CENTER, LLC—See Encompass Health Corporation; *U.S. Public*, pg. 759
RUSMAR INCORPORATED—See Palo Duro Capital, LLC; *U.S. Private*, pg. 3082
RUSMUR FLOORS, INC.; *U.S. Private*, pg. 3505
RUSNAK AUTOMOTIVE GROUP; *U.S. Private*, pg. 3505
RUSNAK WESTLAKE; *U.S. Private*, pg. 3505
RUSNANO CAPITAL LLC—See RUSNANO JSC; *Int'l*, pg. 6429
RUSNANO JSC; *Int'l*, pg. 6429
RUSNANO USA, INC.—See RUSNANO JSC; *Int'l*, pg. 6429
RUSNARBANK JSC; *Int'l*, pg. 6429
RUSOLOVO OAO—See Seligdar OJSC; *Int'l*, pg. 6701
RUSORO MINING LTD.; *Int'l*, pg. 6429
RUSORO MINING LTD.—See Rusoro Mining Ltd.; *Int'l*, pg. 6429
RUSORO MINING LTD.—See Rusoro Mining Ltd.; *Int'l*, pg. 6429
RUSPETRO LIMITED; *Int'l*, pg. 6429
RUSS BASSETT CORP.; *U.S. Private*, pg. 3505
RUSS BLAKELY & ASSOCIATES, LLC—See The Baldwin Insurance Group, Inc.; *U.S. Public*, pg. 2036
RUSS CHEVROLET; *U.S. Private*, pg. 3505
RUSSCO INC.; *U.S. Private*, pg. 3506
RUSS DARROW CHRYSLER & JEEP OF CEDARBURG—See Russ Darrow Group, Inc.; *U.S. Private*, pg. 3505
RUSS DARROW CHRYSLER & JEEP OF MADISON—See Russ Darrow Group, Inc.; *U.S. Private*, pg. 3505
RUSS DARROW CHRYSLER OF APPLETON—See Russ Darrow Group, Inc.; *U.S. Private*, pg. 3505

RUSSCO INC.

CORPORATE AFFILIATIONS

RUSS DARROW DODGE OF MILWAUKEE—See Russ Darrow Group, Inc.; *U.S. Private*, pg. 3505
RUSS DARROW GROUP, INC.; *U.S. Private*, pg. 3505
RUSS DARROW HONDA, NISSAN & SUZUKI OF MILWAUKEE—See Russ Darrow Group, Inc.; *U.S. Private*, pg. 3505
RUSS DARROW KIA OF APPLETON—See Russ Darrow Group, Inc.; *U.S. Private*, pg. 3505
RUSS DARROW KIA OF FOND DU LAC—See Russ Darrow Group, Inc.; *U.S. Private*, pg. 3505
RUSS DARROW KIA OF MADISON—See Russ Darrow Group, Inc.; *U.S. Private*, pg. 3505
RUSS DARROW KIA OF WAUKESHA—See Russ Darrow Group, Inc.; *U.S. Private*, pg. 3505
RUSS DARROW KIA—See Russ Darrow Group, Inc.; *U.S. Private*, pg. 3505
RUSS DARROW MAZDA OF GREENFIELD—See Russ Darrow Group, Inc.; *U.S. Private*, pg. 3506
RUSS DARROW OF WEST BEND—See Russ Darrow Group, Inc.; *U.S. Private*, pg. 3506
RUSS DAVIS WHOLESALE; *U.S. Private*, pg. 3506
RUSSELECTRIC INC.—See Siemens Aktiengesellschaft; *Int'l*, pg. 6889
RUSSELL ATHLETIC—See Berkshire Hathaway Inc.; *U.S. Public*, pg. 305
RUSSELL BARNETT CHRYSLER-DODGE-JEEP, INC.; *U.S. Private*, pg. 3506
RUSSELL BOND & CO. INC.; *U.S. Private*, pg. 3506
RUSSELL BRANDS, LLC—See Berkshire Hathaway Inc.; *U.S. Public*, pg. 305
RUSSELL BREWERIES INC.; *Int'l*, pg. 6430
RUSSELL BREWING COMPANY LTD.—See Russell Breweries Inc.; *Int'l*, pg. 6430
RUSSELL CELLULAR, INC.; *U.S. Private*, pg. 3506
RUSSELL CHEVROLET COMPANY; *U.S. Private*, pg. 3506
RUSSELL CO., LTD.; *Int'l*, pg. 6430
RUSSELL CORP. ALEXANDER CITY—See Berkshire Hathaway Inc.; *U.S. Public*, pg. 305
RUSSELL CORPORATION—See Berkshire Hathaway Inc.; *U.S. Public*, pg. 305
RUSSELL CORROSION CONSULTANTS, INC.—See General Atlantic Service Company, L.P.; *U.S. Private*, pg. 1662
RUSSELL CREDIT LIMITED—See ITC Limited; *Int'l*, pg. 3831
RUSSELL DIALYSIS, LLC—See DaVita Inc.; *U.S. Public*, pg. 642
RUSSELL DUCTILE CASTINGS LIMITED—See Chamberlin plc; *Int'l*, pg. 1439
RUSSELL EUROPE LIMITED—See Berkshire Hathaway Inc.; *U.S. Public*, pg. 305
RUSSELL FOOD EQUIPMENT LIMITED—See Blue Point Capital Partners, LLC; *U.S. Private*, pg. 590
RUSSELL HALL CO.—See Bain Capital, LP; *U.S. Private*, pg. 441
RUSSELL HERDER; *U.S. Private*, pg. 3506
RUSSELL HERDER—See Russell Herder; *U.S. Private*, pg. 3506
RUSSELL HOBBS DEUTSCHLAND GMBH—See Spectrum Brands Holdings, Inc.; *U.S. Public*, pg. 1916
RUSSELL HOBBS, INC.—See Spectrum Brands Holdings, Inc.; *U.S. Public*, pg. 1916
RUSSELL HOBBS LIMITED—See Spectrum Brands Holdings, Inc.; *U.S. Public*, pg. 1916
RUSSELL IMPLEMENTATION SERVICES, INC.—See The Northwestern Mutual Life Insurance Company; *U.S. Private*, pg. 4085
RUSSELL INVESTMENT GROUP LTD—See The Northwestern Mutual Life Insurance Company; *U.S. Private*, pg. 4085
RUSSELL INVESTMENT GROUP PRIVATE LIMITED—See The Northwestern Mutual Life Insurance Company; *U.S. Private*, pg. 4085
RUSSELL INVESTMENT GROUP PTY LIMITED—See The Northwestern Mutual Life Insurance Company; *U.S. Private*, pg. 4085
RUSSELL INVESTMENT MANAGEMENT LTD—See The Northwestern Mutual Life Insurance Company; *U.S. Private*, pg. 4085
RUSSELL INVESTMENTS CANADA LIMITED—See The Northwestern Mutual Life Insurance Company; *U.S. Private*, pg. 4085
RUSSELL INVESTMENTS GROUP, LLC.—See Reverence Capital Partners LLC; *U.S. Private*, pg. 3415
RUSSELL INVESTMENTS GROUP, LLC.—See TA Associates, Inc.; *U.S. Private*, pg. 3918
RUSSELL INVESTMENTS KOREA LIMITED—See The Northwestern Mutual Life Insurance Company; *U.S. Private*, pg. 4085
RUSSELL INVESTMENTS LIMITED—See The Northwestern Mutual Life Insurance Company; *U.S. Private*, pg. 4085
RUSSELL & JILL HEFFNER, INC.; *U.S. Private*, pg. 3506
RUSSELL LANDS INC.; *U.S. Private*, pg. 3506
RUSSELL MEMORIAL CEMETERY LLC—See Axar Capital Management L.P.; *U.S. Private*, pg. 412
RUSSELL-MOORE LUMBER INC; *U.S. Private*, pg. 3507
RUSSELL OIL COMPANY INC.; *U.S. Private*, pg. 3506

RUSSELL PETROLEUM CORPORATION; *U.S. Private*, pg. 3506
RUSSELL PLASTICS TECHNOLOGY COMPANY, INC.—See Sumitomo Bakelite Co., Ltd.; *Int'l*, pg. 7263
RUSSELL REID WASTE HAULING; *U.S. Private*, pg. 3506
RUSSELL REYNOLDS ASSOCIATES, CHICAGO—See Russell Reynolds Associates Inc.; *U.S. Private*, pg. 3506
RUSSELL REYNOLDS ASSOCIATES, FRANCE—See Russell Reynolds Associates Inc.; *U.S. Private*, pg. 3506
RUSSELL REYNOLDS ASSOCIATES, HAMBURG—See Russell Reynolds Associates Inc.; *U.S. Private*, pg. 3507
RUSSELL REYNOLDS ASSOCIATES INC.; *U.S. Private*, pg. 3506
RUSSELL REYNOLDS ASSOCIATES INC.—See Russell Reynolds Associates Inc.; *U.S. Private*, pg. 3506
RUSSELL REYNOLDS ASSOCIATES LTD.—See Russell Reynolds Associates Inc.; *U.S. Private*, pg. 3506
RUSSELL REYNOLDS ASSOCIATES, MENLO PARK—See Russell Reynolds Associates Inc.; *U.S. Private*, pg. 3507
RUSSELL SENIORS, LLC.; *U.S. Private*, pg. 3507
RUSSELL SIGLER INC.; *U.S. Private*, pg. 3507
RUSSELL & SMITH FORD INC.; *U.S. Private*, pg. 3506
RUSSELL STANDARD CORPORATION; *U.S. Private*, pg. 3507
RUSSELL STOVER CANDIES, LLC—See Chocoladefabriken Lindt & Sprungli AG; *Int'l*, pg. 1576
RUSSELL SUB-SURFACE SYSTEMS, LTD.—See NOV, Inc.; *U.S. Public*, pg. 1546
RUSSELL SWINTON OATMAN DESIGN ASSOCIATES, INC.; *U.S. Private*, pg. 3507
RUSSELL T. BUNDY ASSOCIATES; *U.S. Private*, pg. 3507
RUSSELL TRANSPORT, INC.; *U.S. Private*, pg. 3507
RUSSELLVILLE HOSPITAL, INC.—See Curae Health, Inc.; *U.S. Private*, pg. 1124
RUSSELLVILLE NEWSPAPERS INC.—See Paxton Media Group LLC; *U.S. Private*, pg. 3116
RUSSELL-WARNER INC.; *U.S. Private*, pg. 3507
RUSSEL METALS INC.; *Int'l*, pg. 6429
RUSSEL METALS WILLIAMS BAHCALL INC., APPLETON—See Russel Metals Inc.; *Int'l*, pg. 6430
RUSSEL METALS WILLIAMS BAHCALL INC.—See Russel Metals Inc.; *Int'l*, pg. 6430
RUSSIA BALTIC PORK INVEST ASA—See Charoen Pokphand Foods Public Company Limited; *Int'l*, pg. 1453
RUSSIA CORPORATION—See Hyundai Glovis Co., Ltd.; *Int'l*, pg. 3557
RUSSIAN AGRICULTURAL BANK JSC; *Int'l*, pg. 6430
RUSSIAN HELICOPTERS, JSC—See Russian Technologies State Corporation; *Int'l*, pg. 6431
RUSSIAN MACHINES CORPORATION—See Basic Element Company; *Int'l*, pg. 886
RUSSIAN NATIONAL REINSURANCE COMPANY JSC; *Int'l*, pg. 6430
RUSSIAN REGIONAL DEVELOPMENT BANK JSC; *Int'l*, pg. 6430
RUSSIAN STANDARD CREDIT BUREAU LLC—See CJSC Russian Standard Corporation; *Int'l*, pg. 1634
RUSSIAN STANDARD VODKA—See CJSC Russian Standard Corporation; *Int'l*, pg. 1634
RUSSIAN TECHNOLOGIES STATE CORPORATION; *Int'l*, pg. 6430
RUSSIAN TELECOM EQUIPMENT COMPANY CJSC—See Russian Technologies State Corporation; *Int'l*, pg. 6432
RUSSI HEIZUNG-SANITAR AG—See Burkhalter Holding AG; *Int'l*, pg. 1225
RUSSIN LUMBER CORP; *U.S. Private*, pg. 3507
RUSS & JANOT GMBH—See Mercedes-Benz Group AG; *Int'l*, pg. 4829
RUSSKAYA AKVAKULTURA; *Int'l*, pg. 6432
RUSSKAYA ZEMLYA LLC—See Onexim Group Limited; *Int'l*, pg. 5581
RUSSKIYE SAMOTSVETY CORPORATION; *Int'l*, pg. 6432
RUSSNEFT PJSC; *Int'l*, pg. 6432
THE RUSSO FINANCIAL GROUP—See The Northwestern Mutual Life Insurance Company; *U.S. Private*, pg. 4085
RUSSO HARDWARE, INC.; *U.S. Private*, pg. 3507
RUSSO'S NEW YORK PIZZERIA; *U.S. Private*, pg. 3507
RUSS SMALE, INC.; *U.S. Private*, pg. 3506
RUSTAN SUPERCENTERS, INC.—See Robinsons Retail Holdings, Inc.; *Int'l*, pg. 6370
RUST COMMUNICATIONS; *U.S. Private*, pg. 3507
RUST CONSULTING, INC.—See Gainline Capital Partners LP; *U.S. Private*, pg. 1635
RUSTHUIS KRUYENBERG NV—See Ackermans & van Haaren NV; *Int'l*, pg. 106
RUSTIC CANYON PARTNERS; *U.S. Private*, pg. 3507
RUSTIC CRUST; *U.S. Private*, pg. 3507
RUSTIC ESCENTUALS—See Incline MGMT Corp.; *U.S. Private*, pg. 2054

RUSTICI SOFTWARE LLC.—See Learning Technologies Group plc; *Int'l*, pg. 4435
RUST-OLEUM AUSTRALIA & NEW ZEALAND PTY. LTD.—See RPM International Inc.; *U.S. Public*, pg. 1820
RUST-OLEUM AUSTRALIA PTY. LIMITED—See RPM International Inc.; *U.S. Public*, pg. 1820
RUST-OLEUM CORPORATION—See RPM International Inc.; *U.S. Public*, pg. 1817
RUST-OLEUM FRANCE S.A.S.—See RPM International Inc.; *U.S. Public*, pg. 1820
RUST-OLEUM INTERNATIONAL, LLC—See RPM International Inc.; *U.S. Public*, pg. 1817
RUST-OLEUM JAPAN CORPORATION—See RPM International Inc.; *U.S. Public*, pg. 1817
RUST-OLEUM SALES CO., INC.—See RPM International Inc.; *U.S. Public*, pg. 1817
RUST-OLEUM UK LIMITED—See RPM International Inc.; *U.S. Public*, pg. 1820
RUSTON CLINIC COMPANY, LLC—See Community Health Systems, Inc.; *U.S. Public*, pg. 556
RUSTON INDUSTRIAL SUPPLIES, INC.; *U.S. Private*, pg. 3507
RUSTON LOUISIANA HOSPITAL COMPANY, LLC—See Community Health Systems, Inc.; *U.S. Public*, pg. 556
RUSTON PAVING CO. INC.; *U.S. Private*, pg. 3507
RUSTOORD DE VLAAMSE ARDENNEN LLC—See Clariane SE; *Int'l*, pg. 1644
RUSTY ECK FORD, INC.; *U.S. Private*, pg. 3507
RUSTY WALLIS, INC.; *U.S. Private*, pg. 3507
RUSVINYL LLC—See OAO SIBUR Holding; *Int'l*, pg. 5507
RUTAB AB—See Addtech AB; *Int'l*, pg. 135
RUTAB AS—See Addtech AB; *Int'l*, pg. 135
RUTAN REALTY, LLC—See Johnson & Johnson; *U.S. Public*, pg. 1200
RUTAR INTERNATIONAL TRGOVINSKA D.O.O.—See Erste Group Bank AG; *Int'l*, pg. 2499
RUTAS DEL PACIFICO S.A.—See ACS, Actividades de Construccion y Servicios, S.A.; *Int'l*, pg. 112
RUTGERS CASUALTY INSURANCE CO—See American European Group, Inc.; *U.S. Private*, pg. 232
RUTGERS CHEMTRADE GMBH—See Rain Industries Limited; *Int'l*, pg. 6189
RUTGERS GERMANY GMBH—See Rain Industries Limited; *Int'l*, pg. 6189
RUTGERS ORGANICS GMBH—See International Chemical Investors S.E.; *Int'l*, pg. 3745
RUTHENIUM INVESTMENTS LIMITED—See Barclays PLC; *Int'l*, pg. 863
RUTHERFORD ELECTRIC MEMBERSHIP; *U.S. Private*, pg. 3507
RUTHERFORD EQUIPMENT INC.; *U.S. Private*, pg. 3507
RUTHERFORD FARMERS COOPERATIVE INC.; *U.S. Private*, pg. 3508
RUTHERFORD FARM, LLC—See The Southern Company; *U.S. Public*, pg. 2131
RUTHERFORD HILL WINERY—See The Terlato Wine Group; *U.S. Private*, pg. 4126
RUTHMAN PUMP & ENGINEERING INC.; *U.S. Private*, pg. 3508
RUTHRAUFF LLC; *U.S. Private*, pg. 3508
RUTH'S CHRIS STEAK HOUSE FRANCHISE, LLC—See Darden Restaurants, Inc.; *U.S. Public*, pg. 633
RUTH'S HOSPITALITY GROUP, INC.—See Darden Restaurants, Inc.; *U.S. Public*, pg. 633
RUTH VERWALTUNGSGESELLSCHAFT MBH—See Mercedes-Benz Group AG; *Int'l*, pg. 4829
RUTLAND FUND MANAGEMENT LTD.—See Rutland Partners LLP; *Int'l*, pg. 6432
RUTLAND GROUP, INC.—See Avient Corporation; *U.S. Public*, pg. 248
RUTLAND INTERNATIONAL LIMITED—See Avient Corporation; *U.S. Public*, pg. 248
RUTLAND PARTNERS LLP; *Int'l*, pg. 6432
RUTLAND PLASTIC TECHNOLOGIES, INC.—See Avient Corporation; *U.S. Public*, pg. 248
RUTLAND PLYWOOD CORP.; *U.S. Private*, pg. 3508
RUTLAND PRODUCTS CO.; *U.S. Private*, pg. 3508
RUTLAND PRODUCTS, INC.—See Rutland Products Co.; *U.S. Private*, pg. 3508
RUTRONIK BETEILIGUNGSGESELLSCHAFT MBH—See Rutronik Elektronische Bauelemente GmbH; *Int'l*, pg. 6432
RUTRONIK ELECTRONICS ASIA HK LTD—See Rutronik Elektronische Bauelemente GmbH; *Int'l*, pg. 6433
RUTRONIK ELEKTRONISCHE BAUELEMENTE GMBH; *Int'l*, pg. 6432
RUTRONIK ESPANA S.L.—See Rutronik Elektronische Bauelemente GmbH; *Int'l*, pg. 6432
RUTRONIK ITALIA S.R.L.—See Rutronik Elektronische Bauelemente GmbH; *Int'l*, pg. 6433
RUTRONIK MAGYARORSZAG KFT.—See Rutronik Elektronische Bauelemente GmbH; *Int'l*, pg. 6433
RUTRONIK NORDIC AB—See Rutronik Elektronische Bauelemente GmbH; *Int'l*, pg. 6433
RUTRONIK POLSKA SP. Z O.O.—See Rutronik Elektronische Bauelemente GmbH; *Int'l*, pg. 6433
RUTRONIK S.A.S—See Rutronik Elektronische Bauelemente GmbH; *Int'l*, pg. 6433

COMPANY NAME INDEX

RUTRONIK UK LIMITED—See Rutronik Elektronische Bauelemente GmbH; *Int'l*, pg. 6433
RUTSCHI FLUID AG; *Int'l*, pg. 6433
RUTTER INC.; *Int'l*, pg. 6433
RUTTONSHA INTERNATIONAL RECTIFIER LTD.; *Int'l*, pg. 6433
RUUD LIGHTING, INC.—See Wolfspeed, Inc.; *U.S. Public*, pg. 2377
RUUKKI BENELUX B.V.—See SSAB AB; *Int'l*, pg. 7154
RUUKKI CONSTRUCTION OY—See SSAB AB; *Int'l*, pg. 7154
RUUKKI CZ S.R.O.—See SSAB AB; *Int'l*, pg. 7154
RUUKKI DANMARK A/S—See SSAB AB; *Int'l*, pg. 7154
RUUKKI FINANCE B.V.—See SSAB AB; *Int'l*, pg. 7154
RUUKKI FRANCE SARL—See SSAB AB; *Int'l*, pg. 7154
RUUKKI HOLDING B.V.—See SSAB AB; *Int'l*, pg. 7154
RUUKKI HOLDING GMBH—See SSAB AB; *Int'l*, pg. 7154
RUUKKI HUNGARY KFT—See SSAB AB; *Int'l*, pg. 7154
RUUKKI LATVIA S.I.A.—See SSAB AB; *Int'l*, pg. 7154
RUUKKI LITHUANIA—See SSAB AB; *Int'l*, pg. 7154
RUUKKI L.L.C—See SSAB AB; *Int'l*, pg. 7154
RUUKKI METALS POLSKA SP. Z.O.O.—See SSAB AB; *Int'l*, pg. 7154
RUUKKI METALS TOIJALAN—See SSAB AB; *Int'l*, pg. 7154
RUUKKI NORGE—See SSAB AB; *Int'l*, pg. 7154
RUUKKI POLSKA SP. Z.O.O.—See SSAB AB; *Int'l*, pg. 7154
RUUKKI PRODUCT AS—See SSAB AB; *Int'l*, pg. 7154
RUUKKI PRODUCTS AS—See SSAB AB; *Int'l*, pg. 7154
RUUKKI ROMANIA S.R.L.—See SSAB AB; *Int'l*, pg. 7154
RUUKKI SLOVAKIA, S.R.O.—See SSAB AB; *Int'l*, pg. 7154
RUUKKI SPAIN S.L.—See SSAB AB; *Int'l*, pg. 7154
RUUKKI STAINLESS STEEL & ALUMINIUM OY—See SSAB AB; *Int'l*, pg. 7154
RUUKKI SVERIGE AB—See SSAB AB; *Int'l*, pg. 7154
RUUKKI SVERIGE AB—See SSAB AB; *Int'l*, pg. 7154
RUUKKI SVERIGE AB—See SSAB AB; *Int'l*, pg. 7154
RUUKKI UK LTD.—See SSAB AB; *Int'l*, pg. 7154
RUV AGENTURBERATUNGS GMBH—See DZ BANK AG Deutsche Zentral-Genossenschaftsbank; *Int'l*, pg. 2244
RUVAL SA—See Barclays PLC; *Int'l*, pg. 863
RUWAD AL ATHAIBA INTERNATIONAL LLC—See Muehlhan AG; *Int'l*, pg. 5077
R & U WEBER GMBH & CO. KG—See GERRY WEBER International AG; *Int'l*, pg. 2945
RUWEL INTERNATIONAL GMBH—See Unimicron Technology Corporation; *Int'l*, pg. 8050
RUXER FORD LINCOLN MERCURY; *U.S. Private*, pg. 3508
RUYLE MECHANICAL SERVICES, INC—See Partners Group Holding AG; *Int'l*, pg. 5750
RUYS HANDELSVERENIGING B.V—See Francotyp-Postalia Holding AG; *Int'l*, pg. 2761
RUZHOU XINTAI SOLAR POWER TECHNOLOGICAL DEVELOPMENT CO.,LTD.—See HENAN SENYUAN ELECTRIC CO., LTD.; *Int'l*, pg. 3343
RV ACQUISITION CORP.; *U.S. Private*, pg. 3508
RVA INC.—See Robinson Aviation (RVA) Inc.; *U.S. Private*, pg. 3461
R+V ALLGEMEINE VERSICHERUNG AKTIENGESELLSCHAFT—See DZ BANK AG Deutsche Zentral-Genossenschaftsbank; *Int'l*, pg. 2244
RV ASSURANCES SA; *Int'l*, pg. 6433
RVCA CORPORATION—See Leonard Green & Partners, L.P.; *U.S. Private*, pg. 2424
R.V. CLOUD CO.; *U.S. Private*, pg. 3340
RVC MEDICAL IT B.V.—See NEXUS AG; *Int'l*, pg. 5250
RV CONNECTIONS, INC.; *U.S. Private*, pg. 3508
R+V DIENSTLEISTUNGS GMBH—See DZ BANK AG Deutsche Zentral-Genossenschaftsbank; *Int'l*, pg. 2244
R+V DIREKTVERSICHERUNG AG—See DZ BANK AG Deutsche Zentral-Genossenschaftsbank; *Int'l*, pg. 2244
RVE, INC.; *U.S. Private*, pg. 3508
R-VENT NETHERLANDS B.V.—See Lindab International AB; *Int'l*, pg. 4504
RVE REGIONALVERKEHR EUREGIO MAAS-RHEIN GMBH—See Deutsche Bahn AG; *Int'l*, pg. 2052
R.V. EVANS COMPANY; *U.S. Private*, pg. 3340
RVG PARTNERS, LLC—See Porte Brown LLC; *U.S. Private*, pg. 3231
RVG RHEINAUHAFEN VERWALTUNGSGESELLSCHAFT MBH—See Vonovia SE; *Int'l*, pg. 8305
RVH INC.; *Int'l*, pg. 6433
RVISION INC.—See COMSovereign Holding Corp.; *U.S. Public*, pg. 562
RVL HOLDING BV—See LVMH Moet Hennessy Louis Vuitton SE; *Int'l*, pg. 4600
RVL PHARMACEUTICALS PLC; *U.S. Public*, pg. 1827
RVL RESTSTOFFVERWERTUNG LENZING GMBH—See Lenzing Aktiengesellschaft; *Int'l*, pg. 4456
R+V LUXEMBOURG LEBENSVERSICHERUNG S.A.—See DZ BANK AG Deutsche Zentral-Genossenschaftsbank; *Int'l*, pg. 2244
RVM ENTERPRISES, INC.—See JLL Partners, LLC; *U.S. Private*, pg. 2213

R.V. METROPOLIS DIAGNOSTIC & HEALTH CARE CENTER PRIVATE LIMITED—See Metropolis Healthcare Ltd.; *Int'l*, pg. 4863
RVM INC.; *U.S. Private*, pg. 3508
RVM RAIFFEISEN-VERSICHERUNGSMAKLER GMBH—See Raiffeisenlandesbank Oberosterreich Aktiengesellschaft; *Int'l*, pg. 6187
RVM VERSICHERUNGSMAKLER GMBH—See MLP SE; *Int'l*, pg. 5004
RVN REGIONALVERKEHR NIEDERRHEIN GMBH—See Deutsche Bahn AG; *Int'l*, pg. 2052
RVOS FARM MUTUAL INSURANCE COMPANY; *U.S. Private*, pg. 3508
RVP DEVELOPMENT CORPORATION; *U.S. Private*, pg. 3508
RV PEDDLER INC; *U.S. Private*, pg. 3508
RV REPAIR & SALES INC.—See Pollard Enterprises Inc.; *U.S. Private*, pg. 3224
RV RETAILER, LLC—See Redwood Capital Investments, LLC; *U.S. Private*, pg. 3380
RV RHEINBRAUN HANDEL UND DIENSTLEISTUNGEN GMBH—See RWE AG; *Int'l*, pg. 6435
R+V SERVICE CENTER GMBH—See DZ BANK AG Deutsche Zentral-Genossenschaftsbank; *Int'l*, pg. 2244
RV'S NORTHWEST INC.; *U.S. Private*, pg. 3508
RVS REGIONALBUSVERKEHR SUDWEST GMBH—See Deutsche Bahn AG; *Int'l*, pg. 2052
RVT DELLEBRON BVBA—See Clariane SE; *Int'l*, pg. 1644
RV TRADERS; *U.S. Private*, pg. 3508
R V WORLD, INC.—See Markquart Inc.; *U.S. Private*, pg. 2582
RV WORLD, LLC—See Camping World Holdings, Inc.; *U.S. Public*, pg. 428
RV WORLD OF GEORGIA, LLC—See Camping World Holdings, Inc.; *U.S. Public*, pg. 428
RV WORLD OF NOKOMIS INC.; *U.S. Private*, pg. 3508
RWA CONSULTING S.R.L.—See Edenred S.A.; *Int'l*, pg. 2308
RW ADVERTISING, INC.; *U.S. Private*, pg. 3508
RWA HRVATSKA D.O.O.—See BayWa AG; *Int'l*, pg. 918
RWA INTERNATIONAL HOLDING GMBH—See BayWa AG; *Int'l*, pg. 919
RWA MAGYARORSZAG KFT—See BayWa AG; *Int'l*, pg. 918
RWA RAIFFEISEN AGRO D.O.O—See BayWa AG; *Int'l*, pg. 918
RWA RAIFFEISEN AGRO ROMANIA S.R.L.—See BayWa AG; *Int'l*, pg. 918
RWA RAIFFEISEN WARE AUSTRIA AKTIENGESELLSCHAFT—See BayWa AG; *Int'l*, pg. 919
R.W. ARMSTRONG & ASSOCIATES LLC—See H.I.G. Capital, LLC; *U.S. Private*, pg. 1827
RWA SLOVAKIA SPOL. S.R.O.—See BayWa AG; *Int'l*, pg. 918
RWA SLOVENIJA D.O.O.—See BayWa AG; *Int'l*, pg. 918
RWA SRBIJA D.O.O.—See BayWa AG; *Int'l*, pg. 918
RWA UKRAJINA LLC—See BayWa AG; *Int'l*, pg. 918
R.W. BECKETT CORPORATION; *U.S. Private*, pg. 3340
RW BLOCK CONSULTING, INC.—See Accenture plc; *Int'l*, pg. 86
RWB REAL ESTATE INC.; *U.S. Private*, pg. 3508
RWBT INC.; *U.S. Private*, pg. 3508
RWC INC.; *U.S. Private*, pg. 3508
RWC INTERNATIONAL LTD.; *U.S. Private*, pg. 3508
R&W CONCRETE CONTRACTOR; *U.S. Private*, pg. 3333
R/W CONNECTION, INC.—See AEA Investors LP; *U.S. Private*, pg. 115
RW COOKWARE S.L.—See Rena-Ware Distributors Inc.; *U.S. Private*, pg. 3397
RW & CO.—See Reitmans (Canada) Limited; *Int'l*, pg. 6259
R.W. DISTRIBUTORS—See Rena-Ware Distributors Inc.; *U.S. Private*, pg. 3397
RWD SCHLATTER AG—See Arbonia AG; *Int'l*, pg. 538
RWD TECHNOLOGIES LLC; *U.S. Private*, pg. 3509
RWE AG; *Int'l*, pg. 6433
RWE BETEILIGUNGSGESELLSCHAFT MBH—See RWE AG; *Int'l*, pg. 6435
RWE CLEAN ENERGY SOLUTIONS, INC.—See RWE AG; *Int'l*, pg. 6434
RWE CLEAN ENERGY WHOLESALE SERVICES, INC.—See RWE AG; *Int'l*, pg. 6434
RWE DEUTSCHLAND AKTIENGESELLSCHAFT—See RWE AG; *Int'l*, pg. 6435
RWE EFFIZIENZ GMBH—See RWE AG; *Int'l*, pg. 6435
RWE ENERGIE, A.S.—See RWE AG; *Int'l*, pg. 6435
RWE ENERGIE ODNAWIALNE SP. Z O.O.—See RWE AG; *Int'l*, pg. 6435
RWE ENERGY NEDERLAND N.V.—See RWE AG; *Int'l*, pg. 6435
RWE GASNET, S.R.O.—See RWE AG; *Int'l*, pg. 6435
RWE GAS STORAGE CZ, S.R.O.—See RWE AG; *Int'l*, pg. 6435
RWE GENERATION SE—See RWE AG; *Int'l*, pg. 6435
RWE HRVATSKA D.O.O.—See RWE AG; *Int'l*, pg. 6435
RWE INNOGY GMBH—See RWE AG; *Int'l*, pg. 6435
RWE KUNDENSERVICE GMBH—See RWE AG; *Int'l*, pg. 6435

R.W. SIDLEY, INCORPORATED

RWE LJUBLJANA D.O.O.—See RWE AG; *Int'l*, pg. 6435
RWE NPOWER HOLDINGS PLC—See RWE AG; *Int'l*, pg. 6435
RWE NPOWER PLC—See RWE AG; *Int'l*, pg. 6435
RWE NPOWER RENEWABLES LIMITED—See RWE AG; *Int'l*, pg. 6435
RWE NUCLEAR GMBH—See RWE AG; *Int'l*, pg. 6435
RWE PLIN D.O.O.—See RWE AG; *Int'l*, pg. 6435
RWE POWER AKTIENGESELLSCHAFT—See RWE AG; *Int'l*, pg. 6435
RWE RENEWABLES GMBH—See RWE AG; *Int'l*, pg. 6435
RWE RENEWABLES SWEDEN AB—See RWE AG; *Int'l*, pg. 6435
RWE RHEIN-RUHR VERTEILNETZ GMBH—See RWE AG; *Int'l*, pg. 6435
RWE SERVICE GMBH—See RWE AG; *Int'l*, pg. 6435
RWE STOEN OPERATOR SP. Z O.O.—See RWE AG; *Int'l*, pg. 6435
RWE SUPPLY & TRADING ASIA-PACIFIC PTE. LTD.—See RWE AG; *Int'l*, pg. 6435
RWE SUPPLY & TRADING CZ, A.S.—See RWE AG; *Int'l*, pg. 6435
RWE SUPPLY & TRADING CZ GMBH—See RWE AG; *Int'l*, pg. 6435
RWE SUPPLY & TRADING GMBH—See RWE AG; *Int'l*, pg. 6435
RWE SUPPLY & TRADING (INDIA) PRIVATE LIMITED—See RWE AG; *Int'l*, pg. 6435
RWE SUPPLY & TRADING JAPAN KK—See RWE AG; *Int'l*, pg. 6435
RWE SUPPLY & TRADING SWITZERLAND S.A.—See RWE AG; *Int'l*, pg. 6435
RWE TECHNOLOGY INTERNATIONAL GMBH—See RWE AG; *Int'l*, pg. 6435
RWE TRANSGAS, A.S.—See RWE AG; *Int'l*, pg. 6435
RWE VERTRIEB AKTIENGESELLSCHAFT—See RWE AG; *Int'l*, pg. 6435
RWE WESTFALEN-WESER-EMS NETZSERVICE GMBH—See RWE AG; *Int'l*, pg. 6435
RWE WESTFALEN-WESER-EMS VERTEILNETZ GMBH—See RWE AG; *Int'l*, pg. 6435
RWF HEALTH & COMMUNITY DEVELOPERS LIMITED—See HICL Infrastructure PLC; *Int'l*, pg. 3383
R.W. GARCIA CO., INC.—See Utz Brands, Inc.; *U.S. Public*, pg. 2267
RWG GERMANY GMBH—See Arcline Investment Management LP; *U.S. Private*, pg. 314
RWG I ABBRUCH UND TIEFBAU GMBH—See Heidelberg Materials AG; *Int'l*, pg. 3319
RWG I/SCHICHT BAUSTOFFAUFBEREITUNG, LOGISTIK + ENTSORGUNG GMBH—See Heidelberg Materials AG; *Int'l*, pg. 3319
R.W. HARRIS INC.; *U.S. Private*, pg. 3340
RW INOX DE RL DE C.V.—See Rena-Ware Distributors Inc.; *U.S. Private*, pg. 3397
RWI TRANSPORTATION LLC—See Castellini Company, Inc.; *U.S. Private*, pg. 784
RW LOGISTICS OY—See Nurminen Logistics Plc; *Int'l*, pg. 5490
R.W. LYALL & COMPANY INC.—See Hubbell Incorporated; *U.S. Public*, pg. 1067
RWM BETEILIGUNGSVERWALTUNG AUSTRIA GMBH—See Rheinmetall AG; *Int'l*, pg. 6323
RWM CASTERS COMPANY; *U.S. Private*, pg. 3509
R.W. MERCER COMPANY, INC.; *U.S. Private*, pg. 3340
R&W METAL FABRICATING & DESIGN INC.; *Int'l*, pg. 6169
RWM ITALIA S.P.A.—See Rheinmetall AG; *Int'l*, pg. 6323
RWM SCHWEIZ AG—See Rheinmetall AG; *Int'l*, pg. 6323
RWM TECHNOLOGIES LLC—See Piedmont Chemical Industries, Inc.; *U.S. Private*, pg. 3177
RWM ZAUGG AG—See Rheinmetall AG; *Int'l*, pg. 6323
RW NATIONAL HOLDINGS, LLC—See Appreciate Holdings, Inc.; *U.S. Public*, pg. 173
RW PACKAGING LTD.; *Int'l*, pg. 6433
R.W. PRESSPRICH & CO., INCORPORATED; *U.S. Private*, pg. 3340
RWP TRANSFER INC.; *U.S. Private*, pg. 3509
RWR ENTERPRISES INC.; *U.S. Private*, pg. 3509
RW RHINE INC.; *U.S. Private*, pg. 3508
RWR TRUCKING INC.—See Source Energy Services Ltd.; *Int'l*, pg. 7115
RWS & ASSOCIATES ENTERTAINMENT, INC.; *U.S. Private*, pg. 3509
R.W. SAUDER INC.; *U.S. Private*, pg. 3340
RWS ENTERPRISES; *U.S. Private*, pg. 3509
RWS GROUP DEUTSCHLAND GMBH—See RWS Holdings plc; *Int'l*, pg. 6437
RWS HOLDING, LLC; *U.S. Private*, pg. 3509
RWS HOLDINGS PLC - MEDICAL TRANSLATION DIVISION—See RWS Holdings plc; *Int'l*, pg. 6437
RWS HOLDINGS PLC; *Int'l*, pg. 6436
R.W. SIDLEY, INCORPORATED; *U.S. Private*, pg. 3340
RW SILICIUM GMBH—See AMG Critical Materials N.V.; *Int'l*, pg. 426
RWS INFORMATION LIMITED—See RWS Holdings plc; *Int'l*, pg. 6437

R.W. SIDLEY, INCORPORATED

CORPORATE AFFILIATIONS

RWS LIFE SCIENCES, INC.—See RWS Holdings plc; *Int'l*, pg. 6437

R.W. SMITH & CO.—See Warburg Pincus LLC; *U.S. Private*, pg. 4440

RW SPECIALTIES LLC—See Strength Capital Partners, LLC; *U.S. Private*, pg. 3839

RWS TRANSLATIONS LIMITED—See RWS Holdings plc; *Int'l*, pg. 6437

RWTUV AKADEMIE GMBH—See TUV NORD AG; *Int'l*, pg. 7980

RW USA CORP.—See Raymond Weil S.A.; *Int'l*, pg. 6224

RWW RHEINISCH-WESTFALISCHE WASSERWERKSGE-SELLSCHAFT MBH—See RWE AG; *Int'l*, pg. 6435

R.W. ZANT COMPANY; *U.S. Private*, pg. 3340

RXAMERICA LLC—See CVS Health Corporation; *U.S. Public*, pg. 616

RXBENEFITS, INC.; *U.S. Private*, pg. 3509

RXC ACQUISITION COMPANY—See McKesson Corporation; *U.S. Public*, pg. 1408

RX CARE SPECIALTY PHARMACY LLC—See Benzer Pharmacy Holding LLC; *U.S. Private*, pg. 529

RX DIRECT, INC.,—See Centene Corporation; *U.S. Public*, pg. 470

RX FOR FLEAS INC.; *U.S. Private*, pg. 3509

RXHELPLINE, LLC—See Madison Dearborn Partners, LLC; *U.S. Private*, pg. 2540

RX JAPAN CO., LTD.—See RELX plc; *Int'l*, pg. 6266

RXO INC.; *U.S. Public*, pg. 1827

RX OPTICAL LABORATORY INC.; *U.S. Private*, pg. 3509

RX OPTIONS, LLC—See New Rite Aid, LLC; *U.S. Private*, pg. 2906

RX PLASTICS LIMITED—See Aliaxis S.A./N.V.; *Int'l*, pg. 325

RXP SERVICES LIMITED—See Capgemini SE; *Int'l*, pg. 1303

RXP SERVICES LTD.—See Capgemini SE; *Int'l*, pg. 1303

RXR ACQUISITION CORP.; *U.S. Public*, pg. 1827

RXR REALTY, LLC; *U.S. Private*, pg. 3509

RXSAFE LLC—See Illinois Tool Works Inc.; *U.S. Public*, pg. 1110

RXSAVER, INC.—See MacAndrews & Forbes Incorporated; *U.S. Private*, pg. 2532

RXSIGHT, INC.; *U.S. Public*, pg. 1827

RXSOLUTIONS, INC.—See Odyssey Investment Partners, LLC; *U.S. Private*, pg. 2996

RX SYSTEMS INC.; *U.S. Private*, pg. 3509

RX TECHNOLOGIES CORP.; *U.S. Private*, pg. 3509

RX TECHNOLOGY CORP.—See Cenveo, Inc.; *U.S. Private*, pg. 835

RXUSA; *U.S. Private*, pg. 3509

RXVANTAGE, INC.; *U.S. Private*, pg. 3509

RX VITAMINS, INC.—See Swedencare AB; *Int'l*, pg. 7365

R & Y AC COMPRESSOR, INC.; *U.S. Private*, pg. 3331

RYALUX CARPETS LIMITED—See AIREA PLC; *Int'l*, pg. 247

RYANAIR HOLDINGS PLC; *Int'l*, pg. 6438

RYANAIR LIMITED—See Ryanair Holdings PLC; *Int'l*, pg. 6438

RYAN BIGGS CLARK DAVIS, ENGINEERING & SURVEYING, P.C.; *U.S. Private*, pg. 3509

THE RYAN COMPANIES, LLC; *U.S. Private*, pg. 4113

RYAN COMPANIES US, INC.; *U.S. Private*, pg. 3509

RYAN COMPANIES US, INC.—See Ryan Companies US, Inc.; *U.S. Private*, pg. 3510

THE RYAN COMPANY, INC.—See Quanta Services, Inc.; *U.S. Public*, pg. 1753

RYAN COMPANY INC.—See Quanta Services, Inc.; *U.S. Public*, pg. 1753

RYAN CONSTRUCTION CO. INC—See Boyne Capital Management, LLC; *U.S. Private*, pg. 629

RYAN DIRECTIONAL SERVICES, INC.—See Nabors Industries Ltd.; *Int'l*, pg. 5119

RYAN DODGE; *U.S. Private*, pg. 3510

RYAN ENERGY TECHNOLOGIES USA, INC.—See Nabors Industries Ltd.; *Int'l*, pg. 5119

RYAN & FAULDS LLC—See Redniss & Mead, Inc.; *U.S. Private*, pg. 3379

RYAN FIREPROTECTION INC.; *U.S. Private*, pg. 3510

RYANGOLF CORPORATION—See The Ryan Companies, LLC; *U.S. Private*, pg. 4113

RYAN HERCO PRODUCTS CORP.—See Clayton, Dubilier & Rice, LLC; *U.S. Private*, pg. 926

RYAN INCORPORATED CENTRAL; *U.S. Private*, pg. 3510

RYAN INCORPORATED MINING—See The Ryan Companies, LLC; *U.S. Private*, pg. 4113

RYAN LABS ASSET MANAGEMENT INC.—See Sun Life Financial Inc.; *Int'l*, pg. 7305

RYAN LAWN & TREE INC.; *U.S. Private*, pg. 3510

RYAN LINCOLN MERCURY KIA; *U.S. Private*, pg. 3510

RYAN, LLC; *U.S. Private*, pg. 3510

RYAN PARTNERSHIP, LLC; *U.S. Private*, pg. 3510

RYAN PARTNERSHIP—See Ryan Partnership, LLC; *U.S. Private*, pg. 3510

RYAN PARTNERSHIP—See Ryan Partnership, LLC; *U.S. Private*, pg. 3510

RYAN PRINTING, INC; *U.S. Private*, pg. 3510

RYAN RETAIL ZONE—See Ryan Partnership, LLC; *U.S. Private*, pg. 3510

RYAN SALES & SERVICE, INC.—See The Ryan Companies, LLC; *U.S. Private*, pg. 4113

RYANS ALL-GLASS INC.; *U.S. Private*, pg. 3511

RYAN SANDERS BASEBALL, L.P.; *U.S. Private*, pg. 3510

RYAN SEACREST ENTERPRISES, INC.; *U.S. Private*, pg. 3510

RYAN SEACREST PRODUCTIONS, LLC—See Ryan Seacrest Enterprises, Inc.; *U.S. Private*, pg. 3510

RYAN'S EXPRESS TRANSPORTATION SERVICES, INC.—See Century Park Capital Partners, LLC; *U.S. Private*, pg. 834

RYAN SPECIALTY GROUP, LLC - DENMARK—See Ryan Specialty Holdings, Inc.; *U.S. Public*, pg. 1828

RYAN SPECIALTY GROUP, LLC—See Ryan Specialty Holdings, Inc.; *U.S. Public*, pg. 1827

RYAN SPECIALTY GROUP, LLC - SWEDEN—See Ryan Specialty Holdings, Inc.; *U.S. Public*, pg. 1828

RYAN SPECIALTY HOLDINGS, INC.; *U.S. Public*, pg. 1827

RYAN SUPPLY, INC.—See Ace Hardware Corporation; *U.S. Private*, pg. 57

RYAN TRADING CORP.; *U.S. Private*, pg. 3510

RYAN TRANSPORTATION GROUP, INC.—See Auto Expediting Inc.; *U.S. Private*, pg. 397

RYAN TRANSPORTATION INC.—See Auto Expediting Inc.; *U.S. Private*, pg. 397

RYBOVICH BOAT COMPANY LLC—See Sun Communities, Inc.; *U.S. Public*, pg. 1963

RYCAN TECHNOLOGIES INC.—See TruBridge, Inc.; *U.S. Public*, pg. 2198

RYCO GROUP PTY LIMITED—See Amotiv Limited; *Int'l*, pg. 431

RYCON CONSTRUCTION INC.; *U.S. Private*, pg. 3511

RYCOTE MICROPHONE WINDSHIELDS LTD.—See Videndum plc; *Int'l*, pg. 8191

RYDALCH ELECTRIC INC.; *U.S. Private*, pg. 3511

RYDELL CHEVROLET INC.; *U.S. Private*, pg. 3511

RYDELL COMPANY INC.; *U.S. Private*, pg. 3511

RYDER-ASCENT LOGISTICS PTE LTD—See Ryder System, Inc.; *U.S. Public*, pg. 1828

RYDER CAPITAL LIMITED; *Int'l*, pg. 6438

RYDER CONTAINER TERMINALS—See Ryder System, Inc.; *U.S. Public*, pg. 1828

RYDER CRSA LOGISTICS (HK) LIMITED—See Ryder System, Inc.; *U.S. Public*, pg. 1828

RYDER DE MEXICO S.A. DE C.V.—See Ryder System, Inc.; *U.S. Public*, pg. 1828

RYDER ENERGY DISTRIBUTION CORPORATION—See Ryder System, Inc.; *U.S. Public*, pg. 1828

RYDER FUEL SERVICES, LLC—See Ryder System, Inc.; *U.S. Public*, pg. 1828

RYDER GEOTECHNICAL LIMITED—See Tekmar Group plc; *Int'l*, pg. 7527

RYDER, INC. OF FLORIDA—See Ryder System, Inc.; *U.S. Public*, pg. 1828

RYDER INTEGRATED LOGISTICS, INC.—See Ryder System, Inc.; *U.S. Public*, pg. 1828

RYDER LIMITED—See Ryder System, Inc.; *U.S. Public*, pg. 1828

RYDER MEMORIAL HOSPITAL; *U.S. Private*, pg. 3511

RYDER PUERTO RICO, INC.—See Ryder System, Inc.; *U.S. Public*, pg. 1828

RYDER (SHANGHAI) LOGISTICS, CO., LTD.—See Ryder System, Inc.; *U.S. Public*, pg. 1828

RYDER SYSTEM HOLDINGS (UK) LIMITED—See Ryder System, Inc.; *U.S. Public*, pg. 1828

RYDER SYSTEM, INC.; *U.S. Public*, pg. 1828

RYDER TRUCK RENTAL CANADA LTD.—See Ryder System, Inc.; *U.S. Public*, pg. 1828

RYDER TRUCK RENTAL, INC.—See Ryder System, Inc.; *U.S. Public*, pg. 1828

RYDGES BANKSTOWN PTY LIMITED—See Event Hospitality & Entertainment Limited; *Int'l*, pg. 2562

RYDGES CRONULLA PTY LIMITED—See Event Hospitality & Entertainment Limited; *Int'l*, pg. 2562

RYDGES HOBART HOTEL PTY LIMITED—See Event Hospitality & Entertainment Limited; *Int'l*, pg. 2562

RYDGES ROTORUA HOTEL LIMITED—See Event Hospitality & Entertainment Limited; *Int'l*, pg. 2562

RYDON GROUP LTD; *Int'l*, pg. 6438

RYE DIALYSIS, LLC—See DaVita Inc.; *U.S. Public*, pg. 642

RYE & DISTRICT COMMUNITY FINANCIAL SERVICES LIMITED—See Bendigo & Adelaide Bank Ltd.; *Int'l*, pg. 971

RYE FORD INC.; *U.S. Private*, pg. 3511

RYE FUEL COMPANY INC.—See Star Group, L.P.; *U.S. Public*, pg. 1938

RYE PATCH GOLD US INC.—See Argonaut Gold Inc.; *U.S. Public*, pg. 191

RYERSON CANADA, INC.—See Ryerson Holding Corporation; *U.S. Public*, pg. 1829

RYERSON HOLDING CORPORATION; *U.S. Public*, pg. 1828

RYERSON INC. - ATLANTA—See Ryerson Holding Corporation; *U.S. Public*, pg. 1829

RYERSON INC. - BURNS HARBOR—See Ryerson Holding Corporation; *U.S. Public*, pg. 1829

RYERSON INC. - COON RAPIDS—See Ryerson Holding Corporation; *U.S. Public*, pg. 1829

RYERSON INC. - LITTLE ROCK—See Ryerson Holding Corporation; *U.S. Public*, pg. 1829

RYERSON INC. - MEMPHIS—See Ryerson Holding Corporation; *U.S. Public*, pg. 1829

RYERSON INC. - MINNEAPOLIS—See Ryerson Holding Corporation; *U.S. Public*, pg. 1829

RYERSON INC. - SEATTLE—See Ryerson Holding Corporation; *U.S. Public*, pg. 1829

RYERSON INC.—See Ryerson Holding Corporation; *U.S. Public*, pg. 1829

RYESON CORPORATION—See Snap-on Incorporated; *U.S. Public*, pg. 1898

RYE VALLEY FOODS LIMITED—See Kerry Group plc; *Int'l*, pg. 4139

RYHURST LTD—See Rydon Group Ltd; *Int'l*, pg. 6438

RYKADAN CAPITAL LIMITED; *Int'l*, pg. 6438

RYKO PLASTIC PRODUCTS INC.; *U.S. Private*, pg. 3511

THE RYLAND CORPORATION—See Lennar Corporation; *U.S. Public*, pg. 1306

RYLAND HOMES OF CALIFORNIA, INC.—See Lennar Corporation; *U.S. Public*, pg. 1305

RYMAC ENTERPRISES—See Q3 Stamped Metal; *U.S. Private*, pg. 3312

RYMAN HEALTHCARE (AUSTRALIA) PTY. LTD.—See Ryman Healthcare Ltd.; *Int'l*, pg. 6440

RYMAN HEALTHCARE LTD.; *Int'l*, pg. 6439

RYMAN HOSPITALITY PROPERTIES, INC.; *U.S. Public*, pg. 1829

RYM BUSINESS MANAGEMENT CORPORATION; *Int'l*, pg. 6439

RYMES HEATING OILS INC.—See Superior Plus Corp.; *Int'l*, pg. 7338

RYNFIELD TERRACE PROPRIETARY LIMITED—See Dis-Chem Pharmacies Ltd.; *Int'l*, pg. 2131

RYNKEBY FOODS A/S—See Arla Foods amba; *Int'l*, pg. 573

RYNN'S LUGGAGE CORPORATION; *U.S. Private*, pg. 3511

RYNONE MANUFACTURING CORPORATION; *U.S. Private*, pg. 3511

RYOBI ALUMINIUM CASTING (UK), LIMITED—See Ryobi Limited; *Int'l*, pg. 6440

RYOBI ALUMINUM CASTING (UK), LIMITED—See Ryobi Limited; *Int'l*, pg. 6440

RYOBI AUSTRALIA PTY. LTD.—See Ryobi Limited; *Int'l*, pg. 6440

RYOBI COMPUTER BUSINESS CO.—See Ryobi Limited; *Int'l*, pg. 6440

RYOBI DIE CASTING CHANGZHOU CO., LTD.—See Ryobi Limited; *Int'l*, pg. 6440

RYOBI DIE CASTING DALIAN CO., LTD.—See Ryobi Limited; *Int'l*, pg. 6440

RYOBI DIE CASTING (THAILAND) CO., LTD.—See Ryobi Limited; *Int'l*, pg. 6440

RYOBI DIE CASTING (USA), INC.—See Ryobi Limited; *Int'l*, pg. 6440

RYOBI FINANCE CORPORATION—See Ryobi Limited; *Int'l*, pg. 6440

RYOBI GEOTECHNIQUE INTERNATIONAL PTE LTD—See SGS SA; *Int'l*, pg. 6743

RYOBI IMAGIX CO.—See Ryobi Limited; *Int'l*, pg. 6440

RYOBI KISO HOLDINGS LTD.; *Int'l*, pg. 6440

RYOBI LAND DEVELOPMENT LTD.—See Ryobi Limited; *Int'l*, pg. 6440

RYOBI LIFE SERVICES LTD.—See Ryobi Limited; *Int'l*, pg. 6440

RYOBI LIMITED - HIROSHIMA EAST PLANT—See Ryobi Limited; *Int'l*, pg. 6440

RYOBI LIMITED - HIROSHIMA PLANT—See Ryobi Limited; *Int'l*, pg. 6440

RYOBI LIMITED - SHIZUOKA PLANT—See Ryobi Limited; *Int'l*, pg. 6440

RYOBI LIMITED; *Int'l*, pg. 6440

RYOBI LTD. - TOKYO BRANCH—See Ryobi Limited; *Int'l*, pg. 6440

RYOBI MHI GRAPHIC TECHNOLOGY LTD.—See Ryobi Limited; *Int'l*, pg. 6440

RYOBI MIRASAKA CO.—See Ryobi Limited; *Int'l*, pg. 6440

RYOBI MITSUGI CO.—See Ryobi Limited; *Int'l*, pg. 6440

RYOBI POWER TOOL CO.—See Ryobi Limited; *Int'l*, pg. 6440

RYOBI (SHANGHAI) SALES, LTD.—See Ryobi Limited; *Int'l*, pg. 6440

RYOBI-TECH CORPORATION—See Ryobi Limited; *Int'l*, pg. 6440

RYOBI TECHNO INC.—See Mitsubishi Chemical Group Corporation; *Int'l*, pg. 4934

RYODEN CORPORATION; *Int'l*, pg. 6440

RYODEN ELEVATOR CONSTRUCTION, LTD.—See Mitsubishi Electric Corporation; *Int'l*, pg. 4946

RYODEN KASEI CO., LTD.—See Mitsubishi Gas Chemical Company, Inc.; *Int'l*, pg. 4950

RYOEI LIFE SERVICE CO., LTD.—See Mitsubishi Estate Co., Ltd.; *Int'l*, pg. 4947

RYOEN CORP.—See Mitsubishi Materials Corporation; *Int'l*, pg. 4965

RYOHIN KEIKAKU CO., LTD.; *Int'l*, pg. 6441

COMPANY NAME INDEX

RYOHIN-KEIKAKU RELIANCE INDIA PRIVATE LIMITED—See Ryohin Keikaku Co., Ltd.; *Int'l*, pg. 6441
RYOHOKU DENSHI CO., LTD.—See Hokuriku Electric Industry Co., Ltd.; *Int'l*, pg. 3445
RYOJU COLD CHAIN CO., LTD.—See Mitsubishi Heavy Industries, Ltd.; *Int'l*, pg. 4961
RYOJU CORPORATION—See Mitsubishi Chemical Group Corporation; *Int'l*, pg. 4934
RYOJU ESTATE CO., LTD.—See Mitsubishi Heavy Industries, Ltd.; *Int'l*, pg. 4961
RYOKO CHEMICAL CO., LTD.—See Mitsubishi Gas Chemical Company, Inc.; *Int'l*, pg. 4950
RYOKO CO., LTD.—See Mitsubishi Chemical Group Corporation; *Int'l*, pg. 4934
RYOKO LIME INDUSTRY CO., LTD.—See Mitsubishi Materials Corporation; *Int'l*, pg. 4965
RYOKO LOGISTICS CO., LTD.—See Mitsubishi Gas Chemical Company, Inc.; *Int'l*, pg. 4950
RYOKO PLASTIC CO., LTD.—See Mitsubishi Chemical Group Corporation; *Int'l*, pg. 4934
RYOKO SANGYO CORP.—See Mitsubishi Materials Corporation; *Int'l*, pg. 4965
RYOKO SANGYO (THAILAND) CO., LTD.—See Mitsubishi Materials Corporation; *Int'l*, pg. 4965
RYOKO SERVICE CORPORATION—See Mitsubishi Materials Corporation; *Int'l*, pg. 4965
RYOKO SIZING CO., LTD.—See Mitsubishi Chemical Group Corporation; *Int'l*, pg. 4934
RYOKO TEKUNIKA CO., LTD.—See Mitsubishi Chemical Group Corporation; *Int'l*, pg. 4934
RYOMO BUSINESS SUPPORT CO., LTD.—See MITSUBA Corporation; *Int'l*, pg. 4929
RYOMO INTERNET DATA CENTER CO., LTD.—See MITSUBA Corporation; *Int'l*, pg. 4929
RYOMO PHILIPPINES INFORMATION CORP.—See MITSUBA Corporation; *Int'l*, pg. 4929
RYOMO SYSTEMS CO., LTD.—See MITSUBA Corporation; *Int'l*, pg. 4929
RYOMO VIETNAM SOLUTIONS CO., LTD.—See MITSUBA Corporation; *Int'l*, pg. 4929
RYONET CORP.; *U.S. Private*, pg. 3511
RYONETSU CO., LTD.—See Mitsubishi Heavy Industries, Ltd.; *Int'l*, pg. 4961
RYONICHI ENGINEERING CO., LTD.—See Mitsubishi Heavy Industries, Ltd.; *Int'l*, pg. 4961
RYO-SA BUILWARE CO., LTD.—See Mitsubishi Electric Corporation; *Int'l*, pg. 4946
RYOSAN COMPANY, LIMITED; *Int'l*, pg. 6441
RYOSEI AMAGASAKI ELECTRIC WIRE CO., LTD.—See Mitsubishi Materials Corporation; *Int'l*, pg. 4965
RYOSEI KIKO CO., LTD.—See Mitsubishi Materials Corporation; *Int'l*, pg. 4965
RYOSEI SERVICE CO., LTD.—See Mitsubishi Heavy Industries, Ltd.; *Int'l*, pg. 4961
RYOSEI SYSTEMS, LTD.—See Mitsubishi Materials Corporation; *Int'l*, pg. 4965
RYOSEN ENGINEERS CO., LTD.—See Mitsubishi Heavy Industries, Ltd.; *Int'l*, pg. 4961
RYOSHI CO., LTD.—See Mitsubishi Paper Mills Limited; *Int'l*, pg. 4967
RYOSHIN DC CARD COMPANY, LTD.—See Mitsubishi UFJ Financial Group, Inc.; *Int'l*, pg. 4972
RYOSHINDO MANUFACTURING SDN. BHD.—See Mitsubishi Materials Corporation; *Int'l*, pg. 4965
RYOSHIN ELECTRONIC ENGINEERING CORPORATION—See Kanaden Corporation; *Int'l*, pg. 4063
RYOSHO ELECTRONICS (SHANGHAI) CO. LTD.—See Ryoden Corporation; *Int'l*, pg. 6440
RYOSHO EUROPE GMBH—See Ryoden Corporation; *Int'l*, pg. 6441
RYOSHO HONG KONG COMPANY, LIMITED—See Ryoden Corporation; *Int'l*, pg. 6441
RYOSHO HON KONG CO., LTD.—See Ryoden Corporation; *Int'l*, pg. 6441
RYOSHO KOREA CO., LTD.—See Ryoden Corporation; *Int'l*, pg. 6441
RYOSHOKU LIQUOR LTD.—See Mitsubishi Corporation; *Int'l*, pg. 4942
RYOSHO MACHINERY (SHANGHAI) CO., LTD.—See Mitsubishi Corporation; *Int'l*, pg. 4941
RYOSHO MALAYSIA SDN. BHD.—See Ryoden Corporation; *Int'l*, pg. 6441
RYOSHO MEXICO, S.A. DE C.V—See Ryoden Corporation; *Int'l*, pg. 6441
RYOSHO TAIWAN COMPANY, LIMITED—See Ryoden Corporation; *Int'l*, pg. 6441
RYOSHO TECHNO COMPANY, LIMITED—See Ryoden Corporation; *Int'l*, pg. 6441
RYOSHO TECHNO SINGAPORE PRIVATE LIMITED—See Ryoden Corporation; *Int'l*, pg. 6441
RYOSHO (THAILAND) COMPANY, LIMITED—See Ryoden Corporation; *Int'l*, pg. 6440
RYOSHO U.S.A. INCORPORATED—See Ryoden Corporation; *Int'l*, pg. 6441
RYOSHO VIETNAM CO., LTD.—See Ryoden Corporation; *Int'l*, pg. 6441
RYOSO TRANSPORTATION CO.,LTD.—See Mitsubishi Logistics Corporation; *Int'l*, pg. 4963

RYOUEI CO., LTD.—See Mitsubishi Chemical Group Corporation; *Int'l*, pg. 4934
RYOUKOU CO.,LTD.—See Mitsubishi Paper Mills Limited; *Int'l*, pg. 4967
RYOWA CO., LTD.; *Int'l*, pg. 6441
RYOWA CORPORATION—See Mitsubishi Electric Corporation; *Int'l*, pg. 4946
RYOWA ENTERPRISE CO., LTD.—See Mitsubishi Gas Chemical Company, Inc.; *Int'l*, pg. 4950
RYOYO ELECTRO CORPORATION; *Int'l*, pg. 6441
RYOYO ELECTRO HONG KONG LTD.—See Ryoyo Electro Corporation; *Int'l*, pg. 6441
RYOYO ELECTRO (SHANGHAI) CO., LTD.—See Ryoyo Electro Corporation; *Int'l*, pg. 6441
RYOYO ELECTRO SINGAPORE PTE., LTD.—See Ryoyo Electro Corporation; *Int'l*, pg. 6441
RYOYO ELECTRO TAIWAN CO., LTD.—See Ryoyo Electro Corporation; *Int'l*, pg. 6441
RYOYO ELECTRO TRADING (DALIAN) CO., LTD.—See Ryoyo Electro Corporation; *Int'l*, pg. 6441
RYOYO ELECTRO USA, INC.—See Ryoyo Electro Corporation; *Int'l*, pg. 6441
RYOYO TRADING CO., LTD.—See Mitsubishi Gas Chemical Company, Inc.; *Int'l*, pg. 4950
RYOYU INDUSTRIAL CORP.—See Mitsubishi Gas Chemical Company, Inc.; *Int'l*, pg. 4950
RYOYU SYSTEM ENGINEERING CO., LTD.—See Mitsubishi Heavy Industries, Ltd.; *Int'l*, pg. 4961
RYOYU SYSTEMS CO., LTD.; *Int'l*, pg. 6441
THE RYTEX COMPANY—See American Stationery Co., Inc.; *U.S. Private*, pg. 255
RY TIMBER INC.; *U.S. Private*, pg. 3509
RYTMUS AB—See AcadeMedia AB; *Int'l*, pg. 77
RYT-WAY INDUSTRIES, LLC—See Charlesbank Capital Partners, LLC; *U.S. Private*, pg. 855
RYT-WAY INDUSTRIES, LLC—See Partners Group Holding AG; *Int'l*, pg. 5749
RYU APPAREL INC.; *Int'l*, pg. 6441
RYUGIN BUSINESS SERVICE CO., LTD.—See Bank of The Ryukyus, Ltd.; *Int'l*, pg. 849
RYUGIN DC CO., LTD.—See Bank of The Ryukyus, Ltd.; *Int'l*, pg. 849
RYUGIN HOSHO CO., LTD.—See Bank of The Ryukyus, Ltd.; *Int'l*, pg. 849
RYUGIN OFFICE SERVICE CO., LTD.—See Bank of The Ryukyus, Ltd.; *Int'l*, pg. 849
RYUGIN RESEARCH INSTITUTE, LTD.—See Bank of The Ryukyus, Ltd.; *Int'l*, pg. 849
RYUGIN SOUGO KENKYUSHO., LTD.—See Bank of The Ryukyus, Ltd.; *Int'l*, pg. 849
RYUK-IL C&S., LTD.; *Int'l*, pg. 6441
RYUKYU AIR COMMUTER CO., LTD.—See Japan Airlines Co., Ltd.; *Int'l*, pg. 3884
RYUKYU KOKUSAI KOGYO CO., LTD.—See Japan Asia Group Limited; *Int'l*, pg. 3885
RYUKYU LEASING CO., LTD.—See Bank of The Ryukyus, Ltd.; *Int'l*, pg. 849
RYUKYU SEIKAN KAISHA, LTD.—See Toyo Seikan Group Holdings, Ltd.; *Int'l*, pg. 7857
RYUMAI PLASTIC CO., LTD.—See Tensho Electric Industries Co., Ltd.; *Int'l*, pg. 7562
RYUSEKI JUBI CO., LTD.—See Sekisui Chemical Co., Ltd.; *Int'l*, pg. 6694
RYUYAKU CO., LTD.—See Alfresa Holdings Corporation; *Int'l*, pg. 317
RYVYL INC.; *U.S. Public*, pg. 1829
RYZE CLAIM SOLUTIONS LLC; *U.S. Private*, pg. 3511
RYZEX INC.—See Sole Source Capital LLC; *U.S. Private*, pg. 3708
RZB SEKTORBETEILIGUNG GMBH—See Raiffeisen Bank International AG; *Int'l*, pg. 6183
RZ CHEMIE GMBH.—See Uzin Utz AG; *Int'l*, pg. 8103
RZ EKONOMIKA AD; *Int'l*, pg. 6442
RZHEVSKY SUGAR—See Gruppa Kompaniy Rusagro OOO; *Int'l*, pg. 3140
RZ INSTITUT SKOPJE; *Int'l*, pg. 6442
RZ-PRODUCTS GMBH—See MVV Energie AG; *Int'l*, pg. 5109
RZ TEHNICKA KONTROLA AD; *Int'l*, pg. 6442

S

S 11 GROUP PUBLIC COMPANY LIMITED; *Int'l*, pg. 6442
S1 BIOPHARMA, INC.; *U.S. Private*, pg. 3519
S-1 CORPORATION—See ACI Worldwide, Inc.; *U.S. Public*, pg. 35
S2C SHANGHAI CO., LTD.—See SMIT Holdings Limited; *Int'l*, pg. 7007
S2C TAIWAN INC.—See SMIT Holdings Limited; *Int'l*, pg. 7007
S2 FIRE SOLUTIONS LIMITED—See London Security PLC; *Int'l*, pg. 4547
S2MEDICAL AB; *Int'l*, pg. 6458
S2PUBLICOM WEBER SHANDWICK—See The Interpublic Group of Companies, Inc.; *U.S. Public*, pg. 2094
S2 RESOURCES LTD.; *Int'l*, pg. 6457
S2TECH; *U.S. Private*, pg. 3519
S2 YACHTS, INC.; *U.S. Private*, pg. 3519
S360S; *U.S. Private*, pg. 3519

S3C, INC.—See Nagano Keiki Co., Ltd.; *Int'l*, pg. 5125
S3D INTERACTIVE, INC.—See Embracer Group AB; *Int'l*, pg. 2375
S3 MATCHING TECHNOLOGIES, LP; *U.S. Private*, pg. 3519
S3 MEDIA INC.; *U.S. Private*, pg. 3519
S4 CAPITAL PLC; *Int'l*, pg. 6458
S4 COLUMBIA RIDGE RECOVERY, LLC—See Waste Management, Inc.; *U.S. Public*, pg. 2332
S4E S.A.; *Int'l*, pg. 6458
S4 INC.; *U.S. Private*, pg. 3519
S4J MANUFACTURING SERVICES, INC.; *U.S. Private*, pg. 3519
S5 ASIA LIMITED—See S5 North Europe BV; *Int'l*, pg. 6458
S5 NORTH EUROPE BV; *Int'l*, pg. 6458
S8 ENGINEERING INC.—See Tessenderlo Group NV; *Int'l*, pg. 7574
SAAB AB - ELECTRONIC DEFENSE SYSTEMS—See Saab AB; *Int'l*, pg. 6460
SAAB AB; *Int'l*, pg. 6459
SAAB AB—See Saab AB; *Int'l*, pg. 6460
SAAB AEROTECH OF AMERICA LLC—See Saab AB; *Int'l*, pg. 6460
SAAB AIRCRAFT LEASING HOLDINGS AB—See Saab AB; *Int'l*, pg. 6459
SAAB ASIA PACIFIC CO. LTD.—See Saab AB; *Int'l*, pg. 6459
SAAB AUSTRALIA PTY. LTD.—See Saab AB; *Int'l*, pg. 6459
SAAB AVTRONICS AB—See Saab AB; *Int'l*, pg. 6460
SAAB BARRACUDA AB—See Saab AB; *Int'l*, pg. 6459
SAAB BARRACUDA LLC—See Saab AB; *Int'l*, pg. 6460
SAAB BOFORS DYNAMICS AB—See Saab AB; *Int'l*, pg. 6459
SAAB CANADA, INC.—See Saab AB; *Int'l*, pg. 6459
SAAB CZECH S.R.O—See Saab AB; *Int'l*, pg. 6459
SAAB DANMARK A/S—See Saab AB; *Int'l*, pg. 6459
SAAB DYNAMICS AB—See Saab AB; *Int'l*, pg. 6459
SAAB ELECTRONIC DEFENCE SYSTEMS—See Saab AB; *Int'l*, pg. 6459
SAAB FINANCIAL SERVICES CORP.—See General Motors Company; *U.S. Public*, pg. 925
SAAB GRINTEK DEFENCE (PTY.) LTD.—See Saab AB; *Int'l*, pg. 6459
SAAB GRINTEK TECHNOLOGIES (PTY) LTD—See Saab AB; *Int'l*, pg. 6460
SAAB INDIA TECHNOLOGIES PRIVATE LIMITED—See Saab AB; *Int'l*, pg. 6459
SAAB INTERNATIONAL CANADA LTD—See Saab AB; *Int'l*, pg. 6459
SAAB INTERNATIONAL DEUTSCHLAND GMBH—See Saab AB; *Int'l*, pg. 6459
SAAB INTERNATIONAL FINLAND OY—See Saab AB; *Int'l*, pg. 6459
SAAB KOCKUMS AB—See ThyssenKrupp AG; *Int'l*, pg. 7733
SAAB NORDIC DEFENCE INDUSTRIES A/S—See Saab AB; *Int'l*, pg. 6460
SAAB NORTH AMERICA, INC.—See Saab AB; *Int'l*, pg. 6460
SAAB OF KW PREMIUM FINE CARS; *Int'l*, pg. 6460
SAAB PERFORMIT AB—See Saab AB; *Int'l*, pg. 6460
SAAB——See Saab AB; *Int'l*, pg. 6459
SAAB SOUTH AFRICA (PTY) LTD—See Saab AB; *Int'l*, pg. 6460
SAAB SUPPORT & SERVICES—See Saab AB; *Int'l*, pg. 6460
SAAB SYSTEMS PTY. LTD.—See Saab AB; *Int'l*, pg. 6460
SAABTECH AB—See Saab AB; *Int'l*, pg. 6460
SAAB TECHNOLOGIES AUSTRALIA PTY LTD—See Saab AB; *Int'l*, pg. 6460
SAAB TECHNOLOGIES B.V.—See Saab AB; *Int'l*, pg. 6460
SAAB TECHNOLOGIES LTD.—See Saab AB; *Int'l*, pg. 6460
SAAB TECHNOLOGIES NORWAY AS—See Saab AB; *Int'l*, pg. 6460
SAAB TECHNOLOGIES S.R.O.—See Saab AB; *Int'l*, pg. 6460
SAAB TRAINING SYSTEMS AB—See Saab AB; *Int'l*, pg. 6459
SAAB TRAINING SYSTEMS B.V.—See Saab AB; *Int'l*, pg. 6460
SAAB TRANSPONDERTECH AB—See Saab AB; *Int'l*, pg. 6460
SAAB UNDERWATER SYSTEMS AB—See Saab AB; *Int'l*, pg. 6460
SAAD AGRICULTURE—See SAAD Group; *Int'l*, pg. 6460
SAAD AL SANEA CENTRE FOR CHILDREN WITH COMMUNICATION DISORDERS—See SAAD Group; *Int'l*, pg. 6460
SAADANI TRADING & INDUSTRIAL SERVICES S.A.E.—See SMC Corporation; *Int'l*, pg. 7006
SAAD BERKELEY LIMITED—See The Berkeley Group Holdings plc; *Int'l*, pg. 7621
SAAD DESIGN AND ENGINEERING—See SAAD Group; *Int'l*, pg. 6460

SAAD FINANCIAL SERVICES S.A.—See SAAD Group; *Int'l*, pg. 6460
SAAD GROUP; *Int'l*, pg. 6460
SAAD INFORMATION TECHNOLOGY—See SAAD Group; *Int'l*, pg. 6460
SAAD INVESTMENTS COMPANY LIMITED—See SAAD Group; *Int'l*, pg. 6460
SAAD MEDICAL CENTRE—See SAAD Group; *Int'l*, pg. 6460
SAAD NATIONAL SCHOOLS—See SAAD Group; *Int'l*, pg. 6460
SAAD'S HEALTHCARE SERVICES, INC.; *U.S. Private*, pg. 3519
SAAD'S MEDICAL EQUIPMENT INC.—See Saad's Healthcare Services, Inc.; *U.S. Private*, pg. 3519
SAAD'S MEDICAL MANAGEMENT INC.—See Saad's Healthcare Services, Inc.; *U.S. Private*, pg. 3519
SAAD'S NURSING SERVICES INC.—See Saad's Healthcare Services, Inc.; *U.S. Private*, pg. 3519
SAAD TRADING AND CONTRACTING CO.—See SAAD Group; *Int'l*, pg. 6460
SAAD TRANSPORT—See SAAD Group; *Int'l*, pg. 6460
SAAD TRAVEL & TOURISM—See SAAD Group; *Int'l*, pg. 6460
SAAG CONSOLIDATED (M) BHD.; *Int'l*, pg. 6460
SA AGRER NV—See Tecnica Y Proyectos S.A.; *Int'l*, pg. 7515
SA AGRILOIRE; *Int'l*, pg. 6458
S.A. AGRIVOLT; *Int'l*, pg. 6447
SAAG RR INFRA LIMITED—See SAAG Consolidated (M) Bhd.; *Int'l*, pg. 6460
SAAG'S PRODUCTS, LLC—See WH Group Limited; *Int'l*, pg. 8395
S.A. AJINOMOTO OMNICHEM N.V.—See Ajinomoto Company, Inc.; *Int'l*, pg. 257
SAAKSHI MEDTECH & PANELS LIMITED; *Int'l*, pg. 6461
SA ALBA (DECO PAINTS LATIN AMERICA)—See Akzo Nobel N.V.; *Int'l*, pg. 271
S.A. ALCON-COUVREUR N.V.—See Novartis AG; *Int'l*, pg. 5457
SAALEX CORP.; *U.S. Private*, pg. 3520
SAAMA TECHNOLOGIES, INC.; *U.S. Private*, pg. 3520
SAAM DEVELOPMENT PUBLIC COMPANY LIMITED; *Int'l*, pg. 6461
SAAM GUATEMALA S.A.—See Quinenco S.A.; *Int'l*, pg. 6164
SAAM REMOLCADORES COLOMBIA S.A.S.—See Quinenco S.A.; *Int'l*, pg. 6164
SAAM TOWAGE BRASIL S.A.—See Quinenco S.A.; *Int'l*, pg. 6164
SAAM TOWAGE CANADA INC.—See Quinenco S.A.; *Int'l*, pg. 6164
SAAM TOWAGE PANAMA INC.—See Quinenco S.A.; *Int'l*, pg. 6164
SAAND INC. - REXDALE—See Saand Inc.; *Int'l*, pg. 6461
SAAND INC.; *Int'l*, pg. 6461
SAANKHYA LABS PVT. LTD.—See General Motors Company; *U.S. Public*, pg. 928
SAARBRUCKER ZEITUNG VERLAG UND DRUCKEREI GMBH—See Rheinische-Bergische Verlagsgesellschaft mbH; *Int'l*, pg. 6321
SAAR-LAGER-UND PROFILTECHNIK GMBH—See Blackstone Inc.; *U.S. Public*, pg. 348
SAARLANDISCHE HANDELSGESELLSCHAFT MBH—See Knauf Interfer SE; *Int'l*, pg. 4205
SAARLANDISCHE ZEMENT GESELLSCHAFT GMBH—See Heidelberg Materials AG; *Int'l*, pg. 3317
SAARLUX STAHL GMBH & CO. KG—See AG der Dillinger Huttenwerke; *Int'l*, pg. 197
S.A. ARMSTRONG LIMITED; *Int'l*, pg. 6447
SAAR-PFALZ-BUS GMBH—See Deutsche Bahn AG; *Int'l*, pg. 2052
SAAR-PFALZ-MOBIL GMBH—See Deutsche Bahn AG; *Int'l*, pg. 2052
SAAR'S INC.; *U.S. Private*, pg. 3520
SAARSTAHL AG; *Int'l*, pg. 6461
SAARSTAHL AG—See Saarstahl AG; *Int'l*, pg. 6461
SAAR STAHLBAU GMBH—See Saarstahl AG; *Int'l*, pg. 6461
SAARSTAHL-EXPORT GMBH—See Saarstahl AG; *Int'l*, pg. 6461
SAARSTAHL EXPORT INDIA PVT LTD—See Saarstahl AG; *Int'l*, pg. 6461
SAARSTAHL (S.E.A.)—See Saarstahl AG; *Int'l*, pg. 6461
SAARSTAHL SHANGHAI LIMITED—See Saarstahl AG; *Int'l*, pg. 6461
SAARSTAHL S.R.O.—See Saarstahl AG; *Int'l*, pg. 6461
SAARSTEEL INC.—See Saarstahl AG; *Int'l*, pg. 6461
SAASFORCE CONSULTING PRIVATE LIMITED—See Cognizant Technology Solutions Corporation; *U.S. Public*, pg. 525
SAASMAX CORP.; *U.S. Public*, pg. 1832
SAASOPTICS, LLC—See Battery Ventures, L.P.; *U.S. Private*, pg. 489
SAA-SOUTH AFRICAN AIRWAYS—See South African Airways (Pty) Ltd.; *Int'l*, pg. 7115
SAASPLAZA INC.—See Schneider Electric SE; *Int'l*, pg. 6625

SAASPLAZA INC.—See Schneider Electric SE; *Int'l*, pg. 6625
SAASPLAZA INTERNATIONAL B.V.—See Schneider Electric SE; *Int'l*, pg. 6625
SAASPLAZA PTE. LTD.—See Schneider Electric SE; *Int'l*, pg. 6625
SAASPLAZA PTY. LTD.—See Schneider Electric SE; *Int'l*, pg. 6625
SAATCHI BARCELONA—See Publicis Groupe S.A.; *Int'l*, pg. 6108
SAATCHI & SAATCHI ADVERTISING—See Publicis Groupe S.A.; *Int'l*, pg. 6108
SAATCHI & SAATCHI A/S—See Publicis Groupe S.A.; *Int'l*, pg. 6109
SAATCHI & SAATCHI AUSTRALIA—See Publicis Groupe S.A.; *Int'l*, pg. 6108
SAATCHI & SAATCHI BRUSSELS—See Publicis Groupe S.A.; *Int'l*, pg. 6109
SAATCHI & SAATCHI DIRECT—See Publicis Groupe S.A.; *Int'l*, pg. 6108
SAATCHI & SAATCHI DUSSELDORF—See Publicis Groupe S.A.; *Int'l*, pg. 6109
SAATCHI & SAATCHI EGYPT—See Publicis Groupe S.A.; *Int'l*, pg. 6109
SAATCHI & SAATCHI EMEA REGION HEADQUARTERS—See Publicis Groupe S.A.; *Int'l*, pg. 6108
SAATCHI & SAATCHI FALLON TOKYO—See Publicis Groupe S.A.; *Int'l*, pg. 6109
SAATCHI & SAATCHI GROUP LTD.—See Publicis Groupe S.A.; *Int'l*, pg. 6107
SAATCHI & SAATCHI HEALTHCARE ADVERTISING—See Publicis Groupe S.A.; *Int'l*, pg. 6109
SAATCHI & SAATCHI HEALTHCARE CONNECTION—See Publicis Groupe S.A.; *Int'l*, pg. 6109
SAATCHI & SAATCHI HEALTHCARE INNOVATIONS—See Publicis Groupe S.A.; *Int'l*, pg. 6109
SAATCHI & SAATCHI HEALTH—See Publicis Groupe S.A.; *Int'l*, pg. 6109
SAATCHI & SAATCHI LOS ANGELES—See Publicis Groupe S.A.; *Int'l*, pg. 6109
SAATCHI & SAATCHI MALAYSIA—See Publicis Groupe S.A.; *Int'l*, pg. 6109
SAATCHI & SAATCHI MILAN—See Publicis Groupe S.A.; *Int'l*, pg. 6109
SAATCHI & SAATCHI NEW YORK—See Publicis Groupe S.A.; *Int'l*, pg. 6109
SAATCHI & SAATCHI RUSSIA—See Publicis Groupe S.A.; *Int'l*, pg. 6109
SAATCHI & SAATCHI SIMKO—See Publicis Groupe S.A.; *Int'l*, pg. 6106
SAATCHI & SAATCHI SINGAPORE—See Publicis Groupe S.A.; *Int'l*, pg. 6109
SAATCHI & SAATCHI—See Publicis Groupe S.A.; *Int'l*, pg. 6108
SAATCHI & SAATCHI—See Publicis Groupe S.A.; *Int'l*, pg. 6108
SAATCHI & SAATCHI—See Publicis Groupe S.A.; *Int'l*, pg. 6108
SAATCHI & SAATCHI—See Publicis Groupe S.A.; *Int'l*, pg. 6108
SAATCHI & SAATCHI—See Publicis Groupe S.A.; *Int'l*, pg. 6108
SAATCHI & SAATCHI—See Publicis Groupe S.A.; *Int'l*, pg. 6108
SAATCHI & SAATCHI—See Publicis Groupe S.A.; *Int'l*, pg. 6108
SAATCHI & SAATCHI—See Publicis Groupe S.A.; *Int'l*, pg. 6108
SAATCHI & SAATCHI—See Publicis Groupe S.A.; *Int'l*, pg. 6108
SAATCHI & SAATCHI—See Publicis Groupe S.A.; *Int'l*, pg. 6108
SAATCHI & SAATCHI—See Publicis Groupe S.A.; *Int'l*, pg. 6108
SAATCHI & SAATCHI—See Publicis Groupe S.A.; *Int'l*, pg. 6108
SAATCHI & SAATCHI—See Publicis Groupe S.A.; *Int'l*, pg. 6109
SAATCHI & SAATCHI—See Publicis Groupe S.A.; *Int'l*, pg. 6109
SAATCHI & SAATCHI—See Publicis Groupe S.A.; *Int'l*, pg. 6109

SAATCHI & SAATCHI—See Publicis Groupe S.A.; *Int'l*, pg. 6109
SAATCHI & SAATCHI—See Publicis Groupe S.A.; *Int'l*, pg. 6109
SAATCHI & SAATCHI—See Publicis Groupe S.A.; *Int'l*, pg. 6109
SAATCHI & SAATCHI—See Publicis Groupe S.A.; *Int'l*, pg. 6109
SAATCHI & SAATCHI—See Publicis Groupe S.A.; *Int'l*, pg. 6109
SAATCHI & SAATCHI—See Publicis Groupe S.A.; *Int'l*, pg. 6109
SAATCHI & SAATCHI—See Publicis Groupe S.A.; *Int'l*, pg. 6109
SAATCHI & SAATCHI—See Publicis Groupe S.A.; *Int'l*, pg. 6109
SAATCHI & SAATCHI—See Publicis Groupe S.A.; *Int'l*, pg. 6109
SAATCHI & SAATCHI—See Publicis Groupe S.A.; *Int'l*, pg. 6109
SAATCHI & SAATCHI THAILAND—See Publicis Groupe S.A.; *Int'l*, pg. 6109
SAATCHI & SAATCHI WELLNESS—See Publicis Groupe S.A.; *Int'l*, pg. 6109
SAATCHI & SAATCHI WORLDWIDE, INC.—See Publicis Groupe S.A.; *Int'l*, pg. 6107
SAATCHI & SAATCHI X—See Publicis Groupe S.A.; *Int'l*, pg. 6109
SAATCHI & SAATCHI X—See Publicis Groupe S.A.; *Int'l*, pg. 6110
SAATVA, INC.; *U.S. Private*, pg. 3520
SAATZUCHT EDELHOF GMBH—See BayWa AG; *Int'l*, pg. 919
SAATZUCHT GLEISDORF GESELLSCHAFT M.B.H—See BayWa AG; *Int'l*, pg. 919
SABAA INTERNATIONAL COMPANY FOR PHARMACEUTICAL & CHEMICAL INDUSTRY; *Int'l*, pg. 6461
SABA APARCAMIENTOS, S.A.—See Fundacion Bancaria Caixa d'Estalvis i Pensions de Barcelona, la Caixa; *Int'l*, pg. 2845
SABABA SECURITY S.P.A.; *Int'l*, pg. 6461
S.A. BACARDI-MARTINI BELGIUM N.V.—See Bacardi Limited; *Int'l*, pg. 794
SABADELLCAM—See Banco de Sabadell, S.A.; *Int'l*, pg. 821
SABADELL CORPORATE FINANCE, S.L.—See Banco de Sabadell, S.A.; *Int'l*, pg. 821
SABAEK FOR FINANCIAL SERVICES LLC—See Sbaek Invest PLC; *Int'l*, pg. 6603
SABAE MURATA MANUFACTURING CO., LTD.—See Murata Manufacturing Co., Ltd.; *Int'l*, pg. 5098
SABAF APPLIANCE COMPONENTS (KUNSHAN) CO., LTD.—See Sabaf S.p.A.; *Int'l*, pg. 6462
SABAF APPLIANCE COMPONENTS (KUNSHAN) CO. LTD.—See Sabaf S.p.A.; *Int'l*, pg. 6462
SABAF BEYAZ ESYA PARCALARI SANAYI VE TICARET LIMITED SIRTEKI—See Sabaf S.p.A.; *Int'l*, pg. 6462
SABAF DO BRASIL LTDA—See Sabaf S.p.A.; *Int'l*, pg. 6462
SABAF DO BRASIL LTDA—See Sabaf S.p.A.; *Int'l*, pg. 6462
SABAF IMMOBILIARE S.R.L.—See Sabaf S.p.A.; *Int'l*, pg. 6462
SABA FRESH CUTS AB—See BAMA Gruppen AS; *Int'l*, pg. 813
SABAF S.P.A.; *Int'l*, pg. 6461
SABAH COCOA SDN BHD—See Kuala Lumpur Kepong Berhad; *Int'l*, pg. 4319
SABAH ELECTRICITY SDN. BHD.—See Tenaga Nasional Berhad; *Int'l*, pg. 7557
SABAH HOLDINGS CORPORATION SDN BHD—See Kuala Lumpur Kepong Berhad; *Int'l*, pg. 4319
SABAH INTERNATIONAL, INC.; *U.S. Private*, pg. 3520
SABAH PORTS SDN. BHD.—See Suria Capital Holdings Berhad; *Int'l*, pg. 7344
SABAH SHELL PETROLEUM CO. LTD—See Shell plc; *Int'l*, pg. 6797
SABAH SOFTWOODS HYBRID FERTILISER SDN. BHD.—See All Cosmos Bio-Tech Holding Corporation; *Int'l*, pg. 332
SABAH TEA RESORT SDN BHD—See Yee Lee Corporation Bhd.; *Int'l*, pg. 8575
SABAIDEE LEASING CO., LTD.—See Thitikorn Public Company Limited; *Int'l*, pg. 7711
SABA INC.—See Mainco Investments Inc.; *U.S. Private*, pg. 2552
SABA INFRAESTRUCTURAS, S.A.—See Fundacion Bancaria Caixa d'Estalvis i Pensions de Barcelona, la Caixa; *Int'l*, pg. 2845
SABA ITALIA S.R.L.—See Dexelance S.p.A.; *Int'l*, pg. 2092
SABAL FINANCIAL EUROPE LIMITED—See Brookfield Corporation; *Int'l*, pg. 1182
SABAL FINANCIAL GROUP, L.P.—See Brookfield Corporation; *Int'l*, pg. 1182
SABAL HOLDINGS INC.; *U.S. Private*, pg. 3520

COMPANY NAME INDEX

SABAL HOMES, LLC—See Toll Brothers, Inc.; *U.S. Public*, pg. 2162
SABAL PALM BANK; *U.S. Private*, pg. 3520
SABAL TRUST COMPANY—See Sabal Holdings Inc.; *U.S. Private*, pg. 3520
SABANA SHARI'AH COMPLIANT INDUSTRIAL REAL ESTATE INVESTMENT TRUST; *Int'l*, pg. 6462
SABAN CAPITAL GROUP, INC.; *U.S. Private*, pg. 3520
SABAND SOFTWARE TECHNOLOGIES PRIVATE LIMITED—See Cognizant Technology Solutions Corporation; *U.S. Public*, pg. 525
SABART SRL—See Emak S.p.A.; *Int'l*, pg. 2373
SABAS BUNCH LIMITED PARTNERSHIP; *U.S. Private*, pg. 3520
SABA SOFTWARE GMBH—See Clearlake Capital Group, L.P.; *U.S. Private*, pg. 934
SABA SOFTWARE, INC.—See Clearlake Capital Group, L.P.; *U.S. Private*, pg. 934
SABA SOFTWARE SP. Z O.O—See Clearlake Capital Group, L.P.; *U.S. Private*, pg. 934
SABA SOFTWARE (UK) LTD.—See Clearlake Capital Group, L.P.; *U.S. Private*, pg. 934
SABA—See Sodexo S.A.; *Int'l*, pg. 7045
SABA TRADING AB—See Dole plc; *Int'l*, pg. 2157
SAB BIOTHERAPEUTICS, INC.; *U.S. Public*, pg. 1832
SABB TAKAFUL COMPANY—See The Saudi British Bank; *Int'l*, pg. 7680
SABCA BRUSSELS NV—See Societe Anonyme Belge de Constructions Aeronautiques; *Int'l*, pg. 7035
SABCA CASABLANCA NV—See Societe Anonyme Belge de Constructions Aeronautiques; *Int'l*, pg. 7035
SABC AIRWAVE TRAVEL PROPRIETARY LIMITED—See South African Broadcasting Corporation; *Int'l*, pg. 7115
SABCA LIMBURG N.V.—See Societe Anonyme Belge de Constructions Aeronautiques; *Int'l*, pg. 7035
S.A. BEIERSDORF NV—See maxingvest ag; *Int'l*, pg. 4740
SABEL INDUSTRIES INC.; *U.S. Private*, pg. 3520
SABELO BETEILIGUNGSVERWALTUNGS GMBH—See PORR AG; *Int'l*, pg. 5924
SABENA TECHNICS—See TAT Services SASU; *Int'l*, pg. 7466
SABER ACCEPTANCE COMPANY INC.; *U.S. Private*, pg. 3520
SABER HEALTHCARE GROUP LLC; *U.S. Private*, pg. 3520
SABER MANAGEMENT, LLC—See Park Lawn Company Limited; *Int'l*, pg. 5742
SABERO ARGENTINA S.A.—See The Murugappa Group, Ltd.; *Int'l*, pg. 7668
SABERO EUROPE BV—See The Murugappa Group, Ltd.; *Int'l*, pg. 7668
SABER POWER SERVICES, LLC—See Greenbelt Capital Management L.P.; *U.S. Private*, pg. 1774
SABER PROTECTION SOLUTIONS, LLC—See Akal Security, Inc.; *U.S. Private*, pg. 144
SABER REAL ESTATE ADVISORS, LLC; *U.S. Private*, pg. 3520
SABERT CORPORATION; *U.S. Private*, pg. 3520
SABE S.A.S.—See Ag Growth International Inc.; *Int'l*, pg. 198
SABET KHORASAN-FARIMAN SUGAR FACTORY COMPANY; *Int'l*, pg. 6462
SAB EVENTS & GOVERNANCE NOW MEDIA LIMITED; *Int'l*, pg. 6461
SABIANA S.P.A.—See Arbonia AG; *Int'l*, pg. 538
SABIA SPOL. S.R.O.—See Heidelberg Materials AG; *Int'l*, pg. 3319
SABIC AGRI-NUTRIENTS CO.; *Int'l*, pg. 6462
SABIC AMERICAS, INC.—See Saudi Basic Industries Corporation; *Int'l*, pg. 6591
SABIC ASIA PACIFIC LTD.—See Saudi Basic Industries Corporation; *Int'l*, pg. 6591
SABIC ASIA PACIFIC PTE. LTD. - PHILIPPINES OFFICE—See Saudi Basic Industries Corporation; *Int'l*, pg. 6591
SABIC ASIA PACIFIC PTE. LTD.—See Saudi Basic Industries Corporation; *Int'l*, pg. 6591
SABIC AUSTRALIA PTY. LTD.—See Saudi Basic Industries Corporation; *Int'l*, pg. 6591
SABIC CAPITAL B.V.—See Saudi Basic Industries Corporation; *Int'l*, pg. 6591
SABIC (CHINA) RESEARCH & DEVELOPMENT CO., LTD.—See Saudi Basic Industries Corporation; *Int'l*, pg. 6591
SABIC DEUTSCHLAND GMBH—See Saudi Basic Industries Corporation; *Int'l*, pg. 6591
SABIC EASTERN EUROPE OOO—See Saudi Basic Industries Corporation; *Int'l*, pg. 6591
SABIC EURO B.V.—See Saudi Basic Industries Corporation; *Int'l*, pg. 6591
SABIC EUROPE B.V—See Saudi Basic Industries Corporation; *Int'l*, pg. 6591
SABIC FAR EAST LTD.—See Saudi Basic Industries Corporation; *Int'l*, pg. 6591
SABIC FRANCE SAS—See Saudi Basic Industries Corporation; *Int'l*, pg. 6591
SABIC GREECE MEPE—See Saudi Basic Industries Corporation; *Int'l*, pg. 6591
SABIC HONG KONG LTD—See Saudi Basic Industries Corporation; *Int'l*, pg. 6591
SABIC HUNGARY KFT.—See Saudi Basic Industries Corporation; *Int'l*, pg. 6591
SABIC INDIA PVT. LTD.—See Saudi Basic Industries Corporation; *Int'l*, pg. 6591
SABIC INDUSTRIAL INVESTMENT CO.—See Saudi Basic Industries Corporation; *Int'l*, pg. 6591
SABIC INNOVATIVE PLASTICS ABS UK LTD.—See Saudi Basic Industries Corporation; *Int'l*, pg. 6591
SABIC INNOVATIVE PLASTICS ARGENTINA SRL—See Saudi Basic Industries Corporation; *Int'l*, pg. 6591
SABIC INNOVATIVE PLASTICS AUSTRALIA PTY LTD.—See Saudi Basic Industries Corporation; *Int'l*, pg. 6591
SABIC INNOVATIVE PLASTICS AUSTRIA GMBH—See Saudi Basic Industries Corporation; *Int'l*, pg. 6591
SABIC INNOVATIVE PLASTICS BV—See Saudi Basic Industries Corporation; *Int'l*, pg. 6591
SABIC INNOVATIVE PLASTICS CANADA, INC.—See Saudi Basic Industries Corporation; *Int'l*, pg. 6591
SABIC INNOVATIVE PLASTICS (CHINA) CO., LTD.—See Saudi Basic Industries Corporation; *Int'l*, pg. 6591
SABIC INNOVATIVE PLASTICS (CHONGQING) CO., LTD.—See Saudi Basic Industries Corporation; *Int'l*, pg. 6591
SABIC INNOVATIVE PLASTICS CZECH, S.R.O.—See Saudi Basic Industries Corporation; *Int'l*, pg. 6591
SABIC INNOVATIVE PLASTICS DENMARK APS—See Saudi Basic Industries Corporation; *Int'l*, pg. 6591
SABIC INNOVATIVE PLASTICS ESPANA SCPA—See Saudi Basic Industries Corporation; *Int'l*, pg. 6591
SABIC INNOVATIVE PLASTICS FINLAND OY—See Saudi Basic Industries Corporation; *Int'l*, pg. 6591
SABIC INNOVATIVE PLASTICS FRANCE SAC—See Saudi Basic Industries Corporation; *Int'l*, pg. 6591
SABIC INNOVATIVE PLASTICS GP B.V.—See Saudi Basic Industries Corporation; *Int'l*, pg. 6591
SABIC INNOVATIVE PLASTICS HONG KONG LIMITED—See Saudi Basic Industries Corporation; *Int'l*, pg. 6591
SABIC INNOVATIVE PLASTICS IBERICA S.A.—See Saudi Basic Industries Corporation; *Int'l*, pg. 6591
SABIC INNOVATIVE PLASTICS INDIA PRIVATE LTD.—See Saudi Basic Industries Corporation; *Int'l*, pg. 6591
SABIC INNOVATIVE PLASTICS IP B.V.—See Saudi Basic Industries Corporation; *Int'l*, pg. 6591
SABIC INNOVATIVE PLASTICS IP LICENSING B.V.—See Saudi Basic Industries Corporation; *Int'l*, pg. 6591
SABIC INNOVATIVE PLASTICS KERESKEDELMI KFT.—See Saudi Basic Industries Corporation; *Int'l*, pg. 6591
SABIC INNOVATIVE PLASTICS LTD.—See Saudi Basic Industries Corporation; *Int'l*, pg. 6591
SABIC INNOVATIVE PLASTICS MALAYSIA SDN. BHD.—See Saudi Basic Industries Corporation; *Int'l*, pg. 6592
SABIC INNOVATIVE PLASTICS MANAGEMENT (SHANGHAI) CO., LTD.—See Saudi Basic Industries Corporation; *Int'l*, pg. 6592
SABIC INNOVATIVE PLASTICS MT. VERNON, LLC—See Saudi Basic Industries Corporation; *Int'l*, pg. 6592
SABIC INNOVATIVE PLASTICS POLAND SP. Z.O.O—See Saudi Basic Industries Corporation; *Int'l*, pg. 6592
SABIC INNOVATIVE PLASTICS RUS. OOO—See Saudi Basic Industries Corporation; *Int'l*, pg. 6592
SABIC INNOVATIVE PLASTICS (SEA) PTE. LTD.—See Saudi Basic Industries Corporation; *Int'l*, pg. 6592
SABIC INNOVATIVE PLASTICS SERVICIOS MEXICO, S. DE R.L. DE C.V.—See Saudi Basic Industries Corporation; *Int'l*, pg. 6592
SABIC INNOVATIVE PLASTICS SHANGHAI CO., LTD.—See Saudi Basic Industries Corporation; *Int'l*, pg. 6592
SABIC INNOVATIVE PLASTICS SIT HOLDING LIMITED—See Saudi Basic Industries Corporation; *Int'l*, pg. 6592
SABIC INNOVATIVE PLASTICS—See Saudi Basic Industries Corporation; *Int'l*, pg. 6591
SABIC INNOVATIVE PLASTICS—See Saudi Basic Industries Corporation; *Int'l*, pg. 6591
SABIC IRAN—See Saudi Basic Industries Corporation; *Int'l*, pg. 6592
SABIC ITALIA S.P.A.—See Saudi Basic Industries Corporation; *Int'l*, pg. 6592
SABIC JAPAN LTD. - MOKA PLANT—See Saudi Basic Industries Corporation; *Int'l*, pg. 6592
SABIC JAPAN LTD.—See Saudi Basic Industries Corporation; *Int'l*, pg. 6592
SABIC KOREA LTD.—See Saudi Basic Industries Corporation; *Int'l*, pg. 6592
SABIC LEBANON—See Saudi Basic Industries Corporation; *Int'l*, pg. 6592
SABIC MARKETING IBERICA S.A.—See Saudi Basic Industries Corporation; *Int'l*, pg. 6592
SABIC MARKETING IBERICA S.L.—See Saudi Basic Industries Corporation; *Int'l*, pg. 6592

SABINE ROYALTY TRUST

SABIC MOROCCO—See Saudi Basic Industries Corporation; *Int'l*, pg. 6592
SABIC NORDIC A/S—See Saudi Basic Industries Corporation; *Int'l*, pg. 6592
SABIC PAKISTAN PVT. LTD.—See Saudi Basic Industries Corporation; *Int'l*, pg. 6592
SABIC PETROCHEMICALS—See Saudi Basic Industries Corporation; *Int'l*, pg. 6592
SABIC PETROKEMYA TICARET LIMITED—See Saudi Basic Industries Corporation; *Int'l*, pg. 6592
SABIC POLAND SP Z.O.O—See Saudi Basic Industries Corporation; *Int'l*, pg. 6592
SABIC POLYMERLAND MUHENDISLIK PLASTIKLERI SAN. TIC. A.S.—See Saudi Basic Industries Corporation; *Int'l*, pg. 6592
SABIC POLYMERSHAPES MEXICO, S. DE R.L. DE C.V.—See Saudi Basic Industries Corporation; *Int'l*, pg. 6592
SABIC POLYOLEFINE GMBH—See Saudi Basic Industries Corporation; *Int'l*, pg. 6592
SABIC POLYOLESENE GMBH—See Saudi Basic Industries Corporation; *Int'l*, pg. 6591
SABIC SALES EUROPE B.V.—See Saudi Arabian Oil Company; *Int'l*, pg. 6590
SABIC (SHANGHAI) TRADING CO. LTD.—See Tokyo Electron Limited; *Int'l*, pg. 7791
SABIC SOUTH AFRICA (PTY) LTD—See Saudi Basic Industries Corporation; *Int'l*, pg. 6592
SABIC TECHNOLOGY CENTER—See Saudi Basic Industries Corporation; *Int'l*, pg. 6591
SABIC TUNISIA SARL—See Saudi Basic Industries Corporation; *Int'l*, pg. 6592
SABIC TURKEY—See Saudi Basic Industries Corporation; *Int'l*, pg. 6592
SABIC UNITED KINGDOM LTD.—See Saudi Basic Industries Corporation; *Int'l*, pg. 6592
SABIC VIETNAM COMPANY LIMITED—See Saudi Basic Industries Corporation; *Int'l*, pg. 6592
SABIDO INVESTMENTS (PROPRIETARY) LIMITED—See Hosken Consolidated Investments Limited; *Int'l*, pg. 3485
SABIEDRIBA AR IROBEZOTU ATBILDIBU IBM LATVIJA—See International Business Machines Corporation; *U.S. Public*, pg. 1150
SABIEM S.P.A.—See KONE Oyj; *Int'l*, pg. 4250
SABIEN TECHNOLOGY GROUP PLC; *Int'l*, pg. 6462
SABIEN TECHNOLOGY LIMITED—See Sabien Technology Group plc; *Int'l*, pg. 6462
SABIK LTD.—See SPX Technologies, Inc.; *U.S. Public*, pg. 1921
SABIK OU—See SPX Technologies, Inc.; *U.S. Public*, pg. 1921
SABIK OY—See SPX Technologies, Inc.; *U.S. Public*, pg. 1922
SABIK PRIVATE LIMITED—See SPX Technologies, Inc.; *U.S. Public*, pg. 1922
S.A. BILIA EMOND BELGIUM—See Bilia AB; *Int'l*, pg. 1029
SABINA CORPORATION LIMITED; *Int'l*, pg. 6462
SABINA FAREAST CO., LTD—See Sabina Public Company Limited; *Int'l*, pg. 6462
SABINA FARMERS EXCHANGE INC.; *U.S. Private*, pg. 3520
SABINA GOLD & SILVER CORPORATION—See B2Gold Corp.; *U.S. Public*, pg. 790
SABINA PUBLIC COMPANY LIMITED - CHAINAT FACTORY—See Sabina Public Company Limited; *Int'l*, pg. 6462
SABINA PUBLIC COMPANY LIMITED - PHUTTAMONTHON SAI 5 FACTORY—See Sabina Public Company Limited; *Int'l*, pg. 6462
SABINA PUBLIC COMPANY LIMITED; *Int'l*, pg. 6462
SABINA PUBLIC COMPANY LIMITED - YASOTHORN FACTORY—See Sabina Public Company Limited; *Int'l*, pg. 6462
SAB INDUSTRIES LIMITED; *Int'l*, pg. 6461
SABINE BANCSHARES INC.; *U.S. Private*, pg. 3521
SABINE BANK OPERATION CENTER INC.—See Sabine Bancshares Inc.; *U.S. Private*, pg. 3521
THE SABINE MINING COMPANY—See NACCO Industries, Inc.; *U.S. Public*, pg. 1490
SABINE OIL & GAS CORPORATION—See Osaka Gas Co., Ltd.; *Int'l*, pg. 5646
SABINE OIL & GAS HOLDINGS, INC.; *U.S. Private*, pg. 3521
SABINE PASS LIQUEFACTION, LLC; *U.S. Private*, pg. 3521
SABINE PASS LNG, L.P.—See Cheniere Energy, Inc.; *U.S. Public*, pg. 485
SABINE PIPE LINE LLC—See Chevron Corporation; *U.S. Public*, pg. 488
SABINE RIVER AUTHORITY OF TEXAS; *U.S. Private*, pg. 3521
SABINE RIVER AUTHORITY, STATE OF LOUISIANA; *U.S. Private*, pg. 3521
SABINE RIVER & NORTHERN RAILROAD COMPANY—See International Paper Company; *U.S. Public*, pg. 1158
SABINE ROYALTY TRUST; *U.S. Public*, pg. 1833

SABINE STATE BANK & TRUST COMPANY—See Sabine Bancshares Inc.; *U.S. Private*, pg. 3521
SAB INFOTECH LTD.—See Steel Strips Wheels Ltd.; *Int'l*, pg. 7190
SAB INGENIERIE INFORMATIQUE; *Int'l*, pg. 6461
SABIN METAL CORPORATION; *U.S. Private*, pg. 3520
SABIN ROBBINS PAPER CO.; *U.S. Private*, pg. 3520
SABINSA CORPORATION; *U.S. Private*, pg. 3521
SAB INTERNATIONAL SARL; *Int'l*, pg. 6461
SABIO GMBH—See Serviceware SE; *Int'l*, pg. 6726
SABIO HOLDINGS INC.; *Int'l*, pg. 6462
SABIO HOLDINGS INC.; *Int'l*, pg. 6462
SABIO MOBILE, INC.; *U.S. Private*, pg. 3521
SABLE37 DMCC—See DXC Technology Company; *U.S. Public*, pg. 696
SABLE CHEMICAL INDUSTRIES LTD.—See Masawara PLC; *Int'l*, pg. 4720
SABLE CLASSIFIE ET EQUIPEMENT DE WILSON LTEE—See Heidelberg Materials AG; *Int'l*, pg. 3317
SABLE ENVIRONMENTAL, LLC—See Ferrellgas Partners, L.P.; *U.S. Public*, pg. 829
SABLE GROUP HOLDINGS (PTY) LIMITED—See Sable Holdings Limited; *Int'l*, pg. 6462
SABLE HOLDINGS LIMITED; *Int'l*, pg. 6462
SABLE INTERNATIONAL FINANCE LIMITED—See Liberty Global plc; *Int'l*, pg. 4485
SABLE NATURAL RESOURCES CORPORATION; *U.S. Private*, pg. 3521
SABLE OFFSHORE CORP.; *U.S. Public*, pg. 1833
SABLE POLYMER SOLUTIONS, LLC—See RiskOn International, Inc.; *U.S. Public*, pg. 1799
SABLE RESOURCES LTD.; *Int'l*, pg. 6462
SABLE ZINC KABWE LIMITED—See Jubilee Metals Group Plc; *Int'l*, pg. 4021
SABMILLER INDIA LIMITED—See Anheuser-Busch InBev SA/NV; *Int'l*, pg. 464
SABMILLER LATIN AMERICA—See Anheuser-Busch InBev SA/NV; *Int'l*, pg. 464
SABMILLER VIETNAM COMPANY LTD—See Anheuser-Busch InBev SA/NV; *Int'l*, pg. 464
SABO-ARMATUREN SERVICE GMBH—See Emerson Electric Co.; *U.S. Public*, pg. 752
SABO FOAM SRL—See Johnson Controls International plc; *Int'l*, pg. 3987
SABO-MASCHINENFABRIK GMBH; *Int'l*, pg. 6462
SABOO BROTHERS LIMITED; *Int'l*, pg. 6462
SABOO SODIUM CHLORO LTD.; *Int'l*, pg. 6463
SABORES Y FRAGANCIAS S.A.—See International Flavors & Fragrances Inc.; *U.S. Public*, pg. 1154
SA BOUTES; *Int'l*, pg. 6458
SABP ELTEKNIK AB—See Addtech AB; *Int'l*, pg. 135
SAB PIEMONTE S.R.L.—See Deutsche Bahn AG; *Int'l*, pg. 2052
SA BPI-GROUPE—See Caisse des Depots et Consignations; *Int'l*, pg. 1258
SA BPI-GROUPE—See EPIC Bpifrance; *Int'l*, pg. 2460
S.A.B.-PROFIEL B.V.—See Tata Sons Limited; *Int'l*, pg. 7472
S A B PROFIL GMBH—See Tata Sons Limited; *Int'l*, pg. 7472
SABRA DIPPING COMPANY LLC—See PepsiCo, Inc.; *U.S. Public*, pg. 1670
SABRA DIPPING COMPANY LLC—See Strauss Group Ltd.; *Int'l*, pg. 7238
S. ABRAHAM & SONS, INC.; *U.S. Private*, pg. 3514
SABRA HEALTH CARE REIT, INC.; *U.S. Public*, pg. 1833
SABRE AIRLINE SOLUTIONS—See Sabre Corporation; *U.S. Public*, pg. 1833
SABRE ASIA PACIFIC PTE. LTD.—See Sabre Corporation; *U.S. Public*, pg. 1833
SABRE AUSTRIA GMBH—See Sabre Corporation; *U.S. Public*, pg. 1833
SABRE BELGIUM SA—See Sabre Corporation; *U.S. Public*, pg. 1833
SABRE COMMUNICATIONS CORP.—See The Jordan Company, L.P.; *U.S. Private*, pg. 4061
SABRE CORPORATION; *U.S. Public*, pg. 1833
SABRE DEUTSCHLAND MARKETING GMBH—See Sabre Corporation; *U.S. Public*, pg. 1833
SABREFIX (UK) LIMITED—See Simpson Manufacturing Company, Inc.; *U.S. Public*, pg. 1883
SABRE GOLD MINES CORP.; *Int'l*, pg. 6463
SABRE HOLDINGS CORPORATION—See Sabre Corporation; *U.S. Public*, pg. 1833
SABRE HOSPITALITY SOLUTIONS—See Sabre Corporation; *U.S. Public*, pg. 1833
SABRE INDUSTRIES, INC.—See The Jordan Company, L.P.; *U.S. Private*, pg. 4061
SABRE INSURANCE GROUP PLC; *Int'l*, pg. 6463
SABRE ITALIA S.R.L.—See Sabre Corporation; *U.S. Public*, pg. 1833
SABRELINER CORPORATION; *U.S. Private*, pg. 3521
SABRE MANUFACTURING LLC—See Super Steel LLC; *U.S. Private*, pg. 3875
SABRE MARKETING NEDERLAND B.V.—See Sabre Corporation; *U.S. Public*, pg. 1833
SABRE MARKETING; *U.S. Private*, pg. 3521
SABRE POLSKA SP. Z O.O.—See Sabre Corporation; *U.S. Public*, pg. 1833

SABRE RADIO NETWORKS SA (PTY) LTD—See The Carlyle Group Inc.; *U.S. Public*, pg. 2045
SABRE RESOURCES LIMITED; *Int'l*, pg. 6463
SABRE SEYAHAT DAGITIM SISTERNLERI A.S.—See Sabre Corporation; *U.S. Public*, pg. 1833
SABRE SITE SOLUTIONS—See The Jordan Company, L.P.; *U.S. Private*, pg. 4061
SABRE SVERIGE AB—See Sabre Corporation; *U.S. Public*, pg. 1833
SABRE TECHNOLOGY HOLDINGS PTE. LTD.—See Sabre Corporation; *U.S. Public*, pg. 1833
SABRE TELECOM SERVICES—See The Jordan Company, L.P.; *U.S. Private*, pg. 4061
SABRE TOWERS AND POLES—See The Jordan Company, L.P.; *U.S. Private*, pg. 4061
SABRE TRAVEL NETWORK (CENTRAL ASIA) LLP—See Sabre Corporation; *U.S. Public*, pg. 1833
SABRE TRAVEL NETWORK (HONG KONG) LIMITED—See Sabre Corporation; *U.S. Public*, pg. 1833
SABRE TRAVEL NETWORK JORDAN LLC—See Sabre Corporation; *U.S. Public*, pg. 1834
SABRE TRAVEL NETWORK (MALAYSIA) SDN. BHD.—See Sabre Corporation; *U.S. Public*, pg. 1833
SABRE TRAVEL NETWORK MIDDLE EAST W.L.L.—See Sabre Corporation; *U.S. Public*, pg. 1834
SABRE TRAVEL NETWORK ROMANIA S.R.L.—See Sabre Corporation; *U.S. Public*, pg. 1834
SABRE TRAVEL NETWORK—See Sabre Corporation; *U.S. Public*, pg. 1833
SABRE TRAVEL NETWORK (THAILAND) LTD.—See Sabre Corporation; *U.S. Public*, pg. 1834
SABRE TUBULAR STRUCTURES - ELLWOOD CITY FACILITY—See The Jordan Company, L.P.; *U.S. Private*, pg. 4061
SABRE TUBULAR STRUCTURES - SIOUX CITY FACILITY—See The Jordan Company, L.P.; *U.S. Private*, pg. 4062
SABRE TUBULAR STRUCTURES—See The Jordan Company, L.P.; *U.S. Private*, pg. 4061
SABRE UKRAINE LLC—See Sabre Corporation; *U.S. Public*, pg. 1834
SABRE YACHTS; *U.S. Private*, pg. 3521
SABRIMALA INDUSTRIES INDIA LIMITED; *Int'l*, pg. 6463
SABRITAS, S.A. DE R.L. DE C.V.—See PepsiCo, Inc.; *U.S. Public*, pg. 1670
SABROE UK—See Johnson Controls International plc; *Int'l*, pg. 3986
SABROSURA FOODS, LLC—See Centre Partners Management LLC; *U.S. Private*, pg. 828
SABSA HOLDINGS (PTY) LTD.—See Anheuser-Busch InBev SA/NV; *Int'l*, pg. 464
SABTANK - SABIC TERMINAL SERVICE CO.—See Saudi Basic Industries Corporation; *Int'l*, pg. 6592
SABTANK SABIC TERMINAL SERVICES CO.—See Saudi Basic Industries Corporation; *Int'l*, pg. 6592
SABUY TECHNOLOGY PUBLIC COMPANY LIMITED; *Int'l*, pg. 6463
SABVEST LIMITED; *Int'l*, pg. 6463
SAB WABCO (UK) LIMITED—See Westinghouse Air Brake Technologies Corporation; *U.S. Public*, pg. 2358
S.A. CAMP COMPANIES; *U.S. Private*, pg. 3515
SA CARENE ASSURANCE—See Allianz SE; *Int'l*, pg. 355
SACCA CORPORATION; *U.S. Private*, pg. 3521
SACCHERIA F.LLI FRANCESCHETTI S.P.A; *Int'l*, pg. 6463
SACCHIFICIO TORDERA S.P.A.—See Sistema PJSFC; *Int'l*, pg. 6963
SACC INC.—See Alten S.A.; *Int'l*, pg. 390
SAC COMPONENTS (SOUTH ASIA) PTE. LTD.—See WPG Holdings Limited; *Int'l*, pg. 8461
S.A. CEBELOR—See Axel Johnson Gruppen AB; *Int'l*, pg. 765
SACE FCT S.P.A.—See Cassa Depositi e Prestiti S.p.A.; *Int'l*, pg. 1355
SACEM ENERGY AND ENGINEERING SA—See Kuwait Projects Company (Holding) K.S.C.P.; *Int'l*, pg. 4347
SACEM INDUSTRIES S.A.—See Kuwait Projects Company (Holding) K.S.C.P.; *Int'l*, pg. 4347
SACEM SMART SA—See Kuwait Projects Company (Holding) K.S.C.P.; *Int'l*, pg. 4347
SACEN A.D.; *Int'l*, pg. 6463
SACE S.P.A.—See Cassa Depositi e Prestiti S.p.A.; *Int'l*, pg. 1355
SACGASCO LIMITED; *Int'l*, pg. 6463
SACHA INCHI PTE. LTD.—See Sevens Atelier Limited; *Int'l*, pg. 6734
SACHAJUAN HAIRCARE AB—See Unilever PLC; *Int'l*, pg. 8045
SACHAL ENERGY DEVELOPMENT (PRIVATE) LIMITED—See Arif Habib Corporation Limited; *Int'l*, pg. 564
SA CHAUMONTAISE DES AUTOMOBILES MAUBREY; *Int'l*, pg. 6458
SACHEM ACQUISITION CORP.; *U.S. Public*, pg. 1834
SACHEM ASIA LTD.—See SACHEM Inc.; *U.S. Private*, pg. 3521
SACHEM CAPITAL CORP.; *U.S. Public*, pg. 1834

SACHEM EUROPE BV—See SACHEM Inc.; *U.S. Private*, pg. 3521
SACHEM INC.; *U.S. Private*, pg. 3521
SACHETA METALS LIMITED; *Int'l*, pg. 6463
SACHS AUTOMOTIVE COMPONENTS & SYSTEMS (SHANGHAI) CO., LTD.—See ZF Friedrichshafen AG; *Int'l*, pg. 8642
SACHS CIVIL INC.—See Sachs Electric Company; *U.S. Private*, pg. 3521
SACHS ELECTRIC COMPANY; *U.S. Private*, pg. 3521
SACHSEN BANK—See Landesbank Baden-Wurttemberg; *Int'l*, pg. 4405
SACHSENDRUCK GMBH—See Offizin Andersen Nexo Leipzig GmbH; *Int'l*, pg. 5530
SACHSENFONDS INTERNATIONAL EQUITY HOLDING I GMBH—See Landesbank Baden-Wurttemberg; *Int'l*, pg. 4406
SACHSEN GUSS GMBH—See The Carlyle Group Inc.; *U.S. Public*, pg. 2047
SACHSENKRAFT PLUS GMBH—See PNE AG; *Int'l*, pg. 5901
SACHSENMILCH LEPPERSDORF GMBH—See Unternehmensgruppe Theo Muller S.e.c.s.; *Int'l*, pg. 8085
SACHS HOLDING COMPANY; *U.S. Private*, pg. 3521
SACHS INVESTING COMPANY; *U.S. Private*, pg. 3521
SACHSISCHE GRUNDSTUCKSAUKTIONEN AG—See Deutsche Grundstuecksauktionen AG; *Int'l*, pg. 2065
SACHSISCHE SCHWEIZ KLINIKEN GMBH—See Asklepios Kliniken GmbH & Co. KGaA; *Int'l*, pg. 624
SACHS MEDIA GROUP; *U.S. Private*, pg. 3522
SACHS PROPERTIES—See Sachs Holding Company; *U.S. Private*, pg. 3521
SACHS SYSTEMS INC.—See Sachs Electric Company; *U.S. Private*, pg. 3521
SACHTLEBEN BERGBAU VERWALTUNGSGESELL-SCHAFT MIT BESCHRANKTER HAFTUNG—See GEA Group Aktiengesellschaft; *Int'l*, pg. 2903
SACHTLEBEN MINERALS GMBH & CO. KG; *Int'l*, pg. 6463
SACI CFPA—See Sumitomo Corporation; *Int'l*, pg. 7271
SACID S.R.L.—See Savino Del Bene S.p.A.; *Int'l*, pg. 6600
S.A. CITRIQUE BELGE N.V.—See ADCURAM Group AG; *Int'l*, pg. 128
SACKETT NATIONAL HOLDINGS, INC.; *U.S. Private*, pg. 3522
SACK LUMBER COMPANY; *U.S. Private*, pg. 3522
SACK LUNCH PRODUCTIONS INC.; *U.S. Public*, pg. 1834
SACKNER PRODUCTS INC.—See Leggett & Platt, Incorporated; *U.S. Public*, pg. 1303
SACKS PARENTE GOLF, INC.; *U.S. Public*, pg. 1834
SACKVILLE TPEN PROPERTY (GP) LTD.—See Ameriprise Financial, Inc.; *U.S. Public*, pg. 114
SACKVILLE TSP PROPERTY (GP) LTD.—See Ameriprise Financial, Inc.; *U.S. Public*, pg. 114
SACMA ACCIAI SPECIALI S.P.A.—See voestalpine AG; *Int'l*, pg. 8289
SACMI AUTOMATION—See Sacmi Imola S.C.A.R.L.; *Int'l*, pg. 6464
SACMI BEVERAGE DE MEXICO S.A. DE C.V.—See Sacmi Imola S.C.A.R.L.; *Int'l*, pg. 6464
SACMI BEVERAGE VENEZUELA, C.A.—See Sacmi Imola S.C.A.R.L.; *Int'l*, pg. 6464
SACMI CARPMEC S.P.A.—See Sacmi Imola S.C.A.R.L.; *Int'l*, pg. 6464
SACMI (CHANGSHU) MACHINERY EQUIPMENT CO., LTD—See Sacmi Imola S.C.A.R.L.; *Int'l*, pg. 6464
SACMI DE MEXICO S.A. DE C.V.—See Sacmi Imola S.C.A.R.L.; *Int'l*, pg. 6464
SACMI DEUTSCHLAND GMBH—See Sacmi Imola S.C.A.R.L.; *Int'l*, pg. 6464
SACMI DO BRASIL INDUSTRIA E COMERCIO LTDA—See Sacmi Imola S.C.A.R.L.; *Int'l*, pg. 6464
SACMI FILLING S.P.A.—See Sacmi Imola S.C.A.R.L.; *Int'l*, pg. 6464
SACMI FORNI S.P.A.—See Sacmi Imola S.C.A.R.L.; *Int'l*, pg. 6464
SACMI HONG KONG LTD.—See Sacmi Imola S.C.A.R.L.; *Int'l*, pg. 6464
SACMI IBERICA S.A.—See Sacmi Imola S.C.A.R.L.; *Int'l*, pg. 6464
SACMI IBERICA S.A.—See Sacmi Imola S.C.A.R.L.; *Int'l*, pg. 6464
SACMI IMOLA S.C.A.R.L.; *Int'l*, pg. 6463
SACMI IMOLA S.C.—See Sacmi Imola S.C.A.R.L.; *Int'l*, pg. 6464
SACMI IMPIANTI INDIA LIMITED—See Sacmi Imola S.C.A.R.L.; *Int'l*, pg. 6464
SACMI IMPIANTI S.A.—See Sacmi Imola S.C.A.R.L.; *Int'l*, pg. 6464
SACMI IMPIANTI S.P.A.—See Sacmi Imola S.C.A.R.L.; *Int'l*, pg. 6464
SACMI IRAN - SAZEH CERAMIC & MATERIAL IRANIAN CO.—See Sacmi Imola S.C.A.R.L.; *Int'l*, pg. 6464
SACMI ISTANBUL SANAYI VE TIC. LTD STI.—See Sacmi Imola S.C.A.R.L.; *Int'l*, pg. 6464
SACMI KOREA COMPANY—See Sacmi Imola S.C.A.R.L.; *Int'l*, pg. 6465

COMPANY NAME INDEX

SACMI LABELLING SCM S.P.A.—See Sacmi Imola S.C.A.R.L.; *Int'l*, pg. 6465
SACMI LABELLING S.P.A.—See Sacmi Imola S.C.A.R.L.; *Int'l*, pg. 6465
SACMI MACHINERY (FOSHAN NANHAY) CO. LTD.—See Sacmi Imola S.C.A.R.L.; *Int'l*, pg. 6465
SACMI MIDDLE EAST—See Sacmi Imola S.C.A.R.L.; *Int'l*, pg. 6465
SACMI MOLDS & DIES EGYPT—See Sacmi Imola S.C.A.R.L.; *Int'l*, pg. 6465
SACMI MOLDS & DIES PARS CO.—See Sacmi Imola S.C.A.R.L.; *Int'l*, pg. 6464
SACMI MOLDS & DIES S.P.A.—See Sacmi Imola S.C.A.R.L.; *Int'l*, pg. 6465
SACMI MOLDS & DIES USA LTD.—See Sacmi Imola S.C.A.R.L.; *Int'l*, pg. 6465
SACMI PACKAGING S.P.A.—See Sacmi Imola S.C.A.R.L.; *Int'l*, pg. 6465
SACMI PAKIM S.R.L.—See Sacmi Imola S.C.A.R.L.; *Int'l*, pg. 6465
SACMI POLSKA SP Z O.O.—See Sacmi Imola S.C.A.R.L.; *Int'l*, pg. 6465
SACMI PORTUGAL LDA—See Sacmi Imola S.C.A.R.L.; *Int'l*, pg. 6465
SACMI (SHANGHAI) MACHINERY EQUIPMENT CO. LTD.—See Sacmi Imola S.C.A.R.L.; *Int'l*, pg. 6464
SACMI SINGAPORE PTE LTD.—See Sacmi Imola S.C.A.R.L.; *Int'l*, pg. 6465
SACMI (THAILAND) CO. LTD.—See Sacmi Imola S.C.A.R.L.; *Int'l*, pg. 6464
SACMI USA LTD.—See Sacmi Imola S.C.A.R.L.; *Int'l*, pg. 6465
SACMI WEST EUROPE BEVERAGE TECHNOLOGY SA—See Sacmi Imola S.C.A.R.L.; *Int'l*, pg. 6465
SACMO—See Coesia S.p.A.; *Int'l*, pg. 1690
SAC-N-PAC STORES, INC.—See Sunoco LP; *U.S. Public*, pg. 1965
SACO BAY ORTHOPAEDIC AND SPORTS PHYSICAL THERAPY, INC.—See Select Medical Holdings Corporation; *U.S. Public*, pg. 1859
SACO BAY ORTHOPEDIC AND SPORTS PHYSICAL THERAPY, INC.—See Select Medical Holdings Corporation; *U.S. Public*, pg. 1859
SACO & BIDDEFORD SAVINGS INSTITUTION; *U.S. Private*, pg. 3522
SACO FOODS INC.—See Benford Capital Partners, LLC; *U.S. Private*, pg. 526
SACO LOWELL PARTS LLC—See Hercules Engine Components LLC; *U.S. Private*, pg. 1921
SACOM BANK (CAMBODIA) PLC.—See National Bank of Cambodia; *Int'l*, pg. 5152
SACOMBANK LEASING CO., LTD.—See Saigon Thuong Tin Commercial Joint Stock Bank; *Int'l*, pg. 6483
SACOMBANK SECURITIES JOINT STOCK COMPANY; *Int'l*, pg. 6465
S.A. COMPTOIR FINLANDAIS N.V.—See Stora Enso Oyj; *Int'l*, pg. 7223
SACOM REAL ESTATE CORPORATION—See Sam Holdings Corporation; *Int'l*, pg. 6500
S.A. COMUNALE CO., INC.—See EMCOR Group, Inc.; *U.S. Public*, pg. 737
SACOPAN, INC.—See Owens Corning; *U.S. Public*, pg. 1627
SACOPA, S.A.U.—See Fluidra SA; *Int'l*, pg. 2714
SACO POLYMERS INC.; *U.S. Private*, pg. 3522
SACOPOR - SOCIEDADE DE EMBALAGENS E SACOS DE PAPEL S.A.—See Camargo Correa S.A.; *Int'l*, pg. 1268
SACOREC, S.L.—See Sacyr, S.A.; *Int'l*, pg. 6466
SACO RIVER TELEPHONE LLC—See Keystone Group, L.P.; *U.S. Private*, pg. 2299
SACOR MARITIMA, S.A.—See Galp Energia SGPS, S.A.; *Int'l*, pg. 2875
SA CORPORATE REAL ESTATE LIMITED; *Int'l*, pg. 6458
SACOS CORPORATION—See Nishio Holdings Co., Ltd.; *Int'l*, pg. 5365
SACOVEN PLC; *Int'l*, pg. 6465
THE SACRAMENTO BEE—See Chatham Asset Management, LLC; *U.S. Private*, pg. 867
SACRAMENTO COLLISION, INC.—See AutoNation, Inc.; *U.S. Public*, pg. 237
SACRAMENTO EMPLOYMENT & TRAINING AGENCY; *U.S. Private*, pg. 3522
SACRAMENTO KINGS LIMITED PARTNERSHIP—See Ranadive Group; *U.S. Private*, pg. 3352
SACRAMENTO MIDTOWN ENDOSCOPY CENTER, LLC—See Tenet Healthcare Corporation; *U.S. Public*, pg. 2012
SACRAMENTO PACKING, INC.; *U.S. Private*, pg. 3522
SACRAMENTO REGION COMMUNITY FOUNDATION; *U.S. Private*, pg. 3522
SACRAMENTO TELEVISION STATIONS INC.—See National Amusements, Inc.; *U.S. Private*, pg. 2843
SACRED HEART COMMUNITY SERVICE; *U.S. Private*, pg. 3522
SACRED HEART HEALTHCARE SYSTEM—See UnityPoint Health; *U.S. Private*, pg. 4303
SACRED HEART HEALTH SYSTEM—See Ascension Health Alliance; *U.S. Private*, pg. 347

SACRED POWER CORP.; *U.S. Private*, pg. 3522
SACRED SUN ASIA PACIFIC PTE LTD.—See Shandong Sacred Sun Power Sources Company Limited; *Int'l*, pg. 6757
SACRED SUN EUROPE SPRL—See Shandong Sacred Sun Power Sources Company Limited; *Int'l*, pg. 6757
SACRED WIND ENTERPRISES, INC.—See ATN International, Inc.; *U.S. Public*, pg. 224
SACRIA INDUSTRIES; *Int'l*, pg. 6465
SAC SAURER AUTOMOTIVE COMPONENTS B.V.—See OC Oerlikon Corporation AG; *Int'l*, pg. 5514
SAC'S BAR HOLDINGS INC.; *Int'l*, pg. 6463
SACS S.R.L.—See Somfy SA; *Int'l*, pg. 7085
SACUNAS, INC.; *U.S. Private*, pg. 3522
S&A CUSTOM BUILT HOMES INC.; *U.S. Private*, pg. 3512
SAC WIRELESS, LLC—See Nokia Corporation; *Int'l*, pg. 5405
SACYR AGUA CHACABUCO, S.A.—See Sacyr, S.A.; *Int'l*, pg. 6466
SACYR CONCESIONES CHILE, S.A.—See Sacyr, S.A.; *Int'l*, pg. 6466
SACYR CONCESIONES MEXICO, S.A. DE C.V.—See Sacyr, S.A.; *Int'l*, pg. 6466
SACYR CONCESIONES PERU, S.A.C.—See Sacyr, S.A.; *Int'l*, pg. 6466
SACYR CONCESIONES URUGUAY, S.A.—See Sacyr, S.A.; *Int'l*, pg. 6466
SACYR CONSTRUCCION, S.A.U.—See Sacyr, S.A.; *Int'l*, pg. 6466
SACYR INDUSTRIAL, S.L.U.—See Sacyr, S.A.; *Int'l*, pg. 6466
SACYR IRELAND LIMITED—See Sacyr, S.A.; *Int'l*, pg. 6466
SACYR, S.A.; *Int'l*, pg. 6465
SACYR SOCIAL, S.L.—See Sacyr, S.A.; *Int'l*, pg. 6466
SADA AG—See Poenina Holding AG; *Int'l*, pg. 5903
SADAFCO FOR FOODSTUFF UAE—See Saudi Dairy & Foodstuff Co. Ltd.; *Int'l*, pg. 6593
SADAFCO JORDAN FOODSTUFF CO.—See Saudi Dairy & Foodstuff Co. Ltd.; *Int'l*, pg. 6593
SADAFCO QATAR LLC—See Saudi Dairy & Foodstuff Co. Ltd.; *Int'l*, pg. 6593
SADAF SAUDI PETROCHEMICAL CO.—See Saudi Basic Industries Corporation; *Int'l*, pg. 6592
SADAF SAUDI PETROCHEMICAL CO.—See Shell plc; *Int'l*, pg. 6796
SADAJUP SA; *Int'l*, pg. 6466
SADAO P.S. RUBBER CO., LTD.—See Sri Trang Agro-Industry Public Company Limited; *Int'l*, pg. 7150
SADARA CHEMICAL COMPANY—See Saudi Arabian Oil Company; *Int'l*, pg. 6590
SADA SYSTEMS, INC.—See Insight Enterprises, Inc.; *U.S. Public*, pg. 1130
SADBHAV ENGINEERING LTD; *Int'l*, pg. 6466
SADBHAV INFRASTRUCTURE PROJECTS LTD.; *Int'l*, pg. 6466
SADCO, INC.; *U.S. Private*, pg. 3522
SADCO SAMI DANDAN & CO.—See Dar Al Dawa Development & Investment Co.; *Int'l*, pg. 1971
SADDLEBACK ASSOCIATES INC.; *U.S. Private*, pg. 3522
SADDLEBACK DIALYSIS, LLC—See DaVita Inc.; *U.S. Public*, pg. 642
SADDLEBACK MEMORIAL AT SAN CLEMENTE—See Memorial Health Services; *U.S. Public*, pg. 2664
SADDLEBROOK HOLDINGS, INC.; *U.S. Private*, pg. 3522
SADDLEBROOK RESORTS, INC.—See Saddlebrook Holdings, Inc.; *U.S. Private*, pg. 3523
SADDLE CREEK CORPORATION; *U.S. Private*, pg. 3522
SADDLE RANCH MEDIA, INC.; *U.S. Public*, pg. 1834
SADDORIS COMPANIES, INC.; *U.S. Private*, pg. 3523
SADE CGTH—See Veolia Environnement S.A.; *Int'l*, pg. 8161
SADE-COMPAGNIE GENERALE DE TRAVAUX D'HYDRAULIQUE SA—See Veolia Environnement S.A.; *Int'l*, pg. 8154
SADEF FRANCE S.A.R.L.—See voestalpine AG; *Int'l*, pg. 8293
SADEF N.V.—See voestalpine AG; *Int'l*, pg. 8293
SADEM - SOCIETA PER AZIONI—See Deutsche Bahn AG; *Int'l*, pg. 2052
S.A. DE PROMOCIONES Y EDICIONES—See CIL Group SL; *Int'l*, pg. 1607
SA DES EAUX MINERALES D'EVIAN—See Danone; *Int'l*, pg. 1968
SA DESIGNER PARFUMS LTD.; *Int'l*, pg. 6458
SA DETAJOINT NV—See Deceuninck NV; *Int'l*, pg. 2000
SADHANA NITRO CHEM LIMITED; *Int'l*, pg. 6466
SADHNA BROADCAST LTD.; *Int'l*, pg. 6466
SADIA S.A.—See BRF S.A.; *Int'l*, pg. 1151
SADIA URUGUAY S.A.—See BRF S.A.; *Int'l*, pg. 1151
SADIBO; *Int'l*, pg. 6466
SADICO CANTHO JOINT STOCK CORPORATION; *Int'l*, pg. 6466
S.A. D'IETEREN N.V.; *Int'l*, pg. 6447
S.A. D'IETEREN SERVICES N.V.—See s.a. D'Ieteren n.v.; *Int'l*, pg. 6448
S.A. D'IETEREN SPORT N.V.—See s.a. D'Ieteren n.v.; *Int'l*, pg. 6448

S.A. D'IETEREN TREASURY N.V.—See s.a. D'Ieteren n.v.; *Int'l*, pg. 6448
SADIMATO S.A.S.—See L. Possehl & Co. mbH; *Int'l*, pg. 4385
SADIM INVERSIONES S.A.—See Hulleras del Norte, S.A.; *Int'l*, pg. 3528
SADI POLSKA-AGENCJA CELNA SP. Z O.O.—See Stellantis N.V.; *Int'l*, pg. 7197
S A DISTRIBUTION AUTOMOBILE COMPIEGNOISE; *Int'l*, pg. 6442
SADLER'S BAR-B-QUE SALES, LTD.; *U.S. Private*, pg. 3523
SADMITEC S.A.—See Veolia Environnement S.A.; *Int'l*, pg. 8158
SADOFF INVESTMENT MANAGEMENT—See TA Associates, Inc.; *U.S. Private*, pg. 3919
SADOFF & RUDOY INDUSTRIES, LLP; *U.S. Private*, pg. 3523
SADO GAS CO., LTD.—See Shizuokagas Co., Ltd.; *Int'l*, pg. 6856
SADOLIN FARVELAND A/S—See Akzo Nobel N.V.; *Int'l*, pg. 274
SADONG DEVELOPMENT SDN. BHD.—See Advance Synergy Berhad; *Int'l*, pg. 157
SADOSHIMA CORPORATION—See Yodogawa Steel Works, Ltd.; *Int'l*, pg. 8591
SADO STEAM SHIP CO., LTD.; *Int'l*, pg. 6466
SADOVAYA GROUP S.A.; *Int'l*, pg. 6467
SADRA MEDICAL, INC.—See Boston Scientific Corporation; *U.S. Public*, pg. 375
SADTEM; *Int'l*, pg. 6467
S.A. DU CHATEAU D'YQUEM—See LVMH Moet Hennessy Louis Vuitton SE; *Int'l*, pg. 4600
SADUC - SAUDI ARABIAN DUMEZ CO. LTD—See VINCI S.A.; *Int'l*, pg. 8231
SA DUFRA; *Int'l*, pg. 6458
SADVEL SA—See Akzo Nobel N.V.; *Int'l*, pg. 275
SADYBA BEST MALL SP ZOO—See BNP Paribas SA; *Int'l*, pg. 1092
SAE AGENCY PTE. LTD.—See SingAsia Holdings Limited; *Int'l*, pg. 6943
SAE ASTI—See Compagnie de Saint-Gobain SA; *Int'l*, pg. 1727
SAEBE COMPAGNIET APS—See Bunzl plc; *Int'l*, pg. 1219
SAE CIRCUITS COLORADO INC.; *U.S. Private*, pg. 3523
SAECO ARGENTINA S.A.—See Koninklijke Philips N.V.; *Int'l*, pg. 4271
SAECO AUSTRIA AG—See Koninklijke Philips N.V.; *Int'l*, pg. 4271
SAECO CANADA LTEE—See Koninklijke Philips N.V.; *Int'l*, pg. 4271
SAECO CENTROAMERICA SA—See Koninklijke Philips N.V.; *Int'l*, pg. 4271
SAECO DO BRASIL COMERCIO DE EQUIPAMENTOS LTDA—See Koninklijke Philips N.V.; *Int'l*, pg. 4271
SAECO FRANCE S.A.—See Koninklijke Philips N.V.; *Int'l*, pg. 4271
SAECO GMBH—See Koninklijke Philips N.V.; *Int'l*, pg. 4271
SAECO IBERICA S.A.—See Koninklijke Philips N.V.; *Int'l*, pg. 4271
SAECO INTERNATIONAL GROUP AUSTRALIA PTY LTD—See Koninklijke Philips N.V.; *Int'l*, pg. 4271
SAECO INTERNATIONAL GROUP S.P.A.—See Koninklijke Philips N.V.; *Int'l*, pg. 4271
SAE COMPONENTS (CHANGAN) LTD.—See TDK Corporation; *Int'l*, pg. 7487
SAECO POLSKA SP. Z O.O.—See Koninklijke Philips N.V.; *Int'l*, pg. 4271
SAECOPOR-IMPORTACAO E COMERCIO DE APARELHOS ELECTRICOS, LDA—See Koninklijke Philips N.V.; *Int'l*, pg. 4271
SAECO USA INC.—See Koninklijke Philips N.V.; *Int'l*, pg. 4271
SAECO VENDING S.P.A.—See Koninklijke Philips N.V.; *Int'l*, pg. 4271
SAE DIGITAL S.A.—See Dragoneer Investment Group, LLC; *U.S. Private*, pg. 1272
SAE DIGITAL S.A.—See General Atlantic Service Company, L.P.; *U.S. Private*, pg. 1662
SAEDONG CO., LTD.; *Int'l*, pg. 6467
SAEFERDIR EHF.—See Eimskipafelag Islands Hf.; *Int'l*, pg. 2332
S.A. EGON ZEHNDER ASSOCIATES (INTERNATIONAL) N.V.—See Egon Zehnder International Inc.; *U.S. Private*, pg. 1345
SAE-HWASHIN CO., LTD.—See Hwashin Tech Co., Ltd.; *Int'l*, pg. 3543
SA EIFFAGE BENELUX—See Eiffage S.A.; *Int'l*, pg. 2330
SAE (INDIA) LTD.—See SAE International; *U.S. Private*, pg. 3523
SA&E INTERNATIONAL BAG & ACCESSORIES LLC; *U.S. Private*, pg. 3519
SAE INTERNATIONAL; *U.S. Private*, pg. 3523
SAE IT SYSTEMS GMBH & CO KG—See LACROIX S.A.; *Int'l*, pg. 4391
SAE MAGNETICS (H.K.) LTD.—See TDK Corporation; *Int'l*, pg. 7488

SAE INTERNATIONAL — CORPORATE AFFILIATIONS

Company Index

SAEMANGEUM SOLAR POWER CO., LTD.—See Korea Electric Power Corporation; *Int'l*, pg. 4284

SAENGBO REAL ESTATE TRUST CO., LTD.—See Kyobo Life Insurance Co., Ltd.; *Int'l*, pg. 4355

SAENGER ASSOCIATES—See 20/20 Foresight Executive Search LLC; *U.S. Private*, pg. 5

SAENGVITH 2000 CO. LTD.—See Atlas Copco AB; *Int'l*, pg. 684

SAEPAR SERVICOS E PARTICIPACOES S.A.—See Rede D'Or Sao Luiz SA; *Int'l*, pg. 6246

SAEPLAST AMERICAS INC.—See Berry Global Group, Inc; *U.S. Public*, pg. 325

SAEPLAST ICELAND EHF—See Berry Global Group, Inc; *U.S. Public*, pg. 325

SAEPLAST NORWAY AS—See Berry Global Group, Inc; *U.S. Public*, pg. 325

SAEPLAST SPAIN SAU—See Berry Global Group, Inc; *U.S. Public*, pg. 325

SAE POWER COMPANY, INC.—See SAE Power; *U.S. Private*, pg. 3523

SAE POWER INC—See SAE Power; *U.S. Private*, pg. 3523

SAE POWERLINES S.R.L—See Gammon India Limited; *Int'l*, pg. 2879

SAE POWER; *U.S. Private*, pg. 3523

SA EQUUS; *Int'l*, pg. 6458

SAERON AUTOMOTIVE BEIJING CORPORATION—See Nisshinbo Holdings Inc.; *Int'l*, pg. 5375

SAERON AUTOMOTIVE CORP.—See Nisshinbo Holdings Inc.; *Int'l*, pg. 5375

SAERTEX FRANCE SAS—See SAERTEX GmbH & Co. KG; *Int'l*, pg. 6467

SAERTEX GMBH & CO. KG; *Int'l*, pg. 6467

SAERTEX INDIA PRIVATE LIMITED—See SAERTEX GmbH & Co. KG; *Int'l*, pg. 6467

SAERTEX MULTICOM GMBH—See SAERTEX GmbH & Co. KG; *Int'l*, pg. 6467

SAERTEX PORTUGAL, UNIPESSOAL LDA.—See SAERTEX GmbH & Co. KG; *Int'l*, pg. 6467

SAERTEX REINFORCEMENTS DONGYING CO., LTD.—See SAERTEX GmbH & Co. KG; *Int'l*, pg. 6467

SAERTEX SOUTH AFRICA (PTY) LTD.—See SAERTEX GmbH & Co. KG; *Int'l*, pg. 6467

SAERTEX STADE GMBH & CO. KG—See SAERTEX GmbH & Co. KG; *Int'l*, pg. 6467

SAERTEX TECIDOS BRASIL LTDA.—See SAERTEX GmbH & Co. KG; *Int'l*, pg. 6467

SAERTEX USA, LLC—See SAERTEX GmbH & Co. KG; *Int'l*, pg. 6467

S.A. ESAB N.V.—See Enovis Corporation; *U.S. Public*, pg. 771

SAES COATED FILMS S.P.A.—See SAES Getters S.p.A.; *Int'l*, pg. 6467

SAES GETTERS JAPAN CO., LTD.—See SAES Getters S.p.A.; *Int'l*, pg. 6467

SAES GETTERS KOREA—See SAES Getters S.p.A.; *Int'l*, pg. 6467

SAES GETTERS (NANJING) CO., LTD.—See SAES Getters S.p.A.; *Int'l*, pg. 6467

SAES GETTERS SINGAPORE PTE. LTD.—See SAES Getters S.p.A.; *Int'l*, pg. 6467

SAES GETTERS S.P.A.; *Int'l*, pg. 6467

SAES GETTERS/U.S.A., INC.—See SAES Getters S.p.A.; *Int'l*, pg. 6467

SAE—See FAYAT SAS; *Int'l*, pg. 2626

SAES RIAL VACUUM S.R.L.—See SAES Getters S.p.A.; *Int'l*, pg. 6467

S AESTHETICS CLINIC PTE. LTD.—See Republic Healthcare Ltd.; *Int'l*, pg. 6295

S.A. ETABLISSEMENTS N.V. CHARLES WILLE & CO—See ROCKWOOL A/S; *Int'l*, pg. 6381

SAETA YIELD SA; *Int'l*, pg. 6467

SAE TECHNOLOGIES DEVELOPMENT (DONGGUAN) CO., LTD.—See TDK Corporation; *Int'l*, pg. 7487

SAET INDUCTION EQUIPMENT (SHANGHAI) CO. LTD.—See Park-Ohio Holdings Corp.; *U.S. Public*, pg. 1640

SAE TOWERS BRAZIL TORRES DE TRANSMISSION LTDA—See KEC International Limited; *Int'l*, pg. 4113

SAE TOWERS HOLDINGS LLC—See KEC International Limited; *Int'l*, pg. 4113

SAE TOWERS MEXICO S DE RL DE CV—See KEC International Limited; *Int'l*, pg. 4113

SAET S.P.A.—See Park-Ohio Holdings Corp.; *U.S. Public*, pg. 1640

SA EVANGELOU & CO. LLC—See PricewaterhouseCoopers Ltd.; *Int'l*, pg. 5971

SAEXPLORATION (AUSTRALIA) PTY. LTD.—See SAExploration Holdings, Inc.; *U.S. Private*, pg. 3523

SAEXPLORATION (BRASIL) SERVICOS SISMICOS LTDA.—See SAExploration Holdings, Inc.; *U.S. Private*, pg. 3523

SAEXPLORATION (CANADA) LTD.—See SAExploration Holdings, Inc.; *U.S. Private*, pg. 3523

SAEXPLORATION HOLDINGS, INC.; *U.S. Private*, pg. 3523

SAEXPLORATION, INC.—See SAExploration Holdings, Inc.; *U.S. Private*, pg. 3523

SAEXPLORATION SUB, INC.—See SAExploration Holdings, Inc.; *U.S. Private*, pg. 3523

SAFA GOURMET FOOD PTE LTD—See Emerging Glory Sdn Bhd; *Int'l*, pg. 2379

SAFAIR OPERATIONS (PTY) LIMITED—See Aergo Capital Ltd.; *Int'l*, pg. 179

SAFAL HERBS LIMITED; *Int'l*, pg. 6468

SAFA, LLC—See AISIN Corporation; *Int'l*, pg. 251

SAFAL SECURITIES LIMITED; *Int'l*, pg. 6468

SAFANAD INC.—See Safanad Limited; *Int'l*, pg. 6469

SAFANAD LIMITED; *Int'l*, pg. 6469

SAFANAD S.A.—See Safanad Limited; *Int'l*, pg. 6469

SAFANAD (UK) LIMITED—See Safanad Limited; *Int'l*, pg. 6469

SAFARI AFRICAIN DE PORT SAINT PERE SA—See Compagnie des Alpes S.A.; *Int'l*, pg. 1738

SAFARI BOOKS ONLINE, LLC—See O'Reilly Media, Inc.; *U.S. Private*, pg. 2980

SAFARI CIRCUITS, INC.; *U.S. Private*, pg. 3523

SAFARICOM PLC; *Int'l*, pg. 6469

SAFARI INDUSTRIES (INDIA) LTD.; *Int'l*, pg. 6469

SAFARI INVESTMENTS RSA LTD.; *Int'l*, pg. 6469

SAFARILAND LLC - DEFENSE TECHNOLOGY—See Kanders & Company, Inc.; *U.S. Private*, pg. 2259

SAFARILAND, LLC - ONTARIO OFFICE—See Kanders & Company, Inc.; *U.S. Private*, pg. 2259

SAFARILAND, LLC—See Kanders & Company, Inc.; *U.S. Private*, pg. 2259

SAFARI MINERALS INC.; *Int'l*, pg. 6469

SAFARI NRINGSMIDLER AS—See TINE SA; *Int'l*, pg. 7753

SAFARI WORLD PUBLIC COMPANY LIMITED; *Int'l*, pg. 6469

SAFAR TRAVEL SERVICES—See Al Fahim Group; *Int'l*, pg. 277

SAFA SYSTEMS & TECHNOLOGIES LIMITED; *Int'l*, pg. 6468

SAFA TEXTILES LTD.; *Int'l*, pg. 6468

SAFA TRUST INC.; *U.S. Private*, pg. 3523

SAFAVIEH CARPETS OF ISFAHAN; *U.S. Private*, pg. 3523

SAFBON WATER SERVICE (HOLDING) INC., SHANGHAI; *Int'l*, pg. 6469

SAFBON WATER TECHNOLOGY, INC.—See BW Group Ltd.; *Int'l*, pg. 1231

SAFC BIOSCIENCES, INC.—See Merck KGaA; *Int'l*, pg. 4832

SAFC CARLSBAD, INC.—See Merck KGaA; *Int'l*, pg. 4832

SAFC HITECH, INC.—See Merck KGaA; *Int'l*, pg. 4832

SAFC, INC.—See Merck KGaA; *Int'l*, pg. 4832

SAFCO DENTAL SUPPLY LLC—See The PNC Financial Services Group, Inc.; *U.S. Public*, pg. 2120

SAFCO PRODUCTS COMPANY—See Liberty Diversified International Inc.; *U.S. Private*, pg. 2443

SAFCOR PANALPINA (PTY) LTD.—See The Bidvest Group Limited; *Int'l*, pg. 7626

SAF DJAZAIR, SPA—See Compagnie des Levures Lesaffre SA; *Int'l*, pg. 1739

SAF DO BRASIL LTDA—See Compagnie des Levures Lesaffre SA; *Int'l*, pg. 1739

SAFE 1 CREDIT UNION; *U.S. Private*, pg. 3523

SAFEAIR AG—See Stryker Corporation; *U.S. Public*, pg. 1956

SAFE AIR AUSTRALIA PTY LIMITED—See Airbus SE; *Int'l*, pg. 247

SAFE AIR LIMITED—See Airbus SE; *Int'l*, pg. 247

SAFEAIR S.L.—See Systemair AB; *Int'l*, pg. 7391

SAFEAIR TECHNICAL SDN. BHD.—See Destini Berhad; *Int'l*, pg. 2046

SAFE ALARM SYSTEMS INC.; *U.S. Private*, pg. 3523

SAFEAMERICA CREDIT UNION; *U.S. Private*, pg. 3524

SAFE AND GREEN DEVELOPMENT CORPORATION—See Safe & Green Holdings Corp.; *U.S. Public*, pg. 1834

SA.FEATHER CO., INC.—See Bain Capital, LP; *U.S. Private*, pg. 452

SAFE AT SEA AB; *Int'l*, pg. 6469

SAFE AUTO INSURANCE GROUP, INC.; *U.S. Private*, pg. 3523

SAFEBAG - INDUSTRIA COMPONENTES DE SEGURANCA AUTOMOVEL S.A.—See ZF Friedrichshafen AG; *Int'l*, pg. 8645

SAFE BAG S.P.A.; *Int'l*, pg. 6469

SAFEBRANDS S.A.S.—See Team Internet Group plc; *Int'l*, pg. 7500

SAFEBRIDGE CYPRUS LTD.—See Ferd AS; *Int'l*, pg. 2636

SAFEBRIDGE CYPRUS LTD.—See P/F Tjaldur; *Int'l*, pg. 5684

SAFEBRIDGE GMBH—See Ferd AS; *Int'l*, pg. 2636

SAFEBRIDGE GMBH—See P/F Tjaldur; *Int'l*, pg. 5684

SAFEBUILT, INC.; *U.S. Private*, pg. 3524

SAFE BULKERS, INC.; *Int'l*, pg. 6469

SAFE&CEC S.R.L.—See Clean Energy Fuels Corp.; *U.S. Public*, pg. 508

SAFE&CEC S.R.L.—See Landi Renzo S.p.a.; *Int'l*, pg. 4406

SAFE CHAIN SOLUTIONS, LLC—See Benchworks, Inc.; *U.S. Private*, pg. 524

SAFECHARGE INTERNATIONAL GROUP LIMITED—See Nuvei Technologies; *U.S. Private*, pg. 2975

SAFECHEM EUROPE GMBH—See Stirling Square Capital Partners LLP; *Int'l*, pg. 7216

SAFECODE DRUG TECHNOLOGIES CORP.; *Int'l*, pg. 6469

SAFECO INSURANCE COMPANY OF AMERICA-CENTRAL REGION—See Liberty Mutual Holding Company Inc.; *U.S. Private*, pg. 2446

SAFECO INSURANCE COMPANY OF AMERICA-NORTHEAST REGION—See Liberty Mutual Holding Company Inc.; *U.S. Private*, pg. 2446

SAFECO INSURANCE COMPANY OF AMERICA-NORTHWEST REGION—See Liberty Mutual Holding Company Inc.; *U.S. Private*, pg. 2446

SAFECO INSURANCE COMPANY OF AMERICA—See Liberty Mutual Holding Company Inc.; *U.S. Private*, pg. 2446

SAFECO INSURANCE COMPANY OF AMERICA—See Liberty Mutual Holding Company Inc.; *U.S. Private*, pg. 2446

SAFECO INSURANCE COMPANY OF AMERICA-SOUTHEAST REGION—See Liberty Mutual Holding Company Inc.; *U.S. Private*, pg. 2446

SAFECO INSURANCE COMPANY OF AMERICA-SOUTHWEST REGION—See Liberty Mutual Holding Company Inc.; *U.S. Private*, pg. 2446

SAFECOM A/S—See Microsoft Corporation; *U.S. Public*, pg. 1443

SAFECOM GMBH—See Microsoft Corporation; *U.S. Public*, pg. 1443

SAFECOM UK LIMITED—See Microsoft Corporation; *U.S. Public*, pg. 1443

SAFECORE, INC; *U.S. Private*, pg. 3524

SAFECOR HEALTH, LLC—See Vesey Street Capital Partners, L.L.C.; *U.S. Private*, pg. 4371

SAFECORP GROUP LTD.; *Int'l*, pg. 6469

SAFECO SURETY—See Liberty Mutual Holding Company Inc.; *U.S. Private*, pg. 2446

SAFED INDUSTRIEOFEN GMBH—See Berndorf AG; *Int'l*, pg. 987

SAFEDOX, INC.; *U.S. Private*, pg. 3524

SAFED SUISSE S.A.—See Berndorf AG; *Int'l*, pg. 987

SAFEDX S.R.O.—See Hon Hai Precision Industry Co., Ltd.; *Int'l*, pg. 3457

SAFE ELECTRONICS, INC.—See Apollo Global Management, Inc.; *U.S. Public*, pg. 146

SAFE FLEET HOLDINGS LLC—See Genstar Capital, LLC; *U.S. Private*, pg. 1676

SAFE FUEL SYSTEMS, INC.—See Arlington Capital Partners LLC; *U.S. Private*, pg. 327

SAFEGARD MINI STORAGE, LLC—See National Storage Affiliates Trust; *U.S. Public*, pg. 1498

SAFEGARD MINI STORAGE-TIGARD—See National Storage Affiliates Trust; *U.S. Public*, pg. 1498

SAFEGARD SYSTEMS LIMITED—See Investment AB Latour; *Int'l*, pg. 3784

SAFE & GREEN HOLDINGS CORP.; *U.S. Public*, pg. 1834

SAFEGUARD BUSINESS SYSTEMS, INC.—See Deluxe Corporation; *U.S. Public*, pg. 652

SAFEGUARD BUSINESS SYSTEMS LIMITED—See Deluxe Corporation; *U.S. Public*, pg. 652

SAFEGUARD CHEMICAL CORPORATION; *U.S. Private*, pg. 3524

SAFEGUARD FRANCHISE SALES, INC.—See Deluxe Corporation; *U.S. Public*, pg. 653

SAFEGUARD HEALTH ENTERPRISES, INC.—See MetLife, Inc.; *U.S. Public*, pg. 1431

SAFEGUARD HEALTH PLANS, INC.—See MetLife, Inc.; *U.S. Public*, pg. 1431

SAFEGUARD INSURANCE LLC—See GTCR LLC; *U.S. Private*, pg. 1804

SAFEGUARD LANDFILL MANAGEMENT LLC—See BC Partners LLP; *Int'l*, pg. 924

SAFEGUARD MEDICAL, LLC—See Water Street Healthcare Partners, LLC; *U.S. Private*, pg. 4452

SAFEGUARD PEST CONTROL AND ENVIRONMENTAL SERVICES LIMITED—See Rollins, Inc.; *U.S. Public*, pg. 1809

SAFE-GUARD PRODUCTS INTERNATIONAL, LLC—See Stone Point Capital LLC; *U.S. Private*, pg. 3825

SAFEGUARD PROPERTIES, INC.; *U.S. Private*, pg. 3524

SAFEGUARD SCIENTIFICS, INC.; *U.S. Public*, pg. 1834

SAFEGUARD SECURITY SERVICES INC.; *U.S. Private*, pg. 3524

SAFEGUARD SELF STORAGE; *U.S. Private*, pg. 3524

SAFEGUARD SERVICES LLC—See Veritas Capital Fund Management, LLC; *U.S. Private*, pg. 4364

SAFEGUARDS SECURICOR SDN BHD—See Allied Universal Manager LLC; *U.S. Private*, pg. 190

SAFEGUARD WORLD INTERNATIONAL LTD.; *Int'l*, pg. 6470

SAFE HARBOR FINANCIAL, INC.; *U.S. Private*, pg. 3523

SAFEHARBOR KNOWLEDGE SOLUTIONS—See Shackleton Equity Partners LLC; *U.S. Private*, pg. 3622

SAFE HARBOR MARINAS LLC—See Sun Communities, Inc.; *U.S. Public*, pg. 1963

COMPANY NAME INDEX

SAFE HARBOR WATER POWER CORPORATION—See Constellation Energy Corporation; *U.S. Public*, pg. 572
SAFE HARBOR WATER POWER CORPORATION—See LS Power Development, LLC; *U.S. Private*, pg. 2508
SAFE HARBOUR UNDERWRITERS, LLC—See The Progressive Corporation; *U.S. Public*, pg. 2124
SAFE-HIT CORPORATION—See Trinity Industries, Inc.; *U.S. Public*, pg. 2193
SAFEHOLD INC.; *U.S. Public*, pg. 1834
SAFEHOLD SPECIAL RISK, INC.—See Wells Fargo & Company; *U.S. Public*, pg. 2345
SAFE HOUSE INFORMATION MANAGEMENT SOLUTIONS PRIVATE LIMITED—See Iron Mountain Incorporated; *U.S. Public*, pg. 1174
SAFEIT SECURITY SWEDEN AB—See Francisco Partners Management, LP; *U.S. Private*, pg. 1588
SAFEKONT GMBH—See E.ON SE; *Int'l*, pg. 2259
SAFELAND ACTIVE MANAGEMENT LIMITED—See Safeland plc; *Int'l*, pg. 6470
SAFELAND INVESTMENTS LIMITED—See Safeland plc; *Int'l*, pg. 6470
SAFELAND PLC; *Int'l*, pg. 6470
SAFE-LIFE - INDUSTRIA DE COMPONENTES DE SEGURANCA AUTOMOVEL S.A—See ZF Friedrichshafen AG; *Int'l*, pg. 8645
SAFELITE GLASS CORP.—See s.a. D'Ieteren n.v.; *Int'l*, pg. 6448
SAFELITE GROUP, INC.—See s.a. D'Ieteren n.v.; *Int'l*, pg. 6447
SAFELITE SOLUTIONS LLC—See s.a. D'Ieteren n.v.; *Int'l*, pg. 6448
SAFELLO GROUP AB; *Int'l*, pg. 6470
SAFE & MANSFIELD TRAVEL GROUP PTE LTD.—See Sembcorp Industries Ltd.; *Int'l*, pg. 6702
SAFEMARK INC.—See MSouth Equity Partners, LLC; *U.S. Private*, pg. 2808
SAFEMARK SYSTEMS, LP—See ASSA ABLOY AB; *Int'l*, pg. 640
SAFE MIX CONCRETE LIMITED; *Int'l*, pg. 6469
SAFENET ASIA LIMITED—See Thales S.A.; *Int'l*, pg. 7599
SAFENET (AUSTRALIA) PTY. LTD.—See Thales S.A.; *Int'l*, pg. 7599
SAFENET CHINA LTD.—See Thales S.A.; *Int'l*, pg. 7599
SAFENET CONSULTING, LLC—See Stone Point Capital LLC; *U.S. Private*, pg. 3823
SAFENET, INC.—See Thales S.A.; *Int'l*, pg. 7599
SAFENET, INC.—See Thales S.A.; *Int'l*, pg. 7599
SAFENET INDIA PVT. LTD.—See Thales S.A.; *Int'l*, pg. 7599
SAFENET UK LIMITED—See Thales S.A.; *Int'l*, pg. 7599
SAFEOP SURGICAL, INC.—See Alphatec Holdings, Inc.; *U.S. Public*, pg. 84
SAFE ORTHOPAEDICS GMBH—See Safe SA; *Int'l*, pg. 6469
SAFE ORTHOPAEDICS, LLC—See Safe SA; *Int'l*, pg. 6469
SAFE ORTHOPAEDICS LTD.—See Safe SA; *Int'l*, pg. 6469
SAFE ORTHOPAEDICS SAS—See Safe SA; *Int'l*, pg. 6469
SAFEPACK PRODUCTS LTD.—See UPL Limited; *Int'l*, pg. 8089
SAFEPAK CORPORATION—See Custom Vault Corp; *U.S. Private*, pg. 1130
SAFE PASSAGE NEUROMONITORING—See Globus Medical, Inc.; *U.S. Public*, pg. 947
SAFEPLACE LTD.—See ASSA ABLOY AB; *Int'l*, pg. 640
SAFEPRINTS LLC—See AEA Investors LP; *U.S. Private*, pg. 114
SAFE RACK, LLC; *U.S. Private*, pg. 3523
SAFER ALSACE; *Int'l*, pg. 6470
SAFER DE HAUTE-NORMANDIE; *Int'l*, pg. 6470
S.A. FERIA DE LOS AGRICULTORES; *Int'l*, pg. 6448
SAFEROAD AS—See Nordic Capital AB; *Int'l*, pg. 5421
SAFEROADS HOLDINGS LIMITED; *Int'l*, pg. 6470
SAFEROADS PTY LTD—See Saferoads Holdings Limited; *Int'l*, pg. 6470
SAFER PRINTS INC.; *U.S. Private*, pg. 3524
SAFER SYSTEMS LLC—See Fortive Corporation; *U.S. Public*, pg. 871
SAFE-RUN INC—See SMCore Inc.; *Int'l*, pg. 7006
SAFE SA; *Int'l*, pg. 6469
SAFESEARCH PTY LIMITED—See ManpowerGroup Inc.; *U.S. Private*, pg. 1362
SAFESHRED CO., INC.—See Japan Pulp and Paper Company Limited; *Int'l*, pg. 3904
SAFESKIN MEDICAL & SCIENTIFIC (THAILAND) LIMITED—See Kimberly-Clark Corporation; *U.S. Public*, pg. 1231
SAFESOFT SOLUTIONS INC.; *U.S. Private*, pg. 3524
SAFE SPACE NYC INC.; *U.S. Private*, pg. 3524
SAFESPAN PLATFORM SYSTEMS INC.; *U.S. Private*, pg. 3524
SAFE S.P.A.—See Landi Renzo S.p.a.; *Int'l*, pg. 4406
SAFE-START, LLC; *U.S. Private*, pg. 3524
SAFESTAY ATHENS HOSTEL LIMITED—See Safestay Plc; *Int'l*, pg. 6470
SAFESTAY (EDINBURGH) HOSTEL LIMITED—See Safestay Plc; *Int'l*, pg. 6470

SAFESTAY (ELEPHANT & CASTLE) LIMITED—See Safestay Plc; *Int'l*, pg. 6470
SAFESTAY ESPANA S.L—See Safestay Plc; *Int'l*, pg. 6470
SAFESTAY HOSTEL GMBH—See Safestay Plc; *Int'l*, pg. 6470
SAFESTAY HOSTELS MADRID SL—See Safestay Plc; *Int'l*, pg. 6470
SAFESTAY ITALIA SRL—See Safestay Plc; *Int'l*, pg. 6470
SAFESTAY PLC; *Int'l*, pg. 6470
SAFESTAY (YORK) LIMITED—See Safestay Plc; *Int'l*, pg. 6470
SAFE STEP WALK IN TUB, LLC—See Ferguson plc; *Int'l*, pg. 2638
SAFESTORE ACQUISITION LIMITED—See Safestore Holdings plc; *Int'l*, pg. 6470
SAFESTORE HOLDINGS PLC; *Int'l*, pg. 6470
SAFESTYLE UK PLC; *Int'l*, pg. 6470
SAFE SUPPLY STREAMING CO., LTD.; *Int'l*, pg. 6469
SAFE SYSTEMS, INC.; *U.S. Private*, pg. 3524
SAFETEC COMPLIANCE SYSTEMS—See The Riverside Company; *U.S. Private*, pg. 4110
SAFETEC ENTSORGUNGS- UND SICHERHEITSTECHNIK GMBH—See E.ON SE; *Int'l*, pg. 2259
SAFE TECHNOLOGIES, INC.—See Lindsay Corporation; *U.S. Public*, pg. 1320
SAFETELL LIMITED—See Newmark Security Plc; *Int'l*, pg. 5235
SAFETIC AG—See SafeTIC S.A.; *Int'l*, pg. 6470
SAFETIC S.A.; *Int'l*, pg. 6470
SAFE TIME, SPOL. S.R.O.—See Bergman & Beving AB; *Int'l*, pg. 980
SAFETONET LIMITED; *Int'l*, pg. 6470
SAFE TRADE INTERNATIONAL COMPANY LIMITED—See Thiensurat Public Company Limited; *Int'l*, pg. 7709
SAFETURE AB; *Int'l*, pg. 6470
SAFE-T USA INC.—See Alarum Technologies Ltd.; *Int'l*, pg. 291
SAFETY ADHERENCE TECHNOLOGY (PTY) LTD—See CSG Holdings Limited; *Int'l*, pg. 1864
SAFETY AUTOPARTS MEXICO S. DE R.L.DE C.V.—See Ningbo Joyson Electronic Corp.; *Int'l*, pg. 5304
SAFETY BUSINESS LEARNING LIMITED—See K1 Investment Management, LLC; *U.S. Private*, pg. 2252
SAFETYCHAIN SOFTWARE, INC.; *U.S. Private*, pg. 3525
SAFETY, CLAIMS & LITIGATION SERVICES, LLC—See American Financial Group, Inc.; *U.S. Public*, pg. 103
THE SAFETY CO., LTD.—See NK Co., Ltd.; *Int'l*, pg. 5390
SAFETY COMPONENTS FABRIC TECHNOLOGIES, INC.—See Platinum Equity, LLC; *U.S. Private*, pg. 3203
SAFETY CONSULTING ENGINEERS INC.—See DEKRA e.V.; *Int'l*, pg. 2009
SAFETY CONTROLS TECHNOLOGY, INC.—See ScaleCo Management LLC; *U.S. Private*, pg. 3560
SAFETY DIRECT SOLUTIONS PTY. LTD.—See Security & Intelligence Services (INDIA) Limited; *Int'l*, pg. 6677
SAFETY & ECOLOGY CORPORATION—See Perma-Fix Environmental Services, Inc.; *U.S. Public*, pg. 1676
SAFETY FIRST—See O'Keeffe's, Inc.; *U.S. Private*, pg. 2978
SAFETY GODOWN COMPANY LIMITED; *Int'l*, pg. 6471
SAFETY GRID PAVEMENTS LTD.—See VINCI S.A.; *Int'l*, pg. 8218
SAFETY HARBOR SPA SPRINGS, INC.—See S.H.S. Resort, LLC; *U.S. Private*, pg. 3517
SAFETY INSURANCE CO., INC.—See Safety Insurance Group, Inc.; *U.S. Public*, pg. 1835
SAFETY INSURANCE GROUP, INC.; *U.S. Public*, pg. 1834
SAFETY ISLAND CO., LTD.—See Daiei Kankyo Co., Ltd.; *Int'l*, pg. 1924
SAFETY-KLEEN CANADA, INC.—See Clean Harbors, Inc.; *U.S. Public*, pg. 510
SAFETY-KLEEN DE MEXICO, S. DE R.L. DE C.V.—See Clean Harbors, Inc.; *U.S. Public*, pg. 510
SAFETY-KLEEN ENVIROSYSTEMS CO.—See Clean Harbors, Inc.; *U.S. Public*, pg. 510
SAFETY-KLEEN, INC.—See Clean Harbors, Inc.; *U.S. Public*, pg. 510
SAFETY-KLEEN OF CALIFORNIA, INC.—See Clean Harbors, Inc.; *U.S. Public*, pg. 510
SAFETY-KLEEN OIL RECOVERY CO.—See Clean Harbors, Inc.; *U.S. Public*, pg. 510
SAFETY-KLEEN SYSTEMS, INC.—See Clean Harbors, Inc.; *U.S. Public*, pg. 510
SAFETY MANAGEMENT GROUP; *U.S. Private*, pg. 3524
SAFETY NATIONAL CASUALTY CORPORATION—See Tokio Marine Holdings, Inc.; *Int'l*, pg. 7782
SAFETY NETACCESS, INC.; *U.S. Private*, pg. 3524
SAFETY PRODUCTION S.A.S.—See Sandvik AB; *Int'l*, pg. 6530
SAFETY RAILWAY SERVICE—See Commercial Metals Company; *U.S. Public*, pg. 547
SAFETY RESEARCH INSTITUTE FOR CHEMICAL COMPOUNDS CO., LTD.—See Nippon Chemiphar Co., Ltd.; *Int'l*, pg. 5313
SAFETY S.A.S.—See Sandvik AB; *Int'l*, pg. 6530
SAFETY SERVICES COMPANY; *U.S. Private*, pg. 3524

SAFETY SERVICES INCORPORATED; *U.S. Private*, pg. 3525
SAFETY SHOE DISTRIBUTORS; *U.S. Private*, pg. 3525
SAFETY SHOT, INC.; *U.S. Public*, pg. 1835
SAFETY SIGNS INC.—See Gilvin-Terrill Inc.; *U.S. Private*, pg. 1701
SAFETY SOLUTIONS, INC.—See Carousel Capital Partners; *U.S. Private*, pg. 770
SAFETY SOLUTIONS, INC.—See W.W. Grainger, Inc.; *U.S. Public*, pg. 2320
SAFETY SOLUTIONS U.K. LIMITED—See Carrier Global Corporation; *U.S. Public*, pg. 444
SAFETY SOURCE, INC.—See Ritz Safety, LLC; *U.S. Private*, pg. 3442
SAFETY STORAGE INC.; *U.S. Private*, pg. 3525
SAFETY & SUPPLY COMPANY—See Mallory Safety & Supply LLC; *U.S. Private*, pg. 2558
SAFETY & SURVIVAL SYSTEMS INTERNATIONAL LTD.; *U.S. Private*, pg. 3524
SAFETY SYRINGES INC.—See Becton, Dickinson & Company; *U.S. Public*, pg. 292
SAFETY SYSTEMS UK PTE. LTD.—See Pentair plc; *Int'l*, pg. 5791
SAFETY TECHNOLOGY HOLDINGS, INC.—See Bridgepoint Group Plc; *Int'l*, pg. 1155
SAFETY TECHNOLOGY INTERNATIONAL, INC.; *U.S. Private*, pg. 3525
SAFETY TODAY INC.—See Volk Enterprises, Inc.; *U.S. Private*, pg. 4410
SAFETY TUBS LLC—See Sun Capital Partners, Inc.; *U.S. Private*, pg. 3858
SAFETY VISION, LLC; *U.S. Private*, pg. 3525
THE SAFETY ZONE, LLC—See H.I.G. Capital, LLC; *U.S. Private*, pg. 1834
SAFEWARE INC.; *U.S. Private*, pg. 3525
SAFEWAY CONSTRUCTION ENTERPRISES LLC—See VINCI S.A.; *Int'l*, pg. 8226
SAFEWAY FUND LIMITED—See Shakarganj Limited; *Int'l*, pg. 6749
SAFE-WAY GARAGE DOORS LLC—See CapitalWorks, LLC; *U.S. Private*, pg. 742
SAFEWAY GLOBAL SOURCING LIMITED—See Cerberus Capital Management, L.P.; *U.S. Private*, pg. 836
SAFEWAY INC.—See Cerberus Capital Management, L.P.; *U.S. Private*, pg. 836
SAFEWAY INSURANCE COMPANY; *U.S. Private*, pg. 3525
SAFEWAY MOVING & STORAGE INC—See Fister Incorporated; *U.S. Private*, pg. 1535
SAFEWAY PHILTECH INC.—See Cerberus Capital Management, L.P.; *U.S. Private*, pg. 836
SAFEWAY SELECT GIFT SOURCE, INC.—See Cerberus Capital Management, L.P.; *U.S. Private*, pg. 836
SAFEWAY TRANSPORTATION INC.; *U.S. Private*, pg. 3525
SAFEWORKS, LLC—See Brand Industrial Services, Inc.; *U.S. Private*, pg. 636
SAFEX CHEMICALS (INDIA) LIMITED; *Int'l*, pg. 6471
SAFFIL AUTOMOTIVE LIMITED—See Clearlake Capital Group, L.P.; *U.S. Private*, pg. 937
SAFFIL AUTOMOTIVE SOUTH AFRICA (PTY) LIMITED—See Clearlake Capital Group, L.P.; *U.S. Private*, pg. 937
SAFFIL LTD.—See Clearlake Capital Group, L.P.; *U.S. Private*, pg. 937
SAFFORD AUTOMOTIVE GROUP; *U.S. Private*, pg. 3525
SAFFRON INDUSTRIES LIMITED; *Int'l*, pg. 6471
SAFFRON TECHNOLOGY, INC.—See Intel Corporation; *U.S. Public*, pg. 1139
SAF-GARD SAFETY SHOE CO.; *U.S. Private*, pg. 3523
SAF GAYRIMENKUL YATIRIM ORTAKLIGI A.S.—See Akis Gayrimenkul Yatirim Ortakligi A.S.; *Int'l*, pg. 263
SAF-HOLLAND (AUST.) PTY. LTD.—See SAF-Holland S.A.; *Int'l*, pg. 6467
SAF-HOLLAND AUSTRIA GMBH—See SAF-Holland S.A.; *Int'l*, pg. 6468
SAF-HOLLAND BULGARIA EOOD—See SAF-Holland S.A.; *Int'l*, pg. 6468
SAF-HOLLAND CANADA, LTD—See SAF-Holland S.A.; *Int'l*, pg. 6468
SAF-HOLLAND CZECHIA SPOL. S R.O.—See SAF-Holland S.A.; *Int'l*, pg. 6468
SAF-HOLLAND DENMARK APS—See SAF-Holland S.A.; *Int'l*, pg. 6468
SAF-HOLLAND DO BRASIL LTDA.—See SAF-Holland S.A.; *Int'l*, pg. 6468
SAF-HOLLAND EQUIPMENT, LTD.—See SAF-Holland S.A.; *Int'l*, pg. 6468
SAF-HOLLAND ESPANA S.L.—See SAF-Holland S.A.; *Int'l*, pg. 6468
SAF-HOLLAND FRANCE SAS—See SAF-Holland S.A.; *Int'l*, pg. 6468
SAF-HOLLAND GMBH—See SAF-Holland S.A.; *Int'l*, pg. 6467
SAF-HOLLAND GMBH—See SAF-Holland S.A.; *Int'l*, pg. 6468
SAF-HOLLAND HONG KONG LTD.—See SAF-Holland S.A.; *Int'l*, pg. 6467

SAF-GARD SAFETY SHOE CO.   CORPORATE AFFILIATIONS

SAF-HOLLAND INC.—See SAF-Holland S.A.; *Int'l*, pg. 6468
SAF-HOLLAND INDIA PRIVATE LTD.—See SAF-Holland S.A.; *Int'l*, pg. 6468
SAF-HOLLAND INTERNATIONAL DE MEXICO S. DE R.L. DE C.V.—See SAF-Holland S.A.; *Int'l*, pg. 6468
SAF-HOLLAND INTERNATIONAL, INC.—See SAF-Holland S.A.; *Int'l*, pg. 6468
SAF-HOLLAND INTERNATIONAL SERVICES MEXICO S. DE R.L. DE C.V.—See SAF-Holland S.A.; *Int'l*, pg. 6468
SAF-HOLLAND ITALIA S.R.L UNIPERSONALE—See SAF-Holland S.A.; *Int'l*, pg. 6468
SAF-HOLLAND (MALAYSIA) SDN. BHD.—See SAF-Holland S.A.; *Int'l*, pg. 6467
SAF-HOLLAND MIDDLE EAST FZE—See SAF-Holland S.A.; *Int'l*, pg. 6468
SAF-HOLLAND NIPPON, LTD.—See SAF-Holland S.A.; *Int'l*, pg. 6468
SAF-HOLLAND OTOMOTIV SANAYI VE TICARET LIMITED SIRKETI—See SAF-Holland S.A.; *Int'l*, pg. 6468
SAF-HOLLAND POLSKA SP.Z O.O.—See SAF-Holland S.A.; *Int'l*, pg. 6468
SAF-HOLLAND ROMANIA SRL—See SAF-Holland S.A.; *Int'l*, pg. 6468
SAF-HOLLAND RUS OOO—See SAF-Holland S.A.; *Int'l*, pg. 6468
SAF-HOLLAND S.A.; *Int'l*, pg. 6467
SAF-HOLLAND SOUTH AFRICA (PROPRIETARY) LTD—See SAF-Holland S.A.; *Int'l*, pg. 6468
SAF-HOLLAND (THAILAND) CO., LTD.—See SAF-Holland S.A.; *Int'l*, pg. 6467
SAF-HOLLAND USA, INC.-DUMAS—See SAF-Holland S.A.; *Int'l*, pg. 6468
SAF-HOLLAND USA, INC.—See SAF-Holland S.A.; *Int'l*, pg. 6468
SAF-HOLLAND USA, INC.-WARRENTON—See SAF-Holland S.A.; *Int'l*, pg. 6468
SAF-HOLLAND VERKEHRSTECHNIK GMBH—See SAF-Holland S.A.; *Int'l*, pg. 6468
SAF-HOLLAND (XIAMEN) CO., LTD.—See SAF-Holland S.A.; *Int'l*, pg. 6467
SAFIC-ALCAN ADRIATIC D.O.O.—See Safic-Alcan SAS; *Int'l*, pg. 6471
SAFIC-ALCAN BENELUX S.A./N.V.—See Safic-Alcan SAS; *Int'l*, pg. 6471
SAFIC-ALCAN NECARBO B.V.—See Safic-Alcan SAS; *Int'l*, pg. 6471
SAFIC-ALCAN SAS; *Int'l*, pg. 6471
SAFIC-ALCAN UK LTD—See Safic-Alcan SAS; *Int'l*, pg. 6471
SAFICHEM ASSETS, A.S.—See Safichem Group AG; *Int'l*, pg. 6471
SAFICHEM GROUP AG; *Int'l*, pg. 6471
SAFIE INC.; *Int'l*, pg. 6471
SAFIG MOYENS DE PAIEMENT; *Int'l*, pg. 6471
SAFIG STREAMWAY; *Int'l*, pg. 6471
SAFIKA CEMENT HOLDING (PTY) LTD.—See PPC Ltd.; *Int'l*, pg. 5950
SAFILO AMERICA INC.—See Safilo Group S.p.A.; *Int'l*, pg. 6471
SAFILO AUSTRALIA PTY LTD.—See Safilo Group S.p.A.; *Int'l*, pg. 6471
SAFILO AUSTRIA GMBH—See Safilo Group S.p.A.; *Int'l*, pg. 6471
SAFILO BENELUX S.A.—See Safilo Group S.p.A.; *Int'l*, pg. 6471
SAFILO DO BRASIL LTDA—See Safilo Group S.p.A.; *Int'l*, pg. 6471
SAFILO ESPANA SA—See Safilo Group S.p.A.; *Int'l*, pg. 6471
SAFILO FAR EAST LTD.—See Safilo Group S.p.A.; *Int'l*, pg. 6471
SAFILO FRANCE SARL—See Safilo Group S.p.A.; *Int'l*, pg. 6471
SAFILO GMBH—See Safilo Group S.p.A.; *Int'l*, pg. 6471
SAFILO GROUP S.P.A.; *Int'l*, pg. 6471
SAFILO HELLAS OTTICA S.A.—See Safilo Group S.p.A.; *Int'l*, pg. 6472
SAFILO HELLAS S.A.—See Safilo Group S.p.A.; *Int'l*, pg. 6472
SAFILO HONG-KONG LTD—See Safilo Group S.p.A.; *Int'l*, pg. 6471
SAFILO INDIA PRIVATE LIMITED—See Safilo Group S.p.A.; *Int'l*, pg. 6472
SAFILO INTERNATIONAL B.V.—See Safilo Group S.p.A.; *Int'l*, pg. 6472
SAFILO JAPAN CO. LTD.—See Safilo Group S.p.A.; *Int'l*, pg. 6472
SAFILO LATIN AMERICA—See Safilo Group S.p.A.; *Int'l*, pg. 6472
SAFILO NETHERLAND BV—See Safilo Group S.p.A.; *Int'l*, pg. 6472
SAFILO NORDIC AB—See Safilo Group S.p.A.; *Int'l*, pg. 6472
SAFILO OPTICAL SDN. BHD.—See Safilo Group S.p.A.; *Int'l*, pg. 6472
SAFILO PORTUGAL LDA—See Safilo Group S.p.A.; *Int'l*, pg. 6472
SAFILO SERVICES LLC—See Safilo Group S.p.A.; *Int'l*, pg. 6471
SAFILO SINGAPORE PTE LTD.—See Safilo Group S.p.A.; *Int'l*, pg. 6472
SAFILO SPA—See Safilo Group S.p.A.; *Int'l*, pg. 6472
SAFILO SWITZERLAND AG—See Safilo Group S.p.A.; *Int'l*, pg. 6472
SAFILO TRADING SHENZHEN CO. LTD.—See Safilo Group S.p.A.; *Int'l*, pg. 6472
SAFILO UK LTD.—See Safilo Group S.p.A.; *Int'l*, pg. 6472
SAFILO USA INC.—See Safilo Group S.p.A.; *Int'l*, pg. 6472
SAFINCO NEDERLAND BV—See Vandemoortele N.V.; *Int'l*, pg. 8129
SAFINT AUSTRALIA PTY LTD.—See Safilo Group S.p.A.; *Int'l*, pg. 6472
SAFIRA FACILITY SERVICES SA—See Derichebourg S.A.; *Int'l*, pg. 2042
SAFIRE REHABILITATION OF AMHERST, LLC; *U.S. Private*, pg. 3525
SAFI SILVER CORP.—See Trigon Metals, Inc.; *Int'l*, pg. 7922
SAFISIS—See Compagnie des Levures Lesaffre SA; *Int'l*, pg. 1739
SAF IVOIRE SARL—See Compagnie des Levures Lesaffre SA; *Int'l*, pg. 1739
SAFKAR EGE SOGUTMACILIK KLIMA SOGUK HAVA TES.IHR.ITH. A.S.; *Int'l*, pg. 6472
SAFKO SPINNING MILLS LTD.; *Int'l*, pg. 6472
SAFLITE PACKAGING (PTY) LTD—See Berry Global Group, Inc; *U.S. Public*, pg. 324
SAFLOK—See dormakaba Holding AG; *Int'l*, pg. 2177
SAF MAGELLAN AD; *Int'l*, pg. 6467
SAFMAR INDUSTRIAL & FINANCIAL GROUP; *Int'l*, pg. 6472
SAFMARINE CONTAINER LINES N.V.—See A.P. Moller-Maersk A/S; *Int'l*, pg. 27
SAFMARINE (PTY) LTD.—See A.P. Moller-Maersk A/S; *Int'l*, pg. 27
SAFMEX SA DE CV—See Compagnie des Levures Lesaffre SA; *Int'l*, pg. 1739
SAF NEVA OOO - BREAD MAKING IMPROVERS FACTORY—See Compagnie des Levures Lesaffre SA; *Int'l*, pg. 1739
SAF NEVA OOO - KURGAN YEAST FACTORY—See Compagnie des Levures Lesaffre SA; *Int'l*, pg. 1739
SAF NEVA OOO - OUZLOVAYA YEAST FACTORY—See Compagnie des Levures Lesaffre SA; *Int'l*, pg. 1739
SAF NEVA OOO—See Compagnie des Levures Lesaffre SA; *Int'l*, pg. 1739
SAF NORTH AMERICA LLC—See A/S SAF Tehnika; *Int'l*, pg. 28
SAFOCO FOODSTUFF JOINT STOCK COMPANY; *Int'l*, pg. 6472
SAF-OERLIKON MALAYSIA SWDN BHD—See Lincoln Electric Holdings, Inc.; *U.S. Public*, pg. 1318
SAFRA COMPANY LTD.—See Xenel Industries Ltd.; *Int'l*, pg. 8521
SAFRAN AERO BOOSTERS—See Safran SA; *Int'l*, pg. 6473
SAFRAN AEROSYSTEMS - CHATEAUDUN—See Safran SA; *Int'l*, pg. 6473
SAFRAN AEROSYSTEMS - COMPIEGNE—See Safran SA; *Int'l*, pg. 6473
SAFRAN AEROSYSTEMS SERVICES UK LIMITED—See Safran SA; *Int'l*, pg. 6473
SAFRAN AIRCRAFT ENGINES (GUIYANG) CO., LTD.—See Safran SA; *Int'l*, pg. 6473
SAFRAN AIRCRAFT ENGINES SUZHOU CO., LTD.—See Safran SA; *Int'l*, pg. 6473
SAFRA NATIONAL BANK OF NEW YORK; *U.S. Private*, pg. 3525
SAFRAN CABIN BANGKOK LTD.—See Safran SA; *Int'l*, pg. 6473
SAFRAN CABIN BRAZIL LTDA.—See Safran SA; *Int'l*, pg. 6473
SAFRAN CABIN CANADA CO.—See Safran SA; *Int'l*, pg. 6473
SAFRAN CABIN CZ S.R.O.—See Safran SA; *Int'l*, pg. 6473
SAFRAN CABIN, INC. - CARSON—See Safran SA; *Int'l*, pg. 6477
SAFRAN CABIN, INC. - GARDEN GROVE—See Safran SA; *Int'l*, pg. 6477
SAFRAN CABIN, INC. - MARYSVILLE—See Safran SA; *Int'l*, pg. 6477
SAFRAN CABIN, INC.—See Safran SA; *Int'l*, pg. 6477
SAFRAN CABIN LAMPHUN LTD.—See Safran SA; *Int'l*, pg. 6473
SAFRAN CABIN NETHERLANDS N.V.—See Safran SA; *Int'l*, pg. 6473
SAFRAN CABIN STERLING, INC.—See Safran SA; *Int'l*, pg. 6473
SAFRAN COLIBRYS SA—See Safran SA; *Int'l*, pg. 6473
SAFRAN DATA SYSTEMS INC—See Safran SA; *Int'l*, pg. 6473
SAFRAN ELECTRICAL COMPONENTS CANADA - LONDON FACILITY—See Safran SA; *Int'l*, pg. 6474
SAFRAN ELECTRICAL COMPONENTS UK LIMITED—See Safran SA; *Int'l*, pg. 6477
SAFRAN ELECTRICAL COMPONENTS USA, INC.—See Safran SA; *Int'l*, pg. 6477
SAFRAN ELECTRICAL & POWER - CHATOU—See Safran SA; *Int'l*, pg. 6474
SAFRAN ELECTRICAL & POWER CHIHUAHUA SA DE CV—See Safran SA; *Int'l*, pg. 6473
SAFRAN ELECTRICAL & POWER MOROCCO SA—See Safran SA; *Int'l*, pg. 6473
SAFRAN ELECTRICAL & POWER SAS—See Safran SA; *Int'l*, pg. 6473
SAFRAN ELECTRICAL & POWER UK LTD—See Safran SA; *Int'l*, pg. 6474
SAFRAN ELECTRICAL & POWER USA, LLC - EVERETT—See Safran SA; *Int'l*, pg. 6474
SAFRAN ELECTRICAL & POWER USA, LLC—See Safran SA; *Int'l*, pg. 6474
SAFRAN ELECTRONICS CANADA INC—See Safran SA; *Int'l*, pg. 6475
SAFRAN ELECTRONICS & DEFENSE CANADA INC.—See Safran SA; *Int'l*, pg. 6474
SAFRAN ELECTRONICS & DEFENSE GERMANY GMBH—See Safran SA; *Int'l*, pg. 6475
SAFRAN ELECTRONICS & DEFENSE GERMANY GMBH—See Safran SA; *Int'l*, pg. 6474
SAFRAN ELECTRONICS & DEFENSE SERVICES ASIA PTE LTD—See Safran SA; *Int'l*, pg. 6474
SAFRAN ENGINEERING SERVICES GMBH—See Safran SA; *Int'l*, pg. 6474
SAFRAN ENGINEERING SERVICES INDIA PVT LTD—See Safran SA; *Int'l*, pg. 6474
SAFRAN ENGINEERING SERVICES—See Safran SA; *Int'l*, pg. 6474
SAFRAN ENGINEERING SERVICES—See Safran SA; *Int'l*, pg. 6474
SAFRAN ENGINEERING SERVICES—See Safran SA; *Int'l*, pg. 6474
SAFRAN ENGINEERING SERVICES UK LTD—See Safran SA; *Int'l*, pg. 6474
SAFRAN HELICOPTER ENGINES ASIA PTE. LTD.—See Safran SA; *Int'l*, pg. 6476
SAFRAN HELICOPTER ENGINES ASIA PTE. LTD.—See Safran SA; *Int'l*, pg. 6474
SAFRAN HELICOPTER ENGINES AUSTRALIA PTY LTD—See Safran SA; *Int'l*, pg. 6474
SAFRAN HELICOPTER ENGINES BRASIL INDUSTRIA E COMERCIO DO BRASIL LTDA—See Safran SA; *Int'l*, pg. 6474
SAFRAN HELICOPTER ENGINES GERMANY GMBH—See Safran SA; *Int'l*, pg. 6474
SAFRAN HELICOPTER ENGINES—See Safran SA; *Int'l*, pg. 6476
SAFRAN HELICOPTER ENGINES TIANJIN CO. LTD.—See Safran SA; *Int'l*, pg. 6474
SAFRAN HELICOPTER ENGINES UK LIMITED—See Safran SA; *Int'l*, pg. 6476
SAFRAN HELICOPTER ENGINES UK LIMITED—See Safran SA; *Int'l*, pg. 6474
SAFRAN HELICOPTER ENGINES USA, INC.—See Safran SA; *Int'l*, pg. 6474
SAFRAN HELICOPTER ENGINES USA—See Safran SA; *Int'l*, pg. 6476
SAFRAN LANDING SYSTEMS CANADA INC.—See Safran SA; *Int'l*, pg. 6475
SAFRAN LANDING SYSTEMS EVERETT, LLC—See Safran SA; *Int'l*, pg. 6475
SAFRAN LANDING SYSTEMS HOLDINGS SINGAPORE PTE. LTD.—See Safran SA; *Int'l*, pg. 6475
SAFRAN LANDING SYSTEMS KENTUCKY, LLC—See Safran SA; *Int'l*, pg. 6475
SAFRAN LANDING SYSTEMS MALAYSIA SDN. BHD.—See Safran SA; *Int'l*, pg. 6475
SAFRAN LANDING SYSTEMS MEXICO S.A. DE C.V.—See Safran SA; *Int'l*, pg. 6475
SAFRAN LANDING SYSTEMS - QUERETARO FACILITY—See Safran SA; *Int'l*, pg. 6475
SAFRAN LANDING SYSTEMS SERVICES AMERICAS S.A. DE C.V.—See Safran SA; *Int'l*, pg. 6475
SAFRAN LANDING SYSTEMS SERVICES MIAMI, INC.—See Safran SA; *Int'l*, pg. 6475
SAFRAN LANDING SYSTEMS SERVICES SINGAPORE PTE. LTD.—See Safran SA; *Int'l*, pg. 6475
SAFRAN LANDING SYSTEMS SERVICES UK LTD.—See Safran SA; *Int'l*, pg. 6475
SAFRAN LANDING SYSTEMS—See Safran SA; *Int'l*, pg. 6474
SAFRAN LANDING SYSTEMS SUZHOU CO., LTD.—See Safran SA; *Int'l*, pg. 6475
SAFRAN LANDING SYSTEMS UK LTD.—See Safran SA; *Int'l*, pg. 6475
SAFRAN MOTEURS D'HELICOPTERES CANADA INC.—See Safran SA; *Int'l*, pg. 6475
SAFRAN NACELLES LIMITED—See Safran SA; *Int'l*, pg. 6473
SAFRAN NACELLES LIMITED—See Safran SA; *Int'l*, pg. 6475
SAFRAN PASSENGER INNOVATIONS - GERMANY—See Safran SA; *Int'l*, pg. 6475

COMPANY NAME INDEX

SAFRAN POWER UNITS SAN DIEGO, LLC—See Safran SA; *Int'l*, pg. 6475
SAFRAN POWER USA LLC—See Safran SA; *Int'l*, pg. 6474
SAFRAN SA; *Int'l*, pg. 6472
SAFRAN SEATS FRANCE S.A.—See Safran SA; *Int'l*, pg. 6475
SAFRAN SEATS GB LIMITED—See Safran SA; *Int'l*, pg. 6475
SAFRAN SEATS GB LIMITED—See Safran SA; *Int'l*, pg. 6475
SAFRAN SEATS SANTA MARIA LLC—See Safran SA; *Int'l*, pg. 6475
SAFRAN SEATS USA LLC—See Safran SA; *Int'l*, pg. 6475
SAFRAN SOFTWARE SOLUTIONS AS—See Dovre Group Plc; *Int'l*, pg. 2182
SAFRAN TEST CELLS, INC.—See Safran SA; *Int'l*, pg. 6475
SAFRAN USA INC.—See Safran SA; *Int'l*, pg. 6475
SAFRAN VECTRONIX AG—See Safran SA; *Int'l*, pg. 6475
SAFRAN VENTILATION SYSTEMS OKLAHOMA, INC.—See Safran SA; *Int'l*, pg. 6477
SAFRAN VENTILATION SYSTEMS USA, LLC—See Safran SA; *Int'l*, pg. 6475
SAFREMA ENERGY EUROPE—See Safrema Energy LLC; *U.S. Private*, pg. 3525
SAFREMA ENERGY LLC; *U.S. Private*, pg. 3525
SAFRIPOL (PTY) LTD—See Steinhoff International Holdings N.V.; *Int'l*, pg. 7194
SAFROCK FINANCE CORPORATION (QLD) PTY LTD—See Cash Converters International Limited; *Int'l*, pg. 1352
S.A.F. SPECIAL STEEL PUBLIC COMPANY LIMITED; *Int'l*, pg. 6448
SAFT AB—See TotalEnergies SE; *Int'l*, pg. 7837
SAFT AMERICA INC.—See TotalEnergies SE; *Int'l*, pg. 7838
SAFT AMERICA INC.—See TotalEnergies SE; *Int'l*, pg. 7838
SAFT AMERICA INC.—See TotalEnergies SE; *Int'l*, pg. 7838
SAFT AS—See TotalEnergies SE; *Int'l*, pg. 7838
SAFT AUSTRALIA PTY. LTD.—See TotalEnergies SE; *Int'l*, pg. 7838
SAFT BATERIAS SL—See TotalEnergies SE; *Int'l*, pg. 7838
SAFT BATTERIE ITALIA S.R.L.—See TotalEnergies SE; *Int'l*, pg. 7837
SAFT BATTERIEN GMBH—See TotalEnergies SE; *Int'l*, pg. 7838
SAFT BATTERIES PTE. LTD.—See TotalEnergies SE; *Int'l*, pg. 7838
SAFT BATTERIES PTY LTD—See TotalEnergies SE; *Int'l*, pg. 7838
SAFT DO BRASIL LTDA.—See TotalEnergies SE; *Int'l*, pg. 7837
SAFTEC CO., LTD.; *Int'l*, pg. 6477
SAFT FEDERAL SYSTEMS, INC.—See TotalEnergies SE; *Int'l*, pg. 7838
SAFT FERAK AS—See TotalEnergies SE; *Int'l*, pg. 7838
SAFT GROUPE S.A.—See TotalEnergies SE; *Int'l*, pg. 7837
SAFT HONG KONG LTD.—See TotalEnergies SE; *Int'l*, pg. 7838
SAFTI GROUPE SA; *Int'l*, pg. 6477
SAFT JAPAN KK—See TotalEnergies SE; *Int'l*, pg. 7838
SAFT LLC—See TotalEnergies SE; *Int'l*, pg. 7838
SAFT NIFE ME LTD—See TotalEnergies SE; *Int'l*, pg. 7838
SAF-T-PAK INC.—See Kelso & Company, L.P.; *U.S. Private*, pg. 2278
SAFT SWEDEN AB—See TotalEnergies SE; *Int'l*, pg. 7838
SAFT (ZHUHAI FTZ) BATTERIES COMPANY LIMITED—See TotalEnergies SE; *Int'l*, pg. 7837
SAFWA ISLAMIC BANK—See Dubai Islamic Bank PSJ; *Int'l*, pg. 2220
SAFWAN TRADING & CONTRACTING COMPANY K.S.C.C.; *Int'l*, pg. 6477
SAFWAY ATLANTIC LLC—See Brand Industrial Services, Inc.; *U.S. Private*, pg. 636
SAFWOOD S.P.A.; *Int'l*, pg. 6477
SAGA BROADCASTING CORPORATION—See Saga Communications, Inc.; *U.S. Public*, pg. 1835
SAGA CITY-VISION CO., LTD.—See Hisamitsu Pharmaceutical Co., Inc.; *Int'l*, pg. 3406
SAGA COMMUNICATIONS, INC. - COLUMBUS RADIO GROUP—See Saga Communications, Inc.; *U.S. Public*, pg. 1835
SAGA COMMUNICATIONS, INC.; *U.S. Public*, pg. 1835
SAGA COMMUNICATIONS OF IOWA—See Saga Communications, Inc.; *U.S. Public*, pg. 1835
SAGA COMMUNICATIONS OF SOUTH DAKOTA, LLC—See Saga Communications, Inc.; *U.S. Public*, pg. 1835
SAGA DECOR S.A.S.—See Compagnie de Saint-Gobain SA; *Int'l*, pg. 1733
SAGA ELECTRONICS CO. LTD.—See Nisshinbo Holdings Inc.; *Int'l*, pg. 5373
SAGA ENERGY, INC.; *U.S. Private*, pg. 3525
SAGA ENTREPRISE—See VINCI S.A.; *Int'l*, pg. 8237

SAGA FALABELLA SA; *Int'l*, pg. 6477
SAGA FOODS ZRT—See Boparan Holdings Limited; *Int'l*, pg. 1112
SAGAFORM AB—See New Wave Group AB; *Int'l*, pg. 5230
SAGAFORM APS—See New Wave Group AB; *Int'l*, pg. 5230
SAGAFORM A/S—See New Wave Group AB; *Int'l*, pg. 5230
SAGAFORM FORSALJNINGS AB—See New Wave Group AB; *Int'l*, pg. 5230
SAGAFORM GMBH—See New Wave Group AB; *Int'l*, pg. 5230
SAGAFORM INC.—See New Wave Group AB; *Int'l*, pg. 5230
SAG-AFTRA HEALTH PLAN; *U.S. Private*, pg. 3525
SAGA FURS OYJ; *Int'l*, pg. 6477
SAGA GABON SA—See Financière de L'Odet; *Int'l*, pg. 2668
SAGA GROUP LIMITED—See Charterhouse Capital Partners LLP; *Int'l*, pg. 1454
SAGA GROUP LIMITED—See CVC Capital Partners SICAV-FIS S.A.; *Int'l*, pg. 1881
SAGA GROUP LIMITED—See Permira Advisers LLP; *Int'l*, pg. 5802
SAGA HISAMITSU SPRINGS CO., LTD.—See Hisamitsu Pharmaceutical Co., Inc.; *Int'l*, pg. 3406
SAGALIAM ACQUISITION CORP.; *U.S. Public*, pg. 1835
SAGALIO ENERGY LIMITED; *Int'l*, pg. 6478
SAGA MAKMUR INDUSTRI SDN. BHD.—See Ann Joo Resources Berhad; *Int'l*, pg. 473
SAGAMI CHEMICAL INDUSTRY CO., LTD.—See Mitani Sangyo Co., Ltd.; *Int'l*, pg. 4925
SAGAMI GROUP HOLDINGS CO., LTD.—See BELLUNA CO. LTD.; *Int'l*, pg. 967
SAGAMI HOLDINGS CORPORATION; *Int'l*, pg. 6478
SAGAMI LOGISTICS & SERVICE CO., LTD.—See Mitsubishi Heavy Industries, Ltd.; *Int'l*, pg. 4961
SAGAMI RAILWAY CO., LTD.—See Sotetsu Holdings, Inc.; *Int'l*, pg. 7112
SAGAMI RUBBER INDUSTRIES CO., LTD.; *Int'l*, pg. 6478
SAGAMI SERVICE CO LTD—See Sagami Holdings Corporation; *Int'l*, pg. 6478
SAGAMI YOKI CO., LTD.—See Dai Nippon Printing Co., Ltd.; *Int'l*, pg. 1916
SAGAMORE HOTEL; *U.S. Private*, pg. 3525
SAGAMORE INSURANCE COMPANY—See The Progressive Corporation; *U.S. Public*, pg. 2125
SAGAMORE READY MIX, LLC; *U.S. Private*, pg. 3526
SAGA NOK CORPORATION—See NOK Corporation; *Int'l*, pg. 5403
SAGANO SCENIC RAILWAY—See West Japan Railway Company; *Int'l*, pg. 8385
SAGANTEC NORTH AMERICA; *U.S. Private*, pg. 3526
SAGA PLC; *Int'l*, pg. 6477
SAGA PURE ASA; *Int'l*, pg. 6477
SAGA RADIO NETWORKS, LLC—See Saga Communications, Inc.; *U.S. Public*, pg. 1835
SA GARAGE NELLO CHELI; *Int'l*, pg. 6458
SAG ARCADIA, LP—See National Storage Affiliates Trust; *U.S. Public*, pg. 1498
SAGAR CEMENTS LIMITED - PEDAVEEDU VILLAGE PLANT—See Sagar Cements Limited; *Int'l*, pg. 6478
SAGAR CEMENTS LIMITED; *Int'l*, pg. 6478
SAGARD CAPITAL PARTNERS, L.P.—See Power Corporation of Canada; *Int'l*, pg. 5944
SAGARD CAPITAL PARTNERS MANAGEMENT CORP.—See Power Corporation of Canada; *Int'l*, pg. 5944
SAGARDEEP ALLOYS LTD.; *Int'l*, pg. 6478
SAGARD HOLDINGS ULC—See Power Corporation of Canada; *Int'l*, pg. 5944
SAGAR DIAMONDS LIMITED; *Int'l*, pg. 6478
SAGARD SAS—See Power Corporation of Canada; *Int'l*, pg. 5944
SAGA REUNION SA—See Financiere de L'Odet; *Int'l*, pg. 2668
SAGARMATHA LUMBINI INSURANCE COMPANY LIMITED; *Int'l*, pg. 6478
SAGARMATHA SAS—See Hopscotch Groupe S.A.; *Int'l*, pg. 3474
SAGAR POLYCLINIC LLC—See Oman Holdings International Company SAOG; *Int'l*, pg. 5560
SAGARSOFT (INDIA) LIMITED; *Int'l*, pg. 6478
SAGAR SOYA PRODUCTS LTD.; *Int'l*, pg. 6478
SAGAR SYSTECH LIMITED; *Int'l*, pg. 6478
SAGAR TOURIST RESORTS LIMITED; *Int'l*, pg. 6478
SAGA SEAL INDUSTRY CO., LTD—See NOK Corporation; *Int'l*, pg. 5403
SAGA SERVICES LIMITED—See Charterhouse Capital Partners LLP; *Int'l*, pg. 1455
SAGA SERVICES LIMITED—See CVC Capital Partners SICAV-FIS S.A.; *Int'l*, pg. 1882
SAGA SERVICES LIMITED—See Permira Advisers LLP; *Int'l*, pg. 5803
SAGA SHIPHOLDING (NORWAY) AS—See Nippon Yusen Kabushiki Kaisha; *Int'l*, pg. 5359
SAGA TEKKOSHO CO., LTD.—See Piolax Inc.; *Int'l*, pg. 5871

SAGA TERTIAIRE SAS—See VINCI S.A.; *Int'l*, pg. 8226
SAGAWA ADVANCE CO., LTD.—See SG Holdings Co., Ltd.; *Int'l*, pg. 6740
SAGAWA GLOBAL LOGISTICS CO., LTD.—See SG Holdings Co., Ltd.; *Int'l*, pg. 6740
SAGAX FINLAND ASSET MANAGEMENT OY—See AB Sagax; *Int'l*, pg. 41
SAGAX GERMANY HOLDING GMBH—See AB Sagax; *Int'l*, pg. 41
SAGAX NEDERLAND B.V.—See AB Sagax; *Int'l*, pg. 41
SAG & BETONGBORRNING I UDDEVALLA AB—See Storskogen Group AB; *Int'l*, pg. 7228
SAG CONSULTING SERVICES GMBH—See Silver Lake Group, LLC; *U.S. Private*, pg. 3658
SAG DEUTSCHLAND GMBH—See Silver Lake Group, LLC; *U.S. Private*, pg. 3658
SAGE ADVERTISING; *U.S. Private*, pg. 3526
SAGE APPLIANCES FRANCE SAS—See Breville Group Limited; *Int'l*, pg. 1150
SAGE APPLIANCES GMBH—See Breville Group Limited; *Int'l*, pg. 1150
SAG EAST GMBH—See Silver Lake Group, LLC; *U.S. Private*, pg. 3658
SAGE ATC ENVIRONMENTAL CONSULTING LLC—See Bernhard Capital Partners Management, LP; *U.S. Private*, pg. 536
SAGE AUTOMOTIVE INTERIORS, INC. - ABBEVILLE PLANT—See Asahi Kasei Corporation; *Int'l*, pg. 597
SAGE AUTOMOTIVE INTERIORS, INC. - GAYLEY PLANT—See Asahi Kasei Corporation; *Int'l*, pg. 597
SAGE AUTOMOTIVE INTERIORS, INC. - SHARON PLANT—See Asahi Kasei Corporation; *Int'l*, pg. 597
SAGE AUTOMOTIVE INTERIORS, INC.—See Asahi Kasei Corporation; *Int'l*, pg. 597
SAGE AUTOMOTIVE INTERIORS, LTD.—See Asahi Kasei Corporation; *Int'l*, pg. 597
SAGE AUTOMOTIVE INTERIORS, LTD.—See Asahi Kasei Corporation; *Int'l*, pg. 597
SAGE BAEURER GMBH—See The Sage Group plc; *Int'l*, pg. 7679
SAGE BRASIL INTERIORS AUTOMOTIVOS INDUSTRIA E COMERCIO, LTDA.—See Asahi Kasei Corporation; *Int'l*, pg. 597
SAGEBRUSH HEALTHCARE, INC.—See The Ensign Group, Inc.; *U.S. Public*, pg. 2072
SAGEBRUSH SALES COMPANY—See Jefferies Financial Group Inc.; *U.S. Public*, pg. 1188
SAGE BUSINESS GROUP PTY. LTD.—See Azimut Holding SpA; *Int'l*, pg. 779
SAGE CAPITAL LLC; *U.S. Private*, pg. 3526
SAGE COLLECTIVE INC.—See Omnicom Group Inc.; *U.S. Public*, pg. 1593
SAGE COMMUNICATIONS, LLC; *U.S. Private*, pg. 3526
SAGE DATA SECURITY, LLC—See Tyler Technologies, Inc.; *U.S. Public*, pg. 2209
SAGE DINING SERVICES INC.; *U.S. Private*, pg. 3526
SAGE ELECTRIC CORPORATION; *U.S. Private*, pg. 3526
SAGE ELECTROCHROMICS, INC.—See Compagnie de Saint-Gobain SA; *Int'l*, pg. 1730
SAGE FUNERAL SERVICES LIMITED—See Yeah Yeah Group Holdings Limited; *Int'l*, pg. 8575
THE SAGE GROUP PLC; *Int'l*, pg. 7679
THE SAGE GROUP; *U.S. Private*, pg. 4113
SAGE HOLDING COMPANY; *U.S. Private*, pg. 3526
SAGE HOSPITALITY RESOURCES, LLP—See Sage Investment Holdings; *U.S. Private*, pg. 3526
SAGE INTACCT, INC.—See The Sage Group plc; *Int'l*, pg. 7679
SAGE INVESTMENT HOLDINGS; *U.S. Private*, pg. 3526
SAGE LOGIC CONTROL, S.L—See The Sage Group plc; *Int'l*, pg. 7679
SAGE MANAGEMENT ENTERPRISE, LLC; *U.S. Private*, pg. 3526
SAGE MANAGEMENT—See Sage Management Enterprise, LLC; *U.S. Private*, pg. 3526
SAGE MANAGEMENT—See Sage Management Enterprise, LLC; *U.S. Private*, pg. 3526
SAGE MANAGEMENT—See Sage Management Enterprise, LLC; *U.S. Private*, pg. 3526
SAGE MANUFACTURING CORPORATION—See Joshua Green Corporation; *U.S. Private*, pg. 2237
SAGEMCOM BROADBAND GERMANY GMBH—See Charterhouse Capital Partners LLP; *Int'l*, pg. 1456
SAGEMCOM BROADBAND SAS—See Charterhouse Capital Partners LLP; *Int'l*, pg. 1456
SAGEMCOM MAGYARORSZAG ELEKTRONIKAI KFT.—See Charterhouse Capital Partners LLP; *Int'l*, pg. 1456
SAGEM DEFENSE SECURITE SA—See Safran SA; *Int'l*, pg. 6475
SAGEM KARRIE TECHNOLOGIES (HONG KONG) COMPANY LIMITED—See Karrie International Holdings Limited; *Int'l*, pg. 4085
SAGEM SECURITY INTERNATIONAL TRADING CO., LTD.—See Safran SA; *Int'l*, pg. 6475
SAGEM SECURITY IRELAND LTD—See Safran SA; *Int'l*, pg. 6475
SAGENET LLC—See Woodard Technology & Investments LLC; *U.S. Private*, pg. 4557

SAGE MANAGEMENT ENTERPRISE, LLC — CORPORATE AFFILIATIONS

SAGENEX DIAGNOSTICS LABORATORY, LLC—See AAC Holdings, Inc.; *U.S. Private*, pg. 31
SAGEN MI CANADA INC.—See Brookfield Corporation; *Int'l*, pg. 1181
SAGENT AGILA LLC—See Viatris Inc.; *U.S. Public*, pg. 2294
SAGENT AUTO, LLC; *U.S. Private*, pg. 3527
SAGENTIA CATELLA AB—See Science Group plc; *Int'l*, pg. 6647
SAGENTIA INC—See Science Group plc; *Int'l*, pg. 6647
SAGENTIA LTD.—See Science Group plc; *Int'l*, pg. 6647
SAGENTIA SGAI LTD.—See Science Group plc; *Int'l*, pg. 6647
SAGENTIA TECHNOLOGY ADVISORY LIMITED—See Science Group plc; *Int'l*, pg. 6647
SAGENTIC WEB DESIGN; *U.S. Private*, pg. 3527
SAGENT PHARMACEUTICALS, INC.—See Nichi-Iko Pharmaceutical Co., Ltd.; *Int'l*, pg. 5266
SAGENT PHARMACEUTICALS, INC.—See Nichi-Iko Pharmaceutical Co., Ltd.; *Int'l*, pg. 5266
SAGE PARK, INC.; *U.S. Private*, pg. 3526
SAGE PARTNERS, LLC; *U.S. Private*, pg. 3526
SAGE PARTS PLUS, INC.—See Power Corporation of Canada; *Int'l*, pg. 5944
SAGEPATH LLC—See Reply S.p.A.; *Int'l*, pg. 6291
SAGE PAY EUROPE LIMITED—See The Sage Group plc; *Int'l*, pg. 7679
SAGEPOINT FINANCIAL, INC.—See Reverence Capital Partners LLC; *U.S. Private*, pg. 3415
SAGE PORTUGAL SOFTWARE S.A.—See The Sage Group plc; *Int'l*, pg. 7679
SAGE PRODUCTS, LLC—See Stryker Corporation; *U.S. Public*, pg. 1956
SAGE PUBLICATIONS, INC.; *U.S. Private*, pg. 3526
SAGE REFINED PRODUCTS, LTD.—See Kinder Morgan, Inc.; *U.S. Public*, pg. 1234
SAGER ELECTRICAL SUPPLY CO—See Berkshire Hathaway Inc.; *U.S. Public*, pg. 316
SAGE RENEWABLE ENERGY CONSULTING, INC.—See NV5 Global, Inc.; *U.S. Public*, pg. 1557
SAGE RESTAURANT GROUP—See Sage Investment Holdings; *U.S. Private*, pg. 3526
SAGERIS SARL—See Willis Towers Watson Public Limited Company; *Int'l*, pg. 8416
SAGE SAS—See The Sage Group plc; *Int'l*, pg. 7679
SAGE SCHWEIZ AG—See The Sage Group plc; *Int'l*, pg. 7679
SAGE SETTLEMENT CONSULTING, LLC; *U.S. Private*, pg. 3527
SAGE SIMULTAN AG—See The Sage Group plc; *Int'l*, pg. 7679
SAGE SOFTWARE ASIA PTE LTD—See The Sage Group plc; *Int'l*, pg. 7679
SAGE SOFTWARE CANADA LTD—See The Sage Group plc; *Int'l*, pg. 7680
SAGE SOFTWARE GMBH—See The Sage Group plc; *Int'l*, pg. 7680
SAGE SOFTWARE, INC.—See The Sage Group plc; *Int'l*, pg. 7680
SAGE SOFTWARE, INC.—See The Sage Group plc; *Int'l*, pg. 7680
SAGE SOFTWARE INDIA (P) LTD—See The Sage Group plc; *Int'l*, pg. 7680
SAGE SOFTWARE (SHANGHAI) CO. LTD—See The Sage Group plc; *Int'l*, pg. 7679
SAGE SOFTWARE—See The Sage Group plc; *Int'l*, pg. 7680
SAGE—See The Sage Group plc; *Int'l*, pg. 7680
SAGE SP, S.L.—See The Sage Group plc; *Int'l*, pg. 7679
SAGE SP. Z O.O.—See The Sage Group plc; *Int'l*, pg. 7679
SAGE STAFFING, INC.; *U.S. Private*, pg. 3527
SAGE SUSTAINABLE ELECTRONICS LLC—See Closed Loop Partners LLC; *U.S. Private*, pg. 946
SAGE TECHNOLOGIES CO.—See Ferrer Freeman & Company, LLC; *U.S. Private*, pg. 1498
SAGE TELECOMMUNICATIONS CORP. OF COLORADO, LLC—See Dycom Industries, Inc.; *U.S. Public*, pg. 699
SAGE THERAPEUTICS, INC.; *U.S. Public*, pg. 1835
SAGET MAROC/WORMS S.M. GROUP—See Albert Ballin KG; *Int'l*, pg. 296
SAGE TREE LLC—See Leonard Green & Partners, L.P.; *U.S. Private*, pg. 2423
SAGE (UK) LIMITED—See The Sage Group plc; *Int'l*, pg. 7679
SAGE V FOODS, LLC - LITTLE ROCK PLANT—See Sage V Foods, LLC; *U.S. Private*, pg. 3527
SAGE V FOODS, LLC; *U.S. Private*, pg. 3527
SAGE V FOODS, LLC - STUTTGART PLANT—See Producers Rice Mill, Inc.; *U.S. Private*, pg. 3273
SAGEVIEW ADVISORY GROUP LLC; *U.S. Private*, pg. 3527
SAGEVIEW CAPITAL LP; *U.S. Private*, pg. 3527
SAGEWIND CAPITAL LLC; *U.S. Private*, pg. 3527
SAGEWOOD ASSET MANAGEMENT LLC—See Stifel Financial Corp.; *U.S. Public*, pg. 1950
SAGEWORKS, INC.; *U.S. Private*, pg. 3528
SAG GEST - SOLUCOES AUTOMOVEL GLOBAIS, SGPS, S.A.; *Int'l*, pg. 6477

SAGGEZZA INC.; *U.S. Private*, pg. 3528
SAG HARBOR INDUSTRIES, INC.; *U.S. Private*, pg. 3525
SAG HARBOR—See Sun Capital Partners, Inc.; *U.S. Private*, pg. 3859
SA GIANG IMPORT EXPORT CORPORATION - SAGIANG FOOD FACTORY—See Vinh Hoan Corporation; *Int'l*, pg. 8241
SA GIANG IMPORT EXPORT CORPORATION - SAGIANG SHRIMP CHIPS FACTORY 2—See Vinh Hoan Corporation; *Int'l*, pg. 8241
SA GIANG IMPORT EXPORT CORPORATION—See Vinh Hoan Corporation; *Int'l*, pg. 8241
SAGICOR ASSET MANAGEMENT INC.—See Alignvest Management Corporation; *Int'l*, pg. 327
SAGICOR AT LLOYD'S LIMITED—See Alignvest Management Corporation; *Int'l*, pg. 328
SAGICOR BANK JAMAICA LIMITED—See Alignvest Management Corporation; *Int'l*, pg. 327
SAGICOR CLAIMS MANAGEMENT, INC.—See Alignvest Management Corporation; *Int'l*, pg. 328
SAGICOR FINANCE INC.—See Alignvest Management Corporation; *Int'l*, pg. 327
SAGICOR FINANCIAL CORPORATION LIMITED—See Alignvest Management Corporation; *Int'l*, pg. 327
SAGICOR FUNDS INCORPORATED—See Alignvest Management Corporation; *Int'l*, pg. 327
SAGICOR GENERAL INSURANCE INC.—See Alignvest Management Corporation; *Int'l*, pg. 327
SAGICOR GROUP JAMAICA LIMITED—See Alignvest Management Corporation; *Int'l*, pg. 327
SAGICOR INSURANCE BROKERS LIMITED—See Alignvest Management Corporation; *Int'l*, pg. 328
SAGICOR INTERNATIONAL MANAGEMENT SERVICES, INC.—See Alignvest Management Corporation; *Int'l*, pg. 328
SAGICOR INVESTMENTS JAMAICA LIMITED—See Alignvest Management Corporation; *Int'l*, pg. 328
SAGICOR LIFE INC.—See Alignvest Management Corporation; *Int'l*, pg. 328
SAGICOR LIFE INC.—See Alignvest Management Corporation; *Int'l*, pg. 328
SAGICOR LIFE INSURANCE COMPANY—See Alignvest Management Corporation; *Int'l*, pg. 328
SAGICOR LIFE JAMAICA LIMITED—See Alignvest Management Corporation; *Int'l*, pg. 328
SAGICOR LIFE OF THE CAYMAN ISLANDS LIMITED—See Alignvest Management Corporation; *Int'l*, pg. 328
SAGICOR PANAMA SA—See Alignvest Management Corporation; *Int'l*, pg. 328
SAGICOR SYNDICATE HOLDINGS LIMITED—See Alignvest Management Corporation; *Int'l*, pg. 328
SAGICOR UNDERWRITING LIMITED—See Alignvest Management Corporation; *Int'l*, pg. 328
SAGICOR USA, INC.—See Alignvest Management Corporation; *Int'l*, pg. 328
SAGIENT RESEARCH SYSTEMS, INC.—See Informa plc; *Int'l*, pg. 3692
SAGIES - SEGURANCA, HIGIENE E SAUDE NO TRABALHO, S.A.—See Jose de Mello, SGPS, S.A.; *Int'l*, pg. 4001
SAGIMET BIOSCIENCES INC.; *U.S. Public*, pg. 1835
SAGINAW CONTROL & ENGINEERING INC.; *U.S. Private*, pg. 3528
SAGINAW PIPE COMPANY INC.; *U.S. Private*, pg. 3528
SAGINAW VALLEY SPORT & SPINE, LIMITED PARTNERSHIP—See U.S. Physical Therapy, Inc.; *U.S. Public*, pg. 2216
SAGITAS AG GLARUS—See Rothschild & Co SCA; *Int'l*, pg. 6404
SAGITTARIUS BRANDS, INC.—See Charlesbank Capital Partners, LLC; *U.S. Private*, pg. 856
SAGITTARIUS BRANDS, INC.—See Grotech Ventures; *U.S. Private*, pg. 1793
SAGITTARIUS BRANDS, INC.—See Leonard Green & Partners, L.P.; *U.S. Private*, pg. 2429
SAGITTARIUS LIFE SCIENCE CORP.; *Int'l*, pg. 6478
SAGO NETWORKS, LLC; *U.S. Private*, pg. 3528
SAGON-PHIOR—See Sagon-Phior; *U.S. Private*, pg. 3528
SAGON-PHIOR; *U.S. Private*, pg. 3528
SAGON-PHIOR—See Sagon-Phior; *U.S. Private*, pg. 3528
SAGON-PHIOR—See Sagon-Phior; *U.S. Private*, pg. 3528
SAGO SAGO TOYS INC.—See Spin Master Corp.; *Int'l*, pg. 7136
S.A. GRAHAM COMPANY INC.; *U.S. Private*, pg. 3515
SAGREX B.V.—See Heidelberg Materials AG; *Int'l*, pg. 3319
SAGREX FRANCE S.A.S.—See Heidelberg Materials AG; *Int'l*, pg. 3319
SAGREX HOLDING B.V.—See Heidelberg Materials AG; *Int'l*, pg. 3319
SAGREX PRODUCTIE B.V.—See Heidelberg Materials AG; *Int'l*, pg. 3319
SAG SALES CENTRE IRELAND LIMITED—See Silver Lake Group, LLC; *U.S. Private*, pg. 3659
SAG SOFTWARE AG LUXEMBOURG S.A.—See Silver Lake Group, LLC; *U.S. Private*, pg. 3659
SAG SOFTWARE SYSTEMS AG—See Silver Lake Group, LLC; *U.S. Private*, pg. 3659

SAG SOFTWARE SYSTEMS SA—See Silver Lake Group, LLC; *U.S. Private*, pg. 3659
S.A.G. SOLAR GMBH & CO. KG—See Shunfeng International Clean Energy Ltd.; *Int'l*, pg. 6870
SAG SYSTEMS RUS LIMITED LIABILITY COMPANY—See Silver Lake Group, LLC; *U.S. Private*, pg. 3659
SAGUARO ELECTRONICA, S.A. DE C.V.—See Robert Bosch GmbH; *Int'l*, pg. 6368
SAGUARO POWER COMPANY, A LIMITED PARTNERSHIP—See NRG Energy, Inc.; *U.S. Public*, pg. 1551
SAGUARO ROAD RECORDS, INC.—See Mosaic Media Investment Partners LLC; *U.S. Private*, pg. 2792
SA GUIET; *Int'l*, pg. 6458
SAGUNA NETWORKS LTD.—See COMSovereign Holding Corp.; *U.S. Public*, pg. 562
SAGUS INTERNATIONAL LLC; *U.S. Private*, pg. 3528
SAHA ADVANCE NETWORK CO., LTD.—See Advanced Info Service Plc; *Int'l*, pg. 160
SAHACHOL FOOD SUPPLIES CO., LTD.—See Saha Pathanapibul Public Company Limited; *Int'l*, pg. 6479
SAHACOGEN (CHONBURI) PUBLIC CO., LTD.—See RATCH Group Public Company Limited; *Int'l*, pg. 6213
SAHACOGEN GREEN COMPANY LIMITED—See RATCH Group Public Company Limited; *Int'l*, pg. 6213
SAHAGREEN FOREST COMPANY LIMITED—See RATCH Group Public Company Limited; *Int'l*, pg. 6213
SAHAKARN WISAVAKORN CO., LTD.—See TRC Construction Public Company Limited; *Int'l*, pg. 7908
SAHAKOL CHASSIS CO., LTD.—See Thanachart Capital PCL; *Int'l*, pg. 7607
SAHAKOL EQUIPMENT PUBLIC COMPANY LIMITED; *Int'l*, pg. 6480
SAHALE SNACKS, INC.—See The J.M. Smucker Company; *U.S. Public*, pg. 2107
SAHAM GROUP SA; *Int'l*, pg. 6480
SAHAMIT MACHINERY PUBLIC COMPANY LIMITED; *Int'l*, pg. 6480
SAHAMITR PRESSURE CONTAINER PUBLIC COMPANY LIMITED; *Int'l*, pg. 6480
SAHANA SYSTEM LIMITED; *Int'l*, pg. 6480
SAHAND FORKLIFT MFG. CO.; *Int'l*, pg. 6480
SAHA PATHANA INTER-HOLDING PUBLIC COMPANY LIMITED; *Int'l*, pg. 6478
SAHA PATHANAPIBUL PUBLIC COMPANY LIMITED; *Int'l*, pg. 6478
SAHARA ASSET MANAGEMENT COMPANY PVT. LTD.—See Sahara India Pariwar; *Int'l*, pg. 6480
SAHARA BUILDING CONTRACTORS LTD.—See The Al Fadl Group of Companies; *Int'l*, pg. 7613
SAHARA ENERGY LTD.; *Int'l*, pg. 6480
SAHARA ENTERPRISES INC.; *U.S. Private*, pg. 3528
SAHARA HOSPITALITY COMPANY S.A.O.G.; *Int'l*, pg. 6480
SAHARA HOUSINGFINA CORPORATION LIMITED; *Int'l*, pg. 6480
SAHARA IMPORTS, INC.—See AutoNation, Inc.; *U.S. Public*, pg. 237
SAHARA INC.; *U.S. Private*, pg. 3528
SAHARA INDIA COMMERCIAL CORPORATION LIMITED—See Sahara India Pariwar; *Int'l*, pg. 6481
SAHARA INDIA PARIWAR; *Int'l*, pg. 6480
SAHARA INDIA T.V. NETWORK PVT. LTD.—See Sahara India Pariwar; *Int'l*, pg. 6481
SAHARA INTERNATIONAL PETROCHEMICAL COMPANY; *Int'l*, pg. 6481
SAHARA LIFE INSURANCE COMPANY LTD—See Sahara India Pariwar; *Int'l*, pg. 6481
SAHARA NISSAN, INC.—See AutoNation, Inc.; *U.S. Public*, pg. 237
SAHARA ONE MEDIA AND ENTERTAINMENT LIMITED.; *Int'l*, pg. 6481
SAHARA PETROLEUM SERVICES COMPANY S.A.E.—See National Energy Services Reunited Corp.; *U.S. Public*, pg. 1494
SAHARA PRESENTATION SYSTEMS LIMITED—See Boxlight Corporation; *U.S. Public*, pg. 377
SAHARA SURGERY CENTER—See HCA Healthcare, Inc.; *U.S. Public*, pg. 1008
S.A. HASBRO N.V.—See Hasbro, Inc.; *U.S. Public*, pg. 988
SAHA SEIREN CO., LTD. - FACTORY II—See Seiren Co., Ltd.; *Int'l*, pg. 6691
SAHA SEIREN CO., LTD.—See Seiren Co., Ltd.; *Int'l*, pg. 6691
SAHAS TECHNOLOGIES LLC; *U.S. Private*, pg. 3528
SAHATHAI TERMINAL PCL; *Int'l*, pg. 6481
SAHA-UNION HOLDING CO., LTD.—See Saha-Union Public Company Limited; *Int'l*, pg. 6480
SAHA-UNION INTERNATIONAL LTD.—See Saha-Union Public Company Limited; *Int'l*, pg. 6480
SAHA-UNION INVESTMENT (CHINA) CO., LTD.—See Saha-Union Public Company Limited; *Int'l*, pg. 6480
SAHA-UNION PUBLIC COMPANY LIMITED; *Int'l*, pg. 6479
SAHAVIRIYA STEEL INDUSTRIES PUBLIC COMPANY LIMITED; *Int'l*, pg. 6481

COMPANY NAME INDEX

S.A. HEALY COMPANY—See Salini Costruttori S.p.A.; *Int'l*, pg. 6493
S.A. HEAVY RIM IMPORTERS PTY LTD.—See Rimex Supply Ltd.; *Int'l*, pg. 6342
S.A. HELM BENELUX N.V.—See HELM AG; *Int'l*, pg. 3338
SAHKO-BUUMI OY—See Instalco AB; *Int'l*, pg. 3722
SAHLING KENWORTH INC.; *U.S. Private*, pg. 3528
SA HLM LE NOUVEAU LOGIS CENTRE- LIMOUSIN; *Int'l*, pg. 6458
SA H L M PIERRES ET LUMIERES; *Int'l*, pg. 6458
SAHNI ENTERPRISES; *U.S. Private*, pg. 3528
S & A HOMES INC.; *U.S. Private*, pg. 3511
SAH POLYMERS LIMITED—See Sat Industries Ltd.; *Int'l*, pg. 6584
SAHYADRI INDUSTRIES LTD; *Int'l*, pg. 6481
SA HYDRAULIQUE PB; *Int'l*, pg. 6458
SAIA-BURGESS BENELUX B.V.—See Honeywell International Inc.; *U.S. Public*, pg. 1052
SAIA BURGESS CONTROLS AG—See Honeywell International Inc.; *U.S. Public*, pg. 1052
SAIA BURGESS CONTROLS ITALIA S.R.L.—See Honeywell International Inc.; *U.S. Public*, pg. 1052
SAIA BURGESS CONTROLS USA INC.—See Honeywell International Inc.; *U.S. Public*, pg. 1052
SAIA-BURGESS ELECTRONICS HOLDING AG—See Honeywell International Inc.; *U.S. Public*, pg. 1051
SAIA ELECTRIC, INC.; *U.S. Private*, pg. 3528
SAIA, INC.; *U.S. Public*, pg. 1835
SAIA LOGISTICS SERVICES, LLC—See Saia, Inc.; *U.S. Public*, pg. 1835
SAIA MOTOR FREIGHT LINE, INC.—See Saia, Inc.; *U.S. Public*, pg. 1835
SAIA MOTOR FREIGHT LINE, INC.—See Saia, Inc.; *U.S. Public*, pg. 1835
SAIA MOTOR FREIGHT LINE, INC.—See Saia, Inc.; *U.S. Public*, pg. 1835
SAIA MOTOR FREIGHT LINE, INC.—See Saia, Inc.; *U.S. Public*, pg. 1835
SAIAN CORPORATION—See Noritsu Koki Co., Ltd.; *Int'l*, pg. 5429
SAIA TL PLUS—See Saia, Inc.; *U.S. Public*, pg. 1835
SAIA TRASPORTI S.P.A.—See Deutsche Bahn AG; *Int'l*, pg. 2052
SAI AUTO GROUP LLC; *U.S. Private*, pg. 3528
SAI AUTOMOTIVE ALLIBERT S.A.—See FORVIA SE, *Int'l*, pg. 2747
SAI AUTOMOTIVE DO BRASIL LTDA.—See FORVIA SE; *Int'l*, pg. 2747
SAI AUTOMOTIVE FRADLEY LTD.—See FORVIA SE; *Int'l*, pg. 2747
SAI AUTOMOTIVE WASHINGTON LTD.—See FORVIA SE; *Int'l*, pg. 2747
SAI BABA INVESTMENT & COMMERCIAL ENTERPRISE LIMITED; *Int'l*, pg. 6481
SAIB BNP PARIBAS ASSET MANAGEMENT CO., LTD.—See BNP Paribas SA; *Int'l*, pg. 1082
SAIB BNP PARIBAS ASSET MANAGEMENT CO., LTD.—See Saudi Investment Bank; *Int'l*, pg. 6594
SAIBO CO., LTD.; *Int'l*, pg. 6482
S.A.I. BROKER S.A.—See BRK Financial Group S.A.; *Int'l*, pg. 1171
SAIBU GAS HOLDINGS CO., LTD.; *Int'l*, pg. 6482
SAIBU GAS KUMAMOTO CO., LTD.—See Saibu Gas Holdings Co., Ltd.; *Int'l*, pg. 6482
SAIBU GAS NAGASAKI CO., LTD.—See Saibu Gas Holdings Co., Ltd.; *Int'l*, pg. 6482
SAIBU GAS SASEBO CO., LTD.—See Saibu Gas Holdings Co., Ltd.; *Int'l*, pg. 6482
SAIC EUROPE GMBH—See Shanghai Automotive Industry Corporation; *Int'l*, pg. 6761
SAIC FIAT POWERTRAIN HONGYAN CO. LTD.—See CNH Industrial N.V.; *Int'l*, pg. 1676
SAIC GENERAL MOTORS SALES COMPANY LIMITED—See General Motors Company; *U.S. Public*, pg. 928
SAIC GM WULING AUTOMOBILE COMPANY LIMITED—See General Motors Company; *U.S. Public*, pg. 928
SAIC GM WULING CO., LTD.—See Shanghai Automotive Industry Corporation; *Int'l*, pg. 6761
SAI CHAMBLEE V, LLC—See Sonic Automotive, Inc.; *U.S. Public*, pg. 1902
SAIC HONG KONG CO., LTD—See Shanghai Automotive Industry Corporation; *Int'l*, pg. 6761
SAI CLEARWATER T, LLC—See Sonic Automotive, Inc.; *U.S. Public*, pg. 1902
SAIC MOTOR CORPORATION LIMITED—See Shanghai Automotive Industry Corporation; *Int'l*, pg. 6762
SAIC MOTOR-CP CO., LTD.—See Shanghai Automotive Industry Corporation; *Int'l*, pg. 6762
SAICON CONSULTANTS, INC.; *U.S. Private*, pg. 3529
SAIC—See Leidos Holdings, Inc.; *U.S. Public*, pg. 1304
SAIC USA INC.—See Shanghai Automotive Industry Corporation; *Int'l*, pg. 6762
SAI DENVER B, INC.—See Sonic Automotive, Inc.; *U.S. Public*, pg. 1902
SAI DONG URBAN DEVELOPMENT & INVESTMENT JSC—See Vingroup Joint Stock Company; *Int'l*, pg. 8241

SAIEED CONSTRUCTION SYSTEMS; *U.S. Private*, pg. 3529
SAI ERSTE ASSET MANAGEMENT S.A.—See Erste Group Bank AG; *Int'l*, pg. 2499
SAIETTA GROUP PLC; *Int'l*, pg. 6482
SAIF CORP.; *U.S. Private*, pg. 3529
SAIF HEALTHCARE LIMITED—See Saif Holdings Limited; *Int'l*, pg. 6482
SAIF HOLDINGS LIMITED; *Int'l*, pg. 6482
SAI FORT MYERS H, LLC—See Sonic Automotive, Inc.; *U.S. Public*, pg. 1902
SAIF PARTNERS; *Int'l*, pg. 6482
SAIF POWER LIMITED—See Saif Holdings Limited; *Int'l*, pg. 6482
SAIF POWERTEC LIMITED; *Int'l*, pg. 6482
SAIF TEXTILE MILLS LTD.—See Saif Holdings Limited; *Int'l*, pg. 6482
SAI GLOBAL CZECH S.R.O—See EQT AB; *Int'l*, pg. 2471
SAI GLOBAL GMBH—See EQT AB; *Int'l*, pg. 2471
SAI GLOBAL INC.—See EQT AB; *Int'l*, pg. 2471
SAI GLOBAL INDIA—See EQT AB; *Int'l*, pg. 2471
SAI GLOBAL ITALIA SRL—See EQT AB; *Int'l*, pg. 2471
SAI GLOBAL JAPAN CO LTD—See EQT AB; *Int'l*, pg. 2471
SAI GLOBAL LIMITED—See EQT AB; *Int'l*, pg. 2471
SAI GLOBAL PTY. LIMITED—See EQT AB; *Int'l*, pg. 2471
SAI GON AUTOMOBILE CO., LTD—See Saigon General Service Corporation; *Int'l*, pg. 6483
SAIGON BEER ALCOHOL BEVERAGE CORP.; *Int'l*, pg. 6482
SAIGON BEER NAM TRUNG BO TRADING JOINT STOCK COMPANY—See Saigon Beer Alcohol Beverage Corp.; *Int'l*, pg. 6483
SAIGON BEER TRANSPORTATION JOINT STOCK COMPANY; *Int'l*, pg. 6483
SAI GON - DONG XUAN BEER ALCOHOL JOINT STOCK COMPANY—See Saigon Beer Alcohol Beverage Corp.; *Int'l*, pg. 6483
SAIGON FISHING NET JOINT STOCK COMPANY; *Int'l*, pg. 6483
SAI GON FOOD JOINT STOCK COMPANY—See Maruha Nichiro Corporation; *Int'l*, pg. 4712
SAIGON FUEL CORPORATION—See Phu Nhuan Jewelry Joint Stock Company; *Int'l*, pg. 5857
SAI GON FUEL JOINT STOCK COMPANY; *Int'l*, pg. 6481
SAIGON GARMENT MANUFACTURING TRADING JOINT STOCK COMPANY - AN NHON GARMENT FACTORY—See Garmex Saigon Corporation; *Int'l*, pg. 2884
SAIGON GENERAL SERVICE CORPORATION; *Int'l*, pg. 6483
SAI GON GROUND SERVICES JSC; *Int'l*, pg. 6481
SAI GON - HANOI BANK LAOS LIMITED—See Saigon - Hanoi Commercial Joint Stock Bank; *Int'l*, pg. 6482
SAIGON - HANOI COMMERCIAL JOINT STOCK BANK; *Int'l*, pg. 6482
SAI GON - HA NOI SECURITIES JOINT STOCK COMPANY; *Int'l*, pg. 6481
SAIGON HOTEL CORP.; *Int'l*, pg. 6483
SAIGON MARITIME JOINT STOCK CO., LTD.; *Int'l*, pg. 6483
SAIGON PAPER CORPORATION—See Sojitz Corporation; *Int'l*, pg. 7063
SAIGON PETROLEUM CONSTRUCTION AND INVESTMENT JOINT STOCK COMPANY—See Vietnam Oil and Gas Group; *Int'l*, pg. 8203
SAIGON PETROLEUM SERVICE COMPANY; *Int'l*, pg. 6483
SAI GON PLASTICS PACKAGING JOINT STOCK COMPANY; *Int'l*, pg. 6481
SAIGON PRECISION CO., LTD.—See MISUMI Group Inc.; *Int'l*, pg. 4922
SAIGON REAL INVESTMENT AND SERVICE JOINT STOCK COMPANY—See Dat Xanh Group Joint Stock Company; *Int'l*, pg. 1975
SAI GON STAR JSC—See Saigon General Service Corporation; *Int'l*, pg. 6483
SAIGON STEEL SERVICE & PROCESSING CO., LTD.—See Sumitomo Corporation; *Int'l*, pg. 7271
SAI GON TELECOMMUNICATIONS TECHNOLOGY JOINT STOCK COMPANY; *Int'l*, pg. 6481
SAIGON THUONG TIN COMMERCIAL JOINT STOCK BANK; *Int'l*, pg. 6483
SAI GON THUONG TIN REAL ESTATE JOINT STOCK COMPANY; *Int'l*, pg. 6481
SAIGONTOURIST TRANSPORT CORPORATION; *Int'l*, pg. 6483
SAIGON VE WONG CO., LTD.—See Ve Wong Corporation; *Int'l*, pg. 8143
SAI GON VIEN DONG E-COMMERCE SERVICES JSC; *Int'l*, pg. 6481
SAI GON WATER INFRASTRUCTURE CORPORATION; *Int'l*, pg. 6481
SAIHAM COTTON MILLS LTD.; *Int'l*, pg. 6483
SAIHAM TEXTILE MILLS LIMITED; *Int'l*, pg. 6483
SAIIA CONSTRUCTION, LLC—See Insight Equity Holdings LLC; *U.S. Private*, pg. 2086
SAI INDUSTRIES LIMITED; *Int'l*, pg. 6481

SAI INVESTIMENTI SGR S.P.A.—See Unipol Gruppo S.p.A.; *Int'l*, pg. 8056
SAIKAYA DEPARTMENT STORE CO., LTD.; *Int'l*, pg. 6483
SAI KD INVESTMENTS S. A.—See KD Group dd; *Int'l*, pg. 4110
SAIKO RUBBER (MALAYSIA) SDN. BHD.—See Kato Sansho Co., Ltd.; *Int'l*, pg. 4090
SAIKOSHA CO., LTD.—See Shimojima Co., Ltd.; *Int'l*, pg. 6836
SAIL ADVISORS LIMITED—See Search Investment Office Limited; *Int'l*, pg. 6666
SAIL ADVISORS RESEARCH INC.—See Search Investment Office Limited; *Int'l*, pg. 6666
SAILANI TOURS N TRAVELS LIMITED; *Int'l*, pg. 6483
SAILBRI COOPER INC.—See Hebei Sailhero Environmental Protection High-Tech Co., Ltd.; *Int'l*, pg. 3306
SAIL CENTRAL MARKETING ORGANIZATION—See Steel Authority of India Limited; *Int'l*, pg. 7189
SAIL CENTRE FOR ENGINEERING AND TECHNOLOGY—See Steel Authority of India Limited; *Int'l*, pg. 7189
SAIL CONSULTANCY DIVISION—See Steel Authority of India Limited; *Int'l*, pg. 7189
S.A.I. LEISURE GROUP COMPANY LIMITED; *Int'l*, pg. 6449
SAIL ENVIRONMENT MANAGEMENT DIVISION—See Steel Authority of India Limited; *Int'l*, pg. 7189
SAILFISH ROYALTY CORP.; *Int'l*, pg. 6483
SAILING CAPITAL ADVISORS (HONG KONG) LTD.; *Int'l*, pg. 6483
SAILING SRL—See Sesa S.p.A.; *Int'l*, pg. 6729
SAIL INTERNATIONAL TRADE DIVISION—See Steel Authority of India Limited; *Int'l*, pg. 7189
SAIL MAGAZINE—See TEN: The Enthusiast Network, Inc.; *U.S. Private*, pg. 3964
SAIL MANAGEMENT TRAINING INSTITUTE—See Steel Authority of India Limited; *Int'l*, pg. 7189
SAI LOGISTICS LIMITED—See Santova Ltd.; *Int'l*, pg. 6560
SAILOGY S.A.; *Int'l*, pg. 6483
SAILORMEN INC.—See Interfoods of America, Inc.; *U.S. Private*, pg. 2110
THE SAILOR PEN CO., LTD. - ROBOTICS DIVISION—See The Sailor Pen Co., Ltd.; *Int'l*, pg. 7680
THE SAILOR PEN CO., LTD.; *Int'l*, pg. 7680
SAILOR PEN EUROPE—See The Sailor Pen Co., Ltd.; *Int'l*, pg. 7680
SAILPOINT TECHNOLOGIES HOLDINGS, INC.—See Thoma Bravo, L.P.; *U.S. Private*, pg. 4153
SAILPOINT TECHNOLOGIES, INC.—See Thoma Bravo, L.P.; *U.S. Private*, pg. 4153
SAILRAIL AUTOMATED SYSTEMS INC.; *Int'l*, pg. 6483
SAIL RAW MATERIALS DIVISION—See Steel Authority of India Limited; *Int'l*, pg. 7189
SAIL RESEARCH AND DEVELOPMENT CENTRE FOR IRON AND STEEL—See Steel Authority of India Limited; *Int'l*, pg. 7189
SAIL & SKI INC.—See NXTLVL Marine, LLC; *U.S. Private*, pg. 2976
THE SAILS PATTAYA—See Grande Asset Hotels & Property Public Company Limited; *Int'l*, pg. 3057
SAILTHRU, INC.; *U.S. Private*, pg. 3529
SAILUN CO. LTD.; *Int'l*, pg. 6484
SAIMAAN LEHTIPAINO OY—See Sanoma Oyj; *Int'l*, pg. 6553
SAIMA AVANDERO SPA—See DSV A/S; *Int'l*, pg. 2216
SAI-MED PARTNERS LLC—See Northlane Capital Partners, LLC; *U.S. Private*, pg. 2956
SAI MICROELECTRONICS INC.; *Int'l*, pg. 6481
SAIMO TECHNOLOGY CO., LTD.; *Int'l*, pg. 6484
SAI MUNTENIA INVEST SA—See SIF Banat-Crisana S.A.; *Int'l*, pg. 6905
SAIN CONSTRUCTION CO.; *U.S. Private*, pg. 3529
S.A INDUSTRIAS CELULOSA ARAGONESA CIF; *Int'l*, pg. 6447
SAIN ENGINEERING ASSOCIATES, INC.; *U.S. Private*, pg. 3529
SAINERGY; *U.S. Private*, pg. 3529
SAINICHI CO., LTD.—See Aktio Holdings Corporation; *Int'l*, pg. 267
SAINIK FINANCE & INDUSTRIES LIMITED; *Int'l*, pg. 6484
S.A. INMOBILIARIA SPORT FRANCAIS; *Int'l*, pg. 6448
SAINRAPT CONTRACTING CO L.L.C.—See VINCI S.A.; *Int'l*, pg. 8235
SAINSBURY'S SUPERMARKETS LTD.—See J Sainsbury plc; *Int'l*, pg. 3852
SAINT ANTHONY HOSPITAL; *U.S. Private*, pg. 3529
SAINT BARNABAS / HEALTHSOUTH REHABILITATION CENTER LLC—See Encompass Health Corporation; *U.S. Public*, pg. 759
SAINT BARNABAS MEDICAL CENTER—See Barnabas Health, Inc.; *U.S. Private*, pg. 477
SAINT-BARTH ASSURANCES S.A R.L.—See Allianz SE; *Int'l*, pg. 355
SAINT BENEDICT PRESS; *U.S. Private*, pg. 3529

SAINT BENEDICT PRESS

SAINT BERNARD PROPERTIES COMPANY LLC—See Valero Energy Corporation; *U.S. Public*, pg. 2272
SAINT BRICE S.A.—See Otto GmbH & Co. KG; *Int'l*, pg. 5663
SAINT-CARE HOLDING CORPORATION; *Int'l*, pg. 6484
SAINT CLAIR SYSTEMS, INC.; *U.S. Private*, pg. 3529
SAINT CLAIR TEXTILES SAS—See Sioen Industries NV; *Int'l*, pg. 6960
SAINT CROIX HOLDING IMMOBILIER SOCIMI SA; *Int'l*, pg. 6484
SAINT CROIX VALLEY HARDWOODS INC.; *U.S. Private*, pg. 3529
SAINT DOMINIC'S HOME; *U.S. Private*, pg. 3529
SAINTEN PTY LTD—See Corporate Travel Management Limited; *Int'l*, pg. 1806
S.A. INTERGROUP COORDINATION SERVICES N.V.—See Recticel S.A.; *Int'l*, pg. 6242
SAINT FRANCIS CENTER FOR SURGICAL WEIGHT LOSS, L.L.C.—See Tenet Healthcare Corporation; *U.S. Public*, pg. 2003
SAINT FRANCIS HEALTH SYSTEM, INC.; *U.S. Private*, pg. 3529
SAINT FRANCIS HOSPITAL-BARTLETT, INC.—See Tenet Healthcare Corporation; *U.S. Public*, pg. 2008
SAINT FRANCIS HOSPITAL BILLING CENTER, L.L.C.—See Tenet Healthcare Corporation; *U.S. Public*, pg. 2007
SAINT FRANCIS HOSPITAL INPATIENT PHYSICIANS, L.L.C.—See Tenet Healthcare Corporation; *U.S. Public*, pg. 2003
SAINT FRANCIS HOSPITAL MEDICARE ACO, LLC—See Tenet Healthcare Corporation; *U.S. Public*, pg. 2006
SAINT FRANCIS HOSPITAL PRO FEE BILLING, L.L.C.—See Tenet Healthcare Corporation; *U.S. Public*, pg. 2003
SAINT FRANCIS MEDICAL CENTER; *U.S. Private*, pg. 3529
SAINT FRANCIS MEDICAL PARTNERS, EAST, L.L.C.—See Tenet Healthcare Corporation; *U.S. Public*, pg. 2003
SAINT FRANCIS SURGERY CENTER, L.L.C.—See Tenet Healthcare Corporation; *U.S. Public*, pg. 2007
SAINT FRANCIS SURGICAL ASSOCIATES, L.L.C.—See Tenet Healthcare Corporation; *U.S. Public*, pg. 2003
SAINT FRERES CONFECTION SAS—See Sioen Industries NV; *Int'l*, pg. 6960
SAINT FRERES SAS—See Sioen Industries NV; *Int'l*, pg. 6960
SAINT-GEORGES DOORS; *Int'l*, pg. 6484
SAINT-GIRONS INDUSTRIES S.N.C.—See Mativ Holdings, Inc.; *U.S. Public*, pg. 1396
SAINT-GOBAIN ABRASIFS SA—See Compagnie de Saint-Gobain SA; *Int'l*, pg. 1731
SAINT-GOBAIN ABRASIFS—See Compagnie de Saint-Gobain SA; *Int'l*, pg. 1729
SAINT-GOBAIN ABRASIVES AB—See Compagnie de Saint-Gobain SA; *Int'l*, pg. 1731
SAINT-GOBAIN ABRASIVES A/S—See Compagnie de Saint-Gobain SA; *Int'l*, pg. 1731
SAINT-GOBAIN ABRASIVES BV—See Compagnie de Saint-Gobain SA; *Int'l*, pg. 1731
SAINT-GOBAIN ABRASIVES CANADA INC—See Compagnie de Saint-Gobain SA; *Int'l*, pg. 1731
SAINT-GOBAIN ABRASIVES GMBH—See Compagnie de Saint-Gobain SA; *Int'l*, pg. 1731
SAINT-GOBAIN ABRASIVES, INC. - CHICAGO—See Compagnie de Saint-Gobain SA; *Int'l*, pg. 1732
SAINT-GOBAIN ABRASIVES, INC. - PHILADELPHIA—See Compagnie de Saint-Gobain SA; *Int'l*, pg. 1732
SAINT-GOBAIN ABRASIVES, INC—See Compagnie de Saint-Gobain SA; *Int'l*, pg. 1730
SAINT-GOBAIN ABRASIVES LIMITED—See Compagnie de Saint-Gobain SA; *Int'l*, pg. 1731
SAINT-GOBAIN ABRASIVES LTD—See Compagnie de Saint-Gobain SA; *Int'l*, pg. 1731
SAINT-GOBAIN ABRASIVES MALAYSIA—See Compagnie de Saint-Gobain SA; *Int'l*, pg. 1731
SAINT-GOBAIN ABRASIVES NEDERLAND B.V.—See Compagnie de Saint-Gobain SA; *Int'l*, pg. 1729
SAINT GOBAIN ABRASIVES PTY. LTD.—See Compagnie de Saint-Gobain SA; *Int'l*, pg. 1731
SAINT-GOBAIN ABRASIVES (PTY.) LTD.—See Compagnie de Saint-Gobain SA; *Int'l*, pg. 1731
SAINT-GOBAIN ABRASIVES SA/NV—See Compagnie de Saint-Gobain SA; *Int'l*, pg. 1731
SAINT-GOBAIN ABRASIVES S.A.—See Compagnie de Saint-Gobain SA; *Int'l*, pg. 1731
SAINT GOBAIN ABRASIVES—See Compagnie de Saint-Gobain SA; *Int'l*, pg. 1729
SAINT-GOBAIN ABRASIVES S.R.O.—See Compagnie de Saint-Gobain SA; *Int'l*, pg. 1731
SAINT-GOBAIN ABRASIVES (SUZHOU) CO., LTD.—See Compagnie de Saint-Gobain SA; *Int'l*, pg. 1731
SAINT-GOBAIN ABRASIVES THAILAND LTD.—See Compagnie de Saint-Gobain SA; *Int'l*, pg. 1731
SAINT-GOBAIN ABRASIVI S.P.A—See Compagnie de Saint-Gobain SA; *Int'l*, pg. 1731
SAINT-GOBAIN ABRASIVI S.P.A.—See Compagnie de Saint-Gobain SA; *Int'l*, pg. 1731

SAINT-GOBAIN ABRASIVOS ARGENTINA SA—See Compagnie de Saint-Gobain SA; *Int'l*, pg. 1729
SAINT-GOBAIN ABRASIVOS BRASIL LTDA—See Compagnie de Saint-Gobain SA; *Int'l*, pg. 1729
SAINT-GOBAIN ABRASIVOS CA—See Compagnie de Saint-Gobain SA; *Int'l*, pg. 1731
SAINT-GOBAIN ABRASIVOS COLOMBIA LTDA—See Compagnie de Saint-Gobain SA; *Int'l*, pg. 1731
SAINT-GOBAIN ABRASIVOS LDA—See Compagnie de Saint-Gobain SA; *Int'l*, pg. 1731
SAINT-GOBAIN ABRASIVOS LIMITADA—See Compagnie de Saint-Gobain SA; *Int'l*, pg. 1731
SAINT-GOBAIN ABRASIVOS, S.A. DE C.V.—See Compagnie de Saint-Gobain SA; *Int'l*, pg. 1731
SAINT-GOBAIN ABRASIVOS SA—See Compagnie de Saint-Gobain SA; *Int'l*, pg. 1731
SAINT-GOBAIN ACHATS—See Compagnie de Saint-Gobain SA; *Int'l*, pg. 1727
SAINT-GOBAIN ADFORS AMERICA, INC.—See Compagnie de Saint-Gobain SA; *Int'l*, pg. 1730
SAINT-GOBAIN ADFORS AUSTRIA GMBH—See Compagnie de Saint-Gobain SA; *Int'l*, pg. 1729
SAINT-GOBAIN ADFORS CANADA LTD—See Compagnie de Saint-Gobain SA; *Int'l*, pg. 1732
SAINT-GOBAIN ADFORS CZ FABRICS S.R.O.—See Compagnie de Saint-Gobain SA; *Int'l*, pg. 1727
SAINT-GOBAIN ADFORS CZ GLASS MAT S.R.O.—See Compagnie de Saint-Gobain SA; *Int'l*, pg. 1727
SAINT-GOBAIN ADFORS CZ S.R.O.—See Compagnie de Saint-Gobain SA; *Int'l*, pg. 1729
SAINT-GOBAIN ADFORS DEUTSCHLAND GMBH—See Compagnie de Saint-Gobain SA; *Int'l*, pg. 1729
SAINT-GOBAIN ADFORS FRANCE—See Compagnie de Saint-Gobain SA; *Int'l*, pg. 1735
SAINT-GOBAIN ADFORS ITALIA S.P.A.—See Compagnie de Saint-Gobain SA; *Int'l*, pg. 1729
SAINT-GOBAIN ADVANCED CERAMICS CORPORATION—See Compagnie de Saint-Gobain SA; *Int'l*, pg. 1730
SAINT-GOBAIN ADVANCED CERAMICS (SHANGHAI) CO. LTD—See Compagnie de Saint-Gobain SA; *Int'l*, pg. 1729
SAINT GOBAIN AMERICA S.A. DE C.V.—See Compagnie de Saint-Gobain SA; *Int'l*, pg. 1727
SAINT-GOBAIN ASSESSORIA E ADMINISTRACAO LTDA.—See Compagnie de Saint-Gobain SA; *Int'l*, pg. 1727
SAINT-GOBAIN AUTOVER DEUTSCHLAND GMBH—See Compagnie de Saint-Gobain SA; *Int'l*, pg. 1736
SAINT-GOBAIN AUTOVER DIREKTGLAS AB—See Compagnie de Saint-Gobain SA; *Int'l*, pg. 1729
SAINT-GOBAIN AUTOVER DISTRIBUTION SA—See Compagnie de Saint-Gobain SA; *Int'l*, pg. 1736
SAINT-GOBAIN AUTOVER FRANCE S.A.—See Compagnie de Saint-Gobain SA; *Int'l*, pg. 1729
SAINT GOBAIN AUTOVER FRANCE S.A.S.—See Compagnie de Saint-Gobain SA; *Int'l*, pg. 1729
SAINT-GOBAIN AUTOVER FRANCE—See Compagnie de Saint-Gobain SA; *Int'l*, pg. 1729
SAINT-GOBAIN AUTOVER HELLAS S.A.—See Compagnie de Saint-Gobain SA; *Int'l*, pg. 1729
SAINT-GOBAIN AUTOVER INC—See Compagnie de Saint-Gobain SA; *Int'l*, pg. 1732
SAINT-GOBAIN AUTOVER OSTERREICH GMBH—See Compagnie de Saint-Gobain SA; *Int'l*, pg. 1727
SAINT-GOBAIN AUTOVER PORTUGAL S.A.—See Compagnie de Saint-Gobain SA; *Int'l*, pg. 1736
SAINT-GOBAIN AUTOVER—See Compagnie de Saint-Gobain SA; *Int'l*, pg. 1729
SAINT-GOBAIN BOCKMANN A/S—See Mimir Invest AB; *Int'l*, pg. 4898
SAINT GOBAIN BTI—See Compagnie de Saint-Gobain SA; *Int'l*, pg. 1730
SAINT-GOBAIN BUILDING DISTRIBUTION (IRELAND) LTD.—See Compagnie de Saint-Gobain SA; *Int'l*, pg. 1729
SAINT-GOBAIN BUILDING DISTRIBUTION LTD.—See CVC Capital Partners SICAV-FIS S.A.; *Int'l*, pg. 1884
SAINT-GOBAIN BYGGEVARER AS—See Compagnie de Saint-Gobain SA; *Int'l*, pg. 1726
SAINT-GOBAIN BYGGPRODUKTER AB—See Compagnie de Saint-Gobain SA; *Int'l*, pg. 1727
SAINT-GOBAIN CANALIZACAO S.A.—See Compagnie de Saint-Gobain SA; *Int'l*, pg. 1729
SAINT-GOBAIN CANALIZACION CHILE S.A.—See Compagnie de Saint-Gobain SA; *Int'l*, pg. 1727
SAINT-GOBAIN CENTRAL SEKURIT (QINGDAO) CO., LTD.—See Central Glass Co., Ltd.; *Int'l*, pg. 1407
SAINT-GOBAIN CENTRE DE RECHERCHE ET D'ETUDES EUROPEENNES—See Compagnie de Saint-Gobain SA; *Int'l*, pg. 1732
SAINT-GOBAIN CERAMICAS INDUSTRIALES S.A.—See Compagnie de Saint-Gobain SA; *Int'l*, pg. 1731
SAINT-GOBAIN CERAMIC MATERIALS AS—See Compagnie de Saint-Gobain SA; *Int'l*, pg. 1731
SAINT-GOBAIN CERAMIC MATERIALS CANADA INC.—See Compagnie de Saint-Gobain SA; *Int'l*, pg. 1731

CORPORATE AFFILIATIONS

SAINT-GOBAIN CERAMIC MATERIALS GMBH—See Compagnie de Saint-Gobain SA; *Int'l*, pg. 1728
SAINT-GOBAIN CERAMIC MATERIALS WEILERSWIST GMBH—See Compagnie de Saint-Gobain SA; *Int'l*, pg. 1731
SAINT-GOBAIN CERAMIC MATERIALS (ZHENGZHOU) CO., LTD.—See Compagnie de Saint-Gobain SA; *Int'l*, pg. 1729
SAINT-GOBAIN CERAMICS & PLASTICS PLC—See Compagnie de Saint-Gobain SA; *Int'l*, pg. 1729
SAINT-GOBAIN CERAMICS & PLASTICS—See Compagnie de Saint-Gobain SA; *Int'l*, pg. 1732
SAINT-GOBAIN CERAMICS SC—See Compagnie de Saint-Gobain SA; *Int'l*, pg. 1732
SAINT-GOBAIN CERAMICS—See Compagnie de Saint-Gobain SA; *Int'l*, pg. 1732
SAINT-GOBAIN CERAMICS STRUCTURAL CERAMICS INC—See Compagnie de Saint-Gobain SA; *Int'l*, pg. 1732
SAINT-GOBAIN COATING SOLUTIONS—See Compagnie de Saint-Gobain SA; *Int'l*, pg. 1729
SAINT-GOBAIN CONCEPTIONS VERRIERES—See Compagnie de Saint-Gobain SA; *Int'l*, pg. 1727
SAINT-GOBAIN CONDOTTE S.P.A.—See Compagnie de Saint-Gobain SA; *Int'l*, pg. 1729
SAINT-GOBAIN CONSTRUCTION PRODUCT RUSSIA INSULATION—See Compagnie de Saint-Gobain SA; *Int'l*, pg. 1726
SAINT-GOBAIN CONSTRUCTION PRODUCTS BELGIUM NV—See Compagnie de Saint-Gobain SA; *Int'l*, pg. 1726
SAINT-GOBAIN CONSTRUCTION PRODUCTS BELGIUM NV—See Compagnie de Saint-Gobain SA; *Int'l*, pg. 1726
SAINT-GOBAIN CONSTRUCTION PRODUCTS CZ A.S.—See Compagnie de Saint-Gobain SA; *Int'l*, pg. 1726
SAINT-GOBAIN CONSTRUCTION PRODUCTS CZ A.S.—See Compagnie de Saint-Gobain SA; *Int'l*, pg. 1726
SAINT-GOBAIN CONSTRUCTION PRODUCTS FINLAND—See Compagnie de Saint-Gobain SA; *Int'l*, pg. 1726
SAINT-GOBAIN CONSTRUCTION PRODUCTS HUNGARY KFT.—See Compagnie de Saint-Gobain SA; *Int'l*, pg. 1726
SAINT-GOBAIN CONSTRUCTION PRODUCTS (MALAYSIA) SDN BHD—See Compagnie de Saint-Gobain SA; *Int'l*, pg. 1726
SAINT-GOBAIN CONSTRUCTION PRODUCTS NEDERLAND BV—See Compagnie de Saint-Gobain SA; *Int'l*, pg. 1726
SAINT-GOBAIN CONSTRUCTION PRODUCTS ROMANIA SRL—See Compagnie de Saint-Gobain SA; *Int'l*, pg. 1726
SAINT-GOBAIN CONSTRUCTION PRODUCTS SLOVAKIA S.R.O.—See Compagnie de Saint-Gobain SA; *Int'l*, pg. 1726
SAINT-GOBAIN CONSTRUCTION PRODUCTS SOUTH AFRICA LTD.—See Compagnie de Saint-Gobain SA; *Int'l*, pg. 1726
SAINT-GOBAIN CONSTRUCTION PRODUCTS UKRAINE—See Compagnie de Saint-Gobain SA; *Int'l*, pg. 1726
SAINT-GOBAIN CONSTRUCTION PRODUCTS VIETNAM LIMITED—See Compagnie de Saint-Gobain SA; *Int'l*, pg. 1726
SAINT-GOBAIN CONSULTING INFORMATION AND ORGANIZATION—See Compagnie de Saint-Gobain SA; *Int'l*, pg. 1727
SAINT-GOBAIN CORPORATION—See Compagnie de Saint-Gobain SA; *Int'l*, pg. 1729
SAINT-GOBAIN CRISTAUX—See Compagnie de Saint-Gobain SA; *Int'l*, pg. 1732
SAINT-GOBAIN CRYSTALS NV—See Compagnie de Saint-Gobain SA; *Int'l*, pg. 1732
SAINT-GOBAIN DE COLOMBIA SA—See Compagnie de Saint-Gobain SA; *Int'l*, pg. 1727
SAINT-GOBAIN DESJONQUERES MANUFACTURING, INC—See Compagnie de Saint-Gobain SA; *Int'l*, pg. 1732
SAINT-GOBAIN DESJONQUERES—See Compagnie de Saint-Gobain SA; *Int'l*, pg. 1733
SAINT-GOBAIN DEUTSCHE GLAS GMBH—See Compagnie de Saint-Gobain SA; *Int'l*, pg. 1732
SAINT-GOBAIN DEVELOPPEMENT MAROC—See Compagnie de Saint-Gobain SA; *Int'l*, pg. 1727
SAINT-GOBAIN DEVISA S.A.—See Compagnie de Saint-Gobain SA; *Int'l*, pg. 1727
SAINT-GOBAIN DIAMANTWERKZEUGE GMBH & CO. KG—See Compagnie de Saint-Gobain SA; *Int'l*, pg. 1727
SAINT-GOBAIN DISTRIBUCION CONSTRUCCION, S.L—See Compagnie de Saint-Gobain SA; *Int'l*, pg. 1732
SAINT-GOBAIN DISTRIBUTION BATIMENT—See Compagnie de Saint-Gobain SA; *Int'l*, pg. 1732
SAINT-GOBAIN DISTRIBUTION DENMARK A/S—See Compagnie de Saint-Gobain SA; *Int'l*, pg. 1733

COMPANY NAME INDEX

SAINT-GOBAIN DISTRIBUTION NORDIC AB—See Compagnie de Saint-Gobain SA; *Int'l*, pg. 1733
SAINT-GOBAIN DISTRIBUTION THE NETHERLANDS BV—See Compagnie de Saint-Gobain SA; *Int'l*, pg. 1733
SAINT GOBAIN ECOPHON AB—See Compagnie de Saint-Gobain SA; *Int'l*, pg. 1729
SAINT-GOBAIN ECOPHON A/S—See Compagnie de Saint-Gobain SA; *Int'l*, pg. 1733
SAINT-GOBAIN ECOPHON BV—See Compagnie de Saint-Gobain SA; *Int'l*, pg. 1733
SAINT-GOBAIN ECOPHON CZ S.R.O.—See Compagnie de Saint-Gobain SA; *Int'l*, pg. 1733
SAINT-GOBAIN ECOPHON LTD—See Compagnie de Saint-Gobain SA; *Int'l*, pg. 1733
SAINT-GOBAIN ECOPHON PRODUCTION A/S—See Compagnie de Saint-Gobain SA; *Int'l*, pg. 1733
SAINT-GOBAIN EMBALLAGE—See Compagnie de Saint-Gobain SA; *Int'l*, pg. 1733
SAINT-GOBAIN ENVASES SA—See Compagnie de Saint-Gobain SA; *Int'l*, pg. 1733
SAINT-GOBAIN EUROVEDER ITALIA SPA—See Compagnie de Saint-Gobain SA; *Int'l*, pg. 1733
SAINT-GOBAIN EUROVEDER OPERADORA S.A. DE C.V.—See Compagnie de Saint-Gobain SA; *Int'l*, pg. 1733
SAINT-GOBAIN EUROVEDER POLSKA SP. Z O.O.—See Compagnie de Saint-Gobain SA; *Int'l*, pg. 1734
SAINT-GOBAIN FACILITAS PORTUGAL, SOCIEDADE UNIPESS—See Compagnie de Saint-Gobain SA; *Int'l*, pg. 1728
SAINT-GOBAIN FORMULA GMBH—See Compagnie de Saint-Gobain SA; *Int'l*, pg. 1728
SAINT-GOBAIN FOUNDRY CO. LTD.—See Compagnie de Saint-Gobain SA; *Int'l*, pg. 1733
SAINT-GOBAIN FOUNDRY (MA'ANSHAN) CO., LTD.—See Compagnie de Saint-Gobain SA; *Int'l*, pg. 1733
SAINT-GOBAIN GLASS BENELUX SA—See Compagnie de Saint-Gobain SA; *Int'l*, pg. 1733
SAINT-GOBAIN GLASS ESTONIA SE—See Compagnie de Saint-Gobain SA; *Int'l*, pg. 1733
SAINT-GOBAIN GLASS EXPROVER NORTH AMERICA CORP.—See Compagnie de Saint-Gobain SA; *Int'l*, pg. 1730
SAINT-GOBAIN GLASS FINLAND OY—See Compagnie de Saint-Gobain SA; *Int'l*, pg. 1733
SAINT-GOBAIN GLASS FRANCE SA—See Compagnie de Saint-Gobain SA; *Int'l*, pg. 1733
SAINT-GOBAIN GLASS HELLAS—See Compagnie de Saint-Gobain SA; *Int'l*, pg. 1728
SAINT-GOBAIN GLASS INDIA LTD.—See Compagnie de Saint-Gobain SA; *Int'l*, pg. 1734
SAINT-GOBAIN GLASS ITALIA LOGISTICA SERVIZI S.R.L.—See Compagnie de Saint-Gobain SA; *Int'l*, pg. 1734
SAINT-GOBAIN GLASS ITALIA SPA—See Compagnie de Saint-Gobain SA; *Int'l*, pg. 1734
SAINT-GOBAIN GLASS LOGISTICS S.A.S—See Compagnie de Saint-Gobain SA; *Int'l*, pg. 1733
SAINT-GOBAIN GLASS MEXICO, S.A. DE C.V—See Compagnie de Saint-Gobain SA; *Int'l*, pg. 1734
SAINT-GOBAIN GLASS NORDIC A/S—See Compagnie de Saint-Gobain SA; *Int'l*, pg. 1734
SAINT-GOBAIN GLASSOLUTIONS NITRASKLO, S.R.O.—See Compagnie de Saint-Gobain SA; *Int'l*, pg. 1728
SAINT GOBAIN GLASS OPERADORA S.A. DE C.V.—See Compagnie de Saint-Gobain SA; *Int'l*, pg. 1727
SAINT-GOBAIN GLASS POLSKA—See Compagnie de Saint-Gobain SA; *Int'l*, pg. 1734
SAINT-GOBAIN GLASS PORTUGAL VIDRO PLANO SA—See Compagnie de Saint-Gobain SA; *Int'l*, pg. 1734
SAINT-GOBAIN GLASS ROMANIA SRL—See Compagnie de Saint-Gobain SA; *Int'l*, pg. 1734
SAINT-GOBAIN GLASS SOLUTION BURNIAT—See Compagnie de Saint-Gobain SA; *Int'l*, pg. 1734
SAINT-GOBAIN GLASS SOLUTION FRANKENGLAS NV—See Compagnie de Saint-Gobain SA; *Int'l*, pg. 1734
SAINT-GOBAIN GLASS SOLUTION GLORIOUS NV—See Compagnie de Saint-Gobain SA; *Int'l*, pg. 1734
SAINT-GOBAIN GLASS SOLUTION MIROVER NV—See Compagnie de Saint-Gobain SA; *Int'l*, pg. 1734
SAINT-GOBAIN GLASS SOLUTION SAS GLAS—See Compagnie de Saint-Gobain SA; *Int'l*, pg. 1734
SAINT-GOBAIN GLASS SOLUTIONS CZ, S.R.O.—See Compagnie de Saint-Gobain SA; *Int'l*, pg. 1734
SAINT-GOBAIN GLASS SOLUTIONS MENUISIERS INDUSTRIEL—See Compagnie de Saint-Gobain SA; *Int'l*, pg. 1728
SAINT-GOBAIN GLASS SOLUTIONS PARIS - NORMANDIE—See Compagnie de Saint-Gobain SA; *Int'l*, pg. 1728
SAINT-GOBAIN GLASSSOLUTIONS—See Compagnie de Saint-Gobain SA; *Int'l*, pg. 1734
SAINT-GOBAIN GLASS SOLUTIONS SUD-OUEST—See Compagnie de Saint-Gobain SA; *Int'l*, pg. 1728

SAINT-GOBAIN GLASS SOLUTION WAGENER-JOWACO EUPEN—See Compagnie de Saint-Gobain SA; *Int'l*, pg. 1734
SAINT-GOBAIN GLASS UK LTD—See Compagnie de Saint-Gobain SA; *Int'l*, pg. 1734
SAINT-GOBAIN GRADBENI IZDELKI D.O.O.—See Compagnie de Saint-Gobain SA; *Int'l*, pg. 1728
SAINT-GOBAIN GRADEVINSKI PROIZVODI HRVATSKA D.O.O.—See Compagnie de Saint-Gobain SA; *Int'l*, pg. 1728
SAINT-GOBAIN GUSSROHR GMBH & CO. KG—See Compagnie de Saint-Gobain SA; *Int'l*, pg. 1734
SAINT-GOBAIN GUSSROHRVERTIEB OSTERREICH GMBH—See Compagnie de Saint-Gobain SA; *Int'l*, pg. 1728
SAINT-GOBAIN GYPROC BELGIUM NV—See Compagnie de Saint-Gobain SA; *Int'l*, pg. 1726
SAINT-GOBAIN GYPROC INDIA LTD - BENGALURU PLANT—See Compagnie de Saint-Gobain SA; *Int'l*, pg. 1734
SAINT-GOBAIN GYPROC INDIA LTD—See Compagnie de Saint-Gobain SA; *Int'l*, pg. 1734
SAINT-GOBAIN GYPROC NEDERLAND BV—See Compagnie de Saint-Gobain SA; *Int'l*, pg. 1734
SAINT-GOBAIN GYPROC SOUTH AFRICA (PTY) LTD—See Compagnie de Saint-Gobain SA; *Int'l*, pg. 1734
SAINT-GOBAIN GYPSUM (CHANGZHOU) CO., LTD.—See Compagnie de Saint-Gobain SA; *Int'l*, pg. 1734
SAINT-GOBAIN GYPSUM CHINA (SHANGHAI)—See Compagnie de Saint-Gobain SA; *Int'l*, pg. 1734
SAINT-GOBAIN GYPSUM MATERIALS SHANGHAI—See Compagnie de Saint-Gobain SA; *Int'l*, pg. 1734
SAINT GOBAIN GYPSUM OPERADORA SA DE CV—See Compagnie de Saint-Gobain SA; *Int'l*, pg. 1727
SAINT-GOBAIN GYPSUM SA DE CV—See Compagnie de Saint-Gobain SA; *Int'l*, pg. 1734
SAINT-GOBAIN HANGLAS JAPAN K.K.—See Compagnie de Saint-Gobain SA; *Int'l*, pg. 1734
SAINT-GOBAIN HELLAS ABEE—See Compagnie de Saint-Gobain SA; *Int'l*, pg. 1726
SAINT-GOBAIN HES GMBH—See Compagnie de Saint-Gobain SA; *Int'l*, pg. 1735
SAINT-GOBAIN HORNSTEIN GLASTEXTIL GMBH—See Compagnie de Saint-Gobain SA; *Int'l*, pg. 1734
SAINT-GOBAIN HPM POLSKA SP ZOO—See Compagnie de Saint-Gobain SA; *Int'l*, pg. 1734
SAINT-GOBAIN HPM RUS. OOO—See Compagnie de Saint-Gobain SA; *Int'l*, pg. 1728
SAINT-GOBAIN IDAPLAC, S.L.—See Compagnie de Saint-Gobain SA; *Int'l*, pg. 1728
SAINT-GOBAIN INDUSTRIAL CERAMICS INC.—See Compagnie de Saint-Gobain SA; *Int'l*, pg. 1730
SAINT-GOBAIN INDUSTRIAL CERAMICS LTD.—See Compagnie de Saint-Gobain SA; *Int'l*, pg. 1731
SAINT-GOBAIN INDUSTRIAL CERAMICS PTY LTD—See Compagnie de Saint-Gobain SA; *Int'l*, pg. 1728
SAINT-GOBAIN INDUSTRIEKERAMIK ROEDENTAL GMBH—See Compagnie de Saint-Gobain SA; *Int'l*, pg. 1728
SAINT-GOBAIN INTERSERVICES S.A.—See Compagnie de Saint-Gobain SA; *Int'l*, pg. 1728
SAINT-GOBAIN ISOVER AB—See Compagnie de Saint-Gobain SA; *Int'l*, pg. 1726
SAINT-GOBAIN ISOVER ARGENTINA S.A.—See Compagnie de Saint-Gobain SA; *Int'l*, pg. 1726
SAINT-GOBAIN ISOVER A/S—See Compagnie de Saint-Gobain SA; *Int'l*, pg. 1726
SAINT-GOBAIN ISOVER AUSTRIA AG—See Compagnie de Saint-Gobain SA; *Int'l*, pg. 1726
SAINT GOBAIN ISOVER BENELUX—See Compagnie de Saint-Gobain SA; *Int'l*, pg. 1726
SAINT-GOBAIN ISOVER ESPANA—See Compagnie de Saint-Gobain SA; *Int'l*, pg. 1734
SAINT-GOBAIN ISOVER G+H AG—See Compagnie de Saint-Gobain SA; *Int'l*, pg. 1726
SAINT-GOBAIN ISOVER (GU'AN) GLASS WOOL CO., LTD.—See Compagnie de Saint-Gobain SA; *Int'l*, pg. 1734
SAINT GOBAIN ISOVER ITALIA S.P.A.—See Compagnie de Saint-Gobain SA; *Int'l*, pg. 1726
SAINT-GOBAIN ISOVER S.A.—See Compagnie de Saint-Gobain SA; *Int'l*, pg. 1726
SAINT-GOBAIN ISOVER SA—See Compagnie de Saint-Gobain SA; *Int'l*, pg. 1726
SAINT-GOBAIN ISOVER—See Compagnie de Saint-Gobain SA; *Int'l*, pg. 1726
SAINT-GOBAIN K.K.—See Compagnie de Saint-Gobain SA; *Int'l*, pg. 1731
SAINT-GOBAIN LIMITED—See Compagnie de Saint-Gobain SA; *Int'l*, pg. 1735
SAINT-GOBAIN MALAYSIA SDN BHD.—See Compagnie de Saint-Gobain SA; *Int'l*, pg. 1728
SAINT-GOBAIN MATERIAUX CERAMIQUES BENELUX SA—See Compagnie de Saint-Gobain SA; *Int'l*, pg. 1734
SAINT-GOBAIN MATERIAUX CERAMIQUES SA—See Compagnie de Saint-Gobain SA; *Int'l*, pg. 1732

SAINT-GEORGES DOORS

SAINT-GOBAIN MATERIAUX INNOVANTS—See Compagnie de Saint-Gobain SA; *Int'l*, pg. 1734
SAINT-GOBAIN MEXICO S.A. DE C.V.—See Compagnie de Saint-Gobain SA; *Int'l*, pg. 1734
SAINT-GOBAIN MONDEGO S.A.—See Compagnie de Saint-Gobain SA; *Int'l*, pg. 1734
SAINT-GOBAIN NEDERLAND BEHEER BV—See Compagnie de Saint-Gobain SA; *Int'l*, pg. 1734
SAINT-GOBAIN NORPRO GMBH—See Compagnie de Saint-Gobain SA; *Int'l*, pg. 1735
SAINT-GOBAIN NORPRO—See Compagnie de Saint-Gobain SA; *Int'l*, pg. 1730
SAINT-GOBAIN OBERLAND AG—See Compagnie de Saint-Gobain SA; *Int'l*, pg. 1735
SAINT-GOBAIN ORSIL S.R.O.—See Compagnie de Saint-Gobain SA; *Int'l*, pg. 1735
SAINT-GOBAIN PAM CZ S.R.O.—See Compagnie de Saint-Gobain SA; *Int'l*, pg. 1735
SAINT-GOBAIN PAM DEUTSCHLAND GMBH—See Compagnie de Saint-Gobain SA; *Int'l*, pg. 1735
SAINT-GOBAIN PAM ITALIA SPA—See Compagnie de Saint-Gobain SA; *Int'l*, pg. 1735
SAINT-GOBAIN PAM PORTUGAL SA—See Compagnie de Saint-Gobain SA; *Int'l*, pg. 1735
SAINT-GOBAIN PAM S.A.—See Compagnie de Saint-Gobain SA; *Int'l*, pg. 1735
SAINT-GOBAIN PAM UK—See Compagnie de Saint-Gobain SA; *Int'l*, pg. 1735
SAINT-GOBAIN PAM UK—See Compagnie de Saint-Gobain SA; *Int'l*, pg. 1735
SAINT-GOBAIN PAM UK—See Compagnie de Saint-Gobain SA; *Int'l*, pg. 1735
SAINT-GOBAIN PARTICIPACOES LTDA—See Compagnie de Saint-Gobain SA; *Int'l*, pg. 1728
SAINT-GOBAIN PERFORMANCE PLASTICS BRASIL—See Compagnie de Saint-Gobain SA; *Int'l*, pg. 1732
SAINT-GOBAIN PERFORMANCE PLASTICS CHAINEUX SA—See Compagnie de Saint-Gobain SA; *Int'l*, pg. 1731
SAINT-GOBAIN PERFORMANCE PLASTICS COLOGNE GMBH—See Compagnie de Saint-Gobain SA; *Int'l*, pg. 1732
SAINT-GOBAIN PERFORMANCE PLASTICS CORBY LTD.—See Compagnie de Saint-Gobain SA; *Int'l*, pg. 1735
SAINT-GOBAIN PERFORMANCE PLASTICS CORPORATION—See Compagnie de Saint-Gobain SA; *Int'l*, pg. 1731
SAINT GOBAIN PERFORMANCE PLASTICS CORPORATION—See Compagnie de Saint-Gobain SA; *Int'l*, pg. 1731
SAINT-GOBAIN PERFORMANCE PLASTICS CORP.—See Compagnie de Saint-Gobain SA; *Int'l*, pg. 1730
SAINT-GOBAIN PERFORMANCE PLASTICS CORP.—See Compagnie de Saint-Gobain SA; *Int'l*, pg. 1731
SAINT-GOBAIN PERFORMANCE PLASTICS ESPANA S.A.—See Compagnie de Saint-Gobain SA; *Int'l*, pg. 1735
SAINT-GOBAIN PERFORMANCE PLASTICS EUROPE, S.A.—See Compagnie de Saint-Gobain SA; *Int'l*, pg. 1735
SAINT-GOBAIN PERFORMANCE PLASTICS IRELAND LTD—See Compagnie de Saint-Gobain SA; *Int'l*, pg. 1732
SAINT-GOBAIN PERFORMANCE PLASTICS ISOFLUOR GMBH—See Compagnie de Saint-Gobain SA; *Int'l*, pg. 1728
SAINT-GOBAIN PERFORMANCE PLASTICS KONTICH NV—See Compagnie de Saint-Gobain SA; *Int'l*, pg. 1735
SAINT-GOBAIN PERFORMANCE PLASTICS MG SILIKON GMBH—See Trelleborg AB; *Int'l*, pg. 7914
SAINT-GOBAIN PERFORMANCE PLASTICS PAMPUS GMBH—See Compagnie de Saint-Gobain SA; *Int'l*, pg. 1732
SAINT-GOBAIN PERFORMANCE PLASTICS RENCOL LIMITED—See Compagnie de Saint-Gobain SA; *Int'l*, pg. 1735
SAINT-GOBAIN PERFORMANCE PLASTICS SHANGHAI—See Compagnie de Saint-Gobain SA; *Int'l*, pg. 1732
SAINT-GOBAIN PERFORMANCE PLASTICS SIPRO GMBH—See Compagnie de Saint-Gobain SA; *Int'l*, pg. 1735
SAINT-GOBAIN PERFORMANCE PLASTICS VERNERET—See Compagnie de Saint-Gobain SA; *Int'l*, pg. 1735
SAINT GOBAIN PERU SA—See Compagnie de Saint-Gobain SA; *Int'l*, pg. 1727
SAINT-GOBAIN PIPELINE HONG KONG LTD.—See Compagnie de Saint-Gobain SA; *Int'l*, pg. 1735
SAINT-GOBAIN PIPELINES CO. LTD.—See Compagnie de Saint-Gobain SA; *Int'l*, pg. 1735
SAINT-GOBAIN PIPELINES SOUTH AFRICA (PTY) LIMITED—See Compagnie de Saint-Gobain SA; *Int'l*, pg. 1735
SAINT-GOBAIN PIPE SYSTEMS BELGIUM SA/NV—See Compagnie de Saint-Gobain SA; *Int'l*, pg. 1735

SAINT-GOBAIN PIPE SYSTEMS BV—See Compagnie de Saint-Gobain SA; *Int'l*, pg. 1728
SAINT-GOBAIN PIPE SYSTEMS OY—See Compagnie de Saint-Gobain SA; *Int'l*, pg. 1735
SAINT-GOBAIN PLACO SAS—See Compagnie de Saint-Gobain SA; *Int'l*, pg. 1728
SAINT-GOBAIN POLSKA SP. Z O.O.—See Compagnie de Saint-Gobain SA; *Int'l*, pg. 1728
SAINT-GOBAIN PPC ITALIA SPA—See Compagnie de Saint-Gobain SA; *Int'l*, pg. 1735
SAINT-GOBAIN PPL KOREA CO LTD.—See Compagnie de Saint-Gobain SA; *Int'l*, pg. 1735
SAINT-GOBAIN PRODUITS INDUSTRIELS—See Compagnie de Saint-Gobain SA; *Int'l*, pg. 1735
SAINT-GOBAIN PRODUITS POUR LA CONSTRUCTION SAS—See Compagnie de Saint-Gobain SA; *Int'l*, pg. 1728
SAINT-GOBAIN PROPPANTS (GUANGHAN) CO., LTD.—See Compagnie de Saint-Gobain SA; *Int'l*, pg. 1735
SAINT-GOBAIN QUARTZ (JINZHOU) COMPANY LTD.—See Compagnie de Saint-Gobain SA; *Int'l*, pg. 1735
SAINT-GOBAIN QUARTZ S.A.S.—See Compagnie de Saint-Gobain SA; *Int'l*, pg. 1735
SAINT-GOBAIN RAKENNUSTUOTTEET OY—See Compagnie de Saint-Gobain SA; *Int'l*, pg. 1726
SAINT-GOBAIN RIGIPS ALCI SANAYI VE TICARET ANONIM A.S.—See Compagnie de Saint-Gobain SA; *Int'l*, pg. 1735
SAINT-GOBAIN RIGIPS GMBH—See Compagnie de Saint-Gobain SA; *Int'l*, pg. 1726
SAINT-GOBAIN SA—See Compagnie de Saint-Gobain SA; *Int'l*, pg. 1729
SAINT-GOBAIN SCHLEIFMITTEL GMBH—See Compagnie de Saint-Gobain SA; *Int'l*, pg. 1735
SAINT-GOBAIN SEKURIT BENELUX S.A.—See Compagnie de Saint-Gobain SA; *Int'l*, pg. 1736
SAINT-GOBAIN SEKURIT CR SPOL S.R.O.—See Compagnie de Saint-Gobain SA; *Int'l*, pg. 1736
SAINT-GOBAIN SEKURIT DE COLOMBIA S.A.—See Compagnie de Saint-Gobain SA; *Int'l*, pg. 1736
SAINT-GOBAIN SEKURIT DEUTSCHLAND BETEILIGUNGEN GMBH—See Compagnie de Saint-Gobain SA; *Int'l*, pg. 1736
SAINT-GOBAIN SEKURIT FRANCE—See Compagnie de Saint-Gobain SA; *Int'l*, pg. 1736
SAINT-GOBAIN SEKURIT INDIA LIMITED—See Compagnie de Saint-Gobain SA; *Int'l*, pg. 1736
SAINT-GOBAIN SEKURIT MAROC—See Compagnie de Saint-Gobain SA; *Int'l*, pg. 1736
SAINT-GOBAIN SEKURIT MEXICO, S.A. DE C.V.—See Compagnie de Saint-Gobain SA; *Int'l*, pg. 1736
SAINT-GOBAIN SEKURIT PORTUGAL VIDRO AUTOMOVEL SA—See Compagnie de Saint-Gobain SA; *Int'l*, pg. 1736
SAINT-GOBAIN SEKURIT (SHANGHAI) CO., LTD.—See Compagnie de Saint-Gobain SA; *Int'l*, pg. 1736
SAINT-GOBAIN SEKURIT THAILAND CO., LTD.—See Compagnie de Saint-Gobain SA; *Int'l*, pg. 1736
SAINT-GOBAIN SEKURIT USA—See Compagnie de Saint-Gobain SA; *Int'l*, pg. 1732
SAINT-GOBAIN SERVICES AUSTRIA GMBH—See Compagnie de Saint-Gobain SA; *Int'l*, pg. 1728
SAINT-GOBAIN SERVICES RH FRANCE—See Compagnie de Saint-Gobain SA; *Int'l*, pg. 1728
SAINT-GOBAIN SEVA—See Compagnie de Saint-Gobain SA; *Int'l*, pg. 1735
SAINT-GOBAIN SOLAR GARD AUSTRALIA PTY LTD.—See Compagnie de Saint-Gobain SA; *Int'l*, pg. 1728
SAINT-GOBAIN SOLAR GARD CANADA, INC—See Compagnie de Saint-Gobain SA; *Int'l*, pg. 1730
SAINT-GOBAIN SOLAR GARD, LLC—See Compagnie de Saint-Gobain SA; *Int'l*, pg. 1730
SAINT-GOBAIN SOLAR GARD NV—See Compagnie de Saint-Gobain SA; *Int'l*, pg. 1728
SAINT-GOBAIN SOLAR GARD UK, LTD—See Compagnie de Saint-Gobain SA; *Int'l*, pg. 1728
SAINT-GOBAIN SOLAR S.R.L.—See Compagnie de Saint-Gobain SA; *Int'l*, pg. 1735
SAINT-GOBAIN SOLAR SYSTEMS S.A.—See Compagnie de Saint-Gobain SA; *Int'l*, pg. 1728
SAINT-GOBAIN SOLAR SYSTEMS SA—See Compagnie de Saint-Gobain SA; *Int'l*, pg. 1735
SAINT-GOBAIN—See Compagnie de Saint-Gobain SA; *Int'l*, pg. 1730
SAINT-GOBAIN—See Compagnie de Saint-Gobain SA; *Int'l*, pg. 1730
SAINT-GOBAIN SOUTH AFRICA PTY. LTD.—See Compagnie de Saint-Gobain SA; *Int'l*, pg. 1735
SAINT-GOBAIN SOVIS SAS—See Compagnie de Saint-Gobain SA; *Int'l*, pg. 1733
SAINT-GOBAIN STATYBOS GAMINIAI UAB—See Compagnie de Saint-Gobain SA; *Int'l*, pg. 1727
SAINT-GOBAIN STRADAL—See Compagnie de Saint-Gobain SA; *Int'l*, pg. 1736
SAINT-GOBAIN SULLY S.A.S.—See Compagnie de Saint-Gobain SA; *Int'l*, pg. 1733

SAINT-GOBAIN TM K.K.—See Compagnie de Saint-Gobain SA; *Int'l*, pg. 1736
SAINT-GOBAIN TRANSFORMADOS S.A.—See Compagnie de Saint-Gobain SA; *Int'l*, pg. 1736
SAINT-GOBAIN VETRERIE SPA—See Compagnie de Saint-Gobain SA; *Int'l*, pg. 1736
SAINT-GOBAIN VETROTEX DEUTSCHLAND GMBH—See Compagnie de Saint-Gobain SA; *Int'l*, pg. 1736
SAINT-GOBAIN VETROTEX (THAILAND) LTD.—See Compagnie de Saint-Gobain SA; *Int'l*, pg. 1736
SAINT-GOBAIN VICASA SA—See Compagnie de Saint-Gobain SA; *Int'l*, pg. 1736
SAINT-GOBAIN VIDROS S.A.—See Compagnie de Saint-Gobain SA; *Int'l*, pg. 1736
SAINT-GOBAIN VITRAGE—See Compagnie de Saint-Gobain SA; *Int'l*, pg. 1736
SAINT-GOBAIN WANNER SA—See Compagnie de Saint-Gobain SA; *Int'l*, pg. 1736
SAINT-GOBAIN WEBER AG—See Compagnie de Saint-Gobain SA; *Int'l*, pg. 1727
SAINT-GOBAIN WEBER A/S—See Compagnie de Saint-Gobain SA; *Int'l*, pg. 1727
SAINT-GOBAIN WEBER BEAMIX B.V.—See Compagnie de Saint-Gobain SA; *Int'l*, pg. 1727
SAINT-GOBAIN WEBER BELGIUM NV/SA—See Compagnie de Saint-Gobain SA; *Int'l*, pg. 1727
SAINT-GOBAIN WEBER CEMARKSA SA—See Compagnie de Saint-Gobain SA; *Int'l*, pg. 1727
SAINT-GOBAIN WEBER CO., LTD.—See Compagnie de Saint-Gobain SA; *Int'l*, pg. 1727
SAINT-GOBAIN WEBER FRANCE—See Compagnie de Saint-Gobain SA; *Int'l*, pg. 1727
SAINT-GOBAIN WEBER GMBH—See Compagnie de Saint-Gobain SA; *Int'l*, pg. 1727
SAINT-GOBAIN WEBER (INDIA) LTD—See Compagnie de Saint-Gobain SA; *Int'l*, pg. 1728
SAINT-GOBAIN WEBER LIMITED—See Compagnie de Saint-Gobain SA; *Int'l*, pg. 1727
SAINT-GOBAIN WEBER LUJIAN BUILDING MATERIALS (SHANGHAI) CO., LTD.—See Compagnie de Saint-Gobain SA; *Int'l*, pg. 1727
SAINT-GOBAIN WEBER NETSERVICES—See Compagnie de Saint-Gobain SA; *Int'l*, pg. 1727
SAINT-GOBAIN WEBER OY AB—See Compagnie de Saint-Gobain SA; *Int'l*, pg. 1727
SAINT-GOBAIN WEBER PORTUGAL SA—See Compagnie de Saint-Gobain SA; *Int'l*, pg. 1727
SAINT-GOBAIN WEBER—See Compagnie de Saint-Gobain SA; *Int'l*, pg. 1727
SAINT-GOBAIN WEBER SOUTH AFRICA (PTY) LTD. - ALRODE FACTORY—See Compagnie de Saint-Gobain SA; *Int'l*, pg. 1727
SAINT-GOBAIN WEBER SOUTH AFRICA (PTY) LTD. - CAPE TOWN FACTORY—See Compagnie de Saint-Gobain SA; *Int'l*, pg. 1727
SAINT-GOBAIN WEBER SOUTH AFRICA (PTY) LTD. - KWAZULU NATAL FACTORY—See Compagnie de Saint-Gobain SA; *Int'l*, pg. 1727
SAINT-GOBAIN WEBER SOUTH AFRICA (PTY) LTD. - PORT ELIZABETH FACTORY—See Compagnie de Saint-Gobain SA; *Int'l*, pg. 1727
SAINT-GOBAIN WEBER SOUTH AFRICA (PTY) LTD.—See Compagnie de Saint-Gobain SA; *Int'l*, pg. 1727
SAINT-GOBAIN WEBER STAHEL-KELLER AG—See Compagnie de Saint-Gobain SA; *Int'l*, pg. 1727
SAINT-GOBAIN WEBER TERRANOVA, SPOL. S.R.O.—See Compagnie de Saint-Gobain SA; *Int'l*, pg. 1726
SAINT-GOBAIN WEBER YAPI KIMYASALLARI SAN. VE TIC. A.S—See Compagnie de Saint-Gobain SA; *Int'l*, pg. 1727
SAINT-GOBAIN WINTER INC—See Compagnie de Saint-Gobain SA; *Int'l*, pg. 1732
SAINT HONORE CAKE SHOP LIMITED—See Convenience Retail Asia Limited; *Int'l*, pg. 1787
SAINT HONORE HOLDINGS CO. LTD—See Convenience Retail Asia Limited; *Int'l*, pg. 1787
SAINT JAMES HOLDING & INVESTMENT COMPANY TRUST; *U.S. Private*, pg. 3529
SAINT JAMES HOTEL—See Red Wing Shoe Company, Inc.; *U.S. Private*, pg. 3376
SAINT JEAN GROUPE SA; *Int'l*, pg. 6484
SAINT JEAN INDUSTRIES GMBH—See Saint Jean Industries SAS; *Int'l*, pg. 6484
SAINT JEAN INDUSTRIES SAS SAINT JEAN AERO PLANT—See Saint Jean Industries SAS; *Int'l*, pg. 6484
SAINT JEAN INDUSTRIES SAS SAINT JEAN INDUSTRIES LAVAL PLANT—See Saint Jean Industries SAS; *Int'l*, pg. 6484
SAINT JEAN INDUSTRIES SAS SAINT JEAN INDUSTRIES LORRAINE PLANT—See Saint Jean Industries SAS; *Int'l*, pg. 6484
SAINT JEAN INDUSTRIES SAS SAINT JEAN INDUSTRIES POITOU PLANT—See Saint Jean Industries SAS; *Int'l*, pg. 6484
SAINT JEAN INDUSTRIES SAS SAINT JEAN TOOLING PLANT—See Saint Jean Industries SAS; *Int'l*, pg. 6484

SAINT JEAN INDUSTRIES SAS SAINT JEAN WHEELS PLANT—See Saint Jean Industries SAS; *Int'l*, pg. 6484
SAINT JEAN INDUSTRIES SAS; *Int'l*, pg. 6484
SAINT JOHN ICE COMPANY; *U.S. Private*, pg. 3529
SAINT JOHN LNG DEVELOPMENT COMPANY LTD.—See Repsol, S.A.; *Int'l*, pg. 6294
SAINT JOHN PORT AUTHORITY; *Int'l*, pg. 6484
SAINT JOHN'S COMMUNITIES, INC.; *U.S. Private*, pg. 3529
SAINT JOSEPH HOSPITAL; *U.S. Private*, pg. 3529
SAINT JOSEPH MERCY HEALTH SYSTEM—See Trinity Health Corporation; *U.S. Private*, pg. 4234
SAINT LAURENT ARABIA TRADING LLC—See Kering S.A.; *Int'l*, pg. 4136
SAINT LAURENT DENMARK APS—See Kering S.A.; *Int'l*, pg. 4136
SAINT LAURENT DOMINICAN REPUBLIC S.A.S.—See Kering S.A.; *Int'l*, pg. 4136
SAINT LAURENT GREECE A.E.—See Kering S.A.; *Int'l*, pg. 4136
SAINT LAURENT NEW ZEALAND LTD.—See Kering S.A.; *Int'l*, pg. 4136
SAINT LAURENT NORWAY AS—See Kering S.A.; *Int'l*, pg. 4136
SAINT LAURENT POLAND SP. Z O.O—See Kering S.A.; *Int'l*, pg. 4136
SAINT LAURENT PORTUGAL S.L.—See Kering S.A.; *Int'l*, pg. 4136
SAINT LAURENT SWEDEN AB—See Kering S.A.; *Int'l*, pg. 4136
THE SAINT LOUIS BREWERY, LLC.; *U.S. Private*, pg. 4113
SAINT LOUIS CARDINALS, L.P.; *U.S. Private*, pg. 3529
SAINT LOUISE REGIONAL HOSPITAL—See Daughters of Charity Health System; *U.S. Private*, pg. 1167
SAINT LOUIS REGIONAL HEALTH COMMISSION; *U.S. Private*, pg. 3530
SAINT LOUIS SUCRE S.A.—See Suddeutsche Zuckerruben-Verwertungs-Genossenschaft eG; *Int'l*, pg. 7252
SAINT LUKE'S HEALTH SYSTEM, INC.—See BJC Health System; *U.S. Private*, pg. 568
SAINT MAIXENT ENROBES SAS—See VINCI S.A.; *Int'l*, pg. 8226
SAINT MARC HOLDINGS CO., LTD.; *Int'l*, pg. 6484
SAINT-MARTIN ELECTRO CLIM—See Sonepar S.A.; *Int'l*, pg. 7091
SAINT MARY'S PREFERRED HEALTH INSURANCE COMPANY, INC.—See Catholic Health Initiatives; *U.S. Private*, pg. 790
SAINT-MAUR STATIONNEMENT SAS—See Indigo Group S.A.S.; *Int'l*, pg. 3655
SAINT MEDIA, INC.—See Will Group, Inc.; *Int'l*, pg. 8412
SAINT MERRI CHANTILLY; *Int'l*, pg. 6484
SAINT PETERSBURG CITY BANK JSC; *Int'l*, pg. 6484
SAINTS CAPITAL, LLC; *U.S. Private*, pg. 3530
SAINT THOMAS CAMPUS SURGICARE, L.P.—See Tenet Healthcare Corporation; *U.S. Public*, pg. 2012
SAINT THOMAS HEALTH SERVICES—See Ascension Health Alliance; *U.S. Private*, pg. 347
SAINT THOMAS HIGHLANDS HOSPITAL, LLC—See Ascension Health Alliance; *U.S. Private*, pg. 347
SAINT THOMAS MIDTOWN HOSPITAL—See Ascension Health Alliance; *U.S. Private*, pg. 347
SAINT THOMAS STONES RIVER HOSPITAL, LLC—See Ascension Health Alliance; *U.S. Private*, pg. 347
SAINT TROPEZ AF 1993 A/S—See DK Company A/S; *Int'l*, pg. 2138
SAINT VINCENT HOSPITAL, L.L.C.—See Tenet Healthcare Corporation; *U.S. Public*, pg. 2006
SAINT VINCENT PHYSICIAN SERVICES, INC.—See Tenet Healthcare Corporation; *U.S. Public*, pg. 2014
SAINT VINCENT'S; *U.S. Private*, pg. 3530
SAINTY (HK) COMPANY LIMITED—See Jiangsu Sainty Corp., Ltd.; *Int'l*, pg. 3953
SAIPA AZIN COMPANY; *Int'l*, pg. 6484
SAIPA COMPANY; *Int'l*, pg. 6484
SAIPA DIESEL COMPANY; *Int'l*, pg. 6484
SAIPA GLASS COMPANY; *Int'l*, pg. 6485
SAIPA INVESTMENT GROUP COMPANY; *Int'l*, pg. 6485
SAIPEM AMERICA, INC.—See Eni S.p.A.; *Int'l*, pg. 2438
SAIPEM (MALAYSIA) SDN. BHD.—See Eni S.p.A.; *Int'l*, pg. 2438
SAIPEM S.P.A.—See Eni S.p.A.; *Int'l*, pg. 2438
SAIPEM UK LTD.—See Eni S.p.A.; *Int'l*, pg. 2438
SAI PEOPLE SOLUTIONS, INC.; *U.S. Private*, pg. 3528
S.A.I. RAIFFEISEN ASSET MANAGEMENT S.A.—See Raiffeisen Bank International AG; *Int'l*, pg. 6184
SAI REGENCY POWER CORPORATION PRIVATE LIMITED—See KSK Power Ventur plc; *Int'l*, pg. 4314
SAIRE S.R.L—See Compagnia Finanziaria de Benedetti S.p.A.; *Int'l*, pg. 1722
SAI ROCKVILLE L, LLC—See Graham Holdings Company; *U.S. Public*, pg. 956
SAIRP COMPOSITES; *Int'l*, pg. 6485
SAIRYO SERVICE CO.,LTD.—See Mitsubishi Logistics Corporation; *Int'l*, pg. 4963
SAISAN CO., LTD.; *Int'l*, pg. 6485

COMPANY NAME INDEX

SAISHIN IGAKU CO., LTD.—See Shionogi & Co., Ltd.; *Int'l*, pg. 6851
SAI SILKS (KALAMANDIR) LTD; *Int'l*, pg. 6482
SAISON ASSET MANAGEMENT CO., LTD.—See Credit Saison Co., Ltd.; *Int'l*, pg. 1836
SAISON AUTOMOBILE AND FIRE INSURANCE COMPANY, LIMITED—See Sompo Holdings, Inc.; *Int'l*, pg. 7087
SAISON BUSINESS SUPPORT, INC.—See Credit Saison Co., Ltd.; *Int'l*, pg. 1836
SAI SON CEMENT JSC; *Int'l*, pg. 6482
SAISON FUNDEX CORPORATION—See Credit Saison Co., Ltd.; *Int'l*, pg. 1836
SAISON INFORMATION SYSTEMS CO., LTD.—See Credit Saison Co., Ltd.; *Int'l*, pg. 1836
SAISON PARTNERS CO., LTD.—See Credit Saison Co., Ltd.; *Int'l*, pg. 1836
SAISON PERSONALPLUS CO., LTD.—See Credit Saison Co., Ltd.; *Int'l*, pg. 1836
S.A. ISTA N.V.—See CK Asset Holdings Limited; *Int'l*, pg. 1635
SAI SYSTEMS INTERNATIONAL, INC.; *U.S. Private*, pg. 3528
SAITA CORP.; *Int'l*, pg. 6485
SAITAMA CHIIKI KAIHATSU KOHSHA CO., LTD.—See Kumagai Gumi Co., Ltd.; *Int'l*, pg. 4329
SAITAMA DAIICHI TRAFFIC CO., LTD.—See Daiichi Koutsu Sangyo Co., Ltd.; *Int'l*, pg. 1929
SAITAMA GAS CO., LTD.—See INPEX CORPORATION; *Int'l*, pg. 3717
SAITAMAKEN UOICHIBA K.K.—See TOHTO SUISAN Co., Ltd.; *Int'l*, pg. 7778
SAITAMA K-TECHNO CO., LTD—See Kandenko Co., Ltd.; *Int'l*, pg. 4065
SAITAMA MINAMI SENKO LOGI CO., LTD.—See Senko Group Holdings Co., Ltd.; *Int'l*, pg. 6710
SAITAMA MURATA MANUFACTURING CO., LTD.—See Murata Manufacturing Co., Ltd.; *Int'l*, pg. 5098
SAITAMA NITTO DENKO CORPORATION—See Nitto Denko Corporation; *Int'l*, pg. 5387
SAITAMA ORIGIN CO., LTD.—See Origin Co., Ltd.; *Int'l*, pg. 5629
SAITAMA ORIGIN CO., LTD. - YUKI PLANT—See Origin Co., Ltd.; *Int'l*, pg. 5629
SAITAMA RESONA BANK, LTD.—See Resona Holdings, Inc.; *Int'l*, pg. 6298
SAITAMA RIKUSO CO., LTD.—See Mercedes-Benz Group AG; *Int'l*, pg. 4829
SAITAMA SENKO LOGISERVICE CO., LTD.—See Senko Group Holdings Co., Ltd.; *Int'l*, pg. 6710
SAITAMA SENKO TRANSPORT CO., LTD.—See Senko Group Holdings Co., Ltd.; *Int'l*, pg. 6710
SAITAMA SHINKOH MOLD CO., LTD.—See Shin-Etsu Chemical Co. Ltd.; *Int'l*, pg. 6839
SAITAMA UNION SERVICE CO., LTD.—See Nippon Signal Co., Ltd.; *Int'l*, pg. 5333
SA ITAM DISTRIBUTION; *Int'l*, pg. 6459
SAIT BV—See Securitas AB; *Int'l*, pg. 6675
SAI.TECH GLOBAL CORPORATION; *Int'l*, pg. 6482
SAITO SHIKI CO., LTD.—See Rengo Co., Ltd.; *Int'l*, pg. 6281
SAI TYSONS CORNER H, LLC—See Graham Holdings Company; *U.S. Public*, pg. 956
SAIT ZENITEL SA—See Securitas AB; *Int'l*, pg. 6675
SAI US INC.—See SAI.TECH GLOBAL CORPORATION; *Int'l*, pg. 6482
SAIVICHAI DEVELOPMENT COMPANY LIMITED—See Srivichaivejvivat Public Company Limited; *Int'l*, pg. 7152
SAIWA S.R.L.—See Mondelez International, Inc.; *U.S. Public*, pg. 1463
SAIZERIYA AUSTRALIA PTY. LTD.—See Saizeriya Co., Ltd.; *Int'l*, pg. 6485
SAIZERIYA CO., LTD.; *Int'l*, pg. 6485
SAJA GMBH—See Lagercrantz Group AB; *Int'l*, pg. 4395
SAJAKORPI OY—See Lagercrantz Group AB; *Int'l*, pg. 4395
SA JAPAN KK—See Cisco Systems, Inc.; *U.S. Public*, pg. 500
SAJAR PLASTICS, LLC—See Wembly Enterprises LLC; *U.S. Private*, pg. 4480
SAJET SYSTEM TECHNOLOGY (SUZHOU) CO., LTD.—See Chroma ATE Inc.; *Int'l*, pg. 1588
SAJJAD TEXTILE MILLS LIMITED; *Int'l*, pg. 6485
SAJKASKA FABRIKA SECERA A.D.; *Int'l*, pg. 6485
SAJO DAERIM CO., LTD. - ANSAN PLANT—See Sajo Daerim Corp; *Int'l*, pg. 6485
SAJO DAERIM CO., LTD. - BUSAN PLANT—See Sajo Daerim Corp; *Int'l*, pg. 6485
SAJO DAERIM CORP; *Int'l*, pg. 6485
SAJODONGAONE CO., LTD.; *Int'l*, pg. 6485
SAJO HAEPYO - CHILSEO PLANT—See Sajo Haepyo; *Int'l*, pg. 6485
SAJO HAEPYO - INCHEON PLANT—See Sajo Haepyo; *Int'l*, pg. 6485
SAJO HAEPYO; *Int'l*, pg. 6485
SAJO HAEPYO - YEONGCHEON PLANT—See Sajo Haepyo; *Int'l*, pg. 6485

S.A. JOHNSON MATTHEY NV—See Johnson Matthey PLC; *Int'l*, pg. 3993
SAJO INDUSTRY CO., LTD. - CHEONAN PLANT—See Sajo Daerim Corp; *Int'l*, pg. 6485
SAJO INDUSTRY CO., LTD. - GOSEONG PLANT—See Sajo Daerim Corp; *Int'l*, pg. 6485
SAJO INDUSTRY CO., LTD.; *Int'l*, pg. 6485
SAJO INDUSTRY CO., LTD. - SUNCHANG PLANT—See Sajo Daerim Corp; *Int'l*, pg. 6485
SAJON; *Int'l*, pg. 6486
SAJO OYANG CORPORATION—See Sajo Daerim Corp; *Int'l*, pg. 6485
SAJO SEAFOOD CO., LTD. - IKSAN PLANT—See Sajo Seafood Co., Ltd.; *Int'l*, pg. 6485
SAJO SEAFOOD CO., LTD.; *Int'l*, pg. 6485
SAKAB AB—See E.ON SE; *Int'l*, pg. 2259
SAK ABRASIVES LTD—See SAK Industries Pvt Ltd; *Int'l*, pg. 6486
SAKAB SELLBERGS AB—See E.ON SE; *Int'l*, pg. 2255
SAKAE CORPORATION SDN. BHD.—See Gromutual Berhad; *Int'l*, pg. 3087
SAKAE ELECTRONICS CORPORATION; *Int'l*, pg. 6486
SAKAE HOLDINGS LTD.; *Int'l*, pg. 6486
SAKAE SHOKAI CO., LTD.—See Japan Creative Platform Group Co., Ltd.; *Int'l*, pg. 3887
SAKAE UNYU COMPANY LIMITED—See KKR & Co. Inc.; *U.S. Public*, pg. 1259
SAKAI AMATSUJI STEEL BALL MFG. CO., LTD.—See NSK Ltd.; *Int'l*, pg. 5478
SAKAI AMERICA, INC.—See Sakai Heavy Industries Ltd; *Int'l*, pg. 6487
SAKAI AUSTRALIA PTY LTD.—See Sakai Chemical Industry Co., Ltd.; *Int'l*, pg. 6486
SAKAI CHEMICAL INDUSTRY CO., LTD. - ONAHAMA DIVISION—See Sakai Chemical Industry Co., Ltd.; *Int'l*, pg. 6486
SAKAI CHEMICAL INDUSTRY CO., LTD. - OTSURUGI WORKS—See Sakai Chemical Industry Co., Ltd.; *Int'l*, pg. 6486
SAKAI CHEMICAL INDUSTRY CO., LTD. - SAKAI DIVISION—See Sakai Chemical Industry Co., Ltd.; *Int'l*, pg. 6486
SAKAI CHEMICAL INDUSTRY CO., LTD. - SEMBOKU WORKS—See Sakai Chemical Industry Co., Ltd.; *Int'l*, pg. 6486
SAKAI CHEMICAL INDUSTRY CO., LTD.; *Int'l*, pg. 6486
SAKAI CHEMICAL INDUSTRY CO., LTD. - YUMOTO WORKS—See Sakai Chemical Industry Co., Ltd.; *Int'l*, pg. 6486
SAKAI CHEMICAL (VIETNAM) CO., LTD.—See Sakai Chemical Industry Co., Ltd.; *Int'l*, pg. 6486
SAKAI DAIICHI TRAFFIC CO., LTD.—See Daiichi Koutsu Sangyo Co., Ltd.; *Int'l*, pg. 1929
SAKAIDE COSMO KOSAN CO., LTD.—See Cosmo Energy Holdings Co., Ltd.; *Int'l*, pg. 1812
SAKAIDE LNG CO., INC.—See Shikoku Electric Power Co., Incorporated; *Int'l*, pg. 6830
SAKAI ENGINEERING CO., LTD.—See Sakai Heavy Industries Ltd; *Int'l*, pg. 6487
SAKAI HEAVY INDUSTRIES LTD; *Int'l*, pg. 6486
SAKAI HEAVY INDUSTRIES (SHANGHAI) LTD.—See Sakai Heavy Industries Ltd; *Int'l*, pg. 6487
SAKAI HOLDINGS CO., LTD.; *Int'l*, pg. 6487
SAKAI KIKOH CORPORATION—See Sakai Heavy Industries Ltd; *Int'l*, pg. 6487
SAKAI LNG CORP.—See The Kansai Electric Power Co., Inc.; *Int'l*, pg. 7662
SAKAIMINATO GYOKAN CO., LTD.—See Rengo Co., Ltd.; *Int'l*, pg. 6281
SAKAIMINATO UOICHIBA CO., LTD.—See Maruha Nichiro Corporation; *Int'l*, pg. 4712
SAKAI MOVING SERVICE CO., LTD.; *Int'l*, pg. 6487
SAKAI NAGOYA CO., LTD.—See SAKAI OVEX Co., Ltd.; *Int'l*, pg. 6487
SAKAI OVEX CO., LTD. - FISHERY MATERIAL DIVISION—See SAKAI OVEX Co., Ltd.; *Int'l*, pg. 6487
SAKAI OVEX CO., LTD. - GOSEN FACTORY—See SAKAI OVEX Co., Ltd.; *Int'l*, pg. 6487
SAKAI OVEX CO., LTD. - HANANDOH FACTORY—See SAKAI OVEX Co., Ltd.; *Int'l*, pg. 6487
SAKAI OVEX CO., LTD.; *Int'l*, pg. 6487
SAKAI RECYCLE CENTER INC.—See Kyoei Steel Ltd.; *Int'l*, pg. 4362
SAKAI STEEL SHEETS WORKS, LTD.—See Kobe Steel, Ltd.; *Int'l*, pg. 4220
SAKAI TAIWAN CO., LTD.—See Sakai Chemical Industry Co., Ltd.; *Int'l*, pg. 6486
SAKAI TRADING CO., LTD.—See Sakai Chemical Industry Co., Ltd.; *Int'l*, pg. 6486
SAKAI TRADING EUROPE GMBH—See Sakai Chemical Industry Co., Ltd.; *Int'l*, pg. 6486
SAKAI TRADING KOREA CO., LTD.—See Sakai Chemical Industry Co., Ltd.; *Int'l*, pg. 6486
SAKAI TRADING NEW YORK INC.—See Sakai Chemical Industry Co., Ltd.; *Int'l*, pg. 6486
SAKAI TRADING (SHANGHAI) CO., LTD.—See Sakai Chemical Industry Co., Ltd.; *Int'l*, pg. 6486
SAKAI TRADING (THAILAND) CO., LTD.—See Sakai Chemical Industry Co., Ltd.; *Int'l*, pg. 6486

SAK INDUSTRIES PVT LTD

SAKAMOTO PRINTING CO., LTD.—See Asahi Printing Co., Ltd.; *Int'l*, pg. 598
SAKANA DEL PERU S.A—See Maruha Nichiro Corporation; *Int'l*, pg. 4712
SAKANA HOLISTIC HOUSING SOLUTIONS B.S.C.—See Dar Al-Maal Al-Islami Trust; *Int'l*, pg. 1971
S.A. KARDEX NV—See Kardex Holding AG; *Int'l*, pg. 4080
SAKAR HEALTHCARE LTD.; *Int'l*, pg. 6487
SAKAR INTERNATIONAL, INC.; *U.S. Private*, pg. 3530
SAKARI RESOURCES LIMITED—See PTT Public Company Limited; *Int'l*, pg. 6092
SAKATA HOLLAND B.V.—See Sakata Seed Corporation; *Int'l*, pg. 6488
SAKATA INX CORPORATION - HANYU PLANT—See Sakata INX Corporation; *Int'l*, pg. 6487
SAKATA INX CORPORATION - OSAKA PLANT—See Sakata INX Corporation; *Int'l*, pg. 6487
SAKATA INX CORPORATION - SHIGA PLANT—See Sakata INX Corporation; *Int'l*, pg. 6487
SAKATA INX CORPORATION; *Int'l*, pg. 6487
SAKATA INX CORPORATION - TOKYO PLANT—See Sakata INX Corporation; *Int'l*, pg. 6488
SAKATA INX ENG. CO., LTD.—See Sakata INX Corporation; *Int'l*, pg. 6487
SAKATA INX ESPANA S.A.—See Sakata INX Corporation; *Int'l*, pg. 6487
SAKATA INX (INDIA) PRIVATE LIMITED—See Sakata INX Corporation; *Int'l*, pg. 6488
SAKATA INX (MALAYSIA) SDN. BHD.—See Sakata INX Corporation; *Int'l*, pg. 6488
SAKATA INX MINAMI OSAKA CO. LTD.—See Sakata INX Corporation; *Int'l*, pg. 6488
SAKATA INX SHANGHAI CO. LTD.—See Sakata INX Corporation; *Int'l*, pg. 6488
SAKATA INX VIET NAM CO., LTD. - PLANT 2—See Sakata INX Corporation; *Int'l*, pg. 6488
SAKATA INX VIET NAM CO., LTD.—See Sakata INX Corporation; *Int'l*, pg. 6488
SAKATA INX (ZHONGSHAN) CORP.—See Sakata INX Corporation; *Int'l*, pg. 6487
SAKATA KOREA CO., LTD.—See Sakata Seed Corporation; *Int'l*, pg. 6488
SAKATA KYODO POWER CO., LTD.—See Tohoku Electric Power Co., Inc.; *Int'l*, pg. 7777
SAKATA NATURAL GAS CO., LTD.—See INPEX CORPORATION; *Int'l*, pg. 3717
SAKATA RICE SNACKS AUSTRALIA PTY LTD—See PepsiCo, Inc.; *U.S. Public*, pg. 1671
SAKATA SANGYO, LTD.—See Sakata INX Corporation; *Int'l*, pg. 6488
SAKATA SAS CO., LTD.—See extreme Co., Ltd.; *Int'l*, pg. 2592
SAKATA SEED AMERICA, INC.—See Sakata Seed Corporation; *Int'l*, pg. 6488
SAKATA SEED CORPORATION; *Int'l*, pg. 6488
SAKATA SEED DE GUATEMALA, S.A.—See Sakata Seed Corporation; *Int'l*, pg. 6488
SAKATA SEED DE MEXICO, S.A. DE C.V.—See Sakata Seed Corporation; *Int'l*, pg. 6488
SAKATA SEED IBERICA S.L.U.—See Sakata Seed Corporation; *Int'l*, pg. 6488
SAKATA SEED INDIA PVT. LTD.—See Sakata Seed Corporation; *Int'l*, pg. 6488
SAKATA SEED SOUTHERN AFRICA (PTY) LTD.—See Sakata Seed Corporation; *Int'l*, pg. 6488
SAKATA SEED SUDAMERICA LTDA.—See Sakata Seed Corporation; *Int'l*, pg. 6488
SAKATA SIAM SEED CO., LTD.—See Sakata Seed Corporation; *Int'l*, pg. 6488
SAKATA TARIM URUNLERI VE TOHUMCULUK SAN. VE TIC. LTD. STI.—See Sakata Seed Corporation; *Int'l*, pg. 6488
SAKAZUME SEIZAISHO CO., LTD.—See Japan Asia Group Limited; *Int'l*, pg. 3885
SAK CHAISIDHI COMPANY LIMITED—See Thai Oil Public Company Limited; *Int'l*, pg. 7594
SAKELA BETEILIGUNGSVERWALTUNGS GMBH—See PORR AG; *Int'l*, pg. 5925
SAKE NO HANA LTD.—See Sphere Entertainment Co.; *U.S. Public*, pg. 1918
SAKER AVIATION SERVICES, INC.; *U.S. Public*, pg. 1835
SAKHA DIAMOND CORP.; *Int'l*, pg. 6488
SAKHA ENTERPRISES CORP.; *Int'l*, pg. 6488
SAKHA GOLD MINING, CJSC—See OJSC Vysochaishy; *Int'l*, pg. 5884
SAKHALINENERGO PJSC—See PJSC RusHydro; *Int'l*, pg. 5884
SAKHALINNEFTEGASSERVIS LLC—See Fluor Corporation; *U.S. Public*, pg. 859
SAKHALIN OIL & GAS DEVELOPMENT CO., LTD.—See Japan Petroleum Exploration Co. Ltd.; *Int'l*, pg. 3900
SAKHALIN TECHNICAL TRAINING CENTRE—See Petrofac Limited; *Int'l*, pg. 5826
SAKI CORPORATION—See DMG MORI Co., Ltd.; *Int'l*, pg. 2145
SAK INDUSTRIES PVT LTD; *Int'l*, pg. 6486
S.A. KINGSPAN TAREC INDUSTRIAL INSULATION N.V.—See Recticel S.A.; *Int'l*, pg. 6242

SAKOL ENERGY PUBLIC COMPANY LIMITED

SAKOL ENERGY PUBLIC COMPANY LIMITED; *Int'l*, pg. 6488
SAKO LTD.—See Fabbrica d'Armi Pietro Beretta S.p.A.; *Int'l*, pg. 2598
SAKRAND SUGAR MILLS LTD; *Int'l*, pg. 6488
SAKRETE OF NORTH AMERICA, LLC—See CRH plc; *Int'l*, pg. 1845
S.A. KRONES N.V.—See Krones AG; *Int'l*, pg. 4306
SAKSA-BALTI KAUBANDUSKODA EESTIS—See Messe Munchen GmbH; *Int'l*, pg. 4842
SAKS FIFTH AVENUE, INC.—See Abrams Capital, LLC; *U.S. Private*, pg. 40
SAKS FIFTH AVENUE, INC.—See Rhone Group, LLC; *U.S. Private*, pg. 3423
SAKS FIFTH AVENUE, INC.—See WeWork Inc.; *U.S. Public*, pg. 2364
SAKSHI POWERTECH PRIVATE LIMITED—See Sylph Technologies Limited; *Int'l*, pg. 7378
SAKSIAM LEASING PUBLIC COMPANY LIMITED; *Int'l*, pg. 6488
SAKS INCORPORATED—See Abrams Capital, LLC; *U.S. Private*, pg. 40
SAKS INCORPORATED—See Rhone Group, LLC; *U.S. Private*, pg. 3423
SAKS INCORPORATED—See WeWork Inc.; *U.S. Public*, pg. 2364
SAKSOFT GMBH—See Saksoft Ltd; *Int'l*, pg. 6489
SAKSOFT, INC.—See Saksoft Ltd; *Int'l*, pg. 6489
SAKSOFT LTD; *Int'l*, pg. 6488
SAKSOFT PTE. LTD.—See Saksoft Ltd; *Int'l*, pg. 6489
THE SAK—See Indonesian Imports, Inc.; *U.S. Private*, pg. 2064
SAKTHI AUTO COMPONENT LIMITED—See AAPICO Hitech plc; *Int'l*, pg. 37
SAKTHI FINANCE LIMITED; *Int'l*, pg. 6489
SAKTHI PORTUGAL SA—See Sakthi Sugars Limited; *Int'l*, pg. 6489
SAKTHI SUGARS LIMITED - SAKTHI NAGAR UNIT—See Sakthi Sugars Limited; *Int'l*, pg. 6489
SAKTHI SUGARS LIMITED - SIVAGANGA UNIT—See Sakthi Sugars Limited; *Int'l*, pg. 6489
SAKTHI SUGARS LIMITED; *Int'l*, pg. 6489
SAKTHI SUGARS LIMITED - SOYA UNIT—See Sakthi Sugars Limited; *Int'l*, pg. 6489
(SAKU) DAIICHI TRAFFIC LTD.—See Daiichi Koutsu Sangyo Co., Ltd.; *Int'l*, pg. 1928
SAKUMA EXPORTS LIMITED; *Int'l*, pg. 6489
SAKU OLLETEHASE AS—See Carlsberg A/S; *Int'l*, pg. 1341
SAKURABA MOKUZAI CO., LTD.—See Yamaha Corporation; *Int'l*, pg. 8549
SAKURA BATH & KITCHEN PRODUCTS (CHINA) CO., LTD.—See Noritz Corporation; *Int'l*, pg. 5430
SAKURA BUSSAN CO., LTD.—See GSI Creos Corporation; *Int'l*, pg. 3145
SAKURA CARD CO., LTD.—See Sumitomo Mitsui Financial Group, Inc.; *Int'l*, pg. 7294
SAKURA DEVELOPMENT CO., LTD.; *Int'l*, pg. 6489
SAKURA FERROALLOYS SDN. BHD.—See Sumitomo Corporation; *Int'l*, pg. 7271
SAKURA FINETEK EUROPE B.V.—See Sakura Finetek Japan Co., Ltd.; *Int'l*, pg. 6489
SAKURA FINETEK JAPAN CO., LTD.; *Int'l*, pg. 6489
SAKURA FINETEK USA, INC.—See Sakura Finetek Japan Co., Ltd.; *Int'l*, pg. 6489
SAKURAGAWA SOLAR LTD.—See Wah Lee Industrial Corp.; *Int'l*, pg. 8329
SAKURAI KOSAN CO., LTD.—See Daido Steel Co., Ltd.; *Int'l*, pg. 1923
SAKURAI LTD. - HOSOE PLANT—See SAKURAI LTD.; *Int'l*, pg. 6489
SAKURAI LTD.; *Int'l*, pg. 6489
SAKURA INFORMATION SYSTEMS CO., LTD.—See Osaka Gas Co., Ltd.; *Int'l*, pg. 5645
SAKURA INFORMATION SYSTEMS CO., LTD.—See Sumitomo Mitsui Financial Group, Inc.; *Int'l*, pg. 7294
SAKURA INTERNATIONAL KK—See Compagnie Maritime Belge S.A.; *Int'l*, pg. 1746
SAKURA INTERNET INC.; *Int'l*, pg. 6489
SAKURA U.S.A., CO.—See SAKURAI LTD.; *Int'l*, pg. 6489
SAKURAI VIETNAM CO., LTD.—See SAKURAI LTD.; *Int'l*, pg. 6489
SAKURAJIMA FUTO KAISHA LTD.; *Int'l*, pg. 6489
SAKURA KCS CORPORATION—See Sumitomo Mitsui Financial Group, Inc.; *Int'l*, pg. 7294
SAKURA RUBBER COMPANY LIMITED - KANAGAWA PLANT—See SAKURA Rubber Company Limited; *Int'l*, pg. 6489
SAKURA RUBBER COMPANY LIMITED - OHTAWARA PLANT—See SAKURA Rubber Company Limited; *Int'l*, pg. 6489
SAKURA RUBBER COMPANY LIMITED; *Int'l*, pg. 6489
SAKURASAKU PLUS CO., LTD.; *Int'l*, pg. 6489
SAKURA SEIKI CO., LTD.—See Uchida Yoko Co., Ltd.; *Int'l*, pg. 8012
SAKURA SHOKAI CO., LTD.—See Japan Airport Terminal Co., Ltd.; *Int'l*, pg. 3885
SAKURA SHUNDE CO., LTD.—See Taiwan Sakura Corporation; *Int'l*, pg. 7423

SAKURA SOGO REIT INVESTMENT CORPORATION—See Star Asia Investment Corporation; *Int'l*, pg. 7172
SAKUSAKU CO., LTD.—See Cominix Co., Ltd.; *Int'l*, pg. 1714
SALA AZABU CO., LTD.—See Hulic Co., Ltd.; *Int'l*, pg. 3528
SALA BUSINESS SOLUTIONS INC.—See Sala Corporation; *Int'l*, pg. 6490
SALA CARS JAPAN CO., LTD.—See Sala Corporation; *Int'l*, pg. 6490
SALA CORPORATION; *Int'l*, pg. 6489
SALADA FOODS JAMAICA LIMITED; *Int'l*, pg. 6490
SALADINO'S INC.; *U.S. Private*, pg. 3530
SALADMASTER—See Regal Ware, Inc.; *U.S. Private*, pg. 3386
SALADO CREEK SENIOR CARE, INC.—See The Ensign Group, Inc.; *U.S. Public*, pg. 2072
SALADWORKS, LLC—See Centre Lane Partners, LLC; *U.S. Private*, pg. 827
SALA E ENERGY CO., LTD.—See Sala Corporation; *Int'l*, pg. 6490
SALA ENERGY CO., LTD.—See Sala Corporation; *Int'l*, pg. 6490
SALA E POWER CO., LTD.—See Sala Corporation; *Int'l*, pg. 6490
SALA FINANCIAL SERVICE CO., LTD.—See Sala Corporation; *Int'l*, pg. 6490
SALA FINANCIAL SERVICES CO., LTD.—See Sala Corporation; *Int'l*, pg. 6490
SALAFIN SA—See Bank of Africa; *Int'l*, pg. 840
SALA GAS IWATA CO., LTD.—See Sala Corporation; *Int'l*, pg. 6490
SALA HOTELS & RESTAURANTS CO., LTD.—See Sala Corporation; *Int'l*, pg. 6490
SALA HOUSE CO., LTD.—See Sala Corporation; *Int'l*, pg. 6490
SALA HOUSE SUPPORT CO. LTD.—See Sala Corporation; *Int'l*, pg. 6490
SALAISONS DE L'ADOUR; *Int'l*, pg. 6491
SALAISONS PYRENEENNES; *Int'l*, pg. 6491
SALALAH BEACH RESORT SAOG; *Int'l*, pg. 6491
SALALAH METHANOL COMPANY LLC—See QQ S.A.O.C.; *Int'l*, pg. 5607
SALALAH MILLS COMPANY SAOG; *Int'l*, pg. 6491
SALALAH PORT SERVICES CO. SAOG; *Int'l*, pg. 6491
SALAL CREDIT UNION; *U.S. Private*, pg. 3530
SALA LIFESTYLE INNOVATION CO., LTD.—See Sala Corporation; *Int'l*, pg. 6490
SALA LOGISTICS INC.—See Sala Corporation; *Int'l*, pg. 6490
SALAMA COOPERATIVE INSURANCE COMPANY; *Int'l*, pg. 6491
SALAMANDER INNISBROOK, LLC; *U.S. Private*, pg. 3530
SALAMANDER TECHNOLOGIES; *U.S. Private*, pg. 3530
S. ALAM COLD ROLLED STEELS LIMITED; *Int'l*, pg. 6446
SALAM ENTERPRISE COMPANY—See Salam International Investment Limited; *Int'l*, pg. 6491
SALAM ENTERPRISES L.L.C.—See Salam International Investment Limited; *Int'l*, pg. 6491
SALAM INTERNATIONAL INVESTMENT LIMITED; *Int'l*, pg. 6491
SALAM INTERNATIONAL TRANSPORT & TRADING CO. PLC; *Int'l*, pg. 6491
SALAMIS CRUISE LINES—See Salamis Tours Public Ltd; *Int'l*, pg. 6491
SALAMIS SHIPPING S.A.—See Salamis Tours Public Ltd; *Int'l*, pg. 6491
SALAMIS SHIPPING SERVICES LTD—See Salamis Tours Public Ltd; *Int'l*, pg. 6491
SALAMIS TOURS PUBLIC LTD; *Int'l*, pg. 6491
SALAM STUDIO & STORES L.L.C.—See Salam International Investment Limited; *Int'l*, pg. 6491
SALAM STUDIO & STORES O.P.C.—See Salam International Investment Limited; *Int'l*, pg. 6491
S.A. LA NACION; *Int'l*, pg. 6448
SALARISPROFS B.V.—See ManpowerGroup Inc.; *U.S. Public*, pg. 1362
SALARIUS PHARMACEUTICALS, INC.; *U.S. Public*, pg. 1836
SALARY.COM, LLC—See Accel Partners L.P.; *U.S. Private*, pg. 48
SALARY.COM, LLC—See KKR & Co. Inc.; *U.S. Public*, pg. 1238
SALARY PACKAGING SOLUTIONS PTY. LTD.—See Smartgroup Corporation Limited; *Int'l*, pg. 7002
SALASAR EXTERIORS & CONTOUR LIMITED; *Int'l*, pg. 6491
SALASAR TECHNO ENGINEERING LIMITED; *Int'l*, pg. 6491
SALAS O'BRIEN ENGINEERS, INC.; *U.S. Private*, pg. 3530
SALAS O'BRIEN SOUTH, LLC—See Salas O'Brien Engineers, Inc.; *U.S. Private*, pg. 3530
SALA.SPORTS CO., LTD.—See Sala Corporation; *Int'l*, pg. 6490

CORPORATE AFFILIATIONS

SAL AUTOMOTIVE LIMITED—See b4S Solutions Pvt Ltd.; *Int'l*, pg. 791
SALA WATER CO., LTD.—See Sala Corporation; *Int'l*, pg. 6490
SALAZAR RESOURCES LIMITED; *Int'l*, pg. 6491
SALCE CONTRACTING ASSOCIATES, INC.; *U.S. Private*, pg. 3531
SALCEF COSTRUZIONI EDILI E FERROVIARIE SPA; *Int'l*, pg. 6491
SAL CHEMICAL CO. INC.; *U.S. Private*, pg. 3530
SALCHI-RHENACOAT S.R.L.—See SKion GmbH; *Int'l*, pg. 6986
SALCO FOOTWEAR IND. LTD.; *Int'l*, pg. 6491
SALCO LEATHER; *U.S. Private*, pg. 3531
SAL COMMERCIAL VENTURE ONE, S.A. DE C.V.—See Lakeland Industries, Inc.; *U.S. Public*, pg. 1289
SALCOMP HONG KONG LTD—See Lingyi iTech (Guangdong) Company; *Int'l*, pg. 4512
SALCOMP INDUSTRIAL ELETRONICA DA AMAZONIA LTDA—See Lingyi iTech (Guangdong) Company; *Int'l*, pg. 4512
SALCOMP JAPAN—See Lingyi iTech (Guangdong) Company; *Int'l*, pg. 4512
SALCOMP LTDA—See Lingyi iTech (Guangdong) Company; *Int'l*, pg. 4512
SALCOMP MANUFACTURING INDIA PVT LTD—See Lingyi iTech (Guangdong) Company; *Int'l*, pg. 4512
SALCOMP PLC—See Lingyi iTech (Guangdong) Company; *Int'l*, pg. 4512
SALCOMP (SHENZHEN) CO., LTD—See Lingyi iTech (Guangdong) Company; *Int'l*, pg. 4512
SALCOMP TAIWAN CO., LTD—See Lingyi iTech (Guangdong) Company; *Int'l*, pg. 4512
SALCOMP USA, L.L.C.—See Lingyi iTech (Guangdong) Company; *Int'l*, pg. 4512
SALCON BERHAD; *Int'l*, pg. 6491
SALCON INVESTMENT CONSULTATION (SHANGHAI) COMPANY LIMITED—See Salcon Berhad; *Int'l*, pg. 6492
SALCON PETROLEUM SERVICES (ASIA PACIFIC) SDN. BHD.—See Salcon Berhad; *Int'l*, pg. 6492
SALCO PRODUCTS INC.—See Stone Canyon Industries, LLC; *U.S. Private*, pg. 3817
SALDAB IT AB—See Dustin Group AB; *Int'l*, pg. 2235
SALDADOS, S.L.—See Mutter Ventures, S.A.; *Int'l*, pg. 5106
SALDUS CELINIEKS, SIA—See VINCI S.A.; *Int'l*, pg. 8227
SALE AUTO MALL; *U.S. Private*, pg. 3531
SALEBUILD, INC.—See Ziff Davis, Inc.; *U.S. Public*, pg. 2403
SALECOM ELECTRONICS CO., LTD.—See Inalways Corp.; *Int'l*, pg. 3645
SALECYCLE LTD.; *Int'l*, pg. 6492
SALECYCLE LTD.—See SaleCycle Ltd; *Int'l*, pg. 6492
SALEE COLOUR PUBLIC COMPANY LIMITED; *Int'l*, pg. 6492
SALEE INDUSTRY PUBLIC COMPANY LIMITED; *Int'l*, pg. 6492
SALEEM DENIM INDUSTRIES LIMITED; *Int'l*, pg. 6492
SALEEN AUTOMOTIVE, INC.; *U.S. Private*, pg. 3531
SALEE PRINTING PUBLIC COMPANY LIMITED; *Int'l*, pg. 6492
SALEH ALHAMAD ALMANA CO.—See Nissan Motor Co., Ltd.; *Int'l*, pg. 5369
SALEHIYA TRADING COMPANY—See Venus Remedies Limited; *Int'l*, pg. 8153
SALE INSURANCE AGENCY, INC.—See Hellman & Friedman LLC; *U.S. Private*, pg. 1909
SALELIFTER SP. Z O.O.—See Digitree Group S.A.; *Int'l*, pg. 2124
SALEM AREA VISITING NURSE ASSOCIATION; *U.S. Private*, pg. 3531
SALEM CARE & REHABILITATION CENTER—See Formation Capital, LLC; *U.S. Private*, pg. 1571
SALEM COMMUNICATIONS HOLDING CORPORATION—See Salem Media Group, Inc.; *U.S. Public*, pg. 1836
SALEM COMMUNICATIONS TAMPA/SARASOTA—See Salem Media Group, Inc.; *U.S. Public*, pg. 1836
SALEM COMMUNITY HOSPITAL; *U.S. Private*, pg. 3531
SALEM DISTRIBUTING COMPANY INC.; *U.S. Private*, pg. 3531
SALEM ELECTRIC COMPANY—See Victory of West Virginia, Inc.; *U.S. Private*, pg. 4379
SALEM ERODE INVESTMENTS LIMITED—See ICL Fincorp Limited; *Int'l*, pg. 3581
SALEM FARM SUPPLY INC.; *U.S. Private*, pg. 3531
SALEM FIVE BANCORP; *U.S. Private*, pg. 3531
SALEM FIVE CENTS SAVINGS BANK—See Salem Five Bancorp; *U.S. Private*, pg. 3531
SALEM GRAIN COMPANY INC.; *U.S. Private*, pg. 3531
SALEM & GREEN CORP.—See Weintraub Tobin Chediak Coleman Grodin Law Corporation; *U.S. Private*, pg. 4472
SALEM GROUP INC.; *U.S. Private*, pg. 3531
THE SALEM GROUP; *U.S. Private*, pg. 4113
SALEM HOLDING COMPANY; *U.S. Private*, pg. 3531
SALEM HOME CARE, LLC—See UnitedHealth Group Incorporated; *U.S. Public*, pg. 2247

SALEM HOME CARE SERVICES, LLC—See Community Health Systems, Inc.; *U.S. Public*, pg. 556
SALEM HOSPITAL CORPORATION—See Community Health Systems, Inc.; *U.S. Public*, pg. 556
SALEM INVESTMENT CAPITAL LLC; *U.S. Private*, pg. 3531
SALEM LEASING CORP.—See Salem Holding Company; *U.S. Private*, pg. 3531
SALEM MEDIA GROUP, INC.; *U.S. Public*, pg. 1836
SALEM MEDIA OF COLORADO, INC.—See Salem Media Group, Inc.; *U.S. Public*, pg. 1836
SALEM MEDIA OF HAWAII, INC.—See Salem Media Group, Inc.; *U.S. Public*, pg. 1836
SALEM MEDIA OF MASSACHUSETTS, LLC—See Salem Media Group, Inc.; *U.S. Public*, pg. 1836
SALEM MEDIA OF OREGON—See Salem Media Group, Inc.; *U.S. Public*, pg. 1836
SALEM MEDIA OF PENNSYLVANIA—See Salem Media Group, Inc.; *U.S. Public*, pg. 1836
SALEM MEDIA OF TEXAS, INC.—See Salem Media Group, Inc.; *U.S. Public*, pg. 1836
SALEM MUSIC NETWORKS INC—See Salem Media Group, Inc.; *U.S. Public*, pg. 1836
SALEM NATIONALLEASE—See Salem Holding Company; *U.S. Private*, pg. 3531
THE SALEM OR OPHTHALMOLOGY ASC, LLC—See KKR & Co. Inc.; *U.S. Public*, pg. 1248
SALEM PRINTING; *U.S. Private*, pg. 3531
SALEM PUBLISHING, INC.—See Salem Media Group, Inc.; *U.S. Public*, pg. 1836
SALEM RADIO NETWORK INCORPORATED—See Salem Media Group, Inc.; *U.S. Public*, pg. 1836
SALEM RADIO REPRESENTATIVES—See Salem Media Group, Inc.; *U.S. Public*, pg. 1836
SALEM-SPITAL AG—See Remgro Limited; *Int'l*, pg. 6270
SALEM STONE CORPORATION; *U.S. Private*, pg. 3531
SALEM SURGERY CENTER, LIMITED PARTNERSHIP—See HCA Healthcare, Inc.; *U.S. Public*, pg. 1008
SALEM SURGERY CENTER, LLC—See UnitedHealth Group Incorporated; *U.S. Public*, pg. 2250
SALEM TOOLS, INC.; *U.S. Private*, pg. 3531
SALEM TRUCK LEASING INC.; *U.S. Private*, pg. 3531
SALEM TRUST CO.—See Tuesday Morning Corporation; *U.S. Public*, pg. 2204
SALEM TUBE INC.—See Tubacex S.A.; *Int'l*, pg. 7962
SALEM VENT INTERNATIONAL, INC.—See Marsh & McLennan Companies, Inc.; *U.S. Public*, pg. 1376
SALEM-V, LLC—See Lithia Motors, Inc.; *U.S. Public*, pg. 1326
SALEM WEB NETWORK, LLC—See Salem Media Group, Inc.; *U.S. Public*, pg. 1836
SALENDRE RESEAUX SAS—See VINCI S.A.; *Int'l*, pg. 8227
SALENS HOGFJALLSHOTELL AB—See SkiStar AB; *Int'l*, pg. 6990
SALEPOINT INC.; *U.S. Private*, pg. 3531
SALERNO 94 S.A.—See Grupo Catalana Occidente, S.A.; *Int'l*, pg. 3124
SALERNO CONTAINER TERMINAL S.P.A.—See EURO-KAI GmbH & Co. KGaA; *Int'l*, pg. 2553
SALERNO DAIRY PRODUCTS LIMITED—See Gay Lea Foods Co-operative Ltd.; *Int'l*, pg. 2891
SALERNO DUANE INC.; *U.S. Private*, pg. 3531
SALES BENCHMARK INDEX LLC; *U.S. Private*, pg. 3531
THE SALES BOARD, INC.—See RFE Investment Partners; *U.S. Private*, pg. 3419
SALES DEL ISTMO, S.A. DE C.V.—See Cydsa S.A.B. de C.V.; *Int'l*, pg. 1895
SALES DE MAGNESIO LTDA—See Albemarle Corporation; *U.S. Public*, pg. 73
SALES DESIGN VERTRIEBSGESELLSCHAFT MBH—See Villeroy & Boch AG; *Int'l*, pg. 8207
SALES DEVELOPMENT ASSOCIATES, INC.; *U.S. Private*, pg. 3532
SALES EMPOWERMENT GROUP LLC—See RFE Investment Partners; *U.S. Private*, pg. 3419
SALESFACTORY + WOODBINE, INC.; *U.S. Private*, pg. 3532
SALES FOCUS INC.; *U.S. Private*, pg. 3532
SALESFORCE ARGENTINA S.R.L.—See Salesforce, Inc.; *U.S. Public*, pg. 1837
SALESFORCE.COM CANADA CORPORATION—See Salesforce, Inc.; *U.S. Public*, pg. 1837
SALESFORCE.COM DANMARK, FILIAL AF SFDC SWEDEN AB—See Salesforce, Inc.; *U.S. Public*, pg. 1837
SALESFORCE.COM FRANCE S.A.S.—See Salesforce, Inc.; *U.S. Public*, pg. 1837
SALESFORCE.COM GERMANY GMBH—See Salesforce, Inc.; *U.S. Public*, pg. 1837
SALESFORCE.COM ITALY S.R.L.—See Salesforce, Inc.; *U.S. Public*, pg. 1837
SALESFORCE.COM KOREA LIMITED—See Salesforce, Inc.; *U.S. Public*, pg. 1837
SALESFORCE COMMERCE CLOUD—See Salesforce, Inc.; *U.S. Public*, pg. 1837
SALESFORCE.COM SARL—See Salesforce, Inc.; *U.S. Public*, pg. 1838
SALESFORCE.COM SINGAPORE PTE. LTD.—See Salesforce, Inc.; *U.S. Public*, pg. 1838
SALESFORCE, INC.; *U.S. Public*, pg. 1836
SALES FORCE NATIONAL PTY. LTD.; *Int'l*, pg. 6492
SALESFORCE.ORG EMEA LIMITED—See Salesforce, Inc.; *U.S. Public*, pg. 1838
SALESFORCE SYSTEMS SPAIN, S.L.—See Salesforce, Inc.; *U.S. Public*, pg. 1837
SALESFORCE TECHNOLOGIES MOROCCO—See Salesforce, Inc.; *U.S. Public*, pg. 1837
SALESFORCE UK LIMITED—See Salesforce, Inc.; *U.S. Public*, pg. 1837
SALES FORCE WON LTD.; *U.S. Private*, pg. 3532
SALESFUSION INC.—See Accel Partners L.P.; *U.S. Private*, pg. 49
SALESFUSION INC.—See KKR & Co. Inc.; *U.S. Public*, pg. 1238
SALESGENIE.COM, INC.—See CCMP Capital Advisors, LP; *U.S. Private*, pg. 800
SALES GROUP INC.; *U.S. Private*, pg. 3532
SALES HOLDING GMBH—See Stroer SE & Co. KGaA; *Int'l*, pg. 7242
SA LES HOTELS DE PARIS; *Int'l*, pg. 6459
SALESIFY INC.; *U.S. Private*, pg. 3532
SALES IMPACT GMBH—See Axel Springer SE; *Int'l*, pg. 766
SALES INTELLIGENCE SP. Z O.O.—See Digitree Group S.A.; *Int'l*, pg. 2124
SALESLOFT, INC.; *U.S. Private*, pg. 3532
SALESMASTER ASSOCIATES, INC.—See Floor & Decor Holdings, Inc.; *U.S. Public*, pg. 853
SALES MAX INC.; *U.S. Private*, pg. 3532
SALES OPTIMIZER LLC; *U.S. Private*, pg. 3532
SALES PARTNERSHIPS, INC.; *U.S. Private*, pg. 3532
SALES PERFORMANCE INTERNATIONAL, LLC; *U.S. Private*, pg. 3532
SALES READINESS INC.—See Sales Benchmark Index LLC; *U.S. Private*, pg. 3531
SALES SERVICES INTERNATIONAL; *Int'l*, pg. 6492
SALES SIMPLICITY SOFTWARE, INC.—See Berkshire Hathaway Inc.; *U.S. Public*, pg. 312
SALESSTAFF, LLC; *U.S. Private*, pg. 3532
SALES STRETCHER ENTERPRISES (SSE)—See W.H. Maze Company; *U.S. Private*, pg. 4420
SALES SUPPORT GROUP LIMITED—See Akzo Nobel N.V.; *Int'l*, pg. 275
SALES SYSTEMS LIMITED; *U.S. Private*, pg. 3532
SALFACORP S.A.; *Int'l*, pg. 6492
SALFORD GROUP, INC.—See GenNx360 Capital Partners, L.P.; *U.S. Private*, pg. 1672
SALGUTI INDUSTRIES LIMITED; *Int'l*, pg. 6492
SALHIA REAL ESTATE COMPANY K.S.C.; *Int'l*, pg. 6492
SALIBA CONSTRUCTION CO. INC.; *U.S. Private*, pg. 3532
SALIENCE INSIGHT LIMITED—See News Group International Holding; *Int'l*, pg. 5238
SALIENT BUSINESS SOLUTIONS, LTD.—See Walgreens Boots Alliance, Inc.; *U.S. Public*, pg. 2323
SALIENT FEDERAL SOLUTIONS, INC.—See Bridge Growth Partners, LLC; *U.S. Private*, pg. 648
SALIENT FEDERAL SOLUTIONS, INC.—See Frontenac Company LLC; *U.S. Private*, pg. 1614
SALIENT IT INC.—See Tonka Bay Equity Partners LLC; *U.S. Private*, pg. 4185
SALIENT MIDSTREAM & MLP FUND—See Salient Partners, L.P.; *U.S. Private*, pg. 3532
SALIENT MLP & ENERGY INFRASTRUCTURE FUND—See Salient Partners, L.P.; *U.S. Private*, pg. 3532
SALIENT PARTNERS, L.P.; *U.S. Private*, pg. 3532
SALIENT PRODUCTS CORPORATION; *U.S. Private*, pg. 3532
SALIENT SYSTEMS, INC.—See L.B. Foster Company; *U.S. Public*, pg. 1278
SALI FUND MANAGEMENT, LLC—See JTC PLC; *Int'l*, pg. 4016
SALINA DIAMANTE BRANCO LTDA—See K+S Aktiengesellschaft; *Int'l*, pg. 4041
SALINA IRON & METAL CO.—See Allmetal Recycling, LLC; *U.S. Private*, pg. 192
SALINA REGIONAL HEALTH CENTER; *U.S. Private*, pg. 3532
SALINAS NEWSPAPERS LLC—See Gannett Co., Inc.; *U.S. Public*, pg. 899
SALINAS VALLEY FORD; *U.S. Private*, pg. 3532
SALINCO V.O.F.—See Akzo Nobel N.V.; *Int'l*, pg. 275
SALINE COUNTY MEDICAL CENTER; *U.S. Private*, pg. 3532
SALINE LECTRONICS, INC.—See Crestview Partners, L.P.; *U.S. Private*, pg. 1098
SALINE METAL SYSTEMS—See Patriarch Partners, LLC; *U.S. Private*, pg. 3109
SALINES CEREBOS ET DE BAYONNE S.A.—See K+S Aktiengesellschaft; *Int'l*, pg. 4039
SALINI COSTRUTTORI S.P.A.; *Int'l*, pg. 6492
SALINI NIGERIA LTD.—See Salini Costruttori S.p.A.; *Int'l*, pg. 6492
SALINS RESIDUOS AUTOMOCION, S.L.—See ACS, Actividades de Construccion y Servicios, S.A.; *Int'l*, pg. 116
SALISBURY BANCORP, INC.—See NBT Bancorp Inc.; *U.S. Public*, pg. 1501
SALISBURY ELECTRICAL SAFETY L.L.C.—See Honeywell International Inc.; *U.S. Public*, pg. 1052
SALISBURY MOTOR CO. INC.; *U.S. Private*, pg. 3533
SALISBURY RESOURCES LIMITED; *Int'l*, pg. 6493
SALIX ANIMAL HEALTH, LLC—See Spectrum Brands Holdings, Inc.; *U.S. Public*, pg. 1915
SALIX BUSINESS PARTNER AB—See Volati AB; *Int'l*, pg. 8301
SALIX PHARMACEUTICALS, INC.—See Bausch Health Companies Inc.; *Int'l*, pg. 898
SALIX YATIRIM HOLDING AS; *Int'l*, pg. 6493
SAL, JOHNSON & ASSOCIATES, INC.—See Tyler Technologies, Inc.; *U.S. Public*, pg. 2209
SALK, INC.; *U.S. Private*, pg. 3533
SALLE WAGRAM—See Altarea SCA; *Int'l*, pg. 385
SALLIE MAE BANK—See SLM Corporation; *U.S. Public*, pg. 1894
SALLING BANK A/S; *Int'l*, pg. 6493
SALLING GROUP A/S—See Kobmand Herman Sallings Fond; *Int'l*, pg. 4222
SALLY AB—See AS Infortar; *Int'l*, pg. 590
SALLY BEAUTY HOLDINGS, INC.; *U.S. Public*, pg. 1838
SALLY BEAUTY MILITARY SUPPLY LLC—See Sally Beauty Holdings, Inc.; *U.S. Public*, pg. 1839
SALLY BEAUTY NETHERLANDS BV—See Sally Beauty Holdings, Inc.; *U.S. Public*, pg. 1838
SALLY CHILE HOLDING SPA—See Sally Beauty Holdings, Inc.; *U.S. Public*, pg. 1838
SALLY CORPORATION; *U.S. Private*, pg. 3533
SALLY FOURMY & ASSOCIATES—See Cintas Corporation; *U.S. Public*, pg. 496
SALLY HOLDINGS LLC—See Sally Beauty Holdings, Inc.; *U.S. Public*, pg. 1838
SALLY LOU FASHIONS CORPORATION; *U.S. Private*, pg. 3533
SALLYPORT COMMERCIAL FINANCE, LLC; *U.S. Private*, pg. 3533
SALLY SALON SERVICES LTD—See Sally Beauty Holdings, Inc.; *U.S. Public*, pg. 1839
SALLY TEXTILE MILLS LTD.; *Int'l*, pg. 6494
SALMAN NOMAN ENTERPRISES LIMITED; *Int'l*, pg. 6494
SALMANTINA DE SEGURIDAD VIAL, S.A.—See ACS, Actividades de Construccion y Servicios, S.A.; *Int'l*, pg. 116
SALMAR ASA; *Int'l*, pg. 6494
SALMAR JAPAN KK—See Salmar ASA; *Int'l*, pg. 6494
SALMOBREED SALTEN AS—See Benchmark Holdings Plc; *Int'l*, pg. 970
SALMOLUX, INC.—See Dulcich, Inc.; *U.S. Private*, pg. 1286
SALMONES ANTARTICA S.A—See Nissui Corporation; *Int'l*, pg. 5378
SALMONES CAMANCHACA S.A.—See Camanchaca S.A.; *Int'l*, pg. 1267
SALMON EVOLUTION ASA; *Int'l*, pg. 6494
SALMON EVOLUTION SALES AS—See Salmon Evolution ASA; *Int'l*, pg. 6494
SALMON RIVER MOTORS INC.; *U.S. Private*, pg. 3533
SALMON SURGERY CENTER, LLC—See Tenet Healthcare Corporation; *U.S. Public*, pg. 2006
SALMON VALLEY WATER COMPANY—See Northwest Natural Holding Company; *U.S. Public*, pg. 1542
SALMOSEA AS—See Salmar ASA; *Int'l*, pg. 6494
SALM PARTNERS, LLC—See Johnsonville, LLC; *U.S. Private*, pg. 2229
SALOIR DE VIRIEU SAS—See Coop-Gruppe Genossenschaft; *Int'l*, pg. 1790
SA LOISEAU DES VIGNES—See Bernard Loiseau SA; *Int'l*, pg. 986
SA LOISEAU RIVE GAUCHE—See Bernard Loiseau SA; *Int'l*, pg. 986
SALO, LLC—See Korn Ferry; *U.S. Public*, pg. 1275
SALOMON A. ANGEL LTD.; *Int'l*, pg. 6494
SALOMON & BONFIRE SNOWBOARDING, INC.—See ANTA Sports Products Limited; *Int'l*, pg. 481
SALOMON CANADA SPORTS LTD—See ANTA Sports Products Limited; *Int'l*, pg. 480
SALOMONE BROTHERS INC; *U.S. Private*, pg. 3533
SALOMON, LEVIN AND ELSTEIN LTD.—See Teva Pharmaceutical Industries, Ltd.; *Int'l*, pg. 7579
SALOMON S.A.—See ANTA Sports Products Limited; *Int'l*, pg. 480
SALONA COTSPIN LTD.; *Int'l*, pg. 6494
SALONCENTRIC, INC.—See L'Oreal S.A.; *Int'l*, pg. 4380
SALONCENTRIC, INC.—See L'Oreal S.A.; *Int'l*, pg. 4380
SALON DEVELOPMENT CORP.; *U.S. Private*, pg. 3533
SALON INNOVATIONS INC.; *U.S. Private*, pg. 3533
SALON MEDIA GROUP, INC.; *U.S. Public*, pg. 1839
SALON PROFESSIONAL SERVICES, INC.; *U.S. Private*, pg. 3533
SALONQUEST, LLC—See American Securities LLC; *U.S. Private*, pg. 248

SALON PROFESSIONAL SERVICES, INC. — CORPORATE AFFILIATIONS

SALON SERVICES FRANCHISING LTD—See Sally Beauty Holdings, Inc.; *U.S. Public*, pg. 1839
SALON SUCCESS LIMITED—See Sally Beauty Holdings, Inc.; *U.S. Public*, pg. 1839
SALOODO GMBH—See Deutsche Post AG; *Int'l*, pg. 2082
SAL OPPENHEIM FRANCE—See Deutsche Bank Aktiengesellschaft; *Int'l*, pg. 2062
SAL. OPPENHEIM JR. & CIE. AG & CO. KGAA—See Deutsche Bank Aktiengesellschaft; *Int'l*, pg. 2062
SAL. OPPENHEIM JR. & CIE. (SWITZERLAND) LTD.—See Deutsche Bank Aktiengesellschaft; *Int'l*, pg. 2062
SALORA COMPONENTS LIMITED; *Int'l*, pg. 6494
SALORA INTERNATIONAL LIMITED; *Int'l*, pg. 6494
SALORO S.L.U.—See EQ Resources Limited; *Int'l*, pg. 2466
SALO SOLUTIONS, INC.; *U.S. Private*, pg. 3533
SALSA LABS, INC.—See Insight Venture Management, LLC; *U.S. Private*, pg. 2090
SAL SAUDI LOGISTICS SERVICES COMPANY; *Int'l*, pg. 6489
SALSBURY INDUSTRIES; *U.S. Private*, pg. 3533
SALSBURY'S DODGE CITY, LLC.; *U.S. Private*, pg. 3533
SALSNES FILTER AS—See Danaher Corporation; *U.S. Public*, pg. 631
SALSNES NORTH AMERICA INC—See Aqua-Pure Ventures Inc.; *Int'l*, pg. 527
SAL-SON LOGISTICS, INC.—See Saybrook Corporate Opportunity Fund LP; *U.S. Private*, pg. 3558
S.A.L. STEEL LTD.; *Int'l*, pg. 6449
SALTA EXPLORACIONES S.A.—See Cascadero Copper Corporation; *Int'l*, pg. 1349
SALTANGEN PROPERTY INVEST AB; *Int'l*, pg. 6494
SALT ASSOCIATES LLC—See Reinsurance Group of America, Inc.; *U.S. Public*, pg. 1778
SALT BLOCKCHAIN INC.; *U.S. Private*, pg. 3533
SALT BRANDING, LLC—See Tailwind Capital Group, LLC; *U.S. Private*, pg. 3924
SALTBUSH CONSULTING PTY LTD—See DXC Technology Company; *U.S. Public*, pg. 697
SALTCHUK RESOURCES INC.; *U.S. Private*, pg. 3534
SALT CREEK CAPITAL MANAGEMENT, LLC; *U.S. Private*, pg. 3533
SALT CREEK, INC.—See Benchmark Holdings Plc; *Int'l*, pg. 970
SALTEND COGENERATION COMPANY LIMITED—See ENGIE SA; *Int'l*, pg. 2433
SALTEND—See ENGIE SA; *Int'l*, pg. 2434
SALTER BROTHERS EMERGING COMPANIES LIMITED; *Int'l*, pg. 6494
SALTER LABS—See RoundTable Healthcare Management, Inc.; *U.S. Private*, pg. 3489
SALTERMITCHELL, INC.; *U.S. Private*, pg. 3534
SALTGRASS INC.—See Fertitta Entertainment, Inc.; *U.S. Private*, pg. 1499
SALTIGO GMBH—See LANXESS AG; *Int'l*, pg. 4416
SALTIM HERMES SA; *Int'l*, pg. 6494
SALTIRE CAPITAL LTD.; *Int'l*, pg. 6494
SALTIRE TRADE PLASTICS LIMITED—See Epwin Group Plc; *Int'l*, pg. 2466
SALTIVERI OGILVY & MATHER—See WPP plc; *Int'l*, pg. 8488
SALTIVERI OGILVY & OGILVY ONE PROJECTS—See WPP plc; *Int'l*, pg. 8488
SALT LAKE BEES—See Angels Baseball, L.P.; *U.S. Private*, pg. 282
SALT LAKE BEHAVIORAL HEALTH, LLC—See Universal Health Services, Inc.; *U.S. Public*, pg. 2259
SALT LAKE CITY SOUTHERN RAILROAD COMPANY, INC.—See Brookfield Infrastructure Partners L.P.; *Int'l*, pg. 1192
SALT LAKE CITY SOUTHERN RAILROAD COMPANY, INC.—See GIC Pte. Ltd.; *Int'l*, pg. 2967
SALT LAKE LEGAL DEFENDER ASSOCIATION; *U.S. Private*, pg. 3533
SALT LAKE PHYSICAL THERAPY ASSOCIATES, INC.—See Select Rehabilitation, LLC; *U.S. Private*, pg. 3601
SALT LAKE POTASH LIMITED; *Int'l*, pg. 6494
SALT LAKE VALLEY BUICK GMC; *U.S. Private*, pg. 3533
SALTLUX INC.; *Int'l*, pg. 6495
SALTMARSH CLEAVELAND & GUND CPAS; *U.S. Private*, pg. 3534
SALT MOBILE SA; *Int'l*, pg. 6494
SALT OF THE EARTH LTD.—See Fortissimo Capital Management Ltd.; *Int'l*, pg. 2740
SALTON AUSTRALIA PTY LTD.—See Spectrum Brands Holdings, Inc.; *U.S. Public*, pg. 1916
SALTRAM MEADOW PLYMOUTH MANAGEMENT COMPANY LIMITED—See Persimmon plc; *Int'l*, pg. 5817
SALT RIVER AVIATION, LLC—See Weinberg Capital Group, Inc.; *U.S. Private*, pg. 4471
SALT RIVER ELECTRIC COOP CORP; *U.S. Private*, pg. 3533
SALT RIVER MATERIALS GROUP; *U.S. Private*, pg. 3533
SALT RIVER PROJECT; *U.S. Private*, pg. 3534
SALTS HEALTHCARE LTD.; *Int'l*, pg. 6495
SALT TRADING CORPORATION LIMITED; *Int'l*, pg. 6494

SALT UNION LIMITED—See Compass Minerals International, Inc.; *U.S. Public*, pg. 560
SALTUS INDUSTRIAL TECHNIQUE GMBH—See Atlas Copco AB; *Int'l*, pg. 684
SALTUS PARTNERS LLP; *Int'l*, pg. 6495
SALTVILLE GAS STORAGE COMPANY L.L.C.—See Enbridge Inc.; *Int'l*, pg. 2397
SALTWATER COLLECTIVE LLC—See Innovatus Capital Partners LLC; *U.S. Private*, pg. 2083
SALTWORKS, INC.; *U.S. Private*, pg. 3534
SALTX TECHNOLOGY HOLDING AB; *Int'l*, pg. 6495
SALUBRIS (SUZHOU) PHARMACEUTICALS CO., LTD.—See Shenzhen Salubris Pharmaceuticals Co., Ltd.; *Int'l*, pg. 6820
SALUD INTEGRAL EN LA MONTANA, INC.; *U.S. Private*, pg. 3534
SALUD PARA LA GENTE; *U.S. Private*, pg. 3534
SALUNGANO GROUP; *Int'l*, pg. 6495
SALUSANSVAR AB—See Folksam omsesidig sakforsakring; *Int'l*, pg. 2721
SALUS CAPITAL PARTNERS LLC—See Spectrum Brands Holdings, Inc.; *U.S. Public*, pg. 1915
SALUS CONTROLS GMBH—See Computime Group Limited; *Int'l*, pg. 1760
SALUS CONTROLS PLC—See Computime Group Limited; *Int'l*, pg. 1760
SALUS CONTROLS ROMANIA S.R.L.—See Computime Group Limited; *Int'l*, pg. 1760
SALUS LJUBLJANA D.D.; *Int'l*, pg. 6495
SALUS NORDIC A/S—See Computime Group Limited; *Int'l*, pg. 1760
SALUS NORTH AMERICA, INC.—See Computime Group Limited; *Int'l*, pg. 1761
SALUTAGUSE PARMITEHAS A.S.—See Lallemand, Inc.; *Int'l*, pg. 4400
SALUTAS PHARMA GMBH—See Novartis AG; *Int'l*, pg. 5459
SALUTICA ALLIED SOLUTIONS SDN. BHD.; *Int'l*, pg. 6495
SALVADORAN AMERICAN HUMANITARIAN FOUNDATION; *U.S. Private*, pg. 3535
SALVADOR DALI MUSEUM, INC.; *U.S. Private*, pg. 3535
SALVADORE AUTO EXCHANGE INC.; *U.S. Private*, pg. 3535
SALVADORE AUTO GROUP; *U.S. Private*, pg. 3535
SALVADORE TOOL & FINDINGS, INC.; *U.S. Private*, pg. 3535
SALVADORI SPINOTTI S.R.L.—See AMSTED Industries Incorporated; *U.S. Private*, pg. 268
SALVAGE HUNTER AUTO PARTS—See Four Lane Auto Sales; *U.S. Private*, pg. 1582
THE SALVAJOR COMPANY; *U.S. Private*, pg. 4113
SALVA O'RENICK; *U.S. Private*, pg. 3535
SALVAREM—See VINCI S.A.; *Int'l*, pg. 8233
SALVA RESOURCES PTY LTD—See HDR, Inc.; *U.S. Private*, pg. 1890
SALVA RESOURCES PVT LTD—See HDR, Inc.; *U.S. Private*, pg. 1890
SALVARX GROUP PLC; *Int'l*, pg. 6495
SALVAT DO BRASIL LTDA—See Vivendi SE; *Int'l*, pg. 8278
SALVAT EDITORES, S.A.—See Vivendi SE; *Int'l*, pg. 8274
THE SALVATION ARMY INTERNATIONAL TRUST; *Int'l*, pg. 7680
SALVATORE FERRAGAMO SPA; *Int'l*, pg. 6495
SALVATORPLATZ-GRUNDSTUCKSGESELLSCHAFT MBH & CO. OHG SAARLAND—See UniCredit S.p.A.; *Int'l*, pg. 8035
SALVATORPLATZ-GRUNDSTUCKSGESELLSCHAFT MBH—See UniCredit S.p.A.; *Int'l*, pg. 8035
SALVETRIBAL WORLDWIDE—See Omnicom Group Inc.; *U.S. Public*, pg. 1585
SALVE WOHNGRUPPEN GMBH—See ResMed Inc.; *U.S. Public*, pg. 1791
SALVIN DENTAL SPECIALTIES, INC.—See The Jordan Company, L.P.; *U.S. Private*, pg. 4063
SALVO CHEMICAL INDUSTRY LIMITED; *Int'l*, pg. 6495
SALVO TECHNOLOGIES, INC.; *U.S. Private*, pg. 3535
SALYER LAND COMPANY; *U.S. Private*, pg. 3535
SALZBURGER LANDES-HYPOTHEKENBANK AG—See Raiffeisenlandesbank Oberosterreich Aktiengesellschaft; *Int'l*, pg. 6187
SALZBURGER LANDES-VERSICHERUNG AG—See UNIQA Insurance Group AG; *Int'l*, pg. 8058
SALZBURGER RESTSTOFFVERWERTUNG GMBH—See PORR AG; *Int'l*, pg. 5925
SALZBURGER SPARKASSE BANK AG—See Erste Group Bank AG; *Int'l*, pg. 2498
SALZBURGER ZIEGELWERK GMBH & CO KG—See Wienerberger AG; *Int'l*, pg. 8405
SALZBURG SCHOKOLADE- UND SUSSWARENFABRIK GES.M.B.H. & CO. KG; *Int'l*, pg. 6495
SALZER ELECTRONICS LIMITED; *Int'l*, pg. 6495
SALZGEWINNUNGSGESELLSCHAFT WESTFALEN MBH—See Solvay S.A.; *Int'l*, pg. 7080
SALZGITTER AG; *Int'l*, pg. 6495
SALZGITTER AUTOMOTIVE ENGINEERING GMBH & CO.KG—See Salzgitter AG; *Int'l*, pg. 6498

SALZGITTER AUTOMOTIVE ENGINEERING IMMOBILIEN GMBH & CO. KG—See Salzgitter AG; *Int'l*, pg. 6498
SALZGITTER AUTOMOTIVE ENGINEERING IMMOBILIEN VERWALTUNGSGESELLSCHAFT MBH—See Salzgitter AG; *Int'l*, pg. 6498
SALZGITTER AUTOMOTIVE ENGINEERING VERWALTUNGSGESELLSCHAFT MBH—See Salzgitter AG; *Int'l*, pg. 6498
SALZGITTER BAUELEMENTE GMBH—See FALK Building Systems BV; *Int'l*, pg. 2611
SALZGITTER BUSINESS SERVICE GMBH—See Salzgitter AG; *Int'l*, pg. 6498
SALZGITTER DIGITAL SOLUTIONS GMBH—See Salzgitter AG; *Int'l*, pg. 6498
SALZGITTER EUROPLATINEN GESELLSCHAFT MIT BESCHRANKTER HAFTUNG—See Salzgitter AG; *Int'l*, pg. 6498
SALZGITTER HYDROFORMING GMBH & CO. KG—See Salzgitter AG; *Int'l*, pg. 6498
SALZGITTER HYDROFORMING S.R.O.—See Salzgitter AG; *Int'l*, pg. 6498
SALZGITTER HYDROFORMING VERWALTUNGS GMBH—See Salzgitter AG; *Int'l*, pg. 6498
SALZGITTER MAGNESIUM-TECHNOLOGIE GMBH—See Salzgitter AG; *Int'l*, pg. 6498
SALZGITTER MANNESMANN ACELKERESKEDELMI KFT—See Salzgitter AG; *Int'l*, pg. 6498
SALZGITTER MANNESMANN DISTRIBUTIE S.R.L.—See Salzgitter AG; *Int'l*, pg. 6498
SALZGITTER MANNESMANN (ESPANA) S.A.—See Salzgitter AG; *Int'l*, pg. 6498
SALZGITTER MANNESMANN FORSCHUNG GMBH—See Salzgitter AG; *Int'l*, pg. 6498
SALZGITTER MANNESMANN (FRANCE) S.A.R.L.—See Salzgitter AG; *Int'l*, pg. 6498
SALZGITTER MANNESMANN GMBH—See Salzgitter AG; *Int'l*, pg. 6498
SALZGITTER MANNESMANN GROBBLECH GMBH—See Salzgitter AG; *Int'l*, pg. 6498
SALZGITTER MANNESMANN GROSSROHR GMBH—See Salzgitter AG; *Int'l*, pg. 6498
SALZGITTER MANNESMANN HANDEL GMBH—See Salzgitter AG; *Int'l*, pg. 6498
SALZGITTER MANNESMANN INTERNATIONAL (ASIA) PTE.LTD.—See Salzgitter AG; *Int'l*, pg. 6498
SALZGITTER MANNESMANN INTERNATIONAL (CANADA) INC.—See Salzgitter AG; *Int'l*, pg. 6498
SALZGITTER MANNESMANN INTERNATIONAL DO BRASIL LTDA.—See Salzgitter AG; *Int'l*, pg. 6498
SALZGITTER MANNESMANN INTERNATIONAL GMBH—See Salzgitter AG; *Int'l*, pg. 6498
SALZGITTER MANNESMANN INTERNATIONAL (HK) LTD.—See Salzgitter AG; *Int'l*, pg. 6498
SALZGITTER MANNESMANN INTERNATIONAL (MEXICO) S.A. DE C.V.—See Salzgitter AG; *Int'l*, pg. 6498
SALZGITTER MANNESMANN INTERNATIONAL (USA) INC.—See Salzgitter AG; *Int'l*, pg. 6498
SALZGITTER MANNESMANN (ITALIA) S.R.L.—See Salzgitter AG; *Int'l*, pg. 6498
SALZGITTER MANNESMANN LINE PIPE GMBH—See Salzgitter AG; *Int'l*, pg. 6498
SALZGITTER MANNESMANN PENTASTEEL INTERNATIONAL (INDIA) PVT. LTD.—See Salzgitter AG; *Int'l*, pg. 6498
SALZGITTER MANNESMANN PERSONALSERVICE GMBH—See Salzgitter AG; *Int'l*, pg. 6498
SALZGITTER MANNESMANN PRAZISROHR GMBH—See Salzgitter AG; *Int'l*, pg. 6499
SALZGITTER MANNESMANN PRECISION ETIRAGE SAS—See Salzgitter AG; *Int'l*, pg. 6499
SALZGITTER MANNESMANN PRECISION GMBH—See Salzgitter AG; *Int'l*, pg. 6499
SALZGITTER MANNESMANN PRECISION S.A. DE C.V.—See Salzgitter AG; *Int'l*, pg. 6499
SALZGITTER MANNESMANN ROHR SACHSEN GMBH—See Salzgitter AG; *Int'l*, pg. 6499
SALZGITTER MANNESMANN (SCANDINAVIA) AB—See Salzgitter AG; *Int'l*, pg. 6498
SALZGITTER MANNESMANN SEAMLESS TUBES B.V.—See Salzgitter AG; *Int'l*, pg. 6499
SALZGITTER MANNESMANN STAALHANDEL B.V.—See Salzgitter AG; *Int'l*, pg. 6499
SALZGITTER MANNESMANN STAHLHANDEL AUSTRIA GMBH—See Salzgitter AG; *Int'l*, pg. 6498
SALZGITTER MANNESMANN STAHLHANDEL GMBH—See Salzgitter AG; *Int'l*, pg. 6498
SALZGITTER MANNESMANN STAHLHANDEL SP. Z.O.O.—See Salzgitter AG; *Int'l*, pg. 6499
SALZGITTER MANNESMANN STAHLHANDEL S.R.O.—See Salzgitter AG; *Int'l*, pg. 6499
SALZGITTER MANNESMANN STAHLSERVICE GMBH—See Salzgitter AG; *Int'l*, pg. 6499
SALZGITTER MANNESMANN STAINLESS TUBES DEUTSCHLAND GMBH—See Salzgitter AG; *Int'l*, pg. 6499
SALZGITTER MANNESMANN STAINLESS TUBES FRANCE SAS—See Salzgitter AG; *Int'l*, pg. 6499

COMPANY NAME INDEX

SALZGITTER MANNESMANN STAINLESS TUBES GMBH—See Salzgitter AG; *Int'l*, pg. 6499
SALZGITTER MANNESMANN STAINLESS TUBES ITALIA S.R.L.—See Salzgitter AG; *Int'l*, pg. 6499
SALZGITTER MANNESMANN STAINLESS TUBES USA, INC.—See Salzgitter AG; *Int'l*, pg. 6499
SALZGITTER MANNESMANN TRADE (BEIJING) CO. LTD.—See Salzgitter AG; *Int'l*, pg. 6499
SALZGITTER MANNESMANN UK LTD.—See Salzgitter AG; *Int'l*, pg. 6499
SALZGITTER MASCHINENBAU AG—See Salzgitter AG; *Int'l*, pg. 6499
SALZGITTER STAHL GMBH—See Salzgitter AG; *Int'l*, pg. 6499
SALZINGER LLC.; *U.S. Private*, pg. 3535
SALZMANN AG; *Int'l*, pg. 6499
SALZMANN MEDICO—See Salzmann AG; *Int'l*, pg. 6500
SAM-A ALUMINIUM CO., LTD.—See Nippon Light Metal Holdings Company, Ltd.; *Int'l*, pg. 5324
SAM-A ALUMINUM CO., LTD.; *Int'l*, pg. 6500
SAMAB CIA. INDUSTRIA E COMERCIO DE PAPEL—See Stora Enso Oyj; *Int'l*, pg. 7223
SAMAD MISR; *Int'l*, pg. 6500
SAMAGE; *Int'l*, pg. 6501
SAMAIDEN GROUP BERHAD; *Int'l*, pg. 6501
SAMAKIL, S.A.—See Iberpapel Gestion SA; *Int'l*, pg. 3574
S.A. MAKITA N.V.—See Makita Corporation; *Int'l*, pg. 4658
SAMALAJU HOTEL MANAGEMENT SDN. BHD.—See Cahya Mata Sarawak Berhad; *Int'l*, pg. 1251
SAMALAJU INDUSTRIAL PORT SDN. BHD.—See Bintulu Port Holdings Berhad; *Int'l*, pg. 1035
SAMALAJU INDUSTRIES SDN. BHD.—See Cahya Mata Sarawak Berhad; *Int'l*, pg. 1251
SAMALAJU PROPERTIES SDN. BHD.—See Cahya Mata Sarawak Berhad; *Int'l*, pg. 1251
SAMAMA CONTRACTING COMPANY—See Samama Holding Group; *Int'l*, pg. 6501
SAMAMA HOLDING GROUP; *Int'l*, pg. 6501
SAMA MASCHINENBAU GMBH—See Sacmi Imola S.C.A.R.L.; *Int'l*, pg. 6465
SAMAMA TECHNICAL SERVICES (JEDDAH)—See Samama Holding Group; *Int'l*, pg. 6501
SAMANCOR CHROME LTD.—See Jubilee Metals Group plc; *Int'l*, pg. 4021
SAMANDA TRADING SDN. BHD.—See W T K Holdings Berhad; *Int'l*, pg. 8320
S.A. MANPOWER (BELGIUM) N.V.—See ManpowerGroup Inc.; *U.S. Public*, pg. 1362
SAMANTHA THAVASA JAPAN LIMITED—See Konaka Co., Ltd.; *Int'l*, pg. 4245
SAM-A PHARM. CO., LTD.; *Int'l*, pg. 6500
SAMARAAGROPROMPERERABOTKA (SAPP)—See Gruppa Kompaniy Rusagro OOO; *Int'l*, pg. 3140
SAMARA ASSET GROUP PLC; *Int'l*, pg. 6501
SAMARA BROTHERS LLC; *U.S. Private*, pg. 3536
SAMARA CAPITAL MANAGEMENT LTD.; *Int'l*, pg. 6501
SAMARA INDIA ADVISORS PVT. LTD.—See Samara Capital Management Ltd.; *Int'l*, pg. 6501
SAMARANG LLP; *Int'l*, pg. 6501
SAMARA TERMINAL LLC—See OJSC Rosneftegaz; *Int'l*, pg. 5541
SAMARATRANSGAZ—See PJSC Gazprom; *Int'l*, pg. 5880
SAMA RESOURCES INC.; *Int'l*, pg. 6500
SAMARITAN BEHAVIORAL HEALTH, INC.; *U.S. Private*, pg. 3536
SAMARITAN CENTER; *U.S. Private*, pg. 3536
SAMARITAN HEALTHCARE & HOSPICE; *U.S. Private*, pg. 3536
SAMARITAN HEALTH SERVICES, INC.; *U.S. Private*, pg. 3536
SAMARITAN PHYSICAL THERAPY—See UK HealthCare Good Samaritan Hospital; *U.S. Private*, pg. 4275
SAMARITAN REGIONAL HEALTH SYSTEM; *U.S. Private*, pg. 3536
SAMARITANS FEET INTERNATIONAL; *U.S. Private*, pg. 3536
SAMARIUM GROUP CORPORATION; *Int'l*, pg. 6501
SAMARIUM GROUP PTE. LTD.—See Samarium Group Corporation; *Int'l*, pg. 6501
SAMARKANDFASTIGHETER AB—See Eurocommercial Properties N.V.; *Int'l*, pg. 2534
SAMARKAND GLOBAL (JAPAN) KK—See Samarkand Group Plc; *Int'l*, pg. 6501
SAMARKAND GROUP PLC; *Int'l*, pg. 6501
SAMART COMMUNICATION SERVICES CO., LTD.—See Samart Corporation Public Company Limited; *Int'l*, pg. 6502
SAMART COMTECH CO., LTD.—See Samart Corporation Public Company Limited; *Int'l*, pg. 6502
SAMART CORPORATION PUBLIC COMPANY LIMITED; *Int'l*, pg. 6501
SAMART DIGITAL PUBLIC CO., LTD.—See Samart Corporation Public Company Limited; *Int'l*, pg. 6501
SAMART ED TECH CO., LTD.—See Samart Corporation Public Company Limited; *Int'l*, pg. 6502
SAMART ENGINEERING CO., LTD.—See Samart Corporation Public Company Limited; *Int'l*, pg. 6501
SAMART I-MOBILE (MALAYSIA) SDN BHD—See Samart Corporation Public Company Limited; *Int'l*, pg. 6501

SAMART I-MOBILE PLC—See Samart Corporation Public Company Limited; *Int'l*, pg. 6501
SAMART INFONET CO., LTD.—See Samart Corporation Public Company Limited; *Int'l*, pg. 6502
SAMART MULTIMEDIA CO., LTD.—See Samart Corporation Public Company Limited; *Int'l*, pg. 6501
SAMART RADITECH CO., LTD.—See Samart Corporation Public Company Limited; *Int'l*, pg. 6502
SAMART RESEARCH & DEVELOPMENT CO., LTD.—See Samart Corporation Public Company Limited; *Int'l*, pg. 6502
SAMART TELCOMS PUBLIC CO., LTD.—See Samart Corporation Public Company Limited; *Int'l*, pg. 6502
SAMA-SAMA HOTEL KL INTERNATIONAL AIRPORT—See Malaysia Airports Holdings Berhad; *Int'l*, pg. 4661
SAMA S.A.—See Eternit S.A.; *Int'l*, pg. 2521
SAM ASHER COMPUTING SERVICES INC.—See Valsef Group; *Int'l*, pg. 8123
SAM ASH MUSIC CORPORATION; *U.S. Private*, pg. 3535
SAMA SOUND INC.—See Hibino Corporation; *Int'l*, pg. 3383
SAMAS SA—See Vivendi SE; *Int'l*, pg. 8274
SAMATA GHARELU LAGHUBITTA BITTIYA SANSTHA LTD; *Int'l*, pg. 6502
SAMATA LEATHER COMPLEX LIMITED; *Int'l*, pg. 6502
SAMBA FEDERAL EMPLOYEE BENEFIT ASSOCIATION; *U.S. Private*, pg. 3536
SAMBA HOLDINGS, INC.—See ABRY Partners, LLC; *U.S. Private*, pg. 43
SAMBANDAM SPINNING MILLS LIMITED; *Int'l*, pg. 6502
SAMBA TV, INC.; *U.S. Private*, pg. 3536
SAMBA VALLARTA—See Emporio Hotels & Resorts S.A. de C.V.; *Int'l*, pg. 2387
SAMBAZON BRAZIL—See Sambazon, Inc.; *U.S. Private*, pg. 3536
SAMBAZON, INC.; *U.S. Private*, pg. 3536
SAMBE CONSTRUCTION COMPANY; *U.S. Private*, pg. 3536
SAMBHAAV MEDIA LIMITED; *Int'l*, pg. 6502
SAMBO CORRUGATED BOARD CO., LTD.; *Int'l*, pg. 6502
SAMBO FINE CHEMICALS MFG. CO., LTD.—See Dainichiseika Color & Chemicals Mfg. Co., Ltd.; *Int'l*, pg. 1939
SAMBO INDUSTRIAL CO., LTD.; *Int'l*, pg. 6502
SAMBO METALS CORP.—See Mitsubishi Materials Corporation; *Int'l*, pg. 4965
SAMBO MOTORS CO., LTD.; *Int'l*, pg. 6502
SAMBONET PADERNO INDUSTRIE S.P.A.; *Int'l*, pg. 6502
SAMBON (H.K.) ELECTRONICS LIMITED—See Corstone Corporation; *U.S. Private*, pg. 1060
SAMBRAILO PACKAGING INC.; *U.S. Private*, pg. 3536
SAM BROUSSARD TRUCKING COMPANY INC.; *U.S. Private*, pg. 3535
SAMBU CONSTRUCTION CO., LTD.; *Int'l*, pg. 6502
SAMCHAI STEEL INDUSTRIES PUBLIC COMPANY LIMITED; *Int'l*, pg. 6503
SAMCHEM DRILLING FLUIDS & CHEMICALS (PTY) LTD—See Imdex Limited; *Int'l*, pg. 3623
SAMCHEM ENVIRO CYCLE SDN. BHD.—See Samchem Holdings Berhad; *Int'l*, pg. 6503
SAMCHEM HOLDINGS BERHAD; *Int'l*, pg. 6503
SAMCHEM LOGISTIC SERVICES SDN. BHD.—See Samchem Holdings Berhad; *Int'l*, pg. 6503
SAMCHEM SDN. BHD.—See Samchem Holdings Berhad; *Int'l*, pg. 6503
SAMCHEMSPHERE EXPORT SDN. BHD.—See Samchem Holdings Berhad; *Int'l*, pg. 6503
SAMCHEM TN PTE LTD—See Samchem Holdings Berhad; *Int'l*, pg. 6503
SAMCHULLY ASSET MANAGEMENT CO., LTD.—See Samchully Co., Ltd.; *Int'l*, pg. 6503
SAMCHULLY CO., LTD. - GWANGMYEONG COMBINED HEAT & POWER PLANT—See Samchully Co., Ltd.; *Int'l*, pg. 6503
SAMCHULLY CO., LTD.; *Int'l*, pg. 6503
SAMCHULLY ENG CO., LTD.—See Samchully Co., Ltd.; *Int'l*, pg. 6503
SAMCHULLY ES CO., LTD.—See Samchully Co., Ltd.; *Int'l*, pg. 6503
SAMCHULY BICYCLE CO., LTD.; *Int'l*, pg. 6503
SAM CHUN DANG PHARM. CO., LTD.; *Int'l*, pg. 6500
SAM CLAR OFFICE FURNITURE, INC.; *U.S. Private*, pg. 3535
SAMCO GOLD LIMITED; *Int'l*, pg. 6503
SAMCO INC.; *Int'l*, pg. 6503
SAMCO MACHINERY, LTD.; *Int'l*, pg. 6503
SAMCON INC; *Int'l*, pg. 6503
SAMCO-UCP LTD.—See SAMCO INC.; *Int'l*, pg. 6503
SAMDONG INDUSTRY CO., LTD.—See Chonbang Co., Ltd.; *Int'l*, pg. 1578
SAMEBEST CO., LTD.; *Int'l*, pg. 6503
SAMEDAN METHANOL—See Chevron Corporation; *U.S. Public*, pg. 487
SAME DAY SC OF CENTRAL NJ, LLC—See Tenet Healthcare Corporation; *U.S. Public*, pg. 2007
SAME DEUTZ-FAHR FINANCE SAS—See BNP Paribas SA; *Int'l*, pg. 1092

SAMEDI GMBH—See Asklepios Kliniken GmbH & Co. KGaA; *Int'l*, pg. 624
SAMEERA AGRO & INFRA LIMITED; *Int'l*, pg. 6503
SAMEER AFRICA LTD.; *Int'l*, pg. 6503
SAMEERA HOMES PRIVATE LIMITED; *Int'l*, pg. 6504
SAMEKAWA READY-MIXED CONCRETE CO., LTD.—See UBE Corporation; *Int'l*, pg. 8001
SAM ELECTRONICS GMBH—See L3Harris Technologies, Inc.; *U.S. Public*, pg. 1284
SAM ELECTRONICS NEDERLAND B.V.—See L3Harris Technologies, Inc.; *U.S. Public*, pg. 1284
SAMENA CAPITAL HONG KONG LTD—See Samena Capital Management LLP; *Int'l*, pg. 6504
SAMENA CAPITAL INVESTMENTS LTD—See Samena Capital Management LLP; *Int'l*, pg. 6504
SAMENA CAPITAL MANAGEMENT LLP; *Int'l*, pg. 6504
SAM ENGINEERING & EQUIPMENT (M) BERHAD; *Int'l*, pg. 6500
SAMENWERKENDE APOTHEKERS NEDERLAND BV—See Perrigo Company plc; *Int'l*, pg. 5813
SAMEPAGE LABS INC.—See Paylocity Holding Corporation; *U.S. Public*, pg. 1656
SAMES FORD - CHORPUS CHRISTI—See Sames Motor Co., Inc.; *U.S. Private*, pg. 3537
SAMES KREMLIN SAS—See Exel Industries SA; *Int'l*, pg. 2582
SAMES MOTOR CO., INC.; *U.S. Private*, pg. 3536
SAMES RED BARN MOTORS—See Sames Motor Co., Inc.; *U.S. Private*, pg. 3537
SAMET CORPORATION; *U.S. Private*, pg. 3537
SAMETEL CORPORATION; *Int'l*, pg. 6504
SA METER READING SERVICES (PROPRIETARY) LIMITED—See Sebata Holdings; *Int'l*, pg. 6669
SAMETEX SPOL. S.R.O—See Marzotto S.p.A.; *Int'l*, pg. 4718
SAMETO TECHNIFIL; *Int'l*, pg. 6504
SAM FINE O CHEM LTD.—See Transpek Industry Limited; *Int'l*, pg. 7904
SAM GALLOWAY FORD, INC.; *U.S. Private*, pg. 3535
SAMG ENTERTAINMENT CO., LTD.; *Int'l*, pg. 6504
SAM HAE COMMERCIAL CO., LTD.—See CJ Corporation; *Int'l*, pg. 1634
SAMHA HOME APPLIANCE SPA—See Cevital S.p.A.; *Int'l*, pg. 1425
SAMHALLSBYGGNADSBOLAGET I NORDEN AB; *Int'l*, pg. 6504
SAMHAN CO. LTD.—See CR Holdings Co., Ltd.; *Int'l*, pg. 1827
SAMHA SEWON AUTOMATIVE TECHHNOLOGY CO., LTD.—See Sewon Precision Industry Co., Ltd.; *Int'l*, pg. 6737
SAMHA SEWON AUTOMATIVE TECHNOLOGY CO., LTD.—See SEWON CORPORATION CO., Ltd.; *Int'l*, pg. 6737
SAMHERJI HF; *Int'l*, pg. 6504
SAM HIRE LIMITED—See Grafton Group plc; *Int'l*, pg. 3051
SAMHO DEVELOPMENT CO., LTD - DANGJIN FACTORY—See Samho Development Co., Ltd; *Int'l*, pg. 6505
SAMHO DEVELOPMENT CO., LTD; *Int'l*, pg. 6505
SAMHO ENVIRO-TECH INC—See Samho Development Co., Ltd; *Int'l*, pg. 6505
SAMHO GREEN INVESTMENT INC.—See Samho Development Co., Ltd; *Int'l*, pg. 6505
SAM HOLDINGS CORPORATION; *Int'l*, pg. 6500
SAM HOUSTON ELECTRIC CO-OPERATIVE INC.; *U.S. Private*, pg. 3535
SAM HOUSTON RACE PARK LLC; *U.S. Private*, pg. 3535
SAMHWA CROWN & CLOSURE CO., LTD.—See Kumbi Co., Ltd.; *Int'l*, pg. 4330
SAM HWA ELECTRIC CO., LTD.; *Int'l*, pg. 6500
SAM HWA ELECTRONICS CO., LTD.; *Int'l*, pg. 6500
SAMHWA LOGITECH CO., LTD.—See Samhwa Paints Industrial Co., Ltd.; *Int'l*, pg. 6505
SAMHWA NETWORKS CO., LTD.; *Int'l*, pg. 6505
SAMHWA PAINTS INDUSTRIAL CO., LTD. - ANSAN PLANT—See Samhwa Paints Industrial Co., Ltd.; *Int'l*, pg. 6505
SAMHWA PAINTS INDUSTRIAL CO., LTD.; *Int'l*, pg. 6505
SAMHWA PAINTS INDUSTRIAL CO., LTD. - ZHANGJIAGANG FACTORY—See Samhwa Paints Industrial Co., Ltd.; *Int'l*, pg. 6505
SAMHWA PAINTS (M) SDN. BHD.—See Samhwa Paints Industrial Co., Ltd.; *Int'l*, pg. 6505
SAMHWA PAINTS VINA CO., LTD.—See Samhwa Paints Industrial Co., Ltd.; *Int'l*, pg. 6505
SAMHWA PRECISION CO., LTD.—See ASSA ABLOY AB; *Int'l*, pg. 640
SAMHWA TRADING CO., LTD.—See Daeyang Electric Co., Ltd.; *Int'l*, pg. 1911
SAMHYUN STEEL CO., LTD.; *Int'l*, pg. 6505
SAMIBOIS-SAMIPLAST; *Int'l*, pg. 6505
SAMICK ADM CO., LTD.—See Harmonic Drive Systems Inc.; *Int'l*, pg. 3277
SAMICK BECHSTEIN TRADING (SHANGHAI) CO., LTD.—See Samick Musical Instrument Co., Ltd.; *Int'l*, pg. 6505

SAMICK MUSICAL INSTRUMENT CO., LTD.

SAMICK MUSICAL INSTRUMENT CO., LTD.; *Int'l*, pg. 6505
SAMICK MUSIC CORP.—See Samick Musical Instrument Co., Ltd.; *Int'l*, pg. 6505
SAMICK THK CO., LTD.; *Int'l*, pg. 6505
SAMIL CO., LTD.; *Int'l*, pg. 6505
SAMIL C&S CO., LTD.; *Int'l*, pg. 6505
SAMIL ENTERPRISE CO., LTD.; *Int'l*, pg. 6506
SAMIL PHARMACEUTICAL CO., LTD.; *Int'l*, pg. 6506
SAMINCO, INC.; *U.S. Private*, pg. 3537
SAM, INC.; *U.S. Private*, pg. 3536
SAM INDUSTRIES LIMITED; *Int'l*, pg. 6500
SAMIN S.A.—See Compagnie de Saint-Gobain SA; *Int'l*, pg. 1733
S. A. MIRO, INC.; *U.S. Private*, pg. 3514
SAMIR TRADING & MARKETING - CJSC—See HORIBA Ltd.; *Int'l*, pg. 3478
SAMI SHOP S.A.C.—See Credicorp Ltd.; *Int'l*, pg. 1834
SAMITIVEJ CHONBURI CO., LTD.—See Bangkok Dusit Medical Services Public Company Limited; *Int'l*, pg. 834
SAMITIVEJ INTERNATIONAL CO., LTD.—See Bangkok Dusit Medical Services Public Company Limited; *Int'l*, pg. 834
SAMITIVEJ PUBLIC COMPANY LIMITED—See Bangkok Dusit Medical Services Public Company Limited; *Int'l*, pg. 834
SAMITIVEJ SRIRACHA CO., LTD.—See Bangkok Dusit Medical Services Public Company Limited; *Int'l*, pg. 834
SAMJI ELECTRONICS CO., LTD.; *Int'l*, pg. 6506
SAMJIN CO., LTD.; *Int'l*, pg. 6506
SAMJIN LND CO., LTD.; *Int'l*, pg. 6506
SAMJIN PHARMACEUTICAL CO., LTD. - HYANGNAM PLANT—See Samjin Pharmaceutical Co., Ltd.; *Int'l*, pg. 6506
SAMJIN PHARMACEUTICAL CO., LTD. - OSONG PLANT—See Samjin Pharmaceutical Co., Ltd.; *Int'l*, pg. 6506
SAMJIN PHARMACEUTICAL CO., LTD.; *Int'l*, pg. 6506
SAMJO CELLTECH LTD.—See Dongwon Enterprise Co., Ltd.; *Int'l*, pg. 2171
SAM JUNG PLUP CO., LTD.; *Int'l*, pg. 6500
SAM KANE BEEF PROCESSORS, INC.; *U.S. Private*, pg. 3535
SAMKANG M&T CO., LTD - KOREA FACTORY—See SK oceanplant Co., Ltd.; *Int'l*, pg. 6975
SAMKANG M&T CO., LTD - MIRYANG FACTORY—See SK oceanplant Co., Ltd.; *Int'l*, pg. 6975
SAMKEE AUTOMOTIVE CO., LTD. - SEOSAN FACTORY—See Samkee Corp.; *Int'l*, pg. 6506
SAMKEE CORP.; *Int'l*, pg. 6506
SAMKO TIMBER LIMITED; *Int'l*, pg. 6506
SAMKRG PISTONS & RINGS LIMITED; *Int'l*, pg. 6506
SAMKWANG GLASS CO., LTD. - CHEONAN PLANT—See SGC Solutions Co., Ltd.; *Int'l*, pg. 6741
SAM LABORATORY PTE. LTD.—See Clearbridge Health Limited; *Int'l*, pg. 1656
SAM LEMAN CHRYSLER-JEEP-DODGE OF PEORIA; *U.S. Private*, pg. 3535
SAM LEMAN CHRYSLER-PLYMOUTH-DODGE; *U.S. Private*, pg. 3535
SAM LEVIN INC.—See Thomas H. Lee Partners, L.P.; *U.S. Private*, pg. 4156
SAM LEVITZ FURNITURE COMPANY; *U.S. Private*, pg. 3535
SAM LINDER, INC.; *U.S. Private*, pg. 3535
SAMLING FLOORING PRODUCTS SDN BHD—See Samling Strategic Corporation Sdn. Bhd.; *Int'l*, pg. 6506
SAMLING GLOBAL LIMITED—See Samling Strategic Corporation Sdn. Bhd.; *Int'l*, pg. 6507
SAMLING HOUSING PRODUCTS SDN. BHD.—See DIC Corporation; *Int'l*, pg. 2109
SAMLING JAPAN CORPORATION—See Samling Strategic Corporation Sdn. Bhd.; *Int'l*, pg. 6506
SAMLING PLANTATION SDN BHD—See Samling Strategic Corporation Sdn. Bhd.; *Int'l*, pg. 6506
SAMLING PLYWOOD (BARAMAS) SDN BHD—See Samling Strategic Corporation Sdn. Bhd.; *Int'l*, pg. 6506
SAMLING PLYWOOD (BINTULU) SDN BHD—See Samling Strategic Corporation Sdn. Bhd.; *Int'l*, pg. 6506
SAMLING PLYWOOD (LAWAS) SDN BHD—See Samling Strategic Corporation Sdn. Bhd.; *Int'l*, pg. 6506
SAMLING PLYWOOD (MIRI) SDN BHD—See Samling Strategic Corporation Sdn. Bhd.; *Int'l*, pg. 6506
SAMLING RIVERSIDE CO, LTD—See Samling Strategic Corporation Sdn. Bhd.; *Int'l*, pg. 6507
SAMLING SINGAPORE PTE LTD—See Samling Strategic Corporation Sdn. Bhd.; *Int'l*, pg. 6507
SAMLING STRATEGIC CORPORATION SDN. BHD.; *Int'l*, pg. 6506
SAMLOR S.A.—See Industria de Diseno Textil, S.A.; *Int'l*, pg. 3667
SAMMA INTERNATIONAL S.R.L.—See UPL Limited; *Int'l*, pg. 8089
SAMMAKORN PUBLIC COMPANY LIMITED; *Int'l*, pg. 6507
SAM-MAN REALTY, INC.—See Hyman Brickle & Son, Inc.; *U.S. Private*, pg. 2019
SAM M. BUTLER INC.; *U.S. Private*, pg. 3535
SAM MEDICAL PRODUCTS; *U.S. Private*, pg. 3535

SAM MEERKAT (M) SDN. BHD.—See SAM Engineering & Equipment (M) Berhad; *Int'l*, pg. 6500
SAMMET DAMPERS OY—See Addtech AB; *Int'l*, pg. 135
SAM MEYERS INC.; *U.S. Private*, pg. 3535
SAMMOK KANG UP CO., LTD.—See YoungWire Co. Ltd.; *Int'l*, pg. 8604
SAMMOK S-FORM CO., LTD.; *Int'l*, pg. 6507
SAM MONACO YACHT SHOW—See Informa plc; *Int'l*, pg. 3693
SAMMONS ANNUITY GROUP—See Sammons Enterprises, Inc.; *U.S. Private*, pg. 3537
SAMMONS CORPORATION—See Sammons Enterprises, Inc.; *U.S. Private*, pg. 3537
SAMMONS ENTERPRISES, INC.; *U.S. Private*, pg. 3537
SAMMONS FINANCIAL GROUP, INC.—See Sammons Enterprises, Inc.; *U.S. Private*, pg. 3537
SAMMONS RETIREMENT SOLUTIONS, INC.—See Sammons Enterprises, Inc.; *U.S. Private*, pg. 3537
SAMMONS SECURITIES COMPANY, LLC—See Sammons Enterprises, Inc.; *U.S. Private*, pg. 3537
SAMMONS TRUCKING, INC.; *U.S. Private*, pg. 3537
SAM MOORE FURNITURE LLC—See Hooker Furnishings Corporation; *U.S. Public*, pg. 1052
SAMMY CORPORATION—See Sega Sammy Holdings, Inc.; *Int'l*, pg. 6681
SAMMY DESIGN CO., LTD.—See Interlife Holdings Co., Ltd.; *Int'l*, pg. 3741
SAMMY NETWORKS CO., LTD.—See Sega Sammy Holdings, Inc.; *Int'l*, pg. 6681
SAMMYUNG PRECISION (JIAXING) CO., LTD.—See Samyung Trading Co., Ltd.; *Int'l*, pg. 6520
SAMOA BREWERIES LIMITED; *Int'l*, pg. 6507
SAMOA PAINTS LIMITED—See Asian Paints Limited; *Int'l*, pg. 619
SAMOBA GMBH—See 3U Holding AG; *Int'l*, pg. 10
SAMON'S TIGER STORES INC.; *U.S. Private*, pg. 3537
SAMOON-COLLECTION FASHION-CONCEPT GERRY WEBER GMBH—See GERRY WEBER International AG; *Int'l*, pg. 2945
S.A. MORGAN—See Morgan Advanced Materials plc; *Int'l*, pg. 5044
S.A. MORMAN & COMPANY; *U.S. Private*, pg. 3515
SAMOR REALITY LIMITED; *Int'l*, pg. 6507
SAMOS VERMOGENSVERWALTUNGS GMBH—See Deutsche Bank Aktiengesellschaft; *Int'l*, pg. 2061
SAMOYED HOLDING LIMITED; *Int'l*, pg. 6507
SAM PACK'S FIVE STAR FORD; *U.S. Private*, pg. 3535
SAMPANN UTPADAN INDIA LTD.; *Int'l*, pg. 6507
SAM PAO PETCH CO., LTD.—See BTS Group Holdings Public Company Limited; *Int'l*, pg. 1206
SAMPATH BANK PLC; *Int'l*, pg. 6507
SAMPATH CENTER LIMITED—See Sampath Bank PLC; *Int'l*, pg. 6507
SAMPATH INFORMATION TECHNOLOGY SOLUTIONS LIMITED—See Sampath Bank PLC; *Int'l*, pg. 6507
SAMPATH LEASING & FACTORING LTD.—See Sampath Bank PLC; *Int'l*, pg. 6507
SAMPATH SURAKAM LIMITED—See Sampath Bank PLC; *Int'l*, pg. 6507
SAMPCO INC.; *U.S. Private*, pg. 3537
SAMPCO INC.; *U.S. Private*, pg. 3537
SAMPCO OF TEXAS, INC.—See Sampco Inc.; *U.S. Private*, pg. 3537
SAMPENSION KP LIVSFORSIKRING A/S; *Int'l*, pg. 6507
SAMPIERANA S.P.A.—See CNH Industrial N.V.; *Int'l*, pg. 1676
SAM PIEVAC COMPANY INC.; *U.S. Private*, pg. 3536
SAMPLE BROTHERS INC.—See SBI Incorporated; *U.S. Private*, pg. 3560
SAMPLE TECHNOLOGY (H.K.) CO., LIMITED—See Nanjing Sample Technology Company Limited; *Int'l*, pg. 5141
SAMPO BANK PLC—See Danske Bank A/S; *Int'l*, pg. 1969
SAMPO CORPORATION; *Int'l*, pg. 6507
SAMPO FUND MANAGEMENT LTD.—See Sampo plc; *Int'l*, pg. 6508
SAMPO IP, LLC—See Marathon Digital Holdings, Inc.; *U.S. Public*, pg. 1363
SAMPO PLC; *Int'l*, pg. 6507
SAM PRECISION (THAILAND) LIMITED—See SAM Engineering & Equipment (M) Berhad; *Int'l*, pg. 6500
SAMPRE NUTRITIONS LIMITED; *Int'l*, pg. 6508
SAMPSON-BLADEN OIL CO. INC.; *U.S. Private*, pg. 3538
SAMPSON COATINGS INC.—See Penn Color Inc.; *U.S. Private*, pg. 3133
SAMPSON CONSTRUCTION CO. INC.; *U.S. Private*, pg. 3537
THE SAMPSON INDEPENDENT, INC.—See Heartland Publications, LLC; *U.S. Private*, pg. 1900
SAMPSON LUMBER CO. INC.; *U.S. Private*, pg. 3537
SAMPSON VENTURES, LLC—See Dean Foods Company; *U.S. Private*, pg. 1184
SAMP S.P.A.—See Investment AB Latour; *Int'l*, pg. 3783
SAMPYO CEMENT CO., LTD.—See Sampyo Corporation; *Int'l*, pg. 6508
SAMPYO CORPORATION; *Int'l*, pg. 6508
SAMRA MIDAS CO., LTD.; *Int'l*, pg. 6508
SAMRAT FORGINGS LIMITED; *Int'l*, pg. 6508
SAMRAT PHARMACHEM LIMITED; *Int'l*, pg. 6508

CORPORATE AFFILIATIONS

SAMREC PTY LTD—See Groupe Bruxelles Lambert SA; *Int'l*, pg. 3100
SAM RODGERS PROPERTIES, INC.; *U.S. Private*, pg. 3536
SAMRUK-ENERGY JSC; *Int'l*, pg. 6508
SAMRUK GREEN ENERGY LLP—See Samruk-Energy JSC; *Int'l*, pg. 6508
SAMRUK-KAZYNA CONSTRUCTION JSC; *Int'l*, pg. 6508
SAMRYOONG CO LTD. - SIHWA FACTORY—See Samryoong Co Ltd.; *Int'l*, pg. 6508
SAMRYOONG CO LTD.; *Int'l*, pg. 6508
SAMS ADVANCE CLIMATIC TECHNOLOGIES—See ESPEC Corp.; *Int'l*, pg. 2505
SAMSARA INC.; *U.S. Public*, pg. 1839
SAMSARA LUGGAGE, INC.; *U.S. Public*, pg. 1839
SAMSARA NETWORKS LIMITED—See Samsara Inc.; *U.S. Public*, pg. 1839
SAMSARA SCIENCES, INC.—See LifeNet Health, Inc.; *U.S. Private*, pg. 2450
SAMSARA VISION, INC.; *U.S. Private*, pg. 3538
SAM SCHULTE GMBH—See sam Vertriebs GmbH + Co. KG; *Int'l*, pg. 6500
SAM SCHULTE SA—See sam Vertriebs GmbH + Co. KG; *Int'l*, pg. 6500
SAM SCHWARTZ ENGINEERING D.P.C.; *U.S. Private*, pg. 3536
SAM'S CLUB—See Walmart Inc.; *U.S. Public*, pg. 2325
SAM'S EAST, INC.—See Walmart Inc.; *U.S. Public*, pg. 2325
SAM SENSORY INTERNATIONAL FRANCE S.A.S.—See Eurofins Scientific S.E.; *Int'l*, pg. 2551
SAM SENSORY & MARKETING INTERNATIONAL GMBH—See Eurofins Scientific S.E.; *Int'l*, pg. 2551
SAM SENSORY & MARKETING ITALY S.R.L.—See Eurofins Scientific S.E.; *Int'l*, pg. 2551
SAMSE SA; *Int'l*, pg. 6508
SAM SHIPPING & CLEARING CO. LTD.—See Albert Ballin KG; *Int'l*, pg. 296
SAMSIC; *Int'l*, pg. 6509
SAMSILL, INC.; *U.S. Private*, pg. 3538
SAMSKIP HOLDING B.V.; *Int'l*, pg. 6509
SAMSON BRANDS LLC; *U.S. Private*, pg. 3538
SAMSON CAPITAL ADVISORS LLC—See Fiera Capital Corporation; *Int'l*, pg. 2660
SAMSON ENERGY COMPANY, LLC; *U.S. Private*, pg. 3538
SAMSON HOLDING LTD.—See ITOCHU Corporation; *Int'l*, pg. 3841
SAMSON INTERNATIONAL PLC; *Int'l*, pg. 6509
SAMSONITE AB—See Samsonite International S.A.; *Int'l*, pg. 6509
SAMSONITE AG—See Samsonite International S.A.; *Int'l*, pg. 6509
SAMSONITE ASIA LIMITED—See Samsonite International S.A.; *Int'l*, pg. 6509
SAMSONITE A/S—See Samsonite International S.A.; *Int'l*, pg. 6509
SAMSONITE AUSTRALIA PTY LIMITED—See Samsonite International S.A.; *Int'l*, pg. 6509
SAMSONITE BRASIL LTDA.—See Samsonite International S.A.; *Int'l*, pg. 6509
SAMSONITE B.V.—See Samsonite International S.A.; *Int'l*, pg. 6509
SAMSONITE CANADA—See Samsonite International S.A.; *Int'l*, pg. 6509
SAMSONITE CHILE S.A.—See Samsonite International S.A.; *Int'l*, pg. 6509
SAMSONITE COLOMBIA S.A.S.—See Samsonite International S.A.; *Int'l*, pg. 6509
SAMSONITE ESPANA S.A.—See Samsonite International S.A.; *Int'l*, pg. 6509
SAMSONITE EUROPE N.V.—See Samsonite International S.A.; *Int'l*, pg. 6509
SAMSONITE FINLAND OY—See Samsonite International S.A.; *Int'l*, pg. 6509
SAMSONITE GMBH—See Samsonite International S.A.; *Int'l*, pg. 6509
SAMSONITE HUNGARIA BOROND KFT—See Samsonite International S.A.; *Int'l*, pg. 6509
SAMSONITE INTERNATIONAL S.A.; *Int'l*, pg. 6509
SAMSONITE JAPAN CO., LTD.—See Samsonite International S.A.; *Int'l*, pg. 6509
SAMSONITE KOREA LIMITED—See Samsonite International S.A.; *Int'l*, pg. 6510
SAMSONITE LLC—See Samsonite International S.A.; *Int'l*, pg. 6510
SAMSONITE LTD.—See Samsonite International S.A.; *Int'l*, pg. 6510
SAMSONITE MEXICO, S.A. DE C.V—See Samsonite International S.A.; *Int'l*, pg. 6510
SAMSONITE PANAMA S.A.—See Samsonite International S.A.; *Int'l*, pg. 6510
SAMSONITE PERU S.A.C.—See Samsonite International S.A.; *Int'l*, pg. 6510
SAMSONITE PHILIPPINES, INC.—See Samsonite International S.A.; *Int'l*, pg. 6510
SAMSONITE S.A.S.—See Samsonite International S.A.; *Int'l*, pg. 6510

COMPANY NAME INDEX

SAMSONITE SEYAHAT URUNLERI SANAYI VE TICARET ANONIM SIRKETI—See Samsonite International S.A.; *Int'l*, pg. 6510
SAMSONITE SOUTH ASIA PRIVATE LIMITED—See Samsonite International S.A.; *Int'l*, pg. 6510
SAMSONITE SOUTHERN AFRICA LTD.—See Samsonite International S.A.; *Int'l*, pg. 6510
SAMSONITE S.P.A.—See Samsonite International S.A.; *Int'l*, pg. 6510
SAMSONITE (THAILAND) CO., LTD.—See Samsonite International S.A.; *Int'l*, pg. 6509
SAMSON MANAGEMENT CORP.; *U.S. Private*, pg. 3538
SAMSON OIL & GAS LIMITED; *Int'l*, pg. 6509
SAMSON OIL & GAS USA, INC.—See Samson Oil & Gas Limited; *Int'l*, pg. 6509
SAMSON OIL & GAS USA MONTANA, INC.—See Samson Oil & Gas Limited; *Int'l*, pg. 6509
SAMSON PAPER (BEIJING) COMPANY LIMITED—See Samson Paper Holdings Limited; *Int'l*, pg. 6509
SAMSON PAPER COMPANY LIMITED—See Samson Paper Holdings Limited; *Int'l*, pg. 6509
SAMSON PAPER HOLDINGS LIMITED; *Int'l*, pg. 6509
SAMSON PAPER (SHANGHAI) COMPANY LIMITED—See Samson Paper Holdings Limited; *Int'l*, pg. 6509
SAMSON PAPER (SHENZHEN) COMPANY LIMITED—See Samson Paper Holdings Limited; *Int'l*, pg. 6509
SAMSON PRODUCTS INC.—See Activar, Inc.; *U.S. Private*, pg. 68
SAMSON ROPE TECHNOLOGIES—See Wind River Holdings, L.P.; *U.S. Private*, pg. 4536
SAM SPORTS - STARWATCH ARTIST MANAGEMENT GMBH—See ProSiebenSat.1 Media SE; *Int'l*, pg. 6001
SAMS SEA FARM PTY. LTD.—See Sarin Group Pty Ltd; *Int'l*, pg. 6577
SAMSUI SUPPLIES & SERVICES PTE. LTD.—See Soup Holdings Limited; *Int'l*, pg. 7114
SAMSUL MINERACAO LTDA—See Kincora Copper Limited; *Int'l*, pg. 4165
SAMSUNG AMERICA - FASHION & ENTERTAINMENT DIVISION—See Samsung Group; *Int'l*, pg. 6511
SAMSUNG ASIA PTE., LTD—See Samsung Group; *Int'l*, pg. 6511
SAMSUNG ASSET MANAGEMENT CO., LTD.—See Samsung Group; *Int'l*, pg. 6514
SAMSUNG AUSTIN SEMICONDUCTOR, LLC—See Samsung Group; *Int'l*, pg. 6513
SAMSUNG BIOLOGICS CO., LTD.; *Int'l*, pg. 6510
SAMSUNG CARD CO., LTD.—See Samsung Group; *Int'l*, pg. 6511
SAMSUNG (CHINA) INVESTMENT ELECTRONICS CO., LTD.—See Samsung Group; *Int'l*, pg. 6511
SAMSUNG CLIMATE CONTROL CO., LTD.; *Int'l*, pg. 6511
SAMSUNG C&T AMERICA, INC.—See Samsung Group; *Int'l*, pg. 6511
SAMSUNG C&T CORPORATION—See Samsung Group; *Int'l*, pg. 6511
SAMSUNG C&T THAILAND CO., LTD.—See Samsung BioLogics Co., Ltd.; *Int'l*, pg. 6510
SAMSUNG DENMARK RESEARCH CENTER APS—See Samsung Group; *Int'l*, pg. 6511
SAMSUNG DISPLAY CO., LTD.—See Samsung Group; *Int'l*, pg. 6511
SAMSUNG DISPLAY SLOVAKIA S.R.O.—See Samsung Group; *Int'l*, pg. 6511
SAMSUNG DISPLAYS MEXICANA SA DE CV—See Samsung Group; *Int'l*, pg. 6514
SAMSUNG DISPLAY TIANJIN CO., LTD.—See Samsung Group; *Int'l*, pg. 6511
SAMSUNG ECONOMIC RESEARCH INSTITUTE—See Samsung Group; *Int'l*, pg. 6511
SAMSUNG ELECTRO-MECHANICS AMERICA, INC.—See Samsung Group; *Int'l*, pg. 6511
SAMSUNG ELECTRO-MECHANICS CO., LTD.—See Samsung Group; *Int'l*, pg. 6511
SAMSUNG ELECTRONICA COLOMBIA S.A.—See Samsung BioLogics Co., Ltd.; *Int'l*, pg. 6510
SAMSUNG ELECTRONICA DA AMAZONIA LTDA.—See Samsung Group; *Int'l*, pg. 6512
SAMSUNG ELECTRONICS AMERICA, INC.—See Samsung Group; *Int'l*, pg. 6512
SAMSUNG ELECTRONICS ARGENTINA S.A.—See Samsung Group; *Int'l*, pg. 6513
SAMSUNG ELECTRONICS AUSTRALIA PTY LTD—See Samsung Group; *Int'l*, pg. 6513
SAMSUNG ELECTRONICS BALTICS SIA—See Samsung BioLogics Co., Ltd.; *Int'l*, pg. 6513
SAMSUNG ELECTRONICS BENELUX B.V.—See Samsung Group; *Int'l*, pg. 6513
SAMSUNG ELECTRONICS CANADA INC.—See Samsung Group; *Int'l*, pg. 6512
SAMSUNG ELECTRONICS CHILE LIMITADA.—See Samsung Group; *Int'l*, pg. 6513
SAMSUNG ELECTRONICS CO., LTD.—See Samsung Group; *Int'l*, pg. 6511
SAMSUNG ELECTRONICS CZECH AND SLOVAK. S.R.O.—See Samsung Group; *Int'l*, pg. 6513
SAMSUNG ELECTRONICS DISPLAY(M) SDN. BHD.—See Samsung Group; *Int'l*, pg. 6513
SAMSUNG ELECTRONICS EAST AFRICA LTD.—See Samsung Group; *Int'l*, pg. 6513
SAMSUNG ELECTRONICS EUROPE HOLDING—See Samsung Group; *Int'l*, pg. 6513
SAMSUNG ELECTRONICS GMBH—See Samsung Group; *Int'l*, pg. 6513
SAMSUNG ELECTRONICS HOLDING GMBH—See Samsung Group; *Int'l*, pg. 6513
SAMSUNG ELECTRONICS HONG KONG CO., LTD.—See Samsung Group; *Int'l*, pg. 6513
SAMSUNG ELECTRONICS HUIZHOU CO., LTD.—See Samsung Group; *Int'l*, pg. 6513
SAMSUNG ELECTRONICS HUNGARIAN CO., LTD.—See Samsung Group; *Int'l*, pg. 6513
SAMSUNG ELECTRONICS ITALIA S.P.A.—See Samsung Group; *Int'l*, pg. 6513
SAMSUNG ELECTRONICS JAPAN CO., LTD.—See Samsung Group; *Int'l*, pg. 6513
SAMSUNG ELECTRONICS LATINOAMERICA MIAMI, INC.—See Samsung Group; *Int'l*, pg. 6513
SAMSUNG ELECTRONICS LATINOAMERICA—See Samsung Group; *Int'l*, pg. 6513
SAMSUNG ELECTRONICS NEW ZEALAND LTD.—See Samsung Group; *Int'l*, pg. 6513
SAMSUNG ELECTRONICS NORDIC AB—See Samsung Group; *Int'l*, pg. 6513
SAMSUNG ELECTRONICS OVERSEAS B.V.—See Samsung Group; *Int'l*, pg. 6513
SAMSUNG ELECTRONICS PERU S.A.C.—See Samsung Group; *Int'l*, pg. 6513
SAMSUNG ELECTRONICS PHILIPPINES, CO.—See Samsung Group; *Int'l*, pg. 6513
SAMSUNG ELECTRONICS POLSKA, SP.ZO.O.—See Samsung Group; *Int'l*, pg. 6513
SAMSUNG ELECTRONICS PORTUGUESA S.A.—See Samsung Group; *Int'l*, pg. 6513
SAMSUNG ELECTRONICS RUS COMPANY LLC.—See Samsung Group; *Int'l*, pg. 6513
SAMSUNG ELECTRONICS RUS KALUGA LLC.—See Samsung Group; *Int'l*, pg. 6513
SAMSUNG ELECTRONICS SAUDI ARABIA LTD.—See Samsung BioLogics Co., Ltd.; *Int'l*, pg. 6511
SAMSUNG ELECTRONICS SOUTH AFRICA PTY. LTD.—See Samsung Group; *Int'l*, pg. 6513
SAMSUNG ELECTRONICS (SUZHOU) COMPUTER CO., LTD.—See Samsung Group; *Int'l*, pg. 6512
SAMSUNG ELECTRONICS (SUZHOU) SEMICONDUCTOR CO., LTD.—See Samsung Group; *Int'l*, pg. 6512
SAMSUNG ELECTRONICS SWITZERLAND GMBH—See Samsung Group; *Int'l*, pg. 6513
SAMSUNG ELECTRONICS TURKEY LTD.—See Samsung Group; *Int'l*, pg. 6513
SAMSUNG ELECTRONICS (UK) LIMITED—See Samsung Group; *Int'l*, pg. 6512
SAMSUNG ELECTRONICS UKRAINE COMPANY LLC—See Samsung Group; *Int'l*, pg. 6513
SAMSUNG ELECTRONICS VENEZUELA, C.A.—See Samsung Group; *Int'l*, pg. 6513
SAMSUNG ENGINEERING CO., LTD.—See Samsung Group; *Int'l*, pg. 6514
SAMSUNG EVERLAND INC.—See Samsung Group; *Int'l*, pg. 6514
SAMSUNG FIRE & MARINE INSURANCE CO., LTD.—See Samsung Group; *Int'l*, pg. 6514
SAMSUNGFN REIT CO., LTD.; *Int'l*, pg. 6515
SAMSUNG GROUP; *Int'l*, pg. 6511
SAMSUNG GULF ELECTRONICS—See Samsung Group; *Int'l*, pg. 6513
SAMSUNG HEAVY INDUSTRIES CO., LTD.—See Samsung Group; *Int'l*, pg. 6514
SAMSUNG HVAC AMERICA, LLC—See Samsung BioLogics Co., Ltd.; *Int'l*, pg. 6511
SAMSUNG INDIA ELECTRONICS LTD—See Samsung Group; *Int'l*, pg. 6513
SAMSUNG INFORMATION SYSTEMS AMERICA, INC.—See Samsung Group; *Int'l*, pg. 6514
SAMSUNG LIFE INSURANCE CO., LTD.—See Samsung Group; *Int'l*, pg. 6514
SAMSUNG MALAYSIA ELECTRONICS (SME) SDN. BHD—See Samsung Group; *Int'l*, pg. 6513
SAMSUNG MEDISON AMERICA, INC.—See Samsung Group; *Int'l*, pg. 6513
SAMSUNG MEDISON BRASIL LTDA.—See Samsung Group; *Int'l*, pg. 6513
SAMSUNG MEDISON CO., LTD.—See Samsung Group; *Int'l*, pg. 6513
SAMSUNG MEDISON FRANCE S.A.S.—See Samsung Group; *Int'l*, pg. 6513
SAMSUNG MEDISON INDIA PRIVATE LTD.—See Samsung Group; *Int'l*, pg. 6514
SAMSUNG MEDISON JAPAN CO., LTD.—See Samsung Group; *Int'l*, pg. 6514
SAMSUNG MEDISON SHANGHAI MEDICAL INSTRUMENT CO., LTD.—See Samsung Group; *Int'l*, pg. 6514
SAMSUNG MUST SPECIAL PURPOSE ACQUISITION 3 CO., LTD.; *Int'l*, pg. 6514
SAMSUNG PETROCHEMICAL CO., LTD.—See Samsung Group; *Int'l*, pg. 6514
SAMSUNG PHARMACEUTICAL CO., LTD.; *Int'l*, pg. 6515
SAMSUNG PHARM HEALTHCARE CO., LTD.—See GemVax & KAEL Co., Ltd.; *Int'l*, pg. 2916
SAMSUNG PUBLISHING CO., LTD.; *Int'l*, pg. 6515
SAMSUNG R&D INSTITUTE JAPAN CO. LTD.—See Samsung Group; *Int'l*, pg. 6514
SAMSUNG RESEARCH AMERICA, INC.—See Samsung BioLogics Co., Ltd.; *Int'l*, pg. 6511
SAMSUNG SDI AMERICA, INC.—See Samsung Group; *Int'l*, pg. 6514
SAMSUNG SDI BRASIL LTDA.—See Samsung Group; *Int'l*, pg. 6514
SAMSUNG SDI CO., LTD.—See Samsung Group; *Int'l*, pg. 6514
SAMSUNG SDI (HK) LTD.—See Samsung Group; *Int'l*, pg. 6514
SAMSUNG SDI HUNGARY LTD.—See Samsung Group; *Int'l*, pg. 6514
SAMSUNG SDI (MALAYSIA) SDN. BHD.—See Samsung Group; *Int'l*, pg. 6514
SAMSUNG SDI MEXICO SA DE CV—See Samsung Group; *Int'l*, pg. 6514
SAMSUNG SDS CO., LTD.—See Samsung Group; *Int'l*, pg. 6514
SAMSUNG SECURITIES (AMERICA), INC.—See Samsung Group; *Int'l*, pg. 6514
SAMSUNG SECURITIES CO., LTD.—See Samsung Group; *Int'l*, pg. 6514
SAMSUNG SEMICONDUCTOR EUROPE GMBH—See Samsung Group; *Int'l*, pg. 6514
SAMSUNG SEMICONDUCTOR, INC.—See Samsung Group; *Int'l*, pg. 6513
SAMSUNG SEMICONDUCTOR ISRAEL R&D CENTER LTD.—See Samsung Group; *Int'l*, pg. 6514
SAMSUNG SUZHOU MODULE CO., LTD—See Samsung Group; *Int'l*, pg. 6514
SAMSUNG TELECOMMUNICATIONS AMERICA, LLC—See Samsung Group; *Int'l*, pg. 6513
SAMSUNG TOTAL PETROCHEMICALS CO., LTD.—See Samsung Group; *Int'l*, pg. 6511
SAMSUNG TOTAL PETROCHEMICALS CO., LTD.—See TotalEnergies SE; *Int'l*, pg. 7842
SAMSUNG ZHILABS, S.L.—See Samsung BioLogics Co., Ltd.; *Int'l*, pg. 6510
SAM SUSTAINABLE ASSET MANAGEMENT AG—See S&P Global Inc.; *U.S. Public*, pg. 1831
SAM'S WEST, INC.—See Walmart Inc.; *U.S. Public*, pg. 2325
SAM SWOPE VOLKSWAGEN OF CLARKSVILLE; *U.S. Private*, pg. 3536
SAMTACK INC.—See PINE Technology Holdings Limited; *Int'l*, pg. 5868
SAM TAIHANG ELECTRONICS CO LTD—See L3Harris Technologies, Inc.; *U.S. Public*, pg. 1284
SAMTAN CO., LTD.—See Samchully Co., Ltd.; *Int'l*, pg. 6503
SAMTAN USA, INC.—See Samchully Co., Ltd.; *Int'l*, pg. 6503
SAMT CO., LTD.—See Samji Electronics Co., Ltd.; *Int'l*, pg. 6506
SAMTEC ASIA PACIFIC PTE LTD.—See Samtec, Inc.; *U.S. Private*, pg. 3538
SAMTEC FRANCE—See Samtec, Inc.; *U.S. Private*, pg. 3538
SAMTEC HONG KONG LIMITED—See Samtec, Inc.; *U.S. Private*, pg. 3538
SAMTEC, INC.; *U.S. Private*, pg. 3538
SAMTEC TAIWAN LIMITED—See Samtec, Inc.; *U.S. Private*, pg. 3538
SAMTEL INDIA LTD; *Int'l*, pg. 6515
SAMTEX FASHIONS LIMITED; *Int'l*, pg. 6515
SAM TOOLING TECHNOLOGY SDN. BHD.—See SAM Engineering & Equipment (M) Berhad; *Int'l*, pg. 6500
SAM-TRUCK GMBH & CO. KG—See Wilhelm Geiger GmbH & Co. KG; *Int'l*, pg. 8411
SAMTRYGG GROUP AB; *Int'l*, pg. 6515
SAMTY ASSET MANAGEMENT CO., LTD.—See Samty Co., Ltd.; *Int'l*, pg. 6515
SAMTY CO., LTD.; *Int'l*, pg. 6515
SAMTY PROPERTY MANAGEMENT CO., LTD.—See Samty Co., Ltd.; *Int'l*, pg. 6515
SAMTY RESIDENTIAL INVESTMENT CORPORATION; *Int'l*, pg. 6515
SAMUDERA LOGISTICS DWC LLC—See PT Samudera Indonesia Tbk; *Int'l*, pg. 6069
SAMUDERA SHIPPING LINE (INDIA) PVT., LTD.—See PT Samudera Indonesia Tbk; *Int'l*, pg. 6069
SAMUDERA SHIPPING LINE LTD.—See PT Samudera Indonesia Tbk; *Int'l*, pg. 6069
SAMUDRA HEALTHCARE ENTERPRISES LIMITED—See Apollo Hospitals Enterprise Limited; *Int'l*, pg. 518
SAMUEL A. RAMIREZ & CO. INC.; *U.S. Private*, pg. 3538
SAMUEL BANNER & CO.—See Banner Chemicals Limited; *Int'l*, pg. 851
SAMUEL COIL PROCESSING-CALGARY—See Russel Metals Inc.; *Int'l*, pg. 6430
SAMUEL CORALUZZO CO. INC.; *U.S. Private*, pg. 3538
SAMUEL ENGINEERING, INC.; *U.S. Private*, pg. 3538
SAMUEL ET FILS ET CIE LTEE.—See Samuel, Son & Co., Limited; *Int'l*, pg. 6515

SAMUEL ENGINEERING, INC.   CORPORATE AFFILIATIONS

SAMUEL FELDMAN LUMBER CO., INC.—See Bain Capital, LP; *U.S. Private*, pg. 451
SAMUEL FRENCH INC.—See Massachusetts Mutual Life Insurance Company; *U.S. Private*, pg. 2605
SAMUEL GOLDWYN FILMS, LLC - NEW YORK—See Samuel Goldwyn Films, LLC; *U.S. Private*, pg. 3538
SAMUEL GOLDWYN FILMS, LLC; *U.S. Private*, pg. 3538
SAMUEL GROVES LIMITED—See EveryWare Global, Inc; *U.S. Private*, pg. 1441
SAMUEL HEATH & SONS PLC; *Int'l*, pg. 6515
SAMUEL HOBSON HOUSE LIMITED—See MBH Corporation Plc; *Int'l*, pg. 4752
SAMUEL LAWRENCE FURNITURE—See Hooker Furnishings Corporation; *U.S. Public*, pg. 1052
THE SAMUEL MILLS DAMON ESTATE; *U.S. Private*, pg. 4113
SAMUEL PRESSURE VESSEL GROUP—See Samuel, Son & Co., Limited; *Int'l*, pg. 6516
SAMUEL PRESSURE VESSEL GROUP - TOMAHAWK PLANT—See Samuel, Son & Co., Limited; *Int'l*, pg. 6516
SAMUEL SCOTT FINANCIAL GROUP; *U.S. Private*, pg. 3538
SAMUELS GROUP, INC.; *U.S. Private*, pg. 3538
SAMUEL SHAPIRO & COMPANY INC.; *U.S. Private*, pg. 3538
SAMUELSOHN LIMITED—See Grano Retail Investments Inc.; *Int'l*, pg. 3059
SAMUEL, SON & CO., INC.—See Samuel, Son & Co., Limited; *Int'l*, pg. 6516
SAMUEL, SON & CO., LIMITED - CUSTOM PLATE & PROFILES—See Samuel, Son & Co., Limited; *Int'l*, pg. 6516
SAMUEL, SON & CO., LIMITED - NASH METAL TRADING—See Samuel, Son & Co., Limited; *Int'l*, pg. 6516
SAMUEL, SON & CO., LIMITED; *Int'l*, pg. 6515
SAMUELSON COMMUNICATIONS LIMITED—See Viad Corp.; *U.S. Public*, pg. 2291
SAMUEL STAMPING TECHNOLOGIES LLC—See Samuel, Son & Co., Limited; *Int'l*, pg. 6516
SAMUEL STEEL PICKLING COMPANY—See Samuel, Son & Co., Limited; *Int'l*, pg. 6515
SAMUEL STEEL PICKLING COMPANY—See Worthington Industries, Inc.; *U.S. Public*, pg. 2382
SAMUEL STRAPPING (AUSTRALIA) PTY LTD—See Samuel, Son & Co., Limited; *Int'l*, pg. 6515
SAMUEL STRAPPING SYSTEMS INC—See Samuel, Son & Co., Limited; *Int'l*, pg. 6515
SAMUEL STRAPPING SYSTEMS INC—See Samuel, Son & Co., Limited; *Int'l*, pg. 6515
SAMUEL STRAPPING SYSTEMS-U.S.—See Samuel, Son & Co., Limited; *Int'l*, pg. 6515
SAMUEL STRAPPING SYSTEMS-U.S.—See Samuel, Son & Co., Limited; *Int'l*, pg. 6515
SAMUEL TAYLOR LIMITED; *Int'l*, pg. 6515
SAMUEL TERRY ASSET MANAGEMENT PTY LTD.; *Int'l*, pg. 6515
SAMUEL WILKINSON & SONS LIMITED—See Heidelberg Materials AG; *Int'l*, pg. 3319
SAMUKAWA WATER SERVICE CO., LTD.—See Tsukishima Holdings Co., Ltd.; *Int'l*, pg. 7956
SAMURAI 2K AEROSOL LIMITED; *Int'l*, pg. 6516
SAMURAI ADWAYS INC.—See Adways Inc.; *Int'l*, pg. 169
SAMURAI CAPITAL CORP.; *Int'l*, pg. 6516
SAMURAI FARM SAITO CO., LTD.—See Senko Group Holdings Co., Ltd.; *Int'l*, pg. 6710
SAMVARDHANA MOTHERSON AUTOMOTIVE SYSTEMS GROUP B.V.—See Samvardhana Motherson International Limited; *Int'l*, pg. 6518
SAMVARDHANA MOTHERSON AUTO SYSTEM PRIVATE LIMITED—See Samvardhana Motherson International Limited; *Int'l*, pg. 6518
SAMVARDHANA MOTHERSON HEALTH SOLUTIONS LIMITED—See Samvardhana Motherson International Limited; *Int'l*, pg. 6518
SAMVARDHANA MOTHERSON INTERNATIONAL LIMITED; *Int'l*, pg. 6516
SAMVARDHANA MOTHERSON PEGUFORM AUTOMOTIVE TECHNOLOGY PORTUGAL S.A.—See Samvardhana Motherson International Limited; *Int'l*, pg. 6517
SAMVARDHANA MOTHERSON PEGUFORM BARCELONA S.L.U.—See Samvardhana Motherson International Limited; *Int'l*, pg. 6518
SAMVARDHANA MOTHERSON PEGUFORM GMBH—See Samvardhana Motherson International Limited; *Int'l*, pg. 6518
SAMVARDHANA MOTHERSON REYDEL AUTOTECC MOROCCO S.A.S.—See Samvardhana Motherson International Limited; *Int'l*, pg. 6518
SAM VERTRIEBS GMBH + CO. KG; *Int'l*, pg. 6500
SAMWHA CAPACITOR CO., LTD.—See Samwha Capacitor Group; *Int'l*, pg. 6518
SAMWHA CAPACITOR GROUP; *Int'l*, pg. 6518
SAMWHA ELECTRIC CO., LTD. - CHUNGJU PLANT—See Samwha Capacitor Group; *Int'l*, pg. 6518
SAMWHA ELECTRIC CO., LTD.—See Samwha Capacitor Group; *Int'l*, pg. 6518
SAMWHA ELECTRONICS CO., LTD. - JOCHIWON PLANT—See Samwha Capacitor Group; *Int'l*, pg. 6518
SAMWHA ELECTRONICS CO., LTD.—See Samwha Capacitor Group; *Int'l*, pg. 6518
SAMWHA EUROPE GMBH—See Samwha Capacitor Group; *Int'l*, pg. 6518
SAMWHA HI-TECH INTL. TRADING CO., LTD.—See Samwha Capacitor Group; *Int'l*, pg. 6518
SAMWHA HONGKONG CO., LTD.—See Samwha Capacitor Group; *Int'l*, pg. 6518
SAMWHA HUNGARY KFT.—See Samwha Capacitor Group; *Int'l*, pg. 6518
SAMWHA INDIA ENERGY SAVINGS PVT.LTD.—See Samwha Capacitor Group; *Int'l*, pg. 6518
SAMWHAN CAMUS CO., LTD.—See Samwhan Corporation; *Int'l*, pg. 6518
SAMWHAN CORPORATION; *Int'l*, pg. 6518
SAMWHAN MACHINERY CO., LTD.—See Samwhan Corporation; *Int'l*, pg. 6518
SAMWHA POLAND SP.Z.O.O.—See Samwha Capacitor Group; *Int'l*, pg. 6518
SAMWHA TECOM CO., LTD.—See Samwha Capacitor Group; *Int'l*, pg. 6518
SAMWHA THAILAND CO., LTD.—See Samwha Capacitor Group; *Int'l*, pg. 6518
SAMWHA USA INC.—See Samwha Capacitor Group; *Int'l*, pg. 6518
SAMWONSTEEL CO., LTD.; *Int'l*, pg. 6519
SAMWON TECH (EUROPE) LTD—See Aktieselskabet Schouw & Co.; *Int'l*, pg. 266
SAMWON USA INC.—See Tera Science Co., Ltd.; *Int'l*, pg. 7563
SAMWOO COMMUNICATIONS INDUSTRY CO., LTD.—See Sunny Electronics Corp.; *Int'l*, pg. 7318
SAM WOO CONSTRUCTION GROUP LIMITED; *Int'l*, pg. 6500
SAM WOOD LTD.; *Int'l*, pg. 6500
SAMWOO HEAVY INDUSTRIES CO., LTD.—See Hanwha Ocean Co., Ltd.; *Int'l*, pg. 3266
SAMWORTH BROTHERS DISTRIBUTION LIMITED—See Samworth Brothers Ltd.; *Int'l*, pg. 6519
SAMWORTH BROTHERS LTD.; *Int'l*, pg. 6519
SAMXON ELECTRONIC COMPONENTS LLC—See Man Yue Technology Holdings Limited; *Int'l*, pg. 4665
SAMXON ELECTRONICS (DONGGUAN) CO., LTD.—See Man Yue Technology Holdings Limited; *Int'l*, pg. 4665
SAMYAK INTERNATIONAL LIMITED; *Int'l*, pg. 6519
SAMYANG BIOPHARM USA, INC.—See Samyang Holdings Corporation; *Int'l*, pg. 6519
SAMYANG CORPORATION—See Samyang Holdings Corporation; *Int'l*, pg. 6519
SAMYANG EMS CO., LTD.—See Samyang Holdings Corporation; *Int'l*, pg. 6519
SAMYANG ENGINEERING PLASTICS (HUNGARY) CO., LTD.—See Samyang Holdings Corporation; *Int'l*, pg. 6519
SAMYANG ENGINEERING PLASTICS (SHANGHAI) CO., LTD.—See Samyang Holdings Corporation; *Int'l*, pg. 6519
SAMYANG F&D, INC.—See Samyang Holdings Corporation; *Int'l*, pg. 6519
SAMYANG FOODS CO., LTD.; *Int'l*, pg. 6519
SAMYANG HOLDINGS CORPORATION; *Int'l*, pg. 6519
SAMYANG KASEI CO., LTD.—See Samyang Holdings Corporation; *Int'l*, pg. 6519
SAMYANG MILMAX CORPORATION—See Samyang Holdings Corporation; *Int'l*, pg. 6519
SAMYANG PACKAGING CORP.; *Int'l*, pg. 6519
SAMYANG RESEARCH CORPORATION—See Samyang Holdings Corporation; *Int'l*, pg. 6519
SAMYANG TONGSANG CO., LTD. - GUNPO FACTORY—See SAMYANG TONGSANG Co., Ltd.; *Int'l*, pg. 6520
SAMYANG TONGSANG CO., LTD.; *Int'l*, pg. 6519
SAM YODER & SON, LLC.; *U.S. Private*, pg. 3536
SAMYOUNG CHEMICAL - CHEONGJU FACTORY—See Samyoung Co.,Ltd.; *Int'l*, pg. 6520
SAMYOUNG CHEMICAL - DALIAN FACTORY—See Samyoung Co.,Ltd.; *Int'l*, pg. 6520
SAMYOUNG CHEMICAL - GUMI FACTORY—See Samyoung Co.,Ltd.; *Int'l*, pg. 6520
SAMYOUNG CO.,LTD.; *Int'l*, pg. 6520
SAMYOUNG ELECTRONICS CO., LTD. - POSEUNG PLANT 1—See Samyoung Electronics Co., Ltd.; *Int'l*, pg. 6520
SAMYOUNG ELECTRONICS CO., LTD. - QINGDAO FACTORY—See Samyoung Electronics Co., Ltd.; *Int'l*, pg. 6520
SAMYOUNG ELECTRONICS CO., LTD.; *Int'l*, pg. 6520
SAM YOUNG INK & PAINT MFG. CO. LTD.—See Toyo Ink SC Holdings Co., Ltd.; *Int'l*, pg. 7853
SAMYOUNG M-TEK CO., LTD. - FIRST FACTORY—See Samyoung M-TEK Co., Ltd.; *Int'l*, pg. 6520
SAMYOUNG M-TEK CO., LTD. - SECOND FACTORY—See Samyoung M-TEK Co., Ltd.; *Int'l*, pg. 6520
SAMYOUNG M-TEK CO., LTD.; *Int'l*, pg. 6520
SAMYOUNG PURE CHEMICALS CO., LTD.—See Mitsubishi Gas Chemical Company, Inc.; *Int'l*, pg. 4950
SAMYOUNG S&C CO., LTD.—See Samyoung Electronics Co., Ltd.; *Int'l*, pg. 6520
SAMY'S CAMERA INC.; *U.S. Private*, pg. 3538
SAMYUNG ENC CO., LTD.; *Int'l*, pg. 6520
SAMYUNG TRADING CO., LTD.; *Int'l*, pg. 6520
S.A.M YVES SAINT LAURENT OF MONACO—See Kering S.A.; *Int'l*, pg. 4136
SANABEL SECURITY CO.—See Bank of Khartoum; *Int'l*, pg. 845
SANA BIOTECHNOLOGY, INC.; *U.S. Public*, pg. 1839
SANABLE ALKHAIR FOR FINANCIAL INVESTMENT—See Al Baraka Banking Group B.S.C.; *Int'l*, pg. 276
SAN-ACE CO., LTD.—See Shin-Etsu Chemical Co. Ltd.; *Int'l*, pg. 6839
SAN-A CO., LTD.; *Int'l*, pg. 6522
SANAD AERO SOLUTIONS GMBH—See Mubadala Investment Company PJSC; *Int'l*, pg. 5076
SANA-ELVIS A.D.; *Int'l*, pg. 6522
SANAI HEALTH INDUSTRY GROUP COMPANY LIMITED; *Int'l*, pg. 6522
SANA INDUSTRIES LIMITED; *Int'l*, pg. 6522
SAN-AI OBBLI CO., LTD.; *Int'l*, pg. 6522
SANA KISAN BIKAS LAGHUBITTA BITTIYA SANSTHA LIMITED; *Int'l*, pg. 6522
SANA LINEA A.D.; *Int'l*, pg. 6522
SANAM CORPORATION—See Sanyo Chemical Industries, Ltd.; *Int'l*, pg. 6564
SANAM REAL ESTATE CO. (K.S.C.C.); *Int'l*, pg. 6522
SAN ANGELO COMMUNITY MEDICAL CENTER, LLC—See Community Health Systems, Inc.; *U.S. Public*, pg. 556
SAN ANGELO HOSPITAL, L.P.—See Community Health Systems, Inc.; *U.S. Public*, pg. 552
SAN ANGELO STANDARD-TIMES, LLC—See Gannett Co., Inc.; *U.S. Public*, pg. 898
SAN ANN OIL COMPANY—See Supertest Oil Company Inc.; *U.S. Private*, pg. 3881
SAN'AN OPTOELECTRONICS CO., LTD.; *Int'l*, pg. 6522
SAN ANTONIO ANUSA, LLC—See AutoNation, Inc.; *U.S. Public*, pg. 237
SAN ANTONIO ASC, LP—See KKR & Co. Inc.; *U.S. Public*, pg. 1246
SAN ANTONIO BUSINESS JOURNAL—See Advance Publications, Inc.; *U.S. Private*, pg. 85
SAN ANTONIO CHILDREN'S MUSEUM; *U.S. Private*, pg. 3538
SAN ANTONIO DESIGN GROUP INC.—See M&S Engineering, LLC; *U.S. Private*, pg. 2525
SAN ANTONIO ENDOSCOPY, L.P.—See Tenet Healthcare Corporation; *U.S. Public*, pg. 2012
SAN ANTONIO EXPRESS NEWS—See The Hearst Corporation; *U.S. Private*, pg. 4047
SAN ANTONIO MAGAZINE—See The Hearst Corporation; *U.S. Private*, pg. 4045
SAN ANTONIO MASONRY & TOOL SUPPLY, INC.; *U.S. Private*, pg. 3538
SAN ANTONIO NACOGDOCHES MEDICAL CENTER LLC—See Adeptus Health Inc.; *U.S. Private*, pg. 78
SAN ANTONIO RECOVERY SERVICES—See Webster Equity Partners, LLC; *U.S. Private*, pg. 4466
SAN ANTONIO SPURS, LLC—See Spurs Sports & Entertainment; *U.S. Private*, pg. 3765
SAN ANTONIO STOCK SHOW & RODEO; *U.S. Private*, pg. 3539
SAN ANTONIO SURGICENTER, LLC—See HCA Healthcare, Inc.; *U.S. Public*, pg. 1008
SAN ANTONIO THERMO KING, INC.—See Kirby Corporation; *U.S. Public*, pg. 1235
THE SAN ANTONIO TX ENDOSCOPY ASC, L.P.—See KKR & Co. Inc.; *U.S. Public*, pg. 1248
SAN ANTONIO WINERY & MADDALENA RESTAURANT; *U.S. Private*, pg. 3539
SAN ANTONIO ZOO; *U.S. Private*, pg. 3539
SAN-APRO LTD—See Air Products & Chemicals, Inc.; *U.S. Public*, pg. 67
SANARA MEDTECH INC.; *U.S. Public*, pg. 1839
SANARE, LLC—See Bertram Capital Management, LLC; *U.S. Private*, pg. 540
SANASA DEVELOPMENT BANK PLC; *Int'l*, pg. 6522
SANASA TECH FEB LTD.; *Int'l*, pg. 6522
SANATANA RESOURCES INC.; *Int'l*, pg. 6522
SANATHNAGAR ENTERPRISES LTD.; *Int'l*, pg. 6522
SANATIS GMBH—See Medtronic plc; *Int'l*, pg. 4790
SANAVITA MEDICAL, LLC—See Compagnie Generale des Etablissements Michelin SCA; *Int'l*, pg. 1745
SAN BAR CONSTRUCTION CORP.; *U.S. Private*, pg. 3539
SANBASE CORPORATION LIMITED; *Int'l*, pg. 6523
SAN BENITO SUPPLY INCORPORATED; *U.S. Private*, pg. 3539
SAN BERNABE VINEYARDS—See Delicato Vineyards; *U.S. Private*, pg. 1197
SAN BERNARD ELECTRIC COOP; *U.S. Private*, pg. 3539
THE SAN BERNARDINO COUNTY SUN—See Alden Global Capital LLC; *U.S. Private*, pg. 158
SAN BERNARDINO MUNICIPAL WATER DEPARTMENT; *U.S. Private*, pg. 3539
SAN BERNARDO S.P.A.—See Nestle S.A.; *Int'l*, pg. 5206

COMPANY NAME INDEX

SANBIAN SCI-TECH CO., LTD.; *Int'l*, pg. 6523
SANBIO COMPANY LIMITED; *Int'l*, pg. 6523
SANBIO, INC—See SanBio Company Limited; *Int'l*, pg. 6523
SANBISHI CO., LTD.—See Zensho Holdings Co., Ltd.; *Int'l*, pg. 8634
SANBLUE CORPORATION LTD.; *Int'l*, pg. 6523
SANBOLIC, INC.—See Elliott Management Corporation; *U.S. Private*, pg. 1367
SANBOLIC, INC.—See Vista Equity Partners, LLC; *U.S. Private*, pg. 4396
SANBOR CORPORATION; *U.S. Private*, pg. 3542
SANBORN CHEVROLET; *U.S. Private*, pg. 3542
THE SANBORN MAP COMPANY, INC.; *U.S. Private*, pg. 4113
SANBORN TUBE SALES OF WISCONSIN INC.—See Russel Metals Inc.; *Int'l*, pg. 6430
SAN BUENAVENTURA POWER LIMITED—See Manila Electric Company; *Int'l*, pg. 4671
SAN-BUSINESS SERVICES, LTD.—See Mitsui Chemicals, Inc.; *Int'l*, pg. 4983
SAN-BYTE TAIWAN CO., LTD.—See Sanrio Company, Ltd.; *Int'l*, pg. 6554
SANCAI HOLDING GROUP LTD.; *Int'l*, pg. 6523
SAN CAMILLO INC.; *U.S. Private*, pg. 3539
SANCAP LINER TECHNOLOGY, INC.—See Genstar Capital, LLC; *U.S. Private*, pg. 1679
SANCAST, INC.—See Westinghouse Air Brake Technologies Corporation; *U.S. Public*, pg. 2359
SANCELA CHILE S.A.—See Essity Aktiebolag; *Int'l*, pg. 2517
SANCEM INVESTMENT PTE LTD—See EnGro Corporation Limited; *Int'l*, pg. 2435
SANCHAY FINVEST LIMITED; *Int'l*, pg. 6523
SAN CHEMICAL CO., LTD.—See Sanyo Chemical Industries, Ltd.; *Int'l*, pg. 6563
SANCHEZ ALCARAZ S.L.U.—See Coop-Gruppe Genossenschaft; *Int'l*, pg. 1790
SANCHEZ COMPUTER ASSOCIATES, LLC—See Fidelity National Infor; *U.S. Public*, pg. 833
SANCHEZ ENERGY CORPORATION; *U.S. Private*, pg. 3542
SAN CHIH SEMICONDUCTOR COMPANY; *Int'l*, pg. 6520
SAN CHIH SEMICONDUCTOR COMPANY - TAYUAN PLANT—See SAN CHIH Semiconductor Company; *Int'l*, pg. 6520
SAN CHING ENGINEERING COMPANY LTD.—See Lin Yuan Investment Co., Ltd.; *Int'l*, pg. 4500
SANCHO BBDO—See Omnicom Group Inc.; *U.S. Public*, pg. 1577
SANCHUAN WISDOM TECHNOLOGY CO., LTD.; *Int'l*, pg. 6523
SANCIA GLOBAL INFRAPROJECTS LTD.; *Int'l*, pg. 6523
SANCO COGYO CO., LTD.—See Mie Kotsu Group Holdings, Inc.; *Int'l*, pg. 4888
SANCO CREATIVE LIFE CO., LTD.—See Mie Kotsu Group Holdings, Inc.; *Int'l*, pg. 4888
SANCODE TECHNOLOGIES LTD.; *Int'l*, pg. 6523
SANCO DRIVING SCHOOL CO., LTD.—See Mie Kotsu Group Holdings, Inc.; *Int'l*, pg. 4888
SANCO INDUSTRIES LIMITED; *Int'l*, pg. 6523
SANCO INN CO., LTD.—See Mie Kotsu Group Holdings, Inc.; *Int'l*, pg. 4888
SANCO ISESHIMA KOTSU CO., LTD.—See Mie Kotsu Group Holdings, Inc.; *Int'l*, pg. 4888
SAN-CON INDUSTRIES, INC.—See Marietta Silos LLC; *U.S. Private*, pg. 2574
SANCO OIL CO., LTD.—See Mie Kotsu Group Holdings, Inc.; *Int'l*, pg. 4888
SANCOR COOPERATIVAS UNIDAS LIMITADA; *Int'l*, pg. 6523
SANCOR DAIRY CORPORATION—See SanCor Cooperativas Unidas Limitada; *Int'l*, pg. 6523
SANCO REAL ESTATE APPRAISAL CO., LTD.—See Mie Kotsu Group Holdings, Inc.; *Int'l*, pg. 4888
SANCO REAL ESTATE CO., LTD.—See Mie Kotsu Group Holdings, Inc.; *Int'l*, pg. 4888
SANCO TAXI CO., LTD.—See Mie Kotsu Group Holdings, Inc.; *Int'l*, pg. 4888
SANCO TRANS LTD.; *Int'l*, pg. 6523
SAN CRISTOBAL MINING INC.; *Int'l*, pg. 6520
SANCTUARY ASIA; *Int'l*, pg. 6523
THE SANCTUARY AT COVENT GARDEN LTD—See PZ Cussons Plc; *Int'l*, pg. 6129
SANCTUARY AT GRAND MEMORIES SANTA MARIA—See Sunwing Travel Group, Inc.; *Int'l*, pg. 7332
SANCTUARY AT GRAND MEMORIES VARADERO—See Sunwing Travel Group, Inc.; *Int'l*, pg. 7332
SANCTUARY CARE LIMITED—See Sanctuary Housing Association; *Int'l*, pg. 6523
THE SANCTUARY CITY SPAS LTD—See PZ Cussons Plc; *Int'l*, pg. 6128
SANCTUARY HOME MORTGAGE LLC—See Rithm Capital Corp.; *U.S. Public*, pg. 1800
SANCTUARY HOTEL AND SPA—See Menin Hotels, Inc.; *U.S. Private*, pg. 2666
SANCTUARY HOUSING ASSOCIATION; *Int'l*, pg. 6523

SANCTUARY LAND COMPANY LIMITED—See Sanctuary Housing Association; *Int'l*, pg. 6523
SANCTUARY MAINTENANCE CONTRACTORS LIMITED—See Sanctuary Housing Association; *Int'l*, pg. 6523
SANCTUARY MANAGEMENT SERVICES LIMITED—See Sanctuary Housing Association; *Int'l*, pg. 6524
SANCTUARY SCOTLAND HOUSING ASSOCIATION LIMITED—See Sanctuary Housing Association; *Int'l*, pg. 6524
THE SANCTUARY SPA HOLDINGS LTD—See PZ Cussons Plc; *Int'l*, pg. 6128
SANCTUARY WEALTH GROUP LLC—See Azimut Holding SpA; *Int'l*, pg. 779
SANCUS BMS (IRELAND) LIMITED—See Sancus Lending Group Limited; *Int'l*, pg. 6524
SANCUS (GUERNSEY) LIMITED—See Sancus Lending Group Limited; *Int'l*, pg. 6524
SANCUS LENDING (GIBRALTAR) LIMITED; *Int'l*, pg. 6524
SANCUS LENDING GROUP LIMITED; *Int'l*, pg. 6524
SANCUS LENDING (IRELAND) LIMITED—See Sancus Lending Group Limited; *Int'l*, pg. 6524
SANCUS LENDING (JERSEY) LIMITED—See Sancus Lending Group Limited; *Int'l*, pg. 6524
SANCUS LENDING (UK) LIMITED—See Sancus Lending Group Limited; *Int'l*, pg. 6524
SAN DAIICHI TRAFFIC LTD.—See Daiichi Koutsu Sangyo Co., Ltd.; *Int'l*, pg. 1929
SANDAKAN EDIBLE OILS SDN BHD—See Wilmar International Limited; *Int'l*, pg. 8421
SANDA KAN TECHNOLOGY (SHENZHEN) COMPANY LIMITED—See Kader Holdings Company Limited; *Int'l*, pg. 4046
SANDALS RESORTS INTERNATIONAL; *U.S. Private*, pg. 3542
SANDANGER AS—See Apetit Plc; *Int'l*, pg. 509
SANDAS MONTAGE BV—See Schneider Electric SE; *Int'l*, pg. 6629
SANDATA HOLDINGS, INC.; *U.S. Private*, pg. 3542
SANDATA TECHNOLOGIES, LLC—See Sandata Holdings, Inc.; *U.S. Private*, pg. 3543
SANDAWANA CASTINGS LIMITED—See W. Lucy & Co. Ltd.; *Int'l*, pg. 9321
SANDBACKEN DEVELOPMENT AB; *Int'l*, pg. 6524
SANDBERG CAPITAL SPRAV. SPOL., A.S.; *Int'l*, pg. 6524
SANDBERG FURNITURE MANUFACTURING CO.; *U.S. Private*, pg. 3543
SANDBERG STARCOM—See Publicis Groupe S.A.; *Int'l*, pg. 6111
SANDBOX.COM, INC.—See Gamebase, Inc.; *U.S. Private*, pg. 1640
THE SANDBOX GROUP LLC—See Keystone Capital, Inc.; *U.S. Private*, pg. 2295
SANDBOX LOGISTICS, LLC—See Apollo Global Management, Inc.; *U.S. Public*, pg. 165
SANDBOX MEDICAL LLC—See Canadian Hospital Specialties Limited; *Int'l*, pg. 1283
SANDBRIDGE CAPITAL LLC; *U.S. Private*, pg. 3543
SANDBRIDGE X2 CORP.; *U.S. Public*, pg. 1839
SAND BUILDING MATERIALS, INC.; *U.S. Private*, pg. 3542
SAND CREEK POST & BEAM INC.; *U.S. Private*, pg. 3542
SAND DOLLAR CORPORATION; *U.S. Private*, pg. 3542
SAND DOLLAR HOLDINGS INCORPORATED; *U.S. Private*, pg. 3542
SANDEN ADVANCED TECHNOLOGY CORPORATION—See Sanden Corporation; *Int'l*, pg. 6524
SANDEN AIRCONDITIONING (MALAYSIA) SDN. BHD.—See Sanden Corporation; *Int'l*, pg. 6524
SANDEN AUTOMOTIVE CLIMATE SYSTEMS CORPORATION—See Sanden Corporation; *Int'l*, pg. 6524
SANDEN AUTOMOTIVE COMPONENTS CORPORATION—See Sanden Corporation; *Int'l*, pg. 6524
SANDEN AUTOMOTIVE TECHNOLOGY (SHANGHAI) CO., LTD.—See Sanden Corporation; *Int'l*, pg. 6524
SANDEN BRIGHT PARTNER CORPORATION—See Sanden Corporation; *Int'l*, pg. 6524
SANDEN BUSINESS ASSOCIATE CORPORATION—See Sanden Corporation; *Int'l*, pg. 6524
SANDEN CHONGQING AUTOMOTIVE AIR CONDITIONING CO., LTD.—See Sanden Corporation; *Int'l*, pg. 6524
SANDEN CORPORATION; *Int'l*, pg. 6524
SANDEN ENVIRONMENTAL PRODUCTS CORPORATION—See Sanden Corporation; *Int'l*, pg. 6524
SANDEN HOLDINGS CORPORATION—See Sanden Corporation; *Int'l*, pg. 6524
SANDEN HUAYU AUTOMOTIVE AIR-CONDITIONING CO., LTD.—See Sanden Corporation; *Int'l*, pg. 6524
SANDEN INTERNATIONAL AUSTRALIA PTY. LTD.—See Sanden Corporation; *Int'l*, pg. 6525

SANDEN INTERNATIONAL (EUROPE) GMBH—See Sanden Corporation; *Int'l*, pg. 6524
SANDEN INTERNATIONAL (EUROPE) GMBH—See Sanden Corporation; *Int'l*, pg. 6524
SANDEN INTERNATIONAL (EUROPE) GMBH—See Sanden Corporation; *Int'l*, pg. 6524
SANDEN INTERNATIONAL (EUROPE) GMBH—See Sanden Corporation; *Int'l*, pg. 6524
SANDEN INTERNATIONAL (EUROPE) GMBH—See Sanden Corporation; *Int'l*, pg. 6524
SANDEN INTERNATIONAL (EUROPE) GMBH—See Sanden Corporation; *Int'l*, pg. 6524
SANDEN INTERNATIONAL (EUROPE) LTD.—See Sanden Corporation; *Int'l*, pg. 6524
SANDEN INTERNATIONAL LATIN AMERICA EIRELI—See Sanden Corporation; *Int'l*, pg. 6525
SANDEN INTERNATIONAL PHILIPPINES, INC.—See Sanden Corporation; *Int'l*, pg. 6525
SANDEN INTERNATIONAL (SINGAPORE) PTE. LTD.—See Sanden Corporation; *Int'l*, pg. 6524
SANDEN INTERNATIONAL TAIWAN CORPORATION—See Sanden Corporation; *Int'l*, pg. 6525
SANDEN INTERNATIONAL (USA), INC.—See Sanden Corporation; *Int'l*, pg. 6525
SANDEN LIVING & ENVIRONMENTAL SYSTEMS CORPORATION—See Sanden Corporation; *Int'l*, pg. 6525
SANDEN MANUFACTURING EUROPE S.A.—See Sanden Corporation; *Int'l*, pg. 6525
SANDEN MANUFACTURING MEXICO SA DE CV—See Sanden Corporation; *Int'l*, pg. 6525
SANDEN MANUFACTURING POLAND SP. Z O.O.—See Sanden Corporation; *Int'l*, pg. 6525
SANDEN (SUZHOU) PRECISION PARTS CO., LTD.—See Sanden Corporation; *Int'l*, pg. 6524
SANDEN SYSTEM ENGINEERING CORPORATION—See Sanden Corporation; *Int'l*, pg. 6525
SANDEN TECHNICAL CENTER OF VIETNAM CO., LTD.—See Sanden Corporation; *Int'l*, pg. 6525
SANDEN (THAILAND) CO., LTD.—See Sanden Corporation; *Int'l*, pg. 6524
SANDENVENDO AMERICA—See Sanden Corporation; *Int'l*, pg. 6525
SANDENVENDO BENELUX N.V.—See Sanden Corporation; *Int'l*, pg. 6525
SANDENVENDO EUROPE S.P.A.—See Sanden Corporation; *Int'l*, pg. 6525
SANDENVENDO GMBH—See Sanden Corporation; *Int'l*, pg. 6525
SANDEN VIKAS (INDIA) LTD.—See Sanden Corporation; *Int'l*, pg. 6525
SANDEN VIKAS PRECISION PARTS PVT. LTD.—See Sanden Corporation; *Int'l*, pg. 6525
SANDENZAISHA CO., LTD.—See Tokai Rika Co., Ltd.; *Int'l*, pg. 7780
SANDERLING VENTURES; *U.S. Private*, pg. 3543
SANDER SALES ENTERPRISES LTD.; *U.S. Private*, pg. 3543
SANDERS & ASSOCIATES CUSTOM BUILDERS INC.—See Highland Homes Ltd.; *U.S. Private*, pg. 1938
SANDERS BROTHERS CONSTRUCTION CO; *U.S. Private*, pg. 3543
SANDERSFIRE INTERNATIONAL LIMITED—See Goodwin PLC; *Int'l*, pg. 3042
SANDERS FORD INC.; *U.S. Private*, pg. 3543
SANDERS HYLAND CORPORATION; *U.S. Private*, pg. 3543
SANDERS MANUFACTURING CO., INC.; *U.S. Private*, pg. 3543
SANDERS MARKETING GROUP INC.; *U.S. Private*, pg. 3543
SANDERS MORRIS HARRIS INC.—See Lee Equity Partners LLC; *U.S. Private*, pg. 2412
SANDERS OIL COMPANY INC.; *U.S. Private*, pg. 3543
SANDERSON BELLECCI, INC.; *U.S. Private*, pg. 3543
SANDERSON DESIGN GROUP PLC; *Int'l*, pg. 6525
SANDERSON FARMS, INC. - FOODS DIVISION—See Cargill, Inc.; *U.S. Private*, pg. 760
SANDERSON FARMS, INC. - FOODS DIVISION—See Continental Grain Company; *U.S. Private*, pg. 1029
SANDERSON FARMS, INC. - PROCESSING DIVISION—See Cargill, Inc.; *U.S. Private*, pg. 760
SANDERSON FARMS, INC. - PROCESSING DIVISION—See Continental Grain Company; *U.S. Private*, pg. 1029
SANDERSON FARMS, INC.—See Cargill, Inc.; *U.S. Private*, pg. 760
SANDERSON FARMS, INC.—See Continental Grain Company; *U.S. Private*, pg. 1029
SANDERSON FORD INC.; *U.S. Private*, pg. 3543
SANDERSON GROUP PLC—See TA Associates, Inc.; *U.S. Private*, pg. 3914
SANDERSON LIMITED—See TA Associates, Inc.; *U.S. Private*, pg. 3914
SANDERSON LINCOLN; *U.S. Private*, pg. 3543
SANDERSON MULTI-CHANNEL SOLUTIONS LIMITED—See TA Associates, Inc.; *U.S. Private*, pg. 3914

SANDERSON NI LIMITED—See TA Associates, Inc.; *U.S. Private*, pg. 3914
SANDERSON SAFETY SUPPLY CO. INC.; *U.S. Private*, pg. 3543
SANDERSON STEWART—See Sanderson Bellecci, Inc.; *U.S. Private*, pg. 3543
SANDERS PLUMBING SUPPLY INC.; *U.S. Private*, pg. 3543
SANDERS SAWS, INC.—See K2 Diamond Company; *U.S. Private*, pg. 2253
THE SANDESH LIMITED; *Int'l*, pg. 7680
SANDESTIN GOLF & BEACH RESORT; *U.S. Private*, pg. 3543
SANDFIRE RESOURCES AMERICA INC.—See Sandfire Resources Limited; *Int'l*, pg. 6525
SANDFIRE RESOURCES LIMITED; *Int'l*, pg. 6525
SANDFORCE, INC.—See Seagate Technology Holdings PLC; *Int'l*, pg. 6663
SANDFORD OIL COMPANY, INC.; *U.S. Private*, pg. 3543
SANDFORD OIL SOUTH TEXAS—See Sandford Oil Company, Inc.; *U.S. Private*, pg. 3543
SANDFORD PETROLEUM, INC.—See Sunoco LP; *U.S. Public*, pg. 1965
SAND & GRUS AB JEHANDER—See Heidelberg Materials AG; *Int'l*, pg. 3315
SAND & GRUS JEHANDER—See Heidelberg Materials AG; *Int'l*, pg. 3315
SANDHANI LIFE INSURANCE CO. LTD.; *Int'l*, pg. 6525
SANDHAR TECHNOLOGIES LTD.; *Int'l*, pg. 6525
SANDHILLS AREA LAND TRUST—See Three Rivers Land Trust, Inc.; *U.S. Private*, pg. 4164
SANDHILL SCIENTIFIC, INC.—See Medovations, Inc.; *U.S. Private*, pg. 2658
SANDHILLS PUBLISHING COMPANY; *U.S. Private*, pg. 3543
SAND HOLLOW HEALTHCARE, INC.—See The Ensign Group, Inc.; *U.S. Public*, pg. 2072
SANDHURST AUTOPRINT LTD; *Int'l*, pg. 6525
SANDHURST TRUSTEES LIMITED—See Bendigo & Adelaide Bank Ltd.; *Int'l*, pg. 971
SANDIA BMW; *U.S. Private*, pg. 3543
SANDIA CORPORATION—See Lockheed Martin Corporation; *U.S. Public*, pg. 1339
SANDIA OFFICE SUPPLY; *U.S. Private*, pg. 3544
SAN-DIA POLYMERS, LTD.—See Sanyo Chemical Industries, Ltd.; *Int'l*, pg. 6564
SAN-DIA POLYMERS (NANTONG) CO., LTD.—See Sanyo Chemical Industries, Ltd.; *Int'l*, pg. 6563
SAN DIEGO ADDICTION TREATMENT CENTER, INC.—See AAC Holdings, Inc.; *U.S. Private*, pg. 31
SAN DIEGO AUTO AUCTION INC—See Cox Enterprises, Inc.; *U.S. Private*, pg. 1077
SAN DIEGO BUSINESS JOURNAL; *U.S. Private*, pg. 3539
THE SAN DIEGO CA MULTI-SPECIALTY ASC, LLC—See KKR & Co. Inc.; *U.S. Public*, pg. 1248
SAN DIEGO CASH REGISTER COMPANY, INC.—See i3 Verticals, Inc.; *U.S. Public*, pg. 1081
SAN DIEGO CHARGERS FOOTBALL CO.; *U.S. Private*, pg. 3539
SAN DIEGO CITY EMPLOYEES RETIREE MEDICAL TRUST; *U.S. Private*, pg. 3539
SAN DIEGO COMPOSITES, INC.—See AE Industrial Partners, LP; *U.S. Private*, pg. 111
SAN DIEGO COUNTY CREDIT UNION; *U.S. Private*, pg. 3539
SAN DIEGO COUNTY TOBACCO SECURITIZATION CORPORATION; *U.S. Private*, pg. 3539
SAN DIEGO DATA PROCESSING CORPORATION; *U.S. Private*, pg. 3539
SAN DIEGO GAS & ELECTRIC COMPANY—See Sempra; *U.S. Public*, pg. 1863
SAN DIEGO HAT COMPANY—See Mainland Headwear Holdings Ltd.; *Int'l*, pg. 4651
SAN DIEGO HEALTH ALLIANCE—See Acadia Healthcare Company, Inc.; *U.S. Public*, pg. 30
SAN DIEGO HEBREW HOMES; *U.S. Private*, pg. 3539
SAN DIEGO HYDROPONICS & ORGANICS, INC.—See GrowGeneration Corp.; *U.S. Public*, pg. 972
SAN DIEGO-IMPERIAL COUNTIES DEVELOPMENTAL SERVICES INC.; *U.S. Private*, pg. 3540
SAN DIEGO & IMPERIAL VALLEY RAILROAD COMPANY, INC.—See Brookfield Infrastructure Partners L.P.; *Int'l*, pg. 1192
SAN DIEGO & IMPERIAL VALLEY RAILROAD COMPANY, INC.—See GIC Pte. Ltd.; *Int'l*, pg. 2967
THE SAN DIEGO MUSEUM OF ART; *U.S. Private*, pg. 4113
SAN DIEGO MUTUAL TRADING CO., INC.—See Takara Holdings, Inc.; *Int'l*, pg. 7433
SAN DIEGO PUBLIC LIBRARY FOUNDATION; *U.S. Private*, pg. 3539
SAN DIEGO SIGN COMPANY; *U.S. Private*, pg. 3539
SAN DIEGO SYMPHONY ORCHESTRA ASSOCIATION; *U.S. Private*, pg. 3539
SAN DIEGO TRANSIT CORPORATION—See Metropolitan Transit System; *U.S. Private*, pg. 2689
SAN DIEGO TREATMENT SERVICES—See Acadia Healthcare Company, Inc.; *U.S. Public*, pg. 30

SAN DIEGO TROLLEY INC.—See Metropolitan Transit System; *U.S. Private*, pg. 2689
THE SAN DIEGO UNION-TRIBUNE, LLC—See Alden Global Capital LLC; *U.S. Private*, pg. 159
SAN DIEGO VENTURE GROUP—See CONNECT; *U.S. Private*, pg. 1014
SAN DIEGO VISTA STEEL SERVICE CORPORATION—See Hanwa Co., Ltd.; *Int'l*, pg. 3263
SAN DIEGO VOLVO; *U.S. Private*, pg. 3540
SAN DIEGO WORKFORCE PARTNERSHIP; *U.S. Private*, pg. 3540
SAN DIMAS COMMUNITY HOSPITAL—See Prime Healthcare Services, Inc.; *U.S. Private*, pg. 3262
SAN DIMAS HIGHLANDER—See Alden Global Capital LLC; *U.S. Private*, pg. 158
SAN DIMAS LUGGAGE COMPANY—See LVMH Moet Hennessy Louis Vuitton SE; *Int'l*, pg. 4601
SANDI PROPERTIES CO., LTD.; *Int'l*, pg. 6525
SANDISK HONG KONG LIMITED—See Western Digital Corporation; *U.S. Public*, pg. 2355
SANDISK IL LTD.—See Western Digital Corporation; *U.S. Public*, pg. 2355
SANDISK INDIA - BANGALORE—See Western Digital Corporation; *U.S. Public*, pg. 2355
SANDISK INTERNATIONAL LIMITED—See Western Digital Corporation; *U.S. Public*, pg. 2355
SANDISK ISRAEL (TEFEN) LTD.—See Western Digital Corporation; *U.S. Public*, pg. 2355
SANDISK KOREA LIMITED—See Western Digital Corporation; *U.S. Public*, pg. 2355
SANDISK LIMTED—See Western Digital Corporation; *U.S. Public*, pg. 2356
SANDISK LLC—See Western Digital Corporation; *U.S. Public*, pg. 2355
SANDISK MANUFACTURING LIMITED—See Western Digital Corporation; *U.S. Public*, pg. 2356
SANDISK SAS—See Western Digital Corporation; *U.S. Public*, pg. 2356
SANDISK SCOTLAND LIMITED—See Western Digital Corporation; *U.S. Public*, pg. 2356
SANDISK SEMICONDUCTOR (SHANGHAI) CO., LTD.—See JCET Group Co., Ltd.; *Int'l*, pg. 3923
SANDISK STORAGE MALAYSIA SDN. BHD.—See Western Digital Corporation; *U.S. Public*, pg. 2356
SANDISK TAIWAN LIMITED—See Western Digital Corporation; *U.S. Public*, pg. 2356
SANDISK TRADING (SHANGHAI) CO., LTD.—See Western Digital Corporation; *U.S. Public*, pg. 2356
SAND LAKE SURGICENTER, LLC—See UnitedHealth Group Incorporated; *U.S. Public*, pg. 2250
SANDLAPPER SECURITIES, LLC; *U.S. Private*, pg. 3544
SANDLER CAPITAL MANAGEMENT; *U.S. Private*, pg. 3544
SANDLER COM. ELECT. LTDA.—See Sonepar S.A.; *Int'l*, pg. 7091
SANDLER LLC; *U.S. Private*, pg. 3544
SANDLER O'NEILL MORTGAGE FINANCE L.P.—See Piper Sandler Companies; *U.S. Public*, pg. 1694
SANDLER, O'NEILL & PARTNERS, L.P.—See Piper Sandler Companies; *U.S. Public*, pg. 1694
SANDLER PARTNERS; *U.S. Private*, pg. 3544
SANDLER SYSTEMS, INC.; *U.S. Private*, pg. 3544
SANDLEWOOD DEVELOPMENTS LTD.; *Int'l*, pg. 6526
SAND LILY HEALTHCARE, INC.—See The Ensign Group, Inc.; *U.S. Public*, pg. 2072
SANDLIN MOTORS; *U.S. Private*, pg. 3544
SAND MARK CORPORATION—See Berg Equipment Corporation; *U.S. Private*, pg. 530
SANDMARTIN INTERNATIONAL HOLDINGS LIMITED; *Int'l*, pg. 6526
SANDMARTIN (ZHONG SHAN) ELECTRONIC CO., LTD.—See Sandmartin International Holdings Limited; *Int'l*, pg. 6526
SANDMOLD SYSTEMS, INC.—See Sintokogio Ltd.; *Int'l*, pg. 6958
SANDNES SPAREBANK; *Int'l*, pg. 6526
SAND OAK CAPITAL LLC; *U.S. Private*, pg. 3542
SANDO BRAKE CO., LTD.—See SANGSIN BRAKE Co., Ltd.; *Int'l*, pg. 6538
SANDOLL, INC.; *Int'l*, pg. 6526
SAN DOMENICO VETRARIA S.R.L.—See O-I Glass, Inc.; *U.S. Public*, pg. 1560
SANDON CAPITAL INVESTMENTS LIMITED; *Int'l*, pg. 6526
SANDO TECH, INC.—See SANGSIN BRAKE Co., Ltd.; *Int'l*, pg. 6538
SANDOVAL CRUZ COMPANY; *U.S. Private*, pg. 3544
SANDOW MEDIA LLC; *U.S. Private*, pg. 3544
SANDOWN & BOURNE; *Int'l*, pg. 6526
SANDOWN CAPITAL INTERNATIONAL LIMITED—See Zarclear Holdings Limited; *Int'l*, pg. 8625
SANDOWN MOTOR HOLDINGS (PTY.) LTD.—See Mercedes-Benz Group AG; *Int'l*, pg. 4829
SANDOZ A/S—See Sandoz Group AG; *Int'l*, pg. 6527
SANDOZ B.V.—See Sandoz Group AG; *Int'l*, pg. 6527
SANDOZ (CHINA) PHARMACEUTICAL CO., LTD.—See Sandoz Group AG; *Int'l*, pg. 6527
SANDOZ D.D.—See Sandoz Group AG; *Int'l*, pg. 6526
SANDOZ D.D.—See Sandoz Group AG; *Int'l*, pg. 6526

SANDOZ DO BRASIL INDUSTRIA FARMACEUTICA LTDA.—See Sandoz Group AG; *Int'l*, pg. 6527
SANDOZ D.O.O.—See Sandoz Group AG; *Int'l*, pg. 6527
SANDOZ EGYPT PHARMA S.A.E.—See Sandoz Group AG; *Int'l*, pg. 6527
SANDOZ FARMACEUTICA LDA.—See Sandoz Group AG; *Int'l*, pg. 6527
SANDOZ FARMACEUTICA S.A.—See Sandoz Group AG; *Int'l*, pg. 6527
SANDOZ GMBH—See Sandoz Group AG; *Int'l*, pg. 6527
SANDOZ GMBH—See Sandoz Group AG; *Int'l*, pg. 6527
SANDOZ GROUP AG; *Int'l*, pg. 6526
SANDOZ GRUP SAGLIK URUNLERI ILACLARI SANAYI VE TICARET A.S.—See Sandoz Group AG; *Int'l*, pg. 6527
SANDOZ HUNGARIA KFT.—See Sandoz Group AG; *Int'l*, pg. 6527
SANDOZ HUNGARY LIMITED LIABILITY COMPANY—See Sandoz Group AG; *Int'l*, pg. 6527
SANDOZ ILAC SANAYI VE TICARET A.S.—See Sandoz Group AG; *Int'l*, pg. 6527
SANDOZ INC.—See Sandoz Group AG; *Int'l*, pg. 6527
SANDOZ INDUSTRIAL PRODUCTS S.A.—See Sandoz Group AG; *Int'l*, pg. 6527
SANDOZ INTERNATIONAL GMBH—See Sandoz Group AG; *Int'l*, pg. 6526
SANDOZ PHARMACEUTICALS AG—See Sandoz Group AG; *Int'l*, pg. 6527
SANDOZ PHARMACEUTICALS D.D.—See Sandoz Group AG; *Int'l*, pg. 6527
SANDOZ PHARMACEUTICALS GMBH—See Sandoz Group AG; *Int'l*, pg. 6527
SANDOZ PHILIPPINES CORPORATION—See Novartis AG; *Int'l*, pg. 5460
SANDOZ POLSKA SP.Z O.O.—See Sandoz Group AG; *Int'l*, pg. 6526
SANDOZ PRIVATE LIMITED—See Novartis AG; *Int'l*, pg. 5460
SANDOZ PTY LTD.—See Sandoz Group AG; *Int'l*, pg. 6527
SANDOZ S.A. DE C.V.—See Sandoz Group AG; *Int'l*, pg. 6527
SANDOZ S.A.—See Sandoz Group AG; *Int'l*, pg. 6527
SANDOZ S.A.S.—See Sandoz Group AG; *Int'l*, pg. 6527
SANDOZ SOUTH AFRICA (PTY) LTD.—See Sandoz Group AG; *Int'l*, pg. 6527
SANDOZ S.P.A.—See Novartis AG; *Int'l*, pg. 5460
SANDOZ S.R.L.—See Sandoz Group AG; *Int'l*, pg. 6526
SANDOZ S. R. O.—See Sandoz Group AG; *Int'l*, pg. 6527
SANDOZ UKRAINE LLC—See Novartis AG; *Int'l*, pg. 5460
SANDPIPER CI LIMITED—See Duke Street Capital Limited; *Int'l*, pg. 2224
SANDPIPER CI LIMITED—See Mitsubishi Estate Co., Ltd.; *Int'l*, pg. 4947
SANDPIPER CI RETAIL LIMITED—See Duke Street Capital Limited; *Int'l*, pg. 2224
SANDPIPER CI RETAIL LIMITED—See Mitsubishi Estate Co., Ltd.; *Int'l*, pg. 4947
SANDPIPER COVE DIV.—See Purcell Co., Inc.; *U.S. Private*, pg. 3304
SANDPIPER DIGITAL PAYMENTS AG—See Mountain Capital Management AG; *Int'l*, pg. 5057
SANDPIPER TOO, INC.; *U.S. Private*, pg. 3544
SANDRA EVANS & ASSOCIATES; *U.S. Private*, pg. 3544
SAND RESOURCES LIMITED—See Interquest Group plc; *Int'l*, pg. 3757
SANDREW METRONOME AB—See Schibsted ASA; *Int'l*, pg. 6617
SANDREW METRONOME DENMARK A/S—See Schibsted ASA; *Int'l*, pg. 6617
SANDREW METRONOME INTERNATIONAL AB—See Schibsted ASA; *Int'l*, pg. 6617
SANDRIDGE CO2, LLC—See SandRidge Energy, Inc.; *U.S. Public*, pg. 1839
SANDRIDGE ENERGY, INC.; *U.S. Public*, pg. 1839
SANDRIDGE EXPLORATION AND PRODUCTION, LLC—See SandRidge Energy, Inc.; *U.S. Public*, pg. 1839
SANDRIDGE FOOD CORPORATION; *U.S. Private*, pg. 3544
SANDRIDGE HOLDINGS, INC.—See SandRidge Energy, Inc.; *U.S. Public*, pg. 1839
SANDRIDGE MIDSTREAM, INC.—See SandRidge Energy, Inc.; *U.S. Public*, pg. 1839
SANDRIDGE MISSISSIPPIAN TRUST II—See SandRidge Energy, Inc.; *U.S. Public*, pg. 1840
SANDRIDGE MISSISSIPPIAN TRUST I—See SandRidge Energy, Inc.; *U.S. Public*, pg. 1839
SANDRIDGE PERMIAN TRUST—See SandRidge Energy, Inc.; *U.S. Public*, pg. 1840
SANDRINGHAM COMMUNITY FINANCIAL SERVICES LIMITED—See Bendigo & Adelaide Bank Ltd.; *Int'l*, pg. 971
SANDRO ANDY S.A.S.—See SMCP S.A.; *Int'l*, pg. 7006
SANDRO CONSTRUCTION, INC.; *U.S. Private*, pg. 3544
SANDS BETHWORKS GAMING LLC—See PCI Gaming Authority; *U.S. Private*, pg. 3120
SANDS BROS AUTO SALES, INC.; *U.S. Private*, pg. 3544

COMPANY NAME INDEX — SANDVIK AB

SANDS BROTHERS ASSET MANAGEMENT LLC; *U.S. Private*, pg. 3544
SANDS BROTHERS & CO. LTD.—See Sands Brothers Asset Management LLC; *U.S. Private*, pg. 3545
SANDS CHINA LTD.—See Las Vegas Sands Corp.; *U.S. Public*, pg. 1293
SANDS DEVELOPMENT—See St. Kitts Nevis Anguilla Trading & Development Co., Ltd.; *Int'l*, pg. 7159
SAND SEED SERVICE INCORPORATED; *U.S. Private*, pg. 3542
SANDS EXPO & CONVENTION CENTER, INC.—See Las Vegas Sands Corp.; *U.S. Public*, pg. 1293
SANDS INVESTMENT GROUP, INC.; *U.S. Private*, pg. 3545
SANDS MOTOR COMPANY, INC.; *U.S. Private*, pg. 3545
SAND SPRINGS RAILWAY, CO.—See The Broe Companies, Inc.; *U.S. Private*, pg. 4001
SANDS REGENCY CASINO HOTEL—See Jacobs Entertainment, Inc.; *U.S. Private*, pg. 2180
THE SANDS REGENT, LLC—See Jacobs Entertainment, Inc.; *U.S. Private*, pg. 2180
SANDSRX, LLC; *U.S. Private*, pg. 3545
SANDSTON CORPORATION; *U.S. Public*, pg. 1840
SANDSTONE CREEK, LLC—See Blackstone Inc.; *U.S. Public*, pg. 351
SANDSTONE GROUP, INC.; *U.S. Private*, pg. 3545
SANDSTONE SENIOR LIVING, INC.—See The Ensign Group, Inc.; *U.S. Public*, pg. 2070
SANDSTORM DESIGN, INC.; *U.S. Private*, pg. 3545
SANDSTORM GOLD LTD.; *Int'l*, pg. 6527
SANDSTORM MOTOR VEHICLES MANUFACTURING LLC—See Alpha Dhabi Holding PJSC; *Int'l*, pg. 368
SANDTOFT ROOF TILES LTD.—See Wienerberger AG; *Int'l*, pg. 8405
SANDTORP THERMOTRANSPORT AS—See DSV A/S; *Int'l*, pg. 2216
SANDU BROTHERS PVT. LTD.—See Sandu Pharmaceuticals Ltd.; *Int'l*, pg. 6527
SANDU PHARMACEUTICALS LTD.; *Int'l*, pg. 6527
SANDU PHYTOCEUTICALS PRIVATE LIMITED—See Sandu Pharmaceuticals Ltd.; *Int'l*, pg. 6527
SANDU RESEARCH FOUNDATION PVT. LTD.—See Sandu Pharmaceuticals Ltd.; *Int'l*, pg. 6527
SANDUR MANGANESE & IRON ORES LIMITED; *Int'l*, pg. 6528
SANDUSCO, INC.; *U.S. Private*, pg. 3545
SANDUSKY CABINETS INC.; *U.S. Private*, pg. 3545
SANDUSKY DIALYSIS, LLC—See DaVita Inc.; *U.S. Public*, pg. 643
SANDUSKY DISTRIBUTING COMPANY, INC.—See Sandusco, Inc.; *U.S. Private*, pg. 3545
SANDUSKY DOCK CORPORATION—See Norfolk Southern Corporation; *U.S. Public*, pg. 1535
SANDUSKY INTERNATIONAL INC.—See MetalTek International; *U.S. Private*, pg. 2682
SANDUSKY LIMITED—See MetalTek International; *U.S. Private*, pg. 2682
SANDUSKY NEWSPAPERS INC.; *U.S. Private*, pg. 3545
SANDVIK AB; *Int'l*, pg. 6528
SANDVIK A.E.—See Sandvik AB; *Int'l*, pg. 6530
SANDVIK AG—See Sandvik AB; *Int'l*, pg. 6530
SANDVIK ARGENTINA S.A.—See Sandvik AB; *Int'l*, pg. 6530
SANDVIK ASIA LTD.—See Sandvik AB; *Int'l*, pg. 6530
SANDVIK A/S—See Sandvik AB; *Int'l*, pg. 6530
SANDVIK AUSTRALIA PTY. LTD.—See Sandvik AB; *Int'l*, pg. 6530
SANDVIK BENELUX B.V.—See Sandvik AB; *Int'l*, pg. 6530
SANDVIK BENELUX—See Sandvik AB; *Int'l*, pg. 6530
SANDVIK BESOKSSERVICE AB—See Sandvik AB; *Int'l*, pg. 6530
SANDVIK BULGARIA LTD.—See Sandvik AB; *Int'l*, pg. 6530
SANDVIK CANADA, INC.—See Sandvik AB; *Int'l*, pg. 6530
SANDVIK CHILE S.A.—See Sandvik AB; *Int'l*, pg. 6530
SANDVIK CHINA HOLDING CO., LTD.—See Sandvik AB; *Int'l*, pg. 6530
SANDVIK CHINA LTD.—See Sandvik AB; *Int'l*, pg. 6530
SANDVIK CHOMUTOV PRECISION TUBES S.R.O.—See Sandvik AB; *Int'l*, pg. 6528
SANDVIK COLOMBIA S.A.S.—See Sandvik AB; *Int'l*, pg. 6530
SANDVIK COROMANT A/S—See Sandvik AB; *Int'l*, pg. 6534
SANDVIK COROMANT BENELUX BV—See Sandvik AB; *Int'l*, pg. 6534
SANDVIK COROMANT - BRAZIL—See Sandvik AB; *Int'l*, pg. 6533
SANDVIK COROMANT - FRANCE—See Sandvik AB; *Int'l*, pg. 6533
SANDVIK COROMANT - GERMANY—See Sandvik AB; *Int'l*, pg. 6533
SANDVIK COROMANT GMBH—See Sandvik AB; *Int'l*, pg. 6530
SANDVIK COROMANT - ITALY—See Sandvik AB; *Int'l*, pg. 6534
SANDVIK COROMANT PTY LTD—See Sandvik AB; *Int'l*, pg. 6534
SANDVIK COROMANT—See Sandvik AB; *Int'l*, pg. 6530
SANDVIK COROMANT—See Sandvik AB; *Int'l*, pg. 6533
SANDVIK COROMANT—See Sandvik AB; *Int'l*, pg. 6533
SANDVIK COROMANT—See Sandvik AB; *Int'l*, pg. 6533
SANDVIK COROMANT—See Sandvik AB; *Int'l*, pg. 6533
SANDVIK COROMANT—See Sandvik AB; *Int'l*, pg. 6533
SANDVIK COROMANT SVERIGE AB—See Sandvik AB; *Int'l*, pg. 6534
SANDVIK COROMANT - UK—See Sandvik AB; *Int'l*, pg. 6534
SANDVIK COROMANT - US—See Sandvik AB; *Int'l*, pg. 6534
SANDVIK CREDIT AB—See Sandvik AB; *Int'l*, pg. 6530
SANDVIK CZ S.R.O.—See Sandvik AB; *Int'l*, pg. 6530
SANDVIK DEL PERU S.A.—See Sandvik AB; *Int'l*, pg. 6535
SANDVIK DE MEXICO S.A. DE C.V.—See Sandvik AB; *Int'l*, pg. 6535
SANDVIK DO BRASIL S.A.—See Sandvik AB; *Int'l*, pg. 6535
SANDVIK D.O.O.—See Sandvik AB; *Int'l*, pg. 6535
SANDVIK E.M.S. TICARET A.S.—See Sandvik AB; *Int'l*, pg. 6530
SANDVIK ENDUSTRIYEL MAMULLER SANAYI VE TICARET A.S.—See Sandvik AB; *Int'l*, pg. 6530
SANDVIK ESPANOLA S.A., MINING & CONSTRUCTION—See Sandvik AB; *Int'l*, pg. 6531
SANDVIK ESPANOLA S.A.—See Sandvik AB; *Int'l*, pg. 6530
SANDVIK FINANCE B.V.—See Sandvik AB; *Int'l*, pg. 6530
SANDVIK HEATING TECHNOLOGY AB—See Sandvik AB; *Int'l*, pg. 6528
SANDVIK HOLDING FRANCE SAS—See Sandvik AB; *Int'l*, pg. 6530
SANDVIK HOLDING GMBH—See Sandvik AB; *Int'l*, pg. 6531
SANDVIK HOLDINGS LTD.—See Sandvik AB; *Int'l*, pg. 6531
SANDVIK HONG KONG LTD.—See Sandvik AB; *Int'l*, pg. 6531
SANDVIK HYPERION TAIWAN LIMITED—See KKR & Co. Inc.; *U.S. Public*, pg. 1253
SANDVIK HYPERION (WUXI) CO., LTD.—See KKR & Co. Inc.; *U.S. Public*, pg. 1253
SANDVIK IN AUSTRIA GES.M.B.H.—See Sandvik AB; *Int'l*, pg. 6535
SANDVIK, INC.—See Sandvik AB; *Int'l*, pg. 6535
SANDVIK INFORMATION TECHNOLOGY AB—See Sandvik AB; *Int'l*, pg. 6531
SANDVIK INTELLECTUAL PROPERTY AB—See Sandvik AB; *Int'l*, pg. 6531
SANDVIK INTERNATIONAL TRADING (SHANGHAI) CO., LTD.—See Sandvik AB; *Int'l*, pg. 6531
SANDVIK ITALIA S.P.A.—See Sandvik AB; *Int'l*, pg. 6531
SANDVIK K.K.—See Sandvik AB; *Int'l*, pg. 6531
SANDVIK KOREA LTD.—See Sandvik AB; *Int'l*, pg. 6531
SANDVIK LTD.—See Sandvik AB; *Int'l*, pg. 6531
SANDVIK MACHINING SOLUTIONS AB—See Sandvik AB; *Int'l*, pg. 6531
SANDVIK MAGYARORZAGON KFT.—See Sandvik AB; *Int'l*, pg. 6531
SANDVIK MALAYSIA SDN. BHD.—See Sandvik AB; *Int'l*, pg. 6531
SANDVIK MAROC SARL—See Sandvik AB; *Int'l*, pg. 6531
SANDVIK MATERIALS TECHNOLOGY - CANADA—See Sandvik AB; *Int'l*, pg. 6528
SANDVIK MATERIALS TECHNOLOGY DEUTSCHLAND GMBH—See Sandvik AB; *Int'l*, pg. 6528
SANDVIK MATERIALS TECHNOLOGY DO BRASIL S.A. IND. COM.—See Sandvik AB; *Int'l*, pg. 6528
SANDVIK MATERIALS TECHNOLOGY EMEA AB—See Sandvik AB; *Int'l*, pg. 6528
SANDVIK MATERIALS TECHNOLOGY FRANCE S.A.S.—See Sandvik AB; *Int'l*, pg. 6528
SANDVIK MATERIALS TECHNOLOGY - HUNGARY—See Sandvik AB; *Int'l*, pg. 6528
SANDVIK MATERIALS TECHNOLOGY - INDIA—See Sandvik AB; *Int'l*, pg. 6528
SANDVIK MATERIALS TECHNOLOGY UK LIMITED—See Sandvik AB; *Int'l*, pg. 6528
SANDVIK MATERIALS TECHNOLOGY UK—See Sandvik AB; *Int'l*, pg. 6528
SANDVIK MATERIALS TECHNOLOGY - USA—See Sandvik AB; *Int'l*, pg. 6528
SANDVIK MEXICANA S.A. DE C.V.—See Sandvik AB; *Int'l*, pg. 6531
SANDVIK MGS S.A.—See Sandvik AB; *Int'l*, pg. 6531
SANDVIK MIDDLE EAST FZE—See Sandvik AB; *Int'l*, pg. 6531
SANDVIK MINING AND CONSTRUCTION ADELAIDE PTY. LTD.—See Sandvik AB; *Int'l*, pg. 6531
SANDVIK MINING AND CONSTRUCTION ALGERIE SPA—See Sandvik AB; *Int'l*, pg. 6532
SANDVIK MINING AND CONSTRUCTION B.V.—See Sandvik AB; *Int'l*, pg. 6533
SANDVIK MINING AND CONSTRUCTION CENTRAL EUROPE GMBH—See Sandvik AB; *Int'l*, pg. 6532
SANDVIK MINING AND CONSTRUCTION CHAUNY S.A.S.—See Sandvik AB; *Int'l*, pg. 6532
SANDVIK MINING AND CONSTRUCTION CRUSHING TECHNOLOGY GMBH—See Sandvik AB; *Int'l*, pg. 6532
SANDVIK MINING AND CONSTRUCTION DO BRASIL S.A.—See Sandvik AB; *Int'l*, pg. 6533
SANDVIK MINING AND CONSTRUCTION DRC S.P.R.L.—See Sandvik AB; *Int'l*, pg. 6532
SANDVIK MINING AND CONSTRUCTION GMBH—See Sandvik AB; *Int'l*, pg. 6532
SANDVIK MINING AND CONSTRUCTION JAPAN K.K.—See Sandvik AB; *Int'l*, pg. 6532
SANDVIK MINING AND CONSTRUCTION KOPING AB—See Sandvik AB; *Int'l*, pg. 6532
SANDVIK MINING AND CONSTRUCTION LOGISTICS LTD.—See Sandvik AB; *Int'l*, pg. 6533
SANDVIK MINING AND CONSTRUCTION (LUOYANG) CO., LTD.—See Sandvik AB; *Int'l*, pg. 6533
SANDVIK MINING AND CONSTRUCTION (MALAYSIA) SDN. BHD—See Sandvik AB; *Int'l*, pg. 6532
SANDVIK MINING AND CONSTRUCTION MALI SARL—See Sandvik AB; *Int'l*, pg. 6532
SANDVIK MINING AND CONSTRUCTION MATERIALS HANDLING GMBH & CO. KG—See Sandvik AB; *Int'l*, pg. 6532
SANDVIK MINING AND CONSTRUCTION NIGERIA LTD.—See Sandvik AB; *Int'l*, pg. 6532
SANDVIK MINING AND CONSTRUCTION S.E. ASIA PTE. LTD.—See Sandvik AB; *Int'l*, pg. 6533
SANDVIK MINING AND CONSTRUCTION—See Sandvik AB; *Int'l*, pg. 6532
SANDVIK MINING AND CONSTRUCTION TOMAGO PTY. LTD.—See Sandvik AB; *Int'l*, pg. 6531
SANDVIK MINING AND ROCK TECHNOLOGY DO BRASIL LTDA.—See Sandvik AB; *Int'l*, pg. 6533
SANDVIK MINING AND ROCK TECHNOLOGY INDIA PRIVATE LIMITED—See Sandvik AB; *Int'l*, pg. 6533
SANDVIK MINING AND ROCK TECHNOLOGY INDIA PRIVATE LTD.—See Sandvik AB; *Int'l*, pg. 6533
SANDVIK MINING & CONSTRUCTION AB—See Sandvik AB; *Int'l*, pg. 6531
SANDVIK MINING & CONSTRUCTION ARGENTINA S.A.—See Sandvik AB; *Int'l*, pg. 6532
SANDVIK MINING & CONSTRUCTION AUSTRALIA PTY. LTD.—See Sandvik AB; *Int'l*, pg. 6531
SANDVIK MINING & CONSTRUCTION CENTRAL EUROPE GMBH—See Sandvik AB; *Int'l*, pg. 6531
SANDVIK MINING & CONSTRUCTION CHILE S.A.—See Sandvik AB; *Int'l*, pg. 6532
SANDVIK MINING & CONSTRUCTION (CHINA) CO., LTD.—See Sandvik AB; *Int'l*, pg. 6531
SANDVIK MINING & CONSTRUCTION CIS LLC—See Sandvik AB; *Int'l*, pg. 6531
SANDVIK MINING & CONSTRUCTION DE MEXICO S.A. DE C.V.—See Sandvik AB; *Int'l*, pg. 6532
SANDVIK MINING & CONSTRUCTION FINLAND OY—See Sandvik AB; *Int'l*, pg. 6532
SANDVIK MINING & CONSTRUCTION FRANCE S.A.S.—See Sandvik AB; *Int'l*, pg. 6532
SANDVIK MINING & CONSTRUCTION HAPARANDA AB—See Sandvik AB; *Int'l*, pg. 6532
SANDVIK MINING & CONSTRUCTION HOLLOLA OY—See Sandvik AB; *Int'l*, pg. 6532
SANDVIK MINING & CONSTRUCTION HONG KONG—See Sandvik AB; *Int'l*, pg. 6531
SANDVIK MINING & CONSTRUCTION KAZAKHSTAN LTD.—See Sandvik AB; *Int'l*, pg. 6531
SANDVIK MINING & CONSTRUCTION LIMITED—See Sandvik AB; *Int'l*, pg. 6532
SANDVIK MINING & CONSTRUCTION LYON S.A.S.—See Sandvik AB; *Int'l*, pg. 6532
SANDVIK MINING & CONSTRUCTION MIDDLE EAST—See Sandvik AB; *Int'l*, pg. 6532
SANDVIK MINING & CONSTRUCTION MOBILE CRUSHERS & SCREENS LIMITED—See Sandvik AB; *Int'l*, pg. 6532
SANDVIK MINING & CONSTRUCTION OY—See Sandvik AB; *Int'l*, pg. 6532
SANDVIK MINING & CONSTRUCTION OY - TAMPERE PLANT—See Sandvik AB; *Int'l*, pg. 6532
SANDVIK MINING & CONSTRUCTION OY - TURKU—See Sandvik AB; *Int'l*, pg. 6532
SANDVIK MINING & CONSTRUCTION PERTH PTY. LTD.—See Sandvik AB; *Int'l*, pg. 6531
SANDVIK MINING & CONSTRUCTION R.S.A. (PTY) LTD.—See Sandvik AB; *Int'l*, pg. 6532
SANDVIK MINING & CONSTRUCTION SUPPLY GMBH—See Sandvik AB; *Int'l*, pg. 6531
SANDVIK MINING & CONSTRUCTION SVERIGE AB—See Sandvik AB; *Int'l*, pg. 6532
SANDVIK MINING & CONSTRUCTION TOOLS AB—See Sandvik AB; *Int'l*, pg. 6532
SANDVIK MINING & CONSTRUCTION TRADING (SHANGHAI) CO., LTD.—See Sandvik AB; *Int'l*, pg. 6531
SANDVIK MINING & CONSTRUCTION ZAMBIA LTD.—See Sandvik AB; *Int'l*, pg. 6532
SANDVIK MINING & CONSTRUCTION ZIMBABWE (PTY) LTD.—See Sandvik AB; *Int'l*, pg. 6532

SANDVIK AB

CORPORATE AFFILIATIONS

SANDVIK MONGOLIA LLC.—See Sandvik AB; *Int'l*, pg. 6533
SANDVIK NEW ZEALAND LTD.—See Sandvik AB; *Int'l*, pg. 6533
SANDVIK NORA AB—See Sandvik AB; *Int'l*, pg. 6533
SANDVIK NORGE A/S—See Sandvik AB; *Int'l*, pg. 6533
SANDVIK OSPREY LTD.—See Sandvik AB; *Int'l*, pg. 6528
SANDVIK PHILIPPINES, INC.—See Sandvik AB; *Int'l*, pg. 6533
SANDVIK POLSKA SP. Z O.O. - KATOWICE PRODUCTION PLANT—See Sandvik AB; *Int'l*, pg. 6533
SANDVIK POLSKA SP. Z O.O.—See Sandvik AB; *Int'l*, pg. 6533
SANDVIK POWDERMET AB—See Sandvik AB; *Int'l*, pg. 6533
SANDVIK POWDER SOLUTIONS AB—See Sandvik AB; *Int'l*, pg. 6533
SANDVIK P&P GMBH—See Sandvik AB; *Int'l*, pg. 6533
SANDVIK (PTY) LTD.—See Sandvik AB; *Int'l*, pg. 6533
SANDVIK (QINGDAO) LTD.—See Sandvik AB; *Int'l*, pg. 6530
SANDVIK RC TOOLS AUSTRALIA PTY. LTD.—See Sandvik AB; *Int'l*, pg. 6533
SANDVIKS AS; *Int'l*, pg. 6535
SANDVIK SAXON LTD.—See Sandvik AB; *Int'l*, pg. 6533
SANDVIKS HOP, INC.—See Sandviks AS; *Int'l*, pg. 6536
SANDVIKS, INC.—See Sandviks AS; *Int'l*, pg. 6536
SANDVIK SLOVAKIA S.R.O.—See Sandvik AB; *Int'l*, pg. 6533
SANDVIK SMC BREAKERS LAHTI—See Sandvik AB; *Int'l*, pg. 6533
SANDVIK SOUTH EAST ASIA PTE. LTD.—See Sandvik AB; *Int'l*, pg. 6533
SANDVIK SPECIAL METALS LLC—See Sandvik AB; *Int'l*, pg. 6528
SANDVIK SRBIJA D.O.O.—See Sandvik AB; *Int'l*, pg. 6533
SANDVIK SRL—See Sandvik AB; *Int'l*, pg. 6533
SANDVIK SRP AB—See Sandvik AB; *Int'l*, pg. 6533
SANDVIK STAL FORSALJNINGS AB—See Sandvik AB; *Int'l*, pg. 6528
SANDVIK SUHJUN LTD.—See Sandvik AB; *Int'l*, pg. 6533
SANDVIK SYSTEMS DEVELOPMENT AB—See Sandvik AB; *Int'l*, pg. 6533
SANDVIK TAIWAN LTD.—See Sandvik AB; *Int'l*, pg. 6533
SANDVIK TAMROCK A/S—See Sandvik AB; *Int'l*, pg. 6533
SANDVIK THAILAND LTD.—See Sandvik AB; *Int'l*, pg. 6533
SANDVIK THERMAL PROCESS, INC.—See Sandvik AB; *Int'l*, pg. 6535
SANDVIK TOOLING AB—See Sandvik AB; *Int'l*, pg. 6533
SANDVIK TOOLING DEUTSCHLAND GMBH—See Sandvik AB; *Int'l*, pg. 6534
SANDVIK TOOLING FRANCE S.A.S.—See Sandvik AB; *Int'l*, pg. 6534
SANDVIK UTBILDNINGS AB—See Sandvik AB; *Int'l*, pg. 6535
SANDVIK VENTURE AB—See Sandvik AB; *Int'l*, pg. 6535
SANDVIK WIRE & HEATING TECHNOLOGY CORPORATION—See Sandvik AB; *Int'l*, pg. 6528
SANDVIK, ZA TRGOVINU D.O.O.—See Sandvik AB; *Int'l*, pg. 6535
SANDVINE CORPORATION—See Francisco Partners Management, LP; *U.S. Private*, pg. 1591
SANDVINE INCORPORATED ULC—See Francisco Partners Management, LP; *U.S. Private*, pg. 1591
SANDWALK FAR EAST LIMITED—See Elegance Optical International Holdings Ltd.; *Int'l*, pg. 2355
SANDWERKE BIESERN GMBH—See Heidelberg Materials AG; *Int'l*, pg. 3319
THE SANDWICH FACTORY HOLDINGS LIMITED—See Greencore Group plc; *Int'l*, pg. 3074
SANDWICH ISLE PEST SOLUTIONS—See Roark Capital Group Inc.; *U.S. Private*, pg. 3456
SANDWIRE CORP.—See Circle Computer Resources, Inc.; *U.S. Private*, pg. 899
SANDY ALEXANDER, INC.—See Snow Peak Capital, LLC; *U.S. Private*, pg. 3701
SANDY HILL KENNELS, INC.—See General Atlantic Service Company, L.P.; *U.S. Private*, pg. 1663
SANDY HOOK YACHT SALES INC.; *U.S. Private*, pg. 3545
S AND Y INDUSTRIES, INC.; *U.S. Private*, pg. 3512
SANDYMAC S.R.L.—See Biesse S.p.A.; *Int'l*, pg. 1020
SANDY SANSING NISSAN, INC.; *U.S. Private*, pg. 3545
SANDYS ASSOCIATES INC.; *U.S. Private*, pg. 3545
SANDY SPRING BANCORP, INC.; *U.S. Public*, pg. 1840
SANDY SPRING BANK—See Sandy Spring Bancorp, Inc.; *U.S. Public*, pg. 1840
SANDY SPRING INSURANCE CORPORATION—See Sandy Spring Bancorp, Inc.; *U.S. Public*, pg. 1840
SANDZAKTRANS - PUTNICKI SAOBRACAJ A.D.; *Int'l*, pg. 6536
SANDZ SOLUTIONS PHILIPPINES, INC.—See Kronologi Asia Berhad; *Int'l*, pg. 3533
SANECHEM SERVICE SP. Z O.O.—See Impel S.A.; *Int'l*, pg. 3632
SANEF—See ACS, Actividades de Construccion y Servicios, S.A.; *Int'l*, pg. 112

SANEI BD CO., LTD.—See TSI Holdings Co., Ltd.; *Int'l*, pg. 7950
SANEI COLLECTION SERVICE CO., LTD.—See Prudential Financial, Inc.; *U.S. Public*, pg. 1733
SANEI CO., LTD.—See Yuasa Trading Co., Ltd.; *Int'l*, pg. 8609
SAN-EI DAIMARU CORP.—See Nippon Steel Corporation; *Int'l*, pg. 5339
SANEI ECOHOME INC.—See Daiki Axis Co., Ltd.; *Int'l*, pg. 1932
SANEI ELECTRIC INC.—See Toei Co., Ltd.; *Int'l*, pg. 7773
SANEI HYTECHS CO., LTD.—See Innotech Corporation; *Int'l*, pg. 3710
SAN-EI INDUSTRIES CO., LTD.—See Kurita Water Industries Ltd.; *Int'l*, pg. 4341
SANEI INTERNATIONAL CO., LTD.—See TSI Holdings Co., Ltd.; *Int'l*, pg. 7950
SAN-EI LOGISTICS CORPORATION—See Kewpie Corporation; *Int'l*, pg. 4144
SAN EI METAL CO., LTD.—See Hanwa Co., Ltd.; *Int'l*, pg. 3263
SAN-EI SUCROCHEMICAL CO., LTD.—See Mitsui & Co., Ltd.; *Int'l*, pg. 4980
SANEL AUTO PARTS CO.—See Automotive Supply Associates, Inc.; *U.S. Private*, pg. 401
SAN ELECTRO HEAT A/S—See NIBE Industrier AB; *Int'l*, pg. 5262
SAN ELIJO HILLS TOWN CENTER, LLC—See Jefferies Financial Group Inc.; *U.S. Public*, pg. 1188
SAN-EL MUHENDISLIK ELEKTRIK TAAHHUT SANAYI VE TICARET AS; *Int'l*, pg. 6522
SANERGY GROUP LIMITED; *Int'l*, pg. 6536
SANERON CCEL THERAPEUTICS, INC.—See CRYOCELL International, Inc.; *U.S. Public*, pg. 600
SANESALTO SANEAMENTO S.A.; *Int'l*, pg. 6536
SAN ESTERS CORPORATION—See Mitsubishi Chemical Group Corporation; *Int'l*, pg. 4933
SAN-ES TRADING CO., LTD.; *Int'l*, pg. 6522
SAN-ESU CO., LTD.—See Unipres Corporation; *Int'l*, pg. 8056
SAN-ESU INC.—See Mitsubishi Corporation; *Int'l*, pg. 4943
SAN ESU INDUSTRY CO., LTD.—See Taikisha Ltd.; *Int'l*, pg. 7413
SAN-ETSU METALS CO., LTD. - SHIN NITTO PLANT—See CK SAN-ETSU Co., Ltd.; *Int'l*, pg. 1639
SAN-ETSU METALS CO., LTD.—See CK SAN-ETSU Co., Ltd.; *Int'l*, pg. 1639
SAN-ETSU METALS CO., LTD. - TAKAOKA PLANT—See CK SAN-ETSU Co., Ltd.; *Int'l*, pg. 1639
SAN-ETSU METALS (SHANGHAI) CO., LTD.—See CK SAN-ETSU Co., Ltd.; *Int'l*, pg. 1639
SANETSU TRANSPORT CO., LTD.—See AISIN Corporation; *Int'l*, pg. 253
S.A. NEXANS CABLING SOLUTIONS N.V.—See Nexans S.A.; *Int'l*, pg. 5240
SANEXEN ENVIRONMENTAL SERVICES INC.—See Blue Wolf Capital Partners LLC; *U.S. Private*, pg. 595
SANEXEN ENVIRONMENTAL SERVICES INC. - TORONTO—See Blue Wolf Capital Partners LLC; *U.S. Private*, pg. 595
SAN FANG CHEMICAL INDUSTRIAL CO., LTD.; *Int'l*, pg. 6520
SAN FAR PROPERTY LIMITED; *Int'l*, pg. 6520
SANFAT ELECTRIC MANUFACTURING CO., LTD.—See SANYEI CORPORATION; *Int'l*, pg. 6563
SANFAT ELECTRIC MANUFACTURING (DONGGUAN) CO., LTD.—See SANYEI CORPORATION; *Int'l*, pg. 6563
SAN FELASCO NURSERIES, INC.—See Trulieve Cannabis Corp.; *U.S. Public*, pg. 2201
SAN FENG (CAMBODIA) CO., LTD.—See Nien Made Enterprise Co., Ltd.; *Int'l*, pg. 5280
SANFENG INTELLIGENT EQUIPMENT GROUP CO., LTD.; *Int'l*, pg. 6536
SAN FERNANDO ELECTRIC LIGHT & POWER CO., INC.—See Aboitiz Equity Ventures, Inc.; *Int'l*, pg. 67
SAN FERNANDO MARBLE & GRANITE; *U.S. Private*, pg. 3540
SAN FERNANDO SHERATON CORPORATION—See Marriott International, Inc.; *U.S. Public*, pg. 1371
SAN FERNANDO VALLEY ALARM, INC.—See Armet Alarm & Electronics Inc.; *U.S. Private*, pg. 830
SAN FERNANDO VALLEY AUTOMOTIVE, LLC—See General Motors Company; *U.S. Public*, pg. 929
SAN FERNANDO VALLEY SURGERY CENTER, L.P.—See Tenet Healthcare Corporation; *U.S. Public*, pg. 2007
SANFIELD BUILDING CONTRACTORS LIMITED—See Sun Hung Kai Properties Limited; *Int'l*, pg. 7304
SANFILIPPO & SONS INSURANCE SERVICES LLC—See Inszone Insurance Services, LLC; *U.S. Private*, pg. 2096
SAN FILIPPO S.R.L.—See Gruppo MutuiOnline S.p.A; *Int'l*, pg. 3141
SANFORD AUTO DEALERS EXCHANGE, INC.—See OPENLANE, Inc.; *U.S. Public*, pg. 1607
SANFORD-BROWN COLLEGE - BOSTON—See Perdoceo Education Corporation; *U.S. Public*, pg. 1673

SANFORD-BROWN COLLEGE INC.—See Perdoceo Education Corporation; *U.S. Public*, pg. 1673
SANFORD-BROWN COLLEGE, LLC—See Perdoceo Education Corporation; *U.S. Public*, pg. 1673
SANFORD C. BERNSTEIN & CO., LLP—See Equitable Holdings, Inc.; *U.S. Public*, pg. 789
SANFORD C. BERNSTEIN (CREST NOMINEES) LIMITED—See Equitable Holdings, Inc.; *U.S. Public*, pg. 789
SANFORD C. BERNSTEIN (INDIA) PRIVATE LIMITED—See Equitable Holdings, Inc.; *U.S. Public*, pg. 790
SANFORD C. BERNSTEIN LIMITED—See Equitable Holdings, Inc.; *U.S. Public*, pg. 789
SANFORD C. BERNSTEIN (SCHWIEZ) GMBH—See Equitable Holdings, Inc.; *U.S. Public*, pg. 790
SANFORD & HAWLEY, INC.; *U.S. Private*, pg. 3545
SANFORD HEALTH; *U.S. Private*, pg. 3545
THE SANFORD HERALD INC.—See Paxton Media Group LLC; *U.S. Private*, pg. 3116
SANFORD INSTITUTION FOR SAVINGS; *U.S. Private*, pg. 3545
SANFORD INVESTMENTS LIMITED—See Sanford Limited; *Int'l*, pg. 6536
SANFORD LIMITED; *Int'l*, pg. 6536
SANFORD L.P.—See Newell Brands Inc.; *U.S. Public*, pg. 1514
SANFORD RECYCLING AND TRANSFER, INC.—See Waste Connections, Inc.; *Int'l*, pg. 8354
SANFORD RESOURCES CORPORATION; *U.S. Private*, pg. 3546
SANFORD WINERY—See The Terlato Wine Group; *U.S. Private*, pg. 4126
SAN FRANCISCO BALLET; *U.S. Private*, pg. 3540
SAN FRANCISCO BASEBALL ASSOCIATES, L.P.; *U.S. Private*, pg. 3540
SAN FRANCISCO BAY CLUB, INC.—See KKR & Co. Inc.; *U.S. Public*, pg. 1264
SAN FRANCISCO-B, INC.—See Lithia Motors, Inc.; *U.S. Public*, pg. 1326
SAN FRANCISCO BUSINESS TIMES—See Advance Publications, Inc.; *U.S. Private*, pg. 85
SAN FRANCISCO CHRONICLE—See The Hearst Corporation; *U.S. Private*, pg. 4048
SAN FRANCISCO CYBERKNIFE, LLC—See Akumin, Inc.; *U.S. Public*, pg. 70
SAN FRANCISCO EQUITY PARTNERS; *U.S. Private*, pg. 3540
SAN FRANCISCO FORTY NINERS, LTD.—See DeBartolo Corporation; *U.S. Private*, pg. 1186
SAN FRANCISCO FOUNDATION; *U.S. Private*, pg. 3540
SAN FRANCISCO GIANTS BASEBALL CLUB—See San Francisco Baseball Associates, L.P.; *U.S. Private*, pg. 3540
SAN FRANCISCO HERB & NATURAL FOOD CO.; *U.S. Private*, pg. 3540
SAN FRANCISCO KNITWORKS—See Hampshire Group Limited; *U.S. Private*, pg. 1851
SAN FRANCISCO MARKET CORPORATION; *U.S. Private*, pg. 3540
SAN FRANCISCO MUSEUM OF MODERN ART; *U.S. Private*, pg. 3540
THE SAN FRANCISCO MUSIC BOX COMPANY—See Kier Group Holdings, LLC; *U.S. Private*, pg. 2304
SAN FRANCISCO PARKING INC.; *U.S. Private*, pg. 3541
SAN FRANCISCO PARKS ALLIANCE; *U.S. Private*, pg. 3541
SAN FRANCISCO SALT COMPANY—See Wells Fargo & Company; *U.S. Public*, pg. 2344
SAN FRANCISCO SYMPHONY; *U.S. Private*, pg. 3541
SAN FRANCISCO TRAVEL ASSOCIATION; *U.S. Private*, pg. 3541
SAN FU CHEMICAL CO., LTD.; *Int'l*, pg. 6520
SAN GABRIEL VALLEY MEDICAL CENTER—See AHMC & AHMC Healthcare Inc.; *U.S. Private*, pg. 130
SAN GABRIEL VALLEY SURGICAL CENTER, L.P.—See Tenet Healthcare Corporation; *U.S. Public*, pg. 2012
SAN GABRIEL VALLEY TRIBUNE—See Alden Global Capital LLC; *U.S. Private*, pg. 158
SAN GABRIEL VALLEY WATER CO—See Fontana Water Company; *U.S. Private*, pg. 1560
SANG-A FLONTEC CO., LTD. - 3RD PLANT—See SANG-A Frontec Co., Ltd.; *Int'l*, pg. 6536
SANG-A FRONTEC CO., LTD.; *Int'l*, pg. 6536
SANGAL PAPERS LIMITED; *Int'l*, pg. 6536
SANG AM & ASSOCIATES, INC.—See Daesang Corporation; *Int'l*, pg. 1909
SANGAM & ASSOCIATES; *U.S. Private*, pg. 3546
SANGAM FINSERV LIMITED; *Int'l*, pg. 6536
SANGAM HEALTH CARE PRODUCTS LIMITED; *Int'l*, pg. 6536
SANGAM INDIA LTD; *Int'l*, pg. 6536
SANGAM LABORATORIES LTD—See Camlin Fine Sciences Ltd.; *Int'l*, pg. 1273
SANGAMON VALLEY LANDFILL, INC.—See Republic Services, Inc.; *U.S. Public*, pg. 1787
SANGAMO THERAPEUTICS FRANCE S.A.S.—See Sangamo Therapeutics, Inc.; *U.S. Public*, pg. 1840
SANGAMO THERAPEUTICS, INC.; *U.S. Public*, pg. 1840

COMPANY NAME INDEX

SANGANA COMMODITIES (K) LTD.—See Ecom Agroindustrial Corporation Ltd.; *Int'l*, pg. 2296
SANGANI HOSPITALS LIMITED; *Int'l*, pg. 6536
SANGAREE OIL COMPANY INC.; *U.S. Private*, pg. 3546
SANGART, INC.—See Jefferies Financial Group Inc.; *U.S. Public*, pg. 1189
SANGAR VALGA VABRIK AS—See AS Sangar; *Int'l*, pg. 591
SANGATECH CO., LTD.—See Bain Capital, LP; *U.S. Private*, pg. 435
SANG BO CO., LTD. - GIMPO PLANT—See Sang Bo Co., Ltd.; *Int'l*, pg. 6536
SANG BO CO., LTD.; *Int'l*, pg. 6536
SANGERA BUICK, INC.; *U.S. Private*, pg. 3546
SANGER AUSTRALIA PTY LTD—See Bindaree Beef Pty. Limited; *Int'l*, pg. 1033
SANGETSU CO., LTD.; *Int'l*, pg. 6537
SANGETSU GOODRICH CHINA CO.,LTD.—See Sangetsu Co., Ltd.; *Int'l*, pg. 6537
SANGETSU GOODRICH (THAILAND) CO., LTD.—See Sangetsu Co., Ltd.; *Int'l*, pg. 6537
SANGETSU GOODRICH VIETNAM CO., LTD.—See Sangetsu Co., Ltd.; *Int'l*, pg. 6537
SANGETSU (SHANGHAI) CORPORATION—See Sangetsu Co., Ltd.; *Int'l*, pg. 6537
SANGETSU VOSNE CORPORATION—See Sangetsu Co., Ltd.; *Int'l*, pg. 6537
SANGFOR TECHNOLOGIES, INC. - FREMONT BRANCH—See Sangfor Technologies, Inc.; *Int'l*, pg. 6537
SANGFOR TECHNOLOGIES, INC.; *Int'l*, pg. 6537
SANG FROID LABS INDIA LTD.; *Int'l*, pg. 6536
SANGHAI DAEKYO CO., LTD.—See Daekyo Co Ltd; *Int'l*, pg. 1907
SANGHAI FUJIX TRADING CO., LTD.—See FUJIX Ltd.; *Int'l*, pg. 2838
SANGHAMITRA HOSPITALS PRIVATE LIMITED—See Aster DM Healthcare Ltd.; *Int'l*, pg. 654
SANGHAR SUGAR MILLS LIMITED - SANGHAR MILL—See Sanghar Sugar Mills Limited; *Int'l*, pg. 6537
SANGHAR SUGAR MILLS LIMITED; *Int'l*, pg. 6537
SANGHI CORPORATE SERVICES LIMITED; *Int'l*, pg. 6537
SANGHI INDUSTRIES LTD—See Adani Enterprises Limited; *Int'l*, pg. 125
SANG HING HOLDINGS (INTERNATIONAL) LIMITED; *Int'l*, pg. 6536
SANGHVI BRANDS LIMITED; *Int'l*, pg. 6537
SANGHVI FORGING AND ENGINEERING LIMITED - INDIA WORKS—See Sanghvi Forging and Engineering Limited; *Int'l*, pg. 6537
SANGHVI FORGING AND ENGINEERING LIMITED; *Int'l*, pg. 6537
SANGHVI MOVERS LIMITED; *Int'l*, pg. 6537
SANGINITA CHEMICALS LIMITED; *Int'l*, pg. 6537
SANGJATTEN SVERIGE AB—See Beter Bed Holding N.V.; *Int'l*, pg. 1002
SANG JEE TRADING CO.—See Toyota Tsusho Corporation; *Int'l*, pg. 7878
SANGJI CONSTRUCTION, INC.; *Int'l*, pg. 6537
SANGJI SHIPPING CO., LTD.—See GS Holdings Corp.; *Int'l*, pg. 3142
SANGO CO., LTD. - MIYOSHI PLANT—See Sango Co., Ltd.; *Int'l*, pg. 6538
SANGO CO., LTD. - NO.3 MIYOSHI PLANT—See Sango Co., Ltd.; *Int'l*, pg. 6538
SANGO CO., LTD.; *Int'l*, pg. 6537
SANGO CO., LTD. - TAKAOKA PLANT—See Sango Co., Ltd.; *Int'l*, pg. 6538
SANGO CO., LTD. - TOYOHASHI PLANT—See Sango Co., Ltd.; *Int'l*, pg. 6538
SANGO CO., LTD. - TOYOTA PLANT—See Sango Co., Ltd.; *Int'l*, pg. 6538
SANGO CO., LTD. - YAWATAYAMA PLANT—See Sango Co., Ltd.; *Int'l*, pg. 6538
SANGO FAMILY SERVICE CO., LTD.—See Sango Co., Ltd.; *Int'l*, pg. 6537
SANGO HOKKAIDO CO., LTD.—See Sango Co., Ltd.; *Int'l*, pg. 6538
SANGO INDIA AUTOMOTIVE PARTS PVT. LTD.—See Sango Co., Ltd.; *Int'l*, pg. 6538
SANGOMA TECHNOLOGIES CORPORATION; *Int'l*, pg. 6538
SANGOMA TECHNOLOGIES INC.—See Sangoma Technologies Corporation; *Int'l*, pg. 6538
SANGO MIE CO., LTD. - MIE PLANT—See Sango Co., Ltd.; *Int'l*, pg. 6538
SANGO MIE CO., LTD.—See Sango Co., Ltd.; *Int'l*, pg. 6538
SANGO OTOMOTIV URUNLERI SANAYI VE TICARET A.S.—See Sango Co., Ltd.; *Int'l*, pg. 6538
SANGO THAI AUTOMOTIVE PARTS CO., LTD.—See Sango Co., Ltd.; *Int'l*, pg. 6538
SANGRAF ITALY S.R.L.—See Sanergy Group Limited; *Int'l*, pg. 6536
SANGRE DE CRISTO COMMUNICATIONS, INC.—See Evening Post Publishing Co.; *U.S. Private*, pg. 1436
SANGRE DE CRISTO ELECTRIC ASSOCIATION, INC.; *U.S. Private*, pg. 3546

SANGSANGIN CO., LTD.; *Int'l*, pg. 6538
SANGSANGIN HEAVY INDUSTRIES CO., LTD.—See Sangsangin Industry Co., Ltd.; *Int'l*, pg. 6538
SANGSANGIN INDUSTRY CO., LTD.; *Int'l*, pg. 6538
SANGSANGIN INVESTMENT & SECURITIES CO., LTD.—See Sangsangin Industry Co., Ltd.; *Int'l*, pg. 6538
SANGSANGIN INVESTMENT & SECURITIES CO. LTD.; *Int'l*, pg. 6538
SANGSANGIN PLUS CO., LTD.—See Sangsangin Industry Co., Ltd.; *Int'l*, pg. 6538
SANGSANGIN PLUS SAVINGS BANK CO., LTD.—See Sangsangin Industry Co., Ltd.; *Int'l*, pg. 6538
SANGSANGIN SAVINGS BANK CO., LTD.—See Sangsangin Industry Co., Ltd.; *Int'l*, pg. 6538
SANGSANG STAY INC.—See KT&G Corporation; *Int'l*, pg. 4316
SANGSHIN ELECTRONICS CO., LTD.; *Int'l*, pg. 6538
SANGSIN BRAKE AMERICA, INC—See SANGSIN BRAKE Co., Ltd.; *Int'l*, pg. 6538
SANGSIN BRAKE CO., LTD.; *Int'l*, pg. 6538
SANGSIN BRAKE INDIA PRIVATE LIMITED—See SANGSIN BRAKE Co., Ltd.; *Int'l*, pg. 6538
SANGSIN BRAKE (WUXI) CO., LTD—See SANGSIN BRAKE Co., Ltd.; *Int'l*, pg. 6538
SANGSINEDP; *Int'l*, pg. 6539
SANGSIN ENERGY DISPLAY PRECISION CO., LTD.; *Int'l*, pg. 6539
SANGSIN ENERTECH SDN BHD—See SangsinEDP; *Int'l*, pg. 6539
SANGSING ENG—See SANGSIN BRAKE Co., Ltd.; *Int'l*, pg. 6539
SANGSOM CO., LTD.—See Thai Beverage Public Company Limited; *Int'l*, pg. 7591
SANGSTER MOTORS, INC.; *U.S. Private*, pg. 3546
SANGSTER'S HEALTH CENTRES; *Int'l*, pg. 6539
SANG TECH INDUSTRIES LIMITED—See Techtronic Industries Co., Ltd.; *Int'l*, pg. 7512
SANGUIBIOTECH GMBH—See Sangui Biotech International, Inc.; *Int'l*, pg. 6539
SANGUI BIOTECH INTERNATIONAL, INC.; *Int'l*, pg. 6539
SANGUINE MEDIA LIMITED; *Int'l*, pg. 6539
SANGUIN INTERNATIONAL INC.—See Stratec SE; *Int'l*, pg. 7235
SAN CWAKKIN LIMITED—See TUM Finance PLC; *Int'l*, pg. 7970
SANHE DOPPELMAYR TRANSPORT SYSTEMS CO., LTD.—See Doppelmayr Group; *Int'l*, pg. 2175
SANHE TONGFEI REFRIGERATION CO., LTD.; *Int'l*, pg. 6539
SANHE XIANGDA CAMEL FEED CO., LTD—See Tangrenshen Group Co., Ltd.; *Int'l*, pg. 7458
SANHE XIANGDE REAL ESTATE DEVELOPMENT CO., LTD.—See Sanxiang Impression Co., Ltd.; *Int'l*, pg. 6561
SANHE YANJIAO SEMBCORP WATER CO LTD—See Sembcorp Industries Ltd.; *Int'l*, pg. 6702
SAN HO AUTOMOTIVE SALES CO.,LTD.—See Universal Cement Corporation; *Int'l*, pg. 8078
SANHO CORPORATION—See Targus Group International, Inc.; *U.S. Private*, pg. 3934
SAN HOLDINGS, INC.; *Int'l*, pg. 6520
SANHUA AWECO APPLIANCE SYSTEMS GMBH—See Zhejiang Sanhua Intelligent Controls Co., Ltd.; *Int'l*, pg. 8662
SANHUA INTERNATIONAL EUROPE, S.L—See Zhejiang Sanhua Intelligent Controls Co., Ltd.; *Int'l*, pg. 8662
SANHUA INTERNATIONAL, INC.—See Zhejiang Sanhua Intelligent Controls Co., Ltd.; *Int'l*, pg. 8662
SANIBEL CAPTIVA COMMUNITY BANK; *U.S. Private*, pg. 3546
SANIBEL CAPTIVA INVESTMENT ADVISERS, INC.—See The Sanibel Captiva Trust Company; *U.S. Private*, pg. 4114
THE SANIBEL CAPTIVA TRUST COMPANY; *U.S. Private*, pg. 4114
SANIBEL VENTURES CORP.; *Int'l*, pg. 6539
SANICANI A.D.; *Int'l*, pg. 6539
SAN-I CHEMICAL CO., LTD.—See Yushiro Chemical Industry Co., Ltd.; *Int'l*, pg. 8617
SANICHI MOULD (THAILAND) CO., LTD.—See Sanichi Technology Berhad; *Int'l*, pg. 6539
SANICHI PROPERTY SDN. BHD.—See Sanichi Technology Berhad; *Int'l*, pg. 6539
SANICHI TECHNOLOGY BERHAD; *Int'l*, pg. 6539
SANIFLEX AB—See Indutrade AB; *Int'l*, pg. 3681
SANIFOAM SUNGER SANAYI VE TICARET A.S.; *Int'l*, pg. 6539
SANILAC MUTUAL INSURANCE CO, INC.—See Farmers Alliance Mutual Insurance Co., Inc.; *U.S. Private*, pg. 1476
SANIMA BANK LIMITED; *Int'l*, pg. 6539
SANIMA CAPITAL LIMITED—See Sanima Bank Limited; *Int'l*, pg. 6539
SANIMA HYDROPOWER PRIVATE LIMITED; *Int'l*, pg. 6539
SANI-MARC INC.; *Int'l*, pg. 6539
SANI-MATIC, INC.; *U.S. Private*, pg. 3546
SANIMAX INDUSTRIES INC.; *Int'l*, pg. 6539

SANIMAX MARKETING LIMITED—See Sanimax Industries Inc.; *Int'l*, pg. 6539
SANIMAX USA LLC—See Sanimax Industries Inc.; *Int'l*, pg. 6539
SANIMED GMBH—See PAUL HARTMANN AG; *Int'l*, pg. 5761
SANIN ASICS INDUSTRY CORP.—See ASICS Corporation; *Int'l*, pg. 621
SAN-IN ECONOMICS & MANAGEMENT INSTITUTE CO., LTD.—See The San-In Godo Bank, Ltd.; *Int'l*, pg. 7680
THE SAN-IN GODO BANK, LTD.; *Int'l*, pg. 7680
SANIN SEKISUI SHOJI CO., LTD.—See Sekisui Chemical Co., Ltd.; *Int'l*, pg. 6694
THE SAN-IN-SERVICING CO., LTD.—See The San-In Godo Bank, Ltd.; *Int'l*, pg. 7680
SANIONA AB; *Int'l*, pg. 6539
SANIPA BADMOBEL TREUCHTLINGEN GMBH—See Villeroy & Boch AG; *Int'l*, pg. 8207
SANIPAC, INC.—See Waste Connections, Inc.; *Int'l*, pg. 8354
SAN ISABEL ELECTRIC ASSOCIATION INC; *U.S. Private*, pg. 3541
SANISERV—See The Affinis Group; *U.S. Private*, pg. 3983
SANISITT-COMUTHERM; *Int'l*, pg. 6540
SANISTAL A/S—See Ahlsell AB; *Int'l*, pg. 223
SANITAIRE ACCESSOIRES SERVICES S.A.S.—See Aliaxis S.A./N.V.; *Int'l*, pg. 325
SANITAIRE COMTOIS—See Compagnie de Saint-Gobain SA; *Int'l*, pg. 1736
SANITAIRE DIVISION—See Xylem Inc.; *U.S. Public*, pg. 2396
SANITAR COMPANY LTD.; *Int'l*, pg. 6540
SANITARIOS DOMINICANOS, S.A.—See Sun Capital Partners, Inc.; *U.S. Private*, pg. 3858
SANITARIOS LAMOSA, S.A. DE C.V.—See Organizacion Corona SA; *Int'l*, pg. 5618
SANITARIUM HEALTH FOOD COMPANY; *Int'l*, pg. 6540
SANITARTECHNIK EISENBERG GMBH—See Aliaxis S.A./N.V.; *Int'l*, pg. 325
SANITAS KRANKENVERSICHERUNG; *Int'l*, pg. 6540
SANITAS SA—See Viohalco SA/NV; *Int'l*, pg. 8243
SANITAS TROESCH AG—See Compagnie de Saint-Gobain SA; *Int'l*, pg. 1736
SANITEC CORPORATION—See Geberit AG; *Int'l*, pg. 2905
SANI-TECH WEST, INC.—See 3i Group plc; *Int'l*, pg. 9
SANITEKS D.D.; *Int'l*, pg. 6540
SANITHERM INC.—See Clean Harbors, Inc.; *U.S. Public*, pg. 510
SANITHERM USA, INC.—See Clean Harbors, Inc.; *U.S. Public*, pg. 510
SANITIZED AG; *Int'l*, pg. 6540
SANITIZED, INC.—See Sanitized AG; *Int'l*, pg. 6540
SANITY SOLUTIONS INC.; *U.S. Private*, pg. 3546
SANIX ENERGY INCORPORATED K.K—See Sanix Incorporated; *Int'l*, pg. 6540
SANIX INCORPORATED; *Int'l*, pg. 6540
SANIX SOFTWARE DESIGN INCORPORATED K.K—See Sanix Incorporated; *Int'l*, pg. 6540
SANJEN JALAVIDHYUT COMPANY LIMITED—See Chilime Hydropower Company Limited; *Int'l*, pg. 1478
SANJIANG SHOPPING CLUB CO., LTD.; *Int'l*, pg. 6540
SAN-J INTERNATIONAL, INC.—See San-Jirushi Corp.; *Int'l*, pg. 6522
SAN-JIRUSHI CORP.; *Int'l*, pg. 6522
SANJIVANI PARENTERAL LIMITED; *Int'l*, pg. 6540
SANJIVANI PARENTERAL LIMITED - DEHRADUN PLANT—See Sanjivani Parenteral Limited; *Int'l*, pg. 6540
SANJIVANI PARENTERAL LIMITED - MUMBAI PLANT—See Sanjivani Parenteral Limited; *Int'l*, pg. 6540
SAN JOAQUIN ENERGY, LLC—See NRG Energy, Inc.; *U.S. Public*, pg. 1551
SAN JOAQUIN FIGS, INC.; *U.S. Private*, pg. 3541
SAN JOAQUIN GENERAL HOSPITAL; *U.S. Private*, pg. 3541
SAN JOAQUIN HELICOPTERS INC.; *U.S. Private*, pg. 3541
SAN JOAQUIN LUMBER CO.; *U.S. Private*, pg. 3541
SAN JOAQUIN REFINING CO., INC.; *U.S. Private*, pg. 3541
SAN JOAQUIN TOMATO GROWERS, INC.; *U.S. Private*, pg. 3541
SAN JOAQUIN VALLEY RAILROAD CO.—See Brookfield Infrastructure Partners L.P.; *Int'l*, pg. 1192
SAN JOAQUIN VALLEY RAILROAD CO.—See GIC Pte. Ltd.; *Int'l*, pg. 2967
SANJOLE INC.—See Keysight Technologies, Inc.; *U.S. Public*, pg. 1227
SAN JOSE BUSINESS JOURNAL—See Advance Publications, Inc.; *U.S. Private*, pg. 85
SANJOSE CONCESIONES Y SERVICIOS, S.A.U—See Grupo Empresarial San Jose, S.A.; *Int'l*, pg. 3128
SANJOSE CONTRACTING, L.L.C.—See Grupo Empresarial San Jose, S.A.; *Int'l*, pg. 3128
SANJOSE ENERGIA Y MEDIO AMBIENTE S A.—See Grupo Empresarial San Jose, S.A.; *Int'l*, pg. 3128
THE SAN JOSE GROUP LTD.; *U.S. Private*, pg. 4113

THE SAN JOSE GROUP LTD.

CORPORATE AFFILIATIONS

SAN JOSE HEALTHCARE SYSTEM, LP—See HCA Healthcare, Inc.; *U.S. Public*, pg. 1008
SANJOSE INMOBILIARIA—See Grupo Empresarial San Jose, S.A.; *Int'l*, pg. 3128
SAN JOSE MERCURY NEWS—See Alden Global Capital LLC; *U.S. Private*, pg. 155
SANJOSE PANAMA, S.A.—See Grupo Empresarial San Jose, S.A.; *Int'l*, pg. 3128
SAN JOSE SHARKS, LLC; *U.S. Private*, pg. 3541
SAN JOSE SURGICAL SUPPLY INC.; *U.S. Private*, pg. 3541
SAN JOSE WATER COMPANY—See SJW Group; *U.S. Public*, pg. 1891
SAN JUAN ABSTRACT COMPANY, INC.—See Stewart Information Services Corporation; *U.S. Public*, pg. 1948
SAN JUAN BASIN ROYALTY TRUST; *U.S. Public*, pg. 1839
SAN JUAN CAPESTRANO HOSPITAL, INC.—See Acadia Healthcare Company, Inc.; *U.S. Public*, pg. 30
SAN JUAN CONSTRUCTION INC.; *U.S. Private*, pg. 3541
SAN JUAN REGIONAL MEDICAL CENTER; *U.S. Private*, pg. 3541
SAN JUAN TRADING CO. INC.; *U.S. Private*, pg. 3541
SAN JU SAN FINANCIAL GROUP, INC.; *Int'l*, pg. 6521
SANJU SAN INSTITUTE OF RESEARCH, LTD.—See San ju San Financial Group, Inc.; *Int'l*, pg. 6521
SANKALP SEMICONDUCTOR PRIVATE LIMITED—See HCL Technologies Ltd.; *Int'l*, pg. 3299
SANKALP USA INC.—See HCL Technologies Ltd.; *Int'l*, pg. 3299
SANKATY ADVISORS (AUSTRALIA), PTY. LTD—See Bain Capital, LP; *U.S. Private*, pg. 444
SANKATY ADVISORS ILLINOIS, LLC—See Bain Capital, LP; *U.S. Private*, pg. 444
SANKATY ADVISORS, LLC—See Bain Capital, LP; *U.S. Private*, pg. 444
SANKATY ADVISORS LTD.—See Bain Capital, LP; *U.S. Private*, pg. 444
SANKATY ADVISORS (NY), LLC—See Bain Capital, LP; *U.S. Private*, pg. 444
SANKATY EUROPEAN INVESTMENTS, S.A.R.L.—See Bain Capital, LP; *U.S. Private*, pg. 444
THE SANKEI BLDG TECHNO CO., LTD.—See Fuji Media Holdings, Inc.; *Int'l*, pg. 2814
SANKEI BUILDING ASSET MANAGEMENT CO., LTD.—See Fuji Media Holdings, Inc.; *Int'l*, pg. 2814
THE SANKEI BUILDING CO., LTD.—See Fuji Media Holdings, Inc.; *Int'l*, pg. 2814
THE SANKEI BUILDING MANAGEMENT CO., LTD.—See Fuji Media Holdings, Inc.; *Int'l*, pg. 2814
SANKEI BUILDING WELL CARE CO., LTD.—See Fuji Media Holdings, Inc.; *Int'l*, pg. 2814
SANKEI CO., LTD.—See ITOCHU Corporation; *Int'l*, pg. 3841
SANKEI HUMAN LEARNING CO., LTD.—See Transcosmos Inc.; *Int'l*, pg. 7898
SANKEI KAIKAN CO., LTD.—See Fuji Media Holdings, Inc.; *Int'l*, pg. 2814
SANKEI LIVING SHIMBUN INC.—See RIZAP GROUP, Inc.; *Int'l*, pg. 6354
SANKEI REAL ESTATE, INC.; *Int'l*, pg. 6540
SANKEN BUSINESS SERVICE CO., LTD.—See Sanken Electric Co., Ltd.; *Int'l*, pg. 6541
SANKEN DENSETSU CO., LTD.—See Sanken Electric Co., Ltd.; *Int'l*, pg. 6541
SANKEN ELECTRIC CO., LTD.; *Int'l*, pg. 6540
SANKEN ELECTRIC HONG KONG CO., LTD.—See Sanken Electric Co., Ltd.; *Int'l*, pg. 6541
SANKEN ELECTRIC KOREA CO., LTD.—See Sanken Electric Co., Ltd.; *Int'l*, pg. 6541
SANKEN ELECTRIC (SHANGHAI) CO., LTD.—See Sanken Electric Co., Ltd.; *Int'l*, pg. 6541
SANKEN ELECTRIC SINGAPORE PTE. LTD.—See Sanken Electric Co., Ltd.; *Int'l*, pg. 6541
SANKEN ELECTRIC (THAILAND) CO., LTD.—See Sanken Electric Co., Ltd.; *Int'l*, pg. 6541
SANKEN LD CO., LTD.—See Sanken Electric Co., Ltd.; *Int'l*, pg. 6541
SANKEN L.D. ELECTRIC (JIANGYIN) CO., LTD.—See Sanken Electric Co., Ltd.; *Int'l*, pg. 6541
SANKEN LOGISTICS CO., LTD.—See Sanken Electric Co., Ltd.; *Int'l*, pg. 6541
SANKEN OPTOPRODUCTS CO., LTD.—See Sanken Electric Co., Ltd.; *Int'l*, pg. 6541
SANKEY AUSTRALIA—See CMG Pty. Ltd.; *Int'l*, pg. 1670
SANKGUJ SEMICONDUCTOR PRIVATE LIMITED—See HCL Technologies Ltd.; *Int'l*, pg. 3299
SANKHYA INFOTECH LTD.; *Int'l*, pg. 6541
SANKI CO LTD—See Daiken Corporation; *Int'l*, pg. 1931
SANKI EASTERN (THAILAND) CO., LTD.—See STG Co., Ltd.; *Int'l*, pg. 7213
SANKI ENGINEERING CO., LTD.—See Mitsui & Co., Ltd.; *Int'l*, pg. 4980
SANKI FINE TECHNOLOGY (HONG KONG) CO., LTD.—See STG Co., Ltd.; *Int'l*, pg. 7213
SANKI KEISO CO., LTD.—See CHINO Corporation; *Int'l*, pg. 1571
SANKI SERVICE CORPORATION; *Int'l*, pg. 6541

SANKI TECHNOS CO., LTD.—See Hitachi, Ltd.; *Int'l*, pg. 3424
SANKI WELLBE CO., LTD.—See Suzuken Co., Ltd.; *Int'l*, pg. 7353
SANKO AD CO., LTD.—See ZIGExN Co., Ltd.; *Int'l*, pg. 8682
SANKO AMERICA CORPORATION—See Tensho Electric Industries Co., Ltd.; *Int'l*, pg. 7562
SANKO CO., LTD.; *Int'l*, pg. 6541
SANKO CONSTRUCTION CO—See MITSUBA Corporation; *Int'l*, pg. 4929
SANKO DIECASTING (THAILAND) PUBLIC COMPANY LIMITED; *Int'l*, pg. 6541
SANKO ELECTRIC CO., LTD.—See MITSUBA Corporation; *Int'l*, pg. 4929
SANKO FASTEM (THAILAND) LTD.—See SANKO TECHNO CO., LTD.; *Int'l*, pg. 6542
SANKO FASTEM (VIETNAM) LTD.—See SANKO TECHNO CO., LTD.; *Int'l*, pg. 6542
SANKO GOSEI CRECH, S.R.O.—See Sanko Gosei Ltd.; *Int'l*, pg. 6542
SANKO GOSEI LTD. - GUNMA FACTORY—See Sanko Gosei Ltd.; *Int'l*, pg. 6542
SANKO GOSEI LTD. - KUMAGAYA FACTORY—See Sanko Gosei Ltd.; *Int'l*, pg. 6542
SANKO GOSEI LTD. - SHIGA FACTORY—See Sanko Gosei Ltd.; *Int'l*, pg. 6542
SANKO GOSEI LTD. - SHIZUOKA FACTORY—See Sanko Gosei Ltd.; *Int'l*, pg. 6542
SANKO GOSEI LTD.; *Int'l*, pg. 6541
SANKO GOSEI LTD. - TOOL & ENGINEERING BUSINESS UNIT—See Sanko Gosei Ltd.; *Int'l*, pg. 6542
SANKO GOSEI MEXICO, S.A.DE C. V.—See Sanko Gosei Ltd.; *Int'l*, pg. 6541
SANKO GOSEI PHILIPPINES, INC.—See Sanko Gosei Ltd.; *Int'l*, pg. 6541
SANKO GOSEI TECHNOLOGIES USA INC—See Sanko Gosei Ltd.; *Int'l*, pg. 6542
SANKO GOSEI TECHNOLOGY INDIA PRIVATE LTD.—See Sanko Gosei Ltd.; *Int'l*, pg. 6541
SANKO GOSEI TECHNOLOGY (SINGAPORE) PTE. LTD.—See Sanko Gosei Ltd.; *Int'l*, pg. 6542
SANKO GOSEI TECHNOLOGY TECHNOLOGY INDIA PRIVATE LTD.—See Sanko Gosei Ltd.; *Int'l*, pg. 6542
SANKO GOSEI TECHNOLOGY (THAILAND) LTD.—See Sanko Gosei Ltd.; *Int'l*, pg. 6541
SANKO GOSEI (THAILAND) LTD.—See Sanko Gosei Ltd.; *Int'l*, pg. 6541
SANKO GOSEI UK LTD.—See Sanko Gosei Ltd.; *Int'l*, pg. 6542
SANKOH ENGINEERING CORPORATION—See Kaga Electronics Co., Ltd.; *Int'l*, pg. 4049
SANKOH MACHINERY CO., LTD.—See Nippon Koei Co., Ltd.; *Int'l*, pg. 5322
SANKO, INC.—See KAYAC Inc.; *Int'l*, pg. 4101
SANKO INTERNATIONAL INC.; *U.S. Private*, pg. 3546
SANKO KIKO CO., LTD.—See Kurimoto Ltd; *Int'l*, pg. 4340
SANKO MABIS (BEIJING) CORP.—See Kamei Corporation; *Int'l*, pg. 4062
SANKO MARKETING FOODS CO., LTD.; *Int'l*, pg. 6542
SANKO METAL INDUSTRIAL CO., LTD.; *Int'l*, pg. 6542
SANKO PAZARLAMA ITHALAT IHRACAT AS; *Int'l*, pg. 6542
SANKO PLASTICS MEXICO CORPORATION S.A. DE C.V.—See Tensho Electric Industries Co., Ltd.; *Int'l*, pg. 7562
SANKO PROGRESS MABIS CORPORATION—See Kamei Corporation; *Int'l*, pg. 4062
SANKO SANGYO (BANGKOK) CO.,LTD.—See SANKO SANGYO CO., LTD.; *Int'l*, pg. 6542
SANKO SANGYO CO., LTD.; *Int'l*, pg. 6542
SANKO SANGYO (MALAYSIA) SDN.BHD.—See SANKO SANGYO CO., LTD.; *Int'l*, pg. 6542
SANKO SANGYO (SHEN ZHEN) LTD.—See SANKO SANGYO CO., LTD.; *Int'l*, pg. 6542
SANKO SECURITIES CO., LTD.—See Okasan Securities Group Inc.; *Int'l*, pg. 5545
SANKO SEISAKUSHO CO., LTD.—See THK CO., LTD.; *Int'l*, pg. 7712
SANKOSHA CO., LTD.—See Sankosha Corporation; *Int'l*, pg. 6542
SANKOSHA CO., LTD.; *Int'l*, pg. 6542
SANKOSHA CO., LTD.—See Sankosha Co., Ltd.; *Int'l*, pg. 6542
SANKOSHA CO., LTD.—See Sankosha Co., Ltd.; *Int'l*, pg. 6542
SANKOSHA CO., LTD.—See Sankosha Co., Ltd.; *Int'l*, pg. 6542
SANKOSHA CO., LTD.—See Sankosha Co., Ltd.; *Int'l*, pg. 6542
SANKOSHA CORPORATION; *Int'l*, pg. 6542
SANKOSHA ENGINEERING SINGAPORE PTE. LTD.—See Sankosha Corporation; *Int'l*, pg. 6542
SANKOSHA GUANGZHOU INC.—See Sankosha Corporation; *Int'l*, pg. 6542
SANKOSHA KOREA CORPORATION—See Sankosha Corporation; *Int'l*, pg. 6542
SANKOSHA LAUNDRY CENTER CO., LTD.—See Yoshinoya Holdings Co., Ltd.; *Int'l*, pg. 8600

SANKOSHA THAILAND CO.,LTD.—See Sankosha Corporation; *Int'l*, pg. 6542
SANKOSHA U.S.A., INC.—See Sankosha Corporation; *Int'l*, pg. 6543
SANKOSHA VIETNAM LLC—See Sankosha Corporation; *Int'l*, pg. 6543
SANKOSHA YANGJIANG INC.—See Sankosha Corporation; *Int'l*, pg. 6543
SANKO SVANCE JRG TOOLING INDIA PRIVATE LTD.—See Sanko Gosei Ltd.; *Int'l*, pg. 6541
SANKO TECHNO CO., LTD.; *Int'l*, pg. 6542
SANKO TRUCKING CO., LTD.—See Mitsui-Soko Holdings Co., Ltd.; *Int'l*, pg. 4993
SANKO ULVAC CO., LTD.—See ULVAC, Inc.; *Int'l*, pg. 8020
SANKO BUTSURYU NIYAKU CO., LTD.—See Senko Group Holdings Co., Ltd.; *Int'l*, pg. 6711
SANKYO DANBORU CO., LTD.—See Rengo Co., Ltd.; *Int'l*, pg. 6281
SANKYO ELECTRONICS, CO., LTD.—See Sansei Co., Ltd.; *Int'l*, pg. 6555
SANKYO FREIGHT CO., LTD.—See Senko Group Holdings Co., Ltd.; *Int'l*, pg. 6711
SANKYO FRONTIER. CO., LTD.; *Int'l*, pg. 6543
SANKYO FRONTIER MALAYSIA SDN. BHD.—See Sankyo Frontier. Co., Ltd.; *Int'l*, pg. 6543
SANKYO FRONTIER MYANMAR CO., LTD.—See Sankyo Frontier. Co., Ltd.; *Int'l*, pg. 6543
SANKYO FRONTIER TECHNOLOGIES MYANMAR CO., LTD.—See Sankyo Frontier. Co., Ltd.; *Int'l*, pg. 6543
SANKYO KASEI CORPORATION; *Int'l*, pg. 6543
SANKYO KASEI INDUSTRY CORPORATION—See Tosoh Corporation; *Int'l*, pg. 7833
SANKYO KASEI (SHANGHAI) CO., LTD.—See Sankyo Kasei Corporation; *Int'l*, pg. 6543
SANKYO KASEI SINGAPORE PTE. LTD.—See Sankyo Kasei Corporation; *Int'l*, pg. 6543
SANKYO KASEI (THAILAND) CO., LTD.—See Sankyo Kasei Corporation; *Int'l*, pg. 6543
SANKYO KOUN CO., LTD.—See Sankyu, Inc.; *Int'l*, pg. 6544
SANKYO LOGI ASSOCIATE. CO., LTD.—See Bain Capital, LP; *U.S. Private*, pg. 435
SANKYO MANUFACTURING CO., LTD.—See Togami Electric Mfg. Co., Ltd.; *Int'l*, pg. 7774
SANKYO MEAT CO., LTD.—See Itoham Yonekyu Holdings Inc.; *Int'l*, pg. 3843
SANKYO NORITAKE STEEL CO., LTD.—See Onoken Co., Ltd.; *Int'l*, pg. 5583
SANKYO RADIATOR CO., LTD.—See Denso Corporation; *Int'l*, pg. 2033
SANKYO SEIKO APPAREL FASHION CO., LTD.—See Sankyo Seiko Co., Ltd.; *Int'l*, pg. 6543
SANKYO SEIKO CO., LTD.; *Int'l*, pg. 6543
SANKYO SEIKO FASHION SERVICE CO., LTD.—See Sankyo Seiko Co., Ltd.; *Int'l*, pg. 6543
SANKYO TATEYAMA INC.; *Int'l*, pg. 6543
SANKYO UNYU KOGYO CO., LTD.—See Taiheiyo Cement Corporation; *Int'l*, pg. 7412
SANKYU AIR (HONG KONG) LTD.—See Sankyu, Inc.; *Int'l*, pg. 6544
SANKYU ARCC SAUDI CO.—See Sankyu, Inc.; *Int'l*, pg. 6544
SANKYU ASIA-PACIFIC QINGDAO LOGISTICS CO., LTD.—See Sankyu, Inc.; *Int'l*, pg. 6544
SANKYU BUSINESS SERVICE CO., LTD.—See Sankyu, Inc.; *Int'l*, pg. 6544
SANKYU CHUBU SERVICE CO., LTD.—See Sankyu, Inc.; *Int'l*, pg. 6544
SANKYU CLEARING CO., LTD.—See Sankyu, Inc.; *Int'l*, pg. 6544
SANKYU DELIVERY & SERVICE CO., LTD.—See Sankyu, Inc.; *Int'l*, pg. 6544
SANKYU DESIGN & ENGINEERING SERVICE CO., LTD.—See Sankyu, Inc.; *Int'l*, pg. 6544
SANKYU EASTERN INTERNATIONAL (HK) COMPANY LIMITED—See Sankyu, Inc.; *Int'l*, pg. 6544
SANKYU EUROPE BV—See Sankyu, Inc.; *Int'l*, pg. 6544
SANKYU GUANGZHOU LOGISTICS CO., LTD.—See Sankyu, Inc.; *Int'l*, pg. 6544
SANKYU HIGASHI NIHON SERVICE CO., LTD.—See Sankyu, Inc.; *Int'l*, pg. 6544
SANKYU, INC.; *Int'l*, pg. 6543
SANKYU INDIA LOGISTICS & ENGINEERING PRIVATE LIMITED—See Sankyu, Inc.; *Int'l*, pg. 6544
SANKYU INSURANCE SERVICE CORPORATION—See Sankyu, Inc.; *Int'l*, pg. 6544
SANKYU JIANGSU LOGISTICS CO., LTD.—See Sankyu, Inc.; *Int'l*, pg. 6544
SANKYU JUKIKO CO., LTD.—See Sankyu, Inc.; *Int'l*, pg. 6544
SANKYU-JVAN AN INTERNATIONAL LOGISTICS CO., LTD.—See Sankyu, Inc.; *Int'l*, pg. 6545
SANKYU KAIRIKU CO., LTD.—See Sankyu, Inc.; *Int'l*, pg. 6544
SANKYU KINKI SERVICE CO., LTD.—See Sankyu, Inc.; *Int'l*, pg. 6544
SANKYU LAEM CHABANG (THAILAND) COMPANY LIMITED—See Sankyu, Inc.; *Int'l*, pg. 6544

COMPANY NAME INDEX

SANKYU LOGISTICS BRAZIL. A.V.—See Sankyu, Inc.; *Int'l*, pg. 6544
SANKYU LOGISTICS (VIETNAM) CO., LTD.—See Sankyu, Inc.; *Int'l*, pg. 6544
SANKYU L&T (ZFTZ) CO., LTD.—See Sankyu, Inc.; *Int'l*, pg. 6544
SANKYU (MALAYSIA) SDN BHD—See Sankyu, Inc.; *Int'l*, pg. 6544
SANKYU MEXICO S.A. DE C.V.—See Sankyu, Inc.; *Int'l*, pg. 6544
SANKYU OITA BUSINESS INC.—See Sankyu, Inc.; *Int'l*, pg. 6544
SANKYU PLANT ENGINEERING SHANGHAI CO., LTD.—See Sankyu, Inc.; *Int'l*, pg. 6544
SANKYU PLANT TECHNO CO., LTD.—See Sankyu, Inc.; *Int'l*, pg. 6544
SANKYU RESEARCH & CREATE CO., LTD.—See Sankyu, Inc.; *Int'l*, pg. 6544
SANKYU ROAD ENGINEERING CO., LTD.—See Sankyu, Inc.; *Int'l*, pg. 6544
SANKYU S.A.—See Sankyu, Inc.; *Int'l*, pg. 6544
SANKYU SAUDI ARABIA CO., LTD.—See Sankyu, Inc.; *Int'l*, pg. 6544
SANKYU SHIPPING INC.—See Sankyu, Inc.; *Int'l*, pg. 6544
SANKYU (SINGAPORE) PTE. LTD.—See Sankyu, Inc.; *Int'l*, pg. 6544
SANKYU SOUTHEAST ASIA HOLDINGS PTE. LTD.—See Sankyu, Inc.; *Int'l*, pg. 6544
SANKYU-THAI COMPANY LIMITED—See Sankyu, Inc.; *Int'l*, pg. 6545
SANKYU TRANSPORT CHUBU CO., LTD.—See Sankyu, Inc.; *Int'l*, pg. 6544
SANKYU TRANSPORT CHUGOKU CO., LTD.—See Sankyu, Inc.; *Int'l*, pg. 6544
SANKYU TRANSPORT HIGASHINIHON CO., LTD.—See Sankyu, Inc.; *Int'l*, pg. 6544
SANKYU TRANSPORT KANSAI CO., LTD.—See Sankyu, Inc.; *Int'l*, pg. 6545
SANKYU TRANSPORT KYUSHU CO., LTD.—See Sankyu, Inc.; *Int'l*, pg. 6545
SANKYU TRANSPORT TOKYO CO., LTD.—See Sankyu, Inc.; *Int'l*, pg. 6545
SANKYU USA INCORPORATED—See Sankyu, Inc.; *Int'l*, pg. 6545
SANKYU (VIETNAM) CO., LTD.—See Sankyu, Inc.; *Int'l*, pg. 6544
SANLAM ASSET MANAGEMENT (IRELAND) LIMITED—See Sanlam Limited; *Int'l*, pg. 6545
SANLAM GENERAL INSURANCE LIMITED—See Sanlam Kenya Plc; *Int'l*, pg. 6545
SANLAM INVESTMENT HOLDINGS LIMITED—See Sanlam Limited; *Int'l*, pg. 6545
SANLAM INVESTMENT MANAGEMENT (PTY) LIMITED—See Sanlam Limited; *Int'l*, pg. 6545
SANLAM KENYA PLC; *Int'l*, pg. 6545
SANLAM LIMITED; *Int'l*, pg. 6545
SANLAM MAROC S.A.—See Sanlam Limited; *Int'l*, pg. 6545
SANLAM NETHERLANDS HOLDING BV—See Sanlam Limited; *Int'l*, pg. 6545
SANLAM PRIVATE WEALTH (UK)—See Sanlam Limited; *Int'l*, pg. 6545
SANLAM SPEC (PTY) LIMITED—See Sanlam Limited; *Int'l*, pg. 6545
SANLAM UK LTD—See Sanlam Limited; *Int'l*, pg. 6545
SAN LEON ENERGY PLC; *Int'l*, pg. 6521
SAN LETS CO., LTD.—See Sankyo Seiko Co.; *Int'l*, pg. 6543
SANLIC INTERNATIONAL (PTY) LIMITED—See The Bidvest Group Limited; *Int'l*, pg. 7626
SANLI E&C PTE. LTD.—See Sanli Environmental Limited; *Int'l*, pg. 6546
SANLIEN TECHNOLOGY CORP.; *Int'l*, pg. 6546
SANLI ENVIRONMENTAL LIMITED; *Int'l*, pg. 6545
SANLI ENVIRONMENTAL (MYANMAR) CO. LTD.—See Sanli Environmental Limited; *Int'l*, pg. 6546
SANLI M&E ENGINEERING PTE. LTD.—See Sanli Environmental Limited; *Int'l*, pg. 6546
SANLI M&E ENGINEERING SDN. BHD.—See Sanli Environmental Limited; *Int'l*, pg. 6546
SANLO, INC.—See Central Wire Industries Ltd; *Int'l*, pg. 1410
SAN LOMA, INC.—See Platinum Equity, LLC; *U.S. Private*, pg. 3209
SANLORENZO CHINA CO., LTD.—See Sundiro Holding Co., Ltd.; *Int'l*, pg. 7312
SANLORENZO OF THE AMERICAS LLC—See Sanlorenzo S.p.A.; *Int'l*, pg. 6546
SANLORENZO S.P.A.; *Int'l*, pg. 6546
SAN LOTUS HOLDING INC.; *U.S. Private*, pg. 3541
SANLUIS CO-INTER, S. A.—See Rassini S.A.B. de C.V.; *Int'l*, pg. 6213
SAN LUIS GARBAGE COMPANY—See Waste Connections, Inc.; *Int'l*, pg. 8354
THE SAN LUIS OBISPO CA ENDOSCOPY ASC, L.P.—See KKR & Co. Inc.; *U.S. Public*, pg. 1248
SAN LUIS OBISPO COUNTY FARM SUPPLY; *U.S. Private*, pg. 3541

SAN LUIS OBISPO TRIBUNE, LLC—See Chatham Asset Management, LLC; *U.S. Private*, pg. 867
SANLUIS RASSINI AUTOPARTES, S.A. DE C.V.—See Rassini S.A.B. de C.V.; *Int'l*, pg. 6213
SANLUIS RASSINI S.A. DE C.V.—See Rassini S.A.B. de C.V.; *Int'l*, pg. 6213
THE SAN LUIS RESORT, SPA & CONFERENCE CENTER—See Fertitta Entertainment, Inc.; *U.S. Private*, pg. 1499
SAN LUIS VALLEY RURAL ELECTRIC COOPERATIVE, INC.; *U.S. Private*, pg. 3541
SANLUX CO., LTD.; *Int'l*, pg. 6546
SANMAN CAPITAL MARKETS—See Sanlam Limited; *Int'l*, pg. 6545
SAN MANUEL INDIAN BINGO & CASINO; *U.S. Private*, pg. 3541
SAN MAR CORPORATION; *U.S. Private*, pg. 3542
SAN MARCOS AIR CONDITIONING, INC.—See Novak Group LLC; *U.S. Private*, pg. 2966
SAN MARCOS ASC, LLC—See HCA Healthcare, Inc.; *U.S. Public*, pg. 1008
SAN MARCOS DIALYSIS, LLC—See DaVita Inc.; *U.S. Public*, pg. 643
SAN MARCOS SURGERY CENTER—See HCA Healthcare, Inc.; *U.S. Public*, pg. 1008
SANMAR ENGINEERING CORPORATION LTD.—See Sanmar Holdings Ltd.; *Int'l*, pg. 6546
SANMAR ENGINEERING CORP.—See Sanmar Holdings Ltd.; *Int'l*, pg. 6546
SANMAR ENGINEERING SERVICES-CHENNAI—See Sanmar Holdings Ltd.; *Int'l*, pg. 6546
SANMAR FOUNDRIES LTD.—See Sanmar Holdings Ltd.; *Int'l*, pg. 6546
SANMAR HOLDINGS LTD.; *Int'l*, pg. 6546
SANMAR SHIPPING LTD.—See Sanmar Holdings Ltd.; *Int'l*, pg. 6546
SANMAR SPECIALITY CHEMICALS LIMITED - BERIGAI PLANT—See Sanmar Holdings Ltd.; *Int'l*, pg. 6547
SANMAR SPECIALITY CHEMICALS LTD.—See Sanmar Holdings Ltd.; *Int'l*, pg. 6546
SAN MARTIN CONTRATISTAS GENERALES S.A.—See Empresas ICA S.A.B. de C.V.; *Int'l*, pg. 2391
SAN MARTIN SURGERY CENTER, LLC—See Tenet Healthcare Corporation; *U.S. Public*, pg. 2012
SAN MATEO COUNTY TIMES—See Alden Global Capital LLC; *U.S. Private*, pg. 155
SAN MATEO COUNTY TRANSIT; *U.S. Private*, pg. 3542
SAN MATEO CREDIT UNION; *U.S. Private*, pg. 3542
SAN MATEO FORWARDING; *U.S. Private*, pg. 3542
SANMAX TECHNOLOGIES INC.—See Minato Holdings Inc.; *Int'l*, pg. 4899
SANMENXIA TIANYUAN ALUMINUM COMPANY LIMITED—See Tianrui Group Co., Ltd.; *Int'l*, pg. 7741
SANMENXIA ZHONGYU GAS CO., LTD.—See Zhongyu Energy Holdings Limited; *Int'l*, pg. 8676
SAN-MIC TRADING CO., (H.K.) LTD.—See Nippon Paper Industries Co., Ltd.; *Int'l*, pg. 5328
SAN-MIC TRADING CO., (SHENZHEN) LTD.—See Nippon Paper Industries Co., Ltd.; *Int'l*, pg. 5328
SAN MIGUEL BREWERY HONG KONG LTD.—See Top Frontier Investment Holdings, Inc.; *Int'l*, pg. 7811
SAN MIGUEL BREWERY INC.—See Top Frontier Investment Holdings, Inc.; *Int'l*, pg. 7811
SAN MIGUEL CLINIC CORP.—See Quorum Health Corporation; *U.S. Private*, pg. 3330
SAN MIGUEL CORPORATION—See Top Frontier Investment Holdings, Inc.; *Int'l*, pg. 7811
SAN MIGUEL FOOD AND BEVERAGE, INC.—See Top Frontier Investment Holdings, Inc.; *Int'l*, pg. 7812
SAN MIGUEL FOODS, INC.—See Top Frontier Investment Holdings, Inc.; *Int'l*, pg. 7812
SAN MIGUEL (GUANGDONG) BREWERY CO., LTD.—See Top Frontier Investment Holdings, Inc.; *Int'l*, pg. 7812
SAN MIGUEL POWER ASSOCIATION; *U.S. Private*, pg. 3542
SAN MIGUEL PROPERTIES, INC.—See Top Frontier Investment Holdings, Inc.; *Int'l*, pg. 7812
SAN MIGUEL YAMAMURA ASIA CORPORATION—See Top Frontier Investment Holdings, Inc.; *Int'l*, pg. 7812
SAN MIGUEL YAMAMURA PACKAGING CORPORATION—See Top Frontier Investment Holdings, Inc.; *Int'l*, pg. 7812
SANMINA CORPORATION - KUNSHAN—See Sanmina Corporation; *U.S. Public*, pg. 1840
SANMINA CORPORATION—See Sanmina Corporation; *U.S. Public*, pg. 1840
SANMINA CORPORATION; *U.S. Public*, pg. 1840
SANMINADE MEXICO S.A. DE C.V.—See Sanmina Corporation; *U.S. Public*, pg. 1841
SANMINA FRANCE SAS—See Sanmina Corporation; *U.S. Public*, pg. 1840
SANMINA SAS—See Sanmina Corporation; *U.S. Public*, pg. 1840
SANMINA-SCI AB—See Sanmina Corporation; *U.S. Public*, pg. 1840
SANMINA-SCI DE MEXICO S.A. DE C.V.—See Sanmina Corporation; *U.S. Public*, pg. 1841

SANMINA-SCI DO BRAZIL LDTA.—See Sanmina Corporation; *U.S. Public*, pg. 1841
SANMINA-SCI EMS HAUKIPUDAS OY—See Sanmina Corporation; *U.S. Public*, pg. 1840
SANMINA-SCI ENCLOSURE SYSTEMS (ASIA) LTD.—See Sanmina Corporation; *U.S. Public*, pg. 1840
SANMINA-SCI ENCLOSURE SYSTEMS OY—See Sanmina Corporation; *U.S. Public*, pg. 1840
SANMINA-SCI ENCLOSURE SYSTEMS (SHENZHEN) LTD.—See Sanmina Corporation; *U.S. Public*, pg. 1840
SANMINA-SCI GERMANY GMBH—See Sanmina Corporation; *U.S. Public*, pg. 1840
SANMINA-SCI GMBH—See Sanmina Corporation; *U.S. Public*, pg. 1840
SANMINA-SCI HOLDING GMBH & CO. KG—See Sanmina Corporation; *U.S. Public*, pg. 1840
SANMINA-SCI HUNGARY ELECTRONICS MANUFACTURING LIMITED LIABILITY COMPANY—See Sanmina Corporation; *U.S. Public*, pg. 1840
SANMINA-SCI IRELAND—See Sanmina Corporation; *U.S. Public*, pg. 1841
SANMINA-SCI ISRAEL MEDICAL SYSTEMS, LTD.—See Sanmina Corporation; *U.S. Public*, pg. 1841
SANMINA-SCI MANCHESTER PLANT—See Sanmina Corporation; *U.S. Public*, pg. 1841
SANMINA-SCI OPTICAL TECHNOLOGY (SHENZHEN) LTD.—See Sanmina Corporation; *U.S. Public*, pg. 1841
SANMINA-SCI RSP DE MEXICO S.A. DE C.V.—See Sanmina Corporation; *U.S. Public*, pg. 1841
SANMINA-SCI (SHENZHEN) LIMITED—See Sanmina Corporation; *U.S. Public*, pg. 1840
SANMINA-SCI SYSTEMS DE MEXICO S.A. DE C.V.—See Sanmina Corporation; *U.S. Public*, pg. 1841
SANMINA-SCI SYSTEMS JAPAN, LTD.—See Sanmina Corporation; *U.S. Public*, pg. 1841
SANMINA-SCI SYSTEMS (MALAYSIA) SND BHD—See Sanmina Corporation; *U.S. Public*, pg. 1841
SANMINA-SCI SYSTEMS SINGAPORE PTE. LTD.—See Sanmina Corporation; *U.S. Public*, pg. 1841
SANMINA-SCI SYSTEMS (THAILAND) LIMITED—See Sanmina Corporation; *U.S. Public*, pg. 1841
SANMINA-SCI TECHNOLOGY INDIA PRIVATE LIMITED—See Sanmina Corporation; *U.S. Public*, pg. 1841
SANMIT INFRA LIMITED; *Int'l*, pg. 6547
SANMITRA COMMERCIAL LIMITED; *Int'l*, pg. 6547
SANNA MATTSON MACLEOD, INC.; *U.S. Private*, pg. 3546
SANNECT CO., LTD.—See COMSYS Holdings Corporation; *Int'l*, pg. 1762
SANNENG APPLIANCE (WUXI) CO., LTD.—See San Neng Group Holdings Co., Ltd.; *Int'l*, pg. 6521
SANNENG BAKEWARE CORPORATION—See San Neng Group Holdings Co., Ltd.; *Int'l*, pg. 6521
SANNENG BAKEWARE (WUXI) CO., LTD.—See San Neng Group Holdings Co., Ltd.; *Int'l*, pg. 6521
SANNENG FOOD APPLIANCE CO., LTD.—See San Neng Group Holdings Co., Ltd.; *Int'l*, pg. 6521
SAN NENG GROUP HOLDINGS CO., LTD.; *Int'l*, pg. 6521
SANNENG JAPAN BAKEWARE CO., LTD.—See San Neng Group Holdings Co., Ltd.; *Int'l*, pg. 6521
SANNENG JAPAN FOOD EQUIPMENT CO., LTD.—See San Neng Group Holdings Co., Ltd.; *Int'l*, pg. 6521
SANNER GMBH—See GHO Capital Partners LLP; *Int'l*, pg. 2959
SANNO CO., LTD.; *Int'l*, pg. 6547
SANNOMIYA TERMINAL BUILDING CO., LTD.—See West Japan Railway Company; *Int'l*, pg. 8385
SAN NOPCO KOREA LTD.—See Sanyo Chemical Industries, Ltd.; *Int'l*, pg. 6563
SAN NOPCO LIMITED—See Sanyo Chemical Industries, Ltd.; *Int'l*, pg. 6563
SAN NOPCO (SHANGHAI) TRADING CO., LTD—See Sanyo Chemical Industries, Ltd.; *Int'l*, pg. 6563
SANNOVA CO., LTD.—See Eisai Co., Ltd.; *Int'l*, pg. 2335
SANO ASSOCIATES, INC.; *U.S. Private*, pg. 3546
SANO BRUNO'S ENTERPRISES LTD.; *Int'l*, pg. 6547
SANOCHEMIA PHARMAZEUTIKA AG; *Int'l*, pg. 6547
SANOCKIE ZAKLADY PRZEMYSLU GUMOWEGO STOMIL SANOK S.A.; *Int'l*, pg. 6547
SANOFI AB—See Sanofi; *Int'l*, pg. 6548
SANOFI ARABIA TRADING COMPANY LIMITED—See Sanofi; *Int'l*, pg. 6548
SANOFI A/S—See Sanofi; *Int'l*, pg. 6548
SANOFI AUSTRALIA PTY LIMITED—See Sanofi; *Int'l*, pg. 6548
SANOFI-AVENTIS AB—See Sanofi; *Int'l*, pg. 6550
SANOFI-AVENTIS A.E.B.E.—See Sanofi; *Int'l*, pg. 6550
SANOFI-AVENTIS ALGERIE SPA—See Sanofi; *Int'l*, pg. 6550
SANOFI-AVENTIS AMERIQUE DU NORD S.A.S.—See Sanofi; *Int'l*, pg. 6550
SANOFI-AVENTIS ARGENTINA S.A.—See Sanofi; *Int'l*, pg. 6550
SANOFI-AVENTIS BANGLADESH LTD—See Sanofi; *Int'l*, pg. 6551
SANOFI-AVENTIS CROATIA D.O.O.—See Sanofi; *Int'l*, pg. 6551

2371

SANOFI-AVENTIS CYPRUS LTD.—See Sanofi; *Int'l*, pg. 6551
SANOFI-AVENTIS DE CHILE SA—See Sanofi; *Int'l*, pg. 6551
SANOFI-AVENTIS DEL PERU S.A.—See Sanofi; *Int'l*, pg. 6551
SANOFI-AVENTIS DE MEXICO S.A. DE C.V.—See Sanofi; *Int'l*, pg. 6551
SANOFI-AVENTIS DENMARK A/S—See Sanofi; *Int'l*, pg. 6550
SANOFI-AVENTIS DE PANAMA S.A.—See Sanofi; *Int'l*, pg. 6551
SANOFI-AVENTIS DEUTSCHLAND GMBH—See Sanofi; *Int'l*, pg. 6550
SANOFI-AVENTIS DE VENEZUELA S.A.—See Sanofi; *Int'l*, pg. 6552
SANOFI-AVENTIS D.O.O—See Sanofi; *Int'l*, pg. 6551
SANOFI-AVENTIS ECUADOR—See Sanofi; *Int'l*, pg. 6551
SANOFI-AVENTIS ESTONIA OU—See Sanofi; *Int'l*, pg. 6551
SANOFI-AVENTIS FARMACEUTICA LTDA—See Sanofi; *Int'l*, pg. 6550
SANOFI-AVENTIS FRANCE S.A.—See Sanofi; *Int'l*, pg. 6550
SANOFI-AVENTIS GMBH—See Sanofi; *Int'l*, pg. 6550
SANOFI-AVENTIS GROUPE S.A.—See Sanofi; *Int'l*, pg. 6550
SANOFI-AVENTIS GULF—See Sanofi; *Int'l*, pg. 6551
SANOFI-AVENTIS HONG KONG LIMITED—See Sanofi; *Int'l*, pg. 6550
SANOFI-AVENTIS ILACLARI LIMITED SIRKETI—See Sanofi; *Int'l*, pg. 6550
SANOFI-AVENTIS IRELAND LTD.—See Sanofi; *Int'l*, pg. 6550
SANOFI-AVENTIS ISRAEL—See Sanofi; *Int'l*, pg. 6550
SANOFI-AVENTIS KAZAKHSTAN LLP—See Sanofi; *Int'l*, pg. 6551
SANOFI-AVENTIS KOREA CO. LTD—See Sanofi; *Int'l*, pg. 6550
SANOFI-AVENTIS LIBAN S.A.L.—See Sanofi; *Int'l*, pg. 6551
SANOFI-AVENTIS (MALAYSIA) SDN. BHD.—See Sanofi; *Int'l*, pg. 6550
SANOFI-AVENTIS-MEIJI PHARMACEUTICALS CO., LTD.—See Meiji Holdings Co., Ltd.; *Int'l*, pg. 4801
SANOFI-AVENTIS NETHERLANDS B.V.—See Sanofi; *Int'l*, pg. 6550
SANOFI-AVENTIS NIGERIA LTD.—See Sanofi; *Int'l*, pg. 6551
SANOFI-AVENTIS NORGE AS—See Sanofi; *Int'l*, pg. 6550
SANOFI-AVENTIS OY—See Sanofi; *Int'l*, pg. 6551
SANOFI-AVENTIS PHARMA SLOVAKIA S.R.O.—See Sanofi; *Int'l*, pg. 6551
SANOFI-AVENTIS PHARMA TUNISIE SA—See Sanofi; *Int'l*, pg. 6551
SANOFI-AVENTIS PHILIPPINES INC.—See Sanofi; *Int'l*, pg. 6551
SANOFI-AVENTIS PRIVATE CO., LTD.—See Sanofi; *Int'l*, pg. 6551
SANOFI-AVENTIS RESEARCH & DEVELOPMENT—See Sanofi; *Int'l*, pg. 6551
SANOFI-AVENTIS S.A. DE C.V.—See Sanofi; *Int'l*, pg. 6551
SANOFI-AVENTIS S.A.—See Sanofi; *Int'l*, pg. 6551
SANOFI-AVENTIS S.A.U—See Sanofi; *Int'l*, pg. 6551
SANOFI-AVENTIS SINGAPORE PTE. LTD—See Sanofi; *Int'l*, pg. 6551
SANOFI-AVENTIS—See Sanofi; *Int'l*, pg. 6551
SANOFI-AVENTIS—See Sanofi; *Int'l*, pg. 6551
SANOFI-AVENTIS—See Sanofi; *Int'l*, pg. 6551
SANOFI-AVENTIS—See Sanofi; *Int'l*, pg. 6551
SANOFI-AVENTIS—See Sanofi; *Int'l*, pg. 6551
SANOFI-AVENTIS—See Sanofi; *Int'l*, pg. 6550
SANOFI-AVENTIS—See Sanofi; *Int'l*, pg. 6551
SANOFI-AVENTIS SOUTH AFRICA (PROPRIETARY) LTD—See Sanofi; *Int'l*, pg. 6551
SANOFI-AVENTIS SPA—See Sanofi; *Int'l*, pg. 6551
SANOFI-AVENTIS SP Z.O.O.—See Sanofi; *Int'l*, pg. 6551
SANOFI-AVENTIS S.R.O.—See Sanofi; *Int'l*, pg. 6551
SANOFI-AVENTIS (SUISSE) SA—See Sanofi; *Int'l*, pg. 6550
SANOFI-AVENTIS TAIWAN CO. LTD—See Sanofi; *Int'l*, pg. 6551
SANOFI-AVENTIS THAILAND LTD.—See Sanofi; *Int'l*, pg. 6551
SANOFI-AVENTIS TUNISIE—See Sanofi; *Int'l*, pg. 6551
SANOFI-AVENTIS UK HOLDINGS LIMITED—See Sanofi; *Int'l*, pg. 6550
SANOFI-AVENTIS URUGUAY S.A.—See Sanofi; *Int'l*, pg. 6551
SANOFI-AVENTIS US LLC—See Sanofi; *Int'l*, pg. 6552
SANOFI-AVENTIS VIETNAM COMPANY LIMITED—See Sanofi; *Int'l*, pg. 6551
SANOFI-AVENTIS VOSTOK ZAO—See Sanofi; *Int'l*, pg. 6551
SANOFI-AVENTIS ZRT.—See Sanofi; *Int'l*, pg. 6551
SANOFI BELGIUM—See Sanofi; *Int'l*, pg. 6550
SANOFI CHIMIE S.A.—See Sanofi; *Int'l*, pg. 6548

SANOFI (CHINA) INVESTMENT CO., LTD.—See Sanofi; *Int'l*, pg. 6548
SANOFI CHINA—See Sanofi; *Int'l*, pg. 6548
SANOFI DE GUATEMALA S.A.—See Sanofi; *Int'l*, pg. 6550
SANOFI EGYPT S.A.E.—See Sanofi; *Int'l*, pg. 6548
SANOFI FRANCE—See Sanofi; *Int'l*, pg. 6550
SANOFI INDIA LIMITED—See Sanofi; *Int'l*, pg. 6548
SANOFI K.K.—See Sanofi; *Int'l*, pg. 6548
SANOFI OY—See Sanofi; *Int'l*, pg. 6548
SANOFI PASTEUR INC.—See Sanofi; *Int'l*, pg. 6549
SANOFI PASTEUR K.K.—See Sanofi; *Int'l*, pg. 6549
SANOFI PASTEUR LIMITED—See Sanofi; *Int'l*, pg. 6549
SANOFI PASTEUR LTDA.—See Sanofi; *Int'l*, pg. 6549
SANOFI PASTEUR LTD—See Sanofi; *Int'l*, pg. 6549
SANOFI PASTEUR MSD AG—See Merck & Co., Inc.; *U.S. Public*, pg. 1421
SANOFI PASTEUR MSD AG—See Sanofi; *Int'l*, pg. 6549
SANOFI PASTEUR MSD GMBH—See Merck & Co., Inc.; *U.S. Public*, pg. 1421
SANOFI PASTEUR MSD GMBH—See Merck & Co., Inc.; *U.S. Public*, pg. 1421
SANOFI PASTEUR MSD GMBH—See Sanofi; *Int'l*, pg. 6549
SANOFI PASTEUR MSD GMBH—See Sanofi; *Int'l*, pg. 6549
SANOFI PASTEUR MSD N.V.—See Merck & Co., Inc.; *U.S. Public*, pg. 1421
SANOFI PASTEUR MSD N.V.—See Sanofi; *Int'l*, pg. 6549
SANOFI PASTEUR MSD OY—See Merck & Co., Inc.; *U.S. Public*, pg. 1421
SANOFI PASTEUR MSD OY—See Sanofi; *Int'l*, pg. 6549
SANOFI PASTEUR MSD, SA—See Merck & Co., Inc.; *U.S. Public*, pg. 1421
SANOFI PASTEUR MSD, SA—See Sanofi; *Int'l*, pg. 6549
SANOFI PASTEUR MSD, SNC—See Merck & Co., Inc.; *U.S. Public*, pg. 1421
SANOFI PASTEUR MSD, SNC—See Sanofi; *Int'l*, pg. 6549
SANOFI PASTEUR MSD—See Merck & Co., Inc.; *U.S. Public*, pg. 1421
SANOFI PASTEUR MSD—See Sanofi; *Int'l*, pg. 6549
SANOFI PASTEUR MSD SPA—See Merck & Co., Inc.; *U.S. Public*, pg. 1421
SANOFI PASTEUR MSD SPA—See Sanofi; *Int'l*, pg. 6549
SANOFI PASTEUR SA—See Sanofi; *Int'l*, pg. 6548
SANOFI PASTEUR SA—See Sanofi; *Int'l*, pg. 6549
SANOFI PASTEUR S.A.—See Sanofi; *Int'l*, pg. 6549
SANOFI PASTEUR S.A.—See Sanofi; *Int'l*, pg. 6549
SANOFI PASTEUR S.A.—See Sanofi; *Int'l*, pg. 6549
SANOFI PASTEUR—See Sanofi; *Int'l*, pg. 6549
SANOFI PASTEUR—See Sanofi; *Int'l*, pg. 6548
SANOFI PASTEUR—See Sanofi; *Int'l*, pg. 6548
SANOFI PASTEUR—See Sanofi; *Int'l*, pg. 6549
SANOFI PASTEUR—See Sanofi; *Int'l*, pg. 6549
SANOFI PASTEUR—See Sanofi; *Int'l*, pg. 6549
SANOFI PASTEUR—See Sanofi; *Int'l*, pg. 6549
SANOFI PASTEUR—See Sanofi; *Int'l*, pg. 6549
SANOFI PASTEUR—See Sanofi; *Int'l*, pg. 6549
SANOFI PASTEUR—See Sanofi; *Int'l*, pg. 6549
SANOFI PASTEUR—See Sanofi; *Int'l*, pg. 6549
SANOFI PASTEUR—See Sanofi; *Int'l*, pg. 6549
SANOFI PASTEUR—See Sanofi; *Int'l*, pg. 6549
SANOFI PASTEUR—See Sanofi; *Int'l*, pg. 6549
SANOFI PASTEUR VAXDESIGN CORPORATION—See Sanofi; *Int'l*, pg. 6549
SANOFI PRODUTOS FARMACEUTICOS, LDA—See Sanofi; *Int'l*, pg. 6550
SANOFI ROMANIA SRL—See Sanofi; *Int'l*, pg. 6549
SANOFI SAGLIK URUNLERI LIMITED SIRKETI—See Sanofi; *Int'l*, pg. 6549
SANOFI SANTE GRAND PUBLIC INC.—See Sanofi; *Int'l*, pg. 6549
SANOFI; *Int'l*, pg. 6547
SANOFI-SYNTHELABO DE HONDURAS S.A.—See Sanofi; *Int'l*, pg. 6552
SANOFI SYNTHELABO H.K. LTD—See Sanofi; *Int'l*, pg. 6549
SANOFI-SYNTHELABO, INC.—See Sanofi; *Int'l*, pg. 6552
SANOFI-SYNTHELABO (INDIA) LIMITED—See Sanofi; *Int'l*, pg. 6552
SANOFI-SYNTHELABO LIMITED—See Sanofi; *Int'l*, pg. 6552
SANOFI-SYNTHELABO-TAISHO PHARMACEUTICALS CO., LTD.—See Sanofi; *Int'l*, pg. 6549
SANOFI-SYNTHELABO-TAISHO PHARMACEUTICALS CO., LTD.—See Taisho Pharmaceutical Holdings Co., Ltd; *Int'l*, pg. 7417
SANOFI-SYNTHELABO UK LTD—See Sanofi; *Int'l*, pg. 6552
SANOFI-TOPAZ, INC.—See Sanofi; *Int'l*, pg. 6552
SANOFI WINTHROP INDUSTRIE S.A.—See Sanofi; *Int'l*, pg. 6549
SANOH AMERICA, INC. - FINDLAY PLANT—See Sanoh Industrial Co., Ltd.; *Int'l*, pg. 6552

SANOH CANADA, LTD.—See Sanoh Industrial Co., Ltd.; *Int'l*, pg. 6552
SAN OH CO., LTD. - CHIBA FACTORY—See Nishio Holdings Co., Ltd.; *Int'l*, pg. 5365
SAN OH CO., LTD. - SHIGA FACTORY—See Nishio Holdings Co., Ltd.; *Int'l*, pg. 5366
SAN OH CO., LTD.—See Nishio Holdings Co., Ltd.; *Int'l*, pg. 5365
SANOH COMMUNICATIONS CORP.—See Sanoh Industrial Co., Ltd.; *Int'l*, pg. 6552
SANOH EUROPE (FRANCE) EURL—See Sanoh Industrial Co., Ltd.; *Int'l*, pg. 6552
SANOH EUROPE GMBH—See Sanoh Industrial Co., Ltd.; *Int'l*, pg. 6552
SANOH FULTON (PHILIPPINES) INC.—See Sanoh Industrial Co., Ltd.; *Int'l*, pg. 6552
SANOH INDUSTRIAL CO., LTD. - KOGA FACTORY—See Sanoh Industrial Co., Ltd.; *Int'l*, pg. 6552
SANOH INDUSTRIAL CO., LTD.; *Int'l*, pg. 6552
SANOH INDUSTRIAL DE MEXICO S.A. DE C.V.—See Sanoh Industrial Co., Ltd.; *Int'l*, pg. 6552
SANOH INDUSTRIAL (WUHAN) CO., LTD.—See Sanoh Industrial Co., Ltd.; *Int'l*, pg. 6552
SANOH INDUSTRIAL (WUXI) CO., LTD.—See Sanoh Industrial Co., Ltd.; *Int'l*, pg. 6552
SANOH MAGYAR KFT—See Sanoh Industrial Co., Ltd.; *Int'l*, pg. 6552
SANOH MANUFACTURING DE MEXICO S.A. DE C.V.—See Sanoh Industrial Co., Ltd.; *Int'l*, pg. 6552
SANOH UK MANUFACTURING LTD.—See Sanoh Industrial Co., Ltd.; *Int'l*, pg. 6552
SANOLABOR D.D.; *Int'l*, pg. 6553
SANOMA BUDAPEST ZRT—See DPG Media Group NV; *Int'l*, pg. 2188
SANOMA DATA OY—See Sanoma Oyj; *Int'l*, pg. 6553
SANOMA DIGITAL OY—See Sanoma Oyj; *Int'l*, pg. 6553
SANOMA DIGITAL THE NETHERLANDS B.V.—See DPG Media Group NV; *Int'l*, pg. 2188
SANOMA EDUCACION, S.L.—See Sanoma Oyj; *Int'l*, pg. 6553
SANOMA ENTERTAINMENT LTD.—See DPG Media Group NV; *Int'l*, pg. 2188
SANOMA ITALIA S.P.A.—See Sanoma Oyj; *Int'l*, pg. 6553
SANOMALA OY—See Sanoma Oyj; *Int'l*, pg. 6553
SANOMA LEARNING B.V.—See Sanoma Oyj; *Int'l*, pg. 6553
SANOMALEHTI ILKKA OY—See Ilkka Yhtymae Oyj; *Int'l*, pg. 3615
SANOMA MAGAZINES BELGIUM NV—See DPG Media Group NV; *Int'l*, pg. 2188
SANOMA MAGAZINES FINLAND CORPORATION—See DPG Media Group NV; *Int'l*, pg. 2188
SANOMA MAGAZINES INTERNATIONAL B.V.—See DPG Media Group NV; *Int'l*, pg. 2188
SANOMA MANU OY—See Sanoma Oyj; *Int'l*, pg. 6553
SANOMA MEDIA B.V.—See DPG Media Group NV; *Int'l*, pg. 2188
SANOMA MEDIA NETHERLANDS B.V.—See Sanoma Oyj; *Int'l*, pg. 6553
SANOMA MEDIA UKRAINE—See DPG Media Group NV; *Int'l*, pg. 2188
SANOMA NEWS LTD.—See Sanoma Oyj; *Int'l*, pg. 6553
SANOMA OYJ; *Int'l*, pg. 6553
SANOMAPAINO OY—See Sanoma Oyj; *Int'l*, pg. 6553
SANOMA PRO LTD.—See Sanoma Oyj; *Int'l*, pg. 6553
SANOMA PRO OY—See Bonnier AB; *Int'l*, pg. 1108
SANOMA TELEVISION OY—See DPG Media Group NV; *Int'l*, pg. 2188
SANOMEDICS, INC.; *U.S. Private*, pg. 3546
SANOMED SANITATSHAUS FUR ORTHOPADIE UND REHABILITATIONSTECHNIK GMBH—See Asklepios Kliniken GmbH & Co. KGaA; *Int'l*, pg. 624
SANOOK ENTERPRISES, INC.; *Int'l*, pg. 6554
SANOOK ONLINE LIMITED—See Naspers Limited; *Int'l*, pg. 5148
SANOTACT GMBH; *Int'l*, pg. 6554
SANOTACT (HK) LIMITED—See sanotact GmbH; *Int'l*, pg. 6554
SANO UNYU CO., LTD.—See Konoike Transport Co., Ltd.; *Int'l*, pg. 4275
S.A NOVACEL BELGIUM NV—See Chargeurs SA; *Int'l*, pg. 1449
SANOVAL; *Int'l*, pg. 6554
SANOVAS, INC.; *U.S. Private*, pg. 3546
SANOVO EIPRODUKTE GMBH & CO. KG—See Thornico A/S; *Int'l*, pg. 7720
SANOVO FOODS A/S—See Thornico A/S; *Int'l*, pg. 7720
SANOVO GREENPACK BRAZIL—See Thornico A/S; *Int'l*, pg. 7720
SANOVO INTERNATIONAL ASIA PACIFIC CO. LTD.—See Thornico A/S; *Int'l*, pg. 7720
SANOVO INTERNATIONAL LTD.—See Thornico A/S; *Int'l*, pg. 7720
S.A. NOVO NORDISK PHARMA N.V.—See Novo Nordisk Fonden; *Int'l*, pg. 5465
SANOVO TECHNOLOGY A/S—See Thornico A/S; *Int'l*, pg. 7720
SANOVO VAX INC.—See Thornico A/S; *Int'l*, pg. 7720

COMPANY NAME INDEX

SANOYAS BUSINESS PARTNER CORPORATION—See Sanoyas Holdings Corporation; *Int'l*, pg. 6554
SANOYAS CONSTRUCTION MACHINERY CORPORATION - HIROSHIMA FACTORY—See Sanoyas Holdings Corporation; *Int'l*, pg. 6554
SANOYAS ENGINEERING CORPORATION—See Sanoyas Holdings Corporation; *Int'l*, pg. 6554
SANOYAS HOLDINGS CORPORATION; *Int'l*, pg. 6554
SANOYAS RIDES CORPORATION - KYUSHU FACTORY—See Sanoyas Holdings Corporation; *Int'l*, pg. 6554
SANOYAS RIDES CORPORATION - OSAKA FACTORY—See Sanoyas Holdings Corporation; *Int'l*, pg. 6554
SANOYAS RIDES SERVICE CORPORATION—See Sanoyas Holdings Corporation; *Int'l*, pg. 6554
SANOYAS SANGYO CO., LTD.—See Sanoyas Holdings Corporation; *Int'l*, pg. 6554
SANOYAS SHIPBUILDING CORPORATION - TECHNICAL & DESIGN DIVISION—See Sanoyas Holdings Corporation; *Int'l*, pg. 6554
SANPAK ENGINEERING INDUSTRIES (PVT.) LTD.—See Sanden Corporation; *Int'l*, pg. 6525
SANPAN ISITMA SISTEMLERI SAN VE TIC A.S.—See Zehnder Group AG; *Int'l*, pg. 8630
SANPAOLO IMI BANK IRELAND PLC—See Intesa Sanpaolo S.p.A.; *Int'l*, pg. 3766
SANPAOLO IMI S.P.A—See Intesa Sanpaolo S.p.A.; *Int'l*, pg. 3766
SANPAOLO IMI S.P.A.—See Intesa Sanpaolo S.p.A.; *Int'l*, pg. 3766
SAN PATRICIO ELECTRIC COOPERATIVE, INC.; *U.S. Private*, pg. 3542
SAN PATRICIO PIPELINE LLC—See Occidental Petroleum Corporation; *U.S. Public*, pg. 1562
SAN PEDRO BAY PIPELINE COMPANY—See Amplify Energy Corp.; *U.S. Public*, pg. 133
SANPEI KOGYO CO., LTD.—See Japan Pulp and Paper Company Limited; *Int'l*, pg. 3904
SANPELLEGRINO POLSKA SP. Z O.O.—See CSP International Fashion Group S.p.A.; *Int'l*, pg. 1867
SANPELLEGRINO S.P.A.—See Nestle S.A.; *Int'l*, pg. 5210
SANPOWER GROUP CO., LTD.; *Int'l*, pg. 6554
SANPRO - APT SP. Z O.O.—See Impel S.A.; *Int'l*, pg. 3632
SANPRO JOB SERVICE SP. Z O.O.—See Impel S.A.; *Int'l*, pg. 3632
SANPULSE TECHNOLOGIES INC.; *U.S. Private*, pg. 3546
SANQUAN FOOD CO., LTD.; *Int'l*, pg. 6554
SAN RAFAEL ROCK QUARRY LLC—See The Dutra Group Inc.; *U.S. Private*, pg. 4024
SAN RAMON BOAT CENTER INC.; *U.S. Private*, pg. 3542
SAN RAMON REGIONAL MEDICAL CENTER, INC.—See Tenet Healthcare Corporation; *U.S. Public*, pg. 2003
SAN RAMON SURGERY CENTER, LLC—See Tenet Healthcare Corporation; *U.S. Public*, pg. 2003
SAN REMO DISTRICT FINANCIAL SERVICES LTD—See Bendigo & Adelaide Bank Ltd.; *Int'l*, pg. 971
SAN REMO MACARONI COMPANY PTY LTD—See SYSU International, Inc.; *Int'l*, pg. 7394
SANREX CORPORATION—See Sansha Electric Manufacturing Co., Ltd.; *Int'l*, pg. 6555
SANREX LIMITED—See Sansha Electric Manufacturing Co., Ltd.; *Int'l*, pg. 6555
SAN RIGA—See WPP plc; *Int'l*, pg. 8481
SANRIKU TOYO KAISHA, LTD.—See Toyo Suisan Kaisha, Ltd.; *Int'l*, pg. 7858
SANRIN CO., LTD.; *Int'l*, pg. 6554
SANRIO ASIA MERCHANDISE CO., LTD.—See Sanrio Company, Ltd.; *Int'l*, pg. 6554
SANRIO CAR LEASE CO., LTD.—See Sanrio Company, Ltd.; *Int'l*, pg. 6554
SANRIO COMPANY, LTD.; *Int'l*, pg. 6554
SANRIO DO BRASIL COMERCIO E REPRESENTACOES LTDA—See Sanrio Company, Ltd.; *Int'l*, pg. 6554
SANRIO ENTERTAINMENT CO., LTD.—See Sanrio Company, Ltd.; *Int'l*, pg. 6554
SANRIO FAR EAST CO., LTD.—See Sanrio Company, Ltd.; *Int'l*, pg. 6554
SANRIO GMBH—See Sanrio Company, Ltd.; *Int'l*, pg. 6555
SANRIO (HONG KONG) COMPANY LIMITED—See Sanrio Company, Ltd.; *Int'l*, pg. 6554
SANRIO, INC.—See Sanrio Company, Ltd.; *Int'l*, pg. 6555
SANRIO LICENSE GMBH—See Sanrio Company, Ltd.; *Int'l*, pg. 6555
SANRIO MUSIC PUBLICATIONS CO., LTD.—See Sanrio Company, Ltd.; *Int'l*, pg. 6555
SANRIO PUROLAND, K.K.—See Sanrio Company, Ltd.; *Int'l*, pg. 6555
SANRIO TAIWAN CO , LTD.—See Sanrio Company, Ltd.; *Int'l*, pg. 6555
SANRIO WAVE CO., LTD.—See Sanrio Company, Ltd.; *Int'l*, pg. 6555
SANRIO WAVE HONG KONG CO., LTD.—See Sanrio Company, Ltd.; *Int'l*, pg. 6555
SANRITSU CORPORATION; *Int'l*, pg. 6555

SANRITZ AUTOMATION CO., LTD.—See Optex Group Co., Ltd.; *Int'l*, pg. 5602
SANRITZ CORPORATION—See Sumitomo Chemical Company, Limited; *Int'l*, pg. 7264
SAN ROQUE POWER CORPORATION—See Marubeni Corporation; *Int'l*, pg. 4709
SAN SABA PECAN, INC.; *U.S. Private*, pg. 3542
SAN SAC GROUP AB—See Accent Equity Partners AB; *Int'l*, pg. 81
SANSAN, INC.; *Int'l*, pg. 6555
SAN SEBASTIAN GOLD MINES, INC.—See Commerce Group Corp.; *U.S. Public*, pg. 545
SANSEGAL SPORTSWEAR, INC.; *U.S. Private*, pg. 3546
SANSEI CO., LTD.; *Int'l*, pg. 6555
SANSEI INDUSTRY CO., LTD.—See Sankyo Tateyama Inc.; *Int'l*, pg. 6543
SANSEIKAIHATSU CO., LTD.—See Mitsui Chemicals, Inc.; *Int'l*, pg. 4983
SANSEI LANDIC CO., LTD.; *Int'l*, pg. 6555
SANSEI MAINTENANCE CO., LTD.—See Sansei Technologies Inc.; *Int'l*, pg. 6555
SANSEI PRINTING LTD.—See TOPPAN Holdings Inc.; *Int'l*, pg. 7817
SANSEI - SHOWA CO., LTD.—See SHOWA SHINKU CO., LTD.; *Int'l*, pg. 6862
SANSEI TECHNOLOGIES INC - KOBE PLANT—See Sansei Technologies Inc.; *Int'l*, pg. 6555
SANSEI TECHNOLOGIES INC.; *Int'l*, pg. 6555
SANSEI VIETNAM TRADING CO., LTD.—See Sansei Co., Ltd.; *Int'l*, pg. 6555
SANSEMISA, S.A.—See Nefinsa S.A.; *Int'l*, pg. 5192
SANSERA ENGINEERING LIMITED; *Int'l*, pg. 6555
SANS FIBERS INCORPORATED—See AECI Limited; *Int'l*, pg. 171
SANSHA ELECTRIC MANUFACTURING CO., LTD. - OKAYAMA PLANT—See Sansha Electric Manufacturing Co., Ltd.; *Int'l*, pg. 6555
SANSHA ELECTRIC MANUFACTURING CO., LTD. - SHIGA PLANT—See Sansha Electric Manufacturing Co., Ltd.; *Int'l*, pg. 6555
SANSHA ELECTRIC MANUFACTURING CO., LTD.; *Int'l*, pg. 6555
SANSHA ELECTRIC MFG. (GUANGDONG) CO., LTD.—See Sansha Electric Manufacturing Co., Ltd.; *Int'l*, pg. 6555
SANSHA ELECTRIC MFG. (SHANGHAI) CO., LTD.—See Sansha Electric Manufacturing Co., Ltd.; *Int'l*, pg. 6555
SANSHA SOLUTION SERVICE CO., LTD.—See Sansha Electric Manufacturing Co., Ltd.; *Int'l*, pg. 6555
SANSHELL PRODUCTS, INC.—See Frank Calandra, Inc.; *U.S. Private*, pg. 1594
SANSHENG HOLDINGS (GROUP) CO., LTD.; *Int'l*, pg. 6556
SANSHENG INTELLECTUAL EDUCATION TECHNOLOGY CO., LTD.; *Int'l*, pg. 6556
SANSHIN CORPORATION—See Aktio Holdings Corporation; *Int'l*, pg. 267
SANSHIN ELECTRIC CO., LTD.—See Bain Capital, LP; *U.S. Private*, pg. 435
SANSHIN ELECTRIC CO., LTD.; *Int'l*, pg. 6556
SANSHIN ELECTRIC CORPORATION - ADACHI FACTORY—See Sanshin Electric Corporation; *Int'l*, pg. 6556
SANSHIN ELECTRIC CORPORATION - ISE FACTORY—See Sanshin Electric Corporation; *Int'l*, pg. 6556
SANSHIN ELECTRIC CORPORATION; *Int'l*, pg. 6556
SANSHIN ELECTRONICS CO., LTD.; *Int'l*, pg. 6556
SANSHIN ELECTRONICS CORPORATION—See Sanshin Electronics Co., Ltd.; *Int'l*, pg. 6556
SANSHIN ELECTRONICS (HONG KONG) CO., LTD.—See Sanshin Electronics Co., Ltd.; *Int'l*, pg. 6556
SANSHIN ELECTRONICS KOREA CO., LTD.—See Sanshin Electronics Co., Ltd.; *Int'l*, pg. 6556
SAN SHIN ELECTRONICS (MALAYSIA) SDN. BHD.—See Sanshin Electronics Co., Ltd.; *Int'l*, pg. 6556
SANSHIN ELECTRONICS (SHANGHAI) CO., LTD.—See Sanshin Electronics Co., Ltd.; *Int'l*, pg. 6556
SANSHIN ELECTRONICS (SHENZHEN) CO., LTD.—See Sanshin Electronics Co., Ltd.; *Int'l*, pg. 6556
SANSHIN ELECTRONICS SINGAPORE (PTE.) LTD.—See Sanshin Electronics Co., Ltd.; *Int'l*, pg. 6556
SANSHIN ELECTRONICS (THAILAND) CO., LTD.—See Sanshin Electronics Co., Ltd.; *Int'l*, pg. 6556
SANSHIN ELECTRONICS (U.S.A.) CORPORATION—See Sanshin Electronics Co., Ltd.; *Int'l*, pg. 6556
SAN SHING FASTECH CORP.; *Int'l*, pg. 6521
SANSHIN (MALAYSIA) SDN. BHD.—See Bain Capital, LP; *U.S. Private*, pg. 435
SANSHIN MEDIA SOLUTIONS CO., LTD.—See Sanshin Electronics Co., Ltd.; *Int'l*, pg. 6556
SANSHIN NETWORK SERVICE CO., LTD.—See Sanshin Electronics Co., Ltd.; *Int'l*, pg. 6556
SANSHIN SANGYO CO., LTD.—See Kyoritsu Electric Corporation; *Int'l*, pg. 4365
SANSHIN SYSTEM DESIGN CO., LTD.—See Sanshin Electronics Co., Ltd.; *Int'l*, pg. 6556
SANSHIN TSUSHO CO., LTD.—See UBE Corporation; *Int'l*, pg. 8001

SANTA FE MINERALS LTD.

SAN SIMEON BY THE SOUND NURSING & REHABILITATION; *U.S. Private*, pg. 3542
SANSIRI LAND LIMITED—See Sansiri pcl; *Int'l*, pg. 6557
SANSIRI PCL; *Int'l*, pg. 6556
SANSIRI RAM-INDRA LIMITED—See Sansiri pcl; *Int'l*, pg. 6557
SANSIRI VENTURE CO., LTD.—See Sansiri pcl; *Int'l*, pg. 6557
SANSO ELECTRIC CO., LTD.; *Int'l*, pg. 6557
SANSO K.K.—See Mitsui-Soko Holdings Co., Ltd.; *Int'l*, pg. 4993
SANSO KOUUN CO., LTD.—See Mitsui-Soko Holdings Co., Ltd.; *Int'l*, pg. 4993
SANSONE AUTO MALL; *U.S. Private*, pg. 3546
SANSONE GROUP LLC; *U.S. Private*, pg. 3546
SAN SOON SENG FOOD INDUSTRIES SDN. BHD.—See Three-A Resources Berhad; *Int'l*, pg. 7721
SANSO SEIKO ELECTRIC CO., LTD.—See Sanso Electric Co., Ltd.; *Int'l*, pg. 6557
SANSO UNYU CO., LTD.—See Nippon Soda Co., Ltd.; *Int'l*, pg. 5334
SANS TECHNICAL FIBERS LLC—See AECI Limited; *Int'l*, pg. 171
SANSTEEL MINGUANG CO., LTD.; *Int'l*, pg. 6557
SANSURE BIOTECH, INC.; *Int'l*, pg. 6557
SANSUY S.A. - EMBU INDUSTRIAL UNIT—See Sansuy S.A.; *Int'l*, pg. 6557
SANSUY S.A.; *Int'l*, pg. 6557
SAN SWISS ARMS AG; *Int'l*, pg. 6521
SANTA ANA BUSINESS BANK; *U.S. Private*, pg. 3546
THE SANTA ANITA COMPANIES, INC.—See The Stronach Group Inc.; *Int'l*, pg. 7689
SANTA BARBARA APPLIED RESEARCH INC.; *U.S. Private*, pg. 3546
SANTA BARBARA ASSET MANAGEMENT, LLC—See Teachers Insurance Association - College Retirement Fund; *U.S. Private*, pg. 3947
SANTA BARBARA BREWING CO.; *U.S. Private*, pg. 3546
SANTA BARBARA CATERING COMPANY; *U.S. Private*, pg. 3547
SANTA BARBARA HUMANE SOCIETY—See Santa Maria Valley Humane Society; *U.S. Private*, pg. 3547
SANTA BARBARA INFRARED, INC.—See HEICO Corporation; *U.S. Public*, pg. 1020
SANTA BARBARA NEWS-PRESS; *U.S. Private*, pg. 3547
SANTA BARBARA OUTPATIENT SURGERY CENTER, LLC—See Tenet Healthcare Corporation; *U.S. Public*, pg. 2007
SANTA BARBARA SISTEMAS S.A.—See General Dynamics Corporation; *U.S. Public*, pg. 914
SANTA BARBARA SPECIALTY PHARMACY, LLC—See Elevance Health, Inc.; *U.S. Public*, pg. 730
SANTA BUCKLEY ENERGY, INC.—See Santa Energy Corporation; *U.S. Private*, pg. 3547
SANTAC CO., LTD.—See Nakamoto Packs Co., Ltd.; *Int'l*, pg. 5132
SANTA CLARA INC.—See Imperial Brands PLC; *Int'l*, pg. 3634
SANTA CLARA NUT COMPANY INC.; *U.S. Private*, pg. 3547
SANTA CLARITA SURGERY CENTER, L.P.—See Tenet Healthcare Corporation; *U.S. Public*, pg. 2012
SANTA CRUZ COUNTY BANK—See West Coast Community Bancorp; *U.S. Public*, pg. 2352
THE SANTA CRUZ COUNTY SENTINEL, INC.—See Gannett Co., Inc.; *U.S. Public*, pg. 905
SANTA CRUZ ENDOSCOPY CENTER, LLC—See UnitedHealth Group Incorporated; *U.S. Public*, pg. 2250
SANTA CRUZ HEALTHCARE CENTER—See Apollo Global Management, Inc.; *U.S. Public*, pg. 157
SANTA CRUZ NISSAN DODGE; *U.S. Private*, pg. 3547
SANTA CRUZ SEASIDE COMPANY; *U.S. Private*, pg. 3547
SANTA CRUZ SENTINEL—See Alden Global Capital LLC; *U.S. Private*, pg. 155
SANTACRUZ SILVER MINING LTD.; *Int'l*, pg. 6557
SANTA ENERGY CORPORATION; *U.S. Private*, pg. 3547
SANTA FE BELGRADE—See EAC Invest AS; *Int'l*, pg. 2262
SANTA FE COMMUNITY FOUNDATION; *U.S. Private*, pg. 3547
SANTA FE FINANCIAL CORPORATION—See InterGroup Corporation; *U.S. Public*, pg. 1144
SANTA FE GOLD CORP.; *U.S. Public*, pg. 1841
SANTAFE HEALTHCARE, INC.; *U.S. Private*, pg. 3547
SANTA FE HOLDINGS LTD.—See Mobilitas SA; *Int'l*, pg. 5011
SANTA FE INDIA PRIVATE LIMITED—See EAC Invest AS; *Int'l*, pg. 2262
SANTA FE INTERNATIONAL PROJECTS LIMITED—See EAC Invest AS; *Int'l*, pg. 2262
SANTA FE LEATHER CORPORATION; *U.S. Private*, pg. 3547
SANTA FE MINERALS LTD.; *Int'l*, pg. 6557
SANTA FE MOVING AND RELOCATION SERVICES PHILS., INC.—See EAC Invest AS; *Int'l*, pg. 2262
SANTA FE NATURAL TOBACCO COMPANY, INC.—See British American Tobacco plc; *Int'l*, pg. 1168

SANTA FE MINERALS LTD.
CORPORATE AFFILIATIONS

SANTA FE PACKAGING CORP.—See Alpha Industries, Inc.; *U.S. Private*, pg. 198
SANTA FE PETROLEUM, INC.; *U.S. Private*, pg. 3547
SANTA FE RELOCATION SERVICES JAPAN K.K.—See EAC Invest AS; *Int'l*, pg. 2262
SANTA FE RELOCATION SERVICES KOREA CO., LTD.—See EAC Invest AS; *Int'l*, pg. 2262
SANTA FE RELOCATION SERVICES LLC—See EAC Invest AS; *Int'l*, pg. 2262
SANTA FE RELOCATION SERVICES SDN. BHD.—See EAC Invest AS; *Int'l*, pg. 2262
SANTA FE RELOCATION SERVICES SINGAPORE PVT. LTD.—See EAC Invest AS; *Int'l*, pg. 2262
SANTA FE RELOCATION SERVICES—See EAC Invest AS; *Int'l*, pg. 2262
SANTA FE RELOCATION SERVICES—See EAC Invest AS; *Int'l*, pg. 2262
SANTA FE RELOCATION SERVICES TAIWAN CO., LTD—See EAC Invest AS; *Int'l*, pg. 2262
SANTAFE SENIOR LIVING—See SantaFe Healthcare, Inc.; *U.S. Private*, pg. 3547
SANTA FE SHUTTERS LIMITED—See Nien Made Enterprise Co., Ltd.; *Int'l*, pg. 5280
SANTA FE SPRINGS DIALYSIS, LLC—See DaVita Inc.; *U.S. Public*, pg. 643
SANTA FE (THAILAND) LTD.—See EAC Invest AS; *Int'l*, pg. 2262
SANTAFE TILE CORP.; *U.S. Private*, pg. 3548
SANTA FE TRANSPORT INTERNATIONAL LIMITED—See EAC Invest AS; *Int'l*, pg. 2262
SANTA FE VAN LINES CO. LTD.—See EAC Invest AS; *Int'l*, pg. 2262
SANTA FE WINWATER; *U.S. Private*, pg. 3547
SANTA FE WRIDGWAYS—See EAC Invest AS; *Int'l*, pg. 2262
SANTA FUEL, INC.—See Santa Energy Corporation; *U.S. Private*, pg. 3547
SANTA HELENA ASSISTENCIA MEDICA S.A.—See UnitedHealth Group Incorporated; *U.S. Public*, pg. 2250
SAN TAI DISTRIBUTION CO., LTD.—See Global Brands Manufacture Ltd.; *Int'l*, pg. 2993
SANTA INES EMPREENDIMENTOS IMOBILIARIOS LTDA.—See Direcional Engenharia S.A.; *Int'l*, pg. 2129
SANTA ISABEL S.A.—See Cencosud S.A.; *Int'l*, pg. 1401
SANTA IZABEL AGRO INDUSTRIA LTDA.—See Alamo Group Inc.; *U.S. Public*, pg. 71
SANTAK ELECTRONICS (SHENZHEN) CO., LTD.—See Eaton Corporation plc; *Int'l*, pg. 2282
SANTA LAURA EXPORTADORA DE CAFE S.L.E.C SA—See Segafredo Zanetti S.p.A.; *Int'l*, pg. 6682
SANTA MARIA ENERGIAS RENOVAVEIS S.A.—See Companhia Paranaense de Energia; *Int'l*, pg. 1748
SANTA MARIA FOODS ULC—See Sofina Foods Inc.; *Int'l*, pg. 7050
SANTA MARIA FORD INC.; *U.S. Private*, pg. 3547
SANTA MARIA MANUELA TURISMO, S.A.—See Jeronimo Martins SGPS SA; *Int'l*, pg. 3931
SANTA MARIA SEEDS INC.; *U.S. Private*, pg. 3547
SANTA MARIA SUITES RESORT—See Forbes Hamilton Management Company; *U.S. Private*, pg. 1562
SANTA MARIA TIMES, INC.—See Lee Enterprises, Incorporated; *U.S. Public*, pg. 1300
SANTA MARIA VALLEY HUMANE SOCIETY; *U.S. Private*, pg. 3547
SANTAM INSURANCE LTD.—See Sanlam Limited; *Int'l*, pg. 6545
SANTAMIX IBERICA SL—See Element Solutions Inc.; *U.S. Public*, pg. 728
SANTAM LIMITED—See Sanlam Limited; *Int'l*, pg. 6545
SANTA MONICA FORD COMPANY; *U.S. Private*, pg. 3547
SANTA MONICA SEAFOOD CO.; *U.S. Private*, pg. 3547
SANTAM STRUCTURED INSURANCE (PTY) LTD.—See Sanlam Limited; *Int'l*, pg. 6545
SANTANA MINERALS LIMITED; *Int'l*, pg. 6557
SANTANA S.A. DROGARIA FARMACIAS—See Brazil Pharma S.A.; *Int'l*, pg. 1143
SANTANDER ASSET MANAGEMENT CHILE S.A.—See Banco Santander, S.A.; *Int'l*, pg. 826
SANTANDER ASSET MANAGEMENT, S.A., S.G.I.I.C.—See Banco Santander, S.A.; *Int'l*, pg. 826
SANTANDER ASSET MANAGEMENT, S.A.—See Banco Santander, S.A.; *Int'l*, pg. 826
SANTANDER ASSET MANAGEMENT UK LIMITED—See Banco Santander, S.A.; *Int'l*, pg. 826
SANTANDER BANCORP—See First BanCorp; *U.S. Public*, pg. 839
SANTANDER BANESPA GRUPO—See Banco Santander, S.A.; *Int'l*, pg. 826
SANTANDER BANK AND TRUST (BAHAMAS), LTD.—See Banco Santander, S.A.; *Int'l*, pg. 826
SANTANDER BANK, N.A.—See Banco Santander, S.A.; *Int'l*, pg. 827
SANTANDER BANK POLSKA S.A.—See Banco Santander, S.A.; *Int'l*, pg. 826
SANTANDER BANK & TRUST, LTD.—See Banco Santander, S.A.; *Int'l*, pg. 826
SANTANDER BENELUX SA/NV—See Banco Santander, S.A.; *Int'l*, pg. 826

SANTANDER CARDS UK LTD.—See Banco Santander, S.A.; *Int'l*, pg. 827
SANTANDER CONSUMER BANK AG—See Banco Santander, S.A.; *Int'l*, pg. 826
SANTANDER CONSUMER BANK AS—See Banco Santander, S.A.; *Int'l*, pg. 826
SANTANDER CONSUMER BANK GMBH—See Banco Santander, S.A.; *Int'l*, pg. 826
SANTANDER CONSUMER BANK S.A.—See Banco Santander, S.A.; *Int'l*, pg. 826
SANTANDER CONSUMER BANQUE S.A.—See Banco Santander, S.A.; *Int'l*, pg. 827
SANTANDER CONSUMER CREDIT SERVICES LIMITED—See Banco Santander, S.A.; *Int'l*, pg. 827
SANTANDER CONSUMER, EFC, S.A.—See Banco Santander, S.A.; *Int'l*, pg. 827
SANTANDER CONSUMER FINANCE BENELUX B.V.—See Banco Santander, S.A.; *Int'l*, pg. 827
SANTANDER CONSUMER FINANCE, S.A.—See Banco Santander, S.A.; *Int'l*, pg. 827
SANTANDER CONSUMER HOLDING GMBH—See Banco Santander, S.A.; *Int'l*, pg. 827
SANTANDER CONSUMER LEASING GMBH—See Banco Santander, S.A.; *Int'l*, pg. 827
SANTANDER CONSUMER LEASING S.R.O.—See Banco Santander, S.A.; *Int'l*, pg. 827
SANTANDER CONSUMER RENTING, S.L.—See Banco Santander, S.A.; *Int'l*, pg. 827
SANTANDER CONSUMER S.A.S.—See Banco Santander, S.A.; *Int'l*, pg. 827
SANTANDER CONSUMER USA HOLDINGS INC.—See Banco Santander, S.A.; *Int'l*, pg. 827
SANTANDER CONSUMER USA INC.—See Banco Santander, S.A.; *Int'l*, pg. 827
SANTANDER CORPORATE & INVESTMENT BANKING—See Banco Santander, S.A.; *Int'l*, pg. 827
SANTANDER ENTERPRISES INC.; *U.S. Private*, pg. 3548
SANTANDER FINANCIAL PRODUCTS, LTD.—See Banco Santander, S.A.; *Int'l*, pg. 827
SANTANDER FINANCIAL SERVICES PLC—See Banco Santander, S.A.; *Int'l*, pg. 827
SANTANDER GENERALES SEGUROS Y REASEGUROS, S.A.—See Aegon N.V.; *Int'l*, pg. 175
SANTANDER GLOBAL PROPERTY, S.L.—See Banco Santander, S.A.; *Int'l*, pg. 827
SANTANDER HOLDINGS USA, INC.—See Banco Santander, S.A.; *Int'l*, pg. 827
SANTANDER INSURANCE AGENCY, U.S., LLC—See Banco Santander, S.A.; *Int'l*, pg. 827
SANTANDER INSURANCE SERVICES UK LIMITED—See Banco Santander, S.A.; *Int'l*, pg. 827
SANTANDER INVESTMENT SECURITIES INC.—See Banco Santander, S.A.; *Int'l*, pg. 827
SANTANDER SECURITIES CORPORATION—See First BanCorp; *U.S. Public*, pg. 839
SANTANDER SEGUROS Y REASEGUROS, COMPANIA ASEGURADORA, S.A.—See Banco Santander, S.A.; *Int'l*, pg. 827
SANTANDER TOTTA SEGUROS, COMPANHIA DE SEGUROS DE VIDA, S.A.—See Banco Santander, S.A.; *Int'l*, pg. 827
SANTANDER TOWARZYSTWO FUNDUSZY INWESTYCYJNYCH S.A.—See Banco Santander, S.A.; *Int'l*, pg. 827
SANTANDER UK GROUP HOLDINGS PLC—See Banco Santander, S.A.; *Int'l*, pg. 827
SANTANDER UK PLC - ISLE OF MAN BRANCH—See Banco Santander, S.A.; *Int'l*, pg. 827
SANTANDER UK PLC—See Banco Santander, S.A.; *Int'l*, pg. 827
SANTANDREA TERMINALI SPECIALIZZATI S.R.L.—See B. Pacorini S.p.A.; *Int'l*, pg. 789
SANT'ANDREA TEXTILES MACHINES SRL—See NSC Groupe SA; *Int'l*, pg. 5476
SANT'ANNA GOLF S.R.L.—See BPER BANCA S.p.A; *Int'l*, pg. 1132
SANTANNA NATURAL GAS CORP.; *U.S. Private*, pg. 3548
SANTAPAUL CORP.—See Ares Management Corporation; *U.S. Public*, pg. 189
SANTA QUITERIA ENERGIA, S.L.U.—See EDP - Energias de Portugal, S.A.; *Int'l*, pg. 2315
SANTARELLI & SONS OIL CO., INC.; *U.S. Private*, pg. 3548
SANTA RITA HARINAS, S.L.—See Ebro Foods S.A.; *Int'l*, pg. 2287
SANTARO INDUSTRIES INC.; *U.S. Private*, pg. 3548
SANTA ROSA CAMPWAY, INC.; *U.S. Private*, pg. 3547
SANTA ROSA CONSULTING, INC.; *U.S. Private*, pg. 3547
SANTA ROSA ENERGY CENTER, LLC—See LS Power Development, LLC; *U.S. Private*, pg. 2508
SANTA ROSA LEAD PRODUCTS INC.—See Metalico Inc.; *U.S. Private*, pg. 2681
SANTA'S BEST CRAFT, LTD.; *U.S. Private*, pg. 3547
SAN TECHNOLOGY, INC.—See Hitachi, Ltd.; *Int'l*, pg. 3424
SANTEC HOLDINGS CORPORATION—See EXEO Group Inc.; *Int'l*, pg. 2584
SANTECLAIR—See Covea Groupe S.A.S.; *Int'l*, pg. 1820

SANTEE DAIRIES, INC.—See Dean Foods Company; *U.S. Private*, pg. 1184
SANTEE PRINT WORKS, INC.; *U.S. Private*, pg. 3548
SAN TEH LTD.; *Int'l*, pg. 6521
SANTEK ENVIRONMENTAL LLC; *U.S. Private*, pg. 3548
SANTEK WASTE SERVICES LLC—See Republic Services, Inc.; *U.S. Public*, pg. 1787
SANTEN BUSINESS SERVICES CO., LTD.—See Santen Pharmaceutical Co., Ltd.; *Int'l*, pg. 6557
SANTEN CANADA INC.—See Santen Pharmaceutical Co., Ltd.; *Int'l*, pg. 6557
SANTEN GMBH—See Santen Pharmaceutical Co., Ltd.; *Int'l*, pg. 6557
SANTEN HOLDINGS U.S. INC—See Santen Pharmaceutical Co., Ltd.; *Int'l*, pg. 6557
SANTEN INC.—See Santen Pharmaceutical Co., Ltd.; *Int'l*, pg. 6557
SANTEN INDIA PRIVATE LIMITED—See Santen Pharmaceutical Co., Ltd.; *Int'l*, pg. 6557
SANTEN ITALY S.R.L.—See Santen Pharmaceutical Co., Ltd.; *Int'l*, pg. 6557
SANTEN LIMITED LIABILITY COMPANY—See Santen Pharmaceutical Co., Ltd.; *Int'l*, pg. 6557
SANTEN OY—See Santen Pharmaceutical Co., Ltd.; *Int'l*, pg. 6558
SANTENPHARMA AB—See Santen Pharmaceutical Co., Ltd.; *Int'l*, pg. 6558
SANTEN PHARMACEUTICAL ASIA PTE. LTD.—See Santen Pharmaceutical Co., Ltd.; *Int'l*, pg. 6558
SANTEN PHARMACEUTICAL (CHINA) CO., LTD.—See Santen Pharmaceutical Co., Ltd.; *Int'l*, pg. 6558
SANTEN PHARMACEUTICAL CO., LTD. - NOTO PLANT—See Santen Pharmaceutical Co., Ltd.; *Int'l*, pg. 6558
SANTEN PHARMACEUTICAL CO., LTD. - OSAKA PLANT—See Santen Pharmaceutical Co., Ltd.; *Int'l*, pg. 6558
SANTEN PHARMACEUTICAL CO., LTD. - SHIGA PLANT—See Santen Pharmaceutical Co., Ltd.; *Int'l*, pg. 6558
SANTEN PHARMACEUTICAL CO., LTD.; *Int'l*, pg. 6557
SANTEK PHARMACEUTICAL (HONG KONG) LIMITED—See Santen Pharmaceutical Co., Ltd.; *Int'l*, pg. 6558
SANTEN PHARMACEUTICAL KOREA, CO., LTD—See Santen Pharmaceutical Co., Ltd.; *Int'l*, pg. 6558
SANTEN PHARMACEUTICAL SPAIN, S.L.—See Santen Pharmaceutical Co., Ltd.; *Int'l*, pg. 6558
SANTEN PHARMA MALAYSIA SDN. BHD.—See Santen Pharmaceutical Co., Ltd.; *Int'l*, pg. 6558
SANTEN PHILIPPINES INC.—See Santen Pharmaceutical Co., Ltd.; *Int'l*, pg. 6558
SANTEN S.A.S.—See Santen Pharmaceutical Co., Ltd.; *Int'l*, pg. 6558
SANTEN (THAILAND) CO., LTD.—See Santen Pharmaceutical Co., Ltd.; *Int'l*, pg. 6557
SANTEN UK LIMITED—See Santen Pharmaceutical Co., Ltd.; *Int'l*, pg. 6558
SANTEON GROUP, INC.; *U.S. Public*, pg. 1841
SANTERNE ALSACE SAS—See VINCI S.A.; *Int'l*, pg. 8227
SANTERNE AQUITAINE SAS—See VINCI S.A.; *Int'l*, pg. 8227
SANTERNE BRETAGNE SAS—See VINCI S.A.; *Int'l*, pg. 8227
SANTERNE CAMARGUE SAS—See VINCI S.A.; *Int'l*, pg. 8227
SANTERNE CENTRE EST ENERGIES SAS—See VINCI S.A.; *Int'l*, pg. 8227
SANTERNE CENTRE EST—See VINCI S.A.; *Int'l*, pg. 8238
SANTERNE ENERGIES EST SAS—See VINCI S.A.; *Int'l*, pg. 8227
SANTERNE EST TELECOMS SAS—See VINCI S.A.; *Int'l*, pg. 8227
SANTERNE ILE-DE-FRANCE SAS—See VINCI S.A.; *Int'l*, pg. 8227
SANTERNE MARSEILLE SAS—See VINCI S.A.; *Int'l*, pg. 8227
SANTERNE MAYENNE SAS—See VINCI S.A.; *Int'l*, pg. 8227
SANTERNE MEDITERRANEE SAS—See VINCI S.A.; *Int'l*, pg. 8227
SANTERNE NORD PICARDIE INFRA SAS—See VINCI S.A.; *Int'l*, pg. 8227
SANTERNE NORD TERTIAIRE SAS—See VINCI S.A.; *Int'l*, pg. 8227
SANTERNE TOULOUSE SAS—See VINCI S.A.; *Int'l*, pg. 8227
SANTERRA CO., LTD.—See Sumitomo Chemical Company, Limited; *Int'l*, pg. 7264
SANTEX S.P.A.; *Int'l*, pg. 6558
SANTEX TRUCK CENTER LTD.; *U.S. Private*, pg. 3548
SAN-THAP INTERNATIONAL CO.—See Sanyo Trading Co., Ltd.; *Int'l*, pg. 6565
SANTHERA PHARMACEUTICALS (GERMANY) GMBH—See Santhera Pharmaceuticals Holding AG; *Int'l*, pg. 6558

COMPANY NAME INDEX

SANTHERA PHARMACEUTICALS HOLDING AG; *Int'l,* pg. 6558
SANTHERA PHARMACEUTICALS (SWITZERLAND) LTD—See Santhera Pharmaceuticals Holding AG; *Int'l,* pg. 6558
SANTHERA PHARMACEUTICALS (USA), INC.—See Santhera Pharmaceuticals Holding AG; *Int'l,* pg. 6558
SANTHER FABRICA DE PAPEL SANTA THEREZINHA S.A.; *Int'l,* pg. 6558
SANTIAM DIALYSIS, LLC—See DaVita Inc.; *U.S. Public,* pg. 643
SANTIAM DRUG INC.; *U.S. Private,* pg. 3548
SANTIER INC.—See Egide SA; *Int'l,* pg. 2324
SANTIERUL NAVAL 2 MAI S.A.; *Int'l,* pg. 6558
SANTIERUL NAVAL CONSTANTA S.A.; *Int'l,* pg. 6558
SANTILLANA CANARIAS, S.L.—See Promotora de Informaciones S.A.; *Int'l,* pg. 5995
SANTILLANA COSTA RICA—See Promotora de Informaciones S.A.; *Int'l,* pg. 5996
SANTILLANA DE EDICIONES, S.A.—See Promotora de Informaciones S.A.; *Int'l,* pg. 5996
SANTILLANA DE SEGURIDAD VIGILANCIA PRIVADA LTDA.—See Bain Capital, LP; *U.S. Private,* pg. 435
SANTILLANA EDUCACAO, LTDA.—See Promotora de Informaciones S.A.; *Int'l,* pg. 5996
SANTILLANA, S.A.—See Promotora de Informaciones S.A.; *Int'l,* pg. 5996
SANTILLANA, S.A.—See Promotora de Informaciones S.A.; *Int'l,* pg. 5996
SANTILLANA, S.A.—See Promotora de Informaciones S.A.; *Int'l,* pg. 5996
SANTILLANA USA PUBLISHING CO. INC.—See Promotora de Informaciones S.A.; *Int'l,* pg. 5996
SANTINELLI INTERNATIONAL INC.; *U.S. Private,* pg. 3548
SANTINI TRANSFER & STORAGE; *U.S. Private,* pg. 3548
SA NTI—See Hiolle Industries S.A.; *Int'l,* pg. 3401
SANTISTA JEANSWEAR S.A.—See Camargo Correa S.A.; *Int'l,* pg. 1268
SANTIST CO., LTD.—See MITSUBA Corporation; *Int'l,* pg. 4929
SANTMYER OIL CO. INC.; *U.S. Private,* pg. 3548
SANTMYER OIL CO. OF ASHLAND INC.—See Santmyer Oil Co. Inc.; *U.S. Private,* pg. 3548
SANTO ANTONIO ENERGIA S.A.; *Int'l,* pg. 6558
SANTO BUENOS AIRES—See WPP plc; *Int'l,* pg. 8466
SANTO CO., LTD.; *Int'l,* pg. 6558
SANTOGYN (PTY) LIMITED—See Reunert Limited; *Int'l,* pg. 6312
SANTO INDUSTRIES LIMITED—See Techtronic Industries Co., Ltd.; *Int'l,* pg. 7512
SANTO INSURANCE & FINANCIAL SERVICES, INC.—See Aquiline Capital Partners LLC; *U.S. Private,* pg. 305
SANTOKU BASF PTE. LTD.—See BASF SE; *Int'l,* pg. 878
SANTOKU COMPUTER SERVICE CO., LTD.—See Nippon Steel Corporation; *Int'l,* pg. 5340
SANTOKU CORPORATION—See Hitachi, Ltd.; *Int'l,* pg. 3424
SANTOKU SEIKEN CO., LTD.—See Nippon Steel Corporation; *Int'l,* pg. 5340
SANTOKU TECH CO., LTD.—See Nippon Steel Corporation; *Int'l,* pg. 5340
SANTON CIRCUIT BREAKER SERVICES B.V.—See discoverIE Group plc; *Int'l,* pg. 2133
SANTON GMBH—See discoverIE Group plc; *Int'l,* pg. 2133
SANTON HOLLAND B.V.—See discoverIE Group plc; *Int'l,* pg. 2133
SANTON INTERNATIONAL B.V.—See discoverIE Group plc; *Int'l,* pg. 2133
SANTONI'S INC.; *U.S. Private,* pg. 3548
SANTON SWITCHGEAR LIMITED—See discoverIE Group plc; *Int'l,* pg. 2133
SANTORA KAFFEE GMBH—See JAB Holding Company S.a.r.l.; *Int'l,* pg. 3863
SANTORO OIL COMPANY INC—See Domestic Industries Inc.; *U.S. Private,* pg. 1255
SANTOS ASIA PACIFIC PTY LTD.—See Santos Limited; *Int'l,* pg. 6559
SANTOS BRASIL PARTICIPACOES SA - LOGISTICS - DISTRIBUTION CENTER—See Santos Brasil Participacoes SA; *Int'l,* pg. 6558
SANTOS BRASIL PARTICIPACOES SA - LOGISTICS - FOREIGN TRADE - CLIA GUARUJA—See Santos Brasil Participacoes SA; *Int'l,* pg. 6558
SANTOS BRASIL PARTICIPACOES SA - LOGISTICS - FOREIGN TRADE - CLIA SANTOS—See Santos Brasil Participacoes SA; *Int'l,* pg. 6558
SANTOS BRASIL PARTICIPACOES SA - LOGISTICS - FOREIGN TRADE - IPA XXXLL—See Santos Brasil Participacoes SA; *Int'l,* pg. 6558
SANTOS BRASIL PARTICIPACOES SA; *Int'l,* pg. 6558
SANTOS BRASIL PARTICIPACOES SA - TECON IMBITUBA—See Santos Brasil Participacoes SA; *Int'l,* pg. 6558

SANTOS BRASIL PARTICIPACOES SA-TECON VILA DO CONDE—See Santos Brasil Participacoes SA; *Int'l,* pg. 6558
SANTOS ENTERPRISES; *U.S. Private,* pg. 3548
SANTOSH FINE-FAB LIMITED; *Int'l,* pg. 6559
SANTOSH INDUSTRIES LIMITED; *Int'l,* pg. 6559
SANTOS INTERNATIONAL OPERATIONS PTY LTD.—See Santos Limited; *Int'l,* pg. 6559
SANTOS LIMITED; *Int'l,* pg. 6559
SANTOS PETROLEUM PTY. LTD.—See Santos Limited; *Int'l,* pg. 6559
SANTOS RESOURCES PTY. LTD.—See Santos Limited; *Int'l,* pg. 6559
SANTO STEEL CO., LTD.—See Hanwa Co., Ltd.; *Int'l,* pg. 3263
SANTOS USA CORPORATION—See Santos Limited; *Int'l,* pg. 6559
SANTOS VIETNAM PTY LTD.—See Santos Limited; *Int'l,* pg. 6559
SANTOS WA ASSET HOLDINGS PTY. LTD.—See Santos Limited; *Int'l,* pg. 6559
SANTOS WA ENERGY HOLDINGS PTY. LTD.—See Santos Limited; *Int'l,* pg. 6559
SANTOS WA ENERGY LIMITED—See Santos Limited; *Int'l,* pg. 6559
SANTOS WA NORTHWEST PTY. LTD.—See Santos Limited; *Int'l,* pg. 6559
SANTOS WA PVG HOLDINGS PTY. LTD.—See Santos Limited; *Int'l,* pg. 6559
SANTO TATEMONO SERVICE CO., LTD.—See Mitsui O.S.K. Lines, Ltd.; *Int'l,* pg. 4989
SANTOUKA KAMEI CANADA FOODS LTD.—See Kamei Corporation; *Int'l,* pg. 4062
SANTOVA FINANCIAL SERVICES (PTY) LIMITED—See Santova Ltd.; *Int'l,* pg. 6559
SANTOVA INTERNATIONAL TRADE SOLUTIONS (PTY) LIMITED—See Santova Ltd.; *Int'l,* pg. 6559
SANTOVA LOGISTICS B.V.—See Santova Ltd.; *Int'l,* pg. 6559
SANTOVA LOGISTICS GMBH—See Santova Ltd.; *Int'l,* pg. 6559
SANTOVA LOGISTICS LIMTED—See Santova Ltd.; *Int'l,* pg. 6559
SANTOVA LOGISTICS LIMTED—See Santova Ltd.; *Int'l,* pg. 6559
SANTOVA LOGISTICS (PTY) LIMITED—See Santova Ltd.; *Int'l,* pg. 6559
SANTOVA LTD.; *Int'l,* pg. 6559
SANTOYOKO (HONG KONG) CO., LTD.—See Toyobo Co., Ltd.; *Int'l,* pg. 7860
SANTRADE LTD.—See Sandvik AB; *Int'l,* pg. 6530
SANTROL (YIXING) PROPPANT CO. LTD—See Covia Holdings Corporation; *U.S. Public,* pg. 1072
SANTSU KENSETSU KOJI CO., LTD.—See COMSYS Holdings Corporation; *Int'l,* pg. 1762
SANTUMAS SHAREHOLDINGS PLC; *Int'l,* pg. 6560
SANU GOLD CORP.; *Int'l,* pg. 6560
SANUWAVE AG—See SANUWAVE Health, Inc.; *U.S. Public,* pg. 1841
SANUWAVE HEALTH, INC.; *U.S. Public,* pg. 1841
SANVAC (BEIJING) MAGNETICS CO., LTD.—See Beijing Zhong Ke San Huan High-tech Co., Ltd.; *Int'l,* pg. 961
SAN VAL INC.—See GL Group, Inc.; *U.S. Private,* pg. 1704
SANVIC INC.—See Kaneka Corporation; *Int'l,* pg. 4067
SAN VILNIUS—See WPP plc; *Int'l,* pg. 8481
SANWA BUHIN CO., LTD.—See Topy Industries, Ltd.; *Int'l,* pg. 7822
SANWA CHEMICAL CO., LTD.—See NIPPON CARBIDE INDUSTRIES CO., INC.; *Int'l,* pg. 5311
SANWA COATEX CORPORATION—See Sanden Corporation; *Int'l,* pg. 6525
SANWA CO., LTD. - KASHIMA FACTORY—See Tomoegawa Co., Ltd.; *Int'l,* pg. 7801
SANWA CO., LTD. - OKAYAMA FACTORY—See Tomoegawa Co., Ltd.; *Int'l,* pg. 7801
SANWA CO., LTD.—See Tomoegawa Co., Ltd.; *Int'l,* pg. 7801
SANWA COMPANY LTD.; *Int'l,* pg. 6560
SANWA COMPANY RS TAIWAN LTD.—See Sanwa Company Ltd.; *Int'l,* pg. 6560
SANWA COMSYS ENGINEERING CORPORATION—See COMSYS Holdings Corporation; *Int'l,* pg. 1762
SANWA DENSHI INC.—See COMSYS Holdings Corporation; *Int'l,* pg. 1762
SANWA DENZAI CO., LTD.—See Kondotec Inc.; *Int'l,* pg. 4247
SANWA ELECTRIC PHILIPPINES, INC.—See Panasonic Holdings Corporation; *Int'l,* pg. 5724
SANWA ELECTRON CO., LTD.—See KYOSHA CO., LTD.; *Int'l,* pg. 4365
SANWA ELECTRONICS ENGINEERING CO., LTD.—See Sanwa Holdings Corporation; *Int'l,* pg. 6561
SANWA ESTATE PHILIPPINES, INC.—See Panasonic Holdings Corporation; *Int'l,* pg. 5724
SANWA EXTERIOR NIIGATA PLANT CO., LTD.—See Sanwa Holdings Corporation; *Int'l,* pg. 6561
SANWA GROWERS INC.; *U.S. Private,* pg. 3548
SANWA HOLDINGS CORPORATION; *Int'l,* pg. 6560

SANWA KAGAKU KENKYUSHO CO., LTD.—See Suzuken Co., Ltd.; *Int'l,* pg. 7353
SANWA KIKAI LEASE CO., LTD.—See Kanamoto Co., Ltd.; *Int'l,* pg. 4064
SANWA KOGYO CO., LTD.—See Topy Industries, Ltd.; *Int'l,* pg. 7822
SANWA MITAKA K.K.—See Sanwa Holdings Corporation; *Int'l,* pg. 6561
SANWARIA CONSUMER LIMITED; *Int'l,* pg. 6561
SANWA SEIKI CO., LTD.—See OSG Corporation; *Int'l,* pg. 5649
SANWA SEISAKUSYO LTD.—See Minebea Mitsumi Inc.; *Int'l,* pg. 4905
SANWA SHUTTER CORPORATION—See Sanwa Holdings Corporation; *Int'l,* pg. 6561
SANWA SHUTTER (H.K.) LTD.—See Sanwa Holdings Corporation; *Int'l,* pg. 6561
SANWA SIGNWORKS CO., LTD.—See ITOCHU Corporation; *Int'l,* pg. 3835
SANWA SOKO CO., LTD.—See Nippon Soda Co., Ltd.; *Int'l,* pg. 5334
SANWA STEEL CO., LTD.—See Nippon Steel Corporation; *Int'l,* pg. 5339
SANWA SYSTEM WALL CO., LTD.—See Sanwa Holdings Corporation; *Int'l,* pg. 6561
SANWA TAJIMA CORPORATION—See Sanwa Holdings Corporation; *Int'l,* pg. 6561
SANWA TEKKO CO., LTD.—See Kobe Steel, Ltd.; *Int'l,* pg. 4220
SANWECO INC.; *U.S. Private,* pg. 3548
SANWEI HOLDING GROUP CO., LTD.; *Int'l,* pg. 6561
SANWIL HOLDING S.A.; *Int'l,* pg. 6561
SANWIRE CORP.; *U.S. Private,* pg. 3548
SANWU BANDO INC.—See Bando Chemical Industries, Ltd.; *Int'l,* pg. 831
SANXIANG ADVANCED MATERIALS CO., LTD.; *Int'l,* pg. 6561
SANXIANG IMPRESSION CO., LTD.; *Int'l,* pg. 6561
SANXIA WAI CHI OPTO TECHNOLOGY (YICHANG) LIMITED—See Wai Chi Holdings Company Limited; *Int'l,* pg. 8331
SANXIN FACADE TECHNOLOGY LTD.—See Hainan Development Holdings Nanhai Co., Ltd.; *Int'l,* pg. 3212
SANXUN HOLDINGS GROUP LIMITED; *Int'l,* pg. 6562
SANYA HNA REA-ESTATE DEVELOPMENT CO., LTD.—See Hainan Traffic Administration Holding Co., Ltd.; *Int'l,* pg. 3216
SANY ALGERIA CO, LTD—See Sany Group Co., Ltd.; *Int'l,* pg. 6562
SANY AMERICA, INC.—See Sany Group Co., Ltd.; *Int'l,* pg. 6563
SAN YANG MA (CHONGQING) LOGISTICS CO., LTD.; *Int'l,* pg. 6521
SANY ANGOLA—See Sany Group Co., Ltd.; *Int'l,* pg. 6562
SANYA PHOENIX INTERNATIONAL AIRPORT CO., LTD.—See Hainan Traffic Administration Holding Co., Ltd.; *Int'l,* pg. 3216
SANY ARGENTINA—See Sany Group Co., Ltd.; *Int'l,* pg. 6562
SANYA SHANGRI-LA HOTEL CO., LIMITED—See Shangri-La Asia Limited; *Int'l,* pg. 6783
SANY ASIA-PACIFIC HONG KONG CO. LTD—See Sany Group Co., Ltd.; *Int'l,* pg. 6562
SANY ASIA PACIFIC (PHILIPPINES) CO. LTD—See Sany Group Co., Ltd.; *Int'l,* pg. 6562
SANY AUSTRALIA PTY. LTD.—See Sany Group Co., Ltd.; *Int'l,* pg. 6562
SANY CAMBODIA—See Sany Group Co., Ltd.; *Int'l,* pg. 6562
SANY CHILE—See Sany Group Co., Ltd.; *Int'l,* pg. 6562
SANYCO GRAND INDUSTRIES SDN. BHD.—See SMIS Corporation Berhad; *Int'l,* pg. 7007
SANY COLOMBIA SAS—See Sany Group Co., Ltd.; *Int'l,* pg. 6562
SANY COSTA RICA—See Sany Group Co., Ltd.; *Int'l,* pg. 6562
SANY DO BRASIL LTDA.—See Sany Group Co., Ltd.; *Int'l,* pg. 6563
SANY EAST ASIA CO., LTD.—See Sany Group Co., Ltd.; *Int'l,* pg. 6562
SANY ECUADOR—See Sany Group Co., Ltd.; *Int'l,* pg. 6562
SANYEI CORPORATION; *Int'l,* pg. 6563
SANY ETHIOPIA—See Sany Group Co., Ltd.; *Int'l,* pg. 6562
SANY GERMANY GMBH—See Sany Group Co., Ltd.; *Int'l,* pg. 6563
SANY GHANA CO., LTD—See Sany Group Co., Ltd.; *Int'l,* pg. 6562
SANY GROUP CO., LTD.; *Int'l,* pg. 6562
SANY GUINEA—See Sany Group Co., Ltd.; *Int'l,* pg. 6562
SANY HEAVY EQUIPMENT INTERNATIONAL HOLDINGS CO., LTD.—See Sany Group Co., Ltd.; *Int'l,* pg. 6562
SANY HEAVY INDUSTRY CO., LTD.—See Sany Group Co., Ltd.; *Int'l,* pg. 6562
SANY HEAVY INDUSTRY INDIA PVT. LTD.—See Sany Group Co., Ltd.; *Int'l,* pg. 6563
SANY HEAVY INDUSTRY (KENYA) CO., LTD—See Sany Group Co., Ltd.; *Int'l,* pg. 6562

SANY GROUP CO., LTD.   CORPORATE AFFILIATIONS

SANY HEAVY INDUSTRY SAUDI ARABIA CO., LTD.—See Sany Group Co., Ltd.; *Int'l*, pg. 6562
SANY HEAVY INDUSTRY (THAILAND) CO., LTD—See Sany Group Co., Ltd.; *Int'l*, pg. 6562
SANY IMPORTACAO E EXPORTACAO DA AMERICA DO SUL LTDA.—See Sany Group Co., Ltd.; *Int'l*, pg. 6563
SANY JAPAN CO., LTD—See Sany Group Co., Ltd.; *Int'l*, pg. 6562
SANY KUWAIT—See Sany Group Co., Ltd.; *Int'l*, pg. 6562
SANY LLP—See Sany Group Co., Ltd.; *Int'l*, pg. 6562
SANY MALAYSIA—See Sany Group Co., Ltd.; *Int'l*, pg. 6562
SANY MIDDLE & WEST AFRICA COMPANY LTD.—See Sany Group Co., Ltd.; *Int'l*, pg. 6563
SANY (NIG.) LTD—See Sany Group Co., Ltd.; *Int'l*, pg. 6562
SANYO AIRCONDITIONERS EUROPE S.R.L.—See Panasonic Holdings Corporation; *Int'l*, pg. 5724
SANYO AIRCONDITIONERS MANUFACTURING SINGAPORE PTE., LTD.—See Panasonic Holdings Corporation; *Int'l*, pg. 5724
SANYO ARGO CLIMA S.R.L.—See Panasonic Holdings Corporation; *Int'l*, pg. 5724
SANYO ARMCO (KENYA) LIMITED—See Panasonic Holdings Corporation; *Int'l*, pg. 5724
SANYO ASIA PTE LTD—See Panasonic Holdings Corporation; *Int'l*, pg. 5724
SANYO AUTOMEDIA SDN. BHD.—See Panasonic Holdings Corporation; *Int'l*, pg. 5724
SANYO AUTOMEDIA SDN. BHD.—See Panasonic Holdings Corporation; *Int'l*, pg. 5724
SANYO BURO-ELECTRONIC EUROPE-VERTRIEB GMBH—See Panasonic Holdings Corporation; *Int'l*, pg. 5724
SANYO BUSSAN CO., LTD.—See Kato Sangyo Co., Ltd.; *Int'l*, pg. 4090
SANYO CANADA HOLDINGS 1990 INC.—See Panasonic Holdings Corporation; *Int'l*, pg. 5724
SANYO CHEMICAL AMERICA INCORPORATED—See Sanyo Chemical Industries, Ltd.; *Int'l*, pg. 6564
SANYO CHEMICAL INDUSTRIES, LTD.; *Int'l*, pg. 6563
SANYO CHEMICAL (SHANGHAII) TRADING CO., LTD.—See Sanyo Chemical Industries, Ltd.; *Int'l*, pg. 6564
SANYO CHEMICAL (SHANGHAI) TRADING CO., LTD.—See Sanyo Chemical Industries, Ltd.; *Int'l*, pg. 6564
SANYO CHEMICAL TEXAS INDUSTRIES, LLC—See Sanyo Chemical Industries, Ltd.; *Int'l*, pg. 6564
SANYO COMMERCIAL REFRIGERATION INTERNATIONAL CO., LTD.—See Panasonic Holdings Corporation; *Int'l*, pg. 5724
SANYO COMMERCIAL SOLUTIONS (THAILAND) CO., LTD.—See Panasonic Holdings Corporation; *Int'l*, pg. 5723
SANYO CORPORATION—See Sanyo Trading Co., Ltd.; *Int'l*, pg. 6565
SANYO CUSTOMS BROKERAGE, INC.—See Panasonic Holdings Corporation; *Int'l*, pg. 5724
SANYO CUSTOMS BROKERAGE S.A. DE C.V.—See Panasonic Holdings Corporation; *Int'l*, pg. 5724
SANYODENKI CO. LTD. - FUJIYAMA UNIT—See SANYO DENKI Co., Ltd.; *Int'l*, pg. 6564
SANYODENKI CO. LTD. - KANGAWA WORKS—See SANYO DENKI Co., Ltd.; *Int'l*, pg. 6564
SANYODENKI CO. LTD. - SHIODA UNIT—See SANYO DENKI Co., Ltd.; *Int'l*, pg. 6564
SANYO DENKI CO., LTD.; *Int'l*, pg. 6564
SANYO DENKI ENGINEERING (SHANGHAI) CO., LTD.—See SANYO DENKI Co., Ltd.; *Int'l*, pg. 6564
SANYO DENKI ENGINEERING (SHENZHEN) CO., LTD.—See SANYO DENKI Co., Ltd.; *Int'l*, pg. 6564
SANYO DENKI EUROPE S.A.—See SANYO DENKI Co., Ltd.; *Int'l*, pg. 6564
SANYO DENKI GERMANY GMBH—See SANYO DENKI Co., Ltd.; *Int'l*, pg. 6564
SANYO DENKI (H.K.) CO., LIMITED—See SANYO DENKI Co., Ltd.; *Int'l*, pg. 6564
SANYO DENKI INDIA PRIVATE LIMITED—See SANYO DENKI Co., Ltd.; *Int'l*, pg. 6564
SANYO DENKI IT SOLUTION CO., LTD.—See SANYO DENKI Co., Ltd.; *Int'l*, pg. 6564
SANYO DENKI KOREA CO., LTD.—See SANYO DENKI Co., Ltd.; *Int'l*, pg. 6564
SANYO DENKI SHANGHAI CO., LTD.—See SANYO DENKI Co., Ltd.; *Int'l*, pg. 6564
SANYO DENKI (SHENZHEN) CO., LTD.—See SANYO DENKI Co., Ltd.; *Int'l*, pg. 6564
SANYO DENKI SINGAPORE PTE. LTD.—See SANYO DENKI Co., Ltd.; *Int'l*, pg. 6564
SANYO DENKI TAIWAN CO., LTD.—See SANYO DENKI Co., Ltd.; *Int'l*, pg. 6564
SANYO DENKI TECHNO SERVICE CO., LTD.—See SANYO DENKI Co., Ltd.; *Int'l*, pg. 6564
SANYO DENKI (THAILAND) CO., LTD.—See SANYO DENKI Co., Ltd.; *Int'l*, pg. 6564
SANYO DENKI (TIANJIN) CO., LTD.—See SANYO DENKI Co., Ltd.; *Int'l*, pg. 6564
SANYO DENSO INDUSTRIES (SINGAPORE) PTE., LTD.—See Panasonic Holdings Corporation; *Int'l*, pg. 5724
SANYO DEPARTMENT STORE CO., LTD.—See Sanyo Electric Railway Co., Ltd.; *Int'l*, pg. 6564
SANYODO HOLDINGS INC.; *Int'l*, pg. 6565
SANYO E & E CORPORATION—See Panasonic Holdings Corporation; *Int'l*, pg. 5724
SANYO E&E S.A. DE C.V.—See Panasonic Holdings Corporation; *Int'l*, pg. 5724
SANYO ELECTRIC CO., LTD.—See Panasonic Holdings Corporation; *Int'l*, pg. 5723
SANYO ELECTRIC INTERNATIONAL FINANCE (UK) PLC—See Panasonic Holdings Corporation; *Int'l*, pg. 5724
SANYO ELECTRIC RAILWAY CO., LTD.; *Int'l*, pg. 6564
SANYO ELECTRIC (TAIWAN) CO., LTD.; *Int'l*, pg. 6564
SANYO ELECTRONIC COMPONENTS (S) PTE. LTD.—See Panasonic Holdings Corporation; *Int'l*, pg. 5724
SANYO ELECTRONIC DEVICE SALES (USA) CORPORATION—See Panasonic Holdings Corporation; *Int'l*, pg. 5724
SANYO ELECTRONIC DEVICE (U.S.A.) CORPORATION—See Panasonic Holdings Corporation; *Int'l*, pg. 5724
SANYO ELECTRONICS S.A.—See Panasonic Holdings Corporation; *Int'l*, pg. 5724
SANYO ELECTRONIC (TAICHUNG) CO., LTD.—See Panasonic Holdings Corporation; *Int'l*, pg. 5724
SANYO ENERGY, S.A. DE C.V.—See Panasonic Holdings Corporation; *Int'l*, pg. 5724
SANYO ENERGY (SINGAPORE) CORPORATION PTE., LTD.—See Panasonic Holdings Corporation; *Int'l*, pg. 5724
SANYO ENERGY (SINGAPORE) CORP, PTE. LTD.—See Panasonic Holdings Corporation; *Int'l*, pg. 5724
SANYO ENERGY (SUZHOU) CO., LTD.—See Panasonic Holdings Corporation; *Int'l*, pg. 5725
SANYO ENERGY (U.S.A.) CORPORATION - HEV BATTERY BUSINESS DIVISION—See Panasonic Holdings Corporation; *Int'l*, pg. 5724
SANYO ENERGY (U.S.A.) CORPORATION - KANSAS CITY HEV JIT FACILITY—See Panasonic Holdings Corporation; *Int'l*, pg. 5724
SANYO ENERGY (U.S.A.) CORPORATION - MOBILE ENERGY BUSINESS DIVISION—See Panasonic Holdings Corporation; *Int'l*, pg. 5724
SANYO ENERGY (U.S.A.) CORPORATION—See Panasonic Holdings Corporation; *Int'l*, pg. 5724
SANYO ENGINEERING & CONSTRUCTION INC.; *Int'l*, pg. 6564
SANYO E.T. CANADA, INC.—See Panasonic Holdings Corporation; *Int'l*, pg. 5724
SANYO EXTENDED SYSTEM SERVICES LIMITED—See Computer & Technologies Holdings Limited; *Int'l*, pg. 1758
SANYO FINE CO.,LTD.—See Osaka Soda Co., Ltd.; *Int'l*, pg. 5646
SANYO FISHER COMPANY—See Panasonic Holdings Corporation; *Int'l*, pg. 5724
SANYO FISHER HOME APPLIANCE & CONSUMER PRODUCTS DIV.—See Panasonic Holdings Corporation; *Int'l*, pg. 5724
SANYO FISHER VERTRIEBS GMBH—See Panasonic Holdings Corporation; *Int'l*, pg. 5724
SANYO FOODS CO., LTD.—See Mitsubishi Corporation; *Int'l*, pg. 4943
SANYO HOMES CORPORATION; *Int'l*, pg. 6565
SANYO - IK COLOR (DG) LTD.—See Inabata & Co., Ltd.; *Int'l*, pg. 3644
SANYO - IK COLOR (H.K.) LTD. - DONG GUAN PLANT—See Inabata & Co. Ltd.; *Int'l*, pg. 3644
SANYO-IK COLOR (H.K.) LTD.—See Inabata & Co. Ltd.; *Int'l*, pg. 3644
SANYO-IK COLOR (PTE.) LTD.—See Inabata & Co. Ltd.; *Int'l*, pg. 3644
SANYO INDUSTRIES, LTD.; *Int'l*, pg. 6565
SANYO JIDOSHA UNSO CO., LTD.—See Hankyu Hanshin Holdings Co., Ltd.; *Int'l*, pg. 3256
SANYO KASEI KOREA, LTD—See Sanyo Chemical Industries, Ltd.; *Int'l*, pg. 6564
SANYO KASEI (NANTONG) CO., LTD.—See Sanyo Chemical Industries, Ltd.; *Int'l*, pg. 6564
SANYO KASEI (TAIWAN) LTD.—See Sanyo Chemical Industries, Ltd.; *Int'l*, pg. 6564
SANYO KASEI (THAILAND) LTD.—See Sanyo Chemical Industries, Ltd.; *Int'l*, pg. 6564
SANYO KOGYO CO., LTD.—See Wealth Management Inc.; *Int'l*, pg. 8363
SANYO KOSAN CO., LTD.—See Chugoku Marine Paints, Ltd.; *Int'l*, pg. 1595
SANYO KOUZAI CO., LTD.—See Hanwa Co., Ltd.; *Int'l*, pg. 3263
SANYO LOGISTICS CORPORATION—See Panasonic Holdings Corporation; *Int'l*, pg. 5725
SANYO LSI TECHNOLOGY INDIA PRIVATE LIMITED—See Panasonic Holdings Corporation; *Int'l*, pg. 5724
SANYO MACHINERY CO., LTD.—See Sanyo Trading Co., Ltd.; *Int'l*, pg. 6565
SANYO NORTH AMERICAN CORPORATION—See Panasonic Holdings Corporation; *Int'l*, pg. 5724
SANYO OCEANIA PTY. LTD.—See Panasonic Holdings Corporation; *Int'l*, pg. 5725
SANYO OKAMURA CORPORATION—See Okamura Corporation; *Int'l*, pg. 5545
SANYO OPTICAL INSTRUMENTS CO.—See Ryobi Limited; *Int'l*, pg. 6440
SANYO PETROCHEMICAL CO., LTD.—See Asahi Kasei Corporation; *Int'l*, pg. 597
SANYO PORTUGAL ELECTRONICA S.A.—See Panasonic Holdings Corporation; *Int'l*, pg. 5725
SANYO PRECISION SINGAPORE PTE., LTD.—See Panasonic Holdings Corporation; *Int'l*, pg. 5725
SANYO REFORM CORPORATION—See Sanyo Homes Corporation; *Int'l*, pg. 6565
SANYO SALES & SERVICE SDN. BHD.—See Panasonic Holdings Corporation; *Int'l*, pg. 5725
SANYO SEMICONDUCTOR CO., LTD.—See ON Semiconductor Corporation; *U.S. Public*, pg. 1601
SANYO SEMICONDUCTOR CORPORATION—See ON Semiconductor Corporation; *U.S. Public*, pg. 1601
SANYO SEMICONDUCTOR (H.K.) CO., LTD.—See ON Semiconductor Corporation; *U.S. Public*, pg. 1601
SANYO SEMICONDUCTOR MANUFACTURING PHILIPPINES CORPORATION—See ON Semiconductor Corporation; *U.S. Public*, pg. 1601
SANYO SEMICONDUCTOR (THAILAND) CO., LTD.—See ON Semiconductor Corporation; *U.S. Public*, pg. 1601
SANYO SEMICONDUCTOR (VIETNAM) CO., LTD.—See Panasonic Holdings Corporation; *Int'l*, pg. 5724
SANYO SENKO TRANSPORT CO., LTD.—See Senko Group Holdings Co., Ltd.; *Int'l*, pg. 6711
SANYO SHOKAI LTD.; *Int'l*, pg. 6565
SANYO SHOKAI NEW YORK, INC.—See Sanyo Shokai Ltd.; *Int'l*, pg. 6565
SANYO SINGAPORE PTE LTD.—See Panasonic Holdings Corporation; *Int'l*, pg. 5725
SANYO SOLAR OF OREGON L.L.C.—See Panasonic Holdings Corporation; *Int'l*, pg. 5724
SANYO SOUTH AFRICA (PTY) LTD.—See Panasonic Holdings Corporation; *Int'l*, pg. 5725
SANYO SPECIAL STEEL CO LTD—See Nippon Steel Corporation; *Int'l*, pg. 5340
SANYO SPECIAL STEEL TRADING (SHANGHAI) CO., LTD—See Nippon Steel Corporation; *Int'l*, pg. 5340
SANYO SPECIAL STEEL U.S.A., INC.—See Nippon Steel Corporation; *Int'l*, pg. 5340
SANYO STEEL DRUM INDUSTRY CO., LTD.—See Nippon Steel Corporation; *Int'l*, pg. 5335
SANYO TECHNOS CO., LTD.—See Sanyo Trading Co., Ltd.; *Int'l*, pg. 6565
SANYO TOKUYAMA READY MIXED CONCRETE CO., LTD.—See Tokuyama Corporation; *Int'l*, pg. 7787
SANYO-TOUCHI (SHANGHAI) RUBBER CO., LTD.—See Sanyo Trading Co., Ltd.; *Int'l*, pg. 6565
SANYO TRADING CO., LTD.; *Int'l*, pg. 6565
SANYO TRADING INDIA PRIVATE LTD.—See Sanyo Trading Co., Ltd.; *Int'l*, pg. 6565
SANYO TRADING INTERNATIONAL (HONG KONG) CO., LTD.—See Sanyo Trading Co., Ltd.; *Int'l*, pg. 6565
SANYO TRADING (SHANGHAI) CO., LTD.—See Sanyo Trading Co., Ltd.; *Int'l*, pg. 6565
SANYO TRADING (VIETNAM) CO., LTD.—See Sanyo Trading Co., Ltd.; *Int'l*, pg. 6565
SANYO UBE CO., LTD.—See UBE Corporation; *Int'l*, pg. 8001
SANYOU CORPORATION LIMITED; *Int'l*, pg. 6565
SANYOU ELECTRICAL APPLIANCES GMBH—See Sanyou Corporation Limited; *Int'l*, pg. 6565
SANYO UNIVERSAL ELECTRIC PUBLIC CO., LTD.—See Panasonic Holdings Corporation; *Int'l*, pg. 5725
SANYO VIDEO VERTRIEB AG—See Burg-Wachter KG; *Int'l*, pg. 1223
SANYO VLSI ENGINEERING CO., LTD.—See Panasonic Holdings Corporation; *Int'l*, pg. 5725
SANYO WHITE CEMENT CO., LTD.—See Taiheiyo Cement Corporation; *Int'l*, pg. 7412
SANY PAKISTAN—See Sany Group Co., Ltd.; *Int'l*, pg. 6562
SANY PANAMA—See Sany Group Co., Ltd.; *Int'l*, pg. 6562
SANY PERU S.A.C—See Sany Group Co., Ltd.; *Int'l*, pg. 6562
SANYPICK PLASTIC, S.A.—See ACS, Actividades de Construccion y Servicios, S.A.; *Int'l*, pg. 116
SANY QATAR—See Sany Group Co., Ltd.; *Int'l*, pg. 6562
SANY RUSSIA—See Sany Group Co., Ltd.; *Int'l*, pg. 6562
SANY SOUTHEAST ASIA PTE. LTD.—See Sany Group Co., Ltd.; *Int'l*, pg. 6563
SANY SOUTH KOREA—See Sany Group Co., Ltd.; *Int'l*, pg. 6562
SANY TAIWAN—See Sany Group Co., Ltd.; *Int'l*, pg. 6562
SANY TURKEY—See Sany Group Co., Ltd.; *Int'l*, pg. 6562
SANY U.A.E—See Sany Group Co., Ltd.; *Int'l*, pg. 6562
SANYUANDA HOLDINGS CO., LTD.; *Int'l*, pg. 6565
SANYU CO., LTD.; *Int'l*, pg. 6565

COMPANY NAME INDEX

SANYU INDUSTRY (HONG KONG) COMPANY LIMITED—See Nitta Corporation; *Int'l*, pg. 5382
SANYU SERVICE CO., LTD.—See Mitsui-Soko Holdings Co., Ltd.; *Int'l*, pg. 4993
SANY VENEZUEL—See Sany Group Co., Ltd.; *Int'l*, pg. 6562
SANY (VIETNAM) MACHINERY CO., LTD—See Sany Group Co., Ltd.; *Int'l*, pg. 6562
SANY ZAMBIA—See Sany Group Co., Ltd.; *Int'l*, pg. 6562
SANZEN SEIYAKU K.K.—See Katakura Industries Co., Ltd.; *Int'l*, pg. 4089
SANZO BUSINESS CREATIVE CO., LTD.—See Mitsui E&S Holdings Co., Ltd.; *Int'l*, pg. 4986
SANZO ENTERPRISE CO., LTD.—See Mitsui E&S Holdings Co., Ltd.; *Int'l*, pg. 4986
SANZO KOSAN CO., LTD.—See Mitsui E&S Holdings Co., Ltd.; *Int'l*, pg. 4986
SANZO MANUFACTURING & CONSTRUCTION CO., LTD.—See Mitsui E&S Holdings Co., Ltd.; *Int'l*, pg. 4986
SAO BENTO MINERACAO SA—See Eldorado Gold Corporation; *Int'l*, pg. 2347
SAOBRACAJ A.D.; *Int'l*, pg. 6566
SAOBRACAJ I TRANSPORT A.D.; *Int'l*, pg. 6566
SAO CARLOS EMPREENDIMENTOS E PARTICIPACOES S.A.; *Int'l*, pg. 6565
SA OKTOPUS NV—See Johnson Controls International plc; *Int'l*, pg. 3986
SAO MAI GROUP CORPORATION; *Int'l*, pg. 6565
SAO MARTINHO S.A. - BOA VISTA MILL—See Sao Martinho S.A.; *Int'l*, pg. 6566
SAO MARTINHO S.A. - IRACEMA MILL—See Sao Martinho S.A.; *Int'l*, pg. 6566
SAO MARTINHO S.A.; *Int'l*, pg. 6566
SAO MIGUEL HOLDING E INVESTIMENTOS S.A.; *Int'l*, pg. 6566
SAONGROUP LIMITED—See Axel Springer SE; *Int'l*, pg. 766
SAO PAULO INVESTMENT COMPANY INC.—See Hyatt Hotels Corporation; *U.S. Public*, pg. 1078
SAO PAULO TURISMO S/A; *Int'l*, pg. 6566
SAO PROFINE RUS—See Arcapita Group Holdings Limited; *Int'l*, pg. 542
SAO TA FOODS JOINT STOCK COMPANY; *Int'l*, pg. 6566
SAOTHAIR CAPITAL PARTNERS LLC; *U.S. Private*, pg. 3548
SAO THANG LONG INVESTMENT JOINT STOCK COMPANY; *Int'l*, pg. 6566
SAO VANG RUBBER JOINT STOCK COMPANY; *Int'l*, pg. 6566
SAO VIET SECURITIES CORPORATION; *Int'l*, pg. 6566
SAPA AB—See Norsk Hydro ASA; *Int'l*, pg. 5435
SAPA ALUMINIUM PROFILE AG—See Norsk Hydro ASA; *Int'l*, pg. 5435
SAPA ALUMINIUM SP.Z O.O.—See Norsk Hydro ASA; *Int'l*, pg. 5435
SAPA AS—See Norsk Hydro ASA; *Int'l*, pg. 5435
SAPA BUILDING SYSTEM AB—See Norsk Hydro ASA; *Int'l*, pg. 5435
SAPA BUILDING SYSTEM NV—See Norsk Hydro ASA; *Int'l*, pg. 5436
SAPA BUILDING SYSTEMS AG—See Norsk Hydro ASA; *Int'l*, pg. 5436
SAPA BUILDING SYSTEMS BV—See Norsk Hydro ASA; *Int'l*, pg. 5436
SAPA BUILDING SYSTEMS GMBH—See Norsk Hydro ASA; *Int'l*, pg. 5436
SAPA BUILDING SYSTEMS LIMITED—See Norsk Hydro ASA; *Int'l*, pg. 5436
SAPA BUILDING SYSTEMS SAS—See Norsk Hydro ASA; *Int'l*, pg. 5436
SAPA BUILDING SYSTEMS SPOL. S R.O.—See Norsk Hydro ASA; *Int'l*, pg. 5436
SAPA BUILDING SYSTEMS (WAKEFIELD) LIMITED—See Norsk Hydro ASA; *Int'l*, pg. 5436
SAPA BUILDING SYSTEM VERTRIEBS GMBH—See Norsk Hydro ASA; *Int'l*, pg. 5436
SAPA CANADA INC.—See Norsk Hydro ASA; *Int'l*, pg. 5436
SAPA COMPONENTS UK LIMITED—See Norsk Hydro ASA; *Int'l*, pg. 5436
SAPA EXTRUDER INC.—See Norsk Hydro ASA; *Int'l*, pg. 5436
SAPA EXTRUDER INC.—See Norsk Hydro ASA; *Int'l*, pg. 5436
SAPA EXTRUSION RAEREN S.A.—See Norsk Hydro ASA; *Int'l*, pg. 5436
SAPA EXTRUSION - SANTA OLIVA—See Norsk Hydro ASA; *Int'l*, pg. 5436
SAPA EXTRUSIONS - CRESSONA OPERATION—See Norsk Hydro ASA; *Int'l*, pg. 5436
SAPA EXTRUSIONS NORTH AMERICA - BELTON—See Norsk Hydro ASA; *Int'l*, pg. 5436
SAPA EXTRUSIONS NORTH AMERICA - KALAMAZOO—See Norsk Hydro ASA; *Int'l*, pg. 5436
SAPA EXTRUSIONS NORTH AMERICA, LLC—See Norsk Hydro ASA; *Int'l*, pg. 5436
SAPA EXTRUSIONS NORTH AMERICA - MONETT—See Norsk Hydro ASA; *Int'l*, pg. 5436
SAPA EXTRUSIONS NORTH AMERICA - NORTH LIBERTY—See Norsk Hydro ASA; *Int'l*, pg. 5436
SAPA EXTRUSIONS NORTH AMERICA - PHOENIX—See Norsk Hydro ASA; *Int'l*, pg. 5436
SAPA EXTRUSIONS NORTH AMERICA - SIDNEY—See Norsk Hydro ASA; *Int'l*, pg. 5436
SAP AFRICA (PTY.) LTD. - KENYA—See SAP SE; *Int'l*, pg. 6570
SAP AFRICA (PTY.) LTD. - NAMIBIA—See SAP SE; *Int'l*, pg. 6570
SAP AGENCIA EN CHILE—See SAP SE; *Int'l*, pg. 6568
SAPA H E TUBING MONTERREY OPERATION SA DE CV—See Norsk Hydro ASA; *Int'l*, pg. 5436
SAPA HOLDINGS SL—See Norsk Hydro ASA; *Int'l*, pg. 5436
SAPA II PERFIS SA—See Norsk Hydro ASA; *Int'l*, pg. 5436
SAPAL S.A.—See CVC Capital Partners SICAV-FIS S.A.; *Int'l*, pg. 1884
SAP AMERICA, INC.—See SAP SE; *Int'l*, pg. 6567
SAPAN CHEMICALS LIMITED; *Int'l*, pg. 6571
SAP ANDINA Y DEL CARIBE, C.A.—See SAP SE; *Int'l*, pg. 6568
SAPA PRECISION TUBING ROCKLEDGE, LLC—See Norsk Hydro ASA; *Int'l*, pg. 5436
SAPA PRECISION TUBING TONDER A/S—See Norsk Hydro ASA; *Int'l*, pg. 5436
SAPA PRODOTTI PLASTICI SAGL—See Baxter International Inc.; *U.S. Public*, pg. 284
SAPA PROFIILID AS—See Norsk Hydro ASA; *Int'l*, pg. 5436
SAPA PROFIILIT OY—See Norsk Hydro ASA; *Int'l*, pg. 5436
SAPA PROFILER AB—See Norsk Hydro ASA; *Int'l*, pg. 5435
SAPA PROFILES ALBI SAS—See Norsk Hydro ASA; *Int'l*, pg. 5436
SAPA PROFILES BANBURY LTD.—See Norsk Hydro ASA; *Int'l*, pg. 5436
SAPA PROFILES - HARDERWIJK—See Norsk Hydro ASA; *Int'l*, pg. 5436
SAPA PROFILES INC.—See Norsk Hydro ASA; *Int'l*, pg. 5436
SAPA PROFILES KFT—See Norsk Hydro ASA; *Int'l*, pg. 5436
SAPA PROFILES NL B.V.—See Norsk Hydro ASA; *Int'l*, pg. 5436
SAPA PROFILES NORD/OUEST - LUCE—See Norsk Hydro ASA; *Int'l*, pg. 5436
SAPA PROFILES PERIFALSA S.R.L.—See Norsk Hydro ASA; *Int'l*, pg. 5436
SAPA PROFILES UK LIMITED - BIRTLEY—See Norsk Hydro ASA; *Int'l*, pg. 5436
SAPA PROFILES UK LIMITED—See Norsk Hydro ASA; *Int'l*, pg. 5436
SAPA PROFILI S.R.L.—See Norsk Hydro ASA; *Int'l*, pg. 5436
SAP ARGENTINA S.A.—See SAP SE; *Int'l*, pg. 6568
SAP ASIA PTE. LTD.—See SAP SE; *Int'l*, pg. 6568
SAPA THERMAL MANAGEMENT AB—See Norsk Hydro ASA; *Int'l*, pg. 5435
SAP AUSTRALIA PTY. LTD.—See SAP SE; *Int'l*, pg. 6568
SAP AZ LLC—See SAP SE; *Int'l*, pg. 6567
SAP (BEIJING) SOFTWARE SYSTEM CO., LTD.—See SAP SE; *Int'l*, pg. 6568
SAP BELGIUM - SYSTEMS APPLICATIONS & PRODUCTS NV/SA—See SAP SE; *Int'l*, pg. 6568
SAP BETEILIGUNGS GMBH—See SAP SE; *Int'l*, pg. 6569
SAP BRASIL LTDA.—See SAP SE; *Int'l*, pg. 6568
SAPB—See FAYAT SAS; *Int'l*, pg. 2626
SAP BULGARIA EOOD—See SAP SE; *Int'l*, pg. 6569
SAP BUSINESS SERVICES CENTER EUROPE, S.R.O.—See SAP SE; *Int'l*, pg. 6569
SAP BUSINESS SERVICES CENTER NEDERLAND B.V.—See SAP SE; *Int'l*, pg. 6567
SAP CANADA INC.—See SAP SE; *Int'l*, pg. 6567
SAP COLOMBIA S.A.S.—See SAP SE; *Int'l*, pg. 6568
SAP COSTA RICA, S.A.—See SAP SE; *Int'l*, pg. 6569
SAPCOTE GROUP PLC; *Int'l*, pg. 6571
SAP CR, SPOL. S.R.O.—See SAP SE; *Int'l*, pg. 6569
SAP CYPRUS LTD.—See SAP SE; *Int'l*, pg. 6569
SAP DANMARK A/S—See SAP SE; *Int'l*, pg. 6569
SAP DEUTSCHLAND SE & CO. KG—See SAP SE; *Int'l*, pg. 6569
SAP D.O.O.—See SAP SE; *Int'l*, pg. 6570
SAP DRITTE BETEILIGUNGS- UND VERMOGENSVERWALTUNG GMBH—See SAP SE; *Int'l*, pg. 6569
SAP EAST AFRICA LIMITED—See SAP SE; *Int'l*, pg. 6569
SAPEC AGRO MACAU LTD.—See Bridgepoint Group Plc; *Int'l*, pg. 1155
SAPEC AGRO S.A.—See Bridgepoint Group Plc; *Int'l*, pg. 1155
SAPEC AGRO, S.A.U.—See Bridgepoint Group Plc; *Int'l*, pg. 1155
SAPEC-QUIMICA SA—See REHAU Verwaltungszentrale AG; *Int'l*, pg. 6256
SAPEC S.A.; *Int'l*, pg. 6571

SAPIENT INVESTIGATIONS INC.

SAP EGYPT LLC—See SAP SE; *Int'l*, pg. 6569
SAP EMEA INSIDE SALES S.L.—See SAP SE; *Int'l*, pg. 6569
SAPEON INC.—See SK Inc.; *Int'l*, pg. 6972
SAPERE CONSULTING, INC.; *U.S. Private*, pg. 3548
SAPERIUM, INC.—See OPENLANE, Inc.; *U.S. Public*, pg. 1607
SAP ERSTE BETEILIGUNGS- UND VERMOGENSVERWALTUNG GMBH—See SAP SE; *Int'l*, pg. 6569
SAP ESPANA, S.A.—See SAP SE; *Int'l*, pg. 6569
SAP ESTONIA OU—See SAP SE; *Int'l*, pg. 6569
S.A. PEUGEOT DISTRIBUTION SERVICE N.V.—See Stellantis N.V.; *Int'l*, pg. 7203
SAP FINLAND OY—See SAP SE; *Int'l*, pg. 6569
SAP FOREIGN HOLDINGS GMBH—See SAP SE; *Int'l*, pg. 6569
SAP FRANCE HOLDING S.A.—See SAP SE; *Int'l*, pg. 6569
SAP FRANCE S.A.—See SAP SE; *Int'l*, pg. 6569
SAP GLOBAL MARKETING INC.—See SAP SE; *Int'l*, pg. 6568
SAP GOVERNANCE RISK & COMPLIANCE, INC.—See SAP SE; *Int'l*, pg. 6568
SAP GOVERNMENT SUPPORT & SERVICES, INC.—See SAP SE; *Int'l*, pg. 6568
SAP HELLAS SYSTEMS APPLICATIONS & DATA PROCESSING S.A.—See SAP SE; *Int'l*, pg. 6569
SAPHEON LLC—See Medtronic plc; *Int'l*, pg. 4790
SAP HONG KONG CO. LTD.—See SAP SE; *Int'l*, pg. 6568
SAPHORE EQUIPEMENTS; *Int'l*, pg. 6571
SAP HOSTING BETEILIGUNGS GMBH—See SAP SE; *Int'l*, pg. 6569
SA PHOTONICS, INC.; *U.S. Private*, pg. 3519
SAP HUNGARY RENDSZEREK, ALKALMAZASOK ES TERMEKEK AZ ADATFELDOLGOZASBAN INFORMATIKAI KFT.—See SAP SE; *Int'l*, pg. 6569
SAPHYTO SA—See Element Solutions Inc.; *U.S. Public*, pg. 728
SAPIEN BIOSCIENCES PRIVATE LIMITED—See Apollo Hospitals Enterprise Limited; *Int'l*, pg. 518
SAPIENS AMERICAS CORPORATION—See Sapiens International Corporation N.V.; *Int'l*, pg. 6571
SAPIENS DENMARK A/S—See Sapiens International Corporation N.V.; *Int'l*, pg. 6571
SAPIENS INTERNATIONAL CORPORATION N.V.; *Int'l*, pg. 6571
SAPIENS ISRAEL SOFTWARE SYSTEMS LTD.—See Sapiens International Corporation N.V.; *Int'l*, pg. 6571
SAPIENS LNFORMATION TECHNOLOGY (SHANGHAI) CO., LTD.—See Sapiens International Corporation N.V.; *Int'l*, pg. 6571
SAPIENS SOFTWARE SOLUTIONS (POLAND) SP. Z O.O.—See Sapiens International Corporation N.V.; *Int'l*, pg. 6571
SAPIENS TECHNOLOGIES LTD.—See Sapiens International Corporation N.V.; *Int'l*, pg. 6571
SAPIENS TECHNOLOGY JAPAN CO., LTD.—See Sapiens International Corporation N.V.; *Int'l*, pg. 6571
SAPIENS (UK) LIMITED—See Sapiens International Corporation N.V.; *Int'l*, pg. 6571
SAPIENT CANADA INC.—See Publicis Groupe S.A.; *Int'l*, pg. 6110
SAPIENT CORPORATION - ATLANTA—See Publicis Groupe S.A.; *Int'l*, pg. 6110
SAPIENT CORPORATION - CHICAGO—See Publicis Groupe S.A.; *Int'l*, pg. 6110
SAPIENT CORPORATION - HOUSTON—See Publicis Groupe S.A.; *Int'l*, pg. 6110
SAPIENT CORPORATION - LOS ANGELES—See Publicis Groupe S.A.; *Int'l*, pg. 6110
SAPIENT CORPORATION - MIAMI/FALLS—See Publicis Groupe S.A.; *Int'l*, pg. 6110
SAPIENT CORPORATION - NEW YORK—See Publicis Groupe S.A.; *Int'l*, pg. 6110
SAPIENT CORPORATION PRIVATE LIMITED—See Publicis Groupe S.A.; *Int'l*, pg. 6110
SAPIENT CORPORATION PVT. LTD. - BENGALURU—See Publicis Groupe S.A.; *Int'l*, pg. 6110
SAPIENT CORPORATION PVT. LTD. - NOIDA—See Publicis Groupe S.A.; *Int'l*, pg. 6110
SAPIENT CORPORATION - SAN FRANCISCO—See Publicis Groupe S.A.; *Int'l*, pg. 6110
SAPIENT CORPORATION—See Publicis Groupe S.A.; *Int'l*, pg. 6110
SAPIENT CORPORATION - WASHINGTON, DC—See Publicis Groupe S.A.; *Int'l*, pg. 6110
SAPIENT GMBH—See Publicis Groupe S.A.; *Int'l*, pg. 6110
SAPIENT GOVERNMENT SERVICES, INC.—See Publicis Groupe S.A.; *Int'l*, pg. 6110
SAPIENT INVESTIGATIONS INC.; *U.S. Private*, pg. 3548
SAPIENT ITALY S.R.L.—See Publicis Groupe S.A.; *Int'l*, pg. 6110
SAPIENT LIMITED—See Publicis Groupe S.A.; *Int'l*, pg. 6110
SAPIENT (M)PHASIZE—See Publicis Groupe S.A.; *Int'l*, pg. 6110

SAPIENT INVESTIGATIONS INC.   CORPORATE AFFILIATIONS

SAPIENT NETHERLANDS B.V.—See Publicis Groupe S.A.; *Int'l*, pg. 6111
SAPIENTNITRO ATLANTA—See Publicis Groupe S.A.; *Int'l*, pg. 6110
SAPIENTNITRO HONG KONG LIMITED—See Publicis Groupe S.A.; *Int'l*, pg. 6110
SAPIENTNITRO LIMITED—See Publicis Groupe S.A.; *Int'l*, pg. 6110
SAPIENTNITRO PTY. LTD.—See Publicis Groupe S.A.; *Int'l*, pg. 6110
SAPIENTNITRO USA, INC.—See Publicis Groupe S.A.; *Int'l*, pg. 6110
SAPIENT SWEDEN AB—See Publicis Groupe S.A.; *Int'l*, pg. 6111
SAPIENT SWITZERLAND GMBH—See Publicis Groupe S.A.; *Int'l*, pg. 6111
SAP INDIA PVT. LTD.—See SAP SE; *Int'l*, pg. 6569
SAP INDUSTRIES, INC.—See SAP SE; *Int'l*, pg. 6568
SAP INTERNATIONAL, INC.—See SAP SE; *Int'l*, pg. 6568
SAP INTERNATIONAL PANAMA, S.A.—See SAP SE; *Int'l*, pg. 6569
SAPIO AB—See Nexbis Limited; *Int'l*, pg. 5242
SAP IRELAND LIMITED—See SAP SE; *Int'l*, pg. 6567
SAP ISRAEL LTD.—See SAP SE; *Int'l*, pg. 6569
SAP ITALIA SISTEMI APPLICAZIONI PRODOTTI IN DATA PROCESSING S.P.A.—See SAP SE; *Int'l*, pg. 6569
SAP KOREA LTD.—See SAP SE; *Int'l*, pg. 6568
SAP LABS BULGARIA EOOD—See SAP SE; *Int'l*, pg. 6569
SAP LABS CANADA - MONTREAL—See SAP SE; *Int'l*, pg. 6567
SAP LABS CANADA - TORONTO—See SAP SE; *Int'l*, pg. 6567
SAP LABS CHINA—See SAP SE; *Int'l*, pg. 6568
SAP LABS FINLAND OY—See SAP SE; *Int'l*, pg. 6569
SAP LABS FRANCE S.A.S—See SAP SE; *Int'l*, pg. 6569
SAP LABS HUNGARY—See SAP SE; *Int'l*, pg. 6569
SAP LABS INDIA PVT. LTD.—See SAP SE; *Int'l*, pg. 6569
SAP LABS ISRAEL LTD.—See SAP SE; *Int'l*, pg. 6569
SAP LABS KOREA, INC.—See SAP SE; *Int'l*, pg. 6569
SAP LABS, LLC—See SAP SE; *Int'l*, pg. 6568
SAP LABS U.S. - ALPHARETTA—See SAP SE; *Int'l*, pg. 6568
SAP LABS U.S. - BOSTON—See SAP SE; *Int'l*, pg. 6568
SAP LABS U.S. - LOS ANGELES—See SAP SE; *Int'l*, pg. 6568
SAP LATVIA SIA—See SAP SE; *Int'l*, pg. 6569
SAPLING LEARNING, INC.—See Verlagsgruppe Georg von Holtzbrinck GmbH; *Int'l*, pg. 8171
SAP LUXEMBOURG—See SAP SE; *Int'l*, pg. 6569
SAP MALAYSIA SDN. BHD.—See SAP SE; *Int'l*, pg. 6568
SAPMER S.A.; *Int'l*, pg. 6571
SAP MEXICO S.A. DE C.V. - MONTERREY—See SAP SE; *Int'l*, pg. 6568
SAP MEXICO S.A. DE C.V.—See SAP SE; *Int'l*, pg. 6568
SAP MIDDLE EAST & NORTH AFRICA LLC—See SAP SE; *Int'l*, pg. 6569
SAP NATIONAL SECURITY SERVICES, INC.—See SAP SE; *Int'l*, pg. 6569
SAP NEDERLAND B.V.—See SAP SE; *Int'l*, pg. 6570
SAP NEDERLAND HOLDING B.V.—See SAP SE; *Int'l*, pg. 6570
SAP NEW ZEALAND LIMITED—See SAP SE; *Int'l*, pg. 6568
SAP NORGE AS—See SAP SE; *Int'l*, pg. 6570
SAP NORTH WEST AFRICA LTD—See SAP SE; *Int'l*, pg. 6570
SAPOLOGI CO., LTD.—See Senko Group Holdings Co., Ltd.; *Int'l*, pg. 6711
SAPONA MANUFACTURING COMPANY, INC.—See Acme-McCrary Corporation; *U.S. Private*, pg. 61
SAPONIA D.D.; *Int'l*, pg. 6571
SAPORITO FINISHING COMPANY; *U.S. Private*, pg. 3548
SAP OSTERREICH GMBH—See SAP SE; *Int'l*, pg. 6570
SA POWER NETWORKS—See CK Hutchison Holdings Limited; *Int'l*, pg. 1637
SA POWER NETWORKS—See Power Assets Holdings Limited; *Int'l*, pg. 5943
S.A. POWER SERVICES (PTY) LTD.; *Int'l*, pg. 6448
SAPOZNIK INSURANCE & ASSOCIATES, INC.—See World Insurance Associates LLC; *U.S. Private*, pg. 4566
S. APPAREL CO., LTD.—See Thanulux Public Company Limited; *Int'l*, pg. 7608
SAPP BROS PETROLEUM, INC.; *U.S. Private*, pg. 3548
SAPPE PUBLIC COMPANY LIMITED; *Int'l*, pg. 6571
SAPPERS IBERIA S.L—See Nedap N.V.; *Int'l*, pg. 5187
SAP PERU S.A.C.—See SAP SE; *Int'l*, pg. 6569
SAP PHILIPPINES INC.—See SAP SE; *Int'l*, pg. 6568
SAPPHIRE B.V.—See Randstad N.V.; *Int'l*, pg. 6202
SAPPHIRE CONSTRUCTION & DEVELOPMENT PTE. LTD.—See Sapphire Corporation Limited; *Int'l*, pg. 6572
SAPPHIRE CORPORATION LIMITED; *Int'l*, pg. 6571
SAPPHIRE FIBRES LIMITED; *Int'l*, pg. 6572
SAPPHIRE FOODS INDIA LTD.; *Int'l*, pg. 6572
SAPPHIRE MINERAL RESOURCES PTE. LTD.—See Sapphire Corporation Limited; *Int'l*, pg. 6572

SAPPHIRE RETAIL LIMITED—See Sapphire Textile Mills Ltd.; *Int'l*, pg. 6572
SAPPHIRE SCIENTIFIC INC.—See RPM International Inc.; *U.S. Public*, pg. 1820
SAPPHIRE TECHNOLOGIES—See Randstad N.V.; *Int'l*, pg. 6204
SAPPHIRE TEXTILE MILLS LTD.; *Int'l*, pg. 6572
SAPPHIRE WIND POWER COMPANY LIMITED—See Sapphire Textile Mills Ltd.; *Int'l*, pg. 6572
SAPPI ALFELD GMBH—See Sappi Limited; *Int'l*, pg. 6572
SAPPI AUSTRIA PRODUKTIONS GMBH & CO. KG—See Sappi Limited; *Int'l*, pg. 6572
SAPPI CLOQUET LLC—See Sappi Limited; *Int'l*, pg. 6572
SAPPI DEUTSCHLAND GMBH—See Sappi Limited; *Int'l*, pg. 6572
SAPPI EHINGEN GMBH—See Sappi Limited; *Int'l*, pg. 6572
SAPPI EUROPE S.A.—See Sappi Limited; *Int'l*, pg. 6572
SAPPI FINE PAPER NORTH AMERICA—See Sappi Limited; *Int'l*, pg. 6572
SAPPI FINE PAPER SOUTH AFRICA—See Sappi Limited; *Int'l*, pg. 6572
SAPPI FORESTS (PTY) LTD—See Sappi Limited; *Int'l*, pg. 6572
SAPPI HOLDING GMBH—See Sappi Limited; *Int'l*, pg. 6572
SAPPI LANAKEN N.V.—See Sappi Limited; *Int'l*, pg. 6572
SAPPI LANAKEN PRESS PAPER NV—See Sappi Limited; *Int'l*, pg. 6572
SAPPI LIMITED; *Int'l*, pg. 6572
SAPPI MAASTRICHT B.V.—See Sappi Limited; *Int'l*, pg. 6572
SAPPI MANUFACTURING (PTY) LIMITED—See Sappi Limited; *Int'l*, pg. 6572
SAPPI NORTH AMERICA INC.—See Sappi Limited; *Int'l*, pg. 6572
SAPPI PAPIER HOLDING GMBH—See Sappi Limited; *Int'l*, pg. 6572
SAPPI SOUTHERN AFRICA—See Sappi Limited; *Int'l*, pg. 6572
SAPPI STOCKSTADT GMBH—See Sappi Limited; *Int'l*, pg. 6572
SAPPI TIMBER INDUSTRIES NEW BUSINESS DEVELOPMENT—See Sappi Limited; *Int'l*, pg. 6572
SAPPI TIMBER INDUSTRIES PTY LTD—See Sappi Limited; *Int'l*, pg. 6572
SAPPI TRADING AFRICA PTY LTD—See Sappi Limited; *Int'l*, pg. 6572
SAPPI TRADING AUSTRALIA PTY LTD—See Sappi Limited; *Int'l*, pg. 6572
SAPPI TRADING DO BRASIL LTDA—See Sappi Limited; *Int'l*, pg. 6572
SAPPI TRADING LTD.—See Sappi Limited; *Int'l*, pg. 6572
SAPPI TRENFOR TRADING LTD—See Sappi Limited; *Int'l*, pg. 6573
SAPPLICATOR LTD—See Acrison, Inc.; *U.S. Private*, pg. 65
SAP POLSKA SP. Z O.O.—See SAP SE; *Int'l*, pg. 6570
SAPPORO AGENCY LIMITED—See Sapporo Holdings Limited; *Int'l*, pg. 6573
SAPPORO BEER'S BEVERAGE CO., LTD.—See Sapporo Holdings Limited; *Int'l*, pg. 6573
SAPPORO BEVERAGE CO., LTD—See Sapporo Holdings Limited; *Int'l*, pg. 6573
SAPPORO BREWERIES LIMITED—See Sapporo Holdings Limited; *Int'l*, pg. 6573
SAPPORO CANADA INC.—See Sapporo Holdings Limited; *Int'l*, pg. 6573
SAPPORO CLINICAL LABORATORY INC.; *Int'l*, pg. 6573
SAPPORO DAIICHI TRAFFIC CO., LTD.—See Daiichi Koutsu Sangyo Co., Ltd.; *Int'l*, pg. 1929
SAPPORO DRUG STORE CO., LTD.; *Int'l*, pg. 6573
SAPPORO ENGINEERING LIMITED—See Sapporo Holdings Limited; *Int'l*, pg. 6573
SAPPORO FINE FOODS CO., LTD—See Sapporo Holdings Limited; *Int'l*, pg. 6573
SAPPORO FOODS NET CO., LTD—See Sapporo Holdings Limited; *Int'l*, pg. 6573
SAPPORO GROUP LOGISTICS COMPANY LIMITED—See Sapporo Holdings Limited; *Int'l*, pg. 6573
SAPPORO GROUP MANAGEMENT CO., LTD.—See Sapporo Holdings Limited; *Int'l*, pg. 6573
SAPPORO HOKUYO CARD CO., LTD.—See North Pacific Bank, Ltd.; *Int'l*, pg. 5441
SAPPORO HOKUYO LEASE CO., LTD.—See North Pacific Bank, Ltd.; *Int'l*, pg. 5441
SAPPORO HOLDINGS LIMITED; *Int'l*, pg. 6573
SAPPORO HOTEL ENTERPRISE LIMITED—See Sapporo Holdings Limited; *Int'l*, pg. 6573
SAPPORO INTERNATIONAL INC.—See Sapporo Holdings Limited; *Int'l*, pg. 6573
SAPPORO KAMI RYUTSU CENTER CO., LTD.—See Japan Pulp and Paper Company Limited; *Int'l*, pg. 3904
SAPPORO KAWASAKI ROLLING STOCK ENGINEERING CO., LTD.—See Kawasaki Heavy Industries, Ltd.; *Int'l*, pg. 4098
SAPPORO LION LIMITED—See Sapporo Holdings Limited; *Int'l*, pg. 6573

SAPPORO LOGISTICS SYSTEM CO., LTD.—See Sapporo Holdings Limited; *Int'l*, pg. 6573
SAPPORO LOGISTICS SYSTEMS CO., LTD.—See Sapporo Holdings Limited; *Int'l*, pg. 6573
SAPPORO MARUI MITSUKOSHI LTD.—See Isetan Mitsukoshi Holdings Ltd.; *Int'l*, pg. 3815
SAPPORO MITSUKOSHI LTD.—See Isetan Mitsukoshi Holdings Ltd.; *Int'l*, pg. 3815
SAPPORO NICHIREI SERVICE INC.—See Nichirei Corporation; *Int'l*, pg. 5270
SAPPORO NISSHIN ELECTRONICS CO., LTD.—See Nippon Signal Co., Ltd.; *Int'l*, pg. 5334
SAPPORO PARIS CO., LTD—See Yamazaki Baking Co., Ltd.; *Int'l*, pg. 8556
SAPPORO REAL ESTATE CO.,LTD.—See Sapporo Holdings Limited; *Int'l*, pg. 6573
SAPPORO SENKO TRANSPORT CO., LTD.—See Senko Group Holdings Co., Ltd.; *Int'l*, pg. 6711
SAPPORO TOHUN CO., LTD.—See Tomoku Co., Ltd.; *Int'l*, pg. 7801
SAPPORO U.S.A., INC.—See Sapporo Holdings Limited; *Int'l*, pg. 6573
SAPPORO U.S.A., INC.—See Sapporo Holdings Limited; *Int'l*, pg. 6573
SAPPORO VIETNAM LIMITED—See Sapporo Holdings Limited; *Int'l*, pg. 6573
SAPPORO WINES LIMITED—See Sapporo Holdings Limited; *Int'l*, pg. 6573
SAP PORTALS EUROPE GMBH—See SAP SE; *Int'l*, pg. 6570
SAP PORTALS ISRAEL LTD.—See SAP SE; *Int'l*, pg. 6569
SAP PORTUGAL - SISTEMAS, APLICACOES E PRODUTOS INFORMATICOS, SOCIEDADE UNIPESSOAL, LDA—See SAP SE; *Int'l*, pg. 6570
SAP PORTUGAL - SISTEMAS, APLICAGOES E PRODUTOS INFORMATICOS SOCIEDADE UNIPESSOAL LDA—See SAP SE; *Int'l*, pg. 6570
SAP PROJEKTVERWALTUNGS- UND BETEILIGUNGS GMBH—See SAP SE; *Int'l*, pg. 6570
SAP PUBLIC SERV. HUNGARY—See SAP SE; *Int'l*, pg. 6569
SAP PUBLIC SERVICES, INC.—See SAP SE; *Int'l*, pg. 6568
SAPRA-LANDAUER, LTDA.—See Fortive Corporation; *U.S. Public*, pg. 871
SAPRATIN TECHNOLOGIES S.A.S.—See Schunk GmbH; *Int'l*, pg. 6641
SAP R&D CENTER KOREA, INC.—See SAP SE; *Int'l*, pg. 6568
SAPREF AG—See RHI Magnesita N.V.; *Int'l*, pg. 6326
SAP RESEARCH GROUP - SOUTH AFRICA—See SAP SE; *Int'l*, pg. 6569
SAP RETAIL SOLUTIONS BETEILIGUNGSGESELL-SCHAFT MBH—See SAP SE; *Int'l*, pg. 6570
SAP ROMANIA SRL—See SAP SE; *Int'l*, pg. 6570
S.A. PROSEAT N.V.—See Recticel S.A.; *Int'l*, pg. 6242
SAP SAUDI ARABIA SOFTWARE SERVICES CO. LTD.—See SAP SE; *Int'l*, pg. 6569
SAP SAUDI ARABIA SOFTWARE TRADING LTD.—See SAP SE; *Int'l*, pg. 6570
SAP (SCHWEIZ) AG—See SAP SE; *Int'l*, pg. 6567
SAP SECHSTE BETEILIGUNGS- UND VERMOGENS-VERWALTUNGS GMBH—See SAP SE; *Int'l*, pg. 6570
SAP SERVICES S.R.O.—See SAP SE; *Int'l*, pg. 6570
SAP SERVICE & SUPPORT (IRELAND) LTD.—See SAP SE; *Int'l*, pg. 6567
SAP SE - SERVICE CENTER ROT—See SAP SE; *Int'l*, pg. 6570
SAP SE; *Int'l*, pg. 6566
SAP SISTEMI, APLIKACIJE IN PRODUKTI ZA OB-DELAVO PODATKOV D.O.O.—See SAP SE; *Int'l*, pg. 6570
SAP SISTEMI, APLIKACIJJE IN PRODUKTI ZA OB-DELAVO PODATKOV D.O.O.—See SAP SE; *Int'l*, pg. 6570
SAP SLOVENSKO S.R.O.—See SAP SE; *Int'l*, pg. 6570
SAP SVENSKA AB—See SAP SE; *Int'l*, pg. 6570
SAP SYSTEMS, APPLICATIONS & PRODUCTS IN DATA PROCESSING (THAILAND) LTD.—See SAP SE; *Int'l*, pg. 6568
SAP TAIWAN CO., LTD.—See SAP SE; *Int'l*, pg. 6568
SAPTAK CHEM AND BUSINESS LIMITED; *Int'l*, pg. 6574
SAP TAKISAWA MACHINE TOOLS PRIVATE LTD.—See Nidec Corporation; *Int'l*, pg. 5280
SAPTASHVA SOLAR S.A.—See XL Energy Ltd.; *Int'l*, pg. 8535
SAPTHIP GREEN ENERGY CO., LTD.—See PTT Public Company Limited; *Int'l*, pg. 6093
SAP TURKIYE YAZILIM URETIM VE TICARET A.S.—See SAP SE; *Int'l*, pg. 6570
SAP UAB (LITHUANIA)—See SAP SE; *Int'l*, pg. 6570
SAP (UK) LIMITED—See SAP SE; *Int'l*, pg. 6567
SAP (UK) LIMITED—See SAP SE; *Int'l*, pg. 6567
SAPURA AERO SDN. BHD.—See Sapura Holdings Sdn. Bhd.; *Int'l*, pg. 6574
SAPURA BAKER HUGHES TPS SDN. BHD.—See Sapura Energy Berhad; *Int'l*, pg. 6574
SAPURA ENERGY BERHAD; *Int'l*, pg. 6574

COMPANY NAME INDEX

SAPURA ENERGY SDN. BHD.—See Sapura Energy Berhad; *Int'l*, pg. 6574
SAPURA HOLDINGS SDN. BHD.; *Int'l*, pg. 6574
SAPURA INDUSTRIAL BERHAD—See Sapura Holdings Sdn. Bhd.; *Int'l*, pg. 6574
SAPURAKENCANA ALLIED MARINE SDN BHD—See Sapura Energy Berhad; *Int'l*, pg. 6574
SAPURAKENCANA ENERGY MALAYSIA INC.—See Sapura Energy Berhad; *Int'l*, pg. 6574
SAPURAOMV BLOCK 30, S. DE R.L. DE C.V.—See OMV Aktiengesellschaft; *Int'l*, pg. 5570
SAPURAOMV UPSTREAM (WESTERN AUSTRALIA) PTY LTD.—See OMV Aktiengesellschaft; *Int'l*, pg. 5570
SAPURA PETROLEUM (AUSTRALIA) PTY LTD—See Sapura Energy Berhad; *Int'l*, pg. 6574
SAPURA POWER SERVICES SDN BHD—See Sapura Energy Berhad; *Int'l*, pg. 6574
SAPURA RESOURCES BERHAD—See Sapura Holdings Sdn. Bhd.; *Int'l*, pg. 6574
SAPURA RETAIL SOLUTIONS SDN BHD—See Sapura Energy Berhad; *Int'l*, pg. 6574
SAPUTO CHEESE USA INC.—See Saputo Inc.; *Int'l*, pg. 6575
SAPUTO DAIRY FOODS USA, LLC—See Saputo Inc.; *Int'l*, pg. 6575
SAPUTO DAIRY FOODS USA—See Saputo Inc.; *Int'l*, pg. 6575
SAPUTO DAIRY FOODS USA—See Saputo Inc.; *Int'l*, pg. 6575
SAPUTO DAIRY PRODUCTS CANADA G.P.—See Saputo Inc.; *Int'l*, pg. 6575
SAPUTO DAIRY PRODUCTS—See Saputo Inc.; *Int'l*, pg. 6575
SAPUTO DESIGN, INC.; *U.S. Private*, pg. 3548
SAPUTO INC.; *Int'l*, pg. 6575
SAP VIERTE BETEILIGUNGS- UND VERMOGENSVERWALTUNG GMBH—See SAP SE; *Int'l*, pg. 6570
SAP VIETNAM COMPANY LIMITED—See SAP SE; *Int'l*, pg. 6570
SAPV (MAURITIUS)—See SAP SE; *Int'l*, pg. 6570
SAP WEST BALKANS D.O.O.—See SAP SE; *Int'l*, pg. 6570
SAPY DANONE—See Danone; *Int'l*, pg. 1968
SAP ZWEITE BETEILIGUNGS- UND VERMOGENSVER WALTUNG GMBH—See SAP SE; *Int'l*, pg. 6570
SARA BAY COUNTRY CLUB, INC.; *U.S. Private*, pg. 3549
SARABAY REAL ESTATE, INC.; *U.S. Private*, pg. 3549
SARABHAI CHEMICALS (INDIA) PVT. LTD.—See Ambalal Sarabhai Enterprises Ltd.; *Int'l*, pg. 413
SARACEN FUND MANAGERS LIMITED—See AssetCo plc; *Int'l*, pg. 643
SARACEN MINERAL HOLDINGS LIMITED—See Northern Star Resources Ltd; *Int'l*, pg. 5444
SARA ENTERPRISES—See Corporate Travel Management Limited; *Int'l*, pg. 1806
SARAFIN S.P.A.; *Int'l*, pg. 6575
SARAH BRAYTON GENERAL PARTNERSHIP—See Welltower Inc.; *U.S. Public*, pg. 2349
SARAH BUSH LINCOLN HEALTH CENTER; *U.S. Private*, pg. 3549
SARAH CANNON DEVELOPMENT INNOVATIONS, LLC—See HCA Healthcare, Inc.; *U.S. Public*, pg. 1008
SARAH CANNON RESEARCH INSTITUTE, LLC—See HCA Healthcare, Inc.; *U.S. Public*, pg. 1008
SARAH CANNON RESEARCH INSTITUTE UK LIMITED—See HCA Healthcare, Inc.; *U.S. Public*, pg. 1008
SARAH CANNON RESEARCH UK LIMITED—See HCA Healthcare, Inc.; *U.S. Public*, pg. 1008
SARAIVA S.A. LIVREIROS EDITORES; *Int'l*, pg. 6575
SARAJEVO GAS A.D.; *Int'l*, pg. 6575
SARAJEVO OSIGURANJE D.D.; *Int'l*, pg. 6575
SARAJEVO PUBLISHING D.D.; *Int'l*, pg. 6575
SARAJEVOPUTEVI D.D. SARAJEVO; *Int'l*, pg. 6576
SARAJEVOSTAN D.O.O.—See Zavarovalnica Triglav, d.d.; *Int'l*, pg. 8626
THE SARAJEVO STOCK EXCHANGE—See Zagrebacka burza d.d.; *Int'l*, pg. 8619
SARAJEVSKA PIVARA D.D.; *Int'l*, pg. 6576
SARAJISHVILI JOINT STOCK COMPANY; *Int'l*, pg. 6576
SARA JSC; *Int'l*, pg. 6575
SARA LEE AUSTRALIA PTY LTD.—See JAB Holding Company S.a.r.l.; *Int'l*, pg. 3863
SARA LEE BALTIC, S.I.A.—See JAB Holding Company S.a.r.l.; *Int'l*, pg. 3863
SARA LEE COFFEE AND TEA HELLAS S.A.—See JAB Holding Company S.a.r.l.; *Int'l*, pg. 3863
SARA LEE COFFEE & TEA FRANCE SNC—See JAB Holding Company S.a.r.l.; *Int'l*, pg. 3863
SARA LEE COFFEE & TEA GERMANY GMBH—See JAB Holding Company S.a.r.l.; *Int'l*, pg. 3862
SARA LEE CZECH REPUBLIC, S.R.O.—See JAB Holding Company S.a.r.l.; *Int'l*, pg. 3863
SARA LEE FINANCE SPAIN S.L.—See JAB Holding Company S.a.r.l.; *Int'l*, pg. 3862
SARA LEE FOOD HOLDINGS PTY. LTD.—See JAB Holding Company S.a.r.l.; *Int'l*, pg. 3863
SARA LEE FOODS, LLC—See Tyson Foods, Inc.; *U.S. Public*, pg. 2210
SARA LEE FROZEN BAKERY, LLC—See KKR & Co. Inc.; *U.S. Public*, pg. 1263
SARA LEE GROUP (AUSTRALIA) PTY. LTD.—See JAB Holding Company S.a.r.l.; *Int'l*, pg. 3863
SARA LEE HONG KONG LTD.—See JAB Holding Company S.a.r.l.; *Int'l*, pg. 3863
SARA LEE HUNGARY KAVE ES TEA KFT—See JAB Holding Company S.a.r.l.; *Int'l*, pg. 3863
SARA LEE JAPAN, LTD.—See JAB Holding Company S.a.r.l.; *Int'l*, pg. 3863
SARA LEE (MALAYSIA) SDN. BHD.—See JAB Holding Company S.a.r.l.; *Int'l*, pg. 3863
SARA LEE NEW ZEALAND LIMITED—See JAB Holding Company S.a.r.l.; *Int'l*, pg. 3863
SARA LEE TRADEMARK HOLDINGS AUSTRALASIA LLC—See Tyson Foods, Inc.; *U.S. Public*, pg. 2210
SARA LEE UK HOLDINGS LIMITED—See JAB Holding Company S.a.r.l.; *Int'l*, pg. 3863
SARAL PUBLICATIONS, INC.—See Grupo Televisa, S.A.B.; *Int'l*, pg. 3136
SARAMANIS LIMITED; *Int'l*, pg. 6576
SARAMA RESOURCES LTD.; *Int'l*, pg. 6576
SARAMAX APPAREL GROUP INC.; *U.S. Private*, pg. 3549
SARAMIN CO., LTD.; *Int'l*, pg. 6576
SARANTICS CZECH REPUBLIC SRO—See Gr. Sarantis S.A.; *Int'l*, pg. 3047
SARANTIS BANJA LUKA D.O.O.—See Gr. Sarantis S.A.; *Int'l*, pg. 3047
SARANTIS BELGRADE D.O.O.—See Gr. Sarantis S.A.; *Int'l*, pg. 3047
SARANTIS BULGARIA LTD—See Gr. Sarantis S.A.; *Int'l*, pg. 3047
SARANTIS D.O.O.—See Gr. Sarantis S.A.; *Int'l*, pg. 3047
SARANTIS HUNGARY KFT.—See Gr. Sarantis S.A.; *Int'l*, pg. 3047
SARANTIS POLSKA S.A.—See Gr. Sarantis S.A.; *Int'l*, pg. 3047
SARANTIS ROMANIA S.A.—See Gr. Sarantis S.A.; *Int'l*, pg. 3047
SARANTIS SERBIA LTD—See Gr. Sarantis S.A.; *Int'l*, pg. 3047
SARANTIS-SKOPJE D.O.O.—See Gr. Sarantis S.A.; *Int'l*, pg. 3048
SARAPUL ELECTROGENERATOR PLANT JSC—See Russian Technologies State Corporation; *Int'l*, pg. 6432
SARA SAE PVT. LTD.; *Int'l*, pg. 6575
SARASOTA 500 INC.; *U.S. Private*, pg. 3549
SARASOTA AMBULATORY SURGERY CENTER, LTD.—See Bain Capital, LP; *U.S. Public*, pg. 446
SARASOTA COUNTY PUBLIC HOSPITAL DISTRICT; *U.S. Private*, pg. 3549
SARASOTA DOCTORS HOSPITAL, INC.—See HCA Healthcare, Inc.; *U.S. Public*, pg. 1008
THE SARASOTA ENDOSCOPY ASC, LLC—See KKR & Co. Inc.; *U.S. Public*, pg. 1248
SARASOTA FUN MACHINES INC.; *U.S. Private*, pg. 3549
SARASOTA MANAGEMENT AND LEASING; *U.S. Private*, pg. 3549
SARASOTA MANATEE JEWISH HOUSING COUNCIL, INC.; *U.S. Private*, pg. 3549
SARASOTA MILITARY ACADEMY, INC.; *U.S. Private*, pg. 3549
THE SARASOTA OPHTHALMOLOGY ASC, LLC—See KKR & Co. Inc.; *U.S. Public*, pg. 1248
SARASOTA PHYSICIANS SURGICAL CENTER, LLC—See KKR & Co. Inc.; *U.S. Public*, pg. 1246
SARASOTA POLO CLUB—See Schroeder-Manatee Ranch, Inc.; *U.S. Private*, pg. 3569
SARASOTA RARE COIN GALLERY, INC.; *U.S. Private*, pg. 3549
SAR AS—See Stirling Square Capital Partners LLP; *Int'l*, pg. 7216
SARAS S.P.A.—See Angelo Moratti S.A.P.A.; *Int'l*, pg. 460
SARASWATI COMMERCIAL (INDIA) LIMITED; *Int'l*, pg. 6576
SARAT FORD SALES INC.; *U.S. Private*, pg. 3549
SARATOGA CAPITAL INC.—See Pacific Properties III; *U.S. Private*, pg. 3070
SARATOGA EAGLE SALES & SERVICES—See Try-It Distributing Co. Inc.; *U.S. Private*, pg. 4251
SARATOGA HARNESS RACING INC.; *U.S. Private*, pg. 3549
SARATOGA HOSPITAL; *U.S. Private*, pg. 3549
SARATOGA INDUSTRIES DIVISION—See Espey Mfg. & Electronics Corp.; *U.S. Public*, pg. 794
SARATOGA INVESTMENT CORP.; *U.S. Public*, pg. 1841
SARATOGA MOTORS INC.; *U.S. Private*, pg. 3549
SARATOGA NATIONAL BANK & TRUST COMPANY—See Arrow Financial Corporation; *U.S. Public*, pg. 200
SARATOGA PARTNERS L.P.; *U.S. Private*, pg. 3549
SARATOGA RESOURCES, INC.; *U.S. Private*, pg. 3550
SARATOGA SOFTWARE (PTY) LTD—See African Equity Empowerment Investmts Limited; *Int'l*, pg. 191
SARATOGA SPRING WATER COMPANY—See Metropoulos & Co.; *U.S. Private*, pg. 2691
SARATOGA SPRING WATER COMPANY—See One Rock Capital Partners, LLC; *U.S. Private*, pg. 3021
SARATOGA TECHNOLOGIES, INC.—See Hon Hai Precision Industry Co., Ltd.; *Int'l*, pg. 3458
SARATOVENERGO AO; *Int'l*, pg. 6576
SARATOVSKIY NPZ AO; *Int'l*, pg. 6576
SAR AUTO PRODUCTS LIMITED; *Int'l*, pg. 6575
SARA VIETNAM JSC; *Int'l*, pg. 6575
SARAWAK CABLE BERHAD; *Int'l*, pg. 6576
SARAWAK CONSOLIDATED INDUSTRIES BERHAD; *Int'l*, pg. 6576
SARAWAK MOULDING INDUSTRIES BERHAD—See W T K Holdings Berhad; *Int'l*, pg. 8320
SARAWAK OIL PALMS BERHAD; *Int'l*, pg. 6576
SARAWAK PLANTATION BERHAD; *Int'l*, pg. 6576
SARAWAK SHELL BERHAD—See Shell plc; *Int'l*, pg. 6795
SARAY MATBAACILIK KAGITCILIK KIRTASIYECILIK TICARET VE SANAYI AS; *Int'l*, pg. 6576
SARAY MATBAACILIK KAGTCILIK KIRTASIYECILIK TICARET VE SANAYI A.S.; *Int'l*, pg. 6576
SARCHIONE AUTOMOTIVE GROUP; *U.S. Private*, pg. 3550
SARCLAD LTD.—See The Heico Companies, L.L.C.; *U.S. Private*, pg. 4051
SARCLAD NORTH AMERICA LP—See The Heico Companies, L.L.C.; *U.S. Private*, pg. 4051
SARDA DAGITIM VE TICARET A.S.—See Sarkuysan Elektrolitik Bakir Sanayi Ve Ticaret A.S.; *Int'l*, pg. 6578
SARDA ENERGY & MINERALS HONGKONG LIMITED—See Sarda Energy & Minerals Ltd; *Int'l*, pg. 6577
SARDA ENERGY & MINERALS LTD; *Int'l*, pg. 6577
SARDALEASING S.P.A.—See BPER BANCA S.p.A; *Int'l*, pg. 1132
SARDA METALS & ALLOYS LIMITED—See Sarda Energy & Minerals Ltd; *Int'l*, pg. 6577
SARDA PLYWOOD INDUSTRIES LTD. - RAJKOT FACTORY—See Duroply Industries Ltd.; *Int'l*, pg. 2230
SARDA PROTEINS LIMITED; *Int'l*, pg. 6577
SARDES NIKEL MADENCILIK A.S—See DMCI Holdings, Inc.; *Int'l*, pg. 2143
SARDINIA CONCRETE COMPANY; *U.S. Private*, pg. 3550
SARDUS LATTA MALTIDER AB—See Atria Plc; *Int'l*, pg. 694
SARECO ENGINEERING (PTY.) LTD.—See Yankuang Group Co., Limited; *Int'l*, pg. 8562
S.A. RECTICEL INTERNATIONAL SERVICES N.V.—See Recticel S.A.; *Int'l*, pg. 6242
S.A. RECTICEL MANAGEMENT SERVICES N.V.—See Recticel S.A.; *Int'l*, pg. 6242
SAREC TOULOUSE—See FAYAT SAS; *Int'l*, pg. 2626
SA RECYCLING LLC—See Sims Limited; *U.S. Public*, pg. 1883
SAREEN & ASSOCIATES, INC.; *U.S. Private*, pg. 3550
SAREGAMA INDIA LIMITED; *Int'l*, pg. 6577
SAREGAMA LIMITED—See Saregama India Limited; *Int'l*, pg. 6577
SAREGAMA PLC.—See Saregama India Limited; *Int'l*, pg. 6577
SARE HOLDING, S.A.B. DE C.V.; *Int'l*, pg. 6577
SAREL - APPAREILLAGE ELECTRIQUE SAS—See Schneider Electric SE; *Int'l*, pg. 6629
SARELEM—See Altawest Group; *Int'l*, pg. 388
SAREL LTD—See Schneider Electric SE; *Int'l*, pg. 6629
SARENET S.A.U; *Int'l*, pg. 6577
SAREPTA THERAPEUTICS, INC.; *U.S. Public*, pg. 1841
SARES-REGIS GROUP; *U.S. Private*, pg. 3550
SAREUM HOLDINGS PLC; *Int'l*, pg. 6577
SAREUM LIMITED—See Sareum Holdings plc; *Int'l*, pg. 6577
SARGENT AEROSPACE & DEFENSE, LLC—See RBC Bearings Incorporated; *U.S. Public*, pg. 1766
SARGENT BICKHAM LAGUDIS LLC—See Colorado Financial Management, Inc.; *U.S. Private*, pg. 974
SARGENT CORPORATION; *U.S. Private*, pg. 3550
SARGENT ELECTRIC COMPANY; *U.S. Private*, pg. 3550
SARGENT & GREENLEAF, INC.—See OpenGate Capital Management, LLC; *U.S. Private*, pg. 3031
SARGENT & GREENLEAF S.A.—See OpenGate Capital Management, LLC; *U.S. Private*, pg. 3031
SARGENT & LUNDY LLC; *U.S. Private*, pg. 3550
SARGENT MANUFACTURING COMPANY—See ASSA ABLOY AB; *Int'l*, pg. 636
SARGENT METAL FABRICATING—See Todd & Sargent, Inc.; *U.S. Private*, pg. 4181
SARGENTO FOODS INC. - CONSUMER PRODUCTS DIVISION—See Sargento Foods Inc.; *U.S. Private*, pg. 3550
SARGENTO FOODS INC. - FOOD SERVICE DIVISION—See Sargento Foods Inc.; *U.S. Private*, pg. 3550
SARGENTO FOODS INC.; *U.S. Private*, pg. 3550
SARGENTO FOODS INC.—See Sargento Foods Inc.; *U.S. Private*, pg. 3550
SARGENT S.A.; *Int'l*, pg. 6577
SARGENT TRUCKING INC.; *U.S. Private*, pg. 3550
SARGODHA SPINNING MILLS LIMITED; *Int'l*, pg. 6577
SARGON CAPITAL PTY LTD.; *Int'l*, pg. 6577
SARHAD TEXTILE MILLS LIMITED; *Int'l*, pg. 6577

SARIA BIO-INDUSTRIES AG & CO. KG—See RETHMANN AG & Co. KG; *Int'l*, pg. 6309
SARIA BIO-INDUSTRIES BELARUS—See RETHMANN AG & Co. KG; *Int'l*, pg. 6309
SARIA BIO-INDUSTRIES ESPANA, S.L.U.—See RETHMANN AG & Co. KG; *Int'l*, pg. 6309
SARIA BIO-INDUSTRIES VOLGA LTD.—See RETHMANN AG & Co. KG; *Int'l*, pg. 6309
SARIA HUNGARY KFT.—See RETHMANN AG & Co. KG; *Int'l*, pg. 6309
SARIA INDUSTRIES SAS—See RETHMANN AG & Co. KG; *Int'l*, pg. 6309
SARIA MALOPOLSKA SP.Z.O.O.—See RETHMANN AG & Co. KG; *Int'l*, pg. 6309
SARIA POLSKA SP. Z O.O.—See RETHMANN AG & Co. KG; *Int'l*, pg. 6309
SARIA SE & CO KG—See RETHMANN AG & Co. KG; *Int'l*, pg. 6309
SARI FOODS, LLC—See Aterian, Inc.; *U.S. Public*, pg. 221
SARINA & DISTRICT COMMUNITY FINANCIAL SERVICES LIMITED—See Bendigo & Adelaide Bank Ltd.; *Int'l*, pg. 971
SARINE TECHNOLOGIES LTD.; *Int'l*, pg. 6577
SARIN GROUP PTY LTD; *Int'l*, pg. 6577
SARIO GRUNDSTUCKS-VERMIETUNGSGESELLSCHAFT MBH & CO. OBJEKT ELFI—See Ball Corporation; *U.S. Public*, pg. 268
THE SARI PAN PACIFIC JAKARTA—See UOL Group Limited; *Int'l*, pg. 8086
SARI SA—See Ermewa Interservices Sarl; *Int'l*, pg. 2494
SARIS CYCLING GROUP, INC.—See C&A Marketing, Inc.; *U.S. Private*, pg. 702
SARISSA CAPITAL ACQUISITION CORP.; *U.S. Public*, pg. 1841
SARISSA RESOURCES, INC.; *Int'l*, pg. 6577
SARITOW SPINNING MILLS LIMITED; *Int'l*, pg. 6577
SARIYER TANKERCILIK A.S.—See Koc Holding A.S.; *Int'l*, pg. 4223
SARKES TARZIAN INC.; *U.S. Private*, pg. 3550
SARKIS GROUP INTERNATIONAL SAL; *Int'l*, pg. 6577
SARKUYSAN ELEKTROLITIK BAKIR SANAYI VE TICARET A.S.; *Int'l*, pg. 6578
SARKUYSAN S.P.A—See Sarkuysan Elektrolitik Bakir Sanayi Ve Ticaret A.S.; *Int'l*, pg. 6578
SARLA EUROPE LDA—See Sarla Performance Fibers Limited; *Int'l*, pg. 6578
SARLAFLEX INC.—See Sarla Performance Fibers Limited; *Int'l*, pg. 6578
SARLA PERFORMANCE FIBERS LIMITED; *Int'l*, pg. 6578
SARL BUSINESS & DECISION LILLE—See Orange S.A.; *Int'l*, pg. 5608
SARL CHAMEXPRESS.COM—See Mobico Group PLC.; *Int'l*, pg. 5009
SARL CIEPTAL—See Catering International & Services S.A.; *Int'l*, pg. 1360
SARL CLINIQUE MAISON BLANCHE—See Clariane SE; *Int'l*, pg. 1644
SARL COMI SERVICE—See Altrad Investment Authority SAS; *Int'l*, pg. 398
SARL CONEC FRANCE—See Amphenol Corporation; *U.S. Public*, pg. 132
SARL DENTIUM MAROC—See Dentium Co., Ltd; *Int'l*, pg. 2034
SARLEC SAS—See VINCI S.A.; *Int'l*, pg. 8227
SARL EMMETI - FIV FRANCE—See Rettig Group Ltd.; *Int'l*, pg. 6311
SARL ESPACE EXPANSION IMMOBILIERE—See Unibail-Rodamco-Westfield SE; *Int'l*, pg. 8030
SARL FONCIERE ATLAND REIM—See Fonciere Atland SA; *Int'l*, pg. 2724
SARL GLOBAL SERVICE INDUSTRY—See Doga; *Int'l*, pg. 2154
SARL HIRAM—See Lloyds Banking Group plc; *Int'l*, pg. 4538
SARL JEAN-MARC BROCARD; *Int'l*, pg. 6578
S.A.R.L JUST SEARCH—See Oniva Online Group Europe AB; *Int'l*, pg. 5581
SARL KIRIACOULIS POINT D' AMURE—See Kiriacoulis Mediterranean Cruises Shipping S.A.; *Int'l*, pg. 4186
SARL LEMEE—See EDP - Energias de Portugal, S.A.; *Int'l*, pg. 2315
SARL LOISEAU DES DUCS—See Bernard Loiseau SA; *Int'l*, pg. 986
SARL MSCA MEDITERRANEAN SHIPPING COMPANY—See Mediterranean Shipping Company, S.A.; *Int'l*, pg. 4784
SARL NATURAL SWEDISH COSMETICS—See Oriflame Cosmetics S.A.; *Int'l*, pg. 5628
SARL OUTILUX—See Einhell Germany AG; *Int'l*, pg. 2334
S.A.R.L. PACIFIQUE PNEUS—See Bridgestone Corporation; *Int'l*, pg. 1160
SARL RED SEA HOUSING SERVICES ALGERIA LIMITED—See Dabbagh Group Holding Company Ltd.; *Int'l*, pg. 1903
SARL RESIDENCE DE BALBIGNY—See Emeis SA; *Int'l*, pg. 2376

S.A.R.L. ROOM SERVICE—See Delivery Hero SE; *Int'l*, pg. 2013
SARL SCHNEIDER ELECTRIC ALGERIE—See Schneider Electric SE; *Int'l*, pg. 6629
SARL SOTRANASA-TELEVIDEOCOM—See Solutions 30 SE; *Int'l*, pg. 7077
SARL THERMES DE CONTREXEVILLE—See Groupe Partouche S.A.; *Int'l*, pg. 3109
SARLUX S.R.L.—See Angelo Moratti S.A.P.A.; *Int'l*, pg. 460
SARL VENT PORTANT—See Kiriacoulis Mediterranean Cruises Shipping S.A.; *Int'l*, pg. 4186
SARMA AFARIN COMPANY; *Int'l*, pg. 6578
SARMAKINA SANAYI VE TICARET A.S.—See Sarkuysan Elektrolitik Bakir Sanayi Ve Ticaret A.S.; *Int'l*, pg. 6578
SARNAFIL LTD.—See Sika AG; *Int'l*, pg. 6917
SARNOFF CORPORATION—See SRI International; *U.S. Private*, pg. 3768
SARNOVA, INC.—See Investor AB; *Int'l*, pg. 3787
SA RODAMCO FRANCE—See Unibail-Rodamco-Westfield SE; *Int'l*, pg. 8030
SAROJA PHARMA INDUSTRIES INDIA LIMITED; *Int'l*, pg. 6578
SAROPH SWEDEN AB—See Thermo Fisher Scientific Inc.; *U.S. Public*, pg. 2152
SAROVA HOTEL GROUP LTD.; *Int'l*, pg. 6578
SAROYAN LUMBER COMPANY INC.; *U.S. Private*, pg. 3550
SARPES BEVERAGES, LLC—See Hygrovest Limited; *Int'l*, pg. 3549
THE SARPES GROUP, INC.; *U.S. Private*, pg. 4114
SARPI DOROG KFT.—See Veolia Environnement S.A.; *Int'l*, pg. 8159
SARP INDUSTRIES-LIMAY—See Veolia Environnement S.A.; *Int'l*, pg. 8159
SARRACCO MECHANICAL SERVICES INC.; *U.S. Private*, pg. 3550
SARRASOLA SAS—See VINCI S.A.; *Int'l*, pg. 8227
SARREID, LTD.; *U.S. Private*, pg. 3550
SARRELL DENTAL; *U.S. Private*, pg. 3550
SARSYS-ASFT AB; *Int'l*, pg. 6578
SARTEN AMBALAJ SANAYI VE TICARET A.S.; *Int'l*, pg. 6578
SARTEN AMBALAJ SRL—See Sarten Ambalaj Sanayi ve Ticaret A.S.; *Int'l*, pg. 6578
SARTEN AMBALAZA DOO—See Sarten Ambalaj Sanayi ve Ticaret A.S.; *Int'l*, pg. 6578
SARTEN BULGARIA LTD.—See Sarten Ambalaj Sanayi ve Ticaret A.S.; *Int'l*, pg. 6578
SARTEN PACKAGING NETHERLANDS B.V.—See Sarten Ambalaj Sanayi ve Ticaret A.S.; *Int'l*, pg. 6578
SARTHAK INDUSTRIES LIMITED; *Int'l*, pg. 6578
SARTHAK METALS LIMITED; *Int'l*, pg. 6578
SARTHE AUTOMOBILES; *Int'l*, pg. 6578
SARTIN LEE TRUCKING CO. INC.; *U.S. Private*, pg. 3551
SARTOGOSM ZAO—See Sartorius AG; *Int'l*, pg. 6579
SARTOMA S.A.—See Sartorius AG; *Int'l*, pg. 6579
SARTOMER ASIA LIMITED—See Arkema S.A.; *Int'l*, pg. 569
SARTOMER (GUANGZHOU) CHEMICALS CO., LTD.—See Arkema S.A.; *Int'l*, pg. 571
SARTOMER USA, LLC—See Arkema S.A.; *Int'l*, pg. 569
SARTOMER USA, LLC—See Arkema S.A.; *Int'l*, pg. 569
SARTOMER USA, LLC—See Arkema S.A.; *Int'l*, pg. 569
SARTORI COMPANY; *U.S. Private*, pg. 3551
SARTORI INSPIRATIONS, LLC—See Sartori Company; *U.S. Private*, pg. 3551
SARTORI SUD S.R.L.—See Salini Costruttori S.p.A.; *Int'l*, pg. 6493
SARTORIUS AG; *Int'l*, pg. 6578
SARTORIUS ARGENTINA S.A.—See Sartorius AG; *Int'l*, pg. 6579
SARTORIUS AUSTRALIA PTY. LTD.—See Sartorius AG; *Int'l*, pg. 6579
SARTORIUS AUSTRIA GMBH—See Sartorius AG; *Int'l*, pg. 6579
SARTORIUS BELGIUM N.V.—See Sartorius AG; *Int'l*, pg. 6579
SARTORIUS BIOHIT LIQUID HANDLING OY—See Sartorius AG; *Int'l*, pg. 6579
SARTORIUS CANADA INC.—See Sartorius AG; *Int'l*, pg. 6579
SARTORIUS CORPORATE ADMINISTRATION GMBH—See Sartorius AG; *Int'l*, pg. 6579
SARTORIUS CORPORATION—See Sartorius AG; *Int'l*, pg. 6579
SARTORIUS CORPORATION—See Sartorius AG; *Int'l*, pg. 6580
SARTORIUS DE MEXICO S.A. DE C.V.—See Sartorius AG; *Int'l*, pg. 6579
SARTORIUS DO BRASIL LTDA.—See Sartorius AG; *Int'l*, pg. 6579
SARTORIUS FRANCE S.A.S.—See Sartorius AG; *Int'l*, pg. 6579
SARTORIUS HONG KONG LTD.—See Sartorius AG; *Int'l*, pg. 6579
SARTORIUS HUNGARY KFT.—See Sartorius AG; *Int'l*, pg. 6579

SARTORIUS ICR OOO—See Sartorius AG; *Int'l*, pg. 6579
SARTORIUS INDIA PVT. LTD.—See Sartorius AG; *Int'l*, pg. 6579
SARTORIUS INTEC—See Sartorius AG; *Int'l*, pg. 6579
SARTORIUS IRELAND LTD.—See Sartorius AG; *Int'l*, pg. 6579
SARTORIUS ITALY S.R.L.—See Sartorius AG; *Int'l*, pg. 6579
SARTORIUS JAPAN K.K.—See Sartorius AG; *Int'l*, pg. 6579
SARTORIUS KOREA BIOTECH CO., LTD.—See Sartorius AG; *Int'l*, pg. 6579
SARTORIUS KOREA LTD.—See Sartorius AG; *Int'l*, pg. 6579
SARTORIUS LAB HOLDING GMBH—See Sartorius AG; *Int'l*, pg. 6579
SARTORIUS LAB INSTRUMENTS GMBH & CO. KG—See Sartorius AG; *Int'l*, pg. 6579
SARTORIUS MALAYSIA SDN. BHD.—See Sartorius AG; *Int'l*, pg. 6579
SARTORIUS MECHATRONICS AUSTRALIA PTY. LTD.—See Sartorius AG; *Int'l*, pg. 6579
SARTORIUS MECHATRONICS AUSTRIA GMBH—See Sartorius AG; *Int'l*, pg. 6579
SARTORIUS MECHATRONICS BELGIUM N.V.—See Sartorius AG; *Int'l*, pg. 6579
SARTORIUS MECHATRONICS CANADA INC.—See Sartorius AG; *Int'l*, pg. 6580
SARTORIUS MECHATRONICS C&D GMBH & CO. KG—See Sartorius AG; *Int'l*, pg. 6579
SARTORIUS MECHATRONICS HONG KONG LTD.—See Sartorius AG; *Int'l*, pg. 6579
SARTORIUS MECHATRONICS HUNGARIA KFT.—See Sartorius AG; *Int'l*, pg. 6579
SARTORIUS MECHATRONICS ITALY S.R.L.—See Sartorius AG; *Int'l*, pg. 6579
SARTORIUS MECHATRONICS JAPAN K.K.—See Sartorius AG; *Int'l*, pg. 6579
SARTORIUS MECHATRONICS KOREA LTD.—See Sartorius AG; *Int'l*, pg. 6579
SARTORIUS MECHATRONICS PHILIPPINES INC.—See Sartorius AG; *Int'l*, pg. 6579
SARTORIUS MECHATRONICS SPAIN S.A.—See Sartorius AG; *Int'l*, pg. 6579
SARTORIUS MECHATRONICS SWITZERLAND AG—See Sartorius AG; *Int'l*, pg. 6579
SARTORIUS NETHERLANDS B.V.—See Sartorius AG; *Int'l*, pg. 6580
SARTORIUS NORDIC A/S—See Sartorius AG; *Int'l*, pg. 6580
SARTORIUS NORTH AMERICA INC.—See Sartorius AG; *Int'l*, pg. 6580
SARTORIUS POLAND SP. Z O.O.—See Sartorius AG; *Int'l*, pg. 6580
SARTORIUS S.A.—See Sartorius AG; *Int'l*, pg. 6580
SARTORIUS SCIENTIFIC INSTRUMENTS (BEIJING) CO. LTD—See Sartorius AG; *Int'l*, pg. 6580
SARTORIUS SINGAPORE PTE. LTD.—See Sartorius AG; *Int'l*, pg. 6580
SARTORIUS SINGAPORE PTE. LTD.—See Sartorius AG; *Int'l*, pg. 6580
SARTORIUS SPAIN S.A.—See Sartorius AG; *Int'l*, pg. 6580
SARTORIUS STEDIM ASEPTICS S.A.—See Sartorius AG; *Int'l*, pg. 6580
SARTORIUS STEDIM AUSTRALIA PTY. LTD.—See Sartorius AG; *Int'l*, pg. 6580
SARTORIUS STEDIM AUSTRIA GMBH—See Sartorius AG; *Int'l*, pg. 6580
SARTORIUS STEDIM BELGIUM N.V.—See Sartorius AG; *Int'l*, pg. 6580
SARTORIUS STEDIM BIOOUTSOURCE LTD.—See Sartorius AG; *Int'l*, pg. 6580
SARTORIUS STEDIM BIOPROCESS S.A.R.L.—See Sartorius AG; *Int'l*, pg. 6580
SARTORIUS STEDIM BIOTECH (BEIJING) CO. LTD.—See Sartorius AG; *Int'l*, pg. 6580
SARTORIUS STEDIM BIOTECH GMBH—See Sartorius AG; *Int'l*, pg. 6580
SARTORIUS STEDIM BIOTECH S.A.—See Sartorius AG; *Int'l*, pg. 6580
SARTORIUS STEDIM FILTERS INC.—See Sartorius AG; *Int'l*, pg. 6580
SARTORIUS STEDIM FRANCE S.A.S—See Sartorius AG; *Int'l*, pg. 6580
SARTORIUS STEDIM HUNGARIA KFT.—See Sartorius AG; *Int'l*, pg. 6580
SARTORIUS STEDIM INDIA PVT. LTD.—See Sartorius AG; *Int'l*, pg. 6580
SARTORIUS STEDIM IRELAND LTD.—See Sartorius AG; *Int'l*, pg. 6580
SARTORIUS STEDIM ITALY S.P.A.—See Sartorius AG; *Int'l*, pg. 6580
SARTORIUS STEDIM JAPAN K.K.—See Sartorius AG; *Int'l*, pg. 6580
SARTORIUS STEDIM LAB LTD.—See Sartorius AG; *Int'l*, pg. 6580
SARTORIUS STEDIM MALAYSIA SDN. BHD.—See Sartorius AG; *Int'l*, pg. 6580

SARTORIUS STEDIM NETHERLANDS B.V.—See Sartorius AG; *Int'l*, pg. 6580
SARTORIUS STEDIM NORTH AMERICA INC.—See Sartorius AG; *Int'l*, pg. 6580
SARTORIUS STEDIM PLASTICS GMBH—See Sartorius AG; *Int'l*, pg. 6580
SARTORIUS STEDIM POLAND SP. Z O.O.—See Sartorius AG; *Int'l*, pg. 6580
SARTORIUS STEDIM SINGAPORE PTE. LTD.—See Sartorius AG; *Int'l*, pg. 6580
SARTORIUS STEDIM SPAIN S.A.—See Sartorius AG; *Int'l*, pg. 6580
SARTORIUS STEDIM SUS INC.—See Sartorius AG; *Int'l*, pg. 6580
SARTORIUS STEDIM SWITZERLAND AG—See Sartorius AG; *Int'l*, pg. 6580
SARTORIUS STEDIM SYSTEMS GMBH—See Sartorius AG; *Int'l*, pg. 6580
SARTORIUS STEDIM UK LTD.—See Sartorius AG; *Int'l*, pg. 6580
SARTORIUS TCC COMPANY—See Sartorius AG; *Int'l*, pg. 6580
SARTORIUS TECHNOLOGIES N.V.—See Sartorius AG; *Int'l*, pg. 6580
SARTORIUS (THAILAND) CO. LTD.—See Sartorius AG; *Int'l*, pg. 6579
SARTORIUS UK LIMITED—See Sartorius AG; *Int'l*, pg. 6580
SARTORIUS UK LTD.—See Sartorius AG; *Int'l*, pg. 6580
SARTORIUS VIETNAM CO. LTD.—See Sartorius AG; *Int'l*, pg. 6581
SARTORIUS WEIGHING INDIA PVT. LTD.—See Sartorius AG; *Int'l*, pg. 6581
SARTORIUS WEIGHING TECHNOLOGY GMBH—See Sartorius AG; *Int'l*, pg. 6581
SARTOR STORSENTER AS—See Olav Thon Eiendomsselskap ASA; *Int'l*, pg. 5552
SARTRA INTERNATIONAL LTD; *Int'l*, pg. 6581
SARULLA OPERATION LTD.—See PT Medco Energi Internasional Tbk; *Int'l*, pg. 6055
SARUP INDUSTRIES LIMITED; *Int'l*, pg. 6581
THE SARUT GROUP; *U.S. Private*, pg. 4114
SARVAMANGAL MERCANTILE COMPANY LIMITED; *Int'l*, pg. 6581
SARVESHWAR FOODS LTD.; *Int'l*, pg. 6581
SARVIK CORP.; *U.S. Private*, pg. 3551
SARVOTTAM FINVEST LIMITED; *Int'l*, pg. 6581
SARWAJA TIMUR SDN. BHD.—See Sarawak Cable Berhad; *Int'l*, pg. 6576
SARY KAZNA LLP—See Central Asia Metals plc; *Int'l*, pg. 1404
SARYTOGAN GRAPHITE LIMITED; *Int'l*, pg. 6581
S.A.S 3DCERAM-SINTO—See Sintokogio Ltd.; *Int'l*, pg. 6958
SASA APAC PTE. LTD.—See BH Global Corporation Limited; *Int'l*, pg. 1009
SASA BROTHERS, INC.; *U.S. Private*, pg. 3552
SAS AB; *Int'l*, pg. 6581
SASA COSMETICS AGRICULTURAL COOPERATIVE SOCIETY LTD.—See Shaniv Paper Industries Ltd.; *Int'l*, pg. 6784
SA SA INTERNATIONAL HOLDINGS LIMITED; *Int'l*, pg. 6459
SAS AIRLINE—See SAS AB; *Int'l*, pg. 6581
SASAKI ASSOCIATES INC.; *U.S. Private*, pg. 3552
SASAKI—See Sasaki Associates Inc.; *U.S. Private*, pg. 3552
SASAKURA ENGINEERING CO., LTD.; *Int'l*, pg. 6582
SASAKURA INTERNATIONAL (H.K.) CO., LTD.—See Sasakura Engineering Co., Ltd.; *Int'l*, pg. 6582
SASAKURA TAIWAN CO., LTD.—See Sasakura Engineering Co., Ltd.; *Int'l*, pg. 6582
SAS ALTAVIA SAINT-ETIENNE—See Altavia S.A.; *Int'l*, pg. 388
SAS AMIENS GLISY—See Eurazeo SE; *Int'l*, pg. 2529
SAS AND COMPANY LIMITED—See MacAndrews & Forbes Incorporated; *U.S. Private*, pg. 2533
SASANI FILMS CORP.; *U.S. Private*, pg. 3552
S.A. SAN MIGUEL A.G.I.C.I. Y F; *Int'l*, pg. 6448
SASA POLYESTER SANAYI AS; *Int'l*, pg. 6582
SASATECH AGRICULTURAL COOPERATIVE SOCIETY LTD.—See Shaniv Paper Industries Ltd.; *Int'l*, pg. 6784
SASATOKU PRINTING CO., LTD.; *Int'l*, pg. 6582
SAS AUTOMATION LLC—See Investor AB; *Int'l*, pg. 3787
SAS AUTOSYSTEMTECHNIK VERWALTUNGS GMBH—See Samvardhana Motherson International Limited; *Int'l*, pg. 6518
SASAYA SHOTEN CO., LTD—See Nissui Corporation; *Int'l*, pg. 5379
SASBADI HOLDINGS BERHAD; *Int'l*, pg. 6582
SAS BELAIR—See ELGI Equipments Limited; *Int'l*, pg. 2360
S.A.S. BELTER—See Kering S.A.; *Int'l*, pg. 4136
SAS CARBIOLICE—See Carbios SACA; *Int'l*, pg. 1320
SASCAR TECNOLOGIA E SEGURANZA AUTOMOTIVA S.A.—See Compagnie Generale des Etablissements Michelin SCA; *Int'l*, pg. 1745

SAS CENTRE EUROPEEN DE SERVICE HORLOGER—See The Swatch Group Ltd.; *Int'l*, pg. 7692
S.A. SCHIESSER INTERNATIONAL N.V.—See GMM Capital LLC; *U.S. Private*, pg. 1722
S.A. SCHINDLER N.V.—See Schindler Holding AG; *Int'l*, pg. 6619
SAS CLIPS HIOLLE—See Hiolle Industries S.A.; *Int'l*, pg. 3401
SASCO CHEMICAL GROUP, LLC—See Polymer Solutions (PSI); *U.S. Private*, pg. 3226
SASCO ELECTRIC; *U.S. Private*, pg. 3552
SASCO ELECTRIC—See Sasco Electric; *U.S. Private*, pg. 3552
SASCO ELECTRIC—See Sasco Electric; *U.S. Private*, pg. 3552
SASCO INSURANCE SERVICES INC.; *U.S. Private*, pg. 3552
S.A.S COLRUYT DISTRIBUTION FRANCE—See Colruyt Group N.V.; *Int'l*, pg. 1705
SASCO SARL—See CVC Capital Partners SICAV-FIS S.A.; *Int'l*, pg. 1882
SAS CRISTALLERIE DE SAINT PAUL—See Cerinnov Group SA; *Int'l*, pg. 1422
SAS DECTRON COMPANY—See Madison Industries Holdings LLC; *U.S. Private*, pg. 2543
SAS DECTRON COMPANY—See Madison Industries Holdings LLC; *U.S. Private*, pg. 2543
SAS DES DOMAINES DE LA BASTIDE ET DE LA CROIX—See Financiere de L'Odet; *Int'l*, pg. 2667
SAS DOMAINE ROLLAN DE BY; *Int'l*, pg. 6581
S.A.S. DORIA AUTOMOBILES; *Int'l*, pg. 6449
S.A.S. DRAGON HOLDINGS LIMITED; *Int'l*, pg. 6449
SAS DU PETIT LAC—See Derichebourg S.A.; *Int'l*, pg. 2042
SAS EAUDISSE; *Int'l*, pg. 6581
SASEBO HEAVY INDUSTRIES CO., LTD.—See Namura Shipbuilding Co., Ltd.; *Int'l*, pg. 5136
SASEBO METAL CO., LTD.—See Kurimoto Ltd; *Int'l*, pg. 4340
S.A.S. E.C.M.,—See Noveko International Inc.; *Int'l*, pg. 5461
SASE COMPANY, LLC—See Blue Point Capital Partners, LLC; *U.S. Private*, pg. 590
SAS EGYPT LLC—See SAS Institute Inc.; *U.S. Private*, pg. 3551
S.A.S. ELECTRONIC COMPANY LIMITED—See S.A.S. Dragon Holdings Limited; *Int'l*, pg. 6449
S.A.S. ENTERPRISES COMPANY LIMITED—See S.A.S. Dragon Holdings Limited; *Int'l*, pg. 6449
S.A.S. ENTERPRISES COMPANY LIM—See S.A.S. Dragon Holdings Limited; *Int'l*, pg. 6449
SAS ERE PLASTIQUE—See Plastiques du Val de Loire S.A.; *Int'l*, pg. 5892
S & A SERVICE UND ANWENDUNGSTECHNIK GMBH—See Rentokil Initial plc; *Int'l*, pg. 6289
SAS EUROPE AUTO; *Int'l*, pg. 6581
SAS EUROSALMO—See Austevoll Seafood ASA; *Int'l*, pg. 717
SAS FABRICAUTO—See 3M Company; *U.S. Public*, pg. 6
SASFIN ASIA LIMITED—See Sasfin Holdings Limited; *Int'l*, pg. 6582
SASFIN ASSET MANAGERS (PTY) LIMITED—See Sasfin Holdings Limited; *Int'l*, pg. 6582
SASFIN BANK LIMITED—See Sasfin Holdings Limited; *Int'l*, pg. 6582
SASFIN FINANCIAL ADVISORY SERVICES (PTY) LIMITED—See Sasfin Holdings Limited; *Int'l*, pg. 6582
SASFIN HOLDINGS LIMITED; *Int'l*, pg. 6582
SASFIN INSURANCE BROKERS (PTY) LIMITED—See Sasfin Holdings Limited; *Int'l*, pg. 6582
SASFIN WEALTH (PTY). LTD.—See Sasfin Holdings Limited; *Int'l*, pg. 6582
SAS FRIGNIDIS; *Int'l*, pg. 6581
SAS GASCOGNE FLEXIBLE—See Gascogne SA; *Int'l*, pg. 2888
S A S GAUTHIER; *Int'l*, pg. 6442
SAS GLOBAL; *U.S. Private*, pg. 3551
SASHA HANDBAGS INC.; *U.S. Private*, pg. 3552
SAS HOTEL LE RECIF—See Lux Island Resorts Ltd; *Int'l*, pg. 4587
SASHWAT TECHNOCRATS LIMITED; *Int'l*, pg. 6582
SASIB S.P.A.—See MPAC Group PLC; *Int'l*, pg. 5060
SASID; *U.S. Private*, pg. 3552
SASIL S.P.A.—See Gruppo Minerali Maffei S.p.A.; *Int'l*, pg. 3140
SASINI PLC; *Int'l*, pg. 6582
SAS INNOVATION COMPANY LIMITED—See SNC Holding Company Limited; *Int'l*, pg. 7025
SAS INSCHOOL—See SAS Institute Inc.; *U.S. Private*, pg. 3552
SAS INSTITUTE AB—See SAS Institute Inc.; *U.S. Private*, pg. 3551
SAS INSTITUTE AG—See SAS Institute Inc.; *U.S. Private*, pg. 3551
SAS INSTITUTE A/S—See SAS Institute Inc.; *U.S. Private*, pg. 3551
SAS INSTITUTE A/S—See SAS Institute Inc.; *U.S. Private*, pg. 3551

SAS INSTITUTE AUSTRALIA PTY. LTD.—See SAS Institute Inc.; *U.S. Private*, pg. 3551
SAS INSTITUTE B.V.—See SAS Institute Inc.; *U.S. Private*, pg. 3551
SAS INSTITUTE (CANADA), INC.—See SAS Institute Inc.; *U.S. Private*, pg. 3551
SAS INSTITUTE CR, S.R.O.—See SAS Institute Inc.; *U.S. Private*, pg. 3551
SAS INSTITUTE GMBH—See SAS Institute Inc.; *U.S. Private*, pg. 3551
SAS INSTITUTE INC. - SHERMAN OAKS—See SAS Institute Inc.; *U.S. Private*, pg. 3551
SAS INSTITUTE INC.; *U.S. Private*, pg. 3551
SAS INSTITUTE INC.—See SAS Institute Inc.; *U.S. Private*, pg. 3551
SAS INSTITUTE INC.—See SAS Institute Inc.; *U.S. Private*, pg. 3551
SAS INSTITUTE (INDIA) PVT. LTD.—See SAS Institute Inc.; *U.S. Private*, pg. 3551
SAS INSTITUTE JAPAN LTD.—See SAS Institute Inc.; *U.S. Private*, pg. 3551
SAS INSTITUTE KFT.—See SAS Institute Inc.; *U.S. Private*, pg. 3551
SAS INSTITUTE LTD.—See SAS Institute Inc.; *U.S. Private*, pg. 3551
SAS INSTITUTE LTD.—See SAS Institute Inc.; *U.S. Private*, pg. 3551
SAS INSTITUTE LTD.—See SAS Institute Inc.; *U.S. Private*, pg. 3551
SAS INSTITUTE N.V.—See SAS Institute Inc.; *U.S. Private*, pg. 3551
SAS INSTITUTE (NZ) LTD.—See SAS Institute Inc.; *U.S. Private*, pg. 3551
SAS INSTITUTE OU—See SAS Institute Inc.; *U.S. Private*, pg. 3551
SAS INSTITUTE OY—See SAS Institute Inc.; *U.S. Private*, pg. 3551
SAS INSTITUTE (PHILIPPINES), INC.—See SAS Institute Inc.; *U.S. Private*, pg. 3551
SAS INSTITUTE PTE. LTD.—See SAS Institute Inc.; *U.S. Private*, pg. 3552
SAS INSTITUTE SARL—See SAS Institute Inc.; *U.S. Private*, pg. 3552
SAS INSTITUTE SA—See SAS Institute Inc.; *U.S. Private*, pg. 3552
SAS INSTITUTE S.A.U.—See SAS Institute Inc.; *U.S. Private*, pg. 3552
SAS INSTITUTE SDN. BHD.—See SAS Institute Inc.; *U.S. Private*, pg. 3552
SAS INSTITUTE—See SAS Institute Inc.; *U.S. Private*, pg. 3551
SAS INSTITUTE SRL—See SAS Institute Inc.; *U.S. Private*, pg. 3552
SAS INSTITUTE TAIWAN LTD.—See SAS Institute Inc.; *U.S. Private*, pg. 3552
SAS INTERNATIONAL APOLLO PARK FACTORY—See SAS International; *Int'l*, pg. 6581
SAS INTERNATIONAL BRIDGEND FACTORY—See SAS International; *Int'l*, pg. 6581
SAS INTERNATIONAL—See SAS International; *Int'l*, pg. 6581
SAS INTERNATIONAL; *Int'l*, pg. 6581
SAS ISEULT—See Unibail-Rodamco-Westfield SE; *Int'l*, pg. 8030
S.A.S. JAMBON ET FILS; *Int'l*, pg. 6449
S.A.S. JSC; *Int'l*, pg. 6449
SASKATCHEWAN GOVERNMENT INSURANCE—See Crown Investments Corporation of Saskatchewan; *Int'l*, pg. 1857
SASKATCHEWAN MINERALS INC.; *Int'l*, pg. 6582
SASKATCHEWAN OPPORTUNITIES CORPORATION—See Crown Investments Corporation of Saskatchewan; *Int'l*, pg. 1857
SASKATCHEWAN POWER CORPORATION—See Crown Investments Corporation of Saskatchewan; *Int'l*, pg. 1857
SASKATCHEWAN TELECOMMUNICATIONS HOLDINGS CORPORATION—See Crown Investments Corporation of Saskatchewan; *Int'l*, pg. 1857
SASKATCHEWAN TRANSPORTATION COMPANY—See Crown Investments Corporation of Saskatchewan; *Int'l*, pg. 1857
SASKATCHEWAN WATER CORPORATION—See Crown Investments Corporation of Saskatchewan; *Int'l*, pg. 1857
SASKATOON COLOSTRUM COMPANY LTD.—See Koepon Holdings B.V.; *Int'l*, pg. 4227
SASKATOON MOTOR PRODUCTS LTD.—See AutoCanada Inc.; *Int'l*, pg. 726
SASKCAN HORIZON TRADING INC.—See AGT Food and Ingredients Inc.; *Int'l*, pg. 221
SASKENERGY INC.—See Crown Investments Corporation of Saskatchewan; *Int'l*, pg. 1857
SASKEN TECHNOLOGIES LIMITED; *Int'l*, pg. 6582
SASKO PASTA (PTY) LTD—See PepsiCo, Inc.; *U.S. Public*, pg. 1672
SASKPOWER INTERNATIONAL—See Crown Investments Corporation of Saskatchewan; *Int'l*, pg. 1857
SAS LA LOUISIANE—See Clariane SE; *Int'l*, pg. 1644

SAS LA TOISON D'OR—See Unibail-Rodamco-Westfield SE; *Int'l*, pg. 8030
SAS LA VILLA DU PARC—See Clariane SE; *Int'l*, pg. 1644
SAS LE CHATEAU D'EBBLINGHEM—See Cox & Kings Limited; *Int'l*, pg. 1823
SAS LEROY SEAFOOD FRANCE—See Austevoll Seafood ASA; *Int'l*, pg. 717
S.A.S. LIGHTING COMPANY LIMITED—See S.A.S. Dragon Holdings Limited; *Int'l*, pg. 6449
SAS LOISEAU DES SENS—See Bernard Loiseau SA; *Int'l*, pg. 986
SAS LYON MEZIEU—See Eurazeo SE; *Int'l*, pg. 2529
SAS MAYBOLE—See SAS International; *Int'l*, pg. 6581
SAS MECATEL—See Hiolle Industries S.A.; *Int'l*, pg. 3401
SAS MICHEZ; *Int'l*, pg. 6581
SAS MURUETS; *Int'l*, pg. 6582
SAS NORMANDIE HABITAT—See Societe Generale S.A.; *Int'l*, pg. 7040
SASOL AUGUSTA S.P.A.—See Sasol Limited; *Int'l*, pg. 6582
SASOL CHEMICAL INDUSTRIES LTD.—See Sasol Limited; *Int'l*, pg. 6582
SASOL CHEMICALS EUROPE LIMITED—See Sasol Limited; *Int'l*, pg. 6583
SASOL CHEMICALS PACIFIC LIMITED—See Sasol Limited; *Int'l*, pg. 6583
SASOL CHEMIE GMBH—See Sasol Limited; *Int'l*, pg. 6583
SASOL CHIMICA D.A.C. S.P.A.—See Sasol Limited; *Int'l*, pg. 6583
SASOL FINANCING (PTY) LTD—See Sasol Limited; *Int'l*, pg. 6583
SASOL FUEL OIL—See Sasol Limited; *Int'l*, pg. 6583
SASOL GAS HOLDINGS (PTY) LTD—See Sasol Limited; *Int'l*, pg. 6583
SASOL GAS LIMITED—See Sasol Limited; *Int'l*, pg. 6583
SASOL GERMANY GMBH—See Sasol Limited; *Int'l*, pg. 6583
SASOL GROUP SERVICES (PTY) LTD—See Sasol Limited; *Int'l*, pg. 6583
SASOL-HUNTSMAN VERWALTUNGS-GMBH—See Huntsman Corporation; *U.S. Public*, pg. 1075
SASOL INVESTMENT COMPANY (PTY) LTD—See Sasol Limited; *Int'l*, pg. 6583
SASOL ITALY SPA—See Sasol Limited; *Int'l*, pg. 6583
SASOL LIMITED; *Int'l*, pg. 6582
SASOL MINING HOLDINGS (PTY) LTD—See Sasol Limited; *Int'l*, pg. 6583
SASOL MINING—See Sasol Limited; *Int'l*, pg. 6583
SASOL NANJING CHEMICAL COMPANY—See Sasol Limited; *Int'l*, pg. 6583
SASOL NITRO—See Sasol Limited; *Int'l*, pg. 6583
SASOL NORTH AMERICA INC.—See Sasol Limited; *Int'l*, pg. 6583
SASOL OIL (PTY) LTD.—See Sasol Limited; *Int'l*, pg. 6583
SASOL OIL—See Sasol Limited; *Int'l*, pg. 6583
SASOL PETROLEUM INTERNATIONAL (PTY) LTD.—See Sasol Limited; *Int'l*, pg. 6583
SASOL POLYMERS INTERNATIONAL INVESTMENTS (PTY) LTD—See Sasol Limited; *Int'l*, pg. 6583
SASOL SOLVENTE—See Sasol Limited; *Int'l*, pg. 6583
SASOL SOLVENT OLEFINS & SURFACTANTS—See Sasol Limited; *Int'l*, pg. 6583
SASOL SOLVENTS & OLEFINS SURFACTANTS—See Sasol Limited; *Int'l*, pg. 6583
SASOL SOLVENTS O&S SOUTH AFRICA—See Sasol Limited; *Int'l*, pg. 6583
SASOL SYNFUELS INTERNATIONAL (PTY) LIMITED—See Sasol Limited; *Int'l*, pg. 6583
SASOL SYNFUELS (PTY) LTD—See Sasol Limited; *Int'l*, pg. 6583
SASOL SYNTHETIC FUELS (PTY.) LTD.—See Sasol Limited; *Int'l*, pg. 6583
SASOL TECHNOLOGY (PTY) LTD—See Sasol Limited; *Int'l*, pg. 6583
SASOL TECHNOLOGY PTY LTD—See Sasol Limited; *Int'l*, pg. 6583
SASOL WAX INTERNATIONAL AG—See Sasol Limited; *Int'l*, pg. 6583
SASOL WAX PTY. LTD.—See Sasol Limited; *Int'l*, pg. 6583
SAS ONDULYS—See VPK Packaging Group NV; *Int'l*, pg. 8312
S.A. SPADEL N.V.; *Int'l*, pg. 6448
SAS PV SENIORIALES PROMOTION ET COMMERCIALISATION—See Pierre & Vacances SA; *Int'l*, pg. 5864
SASQUATCH BOOKS LLC—See Bertelsmann SE & Co. KGaA; *Int'l*, pg. 996
SAS RELEVANT TRAFFIC—See Kinnevik AB; *Int'l*, pg. 4182
SAS RESEARCH & DEVELOPMENT (INDIA) PVT. LTD.—See SAS Institute Inc.; *U.S. Private*, pg. 3552
SAS RESTO BESANCON—See Eurazeo SE; *Int'l*, pg. 2529
SAS RESTO DEV LEON 6 - ARRAS—See Eurazeo SE; *Int'l*, pg. 2529
SAS RESTO METZ—See Eurazeo SE; *Int'l*, pg. 2529
SAS RESTO NANTES—See Eurazeo SE; *Int'l*, pg. 2529

SAS RETAIL SERVICES, LLC—See Bain Capital, LP; *U.S. Private*, pg. 439
SAS RHENUS SVORIS—See RETHMANN AG & Co. KG; *Int'l*, pg. 6309
SAS RUBBER COMPANY—See The Yokohama Rubber Co., Ltd.; *Int'l*, pg. 7703
SASR WORKFORCE SOLUTIONS, LLC; *U.S. Private*, pg. 3552
SAS SAFETY CORP.—See Bunzl plc; *Int'l*, pg. 1218
SASS & BIDE PTY LTD—See Myer Pty Ltd; *Int'l*, pg. 5112
SASS & BIDE RETAIL PTY LTD—See Myer Pty Ltd; *Int'l*, pg. 5112
SAS SB TRADUCTION—See CDS Co., Ltd.; *Int'l*, pg. 1371
S.A.S. SEB—See SEB S.A.; *Int'l*, pg. 6667
SASSER FAMILY HOLDINGS, INC.; *U.S. Private*, pg. 3552
SASSEUR REAL ESTATE INVESTMENT TRUST; *Int'l*, pg. 6583
SAS SFAM—See Unibail-Rodamco-Westfield SE; *Int'l*, pg. 8030
SAS SHIPPING AGENCIES SERVICES SARL—See Mediterranean Shipping Company, S.A.; *Int'l*, pg. 4784
SASSI BTP SAS—See VINCI S.A.; *Int'l*, pg. 8227
SAS SLOVAKIA, S.R.O.—See SAS Institute Inc.; *U.S. Private*, pg. 3552
SASSNITZ FISCH GMBH—See Thai Union Group Public Company Limited; *Int'l*, pg. 7597
SAS SOCIEDADE ADMINISTRADORA DE CENTROS COMERCIAIS LTDA.—See Allos SA; *Int'l*, pg. 359
SAS SOCIETE DE LANCEMENT DE MAGASINS A L'USINE—See Unibail-Rodamco-Westfield SE; *Int'l*, pg. 8030
SAS SOFTWARE KOREA LTD.—See SAS Institute Inc.; *U.S. Private*, pg. 3552
SAS SOFTWARE, LTD.—See SAS Institute Inc.; *U.S. Private*, pg. 3552
SAS SOFTWARE (THAILAND) COMPANY LIMITED.—See SAS Institute Inc.; *U.S. Private*, pg. 3552
SAS SOJAY; *Int'l*, pg. 6582
SASSOU CO.,LTD.—See Nippon Telegraph & Telephone Corporation; *Int'l*, pg. 5355
SAS STERILIZASYON SERVISLERI A.S.—See Servizi Italia SpA; *Int'l*, pg. 6726
SASSY GOLD CORPORATION; *Int'l*, pg. 6583
SASSY, INC.—See Angelcare Holding Inc.; *Int'l*, pg. 459
SASTASUNDAR VENTURES LIMITED; *Int'l*, pg. 6583
SA STONE WEALTH MANAGEMENT INC.—See StoneX Group Inc.; *U.S. Public*, pg. 1953
S&A STORES INC.; *U.S. Private*, pg. 3512
SAS TRADING—See SAS AB; *Int'l*, pg. 6581
SASU BFC CROISSANCE—See Groupe BPCE; *Int'l*, pg. 3099
S&A SUPPLY COMPANY INC.—See Daikin Industries, Ltd.; *Int'l*, pg. 1935
SAS VIPARIS - NORD VILLEPINTE—See Unibail-Rodamco-Westfield SE; *Int'l*, pg. 8030
SAT.1 NORDDEUTSCHLAND GMBH—See ProSiebenSat.1 Media SE; *Int'l*, pg. 6001
SAT.1 SATELLITEN FERNSEHEN GMBH—See ProSiebenSat.1 Media SE; *Int'l*, pg. 6001
SAT.1 SCHWEIZ AG—See ProSiebenSat.1 Media SE; *Int'l*, pg. 6001
SAT.1 SCHWEIZ AG—See Ringier Holding AG; *Int'l*, pg. 6344
SATA CONSTRUCTION CO., LTD.; *Int'l*, pg. 6584
SATA GMBH & CO. KG; *Int'l*, pg. 6584
SATAGO FINANCIAL SOLUTIONS LIMITED—See TruFin plc; *Int'l*, pg. 7941
SATAIR A/S—See Airbus SE; *Int'l*, pg. 244
SATAIR CHINA—See Airbus SE; *Int'l*, pg. 244
SATAIR PTE. LTD.—See Airbus SE; *Int'l*, pg. 244
SATAIR UK—See Airbus SE; *Int'l*, pg. 244
SATAIR USA INC. - MIAMI—See Airbus SE; *Int'l*, pg. 244
SATAIR USA INC.—See Airbus SE; *Int'l*, pg. 244
SAT ALBATROSS SEA AIR TRANSPORT FZE—See Japan Post Holdings Co., Ltd.; *Int'l*, pg. 3901
SATAP S.P.A.—See Argo Finanziaria S.p.A.; *Int'l*, pg. 562
SATA SARL—See Endress+Hauser (International) Holding AG; *Int'l*, pg. 2409
SA TAXI FINANCE HOLDINGS (PTY) LTD—See Transaction Capital Limited; *Int'l*, pg. 7895
SA TAXI PROTECT PROPRIETARY LIMITED—See Transaction Capital Limited; *Int'l*, pg. 7895
SATCHMO HOLDINGS LIMITED; *Int'l*, pg. 6584
SATCO CAPITAL MARKETS LIMITED—See Mangal Credit & Fincorp Limited; *Int'l*, pg. 4669
SAT & CO. HOLDING A.S.—See Fincraft Resources JSC; *Int'l*, pg. 2672
SAT CO., LTD.; *Int'l*, pg. 6584
SATCOM RESOURCES; *U.S. Private*, pg. 3553
SATCO PRODUCTS INC.; *U.S. Private*, pg. 3552
SATCO PRODUCTS INC.—See Satco Products Inc.; *U.S. Private*, pg. 3553
SAT CORPORATION—See Kratos Defense & Security Solutions, Inc.; *U.S. Public*, pg. 1277
SAT COSTA DE NIJAR; *Int'l*, pg. 6584
SATCO WEALTH MANAGER PRIVATE LTD.—See Mangal Credit & Fincorp Limited; *Int'l*, pg. 4669
SATECH K.K.—See Troax Group AB; *Int'l*, pg. 7937

SA TECHNOLOGIES, INC.; *U.S. Private*, pg. 3519
SATECH SAFETY TECHNOLOGY GMBH—See Troax Group AB; *Int'l*, pg. 7937
SATECH SAFETY TECHNOLOGY SARL—See Troax Group AB; *Int'l*, pg. 7938
SATECH SAFETY TECHNOLOGY SPA—See Troax Group AB; *Int'l*, pg. 7938
SATEF HUETTENES ALBERTUS S.P.A.—See Huettenes-Albertus Chemische Werke GmbH; *Int'l*, pg. 3523
SATELCO AG—See Bogen Communications International Inc.; *U.S. Public*, pg. 367
SATELEC—See FAYAT SAS; *Int'l*, pg. 2626
SATEL-FEI, S.A.—See Frequency Electronics, Inc.; *U.S. Public*, pg. 885
SATEL FERNSEH- UND FILMPRODUKTIONS GMBH—See Bavaria Film GmbH; *Int'l*, pg. 899
SATELITES MEXICANOS S.A DE C.V.—See Eutelsat Communications SA; *Int'l*, pg. 2559
SATELIT PRODUTOS PARA LABORATORIOS LTDA—See HORIBA Ltd; *Int'l*, pg. 3478
SATELLITE CHANNELS INC.; *Int'l*, pg. 6584
SATELLITE CHEMICAL CO., LTD.; *Int'l*, pg. 6584
SATELLITE COMM SYSTEMS; *U.S. Private*, pg. 3553
SATELLITE COMMUNICATION LTD.—See Brithol Michcoma Mozambique Limited; *Int'l*, pg. 1165
SATELLITE ENGINEERING GROUP—See WESCO International, Inc.; *U.S. Public*, pg. 2352
SATELLITE HOLDINGS, INC.; *U.S. Private*, pg. 3553
SATELLITE LOGISTICS GROUP, INC.—See Deutsche Post AG; *Int'l*, pg. 2081
SATELLITE SERVICE CO., LTD.—See Fuji Media Holdings, Inc.; *Int'l*, pg. 2814
SATELLOGIC INC.; *U.S. Public*, pg. 1841
SATELLOS BIOSCIENCE INC.; *Int'l*, pg. 6584
SATHAVAHANA ISPAT LIMITED—See Jindal Holdings Limited; *Int'l*, pg. 3966
SATHOSA MOTORS PLC; *Int'l*, pg. 6584
SATIA INDUSTRIES LIMITED; *Int'l*, pg. 6584
SATIC, INC.; *U.S. Private*, pg. 3553
SATICOY FOODS CORPORATION—See Moody Dunbar Inc.; *U.S. Private*, pg. 2778
SATILLA RURAL ELECTRIC MEMBERSHIP CORPORATION; *U.S. Private*, pg. 3553
SATIMO INDUSTRIES, SA—See Microwave Vision SA; *Int'l*, pg. 4882
SATIN CREDITCARE NETWORK LIMITED; *Int'l*, pg. 6584
SAT INDUSTRIES LTD.; *Int'l*, pg. 6584
SATIN HOUSING FINANCE LIMITED—See Satin Creditcare Network Limited; *Int'l*, pg. 6584
SATIOGEN PHARMACEUTICALS, INC.—See Mirum Pharmaceuticals, Inc.; *U.S. Public*, pg. 1450
SATIPHARM AG—See Hygrovest Limited; *Int'l*, pg. 3549
SATISFIED BRAKE PRODUCTS INC.; *Int'l*, pg. 6584
SATIS GROUP SA; *Int'l*, pg. 6584
SATISLOH AG—See EssilorLuxottica SA; *Int'l*, pg. 2516
SATISLOH ASIA LTD.—See EssilorLuxottica SA; *Int'l*, pg. 2516
SATISLOH DO BRASIL LTDA—See EssilorLuxottica SA; *Int'l*, pg. 2516
SATISLOH GMBH—See EssilorLuxottica SA; *Int'l*, pg. 2516
SATISLOH IBERICA SL—See EssilorLuxottica SA; *Int'l*, pg. 2516
SATISLOH ITALY SPA—See EssilorLuxottica SA; *Int'l*, pg. 2516
SATISLOH NORTH AMERICA INC—See EssilorLuxottica SA; *Int'l*, pg. 2514
SATISLOH PHOTONICS AG—See EssilorLuxottica SA; *Int'l*, pg. 2516
SATISLOH ZHONGSHAN LTD—See EssilorLuxottica SA; *Int'l*, pg. 2516
SATIVA WELLNESS GROUP INC.; *Int'l*, pg. 6584
SATIVUS TECH CORP.; *U.S. Public*, pg. 1841
SATIXFY COMMUNICATIONS LTD.; *Int'l*, pg. 6584
SATKAR FINLEASE LIMITED; *Int'l*, pg. 6585
SATLAN SP. Z.O.O—See Teleste Corporation; *Int'l*, pg. 7541
SATMA—See Vicat S.A.; *Int'l*, pg. 8185
SATMATIC OY—See Harju Elekter AS; *Int'l*, pg. 3277
SATMETRIX SYSTEMS, INC.; *U.S. Private*, pg. 3553
SATO AMERICA, INC.—See SATO Holdings Corporation; *Int'l*, pg. 6585
SATO AMOY CONSTRUCTION (MALAYSIA)—See Toda Corporation; *Int'l*, pg. 7772
SATO ARGENTINA S.A.—See SATO Holdings Corporation; *Int'l*, pg. 6585
SATO ARGOX INDIA PVT. LTD.—See SATO Holdings Corporation; *Int'l*, pg. 6585
SATO ASIA PACIFIC PTE LTD.—See SATO Holdings Corporation; *Int'l*, pg. 6585
SATO AUSTRALIA PTY LTD.—See SATO Holdings Corporation; *Int'l*, pg. 6585
SATO AUTO-ID DO BRASIL LTDA.—See SATO Holdings Corporation; *Int'l*, pg. 6585
SATO AUTO-ID INDIA PRIVATE LIMITED—See SATO Holdings Corporation; *Int'l*, pg. 6585
SATO AUTO-ID MALAYSIA SDN. BHD.—See SATO Holdings Corporation; *Int'l*, pg. 6585

COMPANY NAME INDEX

SATO AUTO-ID (THAILAND) CO., LTD.—See SATO Holdings Corporation; *Int'l*, pg. 6585
SATOB CONSTRUCTION BOIS—See VINCI S.A.; *Int'l*, pg. 8226
SATO BENELUX B.V.—See SATO Holdings Corporation; *Int'l*, pg. 6585
SATO CHEMICAL GLASS (SUZHOU) CO., LTD.—See Sato shoji Corporation; *Int'l*, pg. 6586
SATO CHEMIGLASS CORPORATION—See Sato shoji Corporation; *Int'l*, pg. 6586
SATO CORPORATION—See SATO Holdings Corporation; *Int'l*, pg. 6585
SATO EUROPE GMBH—See SATO Holdings Corporation; *Int'l*, pg. 6585
SATO FOODS CO., LTD.; *Int'l*, pg. 6585
SATO FOODS INDUSTRIES CO.,LTD.; *Int'l*, pg. 6585
SATO FRANCE S.A.S.—See SATO Holdings Corporation; *Int'l*, pg. 6585
SATO GENETEC CORPORATION—See Sato shoji Corporation; *Int'l*, pg. 6586
SATO GERMANY GMBH—See SATO Holdings Corporation; *Int'l*, pg. 6585
SATOH & CO., LTD.; *Int'l*, pg. 6586
SATO HEALTHCARE CO., LTD.—See SATO Holdings Corporation; *Int'l*, pg. 6585
SATO HOLDINGS CORPORATION; *Int'l*, pg. 6585
SATO IBERIA S. A. U.—See SATO Holdings Corporation; *Int'l*, pg. 6585
SATO IMPRESS CO., LTD.—See SATO Holdings Corporation; *Int'l*, pg. 6585
SATO INTERNATIONAL EUROPE N. V.—See SATO Holdings Corporation; *Int'l*, pg. 6585
SATO KOGYO BANGKOK CO., LTD.—See Toda Corporation; *Int'l*, pg. 7773
SATO KOGYO (CAMBODIA) CO., LTD.—See Toda Corporation; *Int'l*, pg. 7772
SATO KOGYO CO., LTD.—See Toda Corporation; *Int'l*, pg. 7772
SATO KOGYO (M) SDN. BHD.—See Toda Corporation; *Int'l*, pg. 7773
SATO KOGYO (SINGAPORE) PTE.LTD.—See Toda Corporation; *Int'l*, pg. 7773
SATO KOGYO (XI'AN) CO., LTD.—See Toda Corporation; *Int'l*, pg. 7773
SATO LABELLING POLAND SP. Z O. O.—See SATO Holdings Corporation; *Int'l*, pg. 6585
SATO LOGISTICS CO., LTD.—See SATO Holdings Corporation; *Int'l*, pg. 6585
SATO MALAYSIA ELECTRONICS MANUFACTURING SDN. BHD.—See SATO Holdings Corporation; *Int'l*, pg. 6585
SATO MUSEN CO., LTD.—See Yamada Holdings Co., Ltd.; *Int'l*, pg. 8548
SATO NEW ZEALAND LTD.—See SATO Holdings Corporation; *Int'l*, pg. 6585
SATO PHILIPPINES AIDC SOLUTIONS INC.; *Int'l*, pg. 6586
SATO PHILIPPINES AUTO-ID SP INC.; *Int'l*, pg. 6586
SATO PRINT CONNECT HONG KONG LTD.—See SATO Holdings Corporation; *Int'l*, pg. 6585
SATO PRODUCTIVITY SOLUTIONS MEXICO S.A. DE C.V.—See SATO Holdings Corporation; *Int'l*, pg. 6586
SATOR HOLDING B.V.—See LKQ Corporation; *U.S. Public*, pg. 1336
SATORI CAPITAL, LLC; *U.S. Private*, pg. 3553
SATORI ELECTRIC CO., LTD.; *Int'l*, pg. 6586
SATORI ELECTRIC GERMANY GMBH—See SATORI ELECTRIC CO., LTD.; *Int'l*, pg. 6587
SATORI E-TECHNOLOGY (AMERICA) INC.—See SATORI ELECTRIC CO., LTD.; *Int'l*, pg. 6587
SATORI PINICS CO., LTD.—See SATORI ELECTRIC CO., LTD.; *Int'l*, pg. 6587
SATORI PINICS HONG KONG CO., LTD—See SATORI ELECTRIC CO., LTD.; *Int'l*, pg. 6587
SATORI PINICS (SINGAPORE) PTE LTD.—See SATORI ELECTRIC CO., LTD.; *Int'l*, pg. 6587
SATORI PINICS (THAILAND) CO., LTD.—See SATORI ELECTRIC CO., LTD.; *Int'l*, pg. 6587
SATORI RESOURCES INC.; *Int'l*, pg. 6587
SATORI SOFTWARE INC.—See Platinum Equity, LLC; *U.S. Private*, pg. 3202
SATORI SP TECHNOLOGY CO., LTD.—See SATORI ELECTRIC CO., LTD.; *Int'l*, pg. 6587
SATORY GLOBAL, LLC; *U.S. Private*, pg. 3553
SATOSANGYO CO., LTD.; *Int'l*, pg. 6587
SATO SANGYO VIETNAM CO., LTD.—See SatoSangyo Co., Ltd.; *Int'l*, pg. 6587
SATO S.A.; *Int'l*, pg. 6586
SATO SCHNEIDSYSTEME ANTON HUBERT E. K.; *Int'l*, pg. 6586
SATOSEN CO., LTD.—See Arisawa Manufacturing Co., Ltd.; *Int'l*, pg. 566
SATO SHANGHAI CO., LTD.—See SATO Holdings Corporation; *Int'l*, pg. 6585
SATO SHOJI ASIA PACIFIC PTE. LTD.—See Sato shoji Corporation; *Int'l*, pg. 6586
SATO-SHOJI (CAMBODIA) CO., LTD.—See Sato shoji Corporation; *Int'l*, pg. 6586
SATO SHOJI CORPORATION; *Int'l*, pg. 6586

SATO SHOJI (GUANGZHOU) CO., LTD.—See Sato shoji Corporation; *Int'l*, pg. 6586
SATO SHOJI HONG KONG CO., LTD.—See Sato shoji Corporation; *Int'l*, pg. 6586
SATO-SHOJI INDIA PRIVATE LIMITED—See Sato shoji Corporation; *Int'l*, pg. 6586
SATO SHOJI KOREA CO., LTD.—See Sato shoji Corporation; *Int'l*, pg. 6586
SATO SHOJI SHANGHAI CO., LTD.—See Sato shoji Corporation; *Int'l*, pg. 6586
SATO SHOJI (SHENZHEN) CO., LTD.—See Sato shoji Corporation; *Int'l*, pg. 6586
SATO-SHOJI(THAILAND) CO., LTD.—See Sato shoji Corporation; *Int'l*, pg. 6586
SATO-SHOJI (VIETNAM) CO., LTD.—See Sato shoji Corporation; *Int'l*, pg. 6586
SATO SOLUTION ARCHITECTS CO., LTD.—See SATO Holdings Corporation; *Int'l*, pg. 6586
SATO TAIWAN CO., LTD.; *Int'l*, pg. 6586
SATO TECHNO LAB EUROPE AB—See SATO Holdings Corporation; *Int'l*, pg. 6585
SATO TECHNO SERVICE (THAILAND) CO., LTD.—See Sato shoji Corporation; *Int'l*, pg. 6586
SATO UK LTD.—See SATO Holdings Corporation; *Int'l*, pg. 6585
SATO VICINITY PTY. LTD.—See SATO Holdings Corporation; *Int'l*, pg. 6585
SATO VIETNAM CO., LTD.—See SATO Holdings Corporation; *Int'l*, pg. 6585
SATO VIETNAM SOLUTIONS CO., LTD.—See SATO Holdings Corporation; *Int'l*, pg. 6585
SATRAC ENGINEERING PRIVATE LIMITED—See Kyokuto Kaihatsu Kogyo Co. Ltd.; *Int'l*, pg. 4363
SA TRANSPORTS AUTOMOBILES DE SOLOGNE; *Int'l*, pg. 6459
SATRA PROPERTIES (INDIA) LTD.; *Int'l*, pg. 6587
SATRA SA—See Eiffage S.A.; *Int'l*, pg. 2331
SATREC INITIATIVE CO., LTD.; *Int'l*, pg. 6587
SATS AERO LAUNDRY PTE. LTD.—See Temasek Holdings (Private) Limited; *Int'l*, pg. 7550
SATS AIRPORT SERVICES PTE.LTD.—See Temasek Holdings (Private) Limited; *Int'l*, pg. 7550
SATS ACA; *Int'l*, pg. 6587
SATSERVICE GESELLSCHAFT FUR KOMMUNIKATIONS-SYSTEME MBH—See Calian Group Ltd.; *Int'l*, pg. 1264
SATS HK LIMITED—See Hainan Traffic Administration Holding Co., Ltd.; *Int'l*, pg. 3215
SATS HK LIMITED—See Temasek Holdings (Private) Limited; *Int'l*, pg. 7550
SATS LTD.—See Temasek Holdings (Private) Limited; *Int'l*, pg. 7550
SAT SP. Z O.O—See STRABAG SE; *Int'l*, pg. 7232
SAT S.R.O.—See STRABAG SE; *Int'l*, pg. 7232
SAT STRASSENSANIERUNG GMBH—See STRABAG SE; *Int'l*, pg. 7232
SATSUKI KIZAI CO., LTD.—See Futaba Corporation; *Int'l*, pg. 2851
SATSUMA PHARMACEUTICALS, INC.—See Shin Nippon Biomedical Laboratories, Ltd.; *Int'l*, pg. 6837
SATSUMA SUISAN CO., LTD.—See Nissui Corporation; *Int'l*, pg. 5379
SAT (SURFACE ALUMINIUM TECHNOLOGIES) S.R.L.—See Graco, Inc.; *U.S. Public*, pg. 954
SAT SYSTEMY AUTOMATIZACNEJ TECHNIKY SPOL. S.R.O.—See Siemens Aktiengesellschaft; *Int'l*, pg. 6888
SATTERFIELD & PONTIKES CONSTRUCTION, INC.; *U.S. Private*, pg. 3553
SATTERWHITE COMPANIES INC.; *U.S. Private*, pg. 3553
SATTLER AG; *Int'l*, pg. 6587
SATTLER CENO BIOGAS GMBH—See SATTLER AG; *Int'l*, pg. 6587
SATTLER CORPORATION—See SATTLER AG; *Int'l*, pg. 6587
SATTLER GMBH—See SATTLER AG; *Int'l*, pg. 6587
SATTLER ITALIA S.R.L.—See SATTLER AG; *Int'l*, pg. 6587
SATTLER ROMANIA S.R.L.—See SATTLER AG; *Int'l*, pg. 6587
SATTLER SCHWEIZ GMBH—See SATTLER AG; *Int'l*, pg. 6587
SATTLER TEXTILES SARL—See SATTLER AG; *Int'l*, pg. 6587
SATUDORA HOLDINGS CO., LTD.; *Int'l*, pg. 6587
SATU HOLDINGS LIMITED; *Int'l*, pg. 6587
SATUIT TECHNOLOGIES, INC.—See Dura Software Series A Qof LLC; *U.S. Private*, pg. 1292
SATURDAY CO., LTD.; *Int'l*, pg. 6587
SATURDAY EVENING POST SOCIETY; *U.S. Private*, pg. 3553
SATURDAY GROUP LTD; *Int'l*, pg. 6588
SATURDAY KNIGHT LTD.; *U.S. Private*, pg. 3553
SATURNA CAPITAL CORPORATION; *U.S. Private*, pg. 3553
SATURN BRUGGE NV—See Ceconomy AG; *Int'l*, pg. 1385

SATURN CORPORATION

SATURN BUDA VIDEO TV HIFI ELEKTRO PHOTO COMPUTER KERESKEDELMI KFT.—See Ceconomy AG; *Int'l*, pg. 1385
SATURN BUSINESS SYSTEMS INC.; *U.S. Private*, pg. 3553
SATURN CORPORATION; *U.S. Private*, pg. 3553
SATURN DUNA VIDEO TV HIFI ELEKTRO PHOTO COMPUTER KERESKEDELMI KFT.—See Ceconomy AG; *Int'l*, pg. 1385
SATURN ELECTRO-HANDELSGESELLSCHAFT MBH AUGSBURG—See Ceconomy AG; *Int'l*, pg. 1385
SATURN ELECTRO-HANDELSGESELLSCHAFT MBH BAD HOMBURG—See Ceconomy AG; *Int'l*, pg. 1385
SATURN ELECTRO-HANDELSGESELLSCHAFT MBH BAUNATAL—See Ceconomy AG; *Int'l*, pg. 1385
SATURN ELECTRO-HANDELSGESELLSCHAFT MBH BERLIN-KOPENICK—See Ceconomy AG; *Int'l*, pg. 1385
SATURN ELECTRO-HANDELSGESELLSCHAFT MBH BERLIN-LEIPZIGER PLATZ—See Ceconomy AG; *Int'l*, pg. 1385
SATURN ELECTRO-HANDELSGESELLSCHAFT MBH BERLIN-MARKISCHE ZEILE—See Ceconomy AG; *Int'l*, pg. 1385
SATURN ELECTRO-HANDELSGESELLSCHAFT MBH BERLIN-MARZAHN—See Ceconomy AG; *Int'l*, pg. 1385
SATURN ELECTRO-HANDELSGESELLSCHAFT MBH BERLIN-SCHLO15STRA15E—See Ceconomy AG; *Int'l*, pg. 1385
SATURN ELECTRO-HANDELSGESELLSCHAFT MBH BERLIN-TREPTOW—See Ceconomy AG; *Int'l*, pg. 1385
SATURN ELECTRO-HANDELSGESELLSCHAFT MBH BOCHOLT—See Ceconomy AG; *Int'l*, pg. 1385
SATURN ELECTRO-HANDELSGESELLSCHAFT MBH BOCHUM—See Ceconomy AG; *Int'l*, pg. 1385
SATURN ELECTRO-HANDELSGESELLSCHAFT MBH BRAUNSCHWEIG—See Ceconomy AG; *Int'l*, pg. 1385
SATURN ELECTRO-HANDELSGESELLSCHAFT MBH BREMEN-HABENHAUSEN—See Ceconomy AG; *Int'l*, pg. 1385
SATURN ELECTRO-HANDELSGESELLSCHAFT MBH BREMEN—See Ceconomy AG; *Int'l*, pg. 1385
SATURN ELECTRO-HANDELSGESELLSCHAFT MBH CELLE—See Ceconomy AG; *Int'l*, pg. 1385
SATURN ELECTRO-HANDELSGESELLSCHAFT MBH CHEMNITZ—See Ceconomy AG; *Int'l*, pg. 1386
SATURN ELECTRO-HANDELSGESELLSCHAFT MBH CHEMNITZ-ZENTRUM—See Ceconomy AG; *Int'l*, pg. 1386
SATURN ELECTRO-HANDELSGESELLSCHAFT MBH DARMSTADT—See Ceconomy AG; *Int'l*, pg. 1386
SATURN ELECTRO-HANDELSGESELLSCHAFT MBH DELMENHORST—See Ceconomy AG; *Int'l*, pg. 1386
SATURN ELECTRO-HANDELSGESELLSCHAFT MBH DORTMUND-EVING—See Ceconomy AG; *Int'l*, pg. 1386
SATURN ELECTRO-HANDELSGESELLSCHAFT MBH DORTMUND—See Ceconomy AG; *Int'l*, pg. 1386
SATURN ELECTRO-HANDELSGESELLSCHAFT MBH DRESDEN—See Ceconomy AG; *Int'l*, pg. 1386
SATURN ELECTRO-HANDELSGESELLSCHAFT MBH DUISBURG—See Ceconomy AG; *Int'l*, pg. 1386
SATURN ELECTRO-HANDELSGESELLSCHAFT MBH ERFURT—See Ceconomy AG; *Int'l*, pg. 1386
SATURN ELECTRO-HANDELSGESELLSCHAFT MBH ERLANGEN—See Ceconomy AG; *Int'l*, pg. 1386
SATURN ELECTRO-HANDELSGESELLSCHAFT MBH ESSEN—See Ceconomy AG; *Int'l*, pg. 1386
SATURN ELECTRO-HANDELSGESELLSCHAFT MBH ESSLINGEN—See Ceconomy AG; *Int'l*, pg. 1386
SATURN ELECTRO-HANDELSGESELLSCHAFT MBH EUSKIRCHEN—See Ceconomy AG; *Int'l*, pg. 1386
SATURN ELECTRO-HANDELSGESELLSCHAFT MBH FLENSBURG—See Ceconomy AG; *Int'l*, pg. 1386
SATURN ELECTRO-HANDELSGESELLSCHAFT MBH FRANKFURT/MAIN—See Ceconomy AG; *Int'l*, pg. 1386
SATURN ELECTRO-HANDELSGESELLSCHAFT MBH FREIBURG—See Ceconomy AG; *Int'l*, pg. 1386
SATURN ELECTRO-HANDELSGESELLSCHAFT MBH FREISING—See Ceconomy AG; *Int'l*, pg. 1386
SATURN ELECTRO-HANDELSGESELLSCHAFT MBH FURTH—See Ceconomy AG; *Int'l*, pg. 1386
SATURN ELECTRO-HANDELSGESELLSCHAFT MBH GOTTINGEN—See Ceconomy AG; *Int'l*, pg. 1386
SATURN ELECTRO-HANDELSGESELLSCHAFT MBH GUMMERSBACH—See Ceconomy AG; *Int'l*, pg. 1386
SATURN ELECTRO-HANDELSGESELLSCHAFT MBH HAGEN—See Ceconomy AG; *Int'l*, pg. 1386
SATURN ELECTRO-HANDELSGESELLSCHAFT MBH HAMBURG-ALTSTADT—See Ceconomy AG; *Int'l*, pg. 1386
SATURN ELECTRO-HANDELSGESELLSCHAFT MBH HAMM—See Ceconomy AG; *Int'l*, pg. 1386
SATURN ELECTRO-HANDELSGESELLSCHAFT MBH HANAU—See Ceconomy AG; *Int'l*, pg. 1386

SATURN CORPORATION — CORPORATE AFFILIATIONS

SATURN ELECTRO-HANDELSGESELLSCHAFT MBH HANNOVER—See Ceconomy AG; *Int'l*, pg. 1386
SATURN ELECTRO-HANDELSGESELLSCHAFT MBH HATTINGEN—See Ceconomy AG; *Int'l*, pg. 1386
SATURN ELECTRO-HANDELSGESELLSCHAFT MBH HILDEN—See Ceconomy AG; *Int'l*, pg. 1386
SATURN ELECTRO-HANDELSGESELLSCHAFT MBH INGOLSTADT—See Ceconomy AG; *Int'l*, pg. 1386
SATURN ELECTRO-HANDELSGESELLSCHAFT MBH ISERNHAGEN—See Ceconomy AG; *Int'l*, pg. 1386
SATURN ELECTRO-HANDELSGESELLSCHAFT MBH JENA—See Ceconomy AG; *Int'l*, pg. 1386
SATURN ELECTRO-HANDELSGESELLSCHAFT MBH KAISERSLAUTERN—See Ceconomy AG; *Int'l*, pg. 1386
SATURN ELECTRO-HANDELSGESELLSCHAFT MBH KARLSRUHE-DURLACH—See Ceconomy AG; *Int'l*, pg. 1386
SATURN ELECTRO-HANDELSGESELLSCHAFT MBH KASSEL—See Ceconomy AG; *Int'l*, pg. 1386
SATURN ELECTRO-HANDELSGESELLSCHAFT MBH KEMPTEN—See Ceconomy AG; *Int'l*, pg. 1386
SATURN ELECTRO-HANDELSGESELLSCHAFT MBH KERPEN—See Ceconomy AG; *Int'l*, pg. 1386
SATURN ELECTRO-HANDELSGESELLSCHAFT MBH KIEL—See Ceconomy AG; *Int'l*, pg. 1386
SATURN ELECTRO-HANDELSGESELLSCHAFT MBH KLEVE—See Ceconomy AG; *Int'l*, pg. 1386
SATURN ELECTRO-HANDELSGESELLSCHAFT MBH KOBLENZ—See Ceconomy AG; *Int'l*, pg. 1386
SATURN ELECTRO-HANDELSGESELLSCHAFT MBH KREFELD—See Ceconomy AG; *Int'l*, pg. 1386
SATURN ELECTRO-HANDELSGESELLSCHAFT MBH LANDSHUT—See Ceconomy AG; *Int'l*, pg. 1386
SATURN ELECTRO-HANDELSGESELLSCHAFT MBH LEIPZIG-HAUPTBAHNHOF—See Ceconomy AG; *Int'l*, pg. 1386
SATURN ELECTRO-HANDELSGESELLSCHAFT MBH LEIPZIG—See Ceconomy AG; *Int'l*, pg. 1386
SATURN ELECTRO-HANDELSGESELLSCHAFT MBH LEONBERG—See Ceconomy AG; *Int'l*, pg. 1386
SATURN ELECTRO-HANDELSGESELLSCHAFT MBH LUBECK—See Ceconomy AG; *Int'l*, pg. 1386
SATURN ELECTRO-HANDELSGESELLSCHAFT MBH LUDENSCHEID—See Ceconomy AG; *Int'l*, pg. 1387
SATURN ELECTRO-HANDELSGESELLSCHAFT MBH LUDWIGSBURG—See Ceconomy AG; *Int'l*, pg. 1387
SATURN ELECTRO-HANDELSGESELLSCHAFT MBH LUDWIGSHAFEN—See Ceconomy AG; *Int'l*, pg. 1387
SATURN ELECTRO-HANDELSGESELLSCHAFT MBH LUNEN—See Ceconomy AG; *Int'l*, pg. 1387
SATURN ELECTRO-HANDELSGESELLSCHAFT MBH MAGDEBURG—See Ceconomy AG; *Int'l*, pg. 1387
SATURN ELECTRO-HANDELSGESELLSCHAFT MBH MAINZ—See Ceconomy AG; *Int'l*, pg. 1387
SATURN ELECTRO-HANDELSGESELLSCHAFT MBH MANNHEIM—See Ceconomy AG; *Int'l*, pg. 1387
SATURN ELECTRO-HANDELSGESELLSCHAFT MBH MARL—See Ceconomy AG; *Int'l*, pg. 1387
SATURN ELECTRO-HANDELSGESELLSCHAFT MBH MOERS—See Ceconomy AG; *Int'l*, pg. 1387
SATURN ELECTRO-HANDELSGESELLSCHAFT MBH MULHEIM—See Ceconomy AG; *Int'l*, pg. 1387
SATURN ELECTRO-HANDELSGESELLSCHAFT MBH MUNCHEN—See Ceconomy AG; *Int'l*, pg. 1387
SATURN ELECTRO-HANDELSGESELLSCHAFT MBH MUNSTER—See Ceconomy AG; *Int'l*, pg. 1387
SATURN ELECTRO-HANDELSGESELLSCHAFT MBH NECKARSULM—See Ceconomy AG; *Int'l*, pg. 1387
SATURN ELECTRO-HANDELSGESELLSCHAFT MBH NEU-ISENBURG—See Ceconomy AG; *Int'l*, pg. 1387
SATURN ELECTRO-HANDELSGESELLSCHAFT MBH NORDERSTEDT—See Ceconomy AG; *Int'l*, pg. 1387
SATURN ELECTRO-HANDELSGESELLSCHAFT MBH NURNBERG—See Ceconomy AG; *Int'l*, pg. 1387
SATURN ELECTRO-HANDELSGESELLSCHAFT MBH OBERHAUSEN—See Ceconomy AG; *Int'l*, pg. 1387
SATURN ELECTRO-HANDELSGESELLSCHAFT MBH OLDENBURG—See Ceconomy AG; *Int'l*, pg. 1387
SATURN ELECTRO-HANDELSGESELLSCHAFT MBH PADERBORN—See Ceconomy AG; *Int'l*, pg. 1387
SATURN ELECTRO-HANDELSGESELLSCHAFT MBH PASSAU—See Ceconomy AG; *Int'l*, pg. 1387
SATURN ELECTRO-HANDELSGESELLSCHAFT MBH PFORZHEIM—See Ceconomy AG; *Int'l*, pg. 1387
SATURN ELECTRO-HANDELSGESELLSCHAFT MBH POTSDAM—See Ceconomy AG; *Int'l*, pg. 1387
SATURN ELECTRO-HANDELSGESELLSCHAFT MBH REGENSBURG—See Ceconomy AG; *Int'l*, pg. 1387
SATURN ELECTRO-HANDELSGESELLSCHAFT MBH REMSCHEID—See Ceconomy AG; *Int'l*, pg. 1387
SATURN ELECTRO-HANDELSGESELLSCHAFT MBH REUTLINGEN—See Ceconomy AG; *Int'l*, pg. 1387
SATURN ELECTRO-HANDELSGESELLSCHAFT MBH ROSTOCK—See Ceconomy AG; *Int'l*, pg. 1387
SATURN ELECTRO-HANDELSGESELLSCHAFT MBH SAARBRUCKEN—See Ceconomy AG; *Int'l*, pg. 1387
SATURN ELECTRO-HANDELSGESELLSCHAFT MBH SCHWEINFURT—See Ceconomy AG; *Int'l*, pg. 1387
SATURN ELECTRO-HANDELSGESELLSCHAFT MBH SENDEN—See Ceconomy AG; *Int'l*, pg. 1387
SATURN ELECTRO-HANDELSGESELLSCHAFT MBH STUTTGART-CITY—See Ceconomy AG; *Int'l*, pg. 1387
SATURN ELECTRO-HANDELSGESELLSCHAFT MBH TROISDORF—See Ceconomy AG; *Int'l*, pg. 1387
SATURN FASTENERS INC.—See Fontana Luigi S.p.A.; *Int'l*, pg. 2726
SATURN FREIGHT SYSTEMS INC.; *U.S. Private*, pg. 3553
SATURN GERASDORF ELECTRO-HANDELSGES.M.B.H.—See Ceconomy AG; *Int'l*, pg. 1387
SATURN GRAZ V VERTRIEBSGMBH—See Ceconomy AG; *Int'l*, pg. 1387
SATURN GRONINGEN B.V.—See Ceconomy AG; *Int'l*, pg. 1387
SATURN HAID ELECTRO-HANDELSGES.M.B.H—See Ceconomy AG; *Int'l*, pg. 1387
SATURN HEERHUGOWAARD B.V.—See Ceconomy AG; *Int'l*, pg. 1387
SATURN HOOFDDORP B.V.—See Ceconomy AG; *Int'l*, pg. 1387
SATURN INFOTECH, INC.—See Jade Global, Inc.; *U.S. Private*, pg. 2181
SATURN INNSBRUCK ELECTRO-HANDELSGES .M.B.H.—See Ceconomy AG; *Int'l*, pg. 1387
SATURN INTEGRATED LOGISTICS INC.—See Deutsche Post AG; *Int'l*, pg. 2082
SATURN KLAGENFURT ELECTRO-HANDELSGES .M.B.H.—See Ceconomy AG; *Int'l*, pg. 1387
SATURN KORTRIJK N.V.—See Ceconomy AG; *Int'l*, pg. 1387
SATURN LIEGE MEDIACITE N.V.—See Ceconomy AG; *Int'l*, pg. 1385
SATURN LUXEMBOURG S.A.—See Ceconomy AG; *Int'l*, pg. 1387
SATURN MADRID-PLENILUNIO ELEKTRO, S.A.—See Ceconomy AG; *Int'l*, pg. 1385
SATURN-MEGA MARKT GMBH HALLE—See Ceconomy AG; *Int'l*, pg. 1388
SATURN-MEGA MARKT GMBH TRIER—See Ceconomy AG; *Int'l*, pg. 1388
SATURN MEGA MARKT GMBH WUPPERTAL—See Ceconomy AG; *Int'l*, pg. 1387
SATURN MEIR ANTWERPEN—See Ceconomy AG; *Int'l*, pg. 1385
SATURN METALS LIMITED; *Int'l*, pg. 6588
SATURN MONS N.V.—See Ceconomy AG; *Int'l*, pg. 1387
SATURNO DE MEXICO, SA DE CV—See Industrial Dielectrics Holdings, Inc.; *U.S. Private*, pg. 2065
SATURN OF RICHMOND, INC.; *U.S. Private*, pg. 3553
SATURN OIL & GAS INC.; *Int'l*, pg. 6588
SATURN PEST VIDEO TV HIFI ELEKTRO PHOTO COMPUTER KERESKEDELMI KFT.—See Ceconomy AG; *Int'l*, pg. 1385
SATURN PLANET SP. Z O.O. KRAKOW I SPOLKA KOMANDYTOWA—See Ceconomy AG; *Int'l*, pg. 1387
SATURN PLANET SP. Z O.O.—See Ceconomy AG; *Int'l*, pg. 1385
SATURN PLANET SP. Z O.O. TYCHY SPOLKA KOMANDYTOWA—See Ceconomy AG; *Int'l*, pg. 1387
SATURN PLANET SP. Z O.O. WARSZAWA III SPOLKA KOMANDYTOWA—See Ceconomy AG; *Int'l*, pg. 1387
SATURN PLANET SP. Z O.O. WROCLAW II SPOLKA KOMANDYTOWA—See Ceconomy AG; *Int'l*, pg. 1388
SATURN ROTTERDAM ZUIDPLEIN B.V.—See Ceconomy AG; *Int'l*, pg. 1388
SATURN SYSTEMS, INC.—See RBA, Inc.; *U.S. Private*, pg. 3360
SATURN TECHNO-ELECTRO-HANDELSGESELLSCHAFT MBH—See Ceconomy AG; *Int'l*, pg. 1388
SATURN TECHNO-MARKT ELECTRO GMBH & CO. OHG—See Ceconomy AG; *Int'l*, pg. 1388
SATURN TECHNO-MARKT ELECTRO-HANDELSGESELLSCHAFT MBH DUSSELDORF - FLINGERN—See Ceconomy AG; *Int'l*, pg. 1388
SATURN TECHNO-MARKT ELECTRO-HANDELSGESELLSCHAFT MBH—See Ceconomy AG; *Int'l*, pg. 1388
SATURN TENERIFE 3 DE MAYO ELECTRO, S.A.—See Ceconomy AG; *Int'l*, pg. 1385
SATURN TILBURG B.V.—See Ceconomy AG; *Int'l*, pg. 1388
SATURN VOLKETSWIL AG—See Ceconomy AG; *Int'l*, pg. 1385
SATURN WIEN XIV ELECTRO-HANDELSGES.M.B.H.—See Ceconomy AG; *Int'l*, pg. 1388
SATURN WIEN X VERTRIEBSGMBH—See Ceconomy AG; *Int'l*, pg. 1388
SATURN WIEN XXII ELECTRO-HANDELSGES .M.B.H.—See Ceconomy AG; *Int'l*, pg. 1388
SATURN WIEN XXIII ELECTRO-HANDELSGES .M.B.H.—See Ceconomy AG; *Int'l*, pg. 1388
SATURN WIEN XX VERTRIEBSGMBH—See Ceconomy AG; *Int'l*, pg. 1388
SATURN WILRIJK NV—See Ceconomy AG; *Int'l*, pg. 1385
SATUSA CORPORATION; *U.S. Private*, pg. 3553
SAT UTJAVITO KFT.—See STRABAG SE; *Int'l*, pg. 7232
SATYA DEVELOPERS PVT. LTD.; *Int'l*, pg. 6588
SATYA MINERS & TRANSPORTERS LIMITED; *Int'l*, pg. 6588
SATYAM SILK MILLS LIMITED; *Int'l*, pg. 6588
SAUBER MANUFACTURING CO; *U.S. Private*, pg. 3554
SAUCON VALLEY COUNTRY CLUB; *U.S. Private*, pg. 3554
SAUCONY, INC.—See Wolverine World Wide, Inc.; *U.S. Public*, pg. 2377
SAUD AUJAN & BROS. CO.—See Aujan Industries Co., L.L.C.; *Int'l*, pg. 704
SAUDEE GROUP BERHAD; *Int'l*, pg. 6588
SAUDER FUNERAL PRODUCTS—See Sauder Woodworking Co.; *U.S. Private*, pg. 3554
SAUDER MANUFACTURING COMPANY—See Sauder Woodworking Co.; *U.S. Private*, pg. 3554
SAUDER RTA—See Sauder Woodworking Co.; *U.S. Private*, pg. 3554
SAUDER WOODWORKING CO.; *U.S. Private*, pg. 3554
SAUDI ADVANCED INDUSTRIES COMPANY; *Int'l*, pg. 6588
SAUDI AIRLINES CARGO—See Saudi Arabian Airlines; *Int'l*, pg. 6588
SAUDI AMERICAN GLASS COMPANY—See Dubai Investments PJSC; *Int'l*, pg. 2219
SAUDI AMERICAN HOLDINGS CORP.; *U.S. Private*, pg. 3554
SAUDI ARABIA CONCRETE PRODUCTS LTD.—See NOV, Inc.; *U.S. Public*, pg. 1544
SAUDI ARABIA INVESTMENT COMPANY—See Groupe BPCE; *Int'l*, pg. 3099
SAUDI ARABIAN AIRLINES; *Int'l*, pg. 6588
SAUDI ARABIAN AMIANTIT COMPANY; *Int'l*, pg. 6588
SAUDI ARABIAN CHEVRON INC.—See Chevron Corporation; *U.S. Public*, pg. 488
SAUDI ARABIAN COOPERATIVE INSURANCE COMPANY; *Int'l*, pg. 6588
SAUDI ARABIAN DUMEZ CO. LTD—See VINCI S.A.; *Int'l*, pg. 8235
SAUDI ARABIAN INTEGRATED LOGISTIC SYSTEMS—See Al-Hejailan Group; *Int'l*, pg. 286
SAUDI ARABIAN MARKETS LTD.; *Int'l*, pg. 6588
SAUDI ARABIAN MILITARY INDUSTRIES; *Int'l*, pg. 6588
SAUDI ARABIAN MINING COMPANY - MA'ADEN; *Int'l*, pg. 6589
SAUDI ARABIAN MONETARY AGENCY; *Int'l*, pg. 6589
SAUDI ARABIAN OIL COMPANY; *Int'l*, pg. 6589
SAUDI ARABIAN REFINERIES COMPANY; *Int'l*, pg. 6590
SAUDI ARAMCO LUBRICATING OIL REFINING COMPANY—See Exxon Mobil Corporation; *U.S. Public*, pg. 817
SAUDI ARAMCO LUBRICATING OIL REFINING COMPANY—See Saudi Arabian Oil Company; *Int'l*, pg. 6590
SAUDI ARAMCO MOBIL REFINERY COMPANY LTD.—See Exxon Mobil Corporation; *U.S. Public*, pg. 817
SAUDI ARAMCO MOBIL REFINERY COMPANY LTD.—See Saudi Arabian Oil Company; *Int'l*, pg. 6590
SAUDI ARAMCO PRODUCT TRADING COMPANY—See Saudi Arabian Oil Company; *Int'l*, pg. 6590
SAUDI ARAMCO SHELL REFINERY COMPANY—See Saudi Arabian Oil Company; *Int'l*, pg. 6590
SAUDI ARAMCO SHELL REFINERY COMPANY—See Shell plc; *Int'l*, pg. 6797
SAUDI ARAMCO TOTAL REFINING AND PETROCHEMICAL COMPANY—See Saudi Arabian Oil Company; *Int'l*, pg. 6590
SAUDI ARAMCO TOTAL REFINING AND PETROCHEMICAL COMPANY—See TotalEnergies SE; *Int'l*, pg. 7838
SAUDI ASMA ENVIRONMENTAL SOLUTION LLC—See Progressive Impact Corporation Berhad; *Int'l*, pg. 5991
SAUDI AUTOMOBILE & TOURING ASSOCIATION CO.—See Saudi Automotive Services Co.; *Int'l*, pg. 6590
SAUDI AUTOMOTIVE SERVICES CO.; *Int'l*, pg. 6590
SAUDI BASF FOR BUILDING MATERIALS CO. LTD.—See BASF SE; *Int'l*, pg. 884
SAUDI BASIC INDUSTRIES CORPORATION; *Int'l*, pg. 6590
SAUDI BAUER FOUNDATION CONTRACTORS LTD.—See BAUER Aktiengesellschaft; *Int'l*, pg. 894
THE SAUDI BRITISH BANK; *Int'l*, pg. 7680
SAUDI BUILDING SYSTEMS, LTD.—See BlueScope Steel Limited; *Int'l*, pg. 1073
SAUDI CABLE COMPANY—See Xenel Industries Ltd.; *Int'l*, pg. 8521
SAUDI CARBONATE CO. LTD.—See Omya (Schweiz) AG; *Int'l*, pg. 5572
SAUDI CEMENT COMPANY; *Int'l*, pg. 6592
SAUDI CERAMIC COMPANY; *Int'l*, pg. 6592
SAUDI CHEMICAL HOLDING COMPANY; *Int'l*, pg. 6592
SAUDI COMPANY FOR HARDWARE SJSC; *Int'l*, pg. 6593
SAUDI CONSULTING SA—See Saudi Consulting Services; *Int'l*, pg. 6593
SAUDI CONSULTING SERVICES; *Int'l*, pg. 6593

COMPANY NAME INDEX

SAUDI CONSULTING SERVICES—See Saudi Consulting Services; *Int'l*, pg. 6593
SAUDI CRANES & STEEL WORKS FACTORY LLC—See Konecranes Plc; *Int'l*, pg. 4253
SAUDI CRAWFORD DOORS FACTORY LTD.—See ASSA ABLOY AB; *Int'l*, pg. 635
SAUDI CREALOGIX SINGLE-PARTNER LLC—See Constellation Software Inc.; *Int'l*, pg. 1772
SAUDI DAIRY & FOODSTUFF CO. LTD.; *Int'l*, pg. 6593
SAUDI DIGITAL PAYMENTS COMPANY—See Saudi Telecom Company; *Int'l*, pg. 6595
SAUDI EGYPTIAN LOGISTICS AND ELECTRONICS COMPANY, S.A.E.—See Dabbagh Group Holding Company Ltd.; *Int'l*, pg. 1903
SAUDI ELECTRICITY COMPANY; *Int'l*, pg. 6593
SAUDI ELECTRIC SUPPLY COMPANY; *Int'l*, pg. 6593
SAUDI EMIRATES PULVERIZATION INDUSTRIES COMPANY—See RTE Group; *Int'l*, pg. 6420
SAUDI ENAYA COOPERATIVE INSURANCE COMPANY; *Int'l*, pg. 6593
SAUDI ERICSSON COMMUNICATIONS CO.—See Telefonaktiebolaget LM Ericsson; *Int'l*, pg. 7534
SAUDI FACTORY FOR ELECTRICAL APPLIANCES COMPANY LTD.—See Mitsubishi Heavy Industries, Ltd.; *Int'l*, pg. 4961
SAUDI FISHERIES COMPANY; *Int'l*, pg. 6593
SAUDI FLSMIDTH CO.—See FLSmidth & Co. A/S; *Int'l*, pg. 2712
SAUDI FOOD INDUSTRIES LTD.—See Nestle S.A.; *Int'l*, pg. 5211
SAUDI FRANSI CAPITAL LLC—See Banque Saudi Fransi; *Int'l*, pg. 854
SAUDI GROUND SERVICES COMPANY LIMITED; *Int'l*, pg. 6593
SAUDI GULF HYDRAULICS CO., LTD.—See Hydac International GmbH; *Int'l*, pg. 3545
SAUDI HOLLANDI CAPITAL COMPANY—See The Saudi British Bank; *Int'l*, pg. 7680
SAUDI INDUSTRIAL DEVELOPMENT COMPANY; *Int'l*, pg. 6593
SAUDI INDUSTRIAL EXPORT COMPANY; *Int'l*, pg. 6593
SAUDI INDUSTRIAL GAS COMPANY LTD—See Linde plc; *Int'l*, pg. 4508
SAUDI INDUSTRIAL INVESTMENT GROUP; *Int'l*, pg. 6593
SAUDI INDUSTRIAL RESINS LTD.; *Int'l*, pg. 6593
SAUDI INNOVATIVE PLASTICS SWEDEN AB—See Saudi Basic Industries Corporation; *Int'l*, pg. 6592
SAUDI INTEGRATED TELECOM COMPANY; *Int'l*, pg. 6594
SAUDI INVESTMENT BANK; *Int'l*, pg. 6594
SAUDI JOHNSON CO. LTD.—See S.C. Johnson & Son, Inc.; *U.S. Private*, pg. 3517
SAUDI KAYAN PETROCHEMICAL COMPANY; *Int'l*, pg. 6594
SAUDI KNM LTD.—See KNM Group Berhad; *Int'l*, pg. 4209
SAUDI KOREAN HEALTH INFORMATICS COMPANY—See ezCaretech Co., Ltd.; *Int'l*, pg. 2593
SAUDI KUWAITI FINANCE HOUSE KSCC—See Kuwait Finance House K.S.C.; *Int'l*, pg. 4345
SAUDI LIEBHERR COMPANY LTD.—See Liebherr-International AG; *Int'l*, pg. 4491
SAUDI LIME INDUSTRIES COMPANY; *Int'l*, pg. 6594
SAUDI MAINTENANCE & SUPPLY CHAIN MANAGEMENT COMPANY LIMITED—See BAE Systems plc; *Int'l*, pg. 799
SAUDI MAIS COMPANY FOR MEDICAL PRODUCTS—See Arab Supply & Trading Co.; *Int'l*, pg. 532
SAUDI MARKETING COMPANY; *Int'l*, pg. 6594
SAUDI MARTIFER CONSTRUCTIONS LLC—See Martifer SGPS S.A.; *Int'l*, pg. 4703
SAUDI MECHANICAL INDUSTRIES CO.—See Arab Petroleum Investments Corporation; *Int'l*, pg. 531
SAUDI MECHANICAL INDUSTRIES CO.—See Jadwa Investment Company; *Int'l*, pg. 3869
SAUDI METHANOL COMPANY—See Mitsubishi Gas Chemical Company, Inc.; *Int'l*, pg. 4950
SAUDI MODERN COMPANY FOR CABLES INDUSTRY LTD.—See A.K. Al-Muhaidib & Sons Group of Companies; *Int'l*, pg. 24
SAUDI MODERN COMPANY FOR METALS, CABLES AND PLASTIC INDUSTRY LTD.—See A.K. Al-Muhaidib & Sons Group of Companies; *Int'l*, pg. 24
SAUDI MODERN COMPANY FOR SPECIAL ELECTRIC WIRE & CABLES INDUSTRY LTD.—See A.K. Al-Muhaidib & Sons Group of Companies; *Int'l*, pg. 24
SAUDI MODERN COMPANY FOR TELEPHONE CABLE INDUSTRY LTD.—See A.K. Al-Muhaidib & Sons Group of Companies; *Int'l*, pg. 24
SAUDI NETWORKERS SERVICES COMPANY; *Int'l*, pg. 6594
SAUDI NEW ZEALAND MILK PRODUCTS COMPANY LIMITED—See Fonterra Co-Operative Group Ltd.; *Int'l*, pg. 2726
SAUDI ORIX LEASING COMPANY—See ORIX Corporation; *Int'l*, pg. 5636

SAUDI PAK INDUSTRIAL & AGULTURAL INVESTMENT COMPANY LIMITED—See Saudi Pak Leasing Company Limited; *Int'l*, pg. 6594
SAUDI PAK LEASING COMPANY LIMITED; *Int'l*, pg. 6594
SAUDI PAPER MANUFACTURING COMPANY; *Int'l*, pg. 6594
SAUDI PHARMACEUTICAL DISTRIBUTION CO. LTD.—See Novartis AG; *Int'l*, pg. 5459
SAUDI PHARMACEUTICAL INDUSTRIES & MEDICAL APPLIANCES CORPORATION; *Int'l*, pg. 6594
SAUDI PLASTIC PACKAGING SYSTEM COMPANY—See Takween Advanced Industries; *Int'l*, pg. 7443
SAUDI POLYMERS COMPANY—See SAUDI INDUSTRIAL INVESTMENT GROUP; *Int'l*, pg. 6593
SAUDI POLYOLEFINS CO.LTD—See National Industrialization Company; *Int'l*, pg. 5159
SAUDI POWER TRANSFORMER COMPANY LIMITED—See Electrical Industries Company; *Int'l*, pg. 2350
SAUDI PREINSULATED PIPES INDUSTRIES LLC—See Zamil Industrial Investment Company; *Int'l*, pg. 8623
SAUDI PUBLIC TRANSPORT COMPANY; *Int'l*, pg. 6594
SAUDI REAL ESTATE CONSTRUCTION COMPANY—See Saudi Real Estate Co.; *Int'l*, pg. 6594
SAUDI REAL ESTATE CO.; *Int'l*, pg. 6594
SAUDI REAL ESTATE INFRASTRUCTURE COMPANY—See Saudi Real Estate Co.; *Int'l*, pg. 6594
SAUDI REFINING, INC.—See Saudi Arabian Oil Company; *Int'l*, pg. 6589
SAUDI REFRIGERATORS MANUFACTURING CO.LTD.—See E.A. Juffali & Brothers Company; *Int'l*, pg. 2251
SAUDI REINSURANCE COMPANY; *Int'l*, pg. 6594
SAUDI SERVICES AND OPERATIONS COMPANY LTD.—See Xenel Industries Ltd.; *Int'l*, pg. 8521
SAUDI SERVICING—See Saudi Consulting Services; *Int'l*, pg. 6593
SAUDI SINIORA TRADING COMPANY L.L.C.—See Siniora Food Industries P.L.C.; *Int'l*, pg. 6945
SAUDI SNACK FOODS COMPANY LIMITED—See PepsiCo, Inc.; *U.S. Public*, pg. 1671
SAUDI STEEL PIPE COMPANY; *Int'l*, pg. 6594
SAUDI SUDANESE BANK; *Int'l*, pg. 6594
SAUDI TECHINT LTD—See Techint S.p.A.; *Int'l*, pg. 7503
SAUDI TECHNOLOGY & LOGISTICS SERVICES LIMITED—See BAE Systems plc; *Int'l*, pg. 799
SAUDI TELECOM COMPANY; *Int'l*, pg. 6594
SAUDI TOP TRADING COMPANY; *Int'l*, pg. 6595
SAUDI TOTAL PETROLEUM PRODUCTS CO., LTD.—See TotalEnergies SE; *Int'l*, pg. 7838
SAUDI TOYO ENGINEERING COMPANY—See Toyo Engineering Corporation; *Int'l*, pg. 7853
SAUDI TRANSFORMER COMPANY LIMITED—See Electrical Industries Company; *Int'l*, pg. 2350
SAUDI TUNISIAN COMPANY—See Ajwa Group for Food Industries Holding Ltd. Co.; *Int'l*, pg. 259
SAUDI UNITED COOPERATIVE INSURANCE COMPANY; *Int'l*, pg. 6595
SAUDI VALVES MANUFACTURING CO. LTD.—See AVK Holding A/S; *Int'l*, pg. 748
SAUDI VITRIFIED CLAY PIPE CO.; *Int'l*, pg. 6595
SAUDI YANPET PETROCHEMICAL CO.—See Saudi Basic Industries Corporation; *Int'l*, pg. 6592
SAUER BIBUS GMBH—See Daikin Industries, Ltd.; *Int'l*, pg. 1936
SAUER BRANDS, INC.—See Falfurrias Capital Partners, LP; *U.S. Private*, pg. 1467
SAUER-DANFOSS AB—See Danfoss A/S; *Int'l*, pg. 1960
SAUER-DANFOSS APS—See Danfoss A/S; *Int'l*, pg. 1960
SAUER-DANFOSS A.S.—See Danfoss A/S; *Int'l*, pg. 1961
SAUER-DANFOSS AS—See Danfoss A/S; *Int'l*, pg. 1960
SAUER-DANFOSS BVBA—See Danfoss A/S; *Int'l*, pg. 1961
SAUER-DANFOSS CHINA HOLDING COMPANY APS—See Danfoss A/S; *Int'l*, pg. 1961
SAUER-DANFOSS-DAIKIN LTD.—See Danfoss A/S; *Int'l*, pg. 1961
SAUER-DANFOSS-DAIKIN MOBILE HYDRAULICS (SHANGHAI) CO., LTD.—See Danfoss A/S; *Int'l*, pg. 1961
SAUER-DANFOSS-DAIKIN PTE. LTD.—See Danfoss A/S; *Int'l*, pg. 1961
SAUER-DANFOSS GMBH & CO. OHG—See Danfoss A/S; *Int'l*, pg. 1961
SAUER-DANFOSS GMBH—See Danfoss A/S; *Int'l*, pg. 1961
SAUER-DANFOSS HIDRAULICA MOBIL LTDA.—See Danfoss A/S; *Int'l*, pg. 1961
SAUER-DANFOSS S.A.S.—See Danfoss A/S; *Int'l*, pg. 1961
SAUER-DANFOSS (SHANGHAI) CO. LTD.—See Danfoss A/S; *Int'l*, pg. 1960
SAUER-DANFOSS (US) COMPANY—See Danfoss A/S; *Int'l*, pg. 1960
SAUER ENERGY, INC.—See Better For You Wellness, Inc.; *U.S. Public*, pg. 326

SAUSSY BURBANK, LLC.

SAUERESSIG BASKI ONCESI HAZIRLIK SISTEMIER SANAJI VE TRICARCT AMONIN SIRKETI—See Matthews International Corporation; *U.S. Public*, pg. 1401
SAUERESSIG DESIGN STUDIO GMBH—See Matthews International Corporation; *U.S. Public*, pg. 1401
SAUERESSIG FLEXO GMBH—See Matthews International Corporation; *U.S. Public*, pg. 1401
SAUERESSIG GMBH & CO. KG—See Matthews International Corporation; *U.S. Public*, pg. 1401
SAUERESSIG LTD.—See Matthews International Corporation; *U.S. Public*, pg. 1401
SAUERESSIG OOO—See Matthews International Corporation; *U.S. Public*, pg. 1401
SAUERESSIG POLSKA SP. Z.O.O.—See Matthews International Corporation; *U.S. Public*, pg. 1401
SAUER GMBH—See DMG MORI Co., Ltd.; *Int'l*, pg. 2144
SAUERLAND GETRANKE GMBH & CO KG—See Warsteiner Brauerei Haus Cramer KG; *Int'l*, pg. 8346
SAUERMANN INDUSTRIE S.A.—See Verder International B.V.; *Int'l*, pg. 8167
SAUERSTOFF UND STICKSTOFFROHRLEITUNGS—See Mitsubishi Chemical Group Corporation; *Int'l*, pg. 4937
SAUFLON CL LTD—See The Cooper Companies, Inc.; *U.S. Public*, pg. 2066
SAUGATUCK CAPITAL COMPANY; *U.S. Private*, pg. 3554
SAUGATUCK TECHNOLOGY INC.—See Information Services Group, Inc.; *U.S. Public*, pg. 1118
SAUGBRUGSFORENINGEN AS—See Norske Skog ASA; *Int'l*, pg. 5438
SAUGBRUG TRELAST A/S—See Norske Skog ASA; *Int'l*, pg. 5438
SAUGUS ADVERTISER—See Gannett Co., Inc.; *U.S. Public*, pg. 903
SAUGUS AVALON RETAIL, LLC—See AvalonBay Communities, Inc.; *U.S. Public*, pg. 240
SAUIPE S.A.; *Int'l*, pg. 6595
SAUJANA TRIANGLE SDN. BHD.—See M K Land Holdings Berhad; *Int'l*, pg. 4610
SAUK PRAIRIE HEALTHCARE; *U.S. Private*, pg. 3554
SAUL CENTERS, INC.; *U.S. Public*, pg. 1842
SAUL EWING ARNSTEIN & LEHR LLP; *U.S. Private*, pg. 3554
SAUL-GABAUER FUNERAL HOME, INC.—See Service Corporation International; *U.S. Public*, pg. 1870
SAULSBURY ELECTRIC CO., INC.—See Saulsbury Industries; *U.S. Private*, pg. 3554
SAULSBURY INDUSTRIES; *U.S. Private*, pg. 3554
THE SAULT STAR—See Chatham Asset Management, LLC; *U.S. Public*, pg. 861
SAUMYA CONSULTANTS LIMITED; *Int'l*, pg. 6595
SAUNA360 GROUP OY—See Masco Corporation; *U.S. Public*, pg. 1392
SAUNA-EUROX OY—See Harvia Oyj; *Int'l*, pg. 3281
SAUNALAHTI GROUP OYJ—See Elisa Corporation; *Int'l*, pg. 2361
SAUNAMAX OY—See Harvia Oyj; *Int'l*, pg. 3281
SAUNDERS BROTHERS; *U.S. Private*, pg. 3554
SAUNDERS INTERNATIONAL LIMITED; *Int'l*, pg. 6595
SAUNDERSON HOUSE LIMITED—See Rathbones Group Plc; *Int'l*, pg. 6214
SAUNDERS PLANTWEAVE PTY. LTD.—See Saunders International Limited; *Int'l*, pg. 6595
SAUNDERS UNSWORTH LIMITED—See Daniel J. Edelman, Inc.; *U.S. Private*, pg. 1155
SAUNDERS YACHTWORKS; *U.S. Private*, pg. 3554
SAUNIER DUVAL BELGIQUE S.A.—See Vaillant GmbH; *Int'l*, pg. 8109
SAUNIER DUVAL EAU CHAUDE CHAUFFAGE SA—See Vaillant GmbH; *Int'l*, pg. 8109
SAURAMPS & CIE S A; *Int'l*, pg. 6595
SAURASHTRA CEMENT LTD.; *Int'l*, pg. 6595
SAURER AG—See Jiangsu Jinsheng Industry Co., Ltd.; *Int'l*, pg. 3949
SAURER AG—See OC Oerlikon Corporation AG; *Int'l*, pg. 5514
SAURER COMPONENTS GMBH—See Jiangsu Jinsheng Industry Co., Ltd.; *Int'l*, pg. 3949
SAURER COMPONENTS PTE LTD.—See Jiangsu Jinsheng Industry Co., Ltd.; *Int'l*, pg. 3949
SAURER FAR EAST LTD.—See OC Oerlikon Corporation AG; *Int'l*, pg. 5514
SAURER FIBREVISION LTD.—See Jiangsu Jinsheng Industry Co., Ltd.; *Int'l*, pg. 3949
SAURER MANAGEMENT AG—See OC Oerlikon Corporation AG; *Int'l*, pg. 5514
SAURER TEXTILE SYSTEMS (SUZHOU) CO. LTD.—See OC Oerlikon Corporation AG; *Int'l*, pg. 5514
SAUR SA—See Ardian SAS; *Int'l*, pg. 556
SAUR SA—See Caisse des Depots et Consignations; *Int'l*, pg. 1258
SAU SAN TONG HOLDINGS LIMITED; *Int'l*, pg. 6588
SAU-SEA FOODS, INC.; *U.S. Private*, pg. 3554
SAUSE BROS INC.—See Sause Bros. Ocean Towing Co. Inc.; *U.S. Private*, pg. 3555
SAUSE BROS. OCEAN TOWING CO. INC.; *U.S. Private*, pg. 3555
SAUSSY BURBANK, LLC.; *U.S. Private*, pg. 3555
SAUTEC AS—See Epiroc AB; *Int'l*, pg. 2463

SAUSSY BURBANK, LLC.   CORPORATE AFFILIATIONS

S AUTOLEASING A.S.—See Erste Group Bank AG; *Int'l*, pg. 2499
S AUTOLEASING GMBH—See Erste Group Bank AG; *Int'l*, pg. 2499
SAVA A.D.; *Int'l*, pg. 6595
SAVA A.D.; *Int'l*, pg. 6595
SAVA A.D.; *Int'l*, pg. 6595
SAVA D.D.; *Int'l*, pg. 6595
SAVAGE ARMS (CANADA) INC.—See Vista Outdoor Inc.; *U.S. Public*, pg. 2305
SAVAGE ARMS, INC.—See Vista Outdoor Inc.; *U.S. Public*, pg. 2305
SAVAGE DODGE CHRYSLER JEEP; *U.S. Private*, pg. 3555
SAVAGE INLAND MARINE, LLC—See Savage Services Corporation; *U.S. Private*, pg. 3555
SAVAGE RANGE SYSTEMS, INC.—See Vista Outdoor Inc.; *U.S. Public*, pg. 2305
SAVAGE SERVICES CORPORATION; *U.S. Private*, pg. 3555
SAVAGE & SON, INC.; *U.S. Private*, pg. 3555
SAVAGE SPORTS CORPORATION—See Vista Outdoor Inc.; *U.S. Public*, pg. 2305
SAVAGE UNIVERSAL CORPORATION—See Videndum plc; *Int'l*, pg. 8191
SAVAGLIO TBWA—See Omnicom Group Inc.; *U.S. Public*, pg. 1594
SAVA - GTI D.O.O.—See Sava d.d.; *Int'l*, pg. 6595
SAVA IP, D.O.O.—See Sava d.d.; *Int'l*, pg. 6595
SAVA IT D.O.O.—See Sava d.d.; *Int'l*, pg. 6595
SAVA KOVACEVIC A.D.; *Int'l*, pg. 6596
SAVAL B.V.—See Electricite de France S.A.; *Int'l*, pg. 2352
SAVAL FOODS CORPORATION; *U.S. Private*, pg. 3555
SAVA, LLC—See Nana Regional Corporation, Inc.; *U.S. Private*, pg. 2832
SAVAL N.V.—See Electricite de France S.A.; *Int'l*, pg. 2352
SAVAL; *Int'l*, pg. 6596
SAVA MEDICAL IN STORITVE D.O.O.—See Sava d.d.; *Int'l*, pg. 6595
S.A. VANDEMOORTELE—See Vandemoortele N.V.; *Int'l*, pg. 8128
SAVANI FINANCIALS LIMITED; *Int'l*, pg. 6596
SAVANNA AG—See Hansa Chemie International AG; *Int'l*, pg. 3259
SAVANNA CAPITAL CORP.; *Int'l*, pg. 6596
SAVANNA DRILLING LLC—See Total Energy Services Inc.; *Int'l*, pg. 7835
SAVANNA ENERGY SERVICES CORP.—See Total Energy Services Inc.; *Int'l*, pg. 7835
SAVANNA ENERGY SERVICES PTY. LTD.—See Total Energy Services Inc.; *Int'l*, pg. 7835
SAVANNAH BEE COMPANY INC; *U.S. Private*, pg. 3555
SAVANNAH COCA-COLA BOTTLING COMPANY—See Coca-Cola Bottling Co. United, Inc.; *U.S. Private*, pg. 958
SAVANNAH DISTRIBUTING CO. INC.; *U.S. Private*, pg. 3555
SAVANNAH ENERGY PLC; *Int'l*, pg. 6596
SAVANNAH FOOD COMPANY, INC.; *U.S. Private*, pg. 3555
SAVANNAH FOODS INDUSTRIAL, INC.—See Louis Dreyfus S.A.S.; *Int'l*, pg. 4562
SAVANNAH GOLDFIELDS LIMITED; *Int'l*, pg. 6596
SAVANNAH INTERNATIONAL MOTORS; *U.S. Private*, pg. 3556
SAVANNAH INVESTMENT COMPANY—See Louis Dreyfus S.A.S.; *Int'l*, pg. 4562
SAVANNAH MORNING NEWS—See Gannett Co., Inc.; *U.S. Public*, pg. 904
SAVANNAH NICKEL MINES PTY LTD—See Panoramic Resources Limited; *Int'l*, pg. 5729
SAVANNAH PHARMACEUTICAL INDUSTRIES CO. LTD.—See Hikma Pharmaceuticals PLC; *Int'l*, pg. 3390
SAVANNAH PORT TERMINAL RAILROAD, INC.—See Brookfield Infrastructure Partners L.P.; *Int'l*, pg. 1192
SAVANNAH PORT TERMINAL RAILROAD, INC.—See GIC Pte. Ltd.; *Int'l*, pg. 2967
SAVANNAH PROPERTIES LIMITED—See ENL Limited; *Int'l*, pg. 2441
SAVANNAH RESOURCES PLC; *Int'l*, pg. 6596
SAVANNAH RESTAURANTS CORP.; *U.S. Private*, pg. 3556
SAVANNAH RIVER NUCLEAR SOLUTIONS, LLC—See Fluor Corporation; *U.S. Public*, pg. 859
SAVANNAH RIVER NUCLEAR SOLUTIONS, LLC—See Huntington Ingalls Industries, Inc.; *U.S. Public*, pg. 1072
THE SAVANNAH SUGAR MILLING COMPANY LTD.—See ENL Limited; *Int'l*, pg. 2441
SAVANNAH SUGAR REFINING CORP.—See Louis Dreyfus S.A.S.; *Int'l*, pg. 4562
SAVANNAH TIRE & RUBBER COMPANY, INC.—See Golden Gate Capital Management II, LLC; *U.S. Private*, pg. 1731
SAVANNAKHET SUGAR CORPORATION—See Khon Kaen Sugar Industry Public Company Limited; *Int'l*, pg. 4155
SAVANNA WELL SERVICING CORP.—See Total Energy Services Inc.; *Int'l*, pg. 7835

SAVANNA WELL SERVICING INC.—See Total Energy Services Inc.; *Int'l*, pg. 7835
SAVANO DIRECT CAPITAL PARTNERS LLC; *U.S. Private*, pg. 3556
SAVANTAGE SOLUTIONS INC.; *U.S. Private*, pg. 3556
SAVANTA GROUP LIMITED—See Next 15 Group plc; *Int'l*, pg. 5246
SAVANT CAPITAL, LLC; *U.S. Private*, pg. 3556
SAVANT CONSTRUCTION; *U.S. Private*, pg. 3556
SAVANT INFOCOMM LIMITED; *Int'l*, pg. 6596
SAVANTIS SOLUTIONS LLC - EXTON—See Savantis Solutions LLC; *U.S. Private*, pg. 3556
SAVANTIS SOLUTIONS LLC; *U.S. Private*, pg. 3556
SAVANT SYSTEMS, INC.; *U.S. Private*, pg. 3556
SAVANT TECHNOLOGIES, LLC—See Savant Systems, Inc.; *U.S. Private*, pg. 3556
SAVA OSIGURUVANJE A.D.—See Pozavarovalnica Sava, d.d.; *Int'l*, pg. 5949
SAVA POKOJNINSKA DRUZBA, D.D.—See Pozavarovalnica Sava, d.d.; *Int'l*, pg. 5949
SAVARA INC.; *U.S. Public*, pg. 1842
SAVARIA CONCORD LIFTS INC.—See Savaria Corporation; *Int'l*, pg. 6596
SAVARIA CORPORATION; *Int'l*, pg. 6596
SAVARI, INC.—See Samsung Group; *Int'l*, pg. 6512
SAVA-ROL D.O.O.—See Sava d.d.; *Int'l*, pg. 6595
SAVAR REFRACTORIES PLC; *Int'l*, pg. 6596
SAVAS ENGINEERING COMPANY PRIVATE LIMITED—See Transformers & Rectifiers India Ltd; *Int'l*, pg. 7900
SAVA SENIOR CARE LLC; *U.S. Private*, pg. 3556
SAV-A STEP FOOD MARTS INC.; *U.S. Private*, pg. 3555
SAVATECH CORP.—See Sava d.d.; *Int'l*, pg. 6595
SAVATECH D.O.O.—See Sava d.d.; *Int'l*, pg. 6595
SAVATECH TRADE LTD.—See Sava d.d.; *Int'l*, pg. 6596
SAVA TRADE GMBH—See Sava d.d.; *Int'l*, pg. 6595
SAVA TRADE INC—See Sava d.d.; *Int'l*, pg. 6595
SAVA TRADE SPOL.S.O.O—See Sava d.d.; *Int'l*, pg. 6595
SAVA TRADE SP Z.O.O.—See Sava d.d.; *Int'l*, pg. 6595
SAVA TRADE VERTRIEBSGES, MBH—See Sava d.d.; *Int'l*, pg. 6595
SAVATRANSPORT A.D.; *Int'l*, pg. 6596
SAVATREE, LLC—See Apax Partners LLP; *Int'l*, pg. 505
SAVA TURIZEM D.D.—See Sava d.d.; *Int'l*, pg. 6595
SAVA ZIVOTNO OSIGURANJE A. D. O.—See Pozavarovalnica Sava, d.d.; *Int'l*, pg. 5949
SAVCOR FACE (BEIJING) TECHNOLOGIES CO., LTD.—See Valoe Oyj; *Int'l*, pg. 8121
SAVCOR FACE (GUANGZHOU) TECHNOLOGIES CO., LTD.—See Valoe Oyj; *Int'l*, pg. 8122
SAVCOR FOREST INC.—See Trimble, Inc.; *U.S. Public*, pg. 2191
SAVCOR FOREST LIMITADA—See Trimble, Inc.; *U.S. Public*, pg. 2191
SAVCOR OY—See Trimble, Inc.; *U.S. Public*, pg. 2191
SAVDA AUTOSERVIZI VALLE D'AOSTA S.P.A.—See Deutsche Bahn AG; *Int'l*, pg. 2052
SAVDEN GROUP CORP.; *Int'l*, pg. 6596
SAVE-A-LOAD, INC.—See Fleet Engineers, Inc.; *U.S. Private*, pg. 1541
SAVE-A-LOT FOOD STORES, LTD.—See ONEX Corporation; *Int'l*, pg. 5578
SAVE-A-LOT—See Houchens Industries, Inc.; *U.S. Private*, pg. 1990
SAVEAROUND; *U.S. Private*, pg. 3556
SAVECO GERMANY GMBH—See WAMGROUP S.p.A.; *Int'l*, pg. 8338
SAVECO IBERICA SL—See WAMGROUP S.p.A.; *Int'l*, pg. 8338
SAVECO MIDDLE EAST FZE—See WAMGROUP S.p.A.; *Int'l*, pg. 8338
SAVECO NORTH AMERICA INC.—See WAMGROUP S.p.A.; *Int'l*, pg. 8338
SAVECO S.A.S.—See WAMGROUP S.p.A.; *Int'l*, pg. 8338
SAVECO S.R.L.—See WAMGROUP S.p.A.; *Int'l*, pg. 8338
SAVECO UK LTD.—See WAMGROUP S.p.A.; *Int'l*, pg. 8338
SAVEDAILY.COM, INC.—See SaveDaily, Inc.; *U.S. Private*, pg. 3556
SAVEDAILY, INC.; *U.S. Private*, pg. 3556
SAVE BY THE DRESS, INC.; *U.S. Private*, pg. 3556
SAVE DRUG CENTER CO., LTD.—See Bangkok Dusit Medical Services Public Company Limited; *Int'l*, pg. 834
SAVEENE GROUP CORP.; *Int'l*, pg. 6597
SAVE ENGINEERING S.P.A.—See InfraVia Capital Partners SAS; *Int'l*, pg. 3699
SAVEERA INSTITUTE OF MEDICAL SCIENCES PRIVATE LIMITED—See Krishna Institute of Medical Sciences Limited; *Int'l*, pg. 4302
SAVELEND GROUP AB; *Int'l*, pg. 6597
SAVELYS GDF SUEZ—See ENGIE SA; *Int'l*, pg. 2434
SAVELYS GROUP—See ENGIE SA; *Int'l*, pg. 2434
THE SAVE MART COMPANIES, LLC—See Kingswood Capital Management LLC; *U.S. Private*, pg. 2312
SAVE MART SUPERMARKETS—See Kingswood Capital Management LLC; *U.S. Private*, pg. 2312
SAVENCIA FROMAGE & DAIRY CZECH REPUBLIC, A.S.—See Savencia Fromage & Dairy; *Int'l*, pg. 6597

SAVENCIA FROMAGE & DAIRY DEUTSCHLAND GMBH—See Savencia Fromage & Dairy; *Int'l*, pg. 6597
SAVENCIA FROMAGE & DAIRY; *Int'l*, pg. 6597
SAVEN TECHNOLOGIES LIMITED; *Int'l*, pg. 6597
SAVE-ON DENTAL CARE—See CPF Dental, LLC; *U.S. Private*, pg. 1080
SAVEONRESORTS.COM, LLC; *U.S. Private*, pg. 3556
SAVERA HOTEL—See Savera Industries Limited; *Int'l*, pg. 6597
SAVERA INDUSTRIES LIMITED; *Int'l*, pg. 6597
SAVERDIS; *Int'l*, pg. 6597
SAVERGLASS AUSTRALIA PTY LTD—See Orora Limited; *Int'l*, pg. 5643
SAVERGLASS CHAMPAGNE—See Orora Limited; *Int'l*, pg. 5643
SAVERGLASS COGNAC—See Orora Limited; *Int'l*, pg. 5643
SAVERGLASS IBERICA LDA—See Orora Limited; *Int'l*, pg. 5643
SAVERGLASS IBERICA LDT—See Orora Limited; *Int'l*, pg. 5643
SAVERGLASS INC.—See Orora Limited; *Int'l*, pg. 5643
SAVERGLASS ITALIA SRL—See Orora Limited; *Int'l*, pg. 5643
SAVERGLASS MEXICO—See Orora Limited; *Int'l*, pg. 5643
SAVERGLASS MOSCOU—See Orora Limited; *Int'l*, pg. 5643
SAVERGLASS (NZ) LTD.—See Orora Limited; *Int'l*, pg. 5643
SAVERGLASS PTY LTD.—See Orora Limited; *Int'l*, pg. 5643
SAVERGLASS SAS—See Orora Limited; *Int'l*, pg. 5643
S.A. VERMEIRE-BELTING N.V.—See THK CO., LTD.; *Int'l*, pg. 7712
SAVERONE 2014 LTD.; *Int'l*, pg. 6597
SAVERS COOPERATIVE BANK; *U.S. Private*, pg. 3556
SAVERS, INC.; *U.S. Private*, pg. 3556
SAVERSUD—See Orora Limited; *Int'l*, pg. 5643
SAVERS VALUE VILLAGE, INC.; *U.S. Public*, pg. 1842
SAVER SYSTEMS INC.; *U.S. Private*, pg. 3556
SAVER SYSTEMS OF OHIO, INC.—See Saver Systems Inc.; *U.S. Private*, pg. 3556
SAVE S.P.A.—See InfraVia Capital Partners SAS; *Int'l*, pg. 3699
SAVE THE CHILDREN JAPAN; *Int'l*, pg. 6596
SAVE THE CHIMPS; *U.S. Private*, pg. 3556
SAVE TIME CONVENIENCE STORES INC.—See Melling Tool Company Inc.; *U.S. Private*, pg. 2662
SA VETO-PHARMA—See Element Solutions Inc.; *U.S. Public*, pg. 728
SAVEUR FOOD GROUP, LLC; *U.S. Private*, pg. 3556
SAVEWAY COMPOUNDING PHARMACY, LLC—See Myonex, LLC; *U.S. Private*, pg. 2825
SAVEWAY PETROLEUM INC.; *U.S. Private*, pg. 3557
SAVEX TECHNOLOGIES PVT. LTD.; *Int'l*, pg. 6597
SAVEZONE I&C CORPORATION; *Int'l*, pg. 6597
SAV HOSPITALITY LIMITED—See Chuang's Consortium International Limited; *Int'l*, pg. 1590
SAVIA, S.A. DE C.V.; *Int'l*, pg. 6597
SAVICOM, INC.; *U.S. Private*, pg. 3557
SA VICTIRIA INTERNATIONAL TECHNOLOGY PTY. LTD.—See Eastern Platinum Limited; *Int'l*, pg. 2273
SAVI FINANCIAL CORPORATION; *U.S. Public*, pg. 1842
SA VIGNOBLES DE LAROSE—See Allianz SE; *Int'l*, pg. 355
SAVILLE ASSESSMENT LIMITED—See Willis Towers Watson Public Limited Company; *Int'l*, pg. 8415
SAVILLE & HOLDSWORTH LIMITED—See Exponent Private Equity LLP; *Int'l*, pg. 2589
SAVILLE RESOURCES INC.; *Int'l*, pg. 6597
SAVILLS (ACT) PTY. LIMITED—See Savills plc; *Int'l*, pg. 6598
SAVILLS AGENCY B.V.—See Savills plc; *Int'l*, pg. 6598
SAVILLS AGUIRRE NEWMAN BARCELONA SAU—See Savills plc; *Int'l*, pg. 6598
SAVILLS ASIA PACIFIC LIMITED.—See Savills plc; *Int'l*, pg. 6598
SAVILLS ASSET ADVISORY COMPANY LTD.—See Savills plc; *Int'l*, pg. 6598
SAVILLS (AUST) PTY. LIMITED—See Savills plc; *Int'l*, pg. 6598
SAVILLS BELUX GROUP SA—See Savills plc; *Int'l*, pg. 6599
SAVILLS B.V.—See Savills plc; *Int'l*, pg. 6598
SAVILLS CATERING LTD.—See Savills plc; *Int'l*, pg. 6599
SAVILLS COMMERCIAL (LEEDS) LTD.—See Savills plc; *Int'l*, pg. 6599
SAVILLS COMMERCIAL LTD.—See Savills plc; *Int'l*, pg. 6599
SAVILLS CONSULTANCY B.V.—See Savills plc; *Int'l*, pg. 6599
SAVILLS CONSULTORES INMOBILIARIOS SA—See Savills plc; *Int'l*, pg. 6598
SAVILLS (DORMANT 1) LTD.—See Savills plc; *Int'l*, pg. 6598
SAVILLS ENGINEERING LIMITED.—See Savills plc; *Int'l*, pg. 6598

COMPANY NAME INDEX

SAVILLS FINANCE HOLDINGS PLC—See Savills plc; *Int'l*, pg. 6599
SAVILLS FINANCE LTD.—See Savills plc; *Int'l*, pg. 6599
SAVILLS FINANCIAL SERVICES PLC—See Savills plc; *Int'l*, pg. 6599
SAVILLS FUND MANAGEMENT GMBH—See Savills plc; *Int'l*, pg. 6599
SAVILLS GUARDIAN (HOLDINGS) LIMITED.—See Savills plc; *Int'l*, pg. 6598
SAVILLS HELLAS LTD.—See Savills plc; *Int'l*, pg. 6599
SAVILLS HOLDINGS B.V.—See Savills plc; *Int'l*, pg. 6599
SAVILLS (HONG KONG) LIMITED—See Savills plc; *Int'l*, pg. 6598
SAVILLS HUNGARY LLC—See Savills plc; *Int'l*, pg. 6599
SAVILLS IMMOBILIEN-BERATUNGS GMBH—See Savills plc; *Int'l*, pg. 6599
SAVILLS IMMOBILIEN-BERATUNGS GMBH—See Savills plc; *Int'l*, pg. 6599
SAVILLS INVESTMENT MANAGEMENT AB—See Savills plc; *Int'l*, pg. 6599
SAVILLS INVESTMENT MANAGEMENT (KVG) GMBH—See Savills plc; *Int'l*, pg. 6599
SAVILLS INVESTMENT MANAGEMENT (KVG) GMBH—See Savills plc; *Int'l*, pg. 6599
SAVILLS INVESTMENT MANAGEMENT (LUXEMBOURG) S.A.R.L.—See Savills plc; *Int'l*, pg. 6599
SAVILLS INVESTMENT MANAGEMENT PTE LTD—See Savills plc; *Int'l*, pg. 6599
SAVILLS INVESTMENT MANAGEMENT S.L.—See Savills plc; *Int'l*, pg. 6599
SAVILLS INVESTMENT MANAGEMENT SP ZOO—See Savills plc; *Int'l*, pg. 6599
SAVILLS INVESTMENTS B.V.—See Savills plc; *Int'l*, pg. 6599
SAVILLS ITALY SRL—See Savills plc; *Int'l*, pg. 6599
SAVILLS JAPAN COMPANY LTD.—See Savills plc; *Int'l*, pg. 6599
SAVILLS JAPAN LIMITED KK—See Savills plc; *Int'l*, pg. 6598
SAVILLS KOREA CO. LIMITED—See Savills plc; *Int'l*, pg. 6599
SAVILLS LLC—See Savills plc; *Int'l*, pg. 6599
SAVILLS (L&P) LTD.—See Savills plc; *Int'l*, pg. 6598
SAVILLS (MACAO) LIMITED.—See Savills plc; *Int'l*, pg. 6598
SAVILLS MANAGEMENT RESOURCES LTD.—See Savills plc; *Int'l*, pg. 6599
SAVILLS MANAGEMENT SERVICES LIMITED.—See Savills plc; *Int'l*, pg. 6598
SAVILLS NEDERLAND HOLDING BV—See Savills plc; *Int'l*, pg. 6599
SAVILLS NETHERLAND B.V.—See Savills plc; *Int'l*, pg. 6599
SAVILLS (NSW) PTY. LIMITED.—See Savills plc; *Int'l*, pg. 6598
SAVILLS (OVERSEAS HOLDINGS) LTD.—See Savills plc; *Int'l*, pg. 6598
SAVILLS PLC; *Int'l*, pg. 6597
SAVILLS PRIVATE FINANCE LTD.—See Savills plc; *Int'l*, pg. 6599
SAVILLS PROJECT CONSULTANCY LIMITED.—See Savills plc; *Int'l*, pg. 6598
SAVILLS PROPERTY MANAGEMENT HOLDINGS LIMITED.—See Savills plc; *Int'l*, pg. 6598
SAVILLS PROPERTY MANAGEMENT LIMITED—See Savills plc; *Int'l*, pg. 6598
SAVILLS PROPERTY SERVICES (CHENGDU) COMPANY LTD.—See Savills plc; *Int'l*, pg. 6598
SAVILLS PROPERTY SERVICES (SHANGHAI) COMPANY LTD.—See Savills plc; *Int'l*, pg. 6599
SAVILLS (QLD) PTY. LIMITED—See Savills plc; *Int'l*, pg. 6598
SAVILLS REALTY LIMITED.—See Savills plc; *Int'l*, pg. 6598
SAVILLS RESIDENTIAL (IRELAND) LIMITED—See Savills plc; *Int'l*, pg. 6599
SAVILLS RESIDENTIAL (S) PTE. LTD.—See Savills plc; *Int'l*, pg. 6598
SAVILLS (SA) PTY. LIMITED—See Savills plc; *Int'l*, pg. 6598
SAVILLS SA—See Savills plc; *Int'l*, pg. 6599
SAVILLS S.A.S.—See Savills plc; *Int'l*, pg. 6599
SAVILLS SHOWCASE LIMITED.—See Savills plc; *Int'l*, pg. 6598
SAVILLS (SINGAPORE) PTE LIMITED—See Savills plc; *Int'l*, pg. 6598
SAVILLS SPOLKA Z ORGANICZONA—See Savills plc; *Int'l*, pg. 6599
SAVILLS SP. Z O.O—See Savills plc; *Int'l*, pg. 6599
SAVILLS-STUDLEY, LLC—See Savills plc; *Int'l*, pg. 6599
SAVILLS STUDLEY OCCUPIER SERVICES, INC.—See Savills plc; *Int'l*, pg. 6600
SAVILLS SWEDEN AB—See Savills plc; *Int'l*, pg. 6599
SAVILLS (TAIWAN) LIMITED—See Savills plc; *Int'l*, pg. 6598
SAVILLS (THAILAND) LIMITED.—See Savills plc; *Int'l*, pg. 6598
SAVILLS VALUATION AND PROFESSIONAL SERVICES LTD.—See Savills plc; *Int'l*, pg. 6598

SAVILLS VALUATION SAS—See Savills plc; *Int'l*, pg. 6599
SAVILLS (VIC) PTY. LIMITED—See Savills plc; *Int'l*, pg. 6598
SAVILLS (VIETNAM) LIMITED—See Savills plc; *Int'l*, pg. 6598
SAVILLS (WA) PTY. LIMITED.—See Savills plc; *Int'l*, pg. 6598
SAVIMEX CORPORATION; *Int'l*, pg. 6600
S.A. VINA SANTA RITA—See Cristalerias de Chile S.A.; *Int'l*, pg. 1850
SAVIN CORPORATION—See Ricoh Company, Ltd.; *Int'l*, pg. 6336
SAVINGS BANK MENDOCINO COUNTY; *U.S. Private*, pg. 3557
SAVINGS BANK OF DANBURY; *U.S. Private*, pg. 3557
THE SAVINGS BANK OF ROCKVILLE; *U.S. Private*, pg. 4114
SAVINGS BANK OF WALPOLE; *U.S. Private*, pg. 3557
THE SAVINGS BANK; *U.S. Private*, pg. 4114
SAVINGS.COM—See Platinum Equity, LLC; *U.S. Private*, pg. 3201
SAVINGS & LOAN KENYA LTD.—See KCB Group PLC; *Int'l*, pg. 4108
SAVINGS OIL COMPANY INC.; *U.S. Private*, pg. 3557
SAVINGS PROS, INC.—See ST Dupont S.A.; *Int'l*, pg. 7158
SAVINO DEL BENE ARGENTINA S.A.—See Savino Del Bene S.p.A.; *Int'l*, pg. 6600
SAVINO DEL BENE AUSTRALIA PTY LTD—See Savino Del Bene S.p.A.; *Int'l*, pg. 6600
SAVINO DEL BENE BULGARIA EAD—See Savino Del Bene S.p.A.; *Int'l*, pg. 6600
SAVINO DEL BENE CHILE S.A.—See Savino Del Bene S.p.A.; *Int'l*, pg. 6600
SAVINO DEL BENE CHINA LTD—See Savino Del Bene S.p.A.; *Int'l*, pg. 6600
SAVINO DEL BENE COLOMBIA LTDA—See Savino Del Bene S.p.A.; *Int'l*, pg. 6600
SAVINO DEL BENE CORP. CANADA—See Savino Del Bene S.p.A.; *Int'l*, pg. 6600
SAVINO DEL BENE COSTA RICA S.A.—See Savino Del Bene S.p.A.; *Int'l*, pg. 6601
SAVINO DEL BENE DEL PERU S.A.C—See Savino Del Bene S.p.A.; *Int'l*, pg. 6601
SAVINO DEL BENE DO BRASIL LTDA—See Savino Del Bene S.p.A.; *Int'l*, pg. 6601
SAVINO DEL BENE D.O.O.—See Savino Del Bene S.p.A.; *Int'l*, pg. 6601
SAVINO DEL BENE FLORIDA, INC.—See Savino Del Bene S.p.A.; *Int'l*, pg. 6601
SAVINO DEL BENE FRANCE S.A.—See Savino Del Bene S.p.A.; *Int'l*, pg. 6601
SAVINO DEL BENE FREIGHT FORWARDERS (INDIA) PVT. LTD.—See Savino Del Bene S.p.A.; *Int'l*, pg. 6601
SAVINO DEL BENE GMBH—See Savino Del Bene S.p.A.; *Int'l*, pg. 6601
SAVINO DEL BENE INDIA PVT. LTD.—See Savino Del Bene S.p.A.; *Int'l*, pg. 6601
SAVINO DEL BENE ISRAEL LTD.—See Savino Del Bene S.p.A.; *Int'l*, pg. 6601
SAVINO DEL BENE JAPAN CO LTD—See Savino Del Bene S.p.A.; *Int'l*, pg. 6601
SAVINO DEL BENE (JB) SDN BHD—See Savino Del Bene S.p.A.; *Int'l*, pg. 6600
SAVINO DEL BENE KOREA CO. LTD—See Savino Del Bene S.p.A.; *Int'l*, pg. 6601
SAVINO DEL BENE (MALAYSIA) SDN. BHD.—See Savino Del Bene S.p.A.; *Int'l*, pg. 6600
SAVINO DEL BENE MEXICO, S.A.DE C.V.—See Savino Del Bene S.p.A.; *Int'l*, pg. 6601
SAVINO DEL BENE NAKLIYAT LTD STI—See Savino Del Bene S.p.A.; *Int'l*, pg. 6601
SAVINO DEL BENE NETHERLANDS B.V.—See Savino Del Bene S.p.A.; *Int'l*, pg. 6601
SAVINO DEL BENE PANAMA SA—See Savino Del Bene S.p.A.; *Int'l*, pg. 6601
SAVINO DEL BENE POLAND SP.Z O.O.—See Savino Del Bene S.p.A.; *Int'l*, pg. 6601
SAVINO DEL BENE PORTUGUESA LDA—See Savino Del Bene S.p.A.; *Int'l*, pg. 6601
SAVINO DEL BENE QUEBEC INC.—See Savino Del Bene S.p.A.; *Int'l*, pg. 6601
SAVINO DEL BENE RUSSIA, LLC—See Savino Del Bene S.p.A.; *Int'l*, pg. 6601
SAVINO DEL BENE S.A.—See Savino Del Bene S.p.A.; *Int'l*, pg. 6601
SAVINO DEL BENE SHANGHAI CO., LTD—See Savino Del Bene S.p.A.; *Int'l*, pg. 6601
SAVINO DEL BENE S.L.—See Savino Del Bene S.p.A.; *Int'l*, pg. 6601
SAVINO DEL BENE SOUTH AFRICA (PTY) LTD.—See Savino Del Bene S.p.A.; *Int'l*, pg. 6601
SAVINO DEL BENE S.P.A.; *Int'l*, pg. 6600
SAVINO DEL BENE (S) PTE LTD.—See Savino Del Bene S.p.A.; *Int'l*, pg. 6601
SAVINO DEL BENE SWITZERLAND AG—See Savino Del Bene S.p.A.; *Int'l*, pg. 6601
SAVINO DEL BENE (TEXAS), INC.—See Savino Del Bene S.p.A.; *Int'l*, pg. 6600

SAVINO DEL BENE (U.K.) LTD—See Savino Del Bene S.p.A.; *Int'l*, pg. 6600
SAVINO DEL BENE URUGUAY S.A.—See Savino Del Bene S.p.A.; *Int'l*, pg. 6601
SAVINO DEL BENE U.S.A. INC.—See Savino Del Bene S.p.A.; *Int'l*, pg. 6601
SAVINO DEL BENE U.S.A. INC.—See Savino Del Bene S.p.A.; *Int'l*, pg. 6601
SAVIO MACCHINE TESSILI S.P.A.—See Alpha Associes Conseil SAS; *Int'l*, pg. 366
SAVIOR LIFETEC CORP.; *Int'l*, pg. 6601
SAVI SHOP LTD.—See ENL Limited; *Int'l*, pg. 2441
SAVI S.R.L.—See WAMGROUP S.p.A.; *Int'l*, pg. 8338
SAVITA OIL TECHNOLOGIES LIMITED - LUBES DIVISION—See Savita Oil Technologies Limited; *Int'l*, pg. 6601
SAVITA OIL TECHNOLOGIES LIMITED; *Int'l*, pg. 6601
SAVITECH CORP.—See Diodes Incorporated; *U.S. Public*, pg. 667
SAVI TECHNOLOGIES , INC; *U.S. Private*, pg. 3557
SAVITRANSPORT TRIVENETO S.R.L.—See Savino Del Bene S.p.A.; *Int'l*, pg. 6601
SAVIT S.R.L.—See Ferrovie dello Stato Italiane S.p.A.; *Int'l*, pg. 2645
SAVITZ ORGANIZATION, INCORPORATED—See CBIZ, Inc.; *U.S. Public*, pg. 457
SAVITZ RESEARCH CENTER INC.; *U.S. Private*, pg. 3557
SAVIYNT, INC.; *U.S. Private*, pg. 3557
THE SAVOGRAN COMPANY; *U.S. Private*, pg. 4114
THE SAVO GROUP, LTD—See Seismic Software, Inc.; *U.S. Private*, pg. 3600
SAVOIE REFRACTAIRES—See Compagnie de Saint-Gobain SA; *Int'l*, pg. 1732
SAVOIE'S SAUSAGE & FOOD PRODUCTS, INC.; *U.S. Private*, pg. 3557
SAVOLA EDIBLE OILS COMPANY LTD.—See Savola Group; *Int'l*, pg. 6602
SAVOLA EDIBLE OILS (SUDAN) LTD.—See Savola Group; *Int'l*, pg. 6602
SAVOLA GIDA SANAYI VE TICARET ANONIM SIRKETI—See Savola Group; *Int'l*, pg. 6602
SAVOLA GROUP; *Int'l*, pg. 6601
SAV-O-MAT, INC.—See Stinker Stores, Inc.; *U.S. Private*, pg. 3813
SAVONA FOODS, INC.; *U.S. Private*, pg. 3557
SAVON AURINKOENERGIA OY—See Bravida Holding AB; *Int'l*, pg. 1142
SAV-ON DRUGS OF ARK, INC.; *U.S. Private*, pg. 3555
SAVONLINNA WORKS OY—See ANDRITZ AG; *Int'l*, pg. 454
SAV-ON PLATING, INC.; *U.S. Private*, pg. 3555
SAV-ON PLATING OF ARIZONA INC.—See Sav-On Plating, Inc.; *U.S. Private*, pg. 3555
SAVOO LTD.—See Platinum Equity, LLC; *U.S. Private*, pg. 3201
SAVOREAT LTD.; *Int'l*, pg. 6602
SAVOR GROUP LIMITED; *Int'l*, pg. 6602
SAVOR STREET FOODS INC.; *U.S. Private*, pg. 3557
SAVOSOLAR APS—See Savo-Solar Oy; *Int'l*, pg. 6601
SAVOSOLAR GMBH—See Savo-Solar Oy; *Int'l*, pg. 6601
SAVO-SOLAR OY; *Int'l*, pg. 6601
SAVO-TECHNIK ROTATIONSGUSS GMBH—See L. Possehl & Co. mbH; *Int'l*, pg. 4385
SAVOURY CATERING PTE. LTD.—See Neo Group Limited; *Int'l*, pg. 5196
SAVOURY FLAVOURS LTD.—See International Flavors & Fragrances Inc.; *U.S. Public*, pg. 1154
SAVOURY SYSTEMS INTERNATIONAL, INC.; *U.S. Private*, pg. 3557
SAVOX COMMUNICATIONS LTD.—See Savox Communications Oy Ab; *Int'l*, pg. 6602
SAVOX COMMUNICATIONS OY AB; *Int'l*, pg. 6602
SAVOYE GMBH—See Noblelift Intelligent Equipment Co.,Ltd; *Int'l*, pg. 5398
SAVOYE LLC—See UDR, Inc.; *U.S. Public*, pg. 2218
SAVOYE LOGISTICS SL—See Noblelift Intelligent Equipment Co.,Ltd; *Int'l*, pg. 5398
SAVOYE LTD.—See Noblelift Intelligent Equipment Co.,Ltd; *Int'l*, pg. 5398
SAVOY ENERGY CORPORATION; *U.S. Public*, pg. 1842
SAVOYE S.A.—See Noblelift Intelligent Equipment Co.,Ltd; *Int'l*, pg. 5398
SAVOY HEALTHCARE, INC.—See The Ensign Group, Inc.; *U.S. Public*, pg. 2072
SAVOY HOTEL BAUR EN VILLE AG—See UBS Group AG; *Int'l*, pg. 8007
THE SAVOY HOTEL—See Coral Hospitality, LLC; *U.S. Private*, pg. 1046
SAV-RAHOITUS OYJ—See Oma Saastopankki Oyj; *Int'l*, pg. 5559
SAVREMENA A.D.; *Int'l*, pg. 6602
SAVRE SA—See SKion GmbH; *Int'l*, pg. 6987
SAV SAS PLANT MAZINGARBE—See Tessenderlo Group NV; *Int'l*, pg. 7574
SAV S.P.A.—See Argo Finanziaria S.p.A.; *Int'l*, pg. 562
SAV-TECH SOLVENT, INC—See J.F. Lehman & Company, Inc.; *U.S. Private*, pg. 2163

SAVVICA INC.—See Educomp Solutions, Ltd.; *Int'l*, pg. 2315
SAVVION, INC.—See Progress Software Corporation; *U.S. Public*, pg. 1726
SAVVIS COMMUNICATIONS K.K.—See Lumen Technologies, Inc.; *U.S. Public*, pg. 1347
SAVVIS FEDERAL SYSTEMS, INC.—See Lumen Technologies, Inc.; *U.S. Public*, pg. 1347
SAVVIS GERMANY GMBH—See Lumen Technologies, Inc.; *U.S. Public*, pg. 1347
SAVVIS HONG KONG LIMITED—See Lumen Technologies, Inc.; *U.S. Public*, pg. 1347
SAVVIS, INC—See Lumen Technologies, Inc.; *U.S. Public*, pg. 1347
SAVVIS SINGAPORE COMPANY PTE. LTD.—See Lumen Technologies, Inc.; *U.S. Public*, pg. 1347
SAVVIS SINGAPORE—See Lumen Technologies, Inc.; *U.S. Public*, pg. 1347
SAVVIS UNITED KINGDOM—See Lumen Technologies, Inc.; *U.S. Public*, pg. 1347
SAVVY INC.; *U.S. Private*, pg. 3557
SAVVYPHONE, LLC; *U.S. Private*, pg. 3557
SAVVY REST INC.; *U.S. Private*, pg. 3557
SAVVYSHERPA, LLC—See UnitedHealth Group Incorporated; *U.S. Public*, pg. 2250
SAVWATT USA, INC; *U.S. Private*, pg. 3557
SAV WORKHOLDING AND AUTOMATION GMBH.—See Tyrol Equity AG; *Int'l*, pg. 7996
SAVYON LTD.—See Gamida for Life B.V.; *Int'l*, pg. 2878
SAWACA BUSINESS MACHINES LIMITED; *Int'l*, pg. 6602
SAWADEE AMSTERDAM BV—See TUI AG; *Int'l*, pg. 7966
SAWAFUJI ELECTRIC CO., LTD.; *Int'l*, pg. 6602
SAWAFUJI SOFTWARE DEVELOPMENT CO., LTD.—See Sawafuji Electric Co., Ltd.; *Int'l*, pg. 6602
SAWAI GROUP HOLDINGS CO., LTD.; *Int'l*, pg. 6602
SAWAI PHARMACEUTICAL CO., LTD.—See Sawai Group Holdings Co., Ltd.; *Int'l*, pg. 6602
SAWANG EXPORT PUBLIC COMPANY LIMITED; *Int'l*, pg. 6602
SAWARA DAIICHI TRAFFIC LTD—See Daiichi Koutsu Sangyo Co., Ltd.; *Int'l*, pg. 1929
SA WATER CYCLE GROUP (PROPRIETARY) LIMITED—See The Bidvest Group Limited; *Int'l*, pg. 7625
SAWBROOK STEEL CASTINGS CO.; *U.S. Private*, pg. 3557
S.A. WEISHAUPT N.V.—See Max Weishaupt GmbH; *Int'l*, pg. 4735
SAW GMBH; *Int'l*, pg. 6602
SAWGRASS ASSET MANAGEMENT LLC; *U.S. Private*, pg. 3557
SAW MART LTD—See Addison Saws Limited; *Int'l*, pg. 129
SAW MILL CAPITAL LLC; *U.S. Private*, pg. 3557
SAWMILL CREEK RESORT, LTD.—See Six Flags Entertainment Corporation; *U.S. Public*, pg. 1890
SAWNEE ELECTRIC MEMBERSHIP CORPORATION; *U.S. Private*, pg. 3558
SAW SERVICE OF AMERICA INC.; *U.S. Private*, pg. 3557
SAWSTOP, LLC; *U.S. Private*, pg. 3558
THE SAWTOOTH GROUP; *U.S. Private*, pg. 4114
SAWTOOTH ORTHOTICS AND PROSTHETICS, INC.—See Patient Square Capital, L.P.; *U.S. Private*, pg. 3107
SAWTST, LLC; *U.S. Private*, pg. 3558
SAWYER DISPOSAL SERVICES, LLC—See Clean Harbors, Inc.; *U.S. Public*, pg. 510
SAWYER EXTERMINATING, INC.—See Rollins, Inc.; *U.S. Public*, pg. 1809
SAWYER GAS—See UGI Corporation; *U.S. Public*, pg. 2222
SAWYER MILLER ADVERTISING—See The Interpublic Group of Companies, Inc.; *U.S. Public*, pg. 2105
SAWYER MILLER ADVERTISING—See The Interpublic Group of Companies, Inc.; *U.S. Public*, pg. 2105
SAWYER REALTY HOLDINGS LLC; *U.S. Private*, pg. 3558
SAXA ADVANCED SUPPORT INC.—See SAXA Holdings Inc.; *Int'l*, pg. 6602
SAXA BUSINESS SYSTEM INC.—See SAXA Holdings Inc.; *Int'l*, pg. 6602
SAXA HOLDINGS INC.; *Int'l*, pg. 6602
SAXA INC.—See SAXA Holdings Inc.; *Int'l*, pg. 6602
SAXA PRECISION INC.—See SAXA Holdings Inc.; *Int'l*, pg. 6603
SAXA PROASSIST INC.—See SAXA Holdings Inc.; *Int'l*, pg. 6602
SAX ARTS & CRAFTS, INC.—See School Specialty, Inc.; *U.S. Public*, pg. 1848
SAXA TECHNO INC.—See SAXA Holdings Inc.; *Int'l*, pg. 6603
SAXCO INTERNATIONAL, LLC—See Atlas Holdings, LLC; *U.S. Private*, pg. 378
SAXIN CORPORATION—See Mitsui Chemicals, Inc.; *Int'l*, pg. 4984
SAXLUND GROUP AB; *Int'l*, pg. 6603
SAX MOTOR COMPANY; *U.S. Private*, pg. 3558
SAXO BANK A/S—See Zhejiang Geely Holding Group Co., Ltd.; *Int'l*, pg. 8653

SAXO BANK (DUBAI) LIMITED—See Zhejiang Geely Holding Group Co., Ltd.; *Int'l*, pg. 8653
SAXO BANK FX SECURITIES K.K.—See Zhejiang Geely Holding Group Co., Ltd.; *Int'l*, pg. 8653
SAXO BANK NEDERLAND—See Zhejiang Geely Holding Group Co., Ltd.; *Int'l*, pg. 8653
SAXO BANK (SCHWEIZ) AG—See Zhejiang Geely Holding Group Co., Ltd.; *Int'l*, pg. 8653
SAXO BANQUE FRANCE SAS—See Zhejiang Geely Holding Group Co., Ltd.; *Int'l*, pg. 8653
SAXO CAPITAL MARKETS, AGENTE DE VALORES S.A.—See Zhejiang Geely Holding Group Co., Ltd.; *Int'l*, pg. 8653
SAXO CAPITAL MARKETS (AUSTRALIA) PTY. LTD.—See Zhejiang Geely Holding Group Co., Ltd.; *Int'l*, pg. 8653
SAXO CAPITAL MARKETS CY LTD.—See Zhejiang Geely Holding Group Co., Ltd.; *Int'l*, pg. 8653
SAXO CAPITAL MARKETS HK LIMITED—See Zhejiang Geely Holding Group Co., Ltd.; *Int'l*, pg. 8653
SAXO CAPITAL MARKETS MENKUL DEGERLER A.S.—See Zhejiang Geely Holding Group Co., Ltd.; *Int'l*, pg. 8653
SAXO CAPITAL MARKETS PTE. LTD.—See Zhejiang Geely Holding Group Co., Ltd.; *Int'l*, pg. 8653
SAXO CAPITAL MARKETS UK LTD.—See Zhejiang Geely Holding Group Co., Ltd.; *Int'l*, pg. 8653
SAXO FINANCIAL SERVICES PRIVATE LIMITED—See Zhejiang Geely Holding Group Co., Ltd.; *Int'l*, pg. 8653
SAXON AGRICULTURE, LTD.—See GrainCorp Limited; *Int'l*, pg. 3052
SAXON BUSINESS SYSTEMS, INC.—See Xerox Holdings Corporation; *U.S. Public*, pg. 2389
SAXON CAPITAL GROUP, INC.; *U.S. Public*, pg. 1842
SAXON-CLARK INC.; *U.S. Private*, pg. 3558
SAXON ENERGY SERVICES DEL ECUADOR S.A.—See Schlumberger Limited; *U.S. Public*, pg. 1844
SAXON ENERGY SERVICES INC.—See Schlumberger Limited; *U.S. Public*, pg. 1844
SAXON GLOBAL INC.; *U.S. Private*, pg. 3558
SAXON HUMAN RESOURCES PVT. LTD.—See Saxon Global Inc.; *U.S. Private*, pg. 3558
SAXONIA ENTERTAINMENT GMBH—See Bavaria Film GmbH; *Int'l*, pg. 899
SAXONIA MEDIA FILMPRODUKTION GMBH—See Bavaria Film GmbH; *Int'l*, pg. 899
SAXON MORTGAGE, INC.—See Morgan Stanley; *U.S. Public*, pg. 1475
SAXON OFFICE TECHNOLOGY—See Panasonic Holdings Corporation; *Int'l*, pg. 5721
SAXONS CHASE (HEADCORN) RESIDENTS MANAGEMENT COMPANY LIMITED—See Persimmon plc; *Int'l*, pg. 5817
SAXON SHOES, INC.—See Comfort One Shoes L-1 Corporation; *U.S. Private*, pg. 981
SAXONY PARTNERS LLC; *U.S. Private*, pg. 3558
SAXO PAYMENTS A/S—See Zhejiang Geely Holding Group Co., Ltd.; *Int'l*, pg. 8653
SAXO-PHON GMBH—See Bertelsmann SE & Co. KGaA; *Int'l*, pg. 996
SAXOPRINT AG—See CEWE Stiftung & Co. KGaA; *Int'l*, pg. 1425
SAXOPRINT EURL—See CEWE Stiftung & Co. KGaA; *Int'l*, pg. 1425
SAXOPRINT GMBH—See CEWE Stiftung & Co. KGaA; *Int'l*, pg. 1425
SAXOPRINT LTD.—See CEWE Stiftung & Co. KGaA; *Int'l*, pg. 1425
SAXORE BERGBAU GMBH—See First Tin Plc; *Int'l*, pg. 2688
SAX SANITAIR N.V.—See CRH plc; *Int'l*, pg. 1848
SAXTON, BRADLEY, INC; *U.S. Private*, pg. 3558
SAXTON HORNE ADVERTISING; *U.S. Private*, pg. 3558
SAXTON PIERCE RESTAURANT CORP; *U.S. Private*, pg. 3558
SAXUM PUBLIC RELATIONS; *U.S. Private*, pg. 3558
SAYAJI HOTELS LIMITED; *Int'l*, pg. 6603
SAYAJI HOTELS(PUNE) LIMITED—See SAYAJI HOTELS LIMITED; *Int'l*, pg. 6603
SAYAJI INDUSTRIES LIMITED; *Int'l*, pg. 6603
SAYAMA CORPORATION—See Air Water Inc.; *Int'l*, pg. 240
SAYAMA MANUFACTURING FACILITY—See Honda Motor Co., Ltd.; *Int'l*, pg. 3464
SAYAMA SOKEN CO., LTD.—See Soken Chemical & Engineering Co.,Ltd.; *Int'l*, pg. 7066
SAYBOLT BELGIUM N.V.—See Core Laboratories N.V.; *Int'l*, pg. 1798
SAYBOLT, LP—See Core Laboratories N.V.; *Int'l*, pg. 1798
SAYBOLT NEDERLAND B.V.—See Core Laboratories N.V.; *Int'l*, pg. 1798
SAYBOLT (SINGAPORE) PTE LTD.—See China Leon Inspection Holding Limited; *Int'l*, pg. 1514
SAYBROOK CORPORATE OPPORTUNITY FUND LP; *U.S. Private*, pg. 3558
SAYERS GROUP LLC; *U.S. Private*, pg. 3558
SAYLENT TECHNOLOGIES, INC.; *U.S. Private*, pg. 3558
SAYLE OIL COMPANY INC.; *U.S. Private*, pg. 3558
SAYLER LEGAL SERVICE, INC.—See Gemini Legal Support, Inc.; *U.S. Private*, pg. 1658

SAYLOR ADVERTISING, INC.; *Int'l*, pg. 6603
SAY MEDIA, INC.—See The Arena Group Holdings, Inc; *U.S. Public*, pg. 2035
SAYONA MINING LIMITED; *Int'l*, pg. 6603
SAYONA QUEBEC INC.—See Sayona Mining Limited; *Int'l*, pg. 6603
SAYRES & ASSOCIATES, LLC—See Broadtree Partners, LLC; *U.S. Private*, pg. 659
SAYVA SOLUTIONS INC.; *U.S. Private*, pg. 3558
SAYWELL CONTRACTING LTD.; *Int'l*, pg. 6603
SAYWELL INTERNATIONAL; *Int'l*, pg. 6603
SAY YENILENEBILIR ENERJI EKIPMANLARI SANAYI VE TICARET A.S.; *Int'l*, pg. 6603
SAZERAC COMPANY, INC.; *U.S. Private*, pg. 3559
SAZONADORES DEL PACIFICO C. LTDA.—See Ajinomoto Company, Inc.; *Int'l*, pg. 257
SA ZUB; *Int'l*, pg. 6459
SBA COMMUNICATIONS CORPORATION; *U.S. Public*, pg. 1842
SBAEK INVEST PLC; *Int'l*, pg. 6603
SB AGENCY INC.—See Nippon Steel Corporation; *Int'l*, pg. 5338
S-BAHN BERLIN GMBH—See Deutsche Bahn AG; *Int'l*, pg. 2052
S-BAHN HAMBURG GMBH—See Deutsche Bahn AG; *Int'l*, pg. 2052
SBA NETWORK SERVICES, INC.—See SBA Communications Corporation; *U.S. Public*, pg. 1842
SBANKEN ASA—See DNB Bank ASA; *Int'l*, pg. 2148
SBARRO LLC; *U.S. Private*, pg. 3559
SBAR'S, INC.; *U.S. Private*, pg. 3559
SBAS (HK) LTD.—See Fortune Information Systems Corp.; *Int'l*, pg. 2743
SBAS (HONG KONG) LTD.; *Int'l*, pg. 6603
SBA—See NSC Groupe SA; *Int'l*, pg. 5476
SBA TELECOMMUNICATIONS, INC.—See SBA Communications Corporation; *U.S. Public*, pg. 1842
SBA TOWERS IV, LLC—See SBA Communications Corporation; *U.S. Public*, pg. 1842
SBA ZASO KUPALA—See Vienna Insurance Group AG Wiener Versicherung Gruppe; *Int'l*, pg. 8195
S B BALLARD CONSTRUCTION CO.; *U.S. Private*, pg. 3512
SBB BEUTLER & LANG GMBH & CO—See Beutler & Lang Schalungs- und Behalter-Bau GmbH; *Int'l*, pg. 1004
SBB CARGO DEUTSCHLAND GMBH—See Schweizerische Bundesbahnen SBB AG; *Int'l*, pg. 6646
SBB CARGO GMBH—See Schweizerische Bundesbahnen SBB AG; *Int'l*, pg. 6646
SBB CARGO ITALIA S.R.L.—See Schweizerische Bundesbahnen SBB AG; *Int'l*, pg. 6646
SBB ELDSBODA AB—See Samhallsbyggnadsbolaget I Norden AB; *Int'l*, pg. 6504
SBB FLUGSVAMPEN 7 FASTIGHETS AB—See Samhallsbyggnadsbolaget I Norden AB; *Int'l*, pg. 6504
SB&B FOODS INC.; *U.S. Private*, pg. 3559
SBB GORVALN 1 FASTIGHETS AB—See Samhallsbyggnadsbolaget I Norden AB; *Int'l*, pg. 6504
SBB GROTTAN 7 FASTIGHETS AB—See Samhallsbyggnadsbolaget I Norden AB; *Int'l*, pg. 6504
SBB GULDFISKEN I HOGANAS AB—See Samhallsbyggnadsbolaget I Norden AB; *Int'l*, pg. 6504
SBB GULLBERNAHULT 23 AB—See Samhallsbyggnadsbolaget I Norden AB; *Int'l*, pg. 6504
SBB GULLBERNAHULT 82 AB—See Samhallsbyggnadsbolaget I Norden AB; *Int'l*, pg. 6504
SBB HALLONET 1 FASTIGHETS AB—See Samhallsbyggnadsbolaget I Norden AB; *Int'l*, pg. 6504
SBB HULTET 5 FASTIGHETS AB—See Samhallsbyggnadsbolaget I Norden AB; *Int'l*, pg. 6504
SBB KONTORSSKYLTEN 7 FASTIGHETS AB—See Samhallsbyggnadsbolaget I Norden AB; *Int'l*, pg. 6504
SBB LAKAREN 5 FASTIGHETS AB—See Samhallsbyggnadsbolaget I Norden AB; *Int'l*, pg. 6504
SBB LANDSDOMAREN 15 FASTIGHETS AB—See Samhallsbyggnadsbolaget I Norden AB; *Int'l*, pg. 6504
SBB LEJONET 9 FASTIGHETS AB—See Samhallsbyggnadsbolaget I Norden AB; *Int'l*, pg. 6504
SBB MARIEBERG 5 KB—See Samhallsbyggnadsbolaget I Norden AB; *Int'l*, pg. 6504
SBB MARSCHEN 1 FASTIGHETS AB—See Samhallsbyggnadsbolaget I Norden AB; *Int'l*, pg. 6504
SBB MISTELN 13 FASTIGHETS AB—See Samhallsbyggnadsbolaget I Norden AB; *Int'l*, pg. 6504
SBB MJOLKERSKAN 1 AB—See Samhallsbyggnadsbolaget I Norden AB; *Int'l*, pg. 6504
SBB MORTELN 1 FASTIGHETS AB—See Samhallsbyggnadsbolaget I Norden AB; *Int'l*, pg. 6504
SBB NIKLASBERG 13 FASTIGHETS AB—See Samhallsbyggnadsbolaget I Norden AB; *Int'l*, pg. 6504
SBB NJORD 32 FASTIGHETS AB—See Samhallsbyggnadsbolaget I Norden AB; *Int'l*, pg. 6504
SBB NOSHORNINGEN 15 FASTIGHETS AB—See Samhallsbyggnadsbolaget I Norden AB; *Int'l*, pg. 6504
SBB ROOFING INC.; *U.S. Private*, pg. 3559
SBB ROSENFINKEN 2 FASTIGHETS AB—See Samhallsbyggnadsbolaget I Norden AB; *Int'l*, pg. 6504

COMPANY NAME INDEX

SBB SAMFUNNSBYGG AS—See Samhallsbyggnadsbolaget I Norden AB; *Int'l*, pg. 6504
SBB SOLROSEN 17 FASTIGHETS AB—See Samhallsbyggnadsbolaget I Norden AB; *Int'l*, pg. 6504
SBB SPORREN 9 FASTIGHETS AB—See Samhallsbyggnadsbolaget I Norden AB; *Int'l*, pg. 6504
SBB STJARNEBO 1 FASTIGHETS AB—See Samhallsbyggnadsbolaget I Norden AB; *Int'l*, pg. 6504
SBB STOCKHOLM AB—See Samhallsbyggnadsbolaget I Norden AB; *Int'l*, pg. 6504
SBB TORDYVELN 1 FASTIGHETS AB—See Samhallsbyggnadsbolaget I Norden AB; *Int'l*, pg. 6504
SBB VASTHAGEN 1 FASTIGHETS AB—See Samhallsbyggnadsbolaget I Norden AB; *Int'l*, pg. 6504
SBB VINBARET 1 FASTIGHETS AB—See Samhallsbyggnadsbolaget I Norden AB; *Int'l*, pg. 6504
SBB VINGUDEN 1 FASTIGHETS AB—See Samhallsbyggnadsbolaget I Norden AB; *Int'l*, pg. 6504
SBC ADVERTISING; *U.S. Private*, pg. 3559
SB CAPITAL CORPORATION—See Bayer Aktiengesellschaft; *Int'l*, pg. 902
SB CATTLE LTD.—See ENL Limited; *Int'l*, pg. 2441
SBCBSG COMPANY DE MEXICO, S. DE R.I. DE C.V.—See Sally Beauty Holdings, Inc.; *U.S. Public*, pg. 1838
SBCC CLINIC PTE LTD—See OUE Limited; *Int'l*, pg. 5666
SBCC INC; *U.S. Private*, pg. 3559
SBC CORPORATION BERHAD; *Int'l*, pg. 6603
SBC DEUTSCHLAND GMBH—See Honeywell International Inc.; *U.S. Public*, pg. 1052
SBC EXPORTS LTD.; *Int'l*, pg. 6603
SBC GENERAL TRADING & CONTRACTING CO., LTD.—See SK Engineering & Construction Co., Ltd.; *Int'l*, pg. 6970
SB CHINA HOLDINGS PTE. LTD.—See SoftBank Group Corp.; *Int'l*, pg. 7051
SB COIL CENTER (THAILAND) LTD.—See Nippon Steel Corporation; *Int'l*, pg. 5338
S.B. COLLINS INC.; *U.S. Private*, pg. 3515
S.B. COX INC.; *U.S. Private*, pg. 3515
S.B.C.P. BANCORP, INC.; *U.S. Public*, pg. 1832
SBC PROPERTIES, INC.—See First Metro Investment Corporation; *Int'l*, pg. 2685
SBC SVERIGES BOSTADSRATTSCENTRUM AB; *Int'l*, pg. 6603
SB DARRON PTE. LTD.—See Schoeller-Bleckmann Oilfield Equipment AG; *Int'l*, pg. 6638
SBD CAPITAL CORP.; *Int'l*, pg. 6603
SBD ENTERPRISES, LLC—See Kainos Capital, LLC; *U.S. Private*, pg. 2255
SBE BIOENERGIE HANDELS GMBH; *Int'l*, pg. 6604
S.B.E.C.M. SOCIETE DE BOUCHAGES EMBALLAGES CONDITIONNES MODERNE S.A.R.L.—See Nestle S.A.; *Int'l*, pg. 5205
SBEC SUGAR LTD; *Int'l*, pg. 6604
SBEC SYSTEMS (INDIA), LTD.; *Int'l*, pg. 6604
SBEEG HOLDINGS, LLC; *U.S. Private*, pg. 3559
SBE ENTERTAINMENT GROUP, LLC; *U.S. Private*, pg. 3559
S&B ENGINEERS & CONSTRUCTORS, LTD.; *U.S. Private*, pg. 3512
SBERBANK A.D. BANJA LUKA—See OJSC Sberbank of Russia; *Int'l*, pg. 5542
SBERBANK ASSET MANAGEMENT JSC—See OJSC Sberbank of Russia; *Int'l*, pg. 5542
SBERBANK BANKA D.D.—See OJSC Sberbank of Russia; *Int'l*, pg. 5542
SBERBANK BH DD—See OJSC Sberbank of Russia; *Int'l*, pg. 5542
SBERBANK CAPITAL LLC—See OJSC Sberbank of Russia; *Int'l*, pg. 5542
SBERBANK CIB JSC—See OJSC Sberbank of Russia; *Int'l*, pg. 5542
SBERBANK CIB (UK) LIMITED—See OJSC Sberbank of Russia; *Int'l*, pg. 5542
SBERBANK CIB USA, INC.—See OJSC Sberbank of Russia; *Int'l*, pg. 5542
SBERBANK CZ A.S.—See OJSC Sberbank of Russia; *Int'l*, pg. 5542
SBERBANK EUROPE AG—See OJSC Sberbank of Russia; *Int'l*, pg. 5542
SBERBANK LEASING JSC—See OJSC Sberbank of Russia; *Int'l*, pg. 5542
SBERBANK MAGYARORSZAG ZRT—See OJSC Sberbank of Russia; *Int'l*, pg. 5542
SBERBANK SRBIJA AD—See OJSC Sberbank of Russia; *Int'l*, pg. 5542
SBERBANK (SWITZERLAND) AG—See OJSC Sberbank of Russia; *Int'l*, pg. 5542
S-BETEILIGUNGSGESELLSCHAFT HESSEN-THURINGEN MBH—See Helaba Landesbank Hessen-Thuringen; *Int'l*, pg. 3328
SBE-VARVIT S.P.A.; *Int'l*, pg. 6604
SBF AG; *Int'l*, pg. 6604
SBFC FINANCE LIMITED; *Int'l*, pg. 6604
SBF-HAGUSTA GMBH.—See BAUER Aktiengesellschaft; *Int'l*, pg. 893

SB FINANCIAL GROUP, INC.; *U.S. Public*, pg. 1842
S&B FOODS INC.; *Int'l*, pg. 6444
S.B. FOOT TANNING COMPANY CACTUS DIV.—See Red Wing Shoe Company, Inc.; *U.S. Private*, pg. 3376
S.B. FOOT TANNING COMPANY—See Red Wing Shoe Company, Inc.; *U.S. Private*, pg. 3376
SBG INNOVATIE BV—See CNH Industrial N.V.; *Int'l*, pg. 1676
SBG SUDBADENBUS GMBH—See Deutsche Bahn AG; *Int'l*, pg. 2052
SBG TECHNOLOGY SOLUTIONS INC.; *U.S. Private*, pg. 3559
SBH ASSOCIATES, INC.; *U.S. Private*, pg. 3559
S&B HERBA FOODS, LTD.—See Ebro Foods S.A.; *Int'l*, pg. 2287
SBH KIBING SOLAR NEW MATERIALS (M) SDN. BHD.—See Zhuzhou Kibing Group Co., Ltd.; *Int'l*, pg. 8680
SBH SCIENCE, INC.; *U.S. Private*, pg. 3559
SBI ALAPROMO CO., LTD.—See SBI Holdings, Inc.; *Int'l*, pg. 6604
SBI ARSNOVA RESEARCH CO., LTD.—See SBI Holdings, Inc.; *Int'l*, pg. 6604
SBI ARTFOLIO CO., LTD.—See SBI Holdings, Inc.; *Int'l*, pg. 6606
SBI ASSET MANAGEMENT CO., LTD.—See SBI Holdings, Inc.; *Int'l*, pg. 6604
SBI AUTOSUPPORT CO., LTD.—See SBI Holdings, Inc.; *Int'l*, pg. 6604
SBI BANK LLC—See SBI Holdings, Inc.; *Int'l*, pg. 6604
SBI BENEFIT SYSTEMS CO., LTD.—See SBI Holdings, Inc.; *Int'l*, pg. 6604
SBI BIOTECH CO., LTD.—See SBI Holdings, Inc.; *Int'l*, pg. 6604
SBI BITS CO., LTD.—See SBI Holdings, Inc.; *Int'l*, pg. 6604
SBI BUSINESS SOLUTIONS CO., LTD.—See SBI Holdings, Inc.; *Int'l*, pg. 6604
SBI BUSINESS SUPPORT CO., LTD.—See SBI Holdings, Inc.; *Int'l*, pg. 6604
SBI CAPITAL CO., LTD.—See SBI Holdings, Inc.; *Int'l*, pg. 6604
SBI CAPITAL SOLUTIONS CO., LTD.—See SBI Holdings, Inc.; *Int'l*, pg. 6604
SBICAP VENTURES LTD.—See State Bank of India; *Int'l*, pg. 7181
SBI CARD CO., LTD.—See SBI Holdings, Inc.; *Int'l*, pg. 6605
SBI CARDS & PAYMENTS SERVICES PVT. LTD.—See State Bank of India; *Int'l*, pg. 7181
SBI (CHINA) CO., LTD.—See SBI Holdings, Inc.; *Int'l*, pg. 6604
SBI EQUAL CREDIT CO., LTD.—See SBI Holdings, Inc.; *Int'l*, pg. 6605
SBI ESTATE MANAGEMENT CO., LTD.—See SBI Holdings, Inc.; *Int'l*, pg. 6605
SBI FINTECH SOLUTIONS CO., LTD.—See SBI Holdings, Inc.; *Int'l*, pg. 6605
SBI FUND BANK CO., LTD.—See SBI Holdings, Inc.; *Int'l*, pg. 6605
SBI FUNDS MANAGEMENT LIMITED; *Int'l*, pg. 6604
SBI FUTURES CO., LTD.—See SBI Holdings, Inc.; *Int'l*, pg. 6605
SBI FXTRADE CO., LTD.—See SBI Holdings, Inc.; *Int'l*, pg. 6605
SBIGEO MARKETING CO., LTD.—See GEO Holdings Corporation; *Int'l*, pg. 2932
SBI GLOBAL ASSET MANAGEMENT CO., LTD.—See SBI Holdings, Inc.; *Int'l*, pg. 6605
SBI GUARANTEE CO., LTD.—See SBI Holdings, Inc.; *Int'l*, pg. 6605
SBI-HIKARI P.E. CO., LTD.—See Hikari Tsushin, Inc.; *Int'l*, pg. 3390
SBI-HIKARI P.E. CO., LTD.—See SBI Holdings, Inc.; *Int'l*, pg. 6606
SBI HOLDINGS, INC.; *Int'l*, pg. 6604
SBI HOME FINANCE LTD.; *Int'l*, pg. 6606
SBI IKIIKI SSI INC.—See SBI Holdings, Inc.; *Int'l*, pg. 6605
SBI INCORPORATED; *U.S. Private*, pg. 3559
SBI INSURANCE CO., LTD.—See SBI Holdings, Inc.; *Int'l*, pg. 6605
SBI INSURANCE GROUP CO., LTD.—See SBI Holdings, Inc.; *Int'l*, pg. 6605
SBI INVESTMENT CO., LTD.—See SBI Holdings, Inc.; *Int'l*, pg. 6605
SBI INVESTMENT KOREA CO., LTD.—See SBI Holdings, Inc.; *Int'l*, pg. 6605
SBI JAPANNEXT CO., LTD.—See SBI Holdings, Inc.; *Int'l*, pg. 6605
SBI KOREA HOLDINGS CO., LTD.—See SBI Holdings, Inc.; *Int'l*, pg. 6605
SBI LEASE CO., LTD.—See SBI Holdings, Inc.; *Int'l*, pg. 6605
SBI LIFE INSURANCE CO., LTD.—See SBI Holdings, Inc.; *Int'l*, pg. 6605
SBI LIFE INSURANCE COMPANY LIMITED—See State Bank of India; *Int'l*, pg. 7181
SBI LIQUIDITY MARKET CO., LTD.—See SBI Holdings, Inc.; *Int'l*, pg. 6605

SBL INFRATECH LIMITED

SBI LY HOUR BANK PLC.—See SBI Holdings, Inc.; *Int'l*, pg. 6605
SBI MARKETING CO., LTD.—See SBI Holdings, Inc.; *Int'l*, pg. 6605
SBI METROPOL FUND MANAGEMENT COMPANY—See SBI Holdings, Inc.; *Int'l*, pg. 6605
SBI MONEY PLAZA CO., LTD.—See SBI Holdings, Inc.; *Int'l*, pg. 6605
SBI NEO MOBILE SECURITIES CO., LTD.—See SBI Holdings, Inc.; *Int'l*, pg. 6605
SBI NEOTRADE SECURITIES CO., LTD.—See SBI Holdings, Inc.; *Int'l*, pg. 6605
SBI NET SYSTEMS CO., LTD.—See SBI Holdings, Inc.; *Int'l*, pg. 6605
S.B. INFORMATION SYSTEM CO., LTD.—See Sumitomo Bakelite Co., Ltd.; *Int'l*, pg. 7263
S&B INFRASTRUCTURE, LTD.—See S&B Engineers & Constructors, Ltd.; *U.S. Private*, pg. 3512
SBI NIHON SSI CO., LTD.—See SBI Holdings, Inc.; *Int'l*, pg. 6605
S&B INTERNATIONAL CORPORATION—See S&B Foods Inc.; *Int'l*, pg. 6444
S.BIOMEDICS CO., LTD.; *Int'l*, pg. 6449
S*BIO PTE. LTD.—See EDB Investments Pte. Ltd.; *Int'l*, pg. 2304
SBI PHARMACEUTICALS CO., LTD.—See SBI Holdings, Inc.; *Int'l*, pg. 6605
SBI POINT UNION CO., LTD.—See SBI Holdings, Inc.; *Int'l*, pg. 6605
SBI PRISM SSI CO., LTD.—See SBI Holdings, Inc.; *Int'l*, pg. 6605
SBI PROPERTY ADVISORS CO., LTD.—See SBI Holdings, Inc.; *Int'l*, pg. 6605
SBI R3 JAPAN CO., LTD.—See SBI Holdings, Inc.; *Int'l*, pg. 6605
SBI RECEIPT CO., LTD.—See SBI Holdings, Inc.; *Int'l*, pg. 6605
SBI REMIT CO., LTD.—See SBI Holdings, Inc.; *Int'l*, pg. 6605
SBI RESTA SSI CO., LTD.—See SBI Holdings, Inc.; *Int'l*, pg. 6605
SBI RIPPLE ASIA CO., LTD.—See SBI Holdings, Inc.; *Int'l*, pg. 6605
SBI ROYAL SECURITIES PLC.—See SBI Holdings, Inc.; *Int'l*, pg. 6606
SBI (SEA BUNKERING INTERNATIONAL) B. V.—See Marquard & Bahls AG; *Int'l*, pg. 4700
SBI SECURITIES CO., LTD.—See SBI Holdings, Inc.; *Int'l*, pg. 6606
SBI SEGUROS URUGUAY S.A.—See Fairfax Financial Holdings Limited; *Int'l*, pg. 2608
SBI SERVICER CO., LTD.—See SBI Holdings, Inc.; *Int'l*, pg. 6606
SBI SHINSEI BANK, LIMITED; *Int'l*, pg. 6606
SBI SOCIAL LENDING CO., LTD.—See SBI Holdings, Inc.; *Int'l*, pg. 6606
SBI SUMISHIN NET BANK, LTD.—See SBI Holdings, Inc.; *Int'l*, pg. 6606
SBI SUMISHIN NET BANK, LTD.—See Sumitomo Mitsui Trust Holdings, Inc.; *Int'l*, pg. 7296
SBI THAI ONLINE SECURITIES CO., LTD.—See SBI Holdings, Inc.; *Int'l*, pg. 6606
SBI TRANS-SCIENCE CO., LTD.—See SBI Holdings, Inc.; *Int'l*, pg. 6606
SBI VC TRADE CO., LTD.—See SBI Holdings, Inc.; *Int'l*, pg. 6606
SBI VEN CAPITAL PTE. LTD.—See SBI Holdings, Inc.; *Int'l*, pg. 6606
SBI VEN HOLDINGS PTE. LTD.—See SBI Holdings, Inc.; *Int'l*, pg. 6606
SBI VENTURES MALAYSIA SDN. BHD.—See SBI Holdings, Inc.; *Int'l*, pg. 6606
SBI WELLNESS BANK CO., LTD.—See SBI Holdings, Inc.; *Int'l*, pg. 6606
SBJ DNX CO., LTD.—See Shinhan Financial Group Co., Ltd.; *Int'l*, pg. 6844
SB JSC NURBANK MONEY EXPERTS JSC—See Nurbank JSC; *Int'l*, pg. 5489
SB JSC SBERBANK—See OJSC Sberbank of Russia; *Int'l*, pg. 5542
SB-KAWASUMI LABORATORIES, INC.—See Sumitomo Bakelite Co., Ltd.; *Int'l*, pg. 7263
SBL CAPITAL MANAGEMENT LIMITED—See Standard Bank Limited; *Int'l*, pg. 7166
SBL INFRATECH LIMITED; *Int'l*, pg. 6606
SBLI USA MUTUAL LIFE INSURANCE COMPANY, INC.—See Prosperity Group Holdings, LP; *U.S. Private*, pg. 3289
SB LIVING CO., LTD.—See Nippon Steel Corporation; *Int'l*, pg. 5338
SB LIZINGAS UAB—See Siauliu bankas AB; *Int'l*, pg. 6876
S BLOMQUIST ENTREPRENAD AB—See Nordisk Bergteknik AB; *Int'l*, pg. 5424
SBL PVT. LTD—See Boiron Group; *Int'l*, pg. 1101
SBL SPECIALTY COATINGS PRIVATE LIMITED—See Berger Paints India Limited; *Int'l*, pg. 980
SB MANUFACTURING, INC.—See Berry Companies, Inc.; *U.S. Private*, pg. 538

SBL INFRATECH LIMITED / CORPORATE AFFILIATIONS

SBM ASSET MANAGEMENT LIMITED—See State Bank of Mauritius Ltd.; *Int'l*, pg. 7181
SBM CAPITAL MANAGEMENT LIMITED—See State Bank of Mauritius Ltd.; *Int'l*, pg. 7181
SB MEDIA HOLDINGS CORP.—See SoftBank Group Corp.; *Int'l*, pg. 7051
SBM FINANCIALS LIMITED—See State Bank of Mauritius Ltd.; *Int'l*, pg. 7181
SBM GLOBAL INVESTMENT LIMITED—See State Bank of Mauritius Ltd.; *Int'l*, pg. 7181
SBM HOLDING BEOMEDICINA A.D.; *Int'l*, pg. 6606
SBM INTERNATIONAL INVESTMENTS LIMITED—See State Bank of Mauritius Ltd.; *Int'l*, pg. 7181
SBM INVESTMENTS LIMITED—See State Bank of Mauritius Ltd.; *Int'l*, pg. 7181
SBM IT LIMITED—See State Bank of Mauritius Ltd.; *Int'l*, pg. 7181
SBM LEASE LIMITED—See State Bank of Mauritius Ltd.; *Int'l*, pg. 7181
SBM MALAYSIA SDN BHD—See SBM Offshore N.V.; *Int'l*, pg. 6607
SBM MAURITIUS ASSET MANAGERS LTD—See State Bank of Mauritius Ltd.; *Int'l*, pg. 7181
SBM OFFSHORE N.V.; *Int'l*, pg. 6606
SBM OFFSHORE—See SBM Offshore N.V.; *Int'l*, pg. 6607
SBM OFFSHORE USA, INC.—See SBM Offshore N.V.; *Int'l*, pg. 6607
S & B MOTELS, INC.; *U.S. Private*, pg. 3511
SBM SCHOELLER-BLECKMANN-MEDIZINTECHNIK GMBH—See Robert Bosch GmbH; *Int'l*, pg. 6368
SBM SECURITIES LTD—See State Bank of Mauritius Ltd.; *Int'l*, pg. 7181
SBN, INC.—See Macquarie Group Limited; *Int'l*, pg. 4627
SBN NEWS—See Sheridan Broadcasting Corporation; *U.S. Private*, pg. 3633
SBONE SOLUTIONS SDN. BHD.—See TFP Solutions Berhad; *Int'l*, pg. 7587
SB PARTNERS; *U.S. Private*, pg. 3559
SB PEARL FASHION CO., LTD.—See Nippon Steel Corporation; *Int'l*, pg. 5338
S & B PHARMA INC.—See Alkem Laboratories Ltd.; *Int'l*, pg. 330
SBP HOLDINGS INC.—See AEA Investors LP; *U.S. Private*, pg. 115
SB PLANNING CO., LTD.—See Nippon Steel Corporation; *Int'l*, pg. 5338
S&B PLANT SERVICES, LTD.—See S&B Engineers & Constructors, Ltd.; *U.S. Private*, pg. 3512
SBPR CORP.; *U.S. Private*, pg. 3560
S.B. RECYCLE CO., LTD.—See Sumitomo Bakelite Co., Ltd.; *Int'l*, pg. 7263
S.B. RESEARCH CO., LTD.—See Sumitomo Bakelite Co., Ltd.; *Int'l*, pg. 7263
SB RESHELLERS PVT. LIMITED—See The Ugar Sugar Works Limited; *Int'l*, pg. 7697
SBR EVENTS GROUP; *U.S. Private*, pg. 3560
SB/RH HOLDINGS, LLC; *U.S. Private*, pg. 3559
S BROKER AG & CO. KG—See DekaBank; *Int'l*, pg. 2005
SBR SAS—See VINCI S.A.; *Int'l*, pg. 8226
SBS 6—See Talpa Holding B.V.; *Int'l*, pg. 7448
S.B. SAIGON FASHION CO., LTD.—See Nippon Steel Corporation; *Int'l*, pg. 5338
SBSA, INC.—See Lovell Minnick Partners LLC; *U.S. Private*, pg. 2502
SBS ASSET MANAGEMENT CO., LTD.—See SBS Holdings Inc.; *Int'l*, pg. 6607
SBS BELGIUM NV—See Liberty Global plc; *Int'l*, pg. 4485
SBS/BISON BUILDING MATERIALS, LLC—See Builders FirstSource, Inc.; *U.S. Public*, pg. 409
SBS CONTENTS HUB CO., LTD.—See TY Holdings Co. Ltd.; *Int'l*, pg. 7993
SBS DEUTSCHLAND GMBH—See Scandinavian Brake Systems A/S; *Int'l*, pg. 6612
SBS DRIVING SCHOOL CO., LTD.—See SBS Holdings Inc.; *Int'l*, pg. 6607
SBS ENTERPRISES INC.; *U.S. Private*, pg. 3560
SBS FINANCE CO., LTD.—See SBS Holdings Inc.; *Int'l*, pg. 6607
SBS FLEC CO., LTD.—See SBS Holdings Inc.; *Int'l*, pg. 6607
SBS FLECK NET CO., LTD.—See SBS Holdings Inc.; *Int'l*, pg. 6607
SBS FRANCE SAS—See Scandinavian Brake Systems A/S; *Int'l*, pg. 6612
SBS FREIGHT SERVICE CO., LTD.—See SBS Holdings Inc.; *Int'l*, pg. 6607
SBS FURUKAWA LOGISTICS CO., LTD.—See SBS Holdings Inc.; *Int'l*, pg. 6607
SBS GLOBAL NETWORK CO., LTD.—See SBS Holdings Inc.; *Int'l*, pg. 6607
S.B. SHEET WATERPROOF SYSTEMS CO., LTD.—See Sumitomo Bakelite Co., Ltd.; *Int'l*, pg. 7263
SBS HOLDINGS INC.; *Int'l*, pg. 6607
SB SIMPSON GROUP; *Int'l*, pg. 6603
SBS INDUSTRIES, INC.—See Gladstone Management Corporation; *U.S. Private*, pg. 1705
SBS KAMATA ZAIDAN—See SBS Holdings Inc.; *Int'l*, pg. 6607

SBS LOGICOM CO., LTD.—See SBS Holdings Inc.; *Int'l*, pg. 6607
SBS LOGICOM KANTO CO., LTD.—See SBS Holdings Inc.; *Int'l*, pg. 6607
SBS LOGISTICS HONG KONG LTD.—See SBS Holdings Inc.; *Int'l*, pg. 6607
SBS LOGISTICS SINGAPORE PTE. LTD.—See SBS Holdings Inc.; *Int'l*, pg. 6607
SBS LOGISTICS (THAILAND) CO., LTD.—See SBS Holdings Inc.; *Int'l*, pg. 6607
SBS MEDIA HOLDINGS CO., LTD.—See TY Holdings Co. Ltd.; *Int'l*, pg. 7993
SBS NOMINEES PRIVATE LIMITED—See Singapura Finance Ltd.; *Int'l*, pg. 6943
SBS PHILIPPINES CORPORATION; *Int'l*, pg. 6608
SBS RADIO AB—See Warner Bros. Discovery, Inc.; *U.S. Public*, pg. 2326
SBS REALTY SERVICES (PRIVATE) LIMITED—See Singapura Finance Ltd.; *Int'l*, pg. 6943
SBS RICOH LOGISTICS CO., LTD.—See SBS Holdings Inc.; *Int'l*, pg. 6607
SBS RICOH LOGISTICS SYSTEM CO., LTD.—See SBS Holdings Inc.; *Int'l*, pg. 6607
SBS SAN-AI LOGISTICS CO., LTD.—See SBS Holdings Inc.; *Int'l*, pg. 6607
SBS SEGUROS COLOMBIA S.A.—See Fairfax Financial Holdings Limited; *Int'l*, pg. 2608
SBS SOKUHAI SUPPORT CO., LTD.—See SBS Holdings Inc.; *Int'l*, pg. 6607
SBS—See Groupe BPCE; *Int'l*, pg. 3095
SBS STAFF CO., LTD.—See SBS Holdings Inc.; *Int'l*, pg. 6608
SBS STRABAG BAU HOLDING SERVICE GMBH—See STRABAG SE; *Int'l*, pg. 7232
SBS SUPPORT LOGI CO., LTD.—See SBS Holdings Inc.; *Int'l*, pg. 6608
SBS TOSHIBA LOGISTICS CO., LTD.—See SBS Holdings Inc.; *Int'l*, pg. 6608
SBS TOTAL LOGISTICS MALAYSIA SDN. BHD.—See SBS Holdings Inc.; *Int'l*, pg. 6607
SBS TRANSIT DTL PTE. LTD.—See ComfortDelGro Corporation Limited; *Int'l*, pg. 1713
SBS TRANSIT LTD.—See ComfortDelGro Corporation Limited; *Int'l*, pg. 1713
SB SUPPLIES & LOGISTICS SDN. BHD.—See Borneo Oil Berhad; *Int'l*, pg. 1114
SBS VIETNAM CO., LTD.—See SBS Holdings Inc.; *Int'l*, pg. 6608
SBS ZENTSU CO., LTD.—See SBS Holdings Inc.; *Int'l*, pg. 6608
SBTA INCORPORATION—See Sebo Manufacturing Engineering Corp.; *Int'l*, pg. 6670
SBT BANCSHARES, INC.; *U.S. Private*, pg. 3560
S&B TECHNICAL PRODUCTS, INC.; *U.S. Private*, pg. 3512
SB TECHNOLOGY CORP.—See SoftBank Group Corp.; *Int'l*, pg. 7051
S.B. TECHNO PLASTICS CO., LTD.—See Sumitomo Bakelite Co., Ltd.; *Int'l*, pg. 7263
S. B. & T. INTERNATIONAL LIMITED; *Int'l*, pg. 6446
SB TRADUCTION SARL—See CDS Co., Ltd.; *Int'l*, pg. 1371
S - BUDOVY, A.S.—See Vienna Insurance Group AG Wiener Versicherung Gruppe; *Int'l*, pg. 8195
S. BURDE & CO.; *Int'l*, pg. 6446
S-BUSINESS OY—See Suomen Osuuskauppojen Keskuskunta; *Int'l*, pg. 7333
SBW INC.; *Int'l*, pg. 6608
SC2N SA—See Valeo S.A.; *Int'l*, pg. 8113
SC3 LLC—See General Dynamics Corporation; *U.S. Public*, pg. 916
SCA AMERICAS INC.—See Svenska Cellulosa Aktiebolaget SCA; *Int'l*, pg. 7356
SCABAL JAPAN CO., LTD.—See ITOCHU Corporation; *Int'l*, pg. 3841
SC-ABEAM AUTOMOTIVE CONSULTING—See Sumitomo Corporation; *Int'l*, pg. 7270
SCA CAPSOM; *Int'l*, pg. 6610
SCADATA SCIENTIFIC, LLC—See Wireless Ventures LLC; *U.S. Private*, pg. 4547
SC ADIDAS UKRAINE—See adidas AG; *Int'l*, pg. 146
SCA-DORAL, LLC—See UnitedHealth Group Incorporated; *U.S. Public*, pg. 2250
SCA EMBALLAGE FRANCE SAS—See Svenska Cellulosa Aktiebolaget SCA; *Int'l*, pg. 7356
SCAFCO CORPORATION; *U.S. Private*, pg. 3560
SCAFCO STEEL STUD MANUFACTURING CO.—See SCAFCO Corporation; *U.S. Private*, pg. 3560
SCAFFIDI MOTORS INC.; *U.S. Private*, pg. 3560
SCAFFOLD & CONSTRUCTION PRODUCTS—See The Alumasc Group plc; *Int'l*, pg. 7613
SCAFFOLDING RENTAL & ERECTION SERVICES, LLC—See Bernhard Capital Partners Management, LP; *U.S. Private*, pg. 537
SCAFFOLDING RENTAL & ERECTION SERVICES, LLC—See KBR, Inc.; *U.S. Public*, pg. 1216
SCAFFOLD MASTER SDN BHD—See IJM Corporation Berhad; *Int'l*, pg. 3609
SCAFF'S INC.; *U.S. Private*, pg. 3560

SCA FOREST PRODUCTS AB—See Svenska Cellulosa Aktiebolaget SCA; *Int'l*, pg. 7356
SCA FORSAKRINGS AB—See Svenska Cellulosa Aktiebolaget SCA; *Int'l*, pg. 7356
SCA GMBH—See Svenska Cellulosa Aktiebolaget SCA; *Int'l*, pg. 7357
SC AGRANA ROMANIA SA—See AGRANA Beteiligungs-AG; *Int'l*, pg. 214
SCA GRAPHIC PAPER—See Svenska Cellulosa Aktiebolaget SCA; *Int'l*, pg. 7357
SCA GRAPHIC SUNDSVALL AB—See Svenska Cellulosa Aktiebolaget SCA; *Int'l*, pg. 7357
SCA HYGIENE MALAYSIA SDN BHD—See Svenska Cellulosa Aktiebolaget SCA; *Int'l*, pg. 7357
SCA HYGIENE MARKETING (M) SDN BHD—See Svenska Cellulosa Aktiebolaget SCA; *Int'l*, pg. 7357
SCA HYGIENE PRODUCTS AB—See Svenska Cellulosa Aktiebolaget SCA; *Int'l*, pg. 7357
SCA HYGIENE PRODUCTS AE—See Svenska Cellulosa Aktiebolaget SCA; *Int'l*, pg. 7357
SCA HYGIENE PRODUCTS AG—See Svenska Cellulosa Aktiebolaget SCA; *Int'l*, pg. 7357
SCA HYGIENE PRODUCTS A/S—See Svenska Cellulosa Aktiebolaget SCA; *Int'l*, pg. 7357
SCA HYGIENE PRODUCTS GMBH—See Svenska Cellulosa Aktiebolaget SCA; *Int'l*, pg. 7357
SCA HYGIENE PRODUCTS INC—See Svenska Cellulosa Aktiebolaget SCA; *Int'l*, pg. 7356
SCA HYGIENE PRODUCTS KFT—See Svenska Cellulosa Aktiebolaget SCA; *Int'l*, pg. 7357
SCA HYGIENE PRODUCTS MANCHESTER LTD—See Svenska Cellulosa Aktiebolaget SCA; *Int'l*, pg. 7357
SCA HYGIENE PRODUCTS NEDERLAND B.V.—See Svenska Cellulosa Aktiebolaget SCA; *Int'l*, pg. 7357
SCA HYGIENE PRODUCTS RUSSIA LLC—See Svenska Cellulosa Aktiebolaget SCA; *Int'l*, pg. 7357
SCA HYGIENE PRODUCTS SA-NV—See Svenska Cellulosa Aktiebolaget SCA; *Int'l*, pg. 7357
SCA HYGIENE PRODUCTS SA—See Svenska Cellulosa Aktiebolaget SCA; *Int'l*, pg. 7357
SCA HYGIENE PRODUCTS S.L.—See Svenska Cellulosa Aktiebolaget SCA; *Int'l*, pg. 7357
SCA HYGIENE PRODUCTS—See Svenska Cellulosa Aktiebolaget SCA; *Int'l*, pg. 7357
SCA HYGIENE PRODUCTS—See Svenska Cellulosa Aktiebolaget SCA; *Int'l*, pg. 7357
SCA HYGIENE PRODUCTS S.P.A—See Svenska Cellulosa Aktiebolaget SCA; *Int'l*, pg. 7357
SCA HYGIENE PRODUCTS SP. Z.O.O.—See Svenska Cellulosa Aktiebolaget SCA; *Int'l*, pg. 7357
SCA HYGIENE PRODUCTS UK LIMITED—See Svenska Cellulosa Aktiebolaget SCA; *Int'l*, pg. 7357
SCA HYGIENE SPAIN, S.COM. P.A.—See Svenska Cellulosa Aktiebolaget SCA; *Int'l*, pg. 7357
SCAI S.P.A—See Hitachi, Ltd.; *Int'l*, pg. 3416
SCALA BIO CENTER AALBORG APS—See Egmont Fonden; *Int'l*, pg. 2326
SCALA BIO NYKOBONG F APS—See Egmont Fonden; *Int'l*, pg. 2326
SCALABLE NETWORK TECHNOLOGIES, INC.—See Keysight Technologies, Inc.; *U.S. Public*, pg. 1227
SCALABLE SOFTWARE, INC.; *U.S. Private*, pg. 3560
SCALA COMMUNICATIONS, INC.—See SCALA Inc.; *Int'l*, pg. 6610
SCALA DEVELOPMENT S.A.; *Int'l*, pg. 6610
SCALA EVENINGWEAR, INC.; *U.S. Private*, pg. 3560
SCALA INC.; *Int'l*, pg. 6610
SCALA, INC.—See Stratacache Inc.; *U.S. Private*, pg. 3834
SCALA/JWT—See WPP plc; *Int'l*, pg. 8482
SCALAMANDRE, INC.; *U.S. Private*, pg. 3560
SCALA NEXT INC.—See SCALA Inc.; *Int'l*, pg. 6610
SCALA PARTNERS, INC.—See SCALA Inc.; *Int'l*, pg. 6610
SCALA SERVICE, INC.—See SCALA Inc.; *Int'l*, pg. 6610
SCALDIS SALVAGE AND MARINE CONTRACTORS N.V.—See Ackermans & van Haaren NV; *Int'l*, pg. 105
SCALEBASE, INC.—See ESW Capital, LLC; *U.S. Private*, pg. 1430
SCALECO MANAGEMENT LLC; *U.S. Private*, pg. 3560
SCALED COMPOSITES, LLC—See Northrop Grumman Corporation; *U.S. Public*, pg. 1540
SCALE FINANCE LLC—See Belay, Inc.; *U.S. Private*, pg. 516
SCALE GAS SOLUTIONS, S.L.—See Enagas, S.A.; *Int'l*, pg. 2396
SCALES ADVERTISING; *U.S. Private*, pg. 3560
SCALES AIR COMPRESSOR CORP; *U.S. Private*, pg. 3560
SCALES CORPORATION LIMITED; *Int'l*, pg. 6610
SCALES EXPRESS INC.; *U.S. Private*, pg. 3560
SCALES INDUSTRIAL TECHNOLOGIES, INC.—See Atlas Copco AB; *Int'l*, pg. 684
SCALES LOGISTICS AUSTRALIA PTY. LTD.—See Scales Corporation Limited; *Int'l*, pg. 6611
SCALES LOGISTICS LIMITED—See Scales Corporation Limited; *Int'l*, pg. 6611
SCALE SYSTEMS INC.—See B&D Industrial, Inc.; *U.S. Private*, pg. 418

COMPANY NAME INDEX

SCALE-UP SYSTEMS LIMITED—See Mettler-Toledo International, Inc.; *U.S. Public*, pg. 1433
SCALEWORKS, INC.; *U.S. Private*, pg. 3561
S.C. ALIMENTARA S.A.; *Int'l*, pg. 6450
S.C. ALLFLEX ROMANIA S.R.L.—See Merck & Co., Inc.; *U.S. Public*, pg. 1421
S.C. ALPLA PLASTIC S.R.L.—See Alpla-Werke Alwin Lehner GmbH & Co. KG; *Int'l*, pg. 374
SCALZO GROUP; *U.S. Private*, pg. 3561
S.C. AMCO OTOPENI S.A.; *Int'l*, pg. 6450
SC AMGAZ S.A.—See ENGIE SA; *Int'l*, pg. 2434
SCAMP MARINE SL—See Gibunco Group Limited; *Int'l*, pg. 2963
SCAM SPA—See Certina Holding AG; *Int'l*, pg. 1423
SCANA ASA; *Int'l*, pg. 6611
SCANA BJORNEBORG AB—See Scana ASA; *Int'l*, pg. 6611
SCANACON AB—See Alder Fund I AB; *Int'l*, pg. 304
SCANACON ASIA LTD.—See Alder Fund I AB; *Int'l*, pg. 304
SCANACON (SHANGHAI) ENVIRONMENTAL TECHNOLOGIES., LTD.—See Alder Fund I AB; *Int'l*, pg. 304
SCANA CORPORATION—See Dominion Energy, Inc.; *U.S. Public*, pg. 674
SCANA DO BRASIL INDUSTRIAS LTDA.—See Scana ASA; *Int'l*, pg. 6611
SCANA ENERGY MARKETING INC. (SEMI)—See Dominion Energy, Inc.; *U.S. Public*, pg. 674
SCANA ENERGY—See Dominion Energy, Inc.; *U.S. Public*, pg. 674
SCANA KOREA HYDRAULIC—See Scana ASA; *Int'l*, pg. 6611
SCAN ALARMS LTD.—See SECOM Co., Ltd.; *Int'l*, pg. 6671
SCAN ALARMS & SECURITY SYSTEMS (UK) LTD.—See SECOM Co., Ltd.; *Int'l*, pg. 6671
SCAN-AM MARINE SERVICES, INC.—See GenNx360 Capital Partners, L.P.; *U.S. Private*, pg. 1672
SCAN SHANGHAI—See Scana ASA; *Int'l*, pg. 6611
SCANASIA OVERSEAS, INC.—See SM Investments Corporation; *Int'l*, pg. 6998
SCANA SKARPENORD AS—See Scana ASA; *Int'l*, pg. 6611
SCAN ASSOCIATES BERHAD; *Int'l*, pg. 6611
SCANA STAVANGER AS—See Scana ASA; *Int'l*, pg. 6611
SCANA STEEL BJORNEBORG AB—See Scana ASA; *Int'l*, pg. 6611
SCANA STEEL STAVANGER AS—See Scana ASA; *Int'l*, pg. 6611
SCANA SUBSEA AB—See Scana ASA; *Int'l*, pg. 6611
SCANA VOLDA AS—See Scana ASA; *Int'l*, pg. 6611
SCANCABLES AB (SCS)—See Telefonaktiebolaget LM Ericsson; *Int'l*, pg. 7534
SCANCELL HOLDINGS PLC; *Int'l*, pg. 6611
SCANCELL LIMITED—See Scancell Holdings plc; *Int'l*, pg. 6611
SCANCEM CENTRAL AFRICA HOLDING 1 AB—See Heidelberg Materials AG; *Int'l*, pg. 3319
SCANCEM CENTRAL AFRICA HOLDING 3 AB—See Heidelberg Materials AG; *Int'l*, pg. 3319
SCANCEM INTERNATIONAL ANS—See Heidelberg Materials AG; *Int'l*, pg. 3315
SCANCEM INTERNATIONAL DA—See Heidelberg Materials AG; *Int'l*, pg. 3319
SCAN COIN AB—See ACON Investments, LLC; *U.S. Private*, pg. 63
SCAN COIN, INC.—See ACON Investments, LLC; *U.S. Private*, pg. 63
SCANDAL MEDIA GROUP S.R.O.; *Int'l*, pg. 6611
SCANDAL MEDIA S.R.O.—See Scandal Media Group s.r.o.; *Int'l*, pg. 6611
SCANDBOOK HOLDING AB; *Int'l*, pg. 6611
SCAN DESIGN OF FLORIDA INC.; *U.S. Private*, pg. 3561
SCANDFIBRE LOGISTICS AB—See Billerud AB; *Int'l*, pg. 1030
SCANDIA COMPANY LTD—See N.K. Shacolas (Holdings) Ltd.; *Int'l*, pg. 5116
SCANDIA DOWN—See Chelsey Direct, LLC; *U.S. Private*, pg. 870
SCANDIA, INC.; *U.S. Public*, pg. 1842
SCANDIA PLASTICS—See Odyssey Investment Partners, LLC; *U.S. Private*, pg. 2995
SCANDI BYG A/S—See Nordic Wood Industries A/S; *Int'l*, pg. 5423
SCANDIC DISTILLERIES—See European Drinks S.A.; *Int'l*, pg. 2556
SCANDIC HOTEL DEUTSCHLAND GMBH—See EQT AB; *Int'l*, pg. 2479
SCANDIC HOTELS AB—See EQT AB; *Int'l*, pg. 2479
SCANDIC HOTELS AS—See EQT AB; *Int'l*, pg. 2479
SCANDIC HOTELS A/S—See EQT AB; *Int'l*, pg. 2479
SCANDIC HOTELS OY—See EQT AB; *Int'l*, pg. 2479
SCANDIDOS AB; *Int'l*, pg. 6612
SCANDIDOS INC.—See ScandiDos AB; *Int'l*, pg. 6612
SCANDIDOS SAS—See ScandiDos AB; *Int'l*, pg. 6612
SCANDIFLEX DO BRASIL LTDA.—See Eastman Chemical Company; *U.S. Public*, pg. 705
SCANDIGITAL INC.; *U.S. Private*, pg. 3561

SCANDI-GLASS A/S—See Compagnie de Saint-Gobain SA; *Int'l*, pg. 1736
SCANDILATI TERMOPLASTICI AB—See Lati Industria Termoplastici S.p.A.; *Int'l*, pg. 4423
SCANDINAVIAN AIRLINES SYSTEM SAS—See SAS AB; *Int'l*, pg. 6581
SCANDINAVIAN APPLIANCES A.S—See Frigoglass S.A.I.C.; *Int'l*, pg. 2792
SCANDINAVIAN BRAKE SYSTEMS A/S; *Int'l*, pg. 6612
SCANDINAVIAN BUSINESS SEATING AS—See Triton Advisers Limited; *Int'l*, pg. 7933
SCANDINAVIAN BUSINESS SEATING A/S—See Triton Advisers Limited; *Int'l*, pg. 7933
SCANDINAVIAN BUSINESS SEATING GMBH—See Triton Advisers Limited; *Int'l*, pg. 7933
SCANDINAVIAN BUSINESS SEATING SARL—See Triton Advisers Limited; *Int'l*, pg. 7933
SCANDINAVIAN CHEMOTECH AB; *Int'l*, pg. 6612
SCANDINAVIAN ELECTRIC HOLDING AS—See Rolls-Royce Holdings plc; *Int'l*, pg. 6394
SCANDINAVIAN ENVIRO SYSTEMS AB; *Int'l*, pg. 6612
SCANDINAVIAN INVESTMENT GROUP A/S; *Int'l*, pg. 6612
SCANDINAVIAN MEDICAL SOLUTIONS A/S; *Int'l*, pg. 6612
SCANDINAVIAN PHARMACEUTICALS-GENERICS AB—See Viatris Inc.; *U.S. Public*, pg. 2294
SCANDINAVIAN PRIVATE EQUITY A/S; *Int'l*, pg. 6612
SCANDINAVIAN REAL HEART AB; *Int'l*, pg. 6612
SCANDINAVIAN SERVICE PARTNER AB—See SSP Group plc; *Int'l*, pg. 7157
SCANDINAVIAN STUDIOS AB—See Bonnier AB; *Int'l*, pg. 1109
SCANDINAVIAN TANKING SYSTEM A/S—See Kemira Oyj; *Int'l*, pg. 4124
SCANDINAVIAN TOBACCO GROUP ASSENS—See Skandinavisk Holding A/S; *Int'l*, pg. 6977
SCANDINAVIAN TOBACCO GROUP A/S—See Skandinavisk Holding A/S; *Int'l*, pg. 6976
SCANDINAVIAN TOBACCO GROUP AUSTRALIA PTY LTD.—See Skandinavisk Holding A/S; *Int'l*, pg. 6977
SCANDINAVIAN TOBACCO GROUP HOUTHALEN N.V.—See Skandinavisk Holding A/S; *Int'l*, pg. 6977
SCANDINAVIAN TOBACCO GROUP NEW ZEALAND LTD.—See Skandinavisk Holding A/S; *Int'l*, pg. 6977
SCANDINAVIAN TOBACCO GROUP POLSKA SP Z O.O.—See Skandinavisk Holding A/S; *Int'l*, pg. 6977
SCANDINAVIAN TOBACCO GROUP SPAIN S.A.—See Skandinavisk Holding A/S; *Int'l*, pg. 6977
SCANDINAVIAN TOBACCO GROUP TOBACCO SERVICE B.V.—See Skandinavisk Holding A/S; *Int'l*, pg. 6977
SCANDINAVIA ONLINE AS—See Aller Holding A/S; *Int'l*, pg. 336
SCANDION ONCOLOGY A/S; *Int'l*, pg. 6612
SCANDI STANDARD AB; *Int'l*, pg. 6611
SCANDITRON DANMARK A/S—See Amplex AB; *Int'l*, pg. 434
SCANDITRON FINLAND OY—See Amplex AB; *Int'l*, pg. 434
SCANDITRON FINLAND OY—See Fuji Corporation; *Int'l*, pg. 2810
SCANDITRON FINLAND STENCILS—See Amplex AB; *Int'l*, pg. 434
SCANDITRON SP. Z.O.O.—See Amplex AB; *Int'l*, pg. 434
SCANDITRON SVERIGE AB—See Amplex AB; *Int'l*, pg. 434
SCANDITRON SWEDEN STENCILS—See Amplex AB; *Int'l*, pg. 434
SCANDIUM INTERNATIONAL MINING CORP; *U.S. Public*, pg. 1843
SCANDRILL, INC.; *U.S. Private*, pg. 3561
SCANELEC SAS—See Schneider Electric SE; *Int'l*, pg. 6629
SCAN ENERGY A/S; *Int'l*, pg. 6611
SCAN ENERGY IBERICA SLU—See Scan Energy A/S; *Int'l*, pg. 6611
SCAN ENGINEERING (PVT) LTD.—See Daikin Industries, Ltd.; *Int'l*, pg. 1936
SCANFIL ATVIDABERG AB—See Scanfil Plc; *Int'l*, pg. 6613
SCANFIL EMS OY—See Scanfil Plc; *Int'l*, pg. 6612
SCANFIL (HANGZHOU) CO., LTD; *Int'l*, pg. 6612
SCANFIL, INC.—See Scanfil Plc; *Int'l*, pg. 6613
SCANFIL KFT—See Scanfil Plc; *Int'l*, pg. 6612
SCANFIL MALMO AB—See Scanfil Plc; *Int'l*, pg. 6612
SCANFIL OU—See Scanfil Plc; *Int'l*, pg. 6613
SCANFIL PLC; *Int'l*, pg. 6612
SCANFIL POLAND SP. Z.O.O.—See Scanfil Plc; *Int'l*, pg. 6613
SCANFIL (SUZHOU) CO., LTD—See Scanfil Plc; *Int'l*, pg. 6612
SCANFIL SWEDEN AB—See Scanfil Plc; *Int'l*, pg. 6613
SCANFIL VANTAA OY—See Scanfil Plc; *Int'l*, pg. 6613
SCANFIL VELLINGE AB—See Scanfil Plc; *Int'l*, pg. 6613
SCAN FISH DANMARK A/S—See Austevoll Seafood ASA; *Int'l*, pg. 718
SCANFOODS LIMITED—See Café de Coral Holdings Limited; *Int'l*, pg. 1250

SCAN PROJECTS LIMITED

SCAN FRANCE SARL—See Badger Meter, Inc.; *U.S. Public*, pg. 263
SCANGLAS A/S—See Compagnie de Saint-Gobain SA; *Int'l*, pg. 1734
SCANGRIP AS—See Investment AB Latour; *Int'l*, pg. 3784
SCANGRIP NORTH AMERICA INC.—See Investment AB Latour; *Int'l*, pg. 3784
SCAN GROUP; *U.S. Private*, pg. 3561
SCAN HEALTH PLAN—See SCAN Group; *U.S. Private*, pg. 3561
SCAN-HIDE A.M.B.A.—See Danish Crown AmbA; *Int'l*, pg. 1965
SCANIA AB—See Porsche Automobil Holding SE; *Int'l*, pg. 5930
SCANIA ARGENTINA S.A.—See Porsche Automobil Holding SE; *Int'l*, pg. 5930
SCANIA AUSTRALIA PTY LTD—See Porsche Automobil Holding SE; *Int'l*, pg. 5930
SCANIA CV AB—See Porsche Automobil Holding SE; *Int'l*, pg. 5930
SCANIA DEUTSCHLAND GMBH—See Porsche Automobil Holding SE; *Int'l*, pg. 5931
SCANIA (GREAT BRITAIN) LTD.—See Porsche Automobil Holding SE; *Int'l*, pg. 5930
SCANIA SUOMI OY—See Porsche Automobil Holding SE; *Int'l*, pg. 5931
SCANIA USA INC.—See Porsche Automobil Holding SE; *Int'l*, pg. 5931
SCANICO A/S—See The Middleby Corporation; *U.S. Public*, pg. 2115
SCAN INTER PUBLIC COMPANY LIMITED; *Int'l*, pg. 6611
SCANJET ASIA PACIFIC PTE. LTD.—See Alfa Laval AB; *Int'l*, pg. 312
SCANJET MARINE & SYSTEMS AB—See Alfa Laval AB; *Int'l*, pg. 312
SCAN LAMPS AS—See Byggma ASA; *Int'l*, pg. 1235
SCANLANKEMPERBARD COMPANIES, LLC; *U.S. Private*, pg. 3561
SCANLAN & LEO, LTD.—See Sikich LLP; *U.S. Private*, pg. 3651
SCANLINE VFX; *U.S. Private*, pg. 3561
SCANLON AUTO GROUP; *U.S. Private*, pg. 3561
SCANLON LEXUS—See Scanlon Auto Group; *U.S. Private*, pg. 3561
SCANLON PRINTING CO. PTY LIMITED; *Int'l*, pg. 6613
SCANMASKIN DANMARK APS—See Indutrade AB; *Int'l*, pg. 3681
SCANMASKIN FINLAND OY—See Indutrade AB; *Int'l*, pg. 3681
SCANMASKIN MIDDLE EAST FZE—See Indutrade AB; *Int'l*, pg. 3681
SCANMASKIN NORGE AS—See Indutrade AB; *Int'l*, pg. 3681
SCANMASKIN SVERIGE AB—See Indutrade AB; *Int'l*, pg. 3681
SCANMASKIN USA INC.—See Indutrade AB; *Int'l*, pg. 3681
SCANMASTER SYSTEMS, LTD.—See Toyota Industries Corporation; *Int'l*, pg. 7868
SCANMATIC AS—See Arendals Fossekompani ASA; *Int'l*, pg. 559
SCANMATIC ENVIRONMENTAL TECHNOLOGY AB—See Arendals Fossekompani ASA; *Int'l*, pg. 559
SCANMED S.A.—See Abris Capital Partners Sp. z o.o.; *Int'l*, pg. 69
SCAN MODUL BYRUM APS—See Stanley Black & Decker, Inc.; *U.S. Public*, pg. 1934
SCAN MODUL ORGASYSTEM GMBH—See Stanley Black & Decker, Inc.; *U.S. Public*, pg. 1934
SCAN MODUL SYSTEM AG—See Stanley Black & Decker, Inc.; *U.S. Public*, pg. 1934
SCAN-OPTICS, LLC—See Patriarch Partners, LLC; *U.S. Private*, pg. 3109
SCAN-OPTICS, LTD.—See Patriarch Partners, LLC; *U.S. Private*, pg. 3109
SCANOX AS—See Jotun A/S; *Int'l*, pg. 4003
SCANPAC AB—See Compagnie de Saint-Gobain SA; *Int'l*, pg. 1736
SCANPIX SCANDINAVIA AB—See Schibsted ASA; *Int'l*, pg. 6617
SCANPOCON METRIC A/S—See Nimbus B.V.; *Int'l*, pg. 5296
SCANPOCON METRIC A/S—See Pon Holdings B.V.; *Int'l*, pg. 5918
SCANPOINT GEOMATICS LTD.; *Int'l*, pg. 6613
SCANPOINT GMBH—See Osterreichische Post AG; *Int'l*, pg. 5654
SCANPOLE OY—See Iivari Mononen Oy; *Int'l*, pg. 3608
SCAN PROJECTS LIMITED; *Int'l*, pg. 6611
SCANSCOT TECHNOLOGY AB—See Addnode Group AB; *Int'l*, pg. 130
SCANSHIP AMERICAS INC.—See Vow ASA; *Int'l*, pg. 8310
SCANSHIP AS—See Vow ASA; *Int'l*, pg. 8310
SCANSHIP (GHANA) LTD.—See Financiere de L'Odet; *Int'l*, pg. 2668
SCANSHIP POLAND SP Z O.O—See Vow ASA; *Int'l*, pg. 8310

2391

SCAN PROJECTS LIMITED — CORPORATE AFFILIATIONS

Company Index

SCANSOURCE COMMUNICATIONS, INC.—See ScanSource, Inc.; *U.S. Public*, pg. 1843
SCANSOURCE DE MEXICO S DE RL DE CV—See ScanSource, Inc.; *U.S. Public*, pg. 1843
SCANSOURCE EUROPE BV—See ScanSource, Inc.; *U.S. Public*, pg. 1843
SCANSOURCE EUROPE LIMITED—See ScanSource, Inc.; *U.S. Public*, pg. 1843
SCANSOURCE EUROPE SPRL—See ScanSource, Inc.; *U.S. Public*, pg. 1843
SCANSOURCE, INC.; *U.S. Public*, pg. 1843
SCANSOURCE LATIN AMERICA—See ScanSource, Inc.; *U.S. Public*, pg. 1843
SCANSOURCE SECURITY, INC.—See ScanSource, Inc.; *U.S. Public*, pg. 1843
SCAN-SPEAK A/S—See Eastern Holding Limited; *Int'l*, pg. 2272
SCANSTAT TECHNOLOGIES, LLC—See NewSpring Capital LLC; *U.S. Private*, pg. 2918
SCAN STEELS LIMITED; *Int'l*, pg. 6611
SCANTECH APPLICATIONS PTY. LTD.—See Scantech Ltd; *Int'l*, pg. 6613
SCAN TECH AS—See James Fisher & Sons Public Limited Company; *Int'l*, pg. 3876
SCANTECH INTERNATIONAL PTY LTD.—See Scantech Ltd; *Int'l*, pg. 6613
SCANTECH LTD; *Int'l*, pg. 6613
SCANTECH OFFSHORE LTD—See James Fisher & Sons Public Limited Company; *Int'l*, pg. 3876
SCANTECH OFFSHORE PTY. LTD.—See James Fisher & Sons Public Limited Company; *Int'l*, pg. 3876
SCANTIBODIES LABORATORY INC.; *U.S. Private*, pg. 3561
SCANTRANS (INDIA) PVT. LTD.—See International Press Softcom Limited; *Int'l*, pg. 3752
SCANTRANS SP. Z.O.O—See Stora Enso Oyj; *Int'l*, pg. 7224
SCANTRON A/S—See TCS TurControlSysteme AG; *Int'l*, pg. 7486
SCANTRON CORPORATION - DATA MANAGEMENT SOLUTIONS—See Transom Capital Group, LLC; *U.S. Private*, pg. 4210
SCANTRON CORPORATION—See Transom Capital Group, LLC; *U.S. Private*, pg. 4209
SCANVAEGT AB—See Marel hf; *Int'l*, pg. 4691
SCANVAEGT INTERNATIONAL A/S—See Marel hf; *Int'l*, pg. 4691
SCAN-VINO INC.; *U.S. Private*, pg. 3561
SCANWOLF CORPORATION BERHAD; *Int'l*, pg. 6613
SCANWOLF PLASTIC INDUSTRIES SDN. BHD.—See Scanwolf Corporation Berhad; *Int'l*, pg. 6613
SCA OBBOLA—See Svenska Cellulosa Aktiebolaget SCA; *Int'l*, pg. 7356
SCAPA FRANCE S.A.—See Mativ Holdings, Inc.; *U.S. Public*, pg. 1397
SCAPA GROUP PLC—See Mativ Holdings, Inc.; *U.S. Public*, pg. 1396
SCAPA (HK) HOLDINGS LTD—See Mativ Holdings, Inc.; *U.S. Public*, pg. 1397
SCAPA HOLDINGS GMBH—See Mativ Holdings, Inc.; *U.S. Public*, pg. 1397
SCAPA HONG KONG LTD—See Mativ Holdings, Inc.; *U.S. Public*, pg. 1397
SCAPA ITALIA S.P.A.—See Mativ Holdings, Inc.; *U.S. Public*, pg. 1397
SCAPA NORTH AMERICA INC.—See Mativ Holdings, Inc.; *U.S. Public*, pg. 1397
SCAPA (SCHWEIZ) AG—See Mativ Holdings, Inc.; *U.S. Public*, pg. 1397
SCAPA (SHANGHAI) INTERNATIONAL TRADING COMPANY LTD—See Mativ Holdings, Inc.; *U.S. Public*, pg. 1397
SCAPA TAPES (KOREA) CO. LTD—See Mativ Holdings, Inc.; *U.S. Public*, pg. 1397
SCAPA TAPES MALAYSIA SDN BHD—See Mativ Holdings, Inc.; *U.S. Public*, pg. 1397
SCAPA TAPES NORTH AMERICA INC.—See Mativ Holdings, Inc.; *U.S. Public*, pg. 1397
SCAPA TAPES NORTH AMERICA—See Mativ Holdings, Inc.; *U.S. Public*, pg. 1397
SCAPA TAPES UK LTD—See Mativ Holdings, Inc.; *U.S. Public*, pg. 1397
SCAP AUTOMOTIVE; *U.S. Private*, pg. 3561
SCAPE LIVING PLC; *Int'l*, pg. 6613
SCA PERFORMANCE, INC.—See Fox Factory Holding Corp.; *U.S. Public*, pg. 877
SCA PERSONAL CARE, INC—See Svenska Cellulosa Aktiebolaget SCA; *Int'l*, pg. 7356
SCAPE TECHNOLOGIES A/S; *Int'l*, pg. 6613
SCA PHARMACEUTICALS, LLC—See Excellere Capital Management LLC; *U.S. Private*, pg. 1446
SCA PHARMACEUTICALS, LLC—See The Vistria Group, LP; *U.S. Private*, pg. 4132
SCAPINO RETAIL B.V.—See Ziengs Schoenen BV; *Int'l*, pg. 8681
SCA PREMIER SURGERY CENTER OF LOUISVILLE, LLC—See UnitedHealth Group Incorporated; *U.S. Public*, pg. 2250
SCA PROMOTIONS, INC.; *U.S. Private*, pg. 3560

SCA QUALIS; *Int'l*, pg. 6610
SCARABEE AVIATION GROUP B.V.—See Daifuku Co., Ltd.; *Int'l*, pg. 1926
SCARABEE AVIATION GROUP - JAPAN CO., LTD.—See Daifuku Co., Ltd.; *Int'l*, pg. 1926
SCARAB SWEEPERS LIMITED—See FAYAT SAS; *Int'l*, pg. 2626
SCARBOROTOWN CHRYSLER DODGE JEEP RAM; *Int'l*, pg. 6613
SCARBOROUGH DEVELOPMENT LIMITED—See Far East Consortium International Limited; *Int'l*, pg. 2615
SCARBOROUGH EQUITIES PTY. LIMITED—See Bentley Capital Ltd.; *Int'l*, pg. 977
SCARBOROUGH MINERALS INTERNATIONAL BV—See Cyclone Metals Limited; *Int'l*, pg. 1894
SCARBOROUGH NISSAN LTD; *Int'l*, pg. 6613
SCARBROUGH INTERNATIONAL, LTD.; *U.S. Private*, pg. 3561
S.C. ARCOM S.A.; *Int'l*, pg. 6450
S.C. ARCTIC S.A.—See Koc Holding A.S.; *Int'l*, pg. 4222
SCARECROW LATH & PLASTER INC.; *U.S. Private*, pg. 3561
SCARECROW M&C SAATCHI LIMITED—See M&C Saatchi plc; *Int'l*, pg. 4611
SCARECROW PRESS, INC.—See The Rowman & Littlefield Publishing Group, Inc.; *U.S. Private*, pg. 4112
SCARINCI HOLLENBECK, LLC; *U.S. Private*, pg. 3561
SCARLET BELGIUM NV—See Proximus PLC; *Int'l*, pg. 6008
SCARLET BUSINESS NV—See Proximus PLC; *Int'l*, pg. 6008
SCARLET B.V.; *Int'l*, pg. 6613
SCARLET B.V.—See Proximus PLC; *Int'l*, pg. 6008
SCARLET & GRAY CORP.—See Gray America Corp.; *U.S. Private*, pg. 1759
SCARLET NV—See Proximus PLC; *Int'l*, pg. 6008
SCARLET TELECOM BVBA—See Proximus PLC; *Int'l*, pg. 6008
S.C. ARMATURA S.A.; *Int'l*, pg. 6450
S.C. ARMAX GAZ S.A.; *Int'l*, pg. 6450
SCARNA CONSTRUCTION SAS; *Int'l*, pg. 6613
SCARNOSE INTERNATIONAL LIMITED; *Int'l*, pg. 6613
S.C. AROMET S.A.; *Int'l*, pg. 6450
S. Carpenter Construction Co.; *U.S. Private*, pg. 3515
S.C. ARPLAMA ROMANIA S.R.L.—See Arplama N.V.; *Int'l*, pg. 578
SCAR S.C.R.L.—See Salini Costruttori S.p.A.; *Int'l*, pg. 6493
SCARSELLA BROS INC.; *U.S. Private*, pg. 3561
SCAR S.R.L.—See Wurth Verwaltungsgesellschaft mbH; *Int'l*, pg. 8507
SC ARTECA JILAVA SA; *Int'l*, pg. 6608
S.C. ARTEGO S.A.; *Int'l*, pg. 6450
SC ASAM S.A.; *Int'l*, pg. 6608
SCA-SAN LUIS OBISPO, LLC—See UnitedHealth Group Incorporated; *U.S. Public*, pg. 2250
SCA - SCHEDULE COORDINATION AUSTRIA GMBH—See Deutsche Lufthansa AG; *Int'l*, pg. 2066
SCA SERVICE CENTER ALTENWERDER GMBH—See Hamburger Hafen und Logistik AG; *Int'l*, pg. 3237
SC ASIGURAREA ROMANEASCA ASIROM S.A.—See Vienna Insurance Group AG Wiener Versicherung Gruppe; *Int'l*, pg. 8195
S.C. ASIGURARE REASIGURARE ASTRA S.A.; *Int'l*, pg. 6450
SCA SKOG AB—See Svenska Cellulosa Aktiebolaget SCA; *Int'l*, pg. 7357
SCA SOUND SOLUTIONS CO.—See Transition Evergreen; *Int'l*, pg. 7901
SC ASSET CORPORATION PCL; *Int'l*, pg. 6608
S.C. ASTALROM S.A.—See Salini Costruttori S.p.A.; *Int'l*, pg. 6493
S.C. ATC-AGROTOTALCONSTRUCT S.A.; *Int'l*, pg. 6450
SCATEC ASA; *Int'l*, pg. 6613
SCATEC AS; *Int'l*, pg. 6613
SCATEC HYBRID EPC (PTY.) LTD.—See Scatec ASA; *Int'l*, pg. 6613
SCATEC KENHARDT 1 (PTY.) LTD.—See Scatec ASA; *Int'l*, pg. 6614
SCATEC KENHARDT 3 (PTY.) LTD.—See Scatec ASA; *Int'l*, pg. 6614
SCATEC SOLAR SOLUTIONS EGYPT LLC—See Scatec ASA; *Int'l*, pg. 6614
S.C. ATELIERELE CFR GRIVITA S.A; *Int'l*, pg. 6450
SCA TIMBER AB - BOLLSTA SAWMILL—See Svenska Cellulosa Aktiebolaget SCA; *Int'l*, pg. 7357
SCA TIMBER AB - MUNKSUND SAWMILL—See Svenska Cellulosa Aktiebolaget SCA; *Int'l*, pg. 7357
SCA TIMBER AB - RUNDVIK SAWMILL—See Svenska Cellulosa Aktiebolaget SCA; *Int'l*, pg. 7357
SCA TIMBER AB—See Svenska Cellulosa Aktiebolaget SCA; *Int'l*, pg. 7357
SCA TIMBER AB - TUNADAL SAWMILL—See Svenska Cellulosa Aktiebolaget SCA; *Int'l*, pg. 7357
SCA TIMBER AB - VILHELMINA SAWMILL—See Svenska Cellulosa Aktiebolaget SCA; *Int'l*, pg. 7357
SCA TIMBER CHINA & S.E. ASIA LTD.—See Svenska Cellulosa Aktiebolaget SCA; *Int'l*, pg. 7357

SCA TIMBER FRANCE—See Svenska Cellulosa Aktiebolaget SCA; *Int'l*, pg. 7356
SCA TIMBER SUPPLY LTD—See Svenska Cellulosa Aktiebolaget SCA; *Int'l*, pg. 7357
SCAT INC.; *Int'l*, pg. 6613
SCA TISSUE FRANCE SAS—See Svenska Cellulosa Aktiebolaget SCA; *Int'l*, pg. 7357
SCA TISSUE FRANCE SAS—See Svenska Cellulosa Aktiebolaget SCA; *Int'l*, pg. 7357
SCA TISSUE NEDERLAND—See Svenska Cellulosa Aktiebolaget SCA; *Int'l*, pg. 7357
SCA TISSUE NORTH AMERICA, LLC - FLAGSTAFF—See Svenska Cellulosa Aktiebolaget SCA; *Int'l*, pg. 7356
SCA TISSUE NORTH AMERICA, LLC—See Svenska Cellulosa Aktiebolaget SCA; *Int'l*, pg. 7356
S.C. AUTONOVA S.A.; *Int'l*, pg. 6450
SC AUTOSPORTS, LLC—See KANDI TECHNOLOGIES GROUP, INC.; *Int'l*, pg. 4066
SCA-WESTOVER HILLS, LLC—See UnitedHealth Group Incorporated; *U.S. Public*, pg. 2250
SCAW METALS LTD.—See Industrial Development Corporation of South Africa, Ltd.; *Int'l*, pg. 3672
SCA WOOD HONG KONG LTD.—See Svenska Cellulosa Aktiebolaget SCA; *Int'l*, pg. 7357
SC AZUR SA—See ICC Industries, Inc.; *U.S. Private*, pg. 2030
SCB 10X CO., LTD.—See Siam Commercial Bank Public Company Limited; *Int'l*, pg. 6875
SCB ABACUS CO., LTD.—See Siam Commercial Bank Public Company Limited; *Int'l*, pg. 6875
SCB ASSET MANAGEMENT CO., LTD.—See Siam Commercial Bank Public Company Limited; *Int'l*, pg. 6875
S.C. B.A.T. BASCOV S.A.—See International Lazar Company; *Int'l*, pg. 3751
SC BAYER SRL—See Bayer Aktiengesellschaft; *Int'l*, pg. 910
S.C. BEGA TEHNOMET S.A. TIMISOARA; *Int'l*, pg. 6450
SCB INTERNATIONAL HOLDINGS, LLC—See SER Capital Partners LLC; *U.S. Private*, pg. 3612
S.C. BIRZAVA S.A.; *Int'l*, pg. 6450
SC BITUNOVA ROMANIA SRL—See STRABAG SE; *Int'l*, pg. 7232
SCB-JULIUS BAER SECURITIES CO., LTD.—See Siam Commercial Bank Public Company Limited; *Int'l*, pg. 6875
SCB-JULIUS BAER (SINGAPORE) PTE. LTD.—See Siam Commercial Bank Public Company Limited; *Int'l*, pg. 6875
SCB LIFE ASSURANCE PUBLIC COMPANY LIMITED—See Pacific Century Group Holdings Limited; *Int'l*, pg. 5686
S.C BNP PARIBAS REAL ESTATE ADVISORY S.A—See BNP Paribas SA; *Int'l*, pg. 1092
S.C.BOG'ART BUILDING MANAGEMENT S.R.L.—See Bog'Art S.R.L.; *Int'l*, pg. 1100
S.C. BOG'ART STEEL S.R.L.—See Bog'Art S.R.L.; *Int'l*, pg. 1100
S.C.BOG'ART VEST S.R.L.—See Bog'Art S.R.L.; *Int'l*, pg. 1100
SCB POWER TRANSMISSION SDN. BHD.—See Sarawak Cable Berhad; *Int'l*, pg. 6576
SCB PROTECT CO., LTD.—See Siam Commercial Bank Public Company Limited; *Int'l*, pg. 6875
S.C. BRAICONF S.A.; *Int'l*, pg. 6450
S.C. BRD SOGELEASE IFN S.A.—See Societe Generale S.A.; *Int'l*, pg. 7040
SC BRICOMAT SA; *Int'l*, pg. 6608
SCB SECURITIES CO., LTD.—See Siam Commercial Bank Public Company Limited; *Int'l*, pg. 6875
SCB TRAINING CENTER CO., LTD.—See Siam Commercial Bank Public Company Limited; *Int'l*, pg. 6875
SCB TRAINING CENTRE CO., LTD.—See Siam Commercial Bank Public Company Limited; *Int'l*, pg. 6875
SC BTT SA; *Int'l*, pg. 6608
SC BUCHAREST FINANCIAL PLAZZA SRL—See Erste Group Bank AG; *Int'l*, pg. 2499
S.C. BUCURESTI TURISM S.A.; *Int'l*, pg. 6450
S.C. BUCUR OBOR S.A.; *Int'l*, pg. 6450
S.C. BUCUR S.A.; *Int'l*, pg. 6450
SCB X PUBLIC COMPANY LIMITED; *Int'l*, pg. 6614
S.C. CAPITOL SA; *Int'l*, pg. 6450
S.C. CARBOCHIM S.A.; *Int'l*, pg. 6450
SC CAROMET SA—See S.C Serviciile Comerciale Romane S.R.L.; *Int'l*, pg. 6449
SC CARPATGAS S.R.L.—See UGI Corporation; *U.S. Public*, pg. 2222
S.C. CARS S.A.; *Int'l*, pg. 6450
S.C. CASA DE BUCOVINA - CLUB DE MUNTE S.A.; *Int'l*, pg. 6450
SC CASA DE COMPENSARE BUCURESTI SA—See Daimyo AS; *Int'l*, pg. 1938
SC CAVERION BUILDING SERVICES S.R.L.—See Triton Advisers Limited; *Int'l*, pg. 7935
SCC CORPORATION SDN. BHD.—See SCC Holdings Berhad; *Int'l*, pg. 6614
SC CELESTICA (ROMANIA) SRL—See ONEX Corporation; *Int'l*, pg. 5578
S.C. CEMENT CO., LTD.—See Sumitomo Corporation; *Int'l*, pg. 7269

COMPANY NAME INDEX

SC CEPROHART SA; *Int'l*, pg. 6608
SC CERAMICA SA—See Advent International Corporation; *U.S. Private*, pg. 105
S.C. CEREALCOM S.A.—See S.C. InterAgro S.A.; *Int'l*, pg. 6452
SC CHIMCOMPLEX SA—See S.C Serviciile Comerciale Romane S.R.L.; *Int'l*, pg. 6449
S.C. CHIMICA S.A.; *Int'l*, pg. 6450
SCC HOLDINGS BERHAD; *Int'l*, pg. 6614
S.C. CHS AGRITRADE ROMANIA SRL—See CHS INC.; *U.S. Public*, pg. 492
S.C. CICALEX S.A.—See S.C. InterAgro S.A.; *Int'l*, pg. 6452
S.C. CIE MATRICON, S.A.—See Cie Automotive S.A.; *Int'l*, pg. 1605
SC CLH ESTATE SRL—See ELLAKTOR S.A.; *Int'l*, pg. 2365
S.C. CLUB A.RO SRL—See S.C. InterAgro S.A.; *Int'l*, pg. 6452
SC COCOR SA; *Int'l*, pg. 6608
S.C. COMALIM S.A.; *Int'l*, pg. 6450
SC COMES SA SAVINESTI; *Int'l*, pg. 6608
S.C. COMNORD S.A.; *Int'l*, pg. 6451
S.C. COMPANIA DE INFORMATICA APLICATA S.A. CLUJ-NAPOCA; *Int'l*, pg. 6451
SC COMPANIA SOFGEN SRL—See Mahindra & Mahindra Limited; *Int'l*, pg. 4647
S.C. COMTIM GROUP S.R.L.—See WH Group Limited; *Int'l*, pg. 8395
S.C. COMTRAM S.A.; *Int'l*, pg. 6451
S.C. COMTURIST S.A.; *Int'l*, pg. 6451
SC CONNECTRONICS ROMANIA S.R.L.—See IPTE Factory Automation n.v.; *Int'l*, pg. 3802
SC CONNET RO SRL—See Koch Industries, Inc.; *U.S. Private*, pg. 2333
S.C CONPET S.A.; *Int'l*, pg. 6449
S.C. CONTACTOARE S.A.; *Int'l*, pg. 6451
SC CONTAINER TERMINAL ODESSA—See Hamburger Hafen und Logistik AG; *Int'l*, pg. 3237
SC CONTAINER TERMINAL ODESSA—See Hamburger Hafen und Logistik AG; *Int'l*, pg. 3237
S.C. CONTED S.A DOROHOI; *Int'l*, pg. 6451
SC CONTINENTAL AUTOMOTIVE ROMANIA S.R.L.—See Continental Aktiengesellschaft; *Int'l*, pg. 1793
SC COSMOTE ROMANIAN MOBILE TELECOMMUNICATIONS S.A.—See Hellenic Telecommunications Organization S.A.; *Int'l*, pg. 3333
S.C. CROMA ROMANIA SRL—See Bausch Health Companies Inc.; *Int'l*, pg. 898
SCC SERVICES ROMANIA SRL—See Specialist Computer Holdings Ltd.; *Int'l*, pg. 7128
SCC SOFT COMPUTER INC.; *U.S. Private*, pg. 3561
SCCV CLEF DE SOL—See Altarea SCA; *Int'l*, pg. 385
S. C. DACRIS IMPEX SRL—See Pilot Corporation; *Int'l*, pg. 5867
SC. DAR AL DAWAPHARMA SRL—See Dar Al Dawa Development & Investment Co.; *Int'l*, pg. 1971
SC DATA, INC.—See COR365 Information Solutions; *U.S. Private*, pg. 1046
SCD CO., LTD.—See NanJing Sanchao Advanced Materials Co., Ltd.; *Int'l*, pg. 5141
SCD CO., LTD.—See Nidec Corporation; *Int'l*, pg. 5280
SC DINAFIT SRL—See Christof Holding AG; *Int'l*, pg. 1587
SCD INFORMATION TECHNOLOGY, LLC.; *U.S. Private*, pg. 3562
SC DONAU CHEM SRL—See S.C. InterAgro S.A.; *Int'l*, pg. 6452
SC DORNA TURISM SA; *Int'l*, pg. 6608
S.C. DRUMSERV SA—See Swietelsky Baugesellschaft m.b.H.; *Int'l*, pg. 7367
SC DUMBRAVA SA; *Int'l*, pg. 6608
SCE ENTERPRISE PTE. LTD.—See Serial System Ltd.; *Int'l*, pg. 6722
SCE ENVIRONMENTAL GROUP INC.; *U.S. Private*, pg. 3562
SC EFG EUROLIFE ASIGURARI DE VIATA S.A.—See Eurobank Ergasias Services and Holdings S.A.; *Int'l*, pg. 2533
SC EFG EUROLIFE ASIGURARI GENERALE S.A.—See Eurobank Ergasias Services and Holdings S.A.; *Int'l*, pg. 2533
SCE GROUP; *U.S. Private*, pg. 3562
S.C. EL-CO S.A.; *Int'l*, pg. 6451
SC ELDON SRL—See nVent Electric plc; *Int'l*, pg. 5498
S&C ELECTRIC CANADA LTD.—See S&C Electric Company; *U.S. Private*, pg. 3512
S&C ELECTRIC (CHINA) COMPANY LTD.—See S&C Electric Company; *U.S. Private*, pg. 3512
S&C ELECTRIC COMPANY-AUTOMATION SYSTEMS—See S&C Electric Company; *U.S. Private*, pg. 3513
S&C ELECTRIC COMPANY; *U.S. Private*, pg. 3512
S&C ELECTRIC DO BRASIL LIMITADA—See S&C Electric Company; *U.S. Private*, pg. 3513
S&C ELECTRIC EUROPE LTD.—See S&C Electric Company; *U.S. Private*, pg. 3513
S&C ELECTRIC MEXICANA, S. DE R.L. DE C.V.—See S&C Electric Company; *U.S. Private*, pg. 3513

S&C ELECTRIC (SUZHOU) CO. LTD.—See S&C Electric Company; *U.S. Private*, pg. 3512
SC ELECTROLUX ROMANIA SA—See AB Electrolux; *Int'l*, pg. 41
S.C. ELECTROMONTAJ CARPATI S.A.; *Int'l*, pg. 6451
SC ELECTRONIC ARTS ROMANIA SRL—See Electronic Arts Inc.; *U.S. Public*, pg. 724
SC ELECTRONIC SERVICE GMBH—See Hormann KG Verkaufsgesellschaf; *Int'l*, pg. 3481
S.C. ELECTROUTILAJ S.A.; *Int'l*, pg. 6451
SCELERIN HEATERS LLC—See Primoris Services Corporation; *U.S. Public*, pg. 1719
S.C. ELETTRA COMMUNICATIONS SA—See Leonardo S.p.A.; *Int'l*, pg. 4460
S.C. ELMI PRODFARM S.R.L.—See Gr. Sarantis S.A.; *Int'l*, pg. 3047
SCELTA UMAMI B.V.—See Symrise AG; *Int'l*, pg. 7380
SC EMAILUL SA; *Int'l*, pg. 6608
SCEMI SA; *Int'l*, pg. 6614
SCENAPPS M INC; *Int'l*, pg. 6614
SCENARIOS, INC.—See GMA Holdings, Inc.; *Int'l*, pg. 3012
SCENE MODEL MANAGEMENT PTY LTD.—See BKM Management Limited; *Int'l*, pg. 1054
SCENE MODEL MANAGEMENT PTY LTD.—See BKM Management Limited; *Int'l*, pg. 1054
SCENE MODEL MANAGEMENT PTY LTD.—See BKM Management Limited; *Int'l*, pg. 1054
S.C. ENERGOBIT GROUP S.A.—See Innova Capital Sp. z o.o.; *Int'l*, pg. 3711
S.C. ENERGOBIT PROD S.R.L.—See Innova Capital Sp. z o.o.; *Int'l*, pg. 3711
S.C. ENERGOBIT SCHREDER LIGHTING S.R.L.—See Innova Capital Sp. z o.o.; *Int'l*, pg. 3711
S.C. ENERGOBIT TAVRIDA S.R.L.—See Innova Capital Sp. z o.o.; *Int'l*, pg. 3711
SC ENERGOUTILAJ SA; *Int'l*, pg. 6608
S.C. ENEX S.R.L.—See Innova Capital Sp. z o.o.; *Int'l*, pg. 3711
SC ENGINEERING CO., LTD.; *Int'l*, pg. 6608
S&C ENGINE GROUP LIMITED; *Int'l*, pg. 6444
SCENIC AREA DEVELOPMENT AND MANAGEMENT COMPANY—See Huangshan Tourism Development Co., Ltd.; *Int'l*, pg. 3513
SCENIC CHEVROLET; *U.S. Private*, pg. 3562
SCENIC HUDSON, INC.; *U.S. Private*, pg. 3562
SCENIC RIVERS ENERGY COOP; *U.S. Private*, pg. 3562
SCENIC TRAVELER RV CENTERS; *U.S. Private*, pg. 3562
SCENIC WOOD PRODUCTS; *U.S. Private*, pg. 3562
SCENOGRAFIE S.R.O—See Foga System International AB; *Int'l*, pg. 2721
SCENTRE GROUP LIMITED; *Int'l*, pg. 6614
SCENTRE LIMITED—See Scentre Group Limited; *Int'l*, pg. 6614
SCENTRE (NEW ZEALAND) LIMITED—See Scentre Group Limited; *Int'l*, pg. 6614
SCENTSY, INC.; *U.S. Private*, pg. 3562
SC ENVIRONMENTAL SCIENCE CO., LTD.—See Sumitomo Chemical Company, Limited; *Int'l*, pg. 7264
SCEPTER CANADA INC.—See Myers Industries, Inc.; *U.S. Public*, pg. 1488
SCEPTER HOLDINGS, INC.; *U.S. Private*, pg. 3562
SCEPTER HOLDINGS, INC.; *U.S. Public*, pg. 1843
SCEPTER INC.; *U.S. Private*, pg. 3562
SCEPTER TECHNOLOGIES INC.; *U.S. Private*, pg. 3562
SCEPTRE HOSPITALITY RESOURCES, LLC—See Access Technology Group Limited; *Int'l*, pg. 89
SCEPTRE HOSPITALITY RESOURCES; *U.S. Private*, pg. 3562
SCEPTRE INDUSTRIES, INC.—See Compal Electronics, Inc.; *Int'l*, pg. 1746
SCEPTRE TECHNOLOGIES INC.; *U.S. Private*, pg. 3562
SCEPTRE VENTURES INC.; *Int'l*, pg. 6614
SCE-SOCIETE DE CONCEPTION ET D'EDITION SAS—See A.S. Creation Tapeten AG; *Int'l*, pg. 28
SC ESTATE BUILDER BHD; *Int'l*, pg. 6608
SC EUROINS ROMANIA INSURANCE REINSURANCE SA—See Eurohold Bulgaria AD; *Int'l*, pg. 2553
S.C. EURO-URETHANE S.R.L—See PCC SE; *Int'l*, pg. 5767
SC FAIMAR S.A; *Int'l*, pg. 6609
S.C. FAM S.A.; *Int'l*, pg. 6451
SCF ARCTIC—See PAO Sovcomflot; *Int'l*, pg. 5732
S.C. FAUR S.A.; *Int'l*, pg. 6451
S.C. FAVIL S.A.; *Int'l*, pg. 6451
S.C. FEPA S.A.; *Int'l*, pg. 6451
S.C. FIMARO SA; *Int'l*, pg. 6451
SCF MANAGEMENT SERVICES (CYPRUS) LTD.—See PAO Sovcomflot; *Int'l*, pg. 5732
SCF MANAGEMENT SERVICES (DUBAI) LTD.—See PAO Sovcomflot; *Int'l*, pg. 5732
SCF MARINE INC.—See AIP, LLC; *U.S. Private*, pg. 136
SCF MARPETROL S.A.—See PAO Sovcomflot; *Int'l*, pg. 5732
SCF NATURAL SP.Z.O.O.—See Grupa Azoty S.A.; *Int'l*, pg. 3116
SC FONDUL PROPRIETATEA SA; *Int'l*, pg. 6609

SC FOODS CO., LTD.—See Sumitomo Corporation; *Int'l*, pg. 7270
S.C. FORADEX S.A.; *Int'l*, pg. 6451
S.C. FORAJ SONDE S.A.; *Int'l*, pg. 6451
S.C FORCONCID S.A.; *Int'l*, pg. 6449
S.C. FORESTIND S.A.; *Int'l*, pg. 6451
S.C. FOSERCO S.A.—See Weatherford International plc; *U.S. Public*, pg. 2339
SCF PARTNERS LTD.; *U.S. Private*, pg. 3562
SC FRESENIUS KABI ROMANIA SRL—See Fresenius SE & Co. KGaA; *Int'l*, pg. 2781
SCG ACCOUNTING SERVICES CO., LTD.—See The Siam Cement Public Company Limited; *Int'l*, pg. 7683
SC GALAXY TOBACCO SA—See S.C. InterAgro S.A.; *Int'l*, pg. 6452
S.C. GALFINBAND S.A.; *Int'l*, pg. 6451
SCG AMERICA GROUP INC.—See Shanghai Construction Group Co., Ltd.; *Int'l*, pg. 6764
S. C. GAMMA INTERNATIONAL S.R.L.—See TCS TurControlSysteme AG; *Int'l*, pg. 7486
S.C. GARANTA ASIGURARI S.A.—See National Bank of Greece S.A.; *Int'l*, pg. 5153
SCG BUILDING PRODUCTS CO., LTD.—See The Siam Cement Public Company Limited; *Int'l*, pg. 7683
SCG CERAMICS PUBLIC COMPANY LIMITED—See The Siam Cement Public Company Limited; *Int'l*, pg. 7684
SCG CHEMICALS CO., LTD.—See The Siam Cement Public Company Limited; *Int'l*, pg. 7683
SCG CZECH DESIGN CENTER S.R.O.—See ON Semiconductor Corporation; *U.S. Public*, pg. 1601
SCG DECOR PUBLIC COMPANY LIMITED—See The Siam Cement Public Company Limited; *Int'l*, pg. 7684
SC GDF SUEZ ENERGY ROMANIA SA—See ENGIE SA; *Int'l*, pg. 2434
SCG DISTRIBUTION CO., LTD.—See The Siam Cement Public Company Limited; *Int'l*, pg. 7684
SC GEA KLIMATECHNIK SRL—See GEA Group Aktiengesellschaft; *Int'l*, pg. 2903
SCG E-COMMERCE CO., LTD.—See Shanghai Construction Group Co., Ltd.; *Int'l*, pg. 6764
S.C. GENAGRICOLA ROMANIA—See Assicurazioni Generali S.p.A.; *Int'l*, pg. 647
S.C. GENKO MED GROUP S.A.—See Genko Italia srl; *Int'l*, pg. 2924
SC GERMINA AGRIBUSINESS S.A.; *Int'l*, pg. 6609
SCG EXPERIENCE CO., LTD.—See The Siam Cement Public Company Limited; *Int'l*, pg. 7684
SCG FINANCE CORPORATION LIMITED—See Capital Industrial Financial Services Group Limited; *Int'l*, pg. 1311
SCG HONG KONG SAR LTD.—See ON Semiconductor Corporation; *U.S. Public*, pg. 1601
S&C GINNING COMPANY LIMITED—See Sumaria Group; *Int'l*, pg. 7259
SCG INTERNATIONAL CHINA (GUANGZHOU) CO., LTD.—See The Siam Cement Public Company Limited; *Int'l*, pg. 7684
SCG INTERNATIONAL CORPORATION CO., LTD.—See The Siam Cement Public Company Limited; *Int'l*, pg. 7684
SCGJWD LOGISTICS PUBLIC COMPANY LIMITED; *Int'l*, pg. 6614
SC GLOBAL DEVELOPMENTS LIMITED; *Int'l*, pg. 6609
SCG LOGISTICS MANAGEMENT CO., LTD.—See The Siam Cement Public Company Limited; *Int'l*, pg. 7684
SCGM BERHAD; *Int'l*, pg. 6614
SCG PACKAGING COMPANY LIMITED—See The Siam Cement Public Company Limited; *Int'l*, pg. 7684
SCG PACKAGING PUBLIC COMPANY LIMITED—See The Siam Cement Public Company Limited; *Int'l*, pg. 7685
SCG PERFORMANCE CHEMICALS CO., LTD.—See The Siam Cement Public Company Limited; *Int'l*, pg. 7683
SCG PLASTICS CO., LTD.—See The Siam Cement Public Company Limited; *Int'l*, pg. 7683
SC GROUP THAI; *Int'l*, pg. 6609
S.C. GRUPUL INDUSTRIAL ELECTROCONTACT S.A.; *Int'l*, pg. 6451
SCG-SEKISUI SALES CO., LTD.—See The Siam Cement Public Company Limited; *Int'l*, pg. 7685
SCG SINGAPORE TRADING PTE. LTD.—See The Siam Cement Public Company Limited; *Int'l*, pg. 7684
SCG SOLUTIONS CO., LTD.—See Seoul City Gas Co., Ltd.; *Int'l*, pg. 6716
SCG SOLUTIONS THAILAND LIMITED—See Seoul City Gas Co., Ltd.; *Int'l*, pg. 6716
SCGT MALAYSIA SDN. BHD.—See The Siam Cement Public Company Limited; *Int'l*, pg. 7684
SCG TRADING AUSTRALIA PTY. LTD.—See The Siam Cement Public Company Limited; *Int'l*, pg. 7685
SCG TRADING CO., LTD.—See The Siam Cement Public Company Limited; *Int'l*, pg. 7684
SCG TRADING GUANGZHOU CO., LTD.—See The Siam Cement Public Company Limited; *Int'l*, pg. 7684
SCG TRADING HONG KONG LIMITED—See The Siam Cement Public Company Limited; *Int'l*, pg. 7685
SCG TRADING (JORDAN) L.L.C.—See The Siam Cement Public Company Limited; *Int'l*, pg. 7684

Company Index

S.C. GRUPUL INDUSTRIAL ELECTROCONTACT S.A. CORPORATE AFFILIATIONS

SCG TRADING LAO CO., LTD.—See The Siam Cement Public Company Limited; *Int'l*, pg. 7685
SCG TRADING MIDDLE EAST DMCC—See The Siam Cement Public Company Limited; *Int'l*, pg. 7685
SCG TRADING (M) SDN. BHD.—See The Siam Cement Public Company Limited; *Int'l*, pg. 7684
SCG TRADING PHILIPPINES INC.—See The Siam Cement Public Company Limited; *Int'l*, pg. 7684
SCG TRADING USA INC.—See The Siam Cement Public Company Limited; *Int'l*, pg. 7684
SCG VIETNAM CO., LTD.—See The Siam Cement Public Company Limited; *Int'l*, pg. 7685
SCHAAF CONSULTING; *U.S. Private*, pg. 3562
SCHAAKE CORPORATION; *U.S. Private*, pg. 3562
SCHAAL HEATING & COOLING, INC.; *U.S. Private*, pg. 3562
SCHAAP & CITROEN—See KKR & Co. Inc.; *U.S. Public*, pg. 1261
SCHABLONA INDIA LTD.—See Somany Ceramics Limited; *Int'l*, pg. 7083
SCHABMULLER GMBH—See ZAPI S.p.A; *Int'l*, pg. 8625
SCHACHENMANN & CO. AG—See Burkhalter Holding AG; *Int'l*, pg. 1225
SCHACHENMANN & CO. AG—See Burkhalter Holding AG; *Int'l*, pg. 1225
SCHACH MATT HANDELS + VERTRIEBS GMBH—See CRONIMET Holding GmbH; *Int'l*, pg. 1855
SCHACHTBAU NORDHAUSEN BAU GMBH—See BAUER Aktiengesellschaft; *Int'l*, pg. 894
SCHACHTBAU NORDHAUSEN GMBH - CIVIL ENGINEERING DIVISION—See BAUER Aktiengesellschaft; *Int'l*, pg. 894
SCHACHTBAU NORDHAUSEN GMBH - ENVIRONMENTAL TECHNOLOGY DIVISION—See BAUER Aktiengesellschaft; *Int'l*, pg. 894
SCHACHTBAU NORDHAUSEN GMBH - MECHANICAL ENGINEERING DIVISION—See BAUER Aktiengesellschaft; *Int'l*, pg. 893
SCHACHTBAU NORDHAUSEN GMBH - RECONSTRUCTION DIVISION—See BAUER Aktiengesellschaft; *Int'l*, pg. 894
SCHACHTBAU NORDHAUSEN GMBH.—See BAUER Aktiengesellschaft; *Int'l*, pg. 893
SCHACHTBAU NORDHAUSEN GMBH - UNDERGROUND CONSTRUCTION DIVISION—See BAUER Aktiengesellschaft; *Int'l*, pg. 894
SCHACHTBAU NORDHAUSEN STAHLBAU GMBH—See BAUER Aktiengesellschaft; *Int'l*, pg. 894
SCHADEGG MECHANICAL INC.; *U.S. Private*, pg. 3563
SCHADEVERZEKERINGMAATSCHAPPIJ ZEVENWOUDEN U.A.—See O.O.M. Onderlinge Verzekering-Maatschappij U.A; *Int'l*, pg. 5503
THE SCHAECHTER ADVERTISING AGENCY; *U.S. Private*, pg. 4114
SCHAEDLER/YESCO DISTRIBUTION, INC.; *U.S. Private*, pg. 3563
SCHAEFER AGENCY, INC.—See Inszone Insurance Services, LLC; *U.S. Private*, pg. 2096
SCHAEFER AMBULANCE SERVICE; *U.S. Private*, pg. 3563
SCHAEFER AUTOBODY CENTERS—See Susquehanna International Group, LLP; *U.S. Private*, pg. 3886
SCHAEFER EQUIPMENT, INC.—See Westinghouse Air Brake Technologies Corporation; *U.S. Public*, pg. 2359
THE SCHAEFER GROUP, INC.; *U.S. Private*, pg. 4114
SCHAEFER MARINE INC.; *U.S. Private*, pg. 3563
SCHAEFER MEGOMAT DO BRASIL LTDA—See Schaefer Werkzeug- und Sondermaschinenbau GmbH; *Int'l*, pg. 6614
SCHAEFER MEGOMAT USA, INC.—See Schaefer Werkzeug- und Sondermaschinenbau GmbH; *Int'l*, pg. 6614
SCHAEFER PLUMBING SUPPLY CO.; *U.S. Private*, pg. 3563
SCHAEFER REFRIGERATION INC.—See Total Comfort Solutions LLC; *U.S. Private*, pg. 4190
SCHAEFERROLLS INC.—See SchaferRolls GmbH & Co. KG; *Int'l*, pg. 6615
SCHAEFER ROMANIA SRL—See Schaefer Werkzeug- und Sondermaschinenbau GmbH; *Int'l*, pg. 6614
SCHAEFER SOUTH-EAST EUROPE SRL; *Int'l*, pg. 6614
SCHAEFER TECHNOLOGIES LLC—See Schaefer Werkzeug- und Sondermaschinenbau GmbH; *Int'l*, pg. 6614
SCHAEFER TRADING (SHANGHAI) CO., LTD.—See Schaefer Werkzeug- und Sondermaschinenbau GmbH; *Int'l*, pg. 6614
SCHAEFER TRANS INC.; *U.S. Private*, pg. 3563
SCHAEFER TUNISIE SARL—See Schaefer Werkzeug- und Sondermaschinenbau GmbH; *Int'l*, pg. 6615
SCHAEFER WERKZEUG- UND SONDERMASCHINENBAU GMBH; *Int'l*, pg. 6614
SCHAEFFER GMBH—See William Prym GmbH & Co. KG; *Int'l*, pg. 8413
SCHAEFFER INDUSTRIES; *U.S. Private*, pg. 3563
SCHAEFFER MANUFACTURING CO; *U.S. Private*, pg. 3563
SCHAEFFLER AEROSPACE CANADA INC.—See INA-Holding Schaeffler GmbH & Co. KG; *Int'l*, pg. 3639
SCHAEFFLER AEROSPACE GERMANY GMBH & CO. KG—See INA-Holding Schaeffler GmbH & Co. KG; *Int'l*, pg. 3639
SCHAEFFLER AEROSPACE (SINGAPORE) PTE. LTD.—See INA-Holding Schaeffler GmbH & Co. KG; *Int'l*, pg. 3639
SCHAEFFLER AG—See INA-Holding Schaeffler GmbH & Co. KG; *Int'l*, pg. 3640
SCHAEFFLER ANSAN CORPORATION—See INA-Holding Schaeffler GmbH & Co. KG; *Int'l*, pg. 3641
SCHAEFFLER ARGENTINA S.R.L.—See INA-Holding Schaeffler GmbH & Co. KG; *Int'l*, pg. 3641
SCHAEFFLER AUSTRALIA PTY. LTD.—See INA-Holding Schaeffler GmbH & Co. KG; *Int'l*, pg. 3641
SCHAEFFLER AUSTRIA GMBH—See INA-Holding Schaeffler GmbH & Co. KG; *Int'l*, pg. 3641
SCHAEFFLER AUTOMOTIVE AFTERMARKET GMBH&CO. KG—See INA-Holding Schaeffler GmbH & Co. KG; *Int'l*, pg. 3639
SCHAEFFLER AUTOMOTIVE AFTERMARKET MEXICO, S. DE R.L. DE C.V.—See INA-Holding Schaeffler GmbH & Co. KG; *Int'l*, pg. 3641
SCHAEFFLER AUTOMOTIVE AFTERMARKET SERVICES CONSULTING (SHANGHAI) CO.—See INA-Holding Schaeffler GmbH & Co. KG; *Int'l*, pg. 3639
SCHAEFFLER AUTOMOTIVE AFTERMARKET (UK) LIMITED—See INA-Holding Schaeffler GmbH & Co. KG; *Int'l*, pg. 3641
SCHAEFFLER BEARINGS INDONESIA, PT—See INA-Holding Schaeffler GmbH & Co. KG; *Int'l*, pg. 3641
SCHAEFFLER BEARINGS (MALAYSIA) SDN. BHD.—See INA-Holding Schaeffler GmbH & Co. KG; *Int'l*, pg. 3641
SCHAEFFLER BELGIUM SPRL—See INA-Holding Schaeffler GmbH & Co. KG; *Int'l*, pg. 3641
SCHAEFFLER BIO-HYBRID GMBH—See INA-Holding Schaeffler GmbH & Co. KG; *Int'l*, pg. 3640
SCHAEFFLER BRASIL LTDA.—See INA-Holding Schaeffler GmbH & Co. KG; *Int'l*, pg. 3641
SCHAEFFLER BULGARIA OOD—See INA-Holding Schaeffler GmbH & Co. KG; *Int'l*, pg. 3641
SCHAEFFLER CANADA INC. - AUTOMOTIVE UNIT—See INA-Holding Schaeffler GmbH & Co. KG; *Int'l*, pg. 3641
SCHAEFFLER CHAIN DRIVE SYSTEMS SAS—See INA-Holding Schaeffler GmbH & Co. KG; *Int'l*, pg. 3641
SCHAEFFLER CHILE RODAMIENTOS LTDA.—See INA-Holding Schaeffler GmbH & Co. KG; *Int'l*, pg. 3641
SCHAEFFLER (CHINA) CO., LTD.—See INA-Holding Schaeffler GmbH & Co. KG; *Int'l*, pg. 3640
SCHAEFFLER COLOMBIA LTDA.—See INA-Holding Schaeffler GmbH & Co. KG; *Int'l*, pg. 3641
SCHAEFFLER CZ S.R.O.—See INA-Holding Schaeffler GmbH & Co. KG; *Int'l*, pg. 3641
SCHAEFFLER DANMARK APS—See INA-Holding Schaeffler GmbH & Co. KG; *Int'l*, pg. 3641
SCHAEFFLER ELFERSHAUSEN AG & CO. KG—See INA-Holding Schaeffler GmbH & Co. KG; *Int'l*, pg. 3639
SCHAEFFLER ENGINEERING GMBH—See INA-Holding Schaeffler GmbH & Co. KG; *Int'l*, pg. 3640
SCHAEFFLER FINLAND OY—See INA-Holding Schaeffler GmbH & Co. KG; *Int'l*, pg. 3641
SCHAEFFLER FRANCE SAS—See INA-Holding Schaeffler GmbH & Co. KG; *Int'l*, pg. 3641
SCHAEFFLER FRICTION PRODUCTS GMBH—See INA-Holding Schaeffler GmbH & Co. KG; *Int'l*, pg. 3641
SCHAEFFLER FRICTION PRODUCTS (SUZHOU) CO., LTD.—See INA-Holding Schaeffler GmbH & Co. KG; *Int'l*, pg. 3641
SCHAEFFLER GLOBAL SERVICES EUROPE SP. Z O.O.—See INA-Holding Schaeffler GmbH & Co. KG; *Int'l*, pg. 3640
SCHAEFFLER GROUP USA INC—See INA-Holding Schaeffler GmbH & Co. KG; *Int'l*, pg. 3641
SCHAEFFLER HONG KONG COMPANY LIMITED—See INA-Holding Schaeffler GmbH & Co. KG; *Int'l*, pg. 3641
SCHAEFFLER HRVATSKA D.O.O.—See INA-Holding Schaeffler GmbH & Co. KG; *Int'l*, pg. 3641
SCHAEFFLER IBERIA, S.L.U.—See INA-Holding Schaeffler GmbH & Co. KG; *Int'l*, pg. 3641
SCHAEFFLER INDIA LIMITED; *Int'l*, pg. 6615
SCHAEFFLER INDUSTRIAL DRIVES AG & CO. KG—See INA-Holding Schaeffler GmbH & Co. KG; *Int'l*, pg. 3640
SCHAEFFLER ISRAEL LTD.—See INA-Holding Schaeffler GmbH & Co. KG; *Int'l*, pg. 3641
SCHAEFFLER ITALIA S.R.L.—See INA-Holding Schaeffler GmbH & Co. KG; *Int'l*, pg. 3641
SCHAEFFLER JAPAN CO., LTD.—See INA-Holding Schaeffler GmbH & Co. KG; *Int'l*, pg. 3641
SCHAEFFLER KOREA CORPORATION—See INA-Holding Schaeffler GmbH & Co. KG; *Int'l*, pg. 3641
SCHAEFFLER KYSUCE, SPOL. S R.O.—See INA-Holding Schaeffler GmbH & Co. KG; *Int'l*, pg. 3640
SCHAEFFLER MAGYARORSZAG IPARI KFT.—See INA-Holding Schaeffler GmbH & Co. KG; *Int'l*, pg. 3641
SCHAEFFLER MANUFACTURING RUS OOO—See INA-Holding Schaeffler GmbH & Co. KG; *Int'l*, pg. 3642
SCHAEFFLER MANUFACTURING (THAILAND) CO., LTD.—See INA-Holding Schaeffler GmbH & Co. KG; *Int'l*, pg. 3642
SCHAEFFLER MEXICO, S. DE R.L. DE C.V.—See INA-Holding Schaeffler GmbH & Co. KG; *Int'l*, pg. 3642
SCHAEFFLER MONITORING SERVICES GMBH—See INA-Holding Schaeffler GmbH & Co. KG; *Int'l*, pg. 3640
SCHAEFFLER NEDERLAND B.V.—See INA-Holding Schaeffler GmbH & Co. KG; *Int'l*, pg. 3642
SCHAEFFLER (NINGXIA) CO., LTD.—See INA-Holding Schaeffler GmbH & Co. KG; *Int'l*, pg. 3640
SCHAEFFLER NORGE AS—See INA-Holding Schaeffler GmbH & Co. KG; *Int'l*, pg. 3642
SCHAEFFLER PARAVAN TECHNOLOGIE GMBH & CO. KG—See INA-Holding Schaeffler GmbH & Co. KG; *Int'l*, pg. 3640
SCHAEFFLER PHILIPPINES INC.—See INA-Holding Schaeffler GmbH & Co. KG; *Int'l*, pg. 3642
SCHAEFFLER POLSKA SP. Z.O.O.—See INA-Holding Schaeffler GmbH & Co. KG; *Int'l*, pg. 3642
SCHAEFFLER PORTUGAL S.A.—See INA-Holding Schaeffler GmbH & Co. KG; *Int'l*, pg. 3642
SCHAEFFLER PRODUCTION CZ S.R.O.—See INA-Holding Schaeffler GmbH & Co. KG; *Int'l*, pg. 3640
SCHAEFFLER ROMANIA S.R.L.—See INA-Holding Schaeffler GmbH & Co. KG; *Int'l*, pg. 3642
SCHAEFFLER RULMANLARI TICARET LTD. STI.—See INA-Holding Schaeffler GmbH & Co. KG; *Int'l*, pg. 3642
SCHAEFFLER RUS OOO—See INA-Holding Schaeffler GmbH & Co. KG; *Int'l*, pg. 3640
SCHAEFFLER RUSSLAND GMBH—See INA-Holding Schaeffler GmbH & Co. KG; *Int'l*, pg. 3642
SCHAEFFLER SAVARIA KFT.—See INA-Holding Schaeffler GmbH & Co. KG; *Int'l*, pg. 3640
SCHAEFFLER SCHWEIZ GMBH—See INA-Holding Schaeffler GmbH & Co. KG; *Int'l*, pg. 3640
SCHAEFFLER (SINGAPORE) PTE. LTD.—See INA-Holding Schaeffler GmbH & Co. KG; *Int'l*, pg. 3641
SCHAEFFLER SKALICA SPOL. S R.O.—See INA-Holding Schaeffler GmbH & Co. KG; *Int'l*, pg. 3640
SCHAEFFLER SLOVENIJA D.O.O.—See INA-Holding Schaeffler GmbH & Co. KG; *Int'l*, pg. 3642
SCHAEFFLER SOUTH AFRICA (PTY.) LTD.—See INA-Holding Schaeffler GmbH & Co. KG; *Int'l*, pg. 3642
SCHAEFFLER SVERIGE AB—See INA-Holding Schaeffler GmbH & Co. KG; *Int'l*, pg. 3642
SCHAEFFLER TAIWAN CO., LTD.—See INA-Holding Schaeffler GmbH & Co. KG; *Int'l*, pg. 3642
SCHAEFFLER TECHNOLOGIES GMBH & CO. KG—See INA-Holding Schaeffler GmbH & Co. KG; *Int'l*, pg. 3640
SCHAEFFLER (THAILAND) CO., LTD.—See INA-Holding Schaeffler GmbH & Co. KG; *Int'l*, pg. 3640
SCHAEFFLER TRANSMISION, S. DE R.L. DE C.V.—See INA-Holding Schaeffler GmbH & Co. KG; *Int'l*, pg. 3640
SCHAEFFLER TURKEY ENDUSTRI VE OTOMOTIV TICARET LIMITED SIRKETI—See INA-Holding Schaeffler GmbH & Co. KG; *Int'l*, pg. 3640
SCHAEFFLER (UK) LTD.—See INA-Holding Schaeffler GmbH & Co. KG; *Int'l*, pg. 3641
SCHAEFFLER UKRAINE GMBH—See INA-Holding Schaeffler GmbH & Co. KG; *Int'l*, pg. 3642
SCHAEFFLER VENEZUELA, C.A.—See INA-Holding Schaeffler GmbH & Co. KG; *Int'l*, pg. 3642
SCHAEFFLER VERWALTUNG ZWEI GMBH—See INA-Holding Schaeffler GmbH & Co. KG; *Int'l*, pg. 3640
SCHAEFFLER VIETNAM CO., LTD.—See INA-Holding Schaeffler GmbH & Co. KG; *Int'l*, pg. 3642
SCHAEFFLER (XIANGTAN) CO., LTD.—See INA-Holding Schaeffler GmbH & Co. KG; *Int'l*, pg. 3640
SCHAEFF MASCHINEN GMBH & CO. KG; *Int'l*, pg. 6615
SCHAER THUN AG—See TX Group AG; *Int'l*, pg. 7991
THE SCHAFER COMPANY INC.; *U.S. Private*, pg. 4114
SCHAFER CONDON CARTER; *U.S. Private*, pg. 3563
SCHAFER CORPORATION—See AE Industrial Partners, LP; *U.S. Private*, pg. 112
SCHAFER DRIVELINE, LLC—See HBM Holdings Company; *U.S. Private*, pg. 1887
SCHAFER GEAR WORKS ROSCOE, LLC—See HBM Holdings Company; *U.S. Private*, pg. 1887
SCHAFER GMBH—See Compagnie de Saint-Gobain SA; *Int'l*, pg. 1736
SCHAFER INC.; *U.S. Private*, pg. 3563
SCHAFER INDUSTRIES, INC.—See HBM Holdings Company; *U.S. Private*, pg. 1887
SCHAFER MEGOMAT AG—See Schaefer Werkzeug- und Sondermaschinenbau GmbH; *Int'l*, pg. 6615
SCHAFER OIL COMPANY; *U.S. Private*, pg. 3563
SCHAFERROLLS D.O.O.—See SchaferRolls GmbH & Co. KG; *Int'l*, pg. 6615
SCHAFERROLLS GMBH & CO. KG; *Int'l*, pg. 6615
SCHAFER SYSTEMS, INC.—See Pollard Banknote Limited; *Int'l*, pg. 5910
SCHAFFER CORPORATION LIMITED; *Int'l*, pg. 6615
SCHAFFER MECHANICAL, INC.; *U.S. Private*, pg. 3563
SCHAFFER-POESCHEL VERLAG FUR WIRTSCHAFT, STEUERN, RECHT GMBH—See Rudolf Haufe Verlag GmbH & Co. KG; *Int'l*, pg. 6425
SCHAFFER PRECISION MACHINE SHOP, INC.—See Gremada Industries Inc.; *U.S. Private*, pg. 1783
SCHAFFER PROPERTIES PTY LTD—See Schaffer Corporation Limited; *Int'l*, pg. 6615

COMPANY NAME INDEX

SCHAFFNER DEUTSCHLAND GMBH—See TE Connectivity Ltd.; *Int'l*, pg. 7495
SCHAFFNER EMC AB—See TE Connectivity Ltd.; *Int'l*, pg. 7495
SCHAFFNER EMC CO., LTD.—See TE Connectivity Ltd.; *Int'l*, pg. 7495
SCHAFFNER EMC INC.—See TE Connectivity Ltd.; *Int'l*, pg. 7495
SCHAFFNER EMC K.K.—See TE Connectivity Ltd.; *Int'l*, pg. 7495
SCHAFFNER EMC PTE. LTD.—See TE Connectivity Ltd.; *Int'l*, pg. 7495
SCHAFFNER EMC S.A.S.—See TE Connectivity Ltd.; *Int'l*, pg. 7495
SCHAFFNER EMC S.R.L.—See TE Connectivity Ltd.; *Int'l*, pg. 7495
SCHAFFNER EMV AG—See TE Connectivity Ltd.; *Int'l*, pg. 7495
SCHAFFNER EMV HUNGARY KFT.—See TE Connectivity Ltd.; *Int'l*, pg. 7495
SCHAFFNER HOLDING AG—See TE Connectivity Ltd.; *Int'l*, pg. 7495
SCHAFFNER LTD—See TE Connectivity Ltd.; *Int'l*, pg. 7495
SCHAFFNER OY—See TE Connectivity Ltd.; *Int'l*, pg. 7495
SCHAGRIN GAS CO.; *U.S. Private*, pg. 3563
SCHAKRA, INC.; *U.S. Private*, pg. 3563
SCHALINS RINGAR AB—See Storskogen Group AB; *Int'l*, pg. 7228
SCHALLER AUTO WORLD, INC.; *U.S. Private*, pg. 3563
SCHALLER CORPORATION; *U.S. Private*, pg. 3563
SCHALLER HARDWOOD LUMBER CO.; *U.S. Private*, pg. 3563
SCHALLER MANUFACTURING CORP.; *U.S. Private*, pg. 3563
SCHALTAG AG—See Rieter Holding Ltd.; *Int'l*, pg. 6339
SCHALTBAU ASIA PACIFIC LTD.—See The Carlyle Group Inc.; *U.S. Public*, pg. 2053
SCHALTBAU AUSTRIA GMBH—See The Carlyle Group Inc.; *U.S. Public*, pg. 2053
SCHALTBAU FRANCE S.A.S.—See The Carlyle Group Inc.; *U.S. Public*, pg. 2053
SCHALTBAU HOLDING AG—See The Carlyle Group Inc.; *U.S. Public*, pg. 2052
SCHALTBAU INDIA PVT. LTD.—See The Carlyle Group Inc.; *U.S. Public*, pg. 2053
SCHALTBAU MACHINE ELECTRICS LTD.—See The Carlyle Group Inc.; *U.S. Public*, pg. 2053
SCHALTBAU NORTH AMERICA INC.—See The Carlyle Group Inc.; *U.S. Public*, pg. 2053
SCHALTBAU TRANSPORTATION UK LTD.—See The Carlyle Group Inc.; *U.S. Public*, pg. 2053
SCHALT ELETRO ELETRONICA IND E COM LTDA—See Keyence Corporation; *Int'l*, pg. 4146
S CHAND & COMPANY LIMITED; *Int'l*, pg. 6442
S. CHAND EDUTECH PRIVATE LIMITED—See S Chand & Company Limited; *Int'l*, pg. 6442
SCHAPPE TECHNIQUES; *Int'l*, pg. 6615
SCHARF INVESTMENTS, LLC; *U.S. Private*, pg. 3563
SCHARF MINING MACHINERY (BEIJING) CO. LTD.—See Yankuang Group Co., Limited; *Int'l*, pg. 8562
SCHARF MINING MACHINERY (XUZHOU) LTD.—See Yankuang Group Co., Limited; *Int'l*, pg. 8562
SCHARFSTEIN S.A.—See Aiphone Co., Ltd.; *Int'l*, pg. 235
SCHARRER & ANDRESEN GMBH—See Hoyer GmbH; *Int'l*, pg. 3499
SCHATZL & JUNGMAYR GARTEN- UND LANDSCHAFTSBAU GMBH—See PORR AG; *Int'l*, pg. 5925
SCHAUBACH HOLDINGS INC.; *U.S. Private*, pg. 3563
SCHAUB & CO. GMBH & CO. KG.; *Int'l*, pg. 6615
SCHAUBLIN GMBH—See RBC Bearings Incorporated; *U.S. Public*, pg. 1766
SCHAUFLER TOOLING GMBH & CO. KG; *Int'l*, pg. 6615
SCHAUINSLAND PFLEGEBETRIEB GMBH—See Clariane SE; *Int'l*, pg. 1644
SCHAUMBURG BANK & TRUST COMPANY, N.A.—See Wintrust Financial Corporation; *U.S. Public*, pg. 2375
SCHAUMBURG CASTLE INC.—See Medieval Dinner & Tournament, Inc.; *U.S. Private*, pg. 2656
SCHAWK ASIA PACIFIC PTE. LTD.—See Matthews International Corporation; *U.S. Public*, pg. 1400
SCHAWK CANADA INC.—See Matthews International Corporation; *U.S. Public*, pg. 1401
SCHAWK DE MEXICO SRL DE CV—See Matthews International Corporation; *U.S. Public*, pg. 1401
SCHAWK DIGITAL SOLUTIONS, INC.—See Matthews International Corporation; *U.S. Public*, pg. 1401
SCHAWK HOLDINGS AUSTRALIA PTY. LTD.—See Matthews International Corporation; *U.S. Public*, pg. 1400
SCHAWK IMAGING SDN. BHD.—See Matthews International Corporation; *U.S. Public*, pg. 1401
SCHAWK IMAGING (SHANGHAI) CO. LTD.—See Matthews International Corporation; *U.S. Public*, pg. 1401
SCHAWK INDIA INC.—See Matthews International Corporation; *U.S. Public*, pg. 1400
SCHAWK INDIA PVT. LTD.—See Matthews International Corporation; *U.S. Public*, pg. 1400

SCHAWK JAPAN, LTD.—See Matthews International Corporation; *U.S. Public*, pg. 1401
SCHAWK RETAIL MARKETING—See Matthews International Corporation; *U.S. Public*, pg. 1401
SCHAWK USA, INC. - ATLANTA—See Matthews International Corporation; *U.S. Public*, pg. 1401
SCHAWK USA, INC. - KALAMAZOO—See Matthews International Corporation; *U.S. Public*, pg. 1401
SCHAWK USA, INC. - MINNEAPOLIS—See Matthews International Corporation; *U.S. Public*, pg. 1401
SCHAWK USA, INC. - REDMOND—See Matthews International Corporation; *U.S. Public*, pg. 1401
SCHAWK USA, INC.—See Matthews International Corporation; *U.S. Public*, pg. 1401
SCHB ENGINEERING SERVICES SDN. BHD.—See Suria Capital Holdings Berhad; *Int'l*, pg. 7344
SCHC, INC.—See Shoe Carnival, Inc.; *U.S. Public*, pg. 1875
SCH CORPORATION SDN BHD—See Hextar Industries Berhad; *Int'l*, pg. 3373
SCHC PEDIATRIC ANESTHESIA ASSOCIATES, L.L.C.—See Drexel University; *U.S. Private*, pg. 1276
SCHC PEDIATRIC ANESTHESIA ASSOCIATES, L.L.C.—See Tower Health; *U.S. Public*, pg. 4193
SCHC PEDIATRIC ASSOCIATES, LLC—See Drexel University; *U.S. Private*, pg. 1276
SCHC PEDIATRIC ASSOCIATES, LLC—See Tower Health; *U.S. Public*, pg. 4193
SCHEAR CORPORATION; *U.S. Private*, pg. 3563
SCHECK MECHANICAL CORP.; *U.S. Private*, pg. 3563
SCHECK & SIRESS PROSTHETICS, INC.—See Patient Square Capital, L.P.; *U.S. Private*, pg. 3107
SCHEDA ECOLOGICAL ASSOCIATES, INC.; *U.S. Private*, pg. 3564
SCHEDULED AIRLINES TRAFFIC OFFICES, INC.—See Carlson Companies Inc.; *U.S. Private*, pg. 765
SCHEDULE STAR, LLC—See TEGNA Inc.; *U.S. Public*, pg. 1990
SCHEELITE MANAGEMENT PTY LTD—See Group 6 Metals Limited; *Int'l*, pg. 3088
SCHEELS ALL SPORTS INC.; *U.S. Private*, pg. 3564
SCHEERD.V KERCHOVE N.V.; *Int'l*, pg. 6615
SCHEER GMBH—See Scheer Group GmbH; *Int'l*, pg. 6615
SCHEER GROUP GMBH; *Int'l*, pg. 6615
SCHEER MANAGEMENT BV—See Scheer Group GmbH; *Int'l*, pg. 6615
SCHEER MANAGEMENT DANISMANLIK A.S.—See Scheer Group GmbH; *Int'l*, pg. 6615
SCHEETZ & HOGAN INSURANCE AGENCY, INC.—See Caisse de Depot et Placement du Quebec; *Int'l*, pg. 1256
SCHEETZ & HOGAN INSURANCE AGENCY, INC.—See KKR & Co. Inc.; *U.S. Public*, pg. 1265
SCHEIBEL HALASKA, INC.; *U.S. Private*, pg. 3564
SCHEIDER ELECTRIC - PROFESSIONAL SERVICES—See Schneider Electric SE; *Int'l*, pg. 6634
SCHEID VINEYARDS INC.; *U.S. Public*, pg. 1843
SCHEIN ERNST MISHRA EYE, P.C.—See Henry Schein, Inc.; *U.S. Public*, pg. 1027
SCHELCHER-PRINCE GESTION; *Int'l*, pg. 6615
SCHELDEBOUW B.V.—See Atlas Holdings, LLC; *U.S. Private*, pg. 378
SCHELDE EXOTECH B.V.—See BENCIS Capital Partners B.V.; *Int'l*, pg. 970
SCHELFHOUT N.V.—See CRH plc; *Int'l*, pg. 1848
SC HELIOS SA; *Int'l*, pg. 6609
SCHELLING ANLAGENBAU GMBH; *Int'l*, pg. 6615
SCHELL & KAMPETER, INC.; *U.S. Private*, pg. 3564
SCHEME ENGINE, LLC—See Live Nation Entertainment, Inc.; *U.S. Public*, pg. 1330
SCHENBERGER, TAYLOR, MCCORMICK & JECKER INC.—See Valbridge Property Advisors, Inc.; *U.S. Private*, pg. 4330
SCHENCK CORPORATION—See Durr AG; *Int'l*, pg. 2233
SCHENCK ITALIA S.R.L.—See Durr AG; *Int'l*, pg. 2233
SCHENCK LTD—See Durr AG; *Int'l*, pg. 2233
SCHENCK MEXICO, S.A. DE C.V.—See Durr AG; *Int'l*, pg. 2233
SCHENCK PROCESS AUSTRALIA PTY. LIMITED—See Sandvik AB; *Int'l*, pg. 6535
SCHENCK PROCESS AUSTRAL S.A.—See Sandvik AB; *Int'l*, pg. 6535
SCHENCK PROCESS EQUIPAMENTOS INDUSTRIAIS LTDA.—See Sandvik AB; *Int'l*, pg. 6535
SCHENCK PROCESS FCP EQUIPAMENTOS INDUSTRIAS LTDA.—See Hillenbrand, Inc.; *U.S. Public*, pg. 1037
SCHENCK PROCESS HOLDING GMBH—See Blackstone Inc.; *U.S. Public*, pg. 360
SCHENCK PROCESS LLC—See Blackstone Inc.; *U.S. Public*, pg. 360
SCHENCK PROCESS (THAILAND) LTD.—See Hillenbrand, Inc.; *U.S. Public*, pg. 1037
SCHENCK ROTEC CORPORATION—See Durr AG; *Int'l*, pg. 2233
SCHENCK ROTEC GMBH—See Durr AG; *Int'l*, pg. 2233
SCHENCK ROTEC INDIA LIMITED—See Durr AG; *Int'l*, pg. 2233

SCHENCK SC—See CliftonLarsonAllen LLP; *U.S. Private*, pg. 943
SCHENCK SHANGHAI MACHINERY CORPORATION LTD—See Durr AG; *Int'l*, pg. 2233
SCHENCK TECHNOLOGIE UND INDUSTRIEPARK GMBH—See Durr AG; *Int'l*, pg. 2233
SCHENCK TEST AUTOMATION LTD—See Durr AG; *Int'l*, pg. 2233
SCHENCK TREBEL CORPORATION—See Durr AG; *Int'l*, pg. 2233
SCHENCK USA CORP.—See Durr AG; *Int'l*, pg. 2233
SCHENECTADY AUSTRALIA PTY. LTD.—See SK Capital Partners, LP; *U.S. Private*, pg. 3680
SCHENECTADY BRASIL LIMITADA—See SK Capital Partners, LP; *U.S. Private*, pg. 3680
SCHENECTADY EUROPE, S.A.—See SK Capital Partners, LP; *U.S. Private*, pg. 3680
SCHENECTADY HARDWARE & ELECTRIC CO.; *U.S. Private*, pg. 3564
SCHENECTADY MEXICO, S.A. DE C.V.—See SK Capital Partners, LP; *U.S. Private*, pg. 3680
SCHENKELBERG IMPLEMENT COMPANY; *U.S. Private*, pg. 3564
SCHENKEL & SHULTZ INC.; *U.S. Private*, pg. 3564
SCHENKER AB—See Deutsche Bahn AG; *Int'l*, pg. 2053
SCHENKER AG—See Deutsche Bahn AG; *Int'l*, pg. 2052
SCHENKER AMERICAS, INC.—See Deutsche Bahn AG; *Int'l*, pg. 2054
SCHENKER ARGENTINA S.A.—See Deutsche Bahn AG; *Int'l*, pg. 2053
SCHENKER-ARKAS NAKLIYAT VE TIC. A.S.—See Deutsche Bahn AG; *Int'l*, pg. 2054
SCHENKER A/S—See Deutsche Bahn AG; *Int'l*, pg. 2053
SCHENKER AS—See Deutsche Bahn AG; *Int'l*, pg. 2053
SCHENKER AUSTRALIA PTY. LTD.—See Deutsche Bahn AG; *Int'l*, pg. 2053
SCHENKER (BAX) HOLDING CORP.—See Deutsche Bahn AG; *Int'l*, pg. 2054
SCHENKER BITCC LOGISTICS (BEIJING) CO. LTD.—See Deutsche Bahn AG; *Int'l*, pg. 2053
SCHENKER-BTL LTD.—See Deutsche Bahn AG; *Int'l*, pg. 2054
SCHENKER B.V.—See Deutsche Bahn AG; *Int'l*, pg. 2053
SCHENKER CHILE S.A.—See Deutsche Bahn AG; *Int'l*, pg. 2053
SCHENKER CHINA LTD.—See Deutsche Bahn AG; *Int'l*, pg. 2053
SCHENKER & CO AG—See Deutsche Bahn AG; *Int'l*, pg. 2053
SCHENKER CONSULTING AB—See Deutsche Bahn AG; *Int'l*, pg. 2053
SCHENKER CUSTOMS AGENCY B.V.—See Deutsche Bahn AG; *Int'l*, pg. 2053
SCHENKER DEUTSCHLAND AG—See Deutsche Bahn AG; *Int'l*, pg. 2053
SCHENKER DO BRASIL TRANSPORTES INTERNACIONAIS LTDA.—See Deutsche Bahn AG; *Int'l*, pg. 2054
SCHENKER DOOEL—See Deutsche Bahn AG; *Int'l*, pg. 2053
SCHENKER D.O.O.—See Deutsche Bahn AG; *Int'l*, pg. 2053
SCHENKER D.O.O—See Deutsche Bahn AG; *Int'l*, pg. 2054
SCHENKER D.O.O.—See Deutsche Bahn AG; *Int'l*, pg. 2054
SCHENKER EGYPT LTD.—See Deutsche Bahn AG; *Int'l*, pg. 2053
SCHENKER EOOD—See Deutsche Bahn AG; *Int'l*, pg. 2053
SCHENKER FRANCE SAS—See Deutsche Bahn AG; *Int'l*, pg. 2054
SCHENKER-GEMADEPT LOGISTICS VIETNAM COMPANY LIMITED—See Deutsche Bahn AG; *Int'l*, pg. 2053
SCHENKER HIGH TECH LOGISTICS B.V.—See Deutsche Bahn AG; *Int'l*, pg. 2053
SCHENKER, INC.—See Deutsche Bahn AG; *Int'l*, pg. 2054
SCHENKER, INC.—See Deutsche Bahn AG; *Int'l*, pg. 2054
SCHENKER INDIA PRIVATE LIMITED—See Deutsche Bahn AG; *Int'l*, pg. 2053
SCHENKER INTERNATIONAL HK LIMITED—See Deutsche Bahn AG; *Int'l*, pg. 2053
SCHENKER INTERNATIONAL (HK) LTD.—See Deutsche Bahn AG; *Int'l*, pg. 2054
SCHENKER ITALIANA S.P.A.—See Deutsche Bahn AG; *Int'l*, pg. 2053
SCHENKER JINBEI LOGISTICS (SHENYANG) CO. LTD.—See Deutsche Bahn AG; *Int'l*, pg. 2054
SCHENKER KAZAKHSTAN TOO—See Deutsche Bahn AG; *Int'l*, pg. 2054
SCHENKER KHIMJI'S LLC—See Deutsche Bahn AG; *Int'l*, pg. 2053
SCHENKER KOREA LTD.—See Deutsche Bahn AG; *Int'l*, pg. 2053
SCHENKER (L.L.C)—See Deutsche Bahn AG; *Int'l*, pg. 2053
SCHENKER LOGISTICS AB—See Deutsche Bahn AG; *Int'l*, pg. 2053

SCHENKEL & SHULTZ INC.

SCHENKER LOGISTICS (BANGLADESH) LIMITED—See Deutsche Bahn AG; *Int'l*, pg. 2054
SCHENKER LOGISTICS (GUANGZHOU) COMPANY LTD.—See Deutsche Bahn AG; *Int'l*, pg. 2053
SCHENKER LOGISTICS (JIAXING) CO., LTD.—See Deutsche Bahn AG; *Int'l*, pg. 2054
SCHENKER LOGISTICS (KUNSHAN) CO., LTD.—See Deutsche Bahn AG; *Int'l*, pg. 2054
SCHENKER LOGISTICS L.L.C.—See Deutsche Bahn AG; *Int'l*, pg. 2053
SCHENKER LOGISTICS (MALAYSIA) SDN BHD.—See Deutsche Bahn AG; *Int'l*, pg. 2053
SCHENKER LOGISTICS ROMANIA S.A.—See Deutsche Bahn AG; *Int'l*, pg. 2054
SCHENKER LOGISTICS (SHANGHAI) CO., LTD.—See Deutsche Bahn AG; *Int'l*, pg. 2053
SCHENKER LOGISTICS (SUZHOU) COMPANY LTD.—See Deutsche Bahn AG; *Int'l*, pg. 2053
SCHENKER LOGISTICS VIETNAM CO. LTD.—See Deutsche Bahn AG; *Int'l*, pg. 2053
SCHENKER LOGISTICS (XIAMEN) CO. LTD.—See Deutsche Bahn AG; *Int'l*, pg. 2053
SCHENKER LTD.—See Deutsche Bahn AG; *Int'l*, pg. 2053
SCHENKER LUXEMBURG GMBH—See Deutsche Bahn AG; *Int'l*, pg. 2053
SCHENKER MIDDLE EAST FZE—See Deutsche Bahn AG; *Int'l*, pg. 2053
SCHENKER MYANMAR CO., LTD.—See Deutsche Bahn AG; *Int'l*, pg. 2054
SCHENKER NAMIBIA (PTY) LTD.—See Deutsche Bahn AG; *Int'l*, pg. 2053
SCHENKER N.V.—See Deutsche Bahn AG; *Int'l*, pg. 2053
SCHENKER (NZ) LTD.—See Deutsche Bahn AG; *Int'l*, pg. 2053
SCHENKER OF CANADA LIMITED—See Deutsche Bahn AG; *Int'l*, pg. 2054
SCHENKER OY—See Deutsche Bahn AG; *Int'l*, pg. 2054
SCHENKER PANAMA S.A.—See Deutsche Bahn AG; *Int'l*, pg. 2054
SCHENKER PERU S.R.L.—See Deutsche Bahn AG; *Int'l*, pg. 2054
SCHENKER PHILIPPINES, INC.—See Deutsche Bahn AG; *Int'l*, pg. 2054
SCHENKER PHILIPPINES, INC.—See Deutsche Bahn AG; *Int'l*, pg. 2054
SCHENKER SA—See Deutsche Bahn AG; *Int'l*, pg. 2054
SCHENKER SAUDI ARABIA LLC—See Deutsche Bahn AG; *Int'l*, pg. 2054
SCHENKER SCHWEIZ AG—See Deutsche Bahn AG; *Int'l*, pg. 2054
SCHENKER-SEINO CO. LTD.—See Deutsche Bahn AG; *Int'l*, pg. 2054
SCHENKER SINGAPORE (PTE) LTD.—See Deutsche Bahn AG; *Int'l*, pg. 2054
SCHENKER SOUTH AFRICA (PTY) LTD.—See Deutsche Bahn AG; *Int'l*, pg. 2054
SCHENKER SPOL. S R.O.—See Deutsche Bahn AG; *Int'l*, pg. 2053
SCHENKER S.R.O.—See Deutsche Bahn AG; *Int'l*, pg. 2053
SCHENKER SWITZERLAND AG—See Deutsche Bahn AG; *Int'l*, pg. 2054
SCHENKER (THAI) LTD.—See Deutsche Bahn AG; *Int'l*, pg. 2053
SCHENK PACKING CO. INC.; *U.S. Private*, pg. 3564
S.C. HENNLICH S.R.L.—See THK CO., LTD.; *Int'l*, pg. 7712
SCHEPPS NEW MEXICO DEVELOPMENT CORP.—See Julius Schepps Company, Inc.; *U.S. Private*, pg. 2243
SCHERBAUER SPEDITION GMBH—See Deutsche Post AG; *Int'l*, pg. 2082
S.C. HERCULES S.A.; *Int'l*, pg. 6451
SCHERDEL HERCKELBOUT DAWSON S.A.R.L.; *Int'l*, pg. 6616
SCHERER BROTHERS LUMBER COMPANY; *U.S. Private*, pg. 3564
SCHERER CONSTRUCTION OF WEST FLORIDA, LLC; *U.S. Private*, pg. 3564
SCHERER STAFFING LLC; *U.S. Private*, pg. 3564
SCHERF-PRAZISION EUROPA GMBH—See Gerresheimer AG; *Int'l*, pg. 2944
SCHERING AG REGIONAL SCIENTIFIC OFFICE, MALAYSIA—See Bayer Aktiengesellschaft; *Int'l*, pg. 904
SCHERING AG—See Bayer Aktiengesellschaft; *Int'l*, pg. 904
SCHERING BERLIN INC.—See Bayer Aktiengesellschaft; *Int'l*, pg. 902
SCHERING CHINA LIMITED—See Bayer Aktiengesellschaft; *Int'l*, pg. 904
SCHERING DE CHILE S.A.—See Bayer Aktiengesellschaft; *Int'l*, pg. 905
SCHERING DO BRASIL LTDA.—See Bayer Aktiengesellschaft; *Int'l*, pg. 905
SCHERING GMBH & CO. PRODUKTIONS KG—See Bayer Aktiengesellschaft; *Int'l*, pg. 904
SCHERING NORGE A/S—See Bayer Aktiengesellschaft; *Int'l*, pg. 904

SCHERING PHARMACEUTICAL LIMITED—See Bayer Aktiengesellschaft; *Int'l*, pg. 904
SCHERING-PLOUGH CANADA INC.—See Merck & Co., Inc.; *U.S. Public*, pg. 1421
SCHERING-PLOUGH LABO NV—See Organon & Co.; *U.S. Public*, pg. 1616
SCHERING-PLOUGH SANTE ANIMALE—See Merck & Co., Inc.; *U.S. Public*, pg. 1421
SCHERING PREDSTAVNISTVO U JUGOSLAVIJII—See Bayer Aktiengesellschaft; *Int'l*, pg. 904
SCHERING TAIWAN LTD.—See Bayer Aktiengesellschaft; *Int'l*, pg. 905
SCHERMERHORN BROTHERS CO.; *U.S. Private*, pg. 3564
SCHERMER, INC.; *U.S. Private*, pg. 3564
SCHERRER HAUSTECHNIK AG—See Poenina Holding AG; *Int'l*, pg. 5903
SCHERRMAN'S IMPLEMENT & APPLIANCE; *U.S. Private*, pg. 3564
SCHERWO STEUERUNGSTECHNIK GMBH—See ATON GmbH; *Int'l*, pg. 689
SCHERZER & CO. AG; *Int'l*, pg. 6616
SCHERZ VERLAG AG—See Verlagsgruppe Georg von Holtzbrinck GmbH; *Int'l*, pg. 8171
SCHEUCH GMBH; *Int'l*, pg. 6616
SCHEUERMANN + HEILIG DO BRASIL LTDA—See Scheuermann + Heilig GmbH; *Int'l*, pg. 6616
SCHEUERMANN + HEILIG GMBH; *Int'l*, pg. 6616
SCHEU STEEL SUPPLY COMPANY—See SMC Companies; *U.S. Private*, pg. 3693
SCHEWEL FURNITURE COMPANY, INC.; *U.S. Private*, pg. 3564
SC&H GROUP, LLC; *U.S. Private*, pg. 3560
SCHIAVELLO GROUP PTY LTD; *Int'l*, pg. 6616
SCHIAVELLO SINGAPORE PTY. LTD.—See Schiavello Group Pty Ltd; *Int'l*, pg. 6616
SCHIAVELLO SYSTEMS INTERNATIONAL PTY. LTD.—See Schiavello Group Pty Ltd; *Int'l*, pg. 6616
SCHIAVI LEASING CORPORATION—See Vanguard Modular Building Systems, LLC; *U.S. Private*, pg. 4344
SCHIAVONE CONSTRUCTION CO. LLC—See ACS, Actividades de Construccion y Servicios, S.A.; *Int'l*, pg. 111
SCHIBLEY SOLVENTS & CHEMICAL CO.; *U.S. Private*, pg. 3564
SCHIBSTED ASA; *Int'l*, pg. 6616
SCHIBSTED EIENDOM AS—See Schibsted ASA; *Int'l*, pg. 6617
SCHIBSTED FINANS AS—See Schibsted ASA; *Int'l*, pg. 6617
SCHIBSTED PAYMENT AS—See Schibsted ASA; *Int'l*, pg. 6617
SCHIBSTED SVERIGE AB—See Schibsted ASA; *Int'l*, pg. 6617
SCHIBSTED TECH POLSKA SP. Z.O.O.—See Schibsted ASA; *Int'l*, pg. 6617
SCHIBSTED TILLVAXTMEDIER ANNONSFORSALJNING AB—See Schibsted ASA; *Int'l*, pg. 6617
SCHIBSTED TRYKK OSLO AS—See Schibsted ASA; *Int'l*, pg. 6617
SCHIBSTED VEKST AS—See Schibsted ASA; *Int'l*, pg. 6617
SCHICK ASIA LIMITED—See Edgewell Personal Care Company; *U.S. Public*, pg. 718
SCHICK (GUANGZHOU) COMPANY LTD.—See Edgewell Personal Care Company; *U.S. Public*, pg. 718
SCHICK JAPAN K.K.—See Edgewell Personal Care Company; *U.S. Public*, pg. 718
SCHICK MANUFACTURING INC.—See Edgewell Personal Care Company; *U.S. Public*, pg. 718
SCHICK-WILKINSON SWORD—See Edgewell Personal Care Company; *U.S. Public*, pg. 718
SC HIDROMECANICA SA BRASOV; *Int'l*, pg. 6609
SC HIDRO OLT SRL—See S.C. InterAgro S.A.; *Int'l*, pg. 6452
SCHIEDEL AG—See PAI Partners S.A.S.; *Int'l*, pg. 5701
SCHIEDEL A.S.—See PAI Partners S.A.S.; *Int'l*, pg. 5701
SCHIEDEL GMBH & CO.—See PAI Partners S.A.S.; *Int'l*, pg. 5701
SCHIEDEL KAMINSYSTEME GMBH—See PAI Partners S.A.S.; *Int'l*, pg. 5701
SCHIEDEL KEMENYGYAR KFT.—See PAI Partners S.A.S.; *Int'l*, pg. 5701
SCHIEDEL PROIZVODNJA DIMNJAKA D.O.O.—See PAI Partners S.A.S.; *Int'l*, pg. 5701
SCHIEDEL S.A.R.L.—See PAI Partners S.A.S.; *Int'l*, pg. 5701
SCHIEFER CHOPSHOP—See PopReach Corporation; *Int'l*, pg. 5921
SCHIELD FAMILY BRANDS—See Weathershield Mfg. Inc.; *U.S. Private*, pg. 4463
SCHIERL SALES CORP.—See Team Schierl Companies; *U.S. Private*, pg. 3950
SCHIESSER AG—See GMM Capital LLC; *U.S. Private*, pg. 1722
SCHIESSER BODY FASHION CENTER S.R.O.—See GMM Capital LLC; *U.S. Private*, pg. 1722
SCHIESSER INTERNATIONAL LTD.—See GMM Capital LLC; *U.S. Private*, pg. 1722

CORPORATE AFFILIATIONS

SCHIESSER INTERNATIONAL NEDERLAND BV—See GMM Capital LLC; *U.S. Private*, pg. 1722
SCHIESSER SCHWEIZ AG—See GMM Capital LLC; *U.S. Private*, pg. 1722
SCHIESSL & CO. GMBH; *Int'l*, pg. 6618
SCHIFF ENTERPRISES; *U.S. Private*, pg. 3564
SCHIFF FOOD PRODUCTS CO., INC.; *U.S. Private*, pg. 3564
SCHIFF HARDIN LLP—See ArentFox Schiff LLP; *U.S. Private*, pg. 318
SCHIFFMAYER PLASTICS CORP; *U.S. Private*, pg. 3564
SCHIFF NUTRITION INTERNATIONAL, INC.—See Reckitt Benckiser Group plc; *Int'l*, pg. 6237
SCHIFF'S FOOD SERVICE, INC.; *U.S. Private*, pg. 3564
SCHIFINO/LEE, INC.; *U.S. Private*, pg. 3564
SCHILDBERG CONSTRUCTION CO. INC.; *U.S. Private*, pg. 3565
SCHILD ELEKTRO AG—See Burkhalter Holding AG; *Int'l*, pg. 1225
SCHILDERWERK BEUTHA GMBH; *Int'l*, pg. 6618
SCHILKE MUSIC PRODUCTS, INC.; *U.S. Private*, pg. 3565
SCHILLER GROUNDS CARE, INC.; *U.S. Private*, pg. 3565
SCHILLER HARDWARE INC.; *U.S. Private*, pg. 3565
SCHILLI CORPORATION—See TFI International Inc.; *Int'l*, pg. 7586
SCHILLI DISTRIBUTION SERVICES, INC.—See Daseke, Inc.; *U.S. Private*, pg. 1161
SCHILLI LEASING, INC.—See Daseke, Inc.; *U.S. Private*, pg. 1161
SCHILLI NATIONAL TRUCK LEASING & SALES, INC.—See Daseke, Inc.; *U.S. Private*, pg. 1162
SCHILLING BROS LUMBER CO., INC.; *U.S. Private*, pg. 3565
SCHILLING DISTRIBUTING CO. INC.; *U.S. Private*, pg. 3565
SCHILLING FORGE, INC.—See CUTCO Corporation; *U.S. Private*, pg. 1131
SCHILLING PAPER COMPANY INC.; *U.S. Private*, pg. 3565
SCHILLI SPECIALIZED, INC.—See Daseke, Inc.; *U.S. Private*, pg. 1161
SCHILLI SPECIALIZED OF TEXAS, INC.—See Daseke, Inc.; *U.S. Private*, pg. 1162
SCHILLI TRANSPORTATION SERVICES, INC.—See Daseke, Inc.; *U.S. Private*, pg. 1162
SCHILLI TRANSPORTATION SERVICES, INC.—See Daseke, Inc.; *U.S. Private*, pg. 1161
SCHILL LANDSCAPING & LAWN SERVICES, INC.; *U.S. Private*, pg. 3565
SCHILL + SEILACHER AG; *Int'l*, pg. 6618
SCHILL + SEILACHER CHEMIE GMBH—See Schill + Seilacher AG; *Int'l*, pg. 6618
THE SCHIMBERG GROUP INC.; *U.S. Private*, pg. 4114
SCHIMENTI CONSTRUCTION CO.; *U.S. Private*, pg. 3565
SCHIMMELPFENG CREDITMANAGEMENT GMBH—See Intrum AB; *Int'l*, pg. 3771
SCHIMMELPFENG FORDERUNGSMANAGEMENT GMBH—See Intrum AB; *Int'l*, pg. 3771
SCHIMMER CHEVROLET BUICK, INC.; *U.S. Private*, pg. 3565
SCHIMUNEK FUNERAL HOME, INC.—See Service Corporation International; *U.S. Public*, pg. 1870
SCHINAC B.V.—See Schindler Holding AG; *Int'l*, pg. 6619
SCHINDLER - ASCENSORES E ESCADAS ROLANTES, S.A.—See Schindler Holding AG; *Int'l*, pg. 6619
SCHINDLER AS—See Schindler Holding AG; *Int'l*, pg. 6619
SCHINDLER AUFZUGE AG—See Schindler Holding AG; *Int'l*, pg. 6619
SCHINDLER AUFZUGE & FAHRTREPPEN GMBH—See Schindler Holding AG; *Int'l*, pg. 6619
SCHINDLER AUFZUGE GMBH—See Schindler Holding AG; *Int'l*, pg. 6619
SCHINDLER AUFZUGE. GMBH—See Schindler Holding AG; *Int'l*, pg. 6619
SCHINDLER AUFZUGE UND FAHRTREPPEN AG—See Schindler Holding AG; *Int'l*, pg. 6619
SCHINDLER AUFZUGE UND FAHRTREPPEN GMBH—See Schindler Holding AG; *Int'l*, pg. 6619
SCHINDLER BH D.O.O.—See Schindler Holding AG; *Int'l*, pg. 6619
SCHINDLER BULGARIA EOOD—See Schindler Holding AG; *Int'l*, pg. 6619
SCHINDLER BV—See Schindler Holding AG; *Int'l*, pg. 6619
SCHINDLER CHINA ELEVATOR CO. LTD.—See Schindler Holding AG; *Int'l*, pg. 6620
SCHINDLER CORPORATION OF PUERTO RICO—See Schindler Holding AG; *Int'l*, pg. 6619
SCHINDLER CZ, A.S.—See Schindler Holding AG; *Int'l*, pg. 6619
SCHINDLER DEUTSCHLAND HOLDING GMBH—See Schindler Holding AG; *Int'l*, pg. 6619
SCHINDLER DEVE LIFTS AUSTRALIA—See Schindler Holding AG; *Int'l*, pg. 6619
SCHINDLER D.O.O. BEOGRAD—See Schindler Holding AG; *Int'l*, pg. 6621

COMPANY NAME INDEX

SCHINDLER ELECTRONICS (SUZHOU) CO. LTD.—See Schindler Holding AG; *Int'l*, pg. 6620
SCHINDLER ELEVATOR CORPORATION—See Schindler Holding AG; *Int'l*, pg. 6619
SCHINDLER ELEVATOR CORPORATION—See Schindler Holding AG; *Int'l*, pg. 6619
SCHINDLER ELEVATORER A/S—See Schindler Holding AG; *Int'l*, pg. 6619
SCHINDLER ELEVATOR K.K—See Schindler Holding AG; *Int'l*, pg. 6620
SCHINDLER ENTERPRISES, INC.—See Schindler Holding AG; *Int'l*, pg. 6619
SCHINDLER ESKALATORY S.R.O.—See Schindler Holding AG; *Int'l*, pg. 6619
SCHINDLER FAHRTREPPEN INTERNATIONAL GMBH—See Schindler Holding AG; *Int'l*, pg. 6619
SCHINDLER FENSTER + FASSADEN GMBH; *Int'l*, pg. 6618
SCHINDLER FOR IMPORTATION SERVICES LTD—See Schindler Holding AG; *Int'l*, pg. 6621
SCHINDLER FRANCE—See Schindler Holding AG; *Int'l*, pg. 6619
SCHINDLER HELLAS SA—See Schindler Holding AG; *Int'l*, pg. 6619
SCHINDLER HISS AB—See Schindler Holding AG; *Int'l*, pg. 6619
SCHINDLER HISS AB—See Schindler Holding AG; *Int'l*, pg. 6619
SCHINDLER HOLDING AG; *Int'l*, pg. 6618
SCHINDLER HRVATSKA D.O.O.—See Schindler Holding AG; *Int'l*, pg. 6619
SCHINDLER HUNGARIA KFT—See Schindler Holding AG; *Int'l*, pg. 6620
SCHINDLER IBERICA MANAGEMENT, S.A.—See Schindler Holding AG; *Int'l*, pg. 6620
SCHINDLER INDIA PVT. LTD.—See Schindler Holding AG; *Int'l*, pg. 6620
SCHINDLER INFORMATIK AG—See Schindler Holding AG; *Int'l*, pg. 6620
SCHINDLER KOREA CO. LTD.—See Schindler Holding AG; *Int'l*, pg. 6620
SCHINDLER LATIN AMERICA OPERATIONS—See Schindler Holding AG; *Int'l*, pg. 6620
SCHINDLER LEBANON S.A.L.—See Schindler Holding AG; *Int'l*, pg. 6620
SCHINDLER LIEGENSCHAFTSVERWALTUNGS GMBH—See Schindler Holding AG; *Int'l*, pg. 6620
SCHINDLER LIFTEN B.V.—See Schindler Holding AG; *Int'l*, pg. 6620
SCHINDLER LIFTS AUSTRALIA PTY. LTD.—See Schindler Holding AG; *Int'l*, pg. 6620
SCHINDLER LIFTS (BOTSWANA) (PTY) LTD.—See Schindler Holding AG; *Int'l*, pg. 6620
SCHINDLER LIFTS (HONG KONG) LTD.—See Schindler Holding AG; *Int'l*, pg. 6620
SCHINDLER LIFTS (NAMIBIA) (PTY) LTD.—See Schindler Holding AG; *Int'l*, pg. 6620
SCHINDLER LIFTS NZ LTD.—See Schindler Holding AG; *Int'l*, pg. 6620
SCHINDLER LIFTS SA INVESTMENTS HOLDING (PTY) LTD.—See Schindler Holding AG; *Int'l*, pg. 6620
SCHINDLER LIFTS (SINGAPORE) PTE. LTD.—See Schindler Holding AG; *Int'l*, pg. 6620
SCHINDLER LIFTS SOUTH AFRICA (PTY.) LTD.—See Schindler Holding AG; *Int'l*, pg. 6620
SCHINDLER LIFTS (ZIMBABWE) (PVT) LTD.—See Schindler Holding AG; *Int'l*, pg. 6620
SCHINDLER LTD., EGYPT—See Schindler Holding AG; *Int'l*, pg. 6620
SCHINDLER LTD.—See Schindler Holding AG; *Int'l*, pg. 6620
SCHINDLER LTD.—See Schindler Holding AG; *Int'l*, pg. 6620
SCHINDLER LTD.—See Schindler Holding AG; *Int'l*, pg. 6620
SCHINDLER LTD.—See Schindler Holding AG; *Int'l*, pg. 6620
SCHINDLER MANAGEMENT AG—See Schindler Holding AG; *Int'l*, pg. 6620
SCHINDLER MANAGEMENT AP (SHANGHAI) CO. LTD.—See Schindler Holding AG; *Int'l*, pg. 6620
SCHINDLER MANAGEMENT ASIA/PACIFIC LTD.—See Schindler Holding AG; *Int'l*, pg. 6620
SCHINDLER MAROC S.A.—See Schindler Holding AG; *Int'l*, pg. 6621
SCHINDLER MONACO—See Schindler Holding AG; *Int'l*, pg. 6621
SCHINDLER NECHUSHTAN ELEVATORS LTD.—See Schindler Holding AG; *Int'l*, pg. 6621
SCHINDLER OLAYAN ELEVATOR COMPANY LTD.—See Schindler Holding AG; *Int'l*, pg. 6621
SCHINDLER OY—See Schindler Holding AG; *Int'l*, pg. 6621
SCHINDLER PARS INTERNATIONAL LTD.—See Schindler Holding AG; *Int'l*, pg. 6621
SCHINDLER POLSKA SP. ZOO.—See Schindler Holding AG; *Int'l*, pg. 6621
SCHINDLER ROMANIA S.R.L.—See Schindler Holding AG; *Int'l*, pg. 6621
SCHINDLER S.A.R.L.—See Schindler Holding AG; *Int'l*, pg. 6621
SCHINDLER S.A.—See Schindler Holding AG; *Int'l*, pg. 6621
SCHINDLER, S.A.—See Schindler Holding AG; *Int'l*, pg. 6621
SCHINDLER SCANDINAVIAN HOLDING AB—See Schindler Holding AG; *Int'l*, pg. 6621
SCHINDLER SLOVENIJA D.O.O.—See Schindler Holding AG; *Int'l*, pg. 6621
SCHINDLER S.P.A.—See Schindler Holding AG; *Int'l*, pg. 6621
SCHINDLER STAHL HEISER A/S—See Schindler Holding AG; *Int'l*, pg. 6621
SCHINDLER TECHNIK AG—See Schindler Holding AG; *Int'l*, pg. 6621
SCHINDLER TURKELI ASANSOR SAN A.S.—See Schindler Holding AG; *Int'l*, pg. 6621
SCHINDLER UK—See Schindler Holding AG; *Int'l*, pg. 6621
SCHINDLER VIETNAM LTD.—See Schindler Holding AG; *Int'l*, pg. 6620
SCHINDLER VYTAHY A ESKALATORY A.S.—See Schindler Holding AG; *Int'l*, pg. 6621
THE SCHINNERER GROUP, INC.—See Marsh & McLennan Companies, Inc.; *U.S. Public*, pg. 1388
SCH INSURANCE COMPANY—See InterContinental Hotels Group PLC; *Int'l*, pg. 3738
SCHINVEST (JERSEY) LTD.—See Schindler Holding AG; *Int'l*, pg. 6621
SCHIPHOL AIRPORT RETAIL B.V.—See Schiphol Group NV; *Int'l*, pg. 6621
SCHIPHOL CONNECT B.V.—See Gamma Communications PLC; *Int'l*, pg. 2878
SCHIPHOL GROUP NV; *Int'l*, pg. 6621
SCHIPHOL REAL ESTATE B.V.—See Schiphol Group NV; *Int'l*, pg. 6621
SCHIPHOL TELEMATICS CV—See Schiphol Group NV; *Int'l*, pg. 6621
SCHIRESON ASSOCIATES, INC.—See Known Global LLC; *U.S. Private*, pg. 2324
SCHIRM GMBH-LUBECK—See AECI Limited; *Int'l*, pg. 172
SCHIRM GMBH-SCHONEBECK—See AECI Limited; *Int'l*, pg. 172
SCHIRM GMBH—See AECI Limited; *Int'l*, pg. 171
SCHIRM USA, INC.—See AECI Limited; *Int'l*, pg. 172
SCHIRNHOFER WERKZEUGMASCHINEN & WERKZEUGE GMBH—See Grieshaber Holding GmbH; *Int'l*, pg. 3083
SCHISCHEK GMBH—See Rotork Plc; *Int'l*, pg. 6406
SCHIVO MEDICAL LIMITED; *Int'l*, pg. 6621
SCHJAERVEN 3D—See Schjaerven Reklamebyra; *Int'l*, pg. 6622
SCHJAERVEN FILM—See Schjaerven Reklamebyra; *Int'l*, pg. 6622
SCHJAERVEN INTERACTIVE—See Schjaerven Reklamebyra; *Int'l*, pg. 6622
SCHJAERVEN PR—See Schjaerven Reklamebyra; *Int'l*, pg. 6622
SCHJAERVEN REKLAMEBYRA; *Int'l*, pg. 6622
SCHLAFHORST AUTOCORO GMBH—See OC Oerlikon Corporation AG; *Int'l*, pg. 5515
SCHLAFHORST MARKETING COMPANY LTD.—See OC Oerlikon Corporation AG; *Int'l*, pg. 5515
SCHLAFHORST WINDING SYSTEMS GMBH—See OC Oerlikon Corporation AG; *Int'l*, pg. 5515
SCHLAFHORST ZWEIGNIEDERLASSUNG DER SAURER GERMANY GMBH & CO. KG—See OC Oerlikon Corporation AG; *Int'l*, pg. 5515
SCHLAGE DE MEXICO S.A. DE C.V.—See Ingersoll Rand Inc.; *U.S. Public*, pg. 1122
SCHLAGE ELECTRONIC SECURITY—See Allegion Public Limited Company; *Int'l*, pg. 335
SCHLAGE LOCK COMPANY LLC—See Allegion Public Limited Company; *Int'l*, pg. 335
SCHLAGE LOCK CO.—See Allegion Public Limited Company; *Int'l*, pg. 335
SCHLATHER INSURANCE AGENCY INC.—See Northlane Capital Partners, LLC; *U.S. Private*, pg. 2956
SCHLATTER FRANCE S.A.R.L.—See Schlatter Industries AG; *Int'l*, pg. 6622
SCHLATTER INDUSTRIES AG; *Int'l*, pg. 6622
SCHLATTER INTERNATIONAL GMBH—See Schlatter Industries AG; *Int'l*, pg. 6622
SCHLATTER ITALIANA S.R.L.—See Schlatter Industries AG; *Int'l*, pg. 6622
SCHLATTER LTD.—See Schlatter Industries AG; *Int'l*, pg. 6622
SCHLATTER MAQUINAS DE SOLDAR LTDA.—See Schlatter Industries AG; *Int'l*, pg. 6622
SCHLATTER NORTH AMERICA—See Schlatter Industries AG; *Int'l*, pg. 6622
SCHLATTER SOUTH EAST ASIA SDN. BHD.—See Schlatter Industries AG; *Int'l*, pg. 6622
SCHLAUTHERM GMBH—See RWE AG; *Int'l*, pg. 6435
SCHLEGEL AUSTRALIA PTY LIMITED—See Quanex Building Products Corp.; *U.S. Public*, pg. 1749
SCHLEGEL BELGIUM BVBA—See Quanex Building Products Corp.; *U.S. Public*, pg. 1749
SCHLEGEL BVBA—See Quanex Building Products Corp.; *U.S. Public*, pg. 1749
SCHLEGEL ENGINEERING KK—See Quanex Building Products Corp.; *U.S. Public*, pg. 1749
SCHLEGEL FAR EAST LTD—See Quanex Building Products Corp.; *U.S. Public*, pg. 1749
SCHLEGEL GERMANY GMBH—See Quanex Building Products Corp.; *U.S. Public*, pg. 1749
SCHLEGEL PTY LTD—See Quanex Building Products Corp.; *U.S. Public*, pg. 1749
SCHLEGEL SRL—See Quanex Building Products Corp.; *U.S. Public*, pg. 1750
SCHLEGEL SYSTEMS, INC.—See Quanex Building Products Corp.; *U.S. Public*, pg. 1750
SCHLEGEL TALIANA SL—See Quanex Building Products Corp.; *U.S. Public*, pg. 1750
SCHLEGEL UK (2006) LIMITED—See Quanex Building Products Corp.; *U.S. Public*, pg. 1750
SCHLEGEL (UK) LIMITED—See Quanex Building Products Corp.; *U.S. Public*, pg. 1750
SCHLEHUBER OIL TOOLS, LLC—See Intervale Capital, LLC; *U.S. Private*, pg. 2127
SCHLEICHER BETEILIGUNGS GMBH—See Schleicher Electronic GmbH & Co. KG; *Int'l*, pg. 6622
SCHLEICHER ELECTRONIC GMBH & CO. KG; *Int'l*, pg. 6622
SCHLEICHER ELECTRONIC VERWALTUNGS-GMBH—See Schleicher Electronic GmbH & Co. KG; *Int'l*, pg. 6622
SCHLEIFRING MEDICAL SYSTEMS, LLC—See GE HealthCare Technologies Inc.; *U.S. Public*, pg. 909
SCHLEMMER PHILIPPINES INC.—See Ningbo Huaxiang Electronic Co., Ltd.; *Int'l*, pg. 5302
SCHLESINGER GROUP; *U.S. Private*, pg. 3565
SCHLESWIG-HOLSTEIN NETZ VERWALTUNGS-GMBH—See E.ON SE; *Int'l*, pg. 2259
SCHLEUNIGER AG—See Metall Zug AG; *Int'l*, pg. 4847
SCHLEUNIGER GMBH—See Metall Zug AG; *Int'l*, pg. 4847
SCHLEUNIGER HOLDING AG—See Metall Zug AG; *Int'l*, pg. 4847
SCHLEUNIGER, INC.—See Metall Zug AG; *Int'l*, pg. 4847
SCHLEUNIGER JAPAN CO., LTD.—See Metall Zug AG; *Int'l*, pg. 4847
SCHLEUNIGER MACHINERY (TIANJIN) CO., LTD.—See Metall Zug AG; *Int'l*, pg. 4847
SCHLEUNIGER SOLUTIONS AG—See Metall Zug AG; *Int'l*, pg. 4847
SCHLEUNIGER TEST AUTOMATION GMBH—See Metall Zug AG; *Int'l*, pg. 4847
SCHLEUNIGER TRADING (SHANGHAI) CO., LTD.—See Metall Zug AG; *Int'l*, pg. 4847
SCHLEUPEN AG; *Int'l*, pg. 6622
SCHLOSS BENSBERG MANAGEMENT GMBH—See Aedifica SA; *Int'l*, pg. 173
SCHLOSSBERGPROJEKTENTWICK—See UniCredit S.p.A.; *Int'l*, pg. 8035
SCHLOSSER MOLLER KULDE AS—See Beijer Ref AB; *Int'l*, pg. 945
SCHLOSS HOHENKAMMER GMBH—See Munchener Ruckversicherungs AG; *Int'l*, pg. 5091
SCHLOSS KRICKENBECK GMBH—See Portigon AG; *Int'l*, pg. 5934
SCHLOSSMANN DODGE CITY OF MILWAUKEE—See Schlossmann Investment Corp.; *U.S. Private*, pg. 3565
SCHLOSSMANN IMPORTS INC.—See Schlossmann Investment Corp.; *U.S. Private*, pg. 3565
SCHLOSSMANN INVESTMENT CORP.; *U.S. Private*, pg. 3565
SCHLOSSMANN'S DODGE CITY CHRYSLER JEEP, INC.—See Schlossmann Investment Corp.; *U.S. Private*, pg. 3565
SCHLOSS WACHENHEIM AG; *Int'l*, pg. 6622
SCHLOTTERBECK & FOSS, LLC—See Frontenac Company LLC; *U.S. Private*, pg. 1614
SCHLOTT GRUPPE AG; *Int'l*, pg. 6622
SCHLOTT VERTRIEB GMBH—See Schlott Gruppe AG; *Int'l*, pg. 6622
SCHLOTZSKY'S, LTD.—See Roark Capital Group Inc.; *U.S. Private*, pg. 3455
SCHLUETER CO.; *U.S. Private*, pg. 3565
SCHLUMBERGER BARTLESVILLE PRODUCT CENTER—See Schlumberger Limited; *U.S. Public*, pg. 1846
SCHLUMBERGER B.V.—See Schlumberger Limited; *U.S. Public*, pg. 1844
SCHLUMBERGER CANADA LIMITED—See Schlumberger Limited; *U.S. Public*, pg. 1844
SCHLUMBERGER COMPLETIONS & PRODUCTIVITY—See Schlumberger Limited; *U.S. Public*, pg. 1846
SCHLUMBERGER COMPLETION SYSTEMS—See Schlumberger Limited; *U.S. Public*, pg. 1844
SCHLUMBERGER CONVEYENCE AND DELIVERY TECHNOLOGY CORP.—See Schlumberger Limited; *U.S. Public*, pg. 1844

SCHLUETER CO.   CORPORATE AFFILIATIONS

SCHLUMBERGER DRILLING AND MEASUREMENT—See Schlumberger Limited; *U.S. Public*, pg. 1844
SCHLUMBERGER GMBH & CO. KG—See Schlumberger Limited; *U.S. Public*, pg. 1844
SCHLUMBERGER INDUSTRIES—See Schlumberger Limited; *U.S. Public*, pg. 1846
SCHLUMBERGER INTERNATIONAL—See Schlumberger Limited; *U.S. Public*, pg. 1845
SCHLUMBERGER INTERNATIONAL—See Schlumberger Limited; *U.S. Public*, pg. 1844
SCHLUMBERGER INTERNATIONAL—See Schlumberger Limited; *U.S. Public*, pg. 1844
SCHLUMBERGER INTERNATIONAL—See Schlumberger Limited; *U.S. Public*, pg. 1844
SCHLUMBERGER INTERNATIONAL—See Schlumberger Limited; *U.S. Public*, pg. 1844
SCHLUMBERGER LIMITED - COILED TUBING SERVICES—See Schlumberger Limited; *U.S. Public*, pg. 1845
SCHLUMBERGER LIMITED - DRILL BITS—See Schlumberger Limited; *U.S. Public*, pg. 1845
SCHLUMBERGER LIMITED - HOUMA—See Schlumberger Limited; *U.S. Public*, pg. 1845
SCHLUMBERGER LIMITED—See Schlumberger Limited; *U.S. Public*, pg. 1845
SCHLUMBERGER LIMITED—See Schlumberger Limited; *U.S. Public*, pg. 1845
SCHLUMBERGER LIMITED—See Schlumberger Limited; *U.S. Public*, pg. 1845
SCHLUMBERGER LIMITED—See Schlumberger Limited; *U.S. Public*, pg. 1845
SCHLUMBERGER LIMITED—See Schlumberger Limited; *U.S. Public*, pg. 1845
SCHLUMBERGER LIMITED—See Schlumberger Limited; *U.S. Public*, pg. 1845
SCHLUMBERGER LIMITED—See Schlumberger Limited; *U.S. Public*, pg. 1845
SCHLUMBERGER LIMITED—See Schlumberger Limited; *U.S. Public*, pg. 1845
SCHLUMBERGER LIMITED; *U.S. Public*, pg. 1843
SCHLUMBERGER NETWORK SOLUTIONS—See Schlumberger Limited; *U.S. Public*, pg. 1845
SCHLUMBERGER NORGE AS—See Schlumberger Limited; *U.S. Public*, pg. 1845
SCHLUMBERGER OILFIELD CORP.—See Schlumberger Limited; *U.S. Public*, pg. 1845
SCHLUMBERGER OILFIELD SERVICES—See Schlumberger Limited; *U.S. Public*, pg. 1845
SCHLUMBERGER OILFIELD SERVICES—See Schlumberger Limited; *U.S. Public*, pg. 1845
SCHLUMBERGER OILFIELD SERVICES—See Schlumberger Limited; *U.S. Public*, pg. 1845
SCHLUMBERGER OILFIELD UK PLC—See Schlumberger Limited; *U.S. Public*, pg. 1845
SCHLUMBERGER REDA PRODUCTION SYSTEMS—See Schlumberger Limited; *U.S. Public*, pg. 1846
SCHLUMBERGER RESERVOIR COMPLETIONS CENTER—See Schlumberger Limited; *U.S. Public*, pg. 1846
SCHLUMBERGER SA—See Schlumberger Limited; *U.S. Public*, pg. 1845
SCHLUMBERGER—See Schlumberger Limited; *U.S. Public*, pg. 1844
SCHLUMBERGER—See Schlumberger Limited; *U.S. Public*, pg. 1844
SCHLUMBERGER—See Schlumberger Limited; *U.S. Public*, pg. 1844
SCHLUMBERGER—See Schlumberger Limited; *U.S. Public*, pg. 1844
SCHLUMBERGER TECHNOLOGY CORPORATION—See Schlumberger Limited; *U.S. Public*, pg. 1845
SCHLUMBERGER TECHNOLOGY CORP.—See Schlumberger Limited; *U.S. Public*, pg. 1845
SCHLUMBERGER TECHNOLOGY CORP.—See Schlumberger Limited; *U.S. Public*, pg. 1845
SCHLUMBERGER TECHNOLOGY CORP.—See Schlumberger Limited; *U.S. Public*, pg. 1845
SCHLUMBERGER TECHNOLOGY CORP.—See Schlumberger Limited; *U.S. Public*, pg. 1845
SCHLUMBERGER TECHNOLOGY CORP.—See Schlumberger Limited; *U.S. Public*, pg. 1845
SCHLUMBERGER TECHNOLOGY CORP.—See Schlumberger Limited; *U.S. Public*, pg. 1845
SCHLUMBERGER TECHNOLOGY CORP.—See Schlumberger Limited; *U.S. Public*, pg. 1845
SCHLUMBERGER TECHNOLOGY CORP.—See Schlumberger Limited; *U.S. Public*, pg. 1845
SCHLUMBERGER TECHNOLOGY CORP.—See Schlumberger Limited; *U.S. Public*, pg. 1845
SCHLUMBERGER TECHNOLOGY CORP.—See Schlumberger Limited; *U.S. Public*, pg. 1845
SCHLUMBERGER TECHNOLOGY CORP.—See Schlumberger Limited; *U.S. Public*, pg. 1845
SCHLUMBERGER TECHNOLOGY CORP.—See Schlumberger Limited; *U.S. Public*, pg. 1845

SCHLUMBERGER TECHNOLOGY CORP.—See Schlumberger Limited; *U.S. Public*, pg. 1845
SCHLUMBERGER TECHNOLOGY CORP.—See Schlumberger Limited; *U.S. Public*, pg. 1845
SCHLUMBERGER TECHNOLOGY CORP.—See Schlumberger Limited; *U.S. Public*, pg. 1845
SCHLUMBERGER TECHNOLOGY CORP.—See Schlumberger Limited; *U.S. Public*, pg. 1845
SCHLUMBERGER TECHNOLOGY CORP.—See Schlumberger Limited; *U.S. Public*, pg. 1845
SCHLUMBERGER TECHNOLOGY CORP.—See Schlumberger Limited; *U.S. Public*, pg. 1845
SCHLUMBERGER TECHNOLOGY CORP.—See Schlumberger Limited; *U.S. Public*, pg. 1846
SCHLUMBERGER TECHNOLOGY CORP.—See Schlumberger Limited; *U.S. Public*, pg. 1846
SCHLUMBERGER TECHNOLOGY CORP.—See Schlumberger Limited; *U.S. Public*, pg. 1846
SCHLUMBERGER TECHNOLOGY CORP.—See Schlumberger Limited; *U.S. Public*, pg. 1846
SCHLUMBERGER TECHNOLOGY CORP.—See Schlumberger Limited; *U.S. Public*, pg. 1846
SCHLUMBERGER TECHNOLOGY CORP.—See Schlumberger Limited; *U.S. Public*, pg. 1846
SCHLUMBERGER TECHNOLOGY CORP.—See Schlumberger Limited; *U.S. Public*, pg. 1846
SCHLUMBERGER TECHNOLOGY CORP.—See Schlumberger Limited; *U.S. Public*, pg. 1846
SCHLUMBERGER TECHNOLOGY CORP.—See Schlumberger Limited; *U.S. Public*, pg. 1846
SCHLUMBERGER TECHNOLOGY CORP.—See Schlumberger Limited; *U.S. Public*, pg. 1846
SCHLUMBERGER TECHNOLOGY CORP.—See Schlumberger Limited; *U.S. Public*, pg. 1846
SCHLUMBERGER TECHNOLOGY CORP.—See Schlumberger Limited; *U.S. Public*, pg. 1846
SCHLUMBERGER TECHNOLOGY CORP.—See Schlumberger Limited; *U.S. Public*, pg. 1846
SCHLUMBERGER TECHNOLOGY CORP.—See Schlumberger Limited; *U.S. Public*, pg. 1846
SCHLUMBERGER TECHNOLOGY CORP.—See Schlumberger Limited; *U.S. Public*, pg. 1845
SCHLUMBERGER TECHNOLOGY CORP.—See Schlumberger Limited; *U.S. Public*, pg. 1845
SCHLUMBERGER TECHNOLOGY CORP.—See Schlumberger Limited; *U.S. Public*, pg. 1845
SCHLUMBERGER TECHNOLOGY CORP.—See Schlumberger Limited; *U.S. Public*, pg. 1845
SCHLUMBERGER TECHNOLOGY CORP.—See Schlumberger Limited; *U.S. Public*, pg. 1846
SCHLUMBERGER WELL COMPLETIONS—See Schlumberger Limited; *U.S. Public*, pg. 1846
SCHLUMBERGER WELL SERVICES—See Schlumberger Limited; *U.S. Public*, pg. 1846
SCHLUMBERGER WIRELINE & TESTING—See Schlumberger Limited; *U.S. Public*, pg. 1846
SCHLUMPF INDUSTRIEPRODUKTE GMBH—See Convum Ltd.; *Int'l*, pg. 1788
SCHLUND TECHNOLOGIES GMBH—See United Internet AG; *Int'l*, pg. 8069
SCHMACK BIOGAS GMBH—See Viessmann Werke GmbH & Co. KG; *Int'l*, pg. 8196
SCHMACK BIOGAS KOMPONENTEN GMBH—See Viessmann Werke GmbH & Co. KG; *Int'l*, pg. 8196
SCHMACK BIOGAS SERVICE GMBH—See Viessmann Werke GmbH & Co. KG; *Int'l*, pg. 8196
SCHMACK BIOGAS S.R.L.—See Hitachi Zosen Corporation; *Int'l*, pg. 3411
SCHMACK BIOGAS UK LTD—See Viessmann Werke GmbH & Co. KG; *Int'l*, pg. 8196
SCHMACK CARBOTECH GMBH—See Viessmann Werke GmbH & Co. KG; *Int'l*, pg. 8196
SCHMALE GMBH & CO. KG; *Int'l*, pg. 6622
SCHMEECKLE BROS CONSTRUCTION CO.; *U.S. Private*, pg. 3565
SCHMEING GMBH & CO. KG—See Groz-Beckert KG; *Int'l*, pg. 3113
SCHMIDBERGER GMBH—See Tsubakimoto Chain Co.; *Int'l*, pg. 7953
SCHMID CONSTRUCTION INC.; *U.S. Private*, pg. 3565
SCHMIDHAUSER AG—See Lenze SE; *Int'l*, pg. 4455
SCHMID RHYNER AG—See SKion GmbH; *Int'l*, pg. 6989
SCHMID SCHRAUBEN HAINFELD GMBH—See Wurth Verwaltungsgesellschaft mbH; *Int'l*, pg. 8507
SCHMIDT ASSOCIATES, INC.; *U.S. Private*, pg. 3565
SCHMIDT BAKING CO., INC.; *U.S. Private*, pg. 3566
SCHMIDT BUILDERS SUPPLY INC.; *U.S. Private*, pg. 3566
SCHMIDT & CO. (HONG KONG) LTD.—See Schmidt Electronics Group Ltd.; *Int'l*, pg. 6623
SCHMIDT DISTRIBUTORS INC.; *U.S. Private*, pg. 3566
SCHMID TELECOM AG; *Int'l*, pg. 6622
SCHMID TELECOM BEIJING LTD.—See Schmid Telecom AG; *Int'l*, pg. 6622
SCHMID TELECOM BRAZIL LTDA—See Schmid Telecom AG; *Int'l*, pg. 6623
SCHMID TELECOM FRANCE LTD.—See Schmid Telecom AG; *Int'l*, pg. 6623

SCHMID TELECOM INDIA PVT. LTD.—See Schmid Telecom AG; *Int'l*, pg. 6623
SCHMID TELECOM RUSSIA LTD.—See Schmid Telecom AG; *Int'l*, pg. 6623
SCHMID TELECOM SINGAPORE PTE. LTD.—See Schmid Telecom AG; *Int'l*, pg. 6623
SCHMIDT ELECTRONICS GROUP LTD.; *Int'l*, pg. 6623
SCHMIDT FINANCIAL GROUP, INC.—See Aon plc; *Int'l*, pg. 497
SCHMIDT FIRE PROTECTION COMPANY, INC.; *U.S. Private*, pg. 3566
SCHMIDT-GOODMAN OFFICE PRODUCTS; *U.S. Private*, pg. 3566
SCHMIDT KOMMUNALFAHRZEUGE GMBH; *Int'l*, pg. 6623
SCHMIDT PRINTING—See Taylor Corporation; *U.S. Private*, pg. 3939
SCHMIDT STRUCTURAL PRODUCTS, INC.—See Summa Holdings, Inc.; *U.S. Private*, pg. 3853
SCHMID & WEZEL GMBH—See Fukuda Corporation; *Int'l*, pg. 2849
SCHMIEDAG GMBH—See Georgsmarienhutte Holding GmbH; *Int'l*, pg. 2941
SCHMIEDEBERGER GIESSEREI GMBH—See DIHAG Holding GmbH; *Int'l*, pg. 2125
SCHMIEDEWERKE GROEDITZ GMBH—See Georgsmarienhutte Holding GmbH; *Int'l*, pg. 2941
SCHMIEDING ARMATUREN GMBH—See Triton Advisers Limited; *Int'l*, pg. 7934
SCHMIEDING ENTERPRISES INC.; *U.S. Private*, pg. 3566
SCHMIT FORD-MERCURY CORPORATION; *U.S. Private*, pg. 3566
SCHMITTER ELEKTRO, ZNL DER ELEKTRO-BAU AG—See Burkhalter Holding AG; *Int'l*, pg. 1225
SCHMITT EUROPE, LTD.—See Schmitt Industries, Inc.; *U.S. Public*, pg. 1846
SCHMITT INDUSTRIES, INC.; *U.S. Public*, pg. 1846
SCHMITT MEASUREMENT SYSTEMS, INC.—See Tokyo Seimitsu Co., Ltd.; *Int'l*, pg. 7795
SCHMITT SALES INC.; *U.S. Private*, pg. 3566
SCHMITT'S AUDI VOLKSWAGEN OF BUFFALO; *U.S. Private*, pg. 3566
SCHMITZ & KRIEGER GMBH; *Int'l*, pg. 6623
SCHMITZ READY MIX INC.; *U.S. Private*, pg. 3566
SCHMITZ REINIGUNGSKUGELN GMBH—See BGR Energy Systems Limited; *Int'l*, pg. 1009
SCHMITZTECHNIK GMBH—See Lagercrantz Group AB; *Int'l*, pg. 4395
SCHMOLZ + BICKENBACH DISTRIBUTIONS GMBH—See Swiss Steel Holding AG; *Int'l*, pg. 7373
SCHMOLZ + BICKENBACH USA INC.—See Swiss Steel Holding AG; *Int'l*, pg. 7373
SCHM SERVICE CO., LTD.—See Hitachi, Ltd.; *Int'l*, pg. 3424
SCHMUCKAL OIL COMPANY INC.—See True North Energy, LLC; *U.S. Private*, pg. 4248
SCHMUESER & ASSOCIATES INC.; *U.S. Private*, pg. 3566
SCHMUESER & ASSOCIATES INC.—See Schmueser & Associates Inc.; *U.S. Private*, pg. 3566
SCHMUESER & ASSOCIATES INC.—See Schmueser & Associates Inc.; *U.S. Private*, pg. 3566
SCHNABEL ENGINEERING, INC.; *U.S. Private*, pg. 3566
SCHNABEL FOUNDATION COMPANY; *U.S. Private*, pg. 3566
SCHNEIDER ASIA PACIFIC LTD.—See Jos. Schneider Optische Werke GmbH; *Int'l*, pg. 4000
SCHNEIDER ASSOCIATES; *U.S. Private*, pg. 3566
SCHNEIDER AUTOMATEN GMBH & CO. KG—See Gauselmann AG; *Int'l*, pg. 2890
SCHNEIDER AUTOMATION, INC.—See Schneider Electric SE; *Int'l*, pg. 6633
SCHNEIDER AUTOMATION SAS—See Schneider Electric SE; *Int'l*, pg. 6629
SCHNEIDER (BEIJING) MEDIUM & LOW VOLTAGE CO., LTD—See Schneider Electric SE; *Int'l*, pg. 6629
SCHNEIDER BOHEMIA SPOL S.R.O.—See Atlas Copco AB; *Int'l*, pg. 684
SCHNEIDER BUSWAY (GUANGZHOU) LTD—See Schneider Electric SE; *Int'l*, pg. 6629
SCHNEIDER DOWNS & CO., INC.; *U.S. Private*, pg. 3566
SCHNEIDER DOWNS & CO.—See Schneider Downs & Co., Inc.; *U.S. Private*, pg. 3566
SCHNEIDER DRUCKLUFT GMBH—See Atlas Copco AB; *Int'l*, pg. 684
SCHNEIDER EGYPT & NORTH EAST AFRICA—See Schneider Electric SE; *Int'l*, pg. 6629
SCHNEIDER ELECTRIC AB—See Schneider Electric SE; *Int'l*, pg. 6629
SCHNEIDER ELECTRIC ADMINISTRACION, S.A. DE C.V.—See Schneider Electric SE; *Int'l*, pg. 6629
SCHNEIDER ELECTRIC A.E.—See Schneider Electric SE; *Int'l*, pg. 6629
SCHNEIDER ELECTRIC ARGENTINA SA—See Schneider Electric SE; *Int'l*, pg. 6629
SCHNEIDER ELECTRIC ASIA PACIFIC LIMITED—See Schneider Electric SE; *Int'l*, pg. 6629

COMPANY NAME INDEX

SCHNEIDER ELECTRIC SE

SCHNEIDER ELECTRIC A/S—See Schneider Electric SE; *Int'l*, pg. 6629
SCHNEIDER ELECTRIC AS—See Schneider Electric SE; *Int'l*, pg. 6629
SCHNEIDER ELECTRIC AUSTRALIA HOLDINGS PTY LTD—See Schneider Electric SE; *Int'l*, pg. 6629
SCHNEIDER ELECTRIC AUSTRALIA PTY LTD—See Schneider Electric SE; *Int'l*, pg. 6629
SCHNEIDER ELECTRIC AUSTRIA GES.MBH—See Schneider Electric SE; *Int'l*, pg. 6630
SCHNEIDER ELECTRIC AUTOMATION DEUTSCHLAND GMBH—See Schneider Electric SE; *Int'l*, pg. 6630
SCHNEIDER ELECTRIC AUTOMATION—See Schneider Electric SE; *Int'l*, pg. 6630
SCHNEIDER ELECTRIC BELGIUM SA/NV—See Schneider Electric SE; *Int'l*, pg. 6630
SCHNEIDER ELECTRIC BEL LTD.—See Schneider Electric SE; *Int'l*, pg. 6630
SCHNEIDER ELECTRIC BENIN—See Schneider Electric SE; *Int'l*, pg. 6630
SCHNEIDER ELECTRIC BILGI TEKNOLOJILERI TICARET VE PAZARLAMA A.S—See Schneider Electric SE; *Int'l*, pg. 6630
SCHNEIDER ELECTRIC BUILDINGS AB—See Schneider Electric SE; *Int'l*, pg. 6630
SCHNEIDER ELECTRIC BUILDINGS AMERICAS - CINCINNATI—See Schneider Electric SE; *Int'l*, pg. 6633
SCHNEIDER ELECTRIC BUILDINGS AMERICAS, INC.—See Schneider Electric SE; *Int'l*, pg. 6633
SCHNEIDER ELECTRIC BUILDINGS AUSTRALIA PTY. LTD.—See Schneider Electric SE; *Int'l*, pg. 6629
SCHNEIDER ELECTRIC BUILDINGS CRITICAL SYSTEMS, INC.—See Schneider Electric SE; *Int'l*, pg. 6633
SCHNEIDER ELECTRIC BUILDINGS DENMARK A/S—See Schneider Electric SE; *Int'l*, pg. 6629
SCHNEIDER ELECTRIC BUILDINGS FINLAND OY—See Schneider Electric SE; *Int'l*, pg. 6630
SCHNEIDER ELECTRIC BUILDINGS GERMANY GMBH—See Schneider Electric SE; *Int'l*, pg. 6631
SCHNEIDER ELECTRIC BUILDINGS IRELAND LTD—See Schneider Electric SE; *Int'l*, pg. 6630
SCHNEIDER ELECTRIC BUILDINGS NORWAY AS—See Schneider Electric SE; *Int'l*, pg. 6630
SCHNEIDER ELECTRIC BUILDINGS POLSKA SP. Z.O.O.—See Schneider Electric SE; *Int'l*, pg. 6630
SCHNEIDER ELECTRIC BUILDINGS SWEDEN AB—See Schneider Electric SE; *Int'l*, pg. 6629
SCHNEIDER ELECTRIC BUILDINGS UK LTD—See Schneider Electric SE; *Int'l*, pg. 6630
SCHNEIDER ELECTRIC BULGARIA EOOD—See Schneider Electric SE; *Int'l*, pg. 6630
SCHNEIDER ELECTRIC BV—See Schneider Electric SE; *Int'l*, pg. 6630
SCHNEIDER ELECTRIC CANADA INC.—See Schneider Electric SE; *Int'l*, pg. 6630
SCHNEIDER ELECTRIC CENTROAMERICA LIMITADA—See Schneider Electric SE; *Int'l*, pg. 6630
SCHNEIDER ELECTRIC CHILE S.A.—See Schneider Electric SE; *Int'l*, pg. 6630
SCHNEIDER ELECTRIC (CHINA) CO., LTD.—See Schneider Electric SE; *Int'l*, pg. 6630
SCHNEIDER ELECTRIC (CHINA) INVESTMENT CO. LTD—See Schneider Electric SE; *Int'l*, pg. 6629
SCHNEIDER ELECTRIC CONSULTING SAS—See Schneider Electric SE; *Int'l*, pg. 6630
SCHNEIDER ELECTRIC CPCS (THAILAND) CO. LTD.—See Schneider Electric SE; *Int'l*, pg. 6630
SCHNEIDER ELECTRIC CZ S.R.O.—See Schneider Electric SE; *Int'l*, pg. 6630
SCHNEIDER ELECTRIC DANMARK A/S—See Schneider Electric SE; *Int'l*, pg. 6630
SCHNEIDER ELECTRIC DE COLOMBIA S.A.S—See Schneider Electric SE; *Int'l*, pg. 6634
SCHNEIDER ELECTRIC DEUTSCHLAND ENERGY GMBH—See Schneider Electric SE; *Int'l*, pg. 6630
SCHNEIDER ELECTRIC DEUTSCHLAND GMBH—See Schneider Electric SE; *Int'l*, pg. 6631
SCHNEIDER ELECTRIC DISTRIBUTION CENTRE AB—See Schneider Electric SE; *Int'l*, pg. 6630
SCHNEIDER ELECTRIC DMS NS—See Schneider Electric SE; *Int'l*, pg. 6630
SCHNEIDER ELECTRIC D.O.O.—See Schneider Electric SE; *Int'l*, pg. 6634
SCHNEIDER ELECTRIC D.O.O.—See Schneider Electric SE; *Int'l*, pg. 6634
SCHNEIDER ELECTRIC D.O.O.—See Schneider Electric SE; *Int'l*, pg. 6634
SCHNEIDER ELECTRIC EAST MEDITERRANEAN SAL—See Schneider Electric SE; *Int'l*, pg. 6630
SCHNEIDER ELECTRIC EESTI AS—See Schneider Electric SE; *Int'l*, pg. 6630
SCHNEIDER ELECTRIC EGYPT SA—See Schneider Electric SE; *Int'l*, pg. 6630
SCHNEIDER ELECTRIC ENERGY AUSTRIA AG—See Schneider Electric SE; *Int'l*, pg. 6630
SCHNEIDER ELECTRIC ENERGY BELGIUM SA—See Schneider Electric SE; *Int'l*, pg. 6630
SCHNEIDER ELECTRIC ENERGY FRANCE SAS—See Schneider Electric SE; *Int'l*, pg. 6630
SCHNEIDER ELECTRIC ENERGY GMBH—See Schneider Electric SE; *Int'l*, pg. 6630
SCHNEIDER ELECTRIC ENERGY MALAYSIA SDN BHD—See Schneider Electric SE; *Int'l*, pg. 6630
SCHNEIDER ELECTRIC ENERGY MANUFACTURING ITALIA SRL—See Schneider Electric SE; *Int'l*, pg. 6630
SCHNEIDER ELECTRIC ENERGY NETHERLANDS BV—See Schneider Electric SE; *Int'l*, pg. 6630
SCHNEIDER ELECTRIC ENERGY POLAND SP. Z.O.O.—See Schneider Electric SE; *Int'l*, pg. 6630
SCHNEIDER ELECTRIC ENERGY SPAIN SL—See Schneider Electric SE; *Int'l*, pg. 6630
SCHNEIDER ELECTRIC ENERGY UK LTD—See Schneider Electric SE; *Int'l*, pg. 6630
SCHNEIDER ELECTRIC ENGINEERING SERVICES, LLC—See Schneider Electric SE; *Int'l*, pg. 6633
SCHNEIDER ELECTRIC EQUIPMENT AN ENGINEERING (X'IAN) CO., LTD.—See Schneider Electric SE; *Int'l*, pg. 6630
SCHNEIDER ELECTRIC ESPANA S.A.—See Schneider Electric SE; *Int'l*, pg. 6630
SCHNEIDER ELECTRIC EXPORT SERVICES PTE. LTD—See Schneider Electric SE; *Int'l*, pg. 6630
SCHNEIDER ELECTRIC FINLAND OY—See Schneider Electric SE; *Int'l*, pg. 6631
SCHNEIDER ELECTRIC FONCIERE SAS—See Schneider Electric SE; *Int'l*, pg. 6631
SCHNEIDER ELECTRIC FRANCE SAS—See Schneider Electric SE; *Int'l*, pg. 6631
SCHNEIDER ELECTRIC FZE—See Schneider Electric SE; *Int'l*, pg. 6631
SCHNEIDER ELECTRIC GMBH—See Schneider Electric SE; *Int'l*, pg. 6631
SCHNEIDER ELECTRIC HOLDING AMERIQUE DU NORD SAS—See Schneider Electric SE; *Int'l*, pg. 6631
SCHNEIDER ELECTRIC HOLDING EUROPE SAS—See Schneider Electric SE; *Int'l*, pg. 6631
SCHNEIDER ELECTRIC (HONG KONG) LIMITED—See Schneider Electric SE; *Int'l*, pg. 6629
SCHNEIDER ELECTRIC HUADIAN SWITCHGEAR (XIAMEN) CO., LTD—See Schneider Electric SE; *Int'l*, pg. 0001
SCHNEIDER ELECTRIC HUNGARIA VILLAMASSAGI ZRT—See Schneider Electric SE; *Int'l*, pg. 6631
SCHNEIDER ELECTRIC II IT PORTUGAL LDA—See Schneider Electric SE; *Int'l*, pg. 6631
SCHNEIDER ELECTRIC INDIA LTD.—See Schneider Electric SE; *Int'l*, pg. 6631
SCHNEIDER ELECTRIC INDUSTRIE ITALIA SPA—See Schneider Electric SE; *Int'l*, pg. 6631
SCHNEIDER ELECTRIC INDUSTRIES (M) SDN BHD—See Schneider Electric SE; *Int'l*, pg. 6631
SCHNEIDER ELECTRIC INDUSTRIES POLSKA SP—See Schneider Electric SE; *Int'l*, pg. 6631
SCHNEIDER ELECTRIC INDUSTRIES SAS—See Schneider Electric SE; *Int'l*, pg. 6625
SCHNEIDER ELECTRIC INFRASTRUCTURE LIMITED; *Int'l*, pg. 6623
SCHNEIDER ELECTRIC INTERNATIONAL SAS—See Schneider Electric SE; *Int'l*, pg. 6631
SCHNEIDER ELECTRIC IRELAND—See Schneider Electric SE; *Int'l*, pg. 6631
SCHNEIDER ELECTRIC IT AMERICA CORP.—See Schneider Electric SE; *Int'l*, pg. 6633
SCHNEIDER ELECTRIC IT (CHINA) CO., LTD—See Schneider Electric SE; *Int'l*, pg. 6631
SCHNEIDER ELECTRIC IT CORPORATION—See Schneider Electric SE; *Int'l*, pg. 6633
SCHNEIDER ELECTRIC IT DENMARK APS—See Schneider Electric SE; *Int'l*, pg. 6631
SCHNEIDER ELECTRIC IT GREECE ABEE—See Schneider Electric SE; *Int'l*, pg. 6631
SCHNEIDER ELECTRIC IT HONG KONG LIMITED—See Schneider Electric SE; *Int'l*, pg. 6631
SCHNEIDER ELECTRIC IT LOGISTICS ASIA PACIFIC PTE. LTD—See Schneider Electric SE; *Int'l*, pg. 6631
SCHNEIDER ELECTRIC IT LOGISTICS EUROPE LTD—See Schneider Electric SE; *Int'l*, pg. 6631
SCHNEIDER ELECTRIC IT MALAYSIA SDN BHD—See Schneider Electric SE; *Int'l*, pg. 6631
SCHNEIDER ELECTRIC IT MOROCCO, SA—See Schneider Electric SE; *Int'l*, pg. 6631
SCHNEIDER ELECTRIC IT NORWAY AS—See Schneider Electric SE; *Int'l*, pg. 6631
SCHNEIDER ELECTRIC IT POLAND SP. Z.O.O.—See Schneider Electric SE; *Int'l*, pg. 6631
SCHNEIDER ELECTRIC IT SINGAPORE PTE. LTD—See Schneider Electric SE; *Int'l*, pg. 6631
SCHNEIDER ELECTRIC IT SOUTH AFRICA (PTY) LTD—See Schneider Electric SE; *Int'l*, pg. 6631
SCHNEIDER ELECTRIC IT, SPAIN SL—See Schneider Electric SE; *Int'l*, pg. 6631
SCHNEIDER ELECTRIC IT SWEDEN AB—See Schneider Electric SE; *Int'l*, pg. 6631
SCHNEIDER ELECTRIC IT SWITZERLAND AG—See Schneider Electric SE; *Int'l*, pg. 6631
SCHNEIDER ELECTRIC IT UK LTD—See Schneider Electric SE; *Int'l*, pg. 6631
SCHNEIDER ELECTRIC IT USA, INC.—See Schneider Electric SE; *Int'l*, pg. 6633
SCHNEIDER ELECTRIC IT (XIAMEN) CO., LTD.—See Schneider Electric SE; *Int'l*, pg. 6631
SCHNEIDER ELECTRIC JAPAN HOLDINGS LTD—See Schneider Electric SE; *Int'l*, pg. 6631
SCHNEIDER ELECTRIC KOREA LTD—See Schneider Electric SE; *Int'l*, pg. 6632
SCHNEIDER ELECTRIC LANKA (PRIVATE) LIMITED—See Schneider Electric SE; *Int'l*, pg. 6632
SCHNEIDER ELECTRIC LATVIJA SIA—See Schneider Electric SE; *Int'l*, pg. 6632
SCHNEIDER ELECTRIC LIMITED—See Schneider Electric SE; *Int'l*, pg. 6632
SCHNEIDER ELECTRIC LLP—See Schneider Electric SE; *Int'l*, pg. 6632
SCHNEIDER ELECTRIC LOGISTIC CENTRE BV—See Schneider Electric SE; *Int'l*, pg. 6632
SCHNEIDER ELECTRIC LOW VOLTAGE (TIANJIN) CO., LTD.—See Schneider Electric SE; *Int'l*, pg. 6632
SCHNEIDER ELECTRIC MADAGASCAR—See Schneider Electric SE; *Int'l*, pg. 6632
SCHNEIDER ELECTRIC MANUFACTURING BOURGUEBUS SAS—See Schneider Electric SE; *Int'l*, pg. 6632
SCHNEIDER ELECTRIC MANUFACTURING (CHONGQING) CO., LTD.—See Schneider Electric SE; *Int'l*, pg. 6632
SCHNEIDER ELECTRIC MANUFACTURING THE NETHERLANDS BV—See Schneider Electric SE; *Int'l*, pg. 6632
SCHNEIDER ELECTRIC MANUFACTURING (WUHAN) CO., LTD.—See Schneider Electric SE; *Int'l*, pg. 6632
SCHNEIDER ELECTRIC MAROC—See Schneider Electric SE; *Int'l*, pg. 6632
SCHNEIDER ELECTRIC MEXICO, S.A. DE C.V.—See Schneider Electric SE; *Int'l*, pg. 6632
SCHNEIDER ELECTRIC MOTION DEUTSCHLAND GMBH—See Schneider Electric SE; *Int'l*, pg. 6632
SCHNEIDER ELECTRIC MOTION USA, INC.—See Novanta Inc.; *U.S. Public*, pg. 1548
SCHNEIDER ELECTRIC NEW ZEALAND LIMITED—See Schneider Electric SE; *Int'l*, pg. 6632
SCHNEIDER ELECTRIC NEW ZEALAND LIMITED—See Schneider Electric SE; *Int'l*, pg. 6632
SCHNEIDER ELECTRIC NEW ZEALAND—See Schneider Electric SE; *Int'l*, pg. 6632
SCHNEIDER ELECTRIC NIGERIA LTD—See Schneider Electric SE; *Int'l*, pg. 6632
SCHNEIDER ELECTRIC NORWAY AS—See Schneider Electric SE; *Int'l*, pg. 6632
SCHNEIDER ELECTRIC PAKISTAN (PRIVATE) LIMITED—See Schneider Electric SE; *Int'l*, pg. 6632
SCHNEIDER ELECTRIC PERU S.A.—See Schneider Electric SE; *Int'l*, pg. 6632
SCHNEIDER ELECTRIC (PHILIPPINES) INC.—See Schneider Electric SE; *Int'l*, pg. 6632
SCHNEIDER ELECTRIC POLSKA SP. Z.O.O.—See Schneider Electric SE; *Int'l*, pg. 6632
SCHNEIDER ELECTRIC PORTUGAL LDA.—See Schneider Electric SE; *Int'l*, pg. 6632
SCHNEIDER ELECTRIC POWER DRIVES GMBH—See Schneider Electric SE; *Int'l*, pg. 6632
SCHNEIDER ELECTRIC PRESIDENT SYSTEMS LTD.—See Schneider Electric SE; *Int'l*, pg. 6632
SCHNEIDER ELECTRIC - PROCESS AUTOMATION—See Schneider Electric SE; *Int'l*, pg. 6627
SCHNEIDER ELECTRIC PROTECTION ET CONTROLE SAS—See Schneider Electric SE; *Int'l*, pg. 6632
SCHNEIDER ELECTRIC RAK FZE—See Schneider Electric SE; *Int'l*, pg. 6632
SCHNEIDER ELECTRIC ROMANIA SRL—See Schneider Electric SE; *Int'l*, pg. 6632
SCHNEIDER ELECTRIC SACHSENWERK GMBH—See Schneider Electric SE; *Int'l*, pg. 6632
SCHNEIDER ELECTRIC'S AGENCY; *U.S. Private*, pg. 3566
SCHNEIDER ELECTRIC SAS—See Schneider Electric SE; *Int'l*, pg. 6632
SCHNEIDER ELECTRIC (SCHWEIZ) AG—See Schneider Electric SE; *Int'l*, pg. 6629
SCHNEIDER ELECTRIC SERVICES INTERNATIONAL SPRL—See Schneider Electric SE; *Int'l*, pg. 6632
SCHNEIDER ELECTRIC SE; *Int'l*, pg. 6623
SCHNEIDER ELECTRIC SINGAPORE PRIVATE LIMITED—See Schneider Electric SE; *Int'l*, pg. 6632
SCHNEIDER ELECTRIC SLOVAKIA SPOL S.R.O.—See Schneider Electric SE; *Int'l*, pg. 6633
SCHNEIDER ELECTRIC SOFTWARE - SIMSCI—See Schneider Electric SE; *Int'l*, pg. 6627
SCHNEIDER ELECTRIC SOFTWARE—See Schneider Electric SE; *Int'l*, pg. 6627
SCHNEIDER ELECTRIC—See Schneider Electric SE; *Int'l*, pg. 6629
SCHNEIDER ELECTRIC SOUTH AFRICA PTY. LTD.—See Schneider Electric SE; *Int'l*, pg. 6633

SCHNEIDER ELECTRIC SE

SCHNEIDER ELECTRIC SPA—See Schneider Electric SE; *Int'l*, pg. 6633
SCHNEIDER ELECTRIC SVERIGE AB—See Schneider Electric SE; *Int'l*, pg. 6633
SCHNEIDER ELECTRIC SYSTEMS (AUSTRALIA) PTY LIMITED—See Schneider Electric SE; *Int'l*, pg. 6627
SCHNEIDER ELECTRIC SYSTEMS GERMANY - EUROTHERM—See Schneider Electric SE; *Int'l*, pg. 6631
SCHNEIDER ELECTRIC SYSTEMS GERMANY GMBH—See Schneider Electric SE; *Int'l*, pg. 6631
SCHNEIDER ELECTRIC SYSTEMS IBERICA, S.L.U. - EUROTHERM DIVISION—See Schneider Electric SE; *Int'l*, pg. 6627
SCHNEIDER ELECTRIC SYSTEMS ITALIA SPA—See Schneider Electric SE; *Int'l*, pg. 6627
SCHNEIDER ELECTRIC SYSTEMS NETHERLANDS N.V.—See Schneider Electric SE; *Int'l*, pg. 6627
SCHNEIDER ELECTRIC SYSTEMS UK LIMITED—See Schneider Electric SE; *Int'l*, pg. 6627
SCHNEIDER ELECTRIC SYSTEMS USA, INC—See Schneider Electric SE; *Int'l*, pg. 6635
SCHNEIDER ELECTRIC TAIWAN CO., LTD.—See Schneider Electric SE; *Int'l*, pg. 6633
SCHNEIDER ELECTRIC TELECONTROL SAS—See Schneider Electric SE; *Int'l*, pg. 6633
SCHNEIDER ELECTRIC TRANSFORMERS POLAND SP. Z.O.O.—See Schneider Electric SE; *Int'l*, pg. 6633
SCHNEIDER ELECTRIC TUNISIA—See Schneider Electric SE; *Int'l*, pg. 6633
SCHNEIDER ELECTRIC TURKEY—See Schneider Electric SE; *Int'l*, pg. 6633
SCHNEIDER ELECTRIC (UK) LTD—See Schneider Electric SE; *Int'l*, pg. 6629
SCHNEIDER ELECTRIC UKRAINE LLC—See Schneider Electric SE; *Int'l*, pg. 6634
SCHNEIDER ELECTRIC URUGUAY S.A.—See Schneider Electric SE; *Int'l*, pg. 6634
SCHNEIDER ELECTRIC USA, INC. - BORDENTOWN—See Schneider Electric SE; *Int'l*, pg. 6633
SCHNEIDER ELECTRIC USA, INC. - CEDAR RAPIDS—See Schneider Electric SE; *Int'l*, pg. 6633
SCHNEIDER ELECTRIC USA, INC. - CINCINNATI—See Schneider Electric SE; *Int'l*, pg. 6633
SCHNEIDER ELECTRIC USA, INC. - COLUMBIA—See Schneider Electric SE; *Int'l*, pg. 6634
SCHNEIDER ELECTRIC USA, INC. - DALLAS—See Schneider Electric SE; *Int'l*, pg. 6634
SCHNEIDER ELECTRIC USA, INC. - GREEN BAY—See Schneider Electric SE; *Int'l*, pg. 6634
SCHNEIDER ELECTRIC USA, INC. - GREENSBORO—See Schneider Electric SE; *Int'l*, pg. 6634
SCHNEIDER ELECTRIC USA, INC. - HOPKINS—See Schneider Electric SE; *Int'l*, pg. 6634
SCHNEIDER ELECTRIC USA, INC. - HUNTINGTON—See Schneider Electric SE; *Int'l*, pg. 6634
SCHNEIDER ELECTRIC USA, INC. - KENNESAW—See Schneider Electric SE; *Int'l*, pg. 6634
SCHNEIDER ELECTRIC USA, INC. - LEXINGTON—See Schneider Electric SE; *Int'l*, pg. 6634
SCHNEIDER ELECTRIC USA, INC. - LINCOLN—See Schneider Electric SE; *Int'l*, pg. 6634
SCHNEIDER ELECTRIC USA, INC. - MILWAUKEE—See Schneider Electric SE; *Int'l*, pg. 6634
SCHNEIDER ELECTRIC USA, INC. - NASHVILLE—See Schneider Electric SE; *Int'l*, pg. 6634
SCHNEIDER ELECTRIC USA, INC. - NORCROSS—See Schneider Electric SE; *Int'l*, pg. 6634
SCHNEIDER ELECTRIC USA, INC. - OXFORD—See Schneider Electric SE; *Int'l*, pg. 6634
SCHNEIDER ELECTRIC USA, INC. - PERU—See Schneider Electric SE; *Int'l*, pg. 6634
SCHNEIDER ELECTRIC USA, INC. - PUERTO RICO—See Schneider Electric SE; *Int'l*, pg. 6634
SCHNEIDER ELECTRIC USA, INC. - RALEIGH—See Schneider Electric SE; *Int'l*, pg. 6634
SCHNEIDER ELECTRIC USA, INC. - SALISBURY—See Schneider Electric SE; *Int'l*, pg. 6634
SCHNEIDER ELECTRIC USA, INC. - SEATTLE—See Schneider Electric SE; *Int'l*, pg. 6634
SCHNEIDER ELECTRIC USA, INC. - SENECA—See Schneider Electric SE; *Int'l*, pg. 6634
SCHNEIDER ELECTRIC USA, INC.—See Schneider Electric SE; *Int'l*, pg. 6633
SCHNEIDER ELECTRIC USA, INC. - TAMPA—See Schneider Electric SE; *Int'l*, pg. 6634
SCHNEIDER ELECTRIC USA, INC. - YORK—See Schneider Electric SE; *Int'l*, pg. 6634
SCHNEIDER ELECTRIC VENEZUELA SA—See Schneider Electric SE; *Int'l*, pg. 6634
SCHNEIDER ELECTRIC VIETNAM CO. LTD—See Schneider Electric SE; *Int'l*, pg. 6634
SCHNEIDER ELECTRIC (XIAMEN) SWITCHGEAR CO. LTD—See Schneider Electric SE; *Int'l*, pg. 6629
SCHNEIDER ELEKTRIK SANAYI VE TICARET A.S.—See Schneider Electric SE; *Int'l*, pg. 6634
SCHNEIDER ENERJI ENDUSTRISI SANAYI VE TICARET A.S—See Schneider Electric SE; *Int'l*, pg. 6634
SCHNEIDER FAHRZEUG- UND CONTAINERTECHNIK GMBH; *Int'l*, pg. 6636
SCHNEIDER FINANCE, INC.—See Schneider National, Inc.; *U.S. Public*, pg. 1846
SCHNEIDER HOMES INC.; *U.S. Private*, pg. 3566
SCHNEIDER INDUSTRIAL TLAXCALA, S.A. DE C.V.—See Schneider Electric SE; *Int'l*, pg. 6634
SCHNEIDER INTERCOM GMBH—See TKH Group N.V.; *Int'l*, pg. 7764
SCHNEIDER LOGISTICS, INC.—See Schneider National, Inc.; *U.S. Public*, pg. 1847
SCHNEIDER LOGISTICS TRANSLOADING AND DISTRIBUTION, INC.—See Schneider National, Inc.; *U.S. Public*, pg. 1847
SCHNEIDERMAN'S FURNITURE, INC.; *U.S. Private*, pg. 3567
SCHNEIDER MILLS, INC.; *U.S. Private*, pg. 3566
SCHNEIDER NATIONAL BULK CARRIERS, INC.—See Schneider National, Inc.; *U.S. Public*, pg. 1847
SCHNEIDER NATIONAL, INC.; *U.S. Public*, pg. 1846
SCHNEIDER NOVUS VERTRIEBS GMBH—See Schneider Schreibgerate GmbH; *Int'l*, pg. 6636
SCHNEIDER OPTICAL TECHNOLOGIES (SHENZHEN) CO., LTD.—See Jos. Schneider Optische Werke GmbH; *Int'l*, pg. 4000
SCHNEIDER OPTICS INC.—See Jos. Schneider Optische Werke GmbH; *Int'l*, pg. 4000
SCHNEIDER POWER INC—See Quantum Fuel Systems Technologies Worldwide, Inc.; *U.S. Public*, pg. 1754
SCHNEIDER R&D, S.A. DE C.V.—See Schneider Electric SE; *Int'l*, pg. 6634
SCHNEIDER RECURSOS HUMANOS, S.A. DE C.V.—See Schneider Electric SE; *Int'l*, pg. 6635
SCHNEIDER SCHREIBGERATE GMBH; *Int'l*, pg. 6636
SCHNEIDER'S DAIRY HOLDINGS; *U.S. Private*, pg. 3567
SCHNEIDER'S DAIRY, INC.—See Schneider's Dairy Holdings; *U.S. Private*, pg. 3567
SCHNEIDER SHANGHAI APPARATUS PARTS MANUFACTURING CO. LTD—See Schneider Electric SE; *Int'l*, pg. 6635
SCHNEIDER SHANGHAI INDUSTRIAL CONTROL CO. LTD—See Schneider Electric SE; *Int'l*, pg. 6635
SCHNEIDER (SHANGHAI) SUPPLY CO. LTD—See Schneider Electric SE; *Int'l*, pg. 6629
SCHNEIDER-SLOVENSKO TLAKOVA VZDUCHOTECHNIKA SPOL. S R.O.—See Atlas Copco AB; *Int'l*, pg. 684
SCHNEIDER (SUZHOU) DRIVES COMPANY LTD—See Schneider Electric SE; *Int'l*, pg. 6629
SCHNEIDER (SUZHOU) TRANSFORMERS CO. LTD—See Schneider Electric SE; *Int'l*, pg. 6629
SCHNEIDER SWITCHGEAR (SUZHOU) CO, LTD—See Schneider Electric SE; *Int'l*, pg. 6635
SCHNEIDER (THAILAND) LTD.—See Schneider Electric SE; *Int'l*, pg. 6629
SCHNEIDER TOSHIBA INVERTER EUROPE S.A.S.—See Japan Industrial Partners, Inc.; *Int'l*, pg. 3890
SCHNEIDER TRANSPORT, INC.—See Schneider National, Inc.; *U.S. Public*, pg. 1847
SCHNEIDER VALLEY FARMS DAIRY—See Schneider's Dairy Holdings; *U.S. Private*, pg. 3567
SCHNEIDER VERSAND GMBH—See Silverfleet Capital Limited; *Int'l*, pg. 6925
SCHNEIDER WINGOAL (TIANJIN) ELECTRIC EQUIPMENT CO. LTD—See Schneider Electric SE; *Int'l*, pg. 6629
SCHNELLECKE BOHEMIA SERVICES S.R.O.—See Schnellecke Group AG & Co. KG; *Int'l*, pg. 6636
SCHNELLECKE BRASIL LTDA.—See Schnellecke Group AG & Co. KG; *Int'l*, pg. 6636
SCHNELLECKE GROUP AG & CO. KG; *Int'l*, pg. 6636
SCHNELLECKE HUNGARY KFT.—See Schnellecke Group AG & Co. KG; *Int'l*, pg. 6636
SCHNELLECKE ITALIA S.R.L.—See Schnellecke Group AG & Co. KG; *Int'l*, pg. 6636
SCHNELLECKE JEENA LOGISTICS INDIA PVT. LTD.—See Schnellecke Group AG & Co. KG; *Int'l*, pg. 6636
SCHNELLECKE LOGISTICS DINGOLFING GMBH—See Schnellecke Group AG & Co. KG; *Int'l*, pg. 6636
SCHNELLECKE LOGISTIC SERVICES (PTY) LTD.—See Schnellecke Group AG & Co. KG; *Int'l*, pg. 6636
SCHNELLECKE LOGISTICS ESPANA, S.A.—See Schnellecke Group AG & Co. KG; *Int'l*, pg. 6636
SCHNELLECKE LOGISTICS GERMANY GMBH—See Schnellecke Group AG & Co. KG; *Int'l*, pg. 6636
SCHNELLECKE LOGISTICS SACHSEN GMBH—See Schnellecke Group AG & Co. KG; *Int'l*, pg. 6636
SCHNELLECKE LOGISTICS USA LLC—See Schnellecke Group AG & Co. KG; *Int'l*, pg. 6636
SCHNELLECKE LOGISTICS WOLFSBURG GMBH—See Schnellecke Group AG & Co. KG; *Int'l*, pg. 6636
SCHNELLECKE MODUL GMBH—See Schnellecke Group AG & Co. KG; *Int'l*, pg. 6636
SCHNELLECKE MODUL- UND LIEFERANTENZENTRUM GMBH—See Schnellecke Group AG & Co. KG; *Int'l*, pg. 6636
SCHNELLECKE POLSKA SP. Z O.O.—See Schnellecke Group AG & Co. KG; *Int'l*, pg. 6636
SCHNELLECKE PORTUGAL LDA.—See Schnellecke Group AG & Co. KG; *Int'l*, pg. 6636
SCHNELLECKE SACHSEN GMBH - LOGISTIK BMW LEIPZIG UNIT—See Schnellecke Group AG & Co. KG; *Int'l*, pg. 6636
SCHNELLECKE SACHSEN GMBH - LOGISTIK PORSCHE LEIPZIG UNIT—See Schnellecke Group AG & Co. KG; *Int'l*, pg. 6636
SCHNELLECKE SACHSEN GMBH—See Schnellecke Group AG & Co. KG; *Int'l*, pg. 6636
SCHNELLECKE SLOVAKIA S.R.O.—See Schnellecke Group AG & Co. KG; *Int'l*, pg. 6636
SCHNELLECKE TRANSPORTLOGISTIK GMBH—See Schnellecke Group AG & Co. KG; *Int'l*, pg. 6636
SCHNELLECKE TRANSPORT SLOVAKIA S.R.O.—See Schnellecke Group AG & Co. KG; *Int'l*, pg. 6636
SCHNELLER ASIA PTE. LTD.—See TransDigm Group Incorporated; *U.S. Public*, pg. 2183
SCHNELLER FLORIDA—See TransDigm Group Incorporated; *U.S. Public*, pg. 2183
SCHNELLER LLC—See TransDigm Group Incorporated; *U.S. Public*, pg. 2183
SCHNELLER S.A.R.L.—See TransDigm Group Incorporated; *U.S. Public*, pg. 2183
SCHNITZER FRESNO, INC.—See Radius Recycling, Inc.; *U.S. Public*, pg. 1760
SCHNITZER NORTHEAST-CONCORD—See Radius Recycling, Inc.; *U.S. Public*, pg. 1760
SCHNITZER PUERTO RICO, INC.—See Radius Recycling, Inc.; *U.S. Public*, pg. 1760
SCHNITZER SOUTHEAST - ATLANTA—See Radius Recycling, Inc.; *U.S. Public*, pg. 1760
SCHNITZER SOUTHEAST, LLC—See Radius Recycling, Inc.; *U.S. Public*, pg. 1760
SCHNITZER SOUTHEAST - MACON—See Radius Recycling, Inc.; *U.S. Public*, pg. 1760
SCHNITZER STEEL BC, INC.—See Radius Recycling, Inc.; *U.S. Public*, pg. 1760
SCHNITZER STEEL BILLINGS—See Radius Recycling, Inc.; *U.S. Public*, pg. 1760
SCHNITZER STEEL HAWAII CORP.—See Radius Recycling, Inc.; *U.S. Public*, pg. 1760
SCHNITZER STEEL INDUSTRIES, INC.-WOODINVILLE—See Radius Recycling, Inc.; *U.S. Public*, pg. 1760
SCHNITZER WEST, LLC.; *U.S. Private*, pg. 3567
SCHNOEBELEN, INC.—See Tym Corporation; *Int'l*, pg. 7995
SCHNORR ESPANA S.L.U.—See Schnorr GmbH; *Int'l*, pg. 6636
SCHNORR GMBH; *Int'l*, pg. 6636
SCHNORR GROUP FRANCE S.A.R.L.—See Schnorr GmbH; *Int'l*, pg. 6636
SCHNORR GROUP MEXICO S.DE R.L.DE C.V.—See Schnorr GmbH; *Int'l*, pg. 6636
SCHNORR ITALIA S.R.L.—See Schnorr GmbH; *Int'l*, pg. 6636
SCHNORR KOREA CO. LTD—See Schnorr GmbH; *Int'l*, pg. 6636
SCHNORR SHANGHAI TRADING CO., LTD.—See Schnorr GmbH; *Int'l*, pg. 6636
SCHNUCK MARKETS, INC.—See The Kroger Co.; *U.S. Public*, pg. 2109
SCHOBRUNN PARIS SA; *Int'l*, pg. 6636
SCHOCH HOLDING AG—See PPG Industries, Inc.; *U.S. Public*, pg. 1710
SCHOCKEN BOOKS—See Bertelsmann SE & Co. KGaA; *Int'l*, pg. 991
THE SCHOCKMAN LUMBER COMPANY, INC.; *U.S. Private*, pg. 4114
SCHOELLER ALLIBERT AB—See OEP Capital Advisors, L.P.; *U.S. Private*, pg. 3000
SCHOELLER ALLIBERT LIMITED—See OEP Capital Advisors, L.P.; *U.S. Private*, pg. 3000
SCHOELLER ALLIBERT—See OEP Capital Advisors, L.P.; *U.S. Private*, pg. 3000
SCHOELLER ARCA SYSTEMS BV—See OEP Capital Advisors, L.P.; *U.S. Private*, pg. 3000
SCHOELLER ARCA SYSTEMS GMBH—See OEP Capital Advisors, L.P.; *U.S. Private*, pg. 3000
SCHOELLER ARCA SYSTEMS GMBH—See OEP Capital Advisors, L.P.; *U.S. Private*, pg. 3000
SCHOELLER ARCA SYSTEMS GROUP B.V.—See OEP Capital Advisors, L.P.; *U.S. Private*, pg. 3000
SCHOELLER ARCA SYSTEMS INC.—See OEP Capital Advisors, L.P.; *U.S. Private*, pg. 3000
SCHOELLER ARCA SYSTEMS LIMITED—See OEP Capital Advisors, L.P.; *U.S. Private*, pg. 3000
SCHOELLER ARCA SYSTEMS OY—See OEP Capital Advisors, L.P.; *U.S. Private*, pg. 3000
SCHOELLER ARCA SYSTEMS S.A.—See OEP Capital Advisors, L.P.; *U.S. Private*, pg. 3000
SCHOELLER ARCA SYSTEMS S.L.—See OEP Capital Advisors, L.P.; *U.S. Private*, pg. 3000
SCHOELLER ARCA SYSTEMS, SPOL S.R.O.—See OEP Capital Advisors, L.P.; *U.S. Private*, pg. 3000

COMPANY NAME INDEX — SCHOTTENSTEIN STORES CORPORATION

SCHOELLER ARCA SYSTEMS ZAO—See OEP Capital Advisors, L.P.; *U.S. Private*, pg. 3000
SCHOELLER ASIA CO., LTD.—See FORMOSA TAFFETA CO., LTD.; *Int'l*, pg. 2736
SCHOELLERBANK AKTIENGESELLSCHAFT—See UniCredit S.p.A.; *Int'l*, pg. 8040
SCHOELLERBANK INVEST AG—See UniCredit S.p.A.; *Int'l*, pg. 8040
SCHOELLER - BLECKMAN AS—See Tubacex S.A.; *Int'l*, pg. 7962
SCHOELLER - BLECKMAN EDELSTAHLROHR DEUTSCHLAND, GMBH—See Tubacex S.A.; *Int'l*, pg. 7962
SCHOELLER - BLECKMAN EDELSTAHLROHR, GMBH—See Tubacex S.A.; *Int'l*, pg. 7962
SCHOELLER - BLECKMAN EDELSTAHLROHR PHONIX KFT—See Tubacex S.A.; *Int'l*, pg. 7962
SCHOELLER-BLECKMANN AMERICA INC.—See Schoeller-Bleckmann Oilfield Equipment AG; *Int'l*, pg. 6638
SCHOELLER-BLECKMANN DARRON (ABERDEEN) LIMITED—See Schoeller-Bleckmann Oilfield Equipment AG; *Int'l*, pg. 6638
SCHOELLER-BLECKMANN DARRON LIMITED—See Schoeller-Bleckmann Oilfield Equipment AG; *Int'l*, pg. 6638
SCHOELLER-BLECKMANN DARRON LTD.—See Schoeller-Bleckmann Oilfield Equipment AG; *Int'l*, pg. 6638
SCHOELLER-BLECKMANN DE MEXICO S.A. DE C.V.—See Schoeller-Bleckmann Oilfield Equipment AG; *Int'l*, pg. 6638
SCHOELLER-BLECKMANN DO BRASIL LTDA.—See Schoeller-Bleckmann Oilfield Equipment AG; *Int'l*, pg. 6638
SCHOELLER-BLECKMANN ENERGY SERVICES L.L.C.—See Schoeller-Bleckmann Oilfield Equipment AG; *Int'l*, pg. 6638
SCHOELLER-BLECKMANN NITEC GMBH—See Christof Holding AG; *Int'l*, pg. 1587
SCHOELLER-BLECKMANN OILFIELD EQUIPMENT AG; *Int'l*, pg. 6637
SCHOELLER-BLECKMANN OILFIELD EQUIPMENT MIDDLE EAST FZE—See Schoeller-Bleckmann Oilfield Equipment AG; *Int'l*, pg. 6638
SCHOELLER-BLECKMANN OILFIELD EQUIPMENT VIETNAM L.L.C.—See Schoeller-Bleckmann Oilfield Equipment AG; *Int'l*, pg. 6638
SCHOELLER-BLECKMANN OILFIELD TECHNOLOGY GMBH & CO. KG—See Schoeller-Bleckmann Oilfield Equipment AG; *Int'l*, pg. 6638
SCHOELLER-BLECKMANN SALES CO. L.P.—See Schoeller-Bleckmann Oilfield Equipment AG; *Int'l*, pg. 6638
SCHOELLER-BLECKMANN (UK) LIMITED—See voestalpine AG; *Int'l*, pg. 8287
SCHOELLER - BLECKMAN TUBE FRANCE—See Tubacex S.A.; *Int'l*, pg. 7962
SCHOELLER-ELECTRONICS GMBH—See NORD Holding Unternehmensbeteiligungsgesellschaft mbH; *Int'l*, pg. 5416
SCHOELLER GMBH & CO KG—See Indorama Ventures Public Company Limited; *Int'l*, pg. 3659
SCHOELLER HOLDINGS LTD.; *Int'l*, pg. 6636
SCHOELLER INDIA INDUSTRIES PVT. LTD.—See Felix Schoeller Holding GmbH & Co. KG; *Int'l*, pg. 2633
SCHOELLER INDUSTRIES—See Empteezy Ltd; *Int'l*, pg. 2392
SCHOELLER INSTRUMENTS, S.R.O.—See ESPEC Corp.; *Int'l*, pg. 2505
SCHOELLER KRESICE S.R.O.—See Indorama Ventures Public Company Limited; *Int'l*, pg. 3659
SCHOELLER LITVINOV K.S.—See CLC Industries Limited; *Int'l*, pg. 1653
SCHOELLER MUNZHANDEL GMBH—See Oesterreichische Nationalbank; *Int'l*, pg. 5529
SCHOELLER TECHNOCELL GMBH & CO. KG—See Felix Schoeller Holding GmbH & Co. KG; *Int'l*, pg. 2633
SCHOELLER TEXTILE (NETHERLANDS), B.V.—See CLC Industries Limited; *Int'l*, pg. 1653
SCHOELLY, INC.—See Intuitive Surgical, Inc.; *U.S. Public*, pg. 1161
SCHOENECKERS INC.; *U.S. Private*, pg. 3567
SCHOENEMAN BEAUTY SUPPLY INC.—See Sally Beauty Holdings, Inc.; *U.S. Public*, pg. 1839
SCHOENEMAN BROTHERS COMPANY; *U.S. Private*, pg. 3567
SCHOENEWEISS & CO. GMBH—See Mahindra & Mahindra Limited; *Int'l*, pg. 4646
SCHOEPP MOTORS INC.; *U.S. Private*, pg. 3567
SCHOEP'S ICE CREAM CO., INC.—See Brothers International Desserts, Inc.; *U.S. Private*, pg. 665
SCHOETTLER TIRE INC.; *U.S. Private*, pg. 3567
SCHOFFEL SPORTBEKLEIDUNG GMBH; *Int'l*, pg. 6638
SCHOFIELD MEDIA LTD.; *U.S. Private*, pg. 3567
SCHOLARBUYS LLC; *U.S. Private*, pg. 3567
SCHOLARCHIP CARD, LLC—See Valsef Group; *Int'l*, pg. 8123

SCHOLAR CRAFT PRODUCTS, INC.; *U.S. Private*, pg. 3567
SCHOLAR EDUCATION GROUP; *Int'l*, pg. 6638
SCHOLARIS INTERNATIONAL LIMITED; *Int'l*, pg. 6638
SCHOLAR ROCK HOLDING CORPORATION; *U.S. Public*, pg. 1847
SCHOLARSFIRST LLC—See Pensler Capital Corporation; *U.S. Private*, pg. 3139
SCHOLASTIC AT HOME INC.—See Scholastic Corporation; *U.S. Public*, pg. 1847
SCHOLASTIC AUSTRALIA PTY. LTD.—See Scholastic Corporation; *U.S. Public*, pg. 1847
SCHOLASTIC BOOK CLUBS, INC.—See Scholastic Corporation; *U.S. Public*, pg. 1847
SCHOLASTIC BOOKFAIRS CANADA LTD.—See Scholastic Corporation; *U.S. Public*, pg. 1847
SCHOLASTIC BOOK FAIRS, INC.—See Scholastic Corporation; *U.S. Public*, pg. 1847
SCHOLASTIC BOOK FAIRS, LTD.—See Scholastic Corporation; *U.S. Public*, pg. 1847
SCHOLASTIC CANADA LTD.—See Scholastic Corporation; *U.S. Public*, pg. 1847
SCHOLASTIC CORPORATION; *U.S. Public*, pg. 1847
SCHOLASTIC ENTERTAINMENT INC.—See Scholastic Corporation; *U.S. Public*, pg. 1847
SCHOLASTIC HONG KONG LIMITED—See Scholastic Corporation; *U.S. Public*, pg. 1847
SCHOLASTIC INC. INFORMATION CENTER—See Scholastic Corporation; *U.S. Public*, pg. 1847
SCHOLASTIC INC. NATIONAL DISTRIBUTION CENTER—See Scholastic Corporation; *U.S. Public*, pg. 1847
SCHOLASTIC INC.—See Scholastic Corporation; *U.S. Public*, pg. 1847
SCHOLASTIC LIBRARY PUBLISHING INC.—See Scholastic Corporation; *U.S. Public*, pg. 1847
SCHOLASTIC LIMITED—See Scholastic Corporation; *U.S. Public*, pg. 1847
SCHOLASTIC NEW ZEALAND LTD.—See Scholastic Corporation; *U.S. Public*, pg. 1847
THE SCHOLASTIC STORE, INC.—See Scholastic Corporation; *U.S. Public*, pg. 1848
SCHOLASTIC UK LIMITED—See Scholastic Corporation; *U.S. Public*, pg. 1847
SC HOLCZ STILE S.R.L.—See Quaser Machine Tools, Inc.; *Int'l*, pg. 6157
SC HOLDINGS CORP.; *U.S. Public*, pg. 1842
SCHOLFIELD BROS. INC.; *U.S. Private*, pg. 3567
SCHOLFIELD LEXUS LLC—See Scholfield Bros. Inc.; *U.S. Private*, pg. 3567
SCHOLIUM GROUP PLC; *Int'l*, pg. 6638
SCHOLLE CANADA, LTD.—See Scholle Corporation; *U.S. Private*, pg. 3567
SCHOLLE CORPORATION; *U.S. Private*, pg. 3567
SCHOLLE EUROPE, B.V.—See Scholle Corporation; *U.S. Private*, pg. 3567
SCHOLLE EUROPE FRANCE SAS—See Scholle Corporation; *U.S. Private*, pg. 3567
SCHOLLE EUROPE GMBH—See Scholle Corporation; *U.S. Private*, pg. 3567
SCHOLLE EUROPE, LTD.—See Scholle Corporation; *U.S. Private*, pg. 3567
SCHOLLE INDUSTRIES, PTY. LTD.—See Scholle Corporation; *U.S. Private*, pg. 3567
SCHOLLE PACKAGING, INC.—See Scholle Corporation; *U.S. Private*, pg. 3567
SCHOLLE PACKAGING, LTDA.—See Scholle Corporation; *U.S. Private*, pg. 3567
SCHOLLER GMBH & CO. KG—See Matthews International Corporation; *U.S. Public*, pg. 1400
SCHOLLER ICE-CREAM LTD—See Nestle S.A.; *Int'l*, pg. 5211
SCHOLL FOREST INDUSTRIES INC.; *U.S. Private*, pg. 3567
SCHOLL'S WELLNESS CO.—See Yellow Wood Partners LLC; *U.S. Private*, pg. 4587
SCHOLS & VOLKMER GMBH; *Int'l*, pg. 6638
SCHOLTEN'S EQUIPMENT INC.; *U.S. Private*, pg. 3567
SCHOLZEN PRODUCTS COMPANY INC.; *U.S. Private*, pg. 3568
SCHOLZ & FRIENDS GROUP GMBH—See WPP plc; *Int'l*, pg. 8462
SCHOLZ INDUSTRIES PTY LTD.; *Int'l*, pg. 6638
SCHOLZ ROHSTOFFHANDEL GMBH—See voestalpine AG; *Int'l*, pg. 8295
SCHOMAC GROUP INC.; *U.S. Private*, pg. 3568
SCHOMBURG REFRIGERATION CO., INC.—See Benedict Refrigeration Service, Inc.; *U.S. Private*, pg. 525
SC HONDA TRADING ROMANIA SRL—See Honda Motor Co., Ltd.; *Int'l*, pg. 3464
SCHONE EDELMETAAL BV—See Umicore S.A./N.V.; *Int'l*, pg. 8024
SCHONFELD GROUP HOLDINGS, LLC; *U.S. Private*, pg. 3568
SCHONFELD SECURITIES, LLC—See Schonfeld Group Holdings, LLC; *U.S. Private*, pg. 3568
SCHONHOLZER AG—See Burkhalter Holding AG; *Int'l*, pg. 1225

SCHONNING INSURANCE SERVICES, INC.—See Cross Financial Corporation; *U.S. Private*, pg. 1105
SCHONOX GMBH—See Sika AG; *Int'l*, pg. 6916
SCHONSTEDT INSTRUMENT, CO.—See SPX Technologies, Inc.; *U.S. Public*, pg. 1922
SCHON TEXTILES LIMITED; *Int'l*, pg. 6638
SCHOOL APPAREL, INC.; *U.S. Private*, pg. 3568
SCHOOL BOX INC.; *U.S. Private*, pg. 3568
SCHOOL BUS SALES COMPANY; *U.S. Private*, pg. 3568
SCHOOLDUDE.COM; *U.S. Private*, pg. 3568
SCHOOLEY MITCHELL TELECOM CONSULTANTS; *U.S. Private*, pg. 3568
SCHOOL HEALTH CORPORATION; *U.S. Private*, pg. 3568
SCHOOLKIDZ.COM, LLC—See Skyview Capital, LLC; *U.S. Private*, pg. 3686
SCHOOL LINES, INC.—See Girardin Blue Bird Company; *Int'l*, pg. 2979
SCHOOL LUNCH PRODUCTS, INC.—See Alvarez & Marsal, Inc.; *U.S. Private*, pg. 213
SCHOOL LUNCH PRODUCTS, INC.—See Highview Capital, LLC; *U.S. Private*, pg. 1942
SCHOOLMASTERS—See School-Tech, Inc.; *U.S. Private*, pg. 3568
SCHOOLNET, INC.—See Pearson plc; *Int'l*, pg. 5778
SCHOOLNET INDIA LIMITED; *Int'l*, pg. 6638
SCHOOL NUTRITION ASSOCIATION; *U.S. Private*, pg. 3568
SCHOOLS FINANCIAL CREDIT UNION; *U.S. Private*, pg. 3568
SCHOOL—See Project: Worldwide, Inc.; *U.S. Private*, pg. 3281
SCHOOL SPECIALTY CANADA, LTD.—See School Specialty, Inc.; *U.S. Public*, pg. 1848
SCHOOL SPECIALTY, INC.; *U.S. Public*, pg. 1848
SCHOOL STREET ASSOCIATES LIMITED PARTNERSHIP—See Boston Properties, Inc.; *U.S. Public*, pg. 373
SCHOOL-TECH, INC.; *U.S. Private*, pg. 3568
SCHOOL TECH SUPPLY; *U.S. Private*, pg. 3568
SCHOOL TOMAS CO., LTD.—See Hulic Co., Ltd.; *Int'l*, pg. 3528
SCHOOL-TO-SCHOOL INTERNATIONAL; *U.S. Private*, pg. 3568
SCHOOL YEAR ABROAD INC.; *U.S. Private*, pg. 3568
SCHOON CONSTRUCTION INC.; *U.S. Private*, pg. 3568
SCHOONER BAY REALTY INC.; *U.S. Private*, pg. 3568
SCHOONER CAPITAL, CORP.; *Int'l*, pg. 6638
SCHORCH BETEILIGUNGS GMBH—See Wolong Holding Group Co., Ltd.; *Int'l*, pg. 8443
SCHORCH ELEKTRISCHE MASCHINEN UND ANTRIEBE GMBH—See Wolong Holding Group Co., Ltd.; *Int'l*, pg. 8443
SCHORGHUBER SPEZIALTUREN KG—See Hormann KG Verkaufsgesellschaf; *Int'l*, pg. 3481
SCHORGHUBER STIFTUNG & CO. HOLDING KG; *Int'l*, pg. 6638
SCHORN & GROH GMBH; *Int'l*, pg. 6639
SCHORO ELECTRICITE SAS—See VINCI S.A.; *Int'l*, pg. 8227
SCHOSSMETALL GMBH & CO. KG—See Wurth Verwaltungsgesellschaft mbH; *Int'l*, pg. 8507
SCHOTT AG—See Carl-Zeiss-Stiftung; *Int'l*, pg. 1336
SCHOTT BENELUX B.V.—See Carl-Zeiss-Stiftung; *Int'l*, pg. 1336
SCHOTT BRASIL LTDA. DIVISAO VITROFARMA—See Carl-Zeiss-Stiftung; *Int'l*, pg. 1336
SCHOTT BRASIL LTDA.—See Carl-Zeiss-Stiftung; *Int'l*, pg. 1336
SCHOTT BRAZIL—See Carl-Zeiss-Stiftung; *Int'l*, pg. 1336
SCHOTT BROTHERS, INC.; *U.S. Private*, pg. 3568
SCHOTT DE MEXICO, S.A. DE C.V.—See Carl-Zeiss-Stiftung; *Int'l*, pg. 1337
SCHOTT DIAMONDVIEW ARMOR PRODUCTS, LLC—See Carl-Zeiss-Stiftung; *Int'l*, pg. 1337
SCHOTT DISTRIBUTING CO. INC.; *U.S. Private*, pg. 3568
SCHOTTENSTEIN/BERNSTEIN CAPITAL; *U.S. Private*, pg. 3569
SCHOTTENSTEIN PROPERTY GROUP, INC.; *U.S. Private*, pg. 3568
SCHOTTENSTEIN STORES CORPORATION; *U.S. Private*, pg. 3568
SCHOTT ENVASES ARGENTINA S.A.—See Carl-Zeiss-Stiftung; *Int'l*, pg. 1337
SCHOTT ENVASES FARMACEUTICOS S.A.—See Carl-Zeiss-Stiftung; *Int'l*, pg. 1337
SCHOTTER- UND BETONWERK KARL SCHWARZL BETRIEBSGESELLSCHAFT M.B.H.—See PORR AG; *Int'l*, pg. 5925
SCHOTTERWERK GRADENBERG GESELLSCHAFT M.B.H.—See PORR AG; *Int'l*, pg. 5925
SCHOTT FLAT GLASS DO BRASIL LTDA.—See Carl-Zeiss-Stiftung; *Int'l*, pg. 1337
SCHOTT FRANCE PHARMA SYSTEMS SAS—See Carl-Zeiss-Stiftung; *Int'l*, pg. 1337
SCHOTT GEMTRON CANADA CORPORATION—See Carl-Zeiss-Stiftung; *Int'l*, pg. 1337
SCHOTT GEMTRON CORPORATION—See AGC Inc.; *Int'l*, pg. 201

SCHOTT GEMTRON CORPORATION—See Carl-Zeiss-Stiftung; *Int'l*, pg. 1337
SCHOTT GEMTRON CORPORATION—See AGC Inc.; *Int'l*, pg. 201
SCHOTT GEMTRON CORPORATION—See Carl-Zeiss-Stiftung; *Int'l*, pg. 1337
SCHOTT GLAS EXPORT GMBH—See Carl-Zeiss-Stiftung; *Int'l*, pg. 1337
SCHOTT GLASS INDIA PVT. LTD.—See Carl-Zeiss-Stiftung; *Int'l*, pg. 1337
SCHOTT GLASS (MALAYSIA) SDN. BHD.—See Carl-Zeiss-Stiftung; *Int'l*, pg. 1337
SCHOTT GLASS TECHNOLOGIES (SUZHOU) CO., LTD.—See Carl-Zeiss-Stiftung; *Int'l*, pg. 1337
SCHOTT GOVERNMENT SERVICES, LLC—See Carl-Zeiss-Stiftung; *Int'l*, pg. 1337
SCHOTT IBERICA, S.A. COMMERCIAL DIVISION—See Carl-Zeiss-Stiftung; *Int'l*, pg. 1337
SCHOTT IBERICA, S.A.—See Carl-Zeiss-Stiftung; *Int'l*, pg. 1337
SCHOTT ITALVETRO S.P.A.—See Carl-Zeiss-Stiftung; *Int'l*, pg. 1337
SCHOTT MINIFAB PTY LTD—See Carl-Zeiss-Stiftung; *Int'l*, pg. 1337
SCHOTT MUSIC CO. LTD.—See Schott Music GmbH & Co. KG; *Int'l*, pg. 6639
SCHOTT MUSIC CORPORATION—See Schott Music GmbH & Co. KG; *Int'l*, pg. 6639
SCHOTT MUSIC GMBH & CO. KG; *Int'l*, pg. 6639
SCHOTT MUSIC LTD—See Schott Music GmbH & Co. KG; *Int'l*, pg. 6639
SCHOTT MUSIC PUBLISHERS (CANADA) LTD.—See Schott Music GmbH & Co. KG; *Int'l*, pg. 6639
SCHOTT NIPPON K.K.—See Carl-Zeiss-Stiftung; *Int'l*, pg. 1337
SCHOTT NORTH AMERICA, INC. - ARCHITECTURE DIVISION—See Carl-Zeiss-Stiftung; *Int'l*, pg. 1337
SCHOTT NORTH AMERICA, INC. - BARON SYSTEMS & SOLUTIONS DIVISION—See Carl-Zeiss-Stiftung; *Int'l*, pg. 1337
SCHOTT NORTH AMERICA, INC. - ELECTRONIC PACKAGING DIVISION—See Carl-Zeiss-Stiftung; *Int'l*, pg. 1337
SCHOTT NORTH AMERICA, INC. - FLAT GLASS DIVISION—See Carl-Zeiss-Stiftung; *Int'l*, pg. 1337
SCHOTT NORTH AMERICA, INC. - LIGHTING & IMAGING DIVISION—See Carl-Zeiss-Stiftung; *Int'l*, pg. 1337
SCHOTT NORTH AMERICA, INC. - PHARMACEUTICAL PACKAGING DIVISION—See Carl-Zeiss-Stiftung; *Int'l*, pg. 1337
SCHOTT NORTH AMERICA INC—See Carl-Zeiss-Stiftung; *Int'l*, pg. 1337
SCHOTT ORIM CAM SANAYI VE TICARET A.S.—See Carl-Zeiss-Stiftung; *Int'l*, pg. 1337
SCHOTT SCHWEIZ AG—See Carl-Zeiss-Stiftung; *Int'l*, pg. 1337
SCHOTT (SHANGHAI) PRECISION MATERIALS & EQUIPMENT INTERNATIONAL TRADING CO., LTD.—See Carl-Zeiss-Stiftung; *Int'l*, pg. 1336
SCHOTT SINGAPORE PTE. LTD.—See Carl-Zeiss-Stiftung; *Int'l*, pg. 1337
SCHOTT SOLAR S.L.—See Carl-Zeiss-Stiftung; *Int'l*, pg. 1337
SCHOTT SPEZIALGLAS AG—See Carl-Zeiss-Stiftung; *Int'l*, pg. 1337
SCHOTT TAIWAN LTD.—See Carl-Zeiss-Stiftung; *Int'l*, pg. 1337
SCHOTT TECHNICAL GLASS SOLUTIONS GMBH—See Carl-Zeiss-Stiftung; *Int'l*, pg. 1337
SCHOTT TERMOFROST AB—See Carl-Zeiss-Stiftung; *Int'l*, pg. 1337
SCHOTT TERMOFROST AS—See Carl-Zeiss-Stiftung; *Int'l*, pg. 1337
SCHOTT UK LTD.—See Carl-Zeiss-Stiftung; *Int'l*, pg. 1337
SCHOTT VTF SAS—See Carl-Zeiss-Stiftung; *Int'l*, pg. 1337
SCHOTT XINKANG PHARMACEUTICAL PACKAGING CO., LTD.—See Carl-Zeiss-Stiftung; *Int'l*, pg. 1337
SCHOUEST, BAMDAS, SOSHEA & BENMAIER, PLLC; *U.S. Private*, pg. 3569
SCHOUW & CO. FINANS A/S—See Aktieselskabet Schouw & Co.; *Int'l*, pg. 266
SCHOWALTER & JABOURI COMPUTER SOLUTIONS, INC.—See Honkamp Krueger & Co., PC; *U.S. Private*, pg. 1977
SCHOX, PLC; *U.S. Private*, pg. 3569
SCHRADE KABEL- UND ELEKTROTECHNIK GMBH—See TKH Group N.V.; *Int'l*, pg. 7764
SCHRADENBIOGAS GMBH & CO. KG—See BayWa AG; *Int'l*, pg. 919
SCHRADER-BRIDGEPORT INTERNATIONAL, INC.—See Sensata Technologies Holding plc; *U.S. Public*, pg. 1865
SCHRADER CELLARS, LLC—See Constellation Brands, Inc.; *U.S. Public*, pg. 571
SCHRADER DUNCAN LIMITED - PNEUMATICS BUSINESS UNIT—See Duncan Engineering Limited; *Int'l*, pg. 2225

SCHRADER ELECTRONICS LIMITED—See Sensata Technologies Holding plc; *U.S. Public*, pg. 1866
SCHRADER INTERNATIONAL BRASIL LTDA.—See Sensata Technologies Holding plc; *U.S. Public*, pg. 1866
SCHRADER INTERNATIONAL, INC.—See Sensata Technologies Holding plc; *U.S. Public*, pg. 1866
SCHRADER SAS—See Sensata Technologies Holding plc; *U.S. Public*, pg. 1866
SCHRAMEK GMBH; *Int'l*, pg. 6639
SCHRAMM COATINGS GMBH—See Akzo Nobel N.V.; *Int'l*, pg. 275
SCHRAMM COATINGS IBERICA SA—See Akzo Nobel N.V.; *Int'l*, pg. 275
SCHRAMM HOLDING AG—See Akzo Nobel N.V.; *Int'l*, pg. 275
SCHRAMM, INC.; *U.S. Private*, pg. 3569
SCHRAMM SSCP (HANOI) CO LTD.—See Akzo Nobel N.V.; *Int'l*, pg. 275
SCHRAMM SSCP (THAILAND) CO., LTD.—See Akzo Nobel N.V.; *Int'l*, pg. 275
SCHRAUBEN UND DRAHT UNION GMBH; *Int'l*, pg. 6639
SCHRAUWEN SANITAIR EN VERWARMING BVBA—See CRH plc; *Int'l*, pg. 1848
SCHREDER S.A.; *Int'l*, pg. 6639
SCHREIBER FOODS, INC. - FULLERTON—See Schreiber Foods, Inc.; *U.S. Private*, pg. 3569
SCHREIBER FOODS, INC. - SHIPPENSBURG—See Schreiber Foods, Inc.; *U.S. Private*, pg. 3569
SCHREIBER FOODS, INC.; *U.S. Private*, pg. 3569
SCHREIBER FOODS, INC. - WEST BEND—See Schreiber Foods, Inc.; *U.S. Private*, pg. 3569
SCHREIBER LLC—See Axel Johnson Gruppen AB; *Int'l*, pg. 765
SCHREIBER MEXICO, S.A. DE C.V.—See Schreiber Foods, Inc.; *U.S. Private*, pg. 3569
SCHREIBER-RELIUS; *Int'l*, pg. 6639
SCHREIBER & ROMAN, INC.; *U.S. Private*, pg. 3569
SCHREINERMACHER KABELCONFEKTIONEN GMBH—See TKH Group N.V.; *Int'l*, pg. 7764
SCHRETLEN & CO N.V.—See Cooperatieve Centrale Raiffeisen-Boerenleenbank B.A.; *Int'l*, pg. 1792
SCHRODER ADVEQ MANAGEMENT AG—See Schroders plc; *Int'l*, pg. 6640
SCHRODER AIDA SAS—See Schroders plc; *Int'l*, pg. 6640
SCHRODER ASIAN TOTAL RETURN INVESTMENT COMPANY PLC; *Int'l*, pg. 6639
SCHRODER CAYMAN BANK AND TRUST COMPANY LIMITED—See Schroders plc; *Int'l*, pg. 6640
SCHRODER & CO. (ASIA) LIMITED—See Schroders plc; *Int'l*, pg. 6640
SCHRODER & CO BANK AG—See Schroders plc; *Int'l*, pg. 6640
SCHRODER & CO BANQUE SA—See Schroders plc; *Int'l*, pg. 6640
SCHRODER & CO.—See Schroders plc; *Int'l*, pg. 6640
SCHRODER EXECUTOR & TRUSTEE COMPANY LIMITED—See Schroders plc; *Int'l*, pg. 6640
SCHRODER FUND ADVISORS LLC—See Schroders plc; *Int'l*, pg. 6640
SCHRODER INVESTMENT MANAGEMENT A/S—See Schroders plc; *Int'l*, pg. 6640
SCHRODER INVESTMENT MANAGEMENT (AUSTRALASIA) LIMITED—See Schroders plc; *Int'l*, pg. 6640
SCHRODER INVESTMENT MANAGEMENT BENELUX N.V.—See Schroders plc; *Int'l*, pg. 6640
SCHRODER INVESTMENT MANAGEMENT BRASIL DTZM SA—See Schroders plc; *Int'l*, pg. 6640
SCHRODER INVESTMENT MANAGEMENT (EUROPE) S.A.—See Schroders plc; *Int'l*, pg. 6640
SCHRODER INVESTMENT MANAGEMENT FONDSMAEGLERSELSKAB A/S—See Schroders plc; *Int'l*, pg. 6640
SCHRODER INVESTMENT MANAGEMENT GMBH—See Schroders plc; *Int'l*, pg. 6640
SCHRODER INVESTMENT MANAGEMENT (HONG KONG) LIMITED—See Schroders plc; *Int'l*, pg. 6640
SCHRODER INVESTMENT MANAGEMENT (JAPAN) LIMITED—See Schroders plc; *Int'l*, pg. 6640
SCHRODER INVESTMENT MANAGEMENT (LUXEMBOURG) S.A.—See Schroders plc; *Int'l*, pg. 6640
SCHRODER INVESTMENT MANAGEMENT NORTH AMERICA INC.—See Schroders plc; *Int'l*, pg. 6640
SCHRODER INVESTMENT MANAGEMENT NORTH AMERICA INTERNATIONAL INC.—See Schroders plc; *Int'l*, pg. 6640
SCHRODER INVESTMENT MANAGEMENT SA—See Schroders plc; *Int'l*, pg. 6640
SCHRODER INVESTMENT MANAGEMENT (SINGAPORE) LTD.—See Schroders plc; *Int'l*, pg. 6640
SCHRODER INVESTMENT MANAGEMENT (TAIWAN) LIMITED—See Schroders plc; *Int'l*, pg. 6640
SCHRODER INVESTMENT MANAGEMENT (UK) LIMITED—See Schroders plc; *Int'l*, pg. 6640
SCHRODER MASCHINENBAU GMBH & CO KG—See John Bean Technologies Corporation; *U.S. Public*, pg. 1192
SCHRODER PROPERTY INVESTMENT MANAGEMENT LIMITED—See Schroders plc; *Int'l*, pg. 6640

SCHRODER PROPERTY KAPITALANLAGEGESELLSCHAFT MBH—See Schroders plc; *Int'l*, pg. 6640
SCHRODER REAL ESTATE INVESTMENT TRUST LIMITED; *Int'l*, pg. 6639
SCHRODER REAL ESTATE KAPITALVERWALTUNGSGESELLSCHAFT MBH—See Schroders plc; *Int'l*, pg. 6640
SCHRODER REAL ESTATE MANAGERS (JERSEY) LIMITED—See Schroders plc; *Int'l*, pg. 6640
SCHRODER S.A. SOCIEDAD GERENTE DE FONDOS COMUNES DE INVERSION—See Schroders plc; *Int'l*, pg. 6640
SCHRODERS (BERMUDA) LIMITED—See Schroders plc; *Int'l*, pg. 6641
SCHRODERS CAPITAL MANAGEMENT (FRANCE) S.A.S.—See Schroders plc; *Int'l*, pg. 6641
SCHRODERS CHILE SPA—See Schroders plc; *Int'l*, pg. 6641
SCHRODERS (C.I.) LIMITED—See Schroders plc; *Int'l*, pg. 6641
SCHRODERS FRANCE—See Schroders plc; *Int'l*, pg. 6641
SCHRODERS ITALY SIM S.P.A.—See Schroders plc; *Int'l*, pg. 6641
SCHRODERS KOREA LIMITED—See Schroders plc; *Int'l*, pg. 6641
SCHRODERS PLC; *Int'l*, pg. 6639
SCHRODERS PROPERTY MANAGERS (JERSEY) LIMITED—See Schroders plc; *Int'l*, pg. 6641
SCHRODERS (SHANGHAI) FINANCIAL ADVISORY CO. LIMITED—See Schroders plc; *Int'l*, pg. 6641
SCHRODERS TAIWAN LIMITED—See Schroders plc; *Int'l*, pg. 6641
SCHRODER TRUST AG—See Schroders plc; *Int'l*, pg. 6640
SCHRODER UK MID CAP FUND PLC; *Int'l*, pg. 6639
SCHRODER UNIT TRUSTS LIMITED—See Schroders plc; *Int'l*, pg. 6641
SCHRODER US HOLDINGS INC.—See Schroders plc; *Int'l*, pg. 6640
SCHRODINGER, INC.; *U.S. Public*, pg. 1848
SCHROEDAHL-ARAPP SPEZIALARMATUREN GMBH & CO. KG—See KKR & Co. Inc.; *U.S. Public*, pg. 1242
SCHROEDER/LEVERINGTON INC.; *U.S. Private*, pg. 3569
SCHROEDER-MANATEE RANCH, INC.; *U.S. Private*, pg. 3569
SCHROEDER MEASUREMENT TECHNOLOGIES, INC.—See Educational Testing Service Inc.; *U.S. Private*, pg. 1340
SCHROEDER MOVING SYSTEMS; *U.S. Private*, pg. 3569
SCHROEDER PUBLISHING COMPANY - COLLECTOR BOOKS—See Schroeder Publishing Company; *U.S. Private*, pg. 3569
SCHROEDER PUBLISHING COMPANY; *U.S. Private*, pg. 3569
SCHROEDER & TREMAYNE INC.—See SBI Incorporated; *U.S. Private*, pg. 3560
SCHROER MANUFACTURING COMPANY—See Midmark Corporation; *U.S. Private*, pg. 2716
SCHROFF GMBH—See Pentair plc; *Int'l*, pg. 5791
SCHROFF GMBH—See Pentair plc; *Int'l*, pg. 5791
SCHROFF K.K.—See Pentair plc; *Int'l*, pg. 5791
SCHROFF SCANDINAVIA AB—See Pentair plc; *Int'l*, pg. 5791
SCHROFF TECHNOLOGIES INTERNATIONAL, INC.—See RF Industries, Ltd.; *U.S. Public*, pg. 1796
SCHROLE GROUP LIMITED—See ONEX Corporation; *Int'l*, pg. 5580
SCHROMBGENS & STEPHAN GMBH, VERSICHERUNGSMAKLER—See Munchener Ruckversicherungs AG; *Int'l*, pg. 5091
SCHRYVER MEDICAL SALES & MARKETING, INC.; *U.S. Private*, pg. 3569
SCHUBERT COMMUNICATIONS, INC.; *U.S. Private*, pg. 3570
SCHUBERTH GMBH—See Perusa GmbH; *Int'l*, pg. 5821
SCHUBERTH HOLDING GMBH—See Perusa GmbH; *Int'l*, pg. 5821
SCHUBERTH NORTH AMERICA, LLC—See Perusa GmbH; *Int'l*, pg. 5821
SCHUCHART CORPORATION; *U.S. Private*, pg. 3570
SCHUCK & SONS CONSTRUCTION COMPANY, INC.; *U.S. Private*, pg. 3570
SCHUCO USA L.L.L.P.; *U.S. Private*, pg. 3570
SCHUECK STEEL—See Lexicon, Inc.; *U.S. Private*, pg. 2440
SCHUETTE MOVERS; *U.S. Private*, pg. 3570
SCHUETTE STORES, INC.; *U.S. Private*, pg. 3570
SCHUFF STEEL-ATLANTIC, LLC—See INNOVATE Corp.; *U.S. Public*, pg. 1126
SCHUFF STEEL COMPANY—See INNOVATE Corp.; *U.S. Public*, pg. 1125
SCHUFF STEEL-GULF COAST, INC.—See INNOVATE Corp.; *U.S. Public*, pg. 1126
SCHUFF STEEL MANAGEMENT COMPANY SE, LLC—See INNOVATE Corp.; *U.S. Public*, pg. 1126
SCHUFF STEEL MANAGEMENT COMPANY SW, INC.—See INNOVATE Corp.; *U.S. Public*, pg. 1126

COMPANY NAME INDEX

SCHUFF STEEL-PACIFIC, INC.—See INNOVATE Corp.; *U.S. Public*, pg. 1126
SCHUH BODENTECHNIK GMBH—See VINCI S.A.; *Int'l*, pg. 8227
SCHUH BRANDSCHUTZ UND SANIERUNG GMBH—See VINCI S.A.; *Int'l*, pg. 8227
SCHUH LIMITED—See Genesco Inc.; *U.S. Public*, pg. 930
SCHUKAT ELECTRONIC VERTRIEBS GMBH; *Int'l*, pg. 6641
SCHUKEI CHEVROLET, INC.; *U.S. Private*, pg. 3570
SCHUKRA BERNDORF GES.M.B.H.—See Leggett & Platt, Incorporated; *U.S. Public*, pg. 1302
SCHUKRA GERATEBAU GMBH—See Leggett & Platt, Incorporated; *U.S. Public*, pg. 1303
SCHUKRA OF NORTH AMERICA LTD.—See Leggett & Platt, Incorporated; *U.S. Public*, pg. 1303
SCHULE FUR MEDIENINTEGRATION (SMI) AG—See Ringier Holding AG; *Int'l*, pg. 6344
SCHULER AG—See ANDRITZ AG; *Int'l*, pg. 456
SCHULER AUTOMATION GMBH & CO. KG—See ANDRITZ AG; *Int'l*, pg. 456
SCHULER BOOKS & MUSIC, INC., *U.S. Private*, pg. 3570
SCHULER BUSINESS SOLUTIONS S.L.—See Durr AG; *Int'l*, pg. 2232
SCHULER CARTEC ENGINEERING GMBH & CO. KG—See ANDRITZ AG; *Int'l*, pg. 456
SCHULER (CHINA) CO., LTD.—See ANDRITZ AG; *Int'l*, pg. 456
SCHULER CONSULTING GMBH—See Durr AG; *Int'l*, pg. 2232
SCHULER (DALIAN) FORMING TECHNOLOGIES CO., LTD.—See ANDRITZ AG; *Int'l*, pg. 456
SCHULER FRANCE S.A.—See ANDRITZ AG; *Int'l*, pg. 456
SCHULER IBERICA S.A.U.—See ANDRITZ AG; *Int'l*, pg. 456
SCHULER INC.—See ANDRITZ AG; *Int'l*, pg. 456
SCHULER INDIA PRIVATE LIMITED—See ANDRITZ AG; *Int'l*, pg. 456
SCHULER ITALIA S.R.L.—See ANDRITZ AG; *Int'l*, pg. 456
SCHULER POLAND SERVICE SP. Z O.O.—See ANDRITZ AG; *Int'l*, pg. 456
SCHULER PRESSEN GMBH—See ANDRITZ AG; *Int'l*, pg. 456
SCHULER PRESSEN GMBH - WAGHAUSEL—See ANDRITZ AG; *Int'l*, pg. 456
SCHULER PRESSES UK LIMITED—See ANDRITZ AG; *Int'l*, pg. 456
SCHULER SALES & SERVICE (SHANGHAI) CO., LTD.—See ANDRITZ AG; *Int'l*, pg. 456
SCHULER SHOES INC.; *U.S. Private*, pg. 3570
SCHULER SLOVAKIA SERVICES S.R.O.—See ANDRITZ AG; *Int'l*, pg. 456
SCHULER THAILAND CO. LTD.—See ANDRITZ AG; *Int'l*, pg. 456
SCHULHOF COMPANY; *U.S. Private*, pg. 3570
SCHUL INTERNATIONAL CO., LLC—See RPM International Inc.; *U.S. Public*, pg. 1818
SCHULKE FRANCE SARL—See EQT AB; *Int'l*, pg. 2479
SCHULKE INC.—See EQT AB; *Int'l*, pg. 2479
SCHULKE & MAYR AG—See EQT AB; *Int'l*, pg. 2479
SCHULKE & MAYR (ASIA) PTE. LTD.—See EQT AB; *Int'l*, pg. 2479
SCHULKE & MAYR (ASIA) SDN.BHD.—See EQT AB; *Int'l*, pg. 2479
SCHULKE & MAYR BELGIUM NV—See EQT AB; *Int'l*, pg. 2479
SCHULKE & MAYR BENELUX BV—See EQT AB; *Int'l*, pg. 2479
SCHULKE & MAYR GES.M.B.H.—See EQT AB; *Int'l*, pg. 2479
SCHULKE & MAYR GMBH—See EQT AB; *Int'l*, pg. 2479
SCHULKE & MAYR ITALIA S.R.L.—See EQT AB; *Int'l*, pg. 2479
SCHULKE & MAYR UK LTD—See EQT AB; *Int'l*, pg. 2479
SCHULKE POLSKA SP.Z O.O.—See EQT AB; *Int'l*, pg. 2479
SCHULL CONSTRUCTION CO.; *U.S. Private*, pg. 3570
SCHULLER GMBH—See Berkshire Hathaway Inc.; *U.S. Public*, pg. 316
SCHULTE BUILDING SYSTEMS, INC.; *U.S. Private*, pg. 3570
SCHULTE CORPORATION; *U.S. Private*, pg. 3570
SCHULTE ELEKTROTECHNIK GMBH & CO KG; *Int'l*, pg. 6641
SCHULTE-HENKE GMBH; *Int'l*, pg. 6641
SCHULTE, ROTH & ZABEL LLP; *U.S. Private*, pg. 3570
SCHULTES PRECISION MANUFACTURING, INC.—See Helios Technologies, Inc.; *U.S. Public*, pg. 1023
SCHULTHEIS-MOCKLI AG—See Burkhalter Holding AG; *Int'l*, pg. 1225
SCHULTHESS GROUP AG—See NIBE Industrier AB; *Int'l*, pg. 5262
SCHULTHESS MASCHINEN AG—See NIBE Industrier AB; *Int'l*, pg. 5262
SCHULTHESS MASCHINEN GMBH—See NIBE Industrier AB; *Int'l*, pg. 5262
SCHULTZ COMPANY—See Spectrum Brands Holdings, Inc.; *U.S. Public*, pg. 1916

SCHULTZE ASSET MANAGEMENT, LLC; *U.S. Private*, pg. 3570
SCHULTZE SPECIAL PURPOSE ACQUISITION CORP.; *U.S. Public*, pg. 1848
SCHULTZ EYE CLINIC—See Trilogy Eye Medical Group Inc.; *U.S. Private*, pg. 4232
SCHULTZ INDUSTRIAL SERVICES, INC.—See New Mountain Capital, LLC; *U.S. Private*, pg. 2900
THE SCHULTZ ORGANIZATION, LLC; *U.S. Private*, pg. 4115
SCHULTZ STEEL COMPANY; *U.S. Private*, pg. 3570
SCHULTZ SURVEYING & ENGINEERING, INC.; *U.S. Private*, pg. 3570
SCHULZE & BURCH BISCUIT COMPANY; *U.S. Private*, pg. 3570
SCHULZ FISHERIES PTY. LTD.—See Temasek Holdings (Private) Limited; *Int'l*, pg. 7550
SCHULZ S/A; *Int'l*, pg. 6641
SCHUMACHER COMPANY INCORPORATED; *U.S. Private*, pg. 3570
SCHUMACHER DUGAN CONSTRUCTION, INC.; *U.S. Private*, pg. 3571
SCHUMACHER ELECTRIC CORPORATION—See Ripple Industries LLC; *U.S. Private*, pg. 3439
SCHUMACHER ELEVATOR CO. INC.; *U.S. Private*, pg. 3571
THE SCHUMACHER GROUP OF LOUISIANA, INC.—See Subsidium Healthcare, LLC; *U.S. Private*, pg. 3847
SCHUMACHER HOMES, INC.; *U.S. Private*, pg. 3571
SCHUMACHER & SEILER INC.; *U.S. Private*, pg. 3570
SCHUMAG AG—See Hangzhou Meibah Precision Machinery Co., Ltd.; *Int'l*, pg. 3249
SCHUMAG ROMANIA S.R.L.—See Hangzhou Meibah Precision Machinery Co., Ltd.; *Int'l*, pg. 3249
SCHUMAKER & CO. INC.; *U.S. Private*, pg. 3571
SCHUMANN PRINTERS, INC.; *U.S. Private*, pg. 3571
THE SCHUNDLER COMPANY—See Normiska Corporation; *Int'l*, pg. 5431
SCHUNK AG—See Schunk GmbH; *Int'l*, pg. 6642
SCHUNK (AUST) PTY. LTD.—See Schunk GmbH; *Int'l*, pg. 6641
SCHUNK BAHNTECHNIK GMBH—See Schunk GmbH; *Int'l*, pg. 6642
SCHUNK DAI IN UND INDUSTRIETECHNIK GMBH—See Schunk GmbH; *Int'l*, pg. 6642
SCHUNK BENELUX B.V.—See Schunk GmbH; *Int'l*, pg. 6642
SCHUNK CARBON PROCESSING GMBH—See Schunk GmbH; *Int'l*, pg. 6642
SCHUNK CARBON TECHNOLOGY CO. LTD.—See Schunk GmbH; *Int'l*, pg. 6642
SCHUNK CARBON TECHNOLOGY CO., LTD.—See Schunk GmbH; *Int'l*, pg. 6642
SCHUNK CARBON TECHNOLOGY JAPAN KK—See Schunk GmbH; *Int'l*, pg. 6642
SCHUNK CARBON TECHNOLOGY KFT.—See Schunk GmbH; *Int'l*, pg. 6642
SCHUNK CARBON TECHNOLOGY LIMITED—See Schunk GmbH; *Int'l*, pg. 6642
SCHUNK CARBON TECHNOLOGY LIMITED—See Schunk GmbH; *Int'l*, pg. 6642
SCHUNK CARBON TECHNOLOGY LTD.—See Schunk GmbH; *Int'l*, pg. 6642
SCHUNK CARBON TECHNOLOGY PTY LTD—See Schunk GmbH; *Int'l*, pg. 6642
SCHUNK CARBON TECHNOLOGY S.A.S.—See Schunk GmbH; *Int'l*, pg. 6642
SCHUNK CARBON TECHNOLOGY S.R.L.—See Schunk GmbH; *Int'l*, pg. 6642
SCHUNK CARBON TECHNOLOGY SRL—See Schunk GmbH; *Int'l*, pg. 6642
SCHUNK CARBON TECHNOLOGY S.R.O.—See Schunk GmbH; *Int'l*, pg. 6642
SCHUNK CARBON TECHNOLOGY S.R.O. SP. Z O.O.—See Schunk GmbH; *Int'l*, pg. 6642
SCHUNK CARBON TECHNOLOGY (SUZHOU) CO., LTD.—See Schunk GmbH; *Int'l*, pg. 6642
SCHUNK DIENSTLEISTUNGSGES. MBH—See Schunk GmbH; *Int'l*, pg. 6642
SCHUNK DO BRASIL ELETROGRAFITES LTDA.—See Schunk GmbH; *Int'l*, pg. 6643
SCHUNK DO BRASIL LTDA.—See Schunk GmbH; *Int'l*, pg. 6643
SCHUNK ELECTRO CARBON, S.A. DE C.V.—See Schunk GmbH; *Int'l*, pg. 6642
SCHUNK ELECTROGRAPHITE SAS—See Schunk GmbH; *Int'l*, pg. 6642
SCHUNK GENERAL CARBON LTD.—See Schunk GmbH; *Int'l*, pg. 6642
SCHUNK GENERAL CARBON (PANYU) CO., LTD.—See Schunk GmbH; *Int'l*, pg. 6642
SCHUNK GERHARD CARBON TECHNOLOGY GMBH—See Schunk GmbH; *Int'l*, pg. 6642
SCHUNK GMBH; *Int'l*, pg. 6641
SCHUNK GRAPHITE TECHNOLOGY, LLC—See Schunk GmbH; *Int'l*, pg. 6643
SCHUNK HOFFMANN CARBON TECHNOLOGY AG—See Schunk GmbH; *Int'l*, pg. 6642

SCHUSTER COMPANY

SCHUNK IBERICA S.A.—See Schunk GmbH; *Int'l*, pg. 6642
SCHUNK INGENIEURKERAMIK GMBH—See Schunk GmbH; *Int'l*, pg. 6642
SCHUNK ITALIA S.R.L.—See Schunk GmbH; *Int'l*, pg. 6642
SCHUNK METAL & CARBON (I) PVT. LTD.—See Schunk GmbH; *Int'l*, pg. 6642
SCHUNK NORDISKA AB—See Schunk GmbH; *Int'l*, pg. 6642
SCHUNK OF NORTH AMERICA, INC.—See Schunk GmbH; *Int'l*, pg. 6643
SCHUNK PORTUGAL LDA.—See Schunk GmbH; *Int'l*, pg. 6642
SCHUNK PRAHA S R.O.—See Schunk GmbH; *Int'l*, pg. 6642
SCHUNK SINTERMETALLTECHNIK GMBH—See Schunk GmbH; *Int'l*, pg. 6642
SCHUNK SINTERMETAL SA DE CV—See Schunk GmbH; *Int'l*, pg. 6642
SCHUNK SONOSYSTEMS INNOVATIONS GMBH—See Schunk GmbH; *Int'l*, pg. 6642
SCHUNK UK LTD.—See Schunk GmbH; *Int'l*, pg. 6642
SCHUNK ULTRASCHALLTECHNIK GMBH—See Schunk GmbH; *Int'l*, pg. 6642
SCHUNK WIEN GESELLSCHAFT M.B.H.—See Schunk GmbH; *Int'l*, pg. 6642
SCHUNK WIEN GESELLSCHAFT M.B.H.—See Schunk GmbH; *Int'l*, pg. 6642
SCHUNK WIEN GESELLSCHAFT M.B.H.—See Schunk GmbH; *Int'l*, pg. 6643
SCHUNK XYCARB (SHANGHAI) PRECISION CERAMICS TECHNOLOGY CO., LTD.—See Schunk GmbH; *Int'l*, pg. 6643
SCHUNK XYCARB TECHNOLOGY B.V.—See Schunk GmbH; *Int'l*, pg. 6643
SCHUNK XYCARB TECHNOLOGY CO. LTD.—See Schunk GmbH; *Int'l*, pg. 6643
SCHUNK XYCARB TECHNOLOGY CO. LTD.—See Schunk GmbH; *Int'l*, pg. 6643
SCHUNK XYCARB TECHNOLOGY PTE. LTD.—See Schunk GmbH; *Int'l*, pg. 6643
SCHUPAN & SONS, INC.; *U.S. Private*, pg. 3571
SCHUPP COMPANY, INC.; *U.S. Private*, pg. 3571
SCHUR CONFERENCE CENTER A/S—See Schur International a/s; *Int'l*, pg. 6644
SCHUR CONSUMER PRODUCTS A/S—See Schur International a/s; *Int'l*, pg. 6644
SCHUR CONSUMER PRODUCTS INC.—See Schur International a/s; *Int'l*, pg. 6644
SCHUR FLEXIBLES BENELUX B.V.—See UniCredit S.p.A.; *Int'l*, pg. 8039
SCHUR FLEXIBLES DENMARK A/S—See UniCredit S.p.A.; *Int'l*, pg. 8039
SCHUR FLEXIBLES DIXIE GMBH—See UniCredit S.p.A.; *Int'l*, pg. 8039
SCHUR FLEXIBLES FINLAND OY—See UniCredit S.p.A.; *Int'l*, pg. 8039
SCHUR FLEXIBLES GERMANY GMBH—See UniCredit S.p.A.; *Int'l*, pg. 8039
SCHUR FLEXIBLES HOLDING GESMBH—See UniCredit S.p.A.; *Int'l*, pg. 8039
SCHUR FLEXIBLES MONETA—See UniCredit S.p.A.; *Int'l*, pg. 8039
SCHUR FLEXIBLES POLAND SP. Z O.O.—See UniCredit S.p.A.; *Int'l*, pg. 8039
SCHUR FLEXIBLES VACUFOL GMBH—See UniCredit S.p.A.; *Int'l*, pg. 8039
SCHURICHT DISTRELEC GMBH—See Pema Holding AG; *Int'l*, pg. 5785
SCHUR INTERNATIONAL A/S; *Int'l*, pg. 6644
SCHURMAN FINE PAPERS & PAPYRUS FRANCHISE CORPORATION; *U.S. Private*, pg. 3571
SCHUR PACKAGING SYSTEMS AB—See Schur International a/s; *Int'l*, pg. 6644
SCHUR PACKAGING SYSTEMS INC.—See Schur International a/s; *Int'l*, pg. 6644
SCHUR PACK GERMANY GMBH—See Schur International a/s; *Int'l*, pg. 6644
SCHUR PACK NORWAY A/S—See Schur International a/s; *Int'l*, pg. 6644
SCHUR PACK SWEDEN AB—See Schur International a/s; *Int'l*, pg. 6644
SCHUR STAR SYSTEMS GMBH—See Schur International a/s; *Int'l*, pg. 6644
SCHUR TECHNOLOGY A/S—See Schur International a/s; *Int'l*, pg. 6644
SCHUR WAMAC FRANCE SAS—See Schur International a/s; *Int'l*, pg. 6644
SCHURZ COMMUNICATIONS, INC.; *U.S. Private*, pg. 3571
SCHUSSLER NOVACHEM GMBH; *Int'l*, pg. 6644
SCHUST DEVELOPMENT, INC.—See Scheuch GmbH; *Int'l*, pg. 6616
SCHUSTER AGUILO LLC—See Littler Mendelson P.C.; *U.S. Private*, pg. 2472
SCHUSTER COMPANY; *U.S. Private*, pg. 3571
SCHUSTER ELECTRONICS INC.—See TLC Electronics, Inc.; *U.S. Private*, pg. 4178

SCHUSTER ENTERPRISES INC.; *U.S. Private*, pg. 3571
SCHUSTER KLIMA LUFTUNG GMBH & CO. KG—See INDUS Holding AG; *Int'l*, pg. 3664
SCHUSTER THOMSEN ROEHLE; *Int'l*, pg. 6644
SCHUSTER VERSICHERUNGSMAKLER GMBH—See DZ BANK AG Deutsche Zentral-Genossenschaftsbank; *Int'l*, pg. 2244
SCHUTTE LUMBER COMPANY; *U.S. Private*, pg. 3571
SCHUTT SPORTS—See Platinum Equity, LLC; *U.S. Private*, pg. 3208
SCHUTZ CONTAINER SYSTEMS, INC.—See BayernLB Holding AG; *Int'l*, pg. 914
SCHUTZ GROUP GMBH & CO. KG—See BayernLB Holding AG; *Int'l*, pg. 914
SCHUYLER HOUSE INC.—See CompuGroup Medical SE & Co. KGaA; *Int'l*, pg. 1756
SCHUYLER WOOD PELLET, LLC—See Rentech, Inc.; *U.S. Private*, pg. 3400
SCHUYLKILL ENERGY RESOURCES INC.; *U.S. Private*, pg. 3571
SCHUYLKILL OPEN MRI, INC.—See Medical Imaging Corp.; *U.S. Public*, pg. 1412
SCHUYLKILL VALLEY SPORTS; *U.S. Private*, pg. 3571
SCHWAAB INC.; *U.S. Private*, pg. 3571
SCHWABE CZECH REPUBLIC S.R.O.—See Dr. Willmar Schwabe GmbH & Co. KG; *Int'l*, pg. 2195
SCHWABE HUNGARY KFT—See Dr. Willmar Schwabe GmbH & Co. KG; *Int'l*, pg. 2195
SCHWABE NORTH AMERICA, INC.—See Dr. Willmar Schwabe GmbH & Co. KG; *Int'l*, pg. 2195
SCHWABE PHARMA AG—See Dr. Willmar Schwabe GmbH & Co. KG; *Int'l*, pg. 2195
SCHWABE PHARMA ASIA PACIFIC PTE. LTD.—See Dr. Willmar Schwabe GmbH & Co. KG; *Int'l*, pg. 2196
SCHWABE PHARMA (UK) LTD.—See Dr. Willmar Schwabe GmbH & Co. KG; *Int'l*, pg. 2195
SCHWABE SLOVAKIA S.R.O.—See Dr. Willmar Schwabe GmbH & Co. KG; *Int'l*, pg. 2195
SCHWABISCHE BANK AG—See M.M. Warburg & Co. KGaA; *Int'l*, pg. 4616
SCHWABISCH HALL FACILITY MANAGEMENT GMBH—See DZ BANK AG Deutsche Zentral-Genossenschaftsbank; *Int'l*, pg. 2244
SCHWABO CAPITAL CORPORATION; *Int'l*, pg. 6644
SCHWAB PERFORMANCE TECHNOLOGIES INC.—See The Charles Schwab Corporation; *U.S. Public*, pg. 2058
SCHWAB VERSAND GMBH E-COMMERCE—See Otto GmbH & Co. KG; *Int'l*, pg. 5663
SCHWAB VERSAND GMBH—See Otto GmbH & Co. KG; *Int'l*, pg. 5663
SCHWAGER ENERGY S.A.; *Int'l*, pg. 6644
SCHWAIGER GMBH—See VOXX International Corporation; *U.S. Public*, pg. 2311
SCHWALBCHEN MOLKEREI JAKOB BERZ AG; *Int'l*, pg. 6644
SCHWAN COSMETICS CR, S.R.O.—See Schwan-STABILO Cosmetics GmbH & Co. KG; *Int'l*, pg. 6644
SCHWAN COSMETICS DO BRASIL LTDA.—See Schwan-STABILO Cosmetics GmbH & Co. KG; *Int'l*, pg. 6644
SCHWAN COSMETICS KUNSTSTOFFTECHNIK GMBH & CO. KG—See Schwan-STABILO Cosmetics GmbH & Co. KG; *Int'l*, pg. 6644
SCHWAN COSMETICS USA INC.—See Schwan-STABILO Cosmetics GmbH & Co. KG; *Int'l*, pg. 6644
THE SCHWAN FOOD COMPANY; *U.S. Private*, pg. 4115
SCHWANK BE—See Schwank Inc.; *U.S. Private*, pg. 3572
SCHWANK BV—See Schwank Inc.; *U.S. Private*, pg. 3572
SCHWANK GESMBH—See Schwank Inc.; *U.S. Private*, pg. 3572
SCHWANK GMBH—See Schwank Inc.; *U.S. Private*, pg. 3572
SCHWANK INC.; *U.S. Private*, pg. 3572
SCHWANK INC.—See Schwank Inc.; *U.S. Private*, pg. 3572
SCHWANK LTD—See Schwank Inc.; *U.S. Private*, pg. 3572
SCHWANK S.A.R.L.—See Schwank Inc.; *U.S. Private*, pg. 3572
SCHWANK—See Schwank Inc.; *U.S. Private*, pg. 3572
SCHWANK SRL—See Schwank Inc.; *U.S. Private*, pg. 3572
SCHWAN'S BAKERY INC—See The Schwan Food Company; *U.S. Private*, pg. 4115
SCHWAN'S CONSUMER BRANDS, INC.—See The Schwan Food Company; *U.S. Private*, pg. 4115
SCHWAN'S FOOD SERVICE, INC.—See The Schwan Food Company; *U.S. Private*, pg. 4115
SCHWAN'S HOME SERVICE, INC.—See The Schwan Food Company; *U.S. Private*, pg. 4115
SCHWAN'S MAMA ROSA'S, LLC—See Schwan's Shared Services, LLC; *U.S. Private*, pg. 3572
SCHWAN'S SHARED SERVICES, LLC; *U.S. Private*, pg. 3572
SCHWAN-STABILO COSMETICS GMBH & CO. KG; *Int'l*, pg. 6644
SCHWAN-STABILO CREATIVE COLORS DE MEXICO, S.A. DE C.V.—See Schwan-STABILO Cosmetics GmbH & Co. KG; *Int'l*, pg. 6644
SCHWAN-STABILO PROMOTION PRODUCTS GMBH & CO. KG—See Schwan-STABILO Cosmetics GmbH & Co. KG; *Int'l*, pg. 6644
SCHWARTE GROUP A/S—See L. Possehl & Co. mbH; *Int'l*, pg. 4385
SCHWARTE GROUP GMBH—See L. Possehl & Co. mbH; *Int'l*, pg. 4385
SCHWARTE GROUP GMBH—See L. Possehl & Co. mbH; *Int'l*, pg. 4385
SCHWARTE GROUP SP. Z O.O—See L. Possehl & Co. mbH; *Int'l*, pg. 4385
SCHWARTZ BENEFIT SERVICES, INC.—See Aon plc; *Int'l*, pg. 497
SCHWARTZ & BENJAMIN, INC.—See Steven Madden, Ltd.; *U.S. Public*, pg. 1947
THE SCHWARTZBERG COMPANIES; *U.S. Private*, pg. 4115
SCHWARTZ BROTHERS RESTAURANTS; *U.S. Private*, pg. 3572
SCHWARTZ JEWELERS; *U.S. Private*, pg. 3572
SCHWARTZ PUBLIC RELATIONS ASSOCIATES, INC.; *U.S. Private*, pg. 3572
SCHWARTZ VENTURES INC.; *U.S. Private*, pg. 3572
SCHWARZATAL GEMEINNUTZIGE WOHNUNGS-UND SIEDLUNGSANLAGEN-GMBH—See Vienna Insurance Group AG Wiener Versicherung Gruppe; *Int'l*, pg. 8195
SCHWARZECK-VERLAG GMBH—See IQVIA Holdings Inc.; *U.S. Public*, pg. 1169
SCHWARZE INDUSTRIES AUSTRALIA PTY LTD.—See Alamo Group Inc.; *U.S. Public*, pg. 71
SCHWARZ INSURANCE, INC.—See Seeman Holtz Property & Casualty, LLC; *U.S. Private*, pg. 3598
SCHWARZKOPF & HENKEL GMBH—See Henkel AG & Co. KGaA; *Int'l*, pg. 3354
SCHWARZKOPF & HENKEL K.K.—See Henkel AG & Co. KGaA; *Int'l*, pg. 3354
SCHWARZKOPF & HENKEL PRODUCTION MANAGEMENT GMBH—See Henkel AG & Co. KGaA; *Int'l*, pg. 3354
SCHWARZKOPF, INC.—See Henkel AG & Co. KGaA; *Int'l*, pg. 3354
SCHWARZKOPF S.A.—See Henkel AG & Co. KGaA; *Int'l*, pg. 3354
SCHWARZL BETON D.O.O.—See PORR AG; *Int'l*, pg. 5925
SCHWARZL TRANSPORT GMBH—See PORR AG; *Int'l*, pg. 5925
SCHWARZMEER UND OSTSEE VERSICHERUNGS-AG—See PJSC Gazprom; *Int'l*, pg. 5880
SCHWARZ PAPER COMPANY; *U.S. Private*, pg. 3572
SCHWARZ PARTNERS, LP; *U.S. Private*, pg. 3572
SCHWARZ PHARMA MANUFACTURING, INC.—See UCB S.A.; *Int'l*, pg. 8012
SCHWARZSCHILD JEWELERS, INC.; *U.S. Private*, pg. 3572
SCHWARZ UNTERNEHMENSKOMMUNIKATION GMBH & CO. KG—See Schwarz Unternehmenstreuhand KG; *Int'l*, pg. 6645
SCHWARZ UNTERNEHMENSTREUHAND KG; *Int'l*, pg. 6645
SCHWARZ VIVA AG—See Coop-Gruppe Genossenschaft; *Int'l*, pg. 1790
SCHWEBEL BAKING CO. INC.; *U.S. Private*, pg. 3572
SCHWEBEL BAKING CO. OF PENNSYLVANIA INC.—See Schwebel Baking Co. Inc.; *U.S. Private*, pg. 3572
SCHWEIGER DERMATOLOGY GROUP; *U.S. Private*, pg. 3572
SCHWEIGHOUSE ENROBES SAS—See VINCI S.A.; *Int'l*, pg. 8227
SCHWEITER TECHNOLOGIES AG; *Int'l*, pg. 6645
SCHWEITZER ENGINEERING LABORATORIES INC.; *U.S. Private*, pg. 3573
SCHWEITZER-MAUDUIT CANADA, INC.—See Mativ Holdings, Inc.; *U.S. Public*, pg. 1397
SCHWEIZER ELECTRONIC AG; *Int'l*, pg. 6645
SCHWEIZER ELECTRONIC (JIANGSU) CO., LTD.—See Schweizer Electronic AG; *Int'l*, pg. 6645
SCHWEIZER ELECTRONIC SINGAPORE PTE. LTD.—See Schweizer Electronic AG; *Int'l*, pg. 6646
SCHWEIZER FAMILIE AG—See TX Group AG; *Int'l*, pg. 7992
SCHWEIZERISCHE BODENSEE-SCHIFFFAHRTSGES. AG—See Schweizerische Bundesbahnen SBB AG; *Int'l*, pg. 6646
SCHWEIZERISCHE BUNDESBAHNEN SBB AG; *Int'l*, pg. 6646
SCHWEIZERISCHE BUNDESBAHNEN SBB CARGO AG—See Schweizerische Bundesbahnen SBB AG; *Int'l*, pg. 6646
SCHWEIZERISCHE MOBILIAR VERSICHERUNGSGESELLSCHAFT AG; *Int'l*, pg. 6646
SCHWEIZERISCHE NATIONALBANK; *Int'l*, pg. 6646
SCHWEIZERISCHE TELETEXT AG—See SRG SSR Idee Suisse; *Int'l*, pg. 7149
SCHWEIZER MEDIENDATENBANK (SMD) AG—See Ringier Holding AG; *Int'l*, pg. 6344
SCHWEIZER MEDIENDATENBANK (SMD) AG—See SRG SSR Idee Suisse; *Int'l*, pg. 7149
SCHWEIZER MEDIENDATENBANK (SMD) AG—See TX Group AG; *Int'l*, pg. 7992
SCHWEPPES AUSTRALIA PTY LTD—See Asahi Group Holdings Ltd.; *Int'l*, pg. 594
SCHWEPPES S.A.—See Suntory Holdings Limited; *Int'l*, pg. 7327
SCHWEPPES ZIMBABWE LTD.; *Int'l*, pg. 6646
SCHWERIN PLUS TOURISTIK-SERVICE GMBH—See TUI AG; *Int'l*, pg. 7966
SCHWERMAN REAL ESTATE & DEVELOPMENT CORP.—See Tankstar USA, Inc.; *U.S. Private*, pg. 3931
SCHWERMAN TRUCKING CO. INC.—See Tankstar USA, Inc.; *U.S. Private*, pg. 3931
SCHWERMETALL HALBZEUGWERK GMBH & CO. KG—See Aurubis AG; *Int'l*, pg. 715
SCHWESERS STORES INC.; *U.S. Private*, pg. 3573
SCHWEVERS & RAAB STAHL - HOCHBAU GMBH; *Int'l*, pg. 6646
SCHWICKERT'S TECTA AMERICA LLC—See Altas Partners LP; *Int'l*, pg. 386
SCHWICKERT'S TECTA AMERICA LLC - STEWARTVILLE—See Altas Partners LP; *Int'l*, pg. 386
SCHWICKERT'S TECTA AMERICA OF MANKATO LLC—See Altas Partners LP; *Int'l*, pg. 386
SCHWIMMBAD-SAUNA-AUSSTATTUNGS-GROSSHANDELS GESMBH—See Fluidra SA; *Int'l*, pg. 2714
SCHWING AMERICA, INC.—See Xuzhou Construction Machinery Group Co., Ltd.; *Int'l*, pg. 8541
SCHWING BIOSET, INC.; *U.S. Private*, pg. 3573
SCHWING BIOSET—See Schwing Bioset, Inc.; *U.S. Private*, pg. 3573
SCHWING ELECTRICAL SUPPLY CORP.; *U.S. Private*, pg. 3573
SCHWING EQUIPAMENTOS INDUSTRIAIS LTDA.—See Xuzhou Construction Machinery Group Co., Ltd.; *Int'l*, pg. 8541
SCHWING GMBH—See Xuzhou Construction Machinery Group Co., Ltd.; *Int'l*, pg. 8541
SCHWING GMBH—See Xuzhou Construction Machinery Group Co., Ltd.; *Int'l*, pg. 8541
SCHWING STETTER INDIA PVT LTD—See Xuzhou Construction Machinery Group Co., Ltd.; *Int'l*, pg. 8541
SCHWING STETTER OSTRAVA S.R.O.—See Xuzhou Construction Machinery Group Co., Ltd.; *Int'l*, pg. 8541
S.C. HYDAC SRL—See Hydac International GmbH; *Int'l*, pg. 3545
SCIACCA'S LAWYERS PTY. LTD.—See Shine Justice Ltd.; *Int'l*, pg. 6842
SCIA CZ S.R.O.—See Nemetschek SE; *Int'l*, pg. 5195
S.C.I.A.E.—See Vivonio Furniture GmbH; *Int'l*, pg. 8280
SCIA FRANCE S.A.R.L.—See Nemetschek SE; *Int'l*, pg. 5195
SCIA INTERNATIONAL NV—See Nemetschek SE; *Int'l*, pg. 5195
SCIAKY, INC.—See Phillips Service Industries, Inc. (PSI); *U.S. Private*, pg. 3171
SCIAKY WELDING MACHINES LTD.—See Phillips Service Industries, Inc. (PSI); *U.S. Private*, pg. 3171
SCI ALABAMA FUNERAL SERVICES, LLC—See Service Corporation International; *U.S. Public*, pg. 1870
SCIAME CONSTRUCTION, LLC—See F.J. Sciame Construction Co. Inc.; *U.S. Private*, pg. 1456
SCIAME DEVELOPMENT, INC.—See F.J. Sciame Construction Co. Inc.; *U.S. Private*, pg. 1456
SCIANDA (CHANGSHU) PHARMACEUTICALS, LTD.—See ScinoPharm Taiwan, Ltd.; *Int'l*, pg. 6649
SCIANDA SHANGHAI BIOCHEMICAL TECHNOLOGY, LTD.—See ScinoPharm Taiwan, Ltd.; *Int'l*, pg. 6649
SCIA NEDERLAND B.V.—See Nemetschek SE; *Int'l*, pg. 5195
SCIA NV—See Herbalife Nutrition Ltd.; *Int'l*, pg. 3360
SCIA NV—See Nemetschek SE; *Int'l*, pg. 5195
SCIA SARL—See Nemetschek SE; *Int'l*, pg. 5195
S.C. IASITEX S.A.—See S.C Serviciile Comerciale Romane S.R.L.; *Int'l*, pg. 6449
SCIA SK S.R.O.—See Nemetschek SE; *Int'l*, pg. 5195
SCI ASSAS RASPAIL—See Vivendi SE; *Int'l*, pg. 8278
SCIBAL ASSOCIATES, INC.—See The Cigna Group; *U.S. Public*, pg. 2061
SCIBASE HOLDING AB; *Int'l*, pg. 6646
SCIBITE LTD.—See RELX plc; *Int'l*, pg. 6269
SCIC HABITAT—See Caisse des Depots et Consignations; *Int'l*, pg. 1258
SCI CHAMPVERNIER—See BNP Paribas SA; *Int'l*, pg. 1092
SCICLONE PHARMACEUTICALS CHINA LTD.—See SciClone Pharmaceuticals, Inc.; *U.S. Private*, pg. 3573
SCICLONE PHARMACEUTICALS HONG KONG LIMITED—See SciClone Pharmaceuticals, Inc.; *U.S. Private*, pg. 3573
SCICLONE PHARMACEUTICALS, INC.; *U.S. Private*, pg. 3573
SCICLONE PHARMACEUTICALS INTERNATIONAL LTD.—See SciClone Pharmaceuticals, Inc.; *U.S. Private*, pg. 3573
SCI COLORADO FUNERAL SERVICES, LLC—See Service Corporation International; *U.S. Public*, pg. 1870

COMPANY NAME INDEX

SCICOM (MSC) BERHAD; *Int'l*, pg. 6647
SCI COMPANIES—See People Inc.; *U.S. Private*, pg. 3140
SCI CONSULTING SERVICES, INC.; *U.S. Private*, pg. 3573
S.C. ICSIM- S.A.; *Int'l*, pg. 6451
SCIDEV LTD; *Int'l*, pg. 6647
SCI DIRECT, INC.—See Service Corporation International; *U.S. Public*, pg. 1870
SCI DOMAINE DE SAINT JEAN—See VINCI S.A.; *Int'l*, pg. 8226
SCI ECO SERVICES CO., LTD.—See The Siam Cement Public Company Limited; *Int'l*, pg. 7685
SCI EDISON—See LVMH Moet Hennessy Louis Vuitton SE; *Int'l*, pg. 4600
SCI ELECTRIC PUBLIC COMPANY LIMITED; *Int'l*, pg. 6646
SCIENCE 37 HOLDINGS, INC.—See eMed, LLC; *U.S. Private*, pg. 1379
SCIENCE AND TECHNOLOGY CORP.—See STC Group Inc.; *U.S. Private*, pg. 3794
SCIENCE APPLICATIONS INTERNATIONAL CORPORATION - HUNTSVILLE—See Science Applications International Corporation; *U.S. Public*, pg. 1848
SCIENCE APPLICATIONS INTERNATIONAL CORPORATION - HUNTSVILLE—See Science Applications International Corporation; *U.S. Public*, pg. 1848
SCIENCE APPLICATIONS INTERNATIONAL CORPORATION; *U.S. Public*, pg. 1848
SCIENCE + COMPUTING AG—See Atos SE; *Int'l*, pg. 690
SCIENCE DEVELOPMENTS PTY LTD—See SciDev Ltd; *Int'l*, pg. 6647
SCIENCE, ENGINEERING, AND TECHNOLOGY ASSOCIATES CORPORATION—See Leidos Holdings, Inc.; *U.S. Public*, pg. 1304
SCIENCE & ENGINEERING SERVICES, INC.; *U.S. Private*, pg. 3573
SCIENCE GROUP PLC; *Int'l*, pg. 6647
SCIENCE IN SPORT PLC; *Int'l*, pg. 6647
SCIENCE KIT LLC; *U.S. Private*, pg. 3573
SCIENCELOGIC LLC; *U.S. Private*, pg. 3573
SCIENCE-METRIX INC.—See RELX plc; *Int'l*, pg. 6269
SCIENCE MUSEUM OKLAHOMA; *U.S. Private*, pg. 3573
SCIENCENOW LIMITED; *Int'l*, pg. 6647
SCIENCESOFT, INC.; *Int'l*, pg. 6647
SCIENCE STRATEGIC ACQUISITION CORP. ALPHA; *U.S. Public*, pg. 1848
SCIENCE SYSTEMS & APPLICATIONS, INC.; *U.S. Private*, pg. 3573
SCIENCE SYSTEMS (SPACE) LIMITED—See CGI Inc.; *Int'l*, pg. 1434
SCIENCE & TECHNOLOGY INTERNATIONAL; *U.S. Private*, pg. 3573
SCIENERGY, INC.; *U.S. Private*, pg. 3573
SCI ENGINEERED MATERIALS, INC.; *U.S. Public*, pg. 1848
SCIENION GMBH—See BICO Group AB; *Int'l*, pg. 1019
SCIENJOY HOLDING CORP.; *Int'l*, pg. 6647
SCIENS BUILDING SOLUTIONS, LLC—See The Carlyle Group Inc.; *U.S. Public*, pg. 2053
SCIENS CAPITAL MANAGEMENT LLC; *U.S. Private*, pg. 3574
SCIENS INTERNATIONAL INVESTMENTS & HOLDINGS S.A.; *Int'l*, pg. 6647
SCIENS WATER OPPORTUNITIES MANAGEMENT, LLC—See Sciens Capital Management LLC; *U.S. Private*, pg. 3574
SCIENTEC CONSULTING PTE. LTD.—See Will Group, Inc.; *Int'l*, pg. 8412
SCIENTECH CORPORATION - HUKO FACTORY—See Scientech Corporation; *Int'l*, pg. 6647
SCIENTECH CORPORATION; *Int'l*, pg. 6647
SCIENTECH, INC.; *U.S. Private*, pg. 3574
SCIENTECHNIC LLC; *Int'l*, pg. 6647
SCIENTEK CORPORATION—See Zen Voce Corporation; *Int'l*, pg. 8632
SCIENTEX BERHAD; *Int'l*, pg. 6647
SCIENTEX INDUSTRIES GROUP SDN. BHD.—See Scientex Berhad; *Int'l*, pg. 6647
SCIENTEX PACKAGING (AYER KEROH) BERHAD—See Scientex Berhad; *Int'l*, pg. 6648
SCIENTEX PACKAGING FILM SDN. BHD.—See Scientex Berhad; *Int'l*, pg. 6648
SCIENTEX QUATARI SDN. BHD.—See Scientex Berhad; *Int'l*, pg. 6648
SCIENTEX (SKUDAI) SDN. BHD.—See Scientex Berhad; *Int'l*, pg. 6648
SCIENTIA ALHUCEMA, S.L.—See Scientia School, S.A.; *Int'l*, pg. 6648
SCIENTIA DENIA, S.L.—See Scientia School, S.A.; *Int'l*, pg. 6648
SCIENTIA KARMELO, S.L.—See Scientia School, S.A.; *Int'l*, pg. 6648
SCIENTIA LALIN, S.L.—See Scientia School, S.A.; *Int'l*, pg. 6648
SCIENTIA SCHOOL, S.A.; *Int'l*, pg. 6648
SCIENTIFIC ADVANCES, INC.—See Battelle Memorial Institute; *U.S. Private*, pg. 487
SCIENTIFIC ADVANTAGE LLC—See Acquis Consulting Group, LLC; *U.S. Private*, pg. 65

SCIENTIFIC AMERICAN, INC.—See Verlagsgruppe Georg von Holtzbrinck GmbH; *Int'l*, pg. 8171
SCIENTIFIC AMERICAN MAGAZINE—See Verlagsgruppe Georg von Holtzbrinck GmbH; *Int'l*, pg. 8171
SCIENTIFIC AND SEMICONDUCTOR MANUFACTURING EQUIPMENT RECYCLING CO., LTD.—See Screen Holdings Co., Ltd.; *Int'l*, pg. 6655
SCIENTIFIC-ATLANTA, LLC—See Cisco Systems, Inc.; *U.S. Public*, pg. 500
SCIENTIFIC AVIATION, INC.—See ChampionX Corporation; *U.S. Public*, pg. 478
SCIENTIFIC BIOTECH SPECIALTIES INC.—See HORIBA Ltd; *Int'l*, pg. 3478
SCIENTIFIC BOILER WATER CONDITIONING CO, INC.—See Nolan Capital, Inc.; *U.S. Private*, pg. 2934
SCIENTIFIC BRAIN TRAINING SA; *Int'l*, pg. 6648
SCIENTIFIC BRAKE & EQUIPMENT CO.; *U.S. Private*, pg. 3574
SCIENTIFIC CERTIFICATION SYSTEMS, INC.; *U.S. Private*, pg. 3574
SCIENTIFIC COMMERCIALIZATION, LLC—See The CM Group, LLC; *U.S. Private*, pg. 4011
SCIENTIFIC COMPONENTS CORP.; *U.S. Private*, pg. 3574
SCIENTIFIC DESIGN COMPANY, INC.—See Clariant AG; *Int'l*, pg. 1647
SCIENTIFIC DESIGN COMPANY, INC.—See Saudi Basic Industries Corporation; *Int'l*, pg. 6592
SCIENTIFIC DRILLING INTERNATIONAL INC.; *U.S. Private*, pg. 3574
SCIENTIFIC DRILLING—See Applied Technologies Associates; *U.S. Private*, pg. 299
SCIENTIFIC DUST COLLECTORS—See Venturedyne, Ltd.; *U.S. Private*, pg. 4358
SCIENTIFIC ENERGY, INC.; *U.S. Public*, pg. 1848
SCIENTIFIC GAMES (CHINA) COMPANY LIMITED—See Light & Wonder, Inc.; *U.S. Public*, pg. 1314
SCIENTIFIC GAMES DEUTSCHLAND GMBH—See Light & Wonder, Inc.; *U.S. Public*, pg. 1314
SCIENTIFIC GAMES GERMANY GMBH—See Light & Wonder, Inc.; *U.S. Public*, pg. 1314
SCIENTIFIC GAMES HOLDINGS (CANADA) ULC—See Light & Wonder, Inc.; *U.S. Public*, pg. 1314
SCIENTIFIC GAMES INTERNATIONAL—See Light & Wonder, Inc.; *U.S. Public*, pg. 1315
SCIENTIFIC GAMES KFT.—See Light & Wonder, Inc.; *U.S. Public*, pg. 1315
SCIENTIFIC GAMES LOTTERY SERVICES KFT—See Light & Wonder, Inc.; *U.S. Public*, pg. 1315
SCIENTIFIC GAMES NEW JERSEY, LLC—See Light & Wonder, Inc.; *U.S. Public*, pg. 1315
SCIENTIFIC GAMES PUERTO RICO, LLC—See Light & Wonder, Inc.; *U.S. Public*, pg. 1315
SCIENTIFIC GAMES SWEDEN AB—See Light & Wonder, Inc.; *U.S. Public*, pg. 1315
SCIENTIFIC GAMES WORLDWIDE LIMITED—See Light & Wonder, Inc.; *U.S. Public*, pg. 1315
SCIENTIFIC INDUSTRIES, INC.; *U.S. Public*, pg. 1848
SCIENTIFIC INSTRUMENT MANUFACTURING—See IMI plc; *Int'l*, pg. 3624
SCIENTIFIC INSTRUMENT SERVICES, INC.—See IMI plc; *Int'l*, pg. 3624
SCIENTIFIC INSTRUMENTS, INC.; *U.S. Private*, pg. 3574
SCIENTIFIC INSTRUMENTS S.A. DE C.V.—See HORIBA Ltd; *Int'l*, pg. 3478
SCIENTIFIC LEARNING CORPORATION—See CIP Capital Fund, L.P.; *U.S. Private*, pg. 899
SCIENTIFIC MAGNETICS LIMITED—See Avingtrans plc; *Int'l*, pg. 744
SCIENTIFIC & MEDICAL EQUIPMENT HOUSE COMPANY; *Int'l*, pg. 6648
SCIENTIFIC & MEDICAL SUPPLIES CO. (SMS)—See Agilent Technologies, Inc.; *U.S. Public*, pg. 62
SCIENTIFIC MEDICAL SYSTEMS CORP.—See Daxor Corporation; *U.S. Public*, pg. 644
SCIENTIFIC MICROSCOPES INC.; *U.S. Private*, pg. 3574
SCIENTIFIC MOLDING CORPORATION; *U.S. Private*, pg. 3574
SCIENTIFIC PEST MANAGEMENT (AUSTRALIA/PACIFIC) PTY. LTD.—See Rollins, Inc.; *U.S. Public*, pg. 1809
SCIENTIFIC PRODUCTION SERVICES—See Applied Technologies Associates; *U.S. Private*, pg. 299
SCIENTIFIC PROTEIN LABORATORIES, LLC—See Shenzhen Hepalink Pharmaceutical Group Co., Ltd.; *Int'l*, pg. 6811
SCIENTIFIC RESEARCH CORP.; *U.S. Private*, pg. 3574
SCIENTIFIC-RESEARCH INSTITUTE OF COMMUNICATION AND MANAGEMENT OJSC—See Russian Technologies State Corporation; *Int'l*, pg. 6432
SCIENTIFIC RESEARCH PRODUCTS, INC.—See The Stephan Company; *U.S. Public*, pg. 2132
SCIENTIFIC SALES, INC.; *U.S. Private*, pg. 3574
SCIENTIFIC SPRAY SERVICE, INC.—See Senske Lawn & Tree Care, Inc.; *U.S. Private*, pg. 3608
SCIENTIFIC SUPPLIES & TECHNOLOGY INTERNATIONAL INC.; *U.S. Private*, pg. 3574
SCIENTIFIC SYSTEMS INC.—See Teledyne Technologies Incorporated; *U.S. Public*, pg. 1994
SCIENTIGO, INC.; *U.S. Private*, pg. 3574

SCINEX CORPORATION

SCIENT, INC.; *U.S. Public*, pg. 1848
SCIENTURE HOLDINGS, INC.; *U.S. Public*, pg. 1849
SCIENTURE, INC.—See Scienture Holdings, Inc.; *U.S. Public*, pg. 1849
SCIENTURE, LLC—See Scienture Holdings, Inc.; *U.S. Public*, pg. 1849
SCIE-PLAS LTD.—See Harvard Bioscience, Inc.; *U.S. Public*, pg. 987
SCIE PUY DE DOME SAS—See VINCI S.A.; *Int'l*, pg. 8226
SCIERIE PARENT, INC.—See Kruger Inc.; *Int'l*, pg. 4308
SCIES B.G.R. INC.; *Int'l*, pg. 6648
SCI EUROPE I, INC.—See Starbucks Corporation; *U.S. Public*, pg. 1938
SCI FEMTO S.A.S—See Komax Holding AG; *Int'l*, pg. 4241
SCIFIT SYSTEMS, INC.—See Brunswick Corporation; *U.S. Public*, pg. 408
SCI FLIF CHATEAU LANDON—See BNP Paribas SA; *Int'l*, pg. 1092
SCI FLIF EVRY 2—See BNP Paribas SA; *Int'l*, pg. 1092
SCI FLIF LE GALLO—See BNP Paribas SA; *Int'l*, pg. 1092
SCI FLOOR COVERING, INC.—See Rainier Partners LP; *U.S. Private*, pg. 3348
SCIFLUENT COMMUNICATIONS INC—See Arsenal Capital Management LP; *U.S. Private*, pg. 338
SCIFORMIX CORPORATION—See Laboratory Corporation of America Holdings; *U.S. Public*, pg. 1287
SCIFORMIX PHILIPPINES, INC.—See Laboratory Corporation of America Holdings; *U.S. Public*, pg. 1287
SCIFORMIX TECHNOLOGIES PRIVATE LIMITED—See Laboratory Corporation of America Holdings; *U.S. Public*, pg. 1287
SCIGATE TECHNOLOGY CORP.—See BioLASCO Taiwan Co., Ltd.; *Int'l*, pg. 1038
SCIGEN (AUSTRALIA) PTY. LTD.—See Yifan Pharmaceutical Co., Ltd.; *Int'l*, pg. 8582
SCIGEN BIOPHARMA PVT LTD—See BIOTON S.A.; *Int'l*, pg. 1043
SCIGEN LTD.—See Yifan Pharmaceutical Co., Ltd.; *Int'l*, pg. 8582
SCIGINEER INC.; *Int'l*, pg. 6648
SCI GROUP INC.—See Metro Supply Chain Group Inc.; *Int'l*, pg. 4861
SCI INFORMATION SERVICE INC.; *Int'l*, pg. 6646
SCI JACQUOT—See Apollo Global Management, Inc.; *U.S. Public*, pg. 165
SCI JOINT STOCK CO.; *Int'l*, pg. 6646
SCI KORIAN LE GRAND PARC IMMOBILIER—See Clariane SE; *Int'l*, pg. 1644
SCI KORIAN LES CATALAUNES IMMOBILIER—See Clariane SE; *Int'l*, pg. 1644
SCI KORIAN MORNAY IMMOBILIER—See Clariane SE; *Int'l*, pg. 1644
SCILAB KOREA CO., LTD.—See Daihan Scientific Co., Ltd.; *Int'l*, pg. 1926
SCILABWARE LTD.—See OEP Capital Advisors, L.P.; *U.S. Private*, pg. 2999
SCIL ANIMAL CARE COMPANY FRANCE SARL—See Mars, Incorporated; *U.S. Private*, pg. 2588
SCIL ANIMAL CARE COMPANY GMBH—See Mars, Incorporated; *U.S. Private*, pg. 2589
SCIL ANIMAL CARE COMPANY SL—See Mars, Incorporated; *U.S. Private*, pg. 2588
SCIL ANIMAL CARE COMPANY—See Mars, Incorporated; *U.S. Private*, pg. 2589
SCIL ANIMAL CARE COMPANY SRL—See Mars, Incorporated; *U.S. Private*, pg. 2588
SCI LCDL—See Groupe Seche SAS; *Int'l*, pg. 3110
SCIL DIAGNOSTICS SDN. BHD.—See Mars, Incorporated; *U.S. Private*, pg. 2589
SCILDON N.V.—See Chesnara Plc; *Int'l*, pg. 1472
SCILEX HOLDING COMPANY; *U.S. Public*, pg. 1849
SCI L'HERMITAGE—See L. Possehl & Co. mbH; *Int'l*, pg. 4385
SCILLI SPECIALIZED FLATBED DIVISION, INC.—See Daseke, Inc.; *U.S. Private*, pg. 1161
SCI LOUISIANA FUNERAL SERVICES, INC.—See Service Corporation International; *U.S. Public*, pg. 1870
SCI LTD; *Int'l*, pg. 6646
SC ILVAS SA; *Int'l*, pg. 6609
SCI MANGIN—See Orange S.A.; *Int'l*, pg. 5608
SCIMEDICA GROUP; *U.S. Private*, pg. 3574
SCIMETRIKA; *U.S. Private*, pg. 3574
SCI MEZEROLLES—See Groupe Seche SAS; *Int'l*, pg. 3110
SCI MISSOURI FUNERAL SERVICES, INC.—See Service Corporation International; *U.S. Public*, pg. 1870
SC IMOTRUST S.A.; *Int'l*, pg. 6609
SCIM S.A. CONSTANTA; *Int'l*, pg. 6648
SCINAI IMMUNOTHERAPEUTICS LTD.; *Int'l*, pg. 6648
S.C. INAR S.A.; *Int'l*, pg. 6452
SCI INAV SA—See S.C Serviciile Comerciale Romane S.R.L.; *Int'l*, pg. 6449
SC INCERTRANS SA; *Int'l*, pg. 6609
S.C. INDUSTRIE MICA PRAHOVA S.A.; *Int'l*, pg. 6452
SCINETIC ENGINEERING PTE LTD—See Venture Corporation Limited; *Int'l*, pg. 8151
SCINEX CORPORATION; *Int'l*, pg. 6648

SCINOPHARM TAIWAN, LTD.; *Int'l*, pg. 6648
S.C. INSCUT BUCURESTI S.A.—See ELLAKTOR S.A.; *Int'l*, pg. 2365
S.C. INTERAGRO S.A.; *Int'l*, pg. 6452
S.C. INTERAGRO SRL—See S.C. InterAgro S.A.; *Int'l*, pg. 6452
SC INTERGAZ SRL—See S.C. InterAgro S.A.; *Int'l*, pg. 6452
S.C. INTFOR S.A.; *Int'l*, pg. 6452
SCINTILLA AG—See Robert Bosch GmbH; *Int'l*, pg. 6364
SCINTILLA COMMERCIAL & CREDIT LTD.; *Int'l*, pg. 6649
SCINTREX LTD.; *Int'l*, pg. 6649
SCINTRONIX CORPORATION LTD.; *Int'l*, pg. 6649
SCINTRONIX ENGINEERING PTE. LTD.—See Scintronix Corporation Ltd.; *Int'l*, pg. 6649
SCINTRONIX MANUFACTURING PTE. LTD.—See Scintronix Corporation Ltd.; *Int'l*, pg. 6649
SCINTRONIX TECHNOLOGY PTE. LTD.—See Scintronix Corporation Ltd.; *Int'l*, pg. 6649
SCIO AUTOMATION GMBH; *Int'l*, pg. 6649
SCIOCS COMPANY LIMITED—See Sumitomo Chemical Company, Limited; *Int'l*, pg. 7264
SCIO DIAMOND TECHNOLOGY CORP.—See Adamas One Corp.; *U.S. Public*, pg. 37
SCIO HEALTH ANALYTICS (UK) LIMITED—See ExlService Holdings, Inc.; *U.S. Public*, pg. 808
SCI OHIO FUNERAL SERVICES, INC.—See Service Corporation International; *U.S. Public*, pg. 1870
SCI OKLAHOMA FUNERAL SERVICES, INC.—See Service Corporation International; *U.S. Public*, pg. 1870
SCION GROUP LIMITED—See Mears Group PLC; *Int'l*, pg. 4763
SCION INC.; *U.S. Private*, pg. 3574
SCION MEDICAL TECHNOLOGIES, LLC; *U.S. Private*, pg. 3574
S.C. IOR S.A.; *Int'l*, pg. 6452
SCIOTO DOWNS, INC.—See Caesars Entertainment, Inc.; *U.S. Public*, pg. 420
SCI PARCOLOG ISLE D'ABEAU 3—See Assicurazioni Generali S.p.A.; *Int'l*, pg. 647
SCI PAUL CEZANNE—See Inmobiliaria Colonial SOCIMI SA; *Int'l*, pg. 3706
SCI PENNSYLVANIA FUNERAL SERVICES, INC.—See Service Corporation International; *U.S. Public*, pg. 1870
SCI PHARMTECH INC.—See Siegfried Holding AG; *Int'l*, pg. 6884
SCI PHILIPPE AUGUSTE—See Manutan International SA; *Int'l*, pg. 4680
SCIPLAY CORPORATION—See Light & Wonder, Inc.; *U.S. Public*, pg. 1314
S.C. IPROCHIM S.A. BUCURESTI; *Int'l*, pg. 6452
S.C. IPROEB S.A.; *Int'l*, pg. 6452
S.C. IPROMET S.A.; *Int'l*, pg. 6452
SCI QUAI DE NORVEGE—See Derichebourg S.A.; *Int'l*, pg. 2042
SCIQUEST, INC.—See Accel Partners L.P.; *U.S. Private*, pg. 48
SCIQUEST, INC.—See KKR & Co. Inc.; *U.S. Public*, pg. 1238
SCI REAL ESTATE INVESTMENTS, LLC; *U.S. Private*, pg. 3573
SCI-ROEV TEXAS PARTNERS LP; *U.S. Private*, pg. 3573
SCISAFE, INC.—See 1315 Capital LLC; *U.S. Private*, pg. 3
SCIS AIR SECURITY CORPORATION—See Deutsche Lufthansa AG; *Int'l*, pg. 2068
SCI SAM YVES SAINT LAURENT OF MONACO—See Kering S.A.; *Int'l*, pg. 4136
SCI SOLUTIONS INC.—See R1 RCM Inc.; *U.S. Public*, pg. 1758
S.C. ISOPOR SRL—See swisspor Management AG; *Int'l*, pg. 7374
SCI SOUTH CAROLINA FUNERAL SERVICES, INC.—See Service Corporation International; *U.S. Public*, pg. 1870
SCISPARC LTD.; *Int'l*, pg. 6649
SCI/STEELCON INC.; *U.S. Private*, pg. 3573
SCISYS DEUTSCHLAND GMBH—See CGI Inc.; *Int'l*, pg. 1434
SCISYS DEUTSCHLAND GMBH—See CGI Inc.; *Int'l*, pg. 1434
SCISYS GROUP PLC—See CGI Inc.; *Int'l*, pg. 1434
SCISYS UK HOLDING LIMITED—See CGI Inc.; *Int'l*, pg. 1434
SCISYS UK LTD.—See CGI Inc.; *Int'l*, pg. 1434
SCI TECH FARM CO., LTD.—See Nishimatsu Construction Co., Ltd.; *Int'l*, pg. 5365
SCI TECHNOLOGY, INC.—See Sanmina Corporation; *U.S. Public*, pg. 1840
SCITECH SPECIALITIES PRIVATE LIMITED—See Advanced Enzyme Technologies Limited; *Int'l*, pg. 159
SCITEK AUSTRALIA PTY LTD.; *Int'l*, pg. 6649
SCI-TEK INSTRUMENTS LTD.; *Int'l*, pg. 6646
SCI TEXAS FUNERAL SERVICES, INC.—See Service Corporation International; *U.S. Public*, pg. 1870
SCI TF1 EVENTS—See Television Francaise 1 S.A.; *Int'l*, pg. 7617
SCITI ROCS TRUST—See The Bank of Nova Scotia; *Int'l*, pg. 7617

SCITI TRUST—See The Bank of Nova Scotia; *Int'l*, pg. 7617
SCIT TRADING LIMITED—See Shoucheng Holdings Limited; *Int'l*, pg. 6860
SCITUATE MARINER—See Gannett Co., Inc.; *U.S. Public*, pg. 903
SCITUATE SOLAR I, LLC—See The AES Corporation; *U.S. Public*, pg. 2032
SCIUKER FRAMES SPA; *Int'l*, pg. 6649
SCIVAC (ISRAEL) LTD.—See VBI Vaccines Inc.; *U.S. Public*, pg. 2276
SCIVAC LTD.—See VBI Vaccines Inc.; *U.S. Public*, pg. 2276
S.C.I. VAL PROMERY—See AbbVie Inc.; *U.S. Public*, pg. 23
SCIVANTAGE, INC.—See London Stock Exchange Group plc; *Int'l*, pg. 4548
SCIVATION INC.—See Woodbolt Distribution, LLC; *U.S. Private*, pg. 4557
SCIVISION BIOTECH INC.; *Int'l*, pg. 6649
SCI WEST VIRGINIA FUNERAL SERVICES, INC.—See Service Corporation International; *U.S. Public*, pg. 1870
SCI WISCONSIN FUNERAL SERVICES, INC.—See Service Corporation International; *U.S. Public*, pg. 1870
S.C. JOHNSON AG—See S.C. Johnson & Son, Inc.; *U.S. Private*, pg. 3517
SC JOHNSON AND SON CHILE LTDA.—See S.C. Johnson & Son, Inc.; *U.S. Private*, pg. 3517
S.C. JOHNSON AND SON KENYA LIMITED—See Johnson & Johnson; *U.S. Public*, pg. 1200
S.C. JOHNSON CANADA—See S.C. Johnson & Son, Inc.; *U.S. Private*, pg. 3517
S.C. JOHNSON COMPANY LIMITED—See S.C. Johnson & Son, Inc.; *U.S. Private*, pg. 3517
S.C. JOHNSON DE CENTROAMERICA S.A.—See S.C. Johnson & Son, Inc.; *U.S. Private*, pg. 3517
S. C. JOHNSON DE PUERTO RICO, INC.—See S.C. Johnson & Son, Inc.; *U.S. Private*, pg. 3516
S. C. JOHNSON EUROPE SARL—See S.C. Johnson & Son, Inc.; *U.S. Private*, pg. 3516
S.C. JOHNSON GMBH—See S.C. Johnson & Son, Inc.; *U.S. Private*, pg. 3517
S. C. JOHNSON ISRAEL LTD.—See S.C. Johnson & Son, Inc.; *U.S. Private*, pg. 3516
S.C. JOHNSON ITALY SRL PREDSTAVNISTVO—See S.C. Johnson & Son, Inc.; *U.S. Private*, pg. 3517
S.C. JOHNSON ITALY S.R.L.—See S.C. Johnson & Son, Inc.; *U.S. Private*, pg. 3517
S.C. JOHNSON KFT.—See S.C. Johnson & Son, Inc.; *U.S. Private*, pg. 3517
S.C. JOHNSON, LTD.—See S.C. Johnson & Son, Inc.; *U.S. Private*, pg. 3517
S.C. JOHNSON LTD—See S.C. Johnson & Son, Inc.; *U.S. Private*, pg. 3517
S.C. JOHNSON MANUFACTURING (M) SDN BHD—See S.C. Johnson & Son, Inc.; *U.S. Private*, pg. 3517
S.C. JOHNSON SCANDINAVIA AB—See S.C. Johnson & Son, Inc.; *U.S. Private*, pg. 3517
S.C. JOHNSON & SON COLOMBIANA S.A.—See S.C. Johnson & Son, Inc.; *U.S. Private*, pg. 3516
S.C. JOHNSON & SON DE ARGENTINA S.A.I.C.—See S.C. Johnson & Son, Inc.; *U.S. Private*, pg. 3516
S.C. JOHNSON & SON DE VENEZUELA, C.A.—See S.C. Johnson & Son, Inc.; *U.S. Private*, pg. 3516
S.C. JOHNSON & SON (HELLAS) E.P.E.—See S.C. Johnson & Son, Inc.; *U.S. Private*, pg. 3516
S.C. JOHNSON & SON, INC.; *U.S. Private*, pg. 3515
S.C. JOHNSON & SON, INC.—See S.C. Johnson & Son, Inc.; *U.S. Private*, pg. 3517
S.C. JOHNSON & SON, INC. - WASHINGTON, DC—See S.C. Johnson & Son, Inc.; *U.S. Private*, pg. 3517
S.C. JOHNSON & SON, LTD.—See S.C. Johnson & Son, Inc.; *U.S. Private*, pg. 3517
S.C. JOHNSON & SON OF SOUTH AFRICA—See S.C. Johnson & Son, Inc.; *U.S. Private*, pg. 3516
S.C. JOHNSON & SON PTE. LIMITED—See S.C. Johnson & Son, Inc.; *U.S. Private*, pg. 3516
S.C. JOHNSON & SON PTY. LTD.—See S.C. Johnson & Son, Inc.; *U.S. Private*, pg. 3516
S C JOHNSON & SON S.A. DE C.V—See S.C. Johnson & Son, Inc.; *U.S. Private*, pg. 3516
S.C. JOHNSON & SON TAIWAN, LTD.—See S.C. Johnson & Son, Inc.; *U.S. Private*, pg. 3516
S.C. JOHNSON UKRAINE, INC—See S.C. Johnson & Son, Inc.; *U.S. Private*, pg. 3517
S.C. JOHNSON WAX BENELUX N.V./S.A.—See S.C. Johnson & Son, Inc.; *U.S. Private*, pg. 3517
S. C. JOHNSON WAX LTD.—See S.C. Johnson & Son, Inc.; *U.S. Private*, pg. 3516
SC JOHNSON WAX SRL—See S.C. Johnson & Son, Inc.; *U.S. Private*, pg. 3517
SC KEMCRISTAL SRL—See Kemira Oyj; *Int'l*, pg. 4124
SC KINGFLEX CORPORATION; *Int'l*, pg. 6609
S.C. KONECRANES SA TIMISOARA—See Konecranes Plc; *Int'l*, pg. 4252
S.C. LACTA S.A.; *Int'l*, pg. 6452
SC LACTATE NATURA SA; *Int'l*, pg. 6609
SCLAFANI WILLIAMS COURT REPORTERS, INC.—See U.S. Legal Support, Inc.; *U.S. Private*, pg. 4271

S.C. LA QUERCIA S.R.L.—See Assicurazioni Generali S.p.A.; *Int'l*, pg. 647
SC LASSELSBERGER SA—See Lasselsberger GmbH; *Int'l*, pg. 4421
SCLC, INC.—See Shoe Carnival, Inc.; *U.S. Public*, pg. 1875
SCL CONTRACTS PRIVATE LIMITED—See Siddhika Coatings Limited; *Int'l*, pg. 6883
S.C. LEGUME FRUCTE BUZAU S.A.; *Int'l*, pg. 6452
SC LEISURE GROUP LTD.—See InterContinental Hotels Group PLC; *Int'l*, pg. 3739
S.C. LIDO S.A.; *Int'l*, pg. 6452
SC LINE COLOMBIA SAS—See SC Line S.A.; *Int'l*, pg. 6609
SC LINE S.A.; *Int'l*, pg. 6609
SC LINE USA CORPORATION—See SC Line S.A.; *Int'l*, pg. 6609
SC LINE VENEZUELA—See SC Line S.A.; *Int'l*, pg. 6609
SC LINE ZONA FRANCA S.A.S.—See SC Line S.A.; *Int'l*, pg. 6609
S.C. LUCEAFARUL S.A.; *Int'l*, pg. 6452
SC MACHINARY & SERVICE CO., LTD.—See Sumitomo Corporation; *Int'l*, pg. 7270
SC MACHINERY CORP.—See Shimizu Corporation; *Int'l*, pg. 6835
SC MACHINERY & SERVICE CO., LTD.—See Sumitomo Corporation; *Int'l*, pg. 7270
S.C. MACOFIL S.A.; *Int'l*, pg. 6452
S.C. MAGAZIN UNIVERSAL MARAMURES S.A.; *Int'l*, pg. 6452
SC MAKITA EU SRL—See Makita Corporation; *Int'l*, pg. 4658
SC MANPOWER ROMANIA SRL—See ManpowerGroup Inc.; *U.S. Public*, pg. 1362
S.C. MARA COM MIXT S.A.; *Int'l*, pg. 6452
S.C. MARTENS S.A.; *Int'l*, pg. 6452
S.C.M. BLISS SAS—See Haco N.V.; *Int'l*, pg. 3205
SCM CAPITAL LIMITED—See Sterling Bank Plc; *Int'l*, pg. 7211
SCM CONSULTANTS, INC.—See Tetra Tech, Inc.; *U.S. Public*, pg. 2023
SCM DATA INC.; *U.S. Private*, pg. 3574
SCM DMA (PTY) LTD.; *Int'l*, pg. 6649
SC MECANICA CEAHLAU SA; *Int'l*, pg. 6609
S.C. MECANICA CODLEA S.A.; *Int'l*, pg. 6452
S.C. MECANICA ROTES S.A.; *Int'l*, pg. 6453
S.C. MECANICA S.A.; *Int'l*, pg. 6453
S.C. MECANICA SIGHETU S.A.; *Int'l*, pg. 6453
S.C. MECON S.A.; *Int'l*, pg. 6453
S.C. MEDIMFARM S.A.; *Int'l*, pg. 6453
S.C. MEDUMAN S.A.; *Int'l*, pg. 6453
S.C. METALICA S.A.; *Int'l*, pg. 6453
SC METAL LEMN SA; *Int'l*, pg. 6609
S.C. METAV S.A.; *Int'l*, pg. 6453
SCM FINANCIAL GROUP PTY. LTD.—See Azimut Holding SpA; *Int'l*, pg. 779
S.C. MINDO S.A.; *Int'l*, pg. 6453
SC MINERAL RESOURCES PTY. LTD.—See Sumitomo Corporation; *Int'l*, pg. 7270
SCM INSURANCE SERVICES, INC.—See TorQuest Partners Inc.; *Int'l*, pg. 7830
SCM LIFESCIENCE CO., LTD.; *Int'l*, pg. 6649
SCM METAL PRODUCTS, INC.—See Palladium Equity Partners, LLC; *U.S. Private*, pg. 3078
SCM MICROSYSTEMS INDIA PVT. LTD.—See Identiv, Inc.; *U.S. Public*, pg. 1089
SCM MICROSYSTEMS JAPAN, INC.—See Identiv, Inc.; *U.S. Public*, pg. 1089
SCM MICROSYSTEMS LTD.—See Identiv, Inc.; *U.S. Public*, pg. 1089
S.C. MOBAM S.A.; *Int'l*, pg. 6453
S.C. MOBEX S.A.; *Int'l*, pg. 6453
S.C. MOBICRASNA S.A.; *Int'l*, pg. 6453
S.C. MOBILA RADAUTI S.A.; *Int'l*, pg. 6453
S.C. MOBILEXTRA S.A.; *Int'l*, pg. 6453
S.C. MOLDOVA S.A.; *Int'l*, pg. 6453
SC MOTORS SWEDEN AB—See Sumitomo Corporation; *Int'l*, pg. 7270
SCM REF AB—See Beijer Ref AB; *Int'l*, pg. 945
SCM SINGAPORE HOLDINGS PTE. LTD.—See Caterpillar, Inc.; *U.S. Public*, pg. 453
SCM SP. Z O.O.—See AmRest Holdings SE; *Int'l*, pg. 437
SCM STIFTUNG CHRISTLICHE MEDIEN; *Int'l*, pg. 6649
SCM STRATEGIC CAPITAL MANAGEMENT ASIA LTD—See Marsh & McLennan Companies, Inc.; *U.S. Public*, pg. 1388
SCM SUOMI OY—See Schibsted ASA; *Int'l*, pg. 6617
SCM-VERBOOM—See Groupe Gorge S.A.; *Int'l*, pg. 3103
SC NAPOCHIM SA; *Int'l*, pg. 6609
S.C. NATURA QUATTUOR ENERGIA HOLDINGS S.A.; *Int'l*, pg. 6453
SC NEDSENSE SRL—See Constellation Software Inc.; *Int'l*, pg. 1773
SCNEITEK CORPORATION—See Zen Voce Corporation; *Int'l*, pg. 8632
S.C. NEPTUN S.A.; *Int'l*, pg. 6453
S.C. NESS ROMANIA S.R.L—See KKR & Co. Inc.; *U.S. Public*, pg. 1261

SC NEUSOFT EDC SRL—See Neusoft Corporation; *Int'l*, pg. 5220
S.C NEW ENERGY TECHNOLOGY CORPORATION; *Int'l*, pg. 6449
S.C. NIMB CONSMETAL S.R.L.; *Int'l*, pg. 6453
SC NITROPOROS SRL—See S.C. InterAgro S.A.; *Int'l*, pg. 6452
S.C.NORD DRIVESYSTEMS S.R.L.—See Getriebebau NORD GmbH & Co. KG; *Int'l*, pg. 2953
SC NORMARK SPORT ROMANIA S.R.L.—See Rapala VMC Oyj; *Int'l*, pg. 6210
SC NOVA TEXTILE BUMBAC SRL—See S.C Serviciile Comerciale Romane S.R.L.; *Int'l*, pg. 6449
SCN TRUPHONE SL—See Truphone Limited; *Int'l*, pg. 7944
SCN UK GROUP LTD.—See Addtech AB; *Int'l*, pg. 135
S.C. NUTRICOM S.A.; *Int'l*, pg. 6453
S.C. NUTRIENTUL S.A.; *Int'l*, pg. 6453
SCO - AREX HOLDING GES.M.B.H.—See Studen & Co. Holding GmbH; *Int'l*, pg. 7244
SCOBEE FOODS INCORPORATED; *U.S. Private*, pg. 3575
SCOBEY MOVING & STORAGE LTD; *U.S. Private*, pg. 3575
SCODER; *Int'l*, pg. 6649
SCODIX B.V.—See Scodix Ltd.; *Int'l*, pg. 6649
SCODIX INC.—See Scodix Ltd.; *Int'l*, pg. 6649
SCODIX LTD.; *Int'l*, pg. 6649
SCO FAMILY OF SERVICES; *U.S. Private*, pg. 3574
SCOGAT SA SOCIETE POUR LA CONSTRUCTION DU GAZODUC TRANST—See Eni S.p.A.; *Int'l*, pg. 2437
SCOLAREST - ZARIZENI SKOLNIHO STRAVOVANI SPOL. S.R.O—See Compass Group PLC; *Int'l*, pg. 1752
SCOLARI'S WAREHOUSE MARKETS; *U.S. Private*, pg. 3575
SCOLA; *U.S. Private*, pg. 3575
SCOLDING LOCKS CORP; *U.S. Private*, pg. 3575
S-COM A/S—See TKH Group N.V.; *Int'l*, pg. 7764
SCOMAT LIMITEE—See Ireland Blyth Limited; *Int'l*, pg. 3807
SCOM D.O.O.; *Int'l*, pg. 6649
SCOMI ANTICOR S.A.S—See Vink + Co GmbH Handelsgesellschaft und Co KG; *Int'l*, pg. 8241
SCOMI ENERGY SERVICES BERHAD—See Scomi Group Berhad; *Int'l*, pg. 6649
SCOMI EQUIPMENT INC.—See Scomi Group Berhad; *Int'l*, pg. 6650
SCOMI GROUP BERHAD; *Int'l*, pg. 6649
SCOMI MARINE SERVICES PTE LTD—See Scomi Group Berhad; *Int'l*, pg. 6650
SCOMI OILTOOLS SDN. BHD.—See Scomi Group Berhad; *Int'l*, pg. 6650
SCOMI SOSMA SDN. BHD.—See Scomi Group Berhad; *Int'l*, pg. 6650
S-COM SYSTEM (S) PTE LTD—See Trek 2000 International Ltd; *Int'l*, pg. 7910
S.C. OMV PETROM S.A.—See OMV Aktiengesellschaft; *Int'l*, pg. 5568
SC OMV ROMANIA MINERALOEL S.R.L.—See OMV Aktiengesellschaft; *Int'l*, pg. 5570
SCONCE SOLUTIONS PTE. LTD.; *U.S. Private*, pg. 3575
S-CONNECT CO., LTD.; *Int'l*, pg. 6446
SCOOBEE DAY GARMENTS (INDIA) LIMITED; *Int'l*, pg. 6650
SCOOBEEZ GLOBAL, INC.; *U.S. Public*, pg. 1849
SCOOP DESIGNS LTD—See IG Design Group Plc; *Int'l*, pg. 3600
SCOOP MEDIA AND COMMUNICATION COMPANY O.M.C.—See United Development Company PSC; *Int'l*, pg. 8066
SCOOP NYC; *U.S. Private*, pg. 3575
SCOOTERS INDIA LIMITED; *Int'l*, pg. 6650
SCOOTERS PIZZA (PTY) LTD.—See Luxe Holdings Limited; *Int'l*, pg. 4588
SCOOT—See BT Group plc; *Int'l*, pg. 1203
SCO-PAK S.A.; *Int'l*, pg. 6649
SCOPE CARBON CORP; *Int'l*, pg. 6650
SCOPE EDUCATION SERVICES; *U.S. Private*, pg. 3575
SCOPE E-KNOWLEDGE CENTER PVT LTD.—See Partners Group Holding AG; *Int'l*, pg. 5750
SCOPE ENERGY RESOURCES, INC.—See ReConserve, Inc.; *U.S. Private*, pg. 3371
SCOPE FLUIDICS SPOLKA AKCYJNA; *Int'l*, pg. 6650
SCOPE IMPORTS INC.; *U.S. Private*, pg. 3575
SCOPE INDUSTRIES BERHAD; *Int'l*, pg. 6650
SCOPE LEASING, INC.—See Park National Corporation; *U.S. Public*, pg. 1638
SCOPE MANUFACTURERS (M) SDN. BHD.—See Scope Industries Berhad; *Int'l*, pg. 6650
SCOPE MEDICAL CO.—See Mauna Kea Technologies SA; *Int'l*, pg. 4732
SCOPE METALS GROUP LTD.; *Int'l*, pg. 6650
SCOPE ORTHOTICS & PROSTHETICS, INC.—See Patient Square Capital, L.P.; *U.S. Private*, pg. 3107
SCOPE PROPERTIES, INC.—See ReConserve, Inc.; *U.S. Private*, pg. 3371
SCOPE SERVICES INC.; *U.S. Private*, pg. 3575

SCOPE SEVEN LLC—See ZOO Digital Group plc; *Int'l*, pg. 8689
SCOPE TECHNOLOGY CO., LTD.—See Nichidenbo Corporation; *Int'l*, pg. 5268
SCOPEWORKS ASIA, INC.—See Paxys, Inc.; *Int'l*, pg. 5763
SCOPIA CAPITAL MANAGEMENT LP; *U.S. Private*, pg. 3575
SCOPIS GMBH—See Stryker Corporation; *U.S. Public*, pg. 1956
SCOPPECHIO; *U.S. Private*, pg. 3575
SCOPRO OPTICAL CO., INC.—See Asia Optical Co., Inc.; *Int'l*, pg. 613
SCOPUS BIOPHARMA INC.; *U.S. Public*, pg. 1849
SCOPUS-OMNIBADGES S.A.S.—See Amano Corporation; *Int'l*, pg. 411
SCOPUS TECNOLOGIA LTDA—See Banco Bradesco S.A.; *Int'l*, pg. 819
SCOR AFRICA LTD—See SCOR SE; *Int'l*, pg. 6650
SCOR ASIA HOUSE LIMITED PARTNERSHIP—See SCOR SE; *Int'l*, pg. 6650
SCOR BRASIL LTDA—See SCOR SE; *Int'l*, pg. 6650
SCOR CANADA REINSURANCE COMPANY—See SCOR SE; *Int'l*, pg. 6650
SCORE ASSOCIATION; *U.S. Private*, pg. 3575
SCOREBIG.COM—See TicketNetwork, Inc.; *U.S. Private*, pg. 4167
S-CORE CORPORATION—See Noritz Corporation; *Int'l*, pg. 5430
SCORECO - VALORIZACAO DE RESIDUOS LDA—See Camargo Correa S.A.; *Int'l*, pg. 1268
SCORELOOP AG—See BlackBerry Limited; *Int'l*, pg. 1060
SCOREL SAS—See VINCI S.A.; *Int'l*, pg. 8227
SCORE MEDIA AND GAMING INC.—See PENN Entertainment, Inc.; *U.S. Public*, pg. 1662
SCORES HOLDING COMPANY, INC.; *U.S. Public*, pg. 1849
SCORES LICENSING CORP.—See Scores Holding Company, Inc.; *U.S. Public*, pg. 1849
SCOREX SCANDINAVIA—See Experian plc; *Int'l*, pg. 2587
SCOREX (UK) LIMITED—See Experian plc; *Int'l*, pg. 2587
SC ORGANIC CHEMICAL CO., LTD. - ISHIZU FACTORY—See Sakai Chemical Industry Co., Ltd.; *Int'l*, pg. 6486
SC ORGANIC CHEMICAL CO., LTD.—See Sakai Chemical Industry Co., Ltd.; *Int'l*, pg. 6486
SCOR GLOBAL INVESTMENT SE—See SCOR SE; *Int'l*, pg. 6650
SCOR GLOBAL LIFE AUSTRALIA PTY LTD.—See SCOR SE; *Int'l*, pg. 6651
SCOR GLOBAL LIFE CHILE LTDA.—See SCOR SE; *Int'l*, pg. 6651
SCOR GLOBAL LIFE REINSURANCE COMPANY OF AMERICA—See SCOR SE; *Int'l*, pg. 6651
SCOR GLOBAL LIFE REINSURANCE COMPANY OF TEXAS—See SCOR SE; *Int'l*, pg. 6651
SCOR GLOBAL LIFE REINSURANCE IRELAND LTD.—See SCOR SE; *Int'l*, pg. 6651
SCOR GLOBAL LIFE REINSURANCE LTD.—See SCOR SE; *Int'l*, pg. 6651
SCOR GLOBAL LIFE RUCKVERSICHERUNG SCHWEIZ AG—See SCOR SE; *Int'l*, pg. 6651
SCOR GLOBAL LIFE—See SCOR SE; *Int'l*, pg. 6650
SCOR GLOBAL P&C DEUTSCHLAND—See SCOR SE; *Int'l*, pg. 6651
SCOR GLOBAL P&C—See SCOR SE; *Int'l*, pg. 6651
SCOR GLOBAL SOUTH AFRICA (PTY) LTD.—See SCOR SE; *Int'l*, pg. 6651
SCOR HOLDING (SWITZERLAND) LTD—See SCOR SE; *Int'l*, pg. 6651
SCOR ITALIA RIASSICURAZIONI S.P.A.—See SCOR SE; *Int'l*, pg. 6651
SC ORIZONT TURISM SA; *Int'l*, pg. 6609
SCOR PERESTRAKHOVANIYE O.O.O.—See SCOR SE; *Int'l*, pg. 6651
SCORPEX, INC.; *U.S. Private*, pg. 3575
SCORPIO EAST ENTERTAINMENT PTE LTD—See KOP Limited; *Int'l*, pg. 4279
SCORPIO EAST MULTIMEDIA PTE LTD—See KOP Limited; *Int'l*, pg. 4279
SCORPIO GOLD CORPORATION; *Int'l*, pg. 6651
SCORPION DESIGN LLC; *U.S. Private*, pg. 3575
SCORPION MINERALS LIMITED; *Int'l*, pg. 6651
SCORPION PROTECTIVE COATINGS, INC.; *U.S. Private*, pg. 3575
SCORPIO PARTNERSHIP LIMITED—See Aon plc; *Int'l*, pg. 495
SCORPIO TANKERS INC.; *Int'l*, pg. 6651
SCORPIUS HOLDINGS, INC.; *U.S. Public*, pg. 1849
SCOR REINSURANCE ASIA-PACIFIC PTE LTD.—See SCOR SE; *Int'l*, pg. 6651
SCOR REINSURANCE CO. (ASIA) LTD.—See SCOR SE; *Int'l*, pg. 6651
SCOR REINSURANCE COMPANY—See SCOR SE; *Int'l*, pg. 6651
SCOR REPRESENTACIONES S.A.—See SCOR SE; *Int'l*, pg. 6651
SCORR MARKETING; *U.S. Private*, pg. 3575

SCOR SERVICES ASIA PACIFIC PTE LTD—See SCOR SE; *Int'l*, pg. 6651
SCOR SERVICES BELUX SPRL—See SCOR SE; *Int'l*, pg. 6651
SCOR SERVICES JAPAN CO. LTD.—See SCOR SE; *Int'l*, pg. 6651
SCOR SERVICES SWITZERLAND AG—See SCOR SE; *Int'l*, pg. 6651
SCOR SERVICES (UK) LTD—See SCOR SE; *Int'l*, pg. 6651
SCOR SE; *Int'l*, pg. 6650
SCOR SWITZERLAND AG—See SCOR SE; *Int'l*, pg. 6651
SCOR UK COMPANY LTD.—See SCOR SE; *Int'l*, pg. 6651
SCOR UNDERWRITING LTD.—See SCOR SE; *Int'l*, pg. 6651
SCOR U.S. CORPORATION—See SCOR SE; *Int'l*, pg. 6651
SCORVALIA SAS—See Vinci S.A.; *Int'l*, pg. 8227
SCORVALIS SAS—See VINCI S.A.; *Int'l*, pg. 8227
SCOTASH LIMITED—See CRH plc; *Int'l*, pg. 1848
SCOTASH LIMITED—See Iberdrola, S.A.; *Int'l*, pg. 3573
SCOTBILT HOMES, INC.—See Champion Homes, Inc.; *U.S. Public*, pg. 477
SCOTCH CREEK VENTURES, INC.; *Int'l*, pg. 6651
SCOTCH & GULF LUMBER, LLC; *U.S. Private*, pg. 3576
THE SCOTCH MALT WHISKY SOCIETY LIMITED—See The Artisanal Spirits Company Plc; *Int'l*, pg. 7614
THE SCOTCH MALT WHISKY SOCIETY LTD—See LVMH Moet Hennessy Louis Vuitton SE; *Int'l*, pg. 4600
SCOTCHMAN CREDIT CORP.—See Krofam Inc.; *U.S. Private*, pg. 2353
SCOTCHMAN INDUSTRIES, INC.—See Krofam Inc.; *U.S. Private*, pg. 2353
SCOTCH PLYWOOD COMPANY OF ALABAMA; *U.S. Private*, pg. 3576
SCOTCH & SODA B.V.—See Bluestar Alliance LLC; *U.S. Private*, pg. 598
S.C. OTELINOX S.A.—See Samsung BioLogics Co., Ltd.; *Int'l*, pg. 6510
SCOT FORGE COMPANY INC.; *U.S. Private*, pg. 3576
SCOTGEMS PLC; *Int'l*, pg. 6651
SCOTGOLD RESOURCES LIMITED - SCOTLAND—See Scotgold Resources Limited; *Int'l*, pg. 6651
SCOTGOLD RESOURCES LIMITED; *Int'l*, pg. 6651
SCOTGRAIN AGRICULTURE LTD.—See GrainCorp Limited; *Int'l*, pg. 3052
SCOTIA ASSET MANAGEMENT L.P.—See The Bank of Nova Scotia; *Int'l*, pg. 7617
SCOTIABANC INC.—See The Bank of Nova Scotia; *Int'l*, pg. 7618
SCOTIABANK AZUL S.A.—See The Bank of Nova Scotia; *Int'l*, pg. 7618
SCOTIABANK (BAHAMAS) LTD.—See The Bank of Nova Scotia; *Int'l*, pg. 7619
SCOTIABANK (BELIZE) LTD.—See The Bank of Nova Scotia; *Int'l*, pg. 7618
SCOTIABANK BRASIL S.A. BANCO MULTIPLO—See The Bank of Nova Scotia; *Int'l*, pg. 7618
SCOTIABANK CARIBBEAN TREASURY LIMITED—See The Bank of Nova Scotia; *Int'l*, pg. 7619
SCOTIABANK CHILE S.A.—See The Bank of Nova Scotia; *Int'l*, pg. 7618
SCOTIABANK EUROPE PLC—See The Bank of Nova Scotia; *Int'l*, pg. 7618
SCOTIABANK (HONG KONG) LIMITED—See The Bank of Nova Scotia; *Int'l*, pg. 7618
SCOTIABANK INTERNATIONAL LIMITED—See The Bank of Nova Scotia; *Int'l*, pg. 7618
SCOTIABANK (IRELAND) DESIGNATED ACTIVITY COMPANY—See The Bank of Nova Scotia; *Int'l*, pg. 7618
SCOTIABANK PERU HOLDING S.A.—See The Bank of Nova Scotia; *Int'l*, pg. 7618
SCOTIABANK PERU S.A.—See The Bank of Nova Scotia; *Int'l*, pg. 7618
SCOTIABANK REPUBLICA DOMINICANA, S.A.—See The Bank of Nova Scotia; *Int'l*, pg. 7619
SCOTIABANK TRINIDAD & TOBAGO LIMITED—See The Bank of Nova Scotia; *Int'l*, pg. 7619
SCOTIABANK & TRUST (CAYMAN) LIMITED—See The Bank of Nova Scotia; *Int'l*, pg. 7619
SCOTIABANK TURKS & CAICOS LIMITED—See The Bank of Nova Scotia; *Int'l*, pg. 7619
SCOTIABANK URUGUAY S.A.—See The Bank of Nova Scotia; *Int'l*, pg. 7619
SCOTIA CAPITAL (EUROPE) LIMITED—See The Bank of Nova Scotia; *Int'l*, pg. 7617
SCOTIA CAPITAL INC.—See The Bank of Nova Scotia; *Int'l*, pg. 7617
SCOTIA CAPITAL (USA) INC. - HOUSTON—See The Bank of Nova Scotia; *Int'l*, pg. 7617
SCOTIA CAPITAL (USA) INC. - SAN FRANCISCO—See The Bank of Nova Scotia; *Int'l*, pg. 7617
SCOTIA CAPITAL (USA) INC.—See The Bank of Nova Scotia; *Int'l*, pg. 7617
SCOTIA CHRYSLER INC.; *Int'l*, pg. 6651
SCOTIA DEALER ADVANTAGE INC.—See The Bank of Nova Scotia; *Int'l*, pg. 7617

SCOTIA CHRYSLER INC.

SCOTIA EL SALVADOR, S.A.—See The Bank of Nova Scotia; *Int'l*, pg. 7617
SCOTIA FUELS LTD.; *Int'l*, pg. 6652
SCOTIA GENERAL INSURANCE COMPANY—See The Bank of Nova Scotia; *Int'l*, pg. 7617
SCOTIA GROUP JAMAICA LTD.—See The Bank of Nova Scotia; *Int'l*, pg. 7617
SCOTIA HOLDINGS (US) INC.—See The Bank of Nova Scotia; *Int'l*, pg. 7618
SCOTIA INDUSTRIAL PARK, INC.—See Galesi Group; *U.S. Private*, pg. 1637
SCOTIA INSURANCE (BARBADOS) LIMITED—See The Bank of Nova Scotia; *Int'l*, pg. 7618
SCOTIA INTERNATIONAL LIMITED—See The Bank of Nova Scotia; *Int'l*, pg. 7618
SCOTIA INVERLAT CASA DE BOLSA—See The Bank of Nova Scotia; *Int'l*, pg. 7617
SCOTIA JAMAICA BUILDING SOCIETY—See The Bank of Nova Scotia; *Int'l*, pg. 7618
SCOTIA JAMAICA FINANCIAL SERVICES LIMITED—See The Bank of Nova Scotia; *Int'l*, pg. 7618
SCOTIA JAMAICA GENERAL INSURANCE BROKERS LIMITED—See The Bank of Nova Scotia; *Int'l*, pg. 7618
SCOTIA JAMAICA INVESTMENT MANAGEMENT LIMITED—See The Bank of Nova Scotia; *Int'l*, pg. 7618
SCOTIA JAMAICA LIFE INSURANCE COMPANY LIMITED—See The Bank of Nova Scotia; *Int'l*, pg. 7618
SCOTIA LIFE INSURANCE COMPANY—See The Bank of Nova Scotia; *Int'l*, pg. 7618
SCOTIA MANAGED COMPANIES ADMINISTRATION INC.—See The Bank of Nova Scotia; *Int'l*, pg. 7617
SCOTIAMCLEOD DIRECT INVESTING—See The Bank of Nova Scotia; *Int'l*, pg. 7618
SCOTIAMOCATTA DEPOSITORY CORPORATION—See The Bank of Nova Scotia; *Int'l*, pg. 7618
SCOTIAMOCATTA LIMITED—See The Bank of Nova Scotia; *Int'l*, pg. 7618
SCOTIA MORTGAGE CORPORATION—See The Bank of Nova Scotia; *Int'l*, pg. 7618
SCOTIAN GOLD COOPERATIVE LIMITED; *Int'l*, pg. 6652
SCOTIA REALTY LIMITED—See The Bank of Nova Scotia; *Int'l*, pg. 7619
SCOTIA SECURITIES, INC.—See The Bank of Nova Scotia; *Int'l*, pg. 7618
SCOTIATRUST (HONG KONG) LIMITED—See The Bank of Nova Scotia; *Int'l*, pg. 7618
SCOTIATRUST & MERCHANT BANK TRINIDAD & TOBAGO LIMITED—See The Bank of Nova Scotia; *Int'l*, pg. 7619
SCOTIA WATEROUS—See The Bank of Nova Scotia; *Int'l*, pg. 7617
SCOTIA WATEROUS USA INC.—See The Bank of Nova Scotia; *Int'l*, pg. 7617
SCOT INDUSTRIES INC.; *U.S. Private*, pg. 3576
SCOT LABORATORIES—See Berkshire Hathaway Inc.; *U.S. Public*, pg. 300
SCOTLAND EUROPA LIMITED—See Scottish Enterprise; *Int'l*, pg. 6652
SCOTLAND MANUFACTURING CO., INC.—See Reserve Group Management Company; *U.S. Private*, pg. 3404
SCOTLAND TRANSERV—See Balfour Beatty plc; *Int'l*, pg. 808
SCOTLAND TRANSERV—See Kier Group plc; *Int'l*, pg. 4159
SCOTLOAD LTD—See James Fisher & Sons Public Limited Company; *Int'l*, pg. 3876
SCOTMIN NUTRITION LIMITED—See Carr's Group PLC; *Int'l*, pg. 1343
SCOTOIL GROUP PLC; *Int'l*, pg. 6652
SCOTOIL SERVICES LIMITED—See Scotoil Group plc; *Int'l*, pg. 6652
SCOTSBURN CO-OPERATIVE SERVICES LIMITED; *Int'l*, pg. 6652
SCOTSCO INC.; *U.S. Private*, pg. 3576
SCOTSMAN GROUP LLC—See Ali Holding S.r.l; *Int'l*, pg. 321
SCOTSMAN ICE SYSTEMS (SHANGHAI) CO., LTD.—See Ali Holding S.r.l; *Int'l*, pg. 321
SCOTSMAN INDUSTRIES, INC.—See Ali Holding S.r.l; *Int'l*, pg. 321
SCOTSMAN INDUSTRIES (S) PTE LTD.—See Ali Holding S.r.l; *Int'l*, pg. 321
THE SCOTSMAN PUBLICATIONS LTD—See JPIMedia Holdings Limited; *Int'l*, pg. 4007
SCOTT ACCEPTANCE CORPORATION—See The Randall Group Inc.; *U.S. Private*, pg. 4102
SCOTT A. GOFFSTEIN & ASSOCIATES, LLP—See AAFCPAs; *U.S. Private*, pg. 31
SCOTT AND MURPHY, INC.; *U.S. Private*, pg. 3576
SCOTT BRASS, INC.—See Sun Capital Partners, Inc.; *U.S. Private*, pg. 3860
SCOTT BRIDGE COMPANY INC.; *U.S. Private*, pg. 3576
SCOTT & BROAD PTY LTD—See Steadfast Group Limited; *Int'l*, pg. 7187
SCOTT BROWN MEDIA GROUP; *U.S. Private*, pg. 3576

SCOTT CABLE COMMUNICATIONS; *U.S. Private*, pg. 3576
THE SCOTTCARE CORPORATION—See Berkshire Hathaway Inc.; *U.S. Public*, pg. 300
SCOTT (CHINA) CO., LTD.—See Scott Sports SA; *Int'l*, pg. 6652
SCOTT CITRUS MANAGEMENT, INC.; *U.S. Private*, pg. 3576
SCOTT CLARK HONDA; *U.S. Private*, pg. 3576
SCOTT-CLARKS TOYOTA CITY INC.; *U.S. Private*, pg. 3577
SCOTT COOPERATIVE ASSOCIATION; *U.S. Private*, pg. 3576
SCOTT CORPORATION LIMITED—See K&S Corporation Limited; *Int'l*, pg. 4039
SCOTT COUNTY HMA, LLC—See Community Health Systems, Inc.; *U.S. Public*, pg. 556
SCOTT COUNTY READY MIX INC.—See WG Block Co.; *U.S. Private*, pg. 4503
SCOTT CREDIT UNION; *U.S. Private*, pg. 3576
SCOTT CRUMP TOYOTA SCION, INC.; *U.S. Private*, pg. 3576
SCOTT DUNN LIMITED—See Flight Centre Travel Group Limited; *Int'l*, pg. 2706
SCOTT DUNN USA—See Flight Centre Travel Group Limited; *Int'l*, pg. 2706
SCOTT ELECTRIC COMPANY; *U.S. Private*, pg. 3576
SCOTTEL VOICE & DATA, INC.—See Black Box Limited; *Int'l*, pg. 1058
SCOTT ENERGY CO., INC.; *U.S. Private*, pg. 3576
SCOTT & ENGLISH ENERGY PTE. LTD.—See Swissco Holdings Limited; *Int'l*, pg. 7373
SCOTT EQUIPMENT COMPANY, LLC; *U.S. Private*, pg. 3576
SCOTT EQUIPMENT CO.; *U.S. Private*, pg. 3576
SCOTT EQUIPMENT INCORPORATED; *U.S. Private*, pg. 3576
SCOTT EQUIPMENT, LLC—See EVI Industries, Inc.; *U.S. Public*, pg. 803
SCOTT EQUITY EXCHANGE CO.; *U.S. Private*, pg. 3576
SCOTTEVEST INC.; *U.S. Private*, pg. 3578
SCOTT EXTERMINATING CO—See Bug Busters USA, Inc.; *U.S. Private*, pg. 681
SCOTT FABTECH—See JBS S.A.; *Int'l*, pg. 3918
SCOTT FELDER HOMES, LLC—See BR Homebuilding Group, L.P.; *U.S. Private*, pg. 630
SCOTT FETZER COMPANY—See Berkshire Hathaway Inc.; *U.S. Public*, pg. 299
SCOTT FISCHER ENTERPRISES LLC; *U.S. Private*, pg. 3577
SCOTT-GALLAHER, INC.—See Highway Equipment Company; *U.S. Private*, pg. 1942
SCOTT-GROSS COMPANY, INC.; *U.S. Private*, pg. 3577
SCOTT GROUP CUSTOM CARPETS, INC.; *U.S. Private*, pg. 3577
SCOTT HEALTH & SAFETY LIMITED—See 3M Company; *U.S. Public*, pg. 8
SCOTT HEALTH & SAFETY LIMITED—See Johnson Controls International plc; *Int'l*, pg. 3987
SCOTT HILL ACQUISITION CORPORATION; *U.S. Private*, pg. 3577
SCOTTIE RESOURCES CORP.; *Int'l*, pg. 6652
SCOTTIE'S BUILDING SERVICES, LLC—See Valcourt Building Services LLC; *U.S. Private*, pg. 4330
SCOTT INDUSTRIAL SYSTEMS INC.; *U.S. Private*, pg. 3577
SCOTT INDUSTRIES LLC; *U.S. Private*, pg. 3577
SCOTTISH AGRICULTURAL INDUSTRIES LIMITED—See Akzo Nobel N.V.; *Int'l*, pg. 275
SCOTTISH AMERICAN CAPITAL LLC; *U.S. Private*, pg. 3578
SCOTTISH AMERICAN INSURANCE GENERAL AGENCY, INC.; *U.S. Private*, pg. 3578
THE SCOTTISH AMERICAN INVESTMENT COMPANY PLC; *Int'l*, pg. 7681
SCOTTISH BORDERS EDUCATION PARTNERSHIP HOLDINGS LTD.—See Bilfinger SE; *Int'l*, pg. 1028
SCOTTISH BORDERS EDUCATION PARTNERSHIP LTD.—See Bilfinger SE; *Int'l*, pg. 1028
SCOTTISH BUILDING SOCIETY; *Int'l*, pg. 6652
SCOTTISH CITYLINK COACHES LIMITED—See ComfortDelGro Corporation Limited; *Int'l*, pg. 1713
SCOTTISH DAILY RECORD & SUNDAY MAIL LTD.—See Reach PLC; *Int'l*, pg. 6231
SCOTTISH DEVELOPMENT INTERNATIONAL—See Scottish Enterprise; *Int'l*, pg. 6653
SCOTTISH DEVELOPMENT INTERNATIONAL—See Scottish Enterprise; *Int'l*, pg. 6653
SCOTTISH DEVELOPMENT INTERNATIONAL—See Scottish Enterprise; *Int'l*, pg. 6652
SCOTTISH ENTERPRISE AYRSHIRE LTD.—See Scottish Enterprise; *Int'l*, pg. 6653
SCOTTISH ENTERPRISE BORDERS LTD.—See Scottish Enterprise; *Int'l*, pg. 6653
SCOTTISH ENTERPRISE DUMFRIES & GALLOWAY LTD.—See Scottish Enterprise; *Int'l*, pg. 6653
SCOTTISH ENTERPRISE DUNBARTONSHIRE LTD.—See Scottish Enterprise; *Int'l*, pg. 6653

CORPORATE AFFILIATIONS

SCOTTISH ENTERPRISE EDINBURGH & LOTHIAN LTD.—See Scottish Enterprise; *Int'l*, pg. 6653
SCOTTISH ENTERPRISE FIFE LTD.—See Scottish Enterprise; *Int'l*, pg. 6653
SCOTTISH ENTERPRISE FORTH VALLEY LTD.—See Scottish Enterprise; *Int'l*, pg. 6653
SCOTTISH ENTERPRISE GLASGOW LTD.—See Scottish Enterprise; *Int'l*, pg. 6653
SCOTTISH ENTERPRISE GRAMPIAN LTD.—See Scottish Enterprise; *Int'l*, pg. 6653
SCOTTISH ENTERPRISE RENFREWSHIRE LTD.—See Scottish Enterprise; *Int'l*, pg. 6653
SCOTTISH ENTERPRISE; *Int'l*, pg. 6652
SCOTTISH ENTERPRISE TAYSIDE LTD.—See Scottish Enterprise; *Int'l*, pg. 6653
SCOTTISH EQUITY PARTNERS LLP; *Int'l*, pg. 6653
SCOTTISH FOOD SYSTEMS INC.—See ZV Pate Inc.; *U.S. Private*, pg. 4610
SCOTTISH HYDRO ELECTRIC POWER DISTRIBUTION LTD—See SSE Plc; *Int'l*, pg. 7156
SCOTTISH HYDRO ELECTRIC TRANSMISSION LTD—See SSE Plc; *Int'l*, pg. 7156
SCOTTISH LEATHER GROUP LTD.; *Int'l*, pg. 6653
SCOTTISH MORTGAGE INVESTMENT TRUST PLC; *Int'l*, pg. 6653
SCOTTISH MUTUAL INTERNATIONAL LTD.—See Phoenix Group Holdings PLC; *Int'l*, pg. 5851
SCOTTISH & NEWCASTLE PUB COMPANY—See L'Arche Green N.V.; *Int'l*, pg. 4377
THE SCOTTISH ORIENTAL SMALLER COMPANIES TRUST PLC; *Int'l*, pg. 7681
SCOTTISH PACIFIC BUSINESS FINANCE PTY. LIMITED—See Balmain Corp.; *Int'l*, pg. 810
SCOTTISHPOWER ENERGY MANAGEMENT, LTD.—See Iberdrola, S.A.; *Int'l*, pg. 3573
SCOTTISHPOWER ENERGY RETAIL LTD—See Iberdrola, S.A.; *Int'l*, pg. 3573
SCOTTISHPOWER FINANCIAL SERVICES, INC.—See Iberdrola, S.A.; *Int'l*, pg. 3574
SCOTTISHPOWER GROUP HOLDINGS COMPANY—See Iberdrola, S.A.; *Int'l*, pg. 3573
SCOTTISHPOWER NA 1, LTD.—See Iberdrola, S.A.; *Int'l*, pg. 3574
SCOTTISHPOWER OVERSEAS HOLDINGS, LTD.—See Iberdrola, S.A.; *Int'l*, pg. 3574
SCOTTISH POWER PLC—See Iberdrola, S.A.; *Int'l*, pg. 3573
SCOTTISH POWER RENEWABLE ENERGY, LTD.—See Iberdrola, S.A.; *Int'l*, pg. 3573
SCOTTISH POWER RENEWABLE UK, LTD.—See Iberdrola, S.A.; *Int'l*, pg. 3573
SCOTTISHPOWER SP ENERGYNETWORKS—See Iberdrola, S.A.; *Int'l*, pg. 3574
SCOTTISH POWER UK GROUP, LTD.—See Iberdrola, S.A.; *Int'l*, pg. 3573
SCOTTISH POWER UK HOLDINGS, LTD.—See Iberdrola, S.A.; *Int'l*, pg. 3573
THE SCOTTISH SALMON COMPANY LIMITED—See P/F Bakkafrost; *Int'l*, pg. 5683
THE SCOTTISH SALMON COMPANY PLC—See P/F Bakkafrost; *Int'l*, pg. 5683
SCOTTISH STEM CELL NETWORK LIMITED—See Scottish Enterprise; *Int'l*, pg. 6653
SCOTTISH & UNIVERSAL NEWSPAPERS LTD—See Reach PLC; *Int'l*, pg. 6231
SCOTTISH WATER BUSINESS STREAM LIMITED; *Int'l*, pg. 6653
SCOTTISH WIDOWS FUND & LIFE ASSURANCE SOCIETY—See Lloyds Banking Group plc; *Int'l*, pg. 4538
SCOTTISH WIDOWS PLC—See Lloyds Banking Group plc; *Int'l*, pg. 4538
SCOTTISH WIDOWS SCHRODER PERSONAL WEALTH LTD.—See Lloyds Banking Group plc; *Int'l*, pg. 4538
SCOTTISH & YORK INSURANCE CO. LIMITED—See Aviva plc; *Int'l*, pg. 745
SCOTT ITALIA S.R.L.—See Scott Sports SA; *Int'l*, pg. 6652
SCOTT JAPAN INC.—See Scott Sports SA; *Int'l*, pg. 6652
SCOTT KOREA LTD.—See Scott Sports SA; *Int'l*, pg. 6652
SCOTT LOGISTICS CORP.—See ABRY Partners, LLC; *U.S. Private*, pg. 41
SCOTT LUMBER COMPANY; *U.S. Private*, pg. 3577
SCOTT M & A CORPORATION; *U.S. Private*, pg. 3577
SCOTT-MCRAE ADVERTISING INC.—See Scott-McRae Automotive Group Inc.; *U.S. Private*, pg. 3578
SCOTT-MCRAE AUTOMOTIVE GROUP INC.; *U.S. Private*, pg. 3577
SCOTT-MCRAE INVESTMENTS INC.—See Scott-McRae Automotive Group Inc.; *U.S. Private*, pg. 3578
SCOTT-MCRAE PROPERTIES INC.—See Scott-McRae Automotive Group Inc.; *U.S. Private*, pg. 3578
THE SCOTT MOTORS COMPANY—See Jordan Industries, Inc.; *U.S. Private*, pg. 2235
S.C. OTTO BOCK ROMANIA S.R.L.—See Ottobock Holding GmbH & Co. KG; *Int'l*, pg. 5665
SCOTTO BROTHERS ENTERPRISES, INC.—See Scotto's Holding Corp.; *U.S. Private*, pg. 3578

COMPANY NAME INDEX

SCREAMING EAGLE ACQUISITION CORP.

SCOTTO BROTHERS WESTBURY RESTAURANT INC.—See Scotto's Holding Corp.; *U.S. Private*, pg. 3578
SCOTTO BROTHERS WOODBURY RESTAURANT INC.—See Scotto's Holding Corp.; *U.S. Private*, pg. 3578
SCOTT OFFICE SYSTEMS—See Longwood Industries Holdings, LLC; *U.S. Private*, pg. 2493
SCOTTO & MELCHIORRE GROUP LLC; *U.S. Private*, pg. 3578
SCOTTO'S HOLDING CORP.; *U.S. Private*, pg. 3578
SCOTT PARK GROUP PTY. LTD.—See Sumitomo Forestry Co., Ltd.; *Int'l*, pg. 7286
SCOTT PENN, INC.; *U.S. Private*, pg. 3577
SCOTT PET PRODUCTS INC.; *U.S. Private*, pg. 3577
SCOTT PETROLEUM CORPORATION; *U.S. Private*, pg. 3577
SCOTT PEYRON & ASSOCIATES, INC.; *U.S. Private*, pg. 3577
SCOTT PLASTICS LTD.; *Int'l*, pg. 6652
SCOTT PUBLIC RELATIONS; *U.S. Private*, pg. 3577
SCOTT & REID GENERAL CONTRACTORS INC.; *U.S. Private*, pg. 3578
THE SCOTT RESORT & SPA—See Grossman Company Properties, Inc.; *U.S. Private*, pg. 1792
SCOTT RESOURCES—See Geneve Holdings Corp.; *U.S. Private*, pg. 1671
SCOTT RICE OFFICE INTERIORS; *U.S. Private*, pg. 3577
SCOTT RIDDLE AGENCY—See Integrity Marketing Group LLC; *U.S. Private*, pg. 2104
SCOTT ROBINSON HONDA INC.; *U.S. Private*, pg. 3577
SCOTTSBLUFF MOTOR COMPANY—See Rydell Company Inc.; *U.S. Private*, pg. 3511
SCOTTS CANADA LTD.—See The Scotts Miracle-Gro Company; *U.S. Public*, pg. 2127
THE SCOTTS COMPANY LLC—See The Scotts Miracle-Gro Company; *U.S. Public*, pg. 2127
THE SCOTTS COMPANY (MANUFACTURING) LIMITED—See Exponent Private Equity LLP; *Int'l*, pg. 2590
THE SCOTTS COMPANY—See The Scotts Miracle-Gro Company; *U.S. Public*, pg. 2127
THE SCOTTS COMPANY—See The Scotts Miracle-Gro Company; *U.S. Public*, pg. 2127
THE SCOTTS COMPANY—See The Scotts Miracle-Gro Company; *U.S. Public*, pg. 2127
THE SCOTTS COMPANY—See The Scotts Miracle-Gro Company; *U.S. Public*, pg. 2127
THE SCOTTS COMPANY—See The Scotts Miracle-Gro Company; *U.S. Public*, pg. 2127
THE SCOTTS COMPANY—See The Scotts Miracle-Gro Company; *U.S. Public*, pg. 2127
THE SCOTTS COMPANY—See The Scotts Miracle-Gro Company; *U.S. Public*, pg. 2127
THE SCOTTS COMPANY—See The Scotts Miracle-Gro Company; *U.S. Public*, pg. 2127
THE SCOTTS COMPANY—See The Scotts Miracle-Gro Company; *U.S. Public*, pg. 2127
THE SCOTTS COMPANY—See The Scotts Miracle-Gro Company; *U.S. Public*, pg. 2127
THE SCOTTS COMPANY—See The Scotts Miracle-Gro Company; *U.S. Public*, pg. 2127
THE SCOTTS COMPANY—See The Scotts Miracle-Gro Company; *U.S. Public*, pg. 2127
SCOTTSDALE ART FACTORY LLC; *U.S. Private*, pg. 3578
SCOTTSDALE CONSTRUCTION SYSTEMS LIMITED—See Panceltica Holdings Limited; *Int'l*, pg. 5725
SCOTTSDALE CONVENTION & VISITORS BUREAU; *U.S. Private*, pg. 3578
THE SCOTTSDALE CO.; *U.S. Private*, pg. 4115
SCOTTSDALE CULTURAL COUNCIL; *U.S. Private*, pg. 3578
SCOTTSDALE ENDOSCOPY ASC, LLC—See Tenet Healthcare Corporation; *U.S. Public*, pg. 2007
SCOTTSDALE FASHION SQUARE LLC—See The Macerich Company; *U.S. Public*, pg. 2110
SCOTTSDALE FASHION SQUARE PARTNERSHIP—See The Macerich Company; *U.S. Public*, pg. 2110
SCOTTSDALE FERRARI, LLC—See Penske Automotive Group, Inc.; *U.S. Public*, pg. 1666
SCOTTSDALE NURSING CENTER—See Sava Senior Care LLC; *U.S. Private*, pg. 3555
SCOTTSDALE PAINT & BODY, LLC—See Penske Automotive Group, Inc.; *U.S. Public*, pg. 1666
SCOTTSDALE PLAZA RESORT LLC; *U.S. Private*, pg. 3578
SCOTTSDALE RESIDENTIAL CARE INVESTORS—See Pacifica Senior Living; *U.S. Private*, pg. 3072
SCOTTSDALE VETERINARY SERVICES PTY. LTD.—See Apiam Animal Health Limited; *Int'l*, pg. 515

SCOTTS EARTHGRO—See The Scotts Miracle-Gro Company; *U.S. Public*, pg. 2127
SCOTT'S FOOD AND PHARMACY—See The Kroger Co.; *U.S. Public*, pg. 2109
SCOTTS GARMENTS LTD.; *Int'l*, pg. 6653
SCOTT SHERV HUMMER INCORPORATED; *U.S. Private*, pg. 3577
SCOTTS HOLDINGS LIMITED—See Exponent Private Equity LLP; *Int'l*, pg. 2590
SCOTT'S LANDSCAPING INC.—See Ruppert Landscape, LLC; *U.S. Private*, pg. 3504
SCOTT'S LIQUID GOLD- ADVERTISING PROMOTIONS, INC.—See Scott's Liquid Gold-Inc.; *U.S. Public*, pg. 1849
SCOTT'S LIQUID GOLD-INC.; *U.S. Public*, pg. 1849
SCOTTS MANUFACTURING COMPANY—See The Scotts Miracle-Gro Company; *U.S. Public*, pg. 2127
THE SCOTTS MIRACLE-GRO COMPANY; *U.S. Public*, pg. 2126
SCOTT SOLID WASTE DISPOSAL COMPANY—See Waste Connections, Inc.; *Int'l*, pg. 8354
SCOTT SPECIALITY GASES NETHERLANDS B.V.—See L'Air Liquide S.A.; *Int'l*, pg. 4370
SCOTT SPECIALTIES INC.; *U.S. Private*, pg. 3577
SCOTT SPORTS AB—See Scott Sports SA; *Int'l*, pg. 6652
SCOTT SPORTS AFRICA (PTY) LTD—See Scott Sports SA; *Int'l*, pg. 6652
SCOTT SPORTS AG—See Scott Sports SA; *Int'l*, pg. 6652
SCOTT SPORTS AG—See Scott Sports SA; *Int'l*, pg. 6652
SCOTT SPORTS, INC.—See Scott Sports SA; *Int'l*, pg. 6652
SCOTT SPORTS INDIA PRIVATE LIMITED—See Scott Sports SA; *Int'l*, pg. 6652
SCOTT SPORTS SA—See Scott Sports SA; *Int'l*, pg. 6652
SCOTT SPORTS SA; *Int'l*, pg. 6652
SCOTTS PROFESSIONAL PRODUCTS CO.—See The Scotts Miracle-Gro Company; *U.S. Public*, pg. 2127
SCOTTS-SIERRA HORTICULTURAL PRODUCTS CO.—See The Scotts Miracle-Gro Company; *U.S. Public*, pg. 2127
SCOTTS-SIERRA INVESTMENTS, INC.—See The Scotts Miracle-Gro Company; *U.S. Public*, pg. 2127
SCOTTS TEMECULA OPERATIONS, LLC—See The Scotts Miracle-Gro Company; *U.S. Public*, pg. 2127
SCOTT STREET SENIOR HOUSING COMPLEX INC; *U.S. Private*, pg. 3577
SCOTT & STRINGFELLOW, LLC—See Truist Financial Corporation; *U.S. Public*, pg. 2201
SCOTT SYSTEMS INTERNATIONAL, INC.—See JBS S.A.; *Int'l*, pg. 3918
SCOTT TECHNOLOGIES, INC.—See 3M Company; *U.S. Public*, pg. 8
SCOTT TECHNOLOGY LIMITED—See JBS S.A.; *Int'l*, pg. 3918
SCOTT TIMBER CO.—See Roseburg Forest Products; *U.S. Private*, pg. 3482
THE SCOTT TRUST LIMITED; *Int'l*, pg. 7680
SCOTT TURBON MIXER, INC.—See Ebara Corporation; *Int'l*, pg. 2284
SCOTT USA—See Scott Sports SA; *Int'l*, pg. 6652
SCOTT WASTE SERVICES, LLC—See Waste Connections, Inc.; *Int'l*, pg. 8354
SCOTT & WHITE HEALTH PLAN INC.; *U.S. Private*, pg. 3576
SCOTT-WILSON, INC.—See UnitedHealth Group Incorporated; *U.S. Public*, pg. 2244
SCOTT WINTON NOMINEES PTY LTD—See Steadfast Group Limited; *Int'l*, pg. 7187
SCOTTYS CONTRACTING & STONE LLC; *U.S. Private*, pg. 3578
SCOTTYS FASHIONS, INC.; *U.S. Private*, pg. 3578
SCOTVALVE SERVICES LIMITED—See Petrofac Limited; *Int'l*, pg. 5826
SCOTWORK (NA); *U.S. Private*, pg. 3578
THE SCOULAR CO. - MINNEAPOLIS CORPORATE OFFICE—See The Scoular Company; *U.S. Private*, pg. 4115
THE SCOULAR COMPANY; *U.S. Private*, pg. 4115
THE SCOULAR CO. - OVERLAND PARK CORPORATE OFFICE—See The Scoular Company; *U.S. Private*, pg. 4115
SCOUT24 HOLDING GMBH—See Scout24 SE; *Int'l*, pg. 6654
SCOUT24 SE; *Int'l*, pg. 6653
SCOUT BIO, INC.—See Ceva Sante Animale SA; *Int'l*, pg. 1425
SCOUT GAMING GROUP AB; *Int'l*, pg. 6653
SCOUT INVESTMENTS, INC.—See Raymond James Financial, Inc.; *U.S. Public*, pg. 1764
SCOUT MARKETING, INC.—See Stagwell, Inc.; *U.S. Public*, pg. 1928
SCOUT PUBLISHING, LLC—See The Walt Disney Company; *U.S. Public*, pg. 2141
SCOUT RFP LLC—See Workday, Inc.; *U.S. Public*, pg. 2378
SCOUT SECURITY LIMITED; *Int'l*, pg. 6653
S.C. OVB ALLFINANZ ROMANIA BROKER DE ASIGURARE S.R.L.—See OVB Holding AG; *Int'l*, pg. 5671

SCOVILL FASTENERS INC.—See The Gores Group, LLC; *U.S. Private*, pg. 4035
SCOVILL FASTENERS INDIA PRIVATE LIMITED—See The Gores Group, LLC; *U.S. Private*, pg. 4035
SCOVILL HOLDINGS INC.; *U.S. Private*, pg. 3579
SCOYO GMBH—See Bertelsmann SE & Co. KGaA; *Int'l*, pg. 997
SCOZINC LIMITED—See ScoZinc Mining Ltd.; *Int'l*, pg. 6654
SCOZINC MINING LTD.; *Int'l*, pg. 6654
SC PALACE SA; *Int'l*, pg. 6609
S.C. PAUL HARTMANN S.R.L.—See PAUL HARTMANN AG; *Int'l*, pg. 5761
SCP BENELUX SA—See Pool Corporation; *U.S. Public*, pg. 1701
SCP & CO HEALTHCARE ACQUISITION COMPANY; *U.S. Public*, pg. 1849
SCP CONSTRUCTION, LLC; *U.S. Private*, pg. 3579
SCP DISTRIBUTORS LLC—See Pool Corporation; *U.S. Public*, pg. 1702
S.C. PERLA COVASNEI S.A.; *Int'l*, pg. 6453
S & C PERMANENT PLACEMENT INC.—See Sullivan & Cogliano Designers Inc.; *U.S. Private*, pg. 3850
S.C. PETRODESIGN S.A.; *Int'l*, pg. 6453
S.C. PETROUTILAJ S.A.; *Int'l*, pg. 6453
SCP FRANCE SAS—See Pool Corporation; *U.S. Public*, pg. 1702
SCPHARMACEUTICALS, INC.; *U.S. Public*, pg. 1849
SC PIPE SOLUTIONS CO., LTD.—See Sumitomo Corporation; *Int'l*, pg. 7270
S.C. PIRELLI TYRES ROMANIA S.R.L.—See China National Chemical Corporation; *Int'l*, pg. 1529
S.C. PLASTIDRUM S.R.L.; *Int'l*, pg. 6453
SCP MANAGEMENT SDN BHD; *Int'l*, pg. 6654
S.C. PNE WIND ROMANIA ENERGY HOLDING S.R.L.—See PNE AG; *Int'l*, pg. 5901
SCP POOL DISTRIBUTORS SPAIN S.L.—See Pool Corporation; *U.S. Public*, pg. 1702
SCP PRIVATE EQUITY PARTNERS—See Safeguard Scientifics, Inc.; *U.S. Public*, pg. 1834
SC PRACTIC SA; *Int'l*, pg. 6610
SC PRAMAC GENERATORS S.R.L.—See Generac Holdings Inc.; *U.S. Public*, pg. 913
SC PRE-CON CORP.—See Shimizu Corporation; *Int'l*, pg. 6835
S.C. PREFAB S.A.; *Int'l*, pg. 6453
SC PREMIUM SA; *Int'l*, pg. 6610
S.C. PRIMCOM S.A.; *Int'l*, pg. 6454
S.C. PRODLACTA S.A.; *Int'l*, pg. 6454
S.C. PROPERTIES (SINGAPORE) PTE. LTD.—See Shimizu Corporation; *Int'l*, pg. 6835
SCP SAMLIP CO., LTD.; *Int'l*, pg. 6654
SC PUTEREA VERDE S.R.L.—See BayWa AG; *Int'l*, pg. 919
SCP WORLDWIDE; *U.S. Private*, pg. 3579
SCRABBLE DIGITAL LIMITED—See UFO Moviez India Ltd; *Int'l*, pg. 8015
SCRABBLE ENTERTAINMENT LIMITED—See UFO Moviez India Ltd; *Int'l*, pg. 8015
S.C. RAFINARIA STEAUA ROMANA S.A. CAMPINA; *Int'l*, pg. 6454
SCR AIR SERVICES, INC.—See NFI Industries, Inc.; *U.S. Private*, pg. 2923
SCRANTON CLINIC COMPANY, LLC—See Community Health Systems, Inc.; *U.S. Public*, pg. 556
SCRANTON EMERGENCY PHYSICIAN SERVICES, LLC—See Community Health Systems, Inc.; *U.S. Public*, pg. 556
SCRANTON EQUITY EXCHANGE INC.; *U.S. Private*, pg. 3579
SCRANTON GILLETTE COMMUNICATIONS, INC.; *U.S. Private*, pg. 3579
SCRANTON HOSPITALIST PHYSICIAN SERVICES, LLC—See Community Health Systems, Inc.; *U.S. Public*, pg. 556
SCRANTON-LACKAWANNA HUMAN DEVELOPMENT AGENCY, INC.; *U.S. Private*, pg. 3579
SCRANTON MANUFACTURING COMPANY INC.; *U.S. Private*, pg. 3579
SCRANTON PRODUCTS INC.—See The AZEK Company Inc.; *U.S. Public*, pg. 2035
SCRANTON QUINCY AMBULANCE, LLC—See Community Health Systems, Inc.; *U.S. Public*, pg. 556
SCRANTON QUINCY CLINIC COMPANY, LLC—See Community Health Systems, Inc.; *U.S. Public*, pg. 556
SCRANTON QUINCY HOSPITAL COMPANY, LLC—See Community Health Systems, Inc.; *U.S. Public*, pg. 556
SCRANTON TIMES TRIBUNE—See Alden Global Capital LLC; *U.S. Private*, pg. 157
SCRAPENA S.A.—See Commercial Metals Company; *U.S. Public*, pg. 545
SCRAP METAL SERVICES, LLC; *U.S. Private*, pg. 3579
SCRAP YOUR TRIP.COM; *U.S. Private*, pg. 3579
SCRATCH GOLF COMPANY—See The United Company; *U.S. Private*, pg. 4129
SCR CONSTRUCTION CO. INC.; *U.S. Private*, pg. 3579
SCREAMING EAGLE ACQUISITION CORP.; *U.S. Public*, pg. 1849

S.C. RED BULL ROMANIA S.R.L.—See Red Bull GmbH; Int'l, pg. 6244
SCREENBEAM INC.—See Ban Leong Technologies Limited; Int'l, pg. 814
SCREEN BUSINESS EXPERT CO., LTD.—See Screen Holdings Co., Ltd.; Int'l, pg. 6655
SCREENCELL—See BNP Paribas SA; Int'l, pg. 1089
SCREEN DECORAPRINT CO., LTD.—See Nagase & Co., Ltd.; Int'l, pg. 5128
SCREEN DOCTOR PTY. LTD.—See Invicta Holdings Limited; Int'l, pg. 3788
SCREENED IMAGES, INC.—See HH Global Group Limited; Int'l, pg. 3379
SCREEN ELECTRONICS SHA CO., LTD.—See Screen Holdings Co., Ltd.; Int'l, pg. 6655
SCREEN ENTERPRISES LIMITED—See Sky Network Television Limited; Int'l, pg. 6992
SCREEN FINETECH SOLUTIONS CO., LTD.—See Screen Holdings Co., Ltd.; Int'l, pg. 6655
SCREEN FINETECH SOLUTIONS SHANGHAI CO., LTD.—See Screen Holdings Co., Ltd.; Int'l, pg. 6655
SCREENFLEX PORTABLE PARTITION, LLC—See WILsquare Capital LLC; U.S. Private, pg. 4532
SCREEN FT CHANGSHU CO., LTD.—See Screen Holdings Co., Ltd.; Int'l, pg. 6655
SCREEN FT TAIWAN CO., LTD.—See Screen Holdings Co., Ltd.; Int'l, pg. 6655
SCREEN FUTURE S.R.L.—See DB Elettronica Telecomunicazioni SpA; Int'l, pg. 1986
SCREEN GEMS INC.—See Sony Group Corporation; Int'l, pg. 7105
SCREEN GP CHINA CO., LTD.—See Screen Holdings Co., Ltd.; Int'l, pg. 6655
SCREEN GP EUROPE B.V.—See Screen Holdings Co., Ltd.; Int'l, pg. 6655
SCREEN GP HANGZHOU CO., LTD.—See Screen Holdings Co., Ltd.; Int'l, pg. 6655
SCREEN GP IJC LTD.—See Screen Holdings Co., Ltd.; Int'l, pg. 6655
SCREEN GP JAPAN CO., LTD.—See Screen Holdings Co., Ltd.; Int'l, pg. 6655
SCREEN GP SERVICE JAPAN EAST CO., LTD.—See Screen Holdings Co., Ltd.; Int'l, pg. 6655
SCREEN GP SERVICE JAPAN WEST CO., LTD.—See Screen Holdings Co., Ltd.; Int'l, pg. 6655
SCREEN GP SHANGHAI CO., LTD.—See Screen Holdings Co., Ltd.; Int'l, pg. 6655
SCREEN GP TAIWAN CO., LTD.—See Screen Holdings Co., Ltd.; Int'l, pg. 6655
SCREEN HD KOREA CO., LTD.—See Screen Holdings Co., Ltd.; Int'l, pg. 6656
SCREEN HOLDINGS CO., LTD.; Int'l, pg. 6654
SCREEN HOLDINGS CO., LTD. - YASU PLANT—See Screen Holdings Co., Ltd.; Int'l, pg. 6656
SCREEN HOLDINGS SINGAPORE PTE. LTD.—See Screen Holdings Co., Ltd.; Int'l, pg. 6656
SCREENINGONE, INC.; U.S. Private, pg. 3579
THE SCREENING PROS, LLC—See CoStar Group, Inc.; U.S. Public, pg. 586
SCREEN LAMINATECH CO., LTD.—See Screen Holdings Co., Ltd.; Int'l, pg. 6656
SCREEN MEDIA TECHNOLOGY LTD—See Screen Holdings Co., Ltd.; Int'l, pg. 6656
SCREEN MEDIA VENTURES LLC—See Chicken Soup for the Soul Entertainment, Inc.; U.S. Public, pg. 488
SCREENMOBILE CORP.—See Apax Partners LLP; Int'l, pg. 502
SCREEN PE ENGINEERING CO., LTD.—See Screen Holdings Co., Ltd.; Int'l, pg. 6656
SCREEN PE SOLUTIONS CO., LTD.—See Screen Holdings Co., Ltd.; Int'l, pg. 6656
SCREEN SEMICONDUCTOR SOLUTIONS CO., LTD.—See Screen Holdings Co., Ltd.; Int'l, pg. 6656
SCREEN SERVICE AMERICA LLC—See DB Elettronica Telecomunicazioni SpA; Int'l, pg. 1986
SCREEN SERVICE DO BRASIL LTDA.—See DB Elettronica Telecomunicazioni SpA; Int'l, pg. 1986
SCREENSHOT DIGITAL, INC.—See TEGNA Inc.; U.S. Public, pg. 1990
SCREEN SOLUTIONS LTD.—See Gabriel Holding A/S; Int'l, pg. 2867
SCREEN SPE GERMANY GMBH—See Screen Holdings Co., Ltd.; Int'l, pg. 6656
SCREEN SPE KOREA CO., LTD.—See Screen Holdings Co., Ltd.; Int'l, pg. 6656
SCREEN SPE QUARTZ CO., LTD.—See Screen Holdings Co., Ltd.; Int'l, pg. 6656
SCREEN SPE SINGAPORE PTE. LTD.—See Screen Holdings Co., Ltd.; Int'l, pg. 6656
SCREEN SPE TAIWAN CO., LTD.—See Screen Holdings Co., Ltd.; Int'l, pg. 6656
SCREEN SPE WORKS CO., LTD.—See Screen Holdings Co., Ltd.; Int'l, pg. 6656
SCREENTIME LIMITED—See LOV Group Invest SAS; Int'l, pg. 4563
SCREENTIME PTY LTD—See LOV Group Invest SAS; Int'l, pg. 4563
SCREENTONIC S.A.—See Microsoft Corporation; U.S. Public, pg. 1441

SCREEN TRYCK AB—See Bergman & Beving AB; Int'l, pg. 980
SCREENVISION CINEMA NETWORK LLC—See ABRY Partners, LLC; U.S. Private, pg. 43
SCREENWORKS LLC - OPERATIONS & TECHNICAL SUPPORT—See The Carlyle Group Inc.; U.S. Public, pg. 2049
SCREENWORKS LLC—See The Carlyle Group Inc.; U.S. Public, pg. 2049
S.C. REHM SUDARE S.R.L—See REHM GmbH u. Co. KG Schweisstechnik; Int'l, pg. 6256
SC REISSWOLF ROMANIA SRL—See REISSWOLF International AG; Int'l, pg. 6258
S.C. RELEE S.A.; Int'l, pg. 6454
SC. RESEARCH INSTITUTE FOR ADVANCED COATINGS - ICAA S.A.; Int'l, pg. 6610
SC RESERVATIONS (PHILIPPINES) INC—See InterContinental Hotels Group PLC; Int'l, pg. 3738
S.C. RETRASIB S.A. SIBIU—See BC Partners LLP; Int'l, pg. 925
SCR EUROPE SRL—See Merck & Co., Inc.; U.S. Public, pg. 1421
SCREW CONVEYOR INDUSTRIES; U.S. Private, pg. 3579
SCREW CONVEYOR INDUSTRIES - VISALIA PLANT—See Screw Conveyor Industries; U.S. Private, pg. 3579
SCREW CONVEYOR INDUSTRIES - WINONA PLANT—See Screw Conveyor Industries; U.S. Private, pg. 3579
SCREWFAST FOUNDATIONS LIMITED—See Van Elle Holdings PLC; Int'l, pg. 8126
SCREWFIX DIRECT LIMITED—See Kingfisher plc; Int'l, pg. 4173
SCREXS GMBH—See Wurth Verwaltungsgesellschaft mbH; Int'l, pg. 8507
SCRIBBLERS' CLUB; Int'l, pg. 6656
SCRIBBLE TECHNOLOGIES INC.—See e.Bricks Ventures; Int'l, pg. 2251
SCRIBD, INC.; U.S. Private, pg. 3579
SCRIBEAMERICA; U.S. Private, pg. 3579
SCRIBE MANUFACTURING, INC.—See H.I.G. Capital, LLC; U.S. Private, pg. 1831
SCRIBE SOLUTIONS, INC.—See GEE Group Inc.; U.S. Public, pg. 910
SCR, INC.; U.S. Private, pg. 3579
SC RINGIER ROMANIA SRL—See Ringier Holding AG; Int'l, pg. 6344
SCRINSER, S.A.—See Sacyr, S.A.; Int'l, pg. 6466
SCRIP COMPANIES; U.S. Private, pg. 3579
SCRIPHESSCO; U.S. Private, pg. 3579
SCRIPPS ENCINITAS SURGERY CENTER, LLC—See Tenet Healthcare Corporation; U.S. Public, pg. 2012
SCRIPPS HEALTH; U.S. Private, pg. 3580
SCRIPPS MEDIA, INC.—See The E.W. Scripps Company; U.S. Public, pg. 2068
SCRIPPS MERCY HOSPITAL—See Scripps Health; U.S. Private, pg. 3580
SCRIP-SAFE SECURITY PRODUCTS, INC.; U.S. Private, pg. 3579
SCRIPTFLEET, INC.—See Harbour Group Industries, Inc.; U.S. Private, pg. 1860
SCRIPTPRO LLC; U.S. Private, pg. 3580
SCRIPTSENDER, LLC—See RadNet, Inc.; U.S. Public, pg. 1761
SCRIP WORLD, INC.—See CVS Health Corporation; U.S. Public, pg. 615
THE SCRNEN FOUNDATION; U.S. Private, pg. 4115
SCROCCA OPTION TRADING B.V.; Int'l, pg. 6656
S.C. ROFEP S.A.; Int'l, pg. 6454
SCROGGS & GRIZZEL CONTRACTING, INC.; U.S. Private, pg. 3580
SCROLL360 CORPORATION—See Scroll Corporation; Int'l, pg. 6656
SCROLL COMPRESSORS LLC—See Emerson Electric Co.; U.S. Public, pg. 744
SCROLL CORPORATION; Int'l, pg. 6656
SCROLLMOTION, INC.; U.S. Private, pg. 3580
SCROLL TECHNOLOGIES—See Danfoss A/S; Int'l, pg. 1961
S.C. ROMAN S.A.; Int'l, pg. 6454
S.C. ROMCAB S.A.; Int'l, pg. 6454
S.C. ROM - ITAL SRL—See S.C. InterAgro S.A.; Int'l, pg. 6452
SC ROMNITRO EXPLOSIVES SRL—See Incitec Pivot Limited; Int'l, pg. 3648
S.C. ROPHARMA S.A.; Int'l, pg. 6454
SC RPK SVYAZIST—See PJSC Rostelecom; Int'l, pg. 5884
SCR SIBELCO SA; Int'l, pg. 6654
SC RTCOMM.RU—See PJSC Rostelecom; Int'l, pg. 5884
SC RT LABS—See PJSC Rostelecom; Int'l, pg. 5884
SCRUBADUB AUTO WASH CENTERS; U.S. Private, pg. 3580
SCRUB DADDY, INC.; U.S. Private, pg. 3580
SCRUBS & BEYOND LLC; U.S. Private, pg. 3580
SCRUBS ON WHEELS—See Birch Swing Capital LLC; U.S. Private, pg. 564

SCRUFARI CONSTRUCTION CO. INC.; U.S. Private, pg. 3580
THE SCRUGGS COMPANY INC.; U.S. Private, pg. 4115
SCRUGGS CONCRETE COMPANY; U.S. Private, pg. 3580
S.C. RULMENTI S.A.; Int'l, pg. 6454
SCRYB INC.; Int'l, pg. 6656
SCRYPT CORPORATION; U.S. Public, pg. 1850
SCRYPT INC.—See Scrypt Corporation; U.S. Public, pg. 1850
S.C. SALGAZ S.A.—See E.ON SE; Int'l, pg. 2259
S.C. SANTIERUL NAVAL ORSOVA S.A.; Int'l, pg. 6454
SC SAPA PROFILES SRL—See Norsk Hydro ASA; Int'l, pg. 5435
S.C. SATURN S.A.; Int'l, pg. 6454
SCS BOEHRINGER INGELHEIM COMM. V.—See C.H. Boehringer Sohn AG & Co. KG; Int'l, pg. 1243
SC SCHAEFFLER ROMANIA S.R.L.—See INA-Holding Schaeffler GmbH & Co. KG; Int'l, pg. 3640
SC SCHWARZL BETON SRL—See PORR AG; Int'l, pg. 5924
S C S CONTRACTING, INC.; U.S. Private, pg. 3512
SCS DIRECT INC.; U.S. Private, pg. 3580
SC SECURITIES (PVT) LTD.—See Sampath Bank PLC; Int'l, pg. 6507
S.C. SEMBRAZ S.A.; Int'l, pg. 6454
SC SEMROM OLTENIA S.A.; Int'l, pg. 6610
SCS ENGINEERS KOREA, LTD.—See SCS Engineers; U.S. Private, pg. 3580
SCS ENGINEERS OF NEW YORK, PC—See SCS Engineers; U.S. Private, pg. 3580
SCS ENGINEERS - SCS ENERGY DIVISION—See SCS Engineers; U.S. Private, pg. 3580
SCS ENGINEERS; U.S. Private, pg. 3580
SCS ENGINEERS - TAMPA—See SCS Engineers; U.S. Private, pg. 3580
S.C. SERICO S.A.; Int'l, pg. 6454
S.C SERVICIILE COMERCIALE ROMANE S.R.L.; Int'l, pg. 6449
SCS ES CONSULTANTS—See SCS Engineers; U.S. Private, pg. 3580
SC SEVEREN-TELECOM—See PJSC Rostelecom; Int'l, pg. 5884
S.C. SEVERNAV S.A.; Int'l, pg. 6454
SCS FIELD SERVICES—See SCS Engineers; U.S. Private, pg. 3580
SCS FILTRATION PTY LTD—See Atlas Copco AB; Int'l, pg. 684
SCS FOOD SERVICES PTE LTD—See Select Group Limited; Int'l, pg. 6699
SCS FRIGETTE—See Hickman Investments Inc.; U.S. Private, pg. 1933
SCS GLOBEX ENGINEERING—See SCS Engineers; U.S. Private, pg. 3580
SCS GROUP PLC—See Poltronesofa Holding Srl; Int'l, pg. 5913
S.C. SIBAREX S.A.; Int'l, pg. 6454
S.C SIGSTRAT S.A; Int'l, pg. 6449
S.C. SILCOM S.A.; Int'l, pg. 6454
S.C. SILOTRANS S.R.L.—See CHS INC.; U.S. Public, pg. 492
S.C. SIMEROM S.A.; Int'l, pg. 6454
SCS INFORMATION TECHNOLOGY SDN. BHD.—See Temasek Holdings (Private) Limited; Int'l, pg. 7553
SC SINTEROM S.A.; Int'l, pg. 6610
S.C. SINTOFARM S.A.; Int'l, pg. 6454
SCSK CORPORATION—See Sumitomo Corporation; Int'l, pg. 7270
SCS LIEGENSCHAFTSVERWERTUNG GMBH—See Unibail-Rodamco-Westfield SE; Int'l, pg. 8030
SC SMC ROMANIA S.R.L.—See SMC Corporation; Int'l, pg. 7004
SCS MOTOR CITY SUD ERRICHTUNGSGES.MBH—See Unibail-Rodamco-Westfield SE; Int'l, pg. 8030
SC SMR SA; Int'l, pg. 6610
S.C. SOCIETATEA TRAINING IN ASIGURARI S.R.L.—See Vienna Insurance Group AG Wiener Versicherung Gruppe; Int'l, pg. 8195
S.C. SOFERT S.A.—See S.C. InterAgro S.A.; Int'l, pg. 6452
SC SOFT AMERICAS LLC—See Aurionpro Solutions Limited; Int'l, pg. 711
S.C. SOMES S.A.—See S.C Serviciile Comerciale Romane S.R.L.; Int'l, pg. 6449
S.C. SOMETA S.A.; Int'l, pg. 6454
S.C. SOMETRA S.A. COPSA MICA—See Metlen Energy & Metals S.A.; Int'l, pg. 4855
SC SOMFY S.R.L.—See Somfy SA; Int'l, pg. 7085
SC SOMPLAST SA; Int'l, pg. 6610
SCS SKIN CARE STUDIO GMBH—See maxingvest ag; Int'l, pg. 4741
SCS SOFTWARE, INC.—See CrossCountry Consulting LLC; U.S. Private, pg. 1106
S.C. STICLOVAL S.A.; Int'l, pg. 6454
SC STIMAS SA; Int'l, pg. 6610
SCST, INC.; U.S. Private, pg. 3580
S.C. STOFE BUHUSI S.A.; Int'l, pg. 6454
SCS TRACER ENVIRONMENTAL—See SCS Engineers; U.S. Private, pg. 3580

COMPANY NAME INDEX

S.C. SUBANSAMBLE AUTO S.A.; *Int'l*, pg. 6454
SCS UPHOLSTERY LTD.; *Int'l*, pg. 6656
S.C. SWISSPOR S.A.—See swisspor Management AG; *Int'l*, pg. 7374
SCT ACQUISITION, LLC—See Kratos Defense & Security Solutions, Inc.; *U.S. Private*, pg. 1277
S.C. TALC DOLOMITA S.A.; *Int'l*, pg. 6454
S.C. TARNAVA S.A.; *Int'l*, pg. 6454
SCTBIO A.S.—See PPF Group N.V.; *Int'l*, pg. 5951
S.C. TCHIBO BRANDS S.R.L.—See maxingvest ag; *Int'l*, pg. 4741
S.C. TCI CONTRACTOR GENERAL S.A.; *Int'l*, pg. 6455
SCT CO., LTD.—See The Siam Cement Public Company Limited; *Int'l*, pg. 7684
SCT COOLERS CANADA TECHNOLOGY INC—See Sunonwealth Electric Machine Industry Company Limited; *Int'l*, pg. 7319
SCT COPPER INDUSTRY (SHENYANG) CO., LTD.—See Livingstone Health Holdings Limited; *Int'l*, pg. 4532
S.C. TECHNO CO., LTD.—See SANYEI CORPORATION; *Int'l*, pg. 6563
SC TECKENTRUP ROMANIA SRL—See Teckentrup GmbH & Co. KG; *Int'l*, pg. 7514
SCT ELECTRONICS LIMITED—See HNA International Investment Holdings Limited; *Int'l*, pg. 3433
S.C. TELEROM PROIECT INSTITUTUL NATIONAL DE PROIECTARI TELECOMUNICATII S.A.; *Int'l*, pg. 6455
S.C. TESATORIILE REUNITE S.A.; *Int'l*, pg. 6455
SCT EUROPE LTD.—See Westinghouse Air Brake Technologies Corporation; *U.S. Public*, pg. 2359
S.C. TEXTILA OLTUL S.A.; *Int'l*, pg. 6455
SC THONAUER AUTOMATIC S.R.L.—See Komax Holding AG; *Int'l*, pg. 4241
SCT TKT-STROY—See PJSC Rostelecom; *Int'l*, pg. 5884
S.C TMD S.A FILIASI; *Int'l*, pg. 6450
SC TMK-ARTROM SA—See PAO TMK; *Int'l*, pg. 5732
S.C. TOYOTA TSUSHO DO BRASIL LTDA.—See Toyota Tsusho Corporation; *Int'l*, pg. 7877
S.C.T. PTY LTD; *Int'l*, pg. 6456
SC TRAMECO S.A.; *Int'l*, pg. 6610
S.C. TRANSCOM S.A.; *Int'l*, pg. 6455
S.C. TRANSCOM S.A.; *Int'l*, pg. 6455
S.C. TRANSILANA S.A.; *Int'l*, pg. 6455
S.C. TRANSILVANIA CONSTRUCTII S.A.—See Parc Logistic Transilvania SRL; *Int'l*, pg. 5739
S.C. TRANSPORTER S.R.L.—See CHS INC.; *U.S. Public*, pg. 493
SC TREFO SA; *Int'l*, pg. 6610
S.C. TRI-WALL ROMANIA S.R.L.—See Rengo Co., Ltd.; *Int'l*, pg. 6281
S.C. TRUST EURO THERM S.R.L.—See NIBE Industrier AB; *Int'l*, pg. 5262
SCT SUNTAR CERAMIC TECHNOLOGY (XIAMEN) CO., LTD.—See CDH China Management Company Limited; *Int'l*, pg. 1370
SCT TECHNOLOGIES (THAILAND) CO., LTD.—See Livingstone Health Holdings Limited; *Int'l*, pg. 4533
SCT TELECOM S.A.S.—See Astorg Partners S.A.S.; *Int'l*, pg. 657
SC TUBULAR AND STEEL PRODUCTS (M.E.) FZCO—See Sumitomo Corporation; *Int'l*, pg. 7270
SC TUBULARS CO., LTD.—See Sumitomo Corporation; *Int'l*, pg. 7270
S.C. TURISM COVASNA S.A.; *Int'l*, pg. 6455
SC TURISM FELIX SA; *Int'l*, pg. 6610
S.C. TURISM, HOTELURI, RESTAURANTE MAREA NEAGRA S.A.; *Int'l*, pg. 6455
S.C. TURNATORIA CENTRALA ORION S.A.; *Int'l*, pg. 6455
SCT USA.INC.—See Siward Crystal Technology Co., Ltd.; *Int'l*, pg. 6966
S.C. TUSNAD S.A.; *Int'l*, pg. 6455
SCUBAPRO AG—See Johnson Outdoors Inc.; *U.S. Public*, pg. 1201
SCUBAPRO ASIA, LTD.—See Johnson Outdoors Inc.; *U.S. Public*, pg. 1201
SCUBAPRO ASIA PACIFIC LTD.—See Johnson Outdoors Inc.; *U.S. Public*, pg. 1201
SCUBAPRO ESPANA, S.A.—See Johnson Outdoors Inc.; *U.S. Public*, pg. 1201
SCUBAPRO EUROPE BENELUX, S.A.—See Johnson Outdoors Inc.; *U.S. Public*, pg. 1201
SCUBAPRO EUROPE S.R.L—See Johnson Outdoors Inc.; *U.S. Public*, pg. 1201
SCUBAPRO ITALY S.R.L.—See Johnson Outdoors Inc.; *U.S. Public*, pg. 1201
SCUBAPRO-UWATEC AUSTRALIA PTY. LTD.—See Johnson Outdoors Inc.; *U.S. Public*, pg. 1201
SCUBAPRO/UWATEC FRANCE S.A.—See Johnson Outdoors Inc.; *U.S. Public*, pg. 1201
SCUBAPRO-UWATEC FRANCE S.A.—See Johnson Outdoors Inc.; *U.S. Public*, pg. 1201
S-CUBE INC.—See Takachiho Koheki Co., Ltd.; *Int'l*, pg. 7429
SCUBIA GBR—See Axel Springer SE; *Int'l*, pg. 766
SCUD BATTERY CO., LTD.—See Veson Holdings Limited; *Int'l*, pg. 8176

SCUDO GRUNDSTUCKS-VERMIETUNGSGESELLSCHAFT MBH & CO. OBJEKT KLEINE ALEXANDERSTRASSE KG—See Deutsche Bank Aktiengesellschaft; *Int'l*, pg. 2061
SCULLIN OIL CO.; *U.S. Private*, pg. 3581
SCULLY CAPITAL SERVICES, INC.—See Value Recovery Group, Inc.; *U.S. Private*, pg. 4337
SCULLY OIL CO., INC.—See Pops Mart Fuels, LLC; *U.S. Private*, pg. 3229
SCULLY ROYALTY LTD.; *Int'l*, pg. 6656
SCULLY WELDING SUPPLY CORP.—See L'Air Liquide S.A.; *Int'l*, pg. 4372
SCULPTEO SAS—See BASF SE; *Int'l*, pg. 884
SCULPTOR CAPITAL MANAGEMENT EUROPE LIMITED—See Rithm Capital Corp.; *U.S. Public*, pg. 1800
SCULPTOR CAPITAL MANAGEMENT HONG KONG LIMITED—See Rithm Capital Corp.; *U.S. Public*, pg. 1800
SCULPTOR CAPITAL MANAGEMENT, INC.—See Rithm Capital Corp.; *U.S. Public*, pg. 1800
SCULPTZ, INC.; *U.S. Private*, pg. 3581
S.C. UNIREA SHOPPING CENTER S.A.; *Int'l*, pg. 6455
S.C. UNITED ROMANIAN BREWERIES BEREPROD—See Eckes AG; *Int'l*, pg. 2291
S.C. UNITEH S.A.; *Int'l*, pg. 6455
S.C. UNIVERS S.A.; *Int'l*, pg. 6455
SCUNTHORPE VETS4PETS LIMITED—See Pets at Home Group Plc; *Int'l*, pg. 5834
SCUOLA CARABINIERI S.C.R.L.—See Salini Costruttori S.p.A.; *Int'l*, pg. 6493
SCURA PARTNERS SECURITIES LLC; *U.S. Private*, pg. 3581
SC URBANA SA; *Int'l*, pg. 6610
S.C. URB RULMENTI SUCEAVA S.A.; *Int'l*, pg. 6455
SCURLOCK INDUSTRIES; *U.S. Private*, pg. 3581
S.C. UTILAJ GREU S.A.; *Int'l*, pg. 6455
SCUT SA—See Comcm S.A.; *Int'l*, pg. 1709
SCUT SA; *Int'l*, pg. 6656
SCUTUM CAPITAL AG; *Int'l*, pg. 6657
S.C. UZINELE SODICE GOVORA CIECH CHEMICAL GROUP S.A.—See Kulczyk Investments S.A.; *Int'l*, pg. 4328
S.C. UZUC S.A.; *Int'l*, pg. 6455
SC UZUC SA—See S.C Serviciile Comerciale Romane S.R.L.; *Int'l*, pg. 6449
SC VBH ROMCOM SRL—See VBH Holding AG; *Int'l*, pg. 8139
SCV DOMAINE SKIABLE SA—See Compagnie des Alpes S.A.; *Int'l*, pg. 1738
S.C. VEST ENERGO S.A.; *Int'l*, pg. 6455
S.C. VICTORIA S.A.; *Int'l*, pg. 6455
S.C. VICTORIA S.A.; *Int'l*, pg. 6455
SC VILMAR S.A.—See Groupe BPCE; *Int'l*, pg. 3095
S.C. VINALCOOL ARGES S.A.; *Int'l*, pg. 6455
S.C. VIROMET S.A.—See S.C. InterAgro S.A.; *Int'l*, pg. 6452
S.C. VITIMAS S.A. TECUCI; *Int'l*, pg. 6455
SC VITROMETAN SA; *Int'l*, pg. 6610
SCVNGR, INC.—See Just Eat Takeaway.com N.V.; *Int'l*, pg. 4030
SC VPK PACKAGING SRL—See VPK Packaging Group NV; *Int'l*, pg. 8312
S.C. VRANCART S.A.—See SIF Banat-Crisana S.A.; *Int'l*, pg. 6905
SCVX CORP.; *U.S. Public*, pg. 1850
SC WAM ROMANIA S.R.L.—See WAMGROUP S.p.A.; *Int'l*, pg. 8338
SC WESTERN SHIPYARD—See BLRT Grupp AS; *Int'l*, pg. 1066
SCWORX CORP.; *U.S. Public*, pg. 1850
S.C. WURTH INDUSTRIE S.R.L.—See Wurth Verwaltungsgesellschaft mbH; *Int'l*, pg. 8507
S.C.YALCO ROMANIA SRL—See YALCO - SOCRATES D. CONSTANTINOU & SON S.A.; *Int'l*, pg. 8547
S.C. YARNEA S.R.L.—See Radici Partecipazioni S.p.A.; *Int'l*, pg. 6175
SCYNEXIS, INC.; *U.S. Public*, pg. 1850
SCYTL AUSTRALIA PTY. LTD.—See Scytl Secure Electronic Voting SA; *Int'l*, pg. 6657
SCYTL CANADA INC.—See Scytl Secure Electronic Voting SA; *Int'l*, pg. 6657
SCYTL META FZE—See Scytl Secure Electronic Voting SA; *Int'l*, pg. 6657
SCYTL MEXICO, SRL DE CV.—See Scytl Secure Electronic Voting SA; *Int'l*, pg. 6657
SCYTL PERU S.A.C.—See Scytl Secure Electronic Voting SA; *Int'l*, pg. 6657
SCYTL SECURE ELECTRONIC VOTING SA; *Int'l*, pg. 6657
SCYTL USA LLC—See Scytl Secure Electronic Voting SA; *Int'l*, pg. 6657
S.C. ZAREA S.A.; *Int'l*, pg. 6456
S.C. ZECASIN S.A.; *Int'l*, pg. 6456
SC ZIMTUB SA—See S.C. InterAgro S.A.; *Int'l*, pg. 6452
SD3IT, LLC; *U.S. Private*, pg. 3581
SDAAC AUTOMOTIVE AIR-CONDITIONING SYSTEMS CO., LTD.—See Shanghai Aerospace Automobile Electromechanical Co., Ltd.; *Int'l*, pg. 6761

SDII GLOBAL CORPORATION

SDA EXPRESS COURIER—See Poste Italiane S.p.A.; *Int'l*, pg. 5939
SDAI LIMITED; *Int'l*, pg. 6657
SDB ASIA PTE. LTD.—See Selangor Dredging Berhad; *Int'l*, pg. 6699
SDB CISCO (INDIA) LTD.—See Sicagen India Ltd.; *Int'l*, pg. 6877
SDB INFORMATION TECHNOLOGY—See Savino Del Bene S.p.A.; *Int'l*, pg. 6600
SDB INTERNATIONAL B.V.; *Int'l*, pg. 6657
SD BIOSENSOR HEALTHCARE PVT. LTD.—See SD Biosensor, Inc.; *Int'l*, pg. 6657
SD BIOSENSOR, INC.; *Int'l*, pg. 6657
SDBIOTECH CO., LTD.; *Int'l*, pg. 6657
SD BIOTECHNOLOGIES COSMETICS CO., LTD.—See SDBIOTECH Co., Ltd.; *Int'l*, pg. 6657
SD BIOTECHNOLOGIES U.S CORPORATION—See SDBIOTECH Co., Ltd.; *Int'l*, pg. 6657
SDB PROPERTIES SDN. BHD.—See Selangor Dredging Berhad; *Int'l*, pg. 6699
SDB TRADE INTERNATIONAL, LP; *U.S. Private*, pg. 3581
SDB UK LTD—See SDB International B.V.; *Int'l*, pg. 6657
SDC CANADA INC.—See SmileDirectClub, Inc.; *U.S. Public*, pg. 1896
SDC CAPITAL PARTNERS, LLC; *U.S. Private*, pg. 3581
SDC GMBH—See Kulczyk Investments S.A.; *Int'l*, pg. 4328
SDCL EDGE ACQUISITION CORPORATION; *U.S. Private*, pg. 3581
SDCL ENERGY EFFICIENCY INCOME TRUST PLC; *Int'l*, pg. 6657
SDC MATERIALS, INC.—See General Motors Company; *U.S. Public*, pg. 928
S. & D. COFFEE, INC.—See Westrock Coffee Company; *U.S. Public*, pg. 2361
S&D CO.,LTD.; *Int'l*, pg. 6444
SD COSMETICS (QINGDAO) CO., LTD.—See SDBIOTECH Co., Ltd.; *Int'l*, pg. 6657
SD COSMETICS (SHANGHAI) CO., LTD.—See SDBIOTECH Co., Ltd.; *Int'l*, pg. 6657
SDC TECHMEDIA LTD; *Int'l*, pg. 6657
SDC TECHNOLOGIES ASIA PACIFIC, PTE. LTD.—See Mitsui Chemicals, Inc.; *Int'l*, pg. 4983
SDC TECHNOLOGIES, INC.—See Mitsui Chemicals, Inc.; *Int'l*, pg. 4982
SDC TRAILERS LTD.—See CIMC Vehicle (Group) Co., Ltd.; *Int'l*, pg. 1608
SDDA PTE. LTD.—See Temasek Holdings (Private) Limited; *Int'l*, pg. 7551
S.D. DEACON CORP. OF WASHINGTON—See S.D. Deacon Corporation; *U.S. Private*, pg. 3517
S.D. DEACON CORPORATION; *U.S. Private*, pg. 3517
S.D. DEACON CORP.—See S.D. Deacon Corporation; *U.S. Private*, pg. 3517
SDDS HOLDINGS, INC.; *U.S. Private*, pg. 3581
SDEL ATLANTIS SAS—See VINCI S.A.; *Int'l*, pg. 8226
SDEL CONTROLE COMMANDE SAS—See VINCI S.A.; *Int'l*, pg. 8226
SDEL INFI SAS—See VINCI S.A.; *Int'l*, pg. 8226
SDEL MASSIF CENTRAL SAS—See VINCI S.A.; *Int'l*, pg. 8226
SDEL NANTES SAS—See VINCI S.A.; *Int'l*, pg. 8226
SDEL RESEAUX AQUITAINE SAS—See VINCI S.A.; *Int'l*, pg. 8226
SDEL RESEAUX EXTERIEURS SAS—See VINCI S.A.; *Int'l*, pg. 8226
SDEL SAVOIE LEMAN SAS—See VINCI S.A.; *Int'l*, pg. 8226
SDEL TERTIAIRE SAS—See VINCI S.A.; *Int'l*, pg. 8226
SD ENGINEERING (EUROPE) SP. Z.O.O.—See Sumitomo Electric Industries, Ltd.; *Int'l*, pg. 7279
S D ENGINEERING - HUI ZHOU, LTD.—See Sumitomo Electric Industries, Ltd.; *Int'l*, pg. 7279
S.D. ENGINEERING, LTD.—See Sumitomo Electric Industries, Ltd.; *Int'l*, pg. 7279
SD ENTERTAINMENT INC.—See RIZAP GROUP, Inc.; *Int'l*, pg. 6354
SDE (PHILIPPINES) CORP.—See Sumitomo Electric Industries, Ltd.; *Int'l*, pg. 7279
SDG CORPORATION; *U.S. Private*, pg. 3581
SD GERMANY GMBH—See Spectral Dynamics, Inc.; *U.S. Private*, pg. 3751
SD GROUP SERVICE COMPANY LTD.—See Dow Inc.; *U.S. Public*, pg. 686
SDI BRASIL INDUSTRIA E COMERCIO LTDA—See SDI Limited; *Int'l*, pg. 6658
SDIC CAPITAL CO., LTD.; *Int'l*, pg. 6658
SDI CHINA CO., LTD.—See SDI Corporation; *Int'l*, pg. 6657
SDI CORPORATION; *Int'l*, pg. 6657
SDIC POWER HOLDINGS CO., LTD.; *Int'l*, pg. 6658
SDIC ZHONGLU FRUIT JUICE CO., LTD.; *Int'l*, pg. 6658
SDI DENTAL LIMITED—See SDI Limited; *Int'l*, pg. 6658
THE SDI DIVESTITURE CORPORATION—See Bayer Aktiengesellschaft; *Int'l*, pg. 902
SDI EUROPE LIMITED—See OriGene Technologies, Inc.; *U.S. Private*, pg. 3042
SDI GROUP PLC; *Int'l*, pg. 6658
SDII GLOBAL CORPORATION; *U.S. Private*, pg. 3581

SDII GLOBAL CORPORATION

CORPORATE AFFILIATIONS

SDI, INC.—See Independence Capital Partners, LLC; *U.S. Private*, pg. 2056
SDI, INC.—See Pouschine Cook Capital Management LLC; *U.S. Private*, pg. 3236
SDI INNOVATIONS, INC.; *U.S. Private*, pg. 3581
SDI INTERNATIONAL CORP.; *U.S. Private*, pg. 3581
SDI LIMITED; *Int'l*, pg. 6658
SDI MEDIA A/S—See Imagica Group Inc.; *Int'l*, pg. 3619
SDI MEDIA GROUP, INC.—See Imagica Group Inc.; *Int'l*, pg. 3619
SDI MEDIA HOLDINGS GERMANY GMBH—See Imagica Group Inc.; *Int'l*, pg. 3619
SDI MEDIA LTD.—See Imagica Group Inc.; *Int'l*, pg. 3619
SDI MEDIA—See Elevation Partners; *U.S. Private*, pg. 1358
SDI MEDIA SWEDEN AB—See Imagica Group Inc.; *Int'l*, pg. 3619
SDI (NORTH AMERICA) INC.—See SDI Limited; *Int'l*, pg. 6658
SDI PRESENCE LLC; *U.S. Private*, pg. 3581
SDIPTECH AB; *Int'l*, pg. 6658
SDIPTECH AB; *Int'l*, pg. 6658
S.D. IRELAND BROTHERS CORP; *U.S. Private*, pg. 3517
SDI TECHNOLOGIES, INC.; *U.S. Private*, pg. 3581
SDI TRAVEL & INCENTIVES—See SmithBucklin Corporation; *U.S. Private*, pg. 3697
SDIX, LLC—See OriGene Technologies, Inc.; *U.S. Private*, pg. 3042
SDK AGENCIS C.C.—See Schwan-STABILO Cosmetics GmbH & Co. KG; *Int'l*, pg. 6644
SD.- KOLEJOVA DOPRAVA, A.S.—See CEZ, a.s.; *Int'l*, pg. 1428
SD.- KOMES, A.S.—See CEZ, a.s.; *Int'l*, pg. 1428
SDK SERVICES LIMITED—See Kader Holdings Company Limited; *Int'l*, pg. 4046
SDK VASTGOED BV—See Koninklijke VolkerWessels N.V.; *Int'l*, pg. 4272
SDL ALTERIAN—See RWS Holdings plc; *Int'l*, pg. 6437
SDL BELGIUM NV—See RWS Holdings plc; *Int'l*, pg. 6437
SDL CHILE SA—See RWS Holdings plc; *Int'l*, pg. 6437
S.D.L. CO., LTD.—See Tokyo Century Corporation; *Int'l*, pg. 7789
SDLC PARTNERS, L.P.—See CitiusTech Inc.; *U.S. Private*, pg. 902
SDL CZ SRO—See RWS Holdings plc; *Int'l*, pg. 6437
SDL DENHOLM LIMITED—See J&J Denholm Ltd.; *Int'l*, pg. 3853
SDL DO BRASIL SERVICOS DE TRADUCAO LTDA—See RWS Holdings plc; *Int'l*, pg. 6438
SDL DO BRAZIL GLOBAL SOLUTIONS LTDA.—See RWS Holdings plc; *Int'l*, pg. 6438
SDL DOO LJUBLJANA—See RWS Holdings plc; *Int'l*, pg. 6437
SDL FRANCE SARL—See RWS Holdings plc; *Int'l*, pg. 6437
SDL GLOBAL SOLUTIONS (IRELAND) LTD—See RWS Holdings plc; *Int'l*, pg. 6437
SDL HELLAS MEPE—See RWS Holdings plc; *Int'l*, pg. 6437
SDL HOLDINGS BV—See RWS Holdings plc; *Int'l*, pg. 6437
SDL HONG KONG LTD.—See RWS Holdings plc; *Int'l*, pg. 6437
SDL INC.—See RWS Holdings plc; *Int'l*, pg. 6437
SDL INC.—See RWS Holdings plc; *Int'l*, pg. 6437
SDL INTERNATIONAL BELGIUM NV—See RWS Holdings plc; *Int'l*, pg. 6437
SDL INTERNATIONAL (CANADA) INC.—See RWS Holdings; *Int'l*, pg. 6437
SDL INTERNATIONAL NEDERLAND B.V.—See RWS Holdings plc; *Int'l*, pg. 6437
SDL ITALIA SRL—See RWS Holdings plc; *Int'l*, pg. 6437
SDL JAPAN KK—See RWS Holdings plc; *Int'l*, pg. 6437
SDL LIMITED—See Sumaria Group; *Int'l*, pg. 7260
SDL LUXEMBOURG SAR—See RWS Holdings plc; *Int'l*, pg. 6437
SDL MULTILINGUAL SERVICES GMBH & CO KG—See RWS Holdings plc; *Int'l*, pg. 6437
SDL MULTILINGUAL SOLUTIONS PRIVATE LTD.—See RWS Holdings plc; *Int'l*, pg. 6438
SDL MULTI-LINGUAL SOLUTIONS (SINGAPORE) PTE LTD—See RWS Holdings plc; *Int'l*, pg. 6437
SDL NEDERLAND HOLDING BV—See RWS Holdings plc; *Int'l*, pg. 6438
SDL PASSOLO GMBH—See RWS Holdings plc; *Int'l*, pg. 6438
SDL PLC—See RWS Holdings plc; *Int'l*, pg. 6437
SDL POLAND SP. Z O.O.—See RWS Holdings plc; *Int'l*, pg. 6438
SDL PORTUGAL UNIPESSOAL LDA—See RWS Holdings plc; *Int'l*, pg. 6438
SDL QUATRON BV—See RWS Holdings plc; *Int'l*, pg. 6438
SDL SHEFFIELD LIMITED—See RWS Holdings plc; *Int'l*, pg. 6438
SDL SPAIN SL—See RWS Holdings plc; *Int'l*, pg. 6438
SDL SUDDEUTSCHE LEASING AG; *Int'l*, pg. 6659
SDL SWEDEN AB—See RWS Holdings plc; *Int'l*, pg. 6438

SDL TECHNOLOGIES (AUSTRALIA) PTY. LTD.—See RWS Holdings plc; *Int'l*, pg. 6437
SDL TECHNOLOGIES (VIETNAM) CQ. LTD.—See RWS Holdings plc; *Int'l*, pg. 6438
SDL TRADUCERI SRL—See RWS Holdings plc; *Int'l*, pg. 6438
SDL TRIDION BVBA—See RWS Holdings plc; *Int'l*, pg. 6438
SDL TRIDION BV—See RWS Holdings plc; *Int'l*, pg. 6438
SDL TRIDION CORPORATE SERVICES BV—See RWS Holdings plc; *Int'l*, pg. 6438
SDL TRIDION GMBH—See RWS Holdings plc; *Int'l*, pg. 6438
SDL TRIDION HISPANIA SL—See RWS Holdings plc; *Int'l*, pg. 6438
SDL TRIDION HOLDING BV—See RWS Holdings plc; *Int'l*, pg. 6438
SDL TRIDION INC—See RWS Holdings plc; *Int'l*, pg. 6438
SDL TRIDION KK—See RWS Holdings plc; *Int'l*, pg. 6438
SDL TRIDION LTD—See RWS Holdings plc; *Int'l*, pg. 6438
SDL TRIDION SAS—See RWS Holdings plc; *Int'l*, pg. 6438
SDL TURKEY TRANSLATION SERVICES & COMMERCE LTD.—See RWS Holdings plc; *Int'l*, pg. 6438
SDL XOPUS BV—See RWS Holdings plc; *Int'l*, pg. 6438
SDL XYENTERPRISE LLC—See RWS Holdings plc; *Int'l*, pg. 6438
SDL ZAGREB LLC—See RWS Holdings plc; *Int'l*, pg. 6438
SD MAYER & ASSOCIATES LLP; *U.S. Private*, pg. 3581
SDM-BANK PJSC; *Int'l*, pg. 6659
SDM EDUCATION GROUP HOLDINGS LIMITED; *Int'l*, pg. 6659
SD MFG. COMPANY—See OSG Corporation; *Int'l*, pg. 5649
SDMO GENERATING SETS INC.—See Kohler Company; *U.S. Private*, pg. 2340
SDMO GMBH—See Kohler Company; *U.S. Private*, pg. 2340
SDMO INDUSTRIES IBERICA—See Kohler Company; *U.S. Private*, pg. 2340
SDMO INDUSTRIES—See Kohler Company; *U.S. Private*, pg. 2340
SDMO NV/SA—See Kohler Company; *U.S. Private*, pg. 2340
SDM SE; *Int'l*, pg. 6659
SDMS, INC.; *U.S. Private*, pg. 3581
S.D. MYERS, INC.; *U.S. Private*, pg. 3581
SDN COMPANY LTD. - KOREA RENEWABLE ENERGY LABORATORY & GWANGJU ADVANCED SCIENCE FACTORY—See SDN Company Ltd.; *Int'l*, pg. 6659
SDN COMPANY LTD.; *Int'l*, pg. 6659
SD NETWORK CO., LTD.—See Carlit Co., Ltd.; *Int'l*, pg. 1338
SDN GLOBAL, INC.—See Synergy Core LLC; *U.S. Private*, pg. 3904
SDN INSURANCE AGENCY, LLC—See Aon plc; *Int'l*, pg. 497
S.D.O—See Carrefour SA; *Int'l*, pg. 1346
S&D OSTERFELD MECHANICAL CONTRACTORS—See Unitize Company Inc.; *U.S. Private*, pg. 4302
SD PARTNERS LIMITED—See Alten S.A.; *Int'l*, pg. 390
SDP. GLOBAL CO., LTD.—See Sanyo Chemical Industries, Ltd.; *Int'l*, pg. 6563
SDP GLOBAL (MALAYSIA) SDN. BHD.—See Sanyo Chemical Industries, Ltd.; *Int'l*, pg. 6563
SDP JOINT STOCK COMPANY; *Int'l*, pg. 6659
SDP MANUFACTURING SDN BHD—See Sunningdale Tech Ltd; *Int'l*, pg. 7318
SDP TELECOM INC.—See Koch Industries, Inc.; *U.S. Private*, pg. 2335
SDQ, CORP.; *U.S. Private*, pg. 3581
SD - REKULTIVACE, A.S.—See CEZ, a.s.; *Int'l*, pg. 1428
SD RETAIL CONSULTING—See Hilco Trading, LLC; *U.S. Private*, pg. 1944
S.D. RICHMAN SONS, INC.; *U.S. Private*, pg. 3517
SDR PLASTICS, INC.; *U.S. Private*, pg. 3581
SDS BIOTECH KKS—See Idemitsu Kosan Co., Ltd.; *Int'l*, pg. 3592
S&D SERVICE & DISTRIBUTION GMBH—See McNaughton-McKay Electric Company; *U.S. Private*, pg. 2643
SDS GROUP BERHAD; *Int'l*, pg. 6659
SDS GROUP LIMITED; *Int'l*, pg. 6659
SDS HOLDINGS CO., LTD.; *Int'l*, pg. 6659
SDS INDUSTRIES INC.; *U.S. Private*, pg. 3582
S&DS MARKET INC.; *U.S. Private*, pg. 3513
S & D SPECIALTY, INC.; *U.S. Private*, pg. 3511
SDSP INC.; *U.S. Private*, pg. 3582
S.D. STANDARD ETC PLC—See Saga Pure ASA; *Int'l*, pg. 6477
SD SYSTEM CO., LTD; *Int'l*, pg. 6657
SDT THAI CO., LTD.—See Shinden Hightex Corporation; *Int'l*, pg. 6841
SDU TECHNIKA ZLACZENIOWA SLASK SP. Z O.O.—See Schrauben Und Draht Union GmbH; *Int'l*, pg. 6639
SDU UITGEVERS B.V.—See Editions Lefebvre Sarrut SA; *Int'l*, pg. 2311
SDV ESCALATORS LTD.—See ThyssenKrupp AG; *Int'l*, pg. 7725

SD VIETNAM INDUSTRIES LTD.—See Onamba Co., Ltd.; *Int'l*, pg. 5573
SDV INCORPORATED; *U.S. Private*, pg. 3582
SDV INTERNATIONAL LOGISTICS—See Financiere de L'Odet; *Int'l*, pg. 2667
SDV SOLUTIONS, INC.; *U.S. Private*, pg. 3582
SDV (USA) INC.—See Financiere de L'Odet; *Int'l*, pg. 2667
SD WORX GROUP; *Int'l*, pg. 6657
SD WORX UK LIMITED—See SD Worx Group; *Int'l*, pg. 6657
SDX ENERGY PLC; *Int'l*, pg. 6659
SE2 INC.—See Guggenheim Partners, LLC; *U.S. Private*, pg. 1812
SEA-3 INC.—See Trammo, Inc.; *U.S. Private*, pg. 4204
SEA-3 OF FLORIDA INC.—See Trammo, Inc.; *U.S. Private*, pg. 4204
SEA & AIR FREIGHT INTERNATIONAL; *Int'l*, pg. 6660
SEAARK MARINE INC.—See McClendon Resources Inc.; *U.S. Private*, pg. 2628
SEABAY BUILDING GROUP, LLC; *U.S. Private*, pg. 3583
SEABEE CORPORATION CYLINDERS—See Ligon Industries LLC; *U.S. Private*, pg. 2455
SEABEE CORPORATION FOUNDRY—See Ligon Industries LLC; *U.S. Private*, pg. 2455
SEA BIOGAS CORPORATION; *Int'l*, pg. 6660
SEA-BIRD ELECTRONICS, INC.; *U.S. Private*, pg. 3583
SEABIRD EXPLORATION AMERICAS INC—See Seabird Exploration Norway AS; *Int'l*, pg. 6661
SEABIRD EXPLORATION FZ LLC—See Seabird Exploration Norway AS; *Int'l*, pg. 6661
SEABIRD EXPLORATION NORWAY AS; *Int'l*, pg. 6661
SEABOARD CORPORATION; *U.S. Public*, pg. 1850
SEABOARD DE COLOMBIA, S.A.—See Seaboard Corporation; *U.S. Public*, pg. 1851
SEABOARD DE NICARAGUA, S.A.—See Seaboard Corporation; *U.S. Public*, pg. 1851
SEABOARD ENERGIAS RENOVABLES Y ALIMENTOS S.R.L.—See Seaboard Corporation; *U.S. Public*, pg. 1851
SEABOARD ENERGY KANSAS, LLC—See Seaboard Corporation; *U.S. Public*, pg. 1851
SEABOARD ENERGY, LLC—See Seaboard Corporation; *U.S. Public*, pg. 1851
SEABOARD ENERGY OKLAHOMA, LLC—See Seaboard Corporation; *U.S. Public*, pg. 1851
SEABOARD FARMS OF OKLAHOMA INC.—See Seaboard Corporation; *U.S. Public*, pg. 1851
SEABOARD FOLDING BOX CORP.—See Vidya Brands Group LLC; *U.S. Private*, pg. 4381
SEABOARD FOODS LLC—See Seaboard Corporation; *U.S. Public*, pg. 1851
SEABOARD FOODS OF IOWA, LLC—See Seaboard Corporation; *U.S. Public*, pg. 1851
SEABOARD FOODS SERVICES INC.—See Seaboard Corporation; *U.S. Public*, pg. 1851
SEABOARD INDUSTRIES; *U.S. Private*, pg. 3583
SEABOARD INTERNATIONAL FOREST PRODUCTS LLC—See Forest City Trading Group, LLC; *U.S. Private*, pg. 1566
SEABOARD INTERNATIONAL, INC.; *U.S. Private*, pg. 3583
SEABOARD MARINE LTD. INC.—See Seaboard Corporation; *U.S. Public*, pg. 1851
SEABOARD MARINE OF FLORIDA, INC.—See Seaboard Corporation; *U.S. Public*, pg. 1851
SEABOARD OVERSEAS LTD.—See Seaboard Corporation; *U.S. Public*, pg. 1851
SEABOARD OVERSEAS PERU S.A.—See Seaboard Corporation; *U.S. Public*, pg. 1851
SEABOARD OVERSEAS TRADING AND SHIPPING (PTY) LTD.—See Seaboard Corporation; *U.S. Public*, pg. 1851
SEABOARD PRODUCE DISTRIBUTORS; *U.S. Private*, pg. 3583
SEABOARD SALES CORP.—See Seaboard Corporation; *U.S. Public*, pg. 1851
SEABOARD SHIP MANAGEMENT INC.—See Seaboard Corporation; *U.S. Public*, pg. 1851
SEABOARD SOLAR HOLDINGS, LLC; *U.S. Private*, pg. 3583
SEABOARD SOLAR LLC—See Duke Energy Corporation; *U.S. Public*, pg. 691
SEABOARD SOLAR OPERATIONS, LLC—See Seaboard Solar Holdings, LLC; *U.S. Private*, pg. 3583
SEABOARD TRADING & SHIPPING LTD. INC.—See Seaboard Corporation; *U.S. Public*, pg. 1851
SEABOARD TRANSPORT GROUP; *Int'l*, pg. 6661
SEABOARD TRANSPORT LLC—See Seaboard Corporation; *U.S. Public*, pg. 1851
SEA BOX, INC.; *U.S. Private*, pg. 3582
SEABRA GROUP; *U.S. Private*, pg. 3583
SEABREEZE MANAGEMENT COMPANY, INC.; *U.S. Private*, pg. 3583
SEABREEZE PLAZA, LLC—See Saul Centers, Inc.; *U.S. Public*, pg. 1842
SEABREEZE PROPERTIES, INC.—See Levy Group, Inc.; *U.S. Private*, pg. 2437
SEABRIDGE GOLD INC.; *Int'l*, pg. 6661

COMPANY NAME INDEX

SEABRIGHT HOLDINGS, INC.—See Enstar Group Limited; *Int'l*, pg. 2449
SEABRIGHT INSURANCE COMPANY—See Enstar Group Limited; *Int'l*, pg. 2449
SEABRING MARINE INDUSTRIES INC.; *U.S. Private*, pg. 3583
SEABROOK BROTHERS & SONS, INC.; *U.S. Private*, pg. 3583
SEABROOK HOUSE, INC.; *U.S. Private*, pg. 3583
SEABROOK INTERNATIONAL, LLC—See The Jordan Company, L.P.; *U.S. Private*, pg. 4060
SEABROOK ISLAND REALTY—See Club At Seabrook Island Inc.; *U.S. Private*, pg. 948
SEABROOK WALLCOVERINGS, INC.; *U.S. Private*, pg. 3583
SEABULK INTERNATIONAL, INC.—See AIP, LLC; *U.S. Private*, pg. 136
SEABULK TANKERS, INC.—See AIP, LLC; *U.S. Private*, pg. 137
SEABULK TOWING HOLDINGS INC.—See AIP, LLC; *U.S. Private*, pg. 137
SEABULK TOWING SERVICES, INC.—See AIP, LLC; *U.S. Private*, pg. 137
SEABULK TOWING—See AIP, LLC; *U.S. Private*, pg. 137
SEABURY & SMITH, INC.—See Marsh & McLennan Companies, Inc.; *U.S. Public*, pg. 1388
SEA-CAP INC.; *U.S. Private*, pg. 3583
SEACAST AIC—See SeaCast, Inc.; *U.S. Private*, pg. 3583
SEACAST, INC.; *U.S. Private*, pg. 3583
SEACAT L.P.—See Techint S.p.A.; *Int'l*, pg. 7504
SEACERA CARE SDN. BHD.—See Seacera Group Berhad; *Int'l*, pg. 6661
SEACERA GROUP BERHAD; *Int'l*, pg. 6661
SEACERAMART SDN. BHD.—See Seacera Group Berhad; *Int'l*, pg. 6661
SEACFA - CLERMONT-FERRAND AIRPORT—See VINCI S.A.; *Int'l*, pg. 8230
SEA CHANGE ASIA PACIFIC OPERATIONS PTE. LTD.—See SeaChange International, Inc.; *U.S. Public*, pg. 1851
SEACHANGE INDIA PRIVATE, LTD.—See SeaChange International, Inc.; *U.S. Public*, pg. 1851
SEACHANGE INTERNATIONAL, INC.; *U.S. Public*, pg. 1851
SEACHANGE NLG B.V.—See SeaChange International, Inc.; *U.S. Public*, pg. 1851
SEACHANGE POLSKA SP ZOO—See SeaChange International, Inc.; *U.S. Public*, pg. 1851
SEACHEM LABORATORIES INC.; *U.S. Private*, pg. 3583
SEACH MEDICAL GROUP LTD.; *Int'l*, pg. 6661
SEAC LIMITED; *Int'l*, pg. 6661
SEACO AMERICA LLC—See Hainan Traffic Administration Holding Co., Ltd.; *Int'l*, pg. 3213
SEACO ASIA PTE LTD.—See Hainan Traffic Administration Holding Co., Ltd.; *Int'l*, pg. 3213
SEACOAST BANKING CORPORATION OF FLORIDA; *U.S. Public*, pg. 1851
SEACOAST CAPITAL - SAN FRANCISCO—See Seacoast Capital; *U.S. Private*, pg. 3583
SEACOAST CAPITAL; *U.S. Private*, pg. 3583
SEACOAST COMMERCE BANK; *U.S. Private*, pg. 3583
SEACOAST ELECTRIC COMPANY; *U.S. Private*, pg. 3584
SEACOAST NATIONAL BANK—See Seacoast Banking Corporation of Florida; *U.S. Public*, pg. 1851
SEACOAST NEWSPAPERS, INC.—See Gannett Co., Inc.; *U.S. Public*, pg. 904
SEACOAST PATHOLOGY, INC.—See Sonic Healthcare Limited; *Int'l*, pg. 7098
SEACOAST PHYSICAL THERAPY, LIMITED PARTNERSHIP—See U.S. Physical Therapy, Inc.; *U.S. Public*, pg. 2216
SEACOAST SHIPPING SERVICES LTD.; *Int'l*, pg. 6661
SEACOAST SPECIALTY ADMINISTRATORS, INC.—See One80 Intermediaries LLC; *U.S. Private*, pg. 3024
SEACOAST UNDERWRITERS, INC.—See Arthur J. Gallagher & Co.; *U.S. Private*, pg. 207
SEACOAST VOLKSWAGEN, INC.; *U.S. Private*, pg. 3584
SEACO BRITISH ISLES LTD.—See Hainan Traffic Administration Holding Co., Ltd.; *Int'l*, pg. 3213
SEACO CHINA LTD.—See Hainan Traffic Administration Holding Co., Ltd.; *Int'l*, pg. 3213
SEACO FRANCE SARL—See Hainan Traffic Administration Holding Co., Ltd.; *Int'l*, pg. 3213
SEACO GLOBAL AUSTRALIA PTY. LTD.—See Hainan Traffic Administration Holding Co., Ltd.; *Int'l*, pg. 3213
SEACO GLOBAL LTD.—See Hainan Traffic Administration Holding Co., Ltd.; *Int'l*, pg. 3213
SEACO, INC.—See Ergon, Inc.; *U.S. Private*, pg. 1418
SEACO INTERNATIONAL LEASING GMBH—See Hainan Traffic Administration Holding Co., Ltd.; *Int'l*, pg. 3213
SEACO ITALIA SRL—See Hainan Traffic Administration Holding Co., Ltd.; *Int'l*, pg. 3213
SEACOMP DISPLAYS, INC.; *U.S. Private*, pg. 3584
SEACOM SA SPV PROPRIETARY LIMITED—See Remgro Limited; *Int'l*, pg. 6271
SEACON ADVANCED PRODUCTS LLC—See TE Connectivity Ltd.; *Int'l*, pg. 7495

SEA CON BRANTNER & ASSOCIATES INC.—See TE Connectivity Ltd.; *Int'l*, pg. 7497
SEACON (EUROPE) LIMITED—See TE Connectivity Ltd.; *Int'l*, pg. 7496
SEACON PRODUTOS E SERVICOS OPTICOS E ELETRICOS LTDA.—See TE Connectivity Ltd.; *Int'l*, pg. 7496
SEACON SHIPPING GROUP HOLDINGS LIMITED; *Int'l*, pg. 6661
SEACOR AMH LLC—See AIP, LLC; *U.S. Private*, pg. 136
SEACOR CAPACITORS—See Electrocube Incorporated; *U.S. Private*, pg. 1354
SEACOR ENERGY CANADA LIMITED—See AIP, LLC; *U.S. Private*, pg. 136
SEACOR HOLDINGS INC.—See AIP, LLC; *U.S. Private*, pg. 136
SEACOR ISLAND LINES LLC—See AIP, LLC; *U.S. Private*, pg. 136
SEACOR LIFTBOATS LLC—See AIP, LLC; *U.S. Private*, pg. 136
SEACOR MARINE (ASIA) PTE. LTD.—See AIP, LLC; *U.S. Private*, pg. 136
SEACOR MARINE HOLDINGS INC.; *U.S. Public*, pg. 1851
SEACOR MARINE (INTERNATIONAL) LTD.—See AIP, LLC; *U.S. Private*, pg. 136
SEACOR MARINE LLC—See AIP, LLC; *U.S. Private*, pg. 136
SEACOR OFFSHORE DUBAI (L.L.C.)—See AIP, LLC; *U.S. Private*, pg. 136
SEACORP, LLC; *U.S. Private*, pg. 3584
SEACREST PETROLEO BERMUDA LIMITED; *Int'l*, pg. 6662
SEACREST SEAFOODS INC.—See Coastal Corporation Limited; *Int'l*, pg. 1681
SEACREST SERVICES, INC.; *U.S. Private*, pg. 3584
SEAC—See Nufarm Limited; *Int'l*, pg. 5487
SEACUBE CONTAINER LEASING LTD.—See Ontario Teachers' Pension Plan; *Int'l*, pg. 5590
SEACURUS LIMITED—See Arch Capital Group Ltd.; *Int'l*, pg. 547
SEA DEEP SHIPYARD PTE. LTD—See Baker Technology Limited; *Int'l*, pg. 805
SEA DOG BREWING COMPANY; *U.S. Private*, pg. 3582
SEA-DOG CORPORATION—See Patrick Industries, Inc.; *U.S. Public*, pg. 1653
SEADRAGON LTD.; *Int'l*, pg. 6662
SEADREAM YACHT CLUB, INC.; *U.S. Private*, pg. 3584
SEADRIFT COKE L.P.—See Brookfield Corporation; *Int'l*, pg. 1187
SEADRILL AMERICAS INC.—See SeaDrill Limited; *Int'l*, pg. 6662
SEADRILL ASIA LTD.—See SeaDrill Limited; *Int'l*, pg. 6662
SEADRILL DEEPWATER UNITS PTE LTD—See SeaDrill Limited; *Int'l*, pg. 6662
SEADRILL LIMITED; *Int'l*, pg. 6662
SEADRILL MANAGEMENT A.M.E LDT—See SeaDrill Limited; *Int'l*, pg. 6662
SEADRILL MANAGEMENT AS—See SeaDrill Limited; *Int'l*, pg. 6662
SEADRILL MANAGEMENT (S) PTE. LTD.—See SeaDrill Limited; *Int'l*, pg. 6662
SEADRILL MANAGEMENT (S) PTE LTD—See SeaDrill Limited; *Int'l*, pg. 6662
SEADRILL RIG HOLDING COMPANY LTD—See SeaDrill Limited; *Int'l*, pg. 6662
SEADRILL SDN. BHD.—See SeaDrill Limited; *Int'l*, pg. 6662
SEADRILL SERVICOS DE PETROLEO LTDA.—See SeaDrill Limited; *Int'l*, pg. 6662
SEADRILL-TENDER RIG PTE. LTD.—See SeaDrill Limited; *Int'l*, pg. 6662
SEA EAGLE BOATS, INC.—See Harrison-Hoge Industries, Inc.; *U.S. Private*, pg. 1871
SEAFARER EXPLORATION CORP.; *U.S. Public*, pg. 1851
SEAFARERS WELFARE PLAN INC.; *U.S. Private*, pg. 3584
SEAFARMS GROUP LIMITED; *Int'l*, pg. 6662
SEA FARMS, INC.—See Seafresh Industry Public Company Limited; *Int'l*, pg. 6663
SEA FARMS NUTRITION LIMITED—See Seafresh Industry Public Company Limited; *Int'l*, pg. 6663
SEAFAX, INC.—See Stone Point Capital LLC; *U.S. Private*, pg. 3819
SEAFCO (MYANMAR) CO., LTD.—See SEAFCO Public Company Limited; *Int'l*, pg. 6662
SEAFCO PUBLIC COMPANY LIMITED; *Int'l*, pg. 6662
SEA FIBRE NETWORKS LIMITED—See Digital 9 Infrastructure Plc; *Int'l*, pg. 2120
SEAFIELD RESOURCES LTD.; *Int'l*, pg. 6662
SEAFIRE AB; *Int'l*, pg. 6662
SEA FISH INDUSTRY AUTHORITY; *Int'l*, pg. 6660
SEAFLEX AS—See Kongsberg Gruppen ASA; *Int'l*, pg. 4256
SEAFLEX RISER TECHNOLOGY INC.—See Kongsberg Gruppen ASA; *Int'l*, pg. 4256
SEAFOOD CONNECTION HOLDING B.V.—See Maruha Nichiro Corporation; *Int'l*, pg. 4712

SEAFOOD HOLDINGS LTD—See The Bidvest Group Limited; *Int'l*, pg. 7622
SEAFOOD INTERNATIONAL ONE FZCO—See Thai Union Group Public Company Limited; *Int'l*, pg. 7596
SEAFOOD JOINT STOCK COMPANY NO.4; *Int'l*, pg. 6661
SEAFOOD PRODUCERS COOPERATIVE; *U.S. Private*, pg. 3584
SEAFOOD SALES INC.; *U.S. Private*, pg. 3584
SEAFOODS ENTERPRISE CO., LTD—See Charoen Pokphand Foods Public Company Limited; *Int'l*, pg. 1453
SEAFOOD SUPPLY CO. INC.; *U.S. Private*, pg. 3584
SEAFOOD TIP.—See Arendals Fossekompani ASA; *Int'l*, pg. 559
SEAFORD CONSULTING, LLC—See Godspeed Capital Management LP; *U.S. Private*, pg. 1725
SEA FORREST TECHNOLOGIES PTE. LTD.—See BH Global Corporation Limited; *Int'l*, pg. 1009
SEAFORT CAPITAL, INC.; *Int'l*, pg. 6662
SEAFORTH MINERAL & ORE CO., INC.; *U.S. Private*, pg. 3584
SEAFORTH SUPPLY CHAIN SOLUTIONS INC.—See Swiss Water Decaffeinated Coffee Inc.; *Int'l*, pg. 7373
SEAFOX BOAT COMPANY INC.; *U.S. Private*, pg. 3584
SEAFRANCE S.A.—See SNCF; *Int'l*, pg. 7027
SEAFREIGHT AGENCIES INC.; *U.S. Private*, pg. 3584
SEA FREIGHT AGENCIES & STEVEDORING LIMITED—See Goddard Enterprises Limited; *Int'l*, pg. 3019
SEAFRESH GROUP (HOLDINGS) LIMITED—See Seafresh Industry Public Company Limited; *Int'l*, pg. 6663
SEAFRESH INDUSTRY PUBLIC COMPANY LIMITED - CHUMPHON FACTORY—See Seafresh Industry Public Company Limited; *Int'l*, pg. 6663
SEAFRESH INDUSTRY PUBLIC COMPANY LIMITED; *Int'l*, pg. 6663
SEA FRESH USA, INC.—See Oceano Seafood SA; *Int'l*, pg. 5518
SEA FRESH USA INC.—See Oceano Seafood SA; *Int'l*, pg. 5518
SEAFRONT RESOURCES CORPORATION; *Int'l*, pg. 6663
SEA GARDENS BEACH & TENNIS RESORT—See Travel & Leisure Co.; *U.S. Public*, pg. 2186
SEAGAS PIPELINE COMPANY—See Phillips 66 Company; *U.S. Public*, pg. 1688
SEAGATE CLOUD SYSTEMS, INC.—See Seagate Technology Holdings PLC; *Int'l*, pg. 6663
SEAGATE CORPORATION—See Kawasaki Kisen Kaisha, Ltd.; *Int'l*, pg. 4101
SEAGATE FOODS INC.; *U.S. Private*, pg. 3584
SEAGATE HANDLING INC—See Dulany Industries Inc.; *U.S. Private*, pg. 1286
THE SEAGATE HOTEL & SPA; *U.S. Private*, pg. 4115
SEAGATE INTERNATIONAL (JOHOR) SDN. BHD.—See Seagate Technology Holdings PLC; *Int'l*, pg. 6663
SEAGATE RECORDING MEDIA—See Seagate Technology Holdings PLC; *Int'l*, pg. 6663
SEAGATE RECOVERY SERVICES—See Seagate Technology Holdings PLC; *Int'l*, pg. 6663
SEAGATE SINGAPORE INTERNATIONAL HEADQUARTERS PTE. LTD.—See Seagate Technology Holdings PLC; *Int'l*, pg. 6663
SEAGATE SYSTEMS (US) HOLDINGS INC.—See Seagate Technology Holdings PLC; *Int'l*, pg. 6663
SEAGATE TECHNOLOGY HOLDINGS PLC; *Int'l*, pg. 6663
SEAGATE TECHNOLOGY (IRELAND)—See Seagate Technology Holdings PLC; *Int'l*, pg. 6663
SEAGATE TECHNOLOGY KOREA, INC.—See Seagate Technology Holdings PLC; *Int'l*, pg. 6664
SEAGATE TECHNOLOGY LLC - BLOOMINGTON—See Seagate Technology Holdings PLC; *Int'l*, pg. 6663
SEAGATE TECHNOLOGY LLC - OKLAHOMA CITY—See Seagate Technology Holdings PLC; *Int'l*, pg. 6664
SEAGATE TECHNOLOGY LLC—See Seagate Technology Holdings PLC; *Int'l*, pg. 6663
SEAGATE TECHNOLOGY (MARLOW) LIMITED—See Seagate Technology Holdings PLC; *Int'l*, pg. 6663
SEAGATE TECHNOLOGY (NETHERLANDS) B.V.—See Seagate Technology Holdings PLC; *Int'l*, pg. 6663
SEAGATE TECHNOLOGY TAIWAN LTD.—See Seagate Technology Holdings PLC; *Int'l*, pg. 6664
SEAGATE TECHNOLOGY (THAILAND) LIMITED—See Seagate Technology Holdings PLC; *Int'l*, pg. 6663
SEAGATE TECHNOLOGY UK LTD.—See Seagate Technology Holdings PLC; *Int'l*, pg. 6664
SEAGATE TECHNOLOGY (US) HOLDINGS, INC.—See Seagate Technology Holdings PLC; *Int'l*, pg. 6663
SEAGATE US LLC—See Seagate Technology Holdings PLC; *Int'l*, pg. 6664
SEAGEN AUSTRIA GMBH—See Seagen Inc.; *U.S. Public*, pg. 1852
SEAGEN B.V.—See Seagen Inc.; *U.S. Public*, pg. 1852
SEAGEN INC.; *U.S. Public*, pg. 1852
SEAGEN SPAIN, S.L.—See Seagen Inc.; *U.S. Public*, pg. 1852

SEAGEN INC. — CORPORATE AFFILIATIONS

SEAGI - GRENOBLE AIRPORT—See VINCI S.A.; *Int'l*, pg. 8230
SEA GLASBRUK AB—See New Wave Group AB; *Int'l*, pg. 5230
SEAGOE CONCRETE PRODUCTS LIMITED—See Heidelberg Materials AG; *Int'l*, pg. 3319
SEAGOE TECHNOLOGIES LIMITED—See The Glen Dimplex Group; *Int'l*, pg. 7650
SEAGOLD LTD.—See Samherji hf; *Int'l*, pg. 6505
SEAGOOD PTE LTD.—See Sealink International Bhd; *Int'l*, pg. 6665
SEAGRAM DISTILLERIES PTE LTD—See Pernod Ricard S.A.; *Int'l*, pg. 5811
SEAGRAVE FIRE APPARATUS, LLC—See FB Capital Partners, L.P.; *U.S. Private*, pg. 1485
SEA GULL ADVERTISING SDN. BHD.—See Hai-O Enterprise Berhad; *Int'l*, pg. 3209
SEAGULL BOOK & TAPE INC.; *U.S. Private*, pg. 3584
SEAGULL COOLING TECHNOLOGIES (ASIA PACIFIC) SDN. BHD.—See Jiangsu Seagull Cooling Tower Co., Ltd.; *Int'l*, pg. 3953
SEAGULL COOLING TECHNOLOGIES (THAILAND) CO., LTD.—See Jiangsu Seagull Cooling Tower Co., Ltd.; *Int'l*, pg. 3953
SEAGULL K.K.—See Oakley Capital Limited; *Int'l*, pg. 5504
SEAGULL LIGHTING PRODUCTS INC.; *U.S. Private*, pg. 3584
SEA GULL LIGHTING PRODUCTS, LLC—See AEA Investors LP; *U.S. Private*, pg. 114
SEAGULL MARITIME AS—See Oakley Capital Limited; *Int'l*, pg. 5504
SEAGULL MARITIME AS SP. Z O.O.—See Oakley Capital Limited; *Int'l*, pg. 5504
SEAGULL MARITIME INFORMATION TECHNOLOGIES LTD.—See Oakley Capital Limited; *Int'l*, pg. 5504
SEAGULL MARITIME INFORMATION TECHNOLOGY GMBH—See Oakley Capital Limited; *Int'l*, pg. 5504
SEAGULL MARITIME INFORMATION TECHNOLOGY PTE LTD—See Oakley Capital Limited; *Int'l*, pg. 5504
SEAGULL MARITIME INFORMATION TECHNOLOGY—See Oakley Capital Limited; *Int'l*, pg. 5504
SEAGULL SCIENTIFIC, INC.—See Peak Rock Capital LLC; *U.S. Private*, pg. 3124
SEAGULL SHIPPING COMPANY; *Int'l*, pg. 6664
SEAH AEROSPACE & DEFENSE CO., LTD.—See SeAH Holdings Corp.; *Int'l*, pg. 6664
SEA HARVEST CORPORATION LIMITED—See Brimstone Investment Corporation Ltd.; *Int'l*, pg. 1164
SEAH AUTOMOTIVE (NANTONG) CO. LTD.—See SeAH Holdings Corp.; *Int'l*, pg. 6664
SEAHAWK GOLD CORP.; *Int'l*, pg. 6664
SEAH BESTEEL HOLDINGS CORPORATION—See SeAH Holdings Corp.; *Int'l*, pg. 6664
SEAH CHANGWON INTEGRATED SPECIAL STEEL CORPORATION—See SeAH Holdings Corp.; *Int'l*, pg. 6664
SEAH CSS CORP.—See SeAH Holdings Corp.; *Int'l*, pg. 6664
SEAH ENGINEERING CO., LTD.—See SeAH Holdings Corp.; *Int'l*, pg. 6664
SEAH ESAB CO. LTD.—See SeAH Holdings Corp.; *Int'l*, pg. 6664
SEAH E & T CORPORATION—See SeAH Holdings Corp.; *Int'l*, pg. 6664
SEAH FS CO., LTD.—See SeAH Holdings Corp.; *Int'l*, pg. 6664
SEAH GLOBAL INC.—See SeAH Holdings Corp.; *Int'l*, pg. 6664
SEAH GLOBAL THAILAND CO., LTD.—See SeAH Holdings Corp.; *Int'l*, pg. 6664
SEAH HOLDINGS CORP.; *Int'l*, pg. 6664
SEA HIBISCUS SDN BHD—See Hibiscus Petroleum Berhad; *Int'l*, pg. 3383
SEAH METAL CO. LTD—See SeAH Holdings Corp.; *Int'l*, pg. 6664
SEAH M&S CORP.—See SeAH Holdings Corp.; *Int'l*, pg. 6664
SEAH NETWORKS CO., LTD.—See SeAH Holdings Corp.; *Int'l*, pg. 6664
SEA HOLDINGS LIMITED; *Int'l*, pg. 6660
THE SEAHORSE FERRIES CO., LTD.—See Namyong Terminal Public Company Limited; *Int'l*, pg. 5137
THE SEAHORSE FERRY CO., LTD.—See Namyong Terminal Public Company Limited; *Int'l*, pg. 5137
SEAHORSE GEOMATICS, INCORPORATED—See Norbit ASA; *Int'l*, pg. 5415
SEAH PRECISION METAL INDONESIA. PT—See SeAH Holdings Corp.; *Int'l*, pg. 6664
SEAH PRECISION METAL (THAILAND) CO., LTD.—See SeAH Holdings Corp.; *Int'l*, pg. 6664
SEAH PRECISION MEXICO S.A DE C.V.—See SeAH Holdings Corp.; *Int'l*, pg. 6664
SEAH SPECIAL STEEL CO., LTD.—See SeAH Holdings Corp.; *Int'l*, pg. 6664
SEAH STEEL AMERICA, INC.—See SeAH Holdings Corp.; *Int'l*, pg. 6664

SEAH STEEL CORPORATION—See SeAH Holdings Corp.; *Int'l*, pg. 6664
SEAI AMERICA, INC.—See S-Energy Co., Ltd.; *Int'l*, pg. 6446
SEA-INVEST GROUP; *Int'l*, pg. 6661
SEA INVEST SHIPPING AGENCY N.V.—See SEA-invest Group; *Int'l*, pg. 6661
SEA ISLAND CLOTHIERS, LLC—See Brentwood Associates; *U.S. Private*, pg. 646
SEA ISLAND COMPANY; *U.S. Private*, pg. 3582
SEA ISLAND PROPERTIES, INC.—See Sea Island Company; *U.S. Private*, pg. 3582
SEAJACKS INTERNATIONAL LIMITED—See Marubeni Corporation; *Int'l*, pg. 4709
SEA JET INDUSTRIES DE CORP.; *U.S. Private*, pg. 3582
SEA KAY ENGINEERING SERVICES GAUTENG PROVINCE (PTY) LIMITED—See Sea Kay Holdings Ltd.; *Int'l*, pg. 6660
SEA KAY ENGINEERING SERVICES (PTY) LIMITED—See Sea Kay Holdings Ltd.; *Int'l*, pg. 6660
SEA KAY ENGINEERING SERVICES WESTERN CAPE (PTY) LIMITED—See Sea Kay Holdings Ltd.; *Int'l*, pg. 6660
SEA KAY HOLDINGS LTD.; *Int'l*, pg. 6660
SEA KAY PROPERTY DEVELOPMENT (PTY) LIMITED—See Sea Kay Holdings Ltd.; *Int'l*, pg. 6660
SEA KAY PROPERTY DEVELOPMENT WESTERN CAPE (PTY) LIMITED—See Sea Kay Holdings Ltd.; *Int'l*, pg. 6660
SE A&K CORPORATION—See SE Corporation; *Int'l*, pg. 6660
SEAL AFTERMARKET PRODUCTS LLC; *U.S. Private*, pg. 3584
SEAL ANALYTICAL GMBH—See Porvair plc; *Int'l*, pg. 5935
SEAL ANALYTICAL INC.—See Porvair plc; *Int'l*, pg. 5935
SEAL ANALYTICAL LIMITED—See Porvair plc; *Int'l*, pg. 5936
SEALAND CAPITAL GALAXY LIMITED; *Int'l*, pg. 6665
SEALAND CONTRACTORS CORP.; *U.S. Private*, pg. 3584
SEALAND EUROPE A/S—See A.P. Moller-Maersk A/S; *Int'l*, pg. 27
SEALAND MAERSK ASIA PTE. LTD.—See A.P. Moller-Maersk A/S; *Int'l*, pg. 27
SEALAND NATURAL RESOURCES INC.; *U.S. Private*, pg. 3584
SEALAND SECURITIES CO., LTD.; *Int'l*, pg. 6665
SEALANES (1985) PTY LTD—See Quadrant Private Equity Pty. Ltd.; *Int'l*, pg. 6149
SEALANTS EUROPE SAS—See PPG Industries, Inc.; *U.S. Public*, pg. 1710
SEALANT SYSTEMS INTERNATIONAL, INC.—See Illinois Tool Works Inc.; *U.S. Public*, pg. 1110
SEALASKA CONSTRUCTORS, LLC—See Sealaska Corporation; *U.S. Private*, pg. 3585
SEALASKA CORPORATION; *U.S. Private*, pg. 3584
SEALASKA ENVIRONMENTAL SERVICES, LLC—See Sealaska Corporation; *U.S. Private*, pg. 3585
SEALASKA GLOBAL LOGISTICS, LLC—See Sealaska Corporation; *U.S. Private*, pg. 3585
SEALASKA SECURITY HOLDINGS, LLC—See Sealaska Corporation; *U.S. Private*, pg. 3585
SEALASKA TIMBER CORPORATION—See Sealaska Corporation; *U.S. Private*, pg. 3585
SEALCO AIR CONTROLS INC.; *U.S. Private*, pg. 3585
SEALCO ASPHALT, INC.—See Rabine Paving America, LLC; *U.S. Private*, pg. 3341
SEALCOAT TECHNOLOGIES LLC—See BERICAP GmbH & Co. KG; *Int'l*, pg. 981
SEALCO LLC—See Angeles Equity Partners, LLC; *U.S. Private*, pg. 282
SEAL CONSULTING, INC.—See Lumen Technologies, Inc.; *U.S. Public*, pg. 1347
SEALD SWEET LLC—See CVC Capital Partners SICAV-FIS S.A.; *Int'l*, pg. 1886
SEAL DYNAMICS LIMITED—See HEICO Corporation; *U.S. Public*, pg. 1021
SEAL DYNAMICS LLC—See HEICO Corporation; *U.S. Public*, pg. 1021
SEAL DYNAMICS LLC—See HEICO Corporation; *U.S. Public*, pg. 1021
SEALECO AB—See Kingspan Group PLC; *Int'l*, pg. 4178
SEALECO AG—See Kingspan Group PLC; *Int'l*, pg. 4178
SEALECO B.V.—See Kingspan Group PLC; *Int'l*, pg. 4179
SEALECO LTD.—See Kingspan Group PLC; *Int'l*, pg. 4179
SEALECO N.V.—See Kingspan Group PLC; *Int'l*, pg. 4179
SEA-LECT PLASTIC CORP.—See Patrick Industries, Inc.; *U.S. Public*, pg. 1653
SEALED AIR AFRICA (PTY) LTD.—See Sealed Air Corporation; *U.S. Public*, pg. 1854
SEALED AIR AMERICAS MANUFACTURING S. DE R.L. DE C.V—See Sealed Air Corporation; *U.S. Public*, pg. 1854
SEALED AIR ARGENTINA S.A.—See Sealed Air Corporation; *U.S. Public*, pg. 1854
SEALED AIR (ASIA) HOLDINGS B.V.—See Sealed Air Corporation; *U.S. Public*, pg. 1854

SEALED AIR AUSTRALIA (HOLDINGS) PTY. LIMITED—See Sealed Air Corporation; *U.S. Public*, pg. 1854
SEALED AIR AUSTRALIA PTY. LIMITED—See Sealed Air Corporation; *U.S. Public*, pg. 1854
SEALED AIR B.V.—See Sealed Air Corporation; *U.S. Public*, pg. 1854
SEALED AIR (CANADA) CO.—See Sealed Air Corporation; *U.S. Public*, pg. 1854
SEALED AIR (CHINA) CO., LTD.—See Sealed Air Corporation; *U.S. Public*, pg. 1854
SEALED AIR CORPORATION - DANBURY—See Sealed Air Corporation; *U.S. Public*, pg. 1854
SEALED AIR CORPORATION; *U.S. Public*, pg. 1852
SEALED AIR CORPORATION (US)—See Sealed Air Corporation; *U.S. Public*, pg. 1854
SEALED AIR DE MEXICO S. DE R.L. DE C.V—See Sealed Air Corporation; *U.S. Public*, pg. 1855
SEALED AIR DENMARK A/S—See Sealed Air Corporation; *U.S. Public*, pg. 1854
SEALED AIR GMBH—See Sealed Air Corporation; *U.S. Public*, pg. 1854
SEALED AIR GMBH—See Sealed Air Corporation; *U.S. Public*, pg. 1854
SEALED AIR HONG KONG LIMITED—See Sealed Air Corporation; *U.S. Public*, pg. 1854
SEALED AIR HUNGARY KFT.—See Sealed Air Corporation; *U.S. Public*, pg. 1854
SEALED AIR (ISRAEL) LTD.—See Sealed Air Corporation; *U.S. Public*, pg. 1854
SEALED AIR JAPAN G.K.—See Sealed Air Corporation; *U.S. Public*, pg. 1854
SEALED AIR KOREA LIMITED—See Sealed Air Corporation; *U.S. Public*, pg. 1854
SEALED AIR LIMITED—See Sealed Air Corporation; *U.S. Public*, pg. 1854
SEALED AIR LIMITED—See Sealed Air Corporation; *U.S. Public*, pg. 1854
SEALED AIR LUXEMBOURG S.A.R.L—See Sealed Air Corporation; *U.S. Public*, pg. 1854
SEALED AIR NETHERLANDS HOLDINGS IV COOPERATIEF U.A.—See Sealed Air Corporation; *U.S. Public*, pg. 1854
SEALED AIR (NEW ZEALAND)—See Sealed Air Corporation; *U.S. Public*, pg. 1854
SEALED AIR (NEW ZEALAND)—See Sealed Air Corporation; *U.S. Public*, pg. 1854
SEALED AIR (NEW ZEALAND)—See Sealed Air Corporation; *U.S. Public*, pg. 1854
SEALED AIR NORGE AS—See Sealed Air Corporation; *U.S. Public*, pg. 1854
SEALED AIR OY—See Sealed Air Corporation; *U.S. Public*, pg. 1854
SEALED AIR PACKAGING (SHANGHAI) CO. LTD.—See Sealed Air Corporation; *U.S. Public*, pg. 1854
SEALED AIR PACKAGING S.R.L.—See Sealed Air Corporation; *U.S. Public*, pg. 1854
SEALED AIR (PHILIPPINES) INC.—See Sealed Air Corporation; *U.S. Public*, pg. 1854
SEALED AIR POLSKA SP. Z.O.O.—See Sealed Air Corporation; *U.S. Public*, pg. 1855
SEALED AIR S.A.S.—See Sealed Air Corporation; *U.S. Public*, pg. 1855
SEALED AIR SHRINK EQUIPMENT—See Sealed Air Corporation; *U.S. Public*, pg. 1855
SEALED AIR (SINGAPORE) PTE. LTD.—See Sealed Air Corporation; *U.S. Public*, pg. 1854
SEALED AIR S.L.—See Sealed Air Corporation; *U.S. Public*, pg. 1855
SEALED AIR S.R.L.—See Sealed Air Corporation; *U.S. Public*, pg. 1855
SEALED AIR S.R.O—See Sealed Air Corporation; *U.S. Public*, pg. 1855
SEALED AIR SVENSKA A.B.—See Sealed Air Corporation; *U.S. Public*, pg. 1855
SEALED AIR (TAIWAN) LIMITED—See Sealed Air Corporation; *U.S. Public*, pg. 1854
SEALED AIR (THAILAND) LTD.—See Sealed Air Corporation; *U.S. Public*, pg. 1854
SEALED AIR URUGUAY S.A.—See Sealed Air Corporation; *U.S. Public*, pg. 1855
SEALED AIR VERPACKUNGEN GMBH—See Sealed Air Corporation; *U.S. Public*, pg. 1855
SEALED AIR VITEMBAL S.L.—See Sealed Air Corporation; *U.S. Public*, pg. 1855
SEALEGS INTERNATIONAL LIMITED—See Future Mobility Solutions; *Int'l*, pg. 2857
SEALEGS (US) CORPORATION—See Future Mobility Solutions; *Int'l*, pg. 2857
SEAL ENGINEERING SA—See TechnipFMC plc; *Int'l*, pg. 7508
SEA LEVEL SEAFOODS, LLC—See Dulcich, Inc.; *U.S. Private*, pg. 1286
SEALEX, INC.; *U.S. Private*, pg. 3585
SEALEZE—See Jason Industries, Inc.; *U.S. Private*, pg. 2190
SEAL FOR LIFE INDUSTRIES, LLC—See Henkel AG & Co. KGaA; *Int'l*, pg. 3354

COMPANY NAME INDEX — SEARS PETROLEUM & TRANSPORT CORP.

SEAL FURNITURE SYSTEMS SAN DIEGO INC.; *U.S. Private*, pg. 3584
SEALIFE CORP.; *U.S. Public*, pg. 1855
SEA LIFE DEUTSCHLAND GMBH—See Merlin Entertainments plc; *Int'l*, pg. 4838
SEA LIFE HELSINKI OY—See Merlin Entertainments plc; *Int'l*, pg. 4838
SEA LIFE KONSTANZ GMBH—See Merlin Entertainments plc; *Int'l*, pg. 4838
SEA LIFE PARK HAWAII—See Newgate Private Equity LLP; *Int'l*, pg. 5235
SEALIFT CHEMICAL INCORPORATED—See Sealift Holdings Inc.; *U.S. Private*, pg. 3585
SEALIFT HOLDINGS INC.; *U.S. Private*, pg. 3585
SEALIFT INCORPORATED OF DELAWARE—See Sealift Holdings Inc.; *U.S. Private*, pg. 3585
SEALIFT TANKSHIPS INCORPORATED—See Sealift Holdings Inc.; *U.S. Private*, pg. 3585
SEA LIMITED; *Int'l*, pg. 6660
SEAL INCORPORATED BERHAD; *Int'l*, pg. 6665
SEAL INFOTECH PRIVATE LIMITED—See Lumen Technologies, Inc.; *U.S. Public*, pg. 1348
SEALING AGENTS WATERPROOFING, INC.; *U.S. Private*, pg. 3585
SEALING DEVICES INC.; *U.S. Private*, pg. 3585
SEALING EQUIPMENT PRODUCTS COMPANY, INC.; *U.S. Private*, pg. 3585
SEALING TECHNOLOGIES, INC.—See Parsons Corporation; *U.S. Public*, pg. 1651
SEALINK ENGINEERING AND SLIPWAY SDN BHD—See Sealink International Bhd; *Int'l*, pg. 6665
SEALINK INTERNATIONAL BHD; *Int'l*, pg. 6665
SEA LINK INTERNATIONAL IRB, INC.—See New Water Capital, L.P.; *U.S. Private*, pg. 2908
SEALINK SHIPYARD SDN BHD—See Sealink International Bhd; *Int'l*, pg. 6665
SEA LION CORPORATION; *U.S. Private*, pg. 3582
SEALITE SHIPPING CO., LTD.—See Stonepeak Partners L.P.; *U.S. Private*, pg. 3829
SEAL-KRETE INC.—See RPM International Inc.; *U.S. Public*, pg. 1817
SEALMASTER INDUSTRIES INC.; *U.S. Private*, pg. 3585
SEALMATIC INDIA LIMITED; *Int'l*, pg. 6665
SEALNET SDN. BHD.—See Dagang NeXchange Berhad; *Int'l*, pg. 1912
SEALORD GROUP LTD.; *Int'l*, pg. 6665
SEAL SANDS STORAGE LTD.—See Simon Group plc; *Int'l*, pg. 6932
SEAL SCIENCE, INC.—See Arcline Investment Management LP; *U.S. Private*, pg. 314
SEALS ENTERTAINMENT CORPORATION; *U.S. Private*, pg. 3585
SEAL SOFTWARE INC.—See DocuSign, Inc.; *U.S. Public*, pg. 672
SEALSQ CORP.; *Int'l*, pg. 6665
SEALS UNLIMITED HOLDING CO., INC.—See Applied Industrial Technologies, Inc.; *U.S. Public*, pg. 171
SEALS UNLIMITED, INC.—See Genuine Parts Company; *U.S. Public*, pg. 933
SEALTRON ACQUISITION CORP.—See AMETEK, Inc.; *U.S. Public*, pg. 116
SEALTRON INC.—See AMETEK, Inc.; *U.S. Public*, pg. 116
SEALTRON INC.—See AMETEK, Inc.; *U.S. Public*, pg. 116
SEALVE - SOCIEDADE ELECTRICA DE ALVAIAZERE SA—See Enel S.p.A.; *Int'l*, pg. 2414
SEALWELD (USA), INC.—See Entegris, Inc.; *U.S. Public*, pg. 776
SEALY ARGENTINA SRL—See Tempur Sealy International, Inc.; *U.S. Public*, pg. 1999
SEALY ASIA (HONG KONG) LTD—See Dyer Holdings Pty. Ltd.; *Int'l*, pg. 2238
SEALY ASIA (HONG KONG) LTD—See Tempur Sealy International, Inc.; *U.S. Public*, pg. 1999
SEALY ASIA (SINGAPORE) PTE. LTD.—See Dyer Holdings Pty. Ltd.; *Int'l*, pg. 2238
SEALY ASIA (SINGAPORE) PTE. LTD.—See Tempur Sealy International, Inc.; *U.S. Public*, pg. 1999
SEALY CANADA, LTD.—See Tempur Sealy International, Inc.; *U.S. Public*, pg. 1999
SEALY COMPONENTS GROUP - COLORADO SPRINGS—See Tempur Sealy International, Inc.; *U.S. Public*, pg. 1999
SEALY COMPONENTS GROUP - DELANO—See Tempur Sealy International, Inc.; *U.S. Public*, pg. 2000
SEALY CORPORATION—See Tempur Sealy International, Inc.; *U.S. Public*, pg. 1999
SEALY MATTRESS COMPANY OF ALBANY, INC.—See Tempur Sealy International, Inc.; *U.S. Public*, pg. 2000
SEALY MATTRESS COMPANY OF ILLINOIS—See Tempur Sealy International, Inc.; *U.S. Public*, pg. 2000
SEALY MATTRESS COMPANY OF KANSAS CITY, INC.—See Tempur Sealy International, Inc.; *U.S. Public*, pg. 2000
SEALY MATTRESS COMPANY OF PUERTO RICO—See Tempur Sealy International, Inc.; *U.S. Public*, pg. 2000
SEALY MATTRESS COMPANY—See Tempur Sealy International, Inc.; *U.S. Public*, pg. 2000
SEALY MATTRESS CORPORATION—See Tempur Sealy International, Inc.; *U.S. Public*, pg. 2000

SEALY OF AUSTRALIA; *Int'l*, pg. 6665
SEALY OF MARYLAND AND VIRGINIA, INC.—See Tempur Sealy International, Inc.; *U.S. Public*, pg. 2000
SEALY OF MINNESOTA, INC.—See Tempur Sealy International, Inc.; *U.S. Public*, pg. 2000
SEALY REAL ESTATE, INC.—See Tempur Sealy International, Inc.; *U.S. Public*, pg. 2000
SEALY & SMITH FOUNDATION; *U.S. Private*, pg. 3585
SEALY STEARNS & FOSTER MANUFACTURING - ATLANTA—See Tempur Sealy International, Inc.; *U.S. Public*, pg. 2000
SEALY STEARNS & FOSTER MANUFACTURING - HOUSTON—See Tempur Sealy International, Inc.; *U.S. Public*, pg. 2000
SEALY STEARNS & FOSTER MANUFACTURING - ORLANDO—See Tempur Sealy International, Inc.; *U.S. Public*, pg. 2000
SEALY TECHNOLOGY LLC—See Tempur Sealy International, Inc.; *U.S. Public*, pg. 2000
SEAMAN CORPORATION; *U.S. Private*, pg. 3585
SEAMAN PAPER ASIA CO LTD—See Seaman Paper Company of Massachusetts Inc.; *U.S. Private*, pg. 3585
SEAMAN PAPER COMPANY OF MASSACHUSETTS INC.; *U.S. Private*, pg. 3585
SEAMAP LIMITED—See MIND Technology, Inc.; *U.S. Public*, pg. 1448
SEAMAP PTE. LTD.—See MIND Technology, Inc.; *U.S. Public*, pg. 1448
SEAMAP (UK) LTD.—See MIND Technology, Inc.; *U.S. Public*, pg. 1448
SEAMAR MANAGEMENT S.A.—See Pangaea Logistics Solutions Ltd.; *U.S. Public*, pg. 1635
SEAMATES INTERNATIONAL INC.; *U.S. Private*, pg. 3585
SEAMCOM GMBH & CO. KG—See Droege Group AG; *Int'l*, pg. 2205
SEA MECHANICS CO., LTD.; *Int'l*, pg. 6661
SEAMECH INTERNATIONAL, INC.—See Bascom Hunter Technologies Inc.; *U.S. Private*, pg. 484
SEAMEC LIMITED—See HAL Offshore Limited; *Int'l*, pg. 3223
SEAMEN'S SOCIETY FOR CHILDREN AND FAMILIES; *U.S. Private*, pg. 3585
SEAM GROUP LLC—See ABB Ltd.; *Int'l*, pg. 56
SEAMILES LLC—See Intellectual Capital Group Ltd.; *Int'l*, pg. 3733
SEA MINERAL LIMITED—See Tongkah Harbour Public Company Limited; *Int'l*, pg. 7808
SEA MINERALS LIMITED (SML)—See Tongkah Harbour Public Company Limited; *Int'l*, pg. 7808
SEA MIST INC.; *U.S. Private*, pg. 3582
SEAMLESS DISTRIBUTION SYSTEMS AB; *Int'l*, pg. 6665
SEAMLESS EUROPE, LTD.—See Just Eat Takeaway.com N.V.; *Int'l*, pg. 4030
SEAMLESS GREEN CHINA (HOLDINGS) LIMITED; *Int'l*, pg. 6665
SEAMLESS GROUP INC.—See Currenc Group Inc.; *U.S. Public*, pg. 611
SEAMLESS NORTH AMERICA, LLC—See Just Eat Takeaway.com N.V.; *Int'l*, pg. 4030
SEAMLESS PUERTO RICO, INC.—See Hanesbrands Inc.; *U.S. Public*, pg. 983
SEAMLESS TEXTILES, LLC—See Hanesbrands Inc.; *U.S. Public*, pg. 983
SEAMLESS TUBES ASIA PACIFIC PTE LTD—See Vallourec SA; *Int'l*, pg. 8117
SEANAIR MACHINE CO., INC.—See AE Industrial Partners, LP; *U.S. Private*, pg. 112
SEANAIR MACHINE CO., INC.—See Broadtree Partners, LLC; *U.S. Private*, pg. 659
SEANERGY MARITIME HOLDINGS CORP.; *Int'l*, pg. 6665
SEAN JOHN CLOTHING, INC.—See Global Brands Group Holding Ltd; *Int'l*, pg. 2993
SEA OCEAN SHIPPING AGENCY PTE LTD—See Wilmar International Limited; *Int'l*, pg. 8421
SEA OIL PETROLEUM PTE. LTD.—See Sea Oil Public Company Limited; *Int'l*, pg. 6661
SEAOIL PHILIPPINES INC.; *Int'l*, pg. 6665
SEA OIL PUBLIC COMPANY LIMITED; *Int'l*, pg. 6661
SEAONICS AS—See Fincantieri S.p.A.; *Int'l*, pg. 2671
SEA OTTER CLASSIC, INC.—See Lifetime, Inc.; *U.S. Private*, pg. 2451
SEA PAC ENGINEERING, INC.; *U.S. Private*, pg. 3582
SEAPAC INC.; *U.S. Private*, pg. 3585
SEA-PAC SALES COMPANY; *U.S. Private*, pg. 3585
SEAPAK SHRIMP & SEAFOOD COMPANY—See Rich Holdings, Inc.; *U.S. Private*, pg. 3427
SEAPEAK LLC—See Stonepeak Partners L.P.; *U.S. Private*, pg. 3829
SEAPEARL HOTELS PRIVATE LIMITED—See Chalet Hotels Ltd; *Int'l*, pg. 1437
SEA PINES RESORT, LLC—See The Riverstone Group, LLC; *U.S. Private*, pg. 4110
SEAPLAST (INDIA) PRIVATE LIMITED—See Berry Global Group, Inc.; *U.S. Public*, pg. 325
SEAPORT CALIBRE MATERIALS ACQUISITION CORP.; *U.S. Public*, pg. 1855
SEAPORT CAPITAL, LLC; *U.S. Private*, pg. 3586

SEAPORT GLOBAL HOLDINGS LLC; *U.S. Private*, pg. 3586
SEAPORT GLOBAL SECURITIES LLC—See Seaport Global Holdings LLC; *U.S. Private*, pg. 3586
SEAPORT INTERNATIONAL INC.; *U.S. Private*, pg. 3586
SEAPORT MEAT COMPANY—See Pacific Ventures Group, Inc.; *U.S. Public*, pg. 1632
SEAPORT PRODUCTS CORP.; *U.S. Private*, pg. 3586
SEAPORT SOUND TERMINAL LLC—See Targa Resources Corp.; *U.S. Public*, pg. 1981
THE SEAPORT TITLE AGENCY LTD.—See LandStar Title Agency Inc.; *U.S. Private*, pg. 2387
SEAPORT WORLDWIDE SDN. BHD.—See MMC Corporation Berhad; *Int'l*, pg. 5005
SEA PR GMBH—See The Gate Worldwide Limited; *Int'l*, pg. 7649
SEAPRODEX REFRIGERATION INDUSTRY CORPORATION; *Int'l*, pg. 6665
SEA PRODUCTS INTERNATIONAL LTD.—See Westindia AB; *Int'l*, pg. 8390
SEAPS VIETNAM CO., LTD.—See Sumitomo Electric Industries, Ltd.; *Int'l*, pg. 7280
SEAP TRADING PTE. LTD.—See TEM Holdings Limited; *Int'l*, pg. 7546
SEAQC - SOCIETE D'EXPLOITATION DE L'AEROPORT DE QUIMPER—See VINCI S.A.; *Int'l*, pg. 8230
SEAQUIST GENERAL PLASTICS—See AptarGroup, Inc.; *U.S. Public*, pg. 175
SEA RAY BOATS, INC.—See Brunswick Corporation; *U.S. Public*, pg. 407
SEA RAY SPORT YACHTS INC.; *U.S. Private*, pg. 3582
SEARCE, INC.; *U.S. Private*, pg. 3586
THE SEARCH AGENCY—See Stagwell, Inc.; *U.S. Public*, pg. 1928
SEARCHASIA CONSULTING PTE. LTD.—See HRnetGroup Limited; *Int'l*, pg. 3502
SEARCH DISCOVERY, INC.; *U.S. Private*, pg. 3586
SEARCHES UK LIMITED—See NAHL Group plc; *Int'l*, pg. 5130
SEARCHFLOW LIMITED—See Daily Mail & General Trust plc; *Int'l*, pg. 1937
SEARCH FOR COMMON GROUND; *U.S. Private*, pg. 3586
SEARCHINA CO. LTD.—See SBI Holdings, Inc.; *Int'l*, pg. 6606
SEARCH INC.; *U.S. Private*, pg. 3586
SEARCH INFLUENCE, LLC; *U.S. Private*, pg. 3586
SEARCH INVESTMENT OFFICE LIMITED; *Int'l*, pg. 6665
SEARCH LIFE, INC.—See Hakuhodo DY Holdings Incorporated; *Int'l*, pg. 3222
SEARCHLIGHT CAPITAL PARTNERS, L.P.; *U.S. Private*, pg. 3586
SEARCHLIGHT ELECTRIC LTD.; *Int'l*, pg. 6666
SEARCHLIGHT MINERALS CORP.; *U.S. Public*, pg. 1855
SEARCHLIGHT PHARMA, INC.; *Int'l*, pg. 6666
SEARCHLIGHT PICTURES, INC.—See The Walt Disney Company; *U.S. Public*, pg. 2140
SEARCHLIGHT RESOURCES INC.; *Int'l*, pg. 6666
SEARCHMETRICS GMBH—See Verlagsgruppe Georg von Holtzbrinck GmbH; *Int'l*, pg. 8169
SEARCH MINERALS INC.; *Int'l*, pg. 6666
SEARCH MOJO; *U.S. Private*, pg. 3586
SEARCH ORGANIZACION DE SEGURIDAD, S.A.—See Allied Universal Manager LLC; *U.S. Private*, pg. 190
SEARCHPROS SOLUTIONS; *U.S. Private*, pg. 3591
SEARCH REPUBLIC LIMITED—See Webjet Limited; *Int'l*, pg. 8366
SEARCH TECHNOLOGIES LIMITED—See Accenture plc; *Int'l*, pg. 88
SEARCH TECHNOLOGIES, LLC—See Accenture plc; *Int'l*, pg. 88
SEARCH WIZARDS INC.; *U.S. Private*, pg. 3586
SEARCY NEWSPAPERS INC.—See Paxton Media Group LLC; *U.S. Private*, pg. 3116
SEA RESEARCH FOUNDATION INC.; *U.S. Private*, pg. 3582
THE SEARLE COMPANY LIMITED—See International Brands Private Limited; *Int'l*, pg. 3744
SEARLES DOMESTIC WATER COMPANY LLC—See NIRMA LIMITED; *Int'l*, pg. 5363
SEARLES VALLEY MINERALS EUROPE.—See NIRMA LIMITED; *Int'l*, pg. 5363
SEAROCK INC.—See Shandong Heavy Industry Group Co., Ltd.; *Int'l*, pg. 6754
SEARS AUTHORIZED HOMETOWN STORES, LLC—See Sears Hometown and Outlet Stores, Inc.; *U.S. Public*, pg. 1855
SEARS CONTRACT, INC.; *U.S. Private*, pg. 3591
SEARS HOME APPLIANCE SHOWROOMS, LLC—See Sears Hometown and Outlet Stores, Inc.; *U.S. Public*, pg. 1855
SEARS HOMETOWN AND OUTLET STORES, INC.; *U.S. Public*, pg. 1855
SEARS MANUFACTURING COMPANY; *U.S. Private*, pg. 3591
SEARS OUTLET STORES, LLC—See Sears Hometown and Outlet Stores, Inc.; *U.S. Public*, pg. 1855
SEARS PETROLEUM & TRANSPORT CORP.; *U.S. Private*, pg. 3591

SEARS ROEBUCK DE MEXICO, S. A. DE C. V.—See Grupo Carso, S.A.B. de C.V.; *Int'l*, pg. 3123
SEASAFE INC.—See Gibraltar Industries, Inc.; *U.S. Public*, pg. 935
SEA SAFE, INC.—See Gibraltar Industries, Inc.; *U.S. Public*, pg. 936
SEA S.A.—See Etex SA/NV; *Int'l*, pg. 2522
SEASCAPE SURVEYS PTE. LTD.—See Thoresen Thai Agencies Public Company Limited; *Int'l*, pg. 7718
SEASCOPE INSURANCE SERVICES LTD.; *Int'l*, pg. 6666
SEAS FABRIKKER AS—See Merry Electronics Co., Ltd.; *Int'l*, pg. 4838
SEASHORE INSURANCE & ASSOCIATION; *U.S. Private*, pg. 3591
SEASHORE ORGANIC MEDICINE INC.; *Int'l*, pg. 6666
SEASHORE SURGICAL INTITUTE, LLC—See UnitedHealth Group Incorporated; *U.S. Public*, pg. 2251
SEASIDE CHEVROLET LTD.; *Int'l*, pg. 6666
SEASIDE FESTIVAL AG—See CTS Eventim AG & Co. KGAA; *Int'l*, pg. 1873
SEASIDE FURNITURE SHOP INC.; *U.S. Private*, pg. 3591
SEASIDE HEALTH PLAN—See Memorial Health Services; *U.S. Private*, pg. 2664
SEASIDE HOTEL (THAILAND) CO. LTD—See Hotel Properties Limited; *Int'l*, pg. 3488
SEASIDE INSURANCE, INC.—See United Community Banks, Inc.; *U.S. Public*, pg. 2230
SEASIDE NATIONAL BANK & TRUST—See United Community Banks, Inc.; *U.S. Public*, pg. 2230
SEASIDE S.R.L.—See Italgas S.p.A.; *Int'l*, pg. 3828
SEASIDE SURGERY CENTER, LLC—See Tenet Healthcare Corporation; *U.S. Public*, pg. 2007
SEASIDE UTILITIES INC.; *U.S. Private*, pg. 3591
SEASIF EXPLORATION INC.; *Int'l*, pg. 6666
SEAS INDUSTRIES INC.; *U.S. Private*, pg. 3591
SEASONAIR, INC.—See Comfort Systems USA, Inc.; *U.S. Public*, pg. 544
SEASONAL CONCEPTS INC.—See HOM Furniture, Inc.; *U.S. Private*, pg. 1969
SEASON COMPONENTS CO., LTD.—See Season Group International Co., Ltd.; *Int'l*, pg. 6666
SEASON CONFECTIONARY & BAKERY SDN. BHD.—See ABR Holdings, Ltd.; *Int'l*, pg. 67
SEASON GROUP INTERNATIONAL CO., LTD.; *Int'l*, pg. 6666
SEASON GROUP MX S. DE R.L. DE C.V.—See Season Group International Co., Ltd.; *Int'l*, pg. 6666
SEASON GROUP USA LLC—See Season Group International Co., Ltd.; *Int'l*, pg. 6666
SEASON PRODUCE CO. INC.—See S&H Packing & Sales Co. Inc.; *U.S. Private*, pg. 3513
SEASONS APARTMENT HOTEL GROUP PTY. LTD.—See International Equities Corporation Limited; *Int'l*, pg. 3748
SEASONS DIALYSIS, LLC—See DaVita Inc.; *U.S. Public*, pg. 643
SEASONS FURNISHINGS LTD.; *Int'l*, pg. 6666
SEASONS RETIREMENT COMMUNITY—See Senior Lifestyle Corporation; *U.S. Private*, pg. 3607
SEASONS S.R.L.—See RCS MediaGroup S.p.A.; *Int'l*, pg. 6229
SEASONS TEXTILES LIMITED; *Int'l*, pg. 6666
SEASPACE CORP.; *U.S. Private*, pg. 3591
SEASPAN ADVISORY SERVICES LIMITED—See Seaspan Corporation; *Int'l*, pg. 6667
SEASPAN CORPORATION; *Int'l*, pg. 6666
SEASPAN CREW MANAGEMENT (INDIA) PVT. LTD.—See Seaspan Corporation; *Int'l*, pg. 6667
SEASPAN FERRIES CORPORATION—See Washington Corporations; *U.S. Private*, pg. 4446
SEASPAN MANAGEMENT SERVICES LIMITED—See Seaspan Corporation; *Int'l*, pg. 6667
SEASPAN SHIP MANAGEMENT LTD.—See Seaspan Corporation; *Int'l*, pg. 6667
SEASPINE HOLDINGS CORPORATION; *U.S. Private*, pg. 3591
SEASPINE, INC.—See SeaSpine Holdings Corporation; *U.S. Private*, pg. 3591
SEASSURANCE LIMITED—See AIP, LLC; *U.S. Private*, pg. 137
SEA STAR CAPITAL PLC; *Int'l*, pg. 6661
SEASTAR CHEMICALS ULC—See Avantor, Inc.; *U.S. Public*, pg. 242
SEA STAR LINE, LLC; *U.S. Private*, pg. 3582
SEASTAR MEDICAL HOLDING CORPORATION; *U.S. Public*, pg. 1855
SEA STARR ANIMAL HEALTH, LLC.; *U.S. Private*, pg. 3582
SEASTAR SOLUTIONS - PRIME LINE INDUSTRIAL CONTROLS—See Dometic Group AB; *Int'l*, pg. 2160
SEASTEMA S.P.A.—See Fincantieri S.p.A.; *Int'l*, pg. 2671
SEA-STRUCT INTERNATIONAL PTE LTD—See MTQ Corporation Limited; *Int'l*, pg. 5071
SEA-STRUCT PTY LTD—See MTQ Corporation Limited; *Int'l*, pg. 5071
SEA SUB SYSTEMS INC.—See GenNx360 Capital Partners, L.P.; *U.S. Private*, pg. 1672
SEASUCKER; *U.S. Private*, pg. 3591
SEA SWIFT PTY. LTD.; *Int'l*, pg. 6661

SEATAC STORAGE, LLC—See National Storage Affiliates Trust; *U.S. Public*, pg. 1498
SEATADVISOR, INC.—See Providence Equity Partners L.L.C.; *U.S. Private*, pg. 3293
SEA-TANKERS—See SEA-invest Group; *Int'l*, pg. 6661
SEA -TANK FRANCE, SA—See SEA-invest Group; *Int'l*, pg. 6661
SEAT DEUTSCHLAND GMBH—See Porsche Automobil Holding SE; *Int'l*, pg. 5929
SEATECH VENTURES CORP.; *Int'l*, pg. 6667
SEATEC UK LTD.—See Ackermans & van Haaren NV; *Int'l*, pg. 106
SEATEC UK LTD.—See STAR Capital Partners Limited; *Int'l*, pg. 7173
SEATEK COMPANY INC.—See Southwire Company, LLC; *U.S. Private*, pg. 3742
SEATEL, INC.—See Advent International Corporation; *U.S. Private*, pg. 100
SEATER CONSTRUCTION CO. INC.; *U.S. Private*, pg. 3591
SEATEX, LLC—See Cotton Creek Capital Management LLC; *U.S. Private*, pg. 1063
SEATING (PTY) LIMITED—See The Bidvest Group Limited; *Int'l*, pg. 7626
SEATORQUE CONTROL SYSTEMS, LLC; *U.S. Private*, pg. 3591
SEA TOW SERVICES INTERNATIONAL INC.; *U.S. Private*, pg. 3582
SEATRADE INTERNATIONAL COMPANY, INC.—See American Holdco Inc.; *U.S. Private*, pg. 236
SEA TRADE INTERNATIONAL, INC.—See China COSCO Shipping Corporation Limited; *Int'l*, pg. 1494
SEATRADE SHIP MANAGEMENT PTE LTD—See Singapore Shipping Corporation Limited; *Int'l*, pg. 6943
SEA TRAIL CORPORATION; *U.S. Private*, pg. 3582
SEATRAIL GULF RESORT; *U.S. Private*, pg. 3591
SEATRIUM LIMITED—See Sembcorp Industries Ltd.; *Int'l*, pg. 6702
SEATRONICS, INC.—See Buckthorn Partners LLP; *Int'l*, pg. 1210
SEATRONICS, INC.—See OEP Capital Advisors, L.P.; *U.S. Private*, pg. 2997
SEATRONICS LTD—See Buckthorn Partners LLP; *Int'l*, pg. 1210
SEATRONICS LTD.—See OEP Capital Advisors, L.P.; *U.S. Private*, pg. 2997
SEAT, S.A.—See Porsche Automobil Holding SE; *Int'l*, pg. 5929
SEATS INCORPORATED—See Nordic Group of Companies, Ltd.; *U.S. Private*, pg. 2937
SEATTLE AERO LLC; *U.S. Private*, pg. 3591
SEATTLE AQUARIUM; *U.S. Private*, pg. 3591
SEATTLE AUTOMOTIVE DISTRIBUTING; *U.S. Private*, pg. 3591
SEATTLE BOX CO.; *U.S. Private*, pg. 3591
SEATTLE CAPITAL MANAGEMENT COMPANY—See D.A. Davidson Companies; *U.S. Private*, pg. 1140
SEATTLE CEDAR HOMES—See Lindal Cedar Homes, Inc.; *U.S. Private*, pg. 2459
SEATTLE CITY LIGHT; *U.S. Private*, pg. 3591
SEATTLE COFFEE GEAR—See Sunrise Identity; *U.S. Private*, pg. 3870
SEATTLE CRAB CO.; *U.S. Private*, pg. 3591
SEATTLE FISH COMPANY; *U.S. Private*, pg. 3592
SEATTLE FISH COMPANY—See Investcorp Holdings B.S.C.; *Int'l*, pg. 3776
SEATTLE GOODWILL INDUSTRIES; *U.S. Private*, pg. 3592
SEATTLE GOURMET FOODS, INC.; *U.S. Private*, pg. 3592
SEATTLE IRON & METALS CORP.; *U.S. Private*, pg. 3592
SEATTLE KING COUNTY CONVENTION AND VISITORS BUREAU; *U.S. Private*, pg. 3592
SEATTLE MARINE & FISHING SUPPLY CO.; *U.S. Private*, pg. 3592
SEATTLE MARINERS BASEBALL CLUB; *U.S. Private*, pg. 3592
SEATTLE PACIFIC INDUSTRIES, INC.; *U.S. Private*, pg. 3592
SEATTLE PACIFIC INDUSTRIES, INC., UNIONBAY DIVISION—See Seattle Pacific Industries, Inc.; *U.S. Private*, pg. 3592
SEATTLEPI.COM—See The Hearst Corporation; *U.S. Private*, pg. 4048
SEATTLE POST-INTELLIGENCER—See The Hearst Corporation; *U.S. Private*, pg. 4048
SEATTLE'S BEST COFFEE INTERNATIONAL—See Roark Capital Group Inc.; *U.S. Private*, pg. 3455
SEATTLE'S BEST COFFEE LLC—See Starbucks Corporation; *U.S. Public*, pg. 1938
SEATTLE SEAHAWKS—See Vulcan Inc.; *U.S. Private*, pg. 4416
SEATTLE SERVICE BUREAU INC.; *U.S. Private*, pg. 3592
SEATTLE SHRIMP & SEAFOOD COMPANY, INC.—See Hanwa Co., Ltd.; *Int'l*, pg. 3263

SEATTLE SPECIALTY INSURANCE SERVICES, INC.—See QBE Insurance Group Limited; *Int'l*, pg. 6137
SEATTLE SUN TAN; *U.S. Private*, pg. 3592
SEATTLE TIMES COMPANY—See Blethen Corporation; *U.S. Private*, pg. 581
SEATTLE TIMES COMPANY—See Chatham Asset Management, LLC; *U.S. Private*, pg. 867
SEA TV NETWORK LIMITED; *Int'l*, pg. 6661
SEATWAVE NEDERLAND B.V.—See Live Nation Entertainment, Inc.; *U.S. Public*, pg. 1330
SEATWIRL AB; *Int'l*, pg. 6667
SEA UNION INTERNATIONAL LOGISTICS (HONG KONG) LTD.—See Tradia Corporation; *Int'l*, pg. 7889
SEA UNION INTERNATIONAL LOGISTICS (SHENZHEN) CO., LTD.—See Tradia Corporation; *Int'l*, pg. 7889
SEAUTO-E GMBH—See Sumitomo Electric Industries, Ltd.; *Int'l*, pg. 7280
SEAVIEW BUICK GMC; *U.S. Private*, pg. 3592
SEAVIEW RESOURCES INC.; *U.S. Private*, pg. 3592
SEAVIEW SUMMIT APARTMENTS—See Sequoia Equities Inc.; *U.S. Private*, pg. 3612
SEAVIN, INC.; *U.S. Private*, pg. 3592
SEAVUS AB; *Int'l*, pg. 6667
SEAWALL SOLAR 9 LLC—See NRG Energy, Inc.; *U.S. Public*, pg. 1551
SEAWARD SERVICES INC.; *U.S. Private*, pg. 3592
SEA WATCH INTERNATIONAL, LTD. - MAPPSVILLE PLANT—See Sea Watch International, Ltd.; *U.S. Private*, pg. 3583
SEA WATCH INTERNATIONAL, LTD.; *U.S. Private*, pg. 3582
SEAWATER SEAFOOD COMPANY; *U.S. Private*, pg. 3592
SEAWAY CHEVROLET CADILLAC BUICK GMC LTD; *Int'l*, pg. 6667
SEAWAY HEAVY LIFTING CONTRACTING GERMANY GMBH—See Subsea 7 S.A.; *Int'l*, pg. 7249
SEAWAY HEAVY LIFTING LIMITED—See Subsea 7 S.A.; *Int'l*, pg. 7249
SEAWAY HOTELS CORPORATION; *U.S. Private*, pg. 3592
SEAWAY MANUFACTURING CORP.; *U.S. Private*, pg. 3592
SEAWAY MARINE & INDUSTRIAL INC.—See Upper Lakes Group Inc.; *Int'l*, pg. 8093
SEAWAY OFFSHORE CABLES GMBH—See Subsea 7 S.A.; *Int'l*, pg. 7249
SEAWAY OFFSHORE CABLES LIMITED—See Subsea 7 S.A.; *Int'l*, pg. 7249
SEAWAY PLASTICS ENGINEERING, INC.; *U.S. Private*, pg. 3592
SEAWAY PRINTING COMPANY, INC.; *U.S. Private*, pg. 3592
SEAWELL AIR SERVICES LIMITED—See Massy Holdings Ltd.; *Int'l*, pg. 4724
SEAWEND LTD.—See Cedar Enterprises Inc.; *U.S. Private*, pg. 804
SEAWEST PROPERTIES, LLC—See The AES Corporation; *U.S. Public*, pg. 2032
SEA WIRE & CABLE INC.; *U.S. Private*, pg. 3583
SEAWORLD CALIFORNIA—See United Parks & Resorts Inc.; *U.S. Public*, pg. 2234
SEA WORLD OF FLORIDA LLC—See United Parks & Resorts Inc.; *U.S. Public*, pg. 2234
SEA WORLD OF TEXAS LLC—See United Parks & Resorts Inc.; *U.S. Public*, pg. 2234
SEAWORLD PARKS & ENTERTAINMENT LLC—See United Parks & Resorts Inc.; *U.S. Public*, pg. 2234
SEAWRIGHT HOLDINGS, INC.; *U.S. Private*, pg. 3592
SEAZEN GROUP LIMITED; *Int'l*, pg. 6667
SEAZEN HOLDINGS CO., LTD.—See Seazen Group Limited; *Int'l*, pg. 6667
SEBA APROZ S.A.—See The Federation of Migros Cooperatives; *Int'l*, pg. 7643
SEBA BROS. FARMS, INC.; *U.S. Private*, pg. 3592
SEBACS CO., LTD.—See Screen Holdings Co., Ltd.; *Int'l*, pg. 6655
SEB ADMINISTRATIVE SERVICES INC.—See The Co-operators Group Limited; *Int'l*, pg. 7634
SEB ADMINISTRATIVE SERVICES INDIA PRIVATE LTD.—See The Co-operators Group Limited; *Int'l*, pg. 7634
SEBAGO BREWING CO.; *U.S. Private*, pg. 3592
SEB AG—See Skandinaviska Enskilda Banken AB; *Int'l*, pg. 6977
SEBALDUS BETEILIGUNGS GMBH—See Schlott Gruppe AG; *Int'l*, pg. 6622
SEBALDUS GMBH—See Schlott Gruppe AG; *Int'l*, pg. 6622
SEBANG BATTERIES EUROPE GMBH—See Sebang Global Battery Co., Ltd.; *Int'l*, pg. 6669
SEBANG BUSAN NEW PORT CONTAINER DEPOT CO., LTD.—See Sebang Co., Ltd.; *Int'l*, pg. 6669
SEBANG BUSAN NEW PORT LOGISTICS CO., LTD.—See Sebang Co., Ltd.; *Int'l*, pg. 6669
SEBANG CO., LTD.; *Int'l*, pg. 6668
SEBANG ESTATES CO., LTD.—See Sebang Co., Ltd.; *Int'l*, pg. 6669

COMPANY NAME INDEX

SEBANG EXPRESS CO., LTD.—See Sebang Co., Ltd.; *Int'l*, pg. 6669
SEBANG GLOBAL BATTERY CO., LTD.; *Int'l*, pg. 6669
SEBANG GLOBAL (M) SDN BHD—See Sebang Global Battery Co., Ltd.; *Int'l*, pg. 6669
SEBANG GWANGYANG INTERNATIONAL LOGISTICS CO., LTD.—See Sebang Co., Ltd.; *Int'l*, pg. 6669
SEBANG INDUSTRIAL CO., LTD.—See Sebang Co., Ltd.; *Int'l*, pg. 6669
SEBANG LAND TRANSPORT CO., LTD.—See Sebang Co., Ltd.; *Int'l*, pg. 6669
SEBANG VINA CO., LTD.—See Sebang Co., Ltd.; *Int'l*, pg. 6669
SEB ASIA—See SEB S.A.; *Int'l*, pg. 6668
SEB ASSET MANAGEMENT NORGE AS—See Skandinaviska Enskilda Banken AB; *Int'l*, pg. 6977
SEB ASSET MANAGEMENT S.A.—See Skandinaviska Enskilda Banken AB; *Int'l*, pg. 6977
SEBASTIAN & ASSOCIATES, INC.; *U.S. Private*, pg. 3593
SEBASTIAN EQUIPMENT CO. INC.; *U.S. Private*, pg. 3593
SEBASTIAN EUROPE GMBH—See The Procter & Gamble Company; *U.S. Public*, pg. 2123
SEBASTIAN HOLDINGS, INC.; *U.S. Private*, pg. 3593
SEBASTIANI VENTURES CORP.; *Int'l*, pg. 6669
SEBASTIANI VINEYARDS, INC.—See Foley Family Wines Holdings Inc; *U.S. Private*, pg. 1558
SEBATA HOLDINGS; *Int'l*, pg. 6669
SEBATA MUNICIPAL SOLUTIONS (PROPRIETARY) LIMITED—See Sebata Holdings; *Int'l*, pg. 6669
SEB BANK JSC; *Int'l*, pg. 6667
SEB DEVELOPPEMENT S.A.—See SEB S.A.; *Int'l*, pg. 6668
SEBEL FURNITURE HOLDINGS PTY LTD—See GWA Group Limited; *Int'l*, pg. 3190
SEBEL FURNITURE LIMITED (NZ)—See Krueger International, Inc.; *U.S. Private*, pg. 2353
SEBEL FURNITURE LTD.—See Krueger International, Inc.; *U.S. Private*, pg. 2353
SEB ELU- JA PENSIONIKINDLUSTUS AS—See Skandinaviska Enskilda Banken AB; *Int'l*, pg. 6977
SEB ENSKILDA CORPORATE FINANCE OY AB—See Skandinaviska Enskilda Banken AB; *Int'l*, pg. 6977
SEBEREX GROUP LTD.—See TyRex Group, Ltd.; *U.S. Private*, pg. 4269
SEBESTA, INC.—See NV5 Global, Inc.; *U.S. Public*, pg. 1557
SEB FINANS AB—See Skandinaviska Enskilda Banken AB; *Int'l*, pg. 6977
SEB FONDER AB—See Skandinaviska Enskilda Banken AB; *Int'l*, pg. 6977
SEB FORETAGSINVEST—See Skandinaviska Enskilda Banken AB; *Int'l*, pg. 6977
SEB GYLLENBERG FONDBOLAG AB—See Skandinaviska Enskilda Banken AB; *Int'l*, pg. 6977
SEB HONG KONG TRADE SERVICES LTD—See Skandinaviska Enskilda Banken AB; *Int'l*, pg. 6977
SEBIA, INC.—See Caisse de Depot et Placement du Quebec; *Int'l*, pg. 1255
SEBIA, INC.—See CVC Capital Partners SICAV-FIS S.A.; *Int'l*, pg. 1884
SEBIA, INC.—See Tethys Invest SAS; *Int'l*, pg. 7576
SEBIA SA—See Caisse de Depot et Placement du Quebec; *Int'l*, pg. 1255
SEBIA SA—See CVC Capital Partners SICAV-FIS S.A.; *Int'l*, pg. 1884
SEBIA SA—See Tethys Invest SAS; *Int'l*, pg. 7575
SEBIGAS S.P.A.—See Societa Esercizi Commerciali Industriali; *Int'l*, pg. 7034
SEBINO FIRE RO S.R.L.—See Sebino S.p.A.; *Int'l*, pg. 6669
SEBINO SECURITY S.R.L.—See Sebino S.p.A.; *Int'l*, pg. 6669
SEBINO SERVICE S.R.L.—See Sebino S.p.A.; *Int'l*, pg. 6669
SEBINO S.P.A.; *Int'l*, pg. 6669
SEB INTERNAL SUPPLIER AB—See Skandinaviska Enskilda Banken AB; *Int'l*, pg. 6977
SEB INVESTMENT MANAGEMENT AB—See Skandinaviska Enskilda Banken AB; *Int'l*, pg. 6977
SEBITCHEM CO., LTD.; *Int'l*, pg. 6669
SEB KORT AB—See Skandinaviska Enskilda Banken AB; *Int'l*, pg. 6977
SEB LEASING, CJSC—See Skandinaviska Enskilda Banken AB; *Int'l*, pg. 6977
SEB LEASING OY—See Skandinaviska Enskilda Banken AB; *Int'l*, pg. 6977
SEB MERCHANT BANKING—See Skandinaviska Enskilda Banken AB; *Int'l*, pg. 6977
SEB OESTERREICH HANDELS GMBH—See SEB S.A.; *Int'l*, pg. 6668
SEBOL - COMERCIO E INDUSTRIA DE SEBO, S.A.—See SODIM, SGPS, SA; *Int'l*, pg. 7049
SEBO MANUFACTURING ENGINEERING CORP.; *Int'l*, pg. 6669
SEBONG VINA COMPANY LIMITED—See M2I Corporation; *Int'l*, pg. 4617

SE BORDNETZE-BULGARIA EOOD—See Sumitomo Electric Industries, Ltd.; *Int'l*, pg. 7279
SE BORDNETZE-MEXICO S.A. DE C.V.—See Sumitomo Electric Industries, Ltd.; *Int'l*, pg. 7279
SE BORDNETZE MOROCCO S.A.R.L.—See Sumitomo Electric Industries, Ltd.; *Int'l*, pg. 7279
SE BORDNETZE-POLSKA SP. Z.O.O.—See Sumitomo Electric Industries, Ltd.; *Int'l*, pg. 7279
SE BORDNETZE-SLOVAKIA S.R.O.—See Sumitomo Electric Industries, Ltd.; *Int'l*, pg. 7279
SE BORDNETZE TUNISIA S.A.R.L.—See Sumitomo Electric Industries, Ltd.; *Int'l*, pg. 7279
SEB PANK, AS—See Skandinaviska Enskilda Banken AB; *Int'l*, pg. 6977
SEB PRIVATE BANK—See Skandinaviska Enskilda Banken AB; *Int'l*, pg. 6977
SEBRING HOSPITAL MANAGEMENT ASSOCIATES, LLC—See HCA Healthcare, Inc.; *U.S. Public*, pg. 1008
SEBRING SOFTWARE, INC.; *U.S. Private*, pg. 3593
SEBRO PLASTICS, INC.—See Sonoco Products Company; *U.S. Public*, pg. 1906
SEB S.A.; *Int'l*, pg. 6667
SEB SECURITIES, INC.—See Skandinaviska Enskilda Banken AB; *Int'l*, pg. 6978
SEB SECURITIES SERVICE—See Skandinaviska Enskilda Banken AB; *Int'l*, pg. 6978
S.E. CABEZO NEGRO, S.A.—See Siemens Energy AG; *Int'l*, pg. 6902
SECA-LEASING GESELLSCHAFT M.B.H.—See UniCredit S.p.A.; *Int'l*, pg. 8035
SECANDA AG—See Mountain Capital Management AG; *Int'l*, pg. 5057
THE SECANT GROUP, LLC—See Compagnie Generale des Etablissements Michelin SCA; *Int'l*, pg. 1745
SECAP GROUPE PITNEY BOWES—See Pitney Bowes Inc.; *U.S. Public*, pg. 1694
SE CAPITAL, LLC; *U.S. Private*, pg. 3582
S.E. CARBUROS METALICOS S.A.—See Air Products & Chemicals, Inc.; *U.S. Public*, pg. 67
SECA SARL—See Toyota Tsusho Corporation; *Int'l*, pg. 7876
SECASI TECHNOLOGIES S.A.—See Schunk GmbH; *Int'l*, pg. 6643
SECA (SOCIETE D'EXPLOITATION ET DE CONSTRUCTION AERONAUTIQUES)—See Airbus SE; *Int'l*, pg. 246
S.E.C. AUTO SALES & SERVICES PCL; *Int'l*, pg. 6456
SECAUTO S.A—See Eiffage S.A.; *Int'l*, pg. 2331
SECBAT-BREGUET ATLANTIC—See Groupe Industriel Marcel Dassault S.A.; *Int'l*, pg. 3105
SECB SWISS EURO CLEARING BANK GMBH—See SIX Group AG; *Int'l*, pg. 6966
SEC CARBON, LIMITED - KYOTO PLANT—See SEC Carbon, Limited; *Int'l*, pg. 6670
SEC CARBON, LIMITED - OKAYAMA PLANT—See SEC Carbon, Limited; *Int'l*, pg. 6670
SEC CARBON, LIMITED; *Int'l*, pg. 6670
SECCO, INC.; *U.S. Private*, pg. 3593
SEC CONSULT AUSTRIA AG—See Atos SE; *Int'l*, pg. 692
SECCREDO AB—See Securitas AB; *Int'l*, pg. 6675
SECCREDO HOLDING AB—See Securitas AB; *Int'l*, pg. 6675
SEC ELECTRIC MACHINERY CO., LTD.; *Int'l*, pg. 6670
SEC ENERGIA SP. Z O.O.—See E.ON SE; *Int'l*, pg. 2259
SEC ENERGY PRODUCTS & SERVICES, L.P.—See Energy Transfer LP; *U.S. Public*, pg. 763
SECHE ALLIANCE SAS—See Groupe Seche SAS; *Int'l*, pg. 3110
SECHE ECO-INDUSTRIES SAS—See Groupe Seche SAS; *Int'l*, pg. 3110
SECHE ECO-SERVICES SAS—See Groupe Seche SAS; *Int'l*, pg. 3110
SECHE ENVIRONNEMENT SA—See Groupe Seche SAS; *Int'l*, pg. 3110
SECHE TRANSPORTS SAS—See Groupe Seche SAS; *Int'l*, pg. 3110
SECHRIST INDUSTRIES, INC.—See The Jordan Company, L.P.; *U.S. Private*, pg. 4062
SECHSTE VERMOGENSVERWALTUNGSGESELLSCHAFT DVB MBH—See Mercedes-Benz Group AG; *Int'l*, pg. 4829
SEC - IHI POWER GENERATION ENVIRONMENT PROTECTION ENGINEERING CO., LTD.—See Shanghai Electric Group Company Limited; *Int'l*, pg. 6765
SECIL, BETOES E INERTES, S.G.P.S., S.A.—See SODIM, SGPS, SA; *Int'l*, pg. 7049
SECIL BRITAS, S.A.—See SODIM, SGPS, SA; *Int'l*, pg. 7049
SECIL CABO VERDE COMERCIO E SERVICOS, LDA.—See SODIM, SGPS, SA; *Int'l*, pg. 7049
SECIL - COMPANHIA DE CIMENTO DO LOBITO, S.A.—See SODIM, SGPS, SA; *Int'l*, pg. 7049
SECIL - COMPANHIA GERAL DE CAL E CIMENTO, S.A.—See SODIM, SGPS, SA; *Int'l*, pg. 7049
SECILPAR, S.L.—See SODIM, SGPS, SA; *Int'l*, pg. 7049
SECION GMBH—See Allgeier SE; *Int'l*, pg. 337
SECITS HOLDING AB; *Int'l*, pg. 6670
SECKLER AG; *Int'l*, pg. 6670

SECOND HARVEST OF SOUTH GEORGIA, INC.

SEC-KSB PUMP CO., LTD.—See Shanghai Electric Group Company Limited; *Int'l*, pg. 6765
SECLA, SOCIEDADE DE EXPORTACAO E CERAMICA, S.A.; *Int'l*, pg. 6670
SEC LOBEZ SP. Z O.O.—See E.ON SE; *Int'l*, pg. 2259
SECMAIR—See FAYAT SAS; *Int'l*, pg. 2626
SECMARK CONSULTANCY LIMITED; *Int'l*, pg. 6670
SEC MASHIBAH SDN. BHD.—See Sanyo Engineering & Construction Inc.; *Int'l*, pg. 6564
SECM SDN. BHD.—See Sanyo Engineering & Construction Inc.; *Int'l*, pg. 6565
SEC NEWGATE S.P.A.; *Int'l*, pg. 6670
SECOA, INC.—See Wenger Corporation; *U.S. Private*, pg. 4481
SECO ARCHITECTURAL SYSTEM; *U.S. Private*, pg. 3593
SECODI; *Int'l*, pg. 6670
SECOMAK LIMITED - BECKAIR DIVISION—See Secomak Limited; *Int'l*, pg. 6672
SECOMAK LIMITED; *Int'l*, pg. 6672
SECOM ALPHA CO., LTD.—See SECOM Co., Ltd.; *Int'l*, pg. 6671
SECO MANUFACTURING COMPANY INC—See Trimble, Inc.; *U.S. Public*, pg. 2191
SECOM AUSTRALIA PTY. LTD.—See SECOM Co., Ltd.; *Int'l*, pg. 6671
SECOM (CHINA) CO., LTD—See SECOM Co., Ltd.; *Int'l*, pg. 6671
SECOM CO., LTD.; *Int'l*, pg. 6670
SECOM ENGINEERING CO., LTD.—See SECOM Co., Ltd.; *Int'l*, pg. 6671
SECOMFORT CO., LTD.—See SECOM Co., Ltd.; *Int'l*, pg. 6672
SECOMFORT TAMA CO., LTD.—See SECOM Co., Ltd.; *Int'l*, pg. 6672
SECOMFORT WEST CO., LTD.—See SECOM Co., Ltd.; *Int'l*, pg. 6672
SECOM GUARDALL NZ LTD.—See SECOM Co., Ltd.; *Int'l*, pg. 6671
SECOM HOKURIKU CO., LTD.—See SECOM Co., Ltd.; *Int'l*, pg. 6671
SECOM JASTIC CO., LTD.—See SECOM Co., Ltd.; *Int'l*, pg. 6671
SECOM JASTIC HOKURIKU CO., LTD.—See SECOM Co., Ltd.; *Int'l*, pg. 6671
SECOM JASTIC KOCHI CO., LTD.—See SECOM Co., Ltd.; *Int'l*, pg. 6671
SECOM JASTIC MIYAZAKI CO., LTD.—See SECOM Co., Ltd.; *Int'l*, pg. 6671
SECOM JASTIC SANIN CO., LTD.—See SECOM Co., Ltd.; *Int'l*, pg. 6672
SECOM JASTIC YAMANASHI CO., LTD.—See SECOM Co., Ltd.; *Int'l*, pg. 6672
SECOM JOSHINETSU CO., LTD.—See SECOM Co., Ltd.; *Int'l*, pg. 6672
SECOM (MALAYSIA) SDN BHD—See SECOM Co., Ltd.; *Int'l*, pg. 6671
SECOM MEDICAL SYSTEM CO., LTD.—See SECOM Co., Ltd.; *Int'l*, pg. 6672
SECOM MEDIPHARMA CO., LTD.—See SECOM Co., Ltd.; *Int'l*, pg. 6672
SECOM MIE CO., LTD.—See SECOM Co., Ltd.; *Int'l*, pg. 6672
SECOM MIYAZAKI CO., LTD.—See SECOM Co., Ltd.; *Int'l*, pg. 6672
SECOM PLC—See SECOM Co., Ltd.; *Int'l*, pg. 6672
SE COMPOSITES LIMITED—See Suzlon Energy Ltd.; *Int'l*, pg. 7353
SECOM SANIN CO., LTD.—See SECOM Co., Ltd.; *Int'l*, pg. 6672
SECOM SINGAPORE PTE LTD—See SECOM Co., Ltd.; *Int'l*, pg. 6672
SECOM STATIC RYUKYU CO., LTD.—See SECOM Co., Ltd.; *Int'l*, pg. 6672
SECOM TECH SANIN CO., LTD.—See SECOM Co., Ltd.; *Int'l*, pg. 6672
SECOM TOSEC CO., LTD.—See SECOM Co., Ltd.; *Int'l*, pg. 6672
SECOM TRUST SYSTEMS CO., LTD.—See SECOM Co., Ltd.; *Int'l*, pg. 6672
SECOM VIETNAM SECURITY SERVICE JSC—See SECOM Co., Ltd.; *Int'l*, pg. 6672
SECOM YAMANASHI CO., LTD.—See SECOM Co., Ltd.; *Int'l*, pg. 6672
SECOND2 LIMITED—See Reabold Resources Plc; *Int'l*, pg. 6230
SECOND ACT PRODUCTIONS LIMITED—See ITV plc; *Int'l*, pg. 3845
SECOND CHANCE INVESTMENTS PTE LTD—See Second Chance Properties Ltd.; *Int'l*, pg. 6672
SECOND CHANCE PROPERTIES LTD.; *Int'l*, pg. 6672
SECOND CITY CAPITAL PARTNERS; *Int'l*, pg. 6672
SECOND CITY PROPERTIES LIMITED—See Heidelberg Materials AG; *Int'l*, pg. 3319
SECOND CURVE CAPITAL, LLC; *U.S. Private*, pg. 3593
SECOND FAMILY INC.; *U.S. Private*, pg. 3593
SECOND HARVEST OF SOUTH GEORGIA, INC.; *U.S. Private*, pg. 3593

2417

SECOND HARVEST OF SOUTH GEORGIA, INC. CORPORATE AFFILIATIONS

SECOND IMAGE NATIONAL, INC.—See Aquiline Capital Partners LLC; *U.S. Private*, pg. 304
SECOND MEDIA INC.—See VerticalScope Holdings Inc.; *Int'l*, pg. 8175
SECOND NATIONAL BANK—See Park National Corporation; *U.S. Public*, pg. 1638
SECOND NATURE BRANDS, INC.—See CapVest Limited; *Int'l*, pg. 1318
SECOND OPINION INSURANCE SERVICES—See Marsh & McLennan Companies, Inc.; *U.S. Public*, pg. 1383
SECOND SOURCE MEDICAL LLC—See Medeon Biodesign, Inc.; *Int'l*, pg. 4769
SECOND STORY, INC.—See Publicis Groupe S.A.; *Int'l*, pg. 6110
SECOND STORY, INC.—See The Kroger Co.; *U.S. Public*, pg. 2109
SECOND STREET MEDIA, INC.—See Upland Software, Inc.; *U.S. Public*, pg. 2264
SECOND STREET SECURITIES, INC.—See SS&C Technologies Holdings, Inc.; *U.S. Public*, pg. 1922
SECOND TO NONE, INC.; *U.S. Private*, pg. 3593
SECOND WIND AIR PURIFIER COMPANY—See Tiercel Technology Corp.; *Int'l*, pg. 7744
SECON SOLAR LTD.—See Grafton Group plc; *Int'l*, pg. 3051
SE-CONSULTING GMBH—See Broadcom Inc.; *U.S. Public*, pg. 390
SE CONTRACTING NV—See VINCI S.A.; *Int'l*, pg. 8227
SECOO HOLDING LIMITED; *Int'l*, pg. 6673
SECOPA S.L.—See Artinova AB; *Int'l*, pg. 584
SECOP COMPRESSORS (TIANJIN) CO., LTD.—See Orlando Management AG; *Int'l*, pg. 5640
SECOP GMBH—See Orlando Management AG; *Int'l*, pg. 5640
SECOP S.R.O.—See Orlando Management AG; *Int'l*, pg. 5640
SECORE & NIEDZIALEK P.C.—See Eide Bailly LLP; *U.S. Private*, pg. 1347
SECOROC GHANA LTD.—See Epiroc AB; *Int'l*, pg. 2463
SE CORPORATION; *Int'l*, pg. 6660
SECOSAR ETIRAGE S.A.S.—See Saarstahl AG; *Int'l*, pg. 6461
SECOSAR S.A.S.—See Saarstahl AG; *Int'l*, pg. 6461
SECOS GMBH—See Lagercrantz Group AB; *Int'l*, pg. 4395
SECOS GROUP LIMITED; *Int'l*, pg. 6673
SECO S.P.A.; *Int'l*, pg. 6670
SECO TOOLS LLC—See Sandvik AB; *Int'l*, pg. 6535
SECO/WARWICK S.A.; *Int'l*, pg. 6670
SEC RADCON ALLIANCE, LLC—See Perma-Fix Environmental Services, Inc.; *U.S. Public*, pg. 1676
SEC RECRUITMENT LTD—See RDL Corporation Limited; *Int'l*, pg. 6230
SECRETARY PLUS MANAGEMENT SUPPORT BV—See Recruit Holdings Co., Ltd.; *Int'l*, pg. 6240
SECRETARY PLUS MANAGEMENT SUPPORT GMBH—See Recruit Holdings Co., Ltd.; *Int'l*, pg. 6240
SECRET CITY CHRYSLER DODGE JEEP; *U.S. Private*, pg. 3593
THE SECRET OF SECRET GARDEN SDN BHD—See Johor Corporation; *Int'l*, pg. 3994
SECRET SOUNDS GROUP PTY LTD—See Live Nation Entertainment, Inc.; *U.S. Public*, pg. 1330
SECRET SOUNDS GROUP SERVICES PTY LTD—See Live Nation Entertainment, Inc.; *U.S. Public*, pg. 1330
SEC SELECTA ENERGY CONSULTING GMBH—See EWE Aktiengesellschaft; *Int'l*, pg. 2575
SECTA S.A.—See TUV Rheinland Berlin-Brandenburg Pfalz e.V.; *Int'l*, pg. 7982
SECTEK INC.; *U.S. Private*, pg. 3593
SECTIGO LIMITED—See Francisco Partners Management, LP; *U.S. Private*, pg. 1591
SECTIONAL STAMPING, INC.—See Shiloh Industries, Inc.; *U.S. Private*, pg. 3636
SECTION EIGHT, INC.; *U.S. Private*, pg. 3593
SECTOR 10, INC.; *U.S. Public*, pg. 1855
SECTOR 5 DIGITAL, LLC—See The Glimpse Group, Inc.; *U.S. Public*, pg. 2075
SECTOR 5, INC.; *U.S. Public*, pg. 1855
SECTOR7 USA INC.; *U.S. Private*, pg. 3593
SECTOR 9, INC.—See Transom Capital Group, LLC; *U.S. Private*, pg. 4209
SECTOR ALARM AS—See Isanor Invest AS; *Int'l*, pg. 3812
SECTOR AVIATION HOLDINGS LTD. (SAH); *Int'l*, pg. 6673
SECTORIEL SA—See Thermador Groupe; *Int'l*, pg. 7707
SECTOR MD, S.L.—See Vocento, S.A.; *Int'l*, pg. 8284
SEC TP SAS—See VINCI S.A.; *Int'l*, pg. 8226
SECTRA AB; *Int'l*, pg. 6673
SECTRA A/S—See Sectra AB; *Int'l*, pg. 6673
SECTRACK N.V.—See Geotab, Inc.; *Int'l*, pg. 2941
SECTRA COMMUNICATIONS AB—See Sectra AB; *Int'l*, pg. 6673
SECTRA COMMUNICATIONS BV—See Sectra AB; *Int'l*, pg. 6673
SECTRA COMMUNICATIONS OY—See Sectra AB; *Int'l*, pg. 6673
SECTRA GMBH—See Sectra AB; *Int'l*, pg. 6673
SECTRA IMAXPERTS B.V.—See Sectra AB; *Int'l*, pg. 6673

SECTRA IMTEC AB—See Sectra AB; *Int'l*, pg. 6673
SECTRA INC.—See Sectra AB; *Int'l*, pg. 6673
SECTRA ITALIA S.R.L.—See Sectra AB; *Int'l*, pg. 6673
SECTRA LTD—See Sectra AB; *Int'l*, pg. 6673
SECTRA MEDICAL SYSTEMS GMBH—See Sectra AB; *Int'l*, pg. 6673
SECTRA MEDICAL SYSTEMS S.L.—See Sectra AB; *Int'l*, pg. 6673
SECTRA NA, INC.—See Sectra AB; *Int'l*, pg. 6673
SECTRAN SECURITY, INC.; *U.S. Private*, pg. 3593
SECTRA PTY. LTD.—See Sectra AB; *Int'l*, pg. 6673
SECTRA SECURE TRANSMISSION AB—See Sectra AB; *Int'l*, pg. 6673
SECTRA SKANDINAVIEN AB—See Sectra AB; *Int'l*, pg. 6673
SECUAL, INC.—See Vector Inc.; *Int'l*, pg. 8144
SECUAVAIL INC.; *Int'l*, pg. 6673
SECUCEN CO LTD; *Int'l*, pg. 6673
SECULETTER CO., LTD.; *Int'l*, pg. 6673
SECUNDAIRE BOUWSTOFFEN UNIE B.V.—See Sweco AB; *Int'l*, pg. 7363
SECUNDERABAD HEALTHCARE LIMITED; *Int'l*, pg. 6673
SECUNET SECURITY NETWORKS AG—See Giesecke & Devrient GmbH; *Int'l*, pg. 2970
SECUOYA GRUPO DE COMUNICACION, S.A.—See N Mas Uno IBG SA; *Int'l*, pg. 5115
SECUPRINT INC.—See DSS, Inc.; *U.S. Public*, pg. 689
SECURADYNE SYSTEMS LLC—See Allied Universal Manager LLC; *U.S. Private*, pg. 191
SECURA GROUP LIMITED; *Int'l*, pg. 6673
SECURA INSURANCE COMPANY; *U.S. Private*, pg. 3593
SECURAMERICA, LLC—See Allied Universal Manager LLC; *U.S. Private*, pg. 191
SECURAPLANE TECHNOLOGIES INC.—See Parker Hannifin Corporation; *U.S. Public*, pg. 1643
SECURA SINGAPORE PTE. LTD.—See Secura Group Limited; *Int'l*, pg. 6674
SECURA TRAINING ACADEMY PTE. LTD.—See Secura Group Limited; *Int'l*, pg. 6674
SECURBORATION, INC.; *U.S. Private*, pg. 3593
SECURCAPITAL HOLDINGS CORP.; *U.S. Public*, pg. 1855
SECURCARE PROPERTIES II, LLC—See National Storage Affiliates Trust; *U.S. Public*, pg. 1498
SECURCARE SELF STORAGE, INC.—See National Storage Affiliates Trust; *U.S. Public*, pg. 1498
SECURCASH B.V.—See Allied Universal Manager LLC; *U.S. Private*, pg. 190
SECURCASH NEDERLAND B.V.—See Diebold Nixdorf, Inc.; *U.S. Public*, pg. 660
SECUR CREDENTIALS LTD.; *Int'l*, pg. 6673
SECURE-24, LLC—See Nippon Telegraph & Telephone Corporation; *Int'l*, pg. 5345
SECURE2GO GROUP LIMITED; *Int'l*, pg. 6674
SECUREBUY, LLC; *U.S. Private*, pg. 3594
SECURE CASH NETWORK, INC.; *U.S. Private*, pg. 3593
SECURECOM INC.; *U.S. Private*, pg. 3594
SECURE COMMUNICATION SYSTEMS, INC.—See Vance Street Capital LLC; *U.S. Private*, pg. 4342
SECURE DATA EUROPE LTD—See Orange S.A.; *Int'l*, pg. 5610
SECURE DATA, INC.—See Kelso & Company, L.P.; *U.S. Private*, pg. 2278
SECURED CAPITAL INVESTMENT MANAGEMENT CO., LTD.—See PAG Capital; *Int'l*, pg. 5697
SECURE DESIGNS, INC.; *U.S. Private*, pg. 3593
SECURE DIGITAL, INC.; *U.S. Private*, pg. 3593
SECURED LAND TRANSFERS LLC—See Anywhere Real Estate Inc.; *U.S. Public*, pg. 142
SECURED SERVICES, INC.; *U.S. Public*, pg. 1855
SECURE EARTH TECHNOLOGIES LIMITED; *Int'l*, pg. 6674
SECURE ELECTRONIC TECHNOLOGY PLC.; *Int'l*, pg. 6674
SECURE ENERGY SERVICES INC. - EMERSON CLASS IB WATER DISPOSAL FACILITY—See Secure Energy Services Inc.; *Int'l*, pg. 6674
SECURE ENERGY SERVICES INC. - FOX CREEK FULL SERVICE TERMINAL (FST)—See Secure Energy Services Inc.; *Int'l*, pg. 6674
SECURE ENERGY SERVICES INC. - KOTCHO CLASS IB FLUIDS SEPARATION/DISPOSAL FACILITY—See Secure Energy Services Inc.; *Int'l*, pg. 6674
SECURE ENERGY SERVICES INC. - NOSEHILL CLASS IB WATER DISPOSAL FACILITY—See Secure Energy Services Inc.; *Int'l*, pg. 6674
SECURE ENERGY SERVICES INC. - OBED CLASS IB WATER DISPOSAL FACILITY—See Secure Energy Services Inc.; *Int'l*, pg. 6674
SECURE ENERGY SERVICES INC. - PEMBINA CLASS I & CLASS II OILFIELD LANDFILL—See Secure Energy Services Inc.; *Int'l*, pg. 6674
SECURE ENERGY SERVICES INC.; *Int'l*, pg. 6674
SECURE ENERGY SERVICES INC. - SOUTH GRANDE PRAIRIE CLASS II OILFIELD LANDFILL—See Secure Energy Services Inc.; *Int'l*, pg. 6674

SECURE ENERGY SERVICES INC. - WILLESDEN GREEN CLASS II OILFIELD LANDFILL—See Secure Energy Services Inc.; *Int'l*, pg. 6674
SECURE ENTERPRISES, LLC; *U.S. Private*, pg. 3593
SECURE EQUIPMENT TRADING SDN. BHD.—See Nicolas Correa S.A.; *Int'l*, pg. 5273
SECURE EXCHANGE SOLUTIONS, INC.; *U.S. Private*, pg. 3593
SECURE FOUNDATION SYSTEMS, INC; *U.S. Private*, pg. 3593
SECURE GLASS HOLDING AB—See Lindengruppen AB; *Int'l*, pg. 4511
SECUREGUARD GMBH—See Kontron AG; *Int'l*, pg. 4278
SECURE IDEAS, LLC; *U.S. Private*, pg. 3593
SECURE INCOME REIT PLC—See LondonMetric Property Plc; *Int'l*, pg. 4548
SECURE INC.; *Int'l*, pg. 6674
SECURE INFO CO., LTD.—See Samart Corporation Public Company Limited; *Int'l*, pg. 6502
SECUREINFO CORPORATION—See Kratos Defense & Security Solutions, Inc.; *U.S. Public*, pg. 1277
SECURE INFORMATION MANAGEMENT GMBH—See Zech Group SE; *Int'l*, pg. 8628
SECURE INTERNATIONAL FINANCE CO. INC.—See Edward B. Beharry & Co. Ltd.; *Int'l*, pg. 2316
SECUREKLOUD TECHNOLOGIES INC.—See Securekloud Technologies Ltd.; *Int'l*, pg. 6674
SECUREKLOUD TECHNOLOGIES LTD.; *Int'l*, pg. 6674
SECURELEMENT INFRASTRUCTURE SOLUTIONS LLC—See IT Solutions Consulting LLC; *U.S. Private*, pg. 2148
SECURE LINE S.R.L—See Bunzl plc; *Int'l*, pg. 1219
SECURELINK BELGIUM N.V.—See Orange S.A.; *Int'l*, pg. 5610
SECURELINK GROUP N.V.—See Orange S.A.; *Int'l*, pg. 5610
SECURE LIVING PTY. LIMITED—See Peet Limited; *Int'l*, pg. 5780
SECURE LOGIC PTY. LTD.—See Thales S.A.; *Int'l*, pg. 7601
SECUREMETRIC BERHAD; *Int'l*, pg. 6674
SECUREMETRIC TECHNOLOGY, INC.—See Securemetric Berhad; *Int'l*, pg. 6674
SECUREMETRIC TECHNOLOGY PTE. LTD.—See Securemetric Berhad; *Int'l*, pg. 6674
SECURENTA CONSEIL—See Belfius Bank SA/NV; *Int'l*, pg. 963
SECURE NURSING SERVICE, INC.—See Kingsway Financial Services Inc.; *U.S. Public*, pg. 1235
SECURENVOY GMBH—See Shearwater Group plc; *Int'l*, pg. 6792
SECURENVOY, INC.—See Shearwater Group plc; *Int'l*, pg. 6792
SECURENVOY LIMITED—See Shearwater Group plc; *Int'l*, pg. 6792
SECUREONEASIA PTE. LTD.—See Multi-Chem Limited; *Int'l*, pg. 5082
SECURE PARKING CORPORATION SDN. BHD.—See PARK24 Co. Ltd.; *Int'l*, pg. 5743
SECURE PARKING PTY. LTD.—See PARK24 Co. Ltd.; *Int'l*, pg. 5743
SECURE PARKING SINGAPORE PTE. LTD.—See PARK24 Co. Ltd.; *Int'l*, pg. 5743
SECURE PAYMENT SOLUTIONS PTY LTD.—See Global Payments Inc.; *U.S. Public*, pg. 944
SECUREPOST AG—See Die Schweizerische Post AG; *Int'l*, pg. 2113
SECURE PROPERTY DEVELOPMENT & INVESTMENT LIMITED; *Int'l*, pg. 6674
SECURE ROOFING & SOLAR, INC.—See Solar Integrated Roofing Corporation; *U.S. Public*, pg. 1900
SECURE SENTINEL AUSTRALIA PTY LIMITED—See Equifax Inc.; *U.S. Public*, pg. 787
SECURE SENTINEL NEW ZEALAND LIMITED—See Equifax Inc.; *U.S. Public*, pg. 787
SECURE SENTINEL PTY LIMITED—See Suncorp Group Limited; *Int'l*, pg. 7311
SECURE SERVICE S.R.L.—See Bunzl plc; *Int'l*, pg. 1219
SECURESTATE LLC—See RSM US LLP; *U.S. Private*, pg. 3497
SECURE SYSTEMS & TECHNOLOGIES LTD—See AEA Investors LP; *U.S. Private*, pg. 113
SECURE TANGENT SDN. BHD.—See MPHB Capital Berhad; *Int'l*, pg. 5062
SECURE TECHNOLOGY INTEGRATION GROUP LTD.; *U.S. Private*, pg. 3594
SECURE TRUST BANK PLC; *Int'l*, pg. 6674
SECUREUSA INC.—See CVC Capital Partners SICAV-FIS S.A.; *Int'l*, pg. 1886
SECUREVISION, W.S GAUCI LTD.—See Hi Sharp Electronics Co., Ltd.; *Int'l*, pg. 3379
SECUREWORKS CORP.—See Dell Technologies Inc.; *U.S. Public*, pg. 650
SECUREWORKS EUROPE S.R.L.—See Dell Technologies Inc.; *U.S. Public*, pg. 651
SECUREWORKS, INC.—See Dell Technologies Inc.; *U.S. Public*, pg. 651
SECUREX GS PTE. LTD.—See IPS Securex Holdings Limited; *Int'l*, pg. 3798

COMPANY NAME INDEX

SECUREXPERT SOLUTIONS LIMITED—See ISP Holdings Limited; *Int'l*, pg. 3821
SECUREXPRESS SERVICES SDN BHD—See Berjaya Corporation Berhad; *Int'l*, pg. 984
SECURIAN FINANCIAL GROUP, INC.; *U.S. Private*, pg. 3594
SECURIAN FINANCIAL SERVICES, INC.—See Securian Financial Group, Inc.; *U.S. Private*, pg. 3594
SECURICO CO., LTD.—See Howa Machinery, Ltd.; *Int'l*, pg. 3493
SECURICON, LLC.—See Risk Mitigation Consulting Inc.; *U.S. Private*, pg. 3441
SECURIDOR LIMITED—See Quanex Building Products Corp.; *U.S. Public*, pg. 1750
SECURIFUND NV—See Belfius Bank SA/NV; *Int'l*, pg. 963
SECURIGENCE LLC—See Chenega Corporation; *U.S. Private*, pg. 872
SECURIGLOBE INC.—See La Capitale Civil Service Mutual; *Int'l*, pg. 4387
SECURIGUARD, INC.; *U.S. Private*, pg. 3594
SECURIGUARD SERVICES LIMITED; *Int'l*, pg. 6675
SECURINFOR SA—See Compagnie Lebon SA; *Int'l*, pg. 1745
SECURIOT APS—See Novotek AB; *Int'l*, pg. 5471
SECURISERVICES SDN BHD—See Berjaya Corporation Berhad; *Int'l*, pg. 983
SECURISOL, S. A.—See Melia Hotels International, S.A.; *Int'l*, pg. 4810
SECURIS; *U.S. Private*, pg. 3594
SECURISTYLE GROUP HOLDINGS LIMITED—See ASSA ABLOY AB; *Int'l*, pg. 640
SECURITAG ASSEMBLY GROUP CO., LTD.; *Int'l*, pg. 6675
SECURITAS AB; *Int'l*, pg. 6675
SECURITAS AG; *Int'l*, pg. 6676
SECURITAS AKADEMIE GMBH—See Securitas AB; *Int'l*, pg. 6675
SECURITAS ALERT SERVICES GMBH—See Securitas AB; *Int'l*, pg. 6675
SECURITAS ALERT SERVICES POLSKA SP.Z O.O.—See Securitas AB; *Int'l*, pg. 6675
SECURITAS ARGENTINA S.A.—See Securitas AB; *Int'l*, pg. 6676
SECURITAS ASIA HOLDING AB—See Securitas AB; *Int'l*, pg. 6675
SECURITAS AVIATION SERVICE GMBH & CO. KG—See Securitas AB; *Int'l*, pg. 6675
SECURITAS BH D.O.O.—See Securitas AB; *Int'l*, pg. 6675
SECURITAS CANADA LIMITED—See Securitas AB; *Int'l*, pg. 6675
SECURITAS CR, S.R.O.—See Securitas AB; *Int'l*, pg. 6675
SECURITAS DEUTSCHLAND HOLDING GMBH & CO. KG—See Securitas AB; *Int'l*, pg. 6675
SECURITAS DIRECT AB—See Bain Capital, LP; *U.S. Private*, pg. 444
SECURITAS DIRECT AB—See Hellman & Friedman LLC; *U.S. Private*, pg. 1910
SECURITAS DIRECT S.A.—See Securitas AG; *Int'l*, pg. 6676
SECURITAS EESTI AS—See Securitas AB; *Int'l*, pg. 6675
SECURITAS EGYPT LLC—See Securitas AB; *Int'l*, pg. 6675
SECURITAS ELECTRONIC SECURITY INC.—See Securitas AB; *Int'l*, pg. 6675
SECURITAS FLUGVERKEHR SERVICES GMBH—See Securitas AB; *Int'l*, pg. 6675
SECURITAS FRANCE S.A.R.L.—See Securitas AB; *Int'l*, pg. 6676
SECURITAS GMBH MOBIL—See Securitas AB; *Int'l*, pg. 6675
SECURITAS GMBH—See Securitas AB; *Int'l*, pg. 6675
SECURITAS GUARDING SERVICES (SINGAPORE) PTE LTD.—See Securitas AB; *Int'l*, pg. 6676
SECURITAS HOLDINGS INC.; *U.S. Private*, pg. 3594
SECURITAS HRVATSKA D.O.O—See Securitas AB; *Int'l*, pg. 6676
SECURITAS INVEST AB—See Securitas AB; *Int'l*, pg. 6676
SECURITAS (LIECHTENSTEIN) AG—See Securitas AG; *Int'l*, pg. 6676
SECURITAS NV/SA—See Securitas AB; *Int'l*, pg. 6676
SECURITAS N.V.—See Securitas AB; *Int'l*, pg. 6676
SECURITAS OY—See Securitas AB; *Int'l*, pg. 6676
SECURITAS PERSONALMANAGEMENT GMBH—See Securitas AB; *Int'l*, pg. 6675
SECURITAS POLSKA SP. Z O.O.—See Securitas AB; *Int'l*, pg. 6676
SECURITAS SAFETY COOPERATION SERVICE GMBH & CO. KG—See Securitas AB; *Int'l*, pg. 6675
SECURITAS SA HOLDINGS PTY. LTD.—See Securitas AB; *Int'l*, pg. 6676
SECURITAS S.A.—See Securitas AB; *Int'l*, pg. 6676
SECURITAS SA—See Securitas AB; *Int'l*, pg. 6676
SECURITAS SECURITY SERVICES USA, INC.—See Securitas AB; *Int'l*, pg. 6676
SECURITAS SECURITY SERVICES USA, INC.—See Securitas AB; *Int'l*, pg. 6676

SECURITAS SECURITY SERVICES USA, INC. - WESTERN OPERATIONS CENTER—See Securitas AB; *Int'l*, pg. 6676
SECURITAS SEGURIDAD ESPANA, S.A.—See Securitas AB; *Int'l*, pg. 6676
SECURITAS SEGURIDAD HOLDING SL—See Securitas AB; *Int'l*, pg. 6676
SECURITAS SERVICES D.O.O.—See Securitas AB; *Int'l*, pg. 6676
SECURITAS SERVICES HOLDING U.K. LTD.—See Securitas AB; *Int'l*, pg. 6676
SECURITAS SERVICES INTERNATIONAL B.V.—See Securitas AB; *Int'l*, pg. 6676
SECURITAS SERVICES ROMANIA SRL—See Securitas AB; *Int'l*, pg. 6676
SECURITAS - SERVICOS E TECNOLOGIA DE SEGURANCA, S.A—See Securitas AB; *Int'l*, pg. 6675
SECURITAS SICHERHEITSDIENSTE GMBH & CO. KG—See Securitas AB; *Int'l*, pg. 6675
SECURITAS SICHERHEITSDIENSTLEISTUNGEN GMBH—See Securitas AB; *Int'l*, pg. 6675
SECURITAS SICHERHEIT & SERVICE GMBH & CO. KG—See Securitas AB; *Int'l*, pg. 6675
SECURITAS—See Securitas AB; *Int'l*, pg. 6675
SECURITAS SVERIGE AB—See Securitas AB; *Int'l*, pg. 6676
SECURITAS TOOLBOX LTD—See Securitas AB; *Int'l*, pg. 6676
SECURITAS TREASURY IRELAND LTD.—See Securitas AB; *Int'l*, pg. 6676
SECURITAS UK—See Securitas AB; *Int'l*, pg. 6676
SECURITAS URUGUAY SA—See Securitas AB; *Int'l*, pg. 6676
SECURITE CHEMINEES INTERNATIONAL LTEE—See Lennox International Inc.; *U.S. Public*, pg. 1308
SECURITECH GROUP, INC.—See ASSA ABLOY AB; *Int'l*, pg. 640
SECURITEC SCREENING SOLUTIONS, INC.—See Appriss Holdings, Inc.; *U.S. Private*, pg. 300
SECURITEST S.A—See SGS SA; *Int'l*, pg. 6746
SECURITIES AMERICA ADVISORS, INC.—See Reverence Capital Partners LLC; *U.S. Private*, pg. 3415
SECURITIES AMERICA FINANCIAL CORPORATION—See Reverence Capital Partners LLC; *U.S. Private*, pg. 3415
SECURITIES AMERICA, INC.—See Reverence Capital Partners LLC; *U.S. Private*, pg. 3415
SECURITIES CLEARING AUTOMATED NETWORK SERVICES SDN BHD—See Bursa Malaysia Berhad; *Int'l*, pg. 1227
SECURITIES & COMMODITIES AUTHORITY; *Int'l*, pg. 6676
THE SECURITIES HOUSE K.S.C.C.; *Int'l*, pg. 7681
SECURITIES INDUSTRY AUTOMATION CORPORATION—See Intercontinental Exchange, Inc.; *U.S. Public*, pg. 1143
SECURITIES & INVESTMENT COMPANY BSC; *Int'l*, pg. 6676
SECURITIES MANAGEMENT & RESEARCH, INC.—See Brookfield Corporation; *Int'l*, pg. 1174
SECURITIES SERVICE NETWORK INC.—See Reverence Capital Partners LLC; *U.S. Private*, pg. 3415
SECURITISATION ADVISORY SERVICES PTY LIMITED—See Commonwealth Bank of Australia; *Int'l*, pg. 1720
SECURITRANS PUBLIC TRANSPORT SECURITY AG—See Schweizerische Bundesbahnen SBB AG; *Int'l*, pg. 6646
SECURITY & ACCESS SYSTEMS—See Financial Investments Corporation; *U.S. Private*, pg. 1507
SECURITY ADMINISTRATORS, INC.—See Security Mutual Life Insurance Company of New York; *U.S. Private*, pg. 3596
SECURITY ADMINISTRATORS LIMITED (SAL)—See Kingston Wharves Limited; *Int'l*, pg. 4180
SECURITY AGENCY, INC.; *U.S. Private*, pg. 3594
SECURITY ALARM FINANCING ENTERPRISES, INC.—See ICV Partners, LLC; *U.S. Private*, pg. 2034
SECURITY ALLIANCE GROUP, LLC; *U.S. Private*, pg. 3594
SECURITY ALLIANCE OF FLORIDA, LLC—See Sealaska Corporation; *U.S. Private*, pg. 3585
SECURITY AUTO SALES INC.; *U.S. Private*, pg. 3594
SECURITY BANCORP, INC.; *U.S. Public*, pg. 1855
SECURITY BANCORP OF TENNESSEE, INC.; *U.S. Private*, pg. 3594
SECURITY BANK OF KANSAS CITY—See Valley View Bancshares, Inc.; *U.S. Private*, pg. 4336
SECURITY BANK; *U.S. Private*, pg. 3595
SECURITY BANK—See Security BanCorp of Tennessee, Inc.; *U.S. Private*, pg. 3595
SECURITY BANK & TRUST COMPANY; *U.S. Private*, pg. 3595
SECURITY BENEFIT CORPORATION—See Guggenheim Partners, LLC; *U.S. Private*, pg. 1812
SECURITY BENEFIT LIFE INSURANCE COMPANY—See Guggenheim Partners, LLC; *U.S. Private*, pg. 1812
SECURITY BUILDERS LTD. INC.—See Mazzola Financial Services; *U.S. Private*, pg. 2623

SECURITY LEASING CORPORATION LIMITED

SECURITY BY DESIGN INC.; *U.S. Private*, pg. 3595
SECURITY CAPITAL RESEARCH & MANAGEMENT INCORPORATED—See JPMorgan Chase & Co.; *U.S. Public*, pg. 1210
SECURITY CARD SERVICES LLC; *U.S. Private*, pg. 3595
SECURITY CHAIN COMPANY—See The Carlyle Group Inc.; *U.S. Public*, pg. 2055
SECURITY CHECK LLC; *U.S. Private*, pg. 3595
SECURITY CHICAGO CORPORATION; *U.S. Private*, pg. 3595
SECURITYCLEARANCEEXPO.COM; *U.S. Private*, pg. 3597
SECURITY COMPANY SECURITY B.V.—See Live Nation Entertainment, Inc.; *U.S. Public*, pg. 1330
THE SECURITY COMPANY UTRECHT HOLLAND HOLDING BV—See Live Nation Entertainment, Inc.; *U.S. Public*, pg. 1331
SECURITY COMPLIANCE ASSOCIATES LLC; *U.S. Private*, pg. 3595
SECURITY CONSULTANTS GROUP, INC.—See Securitas AB; *Int'l*, pg. 6676
SECURITY CORPORATION; *U.S. Private*, pg. 3595
SECURITYCOVERAGE INC.—See National Rural Telecommunications Cooperative; *U.S. Private*, pg. 2862
SECURITY CREDIT SERVICES, LLC; *U.S. Private*, pg. 3595
SECURITY CREDIT SERVICES—See Security Credit Services, LLC; *U.S. Private*, pg. 3595
SECURITY EQUIPMENT SUPPLY INC.; *U.S. Private*, pg. 3595
SECURITY EXPRESS LTD—See Freightways Group Limited; *Int'l*, pg. 2772
SECURITY FEDERAL BANK—See Security Federal Corporation; *U.S. Public*, pg. 1856
SECURITY FEDERAL CORPORATION; *U.S. Public*, pg. 1855
SECURITY FEDERAL INSURANCE, INC.—See Security Federal Corporation; *U.S. Public*, pg. 1856
SECURITY FEDERAL SAVINGS BANK OF MCMINNVILLE—See Security Bancorp, Inc.; *U.S. Public*, pg. 1855
SECURITY FEDERAL SAVINGS BANK; *U.S. Private*, pg. 3595
SECURITY FINANCE CORPORATION—See Continental Holding Company; *U.S. Private*, pg. 1029
SECURITY FINANCE CORP. SPARTANBURG—See Continental Holding Company; *U.S. Private*, pg. 1029
SECURITY FINANCIAL BANK—See Security Financial Services Corporation; *U.S. Private*, pg. 3595
SECURITY FINANCIAL SERVICES CORPORATION; *U.S. Private*, pg. 3595
SECURITY FIRE PROTECTION COMPANY, INC.—See APi Group Corporation; *Int'l*, pg. 514
SECURITY FIRST ALARM KING—See Kimberlite Corp.; *U.S. Private*, pg. 2305
SECURITY FIRST BANK—See First State Bancshares, Inc.; *U.S. Private*, pg. 1528
SECURITY FIRST BANK—See Stockmens Financial Corporation; *U.S. Private*, pg. 3815
SECURITY FIRST INSURANCE COMPANY, INC.; *U.S. Private*, pg. 3595
SECURITY FIRST INTERNATIONAL HOLDINGS, INC.; *U.S. Public*, pg. 1856
SECURITY FIRST NATIONAL BANK OF HUGO—See Sooner Southwest Bankshares, Inc.; *U.S. Private*, pg. 3715
SECURITY GRADE PROTECTIVE SERVICES, LTD.—See Forian Inc.; *U.S. Public*, pg. 868
SECURITY GUARD INC.—See St. John Holdings Inc.; *U.S. Private*, pg. 3772
SECURITYHUNTER, INC.; *U.S. Private*, pg. 3597
SECURITY IDENTIFICATION SYSTEMS CORPORATION—See ACRE, LLC; *U.S. Private*, pg. 65
SECURITY INDUSTRY SPECIALISTS, INC.; *U.S. Private*, pg. 3596
SECURITY INNOVATIONS INC—See TTIK Inc.; *U.S. Private*, pg. 4255
SECURITY & INTELLIGENCE SERVICES (INDIA) LIMITED; *Int'l*, pg. 6677
SECURITY INVESTMENT BANK LIMITED; *Int'l*, pg. 6677
SECURITY INVESTORS, LLC—See Guggenheim Partners, LLC; *U.S. Private*, pg. 1812
SECURITY & KNOWLEDGE SUPPORT SERVICE, INC.—See INES Corporation; *Int'l*, pg. 3683
SECURITY LAND AND DEVELOPMENT CORPORATION; *U.S. Private*, pg. 3596
SECURITY LEASING CORPORATION LIMITED; *Int'l*, pg. 6677
SECURITY LEASING & FINANCE INC.—See Carriage Corporation; *U.S. Private*, pg. 772
SECURITY LIFE OF DENVER INSURANCE COMPANY—See Voya Financial, Inc.; *U.S. Public*, pg. 2311
SECURITY LIFE OF DENVER INTERNATIONAL LIMITED—See ING Groep N.V.; *Int'l*, pg. 3701
SECURITY LOAN INC.—See C.S. Wo & Sons Ltd.; *U.S. Private*, pg. 709

SECURITY LEASING CORPORATION LIMITED

SECURITY MANUFACTURING CORPORATION—See American Locker Group Incorporated; *U.S. Private*, pg. 240
SECURITY MANUFACTURING CORP—See American Locker Group Incorporated; *U.S. Private*, pg. 240
SECURITY MERCHANTS AUSTRALIA PTY LTD.—See ASSA ABLOY AB; *Int'l*, pg. 640
SECURITY METAL PRODUCTS CORP—See ASSA ABLOY AB; *Int'l*, pg. 636
SECURITYMETRICS, INC.; *U.S. Private*, pg. 3597
SECURITY MONITORING CENTRE B.V.B.A./S.P.R.L—See Carrier Global Corporation; *U.S. Public*, pg. 444
SECURITY MONITORING CENTRE B.V.—See Carrier Global Corporation; *U.S. Public*, pg. 444
SECURITY MUTUAL LIFE INSURANCE COMPANY OF NEW YORK; *U.S. Private*, pg. 3596
SECURITY NATIONAL AUTOMOTIVE ACCEPTANCE COMPANY, LLC; *U.S. Private*, pg. 3596
SECURITY NATIONAL BANK; *U.S. Private*, pg. 3596
SECURITY NATIONAL BANK—See Park National Corporation; *U.S. Public*, pg. 1638
SECURITY NATIONAL CAPITAL, INC.—See Security National Financial Corporation; *U.S. Public*, pg. 1856
SECURITY NATIONAL CORPORATION; *U.S. Private*, pg. 3596
SECURITY NATIONAL FINANCIAL CORPORATION; *U.S. Public*, pg. 1856
SECURITY NATIONAL LIFE INSURANCE COMPANY—See Security National Financial Corporation; *U.S. Public*, pg. 1856
SECURITYNATIONAL MORTGAGE COMPANY—See Security National Financial Corporation; *U.S. Public*, pg. 1856
SECURITY NATIONAL TRUST CO., INC. - LANCASTER—See Security National Trust Co., Inc.; *U.S. Private*, pg. 3596
SECURITY NATIONAL TRUST CO., INC.; *U.S. Private*, pg. 3596
SECURITY NETWORKS LLC—See Ascent Capital Group, Inc.; *U.S. Private*, pg. 348
SECURITY ONE INSURANCE AGENCY—See Kemper Corporation; *U.S. Public*, pg. 1221
SECURITY OPERATIONS ENGINEERING—See Sohgo Security Services Co., Ltd.; *Int'l*, pg. 7059
SECURITY PACKAGING INC.; *U.S. Private*, pg. 3596
SECURITY PAPERS LIMITED; *Int'l*, pg. 6677
SECURITY PLAN FIRE INSURANCE COMPANY—See Citizens, Inc.; *U.S. Public*, pg. 506
SECURITY PLAN LIFE INSURANCE COMPANY—See Citizens, Inc.; *U.S. Public*, pg. 506
SECURITY PLASTICS DIVISION/NMC LLC—See National Molding Corporation; *U.S. Private*, pg. 2859
SECURITY PLUMBING & HEATING SUPPLY CO.—See Winsupply Inc.; *U.S. Private*, pg. 4544
SECURITY PLUS ALARMS, LLC—See Arvig Enterprises, Inc.; *U.S. Private*, pg. 345
SECURITY PREMIUM FINANCE CO.—See Steel Partners Holdings L.P.; *U.S. Public*, pg. 1943
SECURITY PRINTERS (M) SDN. BHD.—See Fima Corporation Berhad; *Int'l*, pg. 2664
SECURITY PRINTING CORPORATION (BANGLADESH) LTD.—See Bangladesh Bank; *Int'l*, pg. 835
SECURITY PRO-TELCO PTE LTD.—See TEE International Limited; *Int'l*, pg. 7519
SECURITY RESEARCH GROUP PLC; *Int'l*, pg. 6677
SECURITY & SAFETY THINGS GMBH—See Robert Bosch GmbH; *Int'l*, pg. 6368
SECURITY SCIB SERVICES CO., LTD.—See Thanachart Capital PCL; *Int'l*, pg. 7607
SECURITY SEED & CHEMICAL LLC; *U.S. Private*, pg. 3596
SECURITY SERVICES HOLDINGS, LLC—See Southfield Capital Advisors, LLC; *U.S. Private*, pg. 3736
SECURITY SHREDDING ENTERPRISES—See Redishred Capital Corp.; *Int'l*, pg. 6248
SECURITY SOLUTIONS & MANAGEMENT LLC—See Ares Management Corporation; *U.S. Public*, pg. 189
SECURITY SOLUTIONS OF AMERICA; *U.S. Private*, pg. 3596
SECURITY STATE BANK—See Mackey Banco, Inc.; *U.S. Private*, pg. 2537
SECURITY STATE BANK—See Old O'Brien Banc Shares, Inc.; *U.S. Private*, pg. 3009
SECURITY STATE BANK—See Security State Corporation; *U.S. Private*, pg. 3596
SECURITY STATE BANK & TRUST; *U.S. Private*, pg. 3596
SECURITY STATE CORPORATION; *U.S. Private*, pg. 3596
THE SECURITY TITLE GUARANTEE CORP; *U.S. Private*, pg. 4115
SECURITY VAN LINES—See Johnson Storage & Moving Company; *U.S. Private*, pg. 2229
SECURITY VAULT WORKS INC; *U.S. Private*, pg. 3596
SECURITY WEAVER; *U.S. Private*, pg. 3596
SECURON AG—See BKW AG; *Int'l*, pg. 1056

SECURON HANSE VERSICHERUNGSMAKLER GMBH—See DZ BANK AG Deutsche Zentral-Genossenschaftsbank; *Int'l*, pg. 2244
SECURON VERSICHERUNGSMAKLER GMBH—See DZ BANK AG Deutsche Zentral-Genossenschaftsbank; *Int'l*, pg. 2244
SECUROS EUROPE GMBH—See Cencora, Inc.; *U.S. Public*, pg. 467
SECURUS INC.—See Reliance Worldwide Corporation Limited; *Int'l*, pg. 6264
SECURUS PAYMENTS; *U.S. Private*, pg. 3597
SECUSTACK GMBH—See Giesecke & Devrient GmbH; *Int'l*, pg. 2970
SECUVE CO., LTD.; *Int'l*, pg. 6677
SECUVITA S.L.—See VITA 34 AG; *Int'l*, pg. 8257
SEDACO DMCC—See BayWa AG; *Int'l*, pg. 919
SEDA CO., LTD.—See Noroo Holdings Co., Ltd.; *Int'l*, pg. 5431
SEDA CONSTRUCTION COMPANY INC.; *U.S. Private*, pg. 3597
THE SEDALIA DEMOCRAT—See Independence Capital Partners, LLC; *U.S. Private*, pg. 2057
SEDANA MEDICAL AB; *Int'l*, pg. 6677
SEDANA MEDICAL LTD.—See Sedana Medical AB; *Int'l*, pg. 6677
SEDANA MEDICAL SARL—See Sedana Medical AB; *Int'l*, pg. 6677
SEDANIA INNOVATOR BERHAD; *Int'l*, pg. 6677
SEDANO'S SUPERMARKET MANAGEMENT, INC.; *U.S. Private*, pg. 3597
SEDAO LIMITED—See Boxlight Corporation; *U.S. Public*, pg. 377
SEDA OUTSPAN IBERIA S.L.—See Temasek Holdings (Private) Limited; *Int'l*, pg. 7549
SEDA PLASTIK VE BOYA SAN. ITH. TIC. LDT. STI—See L'Oreal S.A.; *Int'l*, pg. 4381
SEDARU, INC.—See Danaher Corporation; *U.S. Public*, pg. 631
SEDCO CAPITAL REIT FUND; *Int'l*, pg. 6677
SEDCO DUBAI LLC—See Noble Corporation plc; *Int'l*, pg. 5397
SEDCO LTD.; *U.S. Private*, pg. 3597
SEDE CENTRAL SOFTWARE AG ESPANA S.A.—See Silver Lake Group, LLC; *U.S. Public*, pg. 3659
SEDELEC JURA BERNOIS, SUCCURSALE DE SEDELEC S.A.—See Burkhalter Holding AG; *Int'l*, pg. 1225
SEDELEC LA VALLEE, SUCCURSALE DE SEDELEC S.A.—See Burkhalter Holding AG; *Int'l*, pg. 1225
SEDELEC SAIGNELEGIER, SUCCURSALE DE SEDELEC S.A.—See Burkhalter Holding AG; *Int'l*, pg. 1225
SEDELEC SA LAUSANNE—See Burkhalter Holding AG; *Int'l*, pg. 1225
SEDELEC SA—See Burkhalter Holding AG; *Int'l*, pg. 1225
SEDELEC VEVEY, SUCCURSALE DE SEDELEC S.A.—See Burkhalter Holding AG; *Int'l*, pg. 1225
SEDELEC YVERDON, SUCCURSALE DE SEDELEC S.A.—See Burkhalter Holding AG; *Int'l*, pg. 1225
SEDEM S.A.—See CHINO Corporation; *Int'l*, pg. 1571
SEDERMA GMBH—See Croda International plc; *Int'l*, pg. 1853
SEDERMA INC.—See Croda International plc; *Int'l*, pg. 1853
SEDERMA SA—See Croda International plc; *Int'l*, pg. 1853
SEDEX MINING CORP.; *Int'l*, pg. 6677
SED FLOW CONTROL GMBH—See Aliaxis S.A./N.V.; *Int'l*, pg. 324
SEDGMAN PTY LIMITED—See ACS, Actividades de Construccion y Servicios, S.A.; *Int'l*, pg. 113
SEDGWICK BELGIUM SA—See The Carlyle Group Inc.; *U.S. Public*, pg. 2053
SEDGWICK CLAIMS MANAGEMENT SERVICES, INC.—See The Carlyle Group Inc.; *U.S. Public*, pg. 2053
SEDGWICK COUNTY ZOO; *U.S. Private*, pg. 3597
SEDGWICK (DEUTSCHLAND) GMBH—See Marsh & McLennan Companies, Inc.; *U.S. Public*, pg. 1388
SEDGWICK FACTUAL PHOTO, INC.—See The Carlyle Group Inc.; *U.S. Public*, pg. 2053
SEDGWICK FRANCE S.A.—See The Carlyle Group Inc.; *U.S. Public*, pg. 2053
SEDGWICK INTERNATIONAAL B.V.—See Marsh & McLennan Companies, Inc.; *U.S. Public*, pg. 1388
SEDGWICK INTERNATIONAL UK—See The Carlyle Group Inc.; *U.S. Public*, pg. 2054
SEDGWICK LIMITED—See Marsh & McLennan Companies, Inc.; *U.S. Public*, pg. 1388
SEDGWICK NEDERLAND B.V.—See The Carlyle Group Inc.; *U.S. Public*, pg. 2053
SEDGWICK NOBLE LOWNDES GROUP LIMITED—See Marsh & McLennan Companies, Inc.; *U.S. Public*, pg. 1388
SEDGWICK PTE LTD—See Marsh & McLennan Companies, Inc.; *U.S. Public*, pg. 1388
SEDGWICK RISK SERVICES LIMITED—See The Carlyle Group Inc.; *U.S. Public*, pg. 2054
SEDIA BIOSCIENCES CORPORATION; *U.S. Private*, pg. 3597
SEDIA TEGUH SDN. BHD.—See Muhibbah Engineering (M) Bhd.; *Int'l*, pg. 5079

CORPORATE AFFILIATIONS

SEDIBELO PLATINUM MINES LIMITED; *Int'l*, pg. 6677
SEDIBENG DIAMOND MINE JV—See Petra Diamonds Limited; *Int'l*, pg. 5824
SEDICAL, S.A.—See Max Weishaupt GmbH; *Int'l*, pg. 4735
SEDILEC S.C.R.L.; *Int'l*, pg. 6677
SEDIN ENGINEERING CO., LTD.—See China National Chemical Engineering Co., Ltd.; *Int'l*, pg. 1531
SED INTERNATIONAL DE COLOMBIA LTDA.—See Paragon Technologies, Inc.; *U.S. Public*, pg. 1637
SED INTERNATIONAL HOLDINGS, INC.; *U.S. Private*, pg. 3597
SED INTERNATIONAL, INC.—See SED International Holdings, Inc.; *U.S. Private*, pg. 3597
SEDIS SAS—See The Murugappa Group, Ltd.; *Int'l*, pg. 7669
SE DISTRIBUTION INC.—See Scholastic Corporation; *U.S. Public*, pg. 1847
SEDI TV SNC—See Metropole Television SA; *Int'l*, pg. 4863
SEDIVER INSULATORS (SHANGHAI) CO., LTD.—See Seves S.p.A.; *Int'l*, pg. 6736
SEDIVER S.A.—See Seves S.p.A.; *Int'l*, pg. 6736
SEDIVIO S.A.; *Int'l*, pg. 6677
SEDLABANKI ISLANDS; *Int'l*, pg. 6677
SEDLAK MANAGEMENT CONSULTANTS, INC.; *U.S. Private*, pg. 3597
SEDLMAYR GRUND UND IMMOBILIEN AG; *Int'l*, pg. 6678
SED MAGNA (MIAMI), INC.—See SED International Holdings, Inc.; *U.S. Private*, pg. 3597
SEDO.COM LLC—See United Internet AG; *Int'l*, pg. 8069
SEDO GMBH—See United Internet AG; *Int'l*, pg. 8069
SEDO GRUNDSTUCKS-VERMIETUNGSGESELLSCHAFT MBH—See Deutsche Bank Aktiengesellschaft; *Int'l*, pg. 2061
SEDO HOLDING AG—See United Internet AG; *Int'l*, pg. 8069
SEDONA CORP.—See Dominion Energy, Inc.; *U.S. Public*, pg. 674
SEDONA GOLF RESORT LC—See Pinnacle West Capital Corporation; *U.S. Public*, pg. 1692
SEDONA GROUP; *U.S. Private*, pg. 3597
SEDONA SOUL ADVENTURES, INC.; *U.S. Private*, pg. 3597
SEDOSA PORTUGAL, S.A.—See Indo Internacional S.A.; *Int'l*, pg. 3657
SEDO TREEPOINT GMBH—See Alpha Associes Conseil SAS; *Int'l*, pg. 367
SED S.R.L.—See A2A S.p.A.; *Int'l*, pg. 29
SEDULEN LLC—See PopReach Corporation; *Int'l*, pg. 5921
SEDULOUS CONSULTING SERVICES, LLC; *U.S. Private*, pg. 3597
S EDWARD INC.; *U.S. Private*, pg. 3512
SEEBACH FILTER SOLUTIONS INDIA PVT. LTD.—See Smiths Group plc; *Int'l*, pg. 7011
SEEBACH FILTRATION USA, INC.—See Smiths Group plc; *Int'l*, pg. 7011
SEEBACH GMBH—See Smiths Group plc; *Int'l*, pg. 7011
SEECLICKFIX, INC.—See Insight Venture Management, LLC; *U.S. Private*, pg. 2087
SEEC MEDIA GROUP LIMITED; *Int'l*, pg. 6678
SEECO, INC.—See Expand Energy Corporation; *U.S. Public*, pg. 808
SEECONTROL, INC.—See Autodesk, Inc.; *U.S. Public*, pg. 229
SEEDBURO EQUIPMENT CO.; *U.S. Private*, pg. 3597
SEED CO INTERNATIONAL LIMITED—See Cottco Holdings Limited; *Int'l*, pg. 1817
SEED CO. LIMITED—See Cottco Holdings Limited; *Int'l*, pg. 1817
SEED CO LIMITED—See Cottco Holdings Limited; *Int'l*, pg. 1817
SEED CO., LTD.; *Int'l*, pg. 6678
SEED CONSULTANTS INC.—See Corteva, Inc.; *U.S. Public*, pg. 584
SEED CONTACT LENS ASIA PTE. LTD.—See Seed Co., Ltd.; *Int'l*, pg. 6678
SEED CONTACT LENS (M) SDN BHD—See Seed Co., Ltd.; *Int'l*, pg. 6678
SEED CONTACT LENS TAIWAN CO., LTD.—See Seed Co., Ltd.; *Int'l*, pg. 6678
SEED CORPORATION SDN. BHD.—See Padini Holdings Berhad; *Int'l*, pg. 5694
SEED DIGITAL MEDIA OY—See Nordic Morning Plc; *Int'l*, pg. 5423
SEED DYNAMICS, INC.; *U.S. Private*, pg. 3597
SEEDER CO., LTD.—See Okamura Corporation; *Int'l*, pg. 5545
SEEDHEIWA CO., LTD.; *Int'l*, pg. 6678
SEED HOUSE, INC.—See Wilbur-Ellis Company; *U.S. Private*, pg. 4517
SEED INNOVATIONS LIMITED; *Int'l*, pg. 6678
SEEDINVEST, LLC—See Startengine Crowdfunding, Inc.; *U.S. Private*, pg. 3788
SEEDLING PUBLICATIONS—See Continental Press Inc.; *U.S. Private*, pg. 1030

COMPANY NAME INDEX

SEEDLINGS INDIA PRIVATE LIMITED—See Best Agrolife Ltd.; *Int'l*, pg. 998
SEED OIL HOLDINGS GES.M.B.H.—See Studen & Co. Holding GmbH; *Int'l*, pg. 7244
SEED PRINT—See Excelsior Printing Company; *U.S. Private*, pg. 1446
SEED RESEARCH OF OREGON; *U.S. Private*, pg. 3597
SEEDS CO., LTD.—See BANDAI NAMCO Holdings Inc.; *Int'l*, pg. 829
SEED TECHNOLOGY LIMITED—See BeyondSpring Inc.; *U.S. Public*, pg. 327
SEED TRADING (SHANGHAI) CO., LTD.—See Seed Co., Ltd.; *Int'l*, pg. 6678
SE-EDUCATION PUBLIC CO., LTD.; *Int'l*, pg. 6660
SEED VISION (PTY) LTD.—See S&W Seed Co.; *U.S. Public*, pg. 1832
SEEDWAY, LLC—See Growmark, Inc.; *U.S. Private*, pg. 1795
SEEEN PLC; *Int'l*, pg. 6678
SEEF PROPERTIES B.S.C.; *Int'l*, pg. 6678
SEEGARS FENCE COMPANY INC.; *U.S. Private*, pg. 3597
SEEGENE, INC.; *Int'l*, pg. 6678
SEEGER-ORBIS GMBH & CO. OHG—See Barnes Group Inc.; *U.S. Public*, pg. 277
SEEGER TOYOTA, INC.; *U.S. Private*, pg. 3597
SEE GROUP LTD—See Vivendi SE; *Int'l*, pg. 8278
SEE HUP CONSOLIDATED BERHAD; *Int'l*, pg. 6678
SEE HUP SENG CP PTE LTD—See SHS Holdings Ltd.; *Int'l*, pg. 6867
SEEING MACHINES INCORPORATED—See Seeing Machines Limited; *Int'l*, pg. 6678
SEEING MACHINES LIMITED; *Int'l*, pg. 6678
SEE JANE RUN; *U.S. Private*, pg. 3597
SEEKA LIMITED; *Int'l*, pg. 6679
S.E.E.K ARIZONA; *U.S. Private*, pg. 3517
SEEK CAREERS/STAFFING, INC.; *U.S. Private*, pg. 3598
SEEK COMMERCIAL PTY LTD—See SEEK Limited; *Int'l*, pg. 6678
SEEKER ROD COMPANY—See Parrish Enterprises, Ltd.; *U.S. Private*, pg. 3100
SEEKERS EVENT GMBH—See CTS Eventim AG & Co. KGAA; *Int'l*, pg. 1873
SEEKING ALPHA LTD.; *U.S. Private*, pg. 3598
SEEKINGSITTERS INC; *U.S. Private*, pg. 3598
SEEKINS FORD LINCOLN MERCURY; *U.S. Private*, pg. 3598
SEEKINTOO LTD.—See WELL Health Technologies Corp.; *Int'l*, pg. 8372
SEEK LEARNING PTY LTD—See SEEK Limited; *Int'l*, pg. 6678
SEEK LIMITED; *Int'l*, pg. 6678
SEEK NZ LIMITED—See SEEK Limited; *Int'l*, pg. 6679
SEELER INDUSTRIES INC.; *U.S. Private*, pg. 3598
SEELEY INTERNATIONAL AMERICAS—See Seeley International; *Int'l*, pg. 6679
SEELEY INTERNATIONAL EUROPE (ITALY) S.R.L.—See Seeley International; *Int'l*, pg. 6679
SEELEY INTERNATIONAL (EUROPE) LIMITED—See Seeley International; *Int'l*, pg. 6679
SEELEY INTERNATIONAL FRANCE S.A.R.L.—See Seeley International; *Int'l*, pg. 6679
SEELEY INTERNATIONAL; *Int'l*, pg. 6679
SEELOS THERAPEUTICS, INC.; *U.S. Public*, pg. 1856
SEELYE-EILER INDUSTRIAL PLASTIC PRODUCTS—See Activar, Inc.; *U.S. Private*, pg. 68
SEELY EQUIPMENT & SUPPLY CO., INC.—See Modern Group Ltd.; *U.S. Private*, pg. 2761
SEELYE WRIGHT KIA; *U.S. Private*, pg. 3598
SEELYE-WRIGHT OF SOUTH HAVEN; *U.S. Private*, pg. 3598
SEEMAC INCORPORATED; *U.S. Private*, pg. 3598
SEEMAN HOLTZ PROPERTY & CASUALTY, LLC; *U.S. Private*, pg. 3598
SEEMANN COMPOSITES, INC.; *U.S. Private*, pg. 3598
SEEMANN SUB GMBH & CO KG—See Johnson Outdoors Inc.; *U.S. Public*, pg. 1201
SEEN TEC CO., LTD.; *Int'l*, pg. 6679
SE (ENVELOPE MANUFACTURING) LTD—See Bong AB; *Int'l*, pg. 1107
SEEO, INC.—See Robert Bosch GmbH; *Int'l*, pg. 6367
SEE PROGRESS, INC.—See Vista Equity Partners, LLC; *U.S. Private*, pg. 4401
SEEQUENT AUSTRALIA PTY LIMITED—See Bentley Systems, Inc.; *U.S. Public*, pg. 297
SEEQUENT CHILE SPA—See Bentley Systems, Inc.; *U.S. Public*, pg. 297
SEEQUENT LIMITED—See Bentley Systems, Inc.; *U.S. Public*, pg. 297
SEEQUENT PERU S.A.C—See Bentley Systems, Inc.; *U.S. Public*, pg. 297
SEEQUENT SOUTH AFRICA PTY LIMITED—See Bentley Systems, Inc.; *U.S. Public*, pg. 297
SEEQUENT UK LIMITED—See Bentley Systems, Inc.; *U.S. Public*, pg. 297
SEEQUENT USA INC.—See Bentley Systems, Inc.; *U.S. Public*, pg. 297
SE EQUIPMENT, INC.—See Brandt Holdings Company; *U.S. Private*, pg. 639

SEERA GROUP HOLDING CO.; *Int'l*, pg. 6679
THE SEER GROUP LLC; *U.S. Private*, pg. 4115
SEER, INC.; *U.S. Public*, pg. 1856
SEERS BHD; *Int'l*, pg. 6679
SEE'S CANDIES, INC.—See Berkshire Hathaway Inc.; *U.S. Public*, pg. 316
SEE'S CANDY SHOPS, INC.—See Berkshire Hathaway Inc.; *U.S. Public*, pg. 316
SEE SEN CHEMICAL BHD. - PASIR GUDANG FACILITY—See Batu Kawan Berhad; *Int'l*, pg. 891
SEE SEN CHEMICAL BHD.—See Batu Kawan Berhad; *Int'l*, pg. 891
S.E.E. SISTEMAS INDUSTRIA E COMERCIO LTDA.—See Illinois Tool Works Inc.; *U.S. Public*, pg. 1110
SEE-SUL ENERGIA EOLICA, LDA—See E.ON SE; *Int'l*, pg. 2259
SEETEC GROUP LTD.; *Int'l*, pg. 6679
SEE TICKETS INC.—See Vivendi SE; *Int'l*, pg. 8278
SEEUNITY INC.—See Insight Venture Management, LLC; *U.S. Private*, pg. 2087
SEEVAST CORPORATION; *U.S. Private*, pg. 3598
SEE WIDE LETRIK (SEL) SDN BHD—See KVC Industrial Supplies Sdn. Bhd.; *Int'l*, pg. 4349
SEEYOND ARCHITECTURAL SOLUTIONS—See Liberty Diversified International Inc.; *U.S. Private*, pg. 2444
SEEYOND SA—See Groupe BPCE; *Int'l*, pg. 3099
THE SEFA GROUP INC.—See Heidelberg Materials AG; *Int'l*, pg. 3314
SEFALANA CASH & CARRY (NAMIBIA) (PROPRIETARY) LIMITED—See Sefalana Holdings Company Limited; *Int'l*, pg. 6680
SEFALANA CATERING (PTY.) LIMITED—See Sefalana Holdings Company Limited; *Int'l*, pg. 6680
SEFALANA HOLDINGS COMPANY LIMITED; *Int'l*, pg. 6679
SEFALANA LESOTHO (PROPRIETARY) LIMITED—See Sefalana Holdings Company Limited; *Int'l*, pg. 6680
SEFAR AG—See Sefar Holding AG; *Int'l*, pg. 6680
SEFAR AMERICA, INC.—See Sefar Holding AG; *Int'l*, pg. 6680
SEFAR AMERICA INC.—See Sefar Holding AG; *Int'l*, pg. 6680
SEFAR ASIA PACIFIC CO. LTD.—See Sefar Holding AG; *Int'l*, pg. 6680
SEFAR BDH INC.—See Sefar Holding AG; *Int'l*, pg. 6680
SEFAR B.V.—See Sefar Holding AG; *Int'l*, pg. 6680
SEFAR CO. LTD.—See Sefar Holding AG; *Int'l*, pg. 6680
SEFAR FABRICATION (M) SDN BHD—See Sefar Holding AG; *Int'l*, pg. 6680
SEFAR FILTER SPECIALISTS LTD—See Sefar Holding AG; *Int'l*, pg. 6680
SEFAR FILTRASYON SANAYI & TICARET LTD. SIRKETI—See Sefar Holding AG; *Int'l*, pg. 6680
SEFAR FILTRATION SOLUTIONS (SUZHOU) CO., LTD.—See Sefar Holding AG; *Int'l*, pg. 6680
SEFAR FYLTIS S.A.S.—See Sefar Holding AG; *Int'l*, pg. 6680
SEFAR GMBH—See Sefar Holding AG; *Int'l*, pg. 6680
SEFAR HOLDING AG; *Int'l*, pg. 6680
SEFAR INC.—See Sefar Holding AG; *Int'l*, pg. 6680
SEFAR INDIA PRIVATE LIMITED—See Sefar Holding AG; *Int'l*, pg. 6680
SEFAR (INTERNATIONAL) AG—See Sefar Holding AG; *Int'l*, pg. 6680
SEFAR ITALIA SRL—See Sefar Holding AG; *Int'l*, pg. 6680
SEFAR LTD.—See Sefar Holding AG; *Int'l*, pg. 6680
SEFAR MAISSA S.A.—See Sefar Holding AG; *Int'l*, pg. 6680
SEFAR PRINTING SOLUTIONS INC.—See Sefar Holding AG; *Int'l*, pg. 6680
SEFAR PRINTING SOLUTIONS LTDA—See Sefar Holding AG; *Int'l*, pg. 6680
SEFAR PTY LTD—See Sefar Holding AG; *Int'l*, pg. 6680
SEFAR SA DE CV—See Sefar Holding AG; *Int'l*, pg. 6680
SEFAR SINGAPORE PTE. LTD.—See Sefar Holding AG; *Int'l*, pg. 6680
SEFAR SP. Z O.O.—See Sefar Holding AG; *Int'l*, pg. 6680
SEFAR TRADING (SHENZHEN) CO. LTD.—See Sefar Holding AG; *Int'l*, pg. 6680
SEFAS INNOVACION S.A.—See La Poste S.A.; *Int'l*, pg. 4388
SEFAS INNOVATION INC—See La Poste S.A.; *Int'l*, pg. 4388
SEFAS INNOVATION LTD—See La Poste S.A.; *Int'l*, pg. 4388
SEFA TRANSPORTATION, LLC—See Heidelberg Materials AG; *Int'l*, pg. 3319
SEFCOR INC.—See Aubrey Silvey Enterprises Inc.; *U.S. Private*, pg. 385
SEFEA S.A.—See The Swatch Group Ltd.; *Int'l*, pg. 7692
SEFELEC GMBH—See Eaton Corporation plc; *Int'l*, pg. 2282
SEFELEC SAS—See Eaton Corporation plc; *Int'l*, pg. 2282
SEFERCO DEVELOPMENT S.A.—See Eurobank Ergasias Services and Holdings S.A.; *Int'l*, pg. 2533
SEFE SECURING ENERGY FOR EUROPE GMBH—See PJSC Gazprom; *Int'l*, pg. 5880
SEFI FONTEC—See FAYAT SAS; *Int'l*, pg. 2626

SEFINA SVENSK PANTBELANING AB—See Preato Oy; *Int'l*, pg. 5955
SEFIN MARKETING—See Omnicom Group Inc.; *U.S. Public*, pg. 1578
SEFNCO COMMUNICATIONS, INC.—See MasTec, Inc.; *U.S. Public*, pg. 1393
SEFNCO COMMUNICATIONS, INC.—See MasTec, Inc.; *U.S. Public*, pg. 1393
SE FORGE LIMITED—See Suzlon Energy Ltd.; *Int'l*, pg. 7353
SEFTON RESOURCES, INC.; *Int'l*, pg. 6680
SEGA BEE LINK CO., LTD.—See Sega Sammy Holdings, Inc.; *Int'l*, pg. 6681
SEGA CORPORATION—See Sega Sammy Holdings, Inc.; *Int'l*, pg. 6681
SEGA EUROPE LTD.—See Sega Sammy Holdings, Inc.; *Int'l*, pg. 6681
SEGAFREDO ZANETTI ARGENTINA S.A.—See Segafredo Zanetti S.p.A.; *Int'l*, pg. 6682
SEGAFREDO ZANETTI AUSTRALIA PTY LTD.—See Segafredo Zanetti S.p.A.; *Int'l*, pg. 6682
SEGAFREDO ZANETTI AUSTRIA GES.M.B.H.—See Segafredo Zanetti S.p.A.; *Int'l*, pg. 6682
SEGAFREDO ZANETTI AUSTRIA GMBH—See Massimo Zanetti Beverage Group SpA; *Int'l*, pg. 4723
SEGAFREDO ZANETTI BELGIUM NV/SA—See Segafredo Zanetti S.p.A.; *Int'l*, pg. 6682
SEGAFREDO ZANETTI BELGIUM S.A.—See Massimo Zanetti Beverage Group SpA; *Int'l*, pg. 4723
SEGAFREDO ZANETTI BRASIL—See Segafredo Zanetti S.p.A.; *Int'l*, pg. 6682
SEGAFREDO ZANETTI CHILE S.A.—See Segafredo Zanetti S.p.A.; *Int'l*, pg. 6682
SEGAFREDO ZANETTI COFFEE SYSTEM S.P.A.—See Segafredo Zanetti S.p.A.; *Int'l*, pg. 6682
SEGAFREDO ZANETTI CROATIA D.O.O.—See Massimo Zanetti Beverage Group SpA; *Int'l*, pg. 4723
SEGAFREDO ZANETTI CR SPOL. S.R.O.—See Massimo Zanetti Beverage Group SpA; *Int'l*, pg. 4723
SEGAFREDO ZANETTI CZECH REPUBLIC SPOL.S.R.O.—See Segafredo Zanetti S.p.A.; *Int'l*, pg. 6682
SEGAFREDO ZANETTI DANMARK APS—See Segafredo Zanetti S.p.A.; *Int'l*, pg. 6682
SEGAFREDO ZANETTI DEUTSCHLAND GMBH—See Segafredo Zanetti S.p.A.; *Int'l*, pg. 6682
SEGAFREDO ZANETTI D.O.O.—See Segafredo Zanetti S.p.A.; *Int'l*, pg. 6682
SEGAFREDO ZANETTI ESPANIA S.A.—See Segafredo Zanetti S.p.A.; *Int'l*, pg. 6682
SEGAFREDO ZANETTI ESPRESSO WORLDWIDE JAPAN INC.—See Segafredo Zanetti S.p.A.; *Int'l*, pg. 6682
SEGAFREDO ZANETTI FRANCE SAS—See Segafredo Zanetti S.p.A.; *Int'l*, pg. 6682
SEGAFREDO ZANETTI HELLAS SA—See Segafredo Zanetti S.p.A.; *Int'l*, pg. 6682
SEGAFREDO ZANETTI HUNGARIA KFT.—See Massimo Zanetti Beverage Group SpA; *Int'l*, pg. 4723
SEGAFREDO ZANETTI HUNGARY—See Segafredo Zanetti S.p.A.; *Int'l*, pg. 6682
SEGAFREDO ZANETTI NEW ZEALAND LTD—See Segafredo Zanetti S.p.A.; *Int'l*, pg. 6682
SEGAFREDO ZANETTI POLAND—See Segafredo Zanetti S.p.A.; *Int'l*, pg. 6682
SEGAFREDO ZANETTI POLAND SP. Z O.O.—See Massimo Zanetti Beverage Group SpA; *Int'l*, pg. 4723
SEGAFREDO ZANETTI PORTUGAL—See Segafredo Zanetti S.p.A.; *Int'l*, pg. 6682
SEGAFREDO ZANETTI PORTUGAL - SUCURSAL EM ESPANHA COMERCIALIZACAO E DISTRIBUICAO DE CAFE, SA—See Segafredo Zanetti S.p.A.; *Int'l*, pg. 6682
SEGAFREDO ZANETTI S.P.A.; *Int'l*, pg. 6681
SEGAFREDO ZANETTI SPOL. S.R.O.—See Segafredo Zanetti S.p.A.; *Int'l*, pg. 6682
SEGAFREDO ZANETTI SR SPOL.S.R.O.—See Massimo Zanetti Beverage Group SpA; *Int'l*, pg. 4723
SEGAL ADVISORS—See The Segal Group, Inc.; *U.S. Private*, pg. 4115
SEGAL BENZ—See The Segal Group, Inc.; *U.S. Private*, pg. 4116
THE SEGAL COMPANY (EASTERN STATES), INC.—See The Segal Group, Inc.; *U.S. Private*, pg. 4116
THE SEGAL COMPANY, LTD.—See The Segal Group, Inc.; *U.S. Private*, pg. 4116
THE SEGAL GROUP, INC.; *U.S. Private*, pg. 4115
SEGALL BRYANT & HAMILL LLC—See Thoma Bravo, L.P.; *U.S. Private*, pg. 4153
SEGAL LICENSING—See The Interpublic Group of Companies, Inc.; *U.S. Public*, pg. 2093
SEGA LOGISTICS SERVICE CO., LTD—See Sega Sammy Holdings, Inc.; *Int'l*, pg. 6681
SEGAL S.C.—See ArcelorMittal S.A.; *Int'l*, pg. 546
SEGAL SELECT INSURANCE SERVICES, INC.—See The Segal Group, Inc.; *U.S. Private*, pg. 4116
SEGA NETWORKS CO., LTD.—See Sega Sammy Holdings, Inc.; *Int'l*, pg. 6681

THE SEGAL GROUP, INC. — CORPORATE AFFILIATIONS

Company Index

SEGA NETWORKS INC.—See Sega Sammy Holdings, Inc.; *Int'l*, pg. 6681
SEGA OF AMERICA INC.—See Sega Sammy Holdings, Inc.; *Int'l*, pg. 6681
SEGAPLAST MAROC SA—See Sintex Industries, Ltd.; *Int'l*, pg. 6957
SEGA PUBLISHING EUROPE LTD.—See Sega Sammy Holdings, Inc.; *Int'l*, pg. 6681
SEGARMAS PLANTATIONS SDN BHD—See Wilmar International Limited; *Int'l*, pg. 8421
SEGA ROSSO CO., LTD.—See Sega Sammy Holdings, Inc.; *Int'l*, pg. 6681
SEGA SAMMY CREATION INC.—See Sega Sammy Holdings, Inc.; *Int'l*, pg. 6681
SEGA SAMMY GOLF ENTERTAINMENT INC—See Sega Sammy Holdings, Inc.; *Int'l*, pg. 6681
SEGA SAMMY HOLDINGS, INC.; *Int'l*, pg. 6680
SEGA TOYS CO., LTD—See Sega Sammy Holdings, Inc.; *Int'l*, pg. 6681
SEGECE CESKA REPUBLIKA SRO—See BNP Paribas SA; *Int'l*, pg. 1092
SEGECE ESPANA SLU—See BNP Paribas SA; *Int'l*, pg. 1092
SEGECE HELLAS REAL ESTATE MANAGEMENT SA—See BNP Paribas SA; *Int'l*, pg. 1092
SEGECE POLSKA SP. Z.O.O.—See BNP Paribas SA; *Int'l*, pg. 1092
SEGECO; *Int'l*, pg. 6682
SEGEPER SA—See ENCE Energia y Celulosa, S.A.; *Int'l*, pg. 2401
SEGEPO COMPOSANTS MECANIQUES; *Int'l*, pg. 6682
SEGEPO-REFA SP ZO.O—See Segepo Composants Mecaniques; *Int'l*, pg. 6682
THE SEGERDAHL CORPORATION; *U.S. Private*, pg. 4116
SEGER EUROPE AB—See New Wave Group AB; *Int'l*, pg. 5230
SEGERSTROM CENTER FOR THE ARTS; *U.S. Private*, pg. 3598
SEGESTA SPA—See Clariane SE; *Int'l*, pg. 1644
SEGETIS—See GFBiochemicals Italy SpA; *Int'l*, pg. 2956
SEGEZHA GROUP—See Sistema PJSFC; *Int'l*, pg. 6963
SEGEZHA PACKAGING A/S—See Sistema PJSFC; *Int'l*, pg. 6963
SEGEZHA PACKAGING GMBH—See Sistema PJSFC; *Int'l*, pg. 6963
SEGEZHA PACKAGING LIMITED—See Sistema PJSFC; *Int'l*, pg. 6963
SEGEZHA PACKAGING S.A.S.—See Sistema PJSFC; *Int'l*, pg. 6963
SEGEZHA PACKAGING, S.R.O.—See Sistema PJSFC; *Int'l*, pg. 6963
SEG HAUSGERATE GMBH—See Robert Bosch GmbH; *Int'l*, pg. 6368
SEG INTERNATIONAL BHD.—See Navis Capital Partners Limited; *Int'l*, pg. 5176
SEGI RETECH CO.,LTD, *Int'l*, pg. 6682
SEGI SA—See Ermewa Interservices Sarl; *Int'l*, pg. 2494
SEGLO, S.A. DE C.V.—See Schnellecke Group AG & Co. KG; *Int'l*, pg. 6636
SEG MEDIA GROUP INC.; *U.S. Private*, pg. 3598
SEGMENT, INC.—See OPEN Group, Inc.; *Int'l*, pg. 5596
SEGMENT.IO, INC.—See Twilio Inc.; *U.S. Public*, pg. 2206
SEGNALETICA MORDASINI SA—See INTEGRA Holding AG; *Int'l*, pg. 3729
SEGO RESOURCES INC.; *Int'l*, pg. 6682
SEGOVIA, INC.—See ViaSat, Inc.; *U.S. Public*, pg. 2292
SEGRA GROUP—See Sveaskog AB; *Int'l*, pg. 7356
SEGRA—See EQT AB; *Int'l*, pg. 2480
SEGREST FARMS, INC.; *U.S. Private*, pg. 3598
SEGRO BELGIUM NV—See SEGRO plc; *Int'l*, pg. 6683
SEGRO BV—See SEGRO plc; *Int'l*, pg. 6683
SEGRO CZECH REPUBLIC S.R.O.—See SEGRO plc; *Int'l*, pg. 6683
SEGRO DEVELOPMENTS (FRANCE) SA—See SEGRO plc; *Int'l*, pg. 6683
SEGRO ESTATES HUNGARY KFT—See SEGRO plc; *Int'l*, pg. 6683
SEGRO FRANCE S.A.—See SEGRO plc; *Int'l*, pg. 6683
SEGRO GERMANY GMBH—See SEGRO plc; *Int'l*, pg. 6683
SEGRO ITALY SRL—See SEGRO plc; *Int'l*, pg. 6683
SEGRO (KNBC) LIMITED—See SEGRO plc; *Int'l*, pg. 6683
SEGRO MANAGEMENT N.V.—See SEGRO plc; *Int'l*, pg. 6683
SEGRO N.V.—See SEGRO plc; *Int'l*, pg. 6683
SEGRO PLC; *Int'l*, pg. 6683
SEGRO POLAND SP. Z O.O—See SEGRO plc; *Int'l*, pg. 6683
SEGRO PROPERTIES LIMITED—See SEGRO plc; *Int'l*, pg. 6683
SEGRO (SLOUGH ESTATES CR S.R.O.)—See SEGRO plc; *Int'l*, pg. 6683
SEGRO (SLOUGH ESTATES MAINLAND B.V.)—See SEGRO plc; *Int'l*, pg. 6683
SEG—See Groupe Bruxelles Lambert SA; *Int'l*, pg. 3100
SEGUE ELECTRONICS, INC.; *U.S. Private*, pg. 3598
SEGUE GROUP CO., LTD.; *Int'l*, pg. 6683

SEGUE TECHNOLOGIES, INC.—See Tetra Tech, Inc.; *U.S. Public*, pg. 2023
SEGUIDORES SOLARES SOLTEC S.A. DE C.V.—See Soltec Power Holdings S.A.; *Int'l*, pg. 7076
SEGUIN NATURAL HAIR PRODUCTS, INC.; *U.S. Private*, pg. 3598
SEGULAH IV L.P.—See Segulah Advisor AB; *Int'l*, pg. 6684
SEGULAH ADVISOR AB; *Int'l*, pg. 6684
SEGULA MATRA TECHNOLOGIES—See Segula Technologies SA; *Int'l*, pg. 6683
SEGULA TECHNOLOGIES CANADA, INC.—See Segula Technologies SA; *Int'l*, pg. 6683
SEGULA TECHNOLOGIES HUNGARY KFT.—See Segula Technologies SA; *Int'l*, pg. 6683
SEGULA TECHNOLOGIES, INC.—See Segula Technologies SA; *Int'l*, pg. 6683
SEGULA TECHNOLOGIES ISRAEL LTD.—See Segula Technologies SA; *Int'l*, pg. 6683
SEGULA TECHNOLOGIES ITALIA SRL—See Segula Technologies SA; *Int'l*, pg. 6683
SEGULA TECHNOLOGIES NEDERLAND BV—See Segula Technologies SA; *Int'l*, pg. 6683
SEGULA TECHNOLOGIES RUSSIA, LLC—See Segula Technologies SA; *Int'l*, pg. 6683
SEGULA TECHNOLOGIES SA; *Int'l*, pg. 6683
SEGULA TECHNOLOGIES SWITZERLAND GMBH—See Segula Technologies SA; *Int'l*, pg. 6683
SEGUNDO METAL PRODUCTS, INC.—See MiddleGround Management, LP; *U.S. Private*, pg. 2712
SEGURADORA ROMA, S.A.—See MAPFRE S.A.; *Int'l*, pg. 4684
SEGURCAIXA ADESLAS, S.A. DE SEGUROS Y REASEGUROS—See Lone Star Funds; *U.S. Private*, pg. 2485
SEGURIDAD INTEGRAL METROPOLITANA, S.A.—See ACS, Actividades de Construccion y Servicios, S.A.; *Int'l*, pg. 116
SEGURIDAD PRIVADA ACTIVE SECURITY COMPANY A.S.C. CIA. LTDA.—See Bain Capital, LP; *U.S. Private*, pg. 435
SEGURO DIRECTO GERE COMPANHIA DE SEGUROS SA—See AXA S.A.; *Int'l*, pg. 757
SEGUROS BANAMEX, S.A. DE C.V.—See Citigroup Inc.; *U.S. Public*, pg. 504
SEGUROS BBVA BANCOMER SA DE CV—See Banco Bilbao Vizcaya Argentaria, S.A.; *Int'l*, pg. 818
SEGUROS BILBAO FONDOS S.G.I.I.C.—See Grupo Catalana Occidente, S.A.; *Int'l*, pg. 3124
SEGUROS CATALANA OCCIDENTE, S.A—See Grupo Catalana Occidente, S.A.; *Int'l*, pg. 3124
SEGUROS DE CREDITO Y GARANTIA S.A.; *Int'l*, pg. 6684
SEGUROS DE RIESGOS PROFESIONALES SURAMERICANA S.A.—See Grupo de Inversiones Suramericana S.A.; *Int'l*, pg. 3126
SEGUROS DE VIDA Y PENSIONES ANTARES, S.A.—See Grupo Catalana Occidente, S.A.; *Int'l*, pg. 3124
SEGUROS E INVERSIONES, S.A.—See Citigroup Inc.; *U.S. Public*, pg. 504
SEGUROS GENESIS, S.A.—See Liberty Mutual Holding Company Inc.; *U.S. Private*, pg. 2446
SEGUROS LOGO S.A.—See Apollo Global Management, Inc.; *U.S. Public*, pg. 150
SEGUROS MONTERREY NEW YORK LIFE, S.A.—See New York Life Insurance Company; *U.S. Private*, pg. 2910
SEGUROS PROVINCIAL CA—See Banco Bilbao Vizcaya Argentaria, S.A.; *Int'l*, pg. 818
SEGUROS SIN BARRERAS INSURANCE AGENCY, INC.—See Stone Point Capital LLC; *U.S. Private*, pg. 3819
SEGUROS SURA (BRASIL) S.A.—See Grupo de Inversiones Suramericana S.A.; *Int'l*, pg. 3125
SEGUROS SURAMERICANA S.A.—See Grupo de Inversiones Suramericana S.A.; *Int'l*, pg. 3126
SEGUROS SURA, S.A DE C.V.—See Grupo de Inversiones Suramericana S.A.; *Int'l*, pg. 3126
SEGUROS SURA S.A.—See Grupo de Inversiones Suramericana S.A.; *Int'l*, pg. 3126
SEGUROS TRIPLE-S, INC.—See Triple-S Management Corp.; *U.S. Public*, pg. 2195
SEGUROS VENEZUELA C.A.—See MetLife, Inc.; *U.S. Public*, pg. 1431
SEGUROS VIDA SECURITY PREVISION SA; *Int'l*, pg. 6684
SEGUS SP. Z O.O.—See Tesgas S.A.; *Int'l*, pg. 7572
SEGWAYBOOKING B.V.—See Ninebot Limited; *Int'l*, pg. 5300
SEGWAY INC.—See Ninebot Limited; *Int'l*, pg. 5300
SEGWAY NEW ZEALAND LIMITED.—See Ninebot Limited; *Int'l*, pg. 5300
S.E.G-WAY ORTHOPAEDICS, INC.—See Trice Medical, Inc; *U.S. Private*, pg. 4228
SEGWAY (THAILAND) COMPANY LIMITED—See Ninebot Limited; *Int'l*, pg. 5300
SE GYUNG HI TECH CO., LTD.; *Int'l*, pg. 6660
SEHA CORPORATION—See Haesung Industrial Co., Ltd.; *Int'l*, pg. 3205

SEHA INSAAT MUH. MAD. TUR. SAN. VE TIC. A.S.—See Loras Holding A.S.; *Int'l*, pg. 4557
SEH DESIGN BUILD INC.—See Short Elliott Hendrickson Inc.; *U.S. Private*, pg. 3642
THE SEHK OPTIONS CLEARING HOUSE LIMITED—See Hong Kong Exchanges & Clearing Limited; *Int'l*, pg. 3466
S.E.H. MALAYSIA SDN. BHD—See Shin-Etsu Chemical Co. Ltd.; *Int'l*, pg. 6839
SEH OF INDIANA, LLC—See Short Elliott Hendrickson Inc.; *U.S. Private*, pg. 3642
SE HOLDINGS & INCUBATIONS CO., LTD.; *Int'l*, pg. 6660
S.E.H. (SHAH ALAM) SDN. BHD.—See Shin-Etsu Chemical Co. Ltd.; *Int'l*, pg. 6839
S.E.H. SINGAPORE PTE. LTD.—See Shin-Etsu Chemical Co. Ltd.; *Int'l*, pg. 6839
SEH TECHNOLOGY SOLUTIONS—See Short Elliott Hendrickson Inc.; *U.S. Private*, pg. 3642
S.E. HUFFMAN CORP.—See The Springs Company; *U.S. Private*, pg. 4120
SEI/AARON'S, INC.—See Aaron's Company, Inc.; *U.S. Public*, pg. 13
SEI ANTECH-EUROPE GMBH—See Sumitomo Electric Industries, Ltd.; *Int'l*, pg. 7280
SEI ARCHWAY TECHNOLOGY PARTNERS, LLC—See SEI Investments Company; *U.S. Public*, pg. 1856
SEIBELS, BRUCE & COMPANY—See The Seibels Bruce Group, Inc.; *U.S. Private*, pg. 4116
THE SEIBELS BRUCE GROUP, INC.; *U.S. Private*, pg. 4116
SEIBERLING ASSOCIATES, INC.—See The Haskell Company; *U.S. Private*, pg. 4043
SEIB INSURANCE BROKERS LIMITED—See Ecclesiastical Insurance Office plc; *Int'l*, pg. 2288
SEIBU BUS CO., LTD.—See Seibu Holdings Inc.; *Int'l*, pg. 6685
SEIBU CONSTRUCTION CO., LTD.—See Seibu Holdings Inc.; *Int'l*, pg. 6685
SEIBU CONSTRUCTION SUPPLY CO., LTD.—See Seibu Holdings Inc.; *Int'l*, pg. 6685
THE SEIBU DEPARTMENT STORES, LTD.—See SoftBank Group Corp.; *Int'l*, pg. 7054
SEIBU ELECTRIC INDUSTRY CO., LTD.; *Int'l*, pg. 6684
SEIBU ELECTRIC & MACHINERY CO., LTD.; *Int'l*, pg. 6684
SEIBU GIKEN CO., LTD.; *Int'l*, pg. 6685
SEIBU HOLDINGS INC.; *Int'l*, pg. 6684
SEIBU JUKAN OPERATION CO.,LTD.—See Mitsubishi Heavy Industries, Ltd.; *Int'l*, pg. 4961
SEIBU JUSHI CO., LTD.—See Sumitomo Bakelite Co., Ltd.; *Int'l*, pg. 7263
SEIBU LANDSCAPE CO., LTD.—See Seibu Holdings Inc.; *Int'l*, pg. 6685
SEIBU LIONS INC.—See Seibu Holdings Inc.; *Int'l*, pg. 6685
SEIBU LIONS, INC.—See Seibu Holdings Inc.; *Int'l*, pg. 6685
SEIBU MARUYAMA CO., LTD.—See Maruyama Mfg. Co., Inc.; *Int'l*, pg. 4715
SEIBU PAINT CO., LTD.—See Seibu Electric & Machinery Co., Ltd.; *Int'l*, pg. 6684
SEIBU PROPERTIES, INC.—See Seibu Holdings Inc.; *Int'l*, pg. 6685
SEIBU RAILWAY CO., LTD.—See Seibu Holdings Inc.; *Int'l*, pg. 6685
SEIBU SERVICE CO., LTD.—See Hanwa Co., Ltd.; *Int'l*, pg. 3263
SEI BUSINESS CREATES, INC.—See Sumitomo Electric Industries, Ltd.; *Int'l*, pg. 7280
SEIBU TOKUYAMA READY MIXED CONCRETE CO., LTD.—See Tokuyama Corporation; *Int'l*, pg. 7787
SEIBU TRANSPORTATION CO., LTD—See Seino Holdings Co., Ltd.; *Int'l*, pg. 6691
SEIBU TRAVEL, INC.—See Seibu Holdings Inc.; *Int'l*, pg. 6685
SEIBU WHEELS CO., LTD.—See Topy Industries, Ltd.; *Int'l*, pg. 7822
SEI CARBIDE AUSTRALIA PTY., LTD.—See Sumitomo Electric Industries, Ltd.; *Int'l*, pg. 7280
SEICHOU SENRYAKU INC.—See Funai Soken Holdings Incorporated; *Int'l*, pg. 2845
SEI COATINGS, LLC—See North American Coatings, Inc.; *U.S. Private*, pg. 2940
SEI CONSULTING VIETNAM CO., LTD.—See Sumitomo Electric Industries, Ltd.; *Int'l*, pg. 7280
SEIDEL DIESEL GROUP; *U.S. Private*, pg. 3599
SEIDENADER MASCHINENBAU GMBH—See Korber AG; *Int'l*, pg. 4280
THE SEIDEN GROUP; *U.S. Private*, pg. 4116
SEIDEN KOUSAN CO., LTD.—See Seibu Electric & Machinery Co., Ltd.; *Int'l*, pg. 6684
SEIDENSHA CO., LTD.—See Yamada Holdings Co., Ltd.; *Int'l*, pg. 8548
THE SEIDLER COMPANY, LLC; *U.S. Private*, pg. 4116
SEIDMAN INSURANCE CONSULTANTS LLC; *U.S. Private*, pg. 3599
SEIDOPRO GLOBAL INC.—See Nippon Yusen Kabushiki Kaisha; *Int'l*, pg. 5359

COMPANY NAME INDEX

SEI ELECTRONIC COMPONENTS (VIETNAM), LTD.—See Sumitomo Electric Industries, Ltd.; *Int'l*, pg. 7280
SEI ELECTRONICS INC.; *U.S. Private*, pg. 3598
SEI ELECTRONICS MATERIALS LTD.—See Sumitomo Electric Industries, Ltd.; *Int'l*, pg. 7280
SEIEN CONCRETE INDUSTRIES CO., LTD.—See Sala Corporation; *Int'l*, pg. 6490
SEI EPC ITALIA S.P.A.—See Societe Anonyme d'Explosifs et de Produits Chimiques; *Int'l*, pg. 7035
SEI EUROPEAN SERVICES LIMITED—See SEI Investments Company; *U.S. Public*, pg. 1856
SEIFER, MURKEN, DESPINA, JAMES & TEICHMAN, ALC—See SD Mayer & Associates LLP; *U.S. Private*, pg. 3581
SEI FINANCIAL MANAGEMENT CORPORATION—See SEI Investments Company; *U.S. Public*, pg. 1856
SEI FINANCIAL SERVICES COMPANY—See SEI Investments Company; *U.S. Public*, pg. 1857
SEIGAKUSYA CO., LTD.; *Int'l*, pg. 6685
SEIGER GFELLER LAURIE LLP; *U.S. Private*, pg. 3599
SEIGERMANS FURNITURE SHOWPLACE LLC; *U.S. Private*, pg. 3599
SEIGNOL HUGUENY—See LISI S.A.; *Int'l*, pg. 4524
SEIGO CO., LTD.—See AOYAMA TRADING Co. Ltd.; *Int'l*, pg. 499
SEI GROUP, INC.; *U.S. Private*, pg. 3599
SEI GROUP, LLC—See Quad-C Management, Inc.; *U.S. Private*, pg. 3315
SEIHO KAIUN KAISHA LTD—See Mitsubishi Logistics Corporation; *Int'l*, pg. 4963
SEIHOKU PACKAGE CO., LTD.—See Mitsubishi Gas Chemical Company, Inc.; *Int'l*, pg. 4948
SEIHOKU PAPER DEPOT CO., LTD.—See Japan Pulp and Paper Company Limited; *Int'l*, pg. 3904
SEIHYO CO., LTD.; *Int'l*, pg. 6685
SEI INDUSTRIES LTD.; *Int'l*, pg. 6684
SEI INFORMATION TECHNOLOGY INC.; *U.S. Private*, pg. 3599
SEI INSTITUTIONAL TRANSFER AGENT, INC.—See SEI Investments Company; *U.S. Public*, pg. 1857
SEI INTERCONNECT PRODUCTS (EUROPE), LTD.—See Sumitomo Electric Industries, Ltd.; *Int'l*, pg. 7280
SEI INTERCONNECT PRODUCTS (EUROPE) LTD.—See Sumitomo Electric Industries, Ltd.; *Int'l*, pg. 7280
SEI INTERCONNECT PRODUCTS (EUROPE) LTD.—See Sumitomo Electric Industries, Ltd.; *Int'l*, pg. 7280
SEI INTERCONNECT PRODUCTS (EUROPE) LTD.—See Sumitomo Electric Industries, Ltd.; *Int'l*, pg. 7280
SEI INTERCONNECT PRODUCTS (HUNGARY), KFT.—See Sumitomo Electric Industries, Ltd.; *Int'l*, pg. 7280
SEI INVESTMENTS (ASIA), LIMITED—See SEI Investments Company; *U.S. Public*, pg. 1857
SEI INVESTMENTS CANADA COMPANY—See SEI Investments Company; *U.S. Public*, pg. 1857
SEI INVESTMENTS COMPANY; *U.S. Public*, pg. 1856
SEI INVESTMENTS EUROPE LIMITED—See SEI Investments Company; *U.S. Public*, pg. 1857
SEI INVESTMENTS GLOBAL FUNDS SERVICES—See SEI Investments Company; *U.S. Public*, pg. 1857
SEI INVESTMENTS GLOBAL, LIMITED—See SEI Investments Company; *U.S. Public*, pg. 1857
SEI INVESTMENTS - GUERNSEY LIMITED—See SEI Investments Company; *U.S. Public*, pg. 1857
SEI INVESTMENTS (SOUTH AFRICA) LIMITED—See SEI Investments Company; *U.S. Public*, pg. 1857
SEI INVESTMENTS TRUSTEE & CUSTODIAL SERVICES (IRELAND) LIMITED—See SEI Investments Company; *U.S. Public*, pg. 1857
SEIKA CORPORATION; *Int'l*, pg. 6685
SEIKA DAIYA ENGINE CO., LTD.—See Seika Corporation; *Int'l*, pg. 6685
SEIKA DIGITAL IMAGE CORPORATION—See Seika Corporation; *Int'l*, pg. 6685
SEIKA ENGINEERING CO., LTD.—See Sumitomo Seika Chemicals Company Limited; *Int'l*, pg. 7300
SEIKAGAKU CORPORATION - KURIHAMA PLANT—See Seikagaku Corporation; *Int'l*, pg. 6686
SEIKAGAKU CORPORATION; *Int'l*, pg. 6686
SEIKAGAKU CORPORATION - TAKAHAGI PLANT—See Seikagaku Corporation; *Int'l*, pg. 6686
SEIKA MACHINERY, INC.—See Seika Corporation; *Int'l*, pg. 6685
SEIKA SANGYO GMBH—See Seika Corporation; *Int'l*, pg. 6685
SEIKA SANGYO (THAILAND) CO., LTD.—See Seika Corporation; *Int'l*, pg. 6685
SEIKA SANGYO (VIETNAM) COMPANY LIMITED—See Seika Corporation; *Int'l*, pg. 6685
SEIKA SHANGHAI CO., LTD.—See Seika Corporation; *Int'l*, pg. 6685
SEIKAT OY—See Kingspan Group PLC; *Int'l*, pg. 4179
SEIKA TRADING (SHENZHEN) CO., LTD.—See Seika Corporation; *Int'l*, pg. 6685
SEIKATSU KAGAKU UN-EI CO., LTD.—See Haseko Corporation; *Int'l*, pg. 3283
SEIKA YKC CIRCUIT (THAILAND) CO., LTD.—See Seika Corporation; *Int'l*, pg. 6685

SEIKEI STEEL COLUMN CORP.—See Mitsui & Co., Ltd.; *Int'l*, pg. 4980
SEIKENKOGYO CO., LTD.—See MIRAIT ONE Corporation; *Int'l*, pg. 4918
SEIKI CO., LTD.—See Hanwa Co., Ltd.; *Int'l*, pg. 3263
SEIKITOKYU KOGYO CO., LTD.; *Int'l*, pg. 6686
SEIKO AUSTRALIA PTY. LTD.—See Seiko Group Corporation; *Int'l*, pg. 6688
SEIKO BELGIUM S.A.—See Seiko Group Corporation; *Int'l*, pg. 6688
SEIKO CLOCK INC.—See Seiko Group Corporation; *Int'l*, pg. 6688
SEIKO CLOCK (SHENZHEN) CO., LTD.—See Seiko Group Corporation; *Int'l*, pg. 6688
SEIKO CORPORATION - FUJIKAWA PLANT—See Seiko Corporation; *Int'l*, pg. 6686
SEIKO CORPORATION - MISHIMA PLANT—See Seiko Corporation; *Int'l*, pg. 6686
SEIKO CORPORATION OF AMERICA—See Seiko Group Corporation; *Int'l*, pg. 6688
SEIKO CORPORATION; *Int'l*, pg. 6686
SEIKO DEUTSCHLAND GMBH—See Seiko Group Corporation; *Int'l*, pg. 6688
SEIKO ELECTRIC CO., LTD. - KOGA FACTORY—See Seiko Electric Co., Ltd.; *Int'l*, pg. 6686
SEIKO ELECTRIC CO., LTD.; *Int'l*, pg. 6686
SEIKO ELECTRIC CONSTRUCTION CO., LTD.—See Seiko Electric Co., Ltd.; *Int'l*, pg. 6686
SEIKO EPSON CORPORATION; *Int'l*, pg. 6686
SEIKO FRANCE S.A.—See Seiko Group Corporation; *Int'l*, pg. 6688
SEIKO GROUP CORPORATION; *Int'l*, pg. 6688
SEIKOH GIKEN CO., LTD.; *Int'l*, pg. 6689
SEIKOH GIKEN DALIAN CO., LTD.—See Seikoh Giken Co., Ltd.; *Int'l*, pg. 6689
SEIKOH GIKEN EUROPE GMBH—See Seikoh Giken Co., Ltd.; *Int'l*, pg. 6689
SEIKOH GIKEN HANGZHOU CO., LTD.—See Seikoh Giken Co., Ltd.; *Int'l*, pg. 6690
SEIKOH GIKEN USA, INC.—See Seikoh Giken Co., Ltd.; *Int'l*, pg. 6690
SEIKO HONG KONG LTD—See Seiko Group Corporation; *Int'l*, pg. 6688
SEIKO I INFOTECH INC.—See Seiko Group Corporation; *Int'l*, pg. 6688
SEIKO INSTRUMENTS GMBH—See Seiko Group Corporation; *Int'l*, pg. 6688
SEIKO INSTRUMENTS (H.K.) LTD.—See Seiko Group Corporation; *Int'l*, pg. 6688
SEIKO INSTRUMENTS, INC.—See Seiko Group Corporation; *Int'l*, pg. 6688
SEIKO INSTRUMENTS (SHANGHAI) INC.—See Seiko Group Corporation; *Int'l*, pg. 6688
SEIKO INSTRUMENTS SINGAPORE PTE. LTD.—See Seiko Group Corporation; *Int'l*, pg. 6688
SEIKO INSTRUMENTS TAIWAN, INC.—See Seiko Group Corporation; *Int'l*, pg. 6689
SEIKO INSTRUMENTS TECHNOLOGY (SHANGHAI) INC.—See Seiko Group Corporation; *Int'l*, pg. 6688
SEIKO INSTRUMENTS (THAILAND) LTD.—See Seiko Group Corporation; *Int'l*, pg. 6688
SEIKO INSTRUMENTS TRADING (H.K.) LTD.—See Seiko Group Corporation; *Int'l*, pg. 6688
SEIKO INSTRUMENTS USA, INC.—See Seiko Group Corporation; *Int'l*, pg. 6689
SEIKO ITALIA- SEDE SECONDARIA ITALIANA DI SEIKO FRANCE SAS—See Seiko Group Corporation; *Int'l*, pg. 6689
SEIKO IT SOLUTION CO., LTD.—See Seiko Electric Co., Ltd.; *Int'l*, pg. 6686
SEIKO IT SOLUTIONS PHILIPPINES INC.—See Seiko Electric Co., Ltd.; *Int'l*, pg. 6686
SEIKO MANUFACTURING (H.K.) LTD.—See Seiko Group Corporation; *Int'l*, pg. 6689
SEIKO MANUFACTURING (SINGAPORE) PTE. LTD.—See Seiko Group Corporation; *Int'l*, pg. 6689
SEIKO MEDICAL, INC.—See Ship Healthcare Holdings, Inc.; *Int'l*, pg. 6852
SEIKO NEDERLAND B.V.—See Seiko Group Corporation; *Int'l*, pg. 6689
SEIKO NPC CORPORATION - NASUSHIOBARA UNIT—See Seiko Group Corporation; *Int'l*, pg. 6688
SEIKO NPC CORPORATION—See Seiko Group Corporation; *Int'l*, pg. 6689
SEIKO NPC CORPORATION—See Seiko Group Corporation; *Int'l*, pg. 6688
SEIKO OPTICAL PRODUCTS CO., LTD.—See Seiko Group Corporation; *Int'l*, pg. 6688
SEIKO PANAMA S.A.—See Seiko Group Corporation; *Int'l*, pg. 6689
SEIKO PMC CORPORATION - AKASHI PLANT—See Seiko PMC Corporation; *Int'l*, pg. 6689
SEIKO PMC CORPORATION - CHIBA PLANT—See Seiko PMC Corporation; *Int'l*, pg. 6689
SEIKO PMC CORPORATION - HARIMA PLANT—See Seiko PMC Corporation; *Int'l*, pg. 6689
SEIKO PMC CORPORATION - IWAI PLANT—See Seiko PMC Corporation; *Int'l*, pg. 6689

SEIKO PMC CORPORATION - MIZUSHIMA PLANT—See Seiko PMC Corporation; *Int'l*, pg. 6689
SEIKO PMC CORPORATION - RYUGASAKI PLANT—See Seiko PMC Corporation; *Int'l*, pg. 6689
SEIKO PMC CORPORATION - SHIZUOKA PLANT—See Seiko PMC Corporation; *Int'l*, pg. 6689
SEIKO PMC CORPORATION; *Int'l*, pg. 6689
SEIKO PMC (SHANGHAI) COMMERCE & TRADING CORP.—See Seiko PMC Corporation; *Int'l*, pg. 6689
SEIKO PMC (ZHANGJIAGANG) CORPORATION—See Seiko PMC Corporation; *Int'l*, pg. 6689
SEIKO PRECISION HONG KONG LTD.—See Seiko Group Corporation; *Int'l*, pg. 6689
SEIKO PRECISION (THAILAND) CO., LTD.—See Seiko Group Corporation; *Int'l*, pg. 6689
SEIKO S.A.—See Seiko Group Corporation; *Int'l*, pg. 6689
SEIKO SERVICE CENTER CO., LTD.—See Seiko Group Corporation; *Int'l*, pg. 6689
SEIKO SERVICE & ENGINEERING CO., LTD.—See Seiko Electric Co., Ltd.; *Int'l*, pg. 6686
SEIKO SOLUTIONS INC.—See Seiko Group Corporation; *Int'l*, pg. 6689
SEIKO TAIWAN CO., LTD.—See Seiko Group Corporation; *Int'l*, pg. 6689
SEIKO (THAILAND) CO., LTD.—See Seiko Group Corporation; *Int'l*, pg. 6689
SEIKO TIME LABS CO., LTD.—See Seiko Group Corporation; *Int'l*, pg. 6689
SEIKO TIME SYSTEMS INC.—See Seiko Group Corporation; *Int'l*, pg. 6688
SEIKO UK LIMITED—See Seiko Group Corporation; *Int'l*, pg. 6689
SEIKO WACH EUROPE B.V.—See Seiko Group Corporation; *Int'l*, pg. 6689
SEIKO WATCH CORPORATION—See Seiko Group Corporation; *Int'l*, pg. 6689
SEIKO WATCH INDIA PVT. LTD.—See Seiko Group Corporation; *Int'l*, pg. 6689
SEIKO WATCH OF AMERICA LLC—See Seiko Group Corporation; *Int'l*, pg. 6689
SEIKO WATCH (SHANGHAI) CO., LTD.—See Seiko Group Corporation; *Int'l*, pg. 6689
SEILER INSTRUMENT AND MANUFACTURING CO. INC., *U.S. Private*, pg. 3599
SEILER TANK TRUCK SERVICE INC.—See Elkin Co.; *U.S. Private*, pg. 1363
SEILKOP INDUSTRIES INC.; *U.S. Private*, pg. 3599
SEI LLC—See Solugenix Corp.; *U.S. Private*, pg. 3710
SEILLER WATERMAN LLC; *U.S. Private*, pg. 3599
SEI LOGINET CO., LTD.—See Sumitomo Electric Industries, Ltd.; *Int'l*, pg. 7280
SEILON, INC.; *Int'l*, pg. 6690
SEILOX, INC.; *U.S. Private*, pg. 3599
SEI MANUFACTURING, INC.—See Patrick Industries, Inc.; *U.S. Public*, pg. 1653
SEI MEETINGS AND INCENTIVES; *U.S. Private*, pg. 3599
SEI METALFORMS INC.—See SEI MetalTek; *U.S. Private*, pg. 3599
SEI METALTEK; *U.S. Private*, pg. 3599
SEI MOBIL VERKEHRSGESELLSCHAFT MBH—See Ferrovie dello Stato Italiane S.p.A.; *Int'l*, pg. 2645
SEINAJOKI FESTIVALS OY—See CTS Eventim AG & Co. KGAA; *Int'l*, pg. 1873
SEINE GMBH—See Allianz SE; *Int'l*, pg. 355
SEINE (HOLLAND) B.V.—See Zhuhai Seine Technology Co., Ltd.; *Int'l*, pg. 8678
SEINO AUTO LEASE CO., LTD.—See Seino Holdings Co., Ltd.; *Int'l*, pg. 6690
SEINO AUTO SERVICE KANTO CO., LTD.—See Seino Holdings Co., Ltd.; *Int'l*, pg. 6690
SEINO BUSINESS SUPPORT CO., LTD.—See Seino Holdings Co., Ltd.; *Int'l*, pg. 6690
SEINO CUSTOMS CLEARANCE SERVICE CO., LTD.—See Seino Holdings Co., Ltd.; *Int'l*, pg. 6690
SEINO ECOTRADING INC.—See Seino Holdings Co., Ltd.; *Int'l*, pg. 6690
SEINO ENGINEERING CO., LTD.—See Seino Holdings Co., Ltd.; *Int'l*, pg. 6690
SEINO EXPRESS CO., LTD.—See Seino Holdings Co., Ltd.; *Int'l*, pg. 6690
SEINO FAMILY CO., LTD.—See Seino Holdings Co., Ltd.; *Int'l*, pg. 6690
SEINO HIKKOSHI CO., LTD.—See Seino Holdings Co., Ltd.; *Int'l*, pg. 6690
SEINO HOKKAIDO EXPRESS CO., LTD.—See Seino Holdings Co., Ltd.; *Int'l*, pg. 6690
SEINO HOKURIKU EXPRESS CO., LTD.—See Seino Holdings Co., Ltd.; *Int'l*, pg. 6690
SEINO HOLDINGS CO., LTD.; *Int'l*, pg. 6690
SEINO INFORMATION SERVICE CO., LTD.—See Seino Holdings Co., Ltd.; *Int'l*, pg. 6690
SEINO LOGISTICS HOKKAIDO CO., LTD.—See Seino Holdings Co., Ltd.; *Int'l*, pg. 6690
SEINO LOGIX CO., LTD.—See Seino Holdings Co., Ltd.; *Int'l*, pg. 6690
SEINO NIPPON EXPRESS CO., LTD.—See Seino Holdings Co., Ltd.; *Int'l*, pg. 6690
SEINO OSAKA EXPRESS CO., LTD.—See Seino Holdings Co., Ltd.; *Int'l*, pg. 6690

SEINO SANGYO CO., LTD.—See Seino Holdings Co., Ltd.; *Int'l*, pg. 6690
SEINO STAFF SERVICE CO., LTD.—See Seino Holdings Co., Ltd.; *Int'l*, pg. 6690
SEINO SUPER EXPRESS CO., LTD.—See Seino Holdings Co., Ltd.; *Int'l*, pg. 6690
SEINO TOKYO EXPRESS CO., LTD.—See Seino Holdings Co., Ltd.; *Int'l*, pg. 6690
SEINO TRADING CO., LTD.—See Seino Holdings Co., Ltd.; *Int'l*, pg. 6690
SEINO TRANSPORTATION CO., LTD.—See Seino Holdings Co., Ltd.; *Int'l*, pg. 6690
SEI NOVUS UK—See SEI Investments Company; *U.S. Public*, pg. 1857
SEI OPTICAL FIBER AND CABLE (SHENZHEN) CO., LTD.—See Futong Group Co., Ltd.; *Int'l*, pg. 2852
SEI OPTIFRONTIER CO., LTD. - SAITAMA WORKS—See Sumitomo Electric Industries, Ltd.; *Int'l*, pg. 7280
SEI OPTIFRONTIER CO., LTD. - SHONAN WORKS—See Sumitomo Electric Industries, Ltd.; *Int'l*, pg. 7280
SEI OPTIFRONTIER CO., LTD.—See Sumitomo Electric Industries, Ltd.; *Int'l*, pg. 7280
SEI OPTIFRONTIER CO., LTD. - SUWA WORKS—See Sumitomo Electric Industries, Ltd.; *Int'l*, pg. 7280
SEI OPTIFRONTIER VIETNAM, LTD.—See Sumitomo Electric Industries, Ltd.; *Int'l*, pg. 7280
SEIO TECHNOLOGY CO., LTD.—See Shanghai Newtouch Software Co., Ltd.; *Int'l*, pg. 6776
SEI (PHILIPPINES) INCORPORATED—See Sumitomo Electric Industries, Ltd.; *Int'l*, pg. 7280
SEI PROFESSIONAL STAFFS INC.—See Sumitomo Electric Industries, Ltd.; *Int'l*, pg. 7280
SEIREL AUTOMATION EN—See Gerard Perrier Industrie S.A.; *Int'l*, pg. 2942
SEIREN ALMA CO., LTD.—See Seiren Co., Ltd.; *Int'l*, pg. 6691
SEIREN AUCUS CO., LTD.—See Seiren Co., Ltd.; *Int'l*, pg. 6691
SEIREN CO., LTD. - HONSYA-PLANT—See Seiren Co., Ltd.; *Int'l*, pg. 6691
SEIREN CO., LTD. - NITTA NO.1 PLANT—See Seiren Co., Ltd.; *Int'l*, pg. 6691
SEIREN CO., LTD. - NITTA NO.2 PLANT—See Seiren Co., Ltd.; *Int'l*, pg. 6691
SEIREN CO., LTD - NITTA NO.3 PLANT—See Seiren Co., Ltd.; *Int'l*, pg. 6691
SEIREN CO., LTD. - NITTA NO.5 PLANT—See Seiren Co., Ltd.; *Int'l*, pg. 6691
SEIREN CO., LTD. - NITTA NO.6 PLANT—See Seiren Co., Ltd.; *Int'l*, pg. 6691
SEIREN CO., LTD - NITTA PLAT PLANT—See Seiren Co., Ltd.; *Int'l*, pg. 6691
SEIREN CO., LTD. - SABAE PLANT—See Seiren Co., Ltd.; *Int'l*, pg. 6691
SEIREN CO., LTD.; *Int'l*, pg. 6691
SEIREN COSMO CO., LTD.—See Seiren Co., Ltd.; *Int'l*, pg. 6691
SEIREN DESIGN CENTER NORTH AMERICA, LLC—See Seiren Co., Ltd.; *Int'l*, pg. 6691
SEIREN ELECTRONICS CO., LTD.—See Seiren Co., Ltd.; *Int'l*, pg. 6691
SEIREN ELECTRONICS (SUZHOU) CO., LTD.—See Seiren Co., Ltd.; *Int'l*, pg. 6691
SEIREN GUANGDONG CO., LTD.—See Seiren Co., Ltd.; *Int'l*, pg. 6691
SEIREN HEBEI CO., LTD.—See Seiren Co., Ltd.; *Int'l*, pg. 6691
SEIREN HOUSING CO., LTD.—See Seiren Co., Ltd.; *Int'l*, pg. 6691
SEIREN KP CO., LTD.—See Seiren Co., Ltd.; *Int'l*, pg. 6691
SEIREN KST CORP.—See Seiren Co., Ltd.; *Int'l*, pg. 6692
SEIREN PRODUTOS AUTOMOTIVOS LTDA—See Seiren Co., Ltd.; *Int'l*, pg. 6692
SEIREN SHANGHAI CO., LTD.—See Seiren Co., Ltd.; *Int'l*, pg. 6692
SEIREN SHOJI CO., LTD.—See Seiren Co., Ltd.; *Int'l*, pg. 6692
SEIREN SUZHOU CO., LTD.—See Seiren Co., Ltd.; *Int'l*, pg. 6692
SEIREN SYSTEM SERVICE CO., LTD—See Seiren Co., Ltd.; *Int'l*, pg. 6692
SEIREN VISCOTEC MEXICO S.A. DE C.V.—See Seiren Co., Ltd.; *Int'l*, pg. 6692
SEIRYO ELECTRIC CORPORATION; *Int'l*, pg. 6692
SEIRYO ENGINEERING CO., LTD.—See Mitsubishi Heavy Industries, Ltd.; *Int'l*, pg. 4961
SEISA GEAR, LTD.—See Sumitomo Heavy Industries, Ltd.; *Int'l*, pg. 7287
SEISA MEDICAL, INC.—See Genstar Capital, LLC; *U.S. Private*, pg. 1679
SEISAN GIJUTSU PARTNERS CO., LTD.—See Mitsubishi Corporation; *Int'l*, pg. 4942
SEISHIN CORPORATION—See Kikkoman Corporation; *Int'l*, pg. 4161
SEISHIN SEISAKUSYO CO., LTD.—See Daiki Aluminium Industry Co., Ltd.; *Int'l*, pg. 1932
SEISHIN SERVICE CO., LTD.—See Tokyo Tatemono Co. Ltd.; *Int'l*, pg. 7796

SEISHIN (THAILAND) CO., LTD.—See Daiki Aluminium Industry Co., Ltd.; *Int'l*, pg. 1932
SEISHO CO., LTD.—See Nihon Yamamura Glass Co., Ltd.; *Int'l*, pg. 5288
SEISLAND SURVEYS LTD.; *Int'l*, pg. 6692
SEISMIC ASIA PACIFIC PTY. LTD.—See MIND Technology, Inc.; *U.S. Public*, pg. 1448
SEISMIC ENERGY PRODUCTS LP; *U.S. Private*, pg. 3599
SEISMIC EXCHANGE INC.; *U.S. Private*, pg. 3599
SEISMIC SOFTWARE, INC.; *U.S. Private*, pg. 3599
SEISMIC SUPPORT SERVICES—See CGG; *Int'l*, pg. 1432
SEISSENSCHMIDT AG—See Linamar Corporation; *Int'l*, pg. 4502
SEISSENSCHMIDT CORP.—See Linamar Corporation; *Int'l*, pg. 4502
SEISSENSCHMIDT HEAT TREATMENT GMBH + CO. KG—See Linamar Corporation; *Int'l*, pg. 4502
SEISSENSCHMIDT PRECISION COMPONENTS KFT.—See Linamar Corporation; *Int'l*, pg. 4502
SEITEL DATA, LTD.—See ValueAct Capital Management, L.P.; *U.S. Private*, pg. 4338
SEITEL, INC.—See ValueAct Capital Management, L.P.; *U.S. Private*, pg. 4338
SEITEL SOLUTIONS CANADA, LTD.—See ValueAct Capital Management, L.P.; *U.S. Private*, pg. 4338
SEITER & MILLER ADVERTISING, INC.; *U.S. Private*, pg. 3600
SEITER SERVICES, LLC; *U.S. Private*, pg. 3600
SEI THAI ELECTRIC CONDUCTOR CO., LTD.—See Sumitomo Electric Industries, Ltd.; *Int'l*, pg. 7280
S.E.I. THAI HOLDING CO., LTD.—See Sumitomo Electric Industries, Ltd.; *Int'l*, pg. 7279
SEIT HYDR'EAU SAS—See VINCI S.A.; *Int'l*, pg. 8226
SEITRACK USA, LLC—See Live Nation Entertainment, Inc.; *U.S. Public*, pg. 1330
SEI TRADING INDIA PTE, LTD.—See Sumitomo Electric Industries, Ltd.; *Int'l*, pg. 7280
SEI TRUST COMPANY—See SEI Investments Company; *U.S. Public*, pg. 1857
SEITU, S.A.—See Mondragon Corporation; *Int'l*, pg. 5029
SEITZ LLC—See Andlinger & Company, Inc.; *U.S. Private*, pg. 279
SEIVA S.A. - FLORESTAS E INDUSTRIAS—See Metalurgica Gerdau S.A.; *Int'l*, pg. 4850
SEIWA BUTSURYU CO., LTD.—See Nishikawa Rubber Co., Ltd.; *Int'l*, pg. 5365
SEIWA CHUO HOLDINGS CORPORATION; *Int'l*, pg. 6692
SEIWA CO., LTD.—See Toyota Boshoku Corporation; *Int'l*, pg. 7864
SEIWA ELECTRIC MFG. CO., LTD. - OVERSEAS BUSINESS PROMOTION DIVISION—See Seiwa Electric Mfg. Co., Ltd.; *Int'l*, pg. 6692
SEIWA ELECTRIC MFG. CO., LTD.; *Int'l*, pg. 6692
SEIWA ELECTRIC (VIETNAM) CO., LTD.—See Seiwa Electric Mfg. Co., Ltd.; *Int'l*, pg. 6692
SEIWA HOLDINGS CO., LTD.; *Int'l*, pg. 6692
SEIWA KOGYO CO., LTD.—See Seiwa Holdings Co., Ltd.; *Int'l*, pg. 6692
SEIWA RENEWAL WORKS CO., LTD.—See Taisei Corporation; *Int'l*, pg. 7416
SEIWA SANGYO CO., LTD.—See Alfresa Holdings Corporation; *Int'l*, pg. 317
SEIWA SECURITY SERVICE CO., LTD.—See Sala Corporation; *Int'l*, pg. 6490
SEIWA TECHNOLOGY CO., LTD.—See Seiwa Electric Mfg. Co., Ltd.; *Int'l*, pg. 6692
SEIX INVESTMENT ADVISORS LLC—See Virtus Investment Partners, Inc.; *U.S. Public*, pg. 2301
SEIYO FOOD-COMPASS GROUP, INC.—See Compass Group PLC; *Int'l*, pg. 1752
SEIYU KOUN CO., LTD.—See Mitsui-Soko Holdings Co., Ltd.; *Int'l*, pg. 4993
SEIYU REAL ESTATE CO., LTD.—See Maeda Corporation; *Int'l*, pg. 4635
SEJAL GLASS & GLASS MANUFACTURING PRODUCTS LLC—See Sejal Glass Ltd.; *Int'l*, pg. 6692
SEJAL GLASS HOUSE LTD—See Sejal Glass Ltd.; *Int'l*, pg. 6692
SEJAL GLASS LTD.; *Int'l*, pg. 6692
SEJAL INSURANCE BROKING LTD.—See Sejal Glass Ltd.; *Int'l*, pg. 6692
SEJAL INTERNATIONAL LTD.—See Sejal Glass Ltd.; *Int'l*, pg. 6692
SE JAPAN CO.—See Siward Crystal Technology Co., Ltd.; *Int'l*, pg. 6966
SEJIN AMERICA, INC.—See SJK Co., Ltd.; *Int'l*, pg. 6969
SEJIN ELECTRON INC. - OSAN FACTORY—See SJK Co., Ltd.; *Int'l*, pg. 6969
SEJIN HEAVY INDUSTRIES CO., LTD; *Int'l*, pg. 6692
SEJIN TS CO., LTD - CHEONAN PLANT—See SEJIN TS Co., Ltd; *Int'l*, pg. 6692
SEJIN TS CO., LTD; *Int'l*, pg. 6692
S.E. JOHNSON MANAGEMENT LTD.; *Int'l*, pg. 6456
SEJONG ALABAMA LLC—See SJG Sejong Co., Ltd.; *Int'l*, pg. 6969
SEJONG-AMC CORPORATION CO., LTD.—See Honeywell International Inc.; *U.S. Public*, pg. 1048

SEJONG CZECH S.R.O—See SJG Sejong Co., Ltd.; *Int'l*, pg. 6969
SEJONG EV CO., LTD.—See SJG Sejong Co., Ltd.; *Int'l*, pg. 6969
SEJONG GEORGIA LLC—See SJG Sejong Co., Ltd.; *Int'l*, pg. 6969
SEJONG MATERIALS CO., LTD.; *Int'l*, pg. 6692
SEJONG MEDICAL CO., LTD.; *Int'l*, pg. 6692
SEJONG SLOVAKIA S.R.O—See SJG Sejong Co., Ltd.; *Int'l*, pg. 6969
SEJONG TELECOM INC.; *Int'l*, pg. 6693
SEJOONG CO., LTD.; *Int'l*, pg. 6693
SEJ SERVICES LLC; *U.S. Private*, pg. 3600
SEJUNG CO., LTD.—See SJG Sejong Co., Ltd.; *Int'l*, pg. 6969
SEKAR LAUT TBK; *Int'l*, pg. 6693
SEKAWAN INTIPRATAMA TBK; *Int'l*, pg. 6693
SEKERBANK INTERNATIONAL BANKING UNIT LTD.—See Sekerbank T.A.S.; *Int'l*, pg. 6693
SEKERBANK KIBRIS LTD.—See Sekerbank T.A.S.; *Int'l*, pg. 6693
SEKERBANK T.A.S.; *Int'l*, pg. 6693
SEKER BILISIM SANAYI A.S.—See Sekerbank T.A.S.; *Int'l*, pg. 6693
SEKER FAKTORING A.S.—See Sekerbank T.A.S.; *Int'l*, pg. 6693
SEKER FAKTORING HIZMETLERI A.S.—See Sekerbank T.A.S.; *Int'l*, pg. 6693
SEKER FINANSAL KIRALAMA A.S.—See Sekerbank T.A.S.; *Int'l*, pg. 6693
SEKER FINANSMAN A.S.—See Sekerbank T.A.S.; *Int'l*, pg. 6693
SEKER GAYRIMENKUL YATIRIM ORTAKLIGI A.S.—See Sekerbank T.A.S.; *Int'l*, pg. 6693
SEKER YATIRIM MENKUL DEGERLER A.S.—See Sekerbank T.A.S.; *Int'l*, pg. 6693
SEK & GREY—See WPP plc; *Int'l*, pg. 8472
SEKI ARKEMA CO LTD—See Arkema S.A.; *Int'l*, pg. 571
SEKICHU CO., LTD.; *Int'l*, pg. 6693
SEKI CO., LTD.; *Int'l*, pg. 6693
SEKIDENKO, INC.—See Advanced Energy Industries, Inc.; *U.S. Public*, pg. 47
SEKIDO CO., LTD.; *Int'l*, pg. 6693
SEKIHARA SAKE BREWERY CO., LTD.—See Kobe Bussan Co., Ltd.; *Int'l*, pg. 4217
SEKINE KOZAI K.K.—See Sato shoji Corporation; *Int'l*, pg. 6586
SEKISHOU-UNYU CO., LTD.—See Ishizuka Glass Co., Ltd.; *Int'l*, pg. 3818
SEKISUI ACCOUNTING CENTER CO., LTD.—See Sekisui Chemical Co., Ltd.; *Int'l*, pg. 6694
SEKISUI ALVEO AG—See Sekisui Chemical Co., Ltd.; *Int'l*, pg. 6694
SEKISUI ALVEO (BENELUX) B.V.—See Sekisui Chemical Co., Ltd.; *Int'l*, pg. 6695
SEKISUI ALVEO BS G.M.B.H.—See Sekisui Chemical Co., Ltd.; *Int'l*, pg. 6695
SEKISUI-ALVEO B.V.—See Sekisui Chemical Co., Ltd.; *Int'l*, pg. 6695
SEKISUI ALVEO GMBH—See Sekisui Chemical Co., Ltd.; *Int'l*, pg. 6695
SEKISUI ALVEO LTD.—See Sekisui Chemical Co., Ltd.; *Int'l*, pg. 6695
SEKISUI ALVEO REPRESENTACOES LTDA.—See Sekisui Chemical Co., Ltd.; *Int'l*, pg. 6695
SEKISUI ALVEO S.A.R.L.—See Sekisui Chemical Co., Ltd.; *Int'l*, pg. 6695
SEKISUI-ALVEO S.A.—See Sekisui Chemical Co., Ltd.; *Int'l*, pg. 6695
SEKISUI ALVEO S.R.L.—See Sekisui Chemical Co., Ltd.; *Int'l*, pg. 6695
SEKISUI AMAGASAKI KAKO CO., LTD.—See Sekisui Chemical Co., Ltd.; *Int'l*, pg. 6694
SEKISUI AMERICA CORPORATION—See Sekisui Chemical Co., Ltd.; *Int'l*, pg. 6694
SEKISUI AQUA SYSTEMS CO., LTD.—See Sekisui Chemical Co., Ltd.; *Int'l*, pg. 6694
SEKISUI BOARD CO., LTD.—See Sekisui Chemical Co., Ltd.; *Int'l*, pg. 6694
SEKISUI CHEMICAL (CHINA) CO., LTD.—See Sekisui Chemical Co., Ltd.; *Int'l*, pg. 6694
SEKISUI CHEMICAL CO., LTD. - AMAGASAKI PLANT—See Sekisui Chemical Co., Ltd.; *Int'l*, pg. 6694
SEKISUI CHEMICAL CO., LTD. - GUNMA PLANT—See Sekisui Chemical Co., Ltd.; *Int'l*, pg. 6694
SEKISUI CHEMICAL CO., LTD. - MUSASHI PLANT—See Sekisui Chemical Co., Ltd.; *Int'l*, pg. 6694
SEKISUI CHEMICAL CO., LTD.; *Int'l*, pg. 6693
SEKISUI CHEMICAL CO., LTD. - TOKYO PLANT—See Sekisui Chemical Co., Ltd.; *Int'l*, pg. 6694
SEKISUI CHEMICAL GMBH—See Sekisui Chemical Co., Ltd.; *Int'l*, pg. 6695
SEKISUI CHEMICAL HOKKAIDO CO., LTD.—See Sekisui Chemical Co., Ltd.; *Int'l*, pg. 6694
SEKISUI CHEMICAL INDIA PVT. LTD.—See Sekisui Chemical Co., Ltd.; *Int'l*, pg. 6694
SEKISUI CHEMICAL SINGAPORE (PTE.) LTD.—See Sekisui Chemical Co., Ltd.; *Int'l*, pg. 6694

COMPANY NAME INDEX

SEKISUI CHEMICAL (TAIWAN) CO., LTD.—See Sekisui Chemical Co., Ltd.; *Int'l*, pg. 6694
SEKISUI CHEMICAL (THAILAND) CO., LTD.—See Sekisui Chemical Co., Ltd.; *Int'l*, pg. 6694
SEKISUI (DALIAN) HOUSING TECHNOLOGY CO., LTD.—See Sekisui Chemical Co., Ltd.; *Int'l*, pg. 6694
SEKISUI DIAGNOSTICS - COAGULATION DIVISION - STAMFORD—See Sekisui Chemical Co., Ltd.; *Int'l*, pg. 6695
SEKISUI DIAGNOSTICS GMBH—See Sekisui Chemical Co., Ltd.; *Int'l*, pg. 6695
SEKISUI DIAGNOSTICS, LLC—See Sekisui Chemical Co., Ltd.; *Int'l*, pg. 6695
SEKISUI DIAGNOSTICS P.E.I. INC—See Sekisui Chemical Co., Ltd.; *Int'l*, pg. 6695
SEKISUI DIAGNOSTICS—See Sekisui Chemical Co., Ltd.; *Int'l*, pg. 6695
SEKISUI DIAGNOSTICS (UK) LIMITED—See Sekisui Chemical Co., Ltd.; *Int'l*, pg. 6695
SEKISUI DLJM MOLDING PRIVATE LTD.—See Sekisui Chemical Co., Ltd.; *Int'l*, pg. 6694
SEKISUI ENGINEERING CO., LTD.—See Sekisui Chemical Co., Ltd.; *Int'l*, pg. 6694
SEKISUI ESLON B.V.—See Sekisui Chemical Co., Ltd.; *Int'l*, pg. 6695
SEKISUI EUROPE B.V.—See Sekisui Chemical Co., Ltd.; *Int'l*, pg. 6694
SEKISUI EXTERIOR CO., LTD.—See Sekisui Chemical Co., Ltd.; *Int'l*, pg. 6695
SEKISUI FAMI-S CHUSHIKOKU CO., LTD.—See Sekisui Chemical Co., Ltd.; *Int'l*, pg. 6695
SEKISUI FAMIS KINKI CO., LTD.—See Sekisui Chemical Co., Ltd.; *Int'l*, pg. 6695
SEKISUI FAMI S KYUSHU CO., LTD.—See Sekisui Chemical Co., Ltd.; *Int'l*, pg. 6695
SEKISUI FAMI S SHINETSU CO., LTD.—See Sekisui Chemical Co., Ltd.; *Int'l*, pg. 6695
SEKISUI FILM CO., LTD.—See Sekisui Chemical Co., Ltd.; *Int'l*, pg. 6695
SEKISUI FULLER CO. LTD.—See H.B. Fuller Company; *U.S. Public*, pg. 978
SEKISUI HEIM CHUBU CO., LTD.—See Sekisui Chemical Co., Ltd.; *Int'l*, pg. 6695
SEKISUI HEIM CHUSHIKOKU CO., LTD.—See Sekisui Chemical Co., Ltd.; *Int'l*, pg. 6695
SEKISUI HEIM KINKI CO., LTD.—See Sekisui Chemical Co., Ltd.; *Int'l*, pg. 6695
SEKISUI HEIM KYUSHU CO., LTD.—See Sekisui Chemical Co., Ltd.; *Int'l*, pg. 6695
SEKISUI HEIM SHINETSU CO., LTD.—See Sekisui Chemical Co., Ltd.; *Int'l*, pg. 6695
SEKISUI HEIM SUPPLY CO., LTD.—See Sekisui Chemical Co., Ltd.; *Int'l*, pg. 6695
SEKISUI HEIM TOHOKU CO., LTD.—See Sekisui Chemical Co., Ltd.; *Int'l*, pg. 6695
SEKISUI HIGH PERFORMANCE PACKAGING (LANGFANG) CO., LTD.—See Sekisui Chemical Co., Ltd.; *Int'l*, pg. 6695
SEKISUI HOME TECHNO CO., LTD.—See Sekisui Chemical Co., Ltd.; *Int'l*, pg. 6695
SEKISUI (HONG KONG) LTD.—See Sekisui Chemical Co., Ltd.; *Int'l*, pg. 6694
SEKISUI HOUSE ASSET MANAGEMENT, LTD.—See Sekisui House, Ltd.; *Int'l*, pg. 6697
SEKISUI HOUSE AUSTRALIA HOLDINGS PTY LIMITED—See Sekisui House, Ltd.; *Int'l*, pg. 6697
SEKISUI HOUSE CHANGCHENG (SUZHOU) REAL ESTATE DEVELOPMENT CO. LTD.—See Sekisui House, Ltd.; *Int'l*, pg. 6697
SEKISUI HOUSE FINANCIAL SERVICES CO, LTD.—See Sekisui House, Ltd.; *Int'l*, pg. 6697
SEKISUI HOUSE, LTD.; *Int'l*, pg. 6697
SEKISUI HOUSE REAL ESTATE CHUGOKU & SHIKOKU, LTD—See Sekisui House, Ltd.; *Int'l*, pg. 6697
SEKISUI HOUSE REAL ESTATE KANSAI, LTD—See Sekisui House, Ltd.; *Int'l*, pg. 6697
SEKISUI HOUSE REAL ESTATE KYUSHU,LTD—See Sekisui House, Ltd.; *Int'l*, pg. 6697
SEKISUI HOUSE REAL ESTATE TOHOKU, LTD—See Sekisui House, Ltd.; *Int'l*, pg. 6697
SEKISUI HOUSE REIT, INC.—See Sekisui House, Ltd.; *Int'l*, pg. 6697
SEKISUI HOUSE REMODELING, LTD—See Sekisui House, Ltd.; *Int'l*, pg. 6697
SEKISUI HOUSE SI ASSET MANAGEMENT, LTD—See Sekisui House, Ltd.; *Int'l*, pg. 6698
SEKISUI HOUSE UMEDA OPERATION CO., LTD—See Sekisui House, Ltd.; *Int'l*, pg. 6698
SEKISUI INDUSTRIAL PIPING CO., LTD.—See Sekisui Chemical Co., Ltd.; *Int'l*, pg. 6695
SEKISUI JUSHI CORPORATION; *Int'l*, pg. 6698
SEKISUI KASEI CO., LTD.; *Int'l*, pg. 6698
SEKISUI KOREA CO., LTD.—See Sekisui Chemical Co., Ltd.; *Int'l*, pg. 6695
SEKISUI KOSAN CO., LTD.—See Sekisui Chemical Co., Ltd.; *Int'l*, pg. 6695
SEKISUI KYDEX, LLC—See Sekisui Chemical Co., Ltd.; *Int'l*, pg. 6695

SEKISUI LEASING CO., LTD.—See Mitsubishi HC Capital Inc.; *Int'l*, pg. 4952
SEKISUI MEDICAL CO., LTD.—See Sekisui Chemical Co., Ltd.; *Int'l*, pg. 6695
SEKISUI MEDICAL TECHNOLOGY (CHINA) LTD.—See Sekisui Chemical Co., Ltd.; *Int'l*, pg. 6696
SEKISUI MEDICAL TECHNOLOGY (SUZHOU) CO., LTD.—See Sekisui Chemical Co., Ltd.; *Int'l*, pg. 6696
SEKISUI MINAKUCHI KAKO CO., LTD.—See Sekisui Chemical Co., Ltd.; *Int'l*, pg. 6696
SEKISUI MUSASHI KAKO CO., LTD.—See Sekisui Chemical Co., Ltd.; *Int'l*, pg. 6696
SEKISUI NUVOTEC CO., LTD.—See Sekisui Chemical Co., Ltd.; *Int'l*, pg. 6696
SEKISUI PILON PTY. LTD.—See Sekisui Chemical Co., Ltd.; *Int'l*, pg. 6696
SEKISUI PLASTICS CO., LTD. - CHEMICALS BUSINESS DIVISION—See Sekisui Kasei Co., Ltd.; *Int'l*, pg. 6698
SEKISUI PLASTICS CREATIVE DESIGN (THAILAND) CO., LTD.—See Sekisui Kasei Co., Ltd.; *Int'l*, pg. 6698
SEKISUI PLASTICS EUROPE B.V.—See Sekisui Kasei Co., Ltd.; *Int'l*, pg. 6698
SEKISUI PLASTICS (H.K.) CO., LTD.—See Sekisui Kasei Co., Ltd.; *Int'l*, pg. 6698
SEKISUI PLASTICS INDUSTRIAL MATERIALS (THAILAND) CO., LTD.—See Sekisui Kasei Co., Ltd.; *Int'l*, pg. 6698
SEKISUI PLASTICS (SHANGHAI) INTERNATIONAL TRADING CO., LTD.—See Sekisui Kasei Co., Ltd.; *Int'l*, pg. 6698
SEKISUI PLASTICS U.S.A. INC.—See Sekisui Kasei Co., Ltd.; *Int'l*, pg. 6698
SEKISUI POLYMATECH CO., LTD.—See Sekisui Chemical Co., Ltd.; *Int'l*, pg. 6696
SEKISUI POLYMATECH (SHANGHAI) CO., LTD.—See Sekisui Chemical Co., Ltd.; *Int'l*, pg. 6696
SEKISUI POLYMATECH (SHANGHAI) TRADING CO., LTD.—See Sekisui Chemical Co., Ltd.; *Int'l*, pg. 6696
SEKISUI POLYMATECH (THAILAND) CO., LTD.—See Sekisui Chemical Co., Ltd.; *Int'l*, pg. 6696
SEKISUI POLYMATECH TRADING (THAILAND) CO., LTD.—See Sekisui Chemical Co., Ltd.; *Int'l*, pg. 6696
SEKISUI PRODUCTS, LLC—See Sekisui Chemical Co., Ltd.; *Int'l*, pg. 6694
SEKISUI (QINGDAO) PLASTIC CO., LTD. - HUANGDAO PLANT—See Sekisui Chemical Co., Ltd.; *Int'l*, pg. 6694
SEKISUI (QINGDAO) PLASTIC CO., LTD.—See Sekisui Chemical Co., Ltd.; *Int'l*, pg. 6694
SEKISUI REFRESH CO., LTD.—See Sekisui Chemical Co., Ltd.; *Int'l*, pg. 6696
SEKISUI RIB LOC AUSTRALIA PTY. LTD.—See Sekisui Chemical Co., Ltd.; *Int'l*, pg. 6696
SEKISUI ROOF SYSTEM CO., LTD.—See Sekisui Chemical Co., Ltd.; *Int'l*, pg. 6696
SEKISUI-SCG INDUSTRY CO., LTD.—See Sekisui Chemical Co., Ltd.; *Int'l*, pg. 6696
SEKISUI (SHANGHAI) ENVIRONMENTAL TECHNOLOGY CO., LTD.—See Sekisui Chemical Co., Ltd.; *Int'l*, pg. 6694
SEKISUI (SHANGHAI) INTERNATIONAL TRADING CO., LTD.—See Sekisui Chemical Co., Ltd.; *Int'l*, pg. 6694
SEKISUI SINGAPORE PTE. LTD.—See Sekisui Chemical Co., Ltd.; *Int'l*, pg. 6696
SEKISUI S-LEC AMERICAN, LLC—See Sekisui Chemical Co., Ltd.; *Int'l*, pg. 6694
SEKISUI S-LEC B.V.—See Sekisui Chemical Co., Ltd.; *Int'l*, pg. 6696
SEKISUI S-LEC KOREA LTD.—See Sekisui Chemical Co., Ltd.; *Int'l*, pg. 6696
SEKISUI S-LEC MEXICO S.A. DE C.V.—See Sekisui Chemical Co., Ltd.; *Int'l*, pg. 6696
SEKISUI S-LEC (SUZHOU) CO., LTD.—See Sekisui Chemical Co., Ltd.; *Int'l*, pg. 6696
SEKISUI S-LEC (THAILAND) CO., LTD.—See Sekisui Chemical Co., Ltd.; *Int'l*, pg. 6696
SEKISUI SOUTHEAST ASIA CO., LTD.—See Sekisui Chemical Co., Ltd.; *Int'l*, pg. 6696
SEKISUI SPECIAITY CHEMICALS (THAILAND) CO., LTD.—See Sekisui Chemical Co., Ltd.; *Int'l*, pg. 6696
SEKISUI SPECIALITY CHEMICALS EUROPE S.L.—See Sekisui Chemical Co., Ltd.; *Int'l*, pg. 6696
SEKISUI SPECIALTY CHEMICALS AMERICA, LLC—See Sekisui Chemical Co., Ltd.; *Int'l*, pg. 6694
SEKISUI SPECIALTY CHEMICALS MEXICO'S, DE R.L. DE C.V.—See Sekisui Chemical Co., Ltd.; *Int'l*, pg. 6696
SEKISUI SPR AMERICAS, LLC—See Sekisui Chemical Co., Ltd.; *Int'l*, pg. 6694
SEKISUI SPR ASIA PTE. LTD.—See Sekisui Chemical Co., Ltd.; *Int'l*, pg. 6696
SEKISUI TA INDUSTRIES, INC.—See Sekisui Chemical Co., Ltd.; *Int'l*, pg. 6694
SEKISUI TECHNO SHOJI HIGASHI NIHON CO., LTD.—See Sekisui Chemical Co., Ltd.; *Int'l*, pg. 6696
SEKISUI TECHNO SHOJI NISHI NIHON CO., LTD.—See Sekisui Chemical Co., Ltd.; *Int'l*, pg. 6696
SEKISUI UNIDEA CO., LTD.—See Sekisui Chemical Co., Ltd.; *Int'l*, pg. 6696

SELA ROOFING & REMODELING

SEKISUI VIETNAM CO., LTD.—See Sekisui Chemical Co., Ltd.; *Int'l*, pg. 6696
SEKISUI VIROTECH G.M.B.H.—See Sekisui Chemical Co., Ltd.; *Int'l*, pg. 6696
SEKISUI VOLTEK LLC—See Sekisui Chemical Co., Ltd.; *Int'l*, pg. 6695
SEKISUI (WUXI) PLASTICS TECHNOLOGY CO., LTD.—See Sekisui Chemical Co., Ltd.; *Int'l*, pg. 6694
SEKISUI XENOTECH, LLC—See Sekisui Chemical Co., Ltd.; *Int'l*, pg. 6696
SEKISUI YOUNGBO HPP (WUXI) CO., LTD.—See Sekisui Chemical Co., Ltd.; *Int'l*, pg. 6696
SEKIWA CONSTRUCTION HIGASHI-TOKYO, LTD.—See Sekisui House, Ltd.; *Int'l*, pg. 6698
SEKIWA CONSTRUCTION, LTD—See Sekisui House, Ltd.; *Int'l*, pg. 6698
SEKIWA REAL ESTATE SAPPORO LTD.—See Sekisui House, Ltd.; *Int'l*, pg. 6698
SEKIWA WOOD, LTD—See Sekisui House, Ltd.; *Int'l*, pg. 6698
SEKIWOO CO., LTD.—See Sekisui Kasei Co., Ltd.; *Int'l*, pg. 6698
SEKIYA CO., LTD.—See Tomoku Co., Ltd.; *Int'l*, pg. 7801
SEKO ENTERPRISES, LLC—See Greenbriar Equity Group, L.P.; *U.S. Private*, pg. 1776
SEKONDA—See Time Products Ltd.; *Int'l*, pg. 7751
SEKONIC CORPORATION—See Sekonic Corporation; *Int'l*, pg. 6698
SEKONIC CORPORATION; *Int'l*, pg. 6698
SEKONIC ELECTRONICS (CHANGSHU) CO., LTD.—See Sekonic Corporation; *Int'l*, pg. 6698
SEKONIC ELECTRONICS, INC.—See Sekonic Corporation; *Int'l*, pg. 6698
SEKONIC (HONG KONG) CO., LTD.—See Sekonic Corporation; *Int'l*, pg. 6698
SEKONIX CO., LTD.; *Int'l*, pg. 6698
SEKONIX POLAND SP. Z O.O.—See Sekonix Co., Ltd.; *Int'l*, pg. 6699
SEKOPAC D.O.O.—See Ball Corporation; *U.S. Public*, pg. 268
SEKO S.A.; *Int'l*, pg. 6698
SEKPHARMA (PTY) LTD—See African Equity Empowerment Investmts Limited; *Int'l*, pg. 191
SEKSUI ESLON B.V.—See Sekisui Chemical Co., Ltd.; *Int'l*, pg. 6696
SEKSUN TECHNOLOGY SINGAPORE CO., LTD.—See Suzhou Anjie Technology Co., Ltd.; *Int'l*, pg. 7349
SEKSUN TECHNOLOGY THAILAND CO., LTD.—See Suzhou Anjie Technology Co., Ltd.; *Int'l*, pg. 7349
SEKTKELLEREI J OPPMANN AG; *Int'l*, pg. 6699
SEKUNJALO AQUACULTURE (PTY) LTD—See African Equity Empowerment Investmts Limited; *Int'l*, pg. 191
SEKUNJALO MEDICAL SERVICES (PTY) LTD—See African Equity Empowerment Investmts Limited; *Int'l*, pg. 191
SEKUNJALO TECHNOLOGY SOLUTIONS GROUP (PTY) LTD—See African Equity Empowerment Investmts Limited; *Int'l*, pg. 191
SEKURA INDIA MANAGEMENT LIMITED—See Edelweiss Financial Services Ltd.; *Int'l*, pg. 2306
SEKURIT SAINT-GOBAIN DEUTSCHLAND GMBH & CO. KG—See Compagnie de Saint-Gobain SA; *Int'l*, pg. 1736
SEKURIT SAINT-GOBAIN ITALIA S.R.L.—See Compagnie de Saint-Gobain SA; *Int'l*, pg. 1736
SEKURIT SAINT-GOBAIN SCANDINAVIA AB—See Compagnie de Saint-Gobain SA; *Int'l*, pg. 1737
SEKURIT SAINT-GOBAIN TORGAU GMBH—See Compagnie de Saint-Gobain SA; *Int'l*, pg. 1737
SEKURO PLASTIK AMBALAJ SANAYI AS; *Int'l*, pg. 6699
SEKUR PRIVATE DATA LTD.; *Int'l*, pg. 6699
SEKUR PRIVATE DATA LTD.; *Int'l*, pg. 6699
SELACO ALUMINIUM BERHAD—See Compact Metal Industries Ltd.; *Int'l*, pg. 1721
SELANDIA PARK A/S—See Glunz & Jensen Holding A/S; *Int'l*, pg. 3011
SELAN EXPLORATION TECHNOLOGY LTD.; *Int'l*, pg. 6699
SELANGOR DREDGING BERHAD; *Int'l*, pg. 6699
SELANGOR PROPERTIES BERHAD; *Int'l*, pg. 6699
SELANGOR SPECIALIST HOSPITAL SDN BHD—See KPJ Healthcare Berhad; *Int'l*, pg. 4297
SELAN HOLDING GMBH—See Baader Bank AG; *Int'l*, pg. 791
SELA ROOFING & REMODELING; *U.S. Private*, pg. 3600
SELAS FLUID PROCESSING CORP.—See Linde plc; *Int'l*, pg. 4505
SELAS HEAT TECHNOLOGY COMPANY LLC—See Lionheart Ventures; *U.S. Private*, pg. 2464
SELASIH PERMATA SDN. BHD.—See Oriental Holdings Berhad; *Int'l*, pg. 5625
SELAS-LINDE GMBH—See Linde plc; *Int'l*, pg. 4505
SELAS WAERMETECHNIK GMBH—See Lionheart Ventures; *U.S. Private*, pg. 2464
SELAT MAKMUR SDN BHD—See Berjaya Corporation Berhad; *Int'l*, pg. 983
SELBOURNE FOOD SERVICES SDN BHD—See Kuala Lumpur Kepong Berhad; *Int'l*, pg. 4319

SELBY VETS4PETS LIMITED—See Pets at Home Group Plc; *Int'l*, pg. 5834
SELC AUSTRALIA PTY. LTD.—See Bain Capital, LP; *U.S. Private*, pg. 442
SELC CAREER COLLEGE CANADA LTD.—See Bain Capital, LP; *U.S. Private*, pg. 442
SELC ENGLISH LANGUAGE CENTRE CANADA LTD.—See Bain Capital, LP; *U.S. Private*, pg. 442
SELC GROUP LTD.—See Xylem Inc.; *U.S. Public*, pg. 2394
SELCIA LIMITED—See Eurofins Scientific S.E.; *Int'l*, pg. 2551
SELC IRELAND LTD.—See Itron, Inc.; *U.S. Public*, pg. 1176
SELCI S.A. DE C.V.—See HORIBA Ltd; *Int'l*, pg. 3478
SELCO AS—See Littelfuse, Inc.; *U.S. Public*, pg. 1327
SELCO COMMUNITY CREDIT UNION; *U.S. Private*, pg. 3600
SELCODIS SA; *Int'l*, pg. 6699
SELCO INDUSTRIES, INC.; *U.S. Private*, pg. 3600
SELCO LLC; *U.S. Private*, pg. 3600
SELCO TRADE CENTRES LIMITED—See Grafton Group plc; *Int'l*, pg. 3051
SELCUK ECZA DEPOSU TICARET VE SANAYI AS; *Int'l*, pg. 6699
SELCUK GIDA ENDUSTRI IHRACAT ITHALAT A.S.; *Int'l*, pg. 6699
SELDAC 1. KOMMUNALER-RENDITE-FONDS GMBH & CO. KG—See Munchener Ruckversicherungs AG; *Int'l*, pg. 5091
SELDEN'S INTERIOR FURNISHINGS, INC.; *U.S. Private*, pg. 3600
SELDON SYSTEMS, INC.—See EnerSys; *U.S. Public*, pg. 768
SELECCOES DO READER'S DIGEST (PORTUGAL) S.A.—See RDA Holding Co.; *U.S. Private*, pg. 3363
SELECT 1 TRANSPORT INC.; *U.S. Private*, pg. 3600
SELECTA AG—See Allianz SE; *Int'l*, pg. 355
SELECTA AS—See Allianz SE; *Int'l*, pg. 355
SELECTA A/S—See Allianz SE; *Int'l*, pg. 355
SELECTA BETRIEBSVERPFLEGUNGS GMBH—See Allianz SE; *Int'l*, pg. 355
SELECTA DEUTSCHLAND GMBH—See Allianz SE; *Int'l*, pg. 355
SELECTA EESTI OSAUHING—See Allianz SE; *Int'l*, pg. 355
SELECTAERO—See Applied Avionics, Inc.; *U.S. Private*, pg. 298
SELECTA GROUP B.V.—See Allianz SE; *Int'l*, pg. 355
SELECTA HOLDING AB—See Allianz SE; *Int'l*, pg. 355
SELECTA HOLDING GMBH—See Allianz SE; *Int'l*, pg. 355
SELECTA HOLDING LTD.—See Allianz SE; *Int'l*, pg. 355
SELECTA HUNGARY AUTOMATAUZEMELTETO KFT—See Allianz SE; *Int'l*, pg. 355
SELECTA INFRATECHNIEK B.V.—See Allianz SE; *Int'l*, pg. 355
SELECTA OLLAND B.V.—See Allianz SE; *Int'l*, pg. 355
SELECT APPOINTMENTS B.V.—See Randstad N.V.; *Int'l*, pg. 6205
SELECTA PRODUCTS INC.; *U.S. Private*, pg. 3601
SELECTA PURCHASING AG—See Allianz SE; *Int'l*, pg. 355
SELECTA S.A.—See Allianz SE; *Int'l*, pg. 355
SELECTA TMP AG—See Allianz SE; *Int'l*, pg. 355
SELECTA TYRE LIMITED—See Sumitomo Rubber Industries, Ltd.; *Int'l*, pg. 7299
SELECT AUDIO VISUEEL B.V.—See Randstad N.V.; *Int'l*, pg. 6205
SELECT AUDIO VISUEEL PERSONEEL BV—See Randstad N.V.; *Int'l*, pg. 6205
SELECTA UK LTD.—See Allianz SE; *Int'l*, pg. 355
SELECT AV PERSONEEL B.V.—See Randstad N.V.; *Int'l*, pg. 6205
SELECT BANCORP, INC.—See First Bancorp; *U.S. Public*, pg. 839
SELECT BANK & TRUST COMPANY—See First Bancorp; *U.S. Public*, pg. 839
SELECTBUILD CONSTRUCTION, INC.—See Builders FirstSource, Inc.; *U.S. Public*, pg. 410
SELECTBUILD OF NEVADA—See Builders FirstSource, Inc.; *U.S. Public*, pg. 410
SELECT BUSINESS SYSTEMS, INC.—See GoodSuite; *U.S. Private*, pg. 1740
SELECTCARE OF TEXAS, INC.—See Centene Corporation; *U.S. Public*, pg. 471
SELECT CATERING SERVICES PTE LTD—See Select Group Limited; *Int'l*, pg. 6699
SELECTCOMFORT.COM CORPORATION—See Sleep Number Corporation; *U.S. Public*, pg. 1894
SELECT COMFORT RETAIL CORPORATION—See Sleep Number Corporation; *U.S. Public*, pg. 1894
SELECT COMMUNICATIONS, INC.; *U.S. Private*, pg. 3600
SELECTED ENERGY S.A.; *Int'l*, pg. 6700
SELECTED FUNERAL & LIFE INSURANCE CO.; *U.S. Private*, pg. 3601
SELECTED TEXTILES S.A.; *Int'l*, pg. 6700
SELECTEMP CORPORATION; *U.S. Private*, pg. 3601

SELECT ENERGY SERVICES LLC—See Select Water Solutions, Inc.; *U.S. Public*, pg. 1862
SELECT ENGINEERED PRODUCTS—See Select International Corp.; *U.S. Private*, pg. 3600
SELECT ENGINEERING, INC.; *U.S. Private*, pg. 3600
SELECT ENVIRONMENTAL SERVICES, INC.—See Carylon Corporation; *U.S. Private*, pg. 777
SELECT EXPRESS & LOGISTICS LLC—See AIT Worldwide Logistics, Inc.; *U.S. Private*, pg. 142
SELECT GENERAL AGENCY, LLC—See Brown & Brown, Inc.; *U.S. Public*, pg. 401
SELECT GLASS INDUSTRIES LLC—See Al Hamad Contracting Company LLC; *Int'l*, pg. 278
SELECT GROUP LIMITED; *Int'l*, pg. 6699
SELECT GROUP; *U.S. Private*, pg. 3600
SELECT HARVESTS FOOD PRODUCTS PTY LTD—See Select Harvests Limited; *Int'l*, pg. 6700
SELECT HARVESTS LIMITED; *Int'l*, pg. 6699
SELECTHEALTH, INC.; *U.S. Private*, pg. 3601
SELECT HOTELS GROUP, L.L.C.—See Hyatt Hotels Corporation; *U.S. Public*, pg. 1078
SELECT HUMANEROFORRAS KFT; *Int'l*, pg. 6700
SELECT INCOME REIT—See The RMR Group Inc.; *U.S. Public*, pg. 2126
SELECT INDUSTRIES CORP—See Select International Corp.; *U.S. Private*, pg. 3600
SELECT INN; *U.S. Private*, pg. 3600
SELECT INTERIOR CONCEPTS, INC.—See Sun Capital Partners, Inc.; *U.S. Private*, pg. 3861
SELECT INTERNATIONAL CORP.; *U.S. Private*, pg. 3600
SELECTION DU READER'S DIGEST S.A.—See CIL Group SL; *Int'l*, pg. 1607
SELECTIRENTE SA; *Int'l*, pg. 6700
SELECTIS HEALTH, INC.; *U.S. Public*, pg. 1862
SELECTIVE AUTO INSURANCE COMPANY OF NEW JERSEY—See Selective Insurance Group, Inc.; *U.S. Public*, pg. 1862
SELECTIVE CASUALTY INSURANCE COMPANY—See Selective Insurance Group, Inc.; *U.S. Public*, pg. 1862
SELECTIVE ENTERPRISES INC.; *U.S. Private*, pg. 3601
SELECTIVE INSURANCE COMPANY OF AMERICA—See Selective Insurance Group, Inc.; *U.S. Public*, pg. 1862
SELECTIVE INSURANCE COMPANY OF SOUTH CAROLINA—See Selective Insurance Group, Inc.; *U.S. Public*, pg. 1863
SELECTIVE INSURANCE COMPANY OF THE SOUTHEAST—See Selective Insurance Group, Inc.; *U.S. Public*, pg. 1863
SELECTIVE INSURANCE GROUP, INC.; *U.S. Public*, pg. 1862
SELECTIVEND INC.—See The Wittern Group; *U.S. Private*, pg. 4138
SELECT MANAGED FUNDS LIMITED—See Insignia Financial Ltd.; *Int'l*, pg. 3719
SELECT MANAGEMENT HOLDINGS, INC.; *U.S. Private*, pg. 3600
SELECT MEDICAL CORPORATION—See Select Medical Holdings Corporation; *U.S. Public*, pg. 1859
SELECT MEDICAL HOLDINGS CORPORATION; *U.S. Public*, pg. 1857
SELECT MEDICAL OF MARYLAND, INC.—See Select Medical Holdings Corporation; *U.S. Public*, pg. 1859
SELECT MILK PRODUCERS INC.; *U.S. Private*, pg. 3600
SELECTNY.BERLIN GMBH—See SelectNY L.P.; *U.S. Private*, pg. 3601
SELECTNY GMBH—See SelectNY L.P.; *U.S. Private*, pg. 3601
SELECTNY.KOBLENZ GMBH—See SelectNY L.P.; *U.S. Private*, pg. 3601
SELECTNY.LONDON LTD.—See SelectNY L.P.; *U.S. Private*, pg. 3601
SELECTNY L.P.; *U.S. Private*, pg. 3601
SELECTNY.PARIS—See SelectNY L.P.; *U.S. Private*, pg. 3601
SELECT OFFSHORE SERVICES PTE LTD—See Select Group Limited; *Int'l*, pg. 6699
SELECTO INC.—See Axel Johnson Gruppen AB; *Int'l*, pg. 765
SELECTO PRODUCTS CO. INC.; *U.S. Private*, pg. 3601
SELECT OPTICAL, INC.—See EssilorLuxottica SA; *Int'l*, pg. 2513
SELECTOUR VOYAGES; *Int'l*, pg. 6700
SELECTPART PARTICIPACOES S.A.; *Int'l*, pg. 6700
SELECT PHYSICAL THERAPY - AVON—See Select Medical Holdings Corporation; *U.S. Public*, pg. 1859
SELECT PHYSICAL THERAPY OF ALBUQUERQUE, LTD.—See Select Medical Holdings Corporation; *U.S. Public*, pg. 1859
SELECT PHYSICAL THERAPY OF BLUE SPRINGS LIMITED PARTNERSHIP—See Select Medical Holdings Corporation; *U.S. Public*, pg. 1859
SELECT PHYSICAL THERAPY OF CHICAGO, INC.—See Select Medical Holdings Corporation; *U.S. Public*, pg. 1859
SELECT PHYSICAL THERAPY OF COLORADO SPRINGS LIMITED PARTNERSHIP—See Select Medical Holdings Corporation; *U.S. Public*, pg. 1859

SELECT PHYSICAL THERAPY OF CONNECTICUT LIMITED PARTNERSHIP—See Select Medical Holdings Corporation; *U.S. Public*, pg. 1859
SELECT PHYSICAL THERAPY OF DENVER, LTD.—See Select Medical Holdings Corporation; *U.S. Public*, pg. 1859
SELECT PHYSICAL THERAPY OF KENDALL, LTD.—See Select Medical Holdings Corporation; *U.S. Public*, pg. 1859
SELECT PHYSICAL THERAPY OF LOUISVILLE, LTD.—See Select Medical Holdings Corporation; *U.S. Public*, pg. 1859
SELECT PHYSICAL THERAPY OF PORTOLA VALLEY LIMITED PARTNERSHIP—See Select Medical Holdings Corporation; *U.S. Public*, pg. 1859
SELECT PHYSICAL THERAPY OF ST. LOUIS LIMITED PARTNERSHIP—See Select Medical Holdings Corporation; *U.S. Public*, pg. 1859
SELECT PHYSICAL THERAPY OF WEST DENVER LIMITED PARTNERSHIP—See Select Medical Holdings Corporation; *U.S. Public*, pg. 1859
SELECT PHYSICAL THERAPY TEXAS LIMITED PARTNERSHIP—See Select Medical Holdings Corporation; *U.S. Public*, pg. 1859
SELECT PHYSICIANS SURGERY CENTER, LLC—See Tenet Healthcare Corporation; *U.S. Public*, pg. 2007
SELECT PLANT HIRE COMPANY LIMITED—See Laing O'Rourke Plc; *Int'l*, pg. 4396
SELECT PORTFOLIO SERVICING, INC.; *U.S. Private*, pg. 3600
SELECTQUOTE, INC.; *U.S. Public*, pg. 1863
SELECTQUOTE INSURANCE SERVICES; *U.S. Private*, pg. 3601
SELECT REALTY GROUP; *U.S. Private*, pg. 3600
SELECT RECURSOS HUMANOS, S.A.—See Randstad N.V.; *Int'l*, pg. 6205
SELECT REHABILITATION, LLC; *U.S. Private*, pg. 3601
SELECTREMEDY—See Affiliated Managers Group, Inc.; *U.S. Public*, pg. 54
SELECTREMEDY—See Anchorage Capital Group, L.L.C.; *U.S. Private*, pg. 274
SELECT RESTAURANTS, INC.—See Select Management Holdings, Inc.; *U.S. Private*, pg. 3600
SELECTRODE INDUSTRIES INC.; *U.S. Private*, pg. 3601
SELECTRONICS CORP.; *U.S. Private*, pg. 3602
SELECTRON INDUSTRIAL COMPANY; *U.S. Private*, pg. 3601
SELECTRON SYSTEMS AG—See Knorr-Bremse AG; *Int'l*, pg. 4212
SELECTRON SYSTEMS (BEIJING) CO., LTD.—See Knorr-Bremse AG; *Int'l*, pg. 4212
SELECTRUCKS OF AMERICA LLC—See Mercedes-Benz Group AG; *Int'l*, pg. 4829
SELECTRUCKS OF CLEVELAND L.L.C.—See Mercedes-Benz Group AG; *Int'l*, pg. 4823
SELECTRUCKS OF THE TWIN CITIES—See Mercedes-Benz Group AG; *Int'l*, pg. 4823
SELECTRUCKS OF TORONTO, INC.—See Mercedes-Benz Group AG; *Int'l*, pg. 4829
SELECT SANDS CORP.; *Int'l*, pg. 6700
SELECT SERVICE PARTNER FINLAND OY—See SSP Group plc; *Int'l*, pg. 7157
SELECT SERVICE PARTNER (SCHWEIZ) AG—See SSP Group plc; *Int'l*, pg. 7157
SELECT SIRES INC.; *U.S. Private*, pg. 3601
SELECT SIRES MIDAMERICA, INC.—See Select Sires Inc.; *U.S. Private*, pg. 3601
SELECT SOCIETA DIFORNITURA DILAVORO TEMPORANIO S.P.A.—See Randstad N.V.; *Int'l*, pg. 6203
SELECT SOUND SERVICE, INC.—See Communications Engineering Co.; *U.S. Private*, pg. 988
SELECT SPECIALTY-DOWNRIVER, LLC—See Select Medical Holdings Corporation; *U.S. Public*, pg. 1861
SELECT SPECIALTY HOSPITAL-AKRON, LLC—See Select Medical Holdings Corporation; *U.S. Public*, pg. 1859
SELECT SPECIALTY HOSPITAL-ANN ARBOR, INC.—See Select Medical Holdings Corporation; *U.S. Public*, pg. 1859
SELECT SPECIALTY HOSPITAL-ARIZONA, INC.—See Select Medical Holdings Corporation; *U.S. Public*, pg. 1859
SELECT SPECIALTY HOSPITAL-AUGUSTA, INC.—See Select Medical Holdings Corporation; *U.S. Public*, pg. 1859
SELECT SPECIALTY HOSPITAL-BELHAVEN, LLC—See Select Medical Holdings Corporation; *U.S. Public*, pg. 1860
SELECT SPECIALTY HOSPITAL-BOARDMAN, INC.—See Select Medical Holdings Corporation; *U.S. Public*, pg. 1860
SELECT SPECIALTY HOSPITAL-CENTRAL PENNSYLVANIA, L.P.—See Select Medical Holdings Corporation; *U.S. Public*, pg. 1860
SELECT SPECIALTY HOSPITAL-CHARLESTON, INC.—See Select Medical Holdings Corporation; *U.S. Public*, pg. 1860

SELECT SPECIALTY HOSPITAL-CLEVELAND, LLC—See Select Medical Holdings Corporation; *U.S. Public*, pg. 1860
SELECT SPECIALTY HOSPITAL-COLORADO SPRINGS, INC.—See Select Medical Holdings Corporation; *U.S. Public*, pg. 1860
SELECT SPECIALTY HOSPITAL-COLUMBUS, INC.—See Select Medical Holdings Corporation; *U.S. Public*, pg. 1860
SELECT SPECIALTY HOSPITAL-DALLAS, INC.—See Select Medical Holdings Corporation; *U.S. Public*, pg. 1860
SELECT SPECIALTY HOSPITAL-DANVILLE, INC.—See Select Medical Holdings Corporation; *U.S. Public*, pg. 1860
SELECT SPECIALTY HOSPITAL - DAYTONA BEACH, INC.—See Select Medical Holdings Corporation; *U.S. Public*, pg. 1859
SELECT SPECIALTY HOSPITAL-DENVER, INC.—See Select Medical Holdings Corporation; *U.S. Public*, pg. 1860
SELECT SPECIALTY HOSPITAL-DES MOINES, INC.—See Select Medical Holdings Corporation; *U.S. Public*, pg. 1860
SELECT SPECIALTY HOSPITAL-DURHAM, INC.—See Select Medical Holdings Corporation; *U.S. Public*, pg. 1860
SELECT SPECIALTY HOSPITAL-ERIE INC.—See Select Medical Holdings Corporation; *U.S. Public*, pg. 1860
SELECT SPECIALTY HOSPITAL-EVANSVILLE, INC.—See Select Medical Holdings Corporation; *U.S. Public*, pg. 1860
SELECT SPECIALTY HOSPITAL-EVANSVILLE, LLC—See Select Medical Holdings Corporation; *U.S. Public*, pg. 1860
SELECT SPECIALTY HOSPITAL-FLINT, INC.—See Select Medical Holdings Corporation; *U.S. Public*, pg. 1860
SELECT SPECIALTY HOSPITAL-FORT MYERS, INC.—See Select Medical Holdings Corporation; *U.S. Public*, pg. 1860
SELECT SPECIALTY HOSPITAL-FORT SMITH, INC.—See Select Medical Holdings Corporation; *U.S. Public*, pg. 1860
SELECT SPECIALTY HOSPITAL-FORT WAYNE, INC.—See Select Medical Holdings Corporation; *U.S. Public*, pg. 1860
SELECT SPECIALTY HOSPITAL-GAINESVILLE, INC.—See Select Medical Holdings Corporation; *U.S. Public*, pg. 1860
SELECT SPECIALTY HOSPITAL-GREENSBORO, INC.—See Select Medical Holdings Corporation; *U.S. Public*, pg. 1860
SELECT SPECIALTY HOSPITAL-GROSSE POINTE, INC.—See Select Medical Holdings Corporation; *U.S. Public*, pg. 1860
SELECT SPECIALTY HOSPITAL-GULF COAST, INC.—See Select Medical Holdings Corporation; *U.S. Public*, pg. 1860
SELECT SPECIALTY HOSPITAL-HOUSTON, L.P.—See Select Medical Holdings Corporation; *U.S. Public*, pg. 1860
SELECT SPECIALTY HOSPITAL-JACKSON, INC.—See Select Medical Holdings Corporation; *U.S. Public*, pg. 1860
SELECT SPECIALTY HOSPITAL-JOHNSTOWN, INC.—See Select Medical Holdings Corporation; *U.S. Public*, pg. 1860
SELECT SPECIALTY HOSPITAL-KALAMAZOO, INC.—See Select Medical Holdings Corporation; *U.S. Public*, pg. 1860
SELECT SPECIALTY HOSPITAL-KANSAS CITY, INC.—See Select Medical Holdings Corporation; *U.S. Public*, pg. 1860
SELECT SPECIALTY HOSPITAL-KNOXVILLE, INC.—See Select Medical Holdings Corporation; *U.S. Public*, pg. 1860
SELECT SPECIALTY HOSPITAL-LAUREL HIGHLANDS, INC.—See Select Medical Holdings Corporation; *U.S. Public*, pg. 1860
SELECT SPECIALTY HOSPITAL-LEXINGTON, INC.—See Select Medical Holdings Corporation; *U.S. Public*, pg. 1860
SELECT SPECIALTY HOSPITAL-LINCOLN, INC.—See Select Medical Holdings Corporation; *U.S. Public*, pg. 1860
SELECT SPECIALTY HOSPITAL-LITTLE ROCK, INC.—See Select Medical Holdings Corporation; *U.S. Public*, pg. 1860
SELECT SPECIALTY HOSPITAL-LONGVIEW, INC.—See Select Medical Holdings Corporation; *U.S. Public*, pg. 1860
SELECT SPECIALTY HOSPITAL-MACOMB COUNTY, INC.—See Select Medical Holdings Corporation; *U.S. Public*, pg. 1860
SELECT SPECIALTY HOSPITAL-MADISON, INC.—See Select Medical Holdings Corporation; *U.S. Public*, pg. 1860
SELECT SPECIALTY HOSPITAL-MCKEESPORT, INC.—See Select Medical Holdings Corporation; *U.S. Public*, pg. 1860
SELECT SPECIALTY HOSPITAL-MEMPHIS, INC.—See Select Medical Holdings Corporation; *U.S. Public*, pg. 1860
SELECT SPECIALTY HOSPITAL-MIAMI LAKES, INC.—See Select Medical Holdings Corporation; *U.S. Public*, pg. 1860
SELECT SPECIALTY HOSPITAL-MIDLAND, INC.—See Select Medical Holdings Corporation; *U.S. Public*, pg. 1860
SELECT SPECIALTY HOSPITAL-MIDTOWN ATLANTA, LLC—See Select Medical Holdings Corporation; *U.S. Public*, pg. 1861
SELECT SPECIALTY HOSPITAL-MILWAUKEE, INC.—See Select Medical Holdings Corporation; *U.S. Public*, pg. 1861
SELECT SPECIALTY HOSPITAL-NASHVILLE, INC.—See Select Medical Holdings Corporation; *U.S. Public*, pg. 1861
SELECT SPECIALTY HOSPITAL-NORTHEAST NEW JERSEY, INC.—See Select Medical Holdings Corporation; *U.S. Public*, pg. 1861
SELECT SPECIALTY HOSPITAL-NORTHEAST OHIO, INC.—See Select Medical Holdings Corporation; *U.S. Public*, pg. 1861
SELECT SPECIALTY HOSPITAL-NORTHERN KENTUCKY, LLC—See Select Medical Holdings Corporation; *U.S. Public*, pg. 1861
SELECT SPECIALTY HOSPITAL-NORTH KNOXVILLE, INC.—See Select Medical Holdings Corporation; *U.S. Public*, pg. 1861
SELECT SPECIALTY HOSPITAL-NORTHWEST DETROIT, INC.—See Select Medical Holdings Corporation; *U.S. Public*, pg. 1861
SELECT SPECIALTY HOSPITAL-OKLAHOMA CITY, INC.—See Select Medical Holdings Corporation; *U.S. Public*, pg. 1861
SELECT SPECIALTY HOSPITAL-OMAHA, INC.—See Select Medical Holdings Corporation; *U.S. Public*, pg. 1861
SELECT SPECIALTY HOSPITAL-PALM BEACH, INC. See Select Medical Holdings Corporation; *U.S. Public*, pg. 1861
SELECT SPECIALTY HOSPITAL-PANAMA CITY, INC.—See Select Medical Holdings Corporation; *U.S. Public*, pg. 1861
SELECT SPECIALTY HOSPITAL-PENSACOLA, INC.—See Select Medical Holdings Corporation; *U.S. Public*, pg. 1861
SELECT SPECIALTY HOSPITAL-PHOENIX, INC.—See Select Medical Holdings Corporation; *U.S. Public*, pg. 1861
SELECT SPECIALTY HOSPITAL-PITTSBURGH/UPMC, INC.—See Select Medical Holdings Corporation; *U.S. Public*, pg. 1861
SELECT SPECIALTY HOSPITAL-PONTIAC, INC.—See Select Medical Holdings Corporation; *U.S. Public*, pg. 1861
SELECT SPECIALTY HOSPITAL-QUAD CITIES, INC.—See Select Medical Holdings Corporation; *U.S. Public*, pg. 1861
SELECT SPECIALTY HOSPITAL-RICHMOND, INC.—See Select Medical Holdings Corporation; *U.S. Public*, pg. 1861
SELECT SPECIALTY HOSPITAL-SAGINAW, INC.—See Select Medical Holdings Corporation; *U.S. Public*, pg. 1861
SELECT SPECIALTY HOSPITAL-SAN ANTONIO, INC.—See Select Medical Holdings Corporation; *U.S. Public*, pg. 1861
SELECT SPECIALTY HOSPITAL-SAVANNAH, INC.—See Select Medical Holdings Corporation; *U.S. Public*, pg. 1861
SELECT SPECIALTY HOSPITAL-SIOUX FALLS, INC.—See Select Medical Holdings Corporation; *U.S. Public*, pg. 1861
SELECT SPECIALTY HOSPITAL - SPECTRUM HEALTH—See Select Medical Holdings Corporation; *U.S. Public*, pg. 1859
SELECT SPECIALTY HOSPITAL-SPRINGFIELD, INC.—See Select Medical Holdings Corporation; *U.S. Public*, pg. 1861
SELECT SPECIALTY HOSPITAL-TALLAHASSEE, INC.—See Select Medical Holdings Corporation; *U.S. Public*, pg. 1861
SELECT SPECIALTY HOSPITAL-THE VILLAGES, INC.—See Select Medical Holdings Corporation; *U.S. Public*, pg. 1861
SELECT SPECIALTY HOSPITAL-TRICITIES, INC.—See Select Medical Holdings Corporation; *U.S. Public*, pg. 1861
SELECT SPECIALTY HOSPITAL - TUCSON, LLC—See Community Health Systems, Inc.; *U.S. Public*, pg. 556
SELECT SPECIALTY HOSPITAL-TULSA, INC.—See Select Medical Holdings Corporation; *U.S. Public*, pg. 1861
SELECT SPECIALTY HOSPITAL-TULSA/MIDTOWN, LLC—See Select Medical Holdings Corporation; *U.S. Public*, pg. 1861
SELECT SPECIALTY HOSPITAL-WESTERN MISSOURI, INC.—See Select Medical Holdings Corporation; *U.S. Public*, pg. 1861
SELECT SPECIALTY HOSPITAL-WICHITA, INC.—See Select Medical Holdings Corporation; *U.S. Public*, pg. 1861
SELECT SPECIALTY HOSPITAL-WILMINGTON, INC.—See Select Medical Holdings Corporation; *U.S. Public*, pg. 1861
SELECT SPECIALTY HOSPITAL-WINSTON-SALEM, INC.—See Select Medical Holdings Corporation; *U.S. Public*, pg. 1861
SELECT SPECIALTY HOSPITAL-YOUNGSTOWN, INC.—See Select Medical Holdings Corporation; *U.S. Public*, pg. 1861
SELECT SPECIALTY HOSPITAL-ZANESVILLE, INC.—See Select Medical Holdings Corporation; *U.S. Public*, pg. 1861
SELECT STAFFING—See Affiliated Managers Group, Inc.; *U.S. Public*, pg. 54
SELECT STAFFING—See Anchorage Capital Group, L.L.C.; *U.S. Private*, pg. 274
SELECT STAFFING—See Comarco, Inc.; *U.S. Private*, pg. 980
SELECT SYNERGOS, INC.—See Select Medical Holdings Corporation; *U.S. Public*, pg. 1861
SELECT TEMPORARIES INC.; *U.S. Private*, pg. 3601
SELECTUS PTY. LTD.—See Smartgroup Corporation Ltd.; *Int'l*, pg. 7002
SELECT WATER SOLUTIONS, INC.; *U.S. Public*, pg. 1862
SELEE CORPORATION—See Porvair plc; *Int'l*, pg. 5936
SELEGIE TOWER SDN. BHD.—See Merge Housing Bhd; *Int'l*, pg. 4834
SELEKSI JUANG SDN BHD; *Int'l*, pg. 6700
SELEKTA INOVATIF (M) SDN. BHD.—See Giovanni Agnelli B.V.; *Int'l*, pg. 2978
SELEKTA INOVATIF (M) SDN. BHD.—See PrimeMovers Equity (S) Pte. Ltd.; *Int'l*, pg. 5979
SELEKTVRACHT B.V.—See Deutsche Post AG; *Int'l*, pg. 2082
SELENA BOHEMIA S.R.O.—See SELENA FM S.A.; *Int'l*, pg. 6700
SELENA BULGARIA LTD.—See SELENA FM S.A.; *Int'l*, pg. 6700
SELENA DEUTSCHLAND GMBH—See SELENA FM S.A.; *Int'l*, pg. 6700
SELENA FM S.A.; *Int'l*, pg. 6700
SELENA HUNGARIA KFT.—See SELENA FM S.A.; *Int'l*, pg. 6700
SELENA IBERIA SLU—See SELENA FM S.A.; *Int'l*, pg. 6700
SELENA ITALIA SRL—See SELENA FM S.A.; *Int'l*, pg. 6700
SELENA ROMANIA SRL—See SELENA FM S.A.; *Int'l*, pg. 6700
SELENA S.A.—See SELENA FM S.A.; *Int'l*, pg. 6700
SELENA SULAMERICANA LTDA.—See SELENA FM S.A.; *Int'l*, pg. 6700
SELENA UKRAINE LTD.—See SELENA FM S.A.; *Int'l*, pg. 6700
SELENA USA, INC.—See SELENA FM S.A.; *Int'l*, pg. 6700
SELENA VOSTOK MOSCOW SRL—See SELENA FM S.A.; *Int'l*, pg. 6700
SELENCY—See Prosus N.V.; *Int'l*, pg. 6003
SELEN ELEKTRIK URETIM A.S.—See The AES Corporation; *U.S. Public*, pg. 2032
SELENE SPA—See A2A S.p.A.; *Int'l*, pg. 29
SELERANT CORP.; *U.S. Private*, pg. 3602
SELERANT SRL—See Symphony Technology Group, LLC; *U.S. Private*, pg. 3902
SELET ENTEGRE ET VE SUT URUNLERI SAN. TIC. A.S.—See Loras Holding A.S.; *Int'l*, pg. 4557
SELEX COMMUNICATIONS ROMANIA SRL—See Leonardo S.p.A.; *Int'l*, pg. 4460
SELEX ELSAG S.P.A.—See Leonardo S.p.A.; *Int'l*, pg. 4460
SELEX ENGINEERING SERVICES LIMITED—See Great Eagle Holdings Limited; *Int'l*, pg. 3064
SELEX ES SAUDI ARABIA LTD.—See Leonardo S.p.A.; *Int'l*, pg. 4461
SELEX GALILEO INC.—See Leonardo S.p.A.; *Int'l*, pg. 4461
SELEX GALILEO INFRARED LTD.—See Leonardo S.p.A.; *Int'l*, pg. 4461
SELEX GALILEO (PROJECTS) LTD.—See Leonardo S.p.A.; *Int'l*, pg. 4461
SELEX GALILEO S.P.A.—See Leonardo S.p.A.; *Int'l*, pg. 4460
SELEXIS SA—See JSR Corp.; *Int'l*, pg. 4014
SELEX PENSION SCHEME (TRUSTEE) LIMITED—See Leonardo S.p.A.; *Int'l*, pg. 4461
SELEX SISTEMI INTEGRATI DO BRASIL LTDA—See Leonardo S.p.A.; *Int'l*, pg. 4461
SELEX SISTEMI INTEGRATI GMBH—See Leonardo S.p.A.; *Int'l*, pg. 4461

SELEX SISTEMI INTEGRATI S.P.A.—See Leonardo S.p.A.; *Int'l*, pg. 4461
SELEX SYSTEMS INTEGRATION INC.—See Leonardo S.p.A.; *Int'l*, pg. 4461
SELEX SYSTEMS INTEGRATION LTD.—See Leonardo S.p.A.; *Int'l*, pg. 4461
SELEXYS PHARMACEUTICALS—See Novartis AG; *Int'l*, pg. 5458
SELFDOCTOR BEIJING TECHNOLOGY CO. LTD.; *Int'l*, pg. 6700
SELF ESTEEM BRANDS LLC; *U.S. Private*, pg. 3602
SELFHELP COMMUNITY SERVICES, INC; *U.S. Private*, pg. 3602
SELF-HELP CREDIT UNION; *U.S. Private*, pg. 3602
SELF HELP, INC.; *U.S. Private*, pg. 3602
SELF INDUSTRIES INC.—See Ringmetall AG; *Int'l*, pg. 6344
SELF INDUSTRIES INC.—See Ringmetall AG; *Int'l*, pg. 6344
SELFIO GMBH—See 3U Holding AG; *Int'l*, pg. 10
SELF LEVELING MACHINES, INC.—See Team, Inc.; *U.S. Public*, pg. 1988
SELF MAGAZINE—See Advance Publications, Inc.; *U.S. Private*, pg. 86
SELF OPPORTUNITY, INC.; *U.S. Private*, pg. 3602
SELFRIDGES & CO.—See Central Group Company Limited; *Int'l*, pg. 1407
SELFRIDGES & CO.—See SIGNA Holding GmbH; *Int'l*, pg. 6909
SELF SERVE AUTO DISMANTLERS—See Sims Limited; *U.S. Public*, pg. 1883
SELF SERVE LUMBER CO.; *U.S. Private*, pg. 3602
SELF STORAGE GROUP ASA—See Teachers Insurance Association - College Retirement Fund; *U.S. Private*, pg. 3945
SELFWEALTH LIMITED; *Int'l*, pg. 6700
SELIA—See Groupe Limagrain Holding SA; *Int'l*, pg. 3108
SELIC CORP PCL; *Int'l*, pg. 6700
SELIGDAR OJSC; *Int'l*, pg. 6701
SELIG ENTERPRISES INC.; *U.S. Private*, pg. 3602
SELIGMAN & ASSOCIATES, INC.; *U.S. Private*, pg. 3602
SELIGMAN WESTERN ENTERPRISES LIMITED—See Seligman & Associates, Inc.; *U.S. Private*, pg. 3602
SELI GMBH—See Ste Europeenne Logistique Internationale; *Int'l*, pg. 7186
SELIG MULTIMEDIA INC.; *U.S. Private*, pg. 3602
SELIG SEALING PRODUCTS, INC.—See Henry Crown & Company; *U.S. Private*, pg. 1918
SELINA HOSPITALITY PLC; *Int'l*, pg. 6701
SELINSGROVE MOTORS INC.; *U.S. Private*, pg. 3602
SELINSING PLC—See Carson Cumberbatch PLC; *Int'l*, pg. 1347
SELINSKY FORCE, LLC—See KLH Capital L.P.; *U.S. Private*, pg. 2319
SELI PROTRANS—See Ste Europeenne Logistique Internationale; *Int'l*, pg. 7186
SELKA IC VE DIS TICARET A.S.—See Kartonsan Karton Sanayi ve Ticaret A.S.; *Int'l*, pg. 4085
SELKASAN KAGIT VE PAKETLEME MALZEMELERI IMALATI SAN. VE TIC. A.S.—See Cukurova Holding A.S.; *Int'l*, pg. 1876
SELKASAN KAGIT VE PAKETLEME MALZEMELERI IMALATI SAN. VE TIC. A.S.—See DS Smith Plc; *Int'l*, pg. 2208
SELKIRK CANADA CORPORATION—See Canada Pension Plan Investment Board; *Int'l*, pg. 1282
SELKIRK CHRYSLER (MB) LTD.; *Int'l*, pg. 6701
SELKIRK CORPORATION—See Canada Pension Plan Investment Board; *Int'l*, pg. 1282
SELLA CAPITAL REAL ESTATE LTD.; *Int'l*, pg. 6701
SELLAFIELD LIMITED—See AECOM; *U.S. Public*, pg. 51
SELLAND AUTO TRANSPORT INC.; *U.S. Private*, pg. 3602
SELLAS LIFE SCIENCES GROUP, INC.; *U.S. Public*, pg. 1863
SELLEN CONSTRUCTION COMPANY; *U.S. Private*, pg. 3602
SELLERS 3 PROPERTIES, LLC—See Ralph Sellers Motor Co.; *U.S. Private*, pg. 3350
SELLERS BROS. INCORPORATED; *U.S. Private*, pg. 3602
SELLERS BUICK GMC; *U.S. Private*, pg. 3602
SELLERSBURG STONE COMPANY, INC.—See Gohmann Asphalt & Construction Inc.; *U.S. Private*, pg. 1726
SELLER'S CHOICE, LLC—See Creatd, Inc.; *U.S. Public*, pg. 593
SELLERS EQUIPMENT INC.; *U.S. Private*, pg. 3602
SELLERS EQUIPMENT INC.—See Sellers Equipment Inc.; *U.S. Private*, pg. 3602
SELLERS & JOSEPHSON—See Whippoorwill Associates, Inc.; *U.S. Private*, pg. 4507
SELLERS PETROLEUM; *U.S. Private*, pg. 3602
SELLERS-SEXTON INC—See Morse Operations Inc.; *U.S. Private*, pg. 2790
SELLICK EQUIPMENT LIMITED—See Avis Industrial Corporation; *U.S. Public*, pg. 408
SELLING HALLOWEEN—See RFE Investment Partners; *U.S. Private*, pg. 3419

SELLING SIMPLIFIED GROUP, INC.—See Eagle Publishing Inc.; *U.S. Private*, pg. 1310
SELLING SOLUTIONS, INC.; *U.S. Private*, pg. 3603
SELLING SOURCE, LLC—See London Bay Capital LLC; *U.S. Private*, pg. 2483
SELLING-WARE CO., LTD.; *Int'l*, pg. 6701
SELLMARK CORP.; *U.S. Private*, pg. 3603
SELLMORE INDUSTRIES INC.; *U.S. Private*, pg. 3603
SELLNER HOLDING GMBH—See CBR Management GmbH; *Int'l*, pg. 1366
SELLOFF VACATIONS—See Sunwing Travel Group, Inc.; *Int'l*, pg. 7333
SELL POINTS INC.—See Summit Partners, L.P.; *U.S. Private*, pg. 3856
SELL POINTS INC.—See The Jordan Company, L.P.; *U.S. Private*, pg. 4062
SELLSTROM MANUFACTURING CO. - RTC FALL PROTECTION DIVISION—See Sellstrom Manufacturing Co.; *U.S. Private*, pg. 3603
SELLSTROM MANUFACTURING CO.; *U.S. Private*, pg. 3603
SELLUP INC.; *U.S. Private*, pg. 3603
SELLWELL GMBH & CO, KG—See Bertelsmann SE & Co. KGaA; *Int'l*, pg. 995
SELLWIN TRADERS LIMITED; *Int'l*, pg. 6701
SELMABIPIMME LEASING S.P.A.—See Mediobanca-Banca de Credito Finanziario S.p.A.; *Int'l*, pg. 4778
SELMA CARLSON, INC.—See Tenet Healthcare Corporation; *U.S. Public*, pg. 2005
SELMAN & COMPANY—See One80 Intermediaries LLC; *U.S. Private*, pg. 3024
SEL MANUFACTURING COMPANY LIMITED; *Int'l*, pg. 6699
SELMARQ; *U.S. Private*, pg. 3603
SELMA SA—See Vivendi SE; *Int'l*, pg. 8275
SELMA'S COOKIES, INC.—See Byrd Cookie Co.; *U.S. Private*, pg. 700
SELMERBRIDGE PRINT VEHICLES LIMITED; *Int'l*, pg. 6701
THE SELMER COMPANY—See AF International Corporation; *U.S. Private*, pg. 121
SELMESTA CO., LTD.—See H.U. Group Holdings, Inc.; *Int'l*, pg. 3199
SELMET, INC.—See Warburg Pincus LLC; *U.S. Private*, pg. 4437
SELONDA AQUACULTURE SA; *Int'l*, pg. 6701
SELPI SPA—See Giovanni Agnelli B.V.; *Int'l*, pg. 2978
SELPRO S.A.—See Activa Capital S.A.S.; *Int'l*, pg. 119
SELTECH ELECTRONICS INC.; *Int'l*, pg. 6701
SEL TEXTILES LTD.—See SEL Manufacturing Company Limited; *Int'l*, pg. 6699
SELTRIK ELECTRIC INDIA PRIVATE LIMITED—See Sungarner Energies Limited; *Int'l*, pg. 7314
SELVAAG BOLIG ASA; *Int'l*, pg. 6701
SELVAAG EIENDOMSOPPGJOR AS—See Selvaag Bolig ASA; *Int'l*, pg. 6701
SELVAAG PLUSS SERVICE AS—See Selvaag Bolig ASA; *Int'l*, pg. 6701
SELVA GIDA SANAYI A.S.—See Loras Holding A.S.; *Int'l*, pg. 4557
SELVAS AI CO., LTD.; *Int'l*, pg. 6701
SELVAS HEALTHCARE, INC.; *Int'l*, pg. 6701
SELVER AS—See Tallinna Kaubamaja AS; *Int'l*, pg. 7447
SELVITA S.A.; *Int'l*, pg. 6701
SELWAY CORPORATION; *U.S. Private*, pg. 3603
SELWAY MACHINE TOOL CO. INC.; *U.S. Private*, pg. 3603
SELWOOD GROUP LIMITED - BRISTOL PLANT—See Selwood Group Limited; *Int'l*, pg. 6701
SELWOOD GROUP LIMITED; *Int'l*, pg. 6701
SELWYN CARE LIMITED—See Sheikh Holdings Group (Investments) Limited; *Int'l*, pg. 6794
SELWYNS TRAVEL LTD.—See Regie Autonome des Transports Parisiens; *Int'l*, pg. 6253
SELZER AUTOMOTIVA DO BRASIL LTDA.—See INDUS Holding AG; *Int'l*, pg. 3664
SELZER AUTOMOTIVE RO SRL—See INDUS Holding AG; *Int'l*, pg. 3664
SELZER AUTOMOTIVE SYSTEMS CO., LTD.—See INDUS Holding AG; *Int'l*, pg. 3664
SELZER FERTIGUNGSTECHNIK GMBH & CO. KG—See Mutares SE & Co. KGaA; *Int'l*, pg. 5105
SELZER-ORNST CONSTRUCTION COMPANY LLC; *U.S. Private*, pg. 3603
SEMAC CONSULTANTS LTD.; *Int'l*, pg. 6702
SEMAC & PARTNERS LLC—See Semac Consultants Ltd.; *Int'l*, pg. 6702
SEMAC PRIVATE LIMITED—See Semac Consultants Ltd.; *Int'l*, pg. 6702
SEMA EQUIPMENT, INC; *U.S. Private*, pg. 3603
SEMAFO GUINEE S.A.—See Endeavour Mining plc; *Int'l*, pg. 2402
SEMAFO INC—See Endeavour Mining plc.; *Int'l*, pg. 2402
SEMAFO MINERAL S.A.—See Endeavour Mining plc.; *Int'l*, pg. 2402
SEMAFONE LIMITED; *Int'l*, pg. 6702
SEMAFOR, INC.; *U.S. Private*, pg. 3603
SEMA GMBH—See Atos SE; *Int'l*, pg. 692
SEMANAL MEDIA, LLC; *U.S. Private*, pg. 3603

SEMANA, S.L.; *Int'l*, pg. 6702
SEMANGAT CERGAS SDN BHD—See Berjaya Corporation Berhad; *Int'l*, pg. 983
SEMANTICBITS, LLC—See ICF International, Inc.; *U.S. Public*, pg. 1086
SEMANTICSPACE TECHNOLOGIES; *U.S. Private*, pg. 3603
SEMANTIX FINLAND OY—See Segulah Advisor AB; *Int'l*, pg. 6684
SEMANTIX HOLDINGS AB—See Segulah Advisor AB; *Int'l*, pg. 6684
SEMANTIX, INC.; *Int'l*, pg. 6702
SEMAPA - SOCIEDADE DE INVESTIMENTO E GASTAO SGPS, S.A.—See SODIM, SGPS, SA; *Int'l*, pg. 7048
SEMAQ EMBALLAGES, SA—See Inapa - Investimentos, Participacoes e Gestao, SA; *Int'l*, pg. 3645
SEMASA PARKING SDN. BHD.—See Malaysian Resources Corporation Berhad; *Int'l*, pg. 4662
SEMAT AS; *Int'l*, pg. 6702
SEMATECH, INC.; *U.S. Private*, pg. 3603
SEMATELL GMBH—See IMCap Partners AG; *Int'l*, pg. 3621
SEMATIC ELEVADORES MEXICO S. DE R.L. DE C.V.—See Bain Capital, LP; *U.S. Private*, pg. 452
SEMATIC ELEVATOR PRODUCTS (CHANGSHU) CO., LTD.—See Bain Capital, LP; *U.S. Private*, pg. 452
SEMATIC HUNGARIA KFT—See Bain Capital, LP; *U.S. Private*, pg. 452
SEMATIC S.P.A.—See Bain Capital, LP; *U.S. Private*, pg. 452
SEMATIC S.P.A. - SUISIO PLANT—See Bain Capital, LP; *U.S. Private*, pg. 452
SEMATIC USA, INC.—See Bain Capital, LP; *U.S. Private*, pg. 452
SEMAX ARGENTINA S.A.—See Sulzer Ltd.; *Int'l*, pg. 7257
SEMBA CORPORATION; *Int'l*, pg. 6702
SEMBA MALAYSIA DESIGN & CONSTRUCTION SDN. BHD.—See SEMBA Corporation; *Int'l*, pg. 6702
SEMBA (SHANGHAI) CO., LTD.—See SEMBA Corporation; *Int'l*, pg. 6702
SEMBA SINGAPORE PTE. LTD.—See SEMBA Corporation; *Int'l*, pg. 6702
SEMBA TOHKA INDUSTRIES CO., LTD.; *Int'l*, pg. 6702
SEMBA VIETNAM CO., LTD.—See SEMBA Corporation; *Int'l*, pg. 6702
SEMBAWANG ENGINEERS AND CONSTRUCTORS MIDDLE EAST FZE—See Punj Lloyd Ltd.; *Int'l*, pg. 6119
SEMBAWANG ENGINEERS AND CONSTRUCTORS PTE LTD.—See Punj Lloyd Ltd.; *Int'l*, pg. 6119
SEMBAWANG SHIPYARD PTE LTD—See Sembcorp Industries Ltd.; *Int'l*, pg. 6703
SEMBAWANG (TIANJIN) CONSTRUCTION ENGINEERING CO LTD—See Punj Lloyd Ltd.; *Int'l*, pg. 6119
SEMBAWANG UAE PTE LTD.—See Punj Lloyd Ltd.; *Int'l*, pg. 6119
SEMBCORP AGUAS SANTIAGO S.A.—See Sembcorp Industries Ltd.; *Int'l*, pg. 6703
SEMBCORP AIR PRODUCTS (HYCO) PTE. LTD.—See Sembcorp Industries Ltd.; *Int'l*, pg. 6703
SEMBCORP (ANTIGUA) WATER LTD—See Sembcorp Industries Ltd.; *Int'l*, pg. 6703
SEMBCORP BOURNEMOUTH WATER LIMITED—See Sembcorp Industries Ltd.; *Int'l*, pg. 6704
SEMBCORP COGEN PTE LTD—See Sembcorp Industries Ltd.; *Int'l*, pg. 6703
SEMBCORP DESIGN AND CONSTRUCTION PTE LTD—See Chip Eng Seng Corporation Ltd.; *Int'l*, pg. 1572
SEMBCORP DEVELOPMENT LTD.—See Sembcorp Industries Ltd.; *Int'l*, pg. 6704
SEMBCORP ENVIRONMENT PTE. LTD—See Sembcorp Industries Ltd.; *Int'l*, pg. 6704
SEMBCORP GAS PTE LTD—See Sembcorp Industries Ltd.; *Int'l*, pg. 6704
SEMBCORP GREEN INFRA LIMITED—See Sembcorp Industries Ltd.; *Int'l*, pg. 6704
SEMBCORP HUIYANG NEW ENERGY (SHENZHEN) CO., LTD.—See Sembcorp Industries Ltd.; *Int'l*, pg. 6704
SEMBCORP INDUSTRIES LTD.; *Int'l*, pg. 6702
SEMBCORP MYINGYAN POWER COMPANY LIMITED—See Sembcorp Industries Ltd.; *Int'l*, pg. 6704
SEMBCORP NEWATER PTE. LTD—See Sembcorp Industries Ltd.; *Int'l*, pg. 6704
SEMBCORP NORTH-WEST POWER COMPANY LTD.—See Sembcorp Industries Ltd.; *Int'l*, pg. 6704
SEMBCORP POWER PTE. LTD.—See Sembcorp Industries Ltd.; *Int'l*, pg. 6704
SEMBCORP SALALAH POWER & WATER COMPANY SAOG; *Int'l*, pg. 6704
SEMBCORP SILULUMANZI (PTY) LIMITED—See Sembcorp Industries Ltd.; *Int'l*, pg. 6704
SEMBCORP SIZA WATER CO (PTY) LTD—See Sembcorp Industries Ltd.; *Int'l*, pg. 6704
SEMBCORP TIANJIN LINGANG INDUSTRIAL AREA WASTEWATER TREATMENT CO LTD—See Sembcorp Industries Ltd.; *Int'l*, pg. 6704

COMPANY NAME INDEX

SEMBCORP UTILITIES (CHILE) S.A.—See Sembcorp Industries Ltd.; *Int'l*, pg. 6704
SEMBCORP UTILITIES PTE LTD—See Sembcorp Industries Ltd.; *Int'l*, pg. 6704
SEMBCORP UTILITIES SERVICES LTD—See Sembcorp Industries Ltd.; *Int'l*, pg. 6704
SEMBCORP UTILITIES (SOUTH AFRICA) PTY LIMITED—See Sembcorp Industries Ltd.; *Int'l*, pg. 6704
SEMBCORP UTILITIES (UK) LIMITED—See Sembcorp Industries Ltd.; *Int'l*, pg. 6704
SEMBELLA GMBH—See Recticel S.A.; *Int'l*, pg. 6242
SEMBERA VANAK/FCB—See The Interpublic Group of Companies, Inc.; *U.S. Public*, pg. 2093
SEMBERIJA PD A.D.; *Int'l*, pg. 6704
SEMBIOSYS GENETICS INC.; *Int'l*, pg. 6704
SEMBLE, INC.; *U.S. Private*, pg. 3603
THE SEMBLER COMPANY; *U.S. Private*, pg. 4116
SEMBLEX CORPORATION; *U.S. Private*, pg. 3603
SEMBMARINE SLP LIMITED—See Sembcorp Industries Ltd.; *Int'l*, pg. 6703
SEMBRAMKY ENVIRONMENTAL MANAGEMENT PVT LTD—See Sembcorp Industries Ltd.; *Int'l*, pg. 6703
SEMBRAZ SA—See Transilvania Investments Alliance S.A.; *Int'l*, pg. 7900
SEMBWASTE PTE LTD—See Sembcorp Industries Ltd.; *Int'l*, pg. 6703
SEM-CALACA POWER CORPORATION—See DMCI Holdings, Inc.; *Int'l*, pg. 2143
SEMCAMS ULC—See Energy Transfer LP; *U.S. Public*, pg. 764
SEMCNS CO., LTD.; *Int'l*, pg. 6704
SEMCO ENERGY, INC.—See AltaGas Ltd.; *Int'l*, pg. 384
SEMCO ENERGY VENTURES, INC.—See AltaGas Ltd.; *Int'l*, pg. 384
SEMCOGLAS HOLDING GMBH; *Int'l*, pg. 6704
SEMCO INSTRUMENTS, INC.—See TransDigm Group Incorporated; *U.S. Public*, pg. 2183
SEMCON AB—See Knightec AB; *Int'l*, pg. 4207
SEMCON DO BRASIL LTDA.—See Knightec AB; *Int'l*, pg. 4207
SEMCON ENGINEERING SERVICES NORDIC—See Knightec AB; *Int'l*, pg. 4207
SEMCON ENGINEERING UK LTD—See ASM Technologies Limited; *Int'l*, pg. 627
SEMCON EXTERN ENGINEERING AB—See Knightec AB; *Int'l*, pg. 4207
SEMCON INDIA PVT LTD—See Knightec AB; *Int'l*, pg. 4207
SEMCON INFORMATIC PRODUCTION AB—See Knightec AB; *Int'l*, pg. 4207
SEMCON INFORMATIC PRODUCTION LTD.—See Knightec AB; *Int'l*, pg. 4207
SEMCON INFORMATIC SERVICES AB—See Knightec AB; *Int'l*, pg. 4207
SEMCON INFORMATIC SOLUTIONS AB—See Knightec AB; *Int'l*, pg. 4207
SEMCON INFORMATIC SRT AB—See Knightec AB; *Int'l*, pg. 4207
SEMCON INFORMATIC UK LTD—See Knightec AB; *Int'l*, pg. 4207
SEMCON INFORMATION AND CONSULTING CO., LTD.—See Knightec AB; *Int'l*, pg. 4207
SEMCON INTERNATIONAL AB—See Knightec AB; *Int'l*, pg. 4207
SEMCON KFT—See Knightec AB; *Int'l*, pg. 4207
SEMCON PROJECT MANAGEMENT AB—See Knightec AB; *Int'l*, pg. 4207
SEMCON SWEDEN AB—See Knightec AB; *Int'l*, pg. 4207
SEMCON UK LTD—See Knightec AB; *Int'l*, pg. 4207
SEMCOR (QINGDAO) ELECTRONIC CO., LTD.—See SEMIKRON International GmbH; *Int'l*, pg. 6705
SEMCO TOOL & MANUFACTURING CO., INC.—See The Cly-Del Manufacturing Company; *U.S. Private*, pg. 4011
SEM DAIKIN CO, LTD.—See Daikin Industries, Ltd.; *Int'l*, pg. 1936
SEMEC CORPORATION—See Sumitomo Densetsu Co., Ltd.; *Int'l*, pg. 7276
SEMELAB LIMITED—See TT Electronics plc; *Int'l*, pg. 7959
SEMELEC SAS—See Eaton Corporation plc; *Int'l*, pg. 2282
SEMENCES PROGRAIN INC.; *Int'l*, pg. 6704
SEMENTI DOM DOTTO S.P.A.—See Assicurazioni Generali S.p.A.; *Int'l*, pg. 647
SEMENTI ROSS S.R.L.—See Assicurazioni Generali S.p.A.; *Int'l*, pg. 648
SEMENTRA PLANTATIONS SDN BHD—See Yee Lee Corporation Bhd.; *Int'l*, pg. 8575
SEMENTSVERKSMIDJAN EHF—See Heidelberg Materials AG; *Int'l*, pg. 3319
SEMEQUIP, INC.—See 3M Company; *U.S. Public*, pg. 8
SEMES CO., LTD.—See Samsung Group; *Int'l*, pg. 6511
SEMET MASCHINENBAU GMBH & CO. KG—See INDUS Holding AG; *Int'l*, pg. 3664
SEM FIRE AND RESCUE PTY LTD.; *Int'l*, pg. 6701
SEMFLEX, INC.—See Emerson Electric Co.; *U.S. Public*, pg. 752

SEMGAS, L.P.—See Energy Transfer LP; *U.S. Public*, pg. 764
SEMGIMENENEA S.P.A.—See Assicurazioni Generali S.p.A.; *Int'l*, pg. 643
SEMGROUP CORPORATION—See Energy Transfer LP; *U.S. Public*, pg. 764
SEMGROUP HOLDINGS, L.P.—See Energy Transfer LP; *U.S. Public*, pg. 764
SEM HOLDINGS LIMITED; *Int'l*, pg. 6702
SEMIA GREEN S.R.L.—See Iren S.p.A.; *Int'l*, pg. 3808
SEMICAN INC.; *Int'l*, pg. 6704
SEMICOA CORPORATION—See Vance Street Capital LLC; *U.S. Private*, pg. 4342
SEMICON ASSOCIATES—See 3M Company; *U.S. Public*, pg. 8
SEMICONDUCTOR COMPONENTS INDUSTRIES, LLC—See ON Semiconductor Corporation; *U.S. Public*, pg. 1601
SEMICONDUCTOR COMPONENTS INDUSTRIES OF RHODE ISLAND, INC.—See ON Semiconductor Corporation; *U.S. Public*, pg. 1601
SEMICONDUCTOR COMPONENTS INDUSTRIES SINGAPORE PTE. LTD.—See ON Semiconductor Corporation; *U.S. Public*, pg. 1601
SEMICONDUCTOR MANUFACTURING INTERNATIONAL (BEIJING) CORPORATION—See Semiconductor Manufacturing International Corporation; *Int'l*, pg. 6705
SEMICONDUCTOR MANUFACTURING INTERNATIONAL CORPORATION; *Int'l*, pg. 6704
SEMICONDUCTOR MANUFACTURING INTERNATIONAL (SHENZHEN) CORPORATION—See Semiconductor Manufacturing International Corporation; *Int'l*, pg. 6705
SEMICONDUCTOR MANUFACTURING INTERNATIONAL (TIANJIN) CORPORATION—See Semiconductor Manufacturing International Corporation; *Int'l*, pg. 6705
SEMICONDUCTOR PROCESS EQUIPMENT CORPORATION; *U.S. Private*, pg. 3604
SEMIC SLOVAKIA, S.R.O.—See SEMIKRON International GmbH; *Int'l*, pg. 6705
SEMIC TRADE, S.R.O.—See SEMIKRON International GmbH; *Int'l*, pg. 6705
SEMI DICE, LLC—See Behrman Brothers Management Corp.; *U.S. Private*, pg. 515
SEMIFREDDI'S, INC.; *U.S. Private*, pg. 3604
SEMI GENERAL, INC.; *U.S. Private*, pg. 3603
SEMI-KINETICS INC.—See Gonzalez Design Engineering Company Inc.; *U.S. Private*, pg. 1737
SEMIKRON AB—See SEMIKRON International GmbH; *Int'l*, pg. 6705
SEMIKRON AG—See SEMIKRON International GmbH; *Int'l*, pg. 6705
SEMIKRON B.V.—See SEMIKRON International GmbH; *Int'l*, pg. 6705
SEMIKRON CO., LTD.—See SEMIKRON International GmbH; *Int'l*, pg. 6705
SEMIKRON CO. LTD.—See SEMIKRON International GmbH; *Int'l*, pg. 6705
SEMIKRON DE MEXICO S.A. DE C.V.—See SEMIKRON International GmbH; *Int'l*, pg. 6705
SEMIKRON ELECTRONICS PRIVATE LIMITED—See SEMIKRON International GmbH; *Int'l*, pg. 6705
SEMIKRON ELECTRONICS S.L.—See SEMIKRON International GmbH; *Int'l*, pg. 6705
SEMIKRON ELECTRONICS (ZHU HAI) CO. LTD.—See SEMIKRON International GmbH; *Int'l*, pg. 6705
SEMIKRON GLEICHRICHTERELEMENTE GES.M.B.H.—See SEMIKRON International GmbH; *Int'l*, pg. 6705
SEMIKRON GMBH—See SEMIKRON International GmbH; *Int'l*, pg. 6705
SEMIKRON (HONG KONG) CO. LTD.—See SEMIKRON International GmbH; *Int'l*, pg. 6705
SEMIKRON INC.—See SEMIKRON International GmbH; *Int'l*, pg. 6705
SEMIKRON INTERNATIONAL GMBH; *Int'l*, pg. 6705
SEMIKRON K. K.—See SEMIKRON International GmbH; *Int'l*, pg. 6705
SEMIKRON LTD.—See SEMIKRON International GmbH; *Int'l*, pg. 6705
SEMIKRON LTD.—See SEMIKRON International GmbH; *Int'l*, pg. 6705
SEMIKRON OY—See SEMIKRON International GmbH; *Int'l*, pg. 6705
SEMIKRON PTY. LTD.—See SEMIKRON International GmbH; *Int'l*, pg. 6705
SEMIKRON PTY. LTD.—See SEMIKRON International GmbH; *Int'l*, pg. 6705
SEMIKRON S.A.R.L—See SEMIKRON International GmbH; *Int'l*, pg. 6705
SEMIKRON SEMICONDUTORES LTDA.—See SEMIKRON International GmbH; *Int'l*, pg. 6705
SEMIKRON SP. Z O.O.—See SEMIKRON International GmbH; *Int'l*, pg. 6705
SEMIKRON S.R.L.—See SEMIKRON International GmbH; *Int'l*, pg. 6705
SEMIKRON S.R.O.—See SEMIKRON International GmbH; *Int'l*, pg. 6705
SEMIKRON S.R.O.—See SEMIKRON International GmbH; *Int'l*, pg. 6705

SEMMELMEYER-CORBY COMPANY

SEMILEDS CORPORATION; *Int'l*, pg. 6705
SEMILLAS LIMAGRAIN DE CHILE LTDA.—See Groupe Limagrain Holding SA; *Int'l*, pg. 3108
SEMI MAROC, S.A.—See ACS, Actividades de Construccion y Servicios, S.A.; *Int'l*, pg. 116
SEMINARIS HOTEL- UND KONGRESSSTATTEN-BETRIEBSGESELLSCHAFT MBH—See Munchener Ruckversicherungs AG; *Int'l*, pg. 5091
SEMINARY RIDGE HISTORIC PRESERVATION FOUNDATION; *U.S. Private*, pg. 3604
SEMINIS S DE RL DE CV—See Bayer Aktiengesellschaft; *Int'l*, pg. 910
SEMINIS VEGETABLE SEEDS, INC.—See Bayer Aktiengesellschaft; *Int'l*, pg. 909
SEMINOLE ADVISORY SERVICES, LLC—See Seminole Holdings Group, LLC; *U.S. Private*, pg. 3604
SEMINOLE CAPITAL, LLC—See Seminole Holdings Group, LLC; *U.S. Private*, pg. 3604
SEMINOLE CASINO HOLLYWOOD—See Seminole Tribe of Florida, Inc.; *U.S. Private*, pg. 3604
SEMINOLE COUNTY COALITION FOR SCHOOL READINESS, INC.; *U.S. Private*, pg. 3604
SEMINOLE DIALYSIS, LLC—See DaVita Inc.; *U.S. Public*, pg. 643
SEMINOLE ELECTRIC COOPERATIVE, INC.; *U.S. Private*, pg. 3604
SEMINOLE EQUITY INVESTMENTS, LLC—See Seminole Holdings Group, LLC; *U.S. Private*, pg. 3604
SEMINOLE FEED CO.; *U.S. Private*, pg. 3604
SEMINOLE FINANCIAL SERVICES, LLC—See Seminole Holdings Group, LLC; *U.S. Private*, pg. 3604
SEMINOLE FOODS, INC; *U.S. Private*, pg. 3604
SEMINOLE GAMING—See Seminole Tribe of Florida, Inc.; *U.S. Private*, pg. 3604
SEMINOLE HARD ROCK ENTERTAINMENT, INC.—See Seminole Tribe of Florida, Inc.; *U.S. Private*, pg. 3604
SEMINOLE HMA, LLC—See Community Health Systems, Inc.; *U.S. Public*, pg. 556
SEMINOLE HOLDINGS GROUP, LLC; *U.S. Private*, pg. 3604
SEMINOLE MACHINE & WELDING, INC.; *U.S. Private*, pg. 3604
SEMINOLE PIPELINE COMPANY LLC—See Enterprise Products Partners L.P.; *U.S. Public*, pg. 779
SEMINOLE PIPELINE COMPANY—See Enterprise Products Partners L.P.; *U.S. Public*, pg. 779
SEMINOLE PIPELINE COMPANY—See Enterprise Products Partners L.P.; *U.S. Public*, pg. 779
SEMINOLE PIPELINE COMPANY—See Enterprise Products Partners L.P.; *U.S. Public*, pg. 779
SEMINOLE PRECAST MANUFACTURING, INC.; *U.S. Private*, pg. 3604
SEMINOLE REAL ESTATE SERVICES, LLC—See Seminole Holdings Group, LLC; *U.S. Private*, pg. 3604
SEMINOLE SHORES LIVING CENTER, LLC—See Healthpeak Properties, Inc.; *U.S. Public*, pg. 1016
SEMINOLE TOWNE CENTER LIMITED PARTNERSHIP—See Washington Prime Group Inc.; *U.S. Private*, pg. 4449
SEMINOLE TRIBE OF FLORIDA, INC.; *U.S. Private*, pg. 3604
SEM INTERNET REKLAM HIZMETLERI VE DANISMANLIK A.S.—See Stroer SE & Co. KGaA; *Int'l*, pg. 7242
SEMINUS GMBH—See Groupe Industriel Marcel Dassault S.A.; *Int'l*, pg. 3105
SEMINV, SGPS, S.A.—See SODIM, SGPS, SA; *Int'l*, pg. 7049
SEMI-PRODUTOS DE METAIS, LDA—See Stemcor Holdings Limited; *Int'l*, pg. 7206
SEMIRARA MINING AND POWER CORPORATION—See DMCI Holdings, Inc.; *Int'l*, pg. 2143
SEMI SERVICE, INC.—See J.B. Poindexter & Co., Inc.; *U.S. Private*, pg. 2159
SEMITEC CORPORATION; *Int'l*, pg. 6706
SEMITEC KOREA CO., LTD.—See SEMITEC Corporation; *Int'l*, pg. 6706
SEMITEC USA CORP.—See SEMITEC Corporation; *Int'l*, pg. 6706
SEMITORR GROUP, INC.—See Wynnchurch Capital, L.P.; *U.S. Private*, pg. 4577
SEMI-TRAILER SALES & LEASING; *U.S. Private*, pg. 3603
SEMITRONIX CORPORATION; *Int'l*, pg. 6706
SEMITROPIC WATER STORAGE DISTRICT; *U.S. Private*, pg. 3605
SEMLER B.V.—See Renewi plc; *Int'l*, pg. 6279
SEMLER SCIENTIFIC, INC.; *U.S. Public*, pg. 1863
SEMLING-MENKE COMPANY INC.; *U.S. Private*, pg. 3605
SEMMA THERAPEUTICS, INC.—See Vertex Pharmaceuticals Incorporated; *U.S. Public*, pg. 2287
SEMMEL CONCERTS ENTERTAINMENT GMBH—See CTS Eventim AG & Co. KGAA; *Int'l*, pg. 1873
SEMMELMEYER-CORBY COMPANY; *U.S. Private*, pg. 3605
SEMMELROCK BAUSTOFFINDUSTRIE GMBH—See Wienerberger AG; *Int'l*, pg. 8405
SEMMELROCK INDUSTRIEBETEILIGUNGSVERWALTUNG GMBH—See Wienerberger AG; *Int'l*, pg. 8406

SEMMELROCK STEIN & DESIGN BURKOLATKO KFT.—See Wienerberger AG; *Int'l*, pg. 8406
SEMMELROCK STEIN & DESIGN DLAZBY A.S.—See Wienerberger AG; *Int'l*, pg. 8406
SEMMELROCK STEIN + DESIGN DLAZBY S.R.O.—See Wienerberger AG; *Int'l*, pg. 8405
SEMMELROCK STEIN & DESIGN D.O.O.—See Wienerberger AG; *Int'l*, pg. 8406
SEMMELROCK STEIN & DESIGN KFT.—See Wienerberger AG; *Int'l*, pg. 8406
SEMMELROCK STEIN & DESIGN SP. Z O.O.—See Wienerberger AG; *Int'l*, pg. 8406
SEMMELROCK STEIN + DESIGN S.R.L.—See Wienerberger AG; *Int'l*, pg. 8406
SEMMELROCK STEIN UND DESIGN EOOD—See Wienerberger AG; *Int'l*, pg. 8406
SEMMELROCK TLAKOVCI D.O.O.—See Wienerberger AG; *Int'l*, pg. 8406
SEMO ELECTRICAL COOPERATIVE; *U.S. Private*, pg. 3605
SEMOLINA INC.—See Taste Buds, Inc.; *U.S. Private*, pg. 3935
SEMOLINA MISIR IRMIGI GIDA SANAYI VE TICARET A.S.—See Gruma, S.A.B. de C.V.; *Int'l*, pg. 3114
SEMONIN REALTORS—See Berkshire Hathaway Inc.; *U.S. Public*, pg. 307
SEMO TANK/BAKER EQUIPMENT CO.; *U.S. Private*, pg. 3605
SEMOULERIE DE BELLEVUE—See Danone; *Int'l*, pg. 1968
SEMPCHECK SERVICES LLC—See Energy Overwatch LLC; *U.S. Private*, pg. 1395
SEMPELL GMBH—See Emerson Electric Co.; *U.S. Public*, pg. 751
SEMPER DEVELOPMENT LTD; *U.S. Private*, pg. 3605
SEMPERFLEX SHANGHAI LTD.—See Semperit AG Holding; *Int'l*, pg. 6706
SEMPERFLEX SHANGHAI LTD.—See Sri Trang Agro-Industry Public Company Limited; *Int'l*, pg. 7150
SEMPERFORM KFT.—See Semperit AG Holding; *Int'l*, pg. 6706
SEMPER HOME LOANS; *U.S. Private*, pg. 3605
SEMPERIT AG HOLDING; *Int'l*, pg. 6706
SEMPERIT INDUSTRIAL PRODUCTS INC.—See Semperit AG Holding; *Int'l*, pg. 6706
SEMPERIT REIFEN GESMBH—See Continental Aktiengesellschaft; *Int'l*, pg. 1783
SEMPERIT TECHNISCHE PRODUKTE GES.MBH - SEMPERFLEX DIVISION—See Semperit AG Holding; *Int'l*, pg. 6706
SEMPERIT TECHNISCHE PRODUKTE GES.MBH - SEMPERFORM DIVISION—See Semperit AG Holding; *Int'l*, pg. 6706
SEMPERIT TECHNISCHE PRODUKTE GES.MBH - SEMPERMED DIVISION—See Semperit AG Holding; *Int'l*, pg. 6706
SEMPERIT TECHNISCHE PRODUKTE GES.MBH—See Semperit AG Holding; *Int'l*, pg. 6706
SEMPERMED KFT.—See Semperit AG Holding; *Int'l*, pg. 6706
SEMPERMED USA INC.—See Semperit AG Holding; *Int'l*, pg. 6706
SEMPER PARATUS ACQUISITION CORPORATION; *U.S. Public*, pg. 1863
SEMPERTRANS FRANCE BELTING TECHNOLOGY SAS—See Semperit AG Holding; *Int'l*, pg. 6706
SEMPIO CHINA CO., LTD.—See Sempio Company; *Int'l*, pg. 6706
SEMPIO COMPANY; *Int'l*, pg. 6706
SEMPIO FOOD SERVICE, INC.—See Sempio Company; *Int'l*, pg. 6706
SEMPOL SPOL. S R.O—See BayWa AG; *Int'l*, pg. 919
SEMPRAE LABORATORIES, INC.—See Aytu BioPharma, Inc.; *U.S. Public*, pg. 257
SEMPRA ENERGY HOLDINGS XI B.V.—See Sempra; *U.S. Public*, pg. 1863
SEMPRA ENERGY SERVICES—See Sempra; *U.S. Public*, pg. 1863
SEMPRA ENERGY TRADING CORP.—See Sempra; *U.S. Public*, pg. 1863
SEMPRA MIDSTREAM, INC.—See Sempra; *U.S. Public*, pg. 1863
SEMPRA PIPELINES & STORAGE CORP.—See Sempra; *U.S. Public*, pg. 1863
SEMPRA RENEWABLES, LLC—See American Electric Power Company, Inc.; *U.S. Public*, pg. 100
SEMPRA; *U.S. Public*, pg. 1863
SEMPRA TEXAS HOLDINGS CORP.—See Sempra; *U.S. Public*, pg. 1863
SEMPSA JOYERIA PLATERIA, S.A.—See L. Possehl & Co. mbH; *Int'l*, pg. 4385
SEMPURNA RESORT SDN. BHD.—See Sentoria Group Berhad; *Int'l*, pg. 6715
SEMROCK, INC.—See IDEX Corp; *U.S. Public*, pg. 1092
SEMRUSH HOLDINGS, INC.; *U.S. Public*, pg. 1864
SEMS SDN. BHD.—See LB Aluminium Berhad; *Int'l*, pg. 4428
SEMSYSCO GMBH—See Lam Research Corporation; *U.S. Public*, pg. 1290

SEMSYSCO SINGAPORE PTE. LTD.—See Lam Research Corporation; *U.S. Public*, pg. 1290
SEMTECH ADVANCED SYSTEMS INDIA PRIVATE LIMITED—See Semtech Corporation; *U.S. Public*, pg. 1864
SEMTECH CANADA CORPORATION—See Semtech Corporation; *U.S. Public*, pg. 1864
SEMTECH CORPORATION; *U.S. Public*, pg. 1864
SEMTECH CORPUS CHRISTI S.A. DE C.V.—See Semtech Corporation; *U.S. Public*, pg. 1864
SEMTECH ELECTRONICS LIMITED—See Ruixin International Holdings Limited; *Int'l*, pg. 6427
SEMTECH EMEA LIMITED—See Semtech Corporation; *U.S. Public*, pg. 1864
SEMTECH EUROPE LIMITED—See Semtech Corporation; *U.S. Public*, pg. 1864
SEMTECH GERMANY GMBH—See Semtech Corporation; *U.S. Public*, pg. 1864
SEMTECH (INTERNATIONAL) AG—See Semtech Corporation; *U.S. Public*, pg. 1864
SEMTECH LTD.—See Semtech Corporation; *U.S. Public*, pg. 1864
SEMTECH NETHERLANDS BV—See Semtech Corporation; *U.S. Public*, pg. 1864
SEMTECH SAN DIEGO—See Semtech Corporation; *U.S. Public*, pg. 1864
SEMTECH SEMICONDUCTOR (SHANGHAI) CO., LTD.—See Semtech Corporation; *U.S. Public*, pg. 1864
SEMTECH SEMICONDUCTOR (SHENZHEN) COMPANY LIMITED—See Semtech Corporation; *U.S. Public*, pg. 1864
SEMTEK CO., LTD.; *Int'l*, pg. 6706
SEM TREDI S.A. DE C.V.—See Groupe Seche SAS; *Int'l*, pg. 3110
SEMVAC A/S—See Westinghouse Air Brake Technologies Corporation; *U.S. Public*, pg. 2359
SEM YAYINCILIK A.S—See Global Yatirim Holding A.S.; *Int'l*, pg. 3003
SEMYUNG ELECTRIC MACHINERY CO., LTD. - BUSAN MIEUM PLANT—See Semyung Electric Machinery Co., Ltd.; *Int'l*, pg. 6706
SEMYUNG ELECTRIC MACHINERY CO., LTD. - CHANGWON PLANT—See Semyung Electric Machinery Co., Ltd.; *Int'l*, pg. 6706
SEMYUNG ELECTRIC MACHINERY CO., LTD.; *Int'l*, pg. 6706
SEMYUNG INDUSTRIAL CO., LTD.—See Cheil Grinding Wheel Ind. Co., Ltd.; *Int'l*, pg. 1460
SEMYUNG VETOQUINOL—See Vetoquinol S.A.; *Int'l*, pg. 8181
SENA CASES; *U.S. Private*, pg. 3605
SENA DEVELOPMENT PUBLIC COMPANY LIMITED; *Int'l*, pg. 6706
SENAI AIRPORT TERMINAL SERVICES SDN. BHD.—See MMC Corporation Berhad; *Int'l*, pg. 5005
SENALAMIENTO VIAL DE CENTRO AMERICA, S.A. DE C.V.—See SWARCO AG; *Int'l*, pg. 7361
SENALES GIROD SL—See Signaux Girod S.A.; *Int'l*, pg. 6911
SENA MOTORS LTD.—See Honda Motor Co., Ltd.; *Int'l*, pg. 3464
SENAO INTERNATIONAL CO., LTD.—See Chunghwa Telecom Co., Ltd.; *Int'l*, pg. 1598
SENAO NETWORKS, INC.—See Chunghwa Telecom Co., Ltd.; *Int'l*, pg. 1598
SENA REIDER, INC.; *U.S. Private*, pg. 3605
SENA REIDER, INC.—See Sena Reider, Inc.; *U.S. Private*, pg. 3605
SENASA—See Groupe Limagrain Holding SA; *Int'l*, pg. 3108
SENA SOLAR ENERGY CO., LTD.—See Sena Development Public Company Limited; *Int'l*, pg. 6707
SENA SYSTEMS (INDIA) PVT. LTD.—See Aurionpro Solutions Limited; *Int'l*, pg. 711
SENATA GMBH; *Int'l*, pg. 6707
SENATE CONSTRUCTION CORP.; *U.S. Private*, pg. 3605
SENATE FORWARDING INC—See Ambassador Van Lines Inc.; *U.S. Private*, pg. 217
SENATE GROUP LTD.—See Rexel, S.A.; *Int'l*, pg. 6317
SENATOR FILM PRODUKTION GMBH—See Wild Bunch AG; *Int'l*, pg. 8409
SENATOR INTERNATIONAL LTD; *Int'l*, pg. 6707
SE NAUKANAFTOGAZ—See National Joint-Stock Company Naftogaz of Ukraine; *Int'l*, pg. 5160
SENA VANIJ DEVELOPMENT CO., LTD.—See Sena Development Public Company Limited; *Int'l*, pg. 6707
SENBA SENSING TECHNOLOGY CO., LTD.; *Int'l*, pg. 6707
SENBO INDUSTRIES LIMITED; *Int'l*, pg. 6707
SENCHA, INC.—See HGGC, LLC; *U.S. Private*, pg. 1930
SENCHUK FORD SALES LTD.; *Int'l*, pg. 6707
SENCI ELECTRIC MACHINERY CO., LTD.; *Int'l*, pg. 6707
SENCIO B.V.—See Nimbus B.V.; *Int'l*, pg. 5296
SENCO BRANDS, INC.—See KYOCERA Corporation; *Int'l*, pg. 4360
SENCO GLOBAL JEWELLERY TRADING LLC—See Senco Gold Limited; *Int'l*, pg. 6707
SENCO GOLD ARTISANSHIP PRIVATE LIMITED—See Senco Gold Limited; *Int'l*, pg. 6707

SENCO GOLD LIMITED; *Int'l*, pg. 6707
SENCOMMUNICATIONS, INC.; *U.S. Private*, pg. 3605
SENCORE, INC.—See The Riverside Company; *U.S. Private*, pg. 4110
SEN CORPORATION - EHIME PLANT—See Sumitomo Heavy Industries, Ltd.; *Int'l*, pg. 7287
SEN CORPORATION—See Sumitomo Heavy Industries, Ltd.; *Int'l*, pg. 7287
SENCORPWHITE, INC.—See Connell Limited Partnership; *U.S. Private*, pg. 1017
SENCOTEL S.L.—See Ali Holding S.r.l; *Int'l*, pg. 321
THE SENDAI BANK, LTD.—See Jimoto Holdings, Inc.; *Int'l*, pg. 3964
SENDAI CATV CO., LTD.—See TOKAI Holdings Corporation; *Int'l*, pg. 7779
SENDAI DAIICHI TRAFFIC CO., LTD.—See Daiichi Koutsu Sangyo Co., Ltd.; *Int'l*, pg. 1929
SENDAI INTERNATIONAL AIRPORT CO., LTD.—See Tokyu Corporation; *Int'l*, pg. 7797
SENDAI KOBAYASHI PHARMACEUTICAL CO., LTD.—See Kobayashi Pharmaceutical Co., Ltd.; *Int'l*, pg. 4216
SENDAI MITSUKOSHI LTD.—See Isetan Mitsukoshi Holdings Ltd.; *Int'l*, pg. 3815
SENDAI MORI SHIGYO CO., LTD.—See Oji Holdings Corporation; *Int'l*, pg. 5537
SENDAI NIKON CORPORATION—See Nikon Corporation; *Int'l*, pg. 5294
SENDAI NISSHIN ELECTRONICS CO., LTD.—See Nippon Signal Co., Ltd.; *Int'l*, pg. 5334
SENDA INTERNATIONAL CAPITAL LIMITED—See Zhejiang Longsheng Group Co., Ltd.; *Int'l*, pg. 8659
SENDAI PADO CORP.—See RIZAP GROUP, Inc.; *Int'l*, pg. 6354
SENDAI SERVICE CO.,LTD—See Toyo Tire Corporation; *Int'l*, pg. 7859
SENDAI SHIKI KOGYO CO., LTD.—See Tomoku Co., Ltd.; *Int'l*, pg. 7801
SENDAI TELEVISION INC.—See Fuji Media Holdings, Inc.; *Int'l*, pg. 2814
SENDAI TOHUN CO., LTD.—See Tomoku Co., Ltd.; *Int'l*, pg. 7801
SENDAI TOYOPET CO., LTD.—See Kamei Corporation; *Int'l*, pg. 4062
SENDAYCO, LLC; *U.S. Private*, pg. 3605
SENDEREX CARGO INC.; *U.S. Private*, pg. 3606
SENDERO BUSINESS SERVICES LP; *U.S. Private*, pg. 3606
SENDERO DRILLING COMPANY, LLC—See Pioneer Natural Resources Company; *U.S. Public*, pg. 1693
SENDGRID, INC.—See Twilio Inc.; *U.S. Public*, pg. 2206
SENDHYBRID OPBD GMBH—See Osterreichische Post AG; *Int'l*, pg. 5654
SENDMAIL, INC.—See Thoma Bravo, L.P.; *U.S. Private*, pg. 4151
SENDMAIL KK—See Thoma Bravo, L.P.; *U.S. Private*, pg. 4151
SENDMAIL, LTD.—See Thoma Bravo, L.P.; *U.S. Private*, pg. 4151
SENDMAIL S.A.R.L—See Thoma Bravo, L.P.; *U.S. Private*, pg. 4151
SENDONLINE.COM, INC.—See The Impex Group of Companies; *U.S. Private*, pg. 4055
SENDOUTS LLC—See Insight Venture Management, LLC; *U.S. Private*, pg. 2087
SENDTRAFFIC.COM, INC.—See Protagenic Therapeutics, Inc.; *U.S. Public*, pg. 1729
SENDX MEDICAL, INC.—See Danaher Corporation; *U.S. Public*, pg. 631
SENDYNE CORP.—See Sensata Technologies Holding plc; *U.S. Public*, pg. 1865
SENDZIMIR JAPAN, LTD.—See Sojitz Corporation; *Int'l*, pg. 7063
SENECA BEVERAGE CORPORATION; *U.S. Private*, pg. 3606
SENECA CORPORATION; *U.S. Private*, pg. 3606
SENECA DATA DISTRIBUTORS INC.; *U.S. Private*, pg. 3606
SENECA DIALYSIS CENTER, LLC—See Nautic Partners, LLC; *U.S. Private*, pg. 2871
SENECA DIALYSIS, LLC—See DaVita Inc.; *U.S. Public*, pg. 643
SENECA FALLS MACHINES; *U.S. Private*, pg. 3606
SENECA FAMILY OF AGENCIES; *U.S. Private*, pg. 3606
SENECA FEDERAL SAVINGS & LOAN ASSOCIATION; *U.S. Private*, pg. 3606
SENECA FINANCIAL CORP.; *U.S. Public*, pg. 1864
SENECA FLIGHT OPERATIONS—See Seneca Foods Corporation; *U.S. Public*, pg. 1864
SENECA FOOD CORP.—See General Mills, Inc.; *U.S. Public*, pg. 922
SENECA FOODS-CENTRAL DIV.—See Seneca Foods Corporation; *U.S. Public*, pg. 1865
SENECA FOODS CORPORATION; *U.S. Public*, pg. 1864
SENECA FOODS L.L.C.—See Seneca Foods Corporation; *U.S. Public*, pg. 1865
SENECA FOODS-RIPON—See Seneca Foods Corporation; *U.S. Public*, pg. 1865

COMPANY NAME INDEX

SENECA FOODS—See Seneca Foods Corporation; *U.S. Public*, pg. 1865
SENECA FOODS—See Seneca Foods Corporation; *U.S. Public*, pg. 1865
SENECA FOODS—See Seneca Foods Corporation; *U.S. Public*, pg. 1865
SENECA FOODS—See Seneca Foods Corporation; *U.S. Public*, pg. 1865
SENECA FOODS—See Seneca Foods Corporation; *U.S. Public*, pg. 1865
SENECA GLOBAL FUND, L.P.; *U.S. Private*, pg. 3606
SENECA HAWK HOLDING COMPANY INCORPORATED; *U.S. Private*, pg. 3606
SENECA INSURANCE COMPANY INC.—See Fairfax Financial Holdings Limited; *Int'l*, pg. 2606
SENECA INVESTMENTS; *U.S. Private*, pg. 3606
SENECA MEADOWS, INC.—See Waste Connections, Inc.; *Int'l*, pg. 8354
THE SENECA PA ASC, LLC—See KKR & Co. Inc.; *U.S. Public*, pg. 1248
SENECA PARTNERS INC.; *U.S. Private*, pg. 3606
SENECA PETROLEUM CO. INC.; *U.S. Private*, pg. 3606
SENECA REINSURANCE COMPANY, LLC—See Antarctica Capital, LLC; *U.S. Private*, pg. 287
SENECA RESOURCES CORPORATION—See National Fuel Gas Company; *U.S. Public*, pg. 1494
SENECA RESOURCES, LLC—See Caymus Equity Partners LLC; *U.S. Private*, pg. 795
SENECA SAVINGS—See Seneca Financial Corp.; *U.S. Public*, pg. 1864
SENEC AUSTRALIA PTY. LTD.—See EnBW Energie Baden-Wurttemberg AG; *Int'l*, pg. 2400
SENECA WIRE & MANUFACTURING COMPANY; *U.S. Private*, pg. 3606
SENEC GMBH—See EnBW Energie Baden-Wurttemberg AG; *Int'l*, pg. 2400
SENECO SRL—See ESPEC Corp.; *Int'l*, pg. 2505
SENEFELDER MISSET B.V.—See CirclePrinters Holding BV; *Int'l*, pg. 1618
SENEOS GMBH—See Hitachi, Ltd.; *Int'l*, pg. 3424
S-ENERGY CO., LTD. - FACTORY 1—See S-Energy Co., Ltd.; *Int'l*, pg. 6446
S-ENERGY CO., LTD. - FACTORY 2—See S-Energy Co., Ltd.; *Int'l*, pg. 6446
S-ENERGY CO., LTD.; *Int'l*, pg. 6446
SENERGY HOLDING COMPANY K.P.S.C.; *Int'l*, pg. 6707
S-ENERGY JAPAN CO., LTD.—See S-Energy Co., Ltd.; *Int'l*, pg. 6446
SENER INGENIERIA Y SISTEMAS, SA; *Int'l*, pg. 6707
SENERTEC-CENTER GMBH—See 2G Energy AG; *Int'l*, pg. 5
SENERVAL—See Groupe Seche SAS; *Int'l*, pg. 3110
SENESTECH, INC.; *U.S. Public*, pg. 1865
SENETAS CORPORATION LIMITED; *Int'l*, pg. 6707
SENETAS SECURITY PTY LTD—See Senetas Corporation Limited; *Int'l*, pg. 6707
SENET INTERNATIONAL CORPORATION—See Gaming Laboratories International LLC; *U.S. Private*, pg. 1640
SENEVITA AG—See Emeis SA; *Int'l*, pg. 2376
SENEX ENERGY LIMITED—See POSCO Holdings Inc.; *Int'l*, pg. 5938
SENEX EXPLOSIVES INC.; *U.S. Private*, pg. 3606
SENEX INSURANCE SERVICES, INC.—See Peter C. Foy & Associates Insurance Services, Inc.; *U.S. Private*, pg. 3158
SENFA SAS—See Chargeurs SA; *Int'l*, pg. 1450
SENFI UK LIMITED—See The Siam Cement Public Company Limited; *Int'l*, pg. 7685
SENGER HOLDING GMBH; *Int'l*, pg. 6708
SENGEWALD KLINIKPRODUKTE GMBH—See Monitor Clipper Partners, LLC; *U.S. Private*, pg. 2771
SENG FONG HOLDINGS BERHAD; *Int'l*, pg. 6708
SENG HENG DEVELOPMENT COMPANY LIMITED—See Industrial & Commercial Bank of China Limited; *Int'l*, pg. 3670
SENGIN GENERAL LEASING COMPANY LIMITED—See Senshu Ikeda Holdings, Inc.; *Int'l*, pg. 6713
SENGKANG 266 FOOD HOUSE PTE. LTD.—See Kimly Limited; *Int'l*, pg. 4163
SENG YIP FURNITURE SDN. BHD.—See Mieco Chipboard Berhad; *Int'l*, pg. 4888
SENHENG ELECTRIC (KL) SDN. BHD.—See Senheng New Retail Berhad; *Int'l*, pg. 6708
SENHENG NEW RETAIL BERHAD; *Int'l*, pg. 6708
SENICA AIR CONDITIONING, INC.; *U.S. Private*, pg. 3606
SENIHARTA SDN BHD—See Wing Tai Holdings Limited; *Int'l*, pg. 8427
SENI JAYA CORPORATION BERHAD; *Int'l*, pg. 6708
SENIOR AEROSPACE ABSOLUTE MANUFACTURING—See Senior plc; *Int'l*, pg. 6708
SENIOR AEROSPACE AMT—See Senior plc; *Int'l*, pg. 6708
SENIOR AEROSPACE BIRD BELLOWS—See Senior plc; *Int'l*, pg. 6709
SENIOR AEROSPACE BOSMAN B.V—See Senior plc; *Int'l*, pg. 6708
SENIOR AEROSPACE BWT—See Senior plc; *Int'l*, pg. 6709

SENIOR AEROSPACE CAPO INDUSTRIES—See Senior plc; *Int'l*, pg. 6708
SENIOR AEROSPACE COMPOSITES—See Senior plc; *Int'l*, pg. 6708
SENIOR AEROSPACE DAMAR—See Senior plc; *Int'l*, pg. 6708
SENIOR AEROSPACE ERMETO SAS—See Senior plc; *Int'l*, pg. 6708
SENIOR AEROSPACE KETEMA—See Senior plc; *Int'l*, pg. 6708
SENIOR AEROSPACE METAL BELLOWS—See Senior plc; *Int'l*, pg. 6708
SENIOR AEROSPACE MEXICO—See Senior plc; *Int'l*, pg. 6708
SENIOR AEROSPACE SSP—See Senior plc; *Int'l*, pg. 6708
SENIOR AEROSPACE STERLING MACHINE—See Senior plc; *Int'l*, pg. 6708
SENIOR AEROSPACE (THAILAND) LIMITED—See Senior plc; *Int'l*, pg. 6708
SENIOR AUTOMOTIVE BLOIS SAS—See Senior plc; *Int'l*, pg. 6708
SENIORBRIDGE CARE MANAGEMENT, INC.—See Humana, Inc.; *U.S. Public*, pg. 1070
SENIORBRIDGE FAMILY COMPANIES (FL), INC.—See Humana, Inc.; *U.S. Public*, pg. 1070
SENIORBRIDGE FAMILY COMPANIES (IL), INC.—See Humana, Inc.; *U.S. Public*, pg. 1070
SENIORBRIDGE FAMILY COMPANIES, INC.—See Humana, Inc.; *U.S. Public*, pg. 1070
SENIORBRIDGE FAMILY COMPANIES (MD), INC.—See Humana, Inc.; *U.S. Public*, pg. 1070
SENIORBRIDGE FAMILY COMPANIES (NY), INC.—See Humana, Inc.; *U.S. Public*, pg. 1070
SENIORBRIDGE FAMILY COMPANIES (PA), INC.—See Humana, Inc.; *U.S. Public*, pg. 1070
SENIORBRIDGE-FLORIDA, LLC—See Humana, Inc.; *U.S. Public*, pg. 1070
SENIORBRIDGE (NC), INC.—See Humana, Inc.; *U.S. Public*, pg. 1070
SENIOR CALORSTAT SAS—See Senior plc; *Int'l*, pg. 6708
SENIOR CARE CEDAR HILLS, LLC—See Diversicare Healthcare Services, Inc.; *U.S. Public*, pg. 670
SENIOR CARE CENTERS OF AMERICA, INC.—See Audax Group, Limited Partnership; *U.S. Private*, pg. 389
SENIOR CARE ELDERLY LIMITED—See DreamEast Group Limited; *Int'l*, pg. 2203
SENIOR CARE GROUP INC; *U.S. Private*, pg. 3606
SENIOR CARE, INC.; *U.S. Private*, pg. 3606
SENIORCARE, INC.; *U.S. Private*, pg. 3607
SENIOR CARE NURSING HOME LIMITED—See DreamEast Group Limited; *Int'l*, pg. 2203
SENIOR CARE PARTNERS, INC.—See UnitedHealth Group Incorporated; *U.S. Public*, pg. 2250
SENIOR CONNECTION CENTER, INC.; *U.S. Private*, pg. 3606
SENIOR CRAFTSMAN INC.; *U.S. Private*, pg. 3606
SENIOR CREDIT INVESTMENTS, LLC; *U.S. Private*, pg. 3606
SENIOR DENTAL CARE LLC—See Serent Capital Management Company, LLC; *U.S. Private*, pg. 3613
SENIOR DO BRASIL LTDA.—See Senior plc; *Int'l*, pg. 6709
SENIOREN-DOMIZIL FAMILIE WOHNSIEDLER GMBH—See Clariane SE; *Int'l*, pg. 1644
SENIORENPFLEGE HASSLOCH GMBH—See Clariane SE; *Int'l*, pg. 1644
SENIORENRESIDENZ DETTELBACH GMBH—See Clariane SE; *Int'l*, pg. 1644
SENIOREN- UND FACHPFLEGEZENTRUM GMBH—See Clariane SE; *Int'l*, pg. 1644
SENIORENWOHNANLAGE OETTINGEN GMBH—See Clariane SE; *Int'l*, pg. 1644
SENIOREN-WOHNPARK ARNSBERG GMBH—See MK-Kliniken AG; *Int'l*, pg. 5001
SENIOREN WOHNPARK ASCHERSLEBEN GMBH—See MK-Kliniken AG; *Int'l*, pg. 5001
SENIOREN WOHNPARK BAD LANGENSALZA GMBH—See MK-Kliniken AG; *Int'l*, pg. 5001
SENIOREN-WOHNPARK COSWIG GMBH—See MK-Kliniken AG; *Int'l*, pg. 5001
SENIOREN-WOHNPARK COTTBUS SWP GMBH—See MK-Kliniken AG; *Int'l*, pg. 5001
SENIOREN-WOHNPARK DUSSELDORF VOLKSGARTEN GMBH—See MK-Kliniken AG; *Int'l*, pg. 5001
SENIOREN-WOHNPARK ERKNER GMBH—See MK-Kliniken AG; *Int'l*, pg. 5001
SENIOREN-WOHNPARK FRIEDLAND GMBH—See MK-Kliniken AG; *Int'l*, pg. 5001
SENIOREN-WOHNPARK FRIEDLAND SWP GMBH—See MK-Kliniken AG; *Int'l*, pg. 5001
SENIOREN-WOHNPARK HENNIGSDORF GMBH—See MK-Kliniken AG; *Int'l*, pg. 5002
SENIOREN WOHNPARK KLAUSA GMBH—See MK-Kliniken AG; *Int'l*, pg. 5001
SENIOREN-WOHNPARK KLOTZE GMBH—See MK-Kliniken AG; *Int'l*, pg. 5002

SENIOREN-WOHNPARK KREUZTAL KROMBACH GMBH—See MK-Kliniken AG; *Int'l*, pg. 5002
SENIOREN-WOHNPARK LANDSHUT GMBH—See MK-Kliniken AG; *Int'l*, pg. 5002
SENIOREN-WOHNPARK LANGEN GMBH—See MK-Kliniken AG; *Int'l*, pg. 5001
SENIOREN-WOHNPARK LEIPZIG AM KIRSCHBERG GMBH,—See MK-Kliniken AG; *Int'l*, pg. 5002
SENIOREN-WOHNPARK LEIPZIG EUTRITZSCHER MARKT GMBH,—See MK-Kliniken AG; *Int'l*, pg. 5002
SENIOREN-WOHNPARK LEIPZIG STADTPALAIS GMBH,—See MK-Kliniken AG; *Int'l*, pg. 5002
SENIOREN-WOHNPARK LEMWERDER GMBH—See MK-Kliniken AG; *Int'l*, pg. 5002
SENIOREN-WOHNPARK LESSINGPLATZ GMBH—See MK-Kliniken AG; *Int'l*, pg. 5002
SENIOREN-WOHNPARK LICHTENBERG GMBH—See MK-Kliniken AG; *Int'l*, pg. 5002
SENIOREN WOHNPARK MEERBUSCH GMBH—See MK-Kliniken AG; *Int'l*, pg. 5001
SENIOREN-WOHNPARK MONTABAUR GMBH—See MK-Kliniken AG; *Int'l*, pg. 5002
SENIOREN WOHNPARK NEURUPPIN GMBH—See MK-Kliniken AG; *Int'l*, pg. 5001
SENIOREN-WOHNPARK NEURUPPIN SWP GMBH—See MK-Kliniken AG; *Int'l*, pg. 5002
SENIOREN-WOHNPARK RADENSLEBEN GMBH—See MK-Kliniken AG; *Int'l*, pg. 5002
SENIOREN-WOHNPARK SOZIALE ALTENBETREUUNG GMBH—See MK-Kliniken AG; *Int'l*, pg. 5002
SENIOREN WOHNPARK STUTZERBACH GMBH—See MK-Kliniken AG; *Int'l*, pg. 5001
SENIOREN WOHNPARK TANGERHUTTE GMBH—See MK-Kliniken AG; *Int'l*, pg. 5002
SENIOREN WOHNPARK THALE GMBH—See MK-Kliniken AG; *Int'l*, pg. 5001
SENIOREN WOHNPARK TREUENBRIETZEN GMBH—See MK-Kliniken AG; *Int'l*, pg. 5001
SENIOREN WOHNPARK WOLMIRSTEDT GMBH,—See MK-Kliniken AG; *Int'l*, pg. 5001
SENIORENZENTRUM HENNEF GMBH—See Clariane SE; *Int'l*, pg. 1643
SENIORENZENTRUM ST. CORONA AM SCHOPFL BETRIEBSGESELLSCHAFT M.B.H.—See Fresenius SE & Co. KGaA; *Int'l*, pg. 2781
SENIOR FINANCE PROPRIETARY LIMITED—See Alexander Forbes Group Holdings Limited; *Int'l*, pg. 307
SENIOR FLEXONICS BARTLETT—See Senior plc; *Int'l*, pg. 6708
SENIOR FLEXONICS CRUMLIN—See Senior plc; *Int'l*, pg. 6709
SENIOR FLEXONICS CZECH S.R.O—See Senior plc; *Int'l*, pg. 6708
SENIOR FLEXONICS GAMFG PRECISION—See Senior plc; *Int'l*, pg. 6708
SENIOR FLEXONICS GMBH—See Senior plc; *Int'l*, pg. 6708
SENIOR FLEXONICS PATHWAY - METROFLEX DAMPERS—See Senior plc; *Int'l*, pg. 6709
SENIOR FLEXONICS PATHWAY—See Senior plc; *Int'l*, pg. 6708
SENIOR FLEXONICS SA (PTY) LIMITED—See Senior plc; *Int'l*, pg. 6708
SENIOR FRIENDSHIP CENTERS, INC.; *U.S. Private*, pg. 3606
SENIORGARDEN AB—See JM AB; *Int'l*, pg. 3974
SENIOR GLEANERS INC.; *U.S. Private*, pg. 3607
SENIOR HEALTH ASSOCIATES, LLC—See HCA Healthcare, Inc.; *U.S. Public*, pg. 1008
SENIORHEIM AN DER PAAR GMBH—See Clariane SE; *Int'l*, pg. 1644
SENIOR HOME CARE, INC.—See Apollo Global Management, Inc.; *U.S. Public*, pg. 157
SENIORIE DE MARETAK NV—See Clariane SE; *Int'l*, pg. 1644
SENIOR INDIA PRIVATE LIMITED—See Senior plc; *Int'l*, pg. 6708
SENIOR INSURANCE SPECIALISTS—See Integrity Marketing Group LLC; *U.S. Private*, pg. 2104
SENIOR LIFESTYLE CORPORATION; *U.S. Private*, pg. 3607
SENIOR-LIVING.COM, INC.—See Thoma Bravo, L.P.; *U.S. Private*, pg. 4153
THE SENIOR LIVING FOUNDATION INC; *U.S. Private*, pg. 4116
SENIOR LIVING GROUP NV—See Clariane SE; *Int'l*, pg. 1644
SENIOR LIVING INVESTMENT BROKERAGE, INC.; *U.S. Private*, pg. 3607
SENIOR LIVING OPTIONS INC.; *U.S. Private*, pg. 3607
SENIOR LIVING PROPERTIES, LLC; *U.S. Private*, pg. 3607
SENIOR MANAGEMENT ADVISORS, INC.; *U.S. Private*, pg. 3607
SENIOR MARKET ADVISOR—See Wiesner Publishing, LLC; *U.S. Private*, pg. 4517
SENIOR MARKET SALES, INC.—See Stone Point Capital LLC; *U.S. Private*, pg. 3819

SENIOR MANAGEMENT ADVISORS, INC.   CORPORATE AFFILIATIONS

SENIOR OPERATIONS (CANADA) LIMITED—See Senior plc; *Int'l*, pg. 6708
SENIOR OPERATIONS LLC—See Senior plc; *Int'l*, pg. 6708
SENIOR PLC; *Int'l*, pg. 6708
SENIORS ADVISORY SERVICES INC.—See Stone Point Capital LLC; *U.S. Private*, pg. 3819
SENIOR SERVICES, INC.; *U.S. Private*, pg. 3607
SENIOR SERVICES OF SNOHOMISH COUNTY; *U.S. Private*, pg. 3607
SENIORS HOME CARE LLC; *U.S. Private*, pg. 3607
SENIORS HOUSING INVESTMENT III REIT INC.—See Welltower Inc.; *U.S. Public*, pg. 2349
SENIOR SUPPORT CO., LTD.—See Zensho Holdings Co., Ltd.; *Int'l*, pg. 8634
SENIOR TRUST CAPITAL LIMITED—See Senior Trust Retirement Village Listed Fund; *Int'l*, pg. 6709
SENIOR TRUST RETIREMENT VILLAGE LISTED FUND; *Int'l*, pg. 6709
SENIOR UK LIMITED—See Senior plc; *Int'l*, pg. 6709
SENIOR VISION SERVICES, INC.—See Serent Capital Management Company, LLC; *U.S. Private*, pg. 3613
SENIOR WESLEYAN LIVING; *U.S. Private*, pg. 3607
S-ENJOY SERVICE GROUP CO., LIMITED; *Int'l*, pg. 6446
SENKA (THAILAND) CO., LTD.—See Inabata & Co. Ltd.; *Int'l*, pg. 3644
SENKEN CORPORATION—See JUTEC Holdings Corporation; *Int'l*, pg. 4032
SENKICHI CO., LTD.—See Yoshinoya Holdings Co.; *Int'l*, pg. 8600
SENKO A LINE AMANO CO., LTD.—See Senko Group Holdings Co., Ltd.; *Int'l*, pg. 6711
SENKO ASSET MANAGEMENT CO., LTD.—See Senko Group Holdings Co., Ltd.; *Int'l*, pg. 6711
SENKO BUSINESS SUPPORT CO., LTD.—See Senko Group Holdings Co., Ltd.; *Int'l*, pg. 6711
SENKO CREATIVE MANAGEMENT CO., LTD.—See Senko Group Holdings Co., Ltd.; *Int'l*, pg. 6711
SENKO FACILITIES CO., LTD.—See Senko Group Holdings Co., Ltd.; *Int'l*, pg. 6711
SENKO FASHION LOGISTICS CO., LTD.—See Senko Group Holdings Co., Ltd.; *Int'l*, pg. 6711
SENKO FOODS CO., LTD.—See Senko Group Holdings Co., Ltd.; *Int'l*, pg. 6711
SENKO FORWARDING CO., LTD.—See Senko Group Holdings Co., Ltd.; *Int'l*, pg. 6711
SENKO GROUP HOLDINGS CO., LTD.; *Int'l*, pg. 6709
SENKO HOUSING LOGISTICS CO., LTD.—See Senko Group Holdings Co., Ltd.; *Int'l*, pg. 6711
SENKO INFORMATION SYSTEM CO., LTD.—See Senko Group Holdings Co., Ltd.; *Int'l*, pg. 6711
SENKO INSURANCE SERVICES CO., LTD.—See Senko Group Holdings Co., Ltd.; *Int'l*, pg. 6711
SENKO INTERNATIONAL LOGISTICS (HONG KONG) CO., LTD.—See Senko Group Holdings Co., Ltd.; *Int'l*, pg. 6711
SENKO INTERNATIONAL LOGISTICS (HONG KONG) LTD.—See Senko Group Holdings Co., Ltd.; *Int'l*, pg. 6711
SENKO INTERNATIONAL LOGISTICS PTE. LTD—See Senko Group Holdings Co., Ltd.; *Int'l*, pg. 6711
SENKO INTERNATIONAL TRADING CO., LTD.—See Senko Group Holdings Co., Ltd.; *Int'l*, pg. 6710
SENKO LINE CO., LTD.—See Senko Group Holdings Co., Ltd.; *Int'l*, pg. 6711
SENKO LIVING PLAZA CO., LTD.—See Senko Group Holdings Co., Ltd.; *Int'l*, pg. 6711
SENKO LOGISTICS AUSTRALIA PTY LTD—See Senko Group Holdings Co., Ltd.; *Int'l*, pg. 6711
SENKO LOGISTICS DISTRIBUTION (THAILAND) CO., LTD.—See Senko Group Holdings Co., Ltd.; *Int'l*, pg. 6711
SENKO LOGISTICS MEXICO S.A. DE C.V.—See Senko Group Holdings Co., Ltd.; *Int'l*, pg. 6711
SENKO LOGISTICS (SHANGHAI) CO., LTD.—See Senko Group Holdings Co., Ltd.; *Int'l*, pg. 6711
SENKO LOGISTICS (THAILAND) CO., LTD.—See Senko Group Holdings Co., Ltd.; *Int'l*, pg. 6711
SENKO LOGISTICS VIETNAM CO., LTD.—See Senko Group Holdings Co., Ltd.; *Int'l*, pg. 6710
SENKO MEDICAL LOGISTICS CO., LTD.—See Senko Group Holdings Co., Ltd.; *Int'l*, pg. 6711
SENKO MOVING PLAZA CO., LTD.—See Senko Group Holdings Co., Ltd.; *Int'l*, pg. 6711
SENKO NAGASE LOGISTICS CO., LTD.—See Senko Group Holdings Co., Ltd.; *Int'l*, pg. 6711
SENKON ENTERPRISE CO., LTD.—See SENKON Logistics Co.,Ltd.; *Int'l*, pg. 6712
SENKON LOGISTICS CO.,LTD.; *Int'l*, pg. 6712
SENKON LTD.—See SENKON Logistics Co.,Ltd.; *Int'l*, pg. 6712
SENKON TRADING SHANGHAI LTD.—See SENKON Logistics Co.,Ltd.; *Int'l*, pg. 6712
SENKO PLANTEC CO., LTD.—See Senko Group Holdings Co., Ltd.; *Int'l*, pg. 6711
SENKO PRIVATE REIT INC.—See Senko Group Holdings Co., Ltd.; *Int'l*, pg. 6711
SENKO REAL ESTATE CO., LTD.—See Senko Group Holdings Co., Ltd.; *Int'l*, pg. 6711

SENKO SCHOOL FARM TOTTORI CO., LTD.—See Senko Group Holdings Co., Ltd.; *Int'l*, pg. 6711
SENKO SHOJI CO., LTD.—See Senko Group Holdings Co., Ltd.; *Int'l*, pg. 6711
SENKO SMI MYANMAR CO., LTD.—See Senko Group Holdings Co., Ltd.; *Int'l*, pg. 6711
SENKO (THAILAND) CO., LTD.—See Senko Group Holdings Co., Ltd.; *Int'l*, pg. 6711
SENKO TRADING CO., LTD.—See Senko Group Holdings Co., Ltd.; *Int'l*, pg. 6711
SENKO (U.S.A.) INC.—See Senko Group Holdings Co., Ltd.; *Int'l*, pg. 6710
SENKROMA SA—See Plastika Kritis S.A.; *Int'l*, pg. 5892
SENKRON GUVENLIK VE ILETISIM SISTEMLERI AS; *Int'l*, pg. 6712
SENLIS AUTOMOBILES CAMIONS LOISIRS INDUSTRIE; *Int'l*, pg. 6712
SENMATIC A/S—See Indutrade AB; *Int'l*, pg. 3681
SENMIAO TECHNOLOGY LIMITED; *Int'l*, pg. 6712
SENMIN INTERNATIONAL (PTY) LIMITED—See AECI Limited; *Int'l*, pg. 171
SENNA NAHRUNGSMITTEL GMBH & CO. KG—See Raiffeisenlandesbank Oberosterreich Aktiengesellschaft; *Int'l*, pg. 6188
SEN NARI DAIICHI TRAFFIC CO., LTD.—See Daiichi Koutsu Sangyo Co., Ltd.; *Int'l*, pg. 1929
SENN-DELANEY LEADERSHIP CONSULTING GROUP, LLC—See Heidrick & Struggles International, Inc.; *U.S. Public*, pg. 1023
SENNDER ITALIA SRL—See Poste Italiane S.p.A.; *Int'l*, pg. 5939
SENNEN POTASH CORPORATION; *Int'l*, pg. 6712
SENNHEISER AUDIO LTD.—See Sennheiser Electronic GmbH & Co. KG; *Int'l*, pg. 6712
SENNHEISER AUSTRALIA PTY LIMITED—See Sennheiser Electronic GmbH & Co. KG; *Int'l*, pg. 6712
SENNHEISER AUSTRIA GMBH—See Sennheiser Electronic GmbH & Co. KG; *Int'l*, pg. 6712
SENNHEISER BELUX BVBA—See Sennheiser Electronic GmbH & Co. KG; *Int'l*, pg. 6712
SENNHEISER CANADA INC.—See Sennheiser Electronic GmbH & Co. KG; *Int'l*, pg. 6712
SENNHEISER COMMUNICATIONS A/S—See Demant A/S; *Int'l*, pg. 2024
SENNHEISER COMMUNICATIONS A/S—See Sennheiser Electronic GmbH & Co. KG; *Int'l*, pg. 6712
SENNHEISER ELECTRONIC ASIA PTE LTD—See Sennheiser Electronic GmbH & Co. KG; *Int'l*, pg. 6712
SENNHEISER ELECTRONIC (BEIJING) CO. LTD—See Sennheiser Electronic GmbH & Co. KG; *Int'l*, pg. 6712
SENNHEISER ELECTRONIC CORP.—See Sennheiser Electronic GmbH & Co. KG; *Int'l*, pg. 6712
SENNHEISER ELECTRONIC GMBH & CO. KG; *Int'l*, pg. 6712
SENNHEISER ELECTRONIC (SA) (PTY) LTD—See Sennheiser Electronic GmbH & Co. KG; *Int'l*, pg. 6712
SENNHEISER ELECTRONICS INDIA PVT. LTD—See Sennheiser Electronic GmbH & Co. KG; *Int'l*, pg. 6712
SENNHEISER FRANCE SARL—See Sennheiser Electronic GmbH & Co. KG; *Int'l*, pg. 6712
SENNHEISER HONG KONG LIMITED—See Sennheiser Electronic GmbH & Co. KG; *Int'l*, pg. 6712
SENNHEISER JAPAN K.K.—See Sennheiser Electronic GmbH & Co. KG; *Int'l*, pg. 6712
SENNHEISER NEDERLAND BV—See Sennheiser Electronic GmbH & Co. KG; *Int'l*, pg. 6712
SENNHEISER NEW ZEALAND LTD—See Sennheiser Electronic GmbH & Co. KG; *Int'l*, pg. 6712
SENNHEISER NORDIC A/S—See Sennheiser Electronic GmbH & Co. KG; *Int'l*, pg. 6712
SENNHEISER (SCHWEIZ) AG—See Sennheiser Electronic GmbH & Co. KG; *Int'l*, pg. 6712
SENNINGER IRRIGATION, INC.—See Hunter Industries Incorporated; *U.S. Private*, pg. 2010
SENNINGER PLUMBING COMPANY, INC.; *U.S. Private*, pg. 3607
SENOH CORPORATION—See Mizuno Corporation; *Int'l*, pg. 5000
SENOKO ENERGY PTE LTD.—See ENGIE SA; *Int'l*, pg. 2434
SENOMYX, INC.—See Firmenich International SA; *Int'l*, pg. 2680
SEN PLEX CORPORATION; *U.S. Private*, pg. 3605
SENQCIA CORPORATION—See The Carlyle Group Inc.; *U.S. Public*, pg. 2052
SENQCIA MAXCO, LTD.—See Rising Japan Equity, Inc.; *Int'l*, pg. 6350
SENSA EHF.—See Crayon Group Holding ASA; *Int'l*, pg. 1830
SENSA SOLUTIONS, INC.—See Korn Ferry; *U.S. Public*, pg. 1273
SENSAS SA; *Int'l*, pg. 6713
SENSATA GERMANY GMBH—See Sensata Technologies Holding plc; *U.S. Public*, pg. 1866
SENSATA TECHNOLOGIES AUTOMOTIVE SENSORS (SHANGHAI) CO., LTD.—See Sensata Technologies Holding plc; *U.S. Public*, pg. 1865

SENSATA TECHNOLOGIES BAOYING CO., LTD.—See Sensata Technologies Holding plc; *U.S. Public*, pg. 1865
SENSATA TECHNOLOGIES B.V.—See Sensata Technologies Holding plc; *U.S. Public*, pg. 1865
SENSATA TECHNOLOGIES CHANGZHOU CO., LTD.—See Sensata Technologies Holding plc; *U.S. Public*, pg. 1865
SENSATA TECHNOLOGIES CHINA CO., LTD.—See Sensata Technologies Holding plc; *U.S. Public*, pg. 1865
SENSATA TECHNOLOGIES DE MEXICO S DE RL DE CV—See Sensata Technologies Holding plc; *U.S. Public*, pg. 1866
SENSATA TECHNOLOGIES DOMINICANA, S.R.L.—See Sensata Technologies Holding plc; *U.S. Public*, pg. 1865
SENSATA TECHNOLOGIES GERMANY GMBH—See Sensata Technologies Holding plc; *U.S. Public*, pg. 1865
SENSATA TECHNOLOGIES GMBH—See Sensata Technologies Holding plc; *U.S. Public*, pg. 1866
SENSATA TECHNOLOGIES HOLDING PLC; *U.S. Public*, pg. 1865
SENSATA TECHNOLOGIES HOLLAND B.V.—See Sensata Technologies Holding plc; *U.S. Public*, pg. 1865
SENSATA TECHNOLOGIES, INC. - DIMENSIONS—See Sensata Technologies Holding plc; *U.S. Public*, pg. 1866
SENSATA TECHNOLOGIES, INC.—See Sensata Technologies Holding plc; *U.S. Public*, pg. 1866
SENSATA TECHNOLOGIES INDIANA, INC.—See Sensata Technologies Holding plc; *U.S. Public*, pg. 1866
SENSATA TECHNOLOGIES KOREA LIMITED—See Sensata Technologies Holding plc; *U.S. Public*, pg. 1865
SENSATA TECHNOLOGIES MALAYSIA SDN. BHD.—See Sensata Technologies Holding plc; *U.S. Public*, pg. 1865
SENSATA TECHNOLOGIES MEX DISTRIBUTION, S.A. DE C.V.—See Sensata Technologies Holding plc; *U.S. Public*, pg. 1865
SENSATA TECHNOLOGIES POWER CONTROLS—See Sensata Technologies Holding plc; *U.S. Public*, pg. 1866
SENSATA TECHNOLOGIES SENSORES E CONTROLES DO BRASIL LTDA.—See Sensata Technologies Holding plc; *U.S. Public*, pg. 1865
SENSATA TECHNOLOGIES SINGAPORE PTE. LTD.—See Sensata Technologies Holding plc; *U.S. Public*, pg. 1865
SENSATA TECHNOLOGIES TAIWAN CO., LTD.—See Sensata Technologies Holding plc; *U.S. Public*, pg. 1866
SENSATRONICS, LLC; *U.S. Private*, pg. 3607
SENSCIENT INC.; *U.S. Private*, pg. 3607
SENSCIENT, LTD.—See MSA Safety Incorporated; *U.S. Public*, pg. 1482
SENSEAIR AB—See Asahi Kasei Corporation; *Int'l*, pg. 597
SENSE CORP.; *U.S. Private*, pg. 3607
SENSE EHF—See Origo hf.; *Int'l*, pg. 5630
SENSEFLY SA—See AgEagle Aerial Systems Inc.; *U.S. Public*, pg. 60
SENSEI BIOTHERAPEUTICS, INC.; *U.S. Public*, pg. 1866
SENSEI ENTERPRISES, INC.; *U.S. Private*, pg. 3607
SENSEI, INC.—See Humana, Inc.; *U.S. Public*, pg. 1070
SENSEKI KAKO CO., LTD.—See Sekisui Chemical Co., Ltd.; *Int'l*, pg. 6696
SENSEMETRICS, INC.—See Bentley Systems, Inc.; *U.S. Public*, pg. 297
SENSENICH PROPELLER MANUFACTURING CO., INC.—See The Philadelphia Bourse, Inc.; *U.S. Private*, pg. 4094
SENSENICH WOOD PROPELLER CO., INC.—See The Philadelphia Bourse, Inc.; *U.S. Private*, pg. 4094
SENSEN NETWORKS LIMITED; *Int'l*, pg. 6713
SENSEONICS HOLDINGS, INC.; *U.S. Public*, pg. 1866
SENSERA INC.—See Sensera Limited; *Int'l*, pg. 6713
SENSERA LIMITED; *Int'l*, pg. 6713
SENSES MARKETING INTERNATIONAL LIMITED—See Hillhouse Investment Management Limited; *Int'l*, pg. 3393
SENSES PROPERTY MANAGEMENT COMPANY LIMITED—See Univentures Public Company Limited; *Int'l*, pg. 8077
SENSETALBAHN AG—See Schweizerische Bundesbahnen SBB AG; *Int'l*, pg. 6646
SENSE TECHNOLOGIES INC.; *U.S. Public*, pg. 1866
SENSETIME GROUP INC.; *Int'l*, pg. 6713
SENSHU ELECTRIC CO., LTD.; *Int'l*, pg. 6713
SENSHU ELECTRIC INTERNATIONAL CO., LTD.—See Senshu Electric Co., Ltd.; *Int'l*, pg. 6713
SENSHU ELECTRIC (THAILAND) CO., LTD.—See Senshu Electric Co., Ltd.; *Int'l*, pg. 6713
THE SENSHU IKEDA BANK, LTD.—See Senshu Ikeda Holdings, Inc.; *Int'l*, pg. 6713
SENSHU IKEDA BUSINESS SERVICE CO., LTD.—See Senshu Ikeda Holdings, Inc.; *Int'l*, pg. 6713
SENSHU IKEDA HOLDINGS, INC.; *Int'l*, pg. 6713
SENSHUKAI CO., LTD.; *Int'l*, pg. 6713

COMPANY NAME INDEX

SENSHUKAI GENERAL SERVICES CO., LTD.—See Senshukai Co., Ltd.; *Int'l*, pg. 6713
SENSHUKAI IIHANA CO., LTD.—See Senshukai Co., Ltd.; *Int'l*, pg. 6713
SENSHU LOGISCO CO.,LTD.—See Senshukai Co., Ltd.; *Int'l*, pg. 6713
SENSIA LLC—See Rockwell Automation, Inc.; *U.S. Public*, pg. 1807
SENSIA SALON, INC.; *U.S. Private*, pg. 3607
SENSIBA SAN FILIPPO LLP; *U.S. Private*, pg. 3607
SENSIBILL INC.—See Q2 Holdings, Inc.; *U.S. Public*, pg. 1741
SENSIBLE ASSET MANAGEMENT LIMITED—See Value Partners Group Limited; *Int'l*, pg. 8124
SENSIBLE EVENTS LIMITED—See Live Nation Entertainment, Inc.; *U.S. Public*, pg. 1330
SENSIBLE MEATS INC.; *Int'l*, pg. 6713
SENSIBLE MICRO CORPORATION; *U.S. Private*, pg. 3607
SENSIBLU S.R.L.—See A&D Pharma Holdings S.R.L.; *Int'l*, pg. 19
SENSIENT COLORS CANADA LTD.—See Sensient Technologies Corporation; *U.S. Public*, pg. 1867
SENSIENT COLORS EUROPE GMBH—See Sensient Technologies Corporation; *U.S. Public*, pg. 1867
SENSIENT COLORS LLC—See Sensient Technologies Corporation; *U.S. Public*, pg. 1867
SENSIENT COLORS SA DE CV—See Sensient Technologies Corporation; *U.S. Public*, pg. 1867
SENSIENT COLORS UK LTD.—See Sensient Technologies Corporation; *U.S. Public*, pg. 1867
SENSIENT COSMETIC TECHNOLOGIES E CORANTES, IMPORTACAO E EXPORTACAO DO—See Sensient Technologies Corporation; *U.S. Public*, pg. 1867
SENSIENT COSMETIC TECHNOLOGIES POLAND, SP. Z.O.O.—See Sensient Technologies Corporation; *U.S. Public*, pg. 1867
SENSIENT COSMETIC TECHNOLOGIES—See Sensient Technologies Corporation; *U.S. Public*, pg. 1867
SENSIENT COSMETIC TECHNOLOGIES USA—See Sensient Technologies Corporation; *U.S. Public*, pg. 1867
SENSIENT DEHYDRATED FLAVORS SAS—See Sensient Technologies Corporation; *U.S. Public*, pg. 1867
SENSIENT FLAVORS AND FRAGRANCES SOUTH AFRICA (PROPRIETARY) LTD—See Sensient Technologies Corporation; *U.S. Public*, pg. 1867
SENSIENT FLAVORS AUSTRIA GMBH—See Sensient Technologies Corporation; *U.S. Public*, pg. 1867
SENSIENT FLAVORS & FRAGRANCES INDUSTRY & TRADE LIMITED COMPANY—See Sensient Technologies Corporation; *U.S. Public*, pg. 1867
SENSIENT FLAVORS & FRAGRANCES SAS—See Sensient Technologies Corporation; *U.S. Public*, pg. 1867
SENSIENT FLAVORS INTERNATIONAL, INC.—See Sensient Technologies Corporation; *U.S. Public*, pg. 1867
SENSIENT FLAVORS ITALY S.R.L.—See Sensient Technologies Corporation; *U.S. Public*, pg. 1867
SENSIENT FLAVORS, LLC—See Sensient Technologies Corporation; *U.S. Public*, pg. 1867
SENSIENT FLAVORS LTD.—See Sensient Technologies Corporation; *U.S. Public*, pg. 1867
SENSIENT FOOD COLORS CZECH REPUBLIC CZ S.R.O.—See Sensient Technologies Corporation; *U.S. Public*, pg. 1867
SENSIENT FOOD COLORS ITALY S.R.L.—See Sensient Technologies Corporation; *U.S. Public*, pg. 1867
SENSIENT FOOD COLORS POLAND SP.ZO.O.—See Sensient Technologies Corporation; *U.S. Public*, pg. 1867
SENSIENT FOOD COLORS ROMANIA S.R.L.—See Sensient Technologies Corporation; *U.S. Public*, pg. 1867
SENSIENT FOOD COLORS THE NETHERLANDS BV—See Sensient Technologies Corporation; *U.S. Public*, pg. 1867
SENSIENT FRAGRANCES MEXICO, S.A. DE C.V.—See Sensient Technologies Corporation; *U.S. Public*, pg. 1867
SENSIENT FRAGRANCES, S.A.—See Sensient Technologies Corporation; *U.S. Public*, pg. 1867
SENSIENT HOLDINGS UK—See Sensient Technologies Corporation; *U.S. Public*, pg. 1867
SENSIENT IMAGING TECHNOLOGIES INC.—See Sensient Technologies Corporation; *U.S. Public*, pg. 1867
SENSIENT IMAGING TECHNOLOGIES S.A. DE C.V.—See Sensient Technologies Corporation; *U.S. Public*, pg. 1867
SENSIENT NATURAL EXTRACTION INC.—See Sensient Technologies Corporation; *U.S. Public*, pg. 1867
SENSIENT NATURAL INGREDIENTS LLC—See Sensient Technologies Corporation; *U.S. Public*, pg. 1867
SENSIENT NATURAL INGREDIENTS—See Sensient Technologies Corporation; *U.S. Public*, pg. 1867
SENSIENT NATURAL TECHNOLOGIES LLC—See Sensient Technologies Corporation; *U.S. Public*, pg. 1867
SENSIENT TECHNOLOGIES ASIA PACIFIC PTE. LTD.—See Sensient Technologies Corporation; *U.S. Public*, pg. 1867

SENSIENT TECHNOLOGIES AUSTRALIA PTY LTD.—See Sensient Technologies Corporation; *U.S. Public*, pg. 1867
SENSIENT TECHNOLOGIES CORP. (CHINA) LTD—See Sensient Technologies Corporation; *U.S. Public*, pg. 1867
SENSIENT TECHNOLOGIES CORPORATION (JAPAN)—See Sensient Technologies Corporation; *U.S. Public*, pg. 1867
SENSIENT TECHNOLOGIES CORPORATION; *U.S. Public*, pg. 1867
SENSIENT TECHNOLOGIES EUROPE GMBH—See Sensient Technologies Corporation; *U.S. Public*, pg. 1867
SENSIENT TURKEY DOGAL MADDELER A.S.—See Sensient Technologies Corporation; *U.S. Public*, pg. 1868
SENSILE MEDICAL AG—See Gerresheimer AG; *Int'l*, pg. 2944
SENSIML CORPORATION—See QuickLogic Corporation; *U.S. Public*, pg. 1756
SENSING ENTERPRISES INC.; *U.S. Private*, pg. 3608
SENSIR AG—See Investment AB Latour; *Int'l*, pg. 3783
SENSIR INC.—See Epiroc AB; *Int'l*, pg. 2463
SENSIRION AUTOMOTIVE SOLUTIONS INC.—See Sensirion Holding AG; *Int'l*, pg. 6714
SENSIRION AUTOMOTIVE SOLUTIONS KOREA CO., LTD.—See Sensirion Holding AG; *Int'l*, pg. 6714
SENSIRION AUTOMOTIVE SOLUTIONS (SHANGHAI) CO., LTD.—See Sensirion Holding AG; *Int'l*, pg. 6714
SENSIRION CHINA CO. LTD.—See Sensirion Holding AG; *Int'l*, pg. 6714
SENSIRION HOLDING AG; *Int'l*, pg. 6713
SENSIRION JAPAN CO. LTD.—See Sensirion Holding AG; *Int'l*, pg. 6714
SENSIRION KOREA CO. LTD.—See Sensirion Holding AG; *Int'l*, pg. 6714
SENSIRION TAIWAN CO. LTD.—See Sensirion Holding AG; *Int'l*, pg. 6714
SENSIS INC.; *U.S. Private*, pg. 3608
SENSIS PTY. LTD.—See Thryv Holdings, Inc.; *U.S. Public*, pg. 2157
SENSITEC GMBH—See Korber AG; *Int'l*, pg. 4281
SENSITECH BRASIL LTDA.—See Carrier Global Corporation; *U.S. Public*, pg. 444
SENSITECH CANADA INC.—See Carrier Global Corporation; *U.S. Public*, pg. 444
SENSITECH EMEA B.V.—See Carrier Global Corporation; *U.S. Public*, pg. 444
SENSITECH INC. - REDMOND PLANT—See Carrier Global Corporation; *U.S. Public*, pg. 442
SENSITECH INC.—See Carrier Global Corporation; *U.S. Public*, pg. 442
SENSITECH PTY LIMITED—See Carrier Global Corporation; *U.S. Public*, pg. 444
SENSITRON S.R.L.—See Halma plc; *Int'l*, pg. 3232
SENSIT TECHNOLOGIES LLC—See Halma plc; *Int'l*, pg. 3232
SENSKE LAWN & TREE CARE, INC.; *U.S. Private*, pg. 3608
SENSLAB GMBH—See EKF Diagnostics Holdings PLC; *Int'l*, pg. 2338
SENSL TECHNOLOGIES LIMITED—See ON Semiconductor Corporation; *U.S. Public*, pg. 1601
SENSODETECT AB; *Int'l*, pg. 6714
SENSONOR AS; *Int'l*, pg. 6714
SENSOR CONTROL NORDIC AB—See Addtech AB; *Int'l*, pg. 135
SENSOR ECS A/S—See Addtech AB; *Int'l*, pg. 135
SENSOR ELECTRONIC TECHNOLOGY, INC.—See Seoul Semiconductor Co., Ltd.; *Int'l*, pg. 6717
SENSOR ENTERPRISES INC.; *U.S. Private*, pg. 3608
SENSORE TECHNOLOGIES CORPORATION—See Premier1 Lithium Ltd.; *Int'l*, pg. 5962
SENSOREX CORPORATION—See Halma plc; *Int'l*, pg. 3232
SENSORION SA; *Int'l*, pg. 6714
SENSOR KOGYO CO.,LTD. - GONOHE PLANT—See Ferrotec Holdings Corporation; *Int'l*, pg. 2643
SENSOR KOGYO CO., LTD. - HACHINOHE PLANT—See Ferrotec Holdings Corporation; *Int'l*, pg. 2643
SENSOR KOGYO CO., LTD.—See Ferrotec Holdings Corporation; *Int'l*, pg. 2643
SENSORLINK SDN. BHD.—See Nexgram Holdings Berhad; *Int'l*, pg. 5244
SENSORLOGIC, INC.—See Thales S.A.; *Int'l*, pg. 7599
SENSORMARE AG—See Gefran S.p.A.; *Int'l*, pg. 2912
SENSORMATIC ARGENTINA S.A.—See Johnson Controls International plc; *Int'l*, pg. 3988
SENSORMATIC DEL CARIBE, INC.—See Johnson Controls International plc; *Int'l*, pg. 3988
SENSORMATIC DO BRASIL ELETRONICA LTDA.—See Johnson Controls International plc; *Int'l*, pg. 3988
SENSORMATIC ELECTRONICS CORPORATION (IRELAND) LIMITED—See Johnson Controls International plc; *Int'l*, pg. 3988
SENSORMATIC ELECTRONICS, LLC - LITHIA SPRINGS—See Johnson Controls International plc; *Int'l*, pg. 3988
SENSORMATIC ELECTRONICS, LLC—See Johnson Controls International plc; *Int'l*, pg. 3988

SENSYNE HEALTH PLC

SENSORMATIC HONG KONG LIMITED—See Johnson Controls International plc; *Int'l*, pg. 3988
SENSORMATIC MOSCOW—See Johnson Controls International plc; *Int'l*, pg. 3988
SENSORMATIC PROTECCAO CONTRA FURTO, LDA—See Johnson Controls International plc; *Int'l*, pg. 3988
SENSOR NEDERLAND B.V.—See ION Geophysical Corporation; *U.S. Public*, pg. 1166
SENSOR PARTNERS BVBA—See Indutrade AB; *Int'l*, pg. 3681
SENSOR PARTNERS BV—See Indutrade AB; *Int'l*, pg. 3681
SENSOR SCIENTIFIC, INC.—See CTS Corporation; *U.S. Public*, pg. 603
SENSORS EUROPE GMBH—See Sensors, Inc.; *U.S. Private*, pg. 3608
SENSORS, INC.; *U.S. Private*, pg. 3608
SENSOR SOLUTIONS INC.—See Standex International; *U.S. Public*, pg. 1930
SENSORS & SOFTWARE INC.—See SPX Technologies, Inc.; *U.S. Public*, pg. 1922
SENSORS UNLIMITED, INC.—See RTX Corporation; *U.S. Public*, pg. 1821
SENSOR SYSTEMS INC.—See HEICO Corporation; *U.S. Public*, pg. 1021
SENSOR SYSTEMS LIMITED—See Kingspan Group PLC; *Int'l*, pg. 4179
SENSOR SYSTEMS, LLC; *U.S. Private*, pg. 3608
SENSORTEC AG—See Investment AB Latour; *Int'l*, pg. 3783
SENSORTECHNICS GMBH—See TE Connectivity Ltd.; *Int'l*, pg. 7496
SENSOR TECHNOLOGIES CORP.; *Int'l*, pg. 6714
SENSOR TECHNOLOGY ENGINEERING, LLC—See HEICO Corporation; *U.S. Public*, pg. 1020
SENSORTEK TECHNOLOGY CORP.—See Sitronix Technology Corporation; *Int'l*, pg. 6965
SENSORTHERM GMBH—See Nynomic AG; *Int'l*, pg. 5501
SENSORVIEW CO., LTD.; *Int'l*, pg. 6714
SENSORWISE, INC.—See Sanmina Corporation; *U.S. Public*, pg. 1841
SENSORYEFFECTS CEREAL SYSTEMS, INC.—See Balchem Corporation; *U.S. Public*, pg. 266
SENSORYEFFECTS FLAVOR COMPANY—See Balchem Corporation; *U.S. Public*, pg. 266
SENSORYEFFECTS, INC.—See Balchem Corporation; *U.S. Public*, pg. 266
SENSORYEFFECTS POWDER SYSTEMS, INC.—See Balchem Corporation; *U.S. Public*, pg. 266
SENSORY & MARKETING SPAIN, S.L.U.—See Eurofins Scientific S.E.; *Int'l*, pg. 2551
SENSORY TECHNOLOGIES, LLC—See Diversified Specialties, Inc.; *U.S. Private*, pg. 1243
SENSO SAGYO CO., LTD.—See The Sumitomo Warehouse Co. Ltd.; *Int'l*, pg. 7690
SEN SPIRIT TECHNOLOGY LIMITED—See Karin Technology Holdings Limited; *Int'l*, pg. 4081
SENSTAR TECHNOLOGIES LTD.; *Int'l*, pg. 6714
SENSUP JSC—See Lumibird Group; *Int'l*, pg. 4578
SENSUS AMERICA INC.—See Royal Cosun U.A.; *Int'l*, pg. 6412
SENSUS B.V.—See Royal Cosun U.A.; *Int'l*, pg. 6412
SENSUS CANADA INC.—See Xylem Inc.; *U.S. Public*, pg. 2394
SENSUS & CESKA REPUBLIKA SPOL. S R.O.—See Xylem Inc.; *U.S. Public*, pg. 2394
SENSUS CHILE SA—See Xylem Inc.; *U.S. Public*, pg. 2395
SENSUS ESPANA SA—See Xylem Inc.; *U.S. Public*, pg. 2395
SENSUS FRANCE HOLDINGS SAS—See Xylem Inc.; *U.S. Public*, pg. 2394
SENSUS FRANCE SAS—See Xylem Inc.; *U.S. Public*, pg. 2395
SENSUS GMBH HANNOVER—See Xylem Inc.; *U.S. Public*, pg. 2394
SENSUS HEALTHCARE, INC.; *U.S. Public*, pg. 1868
SENSUS ITALIA SRL—See Xylem Inc.; *U.S. Public*, pg. 2395
SENSUS MANUFACTURING (SHANGHAI) CO., LTD.—See Xylem Inc.; *U.S. Public*, pg. 2395
SENSUS MAROC S.A.—See Xylem Inc.; *U.S. Public*, pg. 2395
SENSUS METERING SYSTEMS (FUZHOU) CO., LTD.—See Xylem Inc.; *U.S. Public*, pg. 2395
SENSUS METERING SYSTEMS INC.—See Xylem Inc.; *U.S. Public*, pg. 2395
SENSUS POLSKA SP. ZOO—See Xylem Inc.; *U.S. Public*, pg. 2395
SENSUS SERVICES DEUTSCHLAND GMBH—See Xylem Inc.; *U.S. Public*, pg. 2395
SENSUS SOUTH AFRICA (PROPRIETARY) LTD.—See Xylem Inc.; *U.S. Public*, pg. 2395
SENSYNE HEALTH PLC; *Int'l*, pg. 6714
SENSYS GATSO AUSTRALIA LTD.—See Sensys Gatso Group AB; *Int'l*, pg. 6714
SENSYS GATSO DEUTSCHLAND GMBH—See Sensys Gatso Group AB; *Int'l*, pg. 6714

SENSYS GATSO GROUP AB

SENSYS GATSO GROUP AB; *Int'l*, pg. 6714
SENSYS GATSO GROUP B.V.—See Sensys Gatso Group AB; *Int'l*, pg. 6714
SENSYS GATSO NETHERLANDS B.V.—See Sensys Gatso Group AB; *Int'l*, pg. 6714
SENSYS GATSO SOFTWARE B.V.—See Sensys Gatso Group AB; *Int'l*, pg. 6714
SENSYS GATSO SWEDEN AB—See Sensys Gatso Group AB; *Int'l*, pg. 6714
SENSYS GATSO USA INC.—See Sensys Gatso Group AB; *Int'l*, pg. 6714
SENSYS NETWORKS, INC.—See TagMaster AB; *Int'l*, pg. 7407
SENTAGE HOLDINGS INC.; *Int'l*, pg. 6714
SENTAIDA TIRE COMPANY LTD.; *U.S. Public*, pg. 1868
SENTA - PROMET A.D.; *Int'l*, pg. 6714
SENTARA HEALTHCARE; *U.S. Private*, pg. 3608
SENTECH SERVICES, INC.; *U.S. Private*, pg. 3608
SENTEC LIMITED—See Xylem Inc.; *U.S. Public*, pg. 2395
SENTEK GLOBAL INCORPORATED; *U.S. Private*, pg. 3608
SENTELIC CORP.; *Int'l*, pg. 6714
SENTE MORTGAGE, INC.; *U.S. Private*, pg. 3608
SENTENIAL B.V.B.A.—See EML Payments Limited; *Int'l*, pg. 2383
SENTENIAL LIMITED—See EML Payments Limited; *Int'l*, pg. 2384
SENTENIAL S.A.R.L.—See EML Payments Limited; *Int'l*, pg. 2384
SENTER PETROLEUM, INC.—See Par Pacific Holdings, Inc.; *U.S. Public*, pg. 1636
SENTHIL INFOTEK LIMITED; *Int'l*, pg. 6714
SENTI BIOSCIENCES, INC.; *U.S. Public*, pg. 1868
SENTICA PARTNERS OY; *Int'l*, pg. 6715
SENTIEN PRINTING FACTORY CO., LTD.; *Int'l*, pg. 6715
SENTIENT ASSET MANAGEMENT AUSTRALIA PTY. LIMITED—See The Sentient Group Limited; *Int'l*, pg. 7681
SENTIENT ENERGY, INC.—See Koch Industries, Inc.; *U.S. Private*, pg. 2332
SENTIENT FLIGHT GROUP, LLC—See Macquarie Group Limited; *Int'l*, pg. 4626
THE SENTIENT GROUP LIMITED; *Int'l*, pg. 7681
SENTIENT JET, LLC—See Macquarie Group Limited; *Int'l*, pg. 4626
SENTIENT SERVICES—See Interviewing Service of America; *U.S. Private*, pg. 2128
SENTIMENTS INC.—See Prospect Hill Growth Partners, L.P.; *U.S. Private*, pg. 3288
SENTINEL ADMINISTRATIVE SERVICES, INC.—See National Life Insurance Company; *U.S. Private*, pg. 2858
SENTINEL ADVISORS CO.—See National Life Insurance Company; *U.S. Private*, pg. 2858
SENTINEL ASSET MANAGEMENT, INC.—See National Life Insurance Company; *U.S. Private*, pg. 2859
SENTINEL BROKERS CO., INC.; *U.S. Private*, pg. 3608
SENTINEL BUILDING SYSTEMS INC.; *U.S. Private*, pg. 3608
SENTINEL CAPITAL PARTNERS, L.L.C.; *U.S. Private*, pg. 3608
THE SENTINEL COMPANY—See NewSpring Capital LLC; *U.S. Private*, pg. 2918
SENTINEL ENERGY SERVICES INC.; *U.S. Private*, pg. 3609
SENTINEL & ENTERPRISE—See Alden Global Capital LLC; *U.S. Private*, pg. 157
SENTINEL FLUID CONTROLS, LLC—See Applied Industrial Technologies, Inc.; *U.S. Public*, pg. 171
SENTINEL HEALTHCARE LLC—See The Pennant Group, Inc.; *U.S. Public*, pg. 2118
SENTINEL HEALTHCARE SERVICES, LLC—See KKR & Co. Inc.; *U.S. Public*, pg. 1250
SENTINEL HOLDINGS B.V.—See Eurocommercial Properties N.V.; *Int'l*, pg. 2534
SENTINEL HOLDINGS II B.V.—See Eurocommercial Properties N.V.; *Int'l*, pg. 2534
SENTINEL INTERNATIONAL CO. LIMITED—See Amuse Group Holding Ltd.; *Int'l*, pg. 442
SENTINELLE MEDICAL USA INC.—See Hologic, Inc.; *U.S. Public*, pg. 1045
SENTINEL OFFENDER SERVICES, LLC—See CSRA Probation Services, Inc.; *U.S. Private*, pg. 1117
SENTINELONE, INC.; *U.S. Public*, pg. 1868
SENTINEL POWER SERVICES, INC.—See Techpro Power Group, Inc.; *U.S. Private*, pg. 3956
SENTINEL PRINTING CO., INC.—See Bang Printing; *U.S. Private*, pg. 465
SENTINEL PRODUCTS CORP.; *U.S. Private*, pg. 3609
SENTINEL REAL ESTATE CORPORATION; *U.S. Private*, pg. 3609
SENTINEL-RECORD—See Wehco Media, Inc.; *U.S. Private*, pg. 4469
SENTINEL SALES & MANAGEMENT LLC; *U.S. Private*, pg. 3610
SENTINEL SECURITY SOLUTIONS, INC.; *U.S. Private*, pg. 3610
SENTINEL SELF-STORAGE CORPORATION—See StorageVault Canada Inc.; *Int'l*, pg. 7225
SENTINEL SILENT ALARM CO., INC.—See Alert Holdings Group, Inc.; *U.S. Private*, pg. 162
SENTINEL SYSTEM, LLC—See Revolution Lighting Technologies, Inc.; *U.S. Public*, pg. 1793
SENTINEL TECHNOLOGIES, INC.; *U.S. Private*, pg. 3610
SENTINEL TRANSPORTATION LLC - BELLE—See Phillips 66 Company; *U.S. Public*, pg. 1688
SENTINEL TRANSPORTATION LLC - LOUISVILLE—See Phillips 66 Company; *U.S. Public*, pg. 1688
SENTINEL TRANSPORTATION LLC—See Phillips 66 Company; *U.S. Public*, pg. 1688
SENTINEL TRANSPORTATION LLC - WASHINGTON—See Phillips 66 Company; *U.S. Public*, pg. 1688
SENTINEL TRANSPORTATION LLC - WESTLAKE—See Phillips 66 Company; *U.S. Public*, pg. 1688
SENTIOTEC GMBH—See Harvia Oyj; *Int'l*, pg. 3282
SENTIRE-ONE CO., LTD.—See Naigai Co., Ltd.; *Int'l*, pg. 5130
SENTIS PTY LTD; *Int'l*, pg. 6715
SENTIS USA, INC.—See Sentis Pty Ltd; *Int'l*, pg. 6715
SENTIVO EITORF GMBH—See Clariane SE; *Int'l*, pg. 1644
SENTIVO MONCHENGLADBACH GMBH—See Clariane SE; *Int'l*, pg. 1644
SENTIVO RHONDORF GMBH—See Clariane SE; *Int'l*, pg. 1644
SENTIVO SOLINGEN GMBH—See Clariane SE; *Int'l*, pg. 1644
SENTON ENERGY CO., LTD.; *Int'l*, pg. 6715
SENTON PRINTING & PACKAGING INCORPORATED; *Int'l*, pg. 6715
SENTORARU DENSHI SEIGYO CO., LTD.—See Futaba Corporation; *Int'l*, pg. 2851
SENTORIA BORNEO LAND SDN. BHD.—See Sentoria Group Berhad; *Int'l*, pg. 6715
SENTORIA GROUP BERHAD; *Int'l*, pg. 6715
SENTOSA PHARMACY SDN BHD—See Batu Kawan Berhad; *Int'l*, pg. 891
SENTRAL REIT; *Int'l*, pg. 6715
SENTRALSLIP AS—See EssilorLuxottica SA; *Int'l*, pg. 2516
SENTRANA INC.; *U.S. Private*, pg. 3610
SENTRA NAMIBIA LTD—See Shoprite Holdings Limited; *Int'l*, pg. 6859
SENTREHEART, INC.—See AtriCure, Inc.; *U.S. Public*, pg. 225
SENTREX COMMUNICATIONS INC.; *Int'l*, pg. 6715
SENTRILLION CORPORATION; *U.S. Private*, pg. 3610
SENTRIX GLOBAL HEALTH COMMUNICATIONS MILAN—See WPP plc; *Int'l*, pg. 8492
SENTRON AG—See Melexis N.V.; *Int'l*, pg. 4809
SENTRX ANIMAL CARE, INC.—See Domes Pharma SA; *Int'l*, pg. 2159
SENTRY ABSTRACT COMPANY—See Old Republic International Corporation; *U.S. Public*, pg. 1569
SENTRY AEROSPACE CORP.—See Acorn Growth Companies, LC; *U.S. Private*, pg. 63
SENTRY ANESTHESIA MANAGEMENT, LLC—See Bain Capital, LP; *U.S. Private*, pg. 446
SENTRY AUTO GROUP; *U.S. Private*, pg. 3610
SENTRYCARE, INC.; *U.S. Private*, pg. 3611
SENTRY CASUALTY COMPANY—See Sentry Insurance Group; *U.S. Private*, pg. 3611
SENTRY CENTERS HOLDINGS LLC; *U.S. Private*, pg. 3610
SENTRY COMMUNICATIONS & SECURITY; *U.S. Private*, pg. 3610
SENTRY CONTROL SYSTEMS LLC—See Kudelski S.A.; *Int'l*, pg. 4323
SENTRY DATA SYSTEMS, INC.—See Craneware plc; *Int'l*, pg. 1828
SENTRY DETECTION INC.; *U.S. Private*, pg. 3610
SENTRY EQUIPMENT CORP; *U.S. Private*, pg. 3610
SENTRY EQUIPMENT ERECTORS INC.—See Leonard Green & Partners, L.P.; *U.S. Private*, pg. 2428
SENTRY FORD LINCOLN, INC.; *U.S. Private*, pg. 3610
SENTRY FORD LINCOLN, INC.—See Sentry Auto Group; *U.S. Private*, pg. 3610
SENTRY GROUP, INC.; *U.S. Private*, pg. 3610
SENTRY GROUP—See Sentry Insurance Group; *U.S. Private*, pg. 3611
SENTRY HOUSEHOLD SHIPPING INC—See The Suddath Companies; *U.S. Private*, pg. 4124
SENTRY INSURANCE BROKERS LTD.—See Canadian Imperial Bank of Commerce; *Int'l*, pg. 1283
SENTRY INSURANCE GROUP; *U.S. Private*, pg. 3610
SENTRY INSURANCE—See Sentry Insurance Group; *U.S. Private*, pg. 3611
SENTRY INVESTMENTS INC.—See CI Financial Corporation; *Int'l*, pg. 1601
SENTRY LEASING INC—See Don Hill Automotive Associates Inc.; *U.S. Private*, pg. 1257
SENTRY LIFE INSURANCE COMPANY—See Sentry Insurance Group; *U.S. Private*, pg. 3611
SENTRY MANAGEMENT INC.; *U.S. Private*, pg. 3611
SENTRY MEDICAL PTY. LTD.—See EBOS Group Limited; *Int'l*, pg. 2285
SENTRY PETROLEUM LTD.; *U.S. Public*, pg. 1868

CORPORATE AFFILIATIONS

SENTRY SAFE, INC.—See Fortune Brands Innovations, Inc.; *U.S. Public*, pg. 873
SENTRYSAFE—See Sentry Group, Inc.; *U.S. Private*, pg. 3610
SENTRY SELECT INSURANCE COMPANY—See Sentry Insurance Group; *U.S. Private*, pg. 3611
SENTRY TECHNOLOGY CANADA INC.—See Sentry Technology Corporation; *U.S. Public*, pg. 1868
SENTRY TECHNOLOGY CORPORATION; *U.S. Public*, pg. 1868
SENTRY WATCH INC.—See Pye-Barker Fire & Safety, LLC; *U.S. Private*, pg. 3309
SENTRY WEST, INC.—See Sentry Auto Group; *U.S. Private*, pg. 3610
SENTURE, LLC—See Kingswood Capital Management LLC; *U.S. Private*, pg. 2312
SENTYNL THERAPEUTICS INC.—See Zydus Lifesciences Limited; *Int'l*, pg. 8700
SENUIN BETEILIGUNGSVERWALTUNGS GMBH—See PORR AG; *Int'l*, pg. 5925
SENVA INC.—See Carel Industries S.p.A.; *Int'l*, pg. 1324
SENVEST BLENDS INC.—See Senvest Capital, Inc.; *Int'l*, pg. 6715
SENVEST CAPITAL, INC.; *Int'l*, pg. 6715
SENVEST INTERNATIONAL L.L.C.—See Senvest Capital, Inc.; *Int'l*, pg. 6715
SENWA MARITIME AGENCY, LTD.—See The Sumitomo Warehouse Co. Ltd.; *Int'l*, pg. 7690
SENYO KOUN CO., LTD.—See The Sumitomo Warehouse Co. Ltd.; *Int'l*, pg. 7690
SENYSOFT INFO-TECH (DALIAN) CO., LTD.; *Int'l*, pg. 6715
SEN YUE HOLDINGS LIMITED—See Print N Etch Pte. Ltd.; *Int'l*, pg. 5981
SEN YU INTERNATIONAL HOLDINGS, INC.; *Int'l*, pg. 6706
SENYUN PRECISION OPTICAL CO., LTD.—See GigaByte Technology Co., Ltd.; *Int'l*, pg. 2971
SENZAGEN AB; *Int'l*, pg. 6715
SENZIME AB; *Int'l*, pg. 6715
SEOAM MACHINERY INDUSTRY CO., LTD.; *Int'l*, pg. 6715
SEOBU T&D CO., LTD.; *Int'l*, pg. 6715
SEO.COM LLC; *U.S. Private*, pg. 3611
SEO ENGINEERING CO., LTD.—See Sumitomo Osaka Cement Co Ltd; *Int'l*, pg. 7297
SEOFABRYKA SP. Z O.O.—See Cyber_Folks S.A.; *Int'l*, pg. 1892
SEOHAN CO., LTD.; *Int'l*, pg. 6715
SEOHAN CONST. & ENG. CO., LTD; *Int'l*, pg. 6715
SEOHAN-NTN DRIVESHAFT USA CORP—See NTN Corporation; *Int'l*, pg. 5483
SEOHANWARNER TURBO SYSTEMS, LTD.—See BorgWarner Inc.; *U.S. Public*, pg. 371
SEOHEE CONSTRUCTION CO., LTD.; *Int'l*, pg. 6716
SEOHO ELECTRIC CO., LTD; *Int'l*, pg. 6716
SEO INC.; *U.S. Private*, pg. 3611
SEOJEON ELECTRIC MACHINERY CO., LTD.; *Int'l*, pg. 6716
SEOJIN INDUSTRIAL - ANSAN—See KPS Capital Partners, LP; *U.S. Private*, pg. 2347
SEOJIN INDUSTRIAL CO., LTD.—See Ecoplastic Corporation; *Int'l*, pg. 2299
SEOJIN SYSTEM CO., LTD.; *Int'l*, pg. 6716
SEO KOATSU KOGYO CO., LTD. - ICHIKAWA WORKS—See Mitsubishi Heavy Industries, Ltd.; *Int'l*, pg. 4961
SEO KOATSU KOGYO CO., LTD. - KAIZUKA WORKS—See Mitsubishi Heavy Industries, Ltd.; *Int'l*, pg. 4961
SEO KOATSU KOGYO CO., LTD. - MIKKAICHI WORKS—See Mitsubishi Heavy Industries, Ltd.; *Int'l*, pg. 4961
SEO KOATSU KOGYO CO., LTD.—See Mitsubishi Heavy Industries, Ltd.; *Int'l*, pg. 4961
SEOMOZ INC.—See Ziff Davis, Inc.; *U.S. Public*, pg. 2404
SEONDO ELECTRIC CO., LTD.; *Int'l*, pg. 6716
SEONDO ELECTRIC CO., LTD. - THE 2ND FACTORY—See Seondo Electric Co., Ltd.; *Int'l*, pg. 6716
SEONG AN CO LTD; *Int'l*, pg. 6716
SEONG AN DYEING CO., LTD—See Seong An Co Ltd; *Int'l*, pg. 6716
SEONG-AN SYNTHETICS CO. LTD.—See Seong An Co Ltd; *Int'l*, pg. 6716
SEONG-AN TRADE CORPORATION—See Seong An Co Ltd; *Int'l*, pg. 6716
SEO ONE INC.; *U.S. Private*, pg. 3611
SEO POWER SP. Z.O.O.—See IQ Partners S.A.; *Int'l*, pg. 3803
SEOP; *U.S. Private*, pg. 3611
SEOSAN CO LTD,; *Int'l*, pg. 6716
SEOULAUCTION HONG KONG LIMITED—See Seoul Auction; *Int'l*, pg. 6716
SEOUL AUCTION; *Int'l*, pg. 6716
SEOUL BROADCASTING SYSTEM—See TY Holdings Co. Ltd.; *Int'l*, pg. 7993
SEOUL CITY GAS CO., LTD.; *Int'l*, pg. 6716

COMPANY NAME INDEX

SEOUL CRO INC.—See CHA Biotech Co., Ltd.; *Int'l*, pg. 1436
SEOULEAGUER CO., LTD.—See ES Cube Co., Ltd.; *Int'l*, pg. 2500
SEOUL ELECTRONICS & TELECOM CO., LTD.; *Int'l*, pg. 6716
SEOUL ELECTRONICS & TELECOMMUNICATIONS (M) SDN. BHD.—See Seoul Electronics & Telecom Co., Ltd.; *Int'l*, pg. 6716
SEOUL FOOD INDUSTRIAL. CO., LTD.; *Int'l*, pg. 6716
SEOULIN BIOSCIENCE CO., LTD.; *Int'l*, pg. 6717
SEOUL KEIWA OPTORONICS CO., LTD.—See Keiwa Incorporated; *Int'l*, pg. 4118
SEOUL PHARMA CO., LTD.; *Int'l*, pg. 6716
SEOUL SEMICONDUCTOR CO., LTD.; *Int'l*, pg. 6717
SEOUL SEMICONDUCTOR EUROPE GMBH—See Seoul Semiconductor Co., Ltd.; *Int'l*, pg. 6717
SEOUL SHIK POOM INC.; *U.S. Private*, pg. 3611
SEOUL TOKO CO., LTD.—See Murata Manufacturing Co., Ltd.; *Int'l*, pg. 5098
SEOUL VIOSYS CO., LTD.—See Seoul Semiconductor Co., Ltd.; *Int'l*, pg. 6717
SEOWON CO., LTD. - HWASEONG FACTORY—See Seowon Co., Ltd.; *Int'l*, pg. 6717
SEOWON CO., LTD.; *Int'l*, pg. 6717
SEOWON INTECH CO., LTD.; *Int'l*, pg. 6717
SEOYEON CO., LTD.; *Int'l*, pg. 6717
SEOYON AUTOVISION CO., LTD.—See SEOYEON Co., Ltd.; *Int'l*, pg. 6717
SEOYON CNF CO., LTD.—See SEOYEON Co., Ltd.; *Int'l*, pg. 6717
SEOYON CO., LTD.; *Int'l*, pg. 6717
SEOYON E-HWA AUTOMOTIVE INDIA PRIVATE LIMITED—See Seoyon E-Hwa Co., Ltd.; *Int'l*, pg. 6717
SEOYON E-HWA AUTOMOTIVE POLAND SP. Z O.O.—See Seoyon E-Hwa Co., Ltd.; *Int'l*, pg. 6717
SEOYON E-HWA AUTOMOTIVE SLOVAKIA S.R.O.—See Seoyon E-Hwa Co., Ltd.; *Int'l*, pg. 6717
SEOYON E-HWA CO., LTD.; *Int'l*, pg. 6717
SEOYON ELECTRONICS CO., LTD. - CHEONAN FACTORY—See Mobase Co., Ltd.; *Int'l*, pg. 5007
SEOYON ELECTRONICS CO., LTD. - MG FACTORY—See Mobase Co., Ltd.; *Int'l*, pg. 5007
SEOYON ELECTRONICS POLAND SP. Z O.O.—See Mobase Co., Ltd.; *Int'l*, pg. 5007
SEOYON INTECH CO., LTD.—See SEOYEON Co., Ltd.; *Int'l*, pg. 6717
SEOYON TOPMETAL CO., LTD.; *Int'l*, pg. 6717
SEPAB FORDONSPRODUKTER AB—See Indutrade AB; *Int'l*, pg. 3681
SEP ACQUISITION CORP.; *U.S. Public*, pg. 1868
SEPAHAN CEMENT; *Int'l*, pg. 6717
SEPAHAN INDUSTRIAL GROUP CO.; *Int'l*, pg. 6718
SEPAHAN ROLLING & TUBE PROFILE CO.—See Sepahan Industrial Group Co.; *Int'l*, pg. 6718
SEPAH INVESTMENT COMPANY; *Int'l*, pg. 6717
SEP ANALYTICAL (SHANGHAI) CO., LTD.; *Int'l*, pg. 6717
SEPARATION DYNAMICS, INC.; *U.S. Private*, pg. 3611
SEPARATION TECHNOLOGIES CANADA LTD—See Titan Cement Company S.A.; *Int'l*, pg. 7759
SEPARATION TECHNOLOGIES LLC—See Titan Cement Company S.A.; *Int'l*, pg. 7760
SEPARATION TECHNOLOGIES U.K. LTD.—See Titan Cement Company S.A.; *Int'l*, pg. 7759
SEPARATION TECHNOLOGY, INC.—See EKF Diagnostics Holdings PLC; *Int'l*, pg. 2338
SEPARTIS HOLDINGS AG—See Biotage AB; *Int'l*, pg. 1043
SEPATU BATA TBK; *Int'l*, pg. 6718
SEPC LIMITED; *Int'l*, pg. 6718
SEP COMMUNICATIONS, LLC—See Southeastern Printing Company Inc.; *U.S. Private*, pg. 3728
SEPECAT—See Groupe Industriel Marcel Dassault S.A.; *Int'l*, pg. 3105
SEPETEC, S. A. DE C.V.—See Industrias Bachoco S.A.B. de C.V.; *Int'l*, pg. 3674
SEPETIBA TECON S.A.—See Companhia Siderurgica Nacional; *Int'l*, pg. 1748
SEP GROWTH HOLDINGS CORP.; *U.S. Private*, pg. 3611
SEPG SERVICE CO., LTD.—See Shanghai Electric Group Company Limited; *Int'l*, pg. 6765
SEPHAKU CEMENT (PTY) LIMITED—See Dangote Group Limited; *Int'l*, pg. 1962
SEPHAKU HOLDINGS LTD.; *Int'l*, pg. 6718
SEPHORA DANMARK APS—See LVMH Moet Hennessy Louis Vuitton SE; *Int'l*, pg. 4596
SEPHORA DEUTSCHLAND GMBH—See LVMH Moet Hennessy Louis Vuitton SE; *Int'l*, pg. 4596
SEPHORA FRANCE SA—See LVMH Moet Hennessy Louis Vuitton SE; *Int'l*, pg. 4596
SEPHORA ITALIA SPA—See LVMH Moet Hennessy Louis Vuitton SE; *Int'l*, pg. 4596
SEPHORA LUXEMBOURG SARL—See LVMH Moet Hennessy Louis Vuitton SE; *Int'l*, pg. 4596
SEPHORA MARINOPOULOS S.A.—See LVMH Moet Hennessy Louis Vuitton SE; *Int'l*, pg. 4596
SEPHORA MIDDLE EAST FZE—See LVMH Moet Hennessy Louis Vuitton SE; *Int'l*, pg. 4600

SEPHORA MONACO SAM—See LVMH Moet Hennessy Louis Vuitton SE; *Int'l*, pg. 4596
SEPHORA NEDERLAND BV—See LVMH Moet Hennessy Louis Vuitton SE; *Int'l*, pg. 4596
SEPHORA POLOGNE SP.ZO.O.—See LVMH Moet Hennessy Louis Vuitton SE; *Int'l*, pg. 4596
SEPHORA PORTUGAL PERFUMERIA LDA—See LVMH Moet Hennessy Louis Vuitton SE; *Int'l*, pg. 4596
SEPHORA—See LVMH Moet Hennessy Louis Vuitton SE; *Int'l*, pg. 4596
SEPHORA SPAIN SA—See LVMH Moet Hennessy Louis Vuitton SE; *Int'l*, pg. 4596
SEPHORA UNITIM KOZMETIK AS—See LVMH Moet Hennessy Louis Vuitton SE; *Int'l*, pg. 4600
SEPHORA USA INC—See LVMH Moet Hennessy Louis Vuitton SE; *Int'l*, pg. 4601
SEPIALINE, INC.; *U.S. Private*, pg. 3611
SEPIC, D.O.O.—See Prevent DEV GmbH; *Int'l*, pg. 5967
SEPI ENGINEERING & CONSTRUCTION, INC.—See OceanSound Partners, LP; *U.S. Private*, pg. 2991
SEPIPROD CASTRES—See L'Air Liquide S.A.; *Int'l*, pg. 4374
SEPLAT ENERGY PLC; *Int'l*, pg. 6718
SEPLAT ENERGY UK LIMITED—See Seplat Energy Plc; *Int'l*, pg. 6718
SE PLUS CO., LTD.—See SE Holdings & Incubations Co., Ltd.; *Int'l*, pg. 6660
SEPPALA OY; *Int'l*, pg. 6718
SEPPELFRICKE ARMATUREN GMBH & CO., OHG—See Aalberts N.V.; *Int'l*, pg. 35
SEPPIC BELGIUM—See L'Air Liquide S.A.; *Int'l*, pg. 4374
SEPPIC CHINA—See L'Air Liquide S.A.; *Int'l*, pg. 4374
SEPPIC GMBH—See L'Air Liquide S.A.; *Int'l*, pg. 4374
SEPPIC INC.—See L'Air Liquide S.A.; *Int'l*, pg. 4374
SEPPIC ITALIA SRL—See L'Air Liquide S.A.; *Int'l*, pg. 4374
SEPPIC S.A.—See L'Air Liquide S.A.; *Int'l*, pg. 4374
SEPPIC UK LTD—See L'Air Liquide S.A.; *Int'l*, pg. 4374
SEPPIM CARAIBES SA—See HORIBA Ltd; *Int'l*, pg. 3478
SEPP'S GOURMET FOODS LTD.—See Conagra Brands, Inc.; *U.S. Public*, pg. 564
SEPR INDIA LIMITED—See Compagnie de Saint-Gobain SA; *Int'l*, pg. 1728
SEPR ITALIA S.P.A.—See Compagnie de Saint-Gobain SA; *Int'l*, pg. 1732
SEPR KERAMIK GMBH & CO KG—See Compagnie de Saint-Gobain SA; *Int'l*, pg. 1728
SEPRO CORPORATION; *U.S. Private*, pg. 3611
SEPROD LIMITED; *Int'l*, pg. 6718
SEPROTECH—See BluMetric Environmental Inc.; *Int'l*, pg. 1075
SEPR REFRACTORIES INDIA LTD—See Compagnie de Saint-Gobain SA; *Int'l*, pg. 1728
SEPTAGON INDUSTRIES INC.; *U.S. Private*, pg. 3611
SEPTEMBER FILMS LIMITED—See DCD Media plc; *Int'l*, pg. 1991
SEPTEMBER FILMS USA, INC.—See DCD Media plc; *Int'l*, pg. 1991
SEPTENI CO., LTD.—See Septeni Holdings Co., Ltd.; *Int'l*, pg. 6718
SEPTENI CROSSGATE CO.,LTD.—See Septeni Holdings Co., Ltd.; *Int'l*, pg. 6718
SEPTENI HOLDINGS CO., LTD.; *Int'l*, pg. 6718
SEPTODONT INC.; *U.S. Private*, pg. 3611
SEPTON ELECTRONIC AB—See DistIT AB; *Int'l*, pg. 2136
SEPT RESINE—See VINCI S.A.; *Int'l*, pg. 8220
SEPULVEDA BUILDING MATERIALS, INC.; *U.S. Private*, pg. 3612
SEPURA DEUTSCHLAND GMBH—See Hytera Communications Corporation Limited; *Int'l*, pg. 3555
SEPURA PLC—See Hytera Communications Corporation Limited; *Int'l*, pg. 3555
SEPUR—See Fondations Capital SA; *Int'l*, pg. 2725
SEQENS SAS—See Eurazeo SE; *Int'l*, pg. 2529
SEQIRUS PTY LTD.—See CSL Limited; *Int'l*, pg. 1866
SEQIRUS—See CSL Limited; *Int'l*, pg. 1866
SEQIRUS UK LIMITED—See CSL Limited; *Int'l*, pg. 1866
SEQIRUS USA INC.—See CSL Limited; *Int'l*, pg. 1866
SEQUACHEE VALLEY ELECTRIC CO-OPERATIVE INC.; *U.S. Private*, pg. 3612
SEQUA CORPORATION—See Veritas Capital Fund Management, LLC; *U.S. Private*, pg. 4364
SEQUA CORP. - PRECOAT METALS DIVISION—See AZZ, Inc.; *U.S. Public*, pg. 260
SEQUANA MEDICAL GMBH—See Sequana Medical NV; *Int'l*, pg. 6719
SEQUANA MEDICAL NV; *Int'l*, pg. 6719
SEQUANA SA; *Int'l*, pg. 6719
SEQUANS COMMUNICATIONS INC—See Sequans Communications S.A.; *Int'l*, pg. 6719
SEQUANS COMMUNICATIONS (ISRAEL) LTD.—See Sequans Communications S.A.; *Int'l*, pg. 6719
SEQUANS COMMUNICATIONS LTD. PTE—See Sequans Communications S.A.; *Int'l*, pg. 6719
SEQUANS COMMUNICATIONS LTD.—See Sequans Communications S.A.; *Int'l*, pg. 6719
SEQUANS COMMUNICATIONS S.A.; *Int'l*, pg. 6719
SEQUA PETROLEUM NV; *Int'l*, pg. 6719

SEQUATCHIE CONCRETE SERVICE INC.; *U.S. Private*, pg. 3612
SEQUATCHIE CONCRETE SERVICE INC.—See Sequatchie Concrete Service Inc.; *U.S. Private*, pg. 3612
SEQUATCHIE VALLEY COAL CORPORATION—See Cloud Peak Energy Inc.; *U.S. Private*, pg. 946
SEQUEL DATA SYSTEMS, INC.; *U.S. Private*, pg. 3612
SEQUEL ELECTRICAL SUPPLY, LLC—See Border States Industries, Inc.; *U.S. Private*, pg. 618
SEQUEL RESPONSE, LLC—See Guggenheim Partners, LLC; *U.S. Private*, pg. 1811
SEQUEL YOUTH AND FAMILY SERVICES, LLC; *U.S. Private*, pg. 3612
SEQUENCE (UK) LIMITED—See The Skipton Building Society; *Int'l*, pg. 7687
SEQUENOM CENTER FOR MOLECULAR MEDICINE, LLC—See Laboratory Corporation of America Holdings; *U.S. Public*, pg. 1287
SEQUENOM, INC.—See Laboratory Corporation of America Holdings; *U.S. Public*, pg. 1287
SEQUENT CHINA/HONG KONG LIMITED—See Green Leader Holdings Group Limited; *Int'l*, pg. 3071
SEQUENT ENERGY MANAGEMENT, L.P.—See The Williams Companies, Inc.; *U.S. Public*, pg. 2142
SEQUENTIAL BRANDS GROUP, INC.; *U.S. Public*, pg. 1868
SEQUENTIAL LLC—See Focusrite plc; *Int'l*, pg. 2720
SEQUENT RESEARCH LIMITED—See SeQuent Scientific Limited; *Int'l*, pg. 6719
SEQUENT SCIENTIFIC LIMITED; *Int'l*, pg. 6719
SEQUENT SCIENTIFIC LTD.—See SeQuent Scientific Limited; *Int'l*, pg. 6719
SEQUEST TECHNOLOGIES, INC.—See Genstar Capital, LLC; *U.S. Private*, pg. 1678
SEQUOIA CAPITAL CHINA—See Sequoia Capital Operations, LLC; *U.S. Private*, pg. 3612
SEQUOIA CAPITAL INDIA—See Sequoia Capital Operations, LLC; *U.S. Private*, pg. 3612
SEQUOIA CAPITAL ISRAEL—See Sequoia Capital Operations, LLC; *U.S. Private*, pg. 3612
SEQUOIA CAPITAL OPERATIONS, LLC; *U.S. Private*, pg. 3612
SEQUOIA ECONOMIC INFRASTRUCTURE INCOME FUND LTD.; *Int'l*, pg. 6719
SEQUOIA ENTERPRISES, INC.; *U.S. Private*, pg. 3612
SEQUOIA EQUITIES INC.; *U.S. Private*, pg. 3612
SEQUOIA FINANCIAL GROUP LIMITED; *Int'l*, pg. 6719
SEQUOIA FINANCIAL GROUP, LLC; *U.S. Private*, pg. 3612
SEQUOIA HOME HEALTH—See The Ensign Group, Inc.; *U.S. Public*, pg. 2072
SEQUOIA HOME LOANS PTY. LTD.—See Sequoia Financial Group Limited; *Int'l*, pg. 6719
SEQUOIA HOSPITAL—See Catholic Health Initiatives; *U.S. Private*, pg. 790
SEQUOIA INSURANCE BROKERS PTY. LTD.; *Int'l*, pg. 6720
SEQUOIA INSURANCE COMPANY—See Stone Point Capital LLC; *U.S. Private*, pg. 3821
SEQUOIA PREMIUM FUNDING PTY. LTD.—See Sequoia Financial Group Limited; *Int'l*, pg. 6719
SEQUOIA RESIDENTIAL FUNDING, INC.—See Redwood Trust, Inc.; *U.S. Public*, pg. 1771
SEQUOIA RETAIL SYSTEMS, INC.—See Class Technologies Inc.; *U.S. Private*, pg. 915
SEQUOIA SPECIALIST INVESTMENTS PTY LTD—See Sequoia Financial Group Limited; *Int'l*, pg. 6719
SEQUOIA SUPERANNUATION PTY LTD—See Sequoia Financial Group Limited; *Int'l*, pg. 6720
SEQUOIA SURGICAL CENTER, L.P.—See Bain Capital, LP; *U.S. Private*, pg. 445
SEQUOIA WEALTH MANAGEMENT PTY LTD—See Sequoia Financial Group Limited; *Int'l*, pg. 6720
SEQUOIA WEALTH MANAGEMENT PTY LTD—See Sequoia Financial Group Limited; *Int'l*, pg. 6720
SERABI GOLD PLC; *Int'l*, pg. 6720
SERACARE LIFE SCIENCES, INC.—See KKR & Co. Inc.; *U.S. Public*, pg. 1258
SERACELL PHARMA GMBH—See VITA 34 AG; *Int'l*, pg. 8257
SERACHEM CO., LTD.—See Hitachi Zosen Corporation; *Int'l*, pg. 3412
SERAD S.A.R.L.—See M2I Corporation; *Int'l*, pg. 4617
SERADYN, INC.—See Thermo Fisher Scientific Inc.; *U.S. Public*, pg. 2152
SERAFINA SA—See Societe Anonyme d'Explosifs et de Produits Chimiques; *Int'l*, pg. 7035
SERAFINI FINANCIAL SERVICE INC.—See TA Associates, Inc.; *U.S. Private*, pg. 3919
SERAFINI NISSAN VOLVO; *U.S. Private*, pg. 3613
SERAFIN UNTERNEHMENSGRUPPE GMBH; *Int'l*, pg. 6720
SERAFON—See The Kusto Group Inc.; *Int'l*, pg. 7663
SERA INGENIERIE SAS—See Sogeclair; *Int'l*, pg. 7058
SERAKU BUSINESS SOLUTIONS CO., LTD.—See SERAKU Co., Ltd.; *Int'l*, pg. 6721
SERAKU CO., LTD.; *Int'l*, pg. 6720
SERAPHIM CAPITAL (GENERAL PARTNER) LLP; *Int'l*, pg. 6721

SERAPHIM CAPITAL (GENERAL PARTNER) LLP

SERAPHIM SOFTWARE, LLC—See Blackbaud, Inc.; *U.S. Public*, pg. 341
SERAPHINE GROUP PLC; *Int'l*, pg. 6721
SERAPID, INC.—See LBO France S.a.r.l.; *Int'l*, pg. 4429
SERA PROGNOSTICS, INC.; *U.S. Public*, pg. 1868
SERASA S.A.—See Experian plc; *Int'l*, pg. 2588
SERA—See Gerard Perrier Industrie S.A.; *Int'l*, pg. 2942
SERBA DINAMIK HOLDINGS BERHAD; *Int'l*, pg. 6721
SER BANKING SOFTWARE SOLUTIONS GMBH—See SER Solutions Deutschland GmbH; *Int'l*, pg. 6720
SERBIA CURT GEORGI NOVI SAD—See Curt Georgi GmbH & Co. KG; *Int'l*, pg. 1880
SERBIA ISCAR TOOLS D.O.O.—See Berkshire Hathaway Inc.; *U.S. Public*, pg. 307
SERBIA ZIJIN COPPER DOO—See Zijin Mining Group Company Limited; *Int'l*, pg. 8683
SERBIA ZIJIN MINING DOO—See Zijin Mining Group Company Limited; *Int'l*, pg. 8683
SER CAPITAL PARTNERS LLC; *U.S. Private*, pg. 3612
SERCEL BEIJING TECHNOLOGICAL SERVICES CO LTD.—See CGG; *Int'l*, pg. 1432
SERCEL CANADA LTD—See CGG; *Int'l*, pg. 1432
SERCEL ENGLAND LTD—See CGG; *Int'l*, pg. 1432
SERCEL-GRC—See CGG; *Int'l*, pg. 1432
SERCEL HOLDING SA—See CGG; *Int'l*, pg. 1432
SERCEL, INC.—See CGG; *Int'l*, pg. 1432
SERCEL - LES ULIS—See CGG; *Int'l*, pg. 1432
SERCEL S.A—See CGG; *Int'l*, pg. 1432
SERCEL SINGAPORE PTE LTD—See CGG; *Int'l*, pg. 1432
SERCK CONTROL AND SAFETY LTD—See Schneider Electric SE; *Int'l*, pg. 6635
SERCK CONTROLS LTD—See Schneider Electric SE; *Int'l*, pg. 6635
SERCK CONTROLS PTY. LTD—See Schneider Electric SE; *Int'l*, pg. 6635
SERCK SERVICES CO. (LLC)—See Unipart Group of Companies Limited; *Int'l*, pg. 8055
SERCK SERVICES (GULF) LIMITED—See Unipart Group of Companies Limited; *Int'l*, pg. 8055
SERCK SERVICES, INC.—See Unipart Group of Companies Limited; *Int'l*, pg. 8055
SERCK SERVICES (OMAN) LLC—See Unipart Group of Companies Limited; *Int'l*, pg. 8055
SERCO AUSTRALIA PTY LIMITED—See Serco Group plc; *Int'l*, pg. 6721
SERCO BELGIUM S.A.—See Serco Group plc; *Int'l*, pg. 6721
SERCO DES, INC.—See Serco Group plc; *Int'l*, pg. 6721
SERCO FACILITIES MANAGEMENT B.V.—See Serco Group plc; *Int'l*, pg. 6721
SERCO GESTION DE NEGOCIOS SL—See Serco Group plc; *Int'l*, pg. 6721
SERCO GROUP (HK) LIMITED—See Serco Group plc; *Int'l*, pg. 6721
SERCO GROUP PLC; *Int'l*, pg. 6721
SERCO GROUP PTY LIMITED—See Serco Group plc; *Int'l*, pg. 6721
SERCO-IAL LIMITED—See Serco Group plc; *Int'l*, pg. 6721
SERCO, INC.—See Serco Group plc; *Int'l*, pg. 6721
SERCO LEISURE OPERATING LIMITED—See Serco Group plc; *Int'l*, pg. 6721
SERCOM DISTRIBUTION LIMITED—See DCC plc; *Int'l*, pg. 1991
SERCOMGAS GAS SOLUTIONS, S.L.—See Enagas, S.A.; *Int'l*, pg. 2396
SERCOMM CORPORATION; *Int'l*, pg. 6721
SERCOMM DEUTSCHLAND GMBH—See SerComm Corporation; *Int'l*, pg. 6721
SERCOMM FRANCE SARL—See SerComm Corporation; *Int'l*, pg. 6721
SERCOMM JAPAN CORP.—See SerComm Corporation; *Int'l*, pg. 6722
SERCOMM PHILIPPINES INC.—See SerComm Corporation; *Int'l*, pg. 6722
SERCOMM RUSSIA LLC—See SerComm Corporation; *Int'l*, pg. 6721
SERCOMM USA INC.—See SerComm Corporation; *Int'l*, pg. 6722
SERCO MOLD INC.; *U.S. Private*, pg. 3613
SERCOM SOLUTIONS LIMITED—See DCC plc; *Int'l*, pg. 1991
SERCO NEDERLAND B.V.—See Serco Group plc; *Int'l*, pg. 6721
SERCOO GROUP GMBH—See CEZ, a.s.; *Int'l*, pg. 1427
SERCO SARL—See Serco Group plc; *Int'l*, pg. 6721
SERCO SERVICES GMBH—See Serco Group plc; *Int'l*, pg. 6721
SERCO SERVICES INC.—See Serco Group plc; *Int'l*, pg. 6721
SERCO SERVICES IRELAND LIMITED—See Serco Group plc; *Int'l*, pg. 6721
SERCO SOLUTIONS—See Serco Group plc; *Int'l*, pg. 6721
SERCO S.P.A.—See Serco Group plc; *Int'l*, pg. 6721
SERCOTEL, S.A. DE C.V.—See America Movil, S.A.B. de C.V.; *Int'l*, pg. 421

SERC RELIABILITY CORPORATION; *U.S. Private*, pg. 3613
SERC RELIABILITY CORPORATION; *U.S. Private*, pg. 3613
SERDIKA PROPERTIES REIT; *Int'l*, pg. 6722
SERDIX (RUSSIA) LTD.—See Les Laboratoires Servier SAS; *Int'l*, pg. 4468
SER EDUCACIONAL S.A.; *Int'l*, pg. 6720
SEREGENTI LAW—See Thomson Reuters Corporation; *Int'l*, pg. 7715
SER EGOVERNMENT EUROPE GMBH—See SER Solutions Deutschland GmbH; *Int'l*, pg. 6720
SER ELEKTRONIK GMBH—See Yankuang Group Co., Limited; *Int'l*, pg. 8562
SEREMBAN 3 PARADISE VALLEY GOLF RESORT SDN. BHD.—See Menang Corporation (M) Berhad; *Int'l*, pg. 4815
SEREMBAN ENGINEERING BERHAD—See CTCI Corporation; *Int'l*, pg. 1870
SEREMBAN TWO HOLDINGS SDN BHD—See IJM Corporation Berhad; *Int'l*, pg. 3609
SERENDEBYTE INC.—See TTEC Holdings, Inc.; *U.S. Public*, pg. 2203
SERENDIB FLOUR MILLS (PVT) LTD.—See Al Ghurair Investment LLC; *Int'l*, pg. 278
SERENDIB HOTELS PLC—See LOLC Holdings PLC; *Int'l*, pg. 4545
SERENDIB INVESTMENTS PTE LIMITED—See Fijian Holdings Limited; *Int'l*, pg. 2662
SERENDIB LAND PLC; *Int'l*, pg. 6722
SERENDIB LEISURE MANAGEMENT LTD.—See Hemas Holdings PLC; *Int'l*, pg. 3341
SERENDIPITY CAPITAL ACQUISITION CORP.; *Int'l*, pg. 6722
SERENDIPITY (WA) PTY LTD—See Quadrant Private Equity Pty. Ltd.; *Int'l*, pg. 6149
SERENE HOLIDAYS (PVT) LTD.—See John Keells Holdings PLC; *Int'l*, pg. 3979
SERENGETI BREWERIES LIMITED—See Diageo plc; *Int'l*, pg. 2103
SERENIC CANADA INC.—See Sylogist Ltd.; *Int'l*, pg. 7378
SERENIC SOFTWARE, INC.—See Sylogist Ltd.; *Int'l*, pg. 7378
SERENISYS SARL—See DigitalBridge Group, Inc.; *U.S. Public*, pg. 665
SERENISYS SARL—See EQT AB; *Int'l*, pg. 2482
SERENITY HOSPICE CARE LLC—See Ridgemont Partners Management LLC; *U.S. Private*, pg. 3432
SERENITY KNOLLS—See Acadia Healthcare Company, Inc.; *U.S. Public*, pg. 30
SERENITY PALLIATIVE CARE & HOSPICE, LLC—See Addus HomeCare Corporation; *U.S. Public*, pg. 40
SERENITY WELLNESS CENTER, LLC—See CLS Holdings USA, Inc.; *U.S. Public*, pg. 515
SERENOA GOLF CLUB—See OnCourse Strategies; *U.S. Private*, pg. 3020
SERENOVA, LLC—See Marlin Equity Partners, LLC; *U.S. Private*, pg. 2585
SERENT CAPITAL MANAGEMENT COMPANY, LLC; *U.S. Private*, pg. 3613
SE REPAIR CO., LTD.—See SE Corporation; *Int'l*, pg. 6660
SERESCO SA; *Int'l*, pg. 6722
SERES ENVIRONNEMENT S.A.S—See Electricite de France S.A.; *Int'l*, pg. 2350
SERES GROUP CO., LTD.; *Int'l*, pg. 6722
SERES SA—See La Poste S.A.; *Int'l*, pg. 4388
SERES THERAPEUTICS, INC.; *U.S. Public*, pg. 1868
SERETRAM—See General Mills, Inc.; *U.S. Public*, pg. 922
SERETTA CONSTRUCTION INC.; *U.S. Private*, pg. 3613
SEREX CORPORATION; *U.S. Private*, pg. 3613
SEREX—See Walgreens Boots Alliance, Inc.; *U.S. Public*, pg. 2322
SERFACTORING S.P.A.—See Eni S.p.A.; *Int'l*, pg. 2438
SERFASS CONSTRUCTION COMPANY INC.; *U.S. Private*, pg. 3613
SERFILCO INTERNATIONAL, LTD.—See SERFILCO, Ltd.; *U.S. Private*, pg. 3613
SERFILCO, LTD.; *U.S. Private*, pg. 3613
SERGEANT'S PET CARE PRODUCTS, INC.—See Bansk Group LLC; *U.S. Private*, pg. 469
SERGE FERRARI AG—See Ferrari S.A.; *Int'l*, pg. 2639
SERGE FERRARI SAS; *Int'l*, pg. 6722
SERGENIANS FLOOR COVERINGS; *U.S. Private*, pg. 3613
SERGEN - SERVICOS GERAIS DE ENGENHARIA S.A.; *Int'l*, pg. 6722
SERGENT SERVICES PTE. LTD.—See Trancom Co., Ltd.; *Int'l*, pg. 7891
SERGIOLIN SPA; *Int'l*, pg. 6722
SERGIO LO STANCO ELEKTRO AG—See Burkhalter Holding AG; *Int'l*, pg. 1225
SERGIO ROSSI S.P.A.—See BI-Invest Advisors S.A.; *Int'l*, pg. 1017
SERGIO TACCHINI FRANCE SA; *Int'l*, pg. 6722
SERGOYNE CAR-PARTS BVBA—See LKQ Corporation; *U.S. Public*, pg. 1336
SER HEALTHCARE SOLUTIONS GMBH—See SER Solutions Deutschland GmbH; *Int'l*, pg. 6720

CORPORATE AFFILIATIONS

SERIA CO., LTD.; *Int'l*, pg. 6722
SERIA ENGINEERING INC.—See Komori Corporation; *Int'l*, pg. 4243
SERI ALAM PROPERTIES SDN. BHD.—See Seleksi Juang Sdn Bhd; *Int'l*, pg. 6700
SERIAL I-TECH (FAR EAST) PTE. LTD.—See Serial System Ltd.; *Int'l*, pg. 6722
SERIAL I-TECH (MIDDLE EAST) PTE. LTD.—See Serial System Ltd.; *Int'l*, pg. 6723
SERIAL MICROELECTRONICS (BEIJING) CO., LTD.—See Serial System Ltd.; *Int'l*, pg. 6723
SERIAL MICROELECTRONICS (HK) LIMITED—See Serial System Ltd.; *Int'l*, pg. 6723
SERIAL MICROELECTRONICS INC.—See Serial System Ltd.; *Int'l*, pg. 6723
SERIAL MICROELECTRONICS KOREA LIMITED—See Serial System Ltd.; *Int'l*, pg. 6723
SERIAL MICROELECTRONICS PTE LTD—See Serial System Ltd.; *Int'l*, pg. 6723
SERIAL MICROELECTRONICS SDN. BHD.—See Serial System Ltd.; *Int'l*, pg. 6723
SERIAL MICROELECTRONICS (SHENZHEN) CO., LTD.—See Serial System Ltd.; *Int'l*, pg. 6723
SERIAL MULTIVISION PTE LTD—See Serial System Ltd.; *Int'l*, pg. 6723
SERIAL SYSTEM LTD.; *Int'l*, pg. 6722
SERIALTEC (JAPAN) CO., LTD.—See Serial System Ltd.; *Int'l*, pg. 6723
SERICA ENERGY CORPORATION—See Serica Energy Plc; *Int'l*, pg. 6723
SERICA ENERGY PLC; *Int'l*, pg. 6723
SERICA ENERGY (UK) LTD—See Serica Energy Plc; *Int'l*, pg. 6723
SERICA HOLDINGS UK LTD—See Serica Energy Plc; *Int'l*, pg. 6723
SERICOL SAS—See FUJIFILM Holdings Corporation; *Int'l*, pg. 2823
SERIE CLUB SA—See Television Francaise 1 S.A.; *Int'l*, pg. 7543
SERIE PRODUCTOS SA—See VINCI S.A.; *Int'l*, pg. 8220
SERIESONE, LLC; *U.S. Private*, pg. 3613
SERIGRAPH, INC.; *U.S. Private*, pg. 3613
SERI INDUSTRIAL SPA; *Int'l*, pg. 6722
SERIJAYA INDUSTRI SDN. BHD.—See Innoprise Plantations Berhad; *Int'l*, pg. 3710
SERIMAX DO BRASIL SERVICOS DE SOLDAGEM E FABRICACAO LTDA.—See Vallourec SA; *Int'l*, pg. 8117
SERIMAX FIELD JOINT COATING LTD.—See Vallourec SA; *Int'l*, pg. 8117
SERIMAX HOLDINGS S.A.S.—See Vallourec SA; *Int'l*, pg. 8117
SERIMAX LTD.—See Vallourec SA; *Int'l*, pg. 8117
SERIMAX NORTH AMERICA LLC—See Vallourec SA; *Int'l*, pg. 8117
SERIMAX OOO—See Vallourec SA; *Int'l*, pg. 8117
SERIMAX S.A.S.—See Vallourec SA; *Int'l*, pg. 8117
SERIMAX—See Vallourec SA; *Int'l*, pg. 8117
SERIMAX WELDING SERVICES MALAYSIA SDN. BHD.—See Vallourec SA; *Int'l*, pg. 8117
SERIM B&G CO., LTD.; *Int'l*, pg. 6723
SERINA THERAPEUTICS, INC.; *U.S. Public*, pg. 1868
SERINA THERAPEUTICS, INC.—See Serina Therapeutics, Inc.; *U.S. Public*, pg. 1869
SER INDUSTRIES LIMITED; *Int'l*, pg. 6720
SERINFOOD INC.—See Shinsegae Food Co., Ltd.; *Int'l*, pg. 6848
SERINO COYNE LLC—See Omnicom Group Inc.; *U.S. Public*, pg. 1593
SERINUS ENERGY PLC—See Kulczyk Investments S.A.; *Int'l*, pg. 4328
SERIO CO., LTD.—See Toyota Motor Corporation; *Int'l*, pg. 7871
SERIO HOLDINGS CO., LTD.—See Senko Group Holdings Co., Ltd.; *Int'l*, pg. 6710
SERIOUS CIGARS—See British American Tobacco plc; *Int'l*, pg. 1168
SERIOUS FOOD (DISTRIBUTION) LIMITED—See Pan-Jam Investment Limited; *Int'l*, pg. 5728
SERIOUS INTEGRATED, INC.—See e2ip Technologies; *Int'l*, pg. 2261
SERIPLAST SA; *Int'l*, pg. 6723
SERI PLAST S.P.A.—See Seri Industrial SpA; *Int'l*, pg. 6722
SERIPRESS; *Int'l*, pg. 6723
SERITAGE GROWTH PROPERTIES; *U.S. Public*, pg. 1869
SER JOBS FOR PROGRESS INC. OF SAN ANTONIO; *U.S. Private*, pg. 3612
SERKO LIMITED; *Int'l*, pg. 6723
SERLE DESIGN; *U.S. Private*, pg. 3614
SERMANFER, S.A.U.—See Construcciones y Auxiliar de Ferrocarriles S.A.; *Int'l*, pg. 1777
SERMATECH INTERNATIONAL CANADA CORP.—See Linde plc; *Int'l*, pg. 4510
SERMA TECHNOLOGIES SA; *Int'l*, pg. 6723
SERMATI CANADA INC.—See Sermati; *Int'l*, pg. 6723
SERMATI; *Int'l*, pg. 6723
SERMES DISTRIBUTION; *Int'l*, pg. 6723

COMPANY NAME INDEX

SERMICRO, S.A.—See ACS, Actividades de Construccion y Servicios, S.A.; *Int'l*, pg. 116
SERMO, INC.—See WorldOne, Inc.; *U.S. Private*, pg. 4569
SERMSANG INFINITE COMPANY LIMITED—See Sermsang Power Corporation PLC; *Int'l*, pg. 6723
SERMSANG POWER CORPORATION PLC; *Int'l*, pg. 6723
SERMSUK BEVERAGE CO., LTD.—See Thai Beverage Public Company Limited; *Int'l*, pg. 7591
THE SERM SUK PUBLIC COMPANY LIMITED—See Thai Beverage Public Company Limited; *Int'l*, pg. 7592
SERMSUK PUBLIC COMPANY LIMITED—See Thai Beverage Public Company Limited; *Int'l*, pg. 7592
SERMSUK TRAINING CO., LTD.—See Thai Beverage Public Company Limited; *Int'l*, pg. 7591
SERNA INSURANCE AGENCY, INC.—See Arthur J. Gallagher & Co.; *U.S. Public*, pg. 207
SERNAM CENTRE S.A.—See Butler Capital Partners SA; *Int'l*, pg. 1229
SERNAM EST S.A.—See Butler Capital Partners SA; *Int'l*, pg. 1229
SERNAM IDF S.A.—See Butler Capital Partners SA; *Int'l*, pg. 1229
SERNAM NORD S.A.—See Butler Capital Partners SA; *Int'l*, pg. 1229
SERNAM OUEST S.A.—See Butler Capital Partners SA; *Int'l*, pg. 1229
SERNAM S.A.—See Butler Capital Partners SA; *Int'l*, pg. 1229
SERNEKE GROUP AB; *Int'l*, pg. 6723
SERNEKE INTERNATIONAL AB—See Serneke Group AB; *Int'l*, pg. 6724
SERNET TECHNOLOGY MEXICO S. DE R.L. DE C.V.—See SerComm Corporation; *Int'l*, pg. 6722
SERN KOU RESOURCES BERHAD; *Int'l*, pg. 6723
SERNOVA CORP.; *Int'l*, pg. 6724
SERNOVA (US) CORP.—See Sernova Corp.; *Int'l*, pg. 6724
SERODUS ASA; *Int'l*, pg. 6724
SEROJA INVESTMENTS LIMITED; *Int'l*, pg. 6724
SEROKA; *U.S. Private*, pg. 3614
SERONICS CO., LTD.; *Int'l*, pg. 6724
SERONO DE MEXICO SA DE CV—See Merck KGaA; *Int'l*, pg. 4831
SERONO FRANCE SA—See Merck KGaA; *Int'l*, pg. 4831
SERONO NORDIC AB—See Merck KGaA; *Int'l*, pg. 4831
SEROPA INDUSTRIES SASU—See Matissart Nord SA; *Int'l*, pg. 4728
SEROYAL INTERNATIONAL INC.; *Int'l*, pg. 6724
SEROYAL USA, LLC—See Nestle S.A.; *Int'l*, pg. 5211
SERPA PACKAGING SOLUTIONS, LLC—See Leonard Green & Partners, L.P.; *U.S. Private*, pg. 2428
S.E.R. PLAST S.R.L.—See ACEA S.p.A.; *Int'l*, pg. 95
SERPRO INC.; *U.S. Private*, pg. 3614
SER PUY DE DOME SAS—See VINCI S.A.; *Int'l*, pg. 8226
SERRA AUTOMOTIVE, INC.; *U.S. Private*, pg. 3614
SERRA CHEVROLET INC.; *U.S. Private*, pg. 3614
SERRA CHEVROLET, LLC—See Serra Automotive, Inc.; *U.S. Private*, pg. 3614
SERRA DA BORDA MINERACAO E METALURGIA S.A.—See Pan American Silver Corp.; *Int'l*, pg. 5713
SERRA ENERGY METALS CORP.; *Int'l*, pg. 6724
SERRA INTERNATIONAL INC.; *U.S. Private*, pg. 3614
SERRA LASER PRECISION, LLC—See LFM Capital LLC; *U.S. Private*, pg. 2441
SERRAMONTE CENTER HOLDING CO. LLC—See Regency Centers Corporation; *U.S. Public*, pg. 1774
SERRANDER COMPANY; *Int'l*, pg. 6724
SERRANO ASSOCIATES, LLC; *U.S. Private*, pg. 3614
SERRANO AZNAR OBRAS PUBLICAS S.L—See Eiffage S.A.; *Int'l*, pg. 2331
SERRANO RESOURCES LTD.; *Int'l*, pg. 6724
SERRAVIEW AUSTRALIA PTY LTD—See Eptura, Inc.; *U.S. Private*, pg. 1414
SERRES GINNING S.A.—See EL. D. MOUZAKIS S.A.; *Int'l*, pg. 2341
SERRUYA PRIVATE EQUITY INC.; *Int'l*, pg. 6724
SERSA B.V.—See Rhomberg Sersa Rail Holding GmbH; *Int'l*, pg. 6327
SERSA GMBH—See Rhomberg Sersa Rail Holding GmbH; *Int'l*, pg. 6327
SERSA GROUP AG—See Rhomberg Sersa Rail Holding GmbH; *Int'l*, pg. 6327
SER SANIERUNG IM ERD- UND RUCKBAU GMBH—See Heidelberg Materials AG; *Int'l*, pg. 3319
SERSA TECHNIK AG—See Rhomberg Sersa Rail Holding GmbH; *Int'l*, pg. 6327
SER SEMINE SAS—See VINCI S.A.; *Int'l*, pg. 8226
SERSOL BERHAD; *Int'l*, pg. 6724
SER SOLUTIONS DEUTSCHLAND GMBH; *Int'l*, pg. 6720
SER SOLUTIONS FRANCE SARL—See SER Solutions Deutschland GmbH; *Int'l*, pg. 6720
S.E.R. SOLUTIONS POLSKA SP. Z O.O.—See SER Solutions Deutschland GmbH; *Int'l*, pg. 6720
SER SOLUTIONS SCHWEIZ AG—See SER Solutions Deutschland GmbH; *Int'l*, pg. 6720
SER SOLUTIONS UNITED KINGDOM LTD.—See SER Solutions Deutschland GmbH; *Int'l*, pg. 6720
SERSTECH AB; *Int'l*, pg. 6724

SER STORAGE & IMAGING TECHNOLOGY GMBH—See SER Solutions Deutschland GmbH; *Int'l*, pg. 6720
SERTA, INC.—See Ares Management Corporation; *U.S. Public*, pg. 190
SERTA, INC.—See Ontario Teachers' Pension Plan; *Int'l*, pg. 5590
SERTA MATTRESS COMPANY—See Ares Management Corporation; *U.S. Public*, pg. 190
SERTA MATTRESS COMPANY—See Ares Management Corporation; *U.S. Public*, pg. 190
SERTA MATTRESS COMPANY—See Ontario Teachers' Pension Plan; *Int'l*, pg. 5590
SERTA MATTRESS COMPANY—See Ontario Teachers' Pension Plan; *Int'l*, pg. 5590
SERTEC CHINA—See Sertec Group Holdings Ltd.; *Int'l*, pg. 6724
SERTEC GROUP HOLDINGS LTD.; *Int'l*, pg. 6724
SERTEC TUBE & PRESSINGS LIMITED—See Sertec Group Holdings Ltd.; *Int'l*, pg. 6724
SERTEK INC.—See WPG Holdings Limited; *Int'l*, pg. 8461
SERT-MST PLC.; *Int'l*, pg. 6724
SERTOMA CENTRE, INC.; *U.S. Private*, pg. 3614
SERTOW OOO—See Solvay S.A.; *Int'l*, pg. 7078
SER TRAVAUX PUBLICS ET ROUTIERS SAS—See VINCI S.A.; *Int'l*, pg. 8226
SERUDONG POWER SDN. BHD.—See Mega First Corporation Berhad; *Int'l*, pg. 4792
SERUMWERK BERNBURG AG; *Int'l*, pg. 6724
SERVAALI OY—See Olvi Oyj; *Int'l*, pg. 5555
SERVAIS S.A.S.—See LDC SA; *Int'l*, pg. 4431
SERVAL CANADA FOODS LTD.—See Serval SAS; *Int'l*, pg. 6724
SERVAL SAS; *Int'l*, pg. 6724
SERVANTAGE—See Air France-KLM S.A.; *Int'l*, pg. 237
SERVANTS, INC.; *U.S. Private*, pg. 3614
SERVARUSRM; *U.S. Private*, pg. 3614
SERVASSURE LIMITED—See Daisy Group Limited; *Int'l*, pg. 1943
SERVATECHNIK AG—See Atlas Copco AB; *Int'l*, pg. 677
SERVATHIN S.A.—See Schunk GmbH; *Int'l*, pg. 6643
SERVCATER INTERNACIONAL LTDA—See Deutsche Lufthansa AG; *Int'l*, pg. 2068
SERVCO FS CO-OPERATIVE; *U.S. Private*, pg. 3614
SERVCO OILFIELD SUPPLY CANADA LTD.—See Applied Industrial Technologies, Inc.; *U.S. Public*, pg. 171
SERVCO PACIFIC INC.; *U.S. Private*, pg. 3614
SERVCORP IS MERKEZI ISLETMECILIGI LIMITED SIRKETI—See Servcorp Limited; *Int'l*, pg. 6724
SERVCORP LIMITED; *Int'l*, pg. 6724
SERVCORP MARINA PTE. LTD.—See Servcorp Limited; *Int'l*, pg. 6724
SERVCORP MAYFAIR LIMITED—See Servcorp Limited; *Int'l*, pg. 6725
SERVCORP SOUTHBANK PTY. LTD.—See Servcorp Limited; *Int'l*, pg. 6725
SERVCO TIRE COMPANY—See Bridgestone Corporation; *Int'l*, pg. 1160
SER VEGANO SDN. BHD.—See Berjaya Corporation Berhad; *Int'l*, pg. 984
SERVEIS CATALANS, SERVEICA, S.A.—See ACS, Actividades de Construccion y Servicios, S.A.; *Int'l*, pg. 116
SERVELEC CONTROLS - ABERDEEN—See CSE Global Ltd.; *Int'l*, pg. 1863
SERVEONE CO., LTD.—See Affinity Equity Partners (HK) Ltd.; *Int'l*, pg. 186
SERVEONE CONSTRUCTION (NANJING) CO., LTD—See Affinity Equity Partners (HK) Ltd.; *Int'l*, pg. 186
SERVERBEACH—See DigitalBridge Group, Inc.; *U.S. Public*, pg. 664
SERVER BOYA MATBAA MUREKKEPLERI VE VERNIK SANAYI VE TICARET A.S.—See Akzo Nobel N.V.; *Int'l*, pg. 275
SERVERCENTRAL; *U.S. Private*, pg. 3614
SERVERCOM (INDIA) PRIVATE LIMITED—See SerComm Corporation; *Int'l*, pg. 6722
SERVERFARM, LLC—See Manulife Financial Corporation; *Int'l*, pg. 4678
SERVERIAI VERSLUI UAB—See Atea ASA; *Int'l*, pg. 667
SERVERLIFT CORP.; *U.S. Private*, pg. 3614
SERVERPLUS LLC; *U.S. Private*, pg. 3614
SERVER PRODUCTS INC.; *U.S. Private*, pg. 3614
SERVERS DIRECT, LLC—See Equus Holdings, Inc.; *U.S. Private*, pg. 1417
SERVER TECHNOLOGY, INC.—See Legrand S.A.; *Int'l*, pg. 4446
SERVERWARE CORPORATION—See FUJISOFT INCORPORATED; *Int'l*, pg. 2830
SERVERWORKS CO., LTD.; *Int'l*, pg. 6725
SERVEST GROUP (PTY) LTD.—See Kagiso Tiso Holdings Proprietary Limited; *Int'l*, pg. 4050
SERVET GAYRIMENKUL YATIRIM ORTAKLIGI A.S.; *Int'l*, pg. 6725
SERVE VIRTUAL ENTERPRISES, INC.—See American Express Company; *U.S. Public*, pg. 102
SERVEX (MALAYSIA) SDN BHD—See Acer Incorporated; *Int'l*, pg. 99
SERVIABERTIS, S.L.—See ACS, Actividades de Construccion y Servicios, S.A.; *Int'l*, pg. 112

SERVIAN PTY LTD—See Cognizant Technology Solutions Corporation; *U.S. Public*, pg. 525
SERVIBANCA S.A.—See Banco GNB Sudameris S.A.; *Int'l*, pg. 823
SERVIBANCA S.A.—See SONDA S.A.; *Int'l*, pg. 7089
SERVICAR CAMPO DE LAS NACIONES SA—See Mubadala Investment Company PJSC; *Int'l*, pg. 5074
SERVICE18 S.A.R.L.—See Rosenbauer International AG; *Int'l*, pg. 6400
SERVICE 7000 AG—See Coop-Gruppe Genossenschaft; *Int'l*, pg. 1790
SERVICE 800 TELEPERFORMANCE SA—See Teleperformance SE; *Int'l*, pg. 7540
SERVICE ACCESS AND MANAGEMENT, INC.; *U.S. Private*, pg. 3614
SERVICEAIDE, INC.; *U.S. Private*, pg. 3616
SERVICE ALIMENTAIRE DESCO INC.; *Int'l*, pg. 6725
SERVICE ALUMINUM CORP.; *U.S. Private*, pg. 3614
SERVICE BIRMINGHAM LIMITED—See Capita plc; *Int'l*, pg. 1309
SERVICEBOLAGET I SVERIGE AB—See Systemair AB; *Int'l*, pg. 7391
SERVICE BROADCASTING LLC; *U.S. Private*, pg. 3614
SERVICE BY AIR, INC.—See Radiant Logistics, Inc.; *U.S. Public*, pg. 1760
SERVICE BY MEDALLION; *U.S. Private*, pg. 3614
SERVICECARE, INC.—See Dominion Energy, Inc.; *U.S. Public*, pg. 674
SERVICE CENTER BURCHARDKAI GMBH—See Hamburger Hafen und Logistik AG; *Int'l*, pg. 3237
SERVICE CENTER GELSENKIRCHEN GMBH—See Tata Sons Limited; *Int'l*, pg. 7472
SERVICE CENTER MILAN S.R.L.—See DEUTZ AG; *Int'l*, pg. 2086
SERVICE CENTRE MAASTRICHT B.V.—See Tata Sons Limited; *Int'l*, pg. 7472
SERVICE CHAMPIONS, INC.—See Odyssey Investment Partners, LLC; *U.S. Private*, pg. 2995
SERVICE CHAMP; *U.S. Private*, pg. 3614
SERVICECHANNEL.COM, INC.—See Fortive Corporation; *U.S. Public*, pg. 871
SERVICE CHEMICAL, LLC—See Clean Harbors, Inc.; *U.S. Public*, pg. 510
SERVICE.COM LLC; *U.S. Private*, pg. 3616
SERVICE COMMUNICATIONS INC.; *U.S. Private*, pg. 3615
THE SERVICE COMPANY LIMITED—See Godfreys Group Limited; *Int'l*, pg. 3020
SERVICE CONCIERGE SAS—See Accor S.A.; *Int'l*, pg. 92
SERVICE CONSTRUCTION SUPPLY, INC.—See Darragh Co; *U.S. Private*, pg. 1159
SERVICE COORDINATION, INC.; *U.S. Private*, pg. 3615
SERVICECORE, LLC—See 1bg LLC; *U.S. Private*, pg. 3
SERVICECORE, LLC—See Mainsail Management Company, LLC; *U.S. Private*, pg. 2553
SERVICE CORPORATION INTERNATIONAL; *U.S. Public*, pg. 1869
SERVICE CORPS OF RETIRED EXECUTIVES ASSOCIATION; *U.S. Private*, pg. 3615
SERVICE CREDIT UNION; *U.S. Private*, pg. 3615
SERVICE DIRECTION INC.; *U.S. Private*, pg. 3615
SERVICE ELECTRIC CABLE T.V. OF NEW JERSEY, INC.—See Altice USA, Inc.; *U.S. Public*, pg. 88
SERVICE ELECTRIC CO., INC.; *U.S. Private*, pg. 3615
SERVICE ELECTRIC COMPANY—See Quanta Services, Inc.; *U.S. Public*, pg. 1752
SERVICE EMPLOYEES INTERNATIONAL UNION; *U.S. Private*, pg. 3615
SERVICE ENERGY LLC; *U.S. Private*, pg. 3615
SERVICE EXPERTS LLC; *U.S. Private*, pg. 3615
SERVICE EXPERTS LLC—See Brookfield Infrastructure Partners L.P.; *Int'l*, pg. 1190
SERVICE EXPRESS, LLC—See Harvest Partners L.P.; *U.S. Private*, pg. 1877
SERVICE FABRICS LIMITED; *Int'l*, pg. 6725
SERVICE FILTRATION OF CANADA LIMITED.—See SERFILCO, LTD.; *U.S. Private*, pg. 3613
SERVICE FINANCIAL, LLC; *U.S. Private*, pg. 3615
SERVICEFINDER SVERIGE AB—See Schibsted ASA; *Int'l*, pg. 6617
SERVICE FIRST CORPORATION; *U.S. Private*, pg. 3615
SERVICE FOOD MARKET INC.; *U.S. Private*, pg. 3615
SERVICE FOODS; *U.S. Private*, pg. 3615
SERVICE FOUR EQUIPMENT COMPANY, INC.; *U.S. Private*, pg. 3615
SERVICE GLOBAL FOOTWEAR LIMITED—See Service Industries Limited; *Int'l*, pg. 6725
SERVICE GRAPHICS LIMITED—See SelmerBridge Print Vehicles Limited; *Int'l*, pg. 6701
SERVICE INDUSTRIES LIMITED; *Int'l*, pg. 6725
SERVICE INDUSTRIES LLC—See Thomas Engineering Inc.; *U.S. Private*, pg. 4155
SERVICE INNOVATION GROUP; *Int'l*, pg. 6725
SERVICE JEWELRY & REPAIR, INC.—See Signet Jewelers Limited; *Int'l*, pg. 6911
SERVICE KING PAINT & BODY, LLC—See Blackstone Inc.; *U.S. Public*, pg. 357
SERVICEKONZEPT AG—See The Innovation Group Ltd.; *Int'l*, pg. 7656

SERVICE LIFE & CASUALTY INSURANCE CO.

CORPORATE AFFILIATIONS

SERVICE LIFE & CASUALTY INSURANCE CO.; *U.S. Private,* pg. 3615
SERVICE LIFE S.R.L.—See Ardian SAS; *Int'l,* pg. 555
SERVICELINE—See Ali Holding S.r.l; *Int'l,* pg. 322
SERVICE LINE WARRANTIES OF AMERICA, INC.—See Brookfield Corporation; *Int'l,* pg. 1188
SERVICE LINE WARRANTIES OF CANADA INC.—See Brookfield Corporation; *Int'l,* pg. 1188
SERVICELINK IP HOLDING COMPANY, LLC.—See Fidelity National Financial, Inc.; *U.S. Public,* pg. 831
SERVICE LINK LP—See Fidelity National Financial, Inc.; *U.S. Public,* pg. 831
SERVICELINK NATIONAL FLOOD, LLC—See Fidelity National Financial, Inc.; *U.S. Public,* pg. 831
SERVICELINK—See Fidelity National Financial, Inc.; *U.S. Public,* pg. 831
SERVICE LITHO-PRINT, INC.; *U.S. Private,* pg. 3615
SERVICE LLOYDS INSURANCE COMPANY; *U.S. Private,* pg. 3615
SERVICEMAGIC LIMITED—See IAC Inc.; *U.S. Public,* pg. 1082
SERVICE MANAGEMENT GROUP, INC.; *U.S. Private,* pg. 3615
SERVICE MANAGEMENT SYSTEMS, INC.—See SMS Holdings Corporation; *U.S. Private,* pg. 3699
SERVICEMASTER COMMERCIAL SOLUTIONS L.L.C.—See Rentokil Initial plc; *Int'l,* pg. 6289
THE SERVICEMASTER COMPANY, LLC—See Roark Capital Group Inc.; *U.S. Private,* pg. 3456
SERVICEMASTER CONSUMER SERVICES LIMITED PARTNERSHIP—See Roark Capital Group Inc.; *U.S. Private,* pg. 3456
SERVICEMASTER HONG KONG LIMITED—See Yanlord Land Group Limited; *Int'l,* pg. 8562
SERVICEMASTER LTD.—See Roark Capital Group Inc.; *U.S. Private,* pg. 3456
SERVICEMASTER OF CANADA LTD.—See Roark Capital Group Inc.; *U.S. Private,* pg. 3456
SERVICEMASTER TOTAL RESTORATION SERVICES; *U.S. Private,* pg. 3616
SERVICEMAX AUSTRALIA PTY. LTD.—See PTC Inc.; *U.S. Public,* pg. 1735
SERVICEMAX GLOBAL LTD.—See PTC Inc.; *U.S. Public,* pg. 1735
SERVICEMAX, INC.—See Silver Lake Group, LLC; *U.S. Private,* pg. 3658
SERVICEMAX TECHNOLOGIES (INDIA) PRIVATE LIMITED—See PTC Inc.; *U.S. Public,* pg. 1735
SERVICE MOTOR COMPANY; *U.S. Private,* pg. 3615
SERVICE NEPTUN 2002 SA; *Int'l,* pg. 6725
SERVICENET, INC.; *U.S. Private,* pg. 3616
SERVICE NET WARRANTY, LLC—See American International Group, Inc.; *U.S. Public,* pg. 106
SERVICENOW A.B. ISRAEL LTD—See ServiceNow, Inc.; *U.S. Public,* pg. 1872
SERVICENOW AUSTRALIA PTY LTD—See ServiceNow, Inc.; *U.S. Public,* pg. 1872
SERVICENOW BELGIUM BVBA—See ServiceNow, Inc.; *U.S. Public,* pg. 1872
SERVICENOW BRASIL GERENCIAMENTO DE SERVICOS LTDA.—See ServiceNow, Inc.; *U.S. Public,* pg. 1872
SERVICENOW FINLAND OY—See ServiceNow, Inc.; *U.S. Public,* pg. 1872
SERVICENOW FRANCE SAS—See ServiceNow, Inc.; *U.S. Public,* pg. 1872
SERVICENOW HONG KONG LIMITED—See ServiceNow, Inc.; *U.S. Public,* pg. 1872
SERVICENOW, INC.; *U.S. Public,* pg. 1872
SERVICENOW ITALY—See ServiceNow, Inc.; *U.S. Public,* pg. 1872
SERVICENOW JAPAN KK—See ServiceNow, Inc.; *U.S. Public,* pg. 1872
SERVICENOW NEDERLAND BV—See ServiceNow, Inc.; *U.S. Public,* pg. 1872
SERVICENOW NORWAY AS—See ServiceNow, Inc.; *U.S. Public,* pg. 1872
SERVICENOW OPERATIONS MEXICO—See ServiceNow, Inc.; *U.S. Public,* pg. 1872
SERVICENOW POLAND SP. Z.O.O.—See ServiceNow, Inc.; *U.S. Public,* pg. 1872
SERVICENOW PTE. LTD.—See ServiceNow, Inc.; *U.S. Public,* pg. 1872
SERVICENOW SOUTH AFRICA (PTY) LTD.—See ServiceNow, Inc.; *U.S. Public,* pg. 1872
SERVICENOW SPAIN S.L.—See ServiceNow, Inc.; *U.S. Public,* pg. 1872
SERVICENOW SWEDEN AB—See ServiceNow, Inc.; *U.S. Public,* pg. 1872
SERVICENOW SWITZERLAND GMBH—See ServiceNow, Inc.; *U.S. Public,* pg. 1872
SERVICENOW TURKEY BILISIM SANAYIVE TICARET LTD—See ServiceNow, Inc.; *U.S. Public,* pg. 1872
SERVICENOW UK LTD.—See ServiceNow, Inc.; *U.S. Public,* pg. 1872
SERVICE OIL COMPANY—See J&H Oil Company Inc.; *U.S. Private,* pg. 2154
SERVICE OIL INC.; *U.S. Private,* pg. 3615

SERVICEONE AG—See Comdat Datasystems AG; *Int'l,* pg. 1709
SERVICE ORGANIZATION OF CONCHO VALLEY; *U.S. Private,* pg. 3615
SERVICE ORGANIZATION OF SAN ANTONIO; *U.S. Private,* pg. 3616
SERVICE PACKING COMPANY-UNITED FOOD GROUP; *U.S. Private,* pg. 3616
SERVICE PAINTING CORPORATION—See Five Arrows Inc.; *U.S. Private,* pg. 1537
SERVICE PARTNERS OF FLORIDA, LLC—See Masco Corporation; *U.S. Public,* pg. 1392
SERVICEPLAN AGENTURGRUPPE FUR INNOVATIVE KOMMUNIKATION GMBH & CO. KG; *Int'l,* pg. 6725
SERVICEPLAN AUSTRIA GMBH—See Serviceplan Agenturgruppe fur Innovative Kommunikation GmbH & Co. KG; *Int'l,* pg. 6725
SERVICE PLANET GMBH—See Stroer SE & Co. KGaA; *Int'l,* pg. 7242
SERVICEPLAN INDIA PVT. LTD.—See Serviceplan Agenturgruppe fur Innovative Kommunikation GmbH & Co. KG; *Int'l,* pg. 6725
SERVICEPLAN ITALIA S.R.L.—See Serviceplan Agenturgruppe fur Innovative Kommunikation GmbH & Co. KG; *Int'l,* pg. 6725
SERVICEPLAN SUISSE AG—See Serviceplan Agenturgruppe fur Innovative Kommunikation GmbH & Co. KG; *Int'l,* pg. 6725
SERVICE PLUS GMBH—See E.ON SE; *Int'l,* pg. 2259
SERVICEPOWER BUSINESS SOLUTIONS LIMITED—See Diversis Capital, LLC; *U.S. Private,* pg. 1244
SERVICEPOWER, INC—See Diversis Capital, LLC; *U.S. Private,* pg. 1244
SERVICEPOWER TECHNOLOGIES LTD—See Diversis Capital, LLC; *U.S. Private,* pg. 1244
SERVICE PRINTERS, INC.—See Hederman Brothers, LLC; *U.S. Private,* pg. 1903
SERVICE PROPERTIES TRUST; *U.S. Public,* pg. 1872
SERVICE ROUNDTABLE; *U.S. Private,* pg. 3616
SERVICES AND PROMOTIONS MIAMI LLC—See Banco Santander, S.A.; *Int'l,* pg. 827
SERVICES CONSEIL EXPERTISE TERRITOIRE S.A.—See Caisse des Depots et Consignations; *Int'l,* pg. 1258
SERVICE SELECT, INC.; *U.S. Private,* pg. 3616
SERVICES FOR THE UNDERSERVED, INC.; *U.S. Private,* pg. 3616
SERVICES GENERAUX DE GESTION S.A.—See Astorg Partners S.A.S.; *Int'l,* pg. 657
SERVICES & GESTION FRANCE SARL—See Generac Holdings Inc.; *U.S. Public,* pg. 913
SERVICES GROUP, INC.; *U.S. Private,* pg. 3616
SERVICES GROUP OF AMERICA, INC.; *U.S. Private,* pg. 3616
SERVICE SHOES LANKA (PRIVATE) LIMITED—See Service Industries Limited; *Int'l,* pg. 6725
SERVICES LOGICIELS D'INTEGRATION BOURSIERE SA—See BNP Paribas SA; *Int'l,* pg. 1092
SERVICES MATREC INC.—See BC Partners LLP; *Int'l,* pg. 924
SERVICESOURCE INTERNATIONAL BULGARIA EOOD—See Concentrix Corporation; *U.S. Public,* pg. 564
SERVICESOURCE INTERNATIONAL JAPAN G.K.—See Concentrix Corporation; *U.S. Public,* pg. 564
SERVICESOURCE INTERNATIONAL SINGAPORE PTE. LTD.—See Concentrix Corporation; *U.S. Public,* pg. 564
SERVICES PETROLIERS SCHLUMBERGER S.A.—See Schlumberger Limited; *U.S. Public,* pg. 1846
SERVICES PETROLIERS TRANSOCEAN—See Transocean Ltd.; *Int'l,* pg. 7903
SERVICES PLUS, INC.—See Kimberly-Clark Corporation; *U.S. Public,* pg. 1230
SERVICE STEEL AEROSPACE CORPORATION—See Reliance Steel & Aluminum Co.; *U.S. Public,* pg. 1781
SERVICES TO ENHANCE POTENTIAL; *U.S. Private,* pg. 3616
SERVICES & TRADE COMPANY LLC—See Sobha Limited; *Int'l,* pg. 7030
SERVICE STREAM COMMUNICATIONS PTY LTD—See Service Stream Limited; *Int'l,* pg. 6725
SERVICE STREAM HOLDINGS PTY LTD—See Service Stream Limited; *Int'l,* pg. 6725
SERVICE STREAM INFRASTRUCTURE SERVICES PTY LTD—See Service Stream Limited; *Int'l,* pg. 6725
SERVICE STREAM LIMITED; *Int'l,* pg. 6725
SERVICE STREAM LIMITED—See Service Stream Limited; *Int'l,* pg. 6725
SERVICE STREAM SOLUTIONS PTY LTD—See Service Stream Limited; *Int'l,* pg. 6725
SERVICE SUPPLY CORPORATION—See Stephenson Equipment, Inc.; *U.S. Private,* pg. 3803
SERVICE SUPPLY LIMITED, INC.; *U.S. Private,* pg. 3616
SERVICE SUPPLY OF VICTORIA, INC.; *U.S. Private,* pg. 3616
SERVICE SYSTEMS ASSOCIATES; *U.S. Private,* pg. 3616

SERVICE TEAM INC.; *U.S. Public,* pg. 1872
SERVICE TEAM INC.; *U.S. Private,* pg. 3616
SERVICE TECH AV; *U.S. Private,* pg. 3616
SERVICE TECHNOLOGY SRL—See Sesa S.p.A.; *Int'l,* pg. 6729
SERVICE TERMINAL ROTTERDAM B.V.—See iCON Infrastructure LLP; *Int'l,* pg. 3583
SERVICE TIRE TRUCK CENTERS, INC.; *U.S. Private,* pg. 3616
SERVICETITAN, INC.; *U.S. Private,* pg. 3616
SERVICE TOOL & DIE, INC.; *U.S. Private,* pg. 3616
SERVICE TRANSFER INC.; *U.S. Private,* pg. 3616
SERVICE TRANSPORT COMPANY—See Adams Resources & Energy, Inc.; *U.S. Public,* pg. 38
SERVICE TRUCKING INC.; *U.S. Private,* pg. 3616
SERVICEWARE SE; *Int'l,* pg. 6725
SERVICEWARE SE UK LTD.—See Serviceware SE; *Int'l,* pg. 6726
SERVICE WEB OFFSET CORPORATION; *U.S. Private,* pg. 3616
SERVICE WIRE CO.—See Arthur's Enterprises, Inc.; *U.S. Private,* pg. 342
SERVICE WORKS GLOBAL NORDIC AB—See Addnode Group AB; *Int'l,* pg. 130
SERVICE WORKS GLOBAL PTY. LTD.—See Addnode Group AB; *Int'l,* pg. 130
SERVICE WORKS, INC.—See Allied Universal Manager LLC; *U.S. Private,* pg. 191
SERVICEXPERT GESELLSCHAFT FUR SERVICE INFORMATIONSSYSTEME MBH—See Cognizant Technology Solutions Corporation; *U.S. Public,* pg. 525
SERVICHAP S.L.—See Stemcor Holdings Limited; *Int'l,* pg. 7206
SERVICII ENERGETICE MUNTENIA SA—See Societatea Energetica Electrica S.A.; *Int'l,* pg. 7035
SERVICII TEHNICE COMUNALE SA; *Int'l,* pg. 6726
SERVICIO AMBIENTAL NACIONAL, S.A. DE C.V.—See Promotora Ambiental S.A.B de C.V.; *Int'l,* pg. 5995
SERVICIO DE VENTA AUTOMATICA S.A. (S.V.A.)—See Imperial Brands PLC; *Int'l,* pg. 3633
SERVICIO PANAMERICANO DE VIGILANCIA CURACAO, N.V.—See The Brink's Company; *U.S. Public,* pg. 2043
SERVICIOS ADMINISTRATIVOS ACCEL, S.A. DE C.V.—See Accel, S.A.B. de C.V.; *Int'l,* pg. 79
SERVICIOS ADMINISTRATIVOS AMERICA S. DE RL DE C.V.—See National Amusements, Inc.; *U.S. Private,* pg. 2843
SERVICIOS ADMINISTRATIVOS API ACAPULCO, S.A. DE C.V.—See Grupo TMM, S.A.B.; *Int'l,* pg. 3137
SERVICIOS ADMINISTRATIVOS CABLEMAS, S.A. DE C.V.—See Grupo Televisa, S.A.B.; *Int'l,* pg. 3136
SERVICIOS ADMINISTRATIVOS CORP. IPASA S.A.—See Stellantis N.V.; *Int'l,* pg. 7203
SERVICIOS ADMINISTRATIVOS INDUSTRIALES SA DE CV—See Apollo Global Management, Inc.; *U.S. Public,* pg. 162
SERVICIOS ADMINISTRATIVOS LAMOSA, S.A. DE C.V.—See Grupo Lamosa S.A. de C.V.; *Int'l,* pg. 3132
SERVICIOS ADMINISTRATIVOS LOS CABOS, S.A. DE C.V.—See Grupo Posadas S.A.B. de C.V.; *Int'l,* pg. 3134
SERVICIOS ADMINISTRATIVOS VOLARIS, S.A. DE C.V.—See Controladora Vuela Compania de Aviacion, S.A.B. de C.V.; *Int'l,* pg. 1786
SERVICIOS A LA INFRAESTRUCTURA AEROPORTUARIA DEL PACIFICO, S.A. DE C.V.—See Grupo Aeroportuario del Pacifico, S.A.B. de C.V.; *Int'l,* pg. 3118
SERVICIOS AMBIENTALES WALSH, S.A.—See WSP Global, Inc.; *Int'l,* pg. 8496
SERVICIOS ANIXTER, S.A. DE C.V.—See WESCO International, Inc.; *U.S. Public,* pg. 2351
SERVICIOS ARGKEL, S.C.—See Kellanova; *U.S. Public,* pg. 1218
SERVICIOS AUDIOVISUALES OVERON, S.L.—See Orient Securities Company Limited; *Int'l,* pg. 5622
SERVICIOS BENETECH C.A.—See Benetech Investments Corp; *U.S. Private,* pg. 525
SERVICIOS CHARTWELL DE NUEVO LAREDO, S.A. DE C.V.—See Minor International PCL; *Int'l,* pg. 4913
SERVICIOS COMERCIALES LAMOSA, S.A. DE C.V.—See Grupo Lamosa S.A. de C.V.; *Int'l,* pg. 3132
SERVICIOS CORPORATIVOS CHARTWELL MONTERREY, S.A. DE C.V.—See Minor International PCL; *Int'l,* pg. 4913
SERVICIOS CORPORATIVOS JAVER, S.A.B. DE C.V.; *Int'l,* pg. 6726
SERVICIOS CORPORATIVOS PORTUARIOS S.A. DE C.V.—See Albert Ballin KG; *Int'l,* pg. 296
SERVICIOS CORPORATIVOS TWC, S.A. DE C.V.—See ACS, Actividades de Construccion y Servicios, S.A.; *Int'l,* pg. 116
SERVICIOS DE ADMINISTRACION DE ADHESIVOS, S.A. DE C.V.—See Grupo Lamosa S.A. de C.V.; *Int'l,* pg. 3132
SERVICIOS DE ADMINISTRACION DE LOCOMOTORAS, S. DE R.L. DE C.V.—See Westinghouse Air Brake Technologies Corporation; *U.S. Public,* pg. 2359

COMPANY NAME INDEX

SERVICIOS DE APOYO MARITIMO DE MEXICO, S. DE R.L. DE C.V.—See Trico Marine Services, Inc.; *U.S. Private*, pg. 4229
SERVICIOS DE DESARROLLO ORIENTADO A SOLUCIONES SL—See Alten S.A.; *Int'l*, pg. 391
SERVICIOS DEDICADOS DE TRANSPORTACION, S.A. DE C.V.—See Grupo TMM, S.A.B.; *Int'l*, pg. 3137
SERVICIOS DE OPERACIONES DE NITROGENO, S.A. DE C.V.—See Linde plc; *Int'l*, pg. 4508
SERVICIOS DEPEC S.L.—See Rentokil Initial plc; *Int'l*, pg. 6289
SERVICIOS DE PRODUCCION SALTILLO, S.A. DE C.V.—See Grupo Industrial Saltillo S.A. de C.V.; *Int'l*, pg. 3130
SERVICIOS DE SALUD IPS SURAMERICANA S.A.—See Grupo de Inversiones Suramericana S.A.; *Int'l*, pg. 3126
SERVICIOS DE TRANSPORTACION JAGUAR, S.A DE C.V.—See Lilium Group LLC; *U.S. Private*, pg. 2455
SERVICIOS DE TRANSPORTACION JAGUAR, S.A DE C.V.—See Luminus Management, LLC; *U.S. Private*, pg. 2514
SERVICIOS EJECUTIVOS PROGRESS S. DE R.L. DE C.V.—See Caterpillar, Inc.; *U.S. Public*, pg. 453
SERVICIOS FORMICA DE MEXICO SA DE CV—See Fletcher Building Limited; *Int'l*, pg. 2701
SERVICIOS HALLIBURTON DE VENEZUELA S.A.—See KBR, Inc.; *U.S. Public*, pg. 1216
SERVICIOS HOTELEROS DE MANZANILLO SRL DE CV—See Barcelo Corporacion Empresarial S.A.; *Int'l*, pg. 859
SERVICIOS HOTELEROS POSADAS, S.A. DE C.V.—See Grupo Posadas S.A.B. de C.V.; *Int'l*, pg. 3134
SERVICIOS HOTELEROS TLALNEPANTLA, S.A. DE C.V.—See Minor International PCL; *Int'l*, pg. 4913
SERVICIOS INFORMATICOS ITELLIGENCE S.A.—See Nippon Telegraph & Telephone Corporation; *Int'l*, pg. 5346
SERVICIOS INTEGRALES DE INFORMACION S.A—See Equifax Inc.; *U.S. Public*, pg. 787
SERVICIOS INTEGRALES DE TRANSITOS Y TRANSFERENCIAS S.A.—See Sociedad Quimica y Minera de Chile S.A.; *Int'l*, pg. 7033
SERVICIOS INTEGRALES KRAFT, S. DE R.L. DE C.V.—See Mondelez International, Inc.; *U.S. Public*, pg. 1464
SERVICIOS LOGISTICOS BENAVIDES, S.A. DE C.V.—See Walgreens Boots Alliance, Inc.; *U.S. Public*, pg. 2323
SERVICIOS MEDICOS UNIVERSITARIOS INC; *U.S. Private*, pg. 3617
SERVICIOS MULTIVENDING LTDA.—See Embotelladora Andina S.A.; *Int'l*, pg. 2375
SERVICIOS NOVASAT, S. DE R.L. DE C.V.—See Grupo Televisa, S.A.B.; *Int'l*, pg. 3136
SERVICIOS NUTRESA S.A.S.—See Grupo Nutresa S.A.; *Int'l*, pg. 3133
SERVICIOS OPERACIONALES BENAVIDES, S.A. DE C.V.—See Walgreens Boots Alliance, Inc.; *U.S. Public*, pg. 2323
SERVICIOS OPERACION EOLOELECTRICA DE MEXICO, S.A. DE C.V.—See Iberdrola, S.A.; *Int'l*, pg. 3572
SERVICIOS OPERBES, S.A. DE C.V.—See Grupo Televisa, S.A.B.; *Int'l*, pg. 3136
SERVICIOS PETROTEC DE S.A. DE C.V.—See Superior Energy Services, Inc.; *U.S. Private*, pg. 3877
SERVICIOS PORTUARIOS PATILLOS S.A.—See K+S Aktiengesellschaft; *Int'l*, pg. 4041
SERVICIOS RENOVADOS DE ALIMENTACION, S.A.U.—See Compass Group PLC; *Int'l*, pg. 1752
SERVICIOS REUNIDOS, S.A.—See Banco de Sabadell, S.A.; *Int'l*, pg. 821
SERVICIOS & SOLUCIONES ELECTROMECANICOS S.A. DE C.V.; *Int'l*, pg. 6726
SERVICIOS TECNICOS SATE S.L.—See Brookfield Corporation; *Int'l*, pg. 1189
SERVICIOS VISA INTERNATIONAL LIMITADA—See Visa, Inc.; *U.S. Public*, pg. 2301
SERVICIOS Y ASISTENCIA OK24, S.L.—See Compagnie Generale des Etablissements Michelin SCA; *Int'l*, pg. 1745
SERVICIOS Y MATERIALES PARA LA CONSTRUCCION S.A.—See Camargo Correa S.A.; *Int'l*, pg. 1268
SERVICIO TECNICO URUENA S.L.—See Brookfield Corporation; *Int'l*, pg. 1189
SERVICIO UNITELLER INC—See Uniteller Financial Services; *U.S. Private*, pg. 4302
SERVICIOUS AEROTECNICOS INSULARES SL—See Binter Canarias, S.A.; *Int'l*, pg. 1034
SERVI-COMPRESORES, C.A.—See Enerflex Ltd.; *Int'l*, pg. 2419
SERVICON SYSTEMS INC.; *U.S. Private*, pg. 3617
SERVICOS DEPEC, S.L.—See Rentokil Initial plc; *Int'l*, pg. 6289
SERVICOS MARITIMOS CONTINENTAL S.A.—See James Fisher & Sons Public Limited Company; *Int'l*, pg. 3876

SERVI CYLINDERSERVICE AS—See Ferd AS; *Int'l*, pg. 2636
SERVIDYNE, INC.—See SCIenergy, Inc.; *U.S. Private*, pg. 3573
SERVIER LABORATORIES LTD.—See Les Laboratoires Servier SAS; *Int'l*, pg. 4468
SERVI GROUP AS—See Ferd AS; *Int'l*, pg. 2636
SERVI HYDRANOR AS—See Ferd AS; *Int'l*, pg. 2636
SERVIKS RIGA SIA—See Impel S.A.; *Int'l*, pg. 3632
SERVILAMINA SUMMIT MEXICANA S.A. DE C.V.—See Sumitomo Corporation; *Int'l*, pg. 7271
SERVILEASE S.A.—See Porsche Automobil Holding SE; *Int'l*, pg. 5929
SERVILOGISTICS DE MEXICO, S.A. DE C.V.—See Accel, S.A.B. de C.V.; *Int'l*, pg. 79
SERVILOG—See Compagnie de Saint-Gobain SA; *Int'l*, pg. 1737
SERVIMED TECNICOS, S.L.U.—See Henry Schein, Inc.; *U.S. Public*, pg. 1027
SERVISFIRST BANCSHARES, INC.; *U.S. Public*, pg. 1872
SERVISFIRST BANK—See ServisFirst Bancshares, Inc.; *U.S. Public*, pg. 1872
SERVIS LIMITED—See Angostura Holdings Limited; *Int'l*, pg. 463
SERVISOURCE HEALTHCARE LIMITED—See Bain Capital, LP; *U.S. Private*, pg. 434
SERVISOURCE RECRUITMENT LIMITED—See Bain Capital, LP; *U.S. Private*, pg. 434
SERVISTEEL S.A.—See Metlen Energy & Metals S.A.; *Int'l*, pg. 4855
SERVITAS CALIDAD SA DE CV—See Apollo Global Management, Inc.; *U.S. Public*, pg. 165
SERVI-TEK, LLC; *U.S. Private*, pg. 3614
SERVITEX LTDA—See NSC Groupe SA; *Int'l*, pg. 5476
SERVITIA S.A.—See Intesa Sanpaolo S.p.A.; *Int'l*, pg. 3765
SERVITROQUEL - NOTTING, S.A. UNIPERSONAL—See voestalpine AG; *Int'l*, pg. 8292
SERVI ULSTEINVIK AS—See Ferd AS; *Int'l*, pg. 2636
SERVIWARE S.A.S—See Prologue S.A.; *Int'l*, pg. 5992
SERVIZI AEREI SPA—See Eni S.p.A.; *Int'l*, pg. 2438
SERVIZI AZIENDALI PIRELLI S.C.P.A.—See China National Chemical Corporation; *Int'l*, pg. 1529
SERVIZI E ATTIVITA DOGANALI PER L'INDUSTRIA S.P.A.—See Stellantis N.V.; *Int'l*, pg. 7197
SERVIZI INDUSTRIALI S.R.L.—See Interpump Group S.p.A.; *Int'l*, pg. 3757
SERVIZI ITALIA SPA; *Int'l*, pg. 6726
SERVIZIO ELETTRICO NAZIONALE SPA—See Enel S.p.A.; *Int'l*, pg. 2414
SERVIZI OSPEDALIERI S.P.A. —See Manutencoop Societa Cooperativa; *Int'l*, pg. 4680
SERVIZIO TITOLI S.P.A.—See Computershare Limited; *Int'l*, pg. 1760
SERVO 360 GMBH—See Uzin Utz AG; *Int'l*, pg. 8103
SERVOCA NURSING & CARE LIMITED—See Servoca Plc; *Int'l*, pg. 6726
SERVOCA PLC; *Int'l*, pg. 6726
SERVODAN A/S—See Niko Group N.V.; *Int'l*, pg. 5291
SERVO DYNAMICS CO., LTD.—See ISDN Holdings Limited; *Int'l*, pg. 3813
SERVO DYNAMICS ENGINEERING COMPANY LIMITED—See ISDN Holdings Limited; *Int'l*, pg. 3813
SERVO DYNAMICS (H.K.) LIMITED—See ISDN Holdings Limited; *Int'l*, pg. 3813
SERVO DYNAMICS PTE LTD—See ISDN Holdings Limited; *Int'l*, pg. 3813
SERVO DYNAMICS SDN. BHD.—See ISDN Holdings Limited; *Int'l*, pg. 3813
SERVO ENGINEERING SDN. BHD.—See ISDN Holdings Limited; *Int'l*, pg. 3813
SERVOMATION REFRESHMENTS INC.; *U.S. Private*, pg. 3617
SERVOMEX ASIA PACIFIC LTD—See Spectris Plc; *Int'l*, pg. 7131
SERVOMEX BV—See Spectris Plc; *Int'l*, pg. 7131
SERVOMEX GROUP LTD—See Spectris Plc; *Int'l*, pg. 7131
SERVOMEX INC—See Spectris Plc; *Int'l*, pg. 7131
SERVOMEX MIDDLE EAST LLC—See Spectris Plc; *Int'l*, pg. 7131
SERVOMEX S.A.—See Spectris Plc; *Int'l*, pg. 7131
SERVOPRAX GMBH; *Int'l*, pg. 6726
SERVO SOUTH, INC.—See Wynnchurch Capital, L.P.; *U.S. Public*, pg. 4577
SERVOTEACH INDUSTRIES LIMITED; *Int'l*, pg. 6726
SERVOTECH INDUSTRIES, INC.—See Westport Fuel Systems Inc.; *Int'l*, pg. 8392
SERVOTECH POWER SYSTEMS LTD.; *Int'l*, pg. 6726
SERVOTRONICS, INC.; *U.S. Public*, pg. 1872
SERVOTRONIX MOTION CONTROL LTD.—See Midea Group Co., Ltd.; *Int'l*, pg. 4886
SERVOTRONIX MOTION TECHNOLOGY DEVELOPMENT, LTD.—See Midea Group Co., Ltd.; *Int'l*, pg. 4886
SERVOWATCH SYSTEMS LIMITED—See Rolls-Royce Holdings plc; *Int'l*, pg. 6394

SES, LLC

SERVPRO INDUSTRIES, LLC—See Blackstone Inc.; *U.S. Public*, pg. 357
SERVPRO OF BETHLEHEM; *U.S. Private*, pg. 3617
SERVPRO OF THE QUAD CITIES, LLC—See Blackstone Inc.; *U.S. Public*, pg. 358
SERVTAG GMBH—See Stroer SE & Co. KGaA; *Int'l*, pg. 7243
S.E.R.V. TRAYVOU INTERVERROUILLAGE SA—See Halma plc; *Int'l*, pg. 3232
SERVUS CREDIT UNION, LTD.; *Int'l*, pg. 6726
SERWER SMS POLSKA SP. Z O.O.—See Cyber_Folks S.A.; *Int'l*, pg. 1892
SERWIS UBEZPIECZENIOWY SP. Z O.O.—See Alior Bank S.A.; *Int'l*, pg. 329
SESACO CORPORATION—See Mitsubishi Corporation; *Int'l*, pg. 4943
SESAC PERFORMING RIGHTS, INC.—See Blackstone Inc.; *U.S. Public*, pg. 357
SES ADVISORS, INC.; *U.S. Private*, pg. 3617
SES AI CORPORATION; *U.S. Public*, pg. 1872
SESA INTERNATIONAL—See Randstad N.V.; *Int'l*, pg. 6205
SESAME BANKHALL GROUP LIMITED—See Aviva plc; *Int'l*, pg. 746
SESAME BANKHALL VALUATION SERVICES LIMITED—See Aviva plc; *Int'l*, pg. 746
SESAME COMMUNICATIONS, INC.—See KKR & Co. Inc.; *U.S. Public*, pg. 1253
SESAME CONSEIL SAS—See BNP Paribas SA; *Int'l*, pg. 1092
SESAMEE MEXICANA, S.A. DE C.V.—See The Eastern Company; *U.S. Public*, pg. 2069
SESAME PLACE—See United Parks & Resorts Inc.; *U.S. Public*, pg. 2234
SES AMERICOM COLORADO, INC.—See SES S.A.; *Int'l*, pg. 6727
SES AMERICOM DO BRASIL SERVICOS DE TELECOMUNICACOES, LTDA—See SES S.A.; *Int'l*, pg. 6727
SES AMERICOM, INC.—See SES S.A.; *Int'l*, pg. 6727
SESAME SERVICES LTD—See Aviva plc; *Int'l*, pg. 746
SESAME WORKSHOP; *U.S. Private*, pg. 3617
SE SAMPO LIFE INSURANCE BALTIC, LATVIAN BRANCH—See Sampo plc; *Int'l*, pg. 6508
SESA SELECT—See Randstad N.V.; *Int'l*, pg. 6205
SESA S.P.A.; *Int'l*, pg. 6728
SES ASTRA 1KR S.A R.L.—See SES S.A.; *Int'l*, pg. 6727
SES ASTRA 1L S.A R.L.—See SES S.A.; *Int'l*, pg. 6727
SES ASTRA 1M S.A R.L.—See SES S.A.; *Int'l*, pg. 6727
SES ASTRA 1N S.A R.L.—See SES S.A.; *Int'l*, pg. 6727
SES ASTRA 2G S.A R.L.—See SES S.A.; *Int'l*, pg. 6727
SES ASTRA 5B S.A R.L.—See SES S.A.; *Int'l*, pg. 6727
SES ASTRA AB—See SES S.A.; *Int'l*, pg. 6727
SES ASTRA CEE SP. Z.O.O—See SES S.A.; *Int'l*, pg. 6727
SES ASTRA IBERICA S.A.—See SES S.A.; *Int'l*, pg. 6727
SES ASTRA (ROMANIA) S.A R.L.—See SES S.A.; *Int'l*, pg. 6727
SES ASTRA S.A.—See SES S.A.; *Int'l*, pg. 6727
SES ASTRA TECHCOM BELGIUM S.A.—See SES S.A.; *Int'l*, pg. 6727
SES ASTRA (U.K.) LTD—See SES S.A.; *Int'l*, pg. 6727
SES AUTOMATION INC.—See SES, LLC; *U.S. Private*, pg. 3617
SES BELGIUM S.P.R.L—See SES S.A.; *Int'l*, pg. 6727
SESCO DATACOMM—See Arthur's Enterprises, Inc.; *U.S. Private*, pg. 342
SESCO EFACEC SDN. BHD.—See Efacec Capital, SGPS, S.A.; *Int'l*, pg. 2318
SESCO ELECTRICAL SERVICES GROUP; *U.S. Private*, pg. 3617
SES COMPANY LIMITED—See Union Capital Limited; *Int'l*, pg. 8052
SESCOM SA; *Int'l*, pg. 6729
SES CONSTRUCTION AND FUEL SERVICES LLC—See Bristol Bay Native Corporation; *U.S. Private*, pg. 656
SESCO—See Sonepar S.A.; *Int'l*, pg. 7091
SES DIGITAL DISTRIBUTION SERVICES AG—See SES S.A.; *Int'l*, pg. 6727
SES ENGINEERING (LUXEMBOURG) S.A R.L.—See SES S.A.; *Int'l*, pg. 6727
SES ENGINEERING (NETHERLANDS) B.V.—See SES S.A.; *Int'l*, pg. 6727
SE SETCO SERVICE COMPANY—See Holden Industries, Inc.; *U.S. Private*, pg. 1962
SE SETCO SERVICE COMPANY—See The Timken Company; *U.S. Public*, pg. 2133
SES FINANCE S.A R.L.—See SES S.A.; *Int'l*, pg. 6727
SES GLOBAL-AMERICAS FINANCE INC.—See SES S.A.; *Int'l*, pg. 6727
SES GLOBAL SOUTH AMERICA HOLDING S.L.—See SES S.A.; *Int'l*, pg. 6727
SES GOVERNMENT SOLUTIONS—See SES S.A.; *Int'l*, pg. 6727
SESHACHAL TECHNOLOGIES LIMITED; *Int'l*, pg. 6729
SESHASAYEE PAPER & BOARDS LTD; *Int'l*, pg. 6729
SESHIN BUFFALO CO., LTD.; *Int'l*, pg. 6729
SES LATIN AMERICA S.A.—See SES S.A.; *Int'l*, pg. 6727
SES, LLC; *U.S. Private*, pg. 3617
SESMAT SRL—See FOS S.p.A.; *Int'l*, pg. 2748

2439

SES, LLC

SES NEW ENERGY TECHNOLOGIES, (SHANGHAI) CO., LTD.—See Synthesis Energy Systems, Inc.; *U.S. Public*, pg. 1972
SES NEW SKIES BV—See SES S.A.; *Int'l*, pg. 6727
SES NEW SKIES—See SES S.A.; *Int'l*, pg. 6727
SESODA CORPORATION; *Int'l*, pg. 6729
SESODA STEAMSHIP CORPORATION—See Sesoda Corporation; *Int'l*, pg. 6729
SESOTEC INC.—See VTC Partners GmbH; *Int'l*, pg. 8316
SESOTEC LTD.—See VTC Partners GmbH; *Int'l*, pg. 8316
SESOTEC SARL—See VTC Partners GmbH; *Int'l*, pg. 8316
SESOTEC S.R.L.—See VTC Partners GmbH; *Int'l*, pg. 8316
SES PARTICIPATIONS S.A.—See SES S.A.; *Int'l*, pg. 6727
SESPE CONSULTING, INC.—See Keystone Group, L.P.; *U.S. Private*, pg. 2299
SE SPEZIAL-ELECTRONIC AG; *Int'l*, pg. 6660
SES PLATFORM SERVICES GMBH—See SES S.A.; *Int'l*, pg. 6727
SES PROPERTIES OF STANLEY, INC.—See Gryphon Investors, LLC; *U.S. Private*, pg. 1800
SESSA KLEIN S.P.A.—See LCI Industries; *U.S. Public*, pg. 1296
SES S.A.; *Int'l*, pg. 6726
SESSIONCAM LTD.—See Glassbox Ltd.; *Int'l*, pg. 2989
SESSIONS INC.; *U.S. Private*, pg. 3617
SESSIONS SPECIALTY COMPANY; *U.S. Private*, pg. 3617
SES SIRIUS AB—See SES S.A.; *Int'l*, pg. 6728
SESSLER INC.; *U.S. Private*, pg. 3617
SES SPACE & DEFENSE, INC.—See SES S.A.; *Int'l*, pg. 6728
SESTA STAHL GMBH—See Salzgitter AG; *Int'l*, pg. 6498
SES TECHCOM S.A.—See SES S.A.; *Int'l*, pg. 6728
SEST-LUVE-POLSKA SP. Z.O.O.—See LU-VE SpA; *Int'l*, pg. 4572
SESTRIERES S.P.A.—See Stellantis N.V.; *Int'l*, pg. 7197
SEST S.P.A.—See LU-VE SpA; *Int'l*, pg. 4572
SE SWISS ESTATES AG; *Int'l*, pg. 6660
SES WORLD SKIES SINGAPORE PTY LTD—See SES S.A.; *Int'l*, pg. 6728
SETA CORPORATION OF BOCA, INC.; *U.S. Private*, pg. 3617
SETAI HOTEL LLC; *U.S. Private*, pg. 3617
SETAIR HAVA TASIMACILIGI VE HIZM AS—See Koc Holding A.S.; *Int'l*, pg. 4224
SETAS COLOMBIANAS S.A.—See Grupo Nutresa S.A.; *Int'l*, pg. 3133
SETA S.P.A.; *Int'l*, pg. 6730
SETCAR S.A.—See Directa Plus PLC; *Int'l*, pg. 2130
SETCO AUTOMOTIVE LTD; *Int'l*, pg. 6730
SETCO AUTOMOTIVE (NA) INC., USA—See Setco Automotive Ltd; *Int'l*, pg. 6730
SETCO AUTOMOTIVE (UK) LIMITED—See Setco Automotive Ltd; *Int'l*, pg. 6730
SETCO GREAT LAKES SERVICE CENTER—See Holden Industries, Inc.; *U.S. Private*, pg. 1962
SETCO, LLC—See Berry Global Group, Inc; *U.S. Public*, pg. 321
SETCO MIDWEST SERVICE CENTER—See Holden Industries, Inc.; *U.S. Private*, pg. 1962
SETCO SALES COMPANY—See Holden Industries, Inc.; *U.S. Private*, pg. 1962
SETCO WESTERN SERVICE CENTER—See Holden Industries, Inc.; *U.S. Private*, pg. 1962
SET CREATIVE; *U.S. Private*, pg. 3617
SETECH (GEOTECHNICAL ENGINEERS) LTD—See HAL Trust N.V.; *Int'l*, pg. 3226
SETEGAP VENTURES PETROLEUM SDN. BHD.—See Uzma Berhad; *Int'l*, pg. 8104
S.E.T. ELECTRONICS AG—See OC Oerlikon Corporation AG; *Int'l*, pg. 5515
SETEMA LTD.—See HORIBA Ltd; *Int'l*, pg. 3478
SETEM S.A.R.L.—See Braime Group Plc; *Int'l*, pg. 1136
SET ENVIRONMENTAL, INC.; *U.S. Private*, pg. 3617
SET EUROPE LTD.—See Sanko Gosei Ltd.; *Int'l*, pg. 6542
SETEX AUTOMOTIVE MEXICO, S.A. DE C.V.—See Tachi-S Co., Ltd.; *Int'l*, pg. 7402
SETEX, INC.—See Tachi-S Co., Ltd.; *Int'l*, pg. 7402
SETGAS - SOCIEDADE DE PRODUCAO E DISTRIBUICAO DE GAS, S.A.—See Galp Energia SGPS, S.A.; *Int'l*, pg. 2875
SETH CHILDS 12 OF KANSAS L.L.C.—See Dalian Wanda Group Corporation Ltd.; *Int'l*, pg. 1953
SETHMAR TRANSPORTATION INC.; *U.S. Private*, pg. 3617
SETHNESS-GREENLEAF, INC.—See Carbery Group; *Int'l*, pg. 1320
SETHNESS PRODUCTS COMPANY; *U.S. Private*, pg. 3617
SETHNESS-ROQUETTE (CHINA) CO., LTD.—See Roquette Freres SA; *Int'l*, pg. 6398
SETHNESS-ROQUETTE INDIA LTD.—See Roquette Freres SA; *Int'l*, pg. 6398
SETHNESS-ROQUETTE SAS—See Roquette Freres SA; *Int'l*, pg. 6399

SETHNESS-ROQUETTE SASU—See Roquette Freres SA; *Int'l*, pg. 6399
SETIA A BECKETT (MELBOURNE) PTY. LTD.—See S P Setia Berhad; *Int'l*, pg. 6444
SETIA ALAM RECREATION SDN BHD—See S P Setia Berhad; *Int'l*, pg. 6444
SETIA ALAMSARI SDN BHD—See S P Setia Berhad; *Int'l*, pg. 6444
SETIABECAMEX JOINT STOCK COMPANY—See S P Setia Berhad; *Int'l*, pg. 6444
SETIA (BUKIT TIMAH) PTE. LTD.—See S P Setia Berhad; *Int'l*, pg. 6443
SETIA CITY DEVELOPMENT SDN BHD—See S P Setia Berhad; *Int'l*, pg. 6444
SETIA ECO GLADES SDN BHD—See S P Setia Berhad; *Int'l*, pg. 6444
SETIA ECOHILL 2 SDN BHD—See S P Setia Berhad; *Int'l*, pg. 6444
SETIA ECOHILL RECREATION SDN BHD—See S P Setia Berhad; *Int'l*, pg. 6444
SETIA ECOHILL SDN BHD—See S P Setia Berhad; *Int'l*, pg. 6444
SETIA ECO TEMPLER RECREATION SDN BHD—See S P Setia Berhad; *Int'l*, pg. 6444
SETIA ECO TEMPLER SDN BHD—See S P Setia Berhad; *Int'l*, pg. 6444
SETIA FONTAINES SDN BHD—See S P Setia Berhad; *Int'l*, pg. 6444
SETIA INDAH SDN BHD—See S P Setia Berhad; *Int'l*, pg. 6444
SETIA MAYURI SDN BHD—See S P Setia Berhad; *Int'l*, pg. 6444
SETIA (MELBOURNE) DEVELOPMENT COMPANY PTY. LTD.—See S P Setia Berhad; *Int'l*, pg. 6444
SETIA PRECAST SDN BHD—See S P Setia Berhad; *Int'l*, pg. 6444
SETIA PROMENADE SDN BHD—See S P Setia Berhad; *Int'l*, pg. 6444
SETIA PUTRAJAYA DEVELOPMENT SDN BHD—See S P Setia Berhad; *Int'l*, pg. 6444
SETIA PUTRAJAYA SDN BHD—See S P Setia Berhad; *Int'l*, pg. 6444
SETIA SAFIRO SDN BHD—See S P Setia Berhad; *Int'l*, pg. 6444
SETIA-WOOD INDUSTRIES SDN BHD—See S P Setia Berhad; *Int'l*, pg. 6444
SETLIFF BROTHERS, INC.; *U.S. Private*, pg. 3617
SETNA NUTRICION SA—See Archer-Daniels-Midland Company; *U.S. Public*, pg. 185
SETNOR, BYER, BOGDANOFF, INC.—See Kelso & Company, L.P.; *U.S. Private*, pg. 2280
SETO DELICA CO., LTD.—See Kewpie Corporation; *Int'l*, pg. 4414
SETO FUTO CO., LTD.—See Mitsubishi Corporation; *Int'l*, pg. 4943
SETO HOLDINGS, INC.; *U.S. Public*, pg. 1872
SETON AUSTRALIA PTY. LTD.—See Brady Corporation; *U.S. Public*, pg. 378
SETON MEDICAL CENTER COASTSIDE—See Daughters of Charity Health System; *U.S. Private*, pg. 1167
SETON MEDICAL CENTER—See Daughters of Charity Health System; *U.S. Private*, pg. 1167
SETON NAME PLATE COMPANY; *U.S. Private*, pg. 3617
SETOUDON CO., LTD.—See Zensho Holdings Co., Ltd.; *Int'l*, pg. 8634
SETO & WAN DENTAL CENTRE LIMITED—See Human Health Holdings Limited; *Int'l*, pg. 3529
SETOZAKI IRON WORKS CO., LTD.—See Hitachi Zosen Corporation; *Int'l*, pg. 3412
SET POINT GROUP LIMITED; *Int'l*, pg. 6729
SETPOINT INTEGRATED SOLUTIONS, INC.—See MiddleGround Management, LP; *U.S. Private*, pg. 2712
SET POINT LABORATORIES—See Set Point Group Limited; *Int'l*, pg. 6730
SETRA SYSTEMS, INC.—See Fortive Corporation; *U.S. Public*, pg. 870
SETSCO CONSULTANCY INTERNATIONAL PTE. LTD.—See ComfortDelGro Corporation Limited; *Int'l*, pg. 1713
SETSCO SERVICES (M) SDN. BHD.—See ComfortDelGro Corporation Limited; *Int'l*, pg. 1713
SETSCO SERVICES PTE. LTD.—See ComfortDelGro Corporation Limited; *Int'l*, pg. 1713
SETSIBI IT SUPPORT SERVICES (PTY) LTD—See Stellar Capital Partners Limited; *Int'l*, pg. 7204
SET SOLUTIONS INC.—See American Securities LLC; *U.S. Private*, pg. 250
SETSUNAN KASEI CO., LTD.—See Nagase & Co., Ltd.; *Int'l*, pg. 5128
SETSUYO ASTEC CORPORATION—See Mitsubishi Electric Corporation; *Int'l*, pg. 4946
SETSUYO ENTERPRISE CO., LTD.—See Mitsubishi Electric Corporation; *Int'l*, pg. 4946
SETTE ASSOCIATES INC.; *U.S. Private*, pg. 3617
SETTER GMBH & CO. PAPIERVERARBEITUNG—See Gesco AG; *Int'l*, pg. 2946
SETTER GMBH & CO.—See Gesco AG; *Int'l*, pg. 2946
SETTERSTIX CORP.—See Gesco AG; *Int'l*, pg. 2946
SETTE—See Quebecor Inc.; *Int'l*, pg. 6159

CORPORATE AFFILIATIONS

THE SETTLEMENT ALLIANCE, LLC—See Sage Settlement Consulting, LLC; *U.S. Private*, pg. 3527
SETTLEMENT PLANNERS INC.; *U.S. Private*, pg. 3618
SETTLEMENTS SA; *Int'l*, pg. 6730
SETTLE MUTER ELECTRIC; *U.S. Private*, pg. 3618
SETTLERS LIFE INSURANCE COMPANY—See National Guardian Life Insurance Company; *U.S. Private*, pg. 2855
SETTLERS TRAIL WIND FARM, LLC—See E.ON SE; *Int'l*, pg. 2259
SETTONS INTERNATIONAL FOODS, INC; *U.S. Private*, pg. 3618
SETTSU CARTON CORPORATION—See Rengo Co., Ltd.; *Int'l*, pg. 6281
SETTSU CARTON VIETNAM CORPORATION—See Rengo Co., Ltd.; *Int'l*, pg. 6281
SETTSU OIL MILL INC.—See The Nisshin OilliO Group, Ltd.; *Int'l*, pg. 7671
SETTSU SEIUN CO., LTD.—See Daiei Kankyo Co., Ltd.; *Int'l*, pg. 1924
SETUBANDHAN INFRASTRUCTURE LIMITED; *Int'l*, pg. 6730
SETUP PERFORMANCE SAS—See BASF SE; *Int'l*, pg. 885
SETUR MARINALARI MARINA VE YAT ISLETMECILIGI—See Koc Holding A.S.; *Int'l*, pg. 4224
SETUR SERVIS TURISTIK A.S.—See Koc Holding A.S.; *Int'l*, pg. 4224
SETUR YALOVA MARINA ISLETMECILIGI A.S.—See Koc Holding A.S.; *Int'l*, pg. 4224
SETUZA A.S.; *Int'l*, pg. 6730
SET VINA CO., LTD.—See Seoul Electronics & Telecom Co., Ltd.; *Int'l*, pg. 6716
SE TYLOSE GMBH & CO. KG—See Shin-Etsu Chemical Co. Ltd.; *Int'l*, pg. 6839
SE TYLOSE USA, INC.—See Shin-Etsu Chemical Co. Ltd.; *Int'l*, pg. 6839
SETZER FOREST PRODUCTS INC. - OROVILLE PLANT—See Setzer Forest Products Inc.; *U.S. Private*, pg. 3618
SETZER FOREST PRODUCTS INC.; *U.S. Private*, pg. 3618
SEUBERT & ASSOCIATES INSURANCE; *U.S. Private*, pg. 3618
SEUM ELECTRONICS CO. LTD.—See Korea Electric Terminal Co., Ltd.; *Int'l*, pg. 4284
SEUNG IL CORPORATION; *Int'l*, pg. 6730
SEUNGIL CORP.; *Int'l*, pg. 6730
SEUSTER KG—See Hormann KG Verkaufsgesellschaf; *Int'l*, pg. 3481
SEV1TECH, LLC—See DFW Capital Partners; *U.S. Private*, pg. 1221
SEV1TECH, LLC—See Enlightenment Capital LLC; *U.S. Private*, pg. 1400
SEVABEL SAS—See Compagnie des Alpes S.A.; *Int'l*, pg. 1738
SEVA ENGENHARIA ELETRONICA S.A.—See Compagnie Generale des Etablissements Michelin SCA; *Int'l*, pg. 1745
SEVA FOUNDATION; *U.S. Private*, pg. 3618
SEVAN 300 PTE LTD—See Magnora ASA; *Int'l*, pg. 4641
SEVAN DRILLING ASA—See Magnora ASA; *Int'l*, pg. 4641
SEVAN DRILLING AS—See Magnora ASA; *Int'l*, pg. 4641
SEVAN DRILLING RIG PTE LTD—See Magnora ASA; *Int'l*, pg. 4641
SEVAN HOLDING I AS—See Magnora ASA; *Int'l*, pg. 4641
SEVAN HOLDING I PTE LTD—See Magnora ASA; *Int'l*, pg. 4641
SEVAN INVEST AS—See Magnora ASA; *Int'l*, pg. 4641
SEVAN MARINE DO BRASIL LTDA—See Magnora ASA; *Int'l*, pg. 4641
SEVAN MULTI-SITE SOLUTIONS, INC.; *U.S. Private*, pg. 3618
SEVAN PRODUCTION AS—See Magnora ASA; *Int'l*, pg. 4641
SEVAN PRODUCTION GENERAL PARTNERSHIP—See Magnora ASA; *Int'l*, pg. 4641
SEVAN PTE LTD—See Magnora ASA; *Int'l*, pg. 4641
SEVATEC, INC.—See Arlington Capital Partners LLC; *U.S. Private*, pg. 328
SEVCON GMBH—See BorgWarner Inc.; *U.S. Public*, pg. 371
SEVCON JAPAN KK—See BorgWarner Inc.; *U.S. Public*, pg. 370
SEVCON NEW ENERGY TECHNOLOGY (HUBEI) COMPANY LIMITED—See BorgWarner Inc.; *U.S. Public*, pg. 371
SEVCON SAS—See BorgWarner Inc.; *U.S. Public*, pg. 370
SEVEAL S.A.—See Vivescia; *Int'l*, pg. 8279
SEVEN ACES LIMITED—See Trive Capital Inc.; *U.S. Private*, pg. 4240
SEVEN ARTS ENTERTAINMENT INC.; *U.S. Public*, pg. 1873
SEVEN BANK LTD.; *Int'l*, pg. 6731
SEVENBAR AVIATION, LLC—See KKR & Co. Inc.; *U.S. Public*, pg. 1252
SEVEN BRIDGES TRADING 14 (PTY) LTD—See Barrick Gold Corporation; *Int'l*, pg. 870

COMPANY NAME INDEX

SEVEN CARD SERVICE CO., LTD.—See Seven & i Holdings Co., Ltd.; *Int'l*, pg. 6731
SEVEN CHEMICAL INC.—See Maeda Kosen Co., Ltd.; *Int'l*, pg. 4635
SEVEN CORNERS CENTER, LLC—See Saul Centers, Inc.; *U.S. Public*, pg. 1842
SEVEN CROWN RESORTS INC.; *U.S. Private*, pg. 3618
SEVEN CS CARD SERVICE CO., LTD.—See Seven & i Holdings Co., Ltd.; *Int'l*, pg. 6731
SEVENCS GMBH—See Teledyne Technologies Incorporated; *U.S. Public*, pg. 1992
SEVEN CULTURE NETWORK CO., LTD.—See Seven & i Holdings Co., Ltd.; *Int'l*, pg. 6731
SEVEN D INDUSTRIES, L.P.—See The DeGol Organization; *U.S. Private*, pg. 4019
SEVEN D WHOLESALE L.L.P.—See The DeGol Organization; *U.S. Private*, pg. 4019
SEVEN-ELEVEN (BEIJING) CO., LTD.—See Seven & i Holdings Co., Ltd.; *Int'l*, pg. 6731
SEVEN-ELEVEN HAWAII, INC.—See Seven & i Holdings Co., Ltd.; *Int'l*, pg. 6731
SEVEN-ELEVEN JAPAN CO., LTD.—See Seven & i Holdings Co., Ltd.; *Int'l*, pg. 6731
SEV.EN ENERGY AG; *Int'l*, pg. 6730
SEVEN FINANCIAL SERVICE CO., LTD.—See Seven & i Holdings Co., Ltd.; *Int'l*, pg. 6731
SEVEN GENERATIONS ENERGY LTD—See ARC Resources Ltd.; *Int'l*, pg. 539
SEVEN GROUP HOLDINGS LIMITED; *Int'l*, pg. 6732
SEVEN HEALTH CARE CO., LTD.—See Seven & i Holdings Co., Ltd.; *Int'l*, pg. 6731
SEVEN HILL INDUSTRIES LIMITED; *Int'l*, pg. 6733
SEVEN HILLS FOUNDATION; *U.S. Private*, pg. 3618
SEVEN HILLS HOSPITAL, INC.—See Acadia Healthcare Company, Inc.; *U.S. Public*, pg. 29
SEVEN HILLS REALTY TRUST—See The RMR Group Inc.; *U.S. Public*, pg. 2126
SEVENICH BUTLER GERLACH BRAZIL, LTD.—See Nepsis Inc.; *U.S. Private*, pg. 2885
SEVEN & I CREATE LINK CO., LTD.—See Seven & i Holdings Co., Ltd.; *Int'l*, pg. 6731
SEVEN & I FOOD SYSTEMS CO., LTD.—See Seven & i Holdings Co., Ltd.; *Int'l*, pg. 6731
SEVEN & I HOLDINGS CO., LTD.; *Int'l*, pg. 6730
SEVEN INDUSTRIES CO., LTD.; *Int'l*, pg. 6733
SEVEN & I NETMEDIA CO., LTD.—See Seven & i Holdings Co., Ltd.; *Int'l*, pg. 6731
SEVEN INTERNET LAB. CO., LTD.—See Seven & i Holdings Co., Ltd.; *Int'l*, pg. 6731
SEVEN INVESTMENT MANAGEMENT LLP—See Ontario Teachers' Pension Plan; *Int'l*, pg. 5586
SEVEN & I PUBLISHING CO., LTD.—See Seven & i Holdings Co., Ltd.; *Int'l*, pg. 6731
SEVEN ISLANDS, INC.; *U.S. Public*, pg. 1873
SEVEN K CONSTRUCTION COMPANY INC.—See Kenny Industries Inc.; *U.S. Private*, pg. 2286
SEVEN KINGS HOLDINGS, INC.; *U.S. Private*, pg. 3618
SEVEN LAKEWAY REFRACTORIES LLC—See RHI Magnesita N.V.; *Int'l*, pg. 6326
SEVEN-MEAL SERVICE CO., LTD.—See Seven & i Holdings Co., Ltd.; *Int'l*, pg. 6731
SEVEN MILE CAPITAL PARTNERS, LLC; *U.S. Private*, pg. 3618
SEVEN NET SHOPPING CO., LTD.—See Seven & i Holdings Co., Ltd.; *Int'l*, pg. 6731
SEVEN NETWORKS, INC.; *U.S. Private*, pg. 3618
SEVENOAKS PRINT FINISHERS LTD—See Kin and Carta plc; *Int'l*, pg. 4164
SEVENONE ADFACTORY GMBH—See ProSiebenSat.1 Media SE; *Int'l*, pg. 6001
SEVEN.ONE ENTERTAINMENT GROUP GMBH—See ProSiebenSat.1 Media SE; *Int'l*, pg. 6001
SEVENONE MEDIA GMBH—See ProSiebenSat.1 Media SE; *Int'l*, pg. 6001
SEVEN ONE SEVEN PARKING SERVICES, INC.; *U.S. Private*, pg. 3618
SEVEN PALMS RESORTS MANAGEMENT PTE LTD—See SC Global Developments Limited; *Int'l*, pg. 6609
SEVEN PAY CO., LTD.—See Seven & i Holdings Co., Ltd.; *Int'l*, pg. 6731
SEVEN PAYMENT SERVICES, LTD.—See Seven Bank Ltd.; *Int'l*, pg. 6731
SEVEN POINT EQUITY PARTNERS, LLC; *U.S. Private*, pg. 3618
SEVEN PRINCIPLES AG; *Int'l*, pg. 6733
SEVEN REFRACTORIES DEUTSCHLAND GMBH—See RHI Magnesita N.V.; *Int'l*, pg. 6326
SEVEN REFRACTORIES D.O.O.—See RHI Magnesita N.V.; *Int'l*, pg. 6326
SEVEN REFRACTORIES S.R.L.—See RHI Magnesita N.V.; *Int'l*, pg. 6326
SEVEN REFRACTORIES (UK) LTD.—See RHI Magnesita N.V.; *Int'l*, pg. 6326
SEVEN RIVERS, INC.—See Harima Chemicals Group, Inc.; *Int'l*, pg. 3276
SEVENS ATELIER LIMITED; *Int'l*, pg. 6734
SEVEN SEAS LIMITED—See Merck KGaA; *Int'l*, pg. 4832

SEVEN SEAS WATER CORPORATION—See Morgan Stanley; *U.S. Public*, pg. 1472
SEVEN SEAS WATER CORPORATION—See Morgan Stanley; *U.S. Public*, pg. 1472
SEVEN SEVENTEEN CREDIT UNION, INC.; *U.S. Private*, pg. 3619
SEVEN SIGNATURES INTERNATIONAL CORPORATION - HONOLULU BRANCH—See Kufu Company Inc.; *Int'l*, pg. 4326
SEVEN SISTERS INC.—See JH Kelly LLC; *U.S. Private*, pg. 2207
SEVENSON ENVIRONMENTAL SERVICES, INC.; *U.S. Private*, pg. 3619
SEVENSON INDUSTRIAL SERVICES, INC.—See Sevenson Environmental Services, Inc.; *U.S. Private*, pg. 3619
SEVENS PAINT & WALLPAPER CO.; *U.S. Private*, pg. 3619
SEVENSPRINGS CO., LTD.—See Samyang Holdings Corporation; *Int'l*, pg. 6519
SEVEN SPRINGS MOUNTAIN RESORT, INC.—See The Nutting Company, Inc.; *U.S. Private*, pg. 4086
SEVEN SQUARED; *Int'l*, pg. 6733
SEVENSTAR SEMICONDUCTOR TECHNOLOGIES CO., LTD.—See NAURA Technology Group Co., Ltd.; *Int'l*, pg. 5172
SEVEN STARS MALL MANAGEMENT COMPANY (2000) LTD.—See The Israel Land Development Co., Ltd.; *Int'l*, pg. 7657
SEVENSTAR YACHT TRANSPORT B.V.—See Spliethoff's Bevrachtingskantoor B.V.; *Int'l*, pg. 7141
SEVEN STUDIOS DISTRIBUTION PTY LTD—See Seven West Media Limited; *Int'l*, pg. 6734
SEVEN TECHNOLOGIES LTD.; *Int'l*, pg. 6733
SEVENTEEN MAGAZINE—See The Hearst Corporation; *U.S. Private*, pg. 4046
SEVENTH GENERATION, INC.—See Unilever PLC; *Int'l*, pg. 8048
SEVENTH POINT; *U.S. Private*, pg. 3619
SEVENTH WAVE LABORATORIES, LLC—See Inotiv, Inc.; *U.S. Public*, pg. 1128
SEVENTURE PARTNERS—See Groupe BPCE; *Int'l*, pg. 3095
SEVENTY2 CAPITAL WEALTH MANAGEMENT LLC; *U.S. Private*, pg. 3619
SEVENTY DAMANSARA SDN. BHD.—See Eastern & Oriental Berhad; *Int'l*, pg. 2271
SEVENTY SEVEN PR—See Fishburn Hedges; *Int'l*, pg. 2692
SEVEN-UP BOTTLING COMPANY RENO; *U.S. Private*, pg. 3619
SEVEN UTILITIES AND POWER PUBLIC CO., LTD.; *Int'l*, pg. 6734
SEVENVAL GMBH—See Yoc AG; *Int'l*, pg. 8591
SEVENVENTURES GMBH—See ProSiebenSat.1 Media SE; *Int'l*, pg. 6001
SEVEN VIEW CHRYSLER DODGE JEEP RAM; *Int'l*, pg. 6734
SEVEN WEST MEDIA LIMITED; *Int'l*, pg. 6734
SEVEN WIRE CO., LTD.—See General Engineering Public Company Limited; *Int'l*, pg. 2918
SEVERCOOP GAMZA HOLDING AD; *Int'l*, pg. 6734
SEVERE SERVICE SPECIALISTS INC.—See Clearlake Capital Group, L.P.; *U.S. Private*, pg. 937
SEVERFIELD (DESIGN & BUILD) LTD.—See Severfield Plc; *Int'l*, pg. 6735
SEVERFIELD PLC; *Int'l*, pg. 6734
SEVERFIELD-REEVE INTERNATIONAL LIMITED—See Severfield Plc; *Int'l*, pg. 6735
SEVERFIELD-REEVE PROJECTS LIMITED—See Severfield Plc; *Int'l*, pg. 6735
SEVERFIELD-REEVE STRUCTURES LIMITED—See Severfield Plc; *Int'l*, pg. 6735
SEVERGROUP OOO; *Int'l*, pg. 6735
SEVER HOLDING AD; *Int'l*, pg. 6734
SEVERIN SHOPPING CENTER SRL—See NEPI Rockcastle N.V.; *Int'l*, pg. 5200
SEVERN BANCORP, INC.—See Shore Bancshares, Inc.; *U.S. Public*, pg. 1875
SEVERN GLOCON LTD.; *Int'l*, pg. 6735
SEVERNI BANAT A.D.; *Int'l*, pg. 6736
SEVERNIPIGAZ—See PJSC Gazprom; *Int'l*, pg. 5880
SEVERN SANDS LIMITED—See Breedon Group plc; *Int'l*, pg. 1144
SEVERN SAVINGS BANK, FSB—See Shore Bancshares, Inc.; *U.S. Public*, pg. 1875
SEVERN SCHOOL, INC; *U.S. Private*, pg. 3619
SEVERN TRENT CAS LTD—See Severn Trent Plc; *Int'l*, pg. 6735
SEVERN TRENT ENGINEERING LTD—See Severn Trent Plc; *Int'l*, pg. 6735
SEVERN TRENT GREEN POWER GROUP LIMITED—See Severn Trent Plc; *Int'l*, pg. 6735
SEVERN TRENT LABORATORIES LIMITED - COVENTRY—See Severn Trent Plc; *Int'l*, pg. 6735
SEVERN TRENT LABORATORIES LIMITED - RUNCORN—See Severn Trent Plc; *Int'l*, pg. 6735
SEVERN TRENT LABORATORIES LIMITED - SCOTLAND—See Severn Trent Plc; *Int'l*, pg. 6735

SEVERN TRENT METERING SERVICES LIMITED—See Severn Trent Plc; *Int'l*, pg. 6735
SEVERN TRENT OVERSEAS HOLDINGS LIMITED—See Severn Trent Plc; *Int'l*, pg. 6735
SEVERN TRENT PLC; *Int'l*, pg. 6735
SEVERN TRENT RETAIL AND UTILITY SERVICES LIMITED—See Severn Trent Plc; *Int'l*, pg. 6735
SEVERN TRENT SERVICES, INC. - KATY OFFICE—See Severn Trent Services, Inc.; *U.S. Private*, pg. 3619
SEVERN TRENT SERVICES, INC.; *U.S. Private*, pg. 3619
SEVERN TRENT WATER INTERNATIONAL LIMITED—See Severn Trent Plc; *Int'l*, pg. 6735
SEVERN TRENT WATER LIMITED-BARLASTON—See Severn Trent Plc; *Int'l*, pg. 6735
SEVERN TRENT WATER LIMITED-BIRMINGHAM—See Severn Trent Plc; *Int'l*, pg. 6735
SEVERN TRENT WATER LIMITED-CARSINGTON—See Severn Trent Plc; *Int'l*, pg. 6735
SEVERN TRENT WATER LIMITED-COVENTRY—See Severn Trent Plc; *Int'l*, pg. 6735
SEVERN TRENT WATER LIMITED-DERBY—See Severn Trent Plc; *Int'l*, pg. 6735
SEVERN TRENT WATER LIMITED-GLOUCESTER—See Severn Trent Plc; *Int'l*, pg. 6736
SEVERN TRENT WATER LIMITED-LEAMINGTON—See Severn Trent Plc; *Int'l*, pg. 6736
SEVERN TRENT WATER LIMITED-LEICESTER—See Severn Trent Plc; *Int'l*, pg. 6736
SEVERN TRENT WATER LIMITED-MINWORTH—See Severn Trent Plc; *Int'l*, pg. 6736
SEVERN TRENT WATER LIMITED-NOTTINGHAM—See Severn Trent Plc; *Int'l*, pg. 6736
SEVERN TRENT WATER LIMITED-SHREWSBURY—See Severn Trent Plc; *Int'l*, pg. 6736
SEVERN TRENT WATER LIMITED—See Severn Trent Plc; *Int'l*, pg. 6735
SEVERN TRENT WATER LIMITED-STOCK BARDOLPH—See Severn Trent Plc; *Int'l*, pg. 6736
SEVERN TRENT WATER LIMITED-STOKE ON TRENT—See Severn Trent Plc; *Int'l*, pg. 6736
SEVERN TRENT WATER LIMITED-WANLIP—See Severn Trent Plc; *Int'l*, pg. 6736
SEVERN TRENT WATER LIMITED-WARWICK—See Severn Trent Plc; *Int'l*, pg. 6736
SEVERN TRENT WATER LIMITED-WOLVERHAMPTON—See Severn Trent Plc; *Int'l*, pg. 6736
SEVERN TRENT WATER LIMITED-WORCESTER—See Severn Trent Plc; *Int'l*, pg. 6736
SEVERN WASTE SERVICES LIMITED—See Fomento de Construcciones y Contratas, S.A.; *Int'l*, pg. 2723
SEVEROCESKE DOLY A.S.—See CEZ, a.s.; *Int'l*, pg. 1428
SEVEROCESKE PISKOVNY A STERKOVNY S.R.O.—See Heidelberg Materials AG; *Int'l*, pg. 3319
SEVEROCESKE VODOVODY A KANALIZACE A.S.—See Veolia Environnement S.A.; *Int'l*, pg. 8154
SEVEROMORAVSKA ENERGETIKA, A.S.—See CEZ, a.s.; *Int'l*, pg. 1428
SEVERSON GROUP INCORPORATED; *U.S. Private*, pg. 3619
SEVERSTAL DISTRIBUTION—See PAO Severstal; *Int'l*, pg. 5732
SEVERSTAL EXPORT GMBH—See PAO Severstal; *Int'l*, pg. 5732
SEVERSTAL LIFTING TECHNOLOGIES LLC—See PAO Severstal; *Int'l*, pg. 5732
SEVERSTAL-PROEKT LLC—See PAO Severstal; *Int'l*, pg. 5732
SEVERSTAL TPZ-SHEKSNA LLC—See PAO Severstal; *Int'l*, pg. 5732
SEVERTRANS A.D.; *Int'l*, pg. 6736
SEVES CANADA INC.—See Seves S.p.A.; *Int'l*, pg. 6736
SEVES SAS—See VINCI S.A.; *Int'l*, pg. 8227
SEVES S.P.A. - NUSCO FACTORY—See Seves S.p.A.; *Int'l*, pg. 6736
SEVES S.P.A.; *Int'l*, pg. 6736
SEVES USA—See Seves S.p.A.; *Int'l*, pg. 6736
SEVIBE CELLS S.L.—See VITA 34 AG; *Int'l*, pg. 8257
SEVIER COUNTY BANCSHARES, INC.; *U.S. Public*, pg. 1873
SEVIER COUNTY BANK—See Sevier County Bancshares, Inc.; *U.S. Public*, pg. 1873
SEVIER FARMERS COOPERATIVE; *U.S. Private*, pg. 3619
SEVILLE CENTRAL MIX CORPORATION; *U.S. Private*, pg. 3619
SEVILLE GOLF & COUNTRY CLUB—See Apollo Global Management, Inc.; *U.S. Public*, pg. 150
SEVILLE OPERATIONS LLC—See RCI Hospitality Holdings, Inc.; *U.S. Public*, pg. 1767
SEVILLE PICTURES INC.—See Lions Gate Entertainment Corp.; *Int'l*, pg. 4520
SEV, INC.; *U.S. Private*, pg. 3618
SEVIROLI FOODS, INC.; *U.S. Private*, pg. 3619
SEVIVON SP. Z O.O.—See PNE AG; *Int'l*, pg. 5901
SEVKAZENERGO JSC; *Int'l*, pg. 6736
SEVKAZENERGOSBYT LLP—See SevKazEnergo JSC; *Int'l*, pg. 6736

SEVKO AD

CORPORATE AFFILIATIONS

SEVKO AD; *Int'l*, pg. 6736
SEVONE, INC.—See Turbonomic, Inc.; *U.S. Private*, pg. 4259
SEV PROJECTS PTE LIMITED—See Digilife Technologies Limited; *Int'l*, pg. 2120
SEWA BIKAS BANK LIMITED—See Kamana Sewa Bikas Bank Ltd.; *Int'l*, pg. 4060
SEWA GMBH—See Itron, Inc.; *U.S. Public*, pg. 1176
SEWARD CO-OP GROCERY & DELI; *U.S. Private*, pg. 3619
SEWARD MOTOR FREIGHT, INC.; *U.S. Private*, pg. 3619
SEWARD (WESSEX) LIMITED—See General Motors Company; *U.S. Public*, pg. 928
SEWART SUPPLY INC.; *U.S. Private*, pg. 3619
SEWCO INC.; *U.S. Private*, pg. 3620
SEWCO TOYS & NOVELTY LIMITED—See Winshine Science Company Limited; *Int'l*, pg. 8430
SEWELL BMW MINI OF PLANO—See Sewell Motor Company; *U.S. Private*, pg. 3620
SEWELL CADILLAC CHEVROLET; *U.S. Private*, pg. 3620
SEWELL CADILLAC OF DALLAS—See Sewell Motor Company; *U.S. Private*, pg. 3620
SEWELL CLOTHING COMPANY INC.; *U.S. Private*, pg. 3620
SEWELL FORD—See Sewell Motor Company; *U.S. Private*, pg. 3620
SEWELL HARDWARE CO., INC.; *U.S. Private*, pg. 3620
SEWELL INFINITI OF DALLAS—See Sewell Motor Company; *U.S. Private*, pg. 3620
SEWELL LEXUS OF DALLAS—See Sewell Motor Company; *U.S. Private*, pg. 3620
SEWELL MOTOR COMPANY; *U.S. Private*, pg. 3620
SEWER EQUIPMENT CO. OF AMERICA; *U.S. Private*, pg. 3620
SEWER SYSTEMS EVALUATIONS, INC.—See Carylon Corporation; *U.S. Private*, pg. 777
SEWER TAP, INC.—See Advanced Drainage Systems, Inc.; *U.S. Public*, pg. 46
SEW-EURODRIVE INC.; *U.S. Private*, pg. 3619
SEWHA P&C INC. - JINCHEON-GUN FACTORY/HEAD OFFICE—See Sewha P&C Inc.; *Int'l*, pg. 6736
SEWHA P&C INC.; *Int'l*, pg. 6736
SE WINGS INCORPORATED—See Sanix Incorporated; *Int'l*, pg. 6540
SE WIRING SYSTEMS EGYPT S.A.E—See Sumitomo Electric Industries, Ltd.; *Int'l*, pg. 7279
SE WIRING SYSTEMS TR TRADING AND SERVICES LTD.—See Sumitomo Electric Industries, Ltd.; *Int'l*, pg. 7279
SEWONCELLONTECH CORP. - CHANGWON HYDRAULICE PLANT—See Sewon E&C Co., Ltd.; *Int'l*, pg. 6737
SEWONCELLONTECH CORP. - PROCESS EQUIPMENT 1ST PLANT—See Sewon E&C Co., Ltd.; *Int'l*, pg. 6737
SEWONCELLONTECH CORP. - RMS PLANT—See Sewon E&C Co., Ltd.; *Int'l*, pg. 6737
SEWON CO LTD; *Int'l*, pg. 6736
SEWON CORPORATION CO., LTD.; *Int'l*, pg. 6736
SEWON E&C CO., LTD.; *Int'l*, pg. 6737
SEWONECS VINA CO,. LTD—See YURATECH Co., Ltd.; *Int'l*, pg. 8617
SEWON E&I CO., LTD.—See SEWON CORPORATION Co., Ltd.; *Int'l*, pg. 6737
SEWON PRECISION CO., LTD.—See Sewon Precision Industry Co., Ltd.; *Int'l*, pg. 6737
SEWON PRECISION INDUSTRY CO., LTD.; *Int'l*, pg. 6737
SEWON TECHNOLOGY CO., LTD.—See SEWON CORPORATION Co., Ltd.; *Int'l*, pg. 6737
SEWOO GLOBAL CO., LTD.; *Int'l*, pg. 6737
SEWOO GLOBAL VIETNAM LTD.—See Sewoo Global Co., Ltd.; *Int'l*, pg. 6737
SEWOOM CO., LTD.—See SJG Sejong Co., Ltd.; *Int'l*, pg. 6969
SEWOONMEDICAL CO. LTD; *Int'l*, pg. 6737
SEWS ASIA TECHNICAL CENTER, LTD.—See Sumitomo Electric Industries, Ltd.; *Int'l*, pg. 7280
SEWS AUSTRALIA PTY LTD.—See Sumitomo Electric Industries, Ltd.; *Int'l*, pg. 7280
SEWS-AUTOMOTIVE WIRE HUNGARY LTD.—See Sumitomo Electric Industries, Ltd.; *Int'l*, pg. 7280
SEWS-CABIND MAROC S.A.S.—See Sumitomo Electric Industries, Ltd.; *Int'l*, pg. 7280
SEWS-CABIND POLAND SP. Z.O.O. - LESNIANKA PLANT—See Sumitomo Electric Industries, Ltd.; *Int'l*, pg. 7280
SEWS-CABIND POLAND SP. Z.O.O.—See Sumitomo Electric Industries, Ltd.; *Int'l*, pg. 7280
SEWS-CABIND S.P.A.—See Sumitomo Electric Industries, Ltd.; *Int'l*, pg. 7280
SEWS CANADA, LTD.—See Sumitomo Electric Industries, Ltd.; *Int'l*, pg. 7280
SEWS-COMPONENTS CHANGSHU LTD.—See Sumitomo Electric Industries, Ltd.; *Int'l*, pg. 7280
SEWS-COMPONENTS EUROPE HUNGARY LTD.—See Sumitomo Electric Industries, Ltd.; *Int'l*, pg. 7280
SEWS-COMPONENTS EUROPE POLSKA SP.ZO.O (POLAND)—See Sumitomo Electric Industries, Ltd.; *Int'l*, pg. 7284

SEWS COMPONENTS (HUIZHOU) LIMITED—See Sumitomo Electric Industries, Ltd.; *Int'l*, pg. 7280
SEWS-COMPONENTS (THAILAND) LTD.—See Sumitomo Electric Industries, Ltd.; *Int'l*, pg. 7280
SEWS-COMPONENTS VIETNAM CO., LTD.—See Sumitomo Electric Industries, Ltd.; *Int'l*, pg. 7280
SEWS HUNGARY WIRING HARNESS, LTD.—See Sumitomo Electric Industries, Ltd.; *Int'l*, pg. 7280
SEWS HUNGARY WIRING HARNESS, LTD.—See Sumitomo Electric Industries, Ltd.; *Int'l*, pg. 7284
SEWS-MAROC SARL—See Sumitomo Electric Industries, Ltd.; *Int'l*, pg. 7280
SEWS MEXICO S.A. DE C.V.—See Sumitomo Electric Industries, Ltd.; *Int'l*, pg. 7280
SEWS POLSKA SP. ZO, O.—See Sumitomo Electric Industries, Ltd.; *Int'l*, pg. 7280
SEWS ROMANIA S.R.L.—See Sumitomo Electric Industries, Ltd.; *Int'l*, pg. 7280
SEWS SOUTH AFRICA PTY LTD.—See Sumitomo Electric Industries, Ltd.; *Int'l*, pg. 7280
SEWS-STC, INC.—See Sumitomo Electric Industries, Ltd.; *Int'l*, pg. 7280
SEWS TAIWAN LTD.—See Sumitomo Electric Industries, Ltd.; *Int'l*, pg. 7280
SEW WHAT, INC.; *U.S. Private*, pg. 3619
THE SEXTANT GROUP, INC.—See NV5 Global, Inc.; *U.S. Public*, pg. 1558
SEXTON AUTOMOTIVE GROUP; *U.S. Private*, pg. 3620
SEXTON CAN CO., INC.; *U.S. Private*, pg. 3620
SEXTON PEST CONTROL, INC.; *U.S. Private*, pg. 3620
SEXT Z IMMOBILIEN LEASING GESELLSCHAFT M.B.H—See UniCredit S.p.A.; *Int'l*, pg. 8035
SEXY HAIR CONCEPTS, LLC—See Henkel AG & Co. KGaA; *Int'l*, pg. 3353
SEYA INDUSTRIES LTD.; *Int'l*, pg. 6737
SEYALEMOGA COMMUNICATIONS (PTY) LTD—See African Media Entertainment Limited; *Int'l*, pg. 192
SEYCHELLE ENVIRONMENTAL TECHNOLOGIES, INC.; *U.S. Public*, pg. 1873
SEYCHELLES BREWERIES LIMITED—See Diageo plc; *Int'l*, pg. 2103
SEYCHELLES INTERNATIONAL MERCANTILE BANKING CORPORATION LIMITED—See Standard Chartered PLC; *Int'l*, pg. 7167
SEYCHELLES TRADING COMPANY LTD.; *Int'l*, pg. 6737
THE SEYDEL COMPANIES; *U.S. Private*, pg. 4117
SEYDEL GMBH—See NSC Groupe SA; *Int'l*, pg. 5476
SEYDEL INTERNATIONAL, INC.—See The Seydel Companies; *U.S. Private*, pg. 4117
SEYDEL-WOOLLEY & COMPANY—See The Seydel Companies; *U.S. Private*, pg. 4117
SEYFARTH SHAW; *U.S. Private*, pg. 3620
SEYFARTH SHAW (UK) LLP—See Seyfarth Shaw; *U.S. Private*, pg. 3620
SEYFERTH & ASSOCIATES INC.; *U.S. Private*, pg. 3620
SEYFERT INTERNATIONAL USA INC.—See Seyfert Ltd.; *Int'l*, pg. 6737
SEYFERT LTD.; *Int'l*, pg. 6737
SEYI-AMERICA INC.—See Shieh Yih Machinery Industry Co., Ltd.; *Int'l*, pg. 6828
SEYI-AMERICA, INC.—See Shieh Yih Machinery Industry Co., Ltd.; *Int'l*, pg. 6828
SEYI PRESSES EUROPE GMBH—See Shieh Yih Machinery Industry Co., Ltd.; *Int'l*, pg. 6828
SEYI (THAILAND) CO., LTD.—See Shieh Yih Machinery Industry Co., Ltd.; *Int'l*, pg. 6827
SEYITLER KIMYA SANAYI AS; *Int'l*, pg. 6737
SEYLAN BANK PLC; *Int'l*, pg. 6737
SEYLAN DEVELOPMENTS PLC—See Seylan Bank PLC; *Int'l*, pg. 6737
SEYLAN MERCHANT BANK LTD.—See Seylan Bank PLC; *Int'l*, pg. 6737
SEYMOUR (CIVIL ENGINEERING CONTRACTORS) LTD.—See Renew Holdings plc; *Int'l*, pg. 6278
SEYMOUR INDUSTRIES LTD.—See American Granby, Inc.; *U.S. Private*, pg. 235
SEYMOUR MANUFACTURING CO., INC.—See Seymour Midwest LLC; *U.S. Private*, pg. 3621
SEYMOUR MANUFACTURING LINK HANDLE DIVISION—See Seymour Midwest LLC; *U.S. Private*, pg. 3621
SEYMOUR MIDWEST LLC; *U.S. Private*, pg. 3621
SEYMOUR N. LOGAN ASSOCIATES; *U.S. Private*, pg. 3621
SEYMOUR OF SYCAMORE, INC.; *U.S. Private*, pg. 3621
SEYMOURPOWELL LIMITED—See Writtle Holdings Limited; *Int'l*, pg. 8495
SEYMOUR TAYLOR AUDIT LIMITED—See Hampden Holdings Limited; *Int'l*, pg. 3239
SEYMOUR WHYTE CONSTRUCTIONS PTY LTD—See VINCI S.A.; *Int'l*, pg. 8231
SEYMOUR WHYTE LTD.—See VINCI S.A.; *Int'l*, pg. 8231
SEZ KOREA LTD.—See Lam Research Corporation; *U.S. Public*, pg. 1290
SEZMI CORPORATION—See Piksel, Inc.; *U.S. Private*, pg. 3180
SEZZLE INC.; *U.S. Public*, pg. 1873
S.FACTORY CO., LTD.—See THK CO., LTD.; *Int'l*, pg. 7712

SFA DESIGN; *U.S. Private*, pg. 3621
SFA ENGINEERING CORP.; *Int'l*, pg. 6737
SFAKIANAKIS S.A.; *Int'l*, pg. 6738
SFAM SOCIETE FRANCAISE D'AMPOULES MECANIQUES SARL—See Carl-Zeiss-Stiftung; *Int'l*, pg. 1337
SFA SEMICON CHINA (SUZHOU) CORPORATION—See SFA Engineering Corp.; *Int'l*, pg. 6738
SFA SEMICON CO., LTD.; *Int'l*, pg. 6738
SFA SEMICON PHILIPPINES CORPORATION—See SFA Semicon Co., Ltd.; *Int'l*, pg. 6738
SF-AUSBAU GMBH—See STRABAG SE; *Int'l*, pg. 7232
SF AUTO AUSTRALIA PTY LIMITED—See SubZero Group Limited; *Int'l*, pg. 7250
S. F. BALLOU, INC.; *U.S. Private*, pg. 3515
SFB BANCORP INC.; *U.S. Public*, pg. 1873
SF BUILDING MAINTENANCE CO., LTD.—See Sun Frontier Fudousan Co. Ltd.; *Int'l*, pg. 7303
SF BUILDING SUPPORT INC.—See Sun Frontier Fudousan Co. Ltd.; *Int'l*, pg. 7303
SFC CO., LTD. - BORYEONG FACTORY—See SFC Co., Ltd.; *Int'l*, pg. 6738
SFC CO., LTD.; *Int'l*, pg. 6738
SFC EKA-INVEST LLP; *Int'l*, pg. 6738
SFC ENERGY AG; *Int'l*, pg. 6738
SFC ENERGY POWER S.R.L.—See SFC Energy AG; *Int'l*, pg. 6738
SFC KOENIG AG—See IDEX Corp; *U.S. Public*, pg. 1092
SFC KOENIG GMBH—See IDEX Corp; *U.S. Public*, pg. 1092
SFC KOENIG LLC—See IDEX Corp; *U.S. Public*, pg. 1092
SFC SMART FUEL CELL, INC.—See SFC Energy AG; *Int'l*, pg. 6738
SFC SOLUTIONS AUTOMOTIVE S. R. L.—See Mutares SE & Co. KGaA; *Int'l*, pg. 5105
SFC SOLUTIONS CZESTOCHOWA SP.Z.O.O.—See Mutares SE & Co. KGaA; *Int'l*, pg. 5105
SFC SOLUTIONS ITALY S. R. L.—See Mutares SE & Co. KGaA; *Int'l*, pg. 5105
SFC SOLUTIONS SPAIN BORJA S.L.—See Mutares SE & Co. KGaA; *Int'l*, pg. 5105
SFC STOCKMEIER GMBH—See Stockmeier Holding GmbH; *Int'l*, pg. 7220
SFC WHOLESALE LTD; *Int'l*, pg. 6738
SFDC AUSTRALIA PTY. LTD.—See Salesforce, Inc.; *U.S. Public*, pg. 1837
SFDC IRELAND LTD.—See Salesforce, Inc.; *U.S. Public*, pg. 1838
SFDC MEXICO S. DE R.L. DE C.V.—See Salesforce, Inc.; *U.S. Public*, pg. 1837
SFDC NETHERLANDS B.V.—See Salesforce, Inc.; *U.S. Public*, pg. 1837
SFDC NORWAY AS—See Salesforce, Inc.; *U.S. Public*, pg. 1837
SFDC SWEDEN AB (FINLAND)—See Salesforce, Inc.; *U.S. Public*, pg. 1837
SFDC SWEDEN AB—See Salesforce, Inc.; *U.S. Public*, pg. 1837
SFDC UK LTD. (LONDON)—See Salesforce, Inc.; *U.S. Public*, pg. 1837
SFDC UK LTD. (STAINES)—See Salesforce, Inc.; *U.S. Public*, pg. 1837
SFD EUROPE SRL—See SF Diamond Co., Ltd.; *Int'l*, pg. 6737
SF DIAMOND CO., LTD.; *Int'l*, pg. 6737
SFDK LABORATORIO DE ANALISE DE PRODUTOS LTDA.—See TUV SUD AG; *Int'l*, pg. 7984
SFD LIMITED—See Kingfisher plc; *Int'l*, pg. 4173
SF ENGINEERING INC.—See Sun Frontier Fudousan Co. Ltd.; *Int'l*, pg. 7303
SFERABIT S.R.L.—See Tinexta S.p.A.; *Int'l*, pg. 7753
SFERACO SARL—See Thermador Groupe; *Int'l*, pg. 7707
SFERA EDITORES ESPANA S.L.—See RCS MediaGroup S.p.A.; *Int'l*, pg. 6229
SFERA EDITORES MEXICO S.A.—See RCS MediaGroup S.p.A.; *Int'l*, pg. 6229
SFERA EDITORE S.P.A.—See RCS MediaGroup S.p.A.; *Int'l*, pg. 6229
SFERA JOVEN, S.A.—See El Corte Ingles, S.A.; *Int'l*, pg. 2340
SFERA SERVICE S.R.L.—See RCS MediaGroup S.p.A.; *Int'l*, pg. 6229
SFERA S.P.A.—See Cremonini S.p.A.; *Int'l*, pg. 1838
S-FER INTERNATIONAL INC.—See Salvatore Ferragamo SpA; *Int'l*, pg. 6495
SFFC, INC.—See WH Group Limited; *Int'l*, pg. 8395
SFFI COMPANY, INC.; *U.S. Private*, pg. 3621
SF FILM FINLAND OY—See Telia Company AB; *Int'l*, pg. 7544
SF FIRE CREDIT UNION; *U.S. Private*, pg. 3621
SFG BALTIKA LLC—See Quaser Machine Tools, Inc.; *Int'l*, pg. 6157
SF GMBH—See Freudenberg SE; *Int'l*, pg. 2790
SFH ASSOCIATES L.P.—See InterContinental Hotels Group PLC; *Int'l*, pg. 3738
SFH FERTIGHAUS AG—See Streif GmbH; *Int'l*, pg. 7240
S.F. HOLDING CO., LTD.; *Int'l*, pg. 6456
SF HOLDING CORP.; *U.S. Private*, pg. 3621
SF HOLDING SP. Z.O.O.—See WH Group Limited; *Int'l*, pg. 8395

COMPANY NAME INDEX

SF HOTELERRICHTUNGSGESELLSCHAFT M.B.H.—See Raiffeisen Bank International AG; *Int'l*, pg. 6184
SFIC—See Compagnie de Saint-Gobain SA; *Int'l*, pg. 1728
SFI ENERGY—See First Reserve Management, L.P.; *U.S. Private*, pg. 1526
SFI FOOD PTE. LTD.—See Temasek Holdings (Private) Limited; *Int'l*, pg. 7550
SFINKS POLSKA S.A.; *Int'l*, pg. 6738
SF INVESTMENTS, INC.; *U.S. Private*, pg. 3621
SFI OF TENNESSEE, L.L.C.; *U.S. Private*, pg. 3621
S FISCHER VERLAG GMBH—See Verlagsgruppe Georg von Holtzbrinck GmbH; *Int'l*, pg. 8171
S. FISHER AND S. THOMAS, INC.—See KKR & Co. Inc.; *U.S. Public*, pg. 1249
SFI SUPERIOR IMPLEMENTS—See First Reserve Management, L.P.; *U.S. Private*, pg. 1526
SFI WAIPOULI LLC—See Safehold Inc.; *U.S. Public*, pg. 1834
SFK CO., LTD.—See Sumitomo Heavy Industries, Ltd.; *Int'l*, pg. 7287
SFK CONSTRUCTION HOLDINGS LIMITED—See Sun Fook Kong Group; *Int'l*, pg. 7303
SFK FOOD A/S—See Ardian SAS; *Int'l*, pg. 555
SFL CORPORATION LTD.—See Frontline plc; *Int'l*, pg. 2796
SFL INTERNATIONAL LIMITED; *Int'l*, pg. 6738
SFM30 SARL—See Solutions 30 SE; *Int'l*, pg. 7077
SF MARKETING INC.; *Int'l*, pg. 6737
SFM, LLC—See Sprouts Farmers Markets, Inc.; *U.S. Public*, pg. 1920
SFM MUTUAL INSURANCE COMPANY; *U.S. Private*, pg. 3621
SF MOTORS, INC.—See Seres Group Co., Ltd.; *Int'l*, pg. 6722
SFMPE - CRITTENDEN, L.L.C.—See Tenet Healthcare Corporation; *U.S. Public*, pg. 2006
SFM SYSTEMS INC—See State Fund Mutual Insurance Co.; *U.S. Private*, pg. 3792
SFM TECHNOLOGY, INC.—See Cadence Design Systems, Inc.; *U.S. Public*, pg. 419
SF NEWSPAPER COMPANY, LLC—See The Anschutz Corporation; *U.S. Private*, pg. 3987
SF NORGE AS—See Telia Company AB; *Int'l*, pg. 7544
SFO FORECAST INC.; *U.S. Private*, pg. 3621
S FOODS INC - FUNABASHI NO 2 FACTORY—See S Foods Inc; *Int'l*, pg. 6442
S FOODS INC - FUNABASHI NO.2 FACTORY—See S Foods Inc; *Int'l*, pg. 6442
S FOODS INC - NISHINOMIYA FACTORY—See S Foods Inc; *Int'l*, pg. 6442
S FOODS INC - NISHINOMIYA NO.2 FACTORY—See S Foods Inc; *Int'l*, pg. 6442
S FOODS INC; *Int'l*, pg. 6442
S FOODS SINGAPORE PTE. LTD.—See S Foods Inc; *Int'l*, pg. 6442
SFP HOLDING, INC.—See BlackRock, Inc.; *U.S. Public*, pg. 346
SFP HOLDINGS CO., LTD.; *Int'l*, pg. 6738
SF POLICE CREDIT UNION; *U.S. Private*, pg. 3621
SFP (SHETLAND FISH PRODUCTS) LIMITED—See Pelagia Shetland Limited; *Int'l*, pg. 5781
SFP TECH HOLDINGS BERHAD; *Int'l*, pg. 6738
S. FREEDMAN & SONS, INC.; *U.S. Private*, pg. 3515
SFSB, INC.; *U.S. Public*, pg. 1873
SFS CARE PTE LTD—See Global Cord Blood Corporation; *Int'l*, pg. 2994
SFS DIENSTLEISTUNGS GMBH—See MK-Kliniken AG; *Int'l*, pg. 5001
SFS DISTRIBUTION SERVICES INC.—See Sales Force Won Ltd.; *U.S. Private*, pg. 3532
SFS FINANCIAL SERVICES GMBH—See UniCredit S.p.A.; *Int'l*, pg. 8035
SFS FIRE SERVICES LIMITED—See Carrier Global Corporation; *U.S. Public*, pg. 441
SFS GROUP AG; *Int'l*, pg. 6738
SFS GROUP AUSTRIA GMBH—See SFS Group AG; *Int'l*, pg. 6739
SFS GROUP CANADA INC.—See SFS Group AG; *Int'l*, pg. 6739
SFS GROUP CZ S.R.O.—See SFS Group AG; *Int'l*, pg. 6739
SFS GROUP FASTENING TECHNOLOGY MEXICO S.A.—See SFS Group AG; *Int'l*, pg. 6739
SFS GROUP FINLAND OY—See SFS Group AG; *Int'l*, pg. 6739
SFS GROUP GERMANY GMBH—See SFS Group AG; *Int'l*, pg. 6739
SFS GROUP HUNGARY KFT.—See SFS Group AG; *Int'l*, pg. 6739
SFS GROUP INDIA PVT. LTD.—See SFS Group AG; *Int'l*, pg. 6739
SFS GROUP ITALY S.R.L.—See SFS Group AG; *Int'l*, pg. 6739
SFS GROUP PAZARLAMA A.S.—See SFS Group AG; *Int'l*, pg. 6739
SFS GROUP PUBLIC COMPANY LIMITED; *Int'l*, pg. 6740
SFS GROUP S.A.S.—See SFS Group AG; *Int'l*, pg. 6739
SFS GROUP SCHWEIZ AG—See SFS Group AG; *Int'l*, pg. 6739

SFS GROUP SP. Z O.O.—See SFS Group AG; *Int'l*, pg. 6739
SFS GROUP SWEDEN AB—See SFS Group AG; *Int'l*, pg. 6739
SFS GROUP THE NETHERLANDS B.V.—See SFS Group AG; *Int'l*, pg. 6739
SFS GROUP TR SAN. VE TIC. A.S.—See SFS Group AG; *Int'l*, pg. 6739
SFS GROUP USA, INC—See SFS Group AG; *Int'l*, pg. 6739
SFS INTEC AG—See SFS Group AG; *Int'l*, pg. 6739
SFS INTEC (CHINA) ADVANCED PRECISION PARTS MANUFACTURING CO., LTD.—See SFS Group AG; *Int'l*, pg. 6739
SFS INTEC GMBH—See SFS Group AG; *Int'l*, pg. 6739
SFS INTEC, INC.—See SFS Group AG; *Int'l*, pg. 6739
SFS INTEC OY—See SFS Group AG; *Int'l*, pg. 6739
SFS MUNICH GMBH & CO. KG—See BlackRock, Inc.; *U.S. Public*, pg. 346
SFS MUNICH GMBH & CO. KG—See Blackstone Inc.; *U.S. Public*, pg. 358
SFS MUNICH GMBH & CO. KG—See Cascade Investment LLC; *U.S. Private*, pg. 780
SF SOFTWARE & FRIENDS GMBH—See Allgeier SE; *Int'l*, pg. 338
S&F SUPPLIES INC.; *U.S. Private*, pg. 3513
SF TOOLING GROUP GMBH—See Storskogen Group AB; *Int'l*, pg. 7228
SF TRANSPORT LTD.—See Vita Plus Corporation; *U.S. Private*, pg. 4405
S-FUELCELL CO., LTD.; *Int'l*, pg. 6446
SFUND INTERNATIONAL HOLDINGS LIMITED; *Int'l*, pg. 6740
SF URBAN PROPERTIES AG; *Int'l*, pg. 6737
SFW CAPITAL PARTNERS LLC; *U.S. Private*, pg. 3622
SFW HOLDING CORP.—See United Natural Foods, Inc.; *U.S. Public*, pg. 2232
SFXE NETHERLANDS HOLDINGS B.V.—See LiveStyle, Inc.; *U.S. Private*, pg. 2473
SFZ FREIZEITBETRIEBS-GMBH AND CO KG—See PORR AG; *Int'l*, pg. 5924
SFZ IMMOBILIEN GMBH AND CO KG—See PORR AG; *Int'l*, pg. 5924
SG360—See The Segerdahl Corporation; *U.S. Private*, pg. 4116
SGA CLOUD SERVICE CO., LTD.; *Int'l*, pg. 6741
SGA CO., LTD.; *Int'l*, pg. 6741
SGA CONVEYOR SYSTEM AB—See L. Possehl & Co. mbH; *Int'l*, pg. 4385
SG ACTIVAMEDIA (M) SDN. BHD.—See AM Group Holdings Limited; *Int'l*, pg. 402
SGA GROUP, PC; *U.S. Private*, pg. 3622
SGA-IBI GROUP ARCHITECTS—See ARCADIS N.V.; *Int'l*, pg. 542
SG ALD AUTOMOTIVE PORTUGAL SOCIEDADE GERAL DE COMERCIO E ALUGUER DE BENZ SA—See Societe Generale S.A.; *Int'l*, pg. 7040
SG ALLIED BUSINESSES LIMITED; *Int'l*, pg. 6740
SG AMERICAS, INC.—See Societe Generale S.A.; *Int'l*, pg. 7040
S-G API BV—See Compagnie de Saint-Gobain SA; *Int'l*, pg. 1725
SGA - SOCIEDADE DO GOLFE DE AMARANTE, S.A.—See Mota-Engil SGPS, S.A.; *Int'l*, pg. 5052
SGA SOLUTIONS CO., LTD.; *Int'l*, pg. 6741
SGA SYSTEMS CO., LTD.—See SGA Co., Ltd.; *Int'l*, pg. 6741
SG AUTOMATISERING B.V.—See Advent International Corporation; *U.S. Private*, pg. 97
SG AUTOMATISERING B.V.—See Centerbridge Partners, L.P.; *U.S. Private*, pg. 813
S.G. AUTOVER ITALIA S.R.L.—See Compagnie de Saint-Gobain SA; *Int'l*, pg. 1737
SGB ALUMA MALAYSIA SDN. BHD.—See Brand Industrial Services, Inc.; *U.S. Private*, pg. 636
SGB ALUMA SINGAPORE PTE. LTD.—See Brand Industrial Services, Inc.; *U.S. Private*, pg. 636
S G BANCSHARES INC.—See First Keyes Bancshares, Inc.; *U.S. Private*, pg. 1520
SGB FINANCE S.A.—See Societe Generale S.A.; *Int'l*, pg. 7041
SG BIKE PTE. LTD.—See ISOTeam Ltd.; *Int'l*, pg. 3821
SGB PACKAGING GROUP, INC.—See Ares Management Corporation; *U.S. Public*, pg. 191
SGB PACKAGING GROUP, INC.—See Ontario Teachers' Pension Plan; *Int'l*, pg. 5591
SGB SECURITAS GLEISBAUSICHERUNG GMBH & CO. KG—See Securitas AB; *Int'l*, pg. 6675
SGB SERVICOS E COMERCIO DE PECAS LTDA—See The Swatch Group Ltd.; *Int'l*, pg. 7692
SG CAPITAL CO. LTD.—See Singer Thailand Public Company Limited; *Int'l*, pg. 6943
SG CAPITAL DEVELOPPEMENT—See Societe Generale S.A.; *Int'l*, pg. 7040
SG CAPITAL PUBLIC COMPANY LIMITED—See Singer Thailand Public Company Limited; *Int'l*, pg. 6943
S&G CARPET AND MORE; *U.S. Private*, pg. 3513
SGCC S.A.—See LBO France S.a.r.l.; *Int'l*, pg. 4430

SG&G CORPORATION

SG CERAMICS MATERIALS CANADA INC.—See Compagnie de Saint-Gobain SA; *Int'l*, pg. 1730
SGC ETEC E&C CO., LTD.; *Int'l*, pg. 6741
SGC HORIZON LLC—See Scranton Gillette Communications, Inc.; *U.S. Private*, pg. 3579
SGC KNOWLEDGE TRANSFER LTD.—See Aerodrome Group Ltd.; *Int'l*, pg. 181
SGCM PTE. LTD.—See Singapore Press Holdings Ltd.; *Int'l*, pg. 6942
SG COAL PROPRIETARY LIMITED—See Super Group Limited; *Int'l*, pg. 7334
S&G COMPANY, LTD.—See Daewon Semiconductor Packaging Industrial Corporation; *Int'l*, pg. 1910
SG COMPANY S.P.A.; *Int'l*, pg. 6740
SG CORPORATION; *Int'l*, pg. 6740
SGC SOLUTIONS CO., LTD.; *Int'l*, pg. 6741
SG DE BANQUES AU BURKINA—See Societe Generale S.A.; *Int'l*, pg. 7040
SG DETACHERING B.V.—See Advent International Corporation; *U.S. Private*, pg. 97
SG DETACHERING B.V.—See Centerbridge Partners, L.P.; *U.S. Private*, pg. 813
S&G DEVELOPMENT PARTNERS OBJEKT LEIPZIG GMBH & CO KG—See PJSC LSR Group; *Int'l*, pg. 5881
SG DISTRIBUZIONE SRL—See Compagnie de Saint-Gobain SA; *Int'l*, pg. 1724
SGD KIPFENBERG GMBH—See China Investment Corporation; *Int'l*, pg. 1513
SGD S.A.—See China Investment Corporation; *Int'l*, pg. 1513
SG E-AUCTION PTE. LTD.—See MoneyMax Financial Services Ltd.; *Int'l*, pg. 5033
SGE-C CONGO SA—See VINCI S.A.; *Int'l*, pg. 8227
SGEL (SOCIEDAD GENERAL ESPANOLA DE LIBRERIA)—See Vivendi SE; *Int'l*, pg. 8276
SG ENTERPRISES II, LLC; *U.S. Private*, pg. 3622
SG EQUIPMENT FINANCE AUSTRIA GMBH—See Societe Generale S.A.; *Int'l*, pg. 7039
SG EQUIPMENT FINANCE BENELUX BV—See Societe Generale S.A.; *Int'l*, pg. 7040
SG EQUIPMENT FINANCE CZECH REPUBLIC S.R.O.—See Societe Generale S.A.; *Int'l*, pg. 7040
SG EQUIPMENT FINANCE HUNGARY—See Societe Generale S.A.; *Int'l*, pg. 7039
SG EQUIPMENT FINANCE IBERIA. E.F.C. S.A.—See Societe Generale S.A.; *Int'l*, pg. 7040
SG EQUIPMENT FINANCE INTERNATIONAL GMBH—See Societe Generale S.A.; *Int'l*, pg. 7040
SG EQUIPMENT FINANCE ITALY S.P.A.—See Societe Generale S.A.; *Int'l*, pg. 7040
SG EQUIPMENT FINANCE LIMITED—See Societe Generale S.A.; *Int'l*, pg. 7040
SG EQUIPMENT FINANCE SA & CO KG—See Societe Generale S.A.; *Int'l*, pg. 7040
SG EQUIPMENT FINANCE S.A.—See Societe Generale S.A.; *Int'l*, pg. 7041
SG EQUIPMENT FINANCE—See Societe Generale S.A.; *Int'l*, pg. 7039
SG EQUIPMENT FINANCE—See Societe Generale S.A.; *Int'l*, pg. 7039
SG EQUIPMENT FINANCE USA CORP.—See Societe Generale S.A.; *Int'l*, pg. 7040
SG EQUIPMENT LEASING POLSKA—See Societe Generale S.A.; *Int'l*, pg. 7039
SG FACILITOR B.V.—See Advent International Corporation; *U.S. Private*, pg. 97
SG FACILITOR B.V.—See Centerbridge Partners, L.P.; *U.S. Private*, pg. 813
SG FACTORING SPA—See Societe Generale S.A.; *Int'l*, pg. 7041
SGF CAPITAL PUBLIC COMPANY LIMITED; *Int'l*, pg. 6741
SG FIELDER CO., LTD.—See SG Holdings Co., Ltd.; *Int'l*, pg. 6740
SG FINANCIAL SERVICES HOLDING SA—See Societe Generale S.A.; *Int'l*, pg. 7041
SG FINANS AS—See Societe Generale S.A.; *Int'l*, pg. 7041
S.G.F.-I.N.C. S.P.A.—See Salini Costruttori S.p.A.; *Int'l*, pg. 6493
SG FINSERVE LIMITED; *Int'l*, pg. 6740
SG FLEET GROUP LIMITED—See Super Group Limited; *Int'l*, pg. 7334
SG FLEET INVESTMENTS PTY LTD—See Super Group Limited; *Int'l*, pg. 7334
SG FLEET PROPRIETARY LIMITED—See Super Group Limited; *Int'l*, pg. 7335
SGFOOTWEAR, INC.; *U.S. Private*, pg. 3622
SG GAMING ASIA LIMITED—See Light & Wonder, Inc.; *U.S. Public*, pg. 1314
SG GAMING AUSTRALIA HOLDINGS I PTY LTD—See Light & Wonder, Inc.; *U.S. Public*, pg. 1314
SG GAMING UK LIMITED—See Light & Wonder, Inc.; *U.S. Public*, pg. 1314
SGG BELGIUM S.A.—See Astorg Partners S.A.S.; *Int'l*, pg. 657
SG&G CORPORATION; *Int'l*, pg. 6741
SGGH, LLC—See Elah Holdings Inc.; *U.S. Public*, pg. 722

SG&G CORPORATION

SG GLOBAL BIOTECH SDN. BHD.—See Hai-O Enterprise Berhad; *Int'l*, pg. 3209
SG GLOBAL CO.,LTD.; *Int'l*, pg. 6740
SGG NETHERLANDS N.V.—See Astorg Partners S.A.S.; *Int'l*, pg. 657
SGGS BELGIUM SA—See Compagnie de Saint-Gobain SA; *Int'l*, pg. 1728
SGGS GLASINDUSTRIE BOERMANS—See Compagnie de Saint-Gobain SA; *Int'l*, pg. 1728
SGG SUISSE S.A.—See Astorg Partners S.A.S.; *Int'l*, pg. 657
SG HAMBROS BANK & TRUST LIMITED—See Societe Generale S.A.; *Int'l*, pg. 7041
SG HAMBROS LIMITED—See Societe Generale S.A.; *Int'l*, pg. 7041
SGH ENERGY PTY LIMITED—See Seven Group Holdings Limited; *Int'l*, pg. 6733
SGH GLOBAL JAPAN CO., LTD.—See SG Holdings Co., Ltd.; *Int'l*, pg. 6740
SG HOLDINGS CO., LTD.; *Int'l*, pg. 6740
SG HOLDINGS GLOBAL PTE. LTD.—See SG Holdings Co., Ltd.; *Int'l*, pg. 6740
SG HOMECARE, INC.—See Sverica Capital Management LP; *U.S. Private*, pg. 3888
SGH UG—See TotalEnergies SE; *Int'l*, pg. 7837
SGI-AVIATION SERVICES B.V.—See FinTech Global Incorporated; *Int'l*, pg. 2677
SGI CANADA INSURANCE SERVICES LTD.—See Crown Investments Corporation of Saskatchewan; *Int'l*, pg. 1857
SGIC GENERAL INSURANCE LIMITED—See Insurance Australia Group Limited; *Int'l*, pg. 3725
SGI INC.; *U.S. Private*, pg. 3622
SG INNOVATION HUB PTE. LTD.—See Rumah & Co. Pte. Ltd.; *Int'l*, pg. 6427
SGI SOCIETE DE GALVANOPLASTIE INDUSTRIELLE S.A.S.—See Aalberts N.V.; *Int'l*, pg. 35
SGIS SONGSHAN CO., LTD.; *Int'l*, pg. 6741
SGI VACATION CLUB BERHAD—See OSK Holdings Berhad; *Int'l*, pg. 5651
SG KLEINWORT HAMBROS BANK (CI) LIMITED—See Societe Generale S.A.; *Int'l*, pg. 7041
SG KLEINWORT HAMBROS BANK (GIBRALTAR) LIMITED—See Societe Generale S.A.; *Int'l*, pg. 7041
SG KLEINWORT HAMBROS BANK LIMITED—See Societe Generale S.A.; *Int'l*, pg. 7041
SGK LLC—See Matthews International Corporation; *U.S. Public*, pg. 1400
SGK SERVICEGESELLSCHAFT KREDITMANAGEMENT MBH—See Norddeutsche Landesbank Girozentrale; *Int'l*, pg. 5417
SG LAB S.R.L.—See Stevanato Group S.p.A.; *Int'l*, pg. 7213
SGL AUTOMOTIVE CARBON FIBERS GMBH & CO. KG—See Bayerische Motoren Werke Aktiengesellschaft; *Int'l*, pg. 913
SGL AUTOMOTIVE CARBON FIBERS GMBH & CO. KG—See SGL Carbon SE; *Int'l*, pg. 6741
SGL BRAKES GMBH—See SGL Carbon SE; *Int'l*, pg. 6741
SGL CARBON ASIA-PACIFIC SDN. BHD.—See SGL Carbon SE; *Int'l*, pg. 6741
SGL CARBON FAR EAST LTD.—See SGL Carbon SE; *Int'l*, pg. 6741
SGL CARBON FIBERS AMERICA LLC—See SGL Carbon SE; *Int'l*, pg. 6741
SGL CARBON FIBERS LTD.—See SGL Carbon SE; *Int'l*, pg. 6741
SGL CARBON GMBH & CO. KG—See SGL Carbon SE; *Int'l*, pg. 6742
SGL CARBON GMBH—See SGL Carbon SE; *Int'l*, pg. 6741
SGL CARBON GRAPHITE TECHNIC CO. LTD.—See SGL Carbon SE; *Int'l*, pg. 6742
SGL CARBON HOLDINGS B.V.—See SGL Carbon SE; *Int'l*, pg. 6742
SGL CARBON HOLDING S.L.—See SGL Carbon SE; *Int'l*, pg. 6742
SGL CARBON INDIA PVT. LTD.—See Resistotech Industries Pvt Ltd; *Int'l*, pg. 6297
SGL CARBON JAPAN LTD.—See SGL Carbon SE; *Int'l*, pg. 6742
SGL CARBON KOREA LTD.—See SGL Carbon SE; *Int'l*, pg. 6742
SGL CARBON, LLC - SAINT MARYS—See SGL Carbon SE; *Int'l*, pg. 6742
SGL CARBON, LLC - SINKING SPRING—See SGL Carbon SE; *Int'l*, pg. 6742
SGL CARBON, LLC—See SGL Carbon SE; *Int'l*, pg. 6742
SGL CARBON LTD.—See SGL Carbon SE; *Int'l*, pg. 6742
SGL CARBON POLSKA S.A.—See SGL Carbon SE; *Int'l*, pg. 6742
SGL CARBON (PTY) LTD.—See SGL Carbon SE; *Int'l*, pg. 6741
SGL CARBON S.A.—See SGL Carbon SE; *Int'l*, pg. 6742
SGL CARBON S.A.S.—See SGL Carbon SE; *Int'l*, pg. 6742
SGL CARBON SE; *Int'l*, pg. 6741

SGL CARBON S.P.A.—See SGL Carbon SE; *Int'l*, pg. 6742
SGL CARBON TECHNIC LLC—See SGL Carbon SE; *Int'l*, pg. 6742
SGL CARBON TECHNIC S.A.S.—See SGL Carbon SE; *Int'l*, pg. 6742
SGL COMPOSITES GMBH & CO. KG—See SGL Carbon SE; *Int'l*, pg. 6742
SGL COMPOSITES GMBH—See SGL Carbon SE; *Int'l*, pg. 6742
SGL COMPOSITES S.A.—See SGL Carbon SE; *Int'l*, pg. 6742
SG LEASING—See Societe Generale S.A.; *Int'l*, pg. 7039
SGL EPO GMBH—See SGL Carbon SE; *Int'l*, pg. 6742
SGL GELTER S.A.—See SGL Carbon SE; *Int'l*, pg. 6742
SGL GRAPHITE SOLUTIONS POLSKA SP. Z O.O.—See SGL Carbon SE; *Int'l*, pg. 6742
SGL GRAPHITE VERDELLO S.R.L.—See SGL Carbon SE; *Int'l*, pg. 6742
SGL PROCESS TECHNOLOGY PTE. LTD.—See SGL Carbon SE; *Int'l*, pg. 6742
SGL QUANHAI CARBON (SHANXI) CO., LTD.—See SGL Carbon SE; *Int'l*, pg. 6742
SGL QUANHAI HIGH-TECH MATERIALS (SHANXI) CO. LTD.—See SGL Carbon SE; *Int'l*, pg. 6742
SGL SPEZIAL- UND BERGBAU-SERVICEGESELLSCHAFT LAUCHHAMMER MBH—See General Atomics; *U.S. Private*, pg. 1664
SGL TECHNIC INC.—See SGL Carbon SE; *Int'l*, pg. 6742
SGL TECHNIC LTD.—See SGL Carbon SE; *Int'l*, pg. 6742
SGL TECHNOLOGIES GMBH—See SGL Carbon SE; *Int'l*, pg. 6742
SGL TECHNOLOGIES LLC—See SGL Carbon SE; *Int'l*, pg. 6742
SGL TOKAI CARBON LTD.—See SGL Carbon SE; *Int'l*, pg. 6742
SG MANAGEMENT GMBH—See Landesbank Baden-Wurttemberg; *Int'l*, pg. 4405
SG MART LTD.; *Int'l*, pg. 6740
S.G. MATERIAUX DE CONSTRUCTION—See Compagnie de Saint-Gobain SA; *Int'l*, pg. 1725
S.G.M. DISTRIBUZIONE S.R.L.—See Rhone Group, LLC; *U.S. Private*, pg. 3424
SG MEDICAL PTE LTD—See ResMed Inc.; *U.S. Public*, pg. 1791
SG METALS PTE. LTD.—See Sin Ghee Huat Corporation Ltd.; *Int'l*, pg. 6935
SG METALS (SUZHOU) LTD.—See Sin Ghee Huat Corporation Ltd.; *Int'l*, pg. 6935
SG MICRO CORP.; *Int'l*, pg. 6740
SGM OPERATION CO., LTD.—See Sekisui House, Ltd.; *Int'l*, pg. 6697
S.G. MORRIS CO., LLC—See Applied Industrial Technologies, Inc.; *U.S. Public*, pg. 171
SG MOTORS CO., LTD.—See SG Holdings Co., Ltd.; *Int'l*, pg. 6740
SG MOVING CO., LTD.—See SG Holdings Co., Ltd.; *Int'l*, pg. 6740
S.G.M. S.R.L.—See CAD It S.p.A.; *Int'l*, pg. 1247
SGN GROUP OY; *Int'l*, pg. 6742
SGN TELECOMS LIMITED; *Int'l*, pg. 6742
SG OPTION EUROPE SA—See Societe Generale S.A.; *Int'l*, pg. 7041
SG POWER LIMITED; *Int'l*, pg. 6741
SG PRIVATE BANKING BELGIQUE—See Societe Generale S.A.; *Int'l*, pg. 7041
SG PRIVATE BANKING (JAPAN) LTD—See Societe Generale S.A.; *Int'l*, pg. 7041
SG PRIVATE BANKING MONACO—See Societe Generale S.A.; *Int'l*, pg. 7041
SG PRIVATE BANKING (SUISSE) SA—See Societe Generale S.A.; *Int'l*, pg. 7041
SG PRIVATE EQUITY CO., LTD.; *Int'l*, pg. 6741
SG PROFESSIONAL SERVICES B.V.—See Advent International Corporation; *U.S. Private*, pg. 97
SG PROFESSIONAL SERVICES B.V.—See Centerbridge Partners, L.P.; *U.S. Private*, pg. 813
SGPY—See Danone; *Int'l*, pg. 1968
S. GRAHAM & ASSOCIATES; *U.S. Private*, pg. 3515
SG REALTY CO., LTD.—See SG Holdings Co., Ltd.; *Int'l*, pg. 6740
SG RESIDENTIAL, INC.—See Safe & Green Holdings Corp.; *U.S. Public*, pg. 1834
S GROUP INC.; *U.S. Private*, pg. 3512
S-GROUP SOLUTIONS AB—See Addnode Group AB; *Int'l*, pg. 130
SGRP MERIDIAN (PTY), LTD.—See SPAR Group, Inc.; *U.S. Public*, pg. 1914
SGRP MERIDIAN—See SPAR Group, Inc.; *U.S. Public*, pg. 1914
SGS ACCUTEST INC—See SGS SA; *Int'l*, pg. 6745
SGS ADRIATICA, D.O.O.—See SGS SA; *Int'l*, pg. 6743
SGS ADVANCED TESTING & ENGINEERING INC.—See SGS SA; *Int'l*, pg. 6745
SGS ARGENTINA S.A.—See SGS SA; *Int'l*, pg. 6743
SGS ASTER SA—See SGS SA; *Int'l*, pg. 6743
SGS AUSTRALIA PTY LTD.—See SGS SA; *Int'l*, pg. 6743
SGS AUSTRIA CONTROLL-CO. GES.M.B.H.—See SGS SA; *Int'l*, pg. 6743

CORPORATE AFFILIATIONS

SGS AUTOMOTIVE ALBANIA SH.P.K.—See SGS SA; *Int'l*, pg. 6743
SGS BANGLADESH LIMITED—See SGS SA; *Int'l*, pg. 6743
SGS BELGIUM N.V.—See SGS SA; *Int'l*, pg. 6743
SGS BEOGRAD D.O.O.—See SGS SA; *Int'l*, pg. 6743
SGS BOLIVIA S.A.—See SGS SA; *Int'l*, pg. 6743
SGS BULGARIA LTD.—See SGS SA; *Int'l*, pg. 6743
SGS BURKINA SA—See SGS SA; *Int'l*, pg. 6743
SGS (CAMBODIA) LTD.—See SGS SA; *Int'l*, pg. 6743
SGS CAMEROUN SA—See SGS SA; *Int'l*, pg. 6743
SGS CANADA INC.—See SGS SA; *Int'l*, pg. 6745
SGS CANADA INC.—See SGS SA; *Int'l*, pg. 6745
SGS CENTRAL AMERICA SA—See SGS SA; *Int'l*, pg. 6743
SGS CHEMICAL SOLUTIONS LABORATORIES INC.—See SGS SA; *Int'l*, pg. 6745
SGS COLOMBIA SAS—See SGS SA; *Int'l*, pg. 6743
SGS CONGO S.A.—See SGS SA; *Int'l*, pg. 6743
SGS CONTROL SERVICES, INC.—See SGS SA; *Int'l*, pg. 6745
SGS CORREL RAIL LTD—See SGS SA; *Int'l*, pg. 6744
SGS-CSTC STANDARDS TECHNICAL SERVICES CO. LTD.—See SGS SA; *Int'l*, pg. 6746
SGS CZECH REPUBLIC S.R.O.—See SGS SA; *Int'l*, pg. 6743
SGS DANMARK A/S—See SGS SA; *Int'l*, pg. 6743
SGS DEL ECUADOR S.A.—See SGS SA; *Int'l*, pg. 6746
SGS DE MEXICO, S.A. DE C.V—See SGS SA; *Int'l*, pg. 6746
SGS DO BRASIL LTDA.—See SGS SA; *Int'l*, pg. 6746
SG SECURITIES (HONG KONG) LIMITED—See Societe Generale S.A.; *Int'l*, pg. 7041
SG SECURITIES KOREA CO., LTD.—See Societe Generale S.A.; *Int'l*, pg. 7041
SG SECURITIES (PARIS) SAS—See Societe Generale S.A.; *Int'l*, pg. 7041
SGS EGYPT LTD—See SGS SA; *Int'l*, pg. 6743
SGS ENGINEERING CO., LTD.—See Nippon Electric Glass Co., Ltd.; *Int'l*, pg. 5314
SGS ENTERPRISES INC.; *U.S. Private*, pg. 3622
SGS ENVIRONMENTAL SERVICES INC.—See SGS SA; *Int'l*, pg. 6745
SG SERVICE PLUS CO. LTD.—See Singer Thailand Public Company Limited; *Int'l*, pg. 6943
SGS SERVICES SA—See Societe Generale S.A.; *Int'l*, pg. 7041
SGS ESPANOLA DE CONTROL S.A.—See SGS SA; *Int'l*, pg. 6743
SGS ESTONIA LTD.—See SGS SA; *Int'l*, pg. 6743
SGS FIMKO OY—See SGS SA; *Int'l*, pg. 6743
SGS FRANCE SAS—See SGS SA; *Int'l*, pg. 6743
SGS GEORGIA LTD.—See SGS SA; *Int'l*, pg. 6743
SGS GERMANY GMBH—See SGS SA; *Int'l*, pg. 6743
SGS GHANA LIMITED—See SGS SA; *Int'l*, pg. 6743
SGS GLOBAL TRADE SOLUTIONS PHILIPPINES, INC.—See SGS SA; *Int'l*, pg. 6743
SGS GOTTFELD NDT SERVICES GMBH—See SGS SA; *Int'l*, pg. 6743
SGS GREECE SA—See SGS SA; *Int'l*, pg. 6743
SGS GROUP MANAGEMENT SA—See SGS SA; *Int'l*, pg. 6744
SGSG SCIENCE&TECHNOLOGY CO LTD ZHUHAI; *Int'l*, pg. 6746
SGS GUAM INC.—See SGS SA; *Int'l*, pg. 6744
SGS GUINEE CONAKRY SA—See SGS SA; *Int'l*, pg. 6744
SGS GULF LIMITED—See SGS SA; *Int'l*, pg. 6744
SGS HONG KONG LIMITED—See SGS SA; *Int'l*, pg. 6744
SGS HORIZON B.V.—See SGS SA; *Int'l*, pg. 6744
SGS HUNGARIA KFT.—See SGS SA; *Int'l*, pg. 6744
SGS IBR LABORATORIES, INC.—See SGS SA; *Int'l*, pg. 6745
SGS-IMME MONGOLIA LLC—See SGS SA; *Int'l*, pg. 6746
SGS INDIA PRIVATE LTD—See SGS SA; *Int'l*, pg. 6744
SGS INDUSTRIAL - INSTALACAOES, TESTES E COMISSIONAMENTOS LTDA.—See SGS SA; *Int'l*, pg. 6744
SGS INSPECTION SERVICES NIGERIA LIMITED—See SGS SA; *Int'l*, pg. 6744
SGS INSPECTION SERVICES OY—See SGS SA; *Int'l*, pg. 6744
SGS INSPECTION SERVICES SAUDI ARABIA LTD.—See SGS SA; *Int'l*, pg. 6744
SGS INSTITUT FRESENIUS GMBH—See SGS SA; *Int'l*, pg. 6744
SGS INTERMODAL TRANSPORTATION SERVICES INC.—See SGS SA; *Int'l*, pg. 6745
SGS INTERNATIONAL CERTIFICATION SERVICES, INC.—See SGS SA; *Int'l*, pg. 6745
SGS INTERNATIONAL, INC.—See HPS Investment Partners, LLC; *U.S. Private*, pg. 1997
SGS IRAN (PRIVATE JOINT STOCK) LIMITED—See SGS SA; *Int'l*, pg. 6744
SGS IRELAND (HOLDINGS) LIMITED—See SGS SA; *Int'l*, pg. 6744
SGS ITALIA S.P.A.—See SGS SA; *Int'l*, pg. 6744
SGS JAPAN INC.—See SGS SA; *Int'l*, pg. 6744
SGS (JORDAN) PRIVATE SHAREHOLDING COMPANY—See SGS SA; *Int'l*, pg. 6743

COMPANY NAME INDEX

SGS KAZAKHSTAN LIMITED—See SGS SA; *Int'l*, pg. 6744
SGS KENYA LIMITED—See SGS SA; *Int'l*, pg. 6744
SGS KLAIPEDA LTD—See SGS SA; *Int'l*, pg. 6744
SGS KOREA CO., LTD—See SGS SA; *Int'l*, pg. 6744
SGS KUWAIT W.L.L.—See SGS SA; *Int'l*, pg. 6744
SGS LANKA (PRIVATE) LIMITED—See SGS SA; *Int'l*, pg. 6744
SGS LATVIJA LIMITED—See SGS SA; *Int'l*, pg. 6744
SGS (LIBAN) S.A.L.—See SGS SA; *Int'l*, pg. 6743
SGS LIBERIA INC—See SGS SA; *Int'l*, pg. 6744
SGS LIFE SCIENCE SERVICES - NORTHVIEW LABORATORY—See SGS SA; *Int'l*, pg. 6745
SGS, LLC.; *U.S. Private*, pg. 3622
SGS LUXEMBOURG S.A—See SGS SA; *Int'l*, pg. 6744
SGS (MALAYSIA) SDN. BHD—See SGS SA; *Int'l*, pg. 6743
SGS MALI SARLU—See SGS SA; *Int'l*, pg. 6744
SGS MAROC SA—See SGS SA; *Int'l*, pg. 6744
SGS (MAURITIUS) LTD—See SGS SA; *Int'l*, pg. 6743
SGS MCNET MOCAMBIQUE LIMITADA—See SGS SA; *Int'l*, pg. 6744
SGS MINERALS RDC SARL—See SGS SA; *Int'l*, pg. 6744
SGS MINSK LTD—See SGS SA; *Int'l*, pg. 6744
S.G. SMITH (MOTORS) BECKENHAM LIMITED—See Marshall of Cambridge (Holdings) Limited; *Int'l*, pg. 4702
S.G. SMITH (MOTORS) CROYDON LIMITED—See Marshall of Cambridge (Holdings) Limited; *Int'l*, pg. 4702
S.G. SMITH (MOTORS) SYDENHAM LIMITED—See Marshall of Cambridge (Holdings) Limited; *Int'l*, pg. 4702
SGS MOCAMBIQUE, LIMITADA—See SGS SA; *Int'l*, pg. 6744
SGS (MOLDOVA) S.A.—See SGS SA; *Int'l*, pg. 6743
SGS MONGOLIA LLC—See SGS SA; *Int'l*, pg. 6744
SGS M-SCAN LIMITED—See SGS SA; *Int'l*, pg. 6744
SGS (MYANMAR) LIMITED—See SGS SA; *Int'l*, pg. 6743
SGS NEDERLAND B.V.—See SGS SA; *Int'l*, pg. 6744
SGS NEW ZEALAND LIMITED—See SGS SA; *Int'l*, pg. 6744
SGS NORGE A/S—See SGS SA; *Int'l*, pg. 6744
SGS NORTH AMERICA INC. - GOVERNMENTS & INSTITUTIONS SERVICES—See SGS SA; *Int'l*, pg. 6745
SGS NORTH AMERICA INC. - MINERAL SERVICES DIVISION, DENVER—See SGS SA; *Int'l*, pg. 6745
SGS NORTH AMERICA INC. - MINERALS SERVICES DIVISION—See SGS SA; *Int'l*, pg. 6745
SGS NORTH AMERICA INC.—See SGS SA; *Int'l*, pg. 6744
SGS OIL, GAS & CHEMICALS, SAS—See SGS SA; *Int'l*, pg. 6745
SGS PAKISTAN (PRIVATE) LIMITED—See SGS SA; *Int'l*, pg. 6745
SGS PANAMA CONTROL SERVICES INC.—See SGS SA; *Int'l*, pg. 6745
SGS PARAGUAY S.A.—See SGS SA; *Int'l*, pg. 6745
SGSP (AUSTRALIA) ASSETS PTY. LTD.—See State Grid Corporation of China; *Int'l*, pg. 7183
SGSP (AUSTRALIA) ASSETS PTY. LTD.—See Temasek Holdings (Private) Limited; *Int'l*, pg. 7551
SG SPECIALTY METALS PTE. LTD.—See Sin Ghee Huat Corporation Ltd.; *Int'l*, pg. 6935
SGS PETROLEUM SERVICE CORPORATION—See SGS SA; *Int'l*, pg. 6745
SGS PHILIPPINES, INC—See SGS SA; *Int'l*, pg. 6745
SGS PNG PTY. LIMITED—See SGS SA; *Int'l*, pg. 6745
SGS POLSKA SP. Z.O.O.—See SGS SA; *Int'l*, pg. 6745
SGS PORTUGAL - SOCIEDADE GERAL DE SUPERINTENDENCIA SA—See SGS SA; *Int'l*, pg. 6745
SGS QUALITEST ALGERIE SPA—See SGS SA; *Int'l*, pg. 6745
SGS QUALITEST INDUSTRIE SAS—See SGS SA; *Int'l*, pg. 6745
SGS RDC SPRL—See SGS SA; *Int'l*, pg. 6745
SGS ROMANIA S.A.—See SGS SA; *Int'l*, pg. 6745
SGS SA; *Int'l*, pg. 6742
SGS SCANNING NIGERIA LIMITED—See SGS SA; *Int'l*, pg. 6745
SGS-SCHWARZHEIDER GASTRONOMIE UND SERVICE GMBH—See BASF SE; *Int'l*, pg. 884
SGS SCIENTIFIC SERVICES PTY LTD—See SGS SA; *Int'l*, pg. 6743
SGSS DEUTSCHLAND KAPITALANLAGEGESELLSCHAFT MBH—See Societe Generale S.A.; *Int'l*, pg. 7041
SGS SENEGAL S.A.—See SGS SA; *Int'l*, pg. 6745
SGS SLOVAKIA SPOL.S.R.O.—See SGS SA; *Int'l*, pg. 6745
SGS SLOVENIJA D.O.O.—See SGS SA; *Int'l*, pg. 6745
SGS SOCIETE GENERALE DE SURVEILLANCE SA—See SGS SA; *Int'l*, pg. 6745
SGS SOLUTIONS GMBH—See Syrma SGS Technology Limited; *Int'l*, pg. 7387
SGS SOUTH AFRICA (PROPRIETARY) LIMITED—See SGS SA; *Int'l*, pg. 6745
SGS SUPERVISE GOZETME ETUD KONTROL SERVISLERI ANONIM SIRKETI—See SGS SA; *Int'l*, pg. 6745
SGS SWEDEN AB—See SGS SA; *Int'l*, pg. 6746

SGS TAIWAN LIMITED—See SGS SA; *Int'l*, pg. 6746
SGS TANZANIA SUPERINTENDENCE CO. LIMITED—See SGS SA; *Int'l*, pg. 6746
SGS TASHKENT LTD.—See SGS SA; *Int'l*, pg. 6746
SGS TECNOS, SA, SOCIEDAD UNIPERSONAL—See SGS SA; *Int'l*, pg. 6746
SGS TECNOS, S.A.—See SGS SA; *Int'l*, pg. 6746
SGS TESTCOM, INC.—See SGS SA; *Int'l*, pg. 6745
SGS TESTING & CONTROL SERVICES SINGAPORE PTE LTD.—See SGS SA; *Int'l*, pg. 6746
SGS (THAILAND) LIMITED—See SGS SA; *Int'l*, pg. 6743
SGS TOGO S.A.—See SGS SA; *Int'l*, pg. 6746
SGS TUNISIE S.A.R.L.—See Concentrix Corporation; *U.S. Public*, pg. 565
SGS TURKMEN LTD.—See SGS SA; *Int'l*, pg. 6746
SGS UGANDA LIMITED—See SGS SA; *Int'l*, pg. 6746
SGS UKRAINE, FOREIGN ENTERPRISE—See SGS SA; *Int'l*, pg. 6746
SGS UNITED KINGDOM LIMITED—See SGS SA; *Int'l*, pg. 6746
SGS URUGUAY LIMITADA—See SGS SA; *Int'l*, pg. 6746
SGS U.S. TESTING COMPANY INC.—See SGS SA; *Int'l*, pg. 6745
SGS VIETNAM LTD.—See SGS SA; *Int'l*, pg. 6746
SGS VOSTOK LIMITED—See KONE Oyj; *Int'l*, pg. 4250
SG SYSTEMS CO., LTD.—See SG Holdings Co., Ltd.; *Int'l*, pg. 6743
SGT 2000 INC.—See TFI International Inc.; *Int'l*, pg. 7586
SG TECH HOLDINGS LIMITED—See CW Group Holdings Limited; *Int'l*, pg. 1890
SG TECHNOLOGIES INC—See Liaoning SG Automotive Group Co., Ltd.; *Int'l*, pg. 4483
S.G. TORRICE CO., INC.—See Ferguson plc; *Int'l*, pg. 2638
SGT SOLUTIONS PROPRIETARY LIMITED—See AYO Technology Solutions Ltd.; *Int'l*, pg. 775
SGT SOLUTIONS PROPRIETARY LIMITED—See AYO Technology Solutions Ltd.; *Int'l*, pg. 775
SGT SOLUTIONS PROPRIETARY LIMITED—See AYO Technology Solutions Ltd.; *Int'l*, pg. 775
SGT SOLUTIONS PROPRIETARY LIMITED—See AYO Technology Solutions Ltd.; *Int'l*, pg. 775
SGUAS PTY LTD—See Steadfast Group Limited; *Int'l*, pg. 7187
SG WHOLESALE ROOFING SUPPLIES; *U.S. Private*, pg. 3622
SGWICUS BANGLADESH LTD.—See SG Corporation; *Int'l*, pg. 6740
SGWICUS CORPORATION - CASUAL WEAR EXPORT DIVISION 1—See SG Corporation; *Int'l*, pg. 6740
SGWICUS CORPORATION - CASUAL WEAR EXPORT DIVISION 2—See SG Corporation; *Int'l*, pg. 6740
SGWICUS CORPORATION - GARMENT EXPORT DIVISION—See SG Corporation; *Int'l*, pg. 6740
SGWICUS CORPORATION - LADIES GARMENT DIVISION—See SG Corporation; *Int'l*, pg. 6740
SGWICUS USA, INC—See SG Corporation; *Int'l*, pg. 6740
SGW INTEGRATED MARKETING COMMUNICATIONS, INC.; *U.S. Private*, pg. 3622
SGX EUROPE SP. Z.O.O.—See Amphenol Corporation; *U.S. Public*, pg. 132
SGX LINK PTE LTD—See Singapore Exchange Limited; *Int'l*, pg. 6940
SGX SENSORTECH CHINA LIMITED—See Amphenol Corporation; *U.S. Public*, pg. 132
SGX SENSORTECH GMBH—See Amphenol Corporation; *U.S. Public*, pg. 132
SGX SENSORTECH LTD.—See Baird Financial Group, Inc.; *U.S. Private*, pg. 453
SGX SENSORTECH SA—See Amphenol Corporation; *U.S. Public*, pg. 132
SHAANXI AEROSPACE POWER HIGH-TECH CO., LTD.; *Int'l*, pg. 6746
SHAANXI AIERFU ACTIVTISSUE ENGINEERING COMPANY LIMITED—See China Regenerative Medicine International Co., Ltd.; *Int'l*, pg. 1547
SHAANXI BAOGUANG VACUUM ELECTRONIC APPARATUS CO., LTD.; *Int'l*, pg. 6746
SHAANXI BEIREN PRINTING MACHINERY CO., LTD.—See Beijing Jingcheng Machinery Electric Holding Co., Ltd.; *Int'l*, pg. 953
SHAANXI BEIYUAN CHEMICAL INDUSTRY GROUP CO., LTD.; *Int'l*, pg. 6746
SHAANXI BROADCAST & TV NETWORK INTERMEDIARY (GROUP) CO., LTD.; *Int'l*, pg. 6747
SHAANXI CHINLINK FINANCIAL GUARANTEE LIMITED—See ChinLink International Holdings Limited; *Int'l*, pg. 1570
SHAANXI CNG NEW TECHNOLOGY CO., LTD.—See China Glass Holdings Limited; *Int'l*, pg. 1504
SHAANXI COAL INDUSTRY COMPANY LIMITED; *Int'l*, pg. 6747
SHAANXI CONSTRUCTION ENGINEERING GROUP CORPORATION LIMITED; *Int'l*, pg. 6747
SHAANXI CONSTRUCTION ENGINEERING INSTALLATION GROUP CO., LTD.—See Shaanxi Construction Engineering Group Corporation Limited; *Int'l*, pg. 6747
SHAANXI CONSTRUCTION MACHINERY CO., LTD.; *Int'l*, pg. 6747

SHAFER COMMERCIAL SEATING INC.

SHAANXI ELECTRIC POWER COMPANY—See State Grid Corporation of China; *Int'l*, pg. 7183
SHAANXI FENGHUO ELECTRONICS CO., LTD.; *Int'l*, pg. 6747
SHAANXI GUANZHONG TOOL MANUFACTURING CO., LTD.—See Qinchuan Machine Tool & Tool Group Share Co., Ltd.; *Int'l*, pg. 6141
SHAANXI HAIFENG ENERGY AUTOMATION CO., LTD.—See Endress+Hauser (International) Holding AG; *Int'l*, pg. 2409
SHAANXI HANDE AXLE CO., LTD.—See Shandong Heavy Industry Group Co., Ltd.; *Int'l*, pg. 6754
SHAANXI HEIMAO COKING CO., LTD.; *Int'l*, pg. 6747
SHAANXI HENGXING FRUIT JUICE CO., LTD.—See QAF Limited; *Int'l*, pg. 6132
SHAANXI HEYANGDER ADHESIVE PRODUCT CO., LTD.—See Yem Chio Co., Ltd.; *Int'l*, pg. 8577
SHAANXI INTERNATIONAL TRUST CO., LTD.; *Int'l*, pg. 6747
SHAANXI JINYE SCIENCE TECHNOLOGY & EDUCATION GROUP CO., LTD.; *Int'l*, pg. 6747
SHAANXI KANGHUI PHARMACEUTICAL CO., LTD.; *Int'l*, pg. 6747
SHAANXI LONGMEN IRON AND STEEL CO., LTD.—See General Steel Holdings, Inc.; *Int'l*, pg. 2920
SHAANXI MEINENG CLEAN ENERGY CORP., LTD.; *Int'l*, pg. 6747
SHAANXI NORTHWEST NEW TECHNOLOGY INDUSTRY COMPANY LIMITED; *Int'l*, pg. 6747
SHAANXI O.R.G. PACKAGING CO., LTD.—See ORG Technology Co., Ltd.; *Int'l*, pg. 5617
SHAANXI PANLONG PHARMACEUTICAL GROUP LIMITED BY SHARE LTD.; *Int'l*, pg. 6747
SHAANXI PROVINCIAL NATURAL GAS CO., LTD.; *Int'l*, pg. 6747
SHAANXI QINMING MEDICAL CO., LTD—See Lepu Medical Technology (Beijing) Co., Ltd.; *Int'l*, pg. 4466
SHAANXI SECOM SECURITY CO., LTD.—See SECOM Co., Ltd.; *Int'l*, pg. 6672
SHAANXI TECHTEAM JINONG HUMIC ACID PRODUCT CO., LTD—See China Green Agriculture, Inc.; *Int'l*, pg. 1505
SHAANXI TOPRAY SOLAR CO., LTD.—See Topray Solar Co., Ltd.; *Int'l*, pg. 7820
SHAANXI TUORI NEW ENERGY TECHNOLOGY CO., LTD.—See Topray Solar Co., Ltd.; *Int'l*, pg. 7820
SHAANXI UNISPLENDOUR LIFE CARE PHARMACEUTICAL CO., LTD.—See Kontafarma China Holdings Limited; *Int'l*, pg. 4276
SHAANXI XINGHUA CHEMISTRY CO., LTD.; *Int'l*, pg. 6747
SHAANXI YANCHANG PETROLEUM GROUP CO., LTD.; *Int'l*, pg. 6747
SHAANXI YANCHANG PETROLEUM MATERIAL CORP. LTD.—See Shaanxi Yanchang Petroleum Group Co., Ltd.; *Int'l*, pg. 6747
SHAANXI YAOBAI SPECIAL CEMENT CO. LTD—See West China Cement Limited; *Int'l*, pg. 8383
SHAANXI ZHONGTIAN ROCKET TECHNOLOGY CO., LTD.; *Int'l*, pg. 6747
SHABA CHEMICALS LIMITED; *Int'l*, pg. 6748
SHABBIR TILES & CERAMICS LTD; *Int'l*, pg. 6748
SHABBIR TILES & CERAMICS LTD - UNIT I—See Shabbir Tiles & Ceramics Ltd; *Int'l*, pg. 6748
SHACKLETON EQUITY PARTNERS LLC; *U.S. Private*, pg. 3622
SHACKS MOTOR GROUP PTY. LTD.; *Int'l*, pg. 6748
SHACOM FUTURES LIMITED—See Shanghai Commercial Bank Limited; *Int'l*, pg. 6763
SHACOM INSURANCE BROKERS LIMITED—See Shanghai Commercial Bank Limited; *Int'l*, pg. 6763
SHADAB TEXTILE MILLS LIMITED; *Int'l*, pg. 6748
SHADDOCK DEVELOPMENT CO.; *U.S. Private*, pg. 3622
SHADE LANDFILL, INC.—See Waste Management, Inc.; *U.S. Public*, pg. 2332
SHADE-O-MATIC LTD.—See 3G Capital Partners L.P.; *U.S. Private*, pg. 12
SHADES OF LIGHT LLC; *U.S. Private*, pg. 3622
SHADIN, LP—See Gardner Standard LLC; *U.S. Private*, pg. 1644
SHADMAN COTTON MILLS LTD.; *Int'l*, pg. 6748
SHADOW CONCEPTS LLC; *U.S. Private*, pg. 3622
SHADOW DIALYSIS, LLC—See DaVita Inc.; *U.S. Public*, pg. 643
SHADOWFAX CORPORATION; *U.S. Private*, pg. 3622
THE SHADOWLIGHT GROUP, LTD—See TC Studios, LLC; *U.S. Private*, pg. 3942
SHADOWLINE INCORPORATED; *U.S. Private*, pg. 3622
SHADOW MOUNTAIN BEHAVIORAL HEALTH SYSTEM, LLC—See Universal Health Services, Inc.; *U.S. Public*, pg. 2259
SHADOWOOD GOLF INC.—See Kocolene Marketing, LLC; *U.S. Private*, pg. 2335
SHADOW WOOD COUNTRY CLUB, INC.; *U.S. Private*, pg. 3622
SHADY LANE, INC.; *U.S. Private*, pg. 3623
SHAFER COMMERCIAL SEATING INC.; *U.S. Private*, pg. 3623

SHAFER, KLINE & WARREN, INC.   CORPORATE AFFILIATIONS

SHAFER, KLINE & WARREN, INC.; *U.S. Private*, pg. 3623
SHAFER PROPERTY COMPANY INC.; *U.S. Private*, pg. 3623
SHAFER SEED COMPANY, INC.—See Wagner's LLC; *U.S. Private*, pg. 4426
SHAFFER DISTRIBUTING COMPANY; *U.S. Private*, pg. 3623
SHAFFER ENTERPRISES INC.; *U.S. Private*, pg. 3623
SHAFFER TRUCKING COMPANY—See Crete Carrier Corp.; *U.S. Private*, pg. 1099
SHAFFER TRUCKING COMPANY—See Crete Carrier Corp.; *U.S. Private*, pg. 1099
SHAFFI CHEMICAL INDUSTRIES LIMITED; *Int'l*, pg. 6748
SHAFFNER-HEANEY ASSOCIATES INC.; *U.S. Private*, pg. 3623
SHAFTESBURY CAPITAL PLC; *Int'l*, pg. 6748
SHAFTESBURY CARNABY LIMITED—See Shaftesbury Plc; *Int'l*, pg. 6748
SHAFTESBURY CHARLOTTE STREET LIMITED—See Shaftesbury Plc; *Int'l*, pg. 6748
SHAFTESBURY CHINATOWN LIMITED—See Shaftesbury Plc; *Int'l*, pg. 6748
SHAFTESBURY COVENT GARDEN LIMITED—See Shaftesbury Plc; *Int'l*, pg. 6748
SHAFTESBURY PLC; *Int'l*, pg. 6748
SHAGANG (AUSTRALIA) CO., LTD.—See Jiangsu Shagang Group Ltd.; *Int'l*, pg. 3954
SHAGANG INTERNATIONAL (SINGAPORE) PTE. LTD.—See Jiangsu Shagang Group Ltd.; *Int'l*, pg. 3954
SHAGANG INTL. MIDDLE EAST CO., LTD.—See Jiangsu Shagang Group Ltd.; *Int'l*, pg. 3954
SHAGANG INTL. (SINGAPORE) CO., LTD.—See Jiangsu Shagang Group Ltd.; *Int'l*, pg. 3954
SHAGANG MINING (AUSTRALIA) PTY LTD—See Jiangsu Shagang Group Ltd.; *Int'l*, pg. 3954
SHAGANG SOUTH-ASIA (HONG KONG) CO., LTD.—See Jiangsu Shagang Group Ltd.; *Int'l*, pg. 3954
SHAGANG SOUTH ASIA (HONGKONG) TRADE CO., LTD.—See Jiangsu Shagang Group Ltd.; *Int'l*, pg. 3954
SHAGANG STEEL & IRON TRADE CO., LTD.—See Jiangsu Shagang Group Ltd.; *Int'l*, pg. 3954
SHAGRIR GROUP VEHICLE SERVICES LTD.; *Int'l*, pg. 6748
SHAGRIR MOTOR VEHICLE SYSTEMS LTD.—See PowerFleet, Inc.; *U.S. Public*, pg. 1706
SHAHAB SHISHEH INDUSTRIAL COMPANY—See Pars Tousheh Investment Company; *Int'l*, pg. 5746
SHAHAB TOUSHEH COMPANY—See Pars Tousheh Investment Company; *Int'l*, pg. 5746
SHAH ALLOYS LIMITED; *Int'l*, pg. 6748
SHAHAM INSURANCE AGENCIES LTD—See Shlomo Eliahu Holdings Ltd.; *Int'l*, pg. 6857
SHAH & ASSOCIATES, INC.; *U.S. Private*, pg. 3623
SHAHAWAN (M) SDN BHD—See Sunway Berhad; *Int'l*, pg. 7328
SHAH CAPITAL PARTNERS, LP; *U.S. Private*, pg. 3623
SHAH CONSTRUCTION COMPANY LIMITED; *Int'l*, pg. 6748
SHAHDAAB; *Int'l*, pg. 6748
SHAHDIRAN INC.; *Int'l*, pg. 6748
SHAHED COMPANY; *Int'l*, pg. 6749
SHAHEEN INSURANCE COMPANY LTD.; *Int'l*, pg. 6749
SHAHE INDUSTRIAL CO., LTD.; *Int'l*, pg. 6749
SHAH FOODS LTD; *Int'l*, pg. 6748
SHAHID BAHONAR COPPER IND. CO.; *Int'l*, pg. 6749
SHAHIN PLASTIC MANUFACTURING COMPANY; *Int'l*, pg. 6749
SHAHI SHIPPING LIMITED; *Int'l*, pg. 6749
SHAHJALAL ISLAMI BANK PLC; *Int'l*, pg. 6749
SHAHJALAL ISLAMI BANK SECURITIES LIMITED—See Shahjalal Islami Bank PLC; *Int'l*, pg. 6749
SHAHLON SILK INDUSTRIES LTD.; *Int'l*, pg. 6749
SHAH METACORP LIMITED.; *Int'l*, pg. 6748
SHAHMURAD SUGAR MILLS LIMITED; *Int'l*, pg. 6749
SHAHNAWAZ (PRIVATE) LIMITED—See SHAHTAJ SUGAR MILLS LIMITED; *Int'l*, pg. 6749
SHAHTAJ SUGAR MILLS LIMITED; *Int'l*, pg. 6749
SHAHTAJ TEXTILE LIMITED; *Int'l*, pg. 6749
SHAH TRADING COMPANY LIMITED; *Int'l*, pg. 6748
SHAHZAD TEXTILE MILLS LTD.; *Int'l*, pg. 6749
SHAILJA COMMERCIAL TRADE FRENZY LTD.; *Int'l*, pg. 6749
SHAILY ENGINEERING PLASTICS LIMITED; *Int'l*, pg. 6749
SHAIVAL REALITY LTD.; *Int'l*, pg. 6749
SHAJING GEM HIGH-TECH CO., LTD—See GEM Co., Ltd.; *Int'l*, pg. 2914
SHAKARGANJ LIMITED; *Int'l*, pg. 6749
SHAKARGANJ MILLS LIMITED - CRESCENT UJALA—See Shakarganj Limited; *Int'l*, pg. 6749
SHAKEN-BANKIN DEPOT INC.—See Autobacs Seven Co., Ltd.; *Int'l*, pg. 726
SHAKENKAN CO., LTD.—See Nissan Tokyo Sales Holdings Co., Ltd.; *Int'l*, pg. 5370
SHAKER CLINIC, LLC—See Acadia Healthcare Company, Inc.; *U.S. Public*, pg. 30

SHAKER RECRUITMENT ADVERTISING & COMMUNICATIONS, INC.; *U.S. Private*, pg. 3623
SHAKER RECRUITMENT ADVERTISING & COMMUNICATIONS, INC.—See Shaker Recruitment Advertising & Communications, Inc.; *U.S. Private*, pg. 3623
SHAKER RESOURCES INC.; *Int'l*, pg. 6749
SHAKERTOWN 1992, INC.—See The Clarke Group; *Int'l*, pg. 7633
SHAKE SHACK ENTERPRISES, LLC—See Shake Shack Inc.; *U.S. Public*, pg. 1873
SHAKE SHACK INC.; *U.S. Public*, pg. 1873
SHAKESPEARE (AUSTRALIA) PTY. LTD.—See One Rock Capital Partners, LLC; *U.S. Private*, pg. 3023
SHAKESPEARE CO., LLC - MONOFILAMENT DIVISION—See One Rock Capital Partners, LLC; *U.S. Private*, pg. 3023
SHAKESPEARE COMPANY, LLC—See One Rock Capital Partners, LLC; *U.S. Private*, pg. 3023
SHAKESPEARE MONOFILAMENT U.K. LTD.—See One Rock Capital Partners, LLC; *U.S. Private*, pg. 3023
SHAKESPEARE SQUARED; *U.S. Private*, pg. 3623
SHAKEY'S PIZZA ASIA VENTURES, INC.; *Int'l*, pg. 6749
SHAKEY'S USA, INC.—See Jacmar Companies, Inc.; *U.S. Private*, pg. 2179
SHAKLEE CANADA, INC.—See Activated Holdings LLC; *U.S. Private*, pg. 68
SHAKLEE CANADA, INC.—See Ripplewood Holdings LLC; *U.S. Private*, pg. 3439
SHAKLEE CORPORATION—See Activated Holdings LLC; *U.S. Private*, pg. 68
SHAKLEE CORPORATION—See Ripplewood Holdings LLC; *U.S. Private*, pg. 3439
SHAKLEE GLOBAL GROUP, INC.; *Int'l*, pg. 6750
SHAKLEE MEXICO, S.A. DE C.V.—See Activated Holdings LLC; *U.S. Private*, pg. 69
SHAKLEE MEXICO, S.A. DE C.V.—See Ripplewood Holdings LLC; *U.S. Private*, pg. 3439
SHAKLEE PRODUCTS (MALAYSIA) SDN. BHD.—See Activated Holdings LLC; *U.S. Private*, pg. 69
SHAKLEE PRODUCTS (MALAYSIA) SDN. BHD.—See Ripplewood Holdings LLC; *U.S. Private*, pg. 3439
SHAKLEE RESEARCH CENTER—See Activated Holdings LLC; *U.S. Private*, pg. 69
SHAKLEE RESEARCH CENTER—See Ripplewood Holdings LLC; *U.S. Private*, pg. 3439
SHAKLEE U.S.—See Activated Holdings LLC; *U.S. Private*, pg. 69
SHAKLEE U.S.—See Ripplewood Holdings LLC; *U.S. Private*, pg. 3440
SHAKOPEE CHEVROLET-OLDSMOBILE-PONTIAC-GEO, INC.; *U.S. Private*, pg. 3623
SHAKTI ENERGY SOLUTIONS PVT. LTD.—See Shakti Pumps (India) Ltd.; *Int'l*, pg. 6750
SHAKTI EV MOBILITY PVT. LTD.—See Shakti Pumps (India) Ltd.; *Int'l*, pg. 6750
SHAKTI HORMANN PRIVATE LIMITED—See Hormann KG Verkaufsgesellschaf; *Int'l*, pg. 3481
SHAKTI PRESS LIMITED; *Int'l*, pg. 6750
SHAKTI PUMPS (BANGLADESH) LTD.—See Shakti Pumps (India) Ltd.; *Int'l*, pg. 6750
SHAKTI PUMPS FZE—See Shakti Pumps (India) Ltd.; *Int'l*, pg. 6750
SHAKTI PUMPS (INDIA) LTD.; *Int'l*, pg. 6750
SHAKTI PUMPS USA LLC—See Shakti Pumps (India) Ltd.; *Int'l*, pg. 6750
SHALAG INDUSTRIES, LTD.; *Int'l*, pg. 6750
SHALAMUKA CAPITAL (PTY) LTD.; *Int'l*, pg. 6750
SHALBY ADVANCED TECHNOLOGIES INC.—See Shalby Limited; *Int'l*, pg. 6750
SHALBY GLOBAL TECHNOLOGIES PTE. LIMITED—See Shalby Limited; *Int'l*, pg. 6750
SHALBY LIMITED; *Int'l*, pg. 6750
SHALDAN (PHILIPPINES) INC.—See S.T. CORPORATION; *Int'l*, pg. 6457
SHALE GAS SERVICES, LLC—See Waste Connections, Inc.; *Int'l*, pg. 8354
SHALE-INLAND HOLDINGS LLC; *U.S. Private*, pg. 3623
SHALEPRO ENERGY SERVICES, LLC; *U.S. Private*, pg. 3623
SHALIBHADRA FINANCE LIMITED; *Int'l*, pg. 6750
SHALIMAR AGENCIES LTD.; *Int'l*, pg. 6750
SHALIMAR (MALAY) PLC—See Carson Cumberbatch PLC; *Int'l*, pg. 1347
SHALIMAR PAINTS LTD; *Int'l*, pg. 6750
SHALIMAR PRODUCTIONS LIMITED; *Int'l*, pg. 6750
SHALIMAR WIRES INDUSTRIES LTD.; *Int'l*, pg. 6750
SHALKIYAZINC LTD JSC—See National Mining Company Tau-Ken Samruk JSC; *Int'l*, pg. 5161
SHALLBETTER, INC.; *U.S. Private*, pg. 3623
SHALLOW FORD CONSTRUCTION CO.; *U.S. Private*, pg. 3623
SHALMET CORPORATION—See Carpenter Technology Corporation; *U.S. Public*, pg. 439
SHAL NETWORKS, LLC—See Windstream Holdings, Inc.; *U.S. Public*, pg. 2373
SHALOM PARK; *U.S. Private*, pg. 3623
SHALTZ FLUID POWER INC.; *U.S. Private*, pg. 3623
SHAMANJWALI METALS PVT. LTD.—See A.A.G. STUCCHI s.r.l.; *Int'l*, pg. 23

SHAMARAN PETROLEUM BV—See ShaMaran Petroleum Corp.; *Int'l*, pg. 6750
SHAMARAN PETROLEUM CORP.; *Int'l*, pg. 6750
SHAMA TECHNOLOGIES (S) PTE LTD.—See HUB Cyber Security Ltd.; *Int'l*, pg. 3516
SHAMAYM IMPROVE LTD.; *Int'l*, pg. 6750
SHAMBAUGH & SON - ED GRACE DIVISION—See EMCOR Group, Inc.; *U.S. Public*, pg. 739
SHAMBAUGH & SON, L.P.—See EMCOR Group, Inc.; *U.S. Public*, pg. 738
SHAMBHALA PUBLICATIONS INC.; *U.S. Private*, pg. 3623
SHAMEL PLASTIC INDUSTRIES LLC—See Oman International Development & Investment Company SAOG; *Int'l*, pg. 5560
SHAMIL BANK OF BAHRAIN B.S.C.—See Dar Al-Maal Al-Islami Trust; *Int'l*, pg. 1971
SHAMIN HOTELS INC.; *U.S. Private*, pg. 3623
SHAMIR INSIGHT, INC.—See EssilorLuxottica SA; *Int'l*, pg. 2516
SHAMIR OPTICAL INDUSTRY LTD.—See EssilorLuxottica SA; *Int'l*, pg. 2516
SHAMIR USA, INC.—See EssilorLuxottica SA; *Int'l*, pg. 2516
SHAMOT PLC.—See Synergon Holding PLC; *Int'l*, pg. 7384
SHAMROCK BANCSHARES, INC.; *U.S. Private*, pg. 3624
SHAMROCK BANK, N.A.—See Shamrock Bancshares, Inc.; *U.S. Private*, pg. 3624
SHAMROCK BANK OF FLORIDA; *U.S. Private*, pg. 3624
SHAMROCK BUILDING SERVICES CORP.; *U.S. Private*, pg. 3624
SHAMROCK CABINET & FIXTURE CORP.; *U.S. Private*, pg. 3624
SHAMROCK CAPITAL ADVISORS, LLC; *U.S. Private*, pg. 3624
SHAMROCK CHICAGO CORP.; *U.S. Private*, pg. 3624
THE SHAMROCK COMPANIES INC.; *U.S. Private*, pg. 4117
THE SHAMROCK COMPANY—See The Shamrock Companies Inc.; *U.S. Private*, pg. 4117
SHAMROCK CONCRETE COMPANY—See Lyman-Richey Corporation; *U.S. Private*, pg. 2520
SHAMROCK CORPORATION; *U.S. Private*, pg. 3624
SHAMROCK CO.; *U.S. Private*, pg. 3624
SHAMROCK ENVIRONMENTAL CORPORATION—See CenterOak Partners LLC; *U.S. Private*, pg. 816
SHAMROCK FARMS DAIRY DIVISION—See Shamrock Foods Company; *U.S. Private*, pg. 3624
SHAMROCK FOODS - ARIZONA FOODS DIVISION—See Shamrock Foods Company; *U.S. Private*, pg. 3624
SHAMROCK FOODS - COLORADO FOODS DIVISION—See Shamrock Foods Company; *U.S. Private*, pg. 3624
SHAMROCK FOODS COMPANY; *U.S. Private*, pg. 3624
SHAMROCK FOODS - NEW MEXICO FOODS DIVISION—See Shamrock Foods Company; *U.S. Private*, pg. 3624
SHAMROCK HOLDINGS, INC.; *U.S. Private*, pg. 3624
SHAMROCK HOLDINGS OF CALIFORNIA, INC.—See Shamrock Holdings, Inc.; *U.S. Private*, pg. 3624
SHAMROCK HOME LOANS, INC.—See Lendbuzz, Inc.; *U.S. Private*, pg. 2421
SHAMROCK INDUSTRIAL CO., LTD.; *Int'l*, pg. 6751
SHAMROCK MATERIALS INC. - BUILDING MATERIALS DIVISION—See Vulcan Materials Company; *U.S. Public*, pg. 2313
SHAMROCK MATERIALS INC. - SAND & GRAVEL DIVISION—See Vulcan Materials Company; *U.S. Public*, pg. 2313
SHAMROCK MATERIALS INC.—See Vulcan Materials Company; *U.S. Public*, pg. 2313
SHAMROCK MATERIALS OF NOVATO INC.—See Vulcan Materials Company; *U.S. Public*, pg. 2313
SHAMROCK OFFICE SOLUTIONS—See Oval Partners; *U.S. Private*, pg. 3052
SHAMROCK SCIENTIFIC SPECIALTY SYSTEMS, INC.; *U.S. Private*, pg. 3624
SHAMROCK SEED COMPANY INC.—See Groupe Limagrain Holding SA; *Int'l*, pg. 3108
SHAMROCK TECHNOLOGIES INC.; *U.S. Private*, pg. 3624
SHAMROCK VALLEY ENTERPRISES LTD.; *Int'l*, pg. 6751
SHAMROCK WATERS OF CANADA INC.—See Penney Group; *Int'l*, pg. 5787
SHAMROCK WOOD INDUSTRIES INC.—See J.T. Shannon Lumber Inc.; *U.S. Private*, pg. 2171
SHAMS TEXTILE MILLS LTD.; *Int'l*, pg. 6751
SHANAHAN ENGINEERING LTD—See John Wood Group PLC; *Int'l*, pg. 3983
SHANAHAN MECHANICAL & ELECTRICAL, INC.—See IES Holdings, Inc.; *U.S. Public*, pg. 1094
SHANAYA ENVIRONMENTAL SERVICES PTE. LTD.—See Shanaya Limited; *Int'l*, pg. 6751
SHANAYA LIMITED; *Int'l*, pg. 6751
SHAN CHIH ASSET DEVELOPMENT CO., LTD.—See Tatung Company; *Int'l*, pg. 7475
SHANDA GAMES LIMITED; *Int'l*, pg. 6751

COMPANY NAME INDEX

SHANDA GROUP PTE. LTD.; *Int'l*, pg. 6751
SHANDA INTERACTIVE ENTERTAINMENT LIMITED; *Int'l*, pg. 6751
SHANDERS PROPERTIES PVT. LTD.; *Int'l*, pg. 6751
THE SHAND GROUP; *U.S. Private*, pg. 4117
SHANDONG AIRLINES CO., LTD.; *Int'l*, pg. 6751
SHANDONG ALLIED WANGCHAO CEMENT LIMITED—See Kontafarma China Holdings Limited; *Int'l*, pg. 4276
SHANDONG AOFU ENVIRONMENTAL TECHNOLOGY CO., LTD.; *Int'l*, pg. 6751
SHANDONG BAILONG CHUANGYUAN BIO-TECH CO., LTD.; *Int'l*, pg. 6751
SHANDONG BAOSHIDA CABLE CO., LTD.—See Baoshida International Holding Group Co., Ltd.; *Int'l*, pg. 856
SHANDONG BINANI RONG AN CEMENT CO. LTD.—See The Braj Binani Group; *Int'l*, pg. 7627
SHANDONG BOAN BIOTECHNOLOGY CO., LTD.; *Int'l*, pg. 6751
SHANDONG BOHUI PAPER CO., LTD.; *Int'l*, pg. 6752
SHANDONG BOHUI PULP CO., LTD.—See Shandong Bohui Paper Co., Ltd.; *Int'l*, pg. 6752
SHANDONG CAOPU ARTS & CRAFTS CO., LTD.; *Int'l*, pg. 6752
SHANDONG CENTURY SUNSHINE PAPER GROUP CO., LTD.—See China Sunshine Paper Holdings Company Limited; *Int'l*, pg. 1556
SHANDONG CHANGKONGYAN AVIATION TECHNOLOGY COMPANY—See Shandong Mining Machinery Group Co., Ltd.; *Int'l*, pg. 6756
SHANDONG CHENMING PAPER HOLDINGS LIMITED; *Int'l*, pg. 6752
SHANDONG CHIWAY INDUSTRY DEVELOPMENT CO., LTD.; *Int'l*, pg. 6752
SHANDONG CONGLIN FRUEHAUF AUTOMOBILE CO., LTD.—See Nippon Light Metal Holdings Company, Ltd.; *Int'l*, pg. 5324
SHANDONG CYNDA CHEMICAL CO., LTD.; *Int'l*, pg. 6752
SHANDONG DAWN POLYMER CO.,LTD.; *Int'l*, pg. 6752
SHANDONG DAYE CO., LTD.; *Int'l*, pg. 6752
SHANDONG DELISI FOOD CO., LTD.; *Int'l*, pg. 6752
SHANDONG DENGHAI SEEDS CO., LTD.; *Int'l*, pg. 6752
SHANDONG DONGHONG PIPE INDUSTRY CO., LTD.; *Int'l*, pg. 6752
SHANDONG DONGKE ENGINEERING DETECTION CO., LTD.—See Zhewen Interactive Group Co Ltd; *Int'l*, pg. 8671
SHANDONG DONGYUE CHEMICAL CO., LTD.—See Dongyue Group Limited; *Int'l*, pg. 2172
SHANDONG DONGYUE ORGANOSILICON MATERIALS CO., LTD.; *Int'l*, pg. 6752
SHANDONG DONGYUE POLYMER MATERIAL CO., LTD—See Dongyue Group Limited; *Int'l*, pg. 2172
SHANDONG ELECTRIC POWER COMPANY—See State Grid Corporation of China; *Int'l*, pg. 7183
SHANDONG ENERGY GROUP CO., LTD.; *Int'l*, pg. 6752
SHANDONG ENERGY LINYI MINING GROUP CO., LTD.—See Shandong Energy Group Co., Ltd.; *Int'l*, pg. 6752
SHANDONG ENERGY LONGKOU MINING GROUP CO., LTD.—See Shandong Energy Group Co., Ltd.; *Int'l*, pg. 6752
SHANDONG ENERGY XINWEN MINING GROUP CO., LTD.—See Shandong Energy Group Co., Ltd.; *Int'l*, pg. 6752
SHANDONG ENERGY ZAOZHUANG MINING GROUP CO., LTD.—See Shandong Energy Group Co., Ltd.; *Int'l*, pg. 6753
SHANDONG ENERGY ZIBO MINING GROUP CO., LTD.—See Shandong Energy Group Co., Ltd.; *Int'l*, pg. 6753
SHANDONG FENGXIANG CO., LTD.; *Int'l*, pg. 6753
SHANDONG FENGYUAN CHEMICAL CO LTD; *Int'l*, pg. 6753
SHANDONG FIBERGLASS GROUP CO., LTD.; *Int'l*, pg. 6753
SHANDONG FUFENG FERMENTATION CO., LTD.—See Fufeng Group Limited; *Int'l*, pg. 2805
SHANDONG FU-ZHEN METAL PACKAGING CO.—See Kingcan Holdings Limited; *Int'l*, pg. 4171
SHANDONG GOLD MINING CO., LTD.; *Int'l*, pg. 6753
SHANDONG GOLD PHOENIX CO., LTD.; *Int'l*, pg. 6753
SHANDONG GRAD GROUP—See Chung-Hsin Electric & Machinery Manufacturing Corp.; *Int'l*, pg. 1597
SHANDONG GUOLIAN TELECOMMUNICATION TECHNOLOGY LIMITED—See Telestone Technologies Corporation; *Int'l*, pg. 7542
SHANDONG HAIHUA CO., LTD.; *Int'l*, pg. 6753
SHANDONG HAIHUA HUALONG NEW MATERIAL CO., LTD.—See Shandong Haihua Co., Ltd.; *Int'l*, pg. 6753
SHANDONG HAIHUA OCEAN ENGINEERING CO., LTD.—See Shandong Haihua Co., Ltd.; *Int'l*, pg. 6753
SHANDONG HAIHUA PLASTIC KNITTING CO., LTD.—See Shandong Haihua Co., Ltd.; *Int'l*, pg. 6753
SHANDONG HAITIAN BIO-CHEMICAL CO., LTD.—See Shandong Jinjing Science & Technology Co., Ltd.; *Int'l*, pg. 6755

SHANDONG HAIWANG CHEMICAL CO., LTD.; *Int'l*, pg. 6753
SHANDONG HAIZE NANO-MATERIALS CO., LTD.—See SHENGDATECH, INC.; *Int'l*, pg. 6801
SHANDONG HANGXIAO STEEL STRUCTURE CO., LTD.—See Hangxiao Steel Structure Co., Ltd.; *Int'l*, pg. 3246
SHANDONG HEAD EUROPE BV—See Shandong Head Group Co., Ltd.; *Int'l*, pg. 6753
SHANDONG HEAD GROUP CO., LTD.; *Int'l*, pg. 6753
SHANDONG HEALSEE CAPSULE LTD.—See Shandong Head Group Co., Ltd.; *Int'l*, pg. 6753
SHANDONG HEAVY INDUSTRY GROUP CO., LTD.; *Int'l*, pg. 6753
SHANDONG HELON CO., LTD.—See China Hi-Tech Group Corporation; *Int'l*, pg. 1508
SHANDONG HENGYUAN PETROCHEMICAL CO. LTD.; *Int'l*, pg. 6754
SHANDONG HIGH SPEED RENEWABLE ENERGY GROUP LIMITED; *Int'l*, pg. 6754
SHANDONG HIKING INTERNATIONAL CO., LTD.; *Int'l*, pg. 6754
SHANDONG HI-SPEED COMPANY LIMITED—See Shandong Hi-Speed Group Co., Ltd.; *Int'l*, pg. 6754
SHANDONG HI-SPEED GROUP CO., LTD.; *Int'l*, pg. 6754
SHANDONG HI-SPEED HOLDINGS GROUP LIMITED; *Int'l*, pg. 6754
SHANDONG HI-SPEED NEW ENERGY GROUP LIMITED—See Beijing Enterprises Water Group Limited; *Int'l*, pg. 950
SHANDONG HI-SPEED ROAD & BRIDGE CO., LTD.—See Shandong Hi-Speed Group Co., Ltd.; *Int'l*, pg. 6754
SHANDONG HNA BUSINESS DEVELOPMENT CO., LTD—See Hainan Traffic Administration Holding Co., Ltd.; *Int'l*, pg. 3216
SHANDONG HOMEY AQUATIC DEVELOPMENT CO., LTD.; *Int'l*, pg. 6754
SHANDONG HONGRI CHEMICAL JOINT STOCK COMPANY LIMITED—See Century Sunshine Group Holdings Limited; *Int'l*, pg. 1419
SHANDONG HONGYU AGRICULTURAL MACHINERY CO., LTD.; *Int'l*, pg. 6754
SHANDONG HUALIANG GLASS TECHNOLOGY LTD.—See Shandong Jinjing Science & Technology Co., Ltd.; *Int'l*, pg. 6755
SHANDONG HUALING ELECTRONICS CO., LTD.—See Shandong New Beiyang Information Technology Co., Ltd.; *Int'l*, pg. 6757
SHANDONG HUALU-HENGSHENG CHEMICAL CO., LTD.; *Int'l*, pg. 6754
SHANDONG HUARI BATTERY CO., LTD.—See GS Yuasa Corporation; *Int'l*, pg. 3143
SHANDONG HUATAI PAPER INDUSTRY SHAREHOLDING CO., LTD.; *Int'l*, pg. 6754
SHANDONG HUAXIA SHENZHOU NEW CO., LTD.—See Dongyue Group Limited; *Int'l*, pg. 2172
SHANDONG HUAXIA SHENZHOU NEW MATERIALS CO., LTD.—See Dongyue Group Limited; *Int'l*, pg. 2172
SHANDONG HUAYUAN LAIDONG INTERNAL COMBUSTION ENGINE CO., LTD.—See China Hi-Tech Group Corporation; *Int'l*, pg. 1508
SHANDONG HUIFA FOODSTUFF CO., LTD.; *Int'l*, pg. 6754
SHANDONG HUMON SMELTING CO., LTD.; *Int'l*, pg. 6754
SHANDONG I-LOGISTICS CO., LTD.—See ITOCHU Corporation; *Int'l*, pg. 3839
SHANDONG INSTITUTE OF QUANTUM SCIENCE & TECHNOLOGY CO., LTD.—See QuantumCTek Co., Ltd.; *Int'l*, pg. 6155
SHANDONG INTERNATIONAL TRUST CO., LTD.; *Int'l*, pg. 6755
SHANDONG IRON AND STEEL COMPANY LTD.; *Int'l*, pg. 6755
SHANDONG JIAJIA INTERNATIONAL FREIGHT & FORWARDING CO., LTD.—See China Logistics Group, Inc.; *Int'l*, pg. 1515
SHANDONG JINCHENG PHARMACEUTICAL GROUP CO., LTD.; *Int'l*, pg. 6755
SHANDONG JINCHENG ZHONGHUA BIO-PHARMACEUTICAL CO., LTD.—See Shandong Jincheng Pharmaceutical Group Co., Ltd.; *Int'l*, pg. 6755
SHANDONG JINDU TALIN FOODS CO., LTD.; *Int'l*, pg. 6755
SHANDONG JINGU AUTO PARTS COMPANY LIMITED—See Zhejiang Jingu Co., Ltd.; *Int'l*, pg. 8657
SHANDONG JINJING SCIENCE & TECHNOLOGY CO., LTD.; *Int'l*, pg. 6755
SHANDONG JINJING SCIENCE & TECHNOLOGY STOCK CO., LTD.—See Shandong Jinjing Science & Technology Co., Ltd.; *Int'l*, pg. 6755
SHANDONG JINLING MINING CO., LTD.; *Int'l*, pg. 6755
SHANDONG JINTAI GROUP CO., LTD.; *Int'l*, pg. 6755
SHANDONG KAIJIA FOOD COMPANY LIMITED—See China Kangda Food Company Limited; *Int'l*, pg. 1514
SHANDONG KAISHENG NEW MATERIALS CO., LTD.; *Int'l*, pg. 6755

SHANDONG KAMA AUTOMOBILE MANUFACTURING CO., LTD.—See China Hi-Tech Group Corporation; *Int'l*, pg. 1508
SHANDONG KANGTAI CHASYS AUTOMOBILE PARTS CO., LTD.—See CHASYS CO., LTD; *Int'l*, pg. 1457
SHANDONG KEDA INFRASTRUCTURE CO., LTD.—See Zhewen Interactive Group Co Ltd; *Int'l*, pg. 8671
SHANDONG KEDA PROPERTY SERVICE CO., LTD.—See Zhewen Interactive Group Co Ltd; *Int'l*, pg. 8671
SHAN DONG KEXING BIOPRODUCTS CO., LTD.; *Int'l*, pg. 6751
SHANDONG KEYSTONE CHINWHIZ FOODS CO. LTD.—See Tyson Foods, Inc.; *U.S. Public*, pg. 2210
SHANDONG KOTEI INFORMATICS CO., LTD.—See Wuhan Kotei Informatics Co., Ltd.; *Int'l*, pg. 8501
SHANDONG KUNTAI NEW MATERIAL TECHNOLOGY CO., LTD.; *Int'l*, pg. 6755
SHANDONG LIANCHENG AGRICULTURAL EQUIPMENT CO., LTD.—See Shandong Liancheng Precision Manufacturing Co., Ltd.; *Int'l*, pg. 6755
SHANDONG LIANCHENG PRECISION MANUFACTURING CO., LTD.; *Int'l*, pg. 6755
SHANDONG LINGLONG TYRE CO., LTD.; *Int'l*, pg. 6755
SHANDONG LINGONG CONSTRUCTION MACHINERY—See AB Volvo; *Int'l*, pg. 42
SHANDONG LINK ADVANCED MATERIALS CO., LTD.—See Shandong Link Science & Technology Co., Ltd.; *Int'l*, pg. 6755
SHANDONG LINK SCIENCE & TECHNOLOGY CO., LTD.; *Int'l*, pg. 6755
SHANDONG LINUO TECHNICAL GLASS CO., LTD.; *Int'l*, pg. 6755
SHANDONG LIULIUSHUN FOOD CO., LTD; *Int'l*, pg. 6756
SHANDONG LONGDA MEISHI CO., LTD.; *Int'l*, pg. 6756
SHANDONG LONGERTEK TECHNOLOGY CO., LTD.; *Int'l*, pg. 6756
SHANDONG LONGHUA NEW MATERIAL CO., LTD.; *Int'l*, pg. 6756
SHANDONG LONGJI MACHINERY CO., LTD.; *Int'l*, pg. 6756
SHANDONG LONGLIVE BIO-TECHNOLOGY CO., LTD.; *Int'l*, pg. 6756
SHANDONG LONGQUAN PIPELINE ENGINEERING CO., LTD.; *Int'l*, pg. 6756
SHANDONG LONGTENG FUJI FOODSTUFFS CO., LTD.—See Fuji Oil Holdings Inc.; *Int'l*, pg. 2815
SHANDONG LUBEI CHEMICAL CO., LTD.; *Int'l*, pg. 6756
SHANDONG LUKANG BIOLOGICAL PESTICIDES CO., LTD.—See Shandong Lukang Pharmaceutical Co., Ltd.; *Int'l*, pg. 6756
SHANDONG LUKANG PHARMACEUTICAL CO., LTD.; *Int'l*, pg. 6756
SHANDONG LUKANG ZERUN PHARMA CO., LTD.—See Shandong Lukang Pharmaceutical Co., Ltd.; *Int'l*, pg. 6756
SHANDONG LUOXIN PHARMACEUTICAL GROUP STOCK CO., LTD.; *Int'l*, pg. 6756
SHANDONG LUSHANG MOON ARCHITECTURE DESIGN CO., LTD.—See Moon Environment Technology Co., Ltd.; *Int'l*, pg. 5038
SHANDONG MEICHEN ECOLOGY & ENVIRONMENT CO.,LTD.; *Int'l*, pg. 6756
SHANDONG MINHE ANIMAL HUSBANDRY CO., LTD.; *Int'l*, pg. 6756
SHANDONG MINING MACHINERY COSMEC CONSTRUCTION MATERIALS MACHINERY CO., LTD.—See Shandong Mining Machinery Group Co., Ltd.; *Int'l*, pg. 6756
SHANDONG MINING MACHINERY GROUP CO., LTD.; *Int'l*, pg. 6756
SHANDONG MOLONG PETROLEUM MACHINERY COMPANY LIMITED; *Int'l*, pg. 6756
SHANDONG NANSHAN ALUMINIUM CO., LTD.; *Int'l*, pg. 6757
SHANDONG NANSHAN ZHISHANG SCI-TECH CO., LTD.; *Int'l*, pg. 6757
SHANDONG NEW BEIYANG INFORMATION TECHNOLOGY CO., LTD.; *Int'l*, pg. 6757
SHANDONG NICHIREI FOODS CO., LTD.—See Nichirei Corporation; *Int'l*, pg. 5270
SHANDONG NIKKEI CONGLIN AUTOMOBILE PARTS CO., LTD.—See Nippon Light Metal Holdings Company, Ltd.; *Int'l*, pg. 5324
SHANDONG NISSIN INDUSTRY CO., LTD.—See Honda Motor Co., Ltd.; *Int'l*, pg. 3463
SHANDONG OCI CO., LTD.—See OCI Holdings Co., Ltd.; *Int'l*, pg. 5519
SHANDONG OCI-JIANYANG CARBON BLACK CO., LTD.—See OCI Holdings Co., Ltd.; *Int'l*, pg. 5519
SHANDONG O.R.G PACKAGING CO., LTD.—See ORG Technology Co., Ltd.; *Int'l*, pg. 5617
SHANDONG ORIENTAL OCEAN SCI-TECH CO., LTD.; *Int'l*, pg. 6757
SHANDONG ORLIFE PHARMACEUTICAL CO., LTD.—See MEDIPOST Co., Ltd.; *Int'l*, pg. 4780

SHANDONG PACIFIC FIBER OPTICS CABLE CO., LTD.—See Asia Pacific Wire & Cable Corporation Limited; *Int'l*, pg. 614
SHANDONG PACIFIC RUBBER CABLE CO., LTD.—See Asia Pacific Wire & Cable Corporation Limited; *Int'l*, pg. 614
SHANDONG PHARMACEUTICAL GLASS CO., LTD.; *Int'l*, pg. 6757
SHANDONG POLYMER BIO-CHEMICALS CO., LTD.; *Int'l*, pg. 6757
SHANDONG POWER EQUIPMENT CO., LTD.—See State Grid Corporation of China; *Int'l*, pg. 7183
SHANDONG POWER (GROUP) CORPORATION—See State Grid Corporation of China; *Int'l*, pg. 7183
SHANDONG PRECEDE PETROLEUM TECHNOLOGY CO., LTD.—See Anton Oilfield Services Group Limited; *Int'l*, pg. 484
SHANDONG PUBLISHING & MEDIA CO., LTD.; *Int'l*, pg. 6757
SHANDONG QILU KELI CHEMICAL RESEARCH INSTITUTE CO., LTD.—See ZIBO QIXIANG TENGDA CHEMICAL CO., LTD.; *Int'l*, pg. 8680
SHANDONG QINGYANG NEW MATERIAL CO., LTD.—See Puyang Huicheng Electronic Material Co., Ltd.; *Int'l*, pg. 6124
SHANDONG RIKE CHEMICAL CO., LTD.; *Int'l*, pg. 6757
SHANDONG RIKE PLASTIC CO., LTD.—See Shandong Rike Chemical Co., Ltd.; *Int'l*, pg. 6757
SHANDONG RILONG FOODSTUFFS CO., LTD.—See NH Foods Ltd.; *Int'l*, pg. 5257
SHANDONG RIZHAO POWER COMPANY LIMITED—See China Huaneng Group Co., Ltd.; *Int'l*, pg. 1509
SHANDONG ROCK DRILLING TOOLS CO., LTD.—See Epiroc AB; *Int'l*, pg. 2463
SHANDONG RUIFENG CHEMICAL CO., LTD.; *Int'l*, pg. 6757
SHANDONG RUIYI WOOLEN GARMENT GROUP CO., LTD.; *Int'l*, pg. 6757
SHANDONG SACRED SUN POWER SOURCES COMPANY LIMITED; *Int'l*, pg. 6757
SHANDONG SAHNDA OUMASOFT CO., LTD.; *Int'l*, pg. 6757
SHANDONG SANJIN GLASS MACHINERY CO., LTD.—See Bucher Industries AG; *Int'l*, pg. 1209
SHANDONG SANXING GROUP CO., LTD.; *Int'l*, pg. 6757
SHANDONG SANYUAN BIOTECHNOLOGY CO., LTD; *Int'l*, pg. 6758
SHANDONG SHANGHAI ALLIED CEMENT CO., LTD.—See Kontafarma China Holdings Limited; *Int'l*, pg. 4276
SHANDONG SHANSHUI CEMENT GROUP LTD. (SUNNSY)—See China Shanshui Cement Group Ltd.; *Int'l*, pg. 1550
SHANDONG SHANTUI MACHINERY CO., LTD.—See Shandong Heavy Industry Group Co., Ltd.; *Int'l*, pg. 6753
SHANDONG SHENGLI BIO-ENGINEERING CO., LTD.—See China Animal Husbandry Industry Co., Ltd.; *Int'l*, pg. 1482
SHANDONG SHENGLI CO., LTD.; *Int'l*, pg. 6758
SHANDONG SHENZHOU REFRIGERATION EQUIPMENT CO., LTD.—See Moon Environment Technology Co., Ltd.; *Int'l*, pg. 5038
SHANDONG SHIDA SHENGHUA CHEMICAL GROUP CO., LTD.; *Int'l*, pg. 6758
SHANDONG SHUANGYI TECHNOLOGY CO., LTD.; *Int'l*, pg. 6758
SHANDONG SIMCERE MEDGENN BIO-PHARMACEUTICAL CO., LTD.—See Simcere Pharmaceutical Group; *Int'l*, pg. 6928
SHANDONG SINO-AGRI UNITED BIOTECHNOLOGY CO., LTD.; *Int'l*, pg. 6758
SHANDONG SINOBIOWAY BIOMEDICINE CORP., LTD.; *Int'l*, pg. 6758
SHANDONG SINOBROM ALBEMARLE BROMINE CHEMICALS COMPANY LIMITED—See Albemarle Corporation; *U.S. Public*, pg. 73
SHANDONG SINOCERA FUNCTIONAL MATERIAL CO., LTD.; *Int'l*, pg. 6758
SHANDONG SK HIGHTECH OIL CO., LTD.—See SK Innovation Co., Ltd.; *Int'l*, pg. 6973
SHANDONG SUN PAPER INDUSTRY CO., LTD.; *Int'l*, pg. 6758
SHANDONG SUNWAY CHEMICAL GROUP CO., LTD.; *Int'l*, pg. 6758
SHANDONG SWAN COTTON INDUSTRIAL MACHINERY STOCK CO., LTD; *Int'l*, pg. 6758
SHANDONG SWAN USA, INC.—See Shandong Swan Cotton Industrial Machinery Stock Co., Ltd; *Int'l*, pg. 6758
SHANDONG TAIBANG BIOLOGICAL PRODUCTS CO. LTD.—See China Biologic Products Holdings, Inc.; *Int'l*, pg. 1486
SHANDONG TAIHE WATER TREATMENT TECHNOLOGIES CO., LTD.; *Int'l*, pg. 6758
SHANDONG TENGJUNXIANG BIOTECHNOLOGY CO., LTD.—See Tengjun Biotechnology Corp.; *U.S. Public*, pg. 2015

SHANDONG T&H GLAZE CO., LTD.—See China Glaze Co., Ltd.; *Int'l*, pg. 1505
SHANDONG TIANHAI HIGH PRESSURE CONTAINER CO., LTD.—See Beijing Jingcheng Machinery Electric Co., Ltd.; *Int'l*, pg. 952
SHANDONG TIANTONG FOOD CO., LTD.—See Tianyun International Holdings Limited; *Int'l*, pg. 7742
SHANDONG TOKYO-UNION TECHNOLOGY DEVELOPMENT CO., LTD.—See Tokyo Sangyo Co., Ltd.; *Int'l*, pg. 7795
SHANDONG TONGDA ISLAND NEW MATERIALS CO., LTD.; *Int'l*, pg. 6758
SHANDONG TYSON-DA LONG FOOD COMPANY LIMITED—See Tyson Foods, Inc.; *U.S. Public*, pg. 2210
SHANDONG VEDAN SNOWFLAKE ENTERPRISE CO., LTD.—See Vedan International (Holdings) Ltd.; *Int'l*, pg. 8145
SHANDONG WEIDA MACHINERY CO., LTD.; *Int'l*, pg. 6758
SHANDONG WEIDA SAW BLADE CO., LTD.—See Shandong Weida Machinery Co., Ltd.; *Int'l*, pg. 6758
SHANDONG WEIFANG RAINBOW CHEMICAL CO., LTD.; *Int'l*, pg. 6758
SHANDONG WEIGAO GROUP MEDICAL POLYMER COMPANY LIMITED; *Int'l*, pg. 6758
SHANDONG WEIGAO ORTHOPAEDIC DEVICE COMPANY LIMITED—See Shandong Weigao Group Medical Polymer Company Limited; *Int'l*, pg. 6759
SHANDONG WEIQIAO GROUP CO., LTD.; *Int'l*, pg. 6759
SHANDONG WIT DYNE HEALTH CO., LTD.; *Int'l*, pg. 6759
SHANDONG WOHUA PHARMACEUTICAL CO., LTD.; *Int'l*, pg. 6759
SHANDONG XIANTAN CO., LTD.; *Int'l*, pg. 6759
SHANDONG XINCHAO ENERGY CORPORATION LIMITED; *Int'l*, pg. 6759
SHANDONG XINHUA PHARMACEUTICAL COMPANY LIMITED; *Int'l*, pg. 6759
SHANDONG XINHUA PHARMACEUTICAL (USA) CO., LTD.—See Shandong Xinhua Pharmaceutical Company Limited; *Int'l*, pg. 6759
SHANDONG XINHUA WANBO CHEMICAL INDUSTRY CO., LTD.—See Shandong Xinhua Pharmaceutical Company Limited; *Int'l*, pg. 6759
SHANDONG XINJUFENG TECHNOLOGY PACKAGING CO., LTD.; *Int'l*, pg. 6759
SHANDONG XINNENG TAISHAN POWER GENERATION CO., LTD.; *Int'l*, pg. 6759
SHANDONG YABO TECHNOLOGY CO., LTD.; *Int'l*, pg. 6759
SHANDONG YANGGUANG ENGINEERING DESIGN INSTITUTE CO., LTD.—See Sunpower Group Ltd.; *Int'l*, pg. 7320
SHANDONG YANGGU HUATAI CHEMICAL CO., LTD.; *Int'l*, pg. 6759
SHANDONG YANGGU HUATAI IMPORT & EXPORT CO., LTD.—See Shandong Yanggu Huatai Chemical Co., Ltd.; *Int'l*, pg. 6759
SHANDONG YINGUANG TECHNOLOGY CO., LTD.—See Lincotrade & Associates Holdings Limited; *Int'l*, pg. 4503
SHANDONG YISHENG LIVESTOCK & POULTRY BREEDING CO., LTD.; *Int'l*, pg. 6759
SHANDONG YOKOHAMA RUBBER INDUSTRIAL PRODUCTS CO., LTD.—See The Yokohama Rubber Co., Ltd.; *Int'l*, pg. 7702
SHANDONG YONGMAOTAI AUTO PARTS CO. LTD.—See Shanghai Yongmaotai Automotive Technology Co., Ltd.; *Int'l*, pg. 6782
SHANDONG YONGTAI CHEMICAL GROUP CO., LTD.; *Int'l*, pg. 6759
SHANDONG YUANLI SCIENCE & TECHNOLOGY CO., LTD.—See Yuanli Chemical Group Co., Ltd.; *Int'l*, pg. 8608
SHANDONG YULONG GOLD CO., LTD.; *Int'l*, pg. 6759
SHANDONG YUMA SUN-SHADING TECHNOLOGY CORP.; *Int'l*, pg. 6760
SHANDONG ZHANGQIU BLOWER CO., LTD.; *Int'l*, pg. 6760
SHANDONG ZHONGKE INDUSTRIAL PARK DEVELOPMENT CO., LTD.—See Zhewen Interactive Group Co Ltd; *Int'l*, pg. 8671
SHANDONG ZHONGLU OCEANIC FISHERIES COMPANY LIMITED; *Int'l*, pg. 6760
SHANE DEMLER MASONRY, INC; *U.S. Private*, pg. 3625
SHANE GLOBAL HOLDING, INC.; *Int'l*, pg. 6760
THE SHANE GROUP, LLC—See Worth Investment Group, LLC; *U.S. Private*, pg. 4570
SHANE HOMES LTD.; *Int'l*, pg. 6760
SHANE INDUSTRIES, INC.—See Corning Incorporated; *U.S. Public*, pg. 579
SHANER CORP.; *U.S. Private*, pg. 3625
SHANE'S RIB SHACK—See Petrus Brands, Inc.; *U.S. Private*, pg. 3163
SHAN FU PAPER (KUNSON) CO., LTD.—See Cheng Loong Corp.; *Int'l*, pg. 1466

SHANGAI IDIADA AUTOMOTIVE TECHNOLOGY SERVICES CO., LTD.—See I Squared Capital Advisors (US) LLC; *U.S. Private*, pg. 2023
SHANGAI IDIADA AUTOMOTIVE TECHNOLOGY SERVICES CO., LTD.—See TDR Capital LLP; *Int'l*, pg. 7492
SHANGAI NTN CORP.—See NTN Corporation; *Int'l*, pg. 5483
SHANGAI SHUANGJE TECHNOLOGY CO., LTD.—See Alten S.A.; *Int'l*, pg. 391
SHANGAR DECOR LIMITED; *Int'l*, pg. 6760
SHANGDONG HUAPENG GLASS CO., LTD.; *Int'l*, pg. 6760
SHANGGONG (EUROPE) HOLDING CORP. GMBH—See Shang Gong Group Co., Ltd.; *Int'l*, pg. 6760
SHANGGONG EXPORT & IMPORT CO., LTD.—See Shang Gong Group Co., Ltd.; *Int'l*, pg. 6760
SHANG GONG GROUP CO., LTD.; *Int'l*, pg. 6760
SHANGHAI 2345 NEWORK HOLDING GROUP CO., LTD.; *Int'l*, pg. 6760
SHANGHAI AAG AUTOMOTIVE PRODUCTS TRADING CO. LTD—See Energizer Holdings, Inc.; *U.S. Public*, pg. 760
SHANGHAI ABBOTT PHARMACEUTICAL CO., LTD.—See Abbott Laboratories; *U.S. Public*, pg. 17
SHANGHAI ABB POWER TRANSMISSION CO., LTD—See ABB Ltd.; *Int'l*, pg. 51
SHANGHAI AB FOOD & BEVERAGES CO., LTD—See The Garfield Weston Foundation; *Int'l*, pg. 7649
SHANGHAI ACE INVESTMENT & DEVELOPMENT CO., LTD.; *Int'l*, pg. 6761
SHANGHAI ACREL CO., LTD.; *Int'l*, pg. 6761
SHANGHAI ACROSS APPAREL PROCESSING CO., LTD.—See Onward Holdings Co., Ltd.; *Int'l*, pg. 5593
SHANGHAI ACTION EDUCATION TECHNOLOGY CO., LTD.; *Int'l*, pg. 6761
SHANGHAI AEROSPACE AUTOMOBILE ELECTROMECHANICAL CO., LTD.; *Int'l*, pg. 6761
SHANGHAI AICHI FORGING CO., LTD.—See Aichi Steel Corporation; *Int'l*, pg. 230
SHANGHAI AIKO SOLAR ENERGY CO., LTD.; *Int'l*, pg. 6761
SHANGHAI AILU PACKAGING CO., LTD.; *Int'l*, pg. 6761
SHANGHAI AIREST CATERING COMPANY LTD.—See InfraVia Capital Partners SAS; *Int'l*, pg. 3699
SHANGHAI AIR WATER INTERNATIONAL TRADING CO., LTD.—See Air Water Inc.; *Int'l*, pg. 240
SHANGHAI AIR WATER MEDICAL GAS CO., LTD.—See Air Water Inc.; *Int'l*, pg. 240
SHANGHAI AIYINGSHI CO., LTD.; *Int'l*, pg. 6761
SHANGHAI AJ GROUP CO., LTD.; *Int'l*, pg. 6761
SHANGHAI AJINOMOTO AMINO ACID CO., LTD.—See Ajinomoto Company, Inc.; *Int'l*, pg. 257
SHANGHAI AJINOMOTO SEASONING CO., LTD.—See Ajinomoto Company, Inc.; *Int'l*, pg. 257
SHANGHAI ALADDIN BIOCHEMICAL TECHNOLOGY CO., LTD.; *Int'l*, pg. 6761
SHANGHAI ALL ACCESS NOTER COMMUNICATION TECHNOLOGY CO., LIMITED—See China All Access (Holdings) Limited; *Int'l*, pg. 1482
SHANGHAI ALLIED CEMENT CO., LTD.—See Kontafarma China Holdings Limited; *Int'l*, pg. 4276
SHANGHAI ALLIED INDUSTRIAL CORP., LTD.; *Int'l*, pg. 6761
SHANGHAI ALLIST PHARMACEUTICALS CO., LTD.; *Int'l*, pg. 6761
SHANGHAI AMARSOFT INFORMATION & TECHNOLOGY CO., LTD.; *Int'l*, pg. 6761
SHANGHAI AMOY FOODS CO. LTD.—See Ajinomoto Company, Inc.; *Int'l*, pg. 257
SHANGHAI AMPHENOL AIRWAVE COMMUNICATION ELECTRONIC, CO., LTD.—See Amphenol Corporation; *U.S. Public*, pg. 128
SHANGHAI ANOKY GROUP CO., LTD.; *Int'l*, pg. 6761
SHANGHAI ANSHIJIE REAL ESTATE CONSULTANT CO., LTD—See IFM Investments Limited; *Int'l*, pg. 3599
SHANGHAI ANTAI-ZHIGAO AMORPHOUS METAL CO., LTD.—See Advanced Technology & Materials Co., Ltd.; *Int'l*, pg. 162
SHANGHAI ANYIJIE CHEMICAL LOGISTIC CO., LTD.—See BRENNTAG SE; *Int'l*, pg. 1149
SHANGHAI AOHUI AUTOMOBILE SALES SERVICES CO., LTD.—See China ZhengTong Auto Services Holdings Limited; *Int'l*, pg. 1566
SHANGHAI AOWEI TECHNOLOGY DEVELOPMENT CO., LTD.—See Chengdu Xinzhu Road & Bridge Machinery Co., Ltd.; *Int'l*, pg. 1469
SHANGHAI APEX ELECTRONICS TECHNOLOGY CO., LTD.—See Koninklijke Philips N.V.; *Int'l*, pg. 4271
SHANGHAI APIC YAMADA CO., LTD.—See Yamaha Corporation; *Int'l*, pg. 8550
SHANGHAI APPLE AROMATECH FLAVORS TECHNOLOGY CO., LTD.—See Apple Flavor & Fragrance Group Co., Ltd.; *Int'l*, pg. 520
SHANGHAI APPLE AROMATIC PLANTATION CO., LTD.—See Apple Flavor & Fragrance Group Co., Ltd.; *Int'l*, pg. 520
SHANGHAI APPLE BOTANIC-TECH CO., LTD.—See Apple Flavor & Fragrance Group Co., Ltd.; *Int'l*, pg. 520

SHANGHAI APPLE FOODS INGREDIENTS CO., LTD.—See Apple Flavor & Fragrance Group Co., Ltd.; *Int'l*, pg. 520
SHANGHAI APPLE FOODS TECH (GROUP) CO., LTD.—See Apple Flavor & Fragrance Group Co., Ltd.; *Int'l*, pg. 520
SHANGHAI ARCOTRONICS COMPONENTS & MACHINERIES CO., LTD.—See Yageo Corporation; *Int'l*, pg. 8545
SHANGHAI ARKEMA GAOYUAN CHEMICALS CO. LTD—See Arkema S.A.; *Int'l*, pg. 571
SHANGHAI ASATSU ADVERTISING CO., LTD.—See Bain Capital, LP; *U.S. Private*, pg. 428
SHANGHAI ASEED CO., LTD.—See Aseed Holdings Co., Ltd.; *Int'l*, pg. 605
SHANGHAI ASIARAY ADVERTISING—See Asiaray Media Group Limited; *Int'l*, pg. 620
SHANGHAI ATECH MACHINERY CO. LTD.—See L.K. Technology Holdings Limited; *Int'l*, pg. 4386
SHANGHAI AUTOMOTIVE INDUSTRY CORPORATION; *Int'l*, pg. 6761
SHANGHAI AXIS COMMUNICATION EQUIPMENT TRADING CO. LTD—See Canon Inc.; *Int'l*, pg. 1293
SHANGHAI AZBIL AUTOMATION CO., LTD.—See Azbil Corporation; *Int'l*, pg. 777
SHANGHAI BAIHE WALSIN LIHWA SPECIALTY STEEL PRODUCTS CO., LTD.—See Walsin Lihwa Corporation; *Int'l*, pg. 8335
SHANGHAI BAILIAN GROUP CO., LTD.—See Bailian Group Co., Ltd.; *Int'l*, pg. 802
SHANGHAI BAIRUN INVESTMENT HOLDING GROUP CO., LTD.; *Int'l*, pg. 6762
SHANGHAI BAOHUA INTERNATIONAL TENDERING CO., LTD.—See China Baowu Steel Group Corp., Ltd.; *Int'l*, pg. 1486
SHANGHAI BAOLING PLASTICS CO., LTD.—See Mitsubishi Chemical Group Corporation; *Int'l*, pg. 4934
SHANGHAI BAOLONG AUTOMOTIVE CORPORATION; *Int'l*, pg. 6762
SHANGHAI BAOMING REFRACTORIES CO., LTD.—See Puyang Refractories Group Co., Ltd.; *Int'l*, pg. 6124
SHANGHAI BAOSHAN PACIFIC CONTAINER CO., LTD.—See Singamas Container Holdings Limited; *Int'l*, pg. 6939
SHANGHAI BAOSIGHT SOFTWARE CO., LTD.—See China Baowu Steel Group Corp., Ltd.; *Int'l*, pg. 1486
SHANGHAI BAOSTEEL CHEMICAL CO., LTD.—See China Baowu Steel Group Corp., Ltd.; *Int'l*, pg. 1486
SHANGHAI BAOSTEEL PACKAGING CO., LTD.; *Int'l*, pg. 6762
SHANGHAI BAOSTEEL-SANWA DOOR CO., LTD.—See Sanwa Holdings Corporation; *Int'l*, pg. 6561
SHANGHAI BAOZEN AUTOMOBILE SALES AND SERVICES CO., LTD.—See China Yongda Automobiles Services Holdings Limited; *Int'l*, pg. 1564
SHANGHAI BAOZEN ZHONGHUAN AUTOMOBILE SALES AND SERVICES CO., LTD.—See China Yongda Automobiles Services Holdings Limited; *Int'l*, pg. 1564
SHANGHAI BASF POLYURETHANE CO., LTD.—See BASF SE; *Int'l*, pg. 877
SHANGHAI BAUER TECHNOLOGIES CO. LTD.—See BAUER Aktiengesellschaft; *Int'l*, pg. 892
SHANGHAI BEAUTY STAR CO., LTD.—See Shenzhen Leaguer Co., Ltd.; *Int'l*, pg. 6816
SHANGHAI BEITE TECHNOLOGY CO., LTD.; *Int'l*, pg. 6762
SHANGHAI BEKAERT-ERGANG CO LTD—See NV Bekaert SA; *Int'l*, pg. 5496
SHANGHAI BELLING CO., LTD.; *Int'l*, pg. 6762
SHANGHAI BENTELER HUIZHONG AUTOMOTIVE COMPANY LTD.—See Benteler International AG; *Int'l*, pg. 977
SHANGHAI BESTECH SOFTWARE CO., LTD.—See Beijing Shiji Information Technology Co., Ltd.; *Int'l*, pg. 956
SHANGHAI BIAOWU HIGH TENSILE FASTENERS COMPANY LIMITED—See Shanghai Electric Group Company Limited; *Int'l*, pg. 6766
SHANGHAI BI BA BATTERIES CO. LTD.—See Gold Peak Technology Group Limited; *Int'l*, pg. 3026
SHANGHAI BIO-HEART BIOLOGICAL TECHNOLOGY CO., LTD.; *Int'l*, pg. 6762
SHANGHAI BOILER WORKS LTD.—See Shanghai Electric Group Company Limited; *Int'l*, pg. 6765
SHANGHAI BOLAITE COMPRESSOR CO LTD—See Atlas Copco AB; *Int'l*, pg. 684
SHANGHAI BONDEX NISSHIN LOGISTICS CO., LTD.—See KKR & Co. Inc.; *U.S. Public*, pg. 1259
SHANGHAI BORGWARNER AUTOMOTIVE (GROUP) CO., LTD.—See BorgWarner Inc.; *U.S. Public*, pg. 371
SHANGHAI BOSCH REXROTH HYDRAULICS & AUTOMATION LTD.—See Robert Bosch GmbH; *Int'l*, pg. 6368
SHANGHAI BREADTALK CO., LTD.—See BreadTalk Group Pte Ltd.; *Int'l*, pg. 1144
SHANGHAI BRIGHT POWER SEMICONDUCTOR CO., LTD.; *Int'l*, pg. 6762
SHANGHAI BROADBAND TECHNOLOGY CO., LTD.; *Int'l*, pg. 6762

SHANGHAI BROADMOBI COMMUNICATION TECHNOLOGY CO., LTD.—See Wutong Holding Group Co., Ltd.; *Int'l*, pg. 8514
SHANGHAI BROADWAY PACKAGING & INSULATION MATERIALS CO., LTD.—See Platinum Equity, LLC; *U.S. Private*, pg. 3201
SHANGHAI BROSE AUTOMOTIVE COMPONENTS CO., LTD.—See Brose Fahrzeugteile GmbH & Co. KG; *Int'l*, pg. 1196
SHANGHAI BROSE ELECTRIC MOTORS CO., LTD.—See Brose Fahrzeugteile GmbH & Co. KG; *Int'l*, pg. 1196
SHANGHAI BUILDING DECORATION ENGINEERING GROUP CO., LTD.—See Shanghai Construction Group Co., Ltd.; *Int'l*, pg. 6764
SHANGHAI BUTTERFLY IMP. & EXP. CO., LTD.—See Shang Gong Group Co., Ltd.; *Int'l*, pg. 6760
SHANGHAI BUTTERFLY IMPORT & EXPORT CO., LTD.—See Shang Gong Group Co., Ltd.; *Int'l*, pg. 6760
SHANGHAI BYD COMPANY LIMITED—See BYD Company Limited; *Int'l*, pg. 1234
SHANGHAI CAI-NEWTOUCH SOFTWARE CO., LTD.—See Shanghai Newtouch Software Co., Ltd.; *Int'l*, pg. 6776
SHANGHAI CAMOZZI AUTOMATION CONTROL CO, LTD.—See Camozzi Group; *Int'l*, pg. 1274
SHANGHAI CANXING CULTURE & MEDIA CO., LTD.—See STAR CM Holdings Limited; *Int'l*, pg. 7173
SHANGHAI CARTHANE CO.,LTD; *Int'l*, pg. 6763
SHANGHAI CCECC ENTERPRISES COMPANY LTD.—See China Railway Construction Corporation Limited; *Int'l*, pg. 1543
SHANGHAI CCI POWER CONTROL EQUIPMENT CO LTD—See IMI plc; *Int'l*, pg. 3625
SHANGHAI CDXJ DIGITAL TECHNOLOGY CO., LTD.; *Int'l*, pg. 6763
SHANGHAI CENTRAL PLAZA PROPERTY CO., LTD.—See Sun Hung Kai Properties Limited; *Int'l*, pg. 7304
SHANGHAI CENTURY ACQUISITION CORPORATION; *Int'l*, pg. 6763
SHANGHAI CEO ENVIRONMENTAL PROTECTION TECHNOLOGY CO., LTD.; *Int'l*, pg. 6763
SHANGHAI CHALLENGE TEXTILE CO., LTD.; *Int'l*, pg. 6763
SHANGHAI CHANGLING COMMUNICATION EQUIPMENT CO., LTD.—See MIRAIT ONE Corporation; *Int'l*, pg. 4918
SHANGHAI CHANG WAH ELECTROMATERIALS INC.—See Chang Wah Technology Co., Ltd.; *Int'l*, pg. 1441
SHANGHAI CHEMI-CON TRADING CO., LTD.—See Nippon Chemi-Con Corporation; *Int'l*, pg. 5313
SHANGHAI CHEMPARTNER CO., LTD.—See TPG Capital, L.P.; *U.S. Public*, pg. 2175
SHANGHAI CHENGGUANG REAL ESTATE CO., LTD.—See Sanxiang Impression Co., Ltd.; *Int'l*, pg. 6561
SHANGHAI CHENGHE INTERNATIONAL CO. LTD.—See GCH Technology Co., Ltd.; *Int'l*, pg. 2895
SHANGHAI CHENGTOU HOLDING CO., LTD.; *Int'l*, pg. 6763
SHANGHAI CHENHUA INTERNATIONAL TRADE CO., LTD.—See Yangzhou Chenhua New Material Co.,Ltd.; *Int'l*, pg. 8561
SHANGHAI CHEVALIER TRADING CO., LTD.—See Chevalier International Holdings Limited; *Int'l*, pg. 1474
SHANGHAI CHICMAX COSMETIC CO., LTD.; *Int'l*, pg. 6763
SHANGHAI CHINACOAL EAST CHINA CO., LTD.—See China Coal Energy Company Limited; *Int'l*, pg. 1490
SHANGHAI CHINAFORTUNE CO., LTD.; *Int'l*, pg. 6763
SHANGHAI CHINASOFT RESOURCES INFORMATION TECHNOLOGY SERVICES LIMITED—See Chinasoft International Ltd.; *Int'l*, pg. 1569
SHANGHAI CHIPSEA INNOVATION TECHNOLOGY CO., LTD.—See Chipsea Technologies (Shenzhen) Corp.; *Int'l*, pg. 1573
SHANGHAI CHLOR-ALKALI CHEMICAL CO., LTD.; *Int'l*, pg. 6763
SHANGHAI CHONGYANG INVESTMENT MANAGEMENT CO., LTD.; *Int'l*, pg. 6763
SHANGHAI CHRISTINE FOODSTUFF CO., LTD.—See Christine International Holdings Limited; *Int'l*, pg. 1587
SHANGHAI CHUANGLI GROUP CO., LTD.; *Int'l*, pg. 6763
SHANGHAI CHUGAI PHARMA CO., LTD.—See Roche Holding AG; *Int'l*, pg. 6373
SHANGHAI CHUNG HAO PAPER CO.—See Cheng Loong Corp.; *Int'l*, pg. 1466
SHANGHAI CHUNG LOONG PAPER CO., LTD.—See Cheng Loong Corp.; *Int'l*, pg. 1466
SHANGHAI CHUN YUAN STEEL INDUSTRY CO., LTD—See Chun Yuan Steel Industry Co., Ltd.; *Int'l*, pg. 1596
SHANGHAI CHUN ZU MACHINERY INDUSTRY CO., LTD.—See Chun Yu Works & Co., Ltd.; *Int'l*, pg. 1596
SHANGHAI CHURUI ENERGY TECHNOLOGY CO., LTD.; *Int'l*, pg. 6763
SHANGHAI C. I. KASEI TRADING COMPANY LTD.—See ITOCHU Corporation; *Int'l*, pg. 3835

SHANGHAI CIK ELECTRONICS CO., LTD.—See ITOCHU Corporation; *Int'l*, pg. 3835
SHANGHAI CIMC BAOWELL INDUSTRIES CO. LTD—See China International Marine Containers (Group) Co., Ltd.; *Int'l*, pg. 1512
SHANGHAI CIMC REEFER CONTAINERS CO., LTD.—See China International Marine Containers (Group) Co., Ltd.; *Int'l*, pg. 1512
SHANGHAI CIMC SPECIAL VEHICLE CO., LTD.—See China International Marine Containers (Group) Co., Ltd.; *Int'l*, pg. 1512
SHANGHAI CIMC YANGSHAN CONTAINER SERVICE CO., LTD.—See China International Marine Containers (Group) Co., Ltd.; *Int'l*, pg. 1512
SHANGHAI CITY LAND (GROUP) CO., LTD.—See Shanghai Chengtou Holding Co., Ltd.; *Int'l*, pg. 6763
SHANGHAI CITY QI AI TAXI SERVICES CO., LTD.—See ComfortDelGro Corporation Limited; *Int'l*, pg. 1713
SHANGHAI CLYDE BERGEMANN MACHINERY COMPANY LTD.—See Clyde Blowers Capital IM LLP; *Int'l*, pg. 1665
SHANGHAI C&M FILTRATION SOLUTIONS LIMITED—See Tex Year Industries Inc.; *Int'l*, pg. 7582
SHANGHAI COATS LIMITED—See Coats Group plc; *Int'l*, pg. 1682
SHANGHAI COBI MOLD & PLASTIC ENGINEERING CO., LTD.—See Xiamen Voke Mold & Plastic Engineering Co., Ltd.; *Int'l*, pg. 8526
SHANGHAI COMMERCIAL BANK LIMITED; *Int'l*, pg. 6763
SHANGHAI COMMERCIAL BANK TRUSTEE LIMITED—See Shanghai Commercial Bank Limited; *Int'l*, pg. 6763
THE SHANGHAI COMMERCIAL & SAVINGS BANK, LTD.; *Int'l*, pg. 7681
SHANGHAI COMTEC SOLAR TECHNOLOGY CO., LTD.—See Comtec Solar Systems Group Limited; *Int'l*, pg. 1762
SHANGHAI CONCH CEMENT CO., LTD.—See Anhui Conch Cement Company Limited; *Int'l*, pg. 467
SHANGHAI CONCH CONSTRUCTION MATERIAL INTERNATIONAL TRADING CO., LTD.—See Anhui Conch Cement Company Limited; *Int'l*, pg. 467
SHANGHAI CONSTRUCTION BUILDING MATERIALS TECHNOLOGY GROUP CO., LTD.—See Shanghai Construction Group Co., Ltd.; *Int'l*, pg. 6764
SHANGHAI CONSTRUCTION DESIGN & RESEARCH GENERAL INSTITUTE CO., LTD.—See Shanghai Construction Group Co., Ltd.; *Int'l*, pg. 6764
SHANGHAI CONSTRUCTION DESIGN & RESEARCH INSTITUTE CO., LTD.—See Shanghai Construction Group Co., Ltd.; *Int'l*, pg. 6764
SHANGHAI CONSTRUCTION GROUP CO., LTD.; *Int'l*, pg. 6763
SHANGHAI CONSTRUCTION NO.1 (GROUP) CO., LTD.—See Shanghai Construction Group Co., Ltd.; *Int'l*, pg. 6764
SHANGHAI CONSTRUCTION NO.2 (GROUP) CO., LTD.—See Shanghai Construction Group Co., Ltd.; *Int'l*, pg. 6764
SHANGHAI CONSTRUCTION NO.4 (GROUP) CO., LTD.—See Shanghai Construction Group Co., Ltd.; *Int'l*, pg. 6764
SHANGHAI CONSTRUCTION NO.5 (GROUP) CO., LTD.—See Shanghai Construction Group Co., Ltd.; *Int'l*, pg. 6764
SHANGHAI CONSTRUCTION NO.7 (GROUP) CO., LTD.—See Shanghai Construction Group Co., Ltd.; *Int'l*, pg. 6764
SHANGHAI CONTAINER TERMINALS CO., LTD.—See Shanghai International Port (Group) Co., Ltd.; *Int'l*, pg. 6771
SHANGHAI COOLTECH POWER CO., LTD.; *Int'l*, pg. 6764
SHANGHAI CORE CO., LTD—See Core Corporation; *Int'l*, pg. 1797
SHANGHAI CORNING ENGINEERING CORPORATION—See Corning Incorporated; *U.S. Public*, pg. 579
SHANGHAI COSAFETY TECHNOLOGY CO., LTD.—See Bunzl plc; *Int'l*, pg. 1219
SHANGHAI COSCO KANSAI PAINT & CHEMICALS CO., LTD.—See Kansai Paint Co., Ltd.; *Int'l*, pg. 4073
SHANGHAI COSCO KAWASAKI HEAVY INDUSTRIES STEEL STRUCTURE CO., LTD.—See Kawasaki Heavy Industries, Ltd.; *Int'l*, pg. 4098
SHANGHAI CPT MACHINERY CO., LTD.—See Sichuan Dawn Precision Technology Co., Ltd.; *Int'l*, pg. 6878
SHANGHAI CTRIP COMMERCE CO., LTD.—See Trip.com Group Ltd.; *Int'l*, pg. 7926
SHANGHAI CUMMINS TRADING CO., LTD.—See Cummins Inc.; *U.S. Public*, pg. 609
SHANGHAI CYECO ENVIRONMENTAL TECHNOLOGY CO., LTD.—See Shanghai Electric Group Company Limited; *Int'l*, pg. 6765
SHANGHAI DACHENG NETWORK TECHNOLOGY CO., LTD.—See KongZhong Corporation; *Int'l*, pg. 4257

SHANGHAI DAEJOO ELECTRONIC MATERIALS CO., LTD.—See Daejoo Electronic Materials Co., Ltd.; *Int'l*, pg. 1907
SHANGHAI DAHUA-CHINO INSTRUMENT CO., LTD.—See CHINO Corporation; *Int'l*, pg. 1571
SHANGHAI DAHUA ELECTRICAL EQUIPMENT CO., LTD.—See Shanghai Electric Group Company Limited; *Int'l*, pg. 6766
SHANGHAI DAICEL POLYMERS, LTD.—See Daicel Corporation; *Int'l*, pg. 1920
SHANGHAI DAICOLOR & FUJI CO., LTD.—See Dainichiseika Color & Chemicals Mfg. Co., Ltd.; *Int'l*, pg. 1939
SHANGHAI DAI-ICHI SEIKO MOULD & PLASTICS CO., LTD. - MINHANG PLANT—See I-PEX Inc.; *Int'l*, pg. 3564
SHANGHAI DAI-ICHI SEIKO MOULD & PLASTICS CO., LTD. - SHANGHAI PLANT 1—See I-PEX Inc.; *Int'l*, pg. 3564
SHANGHAI DAI-ICHI SEIKO MOULD & PLASTICS CO., LTD. - SHANGHAI PLANT 2—See I-PEX Inc.; *Int'l*, pg. 3564
SHANGHAI DAI-ICHI SEIKO MOULD & PLASTICS CO., LTD.—See I-PEX Inc.; *Int'l*, pg. 3564
SHANGHAI DAIKO MAOCU ADVERTISING CO., LTD.—See Hakuhodo DY Holdings Incorporated; *Int'l*, pg. 3220
SHANGHAI DAIKO MAOCU ADVERTISING CO., LTD.—See Hakuhodo DY Holdings Incorporated; *Int'l*, pg. 3220
SHANGHAI DAIMAY AUTOMOTIVE INTERIOR CO., LTD.; *Int'l*, pg. 6764
SHANGHAI DAISHINKU INTERNATIONAL TRADING CO., LTD—See Daishinku Corp.; *Int'l*, pg. 1942
SHANGHAI DAIWA CAN TRADING COMPANY—See Daiwa Can Company; *Int'l*, pg. 1944
SHANGHAI DALING FOOD CO., LTD.—See Mitsubishi Corporation; *Int'l*, pg. 4943
SHANGHAI DARCO ENGINEERING CO. LTD—See Darco Water Technologies Limited; *Int'l*, pg. 1972
SHANGHAI DARCO ENVIROTECH COMPANY LIMITED—See Darco Water Technologies Limited; *Int'l*, pg. 1972
SHANGHAI DA-SHEN CELLULOSE PLASTICS CO., LTD.—See Mazzucchelli 1849 S.p.a.; *Int'l*, pg. 4750
SHANGHAI DASHENG AGRICULTURE FINANCE TECHNOLOGY CO., LTD.; *Int'l*, pg. 6764
SHANGHAI DATA PORT CO., LTD; *Int'l*, pg. 6764
SHANGHAI DATUN ENERGY RESOURCES TECHNOLOGY DEVELOPMENT COMPANY LIMITED—See China Coal Energy Company Limited; *Int'l*, pg. 1490
SHANGHAI DATUN ENERGY RESOURSES CO., LTD.; *Int'l*, pg. 6764
SHANGHAI DAZHONG PUBLIC UTILITIES (GROUP) CO., LTD.; *Int'l*, pg. 6764
SHANGHAI DELPHI AUTOMOTIVE AIR CONDITIONING SYSTEMS CO., LTD.—See Shanghai Aerospace Automobile Electromechanical Co., Ltd.; *Int'l*, pg. 6761
SHANGHAI DESCENTE COMMERCIAL CO., LTD.—See ITOCHU Corporation; *Int'l*, pg. 3836
SHANGHAI DIBAI PLANT PROTECTION CO., LTD—See Jiangsu Huifeng Bio-Agriculture Co., Ltd.; *Int'l*, pg. 3948
SHANGHAI DIC INK CO., INC.—See DIC Corporation; *Int'l*, pg. 2109
SHANGHAI DIC PRESSURE-SENSITIVE ADHESIVE MATERIALS CO., LTD.—See DIC Corporation; *Int'l*, pg. 2109
SHANGHAI DIGITAL CHINA LIMITED—See Digital China Group Co., Ltd.; *Int'l*, pg. 2121
SHANGHAI DOBE CULTURAL & CREATIVE INDUSTRY DEVELOPMENT (GROUP) CO., LTD.; *Int'l*, pg. 6765
SHANGHAI DOLLY PTE LTD—See Perennial Real Estate Holdings Limited; *Int'l*, pg. 5797
SHANGHAI DONGBO-TAIKI CONVEYOR SYSTEM MANUFACTURING CO., LTD.—See Taikisha Ltd.; *Int'l*, pg. 7413
SHANGHAI DONGIL RUBBER BELT CO., LTD—See DRB Holding Co., Ltd.; *Int'l*, pg. 2201
SHANGHAI DONGPENG SAFETY CO., LTD.—See Air Water Inc.; *Int'l*, pg. 240
SHANGHAI DONGSONG INTERNATIONAL TRADING CO., LTD.—See Oriental International Enterprise Limited; *Int'l*, pg. 5625
SHANGHAI DONGZHENG AUTOMOTIVE FINANCE CO., LTD.—See China ZhengTong Auto Services Holdings Limited; *Int'l*, pg. 1566
SHANGHAI DONNELLEY PREMEDIA TECHNOLOGY CO., LTD.—See Chatham Asset Management, LLC; *U.S. Private*, pg. 865
SHANGHAI DOUGLAS MEDICAL DEVICE CO., LTD.—See Zhejiang Orient Gene Biotech Co., Ltd.; *Int'l*, pg. 8661
SHANGHAI DOWELL TRADING CO. LTD.; *Int'l*, pg. 6765
SHANGHAI DRAGON CORPORATION; *Int'l*, pg. 6765
SHANGHAI DRAGONNET TECHNOLOGY CO., LTD.; *Int'l*, pg. 6765
SHANGHAI DYNAX CO., LTD.—See Exedy Corporation; *Int'l*, pg. 2581
SHANGHAI DZH LIMITED; *Int'l*, pg. 6765

SHANGHAI EAGLERIES ELECTRIC & ELECTRONIC CO., LTD.—See Eaglerise Electric & Electronic (China) Co., Ltd.; *Int'l*, pg. 2266
SHANGHAI EAGLE SAFETY EQUIPMENT LTD.—See Johnson Controls International plc; *Int'l*, pg. 3987
SHANGHAI EARTH-PANDA PERMANENT MAGNET TECHNOLOGY CO., LTD.—See Earth-Panda Advance Magnetic Material Co., Ltd.; *Int'l*, pg. 2268
SHANGHAI EAST BEST CONVENTION & EXHIBITION MANAGEMENT CO., LTD.—See DLG Exhibitions & Events Corp Ltd.; *Int'l*, pg. 2141
SHANGHAI EAST CONTAINER TERMINALS CO., LTD.—See Shanghai International Port (Group) Co., Ltd.; *Int'l*, pg. 6771
SHANGHAI EASTERN OJI PACKAGING CO., LTD.—See Oji Holdings Corporation; *Int'l*, pg. 5538
SHANGHAI EASTMAN CONSULTING COMPANY LTD.—See Eastman Chemical Company; *U.S. Public*, pg. 705
SHANGHAI EBARA ENGINEERING AND SERVICES CO., LTD.—See Ebara Corporation; *Int'l*, pg. 2284
SHANGHAI EBARA PRECISION MACHINERY CO., LTD.—See Ebara Corporation; *Int'l*, pg. 2284
SHANGHAI ECHO FASHION CO., LTD.—See Nippon Steel Corporation; *Int'l*, pg. 5339
SHANGHAI EDSCHA MACHINERY CO., LTD.—See Acek Desarrollo y Gestion Industrial SL; *Int'l*, pg. 96
SHANGHAI E-EE TECHNOLOGIES CO. LTD.—See Ningbo Techmation Co., Ltd.; *Int'l*, pg. 5306
SHANGHAI EFTEC CHEMICAL PRODUCTS LTD.—See EMS-Chemie Holding AG; *Int'l*, pg. 2394
SHANGHAI ELECTRICAL APPARATUS RESEARCH INSTITUTE SWITCH APPARATUS CO., LTD.—See Boer Power Holdings Limited; *Int'l*, pg. 1099
SHANGHAI ELECTRIC AUTOMATION GROUP—See Shanghai Electric Group Company Limited; *Int'l*, pg. 6765
SHANGHAI ELECTRIC DESALINATION ENGINEERING TECHNOLOGY CO., LTD.—See Shanghai Electric Group Company Limited; *Int'l*, pg. 6765
SHANGHAI ELECTRIC DIGITAL TECHNOLOGY CO., LTD.—See Shanghai Electric Group Company Limited; *Int'l*, pg. 6765
SHANGHAI ELECTRIC ECONOMY GROUP—See Shanghai Electric Group Company Limited; *Int'l*, pg. 6765
SHANGHAI ELECTRIC ENVIRONMENTAL PROTECTION GROUP—See Shanghai Electric Group Company Limited; *Int'l*, pg. 6765
SHANGHAI ELECTRIC FUJI ELECTRIC POWER TECHNOLOGY CO., LTD.—See Shanghai Electric Group Company Limited; *Int'l*, pg. 6765
SHANGHAI ELECTRIC FUJI ELECTRIC POWER TECHNOLOGY (WUXI) CO., LTD.—See Fuji Electric Co., Ltd.; *Int'l*, pg. 2812
SHANGHAI ELECTRIC GROUP COMPANY LIMITED; *Int'l*, pg. 6765
SHANGHAI ELECTRIC GROUP FINANCE CO., LTD.—See Shanghai Electric Group Company Limited; *Int'l*, pg. 6765
SHANGHAI ELECTRIC GROUP NUCLEAR POWER CORPORATION—See Shanghai Electric Group Company Limited; *Int'l*, pg. 6765
SHANGHAI ELECTRIC GROUP SHANGHAI ELECTRIC MACHINERY CO., LTD.—See Shanghai Electric Group Company Limited; *Int'l*, pg. 6765
SHANGHAI ELECTRIC HEAVY INDUSTRY GROUP—See Shanghai Electric Group Company Limited; *Int'l*, pg. 6765
SHANGHAI ELECTRIC LINGANG HEAVY MACHINERY EQUIPMENT CO., LTD.—See Shanghai Electric Group Company Limited; *Int'l*, pg. 6765
SHANGHAI ELECTRIC NUCLEAR POWER EQUIPMENT CO., LTD.—See Shanghai Electric Group Company Limited; *Int'l*, pg. 6765
SHANGHAI ELECTRIC POWER COMPANY LIMITED; *Int'l*, pg. 6766
SHANGHAI ELECTRIC POWER ELECTRONICS CO., LTD.—See Shanghai Electric Group Company Limited; *Int'l*, pg. 6765
SHANGHAI ELECTRIC POWER FUEL CO., LTD.—See Shanghai Electric Power Company Limited; *Int'l*, pg. 6766
SHANGHAI ELECTRIC POWER GENERATION ENGINEERING COMPANY—See Shanghai Electric Group Company Limited; *Int'l*, pg. 6765
SHANGHAI ELECTRIC POWER GENERATION GROUP - SEPG LINGANG WORKS—See Shanghai Electric Group Company Limited; *Int'l*, pg. 6765
SHANGHAI ELECTRIC POWER GENERATION GROUP - SEPG SHANGHAI GENERATOR WORKS—See Shanghai Electric Group Company Limited; *Int'l*, pg. 6765
SHANGHAI ELECTRIC POWER GENERATION GROUP—See Shanghai Electric Group Company Limited; *Int'l*, pg. 6765
SHANGHAI ELECTRIC POWER T&D ENGINEERING CO., LTD.—See Shanghai Electric Group Company Limited; *Int'l*, pg. 6766

SHANGHAI ELECTRIC POWER T&D GROUP—See Shanghai Electric Group Company Limited; *Int'l*, pg. 6766
SHANGHAI ELECTRIC POWER T&D TESTING CENTER CO., LTD.—See Shanghai Electric Group Company Limited; *Int'l*, pg. 6766
SHANGHAI ELECTRIC SHMP PULVERIZING & SPECIAL EQUIPMENT CO., LTD.—See Shanghai Electric Group Company Limited; *Int'l*, pg. 6765
SHANGHAI ELECTRIC - SPX ENGINEERING & TECHNOLOGIES CO., LTD.—See Shanghai Electric Group Company Limited; *Int'l*, pg. 6765
SHANGHAI ELECTRIC WIND POWER GROUP CO., LTD.—See Shanghai Electric Group Company Limited; *Int'l*, pg. 6766
SHANGHAI ELITECH TECHNOLOGY CO., LTD.—See Wonderful Hi-Tech Co., Ltd.; *Int'l*, pg. 8446
SHANGHAI EMHART FASTENING SYSTEMS LTD.—See Stanley Black & Decker, Inc.; *U.S. Public*, pg. 1934
SHANGHAI EMPEROR OF CLEANING HI-TECH CO., LTD.; *Int'l*, pg. 6766
SHANGHAI ENERGY NEW MATERIAL TECHNOLOGY CO., LTD.—See Yunnan Energy New Material Co., Ltd.; *Int'l*, pg. 8615
SHANGHAI ENG KONG CONTAINER SERVICES LTD—See Eng Kong Holdings Pte Ltd; *Int'l*, pg. 2426
SHANGHAI ENSHU DISTRIBUTION CO., LTD.—See The Sumitomo Warehouse Co. Ltd.; *Int'l*, pg. 7690
SHANGHAI ENVIRONMENT GROUP CO., LTD.—See Shanghai Chengtou Holding Co., Ltd.; *Int'l*, pg. 6763
SHANGHAI EPAM SYSTEMS CO., LTD.—See EPAM Systems, Inc.; *U.S. Public*, pg. 783
SHANGHAI EPSON MAGNETICS CO., LTD.—See Seiko Epson Corporation; *Int'l*, pg. 6687
SHANGHAI ESPEC ENVIRONMENTAL EQUIPMENT CO., LTD.—See ESPEC Corp.; *Int'l*, pg. 2505
SHANGHAI ESTIC CO., LTD.—See Estic Corporation; *Int'l*, pg. 2518
SHANGHAI-ETECHNOLOGY CO., LTD.—See Nippon Express Holdings, Inc.; *Int'l*, pg. 5317
SHANGHAI E-TONG CHEMICAL CO., LTD.—See Zhejiang Yongtai Technology Co., Ltd.; *Int'l*, pg. 8667
SHANGHAI E&T SANKYU DISTRIBUTION CO., LTD.—See Sankyu, Inc.; *Int'l*, pg. 6545
SHANGHAI EUGLENA BIOTECHNOLOGY CO., LTD.—See euglena Co., Ltd.; *Int'l*, pg. 2526
SHANGHAI EURO TECH LTD.—See Euro Tech Holdings Company Limited; *Int'l*, pg. 2531
SHANGHAI EVERBRIGHT CONVENTION AND EXHIBITION CENTRE LIMITED—See China Everbright Group Limited; *Int'l*, pg. 1501
SHANGHAI-FANUC ROBOMACHINE CO., LTD.—See FANUC Corporation; *Int'l*, pg. 2615
SHANGHAI-FANUC ROBOTICS CO., LTD.—See FANUC Corporation; *Int'l*, pg. 2615
SHANGHAI FASHION STORE—See Bailian Group Co., Ltd.; *Int'l*, pg. 802
SHANGHAI FASTENER & WELDING MATERIAL TECHNOLOGY RESEARCH CENTRE COMPANY LIMITED—See Shanghai Electric Group Company Limited; *Int'l*, pg. 6766
SHANGHAI FAVCO ENGINEERING MACHINERY MANUFACTURING CO. LTD.—See Muhibbah Engineering (M) Bhd.; *Int'l*, pg. 5079
SHANGHAI FEIHANG ELECTRIC WIRE & CABLE CO., LTD.—See Shanghai Electric Group Company Limited; *Int'l*, pg. 6766
SHANGHAI FEILO ACOUSTICS CO., LTD.; *Int'l*, pg. 6766
SHANGHAI FENGHWA GROUP CO., LTD.; *Int'l*, pg. 6766
SHANGHAI FENGYUZHU CULTURE TECHNOLOGY CO., LTD.; *Int'l*, pg. 6767
SHANGHAI FILM CO., LTD; *Int'l*, pg. 6767
SHANGHAI FINE CHEMICALS CO., LTD.—See EcoGreen International Group Limited; *Int'l*, pg. 2295
SHANGHAI FIONA CHEN FASHION CO., LTD.—See Anzheng Fashion Group Co., Ltd.; *Int'l*, pg. 487
SHANGHAI FLAT GLASS CO., LTD.—See Flat Glass Group Co., Ltd.; *Int'l*, pg. 2698
SHANGHAI FLEETGUARD FILTER CO., LTD.—See Cummins Inc.; *U.S. Public*, pg. 606
SHANGHAI FLYCO ELECTRICAL APPLIANCE CO., LTD.; *Int'l*, pg. 6767
SHANGHAI FOCI FIBER OPTIC COMMUNICATION EQUIPMENTS, INC.—See Foci Fiber Optic Communications, Inc.; *Int'l*, pg. 2718
SHANGHAI FOCI FIBER OPTIC COMMUNICATIONS, INC.—See Foci Fiber Optic Communications, Inc.; *Int'l*, pg. 2718
SHANGHAI FOREIGN SERVICE HOLDING GROUP CO., LTD.; *Int'l*, pg. 6767
SHANGHAI FORMICA DECORATIVE MATERIAL CO., LTD.—See Fletcher Building Limited; *Int'l*, pg. 2701
SHANGHAI FORTE LAND CO., LTD.—See Fosun International Limited; *Int'l*, pg. 2752
SHANGHAI FORTUNE TECHGROUP CO., LTD; *Int'l*, pg. 6767
SHANGHAI FOSHION MEDICAL SYSTEM CO., LTD.—See Sisram Medical Ltd.; *Int'l*, pg. 6963

COMPANY NAME INDEX

SHANGHAI FOSUN CAPITAL INVESTMENT MANAGEMENT CO., LTD.—See Fosun International Limited; *Int'l*, pg. 2752
SHANGHAI FOSUN PHARMACEUTICAL (GROUP) CO., LTD.; *Int'l*, pg. 6767
SHANGHAI FOUNDATION ENGINEERING GROUP CO., LTD.—See Shanghai Construction Group Co., Ltd.; *Int'l*, pg. 6764
SHANGHAI FRANKFURT AIRPORT CONSULTING SERVICES CO., LTD. (SFACS)—See Fraport AG; *Int'l*, pg. 2764
SHANGHAI FREESKY TECHNOLOGY CO., LTD.—See Shanghai Newtouch Software Co., Ltd.; *Int'l*, pg. 6776
SHANGHAI FRESH LINE EXPRESS CO., LTD.—See Nichirei Corporation; *Int'l*, pg. 5270
SHANGHAI FRIENDESS ELECTRONICS TECHNOLOGY CO., LTD.; *Int'l*, pg. 6767
SHANGHAI FTNON FOOD PROCESSING EQUIPMENT CO., LTD.—See John Bean Technologies Corporation; *U.S. Public*, pg. 1192
SHANGHAI FUCHI HIGH- TECH CO., LTD.—See NBTM New Materials Group Co., Ltd.; *Int'l*, pg. 5179
SHANGHAI FUDAN FORWARD S&T CO., LTD.; *Int'l*, pg. 6767
SHANGHAI FUDAN MICROELECTRONICS GROUP CO., LTD.; *Int'l*, pg. 6767
SHANGHAI FUDAN - MICROELECTRONICS (HK) LIMITED—See Shanghai Fudan Microelectronics Group Co., Ltd.; *Int'l*, pg. 6768
SHANGHAI FUDAN-ZHANGJIANG BIO-PHARMACEUTICAL CO., LTD.; *Int'l*, pg. 6768
SHANGHAI FUHUI TEXTILES TRADING CO., LTD.—See Fountain Set (Holdings) Limited; *Int'l*, pg. 2754
SHANGHAI FUJI ELECTRIC SWITCHGEAR CO., LTD.—See Fuji Electric Co., Ltd.; *Int'l*, pg. 2813
SHANGHAI FUJI ELECTRIC TRANSFORMER CO., LTD.—See Fuji Electric Co., Ltd.; *Int'l*, pg. 2813
SHANGHAI FUJIKURA KASEI COATING CO., LTD.—See Fujikura Kasei Co., Ltd.; *Int'l*, pg. 2827
SHANGHAI FUJIN INVESTMENT MANAGEMENT CO., LTD.—See Fortune Fountain (Beijing) Holding Group Co., Ltd.; *Int'l*, pg. 2743
SHANGHAI FUJI SEIKI CO., LTD.—See Fuji Seiki Co., Ltd.; *Int'l*, pg. 2817
SHANGHAI FUJIX TRADING CO., LTD.—See FUJIX Ltd.; *Int'l*, pg. 2838
SHANGHAI FUKOKU RUBBER & PLASTICS INDUSTRY CO., LTD.—See Fukoku Co., Ltd.; *Int'l*, pg. 2839
SHANGHAI FUKONG INTERACTIVE ENTERTAINMENT CO., LTD.; *Int'l*, pg. 6768
SHANGHAI FULLHAN MICROELECTONICS CO.,LTD.; *Int'l*, pg. 6768
SHANGHAI FUTAILONG AUTO TECH CO., LTD.—See Beijing WKW Automotive Parts Co., Ltd.; *Int'l*, pg. 960
SHANGHAI FU YANG PROPERTY CONSULTANT CO., LIMITED—See Fortune Sun (China) Holdings Limited; *Int'l*, pg. 2744
SHANGHAI FUYULONG AUTO TECH CO., LTD.—See Beijing WKW Automotive Parts Co., Ltd.; *Int'l*, pg. 960
SHANGHAI GANGLIAN E-COMMERCE HOLDINGS CO., LTD.; *Int'l*, pg. 6768
SHANGHAI GAONAN GARMENTS CO., LTD.—See Oriental International Enterprise Limited; *Int'l*, pg. 5625
SHANGHAI GAOQIAO BASF DISPERSIONS CO., LTD.—See BASF SE; *Int'l*, pg. 877
SHANGHAI GAOQIAO BASF DISPERSIONS CO., LTD.—See China Petrochemical Corporation; *Int'l*, pg. 1539
SHANGHAI GAOSIN INTERNATIONAL LOGISTICS CO., LTD.—See Nissin Corporation; *Int'l*, pg. 5376
SHANGHAI GARDEN & LANDSCAPE (GROUP) CO., LTD.—See Shanghai Construction Group Co., Ltd.; *Int'l*, pg. 6764
SHANGHAI GAS WELDING EQUIPMENT CO., LTD.—See Shanghai Hugong Electric (Group) Co., Ltd; *Int'l*, pg. 6771
SHANGHAI GENCH EDUCATION GROUP LIMITED; *Int'l*, pg. 6768
SHANGHAI GENERAL BEARING COMPANY LIMITED—See Shanghai Electric Group Company Limited; *Int'l*, pg. 6766
SHANGHAI GENERAL FUJI REFRIGERATION EQUIPMENT CO., LTD.—See Fuji Electric Co., Ltd.; *Int'l*, pg. 2813
SHANGHAI GENERAL HEALTHY INFORMATION & TECHNOLOGY CO., LTD.; *Int'l*, pg. 6768
SHANGHAI GENERAL MOTORS CORPORATION LTD.—See General Motors Company; *U.S. Public*, pg. 929
SHANGHAI GENEXT MEDICAL TECHNOLOGY CO. LTD.; *Int'l*, pg. 6768
SHANGHAI GENOMICS, INC.—See GNI Group Ltd.; *Int'l*, pg. 3017
SHANGHAI GENOMICS TECHNOLOGY, LTD.—See GNI Group Ltd.; *Int'l*, pg. 3017
SHANGHAI GENTECH CO., LTD.; *Int'l*, pg. 6768
SHANGHAI GES INFORMATION TECHNOLOGY CO., LTD.—See Venture Corporation Limited; *Int'l*, pg. 8151
SHANGHAI GIVAUDAN LTD—See Givaudan S.A.; *Int'l*, pg. 2981
SHANGHAI GLOBAL SOURCING CONSULTING CO., LTD.—See Carrefour SA; *Int'l*, pg. 1346
SHANGHAI GMA FACTORY CO., LTD.—See GMA Accessories/Capelli of New York; *U.S. Private*, pg. 1721
SHANGHAI GM (SHENYANG) NORSOM MOTORS CO. LTD.—See General Motors Company; *U.S. Public*, pg. 929
SHANGHAI GOLDEN BRIDGE INFOTECH CO., LTD.; *Int'l*, pg. 6768
SHANGHAI GOLDEN UNION COMMERCIAL MANAGEMENT CO., LTD.; *Int'l*, pg. 6768
SHANGHAI GOLDWIN CO., LTD.—See Goldwin, Inc.; *Int'l*, pg. 3035
SHANGHAI GONGJIN COMMUNICATIONS TECHNOLOGY CO., LTD.—See Shenzhen Gongjin Electronics Co., Ltd.; *Int'l*, pg. 6810
SHANGHAI GOOD COM BUSINESS CONSULTING CO., LTD.—See Good Com Asset Co., Ltd.; *Int'l*, pg. 3038
SHANGHAI GOULDS PUMPS CO. LTD.—See ITT Inc.; *U.S. Public*, pg. 1178
SHANGHAI GOYU AUTOPARTS CO., LTD.—See Nichias Corporation; *Int'l*, pg. 5267
SHANGHAI G-PULSE ELECTRONICS TECHNOLOGY COMPANY LIMITED—See Intron Technology Holdings Limited; *Int'l*, pg. 3770
SHANGHAI GRAFTECH TRADING CO., LTD.—See Brookfield Corporation; *Int'l*, pg. 1187
SHANGHAI GRAND CANYON LED LIGHTING SYSTEMS CO., LTD.—See StrongLED Lighting System (Cayman) Co., Ltd.; *Int'l*, pg. 7243
SHANGHAI GRAPE KING ENTERPRISE CO., LTD.—See Grape King Bio Ltd.; *Int'l*, pg. 3060
SHANGHAI GREAT WATER ENVIRONMENTAL PROTECTION CO.—See China TianYF Holdings Group Limited; *Int'l*, pg. 1559
SHANGHAI GREENCOURT INVESTMENT GROUP CO., LTD.; *Int'l*, pg. 6768
SHANGHAI GRID ELECTRIC TECHNOLOGY CO., LTD.—See Troy Information Technology Co., Ltd.; *Int'l*, pg. 7940
SHANGHAI GRUMMAN INTERNATIONAL FIRE EQUIPMENT CO., LTD.—See Xuzhou Handler Special Vehicle Co., Ltd.; *Int'l*, pg. 8541
SHANGHAI GUANDONG INTERNATIONAL CONTAINER TERMINAL CO., LTD.—See Shanghai International Port (Group) Co., Ltd.; *Int'l*, pg. 6771
SHANGHAI GUANGDIAN ELECTRIC (GROUP) CO., LTD.; *Int'l*, pg. 6768
SHANGHAI GUANGZHAO FORESTRY DEVELOPMENT CO., LTD—See Guangzhao Industrial Forest Biotechnology Group Limited; *Int'l*, pg. 3164
SHANGHAI GUANGZHAO PLANT FAST GROWING TECHNOLOGY CO., LTD.—See Guangzhao Industrial Forest Biotechnology Group Limited; *Int'l*, pg. 3164
SHANGHAI GUANZHI INDUSTRIAL AUTOMATION CO., LTD.—See CSG Smart Science & Technology Co., Ltd.; *Int'l*, pg. 1865
SHANGHAI GUAO ELECTRONIC TECHNOLOGY CO.,LTD; *Int'l*, pg. 6768
SHANGHAI GUIJIU CO., LTD.; *Int'l*, pg. 6768
SHANGHAI GUNZE NEW PACKAGING CO., LTD.—See Gunze Limited; *Int'l*, pg. 3186
SHANGHAI GUOSHENG (GROUP) CO., LTD.; *Int'l*, pg. 6768
SHANGHAI GUOTAI JUNAN SECURITIES ASSET MANAGEMENT CO., LTD.—See Guotai Junan Securities Co., Ltd.; *Int'l*, pg. 3187
SHANGHAI G&W ELECTRIC LTD.—See G&W Electric Company; *U.S. Private*, pg. 1629
SHANGHAI HAIBO CO., LTD.—See Bright Food (Group) Co., Ltd.; *Int'l*, pg. 1161
SHANGHAI HAIHUANG GARMENT CO., LTD.—See Shanghai Haixin Group Co., Ltd.; *Int'l*, pg. 6769
SHANGHAI HAIHUA SHIPPING CO., LTD.—See Shanghai International Port (Group) Co., Ltd.; *Int'l*, pg. 6772
SHANGHAI HA INTERNATIONAL TRADING CO. LTD.—See Huettenes-Albertus Chemische Werke GmbH; *Int'l*, pg. 3523
SHANGHAI HAISHUN NEW PHARMACEUTICAL PACKAGING CO., LTD.; *Int'l*, pg. 6769
SHANGHAI HAITONG INTERNATIONAL AUTOMOBILE LOGISTICS CO., LTD.—See Shanghai International Port (Group) Co., Ltd.; *Int'l*, pg. 6772
SHANGHAI HAITONG INTERNATIONAL AUTOMOBILE TERMINAL CO., LTD.—See Shanghai International Port (Group) Co., Ltd.; *Int'l*, pg. 6772
SHANGHAI HAITONG SECURITIES ASSET MANAGEMENT COMPANY LIMITED—See Haitong Securities Co., Ltd.; *Int'l*, pg. 3218
SHANGHAI HAIXIN BIOTECHNOLOGY CO., LTD.—See Shanghai Haixin Group Co., Ltd.; *Int'l*, pg. 6769
SHANGHAI HAIXIN GROUP CO., LTD.; *Int'l*, pg. 6769
SHANGHAI HAIXIN PHARMACEUTICAL CO., LTD.—See Shanghai Haixin Group Co., Ltd.; *Int'l*, pg. 6769
SHANGHAI HAJIME ADVANCED MATERIAL TECHNOLOGY CO., LTD.; *Int'l*, pg. 6769
SHANGHAI HAKUDO PERCISION MATERIALS CO., LTD.—See Hakudo Co., Ltd.; *Int'l*, pg. 3220
SHANGHAI HAKUHODO ADVERTISING CO., LTD.—See Hakuhodo DY Holdings Incorporated; *Int'l*, pg. 3222
SHANGHAI HANBELL PRECISE MACHINERY CO.; *Int'l*, pg. 6769
SHANGHAI HANBELL VACUUM TECHNOLOGY CO., LTD.—See Shanghai Hanbell Precise Machinery Co., Ltd.; *Int'l*, pg. 6769
SHANGHAI HANDPAL TRADING CO., LTD.—See 99 Loyalty Limited; *Int'l*, pg. 16
SHANGHAI HANHONG PRECISION MACHINERY CO., LTD.—See Ferrotec Holdings Corporation; *Int'l*, pg. 2643
SHANGHAI HAO CHENG FOOD DEVELOPMENT CO., LTD.—See Global Sweeteners Holdings Limited; *Int'l*, pg. 3001
SHANGHAI HAOHAI BIOLOGICAL TECHNOLOGY CO., LTD.; *Int'l*, pg. 6769
SHANGHAI HAOYUAN BIOTECH CO., LTD.—See Revvity, Inc.; *U.S. Public*, pg. 1795
SHANGHAI HAOYUAN CHEMEXPRESS CO., LTD.; *Int'l*, pg. 6769
SHANGHAI HARADA NEW AUTOMOTIVE ANTENNA CO., LTD.—See HARADA INDUSTRY CO., LTD.; *Int'l*, pg. 3269
SHANGHAI HARBOR FUXING SHIPPING CO. LTD.—See Shanghai International Port (Group) Co., Ltd.; *Int'l*, pg. 6772
SHANGHAI HARBOUR ENGINEERING COMPANY LTD.—See Shanghai International Port (Group) Co., Ltd.; *Int'l*, pg. 6772
SHANGHAI HARVEST MARKET CONSULTING CO., LTD.—See Nippon Telegraph & Telephone Corporation; *Int'l*, pg. 5351
SHANGHAI HDK MICRO DEVICES CO., LTD.—See Hokuriku Electric Industry Co., Ltd.; *Int'l*, pg. 3445
SHANGHAI HEARTCARE MEDICAL TECHNOLOGY CORPORATION LIMITED; *Int'l*, pg. 6769
SHANGHAI HEAVY MACHINERY PLANT CO., LTD.—See Shanghai Electric Group Company Limited; *Int'l*, pg. 6766
SHANGHAI HEBAO PROPERTY SERVICE CO., LTD.—See Daiwa House Industry Co., Ltd.; *Int'l*, pg. 1947
SHANGHAI HELIOS INTERNATIONAL TRADE CO.,LTD.—See Taiyo Kogyo Corporation; *Int'l*, pg. 7425
SHANGHAI HENGPENG ELECTRONIC TECHNOLOGY CO., LTD.—See Ningbo Henghe Precision Industry Co., Ltd.; *Int'l*, pg. 5302
SHANGHAI HENKEL CHEMICALS CO., LTD.—See Henkel AG & Co. KGaA; *Int'l*, pg. 3349
SHANGHAI HENLIUS BIOTECH, INC.; *Int'l*, pg. 6769
SHANGHAI HESIDI COSMETICS COMPANY LIMITED—See China Regenerative Medicine International Co., Ltd.; *Int'l*, pg. 1547
SHANGHAI HEWLETT-PACKARD CO. LTD.—See Hewlett Packard Enterprise Company; *U.S. Public*, pg. 1031
SHANGHAI HIGHLY ELECTRICAL APPLIANCES CO., LTD.—See Shanghai Highly (Group) Co., Ltd.; *Int'l*, pg. 6770
SHANGHAI HIGHLY (GROUP) CO., LTD.; *Int'l*, pg. 6770
SHANGHAI HIGHLY NEW ENERGY TECHNOLOGY CO., LTD.—See Shanghai Highly (Group) Co., Ltd.; *Int'l*, pg. 6770
SHANGHAI HIGH STRENGTH BOLT FACTORY COMPANY LIMITED—See Shanghai Electric Group Company Limited; *Int'l*, pg. 6766
SHANGHAI HILE BIO-TECHNOLOGY CO., LTD.; *Int'l*, pg. 6770
SHANGHAI HINO ENGINE CO., LTD.—See Toyota Motor Corporation; *Int'l*, pg. 7871
SHANGHAI HI-ROAD FOOD TECHNOLOGY CO., LTD.; *Int'l*, pg. 6769
SHANGHAI HITACHI METALS CABLE MATERIALS CO., LTD.—See Hitachi, Ltd.; *Int'l*, pg. 3424
SHANGHAI HI-TECH CONTROL SYSTEM ASSEMBLING CO., LTD.—See Shanghai Hi-Tech Control System CO., LTD.; *Int'l*, pg. 6770
SHANGHAI HI-TECH CONTROL SYSTEM CO., LTD.; *Int'l*, pg. 6770
SHANGHAI HI-TEC METAL PRODUCTS CO., LTD.—See Sumitomo Corporation; *Int'l*, pg. 7271
SHANGHAI HIUV NEW MATERIALS CO., LTD.; *Int'l*, pg. 6770
SHANGHAI HIWAVE ADVANCED MATERIALS TECHNOLOGY CO., LTD.—See Wenzhou Hongfeng Electrical Alloy Co., Ltd.; *Int'l*, pg. 8377
SHANGHAI HKC LTD.—See Huikwang Corp.; *Int'l*, pg. 3526
SHANGHAI HOLLYWAVE ELECTRONIC SYSTEM CO., LTD.; *Int'l*, pg. 6770
SHANGHAI HOLYSTAR INFORMATION TECHNOLOGY CO., LTD.; *Int'l*, pg. 6770
SHANGHAI HONGDA NEW MATERIAL CO., LTD. *Int'l*, pg. 6770

SHANGHAI HONGDE POLYURETHANE CO., LTD.—See Shanghai Huide Science & Technology Shares Co., Ltd.; *Int'l*, pg. 6771
SHANGHAI HONGDIAN INVESTMENT MANAGEMENT CO., LTD.—See HengTai Securities CO., LTD; *Int'l*, pg. 3347
SHANGHAI HONGFA ELECTROACOUSTIC CO., LTD.—See Hongfa Technology Co Ltd; *Int'l*, pg. 3470
SHANGHAI HONGHUA OFFSHORE OIL & GAS EQUIPMENT CO., LTD.; *Int'l*, pg. 6770
SHANGHAI HONGHUI FOOD CO., LTD.—See Great-Sun Foods Co., Ltd.; *Int'l*, pg. 3066
SHANGHAI HONGKAI HYDLAULICS EQUIPMENT CO., LTD.—See Daikin Industries, Ltd.; *Int'l*, pg. 1936
SHANGHAI HONGTONG INDUSTRIAL CO., LTD.—See APT Medical, Inc; *Int'l*, pg. 523
SHANGHAI HOPERUN INFORMATION TECHNOLOGY & SERVICES CO., LTD.—See Jiangsu Hoperun Software Co., Ltd.; *Int'l*, pg. 3948
SHANGHAI HORMEL FOODS CO. LTD.—See Hormel Foods Corporation; *U.S. Public*, pg. 1054
SHANGHAI HOUSE CURRY COCO ICHIBANYA RESTAURANT, INC.—See House Foods Group Inc.; *Int'l*, pg. 3490
SHANGHAI HOUSE PROPERTY DEVELOPMENT CO., LTD.—See Marubeni Corporation; *Int'l*, pg. 4710
SHANGHAI HOUSING ARCHITECTURAL DESIGN INSTITUTE CO., LTD.—See Long Yuan Construction Group Co., Ltd; *Int'l*, pg. 4549
SHANGHAI HOYER SINOBULK TRANSPORT CO., LTD.—See Hoyer GmbH; *Int'l*, pg. 3499
SHANGHAI HUACE NAVIGATION TECHNOLOGY LTD; *Int'l*, pg. 6770
SHANGHAI HUA CHANG TRADING CO., LTD.—See Nagase & Co., Ltd.; *Int'l*, pg. 5128
SHANGHAI HUACHENG SOUTHWEST TRAVEL AGENCY CO., LTD.—See Trip.com Group Ltd.; *Int'l*, pg. 7926
SHANGHAI HUA DONG CONSTRUCTION MACHINERY CO., LTD.—See Shanghai Construction Group Co., Ltd.; *Int'l*, pg. 6764
SHANGHAI HUADONG CONSTRUCTION MACHINERY FACTORY CO., LTD.—See Shanghai Construction Group Co., Ltd.; *Int'l*, pg. 6764
SHANGHAI HUAFON ALUMINIUM CORPORATION; *Int'l*, pg. 6770
SHANGHAI HUAGONGBAO E-COMMERCE CO., LTD.—See China Baowu Steel Group Corp., Ltd.; *Int'l*, pg. 1486
SHANGHAI HUAGUO TRANSPORTATION CO., LTD.—See Mitsui O.S.K. Lines, Ltd.; *Int'l*, pg. 4991
SHANGHAI HUAHONG JITONG SMART SYSTEM CO., LTD.; *Int'l*, pg. 6770
SHANGHAI HUAJIA INT'L FREIGHT FORWARDING CO., LTD.—See Mitsui O.S.K. Lines, Ltd.; *Int'l*, pg. 4991
SHANGHAI HUALIAN COMMERCIAL BUILDING HUANGPU—See Bailian Group Co., Ltd.; *Int'l*, pg. 802
SHANGHAI HUALIAN LAWSON CO.—See AEON Co., Ltd.; *Int'l*, pg. 178
SHANGHAI HUALI PACKAGING CO.—See Overseas Chinese Town (Asia) Holdings Limited; *Int'l*, pg. 5672
SHANGHAI HUAMING INTELLIGENT TERMINAL EQUIPMENT CO., LTD.; *Int'l*, pg. 6770
SHANGHAI HUANGPU BAOZEN AUTOMOBILE SALES CO., LTD—See China Yongda Automobiles Services Holdings Limited; *Int'l*, pg. 1564
SHANGHAI HUAPU CABLE CO., LTD.—See Shanghai Electric Group Company Limited; *Int'l*, pg. 6766
SHANGHAI HUASHENG FUJITEC ESCALATOR CO., LTD.—See Fujitec Co., Ltd.; *Int'l*, pg. 2831
SHANGHAI HUATENG METAL PROCESSING CO., LTD.—See Chun Yuan Steel Industry Co., Ltd.; *Int'l*, pg. 1596
SHANGHAI HUATENG SOFTWARE SYSTEMS CO., LTD.—See Chinasoft International Ltd.; *Int'l*, pg. 1569
SHANGHAI HUA TING GUEST HOUSE COMPANY LIMITED—See Shanghai Jin Jiang Capital Company Limited; *Int'l*, pg. 6772
SHANGHAI HUAXIA DUN & BRADSTREET BUSINESS INFORMATION CONSULTING CO., LIMITED—See Cannae Holdings, Inc.; *U.S. Public*, pg. 430
SHANGHAI HUAXIA DUN & BRADSTREET BUSINESS INFORMATION CONSULTING CO., LIMITED—See CC Capital Partners, LLC; *U.S. Private*, pg. 798
SHANGHAI HUAXIA DUN & BRADSTREET BUSINESS INFORMATION CONSULTING CO., LIMITED—See Intercontinental Exchange, Inc.; *U.S. Public*, pg. 1142
SHANGHAI HUAXIN BIOTECHNOLOGY CO., LTD.—See EPS Holdings, Inc.; *Int'l*, pg. 2466
SHANGHAI HUAYI GROUP CORPORATION LTD.; *Int'l*, pg. 6771
SHANGHAI HUAYI MICROELECTRONIC MATERIAL CO. LTD.—See Linde plc; *Int'l*, pg. 4508
SHANGHAI HUDONG SANZO MARINE MACHINERY CO.—See Mitsui E&S Holdings Co., Ltd.; *Int'l*, pg. 4986
SHANGHAI HUF AUTOMOTIVE LOCK CO., LTD.—See Huf Hulsbeck & Furst GmbH & Co. KG; *Int'l*, pg. 3523

SHANGHAI HU GONG AUTO-ELECTRIC CO., LTD.—See China Security Co., Ltd.; *Int'l*, pg. 1550
SHANGHAI HUGONG ELECTRIC (GROUP) CO., LTD; *Int'l*, pg. 6771
SHANGHAI HUIDE SCIENCE & TECHNOLOGY SHARES CO., LTD.; *Int'l*, pg. 6771
SHANGHAI HUILI BUILDING MATERIALS CO., LTD.; *Int'l*, pg. 6771
SHANGHAI HUIMEI PROPERTY CO LTD—See Metro Holdings Limited; *Int'l*, pg. 4860
SHANGHAI HUIPING CULTURE DEVELOPMENT CO., LTD.—See Tianyang New Materials (Shanghai) Technology Co., Ltd.; *Int'l*, pg. 7742
SHANGHAI HUITONG ENERGY CO., LTD.; *Int'l*, pg. 6771
SHANGHAI HUI YU FINE CHEMICALS CO., LTD.—See Headway Advanced Materials Inc.; *Int'l*, pg. 3302
SHANGHAI HUMAN RESOURCE CO., LTD.—See Human Holdings Co., Ltd.; *Int'l*, pg. 3529
SHANGHAI HUNTSMAN POLYURETHANES SPECIALTIES CO., LTD.—See Huntsman Corporation; *U.S. Public*, pg. 1074
SHANGHAI HUVITZ CO., LTD.—See Huvitz Co., Ltd.; *Int'l*, pg. 3541
SHANGHAI HYDROGEN PROPULSION TECHNOLOGY CO., LTD.—See Shanghai Automotive Industry Corporation; *Int'l*, pg. 6762
SHANGHAI HYP- ARCH ARCHITECTURAL DESIGN CONSULTANT CO., LTD.; *Int'l*, pg. 6771
SHANGHAI HYSTER FORKLIFT, LTD.—See Hyster-Yale Materials Handling, Inc.; *U.S. Public*, pg. 1080
SHANGHAI HYUNDAI ELEVATOR MANUFACTURING CO., LTD.—See Hyundai Group; *Int'l*, pg. 3557
SHANGHAI IDEMITSU LUBE TRADING CO., LTD.—See Idemitsu Kosan Co., Ltd.; *Int'l*, pg. 3592
SHANGHAI IDIADA AUTOMOTIVE TECHNOLOGY SERVICES CO., LTD.—See I Squared Capital Advisors (US) LLC; *U.S. Private*, pg. 2023
SHANGHAI IDIADA AUTOMOTIVE TECHNOLOGY SERVICES CO., LTD.—See TDR Capital LLP; *Int'l*, pg. 7492
SHANGHAI IGUZZINI TRADING CO., LTD.—See Fagerhult Group AB; *Int'l*, pg. 2602
SHANGHAI IMAT AUTOMOTIVE TECHNOLOGY SERVICE CO., LTD.—See Centre Testing International Corporation; *Int'l*, pg. 1411
SHANGHAI IMPERIAL LASER SYSTEMS TRADING CO. LTD.—See Spectrum Technologies PLC; *Int'l*, pg. 7132
SHANGHAI IMSINOEXPO DIGITAL SERVICES CO., LTD.—See Informa plc; *Int'l*, pg. 3693
SHANGHAI INABATA FINE CHEMICAL CO., LTD.—See Inabata & Co. Ltd.; *Int'l*, pg. 3644
SHANGHAI INABATA TRADING CO., LTD.—See Inabata & Co. Ltd.; *Int'l*, pg. 3644
SHANGHAI INDUSTRIAL DEVELOPMENT CO., LTD.—See Shanghai Industrial Holdings Limited; *Int'l*, pg. 6771
SHANGHAI INDUSTRIAL HOLDINGS LIMITED; *Int'l*, pg. 6771
SHANGHAI INDUSTRIAL PHARMACEUTICAL INVESTMENT CO LTD—See Shanghai Industrial Holdings Limited; *Int'l*, pg. 6771
SHANGHAI INDUSTRIAL URBAN DEVELOPMENT GROUP LIMITED; *Int'l*, pg. 6771
SHANGHAI INDUSTRY & COMMERCE EXHIBITION CO., LTD.—See DLG Exhibitions & Events Corp Ltd.; *Int'l*, pg. 2141
SHANGHAI INFOTM MICROELECTRONICS CO., LTD.—See Infotmic Co., Ltd.; *Int'l*, pg. 3696
SHANGHAI INOAC CORPORATION—See INOAC Corporation; *Int'l*, pg. 3714
SHANGHAI INOAC ENGINEERING CO., LTD.—See INOAC Corporation; *Int'l*, pg. 3714
SHANGHAI INOAC NEW MATERIAL CO., LTD.—See INOAC Corporation; *Int'l*, pg. 3714
SHANGHAI INOUE PACKING PRODUCT CO., LTD—See INOAC Corporation; *Int'l*, pg. 3714
SHANGHAI INOUE XIN YI PLASTICS CO., LTD.—See INOAC Corporation; *Int'l*, pg. 3715
SHANGHAI INSTALLATION ENGINEERING GROUP CO., LTD.—See Shanghai Construction Group Co., Ltd.; *Int'l*, pg. 6764
SHANGHAI INSTANTWHIP FOODS CO., LTD.—See Rich Holdings, Inc.; *U.S. Private*, pg. 3427
SHANGHAI INSTITUTE OF MACHINERY BUILDING TECHNOLOGY CO., LTD.—See Shanghai Electric Group Company Limited; *Int'l*, pg. 6765
SHANGHAI INSULATING MATERIALS CO., LTD.; *Int'l*, pg. 6771
SHANGHAI INTERMODA CLOTHING CO., LTD.—See Etam Developpement SCA; *Int'l*, pg. 2520
SHANGHAI INTERNATIONAL AIRPORT CO., LTD.; *Int'l*, pg. 6771
SHANGHAI INTERNATIONAL ASSET MANAGEMENT (HONG KONG) CO., LTD.—See SinoPac Financial Holdings Company Ltd.; *Int'l*, pg. 6954
SHANGHAI INTERNATIONAL ENGINEERING CONSTRUCTION CONSULTING CO., LTD.—See ENN Natural Gas Co., Ltd.; *Int'l*, pg. 2443

SHANGHAI INTERNATIONAL PORT (GROUP) CO., LTD.; *Int'l*, pg. 6771
SHANGHAI INTERNATIONAL REALTY CO., LTD.—See Daiwa House Industry Co., Ltd.; *Int'l*, pg. 1947
SHANGHAI INTERNATIONAL SHANGHAI GROWTH INVESTMENT LIMITED; *Int'l*, pg. 6772
SHANGHAI INTERNATIONAL TRADE PROMOTION CO., LTD.—See DLG Exhibitions & Events Corp Ltd.; *Int'l*, pg. 2141
SHANGHAI INTRON ELECTRONICS COMPANY LIMITED—See Intron Technology Holdings Limited; *Int'l*, pg. 3770
SHANGHAI IPM CO., LTD.—See Nishimoto Co., Ltd.; *Int'l*, pg. 5365
SHANGHAI IRISO ELECTRONICS CO., LTD.—See IRISO ELECTRONICS CO.,LTD; *Int'l*, pg. 3809
SHANGHAI ITW PLASTICS & METAL CO., LTD.—See Illinois Tool Works Inc.; *U.S. Public*, pg. 1110
SHANGHAI IWASAKI ELECTRIC CO., LTD.—See IWASAKI ELECTRIC Co., Ltd.; *Int'l*, pg. 3849
SHANGHAI IWATANI CO., LTD.—See Iwatani Corporation; *Int'l*, pg. 3850
SHANGHAI JACKSONLEA POLISHING MATERIALS CO., LTD.—See Jason Industries, Inc.; *U.S. Private*, pg. 2190
SHANGHAI JAHWA UNITED COMPANY LTD.—See Ping An Insurance (Group) Company of China, Ltd.; *Int'l*, pg. 5869
SHANGHAI JA SOLAR PV TECHNOLOGY CO., LTD.—See JA Solar Technology Co., Ltd.; *Int'l*, pg. 3859
SHANGHAI JIAFENG INFORMATION TECHNOLOGY CO., LTD.—See Japan System Techniques Co., Ltd.; *Int'l*, pg. 3905
SHANGHAI JIAHENG DAILY CHEMICAL CO., LTD.—See Jahen Household Products Co., Ltd.; *Int'l*, pg. 3871
SHANGHAI JIANGXI COPPER MARKETING CO., LTD.—See Jiangxi Copper Company Limited; *Int'l*, pg. 3959
SHANGHAI JIANHAO ENGINEERING CONSULTANCY CO., LTD.—See Shanghai Construction Group Co., Ltd.; *Int'l*, pg. 6764
SHANGHAI JIANSHE LUQIAO MACHINERY CO., LTD.—See Sandvik AB; *Int'l*, pg. 6535
SHANGHAI JIAODA ONLLY CO., LTD.; *Int'l*, pg. 6772
SHANGHAI JIAODA WITHUB INFORMATION INDUSTRIAL COMPANY LIMITED; *Int'l*, pg. 6772
SHANGHAI JIAOYUN GROUP CO., LTD.; *Int'l*, pg. 6772
SHANGHAI JIA RONG TRADING CO., LTD.—See BRENNTAG SE; *Int'l*, pg. 1149
SHANGHAI JIEJIN NEW ELECTRIC MATERIALS CO., LTD.—See Shanghai Electric Group Company Limited; *Int'l*, pg. 6766
SHANGHAI JIELONG ART PRINTING CO., LTD.—See Shanghai Jielong Industry Group Co., Ltd.; *Int'l*, pg. 6772
SHANGHAI JIELONG INDUSTRY GROUP CO., LTD.; *Int'l*, pg. 6772
SHANGHAI JIHAI SHIPPING CO., LTD.—See Shanghai International Port (Group) Co., Ltd.; *Int'l*, pg. 6772
SHANGHAI JINDUN FIRE-FIGHTING INTELLIGENCE SCIENCE AND TECHNOLOGY CO., LTD.—See Johnson Controls International plc; *Int'l*, pg. 3986
SHANGHAI JINFENG WINE COMPANY LIMITED; *Int'l*, pg. 6772
SHANGHAI JING XING INDUSTRIAL INVESTMENT CO., LTD.—See Zhejiang Jingxing Paper Joint Stock Co., Ltd.; *Int'l*, pg. 8658
SHANGHAI JINGXUE INSULATION TECHNOLOGY CO., LTD.—See Jiangsu Jingxue Insulation Technology Co., Ltd.; *Int'l*, pg. 3949
SHANGHAI JINHUA HOTEL CO., LTD.—See Shanghai Jin Jiang International Hotels Co Ltd; *Int'l*, pg. 6772
SHANGHAI JINJIANG BATTERY CO. LTD.—See Gold Peak Technology Group Limited; *Int'l*, pg. 3026
SHANGHAI JIN JIANG CAPITAL COMPANY LIMITED; *Int'l*, pg. 6772
SHANGHAI JIN JIANG INTERNATIONAL HOTELS CO LTD; *Int'l*, pg. 6772
SHANGHAI JINJIANG INTERNATIONAL TRAVEL CO., LTD.; *Int'l*, pg. 6773
SHANGHAI JINJIANG MITSUI-SOKO INTERNATIONAL LOGISTICS CO., LTD.—See Mitsui-Soko Holdings Co., Ltd.; *Int'l*, pg. 4993
SHANGHAI JIN JIANG ONLINE NETWORK SERVICE CO., LTD.; *Int'l*, pg. 6772
SHANGHAI JINJIANG-SUMISO INTERNATIONAL LOGISTICS, CO., LTD.—See The Sumitomo Warehouse Co. Ltd.; *Int'l*, pg. 7690
SHANGHAI JINPAN HOTEL CO., LTD.—See Shanghai Jin Jiang International Hotels Co Ltd; *Int'l*, pg. 6772
SHANGHAI JINQIAO EXPORT PROCESSING ZONE DEVELOPMENT CO., LTD.; *Int'l*, pg. 6773
SHANGHAI JINTAI ENGINEERING MACHINERY CO., LTD.—See Guangxi Liugong Machinery Co., Ltd.; *Int'l*, pg. 3163
SHANGHAI JOHNSON & JOHNSON LTD.—See Johnson & Johnson; *U.S. Public*, pg. 1200

COMPANY NAME INDEX

SHANGHAI JOHNSON & JOHNSON PHARMACEUTICALS, LTD.—See Johnson & Johnson; *U.S. Public*, pg. 1200
SHANGHAI JOHNSON LTD.—See S.C. Johnson & Son, Inc.; *U.S. Private*, pg. 3517
SHANGHAI JOIN BUY CO., LTD.; *Int'l*, pg. 6773
SHANGHAI JOYSPEED GLOBAL CARGO CO., LTD.—See Hon Hai Precision Industry Co., Ltd.; *Int'l*, pg. 3457
SHANGHAI JP CO., LTD.—See Japan Pulp and Paper Company Limited; *Int'l*, pg. 3904
SHANGHAI JP CO., LTD.—See Nippon Paper Industries Co., Ltd.; *Int'l*, pg. 5328
SHANGHAI JRM TRADING CO., LTD.—See Japan Resistor Mfg Co., Ltd.; *Int'l*, pg. 3905
SHANGHAI JTU VENTURE CAPITAL CO., LTD.—See Shanghai Jiaoda Onlly Co., Ltd; *Int'l*, pg. 6772
SHANGHAI JUKI SEWING MACHINE CO., LTD.—See Juki Corporation; *Int'l*, pg. 4024
SHANGHAI JUNSHI BIOSCIENCES CO., LTD.; *Int'l*, pg. 6773
SHANGHAI JUNSHI BIOTECHNOLOGY CO., LTD.—See Shanghai Junshi Biosciences Co., Ltd.; *Int'l*, pg. 6773
SHANGHAI JUYUAN DATA CO., LTD.—See Hundsun Technologies Inc.; *Int'l*, pg. 3534
SHANGHAI KAIBAO PHARMACEUTICAL CO., LTD.; *Int'l*, pg. 6773
SHANGHAI KAICHUANG MARINE INTERNATIONAL CO., LTD.; *Int'l*, pg. 6773
SHANGHAI KAI CUTLERY CO., LTD.—See KAI Corporation; *Int'l*, pg. 4050
SHANGHAI KAIHONG ELECTRONIC CO., LTD.—See Diodes Incorporated; *U.S. Public*, pg. 667
SHANGHAI KAI KAI INDUSTRIAL CO., LTD.; *Int'l*, pg. 6773
SHANGHAI KAINING IMPORT & EXPORT CO., LTD.—See China Hi-Tech Group Corporation; *Int'l*, pg. 1508
SHANGHAI KAI TRADE CO., LTD.—See KAI Corporation; *Int'l*, pg. 4050
SHANGHAI KAIXIN BIOTECH CO., LTD.—See Apple Flavor & Fragrance Group Co., Ltd.; *Int'l*, pg. 520
SHANGHAI KAIZHONG MATERIALS SCIENCE & TECHNOLOGY CO., LTD.—See Shanghai Carthane co.,Ltd; *Int'l*, pg. 6763
SHANGHAI KAMIGUMI LOGISTIC SERVICE CO., LTD.—See Kamigumi Co., Ltd.; *Int'l*, pg. 4063
SHANGHAI KAMIGUMI LOGISTICS SERVICE CO., LTD.—See Kamigumi Co., Ltd.; *Int'l*, pg. 4063
SHANGHAI KARON ECO-VALVE MANUFACTURING CO., LTD.; *Int'l*, pg. 6773
SHANGHAI KAYAKU INTERNATIONAL TRADING CO., LTD.—See Nippon Kayaku Co., Ltd.; *Int'l*, pg. 5321
SHANGHAI KAYTUNE INDUSTRIAL CO., LTD.; *Int'l*, pg. 6773
SHANGHAI KEHUA BIO-ENGINEERING CO., LTD.; *Int'l*, pg. 6773
SHANGHAI KEJIAN APPAREL INSPECTION CO., LTD.—See Maruzen Showa Unyu Co., Ltd.; *Int'l*, pg. 4716
SHANGHAI KELAI MECHATRONICS ENG CO LTD; *Int'l*, pg. 6773
THE SHANGHAI KELANTAN RUBBER ESTATES (1925) LTD—See Kuala Lumpur Kepong Berhad; *Int'l*, pg. 4319
SHANGHAI KENNETH KO DESIGNS LTD.—See Shenzhen Bauing Construction Group Co., Ltd.; *Int'l*, pg. 6805
SHANGHAI KENWOOD ELECTRONICS CO., LTD.—See JVCKENWOOD Corporation; *Int'l*, pg. 4034
SHANGHAI KEXU INTERNATIONAL TRADE CO., LTD.—See Zhewen Interactive Group Co Ltd; *Int'l*, pg. 8671
SHANGHAI KFC CO., LTD.—See Yum China Holdings, Inc.; *U.S. Public*, pg. 2399
SHANGHAI KG MACHINERY CO., LTD.—See Kanamoto Co., Ltd.; *Int'l*, pg. 4064
SHANGHAI KINDLY ENTERPRISE DEVELOPMENT GROUP CO., LTD; *Int'l*, pg. 6773
SHANGHAI KINDLY ENTERPRISE DEVELOPMENT GROUP MEDICAL INSTRUMENTS CO., LTD—See Shanghai Kindly Enterprise Development Group Co., Ltd; *Int'l*, pg. 6773
SHANGHAI KINDLY ENTERPRISE DEVELOPMENT GROUP PHARMACEUTICAL CO., LTD—See Shanghai Kindly Enterprise Development Group Co., Ltd; *Int'l*, pg. 6773
SHANGHAI KINDLY INTERNATIONAL TRADE CO., LTD.—See Shanghai Kindly Enterprise Development Group Co., Ltd; *Int'l*, pg. 6773
SHANGHAI KINDLY MEDICAL INSTRUMENTS CO., LTD.; *Int'l*, pg. 6774
SHANGHAI KINDLY TUBE CO., LTD.—See Shanghai Kindly Enterprise Development Group Co., Ltd; *Int'l*, pg. 6773
SHANGHAI KINETIC MEDICAL CO., LTD.; *Int'l*, pg. 6774
SHANGHAI KINGFA SCI & TECH DVPT CO., LTD.—See Kingfa Sci &Tech Co., Ltd.; *Int'l*, pg. 4172
SHANGHAI KINGTEST ELECTRONIC TECHNOLOGY CO., LTD.—See ViTrox Corporation Berhad; *Int'l*, pg. 8262
SHANGHAI KINLITA CHEMICAL CO., LTD.; *Int'l*, pg. 6774
SHANGHAI KNOW-HOW TECHNOLOGIES CO., LTD.—See Daeyang Electric Co., Ltd.; *Int'l*, pg. 1911
SHANGHAI KOA ELECTRONICS TRADING CO.,LTD.—See Koa Corporation; *Int'l*, pg. 4215
SHANGHAI KOHDEN MEDICAL ELECTRONIC INSTRUMENT CORPORATION—See Nihon Kohden Corporation; *Int'l*, pg. 5286
SHANGHAI KONGSBERG AUTOMOTIVE DONG FENG MORSE, CO., LTD.—See Kongsberg Automotive ASA; *Int'l*, pg. 4254
SHANGHAI KORN/FERRY HUMAN CAPITAL CONSULTING CO., LTD.—See Korn Ferry; *U.S. Public*, pg. 1275
SHANGHAI KOSTAL - HUAYANG AUTOMOTIVE ELECTRIC CO. LTD.—See Leopold Kostal GmbH & Co. KG; *Int'l*, pg. 4466
SHANGHAI KRUPP STAINLESS CO., LTD.—See China Baowu Steel Group Corp., Ltd.; *Int'l*, pg. 1486
SHANGHAI KRUPP STAINLESS CO., LTD.—See Shanghai Lujiazui Finance & Trade Zone Development; *Int'l*, pg. 6774
SHANGHAI KUANGDA PENGDIAN AUTOMOBILE TRIM PARTS CO., LTD.—See Kuangda Technology Group Co., Ltd.; *Int'l*, pg. 4319
SHANGHAI KUNHONG INDUSTRIAL CO., LTD.—See Landsea Green Management Limited; *Int'l*, pg. 4407
SHANGHAI KYOCERA ELECTRONICS CO., LTD—See KYOCERA Corporation; *Int'l*, pg. 4360
SHANGHAI KYOCERA SALES & TRADING CORPORATION—See KYOCERA Corporation; *Int'l*, pg. 4360
SHANGHAI KYOKUTO PRECISION ELECTRONICS LTD.—See SIIX CORPORATION; *Int'l*, pg. 6914
SHANGHAI KYORITSU KEDI TESTSYSTEM CO., LTD.—See Kyoritsu Electric Corporation; *Int'l*, pg. 4365
SHANGHAI KYOTEC ELECTRONIC TRADING CO., LTD—See Restar Holdings Corporation; *Int'l*, pg. 6303
SHANGHAI KYOWA AMINO ACID CO., LTD.—See Kirin Holdings Company, Limited; *Int'l*, pg. 4188
SHANGHAI LABWAY CLINICAL LABORATORY CO., LTD.; *Int'l*, pg. 6774
SHANGHAI LADY FASHION DEPARTMENT STORE—See Bailian Group Co., Ltd; *Int'l*, pg. 802
SHANGHAI LAIMU ELECTRONIC LIMITED; *Int'l*, pg. 6774
SHANGHAI LAIYIFEN CO., LTD; *Int'l*, pg. 6774
SHANGHAI LANG CHEMICAL CO., LTD.—See CD International Enterprises, Inc.; *U.S. Public*, pg. 461
SHANGHAI LANSHENG REAL ESTATE CO., LTD.—See DLG Exhibitions & Events Corp Ltd.; *Int'l*, pg. 2141
SHANGHAI LAUNCH-SK AUTOMOBILE SERVICE CO., LTD.—See SK Networks Co., Ltd.; *Int'l*, pg. 6975
SHANGHAI LEAR AUTOMOTIVE SYSTEMS CO., LTD.—See Lear Corporation; *U.S. Public*, pg. 1298
SHANGHAI LECIEN CO., LTD.—See Wacoal Holdings Corp.; *Int'l*, pg. 8326
SHANGHAI LERADO DAILY ARTICLE CO., LTD.—See Lerado Financial Group Company Limited; *Int'l*, pg. 4466
SHANGHAI LES ENPHANTS CHILDREN ARTICLES CO., LTD.—See Les Enphants Group; *Int'l*, pg. 4467
SHANGHAI LETONG PACKAGING MATERIALS CO., LTD.—See Letong Chemical Co., Ltd.; *Int'l*, pg. 4470
SHANGHAI LIANGXIN ELECTRICAL CO., LTD.; *Int'l*, pg. 6774
SHANGHAI LIANGXIN (NADER) ELECTRICAL U.S. CO. INC.—See Shanghai Liangxin Electrical Co.; *Int'l*, pg. 6774
SHANGHAI LIANMING MACHINERY CO., LTD.; *Int'l*, pg. 6774
SHANGHAI LIFETECH HOUSEHOLD PRODUCTS CO., LTD.—See Sumitomo Chemical Company, Limited; *Int'l*, pg. 7264
SHANGHAI LIFE TECHNOLOGIES BIOTECHNOLOGY CO. LIMITED—See Thermo Fisher Scientific Inc.; *U.S. Public*, pg. 2149
SHANGHAI LIKANG DISINFECTANT HIGH-TECH CO., LTD.; *Int'l*, pg. 6774
SHANGHAI LILI & BEAUTY COSMETICS CO., LTD.; *Int'l*, pg. 6774
THE SHANGHAI LINCOLN ELECTRIC CO., LTD.—See Lincoln Electric Holdings, Inc.; *U.S. Public*, pg. 1318
SHANGHAI LINGANG HOLDINGS CO., LTD.; *Int'l*, pg. 6774
SHANGHAI LINGHUA LOGISTICS CO., LTD.—See Mitsubishi Logistics Corporation; *Int'l*, pg. 4963
SHANGHAI LINGYUN GLOBAL FORWARDING CO., LTD.—See Mitsubishi Logistics Corporation; *Int'l*, pg. 4963
SHANGHAI LINGYUN INDUSTRIES DEVELOPMENT CO., LTD.; *Int'l*, pg. 6774
SHANGHAI LIONTOWN HOSPITAL LOGISTICS MANAGEMENT CO., LTD—See Anxian Yuan China Holdings Limited; *Int'l*, pg. 486
SHANGHAI LIXIN HYDRAULIC CO., LTD.—See Jiangsu Hengli Hydraulic Co., Ltd.; *Int'l*, pg. 3947
SHANGHAI LOCK & LOCK TRADE CO., LTD.—See Lock&Lock Co., Ltd.; *Int'l*, pg. 4540
SHANGHAI LOCK&LOCK TRADING CO., LTD.—See Lock&Lock Co., Ltd.; *Int'l*, pg. 4540
SHANGHAI LONE STAR CABLE CO., LTD.—See Kongsberg Automotive ASA; *Int'l*, pg. 4254
SHANGHAI LONGAN AUTOMOTIVE ELECTRONICS CO., LTD.—See Shanghai Baolong Automotive Corporation; *Int'l*, pg. 6762
SHANGHAI LONGFEI INTERNATIONAL LOGISTICS CO., LTD.—See Mitsui O.S.K. Lines, Ltd.; *Int'l*, pg. 4991
SHANGHAI LONG FENG FOOD ADDITIVES CO., LTD.—See DIC Corporation; *Int'l*, pg. 2109
SHANGHAI LONGSHENG LIANYE INVEST CO., LTD.—See Zhejiang Longsheng Group Co., Ltd.; *Int'l*, pg. 8659
SHANGHAI LONGSHENG REAL ESTATE CO., LTD.—See Zhejiang Longsheng Group Co., Ltd.; *Int'l*, pg. 8659
SHANGHAI LONGYUAN TIANCE ENTERPRISE MANAGEMENT CO., LTD.—See Long Yuan Construction Group Co., Ltd; *Int'l*, pg. 4549
SHANGHAI LONGYUN MEDIA GROUP CO., LTD.; *Int'l*, pg. 6774
SHANGHAI LONYER FUELS CO., LTD.; *Int'l*, pg. 6774
SHANGHAI LUDA AUTOMOBILE SALES SERVICES CO., LTD.—See China ZhengTong Auto Services Holdings Limited; *Int'l*, pg. 1567
SHANGHAI LUJIAZUI FINANCE & TRADE ZONE DEVELOPMENT; *Int'l*, pg. 6774
SHANGHAI LUOMAN LIGHTING TECHNOLOGIES, INC.; *Int'l*, pg. 6775
SHANGHAI MACHINE TOOL WORKS LTD.—See Shanghai Electric Group Company Limited; *Int'l*, pg. 6766
SHANGHAI MAILIN INTERNATIONAL TRADE CO., LTD.—See Jiangsu Wanlin Modern Logistics Co., Ltd.; *Int'l*, pg. 3955
SHANGHAI MALING AQUARIUS CO., LTD.—See Bright Food (Group) Co., Ltd.; *Int'l*, pg. 1161
SHANGHAI MARATHON GEXIN ELECTRIC CO. LTD.—See Regal Rexnord Corporation; *U.S. Public*, pg. 1773
SHANGHAI MARUKYO TRANSPORTATION CO., LTD.—See Mitsui-Soko Holdings Co., Ltd.; *Int'l*, pg. 4993
SHANGHAI MATAI TRADING CO., LTD.—See Rengo Co., Ltd.; *Int'l*, pg. 6280
SHANGHAI MATERIAL TRADING CO., LTD.; *Int'l*, pg. 6775
SHANGHAI MATEX CHEMICALS CO., LTD.—See Matex International Limited; *Int'l*, pg. 4727
SHANGHAI MATSUYA F&B MANAGEMENT CO., LTD.—See Matsuya Foods Holdings Co., Ltd.; *Int'l*, pg. 4730
SHANGHAI MCCORMICK FOODS COMPANY LIMITED—See McCormick & Company, Incorporated; *U.S. Public*, pg. 1404
SHANGHAI MECHANICAL & ELECTRICAL INDUSTRY CO., LTD.—See Shanghai Electric Group Company Limited; *Int'l*, pg. 6766
SHANGHAI MECHANIZED CONSTRUCTION CORPORATION LTD.—See Shanghai Construction Group Co., Ltd.; *Int'l*, pg. 6764
SHANGHAI MECHANIZED CONSTRUCTION GROUP CO., LTD.—See Shanghai Construction Group Co., Ltd.; *Int'l*, pg. 6764
SHANGHAI MEDICAL INSTRUMENTS CO., LTD.—See Shanghai Pharmaceuticals Holding Co., Ltd.; *Int'l*, pg. 6776
SHANGHAI MEDICILON, INC.; *Int'l*, pg. 6775
SHANGHAI MEGMEET ELECTRICAL CO., LTD—See Shenzhen Megmeet Electrical Co.,Ltd; *Int'l*, pg. 6817
SHANGHAI MEIDEN SEMICONDUCTOR CO LTD—See Meidensha Corporation; *Int'l*, pg. 4798
SHANGHAI MEIDENSHA CHANGCHENG SWITCHGEAR CO. LTD.—See Meidensha Corporation; *Int'l*, pg. 4798
SHANGHAI MEIKO INTERNATIONAL LOGISTICS CO., LTD.—See Meiko Trans Co. Ltd.; *Int'l*, pg. 4803
SHANGHAI MEI LONG ZHEN ISETAN DEPARTMENT STORE CO., LTD.—See Isetan Mitsukoshi Holdings Ltd.; *Int'l*, pg. 3815
SHANGHAI MEISHAN IRON & STEEL CO., LTD.—See China Baowu Steel Group Corp., Ltd.; *Int'l*, pg. 1486
SHANGHAI MENGZE TRADING CO., LTD.—See Apple Flavor & Fragrance Group Co., Ltd.; *Int'l*, pg. 520
SHANGHAI MENON ANIMAL NUTRITION TECHNOLOGY CO., LTD.; *Int'l*, pg. 6775
SHANGHAI MENTOR MEDIA CO., LTD—See Carl Bennet AB; *Int'l*, pg. 1332
SHANGHAI MENTOR MEDIA PRINTING CO., LTD—See Carl Bennet AB; *Int'l*, pg. 1332
SHANGHAI MERIDIAN MAGNESIUM PRODUCTS LIMITED—See Wanfeng Auto Holding Group Co., Ltd.; *Int'l*, pg. 8340
SHANGHAI MERRYFIELD LAND CO LTD—See Keppel Corporation Limited; *Int'l*, pg. 4132
SHANGHAI METERSBONWE FASHION & ACCESSORIES CO., LTD.; *Int'l*, pg. 6775

SHANGHAI M&G STATIONERY INC.

SHANGHAI M&G STATIONERY INC.; *Int'l*, pg. 6775
SHANGHAI MHI TURBOCHARGER CO., LTD.—See Mitsubishi Heavy Industries, Ltd.; *Int'l*, pg. 4961
SHANGHAI MICHELIN WARRIOR TIRE CO., LTD.—See Compagnie Generale des Etablissements Michelin SCA; *Int'l*, pg. 1743
SHANGHAI MICROPORT ACCESS MEDTECH CO., LTD.—See MicroPort Scientific Corporation; *Int'l*, pg. 4880
SHANGHAI MICROPORT CARDIOFLOW MEDTECH CO., LTD.—See MicroPort Scientific Corporation; *Int'l*, pg. 4880
SHANGHAI MICROPORT ENDOVASCULAR MEDTECH CO., LTD.—See MicroPort Scientific Corporation; *Int'l*, pg. 4880
SHANGHAI MICROPORT EP MEDTECH CO., LTD.—See MicroPort Scientific Corporation; *Int'l*, pg. 4880
SHANGHAI MICROTEK MEDICAL DEVICE CO., LTD.—See Microtek International, Inc.; *Int'l*, pg. 4881
SHANGHAI MICROTEK TECHNOLOGY CO., LTD.—See Microtek International, Inc.; *Int'l*, pg. 4881
SHANGHAI MICROTEK TRADING CO., LTD.—See Microtek International, Inc.; *Int'l*, pg. 4881
SHANGHAI MILKGROUND FOOD TECH CO., LTD.; *Int'l*, pg. 6775
SHANGHAI MIMAKI TRADING CO., LTD.—See MIMAKI ENGINEERING CO., LTD.; *Int'l*, pg. 4898
SHANGHAI MINGCHEN MOULD & PLASTIC TECHNOLOGY CO., LTD.—See Jiangnan Mould & Plastic Technology Co., Ltd.; *Int'l*, pg. 3943
SHANGHAI MINGDONG CONTAINER TERMINALS LTD.—See Shanghai International Port (Group) Co., Ltd.; *Int'l*, pg. 6772
SHANGHAI MIRACOGEN INC.—See Lepu Biopharma Co., Ltd.; *Int'l*, pg. 4466
SHANGHAI MITSUBISHI ELEVATOR CO., LTD.—See Mitsubishi Electric Corporation; *Int'l*, pg. 4946
SHANGHAI MITSUI PLASTIC COMPOUNDS LTD.—See Dainichiseika Color & Chemicals Mfg. Co., Ltd.; *Int'l*, pg. 1939
SHANGHAI MITSUI PLASTIC COMPOUNDS LTD.—See Mitsui & Co., Ltd.; *Int'l*, pg. 4980
SHANGHAI MIZUNO CORPORATION LTD.—See Mizuno Corporation; *Int'l*, pg. 5000
SHANGHAI MODERN INTERNATIONAL EXHIBITION CO., LTD.—See DLG Exhibitions & Events Corp Ltd.; *Int'l*, pg. 2141
SHANGHAI MOLITEC STEEL CO., LTD.—See Molitec Steel Co., Ltd.; *Int'l*, pg. 5022
SHANGHAI MOONS' ELECTRIC CO., LTD.; *Int'l*, pg. 6775
SHANGHAI MORGAN CARBON COMPANY LIMITED—See Morgan Advanced Materials plc; *Int'l*, pg. 5042
SHANGHAI MORGANITE ELECTRICAL CARBON CO. LIMITED—See Morgan Advanced Materials plc; *Int'l*, pg. 5044
SHANGHAI MORIMATSU PHARMACEUTICAL EQUIPMENT ENGINEERING CO., LTD.—See Morimatsu International Holdings Company Limited; *Int'l*, pg. 5045
SHANGHAI MORN ELECTRIC EQUIPMENT CO., LTD.; *Int'l*, pg. 6775
SHANGHAI MOTION CONTROL TECHNOLOGY CO. LTD.—See Eastern Industrial Automation; *U.S. Private*, pg. 1320
SHANGHAI MUNICIPAL CONSTRUCTION CO., LTD.—See Shanghai Construction Group Co., Ltd.; *Int'l*, pg. 6764
SHANGHAI MUNICIPAL ELECTRIC POWER COMPANY—See State Grid Corporation of China; *Int'l*, pg. 7183
SHANGHAI MUNICIPAL ENGINEERING DESIGN INSTITUTE (GROUP) CO., LTD.—See Shanghai Construction Group Co., Ltd.; *Int'l*, pg. 6764
SHANGHAI NABTESCO BUSINESS MANAGEMENT CO., LTD.—See Nabtesco Corporation; *Int'l*, pg. 5120
SHANGHAI NABTESCO HYDRAULIC CO., LTD.—See Nabtesco Corporation; *Int'l*, pg. 5120
SHANGHAI NABTESCO HYDRAULIC EQUIPMENT TRADING CO., LTD.—See Nabtesco Corporation; *Int'l*, pg. 5120
SHANGHAI NABTESCO MOTION-EQUIPMENT TRADING CO., LTD.—See Nabtesco Corporation; *Int'l*, pg. 5120
SHANGHAI NACHI BEARINGS CO., LTD.—See Nachi-Fujikoshi Corp.; *Int'l*, pg. 5123
SHANGHAI NACHI SAW CO., LTD.—See Nachi-Fujikoshi Corp.; *Int'l*, pg. 5122
SHANGHAI NAGASE TRADING CO., LTD.—See Nagase & Co., Ltd.; *Int'l*, pg. 5128
SHANGHAI NAIGAI TRADING CO., LTD.—See Naigai Co., Ltd.; *Int'l*, pg. 5130
SHANGHAI NAIPU INTERNATIONAL TRADE CO., LTD.—See Naipu Mining Machinery Co., Ltd.; *Int'l*, pg. 5131
SHANGHAI NAJIE COMPLETE ELECTRIC CO., LTD.—See Shanghai Electric Group Company Limited; *Int'l*, pg. 6766

SHANGHAI NAKAMURA CHOUKOU TRADING CO., LTD.—See Nakamura Choukou Co., Ltd.; *Int'l*, pg. 5132
SHANGHAI NAN QIAO TRANSFORMER CO., LTD.—See Shanghai Electric Group Company Limited; *Int'l*, pg. 6766
SHANGHAI NANTIAN COMPUTER SYSTEM CO., LTD.—See Yunnan Nantian Electronics Information Co., Ltd.; *Int'l*, pg. 8616
SHANGHAI NANYANG FUJIKURA CABLE CO., LTD.—See Fujikura Ltd.; *Int'l*, pg. 2829
SHANGHAI NAR INDUSTRIAL CO., LTD. - NANTONG FACTORY—See Shanghai NAR Industrial Co., Ltd.; *Int'l*, pg. 6775
SHANGHAI NAR INDUSTRIAL CO., LTD.; *Int'l*, pg. 6775
SHANGHAI NATIONAL CENTER OF TESTING & INSPECTION FOR ELECTRIC CABLE & WIRE CO., LTD.; *Int'l*, pg. 6775
SHANGHAI NATURAL BEAUTY COSMETICS COMPANY LIMITED—See Natural Beauty Bio Technology Ltd; *Int'l*, pg. 5167
SHANGHAI NAVIEN INTERNATIONAL TRADE CO., LTD.—See KyungDong Navien Co., Ltd.; *Int'l*, pg. 4367
SHANGHAI NELES-JAMESBURY VALVE CO., LTD.—See Shanghai Electric Group Company Limited; *Int'l*, pg. 6766
SHANGHAI NENGHUI TECHNOLOGY CO., LTD.; *Int'l*, pg. 6775
SHANGHAI NEW CENTURION NETWORK CO., LTD.; *Int'l*, pg. 6775
SHANGHAI NEW CULTURE MEDIA GROUP CO., LTD.; *Int'l*, pg. 6776
SHANGHAI NEW FUJIX THREAD LTD.—See FUJIX Ltd.; *Int'l*, pg. 2838
SHANGHAI NEW HUANGPU GROUP CO. LTD.; *Int'l*, pg. 6776
SHANGHAI NEW ISLAND PACKAGING PRINTING CO., LTD.—See China Huajun Group Limited; *Int'l*, pg. 1509
SHANGHAI NEW POWER AUTOMOTIVE TECHNOLOGY CO LTD.—See Shanghai Automotive Industry Corporation; *Int'l*, pg. 6762
SHANGHAI NEWTOUCH INFORMATION TECHNOLOGY CO., LTD.—See Shanghai Newtouch Software Co., Ltd.; *Int'l*, pg. 6776
SHANGHAI NEWTOUCH SOFTWARE CO., LTD.; *Int'l*, pg. 6776
SHANGHAI NEW WORLD CO., LTD.; *Int'l*, pg. 6776
SHANGHAI NGAI HING PLASTIC MATERIALS CO., LTD.—See Ngai Hing Hong Co Ltd; *Int'l*, pg. 5253
SHANGHAI NICHIMURA TRADING CO.,LTD.—See Nomura Micro Science Co., Ltd.; *Int'l*, pg. 5412
SHANGHAI NICHIREI FOODS CO., LTD.—See Nichirei Corporation; *Int'l*, pg. 5270
SHANGHAI NICHIRIN AUTOMOBILE ACCESSORIES CO., LTD.—See Nichirin Co., Ltd.; *Int'l*, pg. 5271
SHANGHAI NICHIYU FORKLIFT MANUFACTURING CO., LTD.—See Mitsubishi Heavy Industries, Ltd.; *Int'l*, pg. 4959
SHANGHAI NIFCO PLASTIC MANUFACTURER CO., LTD.—See Nifco Inc.; *Int'l*, pg. 5281
SHANGHAI NIKKA FINE TECHNO CO., LTD.—See Nippon Kayaku Co., Ltd.; *Int'l*, pg. 5321
SHANGHAI NIKKA METAL PRODUCTS CO., LTD.—See Sumitomo Corporation; *Int'l*, pg. 7271
SHANGHAI NIKKISO NON-SEAL PUMP CO.—See Nikkiso Co., Ltd.; *Int'l*, pg. 5291
SHANGHAI NIKKISO TRADING CO., LTD.—See Nikkiso Co., Ltd.; *Int'l*, pg. 5291
SHANGHAI NIKKU SUNTEC INTERNATIONAL TRADING CO., LTD.—See Nippon Air conditioning Services Co., Ltd.; *Int'l*, pg. 5310
SHANGHAI NIPPON STEEL TRADING AUTOMOTIVE PARTS CO.,LTD.—See Nippon Steel Corporation; *Int'l*, pg. 5339
SHANGHAI NISHIKAWA SEALING SYSTEM CO., LTD.—See Nishikawa Rubber Co., Ltd.; *Int'l*, pg. 5365
SHANGHAI NISSEI DISPLAY SYSTEM CO., LTD.—See Nippon Seiki Co., Ltd.; *Int'l*, pg. 5330
SHANGHAI NISSO HUMAN RESOURCES SERVICE CO., LTD.—See Nisso Corporation; *Int'l*, pg. 5377
SHANGHAI NITRO ADVERTISING CO., LIMITED—See Publicis Groupe S.A.; *Int'l*, pg. 6111
SHANGHAI NITTA GELATIN CO., LTD.—See Nitta Gelatin Inc.; *Int'l*, pg. 5383
SHANGHAI NITTO OPTICAL CO., LTD.—See Nitto Denko Corporation; *Int'l*, pg. 5387
SHANGHAI NO. 1 DEPARTMENT STORE - HUANGPU—See Bailian Group Co., Ltd.; *Int'l*, pg. 802
SHANGHAI NO. 1 DEPARTMENT STORE - SONGJIANG—See Bailian Group Co., Ltd.; *Int'l*, pg. 802
SHANGHAI NO1 MACHINE TOOL FOUNDRY (SUZHOU) CO., LTD.—See Yeong Guan Energy Technology Group Co., Ltd.; *Int'l*, pg. 8577
SHANGHAI NO 1 MACHINE TOOL WORKS CO., LTD.—See Shanghai Electric Group Company Limited; *Int'l*, pg. 6765
SHANGHAI NO.1 PHARMACY CO., LTD.; *Int'l*, pg. 6776

CORPORATE AFFILIATIONS

SHANGHAI NO. 1 YAOHAN CO., LTD.—See Bailian Group Co., Ltd.; *Int'l*, pg. 802
SHANGHAI NOBLE CONCEPTS JEWELRY LIMITED—See Central Development Holdings Ltd.; *Int'l*, pg. 1406
SHANGHAI NOMURA ENGINEERING CO., LTD.—See Nomura Micro Science Co., Ltd.; *Int'l*, pg. 5412
SHANGHAI NONGSHIM FOODS CO., LTD.—See Nongshim Co., Ltd.; *Int'l*, pg. 5414
SHANGHAI NORTH GLASS COATING TECHNOLOGY INDUSTRIAL CO., LTD—See Luoyang North Glass Technology Co., Ltd.; *Int'l*, pg. 4585
SHANGHAI NORTH GLASS TECHNOLOGY INDUSTRIAL CO., LTD.—See Luoyang North Glass Technology Co., Ltd.; *Int'l*, pg. 4585
SHANGHAI NOVANAT BIORESOURCES CO., LTD.—See Shanghai Jiaoda Onlly Co., Ltd.; *Int'l*, pg. 6772
SHANGHAI NOVARESE CO., LTD.—See Polaris Capital Group Co., Ltd.; *Int'l*, pg. 5907
SHANGHAI NOVARTIS TRADING LTD.—See Novartis AG; *Int'l*, pg. 5460
SHANGHAI NTL-LOGISTICS LIMITED—See Naigai Trans Line Ltd.; *Int'l*, pg. 5130
SHANGHAI NTN CORP.—See NTN Corporation; *Int'l*, pg. 5482
SHANGHAI NTT TELECOMMUNICATIONS ENGINEERING CO., LTD.—See Nippon Telegraph & Telephone Corporation; *Int'l*, pg. 5345
SHANGHAI NYLECT ENGINEERING CO., LTD.—See Tai Sin Electric Limited; *Int'l*, pg. 7409
SHANGHAI OCEAN AQUARIUM CO., LTD.—See Straco Corporation, Ltd.; *Int'l*, pg. 7234
SHANGHAI OCEAN SHIPPING CO., LTD.—See China COSCO Shipping Corporation Limited; *Int'l*, pg. 1496
SHANGHAI OCEAN SHIPPING TALLY CO., LTD.—See Shanghai International Port (Group) Co., Ltd.; *Int'l*, pg. 6772
SHANGHAI OILES BEARING INC.—See Oiles Corporation; *Int'l*, pg. 5535
SHANGHAI OKAMURA FURNITURE AND LOGISTIC SYSTEM CO., LTD—See Okamura Corporation; *Int'l*, pg. 5545
SHANGHAI OMRON AUTOMATION SYSTEM CO., LTD.—See OMRON Corporation; *Int'l*, pg. 5567
SHANGHAI OMRON CONTROL COMPONENTS CO., LTD.—See OMRON Corporation; *Int'l*, pg. 5567
SHANGHAI ONLLY ADVERTISING CO., LTD.—See Shanghai Jiaoda Onlly Co., Ltd.; *Int'l*, pg. 6772
SHANGHAI ONSTAR TELEMATICS CO., LTD.—See General Motors Company; *U.S. Public*, pg. 929
SHANGHAI ONWARD FASHION CO., LTD.—See Onward Holdings Co., Ltd.; *Int'l*, pg. 5593
SHANGHAI ORIENTAL ART CENTER MANAGEMENT CORPORATION LIMITED—See Poly Culture Group Corporation Limited; *Int'l*, pg. 5914
SHANGHAI ORIENTAL FUTURES CO., LTD.—See China Rare Earth Resources And Technology Co., Ltd.; *Int'l*, pg. 1546
SHANGHAI ORIENTAL PAWN CO., LTD.—See Shanghai Yimin Commercial Group Co., Ltd.; *Int'l*, pg. 6782
SHANGHAI ORIGINAL ADVANCED COMPOUNDS CO., LTD.; *Int'l*, pg. 6776
SHANGHAI ORIGIN DONBON PAINTS CO., LTD.—See Origin Co., Ltd.; *Int'l*, pg. 5629
SHANGHAI OTSUKA FOODS CO., LTD.—See Otsuka Holdings Co., Ltd.; *Int'l*, pg. 5661
SHANGHAI OVAL INSTRUMENT CO., LTD.—See OVAL Corporation; *Int'l*, pg. 5670
SHANGHAI PACIFIC DEPARTMENT STORE CO., LTD.—See The Far Eastern Group; *Int'l*, pg. 7642
SHANGHAI PACIFIC INTERNATIONAL CONTAINER CO., LTD.—See Singamas Container Holdings Limited; *Int'l*, pg. 6939
SHANGHAI PACIFIC MILLENNIUM PACKAGING & PAPER INDUSTRIES CO., LTD.—See Pacific Millennium Packaging Group Corporation; *Int'l*, pg. 5691
SHANGHAI PAN ASIA SHIPPING COMPANY LIMITED—See China COSCO Shipping Corporation Limited; *Int'l*, pg. 1494
SHANGHAI PARKERIZING CO., LTD.—See Nihon Parkerizing Co., Ltd.; *Int'l*, pg. 5287
SHANGHAI PARKER M&E PARTS CO., LTD.—See Nihon Parkerizing Co., Ltd.; *Int'l*, pg. 5287
SHANGHAI PEER BEARING CO. LTD.—See SKF AB; *Int'l*, pg. 6985
SHANGHAI PEPSICO SNACKS COMPANY LIMITED—See PepsiCo, Inc.; *U.S. Public*, pg. 1671
SHANGHAI PERSONALIS BIOTECHNOLOGY CO., LTD.—See Personalis, Inc.; *U.S. Public*, pg. 1677
SHANGHAI PHARMACEUTICALS HOLDING CO., LTD.; *Int'l*, pg. 6776
SHANGHAI PHILLIPS INDUSTRIES VEHICLE COMPONENTS MANUFACTURING LTD.—See Phillips Industries; *U.S. Private*, pg. 3171
SHANGHAI PHOENIX ENTERPRISE (GROUP) CO., LTD.; *Int'l*, pg. 6776
SHANGHAI PICO EXHIBITION SERVICES CO., LTD.—See Pico Far East Holdings Limited; *Int'l*, pg. 5861

SHANGHAI PILLAR TRADING CO., LTD.—See Nippon Pillar Packing Co., Ltd.; *Int'l*, pg. 5328
SHANGHAI PINGUAN PLASTIC INDUSTRY COMPANY LIMITED—See CPMC Holdings Limited; *Int'l*, pg. 1826
SHANGHAI PIONEER HOLDING LTD.; *Int'l*, pg. 6776
SHANGHAI PIONEER SPEAKERS CO., LTD.—See EQT AB; *Int'l*, pg. 2471
SHANGHAI PIXELS INFORMATION TECHNOLOGY CO., LTD.—See Pico Far East Holdings Limited; *Int'l*, pg. 5861
SHANGHAI PIZZA HUT CO., LTD.—See Yum China Holdings, Inc.; *U.S. Public*, pg. 2399
SHANGHAI PNEUMATIC MACHINERY CO., LTD.—See Nippon Pneumatic Mfg. Co., Ltd.; *Int'l*, pg. 5329
SHANGHAI POLY SAGAWA LOGISTIC CO., LTD.—See China Poly Group Corporation; *Int'l*, pg. 1541
SHANGHAI POLY TECHNOLOGIES CO., LTD.—See China Poly Group Corporation; *Int'l*, pg. 1541
SHANGHAI PORCHER INDUSTRIES CO., LTD.—See Groupe Porcher Industries; *Int'l*, pg. 3110
SHANGHAI PORT INTERNATIONAL CRUISE TERMINAL DEVELOPMENT CO., LTD.—See Shanghai International Port (Group) Co., Ltd.; *Int'l*, pg. 6772
SHANGHAI PORT SKILLED LABOR SERVICE CO., LTD.—See Shanghai International Port (Group) Co., Ltd.; *Int'l*, pg. 6772
SHANGHAI POTEVIO CO., LTD.; *Int'l*, pg. 6776
SHANGHAI POWERMAX TECHNOLOGY, INC.—See Routon Electronic Co., Ltd.; *Int'l*, pg. 6407
SHANGHAI POWER STATION AUXILIARY EQUIPMENT WORKS CO., LTD.—See Shanghai Electric Group Company Limited; *Int'l*, pg. 6766
SHANGHAI POWER STREAM MOBILE MEDIA CO., LTD.—See BC Technology Group Limited; *Int'l*, pg. 925
SHANGHAI POWER TRANSMISSION & DISTRIBUTION CO., LTD.—See Shanghai Electric Group Company Limited; *Int'l*, pg. 6766
SHANGHAI PPS SHENG MAO ENVIRONMENTAL SERVICES LIMITED—See PPS International (Holdings) Limited; *Int'l*, pg. 5951
SHANGHAI PRET COMPOSITES CO., LTD.; *Int'l*, pg. 6776
SHANGHAI PRIMEGENE BIO TECH CO., LTD.—See Bio-Techne Corporation; *U.S. Public*, pg. 334
SHANGHAI PRIME MACHINERY COMPANY LIMITED—See Shanghai Electric Group Company Limited; *Int'l*, pg. 6766
SHANGHAI PROSOLAR RESOURCES DEVELOPMENT CO., LTD.; *Int'l*, pg. 6777
SHANGHAI PUDONG DEVELOPMENT BANK CO., LTD.; *Int'l*, pg. 6777
SHANGHAI PUDONG INTERNATIONAL CONTAINER TERMINALS LTD.—See Shanghai International Port (Group) Co., Ltd.; *Int'l*, pg. 6772
SHANGHAI PUDONG NEW AREA NEWCENTURY DECAL CO., LTD.—See China COSCO Shipping Corporation Limited; *Int'l*, pg. 1496
SHANGHAI PUDONG ROAD & BRIDGE CONSTRUCTION CO., LTD.; *Int'l*, pg. 6777
SHANGHAI PUDONG SCIENCE & TECHNOLOGY INVESTMENT CO., LTD.; *Int'l*, pg. 6777
SHANGHAI PUJIA FOOD TECHNOLOGY CO., LTD.—See Apple Flavor & Fragrance Group Co., Ltd.; *Int'l*, pg. 520
SHANGHAI PUKANG PHARMACEUTICAL CO., LTD.—See China Meheco Group Co., Ltd.; *Int'l*, pg. 1519
SHANGHAI PULING TRANSPORTATION & WAREHOUSE CO., LTD.—See Mitsubishi Logistics Corporation; *Int'l*, pg. 4963
SHANGHAI PULONG CONCRETE PRODUCTS CO., LTD.—See Shanghai Guosheng (Group) Co., Ltd.; *Int'l*, pg. 6769
SHANGHAI PUTAILAI NEW ENERGY TECHNOLOGY CO., LTD.; *Int'l*, pg. 6777
SHANGHAI PUTUO BAOZEN AUTOMOBILE SALES AND SERVICES CO., LTD.—See China Yongda Automobiles Services Holdings Limited; *Int'l*, pg. 1564
SHANGHAI PUYANG BIOTECH CO., LTD.—See Apple Flavor & Fragrance Group Co., Ltd.; *Int'l*, pg. 520
SHANGHAI PUYI CHEMICAL CO., LTD.—See ABA Chemicals Corporation; *Int'l*, pg. 47
SHANGHAI PUYUAN SHIPPING CO., LTD.—See Shanghai International Port (Group) Co., Ltd.; *Int'l*, pg. 6772
SHANGHAI QIAN HU AQUARIUM AND PETS CO., LTD.—See Qian Hu Corporation Limited; *Int'l*, pg. 6140
SHANGHAI QIANLONG NETWORK TECHNOLOGY CO., LIMITED—See National Agricultural Holdings Limited; *Int'l*, pg. 5150
SHANGHAI QIFAN CABLE CO., LTD.; *Int'l*, pg. 6777
SHANGHAI QINGKE WAREHOUSE MANAGEMENT CO., LTD.—See Mitsubishi Logistics Corporation; *Int'l*, pg. 4963
SHANGHAI QINGPU FIRE-FIGHTING EQUIPMENT CO. LTD; *Int'l*, pg. 6777
SHANGHAI QINGTIAN ELECTRONIC TECHNOLOGY CO., LTD.—See China Security Co., Ltd.; *Int'l*, pg. 1550

SHANGHAI QIZE AUTOMOBILE SALES SERVICES CO., LTD.—See China ZhengTong Auto Services Holdings Limited; *Int'l*, pg. 1567
SHANGHAI QUICK MYTS MINGSHENG HR.CONSULTING SERVICE CO., LTD.—See QUICK CO., LTD.; *Int'l*, pg. 6162
SHANGHAI RAAS BLOOD PRODUCTS CO., LTD.; *Int'l*, pg. 6777
SHANGHAI RADIALL ELECTRONIC CO., LTD.—See Radiall S.A.; *Int'l*, pg. 6174
SHANGHAI RADIALL ELECTRONICS CO. LTD.—See Radiall S.A.; *Int'l*, pg. 6174
SHANGHAI REALWAY CAPITAL ASSETS MANAGEMENT CO., LTD.; *Int'l*, pg. 6777
SHANGHAI REEFERCO CONTAINER CO., LTD.—See Singamas Container Holdings Limited; *Int'l*, pg. 6939
SHANGHAI REGAL SHOES CO., LTD.—See REGAL CORPORATION; *Int'l*, pg. 6251
SHANGHAI RENGO PACKAGING CO., LTD.—See Rengo Co., Ltd.; *Int'l*, pg. 6281
SHANGHAI REX PACKAGING CO., LTD.—See Hong Leong Investment Holdings Pte. Ltd.; *Int'l*, pg. 3469
SHANGHAI RICOH OFFICE EQUIPMENT CO., LTD.—See Ricoh Company, Ltd.; *Int'l*, pg. 6336
SHANGHAI RIGHTONGENE BIOTECHNOLOGY CO., LTD.; *Int'l*, pg. 6777
SHANGHAI RIKEN TECHNOS CORPORATION—See Riken Technos Corporation; *Int'l*, pg. 6341
SHANGHAI RINNAI CO., LTD.—See Rinnai Corporation; *Int'l*, pg. 6345
SHANGHAI RONGTAI HEALTH TECHNOLOGY CORPORATION LIMITED; *Int'l*, pg. 6777
SHANGHAI RUNDA MEDICAL TECHNOLOGY CO., LTD.; *Int'l*, pg. 6777
SHANGHAI RUNMAO INTERNATIONAL TRADING CO., LTD.—See Thai Rubber Latex Group Public Company Limited; *Int'l*, pg. 7595
SHANGHAI RURAL COMMERCIAL BANK CO., LTD.; *Int'l*, pg. 6777
SHANGHAI RYCHEN TECHNOLOGIES CO., LTD.; *Int'l*, pg. 6778
SHANGHAI RYOTO TRADING CO., LTD.—See Mitsubishi Gas Chemical Company, Inc.; *Int'l*, pg. 4950
SHANGHAI S3 BUILDING MATERIALS CO LTD—See En-Gro Corporation Limited; *Int'l*, pg. 2436
SHANGHAI SACHS HUIZHONG SHOCK ABSORBER CO., LTD.—See ZF Friedrichshafen AG; *Int'l*, pg. 8642
SHANGHAI SAIFU CHEMICAL DEVELOPMENT CO., LTD.—See BRENNTAG SE; *Int'l*, pg. 1149
SHANGHAI SAMSUNG SEMICONDUCTOR CO., LTD—See Samsung Group; *Int'l*, pg. 6514
SHANGHAI SAMSUNG VACUUM ELECTRON DEVICES CO., LTD.—See Samsung Group; *Int'l*, pg. 6514
SHANGHAI SANCO INSTRUMENT CO., LTD.—See Yunnan Energy International Co. Ltd.; *Int'l*, pg. 8615
SHANGHAI SANHANG ONODA CEMENT CO., LTD—See Taiheiyo Cement Corporation; *Int'l*, pg. 7412
SHANGHAI SANJIN IMPORT & EXPORT CO., LTD.—See Shanghai Sanmao Enterprise (Group) Co., Ltd.; *Int'l*, pg. 6778
SHANGHAI SANKO GOSEI TECHNOLOGY LTD.—See Sanko Gosei Ltd.; *Int'l*, pg. 6542
SHANGHAI SANKYU TRADING CO., LTD.—See Sankyu, Inc.; *Int'l*, pg. 6545
SHANGHAI SANMAO ENTERPRISE (GROUP) CO., LTD.; *Int'l*, pg. 6778
SHANGHAI SANOH AUTOMOTIVE TUBE FABRICATION CO., LTD.—See Sanoh Industrial Co., Ltd.; *Int'l*, pg. 6552
SHANGHAI SANOH MECHANICAL MANUFACTURE CO., LTD.—See Sanoh Industrial Co., Ltd.; *Int'l*, pg. 6553
SHANGHAI SANPLUS PLASTIC CO., LTD.—See ITOCHU Corporation; *Int'l*, pg. 3835
SHANGHAI SANSEI CO., LTD.—See Sansei Co., Ltd.; *Int'l*, pg. 6555
SHANGHAI SANXIANG DECORATION & DESIGN CO., LTD.—See Sanxiang Impression Co., Ltd.; *Int'l*, pg. 6562
SHANGHAI SANXIANG PROPERTY SERVICE CO., LTD.—See Sanxiang Impression Co., Ltd.; *Int'l*, pg. 6562
SHANGHAI SANYOU MEDICAL CO., LTD.; *Int'l*, pg. 6778
SHANGHAI SATORII CO., LTD.—See SATORI ELECTRIC CO., LTD.; *Int'l*, pg. 6587
SHANGHAI SEARCHINA INFORMATION CONSULTING CO., LTD.—See SBI Holdings, Inc.; *Int'l*, pg. 6606
SHANGHAI SECCO PETROCHEMICAL CO., LTD.—See BP plc; *Int'l*, pg. 1131
SHANGHAI SECCO PETROCHEMICAL CO., LTD.—See China Petrochemical Corporation; *Int'l*, pg. 1539
SHANGHAI SENKO INTERNATIONAL FREIGHT CO., LTD.—See Senko Group Holdings Co., Ltd.; *Int'l*, pg. 6711
SHANGHAI SENKO INTERNATIONAL FREIGHT FORWARDING INC.—See Senko Group Holdings Co., Ltd.; *Int'l*, pg. 6711
SHANGHAI SENSHU ELECTRIC INTERNATIONAL CO., LTD.—See Senshu Electric Co., Ltd.; *Int'l*, pg. 6713

SHANGHAI SEPR ZIRCONIUM PRODUCTS CO., LTD.—See Compagnie de Saint-Gobain SA; *Int'l*, pg. 1728
SHANGHAI SEVES GLASS CO., LTD.—See Seves S.p.A.; *Int'l*, pg. 6736
SHANGHAI SHANGLUO SOFTWARE CO., LTD.—See Computer & Technologies Holdings Limited; *Int'l*, pg. 1758
SHANGHAI SHANSHAN TECHNOLOGY CO., LTD.—See Ningbo Shanshan Co., Ltd.; *Int'l*, pg. 5305
SHANGHAI SHAN TONG CO., LTD.—See Shan-Loong Transportation Co., Ltd.; *Int'l*, pg. 6751
SHANGHAI SHAPE MEMORY ALLOY CO., LTD.—See Lepu Medical Technology (Beijing) Co., Ltd.; *Int'l*, pg. 4466
SHANGHAI SHENDA CO., LTD.; *Int'l*, pg. 6778
SHANGHAI SHENGDONG INTERNATIONAL CONTAINER TERMINALS CO., LTD.—See Shanghai International Port (Group) Co., Ltd.; *Int'l*, pg. 6772
SHANGHAI SHENG JIAN ENVIRONMENT TECHNOLOGY CO., LTD.; *Int'l*, pg. 6778
SHANGHAI SHENGYUAN PACKAGING CO., LTD.—See Rengo Co., Ltd.; *Int'l*, pg. 6281
SHANGHAI SHENHE THERMO-MAGNETICS CO., LTD. - PV MATERIAL DIVISION—See Ferrotec Holdings Corporation; *Int'l*, pg. 2643
SHANGHAI SHENHE THERMO-MAGNETICS CO., LTD. - SILICON MATERIAL DIVISION—See Ferrotec Holdings Corporation; *Int'l*, pg. 2643
SHANGHAI SHENHE THERMO-MAGNETICS CO., LTD. - TE DIVISION—See Ferrotec Holdings Corporation; *Int'l*, pg. 2643
SHANGHAI SHEN LIAN BIOMEDICAL CORP.; *Int'l*, pg. 6778
SHANGHAI SHENQI PHARMACEUTICAL INVESTMENT MANAGEMENT CO., LTD.; *Int'l*, pg. 6778
SHANGHAI SHENTONG METRO CO., LTD.; *Int'l*, pg. 6778
SHANGHAI SHENXIE AUTOMOBILE TRADING CO., LTD.—See China ZhengTong Auto Services Holdings Limited; *Int'l*, pg. 1567
SHANGHAI SHIBAURA ELECTRONICS CO., LTD.—See Shibaura Electronics Co., Ltd.; *Int'l*, pg. 6827
SHANGHAI SHIBEI HI-TECH CO., LTD.; *Int'l*, pg. 6778
SHANGHAI SHIGE INDUSTRY CO., LTD.—See Anhui Deli Household Glass Co., Ltd.; *Int'l*, pg. 467
SHANGHAI SHILU INSTRUMENT CO. LTD.—See Danaher Corporation; *U.S. Public*, pg. 631
SHANGHAI SHIMAO CO., LTD.—See Shimao Group Holdings Ltd.; *Int'l*, pg. 6834
SHANGHAI SHINE-LINK INTERNATIONAL LOGISTICS CO., LTD.; *Int'l*, pg. 6778
SHANGHAI SHINKO COMPUTER TECHNOLOGY CO., LTD.—See Kobe Steel, Ltd.; *Int'l*, pg. 4220
SHANGHAI SHINKO TRADING LTD.—See Fujitsu Limited; *Int'l*, pg. 2838
SHANGHAI SHINSHO TRADING CO., LTD.—See Kobe Steel, Ltd.; *Int'l*, pg. 4220
SHANGHAI SHINWON EBENEZER CO., LTD.—See Shinwon Corporation; *Int'l*, pg. 6850
SHANGHAI SHIP-USE CRANKSHAFT CO., LTD.—See Shanghai Electric Group Company Limited; *Int'l*, pg. 6765
SHANGHAI SHOWA AUTO PARTS CO., LTD.—See Hitachi Astemo, Ltd.; *Int'l*, pg. 3409
SHANGHAI SHOWA CHEMICALS CO., LTD.—See Resonac Holdings Corporation; *Int'l*, pg. 6299
SHANGHAI SHOWA ELECTRONICS MATERIALS CO., LTD.—See Resonac Holdings Corporation; *Int'l*, pg. 6299
SHANGHAI SHOWA HIGHPOLYMER CO., LTD.—See Resonac Holdings Corporation; *Int'l*, pg. 6299
SHANGHAI SHOWA HIGHPOLYMER TRADING CO., LTD.—See Resonac Holdings Corporation; *Int'l*, pg. 6299
SHANGHAI SHOWA SPECIALTY GASES PURIFICATION CO., LTD.—See Resonac Holdings Corporation; *Int'l*, pg. 6300
SHANGHAI SHUANGHUA AUTOPARTS CO., LTD—See Shuanghua Holdings Limited; *Int'l*, pg. 6868
SHANGHAI SHUIXING HOME TEXTILE CO., LTD.; *Int'l*, pg. 6778
SHANGHAI SHULING NETWORK TECHNOLOGY CO., LTD.—See Waystream Group AB; *Int'l*, pg. 8361
SHANGHAI SHUNHO NEW MATERIALS TECHNOLOGY CO.,LTD.; *Int'l*, pg. 6778
SHANGHAI SHYNDEC PHARMACEUTICAL CO., LTD.; *Int'l*, pg. 6778
SHANGHAI SIGMA KOKI CO.,LTD.—See Sigma Koki Co., Ltd.; *Int'l*, pg. 6908
SHANGHAI SILERGY MICROELECTRONICS TECHNOLOGY CO., LTD.—See Silergy Corp.; *Int'l*, pg. 6919
SHANGHAI SIM-BCD SEMICONDUCTOR MANUFACTURING CO., LTD.—See Diodes Incorporated; *U.S. Public*, pg. 667
SHANGHAI SIMCONIX ELECTRONIC COMPANY LTD.—See Vishay Intertechnology, Inc.; *U.S. Public*, pg. 2302

Company Index

SHANGHAI SHYNDEC PHARMACEUTICAL CO., LTD. CORPORATE AFFILIATIONS

SHANGHAI SIME DARBY MOTOR SALES & SERVICES CO., LTD.—See Sime Darby Berhad; *Int'l*, pg. 6928
SHANGHAI SIMGUI TECHNOLOGY CO., LTD.—See National Silicon Industry Group Co., Ltd.; *Int'l*, pg. 5163
SHANGHAI SIMMONS BEDDING & FURNITURE SALES LTD.—See Nifco Inc.; *Int'l*, pg. 5281
SHANGHAI SIM TECHNOLOGY LIMITED—See SIM Technology Group Limited; *Int'l*, pg. 6927
SHANGHAI SINBON ELECTRONICS CO., LTD.—See SINBON Electronics Co., Ltd.; *Int'l*, pg. 6937
SHANGHAI SINKO AIR CONDITIONING & EQUIPMENT CO., LTD.—See Sinko Industries Ltd.; *Int'l*, pg. 6946
SHANGHAI SINKO REFRIGERATION MACHINE CO., LTD.—See Sinko Industries Ltd.; *Int'l*, pg. 6946
SHANGHAI SINO-IC MICROELECTRONICS COMPANY LIMITED—See Coslight Technology International Group Limited; *Int'l*, pg. 1810
SHANGHAI SINOPHARM WAIGAOQIAO CO., LTD.—See SINOPHARM Group Co., Ltd.; *Int'l*, pg. 6954
SHANGHAI SINOTEC CO., LTD.; *Int'l*, pg. 6778
SHANGHAI SINYANG SEMICONDUCTOR MATERIALS CO., LTD.; *Int'l*, pg. 6778
SHANGHAI SIWEI CLEANING EQUIPMENT TECHNOLOGY CO., LTD.—See Shandong Liancheng Precision Manufacturing Co., Ltd.; *Int'l*, pg. 6755
SHANGHAI SK AUTOMATION TECHNOLOGY CO., LTD.; *Int'l*, pg. 6778
SHANGHAI SK PETROLEUM & CHEMICAL EQUIPMENT CORPORATION LTD.; *Int'l*, pg. 6779
SHANGHAI SKY INTERNATIONAL TRADING CO., LTD.—See YM Tech Co., Ltd.; *Int'l*, pg. 8590
SHANGHAI SMART COLD SCM CO., LTD.—See China Master Logistics Co., Ltd.; *Int'l*, pg. 1518
SHANGHAI SMART CONTROL CO., LTD.; *Int'l*, pg. 6779
SHANGHAI SMG-CJ HOMESHOPPING CO., LTD.—See CJ Corporation; *Int'l*, pg. 1634
SHANGHAI SMH WATCH SERVICE CENTER CO. LTD—See The Swatch Group Ltd.; *Int'l*, pg. 7692
SHANGHAI SMITH ADHESIVE NEW MATERIAL CO., LTD.; *Int'l*, pg. 6779
SHANGHAI SMRC AUTOMOTIVE INTERIORS TECH CONSULTING CO., LTD.—See Samvardhana Motherson International Limited; *Int'l*, pg. 6518
SHANGHAI SMU WARNER INVESTMENT MANAGEMENT CO., LTD.—See BC Technology Group Limited; *Int'l*, pg. 925
SHANGHAI SODICK SOFTWARE CO., LTD.—See Sodick Co., Ltd.; *Int'l*, pg. 7048
SHANGHAI S.S.I. AUTO TEXTILE INTER-DECORATION CO., LTD.—See ITOCHU Corporation; *Int'l*, pg. 3837
SHANGHAI STAL PRECISION STAINLESS STEEL COMPANY LIMITED—See ATI Inc.; *U.S. Public*, pg. 222
SHANGHAI STANLEY ELECTRIC CO., LTD.—See Stanley Electric Co., Ltd.; *Int'l*, pg. 7170
SHANGHAI STARK TECHNOLOGY INC.—See Stark Technology, Inc.; *Int'l*, pg. 7177
SHANGHAI STAR MODERN AGRICULTURE EQUIPMENT CO., LTD.—See IHI Corporation; *Int'l*, pg. 3606
SHANGHAI STEP ELECTRIC CORPORATION; *Int'l*, pg. 6779
SHANGHAI ST FOOD INDUSTRIES CO., LTD.—See Temasek Holdings (Private) Limited; *Int'l*, pg. 7550
SHANGHAI STOCK EXCHANGE; *Int'l*, pg. 6779
SHANGHAI STO LTD.—See Sto SE & Co. KGaA; *Int'l*, pg. 7219
SHANGHAI STOW STORAGE EQUIPMENT CO. LTD.—See Blackstone Inc.; *U.S. Public*, pg. 348
SHANGHAI SUHUA INDUSTRIAL CONTROL EQUIPMENT CO. LTD.—See Rexel, S.A.; *Int'l*, pg. 6317
SHANGHAI SUMIKIN BUSSAN CO., LTD.—See Nippon Steel Corporation; *Int'l*, pg. 5339
SHANGHAI SUMISETSU TRADING CO., LTD.—See Sumitomo Densetsu Co., Ltd.; *Int'l*, pg. 7276
SHANGHAI SUMISO INTERNATIONAL LOGISTICS CO., LTD.—See The Sumitomo Warehouse Co. Ltd.; *Int'l*, pg. 7690
SHANGHAI SUMMIT METAL PRODUCTS CO., LTD.—See Sumitomo Corporation; *Int'l*, pg. 7271
SHANGHAI SUNCOM LOGISTICS LIMITED—See SIM Technology Group Limited; *Int'l*, pg. 6927
SHANGHAI SUNDIRO LOGISTICS CO., LTD.—See Sundiro Holding Co., Ltd.; *Int'l*, pg. 7312
SHANGHAI SUNDIRO PROPERTY MANAGEMENT CO., LTD.—See Sundiro Holding Co., Ltd.; *Int'l*, pg. 7312
SHANGHAI SUNGLOW PACKAGING TECHNOLOGY CO., LTD.; *Int'l*, pg. 6779
SHANGHAI SUNNEN MECHANICAL COMPANY, LTD.—See Sunnen Products Company; *U.S. Private*, pg. 3868
SHANGHAI SUNPLUS TECHNOLOGY CO., LTD.—See Sunplus Technology Co., Ltd.; *Int'l*, pg. 7320
SHANGHAI SUN-RICH ARTS & CRAFTS CO., LTD.—See Nisshinbo Holdings Inc.; *Int'l*, pg. 5375
SHANGHAI SUN-WA TECHNOS CO., LTD.—See Sun-Wa Technos Corporation; *Int'l*, pg. 7309
SHANGHAI SUPERBAG CO., LTD.—See Superbag Co., Ltd.; *Int'l*, pg. 7336
SHANGHAI SUPER LABELS CO., LTD.—See Xiamen Anne Corporation Limited; *Int'l*, pg. 8523
SHANGHAI SWARCO TRAFFIC MANAGEMENT AND EQUIPMENT CO., LTD.—See SWARCO AG; *Int'l*, pg. 7361
SHANGHAI SYNCMOS SEMICONDUCTOR COMPANY LIMITED—See PacRay International Holdings Limited; *Int'l*, pg. 5693
SHANGHAI SYP ENGINEERING GLASS CO., LTD.—See Shanghai Yaohua Pilkington Glass Group Co., Ltd.; *Int'l*, pg. 6782
SHANGHAI TAIHE WATER TECHNOLOGY DEVELOPMENT CO., LTD.; *Int'l*, pg. 6779
SHANGHAI TAIHUA PETROCHEMICAL CO., LTD.—See Shanghai Dasheng Agriculture Finance Technology Co., Ltd.; *Int'l*, pg. 6764
SHANGHAI TAISHENG POWER ENGINEERING MACHINERY CO., LTD.—See Shanghai Taisheng Wind Power Equipment Co., Ltd.; *Int'l*, pg. 6779
SHANGHAI TAISHENG WIND POWER EQUIPMENT CO., LTD.; *Int'l*, pg. 6779
SHANGHAI TAIYO EIKO CO., LTD.—See TAIYO BUSSAN KAISHA LTD; *Int'l*, pg. 7425
SHANGHAI TAIYO KOGYO CO.,LTD.—See Taiyo Kogyo Corporation; *Int'l*, pg. 7426
SHANGHAI TAIYO NIPPON SANSO GAS CO., LTD.—See Mitsubishi Chemical Group Corporation; *Int'l*, pg. 4937
SHANGHAI TAJIMA EMBROIDERY MACHINERY CO., LTD.—See Tajima Industries Ltd.; *Int'l*, pg. 7428
SHANGHAI TAKARA SHUZO INTERNATIONAL TRADING CO., LTD.—See Takara Holdings, Inc.; *Int'l*, pg. 7432
SHANGHAI TAKASAGO-UNION FRAGRANCES & FLAVORS CO., LTD. - SHANGHAI FACTORY—See Takasago International Corporation; *Int'l*, pg. 7433
SHANGHAI TAKASAGO-UNION FRAGRANCES & FLAVORS CO., LTD.—See Takasago International Corporation; *Int'l*, pg. 7433
SHANGHAI TAKEDA PRINTING CO., LTD.—See Takeda iP Holdings Co.,Ltd.; *Int'l*, pg. 7437
SHANGHAI TAKEMOTO PACKAGES CO., LTD - SHANGHAI FACTORY—See Takemoto Yohki Co., Ltd.; *Int'l*, pg. 7440
SHANGHAI TAKEMOTO PACKAGES CO., LTD—See Takemoto Yohki Co., Ltd.; *Int'l*, pg. 7440
SHANGHAI TAKIRON PLASTICS CO., LTD.—See ITOCHU Corporation; *Int'l*, pg. 3835
SHANGHAI TANGRENSHEN MEAT PRODUCT CO., LTD—See Tangrenshen Group Co., Ltd.; *Int'l*, pg. 7458
SHANGHAI TATEYAMA COMMERCIAL FACILITIES CO., LTD.—See Sankyo Tateyama Inc.; *Int'l*, pg. 6543
SHANGHAI TATEYAMA TRADING CO., LTD.—See Sankyo Tateyama Inc.; *Int'l*, pg. 6543
SHANGHAI TAT HONG EQUIPMENT RENTAL CO., LTD.—See Affirma Capital Limited; *Int'l*, pg. 187
SHANGHAI TAYEE ELECTRIC CO., LTD.—See Schneider Electric SE; *Int'l*, pg. 6635
SHANGHAI TAZMO PRECISION MACHINERY CO., LTD.—See Tazmo Co., Ltd.; *Int'l*, pg. 7479
SHANGHAI TECHCOMP BIO-EQUIPMENT LIMITED—See Yunnan Energy International Co. Ltd.; *Int'l*, pg. 8615
SHANGHAI TECHCOMP INSTRUMENT LTD.—See Yunnan Energy International Co. Ltd.; *Int'l*, pg. 8615
SHANGHAI TECHENGIN MACHINERY & ELECTRONICS CO., LTD.—See ZheJiang MeiLi High Technology CO.,LTD.; *Int'l*, pg. 8660
SHANGHAI TECHNODIA SYSTEM INTEGRATION CO., LTD.—See Computer Institute of Japan Ltd.; *Int'l*, pg. 1759
SHANGHAI TECHWELL BIOPHARMACEUTICAL CO., LTD.—See Shanghai Shyndec Pharmaceutical Co., Ltd.; *Int'l*, pg. 6778
SHANGHAI TECO ELECTRIC & MACHINERY CO., LTD.—See Teco Electric & Machinery Co., Ltd.; *Int'l*, pg. 7518
SHANGHAI TENMA PLATECH & HOUSEWARES CO., LTD.—See Tenma Corporation; *Int'l*, pg. 7560
SHANGHAI TENWOW FOODS (GROUP) CO., LTD.—See Tenwow International Holdings Limited; *Int'l*, pg. 7562
SHANGHAI THALES ELECTRON TUBES LTD—See Thales S.A.; *Int'l*, pg. 7603
SHANGHAI T&H GLAZE CO., LTD.—See China Glaze Co., Ltd.; *Int'l*, pg. 1505
SHANGHAI TIAN AN BEARING COMPANY LIMITED—See Shanghai Electric Group Company Limited; *Int'l*, pg. 6766
SHANGHAI TIANCHEN CO., LTD.; *Int'l*, pg. 6779
SHANGHAI TIANYONG ENGINEERING CO., LTD.; *Int'l*, pg. 6779
SHANGHAI TITAN SCIENTIFIC CO., LTD.; *Int'l*, pg. 6779
SHANGHAI TNHG LIGHTING TECHNOLOGY CO., LTD.—See Tecnon Electronics Co., Ltd.; *Int'l*, pg. 7517
SHANGHAI TOFFLON SCIENCE AND TECHNOLOGY CO., LTD.; *Int'l*, pg. 6779
SHANGHAI TOKAI KONETSU CO., LTD.—See Tokai Carbon Co., Ltd.; *Int'l*, pg. 7778
SHANGHAI TOKUYAMA PLASTICS CO., LTD.—See Tokuyama Corporation; *Int'l*, pg. 7787
SHANGHAI TOMSON HUANGPU REAL ESTATE DEVELOPMENT CO., LTD.—See Tomson Group Limited; *Int'l*, pg. 7804
SHANGHAI TONGDA VENTURE CAPITAL CO., LTD.; *Int'l*, pg. 6779
SHANGHAI TONGJI SCIENCE & TECHNOLOGY INDUSTRIAL CO., LTD.; *Int'l*, pg. 6780
SHANGHAI TONGSHENG TRADING CO., LTD.—See Chun Yu Works & Co., Ltd.; *Int'l*, pg. 1596
SHANGHAI TONGTECH SOFTWARE CO., LTD.—See Beijing Tongtech Company Limited; *Int'l*, pg. 959
SHANGHAI TOOL WORKS COMPANY LIMITED—See Shanghai Electric Group Company Limited; *Int'l*, pg. 6766
SHANGHAI TOPCARE MEDICAL SERVICES CO., LTD.; *Int'l*, pg. 6780
SHANGHAI TOPCON-SOKKIA TECHNOLOGY & TRADING CO., LTD.—See Topcon Corporation; *Int'l*, pg. 7814
SHANGHAI TOPOINT PRECISION TECHNOLOGY CO., LTD.—See Topoint Technology Co., Ltd.; *Int'l*, pg. 7816
SHANGHAI TOPPAN ADVERTISEMENT CO., LTD.—See TOPPAN Holdings Inc.; *Int'l*, pg. 7817
SHANGHAI TOPPAN CO., LTD.—See TOPPAN Holdings Inc.; *Int'l*, pg. 7817
SHANGHAI TOPPAN INTERNATIONAL TRADING CO., LTD.—See TOPPAN Holdings Inc.; *Int'l*, pg. 7817
SHANGHAI TOPPAN PRINTING CO., LTD.—See TOPPAN Holdings Inc.; *Int'l*, pg. 7817
SHANGHAI TOSHIBA MACHINE CO., LTD.—See Japan Industrial Partners, Inc.; *Int'l*, pg. 3891
SHANGHAI TOTOLE FOOD LIMITED—See Nestle S.A.; *Int'l*, pg. 5211
SHANGHAI TOYO INK CO., LTD.—See Toyo Ink SC Holdings Co., Ltd.; *Int'l*, pg. 7853
SHANGHAI TOYO INK MFG. CO., LTD.—See Toyo Ink SC Holdings Co., Ltd.; *Int'l*, pg. 7853
SHANGHAI TOYOTA AUTOMOTIVE PARTS CO. LTD.—See Toyota Boshoku Corporation; *Int'l*, pg. 7864
SHANGHAI TOYO TANSO CO., LTD.—See Toyo Tanso Co., Ltd.; *Int'l*, pg. 7858
SHANGHAI TOYO TANSO INDUSTRIAL CO., LTD.—See Toyo Tanso Co., Ltd.; *Int'l*, pg. 7858
SHANGHAI TOYOTA TSUSHO HOT-LINE LOGISTICS CO., LTD.—See Toyota Tsusho Corporation; *Int'l*, pg. 7877
SHANGHAI TRADE WORKS ASIA LIMITED—See Transaction Co., Ltd.; *Int'l*, pg. 7895
SHANGHAI TRANSLATION PUBLISHING HOUSE—See Vivendi SE; *Int'l*, pg. 8278
SHANGHAI TRENDZONE CONSTRUCTION DECORATION GROUP CO., LTD.; *Int'l*, pg. 6780
SHANGHAI TRISTATE ENTERPRISES CO., LTD.—See Tristate Holdings Limited; *Int'l*, pg. 7927
SHANGHAI TRW AUTOMOTIVE SAFETY SYSTEMS CO., LTD.—See ZF Friedrichshafen AG; *Int'l*, pg. 8645
SHANGHAI TSUBACO CO., LTD.—See Tsubakimoto Kogyo Co., Ltd.; *Int'l*, pg. 7955
SHANGHAI TSUMURA PHARMACEUTICALS CO., LTD.—See Tsumura & Co.; *Int'l*, pg. 7957
SHANGHAI TSURUMI PUMP CO., LTD.—See Tsurumi Manufacturing Co., Ltd.; *Int'l*, pg. 7958
SHANGHAI TUBE-COTE PETROLEUM PIPE COATING CO., LTD.—See Hilong Holding Limited; *Int'l*, pg. 3393
SHANGHAI TUNA MARINE ENVIRONMENT TECHNOLOGY CO., LTD.—See Zhejiang Tuna Environmental Science & Technology Co., Ltd.; *Int'l*, pg. 8664
SHANGHAI TUNG PEI ENTERPRISE CO., LTD.—See NTN Corporation; *Int'l*, pg. 5482
SHANGHAI TUNNEL ENGINEERING CO., LTD.; *Int'l*, pg. 6780
SHANGHAI TURBINE WORKS CO., LTD.—See Shanghai Electric Group Company Limited; *Int'l*, pg. 6766
SHANGHAI TURBO ENTERPRISES LTD.; *Int'l*, pg. 6780
SHANGHAI U9 GAME CO., LTD.; *Int'l*, pg. 6780
SHANGHAI UBI COMPUTER SOFTWARE CO. LTD—See Ubisoft Entertainment S.A.; *Int'l*, pg. 8003
SHANGHAI UBM SHOWSTAR EXHIBITION CO LIMITED—See Informa plc; *Int'l*, pg. 3693
SHANGHAI UBM SINOEXPO INTERNATIONAL EXHIBITIONS COMPANY LIMITED—See Informa plc; *Int'l*, pg. 3693
SHANGHAI UCHEE HARDWARE PRODUCTS CO., LTD—See Chun Yu Works & Co., Ltd.; *Int'l*, pg. 1596
SHANGHAI UNITED BEARING COMPANY LIMITED—See Shanghai Electric Group Company Limited; *Int'l*, pg. 6766
SHANGHAI UNITED CAN CO., LTD.—See Great China Metal Ind. Co., Ltd.; *Int'l*, pg. 3064
SHANGHAI UNIVERSAL BIOTECH CO., LTD.; *Int'l*, pg. 6780
SHANGHAI URBAN ARCHITECTURE DESIGN CO., LTD.; *Int'l*, pg. 6780
SHANGHAI VALQUA FLUOROCARBON PRODUCTS CO., LTD.—See Shenzhen Wote Advanced Materials Co., Ltd.; *Int'l*, pg. 6824
SHANGHAI VBH CONSTRUCTION HARDWARE CO., LTD.—See VBH Holding AG; *Int'l*, pg. 8139
SHANGHAI VC LUBRICATING OIL CO., LTD.—See Saudi Arabian Oil Company; *Int'l*, pg. 6589

COMPANY NAME INDEX — SHANGHAI YUYUAN TOURIST MART (GROUP) CO., LTD.

SHANGHAI VIASYSTEMS EMS COMPANY LIMITED—See TTM Technologies, Inc.; *U.S. Public*, pg. 2203
SHANGHAI VIBROPOWER GENERATORS EQUIPMENT CO. LTD—See VibroPower Corporation Limited; *Int'l*, pg. 8185
SHANGHAI VISHAY SEMICONDUCTORS LTD.—See Vishay Intertechnology, Inc.; *U.S. Public*, pg. 2302
SHANGHAI-VOLKSWAGEN AUTOMOTIVE COMPANY LTD.—See Porsche Automobil Holding SE; *Int'l*, pg. 5929
SHANGHAI-VOLKSWAGEN AUTOMOTIVE COMPANY LTD.—See Shanghai Automotive Industry Corporation; *Int'l*, pg. 6762
SHANGHAI VOLKSWAGEN FUJIAN FUSHEN MOTOR SALES & SERVICE CO., LTD.—See Xiamen ITG Group Corp., Ltd.; *Int'l*, pg. 8524
SHANGHAI V TECHNOLOGY CO., LTD.—See V-Technology Co., Ltd.; *Int'l*, pg. 8105
SHANGHAI WAI GAO QIAO BONDED LOGISTICS ZONE YAMATO WAREHOUSE CO., LTD.—See Yamato Holdings Co., Ltd.; *Int'l*, pg. 8554
SHANGHAI WAIGAOQIAO FREE TRADE ZONE GROUP CO., LTD.; *Int'l*, pg. 6780
SHANGHAI WAIGAOQIAO POWER GENERATION CO., LTD.—See Shanghai Electric Power Company Limited; *Int'l*, pg. 6766
SHANGHAI WALCOM BIO-CHEM CO., LTD.—See Walcom Group Limited; *Int'l*, pg. 8333
SHANGHAI WALSIN LIHWA POWER WIRE & CABLE CO., LTD.—See Walsin Lihwa Corporation; *Int'l*, pg. 8335
SHANGHAI WANXIANG AUTOMOBILE CO., LTD—See Young An Hat Co., Ltd.; *Int'l*, pg. 8602
SHANGHAI WANXIANG FLAVORS & FRAGRANCES CO., LTD.—See Wanxiang International Limited; *Int'l*, pg. 8343
SHANGHAI WANYE ENTERPRISES CO., LTD.; *Int'l*, pg. 6780
SHANGHAI WATERTEK INFORMATION TECHNOLOGY CO., LTD.—See Beijing Watertek Information Technology Co., Ltd.; *Int'l*, pg. 960
SHANGHAI WEAVER NETWORK CO.,LTD.; *Int'l*, pg. 6780
SHANGHAI WEIHONG ELECTRONIC TECHNOLOGY CO., LTD; *Int'l*, pg. 6781
SHANGHAI WEISEN TRADING CO.LTD.—See Ecom Agroindustrial Corporation Ltd.; *Int'l*, pg. 2296
SHANGHAI WEITAI PROPERTIES MANAGEMENT CO., LTD.—See Haitong Securities Co., Ltd.; *Int'l*, pg. 3218
SHANGHAI WELLTECH AUTOMATION CO., LTD.; *Int'l*, pg. 6781
SHANGHAI WELL-TRANS INTERNATIONAL LOGISTICS CO., LTD.—See China Merchants Group Limited; *Int'l*, pg. 1522
SHANGHAI WESTGATE MALL CO., LTD.—See CK Asset Holdings Limited; *Int'l*, pg. 1635
SHANGHAI WEST SHANGHAI JIAWO AUTOMOBILE SALES & SERVICES CO., LTD.—See China Yongda Automobiles Services Holdings Limited; *Int'l*, pg. 1564
SHANGHAI WEST SHANGHAI SHENJIE AUTOMOBILE SALES & SERVICES CO., LTD.—See China Yongda Automobiles Services Holdings Limited; *Int'l*, pg. 1564
SHANGHAI WINNER INFORMATION TECHNOLOGY CO., INC.; *Int'l*, pg. 6781
SHANGHAI WINNER MEDICAL APPARATUS CO., LTD.—See Winner Holding Limited; *Int'l*, pg. 8429
SHANGHAI WOLONG ELECTRIC BICYCLE CO., LTD.—See Wolong Electric Group Co., Ltd.; *Int'l*, pg. 8443
SHANGHAI WONDERTEK SOFTWARE CORP LTD; *Int'l*, pg. 6781
SHANGHAI WOOD BASED PANEL MACHINERY CO., LTD.—See Dieffenbacher Holding GmbH & Co. KG; *Int'l*, pg. 2114
SHANGHAI WORLDTREND INTEGRATED TECHNOLOGIES INC.—See Fortune Information Systems Corp.; *Int'l*, pg. 2743
SHANGHAI WORTH GARDEN CO., LTD.; *Int'l*, pg. 6781
SHANGHAI WSP CONSULTING LIMITED—See WSP Global, Inc.; *Int'l*, pg. 8497
SHANGHAI XIANGDING REAL ESTATE CO., LTD.—See Sanxiang Impression Co., Ltd.; *Int'l*, pg. 6562
SHANGHAI XIANGJUN PROPERTY DEVELOPMENT CO., LTD.—See Sanxiang Impression Co., Ltd.; *Int'l*, pg. 6562
SHANGHAI XIANGLE TAMURA ELECTRO CHEMICAL INDUSTRY CO., LTD.—See Tamura Corporation; *Int'l*, pg. 7451
SHANGHAI XIANGSHENG PROPERTY DEVELOPMENT CO., LTD.—See Sanxiang Impression Co., Ltd.; *Int'l*, pg. 6562
SHANGHAI XIEXIN CUSTOMS DECLARATION CO., LTD.—See KKR & Co. Inc.; *U.S. Public*, pg. 1259
SHANGHAI XINAN CURTAIN WALL BUILDING & DECORATION CO., LTD.—See Long Yuan Construction Group Co., Ltd; *Int'l*, pg. 4549
SHANGHAI XINDIE TANAKA GARMENTS CO., LTD.—See Chori Co., Ltd.; *Int'l*, pg. 1583

SHANGHAI XINGUANG OPTICAL INSTRUMENT CO., LTD.—See Shanghai Yimin Commercial Group Co., Ltd.; *Int'l*, pg. 6782
SHANGHAI XINHUA MEDIA CO., LTD.; *Int'l*, pg. 6781
SHANGHAI XIN LONG INFORMATION TECHNOLOGY CO., LIMITED—See National Agricultural Holdings Limited; *Int'l*, pg. 5150
SHANGHAI XIN PENG INDUSTRY LTD.; *Int'l*, pg. 6781
SHANGHAI XINPENG LIANZHONG AUTOMOTIVE CO., LTD.—See Shanghai Xin Peng Industry Ltd.; *Int'l*, pg. 6781
SHANGHAI XIN PENG METAL PRODUCTS CO., LTD.—See Shanghai Xin Peng Industry Ltd.; *Int'l*, pg. 6781
SHANGHAI XINTONGLIAN PACKAGING CO., LTD.; *Int'l*, pg. 6781
SHANGHAI XINYANG VETERINARY DRUGS CO., LTD.—See Tangrenshen Group Co., Ltd.; *Int'l*, pg. 7458
SHANGHAI XIN YU RESIN CO., LTD.—See Headway Advanced Materials Inc.; *Int'l*, pg. 3302
SHANGHAI XIZHEN INFORMATION TECHNOLOGY CO., LTD.—See Global Infotech Co., Ltd.; *Int'l*, pg. 2997
SHANGHAI XNG HOLDINGS LIMITED; *Int'l*, pg. 6781
SHANGHAI XUERONG BIOTECHNOLOGY CO., LTD.; *Int'l*, pg. 6781
SHANGHAI XU HUI DIAMOND INDUSTRIAL CO., LTD.—See Asahi Diamond Industrial Co. Ltd.; *Int'l*, pg. 592
SHANGHAI XUJIAHUI COMMERCIAL CO., LTD.; *Int'l*, pg. 6781
SHANGHAI XUYANG FOOD CO., LTD.—See Fuji Oil Holdings Inc.; *Int'l*, pg. 2816
SHANGHAI XUYU PROPERTY CO. LTD.—See CIFI Holdings (Group) Co. Ltd.; *Int'l*, pg. 1605
SHANGHAI YAHONG MOULDING CO LTD; *Int'l*, pg. 6781
SHANGHAI YAKULT CO., LTD.—See Yakult Honsha Co., Ltd.; *Int'l*, pg. 8546
SHANGHAI YAMAZAKI BAKING CO.,LTD—See Yamazaki Baking Co., Ltd.; *Int'l*, pg. 8556
SHANGHAI YANGGE TECHNOLOGY CO., LTD.—See Shanghai Fullhan Microelectonics Co.,Ltd.; *Int'l*, pg. 6768
SHANGHAI YANHAI REAL ESTATE DEVELOPMENT CO., LTD.—See Yuzhou Group Holdings Company Limited; *Int'l*, pg. 8619
SHANGHAI YANHUA SMARTECH GROUP CO., LTD.; *Int'l*, pg. 6781
SHANGHAI YANPAI FILTER CLOTH CO., LTD.—See Yanpai Filtration Technology Co., Ltd.; *Int'l*, pg. 8564
SHANGHAI YANPU METAL PRODUCTS CO., LTD.; *Int'l*, pg. 6781
SHANGHAI YANSHI ELECTRONIC TECHNOLOGY CO., LTD.—See Shenzhen Keanda Electronic Technology Corp., Ltd.; *Int'l*, pg. 6815
SHANGHAI YAOHUA PILKINGTON GLASS GROUP CO., LTD.; *Int'l*, pg. 6781
SHANGHAI YAOJI TECHNOLOGY CO., LTD.; *Int'l*, pg. 6782
SHANGHAI YAOLONG ELECTRONIC TECHNOLOGY CO., LTD—See The Place Holdings Limited; *Int'l*, pg. 7674
SHANGHAI YASKAWA DRIVE CO., LTD.—See Yaskawa Electric Corporation; *Int'l*, pg. 8569
SHANG HAI YA TONG CO., LTD.; *Int'l*, pg. 6760
SHANGHAI YAYANG ELECTRIC CO., LTD.—See Asia Pacific Wire & Cable Corporation Limited; *Int'l*, pg. 614
SHANGHAI YCT ELECTRONICS GROUP CO., LTD.; *Int'l*, pg. 6782
SHANGHAI YIKANG CHEMICALS AND INDUSTRIES CO., LTD.—See Wah Lee Industrial Corp.; *Int'l*, pg. 8329
SHANGHAI YIMIN COMMERCIAL GROUP CO., LTD.; *Int'l*, pg. 6782
SHANGHAI YIMIN INDUSTRY CO., LTD.—See Shanghai Yimin Commercial Group Co., Ltd.; *Int'l*, pg. 6782
SHANGHAI YINDA TECHNOLOGY INDUSTRIAL CO. LTD.; *Int'l*, pg. 6782
SHANGHAI YINGWO INVESTMENT MANAGEMENT CO., LTD.—See HengTai Securities CO., LTD; *Int'l*, pg. 3347
SHANGHAI YIQIAN TRADING CO. LTD.; *Int'l*, pg. 6782
SHANGHAI YI RONG INTERNATIONAL TRADING CO., LTD.—See BRENNTAG SE; *Int'l*, pg. 1149
SHANGHAI YISHI TRADING CO., LTD.—See Daiichi Jitsugyo Co. Ltd.; *Int'l*, pg. 1927
SHANGHAI YIYOU METAL PRODUCTS CO., LTD.—See Nippon Steel Corporation; *Int'l*, pg. 5339
SHANGHAI YKK ZIPPER CO., LTD—See YKK Corporation; *Int'l*, pg. 8588
SHANGHAI YONGDA AUTOMOBILE NANHUI SALES AND SERVICES CO., LTD.—See China Yongda Automobiles Services Holdings Limited; *Int'l*, pg. 1564
SHANGHAI YONGDA AUTOMOBILE PUDONG SALES AND SERVICES CO., LTD.—See China Yongda Automobiles Services Holdings Limited; *Int'l*, pg. 1564
SHANGHAI YONGDA AUTOMOBILE PUDONG TRADE CO., LTD.—See China Yongda Automobiles Services Holdings Limited; *Int'l*, pg. 1564
SHANGHAI YONGDA AUTOMOBILE PUXI SALES AND SERVICES CO., LTD.—See China Yongda Automobiles Services Holdings Limited; *Int'l*, pg. 1564

SHANGHAI YONGDA AUTOMOBILE SALES CO., LTD.—See China Yongda Automobiles Services Holdings Limited; *Int'l*, pg. 1564
SHANGHAI YONGDA AUTOMOBILE SONGJIANG SALES AND SERVICES CO.—See China Yongda Automobiles Services Holdings Limited; *Int'l*, pg. 1564
SHANGHAI YONGDA AUTOMOBILE TRADE CENTER CO., LTD.—See China Yongda Automobiles Services Holdings Limited; *Int'l*, pg. 1564
SHANGHAI YONGDA BAOYUNLAI AUTOMOBILE SALES AND SERVICES CO., LTD.—See China Yongda Automobiles Services Holdings Limited; *Int'l*, pg. 1564
SHANGHAI YONGDA BASHI AUTOMOBILE SALES AND SERVICES CO., LTD.—See China Yongda Automobiles Services Holdings Limited; *Int'l*, pg. 1565
SHANGHAI YONGDA HAOJIE AUTOMOBILE SALES AND SERVICES CO., LTD.—See China Yongda Automobiles Services Holdings Limited; *Int'l*, pg. 1565
SHANGHAI YONGDA INFINITI AUTOMOBILE SALES AND SERVICES CO., LTD.—See China Yongda Automobiles Services Holdings Limited; *Int'l*, pg. 1565
SHANGHAI YONGDA INFINITI QIBAO AUTOMOBILE SALES AND SERVICES CO., LTD.—See China Yongda Automobiles Services Holdings Limited; *Int'l*, pg. 1565
SHANGHAI YONGDA LUJIE AUTOMOBILE SALES AND SERVICES CO., LTD.—See China Yongda Automobiles Services Holdings Limited; *Int'l*, pg. 1565
SHANGHAI YONGDA QIDONG AUTOMOBILE SALES AND SERVICES CO., LTD.—See China Yongda Automobiles Services Holdings Limited; *Int'l*, pg. 1565
SHANGHAI YONGDA QIMING AUTOMOBILE SALES & SERVICES CO., LTD.—See China Yongda Automobiles Services Holdings Limited; *Int'l*, pg. 1565
SHANGHAI YONGDA SHENLONG AUTOMOBILE SALES AND SERVICES CO., LTD.—See China Yongda Automobiles Services Holdings Limited; *Int'l*, pg. 1565
SHANGHAI YONGDA TONGBAO AUTOMOBILE SALES AND SERVICES CO., LTD.—See China Yongda Automobiles Services Holdings Limited; *Int'l*, pg. 1565
SHANGHAI YONGDA TONGNING AUTOMOBILE SALES AND SERVICES CO., LTD.—See China Yongda Automobiles Services Holdings Limited; *Int'l*, pg. 1565
SHANGHAI YONGDA TONGSHENG AUTOMOBILE SALES AND SERVICES CO., LTD.—See China Yongda Automobiles Services Holdings Limited; *Int'l*, pg. 1565
SHANGHAI YONGDA TOYOTA AUTOMOBILE SALES AND SERVICES CO., LTD.—See China Yongda Automobiles Services Holdings Limited; *Int'l*, pg. 1565
SHANGHAI YONGDA WEIRONG AUTOMOBILE SALES AND SERVICES CO., LTD.—See China Yongda Automobiles Services Holdings Limited; *Int'l*, pg. 1565
SHANGHAI YONGDA ZHONGXIN AUTOMOBILE SALES AND SERVICES CO., LTD.—See China Yongda Automobiles Services Holdings Limited; *Int'l*, pg. 1565
SHANGHAI YONGGUAN ADHESIVE PRODUCTS CORP LTD.; *Int'l*, pg. 6782
SHANGHAI YONGLI BELTING CO., LTD.; *Int'l*, pg. 6782
SHANGHAI YONGMAOTAI AUTOMOTIVE TECHNOLOGY CO., LTD.; *Int'l*, pg. 6782
SHANGHAI YONGMAOTAI AUTO PARTS CO., LTD.—See Shanghai Yongmaotai Automotive Technology Co., Ltd.; *Int'l*, pg. 6782
SHANGHAI YONGQIAN ELECTRICAL AND MECHANICAL CO., LTD.—See CSG Smart Science & Technology Co., Ltd.; *Int'l*, pg. 1865
SHANGHAI YONGXIN TOYO TANSO CO., LTD.—See Toyo Tanso Co., Ltd.; *Int'l*, pg. 7858
SHANGHAI YOUSHEN INDUSTRY CO., LTD.—See Shuanghua Holdings Limited; *Int'l*, pg. 6868
SHANGHAI YUANDA ALUMINIUM INDUSTRY ENGINEERING CO., LTD.—See Yuanda China Holdings Limited; *Int'l*, pg. 8607
SHANGHAI YUANDUN INDUSTRIAL CO., LTD.—See Sundiro Holding Co., Ltd.; *Int'l*, pg. 7313
SHANGHAI YUESHI RESTAURANT MANAGEMENT LIMITED—See S&P Syndicate Public Company Limited; *Int'l*, pg. 6445
SHANGHAI YUNGTAY ELEVATOR EQUIPMENT CO., LTD.—See Hitachi, Ltd.; *Int'l*, pg. 3425
SHANGHAI YUNGTAY GIE CO., LTD.—See Hitachi, Ltd.; *Int'l*, pg. 3425
SHANGHAI YUNG ZIP PHARM. TRADING CO., LTD.—See YungShin Global Holding Corporation; *Int'l*, pg. 8614
SHANGHAI YUSHIRO CHEMICAL INDUSTRY CO., LTD.—See Yushiro Chemical Industry Co. Ltd.; *Int'l*, pg. 8618
SHANGHAI YUYUAN TOURIST MART (GROUP) CO., LTD.; *Int'l*, pg. 6783
SHANGHAI YU YUE MEDICAL EQUIPMENT CO., LTD.—See Jiangsu Yuyue Medical Equipment & Supply Co., Ltd.; *Int'l*, pg. 3957
SHANGHAI ZANUSSI ELETTROMECCANICA CO., LTD.—See Guangzhou Wanbao Group Co., Ltd.; *Int'l*, pg. 3168

SHANGHAI YUYUAN TOURIST MART (GROUP) CO., LTD. CORPORATE AFFILIATIONS

SHANGHAI ZECHUN INVESTMENT & DEVELOPMENT CO., LTD.—See Haitong Securities Co., Ltd.; *Int'l*, pg. 3218
SHANGHAI ZELGEN PHARMA-TECH CO., LTD.—See Suzhou Zelgen Biopharmaceuticals Co., Ltd.; *Int'l*, pg. 7353
SHANGHAI ZENDAI PROPERTY LIMITED; *Int'l*, pg. 6783
SHANGHAI ZENG KANG ELECTRONIC CO., LTD.—See The Place Holdings Limited; *Int'l*, pg. 7674
SHANGHAI ZEON CO., LTD.—See Zeon Corporation; *Int'l*, pg. 8635
SHANGHAI ZHANGJIANG HI-TECH PARK DEVELOPMENT CO., LTD.; *Int'l*, pg. 6783
SHANGHAI ZHENHUA BEARING FACTORY COMPANY LIMITED—See Shanghai Electric Group Company Limited; *Int'l*, pg. 6766
SHANGHAI ZHENHUA HEAVY INDUSTRY CO., LTD—See China Communications Construction Company Limited; *Int'l*, pg. 1491
SHANGHAI ZHEZHONG GROUP CO., LTD.; *Int'l*, pg. 6783
SHANGHAI ZHICHENG BIOLOGICAL TECHNOLOGY CO., LTD.—See Zhongyuan Union Cell & Gene Engineering Corp., Ltd.; *Int'l*, pg. 8676
SHANGHAI ZHONGGU LOGISTICS CO., LTD.; *Int'l*, pg. 6783
SHANGHAI ZHONGHUA PHARMACEUTICAL CO., LTD.—See Shanghai Pharmaceuticals Holding Co., Ltd.; *Int'l*, pg. 6776
SHANGHAI ZHONG JING IMPORT & EXPORT CORPORATION—See China Machinery Engineering Corporation; *Int'l*, pg. 1516
SHANGHAI ZHONGSHENG FENGXING AUTOMOBILE SALES & SERVICE CO., LTD.—See Zhongsheng Group Holdings Limited; *Int'l*, pg. 8674
SHANGHAI ZHONGSHENG STAR AUTOMOBILE SALES & SERVICE CO., LTD.—See Zhongsheng Group Holdings Limited; *Int'l*, pg. 8674
SHANGHAI ZHONGSHENG XINGHONG AUTOMOBILE SALES & SERVICE CO., LTD.—See Zhongsheng Group Holdings Limited; *Int'l*, pg. 8674
SHANGHAI ZHONGZHOU SPECIAL ALLOY MATERIALS CO., LTD.; *Int'l*, pg. 6783
SHANGHAI ZHUO KAI ELECTRONIC TECHNOLOGY CO., LTD.—See The Place Holdings Limited; *Int'l*, pg. 7674
SHANGHAI ZIJIANG ENTERPRISE GROUP CO., LTD.; *Int'l*, pg. 6783
SHANGHAI ZIMMER INTERNATIONAL TRADING CO. LTD. I.L.—See GEA Group Aktiengesellschaft; *Int'l*, pg. 2903
SHANGHAI ZI RI PACKAGING CO., LTD.—See Shanghai Zijiang Enterprise Group Co., Ltd.; *Int'l*, pg. 6783
SHANGHAI ZJ BIO-TECH CO., LTD.; *Int'l*, pg. 6783
SHANGHIA DELIAN CHEMICAL CO., LTD.—See Guangdong Delian Group Co., Ltd.; *Int'l*, pg. 3153
SHANGHI TAKISAWA MECHATRONICS LTD.—See Nidec Corporation; *Int'l*, pg. 5280
SHANGPHARMA CORPORATION—See TPG Capital, L.P.; *U.S. Public*, pg. 2175
SHANG PROPERTIES, INC.; *Int'l*, pg. 6760
SHANGRAO BAOZE AUTOMOBILE SALES SERVICES CO., LTD.—See China ZhengTong Auto Services Holdings Limited; *Int'l*, pg. 1567
SHANGRAO YUTONG OPTICAL TECHNOLOGY CO., LTD.—See Dongguan Yutong Optical Technology Co., Ltd.; *Int'l*, pg. 2167
SHANGRI-LA ASIA LIMITED; *Int'l*, pg. 6783
SHANGRI-LA DEVELOPMENT BANK CO., LTD.; *Int'l*, pg. 6784
SHANGRI-LA DEVELOPMENT BANK LTD.; *Int'l*, pg. 6784
SHANGRI-LA HOTEL (CAIRNS) PTE. LTD.—See Shangri-La Asia Limited; *Int'l*, pg. 6783
SHANGRI-LA HOTEL (KL) SDN BERHAD—See Shangri-La Asia Limited; *Int'l*, pg. 6783
SHANGRI-LA HOTEL (LHASA) CO., LIMITED—See Shangri-La Asia Limited; *Int'l*, pg. 6783
SHANGRI-LA HOTEL LIMITED—See Shangri-La Asia Limited; *Int'l*, pg. 6783
SHANGRI-LA HOTEL (NANJING) CO., LIMITED—See Shangri-La Asia Limited; *Int'l*, pg. 6783
SHANGRI-LA HOTEL PUBLIC COMPANY LIMITED—See Shangri-La Asia Limited; *Int'l*, pg. 6783
SHANGRI-LA HOTEL (QUFU) CO., LIMITED—See Shangri-La Asia Limited; *Int'l*, pg. 6783
SHANGRI-LA HOTELS JAPAN KK—See Shangri-La Asia Limited; *Int'l*, pg. 6783
SHANGRI-LA HOTELS (MALAYSIA) BERHAD; *Int'l*, pg. 6784
SHANGRI-LA HOTELS PTE. LTD.—See Shangri-La Asia Limited; *Int'l*, pg. 6784
SHANGRI-LA HOTEL (XIAMEN) CO., LIMITED—See Shangri-La Asia Limited; *Int'l*, pg. 6783
SHANGRI-LA INTERNATIONAL HOTEL MANAGEMENT GMBH—See Shangri-La Asia Limited; *Int'l*, pg. 6784
SHANGRI-LA INTERNATIONAL HOTEL MARKETING LTD.—See China Rare Earth Resources And Technology Co., Ltd.; *Int'l*, pg. 1546

SHANGRI-LA INTERNATIONAL HOTELS, INC. - LOS ANGELES—See Shangri-La Hotels (Malaysia) Berhad; *Int'l*, pg. 6784
SHANGRI-LA INTERNATIONAL MARKETING COMPANY—See Shangri-La Asia Limited; *Int'l*, pg. 6784
SHANGRI-LA PLAZA CORPORATION—See Shang Properties, Inc.; *Int'l*, pg. 6760
SHANGRI-LA; *U.S. Private*, pg. 3625
SHANGRI-LA ULAANBAATAR HOTEL LLC—See Shangri-La Asia Limited; *Int'l*, pg. 6784
SHANGRI-LA ULAANBAATAR LLC—See Shangri-La Asia Limited; *Int'l*, pg. 6784
SHANGRI-LA YANGON COMPANY LIMITED—See Shangri-La Asia Limited; *Int'l*, pg. 6784
SHANGTEX HOLDING CO., LTD.; *Int'l*, pg. 6784
SHANGYA TECHNOLOGY CO., LTD.; *Int'l*, pg. 6784
SHANGYING GLOBAL CO., LTD.; *Int'l*, pg. 6784
SHANGYU BRANCH OF O.R.G TECHNOLOGY CO., LTD.—See ORG Technology Co., Ltd.; *Int'l*, pg. 5617
SHANGYU JINGXIN PHARMACEUTICAL CO., LTD.—See Zhejiang Jingxin Pharmaceutical Co., Ltd.; *Int'l*, pg. 8657
SHANHAIGUAN SHIPBUILDING INDUSTRY CO., LTD.—See China Shipbuilding Industry Company Limited; *Int'l*, pg. 1551
SHANIV PAPER INDUSTRIES LTD.; *Int'l*, pg. 6784
SHANKARA BUILDING PRODUCTS LIMITED; *Int'l*, pg. 6784
SHANKAR ELECTRONICS LTD.; *Int'l*, pg. 6784
SHANKAR LAL RAMPAL DYE CHEM LTD.; *Int'l*, pg. 6784
SHANKLAND COX LIMITED—See Aukett Swanke Group Plc; *Int'l*, pg. 704
SHANKLIN CORPORATION—See Sealed Air Corporation; *U.S. Public*, pg. 1855
SHANKS ARGYLL & BUTE LIMITED—See Renewi plc; *Int'l*, pg. 6279
SHANKS BRUSSELS-BRABANT S.A.—See Renewi plc; *Int'l*, pg. 6279
SHANKS B.V.—See Renewi plc; *Int'l*, pg. 6279
SHANKS CHEMICAL SERVICES (SCOTLAND) LTD—See Renewi plc; *Int'l*, pg. 6279
SHANKS CUMBRIA LIMITED—See Renewi plc; *Int'l*, pg. 6279
SHANKS HAINAUT S.A.—See Renewi plc; *Int'l*, pg. 6279
SHANKS LIEGE-LUXEMBOURG S.A.—See Renewi plc; *Int'l*, pg. 6279
SHANKS NEDERLAND B.V.—See Renewi plc; *Int'l*, pg. 6279
SHANKS S.A.—See Renewi plc; *Int'l*, pg. 6279
SHANKS VLAANDEREN N.V.—See Renewi plc; *Int'l*, pg. 6279
SHANKS WASTE MANAGEMENT LIMITED—See Renewi plc; *Int'l*, pg. 6279
SHAN-LOONG INTERNATIONAL & CUSTOMS BROKER CO., LTD.—See Shan-Loong Transportation Co., Ltd.; *Int'l*, pg. 6751
SHAN-LOONG TRANSPORTATION CO., LTD. - CHUNG LI PLANT—See Shan-Loong Transportation Co., Ltd.; *Int'l*, pg. 6751
SHAN-LOONG TRANSPORTATION CO., LTD. - KAOHSIUNG PLANT—See Shan-Loong Transportation Co., Ltd.; *Int'l*, pg. 6751
SHAN-LOONG TRANSPORTATION CO., LTD. - MIAO LI PLANT—See Shan-Loong Transportation Co., Ltd.; *Int'l*, pg. 6751
SHAN-LOONG TRANSPORTATION CO., LTD.; *Int'l*, pg. 6751
SHAN-LOONG TRANSPORTATION CO., LTD. - TAICHUNG PLANT—See Shan-Loong Transportation Co., Ltd.; *Int'l*, pg. 6751
SHANNAHAN CRANE & HOIST INC.—See Rotunda Capital Partners LLC; *U.S. Private*, pg. 3487
SHANNON AEROSPACE LTD.—See Deutsche Lufthansa AG; *Int'l*, pg. 2070
SHANNON FUNDING LLC—See Annaly Capital Management, Inc.; *U.S. Public*, pg. 138
SHANNON HARDWARE CO. LTD.; *U.S. Private*, pg. 3625
SHANNON HEALTH SYSTEM; *U.S. Private*, pg. 3625
SHANNON INDUSTRIAL CORPORATION; *U.S. Private*, pg. 3625
SHANNON MEDICAL CENTER—See Shannon Health System; *U.S. Private*, pg. 3625
SHANNON PRECISION FASTENER, LLC; *U.S. Private*, pg. 3625
SHANNON PRECISION INC.; *U.S. Private*, pg. 3625
SHANNON RIDGE, INC.; *U.S. Private*, pg. 3625
SHANNON SEMICONDUCTOR TECHNOLOGY CO., LTD.; *Int'l*, pg. 6784
SHANNON & WILSON, INC.—See Shannon & Wilson, Inc.; *U.S. Private*, pg. 3625
SHANNON & WILSON, INC.; *U.S. Private*, pg. 3625
SHANON CO., LTD. - HOKKAIDO BRANCH—See Tokuyama Corporation; *Int'l*, pg. 7787
SHANON CO., LTD.—See Tokuyama Corporation; *Int'l*, pg. 7787
SHANON, INC.; *Int'l*, pg. 6785

SHANON TOHOKU TRADING CO., LTD—See Tokuyama Corporation; *Int'l*, pg. 7787
SHANOR ELECTRIC SUPPLY INC.; *U.S. Private*, pg. 3625
SHAN POOLS, INC.; *U.S. Private*, pg. 3625
SHANRI (SHANGHAI) ENERGY SCIENCE & TECHNOLOGY CO., LTD.—See Sanix Incorporated; *Int'l*, pg. 6540
SHANSHAN BRAND MANAGEMENT CO., LTD.; *Int'l*, pg. 6785
SHANTA GOLD LIMITED; *Int'l*, pg. 6785
SHANTAI INDUSTRIES LIMITED; *Int'l*, pg. 6785
SHANTA MINING COMPANY LIMITED—See Shanta Gold Limited; *Int'l*, pg. 6785
SHANTAWOOD MANUFACTURING SDN. BHD.—See DPS Resources Berhad; *Int'l*, pg. 2189
SHANTAWOOD SDN BHD—See DPS Resources Berhad; *Int'l*, pg. 2189
SHANTHALA FMCG PRODUCTS LIMITED; *Int'l*, pg. 6785
SHANTHI GEARS LIMITED - A UNIT—See Shanthi Gears Limited; *Int'l*, pg. 6785
SHANTHI GEARS LIMITED - B UNIT—See Shanthi Gears Limited; *Int'l*, pg. 6785
SHANTHI GEARS LIMITED - C UNIT—See Shanthi Gears Limited; *Int'l*, pg. 6785
SHANTHI GEARS LIMITED - F UNIT—See Shanthi Gears Limited; *Int'l*, pg. 6785
SHANTHI GEARS LIMITED; *Int'l*, pg. 6785
SHANTIDOOT INFRA SERVICES LIMITED; *Int'l*, pg. 6785
SHANTI EDUCATIONAL INITIATIVES LTD.; *Int'l*, pg. 6785
SHANTI GURU INDUSTRIES LIMITED; *Int'l*, pg. 6785
SHANTI OVERSEAS (INDIA) LTD.; *Int'l*, pg. 6785
SHANTIVIJAY IMPEX DMCC—See Shantivijay Jewels Ltd.; *Int'l*, pg. 6785
SHANTIVIJAY JEWELS LTD.; *Int'l*, pg. 6785
SHANTOU AIRLINES COMPANY LIMITED—See China Southern Airlines Co., Ltd.; *Int'l*, pg. 1553
SHANTOU BAOZE AUTOMOBILE SALES SERVICES CO., LTD.—See China ZhengTong Auto Services Holdings Limited; *Int'l*, pg. 1567
SHANTOU BOW YUE DEHONG MOTORS SERVICES CO. LTD.—See Sime Darby Berhad; *Int'l*, pg. 6928
SHANTOU BOW YUE VEHICLE TRADING CO., LTD.—See Sime Darby Berhad; *Int'l*, pg. 6928
SHANTOU DONGFENG PRINTING CO., LTD.; *Int'l*, pg. 6785
SHANTOU EASTCROSS OPTOELECTRONIC MATERIAL CO., LTD.—See Shantou Wanshun New Material Group Co., Ltd.; *Int'l*, pg. 6785
SHANTOU GOWORLD DISPLAY CO., LTD.—See Guangdong Goworld Co., Ltd.; *Int'l*, pg. 3154
SHANTOU HONGXIANG MATERIALS CO., LTD.—See China ZhengTong Auto Services Holdings Limited; *Int'l*, pg. 1567
SHANTOU MITUTOYO CHEMICAL CO., LTD.—See Sunjin Beauty Science Co., Ltd.; *Int'l*, pg. 7316
SHANTOU PLUS INSTRUMENTS CO., LTD.—See PLUS Corporation; *Int'l*, pg. 5899
SHANTOU S. E. Z. HUAJIAN ELECTRONICS CO., LTD—See Murata Manufacturing Co., Ltd.; *Int'l*, pg. 5098
SHANTOU SPECIAL ECONOMIC ZONE YAZAKI AUTO PARTS CO., LTD.—See Yazaki Corporation; *Int'l*, pg. 8572
SHANTOU TONZE ELECTRIC APPLIANCE INDUSTRY CO., LTD.—See Tonze New Energy Technology Co., Ltd.; *Int'l*, pg. 7810
SHANTOU WANSHUN NEW MATERIAL GROUP CO., LTD.; *Int'l*, pg. 6785
SHANTUI CONSTRUCTION MACHINERY CO., LTD.; *Int'l*, pg. 6785
SHANXI AKERS TISCO ROLL CO. LTD.—See Ampco-Pittsburgh Corporation; *U.S. Public*, pg. 126
SHANXI ANTAI GROUP CO., LTD.; *Int'l*, pg. 6786
SHANXI BLUE FLAME HOLDING CO., LTD.; *Int'l*, pg. 6786
SHANXI CHANGCHENG MICROLIGHT EQUIPMENT CO., LTD.; *Int'l*, pg. 6786
SHANXI COAL INTERNATIONAL ENERGY GROUP CO., LTD.; *Int'l*, pg. 6786
SHANXI COAL TRANSPORTATION AND SALES GROUP CO., LTD.; *Int'l*, pg. 6786
SHANXI COKING COAL ENERGY GROUP CO., LTD.; *Int'l*, pg. 6786
SHANXI COKING COAL GROUP CO., LTD.—See Shanxi Coking Co., Ltd.; *Int'l*, pg. 6786
SHANXI COKING CO., LTD.; *Int'l*, pg. 6786
SHANXI C&Y PHARMACEUTICAL GROUP CO., LTD.; *Int'l*, pg. 6786
SHANXI DALI FOODS CO., LTD.—See Dali Foods Group Co. Ltd.; *Int'l*, pg. 1951
SHANXI DATANG INTERNATIONAL SHENTOU POWER GENERATION COMPANY LIMITED—See China Datang Corporation; *Int'l*, pg. 1497
SHANXI DONGMU HUASHENG POWDER METALLURGY CO., LTD.—See NBTM New Materials Group Co., Ltd.; *Int'l*, pg. 5179

SHANXI GUANGSHENG MEDICINAL CAPSULE CO., LTD—See Meihua Holdings Group Co., Ltd.; *Int'l*, pg. 4799
SHANXI GUOHUA JINJIE ENERGY CO., LTD.—See Shenhua Group Corporation Limited; *Int'l*, pg. 6802
SHANXI GUOXIN ENERGY CORPORATION LIMITED; *Int'l*, pg. 6786
SHANXI HI-SPEED GROUP CO., LTD.; *Int'l*, pg. 6786
SHANXI HONGYANG HAIOU WEEE RECOVERY & TREATMENT CO., LTD.—See GEM Co., Ltd.; *Int'l*, pg. 2914
SHANXI HUAXIANG GROUP CO., LTD.; *Int'l*, pg. 6786
SHANXI HUAYANG GROUP NEW ENERGY CO., LTD.; *Int'l*, pg. 6786
SHANXI HUAYANG NEW MATERIAL CO., LTD.; *Int'l*, pg. 6786
SHANXI HUHUA GROUP CO., LTD.; *Int'l*, pg. 6786
SHANXI JAPAN ENERGY LUBRICANTS CO., LTD.—See ENEOS Holdings, Inc.; *Int'l*, pg. 2417
SHANXI JINCHENG ANTHRACITE COAL MINING GROUP CO., LTD.; *Int'l*, pg. 6787
SHANXI JINCHENG ANTHRACITE MINING GROUP INTERNATIONAL TRADING CO., LTD.—See Shanxi Jincheng Anthracite Coal Mining Group Co., Ltd.; *Int'l*, pg. 6787
SHANXI LANHUA SCI-TECH VENTURE CO., LTD.; *Int'l*, pg. 6787
SHANXI LU'AN ENVIRONMENTAL ENERGY DEVELOPMENT CO. LTD.; *Int'l*, pg. 6787
SHANXI LU'AN MINING (GROUP) CO., LTD.; *Int'l*, pg. 6787
SHANXI LUTONG YUCI HIGHWAY CO., LTD.—See Road King Infrastructure Limited; *Int'l*, pg. 6357
SHANXI MEIJIN ENERGY CO., LTD.; *Int'l*, pg. 6787
SHANXI NBTM HUASHENG POWDER METALLURGY CO., LTD.—See NBTM New Materials Group Co., Ltd.; *Int'l*, pg. 5179
SHANXI ORIENTAL MATERIAL HANDLING CO., LTD.; *Int'l*, pg. 6787
SHANXI POLY GRAND THEATRE MANAGEMENT CO., LTD—See Poly Culture Group Corporation Limited; *Int'l*, pg. 5914
SHANXI POLY XINGCHEN COKING CO., LTD.—See China Poly Group Corporation; *Int'l*, pg. 1541
SHANXI RUIXIANG BIOLOGICAL PHARMACEUTICAL CO., LTD.—See Tianjin Ringpu Bio-Technology Co., Ltd.; *Int'l*, pg. 7740
SHANXI SECURITIES CO., LTD.; *Int'l*, pg. 6787
SHANXI SK GUOLIN HI-TECH ROAD MATERIAL CO. LTD.—See SK Engineering & Construction Co., Ltd.; *Int'l*, pg. 6970
SHANXI SYNTHETIC RUBBER GROUP CO LTD—See Bluestar Adisseo Company Limited; *Int'l*, pg. 1074
SHANXI TAIGANG STAINLESS STEEL COMPANY LTD.; *Int'l*, pg. 6787
SHANXI TOND CHEMICAL CO., LTD.; *Int'l*, pg. 6787
SHANXI WEINENG COAL MINE GAS DEVELOPMENT CO., LTD.—See VibroPower Corporation Limited; *Int'l*, pg. 8185
SHANXI XIANGDA CAMEL FEED CO., LTD—See Tangrenshen Group Co., Ltd.; *Int'l*, pg. 7458
SHANXI XINGHUACUN FEN WINE FACTORY CO., LTD.; *Int'l*, pg. 6787
SHANXI YONGDONG CHEMICAL CO., LTD.; *Int'l*, pg. 6787
SHANXI ZHENDONG PHARMACEUTICAL CO., LTD.; *Int'l*, pg. 6787
SHANYING INTERNATIONAL HOLDINGS CO., LTD.; *Int'l*, pg. 6787
SHANYUAN CO., LTD.; *Int'l*, pg. 6787
SHANYU GROUP HOLDINGS COMPANY LIMITED; *Int'l*, pg. 6787
SHAOGUAN CITY SHAORUI HEAVY INDUSTRIES CO. LTD.—See Valmet Oyj; *Int'l*, pg. 8119
SHAOGUAN FORTUNE CREATIVE INDUSTRIES CO., LTD.—See Starlite Holdings Limited; *Int'l*, pg. 7178
SHAOGUAN GREEN RECYCLING RESOURCE DEVELOPMENT CO LIMITED—See Dongjiang Environmental Company Limited; *Int'l*, pg. 2168
SHAORUI HEAVY INDUSTRIES (GUANGDONG) CO. LTD.—See Metso Oyj; *Int'l*, pg. 4868
SHAO TONG CHUANG (PHILIPHINE) FOODSTUFFS CO., LTD—See Hong Kong Kam Kee Foodstuffs Trading Co., Ltd.; *Int'l*, pg. 3466
SHAO TONG CHUAN VEGETARIAN FOODS MFG (SG) PTE. LTD.—See Hong Kong Kam Kee Foodstuffs Trading Co., Ltd.; *Int'l*, pg. 3466
SHAOXING ADVANCE GEARBOX CO., LTD.—See Hangzhou Advance Gearbox Group Co., Ltd.; *Int'l*, pg. 3246
SHAOXING ASAHI BEARING CO., LTD.—See Sojitz Corporation; *Int'l*, pg. 7063
SHAOXING HAITAI CHEMICAL LOGISTICS SERVICE CO., LTD.—See Yongtaiyun Chemical Logistics Co., Ltd.; *Int'l*, pg. 8598
SHAOXING HECHENG HAICHANG AUTOMOBILE SALES AND SERVICE CO., LTD.—See China Yongda Automobiles Services Holdings Limited; *Int'l*, pg. 1565

SHAOXING JISHAN ZHIYE CO., LTD.—See China Jishan Holdings Limited; *Int'l*, pg. 1513
SHAOXING KIBING GLASS CO., LTD.—See Zhuzhou Kibing Group Co., Ltd.; *Int'l*, pg. 8680
SHAOXING O.R.G PACKAGING INDUSTRY CO., LTD.—See ORG Technology Co., Ltd.; *Int'l*, pg. 5617
SHAOXING WEILE GARMENT & ORNAMENT CO., LTD—See Younghyun Trading co.,Ltd; *Int'l*, pg. 8603
SHAOXING YONGDA WUXIAN AUTOMOBILE SALES AND SERVICES CO., LTD.—See China Yongda Automobiles Services Holdings Limited; *Int'l*, pg. 1565
SHAOYANG VICTOR HYDRAULICS CO., LTD.; *Int'l*, pg. 6787
SHAOYANG XIANGDA CAMEL FEED CO., LTD—See Tangrenshen Group Co., Ltd.; *Int'l*, pg. 7458
SHAPCO, INC.; *U.S. Private*, pg. 3625
SHAPE AUSTRALIA CORPORATION LIMITED; *Int'l*, pg. 6787
SHAPE CORP.; *U.S. Private*, pg. 3625
SHAPEDIRECT LIMITED—See Heidelberg Materials AG; *Int'l*, pg. 3319
SHAPE FIDELITY, INC.—See Aerobotix, Inc.; *U.S. Private*, pg. 118
SHAPE, INC.—See H.I.G. Capital, LLC; *U.S. Private*, pg. 1834
SHAPE LLC—See Legrand S.A.; *Int'l*, pg. 4446
SHAPELL INVESTMENT PROPERTIES, INC.; *U.S. Private*, pg. 3625
SHAPE PHARMACEUTICALS PTY LTD—See TetraLogic Pharmaceuticals Corporation; *U.S. Public*, pg. 2025
SHAPE ROBOTICS A/S; *Int'l*, pg. 6787
SHAPERON INC.; *Int'l*, pg. 6788
SHAPERO RARE BOOKS LIMITED—See Scholium Group plc; *Int'l*, pg. 6638
SHAPES/ARCH HOLDINGS, LLC—See H.I.G. Capital, LLC; *U.S. Private*, pg. 1831
SHAPE SECURITY, INC.—See F5, Inc.; *U.S. Public*, pg. 819
SHAPE UP—See Marlin Equity Partners, LLC; *U.S. Private*, pg. 2585
SHAPEWAYS HOLDINGS, INC.; *U.S. Public*, pg. 1873
SHAPEWAYS, INC.—See Shapeways Holdings, Inc.; *U.S. Public*, pg. 1873
SHAPIR ENGINEERING & INDUSTRY LTD.; *Int'l*, pg. 6788
SHAPIRO BREWERY LTD.—See Tempo Beverages Ltd.; *Int'l*, pg. 7556
SHAPIRO, LIFSCHITZ AND SCHRAM, P.C.—See Barclay Damon, LLP; *U.S. Private*, pg. 473
SHAPIRO SALES COMPANY; *U.S. Private*, pg. 3625
SHAPOORJI PALLONJI CO .LTD PVT.—See Shapoorji Pallonji & Co. Ltd.; *Int'l*, pg. 6788
SHAPOORJI PALLONJI & CO. LTD.; *Int'l*, pg. 6788
SHAPOORJI PALLONJI INTERNATIONAL FZE—See Shapoorji Pallonji & Co. Ltd.; *Int'l*, pg. 6788
SHAPOORJI PALLONJI LANKA (PVT) LTD—See Shapoorji Pallonji & Co. Ltd.; *Int'l*, pg. 6788
SHAPOORJI PALLONJI MIDEAST L.L.C.—See Shapoorji Pallonji & Co. Ltd.; *Int'l*, pg. 6788
SHAPOORJI PALLONJI NIGERIA LTD—See Shapoorji Pallonji & Co. Ltd.; *Int'l*, pg. 6788
SHAPOORJI PALLONJI QATAR WLL—See Shapoorji Pallonji & Co. Ltd.; *Int'l*, pg. 6788
SHARAD FIBRES & YARN PROCESSORS LIMITED—See Red Ribbon Asset Management PLC; *Int'l*, pg. 6245
SHARANAM INFRAPROJECT & TRADING LTD.; *Int'l*, pg. 6788
SHARAT INDUSTRIES LIMITED; *Int'l*, pg. 6788
SHARAVSKY COMMUNICATIONS; *U.S. Private*, pg. 3625
SHARBELL DEVELOPMENT CORP.; *U.S. Private*, pg. 3625
SHARC INTERNATIONAL SYSTEMS INC.; *Int'l*, pg. 6788
SHARDA CROPCHEM ESPANA, S.L.—See Sharda Cropchem Limited; *Int'l*, pg. 6788
SHARDA CROPCHEM LIMITED; *Int'l*, pg. 6788
SHARDA DEL ECUADOR CIA. LTDA.—See Sharda Cropchem Limited; *Int'l*, pg. 6788
SHARDA DE MEXICO S. DE RL DE CV—See Sharda Cropchem Limited; *Int'l*, pg. 6788
SHARDA HUNGARY KFT—See Sharda Cropchem Limited; *Int'l*, pg. 6788
SHARDA ISPAT LTD.; *Int'l*, pg. 6789
SHARDA MOTOR INDUSTRIES LIMITED; *Int'l*, pg. 6789
SHARDA PERU SAC—See Sharda Cropchem Limited; *Int'l*, pg. 6789
SHARDA UKRAINE LLC—See Sharda Cropchem Limited; *Int'l*, pg. 6789
SHARDA USA LLC—See Sharda Cropchem Limited; *Int'l*, pg. 6789
SHARDUL SECURITIES LTD; *Int'l*, pg. 6789
SHAREASALE.COM, INC.—See Axel Springer SE; *Int'l*, pg. 765
SHAREBPO PTY LTD—See Apex Fund Services Holdings Ltd.; *Int'l*, pg. 510
SHAREBUILDERS, INC.; *U.S. Private*, pg. 3626
SHARECARE, INC.—See Altaris Capital Partners, LLC; *U.S. Private*, pg. 206
SHARECARE, INC.—See Altaris Capital Partners, LLC; *U.S. Private*, pg. 206

SHARECAT SOLUTIONS AS—See Borea AS; *Int'l*, pg. 1113
SHARE CORPORATION; *U.S. Private*, pg. 3626
SHAREDHR—See ABD Insurance & Financial Services, Inc.; *U.S. Private*, pg. 37
SHAREDLABS, INC.; *U.S. Private*, pg. 3626
SHAREDPHONE INTERNATIONAL (PROPRIETARY) LIMITED—See Blue Label Telecoms Limited; *Int'l*, pg. 1068
SHARED SERVICE SYSTEMS INC.—See Nebraska Methodist Health System Inc.; *U.S. Private*, pg. 2878
SHARED TECHNOLOGY SERVICES GROUP INC.—See The Plymouth Rock Co.; *U.S. Private*, pg. 4097
SHAREDXPERTISE MEDIA, LLC; *U.S. Private*, pg. 3626
SHAREFILE LLC—See Elliott Management Corporation; *U.S. Private*, pg. 1367
SHAREFILE LLC—See Vista Equity Partners, LLC; *U.S. Private*, pg. 4396
SHARE GROUP CO., LTD.—See Property Perfect Public Company Limited; *Int'l*, pg. 5998
SHAREHOLDER SERVICES GROUP—See Altruist Corp; *U.S. Private*, pg. 210
SHAREHOLDERS RELATION SERVICE, INC.—See NSD CO., LTD.; *Int'l*, pg. 5477
SHAREHOLDER VALUE BETEILIGUNGEN AG; *Int'l*, pg. 6789
SHAREHOPE MEDICINE CO., LTD.; *Int'l*, pg. 6789
SHARE INDIA ALGOPLUS PRIVATE LIMITED—See Share India Securities Limited; *Int'l*, pg. 6789
SHARE INDIA SECURITIES LIMITED; *Int'l*, pg. 6789
SHARE INVESTING LIMITED—See Australia & New Zealand Banking Group Limited; *Int'l*, pg. 720
SHAREINVESTOR PTE LTD; *Int'l*, pg. 6789
SHAREKHAN LTD.—See BNP Paribas SA; *Int'l*, pg. 1092
SHARELINK SECURITIES & FINANCIAL SERVICES LTD—See SFS Group Public Company Limited; *Int'l*, pg. 6740
SHARE MICROFIN LIMITED; *Int'l*, pg. 6789
SHARE OUR STRENGTH; *U.S. Private*, pg. 3626
SHARE PLC—See abrdn PLC; *Int'l*, pg. 69
SHAREROCKET, INC.—See Nexstar Media Group, Inc.; *U.S. Public*, pg. 1524
SHAREROOT LIMITED; *Int'l*, pg. 6789
SHARESPOST, INC.; *U.S. Private*, pg. 3626
SHARETHROUGH, INC.; *U.S. Private*, pg. 3626
SHARETRACKER, LLC; *U.S. Private*, pg. 3626
SHARETRONIC DATA TECHNOLOGY CO., LTD.; *Int'l*, pg. 6789
SHAREWEALTH SECURITIES LIMITED; *Int'l*, pg. 6789
SHARIAH CAPITAL, INC.; *U.S. Private*, pg. 3626
SHARIKA ENTERPRISES LTD.; *Int'l*, pg. 6789
SHARIKAT MALAYSIA WOOD INDUSTRIES SDN BHD—See Mohawk Industries, Inc.; *U.S. Public*, pg. 1458
SHARIKAT PERMODALAN KEBANGSAAN BHD; *Int'l*, pg. 6789
SHARING ECONOMY INTERNATIONAL INC; *Int'l*, pg. 6789
SHARING FACTORY CO., LTD.—See Niterra Co., Ltd.; *Int'l*, pg. 5381
SHARING IN GROWTH UK LIMITED—See Rolls-Royce Holdings plc; *Int'l*, pg. 6394
SHARING INNOVATIONS, INC.—See Orchestra Holdings, Inc.; *Int'l*, pg. 5615
SHARING SERVICES GLOBAL CORPORATION; *U.S. Public*, pg. 1873
SHARINGTECHNOLOGY, INC.; *Int'l*, pg. 6789
SHARI'S MANAGEMENT CORPORATION—See CapitalSpring LLC; *U.S. Private*, pg. 742
SHARJAH AIRPORT AUTHORITY; *Int'l*, pg. 6790
SHARJAH CEMENT FACTORY—See Sharjah Cement & Industrial Development Company P.S.C.; *Int'l*, pg. 6790
SHARJAH CEMENT & INDUSTRIAL DEVELOPMENT COMPANY P.S.C.; *Int'l*, pg. 6790
SHARJAH INSURANCE COMPANY (PSC); *Int'l*, pg. 6790
SHARJAH ISLAMIC BANK PJSC; *Int'l*, pg. 6790
SHARJAH ISLAMIC FINANCIAL SERVICES LLC—See Sharjah Islamic Bank PJSC; *Int'l*, pg. 6790
SHARJAH NATIONAL HOTEL CORPORATION—See Sharjah Islamic Bank PJSC; *Int'l*, pg. 6790
SHARK AG—See Osotspa Co., Ltd.; *Int'l*, pg. 5652
SHARK BAY SALT PTY. LTD.—See Mitsui & Co., Ltd.; *Int'l*, pg. 4980
SHARK BRANDING; *U.S. Private*, pg. 3626
SHARK COMPUTERS INK.; *U.S. Private*, pg. 3626
SHARKIA NATIONAL FOOD; *Int'l*, pg. 6790
SHARK INDUSTRIES, LTD.; *U.S. Private*, pg. 3626
SHARKLET TECHNOLOGIES, INC.; *U.S. Private*, pg. 3626
SHARKNINJA APPLIANCE LLC—See SharkNinja, Inc.; *U.S. Public*, pg. 1873
SHARKNINJA CO., LTD.—See SharkNinja, Inc.; *U.S. Public*, pg. 1873
SHARKNINJA EUROPE LIMITED—See SharkNinja, Inc.; *U.S. Public*, pg. 1873
SHARKNINJA, INC.; *U.S. Public*, pg. 1873
SHARKNINJA OPERATING LLC—See SharkNinja, Inc.; *U.S. Public*, pg. 1873
SHARKREACH, INC.; *U.S. Private*, pg. 3626

SHARK S.A.—See Groupe BPCE; *Int'l*, pg. 3095
SHARK USA, INC.—See Osotspa Co., Ltd.; *Int'l*, pg. 5652
SHARLENE REALTY LLC—See Lithia Motors, Inc.; *U.S. Public*, pg. 1326
SHARMA & ASSOCIATES, INC.—See TOPS Software, LLC; *U.S. Private*, pg. 4188
SHARMA EAST INDIA HOSP; *Int'l*, pg. 6790
SHARMAN QUINNEY HOLDINGS LIMITED—See The Skipton Building Society; *Int'l*, pg. 7687
SHARON ADVOCATE—See Gannett Co., Inc.; *U.S. Public*, pg. 903
SHARON BIO-MEDICINE LTD; *Int'l*, pg. 6790
SHARON CLINIC COMPANY, LLC—See Community Health Systems, Inc.; *U.S. Public*, pg. 556
SHARON COATING, LLC—See Novolipetski Metallurgicheski Komb OAO; *Int'l*, pg. 5466
SHARON CREDIT UNION; *U.S. Private*, pg. 3626
SHARON HOME CARE SERVICES, LLC—See Community Health Systems, Inc.; *U.S. Public*, pg. 556
SHARON REGIONAL HEALTH SYSTEM, INC.—See Community Health Systems, Inc.; *U.S. Public*, pg. 556
SHARON TOWERS; *U.S. Private*, pg. 3626
SHARON YOUNG INC.; *U.S. Private*, pg. 3626
SHARPAK AYLESHAM LTD.—See Groupe Guillin SA; *Int'l*, pg. 3104
SHARPAK BRIDGWATER LIMITED—See Groupe Guillin SA; *Int'l*, pg. 3104
SHARPAK YATE LTD.—See Groupe Guillin SA; *Int'l*, pg. 3104
SHARP APPLIANCES (THAILAND) LTD.—See Hon Hai Precision Industry Co., Ltd.; *Int'l*, pg. 3457
SHARP BANCSYSTEMS, INC.—See Nymbus, Inc.; *U.S. Private*, pg. 2976
SHARP BROTHERS SEED COMPANY; *U.S. Private*, pg. 3626
SHARP BUSINESS SYSTEMS (INDIA) PRIVATE LIMITED—See Hon Hai Precision Industry Co., Ltd.; *Int'l*, pg. 3457
SHARP BUSINESS SYSTEMS OF NORTH CAROLINA—See Hon Hai Precision Industry Co., Ltd.; *Int'l*, pg. 3458
SHARP BUSINESS SYSTEMS—See Hon Hai Precision Industry Co., Ltd.; *Int'l*, pg. 3458
SHARP BUSINESS SYSTEMS - WASHINGTON—See Hon Hai Precision Industry Co., Ltd.; *Int'l*, pg. 3458
SHARP CLINICAL SERVICES, INC.—See Clayton, Dubilier & Rice, LLC; *U.S. Private*, pg. 928
SHARP CLINICAL SERVICES (UK) LIMITED—See Clayton, Dubilier & Rice, LLC; *U.S. Private*, pg. 928
SHARP CORPORATION MEXICO S.A DE C.V.—See Hon Hai Precision Industry Co., Ltd.; *Int'l*, pg. 3458
SHARP CORPORATION MEXICO, S.A. DE C.V.—See Hon Hai Precision Industry Co., Ltd.; *Int'l*, pg. 3458
SHARP CORPORATION OF AUSTRALIA PTY. LTD.—See Hon Hai Precision Industry Co., Ltd.; *Int'l*, pg. 3458
SHARP CORPORATION OF NEW ZEALAND LTD.—See Hon Hai Precision Industry Co., Ltd.; *Int'l*, pg. 3458
SHARP CORPORATION—See Hon Hai Precision Industry Co., Ltd.; *Int'l*, pg. 3457
SHARP CORPORATION - TOKYO—See Hon Hai Precision Industry Co., Ltd.; *Int'l*, pg. 3458
SHARP & CO.—See Sensis Inc.; *U.S. Private*, pg. 3608
SHARP DECISIONS INC.; *U.S. Private*, pg. 3626
SHARP DECISIONS—See Sharp Decisions Inc.; *U.S. Private*, pg. 3626
SHARPE BROTHERS, INC.—See Vecellio Group, Inc.; *U.S. Private*, pg. 4349
SHARPE DRY GOODS CO., INC.; *U.S. Private*, pg. 3627
SHARP ELECTRONICA ESPANA S.A.—See Hon Hai Precision Industry Co., Ltd.; *Int'l*, pg. 3458
SHARP ELECTRONICS BENELUX B.V.—See Hon Hai Precision Industry Co., Ltd.; *Int'l*, pg. 3458
SHARP ELECTRONICS CORP. - HUNTINGTON BEACH OFFICE—See Hon Hai Precision Industry Co., Ltd.; *Int'l*, pg. 3458
SHARP ELECTRONICS CORPORATION—See Hon Hai Precision Industry Co., Ltd.; *Int'l*, pg. 3458
SHARP ELECTRONICS (EUROPE) GMBH—See Hon Hai Precision Industry Co., Ltd.; *Int'l*, pg. 3458
SHARP ELECTRONICS (EUROPE) GMBH—See Hon Hai Precision Industry Co., Ltd.; *Int'l*, pg. 3458
SHARP ELECTRONICS (EUROPE) LIMITED—See Hon Hai Precision Industry Co., Ltd.; *Int'l*, pg. 3458
SHARP ELECTRONICS FRANCE S.A.—See Hon Hai Precision Industry Co., Ltd.; *Int'l*, pg. 3458
SHARP ELECTRONICS INCORPORATED OF KOREA—See Hon Hai Precision Industry Co., Ltd.; *Int'l*, pg. 3458
SHARP ELECTRONICS (MALAYSIA) SDN. BHD.—See Hon Hai Precision Industry Co., Ltd.; *Int'l*, pg. 3458
SHARP ELECTRONICS (NORDIC) AB—See Hon Hai Precision Industry Co., Ltd.; *Int'l*, pg. 3458
SHARP ELECTRONICS OF CANADA LTD.—See Hon Hai Precision Industry Co., Ltd.; *Int'l*, pg. 3458
SHARP ELECTRONICS RUSSIA LLC—See Hon Hai Precision Industry Co., Ltd.; *Int'l*, pg. 3458
SHARP ELECTRONICS (SCHWEIZ) AG—See Hon Hai Precision Industry Co., Ltd.; *Int'l*, pg. 3458
SHARP ELECTRONICS (VIETNAM) COMPANY LIMITED—See Hon Hai Precision Industry Co., Ltd.; *Int'l*, pg. 3458
SHARPE MIXERS, INC.—See Ebara Corporation; *Int'l*, pg. 2284
SHARP ENERGY, INC.—See Chesapeake Utilities Corporation; *U.S. Public*, pg. 486
SHARPEN TECHNOLOGIES INC.—See Teleo Capital Management, LLC; *U.S. Private*, pg. 3961
SHARPE RESOURCES CORPORATION; *U.S. Private*, pg. 3627
SHARPER IMPRESSIONS PAINTING COMPANY; *U.S. Private*, pg. 3627
SHARP FINANCE CORPORATION—See Hon Hai Precision Industry Co., Ltd.; *Int'l*, pg. 3458
SHARP HEALTHCARE—See Blackstone Inc.; *U.S. Public*, pg. 359
SHARP HOLDING CO.; *U.S. Private*, pg. 3626
SHARP HONG KONG LIMITED—See Hon Hai Precision Industry Co., Ltd.; *Int'l*, pg. 3458
SHARP IMAGING AND INFORMATION COMPANY OF AMERICA—See Hon Hai Precision Industry Co., Ltd.; *Int'l*, pg. 3458
SHARP INDIA LIMITED—See Hon Hai Precision Industry Co., Ltd.; *Int'l*, pg. 3458
SHARP INTERNATIONAL FINANCE (U.K.) PLC—See Hon Hai Precision Industry Co., Ltd.; *Int'l*, pg. 3458
SHARP INVESTMENTS LIMITED; *Int'l*, pg. 6790
SHARP JUSDA LOGISTICS CORP.—See Hon Hai Precision Industry Co., Ltd.; *Int'l*, pg. 3459
SHARP KOREA CORPORATION LTD.—See Hon Hai Precision Industry Co., Ltd.; *Int'l*, pg. 3458
SHARP LABORATORIES OF AMERICA, INC.—See Hon Hai Precision Industry Co., Ltd.; *Int'l*, pg. 3458
SHARP LABORATORIES OF EUROPE LIMITED—See Hon Hai Precision Industry Co., Ltd.; *Int'l*, pg. 3458
SHARPLINK GAMING, INC.; *U.S. Public*, pg. 1873
SHARPLINK GAMING LTD.—See SharpLink Gaming, Inc.; *U.S. Public*, pg. 1873
SHARP MANUFACTURING FRANCE S.A.—See Hon Hai Precision Industry Co., Ltd.; *Int'l*, pg. 3458
SHARP MANUFACTURING POLAND SP. Z O. O.—See Hon Hai Precision Industry Co., Ltd.; *Int'l*, pg. 3458
SHARP MICROELECTRONICS OF THE AMERICAS—See Hon Hai Precision Industry Co., Ltd.; *Int'l*, pg. 3458
SHARP MIDDLE EAST FREE ZONE ESTABLISHMENT—See Hon Hai Precision Industry Co., Ltd.; *Int'l*, pg. 3458
SHARP MIE CORPORATION—See Hon Hai Precision Industry Co., Ltd.; *Int'l*, pg. 3459
SHARP NEC DISPLAY SOLUTIONS, LTD.—See Hon Hai Precision Industry Co., Ltd.; *Int'l*, pg. 3459
SHARP NEC DISPLAY SOLUTIONS, LTD.—See NEC Corporation; *Int'l*, pg. 5186
SHARP NEC DISPLAY SOLUTIONS OF AMERICA, INC.—See Hon Hai Precision Industry Co., Ltd.; *Int'l*, pg. 3459
SHARP NEC DISPLAY SOLUTIONS OF AMERICA, INC.—See NEC Corporation; *Int'l*, pg. 5187
SHARP NIIGATA ELECTRONICS CORPORATION—See Hon Hai Precision Industry Co., Ltd.; *Int'l*, pg. 3459
SHARP PACKAGING SYSTEMS, LLC—See Warburg Pincus LLC; *U.S. Private*, pg. 4439
SHARP (PHILS.) CORPORATION—See Hon Hai Precision Industry Co., Ltd.; *Int'l*, pg. 3457
SHARP RESIDENTIAL, LLC—See Toll Brothers, Inc.; *U.S. Public*, pg. 2162
SHARPRINT; *U.S. Private*, pg. 3627
SHARP-ROXY SALES & SERVICE CO (M) SDN. BHD.—See Hon Hai Precision Industry Co., Ltd.; *Int'l*, pg. 3457
SHARP-ROXY SALES (SINGAPORE) PTE., LTD.—See Hon Hai Precision Industry Co., Ltd.; *Int'l*, pg. 3459
SHARPS BEDROOMS LIMITED—See Sun Capital Partners, Inc.; *U.S. Private*, pg. 3862
SHARPS COMPLIANCE CORP.—See Aurora Capital Group, LLC; *U.S. Private*, pg. 394
SHARP'S CONSTRUCTION SERVICES 2006 LTD.—See Quanta Services, Inc.; *U.S. Public*, pg. 1753
SHARP SEMICONDUCTOR INDONESIA—See Hon Hai Precision Industry Co., Ltd.; *Int'l*, pg. 3459
SHARPS ENVIRONMENTAL SERVICES, INC.—See Aurora Capital Group, LLC; *U.S. Private*, pg. 394
SHARP SINGAPORE ELECTRONICS CORPORATION PTE. LTD.—See Hon Hai Precision Industry Co., Ltd.; *Int'l*, pg. 3459
SHARP SOFTWARE DEVELOPMENT INDIA PVT LTD.—See Hon Hai Precision Industry Co., Ltd.; *Int'l*, pg. 3459
SHARPS PIXLEY BROKERS INCORPORATED—See Deutsche Bank Aktiengesellschaft; *Int'l*, pg. 2058
SHARPSPRING, INC.; *U.S. Public*, pg. 1874
SHARPS TECHNOLOGY, INC.; *U.S. Public*, pg. 1874
SHARP SUPPORT & SERVICE CORPORATION—See Hon Hai Precision Industry Co., Ltd.; *Int'l*, pg. 3459
SHARPSVILLE CONTAINER CORPORATION—See SSP Industrial Group, Inc.; *U.S. Private*, pg. 3769
SHARP (TAIWAN) ELECTRONICS CORPORATION—See Hon Hai Precision Industry Co., Ltd.; *Int'l*, pg. 3457
SHARPTEXT LIMITED—See DCC plc; *Int'l*, pg. 1991
SHARP THAI CO., LTD.—See Hon Hai Precision Industry Co., Ltd.; *Int'l*, pg. 3459
SHARP TRADING CORPORATION—See Hon Hai Precision Industry Co., Ltd.; *Int'l*, pg. 3459
SHARP TRANSPORT INC.; *U.S. Private*, pg. 3627
SHARP YONAGO CORPORATION—See Hon Hai Precision Industry Co., Ltd.; *Int'l*, pg. 3459
SHARQ EASTERN PETROCHEMICAL CO.—See Saudi Basic Industries Corporation; *Int'l*, pg. 6592
SHARQIYAH DESALINATION CO. SAOC—See Veolia Environnement S.A.; *Int'l*, pg. 8154
SHARRARD, MCGEE & CO., P.A.—See Carr, Riggs & Ingram, LLC; *U.S. Private*, pg. 771
SHARRCEM SH.P.K.—See Titan Cement Company S.A.; *Int'l*, pg. 7759
SHARRETT INC.; *U.S. Private*, pg. 3627
SHARYLAND LP; *U.S. Private*, pg. 3627
SHARYLAND UTILITIES LP—See Hunt Consolidated, Inc.; *U.S. Private*, pg. 2009
SHARYN GOL JSC; *Int'l*, pg. 6790
SHASHA DENIMS LTD.; *Int'l*, pg. 6790
SHASHANK TRADERS LTD.; *Int'l*, pg. 6790
SHASHIJIT INFRAPROJECTS LIMITED; *Int'l*, pg. 6790
SHASHI JIULONG POWER STEERING GEARS CO., LTD.—See China Automotive Systems, Inc.; *Int'l*, pg. 1484
SHASHWAT FURNISHING SOLUTIONS LIMITED; *Int'l*, pg. 6790
SH ASIA PACIFIC PTE. LTD.—See Chang Wah Technology Co., Ltd.; *Int'l*, pg. 1441
SHASING SHAPHENG PRINTING & DYEING CO., LTD.—See Co-Prosperity Holdings Limited; *Int'l*, pg. 1680
SHASON INC.; *U.S. Private*, pg. 3627
SHASTA BEVERAGES, INC.—See National Beverage Corp.; *U.S. Public*, pg. 1494
SHASTA COMMUNITY HEALTH CENTER; *U.S. Private*, pg. 3627
SHASTA HARDEY-DAVIDSON, INC.—See Wise Automotive, Inc.; *U.S. Private*, pg. 4549
SHASTA HOLDINGS COMPANY; *U.S. Private*, pg. 3627
SHASTA, INC.—See National Beverage Corp.; *U.S. Public*, pg. 1494
SHASTA INC.—See Shasta Holdings Company; *U.S. Private*, pg. 3627
SHASTA INDUSTRIES INC.; *U.S. Private*, pg. 3627
SHASTA ORTHOTIC PROSTHETIC SERVICE, INC.—See Patient Square Capital, L.P.; *U.S. Private*, pg. 3107
SHASTA SALES, INC.—See National Beverage Corp.; *U.S. Public*, pg. 1494
SHASTA-SISKIYOU TRANSPORT; *U.S. Private*, pg. 3627
SHASUN (DUDLEY) LTD—See Strides Pharma Science Limited; *Int'l*, pg. 7240
SHASUN PHARMA SOLUTIONS INC.—See Strides Pharma Science Limited; *Int'l*, pg. 7240
SHASUN USA INC.—See Strides Pharma Science Limited; *Int'l*, pg. 7241
SHATO HOLDINGS LTD.; *Int'l*, pg. 6790
SHATTUCK & GRUMMETT INC.; *U.S. Private*, pg. 3627
SHATTUCK LABS, INC.; *U.S. Public*, pg. 1874
SHAUB-ELLISON CO; *U.S. Private*, pg. 3627
SHAUGHNESSY AND AHERN COMPANY—See Apollo Global Management, Inc.; *U.S. Public*, pg. 153
SHAUGHNESSY KAPLAN REHABILITATION HOSPITAL—See Partners HealthCare System, Inc.; *U.S. Private*, pg. 3101
SHAVEKIT LIMITED—See Edgewell Personal Care Company; *U.S. Public*, pg. 718
SHAVER AUTOMOTIVE GROUP, INC.; *U.S. Private*, pg. 3627
SHAVER MANUFACTURING COMPANY—See HCC, Inc.; *U.S. Private*, pg. 1888
SHAVER SHOP GROUP LIMITED; *Int'l*, pg. 6790
SHAW ALLOY PIPING PRODUCTS, LLC—See The Shaw Group Inc.; *U.S. Private*, pg. 4117
SHAWANO DIALYSIS, LLC—See DaVita Inc.; *U.S. Public*, pg. 643
SHAW AREVA MOX SERVICES, LLC; *U.S. Private*, pg. 3627
SHAW BROADCAST SERVICES—See Rogers Communications Inc.; *Int'l*, pg. 6383
SHAW BROTHERS CONSTRUCTION; *U.S. Private*, pg. 3627
SHAW BROTHERS HOLDINGS LIMITED; *Int'l*, pg. 6790
SHAW COMMUNICATIONS INC.—See Rogers Communications Inc.; *Int'l*, pg. 6383
SHAW CORE ENERGY SERVICES—See ShawCor Ltd.; *Int'l*, pg. 6791
SHAWCOR GLOBAL SERVICES LIMITED—See ShawCor Ltd.; *Int'l*, pg. 6791
SHAWCOR LTD. - GUARDIAN DIVISION—See ShawCor Ltd.; *Int'l*, pg. 6791
SHAWCOR LTD.; *Int'l*, pg. 6791
SHAWCOR UK LIMITED - CANUSA SYSTEMS DIVISION—See ShawCor Ltd.; *Int'l*, pg. 6791
SHAW CREATIONS, INC.; *U.S. Private*, pg. 3627
SHAW DEVELOPMENT, LLC—See Madison Dearborn Partners, LLC; *U.S. Private*, pg. 2542

COMPANY NAME INDEX

SHAW ELECTRIC CO.; *U.S. Private*, pg. 3627
SHAW ELECTRIC CO.; *U.S. Private*, pg. 3628
SHAW ELECTRIC INC.; *U.S. Private*, pg. 3628
SHAW ENVIRONMENTAL & INFRASTRUCTURE—See The Shaw Group Inc.; *U.S. Private*, pg. 4117
SHAWFLEX—See ShawCor Ltd.; *Int'l*, pg. 6791
THE SHAW GROUP INC.; *U.S. Private*, pg. 4117
SHAW GROUP UK LIMITED—See The Shaw Group Inc.; *U.S. Private*, pg. 4117
THE SHAW GROUP UK PENSION PLAN LIMITED—See The Shaw Group Inc.; *U.S. Private*, pg. 4117
SHAWHANKINS, INC.; *U.S. Private*, pg. 3628
SHAW INDUSTRIES GROUP, INC.—See Berkshire Hathaway Inc.; *U.S. Public*, pg. 316
SHAW INDUSTRIES GROUP—See Berkshire Hathaway Inc.; *U.S. Public*, pg. 316
SHAW INDUSTRIES HOLDING GMBH—See ShawCor Ltd.; *Int'l*, pg. 6791
SHAW INDUSTRIES INC.—See Berkshire Hathaway Inc.; *U.S. Public*, pg. 316
SHAW & JONES MASONRY, INC.; *U.S. Private*, pg. 3627
SHAWKWEI & PARTNERS LTD.; *Int'l*, pg. 6792
SHAW LANCAS, C.A.—See The Shaw Group Inc.; *U.S. Private*, pg. 4117
SHAW L.P. GAS—See UGI Corporation; *U.S. Public*, pg. 2222
SHAW - LUNDQUIST ASSOCIATES, INC.; *U.S. Private*, pg. 3627
SHAWMUT EQUIPMENT COMPANY INC.; *U.S. Private*, pg. 3628
SHAWMUT WOODWORKING & SUPPLY INC.; *U.S. Private*, pg. 3628
SHAW NAPTECH, INC.—See The Shaw Group Inc.; *U.S. Private*, pg. 4117
SHAW NASS MIDDLE EAST WLL—See Abdulla Ahmed Nass Group WLL; *Int'l*, pg. 58
SHAWNEE CONSTRUCTION & ENGINEERING INC.; *U.S. Private*, pg. 3628
SHAWNEE MILLING CO., INC.; *U.S. Private*, pg. 3628
SHAWNEE NEWS-STAR—See Gannett Co., Inc.; *U.S. Public*, pg. 904
SHAWNLEE CONSTRUCTION, LLC—See UFP Industries, Inc.; *U.S. Public*, pg. 2219
SHAW & PETERSEN INSURANCE INC.; *U.S. Private*, pg. 3627
SHAW PIPELINE SERVICES—See ShawCor Ltd.; *Int'l*, pg. 6791
SHAW PIPE PROTECTION LIMITED—See ShawCor Ltd.; *Int'l*, pg. 6791
SHAW PROCESS FABRICATORS, INC.—See The Shaw Group Inc.; *U.S. Private*, pg. 4117
SHAW ROSS INTERNATIONAL IMPORTERS; *U.S. Private*, pg. 3628
SHAW SATELLITE SERVICES, INC.—See Rogers Communications Inc.; *Int'l*, pg. 6383
SHAWSHEEN RUBBER CO., INC.—See Wembly Enterprises LLC; *U.S. Public*, pg. 4480
SHAWS IPM LIMITED—See Permira Advisers LLP; *Int'l*, pg. 5808
SHAW & SONS INC.; *U.S. Private*, pg. 3627
SHAW'S SOUTHERN BELLE FROZEN FOODS; *U.S. Private*, pg. 3628
SHAW SSS FABRICATORS, INC.—See The Shaw Group Inc.; *U.S. Private*, pg. 4117
SHAW'S SUPERMARKETS, INC.—See Cerberus Capital Management, L.P.; *U.S. Private*, pg. 836
SHAW STEWART LUMBER CO. INC.; *U.S. Private*, pg. 3628
SHAW SUBURBAN MEDIA GROUP, INC.; *U.S. Private*, pg. 3628
SHAW SYSTEMS ASSOCIATES INC.; *U.S. Private*, pg. 3628
SHAW TELECOM INC.—See Rogers Communications Inc.; *Int'l*, pg. 6383
SHAWVER & SON, INC.; *U.S. Private*, pg. 3628
SHAW WUNDERMAN—See WPP plc; *Int'l*, pg. 8482
SHAYANO DIALYSIS, LLC—See DaVita Inc.; *U.S. Public*, pg. 643
SHAYCORE ENTERPRISES INC.; *U.S. Private*, pg. 3628
SHAYKIN & COMPANY; *U.S. Private*, pg. 3628
SHAY OIL COMPANY, INC.; *U.S. Private*, pg. 3628
SHAZAM ENTERTAINMENT LTD.—See Apple Inc.; *U.S. Public*, pg. 169
SHAZAM, INC.; *U.S. Private*, pg. 3628
SHAZAND PETROCHEMICAL CORPORATION; *Int'l*, pg. 6792
SHAZDEH FASHIONS INC.; *U.S. Private*, pg. 3629
SHB CAMBODIA LIMITED LIABILITY BANK—See Saigon - Hanoi Commercial Joint Stock Bank; *Int'l*, pg. 6482
SHB LAOS SINGLE MEMBER LIMITED LIABILITY BANK—See Saigon - Hanoi Commercial Joint Stock Bank; *Int'l*, pg. 6482
SHB SECURITIES COMPANY LIMITED—See Saigon - Hanoi Commercial Joint Stock Bank; *Int'l*, pg. 6482
SHB STAHL- UND HARTGUSSWERK BOESDORF GMBH—See DIHAG Holding GmbH; *Int'l*, pg. 2125
SHB STEINBRUCH + HARTSCHOTTERWERK BLAUSEE-MITHOLZ AG—See Vicat S.A.; *Int'l*, pg. 8186

S & H BUILDING MATERIAL CORP.—See Beacon Roofing Supply, Inc.; *U.S. Public*, pg. 287
SHC CO., LTD.—See Sumitomo Electric Industries, Ltd.; *Int'l*, pg. 7281
SHC-KPH, LP—See Universal Health Services, Inc.; *U.S. Public*, pg. 2259
SHD AG—See COFRA Holding AG; *Int'l*, pg. 1693
S.H. DAYTON LTD.; *Int'l*, pg. 6456
SHEAFFER PEN & ART SUPPLY CO.—See Transom Capital Group, LLC; *U.S. Private*, pg. 4209
SHEA HOMES ARIZONA—See J.F. Shea Co., Inc.; *U.S. Private*, pg. 2165
SHEA HOMES-COLORADO—See J.F. Shea Co., Inc.; *U.S. Private*, pg. 2165
SHEA HOMES LIMITED PARTNERSHIP—See J.F. Shea Co., Inc.; *U.S. Private*, pg. 2164
SHEA HOMES, LLC; *U.S. Private*, pg. 3629
SHEA HOMES NORTHERN CALIFORNIA—See J.F. Shea Co., Inc.; *U.S. Private*, pg. 2164
SHEA HOMES SAN DIEGO—See J.F. Shea Co., Inc.; *U.S. Private*, pg. 2164
SHEA HOMES SOUTHERN CALIFORNIA—See J.F. Shea Co., Inc.; *U.S. Private*, pg. 2164
THE SHEAKLEY GROUP; *U.S. Private*, pg. 4117
SHEALY ELECTRICAL WHOLESALERS, INC.—See Border States Industries, Inc.; *U.S. Private*, pg. 618
SHEALY'S TRUCK CENTER INC.; *U.S. Private*, pg. 3629
SHEA PROPERTIES INC.—See J.F. Shea Co., Inc.; *U.S. Private*, pg. 2165
SHEAR ART SALON & SPA; *U.S. Private*, pg. 3629
SHEAR ENGINEERING CORP.—See Chayah Consulting Group LLC; *U.S. Private*, pg. 868
SHEAR ENTERPRISES, LLC; *U.S. Private*, pg. 3629
SHEARER & ASSOCIATES, INC.; *U.S. Private*, pg. 3629
SHEARER FARM INC.; *U.S. Private*, pg. 3629
SHEARER'S FOODS—See Clayton, Dubilier & Rice, LLC; *U.S. Private*, pg. 927
SHEARMAN CORPORATION; *U.S. Private*, pg. 3629
SHEARMAN & STERLING LLP—See Allen Overy Shearman Sterling LLP; *Int'l*, pg. 336
SHEARSON AMERICAN REIT, INC.; *U.S. Private*, pg. 3629
SHEARWATER GROUP PLC; *Int'l*, pg. 6792
SHEARWATER INSURANCE SERVICES LIMITED—See Brown & Brown, Inc.; *U.S. Public*, pg. 402
SHEBA METAL CASTING; *Int'l*, pg. 6792
SHEBESTER BECHTEL, INC.; *U.S. Private*, pg. 3629
SHEBOYGAN CHEVROLET CADILLAC—See Rydell Company Inc.; *U.S. Private*, pg. 3511
SHEBOYGAN CHRYSLER CENTER—See Rydell Company Inc.; *U.S. Private*, pg. 3511
SHEBOYGAN FALLS INSURANCE COMPANY—See Donegal Group Inc.; *U.S. Public*, pg. 676
SHEBOYGAN PAINT COMPANY; *U.S. Private*, pg. 3629
SHEBOYGAN PAPER BOX CO. INC.; *U.S. Private*, pg. 3629
THE SHEBOYGAN PRESS—See Gannett Co., Inc.; *U.S. Public*, pg. 900
SHEBOYGAN SYMPHONY ORCHESTRA INC.; *U.S. Private*, pg. 3629
SHECKY'S MARKETING; *U.S. Private*, pg. 3629
SHED BOSS NZ LIMITED—See Fletcher Building Limited; *Int'l*, pg. 2701
SHEDE SPIRITS CO., LTD.; *Int'l*, pg. 6792
SHEDIR PHARMA GROUP SPA; *Int'l*, pg. 6792
SHED MEDIA SCOTLAND LIMITED—See Warner Bros. Discovery, Inc.; *U.S. Public*, pg. 2329
SHED MEDIA US—See Warner Bros. Discovery, Inc.; *U.S. Public*, pg. 2329
SHEEDOM CO., LTD.—See Kurabo Industries Ltd.; *Int'l*, pg. 4336
SHEEDY DRAYAGE CO.; *U.S. Private*, pg. 3629
SHEEGO GMBH—See Otto GmbH & Co. KG; *Int'l*, pg. 5663
SHEEHAN BUICK PONTIAC GMC, INC.; *U.S. Private*, pg. 3629
SHEEHAN MACK SALES AND EQUIPMENT INC.; *U.S. Private*, pg. 3629
SHEEHAN MOTORS INC.; *U.S. Private*, pg. 3629
SHEEHAN'S TRUCK CENTRE INC.; *Int'l*, pg. 6792
SHEEHY ASHLAND, INC.—See Sheehy Auto Stores, Inc.; *U.S. Private*, pg. 3629
SHEEHY & ASSOCIATES; *U.S. Private*, pg. 3629
SHEEHY AUTO STORES, INC.; *U.S. Private*, pg. 3629
SHEEHY CONSTRUCTION COMPANY; *U.S. Private*, pg. 3629
SHEEHY FORD OF SPRINGFIELD, INC.—See Sheehy Auto Stores, Inc.; *U.S. Private*, pg. 3629
SHEEHY FORD OF WARRENTON; *U.S. Private*, pg. 3630
SHEEHY MAIL CONTRACTORS, INC.—See EVO Transportation & Energy Services, Inc.; *U.S. Public*, pg. 804
SHEEHY WALDORF; *U.S. Private*, pg. 3630
SHEELA FOAM LIMITED; *Int'l*, pg. 6792
SHEELEY ARCHITECTS, INC.; *U.S. Private*, pg. 3630
SHEEN TAI HOLDINGS GROUP COMPANY LIMITED; *Int'l*, pg. 6793
SHEERTRANS SOLUTIONS, LLC; *U.S. Private*, pg. 3630
SHEERVISION INC.; *U.S. Private*, pg. 3630
SHEETAL COOL PRODUCTS LIMITED; *Int'l*, pg. 6793

SHELCO, LLC

SHEETAL DIAMONDS LIMITED; *Int'l*, pg. 6793
SHEET METAL PRECISION LIMITED—See Comtech Telecommunications Corp.; *U.S. Public*, pg. 563
SHEETS CONSTRUCTION INC.; *U.S. Private*, pg. 3630
SHEETS & CO.; *U.S. Private*, pg. 3630
SHEETS & GRAPHIC SHEETS UNLIMITED; *U.S. Private*, pg. 3630
SHEETS MANUFACTURING CO. INC.—See Hi Temp Insulation Inc.; *U.S. Private*, pg. 1931
SHEETS WHOLESALE INC.; *U.S. Private*, pg. 3630
SHEETZ, INC.; *U.S. Private*, pg. 3630
SHEFA GEMS LTD.; *Int'l*, pg. 6793
THE SHEFFER CORPORATION—See The Ralph J. Stolle Company; *U.S. Private*, pg. 4102
SHEFFIELD COATED STONE—See CEMEX, S.A.B. de C.V.; *Int'l*, pg. 1399
SHEFFIELD DRAKEHOUSE VETS4PETS LIMITED—See Pets at Home Group Plc; *Int'l*, pg. 5834
SHEFFIELD FINANCIAL, LLC—See Truist Financial Corporation; *U.S. Public*, pg. 2201
SHEFFIELD GREEN LTD.; *Int'l*, pg. 6793
SHEFFIELD LABORATORIES—See Faria Corporation; *U.S. Private*, pg. 1474
SHEFFIELD METALS INTERNATIONAL, INC.; *U.S. Private*, pg. 3630
SHEFFIELD NEWSPAPERS LTD—See JPIMedia Holdings Limited; *Int'l*, pg. 4006
SHEFFIELD RESOURCES LIMITED; *Int'l*, pg. 6793
SHEFIT OPERATING COMPANY LLC; *U.S. Private*, pg. 3630
SHEH FUNG SCREWS CO., LTD.; *Int'l*, pg. 6793
SHEH KAI PRECISION CO., LTD.; *Int'l*, pg. 6793
SHEIKH AHMED BIN DALMOOK AL MAKTOUM PRIVATE OFFICE LLC; *Int'l*, pg. 6793
SHEIKH HOLDINGS GROUP (INVESTMENTS) LIMITED; *Int'l*, pg. 6793
SHEILA DONNELLY & ASSOCIATES; *U.S. Private*, pg. 3630
SHEKEL BRAINWEIGH LTD.; *Int'l*, pg. 6794
SHEKEL EU S.A.—See Shekel Brainweigh Ltd.; *Int'l*, pg. 6794
SHEKEL (NINGBO) SCALES LTD.—See Shekel Brainweigh Ltd.; *Int'l*, pg. 6794
SHEKEL SCALES (2008) LTD.—See Shekel Brainweigh Ltd.; *Int'l*, pg. 6794
SHEKEL USA LLC—See Shekel Brainweigh Ltd.; *Int'l*, pg. 6794
SHEKHAWATI POLY-YARN LIMITED; *Int'l*, pg. 6794
SHEKNOWS LLC—See Great Hill Partners, L.P.; *U.S. Private*, pg. 1763
SHEKOU CONTAINER TERMINALS (PHASE III) CO., LTD—See China Merchants Group Limited; *Int'l*, pg. 1521
SHELBA D. JOHNSON TRUCKING, INC.; *U.S. Private*, pg. 3630
SHELBORNE SOUTH BEACH HOTEL—See Cedar Capital Partners Limited; *Int'l*, pg. 1388
SHELBORNE SOUTH BEACH HOTEL—See King Street Real Estate GP, L.L.C.; *U.S. Private*, pg. 2310
SHELBORNE SOUTH BEACH HOTEL—See Westdale Properties; *Int'l*, pg. 8387
SHELBOURN CHEMISTS, INC.—See Insulet Corporation; *U.S. Public*, pg. 1134
SHELBOURNE GROUP LIMITED—See Enstar Group Limited; *Int'l*, pg. 2449
SHELBURNE CORP.; *U.S. Private*, pg. 3630
SHELBY AMERICAN INC.; *U.S. Public*, pg. 1874
SHELBY BAPTIST AMBULATORY SURGERY CENTER, LLC—See Tenet Healthcare Corporation; *U.S. Public*, pg. 2007
SHELBY COUNTY CO-OP; *U.S. Private*, pg. 3630
SHELBY COUNTY STATE BANK; *U.S. Private*, pg. 3630
SHELBY DIALYSIS, LLC—See DaVita Inc.; *U.S. Public*, pg. 643
SHELBY ELASTICS OF NORTH CAROLINA, LLC—See Beocare Group, Inc.; *U.S. Private*, pg. 529
SHELBY GRAVEL INC.; *U.S. Private*, pg. 3630
SHELBY GROUP INTERNATIONAL, INC.—See Bunzl plc; *Int'l*, pg. 1219
SHELBY MECHANICAL, INC.; *U.S. Private*, pg. 3630
SHELBY PROPERTIES LLC—See Scales Corporation Limited; *Int'l*, pg. 6611
SHELBY-REID, INC.; *U.S. Private*, pg. 3630
SHELBYVILLE CLINIC CORP.—See Community Health Systems, Inc.; *U.S. Public*, pg. 556
SHELBYVILLE HOME CARE SERVICES, LLC—See Community Health Systems, Inc.; *U.S. Public*, pg. 556
SHELBYVILLE HOSPITAL CORPORATION—See Community Health Systems, Inc.; *U.S. Public*, pg. 556
SHELBYVILLE POWER, WATER, & SEWAGE SYSTEM; *U.S. Private*, pg. 3630
SHELBY WILLIAMS INDUSTRIES, INC.—See Whippoorwill Associates, Inc.; *U.S. Private*, pg. 4507
SHELCIDY CUSTOM REMODELING, INC.; *U.S. Private*, pg. 3630
SHELCO FOUNDRY—See Gnutti Carlo S.p.A.; *Int'l*, pg. 3017
SHELCO, LLC; *U.S. Private*, pg. 3631

SHELCO, LLC

CORPORATE AFFILIATIONS

SHELDON GAS COMPANY—See Superior Plus Corp.; *Int'l*, pg. 7338
SHELDON GOOD & COMPANY INTERNATIONAL, LLC—See Racebrook Capital Advisors, LLC; *U.S. Private*, pg. 3341
SHELDON GOOD & COMPANY-MOUNTAIN REGION—See Racebrook Capital Advisors, LLC; *U.S. Private*, pg. 3341
SHELDON GROSS REALTY INC.; *U.S. Private*, pg. 3631
SHELDON & HAMMOND PTY LTD; *Int'l*, pg. 6794
SHELDON LABORATORY SYSTEMS INC.—See MISSCO Contract Sales; *U.S. Private*, pg. 2747
SHELDON'S EXPRESS PHARMACY—See Houchens Industries, Inc.; *U.S. Private*, pg. 1990
SHELDONS' INC.; *U.S. Private*, pg. 3631
SHELDONS OF OCEANSIDE INC.; *U.S. Private*, pg. 3631
SH ELECTRONICS CHENGDU CO., LTD.—See Chang Wah Technology Co., Ltd.; *Int'l*, pg. 1441
SH ELECTRONICS SUZHOU CO., LTD.—See Chang Wah Technology Co., Ltd.; *Int'l*, pg. 1441
SHELF DRILLING ADRIATIC SERVICES KFT—See Shelf Drilling, Ltd.; *Int'l*, pg. 6794
SHELF DRILLING, LTD.; *Int'l*, pg. 6794
SHELFGENIE; *U.S. Private*, pg. 3631
SHELF SUBSEA PTY LTD; *Int'l*, pg. 6794
SHELF SUBSEA SOLUTIONS PTE—See Shelf Subsea Pty Ltd; *Int'l*, pg. 6794
SHELL ABU DHABI B.V.—See Shell plc; *Int'l*, pg. 6797
SHELL ADDITIVES HOLDINGS (II) B.V.—See Shell plc; *Int'l*, pg. 6795
SHELL ADRIA D.O.O.—See Shell plc; *Int'l*, pg. 6797
SHELL AMERICAS FUNDING (CANADA) LIMITED—See Shell plc; *Int'l*, pg. 6797
SHELL ARGENTINA S.A.—See Shell plc; *Int'l*, pg. 6795
SHELL AUSTRALIA LIMITED—See Shell plc; *Int'l*, pg. 6797
SHELL AUSTRIA GMBH—See Shell plc; *Int'l*, pg. 6797
SHELL AVIATION SWEDEN AB—See Shell plc; *Int'l*, pg. 6795
SHELLBACK SEMICONDUCTOR TECHNOLOGY—See OEM Group, Inc.; *U.S. Private*, pg. 2997
SHELL BITUMEN (UK) LTD—See Shell plc; *Int'l*, pg. 6797
SHELL BTC—See Shell plc; *Int'l*, pg. 6796
SHELL BULGARIA EAD—See Shell plc; *Int'l*, pg. 6795
SHELL BUSINESS SERVICE CENTRE SDN. BHD.—See Shell plc; *Int'l*, pg. 6795
SHELL CANADA CAROLINE GAS PLANT—See Shell plc; *Int'l*, pg. 6797
SHELL CANADA ENERGY—See Shell plc; *Int'l*, pg. 6797
SHELL CANADA LIMITED - MONTREAL—See Shell plc; *Int'l*, pg. 6797
SHELL CANADA LIMITED—See Shell plc; *Int'l*, pg. 6797
SHELL CANADA LIMITED—See Shell plc; *Int'l*, pg. 6797
SHELL CANADA LIMITED—See Shell plc; *Int'l*, pg. 6797
SHELL CASPIAN B.V.—See Shell plc; *Int'l*, pg. 6795
SHELL CATALYSTS & TECHNOLOGIES LIMITED—See Shell plc; *Int'l*, pg. 6797
SHELL CHEMICAL LP NORCO—See Shell plc; *Int'l*, pg. 6796
SHELL CHEMICAL LP—See Shell plc; *Int'l*, pg. 6796
SHELL CHEMICAL LP—See Shell plc; *Int'l*, pg. 6796
SHELL CHEMICAL LP—See Shell plc; *Int'l*, pg. 6796
SHELL CHEMICALS SERAYA (PTE) LIMITED—See Shell plc; *Int'l*, pg. 6798
SHELL CHEMICALS U.K. LIMITED—See Shell plc; *Int'l*, pg. 6797
SHELL CHINA EXPLORATION AND PRODUCTION COMPANY LIMITED—See Shell plc; *Int'l*, pg. 6797
SHELL CHINA HOLDING GMBH—See Shell plc; *Int'l*, pg. 6797
SHELL (CHINA) LIMITED—See Shell plc; *Int'l*, pg. 6797
SHELL COLOMBIA SA—See Shell plc; *Int'l*, pg. 6797
SHELL COMPANIA ARGENTINA DE PETROLEO S.A.—See Shell plc; *Int'l*, pg. 6797
SHELL COMPANIA DE PETROLEOS ECUADOR S.A.—See Shell plc; *Int'l*, pg. 6797
THE SHELL COMPANY OF AUSTRALIA LTD.—See Shell plc; *Int'l*, pg. 6797
THE SHELL COMPANY OF SRI LANKA LTD.—See Shell plc; *Int'l*, pg. 6799
THE SHELL COMPANY OF THAILAND LTD.—See Shell plc; *Int'l*, pg. 6799
SHELL COMPANY OF TURKEY LTD.—See Shell plc; *Int'l*, pg. 6798
THE SHELL CO. OF THE PHILIPPINES LTD.—See Shell plc; *Int'l*, pg. 6799
SHELL CZECH REPUBLIC A.S.—See Shell plc; *Int'l*, pg. 6798
SHELL DEL PERU S.A.—See Shell plc; *Int'l*, pg. 6799
SHELL DEUTSCHLAND OIL GMBH—See Shell plc; *Int'l*, pg. 6798
SHELL DEVELOPMENT (AUSTRALIA) PROPRIETARY LIMITED—See Shell plc; *Int'l*, pg. 6798
SHELL DEVELOPMENT OMAN LLC—See Shell plc; *Int'l*, pg. 6798
SHELL EASTERN PETROLEUM (PTE) LIMITED—See Shell plc; *Int'l*, pg. 6798
SHELL EGYPT N.V.—See Shell plc; *Int'l*, pg. 6798
SHELL EL SALVADOR S.A.—See Shell plc; *Int'l*, pg. 6798

SHELL ENERGY AUSTRALIA PTY. LTD.—See Shell plc; *Int'l*, pg. 6798
SHELL ENERGY DEUTSCHLAND GMBH—See Shell plc; *Int'l*, pg. 6798
SHELL ENERGY HOLDINGS AUSTRALIA LIMITED—See Shell plc; *Int'l*, pg. 6798
SHELL ENERGY ITALIA S.R.L.—See Shell plc; *Int'l*, pg. 6795
SHELL ENERGY NORTH AMERICA (CANADA) INC.—See Shell plc; *Int'l*, pg. 6800
SHELL ENERGY NORTH AMERICA (US) L.P.—See Shell plc; *Int'l*, pg. 6799
SHELL ENERGY PHILIPPINES INC.—See Shell plc; *Int'l*, pg. 6795
SHELL ENERGY RETAIL GMBH—See Shell plc; *Int'l*, pg. 6795
SHELL ENERGY RETAIL LIMITED—See Shell plc; *Int'l*, pg. 6795
SHELL ENERGY UK LIMITED—See Shell plc; *Int'l*, pg. 6795
SHELL ENERJI A.S.—See Shell plc; *Int'l*, pg. 6798
SHELL EP MIDDLE EAST HOLDINGS B.V.—See Shell plc; *Int'l*, pg. 6795
SHELL EP OFFSHORE VENTURES LIMITED—See Shell plc; *Int'l*, pg. 6798
SHELL ERDOEL UND ERDGAS EXPLORATION GMBH—See Shell plc; *Int'l*, pg. 6798
SHELL ESPANA, S.A.—See Shell plc; *Int'l*, pg. 6798
SHELL EXPLORATION AND PRODUCTION LIBYA GMBH—See Shell plc; *Int'l*, pg. 6798
SHELL EXPLORATION AND PRODUCTION OMAN LIMITED—See Shell plc; *Int'l*, pg. 6798
SHELL EXPLORATION NZ LIMITED—See Shell plc; *Int'l*, pg. 6798
SHELL EXPLORATION & PRODUCTION TANZANIA LIMITED—See Shell plc; *Int'l*, pg. 6795
SHELLEY ELECTRIC INC.; *U.S. Private*, pg. 3631
SHELL FINANCE (NETHERLANDS) B.V.—See Shell plc; *Int'l*, pg. 6795
SHELL GABON—See Shell plc; *Int'l*, pg. 6798
SHELL GARDEN CO., LTD.—See Seven & i Holdings Co., Ltd.; *Int'l*, pg. 6731
SHELL GAS B.V.—See Shell plc; *Int'l*, pg. 6796
SHELL GAS (LPG) HOLDINGS B.V.—See Shell plc; *Int'l*, pg. 6795
SHELL GAS VIETNAM LTD.—See Shell plc; *Int'l*, pg. 6798
SHELL GHANA LTD.—See Shell plc; *Int'l*, pg. 6798
SHELL GLOBAL SOLUTIONS (DEUTSCHLAND) GMBH—See Shell plc; *Int'l*, pg. 6798
SHELL GLOBAL SOLUTIONS UK—See Shell plc; *Int'l*, pg. 6798
SHELL GLOBAL SOLUTIONS (US) INC—See Shell plc; *Int'l*, pg. 6798
SHELL GUATEMALA SA—See Shell plc; *Int'l*, pg. 6798
SHELLHARBOUR PRIVATE HOSPITAL PTY. LTD.—See Luye Medical Group; *Int'l*, pg. 4590
SHELL HELLAS A.E.—See Shell plc; *Int'l*, pg. 6798
SHELL HONG KONG LIMITED—See Shell plc; *Int'l*, pg. 6798
SHELLHORN & HILL INC.; *U.S. Private*, pg. 3631
SHELL HUNGARY RT—See Shell plc; *Int'l*, pg. 6798
SHELL INDIA MARKETS PRIVATE LIMITED - EASTERN PROCESSING PLANT—See Shell plc; *Int'l*, pg. 6798
SHELL INDIA MARKETS PRIVATE LIMITED—See Shell plc; *Int'l*, pg. 6798
SHELL INDIA MARKETS PRIVATE LIMITED - WESTERN PROCESSING PLANT—See Shell plc; *Int'l*, pg. 6798
SHELLING DIALYSIS, LLC—See DaVita Inc.; *U.S. Public*, pg. 643
SHELL INTERNATIONAL B.V.—See Shell plc; *Int'l*, pg. 6795
SHELL INTERNATIONAL FINANCE B.V.—See Shell plc; *Int'l*, pg. 6795
SHELL INTERNATIONAL TRADING & SHIPPING CO. LTD.—See Shell plc; *Int'l*, pg. 6799
SHELL JAPAN LTD.—See Shell plc; *Int'l*, pg. 6798
SHELL JAPAN TRADING LTD.—See Idemitsu Kosan Co., Ltd.; *Int'l*, pg. 3592
SHELL KAZAKHSTAN DEVELOPMENT B.V.—See Shell plc; *Int'l*, pg. 6798
SHELL LUBRICANTS JAPAN K.K.—See Shell plc; *Int'l*, pg. 6795
SHELL LUBRICANTS—See Shell plc; *Int'l*, pg. 6796
SHELL LUBRICANTS—See Shell plc; *Int'l*, pg. 6796
SHELL LUMBER & HARDWARE INC.; *U.S. Private*, pg. 3631
SHELL LUXEMBOURGEOISE SARL—See Shell plc; *Int'l*, pg. 6798
SHELL MALAYSIA TRADING SDN. BHD.—See Shell plc; *Int'l*, pg. 6798
SHELL MARINE PRODUCTS LTD.—See Shell plc; *Int'l*, pg. 6798
SHELL MARKETING ALGERIE S.P.A.—See Shell plc; *Int'l*, pg. 6798
SHELL MARKETS MIDDLE EAST—See Shell plc; *Int'l*, pg. 6798
SHELL MDS SENDIRIAN BERHAD—See Shell plc; *Int'l*, pg. 6798

SHELL MIDSTREAM PARTNERS, L.P.—See Shell plc; *Int'l*, pg. 6795
SHELL & MOH AVIATION FUELS A.E.—See Shell plc; *Int'l*, pg. 6795
SHELL NEDERLAND B.V.—See Shell plc; *Int'l*, pg. 6795
SHELL NEDERLAND CHEMIE B.V.—See Shell plc; *Int'l*, pg. 6795
SHELL NEDERLAND RAFFINADERIJ B.V.—See Shell plc; *Int'l*, pg. 6795
SHELL NEDERLAND VERKOOPMAATSCHAPPIJ B.V.—See Shell plc; *Int'l*, pg. 6795
SHELL NEW ZEALAND LTD.—See Shell plc; *Int'l*, pg. 6799
SHELL NIGERIA GAS LIMITED—See Shell plc; *Int'l*, pg. 6799
SHELL OFFSHORE INC—See Shell plc; *Int'l*, pg. 6796
SHELL OIL COMPANY—See Shell plc; *Int'l*, pg. 6796
SHELL OIL PRODUCTS COMPANY LLC—See Shell plc; *Int'l*, pg. 6796
SHELL OLIE - OG GASUDVINDING DANMARK B.V.—See BlueNord ASA; *Int'l*, pg. 1072
SHELL OMAN MARKETING COMPANY SAOG; *Int'l*, pg. 6794
SHELL OMAN TRADING LIMITED—See Shell plc; *Int'l*, pg. 6799
SHELL OPERACIONES PERU S.A.C.—See Shell plc; *Int'l*, pg. 6795
SHELL OVERSEAS HOLDINGS LIMITED—See Shell plc; *Int'l*, pg. 6799
SHELL OVERSEAS INVESTMENTS B.V.—See Shell plc; *Int'l*, pg. 6796
SHELL OVERSEAS SERVICES LTD.—See Shell plc; *Int'l*, pg. 6799
SHELL PAKISTAN LIMITED—See Asyad Holding Group; *Int'l*, pg. 664
SHELL PANAMA S.A.—See Shell plc; *Int'l*, pg. 6799
SHELL PAPUA NEW GUINEA PTY. LTD.—See Shell plc; *Int'l*, pg. 6799
THE SHELL PETROLEUM COMPANY LIMITED—See Shell plc; *Int'l*, pg. 6796
SHELL PETROLEUM INC.—See Shell plc; *Int'l*, pg. 6796
SHELL PETROLEUM N.V.—See Shell plc; *Int'l*, pg. 6795
SHELL PHILIPPINES EXPLORATION B.V.—See Shell plc; *Int'l*, pg. 6795
SHELL PIPELINE COMPANY LP—See Shell plc; *Int'l*, pg. 6796
SHELL PLC; *Int'l*, pg. 6794
SHELLPOINT PARTNERS LLC—See Rithm Capital Corp.; *U.S. Public*, pg. 1800
SHELL POINT RETIREMENT COMMUNITY—See Christian and Missionary Alliance Foundation, Inc.; *U.S. Private*, pg. 890
SHELL POLSKA SP. Z O.O.—See Shell plc; *Int'l*, pg. 6799
SHELL PORTUGUESA LDA—See Shell plc; *Int'l*, pg. 6799
SHELL REFINING AUSTRALIA PTY. LTD.—See Shell plc; *Int'l*, pg. 6797
SHELL REFINING COMPANY (FEDERATION OF MALAYA) BERHAD—See Shandong Hengyuan Petrochemical Co., Ltd.; *Int'l*, pg. 6754
SHELL ROBERT TRAINING & CONFERENCE CENTER—See ConocoPhillips; *U.S. Public*, pg. 569
SHELL SAKHALIN HOLDINGS B.V.—See Shell plc; *Int'l*, pg. 6796
SHELL SALYM DEVELOPMENT B.V.—See PJSC Gazprom; *Int'l*, pg. 5879
SHELL SLOVAKIA, S.R.O.—See Shell plc; *Int'l*, pg. 6799
SHELL SOUTH AFRICA ENERGY (PTY) LTD. - CHEMICAL DIVISION—See Shell plc; *Int'l*, pg. 6799
SHELL SOUTH AFRICA ENERGY (PTY) LTD.—See Shell plc; *Int'l*, pg. 6799
SHELL SOUTH AFRICA HOLDINGS (PTY) LIMITED—See Shell plc; *Int'l*, pg. 6799
SHELL SOUTH AFRICA MARKETING (PTY) LTD.—See Shell plc; *Int'l*, pg. 6799
SHELL SURINAME VERKOOP MAATSCHAPPIJ NV—See Shell plc; *Int'l*, pg. 6799
SHELL (SWITZERLAND) AG—See Shell plc; *Int'l*, pg. 6797
SHELL TANKERS (SINGAPORE) PRIVATE LIMITED—See Shell plc; *Int'l*, pg. 6800
SHELL TECHNOLOGY NORWAY AS—See Shell plc; *Int'l*, pg. 6799
SHELL TECHNOLOGY VENTURES, INC.—See ConocoPhillips; *U.S. Public*, pg. 569
SHELL THAILAND—See Shell plc; *Int'l*, pg. 6799
SHELL TRADING ROTTERDAM B.V.—See Shell plc; *Int'l*, pg. 6800
SHELL TRADING RUSSIA B.V.—See Shell plc; *Int'l*, pg. 6796
SHELL TRADING (US) COMPANY—See Shell plc; *Int'l*, pg. 6800
THE SHELL TRANSPORT & TRADING CO. LTD.—See Shell plc; *Int'l*, pg. 6799
SHELL TREASURY CENTRE LIMITED—See Shell plc; *Int'l*, pg. 6796
SHELL TREASURY DOLLAR COMPANY LIMITED—See Shell plc; *Int'l*, pg. 6796
SHELL TREASURY LUXEMBOURG SARL—See Shell plc; *Int'l*, pg. 6799

COMPANY NAME INDEX

SHELL TRINIDAD LIMITED—See Shell plc; *Int'l*, pg. 6799
SHELL & TURCAS PETROL A.S.—See Shell plc; *Int'l*, pg. 6795
SHELL UGANDA—See Shell plc; *Int'l*, pg. 6799
SHELL U.K. LTD.—See Shell plc; *Int'l*, pg. 6799
SHELL UKRAINE EXPLORATION & PRODUCTION I LLC—See Shell plc; *Int'l*, pg. 6800
SHELL UPSTREAM INTERNATIONAL LTD. - BACTON GAS PLANT—See Shell plc; *Int'l*, pg. 6799
SHELL UPSTREAM INTERNATIONAL LTD. - FIFE NGL PLANT—See Shell plc; *Int'l*, pg. 6799
SHELL UPSTREAM INTERNATIONAL LTD.—See Shell plc; *Int'l*, pg. 6799
SHELL URUGUAY S.A.—See Shell plc; *Int'l*, pg. 6799
SHELL USA, INC.—See Shell plc; *Int'l*, pg. 6800
SHELL US GAS & POWER LLC—See Shell plc; *Int'l*, pg. 6800
SHELL VENEZUELA PRODUCTOS, C.A.—See Shell plc; *Int'l*, pg. 6799
SHELL VERWALTUNGSGESELLSCHAFT FUR ERDGAS-BETEILIGUNGEN MBH—See Shell plc; *Int'l*, pg. 6799
SHELL VIETNAM LTD. - GO DAU PLANT—See Shell plc; *Int'l*, pg. 6799
SHELL VIETNAM LTD.—See Shell plc; *Int'l*, pg. 6799
SHELL WATERTON COMPLEX—See Shell plc; *Int'l*, pg. 6797
SHELLWESTERN LNG B.V.—See Shell plc; *Int'l*, pg. 6796
SHELL WESTERN SUPPLY & TRADING LTD.—See Shell plc; *Int'l*, pg. 6800
THE SHELLY CO. - COLUMBUS DIVISION—See CRH plc; *Int'l*, pg. 1847
THE SHELLY COMPANY—See CRH plc; *Int'l*, pg. 1847
THE SHELLY CO. - NORTHEAST DIVISION—See CRH plc; *Int'l*, pg. 1847
THE SHELLY CO. - NORTHWEST DIVISION—See CRH plc; *Int'l*, pg. 1847
THE SHELLY CO. - SOUTHERN DIVISION—See CRH plc; *Int'l*, pg. 1847
SHELLY ENTERPRISES, INC.—See Bain Capital, LP; *U.S. Private*, pg. 451
SHELLY MATERIALS, INC.—See CRH plc; *Int'l*, pg. 1847
SHELLY & SANDS INC.; *U.S. Private*, pg. 3631
SHELMAN SWISS-HELLENIC WOOD PRODUCT MANUFACTURERS SA; *Int'l*, pg. 6800
SHEL NIBE MANUFACTURING CO LTD—See NIBE Industrier AB; *Int'l*, pg. 5262
SHELOR MOTOR MILE; *U.S. Private*, pg. 3631
SHELTAIR AVIATION CENTER, LLC; *U.S. Private*, pg. 3631
SHELTER BAY RETAIL GROUP, INC.—See Jones Lang LaSalle Incorporated; *U.S. Public*, pg. 1206
SHELTERCLEAN, INC.—See GTJ REIT, Inc.; *U.S. Private*, pg. 1807
SHELTER CO.; *U.S. Private*, pg. 3631
SHELTER FINANCIAL SERVICES, INC.—See Shelter Mutual Insurance Company; *U.S. Private*, pg. 3631
SHELTER HOME MORTGAGE, LLC—See Rithm Capital Corp.; *U.S. Public*, pg. 1800
SHELTER INFRA PROJECTS LIMITED; *Int'l*, pg. 6800
THE SHELTERING ARMS; *U.S. Private*, pg. 4117
SHELTERING PALMS FOUNDATION INC; *U.S. Private*, pg. 3631
SHELTERLOGIC CORP.; *U.S. Private*, pg. 3631
SHELTER MORTGAGE COMPANY, LLC—See Rithm Capital Corp.; *U.S. Public*, pg. 1800
SHELTER MORTGAGE TJV LLC—See Rithm Capital Corp.; *U.S. Public*, pg. 1800
SHELTER MUTUAL INSURANCE COMPANY; *U.S. Private*, pg. 3631
SHELTER PARTNERSHIP, INC.; *U.S. Private*, pg. 3631
SHELTERPOINT GROUP, INC.; *U.S. Private*, pg. 3632
SHELTER PRODUCTS INC.; *U.S. Private*, pg. 3631
SHELTON CANADA CORP.—See Petrosibir AB; *Int'l*, pg. 5832
SHELTON CAPITAL MANAGEMENT; *U.S. Private*, pg. 3632
SHELTON INTERACTIVE—See Advantage Media Group, Inc.; *U.S. Private*, pg. 94
SHELYS PHARMACEUTICALS LIMITED—See Sumaria Group; *Int'l*, pg. 7260
SHEMAROO CONTENTINO MEDIA LLP—See Shemaroo Entertainment Ltd.; *Int'l*, pg. 6800
SHEMAROO ENTERTAINMENT LTD.; *Int'l*, pg. 6800
SHEMEN INDUSTRIES LTD.; *Int'l*, pg. 6800
SHEMEN OIL & GAS RESOURCES LTD.; *Int'l*, pg. 6800
SHENANDOAH CABLE TELEVISION, LLC—See Shenandoah Telecommunications Co.; *U.S. Public*, pg. 1874
SHENANDOAH LIFE INSURANCE COMPANY; *U.S. Private*, pg. 3632
SHENANDOAH LONG DISTANCE CO. INC.—See Shenandoah Telecommunications Co.; *U.S. Public*, pg. 1874
SHENANDOAH MEMORIAL PARK LLC—See Axar Capital Management L.P.; *U.S. Private*, pg. 412
SHENANDOAH MILLS, INC.; *U.S. Private*, pg. 3632
SHENANDOAH MOBILE CO. INC.—See Shenandoah Telecommunications Co.; *U.S. Public*, pg. 1874

SHENANDOAH NETWORK COMPANY INC.—See Shenandoah Telecommunications Co.; *U.S. Public*, pg. 1874
SHENANDOAH TELECOMMUNICATIONS CO.; *U.S. Public*, pg. 1874
SHENANDOAH TELEPHONE COMPANY INC.—See Shenandoah Telecommunications Co.; *U.S. Public*, pg. 1874
SHENANDOAH TOWER SERVICE LTD.; *U.S. Private*, pg. 3632
SHENANDOAH VALLEY ELECTRIC COOPERATIVE; *U.S. Private*, pg. 3632
SHENANDOAH VALLEY WESTMINSTER-CANTERBURY; *U.S. Private*, pg. 3632
SHENANGO LLC; *U.S. Private*, pg. 3632
SHENDA INTERNATIONAL ENGINEERING CO. LTD.; *Int'l*, pg. 6800
SH ENERGY & CHEMICAL CO, LTD.; *Int'l*, pg. 6746
SHENERGY COMPANY LIMITED; *Int'l*, pg. 6801
SHENGDA NETWORK TECHNOLOGY, INC.; *Int'l*, pg. 6801
SHENGDA RESOURCES CO., LTD.; *Int'l*, pg. 6801
SHENGDATECH, INC.; *Int'l*, pg. 6801
SHENGFENG DEVELOPMENT LIMITED; *Int'l*, pg. 6801
SHENGHE RESOURCES HOLDING CO., LTD.; *Int'l*, pg. 6801
SHENGHONG HOLDING GROUP CO., LTD.; *Int'l*, pg. 6801
SHENGHUA ENTERTAINMENT COMMUNICATION CO., LTD.; *Int'l*, pg. 6801
SHENGHUA GROUP HOLDINGS CO., LTD.; *Int'l*, pg. 6801
SHENGHUA LANDE SCITECH LIMITED—See Zhejiang Shenghua Holdings, Co., Ltd.; *Int'l*, pg. 8663
SHENG HUEI (SHENZHEN) ENGINEERING CO., LTD.—See Acter Co., Ltd.; *Int'l*, pg. 117
SHENGJING BANK CO., LTD.; *Int'l*, pg. 6801
SHENGKAI INNOVATIONS, INC.; *Int'l*, pg. 6801
SHENGLAN TECHNOLOGY CO., LTD.; *Int'l*, pg. 6801
SHENGLI OIL & GAS PIPE HOLDINGS LIMITED; *Int'l*, pg. 6802
SHENG LONG BIO-TECH (INDIA) PVT. LTD.—See Guangdong Haid Group Co., Ltd.; *Int'l*, pg. 3155
SHENGLONG SPLENDECOR INTERNATIONAL LIMITED; *Int'l*, pg. 6802
SHENGQU INFORMATION TECHNOLOGY (SHANGHAI) CO., LTD.—See Shanda Interactive Entertainment Limited; *Int'l*, pg. 6751
SHENG-RAAMCO MANAGEMENT INC.—See Raamco International Incorporated; *U.S. Private*, pg. 3341
SHENG RUI ELECTRONIC TECHNOLOGY (SHANGHAI) CO., LTD.—See Casetek Holdings Limited; *Int'l*, pg. 1351
SHENG SIONG GROUP LIMITED; *Int'l*, pg. 6801
SHENG SIONG SUPERMARKET PTE. LTD.—See Sheng Siong Group Limited; *Int'l*, pg. 6801
SHENGTAI PHARMACEUTICAL, INC.; *Int'l*, pg. 6802
SHENGTAK NEW MATERIAL CO., LTD.; *Int'l*, pg. 6802
SHENGUAN HOLDINGS (GROUP) LIMITED; *Int'l*, pg. 6802
SHENGXING (BEIJING) PACKING CO., LTD.—See Sunrise Group Company Limited; *Int'l*, pg. 7321
SHENGXING (HEBEI) PACKING CO., LTD.—See Sunrise Group Company Limited; *Int'l*, pg. 7321
SHENGXING (HONG KONG) CO., LTD.—See Sunrise Group Company Limited; *Int'l*, pg. 7321
SHENGXING (SHANDONG) PACKING CO., LTD.—See Sunrise Group Company Limited; *Int'l*, pg. 7321
SHENGXING (ZHONGSHAN) PACKING CO., LTD.—See Sunrise Group Company Limited; *Int'l*, pg. 7321
SHENG YE COMMERCIAL FACTORING LIMITED—See SY Holdings Group Limited; *Int'l*, pg. 7377
SHENG YI DEVELOPMENT CO., LTD.; *Int'l*, pg. 6801
SHENGYI ELECTRONICS CO., LTD.—See Shengyi Technology, Co. Ltd.; *Int'l*, pg. 6802
SHENGYI TECHNOLOGY, CO. LTD.; *Int'l*, pg. 6802
SHENGYI TECHNOLOGY (HONG KONG) CO., LTD.—See Shengyi Technology, Co. Ltd.; *Int'l*, pg. 6802
SHENGYUAN ENVIRONMENTAL PROTECTION CO., LTD.; *Int'l*, pg. 6802
SHENG YUAN HOLDINGS LIMITED; *Int'l*, pg. 6801
SHENGYUAN NUTRITIONAL FOOD CO., LTD.—See Synutra International, Inc.; *U.S. Private*, pg. 3905
SHENG YUAN SECURITIES LIMITED—See Sheng Yuan Holdings Limited; *Int'l*, pg. 6801
SHENG YU STEEL CO., LTD.—See Yodogawa Steel Works, Ltd.; *Int'l*, pg. 8591
SHENGZHOU AOZE AUTOMOBILE SALES SERVICES CO., LTD.—See China ZhengTong Auto Services Holdings Limited; *Int'l*, pg. 1567
SHENGZHOU BAOZEN AUTO SALES & SERVICES CO., LTD.—See China Yongda Automobiles Services Holdings Limited; *Int'l*, pg. 1565
SHENHUA AUSTRALIA HOLDINGS PTY LIMITED—See Shenhua Group Corporation Limited; *Int'l*, pg. 6802
SHEN HUA CHEMICAL INDUSTRIAL CO., LTD.—See TSRC Corporation; *Int'l*, pg. 7952
SHENHUA FUJIAN ENERGY CO., LTD.—See Shenhua Group Corporation Limited; *Int'l*, pg. 6802

SHENYANG CUIHUA GOLD AND SILVER JEWELRY CO., LTD.

SHENHUA GROUP CORPORATION LIMITED; *Int'l*, pg. 6802
SHENHUA INTERNATIONAL LIMITED; *Int'l*, pg. 6802
SHENHUA SHENDONG COAL GROUP CO., LTD.—See Shenhua Group Corporation Limited; *Int'l*, pg. 6802
SHENHUA WATERMARK COAL PTY LTD.—See Shenhua Group Corporation Limited; *Int'l*, pg. 6802
SHENJI GROUP KUNMING MACHINE TOOL CO., LTD.; *Int'l*, pg. 6802
SHENJUMIAOSUAN CO., LTD.—See GAtechnologies Co., Ltd.; *Int'l*, pg. 2889
SHENKE SLIDE BEARING CORP.; *Int'l*, pg. 6802
SHENMA INDUSTRY CO., LTD.; *Int'l*, pg. 6802
SHENMAO AMERICA, INC.—See Shenmao Technology Inc.; *Int'l*, pg. 6803
SHENMAO EUROPE GMBH—See Shenmao Technology Inc.; *Int'l*, pg. 6803
SHENMAO SOLDER (MALAYSIA) SDN. BHD—See Shenmao Technology Inc.; *Int'l*, pg. 6803
SHENMAO SOLDER MATERIAL (SUZHOU) CO., LTD.—See Shenmao Technology Inc.; *Int'l*, pg. 6803
SHENMAO TECHNOLOGY INC.; *Int'l*, pg. 6802
SHENMAO TECHNOLOGY (THAILAND) CO., LTD.—See Shenmao Technology Inc.; *Int'l*, pg. 6803
SHENNAN CIRCUIT COMPANY LIMITED - LONGGANG FACTORY—See AVIC International Holdings Limited; *Int'l*, pg. 742
SHENNAN CIRCUIT COMPANY LIMITED—See AVIC International Holdings Limited; *Int'l*, pg. 742
SHENNAN CIRCUITS CO., LTD.—See AVIC International Holdings Limited; *Int'l*, pg. 742
SHEN'S ART PRINTING CO., LTD.; *Int'l*, pg. 6800
SHENTEL MANAGEMENT COMPANY—See Shenandoah Telecommunications Co.; *U.S. Public*, pg. 1874
SHENTON FAMILY MEDICAL CLINIC (BUKIT GOMBAK)—See Khazanah Nasional Berhad; *Int'l*, pg. 4152
SHENTON FAMILY MEDICAL CLINIC (SERANGOON)—See Khazanah Nasional Berhad; *Int'l*, pg. 4152
SHENTON FAMILY MEDICAL CLINIC (TAMPINES)—See Khazanah Nasional Berhad; *Int'l*, pg. 4152
SHENTONG ROBOT EDUCATION GROUP COMPANY LIMITED; *Int'l*, pg. 6803
SHENTONG TECHNOLOGY GROUP CO., LTD.; *Int'l*, pg. 6803
SHENWAN HONGYUAN FINANCING SERVICES CO., LTD.—See Shenwan Hongyuan Group Co., Ltd.; *Int'l*, pg. 6803
SHENWAN HONGYUAN GROUP CO., LTD.; *Int'l*, pg. 6803
SHENWAN HONGYUAN (H.K.) LIMITED; *Int'l*, pg. 6803
SHENWAN HONGYUAN (INTERNATIONAL) HOLDINGS LIMITED—See Shenwan Hongyuan Group Co., Ltd.; *Int'l*, pg. 6803
SHENWAN HONGYUAN SINGAPORE PRIVATE LIMITED—See Shenwan Hongyuan (H.K.) Limited; *Int'l*, pg. 6803
SHENWU ENERGY SAVING CO., LTD.; *Int'l*, pg. 6803
SHENWU ENVIRONMENTAL TECHNOLOGY CO., LTD.; *Int'l*, pg. 6803
SHENYANG AICA-HOPE KOGYO CO., LTD.—See AICA Kogyo Company, Limited; *Int'l*, pg. 229
SHENYANG AOXIN Q & M STOMATOLOGY HOSPITAL CO., LTD.—See Aoxin Q & M Dental Group Limited; *Int'l*, pg. 498
SHENYANG BLUE SILVER INDUSTRY AUTOMATIC EQUIPMENT CO., LTD.; *Int'l*, pg. 6803
SHENYANG BRILLIANCE JINBEI AUTOMOBILE CO., LTD.—See Brilliance China Automotive Holdings Limited; *Int'l*, pg. 1163
SHENYANG BRILLIANCE JINBEI AUTOMOBILE CO., LTD.—See Shenyang Jinbei Automotive Company Limited; *Int'l*, pg. 6804
SHENYANG CAMEL XIANGDA PASTURE CO., LTD—See Tangrenshen Group Co., Ltd.; *Int'l*, pg. 7458
SHENYANG CHANGCHUN AUTOMOTIVE PARTS CO., LTD—See Jiangsu Changshu Automotive Trim Group Co., Ltd.; *Int'l*, pg. 3945
SHENYANG CHEMICAL INDUSTRY CO., LTD.; *Int'l*, pg. 6803
SHENYANG CHIA TAI LIVESTOCK CO., LTD.—See Charoen Pokphand Foods Public Company Limited; *Int'l*, pg. 1453
SHENYANG CLEANBIZ CO., LTD.—See Cleanup Corporation; *Int'l*, pg. 1656
SHENYANG COMFORTDELGRO TAXI CO., LTD.—See ComfortDelGro Corporation Limited; *Int'l*, pg. 1713
SHENYANG COMMERCIAL CITY CO., LTD.; *Int'l*, pg. 6803
SHENYANG CUIHUA GOLD AND SILVER JEWELRY CO., LTD.; *Int'l*, pg. 6803
SHENYANG DAODA AUTOMOBILE DECORATIVE PARTS CO., LTD.—See Jiangnan Mould & Plastic Technology Co., Ltd.; *Int'l*, pg. 3943
SHENYANG DIGITAL CHINA LIMITED—See Digital China Holdings Limited; *Int'l*, pg. 2121
SHENYANG DIMPLEX ELECTRONICS—See The Glen Dimplex Group; *Int'l*, pg. 7650

SHENYANG FAME BIO-TECH CO., LTD.—See Wellhope Foods Co., Ltd.; *Int'l*, pg. 8374
SHENYANG FIDIA NC & MACHINE CO., LTD.—See FIDIA S.p.A.; *Int'l*, pg. 2655
SHENYANG FURUKAWA CABLE CO., LTD.—See The Furukawa Electric Co., Ltd.; *Int'l*, pg. 7647
SHENYANG HAORUNDA ADDITIVE CO., LTD.—See Xinxiang Richful Lube Additive Co., Ltd.; *Int'l*, pg. 8533
SHENYANG HEJIN HOLDING INVESTMENT CO., LTD.—See China CITIC Financial Asset Management Co., Ltd.; *Int'l*, pg. 1489
SHENYANG HEPING Q & M AOXIN STOMATOLOGY POLYCLINIC CO., LTD.—See Aoxin Q & M Dental Group Limited; *Int'l*, pg. 498
SHENYANG HUANGGU AOXIN DENTAL CLINIC CO., LTD.—See Aoxin Q & M Dental Group Limited; *Int'l*, pg. 498
SHENYANG HUITIAN THERMAL POWER CO., LTD.; *Int'l*, pg. 6803
SHENYANG ISETAN CO., LTD.—See Isetan Mitsukoshi Holdings Ltd.; *Int'l*, pg. 3815
SHENYANG JINBEI AUTOMOTIVE COMPANY LIMITED; *Int'l*, pg. 6804
SHENYANG JINBEI HENGLONG AUTOMOTIVE STEERING SYSTEM CO., LTD.—See China Automotive Systems, Inc.; *Int'l*, pg. 1484
SHENYANG KIMOTO INDUSTRIES CO., LTD.—See Kimoto Co., Ltd.; *Int'l*, pg. 4163
SHENYANG LEAR AUTOMOTIVE SEATING AND INTERIOR SYSTEMS CO., LTD.—See Lear Corporation; *U.S. Public*, pg. 1298
SHENYANG LONGTENG ELECTRONIC CO., LTD.—See Keli Sensing Technology Ningbo Co., Ltd.; *Int'l*, pg. 4119
SHENYANG MACHINE TOOL CO., LTD.; *Int'l*, pg. 6804
SHENYANG MAOTAI Q & M MEDICAL EQUIPMENT CO., LTD.—See Aoxin Q & M Dental Group Limited; *Int'l*, pg. 498
SHENYANG MINGHUA MOULD & PLASTIC TECHNOLOGY CO., LTD.—See Jiangnan Mould & Plastic Technology Co., Ltd.; *Int'l*, pg. 3943
SHENYANG NEUSOFT BUSINESS SOFTWARE CO., LTD.—See Japan Industrial Partners, Inc.; *Int'l*, pg. 3890
SHENYANG NONGSHIM FOODS CO., LTD.—See Nongshim Co., Ltd.; *Int'l*, pg. 5414
SHENYANG NORTHEAST STORAGE BATTERY LTD.—See Coslight Technology International Group Limited; *Int'l*, pg. 1810
SHENYANG NSK CO., LTD.—See NSK Ltd.; *Int'l*, pg. 5480
SHENYANG NSK PRECISION CO., LTD.—See NSK Ltd.; *Int'l*, pg. 5480
SHENYANG PACIFIC MILLENNIUM PACKAGING & PAPER INDUSTRIES CO., LTD.—See Pacific Millennium Packaging Group Corporation; *Int'l*, pg. 5691
SHENYANG PARKERIZING CO., LTD.—See Nihon Parkerizing Co., Ltd.; *Int'l*, pg. 5287
SHENYANG PUBLIC UTILITY HOLDINGS COMPANY LIMITED; *Int'l*, pg. 6804
SHENYANG QINGAOMEI ORAL RESTORATIVE TECHNOLOGY CO., LTD.—See Aoxin Q & M Dental Group Limited; *Int'l*, pg. 498
SHENYANG RAILWAY SIGNAL CO., LTD.—See China National Railway Signal & Communication Corp.; *Int'l*, pg. 1534
SHEN YANG RIXIN CARBURETER CORP.—See Nikki CO., LTD.; *Int'l*, pg. 5290
SHENYANG SANDEN AUTOMOTIVE AIR-CONDITIONING CO. LTD.—See Sanden Corporation; *Int'l*, pg. 6525
SHENYANG SANYO AIR CONDITIONER CO., LTD.—See Panasonic Holdings Corporation; *Int'l*, pg. 5725
SHENYANG SCHALTBAU ELECTRICAL CORPORATION LTD.—See The Carlyle Group Inc.; *U.S. Public*, pg. 2053
SHENYANG SEMBCORP WATER CO LTD—See Sembcorp Industries Ltd.; *Int'l*, pg. 6704
SHENYANG SENKO LOGISTICS CO., LTD.—See Senko Group Holdings Co., Ltd.; *Int'l*, pg. 6711
SHENYANG SHENHE AOXIN STOMATOLOGY POLYCLINIC CO., LTD.—See Aoxin Q & M Dental Group Limited; *Int'l*, pg. 498
SHENYANG SHINAGAWA METALLURGY MATERIALS CO., LTD.—See Shinagawa Refractories Co., Ltd.; *Int'l*, pg. 6841
SHENYANG SPICER DRIVESHAFT CO. LTD.—See Dana Incorporated; *U.S. Public*, pg. 623
SHENYANG SUNSHINE PHARMACEUTICAL CO., LIMITED—See 3SBio Inc.; *Int'l*, pg. 9
SHENYANG XINGQI PHARMACEUTICAL CO LTD; *Int'l*, pg. 6804
SHENYANG XUANTAN AUTOMOBILE PARTS CO., LTD.—See Aisan Industry Co., Ltd.; *Int'l*, pg. 251
SHENYANG YUANDA COMPRESSOR CO. LTD.—See Burckhardt Compression Holding AG; *Int'l*, pg. 1221
SHENYANG YUANDA INTELLECTUAL INDUSTRY GROUP CO., LTD.; *Int'l*, pg. 6804
SHENYANG ZHONGFU PREFORM CO., LTD.—See Zhuhai Zhongfu Enterprise Co., Ltd.; *Int'l*, pg. 8679
SHEN YAO HOLDINGS LIMITED; *Int'l*, pg. 6800

SHEN YAO INVESTMENTS PTE. LTD.—See Shen Yao Holdings Limited; *Int'l*, pg. 6800
SHENYIN & WANGUO ALTERNATIVE INVESTMENT CO., LTD.—See Shenwan Hongyuan Group Co., Ltd.; *Int'l*, pg. 6803
SHENYIN & WANGUO INVESTMENT CO., LTD.—See Shenwan Hongyuan Group Co., Ltd.; *Int'l*, pg. 6803
SHENYU COMMUNICATION TECHNOLOGY INC.; *Int'l*, pg. 6804
SHEN YUN PERFORMING ARTS INC.; *U.S. Private*, pg. 3632
SHENZEN CAPITAL GROUP CO., LTD.—See Shanghai Dazhong Public Utilities (Group) Co., Ltd.; *Int'l*, pg. 6764
SHENZEN KORADIOR FASHION CO., LTD.—See EEKA Fashion Holdings Limited; *Int'l*, pg. 2317
SHENZHEN 1WOR UNITED DESIGN CO. LTD.—See Guangdong Bobaolon Co., Ltd.; *Int'l*, pg. 3153
SHENZHEN ABSEN OPTOELECTRONIC COMPANY LIMITED; *Int'l*, pg. 6804
SHENZHEN AGRICULTURAL PRODUCTS GROUP CO., LTD.; *Int'l*, pg. 6804
SHENZHEN AINEAR CORNEA ENGINEERING COMPANY LIMITED—See China Regenerative Medicine International Co., Ltd.; *Int'l*, pg. 1547
SHENZHEN AIRPORT CO., LTD.; *Int'l*, pg. 6804
SHENZHEN AISIDI CO., LTD.; *Int'l*, pg. 6804
SHENZHEN ALCONIX (SHANGHAI) CORP.—See Alconix Corporation; *Int'l*, pg. 302
SHENZHEN ALL LINK TECHNOLOGY CO., LTD.—See Shenzhen Zowee Technology Co., Ltd.; *Int'l*, pg. 6825
SHENZHEN ANCHE TECHNOLOGIES CO., LTD.; *Int'l*, pg. 6804
SHENZHEN ANJIE ELECTRONIC CO., LTD.—See Suzhou Anjie Technology Co., Ltd.; *Int'l*, pg. 7349
SHENZHEN ANNI DIGITAL TECHNOLOGY CO., LTD.—See Xiamen Xinde Co., Ltd.; *Int'l*, pg. 8526
SHENZHEN ANZER INTELLIGENT ENGINEERING CO., LTD.—See SuperRobotics Limited; *Int'l*, pg. 7339
SHENZHEN AONI ELECTRONIC CO., LTD.; *Int'l*, pg. 6804
SHENZHEN AOTO ELECTRONICS CO., LTD.; *Int'l*, pg. 6804
SHENZHEN AOZE AUTOMOBILE SALES SERVICES CO., LTD.—See China ZhengTong Auto Services Holdings Limited; *Int'l*, pg. 1567
SHENZHEN APEXLS OPTOELECTRONIC CO., LTD.—See Ledman Optoelectronic Co., Ltd.; *Int'l*, pg. 4439
SHENZHEN ASIA LINK TECHNOLOGY DEVELOPMENT CO., LTD.; *Int'l*, pg. 6804
SHENZHEN AUSTRALIS ELECTRONIC TECHNOLOGY CO., LTD.; *Int'l*, pg. 6804
SHENZHEN AUTO ELECTRIC POWER PLANT CO., LTD.; *Int'l*, pg. 6805
SHENZHEN AV-DISPLAY CO., LTD.; *Int'l*, pg. 6805
SHENZHEN AXXON AUTOMATION CO, LTD.—See Mycronic AB; *Int'l*, pg. 5112
SHENZHEN BAOMING TECHNOLOGY CO., LTD.; *Int'l*, pg. 6805
SHENZHEN BAONENG INVESTMENT GROUP CO., LTD.; *Int'l*, pg. 6805
SHENZHEN BAOTAIHANG AUTOMOBILE SALES SERVICES CO., LTD.—See China ZhengTong Auto Services Holdings Limited; *Int'l*, pg. 1567
SHENZHEN BAOZE AUTOMOBILE SALES SERVICES CO., LTD.—See China ZhengTong Auto Services Holdings Limited; *Int'l*, pg. 1567
SHENZHEN BATIAN ECOTYPIC ENGINEERING CO., LTD.; *Int'l*, pg. 6805
SHENZHEN BAUING CONSTRUCTION GROUP CO., LTD.; *Int'l*, pg. 6805
SHENZHEN BEIREN PRINTING CO., LTD.—See Beijing Jingcheng Machinery Electric Holding Co., Ltd.; *Int'l*, pg. 953
SHENZHEN BENSON AUTOMOBILE GLASS COMPANY LIMITED—See Xinyi Glass Holdings Limited; *Int'l*, pg. 8534
SHENZHEN BESTEK TECHNOLOGY CO., LTD.; *Int'l*, pg. 6805
SHENZHEN BEST OF BEST HOLDINGS CO., LTD.; *Int'l*, pg. 6805
SHENZHEN BINGCHUAN NETWORK CO LTD; *Int'l*, pg. 6805
SHENZHEN BIOEASY BIOTECHNOLOGY CO., LTD.; *Int'l*, pg. 6805
SHENZHEN BOMIN ELECTRONIC CO., LTD.—See Bomin Electronics Co., Ltd.; *Int'l*, pg. 1105
SHENZHEN BONE MEDICAL DEVICE CO., LTD.—See PW Medtech Group Limited; *Int'l*, pg. 6126
SHENZHEN BOOMINGSHING MEDICAL DEVICE CO., LTD.—See Shenzhen Changhong Technology Co., Ltd.; *Int'l*, pg. 6806
SHENZHEN BOW CHUANG VEHICLE TRADING CO, LTD.—See Sime Darby Berhad; *Int'l*, pg. 6928
SHENZHEN BOWJUM TECHNOLOGY CO., LTD.—See Zhuhai Bojay Electronics Co., Ltd.; *Int'l*, pg. 8677

SHENZHEN BROADWAY TOTAL PACKAGING SOLUTION CO., LTD.—See Platinum Equity, LLC; *U.S. Private*, pg. 3201
SHENZHEN BROS EASTERN TEXTILE CO., LTD.—See Bros Eastern Co., Ltd.; *Int'l*, pg. 1195
SHENZHEN BSC TECHNOLOGY CO., LTD.; *Int'l*, pg. 6805
SHENZHEN CAFE DE CORAL CATERING COMPANY LIMITED—See Cafe de Coral Holdings Limited; *Int'l*, pg. 1250
SHENZHEN CAPCHEM TECHNOLOGY CO., LTD.; *Int'l*, pg. 6805
SHENZHEN CAPOL INTERNATIONAL & ASSOCIATES CO., LTD.; *Int'l*, pg. 6805
SHENZHEN CAPSTONE INDUSTRIAL CO., LTD.; *Int'l*, pg. 6805
SHENZHEN CDL PRECISION TECHNOLOGY CO., LTD.; *Int'l*, pg. 6805
SHENZHEN CENTER POWER TECH. CO., LTD.; *Int'l*, pg. 6806
SHENZHEN CENTRALCON INVESTMENT HOLDING CO., LTD.; *Int'l*, pg. 6806
SHENZHEN CENTURY MAN COMMUNICATION EQUIPMENT CO., LTD.—See TE Connectivity Ltd.; *Int'l*, pg. 7496
SHENZHEN CENTURY PLAZA HOTEL CO., LTD.; *Int'l*, pg. 6806
SHENZHEN CEREALS HOLDINGS CO., LTD.; *Int'l*, pg. 6806
SHENZHEN CERMATE TECHNOLOGIES INC.—See Advantech., Co., Ltd.; *Int'l*, pg. 165
SHENZHEN CESTAR ELECTRONIC TECHNOLOGY CO., LTD.—See P-Duke Technology Co., Ltd.; *Int'l*, pg. 5681
SHENZHEN CHANGCHENG HUIHUA GROUP CO., LTD—See Guangdong Rising Assets Management Co., Ltd.; *Int'l*, pg. 3159
SHENZHEN CHANGFANG GROUP CO., LTD.; *Int'l*, pg. 6806
SHENZHEN CHANGHONG TECHNOLOGY CO., LTD.; *Int'l*, pg. 6806
SHENZHEN CHEE YUEN PLASTIC PRODUCTS COMPANY LIMITED—See China Aerospace International Holdings Limited; *Int'l*, pg. 1481
SHENZHEN CHELIC PNEUMATIC CORP.—See Taiwan Chelic Corp. Ltd.; *Int'l*, pg. 7419
SHENZHEN CHENG CHUNG DESIGN CO., LTD.; *Int'l*, pg. 6806
SHENZHEN CHENGTIAN WEIYE TECHNOLOGY CO., LTD.; *Int'l*, pg. 6806
SHENZHEN CHEN HSONG MACHINERY CO. LTD.—See Chen Hsong Holdings Ltd.; *Int'l*, pg. 1464
SHENZHEN CHINA BICYCLE COMPANY (HOLDINGS) CO., LTD.; *Int'l*, pg. 6806
SHENZHEN CHIPSCREEN BIOSCIENCES CO., LTD.; *Int'l*, pg. 6806
SHENZHEN CHIPSCREEN PHARMACEUTICAL CO., LTD.—See Shenzhen Chipscreen Biosciences Co., Ltd.; *Int'l*, pg. 6806
SHENZHEN CHIPS INFORMATION S&T CO., LTD.—See Shenzhen Kingdom Sci-tech Co., Ltd.; *Int'l*, pg. 6816
SHENZHEN CHIWAN PETROLEUM SUPPLY BASE CO., LTD.; *Int'l*, pg. 6806
SHENZHEN CHUANGWEI-RGB ELECTRONICS CO., LTD.—See Skyworth Group Limited; *Int'l*, pg. 6995
SHENZHEN CHUANGYITONG TECHNOLOGY CO., LTD.; *Int'l*, pg. 6806
SHENZHEN CIMC INDUSTRY & CITY DEVELOPMENT CO., LTD.—See China International Marine Containers (Group) Co., Ltd.; *Int'l*, pg. 1512
SHENZHEN CIMC INVESTMENT HOLDING COMPANY—See China International Marine Containers (Group) Co., Ltd.; *Int'l*, pg. 1512
SHENZHEN CIMC TIANDA AIRPORT EQUIPMENT CO., LTD.—See China International Marine Containers (Group) Co., Ltd.; *Int'l*, pg. 1512
SHENZHEN CIMC VEHICLE SALES CO., LTD.—See CIMC Vehicle (Group) Co., Ltd.; *Int'l*, pg. 1608
SHENZHEN CIMC WOOD CO., LTD.—See China International Marine Containers (Group) Co., Ltd.; *Int'l*, pg. 1512
SHENZHEN CIMC YANTIAN PORT CONTAINER SERVICE CO., LTD—See China International Marine Containers (Group) Co., Ltd.; *Int'l*, pg. 1512
SHENZHEN CITY NEW CHINA WATER ELECTRIC POWER LIMITED—See China Water Industry Group Limited; *Int'l*, pg. 1563
SHENZHEN CLICK TECHNOLOGY CO., LTD.; *Int'l*, pg. 6806
SHENZHEN CLOU ELECTRONICS CO., LTD.; *Int'l*, pg. 6807
SHENZHEN CMEC INDUSTRY CO., LTD.—See China Machinery Engineering Corporation; *Int'l*, pg. 1516
SHENZHEN COLIBRI TECHNOLOGIES CO., LTD.; *Int'l*, pg. 6807
SHENZHEN COMIX GROUP CO., LTD.; *Int'l*, pg. 6807
SHENZHEN CONSYS SCIENCE & TECHNOLOGY CO., LTD.; *Int'l*, pg. 6807

COMPANY NAME INDEX

SHEN ZHEN COPARTNER COMMUNICATION CO LTD—See Copartner Technology Corporation; *Int'l*, pg. 1793
SHENZHEN COSCO INTERNATIONAL SHIPMANAGEMENT CO., LTD.—See China COSCO Shipping Corporation Limited; *Int'l*, pg. 1492
SHENZHEN COSCO LOGISTICS CO., LTD.—See China COSCO Shipping Corporation Limited; *Int'l*, pg. 1493
SHENZHEN COSLIGHT SOFTWARE CO., LTD.—See Coslight Technology International Group Limited; *Int'l*, pg. 1810
SHENZHEN COSON ELECTRONIC CO. LTD.—See China Security & Surveillance Technology, Inc.; *Int'l*, pg. 1550
SHENZHEN COSON TECHNOLOGY CO., LTD.—See China Security Co., Ltd.; *Int'l*, pg. 1550
SHENZHEN COTRAN NEW MATERIAL CO., LTD.; *Int'l*, pg. 6807
SHENZHEN CRASTAL TECHNOLOGY CO., LTD.; *Int'l*, pg. 6807
SHENZHEN CYBER-HARBOUR NETWORK CO. LIMITED—See China Merchants Group Limited; *Int'l*, pg. 1521
SHENZHEN DANBOND TECHNOLOGY CO., LTD.; *Int'l*, pg. 6807
SHENZHEN DASH FINANCIAL LEASING CO., LTD.—See Shenzhen DAS Intellitech Co., Ltd.; *Int'l*, pg. 6807
SHENZHEN DASHI INTERNET OF THINGS TECHNOLOGY CO., LTD.—See Shenzhen DAS Intellitech Co., Ltd.; *Int'l*, pg. 6807
SHENZHEN DAS INTELLITECH CO., LTD.; *Int'l*, pg. 6807
SHENZHEN DAWEI INNOVATION TECHNOLOGY CO., LTD.; *Int'l*, pg. 6807
SHENZHEN DEREN ELECTRONIC CO., LTD.; *Int'l*, pg. 6807
SHENZHEN DEREN OPTICS CO., LTD.—See Shenzhen Deren Electronic Co., Ltd.; *Int'l*, pg. 6808
SHENZHEN DE RUN LI JIA COMPANY LIMITED—See Yestar Healthcare Holdings Company Limited; *Int'l*, pg. 8578
SHENZHEN DESAY BATTERY TECHNOLOGY CO., LTD.; *Int'l*, pg. 6808
SHENZHEN DIC CHEMICALS CO., LTD.—See DIC Corporation; *Int'l*, pg. 2109
SHENZHEN-DIC CO., LTD.—See DIC Corporation; *Int'l*, pg. 2109
SHENZHEN DINGWO AUTOMOBILE SALES SERVICES CO., LTD.—See China ZhengTong Auto Services Holdings Limited; *Int'l*, pg. 1567
SHENZHEN DIWEIXUN CO., LTD.; *Int'l*, pg. 6808
SHENZHEN DONG DI XIN TECHNOLOGY COMPANY LIMITED—See Kingworld Medicines Group Limited; *Int'l*, pg. 4180
SHENZHEN DYNANONIC CO., LTD.; *Int'l*, pg. 6808
SHENZHEN DYNA PRECAST CONCRETE PRODUCTS CO., LIMITED—See Golik Holdings Limited; *Int'l*, pg. 3036
SHENZHEN EASTTOP SUPPLY CHAIN MANAGEMENT CO., LTD.; *Int'l*, pg. 6808
SHENZHEN ECOBEAUTY CO., LTD.; *Int'l*, pg. 6808
SHENZHEN EDADOC TECHNOLOGY CO., LTD.; *Int'l*, pg. 6808
SHENZHEN ELCOM TRADING CO. LTD.—See Phoenix Mecano AG; *Int'l*, pg. 5853
SHENZHEN ELECTRONIC COMMODITY TRADING CENTER CO., LTD.—See Shenzhen Huaqiang Industry Co., Ltd.; *Int'l*, pg. 6812
SHENZHEN ELLASSAY FASHION CO., LTD.; *Int'l*, pg. 6808
SHENZHEN EMBEST TECHNOLOGY CO., LTD.—See Avnet, Inc.; *U.S. Public*, pg. 254
SHENZHEN EMPEROR TECHNOLOGY CO., LTD. - SHENZHEN PLANT—See Shenzhen Emperor Technology Co., Ltd.; *Int'l*, pg. 6808
SHENZHEN EMPEROR TECHNOLOGY CO., LTD.; *Int'l*, pg. 6808
SHENZHEN ENERGY ELECTRICITY SALE COMPANY—See Shenzhen Energy Group Co., Ltd.; *Int'l*, pg. 6808
SHENZHEN ENERGY ENVIRONMENT ENGINEERING CO., LTD.—See Shenzhen Energy Group Co., Ltd.; *Int'l*, pg. 6809
SHENZHEN ENERGY FINANCE CO., LTD.—See Shenzhen Energy Group Co., Ltd.; *Int'l*, pg. 6809
SHENZHEN ENERGY GROUP CO., LTD.; *Int'l*, pg. 6808
SHENZHEN ENERGY HOPEWELL POWER (HEYUAN) CO., LTD.—See Shenzhen Energy Group Co., Ltd.; *Int'l*, pg. 6809
SHENZHEN ENERGY KORLA POWER GENERATION CO., LTD.—See Shenzhen Energy Group Co., Ltd.; *Int'l*, pg. 6809
SHENZHEN ENERGY NANJING HOLDING CO., LTD.—See Shenzhen Energy Group Co., Ltd.; *Int'l*, pg. 6809
SHENZHEN ENERGY NORTH HOLDINGS CO., LTD.—See Shenzhen Energy Group Co., Ltd.; *Int'l*, pg. 6809
SHENZHEN ENERGY POWER SERVICE CO., LTD.—See Shenzhen Energy Group Co., Ltd.; *Int'l*, pg. 6809

SHENZHEN ENERGY RESOURCE COMPREHENSIVE DEVELOPMENT CO., LTD.—See Shenzhen Energy Group Co., Ltd.; *Int'l*, pg. 6809
SHENZHEN ENERGY TRANSPORTATION CO., LTD.—See Shenzhen Energy Group Co., Ltd.; *Int'l*, pg. 6809
SHENZHEN ENVICOOL TECHNOLOGY CO., LTD; *Int'l*, pg. 6809
SHENZHEN ESUN DISPLAY CO., LTD.; *Int'l*, pg. 6809
SHENZHEN ETMADE AUTOMATIC EQUIPMENT CO., LTD.; *Int'l*, pg. 6809
SHENZHEN EVERWIN PRECISION TECHNOLOGY CO., LTD.; *Int'l*, pg. 6809
SHENZHEN EXC-LED TECHNOLOGY CO., LTD.; *Int'l*, pg. 6809
SHENZHEN EXPRESSWAY COMPANY LIMITED—See Shenzhen International Holdings Limited; *Int'l*, pg. 6813
SHENZHEN FARBEN INFORMATION TECHNOLOGY CO., LTD.; *Int'l*, pg. 6809
SHENZHEN FASTPRINT CIRCUIT TECH CO., LTD.; *Int'l*, pg. 6809
SHENZHEN FAUN TEXTILES LIMITED—See Fountain Set (Holdings) Limited; *Int'l*, pg. 2754
SHENZHEN FEIMA INTERNATIONAL SUPPLY CHAIN CO., LTD.; *Int'l*, pg. 6809
SHENZHEN FENDA TECHNOLOGY CO., LTD.; *Int'l*, pg. 6809
SHENZHEN FINE MADE ELECTRONICS GROUP CO., LTD.; *Int'l*, pg. 6810
SHENZHEN FLUENCE TECHNOLOGY PLC; *Int'l*, pg. 6810
SHENZHEN FLYKEY ELECTRONICS TECHNOLOGY CO., LTD.—See P-Duke Technology Co., Ltd.; *Int'l*, pg. 5681
SHENZHEN FORMS SYNTRON INFORMATION CO., LTD.; *Int'l*, pg. 6810
SHENZHEN FORTUNE TREND TECHNOLOGY CO., LTD.; *Int'l*, pg. 6810
SHENZHEN FOUNTAIN CORPORATION; *Int'l*, pg. 6810
SHENZHEN FRD SCIENCE & TECHNOLOGY CO., LTD.; *Int'l*, pg. 6810
SHENZHEN FRIENDCOM TECHNOLOGY DEVELOPMENT CO., LTD.; *Int'l*, pg. 6810
SHENZHEN FUANNA BEDDING & FURNISHING CO., LTD.; *Int'l*, pg. 6810
SHENZHEN FUDAKIN PLASTIC & METAL LTD.; *Int'l*, pg. 6810
SHENZHEN FUDAN MICROELECTRONICS COMPANY LIMITED—See Shanghai Fudan Microelectronics Group Co., Ltd.; *Int'l*, pg. 6768
SHENZHEN FUQI JEWELRY CO., LTD.—See Fuqi International, Inc.; *Int'l*, pg. 2846
SHENZHEN FUTABA METAL PRODUCTS CO., LTD.—See Futaba Industrial Co., Ltd.; *Int'l*, pg. 2851
SHENZHEN GAS CORPORATION LTD.; *Int'l*, pg. 6810
SHENZHEN GEMVARY TECHNOLOGY CO., LTD.—See Guangdong Kinlong Hardware Prdcts Co., Ltd.; *Int'l*, pg. 3157
SHENZHEN GENIUS INFORMATION TECHNOLOGY CO., LTD.—See China Finance Online Co. Limited; *Int'l*, pg. 1502
SHENZHEN GENVICT TECHNOLOGIES CO., LTD.; *Int'l*, pg. 6810
SHENZHEN GIANT ALBERT TECHNOLOGY CO., LTD.—See Xuzhou Handler Special Vehicle Co., Ltd.; *Int'l*, pg. 8541
SHENZHEN GIANTPLUS OPTOELECTRONICS DISPLAY CO., LTD.—See TOPPAN Holdings Inc.; *Int'l*, pg. 7817
SHENZHEN GIFT INTENATIONAL GREETINGS COMPANY LTD—See IG Design Group Plc; *Int'l*, pg. 3601
SHENZHEN GLOBAL DIGITAL CREATIONS TECHNOLOGY LIMITED—See Global Digital Creations Holdings Limited; *Int'l*, pg. 2994
SHENZHEN GLORY MEDICAL CO., LTD.; *Int'l*, pg. 6810
SHENZHEN GOLDEN OCEAN CULTURE & CREATIVE CO., LTD.—See MYS Group Co., Ltd.; *Int'l*, pg. 5114
SHENZHEN GOLDWAY INDUSTRIAL INC.—See Koninklijke Philips N.V.; *Int'l*, pg. 4271
SHENZHEN GONGJIN ELECTRONICS CO., LTD.; *Int'l*, pg. 6810
SHENZHEN GOODIX TECHNOLOGY CO., LTD.; *Int'l*, pg. 6810
SHENZHEN GRANDLAND CURTAIN WALL CO., LTD.—See Shenzhen Grandland Group Co., Ltd.; *Int'l*, pg. 6811
SHENZHEN GRANDLAND DECORATION GROUP CORP. LTD - THE 5TH DIVISION—See Shenzhen Grandland Group Co., Ltd.; *Int'l*, pg. 6811
SHENZHEN GRANDLAND FANGTE FACADE TECHNOLOGY CO., LTD.—See Shenzhen Grandland Group Co., Ltd.; *Int'l*, pg. 6811
SHENZHEN GRANDLAND GROUP CO., LTD.; *Int'l*, pg. 6811
SHENZHEN GRANDLAND HI-TECH NEW MATERIALS CO., LTD.—See Shenzhen Grandland Group Co., Ltd.; *Int'l*, pg. 6811
SHENZHEN GRANDLAND INTELLIGENT TECHNOLOGY CO., LTD.—See Shenzhen Grandland Group Co., Ltd.; *Int'l*, pg. 6811

SHENZHEN GRANDLAND SOFT DECORATION ART CO., LTD.—See Shenzhen Grandland Group Co., Ltd.; *Int'l*, pg. 6811
SHENZHEN GREENTRANS TRANSPORTATION CO., LTD.—See Evergreen Marine Corporation (Taiwan) Ltd.; *Int'l*, pg. 2567
SHENZHEN GRENTECH CO., LTD.—See China GrenTech Corporation Limited; *Int'l*, pg. 1506
SHENZHEN GUANGJU ENERGY CO., LTD.; *Int'l*, pg. 6811
SHENZHEN GUANGSHEN SHAJIAO B POWER CO., LTD.—See Shenzhen Energy Group Co., Ltd.; *Int'l*, pg. 6809
SHENZHEN GUOHUA NETWORK SECURITY TECHNOLOGY CO., LTD.; *Int'l*, pg. 6811
SHENZHEN HAIBIN PHARMACEUTICAL CO., LTD—See Joincare Pharmaceutical Industry Group Co., Ltd; *Int'l*, pg. 3995
SHENZHEN HAILIANG STORAGE PRODUCTS CO., LTD.—See Western Digital Corporation; *U.S. Public*, pg. 2355
SHENZHEN HAN'S CNC TECHNOLOGY CO., LTD.; *Int'l*, pg. 6811
SHENZHEN HAOEN SAFETY TECHNOLOGY CO., LTD.—See China Security Co., Ltd.; *Int'l*, pg. 1550
SHENZHEN HEIDELBERG NETWORX TECHNOLOGY CO., LTD.—See Heidelberger Druckmaschinen AG; *Int'l*, pg. 3322
SHENZHEN HEKEDA PRECISION CLEANING EQUIPMENT CO., LTD.; *Int'l*, pg. 6811
SHENZHEN HEKEDA WATER TREATMENT EQUIPMENT CO., LTD.—See Shenzhen Hekeda Precision Cleaning Equipment Co., Ltd.; *Int'l*, pg. 6811
SHENZHEN HELLO TECH ENERGY CO., LTD.; *Int'l*, pg. 6811
SHENZHEN HEMEI GROUP CO., LTD.; *Int'l*, pg. 6811
SHENZHEN HENGHE XINGAO MACHINERY & ELECTRONICS CO., LTD.—See Ningbo Henghe Precision Industry Co., Ltd.; *Int'l*, pg. 5302
SHENZHEN HENGMINGDA NEW TECHNOLOGY RESEARCH INSTITUTE CO., LTD.—See Suzhou Hengmingda Electronic Technology Co., Ltd.; *Int'l*, pg. 7350
SHENZHEN HEPALINK PHARMACEUTICAL GROUP CO., LTD.; *Int'l*, pg. 6811
SHENZHEN HEUNGKONG HOLDING CO., LTD.; *Int'l*, pg. 6812
SHENZHEN HIFUTURE INFORMATION TECHNOLOGY CO., LTD.; *Int'l*, pg. 6812
SHENZHEN HIGH FLYER INTERNATIONAL TRANSPORTATION COMPANY LIMITED—See Samson Paper Holdings Limited; *Int'l*, pg. 6509
SHENZHEN HIGHPOWER TECHNOLOGY CO., LTD.—See Highpower International, Inc.; *Int'l*, pg. 3388
SHENZHEN HIRISUN TECHNOLOGY INC.; *Int'l*, pg. 6812
SHENZHEN HOLIDE INDUSTRY DEVELOPMENT CO., LTD.; *Int'l*, pg. 6812
SHENZHEN HONGFUHAN TECHNOLOGY CO., LTD.; *Int'l*, pg. 6812
SHENZHEN HONGLIN COMMUNICATION TECHNOLOGY CO., LTD.—See InvesTech Holdings Limited; *Int'l*, pg. 3778
SHENZHEN HONGTAO GROUP CO.,LTD.; *Int'l*, pg. 6812
SHENZHEN HONOR ELECTRONIC CO., LTD.; *Int'l*, pg. 6812
SHENZHEN HOPEWIND ELECTRIC CO., LTD.; *Int'l*, pg. 6812
SHENZHEN H&T INTELLIGENT CONTROL CO., LTD. - FACTORY—See Shenzhen H&T Intelligent Control Co., Ltd.; *Int'l*, pg. 6811
SHENZHEN H&T INTELLIGENT CONTROL CO., LTD.; *Int'l*, pg. 6811
SHENZHEN HUACHANG INDUSTRIAL CO., LTD.—See China Boton Group Company Limited; *Int'l*, pg. 1487
SHENZHEN HUAKONG SEG CO., LTD.—See Shenzhen SEG Group Co., Ltd.; *Int'l*, pg. 6820
SHENZHEN HUALI PACKING & TRADING CO., LTD.—See Overseas Chinese Town (Asia) Holdings Limited; *Int'l*, pg. 5672
SHENZHEN HUALITONG INVESTMENT CO., LTD.—See Shenzhen Baoneng Investment Group Co., Ltd.; *Int'l*, pg. 6805
SHENZHEN HUANGHE DIGITAL TECHNOLOGY CO. LTD—See Cantronic Systems Inc.; *Int'l*, pg. 1300
SHENZHEN HUAQIANG CHINA ELECTRONIC MARKET PRICE INDEX CO., LTD.—See Shenzhen Huaqiang Industry Co., Ltd.; *Int'l*, pg. 6812
SHENZHEN HUAQIANG ELECTRONIC COMMERCE CO., LTD.—See Shenzhen Huaqiang Industry Co., Ltd.; *Int'l*, pg. 6812
SHENZHEN HUAQIANG ELECTRONIC TRADING NETWORK CO., LTD.—See Shenzhen Huaqiang Industry Co., Ltd.; *Int'l*, pg. 6812
SHENZHEN HUAQIANG ELECTRONIC TRADING NETWORKS CO., LTD.—See Shenzhen Huaqiang Industry Co., Ltd.; *Int'l*, pg. 6812
SHENZHEN HUAQIANG ELECTRONIC WORLD MANAGEMENT CO., LTD.—See Shenzhen Huaqiang Industry Co., Ltd.; *Int'l*, pg. 6812

SHENZHEN HUAQIANG INDUSTRY CO., LTD.
CORPORATE AFFILIATIONS

SHENZHEN HUAQIANG INDUSTRY CO., LTD.; *Int'l*, pg. 6812

SHENZHEN HUAQIANG NORTH ELECTRONIC MARKET PRICE INDEX CO., LTD.—See Shenzhen Huaqiang Industry Co., Ltd.; *Int'l*, pg. 6812

SHENZHEN HUAQIANG SANYO TECHNOLOGY DESIGN CO., LTD.—See Panasonic Holdings Corporation; *Int'l*, pg. 5725

SHENZHEN HUAQIANG SQUARE HOLDING CO., LTD.—See Shenzhen Huaqiang Industry Co., Ltd.; *Int'l*, pg. 6812

SHENZHEN HUASHUNBAO AUTOMOBILE SALES SERVICES CO., LTD.—See China ZhengTong Auto Services Holdings Limited; *Int'l*, pg. 1567

SHENZHEN HUASHUNBAO AUTOMOBILE SERVICES CO., LTD.—See China ZhengTong Auto Services Holdings Limited; *Int'l*, pg. 1567

SHENZHEN HUATE PACKING CO., LTD.—See NORINCO International Cooperation Ltd.; *Int'l*, pg. 5427

SHENZHEN HUATE PACKING CO., LTD. - TIN-PLATE CUTTING DIVISION—See NORINCO International Cooperation Ltd.; *Int'l*, pg. 5427

SHENZHEN HUAXING OPTOELECTRONIC TECHNOLOGY CO., LTD.—See TCL Technology Group Corp.; *Int'l*, pg. 7483

SHENZHEN HUAYANGTONG ELECTROMECHANICAL CO., LTD.—See Suzhou Hengmingda Electronic Technology Co., Ltd.; *Int'l*, pg. 7350

SHENZHEN HUI CHUANG DA TECHNOLOGY CO., LTD.; *Int'l*, pg. 6812

SHENZHEN HUIJIE GROUP CO., LTD.; *Int'l*, pg. 6812

SHENZHEN HUTCHISON WHAMPOA CATIC PROPERTIES LIMITED—See CK Asset Holdings Limited; *Int'l*, pg. 1635

SHENZHEN HW AUTOMATION EQUIPMENT CO., LTD.—See CSG Smart Science & Technology Co., Ltd.; *Int'l*, pg. 1865

SHENZHEN HYAN MICROELECTRONICS CO., LTD.—See Anhui Tatfook Technology Co., Ltd; *Int'l*, pg. 469

SHENZHEN IDREAMSKY TECHNOLOGY CO., LTD.; *Int'l*, pg. 6812

SHENZHEN IMAGE ENGINEERING CO., LTD.—See Nynomic AG; *Int'l*, pg. 5501

SHENZHEN INCREASE TECHNOLOGY CO., LTD.; *Int'l*, pg. 6813

SHENZHEN IN-CUBE AUTOMATION CO., LTD.; *Int'l*, pg. 6813

SHENZHEN INFINOVA CO., LTD.; *Int'l*, pg. 6813

SHENZHEN INFOGEM TECHNOLOGIES CO., LTD.; *Int'l*, pg. 6813

SHENZHEN INOVANCE TECHNOLOGY CO., LTD.; *Int'l*, pg. 6813

SHENZHEN INSTITUTE OF BUILDING RESEARCH CO., LTD.; *Int'l*, pg. 6813

SHENZHEN INTERNATIONAL HOLDINGS LIMITED; *Int'l*, pg. 6813

SHENZHEN INTERNATIONAL MODERN LOGISTICS MICROFINANCE CO., LTD.—See Shenzhen International Holdings Limited; *Int'l*, pg. 6813

SHENZHEN INTERNATIONAL WEST LOGISTICS CO., LTD.—See Shenzhen International Holdings Limited; *Int'l*, pg. 6813

SHENZHEN INVESTMENT HOLDINGS BAY AREA DEVELOPMENT COMPANY LIMITED—See Shenzhen Investment Limited; *Int'l*, pg. 6813

SHENZHEN INVESTMENT LIMITED; *Int'l*, pg. 6813

SHENZHEN INVT ELECTRIC CO., LTD.; *Int'l*, pg. 6813

SHENZHEN JAME TECHNOLOGY CORP., LTD.; *Int'l*, pg. 6814

SHENZHEN JASIC TECHNOLOGY CO., LTD.; *Int'l*, pg. 6814

SHENZHEN JDI INC.—See Japan Display Inc.; *Int'l*, pg. 3887

SHENZHEN JIANG & ASSOCIATES CREATIVE DESIGN CO., LTD.; *Int'l*, pg. 6814

SHENZHEN JIANYI DECORATION GROUP CO., LTD.; *Int'l*, pg. 6814

SHENZHEN JIEDE INNOVATION TECHNOLOGY CO., LTD.—See Suzhou Alton Electrical & Mechanical Industry Co., Ltd.; *Int'l*, pg. 7348

SHENZHEN JIESHUN SCIENCE & TECHNOLOGY INDUSTRY CO., LTD.; *Int'l*, pg. 6814

SHENZHEN JIEXUNTENG PRECISION ELECTRONIC SCIENCE & TECHNOLOGY CO., LTD.—See Zhejiang Yonggui Electric Equipment Co., Ltd.; *Int'l*, pg. 8667

SHENZHEN JINGHUA DISPLAYS CO., LTD.—See Shenzhen Investment Limited; *Int'l*, pg. 6813

SHENZHEN JINGQUANHUA ELECTRONICS CO., LTD.; *Int'l*, pg. 6814

SHENZHEN JINGZHOU PRECISION TECHNOLOGY CORP.—See Shenzhen Zhongjin Lingnan Nonfemet Co., Ltd.; *Int'l*, pg. 6825

SHENZHEN JINHANG INDUSTRY CO., LTD.—See Aiphone Co., Ltd.; *Int'l*, pg. 235

SHENZHEN JINJIA GROUP CO., LTD.; *Int'l*, pg. 6814

SHENZHEN JINJIA TECHNOLOGY CO., LTD.—See Shenzhen Jinjia Group Co., Ltd.; *Int'l*, pg. 6814

SHENZHEN JINXINNONG TECHNOLOGY CO., LTD.; *Int'l*, pg. 6814

SHENZHEN JIYIN TECHNOLOGY CO., LTD.; *Int'l*, pg. 6814

SHENZHEN JOVE ENTERPRISE LIMITED; *Int'l*, pg. 6814

SHENZHEN JPT OPTO-ELECTRONICS CO., LTD.; *Int'l*, pg. 6814

SHENZHEN JT AUTOMATION EQUIPMENT COMPANY LIMITED; *Int'l*, pg. 6815

SHENZHEN JUFEI OPTOELECTRONICS CO., LTD.; *Int'l*, pg. 6815

SHENZHEN JUNTIAN HENGXUN TECHNOLOGY CO., LTD.—See Bomin Electronics Co., Ltd.; *Int'l*, pg. 1105

SHENZHEN JUTAL MACHINERY EQUIPMENT CO., LTD.—See Jutal Offshore Oil Services Limited; *Int'l*, pg. 4031

SHENZHEN KAFIA MAGNETIC RECORDING CO., LTD.—See China Electronics Corporation; *Int'l*, pg. 1499

SHENZHEN KAIFA TECHNOLOGY CO., LTD.—See China Electronics Corporation; *Int'l*, pg. 1499

SHENZHEN KAIZHONG PRECISION TECHNOLOGY CO., LTD.; *Int'l*, pg. 6815

SHENZHEN KANGTAI BIOLOGICAL PRODUCTS CO., LTD.; *Int'l*, pg. 6815

SHENZHEN KATOP AUTOMATION TECHNOLOGY CO., LTD.—See Shanghai Putailai New Energy Technology Co., Ltd.; *Int'l*, pg. 6777

SHENZHEN KBF LASER TECH CO., LTD.—See El.En. S.p.A.; *Int'l*, pg. 2342

SHENZHEN KEANDA ELECTRONIC TECHNOLOGY CORP., LTD.; *Int'l*, pg. 6815

SHENZHEN KEANDA RAIL TRANSIT TECHNOLOGY CO., LTD.—See Shenzhen Keanda Electronic Technology Corp., Ltd.; *Int'l*, pg. 6815

SHENZHEN KEANDA SOFTWARE CO., LTD.—See Shenzhen Keanda Electronic Technology Corp., Ltd.; *Int'l*, pg. 6815

SHENZHEN KEANDA TESTING TECHNOLOGH CO., LTD.—See Shenzhen Keanda Electronic Technology Corp., Ltd.; *Int'l*, pg. 6815

SHENZHEN KEANDA TRACK EQUIPMENT CO., LTD.—See Shenzhen Keanda Electronic Technology Corp., Ltd.; *Int'l*, pg. 6815

SHENZHEN KECAI PRINTING CO., LTD.—See Litu Holdings Limited; *Int'l*, pg. 4528

SHENZHEN KEDALI INDUSTRY CO., LTD.; *Int'l*, pg. 6815

SHENZHEN KEHUA TECHNOLOGY CO., LTD.—See Kehua Data Co., Ltd.; *Int'l*, pg. 4116

SHENZHEN KENNETH KO DESIGNS LTD.—See Shenzhen Bauing Construction Group Co., Ltd.; *Int'l*, pg. 6805

SHENZHEN KESONG TECHNOLOGY CO., LTD.—See China Security Co., Ltd.; *Int'l*, pg. 1550

SHENZHEN KEXIN COMMUNICATION TECHNOLOGIES CO., LTD.; *Int'l*, pg. 6815

SHENZHEN KEXING PHARMACEUTICAL CO., LTD.—See Shan Dong Kexing Bioproducts Co., Ltd.; *Int'l*, pg. 6751

SHENZHEN KEYBRIDGE HUANENG COMMUNICATION TECHNOLOGY CO., LTD.—See Shenzhen Asia Link Technology Development Co., Ltd.; *Int'l*, pg. 6804

SHENZHEN KING BROTHER ELECTRONICS TECHNOLOGY CO.; *Int'l*, pg. 6815

SHENZHEN KINGDEE MIDDLEWARE CO., LTD.—See Kingdee International Software Group Company Ltd.; *Int'l*, pg. 4172

SHENZHEN KINGDOM SCI-TECH CO., LTD.; *Int'l*, pg. 6816

SHENZHEN KING EXPLORER SCIENCE & TECHNOLOGY CORPORATION; *Int'l*, pg. 6816

SHENZHEN KING FACADE DECORATION ENGINEERING CO., LTD.—See Shenzhen Zhongjin Lingnan Nonfemet Co., Ltd.; *Int'l*, pg. 6825

SHENZHEN KINGKEY SMART AGRICULTURE TIMES CO., LTD.; *Int'l*, pg. 6816

SHENZHEN KINGSUN SCIENCE & TECHNOLOGY CO., LTD.; *Int'l*, pg. 6816

SHENZHEN KIN LONG HBS INTELLIGENT TECHNOLOGY CO., LTD.—See Guangdong Kinlong Hardware Prdcts Co., Ltd.; *Int'l*, pg. 3157

SHENZHEN KINWONG ELECTRONIC CO., LTD.; *Int'l*, pg. 6816

SHENZHEN KSTAR SCIENCE AND TECHNOLOGY CO., LTD.; *Int'l*, pg. 6816

SHENZHEN K+S TRADING CO. LTD—See K+S Aktiengesellschaft; *Int'l*, pg. 4041

SHENZHEN KTC TECHNOLOGY CO., LTD.; *Int'l*, pg. 6816

SHENZHEN KWANG SUNG ELECTRONICS CO., LTD.—See Times Universal Group Holdings Limited; *Int'l*, pg. 7752

SHENZHEN KWAN WING TRADING COMPANY LIMITED—See Deswell Industries, Inc.; *Int'l*, pg. 2047

SHENZHEN L & A DESIGN HOLDING LIMITED; *Int'l*, pg. 6816

SHENZHEN LAIBAO HI-TECH CO., LTD.; *Int'l*, pg. 6816

SHENZHEN LEADWELL TECHNOLOGY CO. LTD.—See L.K. Technology Holdings Limited; *Int'l*, pg. 4386

SHENZHEN LEAGUER CO., LTD.; *Int'l*, pg. 6816

SHENZHEN LEOCH BATTERY TECHNOLOGY CO., LTD.—See Leoch International Technology Limited; *Int'l*, pg. 4457

SHENZHEN LEXEL BATTERY CO., LTD.—See Coslight Technology International Group Limited; *Int'l*, pg. 1810

SHENZHEN LEYARD OPTO-ELECTRONIC CO., LTD.—See Leyard Optoelectronic Co., Ltd.; *Int'l*, pg. 4472

SHENZHEN LIANDE AUTOMATION EQUIPMENT CO., LTD.; *Int'l*, pg. 6816

SHENZHEN LIANHENG TECHNOLOGY CO., LTD.—See Wuhan Yangtze Communications Industry Group Co.; *Int'l*, pg. 8501

SHENZHEN LIANSHUO AUTOMATION TECHNOLOGY CO., LTD.; *Int'l*, pg. 6816

SHENZHEN LIANTRONICS CO., LTD.; *Int'l*, pg. 6816

SHENZHEN LIANTRONICS LLC—See Shenzhen Liantronics Co., Ltd.; *Int'l*, pg. 6816

SHENZHEN LIFOTRONIC TECHNOLOGY CO., LTD.; *Int'l*, pg. 6816

SHENZHEN LIHEXING CO., LTD.; *Int'l*, pg. 6817

SHENZHEN LINGTAO OPTOELECTRONICS CO., LTD.—See Shenzhen Refond Optoelectronics Co. Ltd.; *Int'l*, pg. 6820

SHENZHEN LINGYANG GLOBAL FORWARDING CO., LTD.—See Mitsubishi Logistics Corporation; *Int'l*, pg. 4963

SHENZHEN LONGDIAN SCIENCE TECHNOLOGY INDUSTRIAL CO., LTD.—See ASSA ABLOY AB; *Int'l*, pg. 640

SHENZHEN LONGHORN SECURITY TECHNOLOGY CO., LTD.—See China Security & Surveillance Technology, Inc.; *Int'l*, pg. 1550

SHENZHEN LONGLI OPTOELECTRONICS TECHNOLOGY DEVELOPMENT CO., LTD.—See Shenzhen Longli Technology Co., Ltd.; *Int'l*, pg. 6817

SHENZHEN LONGLI TECHNOLOGY CO., LTD.; *Int'l*, pg. 6817

SHENZHEN LONGOOD INTELLIGENT ELECTRIC CO., LTD.; *Int'l*, pg. 6817

SHENZHEN LONGSYS ELECTRONICS COMPANY LIMITED; *Int'l*, pg. 6817

SHENZHEN LONGTECH SMART CONTROL CO., LTD.; *Int'l*, pg. 6817

SHENZHEN LVGEM HOTEL CO., LTD.—See LVGEM (China) Real Estate Investment Company Limited; *Int'l*, pg. 4590

SHENZHEN MAGIC DESIGN AND DECORATION ENGINEERING CO., LTD.; *Int'l*, pg. 6817

SHENZHEN MAIN LUCK PHARMACEUTICALS INC.—See Mitsui & Co., Ltd.; *Int'l*, pg. 4974

SHENZHEN MALIMALIBOX TRADING CORPORATION LIMITED—See Eastern Holding Limited; *Int'l*, pg. 2272

SHENZHEN MAOYE DEPARTMENT STORE SHENNAN CO., LTD.—See Maoye International Holding Limited; *Int'l*, pg. 4681

SHENZHEN MARINE DIVING ENGINEERING CO., LTD.—See Jutal Offshore Oil Services Limited; *Int'l*, pg. 4031

SHEN ZHEN MARSA PACIFIC CHAIN ENTERPRISE LIMITED—See Pacific Healthcare Holdings Ltd.; *Int'l*, pg. 5689

SHENZHEN MARY PHOTOELECTRICITY CO., LTD.—See Fujian Furi Electronics Co., Ltd.; *Int'l*, pg. 2818

SHENZHEN MASON TECHNOLOGIES CO., LTD.; *Int'l*, pg. 6817

SHENZHEN MASS POWER ELECTRONIC CO. LTD.; *Int'l*, pg. 6817

SHENZHEN MATCHLESS FOOD CO., LTD—See Four Seas Mercantile Holdings Limited; *Int'l*, pg. 2755

SHENZHEN MAXONIC AUTOMATION CONTROL CO., LTD.; *Int'l*, pg. 6817

SHENZHEN MEGMEET CONTROL TECHNOLOGY CO., LTD.—See Shenzhen Megmeet Electrical Co.,Ltd; *Int'l*, pg. 6817

SHENZHEN MEGMEET ELECTRICAL CO.,LTD; *Int'l*, pg. 6817

SHENZHEN MEGMEET ENERGY TECHNOLOGY CO., LTD.—See Shenzhen Megmeet Electrical Co.,Ltd; *Int'l*, pg. 6817

SHENZHEN MEGMEET WELDING TECHNOLOGY CO., LTD.—See Shenzhen Megmeet Electrical Co.,Ltd; *Int'l*, pg. 6817

SHENZHEN MICRO-DREAM NETWORK TECHNOLOGY CO., LTD.—See Xiamen Anne Corporation Limited; *Int'l*, pg. 8523

SHENZHEN MICROGATE TECHNOLOGY CO. LTD.; *Int'l*, pg. 6818

SHENZHEN MINDE ELECTRONICS TECHNOLOGY LTD.; *Int'l*, pg. 6818

SHENZHEN MINDRAY BIO-MEDICAL ELECTRONICS CO. LTD—See Mindray Medical International Ltd.; *Int'l*, pg. 4902

SHENZHEN MINGDIAO DECORATION CO., LTD.; *Int'l*, pg. 6818

SHENZHEN MINGLIDA PRECISION TECHNOLOGY CO., LTD.; *Int'l*, pg. 6818

COMPANY NAME INDEX — SHENZHEN TELLUS HOLDING CO., LTD.

SHENZHEN MINGWAH AOHAN HIGH TECHNOLOGY CORPORATION LIMITED; *Int'l*, pg. 6818
SHENZHEN MINKAVE TECHNOLOGY CO., LTD.; *Int'l*, pg. 6818
SHENZHEN MOSO POWER SUPPLY TECHNOLOGY CO., LTD.; *Int'l*, pg. 6818
SHENZHEN MTC CO., LTD.; *Int'l*, pg. 6818
SHENZHEN MTC OPTRONICS CO., LTD.—See Shenzhen MTC Co., Ltd.; *Int'l*, pg. 6818
SHENZHEN MUNICPAL ENGINEERING CONSULTING CENTER CO., LTD.—See Shenzhen Institute of Building Research Co., Ltd.; *Int'l*, pg. 6813
SHENZHEN MURATA TECHNOLOGY CO., LTD.—See Murata Manufacturing Co., Ltd.; *Int'l*, pg. 5098
SHENZHEN NANPU INDUSTRIAL CO., LTD.—See Tenwow International Holdings Limited; *Int'l*, pg. 7562
SHENZHEN NANSHAN POWER CO., LTD.; *Int'l*, pg. 6818
SHENZHEN NANTIAN DONGHUA TECHNOLOGY CO., LTD.—See Yunnan Nantian Electronics Information Co., Ltd.; *Int'l*, pg. 8616
SHENZHEN NATIONAL ENGINEERING RESEARCH CENTER OF ADVANCED ENERGY STORAGE MATERIAL CO., LTD.—See Hunan Corun New Energy Co., Ltd.; *Int'l*, pg. 3531
SHENZHEN NEOWAY TECHNOLOGY CO., LTD.; *Int'l*, pg. 6818
SHENZHEN NEPSTAR CHAIN CO., LTD.—See China Nepstar Chain Drugstore Ltd.; *Int'l*, pg. 1534
SHENZHEN NEPTUNUS BIOENGINEERING CO., LTD.; *Int'l*, pg. 6818
SHENZHEN NEPTUNUS INTERLONG BIO-TECHNIQUE CO., LTD.—See Shenzhen Neptunus Bioengineering Co., Ltd.; *Int'l*, pg. 6818
SHENZHEN NEW INDUSTRIES BIOMEDICAL ENGINEERING CO., LTD.; *Int'l*, pg. 6818
SHENZHEN NEW LAND TOOL PLANNING & ARCHITECTURAL DESIGN CO., LTD.; *Int'l*, pg. 6818
SHENZHEN NEW NANSHAN HOLDING GROUP CO., LTD.; *Int'l*, pg. 6819
SHENZHEN NEWTOUCH SOFTWARE CO., LTD.—See Shanghai Newtouch Software Co., Ltd.; *Int'l*, pg. 6776
SHENZHEN NINEFOLD CONSTRUCTION GROUP CO., LTD—See Shenzhen Bauing Construction Group Co., Ltd.; *Int'l*, pg. 6805
SHENZHEN NITTO OPTICAL CO., LTD.—See Nitto Denko Corporation; *Int'l*, pg. 5387
SHENZHEN NONFEMET HI-POWER BATTERY MATERIAL CO., LTD.—See Shenzhen Zhongjin Lingnan Nonfemet Co., Ltd.; *Int'l*, pg. 6825
SHENZHEN NOPOSION CROP SCIENCE CO., LTD.; *Int'l*, pg. 6819
SHENZHEN NS STEEL CENTRE CO., LTD.—See Nippon Steel Corporation; *Int'l*, pg. 5339
SHENZHEN O-FILM TECH CO., LTD.; *Int'l*, pg. 6819
SHENZHEN OPWAY COMMUNICATION CO., LTD.—See Tongyu Communication Inc.; *Int'l*, pg. 7809
SHENZHEN OULUO FURNITURE COMPANY LIMITED—See Hing Lee (HK) Holdings Limited; *Int'l*, pg. 3401
SHENZHEN OVERLAND SUPPLY CHAIN MANAGEMENT CO., LTD.—See Yamato Holdings Co., Ltd.; *Int'l*, pg. 8554
SHENZHEN OVERSEAS CHINESE TOWN CO., LTD.; *Int'l*, pg. 6819
SHENZHEN PAGODA INDUSTRIAL (GROUP) CORPORATION LIMITED; *Int'l*, pg. 6819
SHENZHEN PCI CHUANGHUI INVESTMENT CO., LTD.—See PCI Technology Group Co., Ltd; *Int'l*, pg. 5768
SHENZHEN PHOENIX METROPOLIS MEDIA COMPANY LIMITED—See Phoenix Media Investment (Holdings) Limited; *Int'l*, pg. 5854
SHENZHEN PHOENIX TELECOM TECHNOLOGY CO.,LTD.; *Int'l*, pg. 6819
SHENZHEN POLY CULTURE PLAZA CO., LTD—See China Poly Group Corporation; *Int'l*, pg. 1541
SHENZHEN POLYFAIR CURTAINWALL TECHNOLOGY COMPANY LIMITED—See Polyfair Holdings Ltd.; *Int'l*, pg. 5915
SHENZHEN POSSEHL SEG ELECTRONICS CO., LTD.—See L. Possehl & Co. mbH; *Int'l*, pg. 4384
SHENZHEN PREVAIL TECHNOLOGY CO., LTD.; *Int'l*, pg. 6819
SHENZHEN PRINCE NEW MATERIALS CO., LTD; *Int'l*, pg. 6819
SHENZHEN PROLTO SUPPLY CHAIN MANAGEMENT CO., LTD.; *Int'l*, pg. 6819
SHENZHEN PROPERTIES & RESOURCES DEVELOPMENT (GROUP) LTD.; *Int'l*, pg. 6819
SHENZHEN PYROTEK INC.—See Pyrotek Incorporated; *U.S. Private*, pg. 3311
SHENZHEN QIANGRUI PRECISION TECHNOLOGY CO., LTD.; *Int'l*, pg. 6819
SHENZHEN QIANHAI BLUEBERRY CULTURE COMMUNICATION CO., LTD.—See Shenzhen Jinjia Group Co., Ltd.; *Int'l*, pg. 6814
SHENZHEN QIANHAI PROLTO E-BUSINESS INTEGRATED SERVICES CO., LTD.—See Shenzhen Prolto Supply Chain Management Co., Ltd.; *Int'l*, pg. 6819

SHENZHEN QINGYI PHOTOMASK LTD.; *Int'l*, pg. 6819
SHENZHEN QIXIN GROUP CO., LTD.; *Int'l*, pg. 6819
SHENZHEN QUANSINHAO CO., LTD.; *Int'l*, pg. 6819
SHENZHEN RAPID POWER CO., LTD.—See Waja Konsortium Berhad; *Int'l*, pg. 8331
SHENZHEN RAPID RESIN CO., LTD.—See Waja Konsortium Berhad; *Int'l*, pg. 8331
SHENZHEN RAPOO TECHNOLOGY CO., LTD.; *Int'l*, pg. 6819
SHENZHEN RAYITEK HI-TECH FILM CO., LTD.; *Int'l*, pg. 6820
SHENZHEN REFOND OPTOELECTRONICS CO. LTD.; *Int'l*, pg. 6820
SHENZHEN RIDGE ENGINEERING CONSULTING CO., LTD.; *Int'l*, pg. 6820
SHENZHEN RILAND INDUSTRY CO., LTD.; *Int'l*, pg. 6820
SHENZHEN RINGIER TRADE ADVERTISING LTD.—See Ringier Holding AG; *Int'l*, pg. 6344
SHENZHEN ROADROVER TECHNOLOGY CO.,LTD.—See Zoomlion Heavy Industry Science & Technology Co., Ltd.; *Int'l*, pg. 8690
SHENZHEN ROHDE & SCHWARZ TRADING CO., LTD.—See Rohde & Schwarz GmbH & Co. KG; *Int'l*, pg. 6385
SHENZHEN RONGDA PHOTOSENSITIVE SCIENCE & TECHNOLOGY CO., LTD.—See ShenZhen RongDa Photosensitive Science & Technology Co., Ltd.; *Int'l*, pg. 6820
SHENZHEN RONGDA PHOTOSENSITIVE SCIENCE & TECHNOLOGY CO., LTD.; *Int'l*, pg. 6820
SHENZHEN RUIHE CONSTRUCTION DECORATION CO., LTD.; *Int'l*, pg. 6820
SHENZHEN RUIJING INDUSTRIAL CO. LTD.—See CETC Acoustic-Optic-Electronic Technology Inc.; *Int'l*, pg. 1424
SHENZHEN RUIXING PRINTING COMPANY LTD.—See TOPPAN Holdings Inc.; *Int'l*, pg. 7817
SHENZHEN RUNLITE TECHNOLOGY CO., LTD.—See Fujian Furi Electronics Co., Ltd.; *Int'l*, pg. 2818
SHENZHEN SAKATA INX CO., LTD.—See Sakata INX Corporation; *Int'l*, pg. 6488
SHENZHEN SALUBRIS PHARMACEUTICALS CO., LTD.; *Int'l*, pg. 6820
SHENZHEN SANET ELECTRONIC CO., LTD.—See Shenzhen Huaqiang Industry Co., Ltd.; *Int'l*, pg. 6812
SHENZHEN SANHUI PRECISION HARDWARE CO., LTD.—See STG Co., Ltd.; *Int'l*, pg. 7213
SHENZHEN SANOFI PASTEUR BIOLOGICAL PRODUCTS CO. LTD—See Sanofi; *Int'l*, pg. 6552
SHENZHEN SANXIN FACADE ENGINEERING CO., LTD.—See Hainan Development Holdings Nanhai Co., Ltd.; *Int'l*, pg. 3212
SHENZHEN SANYO HUAQIANG ENERGY CO., LTD.—See Panasonic Holdings Corporation; *Int'l*, pg. 5725
SHENZHEN SANYO HUAQIANG OPTICAL TECHNOLOGY CO., LTD.—See Panasonic Holdings Corporation; *Int'l*, pg. 5725
SHENZHEN SATORI CO., LTD.—See SATORI ELECTRIC CO., LTD.; *Int'l*, pg. 6587
SHENZHEN SAVILLS PROPERTY CONSULTANCY LIMITED.—See Savills plc; *Int'l*, pg. 6598
SHENZHEN SCIPROGEN BIO-PHARMACEUTICAL CO., LTD.—See 3SBio Inc.; *Int'l*, pg. 9
SHENZHEN SDG INFORMATION CO., LTD.; *Int'l*, pg. 6820
SHENZHEN SDGI OPTICAL FIBER CO., LTD.—See Shenzhen SDG Information Co., Ltd.; *Int'l*, pg. 6820
SHENZHEN SDG SERVICE CO., LTD.; *Int'l*, pg. 6820
SHENZHEN SEA STAR TECHNOLOGY CO., LTD.; *Int'l*, pg. 6820
SHENZHEN SECURITIES INFORMATION CO., LTD.—See Shenzhen Stock Exchange; *Int'l*, pg. 6821
SHENZHEN SED INDUSTRY CO., LTD.; *Int'l*, pg. 6820
SHENZHEN SEG CO., LTD.—See Shenzhen SEG Group Co., Ltd.; *Int'l*, pg. 6820
SHENZHEN SEG GROUP CO., LTD.; *Int'l*, pg. 6820
SHENZHEN SEG HI-TECH INDUSTRIAL CO., LTD.—See Shenzhen SEG Group Co., Ltd.; *Int'l*, pg. 6820
SHENZHEN SEKONIC TECHNOLOGIES CO., LTD.—See Sekonic Corporation; *Int'l*, pg. 6698
SHENZHEN SELEN SCIENCE & TECHNOLOGY CO., LTD. - DONGGUAN DALINGSHAN FACTORY—See Xinlun New Materials Co., Ltd.; *Int'l*, pg. 8533
SHENZHEN SENIOR TECHNOLOGY MTRL CO LTD; *Int'l*, pg. 6821
SHENZHEN SHENGBIDA ELECTRICAL MATERIAL CO., LTD.—See SKion GmbH; *Int'l*, pg. 6987
SHENZHEN SHIJIA OPTICAL CABLE TECHNOLOGY CO., LTD.—See Henan Shijia Photons Technology Co., Ltd.; *Int'l*, pg. 3343
SHENZHEN SHUN ZHI TONG INTERNATIONAL LOGISTICS CO., LTD.—See Yamato Holdings Co., Ltd.; *Int'l*, pg. 8554
SHENZHEN SILVER BASIS TECHNOLOGY CO., LTD.; *Int'l*, pg. 6821
SHENZHEN SIME DARBY MOTOR ENTERPRISES CO. LTD.—See Sime Darby Berhad; *Int'l*, pg. 6928

SHENZHEN SINBON ELECTRONICS CO., LTD.—See SINBON Electronics Co., Ltd.; *Int'l*, pg. 6937
SHENZHEN SINE ELECTRIC CO., LTD.; *Int'l*, pg. 6821
SHENZHEN SINEXCEL ELECTRIC CO., LTD.; *Int'l*, pg. 6821
SHENZHEN SINODATA TECHNOLOGY CO LTD—See REXLot Holdings Limited; *Int'l*, pg. 6317
SHENZHEN SINOVATIO TECHNOLOGY CO., LTD.; *Int'l*, pg. 6821
SHENZHEN SKING INTELLIGENT EQUIPMENT CO., LTD.; *Int'l*, pg. 6821
SHENZHEN SKYWORTH DIGITAL TECHNOLOGY CO., LTD.; *Int'l*, pg. 6821
SHENZHEN SMART-CORE TECHNOLOGY CO., LTD.—See Smart-Core Holdings Limited; *Int'l*, pg. 7001
SHENZHEN SMITSENSE TECHNOLOGY CO, LTD.—See SMIT Holdings Limited; *Int'l*, pg. 7007
SHENZHEN SOLING INDUSTRIAL CO., LTD.; *Int'l*, pg. 6821
SHENZHEN SOLUSOFT SOFTWARE CO., LTD.—See Beijing Shiji Information Technology Co., Ltd.; *Int'l*, pg. 956
SHENZHEN SONGXIN SPORTS PRODUCTS CO., LTD.; *Int'l*, pg. 6821
SHENZHEN SOSEN ELECTRONICS CO., LTD.; *Int'l*, pg. 6821
SHENZHEN SOUTH-CHINA INTERNATIONAL LOGISTICS CO., LTD.—See Shenzhen International Holdings Limited; *Int'l*, pg. 6813
SHENZHEN SOUTHERN CIMC CONTAINERS SERVICE CO., LTD.—See China International Marine Containers (Group) Co., Ltd.; *Int'l*, pg. 1512
SHENZHEN SOUTHERN CIMC EASTERN LOGISTICS EQUIPMENT MANUFACTURING CO., LTD.—See China International Marine Containers (Group) Co., Ltd.; *Int'l*, pg. 1512
SHENZHEN SPECIAL ECONOMIC ZONE REAL ESTATE AND PROPERTIES (GROUP) CO., LTD.; *Int'l*, pg. 6821
SHENZHEN STANLEY ELECTRIC CO., LTD—See Stanley Electric Co., Ltd.; *Int'l*, pg. 7170
SHENZHEN STOCK EXCHANGE; *Int'l*, pg. 6821
SHENZHEN STRONGTEAM DECORATION ENGINEERING CO., LTD.; *Int'l*, pg. 6821
SHENZHEN STS MICROELECTRONICS CO. LTD.—See STMicroelectronics N.V.; *Int'l*, pg. 7217
SHENZHEN SUCCESS ELECTRONICS CO., LTD. - YU SHUN ELECTRONICS FACTORY—See Aishida Co., Ltd.; *Int'l*, pg. 251
SHENZHEN SUMITOMO CORPORATION LTD.—See Sumitomo Corporation; *Int'l*, pg. 7271
SHENZHEN SUNLINE TECH CO., LTD.; *Int'l*, pg. 6821
SHENZHEN SUNLORD ELECTRONICS CO., LTD.; *Int'l*, pg. 6822
SHENZHEN SUNMOON MICROELECTRONICS CO., LTD.; *Int'l*, pg. 6822
SHENZHEN SUNNYPOL OPTOELECTRONICS CO., LTD.; *Int'l*, pg. 6822
SHENZHEN SUNRAY (GROUP) CO., LTD.—See China Railway Materials Co., Ltd.; *Int'l*, pg. 1544
SHENZHEN SUNRISE NEW ENERGY CO., LTD.; *Int'l*, pg. 6822
SHENZHEN SUNSHINE LASER & ELECTRONICS TECHNOLOGY CO., LTD.; *Int'l*, pg. 6822
SHENZHEN SUNSHINE LASER TECHNOLOGY LTD.—See Shenzhen Sunshine Laser & Electronics Technology Co., Ltd.; *Int'l*, pg. 6822
SHENZHEN SUNTECH POWER CO., LTD.—See Suntech Power Holdings Co., Ltd.; *Int'l*, pg. 7325
SHENZHEN SUNWAY COMMUNICATION CO., LTD.; *Int'l*, pg. 6822
SHENZHEN SUNWIN INTELLIGENT CO., LTD.; *Int'l*, pg. 6822
SHENZHEN SUNXING LIGHT ALLOY MATERIALS, CO., LTD.; *Int'l*, pg. 6822
SHENZHEN SUNYES ELECTRONIC MANUFACTURING HOLDING CO., LTD.; *Int'l*, pg. 6822
SHENZHEN SUOXINDA DATA TECHNOLOGY CO., LTD.; *Int'l*, pg. 6822
SHENZHEN SYLVA ELECTROCHEMICAL LTD.—See Gold Peak Technology Group Limited; *Int'l*, pg. 3026
SHENZHEN TAGEN GROUP CO., LTD.; *Int'l*, pg. 6822
SHENZHEN TAIFLEX ELECTRONIC CO., LTD.—See Taiflex Scientific Co., Ltd.; *Int'l*, pg. 7410
SHENZHEN TAITAI PHARMACEUTICAL CO., LTD—See Joincare Pharmaceutical Industry Group Co., Ltd; *Int'l*, pg. 3995
SHENZHEN TECHDOW PHARMACEUTICAL CO., LTD.—See Shenzhen Hepalink Pharmaceutical Group Co., Ltd.; *Int'l*, pg. 6812
SHENZHEN TECHWINSEMI TECHNOLOGY CO., LTD.; *Int'l*, pg. 6822
SHENZHEN TECNON EXCO-VISION TECHNOLOGY CO., LTD.—See Tecnon Electronics Co., Ltd.; *Int'l*, pg. 7517
SHENZHEN TECNON LIGHTING TECHNOLOGY CO., LTD.—See Tecnon Electronics Co., Ltd.; *Int'l*, pg. 7517
SHENZHEN TEIJIN KASEI TRADING CO., LTD.—See Teijin Limited; *Int'l*, pg. 7522
SHENZHEN TELLUS HOLDING CO., LTD.; *Int'l*, pg. 6822

SHENZHEN TENCENT COMPUTER SYSTEM LTD—See Tencent Holdings Limited; *Int'l*, pg. 7559
SHENZHEN TEXTILE (HOLDINGS) CO., LTD.; *Int'l*, pg. 6823
SHENZHEN THREE-CIRCLE ELECTRONIC CO., LTD.—See Chaozhou Three-Circle Group Co., Ltd.; *Int'l*, pg. 1447
SHENZHEN TIANYUAN DIC INFORMATION TECHNOLOGY CO., LTD.; *Int'l*, pg. 6823
SHENZHEN TIGER GARMENT LTD—See Giordano International Limited; *Int'l*, pg. 2978
SHENZHEN TIGER INFORMATION TECHNOLOGY DEVELOPMENT CO., LTD.—See HNA International Investment Holdings Limited; *Int'l*, pg. 3433
SHENZHEN TKD INDUSTRIAL CO., LTD.—See TKD Science And Technology Co., Ltd.; *Int'l*, pg. 7762
SHENZHEN TONG'AN PHARMACEUTICAL CO., LTD.—See Shan Dong Kexing Bioproducts Co., Ltd.; *Int'l*, pg. 6751
SHENZHEN TONGDA CHEMICAL CORPORATION—See China National Chemical Corporation; *Int'l*, pg. 1527
SHENZHEN TONGYE TECHNOLOGY CO., LTD.; *Int'l*, pg. 6823
SHENZHEN TONGYI INDUSTRY CO., LTD.; *Int'l*, pg. 6823
SHENZHEN TOPBAND CO., LTD.; *Int'l*, pg. 6823
SHENZHEN TOPWAY VIDEO COMMUNICATION CO., LTD.; *Int'l*, pg. 6823
SHENZHEN TORSHARE TECHNOLOGY CO., LTD.—See Ledman Optoelectronic Co., Ltd.; *Int'l*, pg. 4439
SHENZHEN TOTAL LOGISTICS SERVICES LIMITED—See Shenzhen International Holdings Limited; *Int'l*, pg. 6813
SHENZHEN TOTECH TECHNOLOGIES CO., LTD.—See Aiphone Co., Ltd.; *Int'l*, pg. 235
SHENZHEN TOYO INK CO., LTD.—See Toyo Ink SC Holdings Co., Ltd.; *Int'l*, pg. 7853
SHENZHEN TRANSSION HOLDINGS CO.; *Int'l*, pg. 6823
SHENZHEN TVT DIGITAL TECHNOLOGY CO., LTD. - SHENZHEN FACTORY—See Shenzhen TVT Digital Technology Co., Ltd.; *Int'l*, pg. 6823
SHENZHEN TVT DIGITAL TECHNOLOGY CO., LTD.; *Int'l*, pg. 6823
SHENZHEN TXD TECHNOLOGY CO LTD; *Int'l*, pg. 6823
SHENZHEN UBM HERONG EXHIBITION COMPANY—See Informa plc; *Int'l*, pg. 3693
SHENZHEN UNIQUE LOGISTICS INTERNATIONAL LTD.—See Unique Logistics International Inc.; *U.S. Public*, pg. 2227
SHENZHEN UNITED WINNERS LASER CO., LTD.; *Int'l*, pg. 6823
SHENZHEN UNIVERSE (GROUP) CO., LTD.; *Int'l*, pg. 6823
SHENZHEN UNIWIN INTERNATIONAL LOGISTICS LTD.—See Wan Hai Lines Ltd.; *Int'l*, pg. 8340
SHENZHEN URBAN TRANSPORT PLANNING CENTER CO., LTD.; *Int'l*, pg. 6823
SHENZHEN UROVO TECHNOLOGY CO., LTD.; *Int'l*, pg. 6823
SHENZHEN VEKEN NEW ENERGY SCIENCE & TECHNOLOGY CO., LTD.—See Veken Technology Co., Ltd.; *Int'l*, pg. 8148
SHENZHEN VIGORHOOD ELECTRONICS CO. LTD—See Shen Yao Holdings Limited; *Int'l*, pg. 6800
SHENZHEN VITAL NEW MATERIAL CO., LTD.; *Int'l*, pg. 6823
SHENZHEN VITASOY (GUANG MING) FOODS & BEVERAGE COMPANY LIMITED—See Vitasoy International Holdings Ltd.; *Int'l*, pg. 8259
SHENZHEN V&T TECHNOLOGIES CO., LTD.; *Int'l*, pg. 6823
SHENZHEN WATER PLANNING & DESIGN INSTITUTE CO., LTD.; *Int'l*, pg. 6824
SHENZHEN WATERTEK INFORMATION TECHNOLOGY CO., LTD.—See Beijing Watertek Information Technology Co., Ltd.; *Int'l*, pg. 960
SHENZHEN WAVEGUIDER OPTICAL TELECOM TECHNOLOGY LNC.—See Shenzhen Fenda Technology Co., Ltd.; *Int'l*, pg. 6810
SHENZHEN WEIDA MEDICAL SYSTEM ENGINEERING CO., LTD.—See China Security Co., Ltd.; *Int'l*, pg. 1550
SHENZHEN WEIGUANG BIOLOGICAL PRODUCTS CO., LTD.; *Int'l*, pg. 6824
SHENZHEN WOER HEAT-SHRINKABLE MATERIAL CO., LTD.; *Int'l*, pg. 6824
SHENZHEN WONGTEE INTERNATIONAL ENTERPRISE CO., LTD.; *Int'l*, pg. 6824
SHENZHEN WORLD SURGERY MEDICAL DEVICE TECHNOLOGY CO.—See Double Medical Technology Inc.; *Int'l*, pg. 2181
SHENZHEN WOTE ADVANCED MATERIALS CO., LTD.; *Int'l*, pg. 6824
SHENZHEN XFH TECHNOLOGY CO., LTD.; *Int'l*, pg. 6824
SHENZHEN XINHAO PHOTOELECTRICITY TECHNOLOGY CO., LTD; *Int'l*, pg. 6824

SHENZHEN XINHUAFENG ENVIRONMENT DEVELOPMENT CO., LTD.—See Shenzhen Grandland Group Co., Ltd.; *Int'l*, pg. 6811
SHENZHEN XINWEI ELECTRONIC CO., LTD.—See SUNWODA Electronics Co., Ltd.; *Int'l*, pg. 7333
SHENZHEN XINWEI TELECOM TECHNOLOGY CO., LTD.—See Beijing Xinwei Technology Group Co., Ltd.; *Int'l*, pg. 961
SHENZHEN XINYICHANG TECHNOLOGY CO., LTD.; *Int'l*, pg. 6824
SHENZHEN XUNJIEXING TECHNOLOGY CORP. LTD.; *Int'l*, pg. 6824
SHENZHEN YANMADE TECHNOLOGY, INC.; *Int'l*, pg. 6824
SHENZHEN YAN TIAN PORT HOLDINGS CO., LTD.; *Int'l*, pg. 6824
SHENZHEN YEEBO ELECTRONICS TECHNOLOGY CO., LTD.—See Yeebo (International Holdings) Limited; *Int'l*, pg. 8576
SHENZHEN YHLO BIOTECH CO., LTD.; *Int'l*, pg. 6824
SHENZHEN YIDIAN DOUBLE WAY OF INNOVATION CULTURE MEDIA CORP.; *U.S. Public*, pg. 1874
SHENZHEN YINGHE TECHNOLOGY CO., LTD.; *Int'l*, pg. 6824
SHENZHEN YISHENG INVESTMENT CO., LTD.—See SUNWODA Electronics Co., Ltd.; *Int'l*, pg. 7333
SHENZHEN YITOA INTELLIGENT CONTROL CO., LTD.; *Int'l*, pg. 6824
SHENZHEN YOUYU SMART TECHNOLOGIES LIMITED—See Yunfeng Financial Group Limited; *Int'l*, pg. 8613
SHENZHEN YSSTECH INFO-TECH CO., LTD.; *Int'l*, pg. 6825
SHENZHEN YUSEN LOGISTICS SERVICE CO., LTD.—See Nippon Yusen Kabushiki Kaisha; *Int'l*, pg. 5359
SHENZHEN YUTO PACKAGING TECHNOLOGY CO., LTD.; *Int'l*, pg. 6825
SHENZHEN ZEN SEE INFORMATION TECHNOLOGY CO., LTD.—See Q P Group Holdings Limited; *Int'l*, pg. 6129
SHENZHEN ZHAOWEI MACHINERY & ELECTRONICS CO., LTD.; *Int'l*, pg. 6825
SHENZHEN ZHENYE (GROUP) CO., LTD.; *Int'l*, pg. 6825
SHENZHEN ZHETONG ELECTRONICS COMPANY LIMITED—See Karrie International Holdings Limited; *Int'l*, pg. 4085
SHENZHEN ZHILAI SCIENCE & TECHNOLOGY CO., LTD.; *Int'l*, pg. 6825
SHENZHEN ZHONG HAN SCIENCE & TECH. CO., LTD.—See FSP Technology Inc.; *Int'l*, pg. 2800
SHENZHEN ZHONGHAN TECHNOLOGY CO., LTD.—See FSP Technology Inc.; *Int'l*, pg. 2800
SHENZHEN ZHONGHENG HWAFA CO., LTD.; *Int'l*, pg. 6825
SHENZHEN ZHONGJIN LINGNAN NONFEMET CO., LTD.; *Int'l*, pg. 6825
SHENZHEN ZHONGSHENG STAR AUTOMOBILE SALES & SERVICE CO., LTD.—See Zhongsheng Group Holdings Limited; *Int'l*, pg. 8674
SHENZHEN ZHONGWEI TECHNOLOGY CO., LTD.—See American Education Center, Inc.; *U.S. Public*, pg. 99
SHENZHEN ZHONGZHUANG DESIGN DECORATION ENGINEERING CO., LTD; *Int'l*, pg. 6825
SHENZHEN ZOWEE TECHNOLOGY CO., LTD.; *Int'l*, pg. 6825
SHENZHEN ZQGAME NETWORK CO., LTD.; *Int'l*, pg. 6825
SHENZHOU INTERNATIONAL GROUP HOLDINGS LIMITED; *Int'l*, pg. 6825
SHENZHOU JIDONG CEMENT CO., LTD.—See Tangshan Jidong Cement Co., Ltd.; *Int'l*, pg. 7458
SHENZHOU SPACE PARK GROUP LIMITED; *Int'l*, pg. 6825
SHEPARD AUTO GROUP; *U.S. Private*, pg. 3632
SHEPARD EXPOSITION SERVICES INC.; *U.S. Private*, pg. 3632
SHEPARD INSURANCE—See Aquiline Capital Partners LLC; *U.S. Private*, pg. 305
SHEPARD NILES—See Konecranes Plc; *Int'l*, pg. 4252
SHEPARDS MOTOR; *U.S. Private*, pg. 3632
SHEPARD STEEL CO. INC.; *U.S. Private*, pg. 3632
SHEPARDVILLE CONSTRUCTION, LLC—See UFP Industries, Inc.; *U.S. Public*, pg. 2219
SHEPARD WALTON KING INSURANCE GROUP; *U.S. Private*, pg. 3632
SHEPEARD COMMUNITY BLOOD CENTER; *U.S. Private*, pg. 3632
SHEPHARD'S BEACH RESORT, INC.; *U.S. Private*, pg. 3632
SHEPHARD-WESNITZER, INC.—See Littlejohn & Co., LLC; *U.S. Private*, pg. 2470
SHEPHERD CENTER, INC.; *U.S. Private*, pg. 3632
THE SHEPHERD CHEMICAL COMPANY, INC.; *U.S. Private*, pg. 4117
SHEPHERD CONSTRUCTION CO., INC.; *U.S. Private*, pg. 3632
SHEPHERD ELECTRIC SUPPLY COMPANY—See Graybar Electric Company, Inc.; *U.S. Private*, pg. 1760

SHEPHERD NEAME LIMITED; *Int'l*, pg. 6826
SHEPHERD'S FINANCE, LLC; *U.S. Private*, pg. 3632
SHEPLERS, INC.—See Boot Barn Holdings, Inc.; *U.S. Public*, pg. 368
SHEPLEY ENGINEERS LTD.—See Renew Holdings plc; *Int'l*, pg. 6278
SHEPPARD MULLIN RICHTER & HAMPTON LLP; *U.S. Private*, pg. 3632
SHEPPARTON PARTNERS COLLECTIVE PTY LTD.—See Perma Funds Management; *Int'l*, pg. 5802
SHEPPARTON PARTNERS COLLECTIVE PTY LTD.—See Perma Funds Management; *Int'l*, pg. 5802
SHEPPARTON PARTNERS COLLECTIVE PTY LTD.—See The Eights Group Pty Ltd.; *Int'l*, pg. 7638
SHEPPARTON PARTNERS COLLECTIVE PTY LTD.—See The Eights Group Pty Ltd.; *Int'l*, pg. 7638
SHEPPERTON STUDIOS LIMITED—See Aermont Capital LLP; *Int'l*, pg. 180
SH EQUIPMENT (HK) LIMITED—See Sin Heng Heavy Machinery Limited; *Int'l*, pg. 6935
SH EQUIPMENT (MYANMAR) COMPANY LIMITED—See Sin Heng Heavy Machinery Limited; *Int'l*, pg. 6935
SHERATON BALTIMORE WASHINGTON AIRPORT HOTEL - BWI—See Marriott International, Inc.; *U.S. Public*, pg. 1372
SHERATON BOSTON HOTEL—See Marriott International, Inc.; *U.S. Public*, pg. 1372
SHERATON CENTRE TORONTO HOTEL—See Marriott International, Inc.; *U.S. Public*, pg. 1372
SHERATON COLLEGE PARK NORTH HOTEL—See Marriott International, Inc.; *U.S. Public*, pg. 1372
THE SHERATON CORPORATION—See Marriott International, Inc.; *U.S. Public*, pg. 1372
SHERATON DENVER TECH CENTER HOTEL—See Marriott International, Inc.; *U.S. Public*, pg. 1372
SHERATON DETROIT NOVI—See Marriott International, Inc.; *U.S. Public*, pg. 1372
SHERATON EDISON HOTEL—See Marriott International, Inc.; *U.S. Public*, pg. 1372
SHERATON GRAND PHOENIX LLC—See Marriott International, Inc.; *U.S. Public*, pg. 1371
SHERATON INDIANAPOLIS HOTEL—See Marriott International, Inc.; *U.S. Public*, pg. 1372
SHERATON INTERNATIONAL, LLC—See Marriott International, Inc.; *U.S. Public*, pg. 1372
SHERATON MILWAUKEE BROOKFIELD HOTEL—See Marriott International, Inc.; *U.S. Public*, pg. 1372
SHERATON OPERATING CORPORATION—See Marriott International, Inc.; *U.S. Public*, pg. 1371
SHERATON OVERSEAS MANAGEMENT CORPORATION—See Marriott International, Inc.; *U.S. Public*, pg. 1372
SHERATON PROPERTIES & FINANCE LIMITED; *Int'l*, pg. 6826
SHERATON PROVIDENCE AIRPORT HOTEL—See Marriott International, Inc.; *U.S. Public*, pg. 1372
SHERATON SAIGON HOTEL & TOWERS—See Keck Seng Investments (Hong Kong) Limited; *Int'l*, pg. 4114
SHERATON SAN DIEGO HOTEL & MARINA—See Marriott International, Inc.; *U.S. Public*, pg. 1372
SHERATON SKYLINE HOTEL LONDON HEATHROW—See Marriott International, Inc.; *U.S. Public*, pg. 1372
SHERATON SUITES PHILADELPHIA AIRPORT—See Marriott International, Inc.; *U.S. Public*, pg. 1372
SHERATON SUITES WILMINGTON DOWTOWN—See Marriott International, Inc.; *U.S. Public*, pg. 1372
SHERATON TEXTILES (PTY) LTD—See Industrial Development Corporation of South Africa, Ltd.; *Int'l*, pg. 3672
SHERATON TOWERS SINGAPORE—See Bonvests Holdings Limited; *Int'l*, pg. 1110
SHERATON TUCSON HOTEL & SUITES—See Marriott International, Inc.; *U.S. Public*, pg. 1372
SHERATON TYSONS HOTEL—See Marriott International, Inc.; *U.S. Public*, pg. 1372
SHERATON VISTANA RESORT—See Marriott International, Inc.; *U.S. Public*, pg. 1372
SHERATON WEST PORT INC.; *U.S. Private*, pg. 3633
SHERBORNE INVESTORS (GUERNSEY) A LIMITED; *Int'l*, pg. 6826
SHERBORNE INVESTORS MANAGEMENT LP; *U.S. Private*, pg. 3633
SHERBOURN TECHNOLOGIES, LLC—See Jade Design, Inc.; *U.S. Private*, pg. 2181
SHERBROOKE CAPITAL LLC; *U.S. Private*, pg. 3633
SHERBROOKE O.E.M. LTD; *Int'l*, pg. 6826
SHERCON, INC.—See Windjammer Capital Investors, LLC; *U.S. Private*, pg. 4538
SHERE GROUP LIMITED—See Cellnex Telecom, S.A.; *Int'l*, pg. 1394
SHERE MASTEN B.V.—See Cellnex Telecom, S.A.; *Int'l*, pg. 1394
SHEREX FASTENING SOLUTIONS, LLC—See Tinicum Enterprises, Inc.; *U.S. Private*, pg. 4174
SHERIDAN ANESTHESIA SERVICES OF LOUISIANA, INC.—See KKR & Co. Inc.; *U.S. Public*, pg. 1246
SHERIDAN AUSTRALIA PTY. LIMITED—See Hanesbrands Inc.; *U.S. Public*, pg. 983

COMPANY NAME INDEX

SHERIDAN BOOKS, INC.—See CJK Group, Inc.; *U.S. Private*, pg. 909
SHERIDAN BROADCASTING CORPORATION; *U.S. Private*, pg. 3633
SHERIDAN CAPITAL PARTNERS LLC; *U.S. Private*, pg. 3633
SHERIDAN CONSTRUCTION CORP—See Sheri-Key; *U.S. Private*, pg. 3633
SHERIDAN CORPORATION—See Sheri-Key; *U.S. Private*, pg. 3633
SHERIDAN DEXTER INC.—See CJK Group, Inc.; *U.S. Private*, pg. 909
SHERIDAN FABRICATIONS LIMITED—See Howden Joinery Group Plc; *Int'l*, pg. 3494
THE SHERIDAN GROUP, INC.—See CJK Group, Inc.; *U.S. Private*, pg. 909
THE SHERIDAN GROUP INC; *U.S. Private*, pg. 4117
SHERIDAN LANES, INC.—See Bowlero Corp; *U.S. Public*, pg. 376
SHERIDAN MAGAZINE SERVICES—See CJK Group, Inc.; *U.S. Private*, pg. 909
SHERIDAN NISSAN; *U.S. Private*, pg. 3633
SHERIDAN NURSERIES; *Int'l*, pg. 6826
THE SHERIDAN PRESS—See CJK Group, Inc.; *U.S. Private*, pg. 909
SHERIDAN RADIOLOGY SERVICES OF CENTRAL FLORIDA, INC.—See KKR & Co. Inc.; *U.S. Public*, pg. 1246
SHERIDAN RADIOLOGY SERVICES OF KENTUCKY, INC.—See KKR & Co. Inc.; *U.S. Public*, pg. 1246
SHERIDAN RADIOLOGY SERVICES OF PINELLAS, INC.—See KKR & Co. Inc.; *U.S. Public*, pg. 1246
SHERIDAN RADIOLOGY SERVICES OF VIRGINIA, INC.—See KKR & Co. Inc.; *U.S. Public*, pg. 1246
SHERIDAN U.K. LIMITED—See Hanesbrands Inc.; *U.S. Public*, pg. 983
SHERI-KEY; *U.S. Private*, pg. 3633
SHERLAND & FARRINGTON INC.; *U.S. Private*, pg. 3633
SHERLE WAGNER INTERNATIONAL; *U.S. Private*, pg. 3633
SHERLOCK SERVICES, INC.—See Harvest Partners L.P.; *U.S. Private*, pg. 1877
SHERLOQ SOLUTIONS; *U.S. Private*, pg. 3633
SHERMAN AUTO RENTALS; *U.S. Private*, pg. 3634
SHERMAN BROS TRUCKING; *U.S. Private*, pg. 3634
SHERMAN-CARTER-BARNHART, PSC.; *U.S. Private*, pg. 3634
SHERMAN, CLAY & CO.; *U.S. Private*, pg. 3634
SHERMAN COMMUNICATIONS & MARKETING; *U.S. Private*, pg. 3634
SHERMAN DODGE, INC.; *U.S. Private*, pg. 3634
SHERMAN FINANCIAL GROUP LLC; *U.S. Private*, pg. 3634
SHERMAN & HEMSTREET, INC.; *U.S. Private*, pg. 3633
SHERMAN INDUSTRIES LLC—See Heidelberg Materials AG; *Int'l*, pg. 3319
SHERMAN INTERNATIONAL CORPORATION; *U.S. Private*, pg. 3634
SHERMAN OAKS-A, INC.—See Lithia Motors, Inc.; *U.S. Public*, pg. 1326
SHERMAN PUBLICATIONS, INC.—See JAMS Media LLC; *U.S. Private*, pg. 2186
SHERMAN + REILLY, INC.—See Emerson Electric Co.; *U.S. Public*, pg. 741
SHERMAN + REILLY, INC.—See Emerson Electric Co.; *U.S. Public*, pg. 750
SHERMAN'S BOOKS & STATIONERY, INC.; *U.S. Private*, pg. 3634
SHERMAN'S PLACE INC.; *U.S. Private*, pg. 3634
SHERMAN V. ALLEN INC.; *U.S. Private*, pg. 3634
SHERMAN WAY CAMPUS—See Catholic Health Initiatives; *U.S. Private*, pg. 789
SHERMAN WIRE COMPANY—See Contran Corporation; *U.S. Private*, pg. 1033
SHERMCO INDUSTRIES, INC.—See Gryphon Investors, LLC; *U.S. Private*, pg. 1799
SHERMS THUNDERBIRD MARKET; *U.S. Private*, pg. 3634
SHERO ENTERPRISES INC.; *U.S. Private*, pg. 3634
SHERPA.BE SA—See Live Nation Entertainment, Inc.; *U.S. Public*, pg. 1330
SHERPA CAPITAL SL; *Int'l*, pg. 6826
SHERPA II HOLDINGS CORP; *Int'l*, pg. 6826
SHERPA SOFTWARE GROUP, LP; *U.S. Private*, pg. 3634
SHER PLASTICS, LLC—See William Prym GmbH & Co. KG; *Int'l*, pg. 8413
SHERRIFF-GOSLIN CO.; *U.S. Private*, pg. 3634
SHERRILL FURNITURE COMPANY INC.; *U.S. Private*, pg. 3634
SHERRILL, INC.—See Gridiron Capital, LLC; *U.S. Private*, pg. 1786
SHERRIN HIRE PTY LTD—See Boom Logistics Limited; *Int'l*, pg. 1110
SHERRITT INTERNATIONAL CORPORATION; *Int'l*, pg. 6826
SHERRY-LEHMANN INC.; *U.S. Private*, pg. 3634
SHERRY MANUFACTURING CO. INC.; *U.S. Private*, pg. 3634

SHERRY MATTHEWS ADVOCACY MARKETING; *U.S. Private*, pg. 3634
SHERVANI INDUSTRIAL SYNDICATE LIMITED; *Int'l*, pg. 6826
SHERWAY GARDENS—See The Cadillac Fairview Corporation Limited; *Int'l*, pg. 7630
SHERWIN-WILLIAMS ARGENTINA I.Y C.S.A.—See The Sherwin-Williams Company; *U.S. Public*, pg. 2128
SHERWIN-WILLIAMS AUTOMOTIVE FINISHES CORPORATION—See The Sherwin-Williams Company; *U.S. Public*, pg. 2128
SHERWIN-WILLIAMS BALKAN S.R.L.—See The Sherwin-Williams Company; *U.S. Public*, pg. 2128
SHERWIN-WILLIAMS BEL—See The Sherwin-Williams Company; *U.S. Public*, pg. 2128
SHERWIN-WILLIAMS BENELUX NV—See The Sherwin-Williams Company; *U.S. Public*, pg. 2128
SHERWIN-WILLIAMS CHILE S.A.—See The Sherwin-Williams Company; *U.S. Public*, pg. 2128
SHERWIN-WILLIAMS COATINGS INDIA PRIVATE LIMITED—See The Sherwin-Williams Company; *U.S. Public*, pg. 2128
THE SHERWIN-WILLIAMS CO. - DISTRIBUTION SERVICE CENTER - WACO—See The Sherwin-Williams Company; *U.S. Public*, pg. 2129
SHERWIN-WILLIAMS CO. - DIVERSIFIED BRANDS DIVISION—See The Sherwin-Williams Company; *U.S. Public*, pg. 2128
SHERWIN-WILLIAMS CO. - INDUSTRIAL COATINGS DIVISION—See The Sherwin-Williams Company; *U.S. Public*, pg. 2128
SHERWIN WILLIAMS COLOMBIA S.A.S.—See The Sherwin-Williams Company; *U.S. Public*, pg. 2128
THE SHERWIN-WILLIAMS COMPANY; *U.S. Public*, pg. 2127
SHERWIN-WILLIAMS CONSUMER GROUP—See The Sherwin-Williams Company; *U.S. Public*, pg. 2128
THE SHERWIN-WILLIAMS CO. - SAN DIEGO (FRAZEE PAINT) PLANT—See The Sherwin-Williams Company; *U.S. Public*, pg. 2129
SHERWIN-WILLIAMS CZECH REPUBLIC SPOL. S.R.O.—See The Sherwin-Williams Company; *U.S. Public*, pg. 2128
SHERWIN-WILLIAMS CZECH SPOL. S.R.O.—See The Sherwin-Williams Company; *U.S. Public*, pg. 2129
SHERWIN-WILLIAMS DENMARK A/S—See The Sherwin-Williams Company; *U.S. Public*, pg. 2128
SHERWIN-WILLIAMS DEUTSCHLAND GMBH—See The Sherwin-Williams Company; *U.S. Public*, pg. 2128
SHERWIN-WILLIAMS DIVERSIFIED BRANDS LIMITED—See The Sherwin-Williams Company; *U.S. Public*, pg. 2128
SHERWIN-WILLIAMS DO BRASIL INDUSTRIA E COMERCIO LIMITADA—See The Sherwin-Williams Company; *U.S. Public*, pg. 2129
SHERWIN-WILLIAMS FRANCE FINISHES SAS—See The Sherwin-Williams Company; *U.S. Public*, pg. 2128
SHERWIN-WILLIAMS IRELAND LTD.—See The Sherwin-Williams Company; *U.S. Public*, pg. 2128
SHERWIN-WILLIAMS ITALY S.R.L.—See The Sherwin-Williams Company; *U.S. Public*, pg. 2128
SHERWIN-WILLIAMS JERSEY LIMITED—See The Sherwin-Williams Company; *U.S. Public*, pg. 2128
SHERWIN-WILLIAMS NORWAY AS—See The Sherwin-Williams Company; *U.S. Public*, pg. 2128
SHERWIN-WILLIAMS PAINT GROUP—See The Sherwin-Williams Company; *U.S. Public*, pg. 2128
SHERWIN-WILLIAMS PAINT STORES GROUP—See The Sherwin-Williams Company; *U.S. Public*, pg. 2128
SHERWIN-WILLIAMS PAINT STORES GROUP—See The Sherwin-Williams Company; *U.S. Public*, pg. 2128
SHERWIN-WILLIAMS PERU S.R.L.—See The Sherwin-Williams Company; *U.S. Public*, pg. 2128
SHERWIN-WILLIAMS POLAND SP. Z O.O—See The Sherwin-Williams Company; *U.S. Public*, pg. 2129
SHERWIN-WILLIAMS PROTECTIVE & MARINE COATINGS—See The Sherwin-Williams Company; *U.S. Public*, pg. 2129
SHERWIN-WILLIAMS SERVICES (MALAYSIA) SDN. BHD.—See The Sherwin-Williams Company; *U.S. Public*, pg. 2129
SHERWIN-WILLIAMS (SHANGHAI) LIMITED—See The Sherwin-Williams Company; *U.S. Public*, pg. 2128
SHERWIN-WILLIAMS SPAIN COATINGS S.L.—See The Sherwin-Williams Company; *U.S. Public*, pg. 2128
SHERWIN-WILLIAMS SWEDEN AB—See The Sherwin-Williams Company; *U.S. Public*, pg. 2129
SHERWIN-WILLIAMS (THAILAND) CO., LTD.—See The Sherwin-Williams Company; *U.S. Public*, pg. 2128
SHERWIN-WILLIAMS UK COATINGS LIMITED—See The Sherwin-Williams Company; *U.S. Public*, pg. 2129
SHERWIN-WILLIAMS URUGUAY S.A.—See The Sherwin-Williams Company; *U.S. Public*, pg. 2129
SHERWIN-WILLIAMS (WEST INDIES) LTD.—See The Sherwin-Williams Company; *U.S. Public*, pg. 2128
SHERWOOD AMERICA INC.—See INKEL Corporation; *Int'l*, pg. 3705
SHERWOOD CHEVROLET INC.; *Int'l*, pg. 6826

SHIBAURA ELECTRONICS CO., LTD.

SHERWOOD CONSTRUCTION CO. INC.; *U.S. Private*, pg. 3634
SHERWOOD CO-OPERATIVE ASSOCIATION LIMITED; *Int'l*, pg. 6826
SHERWOOD CORPORATION (THAILAND) PUBLIC COMPANY LIMITED—See TOA Group Holding Co., Ltd.; *Int'l*, pg. 7769
SHERWOOD CORP (THAILAND) PUBLIC CO., LTD.—See TOA Group Holding Co., Ltd.; *Int'l*, pg. 7769
SHERWOOD DEVELOPMENT COMPANY—See Murdock Holdings, LLC; *U.S. Private*, pg. 2815
SHERWOOD FOOD DISTRIBUTORS- CLEVELAND DIV—See Sand Dollar Holdings Incorporated; *U.S. Private*, pg. 3542
SHERWOOD FOOD DISTRIBUTORS, LLC—See Sand Dollar Holdings Incorporated; *U.S. Private*, pg. 3542
SHERWOOD FREIGHTLINER STERLING & WESTERN STAR—See Mercedes-Benz Group AG; *Int'l*, pg. 4823
THE SHERWOOD GROUP, INC.; *U.S. Private*, pg. 4117
SHERWOOD INDUSTRIES LTD.; *Int'l*, pg. 6826
SHERWOOD LUMBER CORPORATION; *U.S. Private*, pg. 3635
SHERWOOD MANAGEMENT CO. INC.—See Sheldons of Oceanside Inc.; *U.S. Private*, pg. 3631
SHERWOOD MANUFACTURING CO., INC.—See Columbus A/S; *Int'l*, pg. 1706
SHERWOOD MEMORIAL PARK & MAUSOLEUM, INC.—See Service Corporation International; *U.S. Public*, pg. 1870
SHERWOOD OF SALISBURY; *U.S. Private*, pg. 3635
SHERWOOD STORAGE, LLC—See National Storage Affiliates Trust; *U.S. Public*, pg. 1498
SHERWOOD-TEMPLETON COAL COMPANY, INC.—See Templeton Coal Company, Inc.; *U.S. Private*, pg. 3963
SHERWOOD VALVE LLC—See Wind Point Advisors LLC; *U.S. Private*, pg. 4536
SHERWOOD VALVE LLC - VALLEY VIEW FACILITY—See Wind Point Advisors LLC; *U.S. Private*, pg. 4536
SHERWOOD VALVE—See Wind Point Advisors LLC; *U.S. Private*, pg. 4536
SHESHADRI INDUSTRIES LTD.; *Int'l*, pg. 6826
SHETRON LIMITED; *Int'l*, pg. 6826
SHETUCKET PLUMBING SUPPLY INC.—See Granite Group Wholesale LLC; *U.S. Private*, pg. 1755
SHEUNG MOON HOLDINGS LIMITED; *Int'l*, pg. 6826
SHEUNG YUE GROUP HOLDINGS LIMITED; *Int'l*, pg. 6826
SHEWAS, INC.; *U.S. Private*, pg. 3635
SHEW ELECTRIC, INC.; *U.S. Private*, pg. 3635
S&H EXPRESS, INC.; *U.S. Private*, pg. 3513
SHEZAN INTERNATIONAL LIMITED; *Int'l*, pg. 6827
SHEZHEN ATLANTIC WELDING CONSUMABLES CO., LTD—See Atlantic China Welding Consumables, Inc.; *Int'l*, pg. 674
SHF CO., LTD.—See Beauty Kadan Co., Ltd.; *Int'l*, pg. 935
SHF COMMUNICATION TECHNOLOGIES AG; *Int'l*, pg. 6827
SHF HOLDINGS, INC.; *U.S. Public*, pg. 1874
SHF JAPAN CORPORATION—See SHF Communication Technologies AG; *Int'l*, pg. 6827
SHFL ENTERTAINMENT (ARGENTINA) S.R.L.—See Light & Wonder, Inc.; *U.S. Public*, pg. 1314
SHF, LLC—See SHF Holdings, Inc.; *U.S. Public*, pg. 1874
S-H FORTY-NINE PROPCO VENTURES, LLC—See Healthpeak Properties, Inc.; *U.S. Public*, pg. 1016
SHG HOLDINGS CORP.; *U.S. Private*, pg. 3635
SHGINS INSURANCE SOLUTIONS LLC; *U.S. Private*, pg. 3635
SH GROUP A/S—See BWB Partners P/S; *Int'l*, pg. 1232
SH GROUP (HOLDINGS) LIMITED; *Int'l*, pg. 6746
SH HEAVY MACHINERY SDN. BHD.—See Sin Heng Heavy Machinery Limited; *Int'l*, pg. 6935
SHH RESOURCES HOLDINGS BERHAD; *Int'l*, pg. 6827
SHI ACCELERATOR SERVICE LTD.—See Sumitomo Heavy Industries, Ltd.; *Int'l*, pg. 7287
SHI AIRPORT SYSTEM CO., LTD.—See Sumitomo Heavy Industries, Ltd.; *Int'l*, pg. 7287
SHIANFU OPTICAL FIBER AND CABLES CO., LTD.—See The Furukawa Electric Co., Ltd.; *Int'l*, pg. 7647
SHIANG PAO PRECISION CO., LTD.—See Citizen Watch Co., Ltd.; *Int'l*, pg. 1625
SHIAN YIH ELECTRONIC INDUSTRY CO., LTD.; *Int'l*, pg. 6827
SHI-ATEX CO., LTD.—See Sumitomo Heavy Industries, Ltd.; *Int'l*, pg. 7288
SHIAWASSEE TELEPHONE CO. INC.—See Telephone & Data Systems, Inc.; *U.S. Public*, pg. 1998
SHIBATA INDUSTRY CO., LTD.—See Ashimori Industry Co., Ltd.; *Int'l*, pg. 607
SHIBAULA MECHATRONICS LTD.—See Japan Industrial Partners, Inc.; *Int'l*, pg. 3890
SHIBAURA ELECTRONICS CO., LTD.; *Int'l*, pg. 6827
SHIBAURA ELECTRONICS EUROPE GMBH—See Shibaura Electronics Co., Ltd.; *Int'l*, pg. 6827
SHIBAURA ELECTRONICS HONG KONG CO., LTD.—See Shibaura Electronics Co., Ltd.; *Int'l*, pg. 6827
SHIBAURA ELECTRONICS KOREA CO., LTD.—See Shibaura Electronics Co., Ltd.; *Int'l*, pg. 6827

2469

SHIBAURA ELECTRONICS CO., LTD.   CORPORATE AFFILIATIONS

SHIBAURA ELECTRONICS OF AMERICA CORPORATION—See Shibaura Electronics Co., Ltd.; *Int'l*, pg. 6827
SHIBAURA MACHINE CO., LTD.—See Japan Industrial Partners, Inc.; *Int'l*, pg. 3890
SHIBAURA MECHATRONICS CORPORATION—See Japan Industrial Partners, Inc.; *Int'l*, pg. 3891
SHIBAURA TECHNOLOGY INTERNATIONAL CORP.; *U.S. Private*, pg. 3635
SHIBUSAWA (HONG KONG) LTD.—See The Shibusawa Warehouse Co., Ltd.; *Int'l*, pg. 7681
SHIBUSAWA LOGISTICS (SHANGHAI) LTD.—See The Shibusawa Warehouse Co., Ltd.; *Int'l*, pg. 7681
SHIBUSAWA LOGISTICS VIETNAM CO., LTD.—See The Shibusawa Warehouse Co., Ltd.; *Int'l*, pg. 7681
THE SHIBUSAWA WAREHOUSE CO., LTD.; *Int'l*, pg. 7681
SHIBUYA CORPORATION; *Int'l*, pg. 6827
SHIBUYA EDI CO., LTD.—See Shibuya Corporation; *Int'l*, pg. 6827
SHIBUYA HOPPMAN CORPORATION—See Shibuya Corporation; *Int'l*, pg. 6827
SHIBUYA PACKAGING SYSTEM CORP.—See Shibuya Corporation; *Int'l*, pg. 6827
SHIBUYA SEIKI CO., LTD.—See Shibuya Corporation; *Int'l*, pg. 6827
SHI CANADA—See SHI International Corp.; *U.S. Private*, pg. 3635
SHICHUAN JINCAI PRINTING & PACKAGING CO., LTD.—See MYS Group Co., Ltd.; *Int'l*, pg. 5114
SHICK ESTEVE—See Hillenbrand, Inc.; *U.S. Public*, pg. 1037
SHICK TUBE-VEYOR CORPORATION—See Equistone Partners Europe Limited; *Int'l*, pg. 2486
SHI CRYOGENICS GROUP—See Sumitomo Heavy Industries, Ltd.; *Int'l*, pg. 7287
SHI CRYOGENICS OF KOREA, LTD.—See Sumitomo Heavy Industries, Ltd.; *Int'l*, pg. 7287
SHIDAX CORPORATION; *Int'l*, pg. 6827
SHI DESIGNING & MANUFACTURING INC.—See Sumitomo Heavy Industries, Ltd.; *Int'l*, pg. 7287
SHIDLER INVESTMENT COMPANY, LLC; *U.S. Private*, pg. 3635
SHI DONG SHANGHAI RUBBER CO., LTD.—See Sri Trang Agro-Industry Public Company Limited; *Int'l*, pg. 7150
SHIEH YIH MACHINERY INDUSTRY CO., LTD.; *Int'l*, pg. 6827
SHIEKH LLC; *U.S. Private*, pg. 3635
SHIELD AI INC.; *U.S. Private*, pg. 3635
SHIELD CORPORATION LIMITED - FACTORY—See Shield Corporation Limited; *Int'l*, pg. 6828
SHIELD CORPORATION LIMITED; *Int'l*, pg. 6828
SHIELD HEALTHCARE CENTERS—See Kobayashi Pharmaceutical Co., Ltd.; *Int'l*, pg. 4216
SHIELD PACKAGING OF CALIFORNIA; *U.S. Private*, pg. 3635
SHIELD REPLY LTD.—See Reply S.p.A.; *Int'l*, pg. 6291
SHIELD RESTRAINT SYSTEMS, INC.—See TransDigm Group Incorporated; *U.S. Public*, pg. 2183
SHIELD RESTRAINT SYSTEMS LTD.—See TransDigm Group Incorporated; *U.S. Public*, pg. 2183
SHIELDS ACQUISITION COMPANY; *U.S. Private*, pg. 3635
SHIELDS AUTO CENTER INC.; *U.S. Private*, pg. 3635
SHIELDS BROKERAGE LLC—See Integrity Marketing Group LLC; *U.S. Private*, pg. 2104
SHIELDS BUSINESS SOLUTIONS INC.; *U.S. Private*, pg. 3635
SHIELDS FOR FAMILIES, INC.; *U.S. Private*, pg. 3636
SHIELDS HARPER & CO. INC.; *U.S. Private*, pg. 3636
SHIELDS ORTHOTIC PROSTHETIC SERVICES, INC.—See Patient Square Capital, L.P.; *U.S. Private*, pg. 3107
SHIELD THERAPEUTICS PLC; *Int'l*, pg. 6828
SHIELD TX (SWITZERLAND) AG—See Shield Therapeutics plc; *Int'l*, pg. 6828
SHI ELECTRO-MECHANICAL SYSTEMS (TAIWAN) CO., LTD.—See Sumitomo Heavy Industries, Ltd.; *Int'l*, pg. 7287
SHIEL MEDICAL LABORATORY, INC.—See Quest Diagnostics, Inc.; *U.S. Public*, pg. 1756
SHI EXAMINATION & INSPECTION, LTD.—See Sumitomo Heavy Industries, Ltd.; *Int'l*, pg. 7287
SHIFA INTERNATIONAL DWC-LLC—See Shifa International Hospitals Ltd.; *Int'l*, pg. 6828
SHIFA INTERNATIONAL HOSPITALS LTD.; *Int'l*, pg. 6828
SHIFA MEDICAL CENTER ISLAMABAD (PVT.) LIMITED—See Shifa International Hospitals Ltd.; *Int'l*, pg. 6828
SHIFANG HOLDING LIMITED; *Int'l*, pg. 6828
SHIFENG CULTURAL DEVELOPMENT CO., LTD.; *Int'l*, pg. 6828
SHIFENG (SHENZHEN) INTERNET TECHNOLOGY LIMITED—See Shifeng Cultural Development Co., Ltd.; *Int'l*, pg. 6828
SHI FRANCE—See SHI International Corp.; *U.S. Private*, pg. 3635
SHIFT44, INC.—See PopReach Corporation; *Int'l*, pg. 5921

SHIFT4 CORPORATION—See Shift4 Payments, Inc.; *U.S. Public*, pg. 1875
SHIFT4 PAYMENTS, INC; *U.S. Public*, pg. 1874
SHIFT4 PAYMENTS, LLC—See Shift4 Payments, Inc.; *U.S. Public*, pg. 1874
SHIFT ADMINISTRATORS, LLC—See QGenda, LLC; *U.S. Private*, pg. 3313
SHIFT ASIA CO., LTD.—See SHIFT, Inc.; *Int'l*, pg. 6828
SHIFTCARBON INC.; *Int'l*, pg. 6828
SHIFT COMMUNICATIONS - NEW YORK—See RES PUBLICA Consulting Group Inc.; *Int'l*, pg. 6295
SHIFT COMMUNICATIONS - SAN FRANCISCO—See RES PUBLICA Consulting Group Inc.; *Int'l*, pg. 6295
SHIFT COMMUNICATIONS—See RES PUBLICA Consulting Group Inc.; *Int'l*, pg. 6295
SHIFT F7 LIMITED—See Macquarie Group Limited; *Int'l*, pg. 4631
SHIFT GLOBAL; *U.S. Private*, pg. 3636
SHIFT, INC.; *Int'l*, pg. 6828
SHIFT INDIA PVT. LTD.—See SHIFT, Inc.; *Int'l*, pg. 6828
SHIFTMED, LLC; *U.S. Private*, pg. 3636
SHIFTPIXY, INC.; *U.S. Public*, pg. 1875
SHIFT PLUS INC.—See AltPlus Inc.; *Int'l*, pg. 397
SHIFTRIGHT, INC.—See Zscaler, Inc.; *U.S. Public*, pg. 2411
SHIFT SECURITY, INC.—See SHIFT, Inc.; *Int'l*, pg. 6828
SHIFT TECHNOLOGIES, INC.; *U.S. Public*, pg. 1874
SHIFTWISE, INC.—See AMN Healthcare Services, Inc.; *U.S. Public*, pg. 125
SHIFTWIZARD, INC.—See HealthStream, Inc.; *U.S. Public*, pg. 1017
SHI FW ENERGIA FAKOP SP. Z.O.O.—See Sumitomo Heavy Industries, Ltd.; *Int'l*, pg. 7288
THE SHIGA BANK, LTD.; *Int'l*, pg. 7681
THE SHIGA DC CARD CO., LTD.—See The Shiga Bank, Ltd.; *Int'l*, pg. 7682
SHIGA DENSHI CORPORATION—See Kaneka Corporation; *Int'l*, pg. 4067
SHIGAGIN BUSINESS SERVICE COMPANY LIMITED, THE—See The Shiga Bank, Ltd.; *Int'l*, pg. 7682
SHIGAGIN COMPUTER SERVICE K.K.—See The Shiga Bank, Ltd.; *Int'l*, pg. 7682
THE SHIGAGIN ECONOMIC & CULTURAL CENTER CO., LTD.—See The Shiga Bank, Ltd.; *Int'l*, pg. 7682
SHIGAGIN JCB, K.K.—See The Shiga Bank, Ltd.; *Int'l*, pg. 7682
SHIGAGIN LEASE & CAPITAL CO., LTD—See The Shiga Bank, Ltd.; *Int'l*, pg. 7682
THE SHIGAGIN REAL ESTATE COMPANY LIMITED—See The Shiga Bank, Ltd.; *Int'l*, pg. 7682
SHIGA HINO MOTOR CO., LTD.—See Seino Holdings Co., Ltd.; *Int'l*, pg. 6691
SHIGA KASHIWABARA AGENCY COMPANY LIMITED—See The Shiga Bank, Ltd.; *Int'l*, pg. 7682
SHIGA KUTSUKI AGENCY COMPANY LIMITED, THE—See The Shiga Bank, Ltd.; *Int'l*, pg. 7682
SHIGA MINING CO., LTD.—See Sumitomo Osaka Cement Co Ltd; *Int'l*, pg. 7297
SHIGA SENKO TRANSPORT CO., LTD.—See Senko Group Holdings Co., Ltd.; *Int'l*, pg. 6711
SHIGA SHOFU INC.—See Shofu Inc.; *Int'l*, pg. 6858
SHIGEMATSU WORKS CO., LTD.; *Int'l*, pg. 6828
SHI GERMANY—See SHI International Corp.; *U.S. Private*, pg. 3635
SHIHASI INVESTMENT CORPORATION—See Northampton Group Inc.; *Int'l*, pg. 5442
SHIHEN TECHNICAL CORPORATION—See Daihen Corporation; *Int'l*, pg. 1927
SHIH HER TECHNOLOGIES, INC.; *Int'l*, pg. 6828
SHIH-KUEN PLASTICS CO., LTD.; *Int'l*, pg. 6828
SHIHLIN DEVELOPMENT CO., LTD.; *Int'l*, pg. 6828
SHIHLIN ELECTRIC (AUSTRALIA) PTY. LTD.—See Shihlin Electric & Engineering Corp.; *Int'l*, pg. 6829
SHIHLIN ELECTRIC & ENGINEERING CORP.; *Int'l*, pg. 6829
SHIHLIN ELECTRIC ENGINEERING EQUIPMENT VIETNAM COMPANY LIMITED—See Shihlin Electric & Engineering Corp.; *Int'l*, pg. 6829
SHIHLIN ELECTRIC (SUZHOU) POWER EQUIPMENT CO., LTD.—See Shihlin Electric & Engineering Corp.; *Int'l*, pg. 6829
SHIHLIN ELECTRIC USA COMPANY LIMITED—See Shihlin Electric & Engineering Corp.; *Int'l*, pg. 6829
SHIHLIN PAPER CORPORATION; *Int'l*, pg. 6829
SHI HOLDINGS PTY LIMITED—See Gowing Brothers Limited; *Int'l*, pg. 3044
SHI HONG KONG—See SHI International Corp.; *U.S. Private*, pg. 3635
SHIHO SCREW INDUSTRIAL CO., LTD.—See Nitto Seiko Co., Ltd.; *Int'l*, pg. 5388
SHIH WEI NAVIGATION CO., LTD.; *Int'l*, pg. 6828
SHI INDUSTRIAL EQUIPMENT (TAIWAN) CO., LTD.—See Sumitomo Heavy Industries, Ltd.; *Int'l*, pg. 7288
SHI INTERNATIONAL CORP.; *U.S. Private*, pg. 3635
SHIJIA U.S.—See Henan Shijia Photons Technology Co., Ltd.; *Int'l*, pg. 3343
SHIJI (AUSTRALIA) PTY LTD—See Beijing Shiji Information Technology Co., Ltd.; *Int'l*, pg. 956

SHIJIAZHUANG BAOHE AUTOMOTIVE SALES & SERVICE CO., LTD.—See China Yongda Automobiles Services Holdings Limited; *Int'l*, pg. 1565
SHIJIAZHUANG CHANGSHAN PHARMACY CO., LTD.—See Hebei Changshan Biochemical Pharmaceutical Co. Ltd.; *Int'l*, pg. 3305
SHIJIAZHUANG CHANGSHAN TEXTILE CO., LTD.; *Int'l*, pg. 6829
SHIJIAZHUANG CHENGFENG COGEN CO., LTD.—See Banpu Public Company Limited; *Int'l*, pg. 852
SHIJIAZHUANG CHIA TAI CO., LTD.—See Charoen Pokphand Foods Public Company Limited; *Int'l*, pg. 1453
SHIJIAZHUANG ENRIC GAS EQUIPMENT CO., LTD.—See China International Marine Containers (Group) Co., Ltd.; *Int'l*, pg. 1512
SHIJIAZHUANG GAOCHENG WEIYE GAS CO., LTD.—See Zhongyu Energy Holdings Limited; *Int'l*, pg. 8676
SHIJIAZHUANG JI-TAI PRECISION CASTING CO., LTD.—See Ta Chen Stainless Pipe, Ltd.; *Int'l*, pg. 7399
SHIJIAZHUANG JUNLEBAO DAIRY CO., LTD.; *Int'l*, pg. 6829
SHIJIAZHUANG KELIN ELECTRIC CO., LTD.; *Int'l*, pg. 6829
SHIJIAZHUANG LUQUAN DISTRICT CHENGUANG GAS CO., LTD.—See Zhongyu Energy Holdings Limited; *Int'l*, pg. 8676
SHIJIAZHUANG NO. 4 PHARMACEUTICAL CO., LTD.—See SSY Group Limited; *Int'l*, pg. 7157
SHIJIAZHUANG SHANGTAI TECHNOLOGY CO., LTD.; *Int'l*, pg. 6829
SHIJIAZHUANG TONHE ELECTRONICS TECHNOLOGIES CO., LTD.; *Int'l*, pg. 6829
SHIJIAZHUANG YILING PHARMACEUTICAL CO., LTD.; *Int'l*, pg. 6829
SHIJI DEUTSCHLAND GMBH—See Beijing Shiji Information Technology Co., Ltd.; *Int'l*, pg. 956
SHIJI GMBH—See Beijing Shiji Information Technology Co., Ltd.; *Int'l*, pg. 956
SHIJI (HONG KONG) LTD.—See Beijing Shiji Information Technology Co., Ltd.; *Int'l*, pg. 956
SHIJI INFORMATION TECHNOLOGY (HONG KONG) LIMITED—See Beijing Shiji Information Technology Co., Ltd.; *Int'l*, pg. 956
SHIJI INFORMATION TECHNOLOGY (PHILIPPINES), INC.—See Beijing Shiji Information Technology Co., Ltd.; *Int'l*, pg. 956
SHIJI INFORMATION TECHNOLOGY SPAIN, S.A.—See Beijing Shiji Information Technology Co., Ltd.; *Int'l*, pg. 956
SHIJI JAPAN CO., LTD.—See Beijing Shiji Information Technology Co., Ltd.; *Int'l*, pg. 956
SHIJI MALAYSIA SDN. BHD.—See Beijing Shiji Information Technology Co., Ltd.; *Int'l*, pg. 956
SHIJI MIDDLE EAST FZ-LLC—See Beijing Shiji Information Technology Co., Ltd.; *Int'l*, pg. 956
SHIJI POLAND SP. Z O.O.—See Beijing Shiji Information Technology Co., Ltd.; *Int'l*, pg. 956
SHIJI PORTUGAL - CONCEPTEK SISTEMAS DE INFORMACAO S.A.—See Beijing Shiji Information Technology Co., Ltd.; *Int'l*, pg. 956
SHIJI SINGAPORE PTE. LTD.—See Beijing Shiji Information Technology Co., Ltd.; *Int'l*, pg. 956
SHIJI SLOVAKIA S.R.O.—See Beijing Shiji Information Technology Co., Ltd.; *Int'l*, pg. 956
SHIJI THAILAND LIMITED—See Beijing Shiji Information Technology Co., Ltd.; *Int'l*, pg. 956
SHIJI (UK) LIMITED—See Beijing Shiji Information Technology Co., Ltd.; *Int'l*, pg. 956
SHIJI (US) INC.—See Beijing Shiji Information Technology Co., Ltd.; *Int'l*, pg. 956
SHIKHAR CONSULTANTS LIMITED; *Int'l*, pg. 6829
SHIKHAR INSURANCE COMPANY LTD.; *Int'l*, pg. 6829
SHIKHAR LEASING & TRADING LIMITED; *Int'l*, pg. 6829
SHIKIBO (HK) LTD.—See Shikibo Ltd.; *Int'l*, pg. 6829
SHIKIBO LINEN CO., LTD.—See Shikibo Ltd.; *Int'l*, pg. 6829
SHIKIBO LTD.; *Int'l*, pg. 6829
SHIKIGAKU CO., LTD.; *Int'l*, pg. 6830
SHIKINO HIGH-TECH CO., LTD.; *Int'l*, pg. 6830
SHIKISHIMA BAKING CO., LTD.; *Int'l*, pg. 6830
SHIKISHIMAKIKI CORPORATION—See Seika Corporation; *Int'l*, pg. 6685
SHIKISHIMA STARCH CO., LTD.—See Showa Sangyo Co., Ltd.; *Int'l*, pg. 6861
SHIKMA—See Kimberly-Clark Corporation; *U.S. Public*, pg. 1229
SHIKOKU ALFRESA CORPORATION—See Alfresa Holdings Corporation; *Int'l*, pg. 317
SHIKOKU ANALYTICAL LABORATORIES—See Shikoku Chemicals Corporation; *Int'l*, pg. 6830
THE SHIKOKU BANK LTD.; *Int'l*, pg. 7682
SHIKOKU CABLE CO LTD—See The Furukawa Electric Co., Ltd.; *Int'l*, pg. 7647
SHIKOKU CHEMICALS CORPORATIION - TOKUSHIMA PLANT (KITAJIMA)—See Shikoku Chemicals Corporation; *Int'l*, pg. 6830

COMPANY NAME INDEX

SHIKOKU CHEMICALS CORPORATION - MARUGAME PLANT—See Shikoku Chemicals Corporation; *Int'l*, pg. 6830
SHIKOKU CHEMICALS CORPORATION; *Int'l*, pg. 6830
SHIKOKU CHEMICALS CORPORATION - TOKUSHIMA PLANT (YOSHINARI)—See Shikoku Chemicals Corporation; *Int'l*, pg. 6830
SHIKOKU COCA-COLA BOTTLING CO., LTD.—See Coca-Cola Bottlers Japan Holdings Inc.; *Int'l*, pg. 1684
SHIKOKU DOCKYARD CO., LTD.; *Int'l*, pg. 6830
SHIKOKU ELECTRIC POWER CO., INCORPORATED; *Int'l*, pg. 6830
SHIKOKU ENVIRONMENTAL BUSINESS COMPANY—See Shikoku Chemicals Corporation; *Int'l*, pg. 6830
SHIKOKU ENVIRONMENT SERVICE CO., LTD.—See Hitachi Zosen Corporation; *Int'l*, pg. 3412
SHIKOKU HITACHI CO., LTD.—See Hitachi, Ltd.; *Int'l*, pg. 3424
SHIKOKU HITACHI SYSTEMS, LTD.—See Hitachi, Ltd.; *Int'l*, pg. 3424
SHIKOKU INSTRUMENTATION CO., LTD.—See Shikoku Electric Power Co., Incorporated; *Int'l*, pg. 6830
SHIKOKU INTERNATIONAL CORPORATION—See Shikoku Chemicals Corporation; *Int'l*, pg. 6830
SHIKOKU KAKOH CO., LTD.—See Moriroku Holdings Company, Ltd.; *Int'l*, pg. 5048
SHIKOKU KEIZAI CORPORATION - NARUTO PLANT—See Shikoku Chemicals Corporation; *Int'l*, pg. 6830
SHIKOKU KEIZAI CORPORATION—See Shikoku Chemicals Corporation; *Int'l*, pg. 6830
SHIKOKU KEIZAI KANTO CORPORATION—See Shikoku Chemicals Corporation; *Int'l*, pg. 6830
SHIKOKU KOSAN CORPORATION—See Shikoku Chemicals Corporation; *Int'l*, pg. 6830
SHIKOKU MARINE CUSTOMER SERVICE CO., LTD.—See Nabtesco Corporation; *Int'l*, pg. 5121
SHIKOKU MARUICHI STEEL TUBE LTD.—See Maruichi Steel Tube Ltd; *Int'l*, pg. 4714
SHIKOKU MEIJI CO., LTD.—See Meiji Holdings Co., Ltd.; *Int'l*, pg. 4801
SHIKOKU MEIJI DAIRIES CORPORATION—See Meiji Holdings Co., Ltd., *Int'l*, pg. 4801
SHIKOKU MORI SHIGYO CO., LTD.—See Oji Holdings Corporation; *Int'l*, pg. 5537
SHIKOKU NICHIREI SERVICE INC.—See Nichirei Corporation; *Int'l*, pg. 5270
SHIKOKU OM (SHANGHAI) CO., LTD.—See Shikoku Chemicals Corporation; *Int'l*, pg. 6830
SHIKOKU SEINO TRANSPORTATION CO., LTD.—See Seino Holdings Co., Ltd.; *Int'l*, pg. 6691
SHIKOKU SYSTEM KOHBOH CORPORATION—See Shikoku Chemicals Corporation; *Int'l*, pg. 6830
SHIKOKU TOHCELLO CO., LTD.—See Mitsui Chemicals, Inc.; *Int'l*, pg. 4984
SHIKOKUTSUKEN CO., LTD.—See MIRAIT ONE Corporation; *Int'l*, pg. 4918
SHIKOKU YAKUGYO CO. LTD.—See Medipal Holdings Corporation; *Int'l*, pg. 4779
SHIKOKU YOSHINOYA CO., LTD.—See Yoshinoya Holdings Co., Ltd.; *Int'l*, pg. 8600
SHIKUN & BINUI LTD.; *Int'l*, pg. 6830
SHIKUN & BINUI REAL ESTATE LTD.—See Shikun & Binui Ltd.; *Int'l*, pg. 6830
SHILCHAR TECHNOLOGIES LTD.; *Int'l*, pg. 6830
SHILDAN USA, INC.; *U.S. Private*, pg. 3636
SHILIN HOTEL OF HUANGSHAN TOURISM DEVELOPMENT CO., LTD.—See Huangshan Tourism Development Co., Ltd.; *Int'l*, pg. 3513
SHILLCRAFT, INC.; *U.S. Private*, pg. 3636
SHILLINGTON BOX COMPANY LLC; *U.S. Private*, pg. 3636
SHILOH CORPORATION; *U.S. Private*, pg. 3636
SHILOH INDUSTRIES AB—See Shiloh Industries, Inc.; *U.S. Private*, pg. 3636
SHILOH INDUSTRIES INC. DICKSON MANUFACTURING DIVISION—See Shiloh Industries, Inc.; *U.S. Private*, pg. 3636
SHILOH INDUSTRIES, INC.; *U.S. Private*, pg. 3636
SHILOH INDUSTRIES ITALIA SRL—See Shiloh Industries, Inc.; *U.S. Private*, pg. 3636
SHILOH INDUSTRIES NETHERLANDS B.V.—See Shiloh Industries, Inc.; *U.S. Private*, pg. 3636
SHILOH INDUSTRIES—See Shiloh Industries, Inc.; *U.S. Private*, pg. 3636
SHILOH INTERNACIONAL S.A. DE C.V.—See Shiloh Industries, Inc.; *U.S. Private*, pg. 3636
SHILOH MANUFACTURING DIVISION-LIVERPOOL—See Shiloh Industries, Inc.; *U.S. Private*, pg. 3636
SHILOH TECHNOLOGIES, LLC—See Rock Solid UK Ltd.; *U.S. Private*, pg. 3465
SHILO MANAGEMENT CORPORATION; *U.S. Private*, pg. 3636
SHILPA BIOLOGICALS PRIVATE LIMITED—See Shilpa Medicare Ltd; *Int'l*, pg. 6831
SHILPA MEDICARE LTD; *Int'l*, pg. 6831
SHILP GRAVURES LTD; *Int'l*, pg. 6831

SHIMA AMERICAN CORP.—See Shima Trading Co. Ltd.; *Int'l*, pg. 6831
SHIMA ASIA PACIFIC (M) SDN. BHD.—See Shima Trading Co. Ltd.; *Int'l*, pg. 6831
SHIMABARA DAIICHI TRAFFIC LTD.—See Daiichi Koutsu Sangyo Co., Ltd.; *Int'l*, pg. 1929
SHIMACHU CO., LTD.; *Int'l*, pg. 6831
SHIMA CO., LTD.—See Daito Trust Construction Co., Ltd.; *Int'l*, pg. 1944
SHIMADA GAS CO., LTD.—See Shizuokagas Co., Ltd.; *Int'l*, pg. 6856
SHIMADAYA CORPORATION—See Melco Holdings Inc.; *Int'l*, pg. 4808
SHIMADZU ANALYTICAL (INDIA) PVT. LTD.—See Shimadzu Corporation; *Int'l*, pg. 6832
SHIMADZU (ASIA PACIFIC) PTE. LTD.—See Shimadzu Corporation; *Int'l*, pg. 6832
SHIMADZU BENELUX B.V.—See Shimadzu Corporation; *Int'l*, pg. 6832
SHIMADZU CORPORATION; *Int'l*, pg. 6831
SHIMADZU DEUTSCHLAND GMBH—See Shimadzu Corporation; *Int'l*, pg. 6832
SHIMADZU DO BRASIL COMERCIO LTDA.—See Shimadzu Corporation; *Int'l*, pg. 6832
SHIMADZU D.O.O.—See Shimadzu Corporation; *Int'l*, pg. 6832
SHIMADZU EUROPA GMBH—See Shimadzu Corporation; *Int'l*, pg. 6832
SHIMADZU FRANCE SAS—See Shimadzu Corporation; *Int'l*, pg. 6832
SHIMADZU (GUANGZHOU) ANALYSIS & TECHNOLOGY SERVICES CO., LTD.—See Shimadzu Corporation; *Int'l*, pg. 6832
SHIMADZU HANDELSGESELLSCHAFT MBH—See Shimadzu Corporation; *Int'l*, pg. 6832
SHIMADZU (HONG KONG) LTD.—See Shimadzu Corporation; *Int'l*, pg. 6832
SHIMADZU ITALIA S.R.L.—See Shimadzu Corporation; *Int'l*, pg. 6832
SHIMADZU KOREA VACUUM EQUIPMENT CO., LTD.—See Shimadzu Corporation; *Int'l*, pg. 6832
SHIMADZU LATIN AMERICA S.A.—See Shimadzu Corporation; *Int'l*, pg. 6832
SHIMADZU MALAYSIA SDN. BHD.—See Shimadzu Corporation; *Int'l*, pg. 6832
SHIMADZU MANUFACTURING ASIA SDN. BHD.—See Shimadzu Corporation; *Int'l*, pg. 6832
SHIMADZU MEDICAL (INDIA) PVT. LTD.—See Shimadzu Corporation; *Int'l*, pg. 6832
SHIMADZU MEDICAL SYSTEMS (OCEANIA) PTY. LTD.—See Shimadzu Corporation; *Int'l*, pg. 6832
SHIMADZU MEDICAL SYSTEMS USA—See Shimadzu Corporation; *Int'l*, pg. 6832
SHIMADZU MIDDLE EAST & AFRICA FZE—See Shimadzu Corporation; *Int'l*, pg. 6832
SHIMADZU PHILIPPINES CORPORATION—See Shimadzu Corporation; *Int'l*, pg. 6832
SHIMADZU PHILIPPINES MANUFACTURING INC.—See Shimadzu Corporation; *Int'l*, pg. 6832
SHIMADZU PRECISION INSTRUMENTS, INC.-MEDICAL SYSTEM DIV.—See Shimadzu Corporation; *Int'l*, pg. 6832
SHIMADZU PRECISION INSTRUMENTS, INC.—See Shimadzu Corporation; *Int'l*, pg. 6832
SHIMADZU RESEARCH LABORATORY (EUROPE) LTD.—See Shimadzu Corporation; *Int'l*, pg. 6832
SHIMADZU RESEARCH LABORATORY (SHANGHAI) CO., LTD.—See Shimadzu Corporation; *Int'l*, pg. 6832
SHIMADZU SCHWEIZ GMBH—See Shimadzu Corporation; *Int'l*, pg. 6832
SHIMADZU SCIENTIFIC INSTRUMENTS, INC.—See Shimadzu Corporation; *Int'l*, pg. 6832
SHIMADZU SCIENTIFIC INSTRUMENTS (OCEANIA) PTY LIMITED—See Shimadzu Corporation; *Int'l*, pg. 6832
SHIMADZU SCIENTIFIC INSTRUMENTS—See Shimadzu Corporation; *Int'l*, pg. 6832
SHIMADZU SCIENTIFIC INSTRUMENTS (TAIWAN) CO., LTD.—See Shimadzu Corporation; *Int'l*, pg. 6832
SHIMADZU SCIENTIFIC KOREA CORPORATION—See Shimadzu Corporation; *Int'l*, pg. 6832
SHIMADZU (SHANGHAI) GLOBAL LABORATORY CONSUMABLES CO., LTD.—See Shimadzu Corporation; *Int'l*, pg. 6832
SHIMADZU SINGAPORE PTE. LTD.—See Shimadzu Corporation; *Int'l*, pg. 6832
SHIMADZU SLOVAKIA O.Z.—See Shimadzu Corporation; *Int'l*, pg. 6832
SHIMADZU SOFTWARE DEVELOPMENT CANADA—See Shimadzu Corporation; *Int'l*, pg. 6832
SHIMADZU SOUTH AFRICA (PTY) LTD.—See Shimadzu Corporation; *Int'l*, pg. 6832
SHIMADZU (SUZHOU) INSTRUMENTS MANUFACTURING CO., LTD.—See Shimadzu Corporation; *Int'l*, pg. 6832
SHIMADZU TAIWAN INDUSTRIAL MACHINERY CO., LTD.—See Shimadzu Corporation; *Int'l*, pg. 6833
SHIMADZU UK LIMITED—See Shimadzu Corporation; *Int'l*, pg. 6833

SHIMANO, INC.

SHIMADZU U.S.A. MANUFACTURING, INC.—See Shimadzu Corporation; *Int'l*, pg. 6833
SHIMADZU VACUUM EQUIPMENT (SHANGHAI) CO., LTD.—See Shimadzu Corporation; *Int'l*, pg. 6833
SHIMADZU VIETNAM CO., LTD.—See Shimadzu Corporation; *Int'l*, pg. 6833
SHIMA ELECTRONIC INDUSTRY (MALAYSIA) SDN. BHD.—See nms Holdings Corporation; *Int'l*, pg. 5393
SHIMA FINE PRESS CO., LTD.—See Shima Seiki Mfg., Ltd.; *Int'l*, pg. 6831
SHIMAL SERVICE MMC—See Einhell Germany AG; *Int'l*, pg. 2334
SHIMAMURA CO., LTD.; *Int'l*, pg. 6833
SHIMANE BANK LTD.; *Int'l*, pg. 6833
SHIMANE EAGLE CO., LTD.—See Eagle Industry Co., Ltd.; *Int'l*, pg. 2266
SHIMANE FUJITSU LIMITED—See Fujitsu Limited; *Int'l*, pg. 2837
SHIMANE HINO MOTOR LTD.—See Toyota Motor Corporation; *Int'l*, pg. 7871
SHIMANE MORI SHIGYO CO., LTD.—See Oji Holdings Corporation; *Int'l*, pg. 5537
SHIMANO ARGENTINA S.A.U.—See Shimano, Inc.; *Int'l*, pg. 6833
SHIMANO AUSTRALIA CYCLING PTY. LTD.—See Shimano, Inc.; *Int'l*, pg. 6833
SHIMANO AUSTRALIA FISHING PTY LTD—See Shimano, Inc.; *Int'l*, pg. 6833
SHIMANO BALIKCILIK MALZEMELERI VE EKIPMANLARI SATIS TICARET ANONIM SIRKETI—See Shimano, Inc.; *Int'l*, pg. 6833
SHIMANO BELGIUM N.V.—See Shimano, Inc.; *Int'l*, pg. 6833
SHIMANO BENELUX B.V.—See Shimano, Inc.; *Int'l*, pg. 6833
SHIMANO BIKE & FISHING MEXICO S.A. DE C.V.—See Shimano, Inc.; *Int'l*, pg. 6833
SHIMANO BISIKLET PARCA VE EKIPMANLARI SATIS SERVIS TICARET ANONIM SIRKETI—See Shimano, Inc.; *Int'l*, pg. 6833
SHIMANO (CAMBODIA) CO., LTD.—See Shimano, Inc.; *Int'l*, pg. 6833
SHIMANO CANADA LTD.—See Shimano, Inc.; *Int'l*, pg. 6833
SHIMANO COMPONENTS (MALAYSIA) SDN. BHD.—See Shimano, Inc.; *Int'l*, pg. 6833
SHIMANO CYCLING WORLD PTE. LTD.—See Shimano, Inc.; *Int'l*, pg. 6833
SHIMANO CZECH REPUBLIC S.R.O—See Shimano, Inc.; *Int'l*, pg. 6834
SHIMANO EUROPE B.V.—See Shimano, Inc.; *Int'l*, pg. 6834
SHIMANO EUROPE B.V.—See Shimano, Inc.; *Int'l*, pg. 6834
SHIMANO EUROPE FISHING HOLDING BV—See Sapporo Holdings Limited; *Int'l*, pg. 6574
SHIMANO EUROPE FISHING HOLDING B.V.—See Shimano, Inc.; *Int'l*, pg. 6834
SHIMANO EUROPE HOLDING B.V.—See Shimano, Inc.; *Int'l*, pg. 6834
SHIMANO FRANCE COMPOSANTS CYCLES S.A.S.—See Shimano, Inc.; *Int'l*, pg. 6834
SHIMANO FRANCE—See Shimano, Inc.; *Int'l*, pg. 6834
SHIMANO GERMANY FISHING GMBH—See Shimano, Inc.; *Int'l*, pg. 6834
SHIMANO IBERIA, S.L.—See Shimano, Inc.; *Int'l*, pg. 6834
SHIMANO, INC.; *Int'l*, pg. 6833
SHIMANO, INC. - YAMAGUCHI FACTORY—See Shimano, Inc.; *Int'l*, pg. 6834
SHIMANO ITALY BICYCLE COMPONENTS S.R.L.—See Shimano, Inc.; *Int'l*, pg. 6834
SHIMANO ITALY FISHING S.R.L.—See Shimano, Inc.; *Int'l*, pg. 6834
SHIMANO KUMAMOTO CO., LTD.—See Shimano, Inc.; *Int'l*, pg. 6834
SHIMANO (KUNSHAN) BICYCLE COMPONENTS CO., LTD.—See Shimano, Inc.; *Int'l*, pg. 6833
SHIMANO (KUNSHAN) FISHING TACKLE CO., LTD.—See Shimano, Inc.; *Int'l*, pg. 6833
SHIMANO LATIN AMERICA REPRESENTACAO COMERCIAL LTDA.—See Shimano, Inc.; *Int'l*, pg. 6833
SHIMANO (LIANYUNGANG) INDUSTRIAL CO., LTD.—See Shimano, Inc.; *Int'l*, pg. 6833
SHIMANO MENAT SPOR ETKINLIKLERI SPOR MALZEMELERI VE EKIPMANLARI TICARET LIMITED SIRKETI—See Shimano, Inc.; *Int'l*, pg. 6834
SHIMANO NEW ZEALAND LTD.—See Shimano, Inc.; *Int'l*, pg. 6834
SHIMANO NORDIC AB—See Shimano, Inc.; *Int'l*, pg. 6834
SHIMANO NORDIC AS—See Shimano, Inc.; *Int'l*, pg. 6834
SHIMANO NORDIC CYCLE AB—See Shimano, Inc.; *Int'l*, pg. 6834
SHIMANO NORDIC CYCLE AS—See Shimano, Inc.; *Int'l*, pg. 6834
SHIMANO NORDIC CYCLE OY—See Shimano, Inc.; *Int'l*, pg. 6834
SHIMANO NORDIC DENMARK APS—See Shimano, Inc.; *Int'l*, pg. 6834

SHIMANO NORDIC OY—See Shimano, Inc.; *Int'l*, pg. 6834
SHIMANO NORTH AMERICA FISHING, INC.—See Shimano, Inc.; *Int'l*, pg. 6834
SHIMANO NORTH AMERICA HOLDING, INC.—See Shimano, Inc.; *Int'l*, pg. 6834
SHIMANO OCEANIA HOLDINGS PTY LTD—See Shimano, Inc.; *Int'l*, pg. 6834
SHIMANO (PHILIPPINES) INC.—See Shimano, Inc.; *Int'l*, pg. 6833
SHIMANO POLSKA SP. Z O.O.—See Shimano, Inc.; *Int'l*, pg. 6834
SHIMANO PTE. LTD.—See Shimano, Inc.; *Int'l*, pg. 6834
SHIMANO SALES CO., LTD.—See Shimano, Inc.; *Int'l*, pg. 6834
SHIMANO (SHANGHAI) BICYCLE COMPONENTS CO., LTD.—See Shimano, Inc.; *Int'l*, pg. 6833
SHIMANO (SHANGHAI) SALES CORPORATION—See Shimano, Inc.; *Int'l*, pg. 6833
SHIMANO (SINGAPORE) PTE. LTD.—See Shimano, Inc.; *Int'l*, pg. 6833
SHIMANO SOUTH ASIA PRIVATE LTD.—See Shimano, Inc.; *Int'l*, pg. 6834
SHIMANO TAIWAN CO., LTD.—See Shimano, Inc.; *Int'l*, pg. 6833
SHIMANO (TIANJIN) BICYCLE COMPONENTS CO., LTD.—See Shimano, Inc.; *Int'l*, pg. 6833
SHIMANO U.K. LTD.—See Shimano, Inc.; *Int'l*, pg. 6834
SHIMANO URUGUAY S.A.—See Shimano, Inc.; *Int'l*, pg. 6834
SHI MANUFACTURING & SERVICES (PHILIPPINES), INC.—See Sumitomo Heavy Industries, Ltd.; *Int'l*, pg. 7288
SHIMAO GROUP HOLDINGS LTD.; *Int'l*, pg. 6834
SHIMAO SERVICES HOLDINGS CO., LTD.; *Int'l*, pg. 6834
SHIMA SEIKI EUROPE LTD.—See Shima Seiki Mfg., Ltd.; *Int'l*, pg. 6831
SHIMA SEIKI FRANCE SARL—See Shima Seiki Mfg., Ltd.; *Int'l*, pg. 6831
SHIMA SEIKI (HONG KONG) LTD.—See Shima Seiki Mfg., Ltd.; *Int'l*, pg. 6831
SHIMA SEIKI ITALIA S.P.A.—See Shima Seiki Mfg., Ltd.; *Int'l*, pg. 6831
SHIMA SEIKI KOREA, INC.—See Shima Seiki Mfg., Ltd.; *Int'l*, pg. 6831
SHIMA SEIKI MFG., LTD.; *Int'l*, pg. 6831
SHIMA SEIKI SPAIN, S.A.U.—See Shima Seiki Mfg., Ltd.; *Int'l*, pg. 6831
SHIMA SEIKI (THAILAND) CO., LTD.—See Shima Seiki Mfg., Ltd.; *Int'l*, pg. 6831
SHIMA SEIKI U.S.A. INC.—See Shima Seiki Mfg., Ltd.; *Int'l*, pg. 6831
SHIMA SEIKI WINWIN DONGGUAN LTD.—See Shima Seiki Mfg., Ltd.; *Int'l*, pg. 6831
SHIMA SEIKI WIN WIN SHANGHAI LTD.—See Shima Seiki Mfg., Ltd.; *Int'l*, pg. 6831
SHI MATERIAL HANDLING MACHINERY (SHANGHAI) CO., LTD.—See Sumitomo Heavy Industries, Ltd.; *Int'l*, pg. 7288
SHIMA TRADING CO. LTD.; *Int'l*, pg. 6831
SHIMA TRADING (SHANGHAI) CO., LTD.—See Shima Trading Co. Ltd.; *Int'l*, pg. 6831
SHIMA TRADING SINGAPORE PTE. LTD.—See Shima Trading Co. Ltd.; *Int'l*, pg. 6831
SHIMAYA CO., LTD.—See Toyo Suisan Kaisha, Ltd.; *Int'l*, pg. 7858
SHIMAYAKOUSAN CO., LTD.—See Konoike Transport Co., Ltd.; *Int'l*, pg. 4275
SHIMIZU ALLOY MFG CO., LTD.—See KITZ CORPORATION; *Int'l*, pg. 4196
SHIMIZU AMERICA, INC.—See Shimizu Corporation; *Int'l*, pg. 6835
SHIMIZU BANK, LTD.; *Int'l*, pg. 6834
SHIMIZU BLC CO., LTD.—See Shimizu Corporation; *Int'l*, pg. 6835
SHIMIZU BUILDING LIFE CARE KANSAI, CO., LTD.—See Shimizu Corporation; *Int'l*, pg. 6835
SHIMIZU BUILDING LIFE CARE KYUSHU, CO., LTD.—See Shimizu Corporation; *Int'l*, pg. 6835
SHIMIZU CANADA ENGINEERING CORPORATION—See Shimizu Corporation; *Int'l*, pg. 6835
THE SHIMIZU CARD SERVICE CO., LTD—See Shimizu Bank, Ltd.; *Int'l*, pg. 6834
SHIMIZU CORPORATION (CHINA) LTD.—See Shimizu Corporation; *Int'l*, pg. 6835
SHIMIZU CORPORATION DE MEXICO—See Shimizu Corporation; *Int'l*, pg. 6835
SHIMIZU CORPORATION INDIA PTE. LTD.—See Shimizu Corporation; *Int'l*, pg. 6835
SHIMIZU CORPORATION; *Int'l*, pg. 6835
SHIMIZU CORPORATION—See Shimizu Corporation; *Int'l*, pg. 6835
SHIMIZU CORPORATION—See Shimizu Corporation; *Int'l*, pg. 6835
SHIMIZU CORPORATION—See Shimizu Corporation; *Int'l*, pg. 6835
SHIMIZU CORPORATION—See Shimizu Corporation; *Int'l*, pg. 6835

SHIMIZU CORPORATION—See Shimizu Corporation; *Int'l*, pg. 6835
SHIMIZU CORPORATION—See Shimizu Corporation; *Int'l*, pg. 6835
SHIMIZU CORPORATION—See Shimizu Corporation; *Int'l*, pg. 6835
SHIMIZU CORPORATION—See Shimizu Corporation; *Int'l*, pg. 6835
SHIMIZU CORPORATION—See Shimizu Corporation; *Int'l*, pg. 6835
SHIMIZU CORPORATION—See Shimizu Corporation; *Int'l*, pg. 6835
SHIMIZU CORPORATION—See Shimizu Corporation; *Int'l*, pg. 6835
SHIMIZU CORPORATION—See Shimizu Corporation; *Int'l*, pg. 6835
SHIMIZU CORPORATION—See Shimizu Corporation; *Int'l*, pg. 6835
SHIMIZU CORPORATION—See Shimizu Corporation; *Int'l*, pg. 6835
SHIMIZU DANBORU CO., LTD.—See Tomoku Co., Ltd.; *Int'l*, pg. 7802
SHIMIZU EUROPE LTD.—See Shimizu Corporation; *Int'l*, pg. 6835
SHIMIZU FINANCE CO., LTD.—See Shimizu Corporation; *Int'l*, pg. 6835
THE SHIMIZU GENERAL COMPUTER SERVICE CO., LTD.—See Shimizu Bank, Ltd.; *Int'l*, pg. 6834
THE SHIMIZUGIN CAREER UP CO., LTD—See Shimizu Bank, Ltd.; *Int'l*, pg. 6834
SHIMIZU HONG KONG CO., LTD.—See Shimizu Corporation; *Int'l*, pg. 6835
SHIMIZU INDUSTRY CO., LTD—See Denso Corporation; *Int'l*, pg. 2032
SHIMIZU INTERNATIONAL CAPITAL (SINGAPORE) PTE. LTD.—See Shimizu Corporation; *Int'l*, pg. 6835
SHIMIZU INTERNATIONAL FINANCE (UK) LTD.—See Shimizu Corporation; *Int'l*, pg. 6835
SHIMIZU INTERNATIONAL FINANCE (U.S.A.), INC.—See Shimizu Corporation; *Int'l*, pg. 6835
SHIMIZU INVESTMENT (ASIA) PTE. LTD.—See Shimizu Corporation; *Int'l*, pg. 6836
THE SHIMIZU JCB CARD CO., LTD—See Shimizu Bank, Ltd.; *Int'l*, pg. 6834
SHIMIZU KAWASAKI TRANSPORTATION CO., LTD—See Kawasaki Kisen Kaisha, Ltd.; *Int'l*, pg. 4101
SHIMIZU LNG CO., LTD.—See Shizuokagas Co., Ltd.; *Int'l*, pg. 6856
SHIMIZU NORTH AMERICA LLC - NEW YORK—See Shimizu Corporation; *Int'l*, pg. 6836
SHIMIZU NORTH AMERICA LLC—See Shimizu Corporation; *Int'l*, pg. 6836
SHIMIZU NORTH AMERICA LLC—See Shimizu Corporation; *Int'l*, pg. 6836
SHIMIZU PHILIPPINE CONTRACTORS, INC.—See Shimizu Corporation; *Int'l*, pg. 6836
THE SHIMIZU REGIONAL ECONOMY RESEARCH CENTER, INC—See Shimizu Bank, Ltd.; *Int'l*, pg. 6834
SHIMIZU SHOJI CO., LTD.—See AEON Co., Ltd.; *Int'l*, pg. 178
SHIMMICK CONSTRUCTION COMPANY, INC.—See AECOM; *U.S. Public*, pg. 51
SHIMMICK CORPORATION; *U.S. Public*, pg. 1875
SHIMNIT UTSCH INDIA PVT. LTD.—See Erich Utsch AG; *Int'l*, pg. 2493
SHIMODA AQUA SERVICE INC.—See Fujita Kanko Inc.; *Int'l*, pg. 2831
SHIMODA CENTRAL CO., LTD.—See Taisho Pharmaceutical Holdings Co., Ltd; *Int'l*, pg. 7417
SHIMODA GAS CO., LTD.—See Shizuokagas Co., Ltd.; *Int'l*, pg. 6856
SHIMOJIMA CO., LTD.; *Int'l*, pg. 6836
SHIMOJIMA KAKOUSHI CO., LTD.—See Shimojima Co., Ltd.; *Int'l*, pg. 6836
SHIMOJIMA PACKAGE CO., LTD.—See Shimojima Co., Ltd.; *Int'l*, pg. 6836
SHIMOJIMA (SHANGHAI) CO., LTD.—See Shimojima Co., Ltd.; *Int'l*, pg. 6836
SHIMOMURA TOKUSHU SEIKO CO., LTD.—See Daido Steel Co., Ltd.; *Int'l*, pg. 1923
SHIMONOSEKI DAIMARU, INC.—See J. Front Retailing Co., Ltd.; *Int'l*, pg. 3855
SHIMONOSEKI GYOKO UNYU INC.—See Nichirei Corporation; *Int'l*, pg. 5270
SHIMONOSEKI MITSUI CHEMICALS, INC.—See Mitsui Chemicals, Inc.; *Int'l*, pg. 4984
SHIMONOSEKI RYOJU ENGINEERING CO., LTD.—See Mitsubishi Heavy Industries, Ltd.; *Int'l*, pg. 4961
SHIMPO DRIVES INCORPORATION—See Nidec Corporation; *Int'l*, pg. 5275
SHIMS BARGAIN INC.; *U.S. Private*, pg. 3636
SHINA CORPORATION—See CNL Strategic Capital Management LLC; *U.S. Private*, pg. 952
SHINAGAWA FINE CERAMICS CO., LTD.—See Shinagawa Refractories Co., Ltd.; *Int'l*, pg. 6841

SHINAGAWA KAIHATSU CO., LTD.—See Shinagawa Refractories Co., Ltd.; *Int'l*, pg. 6841
SHINAGAWA KIGYO CO., LTD.—See Shinagawa Refractories Co., Ltd.; *Int'l*, pg. 6841
SHINAGAWA PRECISION MACHINERY (ZHEJIANG) CO., LTD.—See TSUGAMI CORPORATION; *Int'l*, pg. 7955
SHINAGAWA REFRACTORIES AUSTRALASIA NEW ZEALAND LTD.—See Shinagawa Refractories Co., Ltd.; *Int'l*, pg. 6841
SHINAGAWA REFRACTORIES AUSTRALASIA PTY. LTD.—See Shinagawa Refractories Co., Ltd.; *Int'l*, pg. 6841
SHINAGAWA REFRACTORIES CO., LTD. - AKO WORKS—See Shinagawa Refractories Co., Ltd.; *Int'l*, pg. 6841
SHINAGAWA REFRACTORIES CO., LTD. - FURNACE CONSTRUCTION DIVISION—See Shinagawa Refractories Co., Ltd.; *Int'l*, pg. 6841
SHINAGAWA REFRACTORIES CO., LTD. - OKAYAMA WORKS—See Shinagawa Refractories Co., Ltd.; *Int'l*, pg. 6841
SHINAGAWA REFRACTORIES CO., LTD.; *Int'l*, pg. 6841
SHINAGAWA REFRACTORIES CO., LTD. - YUMOTO WORKS—See Shinagawa Refractories Co., Ltd.; *Int'l*, pg. 6841
SHINAGAWA ROKO CO., LTD.—See Shinagawa Refractories Co., Ltd.; *Int'l*, pg. 6841
SHIN AH LIMITED—See Ace Technologies Corp.; *Int'l*, pg. 95
SHINAM OIL CO., LTD.—See Dongjin Semichem Co., Ltd.; *Int'l*, pg. 2168
SHINANO ELECTRIC REFINING CO., LTD. - KASHIWABARA PLANT—See Shin-Etsu Chemical Co. Ltd.; *Int'l*, pg. 6840
SHINANO ELECTRIC REFINING CO., LTD.—See Shin-Etsu Chemical Co. Ltd.; *Int'l*, pg. 6840
SHINANO ELECTRONICS CO., LTD.—See Inabata & Co. Ltd.; *Int'l*, pg. 3644
SHINANO FUJITSU LIMITED—See FUJITSU COMPONENT LIMITED; *Int'l*, pg. 2832
SHINANO POLYMER CO., LTD.—See Shin-Etsu Chemical Co. Ltd.; *Int'l*, pg. 6840
SHINAN WIND POWER GENERATION CO—See Dongkuk S&C Co., Ltd.; *Int'l*, pg. 2169
SHINBA-EDARAN SDN. BHD.—See Edran Berhad; *Int'l*, pg. 2315
SHINBUNDANG RAILROAD CO., LTD.—See Korea Development Bank; *Int'l*, pg. 4283
SHINCHANG CONNECTOR CO., LTD.—See Mobase Co., Ltd.; *Int'l*, pg. 5007
SHIN CHANG CONNECTOR CO., LTD.—See The Furukawa Electric Co., Ltd.; *Int'l*, pg. 7647
SHIN CHANG INTERNATIONAL INC.—See Doppelmayr Group; *Int'l*, pg. 2175
S&H INCORPORATED; *U.S. Private*, pg. 3513
SHINCO TECHNOLOGIES LIMITED—See Zheng Hsing Industrial Co., Ltd.; *Int'l*, pg. 8669
SHINDAEYANG PAPER CO., LTD.; *Int'l*, pg. 6841
SHINDAGHA PHARMACY LLC—See Aster DM Healthcare Ltd.; *Int'l*, pg. 654
SHIN DAI-ICHI VINYL CORPORATION—See Tokuyama Corporation; *Int'l*, pg. 7787
SHINDENGEN AMERICA INC.—See Shindengen Electric Manufacturing Co., Ltd.; *Int'l*, pg. 6842
SHINDENGEN DEVICE COMMERCE CO., LTD.—See Shindengen Electric Manufacturing Co., Ltd.; *Int'l*, pg. 6842
SHINDENGEN ELECTRIC MANUFACTURING CO., LTD. - HANNO FACTORY—See Shindengen Electric Manufacturing Co., Ltd.; *Int'l*, pg. 6842
SHINDENGEN ELECTRIC MANUFACTURING CO., LTD.; *Int'l*, pg. 6841
SHINDENGEN ENTERPRISE CO., LTD.—See Shindengen Electric Manufacturing Co., Ltd.; *Int'l*, pg. 6842
SHINDENGEN (H.K.) CO., LTD.—See Shindengen Electric Manufacturing Co., Ltd.; *Int'l*, pg. 6842
SHINDENGEN INDIA PVT. LTD.—See Shindengen Electric Manufacturing Co., Ltd.; *Int'l*, pg. 6842
SHINDENGEN KUMAMOTO TECHNORESEARCH CO., LTD.—See Shindengen Electric Manufacturing Co., Ltd.; *Int'l*, pg. 6842
SHINDENGEN MECHATRONICS CO., LTD.—See Musashi Kogyo Co., Ltd.; *Int'l*, pg. 5101
SHINDENGEN MECHATRONICS CO., LTD.—See Shindengen Electric Manufacturing Co., Ltd.; *Int'l*, pg. 6842
SHINDENGEN PHILIPPINES CORP.—See Shindengen Electric Manufacturing Co., Ltd.; *Int'l*, pg. 6842
SHINDENGEN (SHANGHAI) ELECTRIC CO., LTD.—See Shindengen Electric Manufacturing Co., Ltd.; *Int'l*, pg. 6842
SHINDENGEN SINGAPORE PTE LTD.—See Shindengen Electric Manufacturing Co., Ltd.; *Int'l*, pg. 6842
SHINDENGEN (THAILAND) CO., LTD.—See Shindengen Electric Manufacturing Co., Ltd.; *Int'l*, pg. 6842
SHINDENGEN THREE E CO., LTD.—See Shindengen Electric Manufacturing Co., Ltd.; *Int'l*, pg. 6842
SHINDENGEN UK LTD.—See Shindengen Electric Manufacturing Co., Ltd.; *Int'l*, pg. 6842

COMPANY NAME INDEX

SHINDENGEN VIETNAM CO., LTD.—See Shindengen Electric Manufacturing Co., Ltd.; *Int'l*, pg. 6842
SHINDEN HIGHTEX CORPORATION; *Int'l*, pg. 6841
SHINDEN HIGHTEX KOREA CORPORATION—See Shinden Hightex Corporation; *Int'l*, pg. 6841
SHINDEN HONG KONG LIMITED—See Shinden Hightex Corporation; *Int'l*, pg. 6841
SHINDO ENG. LAB., LTD.; *Int'l*, pg. 6842
SHINDONG CORPORATION—See Ilshin Spinning Co., Ltd.; *Int'l*, pg. 3616
SHINDONG WINE CO., LTD.—See Ilshin Spinning Co., Ltd.; *Int'l*, pg. 3616
SHINE (AUST) PTY LIMITED—See LOV Group Invest SAS; *Int'l*, pg. 4565
SHINE AUSTRALIA HOLDINGS PTY LIMITED—See LOV Group Invest SAS; *Int'l*, pg. 4565
SHINE BOX CAPITAL CORP.; *Int'l*, pg. 6842
SHINE BROS CORP.; *U.S. Private*, pg. 3637
SHINECHLEL INVEST JOINT STOCK COMPANY; *Int'l*, pg. 6842
SHINECO, INC.; *Int'l*, pg. 6843
SHINE COMMUNICATIONS LIMITED—See The Academy; *Int'l*, pg. 7610
SHINE DEVELOPMENT BANK LTD.; *Int'l*, pg. 6842
SHINE FASHIONS (INDIA) LTD.; *Int'l*, pg. 6842
SHINE FINLAND OY—See LOV Group Invest SAS; *Int'l*, pg. 4565
SHINE FOOD, INC.; *U.S. Private*, pg. 3637
SHINEFOODS PTE LTD.—See QAF Limited; *Int'l*, pg. 6132
SHINE GERMANY FILM UND FERNSEBPRODUKTION GMBH—See LOV Group Invest SAS; *Int'l*, pg. 4565
SHINE GERMANY FILM- UND FERNSEHPRODUKTION GMBH—See LOV Group Invest SAS; *Int'l*, pg. 4565
SHINE IBERIA SLU—See LOV Group Invest SAS; *Int'l*, pg. 4565
SHINEI ENGINEER CORPORATION—See K&O Energy Group Inc.; *Int'l*, pg. 4038
SHINEI INDUSTRY CO., LTD.—See NOK Corporation; *Int'l*, pg. 5403
SHINEI KIKO CO., LTD.—See Nippon Steel Corporation; *Int'l*, pg. 5339
SHIN-EI SHOJI CO., LTD.—See TERAOKA SEISAKUSHO Co Ltd; *Int'l*, pg. 7563
SHINE JUSTICE LTD.; *Int'l*, pg. 6842
SHINELONG AUTOMOTIVE LIGHTWEIGHT APPLICATION LIMITED; *Int'l*, pg. 6843
SHINE LTD.—See LOV Group Invest SAS; *Int'l*, pg. 4565
SHINE MEDICAL TECHNOLOGIES, LLC; *U.S. Private*, pg. 3637
SHINE MINERALS CORP.; *Int'l*, pg. 6842
SHINEMORE TECHNOLOGY MATERIALS CORPORATION LTD.; *Int'l*, pg. 6843
SHINE NORDIC FORMATS AB—See LOV Group Invest SAS; *Int'l*, pg. 4565
SHINE NORDICS AB—See LOV Group Invest SAS; *Int'l*, pg. 4565
SHIN ENTERPRISES INC.; *U.S. Private*, pg. 3637
SHINEPUKUR CERAMICS LIMITED; *Int'l*, pg. 6843
SHINE RESUNGA DEVELOPMENT BANK LIMITED; *Int'l*, pg. 6842
SHINER INTERNATIONAL, INC.; *Int'l*, pg. 6843
SHINEROAD FOOD TECHNOLOGY (VIETNAM) CO., LTD.—See Shineroad International Holdings Limited; *Int'l*, pg. 6843
SHINEROAD INTERNATIONAL HOLDINGS LIMITED; *Int'l*, pg. 6843
SHINE'S CO., LTD.—See Toyota Industries Corporation; *Int'l*, pg. 7866
SHINE@SPRING PTE. LTD.; *Int'l*, pg. 6842
SHINE STAR (HUBEI) BIOLOGICAL ENGINEERING CO., LTD.—See Fosun International Limited; *Int'l*, pg. 2752
SHINETECH SOFTWARE; *U.S. Private*, pg. 3637
SHIN-ETSU ADVANCED MATERIALS KOREA CO., LTD.—See Shin-Etsu Chemical Co. Ltd.; *Int'l*, pg. 6839
SHIN-ETSU ASTECH CO., LTD.—See Shin-Etsu Chemical Co. Ltd.; *Int'l*, pg. 6839
SHIN-ETSU (CHANGTING) TECHNOLOGY CO., LTD.—See Shin-Etsu Chemical Co. Ltd.; *Int'l*, pg. 6839
SHIN-ETSU CHEMICAL CO. LTD. - GOUBARA PLANT—See Shin-Etsu Chemical Co. Ltd.; *Int'l*, pg. 6839
SHIN-ETSU CHEMICAL CO. LTD. - ISOBE PLANT—See Shin-Etsu Chemical Co. Ltd.; *Int'l*, pg. 6839
SHIN-ETSU CHEMICAL CO., LTD. - KASHIMA PLANT—See Shin-Etsu Chemical Co. Ltd.; *Int'l*, pg. 6839
SHIN-ETSU CHEMICAL CO. LTD. - MATSUIDA PLANT—See Shin-Etsu Chemical Co. Ltd.; *Int'l*, pg. 6839
SHIN-ETSU CHEMICAL CO. LTD. - NAOETSU PLANT—See Shin-Etsu Chemical Co. Ltd.; *Int'l*, pg. 6839
SHIN-ETSU CHEMICAL CO. LTD.; *Int'l*, pg. 6838
SHIN-ETSU CHEMICAL CO. LTD. - TAKEFU PLANT—See Shin-Etsu Chemical Co. Ltd.; *Int'l*, pg. 6839
SHIN-ETSU DO BRASIL REPRESENTACAO DE PRODUTOS QUIMICOS LTDA.—See Shin-Etsu Chemical Co. Ltd.; *Int'l*, pg. 6840
SHIN-ETSU ELECTRONICS (MALAYSIA) SDN. BHD.—See Shin-Etsu Chemical Co. Ltd.; *Int'l*, pg. 6839
SHIN-ETSU ELECTRONICS MATERIALS PENANG SDN. BHD.—See Shin-Etsu Chemical Co. Ltd.; *Int'l*, pg. 6839
SHIN-ETSU ELECTRONICS MATERIALS SINGAPORE PTE. LTD.—See Shin-Etsu Chemical Co. Ltd.; *Int'l*, pg. 6839
SHIN-ETSU ELECTRONICS MATERIALS TAIWAN CO., LTD.—See Shin-Etsu Chemical Co. Ltd.; *Int'l*, pg. 6839
SHIN-ETSU ELECTRONICS MATERIALS VIETNAM CO., LTD.—See Shin-Etsu Chemical Co. Ltd.; *Int'l*, pg. 6839
SHIN-ETSU ENGINEERING CO., LTD.—See Shin-Etsu Chemical Co. Ltd.; *Int'l*, pg. 6839
SHIN-ETSU FILM CO., LTD.—See Shin-Etsu Chemical Co. Ltd.; *Int'l*, pg. 6839
SHIN-ETSU FINETECH CO., LTD.—See Shin-Etsu Chemical Co. Ltd.; *Int'l*, pg. 6840
SHIN-ETSU HANDOTAI AMERICA, INC.—See Shin-Etsu Chemical Co. Ltd.; *Int'l*, pg. 6839
SHIN-ETSU HANDOTAI CO., LTD.—See Shin-Etsu Chemical Co. Ltd.; *Int'l*, pg. 6839
SHIN-ETSU HANDOTAI EUROPE, LTD.—See Shin-Etsu Chemical Co. Ltd.; *Int'l*, pg. 6839
SHIN-ETSU HANDOTAI TAIWAN CO., LTD.—See TOPCO Scientific Co., Ltd.; *Int'l*, pg. 7814
SHIN-ETSU HANDOTAI TAIWAN CO., LTD.—See Shin-Etsu Chemical Co. Ltd.; *Int'l*, pg. 6839
SHIN-ETSU INTERNATIONAL EUROPE B.V.—See Shin-Etsu Chemical Co. Ltd.; *Int'l*, pg. 6839
SHIN-ETSU (JIANGSU) OPTICAL PREFORM CO., LTD.—See Shin-Etsu Chemical Co. Ltd.; *Int'l*, pg. 6839
SHIN-ETSU (JIANGYIN) OPTICAL PREFORM TRADING CO., LTD.—See Shin-Etsu Chemical Co. Ltd.; *Int'l*, pg. 6839
SHIN-ETSU MAGNET CO., LTD.—See Shin-Etsu Chemical Co. Ltd.; *Int'l*, pg. 6839
SHIN-ETSU MAGNETIC MATERIALS VIETNAM CO., LTD.—See Shin-Etsu Chemical Co. Ltd.; *Int'l*, pg. 6839
SHIN-ETSU MAGNETICS EUROPE GMBH—See Shin-Etsu Chemical Co. Ltd.; *Int'l*, pg. 6839
SHIN-ETSU MAGNETICS, INC.—See Shin-Etsu Chemical Co. Ltd.; *Int'l*, pg. 6839
SHIN-ETSU MAGNETICS PHILIPPINES, INC.—See Shin-Etsu Chemical Co. Ltd.; *Int'l*, pg. 6839
SHIN-ETSU MAGNETICS (THAILAND) LTD.—See Shin-Etsu Chemical Co. Ltd.; *Int'l*, pg. 6839
SHIN-ETSU (MALAYSIA) SDN. BHD.—See Shin-Etsu Chemical Co. Ltd.; *Int'l*, pg. 6839
SHIN-ETSU MICROSI, INC.—See Shin-Etsu Chemical Co. Ltd.; *Int'l*, pg. 6840
SHIN-ETSU NEW MATERIALS (THAILAND) LIMITED—See Shin-Etsu Chemical Co. Ltd.; *Int'l*, pg. 6840
SHIN-ETSU OPTO ELECTRONIC CO., LTD.—See TOPCO Scientific Co., Ltd.; *Int'l*, pg. 7814
SHIN-ETSU POLYMER AMERICA, INC.—See Shin-Etsu Chemical Co. Ltd.; *Int'l*, pg. 6840
SHIN-ETSU POLYMER CO., LTD.—See Shin-Etsu Chemical Co. Ltd.; *Int'l*, pg. 6840
SHIN-ETSU POLYMER EUROPE B.V—See Shin-Etsu Chemical Co. Ltd.; *Int'l*, pg. 6840
SHIN-ETSU POLYMER HONG KONG CO., LTD.—See Shin-Etsu Chemical Co. Ltd.; *Int'l*, pg. 6840
SHIN-ETSU POLYMER HUNGARY KFT.—See Shin-Etsu Chemical Co. Ltd.; *Int'l*, pg. 6840
SHIN-ETSU POLYMER INDIA PVT. LTD.—See Shin-Etsu Chemical Co. Ltd.; *Int'l*, pg. 6840
SHIN-ETSU POLYMER (MALAYSIA) SDN. BHD.—See Shin-Etsu Chemical Co. Ltd.; *Int'l*, pg. 6840
SHIN-ETSU POLYMER MEXICO S.A. DE C.V.—See Shin-Etsu Chemical Co. Ltd.; *Int'l*, pg. 6840
SHIN-ETSU POLYMER SHANGHAI CO., LTD.—See Shin-Etsu Chemical Co. Ltd.; *Int'l*, pg. 6840
SHIN-ETSU POLYMER SINGAPORE PTE. LTD.—See Shin-Etsu Chemical Co. Ltd.; *Int'l*, pg. 6840
SHIN-ETSU POLYMER (THAILAND) LTD.—See Shin-Etsu Chemical Co. Ltd.; *Int'l*, pg. 6840
SHIN-ETSU POLYMER VIETNAM CO., LTD.—See Shin-Etsu Chemical Co. Ltd.; *Int'l*, pg. 6840
SHIN-ETSU PVC B.V. - BOTLEK PLANT—See Shin-Etsu Chemical Co. Ltd.; *Int'l*, pg. 6840
SHIN-ETSU PVC B.V. - PERNIS PLANT—See Shin-Etsu Chemical Co. Ltd.; *Int'l*, pg. 6840
SHIN-ETSU PVC B.V.—See Shin-Etsu Chemical Co. Ltd.; *Int'l*, pg. 6840
SHIN-ETSU QUARTZ PRODUCTS CO., LTD.—See Shin-Etsu Chemical Co. Ltd.; *Int'l*, pg. 6840
SHIN-ETSU SILICONE INTERNATIONAL TRADING (SHANGHAI) CO., LTD.—See Shin-Etsu Chemical Co. Ltd.; *Int'l*, pg. 6840
SHIN-ETSU SILICONE KOREA CO., LTD.—See Shin-Etsu Chemical Co. Ltd.; *Int'l*, pg. 6840
SHIN-ETSU SILICONE (NANTONG) CO., LTD.—See Shin-Etsu Chemical Co. Ltd.; *Int'l*, pg. 6840
SHIN-ETSU SILICONES EUROPE B.V—See Shin-Etsu Chemical Co. Ltd.; *Int'l*, pg. 6840
SHIN-ETSU SILICONES INDIA PVT. LTD.—See Shin-Etsu Chemical Co. Ltd.; *Int'l*, pg. 6840
SHIN-ETSU SILICONES OF AMERICA, INC.—See Shin-Etsu Chemical Co. Ltd.; *Int'l*, pg. 6840
SHIN-ETSU SILICONES (THAILAND) LTD—See Shin-Etsu Chemical Co. Ltd.; *Int'l*, pg. 6840
SHIN-ETSU SILICONE TAIWAN CO., LTD - HSIN-CHU FACTORY—See Shin-Etsu Chemical Co. Ltd.; *Int'l*, pg. 6840
SHIN-ETSU SILICONE TAIWAN CO., LTD.—See Shin-Etsu Chemical Co. Ltd.; *Int'l*, pg. 6840
SHIN-ETSU SINGAPORE PTE. LTD.—See Shin-Etsu Chemical Co. Ltd.; *Int'l*, pg. 6840
SHIN-ETSU TECHNOLOGY (SUZHOU) CO., LTD.—See Shin-Etsu Chemical Co. Ltd.; *Int'l*, pg. 6840
SHIN-ETSU UNIT CO., LTD.—See Shin-Etsu Chemical Co. Ltd.; *Int'l*, pg. 6840
SHIN-ETSU YOFC (HUBEI) OPTICAL PREFORM CO., LTD.—See Shin-Etsu Chemical Co. Ltd.; *Int'l*, pg. 6840
SHINE TV LIMITED—See The Walt Disney Company; *U.S. Public*, pg. 2141
SHINEWAVE INTERNATIONAL INC.—See ASUSTeK Computer Inc.; *Int'l*, pg. 664
SHIN FOONG SPECIALTY & APPLIED MATERIALS CO., LTD.; *Int'l*, pg. 6836
SHINFOX CO., LTD.—See Cheng Eui Precision Industry Co., Ltd.; *Int'l*, pg. 1465
SHINFUJI KASEIYAKU CO., LTD.—See Nippon Soda Co., Ltd.; *Int'l*, pg. 5334
SHINGAKAI CO., LTD.—See Hulic Co., Ltd.; *Int'l*, pg. 3528
SHINGAKUKAI HOLDINGS CO., LTD.; *Int'l*, pg. 6843
SHINGATA INC.—See Dentsu Group Inc.; *Int'l*, pg. 2039
SHING HIN CATERING GROUP LTD.—See Compass Group PLC; *Int'l*, pg. 1752
SHING KWAN REALTY (PTE) LIMITED—See Singapore Land Group Limited; *Int'l*, pg. 6940
SHINGLE & GIBB AUTOMATION LLC—See Graybar Electric Company, Inc.; *U.S. Private*, pg. 1760
SHINGOBEE BUILDERS INC.; *U.S. Private*, pg. 3637
SHINGU SANSO ELECTRIC CO., LTD.—See Sanso Electric Co., Ltd.; *Int'l*, pg. 6557
SHIN HAI GAS CORP.; *Int'l*, pg. 6836
SHINHA, INC.; *Int'l*, pg. 6843
SHINHAN 2ND SPECIAL PURPOSE ACQUISITION CO., LTD.; *Int'l*, pg. 6843
SHINHAN 3RD SPECIAL PURPOSE ACQUISITION CO LTD; *Int'l*, pg. 6843
SHINHAN 4TH SPECIAL PURPOSE ACQUISITION CO., LTD.; *Int'l*, pg. 6843
SHINHAN AITAS CO., LTD.—See Shinhan Financial Group Co., Ltd.; *Int'l*, pg. 6844
SHINHAN ALPHA REIT; *Int'l*, pg. 6843
SHINHAN ALTERNATIVE INVESTMENT MANAGEMENT INC.—See Shinhan Financial Group Co., Ltd.; *Int'l*, pg. 6844
SHINHAN ASSET MANAGEMENT (HONG KONG) LTD.—See Shinhan Financial Group Co., Ltd.; *Int'l*, pg. 6844
SHINHAN ASSET TRUST CO., LTD.—See Shinhan Financial Group Co., Ltd.; *Int'l*, pg. 6844
SHINHAN BANK AMERICA—See Shinhan Financial Group Co., Ltd.; *Int'l*, pg. 6844
SHINHAN BANK (CAMBODIA) PLC—See Shinhan Financial Group Co., Ltd.; *Int'l*, pg. 6844
SHINHAN BANK CHINA LTD.—See Shinhan Financial Group Co., Ltd.; *Int'l*, pg. 6844
SHINHAN BANK EUROPE GMBH—See Shinhan Financial Group Co., Ltd.; *Int'l*, pg. 6844
SHINHAN BANK KAZAKHSTAN JSC—See Shinhan Financial Group Co., Ltd.; *Int'l*, pg. 6844
SHINHAN BANK—See Shinhan Financial Group Co., Ltd.; *Int'l*, pg. 6844
SHINHAN BANK VIETNAM LTD.—See Shinhan Financial Group Co., Ltd.; *Int'l*, pg. 6844
SHINHAN BNP PARIBAS ASSET MANAGEMENT CO., LTD.—See BNP Paribas SA; *Int'l*, pg. 1082
SHINHAN BNP PARIBAS ASSET MANAGEMENT CO., LTD.—See Shinhan Financial Group Co., Ltd.; *Int'l*, pg. 6844
SHINHAN CANADA BANK—See Shinhan Financial Group Co., Ltd.; *Int'l*, pg. 6844
SHINHAN CAPITAL CO., LTD.—See Shinhan Financial Group Co., Ltd.; *Int'l*, pg. 6844
SHINHAN CARD CO., LTD.—See Shinhan Financial Group Co., Ltd.; *Int'l*, pg. 6844
SHINHAN CHINA LIMITED—See Shinhan Financial Group Co., Ltd.; *Int'l*, pg. 6844
SHINHAN CREDIT INFORMATION CO., LTD.—See Shinhan Financial Group Co., Ltd.; *Int'l*, pg. 6844
SHINHAN DATA SYSTEM CO., LTD.—See Shinhan Financial Group Co., Ltd.; *Int'l*, pg. 6844
SHINHAN DIAMOND INDUSTRIAL CO., LTD.—See Asahi Diamond Industrial Co., Ltd.; *Int'l*, pg. 592
SHINHAN DS VIETNAM CO., LTD.—See Shinhan Financial Group Co., Ltd.; *Int'l*, pg. 6844
SHINHAN ENG. & CONST. CO., LTD. - BUGANG FACTORY—See Shinhan Eng. & Const. Co., Ltd.; *Int'l*, pg. 6843
SHINHAN ENG. & CONST. CO., LTD.; *Int'l*, pg. 6843
SHINHAN FINANCIAL GROUP CO., LTD.; *Int'l*, pg. 6843
SHINHANG DURR INC.—See Durr AG; *Int'l*, pg. 2233

SHINHAN FINANCIAL GROUP CO., LTD.

CORPORATE AFFILIATIONS

SHINHAN INVESTMENT ASIA LTD.—See Shinhan Financial Group Co., Ltd.; *Int'l*, pg. 6844
SHINHAN INVESTMENT CORP. AMERICA INC.—See Shinhan Financial Group Co., Ltd.; *Int'l*, pg. 6844
SHINHAN INVESTMENT CORP. ASIA LTD.—See Shinhan Financial Group Co., Ltd.; *Int'l*, pg. 6844
SHINHAN KAZAKHSTAN BANK—See Shinhan Financial Group Co., Ltd.; *Int'l*, pg. 6844
SHINHAN KHMER BANK—See Shinhan Financial Group Co., Ltd.; *Int'l*, pg. 6844
SHINHAN LIFE INSURANCE CO., LTD—See Shinhan Financial Group Co., Ltd.; *Int'l*, pg. 6844
SHINHAN MACHINERY CO., LTD.—See Hanwha Ocean Co., Ltd.; *Int'l*, pg. 3267
SHINHAN MICROFINANCE CO., LTD.—See Shinhan Financial Group Co., Ltd.; *Int'l*, pg. 6844
SHINHAN NO. 9 ACQUISITION PURPOSE CO., LTD; *Int'l*, pg. 6844
SHINHAN SECURITIES VIETNAM CO., LTD.—See Shinhan Financial Group Co., Ltd.; *Int'l*, pg. 6844
SHINHAN VIETNAM FINANCE COMPANY—See Shinhan Financial Group Co., Ltd.; *Int'l*, pg. 6844
SHINHEUNG CO.,LTD.—See Shinsung Delta Tech Co., Ltd.; *Int'l*, pg. 6849
SHIN HEUNG ENERGY & ELECTRONICS CO., LTD.; *Int'l*, pg. 6836
SHIN-HEUNG MACHINE CO., LTD. - CHUNGJU FACTORY 1—See SMCore Inc.; *Int'l*, pg. 7006
SHIN-HEUNG MACHINE CO., LTD. - JEONJU FACTORY—See SMCore Inc.; *Int'l*, pg. 7006
SHINHOKOKU STEEL CORPORATION; *Int'l*, pg. 6844
SHINHUNG CO., LTD.; *Int'l*, pg. 6844
SHINHUNG GLOBAL CO., LTD.—See Shinsung Delta Tech Co., Ltd.; *Int'l*, pg. 6849
SHIN HWA CONTECH CO., LTD.; *Int'l*, pg. 6836
SHIN HWA DYNAMICS CO., LTD.; *Int'l*, pg. 6836
SHINHWA PRECISION CO., LTD—See NITTAN Corporation; *Int'l*, pg. 5383
SHINHWA TAKAHASHI PRESS CO., LTD.—See NITTAN Corporation; *Int'l*, pg. 5383
SHIN HWA WORLD LIMITED; *Int'l*, pg. 6836
SHINIH ENTERPRISE CO., LTD. - KUEI SHAN FACTORY—See Shinih Enterprise Co., Ltd.; *Int'l*, pg. 6845
SHINIH ENTERPRISE CO., LTD. - PUT ZU FACTORY—See Shinih Enterprise Co., Ltd.; *Int'l*, pg. 6845
SHINIH ENTERPRISE CO., LTD.; *Int'l*, pg. 6844
SHINIH ENTERPRISE CO., LTD. - YILAN FACTORY—See Shinih Enterprise Co., Ltd.; *Int'l*, pg. 6845
SHINIH FIBER PRODUCTS (SUZHOU) CO., LTD.—See Shinih Enterprise Co., Ltd.; *Int'l*, pg. 6845
SHINIH FIBER PRODUCTS (TANGSHAN) CO., LTD.—See Shinih Enterprise Co., Ltd.; *Int'l*, pg. 6845
SHINIH (VIETNAM) CO., LTD.—See Shinih Enterprise Co., Ltd.; *Int'l*, pg. 6845
SHIN-IKEDA CO., LTD.—See Okaya & Co., Ltd.; *Int'l*, pg. 5547
SHINIL ELECTRONICS CO., LTD.; *Int'l*, pg. 6845
SHINIL-MEXICANA S.A. DE C. V,—See Kasai Kogyo Co., Ltd.; *Int'l*, pg. 4086
SHINING BUILDING BUSINESS CO., LTD.; *Int'l*, pg. 6845
SHINING GOLD FOODSTUFFS (NINGBO) CO., LTD—See Golden Agri-Resources Ltd.; *Int'l*, pg. 3028
SHINING GOLD OILSEED CRUSHING (NINGBO) CO., LTD—See Golden Agri-Resources Ltd.; *Int'l*, pg. 3028
SHINING SECURITIES COMPANY LIMITED—See Rui Feng Group Holdings Company Limited; *Int'l*, pg. 6426
SHINING STAR DIALYSIS, INC.—See DaVita Inc.; *U.S. Public*, pg. 643
SHINJIN ESCO CO., LTD.—See Sinjin SM Co., Ltd.; *Int'l*, pg. 6945
SHINJIN-SM (THAILAND) CO., LTD.—See Sinjin SM Co., Ltd.; *Int'l*, pg. 6945
SHINJUKU CENTER BUILDING MANAGEMENT CO., LTD.—See Tokyo Tatemono Co. Ltd.; *Int'l*, pg. 7796
SHINJUKU NS BUILDING CO., LTD.—See Nippon Life Insurance Company; *Int'l*, pg. 5323
SHINJU SERVICE CO., LTD.—See Nitta Gelatin Inc.; *Int'l*, pg. 5383
SHIN-KANAYA CO,.—See Okaya & Co., Ltd.; *Int'l*, pg. 5547
SHINKA SHOKUHIN CO., LTD.—See Kaneka Corporation; *Int'l*, pg. 4067
SHINKAWA KOREA CO., LTD.—See Yamaha Corporation; *Int'l*, pg. 8551
SHINKAWA (MALAYSIA) SDN. BHD.—See Yamaha Corporation; *Int'l*, pg. 8550
SHINKAWA (SHANGHAI) CO., LTD.—See Yamaha Corporation; *Int'l*, pg. 8551
SHINKAWA SINGAPORE PTE. LTD.—See Yamaha Corporation; *Int'l*, pg. 8551
SHINKAWA TECHNOLOGIES LTD.—See Yamaha Corporation; *Int'l*, pg. 8551
SHINKAWA (THAILAND) CO., LTD.—See Yamaha Corporation; *Int'l*, pg. 8551
SHINKAWA U.S.A., INC.—See Yamaha Corporation; *Int'l*, pg. 8551

SHIN-KEISEI ELECTRIC RAILWAY CO., LTD.—See Keisei Electric Railway Co., Ltd.; *Int'l*, pg. 4118
SHINKEN-AD CO., LTD.—See EQT AB; *Int'l*, pg. 2467
SHINKI BUS CO., LTD.; *Int'l*, pg. 6845
SHINKI CORPORATION—See Kawasaki Kisen Kaisha, Ltd.; *Int'l*, pg. 4101
SHINKIN ASSET MANAGEMENT CO., LTD.—See Shinkin Central Bank; *Int'l*, pg. 6845
THE SHINKIN BANKS INFORMATION SYSTEM CENTER CO., LTD.—See Shinkin Central Bank; *Int'l*, pg. 6845
SHINKIN CAPITAL CO., LTD—See Shinkin Central Bank; *Int'l*, pg. 6845
SHINKIN CENTRAL BANK - BUSINESS PROMOTION DIVISION—See Shinkin Central Bank; *Int'l*, pg. 6845
SHINKIN CENTRAL BANK - CORPORATE BUSINESS PROMOTION DIVISION—See Shinkin Central Bank; *Int'l*, pg. 6845
SHINKIN CENTRAL BANK INTERNATIONAL OPERATIONS CENTER—See Shinkin Central Bank; *Int'l*, pg. 6845
SHINKIN CENTRAL BANK - OPERATIONS DIVISION—See Shinkin Central Bank; *Int'l*, pg. 6845
SHINKIN CENTRAL BANK - SHINKIN BUSINESS SOLUTION DIVISION—See Shinkin Central Bank; *Int'l*, pg. 6845
SHINKIN CENTRAL BANK; *Int'l*, pg. 6845
SHINKIN CENTRAL BANK - STRATEGIC PLANNING DIVISION—See Shinkin Central Bank; *Int'l*, pg. 6845
SHINKIN CENTRAL BANK - TRANSFER & CLEARING DIVISION—See Shinkin Central Bank; *Int'l*, pg. 6845
SHINKIN CENTRAL BANK - TREASURY BUSINESS DIVISION—See Shinkin Central Bank; *Int'l*, pg. 6845
SHINKIN CENTRAL BANK - TREASURY DIVISION—See Shinkin Central Bank; *Int'l*, pg. 6845
SHINKIN CENTRAL BANK - TREASURY OPERATIONS DIVISION—See Shinkin Central Bank; *Int'l*, pg. 6845
SHINKIN GUARANTEE CO., LTD—See Shinkin Central Bank; *Int'l*, pg. 6845
SHINKIN INTERNATIONAL LTD.—See Shinkin Central Bank; *Int'l*, pg. 6845
SHINKIN PARTNERS CO., LTD—See Shinkin Central Bank; *Int'l*, pg. 6845
SHINKIN TRUST BANK, LTD—See Shinkin Central Bank; *Int'l*, pg. 6845
SHINKO ACTEC CO., LTD.—See Kobe Steel, Ltd.; *Int'l*, pg. 4220
SHINKO AIRTECH, LTD.—See Kobe Steel, Ltd.; *Int'l*, pg. 4220
SHINKO ALUMINUM WIRE CO., LTD.—See Kobe Steel, Ltd.; *Int'l*, pg. 4220
SHINKO AUTOMOBILE CO., LTD.—See Kyokuto Kaihatsu Kogyo Co. Ltd.; *Int'l*, pg. 4363
SHIN-KOBE ELECTRIC MACHINERY CO., LTD.—See Resonac Holdings Corporation; *Int'l*, pg. 6299
SHINKO BOLT, LTD.—See Kobe Steel, Ltd.; *Int'l*, pg. 4221
SHINKO CHEMICAL TERMINAL CO., LTD.—See Marubeni Corporation; *Int'l*, pg. 4710
SHINKO CO., LTD.—See Sumitomo Metal Mining Co.; *Int'l*, pg. 7291
SHINKO COMMERCE CO., LTD.—See Mizuho Financial Group, Inc.; *Int'l*, pg. 4998
SHINKO DENKI CO., LTD.; *Int'l*, pg. 6845
SHINKO ELECTRIC AMERICA, INC.—See Fujitsu Limited; *Int'l*, pg. 2838
SHINKO ELECTRIC INDUSTRIES CO., LTD. - ARAI PLANT—See Fujitsu Limited; *Int'l*, pg. 2838
SHINKO ELECTRIC INDUSTRIES CO., LTD. - KYOGASE PLANT—See Fujitsu Limited; *Int'l*, pg. 2838
SHINKO ELECTRIC INDUSTRIES CO., LTD.—See Fujitsu Limited; *Int'l*, pg. 2837
SHINKO ELECTRIC INDUSTRIES CO., LTD. - TAKAOKA PLANT—See Fujitsu Limited; *Int'l*, pg. 2838
SHINKO ELECTRIC INDUSTRIES CO., LTD. - WAKAHO PLANT—See Fujitsu Limited; *Int'l*, pg. 2838
SHINKO ELECTRIC INDUSTRIES (WUXI) CO., LTD.—See Fujitsu Limited; *Int'l*, pg. 2838
SHINKO ELECTRIC WIRE CO.,LTD.—See Riken Technos Corporation; *Int'l*, pg. 6341
SHINKO ELECTRONICS (MALAYSIA) SDN. BHD.—See Fujitsu Limited; *Int'l*, pg. 2838
SHINKO ELECTRONICS (SINGAPORE) PTE. LTD.—See Fujitsu Limited; *Int'l*, pg. 2838
SHINKO ENGINEERING CO., LTD.—See Kobe Steel, Ltd.; *Int'l*, pg. 4221
SHINKO ENGINEERING & MAINTENANCE CO., LTD.—See Kobe Steel, Ltd.; *Int'l*, pg. 4221
SHINKO GYORUI CO., LTD.—See Maruha Nichiro Corporation; *Int'l*, pg. 4712
SHINKOH MOLD CO., LTD.—See Shin-Etsu Chemical Co. Ltd.; *Int'l*, pg. 6840
SHINKO, INC.; *Int'l*, pg. 6846
SHINKO IND. LTD.; *Int'l*, pg. 6846
SHINKO INDUSTRIAL CO., LTD.—See Kobe Steel, Ltd.; *Int'l*, pg. 4221
SHINKO INSPECTION & SERVICE CO., LTD—See Kobe Steel, Ltd.; *Int'l*, pg. 4221
SHINKO INVESTMENT TRUST MANAGEMENT CO., LTD.—See Mizuho Financial Group, Inc.; *Int'l*, pg. 4998

SHINKO KANMON SOHGO SERVICE, LTD.—See Kobe Steel, Ltd.; *Int'l*, pg. 4221
SHINKO KOHAN KAKO, LTD.—See Kobe Steel, Ltd.; *Int'l*, pg. 4221
SHINKO LEADMIKK CO., LTD.—See Kobe Steel, Ltd.; *Int'l*, pg. 4221
SHINKO LEASE CO., LTD.—See SBI Shinsei Bank, Limited; *Int'l*, pg. 6606
SHINKO MACHINERY SERVICE CO., LTD.—See RAIZNEXT Corporation; *Int'l*, pg. 6192
SHINKO METAL PRODUCTS CO., LTD.—See Kobe Steel, Ltd.; *Int'l*, pg. 4221
SHINKO MOKA SOHGO SERVICE LTD.—See Kobe Steel, Ltd.; *Int'l*, pg. 4221
SHINKO MUSIC ENTERTAINMENT CO., LTD.; *Int'l*, pg. 6846
SHINKO MUSIC PUBLISHING CO., LTD.—See Shinko Music Entertainment Co., Ltd.; *Int'l*, pg. 6846
SHIN KONG CHAO FENG CO., LTD.—See Shinkong Insurance Co. Ltd.; *Int'l*, pg. 6846
SHINKONG ENGINEERING CORP.—See Shin Kong Group; *Int'l*, pg. 6837
SHIN KONG FINANCIAL HOLDING CO., LTD.—See Shin Kong Group; *Int'l*, pg. 6886
SHIN KONG GROUP; *Int'l*, pg. 6836
SHINKONG IECOFUN CORPORATION—See Shin Kong Group; *Int'l*, pg. 6837
SHINKONG INSURANCE CO. LTD.; *Int'l*, pg. 6846
SHINKONG INTERNATIONAL LEASING CORP.—See Shin Kong Group; *Int'l*, pg. 6837
SHIN KONG INVESTMENT TRUST CO., LTD.—See Shin Kong Group; *Int'l*, pg. 6837
SHIN KONG LEASING CORP.—See Shin Kong Group; *Int'l*, pg. 6837
SHIN KONG LIFE INSURANCE CO., LTD.—See Shin Kong Group; *Int'l*, pg. 6837
SHIN KONG LIFE REAL ESTATE SERVICE COMPANY—See Shin Kong Group; *Int'l*, pg. 6837
SHINKONG MATERIALS TECHNOLOGY CO., LTD.—See Shin Kong Group; *Int'l*, pg. 6837
SHIN KONG MITSUKOSHI DEPARTMENT STORE CO., LTD.—See Isetan Mitsukoshi Holdings Ltd.; *Int'l*, pg. 3815
SHIN KONG MITSUKOSHI DEPARTMENT STORE CO., LTD.—See Shin Kong Group; *Int'l*, pg. 6837
SHIN KONG (MYANMAR) CONSULTING LTD.—See Taiwan Shin Kong Security Co., Ltd.; *Int'l*, pg. 7424
SHIN KONG SHIEN YA INTERNATIONAL CO., LTD.—See Shinkong Insurance Co. Ltd.; *Int'l*, pg. 6846
SHINKONG SYNTHETIC FIBERS CORPORATION—See Shin Kong Group; *Int'l*, pg. 6837
SHINKONG TEXTILE CO., LTD.; *Int'l*, pg. 6846
SHIN KONG WU HO-SU MEMORIAL HOSPITAL—See Shinkong Insurance Co. Ltd.; *Int'l*, pg. 6846
SHINKO-NORTH CO., LTD.—See Kobe Steel, Ltd.; *Int'l*, pg. 4221
SHINKO ORGANIC CHEMICAL INDUSTRY LTD.—See Osaka Organic Chemical Industry Ltd.; *Int'l*, pg. 5646
SHINKO PARTS CO., LTD.—See Fujitsu Limited; *Int'l*, pg. 2838
SHINKO PRINCIPAL INVESTMENT CO., LTD—See Mizuho Financial Group, Inc.; *Int'l*, pg. 4998
SHINKO (PTE) LTD.—See Shinko Shoji Co., Ltd.; *Int'l*, pg. 6846
SHINKO REAL ESTATE CO., LTD.—See Tokyo Century Corporation; *Int'l*, pg. 7789
SHINKO RESEARCH CO., LTD.—See Kobe Steel, Ltd.; *Int'l*, pg. 4221
SHINKO SAGYO CO., LTD.—See The Sumitomo Warehouse Co. Ltd.; *Int'l*, pg. 7690
SHINKO SECURITIES BUSINESS SERVICES CO., LTD—See Mizuho Financial Group, Inc.; *Int'l*, pg. 4998
SHINKO SEIKI CO., LTD.—See AISIN Corporation; *Int'l*, pg. 253
SHINKO SHOJI CO., LTD.—See Max Weishaupt GmbH; *Int'l*, pg. 4735
SHINKO SHOJI CO., LTD.; *Int'l*, pg. 6846
SHINKO SHOJI LSI DESIGN CENTER CO., LTD.—See Shinko Shoji Co., Ltd.; *Int'l*, pg. 6846
SHINKO SLAG PRODUCTS CO., LTD.—See Kobe Steel, Ltd.; *Int'l*, pg. 4221
SHINKO SOGO SERVICE CO., LTD.—See RAIZNEXT Corporation; *Int'l*, pg. 6192
SHINKO TECHNO ENGINEERING CO., LTD.—See Kobe Steel, Ltd.; *Int'l*, pg. 4221
SHINKO TECHNOSERVE CO., LTD.—See Fujitsu Limited; *Int'l*, pg. 2838
SHINKO TRANSPORTATION AND WAREHOUSE CO., LTD.—See UBE Corporation; *Int'l*, pg. 8001
SHINKO WIRE (GUANGZHOU) SALES CO., LTD.—See Kobelco Wire Co Ltd; *Int'l*, pg. 4221
SHINKO WIRE STAINLESS COMPANY, LTD.—See Kobelco Wire Co Ltd; *Int'l*, pg. 4221
SHINKYO GIKEN CO., LTD.—See Sala Corporation; *Int'l*, pg. 6490
SHINKYOWA CO., LTD.—See Shinyei Kaisha; *Int'l*, pg. 6850
SHINLINE SDN. BHD.—See Shin Yang Shipping Corporation Berhad; *Int'l*, pg. 6838

COMPANY NAME INDEX

SHIN MAINT HOLDINGS CO., LTD.; *Int'l*, pg. 6837
SHINMAYWA AEROBRIDGE MALAYSIA SDN. BHD.—See ShinMaywa Industries, Ltd.; *Int'l*, pg. 6847
SHINMAYWA AEROBRIDGE SINGAPORE PTE. LTD.—See ShinMaywa Industries, Ltd.; *Int'l*, pg. 6847
SHINMAYWA (AMERICA), LTD.—See ShinMaywa Industries, Ltd.; *Int'l*, pg. 6847
SHINMAYWA AQUA TECHNOLOGY SERVICE, LTD.—See ShinMaywa Industries, Ltd.; *Int'l*, pg. 6847
SHINMAYWA AQUA TECHNOLOGY SERVICES, LTD.—See ShinMaywa Industries, Ltd.; *Int'l*, pg. 6847
SHINMAYWA (ASIA) PTE. LTD.—See ShinMaywa Industries, Ltd.; *Int'l*, pg. 6847
SHINMAYWA AUTO ENGINEERING, LTD.—See ShinMaywa Industries, Ltd.; *Int'l*, pg. 6847
SHINMAYWA AUTO SALES, LTD.—See ShinMaywa Industries, Ltd.; *Int'l*, pg. 6847
SHINMAYWA (BANGKOK) CO., LTD.—See ShinMaywa Industries, Ltd.; *Int'l*, pg. 6847
SHINMAYWA (CALIFORNIA), LTD.—See ShinMaywa Industries, Ltd.; *Int'l*, pg. 6847
SHINMAYWA HEARTFUL, LTD.—See ShinMaywa Industries, Ltd.; *Int'l*, pg. 6847
SHINMAYWA INDUSTRIES INDIA PRIVATE LIMITED—See ShinMaywa Industries, Ltd.; *Int'l*, pg. 6847
SHINMAYWA INDUSTRIES, LTD.; *Int'l*, pg. 6846
SHINMAYWA IWAKUNI AIRCRAFT MAINTENANCE, LTD.—See ShinMaywa Industries, Ltd.; *Int'l*, pg. 6847
SHINMAYWA MEXICO S.A. DE C.V.—See ShinMaywa Industries, Ltd.; *Int'l*, pg. 6847
SHINMAYWA PARKING TECHNOLOGIES, LTD.—See ShinMaywa Industries, Ltd.; *Int'l*, pg. 6847
SHINMAYWA (SHANGHAI) HIGH-TECH MACHINERY CO., LTD—See ShinMaywa Industries, Ltd.; *Int'l*, pg. 6847
SHINMAYWA (SHANGHAI) TRADING CO.—See ShinMaywa Industries, Ltd.; *Int'l*, pg. 6847
SHINMAYWA SHOJI, LTD.—See ShinMaywa Industries, Ltd.; *Int'l*, pg. 6847
SHINMAYWA SOFT TECHNOLOGIES, LTD.—See ShinMaywa Industries, Ltd.; *Int'l*, pg. 6847
SHINMAYWA WASTE TECHNOLOGY, LTD.—See ShinMaywa Industries, Ltd.; *Int'l*, pg. 6847
SHINMEI AGRI CO., LTD.—See Shinmei Co., Ltd.; *Int'l*, pg. 6847
SHINMEI CO., LTD.; *Int'l*, pg. 6847
SHINMYUNG HA LTD.—See Huettenes-Albertus Chemische Werke GmbH; *Int'l*, pg. 3523
SHINNAIGAI TEXTILE LTD.—See Shikibo Ltd.; *Int'l*, pg. 6829
SHINN & COMPANY, LLC—See Carr, Riggs & Ingram, LLC; *U.S. Private*, pg. 771
SHINNICHI KOGYO CO., LTD.—See Honda Motor Co., Ltd.; *Int'l*, pg. 3464
SHIN-NICHI TECHNOLOGY CO., LTD.—See Tsuburaya Fields Holdings Inc.; *Int'l*, pg. 7955
SHINNIHON CORPORATION; *Int'l*, pg. 6847
SHINNIHON GAS CORPORATION—See Nippon Gas Co., Ltd.; *Int'l*, pg. 5318
SHIN-NIHON HELICOPTER CO., LTD.—See Chubu Electric Power Co., Inc.; *Int'l*, pg. 1593
SHIN NIHON KOGYO CORPORATION—See JFE Holdings, Inc.; *Int'l*, pg. 3937
SHINNIHON REIKI CO., LTD.—See Marubeni Corporation; *Int'l*, pg. 4710
SHINNIHONSEIYAKU CO., LTD.; *Int'l*, pg. 6847
SHIN-NIHON TATEMONO CO., LTD.; *Int'l*, pg. 6841
SHINNING CENTURY LIMITED; *Int'l*, pg. 6847
SHIN NIPPON AIR TECHNOLOGIES CO., LTD.; *Int'l*, pg. 6837
SHIN NIPPON BIOMEDICAL LABORATORIES, LTD.; *Int'l*, pg. 6837
SHIN-NIPPON INDUSTRIES SDN. BHD.—See Asahi Printing Co., Ltd.; *Int'l*, pg. 598
SHIN-NIPPONKAIYOSHA CORPORATION—See Nippon Yusen Kabushiki Kaisha; *Int'l*, pg. 5359
SHIN NIPPON KOKI CO. LTD. - MISAKI—See Fair Friend Group; *Int'l*, pg. 2605
SHIN NIPPON KOKI CO. LTD.—See Fair Friend Group; *Int'l*, pg. 2604
SHIN NIPPON MACHINERY CO., LTD.—See Sumitomo Heavy Industries, Ltd.; *Int'l*, pg. 7288
SHIN-NIPPON THERMAL CERAMICS CORPORATION—See Morgan Advanced Materials plc; *Int'l*, pg. 5044
SHINOBU FOODS PRODUCTS CO., LTD.; *Int'l*, pg. 6847
SHINOKEN ASSET MANAGEMENT CO., LTD.—See Shinoken Group Co., Ltd.; *Int'l*, pg. 6847
SHINOKEN GROUP CO., LTD.; *Int'l*, pg. 6847
SHINOKEN OFFICE SERVICE CO., LTD.—See Shinoken Group Co., Ltd.; *Int'l*, pg. 6847
SHINOZAKIYA INC.; *Int'l*, pg. 6848
SHINPO CO., LTD. - NAGOYA FACTORY—See Shinpo Co., Ltd.; *Int'l*, pg. 6848
SHINPO CO., LTD.; *Int'l*, pg. 6848
SHINPONT INDUSTRY INC.—See Shin Kong Group; *Int'l*, pg. 6837

SHIN POONG DAEWOO PHARM CO., LTD—See Shin Poong Pharmaceutical Co., Ltd.; *Int'l*, pg. 6838
SHINPOONG INC.; *Int'l*, pg. 6837
SHIN POONG PAPER MANUFACTURING CO., LTD.; *Int'l*, pg. 6837
SHIN POONG PHARMACEUTICAL CO., LTD. - KGMP PLANT 1—See Shin Poong Pharmaceutical Co., Ltd.; *Int'l*, pg. 6838
SHIN POONG PHARMACEUTICAL CO., LTD.; *Int'l*, pg. 6837
SHINPO TRADE CO., LTD.—See Shinpo Co., Ltd.; *Int'l*, pg. 6848
SHINRAI AUTO SERVICES LTD.—See Oricon Enterprises Ltd.; *Int'l*, pg. 5621
SHINRYO CORPORATION—See Mitsubishi Heavy Industries, Ltd.; *Int'l*, pg. 4961
SHINRYO KOUN CO., LTD.—See Mitsubishi Logistics Corporation; *Int'l*, pg. 4963
SHINRY TECHNOLOGIES CO., LTD. - SHENZEN PLANT—See Shinry Technologies Co., Ltd.; *Int'l*, pg. 6848
SHINRY TECHNOLOGIES CO., LTD.; *Int'l*, pg. 6848
SHIN-SANKYO-PD. CO., LTD.—See Toyo Seikan Group Holdings, Ltd.; *Int'l*, pg. 7857
SHIN SAN SHING CO., LTD.—See Toyota Boshoku Corporation; *Int'l*, pg. 7864
SHINSANSO KAGAKU CO.—See Mitsubishi Gas Chemical Company, Inc.; *Int'l*, pg. 4950
SHINSEGAE ENGINEERING & CONSTRUCTION CO., LTD.—See Shinsegae Inc.; *Int'l*, pg. 6848
SHINSEGAE FOOD CO., LTD. - CHEONAN PLANT—See Shinsegae Food Co., Ltd.; *Int'l*, pg. 6848
SHINSEGAE FOOD CO., LTD. - ICHEON PLANT 1—See Shinsegae Food Co., Ltd.; *Int'l*, pg. 6848
SHINSEGAE FOOD CO., LTD. - ICHEON PLANT 2—See Shinsegae Food Co., Ltd.; *Int'l*, pg. 6848
SHINSEGAE FOOD CO., LTD. - OSAN PLANT—See Shinsegae Food Co., Ltd.; *Int'l*, pg. 6848
SHINSEGAE FOOD CO., LTD. - SEONGSU PLANT—See Shinsegae Food Co., Ltd.; *Int'l*, pg. 6848
SHINSEGAE FOOD CO., LTD.; *Int'l*, pg. 6848
SHINSEGAE I&C CO., LTD.—See Shinsegae Inc.; *Int'l*, pg. 6848
SHINSEGAE INC.; *Int'l*, pg. 6848
SHINSEGAE INTERNATIONAL INC.; *Int'l*, pg. 6848
SHINSEI CAPITAL (USA), LTD.—See SBI Shinsei Bank, Limited; *Int'l*, pg. 6606
SHINSEIDO CO., LTD.—See RIZAP GROUP, Inc.; *Int'l*, pg. 6354
SHINSEI FINANCIAL CO., LTD.—See SBI Shinsei Bank, Limited; *Int'l*, pg. 6606
SHINSEI INDUSTRY SDN BHD—See AnnAik Limited; *Int'l*, pg. 473
SHINSEI INVESTMENT MANAGEMENT CO., LTD.—See SBI Shinsei Bank, Limited; *Int'l*, pg. 6606
SHINSEI JAPAN INDUSTRY CO LTD—See AnnAik Limited; *Int'l*, pg. 473
SHINSEI KOGYO., LTD.—See Daido Kogyo Co., Ltd.; *Int'l*, pg. 1921
SHINSEI PERSONAL LOAN CO., LTD.—See SBI Shinsei Bank, Limited; *Int'l*, pg. 6606
SHINSEI SECURITIES CO., LTD.—See SBI Shinsei Bank, Limited; *Int'l*, pg. 6606
SHINSEI SEIKI CO., LTD—See Bunka Shutter Co., Ltd.; *Int'l*, pg. 1216
SHINSEN SEIKI CO., LTD.—See Sumitomo Corporation; *Int'l*, pg. 7275
SHIN SHIN CO., LTD.; *Int'l*, pg. 6838
SHINSHIN CREDIT CORPORATION—See Yulon Finance Corporation; *Int'l*, pg. 8613
SHIN SHIN NATURAL GAS CO., LTD.; *Int'l*, pg. 6838
SHINSHIRO CABLE, LTD.—See Fujikura Ltd.; *Int'l*, pg. 2829
SHINSHO AMERICAN CORPORATION—See Kobe Steel, Ltd.; *Int'l*, pg. 4221
SHINSHO CORPORATION—See Kobe Steel, Ltd.; *Int'l*, pg. 4221
SHINSHO OSAKA SEIKO (NANGTONG) CORPORATION—See Kobe Steel, Ltd.; *Int'l*, pg. 4221
SHINSHO SENPAKU KAISHA, LTD.—See NS United Kaiun Kaisha, Ltd.; *Int'l*, pg. 5476
SHINSHU BEVERAGE CO., LTD.—See Kirin Holdings Company, Limited; *Int'l*, pg. 4189
SHINSHU FUJI ELECTRIC CO., LTD.—See Fuji Electric Co., Ltd.; *Int'l*, pg. 2813
SHINSHU GAS CO., LTD.—See Shizuokagas Co., Ltd.; *Int'l*, pg. 6856
SHINSHU TAKEEI CO., LTD.—See Takeei Corporation; *Int'l*, pg. 7440
SHINSOFT CO., LTD.—See Taiwan Shin Kong Security Co., Ltd.; *Int'l*, pg. 7424
SHIN STEEL CO., LTD.; *Int'l*, pg. 6838
SHINSTROM & NORMAN, INC.—See Hellman & Friedman LLC; *U.S. Private*, pg. 1909
SHINSUNG AUTOMOTIVE CO., LTD.—See Shinsung Delta Tech Co., Ltd.; *Int'l*, pg. 6849
SHINSUNG DELTA TECH CO., LTD.; *Int'l*, pg. 6848
SHINSUNG E&G CO., LTD.; *Int'l*, pg. 6849

SHINSUNG ENG CO., LTD.—See Shinsung E&G Co., Ltd.; *Int'l*, pg. 6849
SHINSUNG FA CORPORATION—See Shinsung E&G Co., Ltd.; *Int'l*, pg. 6849
SHINSUNG MOLD TECH CO.,LTD.—See Shinsung Delta Tech Co., Ltd.; *Int'l*, pg. 6849
SHINSUNG PACKARD COMPANY, LTD.—See General Motors Company; *U.S. Public*, pg. 929
SHINSUNG ST CO., LTD.—See Shinsung Delta Tech Co., Ltd.; *Int'l*, pg. 6849
SHINSUNG TONGSANG CO., LTD.; *Int'l*, pg. 6849
SHINSUNG VIETNAM CO., LTD.—See Shinsung E&G Co., Ltd.; *Int'l*, pg. 6849
SHINSUN HOLDING (GROUP) CO., LTD.; *Int'l*, pg. 6848
SHINSYU-ICHI MISO CO., LTD.—See Sapporo Holdings Limited; *Int'l*, pg. 6574
SHIN TAI INDUSTRY CO., LTD.; *Int'l*, pg. 6838
SHIN TAIWAN AGRICULTURAL MACHINERY CO., LTD.—See Kubota Corporation; *Int'l*, pg. 4322
SHIN-TANIGAKI CO., LTD.—See Okaya & Co., Ltd.; *Int'l*, pg. 5547
SHINTECH INC.—See Shin-Etsu Chemical Co. Ltd.; *Int'l*, pg. 6841
SHINTECH LOUISIANA LLC—See Shin-Etsu Chemical Co. Ltd.; *Int'l*, pg. 6841
SHINTECHNO CORPORATION—See Aktio Holdings Corporation; *Int'l*, pg. 267
SHINTOA CORP.—See Kanematsu Corporation; *Int'l*, pg. 4069
SHINTO COMPANY LIMITED; *Int'l*, pg. 6849
SHINTOKYO GROUP CO., LTD.; *Int'l*, pg. 6849
SHIN-TOMOE ELECTRIC MANUFACTURING CO., LTD.—See Nishio Holdings Co., Ltd.; *Int'l*, pg. 5366
SHIN TOMOEGAWA KAKOH CO., LTD.—See Tomoegawa Co., Ltd.; *Int'l*, pg. 7801
SHINTO PAINT CO., LTD.—See Sumitomo Chemical Company, Limited; *Int'l*, pg. 7264
SHINTORI—See Suntory Holdings Limited; *Int'l*, pg. 7326
SHINTO TSUSHIN CO., LTD.; *Int'l*, pg. 6849
SHINTO - WELBEST MANUFACTURING, INC.—See SIIX CORPORATION; *Int'l*, pg. 6914
SHINVA MEDICAL INSTRUMENT COMPANY, LTD.; *Int'l*, pg. 6849
SHINVEST HOLDING LIMITED; *Int'l*, pg. 6849
SHINWA AGENCY CO., LTD.—See NS United Kaiun Kaisha, Ltd.; *Int'l*, pg. 5476
THE SHINWA BANK, LTD.—See Fukuoka Financial Group, Inc.; *Int'l*, pg. 2840
SHINWA BUSINESS MANAGEMENT KAISHA, LTD.—See NS United Kaiun Kaisha, Ltd.; *Int'l*, pg. 5476
SHINWA CHARTERING CORP.—See NS United Kaiun Kaisha, Ltd.; *Int'l*, pg. 5476
SHINWA CHEMICAL TANKER CO., LTD.—See NS United Kaiun Kaisha, Ltd.; *Int'l*, pg. 5476
SHINWA CO., LTD.; *Int'l*, pg. 6849
SHINWA DENZAI CO., LTD.—See NITTO BOSEKI CO., LTD.; *Int'l*, pg. 5384
SHINWA DIE CO., LTD.—See Fuji Die Co., Ltd.; *Int'l*, pg. 2810
SHINWA ENGINEERING SERVICES CO., LTD.—See NS United Kaiun Kaisha, Ltd.; *Int'l*, pg. 5476
SHINWA (INDIA) ENGINEERING & TRADING PRIVATE LIMITED—See Shinwa Co., Ltd.; *Int'l*, pg. 6849
SHINWA INDUSTRIAL CO., LTD.; *Int'l*, pg. 6850
SHINWA INDUSTRIES (CHINA) LTD.—See JVCKENWOOD Corporation; *Int'l*, pg. 4034
SHINWA INDUSTRIES (CHONGQING) LTD.—See JVCKENWOOD Corporation; *Int'l*, pg. 4034
SHINWA INDUSTRIES (HANGZHOU) LTD.—See JVCKENWOOD Corporation; *Int'l*, pg. 4034
SHINWA INDUSTRIES (H.K.) LTD.—See JVCKENWOOD Corporation; *Int'l*, pg. 4034
SHINWA INDUSTRIES (SHENZHEN) LTD.—See JVCKENWOOD Corporation; *Int'l*, pg. 4034
SHINWA INDUSTRIES (XI'AN) LTD.—See JVCKENWOOD Corporation; *Int'l*, pg. 4034
SHINWA INTEC CO., LTD.—See Shinwa Co., Ltd.; *Int'l*, pg. 6849
SHINWA INTEC MALAYSIA SDN, BHD.—See Shinwa Co., Ltd.; *Int'l*, pg. 6849
SHINWA INTERNATIONAL HOLDINGS LTD.—See JVCKENWOOD Corporation; *Int'l*, pg. 4034
SHINWA KIGYO CO., LTD.—See Nippon Steel Corporation; *Int'l*, pg. 5336
SHINWA KIKOU CO., LTD.—See Sintokogio Ltd.; *Int'l*, pg. 6958
SHIN-WAKO SECURITIES INVESTMENT TRUST & MANAGEMENT CO., LTD.—See Mizuho Financial Group, Inc.; *Int'l*, pg. 4998
SHINWA MACHINERY CO., LTD.—See DAIHO CORPORATION; *Int'l*, pg. 1927
SHINWA MARINE CORP.—See NS United Kaiun Kaisha, Ltd.; *Int'l*, pg. 5476
SHINWA MECHATRONICS (SHENZHEN) LTD.—See JVCKENWOOD Corporation; *Int'l*, pg. 4034
SHINWA MFG. CO.—See EXEO Group, Inc.; *Int'l*, pg. 2584
SHINWA PRECISION (HUNGARY) KFT—See JVCKENWOOD Corporation; *Int'l*, pg. 4034

SHINWA INDUSTRIAL CO., LTD.

CORPORATE AFFILIATIONS

SHINWA REPRESENTACAO COMERCIAL DO BRASIL LTDA.—See Shinwa Co., Ltd.; *Int'l*, pg. 6849
SHINWA SEIKO CO., LTD.—See NSK Ltd.; *Int'l*, pg. 5480
SHINWA (SHANGHAI) CO., LTD.—See Shinwa Co., Ltd.; *Int'l*, pg. 6849
SHINWA SHIKI CO., LTD.—See Rengo Co., Ltd.; *Int'l*, pg. 6281
SHINWA SHIPPING (H.K.) CO., LTD.—See NS United Kaiun Kaisha, Ltd.; *Int'l*, pg. 5476
SHINWA SHOJI KAISHA LTD.—See Nittetsu Mining Co., Ltd.; *Int'l*, pg. 5383
SHINWA SHOJI, LIMITED—See Relo Group, Inc.; *Int'l*, pg. 6265
SHINWA SYSTEMS CO., LTD.—See NS United Kaiun Kaisha, Ltd.; *Int'l*, pg. 5476
SHINWATEC LIMITED—See Shinwa Co., Ltd.; *Int'l*, pg. 6850
SHINWA (U.K.) LTD.—See NS United Kaiun Kaisha, Ltd.; *Int'l*, pg. 5476
SHINWA USA CORP.—See Shinwa Co., Ltd.; *Int'l*, pg. 6849
SHINWA VENTURE CAPITAL CO., LTD.—See Fukuoka Financial Group, Inc.; *Int'l*, pg. 2840
SHINWA WISE HOLDINGS CO., LTD.; *Int'l*, pg. 6850
SHINWHA INTERTEK CORPORATION; *Int'l*, pg. 6850
SHINWHA INTERTEK SLOVAKIA S.R.O—See Shinwha Intertek Corporation; *Int'l*, pg. 6850
SHINWHA INTERTEK (SUZHOU) CO., LTD.—See Shinwha Intertek Corporation; *Int'l*, pg. 6850
SHINWON CONSTRUCTION CO.,LTD.; *Int'l*, pg. 6850
SHINWON CORPORATION (BANGLADESH)—See Shinwon Corporation; *Int'l*, pg. 6850
SHINWON CORPORATION; *Int'l*, pg. 6850
SHINWON DENTAL CO. LTD.—See Shinhung Co., Ltd.; *Int'l*, pg. 6844
SHINWON EBENEZER VIETNAM CO., LTD.—See Shinwon Corporation; *Int'l*, pg. 6850
SHINWOO CO., LTD.—See Kumbi Co., Ltd.; *Int'l*, pg. 4330
SHIN YANG SHIPPING CORPORATION BERHAD; *Int'l*, pg. 6838
SHIN YANG SHIPYARD SDN. BHD.—See Shin Yang Shipping Corporation Berhad; *Int'l*, pg. 6838
SHIN YA WIRE & CABLE (SHENZHEN) CO., LTD.—See Copartner Technology Corporation; *Int'l*, pg. 1793
SHINY CHEMICAL INDUSTRIAL CO., LTD.; *Int'l*, pg. 6850
SHIN YEH RESTAURANT PTE LTD—See Tung Lok Restaurants (2000) Ltd; *Int'l*, pg. 7971
SHINYEI AGRITECH CO., LTD.—See Shinyei Kaisha; *Int'l*, pg. 6850
SHINYEI CAPACITOR CO., LTD. - NAGANO PLANT—See Shinyei Kaisha; *Int'l*, pg. 6850
SHINYEI CAPACITOR CO., LTD.—See Shinyei Kaisha; *Int'l*, pg. 6850
SHINYEI CORPORATION OF AMERICA—See Shinyei Kaisha; *Int'l*, pg. 6850
SHINYEI KAISHA ELECTRONICS (M) SDN. BHD.—See Shinyei Kaisha; *Int'l*, pg. 6850
SHINYEI KAISHA; *Int'l*, pg. 6850
SHINYEI LIFETEX CO., LTD.—See Shinyei Kaisha; *Int'l*, pg. 6850
SHINYEI LIVING INDUSTRY CO., LTD.—See Shinyei Kaisha; *Int'l*, pg. 6850
SHINYEI (SHANGHAI) TRADING CO., LTD.—See Shinyei Kaisha; *Int'l*, pg. 6850
SHINYEI SHOJI (QINGDAO) TRADING CO., LTD.—See Shinyei Kaisha; *Int'l*, pg. 6850
SHINYEI TECHNOLOGY CO., LTD. - FUKUOKA PLANT—See Shinyei Kaisha; *Int'l*, pg. 6850
SHINYEI TECHNOLOGY CO., LTD.—See Shinyei Kaisha; *Int'l*, pg. 6850
SHINY GLORY SERVICES LIMITED—See Lapco Holdings Limited; *Int'l*, pg. 4417
SHINYO KAIUN CORPORATION—See Mitsui O.S.K. Lines, Ltd.; *Int'l*, pg. 4991
SHIN-YOKOHAMA STATION DEVELOPMENT CO., LTD.—See Central Japan Railway Company; *Int'l*, pg. 1408
SHINYOPTICS CORP.—See ASUSTeK Computer Inc.; *Int'l*, pg. 664
SHINYOUNG SECURITIES CO., LTD.; *Int'l*, pg. 6850
SHINYOUNG WACOAL INC.—See Wacoal Holdings Corp.; *Int'l*, pg. 8326
SHIN ZU SHING CO., LTD.; *Int'l*, pg. 6838
SHIODOME URBAN ENERGY CORP.—See Dentsu Group Inc.; *Int'l*, pg. 2039
SHIONOGI ADMINISTRATION SERVICE CO., LTD.—See Shionogi & Co., Ltd.; *Int'l*, pg. 6851
SHIONOGI ANALYSIS CENTER CO., LTD.—See Shionogi & Co., Ltd.; *Int'l*, pg. 6851
SHIONOGI BUSINESS PARTNER CO., LTD.—See Shionogi & Co., Ltd.; *Int'l*, pg. 6851
SHIONOGI CAREER DEVELOPMENT CENTER CO., LTD.—See Shionogi & Co., Ltd.; *Int'l*, pg. 6851
SHIONOGI & CO., LTD. - KANEGASAKI PLANT—See Shionogi & Co., Ltd.; *Int'l*, pg. 6851
SHIONOGI & CO., LTD. - SETTSU PLANT—See Shionogi & Co., Ltd.; *Int'l*, pg. 6851
SHIONOGI & CO., LTD.; *Int'l*, pg. 6851

SHIONOGI DEVELOPMENTAL RESEARCH LABORATORIES—See Shionogi & Co., Ltd.; *Int'l*, pg. 6851
SHIONOGI DIGITAL SCIENCE CO., LTD.—See Shionogi & Co., Ltd.; *Int'l*, pg. 6851
SHIONOGI EUROPE B.V.—See Shionogi & Co., Ltd.; *Int'l*, pg. 6851
SHIONOGI GENERAL SERVICE CO.,LTD.—See Shionogi & Co., Ltd.; *Int'l*, pg. 6851
SHIONOGI HEALTHCARE CO., LTD.—See Shionogi & Co., Ltd.; *Int'l*, pg. 6851
SHIONOGI INC.—See Shionogi & Co., Ltd.; *Int'l*, pg. 6851
SHIONOGI INSTITUTE FOR MEDICAL SCIENCE—See Shionogi & Co., Ltd.; *Int'l*, pg. 6851
SHIONOGI MARKETING SOLUTIONS CO., LTD.—See Shionogi & Co., Ltd.; *Int'l*, pg. 6851
SHIONOGI PHARMA CHEMICALS CO., LTD—See Shionogi & Co., Ltd.; *Int'l*, pg. 6851
SHIONOGI PHARMA CO., LTD—See Shionogi & Co., Ltd.; *Int'l*, pg. 6851
SHIONOGI PHARMACOVIGILANCE CENTER CO., LTD.—See Shionogi & Co., Ltd.; *Int'l*, pg. 6851
SHIONOGI PHARMA, INC.—See Shionogi & Co., Ltd.; *Int'l*, pg. 6851
SHIONOGI QUALICAPS, S.A.—See Shionogi & Co., Ltd.; *Int'l*, pg. 6851
SHIONOGI SMILE HEART CO., LTD.—See Shionogi & Co., Ltd.; *Int'l*, pg. 6851
SHIONOGI TECHNO ADVANCE RESEARCH CO., LTD.—See Shionogi & Co., Ltd.; *Int'l*, pg. 6851
SHIOTANI GLASS CO., LTD.—See Sharingtechnology, Inc.; *Int'l*, pg. 6790
SHIP AHOY LLC—See CMG Holdings Group, Inc.; *U.S. Public*, pg. 518
SHIPBOB, INC.; *U.S. Private*, pg. 3637
SHIPBUILDERS OF WISCONSIN, INC.; *U.S. Private*, pg. 3637
SHIPCHEM LOGISTICS CO., LTD.—See Yongtaiyun Chemical Logistics Co., Ltd.; *Int'l*, pg. 8598
SHIPDOCK B.V.—See Damen Shipyards Group; *Int'l*, pg. 1956
SHIPENGINE INC.—See Thoma Bravo, L.P.; *U.S. Private*, pg. 4154
SHIP HEALTHCARE FOOD, INC.—See Ship Healthcare Holdings, Inc.; *Int'l*, pg. 6852
SHIP HEALTHCARE HOLDINGS, INC.; *Int'l*, pg. 6851
SHIP HEALTHCARE RESEARCH & CONSULTING, INC.—See Ship Healthcare Holdings, Inc.; *Int'l*, pg. 6852
SHI PLASTICS MACHINERY DE MEXICO, S.A.DE C.V.—See Sumitomo Heavy Industries, Ltd.; *Int'l*, pg. 7288
SHI PLASTICS MACHINERY (HONG KONG) LTD—See Sumitomo Heavy Industries, Ltd.; *Int'l*, pg. 7288
SHI PLASTICS MACHINERY (INDIA) PRIVATE LTD.—See Sumitomo Heavy Industries, Ltd.; *Int'l*, pg. 7288
SHI PLASTICS MACHINERY (KOREA) CO, LTD.—See Sumitomo Heavy Industries, Ltd.; *Int'l*, pg. 7288
SHI PLASTICS MACHINERY (MALAYSIA) SDN. BHD.—See Sumitomo Heavy Industries, Ltd.; *Int'l*, pg. 7288
SHI PLASTICS MACHINERY (PHILS) INC.—See Sumitomo Heavy Industries, Ltd.; *Int'l*, pg. 7288
SHI PLASTICS MACHINERY (SHANGHAI) LTD—See Sumitomo Heavy Industries, Ltd.; *Int'l*, pg. 7290
S.H.I. PLASTICS MACHINERY (S) PTE. LTD.—See Sumitomo Heavy Industries, Ltd.; *Int'l*, pg. 7287
SHI PLASTICS MACHINERY (TAIWAN) INC.—See Sumitomo Heavy Industries, Ltd.; *Int'l*, pg. 7288
SHI PLASTICS MACHINERY (THAILAND) LTD.—See Sumitomo Heavy Industries, Ltd.; *Int'l*, pg. 7288
S.H.I. PLASTICS MACHINERY (VIETNAM) LLC—See Sumitomo Heavy Industries, Ltd.; *Int'l*, pg. 7287
SHIPLEY ASSOCIATES; *U.S. Private*, pg. 3637
SHIPLEY DO-NUT FLOUR & SUPPLY CO.—See Peak Rock Capital LLC; *U.S. Private*, pg. 3124
SHIPLEY DO-NUTS FLOUR AND SUPPLY CO.; *U.S. Private*, pg. 3637
SHIPLEY ENERGY COMPANY; *U.S. Private*, pg. 3637
SHIPLEY LIMITED—See Shipley Associates; *U.S. Private*, pg. 3637
SHIPLEY MOTOR EQUIPMENT COMPANY—See Bruckner Truck Sales, Inc.; *U.S. Private*, pg. 671
SHIPLEY (UK) GMBH—See Shipley Associates; *U.S. Private*, pg. 3637
SHIP MANAGEMENT SERVICES INC—See Southern Cross Capital Management SA; *Int'l*, pg. 7118
SHIPMAN ELEVATOR COMPANY; *U.S. Private*, pg. 3637
SHIPMAN & GOODWIN; *U.S. Private*, pg. 3637
SHIPMASTER CONTAINERS LTD.; *Int'l*, pg. 6852
SHIPONS A.D.; *Int'l*, pg. 6852
SHIP-PAC CORP.—See Central National Gottesman Inc.; *U.S. Private*, pg. 823
SHIP-PAC INC.; *U.S. Private*, pg. 3637
SHIP PARTNERS CO., LTD.—See Kawasaki Heavy Industries, Ltd.; *Int'l*, pg. 4098
SHIPPERS EUROPE SRL—See Crown Holdings, Inc.; *U.S. Public*, pg. 599

SHIPPERS SUPPLY COMPANY INC.; *U.S. Private*, pg. 3637
SHIPPERS SUPPLY INC—See Central National Gottesman Inc.; *U.S. Private*, pg. 823
SHIPPERS WAREHOUSE, INC.; *U.S. Private*, pg. 3637
SHIPPERS WAREHOUSE OF GEORGIA—See Shippers Warehouse, Inc.; *U.S. Private*, pg. 3637
SHIPPING CORPORATION OF INDIA LIMITED; *Int'l*, pg. 6852
SHIPPING, TRADING & LIGHTERAGE CO. LLC—See Chugoku Marine Paints, Ltd.; *Int'l*, pg. 1595
SHIPPO ASAHI MOULDS (THAILAND) CO., LTD.—See Daido Metal Corporation; *Int'l*, pg. 1922
SHIP-SERVICE S.A.—See Orlen S.A.; *Int'l*, pg. 5641
SHIPSIDE, INC.—See Lepanto Consolidated Mining Company; *Int'l*, pg. 4466
SHIPSTATION LIMITED—See Thoma Bravo, L.P.; *U.S. Private*, pg. 4154
SHIP SUPPLY OF FLORIDA, INC.; *U.S. Private*, pg. 3637
SHIPSURANCE INSURANCE SERVICES, INC.—See Assurant, Inc.; *U.S. Public*, pg. 215
SHIPWAY STAIRS & RAILINGS; *Int'l*, pg. 6853
SHIPWIRE, INC.—See Hainan Traffic Administration Holding Co., Ltd.; *Int'l*, pg. 3215
SHIPWRECK HERITAGE PRESS LLC—See Odyssey Marine Exploration, Inc.; *U.S. Public*, pg. 1564
SHIPXPRESS, INC.—See General Electric Company; *U.S. Public*, pg. 920
THE SHIPYARD BREWING COMPANY; *U.S. Private*, pg. 4117
THE SHIPYARD COMMUNITIES RETAIL OPERATOR, LLC—See Lennar Corporation; *U.S. Public*, pg. 1307
SHIRAHAMA DAIICHI TRAFFIC CO., LTD.—See Daiichi Koutsu Sangyo Co., Ltd.; *Int'l*, pg. 1929
SHIRAI ELECTRONICS INDUSTRIAL CO., LTD. - MORIYAMA FACTORY—See Shirai Electronics Industrial Co., Ltd.; *Int'l*, pg. 6853
SHIRAI ELECTRONICS INDUSTRIAL CO., LTD.; *Int'l*, pg. 6853
SHIRAI ELECTRONICS INDUSTRIAL CO., LTD. - TOMINAMI FACTORY—See Shirai Electronics Industrial Co., Ltd.; *Int'l*, pg. 6853
SHIRAI ELECTRONICS INDUSTRIAL CO., LTD. - UZUMASA FACTORY—See Shirai Electronics Industrial Co., Ltd.; *Int'l*, pg. 6853
SHIRAI ELECTRONICS TECHNOLOGY (HK) LTD.—See Shirai Electronics Industrial Co., Ltd.; *Int'l*, pg. 6853
SHIRAI ELECTRONICS TECHNOLOGY (ZHUHAI) LTD—See Shirai Electronics Industrial Co., Ltd.; *Int'l*, pg. 6853
SHIRAI ELECTRONICS TRADING (SHANGHAI) CO., LTD.—See Shirai Electronics Industrial Co., Ltd.; *Int'l*, pg. 6853
SHIRAI ELECTRONICS TRADING (SHENZHEN) CO., LTD.—See Shirai Electronics Industrial Co., Ltd.; *Int'l*, pg. 6853
SHIRAI LOGISTICS SERVICE CO., LTD.—See Shirai Electronics Industrial Co., Ltd.; *Int'l*, pg. 6853
SHIRAKAWA NITTO KOHKI CO., LTD.—See NITTO KOHKI Co., Ltd.; *Int'l*, pg. 5388
SHIRAKAWA OLYMPUS CO., LTD.—See Olympus Corporation; *Int'l*, pg. 5558
SHIRAM AUTOMALL INDIA LIMITED—See CarTrade Tech Ltd.; *Int'l*, pg. 1348
SHIRA REAL ESTATE DEVELOPMENT & INVESTMENTS P.L.C; *Int'l*, pg. 6853
SHIRAZI BENEFITS LLC—See Genstar Capital, LLC; *U.S. Private*, pg. 1675
SHIRAZI INVESTMENTS (PRIVATE) LIMITED—See Atlas Group of Companies; *Int'l*, pg. 685
SHIRAZI TRADING COMPANY PRIVATE LIMITED—See Atlas Group of Companies; *Int'l*, pg. 685
SHIRAZ OIL REFINING CO.—See Parsian Oil & Gas Development Co.; *Int'l*, pg. 5747
SHIRAZ PETROCHEMICAL COMPANY; *Int'l*, pg. 6853
SHIRAZ VEGETABLE OIL CO.; *Int'l*, pg. 6853
SHIRBLE DEPARTMENT STORE HOLDINGS (CHINA) LIMITED; *Int'l*, pg. 6853
SHIRDI INDUSTRIES LIMITED; *Int'l*, pg. 6853
SHIRDI SAI ELECTRICALS LTD.; *Int'l*, pg. 6853
SHIRE AG—See Takeda Pharmaceutical Company Limited; *Int'l*, pg. 7437
SHIRE AUSTRALIA PTY LIMITED—See Takeda Pharmaceutical Company Limited; *Int'l*, pg. 7437
SHIRE AUSTRIA GMBH—See Takeda Pharmaceutical Company Limited; *Int'l*, pg. 7437
SHIRE BELGIUM BVBA—See Takeda Pharmaceutical Company Limited; *Int'l*, pg. 7437
SHIRE BIOPHARMACEUTICALS IRELAND LIMITED—See Takeda Pharmaceutical Company Limited; *Int'l*, pg. 7437
SHIRE COLOMBIA S.A.S—See Takeda Pharmaceutical Company Limited; *Int'l*, pg. 7437
SHIRE CZECH S.R.O.—See Takeda Pharmaceutical Company Limited; *Int'l*, pg. 7437
SHIRE DEUTSCHLAND GMBH—See Takeda Pharmaceutical Company Limited; *Int'l*, pg. 7437
SHIRE DEVELOPMENT LLC—See Takeda Pharmaceutical Company Limited; *Int'l*, pg. 7438

COMPANY NAME INDEX

SHIRE FARMACEUTICA BRASIL LTDA—See Takeda Pharmaceutical Company Limited; *Int'l*, pg. 7437
SHIRE FOODS LIMITED—See Volvere plc; *Int'l*, pg. 8304
SHIRE FRANCE SA—See Takeda Pharmaceutical Company Limited; *Int'l*, pg. 7438
SHIRE HOLDINGS LUXEMBOURG S.A R.L.—See Takeda Pharmaceutical Company Limited; *Int'l*, pg. 7438
SHIRE HOTELS LIMITED—See Daniel Thwaites PLC; *Int'l*, pg. 1962
SHIRE HUMAN GENETIC THERAPIES AB—See Takeda Pharmaceutical Company Limited; *Int'l*, pg. 7438
SHIRE HUMAN GENETIC THERAPIES (CANADA) INC.—See Takeda Pharmaceutical Company Limited; *Int'l*, pg. 7438
SHIRE HUMAN GENETIC THERAPIES, INC.—See Takeda Pharmaceutical Company Limited; *Int'l*, pg. 7438
SHIRE HUMAN GENETIC THERAPIES LIMITED—See Takeda Pharmaceutical Company Limited; *Int'l*, pg. 7438
SHIRE HUMAN GENETIC THERAPIES S.A.—See Takeda Pharmaceutical Company Limited; *Int'l*, pg. 7438
SHIRE ILAC TICARET LIMITED SIRKETI—See Takeda Pharmaceutical Company Limited; *Int'l*, pg. 7438
SHIRE INCORPORATED—See Takeda Pharmaceutical Company Limited; *Int'l*, pg. 7438
SHIRE INTERNATIONAL GMBH—See Takeda Pharmaceutical Company Limited; *Int'l*, pg. 7438
SHIRE IP SERVICES CORPORATION—See Takeda Pharmaceutical Company Limited; *Int'l*, pg. 7438
SHIRE ITALIA S.P.A—See Takeda Pharmaceutical Company Limited; *Int'l*, pg. 7438
SHIRE JAPAN KK—See Takeda Pharmaceutical Company Limited; *Int'l*, pg. 7438
SHIRE LUXEMBOURG FINANCE S.A R.L.—See Takeda Pharmaceutical Company Limited; *Int'l*, pg. 7438
SHIRE-MOVETIS NV—See Takeda Pharmaceutical Company Limited; *Int'l*, pg. 7438
SHIRE ORPHAN THERAPIES GMBH—See Takeda Pharmaceutical Company Limited; *Int'l*, pg. 7437
SHIRE PHARMACEUTICAL CONTRACTS LIMITED—See Takeda Pharmaceutical Company Limited; *Int'l*, pg. 7438
SHIRE PHARMACEUTICAL DEVELOPMENT LIMITED—See Takeda Pharmaceutical Company Limited; *Int'l*, pg. 7438
SHIRE PHARMACEUTICALS GROUP LIMITED—See Takeda Pharmaceutical Company Limited; *Int'l*, pg. 7438
SHIRE PHARMACEUTICALS IBERICA S.L.—See Takeda Pharmaceutical Company Limited; *Int'l*, pg. 7438
SHIRE PHARMACEUTICALS IRELAND LTD.—See Takeda Pharmaceutical Company Limited; *Int'l*, pg. 7438
SHIRE PHARMACEUTICALS LLC—See Takeda Pharmaceutical Company Limited; *Int'l*, pg. 7438
SHIRE PHARMACEUTICALS LTD.—See Takeda Pharmaceutical Company Limited; *Int'l*, pg. 7438
SHIRE PHARMACEUTICALS MEXICO SA DE CV—See Takeda Pharmaceutical Company Limited; *Int'l*, pg. 7438
SHIRE PHARMACEUTICALS PORTUGAL, LDA—See Takeda Pharmaceutical Company Limited; *Int'l*, pg. 7438
SHIRE PLC—See Takeda Pharmaceutical Company Limited; *Int'l*, pg. 7437
SHIRE POLSKA SP. Z. O. O.—See Takeda Pharmaceutical Company Limited; *Int'l*, pg. 7438
SHIRE SERVICES BVBA—See Takeda Pharmaceutical Company Limited; *Int'l*, pg. 7438
SHIRES INCOME PLC; *Int'l*, pg. 6853
SHIRE SINGAPORE PTE. LTD.—See Takeda Pharmaceutical Company Limited; *Int'l*, pg. 7438
SHIRES (IRELAND) LIMITED—See Anchorage Capital Group, L.L.C.; *U.S. Private*, pg. 2969
SHIRES (IRELAND) LIMITED—See CVC Capital Partners SICAV-FIS S.A.; *Int'l*, pg. 1888
SHIRE SWEDEN AB—See Takeda Pharmaceutical Company Limited; *Int'l*, pg. 7438
SHIRE SWITZERLAND GMBH—See Takeda Pharmaceutical Company Limited; *Int'l*, pg. 7438
SHIRE US INC.—See Takeda Pharmaceutical Company Limited; *Int'l*, pg. 7438
SHIRE VIROPHARMA INCORPORATED—See Takeda Pharmaceutical Company Limited; *Int'l*, pg. 7438
SHIRLEY CONTRACTING COMPANY LLC—See Clark Enterprises, Inc.; *U.S. Private*, pg. 913
SHIRLEY PHARMACY LIMITED—See Green Cross Health Limited; *Int'l*, pg. 3070
SHIRLEY WIND, LLC—See Duke Energy Corporation; *U.S. Public*, pg. 691
SHIRNS PONTIAC-GMC INC.; *U.S. Private*, pg. 3637
SHIRO CORPORATION PTE LTD—See Aztech Group Ltd.; *Int'l*, pg. 781
SHIROHATO CO., LTD.; *Int'l*, pg. 6853
SHIROKAWA CO., LTD.—See Tokuyama Corporation; *Int'l*, pg. 7787
SHIROKI CORPORATION—See AISIN Corporation; *Int'l*, pg. 253

SHIROKI CORPORATION (THAILAND) LTD.—See AISIN Corporation; *Int'l*, pg. 253
SHIROKI-GA, LLC—See AISIN Corporation; *Int'l*, pg. 253
SHIROKI-GT, LLC—See AISIN Corporation; *Int'l*, pg. 254
SHIROKI NORTH AMERICA, INC.—See AISIN Corporation; *Int'l*, pg. 253
SHIROKI SEIKEI CO., LTD.—See AISIN Corporation; *Int'l*, pg. 254
SHIRONE GAS CO., LTD.—See Japan Petroleum Exploration Co. Ltd.; *Int'l*, pg. 3900
SHIROTORI AICHI ELEC CO., LTD.—See Aichi Electric Co., Ltd.; *Int'l*, pg. 229
SHIRPUR GOLD REFINERY LTD.; *Int'l*, pg. 6853
SHIRTCLIFF OIL CO.; *U.S. Private*, pg. 3637
SHISAKA SMELTING CO., LTD.—See Sumitomo Metal Mining Co., Ltd.; *Int'l*, pg. 7291
SHISALANGA CONSTRUCTION (PTY) LTD.—See Raubex Group Limited; *Int'l*, pg. 6221
SHISAS TRADING CONCERN PVT. LTD.—See HORIBA Ltd; *Int'l*, pg. 3478
SHISEIDO AMERICA INC. - DISTRIBUTION FACILITY—See Shiseido Company, Limited; *Int'l*, pg. 6854
SHISEIDO AMERICA INC.—See Shiseido Company, Limited; *Int'l*, pg. 6854
SHISEIDO AMERICAS CORPORATION—See Shiseido Company, Limited; *Int'l*, pg. 6853
SHISEIDO (AUSTRALIA) PTY. LIMITED—See Shiseido Company, Limited; *Int'l*, pg. 6853
SHISEIDO BEAUTY SALON CO., LTD.—See Shiseido Company, Limited; *Int'l*, pg. 6853
SHISEIDO CHINA CO., LTD.—See Shiseido Company, Limited; *Int'l*, pg. 6853
SHISEIDO CHINA RESEARCH CENTER CO., LTD.—See Shiseido Company, Limited; *Int'l*, pg. 6853
SHISEIDO COMPANY, LIMITED; *Int'l*, pg. 6853
SHISEIDO COSMETICI (ITALIA) S.P.A.—See Shiseido Company, Limited; *Int'l*, pg. 6854
SHISEIDO COSMETICS (CANADA) INC.—See Shiseido Company, Limited; *Int'l*, pg. 6854
SHISEIDO DEUTSCHLAND GMBH—See Shiseido Company, Limited; *Int'l*, pg. 6854
SHISEIDO EUROPE S.A.S.—See Shiseido Company, Limited; *Int'l*, pg. 6854
SHISEIDO HONG KONG LTD.—See Shiseido Company, Limited; *Int'l*, pg. 6853
SHISEIDO INTERNATIONAL EUROPE S.A.—See Shiseido Company, Limited; *Int'l*, pg. 6854
SHISEIDO INTERNATIONAL FRANCE S.A.S.—See Shiseido Company, Limited; *Int'l*, pg. 6854
SHISEIDO INTERNATIONAL INC.—See Shiseido Company, Limited; *Int'l*, pg. 6853
SHISEIDO LIYUAN COSMETICS CO., LTD.—See Shiseido Company, Limited; *Int'l*, pg. 6853
SHISEIDO N.Z. LTD.—See Shiseido Company, Limited; *Int'l*, pg. 6854
SHISEIDO PHARMACEUTICAL CO., LTD.—See Shiseido Company, Limited; *Int'l*, pg. 6854
SHISEIDO PROFESSIONAL CO., LTD.—See Shiseido Company, Limited; *Int'l*, pg. 6854
SHISEIDO SALES CO., LTD.—See Shiseido Company, Limited; *Int'l*, pg. 6854
SHISEIDO STUDIO—See Shiseido Company, Limited; pg. 6854
SHISEIDO U.K. CO., LTD.—See Shiseido Company, Limited; *Int'l*, pg. 6854
SHISEIDO VIETNAM INC.—See Shiseido Company, Limited; *Int'l*, pg. 6854
SHISH INDUSTRIES LIMITED; *Int'l*, pg. 6854
SHI SHI SERVICES LIMITED; *Int'l*, pg. 6827
SHI UK—See SHI International Corp.; *U.S. Private*, pg. 3635
SHIVA CEMENT LIMITED; *Int'l*, pg. 6854
SHIVA COMMUNICATION SASU—See Lonsdale Group; *Int'l*, pg. 4552
SHIVA GLOBAL AGRO INDUSTRIES LTD.; *Int'l*, pg. 6854
SHIVA GLOBAL BIOTECH PVT LTD—See Shiva Global Agro Industries Ltd.; *Int'l*, pg. 6854
SHIVA GRANITO EXPORT LIMITED; *Int'l*, pg. 6854
SHIVAGRICO IMPLEMENTS LTD.; *Int'l*, pg. 6855
SHIVAJIMARG PROPERTIES LIMITED—See DLF Limited; *Int'l*, pg. 2141
SHIVALIK BIMETAL CONTROLS LTD.; *Int'l*, pg. 6855
SHIVALIK ENGINEERED PRODUCTS PRIVATE LIMITED—See Shivalik Bimetal Controls Ltd.; *Int'l*, pg. 6855
SHIVALIK RASAYAN LIMITED; *Int'l*, pg. 6855
SHIVAM AUTOTECH LTD.—See Hero Corp.; *Int'l*, pg. 3364
SHIVAM CEMENTS LIMITED; *Int'l*, pg. 6855
SHIVA MEDICARE LIMITED; *Int'l*, pg. 6854
SHIVA MILLS LTD.; *Int'l*, pg. 6855
SHI VANCOUVER—See SHI International Corp.; *U.S. Private*, pg. 3635
SHIVANSH FINSERVE LTD.; *Int'l*, pg. 6855
SHIVA SUITINGS LIMITED; *Int'l*, pg. 6855
SHIVA TEXYARN LIMITED; *Int'l*, pg. 6855
SHIV AUM STEELS LIMITED; *Int'l*, pg. 6854
SHIVE-HATTERY GROUP INC.; *U.S. Private*, pg. 3638

SHIZUOKAGAS CO., LTD.

SHIVELY BROTHERS INC.; *U.S. Private*, pg. 3638
SHIVELY MOTORS; *U.S. Private*, pg. 3638
SHIVER SECURITY SYSTEMS, INC.—See Pye-Barker Fire & Safety, LLC; *U.S. Private*, pg. 3309
SHIVERS TRADING & OPERATING COMPANY; *U.S. Private*, pg. 3638
SHIV KAMAL IMPEX LIMITED; *Int'l*, pg. 6854
SHIVOM INVESTMENT & CONSULTANCY LTD.; *Int'l*, pg. 6855
SHIVPAD ENGINEERS PVT. LTD.—See Jash Engineering Limited; *Int'l*, pg. 3912
SHIV SHAKTI DEVELOPERS—See Poddar Housing and Development Limited; *Int'l*, pg. 5902
SHIV VANI OIL & GAS CO. LLC.—See SVOGL Oil Gas and Energy Limited; *Int'l*, pg. 7359
SHIVVERS INC.; *U.S. Private*, pg. 3638
SHIWAFORCE.COM INC.—See OTP Bank Plc; *Int'l*, pg. 5658
SHIYAN TAIXIANG INDUSTRY CO., LTD.; *Int'l*, pg. 6855
SHI YOU CHEMICAL (YANGZHOU) CO., LTD.—See Kingboard Holdings Limited; *Int'l*, pg. 4171
SHIYUAN (XIAMEN) LIGHTING TECHNOLOGY CO., LTD.—See Tecnon Electronics Co., Ltd.; *Int'l*, pg. 7517
SHIZUGIN BUSINESS CREATE CO., LTD.—See Shizuoka Financial Group, Inc.; *Int'l*, pg. 6855
SHIZUGIN DC CARD CO., LTD.—See Shizuoka Financial Group, Inc.; *Int'l*, pg. 6855
SHIZUGIN HEARTFUL CO., LTD.—See Shizuoka Financial Group, Inc.; *Int'l*, pg. 6855
SHIZUGIN IT SOLUTION CO., LTD.—See Shizuoka Financial Group, Inc.; *Int'l*, pg. 6855
SHIZUGIN LEASE CO., LTD.—See Shizuoka Financial Group, Inc.; *Int'l*, pg. 6855
SHIZUGIN MANAGEMENT CONSULTING CO., LTD.—See Shizuoka Financial Group, Inc.; *Int'l*, pg. 6856
SHIZUGIN SAISON CARD CO., LTD.—See Shizuoka Financial Group, Inc.; *Int'l*, pg. 6856
SHIZUGIN TM SECURITIES CO., LTD.—See Shizuoka Financial Group, Inc.; *Int'l*, pg. 6856
SHIZUKI ELECTRIC COMPANY, INC.; *Int'l*, pg. 6855
SHIZUKI ELECTRIC (SHANGHAI) TRADING CO., INC.—See Shizuki Electric Company, Inc.; *Int'l*, pg. 6855
SHIZUKI ELECTRIC (THAILAND) CO., LTD.—See Shizuki Electric Company, Inc.; *Int'l*, pg. 6855
SHIZUOKA BANK (EUROPE) S.A.—See Shizuoka Financial Group, Inc.; *Int'l*, pg. 6856
SHIZUOKA BANK, LTD.—See Shizuoka Financial Group, Inc.; *Int'l*, pg. 6855
SHIZUOKA CAPITAL CO., LTD.—See Shizuoka Financial Group, Inc.; *Int'l*, pg. 6856
SHIZUOKACHUBU PLASTICS MOLDING CO., LTD.—See Okaya & Co., Ltd.; *Int'l*, pg. 5547
SHIZUOKA COMPUTER SERVICE CO., LTD.—See Shizuoka Financial Group, Inc.; *Int'l*, pg. 6856
SHIZUOKADENSO CO., LTD.—See Koito Manufacturing Co., Ltd.; *Int'l*, pg. 4231
SHIZUOKA FINANCIAL GROUP, INC.; *Int'l*, pg. 6855
SHIZUOKAGAS CO., LTD.; *Int'l*, pg. 6856
SHIZUOKA GAS CREDIT CO., LTD.—See Shizuokagas Co., Ltd.; *Int'l*, pg. 6856
SHIZUOKA GAS ENERGY CO., LTD.—See Shizuokagas Co., Ltd.; *Int'l*, pg. 6856
SHIZUOKA GAS ENGINEERING CO., LTD.—See Shizuokagas Co., Ltd.; *Int'l*, pg. 6856
SHIZUOKA GAS INSURANCE SERVICE CO., LTD.—See Shizuokagas Co., Ltd.; *Int'l*, pg. 6856
SHIZUOKA GAS LIVING CO., LTD.—See Shizuokagas Co., Ltd.; *Int'l*, pg. 6856
SHIZUOKA GAS & POWER CO., LTD.—See Shizuokagas Co., Ltd.; *Int'l*, pg. 6856
SHIZUOKA GAS SERVICE CO., LTD.—See Shizuokagas Co., Ltd.; *Int'l*, pg. 6856
SHIZUOKA GAS SYSTEM SOLUTION CO., LTD.—See Shizuokagas Co., Ltd.; *Int'l*, pg. 6856
SHIZUOKA HAKUHODO INC.—See Hakuhodo DY Holdings Incorporated; *Int'l*, pg. 3222
SHIZUOKA HANSUNG CO., LTD.—See Shizuoka Seiki Co., Ltd.; *Int'l*, pg. 6856
SHIZUOKA HINO MOTOR LTD.—See Toyota Motor Corporation; *Int'l*, pg. 7871
SHIZUOKA HITACHI CO., LTD.—See Hitachi, Ltd.; *Int'l*, pg. 3424
SHIZUOKA ISETAN CO., LTD.—See Isetan Mitsukoshi Holdings Ltd.; *Int'l*, pg. 3815
SHIZUOKA KOSAN CO., LTD.—See Nippon Light Metal Holdings Company, Ltd.; *Int'l*, pg. 5324
SHIZUOKA KOYO CO., LTD.—See JTEKT Corporation; *Int'l*, pg. 4019
SHIZUOKA K-TECHNO CO., LTD—See Kandenko Co., Ltd.; *Int'l*, pg. 4065
SHIZUOKA LOGISTICS CO., LTD.—See Tokushu Tokai Paper Co., Ltd.; *Int'l*, pg. 7786
SHIZUOKA MAZDA CO., LTD.—See Mazda Motor Corporation; *Int'l*, pg. 4749
SHIZUOKA MORTGAGE SERVICE CO., LTD.—See Shizuoka Financial Group, Inc.; *Int'l*, pg. 6856
SHIZUOKA NDS CO., LTD.—See COMSYS Holdings Corporation; *Int'l*, pg. 1762

2477

SHIZUOKAGAS CO., LTD.

SHIZUOKA NISSAN AUTO CO., LTD.—See VT Holdings Co., Ltd.; *Int'l*, pg. 8315
SHIZUOKA OKI ELECTRIC CO., LTD.—See Oki Electric Industry Co., Ltd.; *Int'l*, pg. 5549
SHIZUOKA SEIKI CO., LTD.; *Int'l*, pg. 6856
SHIZUOKA TELECASTING CO., LTD—See Fuji Media Holdings, Inc.; *Int'l*, pg. 2814
SHIZUOKA TERMINAL DEVELOPMENT COMPANY LIMITED—See Central Japan Railway Company; *Int'l*, pg. 1408
SHIZUOKA WIRE HARNESS CO., LTD.—See Koito Manufacturing Co., Ltd.; *Int'l*, pg. 4231
SHK FINANCE LIMITED—See Allied Group Limited; *Int'l*, pg. 357
SHK HONG KONG INDUSTRIES LIMITED; *Int'l*, pg. 6856
S&H KLIMATEKNIK A/S—See Per Aarsleff Holding A/S; *Int'l*, pg. 5796
SHK MANAGEMENT INC.; *U.S. Private*, pg. 3638
SHL AG—See Exponent Private Equity LLP; *Int'l*, pg. 2589
SHL AUTOMATION INC.—See SHL Automatisierungstechnik AG; *Int'l*, pg. 6856
SHL AUTOMATISIERUNGSTECHNIK AG; *Int'l*, pg. 6856
SHL BELGIUM SA—See Exponent Private Equity LLP; *Int'l*, pg. 2589
SHL CONSOLIDATED BHD.; *Int'l*, pg. 6856
SHL DANMARK A/S—See Exponent Private Equity LLP; *Int'l*, pg. 2589
S.H. LEGGITT COMPANY INC.; *U.S. Private*, pg. 3517
SHL FINANCE COMPANY; *Int'l*, pg. 6856
SHL FRANCE SAS—See Exponent Private Equity LLP; *Int'l*, pg. 2589
SHL GROUP LIMITED—See Exponent Private Equity LLP; *Int'l*, pg. 2589
SHL HONG KONG LIMITED—See Exponent Private Equity LLP; *Int'l*, pg. 2589
SHL-JAPAN LTD.; *Int'l*, pg. 6857
SHL-M SDN. BHD.—See SHL Consolidated Bhd.; *Int'l*, pg. 6856
SHL NEDERLAND BV—See Exponent Private Equity LLP; *Int'l*, pg. 2589
SHL NEW ZEALAND LIMITED—See Exponent Private Equity LLP; *Int'l*, pg. 2589
SHLOMO ELIAHU HOLDINGS LTD.; *Int'l*, pg. 6857
SHL PEOPLE SOLUTIONS LTD.—See Exponent Private Equity LLP; *Int'l*, pg. 2589
SHL POLSKA SP. Z.O.O.—See Exponent Private Equity LLP; *Int'l*, pg. 2589
SHL SAVILLE & HOLDSWORTH (DEUTSCHLAND) GMBH—See Exponent Private Equity LLP; *Int'l*, pg. 2589
SHL; *Int'l*, pg. 6856
SHL SVERIGE AB—See Exponent Private Equity LLP; *Int'l*, pg. 2589
SHL TELEMEDICINE LIMITED; *Int'l*, pg. 6856
SHL TELEMEDIZIN GMBH—See SHL Telemedicine Limited; *Int'l*, pg. 6857
SHL (UK) LIMITED—See Exponent Private Equity LLP; *Int'l*, pg. 2589
SHL US LLC—See Exponent Private Equity LLP; *Int'l*, pg. 2589
SHMALTZ BREWING COMPANY; *U.S. Private*, pg. 3639
SHM ANACAPA ISLE, LLC—See Sun Communities, Inc.; *U.S. Public*, pg. 1961
SHM ANNAPOLIS, LLC—See Sun Communities, Inc.; *U.S. Public*, pg. 1961
SHM AQUALAND, LLC—See Sun Communities, Inc.; *U.S. Public*, pg. 1961
SHM AQUA YACHT, LLC—See Sun Communities, Inc.; *U.S. Public*, pg. 1961
SH MARKETS, INC.—See Sprouts Farmers Markets, Inc.; *U.S. Public*, pg. 1920
SHM BAHIA BLEU, LLC—See Sun Communities, Inc.; *U.S. Public*, pg. 1961
SHM BALLENA ISLE, LLC—See Sun Communities, Inc.; *U.S. Public*, pg. 1961
SHM BEAUFORT, LLC—See Sun Communities, Inc.; *U.S. Public*, pg. 1961
SHM BEAVER CREEK, LLC—See Sun Communities, Inc.; *U.S. Public*, pg. 1961
SHM BELLE MAER, LLC—See Sun Communities, Inc.; *U.S. Public*, pg. 1961
SHM BOHEMIA VISTA, LLC—See Sun Communities, Inc.; *U.S. Public*, pg. 1961
SHM BRADY MOUNTAIN, LLC—See Sun Communities, Inc.; *U.S. Public*, pg. 1961
SHM BRUCE & JOHNSON, LLC—See Sun Communities, Inc.; *U.S. Public*, pg. 1961
SHM BURNSIDE, LLC—See Sun Communities, Inc.; *U.S. Public*, pg. 1961
SHM CABRILLO ISLE, LLC—See Sun Communities, Inc.; *U.S. Public*, pg. 1961
SHM CAPE HARBOUR, LLC—See Sun Communities, Inc.; *U.S. Public*, pg. 1961
SHM CAPRI, LLC—See Sun Communities, Inc.; *U.S. Public*, pg. 1961
SHM CARROLL ISLAND, LLC—See Sun Communities, Inc.; *U.S. Public*, pg. 1962
SHM CHARLESTON BOATYARD, LLC—See Sun Communities, Inc.; *U.S. Public*, pg. 1962

SHM CHARLESTON CITY MARINA, LLC—See Sun Communities, Inc.; *U.S. Public*, pg. 1962
SHM COVE HAVEN, LLC—See Sun Communities, Inc.; *U.S. Public*, pg. 1962
SHM COWESETT, LLC—See Sun Communities, Inc.; *U.S. Public*, pg. 1962
SHM CRYSTAL POINT, LLC—See Sun Communities, Inc.; *U.S. Public*, pg. 1962
SHM DAUNTLESS, LLC—See Sun Communities, Inc.; *U.S. Public*, pg. 1962
SHM DEEP RIVER, LLC—See Sun Communities, Inc.; *U.S. Public*, pg. 1962
SHM DETROIT RIVER, LLC—See Sun Communities, Inc.; *U.S. Public*, pg. 1962
SHM EAGLE COVE, LLC—See Sun Communities, Inc.; *U.S. Public*, pg. 1962
SHM EMERALD COAST, LLC—See Sun Communities, Inc.; *U.S. Public*, pg. 1962
SHM EMERALD POINT, LLC—See Sun Communities, Inc.; *U.S. Public*, pg. 1962
SHM EMERYVILLE, LLC—See Sun Communities, Inc.; *U.S. Public*, pg. 1962
SHMERLING-SYNCHRO ENERGY ENGINEERING LTD.—See 2G Energy AG; *Int'l*, pg. 5
SHM FERRY POINT, LLC—See Sun Communities, Inc.; *U.S. Public*, pg. 1962
SHM FIDDLER'S COVE, LLC—See Sun Communities, Inc.; *U.S. Public*, pg. 1962
SHM GAINES, LLC—See Sun Communities, Inc.; *U.S. Public*, pg. 1962
SHM GLEN COVE, LLC—See Sun Communities, Inc.; *U.S. Public*, pg. 1962
SHM GRAND ISLE, LLC—See Sun Communities, Inc.; *U.S. Public*, pg. 1962
SHM GREAT ISLAND, LLC—See Sun Communities, Inc.; *U.S. Public*, pg. 1962
SHM GREAT LAKES, LLC—See Sun Communities, Inc.; *U.S. Public*, pg. 1962
SHM GREAT OAK LANDING, LLC—See Sun Communities, Inc.; *U.S. Public*, pg. 1962
SHM GREEN HARBOR, LLC—See Sun Communities, Inc.; *U.S. Public*, pg. 1962
SHM GREENPORT, LLC—See Sun Communities, Inc.; *U.S. Public*, pg. 1962
SHM GREENWICH BAY, LLC—See Sun Communities, Inc.; *U.S. Public*, pg. 1962
SHM GRIDER HILL, LLC—See Sun Communities, Inc.; *U.S. Public*, pg. 1962
SHM HACKS POINT, LLC—See Sun Communities, Inc.; *U.S. Public*, pg. 1962
SHM HARBORAGE YC, LLC—See Sun Communities, Inc.; *U.S. Public*, pg. 1962
SHM HARBORS VIEW, LLC—See Sun Communities, Inc.; *U.S. Public*, pg. 1962
SHM HARBORTOWN, LLC—See Sun Communities, Inc.; *U.S. Public*, pg. 1962
SHM HAVERSTRAW, LLC—See Sun Communities, Inc.; *U.S. Public*, pg. 1962
SHM HAWTHORNE COVE, LLC—See Sun Communities, Inc.; *U.S. Public*, pg. 1962
SHM HIDEAWAY BAY, LLC—See Sun Communities, Inc.; *U.S. Public*, pg. 1962
SHM HOLLY CREEK, LLC—See Sun Communities, Inc.; *U.S. Public*, pg. 1962
SHM ISLAMORADA, LLC—See Sun Communities, Inc.; *U.S. Public*, pg. 1962
SHM ISLAND PARK, LLC—See Sun Communities, Inc.; *U.S. Public*, pg. 1962
SHMITT TECHNOLOGIES LLC—See Baymark Partners; *U.S. Private*, pg. 496
SHM JAMESTOWN BOATYARD, LLC—See Sun Communities, Inc.; *U.S. Public*, pg. 1962
SHM JAMESTOWN, LLC—See Sun Communities, Inc.; *U.S. Public*, pg. 1962
SHM JEFFERSON BEACH, LLC—See Sun Communities, Inc.; *U.S. Public*, pg. 1962
SHM KING'S POINT, LLC—See Sun Communities, Inc.; *U.S. Public*, pg. 1962
SHM LAKEFRONT, LLC—See Sun Communities, Inc.; *U.S. Public*, pg. 1962
SHM LOCH LOMOND, LLC—See Sun Communities, Inc.; *U.S. Public*, pg. 1962
SHM MANASQUAN, LLC—See Sun Communities, Inc.; *U.S. Public*, pg. 1962
SHM MARINA BAY, LLC—See Sun Communities, Inc.; *U.S. Public*, pg. 1962
SHM MYSTIC, LLC—See Sun Communities, Inc.; *U.S. Public*, pg. 1962
SHM NARROWS POINT, LLC—See Sun Communities, Inc.; *U.S. Public*, pg. 1962
SHM NEW PORT COVE, LLC—See Sun Communities, Inc.; *U.S. Public*, pg. 1962
SHM NORTH PALM BEACH, LLC—See Sun Communities, Inc.; *U.S. Public*, pg. 1962
SHM OLD PORT COVE, LLC—See Sun Communities, Inc.; *U.S. Public*, pg. 1962
SHM ONSET BAY, LLC—See Sun Communities, Inc.; *U.S. Public*, pg. 1962

CORPORATE AFFILIATIONS

SHM PIER 121, LLC—See Sun Communities, Inc.; *U.S. Public*, pg. 1962
SHM PILOTS POINT, LLC—See Sun Communities, Inc.; *U.S. Public*, pg. 1962
SHM PINELAND, LLC—See Sun Communities, Inc.; *U.S. Public*, pg. 1962
SHM PLYMOUTH, LLC—See Sun Communities, Inc.; *U.S. Public*, pg. 1962
SHM PORT ROYAL, LLC—See Sun Communities, Inc.; *U.S. Public*, pg. 1962
SHM POST ROAD, LLC—See Sun Communities, Inc.; *U.S. Public*, pg. 1962
SHM PUERTO DEL REY, LLC—See Sun Communities, Inc.; *U.S. Public*, pg. 1962
SHM REGATTA POINTE, LLC—See Sun Communities, Inc.; *U.S. Public*, pg. 1962
SHM RESERVE HARBOR, LLC—See Sun Communities, Inc.; *U.S. Public*, pg. 1962
SHM ROCKLAND, LLC—See Sun Communities, Inc.; *U.S. Public*, pg. 1962
SHM RYBOVICH WPB TRS, LLC—See Sun Communities, Inc.; *U.S. Public*, pg. 1962
SHM SAKONNET, LLC—See Sun Communities, Inc.; *U.S. Public*, pg. 1962
SHM SANDUSKY, LLC—See Sun Communities, Inc.; *U.S. Public*, pg. 1962
SHM SEVEN INVESTMENTS LTD.—See MOL Magyar Olaj- es Gazipari Nyrt.; *Int'l*, pg. 5021
SHM SHELBURNE, LLC—See Sun Communities, Inc.; *U.S. Public*, pg. 1962
SHM SHELTER ISLAND, LLC—See Sun Communities, Inc.; *U.S. Public*, pg. 1962
SHM SIESTA KEY, LLC—See Sun Communities, Inc.; *U.S. Public*, pg. 1962
SHM SILVER SPRING, LLC—See Sun Communities, Inc.; *U.S. Public*, pg. 1963
SHM SKIPPERS LANDING, LLC—See Sun Communities, Inc.; *U.S. Public*, pg. 1963
SHM SKULL CREEK, LLC—See Sun Communities, Inc.; *U.S. Public*, pg. 1963
SHM SOUTH BAY, LLC—See Sun Communities, Inc.; *U.S. Public*, pg. 1963
SHM SPORTSMAN, LLC—See Sun Communities, Inc.; *U.S. Public*, pg. 1963
SHM STRATFORD, LLC—See Sun Communities, Inc.; *U.S. Public*, pg. 1963
SHM SUNROAD, LLC—See Sun Communities, Inc.; *U.S. Public*, pg. 1963
SHM SUNSET BAY, LLC—See Sun Communities, Inc.; *U.S. Public*, pg. 1963
SHM TOLEDO BEACH, LLC—See Sun Communities, Inc.; *U.S. Public*, pg. 1963
SHM TRADE WINDS, LLC—See Sun Communities, Inc.; *U.S. Public*, pg. 1963
SHM VENTURA ISLE, LLC—See Sun Communities, Inc.; *U.S. Public*, pg. 1963
SHM VINEYARD HAVEN, LLC—See Sun Communities, Inc.; *U.S. Public*, pg. 1963
SHM WALDEN, LLC—See Sun Communities, Inc.; *U.S. Public*, pg. 1963
SHM WENTWORTH, LLC—See Sun Communities, Inc.; *U.S. Public*, pg. 1963
SHM WESTPORT, LLC—See Sun Communities, Inc.; *U.S. Public*, pg. 1963
SHM WICKFORD COVE, LLC—See Sun Communities, Inc.; *U.S. Public*, pg. 1963
SHM WISDOM DOCK, LLC—See Sun Communities, Inc.; *U.S. Public*, pg. 1963
SHM YACHT HAVEN, LLC—See Sun Communities, Inc.; *U.S. Public*, pg. 1963
SHM ZAHNISERS, LLC—See Sun Communities, Inc.; *U.S. Public*, pg. 1963
SHO-A CORPORATION—See Shoko Co., Ltd.; *Int'l*, pg. 6858
SHO-AIR INTERNATIONAL INC.; *U.S. Private*, pg. 3639
SHOAL POINT ENERGY LTD.; *Int'l*, pg. 6857
SHOALS DIALYSIS, LLC—See DaVita Inc.; *U.S. Public*, pg. 643
SHOALS MPE, LLC; *U.S. Private*, pg. 3639
SHOALS PROVISION INC.; *U.S. Private*, pg. 3639
SHOALS TECHNOLOGIES GROUP, INC.; *U.S. Public*, pg. 1875
SHOALTER AUTOMATION (UK) LIMITED—See Hong Kong Technology Venture Company Limited; *Int'l*, pg. 3467
SHOBIDO CORPORATION; *Int'l*, pg. 6857
SHO-BOND HOLDINGS CO., LTD.; *Int'l*, pg. 6857
SHO-BOND (HONG KONG) LTD.—See SHO-BOND Holdings Co., Ltd.; *Int'l*, pg. 6857
SHOBUNSHA CREATIVE CO., LTD.—See Shobunsha Holdings Inc.; *Int'l*, pg. 6857
SHOBUNSHA HOLDINGS INC.; *Int'l*, pg. 6857
SHOCHIKU CO., LTD.; *Int'l*, pg. 6857
SHOCK ABSORBER US INC—See Hanesbrands Inc.; *U.S. Public*, pg. 983
SHOCK DOCTOR, INC.—See Wells Fargo & Company; *U.S. Public*, pg. 2344
THE SHOCKEY PRECAST GROUP—See Metromont Corporation; *U.S. Private*, pg. 2687

COMPANY NAME INDEX

SHOCKOE COMMERCE GROUP, LLC.; *U.S. Private*, pg. 3639
SHOCKWATCH, INC.—See Harbour Group Industries, Inc.; *U.S. Private*, pg. 1861
SHOCKWAVE MEDICAL, INC.—See Johnson & Johnson; *U.S. Public*, pg. 1200
SHOC MEDIA AGENCY AB—See Bertelsmann SE & Co. KGaA; *Int'l*, pg. 996
SHOCO INC.; *U.S. Private*, pg. 3639
SHO-DEEN CONSTRUCTION, LLC—See Sho-Deen Inc.; *U.S. Private*, pg. 3639
SHO-DEEN INC.; *U.S. Private*, pg. 3639
SHODEN SEIWA CO., LTD.—See The Furukawa Electric Co., Ltd.; *Int'l*, pg. 7647
SHODEX CHINA CO., LTD.—See Resonac Holdings Corporation; *Int'l*, pg. 6300
SHOEAHOLICS LIMITED—See Cinven Limited; *Int'l*, pg. 1612
SHOEBUY.COM, INC.—See CriticalPoint Capital, LLC; *U.S. Private*, pg. 1102
SHOE CARNIVAL, INC.; *U.S. Public*, pg. 1875
SHOE CARNIVAL VENTURES, LLC—See Shoe Carnival, Inc.; *U.S. Public*, pg. 1875
SHOE CITY G.P. INC.; *U.S. Private*, pg. 3639
SHOE CITY (PTY) LTD.—See Steinhoff International Holdings N.V.; *Int'l*, pg. 7195
SHOEDAZZLE.COM, INC.—See Just Fabulous, Inc.; *U.S. Private*, pg. 2245
SHOEFAYRE LIMITED—See Co-operative Group Limited; *Int'l*, pg. 1679
SHOEI CHEMICAL INC.; *Int'l*, pg. 6857
SHOEI CO., LTD.; *Int'l*, pg. 6857
SHOEI CORPORATION; *Int'l*, pg. 6858
SHOEI DENSETSU CORPORARION—See Unipulse Corporation; *Int'l*, pg. 8057
SHOEI DISTRIBUTION GMBH—See Shoei Co., Ltd.; *Int'l*, pg. 6858
SHOEI (EUROPA) GMBH—See Shoei Co., Ltd.; *Int'l*, pg. 6858
SHOEI EUROPE DISTRIBUTION S.A.R.L.—See Shoei Co., Ltd.; *Int'l*, pg. 6858
SHOEI FOODS CORPORATION; *Int'l*, pg. 6858
SHOEI FOODS (U.S.A.), INC.—See Shoei Foods Corporation; *Int'l*, pg. 6858
SHOEI PRINTING CO.,LTD. - KAWASAKI FACTORY—See SHOEI Printing Co., Ltd.; *Int'l*, pg. 6858
SHOEI PRINTING CO., LTD. - OSAKA FACTORY—See SHOEI Printing Co., Ltd.; *Int'l*, pg. 6858
SHOEI PRINTING CO., LTD.; *Int'l*, pg. 6858
SHOEI PRINTING (HONG KONG) CO., LTD.—See SHOEI Printing Co., Ltd.; *Int'l*, pg. 6858
SHOEISHA ACADEMY CO., LTD.—See SE Holdings & Incubations Co., Ltd.; *Int'l*, pg. 6660
SHOEI TRADING (THAILAND) CO., LTD.—See Shoei Yakuhin Co., Ltd.; *Int'l*, pg. 6858
SHOEI YAKUHIN CO., LTD.; *Int'l*, pg. 6858
SHOEMAKER CAPITAL PARTNERS LLC.; *U.S. Private*, pg. 3639
SHOEMAKER CONSTRUCTION CO.—See Butz Enterprises, Inc.; *U.S. Private*, pg. 698
SHOEMAKER CONSTRUCTION—See Butz Enterprises, Inc.; *U.S. Private*, pg. 698
SHOEMAKER FINANCIAL—See Securian Financial Group, Inc.; *U.S. Private*, pg. 3594
SHOEMAKER MANUFACTURING, CO.—See CSW Industrials, Inc.; *U.S. Private*, pg. 602
SHOEME TECHNOLOGIES LTD.—See Hardy Capital Corporation; *Int'l*, pg. 3273
SHOE PALACE CORPORATION—See Pentland Group Limited; *Int'l*, pg. 5792
SHOE SENSATION, INC.—See Prospect Hill Growth Partners, L.P.; *U.S. Private*, pg. 3288
SHOES FOR CREWS, LLC—See CCMP Capital Advisors, LP; *U.S. Private*, pg. 801
SHOE SHOW, INC.; *U.S. Private*, pg. 3639
SHOES & SOX PTY LTD—See Anchorage Capital Partners Pty. Limited; *Int'l*, pg. 448
SHOE STATION INC.—See Shoe Carnival, Inc.; *U.S. Public*, pg. 1875
SHOE SUPERSTORE PTY LTD.—See Accent Group Limited; *Int'l*, pg. 81
SHOE ZONE PLC; *Int'l*, pg. 6857
SHOEZOO.COM LLC; *U.S. Private*, pg. 3639
SHOFERS FURNITURE CO. INC.; *U.S. Private*, pg. 3639
SHOFF DARBY COMPANIES INC.—See Lawley Service Inc.; *U.S. Private*, pg. 2401
SHOFFEE INC.; *U.S. Private*, pg. 3639
SHOFFNERKALTHOFF MECHANICAL ELECTRICAL SERVICE, LLC—See Comfort Systems USA, Inc.; *U.S. Public*, pg. 544
SHOFU BIOFIX INC.—See Shofu Inc.; *Int'l*, pg. 6858
SHOFU DENTAL ASIA-PACIFIC PTE. LTD.—See Shofu Inc.; *Int'l*, pg. 6858
SHOFU DENTAL CORPORATION—See Shofu Inc.; *Int'l*, pg. 6858
SHOFU DENTAL GMBH—See Shofu Inc.; *Int'l*, pg. 6858
SHOFU DENTAL TRADING (SHANGHAI) CO., LTD.—See Shofu Inc.; *Int'l*, pg. 6858
SHOFU INC.; *Int'l*, pg. 6858

SHOFU UK—See Shofu Inc.; *Int'l*, pg. 6858
SHOGA GMBH—See ManpowerGroup Inc.; *U.S. Public*, pg. 1362
SHOGREN HOSIERY MANUFACTURING CO., INC.—See Shogren Industries Inc.; *U.S. Private*, pg. 3639
SHOGREN INDUSTRIES INC.; *U.S. Private*, pg. 3639
SHOGYO INTERNATIONAL CORPORATION; *U.S. Private*, pg. 3639
SHOJI CO., LTD.—See Nishio Holdings Co., Ltd.; *Int'l*, pg. 5366
SHOKAI FAR EAST LTD.; *U.S. Private*, pg. 3639
SHOKANDO CO., LTD.—See Polaris Capital Group Co., Ltd.; *Int'l*, pg. 5907
SHOKETSU-SMC CORPORATION—See SMC Corporation; *Int'l*, pg. 7006
SHOKO AGRI CO., LTD.—See Shoko Co., Ltd.; *Int'l*, pg. 6858
THE SHOKO CHUKIN BANK, LTD.; *Int'l*, pg. 7682
SHOKOCHUKIN COMPUTER SYSTEMS CO., LTD.—See The Shoko Chukin Bank, Ltd.; *Int'l*, pg. 7682
SHOKO CO., LTD.; *Int'l*, pg. 6858
SHOKO FARM NET K. K.—See Shoko Co., Ltd.; *Int'l*, pg. 6858
SHOKO HIGHPOLYMER CO., LTD.—See Shoko Co., Ltd.; *Int'l*, pg. 6858
SHOKO INSURANCE SERVICE CO., LTD.—See Shoko Co., Ltd.; *Int'l*, pg. 6858
SHOKO KOREA CO., LTD.—See Shoko Co., Ltd.; *Int'l*, pg. 6858
SHOKO SCIENCE CO., LTD.—See Shoko Co., Ltd.; *Int'l*, pg. 6859
SHOKO SERVICE, LTD.—See The Shoko Chukin Bank, Ltd.; *Int'l*, pg. 7682
SHOKO (TAIWAN) GLOBAL CORPORATION—See Shoko Co., Ltd.; *Int'l*, pg. 6858
SHOKO (THAILAND) CO., LTD.—See Shoko Co., Ltd.; *Int'l*, pg. 6858
SHOKUBUN CO., LTD.; *Int'l*, pg. 6859
SHOKU EN CO., LTD.—See The Kiyo Bank, Ltd.; *Int'l*, pg. 7663
SHOMAL CEMENT COMPANY; *Int'l*, pg. 6859
SHOMALSHARGH SHAHROOD INDUSTRIAL & MINING COMPANY—See National Iranian Lead & Zinc Company; *Int'l*, pg. 6160
SHO-ME POWER ELECTRIC COOPERATIVE INC.; *U.S. Private*, pg. 3639
SHOMERA INSURANCE COMPANY LTD.—See Menora Mivtachim Holdings Ltd.; *Int'l*, pg. 4817
SHOMOUL HOLDING COMPANY L.L.C.—See Mabanee Company S.A.K.; *Int'l*, pg. 4618
THE SHONAI BANK, LTD.—See FIDEA Holdings Co. Ltd.; *Int'l*, pg. 2654
SHONAI YOROZU CORPORATION—See Yorozu Corporation; *Int'l*, pg. 8599
SHONA MCFARLANE RETIREMENT VILLAGE LIMITED—See Ryman Healthcare Ltd.; *Int'l*, pg. 6440
SHONAN HI-TECH PLANNING CO., LTD.—See Imagica Group Inc.; *Int'l*, pg. 3619
SHONAN KAKOU K.K.—See Sato shoji Corporation; *Int'l*, pg. 6586
SHONAN MONORAIL CO., LTD.—See Industrial Growth Platform, Inc.; *Int'l*, pg. 3672
SHONAN ROBO CARE CENTER CO., LTD.—See Cyberdyne Inc.; *Int'l*, pg. 1893
SHONAN SEMINAR CO., LTD.—See Sprix Inc.; *Int'l*, pg. 7145
SHONAN SEMINAR OCEAN CO., LTD.—See Sprix Inc.; *Int'l*, pg. 7145
SHONAN UNITEC CO., LTD.—See Isuzu Motors Limited; *Int'l*, pg. 3826
SHONAN VANTEC CORPORATION—See KKR & Co. Inc.; *U.S. Public*, pg. 1259
SHONE DIALYSIS, LLC—See DaVita Inc.; *U.S. Private*, pg. 643
SHONEY'S NORTH AMERICA CORP—See Royal Hospitality Corp.; *U.S. Private*, pg. 3492
SHONEY'S OF KNOXVILLE INC.; *U.S. Private*, pg. 3639
SHONEY'S OF RICHMOND INC.; *U.S. Private*, pg. 3639
SHONEY'S RESTAURANT—See Royal Hospitality Corp.; *U.S. Private*, pg. 3492
SHOOK & FLETCHER INSULATION CO., INC. - ATLANTA DIVISION—See Shook & Fletcher Insulation Co., Inc.; *U.S. Private*, pg. 3639
SHOOK & FLETCHER INSULATION CO., INC. - BIRMINGHAM DIVISION—See Shook & Fletcher Insulation Co., Inc.; *U.S. Private*, pg. 3639
SHOOK & FLETCHER INSULATION CO., INC. - CHATTANOOGA DIVISION—See Shook & Fletcher Insulation Co., Inc.; *U.S. Private*, pg. 3639
SHOOK & FLETCHER INSULATION CO., INC. - DECATUR DIVISION—See Shook & Fletcher Insulation Co., Inc.; *U.S. Private*, pg. 3640
SHOOK & FLETCHER INSULATION CO., INC. - KNOXVILLE DIVISION—See Shook & Fletcher Insulation Co., Inc.; *U.S. Private*, pg. 3640
SHOOK & FLETCHER INSULATION CO., INC. - MOBILE DIVISION—See Shook & Fletcher Insulation Co., Inc.; *U.S. Private*, pg. 3640

SHOOK & FLETCHER INSULATION CO., INC.; *U.S. Private*, pg. 3640
SHOOK & FLETCHER SUPPLY CO. OF ALABAMA, INC.—See Shook & Fletcher Insulation Co., Inc.; *U.S. Private*, pg. 3640
SHOOK, HARDY & BACON LLP; *U.S. Private*, pg. 3640
SHOOK, INCORPORATED—See Shook National Corporation; *U.S. Private*, pg. 3640
SHOOK INDIANA DIVISION—See Shook National Corporation; *U.S. Private*, pg. 3640
SHOOK NATIONAL CORPORATION; *U.S. Private*, pg. 3640
SHOOK NORTHERN OHIO DIVISION—See Shook National Corporation; *U.S. Private*, pg. 3640
SHOOK WATER RESOURCES—See Shook National Corporation; *U.S. Private*, pg. 3640
SHOOTERS, INC.; *U.S. Private*, pg. 3640
SHOOTING STAR ACQUISITION CORP.; *Int'l*, pg. 6859
SHOOTING STAR WIND PROJECT, LLC—See Constellation Energy Corporation; *U.S. Public*, pg. 572
SHOPADVISOR, INC.—See Targetable Marketing Services LLC; *U.S. Private*, pg. 3933
SHOP-A-LOTT, INC.—See Lott Oil Company, Inc.; *U.S. Private*, pg. 2497
SHOP APOTHEKE EUROPE N.V.; *Int'l*, pg. 6859
SHOPBOP.COM—See Amazon.com, Inc.; *U.S. Public*, pg. 91
SHOPCBD.COM INC.—See Cannara Biotech, Inc.; *Int'l*, pg. 1292
S-H OPCO CARLSBAD, LLC—See Brookdale Senior Living Inc.; *U.S. Public*, pg. 395
S-H OPCO CLIFF VIEW, LLC—See Brookdale Senior Living Inc.; *U.S. Public*, pg. 395
S-H OPCO COTTAGE VILLAGE, LLC—See Brookdale Senior Living Inc.; *U.S. Public*, pg. 395
S-H OPCO DARTMOUTH VILLAGE, LLC—See Brookdale Senior Living Inc.; *U.S. Public*, pg. 395
S-H OPCO EAST BAY MANOR, LLC—See Brookdale Senior Living Inc.; *U.S. Public*, pg. 395
S-H OPCO FOX RIVER, LLC—See Brookdale Senior Living Inc.; *U.S. Public*, pg. 395
S-H OPCO GREENWICH BAY MANOR, LLC—See Brookdale Senior Living Inc.; *U.S. Public*, pg. 395
SHOPCO LEASING INC—See BHX Inc.; *U.S. Private*, pg. 549
S-H OPCO LINCOLN HEIGHTS, LLC—See Brookdale Senior Living Inc.; *U.S. Public*, pg. 395
S-H OPCO NORTHPARK PLACE, LLC—See Brookdale Senior Living Inc.; *U.S. Public*, pg. 395
SHOPCONSULT BY UMDASCH GMBH—See Umdasch Group AG; *Int'l*, pg. 8023
S-H OPCO PROSPERITY OAKS, LLC—See Brookdale Senior Living Inc.; *U.S. Public*, pg. 395
S-H OPCO SPICEWOOD SPRINGS, LLC—See Brookdale Senior Living Inc.; *U.S. Public*, pg. 395
S-H OPCO SPRING CREEK GARDENS, LLC—See Brookdale Senior Living Inc.; *U.S. Public*, pg. 395
S-H OPCO SPRING POINTE, LLC—See Brookdale Senior Living Inc.; *U.S. Public*, pg. 395
S-H OPCO SPRING VILLAGE, LLC—See Brookdale Senior Living Inc.; *U.S. Public*, pg. 395
S-H OPCO WILSON MOUNTAIN, LLC—See Brookdale Senior Living Inc.; *U.S. Public*, pg. 395
SHOP DIRECT FINANCIAL SERVICES LTD—See Shop Direct Home Shopping Limited; *Int'l*, pg. 6859
SHOP DIRECT HOME SHOPPING LIMITED; *Int'l*, pg. 6859
SHOP DIRECT IRELAND LIMITED—See Shop Direct Home Shopping Limited; *Int'l*, pg. 6859
SHOP EAT LIVE, INC.; *U.S. Private*, pg. 3640
SHOPEE SINGAPORE PRIVATE LIMITED—See Sea Limited; *Int'l*, pg. 6660
SHOPER S.A.; *Int'l*, pg. 6859
SHOPEYE, INC.; *U.S. Private*, pg. 3640
SHOPFORBAGS INC.; *U.S. Private*, pg. 3640
SHOPIFY INC.; *Int'l*, pg. 6859
SHOPINVEST SAS; *Int'l*, pg. 6859
SHOPJIMMY.COM, LLC; *U.S. Private*, pg. 3640
SHOPKICK, INC.—See Trax Technology Solutions Pte Ltd.; *Int'l*, pg. 7908
SHOP KWIK STORE LLC; *U.S. Private*, pg. 3640
SHOP LC GLOBAL INC.—See Vaibhav Global Limited; *Int'l*, pg. 8108
SHOP LC—See Vaibhav Global Limited; *Int'l*, pg. 8108
SHOPLOCAL, LLC—See Liquidus Marketing, Inc.; *U.S. Private*, pg. 2466
SHOP-N-SAVE FOODS INC.; *U.S. Private*, pg. 3640
SHOP 'N SAVE ST. LOUIS, INC.—See United Natural Foods, Inc.; *U.S. Public*, pg. 2232
SHOP 'N SAVE WAREHOUSE FOODS, INC.—See United Natural Foods, Inc.; *U.S. Public*, pg. 2232
SHOPPAS MATERIAL HANDLING; *U.S. Private*, pg. 3640
SHOPPER360 LIMITED; *Int'l*, pg. 6859
SHOPPER360 SDN. BHD.—See Shopper360 Limited; *Int'l*, pg. 6859
SHOPPERPLUS MYANMAR CO., LTD.—See Shopper360 Limited; *Int'l*, pg. 6859
SHOPPERPLUS SINGAPORE PTE. LTD.—See Shopper360 Limited; *Int'l*, pg. 6859

SHOPPER360 LIMITED

SHOPPERSCHOICE.COM, LLC—See Brand Velocity Partners; *U.S. Private*, pg. 637
SHOPPERS DRUG MART CORPORATION—See George Weston Limited; *Int'l*, pg. 2939
SHOPPERS FOOD WAREHOUSE CORP.—See United Natural Foods, Inc.; *U.S. Public*, pg. 2232
THE SHOPPER'S GUIDE—See The Nutting Company, Inc.; *U.S. Private*, pg. 4087
SHOPPERS STOP LIMITED; *Int'l*, pg. 6859
SHOPPERTRAK CENTRAL EUROPE GMBH—See Johnson Controls International plc; *Int'l*, pg. 3986
SHOPPERTRAK IBERICA SL—See Johnson Controls International plc; *Int'l*, pg. 3986
SHOPPERTRAK LIMITED—See Johnson Controls International plc; *Int'l*, pg. 3986
SHOPPERTRAK RCT CORPORATION—See Johnson Controls International plc; *Int'l*, pg. 3987
SHOPPES MANILA, INC.; *Int'l*, pg. 6859
SHOPPING BELA VISTA LTDA.—See JHSF Participacoes S.A.; *Int'l*, pg. 3941
SHOPPING CENTER MANAGEMENT; *U.S. Private*, pg. 3640
SHOPPING CENTER PLANUNGS- UND ENTWICK-LUNGSGESELLSCHAFT MBH & CO. WERBEBERATUNG KG—See Unibail-Rodamco-Westfield SE; *Int'l*, pg. 8030
SHOPPING CENTER PLANUNGS- UND ENTWICK-LUNGSGESELLSCHAFT MBH—See Unibail-Rodamco-Westfield SE; *Int'l*, pg. 8030
SHOPPING CENTER VOSENDORF VERWALTUNGSGESELLSCHAFT MBH—See Unibail-Rodamco-Westfield SE; *Int'l*, pg. 8030
SHOPPING CITY PIATRA NEAMT SRL—See NEPI Rockcastle N.V.; *Int'l*, pg. 5200
SHOPPING.COM INC.—See eBay Inc.; *U.S. Public*, pg. 709
SHOPPING MALL EDEN S.R.O.—See Tesco PLC; *Int'l*, pg. 7572
SHOPPINGPARTNER FR; *Int'l*, pg. 6859
SHOPPING PONTA NEGRA S.A.—See JHSF Participacoes S.A.; *Int'l*, pg. 3941
SHOPPINGTOWN HOTEL (BMG) PTY LTD—See Woolworths Group Limited; *Int'l*, pg. 8451
SHOPPINGTOWN MALL, LLC—See The Macerich Company; *U.S. Public*, pg. 2111
SHOPRIDER JAPAN LTD.—See Pihsiang Machinery MFG. Co., Ltd.; *Int'l*, pg. 5865
SHOPRIDER MOBILITY PRODUCTS, INC.—See Pihsiang Machinery MFG. Co., Ltd.; *Int'l*, pg. 5865
SHOPRITE BEVERAGES, INC.—See Wakefern Food Corporation; *U.S. Private*, pg. 4427
SHOPRITE CHECKERS PROPERTIES LTD—See Shoprite Holdings Limited; *Int'l*, pg. 6860
SHOPRITE CHECKERS (PTY) LTD—See Shoprite Holdings Limited; *Int'l*, pg. 6859
SHOPRITE CHECKERS (PTY) LTD—See Shoprite Holdings Limited; *Int'l*, pg. 6860
SHOPRITE CHECKERS UGANDA LTD—See Shoprite Holdings Limited; *Int'l*, pg. 6860
SHOPRITE GHANA (PTY) LTD—See Shoprite Holdings Limited; *Int'l*, pg. 6860
SHOPRITE HOLDINGS LIMITED; *Int'l*, pg. 6859
SHOP RITE INC.; *U.S. Private*, pg. 3640
SHOPRITE OF BRISTOL LLC; *U.S. Private*, pg. 3640
SHOPRITE SUPERMARKETS, INC.—See Wakefern Food Corporation; *U.S. Private*, pg. 4427
SHOPRITE SUPERMARKETS, INC.—See Wakefern Food Corporation; *U.S. Private*, pg. 4427
SHOPRITE SUPERMERCADOS LDA—See Shoprite Holdings Limited; *Int'l*, pg. 6860
SHOPRITE TRADING LTD—See Shoprite Holdings Limited; *Int'l*, pg. 6860
SHOPRUNNER, INC.—See FedEx Corporation; *U.S. Public*, pg. 828
SHOPS AT FAIRFAX LLC—See Saul Centers, Inc.; *U.S. Public*, pg. 1842
SHOPS AT GRAND AVENUE LLC—See Acadia Realty Trust; *U.S. Public*, pg. 31
THE SHOPS AT MARY BRICKELL VILLAGE—See Caisse de Depot et Placement du Quebec; *Int'l*, pg. 1254
SHOPS AT NORTHEAST MALL, LLC—See Washington Prime Group Inc.; *U.S. Private*, pg. 4449
SHOPSMITH, INC.; *U.S. Private*, pg. 3640
SHOPSTER ECOMMERCE INC.; *Int'l*, pg. 6860
SHOPTECH SOFTWARE CORPORATION; *U.S. Private*, pg. 3640
SHOPTOLOGY, INC.—See Project: Worldwide, Inc.; *U.S. Private*, pg. 3281
SHOPTOUCH, INC.—See IAC Inc.; *U.S. Public*, pg. 1082
SHOP-VAC CORPORATION—See GreatStar Group Co., Ltd.; *Int'l*, pg. 3067
SHORCAN BROKERS LIMITED—See TMX Group Limited; *Int'l*, pg. 7767
SHORE BANCSHARES, INC.; *U.S. Public*, pg. 1875
SHORE CAPITAL AND CORPORATE LIMITED—See Shore Capital Group Plc; *Int'l*, pg. 6860
SHORE CAPITAL FINANCE LIMITED—See Shore Capital Group Plc; *Int'l*, pg. 6860
SHORE CAPITAL GROUP PLC; *Int'l*, pg. 6860

SHORE CAPITAL INTERNATIONAL LIMITED—See Shore Capital Group Plc; *Int'l*, pg. 6860
SHORE CAPITAL INVESTMENTS LIMITED—See Shore Capital Group Plc; *Int'l*, pg. 6860
SHORE CAPITAL PARTNERS, LLC; *U.S. Private*, pg. 3640
SHORE CAPITAL STOCKBROKERS LIMITED—See Shore Capital Group Plc; *Int'l*, pg. 6860
SHORE CAPITAL TRADING LIMITED—See Shore Capital Group Plc; *Int'l*, pg. 6860
SHORE CLUB SOUTH BEACH—See SBEEG Holdings, LLC; *U.S. Private*, pg. 3559
SHORE CONSTRUCTION LLC; *U.S. Private*, pg. 3641
SHORE DISTRIBUTORS INC.; *U.S. Private*, pg. 3641
SHOREHAM TELEPHONE LLC—See Keystone Group, L.P.; *U.S. Private*, pg. 2299
SHOREHILL CAPITAL LLC; *U.S. Private*, pg. 3641
SHORELAND TRANSPORT INC.—See Cooke, Inc.; *Int'l*, pg. 1788
SHORELINE AMPHITHEATRE, LTD.—See Live Nation Entertainment, Inc.; *U.S. Public*, pg. 1330
SHORELINE BUILDERS INC.; *U.S. Private*, pg. 3641
SHORELINE CONTAINER INC.—See Schwarz Partners, LP; *U.S. Private*, pg. 3572
SHORELINE CONTAINER INC.—See The Kraft Group LLC; *U.S. Private*, pg. 4066
SHORELINE EQUITY PARTNERS, LLC; *U.S. Private*, pg. 3641
SHORELINE FINANCIAL ADVISORS, LLC—See Exencial Wealth Advisors, LLC; *U.S. Private*, pg. 1448
SHORELINE FRUIT, LLC; *U.S. Private*, pg. 3641
SHORELINE GAS INC.; *U.S. Private*, pg. 3641
SHORELINE GROUP LLC; *U.S. Private*, pg. 3641
SHORELINE, INC.—See Vizion Health LLC; *U.S. Private*, pg. 4407
SHORELINE INDUSTRIES, INC.—See Otter Tail Corporation; *U.S. Public*, pg. 1624
SHORE LINE NEWSPAPER—See Alden Global Capital LLC; *U.S. Private*, pg. 157
SHORELINE SURGERY CENTER, LLP—See Tenet Healthcare Corporation; *U.S. Public*, pg. 2012
SHORELINE VEHICLE SALES LLC—See Tesla, Inc.; *U.S. Public*, pg. 2021
SHOREMASTER INC.—See High Street Capital Management, Inc.; *U.S. Private*, pg. 1937
SHORE MEASURING SYSTEMS—See Berkshire Hathaway Inc.; *U.S. Public*, pg. 303
SHORENSTEIN COMPANY, L.P.; *U.S. Private*, pg. 3641
SHORENSTEIN HAYS-NEDERLANDER THEATRES LLC; *U.S. Private*, pg. 3641
SHORE OUTPATIENT SURGICENTER, L.L.C.—See Tenet Healthcare Corporation; *U.S. Public*, pg. 2012
SHORE PHARMACEUTICAL PROVIDERS, INC.—See CVS Health Corporation; *U.S. Public*, pg. 616
SHOREPOWER TECHNOLOGIES, INC.; *U.S. Public*, pg. 1875
SHORETEL AUSTRALIA PTY. LTD.—See Searchlight Capital Partners, L.P.; *U.S. Private*, pg. 3589
SHORETEL, INC.—See Searchlight Capital Partners, L.P.; *U.S. Private*, pg. 3589
SHORETEL UK LTD.—See Searchlight Capital Partners, L.P.; *U.S. Private*, pg. 3589
SHORE TERMINALS LLC—See Sunoco LP; *U.S. Public*, pg. 1965
SHORE TO SHORE (PVT) LTD.—See Shoprite Holdings Limited; *Int'l*, pg. 6860
SHORE TOYOTA INC.; *U.S. Private*, pg. 3641
SHORE TRADING COMPANY; *U.S. Private*, pg. 3641
SHORE UNITED BANK—See Shore Bancshares, Inc.; *U.S. Public*, pg. 1875
SHORE UP! INC.; *U.S. Private*, pg. 3641
SHOREVIEW INDUSTRIES, LLC; *U.S. Private*, pg. 3641
SHOREWEST INSURANCE ASSOCIATES, LLC—See Marsh & McLennan Companies, Inc.; *U.S. Public*, pg. 1388
SHOREWEST REALTORS, INC.; *U.S. Private*, pg. 3642
SHOREWOOD PACKAGING LLC - HENDERSONVILLE PLANT—See Atlas Holdings, LLC; *U.S. Private*, pg. 378
SHOREWOOD PACKAGING LLC - LOS ANGELES PLANT—See Atlas Holdings, LLC; *U.S. Private*, pg. 378
SHOREWOOD PACKAGING LLC - LOUISVILLE PLANT—See Atlas Holdings, LLC; *U.S. Private*, pg. 378
SHOREWOOD PACKAGING LLC - MELROSE PARK—See Atlas Holdings, LLC; *U.S. Private*, pg. 378
SHOREWOOD PACKAGING LLC—See Atlas Holdings, LLC; *U.S. Private*, pg. 378
SHOREY PUBLIC RELATIONS LLC; *U.S. Private*, pg. 3642
SHORR PACKAGING CORP.; *U.S. Private*, pg. 3642
SHORT AND PAULK SUPPLY COMPANY; *U.S. Private*, pg. 3642
SHORT BLOCK TECHNOLOGIES, INC.; *U.S. Private*, pg. 3642
SHORT BOOKS LTD.—See Vivendi SE; *Int'l*, pg. 8278
SHORT CIRCUIT ELECTRONICS, INC.—See Wind Point Advisors LLC; *U.S. Private*, pg. 4535
SHORTCUT MEDIA AB; *Int'l*, pg. 6860

CORPORATE AFFILIATIONS

SHORTCUTS SOFTWARE, INC.—See Constellation Software Inc.; *Int'l*, pg. 1773
SHORT ELLIOTT HENDRICKSON INC.; *U.S. Private*, pg. 3642
SHORT GROUND LIMITED—See Universal Health Services, Inc.; *U.S. Public*, pg. 2259
SHORTHAND CENTER TSUKUBA CO., LTD.—See Advanced Media, Inc.; *Int'l*, pg. 161
SHORT HILLS ASSOCIATES, LLC—See Simon Property Group, Inc.; *U.S. Public*, pg. 1881
SHORT HILLS SURGERY CENTER, LLC—See KKR & Co. Inc.; *U.S. Public*, pg. 1246
SHORT RUN STAMPING CO.; *U.S. Private*, pg. 3643
SHORT'S BREWING COMPANY; *U.S. Private*, pg. 3643
SHORTS MARINE INC.; *U.S. Private*, pg. 3643
SHORT'S TRAVEL MANAGEMENT, INC.; *U.S. Private*, pg. 3643
SHORTY'S MEXICAN ROADHOUSE; *U.S. Private*, pg. 3643
SHOSANDO CO., LTD.—See Toyo Seikan Group Holdings, Ltd.; *Int'l*, pg. 7857
SHOSAN ENGINEERING CO., LTD.—See Showa Sangyo Co., Ltd.; *Int'l*, pg. 6862
SHOSAN KAIHATSU CO., LTD.—See Showa Sangyo Co., Ltd.; *Int'l*, pg. 6862
SHOSAN SHOJI CO., LTD.—See Showa Sangyo Co., Ltd.; *Int'l*, pg. 6862
SHOSEKI ENGINEERING & CONSTRUCTION CO., LTD.—See Idemitsu Kosan Co., Ltd.; *Int'l*, pg. 3592
SHOSEKI KAKO K.K.—See Idemitsu Kosan Co., Ltd.; *Int'l*, pg. 3592
SHOSEN KOUN CO., LTD.—See Mitsui O.S.K. Lines, Ltd.; *Int'l*, pg. 4991
SHOSHONE DIALYSIS, LLC—See DaVita Inc.; *U.S. Public*, pg. 643
SHOSHONE SILVER/GOLD MINING COMPANY; *U.S. Private*, pg. 3643
S HOTELS AND RESORTS MANAGEMENT CO., LTD.—See Singha Estate PCL; *Int'l*, pg. 6944
S HOTELS AND RESORTS PUBLICCO., LTD.—See Singha Estate PCL; *Int'l*, pg. 6944
S HOTELS & RESORTS PUBLIC COMPANY LIMITED—See Singha Estate PCL; *Int'l*, pg. 6944
SHOTGUN NEWS—See InterMedia Advisors, LLC; *U.S. Private*, pg. 2112
SHOTIC EUROPA INDUSTRIA DE ALUMINIO LDA.—See Resonac Holdings Corporation; *Int'l*, pg. 6299
SHOTIC MALAYSIA SDN. BHD.—See Resonac Holdings Corporation; *Int'l*, pg. 6300
SHOTIC (SINGAPORE) PTE. LTD.—See Resonac Holdings Corporation; *Int'l*, pg. 6300
SHOTOVER CAMERA SYSTEMS LP—See Helinet Aviation Services LLC; *U.S. Private*, pg. 1906
SHOTOVER SYSTEMS LTD.—See Helinet Aviation Services LLC; *U.S. Private*, pg. 1906
SHOTTENKIRK INC.; *U.S. Private*, pg. 3643
SHOTTON PAPER COMPANY PLC—See UPM-Kymmene Corporation; *Int'l*, pg. 8091
SHOUCHENG HOLDINGS LIMITED; *Int'l*, pg. 6860
SHOUEI FURNITURE CO., LTD.—See Sumitomo Forestry Co., Ltd.; *Int'l*, pg. 7286
SHOUGANG CENTURY HOLDINGS LIMITED; *Int'l*, pg. 6860
SHOUGANG CENTURY (SHANGHAI) MANAGEMENT CO., LTD.—See Shougang Century Holdings Limited; *Int'l*, pg. 6860
SHOUGANG CONCORD SHIPPING HOLDINGS LIMITED—See Shoucheng Holdings Limited; *Int'l*, pg. 6860
SHOUGANG CONCORD SHIPPING SERVICES LIMITED—See Shoucheng Holdings Limited; *Int'l*, pg. 6860
SHOUGANG CONCORD STEEL INTERNATIONAL TRADING CO. LTD.—See Shoucheng Holdings Limited; *Int'l*, pg. 6860
SHOUGANG CONCORD TECHNOLOGY HOLDINGS LIMITED—See HNA International Investment Holdings Limited; *Int'l*, pg. 3433
SHOUGANG FUSHAN RESOURCES GROUP LIMITED; *Int'l*, pg. 6860
SHOUGANG GENERACION ELECTRICA S.A.A.; *Int'l*, pg. 6860
SHOUGANG GROUP CO., LTD.; *Int'l*, pg. 6860
SHOUGANG MOTOMAN ROBOT CO., LTD.—See Iwatani Corporation; *Int'l*, pg. 3850
SHOUGANG NEC ELECTRONICS CO., LTD.—See Shougang Group Co., Ltd.; *Int'l*, pg. 6861
SHOUGUANG LIBEN PAPER MAKING CO., LTD.—See Nippon Paper Industries Co., Ltd.; *Int'l*, pg. 5328
SHOUHANG HIGH-TECH ENERGY CO., LTD.; *Int'l*, pg. 6861
SHOUJI MOLD ENGINEERING CO LTD—See Perfectech International Holdings Limited; *Int'l*, pg. 5799
SHOUJI TOOLING FACTORY LTD - CHINA FACTORY—See Perfectech International Holdings Limited; *Int'l*, pg. 5799
SHOUJI TOOLING FACTORY LTD—See Perfectech International Holdings Limited; *Int'l*, pg. 5799

COMPANY NAME INDEX

SHOULDERUP TECHNOLOGY ACQUISITION CORP.; *U.S. Public,* pg. 1875
SHOULTZ & ASSOCIATES ADVERTISING, INC.; *U.S. Private,* pg. 3643
SHOUTEM, INC.—See RSG Kapital d.o.o.; *Int'l,* pg. 6419
SHOUXIN FINANCIAL LEASING CO., LTD.—See Zhewen Interactive Group Co Ltd; *Int'l,* pg. 8671
SHOWA ADOMINISTRACAO, SERVICOS E COMERCIO LTDA—See Hitachi Astemo, Ltd.; *Int'l,* pg. 3410
SHOWA AIRCRAFT INDUSTRY CO., LTD.—See Bain Capital, LP; *U.S. Private,* pg. 444
SHOWA ALUMINUM CAN CORP. - HIKONE PLANT—See Resonac Holdings Corporation; *Int'l,* pg. 6300
SHOWA ALUMINUM CAN CORP. - OMUTA PLANT—See Resonac Holdings Corporation; *Int'l,* pg. 6300
SHOWA ALUMINUM CAN CORP. - OYAMA PLANT—See Resonac Holdings Corporation; *Int'l,* pg. 6300
SHOWA ALUMINUM CAN CORP.—See Resonac Holdings Corporation; *Int'l,* pg. 6300
SHOWA ALUMINUM CORP OF AMERICA—See Resonac Holdings Corporation; *Int'l,* pg. 6300
SHOWA ALUMINUM MANUFACTURING PHILIPPINES CORPORATION—See Resonac Holdings Corporation; *Int'l,* pg. 6300
SHOWA ALUMINUM (THAILAND) CO., LTD.—See Resonac Holdings Corporation; *Int'l,* pg. 6300
SHOWA AUTOPARTS MEXICO, S.A. DE C.V.—See Hitachi Astemo, Ltd.; *Int'l,* pg. 3410
SHOWA AUTOPARTS (THAILAND) CO., LTD.—See Hitachi Astemo, Ltd.; *Int'l,* pg. 3410
SHOWA AUTO-PARTS VIETNAM CO., LTD.—See Hitachi Astemo, Ltd.; *Int'l,* pg. 3410
SHOWA AUTOPARTS WUHAN CO., LTD.—See Hitachi Astemo, Ltd.; *Int'l,* pg. 3410
SHOWA BAIDO CO., LTD.—See Shoko Co., Ltd.; *Int'l,* pg. 6859
SHOWA BEST GLOVE, INC.—See Showa Glove Co.; *Int'l,* pg. 6861
SHOWA BOSTON INSTITUTE FOR LANGUAGE AND CULTURE; *U.S. Private,* pg. 3643
SHOWA CANADA INC.—See Hitachi Astemo, Ltd.; *Int'l,* pg. 3410
SHOWA CHEMICAL INDUSTRY CO., LTD.; *Int'l,* pg. 6861
SHOWA CHEMICALS OF AMERICA, INC.—See Resonac Holdings Corporation; *Int'l,* pg. 6300
SHOWA CLEANER CO., LTD.—See Sala Corporation; *Int'l,* pg. 6490
SHOWA CONSTRUCTION CO., LTD.—See Toda Corporation; *Int'l,* pg. 7773
SHOWA CORPORATION - ASABA PLANT—See Hitachi Astemo, Ltd.; *Int'l,* pg. 3410
SHOWA CORPORATION - GOTEMBA NO.1 PLANT—See Hitachi Astemo, Ltd.; *Int'l,* pg. 3410
SHOWA CORPORATION - GOTEMBA NO.2 PLANT—See Hitachi Astemo, Ltd.; *Int'l,* pg. 3410
SHOWA CORPORATION - HADANO PLANT—See Hitachi Astemo, Ltd.; *Int'l,* pg. 3410
SHOWA CORPORATION - NAGOYA PLANT—See Hitachi Astemo, Ltd.; *Int'l,* pg. 3410
SHOWA CORPORATION—See Hitachi Astemo, Ltd.; *Int'l,* pg. 3409
SHOWA DENKI SETTEN KOGYOSHO.CO.,LTD—See Nippon Tungsten Co., Ltd.; *Int'l,* pg. 5357
SHOWA DENKO ALUMINUM TRADING K.K.—See Resonac Holdings Corporation; *Int'l,* pg. 6300
SHOWA DENKO AMERICA, INC.—See Resonac Holdings Corporation; *Int'l,* pg. 6300
SHOWA DENKO CARBON AUSTRIA GMBH—See Resonac Holdings Corporation; *Int'l,* pg. 6299
SHOWA DENKO CARBON GERMANY GMBH—See Resonac Holdings Corporation; *Int'l,* pg. 6300
SHOWA DENKO CARBON HOLDING GMBH—See Resonac Holdings Corporation; *Int'l,* pg. 6299
SHOWA DENKO CARBON, INC.—See Resonac Holdings Corporation; *Int'l,* pg. 6300
SHOWA DENKO CARBON MALAYSIA SDN. BHD.—See Resonac Holdings Corporation; *Int'l,* pg. 6299
SHOWA DENKO CARBON PRODUCTS GERMANY GMBH & CO. KG—See Resonac Holdings Corporation; *Int'l,* pg. 6299
SHOWA DENKO CARBON SPAIN S.A.—See Resonac Holdings Corporation; *Int'l,* pg. 6299
SHOWA DENKO CERAMICS CO., LTD.—See Resonac Holdings Corporation; *Int'l,* pg. 6300
SHOWA DENKO (DALIAN) CO., LTD.—See Resonac Holdings Corporation; *Int'l,* pg. 6300
SHOWA DENKO EUROPE GMBH—See Resonac Holdings Corporation; *Int'l,* pg. 6300
SHOWA DENKO GAS PRODUCTS CO., LTD.—See Resonac Holdings Corporation; *Int'l,* pg. 6300
SHOWA DENKO HD (MALAYSIA) SDN.BHD.—See Resonac Holdings Corporation; *Int'l,* pg. 6300
SHOWA DENKO HD SINGAPORE PTE LTD—See Resonac Holdings Corporation; *Int'l,* pg. 6300
SHOWA DENKO HD TRACE CORP.—See Resonac Holdings Corporation; *Int'l,* pg. 6300
SHOWA DENKO HD YAMAGATA K.K.—See Resonac Holdings Corporation; *Int'l,* pg. 6300
SHOWA DENKO KENSO CO., LTD.—See Resonac Holdings Corporation; *Int'l,* pg. 6300
SHOWA DENKO KENZAI K.K. - CHIBA PLANT—See Resonac Holdings Corporation; *Int'l,* pg. 6301
SHOWA DENKO KENZAI K.K. - HIGASHI MATSUYAMA PLANT—See Resonac Holdings Corporation; *Int'l,* pg. 6301
SHOWA DENKO KENZAI K.K. - ISHIOKA PLANT—See Resonac Holdings Corporation; *Int'l,* pg. 6301
SHOWA DENKO KENZAI K.K. - OSAKA PLANT—See Resonac Holdings Corporation; *Int'l,* pg. 6301
SHOWA DENKO KENZAI K.K.—See Resonac Holdings Corporation; *Int'l,* pg. 6301
SHOWA DENKO K.K. - CHIBA PLANT—See Resonac Holdings Corporation; *Int'l,* pg. 6300
SHOWA DENKO K.K. - CHICHIBU PLANT—See Resonac Holdings Corporation; *Int'l,* pg. 6300
SHOWA DENKO K.K. - CHIDORI PLANT—See Resonac Holdings Corporation; *Int'l,* pg. 6300
SHOWA DENKO K.K. - HIGASHINAGAHARA PLANT—See Resonac Holdings Corporation; *Int'l,* pg. 6300
SHOWA DENKO K.K. - HIKONE PLANT—See Resonac Holdings Corporation; *Int'l,* pg. 6300
SHOWA DENKO K.K. - ISESAKI PLANT—See Resonac Holdings Corporation; *Int'l,* pg. 6300
SHOWA DENKO K.K. - KAWASAKI PLANT—See Resonac Holdings Corporation; *Int'l,* pg. 6300
SHOWA DENKO K.K. - KITAKATA PLANT—See Resonac Holdings Corporation; *Int'l,* pg. 6300
SHOWA DENKO K.K. - OMACHI PLANT—See Resonac Holdings Corporation; *Int'l,* pg. 6300
SHOWA DENKO K.K. - OYAMA PLANT (NASU)—See Resonac Holdings Corporation; *Int'l,* pg. 6300
SHOWA DENKO K.K. - OYAMA PLANT—See Resonac Holdings Corporation; *Int'l,* pg. 6300
SHOWA DENKO K.K. - SAKAI PLANT—See Resonac Holdings Corporation; *Int'l,* pg. 6300
SHOWA DENKO K.K. - SHIOJIRI PLANT—See Resonac Holdings Corporation; *Int'l,* pg. 6300
SHOWA DENKO K.K. - TATSUNO PLANT—See Resonac Holdings Corporation; *Int'l,* pg. 6300
SHOWA DENKO K.K. - TOKUYAMA PLANT—See Resonac Holdings Corporation; *Int'l,* pg. 6300
SHOWA DENKO K.K. - YOKOHAMA PLANT—See Resonac Holdings Corporation; *Int'l,* pg. 6300
SHOWA DENKO NEW MATERIAL (ZHUHAI) CO., LTD.—See Resonac Holdings Corporation; *Int'l,* pg. 6301
SHOWA DENKO PACKAGING CO., LTD.—See Resonac Holdings Corporation; *Int'l,* pg. 6300
SHOWA DENKO (SHANGHAI) CO., LTD.—See Resonac Holdings Corporation; *Int'l,* pg. 6300
SHOWA DENKO SICHUAN CARBON INC.—See Resonac Holdings Corporation; *Int'l,* pg. 6301
SHOWA DENKO SINGAPORE (PTE) LTD—See Resonac Holdings Corporation; *Int'l,* pg. 6301
SHOWA DENSHI CO., LTD.—See SMK Corporation; *Int'l,* pg. 7013
SHOWA DEUTSCHLAND GMBH—See Hitachi Astemo, Ltd.; *Int'l,* pg. 3409
SHOWA DISTRIBUTION K.K—See Maruzen Showa Unyu Co., Ltd.; *Int'l,* pg. 4716
SHOWA DO BRASIL LTDA.—See Hitachi Astemo, Ltd.; *Int'l,* pg. 3410
SHOWA DO BRAZIL LTDA.—See Hitachi Astemo, Ltd.; *Int'l,* pg. 3410
SHOWA ENTERPRISE CORPORATION—See SMK Corporation; *Int'l,* pg. 7013
SHOWA ESTATE CO.,LTD—See Toyo Tire Corporation; *Int'l,* pg. 7859
SHOWA FRONT CO., LTD.—See Sanwa Holdings Corporation; *Int'l,* pg. 6561
SHOWA GLOVE CO.; *Int'l,* pg. 6861
SHOWA (GUANGZHOU) AUTO PARTS R&D CO., LTD.—See Hitachi Astemo, Ltd.; *Int'l,* pg. 3409
SHOWA HIGHPOLYMER SINGAPORE PTE. LTD.—See Resonac Holdings Corporation; *Int'l,* pg. 6301
SHOWA HOLDINGS CO., LTD.; *Int'l,* pg. 6861
SHOWA INDIA PVT. LTD.—See Hitachi Astemo, Ltd.; *Int'l,* pg. 3410
SHOWA INDUSTRIA E COMERCIO LTDA.—See Hitachi Astemo, Ltd.; *Int'l,* pg. 3410
SHOWA INFORMATION SYSTEMS CO., LTD.—See Canon Inc.; *Int'l,* pg. 1296
SHOWA KAIHATSU KOGYO CO., LTD.—See Dowa Holdings Co., Ltd.; *Int'l,* pg. 2184
SHOWA KASEIKOGYO CO., LTD.—See Kaneka Corporation; *Int'l,* pg. 4067
SHOWA KDE CO., LTD.—See The Carlyle Group Inc.; *U.S. Public,* pg. 2048
SHOWA KENSAN CO., LTD.—See Sanwa Holdings Corporation; *Int'l,* pg. 6561
SHOWA KIGYO CORPORATION—See JFE Holdings, Inc.; *Int'l,* pg. 3937
SHOWA KINZOKU KOGYO CO., LTD.—See NOF Corporation; *Int'l,* pg. 5400
SHOWA KOSAN CO., LTD.—See Adeka Corporation; *Int'l,* pg. 142
SHOWA KYUSHU CORPORATION—See Hitachi Astemo, Ltd.; *Int'l,* pg. 3410
SHOWA LEASING CO., LTD.—See SBI Shinsei Bank, Limited; *Int'l,* pg. 6606
SHOWALTER MOTOR COMPANY INC.; *U.S. Private,* pg. 3643
SHOWA MARUTSUTSU COMPANY, LTD. - HIROSHIMA PLANT—See Showa Marutsutsu Company, Ltd.; *Int'l,* pg. 6861
SHOWA MARUTSUTSU COMPANY, LTD. - HOKURIKU PLANT—See Showa Marutsutsu Company, Ltd.; *Int'l,* pg. 6861
SHOWA MARUTSUTSU COMPANY, LTD.; *Int'l,* pg. 6861
SHOWA MARUTSUTSU COMPANY, LTD. - SUZUKA PLANT—See Showa Marutsutsu Company, Ltd.; *Int'l,* pg. 6861
SHOWA METAL CO., LTD.—See Hanwa Co., Ltd.; *Int'l,* pg. 3263
SHOWA NITTAN CORP.—See ENEOS Holdings, Inc.; *Int'l,* pg. 2418
SHOWA PACKAGING INDUSTRY CO., LTD.—See Japan Pulp and Paper Company Limited; *Int'l,* pg. 3904
SHOWA PAXXS CORPORATION; *Int'l,* pg. 6861
SHOWA PLASTICS MOLDING CO., LTD.—See Showa Marutsutsu Company, Ltd.; *Int'l,* pg. 6861
SHOWA PRODUCTS COMPANY, LTD.—See Showa Marutsutsu Company, Ltd.; *Int'l,* pg. 6861
SHOWA PRODUCTS COMPANY, LTD.—See Showa Marutsutsu Company, Ltd.; *Int'l,* pg. 6861
SHOWA PRODUCTS COMPANY, LTD.—See Showa Marutsutsu Company, Ltd.; *Int'l,* pg. 6861
SHOWA PRODUCTS COMPANY, LTD.—See Showa Marutsutsu Company, Ltd.; *Int'l,* pg. 6861
SHOWA PRODUCTS COMPANY, LTD.—See Showa Marutsutsu Company, Ltd.; *Int'l,* pg. 6861
SHOWA PRODUCTS COMPANY, LTD.—See Showa Marutsutsu Company, Ltd.; *Int'l,* pg. 6861
SHOWA PRODUCTS COMPANY, LTD.—See Showa Marutsutsu Company, Ltd.; *Int'l,* pg. 6861
SHOWA PRODUCTS COMPANY, LTD.—See Showa Marutsutsu Company, Ltd.; *Int'l,* pg. 6861
SHOWA PRODUCTS COMPANY, LTD.—See Showa Marutsutsu Company, Ltd.; *Int'l,* pg. 6861
SHOWA REGIONAL CENTER (THAILAND) CO., LTD.—See Hitachi Astemo, Ltd.; *Int'l,* pg. 3410
SHOWA RUBBER (MALAYSIA) SDN. BHD.—See Showa Holdings Co., Ltd.; *Int'l,* pg. 6861
SHOWA SANGYO CO., LTD.; *Int'l,* pg. 6861
SHOWA SEIKO CO., LTD.—See Hitachi Astemo, Ltd.; *Int'l,* pg. 3410
SHOWA SHELL BUSINESS & IT SOLUTIONS LIMITED—See Idemitsu Kosan Co., Ltd.; *Int'l,* pg. 3592
SHOWA SHELL SEMPAKU K.K.—See Idemitsu Kosan Co., Ltd.; *Int'l,* pg. 3592
SHOWA SHINKU CO., LTD.; *Int'l,* pg. 6862
SHOWA SHINKU MACHINERY TRADING (SHANGHAI) CO., LTD.—See SHOWA SHINKU CO., LTD.; *Int'l,* pg. 6862
SHOWA SPECIALTY GAS (TAIWAN) CO., LTD.—See Resonac Holdings Corporation; *Int'l,* pg. 6301
SHOWA SYSTEM ENGINEERING CORPORATION; *Int'l,* pg. 6862
SHOWA-TBEA (SHANDONG) CABLE ACCESSORIES CO., LTD.—See SWCC Corporation; *Int'l,* pg. 7363
SHOWA TITANIUM CO., LTD.—See Resonac Holdings Corporation; *Int'l,* pg. 6301
SHOWA UK LTD.—See Hitachi Astemo, Ltd.; *Int'l,* pg. 3410
SHOWA WAREHOUSING CO., LTD.—See Konoike Transport Co., Ltd.; *Int'l,* pg. 4275
SHOWA YAKUHIN KAKO CO., LTD.—See GC Corporation; *Int'l,* pg. 2894
SHOWA YOKKAICHI SEKIYU CO., LTD.—See Idemitsu Kosan Co., Ltd.; *Int'l,* pg. 3592
SHOWBOAT ATLANTIC CITY OPERATING COMPANY, LLC—See Caesars Entertainment, Inc.; *U.S. Public,* pg. 419
SHOWBOX CORP.; *Int'l,* pg. 6862
SHOWCASE INC.; *U.S. Private,* pg. 3643
SHOWCASE INC.; *Int'l,* pg. 6862
SHOWCASE MINERALS INC.; *Int'l,* pg. 6862
SHOWCASE MOTORS INC.; *U.S. Private,* pg. 3643
SHOWCASE NEW ENGLAND INC.; *U.S. Private,* pg. 3643
SHOWCASE TECHNOLOGY, INC.—See Atlantic Street Capital Management LLC; *U.S. Private,* pg. 374
S. HOWES, INC.; *U.S. Private,* pg. 3515
SHOW-FACTORY ENTERTAINMENT GMBH—See CTS Eventim AG & Co. KGAA; *Int'l,* pg. 1873
SHOW GROUP ENTERPRISES PTY LTD—See Helloworld Travel Limited; *Int'l,* pg. 3337
SHOW IMAGING, INC.; *U.S. Private,* pg. 3643
SHOWINGTIME.COM, INC.—See Zillow Group, Inc.; *U.S. Public,* pg. 2405
SHOW ME BREAD, INC.; *U.S. Private,* pg. 3643
SHOW MEDIA; *U.S. Private,* pg. 3643
SHOWORKS INC.; *U.S. Private,* pg. 3643
SHOWPLACE INC.; *U.S. Private,* pg. 3643
SHOWSEC INTERNATIONAL LIMITED—See Live Nation Entertainment, Inc.; *U.S. Public,* pg. 1330
SHOWTIME CONCESSION SUPPLY INC.; *U.S. Private,* pg. 3643

SHOWTIME CONCESSION SUPPLY INC.   CORPORATE AFFILIATIONS

SHOWTIME MARKETING INC.—See National Amusements, Inc.; *U.S. Private*, pg. 2843
SHOWTIME NETWORKS INC.—See National Amusements, Inc.; *U.S. Private*, pg. 2843
SHOWTIME NETWORKS INC. (UK)—See National Amusements, Inc.; *U.S. Private*, pg. 2843
SHOWTIME PICTURES; *U.S. Private*, pg. 3643
SHOWTIME SATELLITE NETWORKS, INC.—See National Amusements, Inc.; *U.S. Private*, pg. 2843
S&H PACKING & SALES CO. INC.; *U.S. Private*, pg. 3513
SH PRECISION CHENGDU CO., LTD.—See Chang Wah Technology Co., Ltd.; *Int'l*, pg. 1441
S&H PRODUCTS, LLC—See B12 Capital Partners LLC; *U.S. Private*, pg. 421
SHRADDHA PRIME PROJECTS LTD; *Int'l*, pg. 6862
SHRADER & MARTINEZ CONSTRUCTION INC.; *U.S. Private*, pg. 3643
SHRADHA INFRAPROJECTS LIMITED; *Int'l*, pg. 6862
SHR CONSULTING GROUP, LLC; *U.S. Private*, pg. 3643
THE SHREDDER COMPANY, LLC—See Inabata & Co. Ltd.; *Int'l*, pg. 3644
SHRED-IT GMBH—See Waste Management, Inc.; *U.S. Public*, pg. 2332
SHRED-TECH INC.—See The Heico Companies, L.L.C.; *U.S. Private*, pg. 4051
SHREE AJIT PULP AND PAPER LIMITED; *Int'l*, pg. 6862
SHREE ASHTAVINAYAK CINE VISION LTD; *Int'l*, pg. 6862
SHREE BHAVYA FABRICS LTD.; *Int'l*, pg. 6862
SHREE BHAWANI PAPER MILLS LIMITED; *Int'l*, pg. 6862
SHREE CEMENT LIMITED; *Int'l*, pg. 6862
SHREE DIGVIJAY CEMENT CO. LTD.—See True North Managers LLP; *Int'l*, pg. 7940
SHREE GANESH BIOTECH INDIA LTD.; *Int'l*, pg. 6862
SHREE GANESH ELASTOPLAST LIMITED; *Int'l*, pg. 6862
SHREE GANESH FORGINGS LTD.; *Int'l*, pg. 6862
SHREE GANESH JEWELLERY HOUSE (I) LIMITED; *Int'l*, pg. 6863
SHREE GANESH REMEDIES LIMITED; *Int'l*, pg. 6863
SHREE GLOBAL TRADEFIN LIMITED; *Int'l*, pg. 6863
SHREE HANUMAN SUGAR & INDUSTRIES LIMITED; *Int'l*, pg. 6863
SHREE HARI CHEMICALS EXPORT LIMITED; *Int'l*, pg. 6863
SHREE INVESTMENT & FINANCE COMPANY LIMITED; *Int'l*, pg. 6863
SHREEJAL INFO HUBS LIMITED; *Int'l*, pg. 6864
SHREEJI TRANSLOGISTICS LIMITED; *Int'l*, pg. 6864
SHREE KARTHIK PAPERS LIMITED; *Int'l*, pg. 6863
SHREE KRISHNA INFRASTRUCTURE LTD.; *Int'l*, pg. 6863
SHREE KRISHNA PAPER MILLS & INDUSTRIES LIMITED; *Int'l*, pg. 6863
SHREE MANUFACTURING COMPANY LIMITED; *Int'l*, pg. 6863
SHREE METALLOYS LIMITED; *Int'l*, pg. 6863
SHREE NARMADA ALUMINIUM INDUSTRIES LIMITED; *Int'l*, pg. 6863
SHREENATH INVESTMENT COMPANY LIMITED; *Int'l*, pg. 6865
SHREE NIDHI TRADING COMPANY LIMITED; *Int'l*, pg. 6863
SHREE OSFM E-MOBILITY LIMITED; *Int'l*, pg. 6863
SHREEOSWAL PSYLLIUM EXPORTS INDIA LIMITED—See ShreeOswal Seeds & Chemicals Limited; *Int'l*, pg. 6865
SHREEOSWAL SEEDS & CHEMICALS LIMITED; *Int'l*, pg. 6865
SHREE PACETRONIX LTD.; *Int'l*, pg. 6863
SHREE PRECOATED STEELS LIMITED; *Int'l*, pg. 6863
SHREE PUSHKAR CHEMICALS & FERTILISERS LTD.; *Int'l*, pg. 6863
SHREE RAJASTHAN SYNTEX LTD. - POLYCOT DIVISION—See Shree Rajasthan Syntex Ltd.; *Int'l*, pg. 6864
SHREE RAJASTHAN SYNTEX LTD.; *Int'l*, pg. 6864
SHREE RAJESHWARANAND PAPER MILLS LIMITED; *Int'l*, pg. 6864
SHREE RAMA MULTI-TECH LIMITED; *Int'l*, pg. 6864
SHREE RAMA NEWSPRINT LIMITED—See Riddhi Siddhi Gluco Biols Ltd.; *Int'l*, pg. 6337
SHREE RAM PROTEINS LTD.; *Int'l*, pg. 6864
SHREE RANG MARK TRAVELS LIMITED; *Int'l*, pg. 6864
SHREE RENUKA SUGARS LIMITED; *Int'l*, pg. 6864
SHREE SALASAR INVESTMENTS LTD.; *Int'l*, pg. 6864
SHREE SECURITIES LIMITED; *Int'l*, pg. 6864
SHREESHAY ENGINEERS LIMITED; *Int'l*, pg. 6865
SHREE SHUBHAM LOGISTICS LIMITED—See Kalpataru Ltd.; *Int'l*, pg. 4058
SHREE STEEL WIRE ROPES LIMITED; *Int'l*, pg. 6864
SHREE TIRUPATI BALAJEE FIBC LTD.; *Int'l*, pg. 6864
SHREE TULSI ONLINE.COM LIMITED; *Int'l*, pg. 6864
SHREE VASU LOGISTICS LIMITED; *Int'l*, pg. 6864
SHREEVATSAA FINANCE & LEASING LIMITED; *Int'l*, pg. 6865
SHRENIK LTD.; *Int'l*, pg. 6865

SHRENO LTD - FACTORY UNIT-1—See Alembic Limited; *Int'l*, pg. 306
SHRENO LTD - FACTORY UNIT-2—See Alembic Limited; *Int'l*, pg. 306
SHRENO LTD—See Alembic Limited; *Int'l*, pg. 306
SHRENUJ & CO., LTD.; *Int'l*, pg. 6865
S.H. RESOURCES & DEVELOPMENT CORP.; *U.S. Public*, pg. 1832
SHREVE CRUMP & LOW COMPANY; *U.S. Private*, pg. 3643
SHREWSBURY CHRONICLE—See Gannett Co., Inc.; *U.S. Public*, pg. 903
SHREWSBURY MOTORS INC—See US Auto Group Limited; *U.S. Private*, pg. 4317
SHREWSBURY SURGERY CENTER, LLC—See Tenet Healthcare Corporation; *U.S. Public*, pg. 2012
SHREYANS INDUSTRIES LIMITED - SHREYANS PAPERS PLANT—See Shreyans Industries Limited; *Int'l*, pg. 6865
SHREYANS INDUSTRIES LIMITED; *Int'l*, pg. 6865
SHREYAS INTERMEDIATES LIMITED; *Int'l*, pg. 6865
SHREYAS SHIPPING & LOGISTICS LIMITED; *Int'l*, pg. 6865
SHRI BAJRANG AGRO PROCESSING LIMITED—See Shri Bajrang Alliance Limited; *Int'l*, pg. 6865
SHRI BAJRANG ALLIANCE LIMITED; *Int'l*, pg. 6865
SHRI BHOLANATH CARPETS LTD.; *Int'l*, pg. 6865
SHRICON INDUSTRIES LIMITED; *Int'l*, pg. 6866
SHRI DAMODAR YARN MANUFACTURING PVT. LTD.—See Damodar Industries Limited; *Int'l*, pg. 1957
SHRI DINESH MILLS LTD.; *Int'l*, pg. 6865
SHRI EDUCARE LIMITED—See Kama Holdings Limited; *Int'l*, pg. 4059
SHRIEVE CHEMICAL COMPANY LLC—See Gemspring Capital Management, LLC; *U.S. Private*, pg. 1659
SHRIEVE CHEMICAL PRODUCTS INC.—See Gemspring Capital Management, LLC; *U.S. Private*, pg. 1659
SHRIEVE CHEMICAL (SHANGHAI) LTD.—See Gemspring Capital Management, LLC; *U.S. Private*, pg. 1659
SHRIEVE PRODUCTS INTERNATIONAL LIMITED—See Gemspring Capital Management, LLC; *U.S. Private*, pg. 1659
SHRIEVE QUIMICA DO BRASIL LTDA.—See Gemspring Capital Management, LLC; *U.S. Private*, pg. 1659
SHRI GANG INDUSTRIES & ALLIED PRODUCTS LIMITED; *Int'l*, pg. 6865
SHRI JAGDAMBA POLYMERS LIMITED; *Int'l*, pg. 6865
SHRIJANA FINANCE (FINANCIAL INSTITUTION) LTD.—See Citizens Bank International Limited; *Int'l*, pg. 1626
SHRIJI POLYMERS (INDIA) LTD.; *Int'l*, pg. 6866
SHRI KALYAN HOLDINGS LIMITED; *Int'l*, pg. 6866
SHRI KESHAV CEMENTS & INFRA LIMITED; *Int'l*, pg. 6866
SHRI KRISHNA DEVCON LTD.; *Int'l*, pg. 6866
SHRI KRISHNA PRASADAM LIMITED; *Int'l*, pg. 6866
SHRI LAKSHMI METAL UDYOG LIMITED—See Apl Apollo Tubes Ltd.; *Int'l*, pg. 515
SHRI MAHALAXMI AGRICULTURAL DEVELOPMENT LTD.; *Int'l*, pg. 6866
SHRINERS HOSPITALS FOR CHILDREN; *U.S. Private*, pg. 3643
SHRI NIWAS LEASING & FINANCE LIMITED; *Int'l*, pg. 6866
SHRINKFLEX (THAILAND) PUBLIC COMPANY LIMITED; *Int'l*, pg. 6866
SHRINK PACKAGING SYSTEMS CORP.; *U.S. Private*, pg. 3644
SHRI RAJIVLOCHAN OIL EXTRACTION LTD.; *Int'l*, pg. 6866
SHRIRAM ASSET MANAGEMENT CO.LTD.; *Int'l*, pg. 6866
SHRIRAM BIOSEED (THAILAND) LIMITED—See DCM Shriram Limited; *Int'l*, pg. 1992
SHRIRAM PROPERTIES LIMITED; *Int'l*, pg. 6866
SHRIRAM TRANSPORT FINANCE COMPANY LIMITED; *Int'l*, pg. 6866
SHRIRO EQUIPMENT LTD.—See Shriro Pacific Ltd.; *Int'l*, pg. 6867
SHRIRO GRAPHIC LIMITED—See Shriro Pacific Ltd.; *Int'l*, pg. 6867
SHRIRO (GUANGZHOU) CO. LTD.—See Shriro Pacific Ltd.; *Int'l*, pg. 6866
SHRIRO (H.K.) LTD.—See Shriro Pacific Ltd.; *Int'l*, pg. 6867
SHRIRO HOLDINGS LIMITED—See Shriro Pacific Ltd.; *Int'l*, pg. 6867
SHRIRO MACHINERY LIMITED—See Shriro Pacific Ltd.; *Int'l*, pg. 6867
SHRIRO (MALAYSIA) SDN BHD.—See Shriro Pacific Ltd.; *Int'l*, pg. 6867
SHRIRO MARKETING (THAILAND) LTD.—See Shriro Pacific Ltd.; *Int'l*, pg. 6867
SHRIRO PACIFIC LTD.; *Int'l*, pg. 6866
SHRIRO SHANGHAI CO. LTD.—See Shriro Pacific Ltd.; *Int'l*, pg. 6867
SHRIRO (SINGAPORE) PTE LTD.—See Shriro Pacific Ltd.; *Int'l*, pg. 6867

SHRIRO TRADING CO. LTD.—See Shriro Pacific Ltd.; *Int'l*, pg. 6867
SHRIRO TRADING (VIETNAM) CO. LTD.—See Shriro Pacific Ltd.; *Int'l*, pg. 6867
SHRIRO WEBB LTD.—See Shriro Pacific Ltd.; *Int'l*, pg. 6867
SHRISTI INFRASTRUCTURE DEVELOPMENT CORPORATION LTD.; *Int'l*, pg. 6867
SHRI VASUPRADA PLANTATIONS LIMITED; *Int'l*, pg. 6866
SHRI VENKATESH REFINERIES LTD.; *Int'l*, pg. 6866
THE SHROPSHIRE NUFFIELD HOSPITAL—See Nuffield Health; *Int'l*, pg. 5488
SHRYDUS INDUSTRIES LIMITED; *Int'l*, pg. 6867
SHS ANTWERP AVIATION N.V.; *Int'l*, pg. 6867
SHS GESELLSCHAFT FUR BETEILIGUNGEN MBH & CO. MITTELSTAND KG—See Landesbank Baden-Wurttemberg; *Int'l*, pg. 4405
SHS GROUP, LTD.; *Int'l*, pg. 6867
SHS HOLDINGS LTD.; *Int'l*, pg. 6867
SHS INTERNATIONAL LTD.—See Danone; *Int'l*, pg. 1966
SHS LOGISTICS GMBH—See Saarstahl AG; *Int'l*, pg. 6461
SHS OFFSHORE PTE. LTD.—See SHS Holdings Ltd.; *Int'l*, pg. 6867
S.H.S. RESORT, LLC; *U.S. Private*, pg. 3517
SHS SALES & MARKETING GB LIMITED—See SHS Group, Ltd.; *Int'l*, pg. 6867
SHS SALES & MARKETING LTD—See SHS Group, Ltd.; *Int'l*, pg. 6867
SHS SERVICES GMBH—See Saarstahl AG; *Int'l*, pg. 6461
SHS - STAHL-HOLDING-SAAR GMBH & CO. KGAA—See Saarstahl AG; *Int'l*, pg. 6461
SHS SYSTEM PTE. LTD.—See SHS Holdings Ltd.; *Int'l*, pg. 6867
SHS VIVEON AG—See SIDETRADE S.A.; *Int'l*, pg. 6884
SHS VIVEON SCHWEIZ AG—See SIDETRADE S.A.; *Int'l*, pg. 6884
S+H SYSTEMTECHNIK GMBH—See Trimble, Inc.; *U.S. Public*, pg. 2191
SH TELEKOMMUNIKATION DEUTSCHLAND GMBH—See mobilezone holding ag; *Int'l*, pg. 5011
S-H THIRTY-FIVE OPCO - POCASSET, LLC—See Brookdale Senior Living Inc.; *U.S. Public*, pg. 395
S-H THIRTY-FIVE OPCO - WILLOWWOOD, LLC—See Brookdale Senior Living Inc.; *U.S. Public*, pg. 395
SH TOURS PTE LTD—See Asiatravel.com Holdings Limited; *Int'l*, pg. 620
SH TRADE OY—See Outokumpu Oyj; *Int'l*, pg. 5669
SHT SCHWABISCH HALL TRAINING GMBH—See DZ BANK AG Deutsche Zentral-Genossenschaftsbank; *Int'l*, pg. 2244
SHUAA CAPITAL INTERNATIONAL LTD.—See SHUAA Capital psc; *Int'l*, pg. 6868
SHUAA CAPITAL PSC; *Int'l*, pg. 6867
SHUAA CAPITAL SAUDI ARABIA, PJSC,—See SHUAA Capital psc; *Int'l*, pg. 6868
SHUAA PARTNERS LTD.—See SHUAA Capital psc; *Int'l*, pg. 6868
SHUAA PARTNERS—See SHUAA Capital psc; *Int'l*, pg. 6868
SHUAA SECURITIES LLC—See International Holdings Company PJSC; *Int'l*, pg. 3750
SHUAIBA INDUSTRIAL COMPANY K.S.C.C.—See Al-Safwa Group Holding Co. K.P.S.C.; *Int'l*, pg. 288
SHUANG-BANG INDUSTRIAL. CORP.; *Int'l*, pg. 6868
SHUANGHUA HOLDINGS LIMITED; *Int'l*, pg. 6868
SHUANGLIANG CLYDE BERGEMANN GMBH—See Shuangliang Eco-Energy Systems Company Limited; *Int'l*, pg. 6868
SHUANGLIANG ECO-ENERGY SYSTEMS COMPANY LIMITED; *Int'l*, pg. 6868
SHUANGLIANG ROYAL TECH CSP TECHNOLOGY CO., LTD.—See Shuangliang Eco-Energy Systems Company Limited; *Int'l*, pg. 6868
SHUANG YUN HOLDINGS LIMITED; *Int'l*, pg. 6868
SHUBARKOL KOMIR JSC; *Int'l*, pg. 6868
SHUBARKOL PREMIUM JSC; *Int'l*, pg. 6868
SHUBEE CUSTOMER CARE WEAR; *U.S. Private*, pg. 3644
SHUBHAM POLYSPIN LTD.; *Int'l*, pg. 6868
SHUBHLAXMI JEWEL ART LTD.; *Int'l*, pg. 6868
SHUBHRAM HOSPITAL SOLUTIONS PRIVATE LTD.—See Servizi Italia SpA; *Int'l*, pg. 6726
SHUBIDO PACIFIC SDN BHD—See Wipro Limited; *Int'l*, pg. 8432
SHUEI YOBIKO CO., LTD.; *Int'l*, pg. 6868
SHUETSU CO., LTD.—See Toyo Suisan Kaisha, Ltd.; *Int'l*, pg. 7858
SHUFERSAL; *Int'l*, pg. 6869
SHUFORD DEVELOPMENT CO. INC.—See CV Industries Inc.; *U.S. Private*, pg. 1132
SHUFORD MILLS LLC; *U.S. Private*, pg. 3644
SHUFUNOTOMO CO., LTD.—See Dai Nippon Printing Co., Ltd.; *Int'l*, pg. 1916
SHUFUNOTOMO INFOS CO., LTD.—See Imagica Group Inc.; *Int'l*, pg. 3619
SHUGART CORPORATION; *U.S. Private*, pg. 3644
SHUGART ENTERPRISES LLC; *U.S. Private*, pg. 3644

COMPANY NAME INDEX

SHUHUA SPORTS CO., LTD.; *Int'l*, pg. 6869
SHUI JUN NURSING CENTRE (YAU TONG) COMPANY LIMITED—See Hang Chi Holdings Limited; *Int'l*, pg. 3244
SHUI-MU INTERNATIONAL CO., LTD.; *Int'l*, pg. 6869
SHUI ON BUILDING CONTRACTORS LIMITED—See Shui On Company Limited; *Int'l*, pg. 6869
SHUI ON BUILDING MATERIALS LIMITED—See Shui On Company Limited; *Int'l*, pg. 6869
SHUI ON COMPANY LIMITED; *Int'l*, pg. 6869
SHUI ON CONSTRUCTION COMPANY LIMITED—See Shui On Company Limited; *Int'l*, pg. 6869
SHUI ON LAND LIMITED—See Shui On Company Limited; *Int'l*, pg. 6869
SHUI ON NURSING CENTRE (KWAI SHING E.) CO., LIMITED—See Hang Chi Holdings Limited; *Int'l*, pg. 3244
SHUI ON ROCK PRODUCTS LIMITED—See Shui On Company Limited; *Int'l*, pg. 6869
SHUKRA JEWELLERY LIMITED; *Int'l*, pg. 6869
SHUKRA PHARMACEUTICALS LIMITED; *Int'l*, pg. 6869
SHULAR COMPANY; *U.S. Private*, pg. 3644
SHULER DISTRIBUTING COMPANY; *U.S. Private*, pg. 3644
SHULLSBURG CREAMERY INC.; *U.S. Private*, pg. 3644
SHULMANS LLP—See Knights Group Holdings PLC; *Int'l*, pg. 4208
SHULTS FORD, INC.; *U.S. Private*, pg. 3644
SHULTS FORD LINCOLN-MERCURY, INC.—See Shults Ford, Inc.; *U.S. Private*, pg. 3644
SHULTS MANAGEMENT GROUP, INC.; *U.S. Private*, pg. 3644
SHULTZ DISTRIBUTING, INC.; *U.S. Private*, pg. 3644
SHUMAN-HERITAGE PRINTING CO. LLC—See Mount Royal Printing & Communications, Inc.; *U.S. Private*, pg. 2798
SHUMANI MILLS COMMUNICATIONS (PTY) LTD.—See Caxton and CTP Publishers and Printers Ltd.; *Int'l*, pg. 1363
SHUMBA COAL LIMITED; *Int'l*, pg. 6869
SHUMEN-TABAC AD; *Int'l*, pg. 6869
SHUM YIP SOUTHERN LAND (HOLDINGS) CO., LTD.—See Shenzhen Investment Limited; *Int'l*, pg. 6813
SHUM YIP TAIFU LOGISTICS GROUP HOLDINGS CO., LTD—See Shenzhen Investment Limited; *Int'l*, pg. 6813
SHUNAN BULK TERMINAL CO., LTD.—See Tokuyama Corporation; *Int'l*, pg. 7787
SHUNAN DAIICHI TRAFFIC CO., LTD.—See Daiichi Koutsu Sangyo Co., Ltd.; *Int'l*, pg. 1929
SHUNAN FINECHEM INCORPORATED—See Mitsui & Co., Ltd.; *Int'l*, pg. 4974
SHUNAN SWIMMING CLUB CO., LTD.—See Tokuyama Corporation; *Int'l*, pg. 7787
SHUNAN SYSTEM SANGYO CO., LTD.—See Tokuyama Corporation; *Int'l*, pg. 7787
SHUNDE KAUTEX PLASTICS TECHNOLOGY CO., LTD.—See PLASTECH Holding GmbH; *Int'l*, pg. 5892
S&H UNDERWRITERS, INC.—See XPT Group LLC; *U.S. Private*, pg. 4582
SHUNDE TUBE & ROD TECHNOLOGY CO.—See Guangdong Jingyi Metal Co., Ltd.; *Int'l*, pg. 3157
SHUNE365 CO.—See NITTAN Corporation; *Int'l*, pg. 5383
SHUNFA HENGYE CORP.; *Int'l*, pg. 6870
SHUNFENG INTERNATIONAL CLEAN ENERGY LTD.; *Int'l*, pg. 6870
SHUNG CHING BEIJING HUASHENG EMERGENCY EQUIPMENT SYSTEMS CO., LTD.—See CIMC-TianDa Holdings Company Limited; *Int'l*, pg. 1609
SHUN HING PAPER COMPANY LIMITED—See Samson Paper Holdings Limited; *Int'l*, pg. 6509
SHUN HO HOLDINGS LIMITED; *Int'l*, pg. 6869
SHUN HO PROPERTY INVESTMENTS LTD; *Int'l*, pg. 6869
SHUNJUSHA CO., LTD.—See Mitsubishi Heavy Industries, Ltd.; *Int'l*, pg. 4961
SHUNKAWA CO., LTD.—See TOPCO Scientific Co., Ltd.; *Int'l*, pg. 7814
SHUNLIBAN INFORMATION SERVICE CO., LTD.; *Int'l*, pg. 6870
SHUNMOON (SHANGHAI) LIGHTING LIMITED—See Sonepar S.A.; *Int'l*, pg. 7091
SHUN ON ELECTRONIC CO., LTD.; *Int'l*, pg. 6869
SHUNSAI DELI CO., LTD.—See Kewpie Corporation; *Int'l*, pg. 4144
SHUNSIN TECHNOLOGY HOLDINGS LIMITED; *Int'l*, pg. 6870
SHUNSIN TECHNOLOGY (ZHONGSHAN) LIMITED—See ShunSin Technology Holdings Limited; *Int'l*, pg. 6870
SHUN TAK HOLDINGS LIMITED; *Int'l*, pg. 6870
SHUN TAK PROPERTY MANAGEMENT LIMITED—See Shun Tak Holdings Limited; *Int'l*, pg. 6870
SHUN TAK REAL ESTATE LTD.—See Shun Tak Holdings Limited; *Int'l*, pg. 6870
SHUN TAK TRAVEL SERVICES LIMITED—See Shun Tak Holdings Limited; *Int'l*, pg. 6870
SHUNTEN INTERNATIONAL (HOLDINGS) LIMITED; *Int'l*, pg. 6870

SHUN THAI RUBBER GLOVES INDUSTRY PUBLIC COMPANY LIMITED; *Int'l*, pg. 6870
SHUN WO GROUP HOLDINGS LIMITED; *Int'l*, pg. 6870
SHUNYA INTERNATIONAL MARTECH BEIJING CO LTD; *Int'l*, pg. 6870
SHUR-CO, LLC; *U.S. Private*, pg. 3644
SHURE ASIA LIMITED—See Shure Incorporated; *U.S. Private*, pg. 3644
SHURE EUROPE GMBH—See Shure Incorporated; *U.S. Private*, pg. 3644
SHURE INCORPORATED; *U.S. Private*, pg. 3644
SHURFLO PUMP MANUFACTURING CO.—See Pentair plc; *Int'l*, pg. 5790
SHURGARD SELF STORAGE S.C.A.—See Public Storage; *U.S. Public*, pg. 1736
SHURGARD SELF STORAGE; *Int'l*, pg. 6870
SHURJO ENERGY PVT. LIMITED—See PAE Limited; *Int'l*, pg. 5695
SHURJOINT AMERICA, INC.—See Johnson Controls International plc; *Int'l*, pg. 3987
SHURJOINT PIPING PRODUCTS, INC.—See Aalberts N.V.; *Int'l*, pg. 35
SHURJOINT TAIWAN, INC.—See Johnson Controls International plc; *Int'l*, pg. 3987
SHUR-LINE—See Nova Capital Management Limited; *Int'l*, pg. 5450
SHUR-LOK COMPANY—See Berkshire Hathaway Inc.; *U.S. Public*, pg. 315
SHUR-LOK INTERNATIONAL S.A.—See Berkshire Hathaway Inc.; *U.S. Public*, pg. 315
SHUR-MARKET DEVELOPMENT CO., INC.—See C&S Wholesale Grocers, Inc.; *U.S. Private*, pg. 704
SHUROOQ INVESTMENT SERVICES COMPANY—See Kuwait Projects Company (Holding) K.S.C.P.; *Int'l*, pg. 4347
SHUROOQ SECURITIES COMPANY LLC—See Kuwait Projects Company (Holding) K.S.C.P.; *Int'l*, pg. 4347
SHURTAPE SPECIALTY COATING, LLC—See STM Industries, Inc.; *U.S. Private*, pg. 3813
SHURTAPE TECHNOLOGIES, LLC—See STM Industries, Inc.; *U.S. Private*, pg. 3813
THE SHURTLEFF & ANDREWS CORP.; *U.S. Private*, pg. 4117
SHURWID INDUSTRIES LTD.; *Int'l*, pg. 6870
SHUSTER CORPORATION—See Genuine Parts Company; *U.S. Public*, pg. 933
SHUTOKEN LEASING CO., LTD.—See Resona Holdings, Inc.; *Int'l*, pg. 6298
SHUTTERFLY, INC.—See Apollo Global Management, Inc.; *U.S. Public*, pg. 159
SHUTTERFLY LIFETOUCH, LLC—See Apollo Global Management, Inc.; *U.S. Public*, pg. 159
SHUTTERSTOCK, INC.; *U.S. Public*, pg. 1876
SHUTTERSTOCK (UK) LTD.—See Shutterstock, Inc.; *U.S. Public*, pg. 1876
SHUTTLE COMPUTER GROUP INC.—See Shuttle Inc.; *Int'l*, pg. 6871
SHUTTLE COMPUTER HANDELS GMBH—See Shuttle Inc.; *Int'l*, pg. 6871
SHUTTLE INC.; *Int'l*, pg. 6871
SHUTTLELIFT, INC.—See Marine Travelift, Inc.; *U.S. Private*, pg. 2575
SHUTTLE PHARMACEUTICALS HOLDINGS, INC.; *U.S. Public*, pg. 1876
SHUTTLE PHARMACEUTICALS, INC.; *U.S. Private*, pg. 3644
SHUTTLEROCK JAPAN, INC.—See Digital Holdings, Inc.; *Int'l*, pg. 2122
SHUTTLEWAGON, INC.—See Westinghouse Air Brake Technologies Corporation; *U.S. Public*, pg. 2359
SHUTTLEWORTH EUROPE N.V.—See Leonard Green & Partners, L.P.; *U.S. Private*, pg. 2428
SHUTTLEWORTH, LLC—See Leonard Green & Partners, L.P.; *U.S. Private*, pg. 2428
SHUTTS & BOWEN LLP; *U.S. Private*, pg. 3644
SHUYU CIVILIAN PHARMACY CORPORATION LTD.; *Int'l*, pg. 6871
SHUZ TUNG MACHINERY INDUSTRIAL CO., LTD.; *Int'l*, pg. 6871
SHV ENERGY N.V.—See SHV Holdings N.V.; *Int'l*, pg. 6872
SHV ENERGY PRIVATE LTD.—See SHV Holdings N.V.; *Int'l*, pg. 6873
SHV GAS BRASIL LTDA.—See SHV Holdings N.V.; *Int'l*, pg. 6873
SHV GAS SUPPLY & RISK MANAGEMENT SAS—See SHV Holdings N.V.; *Int'l*, pg. 6873
SHV HOLDINGS N.V.; *Int'l*, pg. 6871
SHW AG—See Pierer Konzerngesellschaft mbH; *Int'l*, pg. 5863
SHW AUTOMOTIVE GMBH—See Pierer Konzerngesellschaft mbH; *Int'l*, pg. 5864
SH WORLDWIDE, LLC; *U.S. Private*, pg. 3622
SHYAMA INFOSYS LIMITED; *Int'l*, pg. 6873
SHYAM CENTURY FERROUS LTD.; *Int'l*, pg. 6873
SHYAMKAMAL INVESTMENTS LIMITED; *Int'l*, pg. 6873
SHYAM METALICS & ENERGY LTD.; *Int'l*, pg. 6873
SHYAMPUR SUGAR MILLS LTD.; *Int'l*, pg. 6873

SIAB HOLDINGS BERHAD

SHYAM TELECOM INC.—See Shyam Telecom Ltd; *Int'l*, pg. 6873
SHYAM TELECOM LTD; *Int'l*, pg. 6873
SHYE FENG ENTERPRISE (THAILAND) CO., LTD.—See Apex International Co., Ltd.; *Int'l*, pg. 511
SHYFT ANALYTICS, INC.—See Dassault Systemes S.A.; *Int'l*, pg. 1975
SHYFT GLOBAL SERVICES, INC.—See TD Synnex Corp; *U.S. Public*, pg. 1984
THE SHYFT GROUP, INC.; *U.S. Public*, pg. 2130
SHYMKENT CEMENT JSC—See Heidelberg Materials AG; *Int'l*, pg. 3317
SHYMKENT MUNAI ONIMDERI JSC; *Int'l*, pg. 6873
SHYPDIRECT, LLC—See Transportation and Logistics Systems, Inc.; *U.S. Public*, pg. 2184
SHZ GEBAUDETECHNIK AG—See Poenina Holding AG; *Int'l*, pg. 5903
SI2CHIP TECHNOLOGIES PRIVATE LTD.—See Alten S.A.; *Int'l*, pg. 391
SI2 TECHNOLOGIES, INC.—See Antenna Research Associates, Incorporated; *U.S. Private*, pg. 287
SI6 METALS LIMITED; *Int'l*, pg. 6874
SIA ABRAFOAM LTD.—See Robert Bosch GmbH; *Int'l*, pg. 6364
SIA ABRASIVES AUSTRALIA PTY. LTD.—See Robert Bosch GmbH; *Int'l*, pg. 6364
SIA ABRASIVES BELGIUM N.V./S.A.—See Robert Bosch GmbH; *Int'l*, pg. 6364
SIA ABRASIVES DEUTSCHLAND GMBH—See Robert Bosch GmbH; *Int'l*, pg. 6364
SIA ABRASIVES ESPANA S.A.U.—See Robert Bosch GmbH; *Int'l*, pg. 6364
SIA ABRASIVES FRANCE SARL—See Robert Bosch GmbH; *Int'l*, pg. 6364
SIA ABRASIVES (G.B.) LTD.—See Robert Bosch GmbH; *Int'l*, pg. 6364
SIA ABRASIVES GMBH—See Robert Bosch GmbH; *Int'l*, pg. 6364
SIA ABRASIVES HOLDING LTD.—See Robert Bosch GmbH; *Int'l*, pg. 6364
SIA ABRASIVES, INC. USA—See Robert Bosch GmbH; *Int'l*, pg. 6364
SIA ABRASIVES INDUSTRIES AG—See Robert Bosch GmbH; *Int'l*, pg. 6364
SIA ABRASIVES POLSKA SP. Z O.O.—See Robert Bosch GmbH; *Int'l*, pg. 6368
SIA ABRASIVOS INDUSTRIAIS LTDA.—See Robert Bosch GmbH; *Int'l*, pg. 6364
SIA ABRASIVOS MEXICO S.A. DE C.V.—See Robert Bosch GmbH; *Int'l*, pg. 6364
SIA AEROC—See Aeroc International AS; *Int'l*, pg. 180
SIA AKG THERMOTECHNIK LATVIA—See Autokuhler GmbH & Co. KG; *Int'l*, pg. 727
SIA ALFA LAVAL EESTI FILIAAL—See Alfa Laval AB; *Int'l*, pg. 312
SIA ALL MEDIA LATVIA—See Providence Equity Partners L.L.C.; *U.S. Private*, pg. 3291
SIA ALSO LATVIA—See Droege Group AG; *Int'l*, pg. 2205
SIA BALTIC FEED—See Apetit Plc; *Int'l*, pg. 509
SIA BALTIKA LATVIJA—See KJK Capital Oy; *Int'l*, pg. 4197
SIA BALTJAS ELEKTRO SABIEDRIBA—See Wurth Verwaltungsgesellschaft mbH; *Int'l*, pg. 8507
SIA BAYER—See Bayer Aktiengesellschaft; *Int'l*, pg. 910
SIAB HOLDINGS BERHAD; *Int'l*, pg. 6874
SIA BK LATVIA—See Hangzhou Hikvision Digital Technology Co., Ltd.; *Int'l*, pg. 3248
S I A BRENNTAG LATVIA—See BRENNTAG SE; *Int'l*, pg. 1149
SIA BUCHER SCHOERLING BALTIC SA—See Bucher Industries AG; *Int'l*, pg. 1208
SIA CABOT LATVIA—See Cabot Corporation; *U.S. Public*, pg. 417
SIAC DO BRASIL LTDA.—See KPS Capital Partners, LP; *U.S. Public*, pg. 2347
SIA CENTRAL EUROPE. A.S.—See Cassa Depositi e Prestiti S.p.A.; *Int'l*, pg. 1355
SIA CENTRAL EUROPE ZRT.—See Cassa Depositi e Prestiti S.p.A.; *Int'l*, pg. 1354
SIA CITY24—See Alma Media Corporation; *Int'l*, pg. 362
SIA CITY SERVICE ENGINEERING—See City Service SE; *Int'l*, pg. 1627
SIA CLEAR CHANNEL LATVIA—See iHeartMedia, Inc.; *U.S. Public*, pg. 1096
SIA COCA-COLA HBC LATVIA—See Coca-Cola HBC AG; *Int'l*, pg. 1686
SIA CONSOLIS LATVIJA—See Bain Capital, LP; *U.S. Private*, pg. 438
SIA CORDSTRAP BALTIC—See Cordstrap Netherlands B.V.; *Int'l*, pg. 1797
SIA CORUS BUILDING SYSTEMS—See Tata Sons Limited; *Int'l*, pg. 7472
SIA CROATIA D.O.O.—See Cassa Depositi e Prestiti S.p.A.; *Int'l*, pg. 1355
SIAC SERVICES SRL—See Allianz SE; *Int'l*, pg. 355
SIA CZECH REPUBLIC. S.R.O.—See Cassa Depositi e Prestiti S.p.A.; *Int'l*, pg. 1355
SIA DANFOSS—See Danfoss A/S; *Int'l*, pg. 1961
SIAD AUSTRIA GMBH—See Linde plc; *Int'l*, pg. 4510

SIAD BULGARIA EOOD—See Linde plc; *Int'l*, pg. 4510
SIAD CZECH SPOL. S R.O.—See Linde plc; *Int'l*, pg. 4510
SIAD HEALTHCARE S.P.A.—See Linde plc; *Int'l*, pg. 4510
SIAD HUNGARY KFT—See Linde plc; *Int'l*, pg. 4510
SIAD MACCHINE IMPIANTI S.P.A.—See Linde plc; *Int'l*, pg. 4510
SIA DOMMO GRUPA—See INVL Baltic Real Estate AB; *Int'l*, pg. 3790
SIA DOUGLAS LATVIA—See CVC Capital Partners SICAV-FIS S.A.; *Int'l*, pg. 1883
SIAD ROMANIA S.R.L.—See Linde plc; *Int'l*, pg. 4510
SIAD RUS O.O.O.—See Linde plc; *Int'l*, pg. 4510
SIAD SLOVAKIA SPOL. S R.O.—See Linde plc; *Int'l*, pg. 4510
SIAD S.P.A.—See Linde plc; *Int'l*, pg. 4510
SIA DS SMITH PACKAGING LATVIA—See DS Smith Plc; *Int'l*, pg. 2209
SIA ELME MESSER L—See BLRT Grupp AS; *Int'l*, pg. 1066
SIA ELME TRANS L—See BLRT Grupp AS; *Int'l*, pg. 1066
SIA EMPIRE BALTICS—See Kakel Max AB; *Int'l*, pg. 4056
SIA ENGINEERING COMPANY LIMITED—See Temasek Holdings (Private) Limited; *Int'l*, pg. 7551
SIA ENGINEERING JAPAN CORPORATION—See Temasek Holdings (Private) Limited; *Int'l*, pg. 7551
SIA ENGINEERING (PHILIPPINES) CORPORATION—See Temasek Holdings (Private) Limited; *Int'l*, pg. 7551
SIA ENGINEERING (USA), INC.—See Temasek Holdings (Private) Limited; *Int'l*, pg. 7551
SIA EOLUS—See Eolus Vind AB; *Int'l*, pg. 2457
SIA FAZER LATVIJA—See Oy Karl Fazer Ab; *Int'l*, pg. 5677
SIA FIBRAL LTD.—See Robert Bosch GmbH; *Int'l*, pg. 6364
SIA FORTUM JELGAVA—See Fortum Oyj; *Int'l*, pg. 2742
SIA FORUM AUTO—See Tallinna Kaubamaja AS; *Int'l*, pg. 7447
SIA FORUM CINEMAS—See Ratos AB; *Int'l*, pg. 6218
SIA GALLUSMAN—See Ovostar Union N.V.; *Int'l*, pg. 5673
SIA GC LEASING BALTIC—See Grenke AG; *Int'l*, pg. 3081
SIAG INDUSTRIE GMBH—See SIAG Schaaf Industrie AG; *Int'l*, pg. 6874
SIA GLAXOSMITHKLINE LATVIA—See GSK plc; *Int'l*, pg. 3149
SIA GRUNDFOS PUMPS BALTIC EESTI—See The Poul Due Jensen Foundation; *Int'l*, pg. 7676
SIAG SCHAAF INDUSTRIE AG; *Int'l*, pg. 6874
SIA GYPROC—See Compagnie de Saint-Gobain SA; *Int'l*, pg. 1726
SIA HANSAMATRIX INNOVATION—See HansaMatrix AS; *Int'l*, pg. 3259
SIA HANSAMATRIX VENTSPILS—See HansaMatrix AS; *Int'l*, pg. 3259
SIA HT SHIPMANAGEMENT—See AS Infortar; *Int'l*, pg. 590
SIA HUSQVARNA LATVIJA—See Husqvarna AB; *Int'l*, pg. 3540
SIA INDUTEK LV—See Indutrade AB; *Int'l*, pg. 3681
SIA INTER RAO LATVIA—See JSC INTER RAO UES; *Int'l*, pg. 4009
SIA INTRUM GLOBAL TECHNOLOGIES—See Intrum AB; *Int'l*, pg. 3771
SIA ITAB SHOP CONCEPT LATVIA—See ITAB Shop Concept AB; *Int'l*, pg. 3828
SIA KALNOZOLS CELTNIECIBA; *Int'l*, pg. 6874
SIA KENTEK LATVIJA—See Diploma PLC; *Int'l*, pg. 2129
SIA KONEKESKO LATVIA—See Kesko Corporation; *Int'l*, pg. 4142
SIA KONE LIFTI LATVIJA OY—See KONE Oyj; *Int'l*, pg. 4250
SIA KRKA LATVIJA—See Krka, d.d., Novo Mesto; *Int'l*, pg. 4303
SIA LANORDIJA—See Orkla ASA; *Int'l*, pg. 5639
SIA LATGRAN—See Kinnevik AB; *Int'l*, pg. 4182
SIA LATVIJAS NAMSAIMNIEKS—See City Service SE; *Int'l*, pg. 1627
SIA LEIPURIN—See Aspo Oyj; *Int'l*, pg. 631
SIA LEMMINKAINEN LATVIJA—See YIT Corporation; *Int'l*, pg. 8586
SIA LSEZ META-PLAST—See Rochling SE & Co. KG; *Int'l*, pg. 6378
SIALTECH B.V.—See ABO-Group NV/SA; *Int'l*, pg. 66
SIA LUNDBECK LATVIA—See Lundbeckfonden; *Int'l*, pg. 4582
SIAM AISIN CO., LTD.—See AISIN Corporation; *Int'l*, pg. 254
SIAM ARATA CO., LTD.—See Arata Corporation; *Int'l*, pg. 536
SIAM ASAHI TECHNOGLASS CO., LTD.—See AGC Inc.; *Int'l*, pg. 204
SIAM AUTOBACS CO., LTD.—See Autobacs Seven Co., Ltd.; *Int'l*, pg. 726
SIAM AZUMA MULTI-TRANS CO., LTD.—See Azuma Shipping Co., Ltd.; *Int'l*, pg. 782
SIAM BATTERY INDUSTRY COMPANY LIMITED - PATHUMTHANI FACTORY—See Siam Pan Group Public Company Limited; *Int'l*, pg. 6875
SIAMBRATOR CO., LTD.—See Sintokogio Ltd.; *Int'l*, pg. 6958

SIAM CALSONIC CO., LIMITED.—See KKR & Co. Inc.; *U.S. Public*, pg. 1260
SIAM CASTING POWDERS LTD.—See Goodwin PLC; *Int'l*, pg. 3042
SIAM CELLULOSE CO., LTD.—See The Siam Cement Public Company Limited; *Int'l*, pg. 7684
SIAM CEMENT INDUSTRY CO., LTD.—See The Siam Cement Public Company Limited; *Int'l*, pg. 7685
THE SIAM CEMENT (KAENG KHOI) CO., LTD.—See The Siam Cement Public Company Limited; *Int'l*, pg. 7685
THE SIAM CEMENT (LAMPANG) CO., LTD.—See The Siam Cement Public Company Limited; *Int'l*, pg. 7685
THE SIAM CEMENT PUBLIC COMPANY LIMITED; *Int'l*, pg. 7682
THE SIAM CEMENT (THUNG SONG) CO., LTD.—See The Siam Cement Public Company Limited; *Int'l*, pg. 7685
THE SIAM CERAMIC GROUP INDUSTRIES CO., LTD.—See The Siam Cement Public Company Limited; *Int'l*, pg. 7683
SIAM CHEMICAL INDUSTRY CO., LTD.—See DIC Corporation; *Int'l*, pg. 2109
SIAM CITY CEMENT (BANGLADESH) LIMITED—See Siam City Cement Public Company Limited; *Int'l*, pg. 6874
SIAM CITY CEMENT (LANKA) LIMITED—See Siam City Cement Public Company Limited; *Int'l*, pg. 6874
SIAM CITY CEMENT NHON TRACH LIMITED—See Siam City Cement Public Company Limited; *Int'l*, pg. 6874
SIAM CITY CEMENT PUBLIC COMPANY LIMITED - SARABURI FACTORY—See Siam City Cement Public Company Limited; *Int'l*, pg. 6874
SIAM CITY CEMENT PUBLIC COMPANY LIMITED; *Int'l*, pg. 6874
SIAM CITY CEMENT (VIETNAM) LIMITED—See Siam City Cement Public Company Limited; *Int'l*, pg. 6874
SIAM CITY CONCRETE COMPANY LIMITED—See Siam City Cement Public Company Limited; *Int'l*, pg. 6874
SIAM CITY CREDIT FINANCE & SECURITIES CO., LTD.—See Thanachart Capital PCL; *Int'l*, pg. 7607
SIAM CITY FACTORING PUBLIC CO., LTD.; *Int'l*, pg. 6874
SIAM COATED ABRASIVE CO., LTD.—See Noritake Co., Limited; *Int'l*, pg. 5428
SIAM COMMERCIAL BANK PUBLIC COMPANY LIMITED; *Int'l*, pg. 6874
SIAM COMMERCIAL LEASING PUBLIC COMPANY LIMITED—See Siam Commercial Bank Public Company Limited; *Int'l*, pg. 6875
SIAM COMPANY—See Integra Management LLC; *Int'l*, pg. 3730
SIAM COMPRESSOR INDUSTRY CO., LTD.—See Mitsubishi Electric Corporation; *Int'l*, pg. 4946
SIAM CONCRETE & BRICK PRODUCTS CO., LTD.—See Italian-Thai Development pcl; *Int'l*, pg. 3829
THE SIAM CONSTRUCTION STEEL CO., LTD.—See The Siam Cement Public Company Limited; *Int'l*, pg. 7682
SIAM DAIKIN SALES CO., LTD.—See Daikin Industries, Ltd.; *Int'l*, pg. 1936
SIAM DEL MONTE COMPANY LIMITED—See Kikkoman Corporation; *Int'l*, pg. 4161
SIAM DENSO MANUFACTURING CO., LTD.—See Denso Corporation; *Int'l*, pg. 2033
SIAM EAST SOLUTIONS PCL; *Int'l*, pg. 6875
SIA MEDIQ LATVIJAS—See Advent International Corporation; *U.S. Private*, pg. 104
SIAM ENVIRONMENTAL TECHNOLOGY CO., LTD.—See Siam Steel Service Center Public Company Limited; *Int'l*, pg. 6875
SIA MERKS—See AS Merko Ehitus; *Int'l*, pg. 590
SIAMESE ASSET PUBLIC COMPANY LIMITED; *Int'l*, pg. 6875
SIAM ETO CO., LTD.—See Kyokuto Boeki Kaisha, Ltd.; *Int'l*, pg. 4362
SIAM FAMILYMART CO., LTD.—See ITOCHU Corporation; *Int'l*, pg. 3836
THE SIAM FIBERGLASS CO., LTD.—See The Siam Cement Public Company Limited; *Int'l*, pg. 7683
SIAM FIBREBOARD COMPANY LIMITED—See Evergreen Fibreboard Berhad; *Int'l*, pg. 2565
THE SIAM FIBRE-CEMENT CO., LTD.—See The Siam Cement Public Company Limited; *Int'l*, pg. 7683
SIAM FLIGHT SERVICES LTD.—See Deutsche Lufthansa AG; *Int'l*, pg. 2067
SIAM FOOD PRODUCTS PUBLIC COMPANY LIMITED—See Plantheon Co., Ltd.; *Int'l*, pg. 5891
SIAM FOOD SERVICES LIMITED—See C.P. All Public Company Limited; *Int'l*, pg. 1244
SIAM FUKOKU CO., LTD. - KORAT FACTORY 1—See Fukoku Co., Ltd.; *Int'l*, pg. 2839
SIAM FUKOKU CO., LTD. - KORAT FACTORY 2—See Fukoku Co., Ltd.; *Int'l*, pg. 2839
SIAM FUKOKU CO., LTD.—See Fukoku Co., Ltd.; *Int'l*, pg. 2839
SIAM FURUKAWA CO., LTD.—See The Siam Cement Public Company Limited; *Int'l*, pg. 7682
SIAM FURUKAWA TRADING CO., LTD.—See The Furukawa Electric Co., Ltd.; *Int'l*, pg. 7646

SIAM FUTURE DEVELOPMENT PCL—See Central Pattana Public Company Limited; *Int'l*, pg. 1409
SIAMGAS AND PETROCHEMICALS PUBLIC COMPANY LIMITED; *Int'l*, pg. 6876
SIAM GLASS INDUSTRY CO., LTD.—See Osotspa Co., Ltd.; *Int'l*, pg. 5652
SIAM GLOBAL HOUSE PUBLIC COMPANY LIMITED; *Int'l*, pg. 6875
SIAM GOSHI MANUFACTURING CO., LTD.—See Honda Motor Co., Ltd.; *Int'l*, pg. 3464
THE SIAM GYPSUM INDUSTRY CO., LTD.—See The Siam Cement Public Company Limited; *Int'l*, pg. 7683
SIAM HANWA CO., LTD.—See Hanwa Co., Ltd.; *Int'l*, pg. 3263
SIAM HITACHI AUTOMOTIVE PRODUCTS LTD.—See Hitachi, Ltd.; *Int'l*, pg. 3424
SIAM-HITACHI ELEVATOR CO., LTD. - CHONBURI FACTORY—See Hitachi, Ltd.; *Int'l*, pg. 3424
SIAM-HITACHI ELEVATOR CO., LTD.—See Hitachi, Ltd.; *Int'l*, pg. 3424
SIA MIELE LIETUVOS FILIALAS—See Miele & Cie KG; *Int'l*, pg. 4889
SIA MIELE—See Miele & Cie KG; *Int'l*, pg. 4889
THE SIAM INDUSTRIAL WIRE COMPANY LTD.—See Tata Sons Limited; *Int'l*, pg. 7473
SIAM KANAMOTO CO., LTD.—See Kanamoto Co., Ltd.; *Int'l*, pg. 4064
SIAM KAYABA CO., LTD.—See KYB Corporation; *Int'l*, pg. 4354
SIAM KIRIN BEVERAGE CO., LTD.—See Kirin Holdings Company, Limited; *Int'l*, pg. 4189
SIAM KRAFT INDUSTRY CO., LTD.—See The Siam Cement Public Company Limited; *Int'l*, pg. 7684
SIAM KUBOTA CORPORATION CO., LTD.—See Kubota Corporation; *Int'l*, pg. 4322
SIAM KUBOTA CORPORATION CO., LTD.—See The Siam Cement Public Company Limited; *Int'l*, pg. 7682
SIAM KUBOTA LEASING CO., LTD.—See Kubota Corporation; *Int'l*, pg. 4322
SIAM KUBOTA METAL TECHNOLOGY CO., LTD.—See Kubota Corporation; *Int'l*, pg. 4322
SIAM KUBOTA METAL TECHNOLOGY CO., LTD.—See The Siam Cement Public Company Limited; *Int'l*, pg. 7682
SIAM KURABO CO., LTD.—See Kurabo Industries Ltd.; *Int'l*, pg. 4336
SIAM LEMMERZ CO., LTD.—See The Siam Cement Public Company Limited; *Int'l*, pg. 7682
SIAM LOTUS CO., LTD.—See Nippon Steel Corporation; *Int'l*, pg. 5339
SIAM LUCKY MARINE COMPANY LIMITED—See Siamgas and Petrochemicals Public Company Limited; *Int'l*, pg. 6876
SIAMMCO LTD.—See Alam Group of Companies; *Int'l*, pg. 289
SIAM MESCO CO., LTD.—See MESCO Inc; *Int'l*, pg. 4840
THE SIAM MOULDING PLASTER CO., LTD.—See Noritake Co., Limited; *Int'l*, pg. 5429
SIAM MTK CO., LTD.—See Siam Steel Service Center Public Company Limited; *Int'l*, pg. 6875
SIAM MUSIC YAMAHA CO., LTD.—See Yamaha Corporation; *Int'l*, pg. 8549
THE SIAM NAWALOHA FOUNDRY CO., LTD.—See The Siam Cement Public Company Limited; *Int'l*, pg. 7682
SIAM NGK SPARK PLUG CO., LTD.—See Niterra Co., Ltd.; *Int'l*, pg. 5381
SIAM NGK TECHNOCERA CO., LTD.—See NGK Insulators, Ltd.; *Int'l*, pg. 5255
SIAM NISSIN & SEQ LOGISTICS CO., LTD.—See Nissin Corporation; *Int'l*, pg. 5376
SIAM NISTRANS CO., LTD.—See Nissin Corporation; *Int'l*, pg. 5376
SIAM NITORI CO., LTD.—See Nitori Holdings Co., Ltd.; *Int'l*, pg. 5381
SIAM NSK STEERING SYSTEMS CO., LTD.—See NSK Ltd.; *Int'l*, pg. 5480
SIA MOBIL PLUS ADV—See Altia Oyj; *Int'l*, pg. 392
SIAM OKAMOTO CO., LTD.—See Okamoto Industries, Inc.; *Int'l*, pg. 5544
SIAM OKAMURA STEEL CO., LTD.—See Siam Steel International Public Company Limited; *Int'l*, pg. 6875
SIAM OKAYA CHEMICAL CO., LTD.—See Okaya & Co., Ltd.; *Int'l*, pg. 5547
SIAMONS INTERNATIONAL INC.—See RPM International Inc.; *U.S. Public*, pg. 1820
SIAM OXYPLAST CO. LTD.—See Protech Chemicals Ltd.; *Int'l*, pg. 6004
SIAM PACIFIC ELECTRIC WIRE & CABLE CO., LTD.—See Italian-Thai Development pcl; *Int'l*, pg. 3829
SIAM PAN GROUP PUBLIC COMPANY LIMITED; *Int'l*, pg. 6875
SIAM PITIWAT CO., LTD.—See Siam Commercial Bank Public Company Limited; *Int'l*, pg. 6875
SIAM POLYSTYRENE CO., LTD.—See Dow Inc.; *U.S. Public*, pg. 686
SIAM POONGSAN METAL CO., LTD.—See Poongsan Holdings Corporation; *Int'l*, pg. 5920

COMPANY NAME INDEX

SIAM POWER GENERATION PUBLIC COMPANY LIMITED—See Melewar Industrial Group Berhad; *Int'l*, pg. 4808
SIAM PVS CHEMICALS COMPANY LIMITED (SPVS)—See PVS Chemicals, Inc.; *U.S. Private*, pg. 3308
SIAM RAJATHANEE CO., LTD.; *Int'l*, pg. 6875
SIAM REALTY AND SERVICES CO., LTD.—See Mitsubishi UFJ Financial Group, Inc.; *Int'l*, pg. 4969
THE SIAM REFRACTORY INDUSTRY CO., LTD.—See The Siam Cement Public Company Limited; *Int'l*, pg. 7685
SIAM SAMSUNG LIFE INSURANCE CO., LTD.—See Saha Pathanapibul Public Company Limited; *Int'l*, pg. 6479
THE SIAM SANITARY FITTINGS CO., LTD.—See The Siam Cement Public Company Limited; *Int'l*, pg. 7683
THE SIAM SANITARY FITTINGS CO., LTD.—See Toto Ltd.; *Int'l*, pg. 7846
SIAM SANITARY WARE CO., LTD.—See The Siam Cement Public Company Limited; *Int'l*, pg. 7683
SIAM SANITARY WARE CO., LTD.—See Toto Ltd.; *Int'l*, pg. 7845
SIAM SANITARY WARE INDUSTRY CO., LTD.—See The Siam Cement Public Company Limited; *Int'l*, pg. 7685
SIAM SNAIL COMPANY LIMITED—See E for L Aim Public Company Limited; *Int'l*, pg. 2246
SIAM SOMAR CO., LTD. - CHONBURI FACTORY—See Somar Corporation; *Int'l*, pg. 7083
SIAM SOMAR CO., LTD.—See Somar Corporation; *Int'l*, pg. 7083
SIAM SPORT SYNDICATE PUBLIC COMPANY LIMITED; *Int'l*, pg. 6875
SIAM STEEL INTERNATIONAL PUBLIC COMPANY LIMITED; *Int'l*, pg. 6875
SIAM STEEL SERVICE CENTER PUBLIC COMPANY LIMITED; *Int'l*, pg. 6875
SIAM SURIYA CO., LTD.—See Okaya & Co., Ltd.; *Int'l*, pg. 5547
SIAM SYNTHETIC LATEX CO., LTD.—See The Siam Cement Public Company Limited; *Int'l*, pg. 7683
SIAM TAKUMA CO., LTD.—See Takuma Co., Ltd.; *Int'l*, pg. 7442
SIAM TANEE PROPERTY CO., LTD.—See Land & Houses Public Company Limited; *Int'l*, pg. 4403
SIAM TANEE REAL ESTATE CO., LTD.—See Land & Houses Public Company Limited; *Int'l*, pg. 4404
SIAM TELTECH COMPUTER CO., LTD.—See Jasmine International Public Company Limited; *Int'l*, pg. 3912
SIAM TOHCELLO CO., LTD.—See Mitsui Chemicals, Inc.; *Int'l*, pg. 4984
SIAM TOPPAN PACKAGING CO., LTD.—See The Siam Cement Public Company Limited; *Int'l*, pg. 7684
SIAM TOPPAN PACKAGING CO., LTD.—See TOPPAN Holdings Inc.; *Int'l*, pg. 7817
SIAM TOYOTA MANUFACTURING CO., LTD.—See The Siam Cement Public Company Limited; *Int'l*, pg. 7682
SIAM TOYOTA MANUFACTURING CO., LTD.—See Toyota Motor Corporation; *Int'l*, pg. 7872
SIAM UACJ TRADING CO., LTD.—See UACJ Corporation; *Int'l*, pg. 7999
THE SIAM UNITED STEEL CO., LTD.—See POSCO Holdings Inc.; *Int'l*, pg. 5938
SIAM WELLNESS GROUP PUBLIC COMPANY LIMITED; *Int'l*, pg. 6875
THE SIAM WHITE CEMENT CO., LTD.—See The Siam Cement Public Company Limited; *Int'l*, pg. 7685
SIAM WILSON LEARNING CO., LTD.—See WILSON LEARNING WORLDWIDE INC.; *Int'l*, pg. 8423
SIAM WIRE NETTING CO., LTD.—See Nippon Filcon Co., Ltd.; *Int'l*, pg. 5318
SIAM YACHIYO CO., LTD.—See Honda Motor Co., Ltd.; *Int'l*, pg. 3464
SIAM YAMATO STEEL CO., LTD.—See Yamato Kogyo Co. Ltd.; *Int'l*, pg. 8555
SIA NAMU SERVISS APSE—See City Service SE; *Int'l*, pg. 1628
SIA NESTE LATVIJA—See Neste Oyj; *Int'l*, pg. 5202
SIA NINEBOT LATVIA—See Ninebot Limited; *Int'l*, pg. 5300
SIANO APPLIANCE DISTRIBUTORS; *U.S. Private*, pg. 3645
SIA NORMARK LATVIA—See Rapala VMC Oyj; *Int'l*, pg. 6210
SIANTAR TOP TBK; *Int'l*, pg. 6876
SIA OPTOKON BALTIC—See Methode Electronics, Inc.; *U.S. Public*, pg. 1429
SIA ORIOLA RIGA—See Oriola Corporation; *Int'l*, pg. 5631
SIA OVOSTAR EUROPE—See Ovostar Union N.V.; *Int'l*, pg. 5673
SIA PAROC—See Owens Corning; *U.S. Public*, pg. 1628
SIA PARTNERS & COMPANY; *Int'l*, pg. 6874
SIA PARTNERS, LTD.—See Sia Partners & Company; *Int'l*, pg. 6874
SIAPA S.R.L.—See Gowan Company LLC; *U.S. Private*, pg. 1747
SIA P. DUSSMANN—See Dussmann Stiftung & Co. KGaA; *Int'l*, pg. 2235

SIA PHILIP MORRIS LATVIA—See Philip Morris International Inc.; *U.S. Public*, pg. 1687
SIA PIEBALGAS ALUS—See Olvi Oyj; *Int'l*, pg. 5555
SIAPI S.R.L.—See ATS Corporation; *Int'l*, pg. 695
SIA PLOCKMATIC—See Grimaldi Industri AB; *Int'l*, pg. 3086
SIAP S.P.A.—See FLY Srl; *Int'l*, pg. 2716
SIA Q.BEYOND—See q.beyond AG; *Int'l*, pg. 6131
SIA "AON CONSULTING"—See Aon plc; *Int'l*, pg. 495
SIA RAISIO LATVIJA—See Raisio PLC; *Int'l*, pg. 6191
SIA REFONDA—See BLRT Grupp AS; *Int'l*, pg. 1066
SIA RIA TECH—See Iron Mountain Incorporated; *U.S. Public*, pg. 1174
SIA RIGAS KARTE—See Conduent Incorporated; *U.S. Public*, pg. 566
SIA RIGAS KARTE—See Sia Rigas satiksme; *Int'l*, pg. 6874
SIA RIGAS SATIKSME; *Int'l*, pg. 6874
SIA ROCKWOOL—See ROCKWOOL A/S; *Int'l*, pg. 6381
SIA ROMANIA PAYMENT TECHNOLOGIES S.R.L.—See Cassa Depositi e Prestiti S.p.A.; *Int'l*, pg. 1355
SIA ROTTNEROS BALTIC AB—See Arctic Paper S.A.; *Int'l*, pg. 552
SIA RS D.O.O.—See Cassa Depositi e Prestiti S.p.A.; *Int'l*, pg. 1355
SIA RUUKKI LATVIJA—See SSAB AB; *Int'l*, pg. 7154
SIA SANGAR TRADING—See AS Sangar; *Int'l*, pg. 591
SIA SANOFI AVENTIS LATVIA—See Sanofi; *Int'l*, pg. 6550
SIA SBC—See Heidelberg Materials AG; *Int'l*, pg. 3319
SIA SCHENKER—See Deutsche Bahn AG; *Int'l*, pg. 2053
SIA SERGEL—See Telia Company AB; *Int'l*, pg. 7544
S.I.A. SOCIETA ITALIANA AUTOSERVIZI S.P.A.—See Deutsche Bahn AG; *Int'l*, pg. 2052
SIA SPILVA—See Orkla ASA; *Int'l*, pg. 5638
SIA SPORTLAND—See Frasers Group plc; *Int'l*, pg. 2765
SIA STAR FM—See Providence Equity Partners L.L.C.; *U.S. Private*, pg. 3291
SIASUN ROBOT & AUTOMATION CO., LTD.; *Int'l*, pg. 6876
SIAT BRAUN SA; *Int'l*, pg. 6876
SIAT BRAUN SA—See Siat Braun SA; *Int'l*, pg. 6876
SIA TELE2—See Tele2 AB; *Int'l*, pg. 7529
SIA TELIA LATVIJA—See Telia Company AB; *Int'l*, pg. 7544
SIA THE HIMALAYA DRUG COMPANY—See Himalaya Drug Company; *Int'l*, pg. 3396
SIA TIKKURILA—See PPG Industries, Inc.; *U.S. Public*, pg. 1710
SIA TLG HOTELL LALVIJA—See AS Infortar; *Int'l*, pg. 590
SIAT S.A.—See Techint S.p.A.; *Int'l*, pg. 7504
SIAT SOCIETA' INTERNAZIONALE APPLICAZIONI TECNICHE SPA; *Int'l*, pg. 6876
SIAULIU BANKAS AB; *Int'l*, pg. 6876
SIAULIU BANKO INVESTICIJU VALDYMAS UAB—See Siauliu bankas AB; *Int'l*, pg. 6876
SIA UNICREDIT INSURANCE BROKER—See UniCredit S.p.A.; *Int'l*, pg. 8036
SIA UNITREE—See Alna AB; *Int'l*, pg. 364
SIA UPONOR LATVIA—See Georg Fischer AG; *Int'l*, pg. 2937
SIA URALCHEM TRADING—See Uralchem OJSC; *Int'l*, pg. 8094
SIA VALIO INTERNATIONAL—See Valio Ltd.; *Int'l*, pg. 8116
SIA VBH LATVIA LTD.—See VBH Holding AG; *Int'l*, pg. 8139
SIA VERTE AUTO—See Tallinna Kaubamaja AS; *Int'l*, pg. 7447
SIAV S.P.A.; *Int'l*, pg. 6876
SIA WURTH—See Wurth Verwaltungsgesellschaft mbH; *Int'l*, pg. 8507
SIBANNAC, INC.; *U.S. Public*, pg. 1876
SIBANYE-STILLWATER LIMITED; *Int'l*, pg. 6876
SIBAR AUTO PARTS LIMITED; *Int'l*, pg. 6876
SIBAR; *Int'l*, pg. 6876
SIBARTLES LLC—See RusForest AB; *Int'l*, pg. 6429
SIBA S.P.A—See Veolia Environnement S.A.; *Int'l*, pg. 8161
SIBCY CLINE, INC.; *U.S. Private*, pg. 3645
SIB (CYPRUS) LIMITED—See OJSC Sberbank of Russia; *Int'l*, pg. 5542
SIBDEAL PTY LIMITED—See Ramsay Health Care Limited; *Int'l*, pg. 6200
SIBELCO ASIA PTE LTD.—See SCR Sibelco SA; *Int'l*, pg. 6654
SIBELCO AUSTRALIA LIMITED—See SCR Sibelco SA; *Int'l*, pg. 6654
SIBELCO BENELUX B.V.—See SCR Sibelco SA; *Int'l*, pg. 6654
SIBELCO GILFAIR XINHUI MINERALS CO., LTD.—See SCR Sibelco SA; *Int'l*, pg. 6654
SIBELCO GMBH—See SCR Sibelco SA; *Int'l*, pg. 6654
SIBELCO INDIA MINERALS PVT. LTD.—See SCR Sibelco SA; *Int'l*, pg. 6654
SIBELCO ITALIA S.P.A—See SCR Sibelco SA; *Int'l*, pg. 6654
SIBELCO JAPAN LTD.—See SCR Sibelco SA; *Int'l*, pg. 6654

SIBELCO KOREA CO., LTD.—See SCR Sibelco SA; *Int'l*, pg. 6654
SIBELCO MALAYSIA SDN BHD—See SCR Sibelco SA; *Int'l*, pg. 6654
SIBELCO MAOMING KAOLIN CO., LTD.—See SCR Sibelco SA; *Int'l*, pg. 6654
SIBELCO NORDIC OY AB—See SCR Sibelco SA; *Int'l*, pg. 6654
SIBELCO SHANGHAI MINERALS CO., LTD.—See SCR Sibelco SA; *Int'l*, pg. 6654
SIBELGA S.C.R.L.; *Int'l*, pg. 6876
SIBENERGOSETPROEKT LLC.—See JSC ROSSETI; *Int'l*, pg. 4011
SIBERIA AIRLINES PJSC—See CJSC S7 Group; *Int'l*, pg. 1634
SIBERIAN FAIR LLC—See Providence Equity Partners L.L.C.; *U.S. Private*, pg. 3293
SIBERIAN FAIR LLC—See Searchlight Capital Partners, L.P.; *U.S. Private*, pg. 3588
SIBERIAN GOSTINEC PJSC; *Int'l*, pg. 6876
SIBERITE MORTGAGES LIMITED—See Computershare Limited; *Int'l*, pg. 1760
SIBERMEDIA SDN BHD—See Utusan Melayu (Malaysia) Berhad; *Int'l*, pg. 8102
SIBERNAME.COM INC.; *Int'l*, pg. 6876
SIBETH PARTNERSCHAFT—See Arnecke Siebold Rechtsanwalte Partnerschaftsgesellschaft; *Int'l*, pg. 576
SIBEX LIMITED—See Solagran Limited; *Int'l*, pg. 7068
SIB FIXED COST REDUCTION COMPANY, LLC—See O2 Investment Partners, LLC; *U.S. Private*, pg. 2982
SIBIL EDUCATION PRIVATE LIMITED—See Humming Bird Education Ltd.; *Int'l*, pg. 3531
SIBIR ENERGY LIMITED—See PJSC Gazprom; *Int'l*, pg. 5879
SIBIRGASSERVICE; *Int'l*, pg. 6876
SIBIRGROUP AG—See Metall Zug AG; *Int'l*, pg. 4847
SIBL EXCHANGE COMPANY (PVT.) LTD.—See Security Investment Bank Limited; *Int'l*, pg. 6677
SIBLEY NURSING PERSONNEL SERVICE, INC.—See The Lifetime Healthcare Companies; *U.S. Private*, pg. 4070
SIBLEY OIL COMPANY INC.; *U.S. Private*, pg. 3645
SIBL - SOCIETE INDUSTRIELLE BOIS LIEGE—See CORTICEIRA AMORIM, S.G.P.S., S.A.; *Int'l*, pg. 1808
SIBMEDIA INTERACTIVE S.R.L.—See Schibsted ASA; *Int'l*, pg. 6617
SIBMEDICA SRL—See Farmaceutica REMEDIA S.A.; *Int'l*, pg. 2619
SIBNEFTEMASH JSC—See HMS Hydraulic Machines & Systems Group plc; *Int'l*, pg. 3432
SIBOBETON EMS GMBH & CO. KG—See Buzzi SpA; *Int'l*, pg. 1231
SIBOBETON ENGER GMBH & CO. KG—See Buzzi SpA; *Int'l*, pg. 1231
SIBOBETON OSNABRUCK GMBH & CO. KG—See Buzzi SpA; *Int'l*, pg. 1231
SIBOBETON WILHELMSHAVEN GMBH & CO. KG—See Buzzi SpA; *Int'l*, pg. 1231
SIBO-GRUPPE GMBH & CO. KG—See Buzzi SpA; *Int'l*, pg. 1231
SI-BONE DEUTSCHLAND GMBH—See SI-BONE, Inc.; *U.S. Public*, pg. 1876
SI-BONE, INC.; *U.S. Public*, pg. 1876
SI-BONE S.R.L.—See SI-BONE, Inc.; *U.S. Public*, pg. 1876
SI-BONE UK LTD.—See SI-BONE, Inc.; *U.S. Public*, pg. 1876
SIBONEY CONTRACTING CO.; *U.S. Private*, pg. 3645
SIB OPERATIONS & SERVICES LTD.—See The South Indian Bank Limited; *Int'l*, pg. 7688
SIBSON CONSULTING, LLC - LOS ANGELES—See The Segal Group, Inc.; *U.S. Private*, pg. 4116
SIBSON CONSULTING, LLC - PRINCETON—See The Segal Group, Inc.; *U.S. Private*, pg. 4116
SIBSON CONSULTING, LLC - RALEIGH—See The Segal Group, Inc.; *U.S. Private*, pg. 4116
SIBSON CONSULTING, LLC—See The Segal Group, Inc.; *U.S. Private*, pg. 4116
SIBU BEAUTY; *U.S. Private*, pg. 3645
SIBU ISLAND RESORTS SDN BHD—See Johor Corporation; *Int'l*, pg. 3994
SIBU MEDICAL CENTRE CORPORATION SDN BHD—See KPJ Healthcare Berhad; *Int'l*, pg. 4297
SIBURAN RESOURCES LIMITED; *Int'l*, pg. 6877
SIBUR INTERNATIONAL GMBH—See OAO SIBUR Holding; *Int'l*, pg. 5507
SIBUR-KSTOVO LLC—See OAO SIBUR Holding; *Int'l*, pg. 5507
SIBUYAN NICKEL PROPERTIES DEV. CORP.—See Pelican Resources Limited; *Int'l*, pg. 5782
SIBYL COLEFAX & JOHN FOWLER LIMITED—See Colefax Group PLC; *Int'l*, pg. 1697
SICAAP SA; *Int'l*, pg. 6877
SICABLE COTE D'IVOIRE; *Int'l*, pg. 6877
SICABLE - SOCIETE IVOIRIENNE DE CABLES S.A—See Prysmian S.p.A.; *Int'l*, pg. 6012
SICA DE BAGNOLET—See LVMH Moet Hennessy Louis Vuitton SE; *Int'l*, pg. 4600

SICAE DE LA SOMME ET DU CAMBRAISIS

SICAE DE LA SOMME ET DU CAMBRAISIS; *Int'l*, pg. 6877
SI-CAFE CO., LTD.—See S. ISHIMITSU & Co., LTD.; *Int'l*; pg. 6446
SICA FLETCHER, LLC; *U.S. Private*, pg. 3645
SICAGEN INDIA LTD; *Int'l*, pg. 6877
SICA INVEST S.A.; *Int'l*, pg. 6877
SICAL IRON ORE TERMINALS LIMITED—See Sical Logistics Limited; *Int'l*, pg. 6877
SICAL LOGISTICS LIMITED; *Int'l*, pg. 6877
SICA MEDICION SA DE CV—See HORIBA Ltd; *Int'l*, pg. 3478
SICAME SA—See Equistone Partners Europe Limited; *Int'l*, pg. 2487
SICAM S.R.L.—See Stargate Capital GmbH; *Int'l*, pg. 7176
SICAP AFRICA PTY LTD—See Swisscom AG; *Int'l*, pg. 7374
SI CAPITAL & FINANCIAL SERVICES LTD.—See Sharewealth Securities Limited; *Int'l*, pg. 6789
SI CAPITAL PARTNERS LTD; *Int'l*, pg. 6874
SICAP MALAYSIA SDN BHD—See Swisscom AG; *Int'l*, pg. 7374
SICAP SCHWEIZ AG—See Constellation Software Inc.; *Int'l*, pg. 1775
SICARD HOLIDAY CAMPERS; *Int'l*, pg. 6877
SICA SPA; *Int'l*, pg. 6877
SICAT GMBH & CO. KG—See DENTSPLY SIRONA Inc.; *U.S. Public*, pg. 655
SICAT VERWALTUNGS GMBH—See DENTSPLY SIRONA Inc.; *U.S. Public*, pg. 655
SICAVONLINE SA—See Ageas SA/NV; *Int'l*, pg. 205
SICCAR POINT ENERGY LIMITED; *Int'l*, pg. 6877
SICC FRANCE S.A.S.—See SICC S.p.A.; *Int'l*, pg. 6877
SIC CO., LTD.—See METAWATER Co., Ltd.; *Int'l*, pg. 4851
SICC S.P.A.; *Int'l*, pg. 6877
SICC USA INC.—See SICC S.p.A.; *Int'l*, pg. 6877
SICE ENERGIA, S.L.—See ACS, Actividades de Construccion y Servicios, S.A.; *Int'l*, pg. 116
SICE HELLAS SISTEMAS TECNOLOGICOS SOCIEDAD UNIPERSONAL DE RESPONSABILIDAD LIMITADA—See ACS, Actividades de Construccion y Servicios, S.A.; *Int'l*, pg. 116
SICE, INC.—See ACS, Actividades de Construccion y Servicios, S.A.; *Int'l*, pg. 116
SICELUB COLOMBIA LTDA.—See KKR & Co. Inc.; *U.S. Public*, pg. 1242
SICELUB IBERICO S.L.—See KKR & Co. Inc.; *U.S. Public*, pg. 1242
SICE PTY, LTD.—See ACS, Actividades de Construccion y Servicios, S.A.; *Int'l*, pg. 116
SICE TECNOLOGIA Y SISTEMAS, S.A.—See ACS, Actividades de Construccion y Servicios, S.A.; *Int'l*, pg. 116
SIC FILMES, LDA—See Impresa SGPS S.A.; *Int'l*, pg. 3637
SIC FINANCIAL SERVICES LIMITED—See SIC Insurance Company Limited; *Int'l*, pg. 6877
SICGILSOL GASES PRIVATE LTD.—See SOL S.p.A.; *Int'l*, pg. 7067
SICHER ELEVATOR CO., LTD.; *Int'l*, pg. 6877
SICHUAN ACCURACY TEST & ACCREDITATION CO., LTD.—See Sichuan Zhonggng Lightg Prtcn Tech Co., Ltd.; *Int'l*, pg. 6881
SICHUAN ANNING IRON & TITANIUM CO., LTD.; *Int'l*, pg. 6877
SICHUAN APPLE FOODS CO., LTD.—See Apple Flavor & Fragrance Group Co., Ltd.; *Int'l*, pg. 520
SICHUAN BLUESTAR MACHINERY CO., LTD—See China National Chemical Corporation; *Int'l*, pg. 1529
SICHUAN CHANGHONG ELECTRIC CO., LTD.; *Int'l*, pg. 6877
SICHUAN CHANGJIANG ENGINEERING CRANE CO., LTD.—See Terex Corporation; *U.S. Public*, pg. 2019
SICHUAN CHEMICAL WORKS GROUP LTD.—See Sichuan Energy Investment Development Co., Ltd.; *Int'l*, pg. 6878
SICHUAN CHENGFEI INTEGRATION TECHNOLOGY CO., LTD.; *Int'l*, pg. 6877
SICHUAN CHILDREN'S PUBLISHING HOUSE CO., LTD.—See Xinhua Winshare Publishing and Media Co., Ltd.; *Int'l*, pg. 8530
SICHUAN CHUANHUAN TECHNOLOGY CO.,LTD; *Int'l*, pg. 6878
SICHUAN CHUANHUA YONGXIN CONSTRUCTION ENGINEERING CO., LTD.—See Sichuan Energy Investment Development Co., Ltd.; *Int'l*, pg. 6878
SICHUAN CHUANTOU ENERGY CO., LTD.; *Int'l*, pg. 6878
SICHUAN CHUANXI PLASTIC CO. LTD.—See Solvay S.A.; *Int'l*, pg. 7078
SICHUAN CONTEMPORARY AMPEREX TECHNOLOGY LIMITED—See Contemporary Amperex Technology Co., Ltd.; *Int'l*, pg. 1779
SICHUAN CRUN CO., LTD.; *Int'l*, pg. 6878
SICHUAN C&Y TRADITIONAL CHINESE MEDICINECO., LTD.—See Shanxi C&Y Pharmaceutical Group Co., Ltd.; *Int'l*, pg. 6786
SICHUAN DANFU ENVIRONMENT TECHNOLOGY CO.,LTD .; *Int'l*, pg. 6878

SICHUAN DAWN PRECISION TECHNOLOGY CO., LTD.; *Int'l*, pg. 6878
SICHUAN DAZHU CQRC VILLAGE & TOWNSHIP BANK CO., LTD.—See Chongqing Rural Commercial Bank Co., Ltd.; *Int'l*, pg. 1581
SICHUAN DEVELOPMENT GUORUN WATER SUPPLY INVESTMENT CO LTD—See Beijing SPC Environment Protection Tech Co., Ltd.; *Int'l*, pg. 957
SICHUAN DEVELOPMENT LOMON CO., LTD.; *Int'l*, pg. 6878
SICHUAN DEYANG ZHENYUN PLASTICS CO., LTD.—See Mesnac Co., Ltd.; *Int'l*, pg. 4840
SICHUAN DISCOVERY DREAM SCIENCE & TECHNOLOGY CO., LTD.; *Int'l*, pg. 6878
SICHUAN DONGFANG INSULATING MATERIAL CO., LTD.—See Sichuan EM Technology Co., Ltd.; *Int'l*, pg. 6878
SICHUAN DOWELL SCIENCE&TECHNOLOGY INC; *Int'l*, pg. 6878
SICHUAN EII COAL BED METHANE INVESTMENT & DEVELOPMENT CO., LTD.—See Sichuan Energy Investment Development Co., Ltd.; *Int'l*, pg. 6878
SICHUAN EM TECHNOLOGY CO., LTD.; *Int'l*, pg. 6878
SICHUAN ENERGY HUAXI BIOMASS ENERGY DEVELOPMENT CO., LTD.—See Sichuan Energy Investment Development Co., Ltd.; *Int'l*, pg. 6878
SICHUAN ENERGY INDUSTRY INVESTMENT ELECTRIC POWER DEVELOPMENT CO., LTD.—See Sichuan Energy Investment Development Co., Ltd.; *Int'l*, pg. 6878
SICHUAN ENERGY INVESTMENT DEVELOPMENT CO., LTD.; *Int'l*, pg. 6878
SICHUAN ENERGY INVESTMENT DISTRIBUTED ENERGY SYSTEMS CO., LTD.—See Sichuan Energy Investment Development Co., Ltd.; *Int'l*, pg. 6878
SICHUAN ENERGY INVESTMENT HUICHENG TRAINING MANAGEMENT CO., LTD.—See Sichuan Energy Investment Development Co., Ltd.; *Int'l*, pg. 6878
SICHUAN ENERGY INVESTMENT PANZHIHUA HYDROPOWER DEVELOPMENT CO., LTD.—See Sichuan Energy Investment Development Co., Ltd.; *Int'l*, pg. 6878
SICHUAN ENERGY INVESTMENT RUNJIA REAL ESTATE CO., LTD.—See Sichuan Energy Investment Development Co., Ltd.; *Int'l*, pg. 6878
SICHUAN ENERGY NEW-TYPE URBANIZATION INVESTMENT CO., LTD.—See Sichuan Energy Investment Development Co., Ltd.; *Int'l*, pg. 6879
SICHUAN ENERGY WIND POWER CO., LTD.—See Sichuan Energy Investment Development Co., Ltd.; *Int'l*, pg. 6879
SICHUAN ETROL TECHNOLOGIES CO., LTD.; *Int'l*, pg. 6879
SICHUAN EVERBRIGHT ENERGY CONSERVATION & ENVIRONMENTAL PROTECTION INVESTMENT CO., LTD.—See Sichuan Energy Investment Development Co., Ltd.; *Int'l*, pg. 6879
SICHUAN EXPRESSWAY COMPANY LIMITED; *Int'l*, pg. 6879
SICHUAN FUHUA AGRICULTURAL SCIENCE INVESTMENT GROUP; *Int'l*, pg. 6879
SICHUAN FULIN TRANSPORTATION GROUP CO., LTD.; *Int'l*, pg. 6879
SICHUAN FURONG TECHNOLOGY CO., LTD.; *Int'l*, pg. 6879
SICHUAN GOLDEN SUMMIT (GRP) JOINT-STOCK CO., LTD.; *Int'l*, pg. 6879
SICHUAN GOLDSTONE ASIA PHARMACEUTICAL INC.; *Int'l*, pg. 6879
SICHUAN GUANGAN AAA PUBLIC CO., LTD.; *Int'l*, pg. 6879
SICHUAN GUOGUANG AGROCHEMICAL CO., LTD.; *Int'l*, pg. 6879
SICHUAN GUORUN NEW MATERIAL CO., LTD.—See Albemarle Corporation; *U.S. Public*, pg. 73
SICHUAN HAITE HIGH-TECH CO., LTD.; *Int'l*, pg. 6879
SICHUAN HAOWU ELECTROMECHANICAL CO., LTD.; *Int'l*, pg. 6879
SICHUAN HEBANG BIOTECHNOLOGY CO., LTD.; *Int'l*, pg. 6879
SICHUAN HEXIE SHUANGMA CO., LTD.; *Int'l*, pg. 6879
SICHUAN HEZHENG PHARMACY CO., LTD.—See Chongqing Lummy Pharmaceutical Co., Ltd.; *Int'l*, pg. 1580
SICHUAN HEZONG MEDICINE PHARMACEUTICAL CO.; *Int'l*, pg. 6879
SICHUAN HILONG PETROLEUM TECHNOLOGY CO., LTD.—See Hilong Holding Limited; *Int'l*, pg. 3393
SICHUAN HONGDA CO., LTD.; *Int'l*, pg. 6880
SICHUAN HONGDA PETROLEUM & NATURAL GAS CO., LTD.—See Houpu Clean Energy Group Co., Ltd; *Int'l*, pg. 3490
SICHUAN HONGFA RELAY CO., LTD.—See Hongfa Technology Co Ltd; *Int'l*, pg. 3470
SICHUAN HONGHUA ELECTRIC CO., LTD.—See Honghua Group Ltd; *Int'l*, pg. 3471
SICHUAN HONGHUA PETROLEUM EQUIPMENT CO., LTD.—See Honghua Group Ltd; *Int'l*, pg. 3471

SICHUAN HUATI LIGHTING TECHNOLOGY CO., LTD.; *Int'l*, pg. 6880
SICHUAN HUIYUAN OPTICAL COMMUNICATIONS CO., LTD.; *Int'l*, pg. 6880
SICHUAN HYDROPOWER INVESTMENT & MANAGEMENT GROUP, LTD.—See Sichuan Energy Investment Development Co., Ltd.; *Int'l*, pg. 6879
SICHUAN I-HEAR CO., LTD.—See Sonova Holding AG; *Int'l*, pg. 7101
SICHUAN INDUSTRIAL INSTITUTE OF ANTIBIOTICS—See China National Pharmaceutical Group Corporation; *Int'l*, pg. 1534
SICHUAN INJET ELECTRIC CO., LTD.; *Int'l*, pg. 6880
SICHUAN JEREH HENGRI NATURAL GAS ENGINEERING CO., LTD.—See Yantai Jereh Oilfield Services Group Co., Ltd.; *Int'l*, pg. 8565
SICHUAN JIAYUN OIL GAS EQUIPMENT CO., LTD.—See Fujian Snowman Co., Ltd.; *Int'l*, pg. 2819
SICHUAN JINDING INDUSTRIAL & FINANCIAL HOLDING CO., LTD.—See Sichuan Energy Investment Development Co., Ltd.; *Int'l*, pg. 6879
SICHUAN JINGHONG PACKAGING CO. LTD—See Teamway International Group Holdings Limited; *Int'l*, pg. 7501
SICHUAN JINSHI TECHNOLOGY CO., LTD.; *Int'l*, pg. 6880
SICHUAN JIUYUAN YINHAI SOFTWARE CO., LTD.; *Int'l*, pg. 6880
SICHUAN JIUZHOU ELECTRIC CO., LTD.; *Int'l*, pg. 6880
SICHUAN KELUN PHARMACEUTICAL CO., LTD.; *Int'l*, pg. 6880
SICHUAN KEXIN MECHANICAL AND ELECTRICAL EQUIPMENT CO., LTD.; *Int'l*, pg. 6880
SICHUAN KINGFA SCI & TECH DVPT CO., LTD.—See Kingfa Sci &Tech Co., Ltd.; *Int'l*, pg. 4172
SICHUAN LANGSHA HOLDING LTD.; *Int'l*, pg. 6880
SICHUAN LANGUANG DEVELOPMENT CO., LTD.; *Int'l*, pg. 6880
SICHUAN LANGUANG JUSTBON SERVICES GROUP CO., LTD.—See Country Garden Services Holdings Company Limited; *Int'l*, pg. 1818
SICHUAN LESHAN FUHUA CROP PROTECTION TECHNOLOGY INVESTMENT CO., LTD.—See Sichuan Fuhua Agricultural Science Investment Group; *Int'l*, pg. 6879
SICHUAN LEXICOGRAPHICAL PRESS CO., LTD.—See Xinhua Winshare Publishing and Media Co., Ltd.; *Int'l*, pg. 8530
SICHUAN LU-MEI SUPPLY CHAIN MANAGEMENT CO., LTD.—See MYS Group Co., Ltd.; *Int'l*, pg. 5114
SICHUAN LUTIANHUA CO., LTD.; *Int'l*, pg. 6880
SICHUAN LUZHOU LIPENG CAPS MAKING CO., LTD.—See Shandong Chiway Industry Development Co., Ltd.; *Int'l*, pg. 6752
SICHUAN MACCURA INDUSTRY CO., LTD.—See Maccura Biotechnology Co., Ltd.; *Int'l*, pg. 4620
SICHUAN MEIFENG CHEMICAL INDUSTRY CO., LTD.; *Int'l*, pg. 6880
SICHUAN MIANZHU NORWEST PHOSPHATE CHEMICAL CO., LTD.—See AsiaPhos Limited; *Int'l*, pg. 620
SICHUAN MIGAO CHEMICAL FERTILIZER CO., LTD.—See Migao Corporation; *Int'l*, pg. 4890
SICHUAN MINGXING ELECTRIC POWER CO., LTD.; *Int'l*, pg. 6880
SICHUAN NATURAL GAS INVESTMENT CO., LTD.—See Sichuan Energy Investment Development Co., Ltd.; *Int'l*, pg. 6879
SICHUAN NENGTOU E&M MATERIAL TRADE CO., LTD.—See Sichuan Energy Investment Development Co., Ltd.; *Int'l*, pg. 6879
SICHUAN NEW ENERGY POWER COMPANY LIMITED; *Int'l*, pg. 6880
SICHUAN NEW HOPE AGRIBUSINESS (CAMBODIA) CO., LTD—See New Hope Group Co., Ltd.; *Int'l*, pg. 5225
SICHUAN NEWSNET MEDIA (GROUP) CO., LTD.; *Int'l*, pg. 6880
SICHUAN NIPO FINE CHEMICAL CO., LTD.—See Nippon Fine Chemical Co., Ltd.; *Int'l*, pg. 5318
SICHUAN NITROCELL CORPORATION—See China North Industries Group Corporation; *Int'l*, pg. 1536
SICHUAN PHARMACEUTICAL INC.—See Truking Technology Limited; *Int'l*, pg. 7941
SICHUAN PRINTING MATERIAL CO., LTD.—See Xinhua Winshare Publishing and Media Co., Ltd.; *Int'l*, pg. 8530
SICHUAN PUBLISHING & PRINTING CO., LTD.—See Xinhua Winshare Publishing and Media Co., Ltd.; *Int'l*, pg. 8530
SICHUAN QIAOYUAN GAS CO., LTD.; *Int'l*, pg. 6880
SICHUAN QILI PHARMACEUTICAL CO., LTD.—See New Journey Health Technology Group Co., Ltd.; *Int'l*, pg. 5226
SICHUAN QINGMU PHARMACEUTICAL CO., LTD.—See Chengdu Easton Biopharmaceuticals Co., Ltd.; *Int'l*, pg. 1467
SICHUAN ROAD & BRIDGE GROUP CO., LTD.; *Int'l*, pg. 6881

COMPANY NAME INDEX

SICHUAN SANGSIN BRAKE CO., LTD.—See SANGSIN BRAKE Co., Ltd.; *Int'l*, pg. 6539
SICHUAN SECOM SECURITY CO., LTD.—See SECOM Co., Ltd.; *Int'l*, pg. 6672
SICHUAN SHANSHAN NEW MATERIAL CO., LTD.—See Ningbo Shanshan Co., Ltd.; *Int'l*, pg. 6305
SICHUAN SHENGDA FORESTRY INDUSTRY CO., LTD.; *Int'l*, pg. 6881
SICHUAN SHENZHEN ENERGY POWER INVESTMENT HOLDING CO., LTD.—See Shenzhen Energy Group Co., Ltd.; *Int'l*, pg. 6809
SICHUAN SHUDAO EQUIPMENT AND TECHNOLOGY CO., LTD.; *Int'l*, pg. 6881
SICHUAN SUNFOR LIGHT CO., LTD.—See Sichuan Energy Investment Development Co., Ltd.; *Int'l*, pg. 6879
SICHUAN SUNHEAL PHARMACEUTICAL CO., LTD.—See Chengdu Easton Biopharmaceuticals Co., Ltd.; *Int'l*, pg. 1467
SICHUAN SUNTECH POWER CO., LTD.—See Suntech Power Holdings Co., Ltd.; *Int'l*, pg. 7325
SICHUAN SWELLFUN CO., LTD.—See Diageo plc; *Int'l*, pg. 2103
SICHUAN TEWAY FOOD GROUP CO., LTD.; *Int'l*, pg. 6881
SICHUAN TIANYI COMHEART TELECOM CO., LTD.; *Int'l*, pg. 6881
SICHUAN TON YI INDUSTRIAL CO., LTD.—See Uni-President Enterprises Corporation; *Int'l*, pg. 8029
SICHUAN TOYO INK MFG. CO., LTD.—See Toyo Ink SC Holdings Co., Ltd.; *Int'l*, pg. 7854
SICHUAN TW FOOD CO., LTD.—See Tongwei Co., Ltd.; *Int'l*, pg. 7808
SICHUAN WANTAI ALUMINUM CO. LTD.—See Shanghai Yongmaotai Automotive Technology Co., Ltd.; *Int'l*, pg. 6782
SICHUAN WENCHUAN LOGISTICS CO., LTD.—See Xinhua Winshare Publishing and Media Co., Ltd.; *Int'l*, pg. 8530
SICHUAN WESTERN RESOURCES HOLDING CO., LTD.; *Int'l*, pg. 6881
SICHUAN WESTERN SUNNY ELECTRIC POWER DEVELOPMENT CO., LTD.—See Sichuan Energy Investment Development Co., Ltd.; *Int'l*, pg. 6879
SICHUAN XICHANG ELECTRIC POWER CO., LTD.; *Int'l*, pg. 6881
SICHUAN XINHUA CULTURE TRANSMISSION CO., LTD.—See Xinhua Winshare Publishing and Media Co., Ltd.; *Int'l*, pg. 8530
SICHUAN XINJINLU GROUP CO., LTD.; *Int'l*, pg. 6881
SICHUAN XUNYOU NETWORK TECHNOLOGY CO., LTD.; *Int'l*, pg. 6881
SICHUAN YADONG CEMENT CO., LTD.—See Asia Cement Corporation; *Int'l*, pg. 611
SICHUAN YAHUA INDUSTRIAL GROUP CO., LTD.; *Int'l*, pg. 6881
SICHUAN YALI TRANSPORT CO., LTD.—See Asia Cement Corporation; *Int'l*, pg. 611
SICHUAN YI-MEI SUPPLY CHAIN MANAGEMENT CO., LTD.—See MYS Group Co., Ltd.; *Int'l*, pg. 5114
SICHUAN YONGGUI SCIENCE & TECHNOLOGY CO., LTD.—See Zhejiang Yonggui Electric Equipment Co., Ltd.; *Int'l*, pg. 8667
SICHUAN YOU YOU FOODS DEVELOPMENT CO., LTD.—See YouYou Foods Co., Ltd.; *Int'l*, pg. 8604
SICHUAN ZHONGGNG LIGHTG PRTCN TECH CO., LTD.; *Int'l*, pg. 6881
SICHUAN ZHONGHUAN ENERGY CO., LTD.—See TCL Zhonghuan Renewable Energy Technology Co.,Ltd.; *Int'l*, pg. 7484
SICHUAN ZHONGJIN MEDICINAL PACKAGING CO., LTD.—See Rengo Co., Ltd.; *Int'l*, pg. 6281
SICHUAN ZIGONG CONVEYING MACHINE GROUP CO., LTD.; *Int'l*, pg. 6881
SICILIA CONVENTION BUREAU SRL—See UniCredit S.p.A.; *Int'l*, pg. 8035
SICILIAN CHEFS, INC.—See Consolidated Investment Group, LLC; *U.S. Private*, pg. 1021
SICILY BY CAR S.P.A.; *Int'l*, pg. 6881
SIC INSURANCE COMPANY LIMITED; *Int'l*, pg. 6877
SICIT GROUP S.P.A.; *Int'l*, pg. 6881
SICK OPTEX CO., LTD.—See Optex Group Co., Ltd.; *Int'l*, pg. 5602
SICME ORANGE1 S.R.L.—See Orange1 Holding; *Int'l*, pg. 5611
SICMO SAS—See Sintex Industries, Ltd.; *Int'l*, pg. 6957
SICOAC—See Aliaxis S.A./N.V.; *Int'l*, pg. 325
SICO ASIA PTE LTD.—See Sico Incorporated; *U.S. Private*, pg. 3645
SICO CAPITAL COMPANY LTD.—See Securities & Investment Company BSC; *Int'l*, pg. 6676
SICO EUROPE LIMITED—See Sico Incorporated; *U.S. Private*, pg. 3645
SICO FUNDS SERVICES CO. BSC (C)—See Securities & Investment Company BSC; *Int'l*, pg. 6676
SICO FUNDS SERVICES COMPANY BSC—See Securities & Investment Company BSC; *Int'l*, pg. 6677
SICO INCORPORATED; *U.S. Private*, pg. 3645
SICO JAPAN INC.—See Sico Incorporated; *U.S. Private*, pg. 3645

S&I CO., LTD.—See BIPROGY Inc.; *Int'l*, pg. 1045
SICO MIDDLE EAST JLT (LLC)—See Sico Incorporated; *U.S. Private*, pg. 3645
SICOM SYSTEMS, INC.—See Global Payments Inc.; *U.S. Public*, pg. 944
SICON LTD.; *Int'l*, pg. 6881
SICO NORTH AMERICA INC.—See Sico Incorporated; *U.S. Private*, pg. 3645
S&I CONSULTANTS CO., LTD.—See Inabata & Co. Ltd.; *Int'l*, pg. 3644
SICOPLAN N.V—See G. Siempelkamp GmbH & Co. KG; *Int'l*, pg. 2864
SICOR (SOCIETA ITALIANA CORTICOSTEROIDI) S.R.L.—See Teva Pharmaceutical Industries, Ltd.; *Int'l*, pg. 7579
SICOS & CIE—See L'Oreal S.A.; *Int'l*, pg. 4381
SICO SOUTH PACIFIC—See Sico Incorporated; *U.S. Private*, pg. 3645
SICOXS CORPORATION—See Sumitomo Metal Mining Co., Ltd.; *Int'l*, pg. 7291
SICPA ARGENTINA SA—See SICPA Holding SA; *Int'l*, pg. 6882
SICPA ASIA DEVELOPMENT PTE. LTD.—See SICPA Holding SA; *Int'l*, pg. 6882
SICPA ASSAN URUN GUVENLIGI SANAYI VE TICARET A.S.—See SICPA Holding SA; *Int'l*, pg. 6882
SICPA AUSTRALIA PTY LTD—See SICPA Holding SA; *Int'l*, pg. 6882
SICPA BRASIL INDUSTRIA DE TINTAS E SISTEMAS LTDA.—See SICPA Holding SA; *Int'l*, pg. 6882
SICPA ECUADOR GSS SA—See SICPA Holding SA; *Int'l*, pg. 6882
SICPA FRANCE SAS—See SICPA Holding SA; *Int'l*, pg. 6882
SICPA GERMANY GMBH—See SICPA Holding SA; *Int'l*, pg. 6882
SICPA GOVERNMENT SECURITY SOLUTIONS LATAM SPA—See SICPA Holding SA; *Int'l*, pg. 6882
SICPAGSS MOROCCO SA—See SICPA Holding SA; *Int'l*, pg. 6882
SICPA HOLDING SA; *Int'l*, pg. 6882
SICPA INDIA PRIVATE LIMITED—See SICPA Holding SA; *Int'l*, pg. 6882
SICPA INKS PAKISTAN (PRIVATE) LIMITED—See SICPA Holding SA; *Int'l*, pg. 6882
SICPA ITALIA S.P.A.—See SICPA Holding SA; *Int'l*, pg. 6882
SICPA KENYA LIMITED—See SICPA Holding SA; *Int'l*, pg. 6882
SICPA MEXICANA S.A. DE C.V.—See SICPA Holding SA; *Int'l*, pg. 6882
SICPA NORTH AMERICA, INC.—See SICPA Holding SA; *Int'l*, pg. 6882
SICPA PRODUCT SECURITY (BEIJING) CO., LTD.—See SICPA Holding SA; *Int'l*, pg. 6882
SICPA PRODUCT SECURITY, LLC—See SICPA Holding SA; *Int'l*, pg. 6882
SICPA PRODUCT SECURITY SDN. BHD—See SICPA Holding SA; *Int'l*, pg. 6882
SICPA SECURINK CORPORATION—See SICPA Holding SA; *Int'l*, pg. 6882
SICPA SECURINK CORP.—See SICPA Holding SA; *Int'l*, pg. 6882
SICPA SECURITY SOLUTIONS ALBANIA SH.P.K.—See SICPA Holding SA; *Int'l*, pg. 6882
SICPA SECURITY SOLUTIONS ARABIA AFRICA FZ-LLC—See SICPA Holding SA; *Int'l*, pg. 6882
SICPA SECURITY SOLUTIONS CE, A.S.—See SICPA Holding SA; *Int'l*, pg. 6882
SICPA SECURITY SOLUTIONS GEORGIA LLC—See SICPA Holding SA; *Int'l*, pg. 6882
SICPA SERVICES CANADA LTD.—See SICPA Holding SA; *Int'l*, pg. 6882
SICPA SOUTH AFRICA (PTY) LIMITED—See SICPA Holding SA; *Int'l*, pg. 6882
SICPA SPAIN, S.L.U.—See SICPA Holding SA; *Int'l*, pg. 6882
SICPA TOGO SAU—See SICPA Holding SA; *Int'l*, pg. 6882
SICPA TURKEY URUN GUVENLIGI SANAYI VE TICARET A.S.—See SICPA Holding SA; *Int'l*, pg. 6882
SICPA UK LTD—See SICPA Holding SA; *Int'l*, pg. 6882
SIC PLASTICS FRANCE S.A.—See Mazzucchelli 1849 S.p.a.; *Int'l*, pg. 4750
SICRA S.A.—See VINCI S.A.; *Int'l*, pg. 8226
SICREM S.P.A.—See CAG Holding GmbH; *Int'l*, pg. 1250
SICRYSTAL AG—See ROHM Co., Ltd.; *Int'l*, pg. 6386
SIC - SOCIEDADE INDEPENDENTE DE COMUNICACAO, S.A.—See Impresa SGPS S.A.; *Int'l*, pg. 3637
SICURA S.R.L.—See A2A S.p.A.; *Int'l*, pg. 29
SICURGLASS SUD SRL—See Compagnie de Saint-Gobain SA; *Int'l*, pg. 1737
SIDAL, INC.—See Tetra Laval International S.A.; *Int'l*, pg. 7577
SIDAMO; *Int'l*, pg. 6882
SIDAPLAX V.O.F.—See Plastic Suppliers, Inc.; *U.S. Private*, pg. 3199
SIDCUP VETS4PETS LIMITED—See Pets at Home Group Plc; *Int'l*, pg. 5834
SIDDALL, INC.; *U.S. Private*, pg. 3645

SIDDARTH BUSINESSES LIMITED; *Int'l*, pg. 6882
SID DEVELOPPEMENT SAS—See LVMH Moet Hennessy Louis Vuitton SE; *Int'l*, pg. 4592
SIDDHARTHA BANK LIMITED; *Int'l*, pg. 6883
SIDDHARTHA CAPITAL LIMITED—See Siddhartha Bank Limited; *Int'l*, pg. 6883
SIDDHARTHA FINANCE LIMITED; *Int'l*, pg. 6883
SIDDHARTHA INSURANCE LIMITED; *Int'l*, pg. 6883
SIDDHARTHA TUBES LIMITED; *Int'l*, pg. 6883
SIDDHARTH EDUCATION SERVICES LIMITED; *Int'l*, pg. 6883
SIDDHARTH SHRIRAM GROUP; *Int'l*, pg. 6883
SIDDHESWARI GARMENTS LIMITED; *Int'l*, pg. 6883
SIDDHI ACQUISITION CORP.; *U.S. Public*, pg. 1876
SIDDHIKA COATINGS LIMITED; *Int'l*, pg. 6883
SIDDIQSONS TINPLATE LIMITED; *Int'l*, pg. 6883
SIDD SARL—See ADLPartner SA; *Int'l*, pg. 151
SIDEA S.R.L.—See Technogym SpA; *Int'l*, pg. 7510
SIDECHANNEL, INC.; *U.S. Public*, pg. 1876
SIDECH S.A.—See Floridienne S.A.; *Int'l*, pg. 2708
SIDEL ARGENTINA—See Tetra Laval International S.A.; *Int'l*, pg. 7576
SIDEL CANADA, INC.—See Tetra Laval International S.A.; *Int'l*, pg. 7576
SIDEL CHILE SA—See Tetra Laval International S.A.; *Int'l*, pg. 7576
SIDEL DE MEXICO S.A. DE C.V.—See Tetra Laval International S.A.; *Int'l*, pg. 7576
SIDEL DE MEXICO, S.A. DE C.V—See Tetra Laval International S.A.; *Int'l*, pg. 7577
SIDEL DISTRIBUTION (MALAYSIA) SDN BHD—See Tetra Laval International S.A.; *Int'l*, pg. 7577
SIDEL DO BRASIL LTDA.—See Tetra Laval International S.A.; *Int'l*, pg. 7577
SIDEL FILLING ASEPTIC S.A.—See Tetra Laval International S.A.; *Int'l*, pg. 7576
SIDEL GMBH—See Tetra Laval International S.A.; *Int'l*, pg. 7576
SIDEL GMEA—See Tetra Laval International S.A.; *Int'l*, pg. 7577
SIDEL GREATER CHINA—See Tetra Laval International S.A.; *Int'l*, pg. 7576
SIDEL GROUP—See Tetra Laval International S.A.; *Int'l*, pg. 7577
SIDEL IBERICA, S.L.U.—See Tetra Laval International S.A.; *Int'l*, pg. 7577
SIDEL INC.—See Tetra Laval International S.A.; *Int'l*, pg. 7576
SIDEL INDIA PVT. LTD.—See Tetra Laval International S.A.; *Int'l*, pg. 7576
SIDELINE, INC.—See Jones Plastic & Engineering Company, LLC; *U.S. Private*, pg. 2234
SIDEL ITALIA SRL—See Tetra Laval International S.A.; *Int'l*, pg. 7576
SIDEL PACKAGING SOLUTIONS S.A.S.—See Tetra Laval International S.A.; *Int'l*, pg. 7576
SIDEL PACKAGING SYSTEMS SOUTH AFRICA (PTY) LTD—See Tetra Laval International S.A.; *Int'l*, pg. 7577
SIDEL PANAMA CORP.—See Tetra Laval International S.A.; *Int'l*, pg. 7577
SIDEL SALES AND CONVEYOR INDUSTRIES PHILIPPINES, INC.—See Tetra Laval International S.A.; *Int'l*, pg. 7577
SIDEL SA—See Tetra Laval International S.A.; *Int'l*, pg. 7576
SIDEL—See Tetra Laval International S.A.; *Int'l*, pg. 7576
SIDEL SOUTH ASIA-PACIFIC LTD.—See Tetra Laval International S.A.; *Int'l*, pg. 7577
SIDEL UK LTD.—See Tetra Laval International S.A.; *Int'l*, pg. 7576
SIDEMARK; *U.S. Private*, pg. 3645
S.I. DE MEXICO S.A. DE C.V.—See Standex International; *U.S. Public*, pg. 1930
SIDEM LIBYA—See Veolia Environnement S.A.; *Int'l*, pg. 8162
SIDEM SAUDI LTD.—See Veolia Environnement S.A.; *Int'l*, pg. 8162
SIDEM—See Veolia Environnement S.A.; *Int'l*, pg. 8161
SIDENER ENGINEERING COMPANY, INC.—See Exotic Automation & Supply, Inc.; *U.S. Private*, pg. 1449
SIDENOR STEEL INDUSTRY S.A.—See Viohalco SA/NV; *Int'l*, pg. 8243
SIDEO GMBH—See Tetra Laval International S.A.; *Int'l*, pg. 7576
SIDERCA S.A.I.C.—See Techint S.p.A.; *Int'l*, pg. 7504
SIDEREAL CAPITAL GROUP, LLC; *U.S. Private*, pg. 3645
SIDERMAR DI NAVIGAZIONE S.P.A.—See Coeclerici S.p.A.; *Int'l*, pg. 1689
SIDERMES INC.—See Vesuvius plc; *Int'l*, pg. 8179
SIDERMES S.P.A.—See Vesuvius plc; *Int'l*, pg. 8179
SIDERNAVAL EQUIPOS SIDERURGICOS S.A.—See SMS Holding GmbH; *Int'l*, pg. 7016
SIDEROM STEEL SRL—See Viohalco SA/NV; *Int'l*, pg. 8244
SIDERURGICA BALBOA, S.A.—See Alfonso Gallardo S.A.; *Int'l*, pg. 316
SIDERURGICA DEL ORINOCO ALFREDO MANEIRO; *Int'l*, pg. 6883

SIDERURGICA DEL ORINOCO ALFREDO MANEIRO — CORPORATE AFFILIATIONS

SIDERURGICA DEL TURBIO S.A.—See Siderurgica Venezolana Sivensa S.A.; *Int'l*, pg. 6883
SIDERURGICA J.L. ALIPERTI S.A.; *Int'l*, pg. 6883
SIDERURGICA VENEZOLANA SIVENSA S.A.; *Int'l*, pg. 6883
SIDERVAL S.P.A.—See Montanstahl AG; *Int'l*, pg. 5036
SIDES & ASSOCIATES, INC.; *U.S. Private*, pg. 3645
SIDESHOW LTD.; *Int'l*, pg. 6883
SI DETECTION CO., LTD—See Satrec Initiative Co., Ltd.; *Int'l*, pg. 6587
SIDETEL, S.A—See ACS, Actividades de Construccion y Servicios, S.A.; *Int'l*, pg. 116
SIDETRADE S.A.; *Int'l*, pg. 6883
SIDE UK LIMITED—See Pole To Win Holdings, Inc.; *Int'l*, pg. 5909
SIDEV SAS—See Midwich Group Plc; *Int'l*, pg. 4887
SIDEWINDER SUPPLY, INC.—See Hendricks Holding Company, Inc.; *U.S. Private*, pg. 1915
SIDEXA; *Int'l*, pg. 6884
SID GENTLE FILMS LIMITED—See British Broadcasting Corporation; *Int'l*, pg. 1169
SID HARVEY INDUSTRIES, INC.; *U.S. Private*, pg. 3645
SIDH AUTOMOBILES LIMITED; *Int'l*, pg. 6884
SIDIC TECHNOLOGY SDN. BHD.—See Edran Berhad; *Int'l*, pg. 2315
SIDI KERIR PETROCHEMICALS CO.; *Int'l*, pg. 6884
SIDIZ, INC.; *Int'l*, pg. 6884
SID LEE INTERNATIONAL LLC—See Hakuhodo DY Holdings Incorporated; *Int'l*, pg. 3222
SID LEE—See Hakuhodo DY Holdings Incorporated; *Int'l*, pg. 3222
SID LEE—See Hakuhodo DY Holdings Incorporated; *Int'l*, pg. 3222
SID LEE—See Hakuhodo DY Holdings Incorporated; *Int'l*, pg. 3222
SID LEE—See Omnicom Group Inc.; *U.S. Public*, pg. 1593
SID LEE USA—See Hakuhodo DY Holdings Incorporated; *Int'l*, pg. 3222
SIDLEY AUSTIN LLP; *U.S. Private*, pg. 3646
SIDLEY TRUCK & EQUIPMENT—See R.W. Sidley, Incorporated; *U.S. Private*, pg. 3340
SIDMA BULGARIA S.A—See SIDMA Steel S.A.; *Int'l*, pg. 6884
SIDMA ROMANIA SRL—See SIDMA Steel S.A.; *Int'l*, pg. 6884
SIDMA S.A.—See Viohalco SA/NV; *Int'l*, pg. 8244
SIDMA S.A. STEEL PRODUCTS - THESSALONIKI STEEL SERVICE AND DISTRIBUTION CENTER—See SIDMA Steel S.A.; *Int'l*, pg. 6884
SIDMA STEEL S.A.; *Int'l*, pg. 6884
THE SIDNEY ASC, LLC—See KKR & Co. Inc.; *U.S. Public*, pg. 1248
SIDNEY COAL COMPANY, INC.—See Alpha Natural Resources, Inc.; *U.S. Private*, pg. 199
SIDNEY FRANK IMPORTING CO., INC.—See Mast-Jagermeister SE; *Int'l*, pg. 4724
SIDNEY HEALTH CENTER; *U.S. Private*, pg. 3646
SIDNEY RESOURCES CORP.; *U.S. Public*, pg. 1876
SIDNEY RICH ASSOCIATES INC.—See Caleres, Inc.; *U.S. Public*, pg. 422
SIDNEY SUGARS INCORPORATED—See American Crystal Sugar Company; *U.S. Public*, pg. 98
SIDOTI & COMPANY, LLC; *U.S. Private*, pg. 3646
SID PATERSON ADVERTISING, INC.; *U.S. Private*, pg. 3645
SID PETERSON MEMORIAL HOSPITAL; *U.S. Private*, pg. 3645
SID PRESSE SAS—See LVMH Moet Hennessy Louis Vuitton SE; *Int'l*, pg. 4592
SIDRAN INC.; *U.S. Private*, pg. 3646
SID RICHARDSON CARBON & ENERGY LTD.; *U.S. Private*, pg. 3645
SID'S CARPET BARN INC.; *U.S. Private*, pg. 3645
SID SPORTMARKETING & COMMUNICATION SERVICES GMBH—See Agence France-Presse; *Int'l*, pg. 205
SID TOOL CO., INC.—See MSC Industrial Direct Co., Inc.; *U.S. Public*, pg. 1483
SI DU 29 BOULEVARD HAUSSMANN—See Societe Generale S.A.; *Int'l*, pg. 7041
SIDURI WINES, LLC—See Jackson Family Wines, Inc.; *U.S. Private*, pg. 2176
SIDUS FNH CORPORATION—See KT Corporation; *Int'l*, pg. 4315
SIDUS SPACE, INC.; *U.S. Public*, pg. 1876
SIDWAL REFRIGERATION INDUSTRIES PRIVATE LIMITED—See Prataap Snacks Limited; *Int'l*, pg. 5955
SIEBEL INSTITUTE OF TECHNOLOGY—See Lallemand, Inc.; *Int'l*, pg. 4400
SIEBENLIST, GREY & PARTNER GMBH—See Manpower-Group Inc.; *U.S. Public*, pg. 1362
THE SIEBENTHALER CO.; *U.S. Private*, pg. 4118
SIEBERT ADVISORNXT, INC.—See Siebert Financial Corp.; *U.S. Public*, pg. 1876
SIEBERT FINANCIAL CORP.; *U.S. Public*, pg. 1876
SIEBERTHEAD LIMITED; *Int'l*, pg. 6884
SIEB & MEYER AG—See Fukuda Corporation; *Int'l*, pg. 2839
SIEBTER HIMMEL BASTEI LUBBE GMBH—See Bastei Lubbe AG; *Int'l*, pg. 888
SIEBTE VERMOGENSVERWALTUNGS-GESELLSCHAFT DVB MBH—See Mercedes-Benz Group AG; *Int'l*, pg. 4829
SIEBURG INTERNATIONAL, INC.; *U.S. Private*, pg. 3646
SIE COMPUTING SOLUTIONS, INC.—See AbelConn LLC; *U.S. Private*, pg. 37
SIEDOUBS SA—See Stellantis N.V.; *Int'l*, pg. 7203
SIEGAL & SONS INVESTMENT LTD.; *U.S. Private*, pg. 3646
SIEGAL STEEL COMPANY—See Steel Warehouse of Wisconsin, Inc.; *U.S. Private*, pg. 3796
SIEGE AIR LIQUIDO SA—See L'Air Liquide S.A.; *Int'l*, pg. 4375
SIEGE LAVAZZA FRANCE S.A.S.—See Luigi Lavazza S.p.A.; *Int'l*, pg. 4575
SIEGEL+GALE - LOS ANGELES—See Omnicom Group Inc.; *U.S. Public*, pg. 1593
SIEGEL+GALE—See Omnicom Group Inc.; *U.S. Public*, pg. 1593
THE SIEGEL GROUP; *U.S. Private*, pg. 4118
SIEGEL OIL COMPANY; *U.S. Private*, pg. 3646
SIEGEL-ROBERT AUTOMOTIVE (SUZHOU) CO., LTD.—See Koch Industries, Inc.; *U.S. Private*, pg. 2330
SIEGER HEIZSYSTEME GMBH—See Robert Bosch GmbH; *Int'l*, pg. 6368
SIEGERS SEED COMPANY INC.; *U.S. Private*, pg. 3646
SIEGE SIEDLUNGSGESELLSCHAFT FUR DAS VERKEHRSPERSONAL MBH MAINZ—See Vonovia SE; *Int'l*, pg. 8305
SIEGE TECHNOLOGIES, LLC—See Braes Capital LLC; *U.S. Private*, pg. 633
SIEGFRIED AG—See Siegfried Holding AG; *Int'l*, pg. 6884
SIEGFRIED BARBERA S.L.—See Siegfried Holding AG; *Int'l*, pg. 6884
SIEGFRIED EL MASNOU, S.A.—See Siegfried Holding AG; *Int'l*, pg. 6884
SIEGFRIED EVIONNAZ SA—See Siegfried Holding AG; *Int'l*, pg. 6884
SIEGFRIED GENERICS (MALTA) LTD—See Siegfried Holding AG; *Int'l*, pg. 6884
SIEGFRIED HAMELN GMBH—See Siegfried Holding AG; *Int'l*, pg. 6884
SIEGFRIED HOLDING AG; *Int'l*, pg. 6884
SIEGFRIED LTD—See Siegfried Holding AG; *Int'l*, pg. 6884
SIEGFRIED MALTA LTD.—See Siegfried Holding AG; *Int'l*, pg. 6884
SIEGFRIED (NANTONG) PHARMACEUTICALS CO., LTD.—See Siegfried Holding AG; *Int'l*, pg. 6884
SIEGFRIED PHARMACHEMIKALIEN MINDEN GMBH—See Siegfried Holding AG; *Int'l*, pg. 6884
SIEGFRIED SCHLUSSLER FEUERUNGSBAU GMBH—See ThyssenKrupp AG; *Int'l*, pg. 7725
SIEGFRIED SHANGHAI—See Siegfried Holding AG; *Int'l*, pg. 6884
SIEGFRIED ST. VULBAS SAS—See Siegfried Holding AG; *Int'l*, pg. 6884
SIEGFRIED (USA) INC.—See Siegfried Holding AG; *Int'l*, pg. 6884
SIEGFRIED VOGELE INSTITUT. (SVI) - INTERNATIONALE GESELLSCHAFT FUR DIALOGMARKETING MBH—See Deutsche Post AG; *Int'l*, pg. 2082
SIEGLING BRASIL LTDA.—See Forbo Holding Ltd.; *Int'l*, pg. 2730
SIEGLING DANMARK A/S—See Forbo Holding Ltd.; *Int'l*, pg. 2730
SIEGLING ITALIA S.P.A.—See Forbo Holding Ltd.; *Int'l*, pg. 2730
SIEGLING MEXICO S.A. DE C.V.—See Forbo Holding Ltd.; *Int'l*, pg. 2730
SIEGLING NEDERLAND B.V.—See Forbo Holding Ltd.; *Int'l*, pg. 2730
SIEGLING (SCHWEIZ) AG—See Forbo Holding Ltd.; *Int'l*, pg. 2730
SIEGRIED PHARMACHEMIKALIEN MINDEN GMBH—See Siegfried Holding AG; *Int'l*, pg. 6884
SIEGWERK ARGENTINA S.A.—See Siegwerk Druckfarben AG & Co. KGaA; *Int'l*, pg. 6884
SIEGWERK BACKNANG GMBH—See Siegwerk Druckfarben AG & Co. KGaA; *Int'l*, pg. 6885
SIEGWERK BASKI MUREKKEPLERI SAN. VE TIC. A.S.—See Siegwerk Druckfarben AG & Co. KGaA; *Int'l*, pg. 6885
SIEGWERK BENELUX N.V.—See Siegwerk Druckfarben AG & Co. KGaA; *Int'l*, pg. 6885
SIEGWERK BRASIL IND. TINTAS LTDA.—See Siegwerk Druckfarben AG & Co. KGaA; *Int'l*, pg. 6885
SIEGWERK BUDINGEN GMBH—See Siegwerk Druckfarben AG & Co. KGaA; *Int'l*, pg. 6885
SIEGWERK CANADA INC.—See Siegwerk Druckfarben AG & Co. KGaA; *Int'l*, pg. 6885
SIEGWERK CENTROAMERICA S.A.—See Siegwerk Druckfarben AG & Co. KGaA; *Int'l*, pg. 6885
SIEGWERK CHILE S. A.—See Siegwerk Druckfarben AG & Co. KGaA; *Int'l*, pg. 6885
SIEGWERK COLOMBIA LTDA.—See Siegwerk Druckfarben AG & Co. KGaA; *Int'l*, pg. 6885
SIEGWERK DRUCKFARBEN AG & CO. KGAA; *Int'l*, pg. 6884
SIEGWERK EIC LLC - CHICAGO BRANCH—See Siegwerk Druckfarben AG & Co. KGaA; *Int'l*, pg. 6885
SIEGWERK EIC LLC - DALLAS BRANCH—See Siegwerk Druckfarben AG & Co. KGaA; *Int'l*, pg. 6885
SIEGWERK EIC LLC - LOS ANGELES BRANCH—See Siegwerk Druckfarben AG & Co. KGaA; *Int'l*, pg. 6885
SIEGWERK EIC LLC—See Siegwerk Druckfarben AG & Co. KGaA; *Int'l*, pg. 6885
SIEGWERK EL SALVADOR S.A. DE C.V.—See Siegwerk Druckfarben AG & Co. KGaA; *Int'l*, pg. 6885
SIEGWERK ENVIRONMENTAL INKS—See Siegwerk Druckfarben AG & Co. KGaA; *Int'l*, pg. 6885
SIEGWERK FINLAND OY—See Siegwerk Druckfarben AG & Co. KGaA; *Int'l*, pg. 6885
SIEGWERK FRANCE S.A.S—See Siegwerk Druckfarben AG & Co. KGaA; *Int'l*, pg. 6885
SIEGWERK HILVERSUM BV—See Siegwerk Druckfarben AG & Co. KGaA; *Int'l*, pg. 6885
SIEGWERK INDIA PRIVATE LIMITED—See Siegwerk Druckfarben AG & Co. KGaA; *Int'l*, pg. 6885
SIEGWERK ITALY SPA—See Siegwerk Druckfarben AG & Co. KGaA; *Int'l*, pg. 6885
SIEGWERK MALAYSIA SDN BHD—See Siegwerk Druckfarben AG & Co. KGaA; *Int'l*, pg. 6885
SIEGWERK MEXICO S.A. DE C.V.—See Siegwerk Druckfarben AG & Co. KGaA; *Int'l*, pg. 6885
SIEGWERK OOO—See Siegwerk Druckfarben AG & Co. KGaA; *Int'l*, pg. 6885
SIEGWERK PERU S.A.C.—See Siegwerk Druckfarben AG & Co. KGaA; *Int'l*, pg. 6885
SIEGWERK PHILIPPINES INC.—See Siegwerk Druckfarben AG & Co. KGaA; *Int'l*, pg. 6885
SIEGWERK POLAND MARKI SP. Z O.O.—See Siegwerk Druckfarben AG & Co. KGaA; *Int'l*, pg. 6885
SIEGWERK PORTUGAL, UNIPESSOAL LDA.—See Siegwerk Druckfarben AG & Co. KGaA; *Int'l*, pg. 6885
SIEGWERK SCANDINAVIA AB—See Siegwerk Druckfarben AG & Co. KGaA; *Int'l*, pg. 6885
SIEGWERK SHANGHAI LTD.—See Siegwerk Druckfarben AG & Co. KGaA; *Int'l*, pg. 6885
SIEGWERK SINGAPORE PTE. LTD.—See Siegwerk Druckfarben AG & Co. KGaA; *Int'l*, pg. 6885
SIEGWERK SOUTH AFRICA (PROPRIETARY) LIMITED—See Siegwerk Druckfarben AG & Co. KGaA; *Int'l*, pg. 6885
SIEGWERK SPAIN, S.A.—See Siegwerk Druckfarben AG & Co. KGaA; *Int'l*, pg. 6885
SIEGWERK SWITZERLAND AG—See Siegwerk Druckfarben AG & Co. KGaA; *Int'l*, pg. 6885
SIEGWERK (THAILAND) LTD.—See Siegwerk Druckfarben AG & Co. KGaA; *Int'l*, pg. 6884
SIEGWERK UK LTD—See Siegwerk Druckfarben AG & Co. KGaA; *Int'l*, pg. 6885
SIEGWERK USA CO.—See Siegwerk Druckfarben AG & Co. KGaA; *Int'l*, pg. 6885
SIEGWERK USA INC. - BOILING SPRINGS BRANCH—See Siegwerk Druckfarben AG & Co. KGaA; *Int'l*, pg. 6885
SIEGWERK USA INC. - DRUMS BRANCH—See Siegwerk Druckfarben AG & Co. KGaA; *Int'l*, pg. 6885
SIEGWERK VIETNAM COMPANY LIMITED—See Siegwerk Druckfarben AG & Co. KGaA; *Int'l*, pg. 6885
SIEGWERK WEST AFRICA LTD.—See Siegwerk Druckfarben AG & Co. KGaA; *Int'l*, pg. 6885
SIEI AREG GMBH—See WEG S.A.; *Int'l*, pg. 8367
SIEI DRIVES TECHNOLOGY CO., LTD.—See Gefran S.p.A.; *Int'l*, pg. 2912
SI ELECTRONICS LTD.—See Kaga Electronics Co., Ltd.; *Int'l*, pg. 4049
SIEL FINANCIAL SERVICES LIMITED; *Int'l*, pg. 6885
SIELOG SYSTEMLOGIK GMBH—See Siemens Aktiengesellschaft; *Int'l*, pg. 6888
SIELTE ITALIA—See Telefonaktiebolaget LM Ericsson; *Int'l*, pg. 7534
SIEM CAPITAL AB—See Siem Industries Inc.; *Int'l*, pg. 6885
SIEM CAPITAL UK LTD.—See Siem Industries Inc.; *Int'l*, pg. 6885
SIEMENS AB—See The Carlyle Group Inc.; *U.S. Public*, pg. 2047
SIEMENS AB—See Siemens Aktiengesellschaft; *Int'l*, pg. 6888
SIEMENS ADVANCED ENGINEERING PTE LTD.—See Siemens Aktiengesellschaft; *Int'l*, pg. 6888
SIEMENS A.E.—See Siemens Aktiengesellschaft; *Int'l*, pg. 6888
SIEMENS AKTIENGESELLSCHAFT OSTERREICH—See Siemens Aktiengesellschaft; *Int'l*, pg. 6888
SIEMENS AKTIENGESELLSCHAFT; *Int'l*, pg. 6886
SIEMENS APPLIED AUTOMATION—See Siemens Aktiengesellschaft; *Int'l*, pg. 6889
SIEMENS A/S—See Siemens Aktiengesellschaft; *Int'l*, pg. 6888
SIEMENS A/S—See Siemens Aktiengesellschaft; *Int'l*, pg. 6888
SIEMENS AS—See Siemens Aktiengesellschaft; *Int'l*, pg. 6888

COMPANY NAME INDEX

SIEMENS AUDIOLOGIAI TECHNIKA KERESKEDELMI ES SZOLGALTATO KORLATOLT FELELOSSEGU TARSASAG—See Siemens Aktiengesellschaft; *Int'l*, pg. 6888
SIEMENS AUDIOLOGICKA TECHNIKA S.R.O.—See Siemens Aktiengesellschaft; *Int'l*, pg. 6888
SIEMENS AUDIOLOGIE AG—See Siemens Aktiengesellschaft; *Int'l*, pg. 6888
SIEMENS AUDIOLOGIE S.A.S.—See Siemens Aktiengesellschaft; *Int'l*, pg. 6888
SIEMENS AUDIOLOGIE TECHNIEK B.V.—See Siemens Aktiengesellschaft; *Int'l*, pg. 6888
SIEMENS (AUSTRIA) PROIECT SPITAL COLTEA SRL—See Siemens Aktiengesellschaft; *Int'l*, pg. 6888
SIEMENS AUTOMATION & DRIVES GROUP—See Siemens Aktiengesellschaft; *Int'l*, pg. 6888
SIEMENS AUTOMATION & DRIVES—See Siemens Aktiengesellschaft; *Int'l*, pg. 6898
SIEMENS BANGLADESH LTD.—See Siemens Aktiengesellschaft; *Int'l*, pg. 6888
SIEMENS BANK GMBH—See Siemens Aktiengesellschaft; *Int'l*, pg. 6888
SIEMENS BETEILIGUNGEN INLAND GMBH—See Siemens Aktiengesellschaft; *Int'l*, pg. 6888
SIEMENS BETEILIGUNGSVERWALTUNG GMBH & CO. OHG—See Siemens Aktiengesellschaft; *Int'l*, pg. 6888
SIEMENS BUILDING TECHNOLOGIES AB—See Siemens Aktiengesellschaft; *Int'l*, pg. 6888
SIEMENS BUILDING TECHNOLOGIES AG—See Siemens Aktiengesellschaft; *Int'l*, pg. 6889
SIEMENS BUILDING TECHNOLOGIES AG—See Siemens Aktiengesellschaft; *Int'l*, pg. 6889
SIEMENS BUILDING TECHNOLOGIES AG—See Siemens Aktiengesellschaft; *Int'l*, pg. 6889
SIEMENS BUILDING TECHNOLOGIES A/S—See Siemens Aktiengesellschaft; *Int'l*, pg. 6888
SIEMENS BUILDING TECHNOLOGIES AS—See Siemens Aktiengesellschaft; *Int'l*, pg. 6889
SIEMENS BUILDING TECHNOLOGIES LTD.—See Siemens Aktiengesellschaft; *Int'l*, pg. 6889
SIEMENS BUILDING TECHNOLOGIES LTD.—See Siemens Aktiengesellschaft; *Int'l*, pg. 6888
SIEMENS BUILDING TECHNOLOGIES LTD.—See Siemens Aktiengooollcohaft; *Int'l*, pg. 6889
SIEMENS BUILDING TECHNOLOGIES LTD.—See Siemens Aktiengesellschaft; *Int'l*, pg. 6889
SIEMENS BUILDING TECHNOLOGIES OY—See Siemens Aktiengesellschaft; *Int'l*, pg. 6889
SIEMENS BUILDING TECHNOLOGIES (PTY) LTD.—See Siemens Aktiengesellschaft; *Int'l*, pg. 6888
SIEMENS BUILDING TECHNOLOGIES SA—See Siemens Aktiengesellschaft; *Int'l*, pg. 6889
SIEMENS BUILDING TECHNOLOGIES S.P.A.—See Siemens Aktiengesellschaft; *Int'l*, pg. 6889
SIEMENS BUILDING TECHNOLOGIES S.R.O—See Siemens Aktiengesellschaft; *Int'l*, pg. 6889
SIEMENS CANADA LIMITED—See Siemens Aktiengesellschaft; *Int'l*, pg. 6889
SIEMENS CANADA LTD.—See Siemens Aktiengesellschaft; *Int'l*, pg. 6889
SIEMENS CANADA—See Siemens Aktiengesellschaft; *Int'l*, pg. 6889
SIEMENS CAPITAL COMPANY LLC—See Siemens Aktiengesellschaft; *Int'l*, pg. 6889
SIEMENS CERBERUS KFT.—See Siemens Aktiengesellschaft; *Int'l*, pg. 6889
SIEMENS CERBERUS SA—See Siemens Aktiengesellschaft; *Int'l*, pg. 6889
SIEMENS CIRCUIT PROTECTION SYSTEMS LTD.—See Siemens Aktiengesellschaft; *Int'l*, pg. 6889
SIEMENS CONCENTRATED SOLAR POWER LTD.—See Siemens Aktiengesellschaft; *Int'l*, pg. 6889
SIEMENS CORP. - MOUNTAIN VIEW BRANCH—See Siemens Aktiengesellschaft; *Int'l*, pg. 6889
SIEMENS CORPORATE RESEARCH—See Siemens Aktiengesellschaft; *Int'l*, pg. 6889
SIEMENS CORPORATION—See Siemens Aktiengesellschaft; *Int'l*, pg. 6889
SIEMENS D.D.—See Siemens Aktiengesellschaft; *Int'l*, pg. 6900
SIEMENS DEMAG DELAVAL TURBOMACHINERY, INC.—See Siemens Aktiengesellschaft; *Int'l*, pg. 6889
SIEMENS DIAGNOSTICS FINANCE CO. LLC—See Siemens Aktiengesellschaft; *Int'l*, pg. 6889
SIEMENS DIAGNOSTICS HOLDING II B.V.—See Siemens Aktiengesellschaft; *Int'l*, pg. 6891
SIEMENS DIAGNOSTICS LIMITED—See Siemens Aktiengesellschaft; *Int'l*, pg. 6893
SIEMENS DIAGNOSTICS PTY. LTD.—See Siemens Aktiengesellschaft; *Int'l*, pg. 6893
SIEMENS DIAGNOSTICS (SHANGHAI) CO. LTD.—See Siemens Aktiengesellschaft; *Int'l*, pg. 6893
SIEMENS DIGITAL BUSINESS BUILDER GMBH—See Siemens Aktiengesellschaft; *Int'l*, pg. 6891
SIEMENS DIGITAL LOGISTICS GMBH—See Siemens Aktiengesellschaft; *Int'l*, pg. 6891
SIEMENS DIGITAL LOGISTICS SP. Z O.O.—See Siemens Aktiengesellschaft; *Int'l*, pg. 6891
SIEMENS D.O.O. PODGORICA—See Siemens Aktiengesellschaft; *Int'l*, pg. 6900
SIEMENS D.O.O. SARAJEVO—See Siemens Aktiengesellschaft; *Int'l*, pg. 6888
SIEMENS D.O.O.—See Siemens Aktiengesellschaft; *Int'l*, pg. 6900
SIEMENS D.O.O.—See Siemens Aktiengesellschaft; *Int'l*, pg. 6900
SIEMENS D.O.O.—See Siemens Aktiengesellschaft; *Int'l*, pg. 6900
SIEMENS ELECTRICAL APPARATUS LTD.—See Siemens Aktiengesellschaft; *Int'l*, pg. 6891
SIEMENS ELECTRICAL DRIVES LTD.—See Siemens Aktiengesellschaft; *Int'l*, pg. 6891
SIEMENS ELECTRICAL DRIVES (SHANGHAI) LTD.—See Siemens Aktiengesellschaft; *Int'l*, pg. 6897
SIEMENS ELECTRIC MACHINES S.R.O.—See Siemens Aktiengesellschaft; *Int'l*, pg. 6891
SIEMENS ELETROELETRONICA LTDA.—See Siemens Aktiengesellschaft; *Int'l*, pg. 6891
SIEMENS ENERGY AG; *Int'l*, **pg. 6901**
SIEMENS ENERGY A/S—See Siemens Energy AG; *Int'l*, pg. 6902
SIEMENS ENERGY B.V. - GERMANY BRANCH—See Siemens Energy AG; *Int'l*, pg. 6902
SIEMENS ENERGY B.V.—See Siemens Energy AG; *Int'l*, pg. 6902
SIEMENS ENERGY CANADA LIMITED—See Siemens Energy AG; *Int'l*, pg. 6902
SIEMENS ENERGY GLOBAL GMBH & CO. KG—See Siemens Energy AG; *Int'l*, pg. 6902
SIEMENS ENERGY, INC.—See Siemens Energy AG; *Int'l*, pg. 6902
SIEMENS ENERGY K.K.—See Siemens Energy AG; *Int'l*, pg. 6902
SIEMENS ENERGY LIMITED—See Siemens Energy AG; *Int'l*, pg. 6902
SIEMENS ENERGY PTE. LTD.—See Siemens Energy AG; *Int'l*, pg. 6902
SIEMENS ENERGY PTY. LTD.—See Siemens Energy AG; *Int'l*, pg. 6902
SIEMENS ENERGY SDN. BHD.—See Siemens Energy AG; *Int'l*, pg. 6902
SIEMENS FOOD—See Siemens Aktiengesellschaft; *Int'l*, pg. 6891
SIEMENS FACTORY AUTOMATION ENGINEERING LTD.—See Siemens Aktiengesellschaft; *Int'l*, pg. 6891
SIEMENS FINANCE AND LEASING LTD.—See Siemens Aktiengesellschaft; *Int'l*, pg. 6891
SIEMENS FINANCE B.V.—See Siemens Aktiengesellschaft; *Int'l*, pg. 6891
SIEMENS FINANCE SP. Z O.O.—See Siemens Aktiengesellschaft; *Int'l*, pg. 6891
SIEMENS FINANCIAL, INC.—See Siemens Aktiengesellschaft; *Int'l*, pg. 6890
SIEMENS FINANCIAL SERVICES AB—See Siemens Aktiengesellschaft; *Int'l*, pg. 6891
SIEMENS FINANCIAL SERVICES HOLDINGS LTD.—See Siemens Aktiengesellschaft; *Int'l*, pg. 6891
SIEMENS FINANCIAL SERVICES, INC.—See Siemens Aktiengesellschaft; *Int'l*, pg. 6889
SIEMENS FINANCIAL SERVICES LTD.—See Siemens Aktiengesellschaft; *Int'l*, pg. 6891
SIEMENS FINANCIAL SERVICES LTD.—See Siemens Aktiengesellschaft; *Int'l*, pg. 6891
SIEMENS FINANCIAL SERVICES PRIVATE LIMITED—See Siemens Aktiengesellschaft; *Int'l*, pg. 6891
SIEMENS FINANCIERINGSMAATSCHAPPIJ N.V.—See Siemens Aktiengesellschaft; *Int'l*, pg. 6891
SIEMENS FINANSAL KIRALAMA A.S.—See Siemens Aktiengesellschaft; *Int'l*, pg. 6891
SIEMENS FIRE & SECURITIES PRODUCTS—See Siemens Aktiengesellschaft; *Int'l*, pg. 6888
SIEMENS FIRE & SECURITY PRODUCTS, S.A.—See Siemens Aktiengesellschaft; *Int'l*, pg. 6891
SIEMENS FONDS INVEST GMBH—See Siemens Aktiengesellschaft; *Int'l*, pg. 6891
SIEMENS FOSSIL SERVICES, INC.—See Siemens Aktiengesellschaft; *Int'l*, pg. 6890
SIEMENS FRANCE HOLDING S.A.S.—See Siemens Aktiengesellschaft; *Int'l*, pg. 6891
SIEMENS FUEL GASIFICATION TECHNOLOGY GMBH & CO. KG—See Siemens Aktiengesellschaft; *Int'l*, pg. 6891
SIEMENS GAMESA RENEWABLE ENERGY 9REN, S.L.—See Siemens Energy AG; *Int'l*, pg. 6902
SIEMENS GAMESA RENEWABLE ENERGY (BEIJING) CO., LTD.—See Siemens Energy AG; *Int'l*, pg. 6902
SIEMENS GAMESA RENEWABLE ENERGY B.V.—See Siemens Energy AG; *Int'l*, pg. 6903
SIEMENS GAMESA RENEWABLE ENERGY DEUTSCHLAND GMBH—See Siemens Energy AG; *Int'l*, pg. 6903
SIEMENS GAMESA RENEWABLE ENERGY D.O.O.—See Siemens Energy AG; *Int'l*, pg. 6903
SIEMENS GAMESA RENEWABLE ENERGY EGYPT LLC—See Siemens Energy AG; *Int'l*, pg. 6903

SIEMENS ENERGY AG

SIEMENS GAMESA RENEWABLE ENERGY ITALIA S.R.L.—See Siemens Energy AG; *Int'l*, pg. 6903
SIEMENS GAMESA RENEWABLE ENERGY ITALY, S.P.A.—See Siemens Energy AG; *Int'l*, pg. 6903
SIEMENS GAMESA RENEWABLE ENERGY JAPAN K.K.—See Siemens Energy AG; *Int'l*, pg. 6903
SIEMENS GAMESA RENEWABLE ENERGY KFT.—See Siemens Energy AG; *Int'l*, pg. 6903
SIEMENS GAMESA RENEWABLE ENERGY LANKA (PRIVATE) LIMITED—See Siemens Energy AG; *Int'l*, pg. 6903
SIEMENS GAMESA RENEWABLE ENERGY LIMITED—See Siemens Energy AG; *Int'l*, pg. 6903
SIEMENS GAMESA RENEWABLE ENERGY LIMITED—See Siemens Energy AG; *Int'l*, pg. 6903
SIEMENS GAMESA RENEWABLE ENERGY LLC—See Siemens Energy AG; *Int'l*, pg. 6903
SIEMENS GAMESA RENEWABLE ENERGY (PTY) LTD.—See Siemens Energy AG; *Int'l*, pg. 6902
SIEMENS GAMESA RENEWABLE ENERGY SARL—See Siemens Energy AG; *Int'l*, pg. 6903
SIEMENS GAMESA RENEWABLE ENERGY, S.A.—See Siemens Energy AG; *Int'l*, pg. 6902
SIEMENS GAMESA RENEWABLE ENERGY SERVICE GMBH—See Siemens Energy AG; *Int'l*, pg. 6903
SIEMENS GAMESA RENEWABLE ENERGY SERVICE LIMITED—See Siemens Energy AG; *Int'l*, pg. 6903
SIEMENS GAMESA RENEWABLE ENERGY SERVICE S.A.S.—See Siemens Energy AG; *Int'l*, pg. 6903
SIEMENS GAMESA RENEWABLE ENERGY SERVICE S.R.L.—See Siemens Energy AG; *Int'l*, pg. 6903
SIEMENS GAMESA RENEWABLE ENERGY SINGAPORE PRIVATE LIMITED—See Siemens Energy AG; *Int'l*, pg. 6903
SIEMENS GAMESA RENEWABLE ENERGY TECHNOLOGY (CHINA) CO., LTD.—See Siemens Energy AG; *Int'l*, pg. 6903
SIEMENS GEARED MOTORS GMBH—See The Carlyle Group Inc.; *U.S. Public*, pg. 2047
SIEMENS GEBAUDEMANAGEMENT & -SERVICES G.M.B.H.—See EQT AB; *Int'l*, pg. 2469
SIEMENS GENERATION SERVICES COMPANY—See Siemens Energy AG; *Int'l*, pg. 6902
SIEMENS GLOBAL INNOVATION PARTNERS MANAGEMENT GMBH—See Siemens Aktiengesellschaft; *Int'l*, pg. 6891
SIEMENS GOVERNMENT TECHNOLOGIES, INC.—See Siemens Aktiengesellschaft; *Int'l*, pg. 6890
SIEMENS HEALTHCARE AB—See Siemens Aktiengesellschaft; *Int'l*, pg. 6892
SIEMENS HEALTHCARE AG—See Siemens Aktiengesellschaft; *Int'l*, pg. 6892
SIEMENS HEALTHCARE A/S—See Siemens Aktiengesellschaft; *Int'l*, pg. 6892
SIEMENS HEALTHCARE AS—See Siemens Aktiengesellschaft; *Int'l*, pg. 6892
SIEMENS HEALTHCARE DIAGNOSTICS AB—See Siemens Aktiengesellschaft; *Int'l*, pg. 6893
SIEMENS HEALTHCARE DIAGNOSTICS AG—See Siemens Aktiengesellschaft; *Int'l*, pg. 6893
SIEMENS HEALTHCARE DIAGNOSTICS APS—See Siemens Aktiengesellschaft; *Int'l*, pg. 6893
SIEMENS HEALTHCARE DIAGNOSTICS AS—See Siemens Aktiengesellschaft; *Int'l*, pg. 6893
SIEMENS HEALTHCARE DIAGNOSTICS B.V.—See Siemens Aktiengesellschaft; *Int'l*, pg. 6893
SIEMENS HEALTHCARE DIAGNOSTICS GMBH—See Siemens Aktiengesellschaft; *Int'l*, pg. 6893
SIEMENS HEALTHCARE DIAGNOSTICS HOLDING GMBH—See Siemens Aktiengesellschaft; *Int'l*, pg. 6893
SIEMENS HEALTHCARE DIAGNOSTICS INC. - CHICAGO—See Siemens Aktiengesellschaft; *Int'l*, pg. 6893
SIEMENS HEALTHCARE DIAGNOSTICS INC. - FLANDERS—See Siemens Aktiengesellschaft; *Int'l*, pg. 6893
SIEMENS HEALTHCARE DIAGNOSTICS INC.—See Siemens Aktiengesellschaft; *Int'l*, pg. 6893
SIEMENS HEALTHCARE DIAGNOSTICS K.K.—See Siemens Aktiengesellschaft; *Int'l*, pg. 6893
SIEMENS HEALTHCARE DIAGNOSTICS LIMITED—See Siemens Aktiengesellschaft; *Int'l*, pg. 6893
SIEMENS HEALTHCARE DIAGNOSTICS LTDA.—See Siemens Aktiengesellschaft; *Int'l*, pg. 6893
SIEMENS HEALTHCARE DIAGNOSTICS LTD—See Siemens Aktiengesellschaft; *Int'l*, pg. 6893
SIEMENS HEALTHCARE DIAGNOSTICS MANUFACTURING LIMITED—See Siemens Aktiengesellschaft; *Int'l*, pg. 6892
SIEMENS HEALTHCARE DIAGNOSTICS MANUFACTURING LTD—See Siemens Aktiengesellschaft; *Int'l*, pg. 6893
SIEMENS HEALTHCARE DIAGNOSTICS OY—See Siemens Aktiengesellschaft; *Int'l*, pg. 6893
SIEMENS HEALTHCARE DIAGNOSTICS PRODUCTS GMBH—See Siemens Aktiengesellschaft; *Int'l*, pg. 6893

SIEMENS ENERGY AG

CORPORATE AFFILIATIONS

SIEMENS HEALTHCARE DIAGNOSTICS PRODUCTS LTD—See Siemens Aktiengesellschaft; *Int'l*, pg. 6893
SIEMENS HEALTHCARE DIAGNOSTICS (PTY.) LIMITED—See Siemens Aktiengesellschaft; *Int'l*, pg. 6893
SIEMENS HEALTHCARE DIAGNOSTICS SA—See Siemens Aktiengesellschaft; *Int'l*, pg. 6893
SIEMENS HEALTHCARE DIAGNOSTICS S.A.S.—See Siemens Aktiengesellschaft; *Int'l*, pg. 6893
SIEMENS HEALTHCARE DIAGNOSTICS, S. DE R.L. DE C.V.—See Siemens Aktiengesellschaft; *Int'l*, pg. 6892
SIEMENS HEALTHCARE DIAGNOSTICS SP. Z O.O.—See Siemens Aktiengesellschaft; *Int'l*, pg. 6893
SIEMENS HEALTHCARE DIAGNOSTICS S.R.L—See Siemens Aktiengesellschaft; *Int'l*, pg. 6893
SIEMENS HEALTHCARE DIAGNOSTICS, UNIPESSOAL LDA—See Siemens Aktiengesellschaft; *Int'l*, pg. 6893
SIEMENS HEALTHCARE D.O.O.—See Siemens Aktiengesellschaft; *Int'l*, pg. 6892
SIEMENS HEALTHCARE D.O.O.—See Siemens Aktiengesellschaft; *Int'l*, pg. 6892
SIEMENS HEALTHCARE D.O.O.—See Siemens Aktiengesellschaft; *Int'l*, pg. 6892
SIEMENS HEALTHCARE FZ LLC—See Siemens Aktiengesellschaft; *Int'l*, pg. 6892
SIEMENS HEALTHCARE GMBH—See Siemens Aktiengesellschaft; *Int'l*, pg. 6892
SIEMENS HEALTHCARE INC.—See Siemens Aktiengesellschaft; *Int'l*, pg. 6892
SIEMENS HEALTHCARE KFT.—See Siemens Aktiengesellschaft; *Int'l*, pg. 6892
SIEMENS HEALTHCARE K.K.—See Siemens Aktiengesellschaft; *Int'l*, pg. 6892
SIEMENS HEALTHCARE LIMITED—See Siemens Aktiengesellschaft; *Int'l*, pg. 6892
SIEMENS HEALTHCARE LIMITED—See Siemens Aktiengesellschaft; *Int'l*, pg. 6892
SIEMENS HEALTHCARE LIMITED—See Siemens Aktiengesellschaft; *Int'l*, pg. 6892
SIEMENS HEALTHCARE LIMITED—See Siemens Aktiengesellschaft; *Int'l*, pg. 6892
SIEMENS HEALTHCARE LIMITED—See Siemens Aktiengesellschaft; *Int'l*, pg. 6892
SIEMENS HEALTHCARE LTD.—See Siemens Aktiengesellschaft; *Int'l*, pg. 6892
SIEMENS HEALTHCARE LTD.—See Siemens Aktiengesellschaft; *Int'l*, pg. 6892
SIEMENS HEALTHCARE MEDICAL SOLUTIONS LIMITED—See Siemens Aktiengesellschaft; *Int'l*, pg. 6892
SIEMENS HEALTHCARE NEDERLAND B.V.—See Siemens Aktiengesellschaft; *Int'l*, pg. 6892
SIEMENS HEALTHCARE OY—See Siemens Aktiengesellschaft; *Int'l*, pg. 6892
SIEMENS HEALTHCARE PRIVATE LIMITED—See Siemens Aktiengesellschaft; *Int'l*, pg. 6892
SIEMENS HEALTHCARE (PRIVATE) LIMITED—See Siemens Aktiengesellschaft; *Int'l*, pg. 6892
SIEMENS HEALTHCARE PTE. LTD.—See Siemens Aktiengesellschaft; *Int'l*, pg. 6892
SIEMENS HEALTHCARE PTY. LTD.—See Siemens Aktiengesellschaft; *Int'l*, pg. 6892
SIEMENS HEALTHCARE S.A.C.—See Siemens Aktiengesellschaft; *Int'l*, pg. 6892
SIEMENS HEALTHCARE S.A.E.—See Siemens Aktiengesellschaft; *Int'l*, pg. 6892
SIEMENS HEALTHCARE SAGLIK ANONIM SIRKETI—See Siemens Aktiengesellschaft; *Int'l*, pg. 6892
SIEMENS HEALTHCARE SARL—See Siemens Aktiengesellschaft; *Int'l*, pg. 6892
SIEMENS HEALTHCARE S.A.—See Siemens Aktiengesellschaft; *Int'l*, pg. 6892
SIEMENS HEALTHCARE S.A.—See Siemens Aktiengesellschaft; *Int'l*, pg. 6892
SIEMENS HEALTHCARE SAS—See Siemens Aktiengesellschaft; *Int'l*, pg. 6892
SIEMENS HEALTHCARE SDN. BHD.—See Siemens Aktiengesellschaft; *Int'l*, pg. 6892
SIEMENS HEALTHCARE S.R.L.—See Siemens Aktiengesellschaft; *Int'l*, pg. 6892
SIEMENS HEALTHCARE S.R.L.—See Siemens Aktiengesellschaft; *Int'l*, pg. 6892
SIEMENS HEALTHCARE, S.R.O.—See Siemens Aktiengesellschaft; *Int'l*, pg. 6892
SIEMENS HEALTHCARE, S.R.O.—See Siemens Aktiengesellschaft; *Int'l*, pg. 6892
SIEMENS HEALTHCARE, UNIPESSOAL, LDA.—See Siemens Aktiengesellschaft; *Int'l*, pg. 6892
SIEMENS HEALTHINEERS AG—See Siemens Aktiengesellschaft; *Int'l*, pg. 6892
SIEMENS HEALTHINEERS INTERNATIONAL AG—See Siemens Aktiengesellschaft; *Int'l*, pg. 6895
SIEMENS HEALTHINEERS LTD.—See Siemens Aktiengesellschaft; *Int'l*, pg. 6895
SIEMENS HEALTHINEERS NEDERLAND B.V.—See Siemens Aktiengesellschaft; *Int'l*, pg. 6895
SIEMENS HEARING INSTRUMENTS INC.—See Siemens Aktiengesellschaft; *Int'l*, pg. 6890

SIEMENS HEARING INSTRUMENTS INC.—See Siemens Aktiengesellschaft; *Int'l*, pg. 6895
SIEMENS HEARING INSTRUMENTS K.K.—See Siemens Aktiengesellschaft; *Int'l*, pg. 6895
SIEMENS HEARING INSTRUMENTS PTY. LTD.—See Siemens Aktiengesellschaft; *Int'l*, pg. 6895
SIEMENS HEARING INSTRUMENTS (SUZHOU) CO. LTD.—See Siemens Aktiengesellschaft; *Int'l*, pg. 6895
SIEMENS HEARING SOLUTION (PTY.) LTD.—See Siemens Aktiengesellschaft; *Int'l*, pg. 6895
SIEMENS HEAT TRANSFER TECHNOLOGY B.V.—See Siemens Energy AG; *Int'l*, pg. 6902
SIEMENS HEAT TRANSFER TECHNOLOGY FREE ZONE LLC—See Siemens Energy AG; *Int'l*, pg. 6902
SIEMENS HIGH VOLTAGE CIRCUIT BREAKER CO., LTD.—See Siemens Aktiengesellschaft; *Int'l*, pg. 6895
SIEMENS HOREAPPARATER A/S—See Siemens Aktiengesellschaft; *Int'l*, pg. 6895
SIEMENS HOREAPPARATER AS—See Siemens Aktiengesellschaft; *Int'l*, pg. 6895
SIEMENS IMMOBILIEN CHEMNITZ-VOERDE GMBH—See Siemens Aktiengesellschaft; *Int'l*, pg. 6895
SIEMENS, INC.—See Siemens Aktiengesellschaft; *Int'l*, pg. 6900
SIEMENS INDUSTRIAL AUTOMATION LTD.—See Siemens Aktiengesellschaft; *Int'l*, pg. 6895
SIEMENS INDUSTRIAL LLC—See Siemens Aktiengesellschaft; *Int'l*, pg. 6895
SIEMENS INDUSTRIAL SOLUTIONS & SERVICES GROUP—See Siemens Aktiengesellschaft; *Int'l*, pg. 6895
SIEMENS INDUSTRIAL TURBOMACHINERY AB—See Siemens Energy AG; *Int'l*, pg. 6903
SIEMENS INDUSTRIAL TURBOMACHINERY (HULUDAO) CO., LTD.—See Siemens Energy AG; *Int'l*, pg. 6903
SIEMENS INDUSTRIAL TURBOMACHINERY LTD.—See Siemens Energy AG; *Int'l*, pg. 6903
SIEMENS INDUSTRIEGETRIEBE GMBH—See Siemens Aktiengesellschaft; *Int'l*, pg. 6895
SIEMENS INDUSTRIEPARK KARLSRUHE GMBH & CO. KG—See Siemens Aktiengesellschaft; *Int'l*, pg. 6895
SIEMENS INDUSTRY, INC. - NEW YORK—See Siemens Aktiengesellschaft; *Int'l*, pg. 6895
SIEMENS INDUSTRY, INC. - PHILADELPHIA—See Siemens Aktiengesellschaft; *Int'l*, pg. 6895
SIEMENS INDUSTRY, INC.—See Siemens Aktiengesellschaft; *Int'l*, pg. 6895
SIEMENS INDUSTRY SOFTWARE AB—See Siemens Aktiengesellschaft; *Int'l*, pg. 6895
SIEMENS INDUSTRY SOFTWARE AG—See Siemens Aktiengesellschaft; *Int'l*, pg. 6895
SIEMENS INDUSTRY SOFTWARE A/S—See Siemens Aktiengesellschaft; *Int'l*, pg. 6895
SIEMENS INDUSTRY SOFTWARE B.V.—See Siemens Aktiengesellschaft; *Int'l*, pg. 6895
SIEMENS INDUSTRY SOFTWARE GMBH—See Siemens Aktiengesellschaft; *Int'l*, pg. 6895
SIEMENS INDUSTRY SOFTWARE (INDIA) PRIVATE LIMITED—See Siemens Aktiengesellschaft; *Int'l*, pg. 6895
SIEMENS INDUSTRY SOFTWARE K.K.—See Siemens Aktiengesellschaft; *Int'l*, pg. 6895
SIEMENS INDUSTRY SOFTWARE LIMITED—See Siemens Aktiengesellschaft; *Int'l*, pg. 6896
SIEMENS INDUSTRY SOFTWARE LTDA.—See Siemens Aktiengesellschaft; *Int'l*, pg. 6896
SIEMENS INDUSTRY SOFTWARE LTD.—See Siemens Aktiengesellschaft; *Int'l*, pg. 6896
SIEMENS INDUSTRY SOFTWARE LTD.—See Siemens Aktiengesellschaft; *Int'l*, pg. 6896
SIEMENS INDUSTRY SOFTWARE LTD.—See Siemens Aktiengesellschaft; *Int'l*, pg. 6896
SIEMENS INDUSTRY SOFTWARE PTE. LTD.—See Siemens Aktiengesellschaft; *Int'l*, pg. 6896
SIEMENS INDUSTRY SOFTWARE SA (PTY.) LTD.—See Siemens Aktiengesellschaft; *Int'l*, pg. 6896
SIEMENS INDUSTRY SOFTWARE SAS—See Siemens Aktiengesellschaft; *Int'l*, pg. 6896
SIEMENS INDUSTRY SOFTWARE SDN. BHD.—See Siemens Aktiengesellschaft; *Int'l*, pg. 6896
SIEMENS INDUSTRY SOFTWARE (SHANGHAI) CO., LTD.—See Siemens Aktiengesellschaft; *Int'l*, pg. 6895
SIEMENS INDUSTRY SOFTWARE S.L.—See Siemens Aktiengesellschaft; *Int'l*, pg. 6896
SIEMENS INDUSTRY SOFTWARE S.R.L—See Siemens Aktiengesellschaft; *Int'l*, pg. 6896
SIEMENS INDUSTRY SOFTWARE, S.R.O.—See Siemens Aktiengesellschaft; *Int'l*, pg. 6896
SIEMENS INDUSTRY SOFTWARE (TW) CO., LTD.—See Siemens Aktiengesellschaft; *Int'l*, pg. 6895
SIEMENS INMOBILIARIA S.A. DE C.V.—See Siemens Aktiengesellschaft; *Int'l*, pg. 6896
SIEMENS INNOVACIONES S.A. DE C.V.—See Siemens Aktiengesellschaft; *Int'l*, pg. 6896
SIEMENS INTELLIGENT TRANSPORTATION SYSTEMS—See Siemens Aktiengesellschaft; *Int'l*, pg. 6895

SIEMENS INTERNATIONAL TRADING LTD.—See Siemens Aktiengesellschaft; *Int'l*, pg. 6896
SIEMENS ISRAEL LTD.—See Siemens Aktiengesellschaft; *Int'l*, pg. 6896
SIEMENS IT SERVICES S.A.—See Siemens Aktiengesellschaft; *Int'l*, pg. 6895
SIEMENS JAPAN HOLDING K.K.—See Siemens Aktiengesellschaft; *Int'l*, pg. 6896
SIEMENS JAPAN K.K.—See Siemens Aktiengesellschaft; *Int'l*, pg. 6896
SIEMENS KAMEDA HEALTHCARE IT SYSTEMS K.K.—See Siemens Aktiengesellschaft; *Int'l*, pg. 6896
SIEMENS KAPITALANLAGEGESELLSCHAFT MBH—See Siemens Aktiengesellschaft; *Int'l*, pg. 6896
SIEMENS KENYA LTD.—See Siemens Aktiengesellschaft; *Int'l*, pg. 6896
SIEMENS K.K.—See Siemens Aktiengesellschaft; *Int'l*, pg. 6896
SIEMENS KONZERNBETEILIGUNGEN GMBH—See Siemens Aktiengesellschaft; *Int'l*, pg. 6898
SIEMENS LASERWORKS INC.—See Russel Metals Inc.; *Int'l*, pg. 6430
SIEMENS LEASE B.V.—See Siemens Aktiengesellschaft; *Int'l*, pg. 6896
SIEMENS LEASE SERVICES SAS—See Siemens Aktiengesellschaft; *Int'l*, pg. 6891
SIEMENS - LIBYA—See Siemens Aktiengesellschaft; *Int'l*, pg. 6888
SIEMENS LIEGENSCHAFTSVERWALTUNG GMBH—See Siemens Aktiengesellschaft; *Int'l*, pg. 6898
SIEMENS LIMITADA—See Siemens Aktiengesellschaft; *Int'l*, pg. 6896
SIEMENS LIMITED—See Siemens Aktiengesellschaft; *Int'l*, pg. 6896
SIEMENS LIMITED—See Siemens Aktiengesellschaft; *Int'l*, pg. 6896
SIEMENS LIMITED—See Siemens Aktiengesellschaft; *Int'l*, pg. 6896
SIEMENS LIMITED—See Siemens Aktiengesellschaft; *Int'l*, pg. 6896
SIEMENS LIMITED—See Siemens Aktiengesellschaft; *Int'l*, pg. 6896
SIEMENS LLC—See Siemens Aktiengesellschaft; *Int'l*, pg. 6896
SIEMENS LOGISTICS AG—See Siemens Aktiengesellschaft; *Int'l*, pg. 6896
SIEMENS LOGISTICS AUTOMATION SYSTEMS (BEIJING) CO., LTD.—See Siemens Aktiengesellschaft; *Int'l*, pg. 6896
SIEMENS LOGISTICS GMBH—See Siemens Aktiengesellschaft; *Int'l*, pg. 6896
SIEMENS LOGISTICS INDIA PRIVATE LIMITED—See Siemens Aktiengesellschaft; *Int'l*, pg. 6896
SIEMENS LOGISTICS LIMITED—See Siemens Aktiengesellschaft; *Int'l*, pg. 6896
SIEMENS LOGISTICS LLC—See Siemens Aktiengesellschaft; *Int'l*, pg. 6890
SIEMENS LOGISTICS LTD.—See Siemens Aktiengesellschaft; *Int'l*, pg. 6896
SIEMENS LOGISTICS PTE. LTD.—See Siemens Aktiengesellschaft; *Int'l*, pg. 6896
SIEMENS LOGISTICS SAS—See Siemens Aktiengesellschaft; *Int'l*, pg. 6896
SIEMENS LOGISTICS S.L.—See Siemens Aktiengesellschaft; *Int'l*, pg. 6896
SIEMENS LOGISTICS S.R.L.—See Siemens Aktiengesellschaft; *Int'l*, pg. 6896
SIEMENS LTDA—See Siemens Energy AG; *Int'l*, pg. 6903
SIEMENS LTD., CHINA—See Siemens Aktiengesellschaft; *Int'l*, pg. 6897
SIEMENS LTD.—See The Carlyle Group Inc.; *U.S. Public*, pg. 2047
SIEMENS LTD.—See Siemens Aktiengesellschaft; *Int'l*, pg. 6896
SIEMENS LTD.—See Siemens Aktiengesellschaft; *Int'l*, pg. 6896
SIEMENS LTD.—See Siemens Aktiengesellschaft; *Int'l*, pg. 6896
SIEMENS LTD.—See Siemens Aktiengesellschaft; *Int'l*, pg. 6896
SIEMENS LTD.—See Siemens Aktiengesellschaft; *Int'l*, pg. 6896
SIEMENS LTD.—See Siemens Aktiengesellschaft; *Int'l*, pg. 6896
SIEMENS MALAYSIA SDN BHD—See Siemens Aktiengesellschaft; *Int'l*, pg. 6897
SIEMENS MANUFACTURING AND ENGINEERING CENTRE LTD.—See Siemens Aktiengesellschaft; *Int'l*, pg. 6897
SIEMENS MANUFACTURING CO., INC.; *U.S. Private*, pg. 3646
SIEMENS MANUFACTURING S.A.—See Siemens Aktiengesellschaft; *Int'l*, pg. 6897
SIEMENS MEASUREMENT SYSTEMS—See Siemens Aktiengesellschaft; *Int'l*, pg. 6899
SIEMENS MEDICAL EQUIPMENT-NEW YORK—See Siemens Aktiengesellschaft; *Int'l*, pg. 6894
SIEMENS MEDICAL INSTRUMENTS PTE. LTD.—See Siemens Aktiengesellschaft; *Int'l*, pg. 6897

COMPANY NAME INDEX

SIEMENS MEDICAL SOLUTIONS AS—See Siemens Aktiengesellschaft; *Int'l*, pg. 6893
SIEMENS MEDICAL SOLUTIONS DIAGNOSTICS EUROPE LIMITED—See Siemens Aktiengesellschaft; *Int'l*, pg. 6897
SIEMENS MEDICAL SOLUTIONS DIAGNOSTICS HOLDING I B.V.—See Siemens Aktiengesellschaft; *Int'l*, pg. 6897
SIEMENS MEDICAL SOLUTIONS DIAGNOSTICS LTD.—See Siemens Aktiengesellschaft; *Int'l*, pg. 6893
SIEMENS MEDICAL SOLUTIONS DIAGNOSTICS SIA—See Siemens Aktiengesellschaft; *Int'l*, pg. 6898
SIEMENS MEDICAL SOLUTIONS DIAGNOSTICS—See Siemens Aktiengesellschaft; *Int'l*, pg. 6893
SIEMENS MEDICAL SOLUTIONS DIAGNOSTICS—See Siemens Aktiengesellschaft; *Int'l*, pg. 6893
SIEMENS MEDICAL SOLUTIONS DIAGNOSTICS, UNIPESSOAL—See Siemens Aktiengesellschaft; *Int'l*, pg. 6893
SIEMENS MEDICAL SOLUTIONS HEALTH SERVICES GMBH—See Siemens Aktiengesellschaft; *Int'l*, pg. 6893
SIEMENS MEDICAL SOLUTIONS HEALTH SERVICES ITALIA—See Siemens Aktiengesellschaft; *Int'l*, pg. 6893
SIEMENS MEDICAL SOLUTIONS LTDA.—See Siemens Aktiengesellschaft; *Int'l*, pg. 6893
SIEMENS MEDICAL SOLUTIONS ULTRASOUND DIVISION—See Siemens Aktiengesellschaft; *Int'l*, pg. 6894
SIEMENS MEDICAL SOLUTIONS USA, INC.—See Siemens Aktiengesellschaft; *Int'l*, pg. 6893
SIEMENS MEDICINA D.O.O.—See Siemens Aktiengesellschaft; *Int'l*, pg. 6897
SIEMENS MOBILITY AB—See Siemens Aktiengesellschaft; *Int'l*, pg. 6897
SIEMENS MOBILITY AG—See Siemens Aktiengesellschaft; *Int'l*, pg. 6897
SIEMENS MOBILITY AS—See Siemens Aktiengesellschaft; *Int'l*, pg. 6897
SIEMENS MOBILITY A/S—See Siemens Aktiengesellschaft; *Int'l*, pg. 6897
SIEMENS MOBILITY AUSTRIA GMBH—See Siemens Aktiengesellschaft; *Int'l*, pg. 6897
SIEMENS MOBILITY B.V.—See Siemens Aktiengesellschaft; *Int'l*, pg. 6897
SIEMENS MOBILITY D.O.O. CEROVAC—See Siemens Aktiengesellschaft; *Int'l*, pg. 6898
SIEMENS MOBILITY D.O.O.—See Siemens Aktiengesellschaft; *Int'l*, pg. 6898
SIEMENS MOBILITY EOOD—See Siemens Aktiengesellschaft; *Int'l*, pg. 6897
SIEMENS MOBILITY GMBH—See Siemens Aktiengesellschaft; *Int'l*, pg. 6897
SIEMENS MOBILITY GROUP—See Siemens Aktiengesellschaft; *Int'l*, pg. 6897
SIEMENS MOBILITY KFT.—See Siemens Aktiengesellschaft; *Int'l*, pg. 6897
SIEMENS MOBILITY LIMITED—See Siemens Aktiengesellschaft; *Int'l*, pg. 6897
SIEMENS MOBILITY LIMITED—See Siemens Aktiengesellschaft; *Int'l*, pg. 6897
SIEMENS MOBILITY LIMITED—See Siemens Aktiengesellschaft; *Int'l*, pg. 6897
SIEMENS MOBILITY LLC—See Siemens Aktiengesellschaft; *Int'l*, pg. 6897
SIEMENS MOBILITY LLC—See Siemens Aktiengesellschaft; *Int'l*, pg. 6897
SIEMENS MOBILITY LTD.—See Siemens Aktiengesellschaft; *Int'l*, pg. 6898
SIEMENS MOBILITY LTD.—See Siemens Aktiengesellschaft; *Int'l*, pg. 6898
SIEMENS MOBILITY OY—See Siemens Aktiengesellschaft; *Int'l*, pg. 6898
SIEMENS MOBILITY PTE. LTD.—See Siemens Aktiengesellschaft; *Int'l*, pg. 6898
SIEMENS MOBILITY PTY LTD.—See Siemens Aktiengesellschaft; *Int'l*, pg. 6898
SIEMENS MOBILITY RAIL & ROAD TRANSPORTATION SOLUTIONS SINGLE-MEMBER SOCIETE ANONYME—See Siemens Aktiengesellschaft; *Int'l*, pg. 6898
SIEMENS MOBILITY RAIL & ROAD TRANSPORTATION SOLUTIONS SOCIETE ANONYME—See Siemens Aktiengesellschaft; *Int'l*, pg. 6898
SIEMENS MOBILITY S.A.C.—See Siemens Aktiengesellschaft; *Int'l*, pg. 6898
SIEMENS MOBILITY S.A.—See Siemens Aktiengesellschaft; *Int'l*, pg. 6898
SIEMENS MOBILITY SAS—See Siemens Aktiengesellschaft; *Int'l*, pg. 6898
SIEMENS MOBILITY SAUDI LTD.—See Siemens Aktiengesellschaft; *Int'l*, pg. 6898
SIEMENS MOBILITY S. DE R.L. DE C.V.—See Siemens Aktiengesellschaft; *Int'l*, pg. 6898
SIEMENS MOBILITY SDN. BHD.—See Siemens Aktiengesellschaft; *Int'l*, pg. 6898
SIEMENS MOBILITY, S.L.U.—See Siemens Aktiengesellschaft; *Int'l*, pg. 6898
SIEMENS MOBILITY SPA—See Siemens Aktiengesellschaft; *Int'l*, pg. 6898
SIEMENS MOBILITY SP. Z O.O.—See Siemens Aktiengesellschaft; *Int'l*, pg. 6898
SIEMENS MOBILITY S.R.L.—See Siemens Aktiengesellschaft; *Int'l*, pg. 6898
SIEMENS MOBILITY S.R.L.—See Siemens Aktiengesellschaft; *Int'l*, pg. 6898
SIEMENS MOBILITY, S.R.O.—See Siemens Aktiengesellschaft; *Int'l*, pg. 6898
SIEMENS MOBILITY, S.R.O.—See Siemens Aktiengesellschaft; *Int'l*, pg. 6898
SIEMENS MOBILITY ULASIM SISTEMLERI ANONIM SIRKETI—See Siemens Aktiengesellschaft; *Int'l*, pg. 6898
SIEMENS MOBILITY, UNIPESSOAL LDA.—See Siemens Aktiengesellschaft; *Int'l*, pg. 6898
SIEMENS MOLECULAR IMAGING, INC.—See Siemens Aktiengesellschaft; *Int'l*, pg. 6893
SIEMENS NEDERLAND N.V.—See Siemens Aktiengesellschaft; *Int'l*, pg. 6898
SIEMENS (NZ) LIMITED—See Siemens Aktiengesellschaft; *Int'l*, pg. 6888
SIEMENS OESTERREICH AG—See Siemens Aktiengesellschaft; *Int'l*, pg. 6898
SIEMENS OSAKEYHTIOE—See Siemens Aktiengesellschaft; *Int'l*, pg. 6898
SIEMENS OSAKEYHTIO OY—See Siemens Aktiengesellschaft; *Int'l*, pg. 6898
SIEMENS PAKISTAN ENGINEERING CO. LTD.—See Siemens Aktiengesellschaft; *Int'l*, pg. 6898
SIEMENS PENSIONSKASSE AG—See Siemens Aktiengesellschaft; *Int'l*, pg. 6898
SIEMENS PERSONALDIENSTLEISTUNGEN GMBH—See Siemens Aktiengesellschaft; *Int'l*, pg. 6898
SIEMENS PETNET KOREA CO. LTD.—See Siemens Aktiengesellschaft; *Int'l*, pg. 6898
SIEMENS PLANT OPERATIONS TAHADDART SARL—See Siemens Aktiengesellschaft; *Int'l*, pg. 6898
SIEMENS PLC—See Siemens Aktiengesellschaft; *Int'l*, pg. 6900
SIEMENS PLM SOFTWARE COMPUTATIONAL DYNAMICS K.K.—See Siemens Aktiengesellschaft; *Int'l*, pg. 6898
SIEMENS PLM SOFTWARE—See Siemens Aktiengesellschaft; *Int'l*, pg. 6891
SIEMENS PLM SOFTWARE—See Siemens Aktiengesellschaft; *Int'l*, pg. 6890
SIEMENS PLM SOFTWARE—See Siemens Aktiengesellschaft; *Int'l*, pg. 6890
SIEMENS PLM SOFTWARE—See Siemens Aktiengesellschaft; *Int'l*, pg. 6890
SIEMENS POSTAL, PARCEL & AIRPORT LOGISTICS LIMITED—See Siemens Aktiengesellschaft; *Int'l*, pg. 6898
SIEMENS POWER AUTOMATION LTD.—See Siemens Aktiengesellschaft; *Int'l*, pg. 6898
SIEMENS POWER CONTROL GMBH—See Siemens Energy AG; *Int'l*, pg. 6903
SIEMENS POWER OPERATIONS, INC.—See Siemens Energy AG; *Int'l*, pg. 6903
SIEMENS POWER PLANT AUTOMATION LTD.—See Siemens Energy AG; *Int'l*, pg. 6903
SIEMENS PRIVATE FINANCE VERSICHERUNGS- UND KAPITALANLAGENVERMITTLUNGS-GMBH—See Siemens Aktiengesellschaft; *Int'l*, pg. 6898
SIEMENS PROCESS AUTOMATION & DRIVES (U.K.) LTD.—See Siemens Aktiengesellschaft; *Int'l*, pg. 6898
SIEMENS PRODUCT LIFECYCLE MANAGEMENT SOFTWARE 2 (IL) LTD.—See Siemens Aktiengesellschaft; *Int'l*, pg. 6899
SIEMENS PRODUCT LIFECYCLE MANAGEMENT SOFTWARE (DE) GMBH—See Siemens Aktiengesellschaft; *Int'l*, pg. 6891
SIEMENS PRODUCT LIFECYCLE MANAGEMENT SOFTWARE (DE) GMBH—See Siemens Aktiengesellschaft; *Int'l*, pg. 6891
SIEMENS PRODUCT LIFECYCLE MANAGEMENT SOFTWARE II (BE) BVBA—See Siemens Aktiengesellschaft; *Int'l*, pg. 6899
SIEMENS PRODUCT LIFECYCLE MANAGEMENT SOFTWARE II (US) INC.—See Siemens Aktiengesellschaft; *Int'l*, pg. 6891
SIEMENS PRODUCT LIFECYCLE MANAGEMENT SOFTWARE INC.—See Siemens Aktiengesellschaft; *Int'l*, pg. 6891
SIEMENS PROGRAM AND SYSTEM ENGINEERING S.R.O.—See Siemens Aktiengesellschaft; *Int'l*, pg. 6899
SIEMENS PROGRAMM- UND SYSTEMENTWICKLUNG GMBH&CO. KG—See Siemens Aktiengesellschaft; *Int'l*, pg. 6899
SIEMENS PROTECTION DEVICES LIMITED—See Siemens Aktiengesellschaft; *Int'l*, pg. 6899
SIEMENS PTE. LTD.—See Siemens Aktiengesellschaft; *Int'l*, pg. 6889
SIEMENS PUBLIC, INC.—See Siemens Aktiengesellschaft; *Int'l*, pg. 6891
SIEMENS RAIL AUTOMATION HOLDINGS LIMITED—See Siemens Aktiengesellschaft; *Int'l*, pg. 6899
SIEMENS REAL ESTATE CORP.—See Siemens Aktiengesellschaft; *Int'l*, pg. 6891
SIEMENS REAL ESTATE GMBH & CO. OHG—See Siemens Aktiengesellschaft; *Int'l*, pg. 6899
SIEMENS REAL ESTATE LTD.—See Siemens Aktiengesellschaft; *Int'l*, pg. 6899
SIEMENS REAL ESTATE MANAGEMENT (PTY.) LTD.—See Siemens Aktiengesellschaft; *Int'l*, pg. 6899
SIEMENS RENTING S.A.—See Siemens Aktiengesellschaft; *Int'l*, pg. 6899
SIEMENS RT.—See Siemens Aktiengesellschaft; *Int'l*, pg. 6899
SIEMENS SAC—See Siemens Aktiengesellschaft; *Int'l*, pg. 6899
SIEMENS, S.A. DE C.V.—See Siemens Aktiengesellschaft; *Int'l*, pg. 6900
SIEMENS SANAYI VE TICARET A.S—See Siemens Aktiengesellschaft; *Int'l*, pg. 6899
SIEMENS S.A./N.V.—See Siemens Aktiengesellschaft; *Int'l*, pg. 6899
SIEMENS S.A.—See Siemens Aktiengesellschaft; *Int'l*, pg. 6899
SIEMENS SA—See Siemens Aktiengesellschaft; *Int'l*, pg. 6899
SIEMENS S.A.—See Siemens Aktiengesellschaft; *Int'l*, pg. 6899
SIEMENS S.A.—See Siemens Aktiengesellschaft; *Int'l*, pg. 6899
SIEMENS S.A.—See Siemens Energy AG; *Int'l*, pg. 6903
SIEMENS S.A.—See Siemens Aktiengesellschaft; *Int'l*, pg. 6899
SIEMENS S.A.—See Siemens Aktiengesellschaft; *Int'l*, pg. 6899
SIEMENS S.A.—See Siemens Aktiengesellschaft; *Int'l*, pg. 6899
SIEMENS S.A.—See Siemens Aktiengesellschaft; *Int'l*, pg. 6899
SIEMENS S.A.—See Siemens Aktiengesellschaft; *Int'l*, pg. 6899
SIEMENS S.A.—See Siemens Aktiengesellschaft; *Int'l*, pg. 6899
SIEMENS S.A.—See Siemens Aktiengesellschaft; *Int'l*, pg. 6899
SIEMENS SA—See Siemens Aktiengesellschaft; *Int'l*, pg. 6899
SIEMENS S.A.—See Siemens Aktiengesellschaft; *Int'l*, pg. 6899
SIEMENS S.A.—See Siemens Aktiengesellschaft; *Int'l*, pg. 6899
SIEMENS SAS—See Siemens Aktiengesellschaft; *Int'l*, pg. 6888
SIEMENS SCHWEIZ AG—See Siemens Aktiengesellschaft; *Int'l*, pg. 6899
SIEMENS SERVICIOS S.A. DE C.V.—See Siemens Aktiengesellschaft; *Int'l*, pg. 6899
SIEMENS SHANGHAI MEDICAL EQUIPMENT LTD.—See Siemens Aktiengesellschaft; *Int'l*, pg. 6899
SIEMENS SHENZHEN MAGNETIC RESONANCE LTD.—See Siemens Aktiengesellschaft; *Int'l*, pg. 6899
SIEMENS SIA—See Siemens Aktiengesellschaft; *Int'l*, pg. 6899
SIEMENS SIGNALLING CO., LTD.—See Siemens Aktiengesellschaft; *Int'l*, pg. 6899
SIEMENS SOLUCIONES TECNOLOGICAS S.A.—See Siemens Aktiengesellschaft; *Int'l*, pg. 6899
SIEMENS S.P.A.—See Siemens Aktiengesellschaft; *Int'l*, pg. 6899
SIEMENS S.P.A.—See Siemens Aktiengesellschaft; *Int'l*, pg. 6888
SIEMENS SPEZIAL-INVESTMENTAKTIENGESELLSCHAFT MIT TGV—See Siemens Aktiengesellschaft; pg. 6899
SIEMENS SP. Z O.O. - BUILDING TECHNOLOGIES—See Siemens Aktiengesellschaft; *Int'l*, pg. 6889
SIEMENS SP. Z O.O.—See Siemens Aktiengesellschaft; *Int'l*, pg. 6899
SIEMENS SRL—See Siemens Aktiengesellschaft; *Int'l*, pg. 6900
SIEMENS S.R.O.—See Siemens Aktiengesellschaft; *Int'l*, pg. 6900
SIEMENS, S.R.O.—See Siemens Aktiengesellschaft; *Int'l*, pg. 6900
SIEMENS SURGE ARRESTERS LTD.—See Siemens Aktiengesellschaft; *Int'l*, pg. 6900
SIEMENS TECHNOLOGY ACCELERATOR GMBH—See Siemens Aktiengesellschaft; *Int'l*, pg. 6900
SIEMENS TECHNOLOGY TO BUSINESS—See Siemens Aktiengesellschaft; *Int'l*, pg. 6891
SIEMENS TECHNOPARK BERLIN GMBH&CO. KG—See Siemens Aktiengesellschaft; *Int'l*, pg. 6900
SIEMENS TECHNOPARK MULHEIM VERWALTUNGS-GMBH—See Siemens Aktiengesellschaft; *Int'l*, pg. 6900

SIEMENS MANUFACTURING CO., INC.   CORPORATE AFFILIATIONS

SIEMENS TECHNOPARK NURNBERG GMBH & CO. KG—See Siemens Aktiengesellschaft; *Int'l*, pg. 6900
SIEMENS TECHNOPARK NURNBERG VERWALTUNGS GMBH—See Siemens Aktiengesellschaft; *Int'l*, pg. 6900
SIEMENS TOO—See Siemens Aktiengesellschaft; *Int'l*, pg. 6900
SIEMENS TRANSFORMER (JINAN) CO., LTD.—See Siemens Energy AG; *Int'l*, pg. 6903
SIEMENS TRANSFORMERS AUSTRIA GMBH & CO KG—See Siemens Aktiengesellschaft; *Int'l*, pg. 6898
SIEMENS TRANSFORMERS CANADA INC.—See Siemens Energy AG; *Int'l*, pg. 6903
SIEMENS TRANSFORMERS S.R.L.—See Siemens Energy AG; *Int'l*, pg. 6903
SIEMENS TRANSFORMER (WUHAN) COMPANY LTD.—See Siemens Energy AG; *Int'l*, pg. 6903
SIEMENS TRANSMISSION & DISTRIBUTION SAS—See Siemens Aktiengesellschaft; *Int'l*, pg. 6900
SIEMENS TRANSPORTATION SYSTEMS, INC.—See Siemens Aktiengesellschaft; *Int'l*, pg. 6891
SIEMENS TRANSPORTATION SYSTEMS—See Siemens Aktiengesellschaft; *Int'l*, pg. 6897
SIEMENS TREASURY GMBH—See Siemens Aktiengesellschaft; *Int'l*, pg. 6900
SIEMENS UGS TECNOMATIX—See Siemens Aktiengesellschaft; *Int'l*, pg. 6891
SIEMENS UKRAINE—See Siemens Aktiengesellschaft; *Int'l*, pg. 6900
SIEMENS URUGUAY S.A.—See Siemens Aktiengesellschaft; *Int'l*, pg. 6900
SIEMENS USA HOLDINGS, INC.—See Siemens Aktiengesellschaft; *Int'l*, pg. 6891
SIEMENS VAI MANUFACTURING (TAICANG) CO., LTD.—See Siemens Aktiengesellschaft; *Int'l*, pg. 6900
SIEMENS VAI METALS TECHNOLOGIES GMBH & CO—See Siemens Aktiengesellschaft; *Int'l*, pg. 6895
SIEMENS VAI METALS TECHNOLOGIES GMBH—See Siemens Aktiengesellschaft; *Int'l*, pg. 6900
SIEMENS VAI METALS TECHNOLOGIES SAS—See Siemens Aktiengesellschaft; *Int'l*, pg. 6900
SIEMENS VAI METALS TECHNOLOGIES S.R.L.—See Siemens Aktiengesellschaft; *Int'l*, pg. 6900
SIEMENS VENTURE CAPITAL GMBH—See Siemens Aktiengesellschaft; *Int'l*, pg. 6900
SIEMENS WERK UERDINGEN TRANSPORTATION SYSTEMS—See Siemens Aktiengesellschaft; *Int'l*, pg. 6897
SIEMENS WIND POWER BLADES (SHANGHAI) CO., LTD.—See Siemens Aktiengesellschaft; *Int'l*, pg. 6900
SIEMENS WIRING ACCESSORIES SHANDONG LTD.—See Siemens Aktiengesellschaft; *Int'l*, pg. 6900
SIEMENS WLL—See Siemens Aktiengesellschaft; *Int'l*, pg. 6900
SIEMENS W.L.L.—See Siemens Aktiengesellschaft; *Int'l*, pg. 6900
SIEMENS X-RAY VACUUM TECHNOLOGY LTD.—See Siemens Aktiengesellschaft; *Int'l*, pg. 6897
SIEMER ENTERPRISES INC.; *U.S. Private*, pg. 3646
SIEMER MILLING COMPANY - HOPKINSVILLE FACILITY—See Siemer Milling Company; *U.S. Private*, pg. 3646
SIEMER MILLING COMPANY; *U.S. Private*, pg. 3646
SIEMIC INC.—See Bureau Veritas S.A.; *Int'l*, pg. 1222
SIEM INDUSTRIES INC.; *Int'l*, pg. 6885
SIEM KAPITAL AS—See Siem Industries Inc.; *Int'l*, pg. 6886
SIEM OFFSHORE AS; *Int'l*, pg. 6886
SIEM OFFSHORE AUSTRALIA PTY LTD.—See Siem Offshore AS; *Int'l*, pg. 6886
SIEM OFFSHORE DO BRASIL SA—See Siem Offshore AS; *Int'l*, pg. 6886
SIEM OFFSHORE SERVICOS MARITIMOS LTDA.—See Siem Offshore AS; *Int'l*, pg. 6886
THE SIEMON COMPANY; *U.S. Private*, pg. 4118
SIEMPELKAMP BARCELONA—See G. Siempelkamp GmbH & Co. KG; *Int'l*, pg. 2864
SIEMPELKAMP BEHALTERTECHNIK GMBH—See G. Siempelkamp GmbH & Co. KG; *Int'l*, pg. 2864
SIEMPELKAMP CZ S. R. O.—See G. Siempelkamp GmbH & Co. KG; *Int'l*, pg. 2865
SIEMPELKAMP DO BRASIL LTDA.—See G. Siempelkamp GmbH & Co. KG; *Int'l*, pg. 2865
SIEMPELKAMP FRANCE SARL—See G. Siempelkamp GmbH & Co. KG; *Int'l*, pg. 2865
SIEMPELKAMP GIESSEREI GMBH—See G. Siempelkamp GmbH & Co. KG; *Int'l*, pg. 2865
SIEMPELKAMP INDIA PVT. LTD.—See G. Siempelkamp GmbH & Co. KG; *Int'l*, pg. 2865
SIEMPELKAMP ISTANBUL—See G. Siempelkamp GmbH & Co. KG; *Int'l*, pg. 2865
SIEMPELKAMP KRANTECHNIK GMBH—See G. Siempelkamp GmbH & Co. KG; *Int'l*, pg. 2865
SIEMPELKAMP LOGISTICS & SERVICE GMBH—See G. Siempelkamp GmbH & Co. KG; *Int'l*, pg. 2865
SIEMPELKAMP L.P.—See G. Siempelkamp GmbH & Co. KG; *Int'l*, pg. 2865

SIEMPELKAMP MASCHINEN- UND ANLAGENBAU GMBH—See G. Siempelkamp GmbH & Co. KG; *Int'l*, pg. 2865
SIEMPELKAMP MOSCOW OOO—See G. Siempelkamp GmbH & Co. KG; *Int'l*, pg. 2865
SIEMPELKAMP MSDG S.A.S.—See G. Siempelkamp GmbH & Co. KG; *Int'l*, pg. 2865
SIEMPELKAMP NIS INGENIEURGESELLSCHAFT MBH—See G. Siempelkamp GmbH & Co. KG; *Int'l*, pg. 2865
SIEMPELKAMP PRUF-UND GUTACHTER GESELLSCHAFT MBH—See G. Siempelkamp GmbH & Co. KG; *Int'l*, pg. 2865
SIEMPELKAMP PTE. LTD.—See G. Siempelkamp GmbH & Co. KG; *Int'l*, pg. 2865
SIEMPELKAMP PTE. LTD.—See G. Siempelkamp GmbH & Co. KG; *Int'l*, pg. 2865
SIEMPELKAMP PTY. LTD.—See G. Siempelkamp GmbH & Co. KG; *Int'l*, pg. 2865
SIEMPELKAMP (QINGDAO) MACHINERY & EQUIPMENT CO. LTD.—See G. Siempelkamp GmbH & Co. KG; *Int'l*, pg. 2864
SIEMPELKAMP TENSIONING SYSTEMS GMBH—See G. Siempelkamp GmbH & Co. KG; *Int'l*, pg. 2865
SIEMPELKAMP (WUXI) MACHINERY MANUFACTURING CO. LTD.—See G. Siempelkamp GmbH & Co. KG; *Int'l*, pg. 2864
SIEMPRETAX LLC—See B. Riley Financial, Inc.; *U.S. Public*, pg. 261
SIEMPRETAX LLC—See Irradiant Partners, LP; *U.S. Private*, pg. 2141
SIEM SHIPPING INC.—See Siem Industries Inc.; *Int'l*, pg. 6886
SIENA DIALYSIS CENTER, LLC—See DaVita Inc.; *U.S. Public*, pg. 643
SIENERGY, L.P.—See Ridgewood Infrastructure LLC; *U.S. Private*, pg. 3434
SIENNA CANCER DIAGNOSTICS LIMITED; *Int'l*, pg. 6904
SIENNA CAPITAL INTERNATIONAL LTD.—See Groupe Bruxelles Lambert SA; *Int'l*, pg. 3100
SIENNA CAPITAL S.A R.L.—See Groupe Bruxelles Lambert SA; *Int'l*, pg. 3101
SIENNA CORPORATION INC.; *U.S. Private*, pg. 3646
SIENNA ECAD TECHNOLOGIES PVT. LTD.—See Sienna Corporation Inc.; *U.S. Private*, pg. 3646
SIENNA GROUP, LLC—See Thoma Bravo, L.P.; *U.S. Private*, pg. 4146
SIENNA MINERALS SAC—See PPX Mining Corp.; *Int'l*, pg. 5951
SIENNA RESOURCES INC.; *Int'l*, pg. 6904
SIENNA RESOURCES SWEDEN AB—See Sienna Resources Inc.; *Int'l*, pg. 6904
SIENNA-RSH NIAGARA FALLS LP—See Sienna Senior Living Inc.; *Int'l*, pg. 6904
SIENNA SENIOR LIVING INC.; *Int'l*, pg. 6904
SIENTRA, INC.; *U.S. Public*, pg. 1876
SIERRA ACURA OF ALHAMBRA; *U.S. Private*, pg. 3646
SIERRA AIR, INC.—See Odyssey Investment Partners, LLC; *U.S. Private*, pg. 2995
SIERRA ALLOYS COMPANY—See Platte River Ventures, LLC; *U.S. Private*, pg. 3211
SIERRA ALUMINUM COMPANY—See Samuel, Son & Co., Limited; *Int'l*, pg. 6516
SIERRA AUCTION MANAGEMENT, INC.—See Liquidity Services, Inc.; *U.S. Public*, pg. 1321
SIERRA AUTOCARS INCORPORATED; *U.S. Private*, pg. 3646
SIERRA BANCORP; *U.S. Public*, pg. 1877
SIERRA BAY CONTRACTORS INC.; *U.S. Private*, pg. 3646
SIERRA BLANCA MOTOR CO.; *U.S. Private*, pg. 3646
SIERRA BRAVO, CORPORATION; *U.S. Private*, pg. 3646
SIERRA BROADCASTING COMPANY—See Intermountain West Communications Company; *U.S. Private*, pg. 2113
SIERRA BULLETS LLC; *U.S. Private*, pg. 3646
SIERRA CABLES PLC; *Int'l*, pg. 6904
THE SIERRA-CEDAR GROUP, INC.—See Golden Gate Capital Management II, LLC; *U.S. Private*, pg. 1732
SIERRA CELLULAR INC.—See Sierra Telecommunications Group; *U.S. Private*, pg. 3648
SIERRA CENTRAL CREDIT UNION; *U.S. Private*, pg. 3646
SIERRA CHEMICAL CO; *U.S. Private*, pg. 3646
SIERRACIN CORPORATION—See PPG Industries, Inc.; *U.S. Public*, pg. 1707
SIERRA CLUB; *U.S. Private*, pg. 3646
SIERRA COATING TECHNOLOGIES LLC; *U.S. Private*, pg. 3647
SIERRA COMMUNICATIONS LIMITED—See Siteserv Investments Limited; *Int'l*, pg. 6965
SIERRA CONCEPTS MANUFACTURING COMPANY INC.—See Ellison Technologies Inc.; *U.S. Private*, pg. 1374
SIERRA CONSTRUCTION COMPANY, INC.—See Sierra Industries Inc.; *U.S. Private*, pg. 3647
SIERRA CONSTRUCTION; *Int'l*, pg. 6904
SIERRA CREST EQUITIES LLC; *U.S. Private*, pg. 3647

SIERRA DESIGNS, INC.—See Exxel Outdoors, Inc.; *U.S. Private*, pg. 1453
SIERRA ENTERTAINMENT, INC.—See Microsoft Corporation; *U.S. Public*, pg. 1439
SIERRA FOREST PRODUCTS, INC.; *U.S. Private*, pg. 3647
SIERRA GRANDE MINERALS INC.; *Int'l*, pg. 6904
SIERRA HEALTH-CARE OPTIONS, INC.—See UnitedHealth Group Incorporated; *U.S. Public*, pg. 2252
SIERRA HEALTH & LIFE INSURANCE COMPANY, INC.—See UnitedHealth Group Incorporated; *U.S. Public*, pg. 2252
SIERRA HOME MEDICAL PRODUCTS, INC.—See UnitedHealth Group Incorporated; *U.S. Public*, pg. 2250
SIERRA INCOME CORPORATION—See Barings BDC, Inc.; *U.S. Public*, pg. 276
SIERRA INDUSTRIES INC.; *U.S. Private*, pg. 3647
SIERRA INSTRUMENTS INC.; *U.S. Private*, pg. 3647
SIERRA INSULATION CONTRACTORS, INC.—See Installed Building Products, Inc.; *U.S. Public*, pg. 1133
SIERRA INSURANCE ASSOCIATES INC.—See Heffernan Insurance Brokers; *U.S. Private*, pg. 1904
SIERRA INTERNATIONAL GROUP, INC.; *U.S. Private*, pg. 3647
SIERRA INTERNATIONAL LLC—See Dometic Group AB; *Int'l*, pg. 2160
SIERRA LAKE ACQUISITION CORP.; *U.S. Public*, pg. 1877
SIERRA LAND GROUP INC.; *U.S. Private*, pg. 3647
SIERRA LEONE CEMENT CORP. LTD.—See Heidelberg Materials AG; *Int'l*, pg. 3315
SIERRA LUMBER & FENCE—See Pacific States Industries Incorporated; *U.S. Private*, pg. 3071
SIERRA LUMBER & FENCE—See Pacific States Industries Incorporated; *U.S. Private*, pg. 3071
SIERRA LUMBER, INC.—See Owens Corning; *U.S. Public*, pg. 1627
SIERRA MACHINERY, INC.—See SMT Belgium NV; *Int'l*, pg. 7017
SIERRA MAZDA; *U.S. Private*, pg. 3647
SIERRA METALS INC.; *Int'l*, pg. 6904
SIERRA MICROWAVE TECHNOLOGY, LLC—See HEICO Corporation; *U.S. Public*, pg. 1020
SIERRA MONITOR CORPORATION—See MSA Safety Incorporated; *U.S. Public*, pg. 1482
SIERRA NEVADA BREWING CO.; *U.S. Private*, pg. 3647
SIERRA NEVADA CORPORATION; *U.S. Private*, pg. 3647
SIERRA NEVADA GOLD INC.; *U.S. Public*, pg. 1877
SIERRA NEVADA MEMORIAL HOSPITAL—See Catholic Health Initiatives; *U.S. Private*, pg. 790
SIERRA ONCOLOGY CANADA ULC—See Sierra Oncology, Inc.; *Int'l*, pg. 6904
SIERRA ONCOLOGY, INC.; *Int'l*, pg. 6904
SIERRA PACIFIC CONSTRUCTORS; *U.S. Private*, pg. 3647
SIERRA PACIFIC INDUSTRIES; *U.S. Private*, pg. 3647
SIERRA PACIFIC POWER COMPANY—See Berkshire Hathaway Inc.; *U.S. Public*, pg. 301
SIERRA PACIFIC TURF SUPPLY; *U.S. Private*, pg. 3647
SIERRA PACIFIC WINDOWS—See Sierra Pacific Industries; *U.S. Private*, pg. 3647
SIERRAPINE LIMITED - MCKILLICAN AMERICAN - AMERICAN HARDWOODS DIVISION—See SierraPine Limited; *U.S. Private*, pg. 3648
SIERRAPINE LIMITED; *U.S. Private*, pg. 3648
SIERRAPINE - MEDITE DIVISION—See SierraPine Limited; *U.S. Private*, pg. 3648
SIERRA PRECAST, INC.—See Vulcan Materials Company; *U.S. Public*, pg. 2314
SIERRA PROPERTIES; *U.S. Private*, pg. 3647
SIERRA PROVIDENCE HEALTH NETWORK, INC.—See Tenet Healthcare Corporation; *U.S. Public*, pg. 2003
SIERRA RADIOPHARMACY, LLC—See Cardinal Health, Inc.; *U.S. Public*, pg. 434
SIERRA READY MIX, LLC—See Summit Materials, Inc.; *U.S. Public*, pg. 1960
SIERRA RESEARCH, INC.—See Gryphon Investors, LLC; *U.S. Private*, pg. 1799
SIERRA RUTILE HOLDINGS LIMITED; *Int'l*, pg. 6904
SIERRA RUTILE LIMITED—See Iluka Resources Limited; *Int'l*, pg. 3616
SIERRA SELECT DISTRIBUTORS; *U.S. Private*, pg. 3647
SIERRA SPECIALTY INSURANCE SERVICES, INC.—See XPT Group LLC; *U.S. Private*, pg. 4582
SIERRA SYSTEMS - AUSTIN—See Nippon Telegraph & Telephone Corporation; *Int'l*, pg. 5348
SIERRA SYSTEMS - CALGARY MANAGED SERVICES—See Nippon Telegraph & Telephone Corporation; *Int'l*, pg. 5348
SIERRA SYSTEMS - CALGARY—See Nippon Telegraph & Telephone Corporation; *Int'l*, pg. 5348
SIERRA SYSTEMS - EDMONTON—See Nippon Telegraph & Telephone Corporation; *Int'l*, pg. 5348
SIERRA SYSTEMS - EL SEGUNDO—See Nippon Telegraph & Telephone Corporation; *Int'l*, pg. 5348
SIERRA SYSTEMS - FREDERICTON—See Nippon Telegraph & Telephone Corporation; *Int'l*, pg. 5348
SIERRA SYSTEMS GROUP INC.—See Nippon Telegraph & Telephone Corporation; *Int'l*, pg. 5348

COMPANY NAME INDEX

SIERRA SYSTEMS GROUP, INC.—See Nippon Telegraph & Telephone Corporation; *Int'l*, pg. 5348
SIERRA SYSTEMS - HARTFORD—See Nippon Telegraph & Telephone Corporation; *Int'l*, pg. 5348
SIERRA SYSTEMS INC.—See Nippon Telegraph & Telephone Corporation; *Int'l*, pg. 5348
SIERRA SYSTEMS - KIRKLAND—See Nippon Telegraph & Telephone Corporation; *Int'l*, pg. 5348
SIERRA SYSTEMS - OLYMPIA—See Nippon Telegraph & Telephone Corporation; *Int'l*, pg. 5348
SIERRA SYSTEMS - OTTAWA—See Nippon Telegraph & Telephone Corporation; *Int'l*, pg. 5348
SIERRA SYSTEMS - TORONTO—See Nippon Telegraph & Telephone Corporation; *Int'l*, pg. 5348
SIERRA SYSTEMS - VICTORIA—See Nippon Telegraph & Telephone Corporation; *Int'l*, pg. 5348
SIERRA SYSTEMS - WINNIPEG—See Nippon Telegraph & Telephone Corporation; *Int'l*, pg. 5348
SIERRA TECHNOLOGY CORPORATION—See American CyberSystems, Inc.; *U.S. Private*, pg. 230
SIERRA TELECOMMUNICATIONS GROUP; *U.S. Private*, pg. 3647
SIERRA TELEPHONE CO. INC.—See Sierra Telecommunications Group; *U.S. Private*, pg. 3648
SIERRA TILE SUPPLY, INC.; *U.S. Private*, pg. 3648
SIERRA TRADING POST INC.—See The TJX Companies, Inc.; *U.S. Public*, pg. 2134
SIERRA TRUSS, LLC—See Clyde Companies Inc.; *U.S. Private*, pg. 949
SIERRA TUCSON INC.—See Acadia Healthcare Company, Inc.; *U.S. Public*, pg. 30
SIERRA VENTURES; *U.S. Private*, pg. 3648
SIERRA VIEW MEMORIAL PARK—See Axar Capital Management L.P.; *U.S. Private*, pg. 412
SIERRA VISTA CHILD AND FAMILY SERVICES; *U.S. Private*, pg. 3648
SIERRA VISTA HOSPITAL, INC.—See Adventist Health System; *U.S. Private*, pg. 108
SIERRA VISTA MALL; LLC—See Brookfield Corporation; *Int'l*, pg. 1185
SIERRA VOLKSWAGEN INC.—See Bill Walsh Automotive Group; *U.S. Private*, pg. 558
SIERRA WIRELESS AMERICA, INC.—See Sierra Wireless, Inc.; *Int'l*, pg. 6904
SIERRA WIRELESS FRANCE—See Sierra Wireless, Inc.; *Int'l*, pg. 6904
SIERRA WIRELESS, INC.; *Int'l*, pg. 6904
SIERRA WIRELESS SERVICES AMERICA HOLDINGS INC.—See Sierra Wireless, Inc.; *Int'l*, pg. 6904
SIERRA W/O WIRES, INC.; *U.S. Private*, pg. 3648
SIERRITA GAS PIPELINE LLC—See Kinder Morgan, Inc.; *U.S. Public*, pg. 1234
SIE S.R.L.—See NOF Corporation; *Int'l*, pg. 5400
SIES S.R.L.—See Manutencoop Societa Cooperativa; *Int'l*, pg. 4680
SIETEL LIMITED; *Int'l*, pg. 6904
SIEU THANH CORPORATION; *Int'l*, pg. 6904
SIEVEKING INC.; *U.S. Private*, pg. 3648
SIEVERS EQUIPMENT CO.; *U.S. Private*, pg. 3648
SIEVI CAPITAL OYJ; *Int'l*, pg. 6905
SIEWERT EQUIPMENT CO. INC.—See Cummins-Wagner Co., Inc.; *U.S. Private*, pg. 1123
SIEYUAN ELECTRIC CO., LTD.; *Int'l*, pg. 6905
S.I.F.1CO., LTD.—See Singha Estate PCL; *Int'l*, pg. 6944
SI FACTOR LLC—See Agenzia Nazionale per l'Attrazione degli Investimenti e lo Sviluppo d'Impresa SpA; *Int'l*, pg. 206
SIFA LIMITED—See Simplybiz Group plc; *Int'l*, pg. 6934
SIFAS; *Int'l*, pg. 6905
SIFA YEMEK VE GIDA URETIM TESISLERI TIC. A.S.—See Ihlas Holding A.S.; *Int'l*, pg. 3606
SIF BANAT-CRISANA S.A.; *Int'l*, pg. 6905
SIFCA SA; *Int'l*, pg. 6905
SIFCO APPLIED SURFACE CONCEPTS—See SIFCO Industries, Inc.; *U.S. Public*, pg. 1877
SIFCO APPLIED SURFACE CONCEPTS SWEDEN AB—See SIFCO Industries, Inc.; *U.S. Public*, pg. 1877
SIFCO APPLIED SURFACE CONCEPTS (UK), LIMITED—See SIFCO Industries, Inc.; *U.S. Public*, pg. 1877
SIFCO ASC - FRANCE—See SIFCO Industries, Inc.; *U.S. Public*, pg. 1877
SIFCO FORGE GROUP—See SIFCO Industries, Inc.; *U.S. Public*, pg. 1877
SIFCO INDUSTRIES, INC.; *U.S. Public*, pg. 1877
S.I.F. CO., LTD.—See Singha Estate PCL; *Int'l*, pg. 6944
SIFCOM ASSURANCES—See Allianz SE; *Int'l*, pg. 355
SIFCO TURBINE COMPONENT SERVICES—See SIFCO Industries, Inc.; *U.S. Public*, pg. 1877
SIF GROUP BV—See Egeria Capital Management B.V.; *Int'l*, pg. 2323
SIF GROUTBOR S.A.—See VINCI S.A.; *Int'l*, pg. 8227
SIF HOTELURI SA—See SIF Banat-Crisana S.A.; *Int'l*, pg. 6905
SIF ICAP S.A. DE C.V.—See Bolsa Mexicana de Valores, S.A.B. de C.V.; *Int'l*, pg. 1103
SIF ICAP S.A. DE C.V.—See CME Group, Inc.; *U.S. Public*, pg. 517
SIFI CJ LOGISTIC SA; *Int'l*, pg. 6905

SIFI CJ STORAGE S.A.; *Int'l*, pg. 6905
SIFI CLUJ RETAIL S.A.; *Int'l*, pg. 6905
SIF IMOBILIARE PLC—See SIF Banat-Crisana S.A.; *Int'l*, pg. 6905
SI FINANCIAL GROUP, INC.—See Berkshire Hills Bancorp, Inc.; *U.S. Public*, pg. 320
S.I.F. ITALIA S.P.A.; *Int'l*, pg. 6456
SIFIVE, INC.; *U.S. Private*, pg. 3648
SIFLOOR AG—See Uzin Utz AG; *Int'l*, pg. 8103
SIF MUNTENIA S.A.; *Int'l*, pg. 6905
SIF SWISS INVESTMENT FUNDS S.A.—See EFG International AG; *Int'l*, pg. 2321
SIFTO CANADA, INC.—See Compass Minerals International, Inc.; *U.S. Public*, pg. 561
SIFTON PROPERTIES LTD.; *Int'l*, pg. 6906
SIFY TECHNOLOGIES LIMITED; *Int'l*, pg. 6906
SIGACHI INDUSTRIES LIMITED; *Int'l*, pg. 6907
SIGA DEVELOPMENT OPERATIONS—See MacAndrews & Forbes Incorporated; *U.S. Private*, pg. 2534
SIG AIR HANDLING HUNGARY KFT—See AIRVANCE GROUP; *Int'l*, pg. 250
SIG AIR HANDLING N.V.—See AIRVANCE GROUP; *Int'l*, pg. 250
SIG AIR HANDLING ROMANIA SRL—See AIRVANCE GROUP; *Int'l*, pg. 250
SIGAL CONSTRUCTION CORPORATION; *U.S. Private*, pg. 3648
SIGAL LIFE UNIQA GROUP AUSTRIA SH.A.—See UNIQA Insurance Group AG; *Int'l*, pg. 8058
SIGAL UNIQA GROUP AUSTRIA, RR.—See UNIQA Insurance Group AG; *Int'l*, pg. 8058
SIGAL UNIQA GROUP AUSTRIA SH.A.—See UNIQA Insurance Group AG; *Int'l*, pg. 8058
SIGARTH AB—See Rettig Group Ltd.; *Int'l*, pg. 6311
SIGARTH SP.Z O.O.—See Rettig Group Ltd.; *Int'l*, pg. 6311
SIG ASIA INVESTMENTS, LLLP—See Susquehanna International Group, LLP; *U.S. Private*, pg. 3885
SIGA TECHNOLOGIES, INC.—See MacAndrews & Forbes Incorporated; *U.S. Private*, pg. 2534
SIG BEVERAGES BRASIL LTDA.—See Tetra Laval International S.A.; *Int'l*, pg. 7577
SIG BUILDING PRODUCTS LIMITED—See SIG plc; *Int'l*, pg. 6906
SIG (CHINA) BEVERAGES MACHINERY CO. LTD.—See Tetra Laval International S.A.; *Int'l*, pg. 7577
SIG COMBIBLOC FRANCE—See ONEX Corporation; *Int'l*, pg. 5579
SIG COMBIBLOC GMBH—See ONEX Corporation; *Int'l*, pg. 5579
SIG COMBIBLOC GROUP AG—See Rank Group Ltd.; *Int'l*, pg. 6208
SIG COMBIBLOC GROUP LTD.—See ONEX Corporation; *Int'l*, pg. 5579
SIG COMBIBLOC S.A.—See ONEX Corporation; *Int'l*, pg. 5579
SIG COMBIBLOC S.R.L.—See ONEX Corporation; *Int'l*, pg. 5579
SIG COMBIBLOC TAIWAN LTD.—See ONEX Corporation; *Int'l*, pg. 5579
SIGDAL KJOKKEN AS—See Nobia AB; *Int'l*, pg. 5396
SIGDO KOPPERS S.A.; *Int'l*, pg. 6907
SIGDOPACK ARGENTINA S.A.—See Oben Holding Group SAC; *Int'l*, pg. 5510
SIGDOPACK S.A.—See Oben Holding Group SAC; *Int'l*, pg. 5510
SIGDOSCAF S.A.—See Sigdo Koppers S.A.; *Int'l*, pg. 6907
SIGDOTEK S.A.—See Sigdo Koppers S.A.; *Int'l*, pg. 6907
SIGECOM, LLC—See WideOpenWest, Inc.; *U.S. Public*, pg. 2370
SIGELS BEVERAGES LP—See Twin Liquors; *U.S. Private*, pg. 4265
SIGENCI SAS—See Societe Anonyme d'Explosifs et de Produits Chimiques; *Int'l*, pg. 7035
SIGE SEMICONDUCTOR (EUROPE) LIMITED—See Skyworks Solutions, Inc.; *U.S. Public*, pg. 1893
SIGE SEMICONDUCTOR (U.S.), CORP.—See Skyworks Solutions, Inc.; *U.S. Public*, pg. 1893
SIGES—See Sodexo S.A.; *Int'l*, pg. 7045
SIGETRONICS, INC.; *Int'l*, pg. 6907
SIGFIG WEALTH MANAGEMENT, LLC—See Nvest, Inc.; *U.S. Private*, pg. 2975
SIGFOX SA; *Int'l*, pg. 6907
SIG FRANCE S.A.S—See SIG plc; *Int'l*, pg. 6906
SIG GASES BERHAD—See L'Air Liquide S.A.; *Int'l*, pg. 4373
SIG GERMANY GMBH—See SIG plc; *Int'l*, pg. 6906
SIGGINS COMPANY INC.; *U.S. Private*, pg. 3648
SIGG SWITZERLAND AG—See Zhejiang Haers Vacuum Containers Co., Ltd.; *Int'l*, pg. 8654
SIGHTLIFE; *U.S. Private*, pg. 3648
SIGHTLINE COMMERCIAL SOLUTIONS LLC; *U.S. Private*, pg. 3648
SIGHTLINE HEALTH; *U.S. Private*, pg. 3648
SIGHTLINE MEDIA GROUP, LLC—See Regent, L.P.; *U.S. Private*, pg. 3388
SIGHT MEDICAL DOCTORS, PLLC—See Chicago Pacific Founders; *U.S. Private*, pg. 878

SIGHTPLAN, INC.—See SmartRent, Inc.; *U.S. Public*, pg. 1896
SIGHTRON JAPAN INC.; *Int'l*, pg. 6907
SIGHT SCIENCES, INC.; *U.S. Public*, pg. 1877
SIGILON THERAPEUTICS, INC.—See Eli Lilly and Company; *U.S. Public*, pg. 734
SIG INSULATION DUBLIN—See SIG plc; *Int'l*, pg. 6906
SIG INSULATION OMAGH—See SIG plc; *Int'l*, pg. 6906
SIG INTERNATIONAL TRADING LIMITED—See SIG plc; *Int'l*, pg. 6906
SIGIRIYA VILLAGE HOTELS PLC—See Lankem Ceylon PLC; *Int'l*, pg. 4412
SIGLER COMPANIES, INC.; *U.S. Private*, pg. 3648
SIGMA3 INTEGRATED RESERVOIR SOLUTIONS—See Symphony Technology Group, LLC; *U.S. Private*, pg. 3901
SIGMA AB—See Danir Resources AB; *Int'l*, pg. 1963
SIGMA ACQUISITION LLC—See Repay Holdings Corporation; *U.S. Public*, pg. 1784
SIGMA ADACTUM AB—See Danir Resources AB; *Int'l*, pg. 1963
SIGMA A.D.; *Int'l*, pg. 6907
SIGMA AIR CONDITIONING PTY. LTD.—See Knorr-Bremse AG; *Int'l*, pg. 4212
SIGMA-ALDRICH BIOCHEMIE GMBH—See Merck KGaA; *Int'l*, pg. 4832
SIGMA-ALDRICH BVBA/SPRL—See Merck KGaA; pg. 4832
SIGMA-ALDRICH BV—See Merck KGaA; *Int'l*, pg. 4832
SIGMA-ALDRICH CANADA CO.—See Merck KGaA; *Int'l*, pg. 4832
SIGMA-ALDRICH CHEMICALS PRIVATE LTD.—See Merck KGaA; *Int'l*, pg. 4832
SIGMA-ALDRICH CHEMIE GMBH—See Merck KGaA; *Int'l*, pg. 4832
SIGMA-ALDRICH CHEMIE HOLDING GMBH—See Merck KGaA; *Int'l*, pg. 4832
SIGMA-ALDRICH CHEMIE NV—See Merck KGaA; *Int'l*, pg. 4832
SIGMA-ALDRICH CHIMIE S.A.R.L.—See Merck KGaA; *Int'l*, pg. 4832
SIGMA-ALDRICH CHIMIE SNC—See Merck KGaA; *Int'l*, pg. 4832
SIGMA-ALDRICH CO. LTD.—See Merck KGaA; *Int'l*, pg. 4832
SIGMA-ALDRICH COMPANY LTD.—See Merck KGaA; *Int'l*, pg. 4832
SIGMA-ALDRICH CORPORATION—See Merck KGaA; *Int'l*, pg. 4832
SIGMA-ALDRICH GRUNDSTUCKS GMBH & CO. KG—See Merck KGaA; *Int'l*, pg. 4832
SIGMA-ALDRICH IRELAND LTD.—See Merck KGaA; *Int'l*, pg. 4832
SIGMA-ALDRICH ISRAEL, LTD.—See Merck KGaA; *Int'l*, pg. 4832
SIGMA-ALDRICH JAPAN G.K.—See Merck KGaA; *Int'l*, pg. 4832
SIGMA-ALDRICH MANUFACTURING LLC—See Merck KGaA; *Int'l*, pg. 4832
SIGMA-ALDRICH (M) SDN. BHD.—See Merck KGaA; *Int'l*, pg. 4832
SIGMA-ALDRICH OCEANIA PTY. LIMITED—See Merck KGaA; *Int'l*, pg. 4832
SIGMA-ALDRICH PRODUCTION GMBH—See Merck KGaA; *Int'l*, pg. 4832
SIGMA-ALDRICH PTE. LTD.—See Merck KGaA; *Int'l*, pg. 4832
SIGMA-ALDRICH PTY. LIMITED—See Merck KGaA; *Int'l*, pg. 4832
SIGMA-ALDRICH QUIMICA LTDA.—See Merck KGaA; *Int'l*, pg. 4832
SIGMA-ALDRICH RTC, INC.—See Merck KGaA; *Int'l*, pg. 4832
SIGMA-ALDRICH SPOL. S.R.O.—See Merck KGaA; *Int'l*, pg. 4832
SIGMA-ALDRICH SP. Z.O.O.—See Merck KGaA; *Int'l*, pg. 4832
SIGMA-ALDRICH SWEDEN AB—See Merck KGaA; *Int'l*, pg. 4832
SIGMA-ALDRICH (SWITZERLAND) HOLDING AG—See Merck KGaA; *Int'l*, pg. 4832
SIGMA ALIMENTOS NORESTE, S.A. DE C.V.—See ALFA, S.A.B. de C.V.; *Int'l*, pg. 314
SIGMA ALIMENTOS, S.A. DE C.V.—See ALFA, S.A.B. de C.V.; *Int'l*, pg. 313
SIGMA BETON—See Vicat S.A.; *Int'l*, pg. 8186
SIGMABLEYZER INVESTMENT GROUP LLC; *U.S. Private*, pg. 3649
SIGMA BRAVO PTY LTD—See KBR, Inc.; *U.S. Public*, pg. 1216
SIGMABROADBAND CO.; *U.S. Public*, pg. 1877
SIGMA CABLE CO. (PTE) LTD.—See Asia Pacific Wire & Cable Corporation Limited; *Int'l*, pg. 614
SIGMA CAPITAL GROUP PLC—See Pacific Century Group Holdings Limited; *Int'l*, pg. 5687
SIGMA CIRCUITS, INC.—See TE Connectivity Ltd.; *Int'l*, pg. 7497
SIGMA CIVIL AB—See Danir Resources AB; *Int'l*, pg. 1963

SIGMABROADBAND CO.

CORPORATE AFFILIATIONS

SIGMA COACHAIR GROUP (CHINA) CO., LTD.—See Knorr-Bremse AG; *Int'l*, pg. 4212
SIGMA COATINGS PROPRIETARY LIMITED—See PPG Industries, Inc.; *U.S. Public*, pg. 1710
SIGMA COMMUNICATIONS INC.—See Mystar Engineering Corporation; *Int'l*, pg. 5114
SIGMA COMPANY LIMITED NORTHERN TERRITORY—See Sigma Healthcare Ltd.; *Int'l*, pg. 6908
SIGMA COMPANY LIMITED QUEENSLAND—See Sigma Healthcare Ltd.; *Int'l*, pg. 6908
SIGMA COMPANY LIMITED SOUTH AUSTRALIA—See Sigma Healthcare Ltd.; *Int'l*, pg. 6908
SIGMA COMPANY LIMITED TASMANIA—See Sigma Healthcare Ltd.; *Int'l*, pg. 6908
SIGMA COMPANY LIMITED WESTERN AUSTRALIA—See Sigma Healthcare Ltd.; *Int'l*, pg. 6908
SIGMA CONSULTING SOLUTIONS LTD—See Danir Resources AB; *Int'l*, pg. 1963
SIGMA CORPORATION; *U.S. Private*, pg. 3648
SIGMA DEFENSE SYSTEMS LLC—See Sagewind Capital LLC; *U.S. Private*, pg. 3527
SIGMADIS S.A.—See Sonepar S.A.; *Int'l*, pg. 7091
SIGMA DISTRIBUTING COMPANY INCORPORATED; *U.S. Private*, pg. 3648
SIGMA ELECTRIC MANUFACTURING CORPORATION—See Argand Partners, LP; *U.S. Private*, pg. 319
SIGMA ELEVATOR (HK) LIMITED—See Otis Worldwide Corporation; *U.S. Public*, pg. 1623
SIGMA EMPROVE AB—See Danir Resources AB; *Int'l*, pg. 1963
SIGMA ENERGO, S.R.O.—See CEZ, a.s.; *Int'l*, pg. 1428
SIGMA ENGINEERING GMBH—See MAGMA GmbH; *Int'l*, pg. 4638
SIGMA ENGINEERING LTD.—See Synex Renewable Energy Corporation; *Int'l*, pg. 7385
SIGMA-EPAN INTERNATIONAL PTE., LTD.—See Asia Pacific Wire & Cable Corporation Limited; *Int'l*, pg. 614
SIGMA FOODS INC.—See ALFA, S.A.B. de C.V.; *Int'l*, pg. 314
SIGMA FREUDENBERG NOK PVT. LTD. - 2 PLANT—See Freudenberg SE; *Int'l*, pg. 2790
SIGMA FREUDENBERG NOK PVT. LTD.—See Freudenberg SE; *Int'l*, pg. 2790
SIGMA GROUP, INC.; *U.S. Private*, pg. 3648
THE SIGMA GROUP, LLC—See Research America, Inc.; *U.S. Private*, pg. 3403
SIGMA HANDELS GMBH—See Trimble, Inc.; *U.S. Public*, pg. 2191
SIGMA HEALTHCARE LTD.; *Int'l*, pg. 6907
SIGMA HEALTH CARE—See Sigma Healthcare Ltd.; *Int'l*, pg. 6908
SIGMA IMAL PROJEKTLEDNING AB—See Danir Resources AB; *Int'l*, pg. 1963
SIGMA INSPECTION AS—See IKM Gruppen AS; *Int'l*, pg. 3612
SIGMA INTERNATIONAL (POLAND) LTD.—See The Interpublic Group of Companies, Inc.; *U.S. Public*, pg. 2105
SIGMA JAPAN CO., LTD.—See Tokyu Fudosan Holdings Corporation; *Int'l*, pg. 7798
SIGMAKALON NIGERIA LIMITED—See PPG Industries, Inc.; *U.S. Public*, pg. 1710
SIGMA KFT.—See Fotex Holding SE; *Int'l*, pg. 2752
SIGMA KOKI CO., LTD. - HIDAKA PLANT—See Sigma Koki Co., Ltd.; *Int'l*, pg. 6908
SIGMA KOKI CO., LTD. - NOTO PLANT—See Sigma Koki Co., Ltd.; *Int'l*, pg. 6908
SIGMA KOKI CO., LTD.; *Int'l*, pg. 6908
SIGMA KUDOS FINLAND OY—See Danir Resources AB; *Int'l*, pg. 1963
SIGMA LITHIUM CORPORATION; *Int'l*, pg. 6908
SIGMA MARINE & PROTECTIVE COATINGS HOLDING B.V.—See PPG Industries, Inc.; *U.S. Public*, pg. 1710
SIGMA MARKETING GROUP LLC—See DeltaPoint Capital Management, LLC; *U.S. Private*, pg. 1202
SIGMA MAXIFLEX OY—See Danir Resources AB; *Int'l*, pg. 1963
SIGMAMELTEC LTD.—See Applied Materials, Inc.; *U.S. Public*, pg. 172
SIGMANEST GMBH—See Sandvik AB; *Int'l*, pg. 6535
SIGMA NZ LIMITED—See Sigma Healthcare Ltd.; *Int'l*, pg. 6908
SIGMA PARTNERS; *U.S. Private*, pg. 3648
SIGMA PRIME VENTURES, LLC—See Sigma Partners; *U.S. Private*, pg. 3649
SIGMARENOPRO, INC.; *Int'l*, pg. 6908
SIGMAROC PLC; *Int'l*, pg. 6908
SIGMA S.A. DE C.V.; *Int'l*, pg. 6908
SIGMA SAMSUNG COATINGS CO., LTD—See PPG Industries, Inc.; *U.S. Public*, pg. 1710
SIGMA SEVEN LIMITED—See Capita plc; *Int'l*, pg. 1309
SIGMA SH.A—See Vienna Insurance Group AG Wiener Versicherung Gruppe; *Int'l*, pg. 8195
SIGMA SIX SOLUTIONS, INC.—See Gryphon Investors, LLC; *U.S. Private*, pg. 1799
SIGMA SOLUTIONS AB—See Danir Resources AB; *Int'l*, pg. 1963

SIGMA SOLVE LIMITED; *Int'l*, pg. 6908
SIGMA STRETCH FILM - CALIFORNIA PLANT—See Alpha Industries, Inc.; *U.S. Private*, pg. 198
SIGMA STRETCH FILM - CANADA PLANT—See Alpha Industries, Inc.; *U.S. Private*, pg. 198
SIGMA STRETCH FILM - KENTUCKY PLANT—See Alpha Industries, Inc.; *U.S. Private*, pg. 198
SIGMA STRETCH FILM - OKLAHOMA PLANT—See Alpha Industries, Inc.; *U.S. Private*, pg. 198
SIGMA SUPPLY INC.; *U.S. Private*, pg. 3649
SIGMA SURVEILLANCE, INC.; *U.S. Private*, pg. 3649
SIGMASYS CORP.—See inTEST Corporation; *U.S. Public*, pg. 1159
SIGMA SYSTEMS GROUP (USA) INC.—See Hansen Technologies Limited; *Int'l*, pg. 3260
SIGMA SYSTEMS JAPAN K.K.—See Hansen Technologies Limited; *Int'l*, pg. 3260
SIGMATA ELECTRONICS, INC.; *U.S. Public*, pg. 1877
SIGMA-TAU ARZNEIMITTEL GMBH—See Sigma-Tau Industrie Farmaceutiche Riunite S.p.A.; *Int'l*, pg. 6908
SIGMA TAU B.V.—See Sigma-Tau Industrie Farmaceutiche Riunite S.p.A.; *Int'l*, pg. 6908
SIGMA-TAU ESPANA S.A.—See Sigma-Tau Industrie Farmaceutiche Riunite S.p.A.; *Int'l*, pg. 6908
SIGMA-TAU FRANCE S.A.R.L.—See Sigma-Tau Industrie Farmaceutiche Riunite S.p.A.; *Int'l*, pg. 6908
SIGMA-TAU INDUSTRIE FARMACEUTICHE RIUNITE S.P.A.; *Int'l*, pg. 6908
SIGMA-TAU PHARMACEUTICALS, INC.—See Sigma-Tau Industrie Farmaceutiche Riunite S.p.A.; *Int'l*, pg. 6908
SIGMATECH INC.—See HORIBA Ltd; *Int'l*, pg. 3478
SIGMA TECHNOLOGY HUNGARY LTD.—See Danir Resources AB; *Int'l*, pg. 1963
SIGMA TECHNOLOGY MANAGEMENT LTD.—See Pacific Century Group Holdings Limited; *Int'l*, pg. 5687
SIGMA TECHNOLOGY SOLUTIONS, INC.—See Pivot Technology Solutions, Inc.; *U.S. Public*, pg. 1695
SIGMA TECHNOLOGY S.R.L.—See Fair Friend Group; *Int'l*, pg. 2604
SIGMATEC INGENIERIE—See VINCI S.A.; *Int'l*, pg. 8233
SIGMATEK AUSTRALIA PTY. LTD.—See Sandvik AB; *Int'l*, pg. 6535
SIGMATEK CANADA, LLC—See Sandvik AB; *Int'l*, pg. 6535
SIGMATEK JAPAN LTD.—See Sandvik AB; *Int'l*, pg. 6535
SIGMATEK S.R.L.—See Sandvik AB; *Int'l*, pg. 6535
SIGMATEK SYSTEMS BRASIL LTDA.—See Sandvik AB; *Int'l*, pg. 6535
SIGMATEK SYSTEMS CHINA, LLC—See Sandvik AB; *Int'l*, pg. 6535
SIGMATEK SYSTEMS INDIA PRIVATE LIMITED—See Sandvik AB; *Int'l*, pg. 6535
SIGMATEK SYSTEMS, LLC—See Sandvik AB; *Int'l*, pg. 6535
SIGMATRON ELECTRONIC TECHNOLOGY CO., LTD.—See SigmaTron International, Inc.; *U.S. Public*, pg. 1877
SIGMATRON INTERNATIONAL, INC.; *U.S. Public*, pg. 1877
SIGMATRON US - WEST COAST—See SigmaTron International, Inc.; *U.S. Public*, pg. 1877
SIGMA (W.A.) PTY LTD—See Sigma Healthcare Ltd.; *Int'l*, pg. 6908
SIGMAWAYS INC.; *U.S. Private*, pg. 3649
SIGMAWORKS GROUP—See Omnicom Group Inc.; *U.S. Public*, pg. 1594
SIGMAXYZ HOLDINGS INC.; *Int'l*, pg. 6909
SIGMU D.P.T. CO., LTD.—See Taiwan Secom Company Ltd.; *Int'l*, pg. 7423
SIGMUND COHN CORP.; *U.S. Private*, pg. 3649
SIGNA 12 VERWALTUNGS GMBH—See Allianz SE; *Int'l*, pg. 355
SIGNA DEVELOPMENT SERVICES, INC.—See DLR Holding, LLC; *U.S. Private*, pg. 1247
SIGNA ENGINEERING CORP.—See Weatherford International plc; *U.S. Public*, pg. 2339
SIGNA FINANCIAL SERVICES AG—See SIGNA Holding GmbH; *Int'l*, pg. 6909
SIGNAFIRE TECHNOLOGIES INC.—See NowVertical Group Inc.; *Int'l*, pg. 5471
SIGNA HOLDING GMBH; *Int'l*, pg. 6909
SIGNAL ADVANCE, INC.; *U.S. Public*, pg. 1878
SIGNAL AG—See INTEGRA Holding AG; *Int'l*, pg. 3729
SIGNAL ANALYTICS PRIVATE LIMITED—See Xelpmoc Design & Tech Ltd.; *Int'l*, pg. 8521
SIGNAL & BANEBYGGARNA I DALARNA AB—See NRC Group ASA; *Int'l*, pg. 5473
SIGNALBAU HUBER HELLAS A.E.—See SWARCO AG; *Int'l*, pg. 7361
SIGNAL BIZTOSITO ZRT.—See SIGNAL IDUNA Gruppe; *Int'l*, pg. 6910
SIGNAL CAPITAL CORPORATION—See WESCO International, Inc.; *U.S. Public*, pg. 2351
SIGNAL CAPITAL PARTNERS LIMITED; *Int'l*, pg. 6910
SIGNAL COMMUNICATIONS LIMITED—See CircuTech International Holdings Limited; *Int'l*, pg. 1618
SIGNALDEMAND, INC.—See PROS Holdings, Inc.; *U.S. Public*, pg. 1728

SIGNALEN AB—See LKQ Corporation; *U.S. Public*, pg. 1336
SIGNAL ENTERTAINMENT GROUP CORP.; *Int'l*, pg. 6910
SIGNALFIRE TELEMETRY INC.—See The TASI Group; *U.S. Private*, pg. 4126
SIGNAL GOLD INC.; *Int'l*, pg. 6910
THE SIGNAL GROUP, LLC; *U.S. Private*, pg. 4118
SIGNAL HILL ACQUISITION CORP.; *U.S. Public*, pg. 1878
SIGNALHORN AG—See Signalhorn Trusted Networks GmbH; *Int'l*, pg. 6910
SIGNALHORN TRUSTED NETWORKS GMBH; *Int'l*, pg. 6910
SIGNAL IDUNA ASIGURARE REASIGURARE S.A.—See SIGNAL IDUNA Gruppe; *Int'l*, pg. 6910
SIGNAL IDUNA GRUPPE; *Int'l*, pg. 6910
SIGNAL IDUNA GRUPPE—See SIGNAL IDUNA Gruppe; *Int'l*, pg. 6910
SIGNAL IDUNA PENSIONSKASSE AG—See SIGNAL IDUNA Gruppe; *Int'l*, pg. 6910
SIGNAL IDUNA POLSKA TOWARZYSTWO UBEZPIECZEN S.A.—See SIGNAL IDUNA Gruppe; *Int'l*, pg. 6910
SIGNAL IDUNA REINSURANCE LTD—See SIGNAL IDUNA Gruppe; *Int'l*, pg. 6910
SIGNAL INNOVATIONS GROUP INC.—See BAE Systems plc; *Int'l*, pg. 798
SIGNAL LAKE MANAGEMENT LLC; *U.S. Private*, pg. 3649
SIGNALLAMP HEALTH INC.—See Sunstone Partners Management LLC; *U.S. Private*, pg. 3873
SIGNAL LANDMARK—See California Coastal Communities, Inc.; *U.S. Private*, pg. 718
SIGNAL METAL INDUSTRIES INC.; *U.S. Private*, pg. 3649
SIGNAL ONE FIRE AND COMMUNICATION, LLC—See APi Group Corporation; *Int'l*, pg. 514
SIGNAL OUTDOOR ADVERTISING LLC—See MSouth Equity Partners, LLC; *U.S. Private*, pg. 2808
SIGNAL OUTDOOR ADVERTISING—See MSouth Equity Partners, LLC; *U.S. Private*, pg. 2808
SIGNAL OUTDOOR ADVERTISING—See MSouth Equity Partners, LLC; *U.S. Private*, pg. 2808
SIGNAL OUTDOOR ADVERTISING—See MSouth Equity Partners, LLC; *U.S. Private*, pg. 2808
SIGNAL OUTDOOR ADVERTISING—See MSouth Equity Partners, LLC; *U.S. Private*, pg. 2808
SIGNAL OUTDOOR ADVERTISING—See MSouth Equity Partners, LLC; *U.S. Private*, pg. 2808
SIGNAL OUTDOOR ADVERTISING—See MSouth Equity Partners, LLC; *U.S. Private*, pg. 2808
SIGNAL PEAK VENTURE PARTNERS, LLC; *U.S. Private*, pg. 3649
SIGNAL PERFECTION LTD.—See Marlin Equity Partners, LLC; *U.S. Private*, pg. 2583
SIGNAL POINT MARKETING+DESIGN; *U.S. Private*, pg. 3649
SIGNAL POINT SYSTEMS INC.—See BAI Communications Pty Ltd; *Int'l*, pg. 801
SIGNAL RADIO LIMITED—See News Corporation; *U.S. Public*, pg. 1520
SIGNALSCAPE, INC.; *U.S. Private*, pg. 3649
SIGNAL SCIENCES, LLC—See Fastly, Inc.; *U.S. Public*, pg. 824
SIGNALSERVIS A.D.; *Int'l*, pg. 6910
SIGNAL; *U.S. Private*, pg. 3649
SIGNAL TRANSFORMER CO., INC.—See Bel Fuse Inc.; *U.S. Public*, pg. 293
SIGNALTREE MARKETING & ADVERTISING; *U.S. Private*, pg. 3649
SIGNAMAX CONNECTIVITY SYSTEMS CANADA, INC.—See AESP, Inc.; *U.S. Private*, pg. 120
SIGNANT HEALTH MGT LLP; *U.S. Private*, pg. 3649
SIGNAPAY; *U.S. Private*, pg. 3649
SIGNA PRIME SELECTION AG—See SIGNA Holding GmbH; *Int'l*, pg. 6909
SIGN-A-RAMA INC.—See UFG Group, Inc.; *U.S. Private*, pg. 4274
SIGN-A-RAMA; *U.S. Private*, pg. 3649
SIGNA REAL ESTATE CAPITAL PARTNERS—See SIGNA Holding GmbH; *Int'l*, pg. 6909
SIGNA SPORTS UNITED GMBH—See SIGNA Sports United N.V.; *Int'l*, pg. 6909
SIGNA SPORTS UNITED N.V.; *Int'l*, pg. 6909
SIGNATOR INVESTORS INC.—See Reverence Capital Partners LLC; *U.S. Private*, pg. 3415
SIGNATURE ACADEMY SDN BHD—See Signature International Berhad; *Int'l*, pg. 6910
SIGNATURE AGENCY, INC.—See The Allstate Corporation; *U.S. Public*, pg. 2034
SIGNATURE AG; *Int'l*, pg. 6910
SIGNATURE ALUMINIUM SDN BHD—See Signature International Berhad; *Int'l*, pg. 6910
SIGNATURE ALUMINUM CANADA, INC.—See H.I.G. Capital, LLC; *U.S. Private*, pg. 1831
SIGNATURE AVIATION LIMITED—See BlackRock, Inc.; *U.S. Public*, pg. 346
SIGNATURE AVIATION LIMITED—See Blackstone Inc.; *U.S. Public*, pg. 358

SIGNATURE AVIATION LIMITED—See Cascade Investment LLC; *U.S. Private*, pg. 780
SIGNATURE BANK OF ARKANSAS; *U.S. Private*, pg. 3649
SIGNATURE BANK OF GEORGIA; *U.S. Public*, pg. 1878
SIGNATURE BEAUTY B.V.—See B&S Group S.A.; *Int'l*, pg. 784
SIGNATURE BRANDS, LLC—See Marvin Traub Associates, Inc.; *U.S. Private*, pg. 2598
SIGNATURE BREADS, INC.; *U.S. Private*, pg. 3649
SIGNATURE BUSINESS SYSTEMS, INC.; *U.S. Private*, pg. 3650
SIGNATURE CAPITAL INVESTMENTS LIMITED—See RF Capital Pty Ltd.; *Int'l*, pg. 6318
SIGNATURE CLOSERS, LLC—See Stewart Information Services Corporation; *U.S. Public*, pg. 1948
SIGNATURE COMMUNICATIONS; *U.S. Private*, pg. 3650
SIGNATURE CONSULTANTS LLC—See Digital Intelligence Systems, LLC; *U.S. Private*, pg. 1230
SIGNATURE CONTRACTING SERVICES LLC; *U.S. Private*, pg. 3650
SIGNATURE CONTROL SYSTEMS, LLC—See TIBA Parking LLC; *U.S. Private*, pg. 4166
SIGNATURE DEVICES, INC.; *U.S. Public*, pg. 1878
SIGNATURE ESTATE & INVESTMENT ADVISORS, LLC—See Reverence Capital Partners LLC; *U.S. Private*, pg. 3415
SIGNATURE EYEWEAR, INC.; *U.S. Public*, pg. 1878
SIGNATURE (FENCING AND FLOORING) SYSTEMS EUROPE, LTD.—See Myers Industries, Inc.; *U.S. Public*, pg. 1488
SIGNATURE FLEXIBLE PACKAGING, INC.—See H.I.G. Capital, LLC; *U.S. Private*, pg. 1834
SIGNATURE FLEXIBLE PACKAGING—See H.I.G. Capital, LLC; *U.S. Private*, pg. 1834
SIGNATURE FLIGHT SUPPORT - BED—See BlackRock, Inc.; *U.S. Public*, pg. 346
SIGNATURE FLIGHT SUPPORT - BED—See Blackstone Inc.; *U.S. Public*, pg. 358
SIGNATURE FLIGHT SUPPORT - BED—See Cascade Investment LLC; *U.S. Private*, pg. 780
SIGNATURE FLIGHT SUPPORT CORP—See BlackRock, Inc.; *U.S. Public*, pg. 346
SIGNATURE FLIGHT SUPPORT CORP—See Blackstone Inc.; *U.S. Public*, pg. 358
SIGNATURE FLIGHT SUPPORT CORP.—See Cascade Investment LLC; *U.S. Private*, pg. 780
SIGNATURE FLIGHT SUPPORT - MKE—See BlackRock, Inc.; *U.S. Public*, pg. 346
SIGNATURE FLIGHT SUPPORT - MKE—See Blackstone Inc.; *U.S. Public*, pg. 358
SIGNATURE FLIGHT SUPPORT - MKE—See Cascade Investment LLC; *U.S. Private*, pg. 780
SIGNATURE FLIGHT SUPPORT - MMU—See BlackRock, Inc.; *U.S. Public*, pg. 346
SIGNATURE FLIGHT SUPPORT - MMU—See Blackstone Inc.; *U.S. Public*, pg. 358
SIGNATURE FLIGHT SUPPORT - MMU—See Cascade Investment LLC; *U.S. Private*, pg. 780
SIGNATURE FLIGHT SUPPORT PARIS SA—See BlackRock, Inc.; *U.S. Public*, pg. 346
SIGNATURE FLIGHT SUPPORT PARIS SA—See Blackstone Inc.; *U.S. Public*, pg. 358
SIGNATURE FLIGHT SUPPORT PARIS SA—See Cascade Investment LLC; *U.S. Private*, pg. 781
SIGNATURE FLIGHT SUPPORT - PIE—See BlackRock, Inc.; *U.S. Public*, pg. 346
SIGNATURE FLIGHT SUPPORT - PIE—See Blackstone Inc.; *U.S. Public*, pg. 358
SIGNATURE FLIGHT SUPPORT - PIE—See Cascade Investment LLC; *U.S. Private*, pg. 780
SIGNATURE FLIGHT SUPPORT - PWK—See BlackRock, Inc.; *U.S. Public*, pg. 346
SIGNATURE FLIGHT SUPPORT - PWK—See Blackstone Inc.; *U.S. Public*, pg. 358
SIGNATURE FLIGHT SUPPORT - PWK—See Cascade Investment LLC; *U.S. Private*, pg. 781
SIGNATURE FLIGHT SUPPORT - STL—See BlackRock, Inc.; *U.S. Public*, pg. 346
SIGNATURE FLIGHT SUPPORT - STL—See Blackstone Inc.; *U.S. Public*, pg. 358
SIGNATURE FLIGHT SUPPORT - STL—See Cascade Investment LLC; *U.S. Private*, pg. 780
SIGNATURE FLIGHT SUPPORT WASHINGTON NATIONAL, INC.—See BlackRock, Inc.; *U.S. Public*, pg. 346
SIGNATURE FLIGHT SUPPORT WASHINGTON NATIONAL, INC.—See Blackstone Inc.; *U.S. Public*, pg. 358
SIGNATURE FLIGHT SUPPORT WASHINGTON NATIONAL, INC.—See Cascade Investment LLC; *U.S. Private*, pg. 781
SIGNATURE FOODS, INC.; *U.S. Private*, pg. 3650
SIGNATURE FORD OF PERRY, LLC—See Elder Automotive Group; *U.S. Private*, pg. 1350
SIGNATURE GENOMIC LABORATORIES, LLC; *U.S. Private*, pg. 3650
SIGNATUREGLOBAL (INDIA) LIMITED; *Int'l*, pg. 6910

SIGNATURE GRAPHICS—See Omnicom Group Inc.; *U.S. Public*, pg. 1593
SIGNATURE GROUP INC—See The Jansen Group Inc.; *U.S. Private*, pg. 4058
THE SIGNATURE GROUP, LLC—See North Carolina Mutual Life Insurance Company; *U.S. Private*, pg. 2943
SIGNATURE HARDWARE; *U.S. Private*, pg. 3650
SIGNATURE HEALTHCARE AT TOWER ROAD—See Signature HealthCARE LLC; *U.S. Private*, pg. 3650
SIGNATURE HEALTHCARE LLC; *U.S. Private*, pg. 3650
SIGNATURE HEALTHCARE OF COSHOCTON—See Signature HealthCARE LLC; *U.S. Private*, pg. 3650
SIGNATURE HELLAS A.E.—See VINCI S.A.; *Int'l*, pg. 8220
SIGNATURE HOME MORTGAGE, LLC—See Wells Fargo & Company; *U.S. Public*, pg. 2345
SIGNATURE INSURANCE AGENCY, INC.—See Triple-S Management Corp.; *U.S. Private*, pg. 2195
SIGNATURE INTERNATIONAL BERHAD; *Int'l*, pg. 6910
SIGNATURE KITCHEN SDN BHD—See Signature International Berhad; *Int'l*, pg. 6910
SIGNATURE LEARNING RESOURCES, INC.—See American Learning Corporation; *U.S. Private*, pg. 239
SIGNATURE LEISURE, INC.; *U.S. Public*, pg. 1878
SIGNATURE METALS LIMITED—See Shen Yao Holdings Limited; *Int'l*, pg. 6800
SIGNATURE MORTGAGE CORPORATION—See Eustis Mortgage Corp.; *U.S. Private*, pg. 1434
SIGNATURE MOTOR CLUB, INC.—See The Allstate Corporation; *U.S. Public*, pg. 2034
SIGNATURE OBICORP SDN BHD—See Signature International Berhad; *Int'l*, pg. 6910
SIGNATURE OFFSET, INC.; *U.S. Private*, pg. 3650
SIGNATURE PARTNERS, LTD.; *U.S. Private*, pg. 3650
SIGNATURE PHYSICAL THERAPY, LIMITED PARTNERSHIP—See U.S. Physical Therapy, Inc.; *U.S. Public*, pg. 2216
SIGNATURE RESOURCES LTD.; *Int'l*, pg. 6910
SIGNATURE RESOURCES PTY. LTD.—See Strategic Minerals Corporation NL; *Int'l*, pg. 7236
SIGNATURE S.A.—See Burelle S.A.; *Int'l*, pg. 1223
SIGNATURE SAS—See VINCI S.A.; *Int'l*, pg. 8220
SIGNATURE SECURITY GROUP HOLDINGS PTY LIMITED—See Johnson Controls International plc; *Int'l*, pg. 3988
SIGNATURE SECURITY GROUP PTY LIMITED—See Johnson Controls International plc; *Int'l*, pg. 3988
SIGNATURE SKYLIGHTS, LLC; *U.S. Private*, pg. 3650
SIGNATURE SMILE—See CPF Dental, LLC; *U.S. Private*, pg. 1080
SIGNATURES—See Starcrest Products of California; *U.S. Private*, pg. 3786
SIGNATURE STYLES, LLC—See Patriarch Partners, LLC; *U.S. Private*, pg. 3109
SIGNATURE SYSTEMS GROUP, LLC—See Myers Industries, Inc.; *U.S. Public*, pg. 1488
SIGNATURE TECHNOLOGIES INC.—See SITA Inc. N.V.; *Int'l*, pg. 6964
SIGNATURE TECHNOLOGY GROUP, INC.—See TD Synnex Corp; *U.S. Public*, pg. 1986
SIGNATURE THEATRES LLC; *U.S. Private*, pg. 3650
SIGNATURE TRANSPORTATION GROUP, LLC; *U.S. Private*, pg. 3650
SIGNATURE TRUCK SYSTEMS LLC—See TerraVest Industries, Inc.; *Int'l*, pg. 7568
SIGNATURE VACATIONS, INC.—See Sunwing Travel Group, Inc.; *Int'l*, pg. 7332
SIGNATURE VERTICAL ET MOBILITY SOLUTIONS SAS—See VINCI S.A.; *Int'l*, pg. 8227
SIGNATUR FASTIGHETER AB—See Fastighets AB Trianon; *Int'l*, pg. 2622
SIGNAUX GIROD S.A.; *Int'l*, pg. 6910
SIGNCAD SYSTEMS, INC.—See Bentley Systems, Inc.; *U.S. Public*, pg. 297
SIGNCASTER CORPORATION; *U.S. Private*, pg. 3650
SIGNCORP—See The Signcraft Group; *Int'l*, pg. 7686
THE SIGNCRAFT GROUP; *Int'l*, pg. 7685
SIGNCRAFT HONG KONG—See The Signcraft Group; *Int'l*, pg. 7686
SIGNCRAFT VARISIGNS PTY. LTD.—See The Signcraft Group; *Int'l*, pg. 7686
SIGNEOS GMBH—See VINCI S.A.; *Int'l*, pg. 8227
SIGNER BUICK-CADILLAC; *U.S. Private*, pg. 3650
SIGNET ARMORLITE (ASIA) PTE LTD—See EssilorLuxottica SA; *Int'l*, pg. 2516
SIGNET ARMORLITE CANADA, INC—See EssilorLuxottica SA; *Int'l*, pg. 2516
SIGNET ARMORLITE GERMANY HOLDING GMBH—See EssilorLuxottica SA; *Int'l*, pg. 2516
SIGNET ARMORLITE (HOLLAND) BV—See EssilorLuxottica SA; *Int'l*, pg. 2516
SIGNET ARMORLITE IBERICA SA—See EssilorLuxottica SA; *Int'l*, pg. 2516
SIGNET ARMORLITE, INC.—See EssilorLuxottica SA; *Int'l*, pg. 2514
SIGNET ARMORLITE OPTIC GMBH—See EssilorLuxottica SA; *Int'l*, pg. 2516
SIGNET EXCIPIENTS PRIVATE LTD.—See IMCD N.V.; *Int'l*, pg. 3622

SIGNET GROUP LIMITED—See Signet Jewelers Limited; *Int'l*, pg. 6911
SIGNET GROUP SERVICES LIMITED—See Signet Jewelers Limited; *Int'l*, pg. 6911
SIGNET GROUP TREASURY SERVICES INC.—See Signet Jewelers Limited; *Int'l*, pg. 6911
SIGNET HEALTHCARE PARTNERS, LLC; *U.S. Private*, pg. 3650
SIGNET HOLDINGS LIMITED—See Signet Jewelers Limited; *Int'l*, pg. 6911
SIGNETICS CORPORATION; *Int'l*, pg. 6911
SIGNETICS HIGH TECHNOLOGY, INC.—See Signetics Corporation; *Int'l*, pg. 6911
SIGNET INDUSTRIES LIMITED; *Int'l*, pg. 6911
SIGNET JEWELERS LIMITED; *Int'l*, pg. 6911
SIGNET LLC; *U.S. Private*, pg. 3650
SIGNET MARITIME CORP.; *U.S. Private*, pg. 3650
SIGNET MINERALS INC.—See Troilus Gold Corp.; *Int'l*, pg. 7938
SIGNET STAR HOLDINGS, INC.—See W.R. Berkley Corporation; *U.S. Public*, pg. 2318
SIGNET TECHNOLOGY INC—See Fluor Corporation; *U.S. Public*, pg. 859
SIGNET TRADING LTD.—See Signet Jewelers Limited; *Int'l*, pg. 6911
SIGNET UK FINANCE PLC—See Signet Jewelers Limited; *Int'l*, pg. 6911
SIGNIA AEROSPACE—See Arcline Investment Management LP; *U.S. Private*, pg. 315
SIGNIA FINANCIAL GROUP INC—See GraceKennedy Limited; *Int'l*, pg. 3049
SIGNIANT INC.; *U.S. Private*, pg. 3650
SIGNICAST LLC—See Partners Group Holding AG; *Int'l*, pg. 5749
SIGNIFY BELGIUM N.V.—See Signify N.V.; *Int'l*, pg. 6911
SIGNIFY (CHINA) INVESTMENT CO., LTD.—See Signify N.V.; *Int'l*, pg. 6912
SIGNIFY FRANCE S.A.S.—See Signify N.V.; *Int'l*, pg. 6911
SIGNIFY GMBH—See Signify N.V.; *Int'l*, pg. 6911
SIGNIFY HEALTH, INC.—See CVS Health Corporation; *U.S. Public*, pg. 616
SIGNIFY HEALTH LLC; *U.S. Private*, pg. 3651
SIGNIFY HOLDING B.V.—See Signify N.V.; *Int'l*, pg. 6911
SIGNIFY NETHERLANDS B.V.—See Signify N.V.; *Int'l*, pg. 6912
SIGNIFY N.V.; *Int'l*, pg. 6911
SIGNIFY POLAND SP. Z O.O.—See Signify N.V.; *Int'l*, pg. 6912
SIGNIFY SAUDI ARABIA—See Signify N.V.; *Int'l*, pg. 6912
SIGNING CLOUD SDN. BHD.—See Securemetric Berhad; *Int'l*, pg. 6674
SIGNING DAY SPORTS, INC.; *U.S. Public*, pg. 1878
SIGN IN SOLUTIONS INC.—See PSG Equity L.L.C.; *U.S. Private*, pg. 3297
SIGNITY—See Swarovski & Co.; *Int'l*, pg. 7362
SIGNIUS COMMUNICATIONS—See AnswerNet, Inc.; *U.S. Private*, pg. 286
SIGNIUS CORP.—See AnswerNet, Inc.; *U.S. Private*, pg. 286
SIGNIUS INVESTMENT CORPORATION—See AnswerNet, Inc.; *U.S. Private*, pg. 286
SIGNODE ACME INC.—See Crown Holdings, Inc.; *U.S. Public*, pg. 599
SIGNODE BRASILEIRA LTDA.—See Crown Holdings, Inc.; *U.S. Public*, pg. 599
SIGNODE BVBA—See Crown Holdings, Inc.; *U.S. Public*, pg. 599
SIGNODE CANADA—See Crown Holdings, Inc.; *U.S. Public*, pg. 599
SIGNODE DENMARK APS—See Crown Holdings, Inc.; *U.S. Public*, pg. 599
SIGNODE (ESPANA) S.A.—See Crown Holdings, Inc.; *U.S. Public*, pg. 599
SIGNODE FINLAND OY—See Crown Holdings, Inc.; *U.S. Public*, pg. 599
SIGNODE FRANCE S.A.S.—See Crown Holdings, Inc.; *U.S. Public*, pg. 599
SIGNODE HONG KONG LIMITED—See Crown Holdings, Inc.; *U.S. Public*, pg. 599
SIGNODE INDIA LIMITED—See Crown Holdings, Inc.; *U.S. Public*, pg. 599
SIGNODE INDIA LIMITED—See Illinois Tool Works Inc.; *U.S. Public*, pg. 1110
SIGNODE INDUSTRIAL GROUP AB—See Crown Holdings, Inc.; *U.S. Public*, pg. 599
SIGNODE INDUSTRIAL GROUP - ANGLEBOARD—See Crown Holdings, Inc.; *U.S. Public*, pg. 599
SIGNODE INDUSTRIAL GROUP GMBH—See Crown Holdings, Inc.; *U.S. Public*, pg. 599
SIGNODE INDUSTRIAL GROUP LLC—See Crown Holdings, Inc.; *U.S. Public*, pg. 599
SIGNODE INDUSTRIAL GROUP MEXICO, R.L. DE C.V.—See Crown Holdings, Inc.; *U.S. Public*, pg. 600
SIGNODE INDUSTRIAL GROUP US INC—See Crown Holdings, Inc.; *U.S. Public*, pg. 600
SIGNODE KABUSHIKI KAISHA—See Crown Holdings, Inc.; *U.S. Public*, pg. 599
SIGNODE LIMITED—See Crown Holdings, Inc.; *U.S. Public*, pg. 600

SIGNODE NORWAY AS—See Crown Holdings, Inc.; *U.S. Public*, pg. 600
SIGNODE PACKAGING ESPANA, S.L.—See Illinois Tool Works Inc.; *U.S. Public*, pg. 1110
SIGNODE PACKAGING GROUP (MALAYSIA) SDN BHD—See Crown Holdings, Inc.; *U.S. Public*, pg. 599
SIGNODE PACKAGING SYSTEMS EUROPE - UK & IRELAND—See Crown Holdings, Inc.; *U.S. Public*, pg. 600
SIGNODE PACKAGING SYSTEMS LIMITED—See Illinois Tool Works Inc.; *U.S. Public*, pg. 1110
SIGNODE PACKAGING SYSTEMS—See Crown Holdings, Inc.; *U.S. Public*, pg. 599
SIGNODE POLSKA SP. Z O.O.—See Crown Holdings, Inc.; *U.S. Public*, pg. 600
SIGNODE SINGAPORE PTE. LTD.—See Crown Holdings, Inc.; *U.S. Public*, pg. 600
SIGNODE SYSTEM GMBH—See Crown Holdings, Inc.; *U.S. Public*, pg. 600
SIGNODE SYSTEMS (THAILAND) LTD.—See Illinois Tool Works Inc.; *U.S. Public*, pg. 1110
SIGNODE UK LTD.—See Crown Holdings, Inc.; *U.S. Public*, pg. 600
SIGN OF THE BEEFCARVER INC.; *U.S. Private*, pg. 3649
SIGNO INC.; *U.S. Private*, pg. 3651
SIGNON DEUTSCHLAND GMBH—See TUV SUD AG; *Int'l*, pg. 7984
SIGNON OSTERREICH GMBH—See TUV SUD AG; *Int'l*, pg. 7984
SIGNON SCHWEIZ AG—See TUV SUD AG; *Int'l*, pg. 7984
SIGN PARROT, LLC; *U.S. Private*, pg. 3649
SIGNPATH PHARMA INC.; *U.S. Public*, pg. 1878
SIGNPOST CORPORATION; *Int'l*, pg. 6912
SIGNPOST INDIA LIMITED; *Int'l*, pg. 6912
SIGNPOST NV; *Int'l*, pg. 6912
SIGN SATISFACTION, INC.—See MBE Worldwide S.p.A.; *Int'l*, pg. 4751
SIGNS.COM, INC.; *U.S. Private*, pg. 3651
SIGNTALK, LLC; *U.S. Private*, pg. 3651
SIGNTECH ELECTRICAL ADVERTISING; *U.S. Private*, pg. 3651
SIGNTRONIX; *U.S. Private*, pg. 3651
SIGNUM GROUP, LLC; *U.S. Private*, pg. 3651
SIGNUM SYSTEMS CORP.—See IAR Systems Group AB; *Int'l*, pg. 3569
SIGNUM TECHNOLOGY LTD.—See Trelleborg AB; *Int'l*, pg. 7911
SIGNUMTTE A.S.—See Kontrolmatik Teknoloji Enerji ve Muhendislik A.S.; *Int'l*, pg. 4276
SIGN-UP TECHNOLOGIES LTD.; *Int'l*, pg. 6909
SIGN YOU MEDIASCREEN GMBH—See Stroer SE & Co. KGaA; *Int'l*, pg. 7242
SIGN ZONE LLC—See HarbourVest Partners, LLC; *U.S. Private*, pg. 1861
SIGN ZONE LLC—See Pfingsten Partners, LLC; *U.S. Private*, pg. 3164
S.I. GOLDMAN CO., INC.—See Comfort Systems USA, Inc.; *U.S. Public*, pg. 544
SIGONG TECH CO., LTD.; *Int'l*, pg. 6912
SIGORA SOLAR, LLC; *U.S. Private*, pg. 3651
SIGORTAYERI SIGORTA VE REASURANS BROKERLIGI A.S.—See Aktif Yatirim Bankasi A.S.; *Int'l*, pg. 267
SIGOSA S.A. DE C.V.—See Industrias CH, S.A.B. de C.V.; *Int'l*, pg. 3674
SIGOS GMBH—See H.I.G. Capital, LLC; *U.S. Private*, pg. 1833
SIGOURNEY TRACTOR & IMPLEMENT; *U.S. Private*, pg. 3651
SIG PLC; *Int'l*, pg. 6906
SIGRANO NEDERLAND B.V.—See EUROQUARZ GmbH; *Int'l*, pg. 2558
SI GROUP - BETHUNE SAS—See SK Capital Partners, LP; *U.S. Private*, pg. 3679
SI GROUP CRIOS - JUNDIAI - PLANT 2—See SK Capital Partners, LP; *U.S. Private*, pg. 3679
SI GROUP CRIOS - RIO CLARO - PLANT 1—See SK Capital Partners, LP; *U.S. Private*, pg. 3679
SI GROUP, INC.—See SK Capital Partners, LP; *U.S. Private*, pg. 3679
SI GROUP - INDIA LIMITED - LOTE UNIT—See SK Capital Partners, LP; *U.S. Private*, pg. 3680
SI GROUP - INDIA LIMITED - NAVI MUMBAI UNIT—See SK Capital Partners, LP; *U.S. Private*, pg. 3680
SI GROUP - INDIA LIMITED - RANJANGAON UNIT—See SK Capital Partners, LP; *U.S. Private*, pg. 3680
SI GROUP - INDIA LIMITED - RASAL UNIT—See SK Capital Partners, LP; *U.S. Private*, pg. 3680
SI GROUP INDIA LTD—See SK Capital Partners, LP; *U.S. Private*, pg. 3680
SI GROUP KOREA LTD—See SK Capital Partners, LP; *U.S. Private*, pg. 3680
SI-GROUP - SHANGHAI CO, LTD.—See SK Capital Partners, LP; *U.S. Private*, pg. 3680
SI GROUP - SINGAPORE PTD. LTD.—See SK Capital Partners, LP; *U.S. Private*, pg. 3679
SI GROUP SOUTH AFRICA (PTD) LTD—See SK Capital Partners, LP; *U.S. Private*, pg. 3680
SI GROUP-SWITZERLAND—See SK Capital Partners, LP; *U.S. Private*, pg. 3680

SIG SIMONAZZI S.P.A.—See Tetra Laval International S.A.; *Int'l*, pg. 7577
SIG SPORTS, LEISURE AND ENTERTAINMENT RISK PURCHASING GROUP, LLC—See Everest Group, Ltd.; *Int'l*, pg. 2564
SIG SP Z O.O.—See SIG plc; *Int'l*, pg. 6906
SIG TECHNICAL INSULATION - ABERDEEN—See SIG plc; *Int'l*, pg. 6906
SIG TECHNICAL INSULATION - GLASGOW—See SIG plc; *Int'l*, pg. 6906
SIG TECHNICAL INSULATION - LONDON EAST, BECKTON—See SIG plc; *Int'l*, pg. 6906
SIG TECHNICAL INSULATION - NEWTON-LE-WILLOWS—See SIG plc; *Int'l*, pg. 6906
SIG TECHNICAL INSULATION - PLYMOUTH—See SIG plc; *Int'l*, pg. 6906
SIG TECHNICAL INSULATION - PORTSMOUTH—See SIG plc; *Int'l*, pg. 6906
SIG TECHNICAL INSULATION - SWANSEA—See SIG plc; *Int'l*, pg. 6906
SIG TECHNICAL INSULATION - TYNESIDE—See SIG plc; *Int'l*, pg. 6907
SIG TECHNISCHE ISOOLATIESPECIALIST B.V.—See SIG plc; *Int'l*, pg. 6906
SIG TRADING (IRELAND) LTD.—See SIG plc; *Int'l*, pg. 6906
SIG TRADING LIMITED—See SIG plc; *Int'l*, pg. 6906
SIGULDAS CMAS; *Int'l*, pg. 6912
SIGULER GUFF & COMPANY, LP; *U.S. Private*, pg. 3651
SIGUM FAGERBERG AS—See Indutrade AB; *Int'l*, pg. 3681
SIGURD MICROELECTRONICS CORP. - CHUNG-SHING FACTORY—See Sigurd Microelectronics Corp.; *Int'l*, pg. 6913
SIGURD MICROELECTRONICS CORP. - HU-KOU FACTORY—See Sigurd Microelectronics Corp.; *Int'l*, pg. 6913
SIGURD MICROELECTRONICS CORP. - PEI-SHING FACTORY—See Sigurd Microelectronics Corp.; *Int'l*, pg. 6913
SIGURD MICROELECTRONICS CORP.; *Int'l*, pg. 6913
SIGURD UTC CORPORATION—See Sigurd Microelectronics Corp.; *Int'l*, pg. 6913
SIGURNOST AS A.D.; *Int'l*, pg. 6913
SIGURNOST - VRACAR A.D.; *Int'l*, pg. 6913
SIGVARIS HOLDING AG; *Int'l*, pg. 6913
SIGYN THERAPEUTICS, INC.; *U.S. Public*, pg. 1878
SIHI GROUP B.V.—See Flowserve Corporation; *U.S. Public*, pg. 857
SIHI PUMPS, INC.—See TBG Holdings NV; *Int'l*, pg. 7479
SIHL LLC—See ANDRITZ AG; *Int'l*, pg. 455
SIHONG BOSSCO WATER CO., LTD.—See Guangxi Bossco Environmental Protection Technology Co., Ltd.; *Int'l*, pg. 3163
SIHONG WEIYE GAS CO., LTD.—See Zhongyu Energy Holdings Limited; *Int'l*, pg. 8676
SIHUAN PHARMACEUTICAL HOLDINGS GROUP LTD.—See Morgan Stanley; *U.S. Public*, pg. 1473
SIHUI FUJI ELECTRONICS TECHNOLOGY CO., LTD.; *Int'l*, pg. 6913
SII AIX-EN-PROVENCE—See Societe Pour L'Informatique Industrielle; *Int'l*, pg. 7043
SII BELGIUM—See Societe Pour L'Informatique Industrielle; *Int'l*, pg. 7044
SII BREST—See Societe Pour L'Informatique Industrielle; *Int'l*, pg. 7044
SIIC ENVIRONMENT HOLDINGS LTD.; *Int'l*, pg. 6913
SII CRYSTAL TECHNOLOGY INC.—See Seiko Group Corporation; *Int'l*, pg. 6688
SII CZECH REPUBLIC—See Societe Pour L'Informatique Industrielle; *Int'l*, pg. 7044
SII DEUTSCHLAND GMBH—See Societe Pour L'Informatique Industrielle; *Int'l*, pg. 7044
SII ILE-DE-FRANCE—See Societe Pour L'Informatique Industrielle; *Int'l*, pg. 7044
SII INDIA IT & ENGINEERING SERVICES PVT LTD.—See Societe Pour L'Informatique Industrielle; *Int'l*, pg. 7044
SII LE MANS—See Societe Pour L'Informatique Industrielle; *Int'l*, pg. 7044
SIILI SOLUTIONS OYJ; *Int'l*, pg. 6913
SII LOGISTICS INC.—See Mitsubishi Logistics Corporation; *Int'l*, pg. 4962
SII LUXEMBOURG SA—See Societe Pour L'Informatique Industrielle; *Int'l*, pg. 7044
SII LYON—See Societe Pour L'Informatique Industrielle; *Int'l*, pg. 7044
SI IMAGING SERVICES CO., LTD—See Satrec Initiative Co., Ltd.; *Int'l*, pg. 6587
SII NANTES—See Societe Pour L'Informatique Industrielle; *Int'l*, pg. 7044
SII INSURANCE (EUROPE), SA—See Sompo Holdings, Inc.; *Int'l*, pg. 7086
SII POLAND WARSAW—See Societe Pour L'Informatique Industrielle; *Int'l*, pg. 7044
SII PRINTEK INC.—See Seiko Group Corporation; *Int'l*, pg. 6688
SII RENNES—See Societe Pour L'Informatique Industrielle; *Int'l*, pg. 7044

SII SERVICES LIMITED—See Societe Pour L'Informatique Industrielle; *Int'l*, pg. 7044
SII SERVICES MOROCCO—See Societe Pour L'Informatique Industrielle; *Int'l*, pg. 7044
SII SOPHIA-ANTIPOLIS—See Societe Pour L'Informatique Industrielle; *Int'l*, pg. 7044
SII SP. Z O.O.; *Int'l*, pg. 6913
SII STRASBOURG—See Societe Pour L'Informatique Industrielle; *Int'l*, pg. 7044
SII SWEDEN AB—See Societe Pour L'Informatique Industrielle; *Int'l*, pg. 7044
SII SWITZERLAND—See Societe Pour L'Informatique Industrielle; *Int'l*, pg. 7044
SIITE INTERACTIVE LLC; *U.S. Private*, pg. 3651
SII TOULOUSE—See Societe Pour L'Informatique Industrielle; *Int'l*, pg. 7044
SII TOURS—See Societe Pour L'Informatique Industrielle; *Int'l*, pg. 7044
SII VITROLLES—See Societe Pour L'Informatique Industrielle; *Int'l*, pg. 7044
SIIX-AGT MEDTECH PTE. LTD.—See SIIX CORPORATION; *Int'l*, pg. 6914
SIIX BANGKOK CO., LTD.—See SIIX CORPORATION; *Int'l*, pg. 6914
SIIX CORPORATION; *Int'l*, pg. 6913
SIIX COXON PRECISION PHILS., INC.—See SIIX CORPORATION; *Int'l*, pg. 6914
SIIX DO BRASIL LTDA.—See SIIX CORPORATION; *Int'l*, pg. 6914
SIIX ELECTRONICS CO., LTD.—See SIIX CORPORATION; *Int'l*, pg. 6914
SIIX EMS (DONG GUAN) CO., LTD.—See SIIX CORPORATION; *Int'l*, pg. 6914
SIIX EMS MEXICO, S. DE R.L DE C.V.—See SIIX CORPORATION; *Int'l*, pg. 6914
SIIX EMS PHILIPPINES, INC.—See SIIX CORPORATION; *Int'l*, pg. 6914
SIIX EMS (SHANGHAI) CO., LTD.—See SIIX CORPORATION; *Int'l*, pg. 6914
SIIX EMS SLOVAKIA S.R.O.—See SIIX CORPORATION; *Int'l*, pg. 6914
SIIX EMS (THAILAND) CO., LTD.—See SIIX CORPORATION; *Int'l*, pg. 6914
SIIX EUROPE GMBH—See SIIX CORPORATION; *Int'l*, pg. 6914
SIIX H.K. LTD.—See SIIX CORPORATION; *Int'l*, pg. 6914
SIIX HUBEI CO., LTD.—See SIIX CORPORATION; *Int'l*, pg. 6914
SIIX HUNGARY KFT.—See SIIX CORPORATION; *Int'l*, pg. 6914
SIIX LOGISTICS PHILS, INC.—See SIIX CORPORATION; *Int'l*, pg. 6914
SIIX MALAYSIA SDN. BHD.—See SIIX CORPORATION; *Int'l*, pg. 6914
SIIX PHILS., INC.—See SIIX CORPORATION; *Int'l*, pg. 6914
SIIX (SHANGHAI) CO., LTD. JADING LC—See SIIX CORPORATION; *Int'l*, pg. 6914
SIIX (SHANGHAI) CO., LTD.—See SIIX CORPORATION; *Int'l*, pg. 6913
SIIX SINGAPORE PTE., LTD.—See SIIX CORPORATION; *Int'l*, pg. 6914
SIIX TWN CO., LTD.—See SIIX CORPORATION; *Int'l*, pg. 6914
SIIX U.S.A. CORP.—See SIIX CORPORATION; *Int'l*, pg. 6914
SIIX VIETNAM COMPANY LIMITED—See SIIX CORPORATION; *Int'l*, pg. 6914
SIJAS PLANTATIONS SDN BHD—See IJM Corporation Berhad; *Int'l*, pg. 3609
SIJBERIA INDUSTRIES LTD.—See LUDLOW JUTE & SPECIALITIES LIMITED; *Int'l*, pg. 4575
SIJIN INTELLIGENT FORMING MACHINERY CO., LTD.; *Int'l*, pg. 6915
SIKA ABYSSINIA CHEMICALS MANUFACTURING PLC—See Sika AG; *Int'l*, pg. 6915
SIKA AG; *Int'l*, pg. 6914
SIKA ALBANIA SH.P.K.—See Sika AG; *Int'l*, pg. 6915
SIKA ANGOLA (SU), LIMITADA—See Sika AG; *Int'l*, pg. 6915
SIKA ARGENTINA S.A.I.C.—See Sika AG; *Int'l*, pg. 6915
SIKA ASIA PACIFIC MGT. PTE. LTD—See Sika AG; *Int'l*, pg. 6915
SIKA AUSTRALIA PTY. LTD—See Sika AG; *Int'l*, pg. 6915
SIKA AUTOMOTIVE AG—See Sika AG; *Int'l*, pg. 6915
SIKA AUTOMOTIVE BELGIUM SA—See Sika AG; *Int'l*, pg. 6915
SIKA AUTOMOTIVE DEUTSCHLAND GMBH—See Sika AG; *Int'l*, pg. 6915
SIKA AUTOMOTIVE GASTONIA INC.—See Sika AG; *Int'l*, pg. 6915
SIKA AUTOMOTIVE GMBH—See Sika AG; *Int'l*, pg. 6916
SIKA AUTOMOTIVE SLOVAKIA, S.R.O.—See Sika AG; *Int'l*, pg. 6915
SIKA AUTOMOTIVE TERRASSA S.A.—See Sika AG; *Int'l*, pg. 6915
SIKA AUTOMOTIVE (TIANJIN) CO. LTD.—See Sika AG; *Int'l*, pg. 6915
SIKA BALTIC SIA—See Sika AG; *Int'l*, pg. 6915

COMPANY NAME INDEX SILEX SYSTEMS LTD.

SIKA BANGLADESH LIMITED—See Sika AG; *Int'l*, pg. 6915
SIKABAU AG—See Sika AG; *Int'l*, pg. 6918
SIKA BELGIUM NV—See Sika AG; *Int'l*, pg. 6915
S I K A BEL LLC—See Sika AG; *Int'l*, pg. 6915
SIKA BH D.O.O.—See Sika AG; *Int'l*, pg. 6915
SIKA BOLIVIA SA—See Sika AG; *Int'l*, pg. 6916
SIKA BULGARIA EOOD—See Sika AG; *Int'l*, pg. 6916
SIKA (CAMBODIA) LTD.—See Sika AG; *Int'l*, pg. 6915
SIKA CAMEROON SARL—See Sika AG; *Int'l*, pg. 6916
SIKA CANADA INC.—See Sika AG; *Int'l*, pg. 6916
SIKA CHEMICALS GHANA LTD.—See Sika AG; *Int'l*, pg. 6916
SIKA (CHINA) LTD.—See Sika AG; *Int'l*, pg. 6915
SIKA COLOMBIA S.A.S.—See Sika AG; *Int'l*, pg. 6916
SIKA COMPANY FOR GENERAL TRADING LLC—See Sika AG; *Int'l*, pg. 6916
SIKA CORP. - CONYERS PLANT—See Sika AG; *Int'l*, pg. 6916
SIKA CORP. - FAIRLESS HILLS PLANT—See Sika AG; *Int'l*, pg. 6916
SIKA CORPORATION—See Sika AG; *Int'l*, pg. 6916
SIKA CROATIA D.O.O.—See Sika AG; *Int'l*, pg. 6916
SIKA CZ, S.R.O.—See Sika AG; *Int'l*, pg. 6916
SIKA DANMARK A / S—See Sika AG; *Int'l*, pg. 6916
SIKA DEUTSCHLAND GMBH—See Sika AG; *Int'l*, pg. 6916
SIKA DJIBOUTI FZE—See Sika AG; *Int'l*, pg. 6916
SIKA DOMINICANA SA—See Sika AG; *Int'l*, pg. 6916
SIKA D.O.O.—See Sika AG; *Int'l*, pg. 6918
SIKA ECUATORIANA SA—See Sika AG; *Int'l*, pg. 6916
SIKA EGYPT FOR CONSTRUCTION CHEMICALS S.A.E.—See Sika AG; *Int'l*, pg. 6916
SIKA EL DJAZAIR SPA—See Sika AG; *Int'l*, pg. 6916
SIKA ESTONIA OU—See Sika AG; *Int'l*, pg. 6916
SIKA GUANGZHOU LTD—See Sika AG; *Int'l*, pg. 6915
SIKA (GUANGZHOU) TRADING COMPANY LTD—See Sika AG; *Int'l*, pg. 6915
SIKA GUATEMALA SA—See Sika AG; *Int'l*, pg. 6916
SIKA GULF B.S.C.—See Sika AG; *Int'l*, pg. 6916
SIKA HELLAS ABEE—See Sika AG; *Int'l*, pg. 6916
SIKA HOLDING CH AG & CO KG—See Sika AG; *Int'l*, pg. 6916
SIKA HOLDING GMBH—See Sika AG; *Int'l*, pg. 6916
SIKA HONG KONG LTD.—See Sika AG; *Int'l*, pg. 6916
SIKA HUANGARIA KFT—See Sika AG; *Int'l*, pg. 6916
SIKA HUNGARIA KFT.—See Sika AG; *Int'l*, pg. 6916
SIKA INDIA PRIVATE LTD—See Sika AG; *Int'l*, pg. 6916
SIKA INFORMATIONSSYSTEME AG—See Sika AG; *Int'l*, pg. 6916
SIKA INTERPLANT SYSTEMS LTD.—See Danaher Corporation; *U.S. Public*, pg. 626
SIKA IRELAND LTD—See Sika AG; *Int'l*, pg. 6916
SIKA ITALIA S.P.A.—See Sika AG; *Int'l*, pg. 6916
SIKA (JIANGSU) BUILDING MATERIAL LTD.—See Sika AG; *Int'l*, pg. 6915
SIKA (JIANGSU) LNDUSTRIAL MATERIAL LTD.—See Sika AG; *Int'l*, pg. 6915
SIKA KAZAKHSTAN LLP—See Sika AG; *Int'l*, pg. 6916
SIKA KENYA LIMITED—See Sika AG; *Int'l*, pg. 6916
SIKA KIMIA SDN. BHD.—See Sika AG; *Int'l*, pg. 6917
SIKA KOREA LTD—See Sika AG; *Int'l*, pg. 6917
SIKA LANKA (PRIVATE) LIMITED—See Sika AG; *Int'l*, pg. 6917
SIKA LIMITED - SIKA LIQUID PLASTICS—See Sika AG; *Int'l*, pg. 6917
SIKA LIMITED—See Sika AG; *Int'l*, pg. 6917
SIKA LLC—See Sika AG; *Int'l*, pg. 6917
SIKA LTD.—See Sika AG; *Int'l*, pg. 6917
SIKA MANUFACTURING AG—See Sika AG; *Int'l*, pg. 6918
SIKA MANUFACTURING FOR CONSTRUCTION PRODUCTS, S.A.E.—See Sika AG; *Int'l*, pg. 6916
SIKA MANUFACTURING FOR CONSTRUCTION S.A.E.—See Sika AG; *Int'l*, pg. 6917
SIKA MANUFACTURING NIGERIA LIMITED—See Sika AG; *Int'l*, pg. 6917
SIKA MAROC SA—See Sika AG; *Int'l*, pg. 6917
SIKA MAURITIUS LTD—See Sika AG; *Int'l*, pg. 6917
SIKA MEXICANA SA DE CV—See Sika AG; *Int'l*, pg. 6917
SIKA MOCAMBIQUE LIMITADA—See Sika AG; *Int'l*, pg. 6917
SIKA MONGOLIA LLC—See Sika AG; *Int'l*, pg. 6917
SIKA MYANMAR LIMITED—See Sika AG; *Int'l*, pg. 6917
SIKA NEAR EAST SAL—See Sika AG; *Int'l*, pg. 6917
SIKA NEDERLAND BV—See Sika AG; *Int'l*, pg. 6917
SIKA NICARAGUA SOCIEDAD ANONIMA—See Sika AG; *Int'l*, pg. 6917
SIKA NORGE AS—See Sika AG; *Int'l*, pg. 6917
SIKA (NZ) LTD—See Sika AG; *Int'l*, pg. 6915
SIKA OSTERREICH GMBH—See Sika AG; *Int'l*, pg. 6917
SIKA PAKISTAN LTD—See Sika AG; *Int'l*, pg. 6917
SIKA PANAMA SA—See Sika AG; *Int'l*, pg. 6917
SIKA PARAGUAY S.A.—See Sika AG; *Int'l*, pg. 6917
SIKA PERU SA—See Sika AG; *Int'l*, pg. 6917
SIKA PHILIPPINES INC.—See Sika AG; *Int'l*, pg. 6917
SIKA POLAND SP.Z.O.O.—See Sika AG; *Int'l*, pg. 6917
SIKA PORTUGAL - PRODUCTOS CONSTRUCAO E INDUSTRIA SA—See Sika AG; *Int'l*, pg. 6917
SIKA PORTUGAL - PRODUCTOS CONSTRUCAO INDUSTRIA SA—See Sika AG; *Int'l*, pg. 6917
SIKA PRODUCTOS PARA LA CONSTRUCCION S.A.—See Sika AG; *Int'l*, pg. 6917
SIKA QATAR LLC—See Sika AG; *Int'l*, pg. 6917
SIKARIN PUBLIC COMPANY LIMITED; *Int'l*, pg. 6918
SIKA ROMANIA S.R.L.—See Sika AG; *Int'l*, pg. 6917
SIKA SA CHILE—See Sika AG; *Int'l*, pg. 6917
SIKA SARNAFIL WATERPROOFING SYSTEMS (SHANGHAI) LTD.—See Sika AG; *Int'l*, pg. 6915
SIKA SAUDI ARABIA CO., LTD.—See Sika AG; *Int'l*, pg. 6917
SIKA, S.A.U.—See Sika AG; *Int'l*, pg. 6918
SIKA SCHWEIZ AG—See Sika AG; *Int'l*, pg. 6918
SIKA SENEGAL S.U.A.R.L—See Sika AG; *Int'l*, pg. 6918
SIKA (SICHUAN) BUILDING MATERIAL LTD.—See Sika AG; *Int'l*, pg. 6915
SIKA SINGAPORE PTE. LTD.—See Sika AG; *Int'l*, pg. 6918
SIKA SLOVENIJA D.O.O.—See Sika AG; *Int'l*, pg. 6918
SIKA SLOVENSKO SPOL. S.R.O.—See Sika AG; *Int'l*, pg. 6918
SIKA SOUTH AFRICA (PTY) LTD—See Sika AG; *Int'l*, pg. 6918
SIKA SRBIJA D.O.O.—See Sika AG; *Int'l*, pg. 6918
SIKA SUPPLY CENTER AG—See Sika AG; *Int'l*, pg. 6918
SIKA SVERIGE AB—See Sika AG; *Int'l*, pg. 6918
SIKA TAIWAN LTD—See Sika AG; *Int'l*, pg. 6918
SIKA TANZANIA CONSTRUCTION CHEMICALS LIMITED—See Sika AG; *Int'l*, pg. 6918
SIKA TECHNOLOGY AG—See Sika AG; *Int'l*, pg. 6918
SIKA (THAILAND) LTD.—See Sika AG; *Int'l*, pg. 6915
SIKA TROCAL GMBH—See Sika AG; *Int'l*, pg. 6916
SIKA TUNISIENNE SARL—See Sika AG; *Int'l*, pg. 6918
SIKA TURKEY OTOMOTIV SANAYI VE TIC. LTD. STI.—See Sika AG; *Int'l*, pg. 6918
SIKA UAE LLC—See Sika AG; *Int'l*, pg. 6918
SIKA URUGUAY SA—See Sika AG; *Int'l*, pg. 6918
SIKA VENEZUELA SA—See Sika AG; *Int'l*, pg. 6918
SIKA YAPI KIMYASALLARI A.S.—See Sika AG; *Int'l*, pg. 6918
SIK COLOR (M) SDN. BHD.—See Inabata & Co. Ltd.; *Int'l*, pg. 3644
SIKEKELA SKILLS ACADEMY PROPRIETARY LIMITED—See Workforce Holdings Ltd.; *Int'l*, pg. 8456
SIKELELA SKILLS ACADEMY PROPRIETARY LIMITED—See Workforce Holdings Ltd.; *Int'l*, pg. 8456
SIKES SENTER, LLC—See Brookfield Corporation; *Int'l*, pg. 1185
SIKICH LLP; *U.S. Private*, pg. 3651
SIKKENS VERKOOP B.V.—See Akzo Nobel N.V.; *Int'l*, pg. 275
SIKKO INDUSTRIES LTD.; *Int'l*, pg. 6918
SIKO CORPORATION; *Int'l*, pg. 6918
SIKORSKY FINANCIAL CREDIT UNION; *U.S. Private*, pg. 3651
SIKOZY REALTORS LIMITED; *Int'l*, pg. 6918
SIK (THAILAND) LTD.—See Inabata & Co. Ltd.; *Int'l*, pg. 3644
SIKU GMBH—See INDUS Holding AG; *Int'l*, pg. 3664
SIK VIETNAM CO., LTD.—See Inabata & Co. Ltd.; *Int'l*, pg. 3644
SILA A.D.; *Int'l*, pg. 6918
SILABS INDIA PRIVATE LIMITED—See Silicon Laboratories Inc.; *U.S. Public*, pg. 1879
SILA HEATING & AIR CONDITIONING, INC.—See Morgan Stanley; *U.S. Public*, pg. 1474
SILA REALTY TRUST, INC.—See Carter & Associates, LLC; *U.S. Private*, pg. 775
SILARX PHARMACEUTICALS, INC.—See Lannett Company, Inc.; *U.S. Public*, pg. 1293
SILAS CREEK MANOR—See Apollo Global Management, Inc.; *U.S. Public*, pg. 157
SILA SERVICES, LLC—See Morgan Stanley; *U.S. Public*, pg. 1474
SILBERLINE ASIA PACIFIC PTE. LTD.—See Silberline Manufacturing Co., Inc.; *U.S. Private*, pg. 3652
SILBERLINE BRASIL LIMITADA—See Silberline Manufacturing Co., Inc.; *U.S. Private*, pg. 3652
SILBERLINE LIMITED—See Silberline Manufacturing Co., Inc.; *U.S. Private*, pg. 3652
SILBERLINE MANUFACTURING CO., INC. - SILBERLINE MANUFACTURING FACILITY—See Silberline Manufacturing Co., Inc.; *U.S. Private*, pg. 3652
SILBERLINE MANUFACTURING CO., INC.; *U.S. Private*, pg. 3652
SILBERLINE PIGMENTOS, SRL DE CV—See Silberline Manufacturing Co., Inc.; *U.S. Private*, pg. 3652
SILBERLINE PIGMENT (SUZHOU) COMPANY LIMITED—See Silberline Manufacturing Co., Inc.; *U.S. Private*, pg. 3652
SILBERLINE SPECIALTY EFFECT PIGMENTS INDIA PRIVATE LIMITED—See Silberline Manufacturing Co., Inc.; *U.S. Private*, pg. 3652
SILBITZ GROUP GMBH; *Int'l*, pg. 6919
SILBITZ GUSS GMBH—See Silbitz Group GmbH; *Int'l*, pg. 6919
SILBRICO CORPORATION; *U.S. Private*, pg. 3652
SILCA GMBH—See dormakaba Holding AG; *Int'l*, pg. 2177
SILCA KEY SYSTEMS S.A.—See dormakaba Holding AG; *Int'l*, pg. 2177
SILCA LTD.—See dormakaba Holding AG; *Int'l*, pg. 2178
SILCA S.A.S.—See dormakaba Holding AG; *Int'l*, pg. 2178
SILCA SOUTH AMERICA S.A.—See dormakaba Holding AG; *Int'l*, pg. 2178
SILCA S.P.A.—See dormakaba Holding AG; *Int'l*, pg. 2177
SILCO INOX KFT—See ThyssenKrupp AG; *Int'l*, pg. 7729
SILCO OIL COMPANY; *U.S. Private*, pg. 3652
SILCOPLAST AG—See Semperit AG Holding; *Int'l*, pg. 6706
SILCOTEC EUROPE LTD.—See Volex plc; *Int'l*, pg. 8301
SILCOTEC EUROPE (SK) S.R.O.—See Volex plc; *Int'l*, pg. 8301
SILCOTEC, INC.—See Avient Corporation; *U.S. Public*, pg. 248
SILC SA; *Int'l*, pg. 6919
SILEC CABLE, S.A.S.—See Prysmian S.p.A.; *Int'l*, pg. 6012
SILEGO TECHNOLOGY, INC.—See Renesas Electronics Corporation; *Int'l*, pg. 6275
SILEKOL SP. Z O.O.—See Pfleiderer GmbH; *Int'l*, pg. 5836
SILENCE THERAPEUTICS PLC; *Int'l*, pg. 6919
SILENSEED LTD.; *Int'l*, pg. 6919
SILENTBLOC UK LTD—See Dellner Brakes AB; *Int'l*, pg. 2014
SILENT DRIVE, INC.—See Brookfield Corporation; *Int'l*, pg. 1176
SILENTNIGHT GROUP LIMITED - SEALY UK DIVISION—See H.I.G. Capital, LLC; *U.S. Private*, pg. 1828
SILENTNIGHT GROUP LIMITED—See H.I.G. Capital, LLC; *U.S. Private*, pg. 1828
SILEO KAPITAL AB—See B2Holding AS; *Int'l*, pg. 791
SILERGY CORP.; *Int'l*, pg. 6919
SILERGY SEMICONDUCTOR (SAMOA) LIMITED—See Silergy Corp.; *Int'l*, pg. 6919
SILERGY SEMICONDUCTOR TECHNOLOGY (HANGZHOU) CO. LTD.—See Silergy Corp.; *Int'l*, pg. 6919
SILESIA ASFALTY SP Z O.O.—See VINCI S.A.; *Int'l*, pg. 8227
SILESIA B.V.—See Silesia Gerhard Hanke GmbH & Co.KG; *Int'l*, pg. 6919
SILESIA CESKA REPUBLIKA SPOL S.R.O.—See Silesia Gerhard Hanke GmbH & Co.KG; *Int'l*, pg. 6919
SILESIA COLOMBIA LTDA.—See Silesia Gerhard Hanke GmbH & Co.KG; *Int'l*, pg. 6919
SILESIA DE MEXICO S. DE R. L. DE C.V.—See Silesia Gerhard Hanke GmbH & Co.KG; *Int'l*, pg. 6919
SILESIA FLAVOURS AUSTRIA GMBH—See Silesia Gerhard Hanke GmbH & Co.KG; *Int'l*, pg. 6919
SILESIA FLAVOURS ESPAA S.L.—See Silesia Gerhard Hanke GmbH & Co.KG; *Int'l*, pg. 6919
SILESIA FLAVOURS GDA TICARET VE SERVIS LIMITED IRKETI—See Silesia Gerhard Hanke GmbH & Co.KG; *Int'l*, pg. 6919
SILESIA FLAVOURS HUNGARY KFT.—See Silesia Gerhard Hanke GmbH & Co.KG; *Int'l*, pg. 6919
SILESIA FLAVOURS INC.—See Silesia Gerhard Hanke GmbH & Co.KG; *Int'l*, pg. 6919
SILESIA FLAVOURS LTD.—See Silesia Gerhard Hanke GmbH & Co.KG; *Int'l*, pg. 6919
SILESIA FLAVOURS POLSKA SP.Z.O.O.—See Silesia Gerhard Hanke GmbH & Co.KG; *Int'l*, pg. 6919
SILESIA FLAVOURS SCANDINAVIA APS—See Silesia Gerhard Hanke GmbH & Co.KG; *Int'l*, pg. 6919
SILESIA FLAVOURS (SHANGHAI) CO. LTD.—See Silesia Gerhard Hanke GmbH & Co.KG; *Int'l*, pg. 6919
SILESIA FLAVOURS SOUTH EAST ASIA PTE. LTD.—See Silesia Gerhard Hanke GmbH & Co.KG; *Int'l*, pg. 6919
SILESIA FLAVOURS SWITZERLAND GMBH—See Silesia Gerhard Hanke GmbH & Co.KG; *Int'l*, pg. 6919
SILESIA FLAVOURS (THAILAND) LTD—See Silesia Gerhard Hanke GmbH & Co.KG; *Int'l*, pg. 6919
SILESIA FLAVOURS UKRAINE LLC—See Silesia Gerhard Hanke GmbH & Co.KG; *Int'l*, pg. 6919
SILESIA FRANCE S.A.—See Silesia Gerhard Hanke GmbH & Co.KG; *Int'l*, pg. 6919
SILESIA GERHARD HANKE GMBH & CO.KG; *Int'l*, pg. 6919
SILESIA ITALIA S.R.L.—See Silesia Gerhard Hanke GmbH & Co.KG; *Int'l*, pg. 6919
SILESIAN COAL INTERNATIONAL GROUP OF COMPANIES S.A.—See HMS Bergbau AG; *Int'l*, pg. 3432
SILESIA RESIDENTIAL PROJECT SP. Z O.O.—See Immofinanz AG; *Int'l*, pg. 3628
SILEX HOLDINGS, INC.; *U.S. Private*, pg. 3652
SILEX INTERIORS 2, LLC—See Silex Holdings, Inc.; *U.S. Private*, pg. 3652
SILEX SEGURIDAD SL—See Societe Anonyme d'Explosifs et de Produits Chimiques; *Int'l*, pg. 7035
SILEX SYSTEMS LTD.; *Int'l*, pg. 6919
SIL FALA SARL—See Compagnie des Levures Lesaffre SA; *Int'l*, pg. 1739
SILFEX, INCORPORATED—See Lam Research Corporation; *U.S. Public*, pg. 1290
SILGAN CAN COMPANY—See Silgan Holdings, Inc.; *U.S. Public*, pg. 1878

Company Index

SILGAN CLOSURES GMBH—See Silgan Holdings, Inc.; *U.S. Public*, pg. 1878
SILGAN CLOSURES UK LIMITED—See Silgan Holdings, Inc.; *U.S. Public*, pg. 1878
SILGAN CONTAINERS MANUFACTURING CORPORATION—See Silgan Holdings, Inc.; *U.S. Public*, pg. 1878
SILGAN CONTAINERS MANUFACTURING PUERTO RICO LLC—See Silgan Holdings, Inc.; *U.S. Public*, pg. 1878
SILGAN CONTAINERS—See Silgan Holdings, Inc.; *U.S. Public*, pg. 1878
SILGAN DISPENSING SYSTEMS ALKMAAR B.V.—See Silgan Holdings, Inc.; *U.S. Public*, pg. 1878
SILGAN DISPENSING SYSTEMS ALKMAAR B.V.—See Silgan Holdings, Inc.; *U.S. Public*, pg. 1878
SILGAN DISPENSING SYSTEMS ALKMAAR B.V.—See Silgan Holdings, Inc.; *U.S. Public*, pg. 1878
SILGAN DISPENSING SYSTEMS ALKMAAR B.V.—See Silgan Holdings, Inc.; *U.S. Public*, pg. 1879
SILGAN DISPENSING SYSTEMS BARCELONA, S.L.—See Silgan Holdings, Inc.; *U.S. Public*, pg. 1879
SILGAN DISPENSING SYSTEMS CANADA LTD.—See Silgan Holdings, Inc.; *U.S. Public*, pg. 1879
SILGAN DISPENSING SYSTEMS CORPORATION—See Silgan Holdings, Inc.; *U.S. Public*, pg. 1879
SILGAN DISPENSING SYSTEMS FRANCE S.A.S.—See Silgan Holdings, Inc.; *U.S. Public*, pg. 1879
SILGAN DISPENSING SYSTEMS HEMER GMBH—See Silgan Holdings, Inc.; *U.S. Public*, pg. 1879
SILGAN DISPENSING SYSTEMS INDIA PRIVATE LIMITED—See Silgan Holdings, Inc.; *U.S. Public*, pg. 1879
SILGAN DISPENSING SYSTEMS LACROST S.A.S.—See Silgan Holdings, Inc.; *U.S. Public*, pg. 1879
SILGAN DISPENSING SYSTEMS LE TREPORT S.A.S.—See Silgan Holdings, Inc.; *U.S. Public*, pg. 1879
SILGAN DISPENSING SYSTEMS MEXICO OPERADORA, S.A. DE C.V.—See Silgan Holdings, Inc.; *U.S. Public*, pg. 1879
SILGAN DISPENSING SYSTEMS MEXICO, S.A. DE C.V.—See Silgan Holdings, Inc.; *U.S. Public*, pg. 1879
SILGAN DISPENSING SYSTEMS MILANO S.R.L.—See Silgan Holdings, Inc.; *U.S. Public*, pg. 1879
SILGAN DISPENSING SYSTEMS NETHERLANDS B.V.—See Silgan Holdings, Inc.; *U.S. Public*, pg. 1879
SILGAN DISPENSING SYSTEMS & PACKAGING DO BRASIL INDUSTRIA DE EMBALAGENS LTDA.—See Silgan Holdings, Inc.; *U.S. Public*, pg. 1878
SILGAN DISPENSING SYSTEMS STATERSVILLE LLC—See Silgan Holdings, Inc.; *U.S. Public*, pg. 1879
SILGAN DISPENSING SYSTEMS THOMASTON CORPORATION—See Silgan Holdings, Inc.; *U.S. Public*, pg. 1879
SILGAN DISPENSING SYSTEMS VICENZA S.R.L.—See Silgan Holdings, Inc.; *U.S. Public*, pg. 1879
SILGAN DISPENSING SYSTEMS (WUXI) CO., LTD.—See Silgan Holdings, Inc.; *U.S. Public*, pg. 1878
SILGAN EQUIPMENT COMPANY—See Silgan Holdings, Inc.; *U.S. Public*, pg. 1879
SILGAN HOLDINGS AUSTRIA GMBH—See Silgan Holdings, Inc.; *U.S. Public*, pg. 1879
SILGAN HOLDINGS, INC.; *U.S. Public*, pg. 1878
SILGAN METAL PACKAGING ENEM O.O.O.—See Silgan Holdings, Inc.; *U.S. Public*, pg. 1879
SILGAN METAL PACKAGING GERMANY GMBH—See Silgan Holdings, Inc.; *U.S. Public*, pg. 1879
SILGAN METAL PACKAGING LEIPZIG GMBH—See Silgan Holdings, Inc.; *U.S. Public*, pg. 1879
SILGAN METAL PACKAGING STUPINO O.O.O.—See Silgan Holdings, Inc.; *U.S. Public*, pg. 1879
SILGAN METAL PACKAGING TCZEW S.A.—See Silgan Holdings, Inc.; *U.S. Public*, pg. 1879
SILGAN PLASTIC CLOSURE SOLUTIONS—See Silgan Holdings, Inc.; *U.S. Public*, pg. 1879
SILGAN PLASTICS CORPORATION—See Silgan Holdings, Inc.; *U.S. Public*, pg. 1879
SILGAN TUBES LLC—See Silgan Holdings, Inc.; *U.S. Public*, pg. 1879
SILGAN WHITE CAP AMERICAS LLC—See Silgan Holdings, Inc.; *U.S. Public*, pg. 1879
SILGAN WHITE CAP BELGIUM N.V.—See Silgan Holdings, Inc.; *U.S. Public*, pg. 1879
SILGAN WHITE CAP CORPORATION—See Silgan Holdings, Inc.; *U.S. Public*, pg. 1879
SILGAN WHITE CAP DEUTSCHLAND GMBH—See Silgan Holdings, Inc.; *U.S. Public*, pg. 1879
SILGAN WHITE CAP ESPANA S.L.—See Silgan Holdings, Inc.; *U.S. Public*, pg. 1879
SILGAN WHITE CAP FRANCE S.A.S.—See Silgan Holdings, Inc.; *U.S. Public*, pg. 1879
SILGAN WHITE CAP GMBH—See Silgan Holdings, Inc.; *U.S. Public*, pg. 1879
SILGAN WHITE CAP HOLDINGS SPAIN, S.L.—See Silgan Holdings, Inc.; *U.S. Public*, pg. 1879
SILGAN WHITE CAP HOLDINGS SPAIN, S.L.—See Silgan Holdings, Inc.; *U.S. Public*, pg. 1879

SILGAN WHITE CAP ITALIA S.R.L.—See Silgan Holdings, Inc.; *U.S. Public*, pg. 1879
SILGAN WHITE CAP LLC—See Silgan Holdings, Inc.; *U.S. Public*, pg. 1879
SILGAN WHITE CAP NEDERLAND N.V.—See Silgan Holdings, Inc.; *U.S. Public*, pg. 1879
SILGAN WHITE CAP POLSKA SP. Z O.O.—See Silgan Holdings, Inc.; *U.S. Public*, pg. 1879
SILGAN WHITE CAP (SHANGHAI) CO., LTD.—See Silgan Holdings, Inc.; *U.S. Public*, pg. 1879
SILGAN WHITE CAP UK LTD.—See Silgan Holdings, Inc.; *U.S. Public*, pg. 1879
SILGO RETAIL LIMITED; *Int'l*, pg. 6919
SIL GROUP LLC; *Int'l*, pg. 6918
SILHOUETTE BENELUX—See Silhouette International Schmied AG; *Int'l*, pg. 6919
SILHOUETTE FRANCE S.A.R.L.—See Silhouette International Schmied AG; *Int'l*, pg. 6919
SILHOUETTE INTERNATIONAL SCHMIED AG; *Int'l*, pg. 6919
SILHOUETTE ITALIA S.R.L.—See Silhouette International Schmied AG; *Int'l*, pg. 6920
SILHOUETTE NORGE AS—See Silhouette International Schmied AG; *Int'l*, pg. 6920
SILHOUETTE OPTICAL CO. LTD.—See Silhouette International Schmied AG; *Int'l*, pg. 6920
SILHOUETTE OPTICAL ESPANA S.A.—See Silhouette International Schmied AG; *Int'l*, pg. 6920
SILHOUETTE OPTICAL LTD.—See Silhouette International Schmied AG; *Int'l*, pg. 6920
SILHOUETTE SCANDINAVIA A/S—See Silhouette International Schmied AG; *Int'l*, pg. 6920
SILHOUETTE SCHWEIZ GMBH—See Silhouette International Schmied AG; *Int'l*, pg. 6920
SILHOUETTE SVERIGE AB—See Silhouette International Schmied AG; *Int'l*, pg. 6920
SILHOUETTE UK LTD.—See Silhouette International Schmied AG; *Int'l*, pg. 6920
SILHOUETTE VERTRIEBS GMBH—See Silhouette International Schmied AG; *Int'l*, pg. 6920
SILICA APPLIANCE & ELECTRONICS; *U.S. Private*, pg. 3652
SILICATOS Y DERIVADOS S.A. DE C.V.—See The Carlyle Group Inc.; *U.S. Public*, pg. 2052
SILICA VERFAHRENSTECHNIK GMBH—See Berndorf AG; *Int'l*, pg. 987
SILICE DEL ISTMO, S.A. DE C.V.—See Crown Holdings, Inc.; *U.S. Public*, pg. 599
SILICOM CONNECTIVITY SOLUTIONS INC.—See RAD Group; *Int'l*, pg. 6173
SILICOM CONNECTIVITY SOLUTIONS LTD.—See RAD Group; *Int'l*, pg. 6173
SILICOM LTD.—See RAD Group; *Int'l*, pg. 6173
SILICOMP-AQL S.A.S.—See Orange S.A.; *Int'l*, pg. 5610
SILICOMP CANADA INC—See Orange S.A.; *Int'l*, pg. 5610
SILICOMP MANAGEMENT—See Orange S.A.; *Int'l*, pg. 5610
SILICON2 CO., LTD.; *Int'l*, pg. 6921
SILICON APPLICATION CORPORATION—See WPG Holdings Limited; *Int'l*, pg. 8461
SILICON CRAFT TECHNOLOGY PUBLIC COMPANY LIMITED; *Int'l*, pg. 6920
SILICONE ENGINEERING LTD.; *Int'l*, pg. 6921
SILICONE SPECIALTIES, INC.; *U.S. Private*, pg. 3652
SILICONEXPERT TECHNOLOGIES, INC.—See Arrow Electronics, Inc.; *U.S. Public*, pg. 200
SILICONFILE TECHNOLOGIES INC.—See SK hynix Inc.; *Int'l*, pg. 6971
SILICON FOREST ELECTRONICS, INC.; *U.S. Private*, pg. 3652
SILICON IMAGE INDIA RESEARCH AND DEVELOPMENT PRIVATE LTD.—See Lattice Semiconductor Corporation; *U.S. Public*, pg. 1294
SILICON INTEGRATED SYSTEMS CORP.; *Int'l*, pg. 6920
SILICON INTEGRATED SYSTEMS LTD.—See Silicon Integrated Systems Corp.; *Int'l*, pg. 6920
SILICONIX INCORPORATED—See Vishay Intertechnology, Inc.; *U.S. Public*, pg. 2302
SILICON LABORATORIES ASIA PACIFIC, LIMITED—See Silicon Laboratories Inc.; *U.S. Public*, pg. 1879
SILICON LABORATORIES CANADA ULC—See Silicon Laboratories Inc.; *U.S. Public*, pg. 1880
SILICON LABORATORIES DENMARK APS—See Silicon Laboratories Inc.; *U.S. Public*, pg. 1880
SILICON LABORATORIES FINLAND OY—See Silicon Laboratories Inc.; *U.S. Public*, pg. 1880
SILICON LABORATORIES FRANCE SAS—See Silicon Laboratories Inc.; *U.S. Public*, pg. 1880
SILICON LABORATORIES GMBH—See Silicon Laboratories Inc.; *U.S. Public*, pg. 1880
SILICON LABORATORIES INC.; *U.S. Public*, pg. 1879
SILICON LABORATORIES INTERNATIONAL PTE. LTD.—See Silicon Laboratories Inc.; *U.S. Public*, pg. 1880
SILICON LABORATORIES NORWAY AS—See Silicon Laboratories Inc.; *U.S. Public*, pg. 1880
SILICON LABORATORIES UK LIMITED—See Silicon Laboratories Inc.; *U.S. Public*, pg. 1880

SILICON LABORATORIES Y.K.—See Silicon Laboratories Inc.; *U.S. Public*, pg. 1880
SILICON LABS EMBER, INC.—See Silicon Laboratories Inc.; *U.S. Public*, pg. 1880
SILICON LIGHT MACHINES CORP.—See Screen Holdings Co., Ltd.; *Int'l*, pg. 6656
SILICON MECHANICS, INC.—See Cerberus Capital Management, L.P.; *U.S. Private*, pg. 839
SILICON MICROSTRUCTURES INC.—See TE Connectivity Ltd.; *Int'l*, pg. 7495
SILICON MITUS; *Int'l*, pg. 6920
SILICON MITUS TECHNOLOGY INC.—See Silicon Mitus; *Int'l*, pg. 6920
SILICON MOTION, INC.—See Silicon Motion Technology Corporation; *Int'l*, pg. 6920
SILICON MOTION, INC.—See Silicon Motion Technology Corporation; *Int'l*, pg. 6920
SILICON MOTION TECHNOLOGY CORPORATION; *Int'l*, pg. 6920
SILICON MOUNTAIN HOLDINGS, INC.; *U.S. Private*, pg. 3652
SILICON MOUNTAIN MEMORY, INC.—See Silicon Mountain Holdings, Inc.; *U.S. Private*, pg. 3652
SILICON OPTRONICS, INC.; *Int'l*, pg. 6920
SILICON POWER COMPUTER & COMMUNICATION, INC.; pg. 6920
SILICON POWER CORPORATION; *U.S. Private*, pg. 3652
SILICON PRODUCTS RESEARCH ENGINEERING PRODUCTION GMBH—See PV Crystalox Solar plc; *Int'l*, pg. 6125
SILICON QUEST INTERNATIONAL; *U.S. Private*, pg. 3652
SILICON RENTALS SOLUTIONS LIMITED; *Int'l*, pg. 6920
SILICON STORAGE TECHNOLOGY INC.—See Microchip Technology Incorporated; *U.S. Public*, pg. 1437
SILICON STUDIO CORP.; *Int'l*, pg. 6920
SILICON TECHNOLOGY CORPORATION—See Carlit Co., Ltd.; *Int'l*, pg. 1338
SILICON TOUCH TECHNOLOGY, INC.; *Int'l*, pg. 6920
SILICON VALLEY BANK—See Federal Deposit Insurance Corporation; *U.S. Private*, pg. 1487
SILICON VALLEY BANK UK LIMITED—See Federal Deposit Insurance Corporation; *U.S. Private*, pg. 1487
SILICON VALLEY COMMUNITY NEWSPAPERS—See Alden Global Capital LLC; *U.S. Private*, pg. 155
SILICON VALLEY CONCEPTS; *U.S. Private*, pg. 3652
SILICON VALLEY EXPERT WITNESS GROUP, INC.—See Thomson Reuters Corporation; *Int'l*, pg. 7715
SILICON VALLEY INFOTECH LIMITED; *Int'l*, pg. 6920
SILICON VALLEY MICROELECTRONICS INC.; *U.S. Private*, pg. 3652
SILICON VALLEY SHELVING & EQUIPMENT; *U.S. Private*, pg. 3652
SILICON VALLEY SURGERY CENTER, L.P.—See HCA Healthcare, Inc.; *U.S. Public*, pg. 1008
SILICONWARE PRECISION INDUSTRIES CO., LTD. - CHANGHUA FACILITY—See ASE Technology Holding Co., Ltd.; *Int'l*, pg. 605
SILICONWARE PRECISION INDUSTRIES CO., LTD. - HSINCHU IG FACILITY—See ASE Technology Holding Co., Ltd.; *Int'l*, pg. 605
SILICONWARE PRECISION INDUSTRIES CO., LTD. - HSINCHU IIIG FACILITY—See ASE Technology Holding Co., Ltd.; *Int'l*, pg. 605
SILICONWARE PRECISION INDUSTRIES CO., LTD.—See ASE Technology Holding Co., Ltd.; *Int'l*, pg. 605
SILICONWARE TECHNOLOGY (SUZHOU) LIMITED—See ASE Technology Holding Co., Ltd.; *Int'l*, pg. 605
SILICONWARE USA, INC.—See ASE Technology Holding Co., Ltd.; *Int'l*, pg. 605
SILICON WORKSHOP LIMITED—See Legend Upstar Holdings Limited; *Int'l*, pg. 4444
SILIGENCE SAS—See ASUSTeK Computer Inc.; *Int'l*, pg. 663
SILIKONS ADVERTISING NETWORK—See WPP plc; *Int'l*, pg. 8482
S I L INC.; *U.S. Private*, pg. 3512
SIL INSURANCE - INSURANCE CLOSED JOINT STOCK COMPANY—See SIL Group LLC; *Int'l*, pg. 6918
SIL INTERNATIONAL; *U.S. Private*, pg. 3651
SIL INVESTMENTS LTD; *Int'l*, pg. 6918
SILITECH ELECTRONIC (SUZHOU) CO., LTD.—See Silitech Technology Corporation; *Int'l*, pg. 6921
SILITECH (HONG KONG) HOLDING LTD.—See Silitech Technology Corporation; *Int'l*, pg. 6921
SILITECH TECHNOLOGY CORPORATION LIMITED—See Silitech Technology Corporation; *Int'l*, pg. 6921
SILITECH TECHNOLOGY CORPORATION LIMITED—See Silitech Technology Corporation; *Int'l*, pg. 6921
SILITECH TECHNOLOGY CORPORATION SDN. BHD.—See Lite-On Technology Corporation; *Int'l*, pg. 4526
SILITECH TECHNOLOGY CORPORATION; *Int'l*, pg. 6921
SILITECH TECHNOLOGY (EUROPE) LTD.—See Silitech Technology Corporation; *Int'l*, pg. 6921
SILITEK ELEC. (GUANGZHOU) CO., LTD.—See Lite-On Technology Corporation; *Int'l*, pg. 4525

COMPANY NAME INDEX

SILITHERM IMMOBILIARE S.R.L.—See BizLink Holding Inc.; *Int'l*, pg. 1053
SILKAIR (SINGAPORE) PTE. LTD.—See Temasek Holdings (Private) Limited; *Int'l*, pg. 7551
SILKAN SOLUTIONS INC.—See SILKAN; *Int'l*, pg. 6921
SILKAN; *Int'l*, pg. 6921
SILKARGO LOGISTICS (SINGAPORE), PTE., LTD.—See PT Samudera Indonesia Tbk; *Int'l*, pg. 6069
SILKBANK LIMITED; *Int'l*, pg. 6921
SILKEBORG DATA A/S—See Francisco Partners Management, LP; *U.S. Private*, pg. 1589
SILKEBORG IF INVEST A/S; *Int'l*, pg. 6921
SILKE COMMUNICATIONS, INC; *U.S. Private*, pg. 3652
SILK ELEMENTS, INC.—See Sally Beauty Holdings, Inc.; *U.S. Public*, pg. 1839
SILK LASER AUSTRALIA LIMITED—See Wesfarmers Limited; *Int'l*, pg. 8380
SILK LASER CLINIC ELIZABETH PTY LTD.—See Wesfarmers Limited; *Int'l*, pg. 8380
SILK LASER CLINIC HOBART PTY LTD.—See Wesfarmers Limited; *Int'l*, pg. 8380
SILK LASER CLINIC HYDE PARK PTY LTD.—See Wesfarmers Limited; *Int'l*, pg. 8380
SILK LASER CLINIC NORWOOD PTY LTD.—See Wesfarmers Limited; *Int'l*, pg. 8380
SILK LASER CLINIC RUNDLE MALL PTY LTD.—See Wesfarmers Limited; *Int'l*, pg. 8380
SILK LOGISTICS HOLDINGS LIMITED; *Int'l*, pg. 6921
SILKNET JSC—See Silk Road Group S.A.; *Int'l*, pg. 6921
SILK ROAD BANK AD SKOPJE—See Silk Road Capital Ltd.; *Int'l*, pg. 6921
SILK ROAD CAPITAL LTD.; *Int'l*, pg. 6921
SILK ROAD ENERGY INC.; *Int'l*, pg. 6921
SILK ROAD ENERGY SERVICES GROUP LIMITED; *Int'l*, pg. 6921
SILK ROAD ENTERTAINMENT, INC.; *U.S. Public*, pg. 1880
SILK ROAD GROUP S.A.; *Int'l*, pg. 6921
SILK ROAD LOGISTICS HOLDINGS LIMITED; *Int'l*, pg. 6921
SILK ROAD MEDICAL, INC.—See Boston Scientific Corporation; *U.S. Public*, pg. 375
SILKROAD NICKEL LTD.; *Int'l*, pg. 6921
SILK ROAD RESTAURANTS INTERNATIONAL PTE LTD—See Amara Holdings Ltd.; *Int'l*, pg. 411
SILKROAD SUGAR PRIVATE LIMITED—See The Murugappa Group, Ltd.; *Int'l*, pg. 7668
SILKROAD TECHNOLOGY, INC.; *U.S. Private*, pg. 3652
SILK ROAD TRANSPORT, INC.—See ACI Capital Co. LLC; *U.S. Private*, pg. 59
SILKROAD VISUAL TECHNOLOGY CO LTD; *Int'l*, pg. 6922
SILKROUTE; *U.S. Private*, pg. 3653
SILKS CLUB CO., LTD.—See Formosa International Hotels Corp.; *Int'l*, pg. 2734
SILK SCREEN INK LTD.—See Delta Apparel, Inc.; *U.S. Public*, pg. 652
SILKS PLACE TAINAN CO., LTD.—See Formosa International Hotels Corp.; *Int'l*, pg. 2734
SILKS PLACE TAROKO CO., LTD.—See Formosa International Hotels Corp.; *Int'l*, pg. 2734
SILKS PLACE YILAN CO., LTD.—See Formosa International Hotels Corp.; *Int'l*, pg. 2734
SILKWAVE INC.; *Int'l*, pg. 6922
SILKY OAKS PTY LIMITED—See GPT Group; *Int'l*, pg. 3047
SILLA CO., LTD.; *Int'l*, pg. 6922
SILLA ENGINEERING CO., LTD—See Silla Co., Ltd.; *Int'l*, pg. 6922
SILLAJEN BIOTHERAPEUTICS, INC.—See SILLAJEN Inc; *Int'l*, pg. 6922
SILLAJEN INC; *Int'l*, pg. 6922
SILLARS (B. & C.E.) LTD—See Downer EDI Limited; *Int'l*, pg. 2186
SILLARS HOLDINGS LIMITED—See Downer EDI Limited; *Int'l*, pg. 2186
SILLA SG CO., LTD - BUSAN FACTORY—See Silla Co., Ltd.; *Int'l*, pg. 6922
SILLA SG CO., LTD—See Silla Co., Ltd.; *Int'l*, pg. 6922
SILLA TEXTILE CO., LTD.; *Int'l*, pg. 6922
SILLENGER EXPLORATION CORP.; *Int'l*, pg. 6922
SILLER & LAAR SCHRAUBEN- WERKZEUG- UND BESCHLAGE- HANDEL GMBH & CO. KG—See Wurth Verwaltungsgesellschaft mbH; *Int'l*, pg. 8507
SILLERY AND PARTNERS; *U.S. Private*, pg. 3653
SILLERY AND PARTNERS—See Sillery and Partners; *U.S. Private*, pg. 3653
SILLERY AND PARTNERS—See Sillery and Partners; *U.S. Private*, pg. 3653
SILLIKER INC.—See Institut Merieux; *Int'l*, pg. 3724
SILL LEUCHTEN GMBH—See Societe d'Application des Methodes Modernes d'Eclairage SA; *Int'l*, pg. 7037
SILLOH INDUSTRIES INC.; *U.S. Private*, pg. 3653
SILLOH MARKET RESEARCH LLC—See Silloh Industries Inc.; *U.S. Private*, pg. 3653
SILLS CUMMIS & GROSS P.C.; *U.S. Private*, pg. 3653
SILL TERHAR MOTORS, INC; *U.S. Private*, pg. 3653
SILLY MONKS ENTERTAINMENT LTD.; *Int'l*, pg. 6922
SILMAASEMA OYJ; *Int'l*, pg. 6922

SILMAR RESINS—See Interplastic Corporation; *U.S. Private*, pg. 2123
THE SILOAM SPRINGS HERALD LEADER—See Wehco Media, Inc.; *U.S. Private*, pg. 4470
SILOAM SPRINGS METAL RECYCLING INC.—See Yaffe Iron & Metal Company Inc.; *U.S. Private*, pg. 4584
SILOCAF OF NEW ORLEANS INC.—See B. Pacorini S.p.A.; *Int'l*, pg. 789
SILOGRAM LUBRICANTS CORP.; *U.S. Private*, pg. 3653
SILO II LBG 57 - 59 LIEGENSCHAFTSVERWERTUNG GMBH & CO KG—See STRABAG SE; *Int'l*, pg. 7232
SILOKONSULT PROCESSTEKNIK SWEDEN AB—See Volati AB; *Int'l*, pg. 8301
SILOMA JSC.—See Industrial Capital Holding AD-Sofia; *Int'l*, pg. 3671
SILOM MEDICAL CO., LTD.—See Teva Pharmaceutical Industries, Ltd.; *Int'l*, pg. 7579
SILO PHARMA INC.; *U.S. Public*, pg. 1880
SILO P. KRUSE BETRIEBS-GMBH & CO. KG—See Archer-Daniels-Midland Company; *U.S. Public*, pg. 185
SILOS GRANARI DELLA SICILIA S.R.L.—See Heidelberg Materials AG; *Int'l*, pg. 3317
SILOSMASHERS, INC.; *U.S. Private*, pg. 3653
SILPADA DESIGNS LLC—See Berkshire Hathaway Inc.; *U.S. Public*, pg. 316
SILSBEE FORD LINCOLN MERCURY, INC.; *U.S. Private*, pg. 3653
SILTANEN & PARTNERS; *U.S. Private*, pg. 3653
SILTA OY—See Administer Oy; *Int'l*, pg. 151
SILTERRA MALAYSIA SDN BHD—See Dagang NeXchange Berhad; *Int'l*, pg. 1912
SILTERRA SALES & MARKETING (L) LTD.—See Dagang NeXchange Berhad; *Int'l*, pg. 1912
SILTERRA USA INC.—See Dagang NeXchange Berhad; *Int'l*, pg. 1912
SILTIN INDUSTRIES, INC.—See Deeco Metals Corporation; *U.S. Private*, pg. 1189
SILTRONIC AG; *Int'l*, pg. 6922
SILTRONTECH ELECTRONICS CORPORATION; *Int'l*, pg. 6922
SILVACO EUROPE LTD.—See Silvaco Group, Inc.; *U.S. Public*, pg. 1880
SILVACO GROUP, INC.; *U.S. Public*, pg. 1880
SILVACO, INC.—See Silvaco Group, Inc.; *U.S. Public*, pg. 1880
SILVACO JAPAN CO., LTD.—See Silvaco Group, Inc.; *U.S. Public*, pg. 1880
SILVACO KOREA CO. LTD.—See Silvaco Group, Inc.; *U.S. Public*, pg. 1880
SILVACO SINGAPORE PTE LTD—See Silvaco Group, Inc.; *U.S. Public*, pg. 1880
SILVACO TAIWAN CO., LTD.—See Silvaco Group, Inc.; *U.S. Public*, pg. 1880
SILVADDEN AB—See Arla Foods amba; *Int'l*, pg. 572
SILVA ESTATE A/S—See Det Danske Hedeselskab; *Int'l*, pg. 2047
SILVA INTERNATIONAL, INC.—See Universal Corporation; *U.S. Public*, pg. 2254
SILVAIR, INC.; *U.S. Public*, pg. 1880
SILVANA S.A.—See SIF Banat-Crisana S.A.; *Int'l*, pg. 6905
SILVAN A/S—See Aurelius Equity Opportunities SE & Co. KGaA; *Int'l*, pg. 709
SILVANIA RESOURCES INC.; *U.S. Private*, pg. 3653
SILVAN INNOVATION LABS PRIVATE LIMITED—See Polycab India Limited; *Int'l*, pg. 5914
SILVANO FASHION GROUP AS; *Int'l*, pg. 6922
SILVANO FASHION OOO—See Silvano Fashion Group AS; *Int'l*, pg. 6922
SILVANO FASHION SIA—See Silvano Fashion Group AS; *Int'l*, pg. 6922
SILVANO FASHION ZAO—See Silvano Fashion Group AS; *Int'l*, pg. 6922
SILVANT CAPITAL MANAGEMENT, LLC—See Virtus Investment Partners, Inc.; *U.S. Public*, pg. 2301
SILVA PHARMACEUTICALS LTD.; *Int'l*, pg. 6922
SILVASEED CO.—See DroneSeed Co.; *U.S. Private*, pg. 1279
SILVAS OIL CO. INC.; *U.S. Private*, pg. 3653
SILVA SWEDEN AB—See Verdane Capital Advisors AS; *Int'l*, pg. 8165
SILVERADO BUILDING MATERIALS; *U.S. Private*, pg. 3662
SILVERADO CABLE COMPANY—See Phoenix Logistics, Inc.; *U.S. Private*, pg. 3173
SILVERADO SENIOR LIVING ALHAMBRA, INC.—See Welltower Inc.; *U.S. Public*, pg. 2349
SILVERADO SENIOR LIVING DALLAS, INC.—See Welltower Inc.; *U.S. Public*, pg. 2349
SILVERADO SENIOR LIVING, INC.—See Welltower Inc.; *U.S. Public*, pg. 2349
SILVERADO SENIOR LIVING SALT LAKE CITY, INC.—See Welltower Inc.; *U.S. Public*, pg. 2349
SILVERADO SENIOR LIVING SCOTTSDALE, INC.—See Welltower Inc.; *U.S. Public*, pg. 2349
SILVERADO STAGES, INC.; *U.S. Private*, pg. 3662
SILVERADO SYSTEMS, INC.; *U.S. Private*, pg. 3662
SILVERADO VINEYARDS INC.—See Foley Family Wines Holdings Inc; *U.S. Private*, pg. 1558

SILVER AIRWAYS, LLC—See Independence Capital Partners, LLC; *U.S. Private*, pg. 2057
SILVERARROW CAPITAL HOLDING LTD.; *Int'l*, pg. 6925
SILVERAY MANUFACTURERS (PTY) LIMITED—See The Bidvest Group Limited; *Int'l*, pg. 7626
SILVERAY STATMARK COMPANY (PTY) LIMITED—See The Bidvest Group Limited; *Int'l*, pg. 7626
SILVER BASE GROUP HOLDINGS LIMITED; *Int'l*, pg. 6922
SILVER BASE INTERNATIONAL DEVELOPMENT CO., LTD.—See Silver Base Group Holdings Limited; *Int'l*, pg. 6922
SILVER BASIS ENGINEERING GERMANY GMBH—See Shenzhen Silver Basis Technology Co., Ltd.; *Int'l*, pg. 6821
SILVER BASIS (HONGKONG) INVESTMENT DEVELOPMENT CO., LTD.—See Shenzhen Silver Basis Technology Co., Ltd.; *Int'l*, pg. 6821
SILVER BEAR RESOURCES PLC; *Int'l*, pg. 6922
SILVERBERG & ASSOCIATES INC.—See People Corporation; *Int'l*, pg. 5793
SILVERBERG JEWELRY COMPANY; *U.S. Private*, pg. 3662
SILVERBIRCH HOTELS & RESORTS—See British Columbia Investment Management Corp.; *Int'l*, pg. 1169
SILVERBOW RESOURCES, INC.—See KKR & Co. Inc.; *U.S. Public*, pg. 1244
SILVERBRIDGE HOLDINGS LTD.; *Int'l*, pg. 6925
SILVER BUCKLE MINES, INC.; *U.S. Public*, pg. 1880
SILVERBULLET A/S—See IQVIA Holdings Inc.; *U.S. Public*, pg. 1170
SILVER BULLET DATA SERVICES GROUP PLC; *Int'l*, pg. 6923
SILVER BULLET MINES CORP.; *Int'l*, pg. 6923
SILVER BULLET TECHNOLOGY, INC.—See COMSovereign Holding Corp.; *U.S. Public*, pg. 562
SILVER BULL RESOURCES INC.; *Int'l*, pg. 6922
SILVERCAR, INC.—See Porsche Automobil Holding SE; *Int'l*, pg. 5926
SILVERCHAIR INFORMATION SYSTEMS; *U.S. Private*, pg. 3662
SILVER CINEMAS ACQUISITION CO.—See Cohen Media Group, LLC; *U.S. Private*, pg. 963
SILVER CITY DRILLING (QLD) PTY LIMITED—See Apollo Global Management, Inc.; *U.S. Public*, pg. 167
SILVER CITY HOUSING LP—See Edison International; *U.S. Public*, pg. 719
SILVER CITY MINERALS LIMITED; *Int'l*, pg. 6923
SILVER CLOUD INNS & HOTELS; *U.S. Private*, pg. 3653
SILVERCORP METALS INC.; *Int'l*, pg. 6925
SILVER CREEK MANOR NURSING CENTER—See Sava Senior Care LLC; *U.S. Private*, pg. 3555
SILVER CREEK MRI, LLC—See Community Health Systems, Inc.; *U.S. Public*, pg. 557
SILVER CREEK PHARMACEUTICALS, INC.—See Merrimack Pharmaceuticals, Inc.; *U.S. Public*, pg. 1425
SILVERCREST ASSET MANAGEMENT GROUP INC.; *U.S. Public*, pg. 1880
SILVERCREST ASSET MANAGEMENT GROUP LLC—See Silvercrest Asset Management Group Inc.; *U.S. Public*, pg. 1880
THE SILVERCREST CENTER FOR NURSING AND REHABILITATION; *U.S. Private*, pg. 4118
SILVERCREST L.P.—See Silvercrest Asset Management Group Inc.; *U.S. Public*, pg. 1880
SILVERCREST METALS, INC.; *Int'l*, pg. 6925
SILVER CROSS 21 PTE LTD—See OUE Limited; *Int'l*, pg. 5666
SILVER CROSS AMBULATORY SURGERY CENTER, LLC—See Tenet Healthcare Corporation; *U.S. Public*, pg. 2007
SILVER CROSS HEALTHCARE PTE LTD—See OUE Limited; *Int'l*, pg. 5666
SILVER CROSS MEDICAL CENTRE PTE LTD—See OUE Limited; *Int'l*, pg. 5666
SILVER CROSS NORTH PTE LTD—See OUE Limited; *Int'l*, pg. 5666
SILVER CROSS/USP SURGERY CENTER, LLC—See Tenet Healthcare Corporation; *U.S. Public*, pg. 2007
SILVER DENKEN CO., LTD.—See Citizen Watch Co., Ltd.; *Int'l*, pg. 1625
SILVER DINER, INC.; *U.S. Private*, pg. 3653
SILVER DOLLAR GOLF & TRAP CLB—See National Home Communities LLC; *U.S. Private*, pg. 2856
SILVER DOLLAR RESOURCES, INC.; *Int'l*, pg. 6923
SILVER DRAGON RESOURCES INC.; *Int'l*, pg. 6923
SILVER EAGLE DISTRIBUTORS LP; *U.S. Private*, pg. 3653
SILVER EAGLE DISTRIBUTORS LTD.; *U.S. Private*, pg. 3653
SILVEREDGE COOPERATIVE; *U.S. Private*, pg. 3663
SILVEREDGE GOVERNMENT SOLUTIONS—See Godspeed Capital Management LP; *U.S. Private*, pg. 1725
SILVEREDGE, LLC; *U.S. Private*, pg. 3663
SILVEREED (HONG KONG) LIMITED—See Li & Fung Limited; *Int'l*, pg. 4480
SILVER EGG TECHNOLOGY CO., LTD.; *Int'l*, pg. 6923
SILVER ELEPHANT MINING CORP.; *Int'l*, pg. 6923
SILVER FALCON MINING, INC.; *U.S. Private*, pg. 3653

SILVERFERN CAPITAL MANAGEMENT, LLC — CORPORATE AFFILIATIONS

SILVERFERN CAPITAL MANAGEMENT, LLC; *U.S. Private,* pg. 3663
SILVER FERN FARMS GMBH—See Silver Fern Farms Limited; *Int'l,* pg. 6923
SILVER FERN FARMS GMBH—See Silver Fern Farms Limited; *Int'l,* pg. 6923
SILVER FERN FARMS LIMITED; *Int'l,* pg. 6923
SILVER FERN FARMS NV—See Silver Fern Farms Limited; *Int'l,* pg. 6923
SILVER FERN FARMS (UK) LIMITED—See Silver Fern Farms Limited; *Int'l,* pg. 6923
SILVER FIELDS RESOURCES INC.; *Int'l,* pg. 6923
SILVERFISH RESOURCES INC.; *Int'l,* pg. 6925
SILVERFLEET CAPITAL LIMITED; *Int'l,* pg. 6925
SILVERFLEET CAPITAL PARTNERS LLP—See Silverfleet Capital Limited; *Int'l,* pg. 6925
SILVER FOAM DISTRIBUTING CO.; *U.S. Private,* pg. 3653
SILVERGATE CAPITAL CORPORATION; *U.S. Public,* pg. 1880
SILVERGATE PHARMACEUTICALS INC.—See NovaQuest Capital Management, LLC; *U.S. Private,* pg. 2967
SILVER GRAIL RESOURCES LTD.; *Int'l,* pg. 6923
SILVER GRANT INTERNATIONAL HOLDINGS GROUP LTD.; *Int'l,* pg. 6923
SILVER HAMMER MINING CORP.; *Int'l,* pg. 6923
SILVERHAWK CAPITAL PARTNERS, LLC; *U.S. Private,* pg. 3663
SILVER HERITAGE GROUP LIMITED—See HatchAsia Inc.; *U.S. Private,* pg. 3284
SILVER HILL HOSPITAL, INC.; *U.S. Private,* pg. 3653
SILVER HILL QUARRY—See Haines & Kibblehouse Inc.; *U.S. Private,* pg. 1841
SILVER HOLDING CORP.—See Ingersoll Rand Inc.; *U.S. Public,* pg. 1122
SILVER HORSMAN INC.; *U.S. Private,* pg. 3653
SILVERHUB MEDIA UK LTD.; *Int'l,* pg. 6926
SILVER INVESTMENT PARTNERS GMBH & CO. KG; *Int'l,* pg. 6923
SILVERITE CONSTRUCTION CO., INC.; *U.S. Private,* pg. 3663
SILVER KING REFRIGERATION, INC—See Berkshire Hathaway Inc.; *U.S. Public,* pg. 310
SILVER LAKE ASIA LIMITED—See Silver Lake Group, LLC; *U.S. Private,* pg. 3655
SILVER LAKE ASSISTED LIVING, LLC—See Brookdale Senior Living Inc.; *U.S. Public,* pg. 395
SILVERLAKE AXIS LTD.; *Int'l,* pg. 6926
SILVER LAKE CENTER, INC.; *U.S. Private,* pg. 3653
SILVERLAKE DIGITAL ECONOMY SDN. BHD.—See Silverlake Axis Ltd.; *Int'l,* pg. 6926
SILVER LAKE EUROPE, LLP—See Silver Lake Group, LLC; *U.S. Private,* pg. 3655
SILVER LAKE GROUP, LLC; *U.S. Private,* pg. 3653
SILVER LAKE HEALTHCARE, INC.—See The Ensign Group, Inc.; *U.S. Public,* pg. 2072
SILVER LAKE KRAFTWERK MANAGEMENT COMPANY, LLC—See Silver Lake Group, LLC; *U.S. Private,* pg. 3655
SILVER LAKE MALL, LLC—See Brookfield Corporation; *Int'l,* pg. 1185
SILVER LAKE MANAGEMENT COMPANY SUMERU, LLC—See Silver Lake Group, LLC; *U.S. Private,* pg. 3655
SILVER LAKE MANAGEMENT, LLC—See Silver Lake Group, LLC; *U.S. Private,* pg. 3655
SILVER LAKE RESOURCES LIMITED-LAKEWOOD GOLD PROCESSING FACILITY—See Red 5 Limited; *Int'l,* pg. 6243
SILVER LAKE RESOURCES LIMITED—See Red 5 Limited; *Int'l,* pg. 6243
SILVERLAKE SYMMETRI (MALAYSIA) SDN. BHD.—See Silverlake Axis Ltd.; *Int'l,* pg. 6926
SILVERLAKE SYMMETRI (PHILIPPINES) ENTERPRISES, INC.—See Silverlake Axis Ltd.; *Int'l,* pg. 6926
SILVER LANE ADVISORS LLC—See Raymond James Financial, Inc.; *U.S. Public,* pg. 1765
SILVERLEAF ADVISORS LLC; *U.S. Private,* pg. 3663
SILVERLEAF RESORTS, INC.—See Kemmons Wilson, Inc.; *U.S. Private,* pg. 2281
SILVER LIFE CO., LTD.; *Int'l,* pg. 6923
SILVERLIGHT AVIATION, LLC—See 808 Renewable Energy Corp.; *U.S. Public,* pg. 9
SILVERLINE ENDUSTRI VE TICARET A.S.; *Int'l,* pg. 6926
SILVER-LINE PLASTICS CORP.; *U.S. Private,* pg. 3662
SILVERLINE TECHNOLOGIES LTD.; *Int'l,* pg. 6926
SILVERLINING INTERIORS, INC.; *U.S. Private,* pg. 3663
SILVERLINK COMMUNICATIONS, LLC—See Welltok, Inc.; *U.S. Private,* pg. 4478
SILVERLINK HOLDINGS LIMITED—See DLF Limited; *Int'l,* pg. 2141
SILVERLINK PCS SOFTWARE LIMITED—See Alcidion Group Limited; *Int'l,* pg. 301
SILVER MANAGEMENT GROUP, INC.—See Apex Fintech Solutions LLC; *U.S. Private,* pg. 292
SILVERMAN MCGOVERN STAFFING AND RECRUITING; *U.S. Private,* pg. 3663

SILVERMAN MEDIA & MARKETING GROUP, INC.; *U.S. Private,* pg. 3663
SILVERMERE HAVEN LIMITED—See CVS Group Plc; *Int'l,* pg. 1890
SILVER MESA AT PALOMINO PARK L.L.C.—See Moody's Corporation; *U.S. Public,* pg. 1469
SILVER MINES LIMITED; *Int'l,* pg. 6923
SILVER MOUNTAIN MINES INC.; *Int'l,* pg. 6924
SILVER NICETY COMPANY LIMITED—See Hysan Development Company Limited; *Int'l,* pg. 3554
SILVER NORTH RESOURCES LTD.; *Int'l,* pg. 6924
SILVER OAK CASUALTY, INC.—See AMERISAFE, Inc.; *U.S. Public,* pg. 115
SILVEROAK COMMERCIALS LIMITED; *Int'l,* pg. 6926
SILVER OAK (INDIA) LIMITED; *Int'l,* pg. 6924
SILVER OAK SERVICES PARTNERS, LLC; *U.S. Private,* pg. 3661
SILVER ONE RESOURCES INC.; *Int'l,* pg. 6924
SILVER PEAK PARTNERS; *U.S. Private,* pg. 3661
SILVERPEAK STRATEGIC PARTNERS LP; *U.S. Private,* pg. 3663
SILVER PEAK SYSTEMS, INC.—See Hewlett Packard Enterprise Company; *U.S. Public,* pg. 1032
SILVER PEARL HOSPITALITY & LUXURY SPACES LIMITED; *Int'l,* pg. 6924
SILVER PHOENIX RESOURCES INC.; *Int'l,* pg. 6924
SILVER P LESSEE, LLC—See Pebblebrook Hotel Trust; *U.S. Public,* pg. 1660
SILVER POINT CAPITAL FUND INVESTMENTS LLC—See Silver Point Capital, L.P.; *U.S. Private,* pg. 3662
SILVER POINT CAPITAL, L.P.; *U.S. Private,* pg. 3661
SILVERPOINT INFRATECH LIMITED; *Int'l,* pg. 6926
SILVER PREDATOR CORP.—See Till Capital Corporation; *Int'l,* pg. 7748
SILVERRAIL TECHNOLOGIES, INC.—See Expedia Group, Inc.; *U.S. Public,* pg. 810
SILVERRAIL TECHNOLOGIES UK LIMITED—See Expedia Group, Inc.; *U.S. Public,* pg. 810
SILVER RANGE RESOURCES LTD.; *Int'l,* pg. 6924
SILVER RIDGE HOLDINGS BHD; *Int'l,* pg. 6924
SILVER SANDS RESOURCES CORP.; *Int'l,* pg. 6924
SILVERSCAPE TECHNOLOGIES, INC.; *U.S. Private,* pg. 3663
SILVER SCOTT MINES, INC.; *U.S. Public,* pg. 1880
SILVERSCRIPT INSURANCE COMPANY—See CVS Health Corporation; *U.S. Public,* pg. 616
SILVERSEA CRUISES AUSTRALIA PTY. LTD.—See Royal Caribbean Cruises Ltd.; *U.S. Public,* pg. 1815
SILVERSEA CRUISES LTD—See Royal Caribbean Cruises Ltd.; *U.S. Public,* pg. 1815
SILVERSEA CRUISES LTD. - THE AMERICAS REGIONAL OFFICE—See Royal Caribbean Cruises Ltd.; *U.S. Public,* pg. 1815
SILVER SEAS SHIPPING LLC—See Belhasa Group of Companies; *Int'l,* pg. 964
SILVER SEAS YACHTS OF CALIFORNIA, INC.—See MarineMax, Inc.; *U.S. Public,* pg. 1367
SILVERSHEET INC.—See AMN Healthcare Services, Inc.; *U.S. Public,* pg. 125
SILVER SHIPS, INC.; *U.S. Private,* pg. 3662
SILVER SKY CAPITAL, LTD.; *U.S. Private,* pg. 3662
SILVER SLIPPER CASINO VENTURE, LLC—See Full House Resorts, Inc.; *U.S. Public,* pg. 892
SILVERSMITH MANAGEMENT, L.P.; *U.S. Private,* pg. 3663
SILVERSPAC INC.; *U.S. Public,* pg. 1880
SILVER SPIKE INVESTMENT CORP.; *U.S. Public,* pg. 1880
SILVER SPRING FOODS, INC.—See Huntsinger Farms Inc.; *U.S. Private,* pg. 2010
THE SILVER SPRING MD ENDOSCOPY ASC, LLC—See KKR & Co. Inc.; *U.S. Public,* pg. 1248
SILVER SPRINGS BOTTLED WATER CO.; *U.S. Private,* pg. 3662
SILVER SPRINGS CITRUS INC.—See Sapporo Holdings Limited; *Int'l,* pg. 6573
SILVER SPRINGS CITRUS INC.—See Toyota Tsusho Corporation; *Int'l,* pg. 7879
SILVER SPRINGS, INC.—See Newgate Private Equity LLP; *Int'l,* pg. 5234
SILVER SPRINGS ORGANICS L.L.C.—See Waste Connections, Inc.; *U.S. Public,* pg. 8354
SILVER SPRUCE RESOURCES INC.; *Int'l,* pg. 6924
SILVER STAR BRANDS, INC.—See Crosby Rock LLC; *U.S. Private,* pg. 1104
SILVERSTAR CASINO (PTY) LTD.—See Hosken Consolidated Investments Limited; *Int'l,* pg. 3485
SILVER STAR COMMUNICATIONS; *U.S. Private,* pg. 3662
SILVER STAR INSURANCE COMPANY LIMITED; *Int'l,* pg. 6924
SILVER STAR PROPERTIES REIT, INC.; *U.S. Private,* pg. 3662
SILVER STATE ACO, LLC—See Apollo Global Management, Inc.; *U.S. Public,* pg. 157
SILVER STATE COACH, INC.—See Silverado Stages, Inc.; *U.S. Private,* pg. 3662

SILVER STATE INTERNATIONAL—See Interstate International, Inc.; *U.S. Private,* pg. 2125
SILVER STATE RELIEF LLC—See C21 Investments Inc.; *Int'l,* pg. 1245
SILVER STATE SCHOOLS CREDIT UNION; *U.S. Private,* pg. 3662
SILVER STATE WIRE ROPE AND RIGGING, INC.—See Altamont Capital Partners; *U.S. Private,* pg. 205
SILVERSTONE BERHAD—See Toyo Tire Corporation; *Int'l,* pg. 7859
SILVERSTONE MARKETING SDN. BHD.—See Toyo Tire Corporation; *Int'l,* pg. 7859
SILVERSTONE MASTER ISSUER PLC—See Nationwide Building Society; *Int'l,* pg. 5165
SILVERSTREAM CAPITAL, LLC; *U.S. Private,* pg. 3664
SILVER STREAM CENTER—See Formation Capital, LLC; *U.S. Private,* pg. 1571
SILVERSTREAM HEALTH CENTRE LIMITED—See Green Cross Health Limited; *Int'l,* pg. 3070
SILVERSTRIPE LIMITED - AUSTRALIA—See SilverStripe Limited; *Int'l,* pg. 6926
SILVERSTRIPE LIMITED; *Int'l,* pg. 6926
SILVERSUMMIT HEALTHPLAN, INC.—See Centene Corporation; *U.S. Public,* pg. 470
SILVER SUSTAINABLE SOLUTIONS CORP.; *U.S. Private,* pg. 3662
SILVERTECH, INC.; *U.S. Private,* pg. 3664
SILVERTECH MIDDLE EAST FZCO—See Rockwell Automation, Inc.; *U.S. Public,* pg. 1807
SILVER TIDE HOLDINGS LIMITED; *Int'l,* pg. 6924
SILVER TIGER METALS INC.; *Int'l,* pg. 6924
SILVERTIP ASSOCIATES, INC.—See Vance Street Capital LLC; *U.S. Private,* pg. 4342
SILVERTON CONSTRUCTION COMPANY, INC.; *U.S. Private,* pg. 3664
SILVERTON ENERGY, INC.; *U.S. Private,* pg. 3664
SILVERTON HEALTH; *U.S. Private,* pg. 3664
SILVERTON MORTGAGE SPECIALISTS, INC.; *U.S. Private,* pg. 3664
SILVERTON SPINNERS LIMITED; *Int'l,* pg. 6926
SILVERTON TRAVEL (PTY) LTD—See Cullinan Holdings Limited; *Int'l,* pg. 1877
SILVER TOUCH TECHNOLOGIES CANADA LIMITED—See Silver Touch Technologies Limited; *Int'l,* pg. 6924
SILVER TOUCH TECHNOLOGIES INC.—See Silver Touch Technologies Limited; *Int'l,* pg. 6924
SILVER TOUCH TECHNOLOGIES LIMITED; *Int'l,* pg. 6924
SILVER TOWNE LP; *U.S. Private,* pg. 3662
SILVER VENTURES, INC.; *U.S. Private,* pg. 3662
SILVER VERDE MAY MINING CO.; *U.S. Public,* pg. 1880
SILVER VIPER MINERALS CORP.; *Int'l,* pg. 6925
SILVERWARE, INC.—See Velosio, LLC; *U.S. Private,* pg. 4355
SILVERWATER CAFE; *U.S. Private,* pg. 3664
SILVER WEIBULL DO BRASIL—See Silver-Weibull Sweden AB; *Int'l,* pg. 6925
SILVER WEIBULL PRODUCTION AB—See Silver-Weibull Sweden AB; *Int'l,* pg. 6925
SILVER-WEIBULL SWEDEN AB; *Int'l,* pg. 6925
SILVER WHEATON (CAYMANS) LTD.—See Wheaton Precious Metals Corp.; *Int'l,* pg. 8397
SILVER WINGS AEROSPACE, INC.—See HEICO Corporation; *U.S. Public,* pg. 1021
SILVER WOLF EXPLORATION LTD.; *Int'l,* pg. 6925
SILVERWOOD DIALYSIS, LLC—See DaVita Inc.; *U.S. Public,* pg. 643
SILVER X MINING CORP; *Int'l,* pg. 6925
SILVERY DRAGON PRESTRESSED MATERIALS CO., LTD.; *Int'l,* pg. 6926
SILVESTRI INVESTMENTS INC.; *U.S. Private,* pg. 3664
SILVESTRI STUDIO INC.; *U.S. Private,* pg. 3664
SILVEY INFORMATION SYSTEMS INC.—See Aubrey Silvey Enterprises Inc.; *U.S. Private,* pg. 385
SILVON SOFTWARE INC.; *U.S. Private,* pg. 3664
SILVON SOFTWARE, LTD.—See Silvon Software Inc.; *U.S. Private,* pg. 3665
SIMAC 3SERVICES BV—See Simac Techniek NV; *Int'l,* pg. 6927
SIMAC BUSINESS APPLICATIONS BV—See Waysis BV; *Int'l,* pg. 8361
SIMAC BUSINESS SOLUTIONS BV—See Simac Techniek NV; *Int'l,* pg. 6927
SIMAC DOCUMENT SOLUTIONS BV—See Simac Techniek NV; *Int'l,* pg. 6927
SIMAC ELECTRONICS BV—See Simac Techniek NV; *Int'l,* pg. 6927
SIMAC ICT NETHERLANDS B.V.—See Simac Techniek NV; *Int'l,* pg. 6927
SIMAC MASIC & TSS BV—See Simac Techniek NV; *Int'l,* pg. 6927
SIMAC QUADCORE BV—See Simac Techniek NV; *Int'l,* pg. 6927
SIMAC TECHNIEK NV; *Int'l,* pg. 6927
SIMAC TRIANGLE B.V—See Simac Techniek NV; *Int'l,* pg. 6927
SIMAFEX—See Guerbet SA; *Int'l,* pg. 3172
SIMAKAS COMPANY INC.; *U.S. Private,* pg. 3665

COMPANY NAME INDEX

SIMA MARINE SALES INC.; *U.S. Private*, pg. 3665
SIMAM S.P.A.—See ACEA S.p.A.; *Int'l*, pg. 95
SIMAPAC CO., LTD.—See PRG Corporation Public Company Limited; *Int'l*, pg. 5968
SIMA PRIVATE EQUITY 1 BETEILIGUNGS GMBH—See Deutsche Bank Aktiengesellschaft; *Int'l*, pg. 2061
SIMA PRIVATE EQUITY 1 GMBH & CO. KG—See Deutsche Bank Aktiengesellschaft; *Int'l*, pg. 2062
SIMAR NORDOST GRUNDSTUCKS-GMBH—See Siemens Aktiengesellschaft; *Int'l*, pg. 6888
SIMA-SACA—See Haco N.V.; *Int'l*, pg. 3205
SIMA TECHNOLOGY CO., LTD.—See Muramoto Electron (Thailand) PCL; *Int'l*, pg. 5096
SIMATHURAKIJ CO., LTD.—See Thai Beverage Public Company Limited; *Int'l*, pg. 7591
SIMAT LABEL COMPANY LIMITED—See Simat Technologies Public Company Limited; *Int'l*, pg. 6927
SIMAT TECHNOLOGIES PUBLIC COMPANY LIMITED; *Int'l*, pg. 6927
SIMAUTHOR, INC.—See QinetiQ Group plc; *Int'l*, pg. 6142
SIMAVITA LIMITED; *Int'l*, pg. 6927
SIMBA-DICKIE-GROUP GMBH; *Int'l*, pg. 6927
SIMBA ESSEL ENERGY INC.; *Int'l*, pg. 6927
SIMBA (PROPRIETARY) LIMITED—See PepsiCo, Inc.; *U.S. Public*, pg. 1671
SIMBA QUIX SWAZILAND (PTY) LIMITED—See PepsiCo, Inc.; *U.S. Public*, pg. 1672
SIMBETON SA; *Int'l*, pg. 6927
SIMBEX LLC—See Fenway Partners, LLC; *U.S. Private*, pg. 1495
SIMBHAOLI POWER PRIVATE LIMITED—See Simbhaoli Sugars Limited; *Int'l*, pg. 6928
SIMBHAOLI SUGARS LIMITED - BRIJNATHPUR ETHANOL DIVISION—See Simbhaoli Sugars Limited; *Int'l*, pg. 6928
SIMBHAOLI SUGARS LIMITED - CHILWARIA SUGAR DIVISION—See Simbhaoli Sugars Limited; *Int'l*, pg. 6928
SIMBHAOLI SUGARS LIMITED; *Int'l*, pg. 6928
SIMBIONIX LTD.—See Surgical Science Sweden AB; *Int'l*, pg. 7344
SIMBIONIX USA CORPORATION—See Surgical Science Sweden AB; *Int'l*, pg. 7344
SIMDLE COLUTIONS LTD.; *Int'l*, pg. 6928
THE SIMBLIST GROUP INC—See Ivystone Group, LLC; *U.S. Private*, pg. 2152
SIMCENTER ENTERPRISES, INC.; *U.S. Private*, pg. 3665
SIMCERE OF AMERICA INC.—See Simcere Pharmaceutical Group; *Int'l*, pg. 6928
SIMCERE PHARMACEUTICAL CO., LTD.—See Simcere Pharmaceutical Group; *Int'l*, pg. 6928
SIMCERE PHARMACEUTICAL GROUP; *Int'l*, pg. 6928
SIMCOA OPERATIONS PTY. LTD.—See Shin-Etsu Chemical Co. Ltd.; *Int'l*, pg. 6841
SIMCOE LEAF TOBACCO COMPANY, LTD.—See Universal Corporation; *U.S. Public*, pg. 2254
SIMCO ELECTRONICS; *U.S. Private*, pg. 3665
SIMCO GLOBAL TECHNOLOGY & SYSTEMS LTD.—See SAMCO INC.; *Int'l*, pg. 6503
SIMCO INDUSTRIES, INC.—See UFP Technologies, Inc.; *U.S. Public*, pg. 2221
SIMCO-ION, INDUSTRIAL GROUP—See Illinois Tool Works Inc.; *U.S. Public*, pg. 1110
SIMCO JAPAN INC.—See Illinois Tool Works Inc.; *U.S. Public*, pg. 1110
SIMCOM, INC.—See CAE Inc.; *Int'l*, pg. 1249
SIMCOM, INC.—See Directional Capital LLC; *U.S. Private*, pg. 1236
SIMCOM WIRELESS SOLUTIONS LTD.—See Sunsea AIoT Technology Co., Ltd.; *Int'l*, pg. 7322
SIMCONA ELECTRONICS CORP; *U.S. Private*, pg. 3665
SIMCO (NEDERLAND) B.V.—See Illinois Tool Works Inc.; *U.S. Public*, pg. 1110
SIMCONTROL SOLUTIONS LTD.; *Int'l*, pg. 6928
SIMCORP ASIA PTY. LTD.—See Deutsche Borse AG; *Int'l*, pg. 2064
SIMCORP A/S—See Deutsche Borse AG; *Int'l*, pg. 2064
SIMCORP BENELUX SA/NV—See Deutsche Borse AG; *Int'l*, pg. 2064
SIMCORP CANADA INC.—See Deutsche Borse AG; *Int'l*, pg. 2064
SIMCORP DEVELOPMENT CENTRE UK LIMITED—See Deutsche Borse AG; *Int'l*, pg. 2064
SIMCORP FRANCE S.A.S.—See Deutsche Borse AG; *Int'l*, pg. 2064
SIMCORP GMBH—See Deutsche Borse AG; *Int'l*, pg. 2064
SIMCORP HONG KONG LTD.—See Deutsche Borse AG; *Int'l*, pg. 2064
SIMCORP ITALIANA S.R.L.—See Deutsche Borse AG; *Int'l*, pg. 2064
SIMCORP JAPAN KK—See Deutsche Borse AG; *Int'l*, pg. 2064
SIMCORP LTD.—See Deutsche Borse AG; *Int'l*, pg. 2064
SIMCORP LUXEMBOURG S.A.—See Deutsche Borse AG; *Int'l*, pg. 2064
SIMCORP NORGE AS—See Deutsche Borse AG; *Int'l*, pg. 2064
SIMCORP OSTERREICH GMBH—See Deutsche Borse AG; *Int'l*, pg. 2064
SIMCORP SCHWEIZ AG—See Deutsche Borse AG; *Int'l*, pg. 2064
SIMCORP SINGAPORE PTE. LTD.—See Deutsche Borse AG; *Int'l*, pg. 2064
SIMCORP SP Z O.O.—See Deutsche Borse AG; *Int'l*, pg. 2064
SIMCORP SVERIGE AB—See Deutsche Borse AG; *Int'l*, pg. 2064
SIMCORP UKRAINE LLC—See Deutsche Borse AG; *Int'l*, pg. 2064
SIMCORP USA INC—See Deutsche Borse AG; *Int'l*, pg. 2064
SIMCO SALES SERVICE OF PA INC.; *U.S. Private*, pg. 3665
SIMCO SONG DA JOINT STOCK COMPANY; *Int'l*, pg. 6928
SIMCO TECHNOLOGIES INC.—See B&D Industrial, Inc.; *U.S. Private*, pg. 418
SIMCOTE INC.; *U.S. Private*, pg. 3665
SIMCRO LIMITED—See Datamars SA; *Int'l*, pg. 1978
SIMCRO (UK) LIMITED—See Datamars SA; *Int'l*, pg. 1978
SIMDEX EHF—See Origo hf.; *Int'l*, pg. 5630
SIMEA SIBIU S.R.L.—See Siemens Aktiengesellschaft; *Int'l*, pg. 6888
SIMEC ATLANTIS ENERGY LTD; *Int'l*, pg. 6931
SIMEC GROUP LIMITED—See GFG Alliance Limited; *Int'l*, pg. 2956
SIMEC SA; *Int'l*, pg. 6931
SIMEC USKMOUTH POWER LIMITED—See SIMEC Atlantis Energy Ltd; *Int'l*, pg. 6931
SIME DARBY AUSTRALIA LIMITED—See Sime Darby Berhad; *Int'l*, pg. 6930
SIME DARBY AUTO BAVARIA SDN BHD—See Sime Darby Berhad; *Int'l*, pg. 6928
SIME DARBY AUTO CONNEXION SDN BHD—See Sime Darby Berhad; *Int'l*, pg. 6929
SIME DARBY AUTO HYUNDAI SDN BHD—See Sime Darby Berhad; *Int'l*, pg. 6929
SIME DARBY AUTO PERFORMANCE SDN BHD—See Sime Darby Berhad; *Int'l*, pg. 6929
SIME DARBY AUTO SELECTION SDN BHD—See Sime Darby Berhad; *Int'l*, pg. 6929
SIME DARBY BERHAD; *Int'l*, pg. 6928
SIME DARBY BEVERAGES SDN BHD—See Sime Darby Berhad; *Int'l*, pg. 6929
SIME DARBY BIOGANIC SDN. BHD.—See Sime Darby Berhad; *Int'l*, pg. 6929
SIME DARBY (CHINA) ENTERPRISE MANAGEMENT CO. LTD.—See Sime Darby Berhad; *Int'l*, pg. 6928
SIME DARBY ELCO POWER JAPAN LIMITED—See Sime Darby Berhad; *Int'l*, pg. 6929
SIME DARBY ELCO POWER KOREA LIMITED—See Sime Darby Berhad; *Int'l*, pg. 6929
SIME DARBY ENERGY SOLUTIONS SDN BHD—See Sime Darby Berhad; *Int'l*, pg. 6929
SIME DARBY ENERGY & UTILITIES—See Sime Darby Berhad; *Int'l*, pg. 6929
SIME DARBY HONG KONG LIMITED—See Sime Darby Berhad; *Int'l*, pg. 6929
SIME DARBY INDUSTRIAL (B) SDN BHD—See Sime Darby Berhad; *Int'l*, pg. 6929
SIME DARBY INDUSTRIAL POWER SDN BHD—See Sime Darby Berhad; *Int'l*, pg. 6929
SIME DARBY INDUSTRIAL SDN BHD—See Sime Darby Berhad; *Int'l*, pg. 6929
SIME DARBY JOMALINA SDN. BHD.—See Sime Darby Berhad; *Int'l*, pg. 6929
SIME DARBY LOCKTON INSURANCE BROKERS SDN BHD—See Sime Darby Berhad; *Int'l*, pg. 6929
SIME DARBY MANAGING AGENCY (HONG KONG) LIMITED—See Sime Darby Berhad; *Int'l*, pg. 6929
SIME DARBY MATERIAL HANDLING SDN BHD—See Sime Darby Berhad; *Int'l*, pg. 6929
SIME DARBY MOTOR GROUP (NZ) LIMITED—See Sime Darby Berhad; *Int'l*, pg. 6929
SIME DARBY MOTORS GROUP (AUSTRALIA) PTY LIMITED—See Sime Darby Berhad; *Int'l*, pg. 6929
SIME DARBY MOTORS SDN. BHD.—See Sime Darby Berhad; *Int'l*, pg. 6929
SIME DARBY OILS LIVERPOOL REFINERY LTD.—See Sime Darby Berhad; *Int'l*, pg. 6929
SIME DARBY OILS ZWIJNDRECHT REFINERY B.V.—See Sime Darby Berhad; *Int'l*, pg. 6929
SIME DARBY PLANTATION SDN. BHD.—See Sime Darby Berhad; *Int'l*, pg. 6929
SIME DARBY PROPERTY BERHAD—See Sime Darby Berhad; *Int'l*, pg. 6929
SIME DARBY RENT-A-CAR SDN BHD—See Sime Darby Berhad; *Int'l*, pg. 6930
SIME DARBY RESEARCH SDN. BHD.—See Sime Darby Berhad; *Int'l*, pg. 6929
SIME DARBY SERVICES PRIVATE LIMITED—See Sime Darby Berhad; *Int'l*, pg. 6930
SIME DARBY SINGAPORE LIMITED—See Sime Darby Berhad; *Int'l*, pg. 6930
SIME DARBY SWEDISH AUTO SDN BHD—See Sime Darby Berhad; *Int'l*, pg. 6930
SIME DARBY VANTAGE (THAILAND) LIMITED—See Sime Darby Berhad; *Int'l*, pg. 6930
SIMED CIA LTDA.—See HORIBA Ltd; *Int'l*, pg. 3478
SIMED PERU S.A.C.—See HORIBA Ltd; *Int'l*, pg. 3478
SIMEI MEDIA CO. LTD.; *Int'l*, pg. 6931
SIMEIO SOLUTIONS, LLC—See ZelnickMedia Corp.; *U.S. Private*, pg. 4600
SIME KANSAI PAINTS SDN. BHD.—See Kansai Paint Co., Ltd.; *Int'l*, pg. 4073
SIME KUBOTA SDN. BHD.—See Kubota Corporation; *Int'l*, pg. 4322
SIMENO HOLDING AG—See Thoma Bravo, L.P.; *U.S. Private*, pg. 4147
SIMEN UTARA SDN. BHD.—See Oriental Holdings Berhad; *Int'l*, pg. 5625
SIMESA SPA.—See AstraZeneca PLC; *Int'l*, pg. 661
SIMEST S.P.A.—See Cassa Depositi e Prestiti S.p.A.; *Int'l*, pg. 1355
SIMEUS FOODS INTERNATIONAL, INC.; *U.S. Private*, pg. 3665
SIMEX, INC.—See Clayton, Dubilier & Rice, LLC; *U.S. Private*, pg. 921
SIMEX PLUS S.R.L.—See Grup Simex S.R.L.; *Int'l*, pg. 3115
SIMFABRIC SA; *Int'l*, pg. 6931
SIMFLEXI SDN. BHD.—See Handal Energy Berhad; *Int'l*, pg. 3243
SIMFONI, INC.; *U.S. Private*, pg. 3665
SIMFRONT SIMULATION SYSTEMS CORPORATION—See Calian Group Ltd.; *Int'l*, pg. 1264
SIMFY AFRICA PROPRIETARY LIMITED—See MTN Group Limited; *Int'l*, pg. 5071
SIMHAPURI ENERGY PRIVATE LIMITED—See Madhucon Projects Limited; *Int'l*, pg. 4633
SIMICON GMBH—See Mesa Laboratories, Inc.; *U.S. Public*, pg. 1426
SIMIGON, INC.—See Maxify Solutions Inc.; *U.S. Private*, pg. 2618
SIMIGON LTD.—See Maxify Solutions Inc.; *U.S. Private*, pg. 2618
SIMILARWEB LTD.; *Int'l*, pg. 6931
SIMILARWEB SG PTE. LTD.—See Similarweb Ltd.; *Int'l*, pg. 6931
SIMILASAN AG—See Nahrin AG; *Int'l*, pg. 5130
SIMILASAN CORPORATION—See Nahrin AG; *Int'l*, pg. 5130
SIMILCO MINES LTD—See HudBay Minerals Inc.; *Int'l*, pg. 3521
SIM IMPEX D.O.O.—See LKQ Corporation; *U.S. Public*, pg. 1336
SIMINN HF; *Int'l*, pg. 6931
SIMINT S.P.A.—See Giorgio Armani S.p.A.; *Int'l*, pg. 2978
SIMITRI SPECIALTY CHEMICALS (PTY) LIMITED—See AECI Limited; *Int'l*, pg. 172
SIMI WINERY—See Constellation Brands, Inc.; *U.S. Public*, pg. 571
SIMKAR CORPORATION; *U.S. Private*, pg. 3665
SIMKINS CORPORATION; *U.S. Private*, pg. 3665
SIMKINS/HARVARD FOLDING BOX COMPANY INC.; *U.S. Private*, pg. 3665
SIM LEISURE GROUP LTD.; *Int'l*, pg. 6926
SIM LEISURE GULF CONTRACTING LLC—See Sim Leisure Group Ltd.; *Int'l*, pg. 6926
SIM LIAN (BISHAN) PTE. LTD.—See Sim Lian Group Limited; *Int'l*, pg. 6927
SIM LIAN CONSTRUCTION CO. (PTE.) LTD.—See Sim Lian Group Limited; *Int'l*, pg. 6927
SIM LIAN (EAST COAST) PTE. LTD.—See Sim Lian Group Limited; *Int'l*, pg. 6927
SIM LIAN GROUP LIMITED; *Int'l*, pg. 6926
SIM LIAN (HOUGANG) PTE. LTD.—See Sim Lian Group Limited; *Int'l*, pg. 6927
SIM LIAN-KORU BENA JV PTE. LTD.—See Sim Lian Group Limited; *Int'l*, pg. 6927
SIM LIAN (MOUNT FABER) PTE. LTD.—See Sim Lian Group Limited; *Int'l*, pg. 6927
SIM LIAN (NEWTON) PTE. LTD.—See Sim Lian Group Limited; *Int'l*, pg. 6927
SIM LIAN (SIMEI) PTE. LTD.—See Sim Lian Group Limited; *Int'l*, pg. 6927
SIM LIAN (TAMPINES CENTRAL) PTE. LTD.—See Sim Lian Group Limited; *Int'l*, pg. 6927
SIM LIAN (TAMPINES) PTE. LTD.—See Sim Lian Group Limited; *Int'l*, pg. 6927
SIM LIAN (UBI) PTE. LTD.—See Sim Lian Group Limited; *Int'l*, pg. 6927
SIMMEL DIFESA S.P.A.—See GIAT Industries S.A.; *Int'l*, pg. 2962
S IMMO AG; *Int'l*, pg. 6442
S-IMMOBILIEN WEINVIERTLER SPARKASSE GMBH—See Erste Group Bank AG; *Int'l*, pg. 2499
S IMMO GERMANY GMBH—See S IMMO AG; *Int'l*, pg. 6442
S IMMO HUNGARY KFT.—See S IMMO AG; *Int'l*, pg. 6442
SIMMONDS MARSHALL LTD.; *Int'l*, pg. 6931
SIMMONDS PRECISION PRODUCTS INC.—See RTX Corporation; *U.S. Public*, pg. 1822

SIMMONDS RESTAURANT MANAGEMENT — CORPORATE AFFILIATIONS

SIMMONDS RESTAURANT MANAGEMENT; *U.S. Private,* pg. 3665

SIMMONS BANK—See Simmons First National Corporation; *U.S. Public,* pg. 1881

SIMMONS BEDDING & FURNITURE (HK) LTD.—See Nifco Inc.; *Int'l,* pg. 5282

SIMMONS BEDDING & FURNITURE (TAIWAN) LTD.—See Nifco Inc.; *Int'l,* pg. 5282

SIMMONS-BOARDMAN PUBLISHING CORP.; *U.S. Private,* pg. 3665

SIMMONS CO. LTD.—See Nifco Inc.; *Int'l,* pg. 5281

SIMMONS & COMPANY INTERNATIONAL LIMITED—See Piper Sandler Companies; *U.S. Public,* pg. 1694

SIMMONS & COMPANY INTERNATIONAL—See Piper Sandler Companies; *U.S. Public,* pg. 1694

SIMMONS COMPANY—See Ares Management Corporation; *U.S. Public,* pg. 190

SIMMONS COMPANY—See Ontario Teachers' Pension Plan; *Int'l,* pg. 5590

SIMMONS CUSTOM PROCESSING, INC.—See Simmons Foods, Inc.; *U.S. Private,* pg. 3665

SIMMONS ENERGY SOLUTIONS, INC.—See Simmons Foods, Inc.; *U.S. Private,* pg. 3665

SIMMONS EROSION CONTROL, INC.; *U.S. Private,* pg. 3665

SIMMONS FIRST FINANCE COMPANY—See Simmons First National Corporation; *U.S. Public,* pg. 1881

SIMMONS FIRST INVESTMENT GROUP, INC.—See Simmons First National Corporation; *U.S. Public,* pg. 1881

SIMMONS FIRST NATIONAL CORPORATION; *U.S. Public,* pg. 1881

SIMMONS FLINT—See Flint Communications, Inc. & Adfarm; *U.S. Private,* pg. 1545

SIMMONS FOODS, INC.; *U.S. Private,* pg. 3665

SIMMONS HANLY CONROY LLP; *U.S. Private,* pg. 3665

SIMMONS IRRIGATION SUPPLY INC.; *U.S. Private,* pg. 3665

SIMMONS JUVENILE FURNITURE—See Delta Enterprise Corporation; *U.S. Private,* pg. 1200

SIMMONS PET FOOD, INC. - PENNSAUKEN—See Simmons Foods, Inc.; *U.S. Private,* pg. 3665

SIMMONS PET FOOD, INC.—See Simmons Foods, Inc.; *U.S. Private,* pg. 3665

SIMMONS PET FOOD, INC. - STREETSVILLE—See Simmons Foods, Inc.; *U.S. Private,* pg. 3665

SIMMONS PREPARED FOODS, INC.—See Simmons Foods, Inc.; *U.S. Private,* pg. 3665

SIMMONS PRIVATE EQUITY II, L.P.—See Piper Sandler Companies; *U.S. Public,* pg. 1694

SIMMONS-ROCKWELL, INC.; *U.S. Private,* pg. 3666

SIMMONS SIRVEY CORPORATION—See Dover Corporation; *U.S. Public,* pg. 682

SIMMONS (SOUTHEAST ASIA) PTE. LTD.—See Nifco Inc.; *Int'l,* pg. 5282

SIMMS CHEVROLET COMPANY INC.; *U.S. Private,* pg. 3666

SIMMS FISHING PRODUCTS CORP.—See Vista Outdoor Inc.; *U.S. Public,* pg. 2305

SIMMS LUMBER CO. INC.; *U.S. Private,* pg. 3666

SIMMTECH AMERICA INC.—See Simmtech Holdings Co., Ltd.; *Int'l,* pg. 6931

SIMMTECH HOLDINGS CO., LTD.; *Int'l,* pg. 6931

SIMMTECH JAPAN INC.—See Simmtech Holdings Co., Ltd.; *Int'l,* pg. 6931

SIMMTECH NICHING (SUZHOU) CO., LTD.—See Simmtech Holdings Co., Ltd.; *Int'l,* pg. 6931

SIMMTECH (XI'AN) CO., LTD.—See Simmtech Holdings Co., Ltd.; *Int'l,* pg. 6931

SIMOCO AUSTRALASIA PTY. LTD.—See Team Telecommunications Group Ltd.; *Int'l,* pg. 7500

SIMOCO EMEA LTD.—See Team Telecommunications Group Ltd.; *Int'l,* pg. 7500

SIMO INTERNATIONAL; *Int'l,* pg. 6931

SIMONA AG; *Int'l,* pg. 6932

SIMONA AMERICA, INC.—See Simona AG; *Int'l,* pg. 6932

SIMONA ASIA LTD.—See Simona AG; *Int'l,* pg. 6932

SIMONA BOLTARON INC.—See Simona AG; *Int'l,* pg. 6932

SIMONA ENGINEERING PLASTICS (GUANGDONG) CO. LTD.—See Simona AG; *Int'l,* pg. 6932

SIMONA ENGINEERING PLASTICS TRADING CO. LTD.—See Simona AG; *Int'l,* pg. 6932

SIMON AERIALS LTD.—See Simon Group plc; *Int'l,* pg. 6932

SIMONA FAR EAST LTD.—See Simona AG; *Int'l,* pg. 6932

SIMONA IBERICA SEMIELABORADOS S.L.—See Simona AG; *Int'l,* pg. 6932

SIMONA INDIA PRIVATE LIMITED—See Simona AG; *Int'l,* pg. 6932

SIMONA-PLASTICS CZ, S.R.O.—See Simona AG; *Int'l,* pg. 6932

SIMONA PLAST-TECHNIK S.R.O.—See Simona AG; *Int'l,* pg. 6932

SIMONA PMC, LLC—See Simona AG; *Int'l,* pg. 6932

SIMONA POLSKA SP. Z O.O.—See Simona AG; *Int'l,* pg. 6932

SIMON & ARRINGTON INC.; *U.S. Private,* pg. 3666

SIMONA S.A.S.—See Simona AG; *Int'l,* pg. 6932

SIMONA S.R.L.—See Simona AG; *Int'l,* pg. 6932

SIMONA UK LTD.—See Simona AG; *Int'l,* pg. 6932

SIMONAZZI IBERICA—See Tetra Laval International S.A.; *Int'l,* pg. 7577

SIMON BAILES LTD.; *Int'l,* pg. 6931

SIMON BAILES STOCKTON—See Simon Bailes Ltd.; *Int'l,* pg. 6931

SIMON CAPITAL LIMITED PARTNERSHIP—See Simon Property Group, Inc.; *U.S. Public,* pg. 1881

SIMONCOMPUTING, INC.; *U.S. Private,* pg. 3666

SIMON CONTRACTORS INC.; *U.S. Private,* pg. 3666

SIMON CONTRACTORS OF SOUTH DAKOTA INC.—See CRH plc; *Int'l,* pg. 1847

SIMON DENTISTRY LLC—See MB2 Dental Solutions LLC; *U.S. Private,* pg. 2624

SIMON DEVELOPERS & INFRASTRUCTURE PRIVATE LIMITED—See Shree Global Tradefin Limited; *Int'l,* pg. 6863

SIMONDS FARSONS CISK PLC; *Int'l,* pg. 6933

SIMONDS GROUP LIMITED; *Int'l,* pg. 6933

SIMONDS HOMES MELBOURNE PTY. LTD.; *Int'l,* pg. 6933

SIMONDS HOMES NSW PTY LTD—See Simonds Group Limited; *Int'l,* pg. 6933

SIMONDS INTERNATIONAL CORPORATION-PORTLAND—See SCIES B.G.R. INC.; *Int'l,* pg. 6648

SIMONDS INTERNATIONAL, LLC—See SCIES B.G.R. INC.; *Int'l,* pg. 6648

SIMONDS QUEENSLAND CONSTRUCTIONS PTY LTD—See Simonds Group Limited; *Int'l,* pg. 6933

SIMONDS-SHIELDS-THEIS GRAIN CO.; *U.S. Private,* pg. 3666

SIMON DUTRIAUX S.A.S.—See Floridienne SA; *Int'l,* pg. 2708

SIMONE S.P.A.; *Int'l,* pg. 6933

SIMON ET MEMBREZ SA—See The Swatch Group Ltd.; *Int'l,* pg. 7692

SIMON GOLUB & SONS INC.—See Shrenuj & Co., Ltd.; *Int'l,* pg. 6865

SIMON GROUP PLC; *Int'l,* pg. 6931

SIMON HOLDINGS LLC; *U.S. Private,* pg. 3666

SIMON H. STEINER, HOPFEN, GMBH—See S.S. Steiner Inc.; *U.S. Private,* pg. 3518

SIMONINI BUILDERS; *U.S. Private,* pg. 3666

SIMONIZ USA, INC.; *U.S. Private,* pg. 3666

THE SIMON KONOVER COMPANY; *U.S. Private,* pg. 4118

SIMON KONOVER DEVELOPMENT CORPORATION—See The Simon Konover Company; *U.S. Private,* pg. 4118

SIMON-LIFT GMBH—See Simon Group plc; *Int'l,* pg. 6932

SIMON MANAGEMENT ASSOCIATES, LLC—See Simon Property Group, Inc.; *U.S. Public,* pg. 1881

SIMON METALS LLC—See Graham Capital Group, LLC; *U.S. Private,* pg. 1751

SIMON MOKSTER SHIPPING A/S; *Int'l,* pg. 6932

SIMON PEARCE US INC.; *U.S. Private,* pg. 3666

SIMON PREMIUM OUTLETS—See Simon Property Group, Inc.; *U.S. Public,* pg. 1881

SIMON PROPERTY GROUP ACQUISITION HOLDINGS, INC.; *U.S. Public,* pg. 1881

SIMON PROPERTY GROUP (ILLINOIS), L.P.—See Simon Property Group, Inc.; *U.S. Public,* pg. 1881

SIMON PROPERTY GROUP, INC.; *U.S. Public,* pg. 1881

SIMON PROPERTY GROUP, L.P.—See Simon Property Group, Inc.; *U.S. Public,* pg. 1881

SIMON PROPERTY GROUP (TEXAS), L.P.—See Simon Property Group, Inc.; *U.S. Public,* pg. 1881

SIMON ROOFING AND SHEET METAL CORP.; *U.S. Private,* pg. 3666

SIMON & SCHUSTER CHILDREN'S PUBLISHING—See KKR & Co. Inc.; *U.S. Public,* pg. 1264

SIMON & SCHUSTER, INC.—See KKR & Co. Inc.; *U.S. Public,* pg. 1263

SIMON & SCHUSTER (UK) LIMITED—See National Amusements, Inc.; *U.S. Private,* pg. 2843

SIMONSEN & SONS LIMITED—See Morgan Advanced Materials plc; *Int'l,* pg. 5043

SIMONS HARDWARE & BATH, INC.; *U.S. Private,* pg. 3666

SIMONS MICHELSON ZIEVE, INC.; *U.S. Private,* pg. 3666

SIMONSON CONSTRUCTION SERVICES, INC.; *U.S. Private,* pg. 3666

SIMONSON PROPERTIES COMPANY; *U.S. Private,* pg. 3666

SIMONS PETROLEUM INC.—See Berkshire Hathaway Inc.; *U.S. Public,* pg. 313

SIMONS SUPPLY CO. INC.; *U.S. Private,* pg. 3666

SIMONSVOSS SECURITY TECHNOLOGIES (ASIA) PTE. LTD.—See Allegion Public Limited Company; *Int'l,* pg. 335

SIMONSVOSS TECHNOLOGIES AB—See Allegion Public Limited Company; *Int'l,* pg. 335

SIMONSVOSS TECHNOLOGIES AG—See Allegion Public Limited Company; *Int'l,* pg. 335

SIMONSVOSS TECHNOLOGIES BV—See Allegion Public Limited Company; *Int'l,* pg. 335

SIMONSVOSS TECHNOLOGIES FZE—See Allegion Public Limited Company; *Int'l,* pg. 335

SIMONSVOSS TECHNOLOGIES GMBH—See Allegion Public Limited Company; *Int'l,* pg. 335

SIMONSVOSS TECHNOLOGIES LIMITED—See Allegion Public Limited Company; *Int'l,* pg. 335

SIMONSVOSS TECHNOLOGIES SAS—See Allegion Public Limited Company; *Int'l,* pg. 335

SIMONSWERK GMBH; *Int'l,* pg. 6933

SIMON TANKLAGER GESELLSCHAFT MBH—See Brookfield Infrastructure Partners L.P.; *Int'l,* pg. 1193

SIMONTON WINDOWS, INC.—See Clayton, Dubilier & Rice, LLC; *U.S. Private,* pg. 921

SIMON WORLDWIDE, INC.; *U.S. Private,* pg. 3666

SIMOP SAS—See Sintex Industries, Ltd.; *Int'l,* pg. 6957

SIMOSA OIL CORPORATION—See Formosa Petrochemical Corporation; *Int'l,* pg. 2735

SIMOS INSOURCING SOLUTIONS, LLC—See TrueBlue, Inc.; *U.S. Public,* pg. 2198

SIMPAC AMERICA CO. LTD.—See SIMPAC Holdings Co., Ltd; *Int'l,* pg. 6933

SIMPAC HOLDINGS CO., LTD; *Int'l,* pg. 6933

SIMPAC INDIA CO., LTD.—See SIMPAC Holdings Co., Ltd; *Int'l,* pg. 6933

SIMPAC INDUSTRIES CO., LTD. - KAJWA 2 PLANT—See SIMPAC Holdings Co., Ltd; *Int'l,* pg. 6933

SIMPAC INDUSTRIES CO., LTD. - NAMDONG PLANT—See SIMPAC Holdings Co., Ltd; *Int'l,* pg. 6933

SIMPAC INDUSTRIES CO., LTD.—See SIMPAC Holdings Co., Ltd; *Int'l,* pg. 6933

SIMPAC MACHINERY (M) SDN. BHD.—See SIMPAC Holdings Co., Ltd; *Int'l,* pg. 6933

SIMPAC METAL CO., LTD.—See SIMPAC Holdings Co., Ltd; *Int'l,* pg. 6933

SIMPAC METAL CO., LTD.—See SIMPAC Holdings Co., Ltd; *Int'l,* pg. 6933

SIMPAC METALLOY CO., LTD - PLANT 2—See SIMPAC Holdings Co., Ltd; *Int'l,* pg. 6933

SIMPAC THAILAND CO., LTD.—See SIMPAC Holdings Co., Ltd; *Int'l,* pg. 6933

SIMPAC TIANJIN CO., LTD—See SIMPAC Holdings Co., Ltd; *Int'l,* pg. 6933

SIMPAK INTERNATIONAL, LLC; *U.S. Private,* pg. 3666

SIMPANG MAJU ENTERPRISES SDN. BHD.—See Gromutual Berhad; *Int'l,* pg. 3088

SIMPEX-DAMMAM—See VIMPEX Handelsgesellschaft mbH; *Int'l,* pg. 8209

SIMPEX-JEDDAH—See VIMPEX Handelsgesellschaft mbH; *Int'l,* pg. 8209

SIMPEX-RIYADH—See VIMPEX Handelsgesellschaft mbH; *Int'l,* pg. 8209

SIMPLE APPROACH (CANADA) LIMITED—See PDS Limited; *Int'l,* pg. 5771

SIMPLE APPROACH LIMITED—See PDS Limited; *Int'l,* pg. 5771

SIMPLECALL BUSINESS LTD—See Zamir Telecom Ltd.; *Int'l,* pg. 8624

SIMPLE ENERGY, INC.—See Schneider Electric SE; *Int'l,* pg. 6636

SIMPLE ENERGY, INC.—See The AES Corporation; *U.S. Public,* pg. 2032

SIMPLE HEALTH & BEAUTY LIMITED—See Unilever PLC; *Int'l,* pg. 8047

SIMPLEHEALTH, INC.; *U.S. Private,* pg. 3667

SIMPLE MANAGEMENT GROUP, INC.; *U.S. Private,* pg. 3666

SIMPLE MEDS, LLC—See SelectQuote, Inc.; *U.S. Public,* pg. 1863

SIMPLENEXUS, LLC—See nCino, Inc.; *U.S. Public,* pg. 1501

SIMPLEPART, LLC—See Infomedia Ltd; *Int'l,* pg. 3690

SIMPLE PRODUCTS CORPORATION; *U.S. Private,* pg. 3667

SIMPLERAY, LLC; *U.S. Private,* pg. 3667

SIMPLE S.A.; *Int'l,* pg. 6933

SIMPLESERVERS LIMITED—See iomart Group plc; *Int'l,* pg. 3793

SIMPLESIGNAL, INC.; *U.S. Private,* pg. 3667

SIMPLE SUGARS; *U.S. Private,* pg. 3667

SIMPLE SYSTEM GMBH—See SFS Group AG; *Int'l,* pg. 6739

SIMPLETIRE; *U.S. Private,* pg. 3667

SIMPLE TOILETRIES LIMITED—See Unilever PLC; *Int'l,* pg. 8047

SIMPLE TRIBUTE FUNERAL AND CREMATION CENTER—See Service Corporation International; *U.S. Public,* pg. 1871

SIMPLEVIEW, INC.; *U.S. Private,* pg. 3667

SIMPLEX ARMATUREN & SYSTEME GMBH—See Aalberts N.V.; *Int'l,* pg. 35

SIMPLEX ASSET MANAGEMENT CO., LTD.—See Simplex Financial Holdings Co., Ltd.; *Int'l,* pg. 6933

SIMPLEX CASTINGS LTD. - BHILAI WORKS—See Simplex Castings Ltd.; *Int'l,* pg. 6933

SIMPLEX CASTINGS LTD.; *Int'l,* pg. 6933

SIMPLEX CASTINGS LTD. - URLA WORKS—See Simplex Castings Ltd.; *Int'l,* pg. 6933

SIMPLEX CONSTRUCTION CO. INC.—See Simplex Industries Inc; *U.S. Private,* pg. 3667

SIMPLEX FINANCIAL HOLDINGS CO., LTD.; *Int'l,* pg. 6933

COMPANY NAME INDEX

SIMPLEXGRINNELL LP—See Johnson Controls International plc; *Int'l*, pg. 3988
SIMPLEXGRINNELL—See Johnson Controls International plc; *Int'l*, pg. 3988
SIMPLEXGRINNELL—See Johnson Controls International plc; *Int'l*, pg. 3988
SIMPLEX HEALTHCARE, INC.; *U.S. Private*, pg. 3667
SIMPLEX INC.—See The Carlyle Group Inc.; *U.S. Public*, pg. 2055
SIMPLEX INDUSTRIES INC; *U.S. Private*, pg. 3667
SIMPLEX INFRASTRUCTURES LIMITED; *Int'l*, pg. 6933
SIMPLEX INFRASTRUCTURES L.L.C—See Simplex Infrastructures Limited; *Int'l*, pg. 6933
SIMPLEX INSURANCE SOLUTIONS PTY. LTD.—See Steadfast Group Limited; *Int'l*, pg. 7187
SIMPLEX INVESTMENT ADVISORS INC—See Hulic Co., Ltd.; *Int'l*, pg. 3528
SIMPLEXITY, LLC—See Independence Capital Partners, LLC; *U.S. Private*, pg. 2057
SIMPLEXITY TECHNOLOGY & OPERATIONS CENTER—See Independence Capital Partners, LLC; *U.S. Private*, pg. 2057
SIMPLEX PAPERS LTD; *Int'l*, pg. 6934
SIMPLEX REALTY LTD; *Int'l*, pg. 6934
SIMPLEX RENEWABLE RESOURCES PRIVATE LIMITED—See Simplex Realty Ltd; *Int'l*, pg. 6934
SIMPLEX TIME RECORDER CO.—See Johnson Controls International plc; *Int'l*, pg. 3988
SIMPLEX WESTPILE LIMITED—See VINCI S.A.; *Int'l*, pg. 8234
SIMPLEX WILFER GMBH & CO.—See Aalberts N.V.; *Int'l*, pg. 35
SIMPLICITY CONSULTING, INC; *U.S. Private*, pg. 3667
SIMPLICITY CREATIVE CORP.—See IG Design Group Plc; *Int'l*, pg. 3600
SIMPLICITY ENGINEERING, INC.—See Terex Corporation; *U.S. Public*, pg. 2020
SIMPLICITY FINANCIAL MARKETING HOLDINGS INC.; *U.S. Private*, pg. 3667
SIMPLICITY GROUP HOLDINGS—See Simplicity Financial Marketing Holdings Inc.; *U.S. Private*, pg. 3667
SIMPLICITY GROUP; *U.S. Private*, pg. 3667
SIMPLICITY HOLDING LTD.; *Int'l*, pg. 6934
SIMPLICITY MANUFACTURING, INC.—See Briggs & Stratton Corporation; *U.S. Private*, pg. 661
SIMPLICITY MARKETING LTD.; *Int'l*, pg. 6934
SIMPLICITY PATTERN CO. INC.—See Conso International Corporation; *U.S. Private*, pg. 1020
SIMPLICITY PATTERNS INTERNATIONAL LTD. INC.—See Conso International Corporation; *U.S. Private*, pg. 1020
SIMPLICITY PTY LIMITED—See IG Design Group Plc; *Int'l*, pg. 3600
SIMPLICITY V8 HONG KONG LTD.—See Bally's Corporation; *U.S. Public*, pg. 268
SIMPLIFIED BUSINESS SOLUTIONS, INC.—See iSolved HCM LLC; *U.S. Private*, pg. 2146
SIMPLIFI HOLDINGS INC.—See GTCR LLC; *U.S. Private*, pg. 1806
SIMPLIFI, INC.; *U.S. Private*, pg. 3667
SIMPLIFILE LC—See Intercontinental Exchange, Inc.; *U.S. Public*, pg. 1143
SIMPLIFY COMPLIANCE HOLDINGS LLC—See Leeds Equity Partners, LLC; *U.S. Private*, pg. 2415
SIMPLIFY DIGITAL LIMITED—See Currys plc; *Int'l*, pg. 1879
SIMPLILEARN AMERICAS LLC—See Simplilearn Solutions Pvt Ltd; *Int'l*, pg. 6934
SIMPLILEARN SOLUTIONS PVT LTD; *Int'l*, pg. 6934
SIMPLIMATIC ENGINEERING HOLDINGS LLC; *U.S. Private*, pg. 3667
SIMPLION TECHNOLOGIES INC.; *U.S. Private*, pg. 3668
SIMPLITIUM LTD.—See Nasdaq, Inc.; *U.S. Public*, pg. 1492
SIMPLON FAHRRAD GMBH—See HANNOVER Finanz GmbH; *Int'l*, pg. 3257
SIMPLOT AUSTRALIA PTY. LTD.—See J.R. Simplot Company; *U.S. Private*, pg. 2171
SIMPLO TECHNOLOGY CO., LTD.; *Int'l*, pg. 6934
SIMPLOT KOREA INC.—See J.R. Simplot Company; *U.S. Private*, pg. 2171
SIMPLOT PARTNERS—See J.R. Simplot Company; *U.S. Private*, pg. 2171
SIMPLOT PHOSPHATES, LLC—See J.R. Simplot Company; *U.S. Private*, pg. 2171
SIMPLURIS, INC.; *U.S. Private*, pg. 3668
SIMPLUS AUSTRALIA PTY. LTD.—See Infosys Limited; *Int'l*, pg. 3696
SIMPLUS MOBILE PTY LTD—See Temasek Holdings (Private) Limited; *Int'l*, pg. 7553
SIMPLY BETTER BRANDS CORP.; *Int'l*, pg. 6934
SIMPLYBIZ GROUP PLC; *Int'l*, pg. 6934
SIMPLY BIZ MORTGAGES LIMITED—See Simplybiz Group plc; *Int'l*, pg. 6934
SIMPLY BIZ SERVICES LIMITED—See Simplybiz Group plc; *Int'l*, pg. 6934
SIMPLY BUSINESS, INC.—See The Travelers Companies, Inc.; *U.S. Public*, pg. 2136
SIMPLYCAST.COM; *Int'l*, pg. 6934

SIMPLY COLOR LAB INC.; *U.S. Private*, pg. 3668
SIMPLY DENTAL MANAGEMENT, INC.; *U.S. Private*, pg. 3668
SIMPLY FASHION STORES LTD.; *U.S. Private*, pg. 3668
SIMPLYGLOBO INC; *U.S. Private*, pg. 3668
THE SIMPLY GOOD FOODS COMPANY; *U.S. Public*, pg. 2130
SIMPLY GREEN HOME SERVICES INC.—See Simply Group; *Int'l*, pg. 6934
SIMPLY GREEN LAWN SPRINKLERS, INC.—See Ryan Lawn & Tree Inc.; *U.S. Private*, pg. 3510
SIMPLY GROUP; *Int'l*, pg. 6934
SIMPLY HEALTHCARE PLANS, INC.—See Elevance Health, Inc.; *U.S. Public*, pg. 730
SIMPLYHEALTH GROUP LIMITED; *Int'l*, pg. 6934
SIMPLY, INC.; *U.S. Public*, pg. 1882
SIMPLYLIFE LLC—See Mainland Headwear Holdings Ltd.; *Int'l*, pg. 4651
SIMPLY MAC, INC.—See Simply, Inc.; *U.S. Public*, pg. 1882
SIMPLY MEASURED INC.—See Sprout Social, Inc.; *U.S. Public*, pg. 1920
SIMPLY NUC, INC.; *U.S. Private*, pg. 3668
SIMPLY SOLVENTLESS CONCENTRATES LTD.; *Int'l*, pg. 6934
SIMPLY SOUTHERN RESTAURANT GROUP LLC—See Brentwood Associates; *U.S. Private*, pg. 646
SIMPLY STORAGE MANAGEMENT LLC—See Public Storage; *U.S. Public*, pg. 1736
SIMPLYTITLE COMPANY—See Lennar Corporation; *U.S. Public*, pg. 1307
SIMPLY TRAVEL LTD.—See TUI AG; *Int'l*, pg. 7966
SIMPLYWELL INC.—See Marlin Equity Partners, LLC; *U.S. Private*, pg. 2585
SIMPLY WHEELZ LLC—See The Catalyst Capital Group Inc.; *Int'l*, pg. 7631
SIMPLY-X GMBH—See CTS Eventim AG & Co. KGAA; *Int'l*, pg. 1874
SIMPLY ZESTY LIMITED—See News Corporation; *U.S. Public*, pg. 1520
SIMPO A.D.; *Int'l*, pg. 6935
SIMPO LINE D.O.O.—See Simpo A.D.; *Int'l*, pg. 6935
SIMPO SIK D.O.O.—See Simpo A.D.; *Int'l*, pg. 6935
SIMPPLE LTD.; *Int'l*, pg. 6935
SIMPSON & COMPANY LIMITED; *Int'l*, pg. 6935
SIMPSON CONSTRUCTION COMPANY, INC.; *U.S. Private*, pg. 3668
SIMPSON CONSTRUCTION MATERIALS; *U.S. Private*, pg. 3668
SIMPSON CONSTRUCTION SERVICES, INC.; *U.S. Private*, pg. 3668
SIMPSON DOOR COMPANY—See Simpson Investment Company; *U.S. Private*, pg. 3668
SIMPSON ELECTRIC COMPANY; *U.S. Private*, pg. 3668
SIMPSON GARDEN GROVE, INC.—See General Motors Company; *U.S. Public*, pg. 929
SIMPSON GUMPERTZ & HEGER INC.; *U.S. Private*, pg. 3668
SIMPSON HOUSE; *U.S. Private*, pg. 3668
SIMPSON HOUSING LIMITED PARTNERSHIP; *U.S. Private*, pg. 3668
SIMPSON HOUSING SOLUTIONS, LLC; *U.S. Private*, pg. 3668
SIMPSON INVESTMENT COMPANY; *U.S. Private*, pg. 3668
SIMPSON MANUFACTURING COMPANY, INC.; *U.S. Public*, pg. 1882
SIMPSON & MCCRADY LLC; *U.S. Private*, pg. 3668
SIMPSON MILLAR LLP—See Fairpoint Group Plc; *Int'l*, pg. 2609
SIMPSON NORTON CORPORATION—See Connor, Clark & Lunn Financial Group; *Int'l*, pg. 1769
SIMPSON OF MARYLAND, INC.; *U.S. Private*, pg. 3668
SIMPSON PERFORMANCE PRODUCTS INC.—See Carousel Capital Partners; *U.S. Private*, pg. 770
SIMPSON PERFORMANCE PRODUCTS—See Carousel Capital Partners; *U.S. Private*, pg. 770
SIMPSON PLASTERING LLC; *U.S. Private*, pg. 3668
SIMPSON PROPERTY GROUP, LP—See Simpson Housing Limited Partnership; *U.S. Private*, pg. 3668
SIMPSON STRONG-TIE ASIA LIMITED—See Simpson Manufacturing Company, Inc.; *U.S. Public*, pg. 1883
SIMPSON STRONG-TIE AUSTRALIA PTY LIMITED—See Simpson Manufacturing Company, Inc.; *U.S. Public*, pg. 1883
SIMPSON STRONG-TIE (BEIJING) COMPANY LIMITED—See Simpson Manufacturing Company, Inc.; *U.S. Public*, pg. 1883
SIMPSON STRONG-TIE CANADA, LIMITED—See Simpson Manufacturing Company, Inc.; *U.S. Public*, pg. 1883
SIMPSON STRONG-TIE CHILE LIMITADA—See Simpson Manufacturing Company, Inc.; *U.S. Public*, pg. 1883
SIMPSON STRONG-TIE CO., INC.—See Simpson Manufacturing Company, Inc.; *U.S. Public*, pg. 1883
SIMPSON STRONG-TIE EUROPE EURL—See Simpson Manufacturing Company, Inc.; *U.S. Public*, pg. 1883
SIMPSON STRONG-TIE GMBH—See Simpson Manufacturing Company, Inc.; *U.S. Public*, pg. 1883

SIMPSON STRONG-TIE INTERNATIONAL, INC.—See Simpson Manufacturing Company, Inc.; *U.S. Public*, pg. 1883
SIMPSON STRONG-TIE (NEW ZEALAND) LIMITED—See Simpson Manufacturing Company, Inc.; *U.S. Public*, pg. 1883
SIMPSON STRONG-TIE (QUIK DRIVE FACTORY)—See Simpson Manufacturing Company, Inc.; *U.S. Public*, pg. 1883
SIMPSON STRONG-TIE SOUTH AFRICA (PTY) LTD—See Simpson Manufacturing Company, Inc.; *U.S. Public*, pg. 1883
SIMPSON STRONG-TIE SP.Z.O.O.—See Simpson Manufacturing Company, Inc.; *U.S. Public*, pg. 1883
SIMPSON TECHNOLOGIES CORPORATION—See Altor Equity Partners AB; *Int'l*, pg. 395
SIMPSON TECHNOLOGIES GMBH—See Altor Equity Partners AB; *Int'l*, pg. 395
SIMPSON THACHER & BARTLETT LLP; *U.S. Private*, pg. 3668
SIMRAD A/S—See Kongsberg Gruppen ASA; *Int'l*, pg. 4256
SIMRAD FISHERIES—See Kongsberg Gruppen ASA; *Int'l*, pg. 4256
SIMRAD NORTH AMERICA INC.—See Kongsberg Gruppen ASA; *Int'l*, pg. 4256
SIMRAD NORTH AMERICA INC.—See Kongsberg Gruppen ASA; *Int'l*, pg. 4256
SIMRAD OPTRONICS SAS-AUBAGNE—See Rheinmetall AG; *Int'l*, pg. 6324
SIMRAD SPAIN SL—See Kongsberg Gruppen ASA; *Int'l*, pg. 4256
SIMRAN FARMS LIMITED; *Int'l*, pg. 6935
SIMRAX BV—See Freudenberg SE; *Int'l*, pg. 2790
SIMRIS BIOLOGICS GMBH—See Simris Group AB; *Int'l*, pg. 6935
SIMRIS GROUP AB; *Int'l*, pg. 6935
SIMRIT DISTRIBUTION ET CIE—See Freudenberg SE; *Int'l*, pg. 2790
SIMRIT SERVICE CENTER DENMARK EAGLEBURGMANN KE A/S—See Freudenberg SE; *Int'l*, pg. 2790
SIMS ALUMINUM PTY. LIMITED—See Sims Limited; *U.S. Public*, pg. 1884
SIMS BROTHERS INC.; *U.S. Private*, pg. 3669
SIMS BUICK -GMC- TRUCK INC.; *U.S. Private*, pg. 3669
SIMSBURY ASSOCIATES INC.; *U.S. Private*, pg. 3669
SIMS CAB DEPOT CORP.; *Int'l*, pg. 6935
SIMS CLINIC LIMITED—See Virtus Health Limited; *Int'l*, pg. 8249
SIMS CRANE & EQUIPMENT COMPANY; *U.S. Private*, pg. 3669
SIMSCROFT-ECHO FARMS INC.; *U.S. Private*, pg. 3669
SIMS E-RECYCLING (NZ) LIMITED—See Sims Limited; *U.S. Public*, pg. 1884
SIMS E-RECYCLING PTY. LTD.—See Sims Limited; *U.S. Public*, pg. 1884
SIMS GROUP AUSTRALIA HOLDINGS LIMITED—See Sims Limited; *U.S. Public*, pg. 1884
SIMS GROUP CANADA HOLDINGS LIMITED—See Sims Limited; *U.S. Public*, pg. 1883
SIMS GROUP UK HOLDINGS LIMITED—See Sims Limited; *U.S. Public*, pg. 1884
SIMS IMPORT INC.; *U.S. Private*, pg. 3669
SIMS INDUSTRIAL PTY LIMITED—See Sims Limited; *U.S. Public*, pg. 1884
SIMS LIMITED; *U.S. Public*, pg. 1883
SIMS-LOHMAN, INC.; *U.S. Private*, pg. 3669
SIMS MANUFACTURING CO. INC.—See Michelsen Packaging Co. Inc.; *U.S. Private*, pg. 2700
SIMS MANUFACTURING PTY. LTD.—See Sims Limited; *U.S. Public*, pg. 1884
SIMSMETAL INDUSTRIES LIMITED—See Sims Limited; *U.S. Public*, pg. 1884
SIMS METAL MANAGEMENT - JERSEY CITY—See Sims Limited; *U.S. Public*, pg. 1883
SIMS METAL MANAGEMENT LIMITED - AUSTRALIA HEAD OFFICE—See Sims Limited; *U.S. Public*, pg. 1883
SIMS METAL MANAGEMENT - STRATFORD-UPON-AVON—See Sims Limited; *U.S. Public*, pg. 1884
SIMSMETAL SERVICES PTY LIMITED—See Sims Limited; *U.S. Public*, pg. 1884
SIMS M+R GMBH—See Sims Limited; *U.S. Public*, pg. 1884
SIMS PACIFIC METALS LIMITED—See Sims Limited; *U.S. Public*, pg. 1884
SIM SPIELBANKEN INVESTITIONS-, BETEILIGUNGS- UND MANAGEMENT GMBH & CO. KG—See Novomatic AG; *Int'l*, pg. 5467
SIMS RECYCLING SOLUTIONS AB—See Sims Limited; *U.S. Public*, pg. 1884
SIMS RECYCLING SOLUTIONS - CHICAGO REFINING—See Sims Limited; *U.S. Public*, pg. 1884
SIMS RECYCLING SOLUTIONS HOLDINGS INC.—See Sims Limited; *U.S. Public*, pg. 1884
SIMS RECYCLING SOLUTIONS, INC.—See Sims Limited; *U.S. Public*, pg. 1884
SIMS RECYCLING SOLUTIONS NV—See Sims Limited; *U.S. Public*, pg. 1884

SIMS-LOHMAN, INC.

SIMS RECYCLING SOLUTIONS PTE LIMITED—See Sims Limited; *U.S. Public*, pg. 1884
SIMS RECYCLING SOLUTIONS UK HOLDINGS LTD.—See Sims Limited; *U.S. Public*, pg. 1884
SIMS RECYCLING SOLUTIONS UK LTD.—See Sims Limited; *U.S. Public*, pg. 1884
SIMS TRADING COMPANY LTD.—See CITIC Group Corporation; *Int'l*, pg. 1621
SIMS TYRECYCLE PTY. LTD.—See Sims Limited; *U.S. Public*, pg. 1884
SIMS URBAN OASIS PTE. LTD.—See Hong Leong Investment Holdings Pte. Ltd.; *Int'l*, pg. 3468
SIMTAB NEOS—See Richelieu Hardware Ltd.; *Int'l*, pg. 6331
SIM TECHNOLOGY GROUP LIMITED; *Int'l*, pg. 6927
SIMTEC SILICONE PARTS, LLC—See RICO Elastomere Projecting GmbH; *Int'l*, pg. 6333
SIMTEK FENCE, INC.—See Compagnie de Saint-Gobain SA; *Int'l*, pg. 1730
SIMTEX INDUSTRIES LIMITED; *Int'l*, pg. 6935
SIMTRONICS AS—See 3M Company; *U.S. Public*, pg. 8
SIMTRONICS SAS—See 3M Company; *U.S. Public*, pg. 8
SIMU GMBH—See Somfy SA; *Int'l*, pg. 7085
SIMULA TECHNOLOGY CORP.—See Simula Technology Inc.; *Int'l*, pg. 6935
SIMULA TECHNOLOGY INC.; *Int'l*, pg. 6935
SIMULA TECHNOLOGY (SHENZHEN) CO., LTD.—See Simula Technology Inc.; *Int'l*, pg. 6935
SIMULATED ENVIRONMENT CONCEPTS, INC.; *U.S. Public*, pg. 1884
SIMULATIONS PLUS, INC.; *U.S. Public*, pg. 1884
SIMULEON B.V.—See Addnode Group AB; *Int'l*, pg. 130
SIMUL INTERNATIONAL, INC.—See TAKARA & COMPANY LTD.; *Int'l*, pg. 7431
SIMULUS LIMITED—See KKR & Co. Inc.; *U.S. Public*, pg. 1241
SIMU S.A.S.—See Somfy SA; *Int'l*, pg. 7085
SIMUTECH GROUP, INC.—See Amphenol Corporation; *U.S. Public*, pg. 131
SIMUTECH GROUP - TORONTO—See Amphenol Corporation; *U.S. Public*, pg. 131
SIMU USA INC.—See Somfy SA; *Int'l*, pg. 7085
SIMVENTIONSM INC.; *U.S. Private*, pg. 3669
SIMWEB INC.—See HUB Cyber Security Ltd.; *Int'l*, pg. 3516
SIMWON DEVELOPMENT CO., LTD.—See Myoung Shin Industry Co., Ltd.; *Int'l*, pg. 5113
SIMWON TECH INC.—See Myoung Shin Industry Co., Ltd.; *Int'l*, pg. 5113
SINA.COM ONLINE—See SINA Corporation; *Int'l*, pg. 6936
SINA.COM TECHNOLOGY (CHINA) CO., LTD.—See SINA Corporation; *Int'l*, pg. 6936
SINA CORP. - BEIJING—See SINA Corporation; *Int'l*, pg. 6936
SINA CORPORATION; *Int'l*, pg. 6935
SINA CORP. - REDWOOD—See SINA Corporation; *Int'l*, pg. 6936
SINA CORP. - SHANGHAI—See SINA Corporation; *Int'l*, pg. 6936
SINA CORP. - TAIPEI—See SINA Corporation; *Int'l*, pg. 6936
SINA DAROU LABORATORIES COMPANY; *Int'l*, pg. 6936
SINAD HOLDING COMPANY; *Int'l*, pg. 6936
SINAER—See Corpfin Capital SA; *Int'l*, pg. 1802
SINAI CEMENT COMPANY—See Vicat S.A.; *Int'l*, pg. 8186
SINAI HEALTH SYSTEM; *U.S. Private*, pg. 3669
SINAI MANGANESE COMPANY—See Chemical Industries Holding Company; *Int'l*, pg. 1462
SINAI WHITE PORTLAND CEMENT CO. SAE—See Cementir Holding N.V.; *Int'l*, pg. 1397
SINAK PLUMBING COMPANY INC.—See CPS Capital; *Int'l*, pg. 1826
SINANEN BIKE CO., LTD.—See Sinanen Holdings Co., Ltd.; *Int'l*, pg. 6936
SINANEN CO., LTD.—See Sinanen Holdings Co., Ltd.; *Int'l*, pg. 6936
SINANEN ECOWORK CO., LTD.—See Sinanen Holdings Co., Ltd.; *Int'l*, pg. 6936
SINANEN FACILITIES CO., LTD.—See Sinanen Holdings Co., Ltd.; *Int'l*, pg. 6936
SINANEN HOLDINGS CO., LTD.; *Int'l*, pg. 6936
SINANEN MOBILITY PLUS CO., LTD.—See Sinanen Holdings Co., Ltd.; *Int'l*, pg. 6936
SINANEN ZEOMIC CO., LTD.—See Sinanen Holdings Co., Ltd.; *Int'l*, pg. 6936
SINA PEARSON TEXTILES, INC.—See Momentum Textiles Inc.; *U.S. Private*, pg. 2768
SINAPSI INFORMATICA SRL—See Sesa S.p.A.; *Int'l*, pg. 6729
SINAR BERLIAN SDN. BHD.—See Mitsubishi Corporation; *Int'l*, pg. 4943
SINAR INDAH PULP & PAPER PTY. LTD.—See Pabrik Kertas Tjiwi Kimia Tbk; *Int'l*, pg. 5684
SINAR MAJU LOGISTIK SDN. BHD.—See Straits Energy Resources Berhad; *Int'l*, pg. 7234
SINARMAS LAND LIMITED; *Int'l*, pg. 6936

SINASAHI SOLDER (M) SDN. BHD.—See Singapore Asahi Chemical & Solder Industries Pte. Ltd.; *Int'l*, pg. 6940
SINA S.P.A.—See Argo Finanziaria S.p.A.; *Int'l*, pg. 562
SINATEX SA; *Int'l*, pg. 6936
SINA TILE & CERAMIC CO.; *Int'l*, pg. 6936
SINBON ELECTRONICS CO., LTD - MIAOLI FACTORY—See SINBON Electronics Co., Ltd.; *Int'l*, pg. 6936
SINBON ELECTRONICS CO., LTD.; *Int'l*, pg. 6936
SINBON HUNGARY KFT.—See SINBON Electronics Co., Ltd.; *Int'l*, pg. 6937
SINBON OHIO LLC—See SINBON Electronics Co., Ltd.; *Int'l*, pg. 6937
SINBON TECHNOLOGIES TENNESSEE LLC—See SINBON Electronics Co., Ltd.; *Int'l*, pg. 6937
SINBON USA L.L.C.—See SINBON Electronics Co., Ltd.; *Int'l*, pg. 6937
SINCA INDUSTRIES, INC.; *U.S. Private*, pg. 3669
SINCAP GROUP LIMITED; *Int'l*, pg. 6937
SINCERE CO., LTD.; *Int'l*, pg. 6937
THE SINCERE CO. LTD.; *Int'l*, pg. 7686
SINCERE LEASING SDN. BHD.—See Tradewinds Corporation Berhad; *Int'l*, pg. 7888
SINCERELY INCORPORATED—See Qurate Retail, Inc.; *U.S. Public*, pg. 1758
SINCERELY YOGURT FRANCHISING LLC—See Ablak Holdings, LLC; *U.S. Private*, pg. 39
SINCERE NAVIGATION CORPORATION; *Int'l*, pg. 6937
SINCERE TAIWAN CO., LTD.—See Sincere Co., Ltd.; *Int'l*, pg. 6937
SINCERE VISION CO., LTD.—See Sincere Co., Ltd.; *Int'l*, pg. 6937
SINCERE WATCH CO., LTD.—See Sincere Watch (Hong Kong) Limited; *Int'l*, pg. 6937
SINCERE WATCH (HONG KONG) LIMITED; *Int'l*, pg. 6937
SINCERITY APPLIED MATERIALS HOLDINGS CORP.; *Int'l*, pg. 6937
SINCERITY ENGINEERING COMPANY LIMITED; *Int'l*, pg. 6937
SINCERUS B.V.—See Dustin Group AB; *Int'l*, pg. 2235
SINCH AB; *Int'l*, pg. 6937
SINCH AMERICA, INC.—See Sinch AB; *Int'l*, pg. 6937
SIN CHEE HENG (BUTTERWORTH) SDN. BHD.—See Hextar Industries Berhad; *Int'l*, pg. 3373
SIN CHEE HENG (JOHORE) SDN. BHD.—See Hextar Industries Berhad; *Int'l*, pg. 3373
SIN CHEE HENG (KUANTAN) SDN. BHD.—See Hextar Industries Berhad; *Int'l*, pg. 3373
SIN CHEE HENG (SABAH) SDN. BHD.—See Hextar Industries Berhad; *Int'l*, pg. 3373
SIN CHEE HENG (SARAWAK) SDN. BHD.—See Hextar Industries Berhad; *Int'l*, pg. 3373
SIN CHEE HENG SDN. BHD.—See Hextar Industries Berhad; *Int'l*, pg. 3373
SIN CHEW ALARM COMPANY LIMITED—See Aiphone Co., Ltd.; *Int'l*, pg. 235
SIN CHEW MEDIA CORPORATION BERHAD—See Media Chinese International Limited; *Int'l*, pg. 4770
SINCH MOBILE AB—See Sinch AB; *Int'l*, pg. 6937
SIN CHUAN MARKETING SDN. BHD.—See Asia File Corporation Bhd.; *Int'l*, pg. 612
SINCH UK LTD.—See Sinch AB; *Int'l*, pg. 6937
SINCLAIR BROADCAST GROUP—See Sinclair, Inc.; *U.S. Public*, pg. 1885
SINCLAIR CASPER REFINERY—See HF Sinclair Corporation; *U.S. Public*, pg. 1034
SINCLAIR DENTAL/DENTAIRE; *Int'l*, pg. 6937
SINCLAIR ELEVATOR INC.; *U.S. Private*, pg. 3669
SINCLAIR GARAGES (PORT TALBOT) LTD.; *Int'l*, pg. 6937
SINCLAIR GLOBAL GROUP S.R.O.—See Beijer Ref AB; *Int'l*, pg. 945
SINCLAIR, INC.; *U.S. Public*, pg. 1885
SINCLAIR INSURANCE GROUP INC.; *U.S. Private*, pg. 3669
SINCLAIR IS PHARMA MANUFACTURING & LOGISTICS—See Huadong Medicine Co., Ltd.; *Int'l*, pg. 3511
SINCLAIR KNIGHT MERZ (NZ) HOLDINGS LTD—See Jacobs Engineering Group, Inc.; *U.S. Public*, pg. 1186
SINCLAIR MEDIA OF BOISE, LLC—See Sinclair, Inc.; *U.S. Public*, pg. 1886
SINCLAIR MEDIA OF IDAHO, LLC—See Sinclair, Inc.; *U.S. Public*, pg. 1886
SINCLAIR MEDIA SERVICES COMPANY—See Sinclair, Inc.; *U.S. Public*, pg. 1886
SINCLAIR OIL LLC—See HF Sinclair Corporation; *U.S. Public*, pg. 1034
SINCLAIR PHARMACEUTICALS LTD.—See Huadong Medicine Co., Ltd.; *Int'l*, pg. 3511
SINCLAIR PHARMA FRANCE—See Huadong Medicine Co., Ltd.; *Int'l*, pg. 3511
SINCLAIR PHARMA GMBH—See Huadong Medicine Co., Ltd.; *Int'l*, pg. 3511
SINCLAIR PHARMA PLC—See Huadong Medicine Co., Ltd.; *Int'l*, pg. 3511
SINCLAIR PRINTING COMPANY; *U.S. Private*, pg. 3669

CORPORATE AFFILIATIONS

SINCLAIR RESEARCH CENTER, LLC; *U.S. Private*, pg. 3669
SINCLAIR & RUSH, INC.—See Cameron Holdings Corporation; *U.S. Private*, pg. 729
SINCLAIR & RUSH LTD.—See Cameron Holdings Corporation; *U.S. Private*, pg. 729
SINCLAIRS HOTELS LIMITED; *Int'l*, pg. 6937
SINCLAIR SLOVAKIA S.R.O.—See Beijer Ref AB; *Int'l*, pg. 945
SINCLAIR SUPPLY LTD.; *Int'l*, pg. 6937
SINCLAIR TECHNOLOGIES INC.—See Hytera Communications Corporation Limited; *Int'l*, pg. 3555
SINCLAIR TELEVISION GROUP, INC.—See Sinclair, Inc.; *U.S. Public*, pg. 1885
SINCLAIR TELEVISION MEDIA, INC.—See Sinclair, Inc.; *U.S. Public*, pg. 1886
SINCLAIR TELEVISION OF BAKERSFIELD, LLC—See Sinclair, Inc.; *U.S. Public*, pg. 1886
SINCLAIR TELEVISION OF CHARLESTON, INC.—See Sinclair, Inc.; *U.S. Public*, pg. 1886
SINCLAIR TELEVISION OF DAYTON, INC.—See Sinclair, Inc.; *U.S. Public*, pg. 1886
SINCLAIR TELEVISION OF NEVADA, INC.—See Sinclair, Inc.; *U.S. Public*, pg. 1886
SINCLAIR TELEVISION OF OREGON, LLC—See Sinclair, Inc.; *U.S. Public*, pg. 1886
SINCLAIR TELEVISION OF PORTLAND, LLC—See Sinclair, Inc.; *U.S. Public*, pg. 1886
SINCLAIR TELEVISION OF SEATTLE, INC.—See Sinclair, Inc.; *U.S. Public*, pg. 1886
SINCLAIR TELEVISION OF TENNESSEE, INC.—See Sinclair, Inc.; *U.S. Public*, pg. 1886
SINCLAIR TELEVISION OF WASHINGTON, LLC—See Sinclair, Inc.; *U.S. Public*, pg. 1886
SINCLAIR TELEVISION STATIONS, LLC—See Sinclair, Inc.; *U.S. Public*, pg. 1885
SINCLAIR TRACTOR—See Sigourney Tractor & Implement; *U.S. Private*, pg. 3651
SINCLAIR WELL PRODUCTS INC.; *U.S. Private*, pg. 3669
SINCO INC.; *U.S. Private*, pg. 3669
SINCO PHARMACEUTICALS HOLDINGS LTD.; *Int'l*, pg. 6937
SINDAI CO., LTD.—See NHK Spring Co., Ltd.; *Int'l*, pg. 5258
SINDH ABADGAR'S SUGAR MILLS LIMITED; *Int'l*, pg. 6938
SINDH BANK LIMITED; *Int'l*, pg. 6938
SINDH INSURANCE LIMITED—See Sindh Modaraba Management Limited; *Int'l*, pg. 6938
SINDH LEASING COMPANY LIMITED—See Sindh Bank Limited; *Int'l*, pg. 6938
SINDH MODARABA MANAGEMENT LIMITED; *Int'l*, pg. 6938
SINDHU BIKASH BANK LTD.; *Int'l*, pg. 6938
SINDHU TRADE LINKS LIMITED; *Int'l*, pg. 6938
SINDOH CO., LTD.; *Int'l*, pg. 6938
SINDOPOWER GMBH—See SEMIKRON International GmbH; *Int'l*, pg. 6705
SINDORA BERHAD—See Johor Corporation; *Int'l*, pg. 3994
SIND PARTICLE BOARD MILLS LTD.—See B.F. Modaraba; *Int'l*, pg. 789
SINDUS ANDRITZ LTDA.—See ANDRITZ AG; *Int'l*, pg. 456
S INDUSTRIAL ESTATE CO., LTD.—See Singha Estate PCL; *Int'l*, pg. 6944
SINDUTCH CABLE MANUFACTURER SDN. BHD.—See Prysmian S.p.A.; *Int'l*, pg. 6013
SINDU VALLEY TECHNOLOGIES LTD.; *Int'l*, pg. 6938
SINECO S.P.A.—See Argo Finanziaria S.p.A.; *Int'l*, pg. 562
SINELCO INTERNATIONAL BVBA—See Sally Beauty Holdings, Inc.; *U.S. Public*, pg. 1839
SINELCO ITALIANA SRL—See Sally Beauty Holdings, Inc.; *U.S. Public*, pg. 1839
SINELEC S.P.A.—See Argo Finanziaria S.p.A.; *Int'l*, pg. 562
SINENERGY PTE. LTD.—See SHS Holdings Ltd.; *Int'l*, pg. 6867
SINENG ELECTRIC CO., LTD.; *Int'l*, pg. 6938
SINENSIX PHARMA (THAILAND) CO., LTD.—See Insud Pharma, S.L.; *Int'l*, pg. 3725
SINERA AG—See UniCredit S.p.A.; *Int'l*, pg. 8040
SINERGIA S.R.L.—See Hera S.p.A.; *Int'l*, pg. 3356
SINERGIYA INVEST HOLDING AD; *Int'l*, pg. 6938
SINETECH; *Int'l*, pg. 6938
SINEW PHARMA CO., LTD.—See Microbio Co., Ltd.; *Int'l*, pg. 4879
SINFA CABLES SARL—See AKWEL; *Int'l*, pg. 268
SINFONIA ASSET MANAGEMENT LIMITED—See Tatton Asset Management plc; *Int'l*, pg. 7475
SINFONIA MICROTEC (DONGGUAN) CO., LTD.—See Sinfonia Technology Co., Ltd.; *Int'l*, pg. 6938
SINFONIA MICROTEC (HONG KONG) CO., LTD.—See Sinfonia Technology Co., Ltd.; *Int'l*, pg. 6938
SINFONIARX, INC.—See Vora Ventures LLC; *U.S. Private*, pg. 4412
SINFONIA TECHNOLOGY CO., LTD.; *Int'l*, pg. 6938

COMPANY NAME INDEX

SINFONIA TECHNOLOGY (SHANGHAI) CO., LTD.—See Sinfonia Technology Co., Ltd.; *Int'l*, pg. 6938
SINFONIA TECHNOLOGY (SINGAPORE) PTE. LTD.—See Sinfonia Technology Co., Ltd.; *Int'l*, pg. 6938
SINFONIA TECHNOLOGY (THAILAND) CO., LTD.—See Sinfonia Technology Co., Ltd.; *Int'l*, pg. 6938
SINFRARED PTE LTD—See Xenics N.V.; *Int'l*, pg. 8521
SINGA DEVELOPMENT PTE LTD—See BBR Holdings (S) Ltd.; *Int'l*, pg. 921
SINGAMAS CONTAINER HOLDINGS LIMITED; *Int'l*, pg. 6939
SINGAMAS CONTAINER INDUSTRY CO., LTD.—See Singamas Container Holdings Limited; *Int'l*, pg. 6939
SINGAMAS LOGISTICS (QINGDAO) CO., LTD.—See Singamas Container Holdings Limited; *Int'l*, pg. 6939
SINGAMAS LOGISTICS (TIANJIN) CO., LTD.—See Singamas Container Holdings Limited; *Int'l*, pg. 6939
SINGAMAS TERMINALS (HK) LTD.—See Singamas Container Holdings Limited; *Int'l*, pg. 6939
SINGAPORE ACRYLIC PTE LTD—See Nippon Shokubai Co., Ltd.; *Int'l*, pg. 5333
SINGAPORE AEROSPACE KABUSHIKI KAISHA—See Temasek Holdings (Private) Limited; *Int'l*, pg. 7551
SINGAPORE AERO SUPPORT SERVICES PTE. LTD.—See Temasek Holdings (Private) Limited; *Int'l*, pg. 7551
SINGAPORE AIRLINES LIMITED—See Temasek Holdings (Private) Limited; *Int'l*, pg. 7550
SINGAPORE AIRLINES LTD. - US REPRESENTATIVE OFFICE—See Temasek Holdings (Private) Limited; *Int'l*, pg. 7551
SINGAPORE ALE PTE. LTD.—See Nokia Corporation; *Int'l*, pg. 5404
SINGAPORE ASAHI CHEMICAL & SOLDER INDUSTRIES PTE. LTD.; *Int'l*, pg. 6939
SINGAPORE ASAHI PTE. LTD.—See Singapore Asahi Chemical & Solder Industries Pte. Ltd.; *Int'l*, pg. 6940
SINGAPORE AUTOMOTIVE INDUSTRIES PTE. LTD.—See Tan Chong International Limited; *Int'l*, pg. 7453
SINGAPORE BIKEN PTE. LTD.—See Biken Techno Corporation Ltd.; *Int'l*, pg. 1023
SINGAPORE CABLES MANUFACTURERS PTE. LTD.—See Prysmian S.p.A.; *Int'l*, pg. 6013
SINGAPORE CAMBO BIOLOGICAL TECHNOLOGY PTE. LTD.—See China GreenFresh Group Co., Ltd.; *Int'l*, pg. 1505
SINGAPORE CASKET COMPANY (PRIVATE) LIMITED—See TPG Capital, L.P.; *U.S. Public*, pg. 2174
SINGAPORE CHEMI-CON (PTE) LTD.—See Nippon Chemi-Con Corporation; *Int'l*, pg. 5313
SINGAPORE COMMUNICATIONS EQUIPMENT CO. PTE LTD.—See HKC International Holdings Limited; *Int'l*, pg. 3428
SINGAPORE CONTEC PTE. LTD.—See Daifuku Co., Ltd.; *Int'l*, pg. 1926
SINGAPORE DAI-ICHI PTE. LTD.—See I-PEX Inc.; *Int'l*, pg. 3564
SINGAPORE DAI-ICHI PTE. LTD. - WOODLANDS PLANT—See I-PEX Inc.; *Int'l*, pg. 3564
SINGAPORE ELECTRIC VEHICLES PTE. LTD.—See Digilife Technologies Limited; *Int'l*, pg. 2120
SINGAPORE ENGINEERING & CONSTRUCTION PTE. LTD.—See BBR Holdings (S) Ltd.; *Int'l*, pg. 921
SINGAPORE EPSON INDUSTRIAL PTE. LTD.—See Seiko Epson Corporation; *Int'l*, pg. 6688
SINGAPORE EXCHANGE DERIVATIVES CLEARING LIMITED—See Singapore Exchange Limited; *Int'l*, pg. 6940
SINGAPORE EXCHANGE DERIVATIVES TRADING LIMITED—See Singapore Exchange Limited; *Int'l*, pg. 6940
SINGAPORE EXCHANGE LIMITED; *Int'l*, pg. 6940
SINGAPORE EXCHANGE SECURITIES TRADING LIMITED—See Singapore Exchange Limited; *Int'l*, pg. 6940
SINGAPORE FOOD INDUSTRIES LTD.—See Temasek Holdings (Private) Limited; *Int'l*, pg. 7550
SINGAPORE GLACIAL ACRYLIC PTE. LTD.—See Nippon Shokubai Co., Ltd.; *Int'l*, pg. 5333
SINGAPORE HAGIWARA PTE. LTD.—See Hagiwara Electric Holdings Co., Ltd.; *Int'l*, pg. 3207
SINGAPORE INFORMATICS COMPUTER INSTITUTE (PVT) LTD—See Informatics Education Ltd; *Int'l*, pg. 3694
SINGAPORE INFORMATION SERVICES PTE LTD—See Rumah & Co. Pte. Ltd.; *Int'l*, pg. 6427
SINGAPORE INSTITUTE OF ADVANCED MEDICINE HOLDINGS PTE LTD—See Berjaya Corporation Berhad; *Int'l*, pg. 984
SINGAPORE ISLAND BANK LIMITED—See Oversea-Chinese Banking Corporation Limited; *Int'l*, pg. 5672
SINGAPORE JAMCO SERVICES PTE LTD.—See JAMCO Corporation; *Int'l*, pg. 3875
SINGAPORE KITCHEN EQUIPMENT LIMITED; *Int'l*, pg. 6940
SINGAPORE KOBE PTE. LTD.—See Kobe Steel, Ltd.; *Int'l*, pg. 4221
SINGAPORE LAND GROUP LIMITED; *Int'l*, pg. 6940

SINGAPORE LAND LIMITED—See Singapore Land Group Limited; *Int'l*, pg. 6940
SINGAPORE LIFE PTE LTD; *Int'l*, pg. 6940
SINGAPORE MEDIA ACADEMY PTE. LTD.—See Temasek Holdings (Private) Limited; *Int'l*, pg. 7548
SINGAPORE MEDICAL GROUP LIMITED; *Int'l*, pg. 6940
SINGAPORE NOBLE ELECTRONICS PTE., LTD.—See Teikoku Tsushin Kogyo Co., Ltd.; *Int'l*, pg. 7524
SINGAPORE O&G LTD.; *Int'l*, pg. 6941
SINGAPORE OXYGEN AIR LIQUIDE PTE. LTD.—See L'Air Liquide S.A.; *Int'l*, pg. 4376
SINGAPORE PAINCARE CENTER @ NOVENA PTE. LTD.—See Singapore Paincare Holdings Limited; *Int'l*, pg. 6941
SINGAPORE PAINCARE HOLDINGS LIMITED; *Int'l*, pg. 6941
SINGAPORE PAINCARE TCM WELLNESS PTE. LTD.—See Singapore Paincare Holdings Limited; *Int'l*, pg. 6941
SINGAPORE PETROLEUM CO. (HK) LTD.—See China National Petroleum Corporation; *Int'l*, pg. 1533
SINGAPORE PETROLEUM COMPANY LIMITED—See China National Petroleum Corporation; *Int'l*, pg. 1533
SINGAPORE PILING & CIVIL ENGINEERING PRIVATE LIMITED—See BBR Holdings (S) Ltd.; *Int'l*, pg. 921
SINGAPORE POLYTECH COMPONENT PTE. LTD.—See Shun On Electronic Co., Ltd.; *Int'l*, pg. 6869
SINGAPORE POST LIMITED; *Int'l*, pg. 6941
SINGAPORE POWER INTERNATIONAL PTE. LTD.—See Temasek Holdings (Private) Limited; *Int'l*, pg. 7551
SINGAPORE POWER LTD.—See Temasek Holdings (Private) Limited; *Int'l*, pg. 7551
SINGAPORE PRECISION INDUSTRIES PTE. LTD.—See Sembcorp Industries Ltd.; *Int'l*, pg. 6704
SINGAPORE PRESS HOLDINGS LTD.; *Int'l*, pg. 6942
SINGAPORE PRESS, WASHINGTON—See Singapore Press Holdings Ltd.; *Int'l*, pg. 6943
SINGAPORE PRINT MEDIA HUB PTE LTD—See Teckwah Industrial Corporation Ltd; *Int'l*, pg. 7515
SINGAPORE PULP (PTE) LTD.—See CellMark AB; *Int'l*, pg. 1394
SINGAPORE REFINING CO. PTE. LTD.—See Chevron Corporation; *U.S. Public*, pg. 486
SINGAPORE REFINING CO. PTE. LTD.—See China National Petroleum Corporation; *Int'l*, pg. 1533
SINGAPORE REINSURANCE CORPORATION LIMITED—See Fairfax Financial Holdings Limited; *Int'l*, pg. 2608
SINGAPORE-RE MANAGEMENT SERVICES PTE. LTD.—See Fairfax Financial Holdings Limited; *Int'l*, pg. 2608
SINGAPORE RESOURCES, INC.; *U.S. Private*, pg. 3669
SINGAPORE SANYO TRADING PTE. LTD.—See Sanyo Trading Co., Ltd.; *Int'l*, pg. 6565
SINGAPORE SATORI PTE.LTD.—See SATORI ELECTRIC CO., LTD.; *Int'l*, pg. 6587
SINGAPORE SHIPPING CORPORATION LIMITED; *Int'l*, pg. 6943
SINGAPORE TAKADA INDUSTRIES PTE., LTD.—See Takada Corporation; *Int'l*, pg. 7429
SINGAPORE TECHNOLOGIES AEROSPACE LTD.—See Temasek Holdings (Private) Limited; *Int'l*, pg. 7552
SINGAPORE TECHNOLOGIES ELECTRONICS LIMITED—See Temasek Holdings (Private) Limited; *Int'l*, pg. 7552
SINGAPORE TECHNOLOGIES ENGINEERING (EUROPE) LTD.—See Temasek Holdings (Private) Limited; *Int'l*, pg. 7552
SINGAPORE TECHNOLOGIES ENGINEERING LIMITED—See Temasek Holdings (Private) Limited; *Int'l*, pg. 7551
SINGAPORE TECHNOLOGIES ENGINEERING (MIDDLE EAST) LTD.—See Temasek Holdings (Private) Limited; *Int'l*, pg. 7552
SINGAPORE TECHNOLOGIES KINETICS LTD.—See Temasek Holdings (Private) Limited; *Int'l*, pg. 7552
SINGAPORE TECHNOLOGIES MARINE LTD.—See Temasek Holdings (Private) Limited; *Int'l*, pg. 7552
SINGAPORE TECHNOLOGIES TELEMEDIA PTE. LTD.—See Temasek Holdings (Private) Limited; *Int'l*, pg. 7552
SINGAPORE TELECOM CHINA—See Temasek Holdings (Private) Limited; *Int'l*, pg. 7553
SINGAPORE TELECOM CHINA—See Temasek Holdings (Private) Limited; *Int'l*, pg. 7553
SINGAPORE TELECOM EUROPE—See Temasek Holdings (Private) Limited; *Int'l*, pg. 7553
SINGAPORE TELECOM HONG KONG LIMITED—See Temasek Holdings (Private) Limited; *Int'l*, pg. 7553
SINGAPORE TELECOM (INDIA-NEW DELHI)—See Temasek Holdings (Private) Limited; *Int'l*, pg. 7553
SINGAPORE TELECOM INDIA—See Temasek Holdings (Private) Limited; *Int'l*, pg. 7553
SINGAPORE TELECOM (INDONESIA)—See Temasek Holdings (Private) Limited; *Int'l*, pg. 7553
SINGAPORE TELECOM INTERNATIONAL PTE. LTD.—See Temasek Holdings (Private) Limited; *Int'l*, pg. 7553

SINGER TRAVEL

SINGAPORE TELECOM JAPAN—See Temasek Holdings (Private) Limited; *Int'l*, pg. 7553
SINGAPORE TELECOM (KOREA)—See Temasek Holdings (Private) Limited; *Int'l*, pg. 7553
SINGAPORE TELECOM (MALAYSIA)—See Temasek Holdings (Private) Limited; *Int'l*, pg. 7553
SINGAPORE TELECOM MOBILE PTE. LTD.—See Temasek Holdings (Private) Limited; *Int'l*, pg. 7554
SINGAPORE TELECOMMUNICATIONS LIMITED—See Temasek Holdings (Private) Limited; *Int'l*, pg. 7552
SINGAPORE TELECOM (PHILIPPINES)—See Temasek Holdings (Private) Limited; *Int'l*, pg. 7553
SINGAPORE TELECOM (THAILAND)—See Temasek Holdings (Private) Limited; *Int'l*, pg. 7553
SINGAPORE TELECOM USA, INC. - NORTHWEST & SOUTHWEST REGION—See Temasek Holdings (Private) Limited; *Int'l*, pg. 7554
SINGAPORE TELECOM USA, INC.—See Temasek Holdings (Private) Limited; *Int'l*, pg. 7553
SINGAPORE TOURISM BOARD; *Int'l*, pg. 6943
SINGAPORE UNITED ESTATES (PRIVATE) LIMITED—See Bukit Sembawang Estates Ltd; *Int'l*, pg. 1213
SINGAPORE UNITED RUBBER PLANTATIONS LIMITED—See Bukit Sembawang Estates Ltd; *Int'l*, pg. 1213
SINGAPORE WALLCOVERINGS CENTRE (PRIVATE) LIMITED—See Stamford Land Corporation Ltd.; *Int'l*, pg. 7165
SINGAPORE WAREHOUSE COMPANY (PRIVATE) LTD.—See Hwa Hong Corporation Limited; *Int'l*, pg. 3541
SINGAPURA FINANCE LTD.; *Int'l*, pg. 6943
SINGARDO INTERNATIONAL PTE LTD—See Electrosteel Castings Ltd; *Int'l*, pg. 2354
SINGASIA HOLDINGS LIMITED; *Int'l*, pg. 6943
SINGASIA RESOURCES PTE. LTD.—See SingAsia Holdings Limited; *Int'l*, pg. 6943
SINGATRON ENTERPRISE CO., LTD.; *Int'l*, pg. 6943
SINGAWAY FLUIDCONTROLS PTE LTD.—See Darco Water Technologies Limited; *Int'l*, pg. 1972
SING BROTHERS INC.; *U.S. Private*, pg. 3669
SING DA MARINE STRUCTURE CORPORATION—See China Steel Corporation; *Int'l*, pg. 1556
SING-ED GLOBAL SCHOOLHOUSE PTE. LTD.—See Chip Eng Seng Corporation Ltd.; *Int'l*, pg. 1572
SINGER AFRICA MIDDLE EAST LIMITED—See Platinum Equity, LLC; *U.S. Private*, pg. 3208
SINGER AMERICAS TRADING S.A.—See Retail Holdings N.V.; *Int'l*, pg. 6305
SINGER ASIA LIMITED—See Retail Holdings N.V.; *Int'l*, pg. 6305
SINGER ASIA SOURCING LIMITED—See Retail Holdings N.V.; *Int'l*, pg. 6305
SINGER BANGLADESH LIMITED—See Retail Holdings N.V.; *Int'l*, pg. 6305
SINGER BUSINESS SCHOOL (PVT) LTD.—See Hayleys PLC; *Int'l*, pg. 3292
SINGER DIRECT LLC—See Omnicom Group Inc.; *U.S. Public*, pg. 1593
SINGER EQUIPMENT COMPANY; *U.S. Private*, pg. 3670
SINGER EQUITIES INC.—See AEA Investors LP; *U.S. Private*, pg. 115
SINGER FINANCE LANKA PLC; *Int'l*, pg. 6943
THE SINGER GROUP; *U.S. Private*, pg. 4118
SINGER GUYANA INC—See Retail Holdings N.V.; *Int'l*, pg. 6306
SINGER INDIA LIMITED—See Retail Holdings N.V.; *Int'l*, pg. 6305
SINGER INDUSTRIES (CEYLON) PLC—See Hayleys PLC; *Int'l*, pg. 3292
SINGER ISLAND RECOVERY CENTER LLC—See AAC Holdings, Inc.; *U.S. Private*, pg. 31
SINGER ITALIA S.P.A.—See Retail Holdings N.V.; *Int'l*, pg. 6306
SINGER LEWAK GREENBAUM & GOLDSTEIN; *U.S. Private*, pg. 3670
SINGER (MALAYSIA) SDN BHD—See Retail Holdings N.V.; *Int'l*, pg. 6305
SINGER NEDERLAND BV—See Retail Holdings N.V.; *Int'l*, pg. 6306
SINGER NELSON CHARLMERS—See Kelso & Company, L.P.; *U.S. Private*, pg. 2280
SINGER SEWING COMPANY—See Platinum Equity, LLC; *U.S. Private*, pg. 3208
SINGER'S GETRANKE SHOP GMBH & CO. KG—See Live Nation Entertainment, Inc.; *U.S. Public*, pg. 1330
SINGER SHANGHAI SEWING MACHINE COMPANY LTD—See Retail Holdings N.V.; *Int'l*, pg. 6306
SINGER (SRI LANKA) PLC—See Hayleys PLC; *Int'l*, pg. 3292
SINGER THAILAND PUBLIC COMPANY LIMITED; *Int'l*, pg. 6943
SINGER TRAVEL; *U.S. Private*, pg. 3670
SINGER VALVE, LLC—See Mueller Water Products, Inc.; *U.S. Public*, pg. 1486
SINGER VALVE (TAICANG) CO., LTD.—See Mueller Water Products, Inc.; *U.S. Public*, pg. 1485

SINGER TRAVEL

SINGER & XENOS, INC.—See Mariner Wealth Advisors, LLC; *U.S. Private*, pg. 2576
SINGGAS (LPG) PRIVATE LIMITED—See Siamgas and Petrochemicals Public Company Limited; *Int'l*, pg. 6876
SINGHA ESTATE PCL; *Int'l*, pg. 6943
SINGHAGIRI (PVT) LTD.—See Daikin Industries, Ltd.; *Int'l*, pg. 1936
SINGHAIYI GROUP PTE. LTD.—See Zensun Enterprises Limited; *Int'l*, pg. 8635
SINGHA PARATECH PUBLIC COMPANY LIMITED; *Int'l*, pg. 6944
SINGH DEVELOPMENT CO. LTD.; *U.S. Private*, pg. 3670
SIN GHEE HUAT CORPORATION LTD.; *Int'l*, pg. 6935
SINGHE HOSPITALS PLC; *Int'l*, pg. 6944
SING HIAP HIN CO.—See HKS CO., LTD.; *Int'l*, pg. 3429
SINGHOFEN & ASSOCIATES, INC.—See Halff Associates, Inc.; *U.S. Private*, pg. 1842
SING HOLDINGS (BELLERIVE) PTE. LTD.—See Sing Holdings Limited; *Int'l*, pg. 6938
SING HOLDINGS (CAIRNHILL) PTE. LTD.—See Sing Holdings Limited; *Int'l*, pg. 6938
SING HOLDINGS LIMITED; *Int'l*, pg. 6938
SINGHOTEX CO., LTD.—See Max Weishaupt GmbH; *Int'l*, pg. 4735
SING HUAT HARDWARE & MACHINERY PTE., LTD.—See Miki Pulley Co., Ltd.; *Int'l*, pg. 4891
SING HUAT HARDWARE & MACHINERY SDN. BHD.—See Miki Pulley Co., Ltd.; *Int'l*, pg. 4891
SINGING BEACH CLUB INC.; *U.S. Private*, pg. 3670
THE SINGING MACHINE COMPANY, INC.; *U.S. Public*, pg. 2130
SINGING RIVER ELECTRIC POWER ASSOCIATION; *U.S. Private*, pg. 3670
SINGLANDE—See FAYAT SAS; *Int'l*, pg. 2626
SINGLE BUOY MOORINGS—See SBM Offshore N.V.; *Int'l*, pg. 6607
SINGLE DIGITS, INC.—See GI Manager L.P.; *U.S. Private*, pg. 1694
SING LEE SOFTWARE (GROUP) LIMITED; *Int'l*, pg. 6938
SINGLE PATH; *U.S. Private*, pg. 3670
SINGLEPLATFORM, LLC—See TripAdvisor, Inc.; *U.S. Public*, pg. 2195
SINGLE POINT ENERGY AND ENVIRONMENT CO., LTD.—See Nex Point Public Company Limited; *Int'l*, pg. 5239
SINGLEPOINT GROUP INTERNATIONAL, INC.; *Int'l*, pg. 6944
SINGLEPOINT INC.; *U.S. Public*, pg. 1888
SINGLE POINT PARTS (THAILAND) PUBLIC COMPANY LIMITED - FACTORY NO.2—See Nex Point Public Company Limited; *Int'l*, pg. 5239
SINGLER-ERNSTER INC.; *U.S. Private*, pg. 3670
SINGLESOURCE APPAREL, INC.—See GMI Holding, Inc.; *U.S. Private*, pg. 1722
SINGLE SOURCE PACKAGING CO. LLC.; *U.S. Private*, pg. 3670
SINGLE SOURCE ROOFING CORP; *U.S. Private*, pg. 3670
SINGLE SOURCE TECHNOLOGIES, INC.—See Makino Milling Machine Co., Ltd.; *Int'l*, pg. 4656
SINGLE SOURCE TECHNOLOGIES S. DE R.L. DE C.V.—See Makino Milling Machine Co., Ltd.; *Int'l*, pg. 4656
SINGLE STOP USA; *U.S. Private*, pg. 3670
SINGLE TEMPERIERTECHNIK GMBH—See Arbonia AG; *Int'l*, pg. 537
SINGLETON MARINE GROUP - BLUE CREEK MARINA AT LAKE MARTIN—See Singleton Marine Group; *U.S. Private*, pg. 3670
SINGLETON MARINE GROUP OF ATLANTA—See Singleton Marine Group; *U.S. Private*, pg. 3670
SINGLETON MARINE GROUP; *U.S. Private*, pg. 3670
SINGLETON MARINE GROUP YACHT CENTER AT HOLIDAY MARINA—See Singleton Marine Group; *U.S. Private*, pg. 3670
SINGLETON OGILVY & MATHER (HOLDINGS) PTY LIMITED—See WPP plc; *Int'l*, pg. 8462
SINGLETON OGILVY & MATHER PTY. LTD.—See WPP plc; *Int'l*, pg. 8488
SINGLETON OGILVY & MATHER (SYDNEY) PTY LIMITED—See WPP plc; *Int'l*, pg. 8462
SINGLETON & PARTNERS, LTD.; *U.S. Private*, pg. 3670
SINGLETON SEAFOOD—See Red Chamber Co.; *U.S. Private*, pg. 3373
SINGLE WELL INDUSTRIAL CORP.; *Int'l*, pg. 6944
SINGLE WELL METICULOUS INDUSTRY (KUNSHAN) CO., LTD.—See Single Well Industrial Corp.; *Int'l*, pg. 6944
SINGLIFE FINANCIAL ADVISERS PTE. LTD.—See Aviva plc; *Int'l*, pg. 746
SINGNET PTE. LTD.—See Temasek Holdings (Private) Limited; *Int'l*, pg. 7553
SINGSONG HOLDINGS CO., LTD.; *Int'l*, pg. 6944
SING TAO (CANADA) LIMITED—See SING TAO NEWS CORPORATION LIMITED; *Int'l*, pg. 6939
SING TAO NEWS CORPORATION LIMITED; *Int'l*, pg. 6939
SING TAO NEWSPAPER GROUP LIMITED—See SING TAO NEWS CORPORATION LIMITED; *Int'l*, pg. 6939

SING TAO NEWSPAPERS LOS ANGELES LTD.—See SING TAO NEWS CORPORATION LIMITED; *Int'l*, pg. 6939
SING TAO NEWSPAPERS NEW YORK LTD.—See SING TAO NEWS CORPORATION LIMITED; *Int'l*, pg. 6939
SING TAO NEWSPAPERS SAN FRANCISCO LTD.—See SING TAO NEWS CORPORATION LIMITED; *Int'l*, pg. 6939
SING TAO PUBLISHING LIMITED—See SING TAO NEWS CORPORATION LIMITED; *Int'l*, pg. 6939
SING TAO (U.K.) LTD.—See SING TAO NEWS CORPORATION LIMITED; *Int'l*, pg. 6939
SING TEC DEVELOPMENT PTE. LTD.—See SNT Holdings Co., Ltd.; *Int'l*, pg. 7029
SINGTEL INNOV8 VENTURES PTE. LTD.—See Temasek Holdings (Private) Limited; *Int'l*, pg. 7554
SINGTEL OPTUS PTY. LTD.—See Temasek Holdings (Private) Limited; *Int'l*, pg. 7553
SINGTEL STRATEGIC INVESTMENTS PTE LTD.—See Advanced Info Service Plc; *Int'l*, pg. 160
SINGTEL TAIWAN LIMITED—See Temasek Holdings (Private) Limited; *Int'l*, pg. 7553
SINGTEL VIETNAM—See Temasek Holdings (Private) Limited; *Int'l*, pg. 7553
SINGTEX INDUSTRIAL CO., LTD.; *Int'l*, pg. 6944
SINGULAR 3DP PTY. LTD.—See Singular Health Group Ltd.; *Int'l*, pg. 6944
SINGULAR GENOMICS SYSTEMS, INC.; *U.S. Public*, pg. 1888
SINGULAR HEALTH GROUP LTD.; *Int'l*, pg. 6944
SINGULARITY ACQUISITION CORP.; *U.S. Public*, pg. 1888
SINGULARITY FUTURE TECHNOLOGY LTD.; *U.S. Public*, pg. 1888
SINGULARLOGIC BUSINESS SERVICES S.A.—See Marfin Investment Group Holdings S.A.; *Int'l*, pg. 4692
SINGULARLOGIC CYPRUS LTD.—See Marfin Investment Group Holdings S.A.; *Int'l*, pg. 4692
SINGULARLOGIC INTEGRATOR S.A.—See Marfin Investment Group Holdings S.A.; *Int'l*, pg. 4692
SINGULAR LOGIC S.A—See Marfin Investment Group Holdings S.A.; *Int'l*, pg. 4692
SINGULEX, INC.; *U.S. Private*, pg. 3670
SINGULUS MANUFACTURING GUANGZOU LTD.—See Singulus Technologies AG; *Int'l*, pg. 6944
SINGULUS MASTERING B.V.—See Singulus Technologies AG; *Int'l*, pg. 6944
SINGULUS NANO DEPOSITION TECHNOLOGIES GMBH—See Singulus Technologies AG; *Int'l*, pg. 6944
SINGULUS STANGL SOLAR GMBH—See Singulus Technologies AG; *Int'l*, pg. 6944
SINGULUS TECHNOLOGIES AG; *Int'l*, pg. 6944
SINGULUS TECHNOLOGIES ASIA PACIFIC PTE. LTD.—See Singulus Technologies AG; *Int'l*, pg. 6944
SINGULUS TECHNOLOGIES FRANCE S.A.R.L.—See Singulus Technologies AG; *Int'l*, pg. 6945
SINGULUS TECHNOLOGIES IBERICA S.L.—See Singulus Technologies AG; *Int'l*, pg. 6944
SINGULUS TECHNOLOGIES, INC.—See Singulus Technologies AG; *Int'l*, pg. 6945
SINGULUS TECHNOLOGIES ITALIA SRL—See Singulus Technologies AG; *Int'l*, pg. 6945
SINGULUS TECHNOLOGIES LATIN AMERICA LTDA.—See Singulus Technologies AG; *Int'l*, pg. 6945
SINGULUS TECHNOLOGIES SHANGHAI CO., LTD.—See Singulus Technologies AG; *Int'l*, pg. 6945
SINGULUS TECHNOLOGIES TAIWAN LIMITED—See Singulus Technologies AG; *Int'l*, pg. 6944
SINGULUS VIKA CHINA LIMITED—See Singulus Technologies AG; *Int'l*, pg. 6945
SING YANG (OVERSEAS) LIMITED; *Int'l*, pg. 6939
SING YANG SERVICES LIMITED—See Tungtex (Holdings) Co. Ltd.; *Int'l*, pg. 7972
SING YANG TRADING LIMITED—See Tungtex (Holdings) Co. Ltd.; *Int'l*, pg. 7972
SIN HEAP LEE CONSTRUCTION SDN. BHD.—See SHL Consolidated Bhd.; *Int'l*, pg. 6856
SIN HEAP LEE DEVELOPMENT SDN. BHD.—See SHL Consolidated Bhd.; *Int'l*, pg. 6856
SIN HENG AERIAL LIFTS PTE. LTD.—See Sin Heng Heavy Machinery Limited; *Int'l*, pg. 6935
SIN HENG CHAN (MALAYA) BERHAD; *Int'l*, pg. 6935
SIN HENG HEAVY MACHINERY LIMITED; *Int'l*, pg. 6935
SIN HENG VINA CO. LTD.—See Sin Heng Heavy Machinery Limited; *Int'l*, pg. 6935
SINHER TECHNOLOGY INC.; *Int'l*, pg. 6945
SIN HONG HARDWARE PTE LTD—See Shinvest Holding Limited; *Int'l*, pg. 6849
SINHOO GROUP CO., LTD.—See Daeyang Electric Co., Ltd.; *Int'l*, pg. 1911
SINIAT B.V.—See Etex SA/NV; *Int'l*, pg. 2522
SINIAT GMBH—See Etex SA/NV; *Int'l*, pg. 2522
SINIAT INTERNATIONAL SA—See Etex SA/NV; *Int'l*, pg. 2522
SINIAT LIMITED—See Etex SA/NV; *Int'l*, pg. 2522
SINIAT NV—See Etex SA/NV; *Int'l*, pg. 2522
SINIAT SA—See Etex SA/NV; *Int'l*, pg. 2522
SINIAT S.P.A—See Etex SA/NV; *Int'l*, pg. 2522
SINIL PHARMACEUTICAL CO., LTD.; *Int'l*, pg. 6945

CORPORATE AFFILIATIONS

SINIORA FOOD INDUSTRIES COMPANY—See Siniora Food Industries P.L.C.; *Int'l*, pg. 6945
SINIORA FOOD INDUSTRIES P.L.C.; *Int'l*, pg. 6945
SINIORA GULF GENERAL TRADING CO., LLC—See Siniora Food Industries P.L.C.; *Int'l*, pg. 6945
SINIT, A.S.—See CEZ, a.s.; *Int'l*, pg. 1428
SINIUS GMBH—See Siemens Aktiengesellschaft; *Int'l*, pg. 6901
SINJIN LAND LIMITED; *Int'l*, pg. 6945
SINJIA PROPERTIES SDN. BHD.—See Sinjia Land Limited; *Int'l*, pg. 6945
SINJIN SM CO., LTD.; *Int'l*, pg. 6945
SINKANG INDUSTRIES CO., LTD.; *Int'l*, pg. 6945
SINKIANG O.R.G PACKAGING CONTAINER CO., LTD.—See ORG Technology Co., Ltd.; *Int'l*, pg. 5617
SINKO AIR CONDITIONING (H.K.) LIMITED—See Sinko Industries Ltd.; *Int'l*, pg. 6945
SINKO AIR CONDITIONING INDUSTRIES LTD. - KANAGAWA FACTORY—See Sinko Industries Ltd.; *Int'l*, pg. 6945
SINKO AIR CONDITIONING INDUSTRIES LTD.—See Sinko Industries Ltd.; *Int'l*, pg. 6945
SINKO AIR CONDITIONING (THAILAND) CO., LTD.—See Sinko Industries Ltd.; *Int'l*, pg. 6945
SINKO ATMOS CO., LTD.—See Sinko Industries Ltd.; *Int'l*, pg. 6945
SINKO-BANK, LTD.; *Int'l*, pg. 6946
SINKO INDUSTRIES LTD.; *Int'l*, pg. 6945
SINKO KUCHO SERVICE CO., LTD.—See Sinko Industries Ltd.; *Int'l*, pg. 6946
SINLAND DEVELOPMENT PTE, LTD.—See China Machinery Engineering Corporation; *Int'l*, pg. 1516
SIN LINE TEK ELECTRONIC CO. SDN. BHD.—See Taiwan Line Tek Electronic Co., Ltd.; *Int'l*, pg. 7422
SINLIPLAS HOLDING SDN. BHD.—See SLP Resources Berhad; *Int'l*, pg. 6998
SINLIPLAS SDN. BHD.—See SLP Resources Berhad; *Int'l*, pg. 6998
SINLOIHI CO,, LTD.—See Dai Nippon Toryo Co., Ltd.; *Int'l*, pg. 1916
SINMAG EQUIPMENT CORP.; *Int'l*, pg. 6946
SINMAH AXIS HEALTHCARE SDN. BHD.—See Malaysia Airports Holdings Berhad; *Int'l*, pg. 4661
SINMAH CAPITAL BERHAD; *Int'l*, pg. 6946
SINMAH DEVELOPMENT SDN. BHD.—See Sinmah Capital Berhad; *Int'l*, pg. 6946
SINMED B.V.—See Roper Technologies, Inc.; *U.S. Public*, pg. 1813
SINMIX PTE. LTD—See Lian Beng Group Ltd.; *Int'l*, pg. 4481
SINNAR BIDI UDYOG LIMITED; *Int'l*, pg. 6946
SINNERSCHRADER AKTIENGESELLSCHAFT—See Accenture plc; *Int'l*, pg. 88
SINNERSCHRADER COMMERCE GMBH—See Accenture plc; *Int'l*, pg. 88
SINNERSCHRADER CONTENT GMBH—See Accenture plc; *Int'l*, pg. 88
SINNERSCHRADER DEUTSCHLAND GMBH—See Accenture plc; *Int'l*, pg. 88
SINNERSCHRADER PRAHA S.R.O.—See Accenture plc; *Int'l*, pg. 88
SINNSUPTAWEE ASSET MANAGEMENT CO., LTD.—See Bangkok Bank Public Company Limited; *Int'l*, pg. 833
SINO ACHIEVE LIMITED—See Link-Asia International MedTech Group Limited; *Int'l*, pg. 4514
SINO-AGRI LEADING BIOSCIENCES CO., LTD.; *Int'l*, pg. 6948
SINOAGRO CHEMICALS CO., LTD.—See Hailir Pesticides & Chemicals Group; *Int'l*, pg. 3211
SINO AGRO FOOD, INC.; *Int'l*, pg. 6946
SINO AG; *Int'l*, pg. 6946
SINO AMERICAN MACHINERY CORPORATION—See China Machinery Engineering Corporation; *Int'l*, pg. 1516
SINO-AMERICAN OIL COMPANY; *U.S. Public*, pg. 1888
SINO-AMERICAN SHANGHAI SQUIBB PHARMACEUTICALS LTD—See Bristol-Myers Squibb Company; *U.S. Public*, pg. 387
SINO-AMERICAN SILICON PRODUCTS INC.; *Int'l*, pg. 6948
SINO-AMERICAN TIANJIN SMITH KLINE & FRENCH LABORATORIES LTD—See GSK plc; *Int'l*, pg. 3149
SINO ASSURANCE INC.; *Int'l*, pg. 6946
SINOBANGLA INDUSTRIES LIMITED; *Int'l*, pg. 6949
SINO-BELGIAN BEER (SUZHOU) CO., LTD.—See The Far Eastern Group; *Int'l*, pg. 7642
SINO BIOENERGY CORP.; *Int'l*, pg. 6946
SINO BIOLOGICAL EUROPE GMBH—See Sino Biological Inc.; *Int'l*, pg. 6946
SINO BIOLOGICAL INC.; *Int'l*, pg. 6946
SINO BIOLOGICAL JAPAN INC.—See Sino Biological Inc.; *Int'l*, pg. 6946
SINO BIOLOGICAL US INC.—See Sino Biological Inc.; *Int'l*, pg. 6946
SINO BIOPHARMACEUTICAL LIMITED; *Int'l*, pg. 6946
SINOBIOPHARMA, INC.; *Int'l*, pg. 6949
SINO BRIGHT INTERNATIONAL TRADING LIMITED—See EcoGreen International Group Limited; *Int'l*, pg. 2295
SINOCARE INC.; *Int'l*, pg. 6949

COMPANY NAME INDEX

SINOCELLTECH GROUP LTD.; *Int'l*, pg. 6949
SINOCHEM AMERICAN HOLDINGS INC.—See Sinochem Corporation; *Int'l*, pg. 6950
SINOCHEM ASIA HOLDINGS CO., LTD.—See Sinochem Corporation; *Int'l*, pg. 6950
SINOCHEM CORPORATION; *Int'l*, pg. 6949
SINOCHEM ELECTRONIC INFORMATION TECHNOLOGY CO.—See Sinochem Corporation; *Int'l*, pg. 6950
SINOCHEM EUROPE HOLDINGS PLC—See Sinochem Corporation; *Int'l*, pg. 6950
SINOCHEM FERTILIZER CO., LTD.—See Sinochem Corporation; *Int'l*, pg. 6951
SINOCHEM FERTILIZER MACAO COMMERCIAL OFFSHORE LIMITED—See Sinochem Corporation; *Int'l*, pg. 6950
SINOCHEM FINANCE CO., LTD.—See Sinochem Corporation; *Int'l*, pg. 6950
SINOCHEM FRANSHION PROPERTY (BEIJING) CO., LTD.—See Sinochem Corporation; *Int'l*, pg. 6950
SINOCHEM GUANGDONG IMPORT AND EXPORT CORPORATION—See Sinochem Corporation; *Int'l*, pg. 6950
SINOCHEM HEBEI CORPORATION—See Sinochem Corporation; *Int'l*, pg. 6950
SINOCHEM HONG KONG INVESTMENT CO., LTD.—See Sinochem Corporation; *Int'l*, pg. 6950
SINOCHEM INTERNATIONAL ADVERTISING & EXHIBITION CO. LTD.—See Sinochem Corporation; *Int'l*, pg. 6950
SINOCHEM INTERNATIONAL CHEMICALS (HONG KONG) CO. LTD.—See Sinochem Corporation; *Int'l*, pg. 6950
SINOCHEM INTERNATIONAL CORPORATION—See Sinochem Corporation; *Int'l*, pg. 6950
SINOCHEM INTERNATIONAL HOTEL AND PROPERTY MANAGEMENT CO., LTD.—See Sinochem Corporation; *Int'l*, pg. 6950
SINOCHEM INTERNATIONAL INDUSTRY CO. LTD.—See Sinochem Corporation; *Int'l*, pg. 6950
SINOCHEM INTERNATIONAL OIL CO.—See Sinochem Corporation; *Int'l*, pg. 6950
SINOCHEM INTERNATIONAL OIL (HONG KONG) CO., LTD.—See Sinochem Corporation; *Int'l*, pg. 6950
SINOCHEM INTERNATIONAL OIL (LONDON) CO., LTD.—See Sinochem Corporation; *Int'l*, pg. 6950
SINOCHEM INTERNATIONAL OIL (SINGAPORE) PTE. LTD.—See Sinochem Corporation; *Int'l*, pg. 6950
SINOCHEM INTERNATIONAL OIL (TIANJIN) CO., LTD.—See Sinochem Corporation; *Int'l*, pg. 6950
SINOCHEM INTERNATIONAL TENDERING CO., LTD.—See Sinochem Corporation; *Int'l*, pg. 6950
SINOCHEM INVESTMENT (SINGAPORE) CO., LTD.—See Sinochem Corporation; *Int'l*, pg. 6950
SINOCHEM JAPAN CO. LTD.—See Sinochem Corporation; *Int'l*, pg. 6950
SINOCHEM JIANGSU CO., LTD.—See Sinochem Corporation; *Int'l*, pg. 6950
SINOCHEM KOREA CO., LTD.—See Sinochem Corporation; *Int'l*, pg. 6950
SINOCHEM LIAONING—See Sinochem Corporation; *Int'l*, pg. 6950
SINOCHEM NINGBO IMPORT & EXPORT CO.—See Sinochem Corporation; *Int'l*, pg. 6950
SINOCHEM OIL ANHUI CO., LTD.—See Sinochem Corporation; *Int'l*, pg. 6950
SINOCHEM OIL FUJIAN CO., LTD.—See Sinochem Corporation; *Int'l*, pg. 6950
SINOCHEM OIL GUANGDONG CO., LTD.—See Sinochem Corporation; *Int'l*, pg. 6950
SINOCHEM OIL HUNAN CO., LTD.—See Sinochem Corporation; *Int'l*, pg. 6950
SINOCHEM OIL JIANGSU CO., LTD.—See Sinochem Corporation; *Int'l*, pg. 6950
SINOCHEM OIL JIANGXI CO., LTD.—See Sinochem Corporation; *Int'l*, pg. 6951
SINOCHEM OIL LIAONING CO., LTD.—See Sinochem Corporation; *Int'l*, pg. 6951
SINOCHEM OIL SHANDONG CO., LTD.—See Sinochem Corporation; *Int'l*, pg. 6951
SINOCHEM OIL SHANXI CO., LTD.—See Sinochem Corporation; *Int'l*, pg. 6951
SINOCHEM OIL ZHEJIANG CO., LTD.—See Sinochem Corporation; *Int'l*, pg. 6951
SINOCHEM PETROLEO BRAZIL LIMITED—See Sinochem Corporation; *Int'l*, pg. 6951
SINOCHEM PETROLEUM EXPLORATION AND PRODUCTION CO., LTD.—See Sinochem Corporation; *Int'l*, pg. 6951
SINOCHEM PETROLEUM NETHERLANDS COOPERATIEF U.A.—See Sinochem Corporation; *Int'l*, pg. 6951
SINOCHEM PLASTICS CO. LTD.—See Sinochem Corporation; *Int'l*, pg. 6951
SINOCHEM PUDONG TRADING CO., LTD.—See Sinochem Corporation; *Int'l*, pg. 6951
SINOCHEM QINGDAO CO., LTD.—See Sinochem Corporation; *Int'l*, pg. 6951
SINOCHEM QUANZHOU PETROCHEMICAL CO., LTD.—See Sinochem Corporation; *Int'l*, pg. 6951
SINOCHEM SHANGHAI IMPORT AND EXPORT CORP.—See Sinochem Corporation; *Int'l*, pg. 6951
SINOCHEM TIANJIN CO. LTD.—See Sinochem Corporation; *Int'l*, pg. 6951
SINOCHEM TRADING (SINGAPORE) PTE. LTD.—See Sinochem Corporation; *Int'l*, pg. 6951
SINOCHEM (UNITED KINGDOM) LTD.—See Sinochem Corporation; *Int'l*, pg. 6950
SINOCHEM (U.S.A.) INC.—See Sinochem Corporation; *Int'l*, pg. 6950
SINOCHEM XINGZHONG OIL STAGING (ZHOUSHAN) CO., LTD.)—See Sinochem Corporation; *Int'l*, pg. 6950
SINOCHEM YANTAI CROP NUTRITION CO., LTD.—See Sinochem Corporation; *Int'l*, pg. 6951
SINOCHEM YUNLONG CO., LTD.—See Sinochem Corporation; *Int'l*, pg. 6951
SINO CHINA ENTERPRISES LIMITED—See CK Asset Holdings Limited; *Int'l*, pg. 1635
SINO CLEAN ENERGY INC.; *Int'l*, pg. 6946
SINOCLOUD GROUP LIMITED; *Int'l*, pg. 6951
SINOCOM JAPAN CORPORATION—See Glory Sun Financial Group Limited; *Int'l*, pg. 3011
SINOCOM PHARMACEUTICAL, INC.; *Int'l*, pg. 6951
SINO-CRYSTAL PRECISION MANUFACTURING CO., LTD.—See Zhengzhou Sino-Crystal Diamond Co., Ltd.; *Int'l*, pg. 8670
SINO DAREN CO. LTD.; *Int'l*, pg. 6946
SINODATA CO., LTD.; *Int'l*, pg. 6951
SINO DEVELOPMENT (TIANJIN) INTERNATIONAL TRADING CO., LTD.—See Samson Paper Holdings Limited; *Int'l*, pg. 6509
SINO ELECTRONICS LIMITED—See Central Wealth Group Holdings Limited; *Int'l*, pg. 1410
SINOENERGY CORPORATION; *Int'l*, pg. 6951
SINO ENERGY INTERNATIONAL HOLDINGS GROUP LIMITED; *Int'l*, pg. 6946
SINO-ENTERTAINMENT TECHNOLOGY HOLDINGS LTD.; *Int'l*, pg. 6948
SINO ENVIRONMENTAL SERVICES CORP.—See CTCI Corporation; *Int'l*, pg. 1870
SINOFERT HOLDINGS LIMITED—See Sinochem Corporation; *Int'l*, pg. 6951
SINOFIBERS TECHNOLOGY CO., LTD.; *Int'l*, pg. 6951
SINO-FOREST (SUZHOU) TRADING CO. LTD.—See Emerald Plantation Holdings Limited; *Int'l*, pg. 2378
SINOFORTUNE FINANICIAL HOLDINGS LIMITED; *Int'l*, pg. 6951
SINO FRENCH WATER DEVELOPMENT CO. LTD.—See Veolia Environnement S.A.; *Int'l*, pg. 8156
SINO GAS & ENERGY HOLDINGS LIMITED—See Lone Star Global Acquisitions, LLC; *U.S. Private*, pg. 2489
SINO GAS & ENERGY LIMITED—See Lone Star Global Acquisitions, LLC; *U.S. Private*, pg. 2489
SINO GAS HOLDINGS GROUP LIMITED; *Int'l*, pg. 6947
SINOGAS WEST INC.; *Int'l*, pg. 6951
SINO GEOPHYSICAL CO., LTD.; *Int'l*, pg. 6947
SINO-GERMAN UNITED AG; *Int'l*, pg. 6948
SINO-GLOBAL SHIPPING AGENCY LIMITED—See Singularity Future Technology Ltd.; *U.S. Public*, pg. 1888
SINO-GLOBAL SHIPPING CANADA INC.—See Singularity Future Technology Ltd.; *U.S. Public*, pg. 1888
SINO-GLOBAL SHIPPING (HK) LTD.—See Singularity Future Technology Ltd.; *U.S. Public*, pg. 1888
SINO GOLF HOLDINGS LTD.; *Int'l*, pg. 6947
SINO GOLF LEISURE COMPANY LTD.—See Sino Golf Holdings Ltd.; *Int'l*, pg. 6947
SINO GOLF MANUFACTURING CO. LTD.—See Sino Golf Holdings Ltd.; *Int'l*, pg. 6947
SINO GRANDNESS FOOD INDUSTRY GROUP LIMITED; *Int'l*, pg. 6947
SINO GREAT WALL CO., LTD.; *Int'l*, pg. 6947
SINO GREEN LAND CORPORATION; *Int'l*, pg. 6947
SINO HARBOUR HOLDINGS GROUP LIMITED; *Int'l*, pg. 6947
SINOHEALTH HOLDINGS LIMITED; *Int'l*, pg. 6951
SINO-HIGH (CHINA) CO., LTD.; *Int'l*, pg. 6948
SINO HOLDINGS (S'PORE) PTE LTD.—See TA Corporation Ltd.; *Int'l*, pg. 7399
SINOHOPE TECHNOLOGY HOLDINGS LIMITED; *Int'l*, pg. 6951
SINO HORIZON HOLDINGS LIMITED; *Int'l*, pg. 6947
SINO HOTELS (HOLDINGS) LIMITED—See Tsim Sha Tsui Properties Limited; *Int'l*, pg. 7951
SINOHUB ELECTRONICS SHENZHEN, LTD.—See SINOHUB, INC.; *Int'l*, pg. 6952
SINOHUB, INC.; *Int'l*, pg. 6952
SINOHYDRO CORPORATION—See Power Construction Corporation of China; *Int'l*, pg. 5943
SINO IC TECHNOLOGY CO., LTD.—See Shanghai Fudan Microelectronics Group Co., Ltd.; *Int'l*, pg. 6768
SINO ICT HOLDINGS LIMITED; *Int'l*, pg. 6947
SINOI GMBH—See China National Building Material Group Co., Ltd.; *Int'l*, pg. 1526
SINO INVESTMENT SERVICES PTY. LTD.—See Sino Strategic International Limited; *Int'l*, pg. 6947
SINO-I TECHNOLOGY LIMITED; *Int'l*, pg. 6948
SINO-JAPAN CHEMICAL CO., LTD.—See Nippon Shokubai Co., Ltd.; *Int'l*, pg. 5333

SINOMINE RESOURCE GROUP CO., LTD.

SINO-JAPAN STAFFTRAINING & DISPATCH CO., LTD.—See nms Holdings Corporation; *Int'l*, pg. 5393
SINO LAND COMPANY LIMITED—See Tsim Sha Tsui Properties Limited; *Int'l*, pg. 7951
SINO-LIFE GROUP LIMITED; *Int'l*, pg. 6952
SINO LIFE INSURANCE CO., LTD.—See Tokio Marine Holdings, Inc.; *Int'l*, pg. 7783
SINOLIGHT CORPORATION; *Int'l*, pg. 6952
SINOLINK ELECTRIC POWER COMPANY LIMITED—See Oshidori International Holdings Limited; *Int'l*, pg. 5650
SINOLINK FINANCIAL LEASING CO., LTD.—See Vibrant Group Limited; *Int'l*, pg. 8184
SINOLINK INTERNATIONAL INVESTMENT (GROUP) LIMITED—See Sinolink Worldwide Holdings Limited; *Int'l*, pg. 6952
SINOLINK LPG INVESTMENT LIMITED—See Oshidori International Holdings Limited; *Int'l*, pg. 5650
SINOLINK POWER INVESTMENT LTD—See Oshidori International Holdings Limited; *Int'l*, pg. 5650
SINOLINK PROPERTIES AGENT LIMITED—See Sinolink Worldwide Holdings Limited; *Int'l*, pg. 6952
SINOLINK SECURITIES CO., LTD.; *Int'l*, pg. 6952
SINOLINK WORLDWIDE HOLDINGS LIMITED; *Int'l*, pg. 6952
SINOLINK WORLDWIDE LTD—See Sinolink Worldwide Holdings Limited; *Int'l*, pg. 6952
SINOMA ADVANCED MATERIALS CO. LTD.—See China National Materials; *Int'l*, pg. 1532
SINOMAB BIOSCIENCE LIMITED; *Int'l*, pg. 6952
SINOMACH AUTOMOBILE CO., LTD.—See China National Machinery Industry Corporation; *Int'l*, pg. 1531
SINOMACH CAPITAL MANAGEMENT CORPORATION—See China National Machinery Industry Corporation; *Int'l*, pg. 1531
SINOMACH GENERAL MACHINERY SCIENCE & TECHNOLOGY CO., LTD.; *Int'l*, pg. 6952
SINOMACH PRECISION INDUSTRY CO., LTD.; *Int'l*, pg. 6952
SINOMACH PRECISION INDUSTRY CO., LTD.—See China National Machinery Industry Corporation; *Int'l*, pg. 1531
SINOMA ENERGY CONSERVATION LTD.—See China National Building Material Group Co., Ltd.; *Int'l*, pg. 1526
SINOMAG TECHNOLOGY CO., LTD.; *Int'l*, pg. 6952
SINOMA (HANDAN) CONSTRUCTION CO., LTD.—See Sinoma International Engineering Co., Ltd.; *Int'l*, pg. 6952
SINOMA INTERNATIONAL ENGINEERING CO., LTD.; *Int'l*, pg. 6952
SINOMA INTERNATIONAL ENVIRONMENTAL ENGINEERING CO., LTD.—See Sinoma International Engineering Co., Ltd.; *Int'l*, pg. 6952
SINOMA JINJING FIBER GLASS CO., LTD.—See China National Materials; *Int'l*, pg. 1532
SINO MANUFACTURING SERVICE CORPORATION—See nms Holdings Corporation; *Int'l*, pg. 5393
SINO-MAPLE (SHANGHAI) CO., LTD.—See Emerald Plantation Holdings Limited; *Int'l*, pg. 2378
SINO-MAPLE (SHANGHAI) TRADING CO., LTD.—See Emerald Plantation Holdings Limited; *Int'l*, pg. 2378
SINOMART TRANSPORT CO., LTD.—See China Merchants Group Limited; *Int'l*, pg. 1522
SINOMA SCIENCE & TECHNOLOGY CO., LTD.—See China National Materials; *Int'l*, pg. 1532
SINOMA (SUZHOU) CONSTRUCTION CO., LTD.—See Sinoma International Engineering Co., Ltd.; *Int'l*, pg. 6952
SINOMA TANGSHAN HEAVY MACHINERY CO., LTD.—See Sinoma International Engineering Co., Ltd.; *Int'l*, pg. 6952
SINOMAX GROUP LIMITED; *Int'l*, pg. 6953
SINOMAX SECURITIES LIMITED—See Fu Shek Financial Holdings Limited; *Int'l*, pg. 2801
SINOMAX USA, INC.—See Sinomax Group Limited; *Int'l*, pg. 6953
SINOMA YANZHOU MINING ENGINEERING CO., LTD.—See China National Materials; *Int'l*, pg. 1532
SINOMED B.V.—See Sino Medical Sciences Technology, Inc.; *Int'l*, pg. 6947
SINOMEDIA (ASIA PACIFIC) COMPANY LIMITED—See SinoMedia Holding Limited; *Int'l*, pg. 6953
SINOMEDIA GLOBAL PTE. LTD.—See SinoMedia Holding Limited; *Int'l*, pg. 6953
SINOMEDIA HOLDING LIMITED; *Int'l*, pg. 6953
SINO MEDICAL SCIENCES TECHNOLOGY, INC.; *Int'l*, pg. 6947
SINOMED K.K.—See Sino Medical Sciences Technology, Inc.; *Int'l*, pg. 6947
SINOMEM TECHNOLOGY LIMITED—See CDH China Management Company Limited; *Int'l*, pg. 1370
SINOMINE DRC RESOURCES EXPLORATION SARL—See Sinomine Resource Group Co., Ltd.; *Int'l*, pg. 6953
SINOMINE OVERSEAS GEO-TECH SERVICES (TIANJIN) CO., LTD.—See Sinomine Resource Group Co., Ltd.; *Int'l*, pg. 6953
SINOMINE RESOURCE GROUP CO., LTD.; *Int'l*, pg. 6953

Company Index

SINOMINE RESOURCE GROUP CO., LTD. CORPORATE AFFILIATIONS

SINOMINE RESOURCE (MALAYSIA) SDN. BHD.—See Sinomine Resource Group Co., Ltd.; *Int'l*, pg. 6953
SINOMINE SPECIALTY FLUIDS LIMITED—See Sinomine Resource Group Co., Ltd.; *Int'l*, pg. 6953
SINOMINE ZAMBIA TRADING COMPANY LIMITED—See Sinomine Resource Group Co., Ltd.; *Int'l*, pg. 6953
SINON AUSTRALIA PTY. LIMITED—See Sinon Corporation; *Int'l*, pg. 6953
SINON CHEMICAL (CHINA) CO., LTD.—See Sinon Corporation; *Int'l*, pg. 6953
SINON CORPORATION; *Int'l*, pg. 6953
SINON DO BRASIL LTDA—See Sinon Corporation; *Int'l*, pg. 6953
SINON EU GMBH—See Sinon Corporation; *Int'l*, pg. 6953
SINONONFERROUS METALS RESOURCES (ZIMBABWE) (PRIVATE) LTD.—See Sinomine Resource Group Co., Ltd.; *Int'l*, pg. 6953
SINON ORCHID GARDEN, INC.—See Sinon Corporation; *Int'l*, pg. 6953
SINON PROFESSIONAL BASEBALL CO., LTD.—See Sinon Corporation; *Int'l*, pg. 6953
SINON (THAILAND) CO., LTD.—See Sinon Corporation; *Int'l*, pg. 6953
SINON USA, INC.—See Sinon Corporation; *Int'l*, pg. 6953
SINO-OCEAN GROUP HOLDINGS LIMITED; *Int'l*, pg. 6949
SINO OIL AND GAS HOLDINGS LIMITED; *Int'l*, pg. 6947
SINOPAC ASSET MANAGEMENT (ASIA) LTD.—See SinoPac Financial Holdings Company Ltd.; *Int'l*, pg. 6954
SINOPAC ASSET MANAGEMENT CORPORATION—See SinoPac Financial Holdings Company Ltd.; *Int'l*, pg. 6954
SINOPAC CALL CENTER CO., LTD.—See SinoPac Financial Holdings Company Ltd.; *Int'l*, pg. 6954
SINOPAC CAPITAL LTD.—See SinoPac Financial Holdings Company Ltd.; *Int'l*, pg. 6954
SINOPAC CARD SERVICES CO., LTD.—See SinoPac Financial Holdings Company Ltd.; *Int'l*, pg. 6954
SINOPAC FINANCIAL CONSULTING CO., LTD.—See SinoPac Financial Holdings Company Ltd.; *Int'l*, pg. 6954
SINOPAC FINANCIAL HOLDINGS COMPANY LTD.; *Int'l*, pg. 6953
SINOPAC FUTURES (ASIA) LTD.—See SinoPac Financial Holdings Company Ltd.; *Int'l*, pg. 6954
SINOPAC FUTURES CORP.—See SinoPac Financial Holdings Company Ltd.; *Int'l*, pg. 6954
SINOPAC INTERNATIONAL LEASING CORP.—See SinoPac Financial Holdings Company Ltd.; *Int'l*, pg. 6954
SINOPAC LEASING CORPORATION—See SinoPac Financial Holdings Company Ltd.; *Int'l*, pg. 6954
SINOPAC LEASING (TIANJIN) CO., LTD.—See SinoPac Financial Holdings Company Ltd.; *Int'l*, pg. 6954
SINOPAC LIFE INSURANCE AGENT CO., LTD.—See SinoPac Financial Holdings Company Ltd.; *Int'l*, pg. 6954
SINOPAC PROPERTY INSURANCE AGENT CO., LTD.—See SinoPac Financial Holdings Company Ltd.; *Int'l*, pg. 6954
SINOPAC SECURITIES (ASIA) LTD.—See SinoPac Financial Holdings Company Ltd.; *Int'l*, pg. 6954
SINOPAC SECURITIES (ASIA) NOMINEES LTD.—See SinoPac Financial Holdings Company Ltd.; *Int'l*, pg. 6954
SINOPAC SECURITIES CO. LTD.—See SinoPac Financial Holdings Company Ltd.; *Int'l*, pg. 6954
SINOPAC SECURITIES (EUROPE) LTD.—See SinoPac Financial Holdings Company Ltd.; *Int'l*, pg. 6954
SINOPAC SECURITIES INVESTMENT SERVICES CORP.—See SinoPac Financial Holdings Company Ltd.; *Int'l*, pg. 6954
SINOPAC SECURITIES INVESTMENT TRUST CORPORATION—See SinoPac Financial Holdings Company Ltd.; *Int'l*, pg. 6954
SINOPAC SOLUTIONS & SERVICES LTD.—See SinoPac Financial Holdings Company Ltd.; *Int'l*, pg. 6954
SINOPAC VENTURE CAPITAL CO., LTD.—See SinoPac Financial Holdings Company Ltd.; *Int'l*, pg. 6954
SINO-PANEL (ASIA) INC.—See Emerald Plantation Holdings Limited; *Int'l*, pg. 2378
SINO-PANEL (CHINA) INVESTMENTS LIMITED—See Emerald Plantation Holdings Limited; *Int'l*, pg. 2378
SINO-PANEL (GUANGXI) LIMITED—See Emerald Plantation Holdings Limited; *Int'l*, pg. 2378
SINO-PANEL (GUANGZHOU) LIMITED—See Emerald Plantation Holdings Limited; *Int'l*, pg. 2378
SINOPEC ASSETS MANAGEMENT CO LTD; *Int'l*, pg. 6954
SINOPEC BEIJING YANHUA PETROCHEMICAL COMPANY LIMITED—See China Petrochemical Corporation; *Int'l*, pg. 1539
SINOPEC CHEMICAL SALES COMPANY—See China Petrochemical Corporation; *Int'l*, pg. 1539
SINOPEC & CRM OIL MARKETING CO., LTD.—See China Railway Materials Co., Ltd.; *Int'l*, pg. 1544
SINOPEC DAYLIGHT ENERGY LTD.—See China Petrochemical Corporation; *Int'l*, pg. 1540
SINOPEC ENGINEERING (GROUP) CO. LTD.—See China Petrochemical Corporation; *Int'l*, pg. 1540
SINOPEC FUEL OIL SALES CO., LTD—See China Petrochemical Corporation; *Int'l*, pg. 1540
SINOPEC FUEL OIL (SINGAPORE) PTE. LTD.—See China Petrochemical Corporation; *Int'l*, pg. 1540
SINOPEC FUJIAN REFINING & CHEMICAL CO., LTD.—See China Petrochemical Corporation; *Int'l*, pg. 1539
SINOPEC GUANGZHOU COMPANY—See China Petrochemical Corporation; *Int'l*, pg. 1539
SINOPEC (HONG KONG) LIMITED—See China Petrochemical Corporation; *Int'l*, pg. 1539
SINOPEC INTERNATIONAL PETROLEUM EXPLORATION & PRODUCTION CORPORATION—See China Petrochemical Corporation; *Int'l*, pg. 1540
SINOPEC KANTONS HOLDINGS LIMITED; *Int'l*, pg. 6954
SINOPEC OILFIELD EQUIPMENT CORPORATION—See China Petrochemical Corporation; *Int'l*, pg. 1540
SINOPEC OILFIELD SERVICE CORPORATION—See China Petrochemical Corporation; *Int'l*, pg. 1540
SINOPEC QILU PETROCHEMICAL CO., LTD.—See China Petrochemical Corporation; *Int'l*, pg. 1539
SINOPEC SALES COMPANY, LTD.—See China Petrochemical Corporation; *Int'l*, pg. 1539
SINOPEC SHANDONG TAISHAN PETROLEUM CO., LTD.; *Int'l*, pg. 6954
SINOPEC SHANGHAI PETROCHEMICAL COMPANY LIMITED—See China Petrochemical Corporation; *Int'l*, pg. 1539
SINOPEC SHENGLI OILFIELD CO., LTD.—See China Petrochemical Corporation; *Int'l*, pg. 1539
SINOPEC TAISHAN OIL PRODUCTS CO., LTD.—See China Petrochemical Corporation; *Int'l*, pg. 1539
SINOPEC WUHAN PHOENIX CO., LTD.—See China Petrochemical Corporation; *Int'l*, pg. 1540
SINOPEC ZHENHAI REFINING & CHEMICAL CO., LTD.—See China Petrochemical Corporation; *Int'l*, pg. 1540
SINOPEP-ALLSINO BIOPHARMACEUTICAL CO., LTD.; *Int'l*, pg. 6954
SINOPHARM BIO-PHARMACEUTICAL CO., LTD.—See SINOPHARM Group Co., Ltd.; *Int'l*, pg. 6954
SINOPHARM GROUP CO., LTD.; *Int'l*, pg. 6954
SINOPHARM HOLDING GUANGDONG XINLONG CO., LTD.—See SINOPHARM Group Co., Ltd.; *Int'l*, pg. 6954
SINOPHARM HOLDING LIUZHOU CO., LTD.—See SINOPHARM Group Co., Ltd.; *Int'l*, pg. 6954
SINOPHARM HOLDING NANNING CO., LTD.—See SINOPHARM Group Co., Ltd.; *Int'l*, pg. 6954
SINOPHARM HOLDING NINGXIA CO., LTD.—See SINOPHARM Group Co., Ltd.; *Int'l*, pg. 6954
SINOPHARM HOLDING SHENYANG CO., LTD.—See SINOPHARM Group Co., Ltd.; *Int'l*, pg. 6955
SINOPHARM MEDICINE HOLDING CO., LTD.—See China National Pharmaceutical Group Corporation; *Int'l*, pg. 1534
SINOPHARM TECH HOLDINGS LIMITED; *Int'l*, pg. 6955
SINOPHARM UNITED ENGINEERING COMPANY LTD.—See China National Pharmaceutical Group Corporation; *Int'l*, pg. 1534
SINO-PLATINUM METALS CO., LTD.; *Int'l*, pg. 6949
SINOPOWER SEMICONDUCTOR, INC.; *Int'l*, pg. 6955
SINO PROSPER GROUP HOLDINGS LTD.; *Int'l*, pg. 6947
SINOPS, INC.; *Int'l*, pg. 6955
SINORA SDN BHD—See Priceworth International Berhad; *Int'l*, pg. 5973
SINOR ENGINE COMPANY, INC.—See Arcline Investment Management LP; *U.S. Private*, pg. 313
SINO RICHFIELD PTE. LTD.—See Chu Kong Petroleum and Natural Gas Steel Pipe Holdings Limited; *Int'l*, pg. 1589
SINOSAFE GENERAL INSURANCE CO., LTD.; *Int'l*, pg. 6955
SINO SANTA FE INTERNATIONAL SERVICES CORPORATION—See EAC Invest AS; *Int'l*, pg. 2262
SINO SANTA FE REAL ESTATE (BEIJING) CO. LTD.—See EAC Invest AS; *Int'l*, pg. 2262
SINOSEAL HOLDING CO., LTD.; *Int'l*, pg. 6955
SINO SECURITY SERVICES LIMITED—See Tsim Sha Tsui Properties Limited; *Int'l*, pg. 7951
SINOSHEEL XINGTAI MACHINERY & MILL ROLL CO., LTD.—See Sinosteel Corporation; *Int'l*, pg. 6955
SINOSOFT CO., LTD.; *Int'l*, pg. 6955
SINOSOFT TECHNOLOGY GROUP LIMITED; *Int'l*, pg. 6955
SINOSOFT TECHNOLOGY PLC; *Int'l*, pg. 6955
SINO SPLENDID HOLDINGS LIMITED; *Int'l*, pg. 6947
SINOSTAR CABLE CO., LTD.; *Int'l*, pg. 6955
SINOSTAR PEC HOLDINGS LIMITED; *Int'l*, pg. 6955
SINOSTEEL AUSTRALIA PTY. LTD.—See Sinosteel Corporation; *Int'l*, pg. 6955
SINOSTEEL CORPORATION; *Int'l*, pg. 6955
SINOSTEEL ENGINEERING & TECHNOLOGY CO., LTD.; *Int'l*, pg. 6955
SINOSTEEL EQUIPMENT & ENGINEERING (BOLVIA) LTDA.—See Sinosteel Engineering & Technology Co., Ltd.; *Int'l*, pg. 6955
SINOSTEEL EQUIPMENT & ENGINEERING (SAUDI ARABIA) COMPANY—See Sinosteel Engineering & Technology Co., Ltd.; *Int'l*, pg. 6955
SINOSTEEL EQUIPMENT & ENGINEERING (TURKEY) CO., LTD.—See Sinosteel Engineering & Technology Co., Ltd.; *Int'l*, pg. 6955
SINOSTEEL LUOYANG INSTITUTE OF REFRACTORIES RESEARCH CO., LTD.—See Sinosteel Corporation; *Int'l*, pg. 6955
SINOSTEEL METALS & RESOURCES CO., LTD.—See Sinosteel Corporation; *Int'l*, pg. 6955
SINOSTEEL NEW MATERIALS CO., LTD.; *Int'l*, pg. 6955
SINOSTEEL PROJECT & TECHNOLOGY (BRAZIL) LTDA.—See Sinosteel Engineering & Technology Co., Ltd.; *Int'l*, pg. 6955
SINOSTEEL REFRACTORY CO., LTD.—See Sinosteel Corporation; *Int'l*, pg. 6955
SINOSTEEL SHENZHEN CO., LTD.—See Sinosteel Corporation; *Int'l*, pg. 6955
SINOSTEEL XI'AN HEAVY MACHINERY CO., LTD.—See Sinosteel Corporation; *Int'l*, pg. 6955
SINOSTEEL ZHENGZHOU RESEARCH INSTITUTE OF STEEL WIRE & STEEL WIRE PRODUCTS CO., LTD.—See Sinosteel Corporation; *Int'l*, pg. 6955
SINOSTONE (GUANGDONG) CO., LTD.; *Int'l*, pg. 6955
SINO STRATEGIC INTERNATIONAL LIMITED; *Int'l*, pg. 6947
SINO STRIDE TECHNOLOGY CO., LTD—See HNA International Investment Holdings Limited; *Int'l*, pg. 3433
SINOSTRUCT PTY. LTD.—See Monadelphous Group Limited; *Int'l*, pg. 5024
SINOSUN TECHNOLOGY CO., LTD.; *Int'l*, pg. 6956
SINO-SWED PHARMACEUTICAL CORP., LTD.—See China National Pharmaceutical Group Corporation; *Int'l*, pg. 1534
SINO-SWED PHARMACEUTICAL CORP., LTD.—See Fresenius SE & Co. KGaA; *Int'l*, pg. 2778
SINOTAC BUILDER'S (S) PTE LTD—See TA Corporation Ltd.; *Int'l*, pg. 7399
SINO TAC RESOURCES PTE. LTD.—See TA Corporation Ltd.; *Int'l*, pg. 7399
SINO TACTFUL CO., LTD.; *Int'l*, pg. 6948
SINOTECH ASIA LTD.—See Groz-Beckert KG; *Int'l*, pg. 3113
SINOTECH ENERGY LIMITED; *Int'l*, pg. 6956
SINO TECHFIBRE LIMITED; *Int'l*, pg. 6948
SINOTECH POLYARD (BEIJING) RESOURCE SCIENCE & TECHNOLOGY LIMITED—See Polyard Petroleum International Group Limited; *Int'l*, pg. 5914
SINO-THAI ENGINEERING & CONSTRUCTION PUBLIC COMPANY LIMITED; *Int'l*, pg. 6949
SINOTRANS AGENCIES (S) PTE LTD.—See China Merchants Group Limited; *Int'l*, pg. 1522
SINOTRANS AIR TRANSPORTATION DEVELOPMENT CO., LTD.—See China Merchants Group Limited; *Int'l*, pg. 1522
SINOTRANS CANADA INC.—See China Merchants Group Limited; *Int'l*, pg. 1521
SINOTRANS CHANGJIANG COMPANY LIMITED—See China Merchants Group Limited; *Int'l*, pg. 1522
SINOTRANS CHONGQING COMPANY LIMITED—See China Merchants Group Limited; *Int'l*, pg. 1522
SINOTRANS CONTAINER LINES COMPANY LIMITED—See China Merchants Group Limited; *Int'l*, pg. 1522
SINOTRANS & CSC HOLDINGS CO., LTD.—See China Merchants Group Limited; *Int'l*, pg. 1521
SINOTRANS & CSC SHIPBUILDING INDUSTRY CORPORATION - CHINA CHANGJIANG NATIONAL SHIPPING GROUP MOTOR FACTORY—See China Merchants Group Limited; *Int'l*, pg. 1521
SINOTRANS & CSC SHIPBUILDING INDUSTRY CORPORATION - HONGGUANG PORT MACHINERY PLANT—See China Merchants Group Limited; *Int'l*, pg. 1521
SINOTRANS & CSC SHIPBUILDING INDUSTRY CORPORATION—See China Merchants Group Limited; *Int'l*, pg. 1521
SINOTRANS DONGGUAN LOGISTICS CO., LTD.—See China Merchants Group Limited; *Int'l*, pg. 1522
SINOTRANS EASTERN COMPANY LIMITED—See China Merchants Group Limited; *Int'l*, pg. 1522
SINOTRANS FOSHAN EXPRESS MANAGMENT AND CUSTOM BROKERAGE CO., LTD.—See China Merchants Group Limited; *Int'l*, pg. 1522
SINOTRANS FOSHAN LOGISTICS CO., LTD.—See China Merchants Group Limited; *Int'l*, pg. 1523
SINOTRANS FOSHAN SHIPPING CO., LTD.—See China Merchants Group Limited; *Int'l*, pg. 1523
SINOTRANS FOSHAN WAREHOUSE & TERMINAL CO., LTD.—See China Merchants Group Limited; *Int'l*, pg. 1523
SINOTRANS (GERMANY) GMBH—See China Merchants Group Limited; *Int'l*, pg. 1522
SINOTRANS GUANGDONG COMPANY LIMITED—See China Merchants Group Limited; *Int'l*, pg. 1522
SINOTRANS GUANGDONG CUSTOMS BROKER CO., LTD.—See China Merchants Group Limited; *Int'l*, pg. 1523
SINOTRANS GUANGDONG DONGJIANG WAREHOUSE & TERMINAL CO., LTD.—See China Merchants Group Limited; *Int'l*, pg. 1523

COMPANY NAME INDEX

SINOTRANS GUANGDONG HUANGPU WAREHOUSE & TERMINAL CO., LTD.—See China Merchants Group Limited; *Int'l*, pg. 1523
SINOTRANS GUANGDONG INTERNATIONAL FREIGHT FORWARDING CO., LTD.—See China Merchants Group Limited; *Int'l*, pg. 1523
SINOTRANS GUANGDONG PROPERTY MANAGEMENT CO., LTD.—See China Merchants Group Limited; *Int'l*, pg. 1523
SINOTRANS GUANGDONG SHIPPING CO., LTD.—See China Merchants Group Limited; *Int'l*, pg. 1523
SINOTRANS HEAVY-LIFT LOGISTICS COMPANY LIMITED—See China Merchants Group Limited; *Int'l*, pg. 1523
SINOTRANS (HK) LOGISTICS LIMITED—See China Merchants Group Limited; *Int'l*, pg. 1522
SINOTRANS (HONG KONG) HOLDINGS LTD.—See China Merchants Group Limited; *Int'l*, pg. 1522
SINOTRANS JAPAN CO., LTD.—See China Merchants Group Limited; *Int'l*, pg. 1522
SINOTRANS JIANGMEN WAREHOUSE & TERMINAL CO., LTD.—See China Merchants Group Limited; *Int'l*, pg. 1523
SINOTRANS JIANGXI CO., LTD.—See China Merchants Group Limited; *Int'l*, pg. 1522
SINOTRANS KOREA SHIPPING CO., LTD.—See China Merchants Group Limited; *Int'l*, pg. 1522
SINOTRANS LANDBRIDGE TRANSPORTATION COMPANY LIMITED—See China Merchants Group Limited; *Int'l*, pg. 1523
SINOTRANS LIMITED—See China Merchants Group Limited; *Int'l*, pg. 1522
SINOTRANS LOGISTICS (CAMBODIA) CO. LTD.—See China Merchants Group Limited; *Int'l*, pg. 1522
SINOTRANS LOGISTICS (M) SDN. BHD.—See China Merchants Group Limited; *Int'l*, pg. 1522
SINOTRANS MACAO CO., LTD.—See China Merchants Group Limited; *Int'l*, pg. 1523
SINOTRANS NANCHANG CO., LTD.—See China Merchants Group Limited; *Int'l*, pg. 1522
SINOTRANS NANJING EXPORT PROCESSING ZONE LOGISTICS CO., LTD.—See China Merchants Group Limited; *Int'l*, pg. 1522
SINOTRANS NETHERLANDS B.V.—See China Merchants Group Limited; *Int'l*, pg. 1522
SINOTRANS SHANDONG COMPANY LIMITED—See China Merchants Group Limited; *Int'l*, pg. 1523
SINOTRANS SHANTOU CO. LTD.—See China Merchants Group Limited; *Int'l*, pg. 1523
SINOTRANS SHENZHEN CUSTOMS BROKER CO., LTD.—See China Merchants Group Limited; *Int'l*, pg. 1523
SINOTRANS SHENZHEN LOGISTICS CO., LTD.—See China Merchants Group Limited; *Int'l*, pg. 1523
SINOTRANS SHIPPING LIMITED—See China Merchants Group Limited; *Int'l*, pg. 1523
SINOTRANS THAI LOGISTICS COMPANY LIMITED—See China Merchants Group Limited; *Int'l*, pg. 1522
SINOTRANS ZHONGSHAN CUSTOMS BROKER CO., LTD.—See China Merchants Group Limited; *Int'l*, pg. 1523
SINOTRANS ZHONGSHAN LOGISTICS CO., LTD.—See China Merchants Group Limited; *Int'l*, pg. 1523
SINOTRANS ZHONGSHAN WAREHOUSE & TERMINAL CO., LTD.—See China Merchants Group Limited; *Int'l*, pg. 1523
SINOTRUK (HONG KONG) HONGYE LIMITED—See Sinotruk (Hong Kong) Limited; *Int'l*, pg. 6956
SINOTRUK (HONG KONG) INTERNATIONAL INVESTMENT LIMITED—See Sinotruk (Hong Kong) Limited; *Int'l*, pg. 6956
SINOTRUK (HONG KONG) LIMITED; *Int'l*, pg. 6956
SINOTRUK INTERNATIONAL CO., LTD.—See Sinotruk (Hong Kong) Limited; *Int'l*, pg. 6956
SINOTRUK JI'NAN HOWO BUS CO., LTD.—See Sinotruk (Hong Kong) Limited; *Int'l*, pg. 6956
SINOTRUK JINAN TRUCK CO., LTD.; *Int'l*, pg. 6956
SINOTRUK LIUZHOU YUNLI SPECIAL VEHICLES CO., LTD.—See Sinotruk (Hong Kong) Limited; *Int'l*, pg. 6956
SINO-US UNITED METLIFE INSURANCE CO—See MetLife, Inc.; *U.S. Public*, pg. 1431
SINOVAC BIOTECH CO.,LTD.—See Sinovac Biotech Ltd.; *Int'l*, pg. 6956
SINOVAC BIOTECH LTD.; *Int'l*, pg. 6956
SINOVATION VENTURES CO., LTD; *Int'l*, pg. 6956
SINOVEL WIND GROUP CO., LTD; *Int'l*, pg. 6956
SINO VISION WORLDWIDE HOLDINGS LIMITED; *Int'l*, pg. 6948
SINO WATER ENVIRONMENTAL CONSULTANCY (SHANGHAI) CO., LTD.—See Puncak Niaga Holdings Berhad; *Int'l*, pg. 6118
SINO WATER PTE. LTD.—See Puncak Niaga Holdings Berhad; *Int'l*, pg. 6118
SINO WEALTH ELECTRONIC LTD.; *Int'l*, pg. 6948
SINO WEALTH ELECTRONIC(SHANGHAI) CO.—See Sino Wealth Electronic Ltd.; *Int'l*, pg. 6948
SINO WEALTH SECURITIES LIMITED—See Heng Tai Consumables Group Limited; *Int'l*, pg. 3345

SINOWOOD LIMITED—See Emerald Plantation Holdings Limited; *Int'l*, pg. 2378
SINO-WOOD PARTNERS LIMITED—See Emerald Plantation Holdings Limited; *Int'l*, pg. 2378
SINO-WOOD TRADING LIMITED—See Emerald Plantation Holdings Limited; *Int'l*, pg. 2378
SINPAS GAYRIMENKUL YATIRIM ORTAKLIGI AS; *Int'l*, pg. 6956
SINPHAR PHARMACEUTICAL CO., LTD.; *Int'l*, pg. 6956
SINQIA S.A.—See EVERTEC, Inc.; *U.S. Public*, pg. 802
SIN RAE MUANGTHAI CO., LTD—See Italian-Thai Development pcl; *Int'l*, pg. 3829
SINSENMOH TRANSPORTATION PTE. LTD.—See PSA Corporation Pte Ltd.; *Int'l*, pg. 6014
SINSIN PHARMACEUTICAL CO., LTD.; *Int'l*, pg. 6956
SINSIN PHARM.CO., LTD. - ANSAN PLANT—See SinSin Pharm.Co.,Ltd.,; *Int'l*, pg. 6956
SINSIN PHARM.CO.,LTD.; *Int'l*, pg. 6956
SIN SOON HUAT INTERNATIONAL TRADING PTE LTD—See KS Energy Limited; *Int'l*, pg. 4310
SINTAL AGRICULTURE PLC; *Int'l*, pg. 6956
SINTANA ENERGY, INC.; *Int'l*, pg. 6956
SINTAX LOGISTICA, S.A.—See Wilh. Wilhelmsen Holding ASA; *Int'l*, pg. 8410
SINTAX LOGISTICA TRANSPORTES, S.A.—See ACS, Actividades de Construccion y Servicios, S.A.; *Int'l*, pg. 116
SINTAX NAVIGOMES, LTDA.—See ACS, Actividades de Construccion y Servicios, S.A.; *Int'l*, pg. 116
SINTEC KERAMIK USA INC.—See Kennametal Inc.; *U.S. Public*, 1222
SINTECMEDIA AMS B.V.—See Francisco Partners Management, LP; *U.S. Private*, pg. 1591
SINTECMEDIA DV INC.—See Francisco Partners Management, LP; *U.S. Private*, pg. 1591
SINTECMEDIA GLOBAL LTD.—See Francisco Partners Management, LP; *U.S. Private*, pg. 1591
SINTECMEDIA, INC.—See Francisco Partners Management, LP; *U.S. Private*, pg. 1591
SINTECMEDIA SYD PTY LTD—See Francisco Partners Management, LP; *U.S. Private*, pg. 1592
SINTECMEDIA WEM LTD.—See Francisco Partners Management, LP; *U.S. Private*, pg. 1592
SINTEF BUILDING AND INFRASTRUCTURE AS—See SINTEF; *Int'l*, pg. 6957
SINTEF HOLDING AS—See SINTEF; *Int'l*, pg. 6957
SINTEF NBL (NORWEGIAN FIRE RESEARCH LABORATORY) AS—See SINTEF; *Int'l*, pg. 6957
SINTEF PETROLEUM RESEARCH AS—See SINTEF; *Int'l*, pg. 6957
SINTEF RAUFOSS MANUFACTURING AS—See SINTEF; *Int'l*, pg. 6957
SINTEF; *Int'l*, pg. 6956
SINTEF TTO AS—See SINTEF; *Int'l*, pg. 6957
SINTEK INTERNATIONAL AB—See ITAB Shop Concept AB; *Int'l*, pg. 3828
SINTEL S.R.L.—See Cellnex Telecom, S.A.; *Int'l*, pg. 1394
SINTEPLAST S.A.; *Int'l*, pg. 6957
SINTERAMA ASIA LIMITED—See Indorama Ventures Public Company Limited; *Int'l*, pg. 3659
SINTERAMA BULGARIA EOOD—See Indorama Ventures Public Company Limited; *Int'l*, pg. 3659
SINTERAMA DO BRASIL LTDA.—See Indorama Ventures Public Company Limited; *Int'l*, pg. 3659
SINTERAMA S.P.A.—See Indorama Ventures Public Company Limited; *Int'l*, pg. 3659
SINTERAMA YARNS (DONGGUAN) CO., LTD.—See Indorama Ventures Public Company Limited; *Int'l*, pg. 3659
SINTERCAST AB; *Int'l*, pg. 6957
SINTERCAST INC.—See Sintercast AB; *Int'l*, pg. 6957
SINTERCAST LTD.—See Sintercast AB; *Int'l*, pg. 6957
SINTERCOM INDIA LTD.; *Int'l*, pg. 6957
SINTERFIRE, INC.—See Argosy Capital Group, LLC; *U.S. Private*, pg. 321
SINTER IBERICA PACKAGING—See Fluor Corporation; *U.S. Public*, pg. 860
SINTERMETAL S.A. DE C.V.—See Schunk GmbH; *Int'l*, pg. 6643
SINTERMET LLC—See Vergani & Associates, LLC; *U.S. Private*, pg. 4359
SINTER REF SA; *Int'l*, pg. 6957
SINTESA GROUP—See PT Widjajatunggal Sejahtera; *Int'l*, pg. 6082
SINTESI S.P.A.; *Int'l*, pg. 6957
SINTESY PHARMA S.R.L.—See Glenmark Pharmaceuticals Limited; *Int'l*, pg. 2992
SINTEX A/S—See The Poul Due Jensen Foundation; *Int'l*, pg. 7676
SINTEX BAPL LIMITED—See Welspun Group; *Int'l*, pg. 8375
SINTEX HOLDINGS USA, INC.—See Sintex Industries, Ltd.; *Int'l*, pg. 6957
SINTEX INDUSTRIES, LTD.; *Int'l*, pg. 6957
SINTEX NYLON AND COTTON PRODUCTS (PTE) LIMITED—See Chuang's Consortium International Limited; *Int'l*, pg. 1590
SINTEX PLASTICS TECHNOLOGY LIMITED; *Int'l*, pg. 6958

SION POWER CORPORATION

SINTEX PREFAB AND INFRA LIMITED—See Welspun Group; *Int'l*, pg. 8375
SINTEZA S.A.; *Int'l*, pg. 6958
SINTO AMERICA, INC.—See Sintokogio Ltd.; *Int'l*, pg. 6958
SINTO BHARAT MANUFACTURING PRIVATE LIMITED—See Sintokogio Ltd.; *Int'l*, pg. 6958
SINTO BRASIL PRODUTOS LIMITADA—See Sintokogio Ltd.; *Int'l*, pg. 6959
SINTO ENGINEERING, LTD.—See Sintokogio Ltd.; *Int'l*, pg. 6959
SINTO FROHN METAL ABRASIVE (QINGDAO) CO., LTD.—See Sintokogio Ltd.; *Int'l*, pg. 6959
SINTO INFORMATION SYSTEMS LTD.—See Sintokogio Ltd.; *Int'l*, pg. 6959
SINTOKOGIO (KUNSHAN) CO., LTD.—See Sintokogio Ltd.; *Int'l*, pg. 6959
SINTOKOGIO LTD. - ICHINOMIYA WORKS—See Sintokogio Ltd.; *Int'l*, pg. 6959
SINTOKOGIO LTD. - KODA WORKS—See Sintokogio Ltd.; *Int'l*, pg. 6959
SINTOKOGIO LTD. - NISHIHARU WORKS—See Sintokogio Ltd.; *Int'l*, pg. 6959
SINTOKOGIO LTD. - OHARU WORKS—See Sintokogio Ltd.; *Int'l*, pg. 6959
SINTOKOGIO LTD. - OSAKI WORKS—See Sintokogio Ltd.; *Int'l*, pg. 6959
SINTOKOGIO LTD. - SHINSHIRO WORKS—See Sintokogio Ltd.; *Int'l*, pg. 6959
SINTOKOGIO LTD.; *Int'l*, pg. 6958
SINTOKOGIO LTD. - TOYOKAWA WORKS—See Sintokogio Ltd.; *Int'l*, pg. 6959
SINTOKOGIO LTD. - TOYOTA DIVISION—See Sintokogio Ltd.; *Int'l*, pg. 6959
SINTON DAIRY FOODS COMPANY L.L.C.; *U.S. Private*, pg. 3670
SINTONIA S.P.A—See Edizione S.r.l.; *Int'l*, pg. 2312
SINTO S-PRECISION, LTD.—See Sintokogio Ltd.; *Int'l*, pg. 6959
SINTO TURKEY MAKINA SANAYI VE TICARET A.S.—See Sintokogio Ltd.; *Int'l*, pg. 6959
SINTO V-CERAX, LTD.—See Sintokogio Ltd.; *Int'l*, pg. 6958
SINTROL OY; *Int'l*, pg. 6959
SINTRONES TECHNOLOGY CORP.; *Int'l*, pg. 6959
SINTRONIC TECHNOLOGY INC.; *Int'l*, pg. 6959
SINTX TECHNOLOGIES, INC.; *U.S. Public*, pg. 1888
SINTYAL OTSUKA PHARMACEUTICAL S.A.—See Otsuka Holdings Co., Ltd.; *Int'l*, pg. 5661
SINUATE MEDIA, LLC; *U.S. Private*, pg. 3670
SINU, INC.; *U.S. Private*, pg. 3670
SINUS-JEVI ELECTRIC HEATING B.V.—See NIBE Industrier AB; *Int'l*, pg. 5262
SINVENT VENTURE II AS—See SINTEF; *Int'l*, pg. 6957
SINVEST AS—See Aban Offshore Limited; *Int'l*, pg. 48
SINWA AUSTRALIA PTY LIMITED—See Financiere SYZ & CO SA; *Int'l*, pg. 2669
SINWA LIMITED; *Int'l*, pg. 6959
SINWA SHIP SUPPLY (HK) PTE. LTD.—See Sinwa Limited; *Int'l*, pg. 6959
SINWA SINGAPORE PTE LTD; *Int'l*, pg. 6959
SINWA THAILAND LTD.—See Sinwa Limited; *Int'l*, pg. 6959
SIN WEE SENG INDUSTRIES SDN. BHD.; *Int'l*, pg. 6935
SINWHA ADVANCE CO., LTD.—See HLB Life Science Co.,Ltd.; *Int'l*, pg. 3430
SINXON PLASTIC (DONG GUAN) CO., LTD.—See COXON Precise Industrial Co., Ltd.; *Int'l*, pg. 1823
SIN YEN TECHNOLOGIES SDN. BHD.—See FoundPac Group Berhad; *Int'l*, pg. 2754
SINYI REALTY INC.; *Int'l*, pg. 6959
SINYON PLASTIC INDUSTRIAL CO., LTD.—See COXON Precise Industrial Co., Ltd.; *Int'l*, pg. 1823
SIO-ECKES KFT.—See Eckes AG; *Int'l*, pg. 2291
SIOEN BALLISTICS OY—See Sioen Industries NV; *Int'l*, pg. 6960
SIOEN COATED FABRICS (SHANGHAI) TRADING CO. LTD.—See Sioen Industries NV; *Int'l*, pg. 6960
SIOEN FABRICS SA—See Sioen Industries NV; *Int'l*, pg. 6960
SIOEN FRANCE SAS—See Sioen Industries NV; *Int'l*, pg. 6960
SIOEN INDUSTRIES NV; *Int'l*, pg. 6959
SIOEN NEDERLAND BV—See Sioen Industries NV; *Int'l*, pg. 6960
SIOEN NV—See Sioen Industries NV; *Int'l*, pg. 6960
SIOEN TECHNICAL FELTS SA—See Sioen Industries NV; *Int'l*, pg. 6960
SIOEN TUNISIE SARL—See Sioen Industries NV; *Int'l*, pg. 6960
SIOEN ZAGHOUAN SA—See Sioen Industries NV; *Int'l*, pg. 6960
SIOE PHARMACEUTICAL CO., LTD.—See Nippon Shinyaku Co., Ltd.; *Int'l*, pg. 5332
SIONIX CORPORATION; *U.S. Private*, pg. 3670
SION POWER CORPORATION; *U.S. Private*, pg. 3670
THE SIOP INSTITUTE LLC—See Pearson plc; *Int'l*, pg. 5778
SIOS CORPORATION—See SIOS Corp.; *Int'l*, pg. 6960

SIOS CORP.   CORPORATE AFFILIATIONS

SIOS CORP.; *Int'l*, pg. 6960
SIOUNI & ZAR CORP.; *U.S. Private*, pg. 3670
SIOUX AUTOMATION CENTER INC.; *U.S. Private*, pg. 3670
SIOUX CITY BRICK & TILE CO—See Brickworks Limited; *Int'l*, pg. 1152
SIOUX CITY FORD LINCOLN; *U.S. Private*, pg. 3671
SIOUX CITY FOUNDRY CO.; *U.S. Private*, pg. 3671
SIOUX CITY MOTORCARS, LLC—See Vern Eide Motorcars, Inc.; *U.S. Private*, pg. 4367
SIOUX CITY NEWSPAPERS, INC.—See Lee Enterprises, Incorporated; *U.S. Public*, pg. 1300
SIOUX CITY TRUCK SALES INCORPORATED; *U.S. Private*, pg. 3671
SIOUX CITY TRUCK & TRAILER—See North American Truck & Trailer, Inc.; *U.S. Private*, pg. 2941
SIOUX FALLS AUTO AUCTION, INC.—See OPENLANE, Inc.; *U.S. Public*, pg. 1607
SIOUX FALLS CHRISTIAN SCHOOLS; *U.S. Private*, pg. 3671
SIOUX FALLS CONSTRUCTION COMPANY; *U.S. Private*, pg. 3671
SIOUX FALLS FORD INC.; *U.S. Private*, pg. 3671
SIOUX FALLS SPECIALTY HOSPITAL LLP—See Medical Facilities Corporation; *Int'l*, pg. 4775
SIOUX FALLS TRUCK & TRAILER, INC.—See North American Truck & Trailer, Inc.; *U.S. Private*, pg. 2941
SIOUX HONEY ASSOCIATION; *U.S. Private*, pg. 3671
SIOUXLAND ENERGY COOPERATIVE; *U.S. Private*, pg. 3671
SIOUXLAND ETHANOL, LLC.; *U.S. Private*, pg. 3671
SIOUX MANUFACTURING CORP.; *U.S. Private*, pg. 3671
SIOUX-PREME PACKING CO.—See Perdue Farms Incorporated; *U.S. Private*, pg. 3147
SIOUX STEEL COMPANY; *U.S. Private*, pg. 3671
SIOUX VALLEY ENERGY; *U.S. Private*, pg. 3671
SIOUX VALLEY RURAL TELEVISION—See Sioux Valley Energy; *U.S. Private*, pg. 3671
SIOUX VALLEY-SOUTHWESTERN ELECTRIC COOPERATIVE, INC.; *U.S. Private*, pg. 3671
SIOUX VALLEY WIRELESS—See Sioux Valley Energy; *U.S. Private*, pg. 3671
SIOVATION, LLC—See Akoya Capital LLC; *U.S. Private*, pg. 146
SIOVATION, LLC—See Century Park Capital Partners, LLC; *U.S. Private*, pg. 834
SIPAD KOMERC D.D.; *Int'l*, pg. 6960
SIPAD-KRAJINA A.D.; *Int'l*, pg. 6960
SIPAD SRBOBRAN A.D.; *Int'l*, pg. 6960
SIPA EXPLORATION NL—See Sipa Resources Limited; *Int'l*, pg. 6960
SIPAI HEALTH TECHNOLOGY CO., LTD.; *Int'l*, pg. 6960
SIPAR ACEROS S.A.—See Metalurgica Gerdau S.A.; *Int'l*, pg. 4850
SIPA RESOURCES LIMITED; *Int'l*, pg. 6960
SI PARTICIPATIONS S.C.A.—See Groupe Siparex; *Int'l*, pg. 3111
SIPA S.P.A.—See Calvi Holding S.r.l.; *Int'l*, pg. 1266
SIPCAM EUROPE S.P.A—See Adeka Corporation; *Int'l*, pg. 142
SIPCAM NICHINO BRASIL S.A.—See Adeka Corporation; *Int'l*, pg. 142
SIP CHANG HONG OPTOELECTRONICS LTD.—See Wah Hong Industrial Corp.; *Int'l*, pg. 8328
SIPCHEM ASIA PTE. LTD.—See Sahara International Petrochemical Company; *Int'l*, pg. 6481
SIPCO INDUSTRIES CO., LTD—See Toda Corporation; *Int'l*, pg. 7773
SIPCON INSTRUMENT INDUSTRIES PVT. LTD.—See Chien Wei Precise Technology Co., Ltd.; *Int'l*, pg. 1477
SIPCO SERVICES INC.; *U.S. Private*, pg. 3671
SIPEF NV; *Int'l*, pg. 6960
SIPERA SYSTEMS, INC.—See Silver Lake Group, LLC; *U.S. Private*, pg. 3656
SIPERA SYSTEMS, INC.—See TPG Capital, L.P.; *U.S. Public*, pg. 2169
SIPG LOGISTICS CO., LTD.—See Shanghai International Port (Group) Co., Ltd.; *Int'l*, pg. 6771
SIPG LUOJING SUBSIDIARY CO. LTD.—See Shanghai International Port (Group) Co., Ltd.; *Int'l*, pg. 6771
SIPG PASSENGER TRANSPORT CORPORATION LTD.—See Shanghai International Port (Group) Co., Ltd.; *Int'l*, pg. 6771
SIPI METALS CORP.; *U.S. Private*, pg. 3671
S.I.P. INC. OF DELAWARE—See Williams Industries, Inc.; *U.S. Private*, pg. 4526
SIP INDUSTRIES LIMITED; *Int'l*, pg. 6960
SIPING HAOHUA CHEMICAL CO., LTD.—See China National Chemical Corporation; *Int'l*, pg. 1529
SIPLAST ICOPAL INC.—See GAF Materials Corporation; *U.S. Private*, pg. 1634
SIPOREX D.D. TUZLA; *Int'l*, pg. 6961
SI PORTAL.COM SDN BHD—See Singapore Press Holdings Ltd.; *Int'l*, pg. 6942
SIPOS AKTORIK GMBH—See AUMA Riester GmbH & Co. KG; *Int'l*, pg. 705
SIPPEL-TRAVEL GMBH—See Ferrovie dello Stato Italiane S.p.A.; *Int'l*, pg. 2645
SIPP INDUSTRIES, INC.; *U.S. Public*, pg. 1888

SIPRIN S.R.O.—See Siemens Aktiengesellschaft; *Int'l*, pg. 6888
SIPSA SA; *Int'l*, pg. 6961
SIPUP CORPORATION; *Int'l*, pg. 6961
SIPX, INC.—See Cambridge Information Group, Inc.; *U.S. Private*, pg. 727
SIQALO FOODS PROPRIETARY LIMITED—See Remgro Limited; *Int'l*, pg. 6271
SIQ MOUNTAIN INDUSTRIES, INC.; *Int'l*, pg. 6961
SIQUAR HARDWARE INDUSTRY CO., LTD.; *Int'l*, pg. 6961
SIQUAR USA INC.—See Siquar Hardware Industry Co., Ltd.; *Int'l*, pg. 6961
SIQUIS, LTD.; *U.S. Private*, pg. 3671
SIQURA B.V.—See Vector Capital Management, L.P.; *U.S. Private*, pg. 4352
SIRA CONSULTING LIMITED—See CSA Group; *Int'l*, pg. 1861
SIRA ENVIRONMENTAL LIMITED—See CSA Group; *Int'l*, pg. 1861
SIRAI DEUTSCHLAND VERTRIEB ELEKTROMECHANISCHER GERAETE GMBH—See Emerson Electric Co.; *U.S. Public*, pg. 752
SIRAKORN PUBLIC COMPANY LIMITED; *Int'l*, pg. 6961
SIRAM SPA—See Veolia Environnement S.A.; *Int'l*, pg. 8158
SIRAP FRANCE SAS—See Italmobiliare S.p.A.; *Int'l*, pg. 3829
SIRAP GEMA - AMPRICA—See Italmobiliare S.p.A.; *Int'l*, pg. 3829
SIRAP GEMA S.P.A.—See Italmobiliare S.p.A.; *Int'l*, pg. 3829
SIRAP INSULATION S.R.L.—See Italmobiliare S.p.A.; *Int'l*, pg. 3829
SIRAP UK LIMITED—See Italmobiliare S.p.A.; *Int'l*, pg. 3830
SIRAS .COM INC.—See Nintendo Co., Ltd.; *Int'l*, pg. 5308
SIRA TEST AND CERTIFICATION LIMITED—See CSA Group; *Int'l*, pg. 1861
SIRCAL INSTRUMENTS (U.K.) LIMITED—See Judges Scientific plc; *Int'l*, pg. 4021
SIRCA PAINTS INDIA LTD.; *Int'l*, pg. 6961
SIRCHIE FINGERPRINT LABS; *U.S. Private*, pg. 3671
SIR COLIN MACKENZIE ZOOLOGICAL PARK—See Zoological Parks and Gardens Board; *Int'l*, pg. 8689
SIRCONIC GROUP GMBH; *Int'l*, pg. 6961
SIR CORP.; *Int'l*, pg. 6961
SIRCUS S.R.L.—See Gruppo MutuiOnline S.p.A.; *Int'l*, pg. 3141
SIREHNA SA—See Naval Group SA; *Int'l*, pg. 5173
SIREINE AUTO BOURG LA REINE; *Int'l*, pg. 6961
SIREM S.A.S.—See Somfy SA; *Int'l*, pg. 7085
SIRENA MARINE DENIZCILIK SANAYI VE TICARET A.S.—See Kiraca Holding A.S.; *Int'l*, pg. 4185
SIREN GOLD LIMITED; *Int'l*, pg. 6961
SIREN INTERACTIVE, LLC—See Dohmen Co.; *U.S. Private*, pg. 1254
SIRENS MEDIA, LLC—See ITV plc; *Int'l*, pg. 3845
SIRE RECORDS—See Access Industries, Inc.; *U.S. Private*, pg. 52
SI RESOURCES CO., LTD.; *Int'l*, pg. 6874
SIRETUL PASCANI SA; *Int'l*, pg. 6961
SIR FEUERFESTPRODUKTE GMBH—See Vesuvius plc; *Int'l*, pg. 8179
SIRFIA SA; FAYAT SAS; *Int'l*, pg. 2626
SIR GROUT LLC—See Riverside Partners, LLC; *U.S. Private*, pg. 3446
SIRI BELUKAR PACKAGING SDN. BHD.—See LHT Holdings Limited; *Int'l*, pg. 4479
SIRIGEN, INC.—See Becton, Dickinson & Company; *U.S. Public*, pg. 292
SIRIGEN LIMITED—See Becton, Dickinson & Company; *U.S. Public*, pg. 292
SIRIKUL ENGINEERING LTD. PART.—See INDUS Holding AG; *Int'l*, pg. 3664
SIRIM BERHAD; *Int'l*, pg. 6961
SIRIM TECH VENTURE SDN. BHD.—See SIRIM Berhad; *Int'l*, pg. 6961
SIRINA FIRE PROTECTION CORP.; *U.S. Private*, pg. 3672
SIRIO INFORMATICA E SISTEMI SPA—See Sesa S.p.A.; *Int'l*, pg. 6729
SIRIO NORD SRL—See Sesa S.p.A.; *Int'l*, pg. 6729
SIRIO PANEL INC.—See Leonardo S.p.A.; *Int'l*, pg. 4460
SIRIO PANEL SPA—See Leonardo S.p.A.; *Int'l*, pg. 4460
SIRIO PHARMA CO., LTD.; *Int'l*, pg. 6961
SIRIO - SICUREZZA INDUSTRIALE S.C.P.A.—See Stellantis N.V.; *Int'l*, pg. 7203
SIRIO SPA; *Int'l*, pg. 6961
SIRIOS RESOURCES INC.; *Int'l*, pg. 6961
SIRI PHUKET LIMITED—See Sansiri pcl; *Int'l*, pg. 6557
SIRIS CAPITAL GROUP, LLC; *U.S. Private*, pg. 3672
SIRIUS AIR INTERNATIONAL LTD.—See Japan Airlines Co., Ltd.; *Int'l*, pg. 3885
SIRIUS AMERICA INSURANCE CO.—See White Mountains Insurance Group, Ltd.; *U.S. Public*, pg. 2369
SIRIUS BENEFIT PLANS INC.—See People Corporation; *Int'l*, pg. 5793

SIRIUS COMPUTER SOLUTIONS, INC.—See CDW Corporation; *U.S. Public*, pg. 869
SIRIUSDECISIONS, INC.—See Forrester Research, Inc.; *U.S. Public*, pg. 869
SIRIUS FACILITIES GMBH—See Sirius Real Estate Limited; *Int'l*, pg. 6962
SIRIUS IMMOBILIEN- UND PROJEKTENTWICKLUNGS GMBH—See UniCredit S.p.A.; *Int'l*, pg. 8035
SIRIUS INTERNATIONAL INSURANCE CORPORATION—See White Mountains Insurance Group, Ltd.; *U.S. Public*, pg. 2369
SIRIUS MACHINERY AB—See Coesia S.p.A.; *Int'l*, pg. 1690
SIRIUS MINERALS (AUSTRALIA) PTY LIMITED—See Anglo American PLC; *Int'l*, pg. 461
SIRIUS PETROLEUM PLC; *Int'l*, pg. 6962
SIRIUSPOINT LTD.; *Int'l*, pg. 6962
SIRIUS REAL ESTATE LIMITED; *Int'l*, pg. 6962
SIRIUS SOLUTIONS LLC; *U.S. Private*, pg. 3675
SIRIUSVISION CO., LTD.; *Int'l*, pg. 6962
SIRIUSWARE, INC.—See accesso Technology Group Plc; *Int'l*, pg. 89
SIRIUS XM CANADA HOLDINGS INC.; *Int'l*, pg. 6962
SIRIUS XM CANADA INC.—See Sirius XM Canada Holdings Inc.; *Int'l*, pg. 6962
SIRIUS XM HOLDINGS INC.—See Liberty Media Corporation; *U.S. Public*, pg. 1311
SIRIUS XM INNOVATION CENTER—See Liberty Media Corporation; *U.S. Public*, pg. 1311
SIRIUS XM RADIO INC.—See Liberty Media Corporation; *U.S. Public*, pg. 1311
SIRIVIT STANLEY CO., LTD.—See Thai Stanley Electric Public Company Limited; *Int'l*, pg. 7595
SIRMA AD; *Int'l*, pg. 6962
SIRMA ELEKTRIK KOMURLERI SAN. VE TIC. A.S.—See Schunk GmbH; *Int'l*, pg. 6641
SIRMA GROUP HOLDING JSC; *Int'l*, pg. 6962
SIRMA ITT CORP.—See Sirma Group Holding JSC; *Int'l*, pg. 6962
SIRNAOMICS BIOPHARMACEUTICALS (GUANGZHOU) CO., LTD.—See Sirnaomics Ltd.; *Int'l*, pg. 6962
SIRNAOMICS BIOPHARMACEUTICALS (SUZHOU) CO., LTD.—See Sirnaomics Ltd.; *Int'l*, pg. 6962
SIRNAOMICS LTD.; *Int'l*, pg. 6962
SIRNA & SONS, INC.—See Wind Point Advisors LLC; *U.S. Private*, pg. 4534
SIROCO SAS—See Sintex Industries, Ltd.; *Int'l*, pg. 6957
SIROFLEX LTD.—See Arkema S.A.; *Int'l*, pg. 571
SIROHIA & SONS LTD; *Int'l*, pg. 6962
SIRONA BIOCHEM CORP.; *Int'l*, pg. 6962
SIRONA DENTAL A/S—See DENTSPLY SIRONA Inc.; *U.S. Public*, pg. 655
SIRONA DENTAL GMBH—See DENTSPLY SIRONA Inc.; *U.S. Public*, pg. 655
SIRONA DENTAL, INC.—See DENTSPLY SIRONA Inc.; *U.S. Public*, pg. 655
SIRONA DENTAL LIMITED SIRKETI—See DENTSPLY SIRONA Inc.; *U.S. Public*, pg. 655
SIRONA DENTAL MEXICO S. DE R.L. DE C.V.—See DENTSPLY SIRONA Inc.; *U.S. Public*, pg. 655
SIRONA DENTAL SYSTEMS GMBH—See DENTSPLY SIRONA Inc.; *U.S. Public*, pg. 655
SIRONA DENTAL SYSTEMS, INC.—See DENTSPLY SIRONA Inc.; *U.S. Public*, pg. 655
SIRONA DENTAL SYSTEMS K.K.—See DENTSPLY SIRONA Inc.; *U.S. Public*, pg. 655
SIRONA DENTAL SYSTEMS KOREA, LTD.—See DENTSPLY SIRONA Inc.; *U.S. Public*, pg. 655
SIRONA DENTAL SYSTEMS LTD.—See DENTSPLY SIRONA Inc.; *U.S. Public*, pg. 655
SIRONA DENTAL SYSTEMS O.O.O.—See DENTSPLY SIRONA Inc.; *U.S. Public*, pg. 655
SIRONA DENTAL SYSTEMS PRIVATE LTD.—See DENTSPLY SIRONA Inc.; *U.S. Public*, pg. 655
SIRONA DENTAL SYSTEMS PTE. LTD.—See DENTSPLY SIRONA Inc.; *U.S. Public*, pg. 655
SIRONA DENTAL SYSTEMS SAS—See DENTSPLY SIRONA Inc.; *U.S. Public*, pg. 655
SIRONA DENTAL SYSTEMS SOUTH AFRICA (PTY) LTD.—See DENTSPLY SIRONA Inc.; *U.S. Public*, pg. 655
SIRONA DENTAL SYSTEMS S.R.L.—See DENTSPLY SIRONA Inc.; *U.S. Public*, pg. 655
SIRONA DENTAL SYSTEMS TRADING (SHANGHAI) CO. LTD.—See DENTSPLY SIRONA Inc.; *U.S. Public*, pg. 655
SIRONAHEALTH, INC.—See Great Point Partners, LLC; *U.S. Private*, pg. 1767
SIRONA TECHNOLOGIE GMBH & CO. KG—See DENTSPLY SIRONA Inc.; *U.S. Public*, pg. 655
SIRONA VERWALTUNGS GMBH—See DENTSPLY SIRONA Inc.; *U.S. Public*, pg. 655
SIROTA ASIA PACIFIC PTE. LTD.—See Marsh & McLennan Companies, Inc.; *U.S. Public*, pg. 1385
SIROTA CONSULTING LLC—See Marsh & McLennan Companies, Inc.; *U.S. Public*, pg. 1385
SIROTA CONSULTING UK LIMITED—See Marsh & McLennan Companies, Inc.; *U.S. Public*, pg. 1388

COMPANY NAME INDEX

SIRPUR PAPER MILLS LTD. - PLANT—See Sirpur Paper Mills Ltd; *Int'l*, pg. 6962
SIRPUR PAPER MILLS LTD; *Int'l*, pg. 6962
SIR ROYALTY INCOME FUND; *Int'l*, pg. 6961
SIRRUS, INC.—See Nippon Shokubai Co., Ltd.; *Int'l*, pg. 5333
SIRSAI MULTI SOURCING; *U.S. Private*, pg. 3675
SIR SHADI LAL ENTERPRISES LTD; *Int'l*, pg. 6961
SIRSIDYNIX CORPORATION; *U.S. Private*, pg. 3675
SIRSIDYNIX CORPORATION—See SirsiDynix Corporation; *U.S. Private*, pg. 3675
SIRSIDYNIX—See SirsiDynix Corporation; *U.S. Private*, pg. 3675
SIR SPEEDY, INC.—See KOA Holdings Inc.; *U.S. Private*, pg. 2325
SIR STAMFORD AT CIRCULAR QUAY PTY. LTD.—See Stamford Land Corporation Ltd; *Int'l*, pg. 7165
SIRTEC INTERNATIONAL COMPANY LTD.; *Int'l*, pg. 6962
SIRTEX GLOBAL PTY. LTD.—See CDH China Management Company Limited; *Int'l*, pg. 1371
SIRTEX MEDICAL EUROPE GMBH—See CDH China Management Company Limited; *Int'l*, pg. 1371
SIRTEX MEDICAL LIMITED—See CDH China Management Company Limited; *Int'l*, pg. 1370
SIRTEX MEDICAL PRODUCTS PTY. LTD.—See CDH China Management Company Limited; *Int'l*, pg. 1371
SIRTEX SIR-SPHERES PTY. LTD.—See CDH China Management Company Limited; *Int'l*, pg. 1371
SIRTEX TECHNOLOGY PTY. LTD.—See CDH China Management Company Limited; *Int'l*, pg. 1371
SIRTEX WILMINGTON LLC—See CDH China Management Company Limited; *Int'l*, pg. 1371
SIRTI S.P.A.—See TIM S.p.A.; *Int'l*, pg. 7749
SIRTON PHARMACEUTICALS SPA—See 3SBio Inc.; *Int'l*, pg. 9
SIRTRIS PHARMACEUTICALS—See GSK plc; *Int'l*, pg. 3149
SIRUBA LATIN AMERICA INC.—See KAULIN MFG Co., Ltd.; *Int'l*, pg. 4092
SIRVA CANADA LP—See Madison Dearborn Partners, LLC; *U.S. Private*, pg. 2542
SIRVA, INC.—See Madison Dearborn Partners, LLC; *U.S. Private*, pg. 2542
SIRVA MORTGAGE, INC.—See Madison Dearborn Partners, LLC; *U.S. Private*, pg. 2542
SIRVA PTY. LTD—See Madison Dearborn Partners, LLC; *U.S. Private*, pg. 2542
SIRVA RELOCATION LLC—See Madison Dearborn Partners, LLC; *U.S. Private*, pg. 2542
SIRVA WORLDWIDE, INC.—See Madison Dearborn Partners, LLC; *U.S. Private*, pg. 2542
SISAG SA—See Implenia AG; *Int'l*, pg. 3636
SISA HOME AUTOMATISATION LTD.—See Somfy SA; *Int'l*, pg. 7085
SISAL S.P.A.—See Flutter Entertainment plc; *Int'l*, pg. 2715
SISA STUDIO INFORMATICA SA—See WiseTech Global Limited; *Int'l*, pg. 8437
SISBARRO DEALERSHIPS; *U.S. Private*, pg. 3675
SISB PCL; *Int'l*, pg. 6963
SISCO ENTERPRISES INC.; *U.S. Private*, pg. 3675
SIS DISTRIBUTION (THAILAND) PUBLIC COMPANY LIMITED; *Int'l*, pg. 6963
SISECAM AUTOMOTIVE HUNGARY KFT.—See Turkiye Sise ve Cam Fabrikalari A.S.; *Int'l*, pg. 7977
SISECAM AUTOMOTIVE ROMANIA SA—See Turkiye Sise ve Cam Fabrikalari A.S.; *Int'l*, pg. 7977
SISECAM BULGARIA EOOD—See Turkiye Sise ve Cam Fabrikalari A.S.; *Int'l*, pg. 7977
SISECAM CHEMICALS RESOURCES LLC—See Turkiye Is Bankasi A.S.; *Int'l*, pg. 7976
SISECAM ELYAF SANAYII A.C.—See Soda Sanayii A.S.; *Int'l*, pg. 7045
SISECAM RESOURCES LP—See Turkiye Is Bankasi A.S.; *Int'l*, pg. 7976
SISECAM SHANGHAI TRADE CO., LTD.—See Turkiye Sise ve Cam Fabrikalari A.S.; *Int'l*, pg. 7977
SISECAM SIGORTA ARACILIK HIZMETLERI A.S—See Turkiye Sise ve Cam Fabrikalari A.S.; *Int'l*, pg. 7977
SISECAM SODA LUKAVAC D.O.O.—See Turkiye Sise ve Cam Fabrikalari A.S.; *Int'l*, pg. 7977
SISECAM TRADING CO.—See Soda Sanayii A.S.; *Int'l*, pg. 7045
SISENCE INC.; *U.S. Private*, pg. 3675
SISGE MEDICAL SRL—See Apax Partners LLP; *Int'l*, pg. 501
S. ISHIMITSU & CO., LTD.; *Int'l*, pg. 6446
SIS INTERNATIONAL HOLDINGS LIMITED—See SiS Distribution (Thailand) Public Company Limited; *Int'l*, pg. 6963
SIS INTERNATIONAL LTD—See SiS Distribution (Thailand) Public Company Limited; *Int'l*, pg. 6963
SISIS INFORMATIONSSYSTEME GMBH—See Online Computer Library Center, Inc.; *U.S. Private*, pg. 3026
SIS ITALIA S.P.A.—See Solvay S.A.; *Int'l*, pg. 7078
SISK AUTO MALL; *U.S. Private*, pg. 3675
SISK GROUP—See Sicon Ltd.; *Int'l*, pg. 6881

SISKIN STEEL AND SUPPLY CO., INC.—See Reliance Steel & Aluminum Co.; *U.S. Public*, pg. 1781
SISKIYOU FOREST PRODUCTS; *U.S. Private*, pg. 3675
SISKIYOU TELEPHONE CO.; *U.S. Private*, pg. 3675
SISLEYHONDA.COM.; *Int'l*, pg. 6963
SIS MOBILE HOLDINGS LIMITED—See SiS Distribution (Thailand) Public Company Limited; *Int'l*, pg. 6963
SIS NORTHWEST, INC.—See Primoris Services Corporation; *U.S. Public*, pg. 1719
SI SOFTWARE INNOVATION GMBH.—See SPARTA AG; *Int'l*, pg. 7127
SISPORT FIAT S.P.A.—See Stellantis N.V.; *Int'l*, pg. 7200
SISPROD-SISTEMAS DE PRODUCAO ELECTRONICA, LDA.—See ViTrox Corporation Berhad; *Int'l*, pg. 8262
SISRAM MEDICAL LTD.; *Int'l*, pg. 6963
SIS (SCIENCE IN SPORT) LIMITED—See Science in Sport plc; *Int'l*, pg. 6647
SIS, S.C.P.A.—See Sacyr, S.A.; *Int'l*, pg. 6466
SISSETON-WAHPETON SIOUX TRIBE; *U.S. Private*, pg. 3675
SISSONS PAINTS (GRENADA) LIMITED—See ANSA McAL Limited; *Int'l*, pg. 476
SISSONS PAINTS LIMITED—See ANSA McAL Limited; *Int'l*, pg. 476
SISSONS PAINTS (THAILAND) LIMITED—See Yip In Tsoi & Co., Ltd.; *Int'l*, pg. 8585
SIS SPEEDY INDUSTRIAL SUPPLIES SDN. BHD.—See BizLink Holding Inc.; *Int'l*, pg. 1053
SISSY'S LOG CABIN, INC.; *U.S. Private*, pg. 3675
SISTEMA 4B, S.A.—See Banco Santander, S.A.; *Int'l*, pg. 828
SISTEMA DE AHORRO PARA EL RETIRO—See Banco Bilbao Vizcaya Argentaria, S.A.; *Int'l*, pg. 818
SISTEMA EFACTURA S.L.—See Unifiedpost Group SA; *Int'l*, pg. 8043
SISTEMA-HALS DEVELOPMENT COMPANY—See Sistema PJSFC; *Int'l*, pg. 6963
SISTEMA ITALIA 93 S.R.L.—See MBE Worldwide S.p.A.; *Int'l*, pg. 4751
SISTEMA PJSFC; *Int'l*, pg. 6963
SISTEMA PLASTICS LIMITED—See Newell Brands Inc.; *U.S. Public*, pg. 1514
SISTEMA PLASTICS UK LIMITED—See Newell Brands Inc.; *U.S. Public*, pg. 1515
SISTEMAS ANALITICOS S.A.—See HORIBA Ltd; *Int'l*, pg. 3478
SISTEMAS CENTRAL AMERICA, S.A.—See Arcos Dorados Holdings Inc.; *Int'l*, pg. 550
SISTEMAS DE ARNESES K&S MEXICANA, S.A. DE C.V.—See Sumitomo Electric Industries, Ltd.; *Int'l*, pg. 7281
SISTEMAS DE CHASSIS IRACEMAPOLIS LTDA.—See ZF Friedrichshafen AG; *Int'l*, pg. 8641
SISTEMAS DE CONTROL REMOTO, S.L.—See Nippon Telegraph & Telephone Corporation; *Int'l*, pg. 5355
SISTEMAS DE LOCALIZACION S.A. DE C.V.—See Teleperformance SE; *Int'l*, pg. 7540
SISTEMAS DE RESERVACIONES CRS DE VENEZUELA, C.A.—See Amadeus IT Group, S.A.; *Int'l*, pg. 407
SISTEMAS ELECTRICOS Y CONMUTADORES, S.A. DE C.V.—See Aptiv PLC; *Int'l*, pg. 525
SISTEMAS ENERGETICOS CABANELAS, S.A.—See Siemens Energy AG; *Int'l*, pg. 6903
SISTEMAS ENERGETICOS CHANDREXA, S.A.—See Iberdrola, S.A.; *Int'l*, pg. 3574
SISTEMAS ENERGETICOS CUNTIS, S.A.—See Siemens Energy AG; *Int'l*, pg. 6903
SISTEMAS ENERGETICOS DEL SUR, S.A.—See Siemens Energy AG; *Int'l*, pg. 6903
SISTEMAS ENERGETICOS LA GOMERA, S.A.U—See Iberdrola, S.A.; *Int'l*, pg. 3574
SISTEMAS ENERGETICOS LA PLANA, S.A.—See Siemens Energy AG; *Int'l*, pg. 6903
SISTEMAS ENERGETICOS LOMA DEL REPOSO, S.L.—See Siemens Energy AG; *Int'l*, pg. 6903
SISTEMAS ENERGETICOS LOS LIRIOS, S.A.U.—See Iberdrola, S.A.; *Int'l*, pg. 3574
SISTEMAS ENERGETICOS MAS GARULLO, S.A.—See Iberdrola, S.A.; *Int'l*, pg. 3574
SISTEMAS ENERGETICOS SIERRA DE LOURENZA, S.A.—See Siemens Energy AG; *Int'l*, pg. 6903
SISTEMAS ILUMINACION S.A. DE C.V.—See Hella GmbH & Co. KGaA; *Int'l*, pg. 3332
SISTEMAS INFORMATICOS ABIERTOS, S.A.—See Indra Sistemas, S.A.; *Int'l*, pg. 3661
SISTEMAS INTEGRALES DE MANTENIMIENTO, S.A.—See ACS, Actividades de Construccion y Servicios, S.A.; *Int'l*, pg. 116
SISTEMAS INTEGRALES DE MEDICINA, S.A.—See Hoya Corporation; *Int'l*, pg. 3495
SISTEMAS KINEDYNE, S.A. DE C.V.—See Kinedyne Corporation; *U.S. Private*, pg. 2307
SISTEMAS MCDONALD'S PORTUGAL LDA—See McDonald's Corporation; *U.S. Public*, pg. 1406
SISTEMAS ORACLE DE CHILE, S.A.—See Oracle Corporation; *U.S. Public*, pg. 1613
SISTEMAS PHOENIX MECANO ESPANA S. A.—See Phoenix Mecano AG; *Int'l*, pg. 5853

SISTEMAS RADIANTES F. MOYANO, S.A.—See ACS, Actividades de Construccion y Servicios, S.A.; *Int'l*, pg. 116
SISTEMAS SEC, S.A.—See ACS, Actividades de Construccion y Servicios, S.A.; *Int'l*, pg. 116
SISTEMAS Y TECHNICAS DE SEGURIDAD, S.A.—See ASSA ABLOY AB; *Int'l*, pg. 640
SISTEMAS Y VEHICULOS DE ALTA TECNOLOGIA, S.A.—See Fomento de Construcciones y Contratas, S.A.; *Int'l*, pg. 2723
SISTEM FTO 011 A.D.; *Int'l*, pg. 6963
SISTEM INFRAESTRUCTURAS Y OPERACIONES EPC SA—See VINCI S.A.; *Int'l*, pg. 8227
SISTEMI PARABANCARI S.R.L.—See BPER BANCA S.p.A; *Int'l*, pg. 1132
SISTEMI SOSPENSIONI S.P.A.—See Stellantis N.V.; *Int'l*, pg. 7203
SISTEMI TERRITORIALI S.R.L.—See Almawave S.p.A.; *Int'l*, pg. 363
SISTEM MELESUR ENERGIA SAU—See VINCI S.A.; *Int'l*, pg. 8227
SISTEM TELEVISYEN MALAYSIA BERHAD.—See Media Prima Berhad; *Int'l*, pg. 4771
SISTER CIRCLE LLC—See TEGNA Inc.; *U.S. Public*, pg. 1990
SISTERNA B.V.—See Royal Cosun U.A.; *Int'l*, pg. 6412
SISTER SCHUBERT'S HOMEMADE ROLLS, INC.—See Lancaster Colony Corporation; *U.S. Public*, pg. 1292
SISTER SISTER, INC.—See Adjmi Apparel Group, Inc.; *U.S. Private*, pg. 79
SISTERS OF CHARITY HOSPITAL OF BUFFALO, NEW YORK—See Catholic Health System, Inc.; *U.S. Private*, pg. 791
SISTERS OF CHARITY HOSPITAL - ST. JOSEPH CAMPUS—See Catholic Health System, Inc.; *U.S. Private*, pg. 791
SISTERS OF CHARITY OF LEAVENWORTH HEALTH SYSTEM—See Intermountain Healthcare Inc.; *U.S. Private*, pg. 2113
SISTERS OF MERCY HEALTH SYSTEM; *U.S. Private*, pg. 3676
THE SISTERS OF THE THIRD ORDER OF ST. FRANCIS; *U.S. Private*, pg. 4118
SIS-TER S.P.A.—See Fresenius Medical Care AG; *Int'l*, pg. 2775
SISTER'S SANITATION SERVICES, LLC—See Waste Management, Inc.; *U.S. Public*, pg. 2332
SISTHEMA S.P.A.—See Sesa S.p.A.; *Int'l*, pg. 6729
SISTO ARMATUREN S.A.—See KSB SE & Co. KGaA; *Int'l*, pg. 4313
SISU HEALTHCARE IT SOLUTIONS, LLC; *U.S. Private*, pg. 3676
SISU WELLNESS PTY. LTD.—See Wesfarmers Limited; *Int'l*, pg. 8382
SI SYSTEMS, INC.—See Paragon Technologies, Inc.; *U.S. Public*, pg. 1637
S.I. SYSTEMS ULC—See Cornell Capital LLC; *U.S. Private*, pg. 1051
S.I. SYSTEMS ULC—See TorQuest Partners Inc.; *Int'l*, pg. 7830
SITA AUSTRALIA—See Sembcorp Industries Ltd.; *Int'l*, pg. 6702
SITA BELGIUM S.A.—See Veolia Environnement S.A.; *Int'l*, pg. 8155
SITA DEUTSCHLAND GMBH—See Veolia Environnement S.A.; *Int'l*, pg. 8155
SITA ENTERPRISES LIMITED; *Int'l*, pg. 6963
SITA FINLAND OY AB—See Veolia Environnement S.A.; *Int'l*, pg. 8155
SITA FRANCE—See Veolia Environnement S.A.; *Int'l*, pg. 8155
SITAG AG - GERMANY SALES OFFICE—See Nimbus B.V.; *Int'l*, pg. 5296
SITAG AG—See Nimbus B.V.; *Int'l*, pg. 5296
SITAG BUROMOBEL GMBH—See Nimbus B.V.; *Int'l*, pg. 5296
SITAG FORMY SIEDZENIA SP.Z O.O.—See Nimbus B.V.; *Int'l*, pg. 5296
SITAHAL 'HAGAL' (TALIA) PARTNERSHIP—See Kardan N.V.; *Int'l*, pg. 4079
SITA INC. N.V.; *Int'l*, pg. 6963
SITA INC.—See SITA Inc. N.V.; *Int'l*, pg. 6964
SITA INC.—See SITA Inc. N.V.; *Int'l*, pg. 6964
SITA LABORATORIES, INC.—See Marchex, Inc.; *U.S. Public*, pg. 1365
SITAMAS ENVIRONMENTAL SYSTEMS SDN BHD—See Kuok Brothers Sdn. Bhd.; *Int'l*, pg. 4335
SITA POLSKA—See Veolia Environnement S.A.; *Int'l*, pg. 8155
SITARA CHEMICAL INDUSTRIES LTD.; *Int'l*, pg. 6964
SITARA DEVELOPERS (PVT.) LTD—See Sitara Chemical Industries Ltd.; *Int'l*, pg. 6964
SITARA ENERGY LTD.; *Int'l*, pg. 6964
SITARA PEROXIDE LTD.; *Int'l*, pg. 6964
SITAR GROUP—See Imperial Brands PLC; *Int'l*, pg. 3633
SITA SC—See SITA Inc. N.V.; *Int'l*, pg. 6964
SITASHREE FOOD PRODUCTS LTD.; *Int'l*, pg. 6964
SITA SVERIGE AB—See Veolia Environnement S.A.; *Int'l*, pg. 8155

SITA UK—See Veolia Environment S.A.; *Int'l*, pg. 8155
SITA WASTE SERVICES LIMITED—See Veolia Environnement S.A.; *Int'l*, pg. 8155
SITA WASTE SERVICES LTD.—See Veolia Environnement S.A.; *Int'l*, pg. 8155
SITC CONTAINER LINES (SARAWAK) SDN. BHD.—See SITC International Holdings Company Limited; *Int'l*, pg. 6964
SITC INTERNATIONAL HOLDINGS COMPANY LIMITED; *Int'l*, pg. 6964
SITC JAPAN CO., LTD.—See SITC International Holdings Company Limited; *Int'l*, pg. 6964
SITC LOGISTICS (JAPAN) CO., LTD.—See SITC International Holdings Company Limited; *Int'l*, pg. 6964
SITCO IMPORTING CO.; *U.S. Private*, pg. 3676
SITC SHIPPING ASIA PTE. LIMITED—See SITC International Holdings Company Limited; *Int'l*, pg. 6964
SITC STEAMSHIP CO., LTD.—See SITC International Holdings Company Limited; *Int'l*, pg. 6964
SITC VIETNAM CO., LTD.—See SITC International Holdings Company Limited; *Int'l*, pg. 6964
SITE 9, INC.—See Astound Commerce Corp.; *U.S. Private*, pg. 361
SITE CENTERS CORP.; *U.S. Public*, pg. 1888
SITECH ATLANTIC LTD.; *Int'l*, pg. 6964
SITECH DEUTSCHLAND GMBH—See Zeppelin GmbH; *Int'l*, pg. 8637
SITECH DEUTSCHLAND GMBH—See Trimble, Inc.; *U.S. Public*, pg. 2191
SITECH INDIA NORTH & EAST—See TIL Limited; *Int'l*, pg. 7748
SI-TECH INFORMATION TECHNOLOGY CO.,LTD.; *Int'l*, pg. 6874
SITECH MANUFACTURING SERVICES BEHEER BV—See Koninklijke DSM N.V.; *Int'l*, pg. 4266
SITECH SOLUTIONS PTY LIMITED—See Seven Group Holdings Limited; *Int'l*, pg. 6733
SITECH SOUTHERN AFRICA (PTY) LTD—See Trimble, Inc.; *U.S. Public*, pg. 2191
SITECH SOUTH MS, LLC—See Puckett Machinery Company Inc.; *U.S. Private*, pg. 3301
SITECH (WA) PTY LIMITED—See Seven Group Holdings Limited; *Int'l*, pg. 6733
SITEC INDUSTRIETECHNOLOGIE GMBH; *Int'l*, pg. 6964
SITEC LABS PVT. LTD.—See Cipla Ltd.; *Int'l*, pg. 1617
SITECO AYDINLATMA TEKNIGI TIC. VE SAN. LTD, STI.—See Siemens Aktiengesellschaft; *Int'l*, pg. 6900
SITECO BELEUCHTUNGSTECHNIK GMBH—See Siemens Aktiengesellschaft; *Int'l*, pg. 6900
SITECO BELYSNING AS—See Siemens Aktiengesellschaft; *Int'l*, pg. 6900
SITECO FRANCE S.A.S.—See ams AG; *Int'l*, pg. 440
SITECO GMBH—See ams AG; *Int'l*, pg. 440
SITECO LIGHTING AUSTRIA GMBH—See Siemens Aktiengesellschaft; *Int'l*, pg. 6900
SITECO LIGHTING GMBH—See Stern Stewart & Co. GmbH; *Int'l*, pg. 7212
SITECO LIGHTING POLAND SP. Z O.O.—See Siemens Aktiengesellschaft; *Int'l*, pg. 6900
SITECO LIGHTING, S.L.U.—See Siemens Aktiengesellschaft; *Int'l*, pg. 6900
SITECO LIGHTING, SPOL. S R.O.—See Siemens Aktiengesellschaft; *Int'l*, pg. 6900
SITECO LIGHTING SYSTEMS S.R.L.—See Siemens Aktiengesellschaft; *Int'l*, pg. 6900
SITE COMMUNICATIONS, INC.—See Microwave Transmission Systems, Inc.; *U.S. Private*, pg. 2704
SITE CONFIDENCE LIMITED—See NCC Group Plc; *Int'l*, pg. 5181
SITECO NORWAY AS—See ams AG; *Int'l*, pg. 440
SITE CONSULTANTS INC.—See Westwood Professional Services, Inc.; *U.S. Private*, pg. 4502
SITECO OSTERREICH GMBH—See Siemens Aktiengesellschaft; *Int'l*, pg. 6900
SITECO POLAND SP. Z O.O.—See ams AG; *Int'l*, pg. 440
SITECORE AUSTRALIA PTY LTD—See EQT AB; *Int'l*, pg. 2480
SITECORE CANADA LTD—See EQT AB; *Int'l*, pg. 2480
SITECORE CORPORATION A/S—See EQT AB; *Int'l*, pg. 2480
SITECORE DEUTSCHLAND GMBH—See EQT AB; *Int'l*, pg. 2480
SITECORE JAPAN—See EQT AB; *Int'l*, pg. 2480
SITECORE NEDERLAND BV—See EQT AB; *Int'l*, pg. 2480
SITECORE NEW ZEALAND—See EQT AB; *Int'l*, pg. 2480
SITECORE SVERIGE AB—See EQT AB; *Int'l*, pg. 2480
SITECORE UK LTD.—See EQT AB; *Int'l*, pg. 2480
SITECORE USA, INC.—See EQT AB; *Int'l*, pg. 2480
SITECO SCHWEIZ AG—See Siemens Aktiengesellschaft; *Int'l*, pg. 6900
SITECO SISTEMI D.O.O.—See Siemens Aktiengesellschaft; *Int'l*, pg. 6900
SITECO UK LIMITED—See ams AG; *Int'l*, pg. 440
SITE EDUCATION AUSTRALIA PTY LTD—See Site Group International Ltd; *Int'l*, pg. 6964
SITE ENGINEERING INC.; *U.S. Private*, pg. 3676
SITE GROUP HOLDINGS PTY LTD—See Site Group International Ltd; *Int'l*, pg. 6964

SITE GROUP INTERNATIONAL LTD; *Int'l*, pg. 6964
SITE INTEGRATION PLUS INC.; *Int'l*, pg. 6964
SITEK AG—See INTEGRA Holding AG; *Int'l*, pg. 3729
SITEK MARKETING & COMMUNICATIONS; *U.S. Private*, pg. 3676
SITEK-PALVELU OY—See OEM International AB; *Int'l*, pg. 5528
SITEK-SPIKES GMBH & CO. KG—See INDUS Holding AG; *Int'l*, pg. 3664
SITELARK, LLC—See Flotek Industries, Inc.; *U.S. Public*, pg. 853
SIT ELECTRONICS COMPANY LIMITED—See Solartech International Holdings Limited; *Int'l*, pg. 7070
SITEL FRANCE SAS—See Creadev SAS; *Int'l*, pg. 1830
SITEL GMBH—See Creadev SAS; *Int'l*, pg. 1830
SITEL IBERICA TELESERVICES, S.A.—See Creadev SAS; *Int'l*, pg. 1831
SITELINES, INC.; *U.S. Private*, pg. 3676
SITEL NETHERLANDS—See Creadev SAS; *Int'l*, pg. 1831
SITEL NEW ZEALAND LIMITED—See Creadev SAS; *Int'l*, pg. 1831
SITELOGIQ GOVERNMENT SOLUTIONS LLC—See Brookfield Corporation; *Int'l*, pg. 1182
SITEL UK LTD.—See Creadev SAS; *Int'l*, pg. 1831
SITEL WORLDWIDE CORPORATION—See Creadev SAS; *Int'l*, pg. 1830
SITEMAKER SOFTWARE LIMITED; *Int'l*, pg. 6964
SITEMINDER LIMITED—See Bailador Technology Investments Limited; *Int'l*, pg. 802
SITE OIL COMPANY OF MISSOURI; *U.S. Private*, pg. 3676
SITEONE LANDSCAPE SUPPLY, INC.; *U.S. Public*, pg. 1888
SITEONE LANDSCAPE SUPPLY, LLC—See SiteOne Landscape Supply, Inc.; *U.S. Public*, pg. 1889
SITE ORGANIC, LLC; *U.S. Private*, pg. 3676
SITE PERSONNEL SERVICES INC.; *U.S. Private*, pg. 3676
SITE REALTY, INC.—See Pfizer Inc.; *U.S. Public*, pg. 1683
SITESCOUT INC.—See Centro Media, Inc.; *U.S. Private*, pg. 3676
SITESERV ACCESS & FORMWORK—See Siteserv Investments Limited; *Int'l*, pg. 6965
SITESERV INVESTMENTS LIMITED; *Int'l*, pg. 6964
SITESPECT EUROPE—See SiteSpect, Inc.; *U.S. Private*, pg. 3676
SITESPECT GERMANY—See SiteSpect, Inc.; *U.S. Private*, pg. 3676
SITESPECT, INC.; *U.S. Private*, pg. 3676
SITESPECT UK—See SiteSpect, Inc.; *U.S. Private*, pg. 3676
SITESTAR.NET, INC.—See ENDI Corp.; *U.S. Public*, pg. 760
SITESTUFF, INC.—See Yardi Systems, Inc.; *U.S. Private*, pg. 4586
SITE SUPPORT SERVICES, INC.—See Tate Engineering Systems Inc.; *U.S. Private*, pg. 3936
SITE TECHNOLOGY ASIA PACIFIC SDN BHD—See Sime Darby Berhad; *Int'l*, pg. 6930
SITETEL SHANGHAI CO. LTD.—See EnerSys; *U.S. Public*, pg. 767
SITETEL SWEDEN AB—See EnerSys; *U.S. Public*, pg. 767
SITEWIRE; *U.S. Private*, pg. 3676
SITEWIT CORP.; *U.S. Private*, pg. 3676
SITE WORK SPECIALISTS INC.; *U.S. Private*, pg. 3676
SITEWORX, INC.; *U.S. Private*, pg. 3676
SITEX CORPORATION—See Cintas Corporation; *U.S. Public*, pg. 496
SITEX PROPERTIES AG; *Int'l*, pg. 6965
SITEX SA—See SOL S.p.A.; *Int'l*, pg. 7067
SITHE FUEL CO., LTD.—See Marubeni Corporation; *Int'l*, pg. 4710
SITHEGA HOLDINGS (PTY) LTD.; *Int'l*, pg. 6965
SITHE YOSU COGENERATION CO., LTD.—See Marubeni Corporation; *Int'l*, pg. 4710
SITHIPORN ASSOCIATES CO., LTD.—See Waters Corporation; *U.S. Public*, pg. 2335
SITIA BETEILIGUNGS- UND VERWALTUNGS GMBH—See Allianz SE; *Int'l*, pg. 355
SITI BHATIA NETWORK ENTERTAINMENT PRIVATE LIMITED—See Essel Corporate Resources Pvt. Ltd.; *Int'l*, pg. 2510
SITI B&T GROUP S.P.A.; *Int'l*, pg. 6965
SITICABLE BROADBAND SOUTH LIMITED—See Essel Corporate Resources Pvt. Ltd.; *Int'l*, pg. 2510
SITI CABLE TISAI SATELLITE LIMITED—See Essel Corporate Resources Pvt. Ltd.; *Int'l*, pg. 2510
SITICOM GMBH—See Datatec Limited; *Int'l*, pg. 1980
SITI ENERGY LIMITED—See Essel Corporate Resources Pvt. Ltd.; *Int'l*, pg. 2510
SITI GUNTUR DIGITAL NETWORK PRIVATE LIMITED—See Essel Corporate Resources Pvt. Ltd.; *Int'l*, pg. 2510
SITI KRISHNA DIGITAL MEDIA PRIVATE LIMITED—See Essel Corporate Resources Pvt. Ltd.; *Int'l*, pg. 2510
SITI MAURYA CABLE NET PRIVATE LIMITED—See Essel Corporate Resources Pvt. Ltd.; *Int'l*, pg. 2509
SITIME CORP.; *U.S. Public*, pg. 1889

SITI NETWORKS LIMITED—See Essel Corporate Resources Pvt. Ltd.; *Int'l*, pg. 2509
SIT INVESTMENT ASSOCIATES, INC; *U.S. Private*, pg. 3676
SITIO ROYALTIES CORP.; *U.S. Public*, pg. 1889
SITIS S.R.L.—See Planetel S.p.A.; *Int'l*, pg. 5889
SITI VISION DIGITAL MEDIA PRIVATE LIMITED—See Essel Corporate Resources Pvt. Ltd.; *Int'l*, pg. 2510
SITKA GOLD CORP.; *Int'l*, pg. 6965
SITNASUAK NATIVE CORP.; *U.S. Private*, pg. 3676
SITOBIOTECH CO.,LTD.; *Int'l*, pg. 6965
SITOLOR D.O.O.—See Inles d.d.; *Int'l*, pg. 3705
SITO MOBILE LTD.; *U.S. Public*, pg. 1890
SITOUR CESKA REPUBLIKA S.R.O.—See Feratel Media Technologies AG; *Int'l*, pg. 2635
SITOUR ITALIA S.R.L.—See Feratel Media Technologies AG; *Int'l*, pg. 2635
SITOUR JAPAN KK—See Feratel Media Technologies AG; *Int'l*, pg. 2635
SITOUR MARKETING GMBH—See Feratel Media Technologies AG; *Int'l*, pg. 2635
SITOUR SPOL. S R.O.—See Feratel Media Technologies AG; *Int'l*, pg. 2635
SITOUR USA—See Feratel Media Technologies AG; *Int'l*, pg. 2635
SITOY GROUP HOLDINGS LTD.; *Int'l*, pg. 6965
SITOY (HONG KONG) HANDBAG FACTORY LIMITED—See Sitoy Group Holdings Ltd.; *Int'l*, pg. 6965
SITOY (YINGDE) LUGGAGE CO., LTD.—See Sitoy Group Holdings Ltd.; *Int'l*, pg. 6965
SITRA AGENCIES PTE LTD—See Sitra Holdings International Limited; *Int'l*, pg. 6965
SITRA AUTOMAZIONE SRL—See FIDIA S.p.A.; *Int'l*, pg. 2655
SITRADE ITALIA S.P.A.—See GLORY Ltd.; *Int'l*, pg. 3010
SITRA DOVE CONSTRUCTION & LOGISTIC PTE. LTD.—See Sitra Holdings International Limited; *Int'l*, pg. 6965
SITRA HOLDINGS INTERNATIONAL LIMITED; *Int'l*, pg. 6965
SITRAN LLC—See Foresight Energy LP; *U.S. Public*, pg. 867
SITRANS LTDA.—See Ultramar Ltda.; *Int'l*, pg. 8019
SITRICK & CO.; *U.S. Private*, pg. 3676
SITRION ONE—See NewsGator Technologies, Inc.; *U.S. Private*, pg. 2917
SITRONIX TECHNOLOGY CORPORATION; *Int'l*, pg. 6965
SITRONIX TECHNOLOGY (SHENZHEN) CO., LTD.—See Sitronix Technology Corporation; *Int'l*, pg. 6965
SIT SALZGITTER INFORMATION UND TELEKOMMUNIKATION GMBH—See Salzgitter AG; *Int'l*, pg. 6498
S IT SOLUTIONS CZ, S.R.O.—See Erste Group Bank AG; *Int'l*, pg. 2499
S IT SOLUTIONS HR DRUSTVO S OGRANICENOM ODGOVORNOSCU ZA USLUGE INFORMACIJSKIH TEHNOLOGIJA—See Erste Group Bank AG; *Int'l*, pg. 2499
SIT S.P.A.—See Interpump Group S.p.A.; *Int'l*, pg. 3757
SITTAB AB—See Addtech AB; *Int'l*, pg. 135
SITTAB INC.—See Addtech AB; *Int'l*, pg. 135
SITTAB STOL AB—See Addtech AB; *Int'l*, pg. 135
SITTERCITY INC.—See Bain Capital, LP; *U.S. Private*, pg. 437
SITTERLE HOMES; *U.S. Private*, pg. 3677
SITTERS ETC.; *U.S. Private*, pg. 3677
SITTON BUICK GMC SAAB; *U.S. Private*, pg. 3677
SITTON MOTOR LINES, INC.; *U.S. Private*, pg. 3677
SIT-UP LTD.—See Aurelius Equity Opportunities SE & Co. KGaA; *Int'l*, pg. 710
SITUSAMC HOLDINGS CORPORATION—See Stone Point Capital LLC; *U.S. Private*, pg. 3825
SITUS EUROPE LIMITED—See Stone Point Capital LLC; *U.S. Private*, pg. 3825
SITUS GROUP LLC—See Stone Point Capital LLC; *U.S. Private*, pg. 3825
SITUS HOLDINGS, LLC—See Stone Point Capital LLC; *U.S. Private*, pg. 3825
SITUS INTERNATIONAL LIMITED—See Stone Point Capital LLC; *U.S. Private*, pg. 3825
SITV, INC.; *U.S. Private*, pg. 3677
SITV INC.; *U.S. Private*, pg. 3677
SITZMANN, MORRIS & LAVIS INSURANCE AGENCY, INC.—See Brown & Brown, Inc.; *U.S. Public*, pg. 399
S-IU - COR - COMINVESTMENT AG—See Endress+Hauser (International) Holding AG; *Int'l*, pg. 2409
SIU CREDIT UNION; *U.S. Private*, pg. 3677
SIU LLC—See QBE Insurance Group Limited; *Int'l*, pg. 6137
SIVACO ONTARIO PROCESSING DIVISION—See The Heico Companies, L.L.C.; *U.S. Private*, pg. 4051
SIVACO QUEBEC DIVISION—See The Heico Companies, L.L.C.; *U.S. Private*, pg. 4051
SIVACO WIRE GROUP L.L.C. - ONTARIO PLANT—See The Heico Companies, L.L.C.; *U.S. Private*, pg. 4051
SIVACO WIRE GROUP L.P.—See The Heico Companies, L.L.C.; *U.S. Private*, pg. 4051
SIVA EIENDOM HOLDING—See SIVA SF; *Int'l*, pg. 6965

COMPANY NAME INDEX

SIVA INTERNATIONAL MANAGEMENT AS—See SIVA SF; *Int'l*, pg. 6965
SIVALLS, INC. - BROWNWOOD MANUFACTURING PLANT—See Sivalls, Inc.; *U.S. Private*, pg. 3677
SIVALLS, INC. - PAMPA MANUFACTURING PLANT—See Sivalls, Inc.; *U.S. Private*, pg. 3677
SIVALLS, INC.; *U.S. Private*, pg. 3677
SIVANTOS GMBH—See EQT AB; *Int'l*, pg. 2480
SIVANTOS INDIA PVT. LTD.—See EQT AB; *Int'l*, pg. 2480
SIVANTOS LIMITED—See Siemens Aktiengesellschaft; *Int'l*, pg. 6900
SIVAROM REAL ESTATE PUBLIC COMPANY LIMITED; *Int'l*, pg. 6966
SIVA SF; *Int'l*, pg. 6965
SIVA SHIPPING AS—See Siva Ventures Limited; *Int'l*, pg. 6965
SIVA THERAPEUTICS INC.—See Sona Nanotech Inc.; *Int'l*, pg. 7088
SIVA TRUCK LEASING INC.—See Badger Truck and Automotive Group, Inc.; *U.S. Private*, pg. 424
SIVA VENTURES LIMITED; *Int'l*, pg. 6965
SIV CAPITAL LIMITED; *Int'l*, pg. 6965
SIVELGA ASSOCIATED CLOSED JOINT STOCK COMPANY—See VEB.RF; *Int'l*, pg. 8143
SIVENMARK MASKINTJANST AB—See Keller Group plc; *Int'l*, pg. 4121
SIVENT D.D. LJUBLJANA; *Int'l*, pg. 6966
SIVERS SEMICONDUCTORS AB; *Int'l*, pg. 6966
SIVOMATIC B.V.—See Minerals Technologies, Inc.; *U.S. Public*, pg. 1449
SIVOTA PLC; *Int'l*, pg. 6966
SIVYER STEEL CORPORATION RIVERSIDE PRODUCTS DIV.—See Sivyer Steel Corporation; *U.S. Private*, pg. 3677
SIVYER STEEL CORPORATION; *U.S. Private*, pg. 3677
SIWANI MAKMUR TBK; *Int'l*, pg. 6966
SIWARD CRYSTAL TECHNOLOGY CO., LTD.; *Int'l*, pg. 6966
SIWARD CRYSTAL TECHNOLOGY CO., LTD. - WUXI FACTORY—See Siward Crystal Technology Co., Ltd.; *Int'l*, pg. 6966
SIWARD CRYSTAL TECHNOLOGY CO., LTD. - YAMAGATA FACTORY—See Siward Crystal Technology Co., Ltd.; *Int'l*, pg. 6966
SIWARD ELECTRONIC TECHNOLOGY (SHENZHEN) INC.—See Siward Crystal Technology Co., Ltd.; *Int'l*, pg. 6966
SIWARD TECHNOLOGY CO., LTD.—See Siward Crystal Technology Co., Ltd.; *Int'l*, pg. 6966
SI WAREHOUSING COMPANY INC.—See Slay Industries Inc.; *U.S. Private*, pg. 3687
SIWEL CONSULTING INC.; *U.S. Private*, pg. 3677
SIWERTELL AB—See Cargotec Corporation; *Int'l*, pg. 1329
SIX.02 BIOSERVICES, LLC; *U.S. Private*, pg. 3677
SIX3 SYSTEMS, INC.—See CACI International Inc.; *U.S. Public*, pg. 418
SIX88 SOLUTIONS, INC.; *U.S. Private*, pg. 3677
SIX AB—See SIX Group AG; *Int'l*, pg. 6967
SIXARP LLC—See Huizenga Manufacturing Group, Inc.; *U.S. Private*, pg. 2005
SIX BENDS HARLEY-DAVIDSON—See Scott Fischer Enterprises LLC; *U.S. Private*, pg. 3577
SIX CARD SOLUTIONS LTD—See SIX Group AG; *Int'l*, pg. 6966
SIXCO NORTH AMERICA, INC.—See InterContinental Hotels Group PLC; *Int'l*, pg. 3738
SIX CONTINENTS HOTELS DE COLOMBIA SA—See InterContinental Hotels Group PLC; *Int'l*, pg. 3739
SIX CONTINENTS HOTELS, INC.—See InterContinental Hotels Group PLC; *Int'l*, pg. 3738
SIX CONTINENTS INTERNATIONAL HOLDINGS BV—See InterContinental Hotels Group PLC; *Int'l*, pg. 3739
SIX DEGREES TECHNOLOGY GROUP LTD.—See Charlesbank Capital Partners, LLC; *U.S. Private*, pg. 856
SIX DIGITAL EXCHANGE LTD.—See SIX Group AG; *Int'l*, pg. 6966
SIXENSE CANADA INC.—See VINCI S.A.; *Int'l*, pg. 8227
SIXENSE DIGITAL SAS—See VINCI S.A.; *Int'l*, pg. 8227
SIXENSE IBERIA LIMITADA—See VINCI S.A.; *Int'l*, pg. 8227
SIXENSE IBERIA S.A.—See VINCI S.A.; *Int'l*, pg. 8227
SIXENSE LIMITED—See VINCI S.A.; *Int'l*, pg. 8227
SIXENSE LIMITED—See VINCI S.A.; *Int'l*, pg. 8227
SIXENSE MAPING SAS—See VINCI S.A.; *Int'l*, pg. 8227
SIXENSE MAROC SARL—See VINCI S.A.; *Int'l*, pg. 8227
SIXENSE NUMERICAL ENGINEERING ET CONSULTING SERVICES SAS—See VINCI S.A.; *Int'l*, pg. 8227
SIXENSE OCEANIA PTY. LTD.—See VINCI S.A.; *Int'l*, pg. 8227
SIXENSE SOLDATA SAS—See VINCI S.A.; *Int'l*, pg. 8227
SIX EXCHANGE REGULATION LTD.—See SIX Group AG; *Int'l*, pg. 6966
SIX FINANCIAL INFORMATION BELGIUM SA—See SIX Group AG; *Int'l*, pg. 6967
SIX FINANCIAL INFORMATION DENMARK A/S—See SIX Group AG; *Int'l*, pg. 6967
SIX FINANCIAL INFORMATION DEUTSCHLAND GMBH—See SIX Group AG; *Int'l*, pg. 6967
SIX FINANCIAL INFORMATION ESPANA SA—See SIX Group AG; *Int'l*, pg. 6967
SIX FINANCIAL INFORMATION FINLAND OY—See SIX Group AG; *Int'l*, pg. 6967
SIX FINANCIAL INFORMATION FRANCE SAS—See SIX Group AG; *Int'l*, pg. 6967
SIX FINANCIAL INFORMATION HONG KONG LIMITED—See SIX Group AG; *Int'l*, pg. 6967
SIX FINANCIAL INFORMATION ITALIA SRL—See SIX Group AG; *Int'l*, pg. 6967
SIX FINANCIAL INFORMATION JAPAN LTD—See SIX Group AG; *Int'l*, pg. 6967
SIX FINANCIAL INFORMATION LUXEMBOURG S.A.—See SIX Group AG; *Int'l*, pg. 6967
SIX FINANCIAL INFORMATION MONACO SAM—See SIX Group AG; *Int'l*, pg. 6967
SIX FINANCIAL INFORMATION NEDERLAND BV—See SIX Group AG; *Int'l*, pg. 6967
SIX FINANCIAL INFORMATION NORDIC AB—See SIX Group AG; *Int'l*, pg. 6967
SIX FINANCIAL INFORMATION NORWAY AS—See SIX Group AG; *Int'l*, pg. 6967
SIX FINANCIAL INFORMATION SINGAPORE PTE LTD—See SIX Group AG; *Int'l*, pg. 6967
SIX FINANCIAL INFORMATION—See SIX Group AG; *Int'l*, pg. 6966
SIX FINANCIAL INFORMATION UK LTD—See SIX Group AG; *Int'l*, pg. 6967
SIX FINANCIAL INFORMATION USA INC—See SIX Group AG; *Int'l*, pg. 6967
SIX FLAGS AMERICA LP—See Six Flags Entertainment Corp.; *U.S. Public*, pg. 1890
SIX FLAGS DISCOVERY KINGDOM—See Six Flags Entertainment Corp.; *U.S. Public*, pg. 1890
SIX FLAGS ENTERTAINMENT CORPORATION; *U.S. Public*, pg. 1890
SIX FLAGS ENTERTAINMENT CORP.; *U.S. Public*, pg. 1890
SIX FLAGS GREAT ADVENTURE LLC—See Six Flags Entertainment Corp.; *U.S. Public*, pg. 1890
SIX FLAGS GREAT AMERICA, INC.—See Six Flags Entertainment Corp.; *U.S. Public*, pg. 1890
SIX FLAGS HURRICANE HARBOR—See Six Flags Entertainment Corp.; *U.S. Public*, pg. 1890
SIX FLAGS MAGIC MOUNTAIN & HURRICANE HARBOR—See Six Flags Entertainment Corp.; *U.S. Public*, pg. 1890
SIX FLAGS MEXICO S.A. DE C.V.—See Six Flags Entertainment Corp.; *U.S. Public*, pg. 1890
SIX FLAGS OVER GEORGIA, INC.—See Six Flags Entertainment Corp.; *U.S. Public*, pg. 1890
SIX FLAGS OVER TEXAS & HURRICANE HARBOR—See Six Flags Entertainment Corp.; *U.S. Public*, pg. 1890
SIX FLAGS OVER TEXAS, INC.—See Six Flags Entertainment Corp.; *U.S. Public*, pg. 1890
SIX FLAGS ST. LOUIS LLC—See Six Flags Entertainment Corp.; *U.S. Public*, pg. 1890
SIX FLAGS THEME PARKS INC.—See Six Flags Entertainment Corp.; *U.S. Public*, pg. 1890
SIX & GEVING INSURANCE, INC.—See Galiot Insurance Services, Inc.; *U.S. Private*, pg. 1638
SIX GROUP AG; *Int'l*, pg. 6966
SIXIAN ZHONGYU GAS CO., LTD.—See Zhongyu Energy Holdings Limited; *Int'l*, pg. 8676
SIX INTERBANK CLEARING LTD.—See SIX Group AG; *Int'l*, pg. 6967
SIX L'S PACKING COMPANY, INC.—See Lipman & Lipman, Inc.; *U.S. Private*, pg. 2465
SIX MONTH SMILES, INC.—See Huron Capital Partners LLC; *U.S. Private*, pg. 2012
SIXNET, LLC—See HMS Networks AB; *Int'l*, pg. 3433
SIXNET WIRELESS PRODUCT GROUP CANADA—See HMS Networks AB; *Int'l*, pg. 3433
SIXNET WIRELESS PRODUCT GROUP USA—See HMS Networks AB; *Int'l*, pg. 3433
SIX NORGE AS—See SIX Group AG; *Int'l*, pg. 6967
SIX PAYMENT SERVICES (EUROPE) SA—See Worldline SA; *Int'l*, pg. 8458
SIX PAYMENT SERVICES (GERMANY) GMBH—See Worldline SA; *Int'l*, pg. 8458
SIX PAYMENT SERVICES LTD—See Worldline SA; *Int'l*, pg. 8458
SIX PAYMENT SERVICES (SWEDEN) AB—See Worldline SA; *Int'l*, pg. 8458
SIX PAYMENT SERVICES (UK) LTD—See Worldline SA; *Int'l*, pg. 8458
SIX PAYMENT SERVICES (USA) CORP—See SIX Group AG; *Int'l*, pg. 6967
SIX PAYNET LTD.—See SIX Group AG; *Int'l*, pg. 6967
SIX PENN KITCHEN—See Eat'n Park Hospitality Group, Inc.; *U.S. Private*, pg. 1323
SIXPOINT PARTNERS, LLC—See The PNC Financial Services Group, Inc.; *U.S. Public*, pg. 2119
SIX RED MARBLES, LLC—See Jouve, SA; *Int'l*, pg. 4003
SIX ROBBLEES INC.; *U.S. Private*, pg. 3677
SIX SECURITIES SERVICES LTD—See SIX Group AG; *Int'l*, pg. 6967
THE SIX SEMICONDUCTOR INC.—See Openedges Technology, Inc.; *Int'l*, pg. 5599
SIX SIS AG—See SIX Group AG; *Int'l*, pg. 6967
SIX SWISS EXCHANGE LTD.—See SIX Group AG; *Int'l*, pg. 6967
SIXT AG—See Sixt SE; *Int'l*, pg. 6967
SIXT BETEILIGUNGEN GMBH & CO. HOLDING KG—See Sixt SE; *Int'l*, pg. 6968
SIXT B.V.—See Sixt SE; *Int'l*, pg. 6968
SIXT CAR SALES GMBH—See Sixt SE; *Int'l*, pg. 6968
SIXTEENTH STREET COMMUNITY HEALTH CENTER; *U.S. Private*, pg. 3677
SIX TELEKURS (DEUTSCHLAND) GMBH—See SIX Group AG; *Int'l*, pg. 6967
SIX TELEKURS ESPANA SA—See SIX Group AG; *Int'l*, pg. 6967
SIX TELEKURS FINLAND OY—See SIX Group AG; *Int'l*, pg. 6967
SIX TELEKURS FRANCE SAS—See SIX Group AG; *Int'l*, pg. 6967
SIX TELEKURS HONG KONG LTD.—See SIX Group AG; *Int'l*, pg. 6967
SIX TELEKURS ITALIA S.R.L.—See SIX Group AG; *Int'l*, pg. 6967
SIX TELEKURS JAPAN LTD.—See SIX Group AG; *Int'l*, pg. 6967
SIX TELEKURS (U.K.) LTD.—See SIX Group AG; *Int'l*, pg. 6967
SIX TELEKURS USA INC.—See SIX Group AG; *Int'l*, pg. 6967
SIXT FINANCE B.V.—See Sixt SE; *Int'l*, pg. 6968
SIXT GMBH & CO. AUTOVERMIETUNG KG—See Sixt SE; *Int'l*, pg. 6968
SIXTH AVENUE ELECTRONICS, INC.; *U.S. Private*, pg. 3677
SIXTHMAN, LLC; *U.S. Private*, pg. 3678
SIXTH MAN MARKETING—See JEBCommerce LLC; *U.S. Private*, pg. 2196
SIXTH METALLURGICAL CONSTRUCTION COMPANY OF CHINA NONFERROUS METALS INDUSTRY CO., LTD.—See China Aluminum International Engineering Corporation Limited; *Int'l*, pg. 1482
SIXTH OF OCTOBER FOR DEVELOPMENT & INVESTMENT CO.; *Int'l*, pg. 6968
SIXTH STREET ADVISERS, LLC—See Sixth Street Specialty Lending, Inc.; *U.S. Public*, pg. 1891
SIXTH STREET LENDING PARTNERS; *U.S. Private*, pg. 3677
SIXTH STREET PARTNERS LLC; *U.S. Private*, pg. 3677
SIXTH STREET SPECIALTY LENDING, INC.; *U.S. Public*, pg. 1890
SIXTH WAVE INNOVATIONS INC.; *Int'l*, pg. 6968
SIXT KENNING LTD.—See Sixt SE; *Int'l*, pg. 6968
SIXT LEASING G.M.B.H.—See Sixt SE; *Int'l*, pg. 6968
SIXT LEASING (SCHWEIZ) AG—See Sixt SE; *Int'l*, pg. 6968
SIXT LOCATION LONGUE DUREE SARL—See Sixt SE; *Int'l*, pg. 6968
SIXT MOBILITY CONSULTING AG—See Banco Santander, S.A.; *Int'l*, pg. 826
SIXT MOBILITY CONSULTING AG—See Hyundai Motor Company; *Int'l*, pg. 3559
SIXT MOBILITY CONSULTING GMBH—See Banco Santander, S.A.; *Int'l*, pg. 826
SIXT MOBILITY CONSULTING GMBH—See Hyundai Motor Company; *Int'l*, pg. 3559
SIXT MOBILITY CONSULTING S.A.R.L.—See Banco Santander, S.A.; *Int'l*, pg. 826
SIXT MOBILITY CONSULTING S.A.R.L.—See Hyundai Motor Company; *Int'l*, pg. 3559
SIXT PLC—See Sixt SE; *Int'l*, pg. 6968
SIX TRADE REPOSITORY LTD.—See SIX Group AG; *Int'l*, pg. 6967
SIXT R&D PRIVATE LIMITED—See Sixt SE; *Int'l*, pg. 6968
SIXT RENT-A-CAR LLC—See Suhail Bahwan Group (Holding) LLC; *Int'l*, pg. 7254
SIXT RIDE GMBH & CO.—See Sixt SE; *Int'l*, pg. 6968
SIXT SAS—See Sixt SE; *Int'l*, pg. 6968
SIXT SE; *Int'l*, pg. 6967
SIXT VIP SERVICES GMBH—See Sixt SE; *Int'l*, pg. 6968
SIXTY CANADA—See Sixty S.p.A.; *Int'l*, pg. 6968
SIXTY GROUP RUSSIA—See Sixty S.p.A.; *Int'l*, pg. 6968
SIXTY NORTH GOLD MINING LTD.; *Int'l*, pg. 6968
SIXTY PORTUGAL—See Sixty S.p.A.; *Int'l*, pg. 6968
SIXTY-SIX SWITCHGEARS CO PTE. LTD.—See Rotary Engineering Pte. Ltd.; *Int'l*, pg. 6402
SIXTY S.P.A.; *Int'l*, pg. 6968
SIXTY UK LTD—See Sixty S.p.A.; *Int'l*, pg. 6968
SIXXON TECH. CO., LTD.; *Int'l*, pg. 6968
SIYANG TAISOL ELECTRONICS CO., LTD.—See TaiSol Electronics Co., Ltd.; *Int'l*, pg. 7418
SIYAPATHA FINANCE PLC—See Sampath Bank PLC; *Int'l*, pg. 6507
SIYAQHUBEKA FORESTS PROPRIETARY LIMITED—See Mondi plc; *Int'l*, pg. 5027
SIYARAM SILK MILLS LIMITED; *Int'l*, pg. 6968
SIYATA MOBILE, INC.; *Int'l*, pg. 6968
SIZEMASTERS TECHNOLOGY LIMITED; *Int'l*, pg. 6968
SIZEMORE GROUP; *U.S. Private*, pg. 3678
SIZEMORE PERSONNEL INC.—See Sizemore Group; *U.S. Private*, pg. 3678

SIZEMORE GROUP / CORPORATE AFFILIATIONS

SIZEWISE RENTALS, L.L.C.—See Thomas H. Lee Partners, L.P.; *U.S. Private*, pg. 4156
SIZHING ELECTRONIC (SUZHOU) COMPANY LIMITED—See Surface Mount Technology (Holdings) Limited; *Int'l*, pg. 7343
SIZMEK DSP, INC.—See Zeta Interactive Corporation; *U.S. Private*, pg. 4603
SIZMEK INC.—See Vector Capital Management, L.P.; *U.S. Private*, pg. 4352
SIZMEK SPAIN, S.L.—See Vector Capital Management, L.P.; *U.S. Private*, pg. 4352
SIZMEK TECHNOLOGIES GMBH—See Vector Capital Management, L.P.; *U.S. Private*, pg. 4352
SIZMEK TECHNOLOGIES, INC.—See Vector Capital Management, L.P.; *U.S. Private*, pg. 4352
SIZMEK TECHNOLOGIES K.K.—See Vector Capital Management, L.P.; *U.S. Private*, pg. 4353
SIZMEK TECHNOLOGIES LTD.—See Vector Capital Management, L.P.; *U.S. Private*, pg. 4353
SIZMEK TECHNOLOGIES LTD.—See Vector Capital Management, L.P.; *U.S. Private*, pg. 4353
SIZMEK TECHNOLOGIES PTY. LTD.—See Vector Capital Management, L.P.; *U.S. Private*, pg. 4353
SIZUOKA NISSAN AUTO SALES CO., LTD—See VT Holdings Co., Ltd.; *Int'l*, pg. 8315
SIZWE AFRICA IT GROUP (PTY) LTD—See Stellar Capital Partners Limited; *Int'l*, pg. 7204
SIZWE BUSINESS NETWORKING (PTY) LTD—See Stellar Capital Partners Limited; *Int'l*, pg. 7204
SIZZLE ACQUISITION CORP.—See European Lithium Limited; *Int'l*, pg. 2556
SIZZLER USA, INC.; *U.S. Private*, pg. 3678
SIZZLING PLATTER LLC; *U.S. Private*, pg. 3678
SJA INC.; *U.S. Private*, pg. 3678
SJ AMOROSO CONSTRUCTION CO.; *U.S. Private*, pg. 3678
SJB CORPORATE LIMITED—See ManpowerGroup Inc.; *U.S. Public*, pg. 1360
SJB SERVICES, INC.—See Atlantic Testing Laboratories, Ltd.; *U.S. Private*, pg. 374
SJB SERVICES UK LIMITED—See ManpowerGroup Inc.; *U.S. Public*, pg. 1360
SJ CHEM CO., LTD.; *Int'l*, pg. 6968
SJC INC.; *U.S. Private*, pg. 3678
SJ COMMUNICATIONS; *U.S. Private*, pg. 3678
S&J CONSTRUCTION CO. INC.; *U.S. Private*, pg. 3513
SJ CORPORATION LIMITED; *Int'l*, pg. 6968
S&J CORPORATION; *Int'l*, pg. 6444
SJ CREATIONS, INC.—See Platinum Equity, LLC; *U.S. Private*, pg. 3205
S. J. DELPHIA SP. Z.O.O.—See Beneteau S.A; *Int'l*, pg. 973
SJEC CORPORATION; *Int'l*, pg. 6969
SJ ENERTRADE, INC.—See JPMorgan Chase & Co.; *U.S. Public*, pg. 1210
S. JENNINGS LTD.; *Int'l*, pg. 6446
SJESP PLUMBING SERVICES LLC—See Brookfield Corporation; *Int'l*, pg. 1188
SJ FUEL CO., INC.; *U.S. Private*, pg. 3678
SJ GROUP CO., LTD.; *Int'l*, pg. 6969
SJG SEJONG CO., LTD.; *Int'l*, pg. 6969
SJH DISTRIBUTING INC.; *U.S. Private*, pg. 3678
SJI D.O.O.—See Saint Jean Industries SAS; *Int'l*, pg. 6484
SJI FULFILLMENT—See SJI, Inc.; *U.S. Private*, pg. 3678
SJI INC.—See Saint Jean Industries SAS; *Int'l*, pg. 6484
SJI, INC.; *U.S. Private*, pg. 3678
SJI K.K.—See Saint Jean Industries SAS; *Int'l*, pg. 6484
SJI LLC—See RTC Holdings, L.L.C.; *U.S. Private*, pg. 3498
S&J INTERNATIONAL ENTERPRISES PUBLIC COMPANY LIMITED; *Int'l*, pg. 6444
S&J INTERNATIONAL (UK) LTD—See S&J International Enterprises Public Company Limited; *Int'l*, pg. 6445
SJJC AIRLINE SERVICES, LLC—See Macquarie Group Limited; *Int'l*, pg. 4627
SJJC AVIATION SERVICES, LLC—See Macquarie Group Limited; *Int'l*, pg. 4627
SJK CO., LTD.; *Int'l*, pg. 6969
SJL BROADCAST MANAGEMENT CORP.; *U.S. Private*, pg. 3678
S J LOGISTICS (INDIA) LIMITED; *Int'l*, pg. 6442
S.J. LOUIS CONSTRUCTION INC.; *U.S. Private*, pg. 3517
SJL PARTNERS LLC; *Int'l*, pg. 6969
SJL WELL SERVICE, LLC—See Nine Energy Service, Inc.; *U.S. Public*, pg. 1529
SJ MANAGEMENT COMPANY OF SYRACUSE INC.; *U.S. Private*, pg. 3678
SJM CO., LTD.; *Int'l*, pg. 6969
SJM FLEX (PTY) LTD—See SJM CO., LTD.; *Int'l*, pg. 6969
SJM GMBH—See SJM CO., LTD.; *Int'l*, pg. 6969
SJM HOLDINGS CO., LTD.; *Int'l*, pg. 6969
SJM HOLDINGS LIMITED; *Int'l*, pg. 6969
SJM NORTH AMERICA INC.—See SJM CO., LTD.; *Int'l*, pg. 6969
S. JOSEPH & SONS; *U.S. Private*, pg. 3515
SJOSTRAND COFFEE INT AB; *Int'l*, pg. 6969
SJOSTROM & SONS INC.; *U.S. Private*, pg. 3678
SJOTROLL HAVBRUK AS—See Austevoll Seafood ASA; *Int'l*, pg. 718

SJOVA-ALMENNAR TRYGGINGAR HF; *Int'l*, pg. 6970
SJP 1 LIMITED—See Heidelberg Materials AG; *Int'l*, pg. 3319
S.J. PROPERTIES SDN. BHD.—See Sharikat Permodalan Kebangsaan Bhd; *Int'l*, pg. 6789
S&J REED INC.; *U.S. Private*, pg. 3513
SJ SEMICONDUCTOR (HK) LIMITED—See Semiconductor Manufacturing International Corporation; *Int'l*, pg. 6704
SJS ENTERPRISES LIMITED; *Int'l*, pg. 6970
S&J SHEET METAL SUPPLY INC.; *U.S. Private*, pg. 3513
S.J. SMITH CO., INC.; *U.S. Private*, pg. 3517
S&J VILLARI LIVESTOCK; *U.S. Private*, pg. 3513
SJVN ARUN-3 POWER DEVELOPMENT COMPANY PVT. LTD.—See SJVN Ltd.; *Int'l*, pg. 6970
SJVN LTD.; *Int'l*, pg. 6970
SJW GROUP; *U.S. Public*, pg. 1891
SJW LAND COMPANY—See SJW Group; *U.S. Public*, pg. 1891
SK3 GROUP, INC.; *U.S. Private*, pg. 3680
S&K ACQUISITION CORP; *U.S. Private*, pg. 3513
SKAELSKOR ANLAEGSGARTNERE A/S—See Det Danske Hedeselskab; *Int'l*, pg. 2047
SKAERBAEK BYGNINGSINDUSTRI A/S—See VKR Holding A/S; *Int'l*, pg. 8281
SKAFF CRYOGENICS, INC.—See Chart Industries, Inc.; *U.S. Public*, pg. 482
SKAGEN DESIGNS, LTD.—See Fossil Group, Inc.; *U.S. Public*, pg. 875
SKAGERAK ELEKTRO AS—See Statkraft AS; *Int'l*, pg. 7185
SKAGERAK ENERGI AS—See Statkraft AS; *Int'l*, pg. 7185
SKAGFIELD CORPORATION; *U.S. Private*, pg. 3680
SKAGGS AND GRUBER, LTD—See EssilorLuxottica SA; *Int'l*, pg. 2514
SKAGGS COMPANIES, INC.; *U.S. Private*, pg. 3680
SKAGGS-WALSH, INC.; *U.S. Private*, pg. 3680
SKAGIT FARMERS SUPPLY; *U.S. Private*, pg. 3681
SKAGIT RIVER BREWERY; *U.S. Private*, pg. 3681
SKAG-WAY DISCOUNT DEPARTMENT STORES INC.; *U.S. Private*, pg. 3680
SKAHA FORD INC.; *Int'l*, pg. 6976
SKA INVEST AS; *Int'l*, pg. 6976
SK AIRGAS CO., LTD.—See SK Materials Co., Ltd.; *Int'l*, pg. 6974
SKAJAQUODA GROUP INC.; *U.S. Private*, pg. 3681
SKAKO A/S; *Int'l*, pg. 6976
SKAKO CONCRETE A/S—See Skako A/S; *Int'l*, pg. 6976
SKAKO CONCRETE, INC.—See Skako A/S; *Int'l*, pg. 6976
SKAKO CONCRETE S.A.—See Skako A/S; *Int'l*, pg. 6976
SKAKO GMBH—See Skako A/S; *Int'l*, pg. 6976
SKAKO VIBRATION A/S—See Skako A/S; *Int'l*, pg. 6976
SKAKO VIBRATION LTD.—See Skako A/S; *Int'l*, pg. 6976
SKAKO VIBRATION S.A.—See Skako A/S; *Int'l*, pg. 6976
SKALAND GRAPHITE A.S.—See Mineral Commodities Limited; *Int'l*, pg. 4906
SKAMOL AMERICAS, INC.—See FSN Capital Partners AS; *Int'l*, pg. 2800
SKAMOL A/S - CALCIUM SILICATE PLANT—See FSN Capital Partners AS; *Int'l*, pg. 2799
SKAMOL A/S - MOLER BRICK PLANT—See FSN Capital Partners AS; *Int'l*, pg. 2799
SKAMOL A/S—See FSN Capital Partners AS; *Int'l*, pg. 2799
SKAMOL A/S - VERMICULITE PLANT—See FSN Capital Partners AS; *Int'l*, pg. 2800
SKAMOL RUS LLC—See FSN Capital Partners AS; *Int'l*, pg. 2800
SKANAALI—See Publicis Groupe S.A.; *Int'l*, pg. 6111
SKANDEX I BROMMA AB—See Lagercrantz Group AB; *Int'l*, pg. 4395
SKANDIA A/S—See Foreningen AP Pension f.m.b.a.; *Int'l*, pg. 2731
SKANDIA AUSTRIA HOLDING AG—See FWU AG; *Int'l*, pg. 2859
SKANDIABANKEN AKTIEBOLAG—See Livforsakringsaktiebolaget Skandia; *Int'l*, pg. 4532
SKANDIA FONDER AB—See Livforsakringsaktiebolaget Skandia; *Int'l*, pg. 4532
SKANDIA GREENPOWER AS; *Int'l*, pg. 6976
SKANDIA HOLDING DE COLOMBIA S.A.—See Livforsakringsaktiebolaget Skandia; *Int'l*, pg. 4531
SKANDIA, INC.—See TransDigm Group Incorporated; *U.S. Public*, pg. 2183
SKANDIA LEBEN AG—See Mutschler Holding AG; *Int'l*, pg. 5106
SKANDIA LEBEN AG—See Talanx AG; *Int'l*, pg. 7445
SKANDIA LEBENSVERSICHERUNG AG—See Cinven Limited; *Int'l*, pg. 1616
SKANDIA LEBENSVERSICHERUNG AG—See Talanx AG; *Int'l*, pg. 7445
SKANDIA LIFE ASSURANCE (HOLDINGS) LTD.—See Livforsakringsaktiebolaget Skandia; *Int'l*, pg. 4531
SKANDIA LIFE ASSURANCE LTD.—See Livforsakringsaktiebolaget Skandia; *Int'l*, pg. 4531
SKANDIA LIFE INSURANCE CO. (JAPAN) LTD.—See Livforsakringsaktiebolaget Skandia; *Int'l*, pg. 4531
SKANDIA LIFELINE—See Livforsakringsaktiebolaget Skandia; *Int'l*, pg. 4531

SKANDIALINK LIVFORSAKRINGS—See Livforsakringsaktiebolaget Skandia; *Int'l*, pg. 4532
SKANDIALINK MULTIFOND AB—See Livforsakringsaktiebolaget Skandia; *Int'l*, pg. 4532
SKANDIA LINK, S.A. DE SEGUROS Y REASEGUROS—See Livforsakringsaktiebolaget Skandia; *Int'l*, pg. 4532
SKANDIA LIV A/S—See Livforsakringsaktiebolaget Skandia; *Int'l*, pg. 4531
SKANDIA MULTIFUNDS LTD.—See Livforsakringsaktiebolaget Skandia; *Int'l*, pg. 4531
SKANDIA PROPERTY ASSET MANAGEMENT (UK) LTD.—See Livforsakringsaktiebolaget Skandia; *Int'l*, pg. 4531
SKANDIA RETAIL EUROPE HOLDING GMBH—See Cinven Limited; *Int'l*, pg. 1616
SKANDIA RETAIL EUROPE HOLDING GMBH—See Talanx AG; *Int'l*, pg. 7445
SKANDIA SEGUROS DE VIDA S.A.—See Livforsakringsaktiebolaget Skandia; *Int'l*, pg. 4531
SKANDIA SOCIEDAD FIDUCIARIA S.A.—See Livforsakringsaktiebolaget Skandia; *Int'l*, pg. 4531
SKANDIA UK—See Livforsakringsaktiebolaget Skandia; *Int'l*, pg. 4531
SKANDIA VERSICHERUNG MANAGEMENT & SERVICE GMBH—See Cinven Limited; *Int'l*, pg. 1616
SKANDIA VERSICHERUNG MANAGEMENT & SERVICE GMBH—See Talanx AG; *Int'l*, pg. 7445
SKANDIA VIDA S.A. DE SEGUROS Y REASEGUROS—See Livforsakringsaktiebolaget Skandia; *Int'l*, pg. 4531
SKANDIA VITA S.P.A.—See Livforsakringsaktiebolaget Skandia; *Int'l*, pg. 4531
SKANDIFINANZ AG—See Norddeutsche Landesbank Girozentrale; *Int'l*, pg. 5417
SKANDIFORM AB—See Kinnarps AB; *Int'l*, pg. 4181
SKANDINAVISKA BYGGELEMENT AB—See Peab AB; *Int'l*, pg. 5773
SKANDINAVISKA CHUCKFABRIKEN AB—See Investment AB Latour; *Int'l*, pg. 3783
SKANDINAVISKA ENSKILDA BANKEN AB; *Int'l*, pg. 6977
SKANDINAVISKA ENSKILDA BANKEN A/S—See Skandinaviska Enskilda Banken AB; *Int'l*, pg. 6978
SKANDINAVISKA ENSKILDA BANKEN S.A.—See Skandinaviska Enskilda Banken AB; *Int'l*, pg. 6978
SKANDINAVISKA ENSKILDA BANKEN—See Skandinaviska Enskilda Banken AB; *Int'l*, pg. 6978
SKANDINAVISKA ENSKILDA BANKEN SOUTH EAST ASIA LIMITED—See Skandinaviska Enskilda Banken AB; *Int'l*, pg. 6978
SKANDINAVISKA ENSKILDA LTD—See Skandinaviska Enskilda Banken AB; *Int'l*, pg. 6978
SKANDINAVISK HALSOVARD AB—See Lundbeckfonden; *Int'l*, pg. 4583
SKANDINAVISK HOLDING A/S; *Int'l*, pg. 6976
SKANDINAVISK KOMMUNALTEKNIK AB—See Litorina Capital Management AB; *Int'l*, pg. 4528
SKANDINAVISK KOMMUNALTEKNIKK AS—See Litorina Capital Management AB; *Int'l*, pg. 4528
SKANDINAVISK LOGISTIK AS; *Int'l*, pg. 6977
SKANDINAVISK MAT INVEST AS—See Oy Karl Fazer Ab; *Int'l*, pg. 5677
SKANE GRUS AB—See Cementir Holding N.V.; *Int'l*, pg. 1397
SKANEM AS; *Int'l*, pg. 6978
SKANEM BANGKOK CO., LTD.—See Skanem AS; *Int'l*, pg. 6978
SKANEM INTERLABELS INDUSTRIES (P) LTD.—See Skanem AS; *Int'l*, pg. 6978
SKANEM INTERLABELS NAIROBI LTD.—See Skanem AS; *Int'l*, pg. 6978
SKANE-MOLLAN AB; *Int'l*, pg. 6978
SKANEM POZNAN SP. Z. O. O.—See Skanem AS; *Int'l*, pg. 6978
SKANGAS AS—See Gasum Oy; *Int'l*, pg. 2888
SKAN, INC.; *U.S. Private*, pg. 3681
SKANLOG AB—See Skandinavisk Logistik AS; *Int'l*, pg. 6977
SKANRAY TECHNOLOGIES PRIVATE LIMITED; *Int'l*, pg. 6978
SKANSEN BRANDS PTY. LTD.; *Int'l*, pg. 6978
SKANSKA AB; *Int'l*, pg. 6978
SKANSKA BOSTADSUTVECKLING NORDEN AB—See Skanska AB; *Int'l*, pg. 6978
SKANSKA BRASIL LTDA—See Skanska AB; *Int'l*, pg. 6978
SKANSKA BYGGSYSTEM AB—See Skanska AB; *Int'l*, pg. 6978
SKANSKA CHILE S.A.—See Skanska AB; *Int'l*, pg. 6978
SKANSKA COLOMBIA S.A.S—See Skanska AB; *Int'l*, pg. 6978
SKANSKA COMMERCIAL DEVELOPMENT USA INC—See Skanska AB; *Int'l*, pg. 6979
SKANSKA DANMARK A/S—See Skanska AB; *Int'l*, pg. 6978
SKANSKA EMV AS—See Skanska AB; *Int'l*, pg. 6978
SKANSKA ENERGI AB; *Int'l*, pg. 6979
SKANSKA FASTIGHETER GOTEBORG AB—See Skanska AB; *Int'l*, pg. 6979

SKANSKA FASTIGHETER STOCKHOLM AB—See Skanska AB; *Int'l*, pg. 6979
SKANSKA FINANCIAL SERVICES AB—See Skanska AB; *Int'l*, pg. 6978
SKANSKA KOCH—See Skanska AB; *Int'l*, pg. 6979
SKANSKA KOMMERSIELL UTVECKLING NORDEN AB—See Skanska AB; *Int'l*, pg. 6979
SKANSKA LATIN AMERICA SA—See Skanska AB; *Int'l*, pg. 6978
SKANSKA MAGYARORSZAG INGATLAN KFT.—See Skanska AB; *Int'l*, pg. 6978
SKANSKA NORWAY A/S—See Skanska AB; *Int'l*, pg. 6978
SKANSKA OY—See Skanska AB; *Int'l*, pg. 6978
SKANSKA PROPERTY CZECH REPUBLIC, S.R.O.—See Skanska AB; *Int'l*, pg. 6978
SKANSKA PROPERTY POLAND SP. Z.O.O.—See Skanska AB; *Int'l*, pg. 6978
SKANSKAR FINANCIAL SERVICES AB—See Skanska AB; *Int'l*, pg. 6979
SKANSKA S.A.—See Skanska AB; *Int'l*, pg. 6978
SKANSKA SVERIGE AB—See Skanska AB; *Int'l*, pg. 6979
SKANSKA SVERIGE AB—See Skanska AB; *Int'l*, pg. 6978
SKANSKA TECHNOLOGY LIMITED—See Skanska AB; *Int'l*, pg. 6979
SKANSKA TECHNOLOGY LIMITED—See Skanska AB; *Int'l*, pg. 6979
SKANSKA UK PLC—See Skanska AB; *Int'l*, pg. 6979
SKANSKA USA BUILDING INC. - MICHIGAN—See Skanska AB; *Int'l*, pg. 6979
SKANSKA USA BUILDING INC.—See Skanska AB; *Int'l*, pg. 6979
SKANSKA USA BUILDING INC.—See Skanska AB; *Int'l*, pg. 6979
SKANSKA USA BUILDING INC.—See Skanska AB; *Int'l*, pg. 6979
SKANSKA USA BUILDING INC.—See Skanska AB; *Int'l*, pg. 6979
SKANSKA USA BUILDING INC.—See Skanska AB; *Int'l*, pg. 6979
SKANSKA USA CIVIL INC.—See Skanska AB; *Int'l*, pg. 6979
SKANSKA USA CIVIL NORTHEAST INC.—See Skanska AB; *Int'l*, pg. 6979
SKANSKA USA INC.—See Skanska AB; *Int'l*, pg. 6979
SKAN-TOOLING SIA—See Sunningdale Tech Ltd; *Int'l*, pg. 7318
SKAP LOGISTICS PTE. LTD.—See Y Ventures Group Ltd.; *Int'l*, pg. 8543
SKAR AUDIO, INC.; *U.S. Private*, pg. 3681
SKARBIEC HOLDING S.A.; *Int'l*, pg. 6979
SKARBIEC MENNICY POLSKIEJ S.A.—See Mennica Polska S.A.; *Int'l*, pg. 4816
SKARBIEC TOWARZYSTWO FUNDUSZY INWESTYCYJNYCH S.A.—See Skarbiec Holding S.A.; *Int'l*, pg. 6979
SKARDA EQUIPMENT COMPANY, INC.—See Certified Power Solutions; *U.S. Private*, pg. 842
SKARDIN INDUSTRIAL CORP.; *Int'l*, pg. 6979
S. KARGER AG; *Int'l*, pg. 6446
S. KARGER GMBH—See S. Karger AG; *Int'l*, pg. 6447
S. KARGER / KARGER LIBRI—See S. Karger AG; *Int'l*, pg. 6447
S. KARGER PUBLISHERS, INC.—See S. Karger AG; *Int'l*, pg. 6447
SKARNES, INC.—See RMH Systems, Inc.; *U.S. Private*, pg. 3452
S. KAROSSER AB—See KABE Group AB; *Int'l*, pg. 4046
SK ASPHALT (SHANGHAI) CO., LTD.—See SK Innovation Co., Ltd.; *Int'l*, pg. 6973
SKATENATION PLUS; *U.S. Private*, pg. 3681
S.K. AUTO INTERIOR CO., LTD.—See Toyota Boshoku Corporation; *Int'l*, pg. 7864
SK AUTOMOBILE PTE. LTD.—See Autobacs Seven Co., Ltd.; *Int'l*, pg. 726
S K BAJORIA GROUP; *Int'l*, pg. 6442
SKB BANKA D.D.—See OTP Bank Plc; *Int'l*, pg. 5658
SKB-BANK PAO; *Int'l*, pg. 6979
SKB CORPORATION; *U.S. Private*, pg. 3681
SK (BEIJING) ROAD SCIENCE & TECHNOLOGY CO., LTD.—See SK Innovation Co., Ltd.; *Int'l*, pg. 6973
SKB ENVIRONMENTAL, INC.—See Waste Connections, Inc.; *Int'l*, pg. 8354
SKBERGE S.A.—See Sigdo Koppers S.A.; *Int'l*, pg. 6907
SK BIOPHARMACEUTICALS CO., LTD.—See SK Inc.; *Int'l*, pg. 6972
SK BIO-PHARMA TECH (SHANGHAI) CO., LTD.—See SK Inc.; *Int'l*, pg. 6972
SK BIOSCIENCE CO., LTD.; *Int'l*, pg. 6970
SK BIOTEK CO., LTD.—See SK Inc.; *Int'l*, pg. 6972
SK BIOTEK IRELAND LIMITED—See SK Inc.; *Int'l*, pg. 6972
SKB LEASING D.O.O.—See OTP Bank Plc; *Int'l*, pg. 5658
SKB LEASING SELECT D.O.O.—See OTP Bank Plc; *Int'l*, pg. 5658
SKB REAL ESTATE & LEASING LTD.—See OTP Bank Plc; *Int'l*, pg. 5658
SK BROADBAND CO., LTD.—See SK Telecom Co., Ltd.; *Int'l*, pg. 6976

SKB SHUTTERS CORPORATION BERHAD; *Int'l*, pg. 6979
SK BULLION PTE. LTD.—See SK Jewellery Group Limited; *Int'l*, pg. 6974
SK CAPITAL PARTNERS, LP; *U.S. Private*, pg. 3678
SKC (BEIJING) POLYURETHANE CO., LTD.—See SKC Co., Ltd.; *Int'l*, pg. 6979
SKC CO., LTD. - JINCHEON FACTORY—See SKC Co., Ltd.; *Int'l*, pg. 6979
SKC CO., LTD.; *Int'l*, pg. 6979
SKC CO., LTD. - SUWON FACTORY—See SKC Co., Ltd.; *Int'l*, pg. 6979
SKC CO., LTD. - ULSAN FACTORY—See SKC Co., Ltd.; *Int'l*, pg. 6980
SKC ENGINEERING LTD.—See I Squared Capital Advisors (US) LLC; *U.S. Private*, pg. 2023
SKC ENGINEERING LTD.—See TDR Capital LLP; *Int'l*, pg. 7492
SKC ENTERPRISES INC.; *U.S. Private*, pg. 3681
SKC EUROPE GMBH—See SKC Co., Ltd.; *Int'l*, pg. 6980
SKC EUROPE PU SP. Z O.O.—See SKC Co., Ltd.; *Int'l*, pg. 6980
SKCG GROUP, INC.—See GTCR LLC; *U.S. Private*, pg. 1804
SKC GROUP LIMITED—See ANTA Sports Products Limited; *Int'l*, pg. 481
SKC GULF COAST, INC.—See SKC Inc.; *U.S. Private*, pg. 3681
SK HAAS POLSKA SP.Z O. O.—See Dow Inc.; *U.S. Public*, pg. 686
SK CHEMICALS AMERICA, INC.—See SK Discovery Co.,Ltd.; *Int'l*, pg. 6970
SK CHEMICALS CO., LTD. - OSAN PLANT—See SK Discovery Co.,Ltd.; *Int'l*, pg. 6970
SK CHEMICALS GMBH—See SK Discovery Co.,Ltd.; *Int'l*, pg. 6970
SK CHEMICALS QINGDAO LTD.—See SK Discovery Co.,Ltd.; *Int'l*, pg. 6970
SK CHEMICALS SUZHOU CO., LTD.—See SK Discovery Co.,Ltd.; *Int'l*, pg. 6970
SK CHEMTRADE SERVICES PTY LTD—See Cinven Limited; *Int'l*, pg. 1611
SKC INC.; *U.S. Private*, pg. 3681
SKC INC.—See SKC Co., Ltd.; *Int'l*, pg. 6980
SKC KOLON PI, INC. - GUMI PLANT—See Arkema S.A.; *Int'l*, pg. 569
SKC KOLON PI, INC. - JINCHEON PLANT—See Arkema S.A.; *Int'l*, pg. 569
SKC MAQUINARIAS S.A.C.—See Sigdo Koppers S.A.; *Int'l*, pg. 6907
SKC MAQUINARIAS S.A.—See Sigdo Koppers S.A.; *Int'l*, pg. 6907
SKCO INVESTMENTS CORP.; *U.S. Private*, pg. 3681
SKC COMERCIAL S.A.—See Sigdo Koppers S.A.; *Int'l*, pg. 6907
SKC COMMUNICATIONS CO., LTD.—See SK Telecom Co., Ltd.; *Int'l*, pg. 6976
SKC RENTAL LOCACAO DE EQUIPAMENTOS LTDA.—See Sigdo Koppers S.A.; *Int'l*, pg. 6907
SKC RENTAL S.A.—See Sigdo Koppers S.A.; *Int'l*, pg. 6907
SKCS CO., LTD. - 2ND FACTORY—See Vessel Co., Ltd.; *Int'l*, pg. 8176
SKCS CO., LTD.—See Vessel Co., Ltd.; *Int'l*, pg. 8176
SKC-SEJIN OPTO ELECTRONICS (SUZHOU) CO., LTD.—See SEJIN TS Co., Ltd; *Int'l*, pg. 6692
SKC SERVICIOS AUTOMOTRICES S.A.—See Sigdo Koppers S.A.; *Int'l*, pg. 6907
SKC SOLMICS CO., LTD. - ANSEONG PLANT—See SKC Co., Ltd.; *Int'l*, pg. 6980
SKC SOLMICS CO., LTD. - PYEONGTAEK PLANT—See SKC Co., Ltd.; *Int'l*, pg. 6980
SKC SOLMICS CO., LTD.—See SKC Co., Ltd.; *Int'l*, pg. 6980
SKC-WEST, INC.—See SKC Inc.; *U.S. Private*, pg. 3681
SK D&D CO., LTD.; *Int'l*, pg. 6970
SK DISCOVERY CO.,LTD.; *Int'l*, pg. 6970
SKD RESTAURANTS PVT. LTD.—See Total Hospitality Ltd.; *Int'l*, pg. 7835
SK EARTHON CO., LTD.—See SK Inc.; *Int'l*, pg. 6972
SK E&C ANADOLU LLC—See SK Engineering & Construction Co., Ltd.; *Int'l*, pg. 6970
SK E&C BETEK CORP.—See SK Engineering & Construction Co., Ltd.; *Int'l*, pg. 6970
SK E&C CONSULTORES—See SK Engineering & Construction Co., Ltd.; *Int'l*, pg. 6970
SKECHERS COLOMBIA, S.A.S.—See Skechers U.S.A., Inc.; *U.S. Public*, pg. 1891
SKECHERS EDC S.P.R.L.—See Skechers U.S.A., Inc.; *U.S. Public*, pg. 1891
SKECHERS GUANGZHOU CO., LTD.—See Skechers U.S.A., Inc.; *U.S. Public*, pg. 1891
SKECHERS PERU, S.R.L.—See Skechers U.S.A., Inc.; *U.S. Public*, pg. 1891
SKECHERS POLAND SP. Z O.O.—See Skechers U.S.A., Inc.; *U.S. Public*, pg. 1891
SKECHERS RETAIL INDIA PRIVATE LIMITED—See Skechers U.S.A., Inc.; *U.S. Public*, pg. 1891

SKECHERS S.A.R.L.—See Skechers U.S.A., Inc.; *U.S. Public*, pg. 1891
SKECHERS SLOVAKIA S.R.O.—See Skechers U.S.A., Inc.; *U.S. Public*, pg. 1892
SKECHERS USA BENELUX B.V.—See Skechers U.S.A., Inc.; *U.S. Public*, pg. 1892
SKECHERS USA DEUTSCHLAND GMBH—See Skechers U.S.A., Inc.; *U.S. Public*, pg. 1892
SKECHERS USA FRANCE SAS—See Skechers U.S.A., Inc.; *U.S. Public*, pg. 1892
SKECHERS USA IBERIA, S.L.—See Skechers U.S.A., Inc.; *U.S. Public*, pg. 1892
SKECHERS U.S.A., INC.; *U.S. Public*, pg. 1891
SKECHERS USA ITALIA S.R.L.—See Skechers U.S.A., Inc.; *U.S. Public*, pg. 1892
SKECHERS USA LTD.—See Skechers U.S.A., Inc.; *U.S. Public*, pg. 1892
SKECHERS USA PORTUGAL UNIPESSOAL LIMITADA—See Skechers U.S.A., Inc.; *U.S. Public*, pg. 1891
SKECHERS VIETNAM CO. LTD.—See Skechers U.S.A., Inc.; *U.S. Public*, pg. 1892
SKEC INDIA PVT. LTD.—See SK Engineering & Construction Co., Ltd.; *Int'l*, pg. 6970
SK E&C JURONG INVESTMENT PTE. LTD.—See SK Engineering & Construction Co., Ltd.; *Int'l*, pg. 6970
SKE CONSTRUCTION GMBH—See VINCI S.A.; *Int'l*, pg. 8237
SK E&C-SCADO COMPANY—See SK Engineering & Construction Co., Ltd.; *Int'l*, pg. 6970
SKEC THAI LIMITED—See SK Engineering & Construction Co., Ltd.; *Int'l*, pg. 6970
SKEELLER SRL—See Sesa S.p.A.; *Int'l*, pg. 6729
SKEENA RESOURCES LIMITED; *Int'l*, pg. 6980
SKEETER PRODUCTS, INC.—See Yamaha Corporation; *Int'l*, pg. 8549
SKEGGS GROUP LIMITED; *Int'l*, pg. 6980
SKE GROUP ROMANIA SRL—See VINCI S.A.; *Int'l*, pg. 8237
SKE INTERNATIONAL GMBH—See VINCI S.A.; *Int'l*, pg. 8226
SKE INTERNATIONAL, INC.—See VINCI S.A.; *Int'l*, pg. 8237
SKE ITALIE SRL—See VINCI S.A.; *Int'l*, pg. 8226
SKEJBY CRYOBANK APS—See Virtus Health Limited; *Int'l*, pg. 8249
SKE KOREA CO., LTD.—See SK-Electronics Co., Ltd.; *Int'l*, pg. 6976
SKELACK AB—See ITAB Shop Concept AB; *Int'l*, pg. 3828
SK-ELECTRONICS CO., LTD. - KYOTO PLANT—See SK-Electronics Co., Ltd.; *Int'l*, pg. 6976
SK-ELECTRONICS CO., LTD. - SHIGA PLANT—See SK-Electronics Co., Ltd.; *Int'l*, pg. 6976
SK-ELECTRONICS CO., LTD.; *Int'l*, pg. 6976
SK-ELECTRONICS SHANGHAI CO., LTD.—See SK-Electronics Co., Ltd.; *Int'l*, pg. 6976
SKELETAL KINETICS LLC—See Berkshire Hathaway Inc.; *U.S. Public*, pg. 308
SKELJUNGUR HF; *Int'l*, pg. 6980
SKELLERUP HOLDINGS LIMITED; *Int'l*, pg. 6980
SKELLERUP INDUSTRIES LIMITED—See Skellerup Holdings Limited; *Int'l*, pg. 6980
SKELLERUP INDUSTRIES (MALAYSIA) SDN. BHD.—See Johor Corporation; *Int'l*, pg. 3994
SKELLERUP RUBBER PRODUCTS JIANGSU LIMITED—See Skellerup Holdings Limited; *Int'l*, pg. 6980
SKELLERUP RUBBER SERVICES LIMITED—See Skellerup Holdings Limited; *Int'l*, pg. 6980
SKELTON CANADA INC.—See Andlauer Healthcare Group, Inc.; *Int'l*, pg. 451
SKELTON TRUCK LINES, INC.—See Andlauer Healthcare Group, Inc.; *Int'l*, pg. 451
SKE MIDWESTERN INC.; *U.S. Private*, pg. 3681
SKENDER CONSTRUCTION; *U.S. Private*, pg. 3681
SK ENERGY AMERICAS, INC.—See SK Innovation Co., Ltd.; *Int'l*, pg. 6973
SK ENERGY EUROPE LIMITED—See SK Innovation Co., Ltd.; *Int'l*, pg. 6973
SK ENERGY HONG KONG LIMITED—See SK Innovation Co., Ltd.; *Int'l*, pg. 6973
S.K. ENGINEERING CO., LTD.—See Hanwa Co., Ltd.; *Int'l*, pg. 3263
SK ENGINEERING & CONSTRUCTION CO., LTD.; *Int'l*, pg. 6970
SK ENGNEERING CO., LTD.—See Japan Petroleum Exploration Co. Ltd.; *Int'l*, pg. 3900
SK ENMOVE CO., LTD.—See SK Inc.; *Int'l*, pg. 6972
SK ENPULSE CO., LTD.—See SK Inc.; *Int'l*, pg. 6972
SKEPTON CONSTRUCTION, INC.; *U.S. Private*, pg. 3681
SK E&S AMERICAS, INC.—See SK Inc.; *Int'l*, pg. 6972
SKE SCHUL-FACILITY-MANAGEMENT GMBH—See VINCI S.A.; *Int'l*, pg. 8226
SK E&S CO., LTD.—See SK Innovation Co., Ltd.; *Int'l*, pg. 6973
SKE SUPPORT SERVICES GMBH—See VINCI S.A.; *Int'l*, pg. 8226
SKETCHDECK INC.—See 24 Seven, LLC; *U.S. Private*, pg. 6

SKEPTON CONSTRUCTION, INC.
CORPORATE AFFILIATIONS

SKE TECHNICAL SERVICES GMBH—See VINCI S.A.; *Int'l*, pg. 8226
SKET VERSEILMASCHINENBAU GMBH; *Int'l*, pg. 6980
SKF AB - RAIL BUSINESS UNIT—See SKF AB; *Int'l*, pg. 6981
SKF AB; *Int'l*, pg. 6981
SKF ACTUATION & MOTION CONTROL—See SKF AB; *Int'l*, pg. 6985
SKF ACTUATION SYSTEM (LIESTAL) AG—See SKF AB; *Int'l*, pg. 6981
SKF ACTUATION SYSTEM (PINGHU) CO., LTD.—See SKF AB; *Int'l*, pg. 6982
SKF ACTUATION SYSTEM (TAIPEI) CO., LTD.—See SKF AB; *Int'l*, pg. 6981
SKF ACTUATORS AB—See SKF AB; *Int'l*, pg. 6981
SKF AEROENGINE FRANCE S.A.S.U.—See SKF AB; *Int'l*, pg. 6983
SKF AEROENGINE—See SKF AB; *Int'l*, pg. 6985
SKF ARGENTINA S.A.—See SKF AB; *Int'l*, pg. 6981
SKF ASIA & PACIFIC PTE. LTD.—See SKF AB; *Int'l*, pg. 6981
SKF ASSET MANAGEMENT SERVICES, INC.—See SKF AB; *Int'l*, pg. 6985
SKF AUSTRALIA (MANUFACTURING) PTY. LTD.—See SKF AB; *Int'l*, pg. 6981
SKF AUTOBALANCE SYSTEMS AB—See SKF AB; *Int'l*, pg. 6981
SKF AUTOMOTIVE BEARINGS COMPANY LIMITED—See SKF AB; *Int'l*, pg. 6982
SKF AUTOMOTIVE COMPONENTS CORP.—See SKF AB; *Int'l*, pg. 6981
SKF AUTOMOTIVE DIVISION—See SKF AB; *Int'l*, pg. 6985
SKF BEARING IND. (MALAYSIA) SDN. BHD.—See SKF AB; *Int'l*, pg. 6981
SKF BEARING SERVICES TAIWAN LTD.—See SKF AB; *Int'l*, pg. 6982
SKF BEARINGS INDIA LTD.—See SKF AB; *Int'l*, pg. 6982
SKF BELGIUM S.A.—See SKF AB; *Int'l*, pg. 6982
SKF BOSNIA AND HERZEGOVINA—See SKF AB; *Int'l*, pg. 6982
SKF BSS S.P.A.—See SKF AB; *Int'l*, pg. 6981
SKF BULGARIA—See SKF AB; *Int'l*, pg. 6982
SKF B.V.—See SKF AB; *Int'l*, pg. 6981
SKF CANADA LIMITED—See SKF AB; *Int'l*, pg. 6982
SKF CENTRALA HANDLOWO-TECHNICZNA SP.Z.O.O.—See SKF AB; *Int'l*, pg. 6982
SKF CHILENA S.A.I.C.—See SKF AB; *Int'l*, pg. 6982
SKF (CHINA) CO., LTD. - BEIJING OFFICE—See SKF AB; *Int'l*, pg. 6982
SKF (CHINA) CO., LTD. - CHENGDU OFFICE—See SKF AB; *Int'l*, pg. 6982
SKF (CHINA) CO., LTD. - DALIAN OFFICE—See SKF AB; *Int'l*, pg. 6982
SKF (CHINA) CO., LTD. - GUANGZHOU OFFICE—See SKF AB; *Int'l*, pg. 6982
SKF (CHINA) CO., LTD. - NANJING OFFICE—See SKF AB; *Int'l*, pg. 6982
SKF (CHINA) CO., LTD.—See SKF AB; *Int'l*, pg. 6982
SKF (CHINA) CO., LTD. - XI'AN OFFICE—See SKF AB; *Int'l*, pg. 6982
SKF (CHINA) INVESTMENT CO., LTD.—See SKF AB; *Int'l*, pg. 6982
SKF CHINA LIMITED—See SKF AB; *Int'l*, pg. 6982
SKF (CHINA) SALES CO., LTD.—See SKF AB; *Int'l*, pg. 6982
SKF COMMERCE D.O.O.—See SKF AB; *Int'l*, pg. 6982
SKF CONDITION MONITORING INC.—See SKF AB; *Int'l*, pg. 6985
SKF COUPLING SYSTEMS AB—See SKF AB; *Int'l*, pg. 6982
SKF COUPLING SYSTEMS, INC.—See SKF AB; *Int'l*, pg. 6985
SKF CROATIA D.O.O.—See SKF AB; *Int'l*, pg. 6982
SKF CZ, A.S.—See SKF AB; *Int'l*, pg. 6982
SKF (DALIAN) BEARINGS AND PRECISION TECHNOLOGIES CO. LTD.—See SKF AB; *Int'l*, pg. 6982
SKF DANMARK A/S—See SKF AB; *Int'l*, pg. 6982
SKF DATASERVICE AB—See SKF AB; *Int'l*, pg. 6982
SKF DEL PERU S.A.—See SKF AB; *Int'l*, pg. 6985
SKF DE MEXICO, S.A. DE C.V.—See SKF AB; *Int'l*, pg. 6985
SKF DISTRIBUTION (SHANGHAI) CO. LTD.—See SKF AB; *Int'l*, pg. 6982
SKF DO BRASIL LTDA.—See SKF AB; *Int'l*, pg. 6985
SKF ECONOMOS CANADA INC.—See SKF AB; *Int'l*, pg. 6982
SKF ECONOMOS CHINA CO. LTD.—See SKF AB; *Int'l*, pg. 6982
SKF ECONOMOS DENMARK A/S—See SKF AB; *Int'l*, pg. 6982
SKF ECONOMOS DEUTSCHLAND GMBH—See SKF AB; *Int'l*, pg. 6982
SKF ECONOMOS DO BRASIL LTDA.—See SKF AB; *Int'l*, pg. 6985
SKF ECONOMOS GMBH—See SKF AB; *Int'l*, pg. 6982
SKF ECONOMOS NL B.V.—See SKF AB; *Int'l*, pg. 6982
SKF ECONOMOS SCHWEIZ GMBH—See SKF AB; *Int'l*, pg. 6983
SKF ECONOMOS SEALING SOLUTIONS (THAILAND) LTD.—See SKF AB; *Int'l*, pg. 6983
SKF ECONOMOS SVERIGE AB—See SKF AB; *Int'l*, pg. 6983
SKF ECONOMOS UKRAINE LTD.—See SKF AB; *Int'l*, pg. 6983
SKF ECONOMOS USA INC.—See SKF AB; *Int'l*, pg. 6983
SKF ENGINEERING PRODUCTS LIMITED—See SKF AB; *Int'l*, pg. 6981
SKF ENGINEERING & RESEARCH CENTRE B.V.—See SKF AB; *Int'l*, pg. 6984
SKF ESPANOLA S.A.—See SKF AB; *Int'l*, pg. 6983
SKF ESTONIA OU—See SKF AB; *Int'l*, pg. 6983
SKF EUROTRADE AB—See SKF AB; *Int'l*, pg. 6983
SKF FRANCE S.A.—See SKF AB; *Int'l*, pg. 6983
SKF GMBH—See SKF AB; *Int'l*, pg. 6983
SKF GMBH—See SKF AB; *Int'l*, pg. 6983
SKF HELLAS S.A.—See SKF AB; *Int'l*, pg. 6983
SKF HOLDING MEXICANA, S.A. DE C.V.—See SKF AB; *Int'l*, pg. 6983
SKF INDIA LIMITED; *Int'l*, pg. 6985
SKF INDUSTRIAL & SERVICE DIVISION—See SKF AB; *Int'l*, pg. 6985
SKF INDUSTRIAL SERVICE SHANGHAI CO., LTD.—See SKF AB; *Int'l*, pg. 6983
SKF INDUSTRIE S.P.A—See SKF AB; *Int'l*, pg. 6983
SKF INTERNATIONAL AB—See SKF AB; *Int'l*, pg. 6983
SKF IRAN—See SKF AB; *Int'l*, pg. 6983
SKF ISRAEL LTD—See SKF AB; *Int'l*, pg. 6983
SKF JAPAN LTD.—See SKF AB; *Int'l*, pg. 6983
SKF (JAPAN) PRODUCT SERVICE CENTER—See SKF AB; *Int'l*, pg. 6983
SKF KAZAKHSTAN—See SKF AB; *Int'l*, pg. 6983
SKF KENYA LIMITED—See SKF AB; *Int'l*, pg. 6983
SKF KOREA LTD - AD FACTORY—See SKF AB; *Int'l*, pg. 6983
SKF KOREA LTD.—See SKF AB; *Int'l*, pg. 6983
SKF LIETUVA UAB—See SKF AB; *Int'l*, pg. 6983
SKF LINEARSYSTEME GMBH—See SKF AB; *Int'l*, pg. 6983
SKF LOGISTICS SERVICES AB—See SKF AB; *Int'l*, pg. 6983
SKF LOGISTICS SERVICES BELGIUM NV/SA—See SKF AB; *Int'l*, pg. 6983
SKF LOZISKA A.S.—See SKF AB; *Int'l*, pg. 6983
SKF LUBRICATION COMPETENCE CENTER AB—See SKF AB; *Int'l*, pg. 6983
SKF LUBRICATION SYSTEMS CZ S.R.O—See SKF AB; *Int'l*, pg. 6983
SKF LUBRICATION SYSTEMS FRANCE SAS—See SKF AB; *Int'l*, pg. 6983
SKF LUBRICATION SYSTEMS GERMANY AG—See SKF AB; *Int'l*, pg. 6983
SKF LUBRICATION SYSTEMS GERMANY GMBH—See SKF AB; *Int'l*, pg. 6985
SKF LUBRICATION SYSTEMS JAPAN LTD.—See SKF AB; *Int'l*, pg. 6983
SKF LUBRICATION SYSTEMS THE NETHERLANDS B.V.—See SKF AB; *Int'l*, pg. 6984
SKF MACHINE SUPPORT INC.—See SKF AB; *Int'l*, pg. 6985
SKF MAGNETIC BEARINGS—See SKF AB; *Int'l*, pg. 6983
SKF MAGNETIC MECHATRONICS S.A.S.—See SKF AB; *Int'l*, pg. 6983
SKF MAINTENANCE PRODUCTS B.V.—See SKF AB; *Int'l*, pg. 6984
SKF MAKTRADE D.O.O.—See SKF AB; *Int'l*, pg. 6984
SKF MALAYSIA SDN. BHD.—See SKF AB; *Int'l*, pg. 6984
SKF MARINE GMBH—See SKF AB; *Int'l*, pg. 6984
SKF MARINE GMBH—See SKF AB; *Int'l*, pg. 6983
SKF MARINE SINGAPORE PTE. LTD.—See SKF AB; *Int'l*, pg. 6984
SKF MEKAN AB—See SKF AB; *Int'l*, pg. 6984
SKF MIDDLE EAST & NORTH AFRICA—See SKF AB; *Int'l*, pg. 6984
SKF MOSCOW—See SKF AB; *Int'l*, pg. 6984
SKF MULTITEC AB—See SKF AB; *Int'l*, pg. 6984
SKF NEDERLAND B.V.—See SKF AB; *Int'l*, pg. 6984
SKF NEW ZEALAND LIMITED—See SKF AB; *Int'l*, pg. 6984
SKF NIGERIA LIMITED—See SKF AB; *Int'l*, pg. 6984
SKF NORGE A/S—See SKF AB; *Int'l*, pg. 6984
SK FOOD GROUP INC.—See Premium Brands Holdings Corporation; *Int'l*, pg. 5963
SK-FORDERTECHNIK GMBH—See KONE Oyj; *Int'l*, pg. 4250
SK FOREST CO., LTD.—See SK Inc.; *Int'l*, pg. 6972
SKF OSTERREICH AG—See SKF AB; *Int'l*, pg. 6984
SKF PAKISTAN PVT. LTD.—See SKF AB; *Int'l*, pg. 6984
SKF PHILIPPINES, INC.—See SKF AB; *Int'l*, pg. 6984
SKF POLSKA S.A.—See SKF AB; *Int'l*, pg. 6984
SKF POLYSEAL, INC.—See SKF AB; *Int'l*, pg. 6985
SKF PORTUGAL ROLAMENTOS, LDA.—See SKF AB; *Int'l*, pg. 6984
SKF POZNAN S.A.—See SKF AB; *Int'l*, pg. 6984
SKF PRECISION MACHINERY (SHANGHAI) CO. LTD.—See SKF AB; *Int'l*, pg. 6982
SKF REINSURANCE CO. LTD.—See SKF AB; *Int'l*, pg. 6984
SKF RELIABILITY SYSTEMS INC.—See SKF AB; *Int'l*, pg. 6985
SKF RESEARCH & DEVELOPMENT CO.—See SKF AB; *Int'l*, pg. 6984
SKF ROMANIA S.R.L.—See SKF AB; *Int'l*, pg. 6984
SKF (SCHWEIZ) AG—See SKF AB; *Int'l*, pg. 6981
SKF SEALING SOLUTION GMBH—See SKF AB; *Int'l*, pg. 6983
SKF SEALING SOLUTIONS AB—See SKF AB; *Int'l*, pg. 6984
SKF SEALING SOLUTIONS AUSTRIA GMBH—See SKF AB; *Int'l*, pg. 6984
SKF SEALING SOLUTIONS KOREA CO., LTD.—See SKF AB; *Int'l*, pg. 6984
SKF SEALING SOLUTIONS (QINGDAO) CO.—See SKF AB; *Int'l*, pg. 6984
SKF SEALING SOLUTIONS S.A. DE C.V.—See SKF AB; *Int'l*, pg. 6984
SKF SEALING SOLUTIONS—See SKF AB; *Int'l*, pg. 6985
SKF SEALING SOLUTIONS (WUHU) CO. LTD.—See SKF AB; *Int'l*, pg. 6982
SKF SERVICES D.O.O.—See SKF AB; *Int'l*, pg. 6984
SKF (SHANGHAI) AUTOMOTIVE TECHNOLOGY CO. LTD.—See SKF AB; *Int'l*, pg. 6982
SKF (SHANGHAI) BEARINGS LTD.—See SKF AB; *Int'l*, pg. 6981
SKF (SHANGHAI) INVESTMENT CONSULTANCY CO. LTD.—See SKF AB; *Int'l*, pg. 6982
SKF SLOVENIJA D.O.O.—See SKF AB; *Int'l*, pg. 6984
SKF SLOVENIJA D.O.O.—See Vorwerk & Co. KG; *Int'l*, pg. 8307
SKF SLOVENSKO S.R.O.—See SKF AB; *Int'l*, pg. 6984
SKF SOUTH AFRICA (PTY) LIMITED—See SKF AB; *Int'l*, pg. 6984
SKF SVED GOLYOSCSAPAGY RESZVENYTARSASAG—See SKF AB; *Int'l*, pg. 6984
SKF SVED GOLYOSCSAPAGY ZRT—See SKF AB; *Int'l*, pg. 6984
SKF SVERIGE AB—See SKF AB; *Int'l*, pg. 6984
SKF TAIWAN CO, LTD.—See SKF AB; *Int'l*, pg. 6984
SKF TECHNOLOGIES (INDIA) PRIVATE LIMITED—See SKF AB; *Int'l*, pg. 6984
SKF (THAILAND) LTD.—See SKF AB; *Int'l*, pg. 6981
SKF TREASURY CENTRE ASIA PACIFIC PTE LTD.—See SKF AB; *Int'l*, pg. 6981
SKF TURK SANAYI VE TICARET—See SKF AB; *Int'l*, pg. 6984
SKF TVER LTD.—See SKF AB; *Int'l*, pg. 6984
SKF (U.K.) LTD. - AEROENGINE & SUPER PRECISION DIVISION—See SKF AB; *Int'l*, pg. 6981
SKF (U.K.) LTD. - AEROSPACE DIVISION—See SKF AB; *Int'l*, pg. 6981
SKF (U.K.) LTD. - RAILWAY SALES UNIT—See SKF AB; *Int'l*, pg. 6981
SKF (U.K.) LTD.—See SKF AB; *Int'l*, pg. 6981
SKF UKRAINE—See SKF AB; *Int'l*, pg. 6985
S.K. FURNITURE SDN. BHD.—See Sern Kou Resources Berhad; *Int'l*, pg. 6723
SKF URUGUAY S.A.—See SKF AB; *Int'l*, pg. 6985
SKF USA INC. - NORTH AMERICAN TECHNICAL CENTER—See SKF AB; *Int'l*, pg. 6985
SKF USA INC.—See SKF AB; *Int'l*, pg. 6984
SKF VEHICLE PARTS ASIA (PTE) LTD.—See SKF AB; *Int'l*, pg. 6981
SKF VENEZOLANA S.A.—See SKF AB; *Int'l*, pg. 6985
SKF VIETNAM—See SKF AB; *Int'l*, pg. 6985
SKF ZAMBIA LTD.—See SKF AB; *Int'l*, pg. 6985
SKF ZIMBABWE (PVT.) LTD.—See SKF AB; *Int'l*, pg. 6985
SK+G ADVERTISING; *U.S. Private*, pg. 3680
SK GAS CO., LTD.—See SK Discovery Co. Ltd.; *Int'l*, pg. 6970
SK GC AMERICAS, INC.—See SK Inc.; *Int'l*, pg. 6972
SK GEO CENTRIC (BEIJING) HOLDING CO., LTD.—See SK Inc.; *Int'l*, pg. 6972
SK GEO CENTRIC CO., LTD.—See SK Inc.; *Int'l*, pg. 6972
SK GEO CENTRIC INTERNATIONAL TRADING (GUANGZHOU) CO., LTD.—See SK Inc.; *Int'l*, pg. 6972
SK GEO CENTRIC INTERNATIONAL TRADING (SHANGHAI) CO., LTD.—See SK Inc.; *Int'l*, pg. 6972
SK GEO CENTRIC JAPAN CO., LTD.—See SK Inc.; *Int'l*, pg. 6972
SK GEO CENTRIC SINGAPORE PTE. LTD.—See SK Inc.; *Int'l*, pg. 6972
SK GLOBAL CHEMICAL (CHINA) HOLDING CO., LTD.—See SK Innovation Co., Ltd.; *Int'l*, pg. 6973
SK GLOBAL CHEMICAL CO., LTD.—See SK Innovation Co., Ltd.; *Int'l*, pg. 6973
SK GLOBAL CHEMICAL CO., LTD. - ULSAN PLANT—See SK Innovation Co., Ltd.; *Int'l*, pg. 6973
SK GLOBAL CHEMICAL INTERNATIONAL TRADING (GUANGZHOU) CO.,—See SK Innovation Co., Ltd.; *Int'l*, pg. 6973
SK GLOBAL CHEMICAL INTERNATIONAL TRADING (SHANGHAI) CO., LTD.—See SK Innovation Co., Ltd.; *Int'l*, pg. 6973
SK GLOBAL CHEMICAL JAPAN CO., LTD.—See SK Innovation Co., Ltd.; *Int'l*, pg. 6973

COMPANY NAME INDEX

SK GLOBAL CHEMICAL SINGAPORE PTE. LTD.—See SK Innovation Co., Ltd.; *Int'l*, pg. 6973
SK GODELIUS S.A.—See Sigdo Koppers S.A.; *Int'l*, pg. 6907
SKG RADIOLOGY PTY LIMITED—See Sonic Healthcare Limited; *Int'l*, pg. 7098
SK GROWTH OPPORTUNITIES CORPORATION; *U.S. Public*, pg. 1891
SK (GUANGZHOU) METAL CO., LTD.—See SK Networks Co., Ltd.; *Int'l*, pg. 6974
SK HAND TOOL, LLC; *U.S. Private*, pg. 3680
SKH MANAGEMENT CO. INC.; *U.S. Private*, pg. 3681
SK HOLDING COMPANY, INC.—See Clean Harbors, Inc.; *U.S. Public*, pg. 510
S. KHON KAEN FOODS PUBLIC COMPANY LIMITED - BANGPLEE FACTORY—See S. Khon Kaen Foods Public Company Limited; *Int'l*, pg. 6447
S. KHON KAEN FOODS PUBLIC COMPANY LIMITED; *Int'l*, pg. 6447
SK HYENG INC.—See SK hynix Inc.; *Int'l*, pg. 6971
SK HYNIX AMERICA INC.—See SK hynix Inc.; *Int'l*, pg. 6971
SK HYNIX ASIA PTE. LTD.—See SK hynix Inc.; *Int'l*, pg. 6971
SK HYNIX (CHINA) LTD.—See SK hynix Inc.; *Int'l*, pg. 6971
SK HYNIX DEUTSCHLAND GMBH—See SK hynix Inc.; *Int'l*, pg. 6971
SK HYNIX INC.—See SK hynix Inc.; *Int'l*, pg. 6971
SK HYNIX INC.; *Int'l*, pg. 6970
SK HYNIX JAPAN INC.—See SK hynix Inc.; *Int'l*, pg. 6971
SK HYNIX MEMORY SOLUTIONS AMERICA INC—See SK hynix Inc.; *Int'l*, pg. 6971
SK HYNIX MEMORY SOLUTIONS EASTERN EUROPE, LLC—See SK hynix Inc.; *Int'l*, pg. 6971
SK HYNIX MEMORY SOLUTIONS INC.—See SK hynix Inc.; *Int'l*, pg. 6971
SK HYNIX SEMICONDUCTOR (CHINA) LTD.—See SK hynix Inc.; *Int'l*, pg. 6971
SK HYNIX SEMICONDUCTOR HONG KONG LTD.—See SK hynix Inc.; *Int'l*, pg. 6971
SK HYNIX SEMICONDUCTOR INDIA PVT. LTD.—See SK hynix Inc.; *Int'l*, pg. 6971
SK HYNIX SEMICONDUCTOR (SHANGHAI) CO., LTD.—See SK hynix Inc.; *Int'l*, pg. 6971
SK HYNIX SEMICONDUCTOR TAIWAN INC.—See SK hynix Inc.; *Int'l*, pg. 6971
SK HYNIX SYSTEM IC INC.—See SK hynix Inc.; *Int'l*, pg. 6971
SK HYNIX UK LTD.—See SK hynix Inc.; *Int'l*, pg. 6971
SK HYNIX WUXI SEMICONDUCTOR SALES LTD.—See SK hynix Inc.; *Int'l*, pg. 6971
SK HYSTEC INC.—See SK hynix Inc.; *Int'l*, pg. 6971
SKI ALPINE LIMITED—See TUI AG; *Int'l*, pg. 7968
SKIBOUND FRANCE SARL—See TUI AG; *Int'l*, pg. 7966
SKIBOUND HOLIDAYS LIMITED—See TUI AG; *Int'l*, pg. 7968
SKI CHALET INC.; *U.S. Private*, pg. 3681
SKI CLUB OF GREAT BRITAIN LIMITED; *Int'l*, pg. 6985
SKIDATA AG—See ASSA ABLOY AB; *Int'l*, pg. 640
SKIDATA AUSTRALASIA PTY. LTD.—See Kudelski S.A.; *Int'l*, pg. 4323
SKIDATA BENELUX BV—See Kudelski S.A.; *Int'l*, pg. 4323
SKIDATA INC.—See ASSA ABLOY AB; *Int'l*, pg. 640
SKIDATA (SCHWEIZ) AG—See ASSA ABLOY AB; *Int'l*, pg. 640
SKIDAWAY HEALTH AND LIVING SERVICES, INC.; *U.S. Private*, pg. 3681
SKIDMORE GROUP HOLDINGS INC.; *Int'l*, pg. 6985
SKIDMORE OWINGS & MERRILL LLP; *U.S. Private*, pg. 3681
SKIENCE LLC—See Berenson & Company, Inc.; *U.S. Private*, pg. 530
SKIENCE LLC—See Sagewind Capital LLC; *U.S. Private*, pg. 3528
SKIEN STORKJOKKEN AS—See Bunzl plc; *Int'l*, pg. 1219
SKIER'S CHOICE INC.; *U.S. Private*, pg. 3682
SK IE TECHNOLOGY CO., LTD.; *Int'l*, pg. 6971
SKIFFY B.V.—See Essentra plc; *Int'l*, pg. 2511
SKIFFY GMBH—See Essentra plc; *Int'l*, pg. 2511
SKIFFY LTD.—See Essentra plc; *Int'l*, pg. 2512
SKIFFY S.A. (PTY) LTD.—See Essentra plc; *Int'l*, pg. 2512
SKIFFY S.A.S.—See Essentra plc; *Int'l*, pg. 2512
SKI HI ENTERPRISES LTD.; *U.S. Private*, pg. 3681
SKI HI MECHANICAL SERVICES INC.—See Ski Hi Enterprises Ltd.; *U.S. Private*, pg. 3681
SKIINFO.FR S.A.R.L.—See Vail Resorts, Inc.; *U.S. Public*, pg. 2271
S.KIJCHAI ENTERPRISE PUBLIC COMPANY LIMITED; *Int'l*, pg. 6456
SKILCRAFT LLC; *U.S. Private*, pg. 3682
SKIL EUROPE B.V.—See Emerson Electric Co.; *U.S. Public*, pg. 752
SKI LIBERTY OPERATING CORP.—See Vail Resorts, Inc.; *U.S. Public*, pg. 2271
SKIL INFRASTRUCTURE LIMITED; *Int'l*, pg. 6986
SKILLBOX LLC—See VK Company Ltd.; *Int'l*, pg. 8281
SKILLCAST GROUP PLC; *Int'l*, pg. 6986

SKILLED SERVICES CORPORATION—See TrueBlue, Inc.; *U.S. Public*, pg. 2198
SKILLERS WORKWEAR NA INC—See Investment AB Latour; *Int'l*, pg. 3782
SKILLFACTORY LLC—See VK Company Ltd.; *Int'l*, pg. 8281
SKILLFINDER INTERNATIONAL LIMITED; *Int'l*, pg. 6986
SKILLFUL CRAFTSMAN EDUCATION TECHNOLOGY LIMITED; *Int'l*, pg. 6986
SKILL HIRE INDIGENOUS CONTRACTING PTY. LTD.—See Skill Hire WA; *Int'l*, pg. 6986
SKILL HIRE WA PTY. LTD.—See Skill Hire WA; *Int'l*, pg. 6986
SKILL HIRE WA; *Int'l*, pg. 6986
SKILLHOUSE STAFFING SOLUTIONS K.K.—See Empresaria Group Plc; *Int'l*, pg. 2389
SKILLNET OY—See Sanoma Oyj; *Int'l*, pg. 6553
SKILLPAGES HOLDINGS LIMITED; *Int'l*, pg. 6986
SKILLPOWER SERVICES (THAILAND) CO. LTD.—See ManpowerGroup Inc.; *U.S. Public*, pg. 1362
SKILLS DEVELOPMENT INC.—See Ontario Teachers' Pension Plan; *Int'l*, pg. 5587
SKILL SEARCH S.L.—See Synergie SA; *Int'l*, pg. 7383
SKILLS ENTERTAINMENT COMPANY-W.L.L.—See Privatization Holding Company K.S.C.C.; *Int'l*, pg. 5984
SKILLSET GROUP, LLC; *U.S. Private*, pg. 3682
SKILLS, INC.; *U.S. Private*, pg. 3682
SKILLS IN HEALTHCARE GMBH DEUTSCHLAND—See Walgreens Boots Alliance, Inc.; *U.S. Public*, pg. 2323
SKILLSNET, INC.; *U.S. Private*, pg. 3682
SKILLS OF CENTRAL PENNSYLVANIA, INC.; *U.S. Private*, pg. 3682
SKILLSOFT ASIA PACIFIC PTY. LIMITED—See Charterhouse Capital Partners LLP; *Int'l*, pg. 1456
SKILLSOFT CANADA LIMITED—See Charterhouse Capital Partners LLP; *Int'l*, pg. 1456
SKILLSOFT CORPORATION—See Charterhouse Capital Partners LLP; *Int'l*, pg. 1456
SKILLSOFT CORPORATION—See Clarivate PLC; *U.S. Public*, pg. 1650
SKILLSOFT DEUTSCHLAND GMBH—See Charterhouse Capital Partners LLP; *Int'l*, pg. 1456
SKILLSOFT - EMEA HEADQUARTERS—See Charterhouse Capital Partners LLP; *Int'l*, pg. 1456
SKILLSOFT IRELAND LIMITED—See Charterhouse Capital Partners LLP; *Int'l*, pg. 1456
SKILLSOFT LIMITED—See Charterhouse Capital Partners LLP; *Int'l*, pg. 1456
SKILLSOFT UK LIMITED—See Charterhouse Capital Partners LLP; *Int'l*, pg. 1456
SKILLSTORM, INC.; *U.S. Private*, pg. 3682
SKILLSURVEY, INC.—See iCIMS, Inc.; *U.S. Private*, pg. 2031
SKILLTECH CONSULTING SERVICES PTY LTD—See Downer EDI Limited; *Int'l*, pg. 2185
SKILLUP VIDEO TECHNOLOGIES CORPORATION—See Digital Holdings, Inc.; *Int'l*, pg. 2122
SKILLZ INC.; *U.S. Public*, pg. 1892
SKILSTAF INC.; *U.S. Private*, pg. 3682
SKIL-TECH, INC.; *U.S. Private*, pg. 3682
THE SKI MARKET LTD. INC.; *U.S. Private*, pg. 4118
SKIMBIT LTD.—See Symphony Technology Group, LLC; *U.S. Private*, pg. 3900
SKIMLINKS INC.—See Symphony Technology Group, LLC; *U.S. Private*, pg. 3900
SKIN, A MEDICAL SPA—See MD Esthetics, LLC; *U.S. Private*, pg. 2646
SKINBIOTHERAPEUTICS PLC; *Int'l*, pg. 6986
SKINCARESTORE AUSTRALIA PTY LTD—See Walgreens Boots Alliance, Inc.; *U.S. Public*, pg. 2323
SK INCHEON PETROCHEM CO., LTD.—See SK Innovation Co., Ltd.; *Int'l*, pg. 6973
SKINCO COLOMBIT S.A.—See Etex SA/NV; *Int'l*, pg. 2522
SK INC.; *Int'l*, pg. 6971
SK INDUSTRIAL S.A.—See Sigdo Koppers S.A.; *Int'l*, pg. 6907
SKIN ELEMENTS LIMITED; *Int'l*, pg. 6986
SKINKERS LTD.—See Cisco Systems, Inc.; *U.S. Public*, pg. 499
SKINNER & COOK, INC.—See Borgman Capital LLC; *U.S. Private*, pg. 618
SKINNER TRANSFER CORP.; *U.S. Private*, pg. 3682
SK INNOVATION CO., LTD.; *Int'l*, pg. 6973
SKIN N SKIN CO., LTD.; *Int'l*, pg. 6986
SKINNYCORP L.L.C.; *U.S. Private*, pg. 3682
SKINNY TAN PTY LTD.—See Brand Architekts Group plc; *Int'l*, pg. 1139
SKINOURISHMENT, LLC—See Clarus Corporation; *U.S. Public*, pg. 508
SKINOVATION PHARMACEUTICAL INCORPORATED; *U.S. Private*, pg. 3682
SKIN PATHOLOGY ASSOCIATES INC.—See Harvest Partners L.P.; *U.S. Private*, pg. 1876
SKIN SCIENCES, INC.—See FibroGen, Inc.; *U.S. Public*, pg. 830
SKINSMART DERMATOLOGY; *U.S. Private*, pg. 3682
SKINSTORE.COM; *U.S. Private*, pg. 3682
SK INTERNATIONAL EXPORT LIMITED; *Int'l*, pg. 6973

SKM MEDIA CORP.

SK INTERNATIONAL, INC.; *U.S. Private*, pg. 3680
SKINTRUST DERMATOLOGY—See Harvest Partners L.P.; *U.S. Private*, pg. 1876
SKINVET CLINIC, LLC—See Percheron Investment Management LP; *U.S. Private*, pg. 3146
SKINVISIBLE, INC.; *U.S. Public*, pg. 1892
SKION GMBH; *Int'l*, pg. 6986
SKION WATER GMBH—See SKion GmbH; *Int'l*, pg. 6990
SKIP-A-LONG FAMILY AND COMMUNITY SERVICES; *U.S. Private*, pg. 3682
SKIP CONVERSE, INC.; *U.S. Private*, pg. 3682
SKIP HOP, INC.—See Carter's, Inc.; *U.S. Public*, pg. 445
SKIPPER BUDS OF ILLINOIS INC.; *U.S. Private*, pg. 3682
SKIPPER LIMITED; *Int'l*, pg. 6990
SKIPPERS INC.—See Seattle Crab Co.; *U.S. Private*, pg. 3591
SKIPPING STONE, INC.; *U.S. Private*, pg. 3682
SKIPTA, LLC—See Informa plc; *Int'l*, pg. 3693
THE SKIPTON BUILDING SOCIETY; *Int'l*, pg. 7686
SKIPTON BUSINESS FINANCE LIMITED—See The Skipton Building Society; *Int'l*, pg. 7687
SKIPTON FINANCIAL SERVICES LIMITED—See The Skipton Building Society; *Int'l*, pg. 7687
SKIPTON GROUP HOLDINGS LIMITED—See The Skipton Building Society; *Int'l*, pg. 7686
SKIPTON GROUP INC.—See Data Integrity Inc.; *U.S. Public*, pg. 1976
SKIPTON GUERNSEY LIMITED—See The Skipton Building Society; *Int'l*, pg. 7687
SKIPTON INTERNATIONAL LIMITED—See The Skipton Building Society; *Int'l*, pg. 7687
SKIPTON PREMISES LIMITED—See The Skipton Building Society; *Int'l*, pg. 7687
SKIPWITH & ASSOCIATES INSURANCE AGENCIES INC.—See People Corporation; *Int'l*, pg. 5793
SKIRA EDITORE S.P.A.—See Chargeurs SA; *Int'l*, pg. 1450
SKIRBALL CULTURAL CENTER; *U.S. Private*, pg. 3682
SKIS DYNASTAR S.A.S.—See Altor Equity Partners AB; *Int'l*, pg. 396
SKIS ROSSIGNOL DE ESPANA S.A.—See Altor Equity Partners AB; *Int'l*, pg. 396
SKIS ROSSIGNOL S.A.S.—See Altor Equity Partners AB; *Int'l*, pg. 396
SKISTAR AB; *Int'l*, pg. 6990
SKISTAR NORGE AS—See SkiStar AB; *Int'l*, pg. 6990
SKIVA INTERNATIONAL INC.; *U.S. Private*, pg. 3682
SKIYAKI, INC.—See Space Shower Skiyaki Holdings Inc; *Int'l*, pg. 7123
SK JAPAN CO., LTD.; *Int'l*, pg. 6973
SKJERN BANK AS; *Int'l*, pg. 6990
SK JEWELLERY GROUP LIMITED; *Int'l*, pg. 6974
SK KAKEN CO.,LTD.; *Int'l*, pg. 6974
SK KAKEN (M) SDN. BHD.—See SK Kaken Co.,Ltd.; *Int'l*, pg. 6974
SK KAKEN (THAILAND) CO., LTD.—See SK Kaken Co.,Ltd.; *Int'l*, pg. 6974
SKK (HK) CO., LTD.—See SK Kaken Co.,Ltd.; *Int'l*, pg. 6974
SKK (S) PTE. LTD.—See SK Kaken Co.,Ltd.; *Int'l*, pg. 6974
SKLADOVA TEHNIKA AD-GORNA ORYAHOVITSA; *Int'l*, pg. 6990
SKLAR CORPORATION; *U.S. Private*, pg. 3683
SKLAVENITIS J&S S.A.; *Int'l*, pg. 6990
S KLIER' NURSERY, INC.—See Magnuson Sod/Haag Services; *U.S. Private*, pg. 2549
SK LIFE SCIENCE, INC.—See SK Inc.; *Int'l*, pg. 6972
SK LUBRICANTS AMERICAS INC.—See SK Innovation Co., Ltd.; *Int'l*, pg. 6973
SK LUBRICANTS CO., LTD.—See SK Innovation Co., Ltd.; *Int'l*, pg. 6973
SK LUBRICANTS JAPAN CO., LTD.—See SK Innovation Co., Ltd.; *Int'l*, pg. 6973
SK MATERIALS CO., LTD.; *Int'l*, pg. 6974
SK MATERIALS RENEWTECH CO., LTD.—See SK Innovation Co., Ltd.; *Int'l*, pg. 6973
SKM CORPORATION—See Toyota Industries Corporation; *Int'l*, pg. 7866
SKM EGG PRODUCTS EXPORTS (INDIA) LIMITED; *Int'l*, pg. 6990
SKM EUROPE BV—See SKM EGG Products Exports (India) Limited; *Int'l*, pg. 6990
SKM GROUP; *U.S. Private*, pg. 3683
SKM INVESTMENTS AUSTRALIA PTY LTD—See Jacobs Engineering Group, Inc.; *U.S. Public*, pg. 1186
SKM JAPAN CO., LTD.—See SKM EGG Products Exports (India) Limited; *Int'l*, pg. 6990
SKM MEDIA CORP.; *U.S. Private*, pg. 3683
SK MOTORS, LLC—See Penske Automotive Group, Inc.; *U.S. Public*, pg. 1666
SKM (SINGAPORE) PTE LTD—See Jacobs Engineering Group, Inc.; *U.S. Public*, pg. 1186
SKM SKYLINE GMBH—See Zech Group SE; *Int'l*, pg. 8628
SK NETWORKS AMERICA INC.—See SK Networks Co., Ltd.; *Int'l*, pg. 6975

SKM MEDIA CORP.   CORPORATE AFFILIATIONS

SK NETWORKS AUSTRALIA PTY. LTD.—See SK Networks Co., Ltd.; *Int'l*, pg. 6975
SK NETWORKS AUTO SERVICE H.K—See SK Networks Co., Ltd.; *Int'l*, pg. 6975
SK NETWORKS BRAZIL CO., LTD.—See SK Networks Co., Ltd.; *Int'l*, pg. 6975
SK NETWORKS (CHINA) HOLDINGS CO., LTD.—See SK Networks Co., Ltd.; *Int'l*, pg. 6974
SK NETWORKS CO., LTD. - MUMBAI OFFICE—See SK Networks Co., Ltd.; *Int'l*, pg. 6975
SK NETWORKS CO., LTD. - QINGDAO OFFICE—See SK Networks Co., Ltd.; *Int'l*, pg. 6975
SK NETWORKS CO., LTD.-SHANGHAI—See SK Networks Co., Ltd.; *Int'l*, pg. 6975
SK NETWORKS CO., LTD.; *Int'l*, pg. 6974
SK NETWORKS CO., LTD. - TAIWAN OFFICE—See SK Networks Co., Ltd.; *Int'l*, pg. 6975
SK NETWORKS CO., LTD. - WUHAN OFFICE—See SK Networks Co., Ltd.; *Int'l*, pg. 6975
SK NETWORKS DEUTSCHLAND GMBH—See SK Networks Co., Ltd.; *Int'l*, pg. 6975
SK NETWORKS DO BRASIL, LTDA.—See SK Networks Co., Ltd.; *Int'l*, pg. 6975
SK NETWORKS (GUANGZHOU) AUTO SERVICE—See SK Networks Co., Ltd.; *Int'l*, pg. 6974
SK NETWORKS HONG KONG LIMITED—See SK Networks Co., Ltd.; *Int'l*, pg. 6975
SK NETWORKS JAPAN CO., LTD.—See SK Networks Co., Ltd.; *Int'l*, pg. 6975
SK NETWORKS (LIAONING) LOGISTICS CO., LTD.—See SK Networks Co., Ltd.; *Int'l*, pg. 6974
SK NETWORKS METAL (XIAMEN) CO., LTD.—See SK Networks Co., Ltd.; *Int'l*, pg. 6975
SK NETWORKS PS (SHANTOU) CO., LTD.—See SK Networks Co., Ltd.; *Int'l*, pg. 6975
SK NETWORKS (QINGDAO) AUTO SERVICE—See SK Networks Co., Ltd.; *Int'l*, pg. 6974
SK NETWORKS RESOURCES CANADA LTD.—See SK Networks Co., Ltd.; *Int'l*, pg. 6975
SK NETWORKS SERVICE CO., LTD.—See SK Networks Co., Ltd.; *Int'l*, pg. 6975
SK NETWORKS (SHANGHAI) CO., LTD.—See SK Networks Co., Ltd.; *Int'l*, pg. 6974
SK NETWORKS (SHANGHAI) MARKETING CO., LTD.—See SK Networks Co., Ltd.; *Int'l*, pg. 6974
SK NETWORKS (SHENYANG) AUTO SERVICE—See SK Networks Co., Ltd.; *Int'l*, pg. 6974
SK NETWORKS TRADING (MALAYSIA) SDN BHD—See SK Networks Co., Ltd.; *Int'l*, pg. 6975
SK NETWORKS (XIAMEN) STEEL PROCESSING CENTER CO., LTD.—See SK Networks Co., Ltd.; *Int'l*, pg. 6974
SK NETWORKS (ZHANGJIAGANG) METAL PRODUCTS CO., LTD.—See SK Networks Co., Ltd.; *Int'l*, pg. 6974
SK NEXILIS CO., LTD.—See SK Inc.; *Int'l*, pg. 6972
SKN KRAFT AND PAPER CO., LTD.—See S.Kijchai Enterprise Public Company Limited; *Int'l*, pg. 6456
SKN (SHANGHAI) MINING INVESTMENT CO., LTD.—See Shenghe Resources Holding Co., Ltd.; *Int'l*, pg. 6801
SK OCEANPLANT CO.,LTD.; *Int'l*, pg. 6975
SKODA AUTO A.S.—See Porsche Automobil Holding SE; *Int'l*, pg. 5931
SKODA AUTO DEUTSCHLAND GMBH—See Porsche Automobil Holding SE; *Int'l*, pg. 5931
SKODA AUTO INDIA PVT. LTD.—See Porsche Automobil Holding SE; *Int'l*, pg. 5931
SKODA AUTO POLSKA, S.A.—See Porsche Automobil Holding SE; *Int'l*, pg. 5931
SKODAAUTO SLOVENSKO S.R.O.—See Porsche Automobil Holding SE; *Int'l*, pg. 5931
SKODA ELECTRIC A.S.—See PPF Group N.V.; *Int'l*, pg. 5951
SKODA JS A.S.—See Gazprombank JSC; *Int'l*, pg. 2892
SKODA, MINOTTI & CO., CERTIFIED PUBLIC ACCOUNTANTS; *U.S. Private*, pg. 3683
SKODA PARS A.S.—See PPF Group N.V.; *Int'l*, pg. 5951
SKODA POWER PRIVATE LTD.—See Doosan Corporation; *Int'l*, pg. 2174
SKODA PRAHA, A.S.—See CEZ, a.s.; *Int'l*, pg. 1428
SKODA PRAHA INVEST S.R.O.—See CEZ, a.s.; *Int'l*, pg. 1428
SKODA TRANSPORTATION A.S.; *Int'l*, pg. 6991
SKODA TRANSTECH OY—See PPF Group N.V.; *Int'l*, pg. 5951
SKODA VAGONKA A.S.—See PPF Group N.V.; *Int'l*, pg. 5951
SKODA VENTURES, INC.; *Int'l*, pg. 6991
SKO-ENERGO S.R.O.; *Int'l*, pg. 6991
SKOFIN S.R.O.—See Porsche Automobil Holding SE; *Int'l*, pg. 5931
SKOGEN BARNEHAGE AS—See AcadeMedia AB; *Int'l*, pg. 77
SKOGLUND EL & TELE AB—See Bravida Holding AB; *Int'l*, pg. 1142
SKOGMAN CONSTRUCTION COMPANY OF IOWA INC.; *U.S. Private*, pg. 3683
SKOGMAN RALSTON & CARLSON INC.—See Skogman Construction Company of Iowa Inc.; *U.S. Private*, pg. 3683

SKOGMAN REALTY CO. INC.—See Skogman Construction Company of Iowa Inc.; *U.S. Private*, pg. 3683
SKOGVIND AS—See Cloudberry Clean Energy ASA; *Int'l*, pg. 1662
SKOKIE VALLEY BEVERAGE COMPANY; *U.S. Private*, pg. 3683
SKOLNIK INDUSTRIES INC.; *U.S. Private*, pg. 3683
SKOMO A/S—See Lagercrantz Group AB; *Int'l*, pg. 4395
SKOM SDN BHD—See Nam Cheong Limited; *Int'l*, pg. 5133
SK ON CO., LTD.—See SK Inc.; *Int'l*, pg. 6972
SKONEC ENTERTAINMENT CO., LTD.; *Int'l*, pg. 6991
SKOOKUM SERVICES, LLC; *U.S. Private*, pg. 3683
SKOPSKI PAZAR A.D. SKOPJE; *Int'l*, pg. 6991
SKOR CULINARY CONCEPTS INC.—See Colabor Group Inc.; *Int'l*, pg. 1697
SKORO ENTERPRISES LLC—See AdaptHealth Corp.; *U.S. Public*, pg. 39
SKOR WHOLESALE MARKETPLACE—See Colabor Group Inc.; *Int'l*, pg. 1697
SKOVIN AD; *Int'l*, pg. 6991
SKOVIN AG—See Skovin AD; *Int'l*, pg. 6991
SKOVIN S.R.O.—See Skovin AD; *Int'l*, pg. 6991
SKOVSHOVED DYREKLINIK APS—See Vimian Group AB; *Int'l*, pg. 8208
SKOWHEGAN SAVINGS BANK; *U.S. Private*, pg. 3683
SK PERMIAN, LLC—See SK Innovation Co., Ltd.; *Int'l*, pg. 6973
SK PETROCHEMICAL CO., LTD—See SK Discovery Co.,Ltd.; *Int'l*, pg. 6970
SK PETROCHEMICAL CO., LTD - ULSAN PLANT—See SK Discovery Co.,Ltd.; *Int'l*, pg. 6970
SK PHARMA BEIJING CO., LTD.—See SK Discovery Co.,Ltd.; *Int'l*, pg. 6970
SK PHARMTECO INC.—See SK Inc.; *Int'l*, pg. 6972
SK PIC GLOBAL CO., LTD.—See SK Inc.; *Int'l*, pg. 6972
SK PINX CO., LTD.—See SK Networks Co., Ltd.; *Int'l*, pg. 6975
SK PLANET CO., LTD.—See SK Telecom Co., Ltd.; *Int'l*, pg. 6976
SK PLANET, INC.—See SK Square Co., Ltd.; *Int'l*, pg. 6975
S&K POLYTEC CO., LTD.; *Int'l*, pg. 6445
SKP RESOURCES BHD; *Int'l*, pg. 6991
SK PRIMACOR AMERICAS LLC—See SK Innovation Co., Ltd.; *Int'l*, pg. 6973
SK PRIMACOR EUROPE, S.L.U.—See SK Innovation Co., Ltd.; *Int'l*, pg. 6973
SK-PRUZINY, SPOL. S R.O.—See Hutter & Schrantz PMS Ges.m.b.H; *Int'l*, pg. 3540
SKP SECURITIES LIMITED; *Int'l*, pg. 6991
SK PUCORE CO., LTD.—See SK Inc.; *Int'l*, pg. 6972
SK PUCORE USA INC.—See SK Inc.; *Int'l*, pg. 6972
SK REIT(REAL ESTATE INVESTMENT TRUST) CO., LTD; *Int'l*, pg. 6975
SK RENT A CAR CO., LTD.—See Affinity Equity Partners (HK) Ltd.; *Int'l*, pg. 186
SK RETAIL, INC.—See Wayfair Inc.; *U.S. Public*, pg. 2338
SKRETTING CANADA—See SHV Holdings N.V.; *Int'l*, pg. 6872
SKRETTING JAPAN—See SHV Holdings N.V.; *Int'l*, pg. 6872
SKRETTING USA—See SHV Holdings N.V.; *Int'l*, pg. 6872
SKRILL LTD.—See Paysafe Limited; *Int'l*, pg. 5764
S&K ROOFING, SIDING & WINDOWS, INC.; *U.S. Private*, pg. 3513
S.K. ROSENBAUER PTE. LTD.—See Rosenbauer International AG; *Int'l*, pg. 6400
SKRR EXPLORATION INC.; *Int'l*, pg. 6991
SKRUF SNUS AB—See Imperial Brands PLC; *Int'l*, pg. 3634
SK SARAN AMERICAS LLC—See SK Innovation Co., Ltd.; *Int'l*, pg. 6973
SKS CONTROL OY—See Nidec Corporation; *Int'l*, pg. 5276
SK SECURITIES ACPC NO. 7 COMPANY ACQUISITION PURPOSE CO., LTD; *Int'l*, pg. 6975
SK SECURITIES CO., LTD.; *Int'l*, pg. 6975
SK SERVICIOS AMBIENTALES ADMINISTRATIVOS, S. DE R.L. DE C.V.—See Clean Harbors, Inc.; *U.S. Public*, pg. 510
SK SHIELDUS AMERICA, INC.—See SK Inc.; *Int'l*, pg. 6972
SK SHIELDUS CO., LTD.—See SK Telecom Co., Ltd.; *Int'l*, pg. 6976
SK SHIELDUS CO—See SK Telecom Co., Ltd.; *Int'l*, pg. 6976
SK SHIPPING CO., LTD.—See SK Inc.; *Int'l*, pg. 6972
SK SHIPPING EUROPE PLC—See SK Inc.; *Int'l*, pg. 6972
SK SHIPPING JAPAN CO., LTD.—See SK Inc.; *Int'l*, pg. 6972
SK SHIPPING SINGAPORE PTE LTD.—See SK Inc.; *Int'l*, pg. 6972
SKSHU PAINT CO., LTD; *Int'l*, pg. 6991
SK SIGNET INC.; *Int'l*, pg. 6975
SK SILTRON CSS, LLC—See SK Inc.; *Int'l*, pg. 6972
SK SILTRON INC.—See SK Inc.; *Int'l*, pg. 6972
SKS, INC.; *U.S. Private*, pg. 3683

SKS MEKANIIKKA OY—See THK CO., LTD.; *Int'l*, pg. 7712
SK SPECIALTY CO., LTD.—See SK Inc.; *Int'l*, pg. 6972
SK SPECIALTY JAPAN CO., LTD.—See SK Inc.; *Int'l*, pg. 6972
SK SPECIALTY JIANGSU CO., LTD.—See SK Inc.; *Int'l*, pg. 6972
SK SPECIALTY(SHANGHAI) CO., LTD.—See SK Inc.; *Int'l*, pg. 6972
SK SPECIALTY TAIWAN CO., LTD.—See SK Inc.; *Int'l*, pg. 6972
SK SPECIALTY (XIAN) CO., LTD.—See SK Inc.; *Int'l*, pg. 6972
SK SQUARE CO., LTD.; *Int'l*, pg. 6975
SKS STAKUSIT BAUTECHNIK GMBH—See GEI-Immo AG; *Int'l*, pg. 2912
SKS SWEDEN AB—See THK CO., LTD.; *Int'l*, pg. 7712
SKS TECHNOLOGIES GROUP LIMITED; *Int'l*, pg. 6991
SK STEEL AUSTRALIA PTY. LTD.—See SK Networks Co., Ltd.; *Int'l*, pg. 6975
SKS TEHNIKA OU—See THK CO., LTD.; *Int'l*, pg. 7712
S K S TEXTILES LTD.; *Int'l*, pg. 6443
SK STOA CO., LTD.—See SK Inc.; *Int'l*, pg. 6972
SK STOK—See FLSmidth & Co. A/S; *Int'l*, pg. 2712
SKSW ADVERTISING; *U.S. Private*, pg. 3683
SK TARGET GROUP LIMITED; *Int'l*, pg. 6975
SKTD CO., LTD.—See Tong-Tai Machine Tool Co., Ltd.; *Int'l*, pg. 7806
SK TELECOM CHINA HOLDING CO., LTD.—See SK Inc.; *Int'l*, pg. 6972
SK TELECOM CO., LTD.; *Int'l*, pg. 6975
SK TELECOM JAPAN INC.—See SK Inc.; *Int'l*, pg. 6972
SK TELESYS CO., LTD.—See SKC Co., Ltd.; *Int'l*, pg. 6980
SK TELINK CO., LTD.—See SK Telecom Co., Ltd.; *Int'l*, pg. 6976
SK TRADING INTERNATIONAL CO., LTD.—See SK Innovation Co., Ltd.; *Int'l*, pg. 6973
SKT SUOMI OY—See Litorina Capital Management AB; *Int'l*, pg. 4528
SKUBB - SAND + KIES UNION GMBH—See VINCI S.A.; *Int'l*, pg. 8227
SKUE SPAREBANK; *Int'l*, pg. 6991
SKUID, INC.—See TPG Capital, L.P.; *U.S. Public*, pg. 2175
SKULLCANDY AUDIO (SHENZHEN) CO., LTD.—See Mill Road Capital Management LLC; *U.S. Private*, pg. 2730
SKULLCANDY, INC.—See Mill Road Capital Management LLC; *U.S. Private*, pg. 2730
SKULLCANDY INTERNATIONAL GMBH—See Mill Road Capital Management LLC; *U.S. Private*, pg. 2730
SKULLCANDY NORDIC AB—See Mill Road Capital Management LLC; *U.S. Private*, pg. 2730
SKULLS UNLIMITED INTERNATIONAL, INC.; *U.S. Private*, pg. 3683
S. KUMARS NATIONWIDE LIMITED; *Int'l*, pg. 6447
S. KUMARS ONLINE LIMITED; *Int'l*, pg. 6443
SKURKA AEROSPACE INC.—See TransDigm Group Incorporated; *U.S. Public*, pg. 2183
SKURRAYS LIMITED—See General Motors Company; *U.S. Public*, pg. 928
SK U.S.A, INC—See SK Discovery Co.,Ltd.; *Int'l*, pg. 6970
SKUTTLE INDOOR AIR QUALITY PRODUCTS; *U.S. Private*, pg. 3683
SKW EAST ASIA LIMITED; *Int'l*, pg. 6991
SKW METALLURGY SWEDEN AB—See SKW Stahl-Metallurgie Holding AG; *Int'l*, pg. 6992
SKW QUAB CHEMICALS INC.—See SKW Stahl-Metallurgie Holding AG; *Int'l*, pg. 6992
SKW STAHL-METALLURGIE HOLDING AG; *Int'l*, pg. 6991
SKW STICKSTOFFWERKE PIESTERITZ GMBH—See E.ON SE; *Int'l*, pg. 2259
SKW SUBARI SDN. BHD.—See Syarikat Kayu Wangi Berhad; *Int'l*, pg. 7377
SKY440, INC.; *U.S. Public*, pg. 1892
SKY ADVERTISING-CHICAGO—See Sky Advertising, Inc.; *U.S. Private*, pg. 3683
SKY ADVERTISING, INC.; *U.S. Private*, pg. 3683
SKY AIRCRAFT—See GECI International SA; *Int'l*, pg. 2909
SKYA LINK LIMITED—See World-Link Logistics (Asia) Holding Limited; *Int'l*, pg. 8458
SKY ALLIANCE RESOURCES GUINEE S.A.—See WAI Capital Investments Corp.; *Int'l*, pg. 8330
SKYALP FINANSAL TEKNOLOJILER VE DANISMANLIK AS; *Int'l*, pg. 6993
SKYAUCTION.COM, INC.; *U.S. Private*, pg. 3684
SKY BIRD TRAVEL & TOUR INC.; *U.S. Private*, pg. 3683
SKYBITZ, INC.—See AMETEK, Inc.; *U.S. Public*, pg. 122
SKYBITZ PETROLEUM LOGISTICS LLC—See AMETEK, Inc.; *U.S. Public*, pg. 122
SKYBITZ TANK MONITORING CORPORATION—See AMETEK, Inc.; *U.S. Public*, pg. 122
SKY BLUE COURIERS LTD—See CitySprint (UK) Limited; *Int'l*, pg. 1630
SKY BRASIL SERVICOS LTDA.—See AT&T Inc.; *U.S. Public*, pg. 220
SKYBRIDGE AMERICAS, INC.; *U.S. Private*, pg. 3684

COMPANY NAME INDEX

SKYBRIDGE CAPITAL; *U.S. Private*, pg. 3684
SKYBRIDGE RESOURCES, LLC; *U.S. Private*, pg. 3684
SKY BUILDING SERVICE CO., LTD—See ANA Holdings Inc.; *Int'l*, pg. 444
SKY CAC LIMITED—See Alpha Services and Holdings S.A.; *Int'l*, pg. 369
SKY CAPITAL AMERICA INC.—See Sky Solar Holdings, Ltd.; *Int'l*, pg. 6993
SKYCHAIN TECHNOLOGIES INC.; *Int'l*, pg. 6993
SKYCHEF LTD—See Air France-KLM S.A.; *Int'l*, pg. 238
SKY CHEFS DE MEXICO, S.A. DE C.V.—See Deutsche Lufthansa AG; *Int'l*, pg. 2068
SKY CHEFS DE PANAMA, S.A.—See Deutsche Lufthansa AG; *Int'l*, pg. 2068
SKY CHINAFORTUNE HOLDINGS GROUP LIMITED; *Int'l*, pg. 6992
SKYCITY ADELAIDE PTY LIMITED—See Skycity Entertainment Group Limited; *Int'l*, pg. 6993
SKYCITY AUCKLAND HOLDINGS LIMITED—See Skycity Entertainment Group Limited; *Int'l*, pg. 6993
SKYCITY AUCKLAND LIMITED—See Skycity Entertainment Group Limited; *Int'l*, pg. 6993
SKYCITY CASINO MANAGEMENT LIMITED—See Skycity Entertainment Group Limited; *Int'l*, pg. 6993
SKYCITY DARWIN HOLDINGS PTY LIMITED—See Skycity Entertainment Group Limited; *Int'l*, pg. 6993
SKYCITY DARWIN PTY LIMITED—See Skycity Entertainment Group Limited; *Int'l*, pg. 6993
SKYCITY ENTERTAINMENT GROUP LIMITED; *Int'l*, pg. 6993
SKYCITY HAMILTON LIMITED—See Skycity Entertainment Group Limited; *Int'l*, pg. 6993
SKYCITY INVESTMENTS AUSTRALIA LIMITED—See Skycity Entertainment Group Limited; *Int'l*, pg. 6993
SKYCITY INVESTMENTS QUEENSTOWN LIMITED—See Skycity Entertainment Group Limited; *Int'l*, pg. 6993
SKYCITY MANAGEMENT LIMITED—See Skycity Entertainment Group Limited; *Int'l*, pg. 6993
SKYCITY QUEENSTOWN CASINOS LIMITED—See Skycity Entertainment Group Limited; *Int'l*, pg. 6994
SKY CLIFF LIMITED(SCL)—See Tongkah Harbour Public Company Limited; *Int'l*, pg. 7808
SKYCOM CORPORATION—See TKC Corporation; *Int'l*, pg. 7762
SKYCOM (PTY) LTD—See Allied Universal Manager LLC; *U.S. Private*, pg. 190
SKY COMPUTERS, INC.; *U.S. Private*, pg. 3684
SKY COUNTRY TRANSPORTATION SERVICE; *U.S. Private*, pg. 3684
SKY COURIER, INC.—See Deutsche Post AG; *Int'l*, pg. 2082
SKYCREST ENTERPRISES INC.; *U.S. Private*, pg. 3684
SKYDANCE MEDIA LLC—See RedBird Capital Partners L.P.; *U.S. Private*, pg. 3377
SKYDDA I SVERIGE AB—See Bergman & Beving AB; *Int'l*, pg. 980
SKYDECK ACQUISITION CORP.; *U.S. Public*, pg. 1892
SKY DEUTSCHLAND GMBH—See Comcast Corporation; *U.S. Public*, pg. 541
SKY DEUTSCHLAND SERVICE CENTER GMBH—See Comcast Corporation; *U.S. Public*, pg. 541
SKY DIGITAL STORES CORP.; *Int'l*, pg. 6992
SKYDIVE QUEENSTOWN LIMITED—See Experience Co Limited; *Int'l*, pg. 2588
SKYDIVE WANAKA LIMITED—See Experience Co Limited; *Int'l*, pg. 2588
SKYDMEDIS UAB—See Panevezio statybos trestas AB; *Int'l*, pg. 5727
SKYE ASSOCIATES LLC; *U.S. Private*, pg. 3684
SKYE BIOSCIENCE, INC.; *U.S. Public*, pg. 1892
SKY E&M CO., LTD.; *Int'l*, pg. 6992
SKYE PETROLEUM, INC.; *U.S. Public*, pg. 1892
SKYERA, INC.—See Western Digital Corporation; *U.S. Public*, pg. 2355
THE SKY FACTORY, LC.; *U.S. Private*, pg. 4118
SKYFAME REALTY (HOLDINGS) LIMITED; *Int'l*, pg. 6994
SKYFENS SP. Z O.O.—See Arbonia AG; *Int'l*, pg. 538
SKYFII LIMITED; *Int'l*, pg. 6994
SKYFOLD INC.—See dormakaba Holding AG; *Int'l*, pg. 2178
SKY FOX INVESTMENT LIMITED—See Fullsun International Holdings Group Co., Limited; *Int'l*, pg. 2843
SKYFROG CO., LTD.—See Nex Point Public Company Limited; *Int'l*, pg. 5239
SKYGGNIR EHF.—See Origo hf.; *Int'l*, pg. 5630
SKY GOLD CORP.; *Int'l*, pg. 6992
SKY GOURMET - AIRLINE CATERING AND LOGISTICS GMBH—See DO & CO Aktiengesellschaft; *Int'l*, pg. 2152
SKY GREENLAND APS; *Int'l*, pg. 6992
SKY HANDLING PARTNER—See Groupe Crit, S.A.; *Int'l*, pg. 3101
SKY HANDLING PARTNER UK LIMITED—See Groupe Crit, S.A.; *Int'l*, pg. 3101
SKY HARBOUR GROUP CORPORATION; *U.S. Public*, pg. 1892
SKYHARBOUR RESOURCES LTD.; *Int'l*, pg. 6994
SKYHAWKS SPORTS ACADEMY, INC.—See Genstar Capital, LLC; *U.S. Private*, pg. 1678

SKY HEART HOTEL CO., LTD.—See Sun Frontier Fudousan Co. Ltd.; *Int'l*, pg. 7303
SKY HELICOPTERS, INC.; *U.S. Private*, pg. 3684
SKY HIGH FOR ST. JUDE INC.; *U.S. Private*, pg. 3684
SKYHIGH MEMORY CHINA LIMITED—See SK hynix Inc.; *Int'l*, pg. 6971
SKYHIGH MEMORY LIMITED—See SK hynix Inc.; *Int'l*, pg. 6971
SKY HIGH TECHNOLOGY LIMITED—See Tracsis Plc; *Int'l*, pg. 7887
SKY HIGH TECHNOLOGY—See Tracsis Plc; *Int'l*, pg. 7887
SKY HIGH TECHNOLOGY—See Tracsis Plc; *Int'l*, pg. 7887
SKYHIGH TV BV—See Vivendi SE; *Int'l*, pg. 8278
SKY HIGH UNLIMITED INC.; *U.S. Private*, pg. 3684
SKY-HI SCAFFOLDING LTD.—See Andover Capital Corporation; *Int'l*, pg. 451
SKY HOME COMMUNICATIONS LIMITED—See Comcast Corporation; *U.S. Public*, pg. 541
SKYHOOK WIRELESS, INC.—See Liberty Broadband Corporation; *U.S. Public*, pg. 1311
SKYHORSE PUBLISHING CO., INC.; *U.S. Private*, pg. 3684
SKY ICT PUBLIC COMPANY LIMITED; *Int'l*, pg. 6992
SKY INDUSTRIES LTD.; *Int'l*, pg. 6992
SKY INTEC INC.—See TIS Inc.; *Int'l*, pg. 7758
SKY ISLAND CAPITAL LLC; *U.S. Private*, pg. 3684
SKY ISRAEL PRIVATE EQUITY FUND; *Int'l*, pg. 6992
SKY ITALIA S.R.L.—See Comcast Corporation; *U.S. Public*, pg. 541
SKYJACK AB—See Linamar Corporation; *Int'l*, pg. 4502
SKYJACK EQUIPMENT SERVICES INC.—See Linamar Corporation; *Int'l*, pg. 4502
SKYJACK HEBEBUHNEN GMBH—See Linamar Corporation; *Int'l*, pg. 4502
SKYJACK HUNGARY INC—See Linamar Corporation; *Int'l*, pg. 4502
SKYJACK, INC.—See Linamar Corporation; *Int'l*, pg. 4502
SKYJACK SAS—See Linamar Corporation; *Int'l*, pg. 4502
SKYJACK UK LIMITED—See Linamar Corporation; *Int'l*, pg. 4502
SKYKNIGHT CAPITAL LLC; *U.S. Private*, pg. 3684
SKYLA CORPORATION—See Lite-On Technology Corporation; *Int'l*, pg. 4526
SKYLAND ANALYTICS INC.—See Danaher Corporation; *U.S. Public*, pg. 631
SKYLAND AUTOMOTIVE, INC.; *U.S. Private*, pg. 3685
SKYLAND DISTRIBUTING CO., INC.—See Northeast Sales Distributing Inc.; *U.S. Private*, pg. 2951
SKYLAND ENERGY S.R.L.—See Skyland Group S.r.l.; *Int'l*, pg. 6994
SKYLAND GRAIN, LLC—See The Andersons Incorporated; *U.S. Public*, pg. 2034
SKYLAND GROUP S.R.L.; *Int'l*, pg. 6994
SKYLAND PETROLEUM PTY LIMITED; *Int'l*, pg. 6994
SKYLANE OPTICS SA—See Amphenol Corporation; *U.S. Public*, pg. 132
SKYLARK CARE SERVICE CO., LTD.—See Bain Capital, LP; *U.S. Private*, pg. 444
SKYLARK D&M CO., LTD.—See Bain Capital, LP; *U.S. Private*, pg. 444
SKYLARK HOLDINGS CO., LTD.—See Bain Capital, LP; *U.S. Private*, pg. 444
SKYLARK MEATS, LLC—See Rosens Diversified, Inc.; *U.S. Private*, pg. 3484
SKYLER BOYINGTON, INC.—See Omega Healthcare Investors, Inc.; *U.S. Public*, pg. 1571
SKYLIFT B.V.—See ThyssenKrupp AG; *Int'l*, pg. 7726
SKYLIFT CONSOLIDATOR (PTE) LTD.—See Senko Group Holdings Co., Ltd.; *Int'l*, pg. 6711
SKYLIFT DISTRICENTRE (PTE)LTD.—See Senko Group Holdings Co., Ltd.; *Int'l*, pg. 6711
SKYLIGHT BIOTECH, INC.—See Immuno-Biological Laboratories Co., Ltd.; *Int'l*, pg. 3629
SKYLIGHT CONSULTING INC.—See Transcosmos Inc.; *Int'l*, pg. 7898
SKY LIGHT ELECTRONICS (SHENZHEN) LIMITED—See Sky Light Holdings Ltd.; *Int'l*, pg. 6992
SKYLIGHT FINANCIAL, INC.—See Rev Worldwide, Inc.; *U.S. Private*, pg. 3413
SKYLIGHT FINANCIAL, INC.—See Searchlight Capital Partners, L.P.; *U.S. Private*, pg. 3590
SKYLIGHT HEALTH GROUP INC.; *Int'l*, pg. 6994
SKY LIGHT HOLDINGS LTD.; *Int'l*, pg. 6992
SKY LIGHT TECHNOLOGY (HEYUAN) LIMITED—See Sky Light Holdings Ltd.; *Int'l*, pg. 6992
SKY LIMITED—See Comcast Corporation; *U.S. Public*, pg. 541
SKYLINE ADVANCED TECHNOLOGY SERVICES; *U.S. Private*, pg. 3685
SKYLINE AUTO EXCHANGE—See Cox Enterprises, Inc.; *U.S. Private*, pg. 1077
SKYLINE BANKSHARES, INC.; *U.S. Public*, pg. 1892
SKYLINE BIO SP. Z.O.O.—See Skyline Investment S.A.; *Int'l*, pg. 6994
SKYLINE BUILDING SYSTEMS INC.—See Thermal Systems KWC Ltd.; *Int'l*, pg. 7707
SKYLINE CHILI, INC.; *U.S. Private*, pg. 3685

SKYLINE COMMERCIAL INTERIORS; *U.S. Private*, pg. 3685
SKYLINE CONNECTIONS INC.; *U.S. Private*, pg. 3685
SKYLINE CREDIT RIDE INC.; *U.S. Private*, pg. 3685
SKYLINE DFW EXHIBITS & EVENTS; *U.S. Private*, pg. 3685
SKYLINE DISPLAYS INC.; *U.S. Private*, pg. 3685
SKYLINE ENTERTAINMENT NV—See Television Francaise 1 S.A.; *Int'l*, pg. 7543
SKYLINE EQUIPMENT, LLC—See EVI Industries, Inc.; *U.S. Public*, pg. 803
SKYLINE EQUITIES REALTY, LLC; *U.S. Private*, pg. 3685
SKYLINE EXHIBITS OF LOS ANGELES INC.—See Skyline Displays Inc.; *U.S. Private*, pg. 3685
SKYLINE EXHIBITS—See Skyline Displays Inc.; *U.S. Private*, pg. 3685
SKYLINE FUNDING INC.—See Skyline Credit Ride Inc.; *U.S. Private*, pg. 3685
SKYLINE HOMES, INC.—See Champion Homes, Inc.; *U.S. Public*, pg. 477
SKYLINE INTERNATIONAL DEVELOPMENT INC.; *Int'l*, pg. 6994
SKYLINE INVESTMENT S.A.; *Int'l*, pg. 6994
SKYLINE MEDICAL CENTER—See HCA Healthcare, Inc.; *U.S. Public*, pg. 1008
SKYLINE MEDICAL GROUP, LLC—See HCA Healthcare, Inc.; *U.S. Public*, pg. 1008
SKYLINE MILLARS LIMITED; *Int'l*, pg. 6994
SKYLINE NATIONAL BANK—See SKYLINE BANKSHARES, INC.; *U.S. Public*, pg. 1892
SKYLINE NEUROSCIENCE ASSOCIATES, LLC—See HCA Healthcare, Inc.; *U.S. Public*, pg. 1008
SKYLINE PARTNERS TECHNOLOGY, LLC—See COMSovereign Holding Corp.; *U.S. Public*, pg. 562
SKYLINE PROPERTIES; *U.S. Private*, pg. 3685
SKYLINE SALES INC.; *U.S. Private*, pg. 3685
SKYLINE STEEL, INC.—See Endres Manufacturing Co, Inc.; *U.S. Private*, pg. 1392
SKYLINE STEEL, LLC—See Nucor Corporation; *U.S. Public*, pg. 1554
SKYLINE TECHNOLOGIES, INC.—See TE Connectivity Ltd.; *Int'l*, pg. 7496
SKYLINE TELEPHONE MEMBERSHIP CORPORATION; *U.S. Private*, pg. 3685
SKYLINE TRAVEL, TOURISM & SHIPPING—See Juma Al Majid Group; *Int'l*, pg. 4025
SKYLINE ULTD, INC.—See Central Research, Inc.; *U.S. Private*, pg. 824
SKYLINE VENTURES INDIA LIMITED; *Int'l*, pg. 6994
SKYLINE VENTURE SP. Z O.O.—See Skyline Investment S.A.; *Int'l*, pg. 6994
SKYLINK TRAVEL; *U.S. Private*, pg. 3686
SKY LIVING—See Comcast Corporation; *U.S. Public*, pg. 541
SKYLOGIC MEDITERRANEO S.R.L—See Eutelsat Communications SA; *Int'l*, pg. 2560
SKYLOGIC S.P.A.—See Eutelsat Communications SA; *Int'l*, pg. 2560
SKY LOGISTICS AND DISTRIBUTION; *U.S. Private*, pg. 3684
SKYLON ALL ASSET TRUST—See CI Financial Corporation; *Int'l*, pg. 1601
SKYLON INTERNATIONAL ADVANTAGE YIELD TRUST—See CI Financial Corporation; *Int'l*, pg. 1601
SKYLTAR & MARKEN GRUPPEN AB—See Addtech AB; *Int'l*, pg. 135
SKYMALL HOLDINGS, LLC—See C&A Marketing, Inc.; *U.S. Public*, pg. 702
SKYMAN AUTO CHASSIS (WUHU) CO., LTD—See Chongqing Skyman Industry (Group) Co., Ltd.; *Int'l*, pg. 1581
SKYMARK AIRLINES INC.; *Int'l*, pg. 6994
SKYMARK REAL ESTATE INVESTMENTS; *U.S. Private*, pg. 3686
SKYMASTS ANTENNAS LTD.; *Int'l*, pg. 6994
SKY MEDIA GMBH—See Comcast Corporation; *U.S. Public*, pg. 541
SKYMESH PTY. LTD.—See Bigblu Broadband Group PLC; *Int'l*, pg. 1022
SKY METALS LIMITED; *Int'l*, pg. 6992
SKYMISSION GROUP HOLDINGS LIMITED; *Int'l*, pg. 6994
SKY-MOBI LIMITED; *Int'l*, pg. 6993
SKYMOONS TECHNOLOGY, INC.; *Int'l*, pg. 6994
SKY NETWORK (PRIVATE) LIMITED—See Sri Lanka Telecom PLC; *Int'l*, pg. 7150
SKYNETWORKS CO. LTD.—See Skytel Co. Ltd.; *Int'l*, pg. 6994
SKY NETWORK SERVICES LIMITED—See Sky Network Television Limited; *Int'l*, pg. 6992
SKY NETWORK TELEVISION LIMITED; *Int'l*, pg. 6992
SKYNET WORLDWIDE EXPRESS (PVT.) LTD.—See Hemas Holdings PLC; *Int'l*, pg. 3341
SKY NIGHT LLC—See flyExclusive, Inc.; *U.S. Public*, pg. 861
SKY ONE EXPRESS (HK) LIMITED—See Sky One Network (Holding) Ltd.; *Int'l*, pg. 6992
SKY ONE INTERNATIONAL FREIGHT LIMITED—See Sky One Network (Holding) Ltd.; *Int'l*, pg. 6992

SKY NETWORK TELEVISION LIMITED
CORPORATE AFFILIATIONS

SKY ONE LOGISTICS (HK) LIMITED—See Sky One Network (Holding) Ltd.; *Int'l*, pg. 6993
SKY ONE NETWORK (HOLDING) LTD.; *Int'l*, pg. 6992
SKY ONE SSI LOGISTICS LIMITED—See Sky One Network (Holding) Ltd.; *Int'l*, pg. 6992
SKY OSTERREICH FERNSEHEN GMBH—See Comcast Corporation; *U.S. Public*, pg. 541
SKY OSTERREICH GMBH—See Comcast Corporation; *U.S. Public*, pg. 541
SKY OSTERREICH VERWALTUNG GMBH—See Comcast Corporation; *U.S. Public*, pg. 541
SKYPAK SERVICE SPECIALIST LIMITED; *Int'l*, pg. 6994
SKY PARKS BUSINESS CENTER LIMITED—See Flughafen Wien Aktiengesellschaft; *Int'l*, pg. 2713
SKY PARTNERS OU—See Deutsche Bahn AG; *Int'l*, pg. 2054
SKYPASS TRAVEL, INC—See Mondee Holdings, Inc.; *U.S. Public*, pg. 1460
SKYPE COMMUNICATIONS S.A.R.L—See Microsoft Corporation; *U.S. Public*, pg. 1443
SKY PERFECT BROADCASTING CORPORATION—See SKY Perfect JSAT Holdings Inc.; *Int'l*, pg. 6993
SKY PERFECT ENTERTAINMENT CORPORATION—See SKY Perfect JSAT Holdings Inc.; *Int'l*, pg. 6993
SKY PERFECT JSAT CORPORATION—See SKY Perfect JSAT Holdings Inc.; *Int'l*, pg. 6993
SKY PERFECT JSAT HOLDINGS INC.; *Int'l*, pg. 6993
SKYPERSONIC, INC.—See Red Cat Holdings, Inc.; *U.S. Public*, pg. 1769
SKY PETROLEUM, INC.; *U.S. Public*, pg. 1892
SKYPHARM, S.A.—See COSMOS HEALTH INC.; *U.S. Public*, pg. 585
SKYPORT COMPANIES LLC; *U.S. Private*, pg. 3686
SKYPORT SERVICE CORPORATION—See Mitsubishi Corporation; *Int'l*, pg. 4943
SKY POWERSPORTS OF LAKELAND, INC.—See Suzuki of Lake Wales, Inc.; *U.S. Private*, pg. 3887
SKY PUBLICATIONS LIMITED—See Comcast Corporation; *U.S. Public*, pg. 541
SKY RANCH; *U.S. Private*, pg. 3684
SKYRAY INSTRUMENTS USA, INC—See Jiangsu Skyray Instrument Co., Ltd.; *Int'l*, pg. 3954
SKYRAY KOREA CO., LTD.—See Jiangsu Skyray Instrument Co., Ltd.; *Int'l*, pg. 3954
SKYREACH GROUP HOLDINGS PTY LTD—See Nishio Holdings Co., Ltd.; *Int'l*, pg. 5366
SKYREACH PTY LTD—See Nishio Holdings Co., Ltd.; *Int'l*, pg. 5366
SKY RESORT INTERNATIONAL LIMITED; *Int'l*, pg. 6993
SKYRIDGE CLINICAL ASSOCIATES, LLC—See Community Health Systems, Inc.; *U.S. Public*, pg. 557
SKY RIDGE MEDICAL CENTER—See HCA Healthcare, Inc.; *U.S. Public*, pg. 1008
SKY RIDGE SURGERY CENTER, L.P.—See HCA Healthcare, Inc.; *U.S. Public*, pg. 1008
SKY RIDGE SURGICAL CENTER—See HCA Healthcare, Inc.; *U.S. Public*, pg. 1008
SKYRISE PREFAB BUILDING SOLUTIONS INC.—See Sto SE & Co. KGaA; *Int'l*, pg. 7219
SKYRIVER COMMUNICATIONS INC.—See Trive Capital Inc.; *U.S. Private*, pg. 4239
SKYROOMS (PRIVATE) LIMITED—See Pakistan International Airlines Corporation; *Int'l*, pg. 5704
SKYRUN BRECKENRIDGE, LLC; *U.S. Private*, pg. 3686
SKYRUN VACATION RENTALS, LLC; *U.S. Private*, pg. 3686
SKY SANDS (PROPRIETARY) LIMITED—See Group Five Limited; *Int'l*, pg. 3089
SKY SAPIENCE LTD.—See COMSovereign Holding Corp.; *U.S. Public*, pg. 562
SKYSCANNER LIMITED—See Trip.com Group Ltd.; *Int'l*, pg. 7926
SKYSCAPE CAPITAL, INC.; *Int'l*, pg. 6994
SKYSCAPE.COM INC.—See KKR & Co. Inc.; *U.S. Public*, pg. 1253
SKY SERVICE FBO INC—See Exxon Mobil Corporation; *U.S. Public*, pg. 817
SKYSERVICE, INC.—See Skyline Displays Inc.; *U.S. Private*, pg. 3685
SKYSHOP LOGISTICS, INC.; *U.S. Public*, pg. 1892
SKY SILK AO; *Int'l*, pg. 6993
SKYSIS, LLC—See Lloyds Banking Group plc; *Int'l*, pg. 4537
SKY SOLAR BULGARIA CO., EOOD—See Sky Solar Holdings, Ltd.; *Int'l*, pg. 6993
SKY SOLAR HOLDINGS, LTD.; *Int'l*, pg. 6993
SKY SOLAR JAPAN K.K.—See Sky Solar Holdings, Ltd.; *Int'l*, pg. 6993
SKY SOLAR RENEWABLE ENERGY (WUXI) CO., LTD.—See Sky Solar Holdings, Ltd.; *Int'l*, pg. 6993
SKY & SPACE GLOBAL LTD.; *Int'l*, pg. 6992
SKYSTAR AIRPORT SERVICES PTY. LTD.—See Agility; *Int'l*, pg. 210
SKYSTAR BIO-PHARMACEUTICAL COMPANY; *Int'l*, pg. 6994
SKYSTREAM NETWORKS, INC.—See Telefonaktiebolaget LM Ericsson; *Int'l*, pg. 7532
SKYTANKING BORDEAUX SAS—See Marquard & Bahls AG; *Int'l*, pg. 4700

SKYTANKING CALULO LTD.—See Marquard & Bahls AG; *Int'l*, pg. 4700
SKYTANKING GMBH & CO. KG—See Marquard & Bahls AG; *Int'l*, pg. 4700
SKYTANKING HOLDING GMBH—See Marquard & Bahls AG; *Int'l*, pg. 4700
SKYTANKING NICE SAS—See Marquard & Bahls AG; *Int'l*, pg. 4700
SKYTANKING N.V./S.A.—See Marquard & Bahls AG; *Int'l*, pg. 4700
SKYTANKING OSTEND N. V.—See Marquard & Bahls AG; *Int'l*, pg. 4700
SKYTANKING S. R. L.—See Eni S.p.A.; *Int'l*, pg. 2437
SKYTANKING STUTTGART GMBH & CO. KG—See Marquard & Bahls AG; *Int'l*, pg. 4701
SKYTAP, INC.—See Kyndryl Holdings Inc.; *U.S. Public*, pg. 1278
SKYTEC AG—See Allgeier SE; *Int'l*, pg. 337
SKYTECH INC.—See Pilatus Aircraft Ltd.; *Int'l*, pg. 5866
SKYTEL CO. LTD.; *Int'l*, pg. 6994
SKY TELECOM TPC; *U.S. Private*, pg. 3684
SKY THRIVE RAMBAUDI S.R.L.—See Fair Friend Group; *Int'l*, pg. 2604
SKYTOP LODGE CORP.; *U.S. Public*, pg. 1893
SKYTOP LODGE; *U.S. Public*, pg. 1892
SKY TOWER LIMITED—See Skycity Entertainment Group Limited; *Int'l*, pg. 6993
SKY TOWER PUBLIC COMPANY LIMITED—See Capital Engineering Network Public Company Limited; *Int'l*, pg. 1310
SKY TRANSPORTATION SERVICES—See Warehouse Services Inc.; *U.S. Private*, pg. 4442
SKYTRON ENERGY GMBH—See Liberta Partners Holding GmbH; *Int'l*, pg. 4484
SKYTRONICS, INC.—See Phillips Service Industries, Inc. (PSI); *U.S. Private*, pg. 3171
SKYTYPERS, INC.; *U.S. Private*, pg. 3686
SKY UK LIMITED—See Comcast Corporation; *U.S. Public*, pg. 541
SKY UNITED TRADING LIMITED—See China Medical System Holdings Ltd.; *Int'l*, pg. 1518
SKYVIEW CAPITAL, LLC; *U.S. Private*, pg. 3686
SKYVIEW OWNERS CORPORATION; *U.S. Private*, pg. 3686
SKYWALKER COMMUNICATION INC.; *U.S. Private*, pg. 3686
SKYWARD INC.; *U.S. Private*, pg. 3686
SKYWARD INFORMATION SYSTEM CO., LTD.—See Shin-Etsu Chemical Co. Ltd.; *Int'l*, pg. 6841
SKYWARD INFORMATION SYSTEMS CO., LTD—See Shin-Etsu Chemical Co. Ltd.; *Int'l*, pg. 6841
SKYWARD SPECIALTY INSURANCE GROUP, INC.; *U.S. Public*, pg. 1893
SKYWATER TECHNOLOGY, INC.; *U.S. Public*, pg. 1893
SKYWAVE MOBILE COMMUNICATIONS (HK) LIMITED—See ORBCOMM, Inc.; *U.S. Public*, pg. 1614
SKYWAY ADVISORS, LLC—See Skyway Capital Partners, LLC; *U.S. Private*, pg. 3686
SKYWAY AUTO PARTS, INC.—See Metalico Inc.; *U.S. Private*, pg. 2681
SKYWAY CAPITAL PARTNERS, LLC; *U.S. Private*, pg. 3686
SKYWAY CEMENT COMPANY LLC—See Eagle Materials Inc.; *U.S. Public*, pg. 702
SKYWAY HOUSE, LLC—See Acadia Healthcare Company, Inc.; *U.S. Public*, pg. 30
SKYWAY LUGGAGE COMPANY—See Ricardo Beverly Hills, Inc.; *U.S. Private*, pg. 3425
SKYWAYS EXPRESS AB; *Int'l*, pg. 6995
SKYWAY SURGERY CENTER, LLC—See Bain Capital, LP; *U.S. Private*, pg. 445
SKYWAY TECHNOLOGY GROUP, INC.; *U.S. Private*, pg. 3686
SKYWEST AIRLINES, INC. - IDAHO—See Skywest Inc.; *U.S. Public*, pg. 1893
SKYWEST AIRLINES, INC.—See Skywest Inc.; *U.S. Public*, pg. 1893
SKYWEST INC.; *U.S. Public*, pg. 1893
SKYWORD INC.—See Progress Partners, Inc.; *U.S. Private*, pg. 3278
SKYWORD INC.—See Rho Capital Partners, Inc.; *U.S. Private*, pg. 3421
SKYWORK MEDIA LIMITED—See Transmit Entertainment Limited; *Int'l*, pg. 7902
SKYWORKS GLOBAL PTE LTD—See Skyworks Solutions, Inc.; *U.S. Public*, pg. 1893
SKYWORKS LLC; *U.S. Private*, pg. 3686
SKYWORKS SEMICONDUCTOR—See Skyworks Solutions, Inc.; *U.S. Public*, pg. 1893
SKYWORKS SOLUTIONS COMPANY, LIMITED—See Skyworks Solutions, Inc.; *U.S. Public*, pg. 1893
SKYWORKS SOLUTIONS DE MEXICO, S. DE R.L. DE C.V.—See Skyworks Solutions, Inc.; *U.S. Public*, pg. 1893
SKYWORKS SOLUTIONS, INC.; *U.S. Public*, pg. 1893
SKYWORKS SOLUTIONS KOREA LIMITED—See Skyworks Solutions, Inc.; *U.S. Public*, pg. 1893
SKYWORKS SOLUTIONS LIMITED—See Skyworks Solutions, Inc.; *U.S. Public*, pg. 1893

SKYWORKS SOLUTIONS OY—See Skyworks Solutions, Inc.; *U.S. Public*, pg. 1893
SKYWORKS SOLUTIONS WORLDWIDE, INC.—See Skyworks Solutions, Inc.; *U.S. Public*, pg. 1893
SKYWORKS SOLUTIONS WORLDWIDE, INC.—See Skyworks Solutions, Inc.; *U.S. Public*, pg. 1893
SKYWORKS TECHNOLOGIES, INC.; *U.S. Private*, pg. 3686
SKYWORLD DEVELOPMENT BERHAD; *Int'l*, pg. 6995
SKYWORTH ELECTRICAL APPLIANCES (SHENZHEN) CO., LTD.—See Skyworth Group Limited; *Int'l*, pg. 6995
SKYWORTH GROUP LIMITED; *Int'l*, pg. 6995
SKYX PLATFORMS CORP.; *U.S. Public*, pg. 1893
SLAAPGENOTEN—See Beter Bed Holding N.V.; *Int'l*, pg. 1002
SLACAN INDUSTRIES INC.; *Int'l*, pg. 6995
SLACK AND COMPANY, LLC; *U.S. Private*, pg. 3687
SLACK CHEMICAL CO. INC.; *U.S. Private*, pg. 3687
SLACK & CO. CONTRACTING, INC.; *U.S. Private*, pg. 3686
SLACK & COMPANY, LLC; *U.S. Private*, pg. 3686
SLACKER, INC.—See LiveOne, Inc.; *U.S. Public*, pg. 1332
SLACK TECHNOLOGIES, INC.—See Salesforce, Inc.; *U.S. Public*, pg. 1838
SLA CREATION SA; *Int'l*, pg. 6995
SLADE GORTON & CO. INC.; *U.S. Private*, pg. 3687
SLAFTER OIL CO—See Western Cooperative Company; *U.S. Private*, pg. 4492
SLAGELSE LASESERVICE A/S—See ASSA ABLOY AB; *Int'l*, pg. 640
SLAIT CONSULTING, LLC—See ePlus Inc.; *U.S. Public*, pg. 784
SLAKEY BROTHERS INC.; *U.S. Private*, pg. 3687
SL ALABAMA LLC—See SL Corporation; *Int'l*, pg. 6995
THE SLALOM SHOP—See OneWater Marine Holdings LLC; *U.S. Private*, pg. 3026
SLAM CORP.; *U.S. Public*, pg. 1894
SLAM EXPLORATION LTD.; *Int'l*, pg. 6995
SLANCHEV BRYAG AD; *Int'l*, pg. 6995
SLANCHEV BRYAG HOLDING AD; *Int'l*, pg. 6995
SLAND ORTHOPAEDIC CONSULTANTS PTE. LTD.—See OUE Limited; *Int'l*, pg. 5666
THE SLANE COMPANY LLC; *U.S. Private*, pg. 4118
SLANE HOSIERY MILLS, INC.; *U.S. Private*, pg. 3687
SLANEY HEALTHCARE PRIVATE LIMITED—See Shalby Limited; *Int'l*, pg. 6750
SLANG WORLDWIDE, INC.; *Int'l*, pg. 6995
SLANTCHO JSC; *Int'l*, pg. 6995
SLANT/FIN CORPORATION; *U.S. Private*, pg. 3687
SLANT/FIN, LTD/LTEE.—See Slant/Fin Corporation; *U.S. Private*, pg. 3687
SLANTSE STARA ZAGORA TABAC JSC; *Int'l*, pg. 6995
SLAPPY CAKES (SINGAPORE) PTE. LTD.—See Tung Lok Restaurants (2000) Ltd; *Int'l*, pg. 7971
SLASH PINE ELECTRIC MEMBERSHIP CORPORATION; *U.S. Private*, pg. 3687
SLASKIE WESOLE MIASTECZKO SP. Z O. O.—See Tatry Mountain Resorts A.S.; *Int'l*, pg. 7474
SLATE ASSET MANAGEMENT LP; *Int'l*, pg. 6995
SLATE CAPITAL CORP.—See Slate Asset Management LP; *Int'l*, pg. 6995
SLATE CAPITAL GROUP LLC; *U.S. Private*, pg. 3687
SLATE GROCERY REIT—See Slate Asset Management LP; *Int'l*, pg. 6995
THE SLATE GROUP LLC—See Graham Holdings Company; *U.S. Public*, pg. 956
SLATE GROUP; *U.S. Private*, pg. 3687
SLATE MAGAZINE—See Graham Holdings Company; *U.S. Public*, pg. 956
SLATE OFFICE REIT; *Int'l*, pg. 6996
SLATER CONTROLS, INC.; *U.S. Private*, pg. 3687
SLATER DYE WORKS INC.; *U.S. Private*, pg. 3687
SLATER & GORDON LIMITED—See Allegro Funds Pty. Ltd.; *Int'l*, pg. 336
SLATER GORDON SOLUTIONS LEGAL LIMITED—See Allegro Funds Pty. Ltd.; *Int'l*, pg. 336
SLATER & GORDON (UK) LLP—See Allegro Funds Pty. Ltd.; *Int'l*, pg. 336
SLATER MOFFAT ASSOCIATES, LLP—See Sensiba San Filippo LLP; *U.S. Private*, pg. 3607
SLATE ROCK SAFETY LLC; *U.S. Private*, pg. 3687
SLATE SOLUTIONS, INC.—See Genstar Capital, LLC; *U.S. Private*, pg. 1679
SLATINSKA BANKA D.D.; *Int'l*, pg. 6996
SLATON BROS. INC.—See VINCI S.A.; *Int'l*, pg. 8232
SLAUGHTER GROUP; *U.S. Private*, pg. 3687
SLAVEJ AD SKOPJE; *Int'l*, pg. 6996
SLAVE LAKE ZINC CORP.; *Int'l*, pg. 6996
SLAVIA CAPITAL GROUP, A.S.; *Int'l*, pg. 6996
SLAVIA CAPITAL PRAHA, A.S.—See SLAVIA CAPITAL Group, A.S.; *Int'l*, pg. 6996
SLAVIA JSCB; *Int'l*, pg. 6996
SLAVICA PARAFARM A.D.; *Int'l*, pg. 6996
SLAVNEFT-MEGIONNEFTEGAZ OAO; *Int'l*, pg. 6996
SLAVONIC BENEVOLENT ORDER OF THE STATE OF TEXAS; *U.S. Private*, pg. 3687
SLAVONIJA IGM D.O.O.—See Nexe Grupa d.d.; *Int'l*, pg. 5243

COMPANY NAME INDEX

SLAVUTYCH, PJSC; *Int'l*, pg. 6996
SLAVYANSK HIGH VOLTAGE INSULATORS WORKS, PJSC; *Int'l*, pg. 6996
SLAWINSKI & CO. GMBH; *Int'l*, pg. 6996
SLAYDEN PLUMBING & HEATING, INC.; *U.S. Private*, pg. 3688
SLAY INDUSTRIES INC.; *U.S. Private*, pg. 3687
SLAYMAKER RESTAURANT GROUP INC.; *U.S. Private*, pg. 3688
SLAY STEEL, INC.; *U.S. Private*, pg. 3688
SLAY TRANSPORTATION CO INC—See Slay Industries Inc.; *U.S. Private*, pg. 3687
SLB DEVELOPMENT LTD.; *Int'l*, pg. 6996
SL BETEILIGUNGS-GMBH & CO. GRUNDSTUCKSVERWALTUNG KG—See Swiss Life Holding; *Int'l*, pg. 7368
SLC AGRICOLA S.A.; *Int'l*, pg. 6996
SLCA—See Safran SA; *Int'l*, pg. 6473
SLC BELCONNEN PTY LTD.—See Wesfarmers Limited; *Int'l*, pg. 8380
SLC BUNDABERG PTY LTD.—See Wesfarmers Limited; *Int'l*, pg. 8380
SLC BURLEIGH PTY LTD.—See Wesfarmers Limited; *Int'l*, pg. 8380
SLC BURNSIDE PTY LTD.—See Wesfarmers Limited; *Int'l*, pg. 8380
SLC INNALOO PTY LTD.—See Wesfarmers Limited; *Int'l*, pg. 8381
S&L CITY BUILDERS PTE. LTD.—See Sim Lian Group Limited; *Int'l*, pg. 6927
SLC JOONDALUP PTY LTD.—See Wesfarmers Limited; *Int'l*, pg. 8381
SLC MACKAY PTY LTD.—See Wesfarmers Limited; *Int'l*, pg. 8381
SLC MANDURAH PTY LTD.—See Wesfarmers Limited; *Int'l*, pg. 8381
SLC MIDLAND GATE PTY LTD.—See Wesfarmers Limited; *Int'l*, pg. 8381
SLC MORAYFIELD PTY LTD.—See Wesfarmers Limited; *Int'l*, pg. 8381
SLC MORLEY PTY LTD.—See Wesfarmers Limited; *Int'l*, pg. 8381
S & L CONTRACTING INC.—See Strait & Lamp Lumber Co. Inc.; *U.S. Private*, pg. 3833
SL CORPORATION - ANSAN PLANT—See SL Corporation; *Int'l*, pg. 6995
SL CORPORATION - CHEONAN PLANT—See SL Corporation; *Int'l*, pg. 6995
SL CORPORATION - DAGUE PLANT—See SL Corporation; *Int'l*, pg. 6995
SL CORPORATION - HWASUNG PLANT—See SL Corporation; *Int'l*, pg. 6995
SL CORPORATION - JILLYANG PLANT—See SL Corporation; *Int'l*, pg. 6995
SL CORPORATION - SEOSAN PLANT—See SL Corporation; *Int'l*, pg. 6995
SL CORPORATION; *Int'l*, pg. 6995
SL CORPORATION - SUNGSAN PLANT—See SL Corporation; *Int'l*, pg. 6995
SL CORPORATION - ULSAN PLANT—See SL Corporation; *Int'l*, pg. 6995
SLC PERTH PTY LTD.—See Wesfarmers Limited; *Int'l*, pg. 8381
SLC ROCKHAMPTON PTY LTD.—See Wesfarmers Limited; *Int'l*, pg. 8381
SLC ROCKINGHAM PTY LTD.—See Wesfarmers Limited; *Int'l*, pg. 8381
SLC STRATHPINE PTY LTD.—See Wesfarmers Limited; *Int'l*, pg. 8381
SLC WARWICK PTY LTD.—See Wesfarmers Limited; *Int'l*, pg. 8381
SLC WODEN PTY LTD.—See Wesfarmers Limited; *Int'l*, pg. 8381
S.L. DE GESTION MOBILIARIA—See Lone Star Funds; *U.S. Private*, pg. 2485
S.L DELEGACION GALICIA.—See Mondragon Corporation; *Int'l*, pg. 5029
SLD ENTERTAINMENT, INC.; *Int'l*, pg. 6996
S.L. DEVELOPMENT MANAGEMENT PTE LIMITED—See Singapore Land Group Limited; *Int'l*, pg. 6940
SLD LANDFILL, INC.—See Waste Connections, Inc.; *Int'l*, pg. 8354
SLEAD CONSTRUCTION, INC.—See Crossplane Capital Management LP; *U.S. Private*, pg. 1107
SLEAFORD QUALITY FOODS LIMITED.—See Jain Irrigation Systems Limited; *Int'l*, pg. 3872
SLEDD CO.; *U.S. Private*, pg. 3688
SLEDGEHAMMER GAMES, INC—See Microsoft Corporation; *U.S. Public*, pg. 1439
SLEDGE—See Enero Group Limited; *Int'l*, pg. 2424
SLEDGHAMMER GAMES, INC—See Microsoft Corporation; *U.S. Public*, pg. 1439
SLEEK INTERNATIONAL PRIVATE LIMITED—See Asian Paints Limited; *Int'l*, pg. 619
SLEEMAN BREWERIES, LTD.—See Sapporo Holdings Limited; *Int'l*, pg. 6574
SLEEMAN UNIBROUE QUEBEC—See Sapporo Holdings Limited; *Int'l*, pg. 6574
SLEEPAID HOLDING CO.; *Int'l*, pg. 6996
SLEEPCAIR, INC.—See Linde plc; *Int'l*, pg. 4505

SLEEP COUNTRY CANADA HOLDINGS, INC.—See Fairfax Financial Holdings Limited; *Int'l*, pg. 2608
SLEEP COUNTRY CANADA INCOME FUND—See Birch Hill Equity Partners Management Inc.; *Int'l*, pg. 1046
SLEEP COUNTRY CANADA INCOME FUND—See Westerkirk Capital Inc.; *Int'l*, pg. 8388
SLEEP CYCLE AB; *Int'l*, pg. 6996
SLEEPER SEWELL INSURANCE SERVICES, INC.—See Aquiline Capital Partners LLC; *U.S. Private*, pg. 305
SLEEPERS IN SEATTLE; *U.S. Private*, pg. 3688
SLEEP EXPERTS PARTNERS, L.P.—See Steinhoff International Holdings N.V.; *Int'l*, pg. 7195
SLEEP HAVEN, INC.—See Restonic Mattress Corporation; *U.S. Private*, pg. 3409
SLEEP INN HOTELS—See Choice Hotels International, Inc.; *U.S. Public*, pg. 490
SLEEPIQ LABS INC.—See Sleep Number Corporation; *U.S. Public*, pg. 1894
SLEEPMED INC. - SLEEP THERAPY SERVICES OPERATIONS CENTER—See SleepMed Inc; *U.S. Private*, pg. 3688
SLEEPMED INC; *U.S. Private*, pg. 3688
SLEEP NUMBER CORPORATION; *U.S. Public*, pg. 1894
SLEEP PRODUCTS, INC.—See Restonic Mattress Corporation; *U.S. Private*, pg. 3409
SLEEP-RITE INDUSTRIES, INC.—See Restonic Mattress Corporation; *U.S. Private*, pg. 3409
SLEEPSAFE BEDS, LLC; *U.S. Private*, pg. 3688
SLEEP SERVICES OF AMERICA, INC.—See Vicente Capital Partners, LLC; *U.S. Private*, pg. 4376
SLEEPTECH LIMITED—See ResMed Inc.; *U.S. Public*, pg. 1791
SLEEP WELL INC.; *U.S. Private*, pg. 3688
SLEEPWORKS MEDICAL INC.—See WELL Health Technologies Corp.; *Int'l*, pg. 8372
SLEEPY EYE TELEPHONE COMPANY—See Arvig Enterprises, Inc.; *U.S. Private*, pg. 344
SLEEPY EYE TELEPHONE COMPANY—See Blue Earth Valley Communications; *U.S. Private*, pg. 588
SLEEPY EYE TELEPHONE COMPANY—See Nuvera Communications, Inc.; *U.S. Public*, pg. 1556
SLEEPZ AG; *Int'l*, pg. 6996
THE SLEETER GROUP, INC.—See Diversified Communications; *U.S. Private*, pg. 1241
SLEIMAN AGRICULTURAL ESTABLISHMENT; *Int'l*, pg. 6996
SLEM MEDICAL SARL—See HORIBA Ltd; *Int'l*, pg. 3478
SL ENERGY CO., LTD.; *Int'l*, pg. 6995
SLETTEN CONSTRUCTION BOISE—See Sletten Construction Inc.; *U.S. Private*, pg. 3688
SLETTEN CONSTRUCTION INC.; *U.S. Private*, pg. 3688
SLETTEN CONSTRUCTION OF NEVADA, INC.—See Sletten Construction Inc.; *U.S. Private*, pg. 3688
SLETTEN CONSTRUCTION OF WYOMING, INC.—See Sletten Construction Inc.; *U.S. Private*, pg. 3688
SLETTEN CONSTRUCTION PHOENIX—See Sletten Construction Inc.; *U.S. Private*, pg. 3688
SLE WORLDWIDE PTY LIMITED—See The Hanover Insurance Group, Inc.; *U.S. Public*, pg. 2087
SL FINANCIAL SERVICES CORPORATION—See Landesbank Baden-Wurttemberg; *Int'l*, pg. 4405
SLF OF CANADA UK LIMITED—See Phoenix Group Holdings PLC; *Int'l*, pg. 5851
SLF REALISATION FUND LIMITED; *Int'l*, pg. 6996
S.L. FUSCO INC.; *U.S. Private*, pg. 3518
SLG 16 COURT STREET LLC—See SL Green Realty Corp.; *U.S. Public*, pg. 1894
SLG 609 FIFTH LLC—See SL Green Realty Corp.; *U.S. Public*, pg. 1894
SLG 625 LESSEE LLC—See SL Green Realty Corp.; *U.S. Public*, pg. 1894
SLG 711 THIRD LLC—See SL Green Realty Corp.; *U.S. Public*, pg. 1894
SLG BROADCAST AG—See Transition Evergreen; *Int'l*, pg. 7901
SLG CHEMICALS, INC.—See Scott's Liquid Gold-Inc.; *U.S. Public*, pg. 1849
S.L. GILBERT COMPANY INC.; *U.S. Private*, pg. 3518
SLG IRP REALTY LLC—See SL Green Realty Corp.; *U.S. Public*, pg. 1894
SLG PARTNERS, LP II—See Raymond James Financial, Inc.; *U.S. Public*, pg. 1765
SLG PLASTICS, INC.—See Scott's Liquid Gold-Inc.; *U.S. Public*, pg. 1849
SLG RECYCLING—See Coller Capital Ltd.; *Int'l*, pg. 1699
SL GREEN FUNDING LLC—See SL Green Realty Corp.; *U.S. Public*, pg. 1894
SL GREEN MANAGEMENT LLC—See SL Green Realty Corp.; *U.S. Public*, pg. 1894
SL GREEN OPERATING PARTNERSHIP, L.P.—See SL Green Realty Corp.; *U.S. Public*, pg. 1894
SL GREEN REALTY CORP.; *U.S. Public*, pg. 1893
SLG TECHNOLOGY LIMITED—See Scottish Leather Group Ltd.; *Int'l*, pg. 6653
S.L. HOMES PTE. LTD.—See Singapore Land Group Limited; *Int'l*, pg. 6940
S.L. HORSFORD & COMPANY LIMITED; *Int'l*, pg. 6456
S.L. HORSFORD FINANCE COMPANY LIMITED—See S.L. Horsford & Company Limited; *Int'l*, pg. 6456

SLH PHYSICIANS, L.L.C.—See Tenet Healthcare Corporation; *U.S. Public*, pg. 2006
SLH VISTA, INC.—See Tenet Healthcare Corporation; *U.S. Public*, pg. 2006
SLIB S.A.—See Groupe BPCE; *Int'l*, pg. 3097
SLICE TECHNOLOGIES, INC.—See Rakuten Group, Inc.; *Int'l*, pg. 6195
S. LICHTENBERG & CO. INC.; *U.S. Private*, pg. 3515
SLICK CITY MEDIA, INC.—See Just Eat Takeaway.com N.V.; *Int'l*, pg. 4030
SLICKER RECYCLING LIMITED; *Int'l*, pg. 6996
SLICK WILLIE'S FAMILY POOL HALL; *U.S. Private*, pg. 3688
SLI CONSTRUCTION INC.—See SLI Group Inc.; *U.S. Private*, pg. 3688
SLIDE, INC.—See Alphabet Inc.; *U.S. Public*, pg. 84
SLIDEMATIC INDUSTRIES INC.; *U.S. Private*, pg. 3688
SLI DESIGN INC.—See SLI Group Inc.; *U.S. Private*, pg. 3688
SLIDESTORM LLC—See Columbia Ventures Corporation; *U.S. Private*, pg. 978
SLI.DO S.R.O.—See Cisco Systems, Inc.; *U.S. Public*, pg. 501
SLIFER SMITH & FRAMPTON; *U.S. Private*, pg. 3688
SLI FRANCE S.A.—See Havell's India Ltd.; *Int'l*, pg. 3286
SLIGER DESIGNS INC.—See Kontron AG; *Int'l*, pg. 4278
SLIGHTLY MAD STUDIOS LIMITED—See Electronic Arts Inc.; *U.S. Public*, pg. 723
SLIGRO BS BREDA B.V.—See Sligro Food Group N.V.; *Int'l*, pg. 6997
SLIGRO BS DEVENTER B.V.—See Sligro Food Group N.V.; *Int'l*, pg. 6997
SLIGRO BS MAASTRICHT B.V.—See Sligro Food Group N.V.; *Int'l*, pg. 6997
SLIGRO B.V.—See Sligro Food Group N.V.; *Int'l*, pg. 6997
SLIGRO FOOD GROUP NEDERLAND B.V.—See Sligro Food Group N.V.; *Int'l*, pg. 6997
SLIGRO FOOD GROUP N.V.; *Int'l*, pg. 6997
SLIGRO-ISPC BELGIUM N.V.—See Sligro Food Group N.V.; *Int'l*, pg. 6997
SLI GROUP INC.; *U.S. Private*, pg. 3688
SLIM ALUMINIUM S.P.A.—See Jiangsu Dingsheng New Material Joint-Stock Co., Ltd.; *Int'l*, pg. 3945
SLIM CHICKENS DEVELOPMENT CO.; *U.S. Private*, pg. 3688
SLIM-FAST FOODS COMPANY—See Glanbia Co-Operative Society Limited; *Int'l*, pg. 2988
SLIM-FAST NUTRITIONAL FOOD LLC.; *U.S. Private*, pg. 3688
SLIMLINE MANUFACTURING LTD.—See Decisive Dividend Corporation; *Int'l*, pg. 2001
SLIM & TONE—See Kainos Capital, LLC; *U.S. Private*, pg. 2255
SLIMWARE UTILITIES HOLDINGS, INC.—See IAC Inc.; *U.S. Public*, pg. 1082
SL INDUSTRIES, INC.—See Steel Partners Holdings L.P.; *U.S. Public*, pg. 1943
S LINE CO., LTD.; *Int'l*, pg. 6443
S-LINE, LLC—See The Heico Companies, L.L.C.; *U.S. Private*, pg. 4050
SLINGER BAG AMERICAS, INC.—See CONNEXA SPORTS TECHNOLOGIES INC.; *U.S. Public*, pg. 568
SLINGER MANUFACTURING CO., INC.; *U.S. Private*, pg. 3688
SLING GROUP HOLDINGS LIMITED; *Int'l*, pg. 6997
SLING MEDIA, INC.—See EchoStar Corporation; *U.S. Public*, pg. 711
SLINGO, INC.—See RealNetworks, Inc.; *U.S. Private*, pg. 3369
SLINGSHOT, LLC; *U.S. Private*, pg. 3689
SLINGSHOT SEO; *U.S. Private*, pg. 3688
SL INTERNATIONAL LIMITED—See SK Networks Co., Ltd.; *Int'l*, pg. 6975
SL INVESTMENT CORP.—See North Haven Private Income Fund LLC; *U.S. Private*, pg. 2945
SLIPNAXOS AB—See 3M Company; *U.S. Public*, pg. 8
SLIR, S.L.—See Fertigama, S.L.; *Int'l*, pg. 2646
SLI SYLVANIA S.A.—See Havell's India Ltd.; *Int'l*, pg. 3286
SLI SYSTEMS, INC.; *U.S. Private*, pg. 3688
SLI SYSTEMS, INC.—See ESW Capital, LLC; *U.S. Private*, pg. 1430
SLI SYSTEMS, INC.—See SLI Systems, Inc.; *U.S. Private*, pg. 3688
SLITERS; *U.S. Private*, pg. 3689
SLIVACOM D.O.O.—See LS telcom AG; *Int'l*, pg. 4570
SLJUNKARA A.D.; *Int'l*, pg. 6997
SL LIGHTECH CORPORATION—See SL Corporation; *Int'l*, pg. 6995
SL LIGHTING CO., LTD.—See SL Corporation; *Int'l*, pg. 6995
SL LINK CO.,LTD.—See Fortune Oriental Company Limited; *Int'l*, pg. 2744
SLMC FINANCE CORPORATION—See Select Medical Holdings Corporation; *U.S. Public*, pg. 1859
SLM CORPORATION; *U.S. Public*, pg. 1894
S.L.M. DISTRIBUTION—See Carrefour SA; *Int'l*, pg. 1346
SL METALS (M) SDN. BHD.—See Soon Lian Holdings Limited; *Int'l*, pg. 7108

SL METALS PTE LTD—See Soon Lian Holdings Limited; *Int'l*, pg. 7108
SL METALS (SUZHOU) CO., LTD.—See Soon Lian Holdings Limited; *Int'l*, pg. 7108
SL METALS (TAIWAN) CO., LTD.—See Soon Lian Holdings Limited; *Int'l*, pg. 7108
SLM FACILITY SOLUTIONS NATIONWIDE; *U.S. Private*, pg. 3689
SLM FINANCIAL CORP.—See SLM Corporation; *U.S. Public*, pg. 1894
SLM/OGILVY—See WPP plc; *Int'l*, pg. 8488
SL MONTEVIDEO TECHNOLOGY, INC.—See Steel Partners Holdings L.P.; *U.S. Public*, pg. 1943
SLM SOLUTIONS GROUP AG—See Nikon Corporation; *Int'l*, pg. 5294
SLM SOLUTIONS (INDIA) PRIVATE LIMITED—See Nikon Corporation; *Int'l*, pg. 5294
SLM SOLUTIONS (ITALY) S.R.L.—See Nikon Corporation; *Int'l*, pg. 5294
SLM SOLUTIONS NA, INC.—See Nikon Corporation; *Int'l*, pg. 5294
SLM SOLUTIONS SINGAPORE PTE. LTD.—See Nikon Corporation; *Int'l*, pg. 5294
SLOAN CONSTRUCTION COMPANY, INC.—See Reeves Construction Company; *U.S. Private*, pg. 3384
SLOAN DE MEXICO, S. DE R.L. DE C.V.—See Sloan Valve Company; *U.S. Private*, pg. 3689
SLOANE & COMPANY LLC—See Stagwell, Inc.; *U.S. Public*, pg. 1927
SLOAN EQUIPMENT SALES CO. INC.; *U.S. Private*, pg. 3689
SLOANE TOYOTA OF GLENSIDE; *U.S. Private*, pg. 3689
SLOAN FINANCIAL GROUP, LLC; *U.S. Private*, pg. 3689
SLOAN FLUSHMATE—See Sloan Valve Company; *U.S. Private*, pg. 3689
SLOAN FORD; *U.S. Private*, pg. 3689
SLOAN MIYASATO INC.; *U.S. Private*, pg. 3689
SLOAN VALVE COMPANY - ARICHELL TECHNOLOGIES DIVISION—See Sloan Valve Company; *U.S. Private*, pg. 3689
SLOAN VALVE COMPANY, FOUNDRY DIV.—See Sloan Valve Company; *U.S. Private*, pg. 3689
SLOAN VALVE COMPANY; *U.S. Private*, pg. 3689
SLOAN VALVE WATER TECHNOLOGIES (SUZHOU) CO., LTD—See Sloan Valve Company; *U.S. Private*, pg. 3689
SLOAT GARDEN CENTER INC.; *U.S. Private*, pg. 3689
SLOBODA GP A.D.; *Int'l*, pg. 6997
SLOGA A.D.; *Int'l*, pg. 6997
SLOGA A.D.; *Int'l*, pg. 6997
SLOGA A.D.; *Int'l*, pg. 6997
SLOGA A.D.; *Int'l*, pg. 6997
SLOGA A.D.; *Int'l*, pg. 6997
SLOGA A.D.; *Int'l*, pg. 6997
SLOGA A.D.; *Int'l*, pg. 6997
SLOGA A.D.; *Int'l*, pg. 6997
SLOGAN INC.; *Int'l*, pg. 6997
SLO LATVIA LTD.—See Sonepar S.A.; *Int'l*, pg. 7091
SLOMAN NEPTUN SCHIFFAHRTS-AKTIENGESELLSCHAFT; *Int'l*, pg. 6997
SLOMIN'S INC.; *U.S. Private*, pg. 3689
SLONE PONTIAC BUICK GMC TRUCK INC.; *U.S. Private*, pg. 3689
SLO OY—See Sonepar S.A.; *Int'l*, pg. 7091
SLOPAK—See Ball Corporation; *U.S. Public*, pg. 268
SL OPERATING SERVICES GMBH I.L.—See Landesbank Baden-Wurttemberg; *Int'l*, pg. 4405
SLOTTSVIKEN FASTIGHETSAKTIEBOLAG; *Int'l*, pg. 6997
SLOUGH BV—See SEGRO plc; *Int'l*, pg. 6683
SLOVAK AMERICAN CHARITABLE ASSOCIATION; *U.S. Private*, pg. 3689
SLOVAK DIRECT, SPOL. S.R.O.—See ANY Security Printing Company PLC; *Int'l*, pg. 486
SLOVAK PARCEL SERVICE S.R.O.—See Osterreichische Post AG; *Int'l*, pg. 5654
SLOVAK REPUBLIC DZ DRAZICE-SLOVENSKO SPOL.S.R.O.—See NIBE Industrier AB; *Int'l*, pg. 5262
SLOVAK TELEKOM A.S.—See Deutsche Telekom AG; *Int'l*, pg. 2084
SLOVAKTUAL S.R.O.—See Arbonia AG; *Int'l*, pg. 538
SLOVALCO AS—See Norsk Hydro ASA; *Int'l*, pg. 5433
SLOVALCO AS—See Penta Investments Limited; *Int'l*, pg. 5788
SLOVASFALT, SPOL.S.R.O.—See STRABAG SE; *Int'l*, pg. 7233
SLOVECA SPOL. S.R.O.—See Sasol Limited; *Int'l*, pg. 6583
SLOVENE NATIONAL BENEFIT SOCIETY; *U.S. Private*, pg. 3689
SLOVENIJALES D.D.—See Zavarovalnica Triglav, d.d.; *Int'l*, pg. 8626
SLOVENIJALES TRGOVINA D.O.O.—See Zavarovalnica Triglav, d.d.; *Int'l*, pg. 8626
SLOVENSKA SPORITELNA, A.S.—See Erste Group Bank AG; *Int'l*, pg. 2499
SLOVENSKE CUKROVARY S.R.O.—See AGRANA Beteiligungs-AG; *Int'l*, pg. 214

SLOVENSKE ELEKTRARNE AS—See Enel S.p.A.; *Int'l*, pg. 2412
SLOVENSKE ELEKTRARNE FINANCE BV—See Enel S.p.A.; *Int'l*, pg. 2412
SLOVENSKE ENERGETICKE STROJARNE AS; *Int'l*, pg. 6997
SLOVENSKE LOTERIE AS—See INTRALOT S.A.; *Int'l*, pg. 3768
SLOVENSKE TUNELY, A.S.—See Grupo Villar Mir, S.A.U.; *Int'l*, pg. 3139
SLOVENSKE ZELEZNICE, D.O.O.; *Int'l*, pg. 6997
SLOVEXPERTA, S.R.O.—See Vienna Insurance Group AG Wiener Versicherung Gruppe; *Int'l*, pg. 8195
SLOVMAG, A.S.; *Int'l*, pg. 6998
SLOVNAFT A.S.—See MOL Magyar Olaj- es Gazipari Nyrt.; *Int'l*, pg. 5021
SLOVNAFT CESKA REPUBLIKA SPOL SRO—See MOL Magyar Olaj- es Gazipari Nyrt.; *Int'l*, pg. 5021
SLOVNAFT MOBILITY SERVICES, S.R.O.—See MOL Magyar Olaj- es Gazipari Nyrt.; *Int'l*, pg. 5021
SLOVNAFT POLSKA S.A.—See MOL Magyar Olaj- es Gazipari Nyrt.; *Int'l*, pg. 5021
SLOVNAFT TRANS S.A.—See MOL Magyar Olaj- es Gazipari Nyrt.; *Int'l*, pg. 5021
SLOVPAPER RECYCLING S.R.O.—See Mondi plc; *Int'l*, pg. 5027
SLOVRUR SP. Z O.O.—See Zelezrarne Podbrezova a.s.; *Int'l*, pg. 8631
SLOWBOY RACING, INC.; *U.S. Private*, pg. 3689
S.L. PACKAGING INDUSTRIES PTE LTD—See Dynamic Colours Limited; *Int'l*, pg. 2240
SLPM SCHWEIZER LEBEN PENSIONSMANAGEMENT GMBH—See Swiss Life Holding; *Int'l*, pg. 7368
SL POWER ELECTRONICS CORPORATION—See Advanced Energy Industries, Inc.; *U.S. Public*, pg. 47
SLP PERFORMANCE PARTS, INC.; *U.S. Private*, pg. 3689
SLP RESOURCES BERHAD; *Int'l*, pg. 6998
SLP UK LTD.—See Koller Enterprises, Inc.; *U.S. Private*, pg. 2341
SLR CONSULTING AUSTRALIA PTY LTD—See Charterhouse Capital Partners LLP; *Int'l*, pg. 1456
SLR CONSULTING (CANADA) LTD—See Charterhouse Capital Partners LLP; *Int'l*, pg. 1456
SLR CONSULTING (IRELAND) LTD—See Charterhouse Capital Partners LLP; *Int'l*, pg. 1456
SLR CONSULTING LTD.—See Charterhouse Capital Partners LLP; *Int'l*, pg. 1455
SLR CONSULTING (SOUTH AFRICA) PTY LTD—See Charterhouse Capital Partners LLP; *Int'l*, pg. 1456
SLR CONTRACTING & SERVICE COMPANY, INC.; *U.S. Private*, pg. 3689
S.L. REALTY MANAGEMENT SERVICES (HK) LIMITED—See Singapore Land Group Limited; *Int'l*, pg. 6940
SLR INTERNATIONAL CORPORATION—See Charterhouse Capital Partners LLP; *Int'l*, pg. 1456
SLR INVESTMENT CORP.; *U.S. Public*, pg. 1895
SLR LEASING CORP.—See Brookfield Infrastructure Partners L.P.; *Int'l*, pg. 1193
SLR LEASING CORP.—See GIG Pte. Ltd.; *Int'l*, pg. 2967
SLR SENIOR INVESTMENT CORP—See SLR Investment Corp.; *U.S. Public*, pg. 1895
SLS BEARINGS (MALAYSIA) SDN BHD—See THK CO., LTD.; *Int'l*, pg. 7712
SLS BIO CO., LTD.; *Int'l*, pg. 6998
SLS CO LTD; *Int'l*, pg. 6998
SLS CORPORATION—See FLSmidth & Co. A/S; *Int'l*, pg. 2712
S&L SEALING SOLUTIONS PRIVATE LIMITED—See Einhell Germany AG; *Int'l*, pg. 2334
SL SEOBONG CO., LTD.—See SL Corporation; *Int'l*, pg. 6995
SLS GROUP INDUSTRIES INC.; *Int'l*, pg. 6998
S-L SNACKS LOGISTICS, LLC—See Campbell Soup Company; *U.S. Public*, pg. 427
S & L SPECIALTY POLYMERS CO., LTD.—See Sekisui Chemical Co., Ltd.; *Int'l*, pg. 6694
SLS REALTY REIT; *Int'l*, pg. 6998
SLS-TECHNACO S.R.O.—See Descours & Cabaud SA; *Int'l*, pg. 2044
SL SUNGSAN CORPORATION—See SL Corporation; *Int'l*, pg. 6995
SLT CAMPUS (PRIVATE) LIMITED—See Sri Lanka Telecom PLC; *Int'l*, pg. 7150
SLT DIGITAL INFO SERVICES (PRIVATE) LIMITED—See Sri Lanka Telecom PLC; *Int'l*, pg. 7150
SLT DIGITAL SERVICES PVT LTD—See Sri Lanka Telecom PLC; *Int'l*, pg. 7150
SL TENNESSEE, LLC.—See SL Corporation; *Int'l*, pg. 6995
SLT HUMAN CAPITAL SOLUTIONS (PRIVATE) LIMITED—See Sri Lanka Telecom PLC; *Int'l*, pg. 7150
SLT MANPOWER SOLUTIONS (PRIVATE) LIMITED—See Sri Lanka Telecom PLC; *Int'l*, pg. 7150
SLTN B.V.; *Int'l*, pg. 6998
SLTN ZUID NEDERLAND B.V.—See SLTN B.V.; *Int'l*, pg. 6998

SLT PROPERTY MANAGEMENT (PRIVATE) LIMITED—See Sri Lanka Telecom PLC; *Int'l*, pg. 7150
S.L.T. S.R.L.—See Permira Advisers LLP; *Int'l*, pg. 5808
SLT SWEGON GMBH—See Investment AB Latour; *Int'l*, pg. 3784
SLT VISIONCOM (PRIVATE) LIMITED—See Sri Lanka Telecom PLC; *Int'l*, pg. 7150
SLUCHADLOVA AKUSTIKA SPOL S.R.O.—See GN Store Nord A/S; *Int'l*, pg. 3016
SLUH ANESTHESIA PHYSICIANS, L.L.C.—See Tenet Healthcare Corporation; *U.S. Public*, pg. 2006
SLUMBERJACK INC.—See Exxel Outdoors, Inc.; *U.S. Private*, pg. 1453
SLUMBERLAND INC.; *U.S. Private*, pg. 3689
SLUMBERWORLD—See C.S. Wo & Sons Ltd.; *U.S. Private*, pg. 709
SLURRY-21 CO., LTD—See Hitachi Zosen Corporation; *Int'l*, pg. 3412
SLURRY PAVERS INC.; *U.S. Private*, pg. 3690
SLUYTER COMPANY LTD.—See Devjo Industries, Inc.; *Int'l*, pg. 2089
S.L. WILLIAMSON COMPANY INC.; *U.S. Private*, pg. 3518
SLY, INC.; *U.S. Private*, pg. 3690
SM 2016 LTD.—See Informa plc; *Int'l*, pg. 3693
SM2 BALEARES SA—See Atos SE; *Int'l*, pg. 691
SM2 NETWORKS CO., LTD.—See Samhwa Paints Industrial Co., Ltd.; *Int'l*, pg. 6505
SM2 NEWTWORKS CO., LTD.—See Samhwa Paints Industrial Co., Ltd.; *Int'l*, pg. 6505
SMA ALLIANCE, INC.; *U.S. Public*, pg. 1895
SMA ALTENSO GMBH—See SMA Solar Technology AG; *Int'l*, pg. 6999
SMAATO INC.—See FS Development Investment Holdings; *Int'l*, pg. 2797
SMAATO PTE. LTD.—See Verve Group SE; *Int'l*, pg. 8176
SMA AUSTRALIA PTY LTD.—See SMA Solar Technology AG; *Int'l*, pg. 6999
SMA BEIJING COMMERCIAL COMPANY LTD.—See SMA Solar Technology AG; *Int'l*, pg. 6999
SMA BENELUX SPRL.—See SMA Solar Technology AG; *Int'l*, pg. 6999
SMA CANADA, INC.—See SMA Solar Technology AG; *Int'l*, pg. 6999
S MACNEILLIE & SON LIMITED; *Int'l*, pg. 6443
SM&A CORPORATION; *U.S. Private*, pg. 3690
SMAC, SA—See OpenGate Capital Management, LLC; *U.S. Private*, pg. 3031
SMA CZECH REPUBLIC S.R.O.—See SMA Solar Technology AG; *Int'l*, pg. 6999
SMADJURSVETERINAREN A6 AB—See Vimian Group AB; *Int'l*, pg. 8208
S M A D; *Int'l*, pg. 6443
SMA ENGINES, INC.—See Safran SA; *Int'l*, pg. 6473
SMA FAUCHEUX SAS—See Alamo Group Inc.; *U.S. Public*, pg. 70
SMA FRANCE S.A.S.—See SMA Solar Technology AG; *Int'l*, pg. 6999
SMA HELLAS AE.—See SMA Solar Technology AG; *Int'l*, pg. 6999
SMA IBERICA TECNOLOGIA SOLAR, S.L.—See SMA Solar Technology AG; *Int'l*, pg. 6999
SMAIL LINCOLN MERCURY MAZDA; *U.S. Private*, pg. 3690
S.M.A.I.O SA; *Int'l*, pg. 6456
SMA ITALIA S.R.L.—See SMA Solar Technology AG; *Int'l*, pg. 6999
SMAIT CO., LTD.—See Star Mica Holdings Co., Ltd.; *Int'l*, pg. 7174
SMA JAPAN KABUSHIKI KAISHA—See SMA Solar Technology AG; *Int'l*, pg. 6999
SMAKEN AV GRIMSTAD AS—See IKM Gruppen AS; *Int'l*, pg. 3612
SMAKRAFT AS—See Statkraft AS; *Int'l*, pg. 7185
SMALANDSSTENARS MEKANISKA VERKSTAD SMV AB—See Smalandsstenars Mekaniska Verkstad - SMV Industrier AB; *Int'l*, pg. 7000
SMALANDSSTENARS MEKANISKA VERKSTAD - SMV INDUSTRIER AB; *Int'l*, pg. 6999
SMALANDSVILLAN AB—See OBOS BBL; *Int'l*, pg. 5512
SMA'LIA MEDICAL GROUP—See HORIBA Ltd; *Int'l*, pg. 3478
SMALL ARMY, INC.—See Ruder Finn Group, Inc.; *U.S. Private*, pg. 3501
SMALLBIZPROS, INC.; *U.S. Private*, pg. 3690
SMALLBONE & CO (DEVIZES) LIMITED—See Canburg Limited; *Int'l*, pg. 1288
SMALL BONE INNOVATIONS, INC.—See Stryker Corporation; *U.S. Public*, pg. 1956
SMALL BUSINESS DEVELOPMENT GROUP, INC.; *U.S. Public*, pg. 1895
SMALL BUSINESS TRANSPORTATION; *U.S. Private*, pg. 3690
SMALL DOG ELECTRONICS; *U.S. Private*, pg. 3690
SMALL ENTERPRISE FINANCE AGENCY (SOC) LTD.—See Industrial Development Corporation of South Africa, Ltd.; *Int'l*, pg. 3672
SMALLEY & COMPANY INC.; *U.S. Private*, pg. 3690

COMPANY NAME INDEX

SMALLEY STEEL RING COMPANY; *U.S. Private*, pg. 3690
SMALLHD, LLC—See Videndum plc; *Int'l*, pg. 8191
SMALL INDUSTRY CREDIT GUARANTEE CORPORATION; *Int'l*, pg. 7000
SMALL MINE DEVELOPMENT LLC; *U.S. Private*, pg. 3690
SMALL NEWSPAPER GROUP INC.; *U.S. Private*, pg. 3690
SMALL PARTS, INC.; *U.S. Private*, pg. 3690
SMALL PLANET FOODS INC.—See General Mills, Inc.; *U.S. Public*, pg. 922
SMALLPONDS, LLC—See Gale Force Software Corporation; *U.S. Private*, pg. 1636
SMALLS ELECTRICAL CONSTRUCTION, INC.; *U.S. Private*, pg. 3690
THE SMALL WINEMAKER'S COLLECTION INC.—See Andrew Peller Limited; *Int'l*, pg. 451
SMALLWOOD SAWMILL LTD.—See Mill & Timber Products Ltd; *Int'l*, pg. 4895
SMALL WORLD TOYS—See Rivenrock Capital LLC; *U.S. Private*, pg. 3443
SMALL WORLD TRADING CO, INC.; *U.S. Private*, pg. 3690
SMALL WORLD VACATIONS, INC.; *U.S. Private*, pg. 3690
SMALTI PER CERAMICA S.R.L.—See American Securities LLC; *U.S. Private*, pg. 252
SMALTO SA; *Int'l*, pg. 7000
SMA MAGNETICS SP. Z O.O.—See SMA Solar Technology AG; *Int'l*, pg. 6999
S.M.A.METALLTECHNIK GMBH & CO. KG—See INDUS Holding AG; *Int'l*, pg. 3664
SMA MIDDLE EAST LIMITED—See SMA Solar Technology AG; *Int'l*, pg. 6999
SMANS N.V.—See Komax Holding AG; *Int'l*, pg. 4241
SMA RAILWAY TECHNOLOGY GMBH—See Beijing Dinghan Technology Group Co., Ltd.; *Int'l*, pg. 948
SMARDAN-HATCHER COMPANY; *U.S. Private*, pg. 3690
SMARDTV SA—See Kudelski S.A.; *Int'l*, pg. 4323
SMAREGI, INC.; *Int'l*, pg. 7000
S MARK CO., LTD.; *Int'l*, pg. 6443
SMARR EMC; *U.S. Private*, pg. 3690
SMAHSH INC.—See K1 Investment Management, LLC; *U.S. Private*, pg. 2252
SMART & BIGGAR IP AGENCY CO.—See IPH Limited; *Int'l*, pg. 3797
SMART421 TECHNOLOGY GROUP LTD.—See Macquarie Group Limited; *Int'l*, pg. 4626
SMARTAC INTERNATIONAL HOLDINGS LIMITED; *Int'l*, pg. 7001
SMARTAG INTERNATIONAL, INC.; *U.S. Public*, pg. 1895
SMART AGRO LTD.; *Int'l*, pg. 7000
SMARTANALYST INC.—See Clayton, Dubilier & Rice, LLC; *U.S. Private*, pg. 928
SMART AUTOMATION SYSTEMS; *U.S. Private*, pg. 3691
SMART AWARDS LTD.—See Hexatronic Group AB; *Int'l*, pg. 3371
SMART AXIATA CO., LTD.—See Axiata Group Berhad; *Int'l*, pg. 768
SMARTBANK—See SmartFinancial, Inc.; *U.S. Public*, pg. 1895
SMARTBASE SOLUTIONS LLC; *U.S. Private*, pg. 3691
SMART BATTERY SOLUTIONS GMBH—See Gimv NV; *Int'l*, pg. 2976
SMARTBEAN SYSTEMS SDN. BHD.—See OCK Group Berhad; *Int'l*, pg. 5520
SMART BEAR SOFTWARE, INC.; *U.S. Private*, pg. 3691
SMARTBIZ TELECOM LLC—See IQSTEL Inc.; *U.S. Public*, pg. 1167
SMARTBOX COMPANY; *U.S. Private*, pg. 3691
SMARTBOX, LLC—See 424 Capital, LLC; *U.S. Private*, pg. 15
SMARTBOX, LLC—See HealthEdge Investment Partners, LLC; *U.S. Private*, pg. 1896
SMART BOX SUPPORT SERVICES (PTY) LTD—See Stellar Capital Partners Limited; *Int'l*, pg. 7204
SMARTBRIEF, INC.—See Future plc; *Int'l*, pg. 2857
SMARTBROKER HOLDING AG; *Int'l*, pg. 7001
SMARTBUG OPERATING LLC; *U.S. Private*, pg. 3691
SMART BUILDING ENERGIES SA—See VINCI S.A.; *Int'l*, pg. 8227
SMART BUTTON ASSOCIATES, INC.—See Aimia Inc.; *Int'l*, pg. 234
SMART CANNABIS CORP.; *U.S. Public*, pg. 1895
SMART CARD MARKETING SYSTEMS, INC.; *U.S. Public*, pg. 1895
SMART CARPET, INC.; *U.S. Private*, pg. 3691
SMART CELLS INTERNATIONAL LTD.—See VITA 34 AG; *Int'l*, pg. 8257
SMARTCENTRES REAL ESTATE INVESTMENT TRUST; *Int'l*, pg. 7001
SMARTCEO PUBLISHING; *U.S. Private*, pg. 3691
SMARTCHASE CORP.; *Int'l*, pg. 7001
SMARTCHEM TECHNOLOGIES LIMITED—See Deepak Fertilisers & Petrochemicals Corporation Limited; *Int'l*, pg. 2003
SMART CHEVROLET CO.; *U.S. Private*, pg. 3691

SMART CITY DEVELOPMENT HOLDINGS LIMITED—See Deson Development International Holdings Ltd; *Int'l*, pg. 2045
SMART CITY NETWORKS LP—See US Cable Group; *U.S. Private*, pg. 4318
SMART CITY SOLUTIONS, LLC—See US Cable Group; *U.S. Private*, pg. 4318
SMART CITY TELECOMMUNICATIONS LLC—See US Cable Group; *U.S. Private*, pg. 4318
SMARTCLIP EUROPE GMBH—See Bertelsmann SE & Co. KGaA; *Int'l*, pg. 996
SMARTCLIP NORDICS AB—See Bertelsmann SE & Co. KGaA; *Int'l*, pg. 996
SMARTCLIXX, LLC—See TA Associates, Inc.; *U.S. Private*, pg. 3917
SMART CLOSET, INC.; *Int'l*, pg. 7000
SMART COMMUNICATIONS, INC.—See PLDT Inc.; *Int'l*, pg. 5896
SMART COMMUNICATIONS, INC.—See PLDT Inc.; *Int'l*, pg. 5896
SMART COMMUNICATIONS INC.—See Hakuhodo DY Holdings Incorporated; *Int'l*, pg. 3220
THE SMART COMPANIES, INC.—See Rotunda Capital Partners LLC; *U.S. Private*, pg. 3488
SMART CONCRETE PUBLIC COMPANY LIMITED - BANGKOK FACTORY—See Smart Concrete Public Company Limited; *Int'l*, pg. 7000
SMART CONCRETE PUBLIC COMPANY LIMITED; *Int'l*, pg. 7000
SMART CONTROLS INDIA LTD.—See Zeppelin GmbH; *Int'l*, pg. 8637
SMARTCOOL SYSTEMS (EMEA) LTD.—See SmartCool Systems Inc.; *Int'l*, pg. 7001
SMARTCOOL SYSTEMS INC.; *Int'l*, pg. 7001
SMARTCOOL SYSTEMS UK LTD.—See SmartCool Systems Inc.; *Int'l*, pg. 7001
SMARTCOOL SYSTEMS (USA) INC.—See SmartCool Systems Inc.; *Int'l*, pg. 7001
SMART-CORE HOLDINGS LIMITED; *Int'l*, pg. 7001
SMARTCRAFT ASA; *Int'l*, pg. 7001
SMARTDATA ENTERPRISES INC.; *U.S. Private*, pg. 3691
SMARTDATA ENTERPRISES (INDIA) LTD.—See smart-Data Enterprises Inc.; *U.S. Private*, pg. 3692
SMARTDC BV—See Ubisoft Entertainment S.A.; *Int'l*, pg. 8003
SMART DCC LIMITED—See Capita plc; *Int'l*, pg. 1309
SMARTDC HEERLEN BV—See Ubisoft Entertainment S.A.; *Int'l*, pg. 8003
SMART DECISION, INC.; *U.S. Public*, pg. 1895
SMART DESIGN TECHNOLOGY CO., LTD.—See Hotai Motor Co., Ltd.; *Int'l*, pg. 3487
SMART DESTINATIONS, INC.; *U.S. Private*, pg. 3691
SMARTDISPLAYER TECHNOLOGY CO., LTD.; *Int'l*, pg. 7002
SMARTDOG SERVICES, LLC—See Quad-C Management, Inc.; *U.S. Private*, pg. 3315
SMARTDRAW.COM; *U.S. Private*, pg. 3692
SMART DRILLING GMBH—See NOV, Inc.; *U.S. Public*, pg. 1546
SMART DRIVER CLUB LTD.—See CalAmp Corp.; *U.S. Public*, pg. 422
SMARTDRIVE SYSTEMS, INC.; *U.S. Private*, pg. 3692
SMARTEAM CORP—See Dassault Systemes S.A.; *Int'l*, pg. 1975
SMARTECH ELECTRONICS CO., LTD.—See Fuji Corporation; *Int'l*, pg. 2810
SMARTECH ELECTRONICS (SHENZHEN) CO., LTD—See Fuji Corporation; *Int'l*, pg. 2810
SMARTECH ENTERPRISE CO., LTD.—See Fuji Corporation; *Int'l*, pg. 2810
SMARTECH EQUIPMENT (SHENZHEN) CO., LTD.—See Fuji Corporation; *Int'l*, pg. 2810
SMARTEC SA—See Nova Ventures Group Corp.; *U.S. Private*, pg. 2966
SMARTEDGE; *U.S. Private*, pg. 3692
SMART ELECTRONICS & ASSEMBLY, INC.—See Vance Street Capital LLC; *U.S. Private*, pg. 4342
SMART EMPLOYEE BENEFITS INC.—See The Co-operators Group Limited; *Int'l*, pg. 7634
SMARTENCRYPT PTY. LTD.—See Crayon Group Holding ASA; *Int'l*, pg. 1830
SMARTER BUSINESS LIMITED; *Int'l*, pg. 7002
SMARTERER, INC.—See Pluralsight, Inc.; *U.S. Public*, pg. 1699
SMARTERHQ, INC.—See Wunderkind, LLC; *U.S. Private*, pg. 4575
SMARTER MORTGAGES; *U.S. Private*, pg. 3692
SMARTER SECURITY, INC.; *U.S. Private*, pg. 3692
SMARTERTRAVEL.COM—See Cognius, Inc.; *U.S. Private*, pg. 962
SMARTER TRAVEL MEDIA LLC—See Cognius, Inc.; *U.S. Private*, pg. 962
SMARTERWARE CO., LTD.—See Samart Corporation Public Company Limited; *Int'l*, pg. 6502
SMARTERWORK.COM LTD.; *Int'l*, pg. 7002
SMARTESTENERGY LTD.—See Marubeni Corporation; *Int'l*, pg. 4708
SMART EXPO LIMITED—See News Corporation; *U.S. Public*, pg. 1520

SMART EXPRESS LTD.—See Morelli Group Limited; *Int'l*, pg. 5040
SMARTEX SP. Z O.O.—See Dekpol S.A.; *Int'l*, pg. 2006
SMART EYE AB; *Int'l*, pg. 7000
SMART EYE JAPAN CO., LTD.—See Smart Eye AB; *Int'l*, pg. 7000
SMART EYES INTERNATIONAL AB—See Mellby Gard Holding AB; *Int'l*, pg. 4812
SMART FACTORY & SERVICES HOLDINGS (THAILAND) CO., LTD.—See Hitachi, Ltd.; *Int'l*, pg. 3424
SMART & FINAL, INC.—See Apollo Global Management, Inc.; *U.S. Public*, pg. 160
SMART & FINAL STORES, LLC—See Apollo Global Management, Inc.; *U.S. Public*, pg. 160
SMART FINANCIAL CREDIT UNION; *U.S. Private*, pg. 3691
SMARTFINANCIAL, INC.; *U.S. Public*, pg. 1895
SMART FINSEC LTD.; *Int'l*, pg. 7000
SMARTFLEET MANAGEMENT PTY. LTD.—See Smartgroup Corporation Ltd.; *Int'l*, pg. 7002
SMARTFLEX TECHNOLOGY PTE. LTD.—See Novo Tellus Capital Partners Pte. Ltd.; *Int'l*, pg. 5465
SMARTFOCUS GERMANY GMBH—See Altor Equity Partners AB; *Int'l*, pg. 396
SMARTFOCUS HOLDINGS LTD.—See Altor Equity Partners AB; *Int'l*, pg. 395
SMARTFOCUS US INC.—See Altor Equity Partners AB; *Int'l*, pg. 396
SMARTFOODS, INC.—See PepsiCo, Inc.; *U.S. Public*, pg. 1672
SMART FOR LIFE, INC.; *U.S. Public*, pg. 1895
SMART FRANCE SAS—See Mercedes-Benz Group AG; *Int'l*, pg. 4829
SMARTFUN DIGITAL CO., LTD.—See Chunghwa Telecom Co., Ltd.; *Int'l*, pg. 1598
SMART GEARS LIMITED—See Link-Asia International MedTech Group Limited; *Int'l*, pg. 4514
SMARTGEN (ZHENGZHOU) TECHNOLOGY CO., LTD.; *Int'l*, pg. 7002
SMART GLOBE HOLDINGS LIMITED; *Int'l*, pg. 7000
SMART GMBH—See Mercedes-Benz Group AG; *Int'l*, pg. 4829
SMART GOOD THINGS HOLDING S.A.; *Int'l*, pg. 7000
SMART GRID ENERGY SAS—See VINCI S.A.; *Int'l*, pg. 8227
SMARTGROUP CORPORATION LTD.; *Int'l*, pg. 7002
SMART GROUP SERVICES LTD—See Turners Auctions Limited; *Int'l*, pg. 7979
SMARTHEALTH INC.; *U.S. Private*, pg. 3692
SMARTHEAT (SHANGHAI) TRADING CO., LTD.—See Lithium & Boron Technology, Inc.; *Int'l*, pg. 4526
SMART HIGHWAY CO., LTD.—See Jasmine International Public Company Limited; *Int'l*, pg. 3912
SMARTHINKING, INC.—See Pearson plc; *Int'l*, pg. 5778
SMARTHOUSE INTEGRATION, LLC; *U.S. Private*, pg. 3692
SMARTIKS YAZILIM A.S.; *Int'l*, pg. 7002
SMART IMS; *U.S. Private*, pg. 3691
SMART INFRANET CO., LTD.—See RATCH Group Public Company Limited; *Int'l*, pg. 6213
SMART INSIGHT, CORPORATION—See Uchida Yoko Co., Ltd.; *Int'l*, pg. 8012
SMART IN SP. Z O.O. SP. K.—See Introl S.A.; *Int'l*, pg. 3769
SMART INSURANCE & IT SOLUTIONS GMBH—See Helvetia Holding AG; *Int'l*, pg. 3340
SMARTIT STAFFING INC.; *U.S. Private*, pg. 3692
SMART I.T. SYSTEMS BV—See IQVIA Holdings Inc.; *U.S. Public*, pg. 1170
SMARTKEM, INC.; *Int'l*, pg. 7002
SMART LEASING INC.; *U.S. Private*, pg. 3691
SMARTLIFE CARE AG—See Helvetia Holding AG; *Int'l*, pg. 3340
SMARTLINE HOME LOANS PTY. LTD.—See News Corporation; *U.S. Public*, pg. 1520
SMART LINE S.R.L.—See CAD IT S.p.A.; *Int'l*, pg. 1247
SMARTLING, INC.; *U.S. Private*, pg. 3692
SMARTLINK HOLDINGS LIMITED; *Int'l*, pg. 7002
SMARTLINK NETWORK, INC.—See Sony Group Corporation; *Int'l*, pg. 7106
SMARTLITE; *U.S. Private*, pg. 3692
SMART, LLC—See Blackbaud, Inc.; *U.S. Public*, pg. 341
SMARTLOGIC UK; *Int'l*, pg. 7002
SMARTLOGIC US—See Smartlogic UK; *Int'l*, pg. 7002
SMART METERING SOLUTION (CHANGSHA) CO., LTD.—See Wasion Holdings Limited; *Int'l*, pg. 8352
SMART METERING SYSTEMS PLC; *Int'l*, pg. 7000
SMARTMETRIC, INC.; *U.S. Public*, pg. 1895
SMART MODULAR TECHNOLOGIES, INC.—See Penguin Solutions, Inc.; *U.S. Public*, pg. 1661
SMART MODULAR TECHNOLOGIES SDN. BHD.—See Penguin Solutions, Inc.; *U.S. Public*, pg. 1661
SMARTNEY SP. Z O.O.—See Groupe BPCE; *Int'l*, pg. 3099
SMARTONE MOBILE COMMUNICATIONS LIMITED—See Sun Hung Kai Properties Limited; *Int'l*, pg. 7304
SMARTONE TELECOMMUNICATIONS HOLDINGS LIMITED—See Sun Hung Kai Properties Limited; *Int'l*, pg. 7304
SMARTOPS CORP.—See SAP SE; *Int'l*, pg. 6570

SMARTOPTICS AS—See Coherent Corp.; *U.S. Public*, pg. 528
SMARTOPTICS HOLDINGS AS—See Coherent Corp.; *U.S. Public*, pg. 528
SMART ORIENT INVESTMENTS LIMITED—See Sinolink Worldwide Holdings Limited; *Int'l*, pg. 6952
SMART PACKAGING SOLUTIONS NV—See VPK Packaging Group NV; *Int'l*, pg. 8312
SMART PACKAGING SOLUTIONS SAS—See Agfa-Gevaert N.V.; *Int'l*, pg. 209
SMARTPAK EQUINE, LLC—See Clayton, Dubilier & Rice, LLC; *U.S. Private*, pg. 921
SMARTPAK EQUINE, LLC—See TPG Capital, L.P.; *U.S. Public*, pg. 2170
SMARTPANEL AS—See Byggma ASA; *Int'l*, pg. 1235
SMART PARKING LTD.; *Int'l*, pg. 7000
SMART PARKING TECHNOLOGY—See Smart Parking Ltd.; *Int'l*, pg. 7000
SMART PARTS INC.; *U.S. Private*, pg. 3691
SMARTPATIENT GMBH—See Shop Apotheke Europe N.V.; *Int'l*, pg. 6859
SMARTPAY CADMUS LIMITED—See SmartPay Holdings Limited; *Int'l*, pg. 7002
SMARTPAY HOLDINGS LIMITED; *Int'l*, pg. 7002
SMARTPAY NEW ZEALAND LIMITED—See SmartPay Holdings Limited; *Int'l*, pg. 7002
SMARTPETRO INC.—See Vontier Corporation; *U.S. Public*, pg. 2309
SMARTPHONE EXPERTS LLC; *U.S. Private*, pg. 3692
SMARTPHOTO AG—See smartphoto group N.V.; *Int'l*, pg. 7003
SMARTPHOTO GROUP N.V.; *Int'l*, pg. 7003
SMARTPHOTO NEDERLAND BV—See smartphoto group N.V.; *Int'l*, pg. 7003
SMARTPHOTO NORDIC AB—See smartphoto group N.V.; *Int'l*, pg. 7003
SMARTPITCH VENTURES, LLC; *U.S. Private*, pg. 3692
SMARTPLY EUROPE LIMITED—See Coillte Ltd.; *Int'l*, pg. 1696
SMARTPOINT IT CONSULTING GMBH—See Bechtle AG; *Int'l*, pg. 938
SMARTPOOL TRADING LIMITED—See Euronext N.V.; *Int'l*, pg. 2554
SMART POWER CORP.; *Int'l*, pg. 7000
SMARTPRACTICE.COM—See Smarthealth Inc.; *U.S. Private*, pg. 3692
SMARTPRICE SALES & MARKETING INC.; *U.S. Private*, pg. 3692
SMARTPROCURE, INC.—See Endicott Group Equity Partners, L.P.; *U.S. Private*, pg. 1391
SMARTPROCURE, INC.—See Thompson Street Capital Manager LLC; *U.S. Private*, pg. 4161
SMART PRODUCTS NIGERIA PLC; *Int'l*, pg. 7000
SMARTPROS LTD.—See Graham Holdings Company; *U.S. Public*, pg. 956
SMARTQUANTUM GROUP SA; *Int'l*, pg. 7003
SMARTQUANTUM S.A.—See SmartQuantum Group SA; *Int'l*, pg. 7003
SMARTRAC N.V.—See Avery Dennison Corporation; *U.S. Public*, pg. 245
SMARTRAC TECHNOLOGY GMBH—See Avery Dennison Corporation; *U.S. Public*, pg. 245
SMARTRAC TECHNOLOGY LTD.—See Avery Dennison Corporation; *U.S. Public*, pg. 245
SMARTRAC TECHNOLOGY US INC.—See Avery Dennison Corporation; *U.S. Public*, pg. 245
SMART RADAR SYSTEM INC.; *Int'l*, pg. 7000
SMARTREE ROMANIA SRL; *Int'l*, pg. 7003
SMARTRENT, INC.; *U.S. Public*, pg. 1895
SMARTRENT TECHNOLOGIES, INC.—See SmartRent, Inc.; *U.S. Public*, pg. 1896
SMARTREPLY TECHNOLOGIES, INC.—See Permira Advisers LLP; *Int'l*, pg. 5805
SMART RESEARCH CORP.—See HYUNDAI ADM BIO Inc; *Int'l*, pg. 3555
SMARTREVENUE, INC.; *U.S. Private*, pg. 3692
SMARTRG, INC.—See ADTRAN Holdings, Inc; *U.S. Public*, pg. 44
SMART ROBOTICS CO.LTD.—See Bain Capital, LP; *U.S. Private*, pg. 435
SMARTRO CO., LTD.—See KT Corporation; *Int'l*, pg. 4315
SMARTRONIX, LLC—See OceanSound Partners, LP; *U.S. Private*, pg. 2992
SMART ROOFS SOLAR, INC.; *U.S. Private*, pg. 3691
SMART RX SAS—See Cegedim S.A.; *Int'l*, pg. 1390
SMARTSALARY PTY. LIMITED—See Smartgroup Corporation Ltd.; *Int'l*, pg. 7002
SMARTSALARY SOFTWARE SOLUTIONS PTY. LTD.—See Smartgroup Corporation Ltd.; *Int'l*, pg. 7002
SMART SAND, INC.; *U.S. Public*, pg. 1895
SMART SA—See CNTEE TRANSELECTRICA SA; *Int'l*, pg. 1678
SMARTSAT, INC.; *U.S. Private*, pg. 3692
SMART SCORE CO., LTD.; *Int'l*, pg. 7000
SMARTSENSE—See Digi International Inc.; *U.S. Public*, pg. 662
SMART SERVICE & MANAGEMENT CO., LTD.—See AP (Thailand) Public Company Limited; *Int'l*, pg. 499
SMARTSET SERVICES, INC.; *Int'l*, pg. 7003

SMART SHARE GLOBAL LIMITED; *Int'l*, pg. 7001
SMARTSHEET AUSTRALIA PTY. LTD.—See Smartsheet Inc.; *U.S. Public*, pg. 1896
SMARTSHEET INC.; *U.S. Public*, pg. 1896
SMART SHIRTS LTD.—See Youngor Group Co. Ltd.; *Int'l*, pg. 8604
SMARTSIGN.COM LLC; *U.S. Private*, pg. 3692
SMARTSOFT INTERNATIONAL, INC.; *U.S. Private*, pg. 3692
SMART SOFTWARE, INC.—See Clayton, Dubilier & Rice, LLC; *U.S. Private*, pg. 923
SMART SOLUTIONS CO., LTD.; *Int'l*, pg. 7001
SMART SOLUTIONS MARKETING PANAMA, S.A.; *Int'l*, pg. 7001
SMARTSOLUTION TECHNOLOGIES, LP—See FOMO WORLDWIDE, INC.; *U.S. Public*, pg. 863
SMART SOLUTION TECHNOLOGY, INC.—See Star Micronics Co Ltd; *Int'l*, pg. 7174
SMARTSOURCE COMPUTER & AUDIO VISUAL RENTALS—See Abcom Computer Rental, Inc.; *U.S. Private*, pg. 37
SMART SOURCE, LLC—See Guggenheim Partners, LLC; *U.S. Private*, pg. 1812
SMART SOURCE OF GEORGIA, LLC; *U.S. Private*, pg. 3692
SMART SOURCING CO., LTD.—See Aucfan Co., Ltd.; *Int'l*, pg. 699
SMARTSPACE SOFTWARE PLC; *Int'l*, pg. 7003
SMART STABILIZER SYSTEMS LIMITED—See Weatherford International plc; *U.S. Public*, pg. 2339
SMART START, INC.; *U.S. Private*, pg. 3691
SMARTSTOP ASSET MANAGEMENT, LLC—See Strategic Capital Holdings, LLC; *U.S. Private*, pg. 3834
SMARTSTOP SELF STORAGE REIT, INC.—See Strategic Capital Holdings, LLC; *U.S. Private*, pg. 3834
SMARTSTREAM TECHNOLOGIES LTD.—See DIFC Investments Ltd.; *Int'l*, pg. 2118
SMARTS TRUCK & TRAILER EQUIPMENT; *U.S. Private*, pg. 3692
SMARTSTYLE FAMILY HAIR SALONS—See Regis Corporation; *U.S. Public*, pg. 1777
SMART SYSTEMS LTDA.—See America Movil, S.A.B. de C.V.; *Int'l*, pg. 421
SMARTTECH247 GROUP PLC; *Int'l*, pg. 7003
SMART TECHNICS NV—See Colruyt Group N.V.; *Int'l*, pg. 1705
SMART TECHNOLOGIES (GB) LIMITED—See Hon Hai Precision Industry Co., Ltd.; *Int'l*, pg. 3457
SMART TECHNOLOGIES (GERMANY) GMBH—See Hon Hai Precision Industry Co., Ltd.; *Int'l*, pg. 3457
SMART TECHNOLOGIES (MIDDLE EAST) FZE—See Hon Hai Precision Industry Co., Ltd.; *Int'l*, pg. 3457
SMART TECHNOLOGIES (SEATTLE) INC.—See Hon Hai Precision Industry Co., Ltd.; *Int'l*, pg. 3457
SMART TECHNOLOGIES (SINGAPORE) PRIVATE LIMITED—See Hon Hai Precision Industry Co., Ltd.; *Int'l*, pg. 3457
SMART TECHNOLOGIES ULC—See Hon Hai Precision Industry Co., Ltd.; *Int'l*, pg. 3457
SMARTTECH PRODUCTION LTD.—See Aisino Corporation; *Int'l*, pg. 254
SMARTTIP BV—See Bruker Corporation; *U.S. Public*, pg. 407
SMART TRADE INC.—See SerComm Corporation; *Int'l*, pg. 6722
SMART TRAFFIC LTD.; *Int'l*, pg. 7001
SMART TRAFFIC PTY LTD—See Smart Traffic Ltd.; *Int'l*, pg. 7001
SMART TUITION; *U.S. Private*, pg. 3691
SMARTVALUE CO., LTD.; *Int'l*, pg. 7003
SMARTVAULT CORPORATION—See Reckon Limited; *Int'l*, pg. 6237
SMART VERTRIEBS GMBH—See Mercedes-Benz Group AG; *Int'l*, pg. 4829
SMART VISION WORKS, LLC—See Union Park Capital; *U.S. Private*, pg. 4285
SMARTWARE GROUP; *U.S. Private*, pg. 3693
SMARTWARES—See H2 Equity Partners B.V.; *Int'l*, pg. 3199
SMART WATCH ASSETS LIMITED—See China COSCO Shipping Corporation Limited; *Int'l*, pg. 1496
SMARTWATCH SECURITY & SOUND, LLC—See The Carlyle Group LLC; *U.S. Public*, pg. 2053
SMARTWATER CSI, LLC—See SmartWater Technology Limited; *Int'l*, pg. 7003
SMARTWATER MEMPHIS, INC.—See Perpetual Capital, LLC; *U.S. Private*, pg. 3153
SMARTWATER TECHNOLOGY LIMITED; *Int'l*, pg. 7003
SMARTWATT ENERGY, INC.—See Centrica plc; *Int'l*, pg. 1413
SMARTWAVE TECHNOLOGIES CORP.—See Northlane Capital Partners, LLC; *U.S. Private*, pg. 2956
THE SMART-WAY DISPOSAL & RECYCLING COMPANY LTD.—See Zedcor Inc.; *Int'l*, pg. 8629
SMART WIND LIMITED—See Orsted AS; *Int'l*, pg. 5644
SMART WIRES INC.; *U.S. Private*, pg. 3691
SMARTWITNESS USA LLC—See Sensata Technologies Holding plc; *U.S. Public*, pg. 1866

SMART WOOD GERMANY GMBH & CO. KG—See smart wood SAS; *Int'l*, pg. 7001
SMART WOOD SAS; *Int'l*, pg. 7001
SMARTWOOL—See V. F. Corporation; *U.S. Public*, pg. 2268
SMARTWORKS LEARNING CENTRE PTE LTD.—See AEC Education plc; *Int'l*, pg. 171
SMARTWORKS, LLC—See SharedLABS, Inc.; *U.S. Private*, pg. 3626
SMART WORLDWIDE HOLDINGS, INC.—See Penguin Solutions, Inc.; *U.S. Public*, pg. 1661
SMARTYPANTS, INC.—See North Castle Partners, LLC; *U.S. Private*, pg. 2943
SMARTYPIG, L.L.C.—See Q2 Holdings, Inc.; *U.S. Public*, pg. 1741
SMARTZ ANALYTICS, INC.—See Constellation Real Estate Group, Inc.; *U.S. Private*, pg. 1023
SMARTZ PTE LTD—See Eng Kong Holdings Pte Ltd.; *Int'l*, pg. 2426
SMAS AUTO LEASING INDIA PRIVATE LIMITED—See Sumitomo Corporation; *Int'l*, pg. 7270
SMASHING IDEAS, INC.—See Bertelsmann SE & Co. KGaA; *Int'l*, pg. 991
SMA SOLAR INDIA PRIVATE LIMITED—See SMA Solar Technology AG; *Int'l*, pg. 6999
SMA SOLAR TECHNOLOGY AG; *Int'l*, pg. 6999
SMA SOLAR TECHNOLOGY AMERICA, LLC.—See SMA Solar Technology AG; *Int'l*, pg. 6999
SMA SOLAR TECHNOLOGY PORTUGAL, UNIPESSOAL LDA—See SMA Solar Technology AG; *Int'l*, pg. 6999
SMA SOLAR TECHNOLOGY (SHANGHAI) CO., LTD.—See SMA Solar Technology AG; *Int'l*, pg. 6999
SMA SOLAR TECHNOLOGY SOUTH AFRICA (PTY.) LTD.—See SMA Solar Technology AG; *Int'l*, pg. 6999
SMA SOLAR UK LTD.—See SMA Solar Technology AG; *Int'l*, pg. 6999
SMA SOLUTIONS; *U.S. Private*, pg. 3690
SM&A—See SM&A Corporation; *U.S. Private*, pg. 3690
SMA SOUTH AMERICA SPA—See SMA Solar Technology AG; *Int'l*, pg. 6999
SMA TECHNOLOGY AUSTRALIA PTY. LTD.—See SMA Solar Technology AG; *Int'l*, pg. 6999
SMA TECHNOLOGY KOREA CO., LTD.—See SMA Solar Technology AG; *Int'l*, pg. 6999
SMATRA TRAINING HUB PTE. LTD.—See Wong Fong Industries Limited; *Int'l*, pg. 8447
SMATRICS GMBH & CO. KG—See Verbund AG; *Int'l*, pg. 8165
SM AUTO STAMPING LIMITED; *Int'l*, pg. 6998
SM&A-WEST—See SM&A Corporation; *U.S. Private*, pg. 3690
SMB BRIGHTEN SWITCHBOARD ENGINEERING SDN. BHD.—See Fuji Electric Co., Ltd.; *Int'l*, pg. 2812
SMBC AERO ENGINE LEASE B.V.—See Sumitomo Corporation; *Int'l*, pg. 7270
SMBC AVIATION CAPITAL LIMITED—See Sumitomo Corporation; *Int'l*, pg. 7274
SMBC AVIATION CAPITAL LIMITED—See Sumitomo Mitsui Financial Group, Inc.; *Int'l*, pg. 7295
SMBC BUSINESS SERVICING CO., LTD.—See Sumitomo Mitsui Financial Group, Inc.; *Int'l*, pg. 7293
SMBC BUSINESS SUPPORT CO., LTD.—See Sumitomo Mitsui Financial Group, Inc.; *Int'l*, pg. 7293
SMBC CAPITAL MARKETS (ASIA) LIMITED—See Sumitomo Mitsui Financial Group, Inc.; *Int'l*, pg. 7293
SMBC CAPITAL MARKETS, INC.—See Sumitomo Mitsui Financial Group, Inc.; *Int'l*, pg. 7293
SMBC CAPITAL MARKETS LIMITED—See Sumitomo Mitsui Financial Group, Inc.; *Int'l*, pg. 7293
SMBC CENTER SERVICE CO., LTD.—See Sumitomo Mitsui Financial Group, Inc.; *Int'l*, pg. 7294
SMBC CONSULTING CO., LTD.—See Sumitomo Mitsui Financial Group, Inc.; *Int'l*, pg. 7294
SMBC CONSUMER FINANCE CO LTD—See Sumitomo Mitsui Financial Group, Inc.; *Int'l*, pg. 7294
SMBC DELIVERY SERVICE CO., LTD.—See Sumitomo Mitsui Financial Group, Inc.; *Int'l*, pg. 7294
SMBC ELECTRONIC MONETARY CLAIMS RECORDING CO., LTD.—See Sumitomo Mitsui Financial Group, Inc.; *Int'l*, pg. 7294
SMBC FINANCE SERVICE CO., LTD.—See Sumitomo Mitsui Financial Group, Inc.; *Int'l*, pg. 7293
SMBC FRIEND SECURITIES CO., LTD.—See Sumitomo Mitsui Financial Group, Inc.; *Int'l*, pg. 7293
SMBC GREEN SERVICE CO., LTD.—See Sumitomo Mitsui Financial Group, Inc.; *Int'l*, pg. 7294
SMBC GUARANTEE CO., LTD.—See Sumitomo Mitsui Financial Group, Inc.; *Int'l*, pg. 7294
SMBC INTERNATIONAL BUSINESS CO., LTD.—See Sumitomo Mitsui Financial Group, Inc.; *Int'l*, pg. 7294
SMBC LEARNING SUPPORT CO., LTD.—See Sumitomo Mitsui Financial Group, Inc.; *Int'l*, pg. 7294
SMBC LEASING & FINANCE, INC.—See Sumitomo Mitsui Financial Group, Inc.; *Int'l*, pg. 7294
SMBC LOAN BUSINESS SERVICE CO., LTD.—See Sumitomo Mitsui Financial Group, Inc.; *Int'l*, pg. 7294
SMBC LOAN SERVICER CO., LTD.—See Sumitomo Mitsui Financial Group, Inc.; *Int'l*, pg. 7294

COMPANY NAME INDEX

SMBC MARKET SERVICE CO., LTD.—See Sumitomo Mitsui Financial Group, Inc.; *Int'l*, pg. 7294
SMBC METRO INVESTMENT CORP.—See Sumitomo Mitsui Financial Group, Inc.; *Int'l*, pg. 7294
SMBC NIKKO CAPITAL MARKETS LIMITED—See Sumitomo Mitsui Financial Group, Inc.; *Int'l*, pg. 7294
SMBC NIKKO SECURITIES AMERICA, INC.—See Sumitomo Mitsui Financial Group, Inc.; *Int'l*, pg. 7294
SMBC NIKKO SECURITIES INC.—See Sumitomo Mitsui Financial Group, Inc.; *Int'l*, pg. 7294
SMBC PERSONNEL SUPPORT CO., LTD.—See Sumitomo Mitsui Financial Group, Inc.; *Int'l*, pg. 7294
SMBC SECURITIES, INC.—See Sumitomo Mitsui Financial Group, Inc.; *Int'l*, pg. 7294
SMBC SERVICER CO., LTD.—See Sumitomo Mitsui Financial Group, Inc.; *Int'l*, pg. 7294
SMBC STAFF SERVICE CO., LTD.—See Sumitomo Mitsui Financial Group, Inc.; *Int'l*, pg. 7294
SMBC VENTURE CAPITAL CO., LTD.—See Sumitomo Mitsui Financial Group, Inc.; *Int'l*, pg. 7294
SM BENELUX SALES BV—See Skandinavisk Holding A/S; *Int'l*, pg. 6977
SM BEXEL CO, LTD.; *Int'l*, pg. 6998
SMB HARWAL ELECTRIC PTY. LTD.—See Fuji Electric Co., Ltd.; *Int'l*, pg. 2812
SMB KENZAI CO., LTD.; *Int'l*, pg. 7003
SMB MACQUARIE ELECTRIC PTY LTD—See Fuji Electric Co., Ltd.; *Int'l*, pg. 2812
SMB-MEHANIZACIJA I TRANSPORT A.D.; *Int'l*, pg. 7003
SMBOLOGY, INC.; *U.S. Private*, pg. 3693
SMB RESTAURANTS LLC; *U.S. Private*, pg. 3693
SMB SCHWEDE MASCHINENBAU GMBH—See Crown Holdings, Inc.; *U.S. Public*, pg. 599
SMB SCHWERMECHANIK GMBH—See Georgsmarienhutte Holding GmbH; *Int'l*, pg. 2941
SMB SWITCHGEAR & ENGINEERING SDN BHD—See Fuji Electric Co., Ltd.; *Int'l*, pg. 2812
SMBT PUBLISHING (THAILAND) CO., LTD.—See BEC World Public Company Limited; *Int'l*, pg. 936
SMC ARGENTINA S.A.—See SMC Corporation; *Int'l*, pg. 7004
SMC AUSTRIA GMBH—See SMC Corporation; *Int'l*, pg. 7004
SMC AUTOMACAO DO BRASIL LTDA.—See SMC Corporation; *Int'l*, pg. 7004
SMC AUTOMATION AB—See SMC Corporation; *Int'l*, pg. 7004
SMC AUTOMATION AS—See SMC Corporation; *Int'l*, pg. 7004
SMC AUTOMATION BOLIVIA SRL—See SMC Corporation; *Int'l*, pg. 7004
SMC AUTOMATION CHINA CO., LTD.—See SMC Corporation; *Int'l*, pg. 7004
SMC AUTOMATION ISRAEL LTD.—See SMC Corporation; *Int'l*, pg. 7004
SMC AUTOMATION OU—See SMC Corporation; *Int'l*, pg. 7004
SMC AUTOMATION OY—See SMC Corporation; *Int'l*, pg. 7004
SMC AUTOMATION SIA—See SMC Corporation; *Int'l*, pg. 7004
SMC AUTOMATION (TAIWAN) CO., LTD.—See SMC Corporation; *Int'l*, pg. 7004
SMC AUTOMATION UAB—See SMC Corporation; *Int'l*, pg. 7004
SMC (BEIJING) MANUFACTURING CO., LTD - 3RD PLANT OF BEIJING—See SMC Corporation; *Int'l*, pg. 7004
SMC (BEIJING) MANUFACTURING CO. LTD.—See SMC Corporation; *Int'l*, pg. 7004
SMC BELGIUM N.V.—See SMC Corporation; *Int'l*, pg. 7004
SMC (CHINA) CO., LTD. - 1ST PLANT OF BEIJING—See SMC Corporation; *Int'l*, pg. 7004
SMC (CHINA) CO. LTD.—See SMC Corporation; *Int'l*, pg. 7004
SMC COLOMBIA S.A.S.—See SMC Corporation; *Int'l*, pg. 7004
SMC COLOMBIA SUCURSAL DE SMC CHILE S.A.—See SMC Corporation; *Int'l*, pg. 7004
SMC (COMERCIAL OFFSHORE DE MACAU) LIMITADA—See The Singing Machine Company, Inc.; *U.S. Public*, pg. 2130
SMC COMEX INTERNATIONAL DMCC—See SMC Global Securities Limited; *Int'l*, pg. 7006
SMC COMPANIES; *U.S. Private*, pg. 3693
SMC CORPORATION (AUSTRALIA) PTY. LTD.—See SMC Corporation; *Int'l*, pg. 7004
SMC CORPORATION (CHILE), S.A.—See SMC Corporation; *Int'l*, pg. 7004
SMC CORPORATION (INDIA) PVT. LTD.—See SMC Corporation; *Int'l*, pg. 7004
SMC CORPORATION (MEXICO) S.A.DE.C.V.—See SMC Corporation; *Int'l*, pg. 7004
SMC CORPORATION MIDDLE EAST FZE—See SMC Corporation; *Int'l*, pg. 7004
SMC CORPORATION (NZ) LIMITED—See SMC Corporation; *Int'l*, pg. 7004
SMC CORPORATION OF AMERICA—See SMC Corporation; *Int'l*, pg. 7004
SMC CORPORATION PERU S.A.C.—See SMC Corporation; *Int'l*, pg. 7004
SMC CORPORATION (SINGAPORE) PTE. LTD.—See SMC Corporation; *Int'l*, pg. 7004
SMC CORPORATION; *Int'l*, pg. 7003
SMC CORPORATION (VIETNAM) CO., LTD.—See SMC Corporation; *Int'l*, pg. 7004
SMC CORPORATION (ZA) (PTY) LTD.—See SMC Corporation; *Int'l*, pg. 7004
SMC CREDITS LIMITED; *Int'l*, pg. 7006
SMC DANMARK A/S—See SMC Corporation; *Int'l*, pg. 7004
SMC DEUTSCHLAND GMBH—See SMC Corporation; *Int'l*, pg. 7004
SMC ELECTRICAL PRODUCTS INC.; *U.S. Private*, pg. 3693
SMC ELECTRIC LIMITED; *Int'l*, pg. 7006
SMC ELECTRIC SUPPLY—See Southern Materials Company; *U.S. Private*, pg. 3733
SMC ENTERTAINMENT INC.; *U.S. Private*, pg. 3693
SMC ESPANA S.A.—See SMC Corporation; *Int'l*, pg. 7004
SMC FRANCE S.A.—See SMC Corporation; *Int'l*, pg. 7004
SMC GLOBAL IFSC PRIVATE LIMITED—See SMC Global Securities Limited; *Int'l*, pg. 7006
SMC GLOBAL SECURITIES LIMITED; *Int'l*, pg. 7006
SMC HELLAS EPE—See SMC Corporation; *Int'l*, pg. 7004
SMC HUNGARY IPARI AUTOMATIZALASI KFT—See SMC Corporation; *Int'l*, pg. 7004
SM CIGARS INC.—See Philip Morris International Inc.; *U.S. Public*, pg. 1687
SMCI INC.—See MetalTek International; *U.S. Private*, pg. 2682
SMC INDUSTRIAL AUTOMATION BULGARIA EOOD—See SMC Corporation; *Int'l*, pg. 7004
SMC INDUSTRIAL AUTOMATION CZ S.R.O.—See SMC Corporation; *Int'l*, pg. 7004
SMC INDUSTRIAL AUTOMATION D.O.O.—See SMC Corporation; *Int'l*, pg. 7005
SMC INDUSTRIAL AUTOMATION (IRELAND) LIMITED—See SMC Corporation; *Int'l*, pg. 7004
SMC INDUSTRIAL AUTOMATION POLSKA SP.Z.O.O.—See SMC Corporation; *Int'l*, pg. 7005
SMC INDUSTRIJSKA AUTOMATIKA D.O.O.—See SMC Corporation; *Int'l*, pg. 7005
SMC INDUSTRIJSKA AVTOMATIKA D.O.O.—See SMC Corporation; *Int'l*, pg. 7005
SMC INSURANCE BROKERS PRIVATE LIMITED—See SMC Global Securities Limited; *Int'l*, pg. 7006
SMC INVESTMENT TRADING JOINT STOCK COMPANY; *Int'l*, pg. 7006
SMC ITALIA S.P.A. - CARSOLI FACTORY—See SMC Corporation; *Int'l*, pg. 7005
SMC ITALIA S.P.A—See SMC Corporation; *Int'l*, pg. 7005
SMC JAPAN—See Microchip Technology Incorporated; *U.S. Public*, pg. 1437
SMC KOREA CO., LTD.—See SMC Corporation; *Int'l*, pg. 7005
SMC MANUFACTURING (AUSTRALIA) PTY. LTD.—See SMC Corporation; *Int'l*, pg. 7005
SMC MANUFACTURING (SINGAPORE) PTE. LTD.—See SMC Corporation; *Int'l*, pg. 7005
SMC (MYANMAR) CO., LTD.—See SMC Corporation; *Int'l*, pg. 7004
SMC NEDERLAND B.V.—See SMC Corporation; *Int'l*, pg. 7005
SMC NETWORKS INC—See Accton Technology Corporation; *Int'l*, pg. 94
SMC NETWORKS SPAIN SL—See Accton Technology Corporation; *Int'l*, pg. 94
SMC NEUMATICA VENEZUELA S.A.—See SMC Corporation; *Int'l*, pg. 7005
SMCORE INC.; *Int'l*, pg. 7006
SMCP ASIA LIMITED—See SMCP S.A.; *Int'l*, pg. 7006
SMC PNEUMATICOS DO BRASIL LTDA—See SMC Corporation; *Int'l*, pg. 7005
SMC PNEUMATICS (AUSTRALIA) PTY.LTD.—See SMC Corporation; *Int'l*, pg. 7005
SMC PNEUMATICS BOLIVIA S.R.L.—See SMC Corporation; *Int'l*, pg. 7005
SMC PNEUMATICS (CANADA) LTD.—See SMC Corporation; *Int'l*, pg. 7005
SMC PNEUMATICS (CHILE) S.A.—See SMC Corporation; *Int'l*, pg. 7005
SMC PNEUMATICS COLOMBIA.—See SMC Corporation; *Int'l*, pg. 7005
SMC PNEUMATICS FINLAND OY—See SMC Corporation; *Int'l*, pg. 7005
SMC PNEUMATICS (GUANGZHOU) LIMITED—See SMC Corporation; *Int'l*, pg. 7005
SMC PNEUMATICS (HONG KONG) LTD.—See SMC Corporation; *Int'l*, pg. 7005
SMC PNEUMATICS (INDIA) PVT. LTD.—See SMC Corporation; *Int'l*, pg. 7005
SMC PNEUMATICS (IRELAND) LTD.—See SMC Corporation; *Int'l*, pg. 7005
SMC PNEUMATICS KOREA CO.,LTD. - DAEJON FACTORY—See SMC Corporation; *Int'l*, pg. 7005
SMC PNEUMATICS KOREA CO. LTD.—See SMC Corporation; *Int'l*, pg. 7005
SMC PNEUMATICS LATVIA SIA—See SMC Corporation; *Int'l*, pg. 7005
SMC PNEUMATICS (NEW ZEALAND) LTD.—See SMC Corporation; *Int'l*, pg. 7005
SMC PNEUMATICS NORWAY AS—See SMC Corporation; *Int'l*, pg. 7005
SMC PNEUMATICS N.V./S.A.—See SMC Corporation; *Int'l*, pg. 7005
SMC PNEUMATICS (S.E.A.) PTE. LTD.—See SMC Corporation; *Int'l*, pg. 7005
SMC PNEUMATICS (S.E.A) SDN.BHD.—See SMC Corporation; *Int'l*, pg. 7005
SMC PNEUMATICS SWEDEN AB—See SMC Corporation; *Int'l*, pg. 7005
SMC PNEUMATICS (TAIWAN) CO. LTD.—See SMC Corporation; *Int'l*, pg. 7005
SMC PNEUMATICS (TAIWAN) CO., LTD. - TOULIU FACTORY—See SMC Corporation; *Int'l*, pg. 7005
SMC PNEUMATICS (U.K.) LTD.—See SMC Corporation; *Int'l*, pg. 7005
SMC PNEUMATIK AG—See SMC Corporation; *Int'l*, pg. 7005
SMC PNEUMATIK A/S—See SMC Corporation; *Int'l*, pg. 7005
SMC PNEUMATIK GMBH—See SMC Corporation; *Int'l*, pg. 7005
SMC PNEUMATIK LLC—See SMC Corporation; *Int'l*, pg. 7005
SMC PNEUMATIQUE S.A.—See SMC Corporation; *Int'l*, pg. 7006
SMC PNOMATIK SANAYI TICARET VE SERVIS A.S.—See SMC Corporation; *Int'l*, pg. 7006
SMC PRIEMYSELNA AUMTOMATIZACIA SPOL S.R.O.—See SMC Corporation; *Int'l*, pg. 7006
SMC PRIEMYSELNA AUTOMATIZACIA SPOL.S.R.O.—See SMC Corporation; *Int'l*, pg. 7006
SMCP S.A.; *Int'l*, pg. 7006
SMCP USA INC.—See SMCP S.A.; *Int'l*, pg. 7006
SMC REAL ESTATE ADVISORS PRIVATE LIMITED—See SMC Global Securities Limited; *Int'l*, pg. 7006
SMC ROMANIA S.R.L.—See SMC Corporation; *Int'l*, pg. 7006
SMC ROVER—See Bestodeck Ltd.; *Int'l*, pg. 1000
SMC SCHWEIZ AG—See SMC Corporation; *Int'l*, pg. 7006
SMC SOUTH—See Sommer Metalcraft Corporation; *U.S. Private*, pg. 3712
SMC SUCURSAL PORTUGAL S.A.—See SMC Corporation; *Int'l*, pg. 7006
SMC SYSTEMS, INC.—See Gallant Capital Partners, LLC; *U.S. Private*, pg. 1639
SMC THAILAND LTD.—See SMC Corporation; *Int'l*, pg. 7006
SMC TOAMI LLC—See Toami Corporation; *Int'l*, pg. 7770
SMC TURKEY OTOMASYON A.S.—See SMC Corporation; *Int'l*, pg. 7006
SM CULTURE & CONTENTS CO., LTD.—See S.M. Entertainment Co., Ltd.; *Int'l*, pg. 6456
SM CYCLO COLOMBIA, S.A.S.—See Sumitomo Heavy Industries, Ltd.; *Int'l*, pg. 7288
SM-CYCLO DE ARGENTINA S.A.—See Sumitomo Heavy Industries, Ltd.; *Int'l*, pg. 7288
SM-CYCLO DE CHILE, LTDA.—See Sumitomo Heavy Industries, Ltd.; *Int'l*, pg. 7288
SM-CYCLO DE COLOMBIA LTDA.—See Sumitomo Heavy Industries, Ltd.; *Int'l*, pg. 7288
SM-CYCLO DE MEXICO, S.A. DE C.V.—See Sumitomo Heavy Industries, Ltd.; *Int'l*, pg. 7288
SM CYCLO DE PERU S.A.C—See Sumitomo Heavy Industries, Ltd.; *Int'l*, pg. 7288
SM-CYCLO FRANCE S.A.S.—See Sumitomo Heavy Industries, Ltd.; *Int'l*, pg. 7288
SM-CYCLO IBERIA, S.L.—See Sumitomo Heavy Industries, Ltd.; *Int'l*, pg. 7288
SM-CYCLO ITALY SRL—See Sumitomo Heavy Industries, Ltd.; *Int'l*, pg. 7288
SM-CYCLO (MALAYSIA) SDN. BHD.—See Sumitomo Heavy Industries, Ltd.; *Int'l*, pg. 7288
SM-CYCLO OF CANADA, LTD.—See Sumitomo Heavy Industries, Ltd.; *Int'l*, pg. 7288
SM-CYCLO OF CANADA, LTD.—See Sumitomo Heavy Industries, Ltd.; *Int'l*, pg. 7288
SM-CYCLO OF HONG KONG CO., LTD.—See Sumitomo Heavy Industries, Ltd.; *Int'l*, pg. 7288
SM-CYCLO REDUTORES DO BRASIL LTDA.—See Sumitomo Heavy Industries, Ltd.; *Int'l*, pg. 7288
SM-CYCLO (THAILAND) CO., LTD.—See Sumitomo Heavy Industries, Ltd.; *Int'l*, pg. 7288
SM CYCLO TURKEY GUC AKTARIM SIS. TIC. LTD.—See Sumitomo Heavy Industries, Ltd.; *Int'l*, pg. 7288
SM-CYCLO TURKEY LTD. STI.—See Sumitomo Heavy Industries, Ltd.; *Int'l*, pg. 7288
SM-CYCLO UK LTD.—See Sumitomo Heavy Industries, Ltd.; *Int'l*, pg. 7288
SM-CYCLO (VIETNAM) CO., LTD.—See Sumitomo Heavy Industries, Ltd.; *Int'l*, pg. 7288
SM DEUTSCHLAND GMBH—See Philip Morris International Inc.; *U.S. Public*, pg. 1687

SM DEVELOPMENT CORPORATION—See SM Investments Corporation; *Int'l,* pg. 6998
SMD, INC.; *U.S. Private,* pg. 3693
SMD LOGISTICS AB—See Philip Morris International Inc.; *U.S. Private,* pg. 1687
SMD MARINE ELECTRONICS NAMIBIA (PTY) LTD—See Grupo Arbulu S.L.; *Int'l,* pg. 3120
SM D.O.O. ZAGREB—See Skandinavisk Holding A/S; *Int'l,* pg. 6977
SMEAD EUROPE BV—See Smead Manufacturing Company; *U.S. Private,* pg. 3693
SMEAD MANUFACTURING COMPANY; *U.S. Private,* pg. 3693
SMEAL SFA, LLC—See AIP, LLC; *U.S. Private,* pg. 135
SM EASTLAND MALL, LLC—See The Macerich Company; *U.S. Public,* pg. 2110
SMEC AMERICA CORP.—See SMEC Co., Ltd.; *Int'l,* pg. 7007
SMEC CO., LTD. - HYEONPUNG FACTORY—See SMEC Co., Ltd.; *Int'l,* pg. 7007
SMEC CO., LTD.; *Int'l,* pg. 7007
SMEC HOLDINGS LIMITED—See Temasek Holdings (Private) Limited; *Int'l,* pg. 7554
SME CO.,LTD.—See Polaris Capital Group Co., Ltd.; *Int'l,* pg. 5907
SMEC VINA CO., LTD.—See SMEC Co., Ltd.; *Int'l,* pg. 7007
SMEDERNA SVERIGE AB—See Storskogen Group AB; *Int'l,* pg. 7228
SME DEUTSCHLAND GMBH—See Dana Incorporated; *U.S. Public,* pg. 623
SMEDING B. V.—See Mitsubishi Chemical Group Corporation; *Int'l,* pg. 4937
SMEDIO INC.; *Int'l,* pg. 7007
SMEDVIG ASA—See SeaDrill Limited; *Int'l,* pg. 6662
SMEDVIG HOLDING AS—See SeaDrill Limited; *Int'l,* pg. 6662
SMEE AND FORD LIMITED—See Wilmington plc; *Int'l,* pg. 8422
SMEE BUILDERS INC.; *U.S. Private,* pg. 3693
SMEETS COMMUNICATIONS GMBH—See Azerion Group N.V.; *Int'l,* pg. 778
SMEFA ENTREPRENOR AS—See Peab AB; *Int'l,* pg. 5773
S&ME, INC.; *U.S. Private,* pg. 3513
SME, INC.—See Ataïros Group, Inc.; *U.S. Private,* pg. 364
SME INDUSTRIES INC.; *U.S. Private,* pg. 3693
SME INSURANCE SERVICES LIMITED—See Marsh & McLennan Companies, Inc.; *U.S. Public,* pg. 1388
SME LEASING LTD.; *Int'l,* pg. 7006
SM ELECTRONIC GMBH—See Microelectronic NH GmbH; *Int'l,* pg. 4879
SMELTER PLANT—See National Aluminium Company Limited; *Int'l,* pg. 5150
SM ENERGY COMPANY - HOUSTON—See SM Energy Company; *U.S. Public,* pg. 1895
SM ENERGY COMPANY; *U.S. Public,* pg. 1895
SM ENERGY TEKNIK & ELECTRONICS LIMITED; *Int'l,* pg. 6998
S.M. ENTERTAINMENT CO., LTD.; *Int'l,* pg. 6456
SMERALDA RSA DI PADRU SRL—See Clariane SE; *Int'l,* pg. 1644
SMERLING SYNCHRO ENERGY ENGINEERING LTD.—See Taavura Holdings, Ltd.; *Int'l,* pg. 7401
SMERWICK TAIWAN BRANCH LIMITED—See U10 Corp SA; *Int'l,* pg. 7998
SME - SCIENCE MANAGEMENT & ENGINEERING AG—See DXC Technology Company; *U.S. Public,* pg. 696
SME SECURITIES CORPORATION; *Int'l,* pg. 7006
SME SHANGHAI CO., LTD.—See Dana Incorporated; *U.S. Public,* pg. 623
SMETEX GMBH; *Int'l,* pg. 7007
SMETZERS TIRE CENTER INC.; *U.S. Private,* pg. 3693
SMEVA B.V.—See Carrier Global Corporation; *U.S. Public,* pg. 442
SMEV S.R.L.—See Dometic Group AB; *Int'l,* pg. 2160
SMFG CARD & CREDIT, INC.—See Sumitomo Mitsui Financial Group, Inc.; *Int'l,* pg. 7293
SMF INC.; *U.S. Private,* pg. 3693
SMFL LEASING (MALAYSIA) SDN. BHD.—See Sumitomo Corporation; *Int'l,* pg. 7274
SMFL LEASING (MALAYSIA) SDN. BHD.—See Sumitomo Mitsui Financial Group, Inc.; *Int'l,* pg. 7295
SMFL LEASING (THAILAND) CO., LTD.—See Sumitomo Corporation; *Int'l,* pg. 7274
SMFL LEASING (THAILAND) CO., LTD.—See Sumitomo Mitsui Financial Group, Inc.; *Int'l,* pg. 7295
SMFL MIRAI PARTNERS CO., LTD—See Sumitomo Corporation; *Int'l,* pg. 7274
SMFL MIRAI PARTNERS CO., LTD—See Sumitomo Mitsui Financial Group, Inc.; *Int'l,* pg. 7295
SMFL MIRAI PARTNERS INVESTMENT 2 CO., LTD.—See Sumitomo Corporation; *Int'l,* pg. 7274
SMFL MIRAI PARTNERS INVESTMENT 2 CO., LTD.—See Sumitomo Mitsui Financial Group, Inc.; *Int'l,* pg. 7295
S.M. FRANK & CO., INC.; *U.S. Private,* pg. 3518
SMF WEALTH MANAGEMENT PTY LIMITED—See Insignia Financial Ltd.; *Int'l,* pg. 3719

SMG ASSOCIATES—See Ginsburg Development Corp.; *U.S. Private,* pg. 1702
SMG ASTRA WOMEN'S SPECIALISTS PTE. LTD.—See Singapore Medical Group Limited; *Int'l,* pg. 6940
SMG DIRECTORY MARKETING—See Publicis Groupe S.A.; *Int'l,* pg. 6111
SMG EUROPE—See Northlane Capital Partners, LLC; *U.S. Private,* pg. 2956
SMG FOOD & BEVERAGE, LLC—See Northlane Capital Partners, LLC; *U.S. Private,* pg. 2956
SMG GROWING MEDIA, INC.—See The Scotts Miracle-Gro Company; *U.S. Public,* pg. 2127
SMG INDUSTRIES INC.; *U.S. Public,* pg. 1896
SMG NETWORK, INC.—See Northlane Capital Partners, LLC; *U.S. Private,* pg. 2956
S.M. GOLD LIMITED; *Int'l,* pg. 6456
SMG ORTHOPAEDIC GROUP PTE. LTD.—See Singapore Medical Group Limited; *Int'l,* pg. 6941
SMG/P&G—See Publicis Groupe S.A.; *Int'l,* pg. 6111
SMG SPECIALIST CENTRE PTE. LTD.—See Singapore Medical Group Limited; *Int'l,* pg. 6941
SMG UNITED—See Publicis Groupe S.A.; *Int'l,* pg. 6111
SMH CAPITAL ADVISORS, INC.—See Lee Equity Partners LLC; *U.S. Private,* pg. 2412
SMH CUMMER/MOYERS—See Lee Equity Partners LLC; *U.S. Private,* pg. 2412
SMH IMMOBILIEN S.A.—See The Swatch Group Ltd.; *Int'l,* pg. 7692
SM HOTELS & CONVENTIONS CORP.—See SM Investments Corporation; *Int'l,* pg. 6999
SMH SUDDEUTSCHE METALLHANDELSGESELLSCHAFT MIT BESCHRANKTER HAFTUNG—See Diehl Stiftung & Co. KG; *Int'l,* pg. 2115
SMH SWISS WATCH TRADING (SHANGHAI) CO. LTD.—See The Swatch Group Ltd.; *Int'l,* pg. 7692
SMIC AMERICAS—See Semiconductor Manufacturing International Corporation; *Int'l,* pg. 6704
SMIC BEIJING—See Semiconductor Manufacturing International Corporation; *Int'l,* pg. 6704
SMIC EUROPE—See Semiconductor Manufacturing International Corporation; *Int'l,* pg. 6704
SMIC HONG KONG—See Semiconductor Manufacturing International Corporation; *Int'l,* pg. 6704
SMIC JAPAN—See Semiconductor Manufacturing International Corporation; *Int'l,* pg. 6705
SMI CO., LTD.—See Panasonic Holdings Corporation; *Int'l,* pg. 5724
SMIC SHANGHAI—See Semiconductor Manufacturing International Corporation; *Int'l,* pg. 6705
SMIC TIANJIN—See Semiconductor Manufacturing International Corporation; *Int'l,* pg. 6705
SMI CULTURE & TRAVEL GROUP HOLDINGS LIMITED; *Int'l,* pg. 7007
SMIDTH & CO.—See FLSmidth & Co. A/S; *Int'l,* pg. 2712
SMIF EQUIPMENT (TIANJIN) CO., LTD—See Azenta, Inc.; *U.S. Public,* pg. 258
SMIFFY'S UK; *Int'l,* pg. 7007
SMIFS CAPITAL MARKETS LTD.; *Int'l,* pg. 7007
S. MIFSUD & SONS LTD.—See SMS Group Limited; *Int'l,* pg. 7015
SMIGGLE PTY. LIMITED—See Premier Investments Limited; *Int'l,* pg. 5960
SMIGGLE SINGAPORE PTE. LTD.—See Premier Investments Limited; *Int'l,* pg. 5960
SMIGGLE UK LIMITED—See Premier Investments Limited; *Int'l,* pg. 5960
SMI GLOBAL SDN. BHD.—See Meisei Industrial Co., Ltd.; *Int'l,* pg. 4804
SMI HOLDINGS GROUP LIMITED; *Int'l,* pg. 7007
SMILEBOX, INC.—See Perion Network Ltd.; *Int'l,* pg. 5801
SMILE BRANDS, INC.—See Gryphon Investors, LLC; *U.S. Private,* pg. 1799
SMILEBUILDERZ; *U.S. Private,* pg. 3693
SMILE BUSINESS PRODUCTS INC.; *U.S. Private,* pg. 3693
SMILE CORP.—See Senko Group Holdings Co., Ltd.; *Int'l,* pg. 6711
SMILECORP VIETNAM CO., LTD.—See Senko Group Holdings Co., Ltd.; *Int'l,* pg. 6711
SMILEDIRECTCLUB, INC.; *U.S. Public,* pg. 1896
SMILE-LAB CO., LTD.—See Square Enix Holdings Co. Ltd.; *Int'l,* pg. 7147
SMILEMAKERS FOR CHILDREN CO.—See Berkshire Hathaway Inc.; *U.S. Public,* pg. 313
SMILEMAKERS, INC.—See Berkshire Hathaway Inc.; *U.S. Public,* pg. 313
SMILE SAS—See Eurazeo SE; *Int'l,* pg. 2528
SMILES FIDELIDADE SA—See Gol Linhas Aereas Inteligentes S.A.; *Int'l,* pg. 3023
SMILES INCLUSIVE LIMITED; *Int'l,* pg. 7007
SMILE—See Co-operative Group Limited; *Int'l,* pg. 1679
SMILE STAFF CO., LTD.—See Trancom Co., Ltd.; *Int'l,* pg. 7891
SMILE VUN GROUP PVT LTD.—See Dentsu Group Inc.; *Int'l,* pg. 2037
SMILINK SERVICOS ORTODONTICOS LTDA.—See Straumann Holding AG; *Int'l,* pg. 7238
SMINK BEHEER B.V.—See Renewi plc; *Int'l,* pg. 6279
SM INTERNATIONAL D.O.O.—See WPP plc; *Int'l,* pg. 8481

SM INVESTMENTS CORPORATION; *Int'l,* pg. 6998
SMISC HOLDINGS, INC.—See Sonic Financial Corporation; *U.S. Private,* pg. 3713
SMIS CORPORATION BERHAD; *Int'l,* pg. 7007
SMI STEEL INC.—See Commercial Metals Company; *U.S. Public,* pg. 547
SMIT DRAAD NIJMEGEN B V—See IRCE S.p.A.; *Int'l,* pg. 3806
SMI TELECOMS LLC; *Int'l,* pg. 7007
SMIT GROUP LIMITED—See SMIT Holdings Limited; *Int'l,* pg. 7007
SMITHAHN CO.; *U.S. Private,* pg. 3696
SMITH AND NEPHEW HELLAS S.A.—See Smith & Nephew plc; *Int'l,* pg. 7009
SMIT HARBOUR TOWAGE ROTTERDAM B.V.—See HAL Trust N.V.; *Int'l,* pg. 3227
SMITH & ASSOCIATES REAL ESTATE; *U.S. Private,* pg. 3693
SMITHBILT INDUSTRIES INC.; *U.S. Private,* pg. 3696
SMITH-BLAIR, INC.—See Xylem Inc.; *U.S. Public,* pg. 2395
SMITH BRANDON INTERNATIONAL, INC.—See Kreller Group Inc.; *U.S. Private,* pg. 2351
SMITH BROS. & WILSON (BC) LTD.; *Int'l,* pg. 7009
SMITH BROTHERS FARMS, INC.; *U.S. Private,* pg. 3694
SMITH BROTHERS INSURANCE, LLC; *U.S. Private,* pg. 3694
SMITH BROTHERS OF BERNE INC.; *U.S. Private,* pg. 3694
SMITH BROTHERS OIL COMPANY, INC.—See Quality Petroleum Corp.; *U.S. Private,* pg. 3320
SMITH, BRYAN & MYERS INC.; *U.S. Private,* pg. 3696
SMITHBUCKLIN CORPORATION; *U.S. Private,* pg. 3696
SMITH BUS SERVICE, INC.—See Mobico Group PLC.; *Int'l,* pg. 5009
SMITH & BUTTERFIELD CO., INC.—See Champion Industries, Inc.; *U.S. Public,* pg. 478
SMITH-CAIRNS FORD INC.; *U.S. Private,* pg. 3696
SMITH & CARSON; *U.S. Private,* pg. 3693
SMITH CARTER (USA) LLC—See WSP Global, Inc.; *Int'l,* pg. 8498
THE SMITH CENTER; *U.S. Private,* pg. 4118
SMITH CHEVROLET COMPANY INC.; *U.S. Private,* pg. 3694
SMITHCO ENGINEERING INC.; *U.S. Private,* pg. 3697
SMITH & COFFMAN INCORPORATED; *U.S. Private,* pg. 3693
SMITHCO, INC.; *U.S. Private,* pg. 3697
SMITH COMPANIES OF LEXINGTON; *U.S. Private,* pg. 3694
SMITH & COMPANY INC.; *U.S. Private,* pg. 3693
SMITH CONCRETE—See CRH plc; *Int'l,* pg. 1847
SMITH CONSULTING ARCHITECTS—See Godspeed Capital Management LP; *U.S. Private,* pg. 1725
SMITH COOKIE COMPANY—See United States Bakery; *U.S. Private,* pg. 4298
SMITH CORONA CORPORATION—See Pubco Corporation; *U.S. Private,* pg. 3298
SMITHCORP FINANCE LIMITED—See Smiths City Group Limited; *Int'l,* pg. 7009
SMITH DAIRY PRODUCTS COMPANY INC.; *U.S. Private,* pg. 3694
SMITH & DE SHIELDS INC.; *U.S. Private,* pg. 3693
SMITH DOUGLAS HOMES CORP.; *U.S. Public,* pg. 1896
SMITH DRAY LINE & STORAGE CO.; *U.S. Private,* pg. 3694
SMITH DRUG COMPANY—See J.M. Smith Corporation; *U.S. Private,* pg. 2169
SMITH & EDWARDS COMPANY; *U.S. Private,* pg. 3693
SMITH-EDWARDS-DUNLAP COMPANY; *U.S. Private,* pg. 3696
SMITH ELECTRIC VEHICLES CORP.; *U.S. Private,* pg. 3694
SMITH ELECTRIC VEHICLES EUROPE LIMITED—See Smith Electric Vehicles Corp.; *U.S. Private,* pg. 3694
SMITH ELLIOTT KEARNS & COMPANY, LLC; *U.S. Private,* pg. 3694
SMITH-EMERY COMPANY; *U.S. Private,* pg. 3696
SMITH ENGINEERING INC.—See Xylem Inc.; *U.S. Public,* pg. 2394
SMITH EQUIPMENT—See Illinois Tool Works Inc.; *U.S. Public,* pg. 1110
SMITHERS AVANZA—See The Smithers Group; *U.S. Private,* pg. 4118
THE SMITHERS GROUP; *U.S. Private,* pg. 4118
SMITHERS-OASIS ADRIA D.O.O.—See Smithers-Oasis Company; *U.S. Private,* pg. 3697
SMITHERS-OASIS AUSTRALIA PTY LTD—See Smithers-Oasis Company; *U.S. Private,* pg. 3697
SMITHERS-OASIS BELGIUM N.V.—See Smithers-Oasis Company; *U.S. Private,* pg. 3697
SMITHERS-OASIS COMPANY; *U.S. Private,* pg. 3697
SMITHERS-OASIS DE MEXICO S.A. DE C.V.—See Smithers-Oasis Company; *U.S. Private,* pg. 3697
SMITHERS-OASIS FRANCE SARL—See Smithers-Oasis Company; *U.S. Private,* pg. 3697
SMITHERS-OASIS GERMANY GMBH—See Smithers-Oasis Company; *U.S. Private,* pg. 3697

COMPANY NAME INDEX

SMITHERS-OASIS IBERICA, S.L.—See Smithers-Oasis Company; *U.S. Private*, pg. 3697
SMITHERS-OASIS INDIA PVT. LTD.—See Smithers-Oasis Company; *U.S. Private*, pg. 3697
SMITHERS-OASIS JAPAN CO., LTD.—See Smithers-Oasis Company; *U.S. Private*, pg. 3697
SMITHERS-OASIS KOREA CO., LTD.—See Smithers-Oasis Company; *U.S. Private*, pg. 3697
SMITHERS-OASIS MALAYSIA SDN BHD—See Smithers-Oasis Company; *U.S. Private*, pg. 3697
SMITHERS-OASIS NORTH AMERICA—See Smithers-Oasis Company; *U.S. Private*, pg. 3697
SMITHERS-OASIS U.K. LTD.—See Smithers-Oasis Company; *U.S. Private*, pg. 3697
SMITHERS SCIENTIFIC SERVICES, INC.—See The Smithers Group; *U.S. Private*, pg. 4119
SMITH FASTENER CO., INC.—See Kian Capital Partners, LLC; *U.S. Private*, pg. 2302
SMITH FASTENER CO., INC.—See Oakland Standard Co., LLC; *U.S. Private*, pg. 2985
SMITH FEED SERVICE INC.—See Vita Plus Corporation; *U.S. Private*, pg. 4405
SMITH FEIKE MINTON, INC.; *U.S. Private*, pg. 3694
SMITH FIBERCAST—See NOV, Inc.; *U.S. Public*, pg. 1544
SMITHFIELD DELI GROUP—See WH Group Limited; *Int'l*, pg. 8395
SMITHFIELD FERME S.R.L.—See WH Group Limited; *Int'l*, pg. 8395
SMITHFIELD FOODSERVICE GROUP—See WH Group Limited; *Int'l*, pg. 8395
SMITHFIELD FOODS, INC.—See WH Group Limited; *Int'l*, pg. 8394
SMITHFIELD FOODS LTD.—See WH Group Limited; *Int'l*, pg. 8395
SMITHFIELD FRANCE S.A.S.—See WH Group Limited; *Int'l*, pg. 8395
SMITHFIELD FRANCE SERVICES—See WH Group Limited; *Int'l*, pg. 8395
SMITHFIELD GLOBAL PRODUCTS—See WH Group Limited; *Int'l*, pg. 8395
THE SMITHFIELD INN CORPORATION—See WH Group Limited; *Int'l*, pg. 8395
SMITHFIELD INTERNATIONAL INVESTMENTS, INC.—See WH Group Limited; *Int'l*, pg. 8395
THE SMITHFIELD PACKING CO., INC.—See WH Group Limited; *Int'l*, pg. 8396
SMITHFIELD PACKING TRANSPORTATION CO., INC.—See WH Group Limited; *Int'l*, pg. 8395
SMITHFIELD TRANSPORTATION CO., INC.—See WH Group Limited; *Int'l*, pg. 8395
SMITH FILTER CORPORATION—See Audax Group, Limited Partnership; *U.S. Private*, pg. 389
SMITH FINANCIAL CORPORATION; *Int'l*, pg. 7009
SMITH FIRE SYSTEMS INC.; *U.S. Private*, pg. 3694
SMITH FLOORING INC; *U.S. Private*, pg. 3694
SMITH FOOD SALES, INC.—See Smith Frozen Foods, Inc.; *U.S. Private*, pg. 3695
SMITH FROZEN FOODS, INC.; *U.S. Private*, pg. 3694
SMITHGALL DIALYSIS, LLC—See DaVita Inc.; *U.S. Public*, pg. 643
SMITH, GAMBRELL & RUSSELL, LLP—See Smith, Gambrell & Russell; *U.S. Private*, pg. 3696
SMITH, GAMBRELL & RUSSELL; *U.S. Private*, pg. 3696
SMITH GARDENS, INC.; *U.S. Private*, pg. 3695
SMITHGIFFORD; *U.S. Private*, pg. 3697
SMITH, GRAHAM & COMPANY INVESTMENT ADVISORS, LP.; *U.S. Private*, pg. 3696
SMITH-GRAY ELECTRIC CO. INC.; *U.S. Private*, pg. 3696
SMITH & GRAY; *U.S. Private*, pg. 3694
SMITHGROUP COMPANIES, INC.; *U.S. Private*, pg. 3697
SMITHGROUP, INC. - CHICAGO—See SmithGroup Companies, Inc.; *U.S. Private*, pg. 3697
SMITHGROUP, INC. - MADISON—See SmithGroup Companies, Inc.; *U.S. Private*, pg. 3697
SMITHGROUP, INC. - PHOENIX—See SmithGroup Companies, Inc.; *U.S. Private*, pg. 3697
SMITHGROUP, INC. - SAN FRANCISCO—See SmithGroup Companies, Inc.; *U.S. Private*, pg. 3697
SMITHGROUP, INC.—See SmithGroup Companies, Inc.; *U.S. Private*, pg. 3697
SMITHGROUP, INC. - WASHINGTON, DC—See SmithGroup Companies, Inc.; *U.S. Private*, pg. 3698
SMITH HANLEY ASSOCIATES INC.; *U.S. Private*, pg. 3695
SMITH HAVEN CORP.; *U.S. Private*, pg. 3695
SMITH HAYES FINANCIAL SERVICES CORPORATION—See D.A. Davidson Companies; *U.S. Private*, pg. 1140
SMITH IMPLEMENTS INC.; *U.S. Private*, pg. 3695
SMITH INDUSTRIES, INC.—See European Metal Recycling Limited; *Int'l*, pg. 2556
SMITH INSTRUMENT—See The Kendall Group, Inc.; *U.S. Private*, pg. 4064
SMITH INSURANCE ASSOCIATES, INC.—See Brown & Brown, Inc.; *U.S. Public*, pg. 400
SMITH INVESTMENT COMPANY—See A. O. Smith Corporation; *U.S. Public*, pg. 12
SMITH IRONWORKS INC.; *U.S. Private*, pg. 3695
SMITH & JONES; *U.S. Private*, pg. 3694
SMITH/JUNGER/WELLMAN; *U.S. Private*, pg. 3696
SMITH, KAPLAN, ALLEN & REYNOLDS, INC.; *U.S. Private*, pg. 3696
SMITH & KEENE ELECTRIC SERVICE, INC.; *U.S. Private*, pg. 3694
SMITHKLINE BEECHAM CONSUMER BRANDS LIMITED—See GSK plc; *Int'l*, pg. 3149
SMITHKLINE BEECHAM (CORK) LIMITED—See GSK plc; *Int'l*, pg. 3149
SMITHKLINE BEECHAM DE PANAMA S.A.—See GSK plc; *Int'l*, pg. 3149
SMITHKLINE BEECHAM HONDURAS S.A.—See GSK plc; *Int'l*, pg. 3149
SMITHKLINE BEECHAM (IRELAND) LIMITED—See GSK plc; *Int'l*, pg. 3149
SMITHKLINE BEECHAM LIMITED—See GSK plc; *Int'l*, pg. 3149
SMITH, LINDEN & BASSO, LLP—See Windes, Inc.; *U.S. Private*, pg. 4537
SMITH & LOVELESS GEORGIA INC.—See RLR, Inc.; *U.S. Private*, pg. 3451
SMITH & LOVELESS, INC.—See RLR, Inc.; *U.S. Private*, pg. 3451
SMITH & LOVELESS NEW ZEALAND LIMITED—See RLR, Inc.; *U.S. Private*, pg. 3451
SMITH MACK & CO., INC.—See BGC Group, Inc.; *U.S. Public*, pg. 330
SMITH MANAGEMENT CO., INC.; *U.S. Private*, pg. 3695
SMITH MANAGEMENT GROUP, INC.—See All4 LLC; *U.S. Private*, pg. 174
SMITH MARITIME LLC—See Kirby Corporation; *U.S. Public*, pg. 1236
SMITH MEDICAL PARTNERS, LLC—See H.D. Smith Wholesale Drug Co. Inc.; *U.S. Private*, pg. 1825
SMITH METAL PRODUCTS INC—See Plastic Products Company, Inc.; *U.S. Private*, pg. 3199
SMITH MICRO SOFTWARE, INC.; *U.S. Public*, pg. 1896
SMITH MICRO SOFTWARE, INC.—See Smith Micro Software, Inc.; *U.S. Public*, pg. 1896
SMITH MICRO SOFTWARE UK LIMITED—See Smith Micro Software, Inc.; *U.S. Public*, pg. 1896
SMITH MICRO SOFTWARE - WIRELESS & BROADBAND DIVISION—See Smith Micro Software, Inc.; *U.S. Public*, pg. 1896
SMITH-MIDLAND CORPORATION; *U.S. Public*, pg. 1896
SMITH MOORE LLP; *U.S. Private*, pg. 3695
SMITH MOTORS, INC.; *U.S. Private*, pg. 3695
SMITH & NEPHEW AB—See Smith & Nephew plc; *Int'l*, pg. 7008
SMITH & NEPHEW (ALBERTA) INC.—See Smith & Nephew plc; *Int'l*, pg. 7007
SMITH & NEPHEW A/S—See Smith & Nephew plc; *Int'l*, pg. 7008
SMITH & NEPHEW A/S—See Smith & Nephew plc; *Int'l*, pg. 7008
SMITH & NEPHEW COLOMBIA S.A.S.—See Smith & Nephew plc; *Int'l*, pg. 7008
SMITH & NEPHEW ENDOSCOPY KK—See Smith & Nephew plc; *Int'l*, pg. 7008
SMITH & NEPHEW FRANCE SAS—See Smith & Nephew plc; *Int'l*, pg. 7008
SMITH & NEPHEW FZE—See Smith & Nephew plc; *Int'l*, pg. 7008
SMITH & NEPHEW GMBH—See Smith & Nephew plc; *Int'l*, pg. 7008
SMITH & NEPHEW GMBH—See Smith & Nephew plc; *Int'l*, pg. 7008
SMITH & NEPHEW GROUP RESEARCH CENTRE—See Smith & Nephew plc; *Int'l*, pg. 7008
SMITH & NEPHEW HEALTHCARE LIMITED—See Smith & Nephew plc; *Int'l*, pg. 7008
SMITH & NEPHEW HEALTHCARE PRIVATE LIMITED—See Smith & Nephew plc; *Int'l*, pg. 7008
SMITH & NEPHEW HEALTHCARE SDN BERHAD—See Smith & Nephew plc; *Int'l*, pg. 7008
SMITH & NEPHEW, INC. - ADVANCED WOUND MANAGEMENT—See Smith & Nephew plc; *Int'l*, pg. 7009
SMITH & NEPHEW, INC. - ENDOSCOPY DIVISION—See Smith & Nephew plc; *Int'l*, pg. 7009
SMITH & NEPHEW, INC.—See Smith & Nephew plc; *Int'l*, pg. 7008
SMITH & NEPHEW KK—See Smith & Nephew plc; *Int'l*, pg. 7008
SMITH & NEPHEW KOREA—See Smith & Nephew plc; *Int'l*, pg. 7008
SMITH & NEPHEW LDA—See Smith & Nephew plc; *Int'l*, pg. 7008
SMITH & NEPHEW LIMITED—See Smith & Nephew plc; *Int'l*, pg. 7008
SMITH & NEPHEW (MALAYSIA) SDN BHD—See Smith & Nephew plc; *Int'l*, pg. 7008
SMITH & NEPHEW MANUFACTURING AG—See Smith & Nephew plc; *Int'l*, pg. 7008
SMITH & NEPHEW MEDICAL LTD.—See Smith & Nephew plc; *Int'l*, pg. 7008
SMITH & NEPHEW MEDICAL (SHANGHAI) LIMITED—See Smith & Nephew plc; *Int'l*, pg. 7008
SMITH & NEPHEW MEDICAL (SUZHOU) LIMITED—See Smith & Nephew plc; *Int'l*, pg. 7008
SMITH & NEPHEW NEDERLAND CV—See Smith & Nephew plc; *Int'l*, pg. 7008
SMITH & NEPHEW OPERATIONS B.V.—See Smith & Nephew plc; *Int'l*, pg. 7008
SMITH & NEPHEW ORTHOPAEDICS KK—See Smith & Nephew plc; *Int'l*, pg. 7008
SMITH & NEPHEW ORTHOPEDICS GMBH—See Smith & Nephew plc; *Int'l*, pg. 7008
SMITH & NEPHEW ORTHOPEDICS HELLAS SA—See Smith & Nephew plc; *Int'l*, pg. 7008
SMITH & NEPHEW (OVERSEAS) LIMITED—See Smith & Nephew plc; *Int'l*, pg. 7008
SMITH & NEPHEW OY—See Smith & Nephew plc; *Int'l*, pg. 7008
SMITH & NEPHEW PLC; *Int'l*, pg. 7007
SMITH & NEPHEW PTE LIMITED—See Smith & Nephew plc; *Int'l*, pg. 7008
SMITH & NEPHEW (PTY) LIMITED—See Smith & Nephew plc; *Int'l*, pg. 7008
SMITH & NEPHEW PTY LIMITED—See Smith & Nephew plc; *Int'l*, pg. 7008
SMITH & NEPHEW S.A. DE C.V.—See Smith & Nephew plc; *Int'l*, pg. 7008
SMITH & NEPHEW SA-NV—See Smith & Nephew plc; *Int'l*, pg. 7008
SMITH & NEPHEW SAS—See Smith & Nephew plc; *Int'l*, pg. 7008
SMITH & NEPHEW SAU—See Smith & Nephew plc; *Int'l*, pg. 7008
SMITH & NEPHEW SCHWEIZ AG—See Smith & Nephew plc; *Int'l*, pg. 7008
SMITH & NEPHEW SP. Z O. O.—See Smith & Nephew plc; *Int'l*, pg. 7008
SMITH & NEPHEW SRL—See Smith & Nephew plc; *Int'l*, pg. 7008
SMITH & NEPHEW UK LIMITED—See Smith & Nephew plc; *Int'l*, pg. 7008
SMITH & NEPHEW WOUND MANAGEMENT KK—See Smith & Nephew plc; *Int'l*, pg. 7008
THE SMITH & OBY COMPANY; *U.S. Private*, pg. 4118
THE SMITH & OBY SERVICE CO.—See The Smith & Oby Company; *U.S. Private*, pg. 4118
SMITH OFFICE & COMPUTER SUPPLY; *U.S. Private*, pg. 3695
SMITH OFFICE EQUIPMENT INC.; *U.S. Private*, pg. 3695
SMITH OIL CORPORATION; *U.S. Private*, pg. 3695
SMIT HOLDINGS LIMITED; *Int'l*, pg. 7007
SMITH PACKING CO. INC.; *U.S. Private*, pg. 3695
SMITH PETROLEUM INC.; *U.S. Private*, pg. 3695
SMITH PHILLIPS BUILDING SUPPLY; *U.S. Private*, pg. 3695
SMITH, PHILLIPS & DI PIETRO; *U.S. Private*, pg. 3696
SMITH & PICKLE CONSTRUCTION, INC.; *U.S. Private*, pg. 3694
SMITH PIPE & STEEL COMPANY—See Reliance Steel & Aluminum Co.; *U.S. Public*, pg. 1779
SMITH PIPE & SUPPLY INC.; *U.S. Private*, pg. 3695
SMITH POWER PRODUCTS INC.; *U.S. Private*, pg. 3695
SMITH PROTECTIVE SERVICES INC.; *U.S. Private*, pg. 3695
SMITH PUMP COMPANY INC.; *U.S. Private*, pg. 3695
SMITH RANCH CARE CENTER, L.L.C.—See Apollo Global Management, Inc.; *U.S. Public*, pg. 157
SMITH READY MIX INC.; *U.S. Private*, pg. 3695
SMITH ROBERTSON & COMPANY LIMITED—See Agostini's Limited; *Int'l*, pg. 213
SMITH ROGERS OIL CO. INC.; *U.S. Private*, pg. 3695
SMITH'S BEVERAGE OF WYOMING—See The Kroger Co.; *U.S. Public*, pg. 2109
SMITH & SCHAEFER INC.; *U.S. Private*, pg. 3694
SMITH SCHAFER AND ASSOCIATES, LTD.; *U.S. Private*, pg. 3695
SMITHS CITY (CHRISTCHURCH) LIMITED—See Smiths City Group Limited; *Int'l*, pg. 7009
SMITHS CITY GROUP LIMITED; *Int'l*, pg. 7009
SMITHS CITY (NELSON) LIMITED—See Smiths City Group Limited; *Int'l*, pg. 7009
SMITHS CITY PROPERTIES LIMITED—See Smiths City Group Limited; *Int'l*, pg. 7009
SMITHS CITY (SOUTHERN) LIMITED—See Smiths City Group Limited; *Int'l*, pg. 7009
SMITHS CONNECTORS ASIA PTE. LTD.—See Smiths Group plc; *Int'l*, pg. 7011
SMITHS CONSULTING LTD.—See Capita plc; *Int'l*, pg. 1309
SMITHS DETECTION (ASIA PACIFIC) PTE LTD—See Smiths Group plc; *Int'l*, pg. 7011
SMITHS DETECTION (AUSTRALIA) PTE LTD—See Smiths Group plc; *Int'l*, pg. 7011
SMITHS DETECTION BENELUX BV—See Smiths Group plc; *Int'l*, pg. 7011
SMITHS DETECTION EUROPE, AFRICA, MIDDLE EAST HEADQUARTERS—See Smiths Group plc; *Int'l*, pg. 7011
SMITHS DETECTION - FRANCE—See Smiths Group plc; *Int'l*, pg. 7011

SMITHS CITY GROUP LIMITED / CORPORATE AFFILIATIONS

SMITHS DETECTION GMBH—See Smiths Group plc; *Int'l*, pg. 7011
SMITHS DETECTION GROUP LIMITED—See Smiths Group plc; *Int'l*, pg. 7011
SMITHS DETECTION INC.—See Smiths Group plc; *Int'l*, pg. 7011
SMITHS DETECTION ITALIA S.R.L.—See Smiths Group plc; *Int'l*, pg. 7011
SMITHS DETECTION JAPAN GK—See Smiths Group plc; *Int'l*, pg. 7011
SMITHS DETECTION LIMITED—See Smiths Group plc; *Int'l*, pg. 7011
SMITHS DETECTION LIVEWAVE—See Smiths Group plc; *Int'l*, pg. 7011
SMITHS DETECTION MALAYSIA SDN BHD—See Smiths Group plc; *Int'l*, pg. 7012
SMITHS DETECTION MIDDLE EAST FZE—See Smiths Group plc; *Int'l*, pg. 7012
SMITHS DETECTION MONTREAL INC.—See Smiths Group plc; *Int'l*, pg. 7012
SMITHS DETECTION NEW ZEALAND LTD—See Smiths Group plc; *Int'l*, pg. 7011
SMITHS DETECTION RUS LLC—See Smiths Group plc; *Int'l*, pg. 7012
SMITHS DETECTION SYSTEMS PRIVATE LIMITED—See Smiths Group plc; *Int'l*, pg. 7012
SMITHS DETECTION (THAILAND) LTD—See Smiths Group plc; *Int'l*, pg. 7011
SMITHS DETECTION UK LTD—See Smiths Group plc; *Int'l*, pg. 7011
SMITHS DETECTION VEECON SYSTEMS PRIVATE LTD—See Smiths Group plc; *Int'l*, pg. 7011
SMITHS DETECTION WATFORD LTD.—See Smiths Group plc; *Int'l*, pg. 7011
SMITH SECKMAN REID INC.; *U.S. Private*, pg. 3695
SMITHS ELECTRIC MOTORS (PTY) LTD.—See Metair Investments Limited; *Int'l*, pg. 4844
SMITH SERVICES, INC.; *U.S. Private*, pg. 3695
SMITH SERVICES INC.—See The Timken Company; *U.S. Public*, pg. 2133
SMITH'S FOOD & DRUG CENTERS, INC.—See The Kroger Co.; *U.S. Public*, pg. 2108
SMITHS FOOD & DRUGS, INC.—See The Kroger Co.; *U.S. Public*, pg. 2109
SMITHS FOOD GROUP, B.V.—See PepsiCo, Inc.; *U.S. Public*, pg. 1672
SMITHS & FOUNDERS INDIA LIMITED; *Int'l*, pg. 7009
SMITH'S GREENHOUSES, INC.; *U.S. Private*, pg. 3696
SMITHS GROUP AMERICAS LLC—See Smiths Group plc; *Int'l*, pg. 7012
SMITHS GROUP INTERNATIONAL HOLDINGS LIMITED—See Smiths Group plc; *Int'l*, pg. 7012
SMITHS GROUP PLC; *Int'l*, pg. 7009
SMITHS HEIMANN GMBH—See Smiths Group plc; *Int'l*, pg. 7011
SMITHS HEIMANN RUS LLC—See Smiths Group plc; *Int'l*, pg. 7011
SMITHS HEIMANN S.A.S.—See Smiths Group plc; *Int'l*, pg. 7011
SMITH'S INSURANCE AGENCY INC.—See Element Risk Management LLC; *U.S. Private*, pg. 1357
SMITHS INTERCONNECT GROUP LIMITED—See Smiths Group plc; *Int'l*, pg. 7012
SMITHS INTERCONNECT, INC.—See Smiths Group plc; *Int'l*, pg. 7012
SMITHS INTERCONNECT INDIA PRIVATE LIMITED—See Smiths Group plc; *Int'l*, pg. 7012
SMITHS MACHINE, LLC—See The Jordan Company, L.P.; *U.S. Private*, pg. 4060
SMITHS MANUFACTURING (PTY) LTD—See Metair Investments Limited; *Int'l*, pg. 4844
SMITHS MEDICAL ASD INC.—See ICU Medical, Inc.; *U.S. Public*, pg. 1087
SMITHS MEDICAL AUSTRALASIA PTY. LTD.—See ICU Medical, Inc.; *U.S. Public*, pg. 1087
SMITHS MEDICAL (BEIJING) CO., LTD.—See ICU Medical, Inc.; *U.S. Public*, pg. 1087
SMITHS MEDICAL BELGIUM N.V.—See ICU Medical, Inc.; *U.S. Public*, pg. 1087
SMITHS MEDICAL CANADA LTD.—See ICU Medical, Inc.; *U.S. Public*, pg. 1087
SMITHS MEDICAL DANMARK APS—See Smiths Group plc; *Int'l*, pg. 7012
SMITHS MEDICAL DENMARK APS—See ICU Medical, Inc.; *U.S. Public*, pg. 1087
SMITHS MEDICAL DEUTSCHLAND GMBH—See ICU Medical, Inc.; *U.S. Public*, pg. 1087
SMITHS MEDICAL DO BRASIL PRODUTOS HOSPITALARES LTDA.—See Smiths Group plc; *Int'l*, pg. 7012
SMITHS MEDICAL ESPANA, S.R.L.—See ICU Medical, Inc.; *U.S. Public*, pg. 1087
SMITHS MEDICAL FRANCE S.A.—See ICU Medical, Inc.; *U.S. Public*, pg. 1087
SMITHS MEDICAL GROUP LIMITED—See ICU Medical, Inc.; *U.S. Public*, pg. 1087
SMITHS MEDICAL INDIA PRIVATE LIMITED—See Smiths Group plc; *Int'l*, pg. 7012

SMITHS MEDICAL INSTRUMENT (ZHEJIANG) CO., LTD.—See ICU Medical, Inc.; *U.S. Public*, pg. 1087
SMITHS MEDICAL INTERNATIONAL LTD.—See ICU Medical, Inc.; *U.S. Public*, pg. 1087
SMITHS MEDICAL ITALIA S.R.L.—See ICU Medical, Inc.; *U.S. Public*, pg. 1087
SMITHS MEDICAL JAPAN LTD.—See ICU Medical, Inc.; *U.S. Public*, pg. 1087
SMITHS MEDICAL LIMITED—See ICU Medical, Inc.; *U.S. Public*, pg. 1087
SMITHS MEDICAL MD, INC.—See ICU Medical, Inc.; *U.S. Public*, pg. 1087
SMITHS MEDICAL NEDERLAND B.V.—See ICU Medical, Inc.; *U.S. Public*, pg. 1087
SMITHS MEDICAL OSTERREICH GMBH—See Smiths Group plc; *Int'l*, pg. 7012
SMITHS MEDICAL PM INC.—See ICU Medical, Inc.; *U.S. Public*, pg. 1087
SMITHS MEDICAL (PORTUGAL) UNIPESSOAL LDA.—See ICU Medical, Inc.; *U.S. Public*, pg. 1087
SMITHS MEDICAL SCHWEIZ AG—See Smiths Group plc; *Int'l*, pg. 7012
SMITHS MEDICAL—See ICU Medical, Inc.; *U.S. Public*, pg. 1087
SMITHS MEDICAL—See ICU Medical, Inc.; *U.S. Public*, pg. 1087
SMITHS MEDICAL—See ICU Medical, Inc.; *U.S. Public*, pg. 1087
SMITHS MEDICAL—See ICU Medical, Inc.; *U.S. Public*, pg. 1087
SMITHS MEDICAL (SOUTH AFRICA) PTY. LTD.—See ICU Medical, Inc.; *U.S. Public*, pg. 1087
SMITHS MEDICAL SVERIGE AB—See ICU Medical, Inc.; *U.S. Public*, pg. 1087
SMITHS METAL CENTRES LTD.; *Int'l*, pg. 7012
SMITHS NEWS INSTORE LIMITED—See Smiths News PLC; *Int'l*, pg. 7013
SMITHS NEWS PLC; *Int'l*, pg. 7012
SMITHS NEWS TRADING LIMITED—See Smiths News PLC; *Int'l*, pg. 7013
SMITHSONIAN MAGAZINE; *U.S. Private*, pg. 3698
SMITHSON INVESTMENT TRUST PLC; *Int'l*, pg. 7013
SMITH & SONS FOODS, INC.—See Metz Enterprises Inc.; *U.S. Private*, pg. 2691
SMITH; *U.S. Private*, pg. 3693
SMITH—See SMITH; *U.S. Private*, pg. 3693
SMITHS PENSIONS LIMITED—See Smiths Group plc; *Int'l*, pg. 7012
SMITHS PLASTICS (PTY) LTD.—See Metair Investments Limited; *Int'l*, pg. 4844
THE SMITH'S SNACKFOOD COMPANY—See PepsiCo, Inc.; *U.S. Public*, pg. 1670
SMITHS SPECIALTY ENGINEERING—See Smiths Group plc; *Int'l*, pg. 7012
SMITHSTOWN LIGHT ENGINEERING LTD.; *Int'l*, pg. 7013
SMITHS TUBULAR SYSTEMS-LACONIA, INC.—See Smiths Group plc; *Int'l*, pg. 7012
SMITHS TUBULAR SYSTEMS—See Smiths Group plc; *Int'l*, pg. 7012
SMITH SURFACE PREPARATION SYSTEMS INC.—See Graco, Inc.; *U.S. Public*, pg. 954
SMITH SYSTEM DRIVER IMPROVEMENT INSTITUTE INC.—See MidOcean Partners, LLP; *U.S. Private*, pg. 2717
SMITH SYSTEM MANUFACTURING COMPANY—See Steelcase Inc.; *U.S. Public*, pg. 1944
SMITH SYSTEM PINION, LLC; *U.S. Private*, pg. 3695
SMITH TEMPORARIES, INC.; *U.S. Private*, pg. 3696
SMITHTON VETERINARY SERVICE PTY. LTD.—See Apiam Animal Health Limited; *Int'l*, pg. 515
THE SMITHTOWN LIBRARY; *U.S. Private*, pg. 4119
SMITHTOWN NISSAN INC.; *U.S. Private*, pg. 3698
SMITH TRACTOR CO. INC.; *U.S. Private*, pg. 3696
SMITH TRANSPORT, INC.—See Heartland Express, Inc.; *U.S. Public*, pg. 1017
SMITH TURF & IRRIGATION CO.; *U.S. Private*, pg. 3696
SMITH VE NEPHEW MEDIKAL CIHAZLAR TICARET LIMITED SIRKETI—See Smith & Nephew plc; *Int'l*, pg. 7009
SMITH-VICTOR CORPORATION—See Promark International Inc.; *U.S. Private*, pg. 3282
SMITHVILLE TELEPHONE COMPANY INCORPORATED; *U.S. Private*, pg. 3698
SMITH WALKER DESIGN; *U.S. Private*, pg. 3696
SMITH & WESSON BRANDS, INC.; *U.S. Public*, pg. 1896
SMITH & WESSON CORP.—See Smith & Wesson Brands, Inc.; *U.S. Public*, pg. 1896
SMITH & WHITFIELD OILS CO.; *U.S. Private*, pg. 3694
SMITH & WILLIAMSON (CHANNEL ISLANDS) LIMITED—See Permira Advisers LLP; *Int'l*, pg. 5808
SMITH & WILLIAMSON FUND ADMINISTRATION LIMITED—See Permira Advisers LLP; *Int'l*, pg. 5808
SMITH & WILLIAMSON HOLDINGS LIMITED—See Permira Advisers LLP; *Int'l*, pg. 5808
SMITH & WILLIAMSON INVESTMENT MANAGEMENT LIMITED—See Permira Advisers LLP; *Int'l*, pg. 5808
SMITH & WILLIAMSON LIMITED—See Permira Advisers LLP; *Int'l*, pg. 5808

THE SMITH & WOLLENSKY RESTAURANT GROUP, INC.—See Danu Investment Partners Ltd.; *Int'l*, pg. 1969
SMIT INTERNATIONAL (AMERICAS) INC.—See HAL Trust N.V.; *Int'l*, pg. 3227
SMIT INTERNATIONALE N.V.—See HAL Trust N.V.; *Int'l*, pg. 3226
SMIT LAMNALCO TOWAGE (AUSTRALIA) PTY. LTD.—See HAL Trust N.V.; *Int'l*, pg. 3227
SMIT LOGISTICS B.V.—See HAL Trust N.V.; *Int'l*, pg. 3227
SMIT MOBILE EQUIPMENT B.V.—See Berkshire Hathaway Inc.; *U.S. Public*, pg. 299
SMITTY'S SUPPLY INC.; *U.S. Private*, pg. 3698
SMITTY'S SUPPLY—See Smitty's Supply Inc.; *U.S. Private*, pg. 3698
SMI VANTAGE LIMITED; *Int'l*, pg. 7007
SMI WIRE SDN. BHD.—See South Malaysia Industries Berhad; *Int'l*, pg. 7116
SMIZER PERRY; *U.S. Private*, pg. 3698
S.M. JALEEL & CO. LTD.; *Int'l*, pg. 6456
SMJ BEVERAGES ASIA—See S.M. Jaleel & Co. Ltd.; *Int'l*, pg. 6456
S.M.J BEVERAGES (BARBADOS) INC.—See S.M. Jaleel & Co. Ltd.; *Int'l*, pg. 6456
SMJ BEVERAGES SA (PTY) LTD.—See S.M. Jaleel & Co. Ltd.; *Int'l*, pg. 6456
S.M.J BEVERAGES (ST. LUCIA) LTD—See S.M. Jaleel & Co. Ltd.; *Int'l*, pg. 6456
SMK CAREER SERVICE CORPORATION—See SMK Corporation; *Int'l*, pg. 7013
SMK CORPORATION - HITACHI WORKS—See SMK Corporation; *Int'l*, pg. 7013
SMK CORPORATION; *Int'l*, pg. 7013
SMK CORPORATION - TOYAMA WORKS—See SMK Corporation; *Int'l*, pg. 7013
SMK ELECTRONICA S.A. DE C.V.—See SMK Corporation; *Int'l*, pg. 7013
SMK ELECTRONICS CORPORATION—See SMK Corporation; *Int'l*, pg. 7013
SMK ELECTRONICS (DONGGUAN) CO., LTD.—See SMK Corporation; *Int'l*, pg. 7013
SMK ELECTRONICS (EUROPE) LIMITED—See SMK Corporation; *Int'l*, pg. 7013
SMK ELECTRONICS (H.K.) LTD.—See SMK Corporation; *Int'l*, pg. 7013
SMK ELECTRONICS INT'L TRADING (SHANGHAI) CO., LTD.—See SMK Corporation; *Int'l*, pg. 7013
SMK ELECTRONICS (M) SDN BHD—See SMK Corporation; *Int'l*, pg. 7013
SMK ELECTRONICS (PHILS.) CORPORATION—See SMK Corporation; *Int'l*, pg. 7013
SMK ELECTRONICS (SHENZHEN) CO., LTD.—See SMK Corporation; *Int'l*, pg. 7013
SMK ELECTRONICS SINGAPORE PTE. LTD.—See SMK Corporation; *Int'l*, pg. 7013
SMK ELECTRONICS TECHNOLOGY DEVELOPMENT (SHENZHEN) CO., LTD.—See SMK Corporation; *Int'l*, pg. 7013
SMK ELECTRONICS TRADING (SHANGHAI) CO., LTD.—See SMK Corporation; *Int'l*, pg. 7013
SMK ELECTRONICS TRADING (SHENZHEN) CO., LTD.—See SMK Corporation; *Int'l*, pg. 7013
SMK EUROPE N.V.—See SMK Corporation; *Int'l*, pg. 7013
SMK HIGH-TECH TAIWAN TRADING CO., LTD.—See SMK Corporation; *Int'l*, pg. 7013
SMK HUNGARY KFT.—See SMK Corporation; *Int'l*, pg. 7013
SMK IMAGING, LLC; *U.S. Private*, pg. 3698
SMK KOREA CO., LTD.—See SMK Corporation; *Int'l*, pg. 7013
SMK-LINK ELECTRONICS CORPORATION—See SMK Corporation; *Int'l*, pg. 7013
SMK MANUFACTURING, INC.—See SMK Corporation; *Int'l*, pg. 7013
SMK MEXICANA S DE RL DE CV—See SMK Corporation; *Int'l*, pg. 7013
SMK TRADING (H.K.) LTD.—See SMK Corporation; *Int'l*, pg. 7013
SML AGENCY SERVICES, INC.—See Security Mutual Life Insurance Company of New York; *U.S. Private*, pg. 3596
S.M. LAWRENCE COMPANY, INC.—See Comfort Systems USA, Inc.; *U.S. Public*, pg. 544
SML CANADA ACQUISITION CORP.—See Steven Madden, Ltd.; *U.S. Public*, pg. 1947
SML ENTERPRISES INC.—See Angeles Equity Partners, LLC; *U.S. Private*, pg. 282
SML GROUP LTD.; *Int'l*, pg. 7013
SM LIFE DESIGN GROUP CO., LTD.; *Int'l*, pg. 6999
SM LIGHTERS BV—See Philip Morris International Inc.; *U.S. Public*, pg. 1687
SML ISUZU LIMITED; *Int'l*, pg. 7014
SML RELOCATION, LLC—See Porch Group, Inc.; *U.S. Public*, pg. 1702
SMM AUTO FINANCE, INC.—See Sumitomo Mitsui Financial Group, Inc.; *Int'l*, pg. 7294
SMMC MEDICAL GROUP—See Quorum Health Corporation; *U.S. Private*, pg. 3330

SM MESA MALL, LLC—See Washington Prime Group Inc.; *U.S. Private*, pg. 4449
SMM KOREA CO., LTD.—See Sumitomo Metal Mining Co., Ltd.; *Int'l*, pg. 7291
SMM, LTD.—See Graham Holdings Company; *U.S. Public*, pg. 956
S&M MOVING SYSTEMS WEST INC.; *U.S. Private*, pg. 3513
SMM POGO LLC—See Sumitomo Metal Mining Co., Ltd.; *Int'l*, pg. 7292
SMM PRECISION CO., LTD.—See Sumitomo Metal Mining Co., Ltd.; *Int'l*, pg. 7291
SMM SOLOMON LIMITED—See Sumitomo Metal Mining Co., Ltd.; *Int'l*, pg. 7291
SMN CORPORATION—See Sony Group Corporation; *Int'l*, pg. 7107
SM NORGE A/S—See Philip Morris International Inc.; *U.S. Public*, pg. 1687
SMN POWER HOLDING SAOG; *Int'l*, pg. 7014
SMOC INDUSTRIES S.A.S.—See OSG Corporation Co., Ltd.; *Int'l*, pg. 5650
SMO CLINPLUS CO., LTD.; *Int'l*, pg. 7014
SMOE PTE. LTD.—See Sembcorp Industries Ltd.; *Int'l*, pg. 6703
SMOG 'N GO, LLC; *U.S. Private*, pg. 3698
SMOKE AND MIRRORS PRODUCTIONS LIMITED - SHANGHAI UNIT—See Deutsche Post AG; *Int'l*, pg. 2082
SMOKE AND MIRRORS PRODUCTIONS LIMITED—See Deutsche Post AG; *Int'l*, pg. 2082
SMOKE CARTEL, INC.—See High Tide, Inc.; *Int'l*, pg. 3386
SMOKEFREE INNOTEC, INC.; *U.S. Private*, pg. 3698
SMOKE GUARD, INC.—See CSW Industrials, Inc.; *U.S. Public*, pg. 602
SMOKEHOUSE LLC—See Rapala VMC Oyj; *Int'l*, pg. 6210
SMOKE'N PIT CORPORATION—See Brinkmann Corp.; *U.S. Private*, pg. 655
SMOKER CRAFT INC.; *U.S. Private*, pg. 3698
SMOKER FRIENDLY INTERNATIONAL LLC—See The Cigarette Store Corp.; *U.S. Private*, pg. 4010
SMOKESCREEN TECHNOLOGIES PRIVATE LIMITED—See Zscaler, Inc.; *U.S. Public*, pg. 2411
SMOKEWOOD FOODS; *U.S. Private*, pg. 3698
SMOKEY BONES, LLC—See Fog Cutter Capital Group Inc.; *U.S. Private*, pg. 1557
SMOKEY POINT DISTRIBUTING, INC.—See Daseke, Inc.; *U.S. Private*, pg. 1161
SMOKIN' JOES TOBACCO SHOP, INC.; *U.S. Private*, pg. 3698
SMOKY HILLS WIND FARM LLC—See Enel S.p.A.; *Int'l*, pg. 2414
SMOKY HILLS WIND PROJECT II LLC—See Enel S.p.A.; *Int'l*, pg. 2414
SMOKY JENNINGS CHEVROLET; *U.S. Private*, pg. 3698
SMOKY MOUNTAIN BREWERY—See The Copper Cellar Corporation; *U.S. Private*, pg. 4014
SMOKY MOUNTAIN KNIFE WORKS INC.; *U.S. Private*, pg. 3698
SMOKY SYSTEMS, LLC; *U.S. Private*, pg. 3698
SMOLKER BARTLETT SCHLOSSER LOEB & HINDS, P.A.; *U.S. Private*, pg. 3698
SMOLLAN HEADCOUNT—See WPP plc; *Int'l*, pg. 8466
SMOLTEK NANOTECH HOLDING AB; *Int'l*, pg. 7014
SMOLTZ DISTRIBUTING, INC.—See Carolina Wholesale Office Machine Company, Inc.; *U.S. Private*, pg. 769
SMO MOTOR FUELS, INC.—See The Wills Group, Inc.; *U.S. Private*, pg. 4136
SMOOBU GMBH—See HomeToGo SE; *Int'l*, pg. 3456
SMOOCH LABS, INC.—See Spark Networks SE; *Int'l*, pg. 7126
SMOOK CONTRACTORS LTD.—See Mullen Group Ltd.; *Int'l*, pg. 5080
SMOORE INTERNATIONAL HOLDINGS LIMITED; *Int'l*, pg. 7014
SMOOTH FITNESS—See InternetFitness.com, Inc.; *U.S. Private*, pg. 2122
THE SMOOTHIE FACTORY, INC.—See BRIX Holdings, LLC; *U.S. Private*, pg. 658
SMOOTHIE KING CO., INC.—See Affirma Capital Limited; *Int'l*, pg. 187
SMOOTHIE KING FRANCHISES, INC.—See Affirma Capital Limited; *Int'l*, pg. 187
SMOOTHIES KOREA INC.—See Affirma Capital Limited; *Int'l*, pg. 187
SMOOTH INVESTMENT CO., LTD.—See ANEST IWATA Corporation; *Int'l*, pg. 459
SMOOTH OPERATIONS (PRODUCTIONS) LIMITED—See Songtradr, Inc.; *U.S. Private*, pg. 3713
SMOOTH ROCK VENTURES CORP.; *Int'l*, pg. 7014
SMOOTHWATER CAPITAL CORPORATION; *Int'l*, pg. 7014
S MORAVA LEASING, A.S.—See Erste Group Bank AG; *Int'l*, pg. 2499
S.M. OSGOOD COMPANY; *U.S. Private*, pg. 3518
SMOTHER'S MOTORS; *U.S. Private*, pg. 3698
SMOTORS, S.A.—See Teixeira Duarte SA; *Int'l*, pg. 7525

SMP ACCOUNTING & TAX LTD—See Palatine Private Equity LLP; *Int'l*, pg. 5706
SMP ASSET MANAGEMENT, LLC; *U.S. Private*, pg. 3698
SMP AUTOMOTIVE DE MEXICO, S.A. DE C.V.—See Standard Motor Products, Inc.; *U.S. Public*, pg. 1929
SMP AUTOMOTIVE EXTERIOR GMBH—See Samvardhana Motherson International Limited; *Int'l*, pg. 6517
SMP AUTOMOTIVE PRODUTOS AUTOMOTIVOS DO BRASIL LTDA.—See Samvardhana Motherson International Limited; *Int'l*, pg. 6517
SMP AUTOMOTIVE SOLUTIONS SLOVAKIA S.R.O.—See Samvardhana Motherson International Limited; *Int'l*, pg. 6517
SMP AUTOMOTIVE SYSTEMS ALABAMA INC.—See Samvardhana Motherson International Limited; *Int'l*, pg. 6517
SMP AUTOMOTIVE SYSTEMS MEXICO SA DE CV—See Samvardhana Motherson International Limited; *Int'l*, pg. 6517
SMP AUTOMOTIVE TECHNOLOGIES TERUEL SOCIEDAD LIMITADA—See Samvardhana Motherson International Limited; *Int'l*, pg. 6517
SMP AUTOMOTIVE TECHNOLOGY BARCELONA S.L.—See Samvardhana Motherson International Limited; *Int'l*, pg. 6517
SMP AUTOMOTIVE TECHNOLOGY IBERICA, S.L.—See Pierer Konzerngesellschaft mbH; *Int'l*, pg. 5863
SMP BANK JSC; *Int'l*, pg. 7014
SMP CZ A.S.—See VINCI S.A.; *Int'l*, pg. 8231
SMP DEUTSCHLAND GMBH—See Samvardhana Motherson International Limited; *Int'l*, pg. 6517
SMP DEUTSCHLAND GMBH—See Pierer Konzerngesellschaft mbH; *Int'l*, pg. 5863
SMPE GROUP—See Airbus SE; *Int'l*, pg. 246
SMP FOUR SEASONS DE MEXICO, S. DE R.L. DE C.V.—See Standard Motor Products, Inc.; *U.S. Public*, pg. 1929
SMP FUND SERVICES LIMITED—See Palatine Private Equity LLP; *Int'l*, pg. 5706
SMP GOLD CORP.—See Southern Empire Resources Corp.; *Int'l*, pg. 7119
SM PHILIPPINES INC.—See Philip Morris International Inc.; *U.S. Public*, pg. 1687
SMP HOLDINGS, INC.—See Prudential Financial, Inc.; *U.S. Public*, pg. 1733
SMPIC ELECTRONIC COMPANY LIMITED—See Shang Gong Group Co., Ltd.; *Int'l*, pg. 6760
SMPIC IMPORT & EXPORT CO., LTD.—See Shang Gong Group Co., Ltd.; *Int'l*, pg. 6760
S M PLATEK CO., LTD.—See The Japan Steel Works, Ltd.; *Int'l*, pg. 7659
SM PLATEX CO., LTD.—See The Japan Steel Works, Ltd.; *Int'l*, pg. 7659
SMP NET, S.R.O.—See RWE AG; *Int'l*, pg. 6435
SMP PARTNERS ASIA LTD—See Palatine Private Equity LLP; *Int'l*, pg. 5706
SMP PARTNERS LTD.—See Palatine Private Equity LLP; *Int'l*, pg. 5706
SMP PARTNERS SA—See Palatine Private Equity LLP; *Int'l*, pg. 5706
SMP POLAND SP. Z O.O.—See Standard Motor Products, Inc.; *U.S. Public*, pg. 1929
SM PRIME HOLDINGS, INC.—See SM Investments Corporation; *Int'l*, pg. 6998
SMP SCHWEDE MASCHINENBAU WEISCHLITZ GMBH—See Crown Holdings, Inc.; *U.S. Public*, pg. 599
SMR AUTOMOTIVE AUSTRALIA PTY. LTD.—See Samvardhana Motherson International Limited; *Int'l*, pg. 6517
SMR AUTOMOTIVE BRASIL LTDA.—See Samvardhana Motherson International Limited; *Int'l*, pg. 6517
SMR AUTOMOTIVE (LANGFANG) CO., LTD.—See Samvardhana Motherson International Limited; *Int'l*, pg. 6517
SMR AUTOMOTIVE MIRRORS STUTTGART GMBH—See Samvardhana Motherson International Limited; *Int'l*, pg. 6517
SMR AUTOMOTIVE MIRRORS UK LTD.—See Samvardhana Motherson International Limited; *Int'l*, pg. 6517
SMR AUTOMOTIVE MODULES KOREA LTD.—See Samvardhana Motherson International Limited; *Int'l*, pg. 6517
SMR AUTOMOTIVE OPERATIONS JAPAN K.K.—See Samvardhana Motherson International Limited; *Int'l*, pg. 6517
SMR AUTOMOTIVE SYSTEMS FRANCE S.A.—See Samvardhana Motherson International Limited; *Int'l*, pg. 6517
SMR AUTOMOTIVE SYSTEMS SPAIN S.A.U.—See Samvardhana Motherson International Limited; *Int'l*, pg. 6517
SMR AUTOMOTIVE SYSTEMS USA INC.—See Samvardhana Motherson International Limited; *Int'l*, pg. 6517
SMR AUTOMOTIVE SYSTEM (THAILAND) LIMITED—See Samvardhana Motherson International Limited; *Int'l*, pg. 6517

SMR AUTOMOTIVE VISION SYSTEMS MEXICO S.A DE C.V.—See Samvardhana Motherson International Limited; *Int'l*, pg. 6517
SMR AUTOMOTIVE YANCHENG CO., LIMITED—See Samvardhana Motherson International Limited; *Int'l*, pg. 6518
SMRC AUTOMOTIVE INTERIOR MODULES CROATIA D.O.O.—See Samvardhana Motherson International Limited; *Int'l*, pg. 6518
SMRC AUTOMOTIVE MODULES FRANCE SAS—See Samvardhana Motherson International Limited; *Int'l*, pg. 6518
SMRC AUTOMOTIVE SMART INTERIOR TECH (THAILAND) LTD.—See Samvardhana Motherson International Limited; *Int'l*, pg. 6518
SMRC AUTOMOTIVE SOLUTIONS SLOVAKIA S.R.O.—See Samvardhana Motherson International Limited; *Int'l*, pg. 6518
SMRC AUTOMOTIVE TECH ARGENTINA S.A.—See Samvardhana Motherson International Limited; *Int'l*, pg. 6518
SMRC FABRICACAO E COMERCIO DE PRODUTOS AUTOMOTIVOS DO BRASIL LTDA.—See Samvardhana Motherson International Limited; *Int'l*, pg. 6518
S M RESOURCES CORPORATION; *U.S. Private*, pg. 3512
SM RETAIL INC.—See SM Investments Corporation; *Int'l*, pg. 6999
SMR HOLDINGS, LLC; *U.S. Private*, pg. 3698
SMR HR GROUP SDN. BHD.—See Cyberjaya Education Group Berhad; *Int'l*, pg. 1893
SM ROBOTICS INC; *Int'l*, pg. 6999
SMR RESEARCH CORP.; *U.S. Private*, pg. 3698
SMRT AUTOMOTIVE SERVICES PTE. LTD.—See Temasek Holdings (Private) Limited; *Int'l*, pg. 7550
SMRT BUSES LTD.—See Temasek Holdings (Private) Limited; *Int'l*, pg. 7550
SMRT CAPITAL PTE. LTD.—See Temasek Holdings (Private) Limited; *Int'l*, pg. 7550
SMRT CORPORATION LTD.—See Temasek Holdings (Private) Limited; *Int'l*, pg. 7550
SMRT ENGINEERING PTE. LTD.—See Temasek Holdings (Private) Limited; *Int'l*, pg. 7550
SMRT FAR EAST PTE. LTD.—See Temasek Holdings (Private) Limited; *Int'l*, pg. 7550
SMRT HOLDINGS BERHAD; *Int'l*, pg. 7014
SMRT INSTITUTE PTE. LTD.—See Temasek Holdings (Private) Limited; *Int'l*, pg. 7550
SMRT INTERNATIONAL PTE. LTD.—See Temasek Holdings (Private) Limited; *Int'l*, pg. 7550
SMRT INVESTMENTS PTE. LTD.—See Temasek Holdings (Private) Limited; *Int'l*, pg. 7550
SMRT LIGHT RAIL PTE. LTD.—See Temasek Holdings (Private) Limited; *Int'l*, pg. 7550
SMRT ROAD HOLDINGS LTD.—See Temasek Holdings (Private) Limited; *Int'l*, pg. 7550
SMRT TAXIS PTE. LTD.—See Temasek Holdings (Private) Limited; *Int'l*, pg. 7550
SMRT TRAINS LTD.—See Temasek Holdings (Private) Limited; *Int'l*, pg. 7550
SM RUSHMORE MALL, LLC—See Washington Prime Group Inc.; *U.S. Private*, pg. 4449
SMRUTHI ORGANICS LIMITED; *Int'l*, pg. 7014
SMSA CRANE ACQUISITION CORP.; *U.S. Public*, pg. 1896
S&M SAKAMOTO INC.—See S Group Inc.; *U.S. Private*, pg. 3512
SMS ALTERNATIVES INC.; *U.S. Public*, pg. 1896
SMS ASSIST LLC; *U.S. Private*, pg. 3698
SMSA TREEMONT ACQUISITION CORP.; *U.S. Public*, pg. 7017
SMSC ENTERPRISES; *U.S. Private*, pg. 3699
SMS CO., LTD.; *Int'l*, pg. 7014
SMS CONCAST AG—See SMS Holding GmbH; *Int'l*, pg. 7015
SMS CONCAST AMERICA INC.—See SMS Holding GmbH; *Int'l*, pg. 7016
SMS CONCAST IBERICA S.A.—See SMS Holding GmbH; *Int'l*, pg. 7016
SMS DATA PRODUCTS GROUP INCORPORATED; *U.S. Private*, pg. 3698
SMS DIGITAL GMBH—See SMS Holding GmbH; *Int'l*, pg. 7015
SMS ELECTRIC CO., LTD ZHENGZHOU; *Int'l*, pg. 7014
SMS ELEX AG—See SMS Holding GmbH; *Int'l*, pg. 7015
SMS ELOTHERM GMBH—See SMS Holding GmbH; *Int'l*, pg. 7015
SMS ELOTHERM INDIA PVT. LTD.—See SMS Holding GmbH; *Int'l*, pg. 7015
SMS ELOTHERM INDUCTION TECH. CO. LTD.—See SMS Holding GmbH; *Int'l*, pg. 7015
SMS ELOTHERM NORTH AMERICA LLC—See SMS Holding GmbH; *Int'l*, pg. 7015
SMS ELOTHERM S.A.S.—See SMS Holding GmbH; *Int'l*, pg. 7015
SMS ENGINEERING (CHINA) LTD.—See SMS Holding GmbH; *Int'l*, pg. 7015
SMS EQUIPMENT (ALASKA) INC.—See Sumitomo Corporation; *Int'l*, pg. 7270

SMS EQUIPMENT INC.—See Sumitomo Corporation; *Int'l*, pg. 7270
SMS EQUIPMENT INC.—See Sumitomo Corporation; *Int'l*, pg. 7270
SMS EUMUCO GMBH-WAGNER BANNING RING-WALZEN DIVISION—See SMS Holding GmbH; *Int'l*, pg. 7016
SMS FINANCE SA; *Int'l*, pg. 7014
SMS GROUP K.K.—See SMS Holding GmbH; *Int'l*, pg. 7015
SMS GROUP LIMITED; *Int'l*, pg. 7014
SMS GROUP METALURGIA DO BRASIL LTDA.—See SMS Holding GmbH; *Int'l*, pg. 7015
SMS GROUP METALURJI SERVIS SAN. TIC. LTD. STI.—See SMS Holding GmbH; *Int'l*, pg. 7015
SMS GROUP PROCESS TECHNOLOGIES GMBH—See SMS Holding GmbH; *Int'l*, pg. 7015
SMS GROUP S.P.A.—See SMS Holding GmbH; *Int'l*, pg. 7015
SMS GROUP TECHNICAL SERVICES LLC—See SMS Holding GmbH; *Int'l*, pg. 7015
SMS GROUP TECHNICAL SERVICES SOUTH AFRICA (PTY.) LTD.—See SMS Holding GmbH; *Int'l*, pg. 7016
SMS GROUP TECHNICAL SERVICES (UK) LTD.—See SMS Holding GmbH; *Int'l*, pg. 7015
SMS GULF FZE—See SMS Holding GmbH; *Int'l*, pg. 7015
SMS HOLDING GMBH; *Int'l*, pg. 7015
SMS HOLDINGS CORPORATION; *U.S. Private*, pg. 3699
SMS INDIA PVT. LTD.—See SMS Holding GmbH; *Int'l*, pg. 7016
SMS INFOCOMM CORPORATION—See Wistron Corporation; *Int'l*, pg. 8438
SMS INFOCOMM (CZECH) S.R.O.—See Wistron Corporation; *Int'l*, pg. 8438
SMS INFOCOMM (SINGAPORE) PTE. LTD.—See Wistron Corporation; *Int'l*, pg. 8438
SMS INNSE S.P.A.—See SMS Holding GmbH; *Int'l*, pg. 7016
SMS INSURANCE AGENCY LTD—See SMS Group Limited; *Int'l*, pg. 7015
SMS INTERNATIONAL CORPORATION—See Sumitomo Corporation; *Int'l*, pg. 7273
SMS INTERNATIONAL SHORE OPERATIONS US INC—See SMS Group Limited; *Int'l*, pg. 7015
SMSJ TUCSON HOLDINGS, LLC—See Tenet Healthcare Corporation; *U.S. Public*, pg. 2006
SMS (KUNSHAN) CO., LTD.—See Wistron Corporation; *Int'l*, pg. 8438
SMS LIFESCIENCES INDIA LTD.; *Int'l*, pg. 7016
SMS MANAGEMENT & TECHNOLOGY LIMITED—See Nomura Research Institute, Ltd.; *Int'l*, pg. 5413
SMS MEER GMBH—See SMS Holding GmbH; *Int'l*, pg. 7015
SMS MEER SERVICE INC.—See SMS Holding GmbH; *Int'l*, pg. 7016
SMS MEER S.P.A.—See SMS Holding GmbH; *Int'l*, pg. 7016
SMS MEMORY MODULE ASSEMBLY, INC.; *U.S. Private*, pg. 3699
SMS METALLURGICAL SERVICE LLC—See SMS Holding GmbH; *Int'l*, pg. 7016
SMS METALLURGICAL SERVICE LLC—See SMS Holding GmbH; *Int'l*, pg. 7016
SMS METALLURGY POLSKA SP. Z.O.O.—See SMS Holding GmbH; *Int'l*, pg. 7016
SMS METALLURGY ROMANIA S.R.L.—See SMS Holding GmbH; *Int'l*, pg. 7016
SMS MEVAC GMBH—See SMS Holding GmbH; *Int'l*, pg. 7016
SMS MEVAC UK LTD.—See SMS Holding GmbH; *Int'l*, pg. 7016
SMS MINING SERVICES (CANADA) INC.—See Perenti Global Limited; *Int'l*, pg. 5798
SMSMONDIAL—See SMS Group Limited; *Int'l*, pg. 7015
SM SOUTHERN HILLS MALL, LLC—See Washington Prime Group Inc.; *U.S. Private*, pg. 4449
SMS PASSCODE A/S—See Talis Capital Limited; *Int'l*, pg. 7446
SM SPEAKER CORP.—See Gibson Brands, Inc.; *U.S. Private*, pg. 1696
SMS PHARMACEUTICALS LTD; *Int'l*, pg. 7017
SMS PHILIPPINES HEALTHCARE SOLUTIONS INC.—See SMS Co., Ltd.; *Int'l*, pg. 7014
SMS RENTAL (WA) PTY. LTD.—See Rivet Pty. Ltd.; *Int'l*, pg. 6354
SMS S.A.S.—See Advent International Corporation; *U.S. Private*, pg. 100
SMS SAUDI ARABIA LLC—See SMS Holding GmbH; *Int'l*, pg. 7016
SMS SIEMAG AG—See SMS Holding GmbH; *Int'l*, pg. 7016
SMS SIEMAG AG—See SMS Holding GmbH; *Int'l*, pg. 7016
SMS SIEMAG EQUIPAMENTOS E SERVICOS LTDA.—See SMS Holding GmbH; *Int'l*, pg. 7016
SMS SIEMAG LLC—See SMS Holding GmbH; *Int'l*, pg. 7016
SMS SIEMAG SOUTH AFRICA (PTY) LTD.—See SMS Holding GmbH; *Int'l*, pg. 7016

SMS SIEMAG TECHNOLOGY (BEIJING) CO., LTD.—See SMS Holding GmbH; *Int'l*, pg. 7016
SMS SIEMAG TECHNOLOGY (TIANJIN) CO., LTD.—See SMS Holding GmbH; *Int'l*, pg. 7016
SMS TECHNICAL SERVICES GULF S.P.C.—See SMS Holding GmbH; *Int'l*, pg. 7016
SMS TECHNICAL SERVICES LLC—See SMS Holding GmbH; *Int'l*, pg. 7016
SMS TECHNOLOGIES, INC.—See Cal-Comp Electronics (Thailand) pcl; *Int'l*, pg. 1261
SMS TRAVEL & TOURISM UK—See SMS Group Limited; *Int'l*, pg. 7015
THE S.M. STROLLER CORPORATION; *U.S. Private*, pg. 4113
SM SUMMIT HOLDINGS PTE LTD.—See Centurion Corporation Limited; *Int'l*, pg. 1417
SM SUMMIT INVESTMENT PTE. LTD.—See Centurion Corporation Limited; *Int'l*, pg. 1417
SMT BELGIUM NV; *Int'l*, pg. 7017
SMT BIO CO., LTD.—See Sangsangin Industry Co., Ltd.; *Int'l*, pg. 6538
SMTC ASIA LTD.—See H.I.G. Capital, LLC; *U.S. Private*, pg. 1833
SMTC CORPORATION—See H.I.G. Capital, LLC; *U.S. Private*, pg. 1833
SMTC DE CHIHUAHUA S.A. DE C.V.—See H.I.G. Capital, LLC; *U.S. Private*, pg. 1834
SMTC ELECTRONICS DONGGUAN COMPANY LIMITED—See H.I.G. Capital, LLC; *U.S. Private*, pg. 1833
SMTC ELECTRONICS (SUZHOU) COMPANY LIMITED—See H.I.G. Capital, LLC; *U.S. Private*, pg. 1833
SMTC MANUFACTURING CORPORATION OF CALIFORNIA—See H.I.G. Capital, LLC; *U.S. Private*, pg. 1833
SMTC MANUFACTURING CORPORATION OF CANADA—See H.I.G. Capital, LLC; *U.S. Private*, pg. 1834
SMTC MEX HOLDINGS, INC.—See H.I.G. Capital, LLC; *U.S. Private*, pg. 1834
SMTC NOVA SCOTIA COMPANY—See H.I.G. Capital, LLC; *U.S. Private*, pg. 1834
SMT ELECTRONIC TECHNOLOGY LIMITED—See Sandmartin International Holdings Limited; *Int'l*, pg. 6526
SMT FUND SERVICES (IRELAND) LIMITED—See Sumitomo Mitsui Trust Holdings, Inc.; *Int'l*, pg. 7296
SMT HOLDING; *Int'l*, pg. 7017
SMT HONG KONG LIMITED—See Sandmartin International Holdings Limited; *Int'l*, pg. 6526
SMT INDUSTRIES CO. LTD.—See EG Industries Berhad; *Int'l*, pg. 2322
SMTO ENGINEERING, S.A. DE C.V.—See ViTrox Corporation Berhad; *Int'l*, pg. 8262
SMTRACK BERHAD; *Int'l*, pg. 7017
S&M TRANSPORTATION INC; *U.S. Private*, pg. 3513
SMT S.A.; *Int'l*, pg. 7017
SMT SCHARF AFRICA (PTY.) LTD.—See Yankuang Group Co., Limited; *Int'l*, pg. 8562
SMT SCHARF AG—See Yankuang Group Co., Limited; *Int'l*, pg. 8562
SMT SCHARF GMBH—See Yankuang Group Co., Limited; *Int'l*, pg. 8562
SMT SCHARF POLSKA SP. Z O.O.—See Yankuang Group Co., Limited; *Int'l*, pg. 8562
SMT SCHARF SAAR GMBH—See Yankuang Group Co., Limited; *Int'l*, pg. 8562
SMT SCHARF SUDAMERICA SPA—See Yankuang Group Co., Limited; *Int'l*, pg. 8562
S.M.T. - SOCIETA' MANIFATTURA TESSILE S.R.L.—See Pattern SpA; *Int'l*, pg. 5760
SMT SOFTWARE S.A.—See Grupa SMT S.A.; *Int'l*, pg. 3117
SMT TECHNOLOGIES SDN. BHD.—See EG Industries Berhad; *Int'l*, pg. 2322
SMT TRUSTEES (IRELAND) LIMITED—See Sumitomo Mitsui Trust Holdings, Inc.; *Int'l*, pg. 7296
SMUCKER FOODSERVICE, INC.—See The J.M. Smucker Company; *U.S. Public*, pg. 2107
SMUCKER FOODS OF CANADA CORP.—See The J.M. Smucker Company; *U.S. Public*, pg. 2107
SMUCKER NATURAL FOODS, INC.—See The J.M. Smucker Company; *U.S. Public*, pg. 2107
SMUCKER SPECIALTY FOODS COMPANY—See The J.M. Smucker Company; *U.S. Public*, pg. 2107
SMUGGLERS' NOTCH INVESTMENT CO.; *U.S. Private*, pg. 3699
SMUGGLERS' NOTCH MANAGEMENT COMPANY LTD.—See Smugglers' Notch Investment Co.; *U.S. Private*, pg. 3699
SMUGMUG, INC.; *U.S. Private*, pg. 3699
SMULEKOFF FURNITURE COMPANY INC; *U.S. Private*, pg. 3699
SMURFIT CARTON DE COLOMBIA, S.A.—See Smurfit Kappa Group plc; *Int'l*, pg. 7022
SMURFIT CARTON DE VENEZUELA, S.A.—See Smurfit Kappa Group plc; *Int'l*, pg. 7023
SMURFIT CARTON Y PAPEL DE MEXICO S.A. DE C.V.—See Smurfit Kappa Group plc; *Int'l*, pg. 7023

SMURFIT CORRUGATED CASES (CORK) LIMITED—See Smurfit Kappa Group plc; *Int'l*, pg. 7023
SMURFIT CORRUGATED IRELAND LTD.—See Smurfit Kappa Group plc; *Int'l*, pg. 7023
SMURFIT INTERNATIONAL B.V.—See Smurfit Kappa Group plc; *Int'l*, pg. 7023
SMURFIT INTERWELL GMBH & CO. KG—See Smurfit Kappa Group plc; *Int'l*, pg. 7023
SMURFIT KAPPA ALMERIA—See Smurfit Kappa Group plc; *Int'l*, pg. 7023
SMURFIT KAPPA BADEN PACKAGING GMBH—See Smurfit Kappa Group plc; *Int'l*, pg. 7023
SMURFIT KAPPA BAG-IN-BOX MEDITERRANEAN PLASTICOS VICENT—See Smurfit Kappa Group plc; *Int'l*, pg. 7023
SMURFIT KAPPA BAG-IN-BOX—See Smurfit Kappa Group plc; *Int'l*, pg. 7022
SMURFIT KAPPA CARTONNAGE DE COLMAR—See Smurfit Kappa Group plc; *Int'l*, pg. 7022
SMURFIT KAPPA CARTONNERIE DE GETIGNE (SCAO)—See Smurfit Kappa Group plc; *Int'l*, pg. 7023
SMURFIT KAPPA CARTONNERIE DE RENNES—See Smurfit Kappa Group plc; *Int'l*, pg. 7022
SMURFIT KAPPA C.D. HAUPT PAPIER—See Smurfit Kappa Group plc; *Int'l*, pg. 7023
SMURFIT KAPPA CENTRAL RESOURCES—See Smurfit Kappa Group plc; *Int'l*, pg. 7023
SMURFIT KAPPA CERRO GORDO MILL—See Smurfit Kappa Group plc; *Int'l*, pg. 7022
SMURFIT KAPPA COGNAC—See Smurfit Kappa Group plc; *Int'l*, pg. 7023
SMURFIT KAPPA COMPOSITES—See Smurfit Kappa Group plc; *Int'l*, pg. 7024
SMURFIT KAPPA CONNAUGHT PACKAGING—See Smurfit Kappa Group plc; *Int'l*, pg. 7023
SMURFIT KAPPA CORBY—See Smurfit Kappa Group plc; *Int'l*, pg. 7024
SMURFIT KAPPA CORRUGATED BENELUX—See Smurfit Kappa Group plc; *Int'l*, pg. 7018
SMURFIT KAPPA DANMARK - HERFOLGE—See Smurfit Kappa Group plc; *Int'l*, pg. 7022
SMURFIT KAPPA DE ARGENTINA, S.A.—See Smurfit Kappa Group plc; *Int'l*, pg. 7024
SMURFIT KAPPA DEUTSCHLAND GMBH—See Smurfit Kappa Group plc; *Int'l*, pg. 7023
SMURFIT KAPPA DEVELOPMENT CENTRE B.V.—See Smurfit Kappa Group plc; *Int'l*, pg. 7018
SMURFIT KAPPA DISPLAY—See Smurfit Kappa Group plc; *Int'l*, pg. 7023
SMURFIT KAPPA DO BRASIL INDUSTRIA DE EMBALAGENS S.A.—See Smurfit Kappa Group plc; *Int'l*, pg. 7024
SMURFIT KAPPA DROGENBOS—See Smurfit Kappa Group plc; *Int'l*, pg. 7022
SMURFIT KAPPA ELCORR B.V.—See Smurfit Kappa Group plc; *Int'l*, pg. 7018
SMURFIT KAPPA - ELCORR PLANT—See Smurfit Kappa Group plc; *Int'l*, pg. 7018
SMURFIT KAPPA ESPANA, S.A.—See Smurfit Kappa Group plc; *Int'l*, pg. 7023
SMURFIT KAPPA EURO-LOK-WERK HEPPENHEIM—See Smurfit Kappa Group plc; *Int'l*, pg. 7023
SMURFIT KAPPA EUROPE B.V.—See Smurfit Kappa Group plc; *Int'l*, pg. 7023
SMURFIT KAPPA FORT WORTH—See Smurfit Kappa Group plc; *Int'l*, pg. 7023
SMURFIT KAPPA FUNDING PLC—See Smurfit Kappa Group plc; *Int'l*, pg. 7023
SMURFIT KAPPA GROUP IS NEDERLAND B.V.—See Smurfit Kappa Group plc; *Int'l*, pg. 7018
SMURFIT KAPPA GROUP PLC; *Int'l*, pg. 7017
SMURFIT KAPPA GSF B.V.—See Smurfit Kappa Group plc; *Int'l*, pg. 7018
SMURFIT KAPPA GUADALAJARA CORRUGATED—See Smurfit Kappa Group plc; *Int'l*, pg. 7022
SMURFIT KAPPA HERZBERGER PAPIERFABRIK—See Smurfit Kappa Group plc; *Int'l*, pg. 7023
SMURFIT KAPPA HOLDINGS ITALIA, S.P.A.—See Smurfit Kappa Group plc; *Int'l*, pg. 7023
SMURFIT KAPPA HOYA PAPER—See Smurfit Kappa Group plc; *Int'l*, pg. 7022
SMURFIT KAPPA INTERBOX PLANT—See Smurfit Kappa Group plc; *Int'l*, pg. 7022
SMURFIT KAPPA INTERNATIONAL FRANCE SAS—See Smurfit Kappa Group plc; *Int'l*, pg. 7023
SMURFIT KAPPA IRELAND LIMITED—See Smurfit Kappa Group plc; *Int'l*, pg. 7023
SMURFIT KAPPA ITALIA S.P.A. - SAN MARZANO—See Smurfit Kappa Group plc; *Int'l*, pg. 7023
SMURFIT KAPPA ITALIA, S.P.A.—See Smurfit Kappa Group plc; *Int'l*, pg. 7023
SMURFIT KAPPA KRAFTLINER PITEA AB—See Smurfit Kappa Group plc; *Int'l*, pg. 7023
SMURFIT KAPPA LIQUID PACKAGING—See Smurfit Kappa Group plc; *Int'l*, pg. 7023
SMURFIT KAPPA MNL GOLFKARTON B.V.—See Smurfit Kappa Group plc; *Int'l*, pg. 7018
SMURFIT KAPPA MOLD—See Smurfit Kappa Group plc; *Int'l*, pg. 7024

COMPANY NAME INDEX

SMURFIT KAPPA NERVION, S.A.—See Smurfit Kappa Group plc; *Int'l*, pg. 7023
SMURFIT KAPPA NETTINGSDORFER AG & CO. KG—See Smurfit Kappa Group plc; *Int'l*, pg. 7023
SMURFIT KAPPA NEUSS GMBH—See Smurfit Kappa Group plc; *Int'l*, pg. 7023
SMURFIT KAPPA NEWS PRESS LTD—See Smurfit Kappa Group plc; *Int'l*, pg. 7022
SMURFIT KAPPA NORD EMBALLAGES—See Smurfit Kappa Group plc; *Int'l*, pg. 7022
SMURFIT KAPPA OLEN—See Smurfit Kappa Group plc; *Int'l*, pg. 7022
SMURFIT KAPPA ONWELL AB—See Smurfit Kappa Group plc; *Int'l*, pg. 7022
SMURFIT KAPPA ORANGE COUNTY LLC—See Smurfit Kappa Group plc; *Int'l*, pg. 7023
SMURFIT KAPPA ORKO-PAK B.V.—See Smurfit Kappa Group plc; *Int'l*, pg. 7018
SMURFIT KAPPA PACKAGING LLC—See Smurfit Kappa Group plc; *Int'l*, pg. 7023
SMURFIT KAPPA PACKAGING UK LIMITED—See Smurfit Kappa Group plc; *Int'l*, pg. 7023
SMURFIT KAPPA PAPER SALES BENELUX B.V.—See Smurfit Kappa Group plc; *Int'l*, pg. 7018
SMURFIT KAPPA PAPER SERVICES B.V.—See Smurfit Kappa Group plc; *Int'l*, pg. 7018
SMURFIT KAPPA PARTICIPATIONS SAS - CARTONNERIE DE RETHEL—See Smurfit Kappa Group plc; *Int'l*, pg. 7022
SMURFIT KAPPA PARTICIPATIONS SAS—See Smurfit Kappa Group plc; *Int'l*, pg. 7023
SMURFIT KAPPA PETERBOROUGH—See Smurfit Kappa Group plc; *Int'l*, pg. 7024
SMURFIT KAPPA POLSKA SP. Z O.O. ODDZIAL W PRUSZKOWIE—See Smurfit Kappa Group plc; *Int'l*, pg. 7022
SMURFIT KAPPA PROVENCE MEDITERRANEE—See Smurfit Kappa Group plc; *Int'l*, pg. 7023
SMURFIT KAPPA RAPIDCORR EINDHOVEN B.V.—See Smurfit Kappa Group plc; *Int'l*, pg. 7018
SMURFIT KAPPA RECYCLING B.V.—See Smurfit Kappa Group plc; *Int'l*, pg. 7018
SMURFIT KAPPA RECYCLING UK - BLACKBURN PLANT—See Smurfit Kappa Group plc; *Int'l*, pg. 7024
SMURFIT KAPPA RECYCLING UK—See Smurfit Kappa Group plc; *Int'l*, pg. 7024
SMURFIT KAPPA RENA AS—See Smurfit Kappa Group plc; *Int'l*, pg. 7022
SMURFIT KAPPA ROERMOND PAPIER B.V.—See Smurfit Kappa Group plc; *Int'l*, pg. 7018
SMURFIT KAPPA SANGUESA—See Smurfit Kappa Group plc; *Int'l*, pg. 7023
SMURFIT KAPPA SERVICE—See Smurfit Kappa Group plc; *Int'l*, pg. 7022
SMURFIT KAPPA SOLID BOARD B.V. - NIEUWESCHANS PLANT—See Smurfit Kappa Group plc; *Int'l*, pg. 7018
SMURFIT KAPPA SOUTH—See Smurfit Kappa Group plc; *Int'l*, pg. 7022
SMURFIT KAPPA SOUTH WEST—See Smurfit Kappa Group plc; *Int'l*, pg. 7022
SMURFIT KAPPA SPECIALTIES—See Smurfit Kappa Group plc; *Int'l*, pg. 7023
SMURFIT KAPPA SUD - WERK FEUCHT—See Smurfit Kappa Group plc; *Int'l*, pg. 7022
SMURFIT KAPPA SVERIGE AB—See Smurfit Kappa Group plc; *Int'l*, pg. 7022
SMURFIT KAPPA SWISSWELL—See Smurfit Kappa Group plc; *Int'l*, pg. 7022
SMURFIT KAPPA TOWNSEND HOOK—See Smurfit Kappa Group plc; *Int'l*, pg. 7024
SMURFIT KAPPA TREASURY FUNDING LTD.—See Smurfit Kappa Group plc; *Int'l*, pg. 7023
SMURFIT KAPPA TREASURY UNLIMITED COMPANY—See Smurfit Kappa Group plc; *Int'l*, pg. 7023
SMURFIT KAPPA TRIMBACH B.V.—See Smurfit Kappa Group plc; *Int'l*, pg. 7018
SMURFIT KAPPA TROBOX KARTONNAGES B.V.—See Smurfit Kappa Group plc; *Int'l*, pg. 7018
SMURFIT KAPPA TWINCORR—See Smurfit Kappa Group plc; *Int'l*, pg. 7018
SMURFIT KAPPA UK—See Smurfit Kappa Group plc; *Int'l*, pg. 7023
SMURFIT KAPPA VAN DAM GOLFKARTON B.V.—See Smurfit Kappa Group plc; *Int'l*, pg. 7018
SMURFIT KAPPA VANDRA B.V.—See Smurfit Kappa Group plc; *Int'l*, pg. 7018
SMURFITKAPPA WELLPAPPE NORD GMBH—See Smurfit Kappa Group plc; *Int'l*, pg. 7022
SMURFIT KAPPA WELLPAPPENWERK LUBECK GMBH—See Smurfit Kappa Group plc; *Int'l*, pg. 7024
SMURFIT KAPPA WELLPAPPENWERK SCHNEVERDINGEN GMBH—See Smurfit Kappa Group plc; *Int'l*, pg. 7022
SMURFIT KAPPA YATE—See Smurfit Kappa Group plc; *Int'l*, pg. 7024
SMURFIT KAPPA ZEBRAK—See Smurfit Kappa Group plc; *Int'l*, pg. 7022

SMURFIT KAPPA ZEDEK B.V.—See Smurfit Kappa Group plc; *Int'l*, pg. 7018
SMURFIT NEDERLAND HOLDING B.V.—See Smurfit Kappa Group plc; *Int'l*, pg. 7018
SMURFIT PUBLICATIONS LIMITED—See Smurfit Kappa Group plc; *Int'l*, pg. 7024
SMURFIT S.A.—See Smurfit Kappa Group plc; *Int'l*, pg. 7024
SMURFIT SISA S.P.A.—See Smurfit Kappa Group plc; *Int'l*, pg. 7023
SMU S.A.; *Int'l*, pg. 7017
SMVD POLY PACK LTD.; *Int'l*, pg. 7024
SM VINA CO., LTD.; *Int'l*, pg. 6999
SMV PRESSES A/S—See Smalandsstenars Mekaniska Verkstad - SMV Industrier AB; *Int'l*, pg. 6999
SMV PRESSES (UK) LTD—See Smalandsstenars Mekaniska Verkstad - SMV Industrier AB; *Int'l*, pg. 6999
SMV SAS—See VINCI S.A.; *Int'l*, pg. 8227
S.M.V. THAILAND CO., LTD.—See Renaissance Industries SAS; *Int'l*, pg. 6272
S M WILSON & CO.; *U.S. Private*, pg. 3512
SM WIRTSCHAFTSBERATUNGS AG; *Int'l*, pg. 6999
SMW, LTD.—See Iberdrola, S.A.; *Int'l*, pg. 3573
SMW SAND UND MORTELWERK VERWALTUNGS-GMBH—See Heidelberg Materials AG; *Int'l*, pg. 3319
SMX (SECURITY MATTERS) PUBLIC LIMITED COMPANY; *Int'l*, pg. 7024
SMYK S.A.—See Bridgepoint Group Plc; *Int'l*, pg. 1155
SMYL CHEVROLET PONTIAC BUICK GMC; *Int'l*, pg. 7024
SMY MEDIA, INC.; *U.S. Private*, pg. 3699
SMYRNA-F, LLC—See Lithia Motors, Inc.; *U.S. Public*, pg. 1326
SMYTH AUTOMOTIVE INC.; *U.S. Private*, pg. 3699
SMYTH COMPANIES, INC.; *U.S. Private*, pg. 3699
SMYTHE, CRAMER CO.—See Hanna Holdings, Inc.; *U.S. Private*, pg. 1854
SMYTHE EUROPEAN, INC.—See AutoNation, Inc.; *U.S. Public*, pg. 237
SMYTHS TOYS HOLDING UNLIMITED COMPANY; *Int'l*, pg. 7024
SMYTHS TOYS UNLIMITED COMPANY—See Smyths Toys Holding Unlimited Company; *Int'l*, pg. 7024
SNACK EMPIRE HOLDINGS LIMITED; *Int'l*, pg. 7024
SNACK FACTORY, LLC—See Campbell Soup Company; *U.S. Public*, pg. 427
SNACKTIME PLC; *Int'l*, pg. 7024
SNACK VENTURES S.A.—See PepsiCo, Inc.; *U.S. Public*, pg. 1672
SNA EUROPE (CZECH REPUBLIC) S.R.O.—See Snap-on Incorporated; *U.S. Public*, pg. 1898
SNA EUROPE (FRANCE) SARL—See Snap-on Incorporated; *U.S. Public*, pg. 1898
SNA EUROPE—See Snap-on Incorporated; *U.S. Public*, pg. 1898
SNA EUROPE (SPAIN)—See Snap-on Incorporated; *U.S. Public*, pg. 1898
SNAGA D.D. VARES; *Int'l*, pg. 7024
SNAGAJOB.COM, INC.; *U.S. Private*, pg. 3699
SNA GERMANY GMBH—See Snap-on Incorporated; *U.S. Public*, pg. 1898
SNA HOLDINGS INC.—See Schneider Electric SE; *Int'l*, pg. 6633
SNAIL, INC.; *U.S. Public*, pg. 1897
SN AIRHOLDING II NV; *Int'l*, pg. 7024
SNAK CLUB, INC.—See Insignia Capital Group, L.P.; *U.S. Private*, pg. 2091
SNAKE EVEN EMPREENDIMENTOS IMOBILIARIOS LTDA.—See Even Construtora e Incorporadora S.A.; *Int'l*, pg. 2562
SNAKE RIVER SUGAR CO.; *U.S. Private*, pg. 3699
SNAK KING CORP.; *U.S. Private*, pg. 3699
SNAKY CREEK ENTERPRISES, LLC; *U.S. Private*, pg. 3699
SNAM INTERNATIONAL HOLDING A.G.—See Eni S.p.A.; *Int'l*, pg. 2437
SNAM RETE GAS S.P.A.—See Eni S.p.A.; *Int'l*, pg. 2438
SNAM S.p.A.—See Eni S.p.A.; *Int'l*, pg. 2438
SNANDONG HONGCHUANG ALUMINUM INDUSTRY HOLDING COMPANY LIMITED; *Int'l*, pg. 7024
SNAP ADVANCES; *U.S. Private*, pg. 3699
SNAP AGENCY, INC.; *U.S. Private*, pg. 3699
SNAPCOMMS, INC.—See Thoma Bravo, L.P.; *U.S. Private*, pg. 4148
SNAPCOMMS LIMITED—See Thoma Bravo, L.P.; *U.S. Private*, pg. 4147
SNAPCOMMS UK LIMITED—See Thoma Bravo, L.P.; *U.S. Private*, pg. 4147
SNAP CONTRACTING CORPORATION; *U.S. Private*, pg. 3699
SNAPFINGER, INC.; *U.S. Private*, pg. 3700
SNAPFISH LLC—See Apollo Global Management, Inc.; *U.S. Private*, pg. 160
SNAP FITNESS, INC.; *U.S. Private*, pg. 3699
SNAP FRESH PTY LIMITED—See Qantas Airways Limited; *Int'l*, pg. 6132
SNAP GLOBAL, LLC—See Hemisphere Media Group, Inc.; *U.S. Private*, pg. 1913
SNAP INC.; *U.S. Public*, pg. 1897

SNAP, INC.; *U.S. Private*, pg. 3700
SNAP INSTALL, INC.; *U.S. Private*, pg. 3700
SNAPLOCK INDUSTRIES, INC.—See Cobepa S.A.; *Int'l*, pg. 1683
SNAPMART INC.—See Pixta Inc.; *Int'l*, pg. 5877
SNAPNAMES WEB.COM, LLC—See Siris Capital Group, LLC; *U.S. Private*, pg. 3675
SNAP-ON BUSINESS SOLUTIONS GMBH—See Snap-on Incorporated; *U.S. Public*, pg. 1898
SNAP-ON BUSINESS SOLUTIONS, INC.—See Snap-on Incorporated; *U.S. Public*, pg. 1898
SNAP-ON BUSINESS SOLUTIONS INDIA PRIVATE LIMITED—See Snap-on Incorporated; *U.S. Public*, pg. 1898
SNAP-ON BUSINESS SOLUTIONS LIMITED—See Snap-on Incorporated; *U.S. Public*, pg. 1898
SNAP-ON BUSINESS SOLUTIONS, SARL—See Snap-on Incorporated; *U.S. Public*, pg. 1898
SNAP-ON BUSINESS SOLUTIONS, S.A.—See Snap-on Incorporated; *U.S. Public*, pg. 1898
SNAP-ON BUSINESS SOLUTIONS S.L.—See Snap-on Incorporated; *U.S. Public*, pg. 1898
SNAP-ON BUSINESS SOLUTIONS, SRL—See Snap-on Incorporated; *U.S. Public*, pg. 1898
SNAP-ON CLIMATE SOLUTIONS S.R.L.—See Snap-on Incorporated; *U.S. Public*, pg. 1898
SNAP-ON CREDIT LLC—See Snap-on Incorporated; *U.S. Public*, pg. 1898
SNAP-ON DIAGNOSTICS—See Snap-on Incorporated; *U.S. Public*, pg. 1898
SNAP ONE HOLDINGS CORP—See Resideo Technologies, Inc.; *U.S. Public*, pg. 1790
SNAP ONE, LLC—See Resideo Technologies, Inc.; *U.S. Public*, pg. 1790
SNAP-ON EQUIPMENT AUSTRIA GMBH—See Snap-on Incorporated; *U.S. Public*, pg. 1898
SNAP-ON EQUIPMENT GMBH—See Snap-on Incorporated; *U.S. Public*, pg. 1898
SNAP-ON EQUIPMENT HUNGARY KFT.—See Snap-on Incorporated; *U.S. Public*, pg. 1898
SNAP-ON EQUIPMENT INC.—See Snap-on Incorporated; *U.S. Public*, pg. 1898
SNAP-ON EQUIPMENT LTD.—See Snap-on Incorporated; *U.S. Public*, pg. 1898
SNAP-ON EQUIPMENT S.R.L.—See Snap-on Incorporated; *U.S. Public*, pg. 1898
SNAP-ON INCORPORATED; *U.S. Public*, pg. 1897
SNAP-ON INDUSTRIAL—See Snap-on Incorporated; *U.S. Public*, pg. 1898
SNAP-ON POWER TOOLS INC.—See Snap-on Incorporated; *U.S. Public*, pg. 1898
SNAP-ON TOOLS (AUSTRALIA) PTY. LTD.—See Snap-on Incorporated; *U.S. Public*, pg. 1898
SNAP-ON TOOLS HONG KONG LIMITED—See Snap-on Incorporated; *U.S. Public*, pg. 1898
SNAP-ON TOOLS INTERNATIONAL, LTD.—See Snap-on Incorporated; *U.S. Public*, pg. 1898
SNAP-ON TOOLS ITALIA S.R.L.—See Snap-on Incorporated; *U.S. Public*, pg. 1898
SNAP-ON TOOLS JAPAN K.K.—See Snap-on Incorporated; *U.S. Public*, pg. 1898
SNAP-ON TOOLS KOREA LTD.—See Snap-on Incorporated; *U.S. Public*, pg. 1899
SNAP-ON TOOLS LIMITED—See Snap-on Incorporated; *U.S. Public*, pg. 1898
SNAP-ON TOOLS PRIVATE LIMITED—See Snap-on Incorporated; *U.S. Public*, pg. 1899
SNAP-ON TOOLS SINGAPORE PTE LTD—See Snap-on Incorporated; *U.S. Public*, pg. 1899
SNAPP & ASSOCIATES—See GCP Capital Partners Holdings LLC; *U.S. Private*, pg. 1654
SNAPPING SHOALS ELECTRIC MEMBERSHIP CORP.; *U.S. Private*, pg. 3700
SNAPPLE BEVERAGE CORP.—See JAB Holding Company S.a.r.l.; *Int'l*, pg. 3862
SNAPPY COMMUNICATIONS CO. LTD.; *Int'l*, pg. 7024
SNAPPY MARINE INC.—See OneWater Marine Inc.; *U.S. Public*, pg. 1604
SNAPPY SNAPS FRANCHISES LIMITED—See Timpson Group PLC; *Int'l*, pg. 7752
SNAPSHOT GMBH—See Beijing Shiji Information Technology Co., Ltd.; *Int'l*, pg. 956
SNAPTRACK, INC.—See QUALCOMM Incorporated; *U.S. Public*, pg. 1747
SNAS LEBANON SARL—See Deutsche Post AG; *Int'l*, pg. 2082
SNA TOOLS BELGIUM BVBA—See Snap-on Incorporated; *U.S. Public*, pg. 1898
SN AUVERGNE AERONAUTIQUE SAS—See Figeac-Aero SA; *Int'l*, pg. 2661
SNAVELY DEVELOPMENT COMPANY; *U.S. Private*, pg. 3700
SNAVELY FOREST PRODUCTS, INC.—See MacArthur Co.; *U.S. Private*, pg. 2534
SNAX 24 LTD.; *Int'l*, pg. 7024
SNAZAROO HOLDINGS LTD—See Lindengruppen AB; *Int'l*, pg. 4510
SNBC EUROPE B.V.—See Shandong New Beiyang Information Technology Co., Ltd.; *Int'l*, pg. 6757

SNB HOLDINGS, INC.   CORPORATE AFFILIATIONS

SNB HOLDINGS, INC.; *U.S. Private*, pg. 3700
SNBL USA, LTD.—See Shin Nippon Biomedical Laboratories, Ltd.; *Int'l*, pg. 6837
SN BRUSSELS AIRLINES NV—See SN Airholding II NV; *Int'l*, pg. 7024
SN BUILTECH CO., LTD.—See Takamiya Co., Ltd.; *Int'l*, pg. 7430
SNC ATLANTIC HEAT PUMP COMPANY LIMITED—See SNC Holding Company Limited; *Int'l*, pg. 7025
SNC CAPITAL 8—See Unibail-Rodamco-Westfield SE; *Int'l*, pg. 8030
SNC COGEDIM AQUITAINE—See Altarea SCA; *Int'l*, pg. 385
SNC COGEDIM ATLANTIQUE—See Altarea SCA; *Int'l*, pg. 385
SNC COGEDIM EST—See Altarea SCA; *Int'l*, pg. 385
SNC COGEDIM GESTION—See Altarea SCA; *Int'l*, pg. 385
SNC COGEDIM GRAND LYON—See Altarea SCA; *Int'l*, pg. 385
SNC COGEDIM GRENOBLE—See Altarea SCA; *Int'l*, pg. 385
SNC COGEDIM LANGUEDOC ROUSSILLON—See Altarea SCA; *Int'l*, pg. 385
SNC COGEDIM MEDITERRANEE—See Altarea SCA; *Int'l*, pg. 385
SNC COGEDIM MIDI-PYRENEES—See Altarea SCA; *Int'l*, pg. 385
SNC COGEDIM PARIS METROPOLE—See Altarea SCA; *Int'l*, pg. 385
SNC COGEDIM PROVENCE—See Altarea SCA; *Int'l*, pg. 385
SNC COGEDIM SAVOIES-LEMAN—See Altarea SCA; *Int'l*, pg. 385
SNC COGEDIM VENTE—See Altarea SCA; *Int'l*, pg. 385
SNC CO., LTD.—See Sumitomo Osaka Cement Co Ltd; *Int'l*, pg. 7297
SNC COMP PARTS COMPANY LIMITED—See SNC Holding Company Limited; *Int'l*, pg. 7025
SNC COOLING SUPPLY COMPANY LIMITED—See SNC Holding Company Limited; *Int'l*, pg. 7025
SNC FONCIERE ATLAND VALORISATION—See Fonciere Atland SA; *Int'l*, pg. 2724
SNC FORMER PUBLIC COMPANY LIMITED—See SNC Holding Company Limited; *Int'l*, pg. 7024
SNCF; *Int'l*, pg. 7025
SNC FUKUI HOLY INSULATION COMPANY LIMITED—See SNC Holding Company Limited; *Int'l*, pg. 7025
SNC HOLDING COMPANY LIMITED; *Int'l*, pg. 7024
SNC INDUSTRIAL LAMINATES SDN. BHD.—See Sumitomo Bakelite Co., Ltd.; *Int'l*, pg. 7263
SNC-LAVALIN AGRO—See AtkinsRealis Group Inc.; *Int'l*, pg. 671
SNC-LAVALIN ALGERIE EURL—See AtkinsRealis Group Inc.; *Int'l*, pg. 672
SNC-LAVALIN AMERICA, INC.—See AtkinsRealis Group Inc.; *Int'l*, pg. 672
SNC-LAVALIN ARABIA ENGINEERING CONSULTANCY—See AtkinsRealis Group Inc.; *Int'l*, pg. 672
SNC-LAVALIN ARABIA, LLC—See AtkinsRealis Group Inc.; *Int'l*, pg. 672
SNC-LAVALIN AUSTRALIA PTY. LTD.—See AtkinsRealis Group Inc.; *Int'l*, pg. 672
SNC-LAVALIN CAPITAL ENGINEERING LLC—See AtkinsRealis Group Inc.; *Int'l*, pg. 672
SNC-LAVALIN CAPITAL INC.—See AtkinsRealis Group Inc.; *Int'l*, pg. 671
SNC-LAVALIN CHILE S.A.—See AtkinsRealis Group Inc.; *Int'l*, pg. 672
SNC-LAVALIN CONSTRUCTION (ATLANTIC) INC.—See AtkinsRealis Group Inc.; *Int'l*, pg. 671
SNC-LAVALIN CONSTRUCTION INTERNATIONAL SAS—See AtkinsRealis Group Inc.; *Int'l*, pg. 672
SNC-LAVALIN CONSTRUCTION (ONTARIO) INC.—See AtkinsRealis Group Inc.; *Int'l*, pg. 671
SNC-LAVALIN CONSTRUCTORS INC.—See AtkinsRealis Group Inc.; *Int'l*, pg. 672
SNC-LAVALIN DEFENCE PROGRAMS INC.—See AtkinsRealis Group Inc.; *Int'l*, pg. 671
SNC-LAVALIN DOMINICANA S.A.—See AtkinsRealis Group Inc.; *Int'l*, pg. 672
SNC-LAVALIN EGYPT LLC—See AtkinsRealis Group Inc.; *Int'l*, pg. 672
SNC-LAVALIN ENGINEERING INDIA PRIVATE LIMITED—See AtkinsRealis Group Inc.; *Int'l*, pg. 672
SNC-LAVALIN ENGINEERING & TECHNOLOGY PVT LIMITED—See AtkinsRealis Group Inc.; *Int'l*, pg. 672
SNC-LAVALIN ENGINEERS & CONSTRUCTORS, INC.—See AtkinsRealis Group Inc.; *Int'l*, pg. 672
SNC-LAVALIN ENVIRONMENT INC—See AtkinsRealis Group Inc.; *Int'l*, pg. 671
SNC-LAVALIN EURASIA OOO—See AtkinsRealis Group Inc.; *Int'l*, pg. 672
SNC-LAVALIN EUROPE S.A.S.—See AtkinsRealis Group Inc.; *Int'l*, pg. 672
SNC-LAVALIN GULF CONTRACTORS LLC—See AtkinsRealis Group Inc.; *Int'l*, pg. 672

SNC-LAVALIN HEALTH—See AtkinsRealis Group Inc.; *Int'l*, pg. 673
SNC-LAVALIN INC. - CALGARY—See AtkinsRealis Group Inc.; *Int'l*, pg. 671
SNC-LAVALIN INC. - EDMONTON—See AtkinsRealis Group Inc.; *Int'l*, pg. 671
SNC LAVALIN INC. - HALIFAX—See AtkinsRealis Group Inc.; *Int'l*, pg. 671
SNC-LAVALIN INC. - HYDRO DIVISION—See AtkinsRealis Group Inc.; *Int'l*, pg. 671
SNC-LAVALIN INC. - LEVIS—See AtkinsRealis Group Inc.; *Int'l*, pg. 671
SNC-LAVALIN INC. - LONGUEUIL—See AtkinsRealis Group Inc.; *Int'l*, pg. 671
SNC LAVALIN INC. - OTTAWA—See AtkinsRealis Group Inc.; *Int'l*, pg. 671
SNC-LAVALIN INC. - RIMOUSKI—See AtkinsRealis Group Inc.; *Int'l*, pg. 671
SNC-LAVALIN INC. - SARNIA—See AtkinsRealis Group Inc.; *Int'l*, pg. 671
SNC-LAVALIN INC.—See AtkinsRealis Group Inc.; *Int'l*, pg. 671
SNC-LAVALIN INC. - THETFORD MINES—See AtkinsRealis Group Inc.; *Int'l*, pg. 671
SNC-LAVALIN INC. - TORONTO—See AtkinsRealis Group Inc.; *Int'l*, pg. 671
SNC-LAVALIN INC. - VANCOUVER—See AtkinsRealis Group Inc.; *Int'l*, pg. 671
SNC-LAVALIN INC. - WINNIPEG—See AtkinsRealis Group Inc.; *Int'l*, pg. 671
SNC-LAVALIN INFRASTRUCTURE PVT. LTD.—See AtkinsRealis Group Inc.; *Int'l*, pg. 672
SNC-LAVALIN INTERNATIONAL CO. INC.—See AtkinsRealis Group Inc.; *Int'l*, pg. 672
SNC-LAVALIN INTERNATIONAL INC. - BEIJING REPRESENTATIVE OFFICE—See AtkinsRealis Group Inc.; *Int'l*, pg. 671
SNC-LAVALIN INTERNATIONAL INC. - CAMEROON—See AtkinsRealis Group Inc.; *Int'l*, pg. 672
SNC-LAVALIN INTERNATIONAL INC. - HONDURAS—See AtkinsRealis Group Inc.; *Int'l*, pg. 672
SNC-LAVALIN INTERNATIONAL INC. - KAZAKHSTAN—See AtkinsRealis Group Inc.; *Int'l*, pg. 672
SNC-LAVALIN INTERNATIONAL INC. - LIBYA—See AtkinsRealis Group Inc.; *Int'l*, pg. 672
SNC-LAVALIN INTERNATIONAL INC. - RUSSIA—See AtkinsRealis Group Inc.; *Int'l*, pg. 671
SNC-LAVALIN INTERNATIONAL INC.—See AtkinsRealis Group Inc.; *Int'l*, pg. 671
SNC-LAVALIN INTERNATIONAL INC. - THAILAND—See AtkinsRealis Group Inc.; *Int'l*, pg. 672
SNC-LAVALIN INTERNATIONAL INC. - TUNISIA—See AtkinsRealis Group Inc.; *Int'l*, pg. 672
SNC-LAVALIN INTERNATIONAL INC. - VIETNAM—See AtkinsRealis Group Inc.; *Int'l*, pg. 672
SNC-LAVALIN INTERNATIONAL MAROC S.A.S.—See AtkinsRealis Group Inc.; *Int'l*, pg. 672
SNC-LAVALIN INTERNATIONAL—See AtkinsRealis Group Inc.; *Int'l*, pg. 672
SNC-LAVALIN KOREA LIMITED—See AtkinsRealis Group Inc.; *Int'l*, pg. 672
SNC-LAVALIN KUWAIT GENERAL TRADING AND CONTRACTING CO.—See AtkinsRealis Group Inc.; *Int'l*, pg. 672
SNC-LAVALIN MAGYARORSZAG KFT—See AtkinsRealis Group Inc.; *Int'l*, pg. 672
SNC-LAVALIN (MALAYSIA) SDN. BHD.—See AtkinsRealis Group Inc.; *Int'l*, pg. 672
SNC-LAVALIN MINERCONSULT LTDA—See AtkinsRealis Group Inc.; *Int'l*, pg. 672
SNC-LAVALIN MUHENDISLIK VE TAAHHUT LIMITED SIRKETI—See AtkinsRealis Group Inc.; *Int'l*, pg. 673
SNC-LAVALIN NUCLEAR INC.—See AtkinsRealis Group Inc.; *Int'l*, pg. 673
SNC-LAVALIN OPERATIONS & MAINTENANCE INC.—See AtkinsRealis Group Inc.; *Int'l*, pg. 673
SNC-LAVALIN PANAMA, S.A.—See AtkinsRealis Group Inc.; *Int'l*, pg. 673
SNC-LAVALIN PERU S.A.—See AtkinsRealis Group Inc.; *Int'l*, pg. 673
SNC-LAVALIN PHARMA S.A.—See AtkinsRealis Group Inc.; *Int'l*, pg. 673
SNC-LAVALIN POLSKA SP. Z O.O.—See AtkinsRealis Group Inc.; *Int'l*, pg. 673
SNC-LAVALIN PROJECT SERVICES, INC.—See AtkinsRealis Group Inc.; *Int'l*, pg. 672
SNC-LAVALIN PROJETOS LTDA.—See AtkinsRealis Group Inc.; *Int'l*, pg. 673
SNC-LAVALIN (PTY) LTD—See AtkinsRealis Group Inc.; *Int'l*, pg. 672
SNC-LAVALIN ROMANIA S.A.—See AtkinsRealis Group Inc.; *Int'l*, pg. 673
SNC-LAVALIN RURAL DEVELOPMENT—See AtkinsRealis Group Inc.; *Int'l*, pg. 673
SNC-LAVALIN S.A.S.—See AtkinsRealis Group Inc.; *Int'l*, pg. 672
SNC-LAVALIN (SHANGHAI) INTERNATIONAL TRADING CO. LTD.—See AtkinsRealis Group Inc.; *Int'l*, pg. 672

SNC-LAVALIN SOUTH AFRICA (PTY) LTD.—See AtkinsRealis Group Inc.; *Int'l*, pg. 673
SNC-LAVALIN SPAIN SL—See AtkinsRealis Group Inc.; *Int'l*, pg. 673
SNC-LAVALIN TELECOM INC.—See AtkinsRealis Group Inc.; *Int'l*, pg. 673
SNC-LAVALIN TRANSMISSION & DISTRIBUTION—See AtkinsRealis Group Inc.; *Int'l*, pg. 673
SNC-LAVALIN TRANSPORTATION KOREA INC.—See AtkinsRealis Group Inc.; *Int'l*, pg. 673
SNC MANUFACTURING COMPANY, INC.—See Allient Inc.; *U.S. Public*, pg. 80
SNC NMP FRANCE—See Accor S.A.; *Int'l*, pg. 92
S&N COMMUNICATIONS, INC.—See Sun Capital Partners, Inc.; *U.S. Private*, pg. 3860
S&N COMMUNICATIONS—See Sun Capital Partners, Inc.; *U.S. Private*, pg. 3860
SNC PYONGSAN EVOLUTION COMPANY LIMITED—See SNC Holding Company Limited; *Int'l*, pg. 7025
SNC RENAULT DOUAI—See Renault S.A.; *Int'l*, pg. 6274
SNC RESTO CHARTRES—See Eurazeo SE; *Int'l*, pg. 2529
SNC SHIP DESIGN S.R.L.—See Santierul Naval Constanta S.A.; *Int'l*, pg. 6558
SNC SQUARED; *U.S. Private*, pg. 3700
SNC TRAVAUX PUBLICS DE PROVENCE—See Eiffage S.A.; *Int'l*, pg. 2331
SND LIMITED—See Essel Corporate Resources Pvt. Ltd.; *Int'l*, pg. 2509
SNDL INC.; *Int'l*, pg. 7027
SNECMA AMERICA ENGINE SERVICES S.A. DE C.V.—See Safran SA; *Int'l*, pg. 6476
SNECMA MEXICO S.A. DE C.V—See Safran SA; *Int'l*, pg. 6476
SNECMA MOROCCO ENGINE SERVICES—See Royal Air Maroc SA; *Int'l*, pg. 6409
SNECMA MOROCCO ENGINE SERVICES—See Safran SA; *Int'l*, pg. 6476
SNECMA MOTEURS S.A.—See Safran SA; *Int'l*, pg. 6476
SNECMA S.A.—See Safran SA; *Int'l*, pg. 6476
SNECMA SERVICES BRUSSELS NV—See Safran SA; *Int'l*, pg. 6476
SNECMA SERVICES—See Safran SA; *Int'l*, pg. 6476
SNECMA SUZHOU CO. LTD.—See Safran SA; *Int'l*, pg. 6476
SNEDEKER OIL COMPANY INC.; *U.S. Private*, pg. 3700
SNE ENTERPRISES, INC.—See Weathershield Mfg. Inc.; *U.S. Private*, pg. 4463
SNEF SA; *Int'l*, pg. 7027
SNEH MATERIAUX SAS—See VINCI S.A.; *Int'l*, pg. 8226
SNELLING PAPER LIMITED; *Int'l*, pg. 7027
SNELLING PERSONNEL SERVICES—See Patriarch Partners, LLC; *U.S. Private*, pg. 3109
SNELLING STAFFING SERVICES—See Patriarch Partners, LLC; *U.S. Private*, pg. 3109
SNELL SERVICES INC.; *U.S. Private*, pg. 3700
SNELL & WILMER LLP; *U.S. Private*, pg. 3700
SNELSON COMPANIES INC. GAS DISTRIBUTION DIVISION—See Primoris Services Corporation; *U.S. Public*, pg. 1719
SNELSON COMPANIES INC. PIPELINE DIVISION—See Primoris Services Corporation; *U.S. Public*, pg. 1719
SNELSON COMPANIES INC.—See Primoris Services Corporation; *U.S. Public*, pg. 1719
SNELSON STATIONS & FACILITIES DIVISION—See Primoris Services Corporation; *U.S. Public*, pg. 1719
SNEMYR BETONGSPROYTING AS—See Nordisk Bergteknik AB; *Int'l*, pg. 5424
SN ENVIRONMENT TECHNOLOGY CO., LTD—See Hitachi Zosen Corporation; *Int'l*, pg. 3412
SNET SYSTEMS INC.; *Int'l*, pg. 7027
S'NEXT JAPAN CO. LTD.—See Koch Industries, Inc.; *U.S. Private*, pg. 2334
S'NEXT PHILIPPINES—See Koch Industries, Inc.; *U.S. Private*, pg. 2334
SNF AMBIENTAGUA—See SNF SAS; *Int'l*, pg. 7027
SNF ARGENTINA SRL—See SNF SAS; *Int'l*, pg. 7027
SNF (AUSTRALIA) PTY LTD—See SNF SAS; *Int'l*, pg. 7027
SNF CANADA LTD.—See SNF SAS; *Int'l*, pg. 7027
SNF CHILE S.A—See SNF SAS; *Int'l*, pg. 7028
SNF (CHINA) FLOCCULANT CO. LTD.—See SNF SAS; *Int'l*, pg. 7027
SNF DO BRASIL LTDA.—See SNF SAS; *Int'l*, pg. 7028
SNF FINLAND OY—See SNF SAS; *Int'l*, pg. 7028
SNF FLOERGER DE MEXICO SA DE CV—See SNF SAS; *Int'l*, pg. 7028
SNF FLOERGER IBERICA SLU—See SNF SAS; *Int'l*, pg. 7028
SNF FLOERGER PHILIPPINES INC—See SNF SAS; *Int'l*, pg. 7028
SNF FLOERGER TURKEY—See SNF SAS; *Int'l*, pg. 7028
SNF HONGRIE KFT—See SNF SAS; *Int'l*, pg. 7028
SNF (INDIA) PVT. LTD.—See SNF SAS; *Int'l*, pg. 7027
SNF ITALIA S.P.A.—See SNF SAS; *Int'l*, pg. 7028
SNF JAPAN CO. LTD.—See SNF SAS; *Int'l*, pg. 7028
SNF RSA PTY. LTD.—See SNF SAS; *Int'l*, pg. 7028
SNF SAS; *Int'l*, pg. 7027
SNF (UK) LTD.—See SNF SAS; *Int'l*, pg. 7027

COMPANY NAME INDEX

SNF VOSTOK—See SNF SAS; *Int'l*, pg. 7028
S.N.G.N. ROMGAZ S.A.; *Int'l*, pg. 6457
SNIACE S.A.; *Int'l*, pg. 7028
SNICKAR-PER AB—See Ratos AB; *Int'l*, pg. 6220
SNICKERS ORIGINAL LTD—See Investment AB Latour; *Int'l*, pg. 3782
SNICKERS ORIGINAL NV—See Investment AB Latour; *Int'l*, pg. 3782
SNICKERS ORIGINAL SIA—See Investment AB Latour; *Int'l*, pg. 3782
SNICKERS PRODUCTION SIA LATVIA—See Investment AB Latour; *Int'l*, pg. 3782
SNICKERS WORKWEAR LOGISTICS BV—See Investment AB Latour; *Int'l*, pg. 3782
SNICKERS WORKWEAR TRADEWEAR LTD—See Investment AB Latour; *Int'l*, pg. 3782
SNICK EUROINGREDIENTS N.V.—See ACOMO N.V.; *Int'l*, pg. 108
SNI COMPANIES—See GEE Group Inc.; *U.S. Public*, pg. 910
SNIDER ADVISORS; *U.S. Private*, pg. 3700
SNIDER FLEET SOLUTIONS; *U.S. Private*, pg. 3700
SNIDEX AB—See VKR Holding A/S; *Int'l*, pg. 8281
SNIF SYSTEMS—See Pyrotek Incorporated; *U.S. Private*, pg. 3311
SNIKIDDY LLC; *U.S. Private*, pg. 3700
S&N INC.; *U.S. Private*, pg. 3513
SNIP BIOTECH GMBH & CO. KG—See Eurofins Scientific S.E.; *Int'l*, pg. 2551
SNIPER RESOURCES LTD.; *Int'l*, pg. 7028
SNIPES SE—See Deichmann SE; *Int'l*, pg. 2005
SNIPP INTERACTIVE INC.; *Int'l*, pg. 7028
SNJ ENTERPRISES, INC.—See Dometic Group AB; *Int'l*, pg. 2160
SNK AMERICA, INC.—See Fair Friend Group; *Int'l*, pg. 2605
SNK AMERICA, INC.—See Fair Friend Group; *Int'l*, pg. 2605
SNK EG TAIWAN CORPORATION—See Fair Friend Group; *Int'l*, pg. 2605
SNK ENGINEERING KOREA CO, LTD.—See Fair Friend Group; *Int'l*, pg. 2605
SNK GMBH—See Fair Friend Group; *Int'l*, pg. 2605
SNK INDIA PRIVATE LIMITED—See Fair Friend Group; *Int'l*, pg. 2605
SNK NANJING TECHNOLOGY CORPORATION—See Fair Friend Group; *Int'l*, pg. 2605
SNK THAI CO., LTD.—See Fair Friend Group; *Int'l*, pg. 2605
S&N LABELS PROPRIETARY LIMITED—See The Bidvest Group Limited; *Int'l*, pg. 7626
SNL BEARINGS LIMITED—See NRB Bearings Limited; *Int'l*, pg. 5473
SNL DISTRIBUTION INC.; *U.S. Private*, pg. 3700
SNM GLOBAL HOLDINGS; *U.S. Public*, pg. 1899
S.N. NUCLEARELECTRICA S.A.; *Int'l*, pg. 6456
SNODGRASS & SONS CONSTRUCTION CO., INC.; *U.S. Private*, pg. 3700
SNOHOMISH COUNTY PUBLIC UTILITY DISTRICT; *U.S. Private*, pg. 3700
SNOHOMISH PHYSICAL THERAPY, LLC—See U.S. Physical Therapy, Inc.; *U.S. Public*, pg. 2216
SNOKIST GROWERS CO-OP; *U.S. Private*, pg. 3700
SNOLINE EXPRESS, INC.; *U.S. Private*, pg. 3700
SNOLINE S.P.A.—See Lindsay Corporation; *U.S. Public*, pg. 1320
SNOM SOLUTIONS GMBH—See VTech Holdings Ltd.; *Int'l*, pg. 8316
SNOOGOO CORP.; *U.S. Private*, pg. 3700
SNORKEL EUROPE LIMITED—See Tanfield Group Plc; *Int'l*, pg. 7457
SNORKEL EUROPE LIMITED—See Xtreme Manufacturing, LLC; *U.S. Private*, pg. 4583
SNORKEL INTERNATIONAL HOLDINGS, LLC—See Tanfield Group Plc; *Int'l*, pg. 7457
SNORKEL INTERNATIONAL HOLDINGS, LLC—See Xtreme Manufacturing, LLC; *U.S. Private*, pg. 4583
SNORKEL INTERNATIONAL, LLC—See Tanfield Group Plc; *Int'l*, pg. 7457
SNORKEL INTERNATIONAL, LLC—See Xtreme Manufacturing, LLC; *U.S. Private*, pg. 4583
SNORKEL JAPAN CO., LTD.—See Tanfield Group Plc; *Int'l*, pg. 7457
SNORKEL JAPAN CO., LTD.—See Xtreme Manufacturing, LLC; *U.S. Private*, pg. 4583
SNORKEL NEW ZEALAND LIMITED—See Tanfield Group Plc; *Int'l*, pg. 7457
SNORKEL NEW ZEALAND LIMITED—See Xtreme Manufacturing, LLC; *U.S. Private*, pg. 4583
S. NORMAN SANCTON; *Int'l*, pg. 6447
SNORRASON HOLDINGS EHF; *Int'l*, pg. 7028
S.NORTON & CO. LTD.; *Int'l*, pg. 6457
SNOW AND JONES INC.; *U.S. Private*, pg. 3700
SNOWBALL FINANCIAL PTY. LTD.—See Insignia Financial Ltd.; *Int'l*, pg. 3719
SNOWBASIN RESORT COMPANY—See HF Sinclair Corporation; *U.S. Public*, pg. 1034
SNOWBERRY NEW ZEALAND LIMITED—See The Procter & Gamble Company; *U.S. Public*, pg. 2123
SNOWBEST LIMITED—See Panther Securities PLC; *Int'l*, pg. 5731
SNOWBIRD AG; *Int'l*, pg. 7028
SNOWBIRD CORPORATION; *U.S. Private*, pg. 3701
SNOWBOARD DACHSTEIN TAUERN GMBH—See Zumiez Incorporated; *U.S. Public*, pg. 2411
SNOWBOUND SOFTWARE CORP.—See Pegasus Imaging Corporation; *U.S. Private*, pg. 3129
SNOW BRAND AUSTRALIA PTY. LTD.—See MEGMILK SNOW BRAND Co., Ltd.; *Int'l*, pg. 4796
SNOW BRAND HONG KONG CO., LTD.—See MEGMILK SNOW BRAND Co., Ltd.; *Int'l*, pg. 4796
SNOW BRAND MILK PRODUCTS CO., LTD.—See MEGMILK SNOW BRAND Co., Ltd.; *Int'l*, pg. 4796
SNOW BRAND MILK PRODUCTS CO. LTD.—See MEGMILK SNOW BRAND Co., Ltd.; *Int'l*, pg. 4796
SNOW BRAND PILLSBURY, INC.—See General Mills, Inc.; *U.S. Public*, pg. 922
SNOW BRAND SEED CO., LTD.—See MEGMILK SNOW BRAND Co., Ltd.; *Int'l*, pg. 4796
SNOW BRAND SHOJI CO., LTD.—See MEGMILK SNOW BRAND Co., Ltd.; *Int'l*, pg. 4796
SNOW BRAND SIAM LTD—See MEGMILK SNOW BRAND Co., Ltd.; *Int'l*, pg. 4796
SNOW BRAND TAIWAN CO., LTD.—See MEGMILK SNOW BRAND Co., Ltd.; *Int'l*, pg. 4796
SNOW BRAND TRADING AUSTRALIA, PTY.—See MEGMILK SNOW BRAND Co., Ltd.; *Int'l*, pg. 4796
SNOWBUSH MEXICO S.A.P.I. DE C.V.—See Semtech Corporation; *U.S. Public*, pg. 1864
SNOW, CHRISTENSEN & MARTINEAU, P.C.—See Spencer Fane LLP; *U.S. Private*, pg. 3755
SNOW CITY CYCLE MARINE; *Int'l*, pg. 7028
SNOWCREST FOODS LTD.—See TriWest Capital Management Corp.; *Int'l*, pg. 7937
SNOWDEN MINING INDUSTRY CONSULTANTS LIMITED—See Downer EDI Limited; *Int'l*, pg. 2186
SNOWDEN MINING INDUSTRY CONSULTANTS PTY LTD.—See Downer EDI Limited; *Int'l*, pg. 2186
SNOWDEN TECHNOLOGIES PTY LTD—See Downer EDI Limited; *Int'l*, pg. 2186
SNOWDOWN MERCHANDISE (SUZHOU) CO., LTD.—See Kwong Lung Enterprise Co., Ltd.; *Int'l*, pg. 4351
SNOW DRAGON LLC—See Park-Ohio Holdings Corp.; *U.S. Public*, pg. 1640
SNOWED IN STUDIOS, INC.—See Canada Pension Plan Investment Board; *Int'l*, pg. 1280
SNOWED IN STUDIOS, INC.—See EQT AB; *Int'l*, pg. 2483
SNOWED IN STUDIOS, INC.—See Temasek Holdings (Private) Limited; *Int'l*, pg. 7548
SNOW EVEREST CO., LTD.—See Ship Healthcare Holdings, Inc.; *Int'l*, pg. 6852
SNOWFIT GROUP BERHAD; *Int'l*, pg. 7028
SNOWFLAKE COMPUTING PTY. LTD.—See Snowflake Inc.; *U.S. Public*, pg. 1899
SNOWFLAKE INC.; *U.S. Public*, pg. 1899
SNOWHOUSE SOLUTIONS INC.; *Int'l*, pg. 7028
SNOW KING RESORT, INC.; *U.S. Private*, pg. 3700
SNOW LAKE RESOURCES LTD.—See Nova Minerals Limited; *Int'l*, pg. 5452
SNOWLINE GOLD CORP.; *Int'l*, pg. 7028
SNOW-LOTUS CASHMERE CO., LTD—See COFCO Limited; *Int'l*, pg. 1692
SNOWMAN LOGISTICS LTD.—See Adani Enterprises Limited; *Int'l*, pg. 124
SNOWMAN MIDDLE EAST FZCO—See Fujian Snowman Co., Ltd.; *Int'l*, pg. 2819
SNOWMASS VILLAGE SUN—See Swift Communications, Inc.; *U.S. Private*, pg. 3893
SNOW-NABSTEDT POWER TRANSMISSIONS—See Allard Nazarian Group Inc.; *U.S. Private*, pg. 175
SNOW PEAK CAPITAL, LLC; *U.S. Private*, pg. 3701
SNOW PEAK INC.—See Bain Capital, LP; *U.S. Private*, pg. 436
SNOW PEAK KOREA, INC.—See Bain Capital, LP; *U.S. Private*, pg. 436
SNOW PHIPPS GROUP, LLC—See TruArc Partners, L.P.; *U.S. Private*, pg. 4245
SNOWSHOE MOUNTAIN, INC.—See KSL Capital Partners, LLC; *U.S. Private*, pg. 2354
SNOWSKY SALT INDUSTRY GROUP CO., LTD.; *Int'l*, pg. 7028
SNOW TIME, INC.—See Vail Resorts, Inc.; *U.S. Public*, pg. 2271
SNOW VALLEY LLC—See KSL Capital Partners, LLC; *U.S. Private*, pg. 2354
SNOWWORLD LEISURE N.V.—See Value8 N.V.; *Int'l*, pg. 8124
SNOWY HYDRO LIMITED; *Int'l*, pg. 7028
SNOWY HYDRO TRADING PTY. LTD.—See Snowy Hydro Limited; *Int'l*, pg. 7028
SNP AMERICA, INC.—See SNP Schneider-Neureither & Partner AG; *Int'l*, pg. 7029
SNP APPLICATIONS GMBH—See SNP Schneider-Neureither & Partner AG; *Int'l*, pg. 7029
SNP AUSTRIA GMBH—See SNP Schneider-Neureither & Partner AG; *Int'l*, pg. 7029

SNYDER ENVIRONMENTAL, INC.

SNP CONSULTING GMBH—See SNP Schneider-Neureither & Partner AG; *Int'l*, pg. 7029
SNPE SA—See GIAT Industries S.A.; *Int'l*, pg. 2962
SNP GL ASSOCIATES—See SNP Schneider-Neureither & Partner AG; *Int'l*, pg. 7029
SNP HOLDING B.V.—See LOV Group Invest SAS; *Int'l*, pg. 4564
SN POWER AS—See Scatec ASA; *Int'l*, pg. 6613
SN POWER CHILE INVERSIONES ELECTRICAS LTDA.—See Statkraft AS; *Int'l*, pg. 7185
SN POWER ENERGIA DO BRASIL LTDA—See Statkraft AS; *Int'l*, pg. 7185
SNP SCHNEIDER-NEUREITHER & PARTNER AG; *Int'l*, pg. 7028
SNP SCHNEIDER-NEUREITHER & PARTNER ZA (PTY) LIMITED—See SNP Schneider-Neureither & Partner AG; *Int'l*, pg. 7029
SNP (SCHWEIZ) AG—See SNP Schneider-Neureither & Partner AG; *Int'l*, pg. 7029
S.N.P.S. ISRAEL LTD—See Synopsys, Inc.; *U.S. Public*, pg. 1971
S.N.P. SOUTHEAST NETWORK PUBLIC LTD.; *Int'l*, pg. 6457
S&N PUMP (AFRICA) LTDA—See Lone Star Funds; *U.S. Private*, pg. 2485
S&N PUMP AND REWIND LIMITED—See Lone Star Funds; *U.S. Private*, pg. 2486
S & N PUMP COMPANY—See Lone Star Funds; *U.S. Private*, pg. 2485
SNR ARGENTINA S.A—See NTN Corporation; *Int'l*, pg. 5483
SN REFRATECTURE TOKAI CO., LTD.—See Krosaki Harima Corporation; *Int'l*, pg. 4307
SNR ITALIA SPA—See NTN Corporation; *Int'l*, pg. 5483
SNR ROULEMENTS SA—See NTN Corporation; *Int'l*, pg. 5483
SNR ROULEMENTS S.A.—See Renault S.A.; *Int'l*, pg. 6274
SNR WAELZLAGER GMBH—See NTN Corporation; *Int'l*, pg. 5483
SNR WALZLAGER GMBH—See NTN Corporation; *Int'l*, pg. 5483
SNS ASSET MANAGEMENT N.V.—See Stichting Beheer SNS REAAL; *Int'l*, pg. 7214
SNS ASSURADEUREN B.V.—See SNS Bank N.V.; *Int'l*, pg. 7029
SNS ASSURANTIEN B.V.—See SNS Bank N.V.; *Int'l*, pg. 7029
SNS BANK N.V.; *Int'l*, pg. 7029
SNS INVESTMENT COMPANY—See Biglari Holdings Inc.; *U.S. Public*, pg. 331
SNS LOGISTICS, INC.; *U.S. Private*, pg. 3701
SNS MARKETING; *U.S. Private*, pg. 3701
SNS NANO FIBER TECHNOLOGY LLC—See Schill + Seilacher AG; *Int'l*, pg. 6618
SNS NETWORK TECHNOLOGY BERHAD; *Int'l*, pg. 7029
SNS PROPERTY FINANCE—See SNS Bank N.V.; *Int'l*, pg. 7029
SNS REAAL INVEST N.V.—See Stichting Beheer SNS REAAL; *Int'l*, pg. 7214
SNS REGIO BANK N.V.—See SNS Bank N.V.; *Int'l*, pg. 7029
SNS TECHNOLOGY CO., LTD.—See ADTechnology Co., Ltd.; *Int'l*, pg. 154
S.N. TANNOR INC.; *U.S. Private*, pg. 3518
SNTC HOLDING, INC.—See KKR & Co. Inc.; *U.S. Public*, pg. 1254
SNT CORPORATION; *Int'l*, pg. 7029
SNT DEUTSCHLAND AG—See E.ON SE; *Int'l*, pg. 2260
SNT DYNAMICS CO., LTD.—See SNT Holdings Co., Ltd.; *Int'l*, pg. 7029
SN TECH CORPORATION—See Nagase & Co., Ltd.; *Int'l*, pg. 5128
SNTECH, INC.; *U.S. Private*, pg. 3701
SNT HOLDINGS CO., LTD.; *Int'l*, pg. 7029
SNTIAL TECHNOLOGIES, INC.; *U.S. Private*, pg. 3701
SNT MOTIV CO., LTD.—See SNT Holdings Co., Ltd.; *Int'l*, pg. 7029
SNT NOYON—See SNCF; *Int'l*, pg. 7025
SNUGG HOME LLC—See ABRY Partners, LLC; *U.S. Private*, pg. 41
SNUGZ USA INC; *U.S. Private*, pg. 3701
SNVC, L.C.; *U.S. Private*, pg. 3701
SNYDER ASSOCIATED COMPANIES, INC.—See The Snyder Group, Inc.; *U.S. Private*, pg. 4119
SNYDER AUTO WORKS INC.; *U.S. Private*, pg. 3701
SNYDER BROTHERS, INC.—See The Snyder Group, Inc.; *U.S. Private*, pg. 4119
SNYDER CAPITAL MANAGEMENT, L.P.—See Groupe BPCE; *Int'l*, pg. 3096
SNYDER CHEVROLET OLDSMOBILE, INC.; *U.S. Private*, pg. 3701
SNYDER CONCRETE PRODUCTS INC.; *U.S. Private*, pg. 3701
SNYDER CORP.; *U.S. Private*, pg. 3701
SNYDER, CROMPTON & ASSOCIATES, INC.; *U.S. Private*, pg. 3701
SNYDER-DIAMOND; *U.S. Private*, pg. 3701
SNYDER ENVIRONMENTAL, INC.; *U.S. Private*, pg. 3701

SNYDER EQUIPMENT COMPANY, INC.—See Knorr-Bremse AG; *Int'l*, pg. 4212
SNYDER GROUP INCORPORATED; *U.S. Private*, pg. 3701
THE SNYDER GROUP, INC.; *U.S. Private*, pg. 4119
THE SNYDER GROUP; *U.S. Private*, pg. 4119
SNYDER INDUSTRIES, INC. - MANCELONA—See Olympus Partners; *U.S. Private*, pg. 3013
SNYDER INDUSTRIES, INC. - MARKED TREE—See Olympus Partners; *U.S. Private*, pg. 3013
SNYDER INDUSTRIES, INC. - PLASTIC SOLUTIONS DIVISION—See Olympus Partners; *U.S. Private*, pg. 3013
SNYDER INDUSTRIES, INC.—See Olympus Partners; *U.S. Private*, pg. 3013
SNYDER INSURANCE AGENCY, INC.—See R&R Insurance Services, Inc.; *U.S. Private*, pg. 3333
SNYDER INTERNATIONAL BREWING GROUP LLC; *U.S. Private*, pg. 3701
SNYDER LANGSTON LP; *U.S. Private*, pg. 3701
SNYDER OF BERLIN - CANAL FULTON DIVISION—See Utz Brands, Inc.; *U.S. Public*, pg. 2268
SNYDER OF BERLIN—See Utz Brands, Inc.; *U.S. Public*, pg. 2268
SNYDER PAPER CORPORATION; *U.S. Private*, pg. 3701
SNYDER ROOFING & SHEETMETAL INC.; *U.S. Private*, pg. 3701
SNYDER'S-LANCE, INC.—See Campbell Soup Company; *U.S. Public*, pg. 427
SNYDER WIND FARM LLC—See Enel S.p.A.; *Int'l*, pg. 2414
SO ACCURATE GROUP INC.; *U.S. Private*, pg. 3701
S&O AGRAR AG; *Int'l*, pg. 6445
SOAK CITY PTY. LIMITED—See Mulpha International Bhd.; *Int'l*, pg. 5081
SOAL-INDUSTRIAL GASES—See L'Air Liquide S.A.; *Int'l*, pg. 4375
SOALTEE HOTEL LTD.; *Int'l*, pg. 7029
SOANAR PLUS—See Soanar Pty. Ltd.; *Int'l*, pg. 7029
SOANAR PTY. LTD.; *Int'l*, pg. 7029
SOAPBOXSAMPLE—See Interviewing Service of America; *U.S. Private*, pg. 2128
SOAP LINKED BY ISOBAR—See Dentsu Group Inc.; *Int'l*, pg. 2037
SOAP OPERA DIGEST—See Chatham Asset Management, LLC; *U.S. Private*, pg. 860
SOAP OPERA WEEKLY—See TEN: The Enthusiast Network, Inc.; *U.S. Private*, pg. 3964
SOAPROJECTS, INC.; *U.S. Private*, pg. 3702
SOAR COMMUNICATIONS; *U.S. Private*, pg. 3702
SOARES DA COSTA AMERICA INC—See Soares da Costa Construcao, SGPS, S.A.; *Int'l*, pg. 7029
SOARES DA COSTA CONSTRUCAO, SGPS, S.A.; *Int'l*, pg. 7029
SOARE SEKT A.S.—See Schloss Wachenheim AG; *Int'l*, pg. 6622
SOARE SEKT SLOVAKIA S.R.O.—See Schloss Wachenheim AG; *Int'l*, pg. 6622
SOA RINA S.P.A.—See RINA S.p.A.; *Int'l*, pg. 6342
SOAR TECHNOLOGY ACQUISITION CORP.; *U.S. Public*, pg. 1899
SOAR TECHNOLOGY, INC.—See Trive Capital Inc.; *U.S. Private*, pg. 4240
SOARUS L.L.C.—See Mitsubishi Chemical Group Corporation; *Int'l*, pg. 4934
SOAVE ENTERPRISES, LLC; *U.S. Private*, pg. 3702
SOAVE HYDROPONICS COMPANY - GREAT NORTHERN SEEDLINGS DIVISION—See Soave Enterprises, LLC; *U.S. Private*, pg. 3702
SOAVE HYDROPONICS COMPANY—See Soave Enterprises, LLC; *U.S. Private*, pg. 3702
SOBAL CORPORATION; *Int'l*, pg. 7029
SOBC CORP.; *U.S. Private*, pg. 3702
SOBC DARAG HOLDINGS LTD.—See DARAG Group Limited; *Int'l*, pg. 1972
SOBC DARAG HOLDINGS LTD.—See SOBC Corp.; *U.S. Private*, pg. 3702
SOBEA GABON SA—See VINCI S.A.; *Int'l*, pg. 8227
SOBEGI—See L'Air Liquide S.A.; *Int'l*, pg. 4375
SOBEL CO.; *U.S. Private*, pg. 3702
SOBEL WESTEX; *U.S. Private*, pg. 3702
SOBER LIVING BY THE SEA, INC.—See Acadia Healthcare Company, Inc.; *U.S. Public*, pg. 30
SOBE SPORT S.R.L.—See Iervolino & Lady Bacardi Entertainment S.p.A.; *Int'l*, pg. 3597
SOBEYS CAPITAL INCORPORATED.—See Empire Company Limited; *Int'l*, pg. 2387
SOBEYS GROUP INC.—See Empire Company Limited; *Int'l*, pg. 2387
SOBEYS INC.—See Empire Company Limited; *Int'l*, pg. 2387
SOBEYS ONTARIO DIVISION—See Empire Company Limited; *Int'l*, pg. 2387
SOBEYS QUEBEC DIVISION—See Empire Company Limited; *Int'l*, pg. 2387
SOBEYS WEST, INC.—See Empire Company Limited; *Int'l*, pg. 2387
SOBHA CONCRETE PRODUCTS—See Sobha Limited; *Int'l*, pg. 7030

SOBHA CTG SOLUTIONS AUSTRALIA PTY LTD.—See Sobha Renaissance Information Technologies Pvt Ltd; *Int'l*, pg. 7030
SOBHA DEVELOPERS LLC.—See Sobha Limited; *Int'l*, pg. 7030
SOBHA DEVELOPERS LTD. - RESTOPLUS SPRING MATTRESS DIVISION—See Sobha Limited; *Int'l*, pg. 7030
SOBHA DEVELOPERS (PUNE) LIMITED—See Sobha Limited; *Int'l*, pg. 7030
SOBHAGIA SALES PVT. LTD.—See Sportking India Ltd.; *Int'l*, pg. 7142
SOBHA GLAZING & METAL WORKS—See Sobha Limited; *Int'l*, pg. 7030
SOBHAGYA MERCANTILE LTD.; *Int'l*, pg. 7030
SOBHA INTERIORS—See Sobha Limited; *Int'l*, pg. 7030
SOBHA LIMITED; *Int'l*, pg. 7030
SOBHAN DAROU COMPANY—See Alborz Investment Company; *Int'l*, pg. 299
SOBHAN ONCOLOGY PHARMACEUTICAL COMPANY—See Alborz Investment Company; *Int'l*, pg. 299
SOBHAN PHARMACEUTICAL COMPANY; *Int'l*, pg. 7030
SOBHA PROJECTS & TRADE PVT LTD.—See Sobha Limited; *Int'l*, pg. 7030
SOBHA REAL ESTATE LLC.—See Sobha Limited; *Int'l*, pg. 7030
SOBHA RENAISSANCE INFORMATION TECHNOLOGIES PVT LTD; *Int'l*, pg. 7030
SOBI CALENDARS CO., LTD.—See TOPPAN Holdings Inc.; *Int'l*, pg. 7817
SOBI CO., LTD. - IZUMO FACTORY—See SEMBA Corporation; *Int'l*, pg. 6702
SOBI CO., LTD. - KUMAMOTO FACTORY—See SEMBA Corporation; *Int'l*, pg. 6702
SOBI CO., LTD.—See SEMBA Corporation; *Int'l*, pg. 6702
SOBIESKI INTERNATIONAL SP. Z O.O—See Marie Brizard Wine & Spirits S.A.; *Int'l*, pg. 4694
SOBIESKI SARL—See Marie Brizard Wine & Spirits S.A.; *Int'l*, pg. 4694
SOBIESKI TRADE SP. Z.O.O.—See United Beverages S.A.; *Int'l*, pg. 8065
SOBI, INC.—See Swedish Orphan Biovitrum AB; *Int'l*, pg. 7365
SOBI MIDDLE EAST FZ-LLC—See Swedish Orphan Biovitrum AB; *Int'l*, pg. 7365
SOBINBANK JSB; *Int'l*, pg. 7030
SO.BIO SAS—See Carrefour SA; *Int'l*, pg. 1346
SOBI PHARMA (SHANGHAI) COMPANY LIMITED—See Swedish Orphan Biovitrum AB; *Int'l*, pg. 7365
SOBI SINGLE MEMBER I.K.E—See Swedish Orphan Biovitrum AB; *Int'l*, pg. 7365
SOBOTEC LTD.; *Int'l*, pg. 7030
SOBRA D.O.O.—See Bischof + Klein GmbH & Co. KG; *Int'l*, pg. 1049
SOBRAN, INC.; *U.S. Private*, pg. 3702
SOBRECO—See Carrefour SA; *Int'l*, pg. 1346
SO BRIGHT ELECTRONICS CO., LTD.—See Yeh-Chiang Technology Corp.; *Int'l*, pg. 8576
SOBR SAFE, INC.; *U.S. Public*, pg. 1899
SOB STABLES, INC.; *U.S. Private*, pg. 3702
SOBU BUTSURYU CO., LTD.—See Kikkoman Corporation; *Int'l*, pg. 4161
SOBU CO., LTD.—See The Chiba Bank, Ltd.; *Int'l*, pg. 7632
SOBU SERVICE CENTER INC.—See Kikkoman Corporation; *Int'l*, pg. 4161
SOBUTE (BD) CO., LTD.—See Sobute New Materials Co., Ltd.; *Int'l*, pg. 7030
SOBUTE NEW MATERIALS CO., LTD.; *Int'l*, pg. 7030
SOCA BV—See Carrefour SA; *Int'l*, pg. 1345
SOCAFI, S.A. DE C.V—See Sojitz Corporation; *Int'l*, pg. 7063
SOCAL HARVEST, INC.; *U.S. Private*, pg. 3702
SO CALIFORNIA VENTURES LTD.; *U.S. Private*, pg. 3701
SOCAL OFFICE TECHNOLOGIES, INC.—See Xerox Holdings Corporation; *U.S. Public*, pg. 2388
SO CAL SOFT-PAK, INC.—See Dover Corporation; *U.S. Public*, pg. 682
SOCAM DEVELOPMENT LIMITED—See Shui On Company Limited; *Int'l*, pg. 6869
SOCAMEL DEUTSCHLAND GMBH—See Groupe Guillin SA; *Int'l*, pg. 3104
SOCAMEL ESPANA SL—See Groupe Guillin SA; *Int'l*, pg. 3104
SOCAMEL TECHNOLOGIES—See Groupe Guillin SA; *Int'l*, pg. 3104
SOCAMEL UK LIMITED—See Groupe Guillin SA; *Int'l*, pg. 3104
SOCAME SAS—See Sonepar S.A.; *Int'l*, pg. 7091
SOCAMEX, S.A.—See ACS, Actividades de Construccion y Servicios, S.A.; *Int'l*, pg. 116
SOCAMIP—See Eiffage S.A.; *Int'l*, pg. 2330
SOCAPALM S.A.—See Socfinaf SA; *Int'l*, pg. 7031
SOCAPI—See Confederation Nationale du Credit Mutuel; *Int'l*, pg. 1767
SOCAP S.A.S.—See TotalEnergies SE; *Int'l*, pg. 7838

SOCAR ENERGY GEORGIA LLC—See State Oil Co. of Azerbaijan Republic; *Int'l*, pg. 7184
SOCAR ENERGY SWITZERLAND GMBH—See State Oil Co. of Azerbaijan Republic; *Int'l*, pg. 7184
SOCAR ENERGY UKRAINE—See State Oil Co. of Azerbaijan Republic; *Int'l*, pg. 7184
SOCAR GAZ TICARETI A.S.—See State Oil Co. of Azerbaijan Republic; *Int'l*, pg. 7184
SOCAR TURKEY ENERJI A.S.—See State Oil Co. of Azerbaijan Republic; *Int'l*, pg. 7184
SOCAR TURKEY PETROL ENERJI DAGITIM A.S.—See State Oil Co. of Azerbaijan Republic; *Int'l*, pg. 7184
SOCAT LLC—See Sodexo S.A.; *Int'l*, pg. 7045
SOC.CANALISTAS LA FORESTA DE APOQUINDO S; *Int'l*, pg. 7030
SOC CENTRALE BOIS SCIERIES MANCHE SA; *Int'l*, pg. 7030
SOCCERDOME LIMITED—See Tintra PLC; *Int'l*, pg. 7754
SOCCERZONE, INC.—See Let's Play Sports, Inc.; *U.S. Private*, pg. 2433
SOCECAP SA—See Societe Generale S.A.; *Int'l*, pg. 7041
SOCEMBAL SPRL—See Aga Khan Development Network; *Int'l*, pg. 199
SOCEP S.A.; *Int'l*, pg. 7030
SOC. ESPANOLA DE MONTAJES INDUSTRIALES, S.A.—See ACS, Actividades de Construccion y Servicios, S.A.; *Int'l*, pg. 116
SOCFIM SA—See Groupe BPCE; *Int'l*, pg. 3099
SOCFINAF SA; *Int'l*, pg. 7030
SOCFINASIA S.A.; *Int'l*, pg. 7031
SOCFINCO FR S.A.—See Socfinasia S.A.; *Int'l*, pg. 7031
SOCFIN KCD CO., LTD.—See Socfinasia S.A.; *Int'l*, pg. 7031
SOCHINAZ SA—See Bachem Holding AG; *Int'l*, pg. 795
SOCIAL CAPITAL HEDOSOPHIA HOLDINGS CORP. IV; *U.S. Private*, pg. 3702
SOCIAL CAPITAL HEDOSOPHIA HOLDINGS CORP. VI; *U.S. Private*, pg. 3702
THE SOCIAL CHAIN AG; *Int'l*, pg. 7687
SOCIALCHORUS, INC.—See Sumeru Equity Partners LLC; *U.S. Private*, pg. 3852
SOCIALCOM INC.; *U.S. Private*, pg. 3703
SOCIAL CONCERN COMMUNITY DEVELOPMENT CORP; *U.S. Private*, pg. 3703
SOCIAL CUBE INC.; *U.S. Private*, pg. 3703
SOCIAL DETENTION, INC.; *U.S. Public*, pg. 1899
SOCIAL FINANCE, INC.—See SoFi Technologies, Inc.; *U.S. Public*, pg. 1899
SOCIALFLY LLC; *U.S. Private*, pg. 3703
SOCIAL FULCRUM LLC—See ARS Advertising, LLC.; *U.S. Private*, pg. 337
SOCIAL GEAR PTE. LTD.—See Transcosmos Inc.; *Int'l*, pg. 7898
SOCIAL INTEREST SOLUTIONS; *U.S. Private*, pg. 3703
SOCIAL ISLAMI BANK LIMITED; *Int'l*, pg. 7031
SOCIALLITE US AB; *Int'l*, pg. 7031
SOCIAL MEDIA INDIA LIMITED—See Equippp Social Impact Technologies Ltd; *Int'l*, pg. 2485
SOCIAL MEDIA VENTURES, INC.; *U.S. Private*, pg. 3703
SOCIALPLAY USA, INC.; *U.S. Public*, pg. 1899
SOCIAL POINT, S.L.—See Take-Two Interactive Software, Inc.; *U.S. Public*, pg. 1979
SOCIALRADIUS; *U.S. Private*, pg. 3703
SOCIAL SCIENCE ELECTRONIC PUBLISHING, INC.—See RELX plc; *Int'l*, pg. 6268
SOCIAL & SCIENTIFIC SYSTEMS, INC.—See DLH Holdings Corp.; *U.S. Public*, pg. 670
SOCIAL SECURITY ADVOCATES FOR THE DISABLED, LLC—See Brown & Brown, Inc.; *U.S. Public*, pg. 402
SOCIAL SECURITY & NATIONAL INSURANCE TRUST; *Int'l*, pg. 7031
SOCIAL SOLUTIONS GLOBAL INC.; *U.S. Private*, pg. 3703
SOCIAL SPARKLING WINE, LLC; *U.S. Private*, pg. 3703
SOCIAL STUDIES SCHOOL SERVICE; *U.S. Private*, pg. 3703
SOCIALTEXT, INC.; *U.S. Private*, pg. 3703
SOCIAL VALUE INCUBATION LAB CO., LTD.—See Founder's Consultants Holdings, Inc.; *Int'l*, pg. 2753
SOCIALWARE, INC.—See Thoma Bravo, L.P.; *U.S. Private*, pg. 4151
SOCIALWIRE CO., LTD.; *Int'l*, pg. 7031
SOCIAL WORK ASSOCIATES LIMITED—See Empresaria Group Plc; *Int'l*, pg. 2389
SOC IBERICA DE CONSTRUCCIONES ELECTRICAS DE SEGURIDAD, S.L.—See ACS, Actividades de Construccion y Servicios, S.A.; *Int'l*, pg. 116
SOCIEDAD AGRICOLA LA ROSA SOFRUCO S.A.; *Int'l*, pg. 7031
SOCIEDAD ANONIMA ESTATAL DE CAUCION AGRARIA—See Sociedad Estatal de Participaciones Industriales; *Int'l*, pg. 7032
SOCIEDAD ANONIMA TRABAJOS Y OBRAS—See Grupo Villar Mir, S.A.U.; *Int'l*, pg. 3139
SOCIEDAD ASTURIANA DE DIVERSIFICACION MINERA S.A.—See Hulleras del Norte, S.A.; *Int'l*, pg. 3528
SOCIEDAD COMERCIAL DEL PLATA S.A.; *Int'l*, pg. 7031

COMPANY NAME INDEX

SOCIEDAD CONCESIONARIA AUTOPISTA CENTRAL S.A.—See ACS, Actividades de Construccion y Servicios, S.A.; *Int'l*, pg. 112
SOCIEDAD CONCESIONARIA AUTOPISTA DEL SOL, S.A.—See Industry Super Holdings Pty. Ltd.; *Int'l*, pg. 3676
SOCIEDAD CONCESIONARIA AUTOPISTA LOS ANDES, S.A.—See Industry Super Holdings Pty. Ltd.; *Int'l*, pg. 3676
SOCIEDAD CONCESIONARIA AUTOPISTA LOS LIBERTADORES, S.A.—See Industry Super Holdings Pty. Ltd.; *Int'l*, pg. 3676
SOCIEDAD CONCESIONARIA AUTOPISTA NORORIENTE SA—See Edizione S.r.l.; *Int'l*, pg. 2312
SOCIEDAD CONCESIONARIA AUTOPISTA NUEVA VESPUCIO SUR SA—See Edizione S.r.l.; *Int'l*, pg. 2312
SOCIEDAD CONCESIONARIA CENTRO DE JUSTICIA DE SANTIAGO, S.A.—See Grupo Villar Mir, S.A.U.; *Int'l*, pg. 3139
SOCIEDAD CONCESIONARIA CONSTANERA NORTE SA—See Edizione S.r.l.; *Int'l*, pg. 2312
SOCIEDAD CONCESIONARIA DE LOS LAGOS SA—See Edizione S.r.l.; *Int'l*, pg. 2312
SOCIEDAD CONCESIONARIA OPERADORA AEROPORTUARIA INTERNACIONAL S.A.-OPAIN S.A.—See Grupo Argos S.A.; *Int'l*, pg. 3121
SOCIEDAD CONCESIONARIA RUTA DEL CANAL, S.A.—See Empresas Penta S.A.; *Int'l*, pg. 2391
SOCIEDAD CONCESIONARIA VALLES DEL BIO BIO, S.A.—See Sacyr, S.A.; *Int'l*, pg. 6466
SOCIEDAD CONSTRUCTORA Y DE INVERSIONES MARTIN ZAMORA LTD.—See MAPFRE S.A.; *Int'l*, pg. 4685
SOCIEDAD CONTRACTUAL MINERA ATACAMA KOZAN S.A.—See Nittetsu Mining Co., Ltd.; *Int'l*, pg. 5383
SOCIEDAD CONTRACTUAL MINERA EL ABRA—See Corporacion Nacional del Cobre de Chile; *Int'l*, pg. 1805
SOCIEDAD CONTRACTUAL MINERA PUREN—See Corporacion Nacional del Cobre de Chile; *Int'l*, pg. 1805
SOCIEDAD DE CAPACITACION STRUCTURALIA CHILE LIMITADA—See Graham Holdings Company; *U.S. Public*, pg. 956
SOCIEDAD DE CEMENTOS Y MATERIALES DE CONSTRUCCION DE ANDALUCIA S.A.—See Camargo Correa S.A.; *Int'l*, pg. 1268
SOCIEDAD DE COMERCIO, ACHESON COLLOIDS—See Henkel AG & Co. KGaA; *Int'l*, pg. 3353
SOCIEDAD DE GENERACION EOLICA MANCHEGA, S.L.—See ACS, Actividades de Construccion y Servicios, S.A.; *Int'l*, pg. 116
SOCIEDAD DE INVERSIONES CAMPOS CHILENOS SA; *Int'l*, pg. 7031
SOCIEDAD DE INVERSIONES ORO BLANCO S.A.; *Int'l*, pg. 7031
SOCIEDAD DE INVERSIONES PAMPA CALICHERA SA; *Int'l*, pg. 7031
SOCIEDAD DE PARTICIPACION Y PROMOCION EMPRESARIAL CAJA DE MADRID—See Lone Star Funds; *U.S. Private*, pg. 2485
SOCIEDAD DE SERVICIOS PASEO DE SAN FRANCISCO, S.A. DE C.V.—See Industry Super Holdings Pty. Ltd.; *Int'l*, pg. 3675
SOCIEDADE ACOREANA DE ARMAZENAGEM DE GAS, S.A.—See Galp Energia SGPS, S.A.; *Int'l*, pg. 2875
SOCIEDADE ATLAS COPCO DE PORTUGAL LDA—See Atlas Copco AB; *Int'l*, pg. 684
SOCIEDADE CENTRAL DE CERVEJAS E BEBIDAS S.A.—See L'Arche Green N.V.; *Int'l*, pg. 4377
SOCIEDADE COMERCIAL OREY ANTUNES, S.A.; *Int'l*, pg. 7033
SOCIEDADE DAS AGUAS DA CURIA SA; *Int'l*, pg. 7033
SOCIEDADE DE ACTIVITIES EM MULTIMIDIA LTDA.—See CCR S.A.; *Int'l*, pg. 1369
SOCIEDADE GESTORA DO HOSPITAL DE LOURES, S.A.—See Fosun International Limited; *Int'l*, pg. 2751
SOCIEDADE ELECTRICA SANTIAGO S.A.—See The AES Corporation; *U.S. Public*, pg. 2032
SOCIEDADE MINEIRA DE NEVES CORVO S.A.—See Lundin Mining Corporation; *Int'l*, pg. 4584
SOCIEDADE NACIONAL DE COMBUSTIVEIS DE ANGOLA, E.P.; *Int'l*, pg. 7033
SOCIEDADE PORTUGUESA DO AR LIQUIDO LDA.—See L'Air Liquide S.A.; *Int'l*, pg. 4376
SOCIEDADE PORTUGUESA DOS ASCENSORES SCHINDLER LDA.—See Schindler Holding AG; *Int'l*, pg. 6621
SOCIEDADE PRODUTORA DE FIBRAS OPTICAS S.A.—See Prysmian S.p.A.; *Int'l*, pg. 6013
SOCIEDAD ESPANOLA DE CARBUROS METALICOS S.A.—See Air Products & Chemicals, Inc.; *U.S. Public*, pg. 67
SOCIEDAD ESPANOLA DE FRENOS, CALEFACCION Y SENALES, S.A.—See Knorr-Bremse AG; *Int'l*, pg. 4211
SOCIEDAD ESPANOLA DE MONTAJES INDUSTRIALES S.A.—See ACS, Actividades de Construccion y Servicios, S.A.; *Int'l*, pg. 116
SOCIEDAD ESPANOLA ZIG ZAG S.A.—See Miquel y Costas & Miquel, S.A.; *Int'l*, pg. 4915
SOCIEDAD ESTATAL DE PARTICIPACIONES INDUSTRIALES; *Int'l*, pg. 7031

SOCIEDADE TECHNICA DE EQUIPAMENTOS E TRACTORES SA—See Barloworld Ltd.; *Int'l*, pg. 866
SOCIEDAD EXPORTADORA Y COMERCIAL VINA MAIPO LTDA.—See Vina Concha y Toro S.A.; *Int'l*, pg. 8209
SOCIEDAD FINANCIERA Y MINERA S.A. - ANORGA CEMENT FACTORY—See Heidelberg Materials AG; *Int'l*, pg. 3317
SOCIEDAD FINANCIERA Y MINERA S.A. - ARRIGORRIAGA CEMENT FACTORY—See Heidelberg Materials AG; *Int'l*, pg. 3317
SOCIEDAD FINANCIERA Y MINERA S.A. - KUKULARRA PLANT—See Heidelberg Materials AG; *Int'l*, pg. 3317
SOCIEDAD FINANCIERA Y MINERA S.A. - MALAGA CEMENT FACTORY—See Heidelberg Materials AG; *Int'l*, pg. 3317
SOCIEDAD FINANCIERA Y MINERA, SA—See Heidelberg Materials AG; *Int'l*, pg. 3317
SOCIEDAD FINANCIERA Y MINERA S.A.—See Heidelberg Materials AG; *Int'l*, pg. 3317
SOCIEDAD GENERAL DE AGUAS DE BARCELONA, S.A.—See Veolia Environnement S.A.; *Int'l*, pg. 8155
SOCIEDAD GENERAL ESPANOLA DE LIBRERIA S.A.—See Springwater Capital LLC; *Int'l*, pg. 7144
SOCIEDAD GESTORA PARQUES EOLICOS ANDALUCIA, S.A.—See Iberdrola, S.A.; *Int'l*, pg. 3574
SOCIEDAD GNL MEJILLONES S.A.—See ENGIE SA; *Int'l*, pg. 2433
SOCIEDAD HIPODROMO CHILE S.A.; *Int'l*, pg. 7032
SOCIEDAD HIPOTECARIA FEDERAL SNC; *Int'l*, pg. 7032
SOCIEDAD INDUSTRIAL DE TRANSMISSIONES S.A.—See Sumitomo Heavy Industries, Ltd.; *Int'l*, pg. 7288
SOCIEDAD INDUSTRIAL PIZARRENO S.A—See Etex SA/NV; *Int'l*, pg. 2522
SOCIEDAD INDUSTRIAL ROMERAL S.A.—See Etex SA/NV; *Int'l*, pg. 2523
SOCIEDAD INDUSTRIAL TEJAS DE CHENA S.A.—See Etex SA/NV; *Int'l*, pg. 2523
SOCIEDAD INMOBILIARIA VINA DEL MAR S.A.; *Int'l*, pg. 7032
SOCIEDAD INVERSORA DOCK SUD SA—See Enel S.p.A.; *Int'l*, pg. 2412
SOCIEDAD LEGAL MINERA SAN JOSE UNO DE LO VICUNA EL TARTARO Y PIGUCHEN DE PUTAENDO—See Los Andes Copper Ltd.; *Int'l*, pg. 4558
SOCIEDAD MATRIZ BANCO DE CHILE; *Int'l*, pg. 7032
SOCIEDAD MATRIZ SAAM S.A.—See Compania Sudamericana de Vapores, S.A.; *Int'l*, pg. 1749
SOCIEDAD MINERA CAMBIOR PERU SA—See IAMGOLD Corporation; *Int'l*, pg. 3568
SOCIEDAD MINERA EL BROCAL S.A.A.—See Compania de Minas Buenaventura SAA; *Int'l*, pg. 1748
SOCIEDAD MINERA ISLA RIESCO S.A.—See AntarChile S.A.; *Int'l*, pg. 482
SOCIEDAD MINERA ISLA RIESCO S.A.—See Ultramar Ltda.; *Int'l*, pg. 8019
SOCIEDAD MINERA QUINCHIA S.A.S.—See Batero Gold Corp.; *Int'l*, pg. 889
SOCIEDAD MUNDIAL DE ASISTENCIA S.A.—See Allianz SE; *Int'l*, pg. 355
SOCIEDAD NACIONAL DE OLEODUCTOS S.A.—See AntarChile S.A.; *Int'l*, pg. 482
SOCIEDAD PESQUERA COLOSO S.A.; *Int'l*, pg. 7032
SOCIEDAD PORTUARIA EL CAYAO S.A. E.S.P.—See Grupo Aval Acciones y Valores S.A.; *Int'l*, pg. 3121
SOCIEDAD PORTUARIA GOLFO DE MORROSQUILLO S.A—See Grupo Argos S.A.; *Int'l*, pg. 3121
SOCIEDAD PORTUARIA PUERTO BAHIA S.A.—See Frontera Energy Corporation; *Int'l*, pg. 2794
SOCIEDAD PORTUARIA PUERTO WILCHES MUTIPROPOSITO SA—See AIP, LLC; *U.S. Private*, pg. 137
SOCIEDAD PORTUARIA RIO CORDOBA S.A.—See Vale S.A.; *Int'l*, pg. 8111
SOCIEDAD PUNTA DEL COBRE S.A.—See PACIFICO V REGION S.A.; *Int'l*, pg. 5693
SOCIEDAD QUIMICA ALEMANA S.A.—See Avient Corporation; *U.S. Public*, pg. 248
SOCIEDAD QUIMICA Y MINERA DE CHILE S.A.; *Int'l*, pg. 7032
SOCIEDAD RECTORA DE LA BOLSA DE VALORES DE BARCELONA, S.A.—See SIX Group AG; *Int'l*, pg. 6966
SOCIEDAD RECTORA DE LA BOLSA DE VALORES DE DE VALENCIA, S.A.—See SIX Group AG; *Int'l*, pg. 6966
SOCIEDAD SERVICIOS DE SALUD LTDA—See Sociedad Quimica y Minera de Chile S.A.; *Int'l*, pg. 7033
SOCIEDAD URUGUAYA DE CONTROL TECNICO DE AUTOMOTORES SOCIEDAD ANONIMA—See SGS SA; *Int'l*, pg. 6746
SOCIETA AGRICOLA SAN FELICE S.P.A.—See Allianz SE; *Int'l*, pg. 355
SOCIETA AGRICOLA TENIMENTI ANGELINI S.R.L.—See Angelini ACRAF S.p.A.; *Int'l*, pg. 460
SOCIETA AUTOSTRADA TIRRENICA P.A.—See Edizione S.r.l.; *Int'l*, pg. 2312

SOCIETE BIC S.A.

SOCIETA AZIONARIA PER LA CONDOTTA DI ACQUA POTABILI S.P.A.; *Int'l*, pg. 7033
SOCIETA BARIO E DERIVATI S.P.A.—See Solvay S.A.; *Int'l*, pg. 7078
SOCIETA CATTOLICA DI ASSICURAZIONE-SOCIETA COOPERATIVA; *Int'l*, pg. 7033
SOCIETA DEPOSITI COSTIERI - SO.DE.CO. SRL—See UniCredit S.p.A.; *Int'l*, pg. 8034
SOCIETA EDITORIALE IL FATTO S.P.A.; *Int'l*, pg. 7034
SOCIETA EDITRICE PADANA SPA—See Caltagirone Editore S.p.A.; *Int'l*, pg. 1266
SOCIETA ELETTRICA RADICI SPA—See Radici Partecipazioni S.p.A.; *Int'l*, pg. 6176
SOCIETA ELETTRICA SOPRACENERINA SA—See Azienda Elettrica Ticinese; *Int'l*, pg. 779
SOCIETA ELETTROCHIMICA SOLFURI E CLORODERIVATI (ELESO) S.P.A.—See Solvay S.A.; *Int'l*, pg. 7078
SOCIETA ESERCIZI COMMERCIALI INDUSTRIALI; *Int'l*, pg. 7034
SOCIETA GERNERALE PER L'INDUSTRIA DELLA MAGNESIA (SGIM) S.P.A.—See Solvay S.A.; *Int'l*, pg. 7078
SOCIETA INIZIATIVE AUTOSTRADALI E SERVIZI S.P.A.—See Argo Finanziaria S.p.A.; *Int'l*, pg. 562
SOCIETA INTERBANCARIA PER L'AUTOMAZIONE-CEDBORSA S.P.A.—See Cassa Depositi e Prestiti S.p.A.; *Int'l*, pg. 1354
SOCIETA ITALIANA ASSICURAZIONI E REASSICURAZIONI S.P.A.—See Zurich Insurance Group Limited; *Int'l*, pg. 8697
SOCIETA ITALIANA DI REVISIONE E FIDUCIARIA - S.I.RE.F. S.P.A.—See Intesa Sanpaolo S.p.A.; *Int'l*, pg. 3766
SOCIETA ITALIANA PER IL GAS—See Eni S.p.A.; *Int'l*, pg. 2437
SOCIETAL CDMO, INC.—See NovaQuest Capital Management, LLC; *U.S. Private*, pg. 2967
SOCIETA LOMBARDA IMMOBILIARE S.P.A.—See Intesa Sanpaolo S.p.A.; *Int'l*, pg. 3766
SOCIETA REALE MUTUA DI ASSICURAZIONI; *Int'l*, pg. 7034
SOCIETAT CATALANA DE PETROLIS S.A.—See Repsol, S.A.; *Int'l*, pg. 6294
SOCIETATEA COMERCIALA DE TRATAMENT BALNEAR BUZIAS-S.A.; *Int'l*, pg. 7034
SOCIETATEA COMERCIALA STICLA TURDA SA; *Int'l*, pg. 7034
SOCIETATEA DE ASIGURARI-REASIGURARI MOLD-CARGO S.A.; *Int'l*, pg. 7034
SOCIETATEA DE DISTRIBUTIE A ENERGIEI ELECTRICE MUNTENIA NORD SA—See Societatea Energetica Electrica S.A.; *Int'l*, pg. 7035
SOCIETATEA DE DISTRIBUTIE A ENERGIEI ELECTRICE TRANSILVANIA NORD SA—See Societatea Energetica Electrica S.A.; *Int'l*, pg. 7035
SOCIETATEA DE DISTRIBUTIE A ENERGIEI ELECTRICE TRANSILVANIA SUD SA—See Societatea Energetica Electrica S.A.; *Int'l*, pg. 7035
SOCIETATEA DE INVESTITII FINANCIARE OLTENIA S.A.; *Int'l*, pg. 7034
SOCIETATEA ENERGETICA ELECTRICA S.A.; *Int'l*, pg. 7034
SOCIETA VERONESE GESTIONE COMPRAVENDITA IMMOBILI A.R.L.—See UniCredit S.p.A.; *Int'l*, pg. 8035
SOCIETE ABIDJANAISE—See Accor S.A.; *Int'l*, pg. 92
SOCIETE ALSACIENNE DE DEVELOPPEMENT ET D'EXPANSION S.A.—See BNP Paribas SA; *Int'l*, pg. 1084
SOCIETE ANONYME BELGE DE CONSTRUCTIONS AERONAUTIQUES; *Int'l*, pg. 7035
SOCIETE ANONYME D'EXPLOSIFS ET DE PRODUITS CHIMIQUES; *Int'l*, pg. 7035
SOCIETE ARABE INTERNATIONALE DE BANQUE; *Int'l*, pg. 7035
SOCIETE ARMORICAINE DE VALORISATION ENERGETIQUE—See S.V.A. Jean ROZE; *Int'l*, pg. 6457
SOCIETE ATLANTIQUE DE PREFABRICATION—See Compagnie de Saint-Gobain SA; *Int'l*, pg. 1737
SOCIETE AUDOISE DE VEHICULES INDUSTRIELS ET DE MANUTENTION—See Manitou BF S.A.; *Int'l*, pg. 4672
SOCIETE AUTOMATIQUE DE PROFILAGE—See voestalpine AG; *Int'l*, pg. 8294
SOCIETE AZUREENNE DE GRANULATS—See Vicat S.A.; *Int'l*, pg. 8186
SOCIETE BEARNAISE DE SYNTHESE S.A.S.—See Firmenich International SA; *Int'l*, pg. 2681
SOCIETE BENINOISE DES GAZ INDUSTRIELS S.A.—See L'Air Liquide S.A.; *Int'l*, pg. 4376
SOCIETE BIC S.A.; *Int'l*, pg. 7036
SOCIETE BIC (SUISSE) SA—See Societe BIC S.A.; *Int'l*, pg. 7037
SOCIETE BOURBONNAISE DE MAINTENANCE INDUSTRIELLE—See VINCI S.A.; *Int'l*, pg. 8228
SOCIETE BOURBONNAISE DE TP & DE CONSTRUCTION—See VINCI S.A.; *Int'l*, pg. 8228
SOCIETE BOURBONNAISE INDUSTRIELLE D'ENROBES—See VINCI S.A.; *Int'l*, pg. 8227

2535

SOCIETE BIC S.A.

SOCIETE BOURBONNAISE INDUSTRIELLE DE PREFABRICATION ET DE BETON—See VINCI S.A.; *Int'l*, pg. 8227
SOCIETE BSB HLM LES FOYERS; *Int'l*, pg. 7037
SOCIETE BURKINABE DES FIBRES TEXTILES; *Int'l*, pg. 7037
SOCIETE BURKINABE DES GAZ INDUSTRIELS S.A.—See L'Air Liquide S.A.; *Int'l*, pg. 4376
SOCIETE CALEDONIENNE DE BATIMENT—See VINCI S.A.; *Int'l*, pg. 8228
SOCIETE CAMEROUNAISE DE PALMERAIES S.A.—See Socfinasia S.A.; *Int'l*, pg. 7031
SOCIETE CAMEROUNAISE DE PALMERAIES SOCAPALM S.A.—See Societe Financiere des Caoutchoucs SA; *Int'l*, pg. 7038
SOCIETE CARTIER SAS—See Compagnie Financiere Richemont S.A.; *Int'l*, pg. 1741
SOCIETE CHAMPARDENNAISE D'ENTREPRISES ELECTRIQUES—See VINCI S.A.; *Int'l*, pg. 8228
SOCIETE CHAMPENOISE D'ENROBES—See VINCI S.A.; *Int'l*, pg. 8228
SOCIETE CHARPENTE BOIS ET COUVERTURE INDUSTRIALISES—See VINCI S.A.; *Int'l*, pg. 8240
SOCIETE COMMERCIALE DE BRASSERIE SA; *Int'l*, pg. 7037
SOCIETE COMMERCIALE DES POTASSES ET DE L'AZOTE—See Entreprise Miniere et Chimique SA; *Int'l*, pg. 2453
SOCIETE COMMERCIALE ET INDUSTRIELLE DES PRODUITS EN PLASTIQUE; *Int'l*, pg. 7037
SOCIETE COMMERCIALE TARDY ET CIE. S.A.R.L.—See BRENNTAG SE; *Int'l*, pg. 1149
SOCIETE COMTOISE DE SPECIALITES FROMAGERES—See Gimv NV; *Int'l*, pg. 2976
SOCIETE CONCESSIONNAIRE DE LA AEROPORT (SCA)—See VINCI S.A.; *Int'l*, pg. 8230
SOCIETE CONCESSIONNAIRE DES AEROPORTS DU GRAND OUEST—See VINCI S.A.; *Int'l*, pg. 8230
SOCIETE CONGOLAISE DES EXPLOSIFS—See Societe Anonyme d'Explosifs et de Produits Chimiques; *Int'l*, pg. 7035
SOCIETE COOPERATIVE AGRICOLE L'ENVOL DE RETZ; *Int'l*, pg. 7037
SOCIETE CORSE TRAVAUX—See VINCI S.A.; *Int'l*, pg. 8228
SOCIETE D'AFFRETEMENT ET DE TRANSIT S.A.T. SAS—See Die Schweizerische Post AG; *Int'l*, pg. 2113
SOCIETE D'APPLICATION DES METHODES MODERNES D'ECLAIRAGE SA; *Int'l*, pg. 7037
SOCIETE D'APPLICATION ET D'INGENIERIE INDUSTRIELLE ET INFORMATIQUE SAS—See Schneider Electric SE; *Int'l*, pg. 6635
SOCIETE D'APPLICATIONS ROUTIERES—See VINCI S.A.; *Int'l*, pg. 8228
SOCIETE D'ASSAINISSEMENT RATIONNEL ET DE POMPAGE—See Veolia Environnement S.A.; *Int'l*, pg. 8154
SOCIETE D'ASSURANCE-DEPOTS DU CANADA; *Int'l*, pg. 7037
SOCIETE DE BANQUE FRANCAISE ET INTERNATIONALE—See Groupe BPCE; *Int'l*, pg. 3097
SOCIETE DE BOURSE GILBERT DUPONT SNC—See Societe Generale S.A.; *Int'l*, pg. 7042
SOCIETE DE COMMERCIALISATION DE FOURNITURES POUR L'INDUSTRIE ET LA CONSTRUCTION—See Compagnie de Saint-Gobain SA; *Int'l*, pg. 1737
SOCIETE DE CONSERVERIE EN AFRIQUE S.A.—See Dongwon Enterprise Co., Ltd.; *Int'l*, pg. 2171
SOCIETE DE CONSTRUCTION DE CANALISATIONS ET DE LIGNES ELECTRIQUES—See VINCI S.A.; *Int'l*, pg. 8228
SOCIETE DE CONSTRUCTION ET D'ASSEMBLAGES METALLIQUES SAS—See Amplifon S.p.A.; *Int'l*, pg. 436
SOCIETE DE CONSTRUCTION ET DE REPARATION DE MATERIEL AERONAUTIQUE—See Air France-KLM S.A.; *Int'l*, pg. 238
SOCIETE DE CONSTRUCTION GERATEK LTEE; *Int'l*, pg. 7037
SOCIETE DE COULEE CONTINUE DU CUIVRE—See Nexans S.A.; *Int'l*, pg. 5242
SOCIETE D'EDITIONS SCIENTIFIQUES ET CULTURELLES SA—See Informa plc; *Int'l*, pg. 3694
SOCIETE DE LA BOURSE DE LUXEMBOURG S.A.; *Int'l*, pg. 7037
SOCIETE DE LA CITE S.A.; *Int'l*, pg. 7037
SOCIETE DE LA RAFFINERIE DE DUNKERQUE—See OpenGate Capital Management, LLC; *U.S. Private*, pg. 3031
SOCIETE DE LA TOUR EIFFEL SA—See Societe Mutuelle d'Assurance du Batiment et des Travaux Publics; *Int'l*, pg. 7043
SOCIETE DELTA BATIMENT—See Delta Plus Group; *Int'l*, pg. 2020
SOCIETE DE MANUTENTION DU TERMINAL A CONTENEURS DE COTONOU—See Financiere de L'Odet; *Int'l*, pg. 2668
SOCIETE DE MATERIAUX AGGLOMERES GRENOBLOIS—See VINCI S.A.; *Int'l*, pg. 8228

SOCIETE DE MOTORISATIONS AERONAUTIQUES S.A.—See Safran SA; *Int'l*, pg. 6473
SOCIETE D'ENERGIE DE LA BAIE JAMES—See Hydro-Quebec; *Int'l*, pg. 3547
SOCIETE DE PARTICIPATION ET DE FINANCEMENT DANS LA COMM SA; *Int'l*, pg. 7037
SOCIETE DE POLE DE COMPETITIVITE DE MONASTIR - EL FEJJA—See Banque Internationale Arabe de Tunisie; *Int'l*, pg. 854
SOCIETE DE PRESSE FEMININE—See Vivendi SE; *Int'l*, pg. 8275
SOCIETE DE PROMOTION PHARMACEUTIQUE DU MAGHREB S.A.—See Hikma Pharmaceuticals PLC; *Int'l*, pg. 3390
SOCIETE DE PROSPECTION ET D'INVENTIONS TECHNIQUES S.A.S.—See Illinois Tool Works Inc.; *U.S. Public*, pg. 1110
SOCIETE DE PUBLICATIONS NOUVELLES SPN SA—See TX Group AG; *Int'l*, pg. 7992
SOCIETE DE RESTAURATION INDUSTRIELLE—See Air France-KLM S.A.; *Int'l*, pg. 237
SOCIETE DE RESTAURATION MONTPARNASSE SAS—See Eurazeo SE; *Int'l*, pg. 2529
SOCIETE DES ATELIERS LOUIS VUITTON—See LVMH Moet Hennessy Louis Vuitton SE; *Int'l*, pg. 4596
SOCIETE DES BAINS DE MER ET DU CERCLE DES ETRANGERS A MONACO; *Int'l*, pg. 7037
SOCIETE DES CARBONATES PIKETTI—See VINCI S.A.; *Int'l*, pg. 8228
SOCIETE DES CARRIERES DE CHAILLOUE—See VINCI S.A.; *Int'l*, pg. 8228
SOCIETE DES CARRIERES DE DOMPIERRE—See VINCI S.A.; *Int'l*, pg. 8228
SOCIETE DES CARRIERES DE LA 113—See Eiffage S.A.; *Int'l*, pg. 2331
SOCIETE DES CARRIERES DE VIGNATS ET DE NORMANDIE; *Int'l*, pg. 7037
SOCIETE DES CARRIERES DU BOISCHAUT—See VINCI S.A.; *Int'l*, pg. 8228
SOCIETE DES CENTRES D'OC ET D'OIL - SCOO SC—See BNP Paribas SA; *Int'l*, pg. 1092
SOCIETE DES CHEMINS DE FER ET TRAMWAYS DU VAR ET DU GARD SA; *Int'l*, pg. 7038
SOCIETE DES CIMENTS DE GABES, S.A.—See SODIM, SGPS, SA; *Int'l*, pg. 7049
SOCIETE DES EAUX DE MARSEILLE S.A.—See Veolia Environnement S.A.; *Int'l*, pg. 8154
SOCIETE DES EAUX DE MELUN S.C.A.—See Veolia Environnement S.A.; *Int'l*, pg. 8154
SOCIETE DES EAUX MINERALES D'OGEU SAS; *Int'l*, pg. 7038
SOCIETE DES EAUX MINERALES VITTOR S.A.E.—See Nestle S.A.; *Int'l*, pg. 5205
SOCIETE DES ENROBES DE MOULINS ET DES ENVIRONS—See VINCI S.A.; *Int'l*, pg. 8228
SOCIETE DES ENROBES DU CLERMONTOIS—See VINCI S.A.; *Int'l*, pg. 8228
SOCIETE DES ENROBES DU PLATEAU—See VINCI S.A.; *Int'l*, pg. 8228
SOCIETE DE SERVICE DU GAZODUC TRANSTUNISIEN SA - SERGAZ SA—See Eni S.p.A.; *Int'l*, pg. 2438
SOCIETE DE SERVICES DE MAINTENANCE INDUSTRIELS—See Electronic Business System; *Int'l*, pg. 2354
SOCIETE DES ETABLISSEMENTS RESCANIERES—See VINCI S.A.; *Int'l*, pg. 8228
SOCIETE DES FIBRES DE CARBONE S.A.—See Toray Industries, Inc.; *Int'l*, pg. 7823
SOCIETE DES FORCES ELECTRIQUES DE LA GOULE SA—See BKW AG; *Int'l*, pg. 1056
SOCIETE DES GAZ INDUSTRIELS DE LA GUADELOUPE—See L'Air Liquide S.A.; *Int'l*, pg. 4376
SOCIETE DES HOTELS INTERCONTINENTAL FRANCE SNC—See InterContinental Hotels Group PLC; *Int'l*, pg. 3739
SOCIETE DES LECTEURS DU MONDE SA; *Int'l*, pg. 7038
SOCIETE DES MAGASINS LOUIS VUITTON-FRANCE—See LVMH Moet Hennessy Louis Vuitton SE; *Int'l*, pg. 4596
SOCIETE DES MATERIAUX CAENNAIS—See VINCI S.A.; *Int'l*, pg. 8228
SOCIETE DES MATIERES PREMIERES TROPICALES PTE. LTD.—See Compagnie Generale des Etablissements Michelin SCA; *Int'l*, pg. 1743
SOCIETE DES PRODUITS ALIMENTAIRES DE CAUDRY S.A.S.—See Nestle S.A.; *Int'l*, pg. 5211
SOCIETE DES PRODUITS MARNIER-LAPOSTOLLE S.A.—See Alicorcos S.A.; *Int'l*, pg. 327
SOCIETE DES TERRAINS ET IMMEUBLES PARISIENS—See Societe Generale S.A.; *Int'l*, pg. 7041
SOCIETE DES TRANSPORTS DEPARTEMENTAUX DE LA MARNE—See Regie Autonome des Transports Parisiens; *Int'l*, pg. 6253
SOCIETE DES TRANSPORTS SAVREUX—See VINCI S.A.; *Int'l*, pg. 8228
SOCIETE DES TRAVAUX PUBLICS DE L'OUEST—See VINCI S.A.; *Int'l*, pg. 8228

CORPORATE AFFILIATIONS

SOCIETE DES TUYAUX ARMES DE LA CHARENTE—See Compagnie de Saint-Gobain SA; *Int'l*, pg. 1737
SOCIETE DE TAYNINH SA—See Unibail-Rodamco-Westfield SE; *Int'l*, pg. 8030
SOCIETE DE TELEVISION LOCALE SAS—See NRJ Group SA; *Int'l*, pg. 5474
SOCIETE DE TRANSMISSIONS AUTOMATIQUES—See Renault S.A.; *Int'l*, pg. 6274
SOCIETE DE TRANSPORTS DE VEHICULES AUTOMOBILES—See SNCF; *Int'l*, pg. 7027
SOCIETE DE TRAVAUX ET DE ROUTES FRANCILIENNE (STRF) SARL—See VINCI S.A.; *Int'l*, pg. 8220
SOCIETE D'ETUDES ET DE FABRICATIONS ELECTRONIQUES ET ELECTRIQUES—See Amphenol Corporation; *U.S. Public*, pg. 132
SOCIETE D'EXPERTISE ET D'INGENIERIE LGL S.A.—See AtkinsRealis Group Inc.; *Int'l*, pg. 673
SOCIETE D'EXPLOITATION D'ACTIVITES TOURISTIQUES—See Danone; *Int'l*, pg. 1968
SOCIETE D'EXPLOITATION D'AGENCES DE VOYAGES ET DE TOURISME SA—See Accor S.A.; *Int'l*, pg. 92
SOCIETE D'EXPLOITATION DE L'AEROPORT DU PAYS D'ANCENIS—See VINCI S.A.; *Int'l*, pg. 8228
SOCIETE D'EXPLOITATION DE PRODUITS POUR LES INDUSTRIES CHIMIQUES—See L'Air Liquide S.A.; *Int'l*, pg. 4376
SOCIETE D'EXPLOITATION DES MATERIELS MARTIN BAKER SEM MB (SA)—See Safran SA; *Int'l*, pg. 6476
SOCIETE'D EXPLOITATION DES PARCS DE LA DEFENSE—See VINCI S.A.; *Int'l*, pg. 8228
SOCIETE D'EXPLOITATION DU CHALET DE LA PORTE JAUNE SASU—See SSP Group plc; *Int'l*, pg. 7157
SOCIETE D'EXPLOITATION DU PARC DES EXPOSITIONS DE LYON; *Int'l*, pg. 7037
SOCIETE D'INSTALLATIONS ET DE DIFFUSION DE MATERIEL TECHNIQUE S.P.A.—See Adenia Partners Ltd; *Int'l*, pg. 143
SOCIETE D'INSTRUMENTS DE PRECISION SA—See Starrag Group Holding AG; *Int'l*, pg. 7179
SOCIETE DMT SAS; *Int'l*, pg. 7038
SOCIETE D'OXYGENE ET D ACETYLENE D EXTREME-ORIENT SA—See L'Air Liquide S.A.; *Int'l*, pg. 4376
SOCIETE DU BRIQUET JETABLE 75 SASU—See Societe BIC S.A.; *Int'l*, pg. 7037
SOCIETE DU CASINO DE SAINT AMAND S.A.S.—See Groupe Partouche S.A.; *Int'l*, pg. 3109
SOCIETE DU DEPOT DE ST PRIEST—See Rubis SCA; *Int'l*, pg. 6423
SOCIETE DU JOURNAL L'EST REPUBLICAIN SA; *Int'l*, pg. 7038
SOCIETE DU LOUVRE SA—See Starwood Capital Group Global I, LLC; *U.S. Private*, pg. 3789
SOCIETE DU PIPELINE SUD-EUROPEEN—See TotalEnergies SE; *Int'l*, pg. 7838
SOCIETE ECU-LINE TUNISIE SARL—See Allcargo Logistics Limited; *Int'l*, pg. 334
SOCIETE EMCC—See VINCI S.A.; *Int'l*, pg. 8228
SOCIETE EUROPEENE DE COMMUNICATION—See Modern Times Group MTG AB; *Int'l*, pg. 5015
SOCIETE EUROPEENNE DE FINANCEMENT ET D'INVESTISSEMENT SA—See Societe Generale S.A.; *Int'l*, pg. 7041
SOCIETE EUROPEENNE DE GALVANISATION (SEGAL) SA—See Tata Sons Limited; *Int'l*, pg. 7472
SOCIETE EUROPEENNE DES PRODUITS REFRACTAIRES—See Compagnie de Saint-Gobain SA; *Int'l*, pg. 1732
SOCIETE EUROPEENNE DE STOCKAGE—See Rubis SCA; *Int'l*, pg. 6423
SOCIETE FERMIERE DU CASINO MUNICIPAL DE CANNES; *Int'l*, pg. 7038
SOCIETE FINANCIERE DES CAOUTCHOUCS SA; *Int'l*, pg. 7038
SOCIETE FONCIERE ET INDUSTRIELLE S.A.S.—See BASF SE; *Int'l*, pg. 879
SOCIETE FONCIERE, FINANCIERE ET DE PARTICIPATIONS S.A.; *Int'l*, pg. 7038
SOCIETE FONCIERE LYONNAISE S.A.S.—See Inmobiliaria Colonial SOCIMI SA; *Int'l*, pg. 3706
SOCIETE FONCIERE POUR L'EQUIPEMENT—See Stellantis N.V.; *Int'l*, pg. 7203
SOCIETE FRANCAISE DE CASINOS SA; *Int'l*, pg. 7038
SOCIETE FRANCAISE DE COMMERCE EUROPEEN S.A.—See Toyota Tsusho Corporation; *Int'l*, pg. 7876
SOCIETE FRANCAISE DE CONSTRUCTION IMMOBILERE—See SNCF; *Int'l*, pg. 7027
SOCIETE FRANCAISE DE CONSTRUCTION MECANIQUE ET ELECTRIQUE SA—See Schneider Electric SE; *Int'l*, pg. 6635
SOCIETE FRANCAISE DE DISTRIBUTION D'EAU SCA—See Veolia Environnement S.A.; *Int'l*, pg. 8154
SOCIETE FRANCAISE DE GARANTIE S.A.—See Brookfield Corporation; *Int'l*, pg. 863
SOCIETE FRANCAISE DE GESTION ET DE CONSTRUCTION (SFGC) SA—See Barclays PLC; *Int'l*, pg. 863
SOCIETE FRANCAISE DE GESTION ET DINVESTISSEMENT SOFRAGI SA—See Aema Groupe; *Int'l*, pg. 175

COMPANY NAME INDEX

SOCIETE FRANCAISE DE PROMOTION TOURISTIQUE ET HOTELIERE SA—See Accor S.A.; *Int'l*, pg. 92
SOCIETE FRANCAISE DES ASCENSEURS KONE—See KONE Oyj; *Int'l*, pg. 4250
SOCIETE FRANCAISE DES EAUX REGIONALES S.A.S.—See Nestle S.A.; *Int'l*, pg. 5211
SOCIETE FRANCAISE DU RADIOTELEPHONE S.A.—See Tofane Global SAS; *Int'l*, pg. 7774
SOCIETE FRANCAISE GARDY SA—See Schneider Electric SE; *Int'l*, pg. 6635
SOCIETE FRANCAISE KEB SASU—See Karl E. Brinkmann GmbH; *Int'l*, pg. 4081
SOCIETE GASCOGNE SACK TUNISIA—See Gascogne SA; *Int'l*, pg. 2888
SOCIETE GENERALE BANK AND TRUST LUXEMBOURG—See Societe Generale S.A.; *Int'l*, pg. 7041
SOCIETE GENERALE BANK NEDERLAND N.V.—See Societe Generale S.A.; *Int'l*, pg. 7041
SOCIETE GENERALE BANK & TRUST (MIDDLE EAST) FZE—See Societe Generale S.A.; *Int'l*, pg. 7041
SOCIETE GENERALE (CANADA)—See Societe Generale S.A.; *Int'l*, pg. 7041
SOCIETE GENERALE CAPITAL PARTENAIRES SAS—See Societe Generale S.A.; *Int'l*, pg. 7042
SOCIETE GENERALE (CHINA) LIMITED—See Societe Generale S.A.; *Int'l*, pg. 7041
SOCIETE GENERALE CORPORATE & INVESTMENT BANKING AUSTRALIA—See Societe Generale S.A.; *Int'l*, pg. 7039
SOCIETE GENERALE CORPORATE & INVESTMENT BANKING—See Societe Generale S.A.; *Int'l*, pg. 7042
SOCIETE GENERALE DE BANQUE AU LIBAN S.A.L.; *Int'l*, pg. 7038
SOCIETE GENERALE DE BANQUE - JORDANIE—See Societe Generale de Banque au Liban s.a.l.; *Int'l*, pg. 7038
SOCIETE GENERALE DE BANQUES AU SENEGAL—See Societe Generale S.A.; *Int'l*, pg. 7042
SOCIETE GENERALE DE BANQUES EN COTE D'IVOIRE—See Societe Generale S.A.; *Int'l*, pg. 7042
SOCIETE GENERALE DE BANQUES EN GUINEE EQUATORIALE S.A.—See Societe Generale S.A.; *Int'l*, pg. 7042
SOCIETE GENERALE DE BANQUES EN GUINEE-SGBG—See Societe Generale S.A.; *Int'l*, pg. 7042
SOCIETE GENERALE DE LEASING AU MAROC SA—See Societe Generale S.A.; *Int'l*, pg. 7042
SOCIETE GENERALE DE SURVEILLANCE AZERI LTD.—See SGS SA; *Int'l*, pg. 6746
SOCIETE GENERALE ENERGIE SA—See Societe Generale S.A.; *Int'l*, pg. 7041
SOCIETE GENERALE ENERGIE U.S.A.—See Societe Generale S.A.; *Int'l*, pg. 7042
SOCIETE GENERALE EUROPEAN BUSINESS SERVICES S.A.—See Societe Generale S.A.; *Int'l*, pg. 7042
SOCIETE GENERALE FINANCIAL—See Societe Generale S.A.; *Int'l*, pg. 7042
SOCIETE GENERALE FONCIERE SAL—See Fransabank SAL; *Int'l*, pg. 2762
SOCIETE GENERALE-FRANKFURT AM MAIN—See Societe Generale S.A.; *Int'l*, pg. 7042
SOCIETE GENERALE GHANA LIMITED—See Societe Generale S.A.; *Int'l*, pg. 7042
SOCIETE GENERALE GLOBAL SOLUTION CENTRE PRIVATE LIMITED—See Societe Generale S.A.; *Int'l*, pg. 7042
SOCIETE GENERALE INVESTMENTS (U.K.) LIMITED—See Societe Generale S.A.; *Int'l*, pg. 7041
SOCIETE GENERALE-LONDON—See Societe Generale S.A.; *Int'l*, pg. 7042
SOCIETE GENERALE MAROCAINE DE BANQUES SA—See Societe Generale S.A.; *Int'l*, pg. 7042
SOCIETE GENERALE PRIVATE BANKING (SUISSE) S.A.—See Societe Generale S.A.; *Int'l*, pg. 7042
SOCIETE GENERALE PRIVATE WEALTH MANAGEMENT S.A.—See Societe Generale S.A.; *Int'l*, pg. 7042
SOCIETE GENERALE S.A.—See Societe Generale S.A.; *Int'l*, pg. 7042
SOCIETE GENERALE S.A.; *Int'l*, pg. 7038
SOCIETE GENERALE SCF—See Societe Generale S.A.; *Int'l*, pg. 7041
SOCIETE GENERALE SECURITIES (NORTH PACIFIC) LTD—See Societe Generale S.A.; *Int'l*, pg. 7041
SOCIETE GENERALE SECURITIES SERVICES GMBH—See Societe Generale S.A.; *Int'l*, pg. 7042
SOCIETE GENERALE SECURITIES SERVICES HOLDING SA—See Societe Generale S.A.; *Int'l*, pg. 7041
SOCIETE GENERALE SECURITIES SERVICES (IRELAND) LTD.—See Societe Generale S.A.; *Int'l*, pg. 7042
SOCIETE GENERALE SECURITIES SERVICES S.P.A.—See Societe Generale S.A.; *Int'l*, pg. 7042
SOCIETE GENERALE SECURITIES (THAILAND) LTD.—See Societe Generale S.A.; *Int'l*, pg. 7042
SOCIETE GENERALE SENEGAL SA—See Societe Generale S.A.; *Int'l*, pg. 7042
SOCIETE GENERALE SPLITSKA BANKA D.D—See Societe Generale S.A.; *Int'l*, pg. 7041
SOCIETE GENERALE STRAKHOVANIE LLC—See Societe Generale S.A.; *Int'l*, pg. 7042
SOCIETE GENERALE STRAKHOVANIE ZHIZNI LLC—See Societe Generale S.A.; *Int'l*, pg. 7042
SOCIETE GENERALE - TOKYO—See Societe Generale S.A.; *Int'l*, pg. 7041
SOCIETE GENERALE ZWEIGNIEDERLASSUNG WIEN—See Societe Generale S.A.; *Int'l*, pg. 7042
SOCIETE GUADELOUPEENNE DE CARTON ONDULE SAS—See International Paper Company; *U.S. Public*, pg. 1158
SOCIETE GUYANAISE DE L'AIR LIQUIDE—See L'Air Liquide S.A.; *Int'l*, pg. 4376
SOCIETE HOSPITALIERE D'ASSURANCE MUTUELLE; *Int'l*, pg. 7042
SOCIETE HOTELIERE 61 QUAI DE GRENELLE—See Accor S.A.; *Int'l*, pg. 92
SOCIETE HOTELIERE ET IMMOBILIERE DE NICE SA; *Int'l*, pg. 7042
SOCIETE HOTELIERE PARIS VANVES—See Accor S.A.; *Int'l*, pg. 92
SOCIETE HYDROELECTRIQUE DU MIDI—See ENGIE SA; *Int'l*, pg. 2435
SOCIETE HYDRO-ELECTRIQUE DU MIDI—See ENGIE SA; *Int'l*, pg. 2434
SOCIETE IMMOBILIERE BALIMA; *Int'l*, pg. 7043
SOCIETE IMMOBILIERE DE MANDARIN ORIENTAL (GENEVA) SA—See Jardine Matheson Holdings Limited; *Int'l*, pg. 3911
SOCIETE IMMOBILIERE DE NOISIEL S.A.—See Nestle S.A.; *Int'l*, pg. 5211
SOCIETE INDUSTRIELLE DE COMBUSTIBLE NUCLEAIRE ANNECY (SICN) SA—See Orano SA; *Int'l*, pg. 5611
SOCIETE INDUSTRIELLE DE L'OUEST DES PRODUITS ISOLANTS SAS—See SIG plc; *Int'l*, pg. 6907
SOCIETE INDUSTRIELLE DES OLEAGINEUX-SIO—See Archer-Daniels-Midland Company; *U.S. Public*, pg. 185
SOCIETE INDUSTRIELLE DES VITRAGES D'AQUITAINE—See Compagnie de Saint-Gobain SA; *Int'l*, pg. 1736
SOCIETE INDUSTRIELLE DE TRANSFORMATION DE PRODUITS AGRICOLES S.A.S.—See Nestle S.A.; *Int'l*, pg. 5211
SOCIETE INDUSTRIELLE DU TITANE, S.A.—See Contran Corporation; *U.S. Private*, pg. 1033
SOCIETE INDUSTRIELLE ET CHIMIQUE DE L'AISNE S.A.S.—See AMG Critical Materials N.V.; *Int'l*, pg. 426
SOCIETE INDUSTRIELLE ET FINANCIERE DE L'ARTOIS SA; *Int'l*, pg. 7043
SOCIETE INMOBILIAR BBV D—See Banco Bilbao Vizcaya Argentaria, S.A.; *Int'l*, pg. 818
SOCIETE INTERNATIONALE DE CONTROLE ET APPROVISIONNEMENT SASU—See Cobepa S.A.; *Int'l*, pg. 1683
SOCIETE INTERNATIONALE DE PLANTATIONS D'HEVEAS SA—See SIFCA SA; *Int'l*, pg. 6905
SOCIETE INTERNATIONALE DES HOTELS NOVOTEL—See Accor S.A.; *Int'l*, pg. 92
SOCIETE INTERNATIONALE ITALCEMENTI (LUXEMBOURG) S.A.—See Heidelberg Materials AG; *Int'l*, pg. 3317
SOCIETE ITALIANA PER CONDOTTE D'ACQUA S.P.A.—See Ferfina S.p.A.; *Int'l*, pg. 2637
SOCIETE IVOIRIENNE DE MANUTENTION ET DE TRANSIT SA; *Int'l*, pg. 7043
SOCIETE IVOIRIENNE D OXYGENE ET D ACETYLENE—See L'Air Liquide S.A.; *Int'l*, pg. 4376
SOCIETE JAS HENNESSY & CO. S.A.—See LVMH Moet Hennessy Louis Vuitton SE; *Int'l*, pg. 4600
SOCIETE JEAN LEFEBVRE POLYNESIE—See VINCI S.A.; *Int'l*, pg. 8240
SOCIETE LA BIOCHIMIE APPLIQUEE SAS; *Int'l*, pg. 7043
SOCIETE LE NICKEL—See Eramet SA; *Int'l*, pg. 2489
SOCIETE LENSOISE DE CUIVRE—See Nexans S.A.; *Int'l*, pg. 5242
SOCIETE LIBANAISE DE FACTORING SAL—See Bank Audi sal; *Int'l*, pg. 837
SOCIETE LORRAINE D'AGREGATS; *Int'l*, pg. 7043
SOCIETE LORRAINE D'ENROBES—See VINCI S.A.; *Int'l*, pg. 8228
SOCIETE LORRAINE D'EXPLOITATION DE TERRILS—See VINCI S.A.; *Int'l*, pg. 8228
SOCIETE LOUIS VUITTON SERVICES SNC—See LVMH Moet Hennessy Louis Vuitton SE; *Int'l*, pg. 4600
SOCIETE LUXEMBOURGEOISE DE NAVIGATION AERIENNE, S.A.; *Int'l*, pg. 7043
SOCIETE MAGHREBINE DE MONETIQUE - S2M; *Int'l*, pg. 7043
SOCIETE MAHORAISE DES EAUX—See VINCI S.A.; *Int'l*, pg. 8228
SOCIETE MALGACHE DES PETROLES VIVO ENERGY S.A.—See Vitol Holding B.V.; *Int'l*, pg. 8261
SOCIETE MARITIME GENMAR SARL—See Albert Ballin KG; *Int'l*, pg. 296
SOCIETE MAROCAINE DE COOPERATION PHARMACEUTIQUE; *Int'l*, pg. 7043
SOCIETE MAROCAINE DES COLLES—See Arkema S.A.; *Int'l*, pg. 571
SOCIETE MAROCAINE POUR LE DEVELOPPEMENT DES TRANSPORTS TOURISTIQUES S.A.—See TUI AG; *Int'l*, pg. 7966
SOCIETE MARSEILLAISE DE CREDIT SA—See Societe Generale S.A.; *Int'l*, pg. 7042
SOCIETE MARSELLAISE DU TUNNEL PRADO CARENAGE SA; *Int'l*, pg. 7043
SOCIETE MARTINIQUAISE DE CARTON ONDULE—See International Paper Company; *U.S. Public*, pg. 1158
SOCIETE MARTINIQUAISE DE L AIR LIQUIDE—See L'Air Liquide S.A.; *Int'l*, pg. 4376
SOCIETE MECANIQUE AUTOMOBILE DE L'EST—See Stellantis N.V.; *Int'l*, pg. 7203
SOCIETE MEDITERRANEENNE D EMBALLAGES SAS—See International Paper Company; *U.S. Public*, pg. 1158
SOCIETE MISS FRANCE—See LOV Group Invest SAS; *Int'l*, pg. 4565
SOCIETE MODERNE DU PNEUMATIQUE CAMEROUNAIS—See Compagnie Generale des Etablissements Michelin SCA; *Int'l*, pg. 1745
SOCIETE MONEGASQUE JEAN LEFEBVRE—See VINCI S.A.; *Int'l*, pg. 8228
SOCIETE MULTINATIONALE DE BITUMES, LTD; *Int'l*, pg. 7043
SOCIETE MUTUELLE D'ASSURANCE DU BATIMENT ET DES TRAVAUX PUBLICS; *Int'l*, pg. 7043
SOCIETE NATIONALE D'ASSURANCES S.A.L.—See Allianz SE; *Int'l*, pg. 342
SOCIETE NATIONALE DE CREDIT ET D'INVESTISSEMENT; *Int'l*, pg. 7043
SOCIETE NATIONALE D'ELECTROLYSE ET DE PETROCHIMIE EST; *Int'l*, pg. 7043
SOCIETE NATIONALE DE PROPRIETE D'IMMEUBLES SCA; *Int'l*, pg. 7043
SOCIETE NATIONALE DE SIDERURGIE S.A.—See ArcelorMittal S.A.; *Int'l*, pg. 546
SOCIETE NATIONALE IMMOBILIERE—See Caisse des Depots et Consignations; *Int'l*, pg. 1258
SOCIETE NICOISE D'ENROBAGE—See VINCI S.A.; *Int'l*, pg. 8228
SOCIETE NORMANDE DE CARTON ONDULE SAS—See International Paper Company; *U.S. Public*, pg. 1158
SOCIETE NOUVELLE AIR IVOIRE S.A.—See Air France-KLM S.A.; *Int'l*, pg. 238
SOCIETE NOUVELLE CGVL S.A.S.U.—See Mutares SE & Co. KGaA; *Int'l*, pg. 5105
SOCIETE NOUVELLE D'AFFINAGE DES METAUX - SNAM S.A.S.—See Floridienne S.A.; *Int'l*, pg. 2708
SOCIETE NOUVELLE DU GRAND HOTEL SA—See InterContinental Hotels Group PLC; *Int'l*, pg. 3739
SOCIETE ORANAISE DE MAINTENANCE INDUSTRIELLE—See Schindler Holding AG; *Int'l*, pg. 6621
SOCIETE ORBAISIENNE DE PARTICIPATIONS—See BNP Paribas SA; *Int'l*, pg. 1092
SOCIETE PARISIENNE DES HOTELS ECONOMIQUES—See Accor S.A.; *Int'l*, pg. 92
SOCIETE PERINO & BORDONE—See VINCI S.A.; *Int'l*, pg. 8228
SOCIETE PHARMACEUTIQUE DES CARAIBES—See Toyota Tsusho Corporation; *Int'l*, pg. 7876
SOCIETE PHARMACEUTIQUE GABONAISE—See Toyota Tsusho Corporation; *Int'l*, pg. 7876
SOCIETE POLYGONE S.A.; *Int'l*, pg. 7043
SOCIETE POUR LA GESTION DE PLACEMENTS COLLECTIFS GEP SA—See Banque Cantonale Vaudoise; *Int'l*, pg. 853
SOCIETE POUR LE CONDITIONNEMENT DES DECHETS ET EFFLUENTS INDUSTRIELS—See Electricite de France S.A.; *Int'l*, pg. 2352
SOCIETE POUR L'EQUIPEMENT DES INDUSTRIES CHIMIQUES SA—See Schneider Electric SE; *Int'l*, pg. 6635
SOCIETE POUR L'EXPANSION DES VENTES DES PRODUITS AGRICOLES ET ALIMENTAIRES—See Hopscotch Groupe S.A.; *Int'l*, pg. 3474
SOCIETE POUR L'EXPLOITATION DE MANDARIN ORIENTAL (GENEVA) SA—See Jardine Matheson Holdings Limited; *Int'l*, pg. 3911
SOCIETE POUR L'EXPORTATION DES PRODUITS NESTLE S.A.—See Nestle S.A.; *Int'l*, pg. 5211
SOCIETE POUR L'INFORMATIQUE INDUSTRIELLE; *Int'l*, pg. 7043
SOCIETE PROFILAFROID—See voestalpine AG; *Int'l*, pg. 8294
SOCIETE REUNIONNAISE DE PRODUITS PETROLIERS—See Rubis SCA; *Int'l*, pg. 6423
SOCIETE REUNIONNAISE DE RENOVATION—See VINCI S.A.; *Int'l*, pg. 8228
SOCIETE REUNION—See ENL Limited; *Int'l*, pg. 2442
SOCIETE ROUTIERE DU MIDI—See VINCI S.A.; *Int'l*, pg. 8228
SOCIETE SAS—See La Poste S.A.; *Int'l*, pg. 4388

SOCIETE POUR L'INFORMATIQUE INDUSTRIELLE

CORPORATE AFFILIATIONS

SOCIETE SENEGALAISE D OXYGENE ET D ACETYLENE—See L'Air Liquide S.A.; *Int'l*, pg. 4376
SOCIETE SHELL DU LAOS—See Petro Vietnam Oil Corporation; *Int'l*, pg. 5825
SOCIETE SIGNATURE OCEAN INDIEN—See VINCI S.A.; *Int'l*, pg. 8228
SOCIETE SUISSE / SWISS LIFE (FRANCE)—See Swiss Life Holding; *Int'l*, pg. 7369
SOCIETETECHNIQUE D'INGENIERIE ET DE COOPERATION—See Industrielle De Controle Et D Equipement; *Int'l*, pg. 3675
SOCIETE TUNISIENNE D'ASSURANCES ET DE REASSURANCES—See Groupama SA; *Int'l*, pg. 3091
SOCIETE TUNISIENNE DE L'INDUSTRIE DU BOIS—See Poulina Group Holding S.A.; *Int'l*, pg. 5942
SOCIETE TUNISIENNE DE PEINTURES ASTRAL S.A.—See Akzo Nobel N.V.; *Int'l*, pg. 275
SOCIETE TUNISIENNE DE VERRERIES S.A.; *Int'l*, pg. 7044
SOCIETE TUNISO-ANDALOUSE DE CIMENT BLANC—See Cementos Molins S.A.; *Int'l*, pg. 1397
SOCIETE VELLAVE DE TRANSPORTS—See SNCF; *Int'l*, pg. 7025
SOCIETE VERRIERE DE L'ATLANTIQUE—See Compagnie de Saint-Gobain SA; *Int'l*, pg. 1737
SOCIETE VERRIERE D'ENCAPSULATION—See Compagnie de Saint-Gobain SA; *Int'l*, pg. 1737
SOCIETE VERRIERE FRANCAISE—See Compagnie de Saint-Gobain SA; *Int'l*, pg. 1737
SOCIETE VITICOLE DE REIMS SA—See LVMH Moet Hennessy Louis Vuitton SE; *Int'l*, pg. 4600
SOCIETE VIVO ENERGY TUNISIE S.A.—See Vitol Holding B.V.; *Int'l*, pg. 8261
SOCIETE YVELINOISE DE MATERIAUX ET D'ENROBES SAS—See VINCI S.A.; *Int'l*, pg. 8228
SOCIETE ZEGHONDY POUR LE COMMERCE S.A.R.L.—See Einhell Germany AG; *Int'l*, pg. 2334
SOCIETY6, LLC—See Graham Holdings Company; *U.S. Public*, pg. 956
SOCIETY AWARDS; *U.S. Private*, pg. 3703
SOCIETY BRANDS, INC.; *U.S. Private*, pg. 3703
SOCIETY CONSULTING, LLC—See Ernst & Young LLP; *U.S. Private*, pg. 1423
SOCIETY DEVELOPMENT BANK LIMITED; *Int'l*, pg. 7044
SOCIETY FOR LEUKOCYTE BIOLOGY; *U.S. Private*, pg. 3703
SOCIETY FOR NEUROSCIENCE; *U.S. Private*, pg. 3703
SOCIETY FOR SCIENCE & THE PUBLIC; *U.S. Private*, pg. 3703
SOCIETY FOR THE PROTECTION OF NEW HAMP-SHIRE FORESTS; *U.S. Private*, pg. 3703
SOCIETY INSURANCE; *U.S. Private*, pg. 3704
SOCIETY OF BEHAVIORAL MEDICINE; *U.S. Private*, pg. 3704
SOCIETY OF EXPLORATION GEOPHYSICISTS; *U.S. Private*, pg. 3704
SOCIETY OF MANUFACTURING ENGINEERS; *U.S. Private*, pg. 3704
SOCIETY OF PHOTO-OPTICAL INSTRUMENTATION ENGINEERS; *U.S. Private*, pg. 3704
THE SOCIETY OF SAINT ANDREW, INC.; *U.S. Private*, pg. 4119
SOCIETYONE AUSTRALIA PTY. LIMITED—See Moneyme Limited; *Int'l*, pg. 5033
SOCIETY PASS INCORPORATED; *U.S. Public*, pg. 1899
SOCI, INC.; *U.S. Private*, pg. 3702
SOCIO LABS LLC—See Cisco Systems, Inc.; *U.S. Public*, pg. 500
SOCIONEXT AMERICA, INC—See Socionext Inc.; *Int'l*, pg. 7044
SOCIONEXT INC.; *Int'l*, pg. 7044
SOCIONOMUTHYRNING AB—See NGS Group AB; *Int'l*, pg. 5256
SOCIOUS, INC.—See Higher Logic, LLC; *U.S. Private*, pg. 1937
SOCIUS1 LLC—See Velosio, LLC; *U.S. Private*, pg. 4355
SOCIUS INSURANCE SERVICES INC.—See Ryan Specialty Holdings, Inc.; *U.S. Public*, pg. 1828
SOCIUS MARKETING INC.; *U.S. Private*, pg. 3704
SOCK & ACCESSORY BRANDS GLOBAL, INC.—See Huron Capital Partners LLC; *U.S. Private*, pg. 2012
SOC KENZAI CO., LTD.—See Sumitomo Osaka Cement Co Ltd; *Int'l*, pg. 7297
SOCKET HOLDINGS CORP.; *U.S. Private*, pg. 3704
SOCKET MOBILE, INC.; *U.S. Public*, pg. 1899
SOCKETS, INC.; *Int'l*, pg. 7044
SOC LAND DEVELOPMENT CORPORATION—See SOCResources, Inc.; *Int'l*, pg. 7044
SOCLA S.A.S.—See Watts Water Technologies, Inc.; *U.S. Public*, pg. 2337
SOCLA VALVES AND CONTROLS IBERICA SA—See Watts Water Technologies, Inc.; *U.S. Public*, pg. 2337
SOCLI S.A.S.—See Heidelberg Materials AG; *Int'l*, pg. 3316
SOC LOGISTICS CO., LTD.—See Sumitomo Osaka Cement Co Ltd; *Int'l*, pg. 7297
SOC MARINE CO., LTD.—See Sumitomo Osaka Cement Co Ltd; *Int'l*, pg. 7297

SOCMA TRADING (M) SENDIRIAN BERHAD—See PSC Corporation Ltd.; *Int'l*, pg. 6015
SOCOCIM INDUSTRIES—See Vicat S.A.; *Int'l*, pg. 8186
SOCO EXPLORATION (THAILAND) CO., LTD.—See Pharos Energy Plc; *Int'l*, pg. 5842
SOCO GROUP INC.; *U.S. Private*, pg. 3704
SOCOLEC SA—See Sonepar S.A.; *Int'l*, pg. 7091
SOCO MANAGEMENT SERVICES, INC.—See Pharos Energy Plc; *Int'l*, pg. 5842
SOCOMA-PERTEN SAS—See Revvity, Inc.; *U.S. Public*, pg. 1795
SOCOMINTER S.A.—See Techint S.p.A.; *Int'l*, pg. 7503
SOCOMORE S.A.; *Int'l*, pg. 7044
SOCON SONAR CONTROL KAVERNENVERMESSUNG GMBH—See EWE Aktiengesellschaft; *Int'l*, pg. 2575
SOCOPAO RDC SA—See Financiere de L'Odet; *Int'l*, pg. 2668
SOCOPAR SL—See Mubadala Investment Company PJSC; *Int'l*, pg. 5074
SOCOPLAN; *Int'l*, pg. 7044
SOCORAIL SAS—See Getlink SE; *Int'l*, pg. 2953
SOCORRO ELECTRIC COOPERATIVE; *U.S. Private*, pg. 3704
SOCOTEC, INC.—See Cobepa S.A.; *Int'l*, pg. 1683
SOCOTEC SA—See Cobepa S.A.; *Int'l*, pg. 1683
SOCOTHERM BRASIL S.A.—See Techint S.p.A.; *Int'l*, pg. 7504
SOCOTHERM LABARGE; *U.S. Private*, pg. 3704
SOCOVESA S.A.; *Int'l*, pg. 7044
SOCRATA, INC.—See Tyler Technologies, Inc.; *U.S. Public*, pg. 2209
SOCRATES P. KYPRIANIDES LTD.—See Pilot Corporation; *Int'l*, pg. 5867
SOCRATES PRIVATSTIFTUNG; *Int'l*, pg. 7044
SOCRESOURCES, INC.; *Int'l*, pg. 7044
SOC TELEMED, INC.—See Patient Square Capital, L.P.; *U.S. Private*, pg. 3107
SOCUR, S.A.—See Novo Banco, S.A.; *Int'l*, pg. 5462
SODA AROMATIC CO., LTD.—See Toray Industries, Inc.; *Int'l*, pg. 7823
SODA ASH JAPAN CO., LTD.—See Sumitomo Corporation; *Int'l*, pg. 7271
SODA! COMMUNICATIONS INC.—See Tohokushinsha Film Corporation; *Int'l*, pg. 7777
SODA! ITALIA SPA—See ERG S.p.A.; *Int'l*, pg. 2491
SODALI LIMITED; *Int'l*, pg. 7044
SODA NIKKA CO., LTD.; *Int'l*, pg. 7045
SODA NIKKA TRADING (SHANGHAI) CO., LTD.—See Soda Nikka Co., Ltd.; *Int'l*, pg. 7045
SODA NIKKA VIETNAM CO., LTD.—See Soda Nikka Co., Ltd.; *Int'l*, pg. 7045
SODAPEM; *Int'l*, pg. 7045
SODA POLSKA CIECH SP. Z.O.O.—See Kulczyk Investments S.A.; *Int'l*, pg. 4328
SODA SANAYII A.S.; *Int'l*, pg. 7045
SODAS SODYUM SANAYII A.S.; *Int'l*, pg. 7045
SODASTREAM AUSTRALIA PTY. LTD.—See PepsiCo, Inc.; *U.S. Public*, pg. 1672
SODASTREAM CANADA LTD.—See PepsiCo, Inc.; *U.S. Public*, pg. 1672
SODASTREAM DIRECT LLC—See PepsiCo, Inc.; *U.S. Public*, pg. 1672
SODASTREAM ENTERPRISES N.V.—See PepsiCo, Inc.; *U.S. Public*, pg. 1672
SODASTREAM INDUSTRIES LTD.—See PepsiCo, Inc.; *U.S. Public*, pg. 1672
SODASTREAM INTERNATIONAL B.V.—See PepsiCo, Inc.; *U.S. Public*, pg. 1672
SODASTREAM INTERNATIONAL LTD.—See PepsiCo, Inc.; *U.S. Public*, pg. 1672
SODASTREAM ISRAEL LTD.—See PepsiCo, Inc.; *U.S. Public*, pg. 1672
SODASTREAM NORDICS AB—See PepsiCo, Inc.; *U.S. Public*, pg. 1672
SODASTREAM (SA) (PTY) LTD.—See PepsiCo, Inc.; *U.S. Public*, pg. 1672
SODASTREAM (SWITZERLAND) AG—See PepsiCo, Inc.; *U.S. Public*, pg. 1672
SODASTREAM USA, INC.—See PepsiCo, Inc.; *U.S. Public*, pg. 1672
SODAWERK STASSFURT GMBH & CO. KG—See Kulczyk Investments S.A.; *Int'l*, pg. 4328
SODEARIF SA—See Bouygues S.A.; *Int'l*, pg. 1123
SODECIA A.A.; *Int'l*, pg. 7045
SODECIA ARGENTINA S.R.L.—See Sodecia A.A.; *Int'l*, pg. 7045
SODECIA DA AMAZONIA, LTDA.—See Sodecia A.A.; *Int'l*, pg. 7045
SODECIA DA BAHIA, LTDA.—See Sodecia A.A.; *Int'l*, pg. 7045
SODECIA DA GUARDA - SOC.IND.DE METALURGIA DA GUARDA, SA—See Sodecia A.A.; *Int'l*, pg. 7045
SODECIA FSG (DALIAN) CO., LTD.—See Sodecia A.A.; *Int'l*, pg. 7045
SODECIA GLOBAL TECH & AUTOMATION CENTER INC.—See Sodecia A.A.; *Int'l*, pg. 7045
SODECIA INDIA PVT LTD - III UNIT—See Sodecia A.A.; *Int'l*, pg. 7045

SODECIA INDIA PVT LTD—See Sodecia A.A.; *Int'l*, pg. 7045
SODECIA MINAS GERAIS—See Sodecia A.A.; *Int'l*, pg. 7045
SODECIA NORTH AMERICA—See Sodecia A.A.; *Int'l*, pg. 7045
SODECIA SOUTH AFRICA (PTY) LTD—See Sodecia A.A.; *Int'l*, pg. 7045
SODECLIM—See FAYAT SAS; *Int'l*, pg. 2626
SO DELICIOUS DAIRY FREE—See Danone; *Int'l*, pg. 1967
SODEMEX DEVELOPPEMENT—See Caisse de Depot et Placement du Quebec; *Int'l*, pg. 1255
SODENSHA CO., LTD.—See Hanwa Co., Ltd.; *Int'l*, pg. 3263
SODEPA SARL—See LVMH Moet Hennessy Louis Vuitton SE; *Int'l*, pg. 4600
SODERBERG & HAAK MASKIN AB—See Mellby Gard Holding AB; *Int'l*, pg. 4812
SODEREC INTERNATIONAL S.A.—See Vopelius Chemie AG; *Int'l*, pg. 8306
SODER FORESTAL S.A.—See Norske Skog ASA; *Int'l*, pg. 5438
SODERN S.A.—See Airbus SE; *Int'l*, pg. 246
SODES—See Tereos; *Int'l*, pg. 7564
SODEVA; *Int'l*, pg. 7045
SODEXI—See Air France-KLM S.A.; *Int'l*, pg. 238
SODEXO (ANGOLA) LIMITADA—See Sodexo S.A.; *Int'l*, pg. 7046
SODEXO AO—See Sodexo S.A.; *Int'l*, pg. 7046
SODEXO ARGENTINA S.A.—See Sodexo S.A.; *Int'l*, pg. 7046
SODEXO AS—See Sodexo S.A.; *Int'l*, pg. 7046
SODEXO A/S—See Sodexo S.A.; *Int'l*, pg. 7046
SODEXO AUSTRALIA PTY LIMITED—See Sodexo S.A.; *Int'l*, pg. 7046
SODEXO AUSTRALIA PTY LIMITED—See Sodexo S.A.; *Int'l*, pg. 7046
SODEXO BELGIQUE—See Sodexo S.A.; *Int'l*, pg. 7046
SODEXO BELGIUM S.A.—See Sodexo S.A.; *Int'l*, pg. 7046
SODEXO BENEFITS & REWARDS SERVICES AUSTRIA GMBH—See Sodexo S.A.; *Int'l*, pg. 7046
SODEXO CAMEROUN—See Sodexo S.A.; *Int'l*, pg. 7046
SODEXO CANADA INC.—See Sodexo S.A.; *Int'l*, pg. 7046
SODEXO CHILE—See Sodexo S.A.; *Int'l*, pg. 7046
SODEXO COLOMBIA S.A.—See Sodexo S.A.; *Int'l*, pg. 7046
SODEXO DELINJENIERE S.A.—See Sodexo S.A.; *Int'l*, pg. 7046
SODEXO DO BRASIL COMERCIAL LTDA—See Sodexo S.A.; *Int'l*, pg. 7047
SODEXO DO BRAZIL SALES & COMMERCIAL LTDA.—See Sodexo S.A.; *Int'l*, pg. 7047
SODEXO ESPAGNE—See Sodexo S.A.; *Int'l*, pg. 7046
SODEXO FRANCE BUSINESS & INDUSTRY—See Sodexo S.A.; *Int'l*, pg. 7046
SODEXO HEALTHCARE SUPPORT SERVICE (THAILAND) CO., LTD.—See Bangkok Dusit Medical Services Public Company Limited; *Int'l*, pg. 834
SODEXO HONG KONG LTD—See Sodexo S.A.; *Int'l*, pg. 7046
SODEXO, INC—See Sodexo S.A.; *Int'l*, pg. 7047
SODEXO IRELAND LTD.—See Sodexo S.A.; *Int'l*, pg. 7046
SODEXO ITALIA SPA—See Sodexo S.A.; *Int'l*, pg. 7046
SODEXO KOREA—See Sodexo S.A.; *Int'l*, pg. 7046
SODEXO LTD—See Sodexo S.A.; *Int'l*, pg. 7046
SODEXO LTD.—See Sodexo S.A.; *Int'l*, pg. 7046
SODEXO LUXEMBOURG S.A.—See Sodexo S.A.; *Int'l*, pg. 7046
SODEXO MAGYARORSZAG KFT—See Sodexo S.A.; *Int'l*, pg. 7046
SODEXO MALAYSIA—See Sodexo S.A.; *Int'l*, pg. 7046
SODEXO MEXICO SA DE CV—See Sodexo S.A.; *Int'l*, pg. 7046
SODEXO MS CANADA LTD.—See Sodexo S.A.; *Int'l*, pg. 7046
SODEXO NAMIBIA—See Sodexo S.A.; *Int'l*, pg. 7046
SODEXO NEDERLAND B.V.—See Sodexo S.A.; *Int'l*, pg. 7046
SODEXO NOUVELLE-CALEDONIE RESTAURATION FRANCAISE—See Sodexo S.A.; *Int'l*, pg. 7046
SODEXO OY—See Sodexo S.A.; *Int'l*, pg. 7046
SODEXO PASS CHILE S.A—See Sodexo S.A.; *Int'l*, pg. 7046
SODEXO PASS DE COLOMBIA SA—See Sodexo S.A.; *Int'l*, pg. 7047
SODEXO PASS GMBH—See Sodexo S.A.; *Int'l*, pg. 7046
SODEXO PASS HUNGARIA KFT—See Sodexo S.A.; *Int'l*, pg. 7046
SODEXO PASS LUXEMBOURG—See Sodexo S.A.; *Int'l*, pg. 7046
SODEXO PASS—See Sodexo S.A.; *Int'l*, pg. 7046
SODEXO PASS—See Sodexo S.A.; *Int'l*, pg. 7046
SODEXO PASS—See Sodexo S.A.; *Int'l*, pg. 7046
SODEXO PASS—See Sodexo S.A.; *Int'l*, pg. 7046
SODEXO PASS S.R.L.—See Sodexo S.A.; *Int'l*, pg. 7047

COMPANY NAME INDEX

SODEXO PASS SR SRO—See Sodexo S.A.; *Int'l*, pg. 7047
SODEXO PASS VENEZUELA CA—See Sodexo S.A.; *Int'l*, pg. 7047
SODEXO PASS VENEZUELA CA—See Sodexo S.A.; *Int'l*, pg. 7047
SODEXO POLSKA SPOLKA. Z O.O.—See Sodexo S.A.; *Int'l*, pg. 7047
SODEXO POLSKA SP ZOO—See Sodexo S.A.; *Int'l*, pg. 7047
SODEXO PREHRANA IN STORITVE DOO—See Sodexo S.A.; *Int'l*, pg. 7047
SODEXO PRESTIGE—See Sodexo S.A.; *Int'l*, pg. 7047
SODEXO REMOTE SITES SCOTLAND LTD.—See Sodexo S.A.; *Int'l*, pg. 7047
SODEXO REMOTE SITES USA INC.—See Sodexo S.A.; *Int'l*, pg. 7047
SODEXO S.A.; *Int'l*, pg. 7045
SODEXO SCANDINAVIA—See Sodexo S.A.; *Int'l*, pg. 7047
SODEXO SERVICES CO., LTD.—See Sodexo S.A.; *Int'l*, pg. 7047
SODEXO SERVICE SOLUTIONS AUSTRIA GMBH—See Sodexo S.A.; *Int'l*, pg. 7047
SODEXO SINGAPORE PTE. LTD.—See Sodexo S.A.; *Int'l*, pg. 7047
SODEXO—See Sodexo S.A.; *Int'l*, pg. 7047
SODEXO—See Sodexo S.A.; *Int'l*, pg. 7047
SODEXO SOUTHERN AFRICA PTY. LTD.—See Sodexo S.A.; *Int'l*, pg. 7047
SODEXO SPOLEENE STRAVOVANI A SLUZBY SRO—See Sodexo S.A.; *Int'l*, pg. 7047
SODEXO TOPLU YEMEK VE SERVIS A.S.—See Sodexo S.A.; *Int'l*, pg. 7047
SODEXO TUNISIA—See Sodexo S.A.; *Int'l*, pg. 7047
SODEXO TUNISIE—See Sodexo S.A.; *Int'l*, pg. 7047
S.O.D.G.—See Compagnie Generale des Etablissements Michelin SCA; *Int'l*, pg. 1745
SODIAAL INTERNATIONAL SAS; *Int'l*, pg. 7047
SODI AUTOMOTIVE SPA—See Cevital S.p.A.; *Int'l*, pg. 1425
SODICAM 2—See Renault S.A.; *Int'l*, pg. 6274
SODICK AMOY CO., LTD.—See Sodick Co., Ltd.; *Int'l*, pg. 7048
SODICK CO., LTD. - FUKUI PLANT—See Sodick Co., Ltd.; *Int'l*, pg. 7048
SODICK CO., LTD.; *Int'l*, pg. 7048
SODICK DAC CO., LTD.—See Sodick Co., Ltd.; *Int'l*, pg. 7048
SODICK DEUTSCHLAND GMBH—See Sodick Co., Ltd.; *Int'l*, pg. 7048
SODICK DEUTSCHLAND GMBH—See Sodick Co., Ltd.; *Int'l*, pg. 7048
SODICK ELECTROMECHANICAL (SHANGHAI) CO., LTD.—See Sodick Co., Ltd.; *Int'l*, pg. 7048
SODICK ENTERPRISE (SZ) CO., LTD.—See Sodick Co., Ltd.; *Int'l*, pg. 7048
SODICK EUROPE LTD.—See Sodick Co., Ltd.; *Int'l*, pg. 7048
SODICK FA CO., LTD.—See Sodick Co., Ltd.; *Int'l*, pg. 7048
SODICK F.T CO., LTD.—See Sodick Co., Ltd.; *Int'l*, pg. 7048
SODICK HIGHTECH GERMANY GMBH—See Sodick Co., Ltd.; *Int'l*, pg. 7048
SODICK (H.K.) CO., LTD.—See Sodick Co., Ltd.; *Int'l*, pg. 7048
SODICK INC.—See Sodick Co., Ltd.; *Int'l*, pg. 7048
SODICK INTERNATIONAL TRADING (SHANGHAI) CO., LTD.—See Sodick Co., Ltd.; *Int'l*, pg. 7048
SODICK INTERNATIONAL TRADING (SHENZHEN) CO., LTD.—See Sodick Co., Ltd.; *Int'l*, pg. 7048
SODICK JAPAN TRADING CO., LTD.—See Sodick Co., Ltd.; *Int'l*, pg. 7048
SODICK KOREA CO., LTD.—See Sodick Co., Ltd.; *Int'l*, pg. 7048
SODICK PHILIPPINES INC.—See Sodick Co., Ltd.; *Int'l*, pg. 7048
SODICK SINGAPORE PTE., LTD.—See Sodick Co., Ltd.; *Int'l*, pg. 7048
SODICK (TAIWAN) CO., LTD.—See Sodick Co., Ltd.; *Int'l*, pg. 7048
SODICK TECHNOLOGIES INDIA PRIVATE LIMITED—See Sodick Co., Ltd.; *Int'l*, pg. 7048
SODICK TECHNOLOGY (M) SDN. BHD.—See Sodick Co., Ltd.; *Int'l*, pg. 7048
SODICK (THAILAND) CO., LTD.—See Sodick Co., Ltd.; *Int'l*, pg. 7048
SODICK TOM (SHANGHAI) CO., LTD.—See Sodick Co., Ltd.; *Int'l*, pg. 7048
SODICK VIETNAM CO., LTD.—See Sodick Co., Ltd.; *Int'l*, pg. 7048
SODIFRANCE SA—See Sopra Steria Group S.A.; *Int'l*, pg. 7110
SODIGAS BRAGA SOCIEDADE DE DISTRIBUICAO DE GAS, S.A.—See Rubis SCA; *Int'l*, pg. 6423
SODIGAS SEIXAL SOCIEDADE DE DISTRIBUICAO DE GAS S.A.—See Rubis SCA; *Int'l*, pg. 6423
SODILOR SAS—See VINCI S.A.; *Int'l*, pg. 8228

SODIMA SAS—See General Mills, Inc.; *U.S. Public*, pg. 922
SODIM CARAIBES SAS—See VINCI S.A.; *Int'l*, pg. 8228
SODIMEX FR S.A.—See Socfinasia S.A.; *Int'l*, pg. 7031
SODIM SAS—See Korber AG; *Int'l*, pg. 4280
SODIM, SGPS, SA; *Int'l*, pg. 7048
SODIPORC SA; *Int'l*, pg. 7049
SODISCO-HOWDEN GROUP, INC.—See The Futura Corporation; *Int'l*, pg. 7647
SODISCOL SAS—See Bunzl plc; *Int'l*, pg. 1219
SODITA—See Carrefour SA; *Int'l*, pg. 1346
SODITECH SA; *Int'l*, pg. 7049
SODIUM SOLUTIONS INC.—See Bri-Chem Corp.; *Int'l*, pg. 1151
SO DO IT, LLC; *U.S. Private*, pg. 3702
SODRA CELL AB—See Sodra Skogsagarna; *Int'l*, pg. 7050
SODRA CELL TOFTE—See Sodra Skogsagarna; *Int'l*, pg. 7050
SODRA LATVIA SIA—See Sodra Skogsagarna; *Int'l*, pg. 7050
SODRA METSAD OU—See Sodra Skogsagarna; *Int'l*, pg. 7050
SODRA SKOGSAGARNA; *Int'l*, pg. 7049
SODRA SKOGSENERGI—See Sodra Skogsagarna; *Int'l*, pg. 7050
SODRA SKOG—See Sodra Skogsagarna; *Int'l*, pg. 7050
SODRA TIMBER AB—See Sodra Skogsagarna; *Int'l*, pg. 7050
SODREL TRUCK LINES INC.; *U.S. Private*, pg. 3704
SODUFA B.V.—See Solvay S.A.; *Int'l*, pg. 7078
SODX CO., LTD.—See PuraPharm Corporation Limited; *Int'l*, pg. 6121
SOEHNLEN PIPING COMPANY; *U.S. Private*, pg. 3704
SOEI CO., LTD.—See NICHIMO CO. LTD.; *Int'l*, pg. 5269
SOEI FOODS CO., LTD.—See Sotetsu Holdings, Inc.; *Int'l*, pg. 7164
S & O ELECTRONICS (MALAYSIA) SDN. BHD.—See Hon Hai Precision Industry Co., Ltd.; *Int'l*, pg. 3457
SOELLINGEN ADVISORY GROUP, INC.; *U.S. Private*, pg. 3704
SOENEN VERZEKERINGSKANTOOR NV—See Apollo Global Management, Inc.; *U.S. Public*, pg. 147
SOE SOFTWARE CORPORATION—See Scytl Secure Electronic Voting SA; *Int'l*, pg. 6657
SOESSARDIS SARL—See Carrefour SA; *Int'l*, pg. 1346
SOETERMEER FEKKES - ZWIJNDRECHT—See Carisbrooke Shipping Limited; *Int'l*, pg. 1331
SOFACEL SA—See Mersen S.A.; *Int'l*, pg. 4839
SOFADES GINNING MILLS S.A.—See NAFFAKTOS TEXTILE INDUSTRY S.A.; *Int'l*, pg. 5124
SOFALIC SAS—See VINCI S.A.; *Int'l*, pg. 8228
SOFALINE; *Int'l*, pg. 7050
SOFA MART, LLC—See Furniture Row; *U.S. Private*, pg. 1624
SOFAME EUROPE S.A.S.—See Sofame Technologies Inc.; *Int'l*, pg. 7050
SOFAME TECHNOLOGIES INC.; *Int'l*, pg. 7050
SOFAP LTD.—See Taylor Smith Group; *Int'l*, pg. 7478
SOFA WORKSHOP LTD—See New Heights Ltd.; *Int'l*, pg. 5224
SOFAX BANQUE SA—See TotalEnergies SE; *Int'l*, pg. 7838
SOFAXIS—See Societe Hospitaliere d'Assurance Mutuelle; *Int'l*, pg. 7042
SOFCOM SYSTEMS LTD.; *Int'l*, pg. 7050
SOFCO SEAFOODS INC.—See Sojitz Corporation; *Int'l*, pg. 7063
SOFEC, INC.—See Mitsui E&S Holdings Co., Ltd.; *Int'l*, pg. 4985
SOFEMA; *Int'l*, pg. 7050
SOFFSEAL, INC.—See ALP Group; *Int'l*, pg. 365
SOFFT SHOE COMPANY, INC.—See Berkshire Hathaway Inc.; *U.S. Public*, pg. 299
SOFGEN AFRICA LTD—See Mahindra & Mahindra Limited; *Int'l*, pg. 4647
SOFGEN AMERICAS, INC.—See Mahindra & Mahindra Limited; *Int'l*, pg. 4647
SOFGEN AUSTRALIA PTY LTD—See Mahindra & Mahindra Limited; *Int'l*, pg. 4647
SOFGEN CONSULTING AG—See Mahindra & Mahindra Limited; *Int'l*, pg. 4647
SOFGEN HOLDINGS LIMITED—See Mahindra & Mahindra Limited; *Int'l*, pg. 4647
SOFGEN INDIA PRIVATE LTD—See Mahindra & Mahindra Limited; *Int'l*, pg. 4647
SOFGEN S.A.—See Mahindra & Mahindra Limited; *Int'l*, pg. 4647
SOFGEN SDN BHD—See Mahindra & Mahindra Limited; *Int'l*, pg. 4647
SOFGEN SERVICES PTE LTD—See Mahindra & Mahindra Limited; *Int'l*, pg. 4647
SOFGEN (UK) LIMITED—See Mahindra & Mahindra Limited; *Int'l*, pg. 4647
SOFIA-BT A.D.—See Bulgarian Investment Holding; *Int'l*, pg. 1213
SOFIA COMMERCE-PAWN BROKERAGE AD; *Int'l*, pg. 7050
SOFIA GMBH—See Eurofins Scientific S.E.; *Int'l*, pg. 2541
SOFIA HOTEL BALKAN AD; *Int'l*, pg. 7050

SOFTBANK GROUP CORP.

SOFIA MED AD—See Viohalco SA/NV; *Int'l*, pg. 8243
SOFIA MEL EAD—See Raiffeisen-Holding Niederosterreich-Wien reg. Gen.m.b.H.; *Int'l*, pg. 6185
SOFIBEL S.A.S.—See Church & Dwight Co., Inc.; *U.S. Public*, pg. 493
SOFIBOR; *Int'l*, pg. 7050
SOFIBUS PATRIMOINE—See SEGRO plc; *Int'l*, pg. 6683
SOFICA GROUP AD—See TTEC Holdings, Inc.; *U.S. Public*, pg. 2203
SOFIDEL AMERICA CORPORATION—See Sofidel S.p.A; *Int'l*, pg. 7050
SOFIDEL S.P.A; *Int'l*, pg. 7050
SOFIDER SASU—See Groupe BPCE; *Int'l*, pg. 3099
SOFIDIV S.A—See LVMH Moet Hennessy Louis Vuitton SE; *Int'l*, pg. 4600
SOFIDSIM S.P.A.—See Eni S.p.A.; *Int'l*, pg. 2438
SOFIE BIOSCIENCES, INC.; *U.S. Private*, pg. 3704
SOFINA FOODS INC.; *Int'l*, pg. 7050
SOFINANS A/S—See Sydbank A/S; *Int'l*, pg. 7377
SOFINA S.A.; *Int'l*, pg. 7050
SOFIN CONSULTING LTD.—See Mensch und Maschine Software SE; *Int'l*, pg. 4818
SOFINE FOODS BV; *Int'l*, pg. 7050
SOFINEL—See Electricite de France S.A.; *Int'l*, pg. 2352
SOFINIM N.V.—See Ackermans & van Haaren NV; *Int'l*, pg. 106
SOFINNOVA VENTURES, INC.; *U.S. Private*, pg. 3704
SOFINOL S.A.—See Nestle S.A.; *Int'l*, pg. 5211
SOFINTER S.P.A.—See Gammon India Limited; *Int'l*, pg. 2879
SOFIPA SOCIETA DI GESTIONE DEL RISPARMIO (SGR) S.P.A.—See UniCredit S.p.A.; *Int'l*, pg. 8035
SOFIPRIM S.A.S.; *Int'l*, pg. 7050
SOFIPROTEOL S.A.—See Avril SCA; *Int'l*, pg. 750
SOFIS BV—See Halma plc; *Int'l*, pg. 3233
SOFIS GMBH—See Halma plc; *Int'l*, pg. 3233
SOFIS LIMITED—See Halma plc; *Int'l*, pg. 3233
SOFISTIK AG—See Mensch und Maschine Software SE; *Int'l*, pg. 4818
SOFI TECHNOLOGIES, INC.; *U.S. Public*, pg. 1899
SOFITEL CENTRAL HUA HIN RESORT—See Central Plaza Hotel Public Company Limited; *Int'l*, pg. 1409
SOFITEL LUXURY HOTELS FRANCE SAS—See Accor S.A.; *Int'l*, pg. 92
SOFIT-LUX LTD.—See A.A.G. STUCCHI s.r.l.; *Int'l*, pg. 23
SOFIVA GENOMICS CO., LTD.; *Int'l*, pg. 7050
SOFIX CORP.—See Nagase & Co., Ltd.; *Int'l*, pg. 5128
SOFIYSKA VODA AD—See Veolia Environnement S.A.; *Int'l*, pg. 8154
SOFLAN WIZ CO., LTD—See Toyo Tire Corporation; *Int'l*, pg. 7859
SOFO FOOD CO., INC.—See Antonio Sofo & Son Importing Co. Inc.; *U.S. Private*, pg. 288
SOFOTEC GMBH—See AstraZeneca PLC; *Int'l*, pg. 661
SOFRADEN INDUSTRIE SAS—See VINCI S.A.; *Int'l*, pg. 8228
SOFRADIR SAS—See Safran SA; *Int'l*, pg. 6476
SOFRADIR SAS—See Thales S.A.; *Int'l*, pg. 7605
SOFRAFI SA—See Societe Generale S.A.; *Int'l*, pg. 7041
SOFRANCE—See Safran SA; *Int'l*, pg. 6476
SOFRA YEMEK URETIM VE HIZMET A.S.—See Compass Group PLC; *Int'l*, pg. 1752
SOFRECOM ARGENTINA—See Orange S.A.; *Int'l*, pg. 5610
SOFRECOM MAROC—See Orange S.A.; *Int'l*, pg. 5610
SOFRECOM POLSKA SP. Z O.O.—See Orange S.A.; *Int'l*, pg. 5610
SOFRECOM SA—See Orange S.A.; *Int'l*, pg. 5611
SOFREGAZ—See Maire Tecnimont S.p.A.; *Int'l*, pg. 4652
SOF S.P.A.—See Fincantieri S.p.A.; *Int'l*, pg. 2671
SOFT99 CORPORATION - SANDA FACTORY—See Soft99 Corporation; *Int'l*, pg. 7051
SOFT99 CORPORATION; *Int'l*, pg. 7050
SOFT AT HOME—See Orange S.A.; *Int'l*, pg. 5611
SOFTBANK ATWORK CORPORATION—See SoftBank Group Corp.; *Int'l*, pg. 7052
SOFTBANK CAPITAL L.P.—See SoftBank Group Corp.; *Int'l*, pg. 7054
SOFTBANK CORP.—See SoftBank Group Corp.; *Int'l*, pg. 7052
SOFTBANK CREATIVE CORP.—See SoftBank Group Corp.; *Int'l*, pg. 7051
SOFTBANK FRAMEWORKS CORP.—See SoftBank Group Corp.; *Int'l*, pg. 7052
SOFTBANK GROUP CORP.; *Int'l*, pg. 7051
SOFTBANK HOLDINGS, INC.—See SoftBank Group Corp.; *Int'l*, pg. 7052
SOFTBANK HUMAN CAPITAL CORP.—See SoftBank Group Corp.; *Int'l*, pg. 7051
SOFTBANK KOREA CO., LTD.—See SoftBank Group Corp.; *Int'l*, pg. 7054
SOFTBANK PAYMENT SERVICE CORP.—See SoftBank Group Corp.; *Int'l*, pg. 7051
SOFTBANK PLAYERS CORP.—See SoftBank Group Corp.; *Int'l*, pg. 7052
SOFTBANK TELECOM EUROPE LTD.—See SoftBank Group Corp.; *Int'l*, pg. 7052
SOFTBANK TELECOM PARTNERS CORP.—See SoftBank Group Corp.; *Int'l*, pg. 7052

SOFTBANK GROUP CORP. — CORPORATE AFFILIATIONS

SOFTBANK VENTURES KOREA INC.—See SoftBank Group Corp.; *Int'l*, pg. 7054
SOFTBRAIN CO., LTD.; *Int'l*, pg. 7054
SOFTBRAIN INTEGRATION CO., LTD.—See Softbrain Co., Ltd.; *Int'l*, pg. 7054
SOFTBRASIL AUTOMACAO LTDA—See Schneider Electric SE; *Int'l*, pg. 6635
SOFTCAMP CO., LTD.; *Int'l*, pg. 7054
SOFTCAT LTD.; *Int'l*, pg. 7054
SOFTCEN CO., LTD.; *Int'l*, pg. 7054
SOFTCHALK LLC—See Constellation Software Inc.; *Int'l*, pg. 1775
SOFT CHEMICAL CORP.—See Formosan Union Chemical Corp.; *Int'l*, pg. 2736
SOFTCHOICE CORPORATION—See Birch Hill Equity Partners Management Inc.; *Int'l*, pg. 1046
SOFTCOM GROUP INC.—See Hainan Traffic Administration Holding Co., Ltd.; *Int'l*, pg. 3215
SOFT COMPUTER CONSULTANTS INC.; *U.S. Private*, pg. 3704
SOFT COMPUTING SA—See Publicis Groupe S.A.; *Int'l*, pg. 6104
SOFTCON AG—See Allgeier SE; *Int'l*, pg. 337
SOFTCON IT SERVICE S.R.L.—See Allgeier SE; *Int'l*, pg. 337
SOFTCREATE CORPORATION—See Softcreate Holdings Corp.; *Int'l*, pg. 7054
SOFTCREATE HOLDINGS CORP.; *Int'l*, pg. 7054
SOFT DRINK SERVICES COMPANY—See The Coca-Cola Company; *U.S. Public*, pg. 2065
SOFTECH, INC.; *U.S. Public*, pg. 1899
SOFTECH S.R.L.—See SofTech, Inc.; *U.S. Public*, pg. 1899
SOFTECH SYSTEMS (PVT) LIMITED—See Saif Holdings Limited; *Int'l*, pg. 6482
SOFTEC SOLUTIONS, INC.; *U.S. Private*, pg. 3705
SOFTEC S.P.A.—See RCS MediaGroup S.p.A.; *Int'l*, pg. 6229
SOFTEL LTD.—See Belden, Inc.; *U.S. Public*, pg. 294
SOFTEON, INC.; *U.S. Private*, pg. 3705
SOFT-EPI, INC.—See Lumens Co., Ltd.; *Int'l*, pg. 4577
SO.F.TER BRASIL COMPOSTOS TERMOPLASTICOS LTDA.—See Celanese Corporation; *U.S. Public*, pg. 465
SO.F.TER. S.R.L.—See Celanese Corporation; *U.S. Public*, pg. 465
SO.F.TER. US, INC.—See Celanese Corporation; *U.S. Public*, pg. 465
SOFTERWARE, INC.; *U.S. Private*, pg. 3705
SOFT-EX BV—See WidePoint Corporation; *U.S. Public*, pg. 2370
SOFT-EX COMMUNICATIONS LTD.—See WidePoint Corporation; *U.S. Public*, pg. 2370
SOFT-EX UK LIMITED—See WidePoint Corporation; *U.S. Public*, pg. 2370
SOFTFAC TECHNOLOGY SDN. BHD.—See TFP Solutions Berhad; *Int'l*, pg. 7587
SOFTFOBIA, S.R.L.—See Indra Sistemas, S.A.; *Int'l*, pg. 3661
SOFTFRONT HOLDINGS CO., LTD.; *Int'l*, pg. 7054
SOFTFRONT VIETNAM CO., LTD.—See Softfront Holdings Co., Ltd.; *Int'l*, pg. 7054
SOFTGARDEN E-RECRUITING GMBH—See Grupa Pracuj S.A.; *Int'l*, pg. 3117
SOFTGENETICS, LLC—See Insight Venture Management, LLC; *U.S. Private*, pg. 2090
SOFTHALE NV—See Sino Biopharmaceutical Limited; *Int'l*, pg. 6946
SOFTIMAT SA; *Int'l*, pg. 7054
SOFTING AG; *Int'l*, pg. 7055
SOFTING AUTOMOTIVE ELECTRONICS GMBH—See Softing AG; *Int'l*, pg. 7055
SOFTING AUTOMOTIVE ELECTRONICS (KIRCHENTELLINSFURT) GMBH—See Softing AG; *Int'l*, pg. 7055
SOFTING INC.—See Softing AG; *Int'l*, pg. 7055
SOFTING INDUSTRIAL AUTOMATION GMBH—See Softing AG; *Int'l*, pg. 7055
SOFTING ITALIA S.R.L.—See Softing AG; *Int'l*, pg. 7055
SOFTING IT NETWORKS GMBH—See Softing AG; *Int'l*, pg. 7055
SOFTING SINGAPORE PTE. LTD.—See Softing AG; *Int'l*, pg. 7055
SOFTINTEREST HOLDING AG—See Silver Lake Group, LLC; *U.S. Private*, pg. 3659
SOFTIP, A.S.; *Int'l*, pg. 7055
SOFTJIN TECHNOLOGIES PRIVATE LIMITED; *Int'l*, pg. 7055
SOFTLAB9 TECHNOLOGIES, INC.; *Int'l*, pg. 7055
SOFTLAB S.P.A.; *Int'l*, pg. 7055
SOFTLAB SPA.; *Int'l*, pg. 7055
SOFT LANDING LABS LTD; *U.S. Private*, pg. 3704
SOFTLANDING SYSTEMS, INC.—See UNICOM Global, Inc.; *U.S. Private*, pg. 4281
SOFTLAYER TECHNOLOGIES ASIA—See International Business Machines Corporation; *U.S. Public*, pg. 1150
SOFTLAYER TECHNOLOGIES EUROPE—See International Business Machines Corporation; *U.S. Public*, pg. 1150

SOFTLAYER TECHNOLOGIES, INC.—See International Business Machines Corporation; *U.S. Public*, pg. 1150
SOFTLINE AG; *Int'l*, pg. 7055
SOFTLINE (PTY) LTD—See The Sage Group plc; *Int'l*, pg. 7680
SOFTLINE SERVICES GMBH—See Softline AG; *Int'l*, pg. 7055
SOFTLINE SOLUTIONS GMBH—See Softline AG; *Int'l*, pg. 7055
SOFTLINE SOLUTIONS LTD.—See Softline AG; *Int'l*, pg. 7055
SOFTLINE SOLUTIONS NETHERLANDS B.V.—See Softline AG; *Int'l*, pg. 7055
SOFTLINE SOLUTIONS N.V.—See Softline AG; *Int'l*, pg. 7055
SOFT-LITE LLC—See Clayton, Dubilier & Rice, LLC; *U.S. Private*, pg. 920
SOFTLOGIC ASSET MANAGEMENT (PVT) LTD.—See Softlogic Holdings PLC; *Int'l*, pg. 7056
SOFTLOGIC AUSTRALIA (PTY) LTD.—See Softlogic Holdings PLC; *Int'l*, pg. 7056
SOFTLOGIC CAPITAL PLC—See Softlogic Holdings PLC; *Int'l*, pg. 7056
SOFTLOGIC COMPUTERS (PVT) LTD.—See Softlogic Holdings PLC; *Int'l*, pg. 7056
SOFTLOGIC FINANCE PLC—See Softlogic Holdings PLC; *Int'l*, pg. 7056
SOFTLOGIC HOLDINGS PLC; *Int'l*, pg. 7055
SOFTLOGIC INFORMATION TECHNOLOGIES (PVT) LIMITED—See Softlogic Holdings PLC; *Int'l*, pg. 7056
SOFTLOGIC LIFE INSURANCE PLC—See Softlogic Holdings PLC; *Int'l*, pg. 7056
SOFTLOGIC STOCKBROKERS (PVT) LTD.—See Softlogic Holdings PLC; *Int'l*, pg. 7056
SOFTMAN PRODUCTS COMPANY, LLC; *U.S. Private*, pg. 3705
SOFTMAX CO., LTD.; *Int'l*, pg. 7056
SOFTMOBILE TECHNOLOGY CORP.—See SYSTEX Corporation; *Int'l*, pg. 7393
SOFTNAUTICS LLP—See Moschip Technologies Limited; *Int'l*, pg. 5050
SOFTNICE; *U.S. Private*, pg. 3705
SOFTOX SOLUTIONS AS; *U.S. Private*, pg. 3705
SOFT PLAY, LLC—See Littlejohn & Co., LLC; *U.S. Private*, pg. 2471
SOFTPRINT HOLDINGS, INC.; *U.S. Private*, pg. 3705
SOFTPROVIDING AG—See msg group GmbH; *Int'l*, pg. 5067
SOFTRAK VENTURE INVESTMENT LTD.; *Int'l*, pg. 7056
SOFTRAMS LLC—See Sagewind Capital LLC; *U.S. Private*, pg. 3527
SOFTRIDE, INC.—See Allsop, Inc.; *U.S. Private*, pg. 193
SOFTROCK MINERALS LTD; *Int'l*, pg. 7056
SOFTRONIC AB; *Int'l*, pg. 7056
SOFTRONIC BALTIC AS—See Softronic AB; *Int'l*, pg. 7056
SOFTRONIC DANMARK A/S—See Softronic AB; *Int'l*, pg. 7056
SOFT SHEEN/CARSON PRODUCTS, INC.—See L'Oreal S.A.; *Int'l*, pg. 4380
SOFTSHIP AG; *Int'l*, pg. 7056
SOFTSHIP AMERICA, INC.—See Softship AG; *Int'l*, pg. 7056
SOFTSHIP DATA PROCESSING PTE LTD—See Softship AG; *Int'l*, pg. 7056
SOFTSHIP INC.—See Softship AG; *Int'l*, pg. 7056
SOFT SKULL PRESS—See Black Balloon Publishing, LLC; *U.S. Private*, pg. 569
SOFTSOL INDIA LIMITED; *Int'l*, pg. 7056
SOFTSOL RESOURCES; *U.S. Private*, pg. 3705
SOFT SPACE SDN. BHD.—See Transcosmos Inc.; *Int'l*, pg. 7898
SOFTSTAR ENTERTAINMENT, INC.; *Int'l*, pg. 7056
SOFT TEAM CONSULTORIA E INFORMATICA LTDA.—See TOTVS S.A.; *Int'l*, pg. 7846
SOFT TECH CONSULTING INC.; *U.S. Private*, pg. 3705
SOFTTECH DIGITAL PTE. LTD.—See SoftTech Engineers Limited; *Int'l*, pg. 7056
SOFTTECH ENGINEERS LIMITED; *Int'l*, pg. 7056
SOFTTECH GOVERNMENT SOLUTIONS, INC.—See SoftTech Engineers Limited; *Int'l*, pg. 7056
SOFTTECH SOLUTIONS, INC.—See Falfurrias Capital Partners, LP; *U.S. Private*, pg. 1467
SOFTURA, INC; *U.S. Private*, pg. 3705
SOFTWARE24.COM GMBH—See MEDIQON Group AG; *Int'l*, pg. 4780
SOFTWARE ADVICE, INC.—See Gartner, Inc.; *U.S. Public*, pg. 907
SOFTWARE AG ARGENTINA S.R.L.—See Silver Lake Group, LLC; *U.S. Private*, pg. 3659
SOFTWARE AG (ASIA PACIFIC/SINGAPORE) LTD.—See Silver Lake Group, LLC; *U.S. Private*, pg. 3659
SOFTWARE AG AUSTRALIA (HOLDINGS) PTY LTD—See Silver Lake Group, LLC; *U.S. Private*, pg. 3659
SOFTWARE AG AUSTRALIA PTY LTD.—See Silver Lake Group, LLC; *U.S. Private*, pg. 3659
SOFTWARE AG BANGALORE TECHNOLOGIES PRIVATE LTD—See Silver Lake Group, LLC; *U.S. Private*, pg. 3659

SOFTWARE AG BELGIUM S.A.—See Silver Lake Group, LLC; *U.S. Private*, pg. 3659
SOFTWARE AG BILGI SISTEMLERI TICARET A.S—See Silver Lake Group, LLC; *U.S. Private*, pg. 3659
SOFTWARE AG BRASIL INFORMATICA E SERVICOS LTDA—See Silver Lake Group, LLC; *U.S. Private*, pg. 3659
SOFTWARE AG CANADA CORPORATION—See Silver Lake Group, LLC; *U.S. Private*, pg. 3659
SOFTWARE AG (CANADA) INC.—See Silver Lake Group, LLC; *U.S. Private*, pg. 3659
SOFTWARE AG CHENNAI DEVELOPMENT CENTER INDIA PVT LTD—See Silver Lake Group, LLC; *U.S. Private*, pg. 3659
SOFTWARE AG CHILE S.A.—See Silver Lake Group, LLC; *U.S. Private*, pg. 3659
SOFTWARE AG CHINA LTD.—See Silver Lake Group, LLC; *U.S. Private*, pg. 3659
SOFTWARE AG DE PANAMA, S.A—See Silver Lake Group, LLC; *U.S. Private*, pg. 3660
SOFTWARE AG DE PUERTO RICO, INC.—See Silver Lake Group, LLC; *U.S. Private*, pg. 3659
SOFTWARE AG DEVELOPMENT CENTER BULGARIA EOOD—See Silver Lake Group, LLC; *U.S. Private*, pg. 3659
SOFTWARE AG DEVELOPMENT CENTER INDIA PRIVATE LIMITED—See Silver Lake Group, LLC; *U.S. Private*, pg. 3659
SOFTWARE AG DEVELOPMENT CENTRE BULGARIA EOOD—See Silver Lake Group, LLC; *U.S. Private*, pg. 3659
SOFTWARE AG DEVELOPMENT CENTRE SLOVAKIA S.R.O.—See Silver Lake Group, LLC; *U.S. Private*, pg. 3659
SOFTWARE AG ESPANA S.A.—See Silver Lake Group, LLC; *U.S. Private*, pg. 3659
SOFTWARE AG ESPANA SYSTEMHAUS S.L.—See Silver Lake Group, LLC; *U.S. Private*, pg. 3659
SOFTWARE AG FACTORIA S.A.—See Silver Lake Group, LLC; *U.S. Private*, pg. 3659
SOFTWARE AG FINLAND OY—See Silver Lake Group, LLC; *U.S. Private*, pg. 3659
SOFTWARE AG FRANCE S.A.R.L.—See Silver Lake Group, LLC; *U.S. Private*, pg. 3659
SOFTWARE AG FRANCE S.A.—See Silver Lake Group, LLC; *U.S. Private*, pg. 3659
SOFTWARE AG GOVERNMENT SOLUTIONS, INC.—See Silver Lake Group, LLC; *U.S. Private*, pg. 3660
SOFTWARE AG (GULF) S.P.C.—See Silver Lake Group, LLC; *U.S. Private*, pg. 3659
SOFTWARE AG HONG KONG—See Silver Lake Group, LLC; *U.S. Private*, pg. 3659
SOFTWARE AG, INC.—See Silver Lake Group, LLC; *U.S. Private*, pg. 3660
SOFTWARE AG INDIA PVT LTD.—See Silver Lake Group, LLC; *U.S. Private*, pg. 3659
SOFTWARE AG INTERNATIONAL FZ-LLC—See Silver Lake Group, LLC; *U.S. Private*, pg. 3660
SOFTWARE AG INTERNATIONAL INC—See Silver Lake Group, LLC; *U.S. Private*, pg. 3660
SOFTWARE AG (ISRAEL) LTD—See Silver Lake Group, LLC; *U.S. Private*, pg. 3660
SOFTWARE AG ITALIA S.P.A.—See Silver Lake Group, LLC; *U.S. Private*, pg. 3660
SOFTWARE AG KOREA CO., LTD.—See Silver Lake Group, LLC; *U.S. Private*, pg. 3660
SOFTWARE AG LATINOAMERICA S.L.—See Silver Lake Group, LLC; *U.S. Private*, pg. 3660
SOFTWARE AG, LTD.—See Silver Lake Group, LLC; *U.S. Private*, pg. 3660
SOFTWARE AG NEDERLAND B.V.—See Silver Lake Group, LLC; *U.S. Private*, pg. 3660
SOFTWARE AG NEDERLAND B.V.—See Silver Lake Group, LLC; *U.S. Private*, pg. 3660
SOFTWARE AG NORDIC AB—See Silver Lake Group, LLC; *U.S. Private*, pg. 3660
SOFTWARE AG NORDIC A/S—See Silver Lake Group, LLC; *U.S. Private*, pg. 3660
SOFTWARE AG OPERATIONS MALAYSIA SDN BHD—See Silver Lake Group, LLC; *U.S. Private*, pg. 3660
SOFTWARE AG (PHILIPPINES) INC.—See Silver Lake Group, LLC; *U.S. Private*, pg. 3659
SOFTWARE AG POLSKA SP. Z O.O.—See Silver Lake Group, LLC; *U.S. Private*, pg. 3659
SOFTWARE AG PORTUGAL ALTA TECNOLOGIA INFORMATICA LDA—See Silver Lake Group, LLC; *U.S. Private*, pg. 3660
SOFTWARE AG, S.A. DE C.V.—See Silver Lake Group, LLC; *U.S. Private*, pg. 3660
SOFTWARE AG SAUDI ARABIA LLC—See Silver Lake Group, LLC; *U.S. Private*, pg. 3660
SOFTWARE AG (SHENZHEN) CO LTD—See Silver Lake Group, LLC; *U.S. Private*, pg. 3659
SOFTWARE AG (SINGAPORE) PTE LTD—See Silver Lake Group, LLC; *U.S. Private*, pg. 3659
SOFTWARE AG—See Silver Lake Group, LLC; *U.S. Private*, pg. 3658

COMPANY NAME INDEX

SOFTWARE AG SOUTH AFRICA (PTY) LTD—See Silver Lake Group, LLC; *U.S. Private*, pg. 3660
SOFTWARE AG S.R.O.—See Silver Lake Group, LLC; *U.S. Private*, pg. 3660
SOFTWARE AG SWEDEN AB—See Silver Lake Group, LLC; *U.S. Private*, pg. 3660
SOFTWARE AG UK LTD.—See Silver Lake Group, LLC; *U.S. Private*, pg. 3660
SOFTWARE AG UK LTD.—See Silver Lake Group, LLC; *U.S. Private*, pg. 3660
SOFTWARE AG UK LTD.—See Silver Lake Group, LLC; *U.S. Private*, pg. 3660
SOFTWARE AG USA, INC.—See Silver Lake Group, LLC; *U.S. Private*, pg. 3660
SOFTWARE AG VENEZUELA C.A.—See Silver Lake Group, LLC; *U.S. Private*, pg. 3660
SOFTWARE BROKERS OF AMERICA, INC.—See INTCOMEX, Inc.; *U.S. Private*, pg. 2097
SOFTWARE BY DESIGN, INC.—See H.I.G. Capital, LLC; *U.S. Private*, pg. 1833
SOFTWARE CIRCLE PLC.; *Int'l*, pg. 7056
THE SOFTWARE CONSTRUCTION CO. INC.; *U.S. Private*, pg. 4119
SOFTWARE CO-WORK LLC—See DraftKings Inc.; *U.S. Public*, pg. 687
SOFTWARE CREDIT LP—See KKR & Co. Inc.; *U.S. Public*, pg. 1241
SOFTWARE DESIGN SOLUTIONS INC.—See Applied Visions, Inc.; *U.S. Private*, pg. 300
THE SOFTWARE DEVELOPMENT AND TESTING COMPANY, INC.; *U.S. Private*, pg. 4119
SOFTWARE DEVELOPMENT EUROPE, INC.—See 3Pillar Global, Inc.; *U.S. Private*, pg. 14
SOFTWARE DIVERSIFIED SERVICES; *U.S. Private*, pg. 3705
SOFTWARE EFFECTIVE SOLUTIONS CORP.; *Int'l*, pg. 7057
SOFTWARE EXPRESS INFORMATICA LTDA—See Fiserv, Inc.; *U.S. Public*, pg. 851
SOFTWARE FOLKS, INC.; *U.S. Private*, pg. 3705
SOFTWARE GALAXY SYSTEMS, LLC; *U.S. Private*, pg. 3705
SOFTWARE GMBH OSTERREICH—See Silver Lake Group, LLC; *U.S. Private*, pg. 3660
SOFTWARE & INFORMATION INDUSTRY ASSOCIATION, INC.; *U.S. Private*, pg. 3705
SOFTWARE INFORMATION SYSTEMS LLC—See Converge Technology Solutions Corp.; *Int'l*, pg. 1787
SOFTWARE INFORMATION SYSTEMS; *U.S. Private*, pg. 3705
SOFTWARE INNOVATION AS—See TietoEVRY Oyj; *Int'l*, pg. 7745
SOFTWARE MANAGEMENT CONSULTANTS INC.; *U.S. Private*, pg. 3705
SOFTWARENOLOGY, LLC; *U.S. Private*, pg. 3706
SOFTWARE OF EXCELLENCE UNITED KINGDOM LIMITED—See Henry Schein, Inc.; *U.S. Public*, pg. 1027
SOFTWAREONE AB—See SoftwareONE Holding AG; *Int'l*, pg. 7057
SOFTWAREONE ARGENTINA SRL—See SoftwareONE Holding AG; *Int'l*, pg. 7057
SOFTWAREONE AUSTRALIA PTY. LTD.—See SoftwareONE Holding AG; *Int'l*, pg. 7057
SOFTWAREONE BE BV—See SoftwareONE Holding AG; *Int'l*, pg. 7057
SOFTWAREONE BOLIVIA SRL—See SoftwareONE Holding AG; *Int'l*, pg. 7057
SOFTWAREONE BRAZIL CSI LTDA.—See SoftwareONE Holding AG; *Int'l*, pg. 7057
SOFTWAREONE BULGARIA OOD—See SoftwareONE Holding AG; *Int'l*, pg. 7057
SOFTWAREONE CANADA INC.—See SoftwareONE Holding AG; *Int'l*, pg. 7057
SOFTWAREONE CHILE SPA—See SoftwareONE Holding AG; *Int'l*, pg. 7057
SOFTWAREONE COLOMBIA SAS—See SoftwareONE Holding AG; *Int'l*, pg. 7057
SOFTWAREONE COMERCIO E SERVICOS DE INFORMATICA LTDA.—See SoftwareONE Holding AG; *Int'l*, pg. 7057
SOFTWAREONE CZECH REPUBLIC SRO—See SoftwareONE Holding AG; *Int'l*, pg. 7057
SOFTWAREONE DENMARK APS—See SoftwareONE Holding AG; *Int'l*, pg. 7057
SOFTWAREONE DEUTSCHLAND GMBH—See SoftwareONE Holding AG; *Int'l*, pg. 7057
SOFTWAREONE DOMINICAN REPUBLIC SRL—See SoftwareONE Holding AG; *Int'l*, pg. 7057
SOFTWAREONE ECUADOR SOLUCIONES SA—See SoftwareONE Holding AG; *Int'l*, pg. 7057
SOFTWAREONE ESPANA S.A.—See SoftwareONE Holding AG; *Int'l*, pg. 7057
SOFTWAREONE EXPERTS SDN BHD—See SoftwareONE Holding AG; *Int'l*, pg. 7057
SOFTWAREONE EXPERTS SOUTH AFRICA (PTY) LTD.—See SoftwareONE Holding AG; *Int'l*, pg. 7058
SOFTWAREONE FRANCE SAS—See SoftwareONE Holding AG; *Int'l*, pg. 7057

SOFTWAREONE HOLDING AG; *Int'l*, pg. 7057
SOFTWAREONE HONG KONG LTD.—See SoftwareONE Holding AG; *Int'l*, pg. 7057
SOFTWAREONE HUNGARY LTD.—See SoftwareONE Holding AG; *Int'l*, pg. 7057
SOFTWAREONE INDIA PRIVATE LTD.—See SoftwareONE Holding AG; *Int'l*, pg. 7058
SOFTWAREONE, INFORMACIJSKI SISTEMI, DOO—See SoftwareONE Holding AG; *Int'l*, pg. 7058
SOFTWAREONE ITALIA SRL—See SoftwareONE Holding AG; *Int'l*, pg. 7058
SOFTWAREONE JAPAN KK—See SoftwareONE Holding AG; *Int'l*, pg. 7058
SOFTWAREONE KOREA LTD.—See SoftwareONE Holding AG; *Int'l*, pg. 7058
SOFTWAREONE LICENSING EXPERTS SRL—See SoftwareONE Holding AG; *Int'l*, pg. 7058
SOFTWAREONE LUXEMBOURG SARL—See SoftwareONE Holding AG; *Int'l*, pg. 7058
SOFTWAREONE NETHERLANDS B.V.—See SoftwareONE Holding AG; *Int'l*, pg. 7058
SOFTWAREONE NORWAY AS—See SoftwareONE Holding AG; *Int'l*, pg. 7058
SOFTWAREONE OSTERREICH GMBH—See SoftwareONE Holding AG; *Int'l*, pg. 7058
SOFTWAREONE PERU SAC—See SoftwareONE Holding AG; *Int'l*, pg. 7058
SOFTWAREONE PHILIPPINES CORPORATION—See SoftwareONE Holding AG; *Int'l*, pg. 7058
SOFTWAREONE POLSKA SP Z O.O.—See SoftwareONE Holding AG; *Int'l*, pg. 7058
SOFTWAREONE PROJECTS (PRIVATE) LIMITED—See SoftwareONE Holding AG; *Int'l*, pg. 7058
SOFTWAREONE PTE. LTD.—See SoftwareONE Holding AG; *Int'l*, pg. 7058
SOFTWAREONE (SHANGHAI) TRADING CO. LTD.—See SoftwareONE Holding AG; *Int'l*, pg. 7057
SOFTWAREONE SLOVAKIA SRO—See SoftwareONE Holding AG; *Int'l*, pg. 7058
SOFTWAREONE SPAIN SL—See SoftwareONE Holding AG; *Int'l*, pg. 7058
SOFTWAREONE SW1 DOMINICAN REPUBLIC SRL—See SoftwareONE Holding AG; *Int'l*, pg. 7058
SOFTWAREONE TAIWAN LTD.—See SoftwareONE Holding AG; *Int'l*, pg. 7058
SOFTWAREONE THAILAND CO., LTD.—See SoftwareONE Holding AG; *Int'l*, pg. 7058
SOFTWAREONE TURKEY BILISIM TEKNOLOJILERI TICARET ANONIM SIRKETI—See SoftwareONE Holding AG; *Int'l*, pg. 7058
SOFTWAREONE UK LTD.—See SoftwareONE Holding AG; *Int'l*, pg. 7058
SOFTWAREONE UKRAINE LIMITED LIABILITY COMPANY—See SoftwareONE Holding AG; *Int'l*, pg. 7058
SOFTWAREONE URUGUAY SPA—See SoftwareONE Holding AG; *Int'l*, pg. 7058
SOFTWAREONE VIETNAM CO. LIMITED—See SoftwareONE Holding AG; *Int'l*, pg. 7058
SOFTWARE PACKAGING ASSOCIATES INC; *U.S. Private*, pg. 3705
SOFTWARE PARADIGMS INTERNATIONAL GROUP LLC; *U.S. Private*, pg. 3705
SOFTWARE PIPELINE IRELAND LTD.—See SoftwareONE Holding AG; *Int'l*, pg. 7057
SOFTWARE PROFESSIONALS INCORPORATED; *U.S. Private*, pg. 3705
SOFTWAREPUNDITS, INC.; *U.S. Private*, pg. 3706
SOFTWARE RADIO TECHNOLOGY (UK) LIMITED—See SRT Marine Systems plc; *Int'l*, pg. 7152
SOFTWARE RESEARCH ASSOCIATES, INC.—See SRA Holdings Inc; *Int'l*, pg. 7148
SOFTWARE SCIENCE, INC.—See SRA Holdings Inc; *Int'l*, pg. 7148
SOFTWARE SECURE INC.—See Educational Testing Service Inc.; *U.S. Private*, pg. 1340
SOFTWARE SERVICE, INC.; *Int'l*, pg. 7057
SOFTWARE TEAM S.R.L.—See Nihon Kohden Corporation; *Int'l*, pg. 5286
SOFTWARE TECHNICAL SERVICES; *U.S. Private*, pg. 3705
SOFTWARE TECHNOLOGY GROUP INC.—See STG Lifecare Limited; *Int'l*, pg. 7213
SOFTWARE TRANSFORMATIONS, INC.; *U.S. Private*, pg. 3705
SOFTWEB SOLUTIONS INC.—See Avnet, Inc.; *U.S. Public*, pg. 254
SOFTWINK, INC.—See Worklyn Partners; *U.S. Private*, pg. 4564
SOFTWORLD, INC.—See Kelly Services, Inc.; *U.S. Public*, pg. 1220
SOFT-WORLD INTERNATIONAL CORPORATION; *Int'l*, pg. 7050
SOFTWRITERS, INC.—See Roper Technologies, Inc.; *U.S. Public*, pg. 1812
SOGABE (SUZHOU) GEAR REDUCER CO., LTD.—See Sato shoji Corporation; *Int'l*, pg. 6586
SOGAM—See VINCI S.A.; *Int'l*, pg. 8226

SOG-ANDY TAN CLINIC FOR WOMEN PTE. LTD.—See Singapore O&G Ltd.; *Int'l*, pg. 6941
SOGATRA NV—See SEA-invest Group; *Int'l*, pg. 6661
SOGAZ JSC; *Int'l*, pg. 7058
SOGB S.A.—See Socfinasia S.A.; *Int'l*, pg. 7031
SOG-CC TAN BREAST, THYROID & GENERAL SURGERY PTE. LTD.—See Singapore O&G Ltd.; *Int'l*, pg. 6941
SOG-CINDY PANG CLINIC FOR WOMEN PTE. LTD.—See Singapore O&G Ltd.; *Int'l*, pg. 6941
SOG-CLARA ONG CLINIC FOR WOMEN PTE. LTD.—See Singapore O&G Ltd.; *Int'l*, pg. 6941
SOGEA EST—See VINCI S.A.; *Int'l*, pg. 8231
SOGEA GUYANE SAS—See VINCI S.A.; *Int'l*, pg. 8228
SOGEA IDF SAS—See VINCI S.A.; *Int'l*, pg. 8235
SOGEA MAROC—See VINCI S.A.; *Int'l*, pg. 8231
SOGEA MARTINIQUE SAS—See VINCI S.A.; *Int'l*, pg. 8228
SOGEA MAYOTTE SAS—See VINCI S.A.; *Int'l*, pg. 8228
SOGEA NORD HYDRAULIQUE SAS—See VINCI S.A.; *Int'l*, pg. 8235
SOGEA NORD OUEST TP SAS—See VINCI S.A.; *Int'l*, pg. 8235
SOGEA PROVENCE SAS—See VINCI S.A.; *Int'l*, pg. 8235
SOGEA REUNION SAS—See VINCI S.A.; *Int'l*, pg. 8228
SOGEA RHONE ALPES SAS—See VINCI S.A.; *Int'l*, pg. 8235
SOGEA SATOM BENIN SA—See VINCI S.A.; *Int'l*, pg. 8228
SOGEA SATOM CAMEROUN—See VINCI S.A.; *Int'l*, pg. 8231
SOGEA-SATOM GABON—See VINCI S.A.; *Int'l*, pg. 8231
SOGEA-SATOM GUINEE EQUATORIALE—See VINCI S.A.; *Int'l*, pg. 8231
SOGEA SATOM KENYA LTD—See VINCI S.A.; *Int'l*, pg. 8231
SOGEA-SATOM SA—See VINCI S.A.; *Int'l*, pg. 8231
SOGEA SATOM SENEGAL SA—See VINCI S.A.; *Int'l*, pg. 8228
SOGEA-SATOM TANZANIE—See VINCI S.A.; *Int'l*, pg. 8231
SOGEA-SATOM TOGO—See VINCI S.A.; *Int'l*, pg. 8231
SOGEA S.C.A.R.L.—See RINA S.p.A.; *Int'l*, pg. 6343
SOGEA SUD HYDRAULIQUE SAS—See VINCI S.A.; *Int'l*, pg. 8235
SOGEA SUD OUEST HYDRAULIQUE SAS—See VINCI S.A.; *Int'l*, pg. 8235
SOGECAP S.A—See Societe Generale S.A.; *Int'l*, pg. 7041
SOGECLAIR AEROSPACE GMBH—See Sogeclair; *Int'l*, pg. 7058
SOGECLAIR AEROSPACE LTD—See Sogeclair; *Int'l*, pg. 7058
SOGECLAIR AEROSPACE SARL—See Sogeclair; *Int'l*, pg. 7058
SOGECLAIR AEROSPACE SA—See Sogeclair; *Int'l*, pg. 7058
SOGECLAIR; *Int'l*, pg. 7058
SOGEFI FILTRATION ARGENTINA S.A.—See Compagnia Finanziaria de Benedetti S.p.A.; *Int'l*, pg. 1722
SOGEFI FILTRATION D.O.O.—See Compagnia Finanziaria de Benedetti S.p.A.; *Int'l*, pg. 1722
SOGEFI INDUSTRIA DE AUTOPECAS LTDA.—See Compagnia Finanziaria de Benedetti S.p.A.; *Int'l*, pg. 1722
SOGEFINANCEMENT SAS—See Societe Generale S.A.; *Int'l*, pg. 7041
SOGEFI S.P.A.—See Compagnia Finanziaria de Benedetti S.p.A.; *Int'l*, pg. 1722
SOGEI INC.-SAPPORO BRANCH—See Digital Garage, Inc.; *Int'l*, pg. 2121
SOGEI INC.-SENDAI BRANCH—See Digital Garage, Inc.; *Int'l*, pg. 2122
SOGELEASE FRANCE SA—See Societe Generale S.A.; *Int'l*, pg. 7041
SOGELIFE SA—See Societe Generale S.A.; *Int'l*, pg. 7041
SOGEMAR; *Int'l*, pg. 7058
SOGEMAR S.P.A.—See EUROKAI GmbH & Co. KGaA; *Int'l*, pg. 2553
SOGEMI SRL—See Clariane SE; *Int'l*, pg. 1644
SOGEPAR IRELAND LIMITED—See Outokumpu Oyj; *Int'l*, pg. 5669
SO.GE.PA. - SOCIETA GENERALE DI PARTECIPAZIONI SPA—See Leonardo S.p.A.; *Int'l*, pg. 4461
SOGEPROM SA—See Societe Generale S.A.; *Int'l*, pg. 7041
SOGERCO—See La Poste S.A.; *Int'l*, pg. 4388
SOGESSO - SOCIEDADE DE GESSOS DE SOURE, S.A.—See Camargo Correa S.A.; *Int'l*, pg. 1268
SOGESSUR SA—See Societe Generale S.A.; *Int'l*, pg. 7041
SOGESTER - SOCIEDADE GESTORA DE TERMINAIS S.A.—See A.P. Moller-Maersk A/S; *Int'l*, pg. 27
SOGETI BELGIUM—See Capgemini SE; *Int'l*, pg. 1307
SOGETI CORPORATE SERVICES SAS—See Capgemini SE; *Int'l*, pg. 1307
SOGETI DEUTSCHLAND GMBH—See Capgemini SE; *Int'l*, pg. 1307
SOGETI ESPANA SL—See Capgemini SE; *Int'l*, pg. 1307
SOGETI FINLAND OY—See Capgemini SE; *Int'l*, pg. 1307

SOGEMAR

SOGETI FRANCE S.A.S.—See Capgemini SE; *Int'l*, pg. 1307
SOGETI HIGH TECH GMBH—See Capgemini SE; *Int'l*, pg. 1307
SOGETI HIGH TECH S.A.S.—See Capgemini SE; *Int'l*, pg. 1307
SOGETI IRELAND LTD.—See Capgemini SE; *Int'l*, pg. 1307
SOGETI LUXEMBOURG S.A.—See Capgemini SE; *Int'l*, pg. 1307
SOGETI NEDERLAND B.V.—See Capgemini SE; *Int'l*, pg. 1307
SOGETI NORGE AS—See Capgemini SE; *Int'l*, pg. 1307
SOGETI N.V./S.A.—See Capgemini SE; *Int'l*, pg. 1307
SOGETI PSF S.A.—See Capgemini SE; *Int'l*, pg. 1307
SOGETI—See Capgemini SE; *Int'l*, pg. 1307
SOGETI SVERIGE AB—See Capgemini SE; *Int'l*, pg. 1307
SOGETI UK LTD.—See Capgemini SE; *Int'l*, pg. 1307
SOGETI USA LLC—See Capgemini SE; *Int'l*, pg. 1307
SOGETI USA LLC—See Capgemini SE; *Int'l*, pg. 1307
SOGETI USA LLC—See Capgemini SE; *Int'l*, pg. 1307
SOGETI USA LLC—See Capgemini SE; *Int'l*, pg. 1307
SOGETI USA LLC—See Capgemini SE; *Int'l*, pg. 1307
SOGETI USA LLC—See Capgemini SE; *Int'l*, pg. 1307
SOGETI USA LLC—See Capgemini SE; *Int'l*, pg. 1307
SOGETI USA LLC—See Capgemini SE; *Int'l*, pg. 1307
SOGETI USA LLC—See Capgemini SE; *Int'l*, pg. 1307
SOGETI USA LLC—See Capgemini SE; *Int'l*, pg. 1307
SOGEX OMAN CO. L.L.C—See Suhail Bahwan Group (Holding) LLC; *Int'l*, pg. 7254
SOG-HL SIM COLORECTAL, ENDOSCOPY & GENERAL SURGERY PTE. LTD.—See Singapore O&G Ltd.; *Int'l*, pg. 6941
SOGINFO SOCIETE DE GESTION ET D'INVESTISSEMENTS FONCIERS—See Societe Generale S.A.; *Int'l*, pg. 7041
SOG INTERNATIONAL, INC.; *U.S. Private*, pg. 3706
SOGIREST; *Int'l*, pg. 7059
SOGITEC INDUSTRIES—See Groupe Industriel Marcel Dassault S.A.; *Int'l*, pg. 3105
SOGLASIE INSURANCE COMPANY LTD.—See Onexim Group Limited; *Int'l*, pg. 5581
SOG-NATALIE CHUA CLINIC FOR WOMEN PTE. LTD.—See Singapore O&G Ltd.; *Int'l*, pg. 6941
SOGNDALEN FJELLSPRENGING AS—See Nordisk Bergteknik AB; *Int'l*, pg. 5424
SOGNE OG SONGDALEN BUDSTIKKE AS—See Schibsted ASA; *Int'l*, pg. 6617
SOGN SPAREBANK; *Int'l*, pg. 7059
SOGO JIMU SERVICE CO., LTD.—See Honda Motor Co., Ltd.; *Int'l*, pg. 3464
SOGO MEDIA SUPPLY CO., LTD.—See Polaris Capital Group Co., Ltd.; *Int'l*, pg. 5907
SOGO MEDICAL CO. LTD.—See Polaris Capital Group Co., Ltd.; *Int'l*, pg. 5907
SOGO MEDICAL PHARMACY CHUBU CO., LTD.—See Polaris Capital Group Co., Ltd.; *Int'l*, pg. 5907
SOGO MEDIPRO CO., LTD.—See Polaris Capital Group Co., Ltd.; *Int'l*, pg. 5907
SOGO PHARMACEUTICAL CO., LTD.—See Polaris Capital Group Co., Ltd.; *Int'l*, pg. 5907
SOGO & SEIBU CO., LTD.—See SoftBank Group Corp.; *Int'l*, pg. 7054
SOGOTEC ENTERPRISE CO., LTD.—See Anderson Industrial Corporation; *Int'l*, pg. 450
SOGOU INC.—See Tencent Holdings Limited; *Int'l*, pg. 7559
SOG-RADHIKA BREAST & GENERAL SURGICARE PTE. LTD.—See Singapore O&G Ltd.; *Int'l*, pg. 6941
SOG-SC HONG CLINIC FOR WOMEN PTE. LTD.—See Singapore O&G Ltd.; *Int'l*, pg. 6941
SOG-SK LIM BREAST & GENERAL SURGICARE PTE. LTD.—See Singapore O&G Ltd.; *Int'l*, pg. 6941
SOHAR ASHAPURA CHEMICALS LLC—See Ashapura Minechem Limited; *Int'l*, pg. 606
SOHAR GASES COMPANY L.L.C—See Global Financial Investments Holding SAOG; *Int'l*, pg. 2996
SOHAR INTERNATIONAL BANK SAOG; *Int'l*, pg. 7059
SOHAR OPERATION SERVICES LLC—See Sacyr, S.A.; *Int'l*, pg. 6466
SOHAR POULTRY S.A.O.G; *Int'l*, pg. 7059
SOHAR POWER COMPANY—See ENGIE SA; *Int'l*, pg. 2433
SOHAR UNIVERSITY LLC—See Global Financial Investments Holding SAOG; *Int'l*, pg. 2996
SOHBI CRAFT POLAND SP.Z O.O.—See Hanwa Co., Ltd.; *Int'l*, pg. 3263
SOHBI KOHGEI (PHILS) INC.—See Hanwa Co., Ltd.; *Int'l*, pg. 3263
SOHGO HOUSING CO. LTD.—See Dai-ichi Life Holdings, Inc.; *Int'l*, pg. 1918
SOHGOH REAL ESTATE CO., LTD.—See Haseko Corporation; *Int'l*, pg. 3283
SOHGO SECURITY SERVICES CO., LTD.; *Int'l*, pg. 7059

SOH MECHANICAL & ELECTRICAL ENGINEERS CORPORATION—See Ikeshita Sekkei Co. Ltd.; *Int'l*, pg. 3610
SOHM, INC.; *U.S. Public*, pg. 1899
SOHNEN ENTERPRISES INC.; *U.S. Private*, pg. 3706
SOHO CHINA LIMITED; *Int'l*, pg. 7059
SOHO DEVELOPMENT S.A.; *Int'l*, pg. 7059
SOHO FLORDIS INTERNATIONAL PTY LTD.; *Int'l*, pg. 7059
SOHO FLORDIS INTERNATIONAL PTY LTD—See SOHO Group; *Int'l*, pg. 7059
SOHO GROUP; *Int'l*, pg. 7059
SOHO HOLLY CORPORATION; *Int'l*, pg. 7059
SOHO HOUSE & CO INC.; *Int'l*, pg. 7060
SOHO MYRIAD, LLC—See Longwater Opportunities LLC; *U.S. Private*, pg. 2493
SOHONET LIMITED; *Int'l*, pg. 7060
SOHO STUDIO, LLC—See AEA Investors LP; *U.S. Private*, pg. 115
SOHSHIN CO., LTD.—See Toyota Motor Corporation; *Int'l*, pg. 7871
SOHU.COM (HONG KONG) LTD.—See SOHU.com Ltd.; *Int'l*, pg. 7060
SOHU.COM LTD.; *Int'l*, pg. 7060
SO HUDSON 555 MANAGEMENT, INC.—See Vornado Realty Trust; *U.S. Public*, pg. 2310
SOICHER MARIN OF FLORIDA LLC; *U.S. Private*, pg. 3706
SOIKEN HOLDINGS INC.; *Int'l*, pg. 7060
SOIL-AWAY CLEANING & RESTORATION SERVICES—See Insurcomm Construction, Inc.; *U.S. Private*, pg. 2095
SOILBUILD BUSINESS SPACE REIT; *Int'l*, pg. 7060
SOILBUILD CONSTRUCTION GROUP LTD.; *Int'l*, pg. 7060
SOILBUILD CONSTRUCTION (MYANMAR) CO., LTD.—See Soilbuild Construction Group Ltd.; *Int'l*, pg. 7060
SOILBUILD GROUP HOLDINGS LTD.; *Int'l*, pg. 7060
SOILBUILD (MYANMAR) COMPANY LIMITED—See Soilbuild Construction Group Ltd.; *Int'l*, pg. 7060
S-OIL CORPORATION—See Saudi Arabian Oil Company; *Int'l*, pg. 6590
SOILCRETE TECHNOLOGY CO., LTD.—See Thai Solar Energy Public Company Limited; *Int'l*, pg. 7595
SOIL ENGINEERING GEOSERVICES LTD.—See VINCI S.A.; *Int'l*, pg. 8228
SOIL & FOUNDATION (PTE) LIMITED—See Tuan Sing Holdings Limited; *Int'l*, pg. 7962
SOIL INVESTIGATION PTE. LTD.—See CSC Holdings Limited; *Int'l*, pg. 1862
SOIL MACHINE DYNAMICS LTD.; *Int'l*, pg. 7060
SOIL MACHINE DYNAMICS SINGAPORE PTE LTD—See Soil Machine Dynamics Ltd.; *Int'l*, pg. 7060
SOIL & MATERIALS ENGINEERS, INC.; *U.S. Private*, pg. 3706
SOILMEC ALGERIA SARL—See Trevi Finanziaria Industriale SpA.; *Int'l*, pg. 7917
SOILMEC AUSTRALIA PTY. LTD.—See Trevi Finanziaria Industriale SpA.; *Int'l*, pg. 7917
SOILMEC COLOMBIA S.A.S.—See Trevi Finanziaria Industriale SpA.; *Int'l*, pg. 7917
SOILMEC DEUTSCHLAND GMBH—See Trevi Finanziaria Industriale SpA.; *Int'l*, pg. 7917
SOILMEC DO BRASIL S.A.—See Trevi Finanziaria Industriale SpA.; *Int'l*, pg. 7917
SOILMEC F. EQUIPMENT PVT. LTD.—See Trevi Finanziaria Industriale SpA.; *Int'l*, pg. 7917
SOILMEC FRANCE S.A.S.—See Trevi Finanziaria Industriale SpA.; *Int'l*, pg. 7917
SOILMEC H.K. LTD.—See Trevi Finanziaria Industriale SpA.; *Int'l*, pg. 7917
SOILMEC JAPAN CO., LTD.—See Trevi Finanziaria Industriale SpA.; *Int'l*, pg. 7917
SOILMEC NORTH AMERICA INC.—See Trevi Finanziaria Industriale SpA.; *Int'l*, pg. 7917
SOILMEC SINGAPORE PTE. LTD.—See Trevi Finanziaria Industriale SpA.; *Int'l*, pg. 7917
SOILMEC S.P.A.—See Trevi Finanziaria Industriale SpA.; *Int'l*, pg. 7917
SOILMEC U.K. LTD.—See Trevi Finanziaria Industriale SpA.; *Int'l*, pg. 7917
SOIL MIXING GROUP AB—See Nordisk Bergteknik AB; *Int'l*, pg. 5424
SOIL RECOVERY A/S—See NOV, Inc.; *U.S. Public*, pg. 1546
SOIL SAFE, INC.—See BC Partners LLP; *Int'l*, pg. 924
S-OIL SINGAPORE PTE. LTD.—See Saudi Arabian Oil Company; *Int'l*, pg. 6590
SOILTECH AS; *Int'l*, pg. 7060
SOIL WATER SNOW, LLC; *U.S. Private*, pg. 3706
SOIS MENDJINNI INDUSTRIAL TECHNOLOGY (SHANGHAI) CO., LTD.—See AICA Kogyo Company, Limited; *Int'l*, pg. 229
SOITEC JAPAN INC.—See Soitec S.A.; *Int'l*, pg. 7060
SOITEC S.A.; *Int'l*, pg. 7060
SOITEC USA INC.—See Soitec S.A.; *Int'l*, pg. 7060
SOIZA S.A.—See SIF Banat-Crisana S.A.; *Int'l*, pg. 6905

SOJAPROTEIN D.O.O.—See Archer-Daniels-Midland Company; *U.S. Public*, pg. 185
SOJITZ AEROSPACE AMERICA CORPORATION—See Sojitz Corporation; *Int'l*, pg. 7063
SOJITZ AEROSPACE CORPORATION—See Sojitz Corporation; *Int'l*, pg. 7063
SOJITZ AGRO CORPORATION—See Sojitz Corporation; *Int'l*, pg. 7063
SOJITZ AIRCRAFT LEASING B.V.—See Sojitz Corporation; *Int'l*, pg. 7063
SOJITZ ARGENTINA S.A.—See Sojitz Corporation; *Int'l*, pg. 7063
SOJITZ ASIA PTE. LTD.—See Sojitz Corporation; *Int'l*, pg. 7063
SOJITZ ASIA PTE. LTD.—See Sojitz Corporation; *Int'l*, pg. 7063
SOJITZ ASIA PTE. LTD.—See Sojitz Corporation; *Int'l*, pg. 7063
SOJITZ AUSTRALIA LIMITED—See Sojitz Corporation; *Int'l*, pg. 7063
SOJITZ AUSTRALIA LTD.—See Sojitz Corporation; *Int'l*, pg. 7063
SOJITZ AUTO GROUP OSAKA CO., LTD.—See Sojitz Corporation; *Int'l*, pg. 7063
SOJITZ AUTO GROUP TOKYO CO., LTD.—See Sojitz Corporation; *Int'l*, pg. 7063
SOJITZ AUTOMOTIVE & ENGINEERING, INC.—See Sojitz Corporation; *Int'l*, pg. 7063
SOJITZ AUTRANS CORPORATION—See Sojitz Corporation; *Int'l*, pg. 7063
SOJITZ BERALT TIN & WOLFRAM (PORTUGAL) S.A.—See Sojitz Corporation; *Int'l*, pg. 7063
SOJITZ BUILDING MATERIALS CORPORATION—See Sojitz Corporation; *Int'l*, pg. 7063
SOJITZ CANADA CORPORATION—See Sojitz Corporation; *Int'l*, pg. 7063
SOJITZ (CHINA) CO., LTD.—See Sojitz Corporation; *Int'l*, pg. 7063
SOJITZ COAL RESOURCES PTY. LTD.—See Sojitz Corporation; *Int'l*, pg. 7063
SOJITZ COMMERCE DEVELOPMENT CORPORATION—See Sojitz Corporation; *Int'l*, pg. 7063
SOJITZ CORPORATION IRAN LTD.—See Sojitz Corporation; *Int'l*, pg. 7064
SOJITZ CORPORATION OF AMERICA—See Sojitz Corporation; *Int'l*, pg. 7064
SOJITZ CORPORATION OF AMERICA—See Sojitz Corporation; *Int'l*, pg. 7064
SOJITZ CORPORATION; *Int'l*, pg. 7061
SOJITZ COSMETICS CORPORATION—See Sojitz Corporation; *Int'l*, pg. 7064
SOJITZ (DALIAN) CO., LTD.—See Sojitz Corporation; *Int'l*, pg. 7063
SOJITZ DO BRASIL S.A.—See Sojitz Corporation; *Int'l*, pg. 7065
SOJITZ ENERGY AUSTRALIA PTY. LTD.—See Sojitz Corporation; *Int'l*, pg. 7064
SOJITZ ENERGY VENTURE, INC.—See Sojitz Corporation; *Int'l*, pg. 7064
SOJITZ ETAME LTD.—See Sojitz Corporation; *Int'l*, pg. 7064
SOJITZ EUROPE PLC—See Sojitz Corporation; *Int'l*, pg. 7064
SOJITZ FASHION CO., LTD.—See Sojitz Corporation; *Int'l*, pg. 7064
SOJITZ FASHION (SHANGHAI) TRADING CO., LTD.—See Sojitz Corporation; *Int'l*, pg. 7064
SOJITZ FOODS CORPORATION—See Sojitz Corporation; *Int'l*, pg. 7064
SOJITZ FOREST PRODUCTS (EM) SDN. BHD.—See Sojitz Corporation; *Int'l*, pg. 7064
SOJITZ FUSO PHILIPPINES CORPORATION—See Sojitz Corporation; *Int'l*, pg. 7064
SOJITZ GENERAL MERCHANDISE CORPORATION—See Sojitz Corporation; *Int'l*, pg. 7064
SOJITZ GENERAL PROPERTY MANAGEMENT CORPORATION—See Sojitz Corporation; *Int'l*, pg. 7064
SOJITZ GLOBAL TRADING NIGERIA LTD.—See Sojitz Corporation; *Int'l*, pg. 7064
SOJITZ (GUANGZHOU) CO., LTD.—See Sojitz Corporation; *Int'l*, pg. 7063
SOJITZ (HONG KONG) LIMITED—See Sojitz Corporation; *Int'l*, pg. 7063
SOJITZ INDIA PRIVATE LTD.—See Sojitz Corporation; *Int'l*, pg. 7064
SOJITZ INFINITY INC.—See Sojitz Corporation; *Int'l*, pg. 7064
SOJITZ INSTITUTE OF INNOVATIVE TECHNOLOGIES, LTD.—See Sojitz Corporation; *Int'l*, pg. 7064
SOJITZ INSURANCE AGENCY CORPORATION—See Sojitz Corporation; *Int'l*, pg. 7064
SOJITZ INSURANCE BROKERS (HK) LTD.—See Sojitz Corporation; *Int'l*, pg. 7064
SOJITZ JECT CORPORATION—See Sojitz Corporation; *Int'l*, pg. 7064

SOJITZ KELANITISSA (PRIVATE) LIMITED—See Sojitz Corporation; *Int'l*, pg. 7064
SOJITZ KOREA CORPORATION—See Sojitz Corporation; *Int'l*, pg. 7064
SOJITZ KYUSHU CORPORATION—See Sojitz Corporation; *Int'l*, pg. 7064
SOJITZ LOGISTICS CORPORATION—See Sojitz Corporation; *Int'l*, pg. 7064
SOJITZ LOGISTICS VIETNAM CO., LTD.—See Sojitz Corporation; *Int'l*, pg. 7064
SOJITZ LOGITECH CO., LTD.—See Sojitz Corporation; *Int'l*, pg. 7064
SOJITZ MACHINERY CORPORATION—See Sojitz Corporation; *Int'l*, pg. 7064
SOJITZ MACHINERY (SHANGHAI) CORPORATION—See Sojitz Corporation; *Int'l*, pg. 7064
SOJITZ (MALAYSIA) SDN. BHD.—See Sojitz Corporation; *Int'l*, pg. 7063
SOJITZ MARINE & ENGINEERING CORPORATION—See Sojitz Corporation; *Int'l*, pg. 7064
SOJITZ MEXICANA S.A. DE C.V.—See Sojitz Corporation; *Int'l*, pg. 7064
SOJITZ MIDDLE EAST FZE—See Sojitz Corporation; *Int'l*, pg. 7064
SOJITZ MIRAI POWER CORPORATION—See Sojitz Corporation; *Int'l*, pg. 7064
SOJITZ MOBILITY CORPORATION—See Sojitz Corporation; *Int'l*, pg. 7064
SOJITZ MOLY RESOURCES, INC.—See Moon River Moly Ltd.; *Int'l*, pg. 5038
SOJITZ NEW URBAN DEVELOPMENT CORPORATION—See Sojitz Corporation; *Int'l*, pg. 7064
SOJITZ NEW ZEALAND LIMITED—See Sojitz Corporation; *Int'l*, pg. 7065
SOJITZ NOW APPAREL LTD.—See Sojitz Corporation; *Int'l*, pg. 7065
SOJITZ OFFSHORE PROJECT PTE. LTD.—See Sojitz Corporation; *Int'l*, pg. 7065
SOJITZ OIL & GAS (EGYPT) LTD.—See Sojitz Corporation; *Int'l*, pg. 7065
SOJITZ PETROLEUM CO., (SINGAPORE) PTE. LTD.—See Sojitz Corporation; *Int'l*, pg. 7065
SOJITZ PHILIPPINES CORPORATION—See Sojitz Corporation; *Int'l*, pg. 7065
SOJITZ PLA-NET CORPORATION—See Sojitz Corporation; *Int'l*, pg. 7065
SOJITZ PLA-NET HOLDINGS, INC.—See Sojitz Corporation; *Int'l*, pg. 7065
SOJITZ PLASTICS AMERICA INC.—See Sojitz Corporation; *Int'l*, pg. 7064
SOJITZ PLASTICS (CHINA) LTD.—See Sojitz Corporation; *Int'l*, pg. 7065
SOJITZ PRIVATE EQUITY, INC.—See Sojitz Corporation; *Int'l*, pg. 7065
SOJITZ PROMOTION CO., LTD.—See Sojitz Corporation; *Int'l*, pg. 7065
SOJITZ REALNET CORPORATION—See Sojitz Corporation; *Int'l*, pg. 7065
SOJITZ REIT ADVISORS K.K.—See Sojitz Corporation; *Int'l*, pg. 7065
SOJITZ RESEARCH INSTITUTE, LTD.—See Sojitz Corporation; *Int'l*, pg. 7065
SOJITZ RESOURCES (AUSTRALIA) PTY. LTD.—See Sojitz Corporation; *Int'l*, pg. 7065
SOJITZ SAWADA POWER CO., LTD.—See Sojitz Corporation; *Int'l*, pg. 7065
SOJITZ (SHANGHAI) CO., LTD.—See Sojitz Corporation; *Int'l*, pg. 7063
SOJITZ SHARED SERVICE CORPORATION—See Sojitz Corporation; *Int'l*, pg. 7065
SOJITZ SOLAR BETZWEILER GMBH—See Sojitz Corporation; *Int'l*, pg. 7065
SOJITZ SYSTEMS CORPORATION—See Sojitz Corporation; *Int'l*, pg. 7065
SOJITZ TECHNOPLAS CORPORATION—See Sojitz Corporation; *Int'l*, pg. 7065
SOJITZ TEXTILE (SHANGHAI) CO., LTD.—See Sojitz Corporation; *Int'l*, pg. 7065
SOJITZ (THAILAND) CO., LTD.—See Sojitz Corporation; *Int'l*, pg. 7063
SOJITZ TOURIST CORPORATION—See Sojitz Corporation; *Int'l*, pg. 7065
SOJITZ TUNA FARM TAKASHIMA CO., LTD.—See Sojitz Corporation; *Int'l*, pg. 7065
SOJITZ TUNGSTEN RESOURCES, INC.—See Sojitz Corporation; *Int'l*, pg. 7065
SOJITZ VENEZUELA C.A.—See Sojitz Corporation; *Int'l*, pg. 7065
SOJITZ VIETNAM COMPANY LTD.—See Sojitz Corporation; *Int'l*, pg. 7065
SOJITZ YOSHIMOTO RINGYO CORPORATION.—See Sojitz Corporation; *Int'l*, pg. 7065
SOJO ELECTRIC CO., LTD.—See Beijing Sojo Electric Company Limited; *Int'l*, pg. 957
SOJOURNER FARMS LLC—See Clearlake Capital Group, L.P.; *U.S. Private*, pg. 937
SOKC, LLC—See PENN Entertainment, Inc.; *U.S. Public*, pg. 1662
SOKE-HUNGARIA KFT—See Newell Brands Inc.; *U.S. Public*, pg. 1515
SOKEI BUILDING SERVICE CO., LTD.—See Sohgo Security Services Co., Ltd.; *Int'l*, pg. 7059
SOKEN CHEMICAL ASIA CO., LTD.—See Soken Chemical & Engineering Co.,Ltd.; *Int'l*, pg. 7066
SOKEN CHEMICAL & ENGINEERING CO.,LTD.; *Int'l*, pg. 7066
SOKEN CORPORATION—See Meiwa Corporation; *Int'l*, pg. 4805
SOKEN HIGH-TECH MATERIAL (NANJING) CO., LTD.—See Soken Chemical & Engineering Co.,Ltd.; *Int'l*, pg. 7066
SOKENSHA CO LTD; *Int'l*, pg. 7066
SOKHNA PORT DEVELOPMENT COMPANY—See Carrix, Inc.; *U.S. Private*, pg. 773
SOKIGO AB—See Addnode Group AB; *Int'l*, pg. 130
SOKKIA KOREA CO., LTD.—See Topcon Corporation; *Int'l*, pg. 7814
SOK MARKETLER TICARET AS; *Int'l*, pg. 7066
SOKO AIR D.D.; *Int'l*, pg. 7066
SOKO BRAVARSKO LIMARSKO D.D.; *Int'l*, pg. 7066
SOKOCNICA A.D.; *Int'l*, pg. 7066
SOKOFLOK SLOVAKIA S.R.O.—See SNF SAS; *Int'l*, pg. 7028
SOKOFLOK S.R.O.—See SNF SAS; *Int'l*, pg. 7028
SOKO HELIKOPTERI D.D.; *Int'l*, pg. 7066
SOKOL & COMPANY; *U.S. Private*, pg. 3706
SOKOLICA A.D.; *Int'l*, pg. 7066
SOKOLKA SA—See Ratos AB; *Int'l*, pg. 6220
SOKOLOW-LOGISTYKA SP. Z O.O.—See Danish Crown AmbA; *Int'l*, pg. 1965
SOKOLOW—See Danish Crown AmbA; *Int'l*, pg. 1965
SOKOMAN MINERALS CORP.; *Int'l*, pg. 7066
SOKOPREVOZ A.D.; *Int'l*, pg. 7066
SOKO SEIREN CO., LTD.—See Marui Orimono KK; *Int'l*, pg. 4713
SOKOUK HOLDING COMPANY K.S.C.C.; *Int'l*, pg. 7066
SOKOWEB TECHNOLOGIES, S.L.—See Axel Springer SE; *Int'l*, pg. 766
SOKO ZRAKOPLOVSTVO D.D.; *Int'l*, pg. 7066
SOKRATHERM GMBH; *Int'l*, pg. 7067
SOKTAS TEKSTIL SANAYI VE TICARET A.S.; *Int'l*, pg. 7067
SOKUDO CO., LTD.—See Screen Holdings Co., Ltd.; *Int'l*, pg. 6656
SOKUTO CO., LTD.—See Aktio Holdings Corporation; *Int'l*, pg. 267
SOLA BETONG AS—See Heidelberg Materials AG; *Int'l*, pg. 3319
SOLABIOS SA; *Int'l*, pg. 7068
SOLACE CAPITAL PARTNERS, LLC; *U.S. Private*, pg. 3706
SOLACOM TECHNOLOGIES (US), INC.—See Comtech Telecommunications Corp.; *U.S. Public*, pg. 563
SOLAE LLC - PRYOR OFFICE—See DuPont de Nemours, Inc.; *U.S. Public*, pg. 692
SOLAE LLC—See DuPont de Nemours, Inc.; *U.S. Public*, pg. 692
SOLAERO TECHNOLOGIES CORP.—See Rocket Lab USA, Inc.; *U.S. Public*, pg. 1804
SOLAGRAN LIMITED; *Int'l*, pg. 7068
SOLA HOTEL EIENDOM AS—See Avinor AS; *Int'l*, pg. 744
SOLAI & CAMERON INC.; *U.S. Private*, pg. 3706
SOLAIS LIGHTING, INC.—See The Southern Company; *U.S. Public*, pg. 2131
SOLANA AGRO PECUARIA LTDA.—See C.H. Boehringer Sohn AG & Co. KG; *Int'l*, pg. 1242
SOLANA D.D. TUZLA; *Int'l*, pg. 7068
SOLANA ENVIRONMENTAL ASSOCIATES INC.; *U.S. Private*, pg. 3706
SOLANBRIDGE GROUP INC.; *U.S. Public*, pg. 1899
SOLANO COUNTY COMMUNITY HOUSING CORPORATION; *U.S. Private*, pg. 3706
SOLANO GARBAGE COMPANY—See Republic Services, Inc.; *U.S. Public*, pg. 1787
SOLANTIC CORPORATION—See Tenet Healthcare Corporation; *U.S. Public*, pg. 2014
SOLANUM AB—See Lantmannen ek for; *Int'l*, pg. 4414
SOLARA ACTIVE PHARMA SCIENCES LIMITED; *Int'l*, pg. 7069
SOLAR ALLIANCE ENERGY INC.; *Int'l*, pg. 7068
SOLARA MEDICAL SUPPLIES, LLC—See AdaptHealth Corp.; *U.S. Public*, pg. 39
SOLAR APPLIED MATERIALS TECHNOLOGY CORPORATION; *Int'l*, pg. 7068
SOLAR APPLIED MATERIALS TECHNOLOGY (SINGAPORE) PTE. LTD.—See Solar Applied Materials Technology Corporation; *Int'l*, pg. 7069
SOLAR APPLIED MATERIALS USA, INC.—See Solar Applied Materials Technology Corporation; *Int'l*, pg. 7069
SOLAR ART WINDOW FILM, INC.; *U.S. Private*, pg. 3707
SOLARA S.A. DE C.V.—See Strides Pharma Science Limited; *Int'l*, pg. 7240
SOLAR A/S; *Int'l*, pg. 7068
SOLAR ATMOSPHERES, INC.; *U.S. Private*, pg. 3707
SOLARAY CORPORATION; *U.S. Private*, pg. 3707
SOLARBOS—See Gibraltar Industries, Inc.; *U.S. Public*, pg. 936
SOLAR CENTURY HOLDINGS LIMITED; *Int'l*, pg. 7069
SOLAR CHEMICAL APPLIED MATERIAL TECHNOLOGY (KUNSHAN) CO., LTD.—See Solar Applied Materials Technology Corporation; *Int'l*, pg. 7069
SOLARCITY CORP.—See Tesla, Inc.; *U.S. Public*, pg. 2021
SOLAR COMPANY S.A.; *Int'l*, pg. 7069
SOLARDEC CVBA—See Deceuninck NV; *Int'l*, pg. 2000
SOLAREAST HOLDINGS CO., LTD.; *Int'l*, pg. 7069
SOLAREDGE TECHNOLOGIES (AUSTRALIA) PTY LTD—See SolarEdge Technologies, Inc.; *Int'l*, pg. 7069
SOLAREDGE TECHNOLOGIES (BULGARIA) LTD.—See SolarEdge Technologies, Inc.; *Int'l*, pg. 7069
SOLAREDGE TECHNOLOGIES CHINA—See SolarEdge Technologies, Inc.; *Int'l*, pg. 7069
SOLAREDGE TECHNOLOGIES GMBH—See SolarEdge Technologies, Inc.; *Int'l*, pg. 7069
SOLAREDGE TECHNOLOGIES, INC.; *Int'l*, pg. 7069
SOLAREDGE TECHNOLOGIES (INDIA) PRIVATE LIMITED—See SolarEdge Technologies, Inc.; *Int'l*, pg. 7069
SOLAREDGE TECHNOLOGIES ITALY S.R.L.—See SolarEdge Technologies, Inc.; *Int'l*, pg. 7069
SOLAREDGE TECHNOLOGIES (JAPAN) CO., LTD.—See SolarEdge Technologies, Inc.; *Int'l*, pg. 7069
SOLAREDGE TECHNOLOGIES (KOREA) CO. LTD.—See SolarEdge Technologies, Inc.; *Int'l*, pg. 7069
SOLAREDGE TECHNOLOGIES LTD.—See SolarEdge Technologies, Inc.; *Int'l*, pg. 7069
SOLAREDGE TECHNOLOGIES (POLAND) SP. Z O.O.—See SolarEdge Technologies, Inc.; *Int'l*, pg. 7069
SOLAREDGE TECHNOLOGIES (UK) LTD.—See SolarEdge Technologies, Inc.; *Int'l*, pg. 7069
SOLAREDGE TEKNOLOJI. A.S.—See SolarEdge Technologies, Inc.; *Int'l*, pg. 7069
SOLAR ENERJI TEKNOLOJILERI VE METAL SANAYI TICARET A.S.—See Bozlu Holding; *Int'l*, pg. 1125
SOLARES CONTROLS—See Applied Industrial Technologies, Inc.; *U.S. Public*, pg. 171
SOLARFLARE COMMUNICATIONS, INC.—See Advanced Micro Devices, Inc.; *U.S. Public*, pg. 49
SOLAR FRONTIER K.K.—See Idemitsu Kosan Co., Ltd.; *Int'l*, pg. 3592
SOLAR FUNDING SOLUTIONS CORP.; *U.S. Private*, pg. 3707
SOLAR GARD NORDIC AB—See Compagnie de Saint-Gobain SA; *Int'l*, pg. 1729
SOLAR GAS SDN BHD—See KUB Malaysia Berhad; *Int'l*, pg. 4320
SOLARGIGA ENERGY HOLDINGS LIMITED - JINZHOU PLANT—See Solargiga Energy Holdings Limited; *Int'l*, pg. 7069
SOLARGIGA ENERGY HOLDINGS LIMITED; *Int'l*, pg. 7069
SOLAR GOLD LTD.; *U.S. Public*, pg. 1899
SOLAR GREEN MATERIALS TECHNOLOGY CO., LTD.—See Solar Applied Materials Technology Corporation; *Int'l*, pg. 7069
SOLAR GREEN TECHNOLOGY S.P.A.—See SPI Energy Co., Ltd.; *Int'l*, pg. 7135
SOLAR GROUP, INC.—See Gibraltar Industries, Inc.; *U.S. Public*, pg. 936
SOLARHYBRID AG; *Int'l*, pg. 7070
SOLARIA ENERGIA Y MEDIO AMBIENTE, S.A.; *Int'l*, pg. 7070
SOLAR INDUSTRIES INC.; *U.S. Private*, pg. 3707
SOLAR INDUSTRIES INDIA LIMITED; *Int'l*, pg. 7069
SOLAR INNOVATIONS, INC.; *U.S. Private*, pg. 3707
SOLAR INTEGRATED ROOFING CORPORATION; *U.S. Public*, pg. 1899
SOLARINVEST - GREEN ENERGY S.R.O.—See EnBW Energie Baden-Wurttemberg AG; *Int'l*, pg. 2400
SOLARIS ASSET MANAGMENT COMPANY LIMITED—See XSpring Capital Public Company Limited; *Int'l*, pg. 8539
SOLARIS AUSTRIA GMBH—See Construcciones y Auxiliar de Ferrocarriles S.A.; *Int'l*, pg. 1777
SOLARIS BUS & COACH LATVIA LTD.—See Construcciones y Auxiliar de Ferrocarriles S.A.; *Int'l*, pg. 1777
SOLARIS BUS & COACH ROMANIA S.R.L.—See Construcciones y Auxiliar de Ferrocarriles S.A.; *Int'l*, pg. 1777
SOLARIS BUS & COACH, SP. Z O.O.—See Construcciones y Auxiliar de Ferrocarriles S.A.; *Int'l*, pg. 1777
SOLARIS BUS IBERICA, S.L.U.—See Construcciones y Auxiliar de Ferrocarriles S.A.; *Int'l*, pg. 1777
SOLARIS CHEMTECH INDUSTRIES LIMITED—See Avantha Group; *Int'l*, pg. 736
SOLARIS CZECH SPOL. S.R.O.—See Construcciones y Auxiliar de Ferrocarriles S.A.; *Int'l*, pg. 1777
SOLARIS FRANCE S.A.R.L.—See Construcciones y Auxiliar de Ferrocarriles S.A.; *Int'l*, pg. 1777
SOLARIS HEALTHCARE NETWORK LTD—See The Mission Group Public Limited Company; *Int'l*, pg. 7667
SOLARIS, INC.—See Lohmann & Rauscher International GmbH & Co. KG; *Int'l*, pg. 4544
SOLARIS ITALIA S.R.L.—See Construcciones y Auxiliar de Ferrocarriles S.A.; *Int'l*, pg. 1777

SOLAR INTEGRATED ROOFING CORPORATION — CORPORATE AFFILIATIONS

SOLARIS LASER S.A.—See Dover Corporation; *U.S. Public*, pg. 682

SOLARIS MOBILE LTD.—See EchoStar Corporation; *U.S. Public*, pg. 711

SOLARIS NORGE AS—See Construcciones y Auxiliar de Ferrocarriles S.A.; *Int'l*, pg. 1777

SOLARIS OILFIELD INFRASTRUCTURE, INC.; *U.S. Public*, pg. 1900

SOLARIS OILFIELD SITE SERVICES OPERATING, LLC—See Solaris Oilfield Infrastructure, Inc.; *U.S. Public*, pg. 1900

SOLARIS POWER CELLS, INC.; *U.S. Private*, pg. 3707

SOLARIS RESOURCES, INC.; *Int'l*, pg. 7070

SOLARIS SVERIGE AB—See Construcciones y Auxiliar de Ferrocarriles S.A.; *Int'l*, pg. 1777

SOLARIS VERWALTUNGSGESELLSCHAFT MBH & CO. VERMIETUNGS KG—See UniCredit S.p.A.; *Int'l*, pg. 8035

SOLARITY CREDIT UNION; *U.S. Private*, pg. 3708

SOLARIUS DEVELOPMENT, INC.—See Marposs S.p.A.; *Int'l*, pg. 4699

SOLARKRAFTWERK MERZIG GMBH & CO. KG—See Electricite de France S.A.; *Int'l*, pg. 2350

SOLAR LASER SYSTEMS JSC—See HORIBA Ltd; *Int'l*, pg. 3478

SOLARLENS CO., LTD.—See PPG Industries, Inc.; *U.S. Public*, pg. 1710

SOLAR LIBERTY; *U.S. Private*, pg. 3707

SOLAR LINK INTERNATIONAL INC—See Yue Yuen Industrial Holdings Limited; *Int'l*, pg. 8610

SOLAR-LOG GMBH—See BKW AG; *Int'l*, pg. 1056

SOLARMARKT GMBH—See BayWa AG; *Int'l*, pg. 919

SOLAR-MATE SDN. BHD.—See Waterco Limited; *Int'l*, pg. 8356

SOLARMAX TECHNOLOGY, INC.; *U.S. Public*, pg. 1900

SOLAR MILLENNIUM AG; *Int'l*, pg. 7069

SOLAR MILLENNIUM MENA GMBH—See Solar Millennium AG; *Int'l*, pg. 7069

SOLAR MINING SERVICES PTY. LIMITED—See Solar Industries India Limited; *Int'l*, pg. 7069

SOLAR NEDERLAND B.V.—See Solar A/S; *Int'l*, pg. 7068

SOLARNET, LLC—See ITOCHU Corporation; *Int'l*, pg. 3839

SOLAR NITRO CHEMICALS LIMITED—See Solar Industries India Limited; *Int'l*, pg. 7069

SOLAR ONE ENERGY PRIVATE LIMITED—See Fortum Oyj; *Int'l*, pg. 2742

SOLARONE SOLUTIONS, INC.; *U.S. Private*, pg. 3708

SOLARONICS AB—See NV Bekaert SA; *Int'l*, pg. 5496

SOLARONICS SA—See Pomona-Gruppen AB; *Int'l*, pg. 5918

SOLARPACK CORP TECNOLOGICA SA—See EQT AB; *Int'l*, pg. 2483

SOLARPARC GMBH; *Int'l*, pg. 7070

SOLAR PATLAYICI MADDELER SANAYI VE TICARET ANONIM SIRKETI—See Solar Industries India Limited; *Int'l*, pg. 7069

SOLAR PETROLEUM CORP.—See United Salt Corporation; *U.S. Private*, pg. 4297

SOLAR-PLANIT SOFTWARE GMBH—See BayWa AG; *Int'l*, pg. 919

SOLAR PLASTICS LLC—See Olympus Partners; *U.S. Private*, pg. 3013

SOLAR POWER ENGINEERING COMPANY LIMITED—See SPCG Public Company Limited; *Int'l*, pg. 7128

SOLAR POWER MANAGEMENT (THAILAND) COMPANY LIMITED—See BG Container Glass Public Company Limited; *Int'l*, pg. 1007

SOLAR PPM COMPANY LIMITED—See Porn Prom Metal Public Company Limited; *Int'l*, pg. 5922

SOLARPRO HOLDING AD—See Alfa Finance Holding AD; *Int'l*, pg. 307

SOLAR QUARTZ TECHNOLOGIES, INC.; *U.S. Public*, pg. 1900

SOLAR SICILY S.R.L.—See A2A S.p.A.; *Int'l*, pg. 29

SOLAR SOLUTIONS & DISTRIBUTION, LLC.; *U.S. Private*, pg. 3707

SOLAR SOURCES, INC.; *U.S. Private*, pg. 3707

SOLAR SPECTRUM HOLDINGS LLC—See Hercules Capital, Inc.; *U.S. Public*, pg. 1028

SOLAR SPECTRUM HOLDINGS LLC—See Northern Pacific Group; *U.S. Private*, pg. 2954

SOLAR SPECTRUM LLC—See Hercules Capital, Inc.; *U.S. Public*, pg. 1028

SOLAR SPECTRUM LLC—See Northern Pacific Group; *U.S. Private*, pg. 2954

SOLAR SUPPLY, INC.; *U.S. Private*, pg. 3707

SOLAR SUPPLY OF HOUSTON INC.—See Solar Supply, Inc.; *U.S. Private*, pg. 3707

SOLAR SUPPLY OF LAFAYETTE INC.—See Solar Supply, Inc.; *U.S. Private*, pg. 3707

SOLAR SUPPLY OF LAKE CHARLES INC.—See Solar Supply, Inc.; *U.S. Private*, pg. 3707

SOLAR SUPPLY OF LOUISIANA INC.—See Solar Supply, Inc.; *U.S. Private*, pg. 3707

SOLAR SYSTEMS & PERIPHERALS; *U.S. Private*, pg. 3707

SOLARTECH INTERNATIONAL HOLDINGS LIMITED; *Int'l*, pg. 7070

SOLARTECH UNIVERSAL CORP.; *U.S. Private*, pg. 3708

SOLARTRON ANALYTICAL—See AMETEK, Inc.; *U.S. Public*, pg. 118

SOLARTRON METROLOGY LTD.—See AMETEK, Inc.; *U.S. Public*, pg. 118

SOLARTRON PUBLIC COMPANY LIMITED; *Int'l*, pg. 7070

SOLAR TRUST OF AMERICA, LLC—See Solar Millennium AG; *Int'l*, pg. 7069

SOLAR TURBINES CANADA LTD.—See Caterpillar, Inc.; *U.S. Public*, pg. 454

SOLAR TURBINES EUROPE S.A.—See Caterpillar, Inc.; *U.S. Public*, pg. 454

SOLAR TURBINES INCORPORATED—See Caterpillar, Inc.; *U.S. Public*, pg. 453

SOLAR TURBINES INDIA PRIVATE LIMITED—See Caterpillar, Inc.; *U.S. Public*, pg. 454

SOLAR TURBINES INTERNATIONAL COMPANY—See Caterpillar, Inc.; *U.S. Public*, pg. 454

SOLAR TURBINES SERVICES NIGERIA LTD.—See Caterpillar, Inc.; *U.S. Public*, pg. 454

SOLAR TURBINES SERVICES OF ARGENTINA S.R.L.—See Caterpillar, Inc.; *U.S. Public*, pg. 454

SOLAR UNIVERSE LLC; *U.S. Private*, pg. 3707

SOLARUS; *U.S. Private*, pg. 3708

SOLAR VELOCITY; *U.S. Private*, pg. 3707

SOLARVEST BIOENERGY INC.; *Int'l*, pg. 7070

SOLARVEST HOLDINGS BERHAD; *Int'l*, pg. 7070

SOLARVEST (P.E.I.) INC.—See Solarvest BioEnergy Inc.; *Int'l*, pg. 7070

SOLAR WATT SOLUTIONS INC.—See CleanSpark, Inc.; *U.S. Public*, pg. 511

SOLAR WIDE INDUSTRIAL LIMITED—See Techtronic Industries Co., Ltd.; *Int'l*, pg. 7512

SOLAR WIND ENERGY, INC.; *U.S. Private*, pg. 3707

SOLARWINDOW TECHNOLOGIES, INC.; *U.S. Public*, pg. 1900

SOLARWINDS CORPORATION; *U.S. Public*, pg. 1900

SOLARWINDS, INC.—See Silver Lake Group, LLC; *U.S. Private*, pg. 3661

SOLARWINDS, INC.—See Thoma Bravo, L.P.; *U.S. Private*, pg. 4153

SOLARWINDS MSP UK LTD.—See Silver Lake Group, LLC; *U.S. Private*, pg. 3661

SOLARWINDS MSP UK LTD.—See Thoma Bravo, L.P.; *U.S. Private*, pg. 4153

SOLARWINDS WORLDWIDE, LLC—See Silver Lake Group, LLC; *U.S. Private*, pg. 3661

SOLARWINDS WORLDWIDE, LLC—See Thoma Bravo, L.P.; *U.S. Private*, pg. 4153

SOLARX EYEWEAR LLC; *U.S. Private*, pg. 3708

SOLASIA MEDICAL INFORMATION CONSULTING (SHANGHAI) CO. LTD.—See Solasia Pharma, K.K.; *Int'l*, pg. 7070

SOLASIA PHARMA, K.K.; *Int'l*, pg. 7070

SOLAS SHIPPING AGENCY S.R.L.—See Coeclerici S.p.A.; *Int'l*, pg. 1689

SOLASTO CORPORATION; *Int'l*, pg. 7070

SOLAYTEC B.V.—See Amtech Systems, Inc.; *U.S. Public*, pg. 134

SOLBAR INDUSTRIES LTD.—See CHS INC.; *U.S. Public*, pg. 493

SOLBAR NINGBO FOOD CO., LTD.—See CHS INC.; *U.S. Public*, pg. 493

SOLBERG MANUFACTURING INC.; *U.S. Private*, pg. 3708

SOLBERN LLC—See Markel Group Inc.; *U.S. Public*, pg. 1369

SOLBJERG STAALVAREFABRIK A/S—See Ingersoll Tillage Group, Inc.; *Int'l*, pg. 3702

SOLBORN, INC.; *Int'l*, pg. 7070

SOLBRIGHT RENEWABLE ENERGY, LLC—See Iota Communications, Inc.; *U.S. Public*, pg. 1167

SOLCARA LIMITED—See Pulsar Group; *Int'l*, pg. 6116

SOL CARE SERVICES, INC.; *U.S. Private*, pg. 3706

SOLCO BIOMEDICAL CO., LTD.; *Int'l*, pg. 7070

SOLCOM BUSINESS SERVICE CORPORATION—See MIRAIT ONE Corporation; *Int'l*, pg. 4918

SOLCOM CO., LTD.—See MIRAIT ONE Corporation; *Int'l*, pg. 4918

SOLCOMMEISTER CO. LTD.—See MIRAIT ONE Corporation; *Int'l*, pg. 4918

SOLCO PLUMBING SUPPLY INC.; *U.S. Private*, pg. 3708

SOLCO PYROELEC UK LTD.—See Solco Biomedical Co., Ltd.; *Int'l*, pg. 7071

SOLDACENTRO SA—See Enovis Corporation; *U.S. Public*, pg. 773

SOLDADURAS WEST ARCO S.A.S.—See Enovis Corporation; *U.S. Public*, pg. 773

SOLDATA ASIA LTD.—See VINCI S.A.; *Int'l*, pg. 8233

SOLDATA GEOPHYSIC—See VINCI S.A.; *Int'l*, pg. 8234

SOL DATA-NANTERRE—See VINCI S.A.; *Int'l*, pg. 8234

SOLDERA MINING CORP.; *Int'l*, pg. 7071

SOLDEV CO., LTD.—See Saha-Union Public Company Limited; *Int'l*, pg. 6480

SOLDEX S.A.—See Enovis Corporation; *U.S. Public*, pg. 773

SOL DISTRIBUTION PTY. LIMITED—See AGL Energy Limited; *Int'l*, pg. 211

SOLDOUT, INC.—See Hakuhodo DY Holdings Incorporated; *Int'l*, pg. 3222

SOLEBURY TROUT LLC—See The PNC Financial Services Group, Inc.; *U.S. Public*, pg. 2120

SOLECTRAC, INC.—See Ideanomics, Inc.; *U.S. Public*, pg. 1088

SOLEDAD DIALYSIS CENTER, LLC—See DaVita Inc.; *U.S. Public*, pg. 643

SOLE ELITE GROUP LIMITED; *Int'l*, pg. 7071

SOLEGREEN LTD.; *Int'l*, pg. 7071

SOLEIL LEVANT AUTOMOBILES SARL; *Int'l*, pg. 7071

SOLEIL MANAGEMENT, LLC—See The Asny Corporation; *U.S. Private*, pg. 3989

SOLEKIA HONG KONG LIMITED—See SOLEKIA Limited; *Int'l*, pg. 7071

SOLEKIA LIMITED; *Int'l*, pg. 7071

SOLEKIA PLATZ CORP.—See SOLEKIA Limited; *Int'l*, pg. 7071

SOLEKIA SINGAPORE PTE. LTD.—See SOLEKIA Limited; *Int'l*, pg. 7071

SOLEKIA VIETNAM LIMITED—See SOLEKIA Limited; *Int'l*, pg. 7071

SOLEM & ASSOCIATES; *U.S. Private*, pg. 3708

SOL & ENERGITEKNIK SE AB—See NIBE Industrier AB; *Int'l*, pg. 5262

SOLENIS INTERNATIONAL, L.P.—See Platinum Equity, LLC; *U.S. Private*, pg. 3204

SOLENIS LLC—See Platinum Equity, LLC; *U.S. Private*, pg. 3204

SOLENIS TECHNOLOGIES GERMANY GMBH—See Platinum Equity, LLC; *U.S. Private*, pg. 3205

SOLENO THERAPEUTICS, INC.; *U.S. Public*, pg. 1900

SOLENT BLUE LINE LTD.—See GLOBALVIA Inversiones, S.A.U.; *Int'l*, pg. 3005

SOLENT BLUE LINE LTD.—See Kinetic Group Services Pty Ltd.; *Int'l*, pg. 4167

SOLENT COACHES LIMITED—See Mobico Group PLC; *Int'l*, pg. 5009

SOLENTUS; *U.S. Private*, pg. 3708

SOL ENVIRONMENT—See VINCI S.A.; *Int'l*, pg. 8234

SOLEO COMMUNICATIONS, INC.; *U.S. Private*, pg. 3709

SOLERA HOLDINGS, INC.—See Vista Equity Partners, LLC; *U.S. Private*, pg. 4399

SOLERA ITALIA S.R.L.—See Vista Equity Partners, LLC; *U.S. Private*, pg. 4401

SOLERA NATIONAL BANCORP, INC.; *U.S. Public*, pg. 1900

SOLERA NATIONAL BANK—See Solera National Bancorp, Inc.; *U.S. Public*, pg. 1900

SOLERAN, INC.; *U.S. Private*, pg. 3709

SOLERA NORGE AS—See Royal Unibrew A/S; *Int'l*, pg. 6414

SOLERA SVERIGE AB—See Royal Unibrew A/S; *Int'l*, pg. 6414

SOLERA UTELIV AS—See Royal Unibrew A/S; *Int'l*, pg. 6414

SOLES4SOULS; *U.S. Private*, pg. 3709

SOLES ELECTRIC COMPANY INC.; *U.S. Private*, pg. 3709

SOLESIS, INC.—See Altaris Capital Partners, LLC; *U.S. Private*, pg. 206

SOLE SOURCE CAPITAL LLC; *U.S. Private*, pg. 3708

SOLETANCHE BACHY ARGENTINA SA—See VINCI S.A.; *Int'l*, pg. 8234

SOLETANCHE BACHY CANADA LTD.—See VINCI S.A.; *Int'l*, pg. 8228

SOLETANCHE BACHY C.A.—See VINCI S.A.; *Int'l*, pg. 8234

SOLETANCHE BACHY CHILE S.A.—See VINCI S.A.; *Int'l*, pg. 8234

SOLETANCHE BACHY CIMAS S.A.—See VINCI S.A.; *Int'l*, pg. 8228

SOLETANCHE BACHY ECUADOR—See VINCI S.A.; *Int'l*, pg. 8234

SOLETANCHE BACHY FONDATIONS SPECIALES SAS—See VINCI S.A.; *Int'l*, pg. 8228

SOLETANCHE BACHY LLC—See VINCI S.A.; *Int'l*, pg. 8228

SOLETANCHE BACHY PARAGUAY SRL—See VINCI S.A.; *Int'l*, pg. 8228

SOLETANCHE BACHY PERU S.A.—See VINCI S.A.; *Int'l*, pg. 8229

SOLETANCHE BACHY PIEUX—See VINCI S.A.; *Int'l*, pg. 8234

SOLETANCHE BACHY QATAR WLL—See VINCI S.A.; *Int'l*, pg. 8229

SOLETANCHE BACHY ROMANIA SA—See VINCI S.A.; *Int'l*, pg. 8234

SOLETANCHE BACHY—See VINCI S.A.; *Int'l*, pg. 8233

SOLETANCHE BACHY URUGUAY S.A.—See VINCI S.A.; *Int'l*, pg. 8229

SOLETANCHE CESKA REPUBLIKA S.R.O.—See VINCI S.A.; *Int'l*, pg. 8229

SOLETANCHE DO BRAZIL—See VINCI S.A.; *Int'l*, pg. 8233

SOLETANCHE FREYSSINET JORDAN LTD.—See VINCI S.A.; *Int'l*, pg. 8229

COMPANY NAME INDEX

SOLETANCHE FREYSSINET S.A.—See VINCI S.A.; *Int'l*, pg. 8231
SOLETANCHE INC.—See VINCI S.A.; *Int'l*, pg. 8233
SOLETANCHE POLSKA SP. Z O.O.—See VINCI S.A.; *Int'l*, pg. 8233
SOLETANCHE SAM - MONACO—See VINCI S.A.; *Int'l*, pg. 8233
SOLETANCHE S.A.—See VINCI S.A.; *Int'l*, pg. 8233
SOLETANCHE STROY RUSSIE—See VINCI S.A.; *Int'l*, pg. 8233
SOLEVAL NORD-EST S.A.S.—See Tessenderlo Group NV; *Int'l*, pg. 7573
SOLEVAL OUEST S.A.S.—See Tessenderlo Group NV; *Int'l*, pg. 7573
SOLEVAL SUD EST S.A.S.—See Tessenderlo Group NV; *Int'l*, pg. 7573
SOLEVAL SUD OUEST S.A.S.—See Tessenderlo Group NV; *Int'l*, pg. 7573
SOLEX ENERGY LIMITED; *Int'l*, pg. 7071
SOL-EXPERT INTERNATIONAL—See VINCI S.A.; *Int'l*, pg. 8234
SOLFEX LIMITED—See Travis Perkins plc; *Int'l*, pg. 7908
SOL FRANCE SAS—See SOL S.p.A.; *Int'l*, pg. 7067
SOLGAR, INC.—See KKR & Co. Inc.; *U.S. Public*, pg. 1264
SOLGAS DISTRIBUIDORA DE GAS, S.L.—See Repsol, S.A.; *Int'l*, pg. 6292
SOLGAS S.A.—See ENGIE SA; *Int'l*, pg. 2434
SOL-GEL TECHNOLOGIES LTD.; *Int'l*, pg. 7068
SOLGENIA S.P.A.; *Int'l*, pg. 7071
SOL GLOBAL INVESTMENTS CORP.; *Int'l*, pg. 7067
SOLGOLD PLC; *Int'l*, pg. 7071
SOL GROUP, B.V.—See Melia Hotels International, S.A.; *Int'l*, pg. 4810
SOL GROUP CORPORATION—See Melia Hotels International, S.A.; *Int'l*, pg. 4810
SOL GROUP MARKETING COMPANY INC.—See Sumitomo Corporation; *Int'l*, pg. 7268
SOL HYDROPOWER DOO—See SOL S.p.A.; *Int'l*, pg. 7067
SOLHYDRO SPOL SRO—See VINCI S.A.; *Int'l*, pg. 8234
SOLIA CORPORATION—See YCP Holdings (Global) Limited; *Int'l*, pg. 8574
SOLIANCE S.A.—See Givaudan S.A.; *Int'l*, pg. 2982
SOLIANT HEALTH INC.—See Olympus Partners; *U.S. Private*, pg. 3013
SOLIANT, LLC—See Akzo Nobel N.V.; *Int'l*, pg. 275
SOLIA SA; *Int'l*, pg. 7071
SOLIBRI BENELUX B.V.—See Herbalife Nutrition Ltd.; *Int'l*, pg. 3360
SOLIBRI DACH GMBH—See Nemetschek SE; *Int'l*, pg. 5195
SOLIBRI LLC—See Nemetschek SE; *Int'l*, pg. 5195
SOLIBRI OY—See Nemetschek SE; *Int'l*, pg. 5195
SOLIBRI UK LTD.—See Nemetschek SE; *Int'l*, pg. 5195
SOLICOUR INC.—See iA Financial Corporation Inc.; *Int'l*, pg. 3568
SOLID AB—See ASSA ABLOY AB; *Int'l*, pg. 640
SOLID ANGLE LIMITED—See Autodesk, Inc.; *U.S. Public*, pg. 229
SOLID ANGLE, S.L.U.—See Autodesk, Inc.; *U.S. Public*, pg. 229
SOLIDARITY ALLIANCE INSURANCE COMPANY; *Int'l*, pg. 7072
SOLIDARITY BAHRAIN B.S.C.—See First Insurance Co.; *Int'l*, pg. 2684
SOLIDARITY CONTRACTING LLC; *U.S. Private*, pg. 3709
SOLIDARITY GROUP HOLDING BSC; *Int'l*, pg. 7072
SOLIDARITY SAUDI TAKAFUL COMPANY—See Al Jazira Takaful Ta'awuni Company; *Int'l*, pg. 280
SOLIDARITY TAKAFOL S.A.—See Solidarity Group Holding BSC; *Int'l*, pg. 7072
SOLID AUTOMOTIVE BERHAD; *Int'l*, pg. 7071
SOLIDA-WERK WERKZEUGTECHNIK GMBH & CO.; *Int'l*, pg. 7072
SOLID BANK JSC; *Int'l*, pg. 7071
SOLID BENEFIT GUIDANCE LLC—See Arthur J. Gallagher & Co.; *U.S. Public*, pg. 205
SOLID BIOSCIENCES, INC; *U.S. Public*, pg. 1900
SOLID CACTUS INC.—See Siris Capital Group, LLC; *U.S. Private*, pg. 3675
SOLIDCAM ITALIA S.R.L.—See Solid World S.p.A.; *Int'l*, pg. 7072
SOLID CARBIDE TOOLS LIMITED; *Int'l*, pg. 7071
SOLID CEMENT CORP.—See CEMEX, S.A.B. de C.V.; *Int'l*, pg. 1398
SOLID CONTAINERS LTD.; *Int'l*, pg. 7071
SOLIDCORE RESOURCES PLC; *Int'l*, pg. 7072
SOLID CORPORATION SDN BHD—See Solid Automotive Berhad; *Int'l*, pg. 7071
SOLID EARTH, INC.; *U.S. Private*, pg. 3709
SOLIDERE INTERNATIONAL LIMITED—See The Lebanese Company for the Development and Reconstruction of Beirut Central District s.a.l; *Int'l*, pg. 7664
SOLIDFACTORY S.R.L.—See Solid World S.p.A.; *Int'l*, pg. 7072
SOLIDFIRE, INC.—See NetApp, Inc.; *U.S. Public*, pg. 1507
SOLID FORSAKRING AB—See Resurs Holding AB; *Int'l*, pg. 6305
SOLIDGEAR CORPORATION—See TDK Corporation; *Int'l*, pg. 7487
SOLID GOLD PET, LLC—See Health and Happiness (H&H) International Holdings Limited; *Int'l*, pg. 3303
SOLID GROUP, INC.; *Int'l*, pg. 7071
SOLIDIA FINANCE ET PATRIMONIE S.A.—See EFG International AG; *Int'l*, pg. 2320
SOLIDIFI INC.—See Real Matters, Inc.; *Int'l*, pg. 6233
SOLID INC.; *Int'l*, pg. 7072
SOLID INSTANCE, INC.—See Elliott Management Corporation; *U.S. Private*, pg. 1367
SOLID INSTANCE, INC.—See Vista Equity Partners, LLC; *U.S. Private*, pg. 4396
SOLID INTELLIGENCE INC.—See Datasection Inc.; *Int'l*, pg. 1979
SOLIDION TECHNOLOGY INC.; *U.S. Public*, pg. 1901
SOLIDITET AB—See Ratos AB; *Int'l*, pg. 6217
SOLIDITET A/S—See Ratos AB; *Int'l*, pg. 6217
SOLIDITET DECISION AS—See Ratos AB; *Int'l*, pg. 6217
SOLIDITET FINLAND OY—See Ratos AB; *Int'l*, pg. 6217
SOLIDITET POLSKA SP. Z.O.O.—See Ratos AB; *Int'l*, pg. 6217
SOLIDIUM OY; *Int'l*, pg. 7073
SOLID LAGUNA CORPORATION—See Solid Group, Inc.; *Int'l*, pg. 7072
SOLID LINE AG—See Bechtle AG; *Int'l*, pg. 938
SOLID MARKETING INC.; *U.S. Private*, pg. 3709
SOLIDMICRON TECHNOLOGIES PTE LTD—See Fu Yu Corporation Limited; *Int'l*, pg. 2801
SOLIDNOST A.D.; *Int'l*, pg. 7073
SOLIDONE CO., LTD.—See Iida Group Holdings Co., Ltd.; *Int'l*, pg. 3607
SOLID OPTICS EU N.V.—See Amphenol Corporation; *U.S. Public*, pg. 132
SOLID OPTICS LLC—See Amphenol Corporation; *U.S. Public*, pg. 132
SOLIDOR LIMITED—See Owens Corning; *U.S. Public*, pg. 1627
SOLID POWER, INC.; *U.S. Public*, pg. 1900
SOLID POWER OPERATING, INC.—See Solid Power, Inc.; *U.S. Public*, pg. 1900
SOLIDPRO INFORMATIONSSYSTEME GMBH—See Bechtle AG; *Int'l*, pg. 938
SOLID RESTORATION INC.—See Grays Peak Capital LP; *U.S. Private*, pg. 1761
SOLID RESTORATION INC.—See Timoneer Strategic Partners, LLC; *U.S. Private*, pg. 4173
SOLID SAS—See Trimble, Inc.; *U.S. Public*, pg. 2191
SOLIDSCAPE, INC.—See Groupe Gorge S.A.; *Int'l*, pg. 3103
SOLIDS COMPONENTS MIGSA S.L.—See Hosokawa Micron Corporation; *Int'l*, pg. 3486
SOLID SEALING TECHNOLOGY, INC.—See HEICO Corporation; *U.S. Public*, pg. 1021
SOLIDSERVICE ELECTRONICS CORPORATION—See Solid Group, Inc.; *Int'l*, pg. 7072
SOLIDSIM ENGINEERING GMBH—See Emerson Electric Co.; *U.S. Public*, pg. 742
SOLIDSOFT REPLY LTD.—See Reply S.p.A.; *Int'l*, pg. 6291
SOLID SOLUTIONS AG—See Bechtle AG; *Int'l*, pg. 938
SOLID SOURCE REALTY INC.—See HomeSmart International LLC; *U.S. Private*, pg. 1974
SOLIDSTATE CONTROLS, INC. DE ARGENTINA S.R.L.—See AMETEK, Inc.; *U.S. Public*, pg. 121
SOLIDSTATE CONTROLS, LLC—See AMETEK, Inc.; *U.S. Public*, pg. 121
SOLIDSTATE CONTROLS MEXICO, S.A. DE C.V.—See AMETEK, Inc.; *U.S. Public*, pg. 121
SOLID STATE DEVICES, INC.; *U.S. Private*, pg. 3709
SOLID STATE EQUIPMENT LLC; *U.S. Private*, pg. 3709
SOLID STATE INC.; *U.S. Private*, pg. 3709
SOLID STATE MEASUREMENTS INC.; *U.S. Private*, pg. 3709
SOLID STATE PLC; *Int'l*, pg. 7072
SOLID STATE SUPPLIES LIMITED—See Solid State plc; *Int'l*, pg. 7072
SOLID STATE SYSTEM CO., LTD.; *Int'l*, pg. 7072
SOLID STONE COMPANY LIMITED; *Int'l*, pg. 7072
SOLID SURFACES, INC.; *U.S. Private*, pg. 3709
SOLIDSYSTEMS INC.—See Solid Inc.; *Int'l*, pg. 7072
SOLID ULTRABATTERY INC.—See Volt Carbon Technologies Inc.; *Int'l*, pg. 8303
SOLIDUSGOLD INC.; *Int'l*, pg. 7073
SOLIDUS OY—See Eesti Energia AS; *Int'l*, pg. 2318
SOLIDUS SECURITIES S.A.; *Int'l*, pg. 7073
SOLIDUS SOLUTIONS—See Smurfit Kappa Group plc; *Int'l*, pg. 7018
SOLID VIDEO CORPORATION SOLID ELECTRONICS CORPORATION—See Solid Group, Inc.; *Int'l*, pg. 7072
SOLID VIDEO CORPORATION—See Solid Group, Inc.; *Int'l*, pg. 7072
SOLIDWIZARD TECHNOLOGY CO., LTD.; *Int'l*, pg. 7073
SOLIDWORLD MIDDLE EAST DMCC—See Solid World S.p.A.; *Int'l*, pg. 7072
SOLID WORLD S.P.A.; *Int'l*, pg. 7072
SOLIDX AB; *Int'l*, pg. 7073
SOLIDYN SOLUTIONS, LLC—See Parsons Corporation; *U.S. Public*, pg. 1651
SOLIGENIX, INC.; *U.S. Public*, pg. 1901
SOLIGEN TECHNOLOGIES, INC.; *U.S. Public*, pg. 1901
SOLIGENT HOLDINGS INC.; *U.S. Private*, pg. 3709
SOLIGOR GMBH—See Maxwell Electronics Ltd.; *Int'l*, pg. 4743
SOLIKAMSKIY MAGNIYEVYI ZAVOD OAO; *Int'l*, pg. 7073
SOLIMIDE—See The Goldman Sachs Group, Inc.; *U.S. Public*, pg. 2080
SOL-INA D.O.O.—See INA-Industrija Nafte, d.d.; *Int'l*, pg. 3643
SOLINA FRANCE SASU—See Ardian SAS; *Int'l*, pg. 556
SOL, INC.—See Carmanah Technologies Corporation; *Int'l*, pg. 1341
S.O.L INC—See Kohinoor Foods Limited; *Int'l*, pg. 4229
SOL INDIA PRIVATE LTD.—See SOL S.p.A.; *Int'l*, pg. 7067
SOLINE PRIDELAVA SOLI D.O.O.—See Telekom Slovenije, d.d.; *Int'l*, pg. 7538
SOLINFO S.R.L.—See Ardian SAS; *Int'l*, pg. 555
SOL IN ONE GMBH—See BayWa AG; *Int'l*, pg. 919
SOLIS HOLDINGS LIMITED; *Int'l*, pg. 7073
SOLIS MAMMOGRAPHY AT CLEAR LAKE REGIONAL MEDICAL CENTER, LLC—See HCA Healthcare, Inc.; *U.S. Public*, pg. 1008
SOLIS MAMMOGRAPHY AT CONROE REGIONAL MEDICAL CENTER, LLC—See HCA Healthcare, Inc.; *U.S. Public*, pg. 1009
SOLIS MAMMOGRAPHY AT DENTON REGIONAL MEDICAL CENTER, LLC—See HCA Healthcare, Inc.; *U.S. Public*, pg. 1009
SOLIS MAMMOGRAPHY AT HCA HOUSTON TOMBALL, LLC—See HCA Healthcare, Inc.; *U.S. Public*, pg. 1009
SOLIS MAMMOGRAPHY AT KINGWOOD MEDICAL CENTER, LLC—See HCA Healthcare, Inc.; *U.S. Public*, pg. 1009
SOLIS MAMMOGRAPHY AT LAS COLINAS MEDICAL CENTER, LLC—See HCA Healthcare, Inc.; *U.S. Public*, pg. 1009
SOLIS MAMMOGRAPHY AT MEDICAL CENTER ALLIANCE, LLC—See HCA Healthcare, Inc.; *U.S. Public*, pg. 1009
SOLIS MAMMOGRAPHY AT MEDICAL CENTER ARLINGTON, LLC—See HCA Healthcare, Inc.; *U.S. Public*, pg. 1009
SOLIS MAMMOGRAPHY AT MEDICAL CENTER OF LEWISVILLE, LLC—See HCA Healthcare, Inc.; *U.S. Public*, pg. 1009
SOLIS MAMMOGRAPHY AT MEDICAL CENTER OF MCKINNEY, LLC—See HCA Healthcare, Inc.; *U.S. Public*, pg. 1009
SOLIS MAMMOGRAPHY AT MEDICAL CENTER OF PLANO, LLC—See HCA Healthcare, Inc.; *U.S. Public*, pg. 1009
SOLIS MAMMOGRAPHY AT MEDICAL CITY DALLAS, LLC—See HCA Healthcare, Inc.; *U.S. Public*, pg. 1009
SOLIS MAMMOGRAPHY AT OGDEN REGIONAL MEDICAL CENTER, LLC—See HCA Healthcare, Inc.; *U.S. Public*, pg. 1009
SOLIS MAMMOGRAPHY AT PEARLAND MEDICAL CENTER, LLC—See HCA Healthcare, Inc.; *U.S. Public*, pg. 1009
SOLIS MAMMOGRAPHY AT ROSE MEDICAL CENTER, LLC—See HCA Healthcare, Inc.; *U.S. Public*, pg. 1009
SOLIS MAMMOGRAPHY AT SKYLINE MEDICAL CENTER, LLC—See HCA Healthcare, Inc.; *U.S. Public*, pg. 1009
SOLIS MAMMOGRAPHY AT ST. DAVID'S MEDICAL CENTER, LLC—See HCA Healthcare, Inc.; *U.S. Public*, pg. 1009
SOLIS MAMMOGRAPHY AT ST. DAVID'S ROUND ROCK MEDICAL CENTER, LLC—See HCA Healthcare, Inc.; *U.S. Public*, pg. 1009
SOLIS MAMMOGRAPHY AT ST. MARK'S HOSPITAL, LLC—See HCA Healthcare, Inc.; *U.S. Public*, pg. 1009
SOLIS MAMMOGRAPHY AT STONECREST MEDICAL CENTER, LLC—See HCA Healthcare, Inc.; *U.S. Public*, pg. 1009
SOLIS MAMMOGRAPHY AT TIMPANOGOS REGIONAL HOSPITAL, LLC—See HCA Healthcare, Inc.; *U.S. Public*, pg. 1009
SOLIS MAMMOGRAPHY AT WEST HOUSTON MEDICAL CENTER, LLC—See HCA Healthcare, Inc.; *U.S. Public*, pg. 1009
SOLIS MAMMOGRAPHY AT WOMANS HOSPITAL OF TEXAS, LLC—See HCA Healthcare, Inc.; *U.S. Public*, pg. 1009
SOLIS MAMMOGRAPHY OF CEDAR HILL, LLC—See HCA Healthcare, Inc.; *U.S. Public*, pg. 1009
SOLIS MAMMOGRAPHY OF CYFAIR, LLC—See HCA Healthcare, Inc.; *U.S. Public*, pg. 1009
SOLIS MAMMOGRAPHY OF FLOWER MOUND, LLC—See HCA Healthcare, Inc.; *U.S. Public*, pg. 1009
SOLIS MAMMOGRAPHY OF FRISCO, LLC—See HCA Healthcare, Inc.; *U.S. Public*, pg. 1009
SOLIS MAMMOGRAPHY OF GARLAND, LLC—See HCA Healthcare, Inc.; *U.S. Public*, pg. 1009

SOLIS HOLDINGS LIMITED
CORPORATE AFFILIATIONS

SOLIS MAMMOGRAPHY OF GRAND PRAIRIE, LLC—See HCA Healthcare, Inc.; *U.S. Public*, pg. 1009
SOLIS MAMMOGRAPHY OF HOUSTON NW, LLC—See HCA Healthcare, Inc.; *U.S. Public*, pg. 1009
SOLIS MAMMOGRAPHY OF KATY, LLC—See HCA Healthcare, Inc.; *U.S. Public*, pg. 1009
SOLIS MAMMOGRAPHY OF MAINLAND, LLC—See HCA Healthcare, Inc.; *U.S. Public*, pg. 1009
SOLIS MAMMOGRAPHY OF MANSFIELD, LLC—See HCA Healthcare, Inc.; *U.S. Public*, pg. 1009
SOLIS MAMMOGRAPHY OF MESQUITE, LLC—See HCA Healthcare, Inc.; *U.S. Public*, pg. 1009
SOLIS MAMMOGRAPHY OF MONTGOMERY, LLC—See HCA Healthcare, Inc.; *U.S. Public*, pg. 1009
SOLIS MAMMOGRAPHY OF NORTH CYPRESS, LLC—See HCA Healthcare, Inc.; *U.S. Public*, pg. 1009
SOLIS MAMMOGRAPHY OF RED OAK, LLC—See HCA Healthcare, Inc.; *U.S. Public*, pg. 1009
SOLIS MAMMOGRAPHY OF RIVER OAKS, LLC—See HCA Healthcare, Inc.; *U.S. Public*, pg. 1009
SOLIS MAMMOGRAPHY OF ROWLETT, LLC—See HCA Healthcare, Inc.; *U.S. Public*, pg. 1009
SOLIS MAMMOGRAPHY OF SOUTHWEST FORT WORTH, LLC—See HCA Healthcare, Inc.; *U.S. Public*, pg. 1009
SOLIS MAMMOGRAPHY OF SUGAR LAND, LLC—See HCA Healthcare, Inc.; *U.S. Public*, pg. 1009
SOLIS MAMMOGRAPHY OF TOWNE LAKE, LLC—See HCA Healthcare, Inc.; *U.S. Public*, pg. 1010
SOLIS MAMMOGRAPHY OF WEST PLANO, LLC—See HCA Healthcare, Inc.; *U.S. Public*, pg. 1010
SOLIS MAMMOGRAPHY OF WOMANS PLACE, LLC—See HCA Healthcare, Inc.; *U.S. Public*, pg. 1010
SOLIS MARKETING LIMITED; *Int'l*, pg. 7073
SOLIS MINERALS LTD.; *Int'l*, pg. 7073
SOLIS SECURITY INC.—See Frontenac Company LLC; *U.S. Private*, pg. 1614
SOLIS WOMEN'S HEALTH, INC.; *U.S. Private*, pg. 3709
SOLITAIRE GROUP LTD; *Int'l*, pg. 7073
SOLITAIRE HOMES, INC.; *U.S. Private*, pg. 3709
SOLITAIRE MACHINES TOOLS LIMITED - PLANT II—See Solitaire Machines Tools Limited; *Int'l*, pg. 7073
SOLITAIRE MACHINES TOOLS LIMITED - PLANT I—See Solitaire Machines Tools Limited; *Int'l*, pg. 7073
SOLITAIRE MACHINES TOOLS LIMITED; *Int'l*, pg. 7073
SOLITARIO ZINC CORP.; *U.S. Public*, pg. 1901
SOLITE EUROPE LTD—See F.W. Thorpe plc; *Int'l*, pg. 2597
SOLITON, INC.—See AbbVie Inc.; *U.S. Public*, pg. 23
SOLITON SYSTEMS, K.K.; *Int'l*, pg. 7073
SOLITRON DEVICES, INC.; *U.S. Public*, pg. 1901
SOLITUDE MOUNTAIN RESORT, LLC—See KSL Capital Partners, LLC; *U.S. Private*, pg. 2354
SOLIUM CAPITAL INC.—See Morgan Stanley; *U.S. Public*, pg. 1475
SOLIUM CAPITAL LLC—See Morgan Stanley; *U.S. Public*, pg. 1475
SOLIUM CAPITAL UK LIMITED—See Morgan Stanley; *U.S. Public*, pg. 1475
SOLIUM OPTIONEASE, INC.—See Morgan Stanley; *U.S. Public*, pg. 1475
S.OLIVER BERND FREIER GMBH & CO. KG; *Int'l*, pg. 6457
SOLIVITA AT POINCIANA GOLF CLUB, INC.—See Brookfield Corporation; *Int'l*, pg. 1183
SOLIVITA AT POINCIANA, INC.—See Brookfield Corporation; *Int'l*, pg. 1183
SOLIX GROUP AB; *Int'l*, pg. 7073
SOLIX, INC.; *U.S. Private*, pg. 3709
SOLIX TECHNOLOGIES, INC.—See TechNVision Ventures Limited; *Int'l*, pg. 7512
SOLKRAFT EMK AB—See Bravida Holding AB; *Int'l*, pg. 1142
SOLLA EYELET PRODUCTS INC.—See Thyssen'sche Handelsgesellschaft m.b.H.; *Int'l*, pg. 7723
SOLLEDS CO., LTD.—See Partron Co., Ltd.; *Int'l*, pg. 5751
SOLLENSYS CORP.; *U.S. Public*, pg. 1901
SOLLIO COOPERATIVE GROUP; *Int'l*, pg. 7074
SOLMAC INC.; *U.S. Private*, pg. 3709
SOL MANINVEST, B.V.—See Melia Hotels International, S.A.; *Int'l*, pg. 4810
SOLMATES B.V.—See Lam Research Corporation; *U.S. Public*, pg. 1290
SOLMAX INTERNATIONAL, INC.; *Int'l*, pg. 7074
SOLMAX—See ABN AMRO Group N.V.; *Int'l*, pg. 64
SOLMAX—See ABN AMRO Group N.V.; *Int'l*, pg. 64
SOLMAX—See Gilde Buy Out Partners B.V.; *Int'l*, pg. 2974
SOLMAX—See Gilde Buy Out Partners B.V.; *Int'l*, pg. 2974
SOLMAX—See Parcom Capital Management B.V.; *Int'l*, pg. 5740
SOLMAX—See Parcom Capital Management B.V.; *Int'l*, pg. 5740
SOL MELIA BALKANS EAD—See Melia Hotels International, S.A.; *Int'l*, pg. 4810
SOL MELIA DEUTSCHLAND, GMBH—See Melia Hotels International, S.A.; *Int'l*, pg. 4810
SOL MELIA EUROPE, B.V.—See Melia Hotels International, S.A.; *Int'l*, pg. 4810

SOL MELIA FRANCE, S. A. S.—See Melia Hotels International, S.A.; *Int'l*, pg. 4810
SOL MELIA GREECE, HOTEL & TOURISTIC—See Melia Hotels International, S.A.; *Int'l*, pg. 4810
SOL MELIA HOTEL MANAG. SHANGHAI CO., LTD.—See Melia Hotels International, S.A.; *Int'l*, pg. 4810
SOL MELIA INVESTMENT, N.V.—See Melia Hotels International, S.A.; *Int'l*, pg. 4810
SOL MELIA ITALIA SRL—See Melia Hotels International, S.A.; *Int'l*, pg. 4810
SOL MELIA—See Melia Hotels International, S.A.; *Int'l*, pg. 4810
SOL MELIA TRAVEL S.A.—See Melia Hotels International, S.A.; *Int'l*, pg. 4810
SOLMETEX, LLC—See Avista Capital Partners, L.P.; *U.S. Private*, pg. 409
SOLMETRIC CORP.—See Fortive Corporation; *U.S. Public*, pg. 870
SOLNABERG PROPERTY AB; *Int'l*, pg. 7074
SOLNAC CORPORATION—See MCJ Co., Ltd.; *Int'l*, pg. 4759
SOLNE MLYNY, A.S.—See K+S Aktiengesellschaft; *Int'l*, pg. 4041
SOLNET CORPORATION—See JBCC Holdings Inc.; *Int'l*, pg. 3918
SOLO BRANDS, INC.; *U.S. Public*, pg. 1901
SOLOCAL GROUP; *Int'l*, pg. 7074
SOLO CUP COMPANY—See Dart Container Corporation; *U.S. Private*, pg. 1160
SOLO CUP COMPANY—See Dart Container Corporation; *U.S. Private*, pg. 1160
SOLO CUP COMPANY—See Dart Container Corporation; *U.S. Private*, pg. 1160
SOLO CUP COMPANY—See Dart Container Corporation; *U.S. Private*, pg. 1160
SOLO CUP OPERATING CORPORATION—See Dart Container Corporation; *U.S. Private*, pg. 1160
SOLOEL CORPORATION—See ASKUL Corporation; *Int'l*, pg. 625
SOLOFLEX, INC.; *U.S. Private*, pg. 3709
SOLO FOODS, LLC—See Benford Capital Partners, LLC; *U.S. Private*, pg. 526
SOLO GROWTH CORP.; *Int'l*, pg. 7074
SOLO - INVESTIMENTOS EM COMUNICACAO, SGPS, S.A.—See Impresa SGPS S.A.; *Int'l*, pg. 3637
SOLOMAT LOCATION SAS; *Int'l*, pg. 7074
SOLO MECHANICAL MAINTENANCE, INC.—See United Mechanical, Inc.; *U.S. Private*, pg. 4294
SOLOMED PLUS SRL—See MedLife S.A.; *Int'l*, pg. 4785
SOLOMON BUILDERS, INC.; *U.S. Private*, pg. 3709
SOLOMON CHEVROLET CADILLAC; *U.S. Private*, pg. 3709
SOLOMON DATA INTERNATIONAL CORPORATION; *Int'l*, pg. 7074
SOLOMONEDWARDSGROUP, LLC; *U.S. Private*, pg. 3710
SOLOMON EUROPE LIMITED—See Solomon Systech (International) Limited; *Int'l*, pg. 7075
SOLOMON FRIEDMAN ADVERTISING LLC; *U.S. Private*, pg. 3709
SOLOMON GOLDENTEK DISPLAY CORP.—See Solomon Technology Corporation; *Int'l*, pg. 7075
SOLOMON GOLDENTEK DISPLAY (DONGGUAN) LTD.—See Solomon Technology Corporation; *Int'l*, pg. 7075
SOLOMON HOMES, INC.; *U.S. Private*, pg. 3710
SOLOMON ISLANDS TOBACCO COMPANY LIMITED—See British American Tobacco plc; *Int'l*, pg. 1168
SOLOMON MCCOWN & COMPANY, INC.; *U.S. Private*, pg. 3710
SOLOMON-PAGE GROUP LLC; *U.S. Private*, pg. 3710
SOLOMON'S FRESH MARKET LIMITED—See AML Foods Ltd.; *Int'l*, pg. 428
SOLOMON'S SUPERCENTRE (NASSAU) LIMITED—See AML Foods Ltd.; *Int'l*, pg. 428
SOLOMON SYSTECH INC—See Solomon Systech (International) Limited; *Int'l*, pg. 7075
SOLOMON SYSTECH (INTERNATIONAL) LIMITED; *Int'l*, pg. 7074
SOLOMON SYSTECH JAPAN CO., LTD.—See Solomon Systech (International) Limited; *Int'l*, pg. 7075
SOLOMON SYSTECH KOREA LIMITED—See Solomon Systech (International) Limited; *Int'l*, pg. 7075
SOLOMON SYSTECH LIMITED—See Solomon Systech (International) Limited; *Int'l*, pg. 7075
SOLOMON SYSTECH PTE. LTD.—See Solomon Systech (International) Limited; *Int'l*, pg. 7075
SOLOMON SYSTECH (SHENZHEN) LIMITED—See Solomon Systech (International) Limited; *Int'l*, pg. 7075
SOLOMON SYSTECH TAIWAN LIMITED—See Solomon Systech (International) Limited; *Int'l*, pg. 7075
SOLOMON SYSTECH (UK) LIMITED—See Solomon Systech (International) Limited; *Int'l*, pg. 7075
SOLOMON TECHNOLOGY CORPORATION; *Int'l*, pg. 7075
SOLOMON TECHNOLOGY, CORP.—See Solomon Systech (International) Limited; *Int'l*, pg. 7075

SOLOMON WORLDWIDE HOLDINGS LIMITED; *Int'l*, pg. 7075
SOLON CORPORATION—See Microsol International LL FZE; *Int'l*, pg. 4881
SOLON EIENDOM ASA; *Int'l*, pg. 7075
SOLON ENERGY GMBH—See Microsol International LL FZE; *Int'l*, pg. 4881
SOLON INVESTMENTS GMBH.—See Microsol International LL FZE; *Int'l*, pg. 4881
SOLON MOBILITY GMBH—See Microsol International LL FZE; *Int'l*, pg. 4881
SOLON NORD GMBH.—See Microsol International LL FZE; *Int'l*, pg. 4881
SOLON SAS—See Microsol International LL FZE; *Int'l*, pg. 4881
SOLON S.P.A.—See Microsol International LL FZE; *Int'l*, pg. 4881
SOLON SPECIALTY WIRE CO.—See Leggett & Platt, Incorporated; *U.S. Public*, pg. 1303
SOLO OIL AUSTRALIA PTY LTD—See Ampol Limited; *Int'l*, pg. 436
SOLO OIL PLC; *Int'l*, pg. 7074
SOLORO GOLD; *U.S. Private*, pg. 3710
SOLOSAR; *Int'l*, pg. 7075
SOLOS ENDOSCOPY, INC.—See American Medical Group LLC; *U.S. Private*, pg. 241
SOLOSON IMPORT C.A.—See Suzuki Motor Corporation; *Int'l*, pg. 7354
SOLOTHURNER ZEITUNG AG—See BT Holding AG; *Int'l*, pg. 1204
SOLOVIS, INC.—See Nasdaq, Inc.; *U.S. Public*, pg. 1492
SOLOWIN HOLDINGS, LTD.; *Int'l*, pg. 7075
SOLPAC INC.; *U.S. Private*, pg. 3710
SOLPHARM ADRIATIC D.O.O. BEOGRAD—See Takeda Pharmaceutical Company Limited; *Int'l*, pg. 7438
SOLPHARM D.O.O. ZA TRGOVINU I USLUGE—See Takeda Pharmaceutical Company Limited; *Int'l*, pg. 7437
SOL PRODUCTION PVT. LTD—See De Agostini S.p.A.; *Int'l*, pg. 1994
SOLSBURY HILL LLC; *U.S. Private*, pg. 3710
SOL SEE D.O.O.—See SOL S.p.A.; *Int'l*, pg. 7067
SOLS ET FONDATIONS—See FAYAT SAS; *Int'l*, pg. 2626
SOLSIF MAROC S.A.—See VINCI S.A.; *Int'l*, pg. 8233
SOLSONICA—See EEMS Italia S.p.A; *Int'l*, pg. 2317
SOL S.P.A.; *Int'l*, pg. 7067
SOL'S PIPE & STEEL INC.; *U.S. Private*, pg. 3706
SOLSTAD OFFSHORE ASA; *Int'l*, pg. 7075
SOLSTAD OFFSHORE (UK) LTD.—See Solstad Offshore ASA; *Int'l*, pg. 7075
SOLSTAD SHIPPING AS—See Solstad Offshore ASA; *Int'l*, pg. 7075
SOLSTICE BENEFITS, INC.; *U.S. Private*, pg. 3710
SOLSTICE GOLD CORPORATION; *Int'l*, pg. 7075
SOLSTICE MARKETING CONCEPTS, LLC—See Solstice Marketing Corp.; *U.S. Private*, pg. 3710
SOLSTICE MARKETING CORP.; *U.S. Private*, pg. 3710
SOLSTICE MINERALS LIMITED; *Int'l*, pg. 7075
SOLSTICE MOBILE; *U.S. Private*, pg. 3710
SOLSTICE PLANNING AND ARCHITECTURE; *U.S. Private*, pg. 3710
SOLSTICE SAS—See Cognizant Technology Solutions Corporation; *U.S. Public*, pg. 525
SOLSTICE SLEEP PRODUCTS, INC.; *U.S. Private*, pg. 3710
SOLSTISS INC.—See Solstiss; *Int'l*, pg. 7075
SOLSTISS; *Int'l*, pg. 7075
SOLSTRA CAPITAL PARTNERS LLP; *Int'l*, pg. 7075
SOLSYS MEDICAL, LLC—See Bioventus Inc.; *U.S. Public*, pg. 339
SOL SYSTEMS; *U.S. Private*, pg. 3706
SOLTA MEDICAL, INC.—See Bausch Health Companies Inc.; *Int'l*, pg. 898
SOLTEC AMERICA LLC—See Soltec Power Holdings S.A.; *Int'l*, pg. 7076
SOLTEC ARGENTINA, S.R.L.—See Soltec Power Holdings S.A.; *Int'l*, pg. 7076
SOLTEC AUSTRALIA, PTY. LTD.—See Soltec Power Holdings S.A.; *Int'l*, pg. 7076
SOLTEC CHILE S.P.A.—See Soltec Power Holdings S.A.; *Int'l*, pg. 7076
SOLTEC ENERGY SWEDEN AB; *Int'l*, pg. 7076
SOLTEC POWER HOLDINGS S.A.; *Int'l*, pg. 7075
SOLTEK PACIFIC; *U.S. Private*, pg. 3710
SOLTEQ DENMARK A/S—See Solteq Oyj; *Int'l*, pg. 7076
SOLTEQ OYJ; *Int'l*, pg. 7076
SOLTERRA RENEWABLE TECHNOLOGIES, INC.—See Quantum Materials Corp.; *U.S. Public*, pg. 3323
SOL T.G. GMBH—See SOL S.p.A.; *Int'l*, pg. 7067
SOLTHERM EXTERNAL INSULATIONS LIMITED—See Berger Paints India Limited; *Int'l*, pg. 980
SOLTIUS AUSTRALIA PTY. LTD.—See PT. Metrodata Electronics, Tbk.; *Int'l*, pg. 6088
SOLTRX TRANSACTION SERVICES GMBH—See Commerzbank AG; *Int'l*, pg. 1719
SOLTWORKS CO., LTD.; *Int'l*, pg. 7076
SOLTYS SCHNITZLER SCHIRMER LLC; *U.S. Private*, pg. 3710

COMPANY NAME INDEX

SOLUBLE BIOTECH INC.—See Predictive Oncology Inc.; *U.S. Public*, pg. 1713
SOLUBLE THERAPEUTICS, INC.—See Predictive Oncology Inc.; *U.S. Public*, pg. 1713
SOLUCIA PROTECTION JURIDIQUE SARL—See CVC Capital Partners SICAV-FIS S.A.; *Int'l*, pg. 1882
SOLUCION EMPRESA ADMINISTRADORA HIPOTECARIA SA; *Int'l*, pg. 7076
SOLUCIONES CUATROOCHENTA, S.A.; *Int'l*, pg. 7076
SOLUCIONES DE INTEGRACION DE NEGOCIOS S.A.—See Silver Lake Group, LLC; *U.S. Private*, pg. 3660
SOLUCIONES ESTRATEGICAS DE TRANSFORMACION, S.C.—See WILSON LEARNING WORLDWIDE INC.; *Int'l*, pg. 8423
SOLUCIONES EXPERTAS S.A.—See SONDA S.A.; *Int'l*, pg. 7089
SOLUCIONES TECNOLOGICAS AVANZADAS LTDA.—See HORIBA Ltd; *Int'l*, pg. 3478
SOLUCIOUS S.A.—See Colruyt Group N.V.; *Int'l*, pg. 1705
SOLUCOES EM ACO USIMINAS S.A.—See Techint S.p.A.; *Int'l*, pg. 7505
SOLUCORP INDUSTRIES LTD.; *U.S. Public*, pg. 1901
SOLUETA VINA CO., LTD.—See Dasan Solueta Co.,Ltd.; *Int'l*, pg. 1973
SOLUFEED LIMITED; *Int'l*, pg. 7076
SOLUFIP S.A.S.—See Greiner Holding AG; *Int'l*, pg. 3079
SOLUFORCE B.V.—See Wienerberger AG; *Int'l*, pg. 8406
SOLUGENIX CORP; *U.S. Private*, pg. 3710
SOLUMAT ILE-DE-FRANCE SAS—See VINCI S.A.; *Int'l*, pg. 8235
SOLUMAT SAS—See VINCI S.A.; *Int'l*, pg. 8235
SOLUM CO., LTD.; *Int'l*, pg. 7076
SOLUNA AUSTRALIA PTY. LTD.—See Lithium Australia NL; *Int'l*, pg. 4527
SOLUNA HOLDINGS, INC.; *U.S. Public*, pg. 1901
SOLUS ADVANCED MATERIALS CO., LTD.; *Int'l*, pg. 7076
SOLUSCOPE INTERNATIONAL TRADING (SHANGHAI) CO., LTD.—See Ecolab Inc.; *U.S. Public*, pg. 716
SOLUSCOPE SAS—See Ecolab Inc.; *U.S. Public*, pg. 716
SOLUS SCIENTIFIC SOLUTIONS, INC.—See Revvity, Inc.; *U.S. Public*, pg. 1795
SOLUS SCIENTIFIC SOLUTIONS LTD.—See Revvity, Inc.; *U.S. Public*, pg. 1795
SOLUS SECURITY SYSTEMS PRIVATE LIMITED—See dormakaba Holding AG; *Int'l*, pg. 2178
SOLU TECHNOLOGY PARTNERS - PHOENIX OFFICE—See Solu Technology Partners; *U.S. Private*, pg. 3710
SOLU TECHNOLOGY PARTNERS; *U.S. Private*, pg. 3710
SOLUTIA ARGENTINA S.R.L.—See Eastman Chemical Company; *U.S. Public*, pg. 705
SOLUTIA AUSTRALIA PTY. LTD.—See Eastman Chemical Company; *U.S. Public*, pg. 705
SOLUTIA BRASIL LTDA.—See Eastman Chemical Company; *U.S. Public*, pg. 706
SOLUTIA EUROPE BVBA/SPRL—See Eastman Chemical Company; *U.S. Public*, pg. 705
SOLUTIA EUROPE SPRL/BVBA—See Eastman Chemical Company; *U.S. Public*, pg. 706
SOLUTIA HONG KONG LIMITED—See Eastman Chemical Company; *U.S. Public*, pg. 705
SOLUTIA HONG KONG LIMITED—See Eastman Chemical Company; *U.S. Public*, pg. 705
SOLUTIA INC.—See Eastman Chemical Company; *U.S. Public*, pg. 705
SOLUTIA ITALIA S.R.L.—See Eastman Chemical Company; *U.S. Public*, pg. 706
SOLUTIA JAPAN LIMITED—See Eastman Chemical Company; *U.S. Public*, pg. 706
SOLUTIANCE AG; *Int'l*, pg. 7076
SOLUTIA PERFORMANCE PRODUCTS (SUZHOU) CO., LTD.—See Eastman Chemical Company; *U.S. Public*, pg. 706
SOLUTIA SINGAPORE PTE. LTD.—See Eastman Chemical Company; *U.S. Public*, pg. 706
SOLUTIA SOLAR GMBH—See Eastman Chemical Company; *U.S. Public*, pg. 706
SOLUTIA (THAILAND) LTD.—See Eastman Chemical Company; *U.S. Public*, pg. 705
SOLUTIA THERMINOL CO., LTD.—See Eastman Chemical Company; *U.S. Public*, pg. 706
SOLUTIA TLAXCALA S.A. DE C.V.—See Eastman Chemical Company; *U.S. Public*, pg. 706
SOLUTIA UK INVESTMENTS LTD.—See Eastman Chemical Company; *U.S. Public*, pg. 706
SOLUTIA U.K. LIMITED—See Eastman Chemical Company; *U.S. Public*, pg. 706
SOLUTIA VENEZUELA, S.R.L.—See Eastman Chemical Company; *U.S. Public*, pg. 706
SOLUTIONARY, INC.—See Nippon Telegraph & Telephone Corporation; *Int'l*, pg. 5355
SOLUTION BEACON LLC; *U.S. Private*, pg. 3710
SOLUTION CREATION COMPANY LIMITED—See PTT Global Chemical Public Company Limited; *Int'l*, pg. 6091
SOLUTION DYNAMICS LIMITED; *Int'l*, pg. 7076

SOLUTION FINANCIAL (ALBERTA) INC.—See Solution Financial, Inc.; *Int'l*, pg. 7076
SOLUTION FINANCIAL, INC.; *Int'l*, pg. 7076
SOLUTION FONDATION AFRIQUE DE L'OUEST SA—See VINCI S.A.; *Int'l*, pg. 8229
SOLUTION GROUP BERHAD; *Int'l*, pg. 7076
SOLUTIONHEALTH; *U.S. Private*, pg. 3711
SOLUTIONINC TECHNOLOGIES LIMITED; *Int'l*, pg. 7076
SOLUTION IT INC.; *U.S. Private*, pg. 3710
SOLUTION KOREA COMPANY—See Taiwan Line Tek Electronic Co., Ltd.; *Int'l*, pg. 7422
SOLUTION LABO TOKYO CO., LTD.—See Yamatane Corporation; *Int'l*, pg. 8553
SOLUTION MINDS (UK) LIMITED—See 1Spatial Plc; *Int'l*, pg. 3
SOLUTIONPOINT INTERNATIONAL INC.; *U.S. Private*, pg. 3711
SOLUTIONS 30 OPERATIONS GMBH—See Solutions 30 SE; *Int'l*, pg. 7077
SOLUTIONS 30 SE; *Int'l*, pg. 7076
SOLUTIONS 4 MOBILITY LLC—See Allgeier SE; *Int'l*, pg. 337
SOLUTIONS BY DESIGN II, LLC—See Converged Security Solutions LLC; *U.S. Private*, pg. 1035
SOLUTIONS BY DESIGN, INC.; *U.S. Private*, pg. 3711
SOLUTIONS CAPITAL MANAGEMENT SIM S.P.A.; *Int'l*, pg. 7077
THE SOLUTIONSDEVELOPERS CORPORATION; *U.S. Private*, pg. 4119
SOLUTIONSET LLC; *U.S. Private*, pg. 3711
SOLUTIONSET—See SolutionSet LLC; *U.S. Private*, pg. 3711
SOLUTIONS-IES, INC.; *U.S. Private*, pg. 3711
SOLUTIONS-II INCORPORATED; *U.S. Private*, pg. 3711
SOLUTIONS, INC.—See Constellation Software Inc.; *Int'l*, pg. 1774
SOLUTIONS INDUSTRIELLES ULC—See Applied Industrial Technologies, Inc.; *U.S. Public*, pg. 171
SOLUTIONSIQ, LLC—See Accenture plc; *Int'l*, pg. 86
SOLUTIONS RECOVERY INC.—See AAC Holdings, Inc.; *U.S. Private*, pg. 31
SOLUTIONSTAR REALTY SERVICES LLC—See Mr. Cooper Group Inc.; *U.S. Public*, pg. 1480
SOLUTIONSTAR SETTLEMENT SERVICES LLC—See Mr. Cooper Group Inc.; *U.S. Public*, pg. 1480
SOLUTIONS TREATMENT CENTER, LLC—See AAC Holdings, Inc.; *U.S. Private*, pg. 31
SOLUTION STREET, LLC; *U.S. Private*, pg. 3711
SOLUTIONS.TV—See STV Group plc; *Int'l*, pg. 7245
SOLUTIONZ, INC.—See Fernandez Holdings, Inc.; *U.S. Private*, pg. 1497
SOLUTIUS BELGIUM N.V—See Intrum AB; *Int'l*, pg. 3771
SOLUTRONIC ENERGY GMBH—See Shanghai Churui Energy Technology Co., Ltd.; *Int'l*, pg. 6763
SOLUVIA BILLING GMBH—See MVV Energie AG; *Int'l*, pg. 5109
SOLUVIA ENERGY SERVICES GMBH—See MVV Energie AG; *Int'l*, pg. 5109
SOLUVIA IT-SERVICES GMBH—See MVV Energie AG; *Int'l*, pg. 5109
SOLUVIA METERING GMBH—See MVV Energie AG; *Int'l*, pg. 5109
SOLUX CO., LTD.; *Int'l*, pg. 7077
SO LUXURY HMC SARL—See Accor S.A.; *Int'l*, pg. 92
SOLUZIONI PRODOTTI SISTEMI S.R.L.—See TXT e-Solutions S.p.A.; *Int'l*, pg. 7993
SOLVAC S.A.; *Int'l*, pg. 7077
SOLVADIS DEUTSCHLAND GMBH—See Sojitz Corporation; *Int'l*, pg. 7065
SOLVADIS GMBH—See Orlando Management AG; *Int'l*, pg. 5640
SOLVANG ASA; *Int'l*, pg. 7077
SOLVANG LUTHERAN HOME, INC.; *U.S. Private*, pg. 3711
SOLVANG MARITIME AS—See Solvang ASA; *Int'l*, pg. 7077
SOLVAR LIMITED; *Int'l*, pg. 7077
SOLVAY ADVANCED POLYMERS FRANCE S.A.—See Solvay S.A.; *Int'l*, pg. 7079
SOLVAY ADVANCED POLYMERS, L.L.C.—See Solvay S.A.; *Int'l*, pg. 7079
SOLVAY ALEXANDRIA TRADING LLC—See Solvay S.A.; *Int'l*, pg. 7079
SOLVAY ALKOR FOLIE SPOL SR.O.—See Solvay S.A.; *Int'l*, pg. 7079
SOLVAY AMERICA, INC.—See Solvay S.A.; *Int'l*, pg. 7079
SOLVAY ARGENTINA S.A.—See Solvay S.A.; *Int'l*, pg. 7079
SOLVAY ASIA PACIFIC PTE. LTD.—See Solvay S.A.; *Int'l*, pg. 7079
SOLVAY (BANGPOO) SPECIALTY CHEMICALS LTD.—See Solvay S.A.; *Int'l*, pg. 7079
SOLVAY BANK CORP; *U.S. Public*, pg. 1901
SOLVAY BARIO E DERIVATI (SABED) S.P.A.—See Solvay S.A.; *Int'l*, pg. 7079
SOLVAY (BEIJING) ENERGY TECHNOLOGY CO., LTD.—See Solvay S.A.; *Int'l*, pg. 7079
SOLVAY BENVIC & CIE BELGIUM S.N.C.—See Solvay S.A.; *Int'l*, pg. 7079

SOLVAY BANK CORP.

SOLVAY BENVIC EUROPE FRANCE S.A.S.—See Solvay S.A.; *Int'l*, pg. 7079
SOLVAY BULGARIA AD—See Solvay S.A.; *Int'l*, pg. 7079
SOLVAY BUSINESS SERVICES LATVIA SIA—See Solvay S.A.; *Int'l*, pg. 7079
SOLVAY BUSINESS SERVICES PORTUGAL UNIPESSOAL LDA.—See Solvay S.A.; *Int'l*, pg. 7079
SOLVAY CANADA INC.—See Solvay S.A.; *Int'l*, pg. 7079
SOLVAY-CARBONATE-FRANCE S.A.S.—See Solvay S.A.; *Int'l*, pg. 7082
SOLVAY CHEMICALS FINLAND OY—See Solvay S.A.; *Int'l*, pg. 7079
SOLVAY CHEMICALS, INC.—See Solvay S.A.; *Int'l*, pg. 7079
SOLVAY CHEMICALS INTERNATIONAL SA—See Solvay S.A.; *Int'l*, pg. 7079
SOLVAY CHEMICALS LTD.—See Solvay S.A.; *Int'l*, pg. 7079
SOLVAY CHEMICALS (SHANGHAI) CO. LTD.—See Solvay S.A.; *Int'l*, pg. 7079
SOLVAY CHEMIE B.V.—See Solvay S.A.; *Int'l*, pg. 7079
SOLVAY CHIMICA BUSSI S.P.A.—See Solvay S.A.; *Int'l*, pg. 7079
SOLVAY CHIMICA ITALIA S.P.A.—See Solvay S.A.; *Int'l*, pg. 7079
SOLVAY COORDINATION INTERNATIONALE DES CREDITS COMMERCIAUX (CICC) S.A.—See Solvay S.A.; *Int'l*, pg. 7079
SOLVAY & CPC BARIUM STRONTIUM INTERNATIONAL GMBH—See Solvay S.A.; *Int'l*, pg. 7080
SOLVAY & CPC BARIUM STRONTIUM MONTERREY S. DE R.L. DE C.V.—See Solvay S.A.; *Int'l*, pg. 7079
SOLVAY DO BRASIL LTDA—See Solvay S.A.; *Int'l*, pg. 7082
SOLVAY-ELECTROLYSE-FRANCE S.A.—See Solvay S.A.; *Int'l*, pg. 7082
SOLVAY ELEKTROLYSESPEZIALITATEN—See Solvay S.A.; *Int'l*, pg. 7080
SOLVAY ENERGIE FRANCE S.A.S.—See Solvay S.A.; *Int'l*, pg. 7079
SOLVAY ENERGY SERVICES ITALIA S.R.L.—See Solvay S.A.; *Int'l*, pg. 7080
SOLVAY ENERGY SERVICES S.A.S.—See Solvay S.A.; *Int'l*, pg. 7080
SOLVAY ENGINEERED POLYMERS (CANADA), INC.—See Solvay S.A.; *Int'l*, pg. 7080
SOLVAY ENGINEERING PLASTICS POLAND SP. Z O.O.—See Solvay S.A.; *Int'l*, pg. 7081
SOLVAY ENZYMES GMBH & CO.—See Solvay S.A.; *Int'l*, pg. 7080
SOLVAY FARMA LDA.—See Solvay S.A.; *Int'l*, pg. 7080
SOLVAYFARMA LDA.—See Solvay S.A.; *Int'l*, pg. 7082
SOLVAY FINANCE (AMERICA) LLC—See Solvay S.A.; *Int'l*, pg. 7079
SOLVAY FINANCE B.V.—See Solvay S.A.; *Int'l*, pg. 7080
SOLVAY FINANCE FRANCE S.A.—See Solvay S.A.; *Int'l*, pg. 7080
SOLVAY FINANCE IRELAND UNLIMITED—See Solvay S.A.; *Int'l*, pg. 7080
SOLVAY FINANCE (LUXEMBOURG) S.A.—See Solvay S.A.; *Int'l*, pg. 7080
SOLVAY FINANCE S.A.—See Solvay S.A.; *Int'l*, pg. 7080
SOLVAY FINANZIARIA S.P.A.—See Solvay S.A.; *Int'l*, pg. 7080
SOLVAY FINE CHEMICAL ADDITIVES (QINGDAO) CO., LTD.—See Solvay S.A.; *Int'l*, pg. 7080
SOLVAY-FLUORES-FRANCE S.A.S.—See Solvay S.A.; *Int'l*, pg. 7082
SOLVAY FLUOR GMBH—See Solvay S.A.; *Int'l*, pg. 7080
SOLVAY FLUOR ITALIA S.P.A.—See Solvay S.A.; *Int'l*, pg. 7080
SOLVAY FLUOR MEXICO S.A. DE C.V.—See Solvay S.A.; *Int'l*, pg. 7080
SOLVAY FLUX GMBH—See Solvay S.A.; *Int'l*, pg. 7080
SOLVAY GMBH—See Solvay S.A.; *Int'l*, pg. 7080
SOLVAY HEALTHCARE LTD.—See Solvay S.A.; *Int'l*, pg. 7080
SOLVAY HENGCHANG (ZHANGJIAGANG) SPECIALTY CHEMICAL CO., LTD.—See Solvay S.A.; *Int'l*, pg. 7080
SOLVAY INFORMATION SERVICES NAFTA, LLC—See Solvay S.A.; *Int'l*, pg. 7079
SOLVAY INFRA BAD HOENNINGEN GMBH—See Solvay S.A.; *Int'l*, pg. 7080
SOLVAY INTEROX GMBH—See Solvay S.A.; *Int'l*, pg. 7080
SOLVAY INTEROX LTD.—See Solvay S.A.; *Int'l*, pg. 7080
SOLVAY INTEROX - PRODUTOS PEROXIDADOS LDA.—See Solvay S.A.; *Int'l*, pg. 7080
SOLVAY INTEROX PTY. LTD.—See Solvay S.A.; *Int'l*, pg. 7080
SOLVAY INTEROX S.A.—See Solvay S.A.; *Int'l*, pg. 7080
SOLVAY JAPAN K.K.—See Solvay S.A.; *Int'l*, pg. 7080
SOLVAY KOREA CO. LTD.—See KNW Co., Ltd.; *Int'l*, pg. 4214
SOLVAY LANTIAN (QUZHOU) CHEMICALS CO., LTD.—See Solvay S.A.; *Int'l*, pg. 7080
SOLVAY MEXICANA S. DE R.L. DE C.V.—See Solvay S.A.; *Int'l*, pg. 7080

SOLVAY BANK CORP.

SOLVAY MINERALES S.A.—See Solvay S.A.; *Int'l*, pg. 7080
SOLVAY NEW ZEALAND LTD.—See Solvay S.A.; *Int'l*, pg. 7080
SOLVAY NICCA, LTD.—See Nicca Chemical Co., Ltd.; *Int'l*, pg. 5264
SOLVAY NOH—See Solvay S.A.; *Int'l*, pg. 7080
SOLVAY-OLEFINES-FINES S.A.—See Solvay S.A.; *Int'l*, pg. 7082
SOLVAY - ORGANICS - FRANCE S.A.S.—See Solvay S.A.; *Int'l*, pg. 7079
SOLVAY ORGANICS GMBH—See Solvay S.A.; *Int'l*, pg. 7080
SOLVAY OSTERREICH GMBH—See Solvay S.A.; *Int'l*, pg. 7080
SOLVAY PARIS—See Solvay S.A.; *Int'l*, pg. 7081
SOLVAY PARTICIPATIONS FRANCE S.A.—See Solvay S.A.; *Int'l*, pg. 7081
SOLVAY PEROXIDOS PORTUGAL UNIPESSOAL LDA.—See Solvay S.A.; *Int'l*, pg. 7081
SOLVAY PEROXYTHAI LTD—See Solvay S.A.; *Int'l*, pg. 7081
SOLVAY PHARMACEUTICALS, INC.—See Solvay S.A.; *Int'l*, pg. 7079
SOLVAY POLYOLEFINS EUROPE S.A.—See Solvay S.A.; *Int'l*, pg. 7081
SOLVAY PORTUGAL - PRODUTOS QUIMICOS S.A.—See A4F-Algae for Future SA; *Int'l*, pg. 30
SOLVAY PORTUGAL - PRODUTOS QUIMICOS S.A.—See GREEN AQUA Company SGPS, S.A.; *Int'l*, pg. 3069
SOLVAY P&S GMBH—See Solvay S.A.; *Int'l*, pg. 7080
SOLVAY QUIMICA S.A.—See Solvay S.A.; *Int'l*, pg. 7081
SOLVAY QUIMICA S.L.—See Solvay S.A.; *Int'l*, pg. 7081
SOLVAY QUIMICA Y MINERA SERVICIOS SA DE CV—See Solvay S.A.; *Int'l*, pg. 7080
SOLVAY QUIMICA Y MINERA VENTAS SA DE CV—See Solvay S.A.; *Int'l*, pg. 7080
SOLVAY RAYONG HUAY PONG—See Solvay S.A.; *Int'l*, pg. 7078
SOLVAY S.A.; *Int'l*, pg. 7077
SOLVAY (SCHWEIZ) AG—See Solvay S.A.; *Int'l*, pg. 7079
SOLVAY (SHANGHAI) INTERNATIONAL TRADING CO., LTD.—See Solvay S.A.; *Int'l*, pg. 7079
SOLVAY (SHANGHAI) LTD—See Solvay S.A.; *Int'l*, pg. 7079
SOLVAY SISECAM HOLDING AG—See Solvay S.A.; *Int'l*, pg. 7082
SOLVAY SODA DEUTSCHLAND GMBH—See Solvay S.A.; *Int'l*, pg. 7080
SOLVAY SODI AD—See Solvay S.A.; *Int'l*, pg. 7082
SOLVAY SOLEXIS, INC.—See Solvay S.A.; *Int'l*, pg. 7079
SOLVAY SOLEXIS S.P.A.—See Solvay S.A.; *Int'l*, pg. 7082
SOLVAY SOLUTIONS ITALIA S.P.A.—See Solvay S.A.; *Int'l*, pg. 7082
SOLVAY SOLUTIONS UK LIMITED—See Solvay S.A.; *Int'l*, pg. 7081
SOLVAY SOLUTIONS UK LTD.—See Solvay S.A.; *Int'l*, pg. 7082
SOLVAY SPECIAL CHEM JAPAN LTD.—See Solvay S.A.; *Int'l*, pg. 7082
SOLVAY-SPECIALITES-FRANCE S.A.S.—See Solvay S.A.; *Int'l*, pg. 7078
SOLVAY SPECIALITIES INDIA PRIVATE LIMITED—See Solvay S.A.; *Int'l*, pg. 7082
SOLVAY SPECIALITY POLYMERS (CHANGSHU) CO. LTD—See Solvay S.A.; *Int'l*, pg. 7082
SOLVAY SPECIALITY POLYMERS FRANCE S.A.S.—See Solvay S.A.; *Int'l*, pg. 7082
SOLVAY SPECIALTY CHEMICALS ASIA PACIFIC PTE LTD—See Solvay S.A.; *Int'l*, pg. 7082
SOLVAY SPECIALTY CHEMICALS LTD.—See Solvay S.A.; *Int'l*, pg. 7082
SOLVAY SPECIALTY POLYMERS (CHANGSHU) CO. LTD.—See Solvay S.A.; *Int'l*, pg. 7082
SOLVAY SPECIALTY POLYMERS GERMANY GMBH—See Solvay S.A.; *Int'l*, pg. 7080
SOLVAY SPECIALTY POLYMERS GERMANY GMBH—See Solvay S.A.; *Int'l*, pg. 7080
SOLVAY SPECIALTY POLYMERS KOREA COMPANY LTD.—See Solvay S.A.; *Int'l*, pg. 7082
SOLVAY SPECIALTY POLYMERS MANAGEMENT S.R.L.—See Solvay S.A.; *Int'l*, pg. 7082
SOLVAY (THAILAND) LTD.—See Solvay S.A.; *Int'l*, pg. 7079
SOLVAY UK HOLDING COMPANY LTD—See Solvay S.A.; *Int'l*, pg. 7082
SOLVAY UNIVERSITY PARK—See Solvay S.A.; *Int'l*, pg. 7081
SOLVAY USA INC.—See Solvay S.A.; *Int'l*, pg. 7081
SOLVAY VERWALTUNGS-UND VERMITTLUNGS GMBH—See Solvay S.A.; *Int'l*, pg. 7080
SOLVAY VIENNA GMBH—See Solvay S.A.; *Int'l*, pg. 7078
SOLVAY VOSTOK OOO—See Solvay S.A.; *Int'l*, pg. 7082
SOLVAY (ZHENJIANG) CHEMICALS CO., LTD.—See Solvay S.A.; *Int'l*, pg. 7079
SOLVCHEM, INC.; *U.S. Private*, pg. 3711
SOLVE ADVISORS INC.; *U.S. Private*, pg. 3711
SOLVEGY, INC.; *U.S. Private*, pg. 3711
SOLVE IT, INC.; *U.S. Private*, pg. 3711
SOLVENTIS A.V. SA; *Int'l*, pg. 7082
THE SOLVENTS RECOVERY SERVICE OF NEW JERSEY, INC.—See Clean Harbors, Inc.; *U.S. Public*, pg. 510
SOLVENTUM CORPORATION; *U.S. Public*, pg. 1901
SOLVERDE - SOCIEDADE DE INVESTIMENTOS TURISTICOS DA COSTA VERDE, S.A.; *Int'l*, pg. 7082
SOLVER UAB—See Atea ASA; *Int'l*, pg. 667
SOLVIAS AG; *Int'l*, pg. 7082
SOLVIC S.A.—See Solvay S.A.; *Int'l*, pg. 7082
SOLVIK BARNEVERN AS—See Humana AB; *Int'l*, pg. 3530
SOLVIL ET TITUS SA—See Stelux Holdings International Limited; *Int'l*, pg. 7204
SOLVIN FRANCE S.A.—See Solvay S.A.; *Int'l*, pg. 7079
SOLVIN GMBH & CO. KG—See Solvay S.A.; *Int'l*, pg. 7079
SOLVIN HOLDING NEDERLAND B.V.—See Solvay S.A.; *Int'l*, pg. 7079
SOLVIN ITALIA S.P.A.—See Solvay S.A.; *Int'l*, pg. 7079
SOLVIN SA—See Solvay S.A.; *Int'l*, pg. 7078
SOLVIN SPAIN S.L.—See Solvay S.A.; *Int'l*, pg. 7079
SOLVI S.A.; *Int'l*, pg. 7082
SOLVI VALORIZACAO ENERGETICA S.A.—See Solvi S.A.; *Int'l*, pg. 7082
SOLVIX SOLUTIONS, LLC; *U.S. Private*, pg. 3711
SOLVTRANS AS—See Brookfield Corporation; *Int'l*, pg. 1183
SOLVTRANS CHILE S.A.—See Brookfield Corporation; *Int'l*, pg. 1183
SOLVTRANS REDERI AS—See Brookfield Corporation; *Int'l*, pg. 1183
SOLVVY INC.; *Int'l*, pg. 7082
SOLWAY INVESTMENT GROUP LIMITED; *Int'l*, pg. 7082
SOL WELDING SRL—See SOL S.p.A.; *Int'l*, pg. 7067
SOLX, INC.; *U.S. Private*, pg. 3711
SOLXYZ CO., LTD.; *Int'l*, pg. 7083
SOLYTECH ENTERPRISE CORPORATION; *Int'l*, pg. 7083
SOLYTECH JAPAN CO., LTD.—See Solytech Enterprise Corporation; *Int'l*, pg. 7083
SOMACEUTICA, INC.—See Marizyme, Inc.; *U.S. Public*, pg. 1367
SOMACEUTICALS, INC.—See GlobeStar Therapeutics Corporation; *U.S. Public*, pg. 946
SOMAFEL, S.A.—See Teixeira Duarte SA; *Int'l*, pg. 7525
SOMAFEL, S.A.—See Teixeira Duarte SA; *Int'l*, pg. 7525
SOMAFEL, S.A.—See Teixeira Duarte SA; *Int'l*, pg. 7525
SOMAFEL, S.A.—See Teixeira Duarte SA; *Int'l*, pg. 7525
SOMAFEL, S.A.—See Teixeira Duarte SA; *Int'l*, pg. 7525
SOMAGEN DIAGNOSTICS INC.—See Diploma PLC; *Int'l*, pg. 2129
SOMA GMBH—See Leopold Kostal GmbH & Co. KG; *Int'l*, pg. 4466
SOMA GOLD CORP.; *Int'l*, pg. 7083
SOMAGUE ENGENHARIA, S.A.—See HAL Trust N.V.; *Int'l*, pg. 3227
SOMA HEALTH LIMITED—See Spire Healthcare Group plc; *Int'l*, pg. 7139
SOMAHLUTION, INC.—See Marizyme, Inc.; *U.S. Public*, pg. 1367
SOMA INTIMATES, LLC—See Sycamore Partners Management, LP; *U.S. Private*, pg. 3895
SOMAI PHARMACEUTICALS LTD; *Int'l*, pg. 7083
SOMAIR SA—See Orano SA; *Int'l*, pg. 5611
SOMA KYODO POWER CO., LTD.—See Tohoku Electric Power Co., Inc.; *Int'l*, pg. 7777
SOMALOGIC, INC.—See Standard BioTools Inc.; *U.S. Public*, pg. 1928
SOMALOGIC OPERATING CO., INC.—See Standard BioTools Inc.; *U.S. Public*, pg. 1929
SOMA MEDICAL ASSESSMENTS CORP.—See GIC Pte. Ltd.; *Int'l*, pg. 2964
SOMA MEDICAL ASSESSMENTS CORP.—See Leonard Green & Partners, L.P.; *U.S. Private*, pg. 2425
SOMA NETWORKS, INC.; *U.S. Private*, pg. 3711
SOMANY CERAMICS LIMITED - KADI WORKS—See Somany Ceramics Limited; *Int'l*, pg. 7083
SOMANY CERAMICS LIMITED; *Int'l*, pg. 7083
SOMANY GLOBAL LTD.—See Somany Ceramics Limited; *Int'l*, pg. 7083
SOMAPA INFORMATION TECHNOLOGY PUBLIC COMPANY LIMITED; *Int'l*, pg. 7083
SOMA PAPERS & INDUSTRIES LIMITED; *Int'l*, pg. 7083
SOMAPHAR S.A.—See Toyota Tsusho Corporation; *Int'l*, pg. 7876
SOMAR CORPORATION (H.K.) LTD.—See Somar Corporation; *Int'l*, pg. 7084
SOMAR CORPORATION INDIA PVT. LTD.—See Somar Corporation; *Int'l*, pg. 7084
SOMAR CORPORATION - SOKA FACTORY—See Somar Corporation; *Int'l*, pg. 7084
SOMAR CORPORATION; *Int'l*, pg. 7083
SOMAR CORPORATION (TAIWAN) LTD.—See Somar Corporation; *Int'l*, pg. 7084
SOMAREST SARL—See LVMH Moet Hennessy Louis Vuitton SE; *Int'l*, pg. 4596
SOMAR EUROPE B.V.—See Somar Corporation; *Int'l*, pg. 7084

CORPORATE AFFILIATIONS

SOMAR FINE CHEMICALS (ZHUHAI) CO., LTD.—See Somar Corporation; *Int'l*, pg. 7084
SOMARO—See Bouygues S.A.; *Int'l*, pg. 1123
SOMAR VIETNAM CORPORATION—See Somar Corporation; *Int'l*, pg. 7084
SOMASCHINI AUTOMOTIVE, SRL—See Cie Automotive S.A.; *Int'l*, pg. 1605
SOMAT COMPANY—See Illinois Tool Works Inc.; *U.S. Public*, pg. 1110
SOMATEX MEDICAL TECHNOLOGIES GMBH—See Hologic, Inc.; *U.S. Public*, pg. 1045
SOMA TEXTILES & INDUSTRIES LIMITED; *Int'l*, pg. 7083
SOMATHERM S.A.S.; *Int'l*, pg. 7084
SOMATI FIE N.V.—See London Security PLC; *Int'l*, pg. 4547
SOMATRANS LTD.—See Ireland Blyth Limited; *Int'l*, pg. 3807
SOMATRA—See FAYAT SAS; *Int'l*, pg. 2626
SOMA WATER, INC.—See Full Circle Home LLC; *U.S. Private*, pg. 1620
SOMAX BETEILIGUNGSVERWALTUNGS GMBH—See PORR AG; *Int'l*, pg. 5925
SOMBOON ADVANCE TECHNOLOGY PUBLIC COMPANY LIMITED; *Int'l*, pg. 7084
SOMBOON MALLEABLE IRON INDUSTRIAL COMPANY LIMITED—See Somboon Advance Technology Public Company Limited; *Int'l*, pg. 7084
SOMBORSKE NOVINE A.D.; *Int'l*, pg. 7084
SOMBUR TOOL & DIE—See MNP Corporation; *U.S. Private*, pg. 2756
SOM DATT FINANCE CORPORATION LIMITED; *Int'l*, pg. 7083
SOM DISTILLERIES & BREWERIES LTD; *Int'l*, pg. 7083
SOMEC S.P.A.; *Int'l*, pg. 7084
SOMEDIB SARL—See HORIBA Ltd; *Int'l*, pg. 3478
SOME GOOD&CO., INC.—See Sunny Side Up Group Inc.; *Int'l*, pg. 7319
SOMEK & ASSOCIATES LIMITED—See Frenkel Topping Group plc; *Int'l*, pg. 2773
SOMERA CAPITAL MANAGEMENT, LLC; *U.S. Private*, pg. 3711
SOMERA COMMUNICATIONS PTE. LTD.—See Jabil Inc.; *U.S. Public*, pg. 1182
SOMERFORD HOUSE FREDERICK—See AlerisLife Inc.; *U.S. Private*, pg. 162
SOMERFORD PLACE LLC—See AlerisLife Inc.; *U.S. Private*, pg. 162
SOMERLEY CAPITAL HOLDINGS LIMITED; *Int'l*, pg. 7084
SOMERO ENTERPRISES INC.; *U.S. Public*, pg. 1902
SOMERSET BUICK-GMC, INC.; *U.S. Private*, pg. 3711
SOMERSET CAPITAL GROUP, LTD.; *U.S. Private*, pg. 3711
SOMERSET CASUALTY INSURANCE COMPANY—See Brookfield Reinsurance Ltd.; *Int'l*, pg. 1194
SOMERSET CONSUMER SERVICE CORP.—See Somerset Savings Bank, SLA; *U.S. Private*, pg. 3712
SOMERSET CUISINE LIMITED—See Batu Kawan Berhad; *Int'l*, pg. 891
SOMERSET HARDWOOD FLOORING, INC.—See Ernst Gohner Stiftung; *Int'l*, pg. 2495
SOMERSET HARDWOOD LUMBER, INC.—See Ernst Gohner Stiftung; *Int'l*, pg. 2495
SOMERSET HOUSE PUBLISHING INC.; *U.S. Private*, pg. 3712
SOMERSET, INCORPORATED—See Universal Health Services, Inc.; *U.S. Public*, pg. 2259
SOMERSET INDUSTRIES INC.; *U.S. Private*, pg. 3712
SOMERSET MARINE LINES, LLC—See Littlejohn & Co., LLC; *U.S. Private*, pg. 2470
SOMERSET MED SERVICES, INC.—See MedCare Equipment Company, LLC; *U.S. Private*, pg. 2651
SOMERSET MINERALS LIMITED; *Int'l*, pg. 7084
SOMERSET MOTORS, INC.—See Penske Automotive Group, Inc.; *U.S. Public*, pg. 1666
SOMERSET OUTPATIENT SURGERY, LLC—See UnitedHealth Group Incorporated; *U.S. Public*, pg. 2250
SOMERSET PHARMACEUTICALS INC.—See Viatris Inc.; *U.S. Public*, pg. 2294
SOMERSET RAILROAD CORPORATION—See The AES Corporation; *U.S. Public*, pg. 2032
SOMERSET SAVINGS BANK, SLA; *U.S. Private*, pg. 3712
SOMERSET SPORTART; *U.S. Private*, pg. 3712
SOMERSET STEEL ERECTION COMPANY INC—See Riggs Industries, Inc.; *U.S. Private*, pg. 3435
SOMERSET THERAPEUTICS LIMITED—See Veego Pharma LLC; *U.S. Private*, pg. 4353
SOMERSET TRUST CO.; *U.S. Private*, pg. 3712
SOMERSET WELDING AND STEEL, INC. - J&J TRUCK BODIES & TRAILERS DIVISION—See Riggs Industries, Inc.; *U.S. Private*, pg. 3435
SOMERSET WELDING AND STEEL, INC. - J&J TRUCK EQUIPMENT DIVISION—See Riggs Industries, Inc.; *U.S. Private*, pg. 3435
SOMERSET WELDING & STEEL, INC.—See Riggs Industries, Inc.; *U.S. Private*, pg. 3435
SOMERSET WEST AUTOPARK PROPRIETARY LIMITED—See Barclays PLC; *Int'l*, pg. 863

COMPANY NAME INDEX

SOMERSET WOOD PRODUCTS, CO.; *U.S. Private*, pg. 3712
SOMERS LIMITED—See ICM Limited; *Int'l*, pg. 3582
SOMERS OIL SERVICE, INC.—See Taylor Energy, LLC; *U.S. Private*, pg. 3939
SOMERTON CENTER—See Formation Capital, LLC; *U.S. Private*, pg. 1571
SOMERVILLE BANCORP.; *U.S. Private*, pg. 3712
SOMERVILLE BANK—See Somerville Bancorp.; *U.S. Private*, pg. 3712
THE SOMERVILLE BANK & TRUST COMPANY—See Trustmark Corporation; *U.S. Public*, pg. 2202
SOMERVILLE DIALYSIS CENTER, LLC—See DaVita Inc.; *U.S. Public*, pg. 643
SOMERVILLE JOURNAL—See Gannett Co., Inc.; *U.S. Public*, pg. 903
SOMERVILLE MEMORIALS LTD.—See Family Memorials Inc.; *Int'l*, pg. 2612
SOME SEVIT CORPORATION—See Hyosung TNC Co. Ltd.; *Int'l*, pg. 3552
SOMETA; *Int'l*, pg. 7084
SO.MET. ENERGIA S.R.L.—See F2i - Fondi Italiani per le infrastrutture SGR S.p.A.; *Int'l*, pg. 2597
SOMETHINGDIGITAL.COM LLC—See Genpact Limited; *Int'l*, pg. 2927
SOMETHING FUN, INC.—See Will Group, Inc.; *Int'l*, pg. 8412
SOMETHING HOLDINGS CO., LTD.—See ITbook Holdings Co., Ltd.; *Int'l*, pg. 3831
SOMETHING SHIKOKU CO., LTD.—See ITbook Holdings Co., Ltd.; *Int'l*, pg. 3831
SOMETHING UNIQUE, INC.—See Rauen Incorporated; *U.S. Private*, pg. 3357
SOMETRA S.A—See Metlen Energy & Metals S.A.; *Int'l*, pg. 4855
SOMETRICS, INC.—See American Express Company; *U.S. Public*, pg. 102
SOMEWAY NEW MATERIAL (KUNSHAN) CO., LTD.—See J.Pond Precision Technology Co., Ltd.; *Int'l*, pg. 3858
SOMFY ACTIVITES SA—See Somfy SA; *Int'l*, pg. 7085
SOMFY AG—See Somfy SA; *Int'l*, pg. 7085
SOMFY ARGENTINA SRL—See Somfy SA; *Int'l*, pg. 7085
SOMFY BRASIL LTDA.—See Somfy SA; *Int'l*, pg. 7085
SOMFY BULGARIA AD—See Somfy SA; *Int'l*, pg. 7085
SOMFY CHINA CO. LTD.—See Somfy SA; *Int'l*, pg. 7085
SOMFY CO. LTD.—See Somfy SA; *Int'l*, pg. 7085
SOMFY ESPANA S.A.—See Somfy SA; *Int'l*, pg. 7085
SOMFY EV OTOMASYON SISTEMLERI TICALET LTD STI—See Somfy SA; *Int'l*, pg. 7085
SOMFY GMBH—See Somfy SA; *Int'l*, pg. 7085
SOMFY GMBH—See Somfy SA; *Int'l*, pg. 7085
SOMFY HELLAS S.A.—See Somfy SA; *Int'l*, pg. 7085
SOMFY INDIA PVT. LTD.—See Somfy SA; *Int'l*, pg. 7085
SOMFY ITALIA S.R.L.—See Somfy SA; *Int'l*, pg. 7085
SOMFY JOO CO. LTD.—See Somfy SA; *Int'l*, pg. 7085
SOMFY K.F.T.—See Somfy SA; *Int'l*, pg. 7085
SOMFY LATVIA SIA—See Somfy SA; *Int'l*, pg. 7085
SOMFY LLC—See Somfy SA; *Int'l*, pg. 7085
SOMFY LTD.—See Somfy SA; *Int'l*, pg. 7085
SOMFY MAROC S.A.R.L.—See Somfy SA; *Int'l*, pg. 7086
SOMFY MEXICO SA DE CV—See Somfy SA; *Int'l*, pg. 7086
SOMFY MIDDLE EAST CO. LTD.—See Somfy SA; *Int'l*, pg. 7086
SOMFY NEDERLAND B.V.—See Somfy SA; *Int'l*, pg. 7086
SOMFY NORDIC AB—See Somfy SA; *Int'l*, pg. 7086
SOMFY NORWAY AS—See Somfy SA; *Int'l*, pg. 7086
SOMFY PTE. LTD.—See Somfy SA; *Int'l*, pg. 7086
SOMFY PTY. LTD.—See Somfy SA; *Int'l*, pg. 7086
SOMFY SA; *Int'l*, pg. 7084
SOMFY S.A.S.—See Somfy SA; *Int'l*, pg. 7086
SOMFY SOUTH AFRICA PTY. LIMITED—See Somfy SA; *Int'l*, pg. 7086
SOMFY SPOL S.R.O.—See Somfy SA; *Int'l*, pg. 7086
SOMFY SP. Z.O.O.—See Somfy SA; *Int'l*, pg. 7086
SOMFY SYSTEMS INC.—See Somfy SA; *Int'l*, pg. 7086
SOMFY TAIWAN CO. LTD.—See Somfy SA; *Int'l*, pg. 7086
SOMFY (THAILAND) CO., LTD.—See Somfy SA; *Int'l*, pg. 7085
SOMFY ULC—See Somfy SA; *Int'l*, pg. 7086
SOMGAS HOGAR S.L.—See Brookfield Corporation; *Int'l*, pg. 1189
SOMI CONVEYOR BELTINGS LIMITED; *Int'l*, pg. 7086
SOMIFA—See FAYAT SAS; *Int'l*, pg. 2626
SOMINCOR S.A.—See Lundin Mining Corporation; *Int'l*, pg. 4584
SOMLO - METALL KFT.—See Salzgitter AG; *Int'l*, pg. 6499
SOMMER GMBH; *Int'l*, pg. 7086
SOMMER GMBH—See Diploma PLC; *Int'l*, pg. 2129
SOMMER METALCRAFT CORPORATION; *U.S. Private*, pg. 3712
THE SOMMERS COMPANY; *U.S. Private*, pg. 4119
SOMMERSET ASSISTED LIVING RESIDENCE LLC—See Haverland Carter Lifestyle Group; *U.S. Private*, pg. 1880
SOMMER'S MOBILE LEASING, INC.—See WillScot Mobile Mini Holdings Corp.; *U.S. Public*, pg. 2372
SOMMER & STRASSBURGER EDELSTAHLANLAGENBAU GMBH & CO. KG—See Gesco AG; *Int'l*, pg. 2946

SOMNICARE, INC.—See Foundation Healthcare, Inc.; *U.S. Private*, pg. 1580
SOMNIO SOLUTIONS INC.; *U.S. Private*, pg. 3712
SOMNOMED AG—See SomnoMed Limited; *Int'l*, pg. 7086
SOMNOMED FINLAND OY—See SomnoMed Limited; *Int'l*, pg. 7086
SOMNOMED INC.—See SomnoMed Limited; *Int'l*, pg. 7086
SOMNOMED LIMITED; *Int'l*, pg. 7086
SOMOCAR OVERSEAS N.V.—See Coeclerici S.p.A.; *Int'l*, pg. 1689
SOMODY INC.—See Sun Capital Partners, Inc.; *U.S. Private*, pg. 3861
SOMONT GMBH—See Meyer Burger Technology AG; *Int'l*, pg. 4870
SOMOS EDUCACAO S.A.—See Cogna Educacao S.A.; *Int'l*, pg. 1695
SOMOS, INC.; *U.S. Private*, pg. 3712
SOMOTO LTD.—See Nostromo Energy Ltd.; *Int'l*, pg. 5449
SOMPLAST SA—See SIF Banat-Crisana S.A.; *Int'l*, pg. 6905
SOMPO CARE INC.—See Sompo Holdings, Inc.; *Int'l*, pg. 7086
SOMPO CARE NEXT INC.—See Sompo Holdings, Inc.; *Int'l*, pg. 7086
SOMPO HOLDINGS, INC.; *Int'l*, pg. 7086
SOMPO INSURANCE (HONG KONG) COMPANY LIMITED—See Sompo Holdings, Inc.; *Int'l*, pg. 7086
SOMPO INSURANCE (THAILAND) PUBLIC COMPANY LIMITED—See Sompo Holdings, Inc.; *Int'l*, pg. 7087
SOMPO INSURANCE (THAILAND) PUBLIC COMPANY LIMTED—See Sompo Holdings, Inc.; *Int'l*, pg. 7086
SOMPO INTERNATIONAL HOLDINGS LTD.—See Sompo Holdings, Inc.; *Int'l*, pg. 7087
SOMPO JAPAN CLAIM SERVICES (AMERICA), INC.—See Sompo Holdings, Inc.; *Int'l*, pg. 7087
SOMPO JAPAN FIRE & MARINE INSURANCE COMPANY OF AMERICA—See Sompo Holdings, Inc.; *Int'l*, pg. 7087
SOMPO JAPAN HEALTHCARE SERVICES INC.—See Sompo Holdings, Inc.; *Int'l*, pg. 7087
SOMPO JAPAN INSURANCE COMPANY OF AMERICA—See Sompo Holdings, Inc.; *Int'l*, pg. 7087
SOMPO JAPAN NIPPONKOA ASSET MANAGEMENT CO., LTD.—See Sompo Holdings, Inc.; *Int'l*, pg. 7087
SOMPO JAPAN NIPPONKOA CONSULTING (KOREA) INC.—See Sompo Holdings, Inc.; *Int'l*, pg. 7087
SOMPO JAPAN NIPPONKOA CORPORATE MEMBER LIMITED—See Sompo Holdings, Inc.; *Int'l*, pg. 7087
SOMPO JAPAN NIPPONKOA HIMAWARI LIFE INSURANCE, INC.—See Sompo Holdings, Inc.; *Int'l*, pg. 7087
SOMPO JAPAN NIPPONKOA HOLDINGS (AMERICAS) INC.—See Sompo Holdings, Inc.; *Int'l*, pg. 7087
SOMPO JAPAN NIPPONKOA INSURANCE BROKERS (THAILAND) CO., LTD.—See Sompo Holdings, Inc.; *Int'l*, pg. 7087
SOMPO JAPAN NIPPONKOA INSURANCE (CHINA) CO., LTD.—See Sompo Holdings, Inc.; *Int'l*, pg. 7087
SOMPO JAPAN NIPPONKOA INSURANCE COMPANY OF EUROPE LIMITED—See Sompo Holdings, Inc.; *Int'l*, pg. 7087
SOMPO JAPAN NIPPONKOA INSURANCE DE MEXICO, S.A. DE C.V.—See Sompo Holdings, Inc.; *Int'l*, pg. 7087
SOMPO JAPAN NIPPONKOA INSURANCE (HONG KONG) CO., LTD.—See Sompo Holdings, Inc.; *Int'l*, pg. 7087
SOMPO JAPAN NIPPONKOA INSURANCE INC.—See Sompo Holdings, Inc.; *Int'l*, pg. 7087
SOMPO JAPAN NIPPONKOA INSURANCE (TAIWAN) BROKERS CO., LTD.—See Sompo Holdings, Inc.; *Int'l*, pg. 7087
SOMPO JAPAN NIPPONKOA MANAGEMENT (HK) CO., LTD.—See Sompo Holdings, Inc.; *Int'l*, pg. 7087
SOMPO JAPAN NIPPONKOA REINSURANCE COMPANY LIMITED—See Sompo Holdings, Inc.; *Int'l*, pg. 7087
SOMPO JAPAN NIPPONKOA RISK MANAGEMENT INC.—See Sompo Holdings, Inc.; *Int'l*, pg. 7087
SOMPO TAIWAN BROKERS CO., LTD.—See Sompo Holdings, Inc.; *Int'l*, pg. 7087
S-OM SA—See CSL Limited; *Int'l*, pg. 1866
SOMTA TOOLS (PTY) LTD.—See OSG Corporation; *Int'l*, pg. 5649
SONABANK—See Primis Financial Corp.; *U.S. Public*, pg. 1717
SONA BLW PRAZISIONSSCHMIEDE GMBH—See JTEKT India Limited; *Int'l*, pg. 4019
SONA BLW PRECISION FORGINGS LTD.; *Int'l*, pg. 7088
SONAC ALMERE BV—See Darling Ingredients Inc.; *U.S. Public*, pg. 634
SONACA MONTREAL—See SONACA S.A; *Int'l*, pg. 7088
SONACARE MEDICAL, LLC; *U.S. Private*, pg. 3712
SONACA S.A; *Int'l*, pg. 7088
SONAC AUSTRALIA PTY, LTD—See Darling Ingredients Inc.; *U.S. Public*, pg. 634
SONAC BURGUM B.V.—See Darling Ingredients Inc.; *U.S. Public*, pg. 634
SONAC B.V.—See Darling Ingredients Inc.; *U.S. Public*, pg. 634

SONAC EINDHOVEN B.V.—See Darling Ingredients Inc.; *U.S. Public*, pg. 634
SONAC GENT BVBA—See Darling Ingredients Inc.; *U.S. Public*, pg. 634
SONAC HARLINGEN B.V.—See Darling Ingredients Inc.; *U.S. Public*, pg. 634
SONAC KIEL GMBH—See Darling Ingredients Inc.; *U.S. Public*, pg. 634
SONAC LUBIEN KUJAWSKI SPOLKA Z OGRANICZONA ODPOWIEDZIALNOSCIA—See Darling Ingredients Inc.; *U.S. Public*, pg. 634
SONAC OSETNICA SP.Z O.O.—See Darling Ingredients Inc.; *U.S. Public*, pg. 634
SONAC USA—See Darling Ingredients Inc.; *U.S. Public*, pg. 634
SONAC USNICE SP.Z O.O.—See Darling Ingredients Inc.; *U.S. Public*, pg. 634
SONADEZI CHAU DUC SHAREHOLDING COMPANY; *Int'l*, pg. 7088
SONADEZI LONG THANH; *Int'l*, pg. 7088
SONAE CAPITAL, SGPS, SA—See Efanor Investimentos, SGPS, SA; *Int'l*, pg. 2318
SONAECOM SGPS SA; *Int'l*, pg. 7088
SONAE.COM—See Efanor Investimentos, SGPS, SA; *Int'l*, pg. 2319
SONAE INDUSTRIA, SGPS, S.A.—See Efanor Investimentos, SGPS, SA; *Int'l*, pg. 2318
SONAE SGPS, SA—See Efanor Investimentos, SGPS, SA; *Int'l*, pg. 2318
SONAE SIERRA SGPS, SA—See Efanor Investimentos, SGPS, SA; *Int'l*, pg. 2319
SONAG COMPANY, INC.; *U.S. Private*, pg. 3712
SONAGI SGPS SA; *Int'l*, pg. 7088
SONAG READY MIX, LLC—See Sonag Company, Inc.; *U.S. Private*, pg. 3712
SONAK S.A.—See AXON Holdings S.A.; *Int'l*, pg. 770
SONAL ADHESIVES LIMITED; *Int'l*, pg. 7088
SONALI POLARIS FT LTD.—See Intellect Design Arena Limited; *Int'l*, pg. 3733
SONALIS CONSUMER PRODUCTS LIMITED; *Int'l*, pg. 7088
SONAL MERCANTILE LIMITED; *Int'l*, pg. 7088
SONALYSTS, INC.; *U.S. Private*, pg. 3712
SONAMAI COMMERCIAL COMPLEX PVT. LTD.—See Laxmi Bank Limited; *Int'l*, pg. 4426
SONA MEDSPA INTERNATIONAL, INC.—See Pharos Capital Group, LLC; *U.S. Private*, pg. 3166
SONAM LTD.; *Int'l*, pg. 7089
SONA MOBILE HOLDINGS, CORP.; *U.S. Private*, pg. 3712
SONA NANOTECH INC.; *Int'l*, pg. 7088
SONA NANOTECH LTD.—See Sona Nanotech Inc.; *Int'l*, pg. 7088
SONANGOL DISTRIBUIDORA S.A.—See Sociedade Nacional de Combustiveis de Angola, E.P.; *Int'l*, pg. 7033
SONANGOL GAS NATURAL LIMITADA—See Sociedade Nacional de Combustiveis de Angola, E.P.; *Int'l*, pg. 7033
SONANS PRIVATGYMNAS AS—See Lumi Gruppen AS; *Int'l*, pg. 4578
SONANT SYSTEMS, INC.; *U.S. Private*, pg. 3712
SONAR BANGLA CAPITAL MANAGEMENT LTD.—See Sonar Bangla Insurance Limited; *Int'l*, pg. 7089
SONAR BANGLA INSURANCE LIMITED; *Int'l*, pg. 7089
SONARDYNE INTERNATIONAL LTD.; *Int'l*, pg. 7089
SONAR ENTERTAINMENT DISTRIBUTION, LLC—See Chicken Soup for the Soul Entertainment, Inc.; *U.S. Public*, pg. 488
SONAR ENTERTAINMENT, INC.—See Chicken Soup for the Soul Entertainment, Inc.; *U.S. Public*, pg. 488
SONAR ENTERTAINMENT, LLC—See Chicken Soup for the Soul Entertainment, Inc.; *U.S. Public*, pg. 488
SONAROME PRIVATE LIMITED—See International Flavors & Fragrances Inc.; *U.S. Public*, pg. 1154
SONAR OY—See ADDvise Group AB; *Int'l*, pg. 136
SONAR RADIO CORP.; *U.S. Public*, pg. 1902
SONARTECH ATLAS PTY. LTD.—See Airbus SE; *Int'l*, pg. 242
SONARTECH ATLAS PTY. LTD.—See ThyssenKrupp AG; *Int'l*, pg. 7723
SONARWA S.A.—See Industrial & General Insurance Plc; *Int'l*, pg. 3671
SONAR & WELL TESTING SERVICES INC.—See United Salt Corporation; *U.S. Private*, pg. 4297
SONASSI LIMITED—See iomart Group plc; *Int'l*, pg. 3793
SONATA EUROPE LIMITED—See Sonata Software Limited; *Int'l*, pg. 7089
SONATA FINANCE PVT. LTD.—See Kotak Mahindra Bank Limited; *Int'l*, pg. 4292
SONATA LEASING-GESELLSCHAFT M.B.H.—See UniCredit S.p.A.; *Int'l*, pg. 8037
SONATA SOFTWARE FZ-LLC—See Sonata Software Limited; *Int'l*, pg. 7089
SONATA SOFTWARE GMBH—See Sonata Software Limited; *Int'l*, pg. 7089
SONATA SOFTWARE LIMITED; *Int'l*, pg. 7089
SONATA SOFTWARE NORTH AMERICA. INC.—See Sonata Software Limited; *Int'l*, pg. 7089

SONATA SOFTWARE LIMITED

SONATA SOFTWARE (QATAR) LLC—See Sonata Software Limited; *Int'l*, pg. 7089
SONATA SOFTWARE SOLUTIONS LIMITED—See Sonata Software Limited; *Int'l*, pg. 7089
SONATECH INC.—See Blue Wolf Capital Partners LLC; *U.S. Private*, pg. 594
SONATIDE MARINE, LTD—See Tidewater Inc.; *U.S. Public*, pg. 2158
SONATRACH INTERNATIONAL HOLDING CORPORATION; *Int'l*, pg. 7089
SONATYPE, INC—See Hummer Winblad Operating Co., LLC; *U.S. Private*, pg. 2007
SONATYPE, INC—See In-Q-Tel, Inc.; *U.S. Private*, pg. 2052
SONAUTA - SOCIEDADE DE NAVEGACAO, LDA.—See Mota-Engil SGPS, S.A.; *Int'l*, pg. 5052
SONAVOX CANADA INC.—See Merry Electronics Co., Ltd.; *Int'l*, pg. 4838
SONAVOX OZ S.R.O.—See Suzhou Sonavox Electronics Co., Ltd.; *Int'l*, pg. 7352
SONAVOX EUROPE GMBH—See Suzhou Sonavox Electronics Co., Ltd.; *Int'l*, pg. 7352
SONAVOX INDUSTRIA E COMERCIO DE ALTO FALANTES LTD.A.—See Suzhou Sonavox Electronics Co., Ltd.; *Int'l*, pg. 7352
SONCA PRODUCTS LIMITED—See Energizer Holdings, Inc.; *U.S. Public*, pg. 761
SONCO WORLDWIDE, INC.; *U.S. Private*, pg. 3712
SONDA ARGENTINA S.A.—See SONDA S.A.; *Int'l*, pg. 7089
SONDA DE COLOMBIA S.A.—See SONDA S.A.; *Int'l*, pg. 7089
SONDA DEL PERU S.A.—See SONDA S.A.; *Int'l*, pg. 7089
SONDA DO BRASIL S.A.—See SONDA S.A.; *Int'l*, pg. 7089
SONDAGENS RODIO LTDA.—See Empresas ICA S.A.B. de C.V.; *Int'l*, pg. 2391
SONDAGSAVISEN A/S—See North Media A/S; *Int'l*, pg. 5441
SONDA MEXICO S.A. DE C.V.—See SONDA S.A.; *Int'l*, pg. 7089
SONDA S.A.; *Int'l*, pg. 7089
SONDA TECNOL DE COSTA RICA S.A.—See SONDA S.A.; *Int'l*, pg. 7089
SONDA URUGUAY S.A.—See SONDA S.A.; *Int'l*, pg. 7089
SONDE HEALTH, INC.—See PureTech Health plc; *U.S. Public*, pg. 1738
SONDERABFALL SERVICE SUDWEST - 3S GMBH—See Alba SE; *Int'l*, pg. 293
SONDERBORG VAERKTOJSFABRIK A/S—See Flex Ltd.; *Int'l*, pg. 2704
SONDERBORG VRKTOJSFABRIK A/S—See Flex Ltd.; *Int'l*, pg. 2704
SONDERHOFF CHEMICALS GMBH—See Henkel AG & Co. KGaA; *Int'l*, pg. 3354
SONDERHOFF ENGINEERING GMBH—See Henkel AG & Co. KGaA; *Int'l*, pg. 3354
SONDERHOFF HOLDING GMBH—See Henkel AG & Co. KGaA; *Int'l*, pg. 3354
SONDERHOFF ITALIA S.R.L.—See Henkel AG & Co. KGaA; *Int'l*, pg. 3354
SONDERHOFF POLYMER-SERVICES AUSTRIA GMBH—See Henkel AG & Co. KGaA; *Int'l*, pg. 3354
SONDERHOFF SERVICES GMBH—See Henkel AG & Co. KGaA; *Int'l*, pg. 3354
SONDERHOFF (SUZHOU) SEALING SYSTEM CO., LTD.—See Henkel AG & Co. KGaA; *Int'l*, pg. 3354
SONDERHOFF USA LLC—See Henkel AG & Co. KGaA; *Int'l*, pg. 3353
SONDER HOLDINGS, INC.; *U.S. Public*, pg. 1902
SONDERMIND, INC.; *U.S. Private*, pg. 3712
SONDERSCHRAUBEN GULDNER GMBH & CO. KG—See Wurth Verwaltungsgesellschaft mbH; *Int'l*, pg. 8507
SONDERSCHRAUBEN HAMBURG GMBH EIBEN & CO.—See Wurth Verwaltungsgesellschaft mbH; *Int'l*, pg. 8508
SONDEX A/S; *Int'l*, pg. 7089
SONDEX INC.—See Sondex A/S; *Int'l*, pg. 7089
SONDEX LIMITED—See General Electric Company; *U.S. Public*, pg. 920
SONDOTECNICA ENGENHARIA DE SOLOS S.A.; *Int'l*, pg. 7089
SONECABLE—See Sonepar S.A.; *Int'l*, pg. 7091
SONEC CORPORATION; *Int'l*, pg. 7090
SONEE HARDWARE PVT. LTD.—See Leifheit AG; *Int'l*, pg. 4447
SONEL INSTRUMENTS INDIA PRIVATE LIMITED—See Sonel S.A.; *Int'l*, pg. 7090
SONEL S.A.; *Int'l*, pg. 7090
SONEL TEST & MEASUREMENT, INC.; *U.S. Private*, pg. 3712
SONENDO, INC.; *U.S. Public*, pg. 1902
SONEPAR BELGIUM—See Sonepar S.A.; *Int'l*, pg. 7091
SONEPAR CANADA, INC. - SESCO DIVISION—See Sonepar S.A.; *Int'l*, pg. 7091
SONEPAR CANADA, INC. - TEXCAN ONTARIO DIVISION—See Sonepar S.A.; *Int'l*, pg. 7091
SONEPAR CANADA—See Sonepar S.A.; *Int'l*, pg. 7091

SONEPAR CESKA REPUBLIKA SPOL. S. R.O.—See Sonepar S.A.; *Int'l*, pg. 7091
SONEPAR CHINA—See Sonepar S.A.; *Int'l*, pg. 7091
SONEPAR DEUTSCHLAND CABLE SERVICES GMBH—See Sonepar S.A.; *Int'l*, pg. 7092
SONEPAR DEUTSCHLAND ERNEUERBARE ENERGIEN GMBH—See Sonepar S.A.; *Int'l*, pg. 7092
SONEPAR DEUTSCHLAND GMBH—See Sonepar S.A.; *Int'l*, pg. 7092
SONEPAR ELAR—See Sonepar S.A.; *Int'l*, pg. 7092
SONEPAR ELTRA—See Sonepar S.A.; *Int'l*, pg. 7091
SONEPAR FRANCE REGION ILE-DE-FRANCE—See Sonepar S.A.; *Int'l*, pg. 7092
SONEPAR FRANCE REGION MEDITERRANEE—See Sonepar S.A.; *Int'l*, pg. 7092
SONEPAR FRANCE—See Sonepar S.A.; *Int'l*, pg. 7092
SONEPAR HUNGARY KFT—See Sonepar S.A.; *Int'l*, pg. 7092
SONEPAR IBERICA S.A.—See Sonepar S.A.; *Int'l*, pg. 7092
SONEPAR IMMOBILIARE E DI SERVIZI—See Sonepar S.A.; *Int'l*, pg. 7092
SONEPAR ITALIA S.P.A.—See Sonepar S.A.; *Int'l*, pg. 7092
SONEPAR MEXICO—See Sonepar S.A.; *Int'l*, pg. 7092
SONEPAR NEDERLAND INFORMATION SERVICES B.V.—See Sonepar S.A.; *Int'l*, pg. 7092
SONEPAR NEDERLAND—See Sonepar S.A.; *Int'l*, pg. 7092
SONEPAR OSTERREICH GMBH—See Sonepar S.A.; *Int'l*, pg. 7092
SONEPAR PUGLIA S.P.A.—See Sonepar S.A.; *Int'l*, pg. 7092
SONEPAR SARDEGNA S.P.A.—See Sonepar S.A.; *Int'l*, pg. 7092
SONEPAR S.A.; *Int'l*, pg. 7090
SONEPAR SOUTH AMERICA PARTICIPACOES LTDA.—See Sonepar S.A.; *Int'l*, pg. 7092
SONEPAR SWITZERLAND—See Sonepar S.A.; *Int'l*, pg. 7093
SONEPAR USA, INC.—See Sonepar S.A.; *Int'l*, pg. 7093
SONERI BANK LIMITED; *Int'l*, pg. 7094
SONESTA BAYFRONT HOTEL COCONUT GROVE—See The RMR Group Inc.; *U.S. Public*, pg. 2126
SONESTA INTERNATIONAL HOTELS CORPORATION—See The RMR Group Inc.; *U.S. Public*, pg. 2126
SONETEL AB; *Int'l*, pg. 7094
SO-NET ENTERTAINMENT TAIWAN LIMITED—See Sony Group Corporation; *Int'l*, pg. 7107
SONETTE, INC.; *U.S. Private*, pg. 3712
SONGAS LIMITED—See General Atlantic Service Company, L.P.; *U.S. Private*, pg. 1661
SONG BA JOINT STOCK COMPANY; *Int'l*, pg. 7094
SONGCHENG PERFORMANCE DEVELOPMENT CO., LTD.; *Int'l*, pg. 7095
SONG DA 1.01 JSC; *Int'l*, pg. 7094
SONG DA 10 JOINT STOCK COMPANY; *Int'l*, pg. 7094
SONG DA 11 THANG LONG COMPANY LIMITED; *Int'l*, pg. 7094
SONG DA 12 JSC; *Int'l*, pg. 7094
SONG DA 207 JOINT STOCK COMPANY—See Song Da Holdings; *Int'l*, pg. 7095
SONG DA 505 JOINT STOCK COMPANY—See Song Da 5 Joint Stock Company; *Int'l*, pg. 7094
SONG DA 5 JOINT STOCK COMPANY; *Int'l*, pg. 7094
SONGDA 7 JSC; *Int'l*, pg. 7096
SONG DA 9.06 JOINT STOCK COMPANY; *Int'l*, pg. 7095
SONG DA 9 JOINT STOCK COMPANY; *Int'l*, pg. 7094
SONG DA ASSEMBLY CONSTRUCTION & INVESTMENT JSC; *Int'l*, pg. 7095
SONG DA CAO CUONG JSC; *Int'l*, pg. 7095
SONG DA CONSULTING JOINT - STOCK COMPANY; *Int'l*, pg. 7095
SONG DA-HOANG LIEN JSC—See SONG DA 9 JOINT STOCK COMPANY; *Int'l*, pg. 7095
SONG DA HOLDINGS; *Int'l*, pg. 7095
SONG DA INDUSTRY TRADE JOINT STOCK COMPANY; *Int'l*, pg. 7095
SONG DA MECHANICAL-ASSEMBLING JOINT STOCK CO.—See Song Da Holdings; *Int'l*, pg. 7095
SONG DA N 9 MACHINERY AND REPAIRING CO. LTD—See SONG DA 9 JOINT STOCK COMPANY; *Int'l*, pg. 7095
SONG DA NO. 11 JSC; *Int'l*, pg. 7095
SONG DA NO 6 JOINT STOCK COMPANY—See Song Da Holdings; *Int'l*, pg. 7095
SONG DA-THANG LONG JOINT STOCK COMPANY; *Int'l*, pg. 7095
SONG DA - THANH HOA JSC; *Int'l*, pg. 7094
SONG DA TRANSPORTATION CONSTRUCTION JSC; *Int'l*, pg. 7095
SONG DA URBAN & INDUSTRIAL ZONE INVESTMENT & DEVELOPMENT JOINT STOCK COMPANY; *Int'l*, pg. 7095
SONG HO INDUSTRIAL CO., LTD.; *Int'l*, pg. 7095
SONG HONG CONSTRUCTION JOINT STOCK COMPANY; *Int'l*, pg. 7095

CORPORATE AFFILIATIONS

SONGKLA CANNING PCL—See Thai Union Group Public Company Limited; *Int'l*, pg. 7596
SONGKLA FISHING CO., LTD—See Thai Union Group Public Company Limited; *Int'l*, pg. 7597
SONGLIM FOOD CO., LTD.—See CJ Corporation; *Int'l*, pg. 1634
SONG LOGGING COMPANY SENDIRIAN BERHAD—See W T K Holdings Berhad; *Int'l*, pg. 8320
SONG SHANG ELECTRONICS CO., LTD.; *Int'l*, pg. 7095
SONG TIEN SAIGON BEER TRADING JOINT STOCK COMPANY—See Saigon Beer Alcohol Beverage Corp.; *Int'l*, pg. 6483
SONGTRADR, INC.; *U.S. Private*, pg. 3713
SONGWON INDUSTRIAL CO., LTD.; *Int'l*, pg. 7096
SONGWON INTERNATIONAL AG—See Songwon Industrial Co., Ltd.; *Int'l*, pg. 7096
SONGWON INTERNATIONAL AMERICAS, INC.—See Songwon Industrial Co., Ltd.; *Int'l*, pg. 7096
SONGWON INTERNATIONAL - INDIA PVT. LTD.—See Songwon Industrial Co., Ltd.; *Int'l*, pg. 7096
SONGWON INTERNATIONAL - JAPAN K.K.—See Songwon Industrial Co., Ltd.; *Int'l*, pg. 7096
SONGWON SPECIALTY CHEMICALS INDIA PVT. LTD.—See Songwon Industrial Co., Ltd.; *Int'l*, pg. 7096
SONGWON TRADING CO. LTD.—See Songwon Industrial Co., Ltd.; *Int'l*, pg. 7096
SONGZ AUTOMOBILE AIR CONDITIONING CO., LTD.—See Shanghai Dazhong Public Utilities (Group) Co., Ltd.; *Int'l*, pg. 6765
SONGZHI KALLANG AUTOMOTIVE AIR CONDITIONING CO., LTD.; *Int'l*, pg. 7096
SON HA INTERNATIONAL JOINT STOCK COMPANY; *Int'l*, pg. 7087
SON HA SAI GON JSC; *Int'l*, pg. 7087
SON HA SPICE & FLAVORINGS CO., LTD.—See Mitani Corporation; *Int'l*, pg. 4924
SONIA FRIEDMAN PRODUCTIONS LTD—See Ambassador Theatre Group Limited; *Int'l*, pg. 414
SONIBETICA—See Sonepar S.A.; *Int'l*, pg. 7092
SONIC AUTOMATION LTD.—See Sonepar S.A.; *Int'l*, pg. 7094
SONIC AUTOMOTIVE F&I, LLC—See Sonic Automotive, Inc.; *U.S. Public*, pg. 1902
SONIC AUTOMOTIVE, INC.; *U.S. Public*, pg. 1902
SONICBIDS CORPORATION—See Guggenheim Partners, LLC; *U.S. Private*, pg. 1811
SONIC BOOM WELLNESS, INC.—See Ontario Municipal Employees Retirement System; *Int'l*, pg. 5584
SONIC CLINICAL SERVICES PTY LIMITED—See Sonic Healthcare Limited; *Int'l*, pg. 7098
SONIC CLINICAL TRIALS PTY LIMITED—See Sonic Healthcare Limited; *Int'l*, pg. 7098
SONIC CORPORATION—See Roark Capital Group Inc.; *U.S. Private*, pg. 3455
SONIC-CREST CADILLAC, LLC—See Sonic Automotive, Inc.; *U.S. Public*, pg. 1902
SONIC DEVELOPMENT, LLC—See Sonic Automotive, Inc.; *U.S. Public*, pg. 1902
SONIC FINANCIAL CORPORATION; *U.S. Private*, pg. 3713
SONIC FOUNDRY, INC.; *U.S. Public*, pg. 1903
SONIC FOUNDRY INTERNATIONAL B.V.—See Enghouse Systems Limited; *Int'l*, pg. 2427
SONIC FOUNDRY MEDIA SYSTEMS, INC.—See Sonic Foundry, Inc.; *U.S. Public*, pg. 1903
SONIC HEALTHCARE AUSTRALIA PATHOLOGY PTY LIMITED—See Sonic Healthcare Limited; *Int'l*, pg. 7098
SONIC HEALTHCARE AUSTRALIA RADIOLOGY PTY LIMITED—See Sonic Healthcare Limited; *Int'l*, pg. 7098
SONIC HEALTHCARE LIMITED; *Int'l*, pg. 7096
SONIC HEALTHCARE SERVICES PTY LIMITED—See Sonic Healthcare Limited; *Int'l*, pg. 7098
SONIC HEALTHCARE USA, INC.—See Sonic Healthcare Limited; *Int'l*, pg. 7098
SONIC HEALTHPLUS - NAVAL BASE—See Sonic Healthcare Limited; *Int'l*, pg. 7098
SONIC HEALTHPLUS PTY LIMITED—See Sonic Healthcare Limited; *Int'l*, pg. 7098
SONIC INDUSTRIES, INC.—See Roark Capital Group Inc.; *U.S. Private*, pg. 3455
SONIC INNOVATIONS CANADA LTD.—See Demant A/S; *Int'l*, pg. 2024
SONIC INNOVATIONS PTY LTD.—See Demant A/S; *Int'l*, pg. 2024
SONIC INTERFREIGHT PUBLIC CO., LTD.; *Int'l*, pg. 7099
SONIC - LONE TREE CADILLAC, INC.—See Sonic Automotive, Inc.; *U.S. Public*, pg. 1902
SONIC - LUTE RILEY, LP—See Sonic Automotive, Inc.; *U.S. Public*, pg. 1902
SONIC MANAGEMENT; *U.S. Private*, pg. 3713
SONIC MERRITTED GROUP; *U.S. Private*, pg. 3713
SONIC MOMENTUM VWA, LP—See Sonic Automotive, Inc.; *U.S. Public*, pg. 1902
SONIC-NORTH CADILLAC, INC.—See Sonic Automotive, Inc.; *U.S. Public*, pg. 1902
SONIC NURSE CONNECT PTY. LIMITED—See Sonic Healthcare Limited; *Int'l*, pg. 7098
SONIC PATHOLOGY AUSTRALIA PTY LIMITED—See Sonic Healthcare Limited; *Int'l*, pg. 7098

COMPANY NAME INDEX

SONIC PROMOS; *U.S. Private*, pg. 3713
SONICS, INC.; *U.S. Private*, pg. 3714
SONICS & MATERIALS, INC.-EUROPEAN OFFICE—See Sonics & Materials, Inc.; *U.S. Private*, pg. 3713
SONICS & MATERIALS, INC.; *U.S. Private*, pg. 3713
SONIC SOLUTIONS LLC—See Adeia Inc.; *U.S. Public*, pg. 41
SONIC - UNIVERSITY PARK A, LP—See Sonic Automotive, Inc.; *U.S. Public*, pg. 1902
SONICWALL B.V.—See Dell Technologies Inc.; *U.S. Public*, pg. 650
SONIDA SENIOR LIVING, INC.; *U.S. Public*, pg. 1903
SONID INC; *Int'l*, pg. 7099
SONIFI SOLUTIONS, INC.; *U.S. Private*, pg. 3714
SONIL—See VINCI S.A.; *Int'l*, pg. 8229
SONIMED DIAGNOSTICOS LTDA.—See Centro de Imagem Diagnosticos S.A.; *Int'l*, pg. 1414
SONI MEDICARE LIMITED; *Int'l*, pg. 7096
SONIM TECHNOLOGIES, INC.; *U.S. Public*, pg. 1903
SONIM TECHNOLOGIES (INDIA) PRIVATE LIMITED—See Sonim Technologies, Inc.; *U.S. Public*, pg. 1903
SONIM TECHNOLOGIES (SHENZHEN) LIMITED—See Sonim Technologies, Inc.; *U.S. Public*, pg. 1903
SONINFO—See Sonepar S.A.; *Int'l*, pg. 7094
SONION A/S—See Novo Nordisk Fonden; *Int'l*, pg. 5465
SONION US, INC.—See Novo Nordisk Fonden; *Int'l*, pg. 5465
SONION VIETNAM CO LTD—See Novo Nordisk Fonden; *Int'l*, pg. 5465
SONIQUE LTD; *Int'l*, pg. 7099
SONI SOYA PRODUCTS LLC—See Soni Soya Products Ltd.; *Int'l*, pg. 7096
SONI SOYA PRODUCTS LTD.; *Int'l*, pg. 7096
SONITEL S.A.—See Liberty Global plc; *Int'l*, pg. 4485
SONITROL DISTRIBUTION CANADA, INC.—See Stanley Black & Decker, Inc.; *U.S. Public*, pg. 1934
SONITROL FRANCHISE COMPANY, L.L.C.—See Stanley Black & Decker, Inc.; *U.S. Public*, pg. 1934
SONITROL SECURITY SYSTEMS OF BUFFALO, INC.—See Stanley Black & Decker, Inc.; *U.S. Public*, pg. 1934
SONIX, INC.—See Danaher Corporation; *U.S. Public*, pg. 631
SONIX TECHNOLOGY (CHENGDU) CO., LTD.—See Sonix Technology Co., Ltd.; *Int'l*, pg. 7099
SONIX TECHNOLOGY CO., LTD.; *Int'l*, pg. 7099
SONIX TECHNOLOGY KK—See Sonix Technology Co., Ltd.; *Int'l*, pg. 7099
SONIX TECHNOLOGY (SHENZHEN) CO., LTD—See Sonix Technology Co., Ltd.; *Int'l*, pg. 7099
SONJU TWO HARBORS LLC; *U.S. Private*, pg. 3714
SONKE PHARMACEUTICALS PROPRIETARY LIMITED—See Sun Pharmaceutical Industries Ltd.; *Int'l*, pg. 7307
SON LA SUGAR JOINT STOCK COMPANY; *Int'l*, pg. 7088
SONMEZ AIRLINES INC.—See Sonmez Pamuklu Sanayii AS; *Int'l*, pg. 7099
SONMEZ CEMENT BUILDING & MINING INDUSTRY & TRADE INC.—See Sonmez Pamuklu Sanayii AS; *Int'l*, pg. 7099
SONMEZ CONSTRUCTION INC.—See Sonmez Pamuklu Sanayii AS; *Int'l*, pg. 7099
SONMEZ ENERGY ELECTRICITY WHOLESALE TRADE INC.—See Sonmez Pamuklu Sanayii AS; *Int'l*, pg. 7099
SONMEZ FILAMENT SENTETIK IPLIK VE ELYAF SANAYI AS; *Int'l*, pg. 7099
SONMEZ FILAMENT SYNTHETIC THREAD INDUSTRY INC.—See Sonmez Pamuklu Sanayii AS; *Int'l*, pg. 7099
SONMEZ FOOD TOURISM & TRADE INC.—See Sonmez Pamuklu Sanayii AS; *Int'l*, pg. 7099
SONMEZ-KOC AUTOMOTIVE TRADE INC.—See Sonmez Pamuklu Sanayii AS; *Int'l*, pg. 7099
SONMEZ PAMUKLU SANAYII AS; *Int'l*, pg. 7099
SONMEZ PETROL INDUSTRY & TRADE LTD.—See Sonmez Pamuklu Sanayii AS; *Int'l*, pg. 7099
SONNAX INDUSTRIES, INC.; *U.S. Private*, pg. 3714
SONNEBORN, LLC; *U.S. Private*, pg. 3714
SONNEBORN REFINED PRODUCTS B.V.—See Sonneborn, LLC; *U.S. Private*, pg. 3714
SONNEMAN DESIGN GROUP, INC—See Dunes Point Capital, LLC; *U.S. Private*, pg. 1289
SONNENALP PROPERTIES INC.; *U.S. Private*, pg. 3714
SONNENALP REAL ESTATE—See Sonnenalp Properties Inc.; *U.S. Private*, pg. 3714
SONNEN AUDI VOLKSWAGEN; *U.S. Private*, pg. 3714
SONNEN AUSTRALIA PTY LIMITED—See Shell plc; *Int'l*, pg. 6800
SONNEN S.R.L.—See Shell plc; *Int'l*, pg. 6800
SONNET BIOTHERAPEUTICS HOLDINGS, INC.; *U.S. Public*, pg. 1903
SONNET BIOTHERAPEUTICS, INC.—See Sonnet Biotherapeutics Holdings, Inc.; *U.S. Public*, pg. 1904
SONNEVELD FRANCE SARL—See Orkla ASA; *Int'l*, pg. 5639
SONNEVELD GROUP B.V.—See Orkla ASA; *Int'l*, pg. 5639
SONNEVELD KFT.—See Orkla ASA; *Int'l*, pg. 5639

SONNEVELD NVSA—See Orkla ASA; *Int'l*, pg. 5639
SONNEVILLE AG—See Vicat S.A.; *Int'l*, pg. 8186
SONNEX INVESTMENTS (PTY.) LTD.—See Barloworld Ltd.; *Int'l*, pg. 866
SONNHALTER; *U.S. Private*, pg. 3714
SONNICO AS—See Umoe Gruppen AS; *Int'l*, pg. 8026
SONNIMAX A/S—See INDUS Holding AG; *Int'l*, pg. 3664
SONNTAGSZEITUNG AG—See TX Group AG; *Int'l*, pg. 7992
SONNY CANNON AUTO PLAZA INC.; *U.S. Private*, pg. 3714
SONNY'S ENTERPRISES INC.; *U.S. Private*, pg. 3714
SONNY'S FRANCHISE COMPANY INC.; *U.S. Private*, pg. 3714
SONNYS HOME CENTER INC.; *U.S. Private*, pg. 3714
SONNY'S REAL PIT BAR-B-QUE; *U.S. Private*, pg. 3714
SONOACE DEUTSCHLAND GMBH—See Samsung Group; *Int'l*, pg. 6513
SONOCAS S.A.S.; *Int'l*, pg. 7099
SONOCO ALCORE AB—See Sonoco Products Company; *U.S. Public*, pg. 1906
SONOCO ALCORE GMBH—See Sonoco Products Company; *U.S. Public*, pg. 1905
SONOCO ALCORE GMBH—See Sonoco Products Company; *U.S. Public*, pg. 1906
SONOCO ALCORE NV—See Sonoco Products Company; *U.S. Public*, pg. 1906
SONOCO-ALCORE OU—See Sonoco Products Company; *U.S. Public*, pg. 1908
SONOCO-ALCORE OY—See Sonoco Products Company; *U.S. Public*, pg. 1909
SONOCO-ALCORE SP. Z.O.O.—See Sonoco Products Company; *U.S. Public*, pg. 1909
SONOCO ALLOYD-BATAVIA—See Sonoco Products Company; *U.S. Public*, pg. 1905
SONOCO AMBALAJ SANAYI VE TICARET A.S.—See Sonoco Products Company; *U.S. Public*, pg. 1906
SONOCO ASIA L.L.C.—See Sonoco Products Company; *U.S. Public*, pg. 1905
SONOCO AT WHIRLPOOL—See Sonoco Products Company; *U.S. Public*, pg. 1908
SONOCO AUSTRALIA PTY. LTD.—See Sonoco Products Company; *U.S. Public*, pg. 1905
SONOCO AUSTRALIA PTY. LTD.—See Sonoco Products Company; *U.S. Public*, pg. 1905
SONOCO AUSTRALIA PTY. LTD. - WODONGA—See Sonoco Products Company; *U.S. Public*, pg. 1905
SONOCO BAKER—See Sonoco Products Company; *U.S. Public*, pg. 1908
SONOCO BAKER—See Sonoco Products Company; *U.S. Public*, pg. 1908
SONOCO BAKER—See Sonoco Products Company; *U.S. Public*, pg. 1908
SONOCO BOARD MILLS LIMITED—See Sonoco Products Company; *U.S. Public*, pg. 1906
SONOCO CANADA CORPORATION—See Sonoco Products Company; *U.S. Public*, pg. 1905
SONOCO CANADA CORPORATION—See Sonoco Products Company; *U.S. Public*, pg. 1905
SONOCO CANADA CORPORATION—See Sonoco Products Company; *U.S. Public*, pg. 1905
SONOCO CANADA CORPORATION—See Sonoco Products Company; *U.S. Public*, pg. 1905
SONOCO CANADA CORPORATION—See Sonoco Products Company; *U.S. Public*, pg. 1905
SONOCO CANADA CORPORATION—See Sonoco Products Company; *U.S. Public*, pg. 1905
SONOCO CANADA CORPORATION—See Sonoco Products Company; *U.S. Public*, pg. 1905
SONOCO CANADA CORPORATION—See Sonoco Products Company; *U.S. Public*, pg. 1905
SONOCO CANADA CORPORATION—See Sonoco Products Company; *U.S. Public*, pg. 1905
SONOCO CAPREX AG—See Sonoco Products Company; *U.S. Public*, pg. 1906
SONOCO CLEAR PACK—See Sonoco Products Company; *U.S. Public*, pg. 1906
SONOCO COMERCIAL S. DE R.L. DE C.V.—See Sonoco Products Company; *U.S. Public*, pg. 1906
SONOCO CONSUMER PRODUCTS DORDRECHT B.V.—See Sonoco Products Company; *U.S. Public*, pg. 1906
SONOCO CONSUMER PRODUCTS EUROPE GMBH—See Sonoco Products Company; *U.S. Public*, pg. 1906
SONOCO CONSUMER PRODUCTS LTD.—See Sonoco Products Company; *U.S. Public*, pg. 1906
SONOCO CONSUMER PRODUCTS MECHELEN BVBA—See Sonoco Products Company; *U.S. Public*, pg. 1906
SONOCO CONSUMER PRODUCTS MONTANAY SAS—See Sonoco Products Company; *U.S. Public*, pg. 1906
SONOCO CONSUMER PRODUCTS N.V.—See Sonoco Products Company; *U.S. Public*, pg. 1906
SONOCO CONSUMER PRODUCTS—See Sonoco Products Company; *U.S. Public*, pg. 1906

SONOCOM CO., LTD.

SONOCO CONTRACT SERVICES S. DE R.L. DE C.V.—See Sonoco Products Company; *U.S. Public*, pg. 1906
SONOCO-CORRFLEX—See Sonoco Products Company; *U.S. Public*, pg. 1909
SONOCO-CORRFLEX—See Sonoco Products Company; *U.S. Public*, pg. 1909
SONOCO DE COLOMBIA LTDA.—See Sonoco Products Company; *U.S. Public*, pg. 1908
SONOCO DE MEXICO, S.A. DE C.V.—See Sonoco Products Company; *U.S. Public*, pg. 1908
SONOCO DE MEXICO, S.A. DE C.V.—See Sonoco Products Company; *U.S. Public*, pg. 1908
SONOCO DE MEXICO, S.A. DE C.V.—See Sonoco Products Company; *U.S. Public*, pg. 1908
SONOCO DEUTSCHLAND GMBH—See Sonoco Products Company; *U.S. Public*, pg. 1906
SONOCO DEUTSCHLAND HOLDINGS GMBH—See Sonoco Products Company; *U.S. Public*, pg. 1906
SONOCO DISPLAY AND PACKAGING, LLC—See Sonoco Products Company; *U.S. Public*, pg. 1906
SONOCO DO BRASIL PARTICIPACOES LTDA—See Sonoco Products Company; *U.S. Public*, pg. 1908
SONOCO DO BRAZIL LTDA.—See Sonoco Products Company; *U.S. Public*, pg. 1908
SONOCO DO BRAZIL LTDA.—See Sonoco Products Company; *U.S. Public*, pg. 1908
SONOCO DO CHILE S.A.—See Sonoco Products Company; *U.S. Public*, pg. 1908
SONOCO FLEXIBLE PACKAGING CANADA CORPORATION—See Sonoco Products Company; *U.S. Public*, pg. 1906
SONOCO FLEXIBLE PACKAGING LIMITED—See Sonoco Products Company; *U.S. Public*, pg. 1906
SONOCO FLEXIBLE PACKAGING—See Sonoco Products Company; *U.S. Public*, pg. 1906
SONOCO FLEXIBLE PACKAGING—See Sonoco Products Company; *U.S. Public*, pg. 1906
SONOCO FOR PLAS DO BRAZIL LTDA—See Sonoco Products Company; *U.S. Public*, pg. 1906
SONOCO HAYES, INC.—See Sonoco Products Company; *U.S. Public*, pg. 1906
SONOCO HICKORY, INC.—See Sonoco Products Company; *U.S. Public*, pg. 1906
SONOCO HOLDINGS (UK) LTD.—See Sonoco Products Company; *U.S. Public*, pg. 1906
SONOCO HUTCHINSON, LLC—See Sonoco Products Company; *U.S. Public*, pg. 1906
SONOCO, INC.—See Sonoco Products Company; *U.S. Public*, pg. 1908
SONOCO INTERNATIONAL, INC.—See Sonoco Products Company; *U.S. Public*, pg. 1905
SONOCO IPD FRANCE S.A.—See Sonoco Products Company; *U.S. Public*, pg. 1906
SONOCO LTD.—See Sonoco Products Company; *U.S. Public*, pg. 1907
SONOCO LURGAN—See Sonoco Products Company; *U.S. Public*, pg. 1906
SONOCO LUXEMBOURG S.A.R.L.—See Sonoco Products Company; *U.S. Public*, pg. 1906
SONOCO MACHINERY INC.—See Sonoco Products Company; *U.S. Public*, pg. 1905
SONOCOM CO., LTD.; *Int'l*, pg. 7099
SONOCO METAL PACKAGING, LLC—See Sonoco Products Company; *U.S. Public*, pg. 1907
SONOCO MILNROW—See Sonoco Products Company; *U.S. Public*, pg. 1906
SONOCO NETHERLANDS B.V.—See Sonoco Products Company; *U.S. Public*, pg. 1907
SONOCO NEW ZEALAND LTD.—See Sonoco Products Company; *U.S. Public*, pg. 1905
SONOCO NEW ZEALAND LTD.—See Sonoco Products Company; *U.S. Public*, pg. 1905
SONOCO NORGE A/S—See Sonoco Products Company; *U.S. Public*, pg. 1907
SONOCO OF PUERTO RICO, INC.—See Sonoco Products Company; *U.S. Public*, pg. 1908
SONOCO OPV HUELSEN GMBH—See Sonoco Products Company; *U.S. Public*, pg. 1906
SONOCO PACKAGING SERVICES—See Sonoco Products Company; *U.S. Public*, pg. 1907
SONOCO PAPERBOARD SPECIALTIES—See Sonoco Products Company; *U.S. Public*, pg. 1907
SONOCO PAPERBOARD SPECIALTIES—See Sonoco Products Company; *U.S. Public*, pg. 1907
SONOCO PAPER MILL & IPD HELLAS SA—See Sonoco Products Company; *U.S. Public*, pg. 1907
SONOCO PAPER—See Sonoco Products Company; *U.S. Public*, pg. 1907
SONOCO PINA S.A.—See Sonoco Products Company; *U.S. Public*, pg. 1906
SONOCO PLASTICS B.V.—See Sonoco Products Company; *U.S. Public*, pg. 1907
SONOCO PLASTICS GERMANY GMBH—See Sonoco Products Company; *U.S. Public*, pg. 1906
SONOCO PLASTICS GERMANY GMBH—See Sonoco Products Company; *U.S. Public*, pg. 1906

SONOCOM CO., LTD. — CORPORATE AFFILIATIONS

SONOCO PRODUCTS COMPANY - BAKER DIVISION—See Sonoco Products Company; *U.S. Public*, pg. 1908
SONOCO PRODUCTS COMPANY - I.P.D. DIVISION—See Sonoco Products Company; *U.S. Public*, pg. 1908
SONOCO PRODUCTS COMPANY - JACKSON—See Sonoco Products Company; *U.S. Public*, pg. 1908
SONOCO PRODUCTS COMPANY - ORLANDO—See Sonoco Products Company; *U.S. Public*, pg. 1908
SONOCO PRODUCTS COMPANY; *U.S. Public*, pg. 1904
SONOCO PRODUCTS COMPANY—See Sonoco Products Company; *U.S. Public*, pg. 1907
SONOCO PRODUCTS COMPANY—See Sonoco Products Company; *U.S. Public*, pg. 1907
SONOCO PRODUCTS COMPANY—See Sonoco Products Company; *U.S. Public*, pg. 1907
SONOCO PRODUCTS COMPANY—See Sonoco Products Company; *U.S. Public*, pg. 1907
SONOCO PRODUCTS COMPANY—See Sonoco Products Company; *U.S. Public*, pg. 1907
SONOCO PRODUCTS COMPANY—See Sonoco Products Company; *U.S. Public*, pg. 1907
SONOCO PRODUCTS COMPANY—See Sonoco Products Company; *U.S. Public*, pg. 1907
SONOCO PRODUCTS COMPANY—See Sonoco Products Company; *U.S. Public*, pg. 1907
SONOCO PRODUCTS COMPANY—See Sonoco Products Company; *U.S. Public*, pg. 1907
SONOCO PRODUCTS COMPANY—See Sonoco Products Company; *U.S. Public*, pg. 1907
SONOCO PRODUCTS COMPANY—See Sonoco Products Company; *U.S. Public*, pg. 1907
SONOCO PRODUCTS COMPANY—See Sonoco Products Company; *U.S. Public*, pg. 1908
SONOCO PRODUCTS COMPANY—See Sonoco Products Company; *U.S. Public*, pg. 1908
SONOCO PRODUCTS COMPANY—See Sonoco Products Company; *U.S. Public*, pg. 1908
SONOCO PRODUCTS COMPANY—See Sonoco Products Company; *U.S. Public*, pg. 1908
SONOCO PRODUCTS COMPANY—See Sonoco Products Company; *U.S. Public*, pg. 1908
SONOCO PRODUCTS COMPANY—See Sonoco Products Company; *U.S. Public*, pg. 1907
SONOCO PRODUCTS COMPANY—See Sonoco Products Company; *U.S. Public*, pg. 1907
SONOCO PRODUCTS COMPANY—See Sonoco Products Company; *U.S. Public*, pg. 1907
SONOCO PRODUCTS COMPANY—See Sonoco Products Company; *U.S. Public*, pg. 1907
SONOCO PRODUCTS COMPANY—See Sonoco Products Company; *U.S. Public*, pg. 1907
SONOCO PRODUCTS COMPANY—See Sonoco Products Company; *U.S. Public*, pg. 1907
SONOCO PRODUCTS COMPANY—See Sonoco Products Company; *U.S. Public*, pg. 1907
SONOCO PRODUCTS COMPANY—See Sonoco Products Company; *U.S. Public*, pg. 1907
SONOCO PRODUCTS COMPANY—See Sonoco Products Company; *U.S. Public*, pg. 1907
SONOCO PRODUCTS COMPANY—See Sonoco Products Company; *U.S. Public*, pg. 1907
SONOCO PRODUCTS COMPANY—See Sonoco Products Company; *U.S. Public*, pg. 1908
SONOCO PRODUCTS COMPANY—See Sonoco Products Company; *U.S. Public*, pg. 1908
SONOCO PRODUCTS COMPANY—See Sonoco Products Company; *U.S. Public*, pg. 1908
SONOCO PRODUCTS COMPANY—See Sonoco Products Company; *U.S. Public*, pg. 1908
SONOCO PRODUCTS COMPANY—See Sonoco Products Company; *U.S. Public*, pg. 1908
SONOCO PRODUCTS COMPANY—See Sonoco Products Company; *U.S. Public*, pg. 1907
SONOCO PRODUCTS COMPANY—See Sonoco Products Company; *U.S. Public*, pg. 1907
SONOCO PRODUCTS COMPANY—See Sonoco Products Company; *U.S. Public*, pg. 1907
SONOCO PRODUCTS COMPANY—See Sonoco Products Company; *U.S. Public*, pg. 1907
SONOCO PRODUCTS COMPANY—See Sonoco Products Company; *U.S. Public*, pg. 1908
SONOCO PRODUCTS COMPANY—See Sonoco Products Company; *U.S. Public*, pg. 1908
SONOCO PRODUCTS CO. UK UNLIMITED—See Sonoco Products Company; *U.S. Public*, pg. 1907
SONOCO PRODUCTS MALAYSIA SDN BHD—See Sonoco Products Company; *U.S. Public*, pg. 1905
SONOCO RECYCLING, INC.—See Sonoco Products Company; *U.S. Public*, pg. 1908
SONOCO RECYCLING—See Sonoco Products Company; *U.S. Public*, pg. 1907
SONOCO RIGID PLASTICS—See Sonoco Products Company; *U.S. Public*, pg. 1908
SONOCO, S.A. DE C.V.—See Sonoco Products Company; *U.S. Public*, pg. 1908
SONOCO SINGAPORE PTE. LTD.—See Sonoco Products Company; *U.S. Public*, pg. 1905
SONOCO TAIWAN LIMITED—See Sonoco Products Company; *U.S. Public*, pg. 1905
SONOCO THAILAND LIMITED—See Sonoco Products Company; *U.S. Public*, pg. 1905
SONOCO VENEZOLANA C.A.—See Sonoco Products Company; *U.S. Public*, pg. 1908
SONODEPOT, INC.—See Avista Capital Partners, L.P.; *U.S. Private*, pg. 408
SONO GROUP N.V.; *Int'l*, pg. 7099
SONOKONG CO., LTD.; *Int'l*, pg. 7099
SONOL ISRAEL, LTD.; *Int'l*, pg. 7099
SONOMA BRANDS LLC; *U.S. Private*, pg. 3714
SONOMA-CUTRER VINEYARDS, INC.—See The Duckhorn Portfolio, Inc.; *U.S. Public*, pg. 2067
SONOMA GOLF CLUB, LLC—See Goff Capital, Inc.; *U.S. Private*, pg. 1726
SONOMA INTERNET GMBH—See ProSiebenSat.1 Media SE; *Int'l*, pg. 6001
SONOMA MARKET INC.—See Nugget Market Inc.; *U.S. Private*, pg. 2973
SONOMA PARTNERS, LLC; *U.S. Private*, pg. 3714
SONOMA PHARMACEUTICALS, INC.; *U.S. Public*, pg. 1909
SONOMA PHARMACEUTICALS NETHERLANDS B.V.—See Sonoma Pharmaceuticals, Inc.; *U.S. Public*, pg. 1909
SONOMA RISK MANAGEMENT, LLC—See Brookfield Reinsurance Ltd.; *Int'l*, pg. 1194
SONOMA TECHNICAL SERVICE, INC.—See ABM Industries, Inc.; *U.S. Public*, pg. 26
SONOMED, INC.—See Escalon Medical Corp.; *U.S. Public*, pg. 793
SONOPRESS GMBH—See Bertelsmann SE & Co. KGaA; *Int'l*, pg. 996
SONORA BEHAVIORAL HEALTH HOSPITAL, LLC—See Acadia Healthcare Company, Inc.; *U.S. Public*, pg. 30
SONORAN AIR INC.; *U.S. Private*, pg. 3714
SONORAN LLC—See Big Lots, Inc.; *U.S. Public*, pg. 331
SONORAN NATIONAL INSURANCE GROUP—See Franchise Services of North America Inc.; *U.S. Private*, pg. 1587
SONORAN ROOFING INC.; *U.S. Private*, pg. 3714
SONORA RESOURCES CORP.; *Int'l*, pg. 7099
SONOR GMBH & CO. KG—See Matth. Hohner AG; *Int'l*, pg. 4731
SONOR INVESTMENTS LIMITED; *Int'l*, pg. 7099
SONORO ENERGY IRAQ B.V.—See Blue Sky Energy; *U.S. Private*, pg. 593
SONORO ENERGY LTD.; *Int'l*, pg. 7100
SONORO GOLD CORP.; *Int'l*, pg. 7100
SONOROUS CORPORATION—See Shimizu Corporation; *Int'l*, pg. 6836
SONORUKA ENGINEERING CO., LTD.—See Maruka Furusato Corporation; *Int'l*, pg. 4714
SONOSCAN (EUROPE) LTD.—See Nordson Corporation; *U.S. Public*, pg. 1534
SONOSCAN INC.—See Nordson Corporation; *U.S. Public*, pg. 1534
SONOSCAPE MEDICAL CORP.; *Int'l*, pg. 7100
SONOS, INC.; *U.S. Public*, pg. 1909
SONOSITE, INC.—See FUJIFILM Holdings Corporation; *Int'l*, pg. 2823
SONOSITE LTD.—See FUJIFILM Holdings Corporation; *Int'l*, pg. 2823
SONOSITE (SHANGHAI) CO. LTD.—See FUJIFILM Holdings Corporation; *Int'l*, pg. 2823
SONOTECHNIQUE PJL INC.—See Transition Evergreen; *Int'l*, pg. 7901
SONO-TEK CLEANING SYSTEMS, INC.—See Sono-Tek Corporation; *U.S. Public*, pg. 1904
SONO-TEK CORPORATION; *U.S. Public*, pg. 1904
SONOVA AG—See Sonova Holding AG; *Int'l*, pg. 7101
SONOVA CANADA INC.—See Sonova Holding AG; *Int'l*, pg. 7101
SONOVA COMMUNICATIONS AG—See Sonova Holding AG; *Int'l*, pg. 7101
SONOVA DENMARK A/S—See Sonova Holding AG; *Int'l*, pg. 7101
SONOVA HOLDING AG; *Int'l*, pg. 7100
SONOVA IBERICA S.A.U.—See Sonova Holding AG; *Int'l*, pg. 7101
SONOVA KOREA LTD.—See Sonova Holding AG; *Int'l*, pg. 7101
SONOVA NORDIC AB—See Sonova Holding AG; *Int'l*, pg. 7101
SONOVA OPERATION CENTER VIETNAM CO., LTD.—See Sonova Holding AG; *Int'l*, pg. 7101
SONOVA RUS LLC—See Sonova Holding AG; *Int'l*, pg. 7101
SONOVA (SHANGHAI) CO., LTD.—See Sonova Holding AG; *Int'l*, pg. 7101
SONOVA TAIWAN PTE. LTD.—See Sonova Holding AG; *Int'l*, pg. 7101
SONOVIA LTD.; *Int'l*, pg. 7101
SONPO 24 INSURANCE COMPANY LIMITED—See Sompo Holdings, Inc.; *Int'l*, pg. 7087
SONS ACURA; *U.S. Private*, pg. 3714
SONSIO, LLC—See SimpleTire, LLC; *U.S. Private*, pg. 3667
SONSRAY, INC.; *U.S. Private*, pg. 3714
SONSRAY MACHINERY, LLC—See Sonsray, Inc.; *U.S. Private*, pg. 3714
SONSTEGARD FOODS COMPANY; *U.S. Private*, pg. 3714
SONSTEGARD FOODS OF GEORGIA—See Sonstegard Foods Company; *U.S. Private*, pg. 3715
SONSUB LTD.—See Eni S.p.A.; *Int'l*, pg. 2438
SONTAG ADVISORY, LLC—See Aon plc; *U.S. Public*, pg. 497
SONTEK/YSI, INC.—See Xylem Inc.; *U.S. Public*, pg. 2395
SONTIQ, INC.—See TransUnion; *U.S. Public*, pg. 2184
SONUS FABER S.P.A.—See Fine Sounds S.p.A.; *Int'l*, pg. 2673
SONUS NETWORKS AUSTRALIA PTY LTD.—See Ribbon Communications Inc.; *U.S. Public*, pg. 1797
SONUS NETWORKS (INDIA) PRIVATE LIMITED—See Ribbon Communications Inc.; *U.S. Public*, pg. 1797
SONUS USA INC.—See Amplifon S.p.A.; *Int'l*, pg. 435
SONY ASSURANCE INC.—See Sony Group Corporation; *Int'l*, pg. 7106
SONY/ATV MUSIC PUBLISHING LLC—See Sony Group Corporation; *Int'l*, pg. 7104
SONY/ATV TREE MUSIC PUBLISHING NASHVILLE—See Sony Group Corporation; *Int'l*, pg. 7104
SONY AUSTRALIA LIMITED—See Sony Group Corporation; *Int'l*, pg. 7103
SONY AUSTRIA GMBH—See Sony Group Corporation; *Int'l*, pg. 7103
SONY BANK INC.—See Sony Group Corporation; *Int'l*, pg. 7106
SONY BANK SECURITIES INC.—See Sony Group Corporation; *Int'l*, pg. 7106
SONY BENELUX B.V.—See Sony Group Corporation; *Int'l*, pg. 7103
SONY BROADCAST & PROFESSIONAL EUROPE—See Sony Group Corporation; *Int'l*, pg. 7103
SONY BUSINESS SOLUTIONS CORPORATION—See Sony Group Corporation; *Int'l*, pg. 7103
SONY BUSINESS SOLUTIONS & SYSTEMS—See Sony Group Corporation; *Int'l*, pg. 7103
SONY CAPITAL CORPORATION—See Sony Group Corporation; *Int'l*, pg. 7103
SONY (CHINA) LTD.—See Sony Group Corporation; *Int'l*, pg. 7102
SONY COMPUTER SCIENCE LABORATORIES, INC.—See Sony Group Corporation; *Int'l*, pg. 7103
SONY CORPORATE SERVICES (JAPAN) CORPORATION—See Sony Group Corporation; *Int'l*, pg. 7103
SONY CORPORATION OF AMERICA—See Sony Group Corporation; *Int'l*, pg. 7103
SONY CORPORATION OF HONG KONG LTD.—See Sony Group Corporation; *Int'l*, pg. 7105
SONY CORPORATION OF PANAMA, S.A.—See Sony Group Corporation; *Int'l*, pg. 7107
SONY DADC AUSTRIA AG—See Sony Group Corporation; *Int'l*, pg. 7105
SONY DADC CANADA INC.—See Sony Group Corporation; *Int'l*, pg. 7104
SONY DADC CHINA CO., LTD.—See Sony Group Corporation; *Int'l*, pg. 7105
SONY DADC CORPORATION—See Sony Group Corporation; *Int'l*, pg. 7105
SONY DADC COSTA RICA LIMITADA—See Sony Group Corporation; *Int'l*, pg. 7106
SONY DADC CZECH REPUBLIC S.R.O—See Sony Group Corporation; *Int'l*, pg. 7106
SONY DADC FRANCE S.A.S.—See Sony Group Corporation; *Int'l*, pg. 7106
SONY DADC GERMANY GMBH—See Sony Group Corporation; *Int'l*, pg. 7106

COMPANY NAME INDEX

SONY DADC HONG KONG LTD.—See Sony Group Corporation; *Int'l*, pg. 7106
SONY DADC IBERIA S.L.—See Sony Group Corporation; *Int'l*, pg. 7106
SONY DADC ITALIA S.R.L.—See Sony Group Corporation; *Int'l*, pg. 7106
SONY DADC JAPAN INC. - IBARAKI FACILITY (DADJ-I)—See Sony Group Corporation; *Int'l*, pg. 7106
SONY DADC JAPAN INC. - SHIZUOKA FACILITY (DADJ-O) OIGAWA—See Sony Group Corporation; *Int'l*, pg. 7106
SONY DADC JAPAN INC. - SHIZUOKA FACILITY (DADJ-Y) YOSHIDA—See Sony Group Corporation; *Int'l*, pg. 7106
SONY DADC JAPAN INC.—See Sony Group Corporation; *Int'l*, pg. 7106
SONY DADC MANUFACTURING INDIA PRIVATE LIMITED—See Sony Group Corporation; *Int'l*, pg. 7106
SONY DADC—See Sony Group Corporation; *Int'l*, pg. 7105
SONY DADC UK LTD.—See Sony Group Corporation; *Int'l*, pg. 7106
SONY DEUTSCHLAND GMBH—See Sony Group Corporation; *Int'l*, pg. 7106
SONY DIGITAL NETWORK APPLICATIONS INC.—See Sony Group Corporation; *Int'l*, pg. 7106
SONY DIGITAL PRODUCTS (WUXI) CO., LTD.—See Sony Group Corporation; *Int'l*, pg. 7106
SONY ELECTRONICS BROADCAST AND PROFESSIONAL CO.—See Sony Group Corporation; *Int'l*, pg. 7103
SONY ELECTRONICS INC.-DISTRIBUTION CENTER—See Sony Group Corporation; *Int'l*, pg. 7103
SONY ELECTRONICS INC. MEDICAL SYSTEMS DIVISION—See Sony Group Corporation; *Int'l*, pg. 7103
SONY ELECTRONICS, INC.—See Sony Group Corporation; *Int'l*, pg. 7103
SONY ELECTRONICS INC—See Sony Group Corporation; *Int'l*, pg. 7103
SONY ELECTRONICS INC.—See Sony Group Corporation; *Int'l*, pg. 7103
SONY ELECTRONICS (SINGAPORE) PTE. LTD.—See Sony Group Corporation; *Int'l*, pg. 7106
SONY ELECTRONICS VIETNAM COMPANY LTD.—See Sony Group Corporation; *Int'l*, pg. 7106
SONY EMCS CORPORATION—See Sony Group Corporation; *Int'l*, pg. 7106
SONY EMCS (MALAYSIA) SDN. BHD.—See Sony Group Corporation; *Int'l*, pg. 7107
SONY ENGINEERING CORPORATION—See Sony Group Corporation; *Int'l*, pg. 7106
SONY ENTERPRISE CO., LTD.—See Sony Group Corporation; *Int'l*, pg. 7106
SONY ESPANA, S.A.—See Sony Group Corporation; *Int'l*, pg. 7106
SONY EUROPE FINANCE PLC—See Sony Group Corporation; *Int'l*, pg. 7106
SONY EUROPE LIMITED—See Sony Group Corporation; *Int'l*, pg. 7106
SONY FINANCE INTERNATIONAL, INC.—See Sony Group Corporation; *Int'l*, pg. 7106
SONY FINANCIAL HOLDINGS INC.—See Sony Group Corporation; *Int'l*, pg. 7106
SONY GLOBAL TREASURY SERVICES PLC—See Sony Group Corporation; *Int'l*, pg. 7106
SONY GROUP CORPORATION; *Int'l*, pg. 7101
SONY GULF FZE LIMITED—See Sony Group Corporation; *Int'l*, pg. 7106
SONY HOLDING (ASIA) B.V.—See Sony Group Corporation; *Int'l*, pg. 7106
SONY HONDA MOBILITY INC.—See Honda Motor Co., Ltd.; *Int'l*, pg. 3464
SONY HONDA MOBILITY INC.—See Sony Group Corporation; *Int'l*, pg. 7106
SONY HUNGARIA KFT—See Sony Group Corporation; *Int'l*, pg. 7106
SONY INDIA PVT. LTD.—See Sony Group Corporation; *Int'l*, pg. 7106
SONY INTERACTIVE ENTERTAINMENT AMERICA LLC—See Sony Group Corporation; *Int'l*, pg. 7103
SONY INTERACTIVE ENTERTAINMENT EUROPE LTD.—See Sony Group Corporation; *Int'l*, pg. 7103
SONY INTERACTIVE ENTERTAINMENT INC.—See Sony Group Corporation; *Int'l*, pg. 7103
SONY INTERACTIVE ENTERTAINMENT LLC—See Sony Group Corporation; *Int'l*, pg. 7103
SONY INTERNATIONAL (HONG KONG) LTD.—See Sony Group Corporation; *Int'l*, pg. 7106
SONY IRELAND LTD.—See Sony Group Corporation; *Int'l*, pg. 7107
SONY ITALIA S.P.A.—See Sony Group Corporation; *Int'l*, pg. 7107
SONY KOREA CORPORATION—See Sony Group Corporation; *Int'l*, pg. 7107
SONY LATIN AMERICA INC.—See Sony Group Corporation; *Int'l*, pg. 7107
SONY LIFE INSURANCE CO., LTD.—See Sony Group Corporation; *Int'l*, pg. 7106

SONY LSI DESIGN INC.—See Sony Group Corporation; *Int'l*, pg. 7107
SONY MAGNETIC PRODUCTS INC.—See Sony Group Corporation; *Int'l*, pg. 7103
SONY MAGNETIC PRODUCTS INC.—See Sony Group Corporation; *Int'l*, pg. 7103
SONY MALAYSIA SDN. BHD.—See Sony Group Corporation; *Int'l*, pg. 7107
SONY MARKETING (JAPAN) INC.—See Sony Group Corporation; *Int'l*, pg. 7107
SONY MOBILE COMMUNICATIONS AB - KISTA—See Sony Group Corporation; *Int'l*, pg. 7107
SONY MOBILE COMMUNICATIONS AB—See Sony Group Corporation; *Int'l*, pg. 7107
SONY MOBILE COMMUNICATIONS CO., LTD.—See Sony Group Corporation; *Int'l*, pg. 7107
SONY MOBILE COMMUNICATIONS USA INC.—See Sony Group Corporation; *Int'l*, pg. 7107
SONY MUSIC CLASSICAL—See Sony Group Corporation; *Int'l*, pg. 7104
SONY MUSIC COMMUNICATIONS INC.—See Sony Group Corporation; *Int'l*, pg. 7107
SONY MUSIC DISTRIBUTION (JAPAN) INC.—See Sony Group Corporation; *Int'l*, pg. 7107
SONY MUSIC ENTERTAINMENT AB—See Sony Group Corporation; *Int'l*, pg. 7104
SONY MUSIC ENTERTAINMENT A/S—See Sony Group Corporation; *Int'l*, pg. 7104
SONY MUSIC ENTERTAINMENT AUSTRALIA PTY. LTD.—See Sony Group Corporation; *Int'l*, pg. 7104
SONY MUSIC ENTERTAINMENT AUSTRIA GMBH—See Sony Group Corporation; *Int'l*, pg. 7104
SONY MUSIC ENTERTAINMENT BV—See Sony Group Corporation; *Int'l*, pg. 7103
SONY MUSIC ENTERTAINMENT CZECH REPUBLIC S.R.O.—See Sony Group Corporation; *Int'l*, pg. 7104
SONY MUSIC ENTERTAINMENT GERMANY GMBH—See Sony Group Corporation; *Int'l*, pg. 7104
SONY MUSIC ENTERTAINMENT HONG KONG LIMITED—See Sony Group Corporation; *Int'l*, pg. 7104
SONY MUSIC ENTERTAINMENT (JAPAN) INC.—See Sony Group Corporation; *Int'l*, pg. 7107
SONY MUSIC ENTERTAINMENT MAGYARORSZAG KFT.—See Sony Group Corporation; *Int'l*, pg. 7104
SONY MUSIC ENTERTAINMENT MEXICO, S.A. DE C.V.—See Sony Group Corporation; *Int'l*, pg. 7106
SONY MUSIC ENTERTAINMENT NORWAY A/S—See Sony Group Corporation; *Int'l*, pg. 7104
SONY MUSIC ENTERTAINMENT OPERATING (THAILAND) CO., LTD.—See Sony Group Corporation; *Int'l*, pg. 7104
SONY MUSIC ENTERTAINMENT (PHILIPPINES), INC.—See Sony Group Corporation; *Int'l*, pg. 7104
SONY MUSIC ENTERTAINMENT POLAND SP. Z O.O.—See Sony Group Corporation; *Int'l*, pg. 7104
SONY MUSIC ENTERTAINMENT—See Sony Group Corporation; *Int'l*, pg. 7103
SONY MUSIC ENTERTAINMENT SWITZERLAND GMBH—See Sony Group Corporation; *Int'l*, pg. 7104
SONY MUSIC ENTERTAINMENT UK LTD.—See Sony Group Corporation; *Int'l*, pg. 7104
SONY MUSIC HOLDING INC.—See Sony Group Corporation; *Int'l*, pg. 7105
SONY MUSIC NASHVILLE—See Sony Group Corporation; *Int'l*, pg. 7104
SONY NETWORK COMMUNICATIONS INC.—See Sony Group Corporation; *Int'l*, pg. 7107
SONY NETWORK TAIWAN LTD.—See Sony Group Corporation; *Int'l*, pg. 7107
SONY NEW ZEALAND LTD.—See Sony Group Corporation; *Int'l*, pg. 7107
SONY NORDIC A/S—See Sony Group Corporation; *Int'l*, pg. 7102
SONY NUEVO LAREDO, S.A. DE C.V.—See Sony Group Corporation; *Int'l*, pg. 7106
SONY OF CANADA LTD.—See Sony Group Corporation; *Int'l*, pg. 7107
SONY OLYMPUS MEDICAL SOLUTIONS INC.—See Olympus Corporation; *Int'l*, pg. 5558
SONY ONLINE ENTERTAINMENT, INC.—See Sony Group Corporation; *Int'l*, pg. 7105
SONY OPTIARC INC.—See Sony Group Corporation; *Int'l*, pg. 7107
SONY PCL INC.—See Sony Group Corporation; *Int'l*, pg. 7107
SONY PHILIPPINES, INC.—See Sony Group Corporation; *Int'l*, pg. 7107
SONY PICTURES ANIMATION INC.—See Sony Group Corporation; *Int'l*, pg. 7105
SONY PICTURES CLASSICS—See Sony Group Corporation; *Int'l*, pg. 7105
SONY PICTURES DIGITAL—See Sony Group Corporation; *Int'l*, pg. 7105
SONY PICTURES ENTERTAINMENT INC.—See Sony Group Corporation; *Int'l*, pg. 7105
SONY PICTURES ENTERTAINMENT WORLDWIDE PRODUCT FULFILLMENT—See Sony Group Corporation; *Int'l*, pg. 7105

SONY PICTURES FILMVERLEIH GMBH—See Sony Group Corporation; *Int'l*, pg. 7103
SONY PICTURES HOME ENTERTAINMENT—See Sony Group Corporation; *Int'l*, pg. 7105
SONY PICTURES IMAGEWORKS INC.—See Sony Group Corporation; *Int'l*, pg. 7105
SONY PICTURES NETWORKS INDIA PRIVATE LIMITED—See Sony Group Corporation; *Int'l*, pg. 7105
SONY PICTURES RELEASING CORPORATION—See Sony Group Corporation; *Int'l*, pg. 7105
SONY PICTURES RELEASING GMBH—See Sony Group Corporation; *Int'l*, pg. 7105
SONY PICTURES RELEASING OF INDIA LIMITED—See Sony Group Corporation; *Int'l*, pg. 7105
SONY PICTURES TELEVISION INC.—See Sony Group Corporation; *Int'l*, pg. 7105
SONY PRECISION DEVICES (HUIZHOU) CO., LTD.—See Sony Group Corporation; *Int'l*, pg. 7107
SONY PRECISION ENGINEERING CENTER (SINGAPORE) PTE. LTD.—See Sony Group Corporation; *Int'l*, pg. 7107
SONY SOUTH AFRICA (PTY) LIMITED—See Sony Group Corporation; *Int'l*, pg. 7107
SONY SUPPLY CHAIN SOLUTIONS (MALAYSIA) SDN. BHD.—See Sony Group Corporation; *Int'l*, pg. 7107
SONY/TAIYO CORPORATION—See Sony Group Corporation; *Int'l*, pg. 7107
SONY TECHNOLOGY (MALAYSIA) SDN. BHD.—See Sony Group Corporation; *Int'l*, pg. 7107
SONY THAI CO. LTD.—See Sony Group Corporation; *Int'l*, pg. 7107
SONY (U.K.) LTD.—See Sony Group Corporation; *Int'l*, pg. 7102
SOOCHOW SECURITIES CO., LTD.; *Int'l*, pg. 7107
SOO KEE JEWELLERY PTE LTD—See SK Jewellery Group Limited; *Int'l*, pg. 6974
SOO LINE CORPORATION—See Canadian Pacific Kansas City Limited; *Int'l*, pg. 1285
SOO LINE RAILROAD COMPANY—See Canadian Pacific Kansas City Limited; *Int'l*, pg. 1285
SOONER BOLT & SUPPLY INC.; *U.S. Private*, pg. 3715
SOONER COOPERATIVE INC.; *U.S. Private*, pg. 3715
SOONER EQUIPMENT & LEASING, INC.; *U.S. Private*, pg. 3715
SOONER INC.—See ITOCHU Corporation; *Int'l*, pg. 3840
SOONER INC.—See Marubeni Corporation; *Int'l*, pg. 4709
SOONER LANDFILL—See BC Partners LLP; *Int'l*, pg. 924
SOONER LIFT INC.; *U.S. Private*, pg. 3715
SOONER PACKAGING, INC.—See Southern Missouri Container Packaging Group; *U.S. Private*, pg. 3733
SOONER PHYSICAL THERAPY, LIMITED PARTNERSHIP—See U.S. Physical Therapy, Inc.; *U.S. Public*, pg. 2216
SOONER PIPE LLC—See ITOCHU Corporation; *Int'l*, pg. 3840
SOONER PIPE LLC—See Marubeni Corporation; *Int'l*, pg. 4709
SOONER SOUTHWEST BANKSHARES, INC.; *U.S. Private*, pg. 3715
SOONER TRAILER MANUFACTURING COMPANY—See Corporate Partners LLC; *U.S. Private*, pg. 1055
SOON LIAN HOLDINGS LIMITED; *Int'l*, pg. 7108
SOONLY FOOD PROCESSING INDUSTRIES PTE LTD—See Emerging Glory Sdn Bhd; *Int'l*, pg. 2379
SOON MINING LIMITED; *Int'l*, pg. 7108
SOONR, INC.—See Vista Equity Partners, LLC; *U.S. Private*, pg. 4395
SOOO REMONDIS MINSK—See RETHMANN AG & Co. KG; *Int'l*, pg. 6309
SOOR FUEL MARKETING CO. K.S.C.; *Int'l*, pg. 7108
SOOSAN HEAVY INDUSTRIES CO., LTD.; *Int'l*, pg. 7108
SOOSAN INDUSTRIES CO., LTD.; *Int'l*, pg. 7108
SOOSAN INT CO.,LTD.; *Int'l*, pg. 7108
SOOSAN MACHINERY CO., LTD.—See Soosan Heavy Industries Co., Ltd.; *Int'l*, pg. 7108
SOOSAN USA INC.—See Soosan Heavy Industries Co., Ltd.; *Int'l*, pg. 7108
SOOSEOK CO., LTD.—See Dong-A Socio Holdings Co., Ltd.; *Int'l*, pg. 2165
SOO & SOO, LTD.—See Medience Co., Ltd.; *Int'l*, pg. 4777
SOOSUNG LIFT MFG. CO., LTD.; *Int'l*, pg. 7108
SO OTHERS MIGHT EAT; *U.S. Private*, pg. 3702
SOOV OU—See UP Invest OU; *Int'l*, pg. 8087
SOPAF S.P.A.; *Int'l*, pg. 7108
SOPAKCO INC.—See Unaka Company Inc.; *U.S. Private*, pg. 4279
SOPAL—See Eiffage S.A.; *Int'l*, pg. 2331
SOPARCO; *Int'l*, pg. 7108
SOPARK CORP.; *U.S. Private*, pg. 3715
SOPARMA S.A.S.—See Sapmer S.A.; *Int'l*, pg. 6571
SOPECAL HYGIENE SAS—See Bunzl plc; *Int'l*, pg. 1219
SOPELEC RESEAUX SAS—See VINCI S.A.; *Int'l*, pg. 8229
SOPEM SPOLKA Z OGRANICZONA ODPOWIEDZIALNOSCIA—See Somfy SA; *Int'l*, pg. 7086
SOPEXA (CANADA) LTD.—See Hopscotch Groupe S.A.; *Int'l*, pg. 3474

SOPEXA ITALIA S.A.—See Hopscotch Groupe S.A.; *Int'l*, pg. 3474
SOPEXA JAPON CO., LTD.—See Hopscotch Groupe S.A.; *Int'l*, pg. 3474
SOPEXA USA—See Hopscotch Groupe S.A.; *Int'l*, pg. 3474
SOPHARMA AD; *Int'l*, pg. 7108
SOPHARMA ANTILLES—See Toyota Tsusho Corporation; *Int'l*, pg. 7876
SOPHARMA BUILDINGS REIT; *Int'l*, pg. 7108
SOPHARMACY EOOD—See Sopharma AD; *Int'l*, pg. 7108
SOPHARMA PROPERTIES REIT; *Int'l*, pg. 7108
SOPHARMA TRADING JSC—See Sopharma AD; *Int'l*, pg. 7108
SOPHEON GMBH—See Wellspring Worldwide, LLC; *U.S. Private*, pg. 4478
SOPHEON NV—See Wellspring Worldwide, LLC; *U.S. Private*, pg. 4478
SOPHEON PLC—See Wellspring Worldwide, LLC; *U.S. Private*, pg. 4478
SOPHEON UK LTD.—See Wellspring Worldwide, LLC; *U.S. Private*, pg. 4478
SOPHIA CAPITAL S.A.; *Int'l*, pg. 7108
SOPHIA CORPORATION—See GSI Creos Corporation; *Int'l*, pg. 3145
SOPHIA GENETICS SA; *Int'l*, pg. 7109
SOPHIA HOLDINGS CO., LTD.—See Isopra Co., Ltd.; *Int'l*, pg. 3821
SOPHIA LEARNING, LLC—See Strategic Education, Inc.; *U.S. Public*, pg. 1954
SOPHIA TRAEXPO LIMITED; *Int'l*, pg. 7109
SOPHION BIOSCIENCE A/S—See AddLife AB; *Int'l*, pg. 129
SOPHIRIS BIO INC.; *U.S. Private*, pg. 3715
SOPHISTICATED SYSTEMS INC.—See IP Pathways, LLC; *U.S. Private*, pg. 2136
SOPHLOGIC GLOBAL, LLC; *U.S. Private*, pg. 3715
SOPHONO, INC.—See Medtronic plc; *Int'l*, pg. 4790
SOPHORA UNTERNEHMERKAPITAL GMBH; *Int'l*, pg. 7109
SOPHOS AB—See Apax Partners LLP; *Int'l*, pg. 506
SOPHOS ANTI-VIRUS ASIA PTE LTD.—See Apax Partners LLP; *Int'l*, pg. 506
SOPHOS B.V.—See Apax Partners LLP; *Int'l*, pg. 506
SOPHOS GMBH—See Apax Partners LLP; *Int'l*, pg. 506
SOPHOS GROUP PLC—See Apax Partners LLP; *Int'l*, pg. 506
SOPHOS INC.—See Apax Partners LLP; *Int'l*, pg. 506
SOPHOS ITALY S.R.L.—See Apax Partners LLP; *Int'l*, pg. 506
SOPHOS K.K.—See Apax Partners LLP; *Int'l*, pg. 506
SOPHOS LTD.—See Apax Partners LLP; *Int'l*, pg. 506
SOPHOS PTY LTD.—See Apax Partners LLP; *Int'l*, pg. 506
SOPHOS SARL—See Apax Partners LLP; *Int'l*, pg. 506
SOPHRONA SOLUTIONS INC.—See NEXUS AG; *Int'l*, pg. 5250
SOPOCKIE TOWARZYSTWO DORADCZE SP. Z O.O.—See Munchener Ruckversicherungs AG; *Int'l*, pg. 5091
SOPOCKIE TOWARZYSTWO UBEZPIECZEN ERGO HESTIA SPOLKA AKCYJNA—See Munchener Ruckversicherungs AG; *Int'l*, pg. 5091
SOPOCKIE TOWARZYSTWO UBEZPIECZEN NA ZYCIE ERGO HESTIA SPOLKA AKCYJNA—See Munchener Ruckversicherungs AG; *Int'l*, pg. 5087
SOPOCKI INSTYTUT UBEZPIECZEN S.A.—See Munchener Ruckversicherungs AG; *Int'l*, pg. 5091
SOPORCEL - SOCIEDADE PORTUGUESA DE PAPEL, SA.—See SODIM, SGPS, SA; *Int'l*, pg. 7049
SOPOR - SOCIEDADE DISTRIBUIDORA DE COMBUSTIVEIS, S.A.—See Galp Energia SGPS, S.A.; *Int'l*, pg. 2876
SO POSLOVNO SAVJETOVANJE D.O.O.—See Pozavarovalnica Sava, d.d.; *Int'l*, pg. 5949
SOPRA BANKING COTE D'IVOIRE SARL—See Sopra Steria Group S.A.; *Int'l*, pg. 7110
SOPRA BANKING SOFTWARE BELGIUM—See Axway Software SA; *Int'l*, pg. 772
SOPRA BANKING SOFTWARE LUXEMBOURG SA—See Sopra Steria Group S.A.; *Int'l*, pg. 7110
SOPRA BANKING SOFTWARE NETHERLANDS BV—See Sopra Steria Group S.A.; *Int'l*, pg. 7110
SOPRA BANKING SOFTWARE SENEGAL SASU—See Sopra Steria Group S.A.; *Int'l*, pg. 7110
SOPRA BANKING SOFTWARE—See Axway Software SA; *Int'l*, pg. 772
SOPRA FINANCIAL TECHNOLOGY GMBH—See Sopra Steria Group S.A.; *Int'l*, pg. 7110
SOPRA GROUP EUSKADI SL—See Sopra Steria Group S.A.; *Int'l*, pg. 7110
SOPRA GROUP HOLDING LTD.—See Sopra Steria Group S.A.; *Int'l*, pg. 7110
SOPRA GROUP INFORMATICA—See Sopra Steria Group S.A.; *Int'l*, pg. 7110
SOPRA GROUP LIMITED—See Sopra Steria Group S.A.; *Int'l*, pg. 7110
SOPRA HR SOFTWARE GMBH—See Sopra Steria Group S.A.; *Int'l*, pg. 7110

SOPRA HR SOFTWARE SARL—See Sopra Steria Group S.A.; *Int'l*, pg. 7110
SOPRA HR SOFTWARE SARL—See Sopra Steria Group S.A.; *Int'l*, pg. 7110
SOPRA HR SOFTWARE SARL—See Sopra Steria Group S.A.; *Int'l*, pg. 7110
SOPRA HR SOFTWARE SL—See Sopra Steria Group S.A.; *Int'l*, pg. 7110
SOPRA HR SOFTWARE—See Sopra Steria Group S.A.; *Int'l*, pg. 7110
SOPRA HR SOFTWARE SPRL—See Sopra Steria Group S.A.; *Int'l*, pg. 7110
SOPRA HR SOFTWARE SRL—See Sopra Steria Group S.A.; *Int'l*, pg. 7110
SOPRA INDIA PRIVATE LTD—See Sopra Steria Group S.A.; *Int'l*, pg. 7110
SOPRANO DESIGN LIMITED; *Int'l*, pg. 7111
SOPRANO OYJ—See Eiffage S.A.; *Int'l*, pg. 2331
SOPRANTIC CASABLANCA—See Sopra Steria Group S.A.; *Int'l*, pg. 7110
SOPRA STERIA AB—See Sopra Steria Group S.A.; *Int'l*, pg. 7110
SOPRA STERIA AG—See Sopra Steria Group S.A.; *Int'l*, pg. 7110
SOPRA STERIA ASIA PTE. LTD.—See Sopra Steria Group S.A.; *Int'l*, pg. 7110
SOPRA STERIA A/S—See Sopra Steria Group S.A.; *Int'l*, pg. 7110
SOPRA STERIA AS—See Sopra Steria Group S.A.; *Int'l*, pg. 7110
SOPRA STERIA BELGIUM—See Sopra Steria Group S.A.; *Int'l*, pg. 7110
SOPRA STERIA BENELUX SA—See Sopra Steria Group S.A.; *Int'l*, pg. 7110
SOPRA STERIA ESPANA, S.A.—See Sopra Steria Group S.A.; *Int'l*, pg. 7110
SOPRA STERIA GMBH—See Sopra Steria Group S.A.; *Int'l*, pg. 7110
SOPRA STERIA GMBH—See Sopra Steria Group S.A.; *Int'l*, pg. 7110
SOPRA STERIA GROUP S.A.; *Int'l*, pg. 7109
SOPRA STERIA GROUP SPA—See Sopra Steria Group S.A.; *Int'l*, pg. 7110
SOPRA STERIA HOLDINGS LIMITED—See Sopra Steria Group S.A.; *Int'l*, pg. 7111
SOPRA STERIA LIMITED—See Sopra Steria Group S.A.; *Int'l*, pg. 7110
SOPRA STERIA LUXEMBOURG S.A.—See Sopra Steria Group S.A.; *Int'l*, pg. 7111
SOPRA STERIA POLSKA Z O.O.—See Sopra Steria Group S.A.; *Int'l*, pg. 7111
SOPRA STERIA PSF LUXEMBOURG S.A.—See Sopra Steria Group S.A.; *Int'l*, pg. 7111
SOPRA STERIA RECRUITMENT LIMITED—See Sopra Steria Group S.A.; *Int'l*, pg. 7111
SOPRA STERIA SERVICES LIMITED—See Sopra Steria Group S.A.; *Int'l*, pg. 7111
SOPRA STERIA SERVICES—See Sopra Steria Group S.A.; *Int'l*, pg. 7111
SOPRATICO CO., LTD.—See Bushiroad, Inc.; *Int'l*, pg. 1227
SOPREDIS SA—See Vivendi SE; *Int'l*, pg. 8278
SOPREGIM SAS—See Compass Group PLC; *Int'l*, pg. 1752
SOPREMA AG—See SOPREMA SAS; *Int'l*, pg. 7111
SOPREMA CANADA INC. - CHILLIWACK PLANT—See SOPREMA SAS; *Int'l*, pg. 7111
SOPREMA CANADA INC. - DRUMMONDVILLE PLANT—See SOPREMA SAS; *Int'l*, pg. 7111
SOPREMA CANADA INC.—See SOPREMA SAS; *Int'l*, pg. 7111
SOPREMA GMBH—See SOPREMA SAS; *Int'l*, pg. 7111
SOPREMA, INC. - GULFPORT PLANT—See SOPREMA SAS; *Int'l*, pg. 7111
SOPREMA, INC.—See SOPREMA SAS; *Int'l*, pg. 7111
SOPREMA, INC. - SOUTHEAST—See SOPREMA SAS; *Int'l*, pg. 7111
SOPREMA LTDA—See SOPREMA SAS; *Int'l*, pg. 7111
SOPREMA NV - ANDENNE PLANT—See SOPREMA SAS; *Int'l*, pg. 7111
SOPREMA NV—See SOPREMA SAS; *Int'l*, pg. 7111
SOPREMA POLSKA SP. Z O.O.—See SOPREMA SAS; *Int'l*, pg. 7111
SOPREMA, SARL—See SOPREMA SAS; *Int'l*, pg. 7111
SOPREMA SAS BARCELONA PLANT—See SOPREMA SAS; *Int'l*, pg. 7111
SOPREMA SAS CESTAS PLANT—See SOPREMA SAS; *Int'l*, pg. 7111
SOPREMA SAS COLOMIERS PLANT—See SOPREMA SAS; *Int'l*, pg. 7111
SOPREMA SAS IJLST PLANT—See SOPREMA SAS; *Int'l*, pg. 7111
SOPREMA SAS LA CHAPELLE SAINT-LUC PLANT—See SOPREMA SAS; *Int'l*, pg. 7111
SOPREMA SAS SORGUES PLANT—See SOPREMA SAS; *Int'l*, pg. 7111
SOPREMA SAS; *Int'l*, pg. 7111
SOPREMA SAS - VAL DE REUIL PLANT—See SOPREMA SAS; *Int'l*, pg. 7111

SOPREMA SAS ZONA INDUSTRIAL DE ALPIARCA PLANT—See SOPREMA SAS; *Int'l*, pg. 7111
SOPREMA SINGAPORE PTE. LTD—See SOPREMA SAS; *Int'l*, pg. 7111
SOPRO BAUCHEMIE GMBH—See Mapei SpA; *Int'l*, pg. 4683
SOPRO BAUCHEMIE GMBH—See Mapei SpA; *Int'l*, pg. 4683
SOPROCAL CALERIAS & INDUSTRIAS SA; *Int'l*, pg. 7111
SOPROCOS S.A.S.—See L'Oreal S.A.; *Int'l*, pg. 4381
SOPROFEN INDUSTRIE SAS—See Bouyer Leroux SA; *Int'l*, pg. 1121
SOPROFEN SAS—See Bouyer Leroux SA; *Int'l*, pg. 1121
SOPROFEN—See Atrya SAS; *Int'l*, pg. 694
SOPRO HUNGARIA KFT.—See Mapei SpA; *Int'l*, pg. 4683
SOPRO NEDERLAND BV—See Mapei SpA; *Int'l*, pg. 4683
SOPRO NETHERLAND BV—See Mapei SpA; *Int'l*, pg. 4683
SOPRO POLSKA SP. Z O.O.—See Mapei SpA; *Int'l*, pg. 4683
SOPROREAL S.N.C.—See L'Oreal S.A.; *Int'l*, pg. 4381
SOPROVER—See Compagnie de Saint-Gobain SA; *Int'l*, pg. 1737
SOPURA S.A.; *Int'l*, pg. 7111
SOQUIMICH COMERCIAL S.A.—See Sociedad Quimica y Minera de Chile S.A.; *Int'l*, pg. 7032
SORA LABORATORIES, LLC—See Archer-Daniels-Midland Company; *U.S. Public*, pg. 185
SORALUCE AMERICA, INC.—See Mondragon Corporation; *Int'l*, pg. 5031
SORALUCE FRANCE S.A.R.L.—See Mondragon Corporation; *Int'l*, pg. 5031
SORALUCE ITALIA S.R.L.—See Mondragon Corporation; *Int'l*, pg. 5031
SORALUCE, S.COOP.—See Mondragon Corporation; *Int'l*, pg. 5031
SORAMI STEEL SERVICE CO., LTD.—See Okaya & Co., Ltd.; *Int'l*, pg. 5547
SORANA LANKA (PVT.) LTD—See Raigam Marketing Services (Pvt) Ltd.; *Int'l*, pg. 6188
SORB INDUSTRI AB—See Carl Bennet AB; *Int'l*, pg. 1332
SORCE PROPERTIES INC.; *U.S. Private*, pg. 3715
SORCI INSURANCE BROKERAGE, INC.—See Keystone Group, L.P.; *U.S. Private*, pg. 2298
SORDONI CONSTRUCTION CO.—See Sordoni Construction Services, Inc.; *U.S. Private*, pg. 3715
SORDONI CONSTRUCTION SERVICES, INC.; *U.S. Private*, pg. 3715
SOREDIS SA—See Carrefour SA; *Int'l*, pg. 1346
SOREEL—See Kohler Company; *U.S. Private*, pg. 2340
SOREL CORPORATION—See Columbia Sportswear Company; *U.S. Public*, pg. 535
SOREL FORGE CO.—See Swiss Steel Holding AG; *Int'l*, pg. 7372
SOREL MARITIME AGENCIES INC.—See Blue Wolf Capital Partners LLC; *U.S. Private*, pg. 595
SOREN ANDERSSONS EL I DELSBO AKTIEBOLAG—See Bravida Holding AB; *Int'l*, pg. 1142
SORENSEN FLEXIBLE BENEFITS, LTD.; *U.S. Private*, pg. 3715
SORENSEN & KOFOED A/S; *Int'l*, pg. 7111
SORENSEN MOVING & STORAGE COMPANY, INC.—See The Advance Group; *U.S. Private*, pg. 3982
SORENSEN OG BALCHEN AS—See MEKO AB; *Int'l*, pg. 4807
SORENSON BIOSCIENCE, INC.—See Corning Incorporated; *U.S. Public*, pg. 579
SORENSON CAPITAL PARTNERS; *U.S. Private*, pg. 3715
SORENSON MEDIA—See Brookfield Corporation; *Int'l*, pg. 1180
SORENSON MEDIA—See Elliott Management Corporation; *U.S. Private*, pg. 1372
SORENSON TRANSPORTATION CO; *U.S. Private*, pg. 3715
SOREPLA INDUSTRIE S.A.—See Envipco Holding N.V.; *Int'l*, pg. 2453
SOREPLA SRL—See ERG S.p.A.; *Int'l*, pg. 2491
SORETUB SAS—See VINCI S.A.; *Int'l*, pg. 8229
SOR (EUROPE) LTD.—See SOR, Inc.; *U.S. Private*, pg. 3715
SOREVAL S.A.—See Safran SA; *Int'l*, pg. 6476
SOREX HOLDINGS LTD.—See BASF SE; *Int'l*, pg. 882
SOREX LTD.—See BASF SE; *Int'l*, pg. 882
SORG DODGE INC.; *U.S. Private*, pg. 3715
SORGENIA S.P.A—See Asterion Industrial Partners SGEIC SA; *Int'l*, pg. 654
SORGENIA S.p.A—See F2i - Fondi Italiani per le infrastrutture SGR S.p.A.; *Int'l*, pg. 2598
SORGENTE GROUP S.P.A.; *Int'l*, pg. 7111
SORGENTI EMILIANE MODENA SPA; *Int'l*, pg. 7112
SORGHUM JAPAN HOLDINGS CORP.; *Int'l*, pg. 7112
SORGHUM SOLUTIONS SOUTH AFRICA (PTY) LTD.—See S&W Seed Co.; *U.S. Public*, pg. 1832
SORIBADA INC.; *Int'l*, pg. 7112
SORIL INFRA RESOURCES LIMITED; *Int'l*, pg. 7112
SORIN CORP.—See Korea Zinc Company, Ltd.; *Int'l*, pg. 4287

COMPANY NAME INDEX

SORIN CRM S.A.S.—See MicroPort Scientific Corporation; *Int'l*, pg. 4880
SORIN CRM USA, INC.—See MicroPort Scientific Corporation; *Int'l*, pg. 4881
SOR, INC.; *U.S. Private*, pg. 3715
SORIN GROUP ITALIA S.R.L.—See LivaNova PLC; *Int'l*, pg. 4530
SORIN GROUP JAPAN K.K.—See LivaNova PLC; *Int'l*, pg. 4530
SORIN GROUP USA, INC.—See LivaNova PLC; *Int'l*, pg. 4530
SORIN INFORMATION TECHNOLOGY CO., LTD.—See Korea Zinc Company, Ltd.; *Int'l*, pg. 4288
SORINI RING MANUFACTURING INC.—See Ringmetall AG; *Int'l*, pg. 6344
SOR JOINT STOCK COMPANY; *Int'l*, pg. 7111
SORKIN'S RX, LTD.—See KKR & Co. Inc.; *U.S. Public*, pg. 1263
SORL AUTO PARTS, INC.—See Ruili Group Co., Ltd.; *Int'l*, pg. 6427
SORMAS SOGUT REFRAKTER MALZEMELERI ANONIM SIRKETI—See RHI Magnesita N.V.; *Int'l*, pg. 6326
SOR-NORGE ALUMINIUM AS—See Norsk Hydro ASA; *Int'l*, pg. 5436
SOROC TECHNOLOGY INC.; *Int'l*, pg. 7112
SOROS FUND MANAGEMENT LLC; *U.S. Private*, pg. 3715
SORRENTO CAPITAL, INC.; *U.S. Private*, pg. 3716
SORRENTO RESOURCES LTD.; *Int'l*, pg. 7112
SORRISO TECHNOLOGIES, INC.; *U.S. Private*, pg. 3716
SORRY ROBOTS LLC; *U.S. Private*, pg. 3716
SORT CO., LTD.—See Sanyo Trading Co., Ltd.; *Int'l*, pg. 6565
SORTED GROUP HOLDINGS PLC; *Int'l*, pg. 7112
SORTIMAT TECHNOLOGY PVT. LTD.—See ATS Corporation; *Int'l*, pg. 695
SORTIS HOLDINGS, INC.; *U.S. Public*, pg. 1909
SORUM TRACTOR CO., INC.—See AGCO Corporation; *U.S. Public*, pg. 58
SORUN CORPORATION—See TIS Inc.; *Int'l*, pg. 7758
SORUNPURE INC.—See TIS Inc.; *Int'l*, pg. 7758
SOSANDAR PLC; *Int'l*, pg. 7112
SOS BRANDS, INC.—See HealthEdge Investment Partners, LLC, *U.S. Private*, pg. 1090
SOS CONSULTING AND RECRUITMENT; *Int'l*, pg. 7112
SOS CORPORATION; *U.S. Private*, pg. 3716
SOSEI CO. LTD.—See Nxera Pharma Co., Ltd.; *Int'l*, pg. 5499
SOSEI CVC LTD.—See Nxera Pharma Co., Ltd.; *Int'l*, pg. 5499
SOSEI R&D LTD.—See Nxera Pharma Co., Ltd.; *Int'l*, pg. 5499
SOS GLOBAL EXPRESS INC.—See ATL Partners, LLC; *U.S. Private*, pg. 369
SOSHINA ELECTONICS (M) SDN. BHD.—See NGK Insulators, Ltd.; *Int'l*, pg. 5255
SOSHINA ELECTRONICS OF AMERICA INC.—See NGK Insulators, Ltd.; *Int'l*, pg. 5255
SOSHINA ELECTRONICS (SZ) LIMITED—See NGK Insulators, Ltd.; *Int'l*, pg. 5255
SOSHIN DEVICE CO., LTD.—See NGK Insulators, Ltd.; *Int'l*, pg. 5255
SOSHIN ELECTRIC CO., LTD. - ASAMA PLANT—See Walsin Technology Corporation; *Int'l*, pg. 8335
SOSHIN ELECTRIC CO., LTD.—See Walsin Technology Corporation; *Int'l*, pg. 8335
SOSHIN ELECTRONICS EUROPE GMBH—See NGK Insulators, Ltd.; *Int'l*, pg. 5255
SOSHIN ELECTRONICS (HK) LTD.—See NGK Insulators, Ltd.; *Int'l*, pg. 5255
SOSHIN ELECTRONICS (M) SDN. BHD.—See Walsin Technology Corporation; *Int'l*, pg. 8335
SOSHIMAT ELECTRONICS OF AMERICA INC.—See NGK Insulators, Ltd.; *Int'l*, pg. 5255
SOSHIN ELECTRONICS (SZ) LIMITED—See Walsin Technology Corporation; *Int'l*, pg. 8335
SOSHIN POWERTECH CO., LTD—See Walsin Technology Corporation; *Int'l*, pg. 8335
SOS HYDRATION INC.; *U.S. Private*, pg. 3716
SOSILA LOGISTICS REIT, INC.; *Int'l*, pg. 7112
SOS INFORMATION TECHNOLOGY CO., LTD.—See SOS Limited; *Int'l*, pg. 7112
SOS INTERNATIONAL LLC; *U.S. Private*, pg. 3716
SOS INTERNATIONAL LTD.—See SOS International LLC; *U.S. Private*, pg. 3716
SOS LIMITED; *Int'l*, pg. 7112
SOS MECHANICAL LLC—See CPS Capital; *Int'l*, pg. 1826
SOS METALS, INC.—See Berkshire Hathaway Inc.; *U.S. Public*, pg. 314
SOS OF TAMPA BAY, INC.; *U.S. Private*, pg. 3716
S.O.S OILFIELD SAFETY—See Petrowest Corp.; *Int'l*, pg. 5833
SOSO SMART ECO-COMPANY CO., LTD.—See Dowa Holdings Co., Ltd.; *Int'l*, pg. 2184
SOS SECURITY INC—See CDW Corporation; *U.S. Public*, pg. 463
SOS SECURITY LLC—See Allied Universal Manager LLC; *U.S. Private*, pg. 190

SOS TARIFFE S.R.L.—See Gruppo MutuiOnline S.p.A; *Int'l*, pg. 3141
SOSTENEO SGR S.P.A.; *Int'l*, pg. 7112
SOSTENYA GROUP PLC; *Int'l*, pg. 7112
SOSTRAVEL.COM S.P.A.; *Int'l*, pg. 7112
SOSUCO AND GROUP (2008) CO., LTD.—See The Siam Cement Public Company Limited; *Int'l*, pg. 7684
SOSUCO CERAMIC CO., LTD.—See The Siam Cement Public Company Limited; *Int'l*, pg. 7684
SOSYAL YAZILIM VE DANISMANLIK HIZMETLERI AS—See Wynn Resorts Limited; *U.S. Public*, pg. 2384
SOTA ACOUSTICS LIMITED—See Link-Asia International MedTech Group Limited; *Int'l*, pg. 4514
SOTAWALL LIMITED—See Apogee Enterprises, Inc.; *U.S. Public*, pg. 145
SOTC TRAVEL SERVICES PRIVATE LIMITED—See Fairfax Financial Holdings Limited; *Int'l*, pg. 2608
SOTEB—See Gerard Perrier Industrie S.A.; *Int'l*, pg. 2942
SOTEC GMBH—See Clariane SE; *Int'l*, pg. 1644
SOTECNA S.A.—See Floridienne SA; *Int'l*, pg. 2708
SOTECNICA ACORES LIMITADA—See VINCI S.A.; *Int'l*, pg. 8229
SOTECNICA S.A.—See VINCI S.A.; *Int'l*, pg. 8238
SO TELEVISION LIMITED—See ITV plc; *Int'l*, pg. 3845
SOTELMA SA—See Emirates Telecommunications Group Company PJSC; *Int'l*, pg. 2382
SOTEL SYSTEMS, LLC; *U.S. Private*, pg. 3716
SOTEM—See VINCI S.A.; *Int'l*, pg. 8234
SOTERA DEFENSE SOLUTIONS, INC.—See Jacobs Engineering Group, Inc.; *U.S. Public*, pg. 1186
SOTERA HEALTH COMPANY; *U.S. Public*, pg. 1909
SOTERA HEALTH LLC—See Warburg Pincus LLC; *U.S. Private*, pg. 4439
SOTERA WIRELESS, INC.; *U.S. Private*, pg. 3716
SOTERIA KLINIK LEIPZIG GMBH—See Asklepios Kliniken GmbH & Co. KGaA; *Int'l*, pg. 624
SOTERRA LLC—See Greif Inc.; *U.S. Public*, pg. 968
SOTETSU BUILDING MANAGEMENT CO., LTD.—See Sotetsu Holdings, Inc.; *Int'l*, pg. 7112
SOTETSU BUS CO., LTD.—See Sotetsu Holdings, Inc.; *Int'l*, pg. 7112
SOTETSU BUSINESS SERVICE CO., LTD.—See Sotetsu Holdings, Inc.; *Int'l*, pg. 7113
SOTETSU HOLDINGS, INC.; *Int'l*, pg. 7112
SOTETSU HOTEL MANAGEMENT CO., LTD.—See Sotetsu Holdings, Inc.; *Int'l*, pg. 7113
SOTETSU INSURANCE SERVICE CO., LTD.—See Sotetsu Holdings, Inc.; *Int'l*, pg. 7113
SOTETSU INTERNATIONAL KOREA CO., LTD.—See Sotetsu Holdings, Inc.; *Int'l*, pg. 7113
SOTETSU KIGYO CO., LTD.—See Sotetsu Holdings, Inc.; *Int'l*, pg. 7113
SOTETSU LIVING SUPPORT CO., LTD.—See Sotetsu Holdings, Inc.; *Int'l*, pg. 7113
SOTETSU NEXT STAGE CO., LTD.—See Sotetsu Holdings, Inc.; *Int'l*, pg. 7113
SOTETSU PURE WATER CO., LTD.—See Sotetsu Holdings, Inc.; *Int'l*, pg. 7113
SOTETSU REAL ESTATE CO., LTD.—See Sotetsu Holdings, Inc.; *Int'l*, pg. 7113
SOTETSU REAL ESTATE SALES CO., LTD.—See Sotetsu Holdings, Inc.; *Int'l*, pg. 7113
SOTETSU REFORM CO., LTD.—See Sotetsu Holdings, Inc.; *Int'l*, pg. 7113
SOTETSU RENUPS CO., LTD.—See Sotetsu Holdings, Inc.; *Int'l*, pg. 7113
SOTETSU ROSEN CO., LTD.—See Sotetsu Holdings, Inc.; *Int'l*, pg. 7113
SOTETSU ROSEN FRESH FOODS CO., LTD.—See Sotetsu Holdings, Inc.; *Int'l*, pg. 7113
SOTETSU STATION RETAIL CO., LTD.—See Sotetsu Holdings, Inc.; *Int'l*, pg. 7113
SOTETSU URBAN CREATES CO., LTD.—See Sotetsu Holdings, Inc.; *Int'l*, pg. 7113
SOTETSU URBAN CREATORS CO., LTD.—See Sotetsu Holdings, Inc.; *Int'l*, pg. 7113
SOTETSU WISH CO., LTD.—See Sotetsu Holdings, Inc.; *Int'l*, pg. 7113
SOTHEBY'S A.G.—See Sotheby's; *U.S. Public*, pg. 1910
SOTHEBY'S AMSTERDAM BV—See Sotheby's; *U.S. Public*, pg. 1910
SOTHEBY'S FRANCE S.A.S.—See Sotheby's; *U.S. Public*, pg. 1910
SOTHEBY'S GLOBAL TRADING—See Sotheby's; *U.S. Public*, pg. 1910
SOTHEBY'S HONG KONG LTD.—See Sotheby's; *U.S. Public*, pg. 1910
SOTHEBY'S INTERNATIONAL REALTY, INC.—See Anywhere Real Estate Inc.; *U.S. Public*, pg. 141
SOTHEBY'S INTERNATIONAL REALTY—See Anywhere Real Estate Inc.; *U.S. Public*, pg. 141
SOTHEBY'S INTERNATIONAL REALTY—See Anywhere Real Estate Inc.; *U.S. Public*, pg. 141
SOTHEBY'S ITALIA S.R.L.—See Sotheby's; *U.S. Public*, pg. 1910
SOTHEBY'S—See Sotheby's; *U.S. Public*, pg. 1910
SOTHEBY'S; *U.S. Public*, pg. 1909
SOTHEMA; *Int'l*, pg. 7113
SOTHERLY HOTELS INC.; *U.S. Public*, pg. 1910

SOULBRAIN HOLDINGS CO., LTD.

SOTHERLY HOTELS LP—See Sotherly Hotels Inc.; *U.S. Public*, pg. 1910
SOTICO PTY LTD—See Wesfarmers Limited; *Int'l*, pg. 8382
SOTIO A.S.—See PPF Group N.V.; *Int'l*, pg. 5951
SOTIO MEDICAL RESEARCH (BEIJING) CO., LTD.—See PPF Group N.V.; *Int'l*, pg. 5951
SOTIS BUSINESS EQUIPMENT LTD.; *U.S. Private*, pg. 3716
SOTKAMO SILVER AB; *Int'l*, pg. 7113
SOTKAMO SILVER OY—See Sotkamo Silver AB; *Int'l*, pg. 7113
SOTMOZ LIMITADA—See VINCI S.A.; *Int'l*, pg. 8229
SOTOGRANDE S.A.—See Minor International PCL; *Int'l*, pg. 4913
SOTOH CO., LTD.; *Int'l*, pg. 7113
SOTORAM—See Royal Air Maroc SA; *Int'l*, pg. 6409
SOTRANS HA TINH ONE MEMBER LIMITED COMPANY—See Southern International Logistics Joint Stock Company; *Int'l*, pg. 7119
SOTRANS LOGISTICS ONE MEMBER COMPANY LIMITED—See Southern International Logistics Joint Stock Company; *Int'l*, pg. 7120
SOTRA-SEPEREF S.A.S.—See Tessenderlo Group NV; *Int'l*, pg. 7574
SOTRAS SRL—See El.En. S.p.A.; *Int'l*, pg. 2342
SOTRAVO SAS—See Solocal Group; *Int'l*, pg. 7074
SOTREFI ETUPES—See Groupe Seche SAS; *Int'l*, pg. 3111
SOTRIS SPA—See Hera S.p.A.; *Int'l*, pg. 3356
SOTSU CO.,LTD.—See BANDAI NAMCO Holdings Inc.; *Int'l*, pg. 829
SOTSU MUSIC PUBLISHING CO., LTD.—See BANDAI NAMCO Holdings Inc.; *Int'l*, pg. 829
SOTTO INTERNATIONAL, INC.; *U.S. Private*, pg. 3716
SOU 300 GROUP HOLDING CO.; *U.S. Public*, pg. 1910
SOUCY BARON INC.—See Soucy Holding inc.; *Int'l*, pg. 7113
SOUCY BELGEN INC.—See Soucy Holding inc.; *Int'l*, pg. 7113
SOUCY HOLDING INC.; *Int'l*, pg. 7113
SOUCY INDUSTRIES INC.; *U.S. Private*, pg. 3716
SOUCY INTERNATIONAL INC.—See Soucy Holding inc.; *Int'l*, pg. 7113
SOUCY KOUTOU LTEE—See Soucy Holding inc.; *Int'l*, pg. 7113
SOUCY PLASTIQUES INC.—See Soucy Holding inc.; *Int'l*, pg. 7113
SOUCY RIVALAIR INC.—See Soucy Holding inc.; *Int'l*, pg. 7113
SOUCY TECHNO INC—See Soucy Holding inc.; *Int'l*, pg. 7113
SOUDACIER—See Oxymetal SA; *Int'l*, pg. 5676
SOUDAL INC.—See Soudal NV; *Int'l*, pg. 7113
SOUDAL NV; *Int'l*, pg. 7113
SOUDAN METALS COMPANY INC.; *U.S. Private*, pg. 3716
SOUDOKAY S.A.—See voestalpine AG; *Int'l*, pg. 8288
SOUDRONIC, LTD.; *U.S. Private*, pg. 3716
SOUERS CONSTRUCTION INC.; *U.S. Private*, pg. 3716
SOUFFLET AGRICULTE LIMITED—See Etablissements J. Soufflet; *Int'l*, pg. 2519
SOUFFLET AGRO POLSKA SP. Z O.O.—See Etablissements J. Soufflet; *Int'l*, pg. 2519
SOUFFLET AGRO S.R.O.—See Etablissements J. Soufflet; *Int'l*, pg. 2519
SOUFFLET ALIMENTAIRE S.A.—See Etablissements J. Soufflet; *Int'l*, pg. 2519
SOUFFLET BIOTECHNOLOGIES SAS—See Etablissements J. Soufflet; *Int'l*, pg. 2519
SOUFFLET NEGOCE S.A.—See Etablissements J. Soufflet; *Int'l*, pg. 2519
SOUFFLET VIGNE S.A.—See Etablissements J. Soufflet; *Int'l*, pg. 2519
SOUFIAN CEMENT CO.; *Int'l*, pg. 7113
SOUGOU BUSINESS SERVICE CO., LTD.—See Nisshinbo Holdings Inc.; *Int'l*, pg. 5373
SOUGOU SHOUKEN CO., LTD.; *Int'l*, pg. 7113
SOUKEN ACE CO.,LTD.; *Int'l*, pg. 7114
SOULAGE FAVAREL S.A.S.—See Orsero S.p.A.; *Int'l*, pg. 5644
SOUL BIOTECHNOLOGY CORPORATION; *U.S. Private*, pg. 3716
SOULBRAIN CO., LTD. - CHINA PLANT—See Soulbrain Holdings Co., Ltd.; *Int'l*, pg. 7114
SOULBRAIN CO., LTD. - GONGJU PLANT—See Soulbrain Holdings Co., Ltd.; *Int'l*, pg. 7114
SOULBRAIN CO., LTD. - JANGHANG PLANT—See Soulbrain Holdings Co., Ltd.; *Int'l*, pg. 7114
SOULBRAIN CO., LTD. - PAJU PLANT—See Soulbrain Holdings Co., Ltd.; *Int'l*, pg. 7114
SOULBRAIN CO., LTD. - ULSAN PLANT—See Soulbrain Holdings Co., Ltd.; *Int'l*, pg. 7114
SOULBRAIN HOLDINGS CO., LTD.; *Int'l*, pg. 7114
SOULBRAIN LTK CO., LTD.—See Soulbrain Holdings Co., Ltd.; *Int'l*, pg. 7114
SOULBRAIN MI—See Soulbrain Holdings Co., Ltd.; *Int'l*, pg. 7114

SOULBRAIN HOLDINGS CO., LTD.

SOULBRAIN NANOTEC CO., LTD.—See Soulbrain Holdings Co., Ltd.; *Int'l*, pg. 7114
SOULBRAIN OPTOS CO., LTD—See Soulbrain Holdings Co., Ltd.; *Int'l*, pg. 7114
SOULBRAIN SAVINGS BANK—See Soulbrain Holdings Co., Ltd.; *Int'l*, pg. 7114
SOULBRAIN SLD CO., LTD.—See Soulbrain Holdings Co., Ltd.; *Int'l*, pg. 7114
SOUL COMMUNICATIONS PTY. LIMITED—See CK Hutchison Holdings Limited; *Int'l*, pg. 1638
SOUL COMMUNICATIONS PTY. LIMITED—See Vodafone Group Plc; *Int'l*, pg. 8285
SOUL COMMUNITY PLANET, INC.; *U.S. Private*, pg. 3716
SOULCYCLE INC.; *U.S. Private*, pg. 3717
SOULGATE INC.; *Int'l*, pg. 7114
SOUL (LONDON) LTD.—See The Mission Group Public Limited Company; *Int'l*, pg. 7667
SOULPANCAKE—See Participant Productions, LLC; *U.S. Private*, pg. 3100
SOUL PATTINSON TELECOMMUNICATIONS PTY LTD—See CK Hutchison Holdings Limited; *Int'l*, pg. 1638
SOUL PATTINSON TELECOMMUNICATIONS PTY LTD—See Vodafone Group Plc; *Int'l*, pg. 8285
SOULSIGHT, LLC—See Bruins Sports Capital, LLC; *U.S. Private*, pg. 672
SOUL SPACE PROJECTS LIMITED—See B L Kashyap & Sons Limited; *Int'l*, pg. 783
SOULS PRIVATE EQUITY LIMITED—See Washington H. Soul Pattinson & Company Limited; *Int'l*, pg. 8351
SOUNDAIR AVIATION SERVICES, LLC—See HEICO Corporation; *U.S. Public*, pg. 1021
SOUND BANK—See Capital Bancorp, Inc.; *U.S. Public*, pg. 431
SOUNDBITE COMMUNICATIONS, INC.—See Permira Advisers LLP; *Int'l*, pg. 5805
SOUNDBITE COMMUNICATIONS UK, LTD.—See Permira Advisers LLP; *Int'l*, pg. 5805
SOUNDBITE COMMUNICATIONS - WASHINGTON, DC—See Permira Advisers LLP; *Int'l*, pg. 5805
SOUNDCAST COMPANY—See Griswold Industries, Inc.; *U.S. Private*, pg. 1791
SOUNDCAST LLC—See Hancock Park Associates, LP; *U.S. Private*, pg. 1852
SOUND CAVE TECHNOLOGY, INC.; *Int'l*, pg. 7114
SOUNDCHECK, LLC—See Live Nation Entertainment, Inc.; *U.S. Public*, pg. 1330
SOUNDCHIP SA—See Synaptics Incorporated; *U.S. Public*, pg. 1969
THE SOUNDCOAT COMPANY INC.—See Recticel S.A.; *Int'l*, pg. 6242
SOUND COM CORPORATION—See AMETEK, Inc.; *U.S. Public*, pg. 122
SOUND COMMUNICATIONS, INC.; *U.S. Private*, pg. 3717
SOUND COMMUNITY BANK—See Sound Financial Bancorp, Inc.; *U.S. Public*, pg. 1910
SOUNDCONNECT, LLC; *U.S. Private*, pg. 3717
SOUNDCORE CAPITAL PARTNERS, LLC; *U.S. Private*, pg. 3717
SOUNDCRAFT CANADA—See Evertz Microsystems Limited; *Int'l*, pg. 2569
SOUNDCRAFT—See Samsung Group; *Int'l*, pg. 6512
SOUND CREDIT UNION; *U.S. Private*, pg. 3717
SOUND DESIGN TECHNOLOGIES LTD.—See ON Semiconductor Corporation; *U.S. Public*, pg. 1601
SOUNDELUX—See Empire Investment Holdings, LLC; *U.S. Private*, pg. 1385
SOUND ENERGY PLC; *Int'l*, pg. 7114
SOUND ENGINEERING, INC.; *U.S. Private*, pg. 3717
SOUNDEXCHANGE, INC.; *U.S. Private*, pg. 3717
SOUND FINANCIAL BANCORP, INC.; *U.S. Public*, pg. 1910
SOUND FORD, INC.; *U.S. Private*, pg. 3717
SOUNDFOX INTERNATIONAL CO., LTD.—See Transition Evergreen; *Int'l*, pg. 7901
SOUND GLASS SALES, INC.; *U.S. Private*, pg. 3717
SOUND GLOBAL LTD.; *Int'l*, pg. 7114
SOUND GROUP INC.; *Int'l*, pg. 7114
SOUNDHOUND AI, INC.; *U.S. Public*, pg. 1910
SOUND INN STUDIOS INC.—See Nippon Television Holdings Inc.; *Int'l*, pg. 5356
SOUND INPATIENT PHYSICIANS, INC.—See Summit Partners, L.P.; *U.S. Private*, pg. 3856
SOUND MARKETING CONCEPTS OF CT LLC—See The Jordan Company, L.P.; *U.S. Private*, pg. 4062
SOUND MENTAL HEALTH; *U.S. Private*, pg. 3717
SOUND OCEAN SYSTEMS, INC.—See Okeanus Science & Technology, LLC; *U.S. Private*, pg. 3007
SOUND PARTNERS, LLC; *U.S. Private*, pg. 3717
SOUND POINT CAPITAL MANAGEMENT, LP; *U.S. Private*, pg. 3717
SOUND PUBLISHING, INC.—See Black Press Group Ltd.; *Int'l*, pg. 1059
SOUND SEAL, INC.; *U.S. Private*, pg. 3717
SOUND SEAL & PACKING CO.—See Flexaseal Engineered Seals and Systems, LLC; *U.S. Private*, pg. 1543

SOUND SERVICE MSL DISTRIBUTION LIMITED—See ZOOM Corporation; *Int'l*, pg. 8689
SOUND-SERVICE MUSIKANLAGEN-VERTRIEBSGESELLSCHAFT GMBH—See ZOOM Corporation; *Int'l*, pg. 8689
SOUNDS FANTASTIC LTD.; *Int'l*, pg. 7114
SOUND SHORE MEDICAL CENTER OF WESTCHESTER; *U.S. Private*, pg. 3717
SOUND SOLUTIONS AUSTRIA GMBH—See Hon Hai Precision Industry Co., Ltd.; *Int'l*, pg. 3459
SOUND SOLUTIONS INTERNATIONAL CO., LTD.—See Hon Hai Precision Industry Co., Ltd.; *Int'l*, pg. 3459
SOUNDSTORM DIGITAL, INC.; *Int'l*, pg. 7114
SOUND TECHNOLOGIES, INC.—See Mars, Incorporated; *U.S. Private*, pg. 2590
SOUND TECHNOLOGY, INC.—See Altaris Capital Partners, LLC; *U.S. Private*, pg. 205
SOUND TECHNOLOGY LIMITED—See Midwich Group Plc; *Int'l*, pg. 4888
SOUND TELECOM; *U.S. Private*, pg. 3717
SOUNDTHINKING, INC.; *U.S. Public*, pg. 1910
SOUNDVEST SPLIT TRUST; *Int'l*, pg. 7114
SOUND VIDEO SOLUTIONS, INC.; *U.S. Private*, pg. 3717
SOUNDVIEW CONSULTANTS LLC—See Keystone Group, L.P.; *U.S. Private*, pg. 2299
SOUNDVIEW PAPER CO. LLC—See Atlas Holdings, LLC; *U.S. Private*, pg. 378
SOUNDWARE DENMARK A/S—See Transition Evergreen; *Int'l*, pg. 7901
SOUNDWARE NORGE AS—See Transition Evergreen; *Int'l*, pg. 7901
SOUNDWILL HOLDINGS LIMITED; *Int'l*, pg. 7114
SOUPER SALAD, LLC—See BRIX Holdings, LLC; *U.S. Private*, pg. 658
SOUP HOLDINGS LIMITED; *Int'l*, pg. 7114
SOUPMAN, INC.; *U.S. Public*, pg. 1910
SOUP RESTAURANT (CAUSEWAY POINT) PTE. LTD.—See Soup Holdings Limited; *Int'l*, pg. 7114
SOUP RESTAURANT INVESTMENTS PTE. LTD.—See Soup Holdings Limited; *Int'l*, pg. 7115
SOUP RESTAURANT (JURONG POINT) PTE LTD—See Soup Holdings Limited; *Int'l*, pg. 7115
SOUP RESTAURANT SINGAPORE PTE. LTD.—See Soup Holdings Limited; *Int'l*, pg. 7115
SOUQ COMPANY CO., LTD.—See H2O Retailing Corp.; *Int'l*, pg. 3201
SOURCAG AG—See Swisscom AG; *Int'l*, pg. 7374
SOURCE ATLANTIC INDUSTRIAL DISTRIBUTION & SERVICES GROUP; *Int'l*, pg. 7115
THE SOURCE (BELL) ELECTRONICS INC.—See BCE Inc.; *Int'l*, pg. 926
SOURCE BIOSCIENCE LIMITED—See Harwood Capital LLP; *Int'l*, pg. 3282
SOURCEBITS DIGITAL LLC—See Vora Ventures LLC; *U.S. Private*, pg. 4412
SOURCEBOOKS, INC.; *U.S. Private*, pg. 3718
SOURCE CAPITAL, LLC; *U.S. Private*, pg. 3717
SOURCE CODE CORPORATION—See Cerberus Capital Management, L.P.; *U.S. Private*, pg. 839
SOURCE COMMUNICATIONS; *U.S. Private*, pg. 3718
SOURCE COMMUNICATIONS—See Source Communications; *U.S. Private*, pg. 3718
SOURCE EASY LIMITED—See NQIZ Group Limited; *Int'l*, pg. 5401
SOURCE ENERGY SERVICES LTD.; *Int'l*, pg. 7115
SOURCE EVOLUTION INC.—See Alan Allman Associates SA; *Int'l*, pg. 290
SOURCE EXECUTIVE RECRUITMENT SWEDEN AB—See NGS Group AB; *Int'l*, pg. 5256
SOURCEFIRE BRASIL COMERCIO E SEGURANCA DE REDE LTDA.—See Cisco Systems, Inc.; *U.S. Public*, pg. 500
SOURCEFIRE CANADA LTD.—See Cisco Systems, Inc.; *U.S. Public*, pg. 500
SOURCEFIRE, INC.—See Cisco Systems, Inc.; *U.S. Public*, pg. 500
SOURCEFIRE LIMITED—See Cisco Systems, Inc.; *U.S. Public*, pg. 500
SOURCEFIRE SINGAPORE PTE. LTD.—See Cisco Systems, Inc.; *U.S. Public*, pg. 500
THE SOURCE GROUP, INC.—See Apex Companies, LLC; *U.S. Private*, pg. 292
SOURCEHOV L.L.C.—See Gainline Capital Partners LP; *U.S. Private*, pg. 1635
SOURCE INDUSTRIES (INDIA) LIMITED; *Int'l*, pg. 7115
THE SOURCE, LLC; *U.S. Private*, pg. 4119
SOURCE LOGISTICS CENTER CORP.—See Palladium Equity Partners, LLC; *U.S. Private*, pg. 3078
SOURCE MANAGEMENT INC.; *U.S. Private*, pg. 3718
SOURCEMANTRA INC; *U.S. Private*, pg. 3718
SOURCE MARKETING LLC—See Stagwell, Inc.; *U.S. Public*, pg. 1928
SOURCE MEDIA LLC—See Observer Capital LLC; *U.S. Private*, pg. 2988
SOURCE MEDICAL SOLUTIONS, INC.—See Wells Fargo & Company; *U.S. Public*, pg. 2344
SOURCE NATURAL FOODS & HERBAL SUPPLEMENTS LIMITED; *Int'l*, pg. 7115

CORPORATE AFFILIATIONS

SOURCE NATURALS—See Threshold Enterprises, Ltd.; *U.S. Private*, pg. 4164
SOURCENET DISTRIBUTION, INC.; *U.S. Private*, pg. 3718
SOURCENEXT CORPORATION; *Int'l*, pg. 7115
SOURCENTRA, INC.; *U.S. Private*, pg. 3718
SOURCE OFFICE & TECHNOLOGY; *U.S. Private*, pg. 3718
SOURCE ONE DISTRIBUTORS, INC.; *U.S. Private*, pg. 3718
SOURCEONE GLOBAL PARTNERS LLC; *U.S. Private*, pg. 3718
SOURCE ONE MANAGEMENT, INC.; *U.S. Private*, pg. 3718
SOURCE ONE MEDICAL MANAGEMENT; *U.S. Private*, pg. 3718
SOURCE ONE STAFFING LLC; *U.S. Private*, pg. 3718
SOURCE ONE TRANSPORTATION, LLC—See Guttman Holdings, Inc.; *U.S. Private*, pg. 1820
SOURCE OUTDOOR CORP.; *U.S. Private*, pg. 3718
SOURCEPASS, INC.; *U.S. Private*, pg. 3718
SOURCE PHOTONICS, INC.; *U.S. Private*, pg. 3718
SOURCEPOINTE, LLC—See Aquiline Capital Partners LLC; *U.S. Private*, pg. 304
SOURCEPOWER B.V.—See Sopra Steria Group S.A.; *Int'l*, pg. 7115
SOURCE RECOVERY COMPANY INC.; *U.S. Private*, pg. 3718
SOURCE REFRIGERATION & HVAC, INC.—See Audax Group, Limited Partnership; *U.S. Private*, pg. 389
SOURCE ROCK, INC.; *U.S. Private*, pg. 3718
SOURCE SELECT GROUP, LLC; *U.S. Private*, pg. 3718
SOURCE SUPPORT SERVICES, INC.—See Logan Ridge Finance Corporation; *U.S. Public*, pg. 1340
SOURCE TECHNOLOGIES HOLDINGS, LLC—See StoneCalibre, LLC; *U.S. Private*, pg. 3828
SOURCE TECHNOLOGIES, LLC—See StoneCalibre, LLC; *U.S. Private*, pg. 3828
SOURCETOAD, LLC; *U.S. Private*, pg. 3719
SOURCE TWO SPARES INC.; *U.S. Private*, pg. 3718
SOURCEWISE; *U.S. Private*, pg. 3719
SOURCIFY GMBH—See H World Group Limited; *Int'l*, pg. 3191
THE SOURCING GROUP LLC; *U.S. Private*, pg. 4119
SOURCING INTERESTS GROUP (SIG); *U.S. Private*, pg. 3719
SOURDOUGH FUEL, INC.—See Arctic Slope Regional Corporation; *U.S. Private*, pg. 316
SOURIAU JAPAN K.K.—See TransDigm Group Incorporated; *U.S. Public*, pg. 2181
SOURIAU S.A.S.—See TransDigm Group Incorporated; *U.S. Public*, pg. 2181
SOURIAU USA INC.—See TransDigm Group Incorporated; *U.S. Public*, pg. 2181
SOURIREE BIOTECH & PHARM. CO., LTD.—See Standard Chem. & Pharm. Co., Ltd.; *Int'l*, pg. 7168
SOURIS MINI INC.; *Int'l*, pg. 7115
SOURIS RIVER COOPERATIVE; *U.S. Private*, pg. 3719
SO&U SAATCHI & SAATCHI—See Publicis Groupe S.A.; *Int'l*, pg. 6108
SOUSSANA S.A.—See Danish Crown AmbA; *Int'l*, pg. 1964
SOUTER CAPITAL LLP; *Int'l*, pg. 7115
SOUTH32 ALUMINIUM (HOLDINGS) PTY LTD.—See South32 Limited; *Int'l*, pg. 7117
SOUTH32 LIMITED; *Int'l*, pg. 7117
SOUTH32 SA LIMITED—See South32 Limited; *Int'l*, pg. 7117
SOUTH32 SIERRA GORDA S.P.A.—See South32 Limited; *Int'l*, pg. 7117
SOUTH32 WORSLEY ALUMINA PTY. LTD.—See South32 Limited; *Int'l*, pg. 7117
SOUTH49 SOLUTIONS, INC.—See Movista Inc.; *U.S. Private*, pg. 2802
SOUTH AFRICA CUSTODIAL MANAGEMENT INC.—See The GEO Group, Inc.; *U.S. Public*, pg. 2075
SOUTH AFRICAN AIRWAYS (PTY) LTD.; *Int'l*, pg. 7115
SOUTH AFRICAN AIRWAYS—See South African Airways (Pty) Ltd.; *Int'l*, pg. 7115
THE SOUTH AFRICAN BANK OF ATHENS LTD—See AFGRI Limited; *Int'l*, pg. 189
SOUTH AFRICAN BASSIE TRAVEL CENTRE—See South African Airways (Pty) Ltd.; *Int'l*, pg. 7115
THE SOUTH AFRICAN BREWERIES HOP FARMS (PTY) LTD—See Anheuser-Busch InBev SA/NV; *Int'l*, pg. 464
THE SOUTH AFRICAN BREWERIES MALTINGS (PTY) LTD—See Anheuser-Busch InBev SA/NV; *Int'l*, pg. 465
THE SOUTH AFRICAN BREWERIES (PTY) LTD.—See Anheuser-Busch InBev SA/NV; *Int'l*, pg. 464
SOUTH AFRICAN BROADCASTING CORPORATION; *Int'l*, pg. 7115
SOUTH AFRICAN BULK TERMINALS LIMITED—See The Bidvest Group Limited; *Int'l*, pg. 7626
SOUTH AFRICAN CONTAINER DEPOTS (PTY) LIMITED—See The Bidvest Group Limited; *Int'l*, pg. 7626
SOUTH AFRICAN CONTAINER STEVEDORES (PTY) LIMITED—See The Bidvest Group Limited; *Int'l*, pg. 7626

SOUTH AFRICAN CUSTODIAL MANAGEMENT PTY, LTD.—See The GEO Group, Inc.; *U.S. Public*, pg. 2075
SOUTH AFRICAN DIARIES (PTY) LIMITED—See The Bidvest Group Limited; *Int'l*, pg. 7626
SOUTH AFRICAN DISTILLERIES AND WINES (SA) LIMITED—See L'Arche Green N.V.; *Int'l*, pg. 4376
SOUTH AFRICAN FIBRE YARN RUGS (PTY) LIMITED—See Industrial Development Corporation of South Africa, Ltd.; *Int'l*, pg. 3672
SOUTH AFRICAN MICRO-ELECTRONIC SYSTEMS (PTY) LTD—See Labat Africa Ltd; *Int'l*, pg. 4389
SOUTH AFRICAN MINT COMPANY (PTY) LIMITED—See The South African Reserve Bank; *Int'l*, pg. 7687
SOUTH AFRICAN PORT OPERATIONS—See Transnet Ltd.; *Int'l*, pg. 7902
SOUTH AFRICAN PROPERTY OPPORTUNITIES PLC; *Int'l*, pg. 7115
THE SOUTH AFRICAN RESERVE BANK; *Int'l*, pg. 7687
SOUTH AFRICAN TRAVEL CENTRE—See South African Airways (Pty) Ltd.; *Int'l*, pg. 7115
SOUTH AFRICA PALABORA COPPER (PTY) LIMITED—See HBIS Group Co., Ltd.; *Int'l*, pg. 3296
SOUTH ALABAMA BRICK COMPANY; *U.S. Private*, pg. 3719
SOUTH ALABAMA ELECTRIC COOPERATIVE; *U.S. Private*, pg. 3719
SOUTH ALABAMA GAS; *U.S. Private*, pg. 3719
SOUTH AMERICAN GOLD CORP.; *U.S. Public*, pg. 1910
SOUTH AMERICAN LITHIUM CORP; *Int'l*, pg. 7115
SOUTH AMERICAN RESTAURANTS CORP.; *U.S. Private*, pg. 3719
SOUTHAMPTON CONTAINER TERMINALS LIMITED—See Dubai World Corporation; *Int'l*, pg. 2222
SOUTHAMPTON FOOTBALL CLUB LIMITED; *Int'l*, pg. 7117
SOUTHAMPTON INTERNATIONAL—See Ferrovial S.A.; *Int'l*, pg. 2644
SOUTHARD COMMUNICATIONS; *U.S. Private*, pg. 3724
SOUTH ARKANSAS PHYSICIAN SERVICES, LLC—See Community Health Systems, Inc.; *U.S. Public*, pg. 557
SOUTH ARKANSAS YOUTH, SERVICES, INC.; *U.S. Private*, pg. 3719
SOUTH ARLINGTON DIALYSIS CENTER, LLC—See Nautic Partners, LLC; *U.S. Private*, pg. 2871
SOUTH ASIA FM LIMITED—See Sun TV Network Limited; *Int'l*, pg. 7308
SOUTH ASIAN ENTERPRISES LIMITED—See VLS Capital Ltd.; *Int'l*, pg. 8283
SOUTH ASIAN PACIFIC CO., LTD.—See Techtronic Industries Co., Ltd.; *Int'l*, pg. 7513
SOUTH ATLANTIC BANCSHARES, INC.; *U.S. Public*, pg. 1910
SOUTH ATLANTIC BANK—See South Atlantic Bancshares, Inc.; *U.S. Public*, pg. 1911
SOUTH ATLANTIC EQUIPMENT COMPANY, INC.—See The Dickerson Group, Inc.; *U.S. Private*, pg. 4021
SOUTH ATLANTIC FOREST PRODUCTS INC.; *U.S. Private*, pg. 3719
SOUTH ATLANTIC GOLD BRASIL EXPLOTACAO MINERAL LTDA.—See South Atlantic Gold Inc.; *Int'l*, pg. 7115
SOUTH ATLANTIC GOLD INC.; *Int'l*, pg. 7115
SOUTH ATLANTIC LLC; *U.S. Private*, pg. 3719
SOUTH ATLANTIC PACKAGING CORP.; *U.S. Private*, pg. 3719
SOUTH ATLANTIC TRANSPORTATION CORPORATION; *U.S. Private*, pg. 3719
SOUTH AUCKLAND FORD LTD—See The Colonial Motor Company Limited; *Int'l*, pg. 7635
SOUTH AUCKLAND MOTORS LIMITED—See The Colonial Motor Company Limited; *Int'l*, pg. 7635
SOUTH AUGUSTA DIALYSIS CLINIC, LLC—See Nautic Partners, LLC; *U.S. Private*, pg. 2871
SOUTH AUSTIN SURGERY CENTER, LTD.—See HCA Healthcare, Inc.; *U.S. Public*, pg. 1010
THE SOUTH AUSTRALIAN BREWING COMPANY PTY. LIMITED—See Kirin Holdings Company, Limited; *Int'l*, pg. 4189
SOUTH AUSTRALIAN GOVERNMENT FINANCING AUTHORITY; *Int'l*, pg. 7115
SOUTH AUSTRALIAN INSTITUTE OF BUSINESS & TECHNOLOGY PTY LTD.—See Navitas Limited; *Int'l*, pg. 5177
SOUTHBANK FRESH FISH—See The Bidvest Group Limited; *Int'l*, pg. 7622
SOUTH BANKING COMPANY; *U.S. Private*, pg. 3719
SOUTH BARNES DEVELOPMENT CO.; *U.S. Private*, pg. 3719
SOUTH BAY ACCEPTANCE CORPORATION—See Tiptree Inc.; *U.S. Public*, pg. 2159
SOUTH BAY CABLE CORP.; *U.S. Private*, pg. 3719
SOUTH BAY CIRCUITS INC.; *U.S. Private*, pg. 3719
SOUTH BAY FAMILY HEALTH CARE—See Venice Family Clinic; *U.S. Private*, pg. 4356
SOUTH BAY HOSPITAL—See HCA Healthcare, Inc.; *U.S. Public*, pg. 1010
SOUTH BAY IMAGING, LLC—See HCA Healthcare, Inc.; *U.S. Public*, pg. 1010
SOUTH BAY LEXUS; *U.S. Private*, pg. 3719

SOUTH BAY MOTORS LLC; *U.S. Private*, pg. 3719
SOUTHBAY TOYOTA; *U.S. Private*, pg. 3724
SOUTH BAY WORKFORCE INVESTMENT BOARD; *U.S. Private*, pg. 3719
SOUTH BEACH BEVERAGE COMPANY—See PepsiCo, Inc.; *U.S. Public*, pg. 1670
SOUTH BEACH SMOKE LLC—See Turning Point Brands, Inc.; *U.S. Public*, pg. 2205
SOUTH BEACH SPIRITS, INC.; *U.S. Public*, pg. 1911
THE SOUTH BEND CLINIC, LLP; *U.S. Private*, pg. 4119
THE SOUTH BEND IN ENDOSCOPY ASC, LLC—See KKR & Co. Inc.; *U.S. Public*, pg. 1248
SOUTHBEND—See The Middleby Corporation; *U.S. Public*, pg. 2115
SOUTH BOSTON COMMUNITY HEALTH CENTER; *U.S. Private*, pg. 3720
SOUTHBRIDGE COMPANIA DE SEGUROS GENERALES S.A.—See Fairfax Financial Holdings Limited; *Int'l*, pg. 2608
SOUTHBRIDGE INSURANCE COMPANY—See Fairfax Financial Holdings Limited; *Int'l*, pg. 2608
SOUTHBRIDGE SAVINGS BANK—See SSB Community Bancorp MHC; *U.S. Private*, pg. 3768
SOUTH BROADWAY MOTORS, LLC—See AutoNation, Inc.; *U.S. Public*, pg. 237
SOUTH BROWARD HOSPITAL DISTRICT; *U.S. Private*, pg. 3720
SOUTH BURNETT COMMUNITY ENTERPRISES LIMITED—See Bendigo & Adelaide Bank Ltd.; *Int'l*, pg. 971
SOUTH CAN THO INVESTMENT & DEVELOPMENT JSC—See C.E.O Group Joint Stock Company; *Int'l*, pg. 1240
SOUTHCARE PHYSIOTHERAPY PTY LIMITED—See Sonic Healthcare Limited; *Int'l*, pg. 7098
SOUTH CAROLINA AQUARIUM; *U.S. Private*, pg. 3720
SOUTH CAROLINA CENTRAL RAILROAD COMPANY, LLC—See Brookfield Infrastructure Partners L.P.; *Int'l*, pg. 1192
SOUTH CAROLINA CENTRAL RAILROAD COMPANY, LLC—See GIC Pte. Ltd.; *Int'l*, pg. 2967
SOUTH CAROLINA DEPARTMENT OF TRANSPORTATION; *U.S. Private*, pg. 3720
SOUTH CAROLINA ELASTIC—See Industrial Value Partners, LLC; *U.S. Private*, pg. 2069
SOUTH CAROLINA FARM BUREAU MUTUAL INSURANCE COMPANY; *U.S. Private*, pg. 3720
SOUTH CAROLINA FIRST STEPS TO SCHOOL READINESS; *U.S. Private*, pg. 3720
SOUTH CAROLINA INTERACTIVE, LLC—See Tyler Technologies, Inc.; *U.S. Public*, pg. 2209
SOUTH CAROLINA LOGOS, INC.—See Lamar Advertising Company; *U.S. Public*, pg. 1291
SOUTH CAROLINA MANUFACTURING EXTENSION PARTNERSHIP; *U.S. Private*, pg. 3720
SOUTH CAROLINA MENTOR, INC.—See Centerbridge Partners, L.P.; *U.S. Private*, pg. 814
SOUTH CAROLINA PHILHARMONIC ASSOCIATION INC.; *U.S. Private*, pg. 3720
SOUTH CAROLINA PUBLIC SERVICE AUTHORITY; *U.S. Private*, pg. 3720
SOUTH CAROLINA RESEARCH AUTHORITY; *U.S. Private*, pg. 3720
SOUTH CAROLINA SEWEE FAMILY MEDICINE, L.L.C.—See Tenet Healthcare Corporation; *U.S. Public*, pg. 2003
SOUTH CAROLINA STATE PORTS AUTHORITY; *U.S. Private*, pg. 3720
SOUTH CAROLINA STEEL—See Commercial Metals Company; *U.S. Public*, pg. 546
SOUTH CASTLE PROPERTIES LTD.—See Caledonian Trust PLC; *Int'l*, pg. 1263
SOUTH CENTRAL ARKANSAS ELECTRIC COOPERATIVE, INC.; *U.S. Private*, pg. 3720
SOUTH CENTRAL BANK, N.A.—See Verve, a Credit Union; *U.S. Private*, pg. 4371
SOUTH CENTRAL BUILDING SYSTEMS LTD.—See Atlas Engineered Products Ltd.; *Int'l*, pg. 685
SOUTH CENTRAL COMMUNICATIONS CORPORATION; *U.S. Private*, pg. 3720
SOUTH CENTRAL COMPANY INC.; *U.S. Private*, pg. 3720
SOUTH CENTRAL CONNECTICUT REGIONAL WATER AUTHORITY INC.; *U.S. Private*, pg. 3721
SOUTH CENTRAL CO-OP; *U.S. Private*, pg. 3720
SOUTH CENTRAL COOP; *U.S. Private*, pg. 3721
SOUTH CENTRAL FLORIDA DIALYSIS PARTNERS, LLC—See DaVita Inc.; *U.S. Public*, pg. 643
SOUTH CENTRAL FLORIDA EXPRESS, INC.—See United States Sugar Corporation; *U.S. Private*, pg. 4300
SOUTH CENTRAL FS INC.; *U.S. Private*, pg. 3721
SOUTH CENTRAL GRAIN COOPERATIVE; *U.S. Private*, pg. 3721
SOUTH CENTRAL HUMAN RESOURCE AGENCY; *U.S. Private*, pg. 3721
SOUTH CENTRAL INDIANA RURAL ELECTRIC MEMBERSHIP CORPORATION; *U.S. Private*, pg. 3721

SOUTH CENTRAL POWER COMPANY INC.; *U.S. Private*, pg. 3721
SOUTH CENTRAL RURAL TELEPHONE; *U.S. Private*, pg. 3721
SOUTH CENTRAL SERVICE COMPANY; *U.S. Private*, pg. 3721
SOUTH CENTRAL UTAH TELEPHONE ASSOCIATION, INC.; *U.S. Private*, pg. 3721
SOUTH CENTRAL WYOMING HEALTHCARE & REHABILITATION—See Apollo Global Management, Inc.; *U.S. Public*, pg. 157
SOUTH CHESTER TUBE COMPANY; *U.S. Private*, pg. 3721
SOUTH CHICAGO PACKING CO.—See Ed Miniat, Inc.; *U.S. Private*, pg. 1331
SOUTH CHINA ASSETS HOLDINGS LIMITED; *Int'l*, pg. 7116
SOUTHCHINA ENGINEERING & MANUFACTURING LIMITED—See Alltronics Holdings Limited; *Int'l*, pg. 361
SOUTH CHINA FINANCIAL CREDITS LIMITED—See South China Assets Holdings Limited; *Int'l*, pg. 7116
SOUTH CHINA FINANCIAL HOLDINGS LIMITED; *Int'l*, pg. 7116
SOUTH CHINA HOLDINGS COMPANY LIMITED; *Int'l*, pg. 7116
SOUTH CHINA INSURANCE CO., LTD.—See Hua Nan Financial Holdings Co., Ltd.; *Int'l*, pg. 3510
SOUTH CHINA INTERNATIONAL LEASING COMPANY LIMITED—See Capital Industrial Financial Services Group Limited; *Int'l*, pg. 1311
SOUTH CHINA MORNING POST PUBLISHERS LTD.—See Alibaba Group Holding Limited; *Int'l*, pg. 326
THE SOUTH CHINA MORNING POST PUBLISHERS LTD.—See News Corporation; *U.S. Public*, pg. 1520
SOUTH CHINA REBORN RESOURCES (ZHONGSHAN) COMPANY LIMITED—See World Houseware (Holdings) Limited; *Int'l*, pg. 8457
SOUTH CHINA TOWING CO., LTD.—See Tokyo Kisen Co., Ltd.; *Int'l*, pg. 7793
SOUTH CHINA VOCATIONAL EDUCATION GROUP CO., LTD.; *Int'l*, pg. 7116
SOUTH CLEVELAND GARAGES; *Int'l*, pg. 7116
SOUTH COASTAL BANK; *U.S. Private*, pg. 3721
SOUTH COAST BASALT PTY LTD—See Heidelberg Materials AG; *Int'l*, pg. 3319
SOUTH COAST CIRCUITS, INC.—See Summit Interconnect, Inc.; *U.S. Private*, pg. 3855
SOUTH COAST CONSTRUCTION SERVICES; *U.S. Private*, pg. 3721
SOUTH COAST ELECTRIC SYSTEMS, LLC.—See Beier Radio LLC; *U.S. Private*, pg. 516
SOUTH COAST OILS PTY LTD—See Ampol Limited; *Int'l*, pg. 436
SOUTH COAST PLAZA; *U.S. Private*, pg. 3721
SOUTH COAST PRIVATE PTY. LTD.—See Luye Medical Group; *Int'l*, pg. 4590
SOUTH COAST STONE CRUSHERS (PTY) LTD.—See Camargo Correa S.A.; *Int'l*, pg. 1268
SOUTH COAST SUPPLY COMPANY; *U.S. Private*, pg. 3721
SOUTH COAST SURETY INSURANCE SERVICES, LLC—See Boston Omaha Corporation; *U.S. Public*, pg. 372
SOUTH COAST TERMINALS LP; *U.S. Private*, pg. 3721
SOUTH COAST WATER DISTRICT; *U.S. Private*, pg. 3721
SOUTHCO DISTRIBUTING COMPANY; *U.S. Private*, pg. 3724
SOUTHCO, INC.—See South Chester Tube Company; *U.S. Private*, pg. 3721
SOUTHCOMM COMMUNICATIONS, INC.—See SouthComm, Inc.; *U.S. Private*, pg. 3724
SOUTHCOMM, INC.; *U.S. Private*, pg. 3724
SOUTH CONE HOME, INC.; *U.S. Private*, pg. 3721
SOUTH CONE, INC.—See Charlesbank Capital Partners, LLC; *U.S. Private*, pg. 856
SOUTH CONSTRUCTION COMPANY, INC.—See Duke Energy Corporation; *U.S. Public*, pg. 691
SOUTH COTABATO INTEGRATED PORT SERVICES, INC.—See International Container Terminal Services, Inc.; *Int'l*, pg. 3746
SOUTH COUNTRY EQUIPMENT LTD.; *Int'l*, pg. 7116
SOUTH COUNTY INSURANCE AGENCY, LLC—See The Ayres Group, LLC; *U.S. Private*, pg. 3990
SOUTH COUNTY OUTPATIENT ENDOSCOPY SERVICES, L.P.—See Tenet Healthcare Corporation; *U.S. Public*, pg. 2012
SOUTH COUNTY SANITARY SERVICE, INC.—See Waste Connections, Inc.; *Int'l*, pg. 8354
SOUTHCREST BANK, N.A.—See Colony Bankcorp, Inc.; *U.S. Public*, pg. 533
SOUTHCREST DIALYSIS, LLC—See DaVita Inc.; *U.S. Public*, pg. 643
SOUTHCREST FINANCIAL GROUP, INC.—See Colony Bankcorp, Inc.; *U.S. Public*, pg. 533
SOUTH CROFTY LIMITED—See Cornish Metals Inc.; *Int'l*, pg. 1801
SOUTHCROSS ENERGY GP LLC—See Charlesbank Capital Partners, LLC; *U.S. Private*, pg. 856

SOUTH COUNTRY EQUIPMENT LTD.
CORPORATE AFFILIATIONS

SOUTHCROSS ENERGY GP LLC—See EIG Global Energy Partners, LLC; *U.S. Private*, pg. 1347
SOUTHCROSS ENERGY GP LLC—See Tailwater Capital LLC; *U.S. Private*, pg. 3923
SOUTHCROSS ENERGY OPERATING, LLC—See Targa Resources Corp.; *U.S. Public*, pg. 1981
SOUTHCROSS ENERGY PARTNERS,LLC—See Charlesbank Capital Partners, LLC; *U.S. Private*, pg. 856
SOUTHCROSS ENERGY PARTNERS,LLC—See EIG Global Energy Partners, LLC; *U.S. Private*, pg. 1347
SOUTHCROSS ENERGY PARTNERS,LLC—See Tailwater Capital LLC; *U.S. Private*, pg. 3923
SOUTHCROSS HOLDINGS LP—See Charlesbank Capital Partners, LLC; *U.S. Private*, pg. 856
SOUTHCROSS HOLDINGS LP—See EIG Global Energy Partners, LLC; *U.S. Private*, pg. 1347
SOUTHCROSS HOLDINGS LP—See Tailwater Capital LLC; *U.S. Private*, pg. 3923
SOUTHCROSS MISSISSIPPI INDUSTRIAL GAS SALES, L.P.—See Charlesbank Capital Partners, LLC; *U.S. Private*, pg. 856
SOUTHCROSS MISSISSIPPI INDUSTRIAL GAS SALES, L.P.—See EIG Global Energy Partners, LLC; *U.S. Private*, pg. 1347
SOUTHCROSS MISSISSIPPI INDUSTRIAL GAS SALES, L.P.—See Tailwater Capital LLC; *U.S. Private*, pg. 3923
SOUTHCROSS MISSISSIPPI PIPELINE, L.P.—See Charlesbank Capital Partners, LLC; *U.S. Private*, pg. 856
SOUTHCROSS MISSISSIPPI PIPELINE, L.P.—See EIG Global Energy Partners, LLC; *U.S. Private*, pg. 1347
SOUTHCROSS MISSISSIPPI PIPELINE, L.P.—See Tailwater Capital LLC; *U.S. Private*, pg. 3923
SOUTHCROSS NGL PIPELINE LTD.—See Charlesbank Capital Partners, LLC; *U.S. Private*, pg. 856
SOUTHCROSS NGL PIPELINE LTD.—See EIG Global Energy Partners, LLC; *U.S. Private*, pg. 1347
SOUTHCROSS NGL PIPELINE LTD.—See Tailwater Capital LLC; *U.S. Private*, pg. 3923
SOUTH CYPRESS; *U.S. Private*, pg. 3721
SOUTH DADE AUTOMOTIVE INC.; *U.S. Private*, pg. 3722
SOUTH DADE ELECTRICAL SUPPLY; *U.S. Private*, pg. 3722
SOUTH DADE NEONATOLOGY, LLC—See MEDNAX, Inc.; *U.S. Public*, pg. 1413
SOUTH DADE NEWS, INC.; *U.S. Private*, pg. 3722
SOUTH DAKOTA BANCSHARES, INC.; *U.S. Private*, pg. 3722
THE SOUTH DAKOTA GREAT ATLANTIC & PACIFIC TEA CO., INC.—See The Great Atlantic & Pacific Tea Company, Inc.; *U.S. Private*, pg. 4038
SOUTH DAKOTA SOYBEAN PROCESSORS, LLC; *U.S. Private*, pg. 3722
SOUTH DAKOTA SOYBEAN PROCESSORS LLC; *U.S. Public*, pg. 1911
SOUTH DAKOTA STATE UNIVERSITY FOUNDATION; *U.S. Private*, pg. 3722
SOUTH DAKOTA WHEAT GROWERS ASSOCIATION; *U.S. Private*, pg. 3722
SOUTH DAKOTA WHEAT GROWERS—See South Dakota Wheat Growers Association; *U.S. Private*, pg. 3722
SOUTHDATA, INC.; *U.S. Private*, pg. 3724
SOUTH DAVIS COMMUNITY HOSPITAL; *U.S. Private*, pg. 3722
SOUTH DAYTONA TRACTOR & MOWER, INC.—See Ag-Pro, LLC; *U.S. Private*, pg. 125
SOUTH DELTA PLANNING & DEVELOPMENT DISTRICT, INC.; *U.S. Private*, pg. 3722
SOUTHEAST ALABAMA GAS DISTRICT; *U.S. Private*, pg. 3724
SOUTHEAST ALABAMA HOMECARE, LLC—See UnitedHealth Group Incorporated; *U.S. Public*, pg. 2247
SOUTHEAST ALASKA REGIONAL HEALTH CONSORTIUM; *U.S. Private*, pg. 3724
SOUTHEAST ALASKA SMOKED SALMON CO., INC.; *U.S. Private*, pg. 3724
SOUTHEAST AREA COUNCIL—See Dairy Farmers of America; *U.S. Private*, pg. 1146
SOUTH EAST AREA HEALTH EDUCATION CENTER; *U.S. Private*, pg. 3722
SOUTH-EAST ASIA BREWERY LTD.—See Carlsberg A/S; *Int'l*, pg. 1341
SOUTHEAST ASIA ENERGY LIMITED—See CH. Karnchang Public Company Limited; *Int'l*, pg. 1435
SOUTHEAST ASIAN PACKAGING & CANNING LTD.—See Maruha Nichiro Corporation; *Int'l*, pg. 4711
SOUTH EAST ASIA PAPER PRODUCTS SDN BHD—See Yee Lee Corporation Bhd.; *Int'l*, pg. 8575
SOUTHEAST ASIA PROPERTIES & FINANCE LIMITED; *Int'l*, pg. 7117
SOUTHEAST-ATLANTIC BEVERAGE CORP.—See JAB Holding Company S.a.r.l.; *Int'l*, pg. 3862
SOUTH EAST AUSTRALIA GAS PTY LTD—See APA Group; *Int'l*, pg. 500
SOUTHEAST AUTOMOTIVE GROUP PTY LTD—See Eagers Automotive Limited; *Int'l*, pg. 2263
SOUTHEAST BANCSHARES, INC.; *U.S. Private*, pg. 3725
SOUTHEAST BANK PLC; *Int'l*, pg. 7117

SOUTHEAST BEVERAGE COMPANY; *U.S. Private*, pg. 3725
SOUTHEAST BRONX NEIGHBORHOOD CENTERS, INC.; *U.S. Private*, pg. 3725
SOUTHEAST CEMENT CO., LTD.; *Int'l*, pg. 7117
SOUTHEAST COLORADO POWER ASSOCIATION; *U.S. Private*, pg. 3725
SOUTHEAST COMMUNITY WORK CENTER, INC.; *U.S. Private*, pg. 3725
SOUTHEAST COMPUTER SOLUTIONS, INC.—See Net@Work, Inc.; *U.S. Private*, pg. 2887
SOUTHEAST CONNECTIONS LLC—See Kelso & Company, L.P.; *U.S. Private*, pg. 2280
SOUTHEAST CONSTRUCTION PRODUCTS, INC.; *U.S. Private*, pg. 3725
SOUTHEAST COOPERATIVE SERVICE CO.; *U.S. Private*, pg. 3725
SOUTHEAST DIESEL CORP.; *U.S. Private*, pg. 3725
SOUTHEAST DIVISION LOGISTICS, LLC—See Vulcan Materials Company; *U.S. Public*, pg. 2313
SOUTHEASTERN ALUMINUM PRODUCTS, INC.; *U.S. Private*, pg. 3727
SOUTHEASTERN APPLIANCES AND MORE, LLC—See The Climatic Corporation; *U.S. Private*, pg. 4010
SOUTHEASTERN ASSET MANAGEMENT, INC.; *U.S. Private*, pg. 3727
SOUTHEASTERN ASSET MANAGEMENT INTERNATIONAL (UK) LTD.—See Southeastern Asset Management, Inc.; *U.S. Private*, pg. 3727
SOUTHEASTERN AUTOMATIC SPRINKLER CO., INC.—See Comfort Systems USA, Inc.; *U.S. Public*, pg. 543
SOUTHEASTERN AUTOMOTIVE WAREHOUSE; *U.S. Private*, pg. 3727
SOUTHEASTERN BANCORP, INC.; *U.S. Private*, pg. 3727
SOUTHEASTERN BANCORP, INC.; *U.S. Private*, pg. 3727
SOUTHEASTERN BANK INC.—See Southeastern Banking Corp.; *U.S. Public*, pg. 1911
SOUTHEASTERN BANKING CORP.; *U.S. Public*, pg. 1911
SOUTH EASTERN CATTLE BREEDING SOCIETY LIMITED—See Glanbia Co-Operative Society Limited; *Int'l*, pg. 2988
SOUTH EASTERN COALFIELDS LIMITED—See Coal India Limited; *Int'l*, pg. 1680
SOUTHEASTERN COMMUNITY & FAMILY SERVICES, INC.; *U.S. Private*, pg. 3727
SOUTHEASTERN COMPUTER CONSULTANTS, INC.; *U.S. Private*, pg. 3727
SOUTHEASTERN CONSTRUCTION & MAINTENANCE, INC.; *U.S. Private*, pg. 3727
SOUTHEASTERN CONTAINER INC.; *U.S. Private*, pg. 3727
SOUTHEASTERN DATA COOPERATIVE; *U.S. Private*, pg. 3727
SOUTHEASTERN ELECTRICAL DISTRIBUTORS INC.; *U.S. Private*, pg. 3727
SOUTH EASTERN ELECTRIC DEVELOPMENT CORPORATION—See Morgan Stanley; *U.S. Public*, pg. 1475
SOUTHEASTERN EMERGENCY EQUIPMENT, INC.—See Investor AB; *Int'l*, pg. 3787
SOUTHEASTERN ENERGY CORP.; *U.S. Private*, pg. 3727
SOUTHEASTERN EQUIPMENT CO., INC.; *U.S. Private*, pg. 3727
SOUTHEASTERN EQUIPMENT & SUPPLY, INC.; *U.S. Private*, pg. 3727
SOUTHEASTERN EXTRUSION & TOOL, INC.; *U.S. Private*, pg. 3727
SOUTHEASTERN FARMERS COOPERATIVE; *U.S. Private*, pg. 3727
SOUTHEASTERN FINANCIAL INC.; *U.S. Private*, pg. 3727
SOUTHEASTERN FOREST MANAGEMENT, LLC—See Windrock Land Company; *U.S. Public*, pg. 2372
SOUTHEASTERN FREIGHT LINES, INC.; *U.S. Private*, pg. 3728
SOUTHEASTERN GROCERS, INC.—See Aldi Einkauf SE & Co. oHG; *Int'l*, pg. 304
SOUTHEASTERN HAY & NURSERY, LLC—See National Association for Stock Car Auto Racing, Inc.; *U.S. Private*, pg. 2846
SOUTHEASTERN ICE, INC.—See H.I.G. Capital, LLC; *U.S. Private*, pg. 1829
SOUTHEASTERN ILLINOIS ELECTRIC CO-OPERATIVE INC.; *U.S. Private*, pg. 3728
SOUTHEASTERN INDUSTRIAL CONSTRUCTION COMPANY INC.; *U.S. Private*, pg. 3728
SOUTHEASTERN INSTALLATION INC.; *U.S. Private*, pg. 3728
SOUTHEASTERN INTERNATIONAL SALES; *U.S. Private*, pg. 3728
SOUTHEASTERN KIDNEY COUNCIL, INC.; *U.S. Private*, pg. 3728
SOUTHEASTERN MANUFACTURERS AGENTS, INC.; *U.S. Private*, pg. 3728

SOUTHEASTERN MEDEQUIP, INC.; *U.S. Private*, pg. 3728
SOUTHEASTERN METAL PRODUCTS LLC—See Juno Investments LLC; *U.S. Private*, pg. 2244
SOUTHEASTERN METALS MANUFACTURING CO., INC.—See Gibraltar Industries, Inc.; *U.S. Public*, pg. 936
SOUTHEASTERN OIL CO. INC.; *U.S. Private*, pg. 3728
SOUTHEASTERN PACKAGING CO.—See Greif Inc.; *U.S. Public*, pg. 967
SOUTHEASTERN PAPERBOARD INC.; *U.S. Private*, pg. 3728
SOUTHEASTERN PAPERBOARD INC.—See Southeastern Paperboard Inc.; *U.S. Private*, pg. 3728
SOUTHEASTERN PAPER GROUP, INC.; *U.S. Private*, pg. 3728
SOUTHEASTERN PATHOLOGY ASSOCIATES—See PathGroup; *U.S. Private*, pg. 3106
SOUTHEASTERN PENNSYLVANIA TRANSPORTATION AUTHORITY; *U.S. Private*, pg. 3728
SOUTHEASTERN PETROLEUM CO., INC.; *U.S. Private*, pg. 3728
SOUTHEASTERN PHYSICIAN ASSOCIATES, LLC—See Blackstone Inc.; *U.S. Public*, pg. 359
SOUTHEASTERN PLASTICS CORP.—See Alpha Industries, Inc.; *U.S. Public*, pg. 198
SOUTHEASTERN POLE SALES, INC.; *U.S. Private*, pg. 3728
SOUTHEASTERN PRINTING COMPANY INC.; *U.S. Private*, pg. 3728
SOUTHEASTERN PUBLIC SERVICE AUTHORITY; *U.S. Private*, pg. 3728
SOUTHEASTERN REALTY GROUP INC.; *U.S. Private*, pg. 3728
SOUTHEASTERN RISK SPECIALISTS—See American International Group, Inc.; *U.S. Public*, pg. 107
SOUTHEASTERN SALON SUPPLIERS, INC.; *U.S. Private*, pg. 3729
THE SOUTHEASTERN SPINE INSTITUTE SURGERY CENTER, L.L.C.—See Tenet Healthcare Corporation; *U.S. Public*, pg. 2008
SOUTHEASTERN SUPPLY CO. INC.; *U.S. Private*, pg. 3729
SOUTHEASTERN TECHNOLOGY, INC.—See NN, Inc.; *U.S. Public*, pg. 1530
SOUTHEASTERN TELECOM INC.; *U.S. Private*, pg. 3729
SOUTHEASTERN TELECOM OF KNOXVILLE INC.—See Southeastern Telecom Inc.; *U.S. Private*, pg. 3729
SOUTHEASTERN TELECOM—See Southeastern Telecom Inc.; *U.S. Private*, pg. 3729
SOUTHEASTERN UNDERWRITERS, INC.—See W.R. Berkley Corporation; *U.S. Public*, pg. 2318
SOUTHEAST FARM EQUIPMENT CO. INC.—See ZV Pate Inc.; *U.S. Private*, pg. 4610
SOUTHEAST FARMERS ELEVATORS COOP; *U.S. Private*, pg. 3725
SOUTH EAST FIBRE EXPORTS PTY LTD—See Nippon Paper Industries Co., Ltd.; *Int'l*, pg. 5328
SOUTHEAST FINANCIAL CREDIT UNION; *U.S. Private*, pg. 3725
SOUTHEAST FLORIDA BEHAVIORAL HEALTH NETWORK, INC.; *U.S. Private*, pg. 3725
SOUTHEAST FOODS DISTRIBUTION; *U.S. Private*, pg. 3725
SOUTHEAST FOOD SERVICES CORP; *U.S. Private*, pg. 3725
SOUTHEAST FROZEN FOODS COMPANY LP; *U.S. Private*, pg. 3725
SOUTHEAST HARLEY-DAVIDSON, INC.; *U.S. Private*, pg. 3725
SOUTHEAST, INC.; *U.S. Private*, pg. 3727
SOUTHEAST INDUSTRIAL EQUIPMENT, INC.; *U.S. Private*, pg. 3725
SOUTHEAST KANSAS COMMUNITY ACTION PROGRAM, INC.; *U.S. Private*, pg. 3725
SOUTHEAST KANSAS EDUCATION SERVICE CENTER, INC.; *U.S. Private*, pg. 3725
SOUTHEAST KANSAS INDEPENDENT LIVING RESOURCE CENTER, INC.; *U.S. Private*, pg. 3725
SOUTHEAST LAND CONSULTANTS, INC.; *U.S. Private*, pg. 3726
SOUTHEAST LIBRARY BINDERY INC.—See The HF Group LLC; *U.S. Private*, pg. 4052
SOUTHEAST LINEN ASSOCIATES, INC.; *U.S. Private*, pg. 3726
SOUTHEAST LOGISTICS, INC.—See OEP Capital Advisors, L.P.; *U.S. Private*, pg. 2999
SOUTH EAST LONDON & KENT BUS COMPANY LIMITED—See Stagecoach Group plc; *Int'l*, pg. 7163
SOUTHEAST MARINE SALES AND SERVICES, INC.—See Correct Craft, Inc.; *U.S. Private*, pg. 1058
SOUTHEAST MECHANICAL, LLC—See Palladin Consumer Retail Partners, LLC; *U.S. Private*, pg. 3077
SOUTHEAST MEDIA, INC.; *U.S. Private*, pg. 3726
SOUTHEAST MENTAL HEALTH CENTER; *U.S. Private*, pg. 3726
SOUTHEAST MICHIGAN SURGICAL HOSPITAL, LLC—See Bain Capital, LP; *U.S. Private*, pg. 445
SOUTHEAST MILK, INC.; *U.S. Private*, pg. 3726

COMPANY NAME INDEX

SOUTHEAST MISSOURI HOSPITAL ASSOCIATION; *U.S. Private*, pg. 3726
SOUTHEAST MOWER & SAW SHOP—See Ag-Pro, LLC; *U.S. Private*, pg. 125
SOUTHEAST OHIO SURGICAL SUITES, LLC—See Tenet Healthcare Corporation; *U.S. Public*, pg. 2007
SOUTHEAST (OKC) LANDFILL—See Republic Services, Inc.; *U.S. Public*, pg. 1787
SOUTHEAST PERINATAL ASSOCIATES, INC.—See KKR & Co. Inc.; *U.S. Public*, pg. 1246
THE SOUTHEAST PERMANENTE MEDICAL GROUP, INC.—See Kaiser Permanente; *U.S. Private*, pg. 2256
SOUTHEAST PERSONNEL LEASING, INC.; *U.S. Private*, pg. 3726
SOUTHEAST POWER CORPORATION—See The Goldfield Corporation; *U.S. Public*, pg. 2076
SOUTHEAST POWER SYSTEMS OF ORLANDO, INC.; *U.S. Private*, pg. 3726
SOUTHEAST POWER SYSTEMS OF TAMPA—See Southeast Power Systems of Orlando, Inc.; *U.S. Private*, pg. 3726
SOUTHEAST PROPANE, LLC—See CHS INC.; *U.S. Public*, pg. 493
SOUTHEAST QUADRANT MOBILE CRITICAL CARE UNIT INC.; *U.S. Private*, pg. 3726
SOUTH EAST QUEENSLAND FUELS PTY LTD—See Ampol Limited; *Int'l*, pg. 436
SOUTHEAST RESTORATION GROUP; *U.S. Private*, pg. 3726
SOUTH EAST RISK SPECIALTY PROPERTIES—See American International Group, Inc.; *U.S. Public*, pg. 107
SOUTHEAST SELECT SIRES INC.—See Select Sires Inc.; *U.S. Private*, pg. 3601
SOUTHEAST SPREADING COMPANY; *U.S. Private*, pg. 3726
SOUTHEAST TEXAS CLASSIC AUTOMOTIVE; *U.S. Private*, pg. 3726
SOUTHEAST TEXAS INDUSTRIES; *U.S. Private*, pg. 3726
SOUTHEAST TEXAS WORKFORCE DEVELOPMENT BOARD; *U.S. Private*, pg. 3726
SOUTHEAST TOYOTA DISTRIBUTORS, LLC—See JM Family Enterprises Inc.; *U.S. Private*, pg. 2214
SOUTHEAST TOYOTA FINANCE—See JM Family Enterprises Inc.; *U.S. Private*, pg. 2214
SOUTHEAST TRAVEL SERVICES USA CO. LTD.; *U.S. Private*, pg. 3726
SOUTHEAST UNITED DAIRY INDUSTRY ASSOCIATION, INC.; *U.S. Private*, pg. 3726
SOUTHEAST UTILITIES OF GEORGIA, LLC—See Crestview Partners, L.P.; *U.S. Private*, pg. 1098
SOUTHEAST VEIN & LASER CENTER, P.C.—See Cortec Group Management Services, LLC; *U.S. Private*, pg. 1060
SOUTH EAST WATER LIMITED; *Int'l*, pg. 7116
SOUTHEAST WOOD TREATING INC.; *U.S. Private*, pg. 3727
SOUTH EDUCATION - TEXAS LLC—See Dream Center Foundation, a California Nonprofit Corp.; *U.S. Private*, pg. 1273
SOUTH ELECTRONICS COMPANY PLC; *Int'l*, pg. 7116
SOUTH END COMMUNITY HEALTH CENTER—See East Boston Neighborhood Health Center Corp.; *U.S. Private*, pg. 1315
SOUTHEND EXTERIORS, INC.—See Professional Builders Supply, LLC; *U.S. Private*, pg. 3274
SOUTHERN ACIDS (M) BERHAD; *Int'l*, pg. 7117
SOUTHERN ADVERTISING; *Int'l*, pg. 7117
SOUTHERN ADVERTISING—See Southern Advertising; *Int'l*, pg. 7117
SOUTHERN AERO PARTNERS, INC.—See AMETEK, Inc.; *U.S. Public*, pg. 117
SOUTHERN AEROPARTS, INC.—See AMETEK, Inc.; *U.S. Public*, pg. 117
SOUTHERN AG CARRIERS, INC.; *U.S. Private*, pg. 3729
SOUTHERNAG CARRIERS, INC.—See HCI Equity Management, L.P.; *U.S. Private*, pg. 1889
SOUTHERN AGGREGATES, LLC—See Natural Resource Partners L.P.; *U.S. Public*, pg. 1499
SOUTHERN AGRICULTURAL INSECTICIDES, INC.; *U.S. Private*, pg. 3729
SOUTHERN AGRICULTURAL INSECTICIDES—See Southern Agricultural Insecticides, Inc.; *U.S. Private*, pg. 3729
SOUTHERN AGRICULTURAL INSECTICIDES—See Southern Agricultural Insecticides, Inc.; *U.S. Private*, pg. 3729
SOUTHERN AIR, INC.; *U.S. Private*, pg. 3729
SOUTHERN AIRWAYS EXPRESS, LLC—See Surf Air Mobility Inc.; *U.S. Public*, pg. 1967
SOUTHERN ALLEGHENIES LANDFILL, INC.—See Waste Management, Inc.; *U.S. Public*, pg. 2332
SOUTHERN ALLIANCE MINING LTD.; *Int'l*, pg. 7117
SOUTHERN ALUMINUM FINISHING CO. INC.; *U.S. Private*, pg. 3729
SOUTHERN ANCHOR BOLT CO.—See Portland Bolt & Manufacturing Co., LLC; *U.S. Private*, pg. 3232
SOUTHERN ARCHIPELAGO LTD.; *Int'l*, pg. 7117
SOUTHERN ARC MINERALS INC.; *Int'l*, pg. 7117

SOUTHERN ARIZONA REGIONAL REHABILITATION HOSPITAL, L.P.—See Encompass Health Corporation; *U.S. Public*, pg. 759
SOUTHERN ASSISTED LIVING, LLC—See Brookdale Senior Living Inc.; *U.S. Public*, pg. 395
SOUTHERN ASSOCIATION OF COLLEGES & SCHOOLS COMMISSION ON COLLEGES; *U.S. Private*, pg. 3729
SOUTHERN ATLANTIC LABEL CO., INC.—See Platinum Equity, LLC; *U.S. Private*, pg. 3206
SOUTHERN AUSTRALIAN LIVESTOCK PTY. LTD.—See Nutrien Ltd.; *Int'l*, pg. 5493
SOUTHERN AUTOMOTIVE GROUP PTY. LTD.—See Eagers Automotive Limited; *Int'l*, pg. 2264
SOUTHERN AUTO SALES INC.; *U.S. Private*, pg. 3729
SOUTHERN AUTOS - MANUKAU LTD.—See The Colonial Motor Company Limited; *Int'l*, pg. 7635
SOUTHERN AUTO TRANSPORT SERVICES, INC.; *U.S. Private*, pg. 3729
SOUTHERN BAKERIES, INC.—See Flowers Foods, Inc.; *U.S. Public*, pg. 854
THE SOUTHERN BANC COMPANY, INC.; *U.S. Public*, pg. 2130
SOUTHERN BANCORP BANK—See Southern Bancorp, Inc.; *U.S. Private*, pg. 3729
SOUTHERN BANCORP, INC.; *U.S. Private*, pg. 3729
SOUTHERN BANCSHARES (N.C.), INC.; *U.S. Public*, pg. 1911
THE SOUTHERN BANK COMPANY—See The Southern Banc Company, Inc.; *U.S. Public*, pg. 2130
SOUTHERN BANK—See Southern Missouri Bancorp, Inc.; *U.S. Public*, pg. 1912
SOUTHERN BANK & TRUST CO.—See Southern BancShares (N.C.), Inc.; *U.S. Public*, pg. 1911
THE SOUTHERN BASIC CHEMICALS JSC—See Masan Consumer Corp.; *Int'l*, pg. 4719
SOUTHERN BEAUTY ENTERPRISES—See Beauty Enterprises Inc.; *U.S. Private*, pg. 509
SOUTHERN BELLE DAIRY CO. INC.; *U.S. Private*, pg. 3729
SOUTHERN BERKS REGIONAL EMERGENCY MEDICAL SERVICES, INC.—See Tower Health; *U.S. Private*, pg. 4193
SOUTHERN BEVERAGE CO. INC.; *U.S. Private*, pg. 3729
SOUTHERN BEVERAGE PACKERS, INC.; *U.S. Private*, pg. 3729
SOUTHERN BUSINESS SCHOOL PROPRIETARY LIMITED—See Stadio Holdings Ltd.; *Int'l*, pg. 7160
SOUTHERN CABLE GROUP BERHAD; *Int'l*, pg. 7117
SOUTHERN CALIFORNIA BRAIDING, INC.—See Goldberg Lindsay & Co., LLC; *U.S. Private*, pg. 1729
SOUTHERN CALIFORNIA EDISON COMPANY—See Edison International; *U.S. Public*, pg. 719
SOUTHERN CALIFORNIA FLEET SERVICES, INC.—See Velocity Vehicle Group; *U.S. Private*, pg. 4355
SOUTHERN CALIFORNIA GAS COMPANY—See Sempra; *U.S. Public*, pg. 1863
SOUTHERN CALIFORNIA HOUSING DEVELOPMENT CORP.; *U.S. Private*, pg. 3729
SOUTHERN CALIFORNIA MATERIAL HANDLING; *U.S. Private*, pg. 3729
SOUTHERN CALIFORNIA MATRIAL HANDLING INC.—See Caterpillar, Inc.; *U.S. Public*, pg. 454
SOUTHERN CALIFORNIA NEWS GROUP—See Alden Global Capital LLC; *U.S. Private*, pg. 157
SOUTHERN CALIFORNIA PUBLIC RADIO—See American Public Media Group; *U.S. Private*, pg. 245
SOUTHERN CALIFORNIA REGIONAL RAIL AUTHORITY; *U.S. Private*, pg. 3730
SOUTHERN CALIFORNIA SECTION OF THE PGA OF AMERICA; *U.S. Private*, pg. 3730
SOUTHERN CALIFORNIA SOUND IMAGE, INC.; *U.S. Private*, pg. 3730
SOUTHERN CALIFORNIA SPECIALTY CARE, LLC—See Apollo Global Management, Inc.; *U.S. Public*, pg. 250
SOUTHERN CAPITAL GROUP PTE. LTD.; *Int'l*, pg. 7117
SOUTHERN CASCADES FINANCE CORPORATION—See Lithia Motors, Inc.; *U.S. Public*, pg. 1326
SOUTHERN CELLULOSE PRODUCTS, INC.—See Archer-Daniels-Midland Company; *U.S. Public*, pg. 185
SOUTHERN CENTRIFUGAL, INC.—See MetalTek International; *U.S. Private*, pg. 2682
SOUTHERN CHAMPION CONSTRUCTION; *U.S. Private*, pg. 3730
SOUTHERN CHAMPION TRAY CO. INC.; *U.S. Private*, pg. 3730
SOUTHERN CHARM HEALTHCARE, INC.—See The Ensign Group, Inc.; *U.S. Public*, pg. 2071
SOUTHERN CHARTER FINANCIAL GROUP LIMITED; *Int'l*, pg. 7118
SOUTHERN CHINA LIVESTOCK, INC.; *Int'l*, pg. 7118
SOUTHERN CHUTE, INC.; *U.S. Private*, pg. 3730
SOUTHERN COAL CORPORATION; *U.S. Private*, pg. 3730
SOUTHERN COAL (PROPRIETARY) LIMITED—See Canaf Investments Inc.; *Int'l*, pg. 1287
THE SOUTHERN CO., INC.—See The Rosewood Corporation; *U.S. Private*, pg. 4112
SOUTHERN COLOR NORTH AMERICA INC.; *U.S. Private*, pg. 3730

SOUTHERN CROSS GOLD LTD.

SOUTHERN COMMUNICATIONS LTD.; *Int'l*, pg. 7118
SOUTHERN COMMUNICATIONS SERVICES, INC.—See The Southern Company; *U.S. Public*, pg. 2131
SOUTHERN COMMUNITY BANCSHARES, INC.; *U.S. Public*, pg. 1911
SOUTHERN COMMUNITY CAPITAL, LLC—See Trustmark Corporation; *U.S. Public*, pg. 2202
SOUTHERN COMMUNITY LABORATORIES LTD.—See Brookfield Corporation; *Int'l*, pg. 1176
SOUTHERN COMMUNITY NEWSPAPERS INC.; *U.S. Private*, pg. 3730
SOUTHERN COMPANY GAS—See The Southern Company; *U.S. Public*, pg. 2131
SOUTHERN COMPANY SERVICES, INC.—See The Southern Company; *U.S. Public*, pg. 2131
THE SOUTHERN COMPANY; *U.S. Public*, pg. 2130
SOUTHERN COMPONENTS, INC.; *U.S. Private*, pg. 3730
SOUTHERN COMPUTER WAREHOUSE; *U.S. Private*, pg. 3730
SOUTHERN CONCEPTS RESTAURANT GROUP, INC.; *U.S. Public*, pg. 1911
SOUTHERN CONCRETE CONSTRUCTION CO.; *U.S. Private*, pg. 3730
SOUTHERN CONCRETE MATERIALS INC.—See Hedrick Industries Inc.; *U.S. Private*, pg. 1903
SOUTHERN CONCRETE PILE PUBLIC COMPANY LIMITED; *Int'l*, pg. 7118
SOUTHERN CONCRETE PRODUCTS INC.; *U.S. Private*, pg. 3730
SOUTHERN CONE POWER ARGENTINA SA—See Enel S.p.A.; *Int'l*, pg. 2413
THE SOUTHERN CONNECTICUT GAS COMPANY—See Iberdrola, S.A.; *Int'l*, pg. 3571
SOUTHERN CONNECTION SEAFOOD, INC.; *U.S. Private*, pg. 3730
SOUTHERN CONTAINER LLC—See Kelso & Company, L.P.; *U.S. Public*, pg. 2278
SOUTHERN CONTROLS, INC.; *U.S. Private*, pg. 3730
SOUTHERN CONVENTION SERVICES, INC.—See Informa plc; *Int'l*, pg. 3693
SOUTHERN CONVERTERS—See J.R. Cole Industries Inc.; *U.S. Private*, pg. 2170
SOUTHERN COPPER CORPORATION—See Grupo Mexico, S.A.B. de C.V.; *Int'l*, pg. 3132
SOUTHERN COPPER CORPORATION—See Grupo Mexico, S.A.B. de C.V.; *Int'l*, pg. 3133
SOUTHERN CORD INC.—See GI Manager L.P.; *U.S. Private*, pg. 1691
SOUTHERN CORRECTIONS SYSTEM OF WYOMING, LLC—See Corecivic, Inc.; *U.S. Public*, pg. 577
SOUTHERN COUNTIES EXPRESS, INC.—See Universal Logistics Holdings, Inc.; *U.S. Public*, pg. 2261
SOUTHERN COUNTIES OIL CO.; *U.S. Private*, pg. 3730
SOUTHERN CRAFTED HOMES, INC.; *U.S. Private*, pg. 3730
SOUTHERN CRESCENT ANESTHESIOLOGY, PC—See Bain Capital, LP; *U.S. Private*, pg. 446
SOUTHERN CRESCENT NURSE ANESTHESIA, LLC—See Bain Capital, LP; *U.S. Private*, pg. 446
SOUTHERN CROSS AIRPORTS CORPORATION HOLDINGS LIMITED—See Sydney Airport Holdings Pty Ltd; *Int'l*, pg. 7378
SOUTHERN CROSS AVIATION INC.; *U.S. Private*, pg. 3730
SOUTHERN CROSS BOTANICALS PTY. LTD.—See Clariant AG; *Int'l*, pg. 1648
SOUTHERN CROSS BUILDING PRODUCTS, LLC—See Q.E.P. Co., Inc.; *U.S. Public*, pg. 1741
SOUTHERN CROSS CAPITAL MANAGEMENT SA; *Int'l*, pg. 7118
SOUTHERN CROSS CONTRACTING, INC.; *U.S. Private*, pg. 3731
SOUTHERN CROSS DISTRIBUTION SYSTEMS PTY LIMITED—See Elliott Management Corporation; *U.S. Private*, pg. 1373
SOUTHERN CROSS DISTRIBUTION SYSTEMS PTY LIMITED—See Siris Capital Group, LLC; *U.S. Private*, pg. 3674
SOUTHERN CROSS ELECTRICAL ENGINEERING LIMITED-PERTH—See Southern Cross Electrical Engineering Limited; *Int'l*, pg. 7119
SOUTHERN CROSS ELECTRICAL ENGINEERING LIMITED; *Int'l*, pg. 7118
SOUTHERN CROSS ELECTRICAL ENGINEERING (WA) PTY. LTD.—See Southern Cross Electrical Engineering Limited; *Int'l*, pg. 7119
SOUTHERN CROSS EXPLORATION NL; *Int'l*, pg. 7119
SOUTHERN CROSS GOLD LTD.; *Int'l*, pg. 7119
SOUTHERN CROSS GROUP, LLC—See Southern Cross Capital Management SA; *Int'l*, pg. 7118
SOUTHERN CROSS INSURANCE SERVICES, INC.—See Truist Financial Corporation; *U.S. Public*, pg. 2200
SOUTHERN CROSS INSURANCES PTE LIMITED—See Qantas Airways Limited; *Int'l*, pg. 6132
SOUTHERN CROSS INTERNATIONAL PTY LTD.—See Incitec Pivot Limited; *Int'l*, pg. 3648
SOUTHERN CROSS MARINE LIMITED—See Tower Limited; *Int'l*, pg. 7850

2559

SOUTHERN CROSS MEDIA AUSTRALIA PTY LIMITED—See Southern Cross Media Group Limited; Int'l, pg. 7119
SOUTHERN CROSS MEDIA GROUP LIMITED; Int'l, pg. 7119
SOUTHERN CROSS MEDIA—See Southern Cross Media Group Limited; Int'l, pg. 7119
SOUTHERN CROSS PAYMENTS LIMITED; Int'l, pg. 7119
SOUTHERN CROSS RESOURCES AUSTRALIA PTY. LTD.—See State Atomic Energy Corporation ROSATOM; Int'l, pg. 7181
SOUTHERN CROSS STEVEDORING—See Carrix, Inc.; U.S. Private, pg. 773
SOUTHERN CRUSHED CONCRETE LLC—See Ferrovial S.A.; Int'l, pg. 2645
SOUTHERN DATA SOLUTIONS, INC.—See Spire Capital Partners, LLC; U.S. Private, pg. 3757
SOUTHERN DATA STORAGE, INC.; U.S. Private, pg. 3731
SOUTHERN DENTAL INDUSTRIES GMBH—See SDI Limited; Int'l, pg. 6658
SOUTHERN DISCOVERIES LIMITED—See Skeggs Group Limited; Int'l, pg. 6980
SOUTHERN DISTRIBUTING CO. INC.; U.S. Private, pg. 3731
SOUTHERN DIVERSIFIED INDUSTRIES—See Liberty Diversified International Inc.; U.S. Private, pg. 2444
SOUTHERN DIVERSIFIED TECHNOLOGIES, INC.—See Littlejohn & Co., LLC; U.S. Private, pg. 2472
SOUTHERN DIVERSIFIED TECHNOLOGIES, INC.—See New Mountain Capital, LLC; U.S. Private, pg. 2903
SOUTHERN DIVERSIFIED TECHNOLOGIES; U.S. Private, pg. 3731
SOUTHERN EAGLE DISTRIBUTING, INC.; U.S. Private, pg. 3731
SOUTHERN EAGLE DISTRIBUTING, LLC; U.S. Private, pg. 3731
SOUTHERN ELECTRIC CORPORATION—See Quanta Services, Inc.; U.S. Public, pg. 1753
SOUTHERN ELECTRIC GAS LIMITED—See SSE Plc; Int'l, pg. 7156
SOUTHERN ELECTRONICS SUPPLY; U.S. Private, pg. 3731
SOUTHERN EMPIRE RESOURCES CORP.; Int'l, pg. 7119
SOUTHERN ENERGY CORPORATION PTY LTD—See Agrimin Limited; Int'l, pg. 217
SOUTHERN ENERGY CORP.; Int'l, pg. 7119
SOUTHERN ENERGY HOLDINGS GROUP LIMITED; Int'l, pg. 7119
SOUTHERN ENERGY HOMES, INC.—See Berkshire Hathaway Inc.; U.S. Public, pg. 304
SOUTHERN ENERGY HOMES—See Berkshire Hathaway Inc.; U.S. Public, pg. 304
SOUTHERN ENERGY LA, LLC—See Southern Energy Corp.; Int'l, pg. 7119
SOUTHERN EQUIPMENT CO. INC.; U.S. Private, pg. 3731
SOUTHERN EQUIPMENT CORPORATION; U.S. Private, pg. 3731
SOUTHERN EQUIPMENT DISTRIBUTORS, INC.—See Cal-Maine Foods, Inc.; U.S. Public, pg. 421
SOUTHERN ERECTORS INCORPORATED; U.S. Private, pg. 3731
SOUTHERN EXPLORATION PTY LIMITED—See Apollo Minerals Limited; Int'l, pg. 518
SOUTHERN FAMILY MARKETS LLC—See C&S Wholesale Grocers, Inc.; U.S. Private, pg. 704
SOUTHERN FARM BUREAU CASUALTY INSURANCE COMPANY; U.S. Private, pg. 3731
SOUTHERN FARM BUREAU LIFE INSURANCE CO. INC.; U.S. Private, pg. 3731
SOUTHERN FASTENERS & SUPPLY, INC.—See Park-Ohio Holdings Corp.; U.S. Public, pg. 1640
SOUTHERN FASTENING SYSTEMS, INC.; U.S. Private, pg. 3731
SOUTHERN FEDERAL POWER, LLC—See Genie Energy Ltd.; U.S. Public, pg. 931
SOUTHERN FELT COMPANY, INC.—See Lydall, Inc.; U.S. Public, pg. 1350
SOUTHERN FIDELITY INSURANCE CO.; U.S. Private, pg. 3731
SOUTHERN FIDELITY MORTGAGE; U.S. Private, pg. 3731
SOUTHERN FILM EXTRUDERS INC.; U.S. Private, pg. 3731
SOUTHERN FILTER MEDIA LLC; U.S. Private, pg. 3731
SOUTHERN FIRST BANCSHARES, INC.; U.S. Public, pg. 1911
SOUTHERN FIRST BANK—See Southern First Bancshares, Inc.; U.S. Public, pg. 1911
SOUTHERN FLORAL CO.; U.S. Private, pg. 3731
SOUTHERN FLOW COMPANIES, INC.—See IGP Industries, LLC; U.S. Private, pg. 2040
SOUTHERN FOLGER DETENTION EQUIPMENT COMPANY—See Phelps Tointon Inc.; U.S. Private, pg. 3167
SOUTHERN FOOD PARK INCORPORATED; U.S. Private, pg. 3731

SOUTHERN FOODSERVICE MANAGEMENT INC.; U.S. Private, pg. 3732
SOUTHERN FOODS, INC. - HOME DIVISION—See Southern Foods, Inc.; U.S. Private, pg. 3732
SOUTHERN FOODS, INC.; U.S. Private, pg. 3731
SOUTHERN FRAC, LLC—See United Rentals, Inc.; U.S. Public, pg. 2235
SOUTHERN FREIGHT INC.; U.S. Private, pg. 3732
SOUTHERN FS, INC.; U.S. Private, pg. 3732
SOUTHERN FULFILLMENT SERVICES; U.S. Private, pg. 3732
SOUTHERN FUNERAL HOME, INC.—See Service Corporation International; U.S. Public, pg. 1871
SOUTHERN FURNITURE COMPANY OF CONOVER INC.; U.S. Private, pg. 3732
SOUTHERN GAGE INC.—See Alpha Q, Inc.; U.S. Private, pg. 199
SOUTHERN GARDEN CITRUS—See United States Sugar Corporation; U.S. Private, pg. 4300
SOUTHERN GAS & FUELS INC.; U.S. Private, pg. 3732
SOUTHERN GAS JOINT STOCK COMPANY; Int'l, pg. 7119
THE SOUTHERN GAS LIMITED; Int'l, pg. 7688
SOUTHERN GENERAL INSURANCE CO.—See Insurance House; U.S. Private, pg. 2095
SOUTHERN GLAZER'S WINE & SPIRITS, LLC—See Glazer's Family of Companies; U.S. Private, pg. 1707
SOUTHERN GLAZER'S WINE & SPIRITS OF HAWAII—See Glazer's Family of Companies; U.S. Private, pg. 1707
SOUTHERN GLAZER'S WINE & SPIRITS OF ILLINOIS- DIRECT WAREHOUSE SALES—See Glazer's Family of Companies; U.S. Private, pg. 1708
SOUTHERN GLAZER'S WINE & SPIRITS OF ILLINOIS—See Glazer's Family of Companies; U.S. Private, pg. 1708
SOUTHERN GLAZER'S WINE & SPIRITS OF NEW YORK—See Glazer's Family of Companies; U.S. Private, pg. 1708
SOUTHERN GLAZER'S WINE & SPIRITS OF NEW YORK - SYRACUSE—See Glazer's Family of Companies; U.S. Private, pg. 1708
SOUTHERN GLAZER'S WINE & SPIRITS OF PENNSYLVANIA—See Glazer's Family of Companies; U.S. Private, pg. 1708
SOUTHERN GOLD LIMITED; Int'l, pg. 7119
SOUTHERN GRAPHIC SYSTEMS, INC. - FLEXO DIVISON—See HPS Investment Partners, LLC; U.S. Private, pg. 1997
SOUTHERN GRAPHIC SYSTEMS, INC. - GRAVURE DIVISON—See HPS Investment Partners, LLC; U.S. Private, pg. 1997
SOUTHERN GRAPHIC SYSTEMS, INC.—See HPS Investment Partners, LLC; U.S. Private, pg. 1997
SOUTHERN GRAPHIC SYSTEMS, LLC—See Summit Partners, L.P.; U.S. Private, pg. 3856
SOUTHERN GRAPHIC SYSTEMS, LLC—See The Jordan Company, L.P.; U.S. Private, pg. 4062
SOUTHERN GRAPHIC SYSTEMS, LLC—See HPS Investment Partners, LLC; U.S. Private, pg. 1997
SOUTHERN GROUT & MORTARS INC.; U.S. Private, pg. 3732
SOUTHERN GULF LNG COMPANY, L.L.C.—See Kinder Morgan, Inc.; U.S. Public, pg. 1232
SOUTHERN HARVESTERS LTD.—See Claas KGaA mbH; Int'l, pg. 1641
SOUTHERN HARVEST INSURANCE AGENCY INC.—See Stone Point Capital LLC; U.S. Private, pg. 3818
SOUTHERN HEALTH CORPORATION OF DAHLONEGA, INC.—See SunLink Health Systems, Inc.; U.S. Public, pg. 1964
SOUTHERN HEALTH CORPORATION OF ELLIJAY, INC.—See SunLink Health Systems, Inc.; U.S. Public, pg. 1964
SOUTHERN HEALTH CORPORATION OF HOUSTON, INC.—See SunLink Health Systems, Inc.; U.S. Public, pg. 1964
SOUTHERN HEMISPHERE MINING LIMITED; Int'l, pg. 7119
SOUTHERN HEMISPHERE MINING PTY LIMITED—See Southern Hemisphere Mining Limited; Int'l, pg. 7119
SOUTHERN HERITAGE BANK; U.S. Private, pg. 3732
SOUTHERN HERITAGE CASKET CO.—See Matthews International Corporation; U.S. Public, pg. 1399
SOUTHERN HIGHLANDS COMMUNITY MENTAL HEALTH CENTER; U.S. Private, pg. 3732
SOUTHERN HILLS DIALYSIS CENTER, LLC—See DaVita Inc.; U.S. Public, pg. 643
SOUTHERN HILLS HOSPITAL & MEDICAL CENTER—See HCA Healthcare, Inc.; U.S. Public, pg. 1010
SOUTHERN HILLS MEDICAL CENTER—See HCA Healthcare, Inc.; U.S. Public, pg. 1010
SOUTHERN HILLS NEUROLOGY CONSULTANTS, LLC—See HCA Healthcare, Inc.; U.S. Public, pg. 1010
SOUTHERN (HK) PACKAGING COMPANY LIMITED—See Southern Packaging Group Limited; Int'l, pg. 7120
SOUTHERN HOBBY SUPPLY INC.; U.S. Private, pg. 3732

SOUTHERN HOME CARE SERVICES, INC.- MICHIGAN—See KKR & Co. Inc.; U.S. Public, pg. 1263
SOUTHERN HOME CARE SERVICES, INC.—See KKR & Co. Inc.; U.S. Public, pg. 1262
SOUTHERN HOME & RANCH CENTER; U.S. Private, pg. 3732
SOUTHERN HOME RESPIRATORY & EQUIPMENT, INC.—See AdaptHealth Corp.; U.S. Public, pg. 39
SOUTHERN HOME SERVICES LLC—See Gryphon Investors, LLC; U.S. Private, pg. 1799
SOUTHERN HOSPITALITY AUTO GROUP OF VIRGINIA; U.S. Private, pg. 3732
SOUTHERN HYDROPOWER JOINT STOCK COMPANY; Int'l, pg. 7119
SOUTHERN ICE CREAM, CORP.—See Guggenheim Partners, LLC; U.S. Private, pg. 1812
SOUTHERN ICE CREAM SPECIALTIES INC—See The Kroger Co.; U.S. Public, pg. 2109
SOUTHERN IDAHO AMBULATORY SURGERY CENTER, LLC—See KKR & Co. Inc.; U.S. Public, pg. 1246
SOUTHERN IDAHO REGIONAL LABORATORY—See Laboratory Corporation of America Holdings; U.S. Public, pg. 1287
THE SOUTHERN ILLINOISAN—See Paxton Media Group LLC; U.S. Private, pg. 3116
SOUTHERN ILLINOIS HEALTHCARE FOUNDATION; U.S. Private, pg. 3732
SOUTHERN ILLINOIS LAND COMPANY—See R&Q Insurance Holdings Ltd.; Int'l, pg. 6168
SOUTHERN ILLINOIS MEDICAL CARE ASSOCIATES, LLC—See Quorum Health Corporation; U.S. Private, pg. 3330
SOUTHERN ILLINOIS POWER COOP; U.S. Private, pg. 3732
SOUTHERN ILLINOIS RIVERBOAT/CASINO CRUISES, INC.—See Caesars Entertainment, Inc.; U.S. Public, pg. 420
SOUTHERN IML PATHOLOGY SERVICES PTY LIMITED—See Sonic Healthcare Limited; Int'l, pg. 7098
SOUTHERN IMPERIAL INC.; U.S. Private, pg. 3732
SOUTHERN INDIANA ENT LLC—See ENT Partners LLC; U.S. Private, pg. 1402
SOUTHERN INDIANA REHABILITATION HOSPITAL—See Omega Healthcare Investors, Inc.; U.S. Public, pg. 1571
SOUTHERN INDIANA TREATMENT CENTER, LLC—See Acadia Healthcare Company, Inc.; U.S. Public, pg. 30
SOUTHERN INDUSTRIAL CONSTRUCTION INC.—See EMCOR Group, Inc.; U.S. Public, pg. 739
SOUTHERN INDUSTRIAL GAS SDN. BHD.—See L'Air Liquide S.A.; Int'l, pg. 4373
SOUTHERN INDUSTRIAL SALES AND SERVICES, INC.—See IES Holdings, Inc.; U.S. Public, pg. 1094
SOUTHERN INDUSTRIAL TECHNOLOGIES INC.—See Bearing Service Company; U.S. Private, pg. 506
SOUTHERN INFOSYS LIMITED; Int'l, pg. 7119
SOUTHERN INSULATORS, LLC—See Installed Building Products, Inc.; U.S. Public, pg. 1133
SOUTHERN INSURANCE COMPANY OF VIRGINIA—See Donegal Group Inc.; U.S. Public, pg. 676
SOUTHERN INSURANCE UNDERWRITERS INC.; U.S. Private, pg. 3732
SOUTHERN INTERNATIONAL LOGISTICS JOINT STOCK COMPANY; Int'l, pg. 7119
SOUTHERN IONICS, INC.; U.S. Private, pg. 3732
SOUTHERN ISPAT & ENERGY LIMITED; Int'l, pg. 7120
SOUTHERN JET INC.; U.S. Private, pg. 3732
SOUTHERN KENTUCKY MEDICINE ASSOCIATES, LLC—See HCA Healthcare, Inc.; U.S. Public, pg. 1010
SOUTHERN KUZBASS PJSC—See Mechel PAO; Int'l, pg. 4766
SOUTHERN KUZBASS POWER PLANT PAO—See Mechel PAO; Int'l, pg. 4766
SOUTHERN LAKES MOTORS LTD.—See The Colonial Motor Company Limited; Int'l, pg. 7635
SOUTHERN LANDSCAPE SUPPLY LLC—See SiteOne Landscape Supply, Inc.; U.S. Public, pg. 1889
SOUTHERN LATEX LIMITED; Int'l, pg. 7120
SOUTHERN LEATHER COMPANY; U.S. Private, pg. 3732
SOUTHERN LIFE SYSTEMS, INC.—See ADDvise Group AB; Int'l, pg. 136
SOUTHERN LION SDN. BHD.—See Lion Corporation; Int'l, pg. 4518
SOUTHERN LITHOPLATE INC.; U.S. Private, pg. 3732
SOUTHERN LOCK & SUPPLY CO.; U.S. Private, pg. 3732
SOUTHERN LUMBER & MILLWORK CORP.; U.S. Private, pg. 3733
SOUTHERN MAGNESIUM & CHEMICALS LIMITED; Int'l, pg. 7120
SOUTHERN MAINE HEALTH CARE; U.S. Private, pg. 3733
SOUTHERN MANAGEMENT CORPORATION—See Milestone Partners Ltd.; U.S. Private, pg. 2729
SOUTHERN MANAGEMENT CORPORATION; U.S. Private, pg. 3733
SOUTHERN MANUFACTURING TECHNOLOGIES, INC.; U.S. Private, pg. 3733

COMPANY NAME INDEX

SOUTHERN MARKETING AFFILIATES, INC.; *U.S. Private*, pg. 3733
SOUTHERN MARKETING AFFILIATES OF THE SOUTHWEST, INC.—See Southern Marketing Affiliates, Inc.; *U.S. Private*, pg. 3733
SOUTHERN MARYLAND CABLE, INC.—See Argan, Inc.; *U.S. Public*, pg. 191
SOUTHERN MARYLAND ELECTRIC COOPERATIVE INC.; *U.S. Private*, pg. 3733
SOUTHERN MARYLAND NEWSPAPERS—See Nash Holdings LLC; *U.S. Private*, pg. 2835
SOUTHERN MARYLAND OIL, INC.—See The Wills Group, Inc.; *U.S. Private*, pg. 4136
SOUTHERN MARYLAND TRI-COUNTY COMMUNITY ACTION COMMITTEE, INC.; *U.S. Private*, pg. 3733
SOUTHERN MATERIAL HANDLING CO.—See Hugg & Hall Equipment Company; *U.S. Private*, pg. 2003
SOUTHERN MATERIALS COMPANY; *U.S. Private*, pg. 3733
SOUTHERN MEDIA COMMUNICATIONS INC.—See Creek Indian Enterprises; *U.S. Private*, pg. 1092
SOUTHERN MEDICAL HEALTH SYSTEMS INC.; *U.S. Private*, pg. 3733
SOUTHERN (MERTHYR) LIMITED—See General Motors Company; *U.S. Public*, pg. 927
SOUTHERN METALS CO INC.; *U.S. Private*, pg. 3733
SOUTHERN MICHIGAN BANCORP INC.; *U.S. Public*, pg. 1911
SOUTHERN MICHIGAN BANK & TRUST—See Southern Michigan Bancorp Inc.; *U.S. Public*, pg. 1911
SOUTHERN MILLS, INC.—See ABN AMRO Group N.V.; *Int'l*, pg. 64
SOUTHERN MILLS, INC.—See Gilde Buy Out Partners B.V.; *Int'l*, pg. 2974
SOUTHERN MILLS, INC.—See Parcom Capital Management B.V.; *Int'l*, pg. 5740
SOUTHERN MINERALS GROUP LLC—See Strategic Minerals plc; *Int'l*, pg. 7236
SOUTHERN MINNESOTA BEET SUGAR COOPERATIVE; *U.S. Private*, pg. 3733
SOUTHERN MINNESOTA CONSTRUCTION COMPANY—See CRH plc; *Int'l*, pg. 1847
SOUTHERN MISSOURI BANCORP, INC.; *U.S. Public*, pg. 1911
SOUTHERN MISSOURI CONTAINER PACKAGING GROUP; *U.S. Private*, pg. 3733
SOUTHERN MOTION, INC.—See Gainline Capital Partners LP; *U.S. Private*, pg. 1635
SOUTHERN MOTOR CARRIERS ASSOCIATION, INC.; *U.S. Private*, pg. 3733
SOUTHERN MOTORS HONDA; *U.S. Private*, pg. 3733
THE SOUTHERN MULCH COMPANY, LLC; *U.S. Private*, pg. 4119
SOUTHERN MULTIFOODS INC.; *U.S. Private*, pg. 3734
SOUTHERN NATIONAL BANKS, INC.; *U.S. Private*, pg. 3734
SOUTHERN NATIONAL LIFE INSURANCE COMPANY INC.—See Louisiana Health Service & Indemnity Company, Inc.; *U.S. Private*, pg. 2499
SOUTHERN NATURAL GAS COMPANY, L.L.C.—See Kinder Morgan, Inc.; *U.S. Public*, pg. 1232
SOUTHERN NEVADA CONSERVANCY; *U.S. Private*, pg. 3734
SOUTHERN NEVADA HARLEY-DAVIDSON SALES, INC.; *U.S. Private*, pg. 3734
SOUTHERN NEVADA HOME HEALTH CARE, INC.—See The Nathan Adelson Hospice; *U.S. Private*, pg. 4081
THE SOUTHERN NEW ENGLAND TELEPHONE COMPANY—See Frontier Communications Parent, Inc.; *U.S. Public*, pg. 887
SOUTHERN NEWSPAPERS INC.; *U.S. Private*, pg. 3734
SOUTHERN NISSHA SDN. BHD.—See Nissha Co., Ltd.; *Int'l*, pg. 5372
SOUTHERN NUCLEAR OPERATING COMPANY, INC.—See The Southern Company; *U.S. Public*, pg. 2131
SOUTHERN NURSERIES, INC.—See Boyne Capital Management, LLC; *U.S. Private*, pg. 629
SOUTHERN OAK INSURANCE COMPANY; *U.S. Private*, pg. 3734
SOUTHERN OAKS APARTMENT HOMES—See Kennedy-Wilson Holdings, Inc.; *U.S. Public*, pg. 1223
SOUTHERN OAKS HEALTHCARE, INC.—See The Ensign Group, Inc.; *U.S. Public*, pg. 2072
SOUTHERN OCEAN MEDICAL CENTER—See Hackensack Meridian Health, Inc.; *U.S. Private*, pg. 1838
SOUTHERN OIL CO. INC.; *U.S. Private*, pg. 3734
SOUTHERN OIL COMPANY INC.; *U.S. Private*, pg. 3734
SOUTHERN ONLINE BIO TECHNOLOGIES LTD - BIO-DIESEL DIVISION—See Southern Online Bio Technologies Ltd; *Int'l*, pg. 7120
SOUTHERN ONLINE BIO TECHNOLOGIES LTD - INTERNET SERVICES DIVISION—See Southern Online Bio Technologies Ltd; *Int'l*, pg. 7120
SOUTHERN ONLINE BIO TECHNOLOGIES LTD; *Int'l*, pg. 7120
SOUTHERN ONTARIO RAILWAY—See Brookfield Infrastructure Partners L.P.; *Int'l*, pg. 1192

SOUTHERN ONTARIO RAILWAY—See GIC Pte. Ltd.; *Int'l*, pg. 2967
SOUTHERN OREGON SANITATION INC.; *U.S. Private*, pg. 3734
SOUTHERN ORTHOPEDICS AND SPORTS MEDICINE, L.L.C.—See Tenet Healthcare Corporation; *U.S. Public*, pg. 2003
SOUTHERN-OWNERS INSURANCE COMPANY—See Auto-Owners Insurance Group; *U.S. Private*, pg. 398
SOUTHERN PACIFIC HOTEL CORPORATION (BVI) LTD.—See InterContinental Hotels Group PLC; *Int'l*, pg. 3739
SOUTHERN PACKAGING GROUP LIMITED; *Int'l*, pg. 7120
SOUTHERN PACKAGING (JIANGSU) CO., LTD.—See Southern Packaging Group Limited; *Int'l*, pg. 7120
SOUTHERN PALACE GROUP OF COMPANIES (PTY) LTD.; *Int'l*, pg. 7120
SOUTHERN PAN SERVICES COMPANY; *U.S. Private*, pg. 3734
SOUTHERN PARK MALL, LLC—See Washington Prime Group Inc.; *U.S. Private*, pg. 4449
SOUTHERN PC STEEL SDN. BHD.—See Southern Steel Berhad; *Int'l*, pg. 7120
SOUTHERN PEANUT CO. INC.; *U.S. Private*, pg. 3734
SOUTHERN PETROCHEMICAL INDUSTRIES CORPORATION LIMITED; *Int'l*, pg. 7120
SOUTHERN PETROLEUM EQUIPMENT COMPANY, INC.—See Kennedy Tank & Manufacturing Company, Inc.; *U.S. Private*, pg. 2285
SOUTHERN PETROLEUM LABORATORIES, INC.—See Sentinel Capital Partners, L.L.C.; *U.S. Private*, pg. 3609
SOUTHERN PHILIPPINES POWER CORPORATION—See Alcantara Group; *Int'l*, pg. 300
SOUTHERN PHONE COMPANY LIMITED—See AGL Energy Limited; *Int'l*, pg. 211
SOUTHERN PINE ELECTRIC CO-OPERATIVE INC.; *U.S. Private*, pg. 3734
SOUTHERN PINES HEALTHCARE LLC—See The Pennant Group, Inc.; *U.S. Public*, pg. 2118
SOUTHERN PIONEER PROPERTY & CASUALTY INSURANCE COMPANY—See Biglari Holdings Inc.; *U.S. Public*, pg. 331
SOUTHERN PIPE, INC.; *U.S. Private*, pg. 3734
SOUTHERN PIPE INDUSTRY (MALAYSIA) SDN BHD—See Southern Steel Berhad; *Int'l*, pg. 7120
SOUTHERN PIPELINE CONTRACTORS PROPRIETARY LIMITED—See VINCI S.A.; *Int'l*, pg. 8229
SOUTHERN PIPE & SUPPLY CO., INC.; *U.S. Private*, pg. 3734
SOUTHERN PIPING COMPANY; *U.S. Private*, pg. 3734
SOUTHERN PLAINS OIL CORP.; *U.S. Public*, pg. 1912
SOUTHERN POLYMER, INC.—See Audia International, Inc.; *U.S. Private*, pg. 390
SOUTHERN POST COMPANY—See Commercial Metals Company; *U.S. Public*, pg. 546
SOUTHERN POST COMPANY-TEXAS—See Commercial Metals Company; *U.S. Public*, pg. 546
SOUTHERN POST COMPANY-UTAH—See Commercial Metals Company; *U.S. Public*, pg. 546
SOUTHERN POST SOUTH CAROLINA—See Commercial Metals Company; *U.S. Public*, pg. 546
SOUTHERN POWER COMPANY—See The Southern Company; *U.S. Public*, pg. 2131
SOUTHERN POWER & CONTROLS CORP.; *U.S. Private*, pg. 3734
SOUTHERN PRESTIGE INDUSTRIES, INC.; *U.S. Private*, pg. 3734
SOUTHERNPRINT LTD.—See Walstead Investments Ltd.; *Int'l*, pg. 8335
SOUTHERN PRODUCE DISTRIBUTORS, INC.; *U.S. Private*, pg. 3734
SOUTHERN PROMOTIONS, INC.—See Live Nation Entertainment, Inc.; *U.S. Public*, pg. 1330
SOUTHERN PROSTHETIC SUPPLY, INC.—See Patient Square Capital, L.P.; *U.S. Private*, pg. 3107
SOUTHERN PROTECTIVE GROUP, LLC—See The Baldwin Insurance Group, Inc.; *U.S. Public*, pg. 2036
SOUTHERN PROVINCE CEMENT COMPANY; *Int'l*, pg. 7120
SOUTHERN PUBLIC POWER DISTRICT; *U.S. Private*, pg. 3734
SOUTHERN PUBLIC SERVICE CO, INC.—See Ullico Inc.; *U.S. Private*, pg. 4276
SOUTHERN PUBLISHING & MEDIA COMPANY LIMITED; *Int'l*, pg. 7120
SOUTHERN PUMP & TANK COMPANY—See Kian Capital Partners, LLC; *U.S. Private*, pg. 2302
SOUTHERN PUMP & TANK COMPANY—See RFE Investment Partners; *U.S. Private*, pg. 3419
SOUTHERN QUALITY MEATS, INC.—See H.I.G. Capital, LLC; *U.S. Private*, pg. 1831
SOUTHERN QUARRIES PTY LTD—See CRH plc; *Int'l*, pg. 1842
SOUTHERN RAIL TERMINALS, INC.—See Norfolk Southern Corporation; *U.S. Public*, pg. 1536
SOUTHERN RAIL TERMINALS OF NORTH CAROLINA, INC.—See Norfolk Southern Corporation; *U.S. Public*, pg. 1536

SOUTHERN RAILWAY LIMITED—See GLOBALVIA Inversiones, S.A.U.; *Int'l*, pg. 3005
SOUTHERN RAILWAY LIMITED—See Kinetic Group Services Pty Ltd.; *Int'l*, pg. 4167
SOUTHERN RAILWAY OF BRITISH COLUMBIA LIMITED (SRY)—See Washington Corporations; *U.S. Private*, pg. 4446
SOUTHERN RAILWAY OF VANCOUVER ISLAND LIMITED—See Washington Corporations; *U.S. Private*, pg. 4446
SOUTHERN REALTY CO.; *U.S. Public*, pg. 1912
SOUTHERN RECYCLING INC.—See Houchens Industries, Inc.; *U.S. Private*, pg. 1990
SOUTHERN RECYCLING, LLC—See European Metal Recycling Limited; *Int'l*, pg. 2556
SOUTHERN RECYCLING SALES, LLC—See European Metal Recycling Limited; *Int'l*, pg. 2557
SOUTHERN REFRIGERATED TRANSPORT—See Covenant Logistics Group, Inc.; *U.S. Public*, pg. 588
SOUTHERN REFRIGERATION CORP.; *U.S. Private*, pg. 3735
SOUTHERN REGIONAL HEALTH SYSTEM—See Prime Healthcare Services, Inc.; *U.S. Private*, pg. 3262
SOUTHERN REGION COAL TRANSPORT, INC.—See Norfolk Southern Corporation; *U.S. Public*, pg. 1536
SOUTHERN RESIDENTIAL INSTALLATIONS LLC; *U.S. Private*, pg. 3735
SOUTHERN REWINDING & SALES; *U.S. Private*, pg. 3735
SOUTHERN RHODE ISLAND NEWSPAPERS—See R.I.S.N. Operations Inc.; *U.S. Private*, pg. 3336
SOUTHERN ROADWAYS LIMITED—See Sundaram Brake Linings Limited; *Int'l*, pg. 7312
THE SOUTHERN RUBBER INDUSTRY JOINT STOCK COMPANY; *Int'l*, pg. 7688
SOUTHERN SALT (PVT.) LTD.—See Raigam Marketing Services (Pvt) Ltd.; *Int'l*, pg. 6188
SOUTHERN SAMPLE COMPANY—See Sampco Inc.; *U.S. Private*, pg. 3537
SOUTHERN SCORE BUILDERS BERHAD; *Int'l*, pg. 7120
SOUTHERN SCRAP RECYCLING MORGAN CITY, LLC—See European Metal Recycling Limited; *Int'l*, pg. 2557
SOUTHERN SECURITIES LTD.; *U.S. Private*, pg. 3735
SOUTHERN SEED CORPORATION—See The Pan Group Joint Stock Company; *Int'l*, pg. 7673
SOUTHERN SELF STORAGE OF DESTIN, LLC—See National Storage Affiliates Trust; *U.S. Public*, pg. 1498
SOUTHERN SELF STORAGE OF EDGEWATER, LLC—See National Storage Affiliates Trust; *U.S. Public*, pg. 1498
SOUTHERN SELF STORAGE OF GRAYTON, LLC—See National Storage Affiliates Trust; *U.S. Public*, pg. 1498
SOUTHERN SELF STORAGE OF PENSACOLA, LLC—See National Storage Affiliates Trust; *U.S. Public*, pg. 1498
SOUTHERN SHELL FISH CO. INC.; *U.S. Private*, pg. 3735
SOUTHERN SIDING COMPANY INC.; *U.S. Private*, pg. 3735
SOUTHERN SILVER EXPLORATION CORP.; *Int'l*, pg. 7120
SOUTHERN SPARS EUROPE A/S—See Windway Capital Corp.; *U.S. Private*, pg. 4540
SOUTHERN SPARS INTERNATIONAL (PVT) LTD—See Windway Capital Corp.; *U.S. Private*, pg. 4540
SOUTHERN SPARS LTD - CAPE TOWN FACILITY—See Windway Capital Corp.; *U.S. Private*, pg. 4540
SOUTHERN SPARS LTD - RIG PRO RHODE ISLAND FACILITY—See Windway Capital Corp.; *U.S. Private*, pg. 4540
SOUTHERN SPARS LTD—See Windway Capital Corp.; *U.S. Private*, pg. 4540
SOUTHERN SPECIALIST EYE CENTRE SDN. BHD.—See ISEC Healthcare Limited; *Int'l*, pg. 3813
SOUTHERN STAFFING INC.; *U.S. Private*, pg. 3735
SOUTHERN STAIRCASE INCORPORATED; *U.S. Private*, pg. 3735
SOUTHERN STANDARD CARTONS, INC.; *U.S. Private*, pg. 3735
SOUTHERN STAR CENTRAL CORP.—See Caisse de Depot et Placement du Quebec; *Int'l*, pg. 1255
SOUTHERN STAR CENTRAL GAS PIPELINE, INC.—See The Williams Companies, Inc.; *U.S. Public*, pg. 2143
SOUTHERN STAR CENTRAL GAS PIPELINE, INC.—See Morgan Stanley; *U.S. Public*, pg. 1475
SOUTHERN STAR CONCRETE, INC.—See Grupo Argos S.A.; *Int'l*, pg. 3121
SOUTHERN STAR ENERGY CORP.; *U.S. Public*, pg. 1912
SOUTHERN STAR LEASING, LLC—See Grupo Argos S.A.; *Int'l*, pg. 3121
SOUTHERN STATES BANCSHARES, INC.; *U.S. Public*, pg. 1912
SOUTHERN STATES BANK—See Southern States Bancshares, Inc.; *U.S. Public*, pg. 1912
SOUTHERN STATES BDM, LLC; *U.S. Private*, pg. 3735
SOUTHERN STATES CHEMICAL, INC.—See Dulany Industries Inc.; *U.S. Private*, pg. 1286

SOUTHERN STATES CHEMICAL, INC. - WILMINGTON PLANT—See Dulany Industries Inc.; *U.S. Private*, pg. 1286
SOUTHERN STATES COOPERATIVE, INC.; *U.S. Private*, pg. 3735
SOUTHERN STATES MARKETING INC.; *U.S. Private*, pg. 3735
SOUTHERN STATES SIGN COMPANY; *Int'l*, pg. 7120
SOUTHERN STATES TOYOTALIFT—See Florida Lift Systems, Inc.; *U.S. Private*, pg. 1549
SOUTHERN STEEL BERHAD; *Int'l*, pg. 7120
SOUTHERN STEEL COMPANY LLC—See Beta International & Affiliates; *U.S. Private*, pg. 545
SOUTHERN STEEL MESH SDN. BHD.—See Southern Steel Berhad; *Int'l*, pg. 7120
SOUTHERN STEEL SUPPLY, LLC—See Reliance Steel & Aluminum Co.; *U.S. Public*, pg. 1781
SOUTHERN STEEL & WIRE CO. LLC—See Trive Capital Inc.; *U.S. Private*, pg. 4240
SOUTHERN STEEL & WIRE INC.—See Highland Supply Corporation; *U.S. Private*, pg. 1939
SOUTHERN STRIPING SOLUTIONS, LLC; *U.S. Private*, pg. 3735
SOUTHERN SUDAN BEVERAGES LTD—See Anheuser-Busch InBev SA/NV; *Int'l*, pg. 465
SOUTHERNSUN ASSET MANAGEMENT, LLC—See Affiliated Managers Group, Inc.; *U.S. Public*, pg. 55
SOUTHERN SUN HOTELS (PTY) LIMITED—See Hosken Consolidated Investments Limited; *Int'l*, pg. 3485
SOUTHERN SYSTEMS, INC.; *U.S. Private*, pg. 3735
SOUTHERN TANK & MANUFACTURING INC—See Kennedy Tank & Manufacturing Company, Inc.; *U.S. Private*, pg. 2285
SOUTHERN TEA LLC—See Tata Sons Limited; *Int'l*, pg. 7470
SOUTHERN TENNESSEE REGIONAL HEALTH SYSTEM—See Apollo Global Management, Inc.; *U.S. Public*, pg. 158
SOUTHERN THEATRES, LLC; *U.S. Private*, pg. 3735
SOUTHERN TIDE, LLC—See Oxford Industries, Inc.; *U.S. Public*, pg. 1629
SOUTHERN TIER INSULATIONS INC.; *U.S. Private*, pg. 3735
SOUTHERN TILE DISTRIBUTORS, INC.; *U.S. Private*, pg. 3735
SOUTHERN TIRE MART, LLC; *U.S. Private*, pg. 3735
SOUTHERN TITLE INSURANCE CORP.—See ALPS Corporation; *U.S. Private*, pg. 202
SOUTHERN TOOLING, INC.—See LFM Capital LLC; *U.S. Private*, pg. 2441
SOUTHERN TOOL STEEL, INC.—See Ryerson Holding Corporation; *U.S. Public*, pg. 1829
SOUTHERN TOWING COMPANY—See Henry Crown & Company; *U.S. Private*, pg. 1918
SOUTHERN TRACTOR & OUTDOORS—See Sumitomo Corporation; *Int'l*, pg. 7273
SOUTHERN TRAFFIC SERVICES, INC.—See Rekor Systems, Inc.; *U.S. Public*, pg. 1778
SOUTHERN TRAVEL HOLDINGS LIMITED; *Int'l*, pg. 7121
SOUTHERN TRAVELNET LIMITED—See Southern Travel Holdings Limited; *Int'l*, pg. 7121
SOUTHERN TRAVELNET PTY LIMITED—See Southern Travel Holdings Limited; *Int'l*, pg. 7121
SOUTHERN TRIALS (PTY) LTD.—See Thermo Fisher Scientific Inc.; *U.S. Public*, pg. 2147
SOUTHERN TRUST MORTGAGE, LLC; *U.S. Private*, pg. 3735
SOUTHERN TRUST SECURITIES HOLDING CORP.; *U.S. Private*, pg. 3735
SOUTHERN UNITED FIRE INSURANCE COMPANY—See Kingsway Financial Services Inc.; *U.S. Public*, pg. 1235
SOUTHERN URALS NICKEL PLANT OAO—See Mechel PAO; *Int'l*, pg. 4766
SOUTHERN UTAH HOME OXYGEN—See Apollo Global Management, Inc.; *U.S. Public*, pg. 157
SOUTHERN VECTIS OMNIBUS COMPANY LTD.—See GLOBALVIA Inversiones, S.A.U.; *Int'l*, pg. 3005
SOUTHERN VECTIS OMNIBUS COMPANY LTD.—See Kinetic Group Services Pty Ltd.; *Int'l*, pg. 4167
SOUTHERN WALL PRODUCTS INC.—See GMS Inc.; *U.S. Public*, pg. 948
SOUTHERN WASTE SERVICES, L.L.C.—See Waste Management, Inc.; *U.S. Public*, pg. 2332
SOUTHERN WATERBORNE TRANSPORT JOINT STOCK CORPORATION—See Southern International Logistics Joint Stock Company; *Int'l*, pg. 7120
SOUTHERN WAY INSURANCE AGENCY—See Zurich Insurance Group Limited; *Int'l*, pg. 8698
SOUTHERN WEALTH MANAGEMENT LLP—See The CapFinancial Group, LLC; *U.S. Private*, pg. 4004
SOUTHERN WEAVING COMPANY; *U.S. Private*, pg. 3735
SOUTHERN WEST VIRGINIA ASPHALT, INC.—See CRH plc; *Int'l*, pg. 1848
SOUTHERN WHOLESALE FLOORING CO.; *U.S. Private*, pg. 3735
SOUTHERN WISCONSIN BROADCASTING LLC—See Adams Publishing Group, LLC; *U.S. Private*, pg. 74
SOUTHERN WOOL WAREHOUSING PTY. LTD.—See Nutrien Ltd.; *Int'l*, pg. 5493

SOUTH ESSEX INSURANCE BROKERS LIMITED—See Ecclesiastical Insurance Office plc; *Int'l*, pg. 2288
SOUTH EVERSON LUMBER CO., INC.—See Terminal Forest Products Ltd.; *Int'l*, pg. 7565
SOUTHFARM LP—See Benchmark Senior Living, LLC; *U.S. Private*, pg. 524
SOUTH FEATHER WATER & POWER AGENCY; *U.S. Private*, pg. 3722
SOUTHFIELD CAPITAL ADVISORS, LLC; *U.S. Private*, pg. 3735
SOUTHFIELD CHRYSLER JEEP; *U.S. Private*, pg. 3736
SOUTHFIRST BANCSHARES, INC.; *U.S. Private*, pg. 3736
SOUTHFIRST BANK—See FirstBanc of Alabama, Inc.; *U.S. Private*, pg. 1531
SOUTHFIRST MORTGAGE, INC.—See FirstBanc of Alabama, Inc.; *U.S. Private*, pg. 1531
SOUTH FLORIDA AMBULATORY SURGICAL CENTER, LLC—See Tenet Healthcare Corporation; *U.S. Public*, pg. 2005
SOUTH FLORIDA BAKERY, INC.; *U.S. Private*, pg. 3722
SOUTH FLORIDA BAPTIST HOSPITAL—See BayCare Health System Inc.; *U.S. Private*, pg. 496
SOUTH FLORIDA BUSINESS JOURNAL—See Advance Publications, Inc.; *U.S. Private*, pg. 85
SOUTH FLORIDA BUSINESS LEADER—See Business Leader Media; *U.S. Private*, pg. 695
SOUTH FLORIDA INTEGRATED KIDNEY CARE, LLC—See DaVita Inc.; *U.S. Public*, pg. 643
SOUTH FLORIDA MEDIA GROUP, LLC; *U.S. Private*, pg. 3722
SOUTH FLORIDA PARENTING—See Tribune Publishing Company; *U.S. Private*, pg. 4228
SOUTH FLORIDA PBS, INC.; *U.S. Private*, pg. 3722
SOUTHFRESH AQUACULTURE; *U.S. Private*, pg. 3736
SOUTHFRESH FARMS - INDIANOLA PROCESSING PLANT—See Alabama Farmers Cooperative, Inc.; *U.S. Private*, pg. 148
SOUTH GAIN ENTERPRISES LIMITED—See Hung Hing Printing Group Limited; *Int'l*, pg. 3535
SOUTHGATE CHEVROLET BUICK GMC LTD.; *Int'l*, pg. 7121
SOUTH GATE ENGINEERING, LLC; *U.S. Private*, pg. 3722
SOUTHGATE FORD INC.; *U.S. Private*, pg. 3736
SOUTHGATE HOMES - SUBURBAN LIVING, LLC—See Green Brick Partners, Inc.; *U.S. Public*, pg. 963
SOUTHGATE LINCOLN—See Southgate Ford Inc.; *U.S. Private*, pg. 3736
SOUTHGATE TIMBER CO. INC.; *U.S. Private*, pg. 3736
SOUTHGATE VOLKSWAGEN; *Int'l*, pg. 7121
SOUTH GEORGIA PECAN COMPANY INC.; *U.S. Private*, pg. 3722
SOUTHGOBI RESOURCES (HONG KONG) LTD—See Rio Tinto plc; *Int'l*, pg. 6348
SOUTHGOBI RESOURCES LTD.—See Rio Tinto plc; *Int'l*, pg. 6348
SOUTHGOBI SANDS LLC—See Rio Tinto plc; *Int'l*, pg. 6348
SOUTH HAMPTON RESOURCES, INC.—See Balmoral Funds LLC; *U.S. Private*, pg. 462
SOUTH HARZ POTASH LIMITED; *Int'l*, pg. 7116
SOUTH HAVEN COIL INC.—See Humphrey Products Corporation; *U.S. Private*, pg. 2007
SOUTH HAVEN MANOR NURSING HOME—See Sava Senior Care LLC; *U.S. Private*, pg. 3555
SOUTH HAVEN PACKAGING, INC.—See Kindlon Enterprises, Inc.; *U.S. Private*, pg. 2307
SOUTH HILLS HONDA; *U.S. Private*, pg. 3722
THE SOUTH INDIAN BANK LIMITED; *Int'l*, pg. 7688
THE SOUTH INDIA PAPER MILLS LIMITED; *Int'l*, pg. 7688
SOUTHINGTON SUITES, LLC—See KSL Capital Partners, LLC; *U.S. Private*, pg. 2355
SOUTH IOWA MUNICIPAL ELECTRIC COOPERATIVE ASSOCIATION; *U.S. Private*, pg. 3722
SOUTH ISLAND MINING CO BERHAD—See Kuok Brothers Sdn. Bhd.; *Int'l*, pg. 4335
SOUTH ISLAND PLASTICS SDN. BHD.—See Magni-Tech Industries Berhad; *Int'l*, pg. 4640
SOUTH JERSEY CHILDCARE CORP.; *U.S. Private*, pg. 3722
SOUTH JERSEY ENERGY COMPANY—See JPMorgan Chase & Co.; *U.S. Public*, pg. 1210
SOUTH JERSEY ENERGY SERVICES PLUS, LLC—See JPMorgan Chase & Co.; *U.S. Public*, pg. 1210
SOUTH JERSEY ENERGY SOLUTIONS, LLC—See JPMorgan Chase & Co.; *U.S. Public*, pg. 1210
SOUTH JERSEY GAS CO. - GLASSBORO DIVISION—See JPMorgan Chase & Co.; *U.S. Public*, pg. 1210
SOUTH JERSEY GAS COMPANY—See JPMorgan Chase & Co.; *U.S. Public*, pg. 1210
SOUTH JERSEY INDUSTRIES, INC.—See JPMorgan Chase & Co.; *U.S. Public*, pg. 1210
SOUTH JERSEY MARINA INC.; *U.S. Private*, pg. 3722
SOUTH JERSEY PORT CORPORATION; *U.S. Private*, pg. 3723

SOUTH JERSEY PUBS INC—See Metz Enterprises Inc.; *U.S. Private*, pg. 2691
SOUTH JERSEY RESOURCES GROUP, LLC—See JPMorgan Chase & Co.; *U.S. Public*, pg. 1210
SOUTH KENTUCKY RURAL ELECTRIC CO-OPERATIVE CORPORATION; *U.S. Private*, pg. 3723
SOUTHLAKE EQUITY GROUP LLC; *U.S. Private*, pg. 3736
SOUTHLAKE FOOD MART; *U.S. Private*, pg. 3736
SOUTH LAKES SURGICENTER, LLC—See HCA Healthcare, Inc.; *U.S. Public*, pg. 1010
SOUTHLAND ASSOCIATES, INC.—See Truist Financial Corporation; *U.S. Public*, pg. 2199
SOUTHLAND BOX COMPANY—See Tomoku Co., Ltd.; *Int'l*, pg. 7802
SOUTHLAND CENTER, LLC—See Brookfield Corporation; *Int'l*, pg. 1185
SOUTHLAND CREDIT UNION; *U.S. Private*, pg. 3736
SOUTHLAND FINANCE, INC.—See Old National Bancorp; *U.S. Public*, pg. 1567
SOUTHLAND HOLDINGS, INC.; *U.S. Public*, pg. 1912
SOUTHLAND IMPORTS, INC.; *U.S. Private*, pg. 3736
SOUTHLAND INDUSTRIES-MID-ATLANTIC DIVISION—See Southland Industries; *U.S. Private*, pg. 3737
SOUTHLAND INDUSTRIES-NORTHERN CALIFORNIA DIVISION—See Southland Industries; *U.S. Private*, pg. 3737
SOUTHLAND INDUSTRIES; *U.S. Private*, pg. 3737
SOUTHLAND INDUSTRIES-SOUTHERN CALIFORNIA DIVISION—See Southland Industries; *U.S. Private*, pg. 3737
SOUTHLAND INDUSTRIES-SOUTHWEST DIVISION—See Southland Industries; *U.S. Private*, pg. 3737
SOUTHLAND INTERNATIONAL TRUCKS LTD.; *Int'l*, pg. 7121
SOUTHLAND LIGHTING SALES, INC.; *U.S. Private*, pg. 3737
SOUTHLAND MALL, L.P.—See Brookfield Corporation; *Int'l*, pg. 1185
SOUTHLAND MANAGEMENT LLC—See The Ensign Group, Inc.; *U.S. Public*, pg. 2072
SOUTHLAND NATIONAL INSURANCE CORPORATION—See Eli Global, LLC; *U.S. Private*, pg. 1360
SOUTHLAND NURSING HOME—See Sava Senior Care LLC; *U.S. Private*, pg. 3555
SOUTHLAND PLANTATION FOREST COMPANY OF NEW ZEALAND LTD.—See Oji Holdings Corporation; *Int'l*, pg. 5538
SOUTHLAND PLUMBING SUPPLY INC.; *U.S. Private*, pg. 3737
SOUTHLAND PRINTING CO., INC.; *U.S. Private*, pg. 3737
SOUTHLAND TECHNOLOGY, INC.; *U.S. Private*, pg. 3737
THE SOUTHLAND TIMES—See Nine Entertainment Co. Holdings Limited; *Int'l*, pg. 5298
SOUTHLAND TRACTORS LTD—See The Colonial Motor Company Limited; *Int'l*, pg. 7635
SOUTHLAND TRAILER CORP.; *Int'l*, pg. 7121
SOUTHLAND TRANSPORTATION CO.; *U.S. Private*, pg. 3737
SOUTHLAND TUBE, INC.—See Nucor Corporation; *U.S. Public*, pg. 1554
SOUTHLAND VENEERS LTD.—See EAC Invest AS; *Int'l*, pg. 2262
SOUTHLINE METAL PRODUCTS COMPANY—See Greif Inc.; *U.S. Public*, pg. 968
SOUTH-LINK N25 LTD.—See Groupe Egis S.A.; *Int'l*, pg. 3102
SOUTH LONDON INFINITI NISSAN; *Int'l*, pg. 7116
SOUTH LOUISIANA METHANOL LP—See The Todd Corporation Limited; *Int'l*, pg. 7694
SOUTH LUBES INC.; *U.S. Private*, pg. 3723
SOUTH LUZON TOLLWAY CORPORATION—See MTD Capital Bhd.; *Int'l*, pg. 5070
SOUTH MALAYSIA INDUSTRIES BERHAD; *Int'l*, pg. 7116
SOUTH MANGANESE INVESTMENT LIMITED—See CITIC Group Corporation; *Int'l*, pg. 1621
SOUTHMEDIC INC.; *Int'l*, pg. 7121
SOUTH MIAMI HOSPITAL—See Baptist Health South Florida, Inc.; *U.S. Private*, pg. 471
SOUTH MIAMI PHARMACY; *U.S. Private*, pg. 3723
SOUTH MIDDLESEX OPPORTUNITY COUNCIL, INC.; *U.S. Private*, pg. 3723
SOUTH MILL MUSHROOMS SALES, INC.; *U.S. Private*, pg. 3723
SOUTHMINSTER; *U.S. Private*, pg. 3737
SOUTH MISSISSIPPI ELECTRIC & POWER ASSOCIATION; *U.S. Private*, pg. 3723
SOUTH MOON SALES, INC.—See Ames Watson Holding LLC; *U.S. Private*, pg. 262
SOUTH MOTOR COMPANY OF DADE COUNTY; *U.S. Private*, pg. 3723
SOUTH MOTORS INFINITI—See South Motor Company of Dade County; *U.S. Private*, pg. 3723
SOUTH OAK DODGE, INC.; *U.S. Private*, pg. 3723

COMPANY NAME INDEX / SOUTHWEST CONVENIENCE STORES LLC

SOUTH OCEAN ELECTRIC WIRE COMPANY (PROPRIETARY) LIMITED—See South Ocean Holdings Limited; *Int'l*, pg. 7116
SOUTH OCEAN HOLDINGS LIMITED; *Int'l*, pg. 7116
SOUTH OF THE BORDER RESTAURANT INC.—See The Schafer Company Inc.; *U.S. Private*, pg. 4114
SOUTH OTTUMWA SAVINGS BANK; *U.S. Private*, pg. 3723
SOUTH PACIFIC INTERNATIONAL CONTAINER TERMINAL LIMITED—See International Container Terminal Services, Inc.; *Int'l*, pg. 3746
SOUTH PACIFIC MEATS LIMITED—See AFFCO Holdings Limited; *Int'l*, pg. 186
SOUTH PACIFIC POWER PTY. LIMITED—See Electricity Generating Public Co., Ltd.; *Int'l*, pg. 2352
SOUTH PACIFIC STOCK EXCHANGE LIMITED; *Int'l*, pg. 7116
SOUTH PACIFIC WELDING GROUP PTY LIMITED—See Linde plc; *Int'l*, pg. 4507
SOUTHPAC TRUCKS LTD.—See The Colonial Motor Company Limited; *Int'l*, pg. 7635
SOUTH PALM AMBULATORY SURGERY CENTER, LLC—See Baptist Health South Florida, Inc.; *U.S. Private*, pg. 471
SOUTH PARK CORPORATION; *U.S. Private*, pg. 3723
SOUTH PARK MOTOR LINES INC.; *U.S. Private*, pg. 3723
SOUTH PARK STREET INC.—See Symmco Group Inc.; *U.S. Private*, pg. 3899
SOUTHPAW SPORTS & ENTERTAINMENT, INC.; *U.S. Private*, pg. 3737
SOUTH PLAINS BIOMEDICAL SERVICES, INC.; *U.S. Private*, pg. 3723
SOUTH PLAINS ELECTRIC COOPERATIVE; *U.S. Private*, pg. 3723
SOUTH PLAINS ENDOSCOPY ASSOCIATES, LLC—See Tenet Healthcare Corporation; *U.S. Public*, pg. 2007
SOUTH PLAINS FINANCIAL, INC.; *U.S. Public*, pg. 1911
SOUTHPOINT BANCSHARES, INC.; *U.S. Public*, pg. 1912
SOUTHPOINT RISK ADVISORS LLC; *U.S. Private*, pg. 3737
SOUTHPORT ACQUISITION CORPORATION; *U.S. Public*, pg. 1912
SOUTHPORT FINANCIAL CORPORATION; *U.S. Private*, pg. 3737
SOUTH PORT JOINT STOCK COMPANY—See Southern International Logistics Joint Stock Company; *Int'l*, pg. 7120
SOUTH PORTLAND SURGICAL CENTER, LLC—See KKR & Co. Inc.; *U.S. Public*, pg. 1250
SOUTHPORT MAZDA PTY. LIMITED—See Peter Warren Automotive Holdings Ltd.; *Int'l*, pg. 5824
SOUTH PORT NEW ZEALAND LIMITED; *Int'l*, pg. 7116
SOUTH PUGET INTERTRIBAL PLANNING AGENCY; *U.S. Private*, pg. 3723
SOUTH READING BLACKTOP—See Haines & Kibblehouse Inc.; *U.S. Private*, pg. 1841
SOUTHRIDGE TECHNOLOGY GRP, LLC.; *U.S. Private*, pg. 3737
SOUTH RISK MANAGEMENT LLC—See Edwards Capital, LLC; *U.S. Private*, pg. 1342
SOUTH RIVER ELECTRIC MEMBERSHIP CORPORATION; *U.S. Private*, pg. 3723
SOUTH SEAS CYCLE EXCHANGE INC.; *U.S. Private*, pg. 3723
SOUTH SEAS INSPECTION (S) PTE LTD—See NOV, Inc.; *U.S. Public*, pg. 1546
SOUTHSEAS OILS & FATS INDUSTRIAL (CHIWAN) LTD—See Wilmar International Limited; *Int'l*, pg. 8421
SOUTH SHIELDS QUAYS VETS4PETS LIMITED—See Pets at Home Group Plc; *Int'l*, pg. 5834
SOUTH SHORE ASSOCIATION FOR INDEPENDENT LIVING, INC.; *U.S. Private*, pg. 3723
SOUTH SHORE BUILDING SERVICES, INC.—See Valcourt Building Services LLC; *U.S. Private*, pg. 4330
SOUTH SHORE COMMUNITY ACTION COUNCIL, INC.; *U.S. Private*, pg. 3723
SOUTH SHORE DIALYSIS CENTER. L.P.—See DaVita Inc.; *U.S. Public*, pg. 643
SOUTH SHORE FORD INC.; *U.S. Private*, pg. 3723
SOUTH SHORE HARBOUR DEVELOPMENT, LTD.—See Brookfield Corporation; *Int'l*, pg. 1174
SOUTH SHORE HARBOUR RESORT & CONFERENCE CENTER—See Gal-Tex Hotel Corporation; *U.S. Private*, pg. 1635
SOUTH SHORE HOLDINGS LTD.; *Int'l*, pg. 7116
SOUTH SHORE HOME HEALTH SERVICES, INC.—See Addus HomeCare Corporation; *U.S. Public*, pg. 40
SOUTH SHORE HOSPITAL; *U.S. Private*, pg. 3723
SOUTH SHORE HOSPITAL—See Partners HealthCare System, Inc.; *U.S. Private*, pg. 3102
SOUTH SHORE MEDICAL SUPPLY, INC.—See ConvaTec Group PLC; *Int'l*, pg. 1786
SOUTH SHORE MOTORS CORP; *U.S. Private*, pg. 3724
SOUTH SHORE PRODUCTIONS, INC.—See Lions Gate Entertainment Corp.; *Int'l*, pg. 4521
SOUTH SHORE SAVINGS BANK; *U.S. Private*, pg. 3724

SOUTH SHORE TRANSPORTATION CO.; *U.S. Private*, pg. 3724
SOUTHSIDE AUTOS (1981) PTY LTD—See Eagers Automotive Limited; *Int'l*, pg. 2263
SOUTHSIDE BANCSHARES, INC.; *U.S. Public*, pg. 1912
SOUTHSIDE BANK IS A STATE BANK—See Southside Bancshares, Inc.; *U.S. Public*, pg. 1912
SOUTHSIDE BANK—See Southside Bancshares, Inc.; *U.S. Public*, pg. 1912
SOUTH SIDE CONTROL SUPPLY CO.; *U.S. Private*, pg. 3724
SOUTHSIDE DODGE CHRYSLER JEEP & RV CENTRE; *Int'l*, pg. 7121
SOUTHSIDE DODGE SALES INC.; *U.S. Private*, pg. 3737
SOUTHSIDE ELECTRIC COOPERATIVE INC.; *U.S. Private*, pg. 3737
SOUTHSIDE HEALTHCARE, INC.—See The Ensign Group, Inc.; *U.S. Public*, pg. 2072
SOUTHSIDE IMPORTS INC.; *U.S. Private*, pg. 3738
SOUTHSIDE MEDICAL CENTER INC.; *U.S. Private*, pg. 3738
SOUTHSIDE NISSAN LTD; *Int'l*, pg. 7121
SOUTHSIDE OIL LLC—See Sunoco LP; *U.S. Public*, pg. 1965
SOUTHSIDE TIRE CO. INC.; *U.S. Private*, pg. 3738
SOUTH STAFFORDSHIRE PLC—See Arjun Infrastructure Partners Limited; *Int'l*, pg. 568
SOUTH STAFFORDSHIRE WATER PLC—See Arjun Infrastructure Partners Limited; *Int'l*, pg. 568
SOUTH STAR BATTERY METALS CORP.; *Int'l*, pg. 7117
SOUTHSTAR ENERGY SERVICES LLC—See The Southern Company; *U.S. Public*, pg. 2131
SOUTHSTAR EQUIPMENT LTD.—See Komatsu Ltd.; *Int'l*, pg. 4239
SOUTHSTAR EQUIPMENT LTD.—See Komatsu Ltd.; *Int'l*, pg. 4239
SOUTH STATE BANK, N.A.—See SouthState Corporation; *U.S. Public*, pg. 1913
SOUTHSTATE CORPORATION; *U.S. Public*, pg. 1912
SOUTH ST. BURGER CO—See New York Fries; *Int'l*, pg. 5231
SOUTHSTONE BEHAVIORAL HEALTHCARE CENTER, LLC—See Acadia Healthcare Company, Inc.; *U.S. Public*, pg. 30
SOUTHSTONE MINERALS LIMITED; *Int'l*, pg. 7121
SOUTH STREET SEAPORT LIMITED PARTNERSHIP—See Howard Hughes Holdings Inc.; *U.S. Public*, pg. 1060
SOUTH SUBURBAN SURGICAL SUITES, LLC—See Tenet Healthcare Corporation; *U.S. Public*, pg. 2007
SOUTH TAHOE PUBLIC UTILITY DISTRICT; *U.S. Private*, pg. 3724
SOUTHTECH SOLUTIONS INC.—See Court Square Capital Partners, L.P.; *U.S. Private*, pg. 1070
SOUTH TEXAS ACO CLINICAL PARTNERS, LLC—See Universal Health Services, Inc.; *U.S. Public*, pg. 2259
SOUTH TEXAS APPLICATORS, INC.—See Cal-Maine Foods, Inc.; *U.S. Public*, pg. 421
SOUTH TEXAS BROADCASTING, INC.—See Salem Media Group, Inc.; *U.S. Public*, pg. 1836
SOUTH TEXAS ELECTRIC COOPERATIVE, INC.; *U.S. Private*, pg. 3724
SOUTH TEXAS LONE STAR DRYWALL; *U.S. Private*, pg. 3724
SOUTH TEXAS MINING VENTURE, L.L.P.—See Uranium Energy Corp.; *Int'l*, pg. 8094
SOUTHTEX TREATERS, INC.—See Kinder Morgan, Inc.; *U.S. Public*, pg. 1233
SOUTHTOWN HEATING & COOLING, INC.—See Seiter Services, LLC; *U.S. Public*, pg. 3600
SOUTH-TOWN REFRIGERATION INC.—See Haier Smart Home Co., Ltd.; *Int'l*, pg. 3210
SOUTHTRUST BANK, N.A.—See Live Oak Bancshares Corporation; *U.S. Private*, pg. 2473
SOUTH TULSA PHYSICAL THERAPY, LIMITED PARTNERSHIP—See U.S. Physical Therapy, Inc.; *U.S. Public*, pg. 2216
SOUTH UNIVERSITY - COLUMBIA—See Dream Center Foundation, a California Nonprofit Corp.; *U.S. Private*, pg. 1273
SOUTH UNIVERSITY, LLC—See Dream Center Foundation, a California Nonprofit Corp.; *U.S. Private*, pg. 1273
SOUTH UNIVERSITY - MONTGOMERY—See Dream Center Foundation, a California Nonprofit Corp.; *U.S. Private*, pg. 1273
SOUTH UNIVERSITY OF ALABAMA, INC.—See Dream Center Foundation, a California Nonprofit Corp.; *U.S. Private*, pg. 1273
SOUTH UNIVERSITY OF ARIZONA LLC—See Dream Center Foundation, a California Nonprofit Corp.; *U.S. Private*, pg. 1273
SOUTH UNIVERSITY OF CAROLINA, INC.—See Dream Center Foundation, a California Nonprofit Corp.; *U.S. Private*, pg. 1274
SOUTH UNIVERSITY OF FLORIDA, INC.—See Dream Center Foundation, a California Nonprofit Corp.; *U.S. Private*, pg. 1274

SOUTH UNIVERSITY OF MICHIGAN, LLC—See Dream Center Foundation, a California Nonprofit Corp.; *U.S. Private*, pg. 1274
SOUTH UNIVERSITY OF NORTH CAROLINA LLC—See Dream Center Foundation, a California Nonprofit Corp.; *U.S. Private*, pg. 1274
SOUTH UNIVERSITY OF OHIO LLC—See Dream Center Foundation, a California Nonprofit Corp.; *U.S. Private*, pg. 1274
SOUTH UNIVERSITY—See Dream Center Foundation, a California Nonprofit Corp.; *U.S. Private*, pg. 1273
SOUTH UNIVERSITY - WEST PALM BEACH—See Dream Center Foundation, a California Nonprofit Corp.; *U.S. Private*, pg. 1273
SOUTH VALLEY HEALTHCARE, INC.—See The Ensign Group, Inc.; *U.S. Public*, pg. 2072
SOUTH VALLEY MATERIALS, INC. - COALINGA PLANT—See Heidelberg Materials AG; *Int'l*, pg. 3319
SOUTH VALLEY MATERIALS, INC. - EXETER PLANT—See Heidelberg Materials AG; *Int'l*, pg. 3319
SOUTH VALLEY MATERIALS, INC. - PORTERVILLE PLANT—See Heidelberg Materials AG; *Int'l*, pg. 3319
SOUTH VALLEY MATERIALS, INC.—See Heidelberg Materials AG; *Int'l*, pg. 3319
SOUTH VALLEY MATERIALS, INC. - TULARE PLANT—See Heidelberg Materials AG; *Int'l*, pg. 3319
SOUTHVIEW ACURA; *Int'l*, pg. 7121
SOUTH VILLAGE FORD; *U.S. Private*, pg. 3724
SOUTHVILLE CITY SDN. BHD.—See Mah Sing Group Berhad; *Int'l*, pg. 4643
SOUTHWALL EUROPE GMBH—See Eastman Chemical Company; *U.S. Public*, pg. 706
SOUTHWALL TECHNOLOGIES INC.—See Eastman Chemical Company; *U.S. Public*, pg. 706
SOUTHWARE INNOVATIONS, INC.—See Open Systems, Inc.; *U.S. Public*, pg. 3030
SOUTHWARK METAL MANUFACTURING COMPANY - GREENVILLE DIVISION—See Southwark Metal Manufacturing Company; *U.S. Private*, pg. 3738
SOUTHWARK METAL MANUFACTURING COMPANY - IDAHO DIVISION—See Southwark Metal Manufacturing Company; *U.S. Private*, pg. 3738
SOUTHWARK METAL MANUFACTURING COMPANY - INDIANAPOLIS DIVISION—See Southwark Metal Manufacturing Company; *U.S. Private*, pg. 3738
SOUTHWARK METAL MANUFACTURING COMPANY - MISSISSIPPI DIVISION—See Southwark Metal Manufacturing Company; *U.S. Private*, pg. 3738
SOUTHWARK METAL MANUFACTURING COMPANY - NEBRASKA DIVISION—See Southwark Metal Manufacturing Company; *U.S. Private*, pg. 3738
SOUTHWARK METAL MANUFACTURING COMPANY; *U.S. Private*, pg. 3738
SOUTHWAY FORD INC.; *U.S. Private*, pg. 3738
SOUTHWELL RACECOURSE LIMITED—See Reuben Brothers SA; *Int'l*, pg. 6311
SOUTHWEST ADMINISTRATORS INC.; *U.S. Private*, pg. 3738
SOUTHWEST AIRLINES CO.; *U.S. Public*, pg. 1913
SOUTHWEST ARCHITECTURAL BUILDERS, INC.; *U.S. Private*, pg. 3738
SOUTHWEST ARKANSAS DEVELOPMENT COUNCIL; *U.S. Private*, pg. 3738
SOUTHWEST ARKANSAS ELECTRIC COOPERATIVE CORPORATION; *U.S. Private*, pg. 3738
SOUTHWEST ARKANSAS HOMECARE, LLC—See UnitedHealth Group Incorporated; *U.S. Public*, pg. 2247
SOUTHWEST ATLANTA DIALYSIS CENTERS, LLC—See DaVita Inc.; *U.S. Public*, pg. 643
SOUTHWEST BAKING COMPANY, LLC.; *U.S. Private*, pg. 3738
SOUTHWEST BAKING CO.; *U.S. Private*, pg. 3738
SOUTHWEST BANCSHARES, INC.; *U.S. Private*, pg. 3738
SOUTHWEST BATTERY COMPANY—See InvestX Capital Ltd.; *Int'l*, pg. 3788
SOUTHWEST BEVERAGE CO. INC.—See Mockler Beverage Co. LP; *U.S. Private*, pg. 2759
SOUTHWEST BOTTLING & CO-PACKING, LLC—See Regus Advisors, Inc.; *U.S. Private*, pg. 3389
SOUTHWEST BUILDER SUPPLY, INC.—See RP Lumber Co. Inc.; *U.S. Private*, pg. 3495
SOUTHWEST BUILDING MATERIALS, LLC—See GMS Inc.; *U.S. Public*, pg. 948
SOUTHWEST BUSINESS CORPORATION; *U.S. Private*, pg. 3738
SOUTHWEST CANNING & PACKAGING INC—See Kalil Bottling Co., Inc.; *U.S. Private*, pg. 2257
SOUTHWEST CASINO CORP.; *U.S. Private*, pg. 3738
SOUTHWEST COMMUNITY HEALTH CENTER, INC.; *U.S. Private*, pg. 3738
SOUTHWEST CONTRACTORS, INC.; *U.S. Private*, pg. 3738
SOUTHWEST CONVENIENCE STORES LLC; *U.S. Private*, pg. 3738
SOUTHWEST DEALERS SERVICES, INC.—See Spencer Capital Holdings, Ltd.; *U.S. Private*, pg. 3754
SOUTHWEST DISPOSAL SERVICE, INC.—See Republic Services, Inc.; *U.S. Public*, pg. 1787

SOUTHWEST EDUCATIONAL DEVELOPMENT LABORATORY — CORPORATE AFFILIATIONS

SOUTHWEST EDUCATIONAL DEVELOPMENT LABORATORY; *U.S. Private,* pg. 3739
SOUTHWEST ELECTRIC CO. INC.; *U.S. Private,* pg. 3739
SOUTHWEST ELECTRIC COOPERATIVE, INC.; *U.S. Private,* pg. 3739
SOUTHWEST ELECTRONIC ENERGY CORP.—See Ultralife Corporation; *U.S. Public,* pg. 2224
SOUTHWEST ENDOSCOPY, LLC—See Tenet Healthcare Corporation; *U.S. Public,* pg. 2007
SOUTHWEST ENERGY SOLUTIONS, INC.—See Fortis Inc.; *Int'l,* pg. 2740
SOUTHWEST AMBULATORY SURGERY CENTER, LLC—See Tenet Healthcare Corporation; *U.S. Public,* pg. 2012
SOUTHWESTERN BANCORP, INC.; *U.S. Private,* pg. 3741
SOUTHWESTERN BELL TELEPHONE L.P.—See AT&T Inc.; *U.S. Public,* pg. 219
SOUTH-WESTERN CENGAGE LEARNING—See Apax Partners LLP; *Int'l,* pg. 503
SOUTH-WESTERN CENGAGE LEARNING—See Apollo Global Management, Inc.; *U.S. Public,* pg. 168
SOUTH-WESTERN CENGAGE LEARNING—See KKR & Co. Inc.; *U.S. Public,* pg. 1256
SOUTH-WESTERN CENGAGE LEARNING—See Searchlight Capital Partners, L.P.; *U.S. Private,* pg. 3587
SOUTHWESTERN CHILDREN'S HEALTH SERVICES, INC.—See Acadia Healthcare Company, Inc.; *U.S. Public,* pg. 30
SOUTH WESTERN COMMUNICATIONS, INC.—See Koch Enterprises, Inc.; *U.S. Private,* pg. 2326
SOUTHWESTERN COMMUNITY SERVICES, INC.; *U.S. Private,* pg. 3741
THE SOUTHWESTERN COMPANY; *U.S. Private,* pg. 4119
SOUTHWESTERN DIE CASTING, INC.—See ABB Ltd.; *Int'l,* pg. 52
SOUTHWESTERN ELECTRICAL COMPANY INC.; *U.S. Private,* pg. 3741
SOUTHWESTERN ELECTRIC CO-OPERATIVE INC.; *U.S. Private,* pg. 3741
SOUTHWESTERN ELECTRIC POWER COMPANY—See American Electric Power Company, Inc.; *U.S. Public,* pg. 100
SOUTHWESTERN ENERGY COMPANY—See Expand Energy Corporation; *U.S. Public,* pg. 808
SOUTHWESTERN ENERGY PIPELINE SERVICES—See Expand Energy Corporation; *U.S. Public,* pg. 809
SOUTHWESTERN ENERGY PRODUCTION CO.—See Expand Energy Corporation; *U.S. Public,* pg. 809
SOUTHWESTERN ENERGY SERVICES COMPANY—See Expand Energy Corporation; *U.S. Public,* pg. 809
SOUTHWESTERN FINANCIAL CORPORATION; *U.S. Private,* pg. 3741
SOUTH & WESTERN GENERAL AGENCY, INC.—See Brown & Brown, Inc.; *U.S. Public,* pg. 401
SOUTHWESTERN GRAPHITE CO.—See Great Mill Rock LLC; *U.S. Private,* pg. 1766
SOUTHWESTERN ILLINOIS HEALTH FACILITIES, INC.; *U.S. Private,* pg. 3741
SOUTHWESTERN INDUSTRIES, INC.; *U.S. Private,* pg. 3741
SOUTH WESTERN INSURANCE GROUP LIMITED—See ING Groep N.V.; *Int'l,* pg. 3701
SOUTHWESTERN IRRIGATED COTTON GROWERS ASSOCIATION INC.; *U.S. Private,* pg. 3741
SOUTHWESTERN MEDICAL CENTER—See Apollo Global Management, Inc.; *U.S. Public,* pg. 159
SOUTHWESTERN MIDSTREAM SERVICES COMPANY—See Expand Energy Corporation; *U.S. Public,* pg. 809
SOUTHWESTERN MOTOR TRANSPORT INCORPORATED; *U.S. Private,* pg. 3741
SOUTHWESTERN OREGON PUBLISHING CO.—See Lee Enterprises, Incorporated; *U.S. Public,* pg. 1300
SOUTHWESTERN PETROLEUM CANADA LTD.—See Southwestern Petroleum Corporation; *U.S. Private,* pg. 3742
SOUTHWESTERN PETROLEUM CORPORATION; *U.S. Private,* pg. 3742
SOUTHWESTERN POWER GROUP II LLC—See MMR Group Inc.; *U.S. Private,* pg. 2755
SOUTHWESTERN PROPERTY CORP.; *U.S. Private,* pg. 3742
THE SOUTH WESTERN RAILROAD CO.—See Norfolk Southern Corporation; *U.S. Public,* pg. 1536
SOUTHWESTERN SECURITY SERVICES; *U.S. Private,* pg. 3742
SOUTHWESTERN STATIONERY & BANK SUPPLY, INC.; *U.S. Private,* pg. 3742
SOUTHWESTERN SUPPLIERS, INC.; *U.S. Private,* pg. 3742
SOUTHWESTERN TELEPHONE COMPANY—See Telephone & Data Systems, Inc.; *U.S. Public,* pg. 1998
SOUTHWESTERN UNIVERSITY—See PHINMA Corporation; *Int'l,* pg. 5848
SOUTHWESTERN FINANCIAL SERVICES, LTD.—See Real Matters, Inc.; *Int'l,* pg. 6233

SOUTHWEST FLORIDA CABLE CONSTRUCTION, INC.; *U.S. Private,* pg. 3739
SOUTHWEST FLORIDA EMERGENCY MANAGEMENT, LLC—See Blackstone Inc.; *U.S. Public,* pg. 359
SOUTHWEST FLORIDA FRANCHISES INC.; *U.S. Private,* pg. 3739
SOUTHWEST FLORIDA INSURANCE ASSOCIATES, INC.; *U.S. Private,* pg. 3739
SOUTHWEST FORD INC.; *U.S. Private,* pg. 3739
SOUTHWEST FREEWAY SURGERY CENTER MANAGEMENT, LLC—See Nobilis Health Corp.; *U.S. Private,* pg. 2932
SOUTHWEST FREIGHT DISTRIBUTORS, INC.—See Forward Air Corporation; *U.S. Public,* pg. 874
SOUTHWEST FREIGHT INC.; *U.S. Private,* pg. 3739
SOUTHWEST FUEL SYSTEMS LLC—See M International Inc.; *U.S. Private,* pg. 2523
SOUTHWEST FUNDING L.P.; *U.S. Private,* pg. 3739
SOUTHWEST GAS CORPORATION—See Southwest Gas Holdings, Inc.; *U.S. Public,* pg. 1913
SOUTHWEST GAS CORPORATION—See Southwest Gas Holdings, Inc.; *U.S. Public,* pg. 1913
SOUTHWEST GAS HOLDINGS, INC.; *U.S. Public,* pg. 1913
SOUTHWEST GAS TRANSMISSION COMPANY—See Southwest Gas Holdings, Inc.; *U.S. Public,* pg. 1913
SOUTHWEST GENERAL INSURANCE COMPANY—See Gurley Motor Company; *U.S. Private,* pg. 1819
SOUTHWEST GEORGIA COMMUNITY ACTION COUNCIL, INC.; *U.S. Private,* pg. 3739
SOUTHWEST GEORGIA OIL CO., INC.; *U.S. Private,* pg. 3739
SOUTHWEST GROWTH CORPORATION—See Kasco Corporation; *U.S. Private,* pg. 2264
SOUTHWEST HEALTHCARE SERVICES; *U.S. Private,* pg. 3739
SOUTHWEST HEALTHCARE SYSTEM—See Universal Health Services, Inc.; *U.S. Public,* pg. 2260
SOUTHWEST HEALTH CENTER; *U.S. Private,* pg. 3739
SOUTHWEST HEALTH SYSTEM, INC.; *U.S. Private,* pg. 3739
SOUTHWEST HEATER & CONTROLS, INC.—See Gryphon Investors, LLC; *U.S. Private,* pg. 1799
SOUTHWEST HIDE COMPANY; *U.S. Private,* pg. 3739
SOUTH WEST HIGHWAYS LTD.—See VINCI S.A.; *Int'l,* pg. 8229
SOUTHWEST INDIANA DIALYSIS, LLC—See DaVita Inc.; *U.S. Public,* pg. 643
SOUTHWEST INTERNATIONAL TRUCKS, INC.; *U.S. Private,* pg. 3739
SOUTHWEST IOWA RENEWABLE ENERGY, LLC; *U.S. Private,* pg. 3739
SOUTHWEST JACKSONVILLE DIALYSIS CENTER LLC—See Nautic Partners, LLC; *U.S. Private,* pg. 2871
SOUTHWEST KEY PROGRAMS; *U.S. Private,* pg. 3739
SOUTHWEST LANDCOM; *U.S. Private,* pg. 3739
SOUTHWEST LANDFILL TX, LP—See Republic Services, Inc.; *U.S. Public,* pg. 1787
SOUTHWEST LENS CORP.—See EssilorLuxottica SA; *Int'l,* pg. 2514
SOUTHWEST LOUISIANA ELECTRIC MEMBERSHIP CORPORATION; *U.S. Private,* pg. 3739
SOUTHWEST LOUISIANA HOSPITAL ASSOCIATION; *U.S. Private,* pg. 3739
SOUTHWEST MATERIAL HANDLING INC.; *U.S. Private,* pg. 3740
SOUTHWEST MEDIA GROUP, LLC; *U.S. Private,* pg. 3740
SOUTHWEST MEDICAL ASSOCIATES—See UnitedHealth Group Incorporated; *U.S. Public,* pg. 2252
SOUTHWEST MEDICAL CENTER; *U.S. Private,* pg. 3740
SOUTHWEST MEDICAL CENTER SURGICAL GROUP, LLC—See HCA Healthcare, Inc.; *U.S. Public,* pg. 1010
SOUTHWEST MERIDIAN CORP.; *U.S. Private,* pg. 3740
SOUTHWEST METAL FINISHING; *U.S. Private,* pg. 3740
SOUTHWEST MICROWAVE INC.—See Pan American Express Inc.; *U.S. Private,* pg. 3083
SOUTHWEST MISSISSIPPI ELECTRIC POWER ASSOCIATION; *U.S. Private,* pg. 3740
SOUTHWEST MISSOURI BANK; *U.S. Private,* pg. 3740
SOUTHWEST MISSOURI TRUCK CENTER INC.—See TFI International Inc.; *Int'l,* pg. 7586
SOUTHWEST MOLD, INC.—See TruArc Partners, L.P.; *U.S. Private,* pg. 4245
SOUTHWEST MOTORS OF DENVER, LLC—See AutoNation, Inc.; *U.S. Private,* pg. 237
SOUTHWEST MOULDING CO.—See Hardwoods Distribution Inc.; *Int'l,* pg. 3273
SOUTHWEST NATIONAL BANK—See Republic Financial Corporation; *U.S. Private,* pg. 3402
SOUTHWEST OHIO REGIONAL TRANSIT AUTHORITY; *U.S. Private,* pg. 3740
SOUTHWEST OILFIELD CONSTRUCTION COMPANY—See PrimeEnergy Resources Corporation; *U.S. Public,* pg. 1717
SOUTHWEST OILFIELD PRODUCTS, INC.—See CLEANTEK Industries Inc.; *Int'l,* pg. 1655
SOUTHWEST PAPER COMPANY INC.; *U.S. Private,* pg. 3740

SOUTHWEST PET PRODUCTS INC.; *U.S. Private,* pg. 3740
SOUTH WEST PINNACLE EXPLORATION LTD.; *Int'l,* pg. 7117
SOUTHWEST PLASTIC BINDING COMPANY; *U.S. Private,* pg. 3740
SOUTHWEST PLUMBING & WATER HEATERS, INC.—See Koch Industries, Inc.; *U.S. Private,* pg. 2327
SOUTHWEST PLUMBING & WATER HEATERS, INC.—See The Goldman Sachs Group, Inc.; *U.S. Public,* pg. 2077
SOUTHWEST POWER POOL INC.; *U.S. Private,* pg. 3740
SOUTHWEST PRECISION PRINTERS, L.P.; *U.S. Private,* pg. 3740
SOUTHWEST PRODUCTS CORPORATION; *U.S. Private,* pg. 3740
SOUTHWEST PROFESSIONAL VEHICLES; *U.S. Private,* pg. 3740
SOUTHWEST PROPERTIES LTD; *Int'l,* pg. 7121
SOUTHWEST PUBLIC POWER DISTRICT; *U.S. Private,* pg. 3740
SOUTHWEST PUBLISHING & MAILING CORP.—See Moore DM Group, LLC; *U.S. Private,* pg. 2780
SOUTHWEST RAIL INDUSTRIES INC.—See Sojitz Corporation; *Int'l,* pg. 7065
SOUTHWEST REGIONAL REPRESENTATIVES, INC.; *U.S. Private,* pg. 3740
SOUTHWEST REINSURE, INC.—See iA Financial Corporation Inc.; *Int'l,* pg. 3568
SOUTHWEST RESEARCH INSTITUTE; *U.S. Private,* pg. 3740
SOUTHWEST RESIDENTIAL PARTNERS, INC.—See BGC Group, Inc.; *U.S. Public,* pg. 330
SOUTHWEST RISK SERVICES INC.—See W.R. Berkley Corporation; *U.S. Public,* pg. 2318
SOUTHWEST ROCK PRODUCTS, LLC—See Arcosa, Inc.; *U.S. Public,* pg. 186
SOUTHWEST RV CENTERS, LLC—See Camping World Holdings, Inc.; *U.S. Public,* pg. 428
SOUTHWEST SECURITIES CO., LTD.; *Int'l,* pg. 7121
SOUTHWEST SECURITIES INTERNATIONAL SECURITIES LIMITED—See Southwest Securities Co., Ltd.; *Int'l,* pg. 7121
SOUTHWEST SOLUTIONS GROUP; *U.S. Private,* pg. 3741
SOUTHWEST STAIR INC—See SME Industries Inc.; *U.S. Private,* pg. 3693
SOUTHWEST STEEL CASTING COMPANY—See The Greenbrier Companies, Inc.; *U.S. Public,* pg. 2086
SOUTHWEST STEEL COIL INC.—See Calstrip Industries Inc.; *U.S. Private,* pg. 723
SOUTHWEST STEEL FABRICATORS, INC.; *U.S. Private,* pg. 3741
SOUTHWEST STEEL, LLC—See SME Industries Inc.; *U.S. Private,* pg. 3693
SOUTHWEST STEEL PROCESSING LLC—See Park-Ohio Holdings Corp.; *U.S. Public,* pg. 1640
SOUTHWEST STUDENT SERVICES CORP.—See SLM Corporation; *U.S. Public,* pg. 1894
SOUTHWEST SYNTHETIC SYSTEMS, INC.—See Dot Family Holdings LLC; *U.S. Private,* pg. 1264
SOUTHWEST TENNESSEE ELECTRIC MEMBERSHIP CORP.; *U.S. Private,* pg. 3741
SOUTHWEST TEXAS ELECTRIC CO-OP; *U.S. Private,* pg. 3741
SOUTHWEST TEXAS EQUIPMENT DISTRIBUTORS INC.; *U.S. Private,* pg. 3741
THE SOUTHWEST TIMES—See HD Media Company, LLC; *U.S. Private,* pg. 1890
SOUTHWEST TRADERS INCORPORATED; *U.S. Private,* pg. 3741
SOUTHWEST TRADING COMPANY; *U.S. Private,* pg. 3741
SOUTHWEST TRAILERS AND EQUIPMENT LLC; *U.S. Private,* pg. 3741
SOUTHWEST TRAILERS INC.—See Pan American Express Inc.; *U.S. Private,* pg. 3083
SOUTHWEST TRAILS; *U.S. Private,* pg. 3741
SOUTH WEST TRAINS LTD.—See Stagecoach Group plc; *Int'l,* pg. 7163
SOUTHWEST TRANSPLANT ALLIANCE, INC.; *U.S. Private,* pg. 3741
SOUTHWEST TRANSPORT, CO.—See U.S. Venture, Inc.; *U.S. Private,* pg. 4272
SOUTHWEST UNITED CANADA, INC.—See Berkshire Hathaway Inc.; *U.S. Public,* pg. 315
SOUTHWEST UNITED DE MEXICO, S.A. DE C.V.—See Berkshire Hathaway Inc.; *U.S. Public,* pg. 315
SOUTHWEST UNITED INDUSTRIES, INC.—See Berkshire Hathaway Inc.; *U.S. Public,* pg. 315
SOUTHWEST VACUUM DEVICES, INC.—See Video Display Corporation; *U.S. Public,* pg. 2296
SOUTHWEST VALVE & EQUIPMENT—See H.I.G. Capital, LLC; *U.S. Private,* pg. 1834
SOUTHWEST WATER COMPANY—See JPMorgan Chase & Co.; *U.S. Public,* pg. 1207
SOUTHWEST WATER COMPANY—See Water Asset Management, LLC; *U.S. Private,* pg. 4451

COMPANY NAME INDEX

SOUTH WEST WATER LTD.—See Pennon Group PLC; *Int'l*, pg. 5787
SOUTHWEST WATERWORKS CONTRACTORS, INC.—See Bain Capital, LP; *U.S. Private*, pg. 433
SOUTHWEST WIRE ROPE, L.P.—See Dot Family Holdings LLC; *U.S. Private*, pg. 1264
SOUTH WEYMOUTH DODGE; *U.S. Private*, pg. 3724
SOUTHWICK CLOTHING LLC; *U.S. Private*, pg. 3742
SOUTHWICK INC.; *U.S. Private*, pg. 3742
SOUTHWIND FOODS LLC—See Prospect Enterprises Inc.; *U.S. Private*, pg. 3287
SOUTHWIND MANUFACTURING; *U.S. Private*, pg. 3742
SOUTHWIRE CANADA COMPANY—See Southwire Company, LLC; *U.S. Private*, pg. 3742
SOUTHWIRE COMPANY, LLC; *U.S. Private*, pg. 3742
SOUTHWOOD CORPORATION—See Pennichuck Corporation; *U.S. Private*, pg. 3136
SOUTHWOOD EXPORT LIMITED—See ITOCHU Corporation; *Int'l*, pg. 3841
SOUTHWOOD FURNITURE CORP.; *U.S. Private*, pg. 3742
SOUTHWOOD GOLF CLUB—See The St. Joe Company; *U.S. Public*, pg. 2131
SOUTHWOOD PSYCHIATRIC HOSPITAL, INC.—See Acadia Healthcare Company, Inc.; *U.S. Public*, pg. 30
SOUTHWOOD VILLAGE MOBILE HOME PARK, LLC—See Sun Communities, Inc.; *U.S. Public*, pg. 1963
SOUTHWORTH COMPANY INC.; *U.S. Private*, pg. 3742
SOUTHWORTH INTERNATIONAL GROUP INC.; *U.S. Private*, pg. 3742
SOUTHWORTH-MILTON INC.; *U.S. Private*, pg. 3743
SOUTHWORTH PRODUCTS CORP.—See Southworth International Group Inc.; *U.S. Private*, pg. 3743
SOUTH YARRA PHARMA PTY. LTD.—See Apiam Animal Health Limited; *Int'l*, pg. 515
SOUTH YORKSHIRE NEWSPAPERS LTD—See JPIMedia Holdings Limited; *Int'l*, pg. 4006
SOUTH ZAGROS OIL & GAS PRODUCTION COMPANY—See National Iranian Oil Company; *Int'l*, pg. 5160
SOUTO FOODS LLC—See Alex Lee, Inc.; *U.S. Private*, pg. 163
SOUVIGNET; *Int'l*, pg. 7121
SOUYU TE GROUP CO., LTD.; *Int'l*, pg. 7121
SOUZA CRUZ, S.A.—See British American Tobacco plc; *Int'l*, pg. 1168
SOUZHEN TRADING (SHENZHEN) CO., LTD.—See Yamazen Corporation; *Int'l*, pg. 8558
SOVAC GROSSHANDEL UND VERTRETUNGEN IN INDUSTRIEPRODUKTEN GMBH—See Compagnie de Saint-Gobain SA; *Int'l*, pg. 1726
SOVAL SA—See Carrefour SA; *Int'l*, pg. 1346
SOVCOMBANK PJSC; *Int'l*, pg. 7121
SOVCOMFLOT (CYPRUS) LIMITED—See PAO Sovcomflot; *Int'l*, pg. 5732
SOVCOMFLOT (UK) LTD—See PAO Sovcomflot; *Int'l*, pg. 5732
SOVEDYS—See Compagnie de Saint-Gobain SA; *Int'l*, pg. 1737
SOVELIS BETEILIGUNGSVERWALTUNGS GMBH—See PORR AG; *Int'l*, pg. 5925
SOVEMA GLOBAL SERVICES INC.—See ANDRITZ AG; *Int'l*, pg. 456
SOVEMA GROUP S.P.A.—See ANDRITZ AG; *Int'l*, pg. 456
SOVEREIGN AOC OPERATIONS PTY LIMITED—See Brookfield Corporation; *Int'l*, pg. 1189
SOVEREIGN BUSINESS FORMS INC.—See Ennis, Inc.; *U.S. Public*, pg. 769
SOVEREIGN CAPITAL PARTNERS LLP; *Int'l*, pg. 7121
SOVEREIGN CHEMICALS COMPANY—See Henkel AG & Co. KGaA; *Int'l*, pg. 3353
SOVEREIGN CHEMICALS LIMITED—See TotalEnergies SE; *Int'l*, pg. 7843
SOVEREIGN CHEMICALS LTD—See TotalEnergies SE; *Int'l*, pg. 7843
SOVEREIGN CHEMICALS LTD—See TotalEnergies SE; *Int'l*, pg. 7843
SOVEREIGN CLOUD HOLDINGS LIMITED; *Int'l*, pg. 7121
SOVEREIGN CONSULTING INC.; *U.S. Private*, pg. 3743
SOVEREIGN DELAWARE INVESTMENT CORPORATION—See Banco Santander, S.A.; *Int'l*, pg. 827
SOVEREIGN DIAMONDS LIMITED; *Int'l*, pg. 7122
SOVEREIGN DISTRIBUTORS INC.; *U.S. Private*, pg. 3743
SOVEREIGN FOOD INVESTMENTS LTD.—See Capitalworks Investment Partners (Pty) Ltd; *Int'l*, pg. 1314
THE SOVEREIGN GENERAL INSURANCE COMPANY—See The Co-operators Group Limited; *Int'l*, pg. 7634
SOVEREIGN GOLDSEA PTY LIMITED—See Brookfield Corporation; *Int'l*, pg. 1189
SOVEREIGN GROUP INTERNATIONAL; *U.S. Private*, pg. 3743
SOVEREIGN HOMES, LLC—See Berkshire Hathaway Inc.; *U.S. Public*, pg. 304
SOVEREIGN LENDING GROUP, INC.; *U.S. Private*, pg. 3743

SOVEREIGN METALS LIMITED; *Int'l*, pg. 7122
SOVEREIGN PACIFIC BAY PROPERTY MANAGEMENT PTY LIMITED—See Brookfield Corporation; *Int'l*, pg. 1189
SOVEREIGN PALM COVE DEVELOPMENT NOMINEES PTY LIMITED—See Brookfield Corporation; *Int'l*, pg. 1189
SOVEREIGN PROPERTY FUND PTY LIMITED—See Brookfield Corporation; *Int'l*, pg. 1189
SOVEREIGN REAL ESTATE INVESTMENT TRUST—See Banco Santander, S.A.; *Int'l*, pg. 827
SOVEREIGN REIT HOLDINGS, INC.—See Banco Santander, S.A.; *Int'l*, pg. 827
SOVEREIGN REVERSIONS LIMITED—See Grainger plc; *Int'l*, pg. 3052
SOVEREIGN RISK INSURANCE LIMITED—See Chubb Limited; *Int'l*, pg. 1590
SOVEREIGN SECURITIES CORPORATION, LLC—See Banco Santander, S.A.; *Int'l*, pg. 827
SOVEREIGN SERVICES INC.—See Propark, Inc.; *U.S. Private*, pg. 3284
SOVEREIGN SPECIALTY CHEMICALS, INC.—See Henkel AG & Co. KGaA; *Int'l*, pg. 3353
SOVEREIGN SPECIALTY CHEMICALS—See Henkel AG & Co. KGaA; *Int'l*, pg. 3353
SOVEREIGN SPEED GMBH; *Int'l*, pg. 7122
SOVEREIGN SPEED MUC GMBH—See Sovereign Speed GmbH; *Int'l*, pg. 7122
SOVEREIGN SPEED (UK) LTD.—See Sovereign Speed GmbH; *Int'l*, pg. 7122
SOVEREIGN SYSTEMS LLC—See GreenPages, Inc.; *U.S. Private*, pg. 1779
SOVEREIGN TOUR OPERATIONS LIMITED—See TUI AG; *Int'l*, pg. 7968
SOVEREIGN VOLKSWAGEN LLC.; *U.S. Private*, pg. 3743
SOVEREIGN WYNYARD FINANCE PTY LIMITED—See Brookfield Corporation; *Int'l*, pg. 1189
SOVERUS KINGDOM SYSTEMS PTE. LTD.—See Secura Group Limited; *Int'l*, pg. 6674
SOVILEG; *Int'l*, pg. 7122
SOVIME S.R.L.—See Gruppo MutuiOnline S.p.A; *Int'l*, pg. 3141
SOVLINK LLC; *Int'l*, pg. 7122
COVOE BRANDS, INC.—See Campbell Soup Company; *U.S. Public*, pg. 427
SOVOS BRANDS INTERMEDIATE, INC.—See Advent International Corporation; *U.S. Public*, pg. 105
SOVOS COMPLIANCE, LLC—See HgCapital Trust plc; *Int'l*, pg. 3377
SOVRANO LLC; *U.S. Private*, pg. 3743
SOVRN HOLDINGS, INC.; *U.S. Private*, pg. 3743
SOWA SANGYO CO., LTD.—See TS Tech Co Ltd; *Int'l*, pg. 7948
SOWA TECHNO CO., LTD.—See TS Tech Co Ltd; *Int'l*, pg. 7948
SO WATER CO., LTD.—See Thai Beverage Public Company Limited; *Int'l*, pg. 7591
SOWBHAGYA MEDIA LIMITED; *Int'l*, pg. 7122
SOWELL & CO., INC.; *U.S. Private*, pg. 3743
SOW GOOD INC.; *U.S. Public*, pg. 1914
SOWIND JAPAN KK—See Kering S.A.; *Int'l*, pg. 4136
THE SOWLES COMPANY; *U.S. Private*, pg. 4119
SOWLES COMPANY—See The Sowles Company; *U.S. Private*, pg. 4119
SOWLES COMPANY—See The Sowles Company; *U.S. Private*, pg. 4119
SOYAFARM CO., LTD.—See Fuji Oil Holdings Inc.; *Int'l*, pg. 2816
SOYA FARM USA INC.—See Fuji Oil Holdings Inc.; *Int'l*, pg. 2816
SOYEA TECHNOLOGY CO., LTD.; *Int'l*, pg. 7122
SOYER MAGYARORSZAG KFT.—See Heinz Soyer Bolzenschweisstechnik GmbH; *Int'l*, pg. 3325
SOYO CO., LTD.—See NITTO BOSEKI CO., LTD.; *Int'l*, pg. 5384
SO-YOUNG INTERNATIONAL INC.; *Int'l*, pg. 7029
SOYRING CONSULTING, INC.—See Ares Management Corporation; *U.S. Public*, pg. 190
SOYRING CONSULTING, INC.—See Leonard Green & Partners, L.P.; *U.S. Private*, pg. 2427
SOYUZ-SVET LTD.—See A.A.G. STUCCHI s.r.l.; *Int'l*, pg. 23
SOY VAY ENTERPRISES, INC.—See The Clorox Company; *U.S. Public*, pg. 2062
SOZHOU SODICK SPECIAL EQUIPMENT CO., LTD.—See Sodick Co., Ltd.; *Int'l*, pg. 7048
SOZIALBAU GEMEINNUTZIGE WOHNUNGSAKTIENGESELLSCHAFT—See Vienna Insurance Group AG Wiener Versicherung Gruppe; *Int'l*, pg. 8195
SOZIALKONZEPT BARBARAHOF GMBH—See Clariane SE; *Int'l*, pg. 1644
SOZIALKONZEPT CACILIENHOF MBH—See Clariane SE; *Int'l*, pg. 1644
SOZIALKONZEPT DOROTHEENHOF GMBH—See Clariane SE; *Int'l*, pg. 1644
SOZIALKONZEPT FRIEDERIKENHOF GMBH—See Clariane SE; *Int'l*, pg. 1645

SPACEFRAME BUILDINGS PTY. LTD.

SOZIALKONZEPT HELENENHOF GMBH—See Clariane SE; *Int'l*, pg. 1645
SOZIALKONZEPT IM ROSENPARK GMBH—See Clariane SE; *Int'l*, pg. 1645
SOZIALKONZEPT KATHARINENHOF MBH—See Clariane SE; *Int'l*, pg. 1645
SOZIALKONZEPT LORETTAHOF GMBH—See Clariane SE; *Int'l*, pg. 1645
SOZIALKONZEPT LUISENHOF GMBH—See Clariane SE; *Int'l*, pg. 1645
SOZIALKONZEPT MAGDALENENHOF MBH—See Clariane SE; *Int'l*, pg. 1645
SOZIALKONZEPT MARIENHOF GMBH—See Clariane SE; *Int'l*, pg. 1645
SOZIALKONZEPT MARIETTENHOF GMBH—See Clariane SE; *Int'l*, pg. 1645
SOZIALKONZEPT SCHULZE-KATHRINHOF GMBH—See Clariane SE; *Int'l*, pg. 1645
SOZIALKONZEPT SOPHIENHOF GMBH—See Clariane SE; *Int'l*, pg. 1645
SPA AL DAR AL ARABIA POUR LA FABRICATION DE MEDICAMENTS—See Hikma Pharmaceuticals PLC; *Int'l*, pg. 3390
SPAAN TECH, INC.; *U.S. Private*, pg. 3743
SPAARBELEG KAS N.V.—See Aegon N.V.; *Int'l*, pg. 175
SPA ATLAS COPCO ALGERIE—See Atlas Copco AB; *Int'l*, pg. 684
SP ABLEWARE—See Harbour Group Industries, Inc.; *U.S. Private*, pg. 1861
SPA CAPITAL ADVISORS LIMITED—See SPA Capital Services Limited; *Int'l*, pg. 7123
SPA CAPITAL SERVICES LIMITED; *Int'l*, pg. 7123
SPACE4 LIMITED—See Persimmon plc; *Int'l*, pg. 5817
SPACE4 S.P.A.; *Int'l*, pg. 7123
SPACE ADVENTURES LTD.; *U.S. Private*, pg. 3743
SPACE AGE ELECTRONICS, INC.—See DelCam Holdings, LLC; *U.S. Private*, pg. 1196
SPACE AGE FUEL INC.; *U.S. Private*, pg. 3743
SPACE AGE SERVICES, INC.; *U.S. Private*, pg. 3743
SPACEANDPEOPLE GMBH—See SpaceandPeople plc; *Int'l*, pg. 7123
SPACEANDPEOPLE INDIA PVT LTD—See SpaceandPeople plc; *Int'l*, pg. 7123
SPACEANDPEOPLE PLC; *Int'l*, pg. 7123
SPACE & ASSET MANAGEMENT INC.; *U.S. Private*, pg. 3743
SPACEA SYSTEMS/LORAL, LLC—See Advent International Corporation; *U.S. Public*, pg. 104
SPACEBOUND, INC.; *U.S. Private*, pg. 3744
SPACE CARGO SERVICES S.A.—See C.H. Robinson Worldwide, Inc.; *U.S. Public*, pg. 415
SPACE CENTER, INC.—See Helmerich & Payne, Inc.; *U.S. Public*, pg. 1024
SPACE CENTER INC.; *U.S. Private*, pg. 3743
SPACE CITY DIALYSIS CENTER, LLC—See Nautic Partners, LP; *U.S. Public*, pg. 2871
SPACECLAIM CORPORATION—See ANSYS, Inc.; *U.S. Public*, pg. 139
SPACECLAIM JAPAN, K.K.—See ANSYS, Inc.; *U.S. Public*, pg. 139
SPACE COAST BUSINESS, LLC; *U.S. Private*, pg. 3743
SPACE COAST HOLDING CORP.—See Mercedes Homes Inc.; *U.S. Private*, pg. 2668
SPACE COAST SURGERY CENTER LLC—See Bain Capital, LP; *U.S. Private*, pg. 446
SPACE COAST SURGICAL CENTER, LTD.—See HCA Healthcare, Inc.; *U.S. Public*, pg. 1010
SPACE CO., LTD.; *Int'l*, pg. 7123
SPACECON, LLC—See Irex Corporation; *U.S. Private*, pg. 2138
SPACE CONNECT PTY LIMITED—See Smartspace Software Plc; *Int'l*, pg. 7003
SPACECON SOLUTIONS, LLC—See Irex Corporation; *U.S. Private*, pg. 2138
SPACECON SPECIALTY CONTRACTORS LLC—See Irex Corporation; *U.S. Private*, pg. 2138
SPACE CONSTRUCTION & ENGINEERING CO., LTD.—See Space Group Holdings Limited; *Int'l*, pg. 7123
SPACE CONSTRUCTION (PTY) LIMITED—See Raubex Group Limited; *Int'l*, pg. 6221
SPACE-CRAFT MANUFACTURING, INC.; *U.S. Private*, pg. 3744
SPACEDEV INC.—See Sierra Nevada Corporation; *U.S. Private*, pg. 3647
SPACE ELECTRONICS, LLC—See L Squared Capital Management LP; *U.S. Private*, pg. 2362
SPACE ENERGY CORPORATION—See ENEOS Holdings, Inc.; *Int'l*, pg. 2417
SPACE ENGINEERING S.P.A.—See Airbus SE; *Int'l*, pg. 247
SPACE EXPLORATION TECHNOLOGIES CORP.; *U.S. Private*, pg. 3744
SPACE FINANCIAL HOLDINGS LIMITED—See Space Group Holdings Limited; *Int'l*, pg. 7123
SPACE FITTERS INC.; *U.S. Private*, pg. 3744
SPACEFRAME BUILDINGS PTY. LTD.; *Int'l*, pg. 7123
SPACE FURNITURE PTE LIMITED—See Harvey Norman Holdings Ltd; *Int'l*, pg. 3281

2565

SPACEFY, INC.   CORPORATE AFFILIATIONS

SPACEFY, INC.; *Int'l*, pg. 7123
SPACE GROUND SYSTEM SOLUTIONS, INC.—See The O'Neil Group Company, LLC; *U.S. Private*, pg. 4087
SPACE GROUP HOLDINGS LIMITED; *Int'l*, pg. 7123
SPACE HELLAS SA; *Int'l*, pg. 7123
SPACE HOLDING SRL; *Int'l*, pg. 7123
SPACE INCUBATRICS TECHNOLOGIES LIMITED; *Int'l*, pg. 7123
SPACE JAPAN CO., LTD.—See Space Co., Ltd.; *Int'l*, pg. 7123
SPACEJET MONTREAL CENTER, INC.—See Mitsubishi Heavy Industries, Ltd.; *Int'l*, pg. 4961
SPACEKRAFT LTD—See RM plc; *Int'l*, pg. 6356
SPACELABS HEALTHCARE (CANADA), INC.—See OSI Systems, Inc.; *U.S. Public*, pg. 1622
SPACELABS HEALTHCARE, INC.—See OSI Systems, Inc.; *U.S. Public*, pg. 1622
SPACELABS HEALTHCARE, LLC—See OSI Systems, Inc.; *U.S. Public*, pg. 1622
SPACELABS HEALTHCARE LTD.—See OSI Systems, Inc.; *U.S. Public*, pg. 1622
SPACELABS HEALTHCARE SAS—See OSI Systems, Inc.; *U.S. Public*, pg. 1622
SPACELABS MEDICAL, INC.—See OSI Systems, Inc.; *U.S. Public*, pg. 1622
SPACELABS MEDICAL UK S.P.A.—See OSI Systems, Inc.; *U.S. Public*, pg. 1622
SPACE-LOK, INC.—See KKR & Co. Inc.; *U.S. Public*, pg. 1262
SPACEMAKERS INC.; *U.S. Private*, pg. 3744
SPACE MANAGEMENT CO., LTD.—See Relo Group, Inc.; *Int'l*, pg. 6265
SPACEMARKET, INC.; *Int'l*, pg. 7124
SPACE MICRO INC.—See Voyager Space Holdings, Inc.; *U.S. Private*, pg. 4414
SPACE NEEDLE CORPORATION; *U.S. Private*, pg. 3744
SPACENET ENTERPRISES INDIA LIMITED; *Int'l*, pg. 7124
SPACENET, INC.—See Woodard Technology & Investments LLC; *U.S. Private*, pg. 4557
SPACE NORWAY AS; *Int'l*, pg. 7123
THE SPACERS & BAR CHAIRS MANUFACTURER COMPANY LIMITED—See Golik Holdings Limited; *Int'l*, pg. 3036
SPACESAVERCCS INC.—See Spacesaver Solutions, Inc.; *Int'l*, pg. 7124
SPACESAVER CORPORATION—See Krueger International, Inc.; *U.S. Private*, pg. 2353
SPACESAVER SOLUTIONS, INC.; *Int'l*, pg. 7124
SPACESAVER STORAGE SOLUTIONS LLC; *U.S. Private*, pg. 3744
SPACE SHANGHAI CO., LTD.—See Space Co., Ltd.; *Int'l*, pg. 7123
SPACE SHOWER SKIYAKI HOLDINGS INC; *Int'l*, pg. 7123
SPACE SHUTTLE HI-TECH CO., LTD.; *Int'l*, pg. 7123
SPACE SHUTTLE INN—See Best Western International, Inc.; *U.S. Private*, pg. 544
SPACE SHUTTLE (SUZ-HOU) HI-TECH CO., LTD.—See Space Shuttle Hi-Tech Co., Ltd.; *Int'l*, pg. 7123
SPACE SOLUTION INC; *Int'l*, pg. 7123
SPACE S.R.L.—See Dover Corporation; *U.S. Public*, pg. 682
SPACETALK HOLDINGS PTY LTD—See Spacetalk Ltd.; *Int'l*, pg. 7124
SPACETALK LTD.; *Int'l*, pg. 7124
SPACETECH, INC.—See Astrotech Corporation; *U.S. Public*, pg. 218
SPACETIME, INC.; *U.S. Private*, pg. 3744
SPACE VALUE HOLDINGS CO., LTD.—See Polaris Capital Group Co., Ltd.; *Int'l*, pg. 5907
SPACE VALUE (THAILAND) CO., LTD.—See Nissei Build Kogyo Co., Ltd.; *Int'l*, pg. 5370
SPACE VECTOR CORPORATION; *U.S. Private*, pg. 3744
SPACEWELL INTERNATIONAL NV.—See Herbalife Nutrition Ltd.; *Int'l*, pg. 3360
SPACEWELL NETHERLANDS B.V.—See Nemetschek SE; *Int'l*, pg. 5195
SPACEWORKS ENTERPRISES, INC.; *U.S. Private*, pg. 3744
SPA CHAKRA, INC.—See Hercules Capital, Inc.; *U.S. Public*, pg. 1028
SPACIOTEMPO; *Int'l*, pg. 7124
SPACKMAN ENTERTAINMENT GROUP LTD.; *Int'l*, pg. 7124
SPACKMAN EQUITIES GROUP INC.; *Int'l*, pg. 7124
S. PACK & PRINT PUBLIC COMPANY LIMITED—See Oji Holdings Corporation; *Int'l*, pg. 5538
SPACTIV S.P.A.; *Int'l*, pg. 7124
SPADEL NEDERLAND B.V.—See S.A. Spadel N.V.; *Int'l*, pg. 6448
SPADEL UK LTD—See S.A. Spadel N.V.; *Int'l*, pg. 6448
SPADE TECHNOLOGY INC.—See IT Solutions Consulting LLC; *U.S. Private*, pg. 2148
SPADONE ALFA SELF LUBRICATING PRODUCTS, LLC; *U.S. Private*, pg. 3744
SPADONE-HYPEX INC.—See HyPex Inc.; *U.S. Private*, pg. 2020

SP ADVANCED INDUSTRIES LTD.—See Inrom Construction Industries Ltd.; *Int'l*, pg. 3717
SPAENAUR INC.; *Int'l*, pg. 7124
SPAENCOM A/S—See Bain Capital, LP; *U.S. Private*, pg. 438
SPAEQUIP, INC.; *U.S. Private*, pg. 3744
SPAERO TRADE GMBH—See Airbus SE; *Int'l*, pg. 244
SPAETH COMMUNICATIONS, INC.—See Sun West Communications, Inc.; *U.S. Private*, pg. 3864
SPAFAX AIRLINE NETWORK LIMITED—See WPP plc; *Int'l*, pg. 8466
SPAFAX CANADA—See WPP plc; *Int'l*, pg. 8466
SPAFAX MONTREAL—See WPP plc; *Int'l*, pg. 8466
SPAFAX NETWORKS INC.—See WPP plc; *Int'l*, pg. 8466
SPAFAX SINGAPORE—See WPP plc; *Int'l*, pg. 8466
SPAFID CONNECT S.P.A—See Infront ASA; *Int'l*, pg. 3699
SPAFID SOCIETA PER AMMINISTRAZIONI FIDUCIARIE S.P.A.—See Mediobanca-Banca de Credito Finanziario S.p.A.; *Int'l*, pg. 4778
SPAFINDER, INC.; *U.S. Private*, pg. 3744
SPAFINDER WELLNESS UK, LTD.—See SpaFinder, Inc.; *U.S. Private*, pg. 3744
SPAFI—See Compagnie de Saint-Gobain SA; *Int'l*, pg. 1737
SPA GALION ALGERIE—See Berry Global Group, Inc; *U.S. Public*, pg. 325
SPAGHETTI WAREHOUSE, INC.—See Cracken, Harkey & Co., LLC; *U.S. Private*, pg. 1081
SPA-HAKUHODO CO., LTD.—See Hakuhodo DY Holdings Incorporated; *Int'l*, pg. 3222
SPAHN & ROSE LUMBER CO., INC; *U.S. Private*, pg. 3744
SPAIN CURT GEORGI AROMAS Y ESENCIAS S.A.—See Curt Georgi GmbH & Co. KG; *Int'l*, pg. 1880
SPAIN DENTAL EXPRESS S.A.U.—See Henry Schein, Inc.; *U.S. Public*, pg. 1027
SPAL AUTOMOTIVE COMPONENTS (SHANGHAI) CO., LTD.—See SPAL; *Int'l*, pg. 7124
SPAL AUTOMOTIVE UK LIMITED—See SPAL; *Int'l*, pg. 7124
SPAL CHINA—See SPAL; *Int'l*, pg. 7124
SPALDING AUTOMOTIVE INC.; *U.S. Private*, pg. 3744
SPALDING CONSULTING INC.—See Saalex Corp.; *U.S. Private*, pg. 3520
SPALDING DEDECKER ASSOCIATES, INC.; *U.S. Private*, pg. 3744
SPALDING REGIONAL URGENT CARE CENTER AT HERON BAY, L.L.C.—See Tenet Healthcare Corporation; *U.S. Public*, pg. 2005
SPALDING REHABILITATION L.L.C.—See HCA Healthcare, Inc.; *U.S. Public*, pg. 1010
SPALDING—See Berkshire Hathaway Inc.; *U.S. Public*, pg. 305
SPAL DO BRASIL LTDA.—See SPAL; *Int'l*, pg. 7124
SPAL RUS LLC—See SPAL; *Int'l*, pg. 7124
SPAL; *Int'l*, pg. 7124
SPAL USA—See SPAL; *Int'l*, pg. 7124
SPALY BIOQUIMICA, S.A.—See Eli Lilly & Company; *U.S. Public*, pg. 732
SPAMEXPERTS B.V.—See SolarWinds Corporation; *U.S. Public*, pg. 1900
S.P.A.M.I. S.R.L.—See Stevanato Group S.p.A.; *Int'l*, pg. 7212
SPA MONOPOLE SA—See S.A. Spadel N.V.; *Int'l*, pg. 6448
SPAN ALASKA TRANSPORTATION, INC.—See Matson, Inc.; *U.S. Public*, pg. 1398
SPAN-AMERICA MEDICAL SYSTEMS, INC.—See Savaria Corporation; *Int'l*, pg. 6596
SPANBETON B.V.—See Bain Capital, LP; *U.S. Private*, pg. 438
SPANBO NV—See VINCI S.A.; *Int'l*, pg. 8229
SPAN CONSTRUCTION & ENGINEERING INC; *U.S. Private*, pg. 3744
SPANCRETE CORPORATION; *Int'l*, pg. 7124
THE SPANCRETE GROUP, INC.—See Wells Concrete Products Company Inc.; *U.S. Private*, pg. 4476
SPANCRETE INC.—See Wells Concrete Products Company Inc.; *U.S. Private*, pg. 4476
SPANCRETE MACHINERY CORP.—See Wells Concrete Products Company Inc.; *U.S. Private*, pg. 4476
SPANCRETE OF ILLINOIS INC.—See Wells Concrete Products Company Inc.; *U.S. Private*, pg. 4476
SPANDANA SPHOORTY FINANCIAL LIMITED; *Int'l*, pg. 7124
SPANDAUER VELOURS GMBH& CO.KG; *Int'l*, pg. 7124
SPANDEX AG—See Chequers SA; *Int'l*, pg. 1471
SPANDEX BELGIUM NV—See Chequers SA; *Int'l*, pg. 1471
SPANDEX LTD—See Chequers SA; *Int'l*, pg. 1471
SPANDEX USA INC.; *U.S. Private*, pg. 3744
SPAN DIAGNOSTICS LLP—See Span Divergent Ltd.; *Int'l*, pg. 7124
SPAN DIVERGENT LTD.; *Int'l*, pg. 7124
SPAN EHF.—See Landsbankinn hf.; *Int'l*, pg. 4407
SPANG & COMPANY-BOONEVILLE PLANT—See Spang & Company; *U.S. Private*, pg. 3744
SPANG & COMPANY; *U.S. Private*, pg. 3744

S.P. ANGEL & CO. LTD—See Viel & Compagnie SA; *Int'l*, pg. 8192
SPANGLER CANDY COMPANY; *U.S. Private*, pg. 3745
SPANGLER COMPANIES, INC.; *U.S. Private*, pg. 3745
SPANGLER GRAPHICS, LLC—See Chatham Asset Management, LLC; *U.S. Private*, pg. 863
SPANGLER PROPERTIES, LLC—See Spangler Companies, Inc.; *U.S. Private*, pg. 3745
SPANGLERS FLOUR MILLS OF MT. JOY—See Wilkins-Rogers, Inc.; *U.S. Private*, pg. 4520
SPANGLES INC.; *U.S. Private*, pg. 3745
SPANG POWER ELECTRONICS—See Spang & Company; *U.S. Private*, pg. 3745
SPANISH BROADCASTING SYSTEM INC.; *U.S. Public*, pg. 1914
SPANISH BROADCASTING SYSTEM OF CALIFORNIA INC.—See Spanish Broadcasting System Inc.; *U.S. Public*, pg. 1914
SPANISH COVE HOUSING AUTHORITY; *U.S. Private*, pg. 3745
SPANISH MOUNTAIN GOLD LTD.; *Int'l*, pg. 7125
SPANISH POWER, S.L.—See Banco de Sabadell, S.A.; *Int'l*, pg. 821
SPANISH TOWN ESTATE SOLAR 1 LLC—See NRG Energy, Inc.; *U.S. Public*, pg. 1551
SPANISH TRAILS ASSOCIATES LP; *U.S. Private*, pg. 3745
SPANISH WELLS COUNTRY CLUB—See Escalante Golf, Inc.; *U.S. Private*, pg. 1424
SPANJAARD LIMITED; *Int'l*, pg. 7125
SPANNSTAHL AG—See Triton Advisers Limited; *Int'l*, pg. 7929
SPANOLUX SPRL—See Mohawk Industries, Inc.; *U.S. Public*, pg. 1458
SPANOS BARBER JESSE & CO.; *U.S. Private*, pg. 3745
THE SPANOS CORPORATION—See A.G. Spanos Companies; *U.S. Private*, pg. 26
SPAN PACKAGING SERVICES LLC—See Cameron Holdings Corporation; *U.S. Private*, pg. 729
SPANSION LLC—See Infineon Technologies AG; *Int'l*, pg. 3685
SPANSTAAL B.V.—See Ronesans Holding A.S.; *Int'l*, pg. 6396
SPAN SYSTEMS CORPORATION INC.—See TietoEVRY Oyj; *Int'l*, pg. 7745
SPA PARTS PLUS; *U.S. Private*, pg. 3743
SP APPAREL, INC.—See NIKE, Inc.; *U.S. Public*, pg. 1529
S. P. APPARELS LIMITED; *Int'l*, pg. 6447
SPARA CAPITAL PARTNERS INC.; *Int'l*, pg. 7125
SPAR AUSTRALIA LIMITED; *Int'l*, pg. 7125
SPARBOE FARMS; *U.S. Private*, pg. 3745
SPARCALL GMBH—See ecotel communication ag; *Int'l*, pg. 2300
SPAR CANADA COMPANY—See SPAR Group, Inc.; *U.S. Public*, pg. 1914
SPAR CHINA LTD.—See SPAR Group, Inc.; *U.S. Public*, pg. 1914
SPARC HOLDING COMPANY; *U.S. Private*, pg. 3745
SPARC, LLC; *U.S. Private*, pg. 3745
SPARCO.COM; *U.S. Private*, pg. 3745
SPAR CONSTRUCTION LTD.; *Int'l*, pg. 7125
SPARC RESEARCH LLC—See SPARC Holding Company; *U.S. Private*, pg. 3745
SPARC SYSTEMS LIMITED; *Int'l*, pg. 7125
SPARC TECHNOLOGIES LIMITED; *Int'l*, pg. 7125
SPAREBANK 1 FORSIKRING AS—See SpareBank 1 Gruppen AS; *Int'l*, pg. 7125
SPAREBANK 1 GRUPPEN AS; *Int'l*, pg. 7125
SPAREBANK 1 GRUPPEN FINANS AS—See SpareBank 1 Gruppen AS; *Int'l*, pg. 7125
SPAREBANK 1 NORDMORE; *Int'l*, pg. 7125
SPAREBANK 1 NORD-NORGE—See SpareBank 1 Gruppen AS; *Int'l*, pg. 7125
SPAREBANK 1 OESTLANDET; *Int'l*, pg. 7125
SPAREBANK 1 OSTFOLD AKERSHUS; *Int'l*, pg. 7125
SPAREBANK 1 RINGERIKE HADELAND—See SpareBank 1 Gruppen AS; *Int'l*, pg. 7125
SPAREBANK 1 SMN—See SpareBank 1 Gruppen AS; *Int'l*, pg. 7125
SPAREBANKEN MORE; *Int'l*, pg. 7125
SPAREBANKEN OST EIENDOM AS—See Sparebanken Ost; *Int'l*, pg. 7126
SPAREBANKEN OST; *Int'l*, pg. 7125
SPAREBANKEN SOR ASA; *Int'l*, pg. 7126
SPAREBANKEN VEST; *Int'l*, pg. 7126
SPAREKASSEN SJAELLAND-FYN A/S; *Int'l*, pg. 7126
SPARE TIME INC.; *U.S. Private*, pg. 3745
SPAREX AGRIREPUESTOS SL—See AGCO Corporation; *U.S. Public*, pg. 59
SPAREX APS—See AGCO Corporation; *U.S. Public*, pg. 59
SPAREX HANDELS-UND VERTRIEBS GMBH—See AGCO Corporation; *U.S. Public*, pg. 59
SPAREX INC.—See AGCO Corporation; *U.S. Public*, pg. 59
SPAREX LIMITED APS—See AGCO Corporation; *U.S. Public*, pg. 59
SPAREX LIMITED VESTIGING HOLLAND BV—See AGCO Corporation; *U.S. Public*, pg. 59

COMPANY NAME INDEX

SPAREX LTD.—See AGCO Corporation; *U.S. Public*, pg. 59
SPAREX MASCHINENSUBEHOR HANDELSGESELLSCHAFT M.B.H—See AGCO Corporation; *U.S. Public*, pg. 59
SPAREX NEW ZEALAND LTD—See AGCO Corporation; *U.S. Public*, pg. 59
SPAREX POLSKA SP. Z.O.O.—See AGCO Corporation; *U.S. Public*, pg. 59
SPAREX PORTUGAL IMPORTACAO E COMERCIO DE PECAS LDA—See AGCO Corporation; *U.S. Public*, pg. 59
SPAREX S.A.R.L.—See AGCO Corporation; *U.S. Public*, pg. 59
SPAREX (TRACTOR ACCESSORIES) LIMITED—See AGCO Corporation; *U.S. Public*, pg. 59
SPARFACTS AUSTRALIA PTY LTD.—See SPAR Group, Inc.; *U.S. Public*, pg. 1914
SPARFLEX SA—See Cobepa S.A.; *Int'l*, pg. 1683
SPAR FM JAPAN—See SPAR Group, Inc.; *U.S. Public*, pg. 1914
SPARFOND LIVFORSAKRINGS AB—See Swedbank AB; *Int'l*, pg. 7364
SPAR GREECE—See SPAR Group, Inc.; *U.S. Public*, pg. 1914
SPAR GROUP, INC.; *U.S. Public*, pg. 1914
THE SPAR GROUP LIMITED—See Peresec South Africa Proprietary Limited; *Int'l*, pg. 5798
SPARIA FORSAKRINGS AB—See Swedbank AB; *Int'l*, pg. 7364
SPAR, INC.—See SPAR Group, Inc.; *U.S. Public*, pg. 1914
SPARK44 COMMUNICACIONS SL—See Tata Motors Limited; *Int'l*, pg. 7467
SPARK451 INC.—See Jenzabar, Inc.; *U.S. Private*, pg. 2201
THE SPARK AGENCY, INC.; *U.S. Private*, pg. 4120
SPARKASSE BANK D.D.—See Erste Group Bank AG; *Int'l*, pg. 2499
SPARKASSE HAINBURG-BRUCK-NEUSIEDL AG—See Erste Group Bank AG; *Int'l*, pg. 2498
SPARKASSE KOLNBONN; *Int'l*, pg. 7126
SPARKASSE KREMSTAL PYHRN AKTIENGESELLSCHAFT—See Erste Group Bank AG; *Int'l*, pg. 2499
SPARKASSE MUHLVIERTEL WEST BANK AKTIENGESELLSCHAFT—See Erste Group Bank AG; *Int'l*, pg. 2499
SPARKASSENBETEILIGUNGS UND SERVICE AG FUR OBEROSTERREICH UND SALZBURG—See Erste Group Bank AG; *Int'l*, pg. 2499
SPARKASSEN-IMMOBILIEN—See Helaba Landesbank Hessen-Thuringen; *Int'l*, pg. 3328
SPARKASSEN VERSICHERUNG AG—See Vienna Insurance Group AG Wiener Versicherung Gruppe; *Int'l*, pg. 8195
SPARK ATM SYSTEMS PROPRIETARY LIMITED—See NCR Voyix Corporation.; *U.S. Public*, pg. 1502
SPARK & CANNON PTY LIMITED—See VIQ Solutions Inc.; *Int'l*, pg. 8245
SPARK COMMUNICATIONS—See Publicis Groupe S.A.; *Int'l*, pg. 6111
SPARK COMMUNICATIONS—See Omnicom Group Inc.; *U.S. Public*, pg. 1578
SPARK EDUCATION LTD.; *Int'l*, pg. 7126
SPARK ENERGY GAS, LLC—See Via Renewables, Inc.; *U.S. Public*, pg. 2290
SPARK ENERGY MINERALS INC.; *Int'l*, pg. 7126
S. PARKER HARDWARE MANUFACTURING CORP.; *U.S. Private*, pg. 3515
SPARKFACTOR DESIGN; *U.S. Private*, pg. 3745
SPARKFUN ELECTRONICS; *U.S. Private*, pg. 3745
SPARKHOUND, INC.; *U.S. Private*, pg. 3746
SPARKHOUSE—See Augsburg Fortress; *U.S. Private*, pg. 392
SPARK IBERICA S.A.—See VINCI S.A.; *Int'l*, pg. 8238
SPARK INFRASTRUCTURE GROUP; *Int'l*, pg. 7126
SPARK INFRASTRUCTURE HOLDINGS NO. 2 PTY LIMITED—See Spark Infrastructure Group; *Int'l*, pg. 7126
SPARK INFRASTRUCTURE TRUST—See Spark Infrastructure Group; *Int'l*, pg. 7126
SPARKLE, LLC; *U.S. Private*, pg. 3746
SPARKLE LOGISTICS LIMITED—See Kam Hing International Holdings Limited; *Int'l*, pg. 4059
SPARKLE MAINTENANCE, INC.; *U.S. Private*, pg. 3746
SPARKLE MAINTENANCE, INC.—See Silver Oak Services Partners, LLC; *U.S. Private*, pg. 3661
SPARKLE POWER INC.; *U.S. Private*, pg. 3746
SPARKLING (INDIA) FINSHARES LIMITED; *Int'l*, pg. 7126
SPARK NETWORKS INC.—See Spark Networks SE; *Int'l*, pg. 7126
SPARK NETWORKS SE; *Int'l*, pg. 7126
SPARK NEW ZEALAND LIMITED; *Int'l*, pg. 7126
SPARKNOTES, LLC—See Elliott Management Corporation; *U.S. Public*, pg. 1365
SPARK OF GENIUS LIMITED—See Sheikh Holdings Group (Investments) Limited; *Int'l*, pg. 6794
SPARK.ORANGE, LLC; *U.S. Private*, pg. 3745

SPARKPLUG, INC.—See GTT Communications, Inc.; *U.S. Private*, pg. 1808
SPARKPR; *U.S. Private*, pg. 3746
SPAR KROGNOS MARKETING PRIVATE LIMITED—See SPAR Group, Inc.; *U.S. Public*, pg. 1914
SPARKROOM, LLC—See Nelnet, Inc.; *U.S. Public*, pg. 1504
SPARKS BELTING COMPANY—See JSJ Corporation; *U.S. Private*, pg. 2241
SPARKS CUSTOM RETAIL, LLC—See Freeman Decorating Co.; *U.S. Private*, pg. 1605
SPARK SERVICES LTD—See Gresham House Strategic plc; *Int'l*, pg. 3082
SPARKS EVENT MARKETING—See Surge Communications; *Int'l*, pg. 7343
SPARKS EXHIBITS & ENVIRONMENTS CORP.—See Freeman Decorating Co.; *U.S. Private*, pg. 1605
SPARKS FAMILY HOSPITAL, INC.—See Universal Health Services, Inc.; *U.S. Public*, pg. 2259
SPARKS MARKETING GROUP LLC—See Freeman Decorating Co.; *U.S. Private*, pg. 1605
SPARK; *U.S. Private*, pg. 3745
SPARK; *U.S. Private*, pg. 3745
SPARKS PREMIERCARE, L.L.C.—See Community Health Systems, Inc.; *U.S. Public*, pg. 557
SPARK STUDIOS—See SPARK; *U.S. Private*, pg. 3745
SPARKTEC TONO CO., LTD.—See Niterra Co., Ltd.; *Int'l*, pg. 5381
SPARKTEC WKS CO., LTD.—See Niterra Co., Ltd.; *Int'l*, pg. 5381
SPARK THERAPEUTICS, INC.—See Roche Holding AG; *Int'l*, pg. 6376
SPARK VC S.A.; *Int'l*, pg. 7126
SPARKWARE TECHNOLOGIES SRL—See evoke plc; *Int'l*, pg. 2572
SPARKY AD; *Int'l*, pg. 7126
SPARKY ELTOS AD; *Int'l*, pg. 7126
SPARKY'S OCEANICA AMUSEMENT TOYS LLC—See Abdul Mohsen Al-Hokair Group for Tourism and Development Company; *Int'l*, pg. 58
SPARLING, INC.—See Stantec Inc.; *Int'l*, pg. 7172
SPARLING'S PROPANE CO. LTD.—See Parkland Corporation; *Int'l*, pg. 5744
SPAR MARKETING FORCE, INC.—See SPAR Group, Inc.; *U.S. Public*, pg. 1914
SPAR NORD BANK A/S; *Int'l*, pg. 7125
SPAR NORD EJENDOMSSELSKAB A/S—See Spar Nord Bank A/S; *Int'l*, pg. 7125
SPARQ—See Randstad N.V.; *Int'l*, pg. 6205
SPARQ SYSTEMS INC.; *Int'l*, pg. 7126
SPARQUE B.V.—See Intershop Communications AG; *Int'l*, pg. 3760
SPARRER SAUSAGE COMPANY, INC.; *U.S. Private*, pg. 3746
SPAR RETAIL NV—See Colruyt Group N.V.; *Int'l*, pg. 1705
SPARROW CARSON HOSPITAL—See University of Michigan; *U.S. Private*, pg. 4309
SPARROW CLINTON HOSPITAL—See University of Michigan; *U.S. Private*, pg. 4309
SPARROW COMMUNITY CARE—See University of Michigan; *U.S. Private*, pg. 4309
SPARROW EARLY LEARNING PTY LIMITED; *Int'l*, pg. 7126
SPARROW EATON HOSPITAL—See University of Michigan; *U.S. Private*, pg. 4309
SPARROW HEALTH SYSTEM—See University of Michigan; *U.S. Private*, pg. 4309
SPARROW HOSPITAL - ST. LAWRENCE CAMPUS—See University of Michigan; *U.S. Private*, pg. 4309
SPARROW IONIA HOSPITAL—See University of Michigan; *U.S. Private*, pg. 4309
SPARROWS OFFSHORE GROUP LIMITED—See Altrad Investment Authority SAS; *Int'l*, pg. 398
SPARROWS OFFSHORE LLC—See Altrad Investment Authority SAS; *Int'l*, pg. 398
SPARROW SPECIALTY HOSPITAL—See University of Michigan; *U.S. Private*, pg. 4309
SPAR (SHANGHAI) MARKETING MANAGEMENT COMPANY LTD.—See SPAR Group, Inc.; *U.S. Public*, pg. 1914
SPARTA AG; *Int'l*, pg. 7126
SPARTA B.V.—See Accell Group N.V.; *Int'l*, pg. 81
SPARTA CAPITAL LTD.; *Int'l*, pg. 7127
SPARTA CHEVROLET, INC.; *U.S. Private*, pg. 3746
SPARTA COMMERCIAL SERVICES, INC.; *U.S. Public*, pg. 1914
SPARTA COOPERATIVE SERVICES; *U.S. Private*, pg. 3746
SPARTACUS ACQUISITION CORPORATION; *U.S. Private*, pg. 3746
SPARTACUS A/S—See Svenska Handelsbanken AB; *Int'l*, pg. 7358
SPARTA ECUMENICAL COUNCIL ON SENIOR CITIZEN HOUSING INC.; *U.S. Private*, pg. 3746
SPARTA HEALTHCARE ACQUISITION CORP.; *U.S. Public*, pg. 1914
SPARTA, INC.—See Parsons Corporation; *U.S. Public*, pg. 1651

SPARTA INSURANCE HOLDINGS, INC.—See Apollo Global Management, Inc.; *U.S. Public*, pg. 148
SPARTAN ACQUISITION CORP.; *U.S. Public*, pg. 1914
SPARTAN AUTOMATIC RETAILERS; *U.S. Private*, pg. 3746
SPARTAN AUTOS INCORPORATED; *U.S. Private*, pg. 3746
SPARTANBURG COCA-COLA BOTTLING CO.—See Coca-Cola Bottling Co. United, Inc.; *U.S. Private*, pg. 958
SPARTANBURG DIALYSIS, LLC—See Nautic Partners, LLC; *U.S. Private*, pg. 2871
SPARTANBURG FOREST PRODUCTS INC.; *U.S. Private*, pg. 3746
SPARTANBURG HERALD-JOURNAL—See Gannett Co., Inc.; *U.S. Public*, pg. 905
SPARTANBURG MEAT PROCESSING CO., INC.; *U.S. Private*, pg. 3746
SPARTANBURG MEDICAL CENTER—See Spartanburg Regional Health Services District, Inc.; *U.S. Private*, pg. 3747
THE SPARTANBURG REGIONAL HEALTHCARE SYSTEM FOUNDATION—See Spartanburg Regional Health Services District, Inc.; *U.S. Private*, pg. 3747
SPARTANBURG REGIONAL HEALTH SERVICES DISTRICT, INC.; *U.S. Private*, pg. 3746
SPARTANBURG STAINLESS PRODUCTS INC.—See Reserve Group Management Company; *U.S. Private*, pg. 3405
SPARTANBURG STEEL PRODUCTS, INC.—See Reserve Group Management Company; *U.S. Private*, pg. 3404
SPARTANBURG WATER SYSTEM; *U.S. Private*, pg. 3747
SPARTAN CHEMICAL CO. INC.; *U.S. Private*, pg. 3746
SPARTAN CONCRETE, INC.—See Advanced Drainage Systems, Inc.; *U.S. Public*, pg. 46
SPARTAN CONTROLS LTD.; *Int'l*, pg. 7127
SPARTAN DELTA CORP.; *Int'l*, pg. 7127
SPARTAN DISTRIBUTORS INC.; *U.S. Private*, pg. 3746
SPARTAN ENERGY PARTNERS, LP—See Silverhawk Capital Partners, LLC; *U.S. Private*, pg. 3663
SPARTAN FOODS OF AMERICA INC—See B&G Foods, Inc.; *U.S. Public*, pg. 260
SPARTAN GOLD LTD.; *U.S. Private*, pg. 3746
SPARTAN INDUSTRIAL INC.; *U.S. Private*, pg. 3746
SPARTAN LIGHT METAL PRODUCTS; *U.S. Private*, pg. 3746
SPARTAN MOTORS USA, INC.—See AIP, LLC; *U.S. Private*, pg. 135
SPARTAN MOWERS, LLC—See The Toro Company; *U.S. Public*, pg. 2135
SPARTAN PRODUCTS, LLC—See Vulcan Materials Company; *U.S. Public*, pg. 2314
SPARTAN READYMIX & TILES CO. W.L.L—See Taleb Group; *Int'l*, pg. 7446
SPARTAN SCHOOL OF AERONAUTICS; *U.S. Private*, pg. 3746
SPARTAN SECURITY SERVICES, INC. - NEW JERSEY—See ATALIAN Global Services; *Int'l*, pg. 666
SPARTAN SECURITY SERVICES, INC.—See ATALIAN Global Services; *Int'l*, pg. 665
SPARTAN SHOPS INC.; *U.S. Private*, pg. 3746
SPARTAN SHOWCASE, INC.—See Leggett & Platt, Incorporated; *U.S. Public*, pg. 1303
SPARTAN STAFFING, LLC—See TrueBlue, Inc.; *U.S. Public*, pg. 2198
SPARTAN SURFACES, INC.—See Floor & Decor Holdings, Inc.; *U.S. Public*, pg. 853
SPARTAN TOOL—See The Heico Companies, L.L.C.; *U.S. Private*, pg. 4050
SPARTAN TOOL SUPPLY COMPANY, INC.—See Foundation Investment Partners, LLC; *U.S. Private*, pg. 1580
SPARTAN WELLNESS CORPORATION—See MPX International Corporation; *Int'l*, pg. 5063
SPARTA SYSTEMS, INC.—See New Mountain Capital, LLC; *U.S. Private*, pg. 2903
SPARTECH - CAPE GIRARDEAU—See The Jordan Company, L.P.; *U.S. Private*, pg. 4062
SPARTECH - GOODYEAR—See The Jordan Company, L.P.; *U.S. Private*, pg. 4062
SPARTECH - LA MIRADA—See The Jordan Company, L.P.; *U.S. Private*, pg. 4062
SPARTECH LLC—See The Jordan Company, L.P.; *U.S. Private*, pg. 4062
SPARTECH - MCMINNVILLE—See The Jordan Company, L.P.; *U.S. Private*, pg. 4062
SPARTECH - PAULDING—See The Jordan Company, L.P.; *U.S. Private*, pg. 4062
SPARTECH - SALISBURY—See The Jordan Company, L.P.; *U.S. Private*, pg. 4062
SPARTECH - STAMFORD—See The Jordan Company, L.P.; *U.S. Private*, pg. 4062
SPARTECH - TOWNSEND—See The Jordan Company, L.P.; *U.S. Private*, pg. 4062
SPAR TODOPROMO, SAPI, DE CV—See SPAR Group, Inc.; *U.S. Public*, pg. 1914
SPARTON BECKWOOD, LLC—See Elbit Systems Limited; *Int'l*, pg. 2344
SPARTON BROOKSVILLE, LLC—See Elbit Systems Limited; *Int'l*, pg. 2344

SPARTAN SHOPS INC. — CORPORATE AFFILIATIONS

SPARTON CORPORATION—See Elbit Systems Limited; *Int'l*, pg. 2344
SPARTON ELECTRONICS FLORIDA, INC.—See Elbit Systems Limited; *Int'l*, pg. 2344
SPARTON MEDICAL SYSTEMS COLORADO, LLC—See Elbit Systems Limited; *Int'l*, pg. 2345
SPARTON MEDICAL SYSTEMS, INC.—See Elbit Systems Limited; *Int'l*, pg. 2344
SPARTON ONYX, LLC—See Elbit Systems Limited; *Int'l*, pg. 2345
SPARTON RESOURCES INC.; *Int'l*, pg. 7127
SPARTOO SAS; *Int'l*, pg. 7127
SPARTRONICS LLC—See OEP Capital Advisors, L.P.; *U.S. Private*, pg. 3000
SPARX ASIA INVESTMENT ADVISORS LIMITED—See SPARX Group Co., Ltd.; *Int'l*, pg. 7128
SPARX ASSET MANAGEMENT KOREA CO., LTD.—See SPARX Group Co., Ltd.; *Int'l*, pg. 7128
SPARXENT, INC.—See Signal Peak Venture Partners, LLC; *U.S. Private*, pg. 3649
SPARX GREEN ENERGY & TECHNOLOGY CO., LTD.—See SPARX Group Co., Ltd.; *Int'l*, pg. 7128
SPARX GROUP CO., LTD.; *Int'l*, pg. 7127
SPARX HOLDINGS GROUP, INC.; *U.S. Public*, pg. 1914
SPARXOO, LLC—See Big Sea, Inc.; *U.S. Private*, pg. 554
SPASCIANI S.P.A.; *Int'l*, pg. 7128
S&P ASSET COMPANY LIMITED—See S&P Syndicate Public Company Limited; *Int'l*, pg. 6445
SP ASSET MANAGEMENT LLC—See Steel Partners Holdings L.P.; *U.S. Public*, pg. 1943
SPASSGESELLSCHAFT—See Sony Group Corporation; *Int'l*, pg. 7104
SPA STRATEGY LIMITED—See Walgreens Boots Alliance, Inc.; *U.S. Public*, pg. 2323
SPATEN - FRANZISKANER - BRAU GMBH—See Anheuser-Busch InBev SA/NV; *Int'l*, pg. 466
SPATIALAGE SOLUTIONS DIVISION—See Byers Engineering Company; *U.S. Private*, pg. 700
SPATIAL BUSINESS SYSTEMS, INC.—See Peak Rock Capital LLC; *U.S. Private*, pg. 3124
SPATIAL CORP.—See Dassault Systemes S.A.; *Int'l*, pg. 1974
SPATIAL DIMENSION AUSTRALIA PTY. LTD.—See Trimble, Inc.; *U.S. Public*, pg. 2191
SPATIAL DIMENSION CANADA ULC—See Trimble, Inc.; *U.S. Public*, pg. 2191
SPATIAL DIMENSION SISTEMAS DO BRASIL LTDA.—See Trimble, Inc.; *U.S. Public*, pg. 2191
SPATIAL DIMENSION SOUTH AFRICA PTY LTD—See Trimble, Inc.; *U.S. Public*, pg. 2191
SPATIAL ENERGY, LLC—See Advent International Corporation; *U.S. Private*, pg. 103
SPATIAL NETWORKS, INC.; *U.S. Private*, pg. 3747
SPATRONIC GMBH—See Harvia Oyj; *Int'l*, pg. 3281
SPATZ CENTERS INC.; *U.S. Private*, pg. 3747
SPAULDING BRICK COMPANY INC.; *U.S. Private*, pg. 3747
SPAULDING COMPOSITES, INC.; *U.S. Private*, pg. 3747
SPAULDING DECON, LLC; *U.S. Private*, pg. 3747
SPAULDING HOSPITAL - CAMBRIDGE INC.—See Partners HealthCare System, Inc.; *U.S. Private*, pg. 3101
SPAULDING REHABILITATION HOSPITAL CORPORATION—See Partners HealthCare System, Inc.; *U.S. Private*, pg. 3101
SPAULDING REHABILITATION NETWORK—See Partners HealthCare System, Inc.; *U.S. Private*, pg. 3101
SPA UNDERWRITING SERVICES SELECT LIMITED—See Howden Group Holdings Limited; *Int'l*, pg. 3494
SPA VALUATION ADVISORS PRIVATE LTD.—See SPA Capital Services Limited; *Int'l*, pg. 7123
SPAW GLASS CONSTRUCTION CORP.—See Spaw Glass Holding LP; *U.S. Private*, pg. 3747
SPAW GLASS CONTRACTORS INC.—See Spaw Glass Holding LP; *U.S. Private*, pg. 3747
SPAW GLASS HOLDING LP; *U.S. Private*, pg. 3747
SPAWN IDEAS, INC.; *U.S. Private*, pg. 3747
SPAWN LABS, INC.—See GameStop Corp.; *U.S. Public*, pg. 896
SPAY, INC.—See Genstar Capital, LLC; *U.S. Private*, pg. 1678
SPB CANADA INC.; *Int'l*, pg. 7128
SP BEHAVIORAL, LLC—See Universal Health Services, Inc.; *U.S. Public*, pg. 2259
SPB HOSPITALITY LLC—See SoftBank Group Corp.; *Int'l*, pg. 7053
SP BOHEMIA, K.S.—See Heidelberg Materials AG; *Int'l*, pg. 3319
SPB-PC LTD.—See Seshasayee Paper & Boards Ltd; *Int'l*, pg. 6729
SPB SOFTWARE LIMITED—See Yandex N.V.; *Int'l*, pg. 8559
SPB SOFTWARE—See Yandex N.V.; *Int'l*, pg. 8559
SPB SWEDEN AB—See Spectrum Brands Holdings, Inc.; *U.S. Public*, pg. 1916
SPCA INTERNATIONAL, INC.; *U.S. Private*, pg. 3747
SP CAPITAL AB—See E*TRADE Financial Corporation; *U.S. Public*, pg. 1302
S.P. CAPITAL FINANCING LIMITED; *Int'l*, pg. 6457

SPC ARDMONA (GERMANY) GMBH—See Perma Funds Management; *Int'l*, pg. 5802
SPC ARDMONA (GERMANY) GMBH—See Perma Funds Management; *Int'l*, pg. 5802
SPC ARDMONA (GERMANY) GMBH—See The Eights Group Pty Ltd.; *Int'l*, pg. 7638
SPC ARDMONA (GERMANY) GMBH—See The Eights Group Pty Ltd.; *Int'l*, pg. 7638
SPC ARDMONA LIMITED—See Perma Funds Management; *Int'l*, pg. 5802
SPC ARDMONA LIMITED—See Perma Funds Management; *Int'l*, pg. 5802
SPC ARDMONA LIMITED—See The Eights Group Pty Ltd.; *Int'l*, pg. 7638
SPC ARDMONA LIMITED—See The Eights Group Pty Ltd.; *Int'l*, pg. 7638
SPC ARDMONA OPERATIONS LIMITED—See Perma Funds Management; *Int'l*, pg. 5802
SPC ARDMONA OPERATIONS LIMITED—See Perma Funds Management; *Int'l*, pg. 5802
SPC ARDMONA OPERATIONS LIMITED—See The Eights Group Pty Ltd.; *Int'l*, pg. 7638
SPC ARDMONA OPERATIONS LIMITED—See The Eights Group Pty Ltd.; *Int'l*, pg. 7638
SPC ARDMONA (SPAIN), S.L.U.—See Perma Funds Management; *Int'l*, pg. 5802
SPC ARDMONA (SPAIN), S.L.U.—See Perma Funds Management; *Int'l*, pg. 5802
SPC ARDMONA (SPAIN), S.L.U.—See The Eights Group Pty Ltd.; *Int'l*, pg. 7638
SPC ARDMONA (SPAIN), S.L.U.—See The Eights Group Pty Ltd.; *Int'l*, pg. 7638
SPC CAPITAL MANAGEMENT, INC.—See Sonoco Products Company; *U.S. Public*, pg. 1905
SPC CORPORATION-PHILADELPHIA—See Camden Iron & Metal Inc.; *U.S. Private*, pg. 728
SPCG PUBLIC COMPANY LIMITED; *Int'l*, pg. 7128
SP CHEMICALS LIMITED; *Int'l*, pg. 7122
SP CHEMICALS (TAIXING) CO., LTD.—See SP Chemicals Limited; *Int'l*, pg. 7122
SPC INDUSTRIES SDN. BHD.—See Kimlun Corporation Berhad; *Int'l*, pg. 4163
SPC ITALIA SRL—See BT Group plc; *Int'l*, pg. 1203
S&P CLEVER REINFORCEMENT COMPANY BENELUX B.V.—See Simpson Manufacturing Company, Inc.; *U.S. Public*, pg. 1882
S&P CLEVER REINFORCEMENT GMBH—See Simpson Manufacturing Company, Inc.; *U.S. Public*, pg. 1882
SPC MANAGEMENT CO., INC - BEDMINSTER OFFICE—See Swander Pace Capital, LLC; *U.S. Private*, pg. 3890
SPC MANAGEMENT CO., INC.—See Swander Pace Capital, LLC; *U.S. Private*, pg. 3890
SPC MANAGEMENT, INC.—See Sonoco Products Company; *U.S. Public*, pg. 1905
S&P COMPANY INC.; *U.S. Private*, pg. 3513
S-P COMPANY INC.; *U.S. Private*, pg. 3514
SP COMPANY, INC.—See BDT Capital Partners, LLC; *U.S. Private*, pg. 503
SP CORPORATION LIMITED—See Tuan Sing Holdings Limited; *Int'l*, pg. 7962
SPC POWER CORPORATION; *Int'l*, pg. 7128
SPC RESOURCES, INC.—See Sonoco Products Company; *U.S. Public*, pg. 1905
S.P.C. TRANSPORT; *U.S. Private*, pg. 3516
SP DATASERVE, LTD.—See Iberdrola, S.A.; *Int'l*, pg. 3573
SPDB INTERNATIONAL HOLDING, LTD.—See Shanghai Pudong Development Bank Co., Ltd.; *Int'l*, pg. 6777
SPD DEVELOPMENT COMPANY LIMITED—See The Procter & Gamble Company; *U.S. Public*, pg. 2123
SP DELTA FOODS INC.—See SPFS Inc.; *U.S. Private*, pg. 3756
SP DISTRIBUTION, LTD.—See Iberdrola, S.A.; *Int'l*, pg. 3573
SPDJ HOLDINGS, LLC—See Medicus Solutions, LLC; *U.S. Private*, pg. 2656
S&P DJ INDICES UK LTD—See S&P Global Inc.; *U.S. Public*, pg. 1831
S&P DOW JONES INDICES LLC—See S&P Global Inc.; *U.S. Public*, pg. 1831
SPD SWISS PRECISION DIAGNOSTICS GMBH—See The Procter & Gamble Company; *U.S. Public*, pg. 2123
SPD TRUCKING, LLC—See Daseke, Inc.; *U.S. Private*, pg. 1162
SPEA DO BRASIL PROJECTOS E INFRAESTRUTURA LIMITADA—See Edizione S.r.l.; *Int'l*, pg. 2312
SPEAKEASY BERLIN GMBH—See MEDIQON Group AG; *Int'l*, pg. 4780
SPEAKEASY CANNABIS CLUB LTD.; *Int'l*, pg. 7128
SPEAKERBOX COMMUNICATIONS, LLC—See Trinity Hunt Management, L.P.; *U.S. Private*, pg. 4235
SPEAKERBUS, INC.; *U.S. Private*, pg. 3747
SPEAKMAN COMPANY; *U.S. Private*, pg. 3747
SPEAKS CHAPELS LLC—See Birch Hill Equity Partners Management Inc.; *Int'l*, pg. 1046
SPEAKS CHAPELS LLC—See Homesteaders Life Co. Inc.; *U.S. Private*, pg. 1974
SPEAKS OIL CO. INC.; *U.S. Private*, pg. 3747

SPE ALTO IRANI ENERGIA S.A.—See State Grid Corporation of China; *Int'l*, pg. 7182
SPEAR EDUCATION, LLC—See Avista Capital Partners, L.P.; *U.S. Private*, pg. 409
SPEARHALL ADVERTISING & PUBLIC RELATIONS; *U.S. Private*, pg. 3747
SPEARHEAD MACHINERY LTD.—See Alamo Group Inc.; *U.S. Public*, pg. 70
SPEARHEAD PROPERTY HOLDINGS LTD.—See Redefine Properties Limited; *Int'l*, pg. 6246
SPEARING SERVICE L.P.—See Mullen Group Ltd.; *Int'l*, pg. 5080
SPEARMAN BANCSHARES, INC.; *U.S. Private*, pg. 3748
SPEAR MARKETING GROUP LLC; *U.S. Private*, pg. 3747
SPEARMC CONSULTING; *U.S. Private*, pg. 3748
SPEARMINT RESOURCES INC.; *Int'l*, pg. 7128
SPEAR PHYSICAL THERAPY, PLLC.; *U.S. Private*, pg. 3747
SPEAR POWER SYSTEMS AS—See Sensata Technologies Holding plc; *U.S. Public*, pg. 1866
SPEAR POWER SYSTEMS, LLC—See Sensata Technologies Holding plc; *U.S. Public*, pg. 1866
SPEARS MANUFACTURING COMPANY; *U.S. Private*, pg. 3748
SPEARSYSTEM PACKAGING AFRICA (PTY) LTD—See Spear USA LLC; *U.S. Private*, pg. 3747
SPEARSYSTEM PACKAGING ASIA PTE LTD.—See Spear USA LLC; *U.S. Private*, pg. 3747
SPEAR USA LLC—See Spear USA LLC; *U.S. Private*, pg. 3747
SPEAR USA LLC; *U.S. Private*, pg. 3747
SPEAR USA LLC—See Spear USA LLC; *U.S. Private*, pg. 3747
SP EAST HIGHLANDS RANCH—See Westbrook Real Estate Partners, LLC; *U.S. Private*, pg. 4488
SPEC 7 INSULATION CO., LLC—See Installed Building Products, Inc.; *U.S. Public*, pg. 1133
SPECAC INC.—See Ampersand Management LLC; *U.S. Private*, pg. 265
SPECAC LIMITED—See Ampersand Management LLC; *U.S. Private*, pg. 265
SPECHT ELECTRIC CO. INC.; *U.S. Private*, pg. 3748
SPECIAL AEROSPACE SERVICES LLC—See Godspeed Capital Management LP; *U.S. Private*, pg. 1725
SPECIAL APPEARANCE SDN BHD—See Johor Corporation; *Int'l*, pg. 3994
SPECIAL APPLICATIONS TECHNOLOGY INC.—See Hammond, Kennedy, Whitney & Company, Inc.; *U.S. Private*, pg. 1850
SPECIAL BAR MATERIALS LLC—See Special Piping Materials Ltd.; *Int'l*, pg. 7128
SPECIAL CARE HOSPITAL, LLC—See Select Medical Holdings Corporation; *U.S. Public*, pg. 1861
SPECIALCARE HOSPITAL MANAGEMENT CORPORATION—See Webster Equity Partners, LLC; *U.S. Private*, pg. 4467
SPECIAL CONTINGENCY RISKS LIMITED—See GIC Pte. Ltd.; *Int'l*, pg. 2967
SPECIAL COUNSEL INC.—See Adecco Group AG; *Int'l*, pg. 141
SPECIAL COUNSEL INC.—See Adecco Group AG; *Int'l*, pg. 141
SPECIAL DEVICES, INCORPORATED—See Daicel Corporation; *Int'l*, pg. 1918
SPECIAL DEVICES JAPAN LTD.—See Daicel Corporation; *Int'l*, pg. 1920
SPECIAL DEVICES (THAILAND) CO., LTD.—See Daicel Corporation; *Int'l*, pg. 1920
SPECIAL DISPATCH OF SAN ANTONIO, INC.—See J.B. Hunt Transport Services, Inc.; *U.S. Public*, pg. 1180
SPECIAL DISTRICT SERVICES, INC.; *U.S. Private*, pg. 3748
SPECIAL DOMAINS SERVICES, INC.—See KKR & Co. Inc.; *U.S. Public*, pg. 1252
SPECIAL DOMAINS SERVICES, INC.—See Silver Lake Group, LLC; *U.S. Private*, pg. 3657
SPECIAL DOMAINS SERVICES, INC.—See TCMI, Inc.; *U.S. Private*, pg. 3943
SPECIALFALGAR I KUNGSBACKA HOLDING AB—See Storskogen Group AB; *Int'l*, pg. 7228
SPECIAL FASTENERS ENGINEERING CO., LTD.—See Trifast plc; *Int'l*, pg. 7921
SPECIAL FLANGE SERVICES, LTD.—See Groupe BPCE; *Int'l*, pg. 3095
SPECIAL FLANGES SPA—See Wise Equity SGR S.p.A.; *Int'l*, pg. 8435
SPECIAL FLEET SERVICE INC.; *U.S. Private*, pg. 3748
SPECIALISED CLEANING & RESTORATION INDUSTRY ASSOCIATION, INC.; *Int'l*, pg. 7128
SPECIALISED EXHIBITIONS (PTY.) LIMITED—See Angus Montgomery Ltd.; *Int'l*, pg. 463
SPECIALISED PETROLEUM MANUFACTURING LTD—See The Weir Group PLC; *Int'l*, pg. 7699
SPECIALISED WELDING PRODUCTS PTY. LTD.—See Lincoln Electric Holdings, Inc.; *U.S. Public*, pg. 1318
SPECIALIST ANODISING COMPANY LIMITED—See Lendlock Group Limited; *Int'l*, pg. 4453

SPECIALIST COMPUTER CENTRES—See Specialist Computer Holdings Ltd.; *Int'l*, pg. 7128
SPECIALIST COMPUTER CENTRES—See Specialist Computer Holdings Ltd.; *Int'l*, pg. 7128
SPECIALIST COMPUTER HOLDINGS LTD.; *Int'l*, pg. 7128
SPECIALIST DISTRIBUTION GROUP (SDG) LIMITED—See TD Synnex Corp; *U.S. Public*, pg. 1986
SPECIALIST FLEET SERVICES LIMITED—See Rothschild & Co SCA; *Int'l*, pg. 6404
SPECIALIST INVESTMENT PROPERTIES PLC; *Int'l*, pg. 7128
SPECIALISTKLINIKEN FOR DENTALA IMPLANTAT KB—See Apax Partners LLP; *Int'l*, pg. 502
SPECIALIST ORAL SURGEONS PTE. LTD.—See Q&M Dental Group (Singapore) Limited; *Int'l*, pg. 6131
SPECIALIST PEOPLE SERVICES GROUP LTD.—See Lloyds Banking Group plc; *Int'l*, pg. 4538
SPECIALIST PROTECTIVE COATINGS LIMITED—See Billington Holdings Plc; *Int'l*, pg. 1031
THE SPECIALISTS INC.; *U.S. Private*, pg. 4120
SPECIALISTS IN UROLOGY, PA; *U.S. Private*, pg. 3748
SPECIALISTS MARKETING SERVICES, INC.; *U.S. Private*, pg. 3748
SPECIALISTS ON CALL, INC.—See Patient Square Capital, L.P.; *U.S. Private*, pg. 3107
SPECIALIST TECHNOLOGIES LTD.—See ALA SpA; *Int'l*, pg. 289
SPECIALIST UK LTD.—See Omnicom Group Inc.; *U.S. Public*, pg. 1593
THE SPECIALIST WORKS LTD.; *Int'l*, pg. 7688
SPECIALITES INDUSTRIELLES HARVEY ULC—See Applied Industrial Technologies, Inc.; *U.S. Public*, pg. 171
SPECIALITES PET FOOD SA DE C.V—See Symrise AG; *Int'l*, pg. 7380
SPECIALITES PET FOOD SAS—See Symrise AG; *Int'l*, pg. 7380
SPECIALITES PET FOOD SOUTH AFRICA (PTY) LTD.—See Symrise AG; *Int'l*, pg. 7380
SPECIALITIES GROUP HOLDING CO. K.S.C.C.; *Int'l*, pg. 7129
SPECIALITY COATINGS (DARWEN) LTD.—See Lins Trading Ltd.; *Int'l*, pg. 4515
SPECIALITY PRODUCTS AND DISPENSERS PTY. LTD.—See Pro-Pac Packaging Limited; *Int'l*, pg. 5985
SPECIALITY RESTAURANTS LTD; *Int'l*, pg. 7129
SPECIALIZED AUTOMATION SERVICES, LLC.; *U.S. Private*, pg. 3748
SPECIALIZED BICYCLE COMPONENTS; *U.S. Private*, pg. 3748
SPECIALIZED BUSINESS SYSTEM AD; *Int'l*, pg. 7129
SPECIALIZED CARRIER CO. INC.—See General Equipment & Supplies Inc.; *U.S. Private*, pg. 1664
SPECIALIZED COATING SERVICES—See Tide Rock Holdings, LLC; *U.S. Private*, pg. 4168
SPECIALIZED FABRICATION EQUIPMENT GROUP, LLC—See Gladstone Management Corporation; *U.S. Private*, pg. 1705
SPECIALIZED FOR ADVANCED SYSTEMS & CHEMICALS—See Waters Corporation; *U.S. Public*, pg. 2335
SPECIALIZED INVESTMENT COMPOUNDS COMPANY, PLC.; *Int'l*, pg. 7129
SPECIALIZED JORDANIAN INVESTMENTS COMPANY P.L.C.; *Int'l*, pg. 7129
SPECIALIZED LEASE FINANCE CO.—See The Housing Bank for Trade & Finance; *Int'l*, pg. 7653
SPECIALIZED LEASING, INC.; *U.S. Private*, pg. 3749
SPECIALIZED LOAN SERVICING LLC—See Computershare Limited; *Int'l*, pg. 1760
SPECIALIZED MAINTENANCE AND SERVICES, INC.—See Carylon Corporation; *U.S. Private*, pg. 777
SPECIALIZED MEDIA SERVICES, INC.; *U.S. Private*, pg. 3749
SPECIALIZED MEDICAL DEVICES, LLC—See Teleflex Incorporated; *U.S. Public*, pg. 1996
SPECIALIZED MEDICAL SERVICES, INC.—See New Mountain Capital, LLC; *U.S. Private*, pg. 2903
SPECIALIZED MEDICAL SERVICES, INC.—See New Mountain Capital, LLC; *U.S. Private*, pg. 2903
THE SPECIALIZED PACKAGING GROUP, INC—See Altamont Capital Partners; *U.S. Private*, pg. 205
SPECIALIZED PIPE SERVICES, INC.—See Berkshire Hathaway Inc.; *U.S. Public*, pg. 315
SPECIALIZED PRINTED FORMS, INC.—See Ennis, Inc.; *U.S. Public*, pg. 769
SPECIALIZED RAIL SERVICE, INC.—See Universal Logistics Holdings, Inc.; *U.S. Public*, pg. 2261
SPECIALIZED RESPONSE SOLUTIONS, LP—See Republic Services, Inc.; *U.S. Public*, pg. 1788
SPECIALIZED TECHNOLOGY RESOURCES (CONNECTICUT), LLC—See STR Holdings, Inc.; *U.S. Public*, pg. 1953
SPECIALIZED TECHNOLOGY RESOURCES ESPANA S.A.—See STR Holdings, Inc.; *U.S. Public*, pg. 1953
SPECIALIZED TECHNOLOGY RESOURCES, INC.—See STR Holdings, Inc.; *U.S. Public*, pg. 1953

SPECIALIZED TECHNOLOGY RESOURCES (MALAYSIA) SDN. BHD.—See STR Holdings, Inc.; *U.S. Public*, pg. 1953
SPECIALIZED TECHNOLOGY RESOURCES SOLAR (SUZHOU) CO. LIMITED—See STR Holdings, Inc.; *U.S. Public*, pg. 1953
SPECIALIZED TRADING INVESTMENTS CO.; *Int'l*, pg. 7129
SPECIALIZED TRANSPORTATION, INC.—See CRST International, Inc.; *U.S. Private*, pg. 1113
SPECIALIZED TRANSPORTATION SERVICE; *U.S. Private*, pg. 3749
SPECIAL MELTED PRODUCTS LTD.—See Mutares SE & Co. KGaA; *Int'l*, pg. 5105
SPECIAL METALS CORPORATION—See Berkshire Hathaway Inc.; *U.S. Public*, pg. 315
SPECIAL METALS INC.; *U.S. Private*, pg. 3748
SPECIAL METALS WIGGIN LTD.—See Berkshire Hathaway Inc.; *U.S. Public*, pg. 315
SPECIAL METALS WIGGIN TRUSTEES LIMITED—See Berkshire Hathaway Inc.; *U.S. Public*, pg. 315
SPECIAL METHODS & ENGINEERING TECHNIQUES SDN BHD—See Doppelmayr Group; *Int'l*, pg. 2175
SPECIAL MOLD ENGINEERING INC.; *U.S. Private*, pg. 3748
SPECIAL OPERATIONS GROUP INC.; *U.S. Private*, pg. 3748
SPECIAL OPERATIONS SOLUTIONS LLC; *U.S. Private*, pg. 3748
SPECIAL OPERATIONS WARRIOR FOUNDATION, INC.; *U.S. Private*, pg. 3748
SPECIAL OPPORTUNITIES FUND, INC.; *U.S. Public*, pg. 1914
SPECIAL OPTICS, INC.—See AMETEK, Inc.; *U.S. Public*, pg. 121
SPECIAL PHAGE HOLDINGS PTY LTD—See Armata Pharmaceuticals, Inc.; *U.S. Public*, pg. 193
SPECIAL PIPING MATERIALS AUSTRALIA PTY LTD—See Special Piping Materials Ltd.; *Int'l*, pg. 7128
SPECIAL PIPING MATERIALS FZE.—See Special Piping Materials Ltd.; *Int'l*, pg. 7128
SPECIAL PIPING MATERIALS LTD.; *Int'l*, pg. 7128
SPECIAL PIPING MATERIALS (SINGAPORE) PTE LTD—See Special Piping Materials Ltd.; *Int'l*, pg. 7128
SPECIAL PRODUCT COMPANY; *U.S. Private*, pg. 3748
SPECIAL PRODUCTS & MANUFACTURING, INC.; *U.S. Private*, pg. 3748
SPECIAL PROJECTS DIVISION LLC—See BUILD LLC; *U.S. Private*, pg. 681
SPECIAL RISK INSURANCE MANAGERS LTD.—See Brown & Brown, Inc.; *U.S. Public*, pg. 402
SPECIAL RISKS FACILITIES INC.; *U.S. Private*, pg. 3748
SPECIAL SERVICE FOR GROUPS; *U.S. Private*, pg. 3748
SPECIAL SERVICE PARTNERS CORPORATION—See Ennis, Inc.; *U.S. Public*, pg. 769
SPECIAL SITUATIONS HOLDINGS, INC. WESTBRIDGE—See UBS Group AG; *Int'l*, pg. 8006
SPECIAL T'S, INC.; *U.S. Private*, pg. 3748
SPECIALTY A/C PRODUCTS INC.; *U.S. Private*, pg. 3749
SPECIALTY ADHESIVES, INC.; *U.S. Private*, pg. 3749
SPECIALTY ASSOCIATES OF WEST HOUSTON, PLLC—See HCA Healthcare, Inc.; *U.S. Public*, pg. 1010
SPECIALTY BAKERS, INC.; *U.S. Private*, pg. 3749
SPECIALTY BAR PRODUCTS COMPANY—See Dubai Holding LLC; *Int'l*, pg. 2218
SPECIALTY BOTTLE LLC; *U.S. Private*, pg. 3749
SPECIALTY BUILDING PRODUCTS, INC.; *U.S. Private*, pg. 3749
SPECIALTY BUILDING PRODUCTS, LLC; *U.S. Private*, pg. 3749
SPECIALTYCARE, INC.—See Kohlberg & Company, LLC; *U.S. Private*, pg. 2339
SPECIALTY CARTS, INC.—See Levine Leichtman Capital Partners, LLC; *U.S. Private*, pg. 2436
SPECIALTY CASTINGS, INC.—See Bahr Bros Mfg, Inc.; *U.S. Private*, pg. 425
SPECIALTY CEREALS PTY LIMITED—See Kellanova; *U.S. Public*, pg. 1217
SPECIALTY COATING & LAMINATING LLC; *U.S. Private*, pg. 3749
SPECIALTY COATING SYSTEMS, INC.—See KISCO Ltd.; *Int'l*, pg. 4192
SPECIALTY COMMERCE CORP.—See EdgeStone Capital Partners Inc.; *U.S. Private*, pg. 2309
SPECIALTY COMMODITIES, INC.—See Archer-Daniels-Midland Company; *U.S. Public*, pg. 182
SPECIALTY CONSTRUCTION BRANDS, INC.—See H.B. Fuller Company; *U.S. Public*, pg. 978
SPECIALTY CONSTRUCTION BRANDS - PALATINE—See H.B. Fuller Company; *U.S. Public*, pg. 978
SPECIALTY CONSTRUCTION MANAGEMENT, INC.; *U.S. Private*, pg. 3749
SPECIALTY CONTRACTOR'S INSURANCE SERVICES—See Inszone Insurance Services, LLC; *U.S. Private*, pg. 2096

SPECIALTY DESIGN & MANUFACTURING CO.—See Specialty Holdings Corp.; *U.S. Private*, pg. 3750
SPECIALTY ENGINE COMPONENTS L.L.C.; *U.S. Private*, pg. 3749
SPECIALTY ENTERPRISES CO., INC.; *U.S. Private*, pg. 3749
SPECIALTY EXTENDED CARE HOSPITAL OF MONROE, LLC—See UnitedHealth Group Incorporated; *U.S. Public*, pg. 2247
SPECIALTY FEEDS, INC.; *U.S. Private*, pg. 3749
SPECIALTY FERTILIZER PRODUCTS, LLC—See AEA Investors LP; *U.S. Private*, pg. 116
SPECIALTY FOOD ASSOCIATION, INC.; *U.S. Private*, pg. 3749
SPECIALTY FOODS GROUP-FIELD PACKING DIV.—See Mitsubishi Corporation; *Int'l*, pg. 4938
SPECIALTY FOODS GROUP, LLC—See Mitsubishi Corporation; *Int'l*, pg. 4938
SPECIALTY GRANULES INC.; *U.S. Private*, pg. 3749
SPECIALTY GRANULES INC.—See Specialty Granules Inc.; *U.S. Private*, pg. 3749
SPECIALTY GRAPHIC IMAGING ASSOCIATION; *U.S. Private*, pg. 3749
SPECIALTY HEALTHCARE SERVICES, INC.—See Apollo Global Management, Inc.; *U.S. Public*, pg. 157
SPECIALTY HOLDINGS CORP.; *U.S. Private*, pg. 3750
THE SPECIALTY HOSPITAL, L.L.C.—See Apollo Global Management, Inc.; *U.S. Public*, pg. 157
SPECIALTY INDUSTRIES, INC.; *U.S. Private*, pg. 3750
SPECIALTY INSURANCE GROUP, INC.—See Everest Group, Ltd.; *Int'l*, pg. 2564
SPECIALTY INSURANCE SERVICES CORP.—See Munchener Ruckversicherungs AG; *Int'l*, pg. 5090
SPECIALTY INTERIORS INC.; *U.S. Private*, pg. 3750
SPECIALTY LABORATORIES, INC.—See Quest Diagnostics, Inc.; *U.S. Public*, pg. 1755
SPECIALTY LIGHTING INC.; *U.S. Private*, pg. 3750
SPECIALTY LINES OF PENNSYLVANIA, LLC—See Ryan Specialty Holdings, Inc.; *U.S. Public*, pg. 1828
SPECIALTY LIQUID TRANSPORTATION CORP.; *Int'l*, pg. 7129
SPECIALTY MANUFACTURERS, INC.; *U.S. Private*, pg. 3750
SPECIALTY MANUFACTURING CO.; *U.S. Private*, pg. 3750
SPECIALTY MANUFACTURING, INC.—See Arrow International, Inc.; *U.S. Private*, pg. 335
SPECIALTY MATERIALS, INC.; *U.S. Private*, pg. 3750
SPECIALTY MERCHANDISE CORPORATION; *U.S. Private*, pg. 3750
SPECIALTY METALS CORPORATION; *U.S. Private*, pg. 3750
SPECIALTY MICROWAVE CORP.—See Amplitech Group, Inc.; *U.S. Public*, pg. 133
SPECIALTY MINERALS FRANCE S.P.A.S.—See Minerals Technologies, Inc.; *U.S. Public*, pg. 1449
SPECIALTY MINERALS GMBH—See Minerals Technologies, Inc.; *U.S. Public*, pg. 1449
SPECIALTY MINERALS, INC.—See Minerals Technologies, Inc.; *U.S. Public*, pg. 1449
SPECIALTY MINERALS NORDIC OY AB—See Minerals Technologies, Inc.; *U.S. Public*, pg. 1449
SPECIALTY PACKAGING, INC.—See The Pritzker Group - Chicago, LLC; *U.S. Private*, pg. 4099
SPECIALTY PIPE & TUBE CO. OF TEXAS INC.—See Ascent Industries Co.; *U.S. Public*, pg. 210
SPECIALTY PIPE & TUBE INC.—See Ascent Industries Co.; *U.S. Public*, pg. 210
SPECIALTY PIPING CORP.; *U.S. Private*, pg. 3750
SPECIALTY PLASTICS COMPANY—See Parrish Enterprises, Ltd.; *U.S. Private*, pg. 3100
SPECIALTY PLASTICS, INC.—See Future Pipe Industries Group Ltd.; *Int'l*, pg. 2857
SPECIALTY POLYMER COATINGS INC.—See RPM International Inc.; *U.S. Public*, pg. 1818
SPECIALTY POLYMER COATINGS USA, INC.—See RPM International Inc.; *U.S. Public*, pg. 1820
SPECIALTY POLYMERS INC.; *U.S. Private*, pg. 3750
SPECIALTY POWDERS HOLDINGS LTD.; *Int'l*, pg. 7129
SPECIALTY POWDERS LIMITED—See Specialty Powders Holdings Ltd.; *Int'l*, pg. 7129
SPECIALTY PRODUCTS CZECH REPUBLIC S.R.O.—See Celanese Corporation; *U.S. Public*, pg. 465
SPECIALTY PRODUCTS & INSULATION CO.—See Dunes Point Capital, LLC; *U.S. Private*, pg. 1289
SPECIALTY PRODUCTS, S. A. DE C.V.—See Sigma S.A. de C.V.; *Int'l*, pg. 6908
SPECIALTY PRODUCTS—See Nissui Corporation; *Int'l*, pg. 5379
SPECIALTY PRODUCTS TURKEY ENDUSTRI URUNLERI LIMITED SIRKETI—See DuPont de Nemours, Inc.; *U.S. Public*, pg. 694
SPECIALTY PROGRAM GROUP LLC—See Hellman & Friedman LLC; *U.S. Private*, pg. 1909
SPECIALTY RENAL PRODUCTS, INC.—See Nephros, Inc.; *U.S. Public*, pg. 1506
SPECIALTY RENTAL TOOLS & SUPPLY, INC.; *U.S. Private*, pg. 3750

SPECIALTY RESTAURANT GROUP LLC / CORPORATE AFFILIATIONS

SPECIALTY RESTAURANT GROUP LLC; *U.S. Private,* pg. 3750
SPECIALTY RESTAURANTS CORPORATION; *U.S. Private,* pg. 3750
SPECIALTY RESTORATION OF TEXAS; *U.S. Private,* pg. 3750
SPECIALTY RETAILERS, INC.—See Stage Stores, Inc.; *U.S. Public,* pg. 1925
SPECIALTY RETAIL VENTURES LLC; *U.S. Private,* pg. 3750
SPECIALTY SAND CO.—See MineralTech Gulf Coast Abrasives, LLC; *U.S. Private,* pg. 2742
SPECIALTY'S CAFE AND BAKERY; *U.S. Private,* pg. 3751
SPECIALTY SILICONE PRODUCTS, INC.—See HEICO Corporation; *U.S. Public,* pg. 1021
SPECIALTY SPORTS VENTURE LLC—See Vail Resorts, Inc.; *U.S. Public,* pg. 2271
SPECIALTY STEEL TREATING INC.; *U.S. Private,* pg. 3750
SPECIALTY STRIP & OSCILLATING, INC.; *U.S. Private,* pg. 3751
SPECIALTY SURGERY CENTER AT FOUNTAIN VALLEY REGIONAL HOSPITAL, L.L.C.—See UCI Health; *U.S. Private,* pg. 4274
SPECIALTY SURGERY CENTER—See HCA Healthcare, Inc.; *U.S. Public,* pg. 1010
SPECIALTY SURGICAL CENTER, LLC—See Bain Capital, LP; *U.S. Private,* pg. 446
SPECIALTY SURGICAL CENTER OF ARCADIA, LLC—See Bain Capital, LP; *U.S. Private,* pg. 447
SPECIALTY SURGICAL CENTER OF BEVERLY HILLS, L.P.—See Bain Capital, LP; *U.S. Private,* pg. 447
SPECIALTY SURGICAL CENTER OF ENCINO, LLC—See Bain Capital, LP; *U.S. Private,* pg. 447
SPECIALTY SURGICAL CENTER OF IRVINE, LLC—See Bain Capital, LP; *U.S. Private,* pg. 447
SPECIALTY SURGICAL INSTRUMENTATION, INC.—See Audax Group, Limited Partnership; *U.S. Private,* pg. 386
SPECIALTY SYSTEMS, INC.—See Castellum, Inc.; *U.S. Public,* pg. 447
SPECIALTY THERAPEUTIC CARE, GP, LLC—See Centene Corporation; *U.S. Public,* pg. 470
SPECIALTY THERAPEUTIC CARE HOLDINGS, LLC—See Centene Corporation; *U.S. Public,* pg. 470
SPECIALTY TIRES OF AMERICA INC.—See Polymer Enterprises Inc.; *U.S. Private,* pg. 3226
SPECIALTY TOOL, INC.; *U.S. Private,* pg. 3751
SPECIALTY TOOLING SYSTEMS, INC.—See Nachi-Fujikoshi Corp.; *Int'l,* pg. 5123
SPECIALTY TREE SERVICES, LLC—See Tree Medic, LLC; *U.S. Private,* pg. 4216
SPECIALTY WELDING & TURNAROUNDS LLC—See Hastings Equity Partners, LLC; *U.S. Private,* pg. 1879
SPECIALTY WELDING & TURNAROUNDS LLC—See ORIX Corporation; *Int'l,* pg. 5636
SPECIALTY WOOD MANUFACTURING INC.—See Bargreen-Ellingson Inc.; *U.S. Private,* pg. 474
SPECIALTY WOOD PRODUCTS INC.—See Tumac Lumber Co. Inc.; *U.S. Private,* pg. 4258
SPECIASTAL AB—See Jacquet Metal Service SA; *Int'l,* pg. 3868
SPECIFAR S.A.—See Teva Pharmaceutical Industries, Ltd.; *Int'l,* pg. 7579
SPECIFICATION RUBBER PRODUCTS INC.—See American Cast Iron Pipe Company; *U.S. Private,* pg. 226
SPECIFICATION SEALS, INC.—See The Goldman Sachs Group, Inc.; *U.S. Public,* pg. 2080
SPECIFICITY INC.; *U.S. Public,* pg. 1915
SPECIFIC MEDIA INC.; *U.S. Private,* pg. 3751
SPECIFIC RESOURCES SDN. BHD.—See J&Partners L.P.; *Int'l,* pg. 3853
SPECIFIED AIR SOLUTIONS LLC—See Madison Industries Holdings LLC; *U.S. Private,* pg. 2543
SPECIFIED SYSTEMS INC.; *U.S. Private,* pg. 3751
SPECIMEN PAPIR ES NYOMDAIPARI ZRT.—See ANY Security Printing Company PLC; *Int'l,* pg. 486
SPECION SRO—See HORIBA Ltd.; *Int'l,* pg. 3478
SPECITUBES SAS—See Leggett & Platt, Incorporated; *U.S. Public,* pg. 1303
SPECK INSURANCE & FINANCIAL SERVICES PLLC—See Inszone Insurance Services, LLC; *U.S. Private,* pg. 2096
SPECLINE, INC.—See RBC Bearings Incorporated; *U.S. Public,* pg. 1766
SPECMA AB—See Aktieselskabet Schouw & Co.; *Int'l,* pg. 266
SPECMA COMPONENT AB—See Aktieselskabet Schouw & Co.; *Int'l,* pg. 266
SPECMA DO BRASIL LTDA—See Aktieselskabet Schouw & Co.; *Int'l,* pg. 266
SPECMA HYDRAULIC - OEM DIVISION—See Aktieselskabet Schouw & Co.; *Int'l,* pg. 266
SPECMA HYDRAULIC SHANGHAI CO LTD—See Aktieselskabet Schouw & Co.; *Int'l,* pg. 266
SPECMA HYDRAULIC - SYSTEM DIVISION—See Aktieselskabet Schouw & Co.; *Int'l,* pg. 266
SPECMA HYDRAULIC U.S. INC.—See Aktieselskabet Schouw & Co.; *Int'l,* pg. 266
SPECMA HYDRAULIKHUSET AB—See Aktieselskabet Schouw & Co.; *Int'l,* pg. 266
SPECMA OY—See Aktieselskabet Schouw & Co.; *Int'l,* pg. 266
SPECMA SP. Z.O.O.—See Aktieselskabet Schouw & Co.; *Int'l,* pg. 266
SPECMA WIRO AB—See Aktieselskabet Schouw & Co.; *Int'l,* pg. 266
SPECO HIDROTECHNOLOGIA S.L.—See WAMGROUP S.p.A.; *Int'l,* pg. 8339
SPECO LTD.; *Int'l,* pg. 7129
SPECO (SHANGHAI) MACHINERY CO., LTD.—See SPECO Ltd.; *Int'l,* pg. 7129
SPECO WIND POWER S.A. DE. C.V.—See SPECO Ltd.; *Int'l,* pg. 7129
SPECPRO ENVIRONMENTAL SERVICES LLC—See Bristol Bay Native Corporation; *U.S. Private,* pg. 656
SPECPRO INC.—See Bristol Bay Native Corporation; *U.S. Private,* pg. 656
SPECPRO TECHNICAL SERVICES, LLC—See Bristol Bay Native Corporation; *U.S. Private,* pg. 656
SPECSAVERS FINLAND OY—See Specsavers Optical Group Limited; *Int'l,* pg. 7129
SPECSAVERS INTERNATIONAL BV—See Specsavers Optical Group Limited; *Int'l,* pg. 7129
SPECSAVERS NEW ZEALAND LTD—See Specsavers Optical Group Limited; *Int'l,* pg. 7129
SPECSAVERS NORWAY AS—See Specsavers Optical Group Limited; *Int'l,* pg. 7129
SPECSAVERS OPTICAL GROUP LIMITED; *Int'l,* pg. 7129
SPECSAVERS SWEDEN AB—See Specsavers Optical Group Limited; *Int'l,* pg. 7129
SPECS FAMILY PARTNERS LTD.; *U.S. Private,* pg. 3751
SPECTACLE VENTURES LIMITED; *Int'l,* pg. 7129
SPECTACULAR SOLAR, INC.; *U.S. Public,* pg. 1915
SPECTAIRE HOLDINGS INC.; *U.S. Public,* pg. 1915
SPECTAIRE INC.—See Spectaire Holdings Inc.; *U.S. Public,* pg. 1915
SPECTECH FRANCE SAS—See ALA SpA; *Int'l,* pg. 289
SPECTERA INC.—See UnitedHealth Group Incorporated; *U.S. Public,* pg. 2250
SPECTEST SDN. BHD.; *Int'l,* pg. 7129
SPECTOR & ASSOCIATES, INC.; *U.S. Private,* pg. 3751
SPECTOR & EHRENWORTH, P.C.—See Scarinci Hollenbeck, LLC; *U.S. Private,* pg. 3561
SPECTRA360, INC.; *U.S. Private,* pg. 3751
SPECTRA7 MICROSYSTEMS INC.; *U.S. Public,* pg. 1915
SPECTRA ALUMINUM PRODUCTS INC.; *Int'l,* pg. 7129
SPECTRA ANALYSIS INSTRUMENTS, INC.—See DANI Instruments SpA; *Int'l,* pg. 1962
SPECTRA COLOR, INC.—See Arsenal Capital Management LP; *U.S. Private,* pg. 337
SPECTRACURE AB; *Int'l,* pg. 7130
SPECTRA ENERGY CANADA EXCHANGECO INC.—See Enbridge Inc.; *Int'l,* pg. 2397
SPECTRA ENERGY PARTNERS, L.P.—See Enbridge Inc.; *Int'l,* pg. 2397
SPECTRAFORCE TECHNOLOGIES INC.; *U.S. Private,* pg. 3751
SPECTRAGRAPHIC NEW ENGLAND—See Spectra Group Ltd.; *U.S. Private,* pg. 3751
SPECTRA GROUP LTD.; *U.S. Private,* pg. 3751
SPECTRA HOLDINGS, INC.—See ACON Investments, LLC; *U.S. Private,* pg. 62
SPECTRA INC.; *Int'l,* pg. 7129
SPECTRA INDUSTRIES LIMITED; *Int'l,* pg. 7130
SPECTRA INNOVATIONS INC.; *U.S. Private,* pg. 3751
SPECTRAL-AECOM—See AECOM; *U.S. Public,* pg. 51
SPECTRAL AI, INC.; *U.S. Public,* pg. 1915
SPECTRAL CAPITAL CORPORATION; *U.S. Public,* pg. 1915
SPECTRALCAST, INC.; *U.S. Public,* pg. 1915
SPECTRAL DYNAMICS, INC.; *U.S. Private,* pg. 3751
SPECTRAL DYNAMICS (UK) LTD.—See Spectral Dynamics, Inc.; *U.S. Private,* pg. 3751
SPECTRA-LEHRMITTEL-VERLAG GMBH—See Verlagsgruppe Georg von Holtzbrinck GmbH; *Int'l,* pg. 8171
SPECTRA ENGINES OY—See Nynomic AG; *Int'l,* pg. 5501
SPECTRAL ENTERPRISES, INC.; *U.S. Private,* pg. 3751
SPECTRA LIGHTING PTY. LTD.—See IWASAKI ELECTRIC Co., Ltd.; *Int'l,* pg. 3849
SPECTRALINK CORPORATION—See HP Inc.; *U.S. Public,* pg. 1065
SPECTRAL MEDICAL INC.; *Int'l,* pg. 7130
SPECTRAL LOGIC CORPORATION; *U.S. Private,* pg. 3751
SPECTRAL SYSTEMS LLC—See Artemis Capital Partners Management Co., LLC; *U.S. Private,* pg. 341
SPECTRALUX CORPORATION—See Avio Global, Inc.; *U.S. Private,* pg. 407
SPECTRALYTICS, INC.—See The Cretex Companies, Inc.; *U.S. Private,* pg. 4016
SPECTRA MARKETING SYSTEMS, INC.—See Brookfield Corporation; *Int'l,* pg. 1180
SPECTRA MARKETING SYSTEMS, INC.—See Elliott Management Corporation; *U.S. Private,* pg. 1373
SPECTRA MEDICAL DEVICES, LLC—See QHP Capital, L.P.; *U.S. Private,* pg. 3313
SPECTRA METAL SALES INC.; *U.S. Private,* pg. 3751
SPECTRAMI DMCC; *Int'l,* pg. 7130
SPECTRAMI GMBH—See SPECTRAMI DMCC; *Int'l,* pg. 7130
THE SPECTRANETICS CORP.—See Koninklijke Philips N.V.; *Int'l,* pg. 4270
SPECTRANETICS DEUTSCHLAND GMBH—See Koninklijke Philips N.V.; *Int'l,* pg. 4270
SPECTRANETICS INTERNATIONAL B.V.—See Koninklijke Philips N.V.; *Int'l,* pg. 4270
SPECTRANETIX, INC.; *U.S. Private,* pg. 3751
SPECTRA-PHYSICS AB—See Thermo Fisher Scientific Inc.; *U.S. Public,* pg. 2152
SPECTRA-PHYSICS, K.K.—See MKS Instruments, Inc.; *U.S. Public,* pg. 1453
SPECTRA PREMIUM INDUSTRIES INC.; *Int'l,* pg. 7130
SPECTRA PREMIUM (USA) CORP.—See Spectra Premium Industries Inc.; *Int'l,* pg. 7130
SPECTRA PRODUCTS INC.—See Spectra Inc.; *Int'l,* pg. 7130
SPECTRA RESEARCH CORPORATION—See HORIBA Ltd.; *Int'l,* pg. 3478
SPECTRA SCAFFOLDING LTD—See Altrad Investment Authority SAS; *Int'l,* pg. 398
SPECTRASEIS INC.—See Spectris Plc; *Int'l,* pg. 7131
SPECTRASENSORS, INC.—See Endress+Hauser (International) Holding AG; *Int'l,* pg. 2407
SPECTRA SENSORTECH, LTD.—See MKS Instruments, Inc.; *U.S. Public,* pg. 1453
SPECTRASERV INC.; *U.S. Private,* pg. 3751
SPECTRASITE COMMUNICATIONS, LLC—See American Tower Corporation; *U.S. Public,* pg. 111
SPECTRA STRIP CABLE PRODUCTS—See Amphenol Corporation; *U.S. Public,* pg. 132
SPECTRA STRIP LTD.—See Amphenol Corporation; *U.S. Public,* pg. 132
SPECTRA SYSTEMS CORPORATION; *U.S. Public,* pg. 1915
SPECTRA TECHNOLOGIES, LLC—See National Presto Industries, Inc.; *U.S. Public,* pg. 1497
SPECTRATEK TECHNOLOGIES INC.; *U.S. Private,* pg. 3751
SPECTRATEX INC.—See Gildan Activewear Inc.; *Int'l,* pg. 2973
SPECTRATURF INC.—See Ecore International Inc.; *U.S. Private,* pg. 1330
SPECTRA VENUE MANAGEMENT—See Atairos Group, Inc.; *U.S. Public,* pg. 364
SPECTRA VENUE MANAGEMENT—See Comcast Corporation; *U.S. Public,* pg. 538
SPECTRE CAPITAL CORP.; *Int'l,* pg. 7130
SPECTRECOLOGY, LLC—See Salvo Technologies, Inc.; *U.S. Private,* pg. 3535
SPECTREM AIR PTY LTD—See Anglo American PLC; *Int'l,* pg. 462
SPECTREX, INC.—See Emerson Electric Co.; *U.S. Public,* pg. 747
SPECTR INVEST LLC; *Int'l,* pg. 7129
SPECTRIO, LLC—See The Jordan Company, L.P.; *U.S. Private,* pg. 4062
SPECTRIS CANADA INC.—See Spectris Plc; *Int'l,* pg. 7131
SPECTRIS COMPANY LIMITED—See Spectris Plc; *Int'l,* pg. 7132
SPECTRIS DO BRASIL INSTRUMENTOS ELETRONICOS LTDA.—See Spectris Plc; *Int'l,* pg. 7132
SPECTRIS PLC; *Int'l,* pg. 7130
SPECTRO ANALYTICAL INSTRUMENTS (ASIA-PACIFIC) LTD.—See AMETEK, Inc.; *U.S. Public,* pg. 118
SPECTRO ANALYTICAL INSTRUMENTS GMBH—See AMETEK, Inc.; *U.S. Public,* pg. 118
SPECTRO ANALYTICAL INSTRUMENTS INC.—See AMETEK, Inc.; *U.S. Public,* pg. 118
SPECTRO ANALYTICAL LABS LTD.—See Eurofins Scientific S.E.; *Int'l,* pg. 2551
SPECTROGON AB; *Int'l,* pg. 7132
SPECTROGON UK, LTD.—See Spectrogon AB; *Int'l,* pg. 7132
SPECTROGON US, INC.—See Spectrogon AB; *Int'l,* pg. 7132
SPECTROLAB INC.—See The Boeing Company; *U.S. Public,* pg. 2041
SPECTRO LUME INC.; *U.S. Private,* pg. 3752
SPECTRONIC DENMARK A/S—See Advent International Corporation; *U.S. Private,* pg. 100
SPECTRONICS CORPORATION; *U.S. Private,* pg. 3752
SPECTRO RESEARCH LAB VENTURES PRIVATE LIMITED—See Eurofins Scientific S.E.; *Int'l,* pg. 2551
SPECTROS AG—See Metall Zug AG; *Int'l,* pg. 4847
SPECTRO SCIENTIFIC INC.—See AMETEK, Inc.; *U.S. Public,* pg. 122
SPECTRO SSA LABS PRIVATE LIMITED—See Eurofins Scientific S.E.; *Int'l,* pg. 2551
SPECTROTEL, INC.—See Grain Management, LLC; *U.S. Private,* pg. 1751
SPECTRUM 8 THEATRES—See Cohen Media Group, LLC; *U.S. Private,* pg. 963

COMPANY NAME INDEX

SPECTRUM ASA—See TGS ASA; *Int'l*, pg. 7587
SPECTRUM ASB PTY LIMITED—See TGS ASA; *Int'l*, pg. 7588
SPECTRUM ASSET MANAGEMENT, INC.—See Principal Financial Group, Inc.; *U.S. Public*, pg. 1722
SPECTRUM AUTOMATION COMPANY—See Huizenga Manufacturing Group, Inc.; *U.S. Private*, pg. 2004
SPECTRUM AUTOMOTIVE HOLDINGS LLC—See Cornell Capital LLC; *U.S. Private*, pg. 1051
SPECTRUM BRANDS AUSTRALIA PTY. LTD.—See Spectrum Brands Holdings, Inc.; *U.S. Public*, pg. 1916
SPECTRUM BRANDS AUSTRIA GMBH—See Spectrum Brands Holdings, Inc.; *U.S. Public*, pg. 1915
SPECTRUM BRANDS BENELUX B.V.—See Spectrum Brands Holdings, Inc.; *U.S. Public*, pg. 1916
SPECTRUM BRANDS BRASIL INDUSTRIA E COMERCIO DE BENS DE CONSUMO LTDA—See Spectrum Brands Holdings, Inc.; *U.S. Public*, pg. 1916
SPECTRUM BRANDS BULGARIA EOOD—See Spectrum Brands Holdings, Inc.; *U.S. Public*, pg. 1916
SPECTRUM BRANDS CANADA, INC.—See Spectrum Brands Holdings, Inc.; *U.S. Public*, pg. 1916
SPECTRUM BRANDS COLOMBIA S.A.—See Spectrum Brands Holdings, Inc.; *U.S. Public*, pg. 1916
SPECTRUM BRANDS DENMARK A/S—See Spectrum Brands Holdings, Inc.; *U.S. Public*, pg. 1916
SPECTRUM BRANDS EUROPE GMBH—See Spectrum Brands Holdings, Inc.; *U.S. Public*, pg. 1916
SPECTRUM BRANDS HHI MEXICO, S DE RL DE C.V.—See Spectrum Brands Holdings, Inc.; *U.S. Public*, pg. 1916
SPECTRUM BRANDS HHI (SHENZHEN) CO., LTD—See Spectrum Brands Holdings, Inc.; *U.S. Public*, pg. 1916
SPECTRUM BRANDS HHI (ZHONGSHAN) CO., LTD—See Spectrum Brands Holdings, Inc.; *U.S. Public*, pg. 1916
SPECTRUM BRANDS HOLDINGS, INC.; *U.S. Public*, pg. 1915
SPECTRUM BRANDS HRVATSKA D.O.O.—See Spectrum Brands Holdings, Inc.; *U.S. Public*, pg. 1916
SPECTRUM BRANDS HRVATSKA D.O.O.—See Spectrum Brands Holdings, Inc.; *U.S. Public*, pg. 1916
SPECTRUM BRANDS, INC. - FENNIMORE PLANT—See Spectrum Brands Holdings, Inc.; *U.S. Public*, pg. 1916
SPECTRUM BRANDS, INC. - HARDWARE & HOME IMPROVEMENT—See Spectrum Brands Holdings, Inc.; *U.S. Public*, pg. 1916
SPECTRUM BRANDS, INC.—See Spectrum Brands Holdings, Inc.; *U.S. Public*, pg. 1916
SPECTRUM BRANDS ITALIA S.R.L.—See Spectrum Brands Holdings, Inc.; *U.S. Public*, pg. 1916
SPECTRUM BRANDS LEGACY, INC.—See Spectrum Brands Holdings, Inc.; *U.S. Public*, pg. 1916
SPECTRUM BRANDS NEW ZEALAND LTD.—See Spectrum Brands Holdings, Inc.; *U.S. Public*, pg. 1916
SPECTRUM BRANDS NORWAY AS—See Spectrum Brands Holdings, Inc.; *U.S. Public*, pg. 1916
SPECTRUM BRANDS NORWAY AS—See Spectrum Brands Holdings, Inc.; *U.S. Public*, pg. 1916
SPECTRUM BRANDS PET LLC—See Spectrum Brands Holdings, Inc.; *U.S. Public*, pg. 1917
SPECTRUM BRANDS POLAND SP. Z.O.O.—See Spectrum Brands Holdings, Inc.; *U.S. Public*, pg. 1916
SPECTRUM BRANDS ROMANIA S.R.L.—See Spectrum Brands Holdings, Inc.; *U.S. Public*, pg. 1916
SPECTRUM BRANDS SINGAPORE PRIVATE LIMITED—See Spectrum Brands Holdings, Inc.; *U.S. Public*, pg. 1916
SPECTRUM BRANDS SPAIN S.L.—See Spectrum Brands Holdings, Inc.; *U.S. Public*, pg. 1916
SPECTRUM BRANDS TRGOVINA, D.O.O.—See Spectrum Brands Holdings, Inc.; *U.S. Public*, pg. 1916
SPECTRUM BRANDS (UK) LIMITED—See Spectrum Brands Holdings, Inc.; *U.S. Public*, pg. 1916
SPECTRUM BUILDING SYSTEMS, INC.—See Black Diamond Group Limited; *Int'l*, pg. 1059
SPECTRUM BUSINESS SOLUTIONS, LLC; *U.S. Private*, pg. 3752
SPECTRUM CAPITAL ENTERPRISES, INC.; *U.S. Private*, pg. 3752
SPECTRUM CATERING—See Silver Lake Group, LLC; *U.S. Private*, pg. 3658
SPECTRUM CHEMICAL MANUFACTURING CORPORATION; *U.S. Private*, pg. 3752
SPECTRUM CHEMICALS & LABORATORY PRODUCTS, INC.—See Spectrum Chemical Manufacturing Corporation; *U.S. Private*, pg. 3752
SPECTRUM CLUBS INC.; *U.S. Private*, pg. 3752
SPECTRUM COMM. INC.; *U.S. Private*, pg. 3752
SPECTRUM COMMUNICATIONS CABLING SERVICES, INC.; *U.S. Private*, pg. 3752
SPECTRUM CONTRACTING, INC.; *U.S. Private*, pg. 3752
SPECTRUM CONTRACTING SERVICES, INC.—See Minstrell Recruitment Limited; *Int'l*, pg. 4913
SPECTRUM CONTROL DE MEXICO, S.A. DE C.V.—See Allient Inc.; *U.S. Public*, pg. 80
SPECTRUM CONTROL GMBH—See Allient Inc.; *U.S. Public*, pg. 80

SPECTRUM CONTROL, INC.—See Allient Inc.; *U.S. Public*, pg. 80
SPECTRUM CONTROL TECHNOLOGY INC.—See Allient Inc.; *U.S. Public*, pg. 80
SPECTRUM DENTAL, LLC—See Koninklijke Philips N.V.; *Int'l*, pg. 4270
SPECTRUM DERMATOLOGY, PLLC—See Pinnacle Dermatology LLC; *U.S. Private*, pg. 3185
SPECTRUM DIRECT INSURANCE SERVICES, INC.; *U.S. Private*, pg. 3752
SPECTRUMDNA, INC.; *U.S. Private*, pg. 3753
SPECTRUM ELECTRICAL INDUSTRIES LIMITED; *Int'l*, pg. 7132
SPECTRUM ENGINEERING SOLUTIONS, INC.—See M+W Group GmbH; *Int'l*, pg. 4614
SPECTRUM EQUITY INVESTORS, L.P.; *U.S. Private*, pg. 3752
SPECTRUM FOOD SERVICE, INC.; *U.S. Private*, pg. 3752
SPECTRUM FOODS LIMITED; *Int'l*, pg. 7132
SPECTRUM GAMING GROUP; *U.S. Private*, pg. 3752
SPECTRUM GEO DO BRASIL SERVICOS GEOFISICOS LTDA—See TGS ASA; *Int'l*, pg. 7588
SPECTRUM GEO INC—See TGS ASA; *Int'l*, pg. 7588
SPECTRUM GEO LTD—See TGS ASA; *Int'l*, pg. 7588
SPECTRUM GEO PTE LTD—See TGS ASA; *Int'l*, pg. 7588
SPECTRUM GLASS COMPANY INC.; *U.S. Private*, pg. 3752
SPECTRUM GROUP INTERNATIONAL, INC.; *U.S. Public*, pg. 1917
SPECTRUM HEALTHCARE SERVICES, INC.—See Blackstone Inc.; *U.S. Public*, pg. 359
SPECTRUM HEALTH CONTINUING CARE GROUP, INC.; *U.S. Private*, pg. 3752
SPECTRUM HEALTH SYSTEMS; *U.S. Private*, pg. 3752
SPECTRUM IMAGING TECHNOLOGIES, INC.; *U.S. Private*, pg. 3752
SPECTRUM INDUSTRIES, INC. - DECORATIVE FINISHES DIVISION—See Spectrum Industries, Inc.; *U.S. Private*, pg. 3753
SPECTRUM INDUSTRIES, INC.; *U.S. Private*, pg. 3752
SPECTRUM INDUSTRIES, INC.; *U.S. Private*, pg. 3753
SPECTRUM INTERIORS TENNESSEE INC.—See Specialty Interiors Inc.; *U.S. Private*, pg. 3750
SPECTRUM INTERNATIONAL CORPORATION; *U.S. Private*, pg. 3753
SPECTRUM LABEL CORPORATION—See Ares Management Corporation; *U.S. Public*, pg. 191
SPECTRUM LABORATORIES (JOHORE) SDN. BERHAD—See Brite-Tech Berhad; *Int'l*, pg. 1165
SPECTRUM LABORATORIES (PENANG) SDN. BERHAD—See Brite-Tech Berhad; *Int'l*, pg. 1165
SPECTRUM LABS, INC.—See Nextmune AB; *Int'l*, pg. 5249
SPECTRUM LABS INDIA PVT. LTD.—See Repligen Corporation; *U.S. Public*, pg. 1785
SPECTRUM MANAGEMENT HOLDING COMPANY, LLC—See Charter Communications, Inc.; *U.S. Public*, pg. 483
SPECTRUM MANUFACTURING, INC.—See Integer Holdings Corporation; *U.S. Public*, pg. 1135
SPECTRUM MARKETING, INC.; *U.S. Private*, pg. 3753
SPECTRUM METALS LIMITED—See Ramelius Resources Limited; *Int'l*, pg. 6198
SPECTRUM MOLDING—See The Plastek Group; *U.S. Private*, pg. 4096
SPECTRUM MTF OPERATOR GMBH—See IG Group Holdings plc; *Int'l*, pg. 3601
SPECTRUM NEWS NY1—See Charter Communications, Inc.; *U.S. Public*, pg. 483
SPECTRUM NUMISMATICS INTERNATIONAL, INC.—See Spectrum Group International, Inc.; *U.S. Public*, pg. 1917
SPECTRUM ONCOLOGY PRIVATE LIMITED—See Assertio Holdings, Inc.; *U.S. Public*, pg. 214
SPECTRUM OPHTHALMOLOGY LTD.—See AddLife AB; *Int'l*, pg. 130
SPECTRUM ORGANIC PRODUCTS, INC.—See The Hain Celestial Group, Inc.; *U.S. Public*, pg. 2087
SPECTRUM PENSION CONSULTANTS, INC.—See Alliance Benefit Group, LLC; *U.S. Private*, pg. 181
SPECTRUM PHARMACEUTICALS, INC.—See Assertio Holdings, Inc.; *U.S. Public*, pg. 214
SPECTRUM PHYSICAL THERAPY, LIMITED PARTNERSHIP—See U.S. Physical Therapy, Inc.; *U.S. Public*, pg. 2216
THE SPECTRUM PLASTICS GROUP - ATHOL—See Odyssey Investment Partners, LLC; *U.S. Private*, pg. 2995
SPECTRUM PLASTICS GROUP, INC.—See DuPont de Nemours, Inc.; *U.S. Public*, pg. 694
THE SPECTRUM PLASTICS GROUP - MEXICALI PLANT—See Odyssey Investment Partners, LLC; *U.S. Private*, pg. 2995
SPECTRUM POWER MANAGEMENT SYSTEMS—See Allient Inc.; *U.S. Public*, pg. 80
SPECTRUM PRIMARY CARE, INC.—See Blackstone Inc.; *U.S. Public*, pg. 359

SPECTRUM PRINTING INC.—See Mount Royal Printing & Communications, Inc.; *U.S. Public*, pg. 2798
SPECTRUM PRODUCTS LLC—See Court Square Capital Partners, L.P.; *U.S. Private*, pg. 1070
SPECTRUM REACH, LLC—See Charter Communications, Inc.; *U.S. Public*, pg. 483
SPECTRUM RISK MANAGEMENT AND REINSURANCE DMCC—See Brown & Brown, Inc.; *U.S. Public*, pg. 402
SPECTRUM SALES INC.; *U.S. Private*, pg. 3753
SPECTRUM SEI MICROWAVE, INC.—See AEA Investors LP; *U.S. Private*, pg. 113
SPECTRUM SERVICES—See Diamond Chemical Co., Inc.; *U.S. Private*, pg. 1223
SPECTRUM SIGNAL PROCESSING, INC.—See Vecima Networks, Inc.; *Int'l*, pg. 8143
SPECTRUM SIGNAL PROCESSING (USA), INC.—See Vecima Networks, Inc.; *Int'l*, pg. 8143
SPECTRUM SOLUTIONS L.L.C.; *U.S. Private*, pg. 3753
THE SPECTRUM—See Gannett Co., Inc.; *U.S. Public*, pg. 900
SPECTRUM SYSTEMS, INC.; *U.S. Private*, pg. 3753
SPECTRUM TECHNOLOGIES, INC.; *U.S. Private*, pg. 3753
SPECTRUM TECHNOLOGIES, INC.; *U.S. Private*, pg. 3753
SPECTRUM TECHNOLOGIES PLC; *Int'l*, pg. 7132
SPECTRUM TECHNOLOGIES USA, INC.—See Spectrum Technologies PLC; *Int'l*, pg. 7132
SPECTRUM TECHNOLOGIES USA, INC.—See Paragon Energy Solutions, LLC; *U.S. Private*, pg. 3091
SPECTRUM TECHNOLOGY, INC.; *U.S. Private*, pg. 3753
SPECTRUM TRACER SERVICES, LLC—See NCS Multistage Holdings, Inc.; *U.S. Public*, pg. 1503
SPECTRUM TRANSPORTATION; *U.S. Private*, pg. 3753
SPECTRUM VERF B.V.—See LKQ Corporation; *U.S. Public*, pg. 1336
SPECTRUM VISION PARTNERS LLC—See Blue Sea Capital Management LLC; *U.S. Private*, pg. 592
SPECTRUM WINE AUCTIONS, LLC—See Spectrum Group International, Inc.; *U.S. Public*, pg. 1917
SPECTRUM WIRELESS SOLUTIONS, INC. - EF&I DIVISION—See Dycom Industries, Inc.; *U.S. Public*, pg. 699
SPECTRUM WIRELESS SOLUTIONS, INC.—See Dycom Industries, Inc.; *U.S. Public*, pg. 699
SPECTUR LIMITED; *Int'l*, pg. 7132
SPECTUS MANUFACTURING LIMITED; *Int'l*, pg. 7132
SPECTUS WINDOW SYSTEMS LIMITED—See Spectus Manufacturing Limited; *Int'l*, pg. 7132
SPECULATIVE PRODUCT DESIGN, LLC; *U.S. Private*, pg. 3753
SPEC WEST, INC.—See The Sterling Group, L.P.; *U.S. Private*, pg. 4122
SPEDITION ANSORGE GMBH & CO.KG; *Int'l*, pg. 7132
SPEDITION SERVICES LTD; *Int'l*, pg. 7132
SPEDITIONS HOLDING AG—See OBB-Holding AG; *Int'l*, pg. 5510
SPEDITIONS-PARTNER GMBH SCHNEIDER & PEKLAR—See Intereuropa d.d.; *Int'l*, pg. 3740
SPEECE LEWIS ENGINEERS, INC.—See Bowman Consulting Group Ltd.; *U.S. Public*, pg. 376
SPEECH DESIGN CARRIER SYSTEMS GMBH—See Bogen Communications International Inc.; *U.S. Public*, pg. 367
SPEECH DESIGN GMBH—See Bogen Communications International Inc.; *U.S. Public*, pg. 367
SPEECH IQ, LLC—See NICE Ltd.; *Int'l*, pg. 5265
SPEECHLY OY—See Roblox Corporation; *U.S. Public*, pg. 1804
SPEECH MODULES LTD.; *Int'l*, pg. 7132
SPEECH TECHNOLOGY MEDIA—See Information Today Inc.; *U.S. Private*, pg. 2073
SPEECO, INC.—See American Securities LLC; *U.S. Private*, pg. 247
SPEECO, INC.—See P2 Capital Partners, LLC; *U.S. Private*, pg. 3062
SPEEDAGE COMMERCIALS LIMITED; *Int'l*, pg. 7132
THE SPEED ART MUSEUM; *U.S. Private*, pg. 4120
SPEEDA SHIPPING COMPANY (S) PTE LTD—See Richfield International Limited; *Int'l*, pg. 6331
SPEEDCAST COMMUNICATIONS, INC.—See SpeedCast International Limited; *Int'l*, pg. 7133
SPEEDCAST INTERNATIONAL LIMITED; *Int'l*, pg. 7132
SPEEDCO INC—See Love's Travel Stops & Country Stores, Inc.; *U.S. Private*, pg. 2501
SPEED COMMERCE, INC. - CANADA—See Speed Commerce, Inc.; *U.S. Public*, pg. 1917
SPEED COMMERCE, INC.; *U.S. Public*, pg. 1917
SPEED COMMUNICATIONS AGENCY LIMITED—See The Mission Group Public Limited Company; *Int'l*, pg. 7667
SPEE-DEE DELIVERY SERVICE INC.; *U.S. Private*, pg. 3753
SPEED-E-GAS (NSW) PTY LIMITED—See Origin Energy Ltd.; *Int'l*, pg. 5630
SPEEDEMISSIONS, INC.; *U.S. Public*, pg. 1917
SPEED FAB-CRETE; *U.S. Private*, pg. 3753
SPEEDFAM CLEAN SYSTEM CO., LTD. - YAMAGATA FACTORY—See Obara Group Incorporated; *Int'l*, pg. 5508

SPEED FAB-CRETE

SPEEDFAM CO., LTD.—See Obara Group Incorporated; *Int'l*, pg. 5508
SPEEDFAM COMPANY LIMITED—See Obara Group Incorporated; *Int'l*, pg. 5508
SPEEDFAM CORPORATION—See Obara Group Incorporated; *Int'l*, pg. 5508
SPEEDFAM INC.—See Obara Group Incorporated; *Int'l*, pg. 5508
SPEEDFAM (INDIA) PVT. LTD.—See Obara Group Incorporated; *Int'l*, pg. 5508
SPEEDFAM KOREA LTD.—See Obara Group Incorporated; *Int'l*, pg. 5508
SPEEDFAM MECHATRONICS (SHANGHAI) LTD.—See Obara Group Incorporated; *Int'l*, pg. 5508
SPEEDFAM NAGANO CO., LTD.—See Obara Group Incorporated; *Int'l*, pg. 5508
SPEEDGRIP CHUCK, INC.—See The Stratford-Cambridge Group Co.; *U.S. Private*, pg. 4123
SPEEDIMPEX USA INC.; *U.S. Private*, pg. 3753
SPEED INTERNATIONAL INC.—See Bank of the Philippine Islands; *Int'l*, pg. 849
SPEED (KOREA) WIRELESS TECHNOLOGY CO., LTD.—See Huizhou Speed Wireless Technology Co., Ltd.; *Int'l*, pg. 3527
SPEED LINE SOUTH AFRICA (PTY) LTD.—See Emak S.p.A.; *Int'l*, pg. 2373
SPEEDLINE TECHNOLOGIES GMBH—See Illinois Tool Works Inc.; *U.S. Public*, pg. 1110
SPEEDLING INCORPORATED-ALAMO TRANSPLANTS DIVISION—See Speedling Incorporated; *U.S. Private*, pg. 3753
SPEEDLING INCORPORATED-BUSHNELL DIVISION—See Speedling Incorporated; *U.S. Private*, pg. 3753
SPEEDLING, INCORPORATED-SAN JUAN BAUTISTA NURSERY—See Speedling Incorporated; *U.S. Private*, pg. 3753
SPEEDLING, INCORPORATED—See Speedling Incorporated; *U.S. Private*, pg. 3753
SPEEDLING INCORPORATED; *U.S. Private*, pg. 3753
SPEEDLING, INCORPORATED—See Speedling Incorporated; *U.S. Private*, pg. 3753
SPEEDLING, INCORPORATED-SUN CITY NURSERY DIVISION—See Speedling Incorporated; *U.S. Private*, pg. 3754
SPEEDLOCK EQUIPMENT SDN. BHD.—See SHS Holdings Ltd.; *Int'l*, pg. 6867
SPEED LUBE LLC; *U.S. Private*, pg. 3753
SPEEDMARK TRANSPORTATION INC.; *U.S. Private*, pg. 3754
SPEEDNET, LLC—See TPT Global Tech, Inc.; *U.S. Public*, pg. 2178
SPEED NORTH AMERICA INC.—See Emak S.p.A.; *Int'l*, pg. 2373
SPEEDO INTERNATIONAL LTD.—See Pentland Group Limited; *Int'l*, pg. 5792
SPEED-O-TACH, INC.; *U.S. Private*, pg. 3753
SPEEDOTRON CORPORATION—See Promark International Inc.; *U.S. Private*, pg. 3282
SPEEDPAY, INC.—See ACI Worldwide, Inc.; *U.S. Public*, pg. 35
SPEED POWER LIMITED—See SMC Electric Limited; *Int'l*, pg. 7006
SPEEDPROP GLOBAL, INC.; *Int'l*, pg. 7133
SPEED RABBIT PIZZA SA; *Int'l*, pg. 7132
SPEEDRACK PRODUCTS GROUP, LTD.; *U.S. Private*, pg. 3754
SPEED SOUTH AMERICA S.P.A.—See Emak S.p.A.; *Int'l*, pg. 2373
SPEED (TAIWAN) WIRELESS TECHNOLOGY CO., LTD.—See Huizhou Speed Wireless Technology Co., Ltd.; *Int'l*, pg. 3527
SPEED TECH CORP.; *Int'l*, pg. 7132
SPEEDTECH INTERNATIONAL, INC.; *U.S. Private*, pg. 3754
SPEED TECHNOLOGY (USA) CO., LTD.—See Huizhou Speed Wireless Technology Co., Ltd.; *Int'l*, pg. 3527
SPEEDUS CORP.; *U.S. Public*, pg. 1917
SPEEDWAY FUNDING, LLC—See Sonic Financial Corporation; *U.S. Private*, pg. 3713
SPEEDWAY LLC—See Seven & i Holdings Co., Ltd.; *Int'l*, pg. 6731
SPEEDWAY MOTORSPORTS, LLC—See Sonic Financial Corporation; *U.S. Private*, pg. 3713
SPEEDWAY PREPAID CARD LLC—See Marathon Petroleum Corporation; *U.S. Public*, pg. 1364
SPEEDWAY SONOMA LLC—See Sonic Financial Corporation; *U.S. Private*, pg. 3713
SPEEDWELL ENGINEERS PVT. LTD.—See Ace Software Exports Ltd.; *Int'l*, pg. 95
SPEED WIN LIMITED—See Chinese Estates Holdings Limited; *Int'l*, pg. 1569
SPEEDY AD; *Int'l*, pg. 7133
SPEEDY ASSET SERVICES LIMITED—See Speedy Hire Plc; *Int'l*, pg. 7133
SPEEDY BILSERVICE HOGSBO AB—See MEKO AB; *Int'l*, pg. 4807
SPEEDY BILSERVICE OSTERMALM AB—See MEKO AB; *Int'l*, pg. 4807

SPEEDY BILSERVICE PA LIMHAMN AB—See MEKO AB; *Int'l*, pg. 4807
SPEEDY ENGINEERING & TRADING COMPANY LIMITED—See Dimmi Life Holdings Limited; *Int'l*, pg. 2126
SPEEDY FRANCE SAS—See Bridgestone Corporation; *Int'l*, pg. 1159
SPEEDY GENERATORS LIMITED—See Speedy Hire Plc; *Int'l*, pg. 7133
SPEEDY GLOBAL HOLDINGS LIMITED; *Int'l*, pg. 7133
SPEEDY HIRE CENTRES (NORTHERN) LIMITED—See Speedy Hire Plc; *Int'l*, pg. 7133
SPEEDY HIRE CENTRES (SOUTHERN) LIMITED—See Speedy Hire Plc; *Int'l*, pg. 7133
SPEEDY HIRE CENTRES (WESTERN) LIMITED—See Speedy Hire Plc; *Int'l*, pg. 7133
SPEEDY HIRE DIRECT LIMITED—See Speedy Hire Plc; *Int'l*, pg. 7133
SPEEDY HIRE (IRELAND) LIMITED—See Speedy Hire Plc; *Int'l*, pg. 7133
SPEEDY HIRE PLC; *Int'l*, pg. 7133
SPEEDY INDUSTRIAL SUPPLIES PTE. LTD.—See BizLink Holding Inc.; *Int'l*, pg. 1053
SPEEDY INTERNATIONAL ASSET SERVICES EQUIPMENT RENTAL LLC—See Speedy Hire Plc; *Int'l*, pg. 7133
SPEEDY INTERNATIONAL ASSET SERVICES LLC—See Speedy Hire Plc; *Int'l*, pg. 7133
SPEEDY LCH GENERATORS LIMITED—See Speedy Hire Plc; *Int'l*, pg. 7133
SPEEDY LGH LIMITED—See Speedy Hire Plc; *Int'l*, pg. 7133
SPEEDY LIFTING LIMITED—See Speedy Hire Plc; *Int'l*, pg. 7133
SPEEDY POWER LIMITED—See Speedy Hire Plc; *Int'l*, pg. 7133
SPEEDY PUMPS LIMITED—See Speedy Hire Plc; *Int'l*, pg. 7133
SPEEDY Q MARKETS; *U.S. Private*, pg. 3754
SPEEDY STOP FOOD STORES, LLC—See C.L. Thomas, Inc.; *U.S. Private*, pg. 708
SPEEDY SUPPORT SERVICES LIMITED—See Speedy Hire Plc; *Int'l*, pg. 7133
SPEEDY TRANSPORT LIMITED—See Speedy Hire Plc; *Int'l*, pg. 7133
SPEEE, INC.; *Int'l*, pg. 7133
SPEETEC IMPLANTATE GMBH—See Enovis Corporation; *U.S. Public*, pg. 773
SPE HB BROKERS - GESTAO IMOBILIARIA LTDA.—See Helbor Empreendimentos S.A.; *Int'l*, pg. 3328
SPEICHIM PROCESSING S.A.—See Groupe Seche SAS; *Int'l*, pg. 3110
SPEIRA GMBH—See Norsk Hydro ASA; *Int'l*, pg. 5437
SPEIRS FOODS LIMITED—See Speirs Group Limited; *Int'l*, pg. 7134
SPEIRS GROUP LIMITED; *Int'l*, pg. 7134
SPEIRS & JEFFREY LIMITED—See Rathbones Group Plc; *Int'l*, pg. 6214
SPEKTA A.D.; *Int'l*, pg. 7134
SPEKTAR INVEST AD; *Int'l*, pg. 7134
SPEKTRA AGRI SRL—See Trimble, Inc.; *U.S. Public*, pg. 2191
SPEKTRA AGRI SRL—See Trimble, Inc.; *U.S. Public*, pg. 2191
SPEKTRA S.P.A.—See Trimble, Inc.; *U.S. Public*, pg. 2191
SPELLBINDERS PAPER ARTS LLC; *U.S. Private*, pg. 3754
SPELL CAPITAL PARTNERS, LLC; *U.S. Private*, pg. 3754
SPELLMAN BRADY & COMPANY; *U.S. Private*, pg. 3754
SPELLMAN HARDWOODS INC.; *U.S. Private*, pg. 3754
SPELLMAN HIGH VOLTAGE ELECTRONICS CORPORATION; *U.S. Private*, pg. 3754
SPELLMAN HIGH VOLTAGE ELECTRONICS CORP. - VALHALLA—See Spellman High Voltage Electronics Corporation; *U.S. Private*, pg. 3754
SPELNA, INC.; *U.S. Private*, pg. 3754
SPEL SEMICONDUCTOR LTD—See Natronix Semiconductor Technology Ltd.; *Int'l*, pg. 5165
SPELTA - PRODUTOS PETROLIFEROS S.A.—See Rubis SCA; *Int'l*, pg. 6423
SPELZON CORP.; *U.S. Private*, pg. 3754
SPEM AERO S.A.S.—See JPP Holding Co., Ltd.; *Int'l*, pg. 4007
SPEM COMMUNICATION GROUP—See Omnicom Group Inc.; *U.S. Public*, pg. 1592
SPEM PORTER NOVELLI-CROATIA—See Omnicom Group Inc.; *U.S. Public*, pg. 1592
SPENARD BUILDERS SUPPLY LLC—See Builders FirstSource, Inc.; *U.S. Public*, pg. 410
SPENCE/BANKS INC.; *U.S. Private*, pg. 3754
SPENCE & CO., LTD.—See Alliance Select Foods International, Inc.; *Int'l*, pg. 341
SPENCE ENGINEERING CO., INC.—See Emerson Electric Co.; *U.S. Public*, pg. 752
SPENCE, MARSTON, BUNCH, MORRIS & CO.; *U.S. Private*, pg. 3754
SPENCER CAPITAL HOLDINGS, LTD.; *U.S. Private*, pg. 3754

CORPORATE AFFILIATIONS

SPENCER COMPANIES INC.; *U.S. Private*, pg. 3754
SPENCER DISTRIBUTING LP; *U.S. Private*, pg. 3755
SPENCER FABRICATIONS, INC.; *U.S. Private*, pg. 3755
SPENCER FANE LLP; *U.S. Private*, pg. 3755
SPENCER FLUID POWER—See Applied Industrial Technologies, Inc.; *U.S. Public*, pg. 171
SPENCER GIFTS LLC—See ACON Investments, LLC; *U.S. Private*, pg. 62
SPENCER-HARRIS MACHINE & TOOL CO.—See FEMCO Holdings, LLC; *U.S. Private*, pg. 1494
SPENCER INDUSTRIES INC.; *U.S. Private*, pg. 3755
SPENCER MAC CORPORATION; *U.S. Private*, pg. 3755
SPENCER OIL COMPANY; *U.S. Private*, pg. 3755
SPENCER PRODUCTS CO. INC.—See Tuttle Group Inc.; *U.S. Private*, pg. 4263
SPENCER QUARRIES, INC.; *U.S. Private*, pg. 3755
SPENCER REED GROUP, LLC; *U.S. Private*, pg. 3755
SPENCER'S AIR CONDITIONING & APPLIANCE; *U.S. Private*, pg. 3755
SPENCER SAVINGS BANK, SLA; *U.S. Private*, pg. 3755
SPENCER SAVINGS BANK—See SSB Community Bancorp MHC; *U.S. Private*, pg. 3768
SPENCERS ESTATE AGENTS LIMITED—See The Skipton Building Society; *Int'l*, pg. 7687
SPENCER'S RETAIL LIMITED—See CESC Limited; *Int'l*, pg. 1424
SPENCER TECHNOLOGIES INC.; *U.S. Private*, pg. 3755
SPENCER TRASK & CO.; *U.S. Private*, pg. 3755
SPENCER TRASK VENTURES, INC.—See Spencer Trask & Co.; *U.S. Private*, pg. 3755
THE SPENCER TURBINE CO.—See Alliance Holdings, Inc.; *U.S. Private*, pg. 183
SPENCO ENGINEERING COMPANY LTD—See AGCO Corporation; *U.S. Public*, pg. 59
SPENCO MEDICAL CORPORATION; *U.S. Private*, pg. 3755
SPENDA LIMITED; *Int'l*, pg. 7134
SPENDIFFERENCE LLC—See Compass Group PLC; *Int'l*, pg. 1752
SPEND MANAGEMENT EXPERTS, LLC—See Gryphon Investors, LLC; *U.S. Private*, pg. 1800
SPEND MATTERS—See Azul Partners, Inc.; *U.S. Private*, pg. 416
SPENDMEND LLC—See Morgan Stanley; *U.S. Public*, pg. 1474
SPENDSMART NETWORKS, INC.; *U.S. Private*, pg. 3755
SPE NETWORKS - ASIA PTE. LTD.—See Sony Group Corporation; *Int'l*, pg. 7105
SPENGLER GMBH & CO. KG—See Ali Holding S.r.l; *Int'l*, pg. 323
SPENNCON AS—See Bain Capital, LP; *U.S. Private*, pg. 438
SPENSALL ENGINEERING LIMITED—See Pentair plc; *Int'l*, pg. 5791
SPENTA INTERNATIONAL LTD.; *Int'l*, pg. 7134
SPENTEX INDUSTRIES LIMITED - BARAMATI UNIT—See CLC Industries Limited; *Int'l*, pg. 1653
SPENTEX INDUSTRIES LIMITED - SOLAPUR UNIT—See CLC Industries Limited; *Int'l*, pg. 1653
SPENTEX TASHKENT TOYTEPA LLC—See CLC Industries Limited; *Int'l*, pg. 1653
SPENUZZA BROTHERS INC.; *U.S. Private*, pg. 3755
SPEOS BELGIUM SA/NV—See bpost NV/SA; *Int'l*, pg. 1133
SPEQTA AB; *Int'l*, pg. 7134
SPERBER LANDSCAPE COS. LLC; *U.S. Private*, pg. 3755
SPERIAN PROTECTION APPAREL LTD.—See Honeywell International Inc.; *U.S. Public*, pg. 1049
SPERIAN PROTECTION ARMOR SAS—See Honeywell International Inc.; *U.S. Public*, pg. 1049
SPERIAN PROTECTION CLOTHING S.A.—See Honeywell International Inc.; *U.S. Public*, pg. 1049
SPERIAN PROTECTION WORKWEAR SRL—See Honeywell International Inc.; *U.S. Public*, pg. 1049
SPERIDIAN TECHNOLOGIES, LLC; *U.S. Private*, pg. 3756
SPERIDIAN TECHNOLOGIES LLC—See Speridian Technologies, LLC; *U.S. Private*, pg. 3756
SPERIDIAN TECHNOLOGIES PVT LTD—See Speridian Technologies, LLC; *U.S. Private*, pg. 3756
SPERIDIAN TECHNOLOGIES PVT LTD—See Speridian Technologies, LLC; *U.S. Private*, pg. 3756
SPERLARI, S.R.L.—See Cloetta AB; *Int'l*, pg. 1661
SPERLING & KUPFER EDITORI S.P.A.—See Fininvest S.p.A.; *Int'l*, pg. 2675
SPERO THERAPEUTICS, INC.; *U.S. Public*, pg. 1917
SPERRHOLZ KOCH GMBH—See Enno Roggemann GmbH & Co. KG; *Int'l*, pg. 2443
SPERRY MARINE CANADA LIMITED—See Northrop Grumman Corporation; *U.S. Public*, pg. 1540
SPERRY MARINE INC—See Northrop Grumman Corporation; *U.S. Public*, pg. 1540
SPERRY RAIL, INC.—See Rockwood Holdings Limited Partnership; *U.S. Private*, pg. 3468
SPERRY & RICE LLC; *U.S. Private*, pg. 3756
SPERRY TOP-SIDER, INC.—See Wolverine World Wide, Inc.; *U.S. Public*, pg. 2377
SPERRY UNION STORE, INC.; *U.S. Private*, pg. 3756

COMPANY NAME INDEX

SPERRY VAN NESS INTERNATIONAL CORP.; *U.S. Private,* pg. 3756
SPE SANTA LUCIA TRANSMISSORA DE ENERGIA S.A.—See Terna S.p.A. - Rete Elettrica Nazionale; *Int'l,* pg. 7566
SPE SANTA MARIA TRANSMISSORA DE ENERGIA S.A.—See Terna S.p.A. - Rete Elettrica Nazionale; *Int'l,* pg. 7566
SPESA SPEZIALBAU UND SANIERUNG GMBH.—See BAUER Aktiengesellschaft; *Int'l,* pg. 894
SPESCHA HAUSTECHNIK AG—See Poenina Holding AG; *Int'l,* pg. 5903
SPESCOM MOBILE SOLUTIONS (PROPRIETARY) LIMITED—See Jasco Electronics Holdings Limited; *Int'l,* pg. 3911
SPE S.P.A—See Monrif S.p.A.; *Int'l,* pg. 5035
SPETNER ASSOCIATES, INC.; *U.S. Private,* pg. 3756
SPETSGAZAVTOTRANS—See PJSC Gazprom; *Int'l,* pg. 5880
SPEX CLOTHING COMPANY INC.; *U.S. Private,* pg. 3756
SPEXIMO AB—See International Flavors & Fragrances Inc.; *U.S. Public,* pg. 1154
SPEXIS LTD; *Int'l,* pg. 7134
SPEX SERVICES LTD.; *Int'l,* pg. 7134
SPEYMILL DEUTSCHLAND IMMOBILIEN COMPANY PLC; *Int'l,* pg. 7134
SPEY RESOURCES CORP.; *Int'l,* pg. 7134
SPEYSIDE COOPERAGE—See Tonnellerie Francois Freres; *Int'l,* pg. 7810
SPEYSIDE EQUITY LLC; *U.S. Private,* pg. 3756
SPEZIALGUSS WETZLAR GMBH—See DIHAG Holding GmbH; *Int'l,* pg. 2125
SPEZIAL-PFLEGEHEIM HENNIGSDORF GMBH—See MK-Kliniken AG; *Int'l,* pg. 5002
SPEZIALTECHNIK DRESDEN GMBH—See General Atomics; *U.S. Private,* pg. 1663
SPF (BEIJING) BIOTECHNOLOGY CO., LTD.—See Kontafarma China Holdings Limited; *Int'l,* pg. 4276
SPF-DANMARK A/S—See Danish Crown AmbA; *Int'l,* pg. 1965
SPF NORTH AMERICA, INC.; *U.S. Private,* pg. 3756
S&P FOOD SOLUTION COMPANY LIMITED—See S&P Syndicate Public Company Limited; *Int'l,* pg. 6445
SPFS INC.; *U.S. Private,* pg. 3756
SPF WATER ENGINEERING, LLC—See Lindsay Corporation; *U.S. Public,* pg. 1320
SPG ANDERSON MALL, LLC—See Washington Prime Group Inc.; *U.S. Private,* pg. 4449
SPG CO., LTD.; *Int'l,* pg. 7134
SPG (GUIANA)—See Toyota Tsusho Corporation; *Int'l,* pg. 7876
SP&G INSURANCE BROKERS SDN BHD—See Arthur J. Gallagher & Co.; *U.S. Public,* pg. 207
SPGL ACQUISITION CORPORATION; *U.S. Private,* pg. 3756
S&P GLOBAL COMMODITIES UK LIMITED—See S&P Global Inc.; *U.S. Public,* pg. 1831
S&P GLOBAL COMPANY LIMITED—See S&P Syndicate Public Company Limited; *Int'l,* pg. 6445
SP GLOBAL FINANCIAL IBERIA, S.L.U.—See S&P Global Inc.; *U.S. Public,* pg. 1831
S&P GLOBAL GERMANY GMBH—See S&P Global Inc.; *U.S. Public,* pg. 1831
S&P GLOBAL INC.; *U.S. Public,* pg. 1830
SP GLOBAL INTERNATIONAL PTE. LTD.—See Tuan Sing Holdings Limited; *Int'l,* pg. 7962
S&P GLOBAL ITALY S.R.L.—See S&P Global Inc.; *U.S. Public,* pg. 1831
S&P GLOBAL MARKET INTELLIGENCE INC.—See S&P Global Inc.; *U.S. Public,* pg. 1831
S&P GLOBAL MARKET INTELLIGENCE INFORMATION MANAGEMENT CONSULTING (BEIJING) CO., LTD.—See S&P Global Inc.; *U.S. Public,* pg. 1831
S&P GLOBAL PLATTS—See S&P Global Inc.; *U.S. Public,* pg. 1831
S&P GLOBAL RATINGS FRANCE SAS—See S&P Global Inc.; *U.S. Public,* pg. 1831
S&P GLOBAL RATINGS SINGAPORE PTE. LTD.—See S&P Global Inc.; *U.S. Public,* pg. 1831
S&P GLOBAL SWEDEN AB—See S&P Global Inc.; *U.S. Public,* pg. 1831
SPG NETHERLANDS B.V.—See Illinois Tool Works Inc.; *U.S. Public,* pg. 1110
SPG PACKAGING SYSTEMS GMBH—See Crown Holdings, Inc.; *U.S. Public,* pg. 599
SPG PACKAGING UK LTD—See Illinois Tool Works Inc.; *U.S. Public,* pg. 1110
SPGPRINTS AMERICA, INC.—See Investcorp Holdings B.S.C.; *Int'l,* pg. 3776
SPGPRINTS AUSTRIA GMBH—See Investcorp Holdings B.S.C.; *Int'l,* pg. 3776
SPGPRINTS BRASIL LTDA.—See Investcorp Holdings B.S.C.; *Int'l,* pg. 3776
SPGPRINTS B.V.—See Investcorp Holdings B.S.C.; *Int'l,* pg. 3776
SPGPRINTS JAPAN K.K.—See Investcorp Holdings B.S.C.; *Int'l,* pg. 3776
SPGPRINTS PAKISTAN (PVT) LTD.—See Investcorp Holdings B.S.C.; *Int'l,* pg. 3776

SP GROUP A/S; *Int'l,* pg. 7122
SP GROUP LIMITED—See SelmerBridge Print Vehicles Limited; *Int'l,* pg. 6701
SPG SOLAR INC.; *U.S. Private,* pg. 3756
SPG - SOL PLIN GORENJSKA D.O.O.—See SOL S.p.A.; *Int'l,* pg. 7067
SPG USA, INC.—See SPG Co., Ltd.; *Int'l,* pg. 7134
SPH ALPHAONE PTE LTD—See Singapore Press Holdings Ltd.; *Int'l,* pg. 6942
SPH ASIAONE LTD—See Singapore Press Holdings Ltd.; *Int'l,* pg. 6942
SPHEOS GMBH & CO. KG—See msg group GmbH; *Int'l,* pg. 5067
SPHERA FRANCHISE GROUP SA; *Int'l,* pg. 7134
SPHERE 3D CORPORATION; *Int'l,* pg. 7134
SPHERE 3D INC.—See Sphere 3D Corporation; *Int'l,* pg. 7134
SPHEREA TEST & SERVICES LTD.—See Andera Partners SCA; *Int'l,* pg. 450
SPHEREA TEST & SERVICES LTD.—See Coller Capital Ltd.; *Int'l,* pg. 1699
SPHEREA TEST & SERVICES S.A.S.—See Andera Partners SCA; *Int'l,* pg. 450
SPHEREA TEST & SERVICES S.A.S.—See Coller Capital Ltd.; *Int'l,* pg. 1699
SPHERE BELGIUM S.A.—See Sphere SA; *Int'l,* pg. 7134
SPHERE CONSUMER PRODUCTS PLC—See Sphere SA; *Int'l,* pg. 7134
SPHERE DRILLING SUPPLIES LTD.—See Vertex Resource Group Ltd.; *Int'l,* pg. 8174
SPHERE ENTERTAINMENT CO.; *U.S. Public,* pg. 1918
SPHERE EXHIBITS MALAYSIA SDN. BHD.—See Singapore Press Holdings Ltd.; *Int'l,* pg. 6943
SPHERE EXHIBITS PTE LTD—See Singapore Press Holdings Ltd.; *Int'l,* pg. 6942
SPHERE EXHIBITS PTE LTD—See Temasek Holdings (Private) Limited; *Int'l,* pg. 7547
SPHERE GERMANY GMBH—See Sphere SA; *Int'l,* pg. 7134
SPHERE GLOBAL SERVICES LIMITED; *Int'l,* pg. 7134
SPHERE GROUP SPAIN S.L.—See Sphere SA; *Int'l,* pg. 7134
SPHERE LEGAL PTY LIMITED—See Pioneer Credit Limited; *Int'l,* pg. 5871
SPHERE NEDERLAND B.V.—See Sphere SA; *Int'l,* pg. 7135
SPHERE POWER INC.; *Int'l,* pg. 7134
SPHERE PROFESSIONAL UK LTD—See Sphere SA; *Int'l,* pg. 7135
SPHERE SA; *Int'l,* pg. 7134
SPHERIA EMERGING COMPANIES LIMITED; *Int'l,* pg. 7135
SPHERICAL OPTICS (PTY) LTD.—See EssilorLuxottica SA; *Int'l,* pg. 2516
SPHERION OBJEKT GMBH & CO. KG—See Allianz SE; *Int'l,* pg. 356
SPHERION OF LIMA INC.; *U.S. Private,* pg. 3756
SPHINX INVESTMENT CORP.; *Int'l,* pg. 7135
SPHINX RESOURCES LTD.; *Int'l,* pg. 7135
SPH KUNDALILA (PTY) LIMITED—See Raubex Group Limited; *Int'l,* pg. 6221
SPH MAGAZINES PTE LTD.—See Singapore Press Holdings Ltd.; *Int'l,* pg. 6942
SPH MEDIABOXOFFICE PTE LTD.—See Singapore Press Holdings Ltd.; *Int'l,* pg. 6943
SPH MULTIMEDIA PRIVATE LIMITED—See Singapore Press Holdings Ltd.; *Int'l,* pg. 6943
SPH RADIO PRIVATE LIMITED—See Singapore Press Holdings Ltd.; *Int'l,* pg. 6943
SPH REIT MANAGEMENT PTE. LTD.—See Singapore Press Holdings Ltd.; *Int'l,* pg. 6943
SPH UNIONWORKS PTE LTD—See Singapore Press Holdings Ltd.; *Int'l,* pg. 6943
SPICA SRL—See Groupe Bruxelles Lambert SA; *Int'l,* pg. 3100
SPIC DONGFANG NEW ENERGY CORP.; *Int'l,* pg. 7135
SPICE CHAIN CORPORATION—See iSpice LLC; *U.S. Private,* pg. 2146
SPICE CSL INTERNATIONAL SDN. BHD.—See Digilife Technologies Limited; *Int'l,* pg. 2120
SPICE FINANCE LTD.—See United Investments Ltd.; *Int'l,* pg. 8070
THE SPICE HUNTER—See Falfurrias Capital Partners, LP; *U.S. Private,* pg. 1467
SPICE INC.—See Miroku Jyoho Service Co., Ltd.; *Int'l,* pg. 4920
SPICE ISLANDS APPARELS LIMITED; *Int'l,* pg. 7135
SPICEJET LTD.; *Int'l,* pg. 7135
SPICEJET TECHNIC PRIVATE LIMITED—See SpiceJet Ltd.; *Int'l,* pg. 7135
SPICEOLOGY, INC.; *U.S. Private,* pg. 3756
SPICE PRIVATE EQUITY LTD.—See GP Investments, Ltd.; *Int'l,* pg. 3045
SPICER GELENKWELLENBAU GMBH & CO. KG—See GKN plc; *Int'l,* pg. 2986
SPICER OFF-HIGHWAY BELGIUM N.V.—See Dana Incorporated; *U.S. Public,* pg. 623
SPICERS ADMINISTRACION Y SERVICIOS, S.L.—See ADVEO Group International, S.A.; *Int'l,* pg. 167

SPICERS BELGIUM NV—See ADVEO Group International, S.A.; *Int'l,* pg. 167
SPICERS CANADA ULC—See Central National Gottesman Inc.; *U.S. Private,* pg. 823
SPICERS DEUTSCHLAND GMBH—See ADVEO Group International, S.A.; *Int'l,* pg. 167
SPICERS FRANCE SAS—See ADVEO Group International, S.A.; *Int'l,* pg. 167
SPICERS (IRELAND) LIMITED—See Heritage Group Ltd.; *Int'l,* pg. 3362
SPICERS LIMITED—See KPP Group Holdings Co., Ltd.; *Int'l,* pg. 4297
SPICERS LTD.—See Heritage Group Ltd.; *Int'l,* pg. 3361
SPICERS PAPER (HONG KONG) LTD—See KPP Group Holdings Co., Ltd.; *Int'l,* pg. 4298
SPICERS PAPER LTD.—See KPP Group Holdings Co., Ltd.; *Int'l,* pg. 4298
SPICERS PAPER (MALAYSIA) SDN BHD—See Japan Pulp and Paper Company Limited; *Int'l,* pg. 3904
SPICERS PAPER (SINGAPORE) PTE LTD—See Japan Pulp and Paper Company Limited; *Int'l,* pg. 3904
SPICES INTERNATIONAL PTE LTD.—See QAF Limited; *Int'l,* pg. 6132
SPICES & SEASONINGS SPECIALITIES SDN. BHD.—See OCB Berhad; *Int'l,* pg. 5515
SPICEWOOD SURGERY CENTER LLC—See Tenet Healthcare Corporation; *U.S. Public,* pg. 2007
SPICEWORKS, INC.—See Ziff Davis, Inc.; *U.S. Public,* pg. 2404
SPI CHINA—See SPI Energy Co., Ltd.; *Int'l,* pg. 7135
SPI CRM INC.—See PLDT Inc.; *Int'l,* pg. 5896
THE SPIC & SPAN COMPANY—See Prestige Consumer Healthcare Inc.; *U.S. Public,* pg. 1716
SPICY CO., LTD.—See Nippon Parking Development Co., Ltd.; *Int'l,* pg. 5328
SPICY ENTERTAINMENT & MEDIA LIMITED; *Int'l,* pg. 7135
SPIC YUANDA ENVIRONMENTAL-PROTECTION CO., LTD.—See State Power Investment Corporation; *Int'l,* pg. 7184
SPIDAWEB LLC—See Bentley Systems, Inc.; *U.S. Public,* pg. 297
SPIDELL PUBLISHING, INC.—See Leeds Equity Partners, LLC; *U.S. Private,* pg. 2414
SPIDER ACCESS CLADDING WORKS & BUILDING CLEANING LLC—See EdiliziAcrobatica S.p.A.; *Int'l,* pg. 2310
SPIDERCLOUD WIRELESS, INC.—See Corning Incorporated; *U.S. Public,* pg. 579
SPIDER ITALIA S.R.L.—See Spider N. Petsios & Sons S.A.; *Int'l,* pg. 7135
SPIDER N. PETSIOS & SONS S.A. - KARDAMITSIA FACTORY—See Spider N. Petsios & Sons S.A.; *Int'l,* pg. 7135
SPIDER N. PETSIOS & SONS S.A.; *Int'l,* pg. 7135
SPIDERPLUS & CO.; *Int'l,* pg. 7135
SPIDER UK LTD.—See Spider N. Petsios & Sons S.A.; *Int'l,* pg. 7135
SPIDERWORT INC.—See Zim Corporation; *Int'l,* pg. 8683
SPIE BELGIUM SA-ICS DIVISION—See Clayton, Dubilier & Rice, LLC; *U.S. Private,* pg. 926
SPIE BUILDING SOLUTIONS SP. Z O.O—See SPIE Nucleaire SAS; *Int'l,* pg. 7135
SPIECAPAG S.A.—See VINCI S.A.; *Int'l,* pg. 8217
SPIECAPAG UK LTD—See VINCI S.A.; *Int'l,* pg. 8217
SPIE CITYNETWORKS SAS—See SPIE Nucleaire SAS; *Int'l,* pg. 7135
SPIE COMMUNICATIONS SA—See Clayton, Dubilier & Rice, LLC; *U.S. Private,* pg. 926
SPIE COMMUNICATIONS—See Clayton, Dubilier & Rice, LLC; *U.S. Private,* pg. 926
SPIE DEUTSCHLAND & ZENTRALEUROPA GMBH—See SPIE Nucleaire SAS; *Int'l,* pg. 7135
SPIE ENERGY SOLUTIONS GMBH—See Clayton, Dubilier & Rice, LLC; *U.S. Private,* pg. 926
SPIE FLEISCHHAUER GMBH—See Caisse de Depot et Placement du Quebec; *Int'l,* pg. 1255
SPIEGEL BRANDS, INC.—See Patriarch Partners, LLC; *U.S. Private,* pg. 3109
SPIEGELNET GMBH—See SPIEGEL-Verlag Rudolf Augstein GmbH & Co.; *Int'l,* pg. 7136
SPIEGEL ONLINE GMBH—See SPIEGEL-Verlag Rudolf Augstein GmbH & Co.; *Int'l,* pg. 7136
SPIEGEL TV GMBH—See SPIEGEL-Verlag Rudolf Augstein GmbH & Co.; *Int'l,* pg. 7135
SPIEGEL-VERLAG RUDOLF AUGSTEIN GMBH & CO.; *Int'l,* pg. 7135
SPIE ICS AG—See Clayton, Dubilier & Rice, LLC; *U.S. Private,* pg. 926
SPIELBANK BERLIN GUSTAV JAENECKE GMBH & CO. KG—See Trust International Insurance Company E.C.; *Int'l,* pg. 7944
SPIELE MAX GMBH—See Penta Investments Limited; *Int'l,* pg. 5788
SPIELKARTENFABRIK ALTENBURG GMBH—See Cartamundi N.V.; *Int'l,* pg. 1348
SPIE NEDERLAND B.V.—See SPIE Nucleaire SAS; *Int'l,* pg. 7135

SPIEGEL-VERLAG RUDOLF AUGSTEIN GMBH & CO. CORPORATE AFFILIATIONS

SPI ENERGIE S.A.S.—See KSB SE & Co. KGaA; *Int'l*, pg. 4313
SPI ENERGY CO., LTD.; *Int'l*, pg. 7135
SPIE NUCLEAIRE SAS; *Int'l*, pg. 7135
SPIE SA—See Clayton, Dubilier & Rice, LLC; *U.S. Private*, pg. 926
SPIES CORPORATION; *U.S. Private*, pg. 3756
SPIESS EUROPE SAS—See Orior AG; *Int'l*, pg. 5633
SPIE SWITZERLAND AG—See SPIE Nucleaire SAS; *Int'l*, pg. 7135
SPIE UK LIMITED—See SPIE Nucleaire SAS; *Int'l*, pg. 7135
SPIE WHS LIMITED—See Clayton, Dubilier & Rice, LLC; *U.S. Private*, pg. 926
SPIFFBET AB; *Int'l*, pg. 7136
SPIGAS S.R.L.—See EnBW Energie Baden-Wurttemberg AG; *Int'l*, pg. 2400
SPIG COOLING TOWERS INDIA PRIVATE LIMITED—See Babcock & Wilcox Enterprises, Inc.; *U.S. Public*, pg. 263
SPIGEL PROPERTIES INC.; *U.S. Private*, pg. 3756
SPIGEN KOREA CO., LTD.; *Int'l*, pg. 7136
SPIG KOREA LTD.—See Babcock & Wilcox Enterprises, Inc.; *U.S. Public*, pg. 263
SPIG KUHLTURMTECHNOLOGIEN GMBH—See Babcock & Wilcox Enterprises, Inc.; *U.S. Public*, pg. 263
SPI GLOBAL SOLUTIONS CORPORATION—See Partners Group Holding AG; *Int'l*, pg. 5750
SPI GLOBAL (XI'AN) INFORMATION TECHNOLOGY LTD.—See Partners Group Holding AG; *Int'l*, pg. 5750
SPI GROUP LLC—See Ruder Finn Group, Inc.; *U.S. Private*, pg. 3501
SPIG SOGUTMA SISTEMLERI TLC LDT—See Babcock & Wilcox Enterprises, Inc.; *U.S. Public*, pg. 263
SPIG S.P.A.—See Babcock & Wilcox Enterprises, Inc.; *U.S. Public*, pg. 263
SPIG TORRES DE RESFRIAMENTO LTDA.—See Babcock & Wilcox Enterprises, Inc.; *U.S. Public*, pg. 263
SPI INSTRUMENT LTD.—See Einhell Germany AG; *Int'l*, pg. 2334
SPIIRE AUSTRALIA PTY LTD; *Int'l*, pg. 7136
SPII S.P.A.—See The Carlyle Group Inc.; *U.S. Public*, pg. 2053
SPIKE ADVERTISING INC.; *U.S. Private*, pg. 3757
SPIKE/DDB—See Omnicom Group Inc.; *U.S. Public*, pg. 1582
SPIKER COMMUNICATIONS, INC.; *U.S. Private*, pg. 3757
SPIKE REPLY GMBH—See Reply S.p.A.; *Int'l*, pg. 6291
SPIKE REPLY LTD.—See Reply S.p.A.; *Int'l*, pg. 6291
SPIKES BASEBALL LP—See Greenberg Sports Group Inc.; *U.S. Private*, pg. 1775
SPIKES CAVELL ANALYTIC INC.—See DXC Technology Company; *U.S. Public*, pg. 697
SPIKE'S HOLDING, LLC—See Pentland Group Limited; *Int'l*, pg. 5792
SPIKES, INC.—See Aurionpro Solutions Limited; *Int'l*, pg. 711
SPIKE TECHNOLOGIES LLC—See QUALCOMM Incorporated; *U.S. Public*, pg. 1748
SPI LASERS KOREA LTD.—See TRUMPF SE + Co. KG; *Int'l*, pg. 7942
SPI LASERS LLC—See TRUMPF SE + Co. KG; *Int'l*, pg. 7942
SPI LASERS PLC—See TRUMPF SE + Co. KG; *Int'l*, pg. 7942
SPI LIGHTING INC.; *U.S. Private*, pg. 3756
SPILKER FRANCE S.A.R.L.—See Spilker GmbH; *Int'l*, pg. 7136
SPILKER GMBH; *Int'l*, pg. 7136
SPILKER ITALIA S.R.L.—See Spilker GmbH; *Int'l*, pg. 7136
SPILKER POLSKA SP. Z O.O.—See Spilker GmbH; *Int'l*, pg. 7136
SPILKER UK LTD.—See Spilker GmbH; *Int'l*, pg. 7136
SPILLER FURNITURE COMPANY; *U.S. Private*, pg. 3757
SPILLMANN/FELSER/LEO BURNETT—See Publicis Groupe S.A.; *Int'l*, pg. 6102
SPILLMAN TECHNOLOGIES, INC.—See Motorola Solutions, Inc.; *U.S. Public*, pg. 1479
SPILLTECH ENVIRONMENTAL INC—See New Pendulum Corporation; *U.S. Private*, pg. 2905
SP IMAGES LLC; *U.S. Private*, pg. 3743
SPINA CO., LTD.—See Nishi-Nippon Railroad Co., Ltd.; *Int'l*, pg. 5364
SPINAL DIAGNOSTICS AND TREATMENT CENTERS, L.L.C.—See Tenet Healthcare Corporation; *U.S. Public*, pg. 2013
SPINAL ELEMENTS HOLDINGS, INC.; *U.S. Private*, pg. 3757
SPINAL ELEMENTS, INC.—See Kohlberg & Company, LLC; *U.S. Private*, pg. 2337
SPINALGRAFT TECHNOLOGIES, LLC—See Medtronic plc; *Int'l*, pg. 4790
SPINAL KINETICS, LLC—See Orthofix Medical Inc.; *U.S. Public*, pg. 1619
SPINCONTROL AMERIQUE DU NORD, INC.—See Eurofins Scientific S.E.; *Int'l*, pg. 2551
SPINCONTROL S.A.S.—See Eurofins Scientific S.E.; *Int'l*, pg. 2551

SPINCRAFT—See Standex International; *U.S. Public*, pg. 1930
SPINCRAFT WISCONSIN—See Standex International; *U.S. Public*, pg. 1930
SPINDANCE, INC.—See Century Technology Group; *U.S. Private*, pg. 834
SPINDELFABRIK SUESSEN GMBH—See Rieter Holding Ltd.; *Int'l*, pg. 6339
SPINDEX INDUSTRIES (HANOI) CO., LTD.—See Spindex Industries Limited; *Int'l*, pg. 7136
SPINDEX INDUSTRIES LIMITED; *Int'l*, pg. 7136
SPINDEX PRECISION ENGINEERING (SHANGHAI) CO., LTD.—See Spindex Industries Limited; *Int'l*, pg. 7136
SPINDEX PRECISION ENGINEERING (SUZHOU) CO., LTD.—See Spindex Industries Limited; *Int'l*, pg. 7137
SPINDLETOP CAPITAL MANAGEMENT LLC; *U.S. Private*, pg. 3757
SPINDLETOP DRILLING COMPANY—See SPINDLETOP OIL & GAS CO.; *U.S. Public*, pg. 1918
SPINDLETOP HEALTH ACQUISITION CORP.; *U.S. Public*, pg. 1918
SPINDLETOP OIL & GAS CO.; *U.S. Public*, pg. 1918
SP INDUSTRIES INC.—See Harbour Group Industries, Inc.; *U.S. Private*, pg. 1861
S & P INDUSTRIES SDN. BHD.—See S&P International Holding Limited; *Int'l*, pg. 6445
SPINDUSTRY INTERACTIVE, INC.; *U.S. Private*, pg. 3757
SPINEEX, INC.; *U.S. Private*, pg. 3757
SPINEGUARD S.A.; *Int'l*, pg. 7137
SPINELLI S.R.L.; *Int'l*, pg. 7137
SPINEMEDICA, LLC—See MiMedx Group, Inc.; *U.S. Public*, pg. 1448
SPINE SOLUTIONS GMBH—See Johnson & Johnson; *U.S. Public*, pg. 1200
SPINE & SPORT PHYSICAL THERAPY, LIMITED PARTNERSHIP—See U.S. Physical Therapy, Inc.; *U.S. Public*, pg. 2216
SPINE & SPORT; *U.S. Private*, pg. 3757
SPINETEX AG—See BNP Paribas SA; *Int'l*, pg. 1089
SPINEWAY SA; *Int'l*, pg. 7137
SPINIC MANUFACTURING COMPANY, LTD.—See Linamar Corporation; *Int'l*, pg. 4502
SPINIELLO COMPANIES; *U.S. Private*, pg. 3757
SPINIFEX GROUP—See Project: Worldwide, Inc.; *U.S. Private*, pg. 3281
SPIN INTERNATIONAL INC.—See J.J. Exporters Ltd.; *Int'l*, pg. 3858
SPINK SHREVES GALLERIES, INC.; *U.S. Private*, pg. 3757
SPINKS—See DBAY Advisors Limited; *Int'l*, pg. 1987
SPIN MASTER CORP.; *Int'l*, pg. 7136
SPIN MASTER DONGGUAN TECHNICAL CONSULTANCY SERVICING CO., LTD.—See Spin Master Corp.; *Int'l*, pg. 7136
SPIN MASTER FRANCE—See Spin Master Corp.; *Int'l*, pg. 7136
SPIN MASTER, INC.—See Spin Master Corp.; *Int'l*, pg. 7136
SPIN MASTER INTERNATIONAL S.A.R.L.—See Spin Master Corp.; *Int'l*, pg. 7136
SPIN MASTER ITALY S.R.L.—See Spin Master Corp.; *Int'l*, pg. 7136
SPIN MASTER LTD.—See Spin Master Corp.; *Int'l*, pg. 7136
SPIN MASTER MEXICO, S.A. DE C.V.—See Spin Master Corp.; *Int'l*, pg. 7136
SPIN MASTER TOYS FAR EAST LIMITED—See Spin Master Corp.; *Int'l*, pg. 7136
SPIN MASTER TOYS UK LTD.—See Spin Master Corp.; *Int'l*, pg. 7136
SPINNAKER CAPITAL (ASIA) PTE LTD—See Spinnaker Capital Group; *Int'l*, pg. 7137
SPINNAKER CAPITAL C.G.R. LTDA.—See Spinnaker Capital Group; *Int'l*, pg. 7137
SPINNAKER CAPITAL GROUP; *Int'l*, pg. 7137
SPINNAKER CAPITAL (HONG KONG) LIMITED—See Spinnaker Capital Group; *Int'l*, pg. 7137
SPINNAKER CAPITAL (MIDDLE EAST) LIMITED—See Spinnaker Capital Group; *Int'l*, pg. 7137
SPINNAKER COATING, LLC - PLANT 2—See LINTEC Corporation; *Int'l*, pg. 4516
SPINNAKER COATING, LLC—See LINTEC Corporation; *Int'l*, pg. 4516
SPINNAKER CONSULTING GROUP LLC; *U.S. Private*, pg. 3757
SPINNAKER INDUSTRIES INC.; *Int'l*, pg. 7137
SPINNAKER MANAGEMENT GROUP, LLC; *U.S. Private*, pg. 3757
SPINNAKER RECYCLING CORP.—See Waste Management, Inc.; *U.S. Public*, pg. 2332
SPINNAKER SCA—See Black Lake Capital, LLC; *U.S. Private*, pg. 572
SPINNAKER SUPPORT, LLC—See Spinnaker Management Group, LLC; *U.S. Private*, pg. 3757
SPINNEYBECK ENTERPRISES, INC.—See MillerKnoll, Inc.; *U.S. Public*, pg. 1447
SPINNEYBECK IRELAND—See MillerKnoll, Inc.; *U.S. Public*, pg. 1447

SPINNEYBECK LIMITED—See MillerKnoll, Inc.; *U.S. Public*, pg. 1447
SPINNOVA PLC; *Int'l*, pg. 7137
SPINNOVA AB—See Indutrade AB; *Int'l*, pg. 3681
SPIN PRODUCTS, INC.—See Olympus Partners; *U.S. Private*, pg. 3013
SPINREACT SA—See Toyobo Co., Ltd.; *Int'l*, pg. 7860
SPINREACT, S.A.U.—See Toyobo Co., Ltd.; *Int'l*, pg. 7861
SPIN RECRUITMENT ADVERTISING; *U.S. Private*, pg. 3757
SPINRITE LP—See Comvest Group Holdings LLC; *U.S. Private*, pg. 1007
SPIN SYSTEMS INC.—See Dine Development Corporation; *U.S. Private*, pg. 1233
SPIN TECHNOLOGIES PVT. LTD.—See Cadence Design Systems, Inc.; *U.S. Public*, pg. 419
S&P INTERNATIONAL FOODS (CAMBODIA) COMPANY LIMITED—See S&P Syndicate Public Company Limited; *Int'l*, pg. 6445
S&P INTERNATIONAL FOODS COMPANY LIMITED—See S&P Syndicate Public Company Limited; *Int'l*, pg. 6445
S&P INTERNATIONAL HOLDING LIMITED; *Int'l*, pg. 6445
THE SPINX COMPANY INC.; *U.S. Private*, pg. 4120
SPI PHARMA, INC.—See The Garfield Weston Foundation; *Int'l*, pg. 7649
SPIRAL BINDING LLC—See Hilltop Private Capital, LLC; *U.S. Private*, pg. 1947
SPIRAL BINDING LLC—See KCB Management LLC; *U.S. Private*, pg. 2269
SPIRAL BIOTECH, INC.—See Investor AB; *Int'l*, pg. 3786
SPIRAL GROUP; *Int'l*, pg. 7137
SPIRAL HELIX INC.—See Lindab International AB; *Int'l*, pg. 4504
SPIRALOCK CORPORATION—See Stanley Black & Decker, Inc.; *U.S. Public*, pg. 1934
SPIRALOCK DO BRASIL LTDA—See Stanley Black & Decker, Inc.; *U.S. Public*, pg. 1935
SPIRA-LOC—See EMCOR Group, Inc.; *U.S. Public*, pg. 737
SPIRATEX COMPANY INC.; *U.S. Private*, pg. 3757
SPIRATION, INC.—See Olympus Corporation; *Int'l*, pg. 5556
SPIRAX INTER VALF SANAYI VE TICARET LTD—See Spirax-Sarco Engineering plc; *Int'l*, pg. 7137
SPIRAX OY—See Spirax-Sarco Engineering plc; *Int'l*, pg. 7137
SPIRAX-SARCO A.B.—See Spirax-Sarco Engineering plc; *Int'l*, pg. 7138
SPIRAX-SARCO A.G.—See Spirax-Sarco Engineering plc; *Int'l*, pg. 7138
SPIRAX-SARCO AS—See Spirax-Sarco Engineering plc; *Int'l*, pg. 7138
SPIRAX-SARCO CANADA LTD.—See Spirax-Sarco Engineering plc; *Int'l*, pg. 7138
SPIRAX-SARCO CHILE LTDA.—See Spirax-Sarco Engineering plc; *Int'l*, pg. 7138
SPIRAX SARCO CO. LTD.—See Spirax-Sarco Engineering plc; *Int'l*, pg. 7138
SPIRAX SARCO EAST AFRICA LTD.—See Spirax-Sarco Engineering plc; *Int'l*, pg. 7138
SPIRAX SARCO EGYPT L.L.C.—See Spirax-Sarco Engineering plc; *Int'l*, pg. 7138
SPIRAX SARCO ENGINEERING (CHINA) LTD.—See Spirax-Sarco Engineering plc; *Int'l*, pg. 7138
SPIRAX SARCO ENGINEERING LLC—See Spirax-Sarco Engineering plc; *Int'l*, pg. 7138
SPIRAX-SARCO ENGINEERING PLC; *Int'l*, pg. 7137
SPIRAX SARCO ENGINEERING S.L.—See Spirax-Sarco Engineering plc; *Int'l*, pg. 7138
SPIRAX-SARCO EUROPE LTD.—See Spirax-Sarco Engineering plc; *Int'l*, pg. 7138
SPIRAX SARCO GES. MBH—See Spirax-Sarco Engineering plc; *Int'l*, pg. 7138
SPIRAX-SARCO GMBH—See Spirax-Sarco Engineering plc; *Int'l*, pg. 7138
SPIRAX SARCO, INC.—See Spirax-Sarco Engineering plc; *Int'l*, pg. 7138
SPIRAX SARCO IND. E COM. LTDA.—See Spirax-Sarco Engineering plc; *Int'l*, pg. 7138
SPIRAX-SARCO INDIA PRIVATE LTD.—See Spirax-Sarco Engineering plc; *Int'l*, pg. 7138
SPIRAX-SARCO INTERNATIONAL LTD.—See Spirax-Sarco Engineering plc; *Int'l*, pg. 7138
SPIRAX-SARCO INVESTMENTS LTD.—See Spirax-Sarco Engineering plc; *Int'l*, pg. 7138
SPIRAX SARCO (JAPAN) LTD.—See Spirax-Sarco Engineering plc; *Int'l*, pg. 7138
SPIRAX-SARCO KFT—See Spirax-Sarco Engineering plc; *Int'l*, pg. 7138
SPIRAX-SARCO (KOREA) LTD.—See Spirax-Sarco Engineering plc; *Int'l*, pg. 7138
SPIRAX SARCO LTD.—See Spirax-Sarco Engineering plc; *Int'l*, pg. 7138
SPIRAX SARCO MAGHREB—See Spirax-Sarco Engineering plc; *Int'l*, pg. 7138
SPIRAX-SARCO MEXICANA S.A. DE C.V.—See Spirax-Sarco Engineering plc; *Int'l*, pg. 7138
SPIRAX-SARCO NETHERLANDS BV—See Spirax-Sarco Engineering plc; *Int'l*, pg. 7138

COMPANY NAME INDEX

SPIRAX-SARCO N.V.—See Spirax-Sarco Engineering plc; *Int'l*, pg. 7138
SPIRAX-SARCO OVERSEAS LTD.—See Spirax-Sarco Engineering plc; *Int'l*, pg. 7138
SPIRAX SARCO PERU SAC—See Spirax-Sarco Engineering plc; *Int'l*, pg. 7138
SPIRAX-SARCO PHILIPPINES INC.—See Spirax-Sarco Engineering plc; *Int'l*, pg. 7138
SPIRAX-SARCO (PRIVATE) LTD.—See Spirax-Sarco Engineering plc; *Int'l*, pg. 7138
SPIRAX-SARCO PTY. LTD.—See Spirax-Sarco Engineering plc; *Int'l*, pg. 7138
SPIRAX SARCO S.A.—See Spirax-Sarco Engineering plc; *Int'l*, pg. 7138
SPIRAX-SARCO S.A.S.—See Spirax-Sarco Engineering plc; *Int'l*, pg. 7138
SPIRAX-SARCO SAU—See Spirax-Sarco Engineering plc; *Int'l*, pg. 7138
SPIRAX-SARCO SDN. BHD.—See Spirax-Sarco Engineering plc; *Int'l*, pg. 7138
SPIRAX-SARCO SOUTH AFRICA (PTY.) LTD.—See Spirax-Sarco Engineering plc; *Int'l*, pg. 7138
SPIRAX SARCO SPOL. S R.O.—See Spirax-Sarco Engineering plc; *Int'l*, pg. 7138
SPIRAX SARCO SP. Z O.O.—See Spirax-Sarco Engineering plc; *Int'l*, pg. 7138
SPIRAX-SARCO S.R.L.—See Spirax-Sarco Engineering plc; *Int'l*, pg. 7138
SPIRAX SARCO (THAILAND) LTD.—See Spirax-Sarco Engineering plc; *Int'l*, pg. 7138
SPIRAX SARCO VALF SANAYI VE TICARET A.S.—See Spirax-Sarco Engineering plc; *Int'l*, pg. 7138
SPIRAX SARCO VIETNAM CO. LTD.—See Spirax-Sarco Engineering plc; *Int'l*, pg. 7138
SPIR COMMUNICATION SA—See Societe de Participation et de Financement dans la Comm SA; *Int'l*, pg. 7037
SPIRE ALABAMA INC.—See Spire, Inc; *U.S. Public*, pg. 1918
SPIRE AUTOMOTIVE LIMITED—See Group 1 Automotive, Inc.; *U.S. Public*, pg. 972
SPIRE CAPITAL PARTNERS, LLC; *U.S. Private*, pg. 3757
SPIRE CORPORATION; *U.S. Private*, pg. 3757
SPIRE GLOBAL CANADA SUBSIDIARY CORP.—See Spire Global, Inc.; *U.S. Public*, pg. 1918
SPIRE GLOBAL, INC.; *U.S. Public*, pg. 1918
SPIRE GLOBAL LUXEMBOURG S.A.R.L.—See Spire Global, Inc.; *U.S. Public*, pg. 1918
SPIRE GLOBAL SINGAPORE PTE LTD—See Spire Global, Inc.; *U.S. Public*, pg. 1918
SPIRE GLOBAL SUBSIDIARY, INC.—See Spire Global, Inc.; *U.S. Public*, pg. 1918
SPIRE GLOBAL UK LTD.—See Spire Global, Inc.; *U.S. Public*, pg. 1918
SPIRE HEALTHCARE GROUP PLC; *Int'l*, pg. 7139
SPIRE HOSPITALITY, LLC—See Winston Harton Holdings, LLC; *U.S. Private*, pg. 4544
SPIRE, INC; *U.S. Public*, pg. 1918
SPIRE INVESTMENT PARTNERS LLC; *U.S. Private*, pg. 3757
SPIRELLA FRANCE S.A.R.L.—See Menage Selection Valnet S.A.S; *Int'l*, pg. 4815
SPIRELLA GMBH—See Menage Selection Valnet S.A.S; *Int'l*, pg. 4815
SPIRELLA SA—See Menage Selection Valnet S.A.S; *Int'l*, pg. 4815
SPIREL S.A.S.—See Somfy SA; *Int'l*, pg. 7086
SPIREMEDIA, INC.—See BC Partners LLP; *Int'l*, pg. 925
SPIRE MISSOURI INC.—See Spire, Inc; *U.S. Public*, pg. 1919
SPIRENT COMMUNICATIONS (ASIA) LIMITED—See Spirent Communications plc; *Int'l*, pg. 7140
SPIRENT COMMUNICATIONS - CEM—See Spirent Communications plc; *Int'l*, pg. 7139
SPIRENT COMMUNICATIONS - GERMANTOWN—See Spirent Communications plc; *Int'l*, pg. 7140
SPIRENT COMMUNICATIONS - HONOLULU—See Spirent Communications plc; *Int'l*, pg. 7140
SPIRENT COMMUNICATIONS (INDIA) PVT LIMITED—See Spirent Communications plc; *Int'l*, pg. 7140
SPIRENT COMMUNICATIONS PLC; *Int'l*, pg. 7139
SPIRENT COMMUNICATIONS SAS—See Spirent Communications plc; *Int'l*, pg. 7140
SPIRENT COMMUNICATIONS—See Spirent Communications plc; *Int'l*, pg. 7139
SPIRENT COMMUNICATIONS - TAS—See Spirent Communications plc; *Int'l*, pg. 7140
SPIRENT COMMUNICATIONS TECHNOLOGY (BEIJING) LIMITED—See Spirent Communications plc; *Int'l*, pg. 7140
SPIRENT FEDERAL SYSTEMS INC.—See Spirent Communications plc; *Int'l*, pg. 7140
SPIREON, INC.—See Greenbriar Equity Group, L.P.; *U.S. Private*, pg. 1776
SPIRE PAYMENTS ESPANA—See KleinPartners Capital Corp.; *U.S. Private*, pg. 2319
SPIRE PAYMENTS LTD.—See KleinPartners Capital Corp.; *U.S. Private*, pg. 2319
SPIRES RESTAURANTS INC.; *U.S. Private*, pg. 3758

SPIRE TECHNOLOGIES PTE LTD—See ASTI Holdings Limited; *Int'l*, pg. 655
SPIRE TECHNOLOGIES (TAIWAN) LTD.—See ASTI Holdings Limited; *Int'l*, pg. 655
SPIRE THAMES VALLEY HOSPITAL LIMITED—See Spire Healthcare Group plc; *Int'l*, pg. 7139
SPIREX CORPORATION—See Nordson Corporation; *U.S. Public*, pg. 1534
SPIR GROUP ASA; *Int'l*, pg. 7137
SPIRIANT GMBH—See Deutsche Lufthansa AG; *Int'l*, pg. 2067
SPIRIT AEROSYSTEMS (EUROPE) LIMITED—See ONEX Corporation; *Int'l*, pg. 5580
SPIRIT AEROSYSTEMS FINANCE, INC.—See ONEX Corporation; *Int'l*, pg. 5580
SPIRIT AEROSYSTEMS HOLDINGS, INC.—See ONEX Corporation; *Int'l*, pg. 5580
SPIRIT AEROSYSTEMS, INC.—See ONEX Corporation; *Int'l*, pg. 5580
SPIRIT AEROSYSTEMS INTERNATIONAL HOLDINGS, INC.—See ONEX Corporation; *Int'l*, pg. 5580
SPIRIT AEROSYSTEMS MALAYSIA SDN BHD—See ONEX Corporation; *Int'l*, pg. 5580
SPIRIT AEROSYSTEMS NORTH CAROLINA, INC.—See ONEX Corporation; *Int'l*, pg. 5580
SPIRIT AEROSYSTEMS OPERATIONS INTERNATIONAL, INC.—See ONEX Corporation; *Int'l*, pg. 5580
SPIRIT AEROSYSTEMS SINGAPORE PTE. LTD.—See ONEX Corporation; *Int'l*, pg. 5580
SPIRIT AIRLINES, INC.; *U.S. Public*, pg. 1919
SPIRIT BLOCKCHAIN CAPITAL INC.; *Int'l*, pg. 7140
SPIRIT CHRYSLER JEEP; *U.S. Private*, pg. 3758
SPIRIT CONSTRUCTION SERVICES INC.—See VHC Inc.; *U.S. Private*, pg. 4375
SPIRIT CRUISES LLC—See The Pritzker Group - Chicago, LLC; *U.S. Private*, pg. 4098
SPIRIT DEFENSE, INC.—See ONEX Corporation; *Int'l*, pg. 5580
SPIRITE INDUSTRIES, INC.; *U.S. Private*, pg. 3758
SPIRIT ENERGY DANMARK APS—See Centrica plc; *Int'l*, pg. 1413
SPIRIT ENERGY LIMITED—See Centrica plc; *Int'l*, pg. 1413
SPIRIT ENERGY NEDERLAND BV—See Centrica plc; *Int'l*, pg. 1413
SPIRIT ENERGY NORGE AS—See Centrica plc; *Int'l*, pg. 1413
SPIRIT EXPLORATION, INC.; *Int'l*, pg. 7140
SPIRIT FABS INC.—See VHC Inc.; *U.S. Private*, pg. 4375
SPIRIT FORD INC.; *U.S. Private*, pg. 3758
SPIRIT GLOBAL ENERGY SOLUTIONS CANADA LTD.—See Dover Corporation; *U.S. Public*, pg. 682
SPIRIT GLOBAL ENERGY SOLUTIONS, INC.—See Dover Corporation; *U.S. Public*, pg. 682
SPIRIT INTERNATIONAL INC.; *U.S. Private*, pg. 3758
THE SPIRIT JINYU BIOLOGICAL PHARMACEUTICAL CO., LTD—See Jinyu Bio-technology Co., Ltd.; *Int'l*, pg. 3970
SPIRIT MANAGEMENT COMPANY II—See Spirit Realty Capital, Inc.; *U.S. Public*, pg. 1919
SPIRIT MTA REIT; *U.S. Private*, pg. 3758
SPIRIT OF BOSTON—See The Pritzker Group - Chicago, LLC; *U.S. Private*, pg. 4098
SPIRIT OF CHICAGO—See The Pritzker Group - Chicago, LLC; *U.S. Private*, pg. 4099
SPIRIT OF NEW YORK—See The Pritzker Group - Chicago, LLC; *U.S. Private*, pg. 4099
SPIRIT OF NORFOLK—See The Pritzker Group - Chicago, LLC; *U.S. Private*, pg. 4099
SPIRIT OF PHILADELPHIA—See The Pritzker Group - Chicago, LLC; *U.S. Private*, pg. 4099
SPIRIT OF TEXAS BANCSHARES, INC.—See Sentinel Capital Partners, L.L.C.; *U.S. Private*, pg. 3609
SPIRIT OF WASHINGTON—See The Pritzker Group - Chicago, LLC; *U.S. Private*, pg. 4099
SPIRIT OF YORK DISTILLERY INC.—See Northfield Capital Corporation; *Int'l*, pg. 5445
THE SPIRIT PUBLISHING COMPANY—See Horizon Publications Inc.; *U.S. Private*, pg. 1982
SPIRIT REALTY CAPITAL, INC.; *U.S. Public*, pg. 1919
SPIRIT REALTY, L.P.—See Spirit Realty Capital, Inc.; *U.S. Public*, pg. 1919
SPIRITRUST LUTHERAN; *U.S. Private*, pg. 3758
SPIRIT & SANZONE DISTRIBUTING CO.; *U.S. Private*, pg. 3758
SPIRIT SEARCH SAS—See ManpowerGroup Inc.; *U.S. Public*, pg. 1360
SPIRITS PARTNERS SAS—See Pernod Ricard S.A.; *Int'l*, pg. 5811
SPIRIT SPE PORTFOLIO 2012-1, LLC—See Spirit Realty Capital, Inc.; *U.S. Public*, pg. 1919
SPIRITS TIME INTERNATIONAL, INC.; *U.S. Public*, pg. 1919
SPIRITUS MUNDI PLC; *Int'l*, pg. 7140
SPIRKA SCHNELLFLECHTER GMBH—See SKET Verseilmaschinenbau GmbH; *Int'l*, pg. 6981
SPIRKA SCHNELLFLECHTER GMBH—See SKET Verseilmaschinenbau GmbH; *Int'l*, pg. 6981
SPIRK BROTHERS INC.; *U.S. Private*, pg. 3758

SPL ASSOCIATES INC.

SPIRO & ASSOCIATES MARKETING, ADVERTISING & PUBLIC RELATIONS; *U.S. Private*, pg. 3758
SPIRO HEALTH SERVICES, LLC—See AdaptHealth Corp.; *U.S. Public*, pg. 39
SPIRO INTERNATIONAL S.A.—See Lindab International AB; *Int'l*, pg. 4504
SPIROL INDUSTRIES, LTD.—See Spirol International Corporation; *U.S. Private*, pg. 3758
SPIROL INDUSTRIES, LTD.—See Spirol International Corporation; *U.S. Private*, pg. 3758
SPIROL INTERNATIONAL CORPORATION; *U.S. Private*, pg. 3758
SPIROL INTERNATIONAL CORPORATION - STOW—See Spirol International Corporation; *U.S. Private*, pg. 3758
SPIROLITE (M) SDN. BHD.—See Wah Seong Corporation Berhad; *Int'l*, pg. 8329
SPIROLITE (MYANMAR) COMPANY LIMITED—See Wah Seong Corporation Berhad; *Int'l*, pg. 8329
SPIROL SAS—See Spirol International Corporation; *U.S. Private*, pg. 3758
SPIROL WEST, INC.—See Spirol International Corporation; *U.S. Private*, pg. 3758
SPIRO SWEDEN AB—See Lindab International AB; *Int'l*, pg. 4504
SPIROX CORPORATION MALAYSIA SDN. BHD.—See Spirox Corporation; *Int'l*, pg. 7140
SPIROX CORPORATION; *Int'l*, pg. 7140
SPIROX CORPORATION USA INC.—See Spirox Corporation; *Int'l*, pg. 7140
SPIROX (SHANGHAI) CORPORATION—See Spirox Corporation; *Int'l*, pg. 7140
SPIRTAS WRECKING CO. INC.; *U.S. Private*, pg. 3758
SPIT BUCOVINA SA; *Int'l*, pg. 7140
SPI TECHNOLOGIES INDIA PRIVATE LIMITED—See Partners Group Holding AG; *Int'l*, pg. 5750
SPITEX PERSPECTA AG—See SOL S.p.A.; *Int'l*, pg. 7068
SPITFIRE CONTROLS (VIETNAM) CO. LTD.—See Sigma-Tron International, Inc.; *U.S. Public*, pg. 1878
SPITFIRE GROUP, LLC; *U.S. Private*, pg. 3758
SPITFIRE OIL LIMITED; *Int'l*, pg. 7140
SPITS B.V.—See Walgreens Boots Alliance, Inc.; *U.S. Public*, pg. 2323
SPITT D.O.O.—See Unior Kovaska industrija d.d.; *Int'l*, pg. 8055
SPITZER AUTOWORLD HOMESTEAD, INC.—See Spitzer Management, Inc.; *U.S. Private*, pg. 3758
SPITZER CHEVROLET COMPANY; *U.S. Private*, pg. 3758
SPITZER CHEVY NORTHFIELD; *U.S. Private*, pg. 3758
SPITZER MANAGEMENT, INC.; *U.S. Private*, pg. 3758
SPITZ INC.—See Elevate Entertainment, Inc.; *U.S. Private*, pg. 1358
SPIVEY ENTERPRISES INC.; *U.S. Private*, pg. 3758
SPIVEY UTILITY CONSTRUCTION CO. INC.; *U.S. Private*, pg. 3758
SPK ACQUISITION CORP.; *Int'l*, pg. 7140
SPK CORPORATION; *Int'l*, pg. 7140
SPK EUROPE B.V.—See SPK Corporation; *Int'l*, pg. 7140
S.P. KINNEY ENGINEERS, INC.; *U.S. Private*, pg. 3518
SPK MOTORPARTS CO., LTD.—See SPK Corporation; *Int'l*, pg. 7140
SPK OIL & GAS SUPPLIES AND SERVICES SDN BHD—See Sharikat Permodalan Kebangsaan Bhd; *Int'l*, pg. 6789
SPK SINGAPORE PTE. LTD.—See SPK Corporation; *Int'l*, pg. 7140
SPK VEHICLE PRODUCTS SDN. BHD.—See SPK Corporation; *Int'l*, pg. 7140
SP LABORATORIJA A.D.—See Victoria Group a.d.; *Int'l*, pg. 8188
SPLASH BEVERAGE GROUP, INC.; *U.S. Public*, pg. 1919
SPLASH CAR WASH, INC.; *U.S. Private*, pg. 3759
SPLASH CORPORATION—See Wipro Limited; *Int'l*, pg. 8433
SPLASH INTERACTIVE COMPANY LTD.—See The Mission Group Public Limited Company; *Int'l*, pg. 7667
SPLASH INTERACTIVE LTD.—See The Mission Group Public Limited Company; *Int'l*, pg. 7667
SPLASH INTERACTIVE LTD.—See The Mission Group Public Limited Company; *Int'l*, pg. 7667
SPLASH INTERACTIVE SDN. BHD.—See The Mission Group Public Limited Company; *Int'l*, pg. 7667
SPLASHLIGHT LLC; *U.S. Private*, pg. 3759
SPLASHLINE EVENT UND VERMARKTUNGS GMBH—See TUI AG; *Int'l*, pg. 7966
SPLASH MEDIA LP; *U.S. Private*, pg. 3759
SPLASH NEWS & PICTURE AGENCY, LLC—See Rcapital Partners LLP; *Int'l*, pg. 6227
SPLASH PRODUCTS INC.; *U.S. Private*, pg. 3759
SPLASH SUPERPOOLS LTD.—See Ecomembrane S.p.A.; *Int'l*, pg. 2296
SPLASH TRANSPORT, INC.—See JAB Holding Company S.a.r.l.; *Int'l*, pg. 3862
SPL ASSOCIATES INC.; *U.S. Private*, pg. 3759
SPLENDID ENTERTAINMENT GMBH—See Splendid Medien AG; *Int'l*, pg. 7141
SPLENDID FILM B.V.—See Splendid Medien AG; *Int'l*, pg. 7141

SPL ASSOCIATES INC.

CORPORATE AFFILIATIONS

SPLENDID FILM GMBH.—See Splendid Medien AG; *Int'l*, pg. 7141
SPLENDID MEDIEN AG; *Int'l*, pg. 7140
SPLENDID METAL PRODUCTS LIMITED; *Int'l*, pg. 7141
SPLENDID PAVILION SDN BHD—See Gadang Holdings Berhad; *Int'l*, pg. 2868
SPLENDID—See GMM Capital LLC; *U.S. Private*, pg. 1722
SPLENDID STUDIOS GMBH—See Splendid Medien AG; *Int'l*, pg. 7141
SPLENDID SYNCHRON GMBH—See Splendid Medien AG; *Int'l*, pg. 7141
SPLENDOR DESIGN GROUP, INC.; *U.S. Private*, pg. 3759
SPLENDOR MEDIA (PVT) LTD.—See Melstacorp PLC; *Int'l*, pg. 4813
SPLENDRIS PHARMACEUTICALS GMBH—See Shenzhen Salubris Pharmaceuticals Co., Ltd.; *Int'l*, pg. 6820
SPLICE COMMUNICATIONS
SPLIETHOFF'S BEVRACHTINGSKANTOOR B.V.; *Int'l*, pg. 7141
SPLIFAR S.A.—See Recticel S.A.; *Int'l*, pg. 6242
SPL INDUSTRIES LIMITED; *Int'l*, pg. 7140
SPLINE CORPORATION—See Medipal Holdings Corporation; *Int'l*, pg. 4779
SPLINE GAUGES LTD.—See Danaher Corporation; *U.S. Public*, pg. 631
SPLITIT PAYMENTS LTD.; *Int'l*, pg. 7141
SPLIT ROCK PARTNERS, LLC—See The Travelers Companies, Inc.; *U.S. Public*, pg. 2136
SPL SOFTWARE ALLIANCE LLC—See Caterpillar, Inc.; *U.S. Public*, pg. 453
SPLU EXPERTS GMBH—See ManpowerGroup Inc.; *U.S. Public*, pg. 1362
SPLUNK INC.—See Cisco Systems, Inc.; *U.S. Public*, pg. 500
SPLUNK INFORMATION TECHNOLOGY (SHANGHAI) CO., LTD.—See Cisco Systems, Inc.; *U.S. Public*, pg. 500
SPLUNK SERVICES FRANCE SAS—See Cisco Systems, Inc.; *U.S. Public*, pg. 500
SPLUNK SERVICES FZ-LLC—See Cisco Systems, Inc.; *U.S. Public*, pg. 500
SPLUNK SERVICES GERMANY GMBH—See Cisco Systems, Inc.; *U.S. Public*, pg. 500
SPLUNK SERVICES HONG KONG LTD.—See Cisco Systems, Inc.; *U.S. Public*, pg. 500
SPLUNK SERVICES JAPAN GK—See Cisco Systems, Inc.; *U.S. Public*, pg. 500
SPLUNK SERVICES KOREA—See Cisco Systems, Inc.; *U.S. Public*, pg. 500
SPLUNK SERVICES SWEDEN AB—See Cisco Systems, Inc.; *U.S. Public*, pg. 500
SPLUNK SERVICES UK LIMITED—See Cisco Systems, Inc.; *U.S. Public*, pg. 500
SPLUNK TECHNOLOGY CONSULTING (BEIJING) CO., LTD.—See Cisco Systems, Inc.; *U.S. Public*, pg. 500
SPLV CAMEROUN—See Toyota Tsusho Corporation; *Int'l*, pg. 7876
SPL WORLDGROUP, INC.—See Oracle Corporation; *U.S. Public*, pg. 1613
SP MARINE SERVICES SDN. BHD.—See Suria Capital Holdings Berhad; *Int'l*, pg. 7344
SPM AUTOMOTIVE TEXTILE CO., LTD.—See Suminoe Textile Co., Ltd.; *Int'l*, pg. 7262
SPM AUTO PARTS S.A. DE C.V.—See Pungkang Co., Ltd; *Int'l*, pg. 6119
SP MEDICAL SP. Z O.O.—See SP Group A/S; *Int'l*, pg. 7122
SPM FOODS AND BEVERAGES CO., LTD.—See Thai Beverage Public Company Limited; *Int'l*, pg. 7591
SPM JOINT STOCK COMPANY; *Int'l*, pg. 7141
SPML INFRA LIMITED; *Int'l*, pg. 7141
SPML TECHNOLOGIES LIMITED—See SPML Infra Limited; *Int'l*, pg. 7141
SPM MARKETING & COMMUNICATIONS, LLC—See Amulet Capital Partners, L.P.; *U.S. Private*, pg. 268
SPM OIL & GAS INC.—See Caterpillar, Inc.; *U.S. Public*, pg. 453
SP NEW ENERGY CORPORATION; *Int'l*, pg. 7122
SPNP PAPER & PACK PVT. LTD.—See Nidhi Granites Limited; *Int'l*, pg. 5280
SPN WELL SERVICES, INC.—See Superior Energy Services, Inc.; *U.S. Private*, pg. 3877
SPOBAG AG; *Int'l*, pg. 7141
SPODE LIMITED; *Int'l*, pg. 7141
SPOETZL BREWERY—See The Gambrinus Company; *U.S. Private*, pg. 4032
SPOFADENTAL A.S.—See Danaher Corporation; *U.S. Public*, pg. 631
SPO GLOBAL INC.; *Int'l*, pg. 7141
SPOHN & BURKHARDT GMBH & CO. KG; *Int'l*, pg. 7141
SPOHN RANCH, INC.; *U.S. Private*, pg. 3759
SPOKANE FOOD SERVICES, INC.; *U.S. Private*, pg. 3759
SPOKANE HARDWARE SUPPLY, INC.; *U.S. Private*, pg. 3759
SPOKANE INDUSTRIES INC.; *U.S. Private*, pg. 3759

SPOKANE INTERNATIONAL AIRPORT; *U.S. Private*, pg. 3759
SPOKANE MACHINERY COMPANY—See Capital Machine Technologies, Inc.; *U.S. Private*, pg. 741
SPOKANE SEED COMPANY; *U.S. Private*, pg. 3760
SPOKANE SYMPHONY ORCHESTRA; *U.S. Private*, pg. 3760
SPOKANE TEACHERS CREDIT UNION; *U.S. Private*, pg. 3760
SPOKANE TELEVISION INC.; *U.S. Private*, pg. 3760
SPOKANE UNITED METHODIST HOMES; *U.S. Private*, pg. 3760
SPOKANE VALLEY WASHINGTON HOSPITAL COMPANY, LLC—See Community Health Systems, Inc.; *U.S. Public*, pg. 557
SPOK HOLDINGS, INC.; *U.S. Public*, pg. 1919
SPOLANA, S.R.O.—See Orlen S.A.; *Int'l*, pg. 5641
SPOLDZIELNIA USLUGOWA VIG EKSPERT W WARSZAWIE—See Vienna Insurance Group AG Wiener Versicherung Gruppe; *Int'l*, pg. 8195
SPOLEM TYCHY SP. Z O.O.—See Emperia Holding S.A.; *Int'l*, pg. 2386
SPOLYTECH CO., LTD.; *Int'l*, pg. 7142
SPONDA KIINTEISTOT OY—See Blackstone Inc.; *U.S. Public*, pg. 351
SPONDA OYJ—See Blackstone Inc.; *U.S. Public*, pg. 350
SPONGE-CUSHION, INC.—See Leggett & Platt, Incorporated; *U.S. Public*, pg. 1303
SPONSOR CAPITAL OY; *Int'l*, pg. 7142
SPONSORSONE INC.; *Int'l*, pg. 7142
SPONTE SALES, INC.—See Hawk Auto Group; *U.S. Private*, pg. 1882
SPONTEX S.A.S.—See Newell Brands Inc.; *U.S. Public*, pg. 1515
SPOOKFISH LIMITED—See Vista Equity Partners, LLC; *U.S. Private*, pg. 4396
S-POOL HUMAN SOLUTIONS, INC.—See S-Pool, Inc.; *Int'l*, pg. 6446
S-POOL, INC.; *Int'l*, pg. 6446
SPOON AS—See Bonnier AB; *Int'l*, pg. 1109
SPOONER HEALTH SYSTEM; *U.S. Private*, pg. 3760
SPOONER INDUSTRIES LTD.; *Int'l*, pg. 7142
SPOONFLOWER, INC.—See Apollo Global Management, Inc.; *U.S. Public*, pg. 159
SPOON MEDIA, INC.—See Her Campus Media, LLC; *U.S. Private*, pg. 1920
SPOON PUBLISHING AB—See Bonnier AB; *Int'l*, pg. 1109
SPORLAN VALVE COMPANY—See Parker Hannifin Corporation; *U.S. Public*, pg. 1644
SPOROCO INC.; *U.S. Private*, pg. 3760
SPORT1 GMBH—See Highlight Communications AG; *Int'l*, pg. 3388
SPORT1 MEDIA GMBH—See Highlight Communications AG; *Int'l*, pg. 3388
SPORT1 MEDIEN AG; *Int'l*, pg. 7142
SPORT ABROAD (UK) LIMITED—See TUI AG; *Int'l*, pg. 7966
SPORTAL GMBH—See Vista Equity Partners, LLC; *U.S. Private*, pg. 4401
SPORTAL NEW ZEALAND PTY LTD—See Vista Equity Partners, LLC; *U.S. Private*, pg. 4401
SPORTAMORE AB—See Footway Group AB; *Int'l*, pg. 2728
SPORTCAL GLOBAL COMMUNICATIONS LIMITED—See GlobalData Plc; *Int'l*, pg. 3003
SPORT CHALET, INC.—See Independence Capital Partners, LLC; *U.S. Private*, pg. 2057
SPORT CHEVROLET CO. INC.; *U.S. Private*, pg. 3760
SPORT CLIPS, INC.; *U.S. Private*, pg. 3760
SPORT CLUB 18, S.A.—See Banco Bilbao Vizcaya Argentaria, S.A.; *Int'l*, pg. 818
SPORT COURT INTERNATIONAL INC.—See The Riverside Company; *U.S. Private*, pg. 4110
SPORTECH GAMING LIMITED—See Sportech PLC; *Int'l*, pg. 7142
SPORTECH, LLC—See Monomoy Capital Partners LLC; *U.S. Private*, pg. 2772
SPORTECH PLC; *Int'l*, pg. 7142
SPORTECH POOLS COMPETITIONS LIMITED—See Op-Capita LLP; *Int'l*, pg. 5595
SPORTECH RACING GMBH—See Sportech PLC; *Int'l*, pg. 7142
SPORTECH RACING GMBH—See Sportech PLC; *Int'l*, pg. 7142
SPORTECH RACING LLC—See Sportech PLC; *Int'l*, pg. 7142
SPORTECH TRUSTEES LIMITED—See Sportech PLC; *Int'l*, pg. 7142
SPORTECH VENUES INC—See Sportech PLC; *Int'l*, pg. 7142
S'PORTER LTD; *Int'l*, pg. 6446
SPORTFIVE ASIA SDN BHD—See Vivendi SE; *Int'l*, pg. 8277
SPORTFIVE EOOD—See Vivendi SE; *Int'l*, pg. 8277
SPORTFIVE GMBH & CO. KG—See Vivendi SE; *Int'l*, pg. 8277
SPORTFIVE INTERMEDIATE GMBH—See Vivendi SE; *Int'l*, pg. 8277

SPORTFIVE INTERNATIONAL SA—See Vivendi SE; *Int'l*, pg. 8277
SPORTFIVE ITALY SA—See Vivendi SE; *Int'l*, pg. 8277
SPORTFIVE MEDIA SOLUTIONS SAS—See Vivendi SE; *Int'l*, pg. 8277
SPORTFIVE SINGAPORE PTE LTD—See Vivendi SE; *Int'l*, pg. 8277
SPORTFIVE UK LTD—See Vivendi SE; *Int'l*, pg. 8277
SPORTFIVE VERWALTUNGS GMBH—See Vivendi SE; *Int'l*, pg. 8277
SPORT HALEY HOLDINGS, INC.; *U.S. Private*, pg. 3760
SPORT & HEALTH CLUBS, L.C.; *U.S. Private*, pg. 3760
SPORTIF USA INC.; *U.S. Private*, pg. 3760
SPORT-INFORMATIONS-DIENST GMBH UND CO. KG—See Agence France-Presse; *Int'l*, pg. 205
SPORTINGBET AUSTRALIA PTY LIMITED—See Entain PLC; *Int'l*, pg. 2450
SPORTING CLUBE DE BRAGA; *Int'l*, pg. 7142
SPORTING CLUBE DE PORTUGAL - FUTEBOL, SAD; *Int'l*, pg. 7142
SPORTING LIFE INC.—See Fairfax Financial Holdings Limited; *Int'l*, pg. 2608
SPORTING NEWS RADIO—See Advance Publications, Inc.; *U.S. Private*, pg. 85
THE SPORTING NEWS—See Advance Publications, Inc.; *U.S. Private*, pg. 85
SPORTKING INDIA LTD.; *Int'l*, pg. 7142
SPORTLAND EESTIE A.S.—See Frasers Group plc; *Int'l*, pg. 2765
SPORT LISBOA E BENFICA - FUTEBOL SAD; *Int'l*, pg. 7142
SPORT MASKA INC.—See Birch Hill Equity Partners Management Inc.; *Int'l*, pg. 1046
SPORT OBERMEYER LTD.; *U.S. Private*, pg. 3760
SPORTO CORP.; *U.S. Private*, pg. 3760
SPORTODDS SYSTEMS PTY LIMITED—See William Hill Plc; *Int'l*, pg. 8413
SPORTON INTERNATIONAL, INC.; *Int'l*, pg. 7142
SPORTRADAR AB—See Sportradar Group AG; *Int'l*, pg. 7142
SPORTRADAR AS—See Sportradar Group AG; *Int'l*, pg. 7142
SPORTRADAR GERMANY GMBH—See Sportradar Group AG; *Int'l*, pg. 7142
SPORTRADAR GROUP AG; *Int'l*, pg. 7142
SPORTRADAR INFORMACIJSKE TEHNOLOGIJE D.O.O.—See Sportradar Group AG; *Int'l*, pg. 7142
SPORTRADAR MEDIA SERVICES GMBH—See Sportradar Group AG; *Int'l*, pg. 7143
SPORTRADAR OU—See Sportradar Group AG; *Int'l*, pg. 7143
SPORTRADAR SA (PTY.) LTD.—See Sportradar Group AG; *Int'l*, pg. 7143
SPORTRADAR VIRTUAL GAMING GMBH—See Sportradar Group AG; *Int'l*, pg. 7143
SPORTS AFIELD, INC.; *U.S. Private*, pg. 3761
SPORTS ANALYTICS LLC—See FTI Consulting, Inc.; *U.S. Public*, pg. 891
SPORTS AND IMPORTS, INC.; *U.S. Private*, pg. 3761
SPORTSBET PTY LIMITED—See Flutter Entertainment plc; *Int'l*, pg. 2715
SPORTS & BYTES GMBH—See Borussia Dortmund GmbH & Co. KGaA; *Int'l*, pg. 1115
SPORTS CAR CLUB OF AMERICA; *U.S. Private*, pg. 3761
SPORT-SCHECK GMBH—See Otto GmbH & Co. KG; *Int'l*, pg. 5662
SPORTSCHECK GMBH—See SIGNA Holding GmbH; *Int'l*, pg. 6909
SPORTS CLUB NAS CO., LTD.—See Daiwa House Industry Co., Ltd.; *Int'l*, pg. 1947
SPORTS CORNER LIMITED—See Win Hanverky Holdings Limited; *Int'l*, pg. 8424
SPORTSDIRECT.COM FITNESS LIMITED—See Frasers Group plc; *Int'l*, pg. 2765
SPORTS DIRECT MST SDN. BHD.—See Frasers Group plc; *Int'l*, pg. 2765
SPORTS DIRECT SPAIN, S.L.U.—See Frasers Group plc; *Int'l*, pg. 2765
SPORT SEASONS LP; *U.S. Private*, pg. 3760
THE SPORTS EDIT LIMITED—See Marks & Spencer Group plc; *Int'l*, pg. 4697
SPORTS ENDEAVORS INC.; *U.S. Private*, pg. 3761
SPORTSENGINE, INC.—See Comcast Corporation; *U.S. Public*, pg. 540
SPORTS ENTERTAINMENT ACQUISITION CORP.; *U.S. Public*, pg. 1919
SPORTS EXCELLENCE CORPORATION INC.; *Int'l*, pg. 7143
SPORTS & EXHIBITION AUTHORITY OF PITTSBURGH & ALLEGHENY COUNTY; *U.S. Private*, pg. 3760
THE SPORTS FACILITIES ADVISORY; *U.S. Private*, pg. 4120
SPORTSFIELD CO., LTD.; *Int'l*, pg. 7143
SPORTS FIELD HOLDINGS, INC.; *U.S. Private*, pg. 3761
SPORTSHOE CENTER, INC.; *U.S. Private*, pg. 3761
SPORTSHUB GAMES NETWORK INC.—See SharpLink Gaming, Inc.; *U.S. Public*, pg. 1874

COMPANY NAME INDEX

SPORTS HUB PRIVATE LIMITED—See Sportech PLC; *Int'l*, pg. 7142
SPORTS HUMANITARIAN GROUP INC.; *U.S. Private*, pg. 3761
SPORTS ILLUSTRATED—See Meredith Corporation; *U.S. Public*, pg. 1423
SPORTS IMAGE INC.; *U.S. Private*, pg. 3761
SPORTS INTERACTIVE LTD.—See Entain PLC; *Int'l*, pg. 2450
SPORTS LICENSED DIVISION OF THE ADIDAS GROUP, LLC—See adidas AG; *Int'l*, pg. 146
SPORTS LOGISTICS CO., LTD.—See Alpen Co., Ltd.; *Int'l*, pg. 366
THE SPORTSMAN CHANNEL, INC.—See InterMedia Advisors, LLC; *U.S. Private*, pg. 2112
THE SPORTSMAN CLUB LIMITED—See Caesars Entertainment, Inc.; *U.S. Public*, pg. 420
THE SPORTSMAN'S GUIDE, INC.—See Northern Tool & Equipment Company, Inc.; *U.S. Private*, pg. 2954
THE SPORTSMAN'S GUIDE OUTLET, INC.—See Northern Tool & Equipment Company, Inc.; *U.S. Private*, pg. 2954
SPORTSMAN SUPPLY INC.; *U.S. Private*, pg. 3761
SPORTSMAN'S WAREHOUSE HOLDINGS, INC.; *U.S. Public*, pg. 1919
SPORTSMAN'S WAREHOUSE, INC.—See Sportsman's Warehouse Holdings, Inc.; *U.S. Public*, pg. 1919
SPORTSMAP TECH ACQUISITION CORP.; *U.S. Public*, pg. 1919
SPORTS MEDIA ADVISORS LLC—See Vivendi SE; *Int'l*, pg. 8277
SPORTSMEDIA TECHNOLOGY CORP.; *U.S. Private*, pg. 3761
SPORTSMED SA HOSPITALS PTY LTD—See Burnside War Memorial Hospital Inc.; *Int'l*, pg. 1226
SPORTSMEMORABLIA.COM, LLC; *U.S. Private*, pg. 3761
SPORTS MOLDING, LLC—See Nordstjernan AB; *Int'l*, pg. 5426
SPORTSNET NEW YORK, LLC—See Charter Communications, Inc.; *U.S. Public*, pg. 483
SPORTSNET NEW YORK, LLC—See Comcast Corporation; *U.S. Public*, pg. 539
SPORTSNET NEW YORK, LLC—See Sterling Equities, Inc.; *U.S. Private*, pg. 0005
SPORTSNET; *Int'l*, pg. 7143
THE SPORTS NETWORK INC.—See BCE Inc.; *Int'l*, pg. 927
SPORTSOUL CO., LTD.; *Int'l*, pg. 7143
SPORT & SPINE CLINIC, L.P.—See U.S. Physical Therapy, Inc.; *U.S. Public*, pg. 2216
SPORT & SPINE CLINIC OF AUBURNDALE, LIMITED PARTNERSHIP—See U.S. Physical Therapy, Inc.; *U.S. Public*, pg. 2216
SPORT & SPINE REHAB; *U.S. Private*, pg. 3760
THE SPORTS PROMOTERS GMBH—See Vivendi SE; *Int'l*, pg. 8277
SPORTS RECRUITMENT INTERNATIONAL LTD.; *Int'l*, pg. 7143
SPORTS SYSTEMS SERVICES, INC.—See Spotlight Ticket Management, Inc.; *U.S. Private*, pg. 3762
SPORTSTEK ACQUISITION CORP.; *U.S. Public*, pg. 1919
SPORT STIX INC.; *U.S. Private*, pg. 3760
SPORTS TOTO BERHAD—See Berjaya Corporation Berhad; *Int'l*, pg. 983
SPORTS TOTO VIETNAM JOINT STOCK COMPANY—See Development Investment Construction JSC; *Int'l*, pg. 2088
SPORTSTRUST ADVISORS, LLC; *U.S. Private*, pg. 3761
SPORTS UNDERWRITING AUSTRALIA PTY. LTD.—See Steadfast Group Limited; *Int'l*, pg. 7187
SPORTS UNLIMITED, INC.; *U.S. Private*, pg. 3761
SPORT SUPPLY GROUP, INC.—See ONEX Corporation; *Int'l*, pg. 5580
SPORTS VENTURES ACQUISITION CORP.; *U.S. Public*, pg. 1919
SPORTSWEAR STORE INC.; *U.S. Private*, pg. 3761
SPORTSWIFT LIMITED; *Int'l*, pg. 7143
SPORTSWORLD GROUP LIMITED—See TUI AG; *Int'l*, pg. 7968
SPORTSWORLD HOSPITALITY LIMITED—See TUI AG; *Int'l*, pg. 7966
SPORTSWORLD MEDIA GROUP PLC; *Int'l*, pg. 7143
SPORTSWORLD TRAVEL LIMITED—See TUI AG; *Int'l*, pg. 7966
SPORTS ZONE INC.; *U.S. Private*, pg. 3761
SPORTTOTAL AG; *Int'l*, pg. 7143
SPORTTOTAL CONTENT MARKETING GMBH—See SPORTTOTAL AG; *Int'l*, pg. 7143
SPORTTOTAL EVENT GMBH—See SPORTTOTAL AG; *Int'l*, pg. 7143
SPORTTOTAL VENUES GMBH—See SPORTTOTAL AG; *Int'l*, pg. 7143
SPORT TRUCK USA, INC.—See Fox Factory Holding Corp.; *U.S. Public*, pg. 877
SPORT UND REHABILITATIONSZENTRUM HARZ GMBH—See MK-Kliniken AG; *Int'l*, pg. 5002
SPORTVISION, INC.—See Sportsmedia Technology Corp.; *U.S. Private*, pg. 3761

SPORTV MEDYA HIZMETLERI ANONIM SIRKETI—See Warner Bros. Discovery, Inc.; *U.S. Public*, pg. 2327
SPOT BEHAVIOR MEDIA, LLC; *U.S. Private*, pg. 3761
SPOT BUSINESS SYSTEMS, LLC.—See Clearent LLC; *U.S. Private*, pg. 932
SPOT COFFEE (CANADA) LTD.; *Int'l*, pg. 7143
SPOT COFFEE GLEN—See Spot Coffee (Canada) Ltd.; *Int'l*, pg. 7143
SPOT COFFEE SARATOGA LLC—See Spot Coffee (Canada) Ltd.; *Int'l*, pg. 7143
SPOT COFFEE TRANSIT INC.—See Spot Coffee (Canada) Ltd.; *Int'l*, pg. 7143
SPOT COOLERS INC.; *U.S. Private*, pg. 3761
SPOT FREIGHT, INC.; *U.S. Private*, pg. 3761
SPOTHERO, INC.; *U.S. Private*, pg. 3761
SPOTIFY AB; *Int'l*, pg. 7143
SPOTIFY HONG KONG LTD.—See Spotify AB; *Int'l*, pg. 7143
SPOTIFY LIMITED—See Spotify AB; *Int'l*, pg. 7143
SPOTIFY TECHNOLOGY S.A.; *Int'l*, pg. 7143
SPOTIFY USA INC.—See Spotify AB; *Int'l*, pg. 7143
SPOT IMAGE CORPORATION, INC.—See Airbus SE; *Int'l*, pg. 243
SPOT IMAGE S.A.S.—See Airbus SE; *Int'l*, pg. 246
SPOTING SA—See VINCI S.A.; *Int'l*, pg. 8229
SPOTINIST LLC—See NetApp, Inc.; *U.S. Public*, pg. 1507
SPOTINST LLC—See NetApp, Inc.; *U.S. Public*, pg. 1507
SPOTLESS DEFENCE SERVICES PTY. LTD.—See Downer EDI Limited; *Int'l*, pg. 2185
SPOTLESS FACILITY SERVICES PTY LTD—See Downer EDI Limited; *Int'l*, pg. 2185
SPOTLESS GROUP HOLDINGS LIMITED—See Downer EDI Limited; *Int'l*, pg. 2185
SPOTLESS GROUP LIMITED—See Downer EDI Limited; *Int'l*, pg. 2185
SPOTLESS SERVICES AUSTRALIA LIMITED—See Downer EDI Limited; *Int'l*, pg. 2185
SPOTLESS SERVICES (NZ) LTD.—See Downer EDI Limited; *Int'l*, pg. 2185
SPOTLIGHT ADVERTISING; *U.S. Private*, pg. 3761
SPOTLIGHT CAPITAL HOLDINGS, INC.; *U.S. Public*, pg. 1919
SPOTLIGHT FINANCIAL, INC.—See Informa plc; *Int'l*, pg. 3693
SPOTLIGHT INNOVATION INC.; *U.S. Private*, pg. 3761
SPOTLIGHT PTY. LTD.; *Int'l*, pg. 7143
SPOTLIGHT TICKET MANAGEMENT, INC.; *U.S. Private*, pg. 3762
SPOTLIGHT-VERLAG GMBH—See Verlagsgruppe Georg von Holtzbrinck GmbH; *Int'l*, pg. 8171
SPOTLIO A.S.; *Int'l*, pg. 7143
SPOTLITE360 IOT SOLUTIONS, INC.; *Int'l*, pg. 7143
SPOT ON PUBLIC RELATIONS—See Omnicom Group Inc.; *U.S. Public*, pg. 1578
SPOT—See Sonepar S.A.; *Int'l*, pg. 7094
SPOTSYLVANIA MULTI-SPECIALTY GROUP, LLC—See HCA Healthcare, Inc.; *U.S. Public*, pg. 1010
SPOTSYLVANIA REGIONAL MEDICAL CENTER—See HCA Healthcare, Inc.; *U.S. Public*, pg. 1010
SPOTSYLVANIA REGIONAL MEDICAL CENTER—See HCA Healthcare, Inc.; *U.S. Public*, pg. 1010
SPOTWAVE WIRELESS, LTD.—See Kavveri Telecom Products Ltd; *Int'l*, pg. 4093
SPOTXCHANGE INC—See Bertelsmann SE & Co. KGaA; *Int'l*, pg. 995
SPOTZOT, INC.—See MacAndrews & Forbes Incorporated; *U.S. Private*, pg. 2532
SPOUTING ROCK ALTERNATIVE CREDIT, LLC—See Spouting Rock Financial Partners LLC; *U.S. Private*, pg. 3762
SPOUTING ROCK ASSET MANAGEMENT LLC—See Spouting Rock Financial Partners LLC; *U.S. Private*, pg. 3762
SPOUTING ROCK FINANCIAL PARTNERS LLC; *U.S. Private*, pg. 3762
SPOV LTD.—See Canada Pension Plan Investment Board; *Int'l*, pg. 1280
SPOV LTD.—See EQT AB; *Int'l*, pg. 2483
SPOV LTD.—See Temasek Holdings (Private) Limited; *Int'l*, pg. 7548
SPOWER GMBH—See Proton Motor Power Systems Plc; *Int'l*, pg. 6006
SP PARTS CO., LTD. - KANSAI PLANT—See MISUMI Group Inc.; *Int'l*, pg. 4922
SP PARTS CO., LTD.—See MISUMI Group Inc.; *Int'l*, pg. 4922
SPP DG DEVCO 4A, LLC—See NRG Energy, Inc.; *U.S. Public*, pg. 1551
SPP FASTIGHETER AB—See Storebrand ASA; *Int'l*, pg. 7226
SP-PLANNING, INC.—See Kobayashi Pharmaceutical Co., Ltd.; *Int'l*, pg. 4216
SPP LIVFORSAKRING AB—See Storebrand ASA; *Int'l*, pg. 7226
SP PLUS CORPORATION—See Eldridge Industries LLC; *U.S. Private*, pg. 1351
SP PLUS PROPERTY MANAGEMENT, INC.—See Eldridge Industries LLC; *U.S. Private*, pg. 1351

SPREEN, INC.

SP PLUS SECURITY SERVICES, INC.—See Eldridge Industries LLC; *U.S. Private*, pg. 1351
SPP MANAGEMENT SERVICES, LLC; *U.S. Private*, pg. 3762
S&P POLSKA SP. Z.O.O.—See Simpson Manufacturing Company, Inc.; *U.S. Public*, pg. 1883
SPP PUMPS (ASIA) CO. LIMITED—See Kirloskar Brothers Limited; *Int'l*, pg. 4191
SPP PUMPS LIMITED—See Kirloskar Brothers Limited; *Int'l*, pg. 4191
SPP PUMPS MENA LLC—See Kirloskar Brothers Limited; *Int'l*, pg. 4191
SPP PUMPS (SOUTH AFRICA) (PTY). LIMITED—See Kirloskar Brothers Limited; *Int'l*, pg. 4191
SPRACKLEN PHYSICAL THERAPY, LP—See U.S. Physical Therapy, Inc.; *U.S. Public*, pg. 2216
SPRADLEY BARR FORD LINCOLN OF GREELEY INC.; *U.S. Private*, pg. 3762
SPRADLEY CHEVROLET-HYUNDAI; *U.S. Private*, pg. 3762
SPRAGUE DEVICES, INC.—See Commercial Vehicle Group, Inc.; *U.S. Public*, pg. 547
SPRAGUE ENERGY SOLUTIONS INC.—See Brookfield Corporation; *Int'l*, pg. 1182
SPRAGUE OPERATING RESOURCES LLC—See Brookfield Corporation; *Int'l*, pg. 1182
SPRAGUE PEST SOLUTIONS, INC.; *U.S. Private*, pg. 3762
SPRAGUE RESOURCES LP—See Brookfield Corporation; *Int'l*, pg. 1182
SPRAGUES' ROCK & SAND CO.; *U.S. Private*, pg. 3762
SPRASIA, INC.—See Hakuten Corporation; *Int'l*, pg. 3222
SPRAVBYTKOMFORT, A.S.—See CEZ, a.s.; *Int'l*, pg. 1428
SPRAYCOM COMERCIO DE PECAS PARA AGRICOLTURA S.A.—See Emak S.p.A.; *Int'l*, pg. 2373
SPRAYCOOL, INC.—See Parker Hannifin Corporation; *U.S. Public*, pg. 1643
SPRAY EQUIPMENT & SERVICE CENTER, INC.; *U.S. Private*, pg. 3762
SPRAYING SYSTEMS CO.; *U.S. Private*, pg. 3762
SPRAYING SYSTEMS DEUTSCHLAND GMBH—See Spraying Systems Co.; *U.S. Private*, pg. 3762
SPRAYING SYSTEMS JAPAN CO. LTD.—See Spraying Systems Co.; *U.S. Private*, pg. 3762
SPRAY INSULATIONS, INC.—See Paul J. Krez Company; *U.S. Private*, pg. 3113
SPRAYKING AGRO EQUIPMENT LIMITED; *Int'l*, pg. 7143
SPRAYLAT COATINGS (SHANGHAI) LIMITED—See PPG Industries, Inc.; *U.S. Public*, pg. 1710
SPRAY NINE CORPORATION—See Illinois Tool Works Inc.; *U.S. Public*, pg. 1107
SPRAY PAVE (PTY) LIMITED—See AECI Limited; *Int'l*, pg. 171
SPRAYSAFE AUTOMATIC SPRINKLERS LIMITED—See Johnson Controls International plc; *Int'l*, pg. 3989
SPRAY SYSTEMS ARIZONA INC.; *U.S. Private*, pg. 3762
SPRAYTEK, INC.—See Magni Group Inc.; *U.S. Private*, pg. 2548
SPRAYWAY, INC.—See The Pritzker Group - Chicago, LLC; *U.S. Private*, pg. 4099
SPREADSHIRT, INC.; *U.S. Private*, pg. 3762
SPREADTRUM COMMUNICATIONS, INC.—See Tsinghua Holdings Co., Ltd.; *Int'l*, pg. 7951
SPREADTRUM COMMUNICATIONS (SHANGHAI) CO., LTD.—See Tsinghua Holdings Co., Ltd.; *Int'l*, pg. 7951
SPREADTRUM COMMUNICATIONS (TIANJIN) CO., LTD.—See Tsinghua Holdings Co., Ltd.; *Int'l*, pg. 7951
SPREADTRUM COMMUNICATIONS USA INC.—See Tsinghua Holdings Co., Ltd.; *Int'l*, pg. 7951
SPREA EDITORI S.P.A.; *Int'l*, pg. 7144
SPREAFICO AUTOMATION S.R.L.—See I.M.A. Industria Macchine Automatiche S.p.A.; *Int'l*, pg. 3566
SPREA MEDIA ITALY SPA—See Sprea Editori S.p.A.; *Int'l*, pg. 7144
SPRECHER AG—See Burkhalter Holding AG; *Int'l*, pg. 1225
SPRECHER BREWING COMPANY, LLC; *U.S. Private*, pg. 3762
SPRECHER & SCHUH, INC.—See Rockwell Automation, Inc.; *U.S. Public*, pg. 1807
SPRECKELS SUGAR COMPANY, INC.—See Southern Minnesota Beet Sugar Cooperative; *U.S. Private*, pg. 3733
SPREDFAST, INC.—See Vista Equity Partners, LLC; *U.S. Private*, pg. 4398
SPREEGAS GESELLSCHAFT FUR GASVERSORGUNG UND ENERGIEDIENSTLEISTUNG MBH—See ENGIE SA; *Int'l*, pg. 2429
SPREEGAS GESELLSCHAFT FUR GASVERSORGUNG UND ENERGIEDIENSTLEISTUNG MBH—See E.ON SE; *Int'l*, pg. 2257
SPREEGAS GESELLSCHAFT FUR GASVERSORGUNG UND ENERGIEDIENSTLEISTUNG MBH—See Vattenfall AB; *Int'l*, pg. 8137
SPREE HOTELS AND REAL ESTATE PRIVATE LIMITED—See Easy Trip Planners Limited; *Int'l*, pg. 2276
SPREEN, INC.; *U.S. Private*, pg. 3763

SPREEN, INC.

SPREEWERK LUBBEN GMBH—See General Atomics; *U.S. Private*, pg. 1664
SP REFRACTORIES LIMITED; *Int'l*, pg. 7122
SPREHE GEFLUGEL- UND TIEFKUHLFEINKOST HANDELS GMBH & CO. KG - CLOPPENBURG PLANT—See Sprehe Geflugel- und Tiefkuhlfeinkost Handels GmbH & Co. KG; *Int'l*, pg. 7144
SPREHE GEFLUGEL- UND TIEFKUHLFEINKOST HANDELS GMBH & CO. KG; *Int'l*, pg. 7144
S&P REINFORCEMENT FRANCE—See Simpson Manufacturing Company, Inc.; *U.S. Public*, pg. 1883
S&P REINFORCEMENT NORDIC APS—See Simpson Manufacturing Company, Inc.; *U.S. Public*, pg. 1883
S&P REINFORCEMENT SPAIN, S.L.—See Simpson Manufacturing Company, Inc.; *U.S. Public*, pg. 1883
S&P REINFORCEMENT SP. Z O.O.—See Simpson Manufacturing Company, Inc.; *U.S. Public*, pg. 1883
SP RESOURCES INTERNATIONAL PTE. LTD.—See Tuan Sing Holdings Limited; *Int'l*, pg. 7962
S&P RESTAURANT COMPANY LIMITED—See S&P Syndicate Public Company Limited; *Int'l*, pg. 6445
S. P. RICHARDS CO. CANADA INC.—See Genuine Parts Company; *U.S. Public*, pg. 933
S.P. RICHARDS CO. CANADA, INC.—See Novexco, Inc.; *Int'l*, pg. 5462
S.P. RICHARDS COMPANY; *U.S. Private*, pg. 3518
SPRIG ELECTRIC CO.; *U.S. Private*, pg. 3763
SPRIG HEALTH, INC.—See Cambia Health Solutions, Inc.; *U.S. Private*, pg. 726
SPRIG & TRANSPORT NEEDS MANUFACTURING CO—See Chemical Industries Holding Company; *Int'l*, pg. 1462
SPR INC.; *U.S. Private*, pg. 3762
SPRIND D.D. SARAJEVO; *Int'l*, pg. 7144
SPRING11 ADVISORY SERVICES LIMITED—See Newmark Group, Inc.; *U.S. Public*, pg. 1516
SPRING 11 LLC—See Newmark Group, Inc.; *U.S. Public*, pg. 1516
SPRINGAHEAD; *U.S. Private*, pg. 3763
SPRING AIRLINES CO., LTD.; *Int'l*, pg. 7144
SPRING ARBOR DISTRIBUTORS INC.—See Ingram Industries, Inc.; *U.S. Private*, pg. 2076
SPRING ART HOLDINGS BERHAD; *Int'l*, pg. 7144
SPRING ASSET MANAGEMENT LTD.—See Mercuria Investment Co., Ltd.; *Int'l*, pg. 4833
SPRING BANCORP, INC.; *U.S. Private*, pg. 3763
SPRINGBIG HOLDINGS, INC.; *U.S. Public*, pg. 1919
SPRINGBIG, INC.—See SpringBig Holdings, Inc.; *U.S. Public*, pg. 1919
SPRINGBOARD CAPITAL, LLC; *U.S. Private*, pg. 3763
SPRINGBOARD COMMUNICATIONS; *U.S. Private*, pg. 3763
SPRINGBOARD CORPORATE FINANCE LLP—See Begbies Traynor Group plc; *Int'l*, pg. 941
SPRINGBOARD NONPROFIT CONSUMER CREDIT MANAGEMENT, INC.; *U.S. Private*, pg. 3763
SPRINGBOARD; *U.S. Private*, pg. 3763
SPRINGBOARD TELECOM, LLC—See Comporium Group; *U.S. Private*, pg. 1002
SPRINGBOK ATLAS NAMIBIA (PTY) LTD—See Cullinan Holdings Limited; *Int'l*, pg. 1877
SPRINGBOK ATLAS TOURS & SAFARIS PTY LTD—See Cullinan Holdings Limited; *Int'l*, pg. 1877
SPRINGBORN SMITHERS LABS LLC—See Charles River Laboratories International, Inc.; *U.S. Public*, pg. 480
SPRINGBOX, LTD.; *U.S. Private*, pg. 3763
SPRINGBROOK; *U.S. Private*, pg. 3763
SPRING CITY ELECTRICAL MFG. CO., INC; *U.S. Private*, pg. 3763
SPRINGCM INC.—See DocuSign, Inc.; *U.S. Public*, pg. 672
SPRING COMMUNICATIONS HOLDING, INC.—See Prime Communications LP; *U.S. Private*, pg. 3261
SPRING COMMUNICATIONS—See Prime Communications LP; *U.S. Private*, pg. 3261
SPRING CREEK COAL LLC—See Cloud Peak Energy Inc.; *U.S. Private*, pg. 946
SPRINGDALE MORNING NEWS—See Wehco Media, Inc.; *U.S. Private*, pg. 4470
SPRINGDALE TRACTOR COMPANY INC.; *U.S. Private*, pg. 3764
SPRINGDAY PTY. LTD.—See Madison Dearborn Partners, LLC; *U.S. Private*, pg. 2540
SPRING ENGINEERING, INC.; *U.S. Private*, pg. 3763
SPRING ENGINEERS OF HOUSTON LTD.—See SEI MetalTek; *U.S. Private*, pg. 3599
SPRING EQUITY, LLC—See Rithm Capital Corp.; *U.S. Public*, pg. 1800
SPRINGER DEVELOPMENT LLC—See Banner Corporation; *U.S. Public*, pg. 275
SPRINGER FACHMEDIEN MUNCHEN GMBH—See Verlagsgruppe Georg von Holtzbrinck GmbH; *Int'l*, pg. 8170
SPRINGER FACHMEDIEN WIESBADEN GMBH—See Verlagsgruppe Georg von Holtzbrinck GmbH; *Int'l*, pg. 8170
SPRINGER & JACOBY EL LABORATORIO S.L.—See Springer & Jacoby Osterreich GmbH; *Int'l*, pg. 7144

SPRINGER & JACOBY INTERNATIONAL B.V.—See Springer & Jacoby Osterreich GmbH; *Int'l*, pg. 7144
SPRINGER & JACOBY OSTERREICH GMBH; *Int'l*, pg. 7144
SPRINGER MAGRATH COMPANY—See Frandsen Corporation; *U.S. Private*, pg. 1593
SPRINGER MEDIA B.V.—See BC Partners LLP; *Int'l*, pg. 925
SPRINGER-MILLER INTERNATIONAL, LLC—See Constellation Software Inc.; *Int'l*, pg. 1773
SPRINGER-MILLER SYSTEMS - NEVADA—See Constellation Software Inc.; *Int'l*, pg. 1773
SPRINGER-MILLER SYSTEMS—See Constellation Software Inc.; *Int'l*, pg. 1773
SPRINGER MINING COMPANY—See Till Capital Corporation; *Int'l*, pg. 7748
SPRINGER PUBLISHING COMPANY, LLC—See Mannheim, LLC; *U.S. Private*, pg. 2565
SPRINGER SCIENCE+BUSINESS MEDIA B.V.—See BC Partners LLP; *Int'l*, pg. 925
SPRINGER SCIENCE+BUSINESS MEDIA DEUTSCHLAND GMBH—See Verlagsgruppe Georg von Holtzbrinck GmbH; *Int'l*, pg. 8170
SPRINGER SCIENCE+BUSINESS MEDIA, LLC—See Verlagsgruppe Georg von Holtzbrinck GmbH; *Int'l*, pg. 8170
SPRINGER SCIENCE+BUSINESS MEDIA S.A.—See BC Partners LLP; *Int'l*, pg. 925
SPRINGER-VERLAG GMBH—See Verlagsgruppe Georg von Holtzbrinck GmbH; *Int'l*, pg. 8170
SPRINGFIELD AUTO SUPPLY INC.; *U.S. Private*, pg. 3764
SPRINGFIELD DEVELOPMENT CORP LLC—See United Natural Foods, Inc.; *U.S. Public*, pg. 2231
SPRINGFIELD ELECTRIC SUPPLY COMPANY; *U.S. Private*, pg. 3764
SPRINGFIELD FIRST COMMUNITY BANK—See QCR Holdings, Inc.; *U.S. Public*, pg. 1742
SPRINGFIELD FLYING SERVICE INCORPORATED—See Harry Cooper Supply Company; *U.S. Private*, pg. 1871
SPRINGFIELD GAMING AND REDEVELOPMENT, LLC—See PENN Entertainment, Inc.; *U.S. Public*, pg. 1662
SPRINGFIELD HYUNDAI; *U.S. Private*, pg. 3764
SPRINGFIELD LLC—See Milliken & Company; *U.S. Private*, pg. 2737
SPRINGFIELD LODGE DAY NURSERY (DARTFORD) LTD.—See Bain Capital, LP; *U.S. Private*, pg. 437
SPRINGFIELD LODGE DAY NURSERY (SWANSCOMBE) LTD.—See Bain Capital, LP; *U.S. Private*, pg. 437
SPRINGFIELD MANUFACTURING LLC—See The Springs Company; *U.S. Private*, pg. 4120
SPRINGFIELD NEWSPAPERS, INC.—See Apollo Global Management, Inc.; *U.S. Public*, pg. 163
SPRINGFIELD PARK VIEW HOSPITAL, L.L.C.—See Apollo Global Management, Inc.; *U.S. Public*, pg. 157
SPRINGFIELD PEPSI COLA BOTTLING CO. INC.; *U.S. Private*, pg. 3764
SPRINGFIELD PROPERTIES PLC; *Int'l*, pg. 7144
SPRINGFIELD REMANUFACTURING CORP. HEAVY DUTY DIV—See SRC Holdings Corporation; *U.S. Private*, pg. 3767
SPRINGFIELD RESOURCE RECOVERY, INC.—See Fluor Corporation; *U.S. Public*, pg. 859
SPRINGFIELD URBAN LEAGUE, INC.; *U.S. Private*, pg. 3764
SPRINGFIELD UTILITY BOARD INC.; *U.S. Private*, pg. 3764
SPRINGFIELD WATER & SEWER COMMISSION; *U.S. Private*, pg. 3764
SPRINGFIELD WIRE INC.; *U.S. Private*, pg. 3764
SPRING GARDENS LIMITED—See CLS Holdings plc; *Int'l*, pg. 1664
SPRING-GREEN LAWN CARE CORPORATION; *U.S. Private*, pg. 3763
SPRING GROUP AUSTRALIA PTY LIMITED—See Adecco Group AG; *Int'l*, pg. 138
SPRING GROUP LIMITED—See Adecco Group AG; *Int'l*, pg. 138
SPRING GROVE RESOURCE RECOVERY, INC.—See Clean Harbors, Inc.; *U.S. Public*, pg. 510
SPRINGHILL HEALTH SERVICES INC.—See Southern Medical Health Systems Inc.; *U.S. Private*, pg. 3733
SPRINGHILL HOSPITALS, INC.—See Southern Medical Health Systems Inc.; *U.S. Private*, pg. 3733
SPRING HILL IMAGING, LLC—See HCA Healthcare, Inc.; *U.S. Public*, pg. 1010
SPRINGHILL LAKE INVESTORS LIMITED PARTNERSHIP CO.—See Blackstone Inc.; *U.S. Public*, pg. 350
SPRING HILL MALL L.L.C.—See Brookfield Corporation; *Int'l*, pg. 1185
SPRINGHILL MEDICAL COMPLEX INC.—See Southern Medical Health Systems Inc.; *U.S. Private*, pg. 3733
SPRINGHILL MEDICAL SERVICES, INC.; *U.S. Private*, pg. 3764
SPRINGHILL MEMORY GARDENS LLC—See Axar Capital Management L.P.; *U.S. Private*, pg. 412
SPRING HILL PHYSICIANS, LLC—See HCA Healthcare, Inc.; *U.S. Public*, pg. 1010

CORPORATE AFFILIATIONS

SPRINGHILL SMC, LLC—See Marriott International, Inc.; *U.S. Public*, pg. 1371
SPRING HILL SPECIALIST DAY HOSPITAL P.TY LIMITED—See Virtus Health Limited; *Int'l*, pg. 8249
SPRINGHILL SUITES (BY MARRIOTT) - CONVENTION CENTER/INTERNATIONAL DRIVE AREA—See Marriott International, Inc.; *U.S. Public*, pg. 1371
SPRINGHILL SUITES (BY MARRIOTT) - TARRYTOWN GREENBURGH—See Marriott International, Inc.; *U.S. Public*, pg. 1371
SPRING HOUSE ENTERTAINMENT TECH. INC.—See Chunghwa Telecom Co., Ltd.; *Int'l*, pg. 1598
SPRINGHOUSE, L.L.C.—See Altisource Portfolio Solutions S.A.; *Int'l*, pg. 393
SPRING LAKE CONSULTING—See Mitchell Martin, Inc.; *U.S. Private*, pg. 2751
SPRINGLAND INTERNATIONAL HOLDINGS LIMITED; *Int'l*, pg. 7144
SPRINGMASTERS—See American Securities LLC; *U.S. Private*, pg. 250
SPRING MEDICAL CENTRE LTD.—See WELL Health Technologies Corp.; *Int'l*, pg. 8372
SPRING MESSE MANAGEMENT GMBH—See Deutsche Messe AG; *Int'l*, pg. 2071
SPRING METRICS, INC.; *U.S. Private*, pg. 3763
SPRING MOBIL AB—See Tele2 AB; *Int'l*, pg. 7529
SPRINGMOOR LIFE CARE RETIREMENT COMMUNITY; *U.S. Private*, pg. 3764
SPRING MOUNTAIN ADVENTURE CORP.; *U.S. Private*, pg. 3763
SPRING MOUNTAIN VINEYARDS, INC.—See MGG Investment Group, LP; *U.S. Private*, pg. 2694
SPRING NEAR EAST MANUFACTURING COMPANY LIMITED—See PDS Limited; *Int'l*, pg. 5771
SPRING, O'BRIEN & CO. INC.; *U.S. Private*, pg. 3763
SPRINGPATH LLC—See Cisco Systems, Inc.; *U.S. Public*, pg. 500
SPRING PERSONNEL LIMITED—See Adecco Group AG; *Int'l*, pg. 138
SPRING PHARMACEUTICAL GROUP, INC.; *Int'l*, pg. 7144
SPRINGPOINT SENIOR LIVING; *U.S. Private*, pg. 3764
SPRINGPOINT TECHNOLOGIES; *U.S. Private*, pg. 3764
SPRING PROFESSIONAL LUXEMBOURG SA.—See Adecco Group AG; *Int'l*, pg. 141
SPRING PROFESSIONAL SINGAPORE PTE LTD—See Adecco Group AG; *Int'l*, pg. 138
SPRING RICH LIMITED—See Taiwan Paiho Limited; *Int'l*, pg. 7423
SPRINGS AT CLACKAMAS WOODS, LLC—See Ventas, Inc.; *U.S. Public*, pg. 2278
SPRINGS BRANDS, LLC—See Coteminas Companhia de Tecidos Norte de Minas; *Int'l*, pg. 1817
SPRINGS CANADA, LTD.—See Coteminas Companhia de Tecidos Norte de Minas; *Int'l*, pg. 1817
SPRINGS CANADA, LTD.—See Springs Global, Inc.; *U.S. Private*, pg. 3764
THE SPRINGS COMPANY; *U.S. Private*, pg. 4120
SPRINGS DE MEXICO, S.A. DE C.V.—See Coteminas Companhia de Tecidos Norte de Minas; *Int'l*, pg. 1817
SPRINGS DE MEXICO, S.A. DE C.V.—See Springs Global, Inc.; *U.S. Private*, pg. 3764
SPRINGS FABRICATION, INC. - ADVANCED TECHNOLOGY GROUP—See Springs Fabrication, Inc.; *U.S. Private*, pg. 3764
SPRINGS FABRICATION, INC.; *U.S. Private*, pg. 3764
SPRINGS GLOBAL, INC. - BATH FASHIONS DIVISION—See Springs Global, Inc.; *U.S. Private*, pg. 3764
SPRINGS GLOBAL, INC.; *U.S. Private*, pg. 3764
SPRINGS GLOBAL PARTICIPACOES S.A.—See Coteminas Companhia de Tecidos Norte de Minas; *Int'l*, pg. 1817
SPRINGS GLOBAL PARTICIPACOES S.A.—See Springs Global, Inc.; *U.S. Private*, pg. 3764
SPRINGS GLOBAL US, INC.—See Coteminas Companhia de Tecidos Norte de Minas; *Int'l*, pg. 1817
SPRINGS GLOBAL US, INC.—See Springs Global, Inc.; *U.S. Private*, pg. 3764
SPRINGS INC.—See Activar, Inc.; *U.S. Private*, pg. 68
SPRINGS ROOFING LIMITED—See Northern Bear Plc; *Int'l*, pg. 5443
SPRINGSTONE, INC.—See Apollo Global Management, Inc.; *U.S. Public*, pg. 158
SPRINGS VALLEY BANK & TRUST CO.—See SVB&T Corporation; *U.S. Private*, pg. 3888
SPRINGS WATER FACTORY CO. LTD—See Nestle S.A.; *Int'l*, pg. 5211
SPRINGS WINDOW FASHIONS LLC—See AEA Investors LP; *U.S. Private*, pg. 115
SPRINGS WINDOW FASHIONS LLC—See British Columbia Investment Management Corp.; *Int'l*, pg. 1169
SPRING TECHNOLOGY STAFFING SERVICES LIMITED—See Adecco Group AG; *Int'l*, pg. 138
SPRINGTHYME OILS LIMITED—See Kerry Group plc; *Int'l*, pg. 4139
SPRING TOLLMAN COMPANY, INC.; *U.S. Private*, pg. 3763
SPRINGTREE FARM GROUP; *U.S. Private*, pg. 3764

COMPANY NAME INDEX

SPRINGVALE COAL PTY LIMITED—See Banpu Public Company Limited; *Int'l*, pg. 852
SPRING VALLEY PRODUCE, INC.—See GrubMarket, Inc.; *U.S. Private*, pg. 1797
SPRING VENTURE GROUP, LLC; *U.S. Private*, pg. 3763
SPRING VENTURES LTD.; *Int'l*, pg. 7144
SPRING VIEW HOSPITAL, LLC—See Apollo Global Management, Inc.; *U.S. Public*, pg. 158
SPRINGVILLE PHARMACY INFUSION THERAPY, INC.—See Walgreens Boots Alliance, Inc.; *U.S. Public*, pg. 2323
SPRINGWALL SLEEP PRODUCTS INC.; *Int'l*, pg. 7144
SPRINGWATER CAPITAL LLC; *Int'l*, pg. 7144
SPRINGWORKS THERAPEUTICS, INC.; *U.S. Public*, pg. 1919
SPRING WORKS UTAH; *U.S. Private*, pg. 3763
SPRINKLERBOLAGET STOCKHOLM AB—See Instalco AB; *Int'l*, pg. 3722
SPRINKLERBOLAGET SYD I HELSINGBORG AB—See Instalco AB; *Int'l*, pg. 3722
SPRINKLR, INC.; *U.S. Public*, pg. 1920
SPRINT BIOSCIENCE AB; *Int'l*, pg. 7144
SPRINT COMMUNICATIONS, INC.—See Deutsche Telekom AG; *Int'l*, pg. 2084
SPRINT CORPORATION—See Deutsche Telekom AG; *Int'l*, pg. 2084
SPRINT ENERGY SERVICES—See Republic Services, Inc.; *U.S. Public*, pg. 1788
SPRINTEX CLEAN AIR (MALAYSIA) SDN. BHD.—See Sprintex Limited; *Int'l*, pg. 7144
SPRINTEX LIMITED; *Int'l*, pg. 7144
SPRINTEX USA, INC.—See Sprintex Limited; *Int'l*, pg. 7144
SPRINT INDUSTRIAL HOLDINGS LLC; *U.S. Private*, pg. 3764
SPRINT INDUSTRIAL SERVICES, LLC—See Sprint Industrial Holdings LLC; *U.S. Private*, pg. 3765
SPRINT OIL COMPANY; *U.S. Private*, pg. 3765
SPRINTQUIP PTY. LTD.; *Int'l*, pg. 7144
SPRINT SAFETY, INC.—See Littlejohn & Co., LLC; *U.S. Private*, pg. 2472
SPRINT SANIERUNG GMBH—See DZ BANK AG Deutsche Zentral-Genossenschaftsbank; *Int'l*, pg. 2244
SPRINT SPOL S.R.O.—See Goldwin, Inc.; *Int'l*, pg. 3035
SPRINTZ FURNITURE SHOWROOM INC.; *U.S. Private*, pg. 3765
SPRITZER BHD.; *Int'l*, pg. 7145
SPRIX INC.; *Int'l*, pg. 7145
SPRIZA, INC.; *U.S. Public*, pg. 1920
SPRL BRUNELLO CUCINELLI BELGIUM—See Brunello Cucinelli S.p.A.; *Int'l*, pg. 1200
SPRL FERME DE WISEMPIERRE—See Heidelberg Materials AG; *Int'l*, pg. 3319
S-PROCESS EQUIPMENT AUSTRALIA PTY. LIMITED—See Sandvik AB; *Int'l*, pg. 6530
SPROCOMM INTELLIGENCE LIMITED; *Int'l*, pg. 7145
SPRONKEN ORTHOPEDIE NV; *Int'l*, pg. 7145
S PROSERV HUNGARY - PROCUREMENT SERVICES HU KFT.—See Erste Group Bank AG; *Int'l*, pg. 2499
S PROSERV SLOVAKIA - PROCUREMENT SERVICES SK, S.R.O.—See Erste Group Bank AG; *Int'l*, pg. 2499
SPROTT ASSET MANAGEMENT LP—See Sprott Inc.; *Int'l*, pg. 7145
SPROTT FOCUS TRUST, INC.; *Int'l*, pg. 7145
SPROTT INC.; *Int'l*, pg. 7145
SPROTT PHYSICAL GOLD AND SILVER TRUST—See Sprott Inc.; *Int'l*, pg. 7145
SPROTT PHYSICAL GOLD TRUST—See Sprott Inc.; *Int'l*, pg. 7145
SPROTT PHYSICAL PLATINUM AND PALLADIUM TRUST—See Sprott Inc.; *Int'l*, pg. 7145
SPROTT PHYSICAL SILVER TRUST—See Sprott Inc.; *Int'l*, pg. 7145
SPROTT PRIVATE WEALTH LP—See Sprott Inc.; *Int'l*, pg. 7145
SPROTT RESOURCE LENDING CORP.—See Sprott Inc.; *Int'l*, pg. 7145
SPROTT SHAW COLLEGE CORP.—See Global Education Communities Corp; *Int'l*, pg. 2995
SPROULE HOLDINGS LIMITED; *Int'l*, pg. 7145
SPROUT FOODS, INC.—See Neptune Wellness Solutions, Inc.; *Int'l*, pg. 5201
SPROUT GROUP—See UBS Group AG; *Int'l*, pg. 8006
SPROUTLOUD MEDIA NETWORKS, LLC—See Ansira Partners, Inc.; *U.S. Private*, pg. 286
SPROUTLY CANADA, INC.; *Int'l*, pg. 7145
SPROUTS FARMERS MARKETS, INC.; *U.S. Public*, pg. 1920
SPROUT SOCIAL, INC.; *U.S. Public*, pg. 1920
SPROUT TINY HOMES, INC.; *U.S. Public*, pg. 1920
SPR PROCUREMENT COMPANY—See Genuine Parts Company; *U.S. Public*, pg. 933
SPRUCE BIOSCIENCES, INC.; *U.S. Public*, pg. 1920
SPRUCE CREEK DEVELOPMENT CO. OF OCALA; *U.S. Private*, pg. 3765
SPRUCELAND FORD SALES LTD.; *Int'l*, pg. 7145
SPRUCE POWER HOLDING CORPORATION; *U.S. Public*, pg. 1920

SPRUCE PRIVATE INVESTORS LLC; *U.S. Private*, pg. 3765
SPRUCE RIDGE, INC.—See Waste Management, Inc.; *U.S. Public*, pg. 2332
SPRUCE RIDGE RESOURCES LTD.; *Int'l*, pg. 7145
SPRUCE VAKUUTUS OY—See Kemira Oyj; *Int'l*, pg. 4124
SPRUGEL HOMETEX GMBH—See Steilmann Holding AG; *Int'l*, pg. 7193
SPRUIT TRANSMISSIES BV—See Axel Johnson Gruppen AB; *Int'l*, pg. 763
SPRUSON & FERGUSON (ASIA) PTE. LIMITED—See IPH Limited; *Int'l*, pg. 3797
SPRUSON & FERGUSON INTELLECTUAL PROPERTY AGENCY (BEIJING) CO.—See IPH Limited; *Int'l*, pg. 3797
SPRUSON & FERGUSON LAWYERS PTY. LIMITED—See IPH Limited; *Int'l*, pg. 3797
SPRUSON & FERGUSON (M) SDN. BHD.—See IPH Limited; *Int'l*, pg. 3797
SPRUYT HILLEN BV—See Fagron NV; *Int'l*, pg. 2603
SPRYLOGIC TECHNOLOGIES LTD—See Aplab Limited; *Int'l*, pg. 515
SPS AEROSTRUCTURES LIMITED—See Berkshire Hathaway Inc.; *U.S. Public*, pg. 315
S.P. SATRIA LOGISTICS SDN. BHD.—See Suria Capital Holdings Berhad; *Int'l*, pg. 7344
S.P. SATRIA SDN. BHD.—See Suria Capital Holdings Berhad; *Int'l*, pg. 7344
SPS BETEILIGUNGEN ALPHA AG—See Swiss Prime Site AG; *Int'l*, pg. 7370
SPS B.V.—See RPM International Inc.; *U.S. Public*, pg. 1820
SPS COMMERCE CANADA, LTD.—See SPS Commerce, Inc.; *U.S. Public*, pg. 1920
SPS COMMERCE, INC.; *U.S. Public*, pg. 1920
SPS COMPANIES INC.; *U.S. Private*, pg. 3765
SPS CORPORATION, CURTAIN WALL DIVISION—See SPS Corporation; *U.S. Private*, pg. 3765
SPS CORPORATION, RETROFIT DIVISION—See SPS Corporation; *U.S. Private*, pg. 3765
SPS CORPORATION; *U.S. Private*, pg. 3765
S P SETIA BERHAD; *Int'l*, pg. 6443
S P SETIA ECO-PROJECTS MANAGEMENT SDN BHD—See S P Setia Berhad; *Int'l*, pg. 6443
S P SETIA MARKETING SDN BHD—See S P Setia Berhad; *Int'l*, pg. 6443
S P SETIA PROPERTY SERVICES SDN BHD—See S P Setia Berhad; *Int'l*, pg. 6443
SPS FINQUEST LIMITED; *Int'l*, pg. 7146
SPS IMMOBILIEN AG—See Swiss Prime Site AG; *Int'l*, pg. 7370
SPS IMMOBILIEN LTD—See Swiss Prime Site AG; *Int'l*, pg. 7370
SPS INDUSTRIAL INC.; *U.S. Private*, pg. 3765
SPS INTERNATIONAL LIMITED; *Int'l*, pg. 7146
S&P SISTEMAS DE VENTILACIÓN, S.L.U.; *Int'l*, pg. 6445
SPS MEDICAL SUPPLY CORP.—See STERIS plc; *Int'l*, pg. 7209
SPSS CHINA (SHANGHAI) LIMITED—See Openbase Inc.; *Int'l*, pg. 5599
SPSS INC. - ROCHESTER—See International Business Machines Corporation; *U.S. Public*, pg. 1148
SPSS INC.—See International Business Machines Corporation; *U.S. Public*, pg. 1148
SPSS KOREA DATASOLUTION INC.—See Openbase Inc.; *Int'l*, pg. 5599
SPS S.R.L.—See Sesa S.p.A.; *Int'l*, pg. 6729
SPSS SOUTH ASIA (PVT.) LTD.—See International Business Machines Corporation; *U.S. Public*, pg. 1148
SPS STUDIOS, INC.; *U.S. Private*, pg. 3765
SPS TECHNOLOGIES - GREER STOP NUT—See Berkshire Hathaway Inc.; *U.S. Public*, pg. 315
SPS TECHNOLOGIES LIMITED—See Berkshire Hathaway Inc.; *U.S. Public*, pg. 315
SPS TECHNOLOGIES, LLC—See Berkshire Hathaway Inc.; *U.S. Public*, pg. 314
S&P STEEL PRODUCTS INC.; *U.S. Private*, pg. 3513
S&P SYNDICATE PUBLIC COMPANY LIMITED; *Int'l*, pg. 6445
SP SYSTEMS CO., LTD.; *Int'l*, pg. 7123
SP TELECOMMUNICATIONS PTE. LTD.—See Temasek Holdings (Private) Limited; *Int'l*, pg. 7551
SPT ENERGY GROUP INC.; *Int'l*, pg. 7146
SPT FINANCIAL SERVICES PTY. LTD.—See AUB Group Limited; *Int'l*, pg. 698
SPT HOLDINGS INC.—See Rexel, S.A.; *Int'l*, pg. 6317
SPT INKASSO OU—See Axactor SE; *Int'l*, pg. 761
SPT INTERNATIONAL, LTD.—See ScinoPharm Taiwan, Ltd.; *Int'l*, pg. 6649
SPT LABTECH LIMITED; *U.S. Private*, pg. 3765
SPT-PAINTING OY—See Kingspan Group PLC; *Int'l*, pg. 4178
S&P TRAINING CO., LTD.—See S&P Syndicate Public Company Limited; *Int'l*, pg. 6445
SPTS K.K.—See KLA Corporation; *U.S. Public*, pg. 1268
S.P.T. - SOCIETA PASSANTE TORINO S.C.R.L.—See Salini Costruttori S.p.A.; *Int'l*, pg. 6493
SPTS TECHNOLOGIES GMBH—See KLA Corporation; *U.S. Public*, pg. 1268

S P V I PUBLIC COMPANY LIMITED

SPTS TECHNOLOGIES, INC.—See KLA Corporation; *U.S. Public*, pg. 1268
SPTS TECHNOLOGIES - KOREA—See KLA Corporation; *U.S. Public*, pg. 1268
SPTS TECHNOLOGIES LTD.—See KLA Corporation; *U.S. Public*, pg. 1268
SPTS TECHNOLOGIES LTD.—See KLA Corporation; *U.S. Public*, pg. 1269
SPTS TECHNOLOGIES - MALAYSIA—See KLA Corporation; *U.S. Public*, pg. 1268
SPTS TECHNOLOGIES PTE. LTD.—See KLA Corporation; *U.S. Public*, pg. 1268
SPTS TECHNOLOGIES SAS—See KLA Corporation; *U.S. Public*, pg. 1269
SPTS TECHNOLOGIES (SHANGHAI) INC.—See KLA Corporation; *U.S. Public*, pg. 1268
SPTS TECHNOLOGIES - TAIWAN—See KLA Corporation; *U.S. Public*, pg. 1268
SPT TELECOMMUNICATIONS PTY LTD—See CK Hutchison Holdings Limited; *Int'l*, pg. 1638
SPT TELECOMMUNICATIONS PTY LTD—See Vodafone Group Plc; *Int'l*, pg. 8285
SPT WAH WELLINGTON LLC—See Starwood Property Trust, Inc.; *U.S. Public*, pg. 1940
SPUDNIK EQUIPMENT COMPANY; *U.S. Private*, pg. 3765
SPUHL AG—See Leggett & Platt, Incorporated; *U.S. Public*, pg. 1303
SPUHL GMBH—See Leggett & Platt, Incorporated; *U.S. Public*, pg. 1303
SPUN METALS, INC.—See Dubai Holding LLC; *Int'l*, pg. 2218
SPUR CORPORATION AUSTRALIA PTY LTD—See Spur Corporation; *Int'l*, pg. 7146
SPUR CORPORATION; *Int'l*, pg. 7146
SPUR ENERGY PARTNERS LLC—See KKR & Co. Inc.; *U.S. Public*, pg. 1264
SPURLIN INDUSTRIES INC.; *U.S. Private*, pg. 3765
SPURLINO MATERIALS, LLC; *U.S. Private*, pg. 3765
SPURLOCK SCRAP INC.; *U.S. Private*, pg. 3765
SPURR CHEVROLET INC & COURTESY PONTIAC-GMC; *U.S. Private*, pg. 3765
SPURRIER CHEMICAL COMPANIES, INC.; *U.S. Private*, pg. 3765
SPURS SPORTS & ENTERTAINMENT; *U.S. Private*, pg. 3765
SPURWAY COOKE INDUSTRIES PTY LTD.—See Nylex Limited; *Int'l*, pg. 5501
SPURWINK SERVICES INCORPORATED; *U.S. Private*, pg. 3765
S&P USA VENTILATION SYSTEMS, LLC—See S&P Sistemas de Ventilación, S.L.U.; *Int'l*, pg. 6445
SPUTNIK ENTERPRISES INC.; *U.S. Public*, pg. 1920
SPV68, S.R.O.—See HTC holding a.s.; *Int'l*, pg. 3508
SPV-DRUCK GESELLSCHAFT M.B.H—See Erste Group Bank AG; *Int'l*, pg. 2499
SPVGG UNTERHACHING FOOTBALL GMBH & CO. KGAA; *Int'l*, pg. 7146
SPV GLOBAL TRADING LIMITED; *Int'l*, pg. 7146
S P V I PUBLIC COMPANY LIMITED; *Int'l*, pg. 6444
SPX COOLING TECHNOLOGIES FRANCE SA—See SPX Technologies, Inc.; *U.S. Public*, pg. 1921
SPX COOLING TECHNOLOGIES INC.—See SPX Technologies, Inc.; *U.S. Public*, pg. 1921
SPX COOLING TECHNOLOGIES—See SPX Technologies, Inc.; *U.S. Public*, pg. 1921
SPX COOLING TECHNOLOGIES TRADING DMCC—See SPX Technologies, Inc.; *U.S. Public*, pg. 1921
SPX COOLING TECHNOLOGIES UK LTD.—See SPX Technologies, Inc.; *U.S. Public*, pg. 1921
SPX COOLING TECHNOLOGIES (ZHANGJIAKOU) CO. LTD—See SPX Technologies, Inc.; *U.S. Public*, pg. 1921
SPX DE MEXICO, S.A. DE C.V.—See Lone Star Funds; *U.S. Private*, pg. 2487
SPX DRY COOLING USA, LLC—See SPX Technologies, Inc.; *U.S. Public*, pg. 1921
SPX FLOW CONTROL—See Lone Star Funds; *U.S. Private*, pg. 2486
SPX FLOW, INC.—See Lone Star Funds; *U.S. Private*, pg. 2485
SPX FLOW TECHNOLOGY AUSTRALIA—See Lone Star Funds; *U.S. Private*, pg. 2486
SPX FLOW TECHNOLOGY BELGIUM NV—See Lone Star Funds; *U.S. Private*, pg. 2486
SPX FLOW TECHNOLOGY CANADA INC—See Lone Star Funds; *U.S. Private*, pg. 2486
SPX FLOW TECHNOLOGY COPENHAGEN A/S—See Lone Star Funds; *U.S. Private*, pg. 2486
SPX FLOW TECHNOLOGY CRAWLEY LIMITED—See Lone Star Funds; *U.S. Private*, pg. 2486
SPX FLOW TECHNOLOGY DANMARK A/S—See Lone Star Funds; *U.S. Private*, pg. 2486
SPX FLOW TECHNOLOGY ETTEN-LEUR B.V.—See Lone Star Funds; *U.S. Private*, pg. 2486
SPX FLOW TECHNOLOGY FINLAND OY—See Lone Star Funds; *U.S. Private*, pg. 2486
SPX FLOW TECHNOLOGY GERMANY GMBH—See Lone Star Funds; *U.S. Private*, pg. 2486

SPX FLOW TECHNOLOGY HANSE GMBH—See Lone Star Funds; *U.S. Private*, pg. 2486
SPX FLOW TECHNOLOGY (INDIA) PRIVATE LIMITED—See Lone Star Funds; *U.S. Private*, pg. 2486
SPX FLOW TECHNOLOGY JAPAN, INC.—See Lone Star Funds; *U.S. Private*, pg. 2486
SPX FLOW TECHNOLOGY KOREA CO., LTD.—See Lone Star Funds; *U.S. Private*, pg. 2486
SPX FLOW TECHNOLOGY LONDON LIMITED—See Lone Star Funds; *U.S. Private*, pg. 2487
SPX FLOW TECHNOLOGY MEXICO S.A. DE C.V.—See Lone Star Funds; *U.S. Private*, pg. 2486
SPX FLOW TECHNOLOGY MOERS GMBH—See Lone Star Funds; *U.S. Private*, pg. 2486
SPX FLOW TECHNOLOGY NEW ZEALAND LIMITED—See Lone Star Funds; *U.S. Private*, pg. 2486
SPX FLOW TECHNOLOGY NORDERSTEDT GMBH—See Lone Star Funds; *U.S. Private*, pg. 2486
SPX FLOW TECHNOLOGY NORWAY AS—See Lone Star Funds; *U.S. Private*, pg. 2486
SPX FLOW TECHNOLOGY (PTY) LIMITED—See Lone Star Funds; *U.S. Private*, pg. 2486
SPX FLOW TECHNOLOGY ROSISTA GMBH—See Lone Star Funds; *U.S. Private*, pg. 2486
SPX FLOW TECHNOLOGY SANTORSO S.R.L.—See Lone Star Funds; *U.S. Private*, pg. 2486
SPX FLOW TECHNOLOGY SAS—See Lone Star Funds; *U.S. Private*, pg. 2486
SPX FLOW TECHNOLOGY SINGAPORE PTE. LTD.—See Lone Star Funds; *U.S. Private*, pg. 2486
SPX FLOW TECHNOLOGY—See Lone Star Funds; *U.S. Private*, pg. 2486
SPX FLOW TECHNOLOGY STOCKHOLM AB—See Lone Star Funds; *U.S. Private*, pg. 2486
SPX FLOW TECHNOLOGY SVERIGE AB—See Lone Star Funds; *U.S. Private*, pg. 2486
SPX FLOW TECHNOLOGY (THAILAND) LIMITED—See Lone Star Funds; *U.S. Private*, pg. 2486
SPX FLOW TECHNOLOGY USA, INC.—See Lone Star Funds; *U.S. Private*, pg. 2486
SPX FLOW TECHNOLOGY WARENDORF GMBH—See Lone Star Funds; *U.S. Private*, pg. 2486
SPX GENFARE—See SPX Technologies, Inc.; *U.S. Public*, pg. 1921
SPX GERMANY HOLDING GMBH—See SPX Technologies, Inc.; *U.S. Public*, pg. 1921
SPX HEAT TRANSFER INC.—See SPX Technologies, Inc.; *U.S. Public*, pg. 1921
SPX HEAT TRANSFER—See SPX Technologies, Inc.; *U.S. Public*, pg. 1921
SPX HYDRAULIC TECHNOLOGIES—See SPX Technologies, Inc.; *U.S. Public*, pg. 1921
SPX IBERICA S.A.—See Lone Star Funds; *U.S. Private*, pg. 2487
SPX INDIA PRIVATE LIMITED—See Lone Star Funds; *U.S. Private*, pg. 2487
SPX INTERNATIONAL LIMITED—See Lone Star Funds; *U.S. Private*, pg. 2487
SPX ITALIA S.R.L—See Lone Star Funds; *U.S. Private*, pg. 2487
SPX MIDDLE EAST FZE—See Lone Star Funds; *U.S. Private*, pg. 2487
SPX NETHERLANDS B.V.—See Lone Star Funds; *U.S. Private*, pg. 2487
SPX PROCESS EQUIPMENT—See SPX Technologies, Inc.; *U.S. Public*, pg. 1921
SPX PROCESS EQUIPMENT—See SPX Technologies, Inc.; *U.S. Public*, pg. 1921
SPX PROCESS EQUIPMENT—See SPX Technologies, Inc.; *U.S. Public*, pg. 1921
SPX (SCHWEIZ) AG—See Lone Star Funds; *U.S. Private*, pg. 2486
SPX SERVICOS INDUSTRIAIS LTDA.—See Lone Star Funds; *U.S. Private*, pg. 2487
SPX (SHANGHAI) FLOW TECHNOLOGY CO., LTD.—See Lone Star Funds; *U.S. Private*, pg. 2486
SPX TECHNOLOGIES, INC.; *U.S. Public*, pg. 1920
SPX TECHNOLOGIES (PTY) LTD.—See SPX Technologies, Inc.; *U.S. Public*, pg. 1921
SPX TRANSFORMER SOLUTIONS, INC. - GOLDSBORO—See SPX Technologies, Inc.; *U.S. Public*, pg. 1921
SPX TRANSFORMER SOLUTIONS, INC.—See SPX Technologies, Inc.; *U.S. Public*, pg. 1921
SPX VALLEY FORGE TECHNICAL INFORMATION SERVICES, INC.—See SPX Technologies, Inc.; *U.S. Public*, pg. 1921
SPYGLASS ENTERTAINMENT GROUP, LLC—See Cerberus Capital Management, L.P.; *U.S. Private*, pg. 839
SPYGLASS RESOURCES CORP.; *Int'l*, pg. 7146
SPY HILL POWER L.P.—See Northland Power Inc.; *Int'l*, pg. 5446
SPY INC.—See Alvarez & Marsal, Inc.; *U.S. Private*, pg. 212
SPYKER AUTOMOBIELEN B.V.—See Spyker N.V.; *Int'l*, pg. 7146

SPYKER EVENTS & BRANDING B.V.—See Spyker N.V.; *Int'l*, pg. 7146
SPYKER N.V.; *Int'l*, pg. 7146
SPYKER OF CHINA LTD.—See China Automobile Trading Co., Ltd.; *Int'l*, pg. 1484
SPYKER OF CHINA LTD.—See Spyker N.V.; *Int'l*, pg. 7146
SPY OPTIC SRL—See Alvarez & Marsal, Inc.; *U.S. Private*, pg. 212
SPYRE THERAPEUTICS, INC.; *U.S. Public*, pg. 1922
SPYR, INC.; *U.S. Public*, pg. 1922
SPYROSOFT ECOMMERCE S.A.—See Spyrosoft S.A.; *Int'l*, pg. 7146
SPYROSOFT S.A.; *Int'l*, pg. 7146
SPYROSOFT SYNERGY S.A.—See Spyrosoft S.A.; *Int'l*, pg. 7146
SPZ ZEMENTWERK EIBERG GMBH & CO. KG—See Rohrdorfer Gruppe; *Int'l*, pg. 6386
SQA SERVICES, INC.; *U.S. Private*, pg. 3765
SQBG, INC.—See Sequential Brands Group, Inc.; *U.S. Public*, pg. 1868
S.Q.I. CORPORATION NV—See Sociedad Quimica y Minera de Chile S.A.; *Int'l*, pg. 7032
SQI DIAGNOSTICS INC.; *Int'l*, pg. 7146
SQID TECHNOLOGIES LIMITED; *Int'l*, pg. 7146
SQLI AGENCY—See DBAY Advisors Limited; *Int'l*, pg. 1987
SQLI BELGIUM SA—See DBAY Advisors Limited; *Int'l*, pg. 1987
SQLI CONSEIL IT—See DBAY Advisors Limited; *Int'l*, pg. 1987
SQLI IMMOBILIER—See DBAY Advisors Limited; *Int'l*, pg. 1987
SQLI INSTITUT—See DBAY Advisors Limited; *Int'l*, pg. 1987
SQLI LUXEMBOURG SA—See DBAY Advisors Limited; *Int'l*, pg. 1987
SQLI NEWBI—See DBAY Advisors Limited; *Int'l*, pg. 1987
SQLI SA—See DBAY Advisors Limited; *Int'l*, pg. 1987
SQL SENTRY, LLC—See SolarWinds Corporation; *U.S. Public*, pg. 1900
SQLSTREAM, INC.—See Thales S.A.; *Int'l*, pg. 7606
SQ-M2 LTD; *Int'l*, pg. 7146
SQM BEIJING COMMERCIAL CO. LTD.—See Sociedad Quimica y Minera de Chile S.A.; *Int'l*, pg. 7032
SQM BRASIL LTDA.—See Sociedad Quimica y Minera de Chile S.A.; *Int'l*, pg. 7032
SQMC INTERNATIONAL LIMITADA—See Sociedad Quimica y Minera de Chile S.A.; *Int'l*, pg. 7033
SQM COMERCIAL DE MEXICO S.A. DE C.V.—See Sociedad Quimica y Minera de Chile S.A.; *Int'l*, pg. 7032
SQM CORPORATION NV—See Sociedad Quimica y Minera de Chile S.A.; *Int'l*, pg. 7032
SQM DUBAI - FZCO.—See Sociedad Quimica y Minera de Chile S.A.; *Int'l*, pg. 7032
SQM ECUADOR S.A.—See Sociedad Quimica y Minera de Chile S.A.; *Int'l*, pg. 7032
SQM EUROPE NV—See Sociedad Quimica y Minera de Chile S.A.; *Int'l*, pg. 7032
SQM IBERIAN S.A.—See Sociedad Quimica y Minera de Chile S.A.; *Int'l*, pg. 7032
SQM INDUSTRIAL S.A.—See Sociedad Quimica y Minera de Chile S.A.; *Int'l*, pg. 7032
SQM INTERNATIONAL N.V.—See Sociedad Quimica y Minera de Chile S.A.; *Int'l*, pg. 7032
SQM INVESTMENT CORPORATION NV—See Sociedad Quimica y Minera de Chile S.A.; *Int'l*, pg. 7032
SQM ITALIA SRL—See Sociedad Quimica y Minera de Chile S.A.; *Int'l*, pg. 7032
SQM JAPAN CO. LTD.—See Sociedad Quimica y Minera de Chile S.A.; *Int'l*, pg. 7032
SQM JAPON CO. LTDA—See Sociedad Quimica y Minera de Chile S.A.; *Int'l*, pg. 7032
SQM KOREA LLC—See Sociedad Quimica y Minera de Chile S.A.; *Int'l*, pg. 7032
SQM NITRATOS MEXICO S.A. DE C.V.—See Sociedad Quimica y Minera de Chile S.A.; *Int'l*, pg. 7033
SQM NITRATOS S.A.—See Sociedad Quimica y Minera de Chile S.A.; *Int'l*, pg. 7033
SQM NORTH AMERICA CORP.—See Sociedad Quimica y Minera de Chile S.A.; *Int'l*, pg. 7033
SQM PERU S.A.—See Sociedad Quimica y Minera de Chile S.A.; *Int'l*, pg. 7033
SQM POTASIO S.A.—See Sociedad Quimica y Minera de Chile S.A.; *Int'l*, pg. 7033
SQM SALAR S.A.—See Sociedad Quimica y Minera de Chile S.A.; *Int'l*, pg. 7033
SQM (SHANGHAI) CHEMICALS CO. LTD.—See Sociedad Quimica y Minera de Chile S.A.; *Int'l*, pg. 7032
SQM THAILAND LIMITED—See Sociedad Quimica y Minera de Chile S.A.; *Int'l*, pg. 7033
SQM VENEZUELA S.A.—See Sociedad Quimica y Minera de Chile S.A.; *Int'l*, pg. 7033
SQM - VITAS BRASIL LTDA.—See Compagnie Financiere et de Participations Roullier SA; *Int'l*, pg. 1740
SQM VITAS PERU S.A.—See Compagnie Financiere et de Participations Roullier SA; *Int'l*, pg. 1740

SQO STADT QUARTIER OFFENBURG GMBH & CO. KG—See Helaba Landesbank Hessen-Thuringen; *Int'l*, pg. 3328
SQRRL DATA, INC.—See Amazon.com, Inc.; *U.S. Public*, pg. 90
SQS SOFTWARE QUALITY SYSTEMS (SCHWEIZ) AG, ZURICH—See Assystem S.A.; *Int'l*, pg. 650
SQUADHELP, INC.; *U.S. Private*, pg. 3765
SQUADRON ENERGY PTY. LTD.—See Tattarang Pty. Ltd.; *Int'l*, pg. 7474
SQUADRON MEDICAL LIMITED—See DCC plc; *Int'l*, pg. 1991
SQUAMISH TERMINALS LTD.; *Int'l*, pg. 7146
SQUAN CONSTRUCTION SERVICES LLC; *U.S. Private*, pg. 3766
SQUARE 1 ASSET MANAGEMENT, INC.—See Banc of California, Inc.; *U.S. Public*, pg. 269
SQUARE 1 PRODUCTS LTD.; *Int'l*, pg. 7146
SQUARE 2 MARKETING, INC.—See RFE Investment Partners; *U.S. Private*, pg. 3419
SQUARE BUTTE ELECTRIC COOPERATIVE—See Minnkota Power Cooperative, Inc.; *U.S. Private*, pg. 2744
SQUARE CANADA, INC.—See Block, Inc.; *U.S. Public*, pg. 362
SQUARE CIRCLE BROKERS LIMITED—See Brown & Brown, Inc.; *U.S. Public*, pg. 402
SQUARE CO., LTD.—See Nomad Foods Limited; *Int'l*, pg. 5409
SQUARE D COMPANY MEXICO, S.A. DE C.V.—See Schneider Electric SE; *Int'l*, pg. 6635
SQUARE DEAL BUILDING SUPPLY; *U.S. Private*, pg. 3766
SQUARE D INVESTMENT COMPANY—See Schneider Electric SE; *Int'l*, pg. 6634
SQUARE DRANKEN NEDERLAND B.V.—See B&S Group S.A.; *Int'l*, pg. 784
SQUARE ENIX (CHINA) CO. LTD.—See Square Enix Holdings Co. Ltd.; *Int'l*, pg. 7147
SQUARE ENIX CO., LTD.—See Square Enix Holdings Co. Ltd.; *Int'l*, pg. 7147
SQUARE ENIX GMBH—See Square Enix Holdings Co. Ltd.; *Int'l*, pg. 7147
SQUARE ENIX HOLDINGS CO. LTD.; *Int'l*, pg. 7147
SQUARE ENIX, INC.—See Square Enix Holdings Co. Ltd.; *Int'l*, pg. 7147
SQUARE ENIX LTD.—See Square Enix Holdings Co. Ltd.; *Int'l*, pg. 7147
SQUARE ENIX MOBILESTUDIO, CO., LTD.—See Square Enix Holdings Co. Ltd.; *Int'l*, pg. 7147
SQUARE FOUR PROJECTS INDIA LIMITED; *Int'l*, pg. 7147
SQUARE-H BRANDS INC.; *U.S. Private*, pg. 4366
SQUARELIFE LEBENSVERSICHERUNGS AKTIENGESELLSCHAFT S.A.; *Int'l*, pg. 7147
SQUARE MILE CAPITAL MANAGEMENT LLC; *U.S. Private*, pg. 3766
SQUAREMOUTH INC.—See Hellman & Friedman LLC; *U.S. Private*, pg. 1909
SQUARE ONE ARMORING SERVICES CO.; *U.S. Private*, pg. 3766
SQUARE ONE GMBH & CO KG—See STRABAG SE; *Int'l*, pg. 7233
SQUARE ONE, INC.; *U.S. Private*, pg. 3766
SQUARE ONE MARKETING; *U.S. Private*, pg. 3766
SQUARE ONE; *U.S. Private*, pg. 3766
SQUAREPEG DISTRIBUTION SERVICES PVT. LTD.—See Tanvi Foods (India) Limited; *Int'l*, pg. 7460
SQUARE PEG PACKAGING & PRINTING, LLC—See Atlas Holdings, LLC; *U.S. Private*, pg. 378
SQUARE PHARMACEUTICALS LTD.; *Int'l*, pg. 7147
SQUARE ROOT, INC.; *U.S. Private*, pg. 3766
SQUARE S HOLDING GMBH—See Starwood Capital Group Global I, LLC; *U.S. Private*, pg. 3789
SQUARESPACE INC.—See Permira Advisers LLP; *Int'l*, pg. 5808
SQUARESTONE BRASIL LIMITED; *Int'l*, pg. 7147
SQUARE TECHNOLOGY GROUP CO., LTD.; *Int'l*, pg. 7147
SQUARE TEXTILE LTD.; *Int'l*, pg. 7147
SQUARETRADE HOLDING COMPANY, INC.—See The Allstate Corporation; *U.S. Public*, pg. 2034
SQUARETRADE, INC.—See The Allstate Corporation; *U.S. Public*, pg. 2032
SQUARETRADE LIMITED—See The Allstate Corporation; *U.S. Public*, pg. 2034
SQUAR MILNER LLP; *U.S. Private*, pg. 3766
SQUATEX ENERGY & RESSOURCES, INC.; *Int'l*, pg. 7147
SQUAW VALLEY SKI HOLDINGS, LLC—See KSL Capital Partners, LLC; *U.S. Private*, pg. 2354
SQUID INK MANUFACTURING, INC.—See Engage Technologies Corp.; *U.S. Public*, pg. 1397
SQUIRE BOONE CAVERNS INCORPORATED; *U.S. Private*, pg. 3766
SQUIRE CORRUGATED CONTAINER CORP.; *U.S. Private*, pg. 3766
SQUIRE PATTON BOGGS (US) LLP; *U.S. Private*, pg. 3766

COMPANY NAME INDEX

SQUIRE PATTON BOGGS (US) LLP - WASHINGTON, DC—See Squire Patton Boggs (US) LLP; *U.S. Private*, pg. 3766
THE SQUIRES GROUP INC; *U.S. Private*, pg. 4120
SQUIRES KITCHEN SUGARCRAFT (WUXI) CO., LTD.—See San Neng Group Holdings Co., Ltd.; *Int'l*, pg. 6521
SQUIRREL BRAND, L.P.—See John B. Sanfilippo & Son, Inc.; *U.S. Public*, pg. 1190
SQUIRRELS UK LIMITED—See Kitwave Group Plc; *Int'l*, pg. 4196
SQUORING TECHNOLOGIES SAS—See Vector Informatik GmbH; *Int'l*, pg. 8144
SQX RESOURCES LIMITED; *Int'l*, pg. 7147
SQZ BIOTECHNOLOGIES COMPANY; *U.S. Public*, pg. 1922
SR2P—See PSB Industries SA; *Int'l*, pg. 6015
SR ACCORD LTD.; *Int'l*, pg. 7147
S-RACMO CO., LTD.—See Sumitomo Chemical Company, Limited; *Int'l*, pg. 7264
SRA (EUROPE) B.V.—See SRA Holdings Inc; *Int'l*, pg. 7148
SRA HOLDINGS INC; *Int'l*, pg. 7147
SRA INDIA PRIVATE LIMITED—See SRA Holdings Inc; *Int'l*, pg. 7147
SRA IP SOLUTIONS (ASIA PACIFIC) PTE. LTD.—See SRA Holdings Inc; *Int'l*, pg. 7147
SRA/MCGRAW HILL—See Platinum Equity, LLC; *U.S. Private*, pg. 3206
SRAM INTERNATIONAL CORPORATION; *U.S. Private*, pg. 3767
SRAM, LLC - COLORADO DEVELOPMENT CENTER—See SRAM International Corporation; *U.S. Private*, pg. 3767
SRAM, LLC—See SRAM International Corporation; *U.S. Private*, pg. 3767
SRAMPORT - TRANSMISSOES MECHANICAS, LDA.—See SRAM International Corporation; *U.S. Private*, pg. 3767
SRAM - TAIWAN—See SRAM International Corporation; *U.S. Private*, pg. 3767
SRA PROFESSIONAL SERVICE, INC.—See SRA Holdings Inc; *Int'l*, pg. 7147
SRA. RUSHMORE—See WPP plc; *Int'l*, pg. 8467
SRA TOHOKU, INC.—See SRA Holdings Inc; *Int'l*, pg. 7147
SRAVATHI ADVANCE PROCESS TECH PRIVATE LIMITED—See Shilpa Medicare Ltd; *Int'l*, pg. 6831
SRAVATHI AI TECHNOLOGY PRIVATE LIMITED—See Shilpa Medicare Ltd; *Int'l*, pg. 6831
SRAX, INC.; *U.S. Public*, pg. 1922
SR BANCORP, INC.; *U.S. Public*, pg. 1922
SRBIJAPUT A.D.; *Int'l*, pg. 7148
SRBIJA TIS A.D.; *Int'l*, pg. 7148
SRBIJATRANSPORT A.D.; *Int'l*, pg. 7148
SRBIJA TURIST A.D.; *Int'l*, pg. 7148
SR BIOTEK, INC.; *Int'l*, pg. 7147
SRB MANAGEMENT PTY. LTD.—See Steadfast Group Limited; *Int'l*, pg. 7187
S.R. BRAY LLC; *U.S. Private*, pg. 3518
SRC AUTOMOTIVE, INC.—See SRC Holdings Corporation; *U.S. Private*, pg. 3767
SRC COMMERCIAL HOLDINGS, INC.—See SRC, Inc.; *U.S. Private*, pg. 3767
SRC CORP.; *U.S. Private*, pg. 3767
SRC ELECTRICAL LLC—See SRC Holdings Corporation; *U.S. Private*, pg. 3767
SRC HAVERHILL—See Aptiv PLC; *Int'l*, pg. 526
SR-CHINA ADVISORY SERVICES CO LTD—See Fairfax Financial Holdings Limited; *Int'l*, pg. 2608
SRC HOLDINGS CORPORATION; *U.S. Private*, pg. 3767
SRC, INC.; *U.S. Private*, pg. 3767
SRC INTERNATIONAL, INC.—See SRC, Inc.; *U.S. Private*, pg. 3767
SRC LOGISTICS, INC.—See SRC Holdings Corporation; *U.S. Private*, pg. 3767
SR COLLECTE S.A.S.—See Tessenderlo Group NV; *Int'l*, pg. 7574
SRC POWER SYSTEMS INC.—See SRC Holdings Corporation; *U.S. Private*, pg. 3767
SRC POWER SYSTEMS—See SRC Holdings Corporation; *U.S. Private*, pg. 3767
SRC—See VINCI S.A.; *Int'l*, pg. 8226
SRCTEC, LLC—See SRC, Inc.; *U.S. Private*, pg. 3767
SRC VENTURES, INC.—See SRC, Inc.; *U.S. Private*, pg. 3767
SR DENTAL AB—See Rentokil Initial plc; *Int'l*, pg. 6289
SRD INC.—See Dos Gringos Inc.; *U.S. Private*, pg. 1264
S R DOOR, INC.; *U.S. Private*, pg. 3512
SRDS, INC.—See Bain Capital, LP; *U.S. Private*, pg. 448
S-REAL MORAVA SPOL S.R.O.—See Erste Group Bank AG; *Int'l*, pg. 2499
S REAL SPARKASSE D.O.O.—See Erste Group Bank AG; *Int'l*, pg. 2499
SRECO-FLEXIBLE INCORPORATED; *U.S. Private*, pg. 3767
SREDNE-VOLZHSKY TRANSNEFTEPRODUCT, JSC—See OAO AK Transneft; *Int'l*, pg. 5505
SREDNJA BACKA A.D.; *Int'l*, pg. 7148

SREDNJI BANAT A.D.; *Int'l*, pg. 7148
SREECHEM RESINS LIMITED; *Int'l*, pg. 7148
SREE JAYALAKSHMI AUTOSPIN LIMITED; *Int'l*, pg. 7148
SREELEATHERS LIMITED; *Int'l*, pg. 7148
SREE MAHALAKSHMI SMELTERS PRIVATE LIMITED—See Indsil Hydro Power And Manganese Ltd.; *Int'l*, pg. 3661
SREE MARUTHI MARINE INDUSTRIES LTD.—See TGV Sraac Limited; *Int'l*, pg. 7588
SREE RAYALASEEMA HI-STRENGTH HYPO LIMITED; *Int'l*, pg. 7148
SREE RAYALSEEMA GALAXY PROJECTS PRIVATE LTD.—See TGV Sraac Limited; *Int'l*, pg. 7588
S REG AB—See Lundbeckfonden; *Int'l*, pg. 4583
SRE GROUP LIMITED; *Int'l*, pg. 7148
SRE HOLDINGS CORPORATION; *Int'l*, pg. 7148
SREI INFRASTRUCTURE FINANCE LTD—See National Asset Reconstruction Company Limited; *Int'l*, pg. 5150
SREI MUTUAL FUND ASSET MANAGEMENT PVT. LTD.—See National Asset Reconstruction Company Limited; *Int'l*, pg. 5151
SREIT CAMRI GREEN APARTMENTS, L.L.C.—See Starwood Real Estate Income Trust, Inc.; *U.S. Private*, pg. 3790
SREIT-COASTAL PARTNERS, L.P.—See Starwood Real Estate Income Trust, Inc.; *U.S. Private*, pg. 3790
SREIT COLUMBIA HILLS, L.L.C.—See Starwood Real Estate Income Trust, Inc.; *U.S. Private*, pg. 3790
SREIT COURTNEY MANOR, L.L.C.—See Starwood Real Estate Income Trust, Inc.; *U.S. Private*, pg. 3790
SREIT CREEKSIDE AT BELLEMEADE, L.P.—See Starwood Real Estate Income Trust, Inc.; *U.S. Private*, pg. 3790
SREIT DOMINION PINES, L.L.C.—See Starwood Real Estate Income Trust, Inc.; *U.S. Private*, pg. 3790
SREIT FALCON POINTE, L.P.—See Starwood Real Estate Income Trust, Inc.; *U.S. Private*, pg. 3790
SREIT FALCON TRACE, L.L.C.—See Starwood Real Estate Income Trust, Inc.; *U.S. Private*, pg. 3790
SREIT GRIFFIN SCOTTSDALE, L.L.C.—See Starwood Real Estate Income Trust, Inc.; *U.S. Private*, pg. 3790
SREIT HATTERAS SOUND, L.L.C.—See Starwood Real Estate Income Trust, Inc.; *U.S. Private*, pg. 3790
SREIT HOLLY COVE APARTMENTS, L.L.C.—See Starwood Real Estate Income Trust, Inc.; *U.S. Private*, pg. 3790
SREIT LAS VILLAS DE KINO, L.L.C.—See Starwood Real Estate Income Trust, Inc.; *U.S. Private*, pg. 3790
SREIT LAS VILLAS DE LEON, L.P.—See Starwood Real Estate Income Trust, Inc.; *U.S. Private*, pg. 3790
SREIT LEIGH MEADOWS APARTMENTS, L.L.C.—See Starwood Real Estate Income Trust, Inc.; *U.S. Private*, pg. 3790
SREIT LEXINGTON CLUB, L.L.C.—See Starwood Real Estate Income Trust, Inc.; *U.S. Private*, pg. 3790
SREIT MADELYN OAKS, L.L.C.—See Starwood Real Estate Income Trust, Inc.; *U.S. Private*, pg. 3790
SREIT OVERLOOK AT SIMMS CREEK, L.P.—See Starwood Real Estate Income Trust, Inc.; *U.S. Private*, pg. 3790
SREIT PATRIOTS POINTE, L.P.—See Starwood Real Estate Income Trust, Inc.; *U.S. Private*, pg. 3790
SREIT PONCE HARBOR, L.L.C.—See Starwood Real Estate Income Trust, Inc.; *U.S. Private*, pg. 3790
SREIT RESERVES AT ARBORETUM, L.L.C.—See Starwood Real Estate Income Trust, Inc.; *U.S. Private*, pg. 3790
SREIT RIVER PARK PLACE, L.L.C.—See Starwood Real Estate Income Trust, Inc.; *U.S. Private*, pg. 3790
SREIT RIVER REACH, L.L.C.—See Starwood Real Estate Income Trust, Inc.; *U.S. Private*, pg. 3790
SREIT SOLDIERS RIDGE, L.L.C.—See Starwood Real Estate Income Trust, Inc.; *U.S. Private*, pg. 3790
SREIT SOUTH MAINE COMMONS, L.L.C.—See Starwood Real Estate Income Trust, Inc.; *U.S. Private*, pg. 3790
SREIT SPINNAKER REACH, L.L.C.—See Starwood Real Estate Income Trust, Inc.; *U.S. Private*, pg. 3790
SREIT STERLING CREST, L.L.C.—See Starwood Real Estate Income Trust, Inc.; *U.S. Private*, pg. 3790
SREIT STONE CREEK, L.P.—See Starwood Real Estate Income Trust, Inc.; *U.S. Private*, pg. 3790
SREIT THOMAS CHASE APARTMENTS, L.L.C.—See Starwood Real Estate Income Trust, Inc.; *U.S. Private*, pg. 3790
SREIT VISTA HAVEN, L.L.C.—See Starwood Real Estate Income Trust, Inc.; *U.S. Private*, pg. 3790
SREMPUT A.D.; *Int'l*, pg. 7148
SRESTHA FINVEST LIMITED; *Int'l*, pg. 7148
SRETEN GUDURIC A.D.; *Int'l*, pg. 7148
SRF LIMITED; *Int'l*, pg. 7148
S.R.G.A. COMPANY LIMITED—See Chow Steel Industries Public Company Limited; *Int'l*, pg. 1584
SRG CLINICAL—See HFBG Holding B.V.; *Int'l*, pg. 3375
SRG ENGINEERING—See HFBG Holding B.V.; *Int'l*, pg. 3375
SRG GLOBAL AUTOMOTIVE, LLC—See Koch Industries, Inc.; *U.S. Private*, pg. 2329
SRG GLOBAL, INC.—See Koch Industries, Inc.; *U.S. Private*, pg. 2329

SRI PANWA HOSPITALITY REAL ESTATE INVESTMENT TRUST

SRG GLOBAL LIMITED; *Int'l*, pg. 7148
SRG HOUSING FINANCE LTD; *Int'l*, pg. 7149
SRG INTERNATIONAL INC.; *Int'l*, pg. 7149
SRG MINING INC.; *Int'l*, pg. 7149
SRG MINING INC.; *Int'l*, pg. 7149
THE SR GROUP (UK) LTD.—See Baird Financial Group, Inc.; *U.S. Public*, pg. 453
S R G SECURITIES FINANCE LIMITED; *Int'l*, pg. 6444
SRG SECURITY RESOURCE GROUP INC.—See SSC Security Services Corp.; *Int'l*, pg. 7155
SRG SERVICES LIMITED—See The Rank Group Plc; *Int'l*, pg. 7678
SRG—See HFBG Holding B.V.; *Int'l*, pg. 3375
SRG SSR IDEE SUISSE; *Int'l*, pg. 7149
SRG WOOLF GROUP, INC.—See HFBG Holding B.V.; *Int'l*, pg. 3375
SRH FACHKRANKENHAUS NERESHEIM GMBH—See SRH Holding GmbH; *Int'l*, pg. 7149
SRH GESUNDHEITSZENTRUM BAD WIMPFEN GMBH—See SRH Holding GmbH; *Int'l*, pg. 7149
SRHHL INDUSTRIES LIMITED; *Int'l*, pg. 7149
SRH HOLDING GMBH; *Int'l*, pg. 7149
SRHI LLC—See D.R. Horton, Inc.; *U.S. Public*, pg. 620
SRH KLINIKUM KARLSBAD-LANGENSTEINBACH GMBH—See SRH Holding GmbH; *Int'l*, pg. 7149
SRH KRANKENHAUS OBERNDORF A.N. GMBH—See SRH Holding GmbH; *Int'l*, pg. 7149
SRH KRANKENHAUS WALTERSHAUSEN-FRIEDRICHRODA GMBH—See SRH Holding GmbH; *Int'l*, pg. 7149
SRH KURPFALZKRANKENHAUS HEIDELBERG GMBH—See SRH Holding GmbH; *Int'l*, pg. 7149
SRH N.V.—See Stichting Beheer SNS REAAL; *Int'l*, pg. 7214
SRH WALD-KLINIKUM GERA GMBH—See SRH Holding GmbH; *Int'l*, pg. 7149
SRH ZENTRALKLINIKUM SUHL GMBH—See SRH Holding GmbH; *Int'l*, pg. 7149
SRI AMARNATH FINANCE LIMITED; *Int'l*, pg. 7149
SRI CHEYENNE, INC.—See Sports Recruitment International Inc.; *U.S. Private*, pg. 7143
SRI-CUTTER'S INSULATION INC.—See Southern Residential Installations LLC; *U.S. Private*, pg. 3735
SRI FIRE SPRINKLER CORP.; *U.S. Private*, pg. 3767
SRI HAVISHA HOSPITALITY & INFRASTRUCTURE LTD.; *Int'l*, pg. 7149
SRI HYBRID LTD.—See Sumitomo Rubber Industries, Ltd.; *Int'l*, pg. 7299
SRI INTERNATIONAL; *U.S. Private*, pg. 3767
SRIJANG INDAH SDN. BHD.—See MKH Berhad; *Int'l*, pg. 5002
SRIJANG KEMAJUAN SDN. BHD.—See MKH Berhad; *Int'l*, pg. 5002
S-RIKO AUTOMOTIVE HOSE DE CHIHUAHUA, S.A.P.I. DE C.V.—See Sumitomo Riko Company Limited; *Int'l*, pg. 7298
SRI KPR INDUSTRIES LIMITED; *Int'l*, pg. 7149
SRI KRISHNA CONSTRUCTIONS (INDIA) LIMITED; *Int'l*, pg. 7149
SRILAKSHMI ENTERPRISE—See Rajvir Industries Limited; *Int'l*, pg. 6194
SRI LAKSHMI SARASWATHI TEXTILES (ARNI) LTD.; *Int'l*, pg. 7150
SRI LANKA INSTITUTE OF NANOTECHNOLOGY (PVT) LTD.—See Hayleys PLC; *Int'l*, pg. 3292
SRILANKAN AIRLINES LTD.; *Int'l*, pg. 7151
SRILANKAN AIRLINES LTD.-THAILAND—See SriLankan Airlines Ltd.; *Int'l*, pg. 7151
SRILANKAN CATERING LIMITED—See SriLankan Airlines Ltd.; *Int'l*, pg. 7151
SRI LANKA TELECOM PLC; *Int'l*, pg. 7150
SRI LANKA TELECOM (SERVICES) LIMITED—See Sri Lanka Telecom PLC; *Int'l*, pg. 7150
SRI MAHASAKTHI MILLS LIMITED—See Sri Srumuga Enterprise Limited; *Int'l*, pg. 7150
SRI MALINI SPINNING MILLS LTD.; *Int'l*, pg. 7150
SRI MANJUNG SPECIALIST CENTRE SDN BHD—See KPJ Healthcare Berhad; *Int'l*, pg. 4296
THE SRI MUANG INSURANCE COMPANY, LIMITED—See Tokio Marine Holdings, Inc.; *Int'l*, pg. 7783
SRI NACHAMMAI COTTON MILLS LIMITED; *Int'l*, pg. 7150
S/R INDUSTRIES INC.; *U.S. Private*, pg. 3519
S.R. INDUSTRIES LIMITED; *Int'l*, pg. 6457
SRINIVASA HATCHERIES LTD. - BROILER DIVISION—See Srinivasa Hatcheries Ltd.; *Int'l*, pg. 7151
SRINIVASA HATCHERIES LTD.; *Int'l*, pg. 7151
SR INTERNATIONAL BUSINESS INSURANCE COMPANY LTD.—See Swiss Re Ltd.; *Int'l*, pg. 7372
SRI PANGLIMA SDN BHD—See Berjaya Corporation Berhad; *Int'l*, pg. 982
SRI PANWA HOSPITALITY REAL ESTATE INVESTMENT TRUST; *Int'l*, pg. 7150
SRI PANWA MANAGEMENT CO., LTD.—See Charn Issara Development Public Company Limited; *Int'l*, pg. 1451

Company Index

SRIRACHA CONSTRUCTION PUBLIC COMPANY LIMITED CORPORATE AFFILIATIONS

SRIRACHA CONSTRUCTION PUBLIC COMPANY LIMITED; *Int'l*, pg. 7151
SRIRACHA TRANSPORT CO., LTD.—See Saha Pathanapibul Public Company Limited; *Int'l*, pg. 6479
SRIRAMA ASSOCIATES LLC; *U.S. Private*, pg. 3768
SRI RAMAKRISHNA MILLS (COIMBATORE) LIMITED; *Int'l*, pg. 7150
SRISAKORNVEJAVIVAT COMPANY LIMITED—See Srivichaivejvivat Public Company Limited; *Int'l*, pg. 7152
SRI SAN ANTONIO, INC.—See Federal Realty Investment Trust; *U.S. Public*, pg. 825
SRISAWAD CAPITAL CO., LTD.—See Srisawad Corporation Public Company Limited; *Int'l*, pg. 7151
SRISAWAD CORPORATION PUBLIC COMPANY LIMITED; *Int'l*, pg. 7151
SRISAWAD FINANCE PUBLIC COMPANY LIMITED; *Int'l*, pg. 7151
SRI SRUMUGA ENTERPRISE LIMITED; *Int'l*, pg. 7150
SRI TAKADA INDUSTRIES (MALAYSIA) SDN. BHD.—See Takada Corporation; *Int'l*, pg. 7429
SRI TELECOM; *U.S. Private*, pg. 3768
SRITHAI MIYAGAWA COMPANY LIMITED—See Srithai Superware Public Company Limited; *Int'l*, pg. 7151
SRITHAI MOULDS COMPANY LIMITED—See Srithai Superware Public Company Limited; *Int'l*, pg. 7151
SRITHAI-OTTO (THAILAND) COMPANY LIMITED—See Srithai Superware Public Company Limited; *Int'l*, pg. 7152
SRITHAI SUPERWARE INDIA LIMITED—See Srithai Superware Public Company Limited; *Int'l*, pg. 7151
SRITHAI SUPERWARE MANUFACTURING PRIVATE LIMITED—See Srithai Superware Public Company Limited; *Int'l*, pg. 7151
SRITHAI SUPERWARE PUBLIC COMPANY LIMITED - AMATA NAKORN CHONBURI FACTORY—See Srithai Superware Public Company Limited; *Int'l*, pg. 7151
SRITHAI SUPERWARE PUBLIC COMPANY LIMITED - BANGPOO FACTORY—See Srithai Superware Public Company Limited; *Int'l*, pg. 7152
SRITHAI SUPERWARE PUBLIC COMPANY LIMITED - KORAT FACTORY—See Srithai Superware Public Company Limited; *Int'l*, pg. 7152
SRITHAI SUPERWARE PUBLIC COMPANY LIMITED; *Int'l*, pg. 7151
SRITHAI (VIETNAM) COMPANY LIMITED—See Srithai Superware Public Company Limited; *Int'l*, pg. 7151
SRI TRANG AGRO-INDUSTRY PUBLIC COMPANY LIMITED; *Int'l*, pg. 7150
SRI TRANG AYEYAR RUBBER INDUSTRY CO., LTD.—See Sri Trang Agro-Industry Public Company Limited; *Int'l*, pg. 7150
SRI TRANG GLOVES GLOBAL PTE. LTD.—See Sri Trang Agro-Industry Public Company Limited; *Int'l*, pg. 7151
SRI TRANG GLOVES (SINGAPORE) PTE. LTD.—See Sri Trang Agro-Industry Public Company Limited; *Int'l*, pg. 7151
SRI TRANG GLOVES (THAILAND) CO., LTD.—See Sri Trang Agro-Industry Public Company Limited; *Int'l*, pg. 7151
SRI TRANG GLOVES VIETNAM CO., LTD.—See Sri Trang Agro-Industry Public Company Limited; *Int'l*, pg. 7151
SRI TRANG IBC CO., LTD.—See Sri Trang Agro-Industry Public Company Limited; *Int'l*, pg. 7151
SRI TRANG INDOCHINA (VIETNAM) CO., LTD.—See Sri Trang Agro-Industry Public Company Limited; *Int'l*, pg. 7151
SRI TRANG INTERNATIONAL PTE. LTD.—See Sri Trang Agro-Industry Public Company Limited; *Int'l*, pg. 7151
SRI TRANG RUBBER & PLANTATION CO., LTD.—See Sri Trang Agro-Industry Public Company Limited; *Int'l*, pg. 7151
SRI TRANG USA, INC.—See Sri Trang Agro-Industry Public Company Limited; *Int'l*, pg. 7151
SRI VAJRA GRANITES LIMITED; *Int'l*, pg. 7151
SRIVARI SPICES & FOODS LIMITED; *Int'l*, pg. 7152
SRIVARI SUPPLY CHAIN PRIVATE LIMITED—See Srivari Spices & Foods Limited; *Int'l*, pg. 7152
SRIVARU HOLDING LIMITED; *Int'l*, pg. 7152
SRIVARU MOTORS PRIVATE LIMITED—See SRIVARU Holding Limited; *Int'l*, pg. 7152
SRIVEN MULTI-TECH LIMITED; *Int'l*, pg. 7152
SRIVEN SYSTEMS, INC.; *U.S. Private*, pg. 3768
SRIVICHAIVEJVIVAT PUBLIC COMPANY LIMITED; *Int'l*, pg. 7152
SRIVICHAI VOCATIONAL COLLEGE COMPANY LIMITED—See Srivichaivejvivat Public Company Limited; *Int'l*, pg. 7152
SRIXON SPORTS AUSTRALASIA PTY LTD.—See Sumitomo Rubber Industries, Ltd.; *Int'l*, pg. 7300
SRIXON SPORTS EUROPE LTD.—See Sumitomo Rubber Industries, Ltd.; *Int'l*, pg. 7299
SRIXON SPORTS MANUFACTURING (THAILAND) CO., LTD.—See Sumitomo Rubber Industries, Ltd.; *Int'l*, pg. 7299
SRIXON SPORTS SOUTH AFRICA (PTY) LTD.—See Sumitomo Rubber Industries, Ltd.; *Int'l*, pg. 7299
SRIXON SPORTS USA INC.—See Sumitomo Rubber Industries, Ltd.; *Int'l*, pg. 7300
SRJ TECHNOLOGIES GROUP PLC; *Int'l*, pg. 7152
SRJ TECHNOLOGY LIMITED—See SRJ Technologies Group plc; *Int'l*, pg. 7152
S R LABS, LLC—See Insight Venture Management, LLC; *U.S. Private*, pg. 2091
SRL, INC. - AKITA SALES DIVISION—See H.U. Group Holdings, Inc.; *Int'l*, pg. 3197
SRL, INC. - AOMORI SALES DIVISION—See H.U. Group Holdings, Inc.; *Int'l*, pg. 3197
SRL, INC. - ASAHIKAWA SALES DIVISION—See H.U. Group Holdings, Inc.; *Int'l*, pg. 3197
SRL, INC. - ATSUGI SALES DIVISION I—See H.U. Group Holdings, Inc.; *Int'l*, pg. 3197
SRL, INC. - CHIBA II SALES DIVISION—See H.U. Group Holdings, Inc.; *Int'l*, pg. 3197
SRL, INC. - CHIBA I SALES DIVISION—See H.U. Group Holdings, Inc.; *Int'l*, pg. 3197
SRL, INC. - FUKUI SALES DIVISION—See H.U. Group Holdings, Inc.; *Int'l*, pg. 3197
SRL, INC. - FUKUOKA NISHI SALES DIVISION—See H.U. Group Holdings, Inc.; *Int'l*, pg. 3197
SRL, INC. - FUKUSHIMA CHUO SALES DIVISION—See H.U. Group Holdings, Inc.; *Int'l*, pg. 3197
SRL, INC. - GIFU SALES DIVISION—See H.U. Group Holdings, Inc.; *Int'l*, pg. 3197
SRL, INC. - GUNMA SALES DIVISION II—See H.U. Group Holdings, Inc.; *Int'l*, pg. 3197
SRL, INC. - HACHINOHE SALES DIVISION—See H.U. Group Holdings, Inc.; *Int'l*, pg. 3197
SRL, INC. - HACHIOJI SALES DIVISION I—See H.U. Group Holdings, Inc.; *Int'l*, pg. 3197
SRL, INC. - HAKODATE SALES DIVISION—See H.U. Group Holdings, Inc.; *Int'l*, pg. 3197
SRL, INC. - HAMAMATSU SALES DIVISION—See H.U. Group Holdings, Inc.; *Int'l*, pg. 3197
SRL, INC. - HIMEJI SALES DIVISION—See H.U. Group Holdings, Inc.; *Int'l*, pg. 3197
SRL, INC. - HIROSHIMA SALES DIVISION—See H.U. Group Holdings, Inc.; *Int'l*, pg. 3197
SRL, INC. - IBARAKI SALES DIVISION II—See H.U. Group Holdings, Inc.; *Int'l*, pg. 3197
SRL, INC. - IWAKI SALES DIVISION—See H.U. Group Holdings, Inc.; *Int'l*, pg. 3197
SRL, INC. - KAGOSHIMA SALES DIVISION—See H.U. Group Holdings, Inc.; *Int'l*, pg. 3197
SRL, INC. - KANAZAWA SALES DIVISION—See H.U. Group Holdings, Inc.; *Int'l*, pg. 3197
SRL, INC. - KAWAGOE SALES DIVISION I—See H.U. Group Holdings, Inc.; *Int'l*, pg. 3197
SRL, INC. - KENKO SALES DIVISION I—See H.U. Group Holdings, Inc.; *Int'l*, pg. 3197
SRL, INC. - KENKO SALES DIVISION—See H.U. Group Holdings, Inc.; *Int'l*, pg. 3197
SRL, INC. - KITA KANTO SALES DIVISION II—See H.U. Group Holdings, Inc.; *Int'l*, pg. 3197
SRL, INC. - KITAKYUSHU SALES DIVISION—See H.U. Group Holdings, Inc.; *Int'l*, pg. 3197
SRL, INC. - KITAMI SALES DIVISION—See H.U. Group Holdings, Inc.; *Int'l*, pg. 3197
SRL, INC. - KOBE SALES DIVISION V—See H.U. Group Holdings, Inc.; *Int'l*, pg. 3197
SRL, INC. - KOCHI SALES DIVISION—See H.U. Group Holdings, Inc.; *Int'l*, pg. 3198
SRL, INC. - KOFU SALES DIVISION II—See H.U. Group Holdings, Inc.; *Int'l*, pg. 3198
SRL, INC. - KUMAMOTO SALES DIVISION—See H.U. Group Holdings, Inc.; *Int'l*, pg. 3198
SRL, INC. - KURUME SALES DIVISION VII—See H.U. Group Holdings, Inc.; *Int'l*, pg. 3198
SRL, INC. - KUSHIRO SALES DIVISION—See H.U. Group Holdings, Inc.; *Int'l*, pg. 3198
SRL, INC. - KYOTO SALES DIVISION—See H.U. Group Holdings, Inc.; *Int'l*, pg. 3198
SRL, INC. - MATSUYAMA SALES DIVISION—See H.U. Group Holdings, Inc.; *Int'l*, pg. 3198
SRL, INC. - MIE SALES DIVISION—See H.U. Group Holdings, Inc.; *Int'l*, pg. 3198
SRL, INC. - MIYAZAKI SALES DIVISION—See H.U. Group Holdings, Inc.; *Int'l*, pg. 3198
SRL, INC. - MORIOKA SALES DIVISION—See H.U. Group Holdings, Inc.; *Int'l*, pg. 3198
SRL, INC. - NAGANO SALES DIVISION II—See H.U. Group Holdings, Inc.; *Int'l*, pg. 3198
SRL, INC. - NAGASAKI SALES DIVISION—See H.U. Group Holdings, Inc.; *Int'l*, pg. 3198
SRL, INC. - NAGOYA I SALES DIVISION—See H.U. Group Holdings, Inc.; *Int'l*, pg. 3198
SRL, INC. - NARA SALES DIVISION—See H.U. Group Holdings, Inc.; *Int'l*, pg. 3198
SRL, INC. - NIIGATA SALES DIVISION II—See H.U. Group Holdings, Inc.; *Int'l*, pg. 3198
SRL, INC. - NOTO SALES DIVISION—See H.U. Group Holdings, Inc.; *Int'l*, pg. 3198
SRL, INC. - OITA SALES DIVISION—See H.U. Group Holdings, Inc.; *Int'l*, pg. 3198
SRL, INC. - OKAYAMA SALES DIVISION—See H.U. Group Holdings, Inc.; *Int'l*, pg. 3198
SRL, INC. - OKAZAKI SALES DIVISION—See H.U. Group Holdings, Inc.; *Int'l*, pg. 3198
SRL, INC. - OKINAWA SALES DIVISION VII—See H.U. Group Holdings, Inc.; *Int'l*, pg. 3198
SRL, INC. - OSAKA CHUO SALES DIVISION—See H.U. Group Holdings, Inc.; *Int'l*, pg. 3198
SRL, INC. - OSAKA KITA SALES DIVISION—See H.U. Group Holdings, Inc.; *Int'l*, pg. 3198
SRL, INC. - OSAKA MINAMI SALES DIVISION—See H.U. Group Holdings, Inc.; *Int'l*, pg. 3198
SRL, INC. - SAGA SALES DIVISION—See H.U. Group Holdings, Inc.; *Int'l*, pg. 3198
SRL, INC. - SAITAMA SALES DIVISION—See H.U. Group Holdings, Inc.; *Int'l*, pg. 3198
SRL, INC. - SAKATA SALES DIVISION—See H.U. Group Holdings, Inc.; *Int'l*, pg. 3198
SRL, INC. - SAPPORO SALES DIVISION—See H.U. Group Holdings, Inc.; *Int'l*, pg. 3198
SRL, INC. - SASEBO SALES DIVISION—See H.U. Group Holdings, Inc.; *Int'l*, pg. 3198
SRL, INC. - SENDAI SALES DIVISION—See H.U. Group Holdings, Inc.; *Int'l*, pg. 3198
SRL, INC. - SHIGA SALES DIVISION—See H.U. Group Holdings, Inc.; *Int'l*, pg. 3198
SRL, INC. - SHIMANE SALES DIVISION—See H.U. Group Holdings, Inc.; *Int'l*, pg. 3198
SRL, INC. - SHIZUOKA SALES DIVISION—See H.U. Group Holdings, Inc.; *Int'l*, pg. 3198
SRL, INC.—See H.U. Group Holdings, Inc.; *Int'l*, pg. 3197
SRL, INC. - TAKAMATSU SALES DIVISION—See H.U. Group Holdings, Inc.; *Int'l*, pg. 3198
SRL, INC. - TOKUSHIMA SALES DIVISION—See H.U. Group Holdings, Inc.; *Int'l*, pg. 3198
SRL, INC. - TOKYO III SALES DIVISION—See H.U. Group Holdings, Inc.; *Int'l*, pg. 3198
SRL, INC. - TOKYO II SALES DIVISION—See H.U. Group Holdings, Inc.; *Int'l*, pg. 3198
SRL, INC. - TOKYO I SALES DIVISION—See H.U. Group Holdings, Inc.; *Int'l*, pg. 3198
SRL, INC. - TOKYO IV SALES DIVISION—See H.U. Group Holdings, Inc.; *Int'l*, pg. 3198
SRL, INC. - TOKYO V SALES DIVISION—See H.U. Group Holdings, Inc.; *Int'l*, pg. 3198
SRL, INC. - TOMAKOMAI SALES DIVISION—See H.U. Group Holdings, Inc.; *Int'l*, pg. 3198
SRL, INC. - TOYAMA SALES DIVISION VII—See H.U. Group Holdings, Inc.; *Int'l*, pg. 3198
SRL, INC. - TSUKUBA SALES DIVISION II—See H.U. Group Holdings, Inc.; *Int'l*, pg. 3198
SRL, INC. - UEDA SALES DIVISION II—See H.U. Group Holdings, Inc.; *Int'l*, pg. 3198
SRL, INC. - UTSUNOMIYA SALES DIVISION II—See H.U. Group Holdings, Inc.; *Int'l*, pg. 3199
SRL, INC. - WAKAYAMA SALES DIVISION—See H.U. Group Holdings, Inc.; *Int'l*, pg. 3199
SRL, INC. - YAMAGATA SALES DIVISION—See H.U. Group Holdings, Inc.; *Int'l*, pg. 3199
SRL, INC. - YAMAGUCHI SALES DIVISION—See H.U. Group Holdings, Inc.; *Int'l*, pg. 3199
SRL, INC. - YOKOHAMA II SALES DIVISION—See H.U. Group Holdings, Inc.; *Int'l*, pg. 3199
SRL, INC. - YOKOHAMA I SALES DIVISION—See H.U. Group Holdings, Inc.; *Int'l*, pg. 3199
SRL, INC. - YOKOSUKA SALES DIVISION I—See H.U. Group Holdings, Inc.; *Int'l*, pg. 3199
SRL INTERNATIONAL, INC.—See H.U. Group Holdings, Inc.; *Int'l*, pg. 3197
SRL KITAKANTO LABORATORY, INC.—See H.U. Group Holdings, Inc.; *Int'l*, pg. 3197
SRL LABORATORIES CREATE, INC.—See H.U. Group Holdings, Inc.; *Int'l*, pg. 3197
SRL MEDISEARCH INC.—See H.U. Group Holdings, Inc.; *Int'l*, pg. 3197
SRL & SHIZUOKA CANCER CENTER COLLABORATIVE LABORATORIES, INC.—See H.U. Group Holdings, Inc.; *Int'l*, pg. 3197
SRL TECHNOSYSTEM, INC.—See H.U. Group Holdings, Inc.; *Int'l*, pg. 3197
SRM ENERGY LIMITED; *Int'l*, pg. 7152
SRM ENTERTAINMENT, INC.; *U.S. Public*, pg. 1922
SRN NEWS—See Salem Media Group, Inc.; *U.S. Public*, pg. 1836
SRO HOUSING CORPORATION; *U.S. Private*, pg. 3768
SR ONE LIMITED—See GSK plc; *Int'l*, pg. 3149
S ROSE INC.; *U.S. Private*, pg. 3512
SRO SOLUTIONS LIMITED—See Bentley Systems, Inc.; *U.S. Public*, pg. 297
S. ROTHSCHILD & CO., INC.; *U.S. Private*, pg. 3515
SRP ADVERTISING CO., LTD.—See Saha Pathanapibul Public Company Limited; *Int'l*, pg. 6479
SRP ENVIRONMENTAL LLC; *U.S. Private*, pg. 3768
SR PERROTT INC.; *U.S. Private*, pg. 3767
SRP GROUPE SA; *Int'l*, pg. 7152
SRPSKA BANKA A.D; *Int'l*, pg. 7152
SRPS, LLC—See UnitedHealth Group Incorporated; *U.S. Public*, pg. 2250
SR RISK MANAGEMENT SERVICES LIMITED—See Swiss Re Ltd.; *Int'l*, pg. 7371
S.R.S. BITZER S.A.R.L.—See BITZER SE; *Int'l*, pg. 1052
SRS CO., LTD.—See Aktio Holdings Corporation; *Int'l*, pg. 267

COMPANY NAME INDEX

SRS CORE LLC; *U.S. Private*, pg. 3768
SRS DISTRIBUTION INC. - SIERRA ROOFING SUPPLY DIVISION—See Leonard Green & Partners, L.P.; *U.S. Private*, pg. 2429
SRS DISTRIBUTION INC.—See Leonard Green & Partners, L.P.; *U.S. Private*, pg. 2428
SRS ECOTHERM GMBH—See RWE AG; *Int'l*, pg. 6435
SRS ENGINEERING, INC.; *U.S. Private*, pg. 3768
SR SERVICE GMBH—See Alba SE; *Int'l*, pg. 293
SRS FINANCE LTD.; *Int'l*, pg. 7152
SRS HOLDINGS CO.,LTD.; *Int'l*, pg. 7152
SRS, INC.; *U.S. Private*, pg. 3768
SRS KOREA CO., LTD.—See KGinicis Co. Ltd.; *Int'l*, pg. 4150
S.R. SMITH, LLC—See Champlain Capital Management LLC; *U.S. Private*, pg. 847
S.R. SNODGRASS, A.C.; *U.S. Private*, pg. 3518
SRS (QINGDAO) CASTING MATERIALS COMPANY LIMITED—See Goodwin PLC; *Int'l*, pg. 3042
SRS REAL ESTATE PARTNERS, LLC - SAN JOSE OFFICE—See Jones Lang LaSalle Incorporated; *U.S. Public*, pg. 1205
SRS REAL ESTATE PARTNERS, LLC—See Jones Lang LaSalle Incorporated; *U.S. Public*, pg. 1205
SRS REAL INFRASTRUCTURE LIMITED; *Int'l*, pg. 7152
SRS SJOLANDERS AB—See Vermogensverwaltung Erben Dr. Karl Goldschmidt GmbH; *Int'l*, pg. 8173
SRSSOFT; *U.S. Private*, pg. 3768
SRT COMMUNICATIONS INC.; *U.S. Private*, pg. 3768
SR TECHNICS AIRFOIL SERVICES LTD.—See Hainan Traffic Administration Holding Co., Ltd.; *Int'l*, pg. 3216
SR TECHNICS AMERICA INC.—See Hainan Traffic Administration Holding Co., Ltd.; *Int'l*, pg. 3216
SR TECHNICS AUSTRALIA PTY LTD—See Hainan Traffic Administration Holding Co., Ltd.; *Int'l*, pg. 3216
SR TECHNICS HOLDCO I GMBH—See Hainan Traffic Administration Holding Co., Ltd.; *Int'l*, pg. 3215
SR TECHNICS MALAYSIA SDN BHD—See Hainan Traffic Administration Holding Co., Ltd.; *Int'l*, pg. 3216
SR TECHNICS MALTA LTD.—See Hainan Traffic Administration Holding Co., Ltd.; *Int'l*, pg. 3216
SR TECHNICS MANAGEMENT AG—See Hainan Traffic Administration Holding Co., Ltd.; *Int'l*, pg. 3216
SR TECHNICS INICE SPAIN SA—See Hainan Traffic Administration Holding Co., Ltd.; *Int'l*, pg. 3216
SR TECHNICS SWITZERLAND AG—See Hainan Traffic Administration Holding Co., Ltd.; *Int'l*, pg. 3216
SR TECHNICS UK LIMITED—See Hainan Traffic Administration Holding Co., Ltd.; *Int'l*, pg. 3216
SRTECHNOPACK CO., LTD. - KUNSAN PLANT—See Samryoong Co Ltd.; *Int'l*, pg. 6508
SRTECHNOPACK CO., LTD.—See Samryoong Co Ltd.; *Int'l*, pg. 6508
SR TELECOM & CO. S.E.C.—See Groupe Lagasse Inc.; *Int'l*, pg. 3106
SRT MARINE SYSTEMS PLC; *Int'l*, pg. 7152
SRT MARINE TECHNOLOGY LIMITED—See SRT Marine Systems plc; *Int'l*, pg. 7152
SRT SOLUTIONS INC.; *U.S. Private*, pg. 3768
SRT-TAIWAN TRADING CORPORATION—See Hitachi Astemo, Ltd.; *Int'l*, pg. 3409
SRU STEELS LIMITED; *Int'l*, pg. 7153
SR-UTOC INTERNATIONAL TRANSPORTATION LOGISTICS (TIANJIN) INC.—See Mitsui O.S.K. Lines, Ltd.; *Int'l*, pg. 4992
SRV BALTIA OY—See SRV Group Plc; *Int'l*, pg. 7153
SRV CONSTRUCTION LTD—See SRV Group Plc; *Int'l*, pg. 7153
SRV EHITUSE AS—See SRV Group Plc; *Int'l*, pg. 7153
SRV GROUP PLC; *Int'l*, pg. 7153
SRV INFRA LTD.—See SRV Yhtiot Oyj; *Int'l*, pg. 7153
SRV KAAKKOIS-SUOMI OY—See SRV Group Plc; *Int'l*, pg. 7153
SRV KALUSTO OY—See Loxam SAS; *Int'l*, pg. 4566
SRV KESKI-SUOMI OY—See SRV Group Plc; *Int'l*, pg. 7153
SRV KINNISVARA AS—See SRV Group Plc; *Int'l*, pg. 7153
SRV LOUNAIS-SUOMI OY—See SRV Group Plc; *Int'l*, pg. 7153
SRV PIRKANMAA OY—See SRV Group Plc; *Int'l*, pg. 7153
SRV POHJOIS-SUOMI OY—See SRV Group Plc; *Int'l*, pg. 7153
SRV RUSSIA OY—See SRV Group Plc; *Int'l*, pg. 7153
SRVS; *U.S. Private*, pg. 3768
SRV STROI OOO—See SRV Group Plc; *Int'l*, pg. 7153
SRV YHTIOT OYJ; *Int'l*, pg. 7153
SR WEBATEX GMBH; *Int'l*, pg. 7147
S.R. WEINER & ASSOCIATES INC.; *U.S. Private*, pg. 3518
SR WHOLESALE B.V.—See Red Light Holland Corp.; *Int'l*, pg. 6244
SRW INDUSTRIES CORPORATION; *U.S. Private*, pg. 3768
SRW PRODUCTS; *U.S. Private*, pg. 3768
SS8 NETWORKS, INC.—See HighBar Management, LLC; *U.S. Private*, pg. 1937
SSAB AB; *Int'l*, pg. 7153

SSA BANGLADESH LTD.—See Carrix, Inc.; *U.S. Private*, pg. 773
SSAB EMEA AB—See SSAB AB; *Int'l*, pg. 7154
SSAB ENTERPRISES, LLC—See SSAB AB; *Int'l*, pg. 7154
SSAB MEROX—See SSAB AB; *Int'l*, pg. 7154
SSAB OXELOSUND—See SSAB AB; *Int'l*, pg. 7154
SSAB SWEDISH STEEL BV—See SSAB AB; *Int'l*, pg. 7154
SSAB SWEDISH STEEL LTD—See SSAB AB; *Int'l*, pg. 7154
SSAB SWEDISH STEEL LTD—See SSAB AB; *Int'l*, pg. 7154
SSAB SWEDISH STEEL, S.L.—See SSAB AB; *Int'l*, pg. 7155
SSAB SWEDISH STEEL TRADING KFT—See SSAB AB; *Int'l*, pg. 7154
SSAB TECHNOLOGY AB—See SSAB AB; *Int'l*, pg. 7155
SSAB TUNNPLAT—See SSAB AB; *Int'l*, pg. 7155
SSAB WEAR SOLUTIONS LLC—See SSAB AB; *Int'l*, pg. 7155
SSAC LLC—See Littelfuse, Inc.; *U.S. Public*, pg. 1327
S&S ACTIVEWEAR LLC—See Clayton, Dubilier & Rice, LLC; *U.S. Private*, pg. 926
SSA INFORMATICA SRL—See Sesa S.p.A.; *Int'l*, pg. 6729
SSA MARINE, INC.—See Carrix, Inc.; *U.S. Private*, pg. 773
SSA MEXICO S.A. DE C.V.—See Carrix, Inc.; *U.S. Private*, pg. 773
SSANGYONG CEMENT INDUSTRIAL CO., LTD. - DONGHAE PLANT—See Hahn & Company; *Int'l*, pg. 3208
SSANGYONG CEMENT INDUSTRIAL CO., LTD.—See Hahn & Company; *Int'l*, pg. 3208
SSANGYONG CEMENT INDUSTRIAL CO., LTD. - SSANGYONG TECHNOLOGY RESEARCH CENTER—See Hahn & Company; *Int'l*, pg. 3208
SSANGYONG CEMENT INDUSTRIAL CO., LTD. - YEONGWOL PLANT—See Hahn & Company; *Int'l*, pg. 3208
SSANGYONG CEMENT SINGAPORE (CHINA) PTE LTD—See EnGro Corporation Limited; *Int'l*, pg. 2436
SSANGYONG CEMENT (S) PTE LTD—See EnGro Corporation Limited; *Int'l*, pg. 2436
SSANGYONG ENGINEERING AND CONSTRUCTIONS COMPANY LTD—See Investment Corporation of Dubai; *Int'l*, pg. 3785
SSANGYONG ENGINEERING & CONSTRUCTION CO., LTD.—See Investment Corporation of Dubai; *Int'l*, pg. 3785
SSANGYONG ENGINEERING & CONSTRUCTION CO., LTD.—See Investment Corporation of Dubai; *Int'l*, pg. 3785
SSANGYONG ENGINEERING & CONSTRUCTION SDN BHD—See Investment Corporation of Dubai; *Int'l*, pg. 3785
SSANGYONG EUROPEAN PARTS CENTER B.V.—See Mahindra & Mahindra Limited; *Int'l*, pg. 4646
SSANGYONG INFORMATION & COMMUNICATIONS CORP.; *Int'l*, pg. 7155
SSARIS ADVISORS, LLC; *U.S. Private*, pg. 3768
S.S.A.S. GOLF RESORT MANAGEMENT SERVICES SDN. BHD.—See Nam Fatt Corporation Berhad; *Int'l*, pg. 5133
SSAS SOLUTIONS (UK) LTD—See Pollen Street Limited; *Int'l*, pg. 5910
S&S AUTOMOTIVE INC.; *U.S. Private*, pg. 3513
SS AUTO SDN. BHD.—See PT Selamat Sempurna Tbk; *Int'l*, pg. 6071
SSAW HOTELS & RESORTS GROUP CO., LTD.; *Int'l*, pg. 7155
SSB BANCORP, INC.; *U.S. Public*, pg. 1924
SSB BANK—See SSB Bancorp, Inc.; *U.S. Public*, pg. 1924
SSB COMMUNITY BANCORP INC.—See SSB Community Bancorp MHC; *U.S. Private*, pg. 3768
SSB COMMUNITY BANCORP MHC; *U.S. Private*, pg. 3768
S&S BEAUTY SUPPLIES INCORPORATED; *U.S. Private*, pg. 3513
SSB HOLDINGS, INC.—See The Rosewood Corporation; *U.S. Private*, pg. 4112
SSB INSURANCE CORP.—See SouthState Corporation; *U.S. Public*, pg. 1913
SSB INVESTMENTS, INC.—See State Street Corporation; *U.S. Public*, pg. 1940
SSB SOFTWARE SERVICE UND BERATUNG GMBH—See Bertelsmann SE & Co. KGaA; *Int'l*, pg. 995
S&S BUILDERS HARDWARE CO.; *U.S. Private*, pg. 3513
S&S BUILDERS, LLC.; *U.S. Private*, pg. 3514
SSB WIND ENERGY TECHNOLOGY (QINGDAO) CO., LTD.—See Emerson Electric Co.; *U.S. Public*, pg. 752
SSB WIND SYSTEMS GMBH & CO. KG—See Emerson Electric Co.; *U.S. Public*, pg. 752
SSB WIND SYSTEMS GMBH & CO. KG—See Emerson Electric Co.; *U.S. Public*, pg. 752
SSC CHILE S.A.—See GomSpace Group AB; *Int'l*, pg. 3037
SS & C FINANCIAL SERVICES LLC—See SS&C Technologies Holdings, Inc.; *U.S. Public*, pg. 1923

SS&C FUND SERVICES (UK) LIMITED—See SS&C Technologies Holdings, Inc.; *U.S. Public*, pg. 1923
SS&C GLOBEOP S.A.R.L.—See SS&C Technologies Holdings, Inc.; *U.S. Public*, pg. 1923
SSC GROUP; *Int'l*, pg. 7155
SS&C HEDGE FUND SERVICES NORTH AMERICA, INC.—See SS&C Technologies Holdings, Inc.; *U.S. Public*, pg. 1924
S-SCIENCE CO., LTD.; *Int'l*, pg. 6446
SSC, INC.—See Zhanjiang Guolian Aquatic Products Co., Ltd.; *Int'l*, pg. 8647
SSC KITAKANTOU CO., LTD.—See Nippon Steel Corporation; *Int'l*, pg. 5339
SSC MANDARIN FINANCIAL SERVICES LIMITED; *Int'l*, pg. 7155
SSCO MANUFACTURING, INC.—See Lincoln Electric Holdings, Inc.; *U.S. Public*, pg. 1318
S&S COMPONENTS CO., LTD.—See Sumitomo Electric Industries, Ltd.; *Int'l*, pg. 7279
SS&C PRIVATE EQUITY SERVICES, INC.—See SS&C Technologies Holdings, Inc.; *U.S. Public*, pg. 1924
SSC SECURITY SERVICES CORP.; *Int'l*, pg. 7155
SSC SERVICE SOLUTIONS—See Compass Group PLC; *Int'l*, pg. 1751
SSC SHIP MANAGEMENT PTE LTD—See Singapore Shipping Corporation Limited; *Int'l*, pg. 6943
SSC SHIPPING AGENCIES PTE LTD—See MYP Ltd.; *Int'l*, pg. 5113
SS&C SOLUTIONS PTY LIMITED—See SS&C Technologies Holdings, Inc.; *U.S. Public*, pg. 1924
SSC SPACE AUSTRALIA PTY LTD.—See GomSpace Group AB; *Int'l*, pg. 3037
SSC SPACE CANADA CORPORATION—See SSC Group; *Int'l*, pg. 7155
SS&C TECHNOLOGIES AUSTRALIA PTY LTD.—See SS&C Technologies Holdings, Inc.; *U.S. Public*, pg. 1924
SS&C TECHNOLOGIES BV—See SS&C Technologies Holdings, Inc.; *U.S. Public*, pg. 1924
SS&C TECHNOLOGIES CANADA CORP.—See SS&C Technologies Holdings, Inc.; *U.S. Public*, pg. 1924
SS&C TECHNOLOGIES HOLDINGS, INC.- HONG KONG—See SS&C Technologies Holdings, Inc.; *U.S. Public*, pg. 1924
SS&C TECHNOLOGIES HOLDINGS, INC.; *U.S. Public*, pg. 1922
SS&C TECHNOLOGIES HONG KONG LIMITED—See SS&C Technologies Holdings, Inc.; *U.S. Public*, pg. 1924
SS&C TECHNOLOGIES, INC.—See SS&C Technologies Holdings, Inc.; *U.S. Public*, pg. 1924
SS&C TECHNOLOGIES, INC.—See SS&C Technologies Holdings, Inc.; *U.S. Public*, pg. 1924
SS&C TECHNOLOGIES, INC.—See SS&C Technologies Holdings, Inc.; *U.S. Public*, pg. 1924
SS&C TECHNOLOGIES, INC.—See SS&C Technologies Holdings, Inc.; *U.S. Public*, pg. 1924
SS&C TECHNOLOGIES INDIA PRIVATE LIMITED—See SS&C Technologies Holdings, Inc.; *U.S. Public*, pg. 1924
SS&C TECHNOLOGIES IRELAND LIMITED—See SS&C Technologies Holdings, Inc.; *U.S. Public*, pg. 1924
SS&C TECHNOLOGIES LTD.—See SS&C Technologies Holdings, Inc.; *U.S. Public*, pg. 1924
SS&C TECHNOLOGIES SDN. BHD.—See SS&C Technologies Holdings, Inc.; *U.S. Public*, pg. 1924
SS&C TECHNOLOGIES (S) PTE LTD.—See SS&C Technologies Holdings, Inc.; *U.S. Public*, pg. 1924
SSDC SERVICES CORP.; *U.S. Private*, pg. 3768
SSDC (TIGERTEX) CO., LTD.—See Saha Pathanapibul Public Company Limited; *Int'l*, pg. 6479
SSD DRIVES, INC.—See Parker Hannifin Corporation; *U.S. Public*, pg. 1644
SSD DRIVES LTD.—See Parker Hannifin Corporation; *U.S. Public*, pg. 1644
SSD RCS ACTIVE TEAM A R.L.—See RCS MediaGroup S.p.A.; *Int'l*, pg. 6229
S&S DRYWALL INC.; *U.S. Private*, pg. 3514
S&S DRYWALL INSTALLERS INC—See S&S Drywall Inc.; *U.S. Private*, pg. 3514
S.S. DWECK & SONS INC.; *U.S. Private*, pg. 3518
SSEAC CO. LTD.—See SEB S.A.; *Int'l*, pg. 6668
SSE AIRTRICITY ENERGY SERVICES (NI) LIMITED—See SSE Plc; *Int'l*, pg. 7155
SSE AIRTRICITY LIMITED—See SSE Plc; *Int'l*, pg. 7155
SSE CONTRACTING LTD.—See Aurelius Equity Opportunities SE & Co. KGaA; *Int'l*, pg. 709
SSE DO BRASIL LTDA—See Allied Universal Manager LLC; *U.S. Private*, pg. 190
SSE E&P UK LIMITED—See SSE Plc; *Int'l*, pg. 7155
SSE GENERATION LTD—See SSE Plc; *Int'l*, pg. 7155
SSE HORNSEA LTD—See SSE Plc; *Int'l*, pg. 7156
S&S ELECTRIC CO., INC.; *U.S. Private*, pg. 3514
SSE PLC; *Int'l*, pg. 7155
SSE POWER DISTRIBUTION LTD—See SSE Plc; *Int'l*, pg. 7156
SSE RENEWABLES HOLDINGS LIMITED—See SSE Plc; *Int'l*, pg. 7156

SSE RENEWABLES HOLDINGS (UK) LIMITED—See SSE Plc; *Int'l*, pg. 7156
SSE RENEWABLES (IRELAND) LIMITED—See SSE Plc; *Int'l*, pg. 7156
SSE RENEWABLES WIND (IRELAND) HOLDINGS LIMITED—See SSE Plc; *Int'l*, pg. 7156
S SERVIS, S.R.O.—See Erste Group Bank AG; *Int'l*, pg. 2499
SSE SERVICES PLC—See SSE Plc; *Int'l*, pg. 7156
SSE TELECOMMUNICATIONS LIMITED—See M&G Group Limited; *Int'l*, pg. 4612
SSE TELECOMMUNICATIONS LIMITED—See SSE Plc; *Int'l*, pg. 7156
SSF HOME GROUP BERHAD; *Int'l*, pg. 7156
SSF IMPORTED AUTO PARTS LLC—See WM SE; *Int'l*, pg. 8441
SSF INC.; *U.S. Private*, pg. 3768
S&S FIRESTONE INC.; *U.S. Private*, pg. 3514
SSF SCHWIMMBAD GMBH—See Kohler Company; *U.S. Private*, pg. 2339
SSG A/S—See BWB Partners P/S; *Int'l*, pg. 1232
S/S/G CORPORATION; *U.S. Private*, pg. 3519
SSG, INC.—See Great Range Capital, LLC; *U.S. Private*, pg. 1767
SSGM INTERNATIONAL UK—See State Street Corporation; *U.S. Public*, pg. 1941
SSH COMMSEC SINGAPORE PTE. LTD.—See SSH Communications Security Corporation; *Int'l*, pg. 7156
SSH COMMUNICATIONS SECURITY CORPORATION; *Int'l*, pg. 7156
SSH CORPORATION LTD.—See KS Energy Limited; *Int'l*, pg. 4310
SSH CORPORATION (PNG) PTE. LTD.—See KS Energy Limited; *Int'l*, pg. 4310
S&S HEALTHCARE HOLDING LTD; *Int'l*, pg. 6445
SSH GROUP LIMITED; *Int'l*, pg. 7156
S. SHLOMO HOLDINGS LTD.; *Int'l*, pg. 6447
SSH MEDICAL CENTER LLC—See Adeptus Health Inc.; *U.S. Private*, pg. 78
SSHT S&T GROUP LTD.; *Int'l*, pg. 7156
SSH (VIETNAM) COMPANY LIMITED—See KS Energy Limited; *Int'l*, pg. 4310
SSIAL FOOD, INC.; *Int'l*, pg. 7156
SSI ASSET MANAGEMENT LTD.—See SSI Securities Corporation; *Int'l*, pg. 7156
SSI CROSS, INC.—See Cross Financial Corporation; *U.S. Private*, pg. 1105
SSI DIAGNOSTICA A/S—See Adelis Equity Partners AB; *Int'l*, pg. 142
SSI GROUP, INC.; *Int'l*, pg. 7156
THE SSI GROUP, INC.; *U.S. Private*, pg. 4120
SSI INCORPORATED; *U.S. Private*, pg. 3769
SSI INTERNATIONAL GMBH—See Head B.V.; *Int'l*, pg. 3300
SSI INTERNATIONAL (HK) LTD.—See Head B.V.; *Int'l*, pg. 3300
SSI INTERNATIONAL, INC.—See Radius Recycling, Inc.; *U.S. Public*, pg. 1760
SSI INVESTMENT MANAGEMENT, INC.—See Kelso & Company, L.P.; *U.S. Private*, pg. 2280
S&S INDUSTRIAL MARKETING; *U.S. Private*, pg. 3514
S.S. INFRASTRUCTURE DEVELOPMENT CONSULTANTS LIMITED; *Int'l*, pg. 6457
S&S INGENIERIA S.A.S.—See HORIBA Ltd; *Int'l*, pg. 3478
SS INNOVATIONS INTERNATIONAL, INC.; *U.S. Public*, pg. 1922
S+S INSPECTION ASIA PTE LTD—See VTC Partners GmbH; *Int'l*, pg. 8316
S+S INSPECTION INDIA PVT. LTD.—See VTC Partners GmbH; *Int'l*, pg. 8316
S&S INTERNATIONAL CORP; *U.S. Private*, pg. 3514
SSI SCHAFER SHOP GMBH; *Int'l*, pg. 7156
SSI SECURITIES CORPORATION; *Int'l*, pg. 7156
SSI SERVICES, LLC; *U.S. Private*, pg. 3769
SSI STRATEGY—See Acquis Consulting Group, LLC; *U.S. Private*, pg. 65
SSI TECHNOLOGIES GMBH—See Amphenol Corporation; *U.S. Public*, pg. 132
S.S.I. TECHNOLOGIES INC.; *U.S. Private*, pg. 3519
SSI TECHNOLOGIES; *U.S. Private*, pg. 3769
SSI TECHNOLOGIES S.R.O—See Amphenol Corporation; *U.S. Public*, pg. 132
SSI (U.S.) INC.; *U.S. Private*, pg. 3769
S.S. KARNSURA CO., LTD.—See Thai Beverage Public Company Limited; *Int'l*, pg. 7591
SSK CORPORATION; *U.S. Private*, pg. 3769
S.S. KEMP & CO., LLC—See Warburg Pincus LLC; *U.S. Private*, pg. 4440
SSK FOODS CO., LTD.; *Int'l*, pg. 7156
SS&KH CORPORATION; *U.S. Private*, pg. 3768
S.S. LAZIO SPA; *Int'l*, pg. 6457
SSLJ.COM LIMITED; *Int'l*, pg. 7156
S.S. LOGAN PACKING COMPANY; *U.S. Private*, pg. 3518
SSMB PACIFIC HOLDING COMPANY, INC.; *U.S. Private*, pg. 3769
SSMC LIMITED—See Platinum Equity, LLC; *U.S. Private*, pg. 3208
SSM GIUDICI S.R.L.—See Rieter Holding Ltd.; *Int'l*, pg. 6339

SSM HEALTH CARE CORPORATION; *U.S. Private*, pg. 3769
SSM HOLDING AB; *Int'l*, pg. 7157
SSM INDUSTRIES INC.; *U.S. Private*, pg. 3769
SSM ITALY S.R.L.—See Rieter Holding Ltd.; *Int'l*, pg. 6339
S. SMITH & SON PTY. LTD.; *Int'l*, pg. 6447
SSM SCHARER SCHWEITER METTLER AG—See Rieter Holding Ltd.; *Int'l*, pg. 6339
SSM SCHARER SCHWEITER METTLER CORPORATION—See Rieter Holding Ltd.; *Int'l*, pg. 6339
SSM SELECT REHAB ST. LOUIS, LLC—See Select Medical Holdings Corporation; *U.S. Public*, pg. 1859
SSM S.R.L.—See RINA S.p.A.; *Int'l*, pg. 6343
SSM ST. CLARE SURGICAL CENTER, L.L.C.—See Tenet Healthcare Corporation; *U.S. Public*, pg. 2012
SSM VERTRIEBS AG—See Rieter Holding Ltd.; *Int'l*, pg. 6339
SSM (ZHONGSHAN) LTD.—See Rieter Holding Ltd.; *Int'l*, pg. 6339
SSN CUBE GMBH—See Consus Real Estate AG; *Int'l*, pg. 1778
SSNEWTECH CO., LTD.; *Int'l*, pg. 7157
SSN GEBAUDETECHNIK GMBH—See Consus Real Estate AG; *Int'l*, pg. 1778
SSOE GROUP; *U.S. Private*, pg. 3769
SSOE KENYA LIMITED—See The Aditya Birla Group; *Int'l*, pg. 7612
S.S.OIL MILLS LIMITED; *Int'l*, pg. 6457
S.S. ORGANICS LIMITED; *Int'l*, pg. 6457
S+—See LVMH Moet Hennessy Louis Vuitton SE; *Int'l*, pg. 4600
SS PALM CITY, LLC—See National Storage Affiliates Trust; *U.S. Public*, pg. 1498
SSP AMERICA GLADCO, INC.—See SSP Group plc; *Int'l*, pg. 7157
SSP AMERICA, INC.—See SSP Group plc; *Int'l*, pg. 7157
SSP CANADA FOOD SERVICES INC.—See SSP Group plc; *Int'l*, pg. 7157
SSP CO. LTD.—See C.H. Boehringer Sohn AG & Co. KG; *Int'l*, pg. 1243
SSPDL LIMITED; *Int'l*, pg. 7157
S&S PETROLEUM INC.; *U.S. Private*, pg. 3514
SSP FITTINGS CORP.; *U.S. Private*, pg. 3769
SSP GROUP PLC; *Int'l*, pg. 7157
SSPI GMBH; *Int'l*, pg. 7157
SSP INDUSTRIAL GROUP, INC.; *U.S. Private*, pg. 3769
SSP INDUSTRIES—See TransDigm Group Incorporated; *U.S. Public*, pg. 2183
SSP INNOVATIONS, LLC—See Warren Equity Partners, LLC; *U.S. Private*, pg. 4443
SSP LIMITED - SOLIHULL—See Lloyds Banking Group plc; *Int'l*, pg. 4538
SSP LIMITED—See Lloyds Banking Group plc; *Int'l*, pg. 4537
SSP NEDERLAND BV—See SSP Group plc; *Int'l*, pg. 7157
SSPN FINANCE LIMITED; *Int'l*, pg. 7157
S&S POWER SWITCHGEAR LIMITED—See Hamilton & Company Limited; *Int'l*, pg. 3237
S & S PRECAST, INC.; *U.S. Private*, pg. 3512
SSP RECLAMATION CO.—See Radius Recycling, Inc.; *U.S. Public*, pg. 1760
SSP TAIWAN LIMITED—See SSP Group plc; *Int'l*, pg. 7157
S&S PUBLIC RELATIONS, INC.; *U.S. Private*, pg. 3514
S&S PUBLIC RELATIONS, INC.—See S&S Public Relations, Inc.; *U.S. Private*, pg. 3514
SSP (USA), INC.—See Lloyds Banking Group plc; *Int'l*, pg. 4537
SSQ GENERAL INSURANCE COMPANY INC.—See La Capitale Civil Service Mutual; *Int'l*, pg. 4387
SSQ, LIFE INSURANCE COMPANY INC.—See La Capitale Civil Service Mutual; *Int'l*, pg. 4387
SSQ REALTY INC.—See La Capitale Civil Service Mutual; *Int'l*, pg. 4387
S+S REGELTECHNIK GMBH—See Investment AB Latour; *Int'l*, pg. 3784
SSR, INC.; *Int'l*, pg. 7157
SSR MINING INC.; *Int'l*, pg. 7157
SSR SCHADSTOFFSANIERUNG ROSTOCK GMBH—See Heidelberg Materials AG; *Int'l*, pg. 3319
S&S SALES CORPORATION; *U.S. Private*, pg. 3514
SSS BIOMEDICAL RESEARCH SUPPORT DIVISION—See DLH Holdings Corp.; *U.S. Public*, pg. 670
SSS COMPUTER SYSTEMS AND DATA ANALYSIS DIVISION—See DLH Holdings Corp.; *U.S. Public*, pg. 670
SSS CONSULTING, INC.—See GrowthPlay LLC; *U.S. Private*, pg. 1796
SSS DEVELOPMENT INC.; *U.S. Private*, pg. 3769
S+S SEPARATION & SORTING TECHNOLOGY GMBH—See VTC Partners GmbH; *Int'l*, pg. 8316
S+S SEPARATION & SORTING TECHNOLOGY (QINGDAO) CO., LTD—See VTC Partners GmbH; *Int'l*, pg. 8316
SSS MANAGEMENT SERVICES LIMITED—See Parfas Limited; *Int'l*, pg. 5741

S&S SPECIALTY SYSTEMS, LLC—See C. G. Bretting Manufacturing Co., Inc.; *U.S. Private*, pg. 705
S & S SPRINKLER CO LLC—See Pye-Barker Fire & Safety, LLC; *U.S. Private*, pg. 3309
S & S STEEL SERVICES—See The Mill Steel Co., Inc.; *U.S. Private*, pg. 4079
S.S. STEINER INC.; *U.S. Private*, pg. 3518
SSS TRUCKING INC.—See Structural Steel Holding Inc.; *U.S. Private*, pg. 3842
S&S SUPPLIES AND SOLUTIONS, INC.—See Littlejohn & Co., LLC; *U.S. Private*, pg. 2472
SST BENEFITS CONSULTING & INSURANCE SERVICES INC.—See Aon plc; *Int'l*, pg. 497
S&S TECH CO., LTD.; *Int'l*, pg. 6445
SST ENERGY CORPORATION; *U.S. Private*, pg. 3770
SSTRIC LIMITED—See Scottish Enterprise; *Int'l*, pg. 6652
S & S TRUCK PARTS, LLC—See Investcorp Holdings B.S.C.; *Int'l*, pg. 3776
SST SIGNAL & SYSTEM TECHNIK GMBH—See voestalpine AG; *Int'l*, pg. 8289
SST SPEDITION GMBH; *Int'l*, pg. 7157
SS VENTURES II INC.; *U.S. Private*, pg. 3768
SSV ENVIRONNEMENT S.A.S.—See Bucher Industries AG; *Int'l*, pg. 1209
SSWB LIMITED—See Pennon Group PLC; *Int'l*, pg. 5787
SS WHITE MEDICAL PRODUCTS—See S.S. White Technologies Inc.; *U.S. Private*, pg. 3518
S.S. WHITE TECHNOLOGIES INC.; *U.S. Private*, pg. 3518
S S WHITE TECHNOLOGIES UK LIMITED—See S.S. White Technologies Inc.; *U.S. Private*, pg. 3518
SSW HOLDING COMPANY, INC.—See Trive Capital Inc.; *U.S. Private*, pg. 4240
S.S.W. MECHANICAL CONSTRUCTION, INC.; *U.S. Private*, pg. 3519
S&S WORLDWIDE, INC.—See Sansei Technologies Inc.; *Int'l*, pg. 6555
S&S WORLDWIDE INC.; *U.S. Private*, pg. 3514
SSW PARTNERS LP; *U.S. Private*, pg. 3770
SSX, L.C.—See European Metal Recycling Limited; *Int'l*, pg. 2557
SSY GROUP LIMITED; *Int'l*, pg. 7157
ST1 NORDIC OY; *Int'l*, pg. 7160
ST1 SVERIGE AB—See St1 Nordic Oy; *Int'l*, pg. 7160
STAAB CONSTRUCTION CORPORATION; *U.S. Private*, pg. 3774
STAACK POOLTANKSTELLEN GMBH & CO. KG—See Marquard & Bahls AG; *Int'l*, pg. 4701
STAALBANKIERS N.V.—See Achmea B.V.; *Int'l*, pg. 103
STAALSERVICE WEERT BV—See VDL Groep B.V.; *Int'l*, pg. 8140
STAAR JAPAN INC—See STAAR Surgical Co.; *U.S. Public*, pg. 1924
STAAR SURGICAL AG NIEDERLASSUNG GERMANY—See STAAR Surgical Co.; *U.S. Public*, pg. 1924
STAAR SURGICAL CHINA CO., LTD.—See STAAR Surgical Co.; *U.S. Public*, pg. 1924
STAAR SURGICAL COMPANY AG—See STAAR Surgical Co.; *U.S. Public*, pg. 1924
STAAR SURGICAL CO.; *U.S. Public*, pg. 1924
STAAR SURGICAL PTE. LTD.—See STAAR Surgical Co.; *U.S. Public*, pg. 1924
STAATL MINERALBRUNNEN AG BAD BRUECKENAU; *Int'l*, pg. 7160
STABALUX GMBH—See Indutrade AB; *Int'l*, pg. 3681
STA BENEFITS, LTD.—See Aon plc; *Int'l*, pg. 497
STABFUND (GP) AG—See Schweizerische Nationalbank; *Int'l*, pg. 6646
STABILCHEM (M) SDN BHD—See IOI Corporation Berhad; *Int'l*, pg. 3792
STABIL DRILL—See Superior Energy Services, Inc.; *U.S. Private*, pg. 3877
STABIL DRILL SPECIALITIES, L.L.C.—See Superior Energy Services, Inc.; *U.S. Private*, pg. 3877
STABIL DRILL SPECIALTIES, L.L.C.—See Superior Energy Services, Inc.; *U.S. Private*, pg. 3877
STABILIS ENERGY, LLC—See STABILIS SOLUTIONS, INC.; *U.S. Public*, pg. 1924
STABILIS SOLUTIONS, INC.; *U.S. Public*, pg. 1924
STABILIT AMERICA, INC.-GLASTEEL DIV.—See Verzatec, S.A.B. de C.V.; *Int'l*, pg. 8176
STABILIT AMERICA, INC.-RESOLITE DIV.—See Verzatec, S.A.B. de C.V.; *Int'l*, pg. 8176
STABILIT AMERICA, INC.—See Verzatec, S.A.B. de C.V.; *Int'l*, pg. 8176
STABILIT S.A. DE C.V.—See Verzatec, S.A.B. de C.V.; *Int'l*, pg. 8176
STABILITY INC.—See MiMedx Group, Inc.; *U.S. Public*, pg. 1448
STABIL PRODUKT ELEKTROTECHNIKAI KFT.—See Standard Motor Products, Inc.; *U.S. Public*, pg. 1929
STABILUS CO. LTD., KOREA—See Triton Advisers Limited; *Int'l*, pg. 7933
STABILUS GMBH—See Triton Advisers Limited; *Int'l*, pg. 7933
STABILUS INC.—See Triton Advisers Limited; *Int'l*, pg. 7933

COMPANY NAME INDEX

STABILUS JAPAN CORPORATION—See Triton Advisers Limited; *Int'l*, pg. 7934
STABILUS (JIANGSU) LTD.—See Triton Advisers Limited; *Int'l*, pg. 7933
STABILUS LTDA.—See Triton Advisers Limited; *Int'l*, pg. 7934
STABILUS LTD.—See Triton Advisers Limited; *Int'l*, pg. 7934
STABILUS PTY. LTD.—See Triton Advisers Limited; *Int'l*, pg. 7934
STABILUS, S.A. DE C.V.—See Triton Advisers Limited; *Int'l*, pg. 7934
STABILUS S.A.—See Triton Advisers Limited; *Int'l*, pg. 7933
STABILUS; *U.S. Private*, pg. 3774
STABILUS S. R. L. ROMANIA—See Triton Advisers Limited; *Int'l*, pg. 7934
STABILUS S.R.L.—See Triton Advisers Limited; *Int'l*, pg. 7934
STABIPLAN BVBA—See Trimble, Inc.; *U.S. Public*, pg. 2191
STABIPLAN B.V.—See Trimble, Inc.; *U.S. Public*, pg. 2191
STABIPLAN GMBH—See Trimble, Inc.; *U.S. Public*, pg. 2191
STABIPLAN S.A.S.—See Trimble, Inc.; *U.S. Public*, pg. 2191
STABIPLAN S.R.L.—See Trimble, Inc.; *U.S. Public*, pg. 2191
STABLE MAGNET WIRE P. LTD—See IRCE S.p.A.; *Int'l*, pg. 3806
STABLE VISION CORPORATION SDN BHD—See AIA Group Limited; *Int'l*, pg. 227
STA BURKINA—See Mahindra & Mahindra Limited; *Int'l*, pg. 4647
STACCATO FOOTWEAR COMPANY LIMITED—See Hillhouse Investment Management Limited; *Int'l*, pg. 3393
STACE PTY LTD.—See Wilh. Werhahn KG; *Int'l*, pg. 8410
STACEY ENTERPRISES INC.; *U.S. Private*, pg. 3774
STACEY MOVING & STORAGE, INC., *U.S. Private*, pg. 3774
STACEY SMITH ENTERPRISES; *U.S. Private*, pg. 3774
STACI CORP.—See Centre Lane Partners, LLC; *U.S. Private*, pg. 827
STACI SAS—See Ardian SAS; *Int'l*, pg. 556
STACK CAPITAL GROUP INC.; *Int'l*, pg. 7160
STACKE HYDRAULIK AB; *Int'l*, pg. 7160
STACK ELECTRONICS LTD—See Stack Electronics; *U.S. Private*, pg. 3774
STACK ELECTRONICS; *U.S. Private*, pg. 3774
STACKHOUSE BENSINGER INC.; *U.S. Private*, pg. 3774
STACKIFY, LLC—See Netreo, Inc.; *U.S. Private*, pg. 2887
STACK, INC.—See Genstar Capital, LLC; *U.S. Private*, pg. 1678
STACK INFRASTRUCTURE, INC.—See ICONIQ Capital, LLC; *U.S. Private*, pg. 2032
STACK INFRASTRUCTURE, INC.—See Iron Point Partners, LLC; *U.S. Private*, pg. 2139
STACKLA PTY. LTD.—See Bailador Technology Investments Limited; *Int'l*, pg. 802
STACKMOB, LLC—See eBay Inc.; *U.S. Public*, pg. 709
STACK-ON PRODUCTS CO. INC.; *U.S. Private*, pg. 3774
STACKPOLE INTERNATIONAL FLUID POWER SOLUTIONS (CHANGZHOU) CO., LTD.—See Johnson Electric Holdings Limited; *Int'l*, pg. 3991
STACKPOLE INTERNATIONAL OTOMOTIV URUNLERI LIMITED SIRKETI—See Johnson Electric Holdings Limited; *Int'l*, pg. 3991
STACKPOLE INTERNATIONAL POWDER METAL, LTD.—See Johnson Electric Holdings Limited; *Int'l*, pg. 3991
STACKPOLE INTERNATIONAL—See Johnson Electric Holdings Limited; *Int'l*, pg. 3991
STACKPOLE LTD. - MISSISSAUGA, ENGINEERED PRODUCTS DIVISION—See Johnson Electric Holdings Limited; *Int'l*, pg. 3991
STACKPOLE LTD. - MISSISSAUGA, POWDER METAL DIVISION—See Johnson Electric Holdings Limited; *Int'l*, pg. 3991
STACKPOLE LTD. - STRATFORD, POWDER METAL DIVISION—See Johnson Electric Holdings Limited; *Int'l*, pg. 3991
STACKPOLE POWERTRAIN INTERNATIONAL GMBH—See Johnson Electric Holdings Limited; *Int'l*, pg. 3991
STACK'S-BOWERS NUMISMATICS, LLC—See Spectrum Group International, Inc.; *U.S. Public*, pg. 1917
STACK'S-BOWERS & PONTERIO, LTD.—See Spectrum Group International, Inc.; *U.S. Public*, pg. 1917
STACKS CONSULTING E INGENIERA EN SOFTWARE SL—See Cegedim S.A.; *Int'l*, pg. 1390
STACKS SERVICIOS TECHNOLOGICOS SL CHILE LTDA—See Cegedim S.A.; *Int'l*, pg. 1390
STACOENERGY PRODUCTS CO.—See Components Corporation of America, Inc.; *U.S. Private*, pg. 1002
THE STACOLE COMPANY, INC.—See The Winebow Group, LLC; *U.S. Private*, pg. 4137
STACO LINK CO., LTD.; *Int'l*, pg. 7160
STA CONTRACTING, LLC—See Solar Millennium AG; *Int'l*, pg. 7069

STACOSWITCH, INC.—See Components Corporation of America, Inc.; *U.S. Private*, pg. 1002
STA COTE D'IVOIRE—See Mahindra & Mahindra Limited; *Int'l*, pg. 4647
STACY ADAMS SHOE COMPANY—See Weyco Group, Inc.; *U.S. Public*, pg. 2365
STACYC, INC.—See Harley-Davidson, Inc.; *U.S. Public*, pg. 985
STACY EQUIPMENT CO.—See MPE Partners, LLC; *U.S. Private*, pg. 2804
STACY'S PITA CHIP COMPANY, INC.—See PepsiCo, Inc.; *U.S. Public*, pg. 1670
STADA ARZNEIMITTEL AG—See Bain Capital, LP; *U.S. Private*, pg. 442
STADA ARZNEIMITTEL AG—See Cinven Limited; *Int'l*, pg. 1613
STADA ARZNEIMITTEL GESELLSCHAFT M.B.H.—See Bain Capital, LP; *U.S. Private*, pg. 443
STADA ARZNEIMITTEL GESELLSCHAFT M.B.H.—See Cinven Limited; *Int'l*, pg. 1613
STADACONA WB L.P.—See Black Diamond Capital Holdings, LLC; *U.S. Private*, pg. 570
STADA CONSUMER HEALTH & STADAPHARM GMBH—See Bain Capital, LP; *U.S. Private*, pg. 443
STADA CONSUMER HEALTH & STADAPHARM GMBH—See Cinven Limited; *Int'l*, pg. 1613
STADA GMBH—See Bain Capital, LP; *U.S. Private*, pg. 443
STADA GMBH—See Cinven Limited; *Int'l*, pg. 1613
STADA HEMOFARM S.R.L.—See Bain Capital, LP; *U.S. Private*, pg. 443
STADA HEMOFARM S.R.L.—See Cinven Limited; *Int'l*, pg. 1613
STADA NORDIC APS—See Bain Capital, LP; *U.S. Private*, pg. 444
STADA NORDIC APS—See Cinven Limited; *Int'l*, pg. 1614
STADA PHARMA BULGARIA EOOD—See Bain Capital, LP; *U.S. Private*, pg. 443
STADA PHARMA BULGARIA EOOD—See Cinven Limited; *Int'l*, pg. 1613
STADA PHARMACEUTICALS (ASIA) LTD.—See Bain Capital, LP; *U.S. Private*, pg. 443
STADA PHARMACEUTICALS (ASIA) LTD.—See Cinven Limited; *Int'l*, pg. 1613
STADA PHARMACEUTICALS (BEIJING) LTD.—See Bain Capital, LP; *U.S. Private*, pg. 443
STADA PHARMACEUTICALS (BEIJING) LTD.—See Cinven Limited; *Int'l*, pg. 1613
STADA PHARMA CZ, S.R.O.—See Bain Capital, LP; *U.S. Private*, pg. 443
STADA PHARMA CZ, S.R.O.—See Cinven Limited; *Int'l*, pg. 1613
STADAPHARM GMBH—See Bain Capital, LP; *U.S. Private*, pg. 444
STADAPHARM GMBH—See Cinven Limited; *Int'l*, pg. 1614
STADA PRODUCTION IRELAND LIMITED—See Mutares SE & Co. KGaA; *Int'l*, pg. 5105
STADA R&D GMBH—See Bain Capital, LP; *U.S. Private*, pg. 443
STADA R&D GMBH—See Cinven Limited; *Int'l*, pg. 1613
STADA SERVICE HOLDING B.V.—See Bain Capital, LP; *U.S. Private*, pg. 443
STADA SERVICE HOLDING B.V.—See Cinven Limited; *Int'l*, pg. 1613
STADCO AUTOMOTIVE INDIA PVT. LTD.—See Stadco Ltd.; *Int'l*, pg. 7160
STADCO LTD.; *Int'l*, pg. 7160
STADCO SAARLOUIS LTD. & CO. KG—See Stadco Ltd.; *Int'l*, pg. 7160
STADCO—See Harlow Aerostructures, LLC; *U.S. Private*, pg. 1865
STADEMOS HOTELS PLC; *Int'l*, pg. 7160
STA DEVELOPMENT, LLC—See Solar Millennium AG; *Int'l*, pg. 7069
STADIO HOLDINGS LTD.; *Int'l*, pg. 7160
STADION MONEY MANAGEMENT, LLC—See TA Associates, Inc.; *U.S. Private*, pg. 3918
STADIUM ASIA—See Cicor Technologies Ltd.; *Int'l*, pg. 1603
STADIUM AUSTRALIA GROUP LTD.—See Foresight Group Holdings Limited; *Int'l*, pg. 2731
STADIUM ELECTRONICS LIMITED—See Cicor Technologies Ltd.; *Int'l*, pg. 1603
STADIUM INTERNATIONAL TRUCKS INC.; *U.S. Private*, pg. 3774
STADIUM PACKING SERVICES LTD—See British Engines Ltd.; *Int'l*, pg. 1171
STADIUM POWER LIMITED—See Cicor Technologies Ltd.; *Int'l*, pg. 1603
STADIUMRED GROUP; *U.S. Private*, pg. 3774
STADIUM TECHNOLOGY GROUP, LLC—See Entain PLC; *Int'l*, pg. 2450
STADIUM TOYOTA SCION; *U.S. Private*, pg. 3774
STADLAUER MALZFABRIK AG—See IREKS GmbH; *Int'l*, pg. 3806
STADLER ALGERIE EURL—See Stadler Rail AG; *Int'l*, pg. 7160

STADTWERKE SOLINGEN GMBH

STADLER ALTENRHEIN AG—See Stadler Rail AG; *Int'l*, pg. 7160
STADLER BUSSNANG AG—See Stadler Rail AG; *Int'l*, pg. 7160
STADLER NETHERLANDS B.V—See Stadler Rail AG; *Int'l*, pg. 7160
STADLER PANKOW GMBH—See Stadler Rail AG; *Int'l*, pg. 7160
STADLER POLSKA SP. Z O.O.—See Stadler Rail AG; *Int'l*, pg. 7160
STADLER PRAHA, S.R.O.—See Stadler Rail AG; *Int'l*, pg. 7160
STADLER RAIL AG; *Int'l*, pg. 7160
STADLER RAIL VALENCIA S.A.U—See Stadler Rail AG; *Int'l*, pg. 7160
STADLER REINICKENDORF GMBH—See Stadler Rail AG; *Int'l*, pg. 7160
STADLER SERVICE SWEDEN AB—See Stadler Rail AG; *Int'l*, pg. 7160
STADLER STAHLGUSS AG—See Stadler Rail AG; *Int'l*, pg. 7160
STADLER SZOLNOK VASUTI JARMUGYARTO KFT.—See Stadler Rail AG; *Int'l*, pg. 7160
STADLER UNGARN KFT.—See Stadler Rail AG; *Int'l*, pg. 7160
STADLER US INC.—See Stadler Rail AG; *Int'l*, pg. 7160
STADLER-VIEGA—See Georg Fischer AG; *Int'l*, pg. 2938
STADLER WINTERTHUR AG—See Stadler Rail AG; *Int'l*, pg. 7160
STADSHYPOTEK AB—See Svenska Handelsbanken AB; *Int'l*, pg. 7358
STADSNIEUWS BV—See DPG Media Group NV; *Int'l*, pg. 2189
STADTENTWASSERUNG BRAUNSCHWEIG GMBH—See Veolia Environnement S.A.; *Int'l*, pg. 8154
STADT-GALERIE HAMELN KG—See Deutsche EuroShop AG; *Int'l*, pg. 2065
STADT-GALERIE PASSAU KG—See Deutsche EuroShop AG; *Int'l*, pg. 2065
STADTISCHE PFANDLEIHANSTALT STUTTGART AKTIENGESELLSCHAF—See Landesbank Baden-Wurttemberg; *Int'l*, pg. 4406
STADTISCHES KRANKENHAUS WITTINGEN GMBH—See Fresenius SE & Co. KGaA; *Int'l*, pg. 2779
STADT OPTIK FIELMANN LANGENTHAL AG—See Fielmann Group AG; *Int'l*, pg. 2659
STADTRAUM SYSTEMS SP.Z O.O—See Astorg Partners S.A.S.; *Int'l*, pg. 657
STADTREINIGUNG DRESDEN GMBH—See Veolia Environnement S.A.; *Int'l*, pg. 8154
STADTREINIGUNG HAMBURG A.O.R.; *Int'l*, pg. 7161
STADTSPARKASSE MUNCHEN GMBH; *Int'l*, pg. 7161
STADTWERKE BIELEFELD GMBH; *Int'l*, pg. 7161
STADTWERKE DUREN GMBH—See RWE AG; *Int'l*, pg. 6435
STADTWERKE DUSSELDORF AG—See EnBW Energie Baden-Wurttemberg AG; *Int'l*, pg. 2400
STADTWERKE DUSSELDORF NETZ GMBH—See EnBW Energie Baden-Wurttemberg AG; *Int'l*, pg. 2400
STADTWERKE FORST GMBH—See ENGIE SA; *Int'l*, pg. 2429
STADTWERKE FORST GMBH—See E.ON SE; *Int'l*, pg. 2257
STADTWERKE FORST GMBH—See Vattenfall AB; *Int'l*, pg. 8137
STADTWERKE GELNHAUSEN GMBH; *Int'l*, pg. 7161
STADTWERKE GORLITZ AKTIENGESELLSCHAFT—See Veolia Environnement S.A.; *Int'l*, pg. 8154
STADTWERKE HANNOVER AG; *Int'l*, pg. 7161
STADTWERKE INGOLSTADT BETEILIGUNGEN GMBH; *Int'l*, pg. 7161
STADTWERKE INGOLSTADT ENERGIE GMBH—See Stadtwerke Ingolstadt Beteiligungen GmbH; *Int'l*, pg. 7161
STADTWERKE JAPAN CO., INC.—See West Holdings Corporation; *Int'l*, pg. 8385
STADTWERKE KIEL AKTIENGESELLSCHAFT—See MVV Energie AG; *Int'l*, pg. 5109
STADTWERKE KOLN GMBH; *Int'l*, pg. 7161
STADTWERKE ELSTERWERDA GMBH—See Stadtwerke Hannover AG; *Int'l*, pg. 7161
STADTWERKE MUNCHEN GMBH; *Int'l*, pg. 7161
STADTWERKE PULHEIM DIENSTE GMBH—See Veolia Environnement S.A.; *Int'l*, pg. 8154
STADTWERKE SCHWERIN GMBH; *Int'l*, pg. 7162
STADTWERKE SINSHEIM VERSORGUNGS GMBH & CO. KG—See EnBW Energie Baden-Wurttemberg AG; *Int'l*, pg. 2400
STADTWERKE SINSHEIM VERWALTUNGS GMBH—See EnBW Energie Baden-Wurttemberg AG; *Int'l*, pg. 2400
STADTWERKE SOLINGEN GMBH; *Int'l*, pg. 7162
STADTWERKE SOLINGEN NETZ GMBH—See Stadtwerke Solingen GmbH; *Int'l*, pg. 7162
STADTWERKE WEISSWASSER GMBH—See Veolia Environnement S.A.; *Int'l*, pg. 8154
STAEDTLER BENELUX N.V./S.A.—See STAEDTLER MARS GmbH & Co KG; *Int'l*, pg. 7162
STAEDTLER DE MEXICO, S.A. DE C.V.—See STAEDTLER MARS GmbH & Co KG; *Int'l*, pg. 7162

STADTWERKE SOLINGEN GMBH

STAEDTLER IBERIA, S.A.—See STAEDTLER MARS GmbH & Co KG; *Int'l*, pg. 7162
STAEDTLER, INC.—See STAEDTLER MARS GmbH & Co KG; *Int'l*, pg. 7162
STAEDTLER ITALIA S.P.A.—See STAEDTLER MARS GmbH & Co KG; *Int'l*, pg. 7162
STAEDTLER (KOREA) CO. LTD.—See STAEDTLER MARS GmbH & Co KG; *Int'l*, pg. 7162
STAEDTLER MARKETING SDN BHD—See STAEDTLER MARS GmbH & Co KG; *Int'l*, pg. 7162
STAEDTLER MARS GMBH & CO KG; *Int'l*, pg. 7162
STAEDTLER NIPPON K.K.—See STAEDTLER MARS GmbH & Co KG; *Int'l*, pg. 7162
STAEDTLER NORDIC A/S—See STAEDTLER MARS GmbH & Co KG; *Int'l*, pg. 7162
STAEDTLER (NZ) LTD.—See STAEDTLER MARS GmbH & Co KG; *Int'l*, pg. 7162
STAEDTLER (PACIFIC) PTY. LTD.—See STAEDTLER MARS GmbH & Co KG; *Int'l*, pg. 7162
STAEDTLER (S.A.) (PTY.) LTD.—See STAEDTLER MARS GmbH & Co KG; *Int'l*, pg. 7162
STAEDTLER (SINGAPORE) PTE. LTD.—See STAEDTLER MARS GmbH & Co KG; *Int'l*, pg. 7162
STAEDTLER (THAILAND) LTD.—See STAEDTLER MARS GmbH & Co KG; *Int'l*, pg. 7162
STAEDTLER (U.K.) LTD.—See STAEDTLER MARS GmbH & Co KG; *Int'l*, pg. 7162
STAENG LIMITED—See Spirent Communications plc; *Int'l*, pg. 7140
ST AEROSPACE ENGINEERING PTE LTD.—See Temasek Holdings (Private) Limited; *Int'l*, pg. 7551
ST AEROSPACE ENGINES PTE LTD.—See Temasek Holdings (Private) Limited; *Int'l*, pg. 7551
ST AEROSPACE MOBILE, INC.—See Temasek Holdings (Private) Limited; *Int'l*, pg. 7552
ST AEROSPACE SOLUTIONS (EUROPE) A/S—See Temasek Holdings (Private) Limited; *Int'l*, pg. 7551
ST AEROSPACE SUPPLIES PTE LTD.—See Temasek Holdings (Private) Limited; *Int'l*, pg. 7551
ST AEROSPACE SYSTEMS PTE LTD.—See Temasek Holdings (Private) Limited; *Int'l*, pg. 7551
STAFAST PRODUCTS INC.; *U.S. Private*, pg. 3774
STAFA WIRZ VENTILATOR AG—See Konrad REITZ Ventilatoren GmbH & Co. KG; *Int'l*, pg. 4275
STAFF BUILDERS HOME HEALTH—See Amedisys, Inc.; *U.S. Public*, pg. 94
STAFFBUILDERSHR, LLC; *U.S. Private*, pg. 3775
STAFF CARE, INC.—See AMN Healthcare Services, Inc.; *U.S. Public*, pg. 125
S-TAFF CO., LTD—See Senko Group Holdings Co., Ltd.; *Int'l*, pg. 6710
STAFF DEVELOPMENT FOR EDUCATORS, INC.—See Highlights for Children, Inc.; *U.S. Private*, pg. 1940
STAFF FORCE INC.; *U.S. Private*, pg. 3774
STAFFGROUP LTD.—See Cordant Group PLC; *Int'l*, pg. 1795
STAFFIELD COUNTRY RESORT BERHAD—See Berjaya Corporation Berhad; *Int'l*, pg. 984
STAFFING 360 SOLUTIONS, INC.; *U.S. Public*, pg. 1924
STAFFING ASSOCIATES INC.; *U.S. Private*, pg. 3775
THE STAFFING GROUP LTD.; *U.S. Private*, pg. 4120
STAFFING NOW, INC.—See GEE Group Inc.; *U.S. Public*, pg. 910
THE STAFFING RESOURCE GROUP, INC.; *U.S. Private*, pg. 4120
STAFFING SERVICES LLC; *U.S. Private*, pg. 3775
STAFFING TECHNOLOGIES, LLC; *U.S. Private*, pg. 3775
STAFFLINE GROUP PLC; *Int'l*, pg. 7162
STAFFLOGIX CORPORATION; *U.S. Private*, pg. 3775
STAFF MANAGEMENT SOLUTIONS, LLC—See TrueBlue, Inc.; *U.S. Public*, pg. 2199
STAFFMARK HOLDINGS, INC.—See Recruit Holdings Co., Ltd.; *Int'l*, pg. 6241
STAFFMARK PROFESSIONAL SERVICES, LLC—See Recruit Holdings Co., Ltd.; *Int'l*, pg. 6241
STAFF MATTERS INC.—See NSC Technologies, Inc.; *U.S. Private*, pg. 2970
STAFF OF LIFE NATURAL FOODS MARKET; *U.S. Private*, pg. 3775
STAFF ONE, INC.—See Paychex, Inc.; *U.S. Public*, pg. 1655
STAFF ON SITE, INC.; *U.S. Private*, pg. 3775
STAFFORD & COMPANY INSURANCE LTD.; *U.S. Private*, pg. 3775
STAFFORD CONSTRUCTION COMPANY, L.L.C.; *U.S. Private*, pg. 3775
STAFFORD CONSULTING ENGINEERS, INC.—See Terracon Consultants, Inc.; *U.S. Private*, pg. 3971
STAFFORD COUNTY FLOUR MILLS CO; *U.S. Private*, pg. 3775
STAFFORD DEVELOPMENT COMPANY; *U.S. Private*, pg. 3775
STAFFORD HOUSE SCHOOL OF ENGLISH LIMITED—See Bright Scholar Education Holdings Limited; *Int'l*, pg. 1162
STAFFORD HOUSE STUDY HOLIDAYS LIMITED—See Bright Scholar Education Holdings Limited; *Int'l*, pg. 1162

STAFFORD MILLER (IRELAND) LIMITED—See GSK plc; *Int'l*, pg. 3149
STAFFORD OIL CO. INC.; *U.S. Private*, pg. 3775
STAFFORD PRESS, INC—See SATO Holdings Corporation; *Int'l*, pg. 6586
STAFFORD PRIVATE EQUITY INC—See Stafford Private Equity Pty. Limited; *Int'l*, pg. 7162
STAFFORD PRIVATE EQUITY LIMITED—See Stafford Private Equity Pty. Limited; *Int'l*, pg. 7162
STAFFORD PRIVATE EQUITY PTY. LIMITED; *Int'l*, pg. 7162
STAFFORD RAILWAY BUILDING SOCIETY; *Int'l*, pg. 7162
THE STAFFORDSHIRE AND WEST MIDLANDS COMMUNITY REHABILITATION COMPANY LIMITED—See ModivCare, Inc.; *U.S. Public*, pg. 1456
STAFFORDSHIRE HYDRAULIC SERVICES LIMITED—See Graco, Inc.; *U.S. Public*, pg. 954
STAFFORD-SMITH INC.; *U.S. Private*, pg. 3775
STAFFORD TEXTILES LIMITED; *Int'l*, pg. 7162
STAFFORD TIMBERLAND LIMITED—See Stafford Private Equity Pty. Limited; *Int'l*, pg. 7162
STAFFPLAN LTD.—See Vista Equity Partners, LLC; *U.S. Private*, pg. 4394
STAFF PLANNING NEDERLANDS B.V.—See Randstad N.V.; *Int'l*, pg. 6205
STAFF PRO INC.; *U.S. Private*, pg. 3775
STAFF PRO SERVICES INC.—See Staff Pro Inc.; *U.S. Private*, pg. 3775
STAFF SERVICE HOLDINGS CO., LTD.—See Recruit Holdings Co., Ltd.; *Int'l*, pg. 6241
STAFF SOLUTIONS AUSTRALIA PTY LTD—See Bain Capital, LP; *U.S. Private*, pg. 435
STAFFWORKS GROUP; *U.S. Private*, pg. 3775
STAGDOK OAO—See Novolipetski Metallurgicheski Komb OAO; *Int'l*, pg. 5466
STAGE 1 VENTURES, LLC; *U.S. Private*, pg. 3775
STAGE 2 NETWORKS; *U.S. Private*, pg. 3775
STAGE 4 SOLUTIONS, INC.; *U.S. Private*, pg. 3775
STAGE CAPITAL LLP; *Int'l*, pg. 7163
STAGECOACH AGENCY (UK) LIMITED—See Stagecoach Theatre Arts Plc; *Int'l*, pg. 7163
STAGECOACH BUS HOLDINGS LIMITED—See Stagecoach Group plc; *Int'l*, pg. 7163
STAGECOACH CAMBRIDGESHIRE—See Stagecoach Group plc; *Int'l*, pg. 7163
STAGECOACH CARTAGE & DISTRIBUTION, LLC.—See JH Rose Logistics Inc.; *U.S. Private*, pg. 2207
STAGECOACH COFFEE, INC.; *U.S. Private*, pg. 3775
STAGECOACH GROUP PLC; *Int'l*, pg. 7163
STAGECOACH SCOTLAND LTD.—See Stagecoach Group plc; *Int'l*, pg. 7163
STAGECOACH SERVICES LIMITED—See Stagecoach Group plc; *Int'l*, pg. 7163
STAGECOACH (SOUTH) LTD.—See Stagecoach Group plc; *Int'l*, pg. 7163
STAGECOACH SOUTH WESTERN TRAINS LTD.—See Stagecoach Group plc; *Int'l*, pg. 7163
STAGECOACH THEATRE ARTS PLC; *Int'l*, pg. 7163
STAGECOACH THEATRE ARTS SCHOOLS GMBH—See Stagecoach Theatre Arts Plc; *Int'l*, pg. 7163
STAGECOACH TRANSPORT HOLDINGS PLC—See Stagecoach Group plc; *Int'l*, pg. 7163
STAGECOACH VINEYARD—See E. & J. Gallo Winery; *U.S. Private*, pg. 1303
STAGECOACH WEST LIMITED—See Stagecoach Group plc; *Int'l*, pg. 7163
STAGE ELECTRICS PARTNERSHIP LTD.; *Int'l*, pg. 7163
STAGE EQUITY PARTNERS, LLC; *U.S. Private*, pg. 3775
STAGE FRONT PRESENTATION SYSTEMS; *U.S. Private*, pg. 3775
THE STAGE FUND, LLC; *U.S. Private*, pg. 4120
STAGE IT CORP.—See VNUE, Inc.; *U.S. Public*, pg. 2308
STAGER ENTERPRISES INC.; *U.S. Private*, pg. 3775
STAGESTEP INC.; *U.S. Private*, pg. 3775
STAGE STORES, INC.; *U.S. Public*, pg. 1925
STAGE SYSTEMS LIMITED—See Havelock Europa PLC; *Int'l*, pg. 3287
STAGE TECHNOLOGIES LIMITED; *Int'l*, pg. 7163
STAGEZERO LIFE SCIENCES, INC.—See StageZero Life Sciences, Ltd.; *Int'l*, pg. 7163
STAGEZERO LIFE SCIENCES, LTD.; *Int'l*, pg. 7163
STAGG FOODS, INC.—See Hormel Foods Corporation; *U.S. Public*, pg. 1054
STAG INDUSTRIAL, INC.; *U.S. Public*, pg. 1925
STAGING CONCEPTS—See Trex Company, Inc.; *U.S. Public*, pg. 2188
STAGING CONNECTIONS GROUP LIMITED—See Freeman Decorating Co.; *U.S. Private*, pg. 1605
STAG MEBANE 1, LLC—See STAG Industrial, Inc.; *U.S. Public*, pg. 1925
ST. AGNES MEDICAL CENTER—See Trinity Health Corporation; *U.S. Private*, pg. 4234
STAG-PARKWAY, INC.; *U.S. Private*, pg. 3775
STAG READING, LLC—See STAG Industrial, Inc.; *U.S. Public*, pg. 1925
STAG'S LEAP WINE CELLARS, LLC—See Marchesi Antinori S.p.A; *Int'l*, pg. 4690

CORPORATE AFFILIATIONS

THE STAGWELL GROUP LLC—See Stagwell, Inc.; *U.S. Public*, pg. 1928
STAGWELL, INC.; *U.S. Public*, pg. 1925
STAHL & ASSOCIATES INSURANCE, INC.—See Galiot Insurance Services, Inc.; *U.S. Private*, pg. 1638
STAHL & ASSOCIATES INSURANCE INC.—See Galiot Insurance Services, Inc.; *U.S. Private*, pg. 1638
STAHL & ASSOCIATES INSURANCE—See Galiot Insurance Services, Inc.; *U.S. Private*, pg. 1638
STAHL, BOWLES & ASSOCIATES, INC.—See Galiot Insurance Services, Inc.; *U.S. Private*, pg. 1638
STAHL B.V.—See Wendel S.A.; *Int'l*, pg. 8376
STAHL-CENTER BAUNATAL GMBH—See Salzgitter AG; *Int'l*, pg. 6499
STAHL CRANESYSTEMS FZE—See Columbus McKinnon Corporation; *U.S. Public*, pg. 536
STAHL CRANESYSTEMS GMBH—See Columbus McKinnon Corporation; *U.S. Public*, pg. 536
STAHL CRANESYSTEMS INC.—See Columbus McKinnon Corporation; *U.S. Public*, pg. 536
STAHL CRANESYSTEMS (INDIA) PVT. LTD.—See Columbus McKinnon Corporation; *U.S. Public*, pg. 536
STAHL CRANESYSTEMS LTD.—See Columbus McKinnon Corporation; *U.S. Public*, pg. 536
STAHL CRANESYSTEMS S.A.S.—See Columbus McKinnon Corporation; *U.S. Public*, pg. 536
STAHL CRANESYSTEMS SHANGHAI CO. LTD.—See Columbus McKinnon Corporation; *U.S. Public*, pg. 536
STAHL CRANESYSTEMS S.L.—See Columbus McKinnon Corporation; *U.S. Public*, pg. 536
STAHL CRANESYSTEMS TRADING (SHANGHAI) CO. LTD.—See Columbus McKinnon Corporation; *U.S. Public*, pg. 536
STAHLER SUISSE SA; *Int'l*, pg. 7163
STAHLGRUBER COMMUNICATION CENTER GMBH—See Brodos AG; *Int'l*, pg. 1173
STAHLGRUBER CZ S.R.O.—See LKQ Corporation; *U.S. Public*, pg. 1336
STAHLGRUBER D.O.O.—See LKQ Corporation; *U.S. Public*, pg. 1336
STAHLGRUBER GES. M.B.H—See LKQ Corporation; *U.S. Public*, pg. 1336
STAHLGRUBER GMBH—See LKQ Corporation; *U.S. Public*, pg. 1336
STAHLGRUBER OTTO GRUBER GMBH & CO. KG; *Int'l*, pg. 7163
STAHLGRUBER S.R.L—See Stahlgruber Otto Gruber GmbH & Co. KG; *Int'l*, pg. 7164
STAHLGRUBER TRGOVINA D.O.O.—See LKQ Corporation; *U.S. Public*, pg. 1336
STAHLGUSS GRODITZ GMBH—See Georgsmarienhutte Holding GmbH; *Int'l*, pg. 2941
STAHLGUSS SAAR GMBH—See Saarstahl AG; *Int'l*, pg. 6461
STAHLHAMMER BOMMERN GMBH—See Columbus McKinnon Corporation; *U.S. Public*, pg. 536
STAHL HOLDINGS B.V.—See Wendel S.A.; *Int'l*, pg. 8376
STAHLIN NON-METALLIC ENCLOSURES INC.—See Robroy Industries Inc.; *U.S. Private*, pg. 3463
STAHL JUDENBURG GMBH—See Georgsmarienhutte Holding GmbH; *Int'l*, pg. 2941
STAHL-MEYER FOODS, INC.; *U.S. Private*, pg. 3776
STAHL N.V.—See R. STAHL AG; *Int'l*, pg. 6170
STAHLO STAHLSERVICE GMBH & CO. KG—See Friedhelm Loh Stiftung & Co. KG; *Int'l*, pg. 2791
STAHLSAITEN BETONWERKE GMBH—See Heidelberg Materials AG; *Int'l*, pg. 3319
STAHL/SCOTT FETZER COMPANY—See Berkshire Hathaway Inc.; *U.S. Public*, pg. 300
STAHL'S INC.; *U.S. Private*, pg. 3776
STAHL-SYBERG AS—See R. STAHL AG; *Int'l*, pg. 6170
STAHL + VERBUNDBAU GMBH—See Hutter & Schrantz PMS Ges.m.b.H; *Int'l*, pg. 3540
STAHLWERK BOUS GMBH—See Georgsmarienhutte Holding GmbH; *Int'l*, pg. 2941
STAHLWERK THURINGEN GMBH—See Companhia Siderurgica Nacional; *Int'l*, pg. 1748
STA-HOME HEALTH & HOSPICE, INC.—See Advent International Corporation; *U.S. Private*, pg. 97
STAIDSON (BEIJING) BIOPHARMACEUTICALS CO., LTD.; *Int'l*, pg. 7164
STAINES VETS4PETS LIMITED—See Pets at Home Group Plc; *Int'l*, pg. 5834
STAINLESS BROADCASTING, LLC—See Northwest Broadcasting, Inc.; *U.S. Private*, pg. 2959
STAINLESS DESIGN CONCEPTS—See CVD Equipment Corporation; *U.S. Public*, pg. 613
STAINLESS FABRICATION, INC—See Exchange Income Corporation; *Int'l*, pg. 2579
STAINLESS FOUNDRY & ENGINEERING INC.—See TMB Industries Inc.; *U.S. Private*, pg. 4179
STAINLESS METALCRAFT (CHATTERIS) LIMITED—See Avingtrans plc; *Int'l*, pg. 744
STAINLESS ONE CORPORATION—See Mitsubishi Corporation; *Int'l*, pg. 4940
STAINLESS ONE CORPORATION—See Sojitz Corporation; *Int'l*, pg. 7062
STAINLESS PIPE KOGYO CO., LTD.—See Hanwa Co., Ltd.; *Int'l*, pg. 3263

COMPANY NAME INDEX

STAINLESS PIPING SYSTEMS, INC.—See Alco Investment Co., Inc.; *U.S. Private*, pg. 154
STAINLESS SERVICE ANDINO S/A—See Aperam SA; *Int'l*, pg. 508
STAINLESS SPECIALISTS INC.; *U.S. Private*, pg. 3776
STAINLESS STEEL & ALUMINUM CORPORATION—See Tiso Blackstar Group SE; *Int'l*, pg. 7759
STAINLESS STEEL FASTENERS LTD—See IMI plc; *Int'l*, pg. 3626
STAINLESS STEEL MIDWEST LLC; *U.S. Private*, pg. 3776
STAINLESS SYSTEMS INC.; *U.S. Private*, pg. 3776
STAINLESS TANK & EQUIPMENT CO., LLC—See Hendricks Holding Company, Inc.; *U.S. Private*, pg. 1915
STA INTERNATIONAL INC.; *U.S. Private*, pg. 3774
STAINTON METAL CO, LTD.—See Valmont Industries, Inc.; *U.S. Public*, pg. 2274
STAIRWAYS BEHAVIORAL HEALTH—See Children's Home of Bradford, PA.; *U.S. Private*, pg. 884
STAJAC INDUSTRIES, INC.; *U.S. Private*, pg. 3776
STAKE CENTER LOCATING INC.; *U.S. Private*, pg. 3776
STAKE FASTENER COMPANY—See Dupree, Inc.; *U.S. Private*, pg. 1291
STAKEHOLDER GOLD CORP.; *Int'l*, pg. 7164
STAKELOGIC B.V.—See Novomatic AG; *Int'l*, pg. 5467
STAKER & PARSON COMPANIES INC.—See CRH plc; *Int'l*, pg. 1847
STAKHANOV RAILWAY CAR BUILDING WORKS, PJSC; *Int'l*, pg. 7164
STAKLOREKLAM A.D.; *Int'l*, pg. 7164
STAKMORE, INC.; *U.S. Private*, pg. 3776
STAKO SP. Z O.O.—See Worthington Industries, Inc.; *U.S. Public*, pg. 2382
STAKU STANZ UND KUNSTSOFF TECHNIK GMBH—See Amphenol Corporation; *U.S. Public*, pg. 132
S&T ALBANIA LTD.—See Kontron AG; *Int'l*, pg. 4277
S&T ALBANIA SH.P.K.—See Kontron AG; *Int'l*, pg. 4277
ST. ALBERT DODGE CHRYSLER LTD.; *Int'l*, pg. 7158
STALCOP L.P.—See 13i Capital Corporation; *U.S. Private*, pg. 3
STALELIFE STUDIOS; *U.S. Private*, pg. 3776
ST. ALEXIUS MEDICAL CENTER; *U.S. Private*, pg. 3770
STALEXPORT AUTOSTRADA MALOPOLSKA S.A.—See Stalexport Autostrady S.A.; *Int'l*, pg. 7164
STALEXPORT AUTOSTRADY S.A.; *Int'l*, pg. 7164
STALEY COMMUNICATION, INC.; *U.S. Private*, pg. 3776
STALEY INC.; *U.S. Private*, pg. 3776
STALFA SP. Z O.O.—See Polimex-Mostostal S.A.; *Int'l*, pg. 5909
STALKUP'S RV SUPERSTORE, INC.; *U.S. Private*, pg. 3776
STALLARD FINANCIAL STRATEGIES, INC.—See Aon plc; *Int'l*, pg. 497
STALLERGENES GREER HOLDINGS INC.—See B-FLEXION Group Holdings SA; *Int'l*, pg. 785
STALLERGENES GREER PLC—See B-FLEXION Group Holdings SA; *Int'l*, pg. 785
STALLERGENES, INC.—See B-FLEXION Group Holdings SA; *Int'l*, pg. 785
STALLERGENES SAS—See B-FLEXION Group Holdings SA; *Int'l*, pg. 785
STALLINGS BROTHERS INC.; *U.S. Private*, pg. 3776
STALLION GOLD CORP.; *Int'l*, pg. 7164
STALLION, INC.; *U.S. Private*, pg. 3776
STALLION NMN LTD.—See Nissan Motor Co., Ltd.; *Int'l*, pg. 5369
STALLION OILFIELD SERVICES, LTD.; *U.S. Private*, pg. 3776
STALLMASTAREN AB—See Merck & Co., Inc.; *U.S. Public*, pg. 1421
STALLWORTH & JOHNSON INC.; *U.S. Private*, pg. 3776
STALOTON KLINKER VERTRIEBS GMBH—See Deutsche Steinzeug Cremer & Breuer AG; *Int'l*, pg. 2083
ST. ALPHONSUS REGIONAL MEDICAL CENTER—See Trinity Health Corporation; *U.S. Private*, pg. 4234
STALPRODUKT S.A.; *Int'l*, pg. 7164
STALPRODUKT-WAMECH SP. Z O.O.—See Stalprodukt S.A.; *Int'l*, pg. 7164
STALPRODUKT-ZAMOSC SP. Z O.O.—See Stalprodukt S.A.; *Int'l*, pg. 7164
STALPROFIL AB—See Indutrade AB; *Int'l*, pg. 3681
STALPROFIL PK AB—See Indutrade AB; *Int'l*, pg. 3681
STALPROFIL S.A.; *Int'l*, pg. 7164
STAL & RORMONTAGE I SOLVESBORG AB—See Storskogen Group AB; *Int'l*, pg. 7228
STALSERVICE PRODUKTION I ANDERSTORP AB—See Aalberts N.V.; *Int'l*, pg. 35
STAL-SERVICE SPOLKA Z OGRANICZONA ODPOWIEDZIALNOSCIA—See PORR AG; *Int'l*, pg. 5925
STA. LUCIA LAND, INC.; *Int'l*, pg. 7160
STAL WARSZTAT SP. Z O.O.—See Tesgas S.A.; *Int'l*, pg. 7572
STALWART SYSTEMS, LLC—See EQT AB; *Int'l*, pg. 2480
STALWART TANKERS INC.; *Int'l*, pg. 7165
STAMAG STADLAUER MALZFABRIK GESMBH—See IREKS GmbH; *Int'l*, pg. 3806
STAMATS; *U.S. Private*, pg. 3776

STAMBAUGH AVIATION, INC.—See Stambaugh's Air Service, Inc.; *U.S. Private*, pg. 3776
STAMBAUGH'S AIR SERVICE, INC.; *U.S. Private*, pg. 3776
STAMCO INDUSTRIES INC.; *U.S. Private*, pg. 3776
STAMEN CO., LTD.; *Int'l*, pg. 7165
STAMFORD CATERING SERVICES PTE LTD—See Select Group Limited; *Int'l*, pg. 6699
STAMFORD COLLEGE BERHAD—See IRIS Corporation Berhad; *Int'l*, pg. 3809
STAMFORD FOOD INDUSTRIES SDN. BHD.—See Ingredion Incorporated; *U.S. Public*, pg. 1124
STAMFORD FORD LINCOLN, LLC; *U.S. Private*, pg. 3776
STAMFORD HEALTH SYSTEM INC.; *U.S. Private*, pg. 3776
STAMFORD HERITAGE PLAZA HOTEL PTY. LTD.—See Stamford Land Corporation Ltd.; *Int'l*, pg. 7165
STAMFORD HERITAGE PTY LTD—See Stamford Land Corporation Ltd.; *Int'l*, pg. 7165
STAMFORD HOMES LIMITED—See Vistry Group PLC; *Int'l*, pg. 8255
STAMFORD HOTELS PTY. LIMITED—See Stamford Land Corporation Ltd.; *Int'l*, pg. 7165
STAMFORD HOTELS & RESORTS PTE. LTD.—See Stamford Land Corporation Ltd.; *Int'l*, pg. 7165
STAMFORD HOTELS & RESORTS PTY LIMITED—See Stamford Land Corporation Ltd.; *Int'l*, pg. 7165
STAMFORD LAND CORPORATION LTD.; *Int'l*, pg. 7165
STAMFORD LAND MANAGEMENT PTE. LTD.—See Stamford Land Corporation Ltd.; *Int'l*, pg. 7165
STAMFORD PARTNERS LLP—See Piper Sandler Companies; *U.S. Public*, pg. 1694
STAMFORD PLAZA AUCKLAND HOTEL—See Stamford Land Corporation Ltd.; *Int'l*, pg. 7165
STAMFORD PLAZA & CONFERENCE CENTER—See Rosdev Management Inc.; *Int'l*, pg. 6399
STAMFORD PLAZA HOTELS PTY. LIMITED—See Stamford Land Corporation Ltd.; *Int'l*, pg. 7165
STAMFORD PLAZA SYDNEY AIRPORT PTY. LTD.—See Stamford Land Corporation Ltd.; *Int'l*, pg. 7165
STAMFORD SALES (PROPRIETARY) LIMITED—See The Bidvest Group Limited; *Int'l*, pg. 7625
STAMFORD SPORT WHEELS COMPANY LIMITED—See Stamford Tyres Corporation Limited; *Int'l*, pg. 7165
STAMFORD STOCKHOLM AB—See Addnode Group AB; *Int'l*, pg. 130
STAMFORD SYDNEY AIRPORT PTY LTD—See Stamford Land Corporation Ltd.; *Int'l*, pg. 7165
STAMFORD TIRES DISTRIBUTOR CO, LTD—See Stamford Tyres Corporation Limited; *Int'l*, pg. 7165
STAMFORD TYRE MART SDN BHD—See Stamford Tyres Corporation Limited; *Int'l*, pg. 7165
STAMFORD TYRES (AFRICA) (PROPRIETARY) LIMITED—See Stamford Tyres Corporation Limited; *Int'l*, pg. 7165
STAMFORD TYRES (AUSTRALIA) PTY LTD—See Stamford Tyres Corporation Limited; *Int'l*, pg. 7165
STAMFORD TYRES (B) SDN. BHD.—See Stamford Tyres Corporation Limited; *Int'l*, pg. 7165
STAMFORD TYRES CORPORATION LIMITED; *Int'l*, pg. 7165
STAMFORD TYRES DISTRIBUTORS INDIA PVT LTD—See Stamford Tyres Corporation Limited; *Int'l*, pg. 7165
STAMFORD TYRES DURBAN—See Stamford Tyres Corporation Limited; *Int'l*, pg. 7165
STAMFORD TYRES GUANGZHOU LIMITED—See Stamford Tyres Corporation Limited; *Int'l*, pg. 7165
STAMFORD TYRES (HONG KONG) LIMITED—See Stamford Tyres Corporation Limited; *Int'l*, pg. 7165
STAMFORD TYRES INTERNATIONAL PTE LTD—See Stamford Tyres Corporation Limited; *Int'l*, pg. 7165
STAMFORD TYRES JOHANNESBURG—See Stamford Tyres Corporation Limited; *Int'l*, pg. 7165
STAMFORD TYRES (M) SDN BHD—See Stamford Tyres Corporation Limited; *Int'l*, pg. 7165
STAMFORD TYRES PTY. LTD.—See Stamford Tyres Corporation Limited; *Int'l*, pg. 7165
STAMFORD TYRES VIETNAM COMPANY LIMITED—See Stamford Tyres Corporation Limited; *Int'l*, pg. 7165
STAMFORD VAN & CAR HIRE LTD—See Turner & Co. (Glasgow) Limited; *Int'l*, pg. 7978
STAM HEERHUGOWAARD HOLDING B.V—See Alliander N.V.; *Int'l*, pg. 341
STAMICARBON BV—See Maire Tecnimont S.p.A.; *Int'l*, pg. 4652
STAMM AG—See SFS Group AG; *Int'l*, pg. 6739
STAMMEN INSURANCE GROUP, LLC; *U.S. Private*, pg. 3777
STAMM INTERNATIONAL CORPORATION; *U.S. Private*, pg. 3777
STAMPAL SB, D.O.O.—See Impol d.d.; *Int'l*, pg. 3636
STAMPA NAPOLI 2015 SRL—See Caltagirone Editore S.p.A.; *Int'l*, pg. 1266
STAMPARIJA BORBA A.D.; *Int'l*, pg. 7165
STAMPARIJA D.D.KLJUC; *Int'l*, pg. 7166
STAMPEDE CAPITAL LIMITED; *Int'l*, pg. 7166
STAMPEDE DRILLING INC.; *Int'l*, pg. 7166

STANDARD BIOTOOLS INC.

STAMPEDE MEAT, INC.—See Wynnchurch Capital, L.P.; *U.S. Private*, pg. 4578
STAMPEDE TRANSPORTATION, LLC—See AET Holdings, LLC; *U.S. Private*, pg. 120
STAMPED PRODUCTS INC.—See Mid-South Industries, Inc.; *U.S. Private*, pg. 2708
STAMPEN AB; *Int'l*, pg. 7166
STAMPEN MEDIA PARTNER AB—See Stampen AB; *Int'l*, pg. 7166
STAMPER OIL & GAS CORP.; *Int'l*, pg. 7166
STAMPFLI AG; *Int'l*, pg. 7166
STAMPFLI POLSKA SP. Z O.O.—See Stampfli AG; *Int'l*, pg. 7166
STAMPFLI VERLAG AG—See Stampfli AG; *Int'l*, pg. 7166
STAMPIN UP INC.; *U.S. Private*, pg. 3777
STAMPS.COM INC.—See Thoma Bravo, L.P.; *U.S. Private*, pg. 4153
STAMPTECH, INC.—See Amzak Capital Management, LLC; *U.S. Private*, pg. 270
STAMPTEC-HOLDING GMBH—See voestalpine AG; *Int'l*, pg. 8289
STAMS LTD.—See Assurant, Inc.; *U.S. Public*, pg. 215
STAM-TERBERG AUTOBEDRIJVEN B. V.—See General Motors Company; *U.S. Public*, pg. 927
STAN ADLER ASSOCIATES, INC.—See CHR Group LLC; *U.S. Private*, pg. 889
STANADYNE CORPORATION—See Kohlberg & Company, LLC; *U.S. Private*, pg. 2339
STANBEE ASIA, LTD.—See Stanbee Company, Inc.; *U.S. Private*, pg. 3777
STANBEE COMPANY, INC.; *U.S. Private*, pg. 3777
STANBIC IBTC ASSET MANAGEMENT LIMITED—See Stanbic IBTC Holdings PLC; *Int'l*, pg. 7166
STANBIC IBTC CAPITAL LIMITED—See Stanbic IBTC Holdings PLC; *Int'l*, pg. 7166
STANBIC IBTC HOLDINGS PLC; *Int'l*, pg. 7166
STANBIC IBTC INSURANCE BROKERS LIMITED—See Stanbic IBTC Holdings PLC; *Int'l*, pg. 7166
STANBIC IBTC INSURANCE LIMITED—See Stanbic IBTC Holdings PLC; *Int'l*, pg. 7166
STANBIC IBTC NOMINEES LIMITED—See Stanbic IBTC Holdings PLC; *Int'l*, pg. 7166
STANBIC IBTC PENSION MANAGERS LIMITED—See Stanbic IBTC Holdings PLC; *Int'l*, pg. 7166
STANBIC IBTC STOCKBROKERS LIMITED—See Stanbic IBTC Holdings PLC; *Int'l*, pg. 7166
STANBIO LABORATORY LP—See EKF Diagnostics Holdings PLC; *Int'l*, pg. 2338
STANBURY UNIFORMS, INC.—See Bain Capital, LP; *U.S. Private*, pg. 452
STANCHEM, INC.—See SK Capital Partners, LP; *U.S. Private*, pg. 3679
STANCHION ENERGY, LLC—See Blackstone Inc.; *U.S. Public*, pg. 359
STANCODEX SDN. BHD.—See S&P International Holding Limited; *Int'l*, pg. 6445
STANCO METAL PRODUCTS, INC.; *U.S. Private*, pg. 3777
STANCORP FINANCIAL GROUP, INC.—See Meiji Yasuda Life Insurance Company; *Int'l*, pg. 4802
STANCORP MORTGAGE INVESTORS, LLC—See Meiji Yasuda Life Insurance Company; *Int'l*, pg. 4802
STANDALE HOME CENTER—See Standale Lumber & Supply Co. Inc.; *U.S. Private*, pg. 3777
STANDALE LUMBER & SUPPLY CO. INC.; *U.S. Private*, pg. 3777
STANDARD A.D.; *Int'l*, pg. 7166
STANDARD A.D.; *Int'l*, pg. 7166
STANDARD ADVERTISING, INC.—See The Interpublic Group of Companies, Inc.; *U.S. Public*, pg. 2092
STANDARDAERO BUSINESS AVIATION SERVICES LLC—See The Carlyle Group Inc.; *U.S. Public*, pg. 2054
STANDARDAERO—See The Carlyle Group Inc.; *U.S. Public*, pg. 2054
STANDARD AIR & LITE CORPORATION; *U.S. Private*, pg. 3777
STANDARD ALLOYS, INC.—See KSB SE & Co. KGaA; *Int'l*, pg. 4313
STANDARD APPLIANCE INC.; *U.S. Private*, pg. 3777
STANDARD AUDIO AB—See Aiphone Co., Ltd.; *Int'l*, pg. 235
STANDARD AUTOMATIC FIRE ENTERPRISES INC.—See APi Group Corporation; *Int'l*, pg. 513
STANDARD AUTO WRECKERS, INC.—See Stellex Capital Management LP; *U.S. Private*, pg. 3800
STANDARD BANK JSC—See Abu Dhabi Group; *Int'l*, pg. 71
STANDARD BANK LIMITED; *Int'l*, pg. 7166
STANDARD BANK, PASB—See Dollar Mutual Bancorp; *U.S. Private*, pg. 1254
STANDARD BANK SECURITIES LTD.—See Standard Bank Limited; *Int'l*, pg. 7166
THE STANDARD BATTERIES LIMITED—See EXIDE INDUSTRIES LIMITED; *Int'l*, pg. 2585
STANDARD BEVERAGE CORPORATION; *U.S. Private*, pg. 3778
STANDARD BIOTOOLS INC.; *U.S. Public*, pg. 1928

STANDARD BIOTOOLS INC. — CORPORATE AFFILIATIONS

STANDARD BOKSIT ISLETMELERI A.S.—See Verusa Holding A.S.; *Int'l*, pg. 8175
STANDARD BUILDERS SUPPLY INC.; *U.S. Private*, pg. 3778
STANDARD BUSINESS SERVICES; *U.S. Private*, pg. 3778
STANDARD CAPITAL MARKETS LIMITED; *Int'l*, pg. 7166
STANDARD CAR TRUCK COMPANY—See Westinghouse Air Brake Technologies Corporation; *U.S. Public*, pg. 2359
STANDARD CASUALTY COMPANY—See Cavco Industries, Inc.; *U.S. Public*, pg. 455
STANDARD CERAMIC INDUSTRIES LTD.; *Int'l*, pg. 7166
STANDARD CHANGE-MAKERS INC.; *U.S. Private*, pg. 3778
STANDARD CHARTERED BANK AG—See Standard Chartered PLC; *Int'l*, pg. 7168
STANDARD CHARTERED BANK ANGOLA S.A.—See Standard Chartered PLC; *Int'l*, pg. 7168
STANDARD CHARTERED BANK AUSTRALIA LIMITED—See Standard Chartered PLC; *Int'l*, pg. 7167
STANDARD CHARTERED BANK BOTSWANA LIMITED—See Standard Chartered PLC; *Int'l*, pg. 7167
STANDARD CHARTERED BANK CAMEROON S.A.—See Standard Chartered PLC; *Int'l*, pg. 7167
STANDARD CHARTERED BANK (CHINA) LIMITED—See Standard Chartered PLC; *Int'l*, pg. 7167
STANDARD CHARTERED BANK - COLOMBIA REPRESENTATIVE OFFICE—See Standard Chartered PLC; *Int'l*, pg. 7167
STANDARD CHARTERED BANK COTE D' IVOIRE SA—See Standard Chartered PLC; *Int'l*, pg. 7168
STANDARD CHARTERED BANK GAMBIA LTD.—See Standard Chartered PLC; *Int'l*, pg. 7167
STANDARD CHARTERED BANK (HONG KONG) LIMITED—See Standard Chartered PLC; *Int'l*, pg. 7167
STANDARD CHARTERED BANK - INDIA REPRESENTATIVE OFFICE—See Standard Chartered PLC; *Int'l*, pg. 7167
STANDARD CHARTERED BANK - JAPAN REPRESENTATIVE OFFICE—See Standard Chartered PLC; *Int'l*, pg. 7167
STANDARD CHARTERED BANK - JERSEY REPRESENTATIVE OFFICE—See Standard Chartered PLC; *Int'l*, pg. 7167
STANDARD CHARTERED BANK KENYA LIMITED—See Standard Chartered PLC; *Int'l*, pg. 7167
STANDARD CHARTERED BANK KOREA LIMITED—See Standard Chartered PLC; *Int'l*, pg. 7167
STANDARD CHARTERED BANK MALAYSIA BERHAD—See Standard Chartered PLC; *Int'l*, pg. 7167
STANDARD CHARTERED BANK NEPAL LIMITED—See Standard Chartered PLC; *Int'l*, pg. 7167
STANDARD CHARTERED BANK PLC—See Standard Chartered PLC; *Int'l*, pg. 7167
STANDARD CHARTERED BANK SIERRA LEONE LTD.—See Standard Chartered PLC; *Int'l*, pg. 7167
STANDARD CHARTERED BANK (SINGAPORE) PTY. LTD.—See Standard Chartered PLC; *Int'l*, pg. 7167
STANDARD CHARTERED BANK—See Standard Chartered PLC; *Int'l*, pg. 7167
STANDARD CHARTERED BANK (TAIWAN) LIMITED—See Standard Chartered PLC; *Int'l*, pg. 7167
STANDARD CHARTERED BANK TANZANIA LIMITED—See Standard Chartered PLC; *Int'l*, pg. 7167
STANDARD CHARTERED BANK THAILAND - GLOBAL MARKETS—See Standard Chartered PLC; *Int'l*, pg. 7167
STANDARD CHARTERED BANK (THAI) PUBLIC CO. LTD.—See Standard Chartered PLC; *Int'l*, pg. 7167
STANDARD CHARTERED BANK UGANDA LTD.—See Standard Chartered PLC; *Int'l*, pg. 7167
STANDARD CHARTERED BANK - USA REPRESENTATIVE OFFICE—See Standard Chartered PLC; *Int'l*, pg. 7167
STANDARD CHARTERED BANK (VIETNAM) LIMITED—See Standard Chartered PLC; *Int'l*, pg. 7168
STANDARD CHARTERED BANK ZAMBIA LTD.—See Standard Chartered PLC; *Int'l*, pg. 7167
STANDARD CHARTERED BANK ZIMBABWE LIMITED—See Standard Chartered PLC; *Int'l*, pg. 7167
STANDARD CHARTERED CAPITAL (SAUDI ARABIA) LTD.—See Standard Chartered PLC; *Int'l*, pg. 7168
STANDARD CHARTERED EQUITOR TRUSTEE SINGAPORE LIMITED—See Standard Chartered PLC; *Int'l*, pg. 7167
STANDARD CHARTERED FINANCE (BRUNEI) BERHAD—See Standard Chartered PLC; *Int'l*, pg. 7167
STANDARD CHARTERED GLOBAL BUSINESS SERVICES SPOLKA Z OGRANICZONA ODPOWIEDZIALNOSCIA—See Standard Chartered PLC; *Int'l*, pg. 7168
STANDARD CHARTERED NOMINEES SOUTH AFRICA PROPRIETARY LIMITED—See Standard Chartered PLC; *Int'l*, pg. 7168
STANDARD CHARTERED PLC; *Int'l*, pg. 7166

STANDARD CHARTERED REPRESENTACAO LTDA.—See Standard Chartered PLC; *Int'l*, pg. 7168
STANDARD CHARTERED SECURITIES (INDIA) LIMITED—See Standard Chartered PLC; *Int'l*, pg. 7168
STANDARD CHARTERED SECURITIES INVESTMENT CONSULTING LTD—See Standard Chartered PLC; *Int'l*, pg. 7168
STANDARD CHARTERED THAILAND LIMITED—See Standard Chartered PLC; *Int'l*, pg. 7168
STANDARD CHARTERED TRUSTEES (UK) LIMITED—See Standard Chartered PLC; *Int'l*, pg. 7168
STANDARD CHARTERED WEALTH MANAGEMENT LIMITED COMPANY—See Standard Chartered PLC; *Int'l*, pg. 7168
STANDARD CHARTERED YATIRIM BANKASI TURK ANONIM SIRKETI—See Standard Chartered PLC; *Int'l*, pg. 7168
STANDARD CHEM. & PHARM. CO., LTD.; *Int'l*, pg. 7168
STANDARD COMMERCIAL PROPERTY DEVELOPMENTS LTD.—See Mitchells & Butlers Plc; *Int'l*, pg. 4925
STANDARD COMMUNICATIONS (NZ) LTD.—See Standard Communications Pty. Ltd.; *Int'l*, pg. 7168
STANDARD COMMUNICATIONS PTY. LTD.; *Int'l*, pg. 7168
STANDARD COMPANIES INC.; *U.S. Private*, pg. 3778
STANDARD COMPANIES INC.—See Bain Capital, LP; *U.S. Private*, pg. 451
STANDARD COMPONENTS DE MEXICO S.A.—See SigmaTron International, Inc.; *U.S. Public*, pg. 1878
STANDARD CONCRETE PRODUCTS, INC.—See Heidelberg Materials AG; *Int'l*, pg. 3313
STANDARD CONCRETE PRODUCTS INC.; *U.S. Private*, pg. 3778
STANDARD CONSTRUCTION COMPANY, INC.; *U.S. Private*, pg. 3778
STANDARD CORP.—See Brother Industries, Ltd.; *Int'l*, pg. 1198
STANDARD DEPO VE RAF SISTEMLERI A.S.—See Blackstone Inc.; *U.S. Public*, pg. 348
STANDARD DEVELOPMENT GROUP LIMITED; *Int'l*, pg. 7168
STANDARD DISTRIBUTING CO. INC.; *U.S. Private*, pg. 3778
STANDARD DISTRIBUTORS LIMITED—See ANSA McAL Limited; *Int'l*, pg. 477
STANDARD DISTRIBUTORS & SALES BARBADOS LIMITED—See ANSA McAL Limited; *Int'l*, pg. 477
STANDARD DIVERSIFIED INC.—See Turning Point Brands, Inc.; *U.S. Public*, pg. 2205
STANDARD DRYWALL INC.; *U.S. Private*, pg. 3778
STANDARD DUPLICATING MACHINES CORPORATION; *U.S. Private*, pg. 3778
STANDARD DUPLICATING MACHINES CORPORATION - STANDARD BUSINESS SYSTEMS DIVISION—See Standard Duplicating Machines Corporation; *U.S. Private*, pg. 3778
STANDARD ELECTRIC COMPANY; *U.S. Private*, pg. 3778
STANDARD ELECTRIC CO.—See Blackfriars Corp.; *U.S. Private*, pg. 574
STANDARD ELECTRIC CO.—See Blackfriars Corp.; *U.S. Private*, pg. 574
STANDARD ELECTRIC CO.—See Blackfriars Corp.; *U.S. Private*, pg. 574
STANDARD ELECTRIC CO.—See Blackfriars Corp.; *U.S. Private*, pg. 574
STANDARD ELECTRIC CO.—See Blackfriars Corp.; *U.S. Private*, pg. 574
STANDARD ELECTRIC CO.—See Blackfriars Corp.; *U.S. Private*, pg. 574
STANDARD ELECTRIC CO.—See Blackfriars Corp.; *U.S. Private*, pg. 575
STANDARD ELECTRIC CO.—See Blackfriars Corp.; *U.S. Private*, pg. 575
STANDARD ELECTRIC CO.—See Blackfriars Corp.; *U.S. Private*, pg. 575
STANDARD ELECTRIC CO.—See Blackfriars Corp.; *U.S. Private*, pg. 575
STANDARD ELECTRIC CO.—See Blackfriars Corp.; *U.S. Private*, pg. 575
STANDARD ELECTRIC HOLDINGS LIMITED - GUIZHOU PLANT—See Kin Yat Holdings Limited; *Int'l*, pg. 4164
STANDARD ELECTRIC HOLDINGS LIMITED - SHAOGUAN PLANT—See Kin Yat Holdings Limited; *Int'l*, pg. 4164
STANDARD ELECTRIC HOLDINGS LIMITED—See Kin Yat Holdings Limited; *Int'l*, pg. 4164
STANDARD ELECTRIC SUPPLY CO. INC.; *U.S. Private*, pg. 3778
STANDARD ELECTRIC SUPPLY CO.—See Blackfriars Corp.; *U.S. Private*, pg. 574
STANDARD ELECTRIC SUPPLY CO.—See Standard Electric Supply Co. Inc.; *U.S. Private*, pg. 3778
STANDARD ENERGY CORP.; *U.S. Public*, pg. 1929
THE STANDARD FIRE INSURANCE COMPANY—See The Travelers Companies, Inc.; *U.S. Public*, pg. 2136
STANDARD FIRM CO., LTD.; *Int'l*, pg. 7168
STANDARD FOODS CORPORATION; *Int'l*, pg. 7168

STANDARD FORGED PRODUCTS, LLC—See Arcosa, Inc.; *U.S. Public*, pg. 186
STANDARD FORMS FRANCE SAS; *Int'l*, pg. 7168
STANDARD FOR SUCCESS, LLC—See Serent Capital Management Company, LLC; *U.S. Private*, pg. 3613
STANDARD FOR TRADING CO.—See Endress+Hauser (International) Holding AG; *Int'l*, pg. 2409
STANDARD FORWARDING CO. INC.—See Deutsche Post AG; *Int'l*, pg. 2082
STANDARD FORWARDING LLC—See Deutsche Post AG; *Int'l*, pg. 2082
STANDARD FREIGHT, LLC; *U.S. Private*, pg. 3778
STANDARD FURNITURE FACTORY D.D.—See Delta Holding; *Int'l*, pg. 2019
STANDARD FURNITURE MANUFACTURING COMPANY INC.; *U.S. Private*, pg. 3778
STANDARD FUSEE CORPORATION; *U.S. Private*, pg. 3778
THE STANDARD GENERAL INSURANCE COMPANY LIMITED—See King Price Financial Services (Proprietary) Limited; *Int'l*, pg. 4169
STANDARD GENERAL LP; *U.S. Private*, pg. 3778
STANDARD GOLD CORP.—See Augusta Gold Corp.; *Int'l*, pg. 704
STANDARD GREASES & SPECIALITIES PVT LTD.; *Int'l*, pg. 7168
STANDARD GROUP LLC—See Sun Capital Partners, Inc.; *U.S. Private*, pg. 3860
STANDARD GUARANTY INSURANCE COMPANY—See Assurant, Inc.; *U.S. Public*, pg. 215
STANDARD HIDRAULICA, S.A.U.—See H.I.G. Capital, LLC; *U.S. Private*, pg. 1828
STANDARD HOMEOPATHIC COMPANY; *U.S. Private*, pg. 3778
STANDARD HORSE NAIL COMPANY, LLC; *U.S. Private*, pg. 3778
STANDARD HOTEL HOLLYWOOD—See Hyatt Hotels Corporation; *U.S. Public*, pg. 1078
STANDARD IMAGING, INC.; *U.S. Private*, pg. 3779
STANDARD INDUSTRIES HOLDINGS INC.; *U.S. Private*, pg. 3779
STANDARD INDUSTRIES LIMITED; *Int'l*, pg. 7168
STANDARD INSTRUMENTATION—See Preiser Scientific, Inc.; *U.S. Private*, pg. 3249
STANDARD INSURANCE AGENCY, INC.—See Cavco Industries, Inc.; *U.S. Public*, pg. 455
STANDARD INSURANCE CO., INC.—See Zurich Insurance Group Limited; *Int'l*, pg. 8697
STANDARD INSURANCE COMPANY LIMITED; *Int'l*, pg. 7168
STANDARD INSURANCE COMPANY—See Meiji Yasuda Life Insurance Company; *Int'l*, pg. 4802
STANDARD INSURANCE LIMITED; *Int'l*, pg. 7169
STANDARD INTERNATIONAL MANAGEMENT LLC—See Hyatt Hotels Corporation; *U.S. Public*, pg. 1078
STANDARD INVESTMENT MANAGEMENT B.V.; *Int'l*, pg. 7169
STANDARD IRON & WIRE WORKS INC.; *U.S. Private*, pg. 3780
STANDARDKESSEL BAUMGARTE CONTRACTING GMBH—See JFE Holdings, Inc.; *Int'l*, pg. 3935
STANDARDKESSEL BAUMGARTE HOLDING GMBH—See JFE Holdings, Inc.; *Int'l*, pg. 3935
STANDARDKESSEL BAUMGARTE UK LTD.—See JFE Holdings, Inc.; *Int'l*, pg. 3935
STANDARDKESSEL GMBH—See JFE Holdings, Inc.; *Int'l*, pg. 3935
STANDARDKESSEL POWER SYSTEMS HOLDING GMBH—See JFE Holdings, Inc.; *Int'l*, pg. 3935
STANDARD-KNAPP, INC.; *U.S. Private*, pg. 3782
STANDARD LABORATORIES INC.; *U.S. Private*, pg. 3780
STANDARD LIFE & ACCIDENT INSURANCE COMPANY—See Core Specialty Insurance Holdings, Inc.; *U.S. Private*, pg. 1049
STANDARD LIFE ASIA LIMITED—See abrdn PLC; *Int'l*, pg. 69
THE STANDARD LIFE ASSURANCE COMPANY—See Phoenix Group Holdings PLC; *Int'l*, pg. 5851
STANDARD LIFE ASSURANCE LIMITED—See Phoenix Group Holdings PLC; *Int'l*, pg. 5851
STANDARD LIFE BANK LIMITED—See Barclays PLC; *Int'l*, pg. 860
THE STANDARD LIFE INSURANCE COMPANY OF NEW YORK—See Meiji Yasuda Life Insurance Company; *Int'l*, pg. 4802
STANDARD LIFE INTERNATIONAL DESIGNATED ACTIVITY COMPANY—See Phoenix Group Holdings PLC; *Int'l*, pg. 5851
STANDARD LIFE INTERNATIONAL LIMITED—See Phoenix Group Holdings PLC; *Int'l*, pg. 5851
STANDARD LIFE INVESTMENT FUNDS LIMITED—See Phoenix Group Holdings PLC; *Int'l*, pg. 5851
STANDARD LIFE INVESTMENTS LIMITED—See Phoenix Group Holdings PLC; *Int'l*, pg. 5851
STANDARD LIFE TRUSTEE COMPANY LIMITED—See Phoenix Group Holdings PLC; *Int'l*, pg. 5851
STANDARD LIFE WEALTH LIMITED—See abrdn PLC; *Int'l*, pg. 69

COMPANY NAME INDEX

STANDARD LITHIUM LTD.; *Int'l*, pg. 7169
STANDARD LOCKNUT, LLC—See Tonka Bay Equity Partners LLC; *U.S. Private*, pg. 4185
STANDARD MACHINE & MANUFACTURING CO.—See Dema Engineering Co.; *U.S. Private*, pg. 1203
STANDARD MANAGEMENT COMPANY; *U.S. Private*, pg. 3780
STANDARD MANUFACTURING CO., INC.; *U.S. Private*, pg. 3781
STANDARD MEAT COMPANY; *U.S. Private*, pg. 3781
STANDARD MEDIA GROUP LLC—See Standard General LP; *U.S. Private*, pg. 3778
STANDARD MERCANTILE ACQUISITION CORP.; *Int'l*, pg. 7169
STANDARD MERCANTILE ACQUISITION CORP.; *Int'l*, pg. 7169
STANDARD MERCHANDISING CO.; *U.S. Private*, pg. 3781
STANDARD MOBILE, INC.; *U.S. Private*, pg. 3781
STANDARD MORTGAGE CORPORATION; *U.S. Private*, pg. 3781
STANDARD MOTOR PRODUCTS GREENVILLE DIV—See Standard Motor Products, Inc.; *U.S. Public*, pg. 1929
STANDARD MOTOR PRODUCTS (HONG KONG) LTD—See Standard Motor Products, Inc.; *U.S. Public*, pg. 1929
STANDARD MOTOR PRODUCTS, INC.; *U.S. Public*, pg. 1929
STANDARD MOTOR PRODUCTS-INDEPENDENCE—See Standard Motor Products, Inc.; *U.S. Public*, pg. 1929
STANDARD MOTOR PRODUCTS-MISHAWAKA—See Standard Motor Products, Inc.; *U.S. Public*, pg. 1929
STANDARD MOTORS LTD.; *Int'l*, pg. 7169
STANDARD NEKRETNINE D.D. SARAJEVO; *Int'l*, pg. 7169
STANDARD NUTRITION COMPANY; *U.S. Private*, pg. 3781
STANDARD OFFICE SUPPLY; *U.S. Private*, pg. 3781
STANDARD OFFICE SYSTEMS ATLANTIC INC.; *U.S. Private*, pg. 3781
STANDARD OFFSET PRINTING CO.; *U.S. Private*, pg. 3781
STANDARD OUTDOOR LLC—See Turning Point Brands, Inc.; *U.S. Public*, pg. 2205
STANDARD PACIFIC OF COLORADO, INC.—See Lennar Corporation; *U.S. Public*, pg. 1305
STANDARD PACIFIC OF THE CAROLINAS, LLC—See Lennar Corporation; *U.S. Public*, pg. 1305
STANDARD PAINT & WALLPAPER; *U.S. Private*, pg. 3781
STANDARD PARKING CORPORATION IL—See Eldridge Industries LLC; *U.S. Private*, pg. 1351
STANDARD PARKING OF CANADA LTD.—See Eldridge Industries LLC; *U.S. Private*, pg. 1351
STANDARD PARTS CORPORATION; *U.S. Private*, pg. 3781
STANDARD PLUMBING & HEATING CO.; *U.S. Private*, pg. 3781
STANDARD PLUMBING SUPPLY COMPANY, INC.; *U.S. Private*, pg. 3781
STANDARD & POOR'S (AUSTRALIA) PTY LTD.—See S&P Global Inc.; *U.S. Public*, pg. 1831
STANDARD & POOR'S COMPUSTAT SERVICES, INC.—See S&P Global Inc.; *U.S. Public*, pg. 1831
STANDARD & POOR'S CREDIT MARKET SERVICES ITALY S.R.L.—See S&P Global Inc.; *U.S. Public*, pg. 1831
STANDARD & POOR'S (DUBAI) LIMITED—See S&P Global Inc.; *U.S. Public*, pg. 1831
STANDARD & POOR'S FINANCIAL SERVICES LLC—See S&P Global Inc.; *U.S. Public*, pg. 1831
STANDARD & POORS HONG KONG LIMITED—See S&P Global Inc.; *U.S. Public*, pg. 1832
STANDARD & POOR'S MAALOT LTD.—See S&P Global Inc.; *U.S. Public*, pg. 1831
STANDARD & POOR'S S.A. DE C.V.—See S&P Global Inc.; *U.S. Public*, pg. 1831
STANDARD & POORS SINGAPORE PTE. LTD.—See S&P Global Inc.; *U.S. Public*, pg. 1832
STANDARD PREMIUM FINANCE HOLDINGS, INC.; *U.S. Public*, pg. 1929
STANDARD PROCESS INC.; *U.S. Private*, pg. 3781
STANDARD PRODUCTS, INC.; *Int'l*, pg. 7169
STANDARD PROPERTY & CASUALTY INSURANCE COMPANY—See The Allstate Corporation; *U.S. Public*, pg. 2034
STANDARD PROPERTY CORPORATION—See Highmark Health; *U.S. Private*, pg. 1941
STANDARD PUBLISHING GROUP LLC—See The Wicks Group of Companies, LLC; *U.S. Private*, pg. 4136
STANDARD PUMP, INC.—See May River Capital, LLC; *U.S. Private*, pg. 2620
STANDARD READY MIX CONCRETE CO.—See Lyman-Richey Corporation; *U.S. Private*, pg. 2520
STANDARD REFRIGERATION CO. INC.; *U.S. Private*, pg. 3781
STANDARD REGISTER, INC.—See Taylor Corporation; *U.S. Private*, pg. 3939

STANDARD RESTAURANT EQUIPMENT COMPANY; *U.S. Private*, pg. 3781
STANDARD ROOFINGS INC.—See Hendricks Holding Company, Inc.; *U.S. Private*, pg. 1915
STANDARD SAFETY EQUIPMENT CO.; *U.S. Private*, pg. 3781
STANDARD SALES CO. INC.; *U.S. Private*, pg. 3781
STANDARD SECURITY INVESTORS CORPORATION—See Geneve Holdings Corp.; *U.S. Private*, pg. 1671
STANDARD SECURITY LIFE INSURANCE COMPANY OF NEW YORK—See Geneve Holdings Corp.; *U.S. Private*, pg. 1670
STANDARD SHOE SOLE & MOULD (INDIA) LIMITED; *Int'l*, pg. 7169
STANDARD SOLAR, INC.—See Brookfield Corporation; *Int'l*, pg. 1186
STANDARD STEEL, LLC—See Nippon Steel Corporation; *Int'l*, pg. 5340
STANDARD STRUCTURES INC.; *U.S. Private*, pg. 3781
STANDARD SUPPLIES—See Ernest Maier, Inc.; *U.S. Private*, pg. 1421
STANDARD SUPPLY AS; *Int'l*, pg. 7169
STANDARD SUPPLY & DISTRIBUTING CO. INC.; *U.S. Private*, pg. 3781
STANDARD SUPPLY & LUMBER CO.—See Bain Capital, LP; *U.S. Public*, pg. 451
STANDARD SURFACTANTS LTD.; *Int'l*, pg. 7169
STANDARD-TAYLOR INDUSTRIES, INC.; *U.S. Private*, pg. 3782
STANDARD TECHNOLOGY INC.; *U.S. Private*, pg. 3781
STANDARD TEL NETWORKS, INC.—See Blueprint Technologies, Inc.; *U.S. Public*, pg. 366
STANDARD TEXTILE BVBA—See Standard Textile Co., Inc.; *U.S. Private*, pg. 3782
STANDARD TEXTILE CO., INC.; *U.S. Private*, pg. 3782
STANDARD TILE DISTRIBUTORS OF NEW HAVEN INC.; *U.S. Private*, pg. 3782
THE STANDARD-TIMES—See R.I.S.N. Operations Inc.; *U.S. Private*, pg. 3337
STANDARD TOOLS & EQUIPMENT CO. INC.—See Florida Capital Partners, Inc.; *U.S. Private*, pg. 1547
STANDARD TRANSPORTATION SERVICES, INC.; *U.S. Private*, pg. 3782
STANDARD TUBE SALES CORPORATION; *U.S. Private*, pg. 3782
STANDARD UNITS SUPPLY (INDIA) PVT. LTD.—See SUS Co., Ltd.; *Int'l*, pg. 7346
STANDARD UNITS SUPPLY PHILIPPINES CORPORATION—See SUS Co., Ltd.; *Int'l*, pg. 7346
STANDARD UNITS SUPPLY VIETNAM COMPANY LIMITED—See SUS Co., Ltd.; *Int'l*, pg. 7346
STANDARD URANIUM LTD.; *Int'l*, pg. 7169
STANDARD VAPE CORPORATION; *U.S. Public*, pg. 1929
STANDARDWARE INC.—See KKR & Co. Inc.; *U.S. Public*, pg. 1240
STANDARDWERK EUGEN REIS GMBH—See GLORY Ltd.; *Int'l*, pg. 3010
STANDARD WIRE & CABLE CO.; *U.S. Private*, pg. 3782
STANDARD WIRE & CABLE CO.—See Standard Wire & Cable Co.; *U.S. Private*, pg. 3782
STANDBY AB—See Pomona-Gruppen AB; *Int'l*, pg. 5918
STANDBY HOLDINGS PTY LTD—See Expedia Group, Inc.; *U.S. Public*, pg. 810
STANDEN ENGINEERING LIMITED—See Ploeger Machines B.V.; *Int'l*, pg. 5897
STAND ENERGY CORPORATION; *U.S. Private*, pg. 3777
STANDEX AIR DISTRIBUTION PRODUCTS, INC. - GEORGIA—See Blue Wolf Capital Partners LLC; *U.S. Private*, pg. 596
STANDEX AIR DISTRIBUTION PRODUCTS, INC.—See Blue Wolf Capital Partners LLC; *U.S. Private*, pg. 596
STANDEX COOKING SOLUTIONS GROUP—See Standex International; *U.S. Public*, pg. 1930
STANDEX DE MEXICO S.A. DE C.V.—See Standex International; *U.S. Public*, pg. 1931
STANDEX ELECTRONICS, INC.—See Standex International; *U.S. Public*, pg. 1930
STANDEX ELECTRONICS JAPAN CORPORATION—See Standex International; *U.S. Public*, pg. 1930
STANDEX ELECTRONICS (UK) LIMITED—See Standex International; *U.S. Public*, pg. 1931
STANDEX FOOD SERVICE EQUIPMENT GROUP—See Standex International; *U.S. Public*, pg. 1930
STANDEX HOLDINGS LIMITED—See Standex International; *U.S. Public*, pg. 1931
STANDEX INTERNATIONAL CORPORATION; *U.S. Public*, pg. 1929
STANDEX INTERNATIONAL GMBH, MOLD-TECH DIVISION SOUTH—See Standex International; *U.S. Public*, pg. 1931
STANDEX INTERNATIONAL GMBH, MOLD-TECH NORTH (GERMANY)—See Standex International; *U.S. Public*, pg. 1931
STANDEX INTERNATIONAL GMBH—See Standex International; *U.S. Public*, pg. 1931
STANDEX INTERNATIONAL LIMITED—See Standex International; *U.S. Public*, pg. 1931

STAN JOHNSON COMPANY

STANDEX INTERNATIONAL S.A./MOLD-TECH DIVISION—See Standex International; *U.S. Public*, pg. 1931
STANDEX INTERNATIONAL S.A.—See Standex International; *U.S. Public*, pg. 1931
STANDEX INTERNATIONAL S.R.L. - INTERNATIONAL ENGRAVING DIVISION—See Standex International; *U.S. Public*, pg. 1930
STANDEX INTERNATIONAL S.R.L. - MOLD-TECH DIVISION—See Standex International; *U.S. Public*, pg. 1931
STANDEX INTERNATIONAL S.R.L. - PROCON DIVISION—See Standex International; *U.S. Public*, pg. 1931
STANDEX INTERNATIONAL S.R.L.—See Standex International; *U.S. Public*, pg. 1931
STANDEX IRELAND LTD.—See Standex International; *U.S. Public*, pg. 1931
STANDEX MEDER ELECTRONICS GMBH—See Standex International; *U.S. Public*, pg. 1931
STANDEX-MEDER ELECTRONICS (SHANGHAI) CO., LTD.—See Standex International; *U.S. Public*, pg. 1931
STAND FAST PACKAGING PRODUCTS INC.; *U.S. Private*, pg. 3777
STANDIFER PLACE PROPERTIES, LLC—See National HealthCare Corporation; *U.S. Public*, pg. 1496
STANDING PARTNERSHIP; *U.S. Private*, pg. 3782
STANDING PARTNERSHIP—See Standing Partnership; *U.S. Private*, pg. 3782
STANDING STONE BANK; *U.S. Public*, pg. 1931
STANDING STONE LLC—See Abbott Laboratories; *U.S. Public*, pg. 19
STANDISH MELLON ASSET MANAGEMENT COMPANY LLC—See The Bank of New York Mellon Corporation; *U.S. Public*, pg. 2038
STANDISH MILLING COMPANY; *U.S. Private*, pg. 3782
STANDLEY'S SYSTEMS, INC; *U.S. Private*, pg. 3782
STANDOUT GMBH—See RELX plc; *Int'l*, pg. 6267
ST. ANDREW BAY LAND COMPANY, LLC—See Jefferies Financial Group, Inc.; *U.S. Public*, pg. 1188
ST. ANDREWS COUNTRY CLUB, INC.; *U.S. Private*, pg. 3770
ST. ANDREW'S INSURANCE PLC—See Lloyds Banking Group plc; *Int'l*, pg. 4538
ST ANDREW'S LIFE ASSURANCE PLC—See Lloyds Banking Group plc; *Int'l*, pg. 4538
STANDRIDGE COLOR CORPORATION; *U.S. Private*, pg. 3782
STANDRIDGE EQUIPMENT CO., INC.; *U.S. Private*, pg. 3782
STANEK TOOL CORP.—See Jacsten Holdings, LLC; *U.S. Private*, pg. 2181
STANELCO RF TECHNOLOGIES LIMITED—See Biome Technologies plc; *Int'l*, pg. 1039
STANFIELD'S LIMITED MARKETING & SALES DIVISION—See Stanfield's Limited; *Int'l*, pg. 7169
STANFIELD'S LIMITED; *Int'l*, pg. 7169
STANFORD FURNITURE CORP.—See Gabriella White LLC; *U.S. Private*, pg. 1632
STANFORD HOTELS CORPORATION; *U.S. Private*, pg. 3782
STANFORD LUMBER COMPANY INC.; *U.S. Private*, pg. 3782
STANFORD MARINE GROUP—See Abraaj Capital Limited; *Int'l*, pg. 67
STANFORD MEADOWS (STANFORD-LE-HOPE) RESIDENTS MANAGEMENT COMPANY LIMITED—See Persimmon plc; *Int'l*, pg. 5817
STANGCO INDUSTRIAL EQUIPMENT INC.—See Mitsubishi Heavy Industries, Ltd.; *Int'l*, pg. 4953
STANGE (JAPAN) K.K.—See McCormick & Company, Incorporated; *U.S. Public*, pg. 1404
STANGER INDUSTRIES; *U.S. Private*, pg. 3782
STANHILL (HONG KONG) LIMITED—See Stanhill Operations Ltd.; *Int'l*, pg. 7169
STANHILL OPERATIONS LTD.; *Int'l*, pg. 7169
STANHOME FRANCE SAS—See Groupe Rocher Operations SAS; *Int'l*, pg. 3110
STANHOME PANAMERICANA, C.A.—See Stanhome World France; *Int'l*, pg. 7169
STANHOME S.A.—See Stanhome World France; *Int'l*, pg. 7169
STANHOME S.P.A.—See Stanhome World France; *Int'l*, pg. 7169
STANHOME WORLD FRANCE; *Int'l*, pg. 7169
STANHOME WORLD MEXICO, S.A. DE C.V.—See Stanhome World France; *Int'l*, pg. 7169
STANHOME WORLD PHILIPPINES, INC.—See Stanhome World France; *Int'l*, pg. 7170
STAN HOUSTON EQUIPMENT CO.; *U.S. Private*, pg. 3777
STANICO A/S—See Thornico A/S; *Int'l*, pg. 7720
STANIFORTH/—See Omnicom Group Inc.; *U.S. Public*, pg. 1596
STANION WHOLESALE ELECTRIC CO. INC.; *U.S. Private*, pg. 3782
STANISLAUS FARM SUPPLY COMPANY; *U.S. Private*, pg. 3782
STAN JOHNSON COMPANY; *U.S. Private*, pg. 3777

STAN KING CHEVROLET; U.S. Private, pg. 3777
STAN KOCH & SONS TRUCKING; U.S. Private, pg. 3777
STANKOWENDT RUSSIA—See 3M Company; U.S. Public, pg. 9
STANLEIGH INTERNATIONAL, INC.—See Kennington Ltd., Inc.; U.S. Private, pg. 2286
STANLEY ACCESS TECHNOLOGIES, LLC—See Allegion Public Limited Company; Int'l, pg. 335
STANLEY AGRICULTURAL GROUP CO., LTD.; Int'l, pg. 7170
STANLEY ASSEMBLY TECHNOLOGIES—See Stanley Black & Decker, Inc.; U.S. Public, pg. 1934
STANLEY AUTOMOTIVE ENTERPRISES, INC.; U.S. Private, pg. 3782
STANLEY BENEFIT SERVICES, INC.—See Mid Atlantic Capital Group, Inc.; U.S. Private, pg. 2705
STANLEY BLACK & DECKER AUSTRIA GMBH—See Stanley Black & Decker, Inc.; U.S. Public, pg. 1934
STANLEY BLACK & DECKER BELGIUM BVBA—See Stanley Black & Decker, Inc.; U.S. Public, pg. 1934
STANLEY BLACK & DECKER CZECH REPUBLIC S.R.O.—See Stanley Black & Decker, Inc.; U.S. Public, pg. 1934
STANLEY BLACK & DECKER DEUTSCHLAND GMBH—See Stanley Black & Decker, Inc.; U.S. Public, pg. 1934
STANLEY BLACK & DECKER FINLAND OY—See Stanley Black & Decker, Inc.; U.S. Public, pg. 1934
STANLEY BLACK & DECKER FRANCE S.A.S.—See Stanley Black & Decker, Inc.; U.S. Public, pg. 1934
STANLEY BLACK & DECKER (HELLAS) EPE—See Stanley Black & Decker, Inc.; U.S. Public, pg. 1934
STANLEY BLACK & DECKER IBERICA, S.L.—See Stanley Black & Decker, Inc.; U.S. Public, pg. 1934
STANLEY BLACK & DECKER, INC.; U.S. Public, pg. 1931
STANLEY BLACK & DECKER IRELAND—See Stanley Black & Decker, Inc.; U.S. Public, pg. 1934
STANLEY BLACK & DECKER LIMITED—See Stanley Black & Decker, Inc.; U.S. Public, pg. 1934
STANLEY BLACK & DECKER LOGISTICS BVBA—See Stanley Black & Decker, Inc.; U.S. Public, pg. 1934
STANLEY BLACK & DECKER NETHERLANDS B.V.—See Stanley Black & Decker, Inc.; U.S. Public, pg. 1934
STANLEY BLACK & DECKER NORWAY AS—See Stanley Black & Decker, Inc.; U.S. Public, pg. 1934
STANLEY BLACK & DECKER POLSKA SP. Z O.O.—See Stanley Black & Decker, Inc.; U.S. Public, pg. 1934
STANLEY BLACK & DECKER SWEDEN AB—See Stanley Black & Decker, Inc.; U.S. Public, pg. 1934
STANLEY BLACK & DECKER UK LIMITED—See Stanley Black & Decker, Inc.; U.S. Public, pg. 1934
STANLEY CONSULTANTS CO.; U.S. Private, pg. 3782
STANLEY CONSULTANTS (ENGINEERS), P.S.C.—See Stanley Consultants Co.; U.S. Private, pg. 3783
STANLEY CONSULTANTS INC—See Stanley Consultants Co.; U.S. Private, pg. 3783
STANLEY CONSULTANTS INDIA PRIVATE LIMITED—See Stanley Consultants Co.; U.S. Private, pg. 3783
STANLEY CONVERGENT SECURITY SOLUTIONS, INC.—See Stanley Black & Decker, Inc.; U.S. Public, pg. 1934
STANLEY DAVIS GROUP LIMITED—See Dye & Durham Limited; Int'l, pg. 2238
STANLEY DENKA CO., LTD.—See Stanley Electric Co., Ltd.; Int'l, pg. 7170
STANLEY DESIGN-BUILD, INC.—See Stanley Consultants Co.; U.S. Private, pg. 3783
STANLEY ELECTRIC (ASIA PACIFIC) LTD.—See Stanley Electric Co., Ltd.; Int'l, pg. 7170
STANLEY ELECTRIC (ASIA PACIFIC) LTD.—See Stanley Electric Co., Ltd.; Int'l, pg. 7170
STANLEY ELECTRIC (ASIA PACIFIC) LTD.—See Stanley Electric Co., Ltd.; Int'l, pg. 7170
STANLEY ELECTRIC CO., LTD. - HAMAMATSU FACTORY—See Stanley Electric Co., Ltd.; Int'l, pg. 7170
STANLEY ELECTRIC CO., LTD. - HATANO FACTORY—See Stanley Electric Co., Ltd.; Int'l, pg. 7170
STANLEY ELECTRIC CO., LTD. - HIROSHIMA FACTORY—See Stanley Electric Co., Ltd.; Int'l, pg. 7170
STANLEY ELECTRIC CO., LTD. - IIDA FACTORY—See Stanley Electric Co., Ltd.; Int'l, pg. 7170
STANLEY ELECTRIC CO., LTD. - OKAZAKI FACTORY—See Stanley Electric Co., Ltd.; Int'l, pg. 7170
STANLEY ELECTRIC CO., LTD.; Int'l, pg. 7170
STANLEY ELECTRIC CO., LTD. - YAMAGATA FACTORY—See Stanley Electric Co., Ltd.; Int'l, pg. 7170
STANLEY ELECTRIC DO BRASIL LTDA.—See Stanley Electric Co., Ltd.; Int'l, pg. 7170
STANLEY ELECTRIC GMBH—See Stanley Electric Co., Ltd.; Int'l, pg. 7170
STANLEY ELECTRIC HOLDING ASIA-PACIFIC PTE. LTD.—See Stanley Electric Co., Ltd.; Int'l, pg. 7170

STANLEY ELECTRIC HOLDING OF AMERICA, INC.—See Stanley Electric Co., Ltd.; Int'l, pg. 7170
STANLEY ELECTRIC HUNGARY KFT—See Stanley Electric Co., Ltd.; Int'l, pg. 7170
STANLEY ELECTRIC KOREA CO., LTD.—See Stanley Electric Co., Ltd.; Int'l, pg. 7170
STANLEY ELECTRIC MANUFACTURING MEXICO S.A. DE C.V.—See Stanley Electric Co., Ltd.; Int'l, pg. 7170
STANLEY ELECTRIC SALES OF AMERICA, INC.—See Stanley Electric Co., Ltd.; Int'l, pg. 7170
STANLEY ELECTRIC (UK) CO., LTD.—See Stanley Electric Co., Ltd.; Int'l, pg. 7170
STANLEY ELECTRIC U.S. CO., INC.—See Stanley Electric Co., Ltd.; Int'l, pg. 7170
STANLEY ENGINEERED FASTENING BENELUX B.V.—See Stanley Black & Decker, Inc.; U.S. Public, pg. 1935
STANLEY ENGINEERED FASTENING EASTERN EUROPE SP. Z O.O.—See Stanley Black & Decker, Inc.; U.S. Public, pg. 1935
STANLEY ENGINEERED FASTENING FRANCE SAS—See Stanley Black & Decker, Inc.; U.S. Public, pg. 1935
STANLEY ENGINEERED FASTENING INDUSTRIAL DEUTSCHLAND GMBH—See Stanley Black & Decker, Inc.; U.S. Public, pg. 1935
STANLEY ENGINEERED FASTENING ITALY S.R.L.—See Stanley Black & Decker, Inc.; U.S. Public, pg. 1935
STANLEY ENGINEERED FASTENING—See Stanley Black & Decker, Inc.; U.S. Public, pg. 1934
STANLEY ENGINEERED FASTENING SPAIN, S.L.U.—See Stanley Black & Decker, Inc.; U.S. Public, pg. 1935
STANLEY FASTENING SYSTEMS, L.P.—See Stanley Black & Decker, Inc.; U.S. Public, pg. 1935
STANLEY FASTENING SYSTEMS POLAND SP. Z O.O.—See Stanley Black & Decker, Inc.; U.S. Public, pg. 1935
STANLEY FERTILIZER CO., LTD.—See Stanley Agricultural Group Co., Ltd.; Int'l, pg. 7170
STANLEY FERTILIZER CO., LTD.—See Stanley Agricultural Group Co., Ltd.; Int'l, pg. 7170
STANLEY FERTILIZER CO., LTD.—See Stanley Agricultural Group Co., Ltd.; Int'l, pg. 7170
STANLEY FERTILIZER CO., LTD.—See Stanley Agricultural Group Co., Ltd.; Int'l, pg. 7170
STANLEY FERTILIZER CO., LTD.—See Stanley Agricultural Group Co., Ltd.; Int'l, pg. 7170
STANLEY FERTILIZER CO., LTD.—See Stanley Agricultural Group Co., Ltd.; Int'l, pg. 7170
STANLEY FORD - MCGREGOR—See Stanley Automotive Enterprises, Inc.; U.S. Private, pg. 3782
THE STANLEY GIBBONS GROUP PLC; Int'l, pg. 7688
STANLEY GIBBONS (GUERNSEY) LIMITED—See The Stanley Gibbons Group Plc; Int'l, pg. 7688
STANLEY GIBBONS LIMITED—See The Stanley Gibbons Group Plc; Int'l, pg. 7688
STANLEY GRUNDSTUCKSVERWALTUNGS GMBH—See Stanley Black & Decker, Inc.; U.S. Public, pg. 1935
STANLEY GRUNDSTUECKSVERWALTUNGS GMBH—See Stanley Black & Decker, Inc.; U.S. Public, pg. 1935
STANLEY HEALTHCARE SOLUTIONS FRANCE SARL—See Stanley Black & Decker, Inc.; U.S. Public, pg. 1935
STANLEY HOME PRODUCTS—See Victory Park Capital Advisors, LLC; U.S. Private, pg. 4379
STANLEY, HUNT, DUPREE & RHINE, INC.—See Truist Financial Corporation; U.S. Public, pg. 2201
STANLEY HYDRAULIC TOOLS—See Stanley Black & Decker, Inc.; U.S. Public, pg. 1935
STANLEY IDESS S.A.S—See Stanley Electric Co., Ltd.; Int'l, pg. 7170
STANLEY INA WORKS CO., LTD.—See Stanley Electric Co., Ltd.; Int'l, pg. 7171
STANLEY INFRASTRUCTURE, LLC—See Epiroc AB; Int'l, pg. 2463
STANLEY INSPECTION, L. L. C.—See Stanley Black & Decker, Inc.; U.S. Public, pg. 1935
STANLEY INSPECTION SOUTH AFRICA (PTY) LIMITED—See Stanley Black & Decker, Inc.; U.S. Public, pg. 1935
STANLEY INSPECTION US, L.L.C.—See Stanley Black & Decker, Inc.; U.S. Public, pg. 1935
STANLEY IWAKI WORKS CO., LTD.—See Stanley Electric Co., Ltd.; Int'l, pg. 7171
STANLEY MACHINING & TOOL CORPORATION; U.S. Private, pg. 3783
STANLEY MARTIN COMPANIES INC.; U.S. Private, pg. 3783
STANLEY MARTIN HOLDINGS, LLC—See Daiwa House Industry Co.; Int'l, pg. 1947
STANLEY MECHANICAL SOLUTIONS—See Stanley Black & Decker, Inc.; U.S. Public, pg. 1935
THE STANLEY MEDICAL RESEARCH INSTITUTE; U.S. Private, pg. 4120

STANLEY MILLER CONSTRUCTION CO.; U.S. Private, pg. 3783
STANLEY MIYAGI WORKS CO., LTD.—See Stanley Electric Co., Ltd.; Int'l, pg. 7171
STANLEY M. PROCTOR COMPANY, LLC—See Applied Industrial Technologies, Inc.; U.S. Public, pg. 171
STANLEY NIIGATA WORKS CO., LTD.—See Stanley Electric Co., Ltd.; Int'l, pg. 7171
STANLEY NISSAN INC.; U.S. Private, pg. 3783
STANLEY PAL CO., LTD.—See Stanley Electric Co., Ltd.; Int'l, pg. 7171
STANLEY PIPELINE INSPECTION, L.L.C.—See Stanley Black & Decker, Inc.; U.S. Public, pg. 1935
STANLEY SECURITY ALARMCENTRALE B.V.—See Stanley Black & Decker, Inc.; U.S. Public, pg. 1935
STANLEY SECURITY AS—See Stanley Black & Decker, Inc.; U.S. Public, pg. 1935
STANLEY SECURITY B.V.—See Stanley Black & Decker, Inc.; U.S. Public, pg. 1935
STANLEY SECURITY DENMARK APS—See Stanley Black & Decker, Inc.; U.S. Public, pg. 1935
STANLEY SECURITY DEUTSCHLAND ADMINISTRATION GMBH—See Stanley Black & Decker, Inc.; U.S. Public, pg. 1935
STANLEY SECURITY DEUTSCHLAND GMBH—See Stanley Black & Decker, Inc.; U.S. Public, pg. 1935
STANLEY SECURITY ESPANA, S. L.—See Stanley Black & Decker, Inc.; U.S. Public, pg. 1935
STANLEY SECURITY EUROPE BVBA—See Stanley Black & Decker, Inc.; U.S. Public, pg. 1935
STANLEY SECURITY ITALIA S.R.L.—See Stanley Black & Decker, Inc.; U.S. Public, pg. 1935
STANLEY SECURITY NEDERLAND B.V.—See Stanley Black & Decker, Inc.; U.S. Public, pg. 1935
STANLEY SECURITY OY—See Stanley Black & Decker, Inc.; U.S. Public, pg. 1935
STANLEY SECURITY PORTUGAL, UNIPESSOAL, LDA—See Stanley Black & Decker, Inc.; U.S. Public, pg. 1935
STANLEY SECURITY SINGAPORE PTE LTD—See Stanley Black & Decker, Inc.; U.S. Public, pg. 1935
STANLEY SECURITY SOLUTIONS AUSTRALIA PTY. LTD.—See Stanley Black & Decker, Inc.; U.S. Public, pg. 1935
STANLEY SECURITY SOLUTIONS EUROPE LTD.—See Stanley Black & Decker, Inc.; U.S. Public, pg. 1935
STANLEY SECURITY SOLUTIONS, INC.—See Stanley Black & Decker, Inc.; U.S. Public, pg. 1935
STANLEY SECURITY SOLUTIONS (NI) LIMITED—See Stanley Black & Decker, Inc.; U.S. Public, pg. 1935
STANLEY SECURITY SOLUTIONS TAIWAN LTD.—See Stanley Black & Decker, Inc.; U.S. Public, pg. 1935
STANLEY SECURITY SVERIGE AB—See Stanley Black & Decker, Inc.; U.S. Public, pg. 1935
STANLEY SECURITY SWITZERLAND SARL—See Stanley Black & Decker, Inc.; U.S. Public, pg. 1935
STANLEY SHIGA WORKS CO., LTD.—See Stanley Electric Co., Ltd.; Int'l, pg. 7171
STANLEY STEEMER ATLANTA—See Stanley Steemer International, Inc.; U.S. Private, pg. 3783
STANLEY STEEMER INTERNATIONAL, INC.; U.S. Private, pg. 3783
STANLEY STEEMER OF CHARLESTON—See Stanley Steemer International, Inc.; U.S. Private, pg. 3783
STANLEY STEPHENS CO. INC.; U.S. Private, pg. 3783
STANLEY STORAGE & WORKSPACE SYSTEMS—See Stanley Black & Decker, Inc.; U.S. Public, pg. 1935
STANLEY STREET TREATMENT & RESOURCES; U.S. Private, pg. 3783
STANLEY SUPPLY & SERVICES, INC.—See Stanley Black & Decker, Inc.; U.S. Public, pg. 1936
STANLEY SVENSKA AB—See Stanley Black & Decker, Inc.; U.S. Public, pg. 1936
STANLEY TOTAL LIVING CENTER, INC.; U.S. Private, pg. 3783
STANLEY TSURUOKA WORKS CO., LTD.—See Stanley Electric Co., Ltd.; Int'l, pg. 7171
STANLEY UK SALES LIMITED—See Stanley Black & Decker, Inc.; U.S. Public, pg. 1936
STANLEY WELL CORP.—See Stanley Electric Co., Ltd.; Int'l, pg. 7171
STANLEY WORKS (EUROPE) AG—See Stanley Black & Decker, Inc.; U.S. Public, pg. 1936
STANLEY WORKS (EUROPE) GMBH—See Stanley Black & Decker, Inc.; U.S. Public, pg. 1936
THE STANLEY WORKS PTY. LTD.—See Stanley Black & Decker, Inc.; U.S. Public, pg. 1936
STAN & LOU ADVERTISING; U.S. Private, pg. 3777
STANMAR INC.; U.S. Private, pg. 3783
STAN MCNABB; U.S. Private, pg. 3777
STANMORE RESOURCES LIMITED; Int'l, pg. 7171
STANNECKER GMBH—See J. Bauer GmbH & Co. KG; Int'l, pg. 3854
ST. ANNE'S CREDIT UNION; U.S. Private, pg. 3770
ST. ANNE'S MATERNITY HOME; U.S. Private, pg. 3770
ST. ANNE'S RETIREMENT COMMUNITY, INC.; U.S. Private, pg. 3770
ST. ANN'S HOME, INC.; U.S. Private, pg. 3770

COMPANY NAME INDEX

STANOGRAD ULAGANJA D.O.O. ZA PROMET NEKRETNINAMA, USLUGE I GRADITELJSTVO—See PORR AG; *Int'l*, pg. 5924
STANOVI D.O.O.—See Luka Rijeka d.d.; *Int'l*, pg. 4576
STANOVI JADRAN D.D; *Int'l*, pg. 7171
STANPACKS (INDIA) LTD.; *Int'l*, pg. 7171
STANPRO LIGHTING SYSTEMS INC.; *Int'l*, pg. 7171
STANRAIL CORPORATION—See Samuel, Son & Co., Limited; *Int'l*, pg. 6516
STANROSE MAFATLAL INVESTMENTS & FINANCE LIMITED; *Int'l*, pg. 7171
STAN'S CONTRACTING INC.; *U.S. Private*, pg. 3777
STANS ENERGY CORP.; *Int'l*, pg. 1715
STANSFIELD VENDING INC.; *U.S. Private*, pg. 3783
STAN'S HEATING & AIR CONDITIONING, INC.—See Catterton Management Company, LLC; *U.S. Private*, pg. 793
STAN'S - LPS MIDWEST; *U.S. Private*, pg. 3777
STANSON HEALTH, INC.—See Premier, Inc.; *U.S. Public*, pg. 1715
STANSOURCE INC.—See Stellar IT Solutions, Inc.; *U.S. Private*, pg. 3799
STANSTED AIRPORT LTD.—See The Manchester Airport Group plc; *Int'l*, pg. 7665
STAN STONER, INC.; *U.S. Private*, pg. 3777
STANT CORP.—See H.I.G. Capital, LLC; *U.S. Private*, pg. 1831
STANTEC AUSTRALIA PTY. LTD.—See Stantec Inc.; *Int'l*, pg. 7172
STANTEC CONSULTING CARIBBEAN LTD.—See Stantec Inc.; *Int'l*, pg. 7172
STANTEC CONSULTING COLOMBIA S.A.S.—See Stantec Inc.; *Int'l*, pg. 7172
STANTEC CONSULTING GROUP INC.—See Stantec Inc.; *Int'l*, pg. 7172
STANTEC CONSULTING INTERNATIONAL LLC—See Stantec Inc.; *Int'l*, pg. 7172
STANTEC CONSULTING INTERNATIONAL LTD.—See Stantec Inc.; *Int'l*, pg. 7172
STANTEC CONSULTING LTD.—See Stantec Inc.; *Int'l*, pg. 7172
STANTEC CONSULTING LTD. - WINNIPEG OFFICE—See Stantec Inc.; *Int'l*, pg. 7172
STANTEC CONSULTING MICHIGAN INC.—See Stantec Inc.; *Int'l*, pg. 7172
STANTEC CONSULTING SERVICES INC. - BAKERSFIELD—See Stantec Inc.; *Int'l*, pg. 7172
STANTEC CONSULTING SERVICES INC. - BATON ROUGE—See Stantec Inc.; *Int'l*, pg. 7172
STANTEC CONSULTING SERVICES INC.—See Stantec Inc.; *Int'l*, pg. 7172
STANTEC CONSULTING SERVICES INC. - TAMPA—See Stantec Inc.; *Int'l*, pg. 7172
STANTEC EXPERTS-CONSEILS LTEE—See Stantec Inc.; *Int'l*, pg. 7172
STANTEC HOLDING (2017) LIMITED—See Stantec Inc.; *Int'l*, pg. 7172
STANTEC INC. - BELGIUM—See Stantec Inc.; *Int'l*, pg. 7171
STANTEC INC. - BELLEVUE—See Stantec Inc.; *Int'l*, pg. 7171
STANTEC INC. - CHINA—See Stantec Inc.; *Int'l*, pg. 7172
STANTEC INC. - CLEVELAND—See Stantec Inc.; *Int'l*, pg. 7171
STANTEC INC. - ILLINOIS—See Stantec Inc.; *Int'l*, pg. 7171
STANTEC INC. - ITALY—See Stantec Inc.; *Int'l*, pg. 7171
STANTEC INC. - MANAMA—See Stantec Inc.; *Int'l*, pg. 7172
STANTEC INC. - NEW ZEALAND—See Stantec Inc.; *Int'l*, pg. 7172
STANTEC INC.; *Int'l*, pg. 7171
STANTEC INC. - TAIWAN—See Stantec Inc.; *Int'l*, pg. 7172
STANTEC INDIA PVT. LTD.—See Stantec Inc.; *Int'l*, pg. 7171
STANTEC NEWFOUNDLAND & LABRADOR LTD.—See Stantec Inc.; *Int'l*, pg. 7172
STANTEC TECHNOLOGY INTERNATIONAL INC.—See Stantec Inc.; *Int'l*, pg. 7172
ST. ANTHONY REGIONAL HOSPITAL & NURSING HOME; *U.S. Private*, pg. 3770
ST. ANTHONY'S HOSPITAL—See BayCare Health System Inc.; *U.S. Private*, pg. 495
ST. ANTHONY'S MEDICAL CENTER; *U.S. Private*, pg. 3770
STANTON CARPET CORPORATION—See Quad-C Management, Inc.; *U.S. Private*, pg. 3315
STANTON COMMUNICATIONS, INC.; *U.S. Private*, pg. 3783
STANTON COMMUNICATIONS INC.—See Stanton Communications, Inc.; *U.S. Private*, pg. 3783
STANTON COMMUNICATIONS INC.—See Stanton Communications, Inc.; *U.S. Private*, pg. 3783
STANTON GROUP LTD.—See Inuvialuit Regional Corporation; *Int'l*, pg. 3772
STANTON LAKE HEALTHCARE, INC.—See The Ensign Group, Inc.; *U.S. Public*, pg. 2071
STANTON MAGNETICS, INC.—See Gibson Brands, Inc.; *U.S. Private*, pg. 1696
STANTON SOUTH LLC—See Constellation Brands, Inc.; *U.S. Public*, pg. 571
THE STANWICH CLUB, INC.; *U.S. Private*, pg. 4120
STANWICK MANAGEMENT CONSULTANTS; *Int'l*, pg. 7172
STANZEN TOYOTETSU INDIA PVT. LTD.—See Toyoda Iron Works Co., Ltd.; *Int'l*, pg. 7863
STAP INC.; *U.S. Private*, pg. 3783
STAPLA ULTRASCHALLTECHNIK GMBH—See Schunk GmbH; *Int'l*, pg. 6643
STAPLA ULTRASONICS CORPORATION—See Schunk GmbH; *Int'l*, pg. 6641
STAPLE COTTON COOPERATIVE ASSOCIATION/ITTA BENA—See Staple Cotton Cooperative Association; *U.S. Private*, pg. 3783
STAPLE COTTON COOPERATIVE ASSOCIATION; *U.S. Private*, pg. 3783
STAPLE COTTON DISCOUNT CORPORATION—See Staple Cotton Cooperative Association; *U.S. Private*, pg. 3783
STAPLES ADVANTAGE IRELAND LTD.—See Sycamore Partners Management, LP; *U.S. Private*, pg. 3897
STAPLES ARGENTINA S.A.; *Int'l*, pg. 7172
STAPLES AUSTRIA GMBH—See Sycamore Partners Management, LP; *U.S. Private*, pg. 3897
STAPLES BELGIUM BVBA—See Sycamore Partners Management, LP; *U.S. Private*, pg. 3897
STAPLES BUSINESS DEPOT—See Sycamore Partners Management, LP; *U.S. Private*, pg. 3897
STAPLES CANADA, ULC—See Sycamore Partners Management, LP; *U.S. Private*, pg. 3897
STAPLES CONTRACT & COMMERCIAL, INC.—See Sycamore Partners Management, LP; *U.S. Private*, pg. 3897
STAPLES DENMARK APS—See Sycamore Partners Management, LP; *U.S. Private*, pg. 3897
STAPLES DEUTSCHLAND GMBH & CO. KG—See Sycamore Partners Management, LP; *U.S. Private*, pg. 3898
STAPLES EUROPE B.V.—See Sycamore Partners Management, LP; *U.S. Private*, pg. 3898
STAPLES FINLAND OY—See Sycamore Partners Management, LP; *U.S. Private*, pg. 3898
STAPLES FRANCE HOLDING SAS—See Sycamore Partners Management, LP; *U.S. Private*, pg. 3898
STAPLES FUTURE OFFICE PRODUCTS LIMITED—See Future Corporate Resources Limited; *Int'l*, pg. 2853
STAPLES, INC.—See Sycamore Partners Management, LP; *U.S. Private*, pg. 3896
STAPLES INTERNATIONAL B.V.—See Sycamore Partners Management, LP; *U.S. Private*, pg. 3897
STAPLES INTERNATIONAL GROUP SERVICES B.V.—See Sycamore Partners Management, LP; *U.S. Private*, pg. 3898
STAPLES NEDERLAND BV—See Sycamore Partners Management, LP; *U.S. Private*, pg. 3898
STAPLES NEDERLAND HOLDING B.V.—See Sycamore Partners Management, LP; *U.S. Private*, pg. 3898
STAPLES NORDIC AS—See Sycamore Partners Management, LP; *U.S. Private*, pg. 3898
STAPLES NORWAY AS—See Sycamore Partners Management, LP; *U.S. Private*, pg. 3898
STAPLES OIL CO. INC.; *U.S. Private*, pg. 3784
STAPLES POLSKA SP.Z.O.O.—See Sycamore Partners Management, LP; *U.S. Private*, pg. 3898
STAPLES PORTUGAL EQUIPAMENTO DE ESCRITORIA, SA—See Sycamore Partners Management, LP; *U.S. Private*, pg. 3898
STAPLES PRODUCTOS DE OFICINA, SL—See The RAJA Group; *Int'l*, pg. 7678
STAPLES PROMOTIONAL PRODUCTS CANADA LTD.—See Sycamore Partners Management, LP; *U.S. Private*, pg. 3898
STAPLES PROMOTIONAL PRODUCTS—See Sycamore Partners Management, LP; *U.S. Private*, pg. 3898
STAPLES PROMOTIONAL PRODUCTS—See Sycamore Partners Management, LP; *U.S. Private*, pg. 3898
STAPLES RETAIL NORWAY AS—See Sycamore Partners Management, LP; *U.S. Private*, pg. 3898
STAPLES SHARED SERVICE CENTER (EUROPE) II, BVBA—See Sycamore Partners Management, LP; *U.S. Private*, pg. 3897
STAPLES SOLUTIONS B.V.—See Cerberus Capital Management, L.P.; *U.S. Private*, pg. 839
STAPLES SWEDEN AB—See Sycamore Partners Management, LP; *U.S. Private*, pg. 3898
STAPLES TECHNOLOGY SOLUTIONS—See Sycamore Partners Management, LP; *U.S. Private*, pg. 3897
STAPLES THE OFFICE SUPERSTORE, LLC.—See Sycamore Partners Management, LP; *U.S. Private*, pg. 3897
STAPLE STREET CAPITAL LLC; *U.S. Private*, pg. 3783
STAPLES UK LIMITED—See Sycamore Partners Management, LP; *U.S. Private*, pg. 3898
STAPLES VERWALTUNGS GMBH—See Sycamore Partners Management, LP; *U.S. Private*, pg. 3898
STAPLETON'S TYRE SERVICES LTD.—See ITOCHU Corporation; *Int'l*, pg. 3837
THE STAPLEX COMPANY, INC.; *U.S. Private*, pg. 4120
STAPOR RESEARCH, INC.—See Kratos Defense & Security Solutions, Inc.; *U.S. Public*, pg. 1277
STAPPERT CESKA REPUBLIKA SPOL. S R.O.—See Jacquet Metal Service SA; *Int'l*, pg. 3867
STAPPERT DEUTSCHLAND GMBH—See Jacquet Metal Service SA; *Int'l*, pg. 3867
STAPPERT DEUTSCHLAND GMBH—See Jacquet Metal Service SA; *Int'l*, pg. 3867
STAPPERT FRANCE SAS—See Jacquet Metal Service SA; *Int'l*, pg. 3867
STAPPERT INTRAMET SA—See Jacquet Metal Service SA; *Int'l*, pg. 3867
STAPPERT MAGYARORSZAG KFT—See Jacquet Metal Service SA; *Int'l*, pg. 3867
STAPPERT NOXON BV—See Jacquet Metal Service SA; *Int'l*, pg. 3867
STAPPERT POLSKA SP. Z O.O.—See Jacquet Metal Service SA; *Int'l*, pg. 3867
STAPPERT SLOVENSKO A.S.—See Jacquet Metal Service SA; *Int'l*, pg. 3868
STAPPERT SVERIGE AB—See Jacquet Metal Service SA; *Int'l*, pg. 3867
STAPPERT UK LTD.—See Jacquet Metal Service SA; *Int'l*, pg. 3867
STAPRING A.S.; *Int'l*, pg. 7172
STAQO TECHNOLOGIES L.L.C.—See Sheela Foam Limited; *Int'l*, pg. 6792
STAQO WORLD PVT. LTD.—See Sheela Foam Limited; *Int'l*, pg. 6792
STAR (1) LIMITED—See Kingmaker Footwear Holdings Limited; *Int'l*, pg. 4174
STAR2STAR COMMUNICATIONS, LLC—See Comcast Corporation; *U.S. Public*, pg. 537
STAR7 GMBH—See Star7 S.p.A.; *Int'l*, pg. 7175
STAR7 S.P.A.; *Int'l*, pg. 7175
STAR8 CORP.; *Int'l*, pg. 7175
STAR ADHESIVES LTD.; *Int'l*, pg. 7172
STAR ADVERTISING SALES LIMITED—See The Walt Disney Company; *U.S. Public*, pg. 2141
STAR AG; *Int'l*, pg. 7172
STAR AIRLINES—See Eimskipafelag Islands Hf.; *Int'l*, pg. 2332
STAR ALLIANCE INTERNATIONAL CORP.; *U.S. Public*, pg. 1936
STAR-APIC SA—See 1Spatial Plc; *Int'l*, pg. 3
STAR-APIC SAS—See 1Spatial Plc; *Int'l*, pg. 3
STARA PLANINA HOLD PLC; *Int'l*, pg. 7175
STARA SA-INDUSTRIA DE IMPLEMENTOS AGRICOLAS; *Int'l*, pg. 7175
STAR ASIA INVESTMENT CORPORATION; *Int'l*, pg. 7172
STARASIA (MALAYSIA) SDN. BHD.—See JAB Holding Company S.a.r.l.; *Int'l*, pg. 3861
STAR-ASIA TECHNOLOGY LTD.—See Star Micronics Co Ltd; *Int'l*, pg. 7175
STAR ASIA VISION CORPORATION; *Int'l*, pg. 7172
STAR ASSET SECURITY, LLC—See Wind Point Advisors LLC; *U.S. Private*, pg. 4535
STAR AVIATION, INC.—See Amphenol Corporation; *U.S. Public*, pg. 129
STARBAND COMMUNICATIONS INC.; *U.S. Private*, pg. 3786
STAR BANK—See Midwest Bancorporation, Inc.; *U.S. Private*, pg. 2720
STARBEV NETHERLANDS BV—See Molson Coors Beverage Company; *U.S. Public*, pg. 1459
STARBOARD CRUISE SERVICES, INC.—See LVMH Moet Hennessy Louis Vuitton SE; *Int'l*, pg. 4601
STARBOARD HOLDINGS LTD—See LVMH Moet Hennessy Louis Vuitton SE; *Int'l*, pg. 4601
STARBOARD IT PTY. LTD.—See ActivePort Group Limited; *Int'l*, pg. 120
STARBOARD MOTORS INC.; *U.S. Private*, pg. 3786
STARBOARD VALUE LP; *U.S. Private*, pg. 3786
STARBOX GROUP HOLDINGS LTD.; *Int'l*, pg. 7176
STARBREEZE AB; *Int'l*, pg. 7176
STAR BRITE CORP.—See OneWater Marine Inc.; *U.S. Public*, pg. 1604
STAR BRITE DISTRIBUTING, INC.—See OneWater Marine Inc.; *U.S. Public*, pg. 1604
STAR BRITE EUROPE, LLC—See OneWater Marine Inc.; *U.S. Public*, pg. 1604
STARBROKER AG—See Deutsche Post AG; *Int'l*, pg. 2082
STAR BRONZE COMPANY, INC.; *U.S. Private*, pg. 3784
STAR BUCK POWER CORPORATION—See Taiwan Cogeneration Corporation; *Int'l*, pg. 7419
STARBUCKS BRASIL COMERCIO DE CAFES LTDA.—See Starbucks Corporation; *U.S. Public*, pg. 1938
STARBUCKS CARD EUROPE LIMITED—See Starbucks Corporation; *U.S. Public*, pg. 1939
STARBUCKS (CHINA) COMPANY LIMITED—See Starbucks Corporation; *U.S. Public*, pg. 1938
STARBUCKS COFFEE ARGENTINA S.R.L.—See Alsea, S.A.B. de C.V.; *Int'l*, pg. 379
STARBUCKS COFFEE ASIA PACIFIC LIMITED—See Starbucks Corporation; *U.S. Public*, pg. 1938
STARBUCKS COFFEE AUSTRIA GMBH—See Starbucks Corporation; *U.S. Public*, pg. 1939

STARBUCKS COFFEE CANADA, INC.—See Starbucks Corporation; *U.S. Public*, pg. 1939
STARBUCKS COFFEE COMPANY AUSTRALIA PTY. LTD.—See Starbucks Corporation; *U.S. Public*, pg. 1938
STARBUCKS COFFEE COMPANY UK LTD.—See Starbucks Corporation; *U.S. Public*, pg. 1939
STARBUCKS COFFEE EMEA BV—See Starbucks Corporation; *U.S. Public*, pg. 1939
STARBUCKS COFFEE ESPANA S.L.—See Alsea, S.A.B. de C.V.; *Int'l*, pg. 379
STARBUCKS COFFEE FRANCE S.A.S.—See Starbucks Corporation; *U.S. Public*, pg. 1939
STARBUCKS COFFEE HOLDINGS (UK) LIMITED—See Starbucks Corporation; *U.S. Public*, pg. 1939
STARBUCKS COFFEE INTERNATIONAL, INC.—See Starbucks Corporation; *U.S. Public*, pg. 1938
STARBUCKS COFFEE JAPAN, LTD.—See Starbucks Corporation; *U.S. Public*, pg. 1939
STARBUCKS COFFEE KOREA CO., LTD.—See Shinsegae Inc.; *Int'l*, pg. 6848
STARBUCKS COFFEE SINGAPORE PTE. LTD.—See Starbucks Corporation; *U.S. Public*, pg. 1939
STARBUCKS COFFEE SWITZERLAND A.G.—See Starbucks Corporation; *U.S. Public*, pg. 1939
STARBUCKS COFFEE SWITZERLAND GMBH—See Starbucks Corporation; *U.S. Public*, pg. 1939
STARBUCKS COFFEE (THAILAND) CO., LTD.—See Starbucks Corporation; *U.S. Public*, pg. 1938
STARBUCKS COFFEE TRADING COMPANY S.A.R.L.—See Starbucks Corporation; *U.S. Public*, pg. 1939
STARBUCKS CORPORATION; *U.S. Public*, pg. 1938
STARBUCKS EMEA HOLDINGS LTD—See Starbucks Corporation; *U.S. Public*, pg. 1939
STARBUCKS MANUFACTURING EMEA B.V.—See Starbucks Corporation; *U.S. Public*, pg. 1939
STAR BUFFET, INC.; *U.S. Public*, pg. 1937
STAR BUICK GMC; *U.S. Private*, pg. 3784
STAR BUILDING SYSTEMS - MONTICELLO—See Clayton, Dubilier & Rice, LLC; *U.S. Private*, pg. 921
STAR BUILDING SYSTEMS—See Clayton, Dubilier & Rice, LLC; *U.S. Private*, pg. 921
STAR BULK CARRIERS CORP.; *Int'l*, pg. 7173
STARBURST HOLDINGS LIMITED—See Nordic Group Limited; *Int'l*, pg. 5422
STAR BUS SALES INC—See Velocity Vehicle Group; *U.S. Private*, pg. 4355
STARCAN CORPORATION; *Int'l*, pg. 7176
STARCAPITAL AG—See Bellevue Group AG; *Int'l*, pg. 967
STAR CAPITAL PARTNERSHIP LLP—See STAR Capital Partners Limited; *Int'l*, pg. 7173
STAR CAPITAL PARTNERS LIMITED; *Int'l*, pg. 7173
STARCAP MARKETING, LLC—See Voxtur Analytics Corp.; *Int'l*, pg. 8311
STAR CASES, LLC—See CE Star Holdings, LLC; *U.S. Private*, pg. 803
STAR CHANNEL, INC.—See Tohokushinsha Film Corporation; *Int'l*, pg. 7777
STARCHIPS TECHNOLOGY INC.—See ASE Technology Holding Co., Ltd.; *Int'l*, pg. 604
STARCHTECH, INC.; *U.S. Private*, pg. 3786
STAR CIRCLIPS & ENGINEERING LTD.—See MMP Industries Ltd.; *Int'l*, pg. 5006
STAR CITY HOLDINGS LIMITED—See The Star Entertainment Group Limited; *Int'l*, pg. 7688
STAR CM HOLDINGS LIMITED; *Int'l*, pg. 7173
STAR CNC MACHINE TOOL CORPORATION—See Star Micronics Co Ltd; *Int'l*, pg. 7174
STARCO BRANDS, INC.; *U.S. Public*, pg. 1939
STARCO CHEMICAL—See Diamond Chemical Co., Inc.; *U.S. Private*, pg. 1223
THE STARCO GROUP, INC.; *U.S. Private*, pg. 4121
STARCO IMPEX INC.; *U.S. Private*, pg. 3786
STAR COIN INC—See United Gaming, LLC; *U.S. Private*, pg. 4293
STAR COLLABORATIVE; *U.S. Private*, pg. 3784
STARCOM ADPLUS AG—See Publicis Groupe S.A.; *Int'l*, pg. 6111
STARCOM BEIJING—See Publicis Groupe S.A.; *Int'l*, pg. 6111
STAR COMBO PHARMA LTD.; *Int'l*, pg. 7173
STARCOM GUANGZHOU—See Publicis Groupe S.A.; *Int'l*, pg. 6111
STARCOM HONG KONG—See Publicis Groupe S.A.; *Int'l*, pg. 6111
STARCOM INFORMATION TECHNOLOGY LTD; *Int'l*, pg. 7176
STARCOM JAKARTA—See Publicis Groupe S.A.; *Int'l*, pg. 6111
STARCOM LATIN AMERICA REGIONAL HEADQUARTERS—See Publicis Groupe S.A.; *Int'l*, pg. 6111
STARCOM MEDIA S.R.L.—See Publicis Groupe S.A.; *Int'l*, pg. 6111
STARCOM MEDIAVEST GROUP MOSCOW—See Publicis Groupe S.A.; *Int'l*, pg. 6112
STARCOM MEDIAVEST GROUP—See Publicis Groupe S.A.; *Int'l*, pg. 6111

STARCOM MEDIAVEST GROUP—See Publicis Groupe S.A.; *Int'l*, pg. 6111
STARCOM MEDIAVEST GROUP—See Publicis Groupe S.A.; *Int'l*, pg. 6112
STARCOM MEDIAVEST—See Publicis Groupe S.A.; *Int'l*, pg. 6111
STARCOM MEDIAVEST—See Publicis Groupe S.A.; *Int'l*, pg. 6111
STARCOM MEDIAVEST—See Publicis Groupe S.A.; *Int'l*, pg. 6111
STARCOM MEDIOS—See Publicis Groupe S.A.; *Int'l*, pg. 6112
STARCOM MELBOURNE—See Publicis Groupe S.A.; *Int'l*, pg. 6112
STARCOM MIDDLE EAST & EGYPT REGIONAL HEADQUARTERS—See Publicis Groupe S.A.; *Int'l*, pg. 6112
STARCOM MOTIVE PARTNERSHIP LONDON—See Publicis Groupe S.A.; *Int'l*, pg. 6112
STARCOM NETWORK INC—See One Caribbean Media Limited; *Int'l*, pg. 5574
STARCOM NORWAY—See Publicis Groupe S.A.; *Int'l*, pg. 6112
STARCOM PAKISTAN—See Publicis Groupe S.A.; *Int'l*, pg. 6112
STARCOM SHANGHAI—See Publicis Groupe S.A.; *Int'l*, pg. 6112
STARCOM—See Publicis Groupe S.A.; *Int'l*, pg. 6111
STARCOM—See Publicis Groupe S.A.; *Int'l*, pg. 6111
STARCOM SP. Z O.O.—See Publicis Groupe S.A.; *Int'l*, pg. 6112
STARCOM TAIPEI—See Publicis Groupe S.A.; *Int'l*, pg. 6112
STAR COMUNICACAO E SERVICOS LTDA.—See Star7 S.p.A.; *Int'l*, pg. 7175
STARCOM USA—See Publicis Groupe S.A.; *Int'l*, pg. 6112
STARCOM WORLDWIDE-ADELAIDE—See Publicis Groupe S.A.; *Int'l*, pg. 6112
STARCOM WORLDWIDE INDIA—See Publicis Groupe S.A.; *Int'l*, pg. 6112
STARCOM WORLDWIDE NORTHEAST ASIA HQ—See Publicis Groupe S.A.; *Int'l*, pg. 6112
STARCOM WORLDWIDE SA DE CV—See Publicis Groupe S.A.; *Int'l*, pg. 6112
STARCOM WORLDWIDE—See Publicis Groupe S.A.; *Int'l*, pg. 6112
STARCOM WORLDWIDE—See Publicis Groupe S.A.; *Int'l*, pg. 6112
STARCOM WORLDWIDE—See Publicis Groupe S.A.; *Int'l*, pg. 6112
STARCOM WORLDWIDE—See Publicis Groupe S.A.; *Int'l*, pg. 6112
STARCOM WORLDWIDE—See Publicis Groupe S.A.; *Int'l*, pg. 6112
STARCOM WORLDWIDE—See Publicis Groupe S.A.; *Int'l*, pg. 6112
STARCOM WORLDWIDE—See Publicis Groupe S.A.; *Int'l*, pg. 6112
STARCOM WORLDWIDE—See Publicis Groupe S.A.; *Int'l*, pg. 6112
STARCOM WORLDWIDE—See Publicis Groupe S.A.; *Int'l*, pg. 6112
STARCOM WORLDWIDE SOUTHEAST ASIA HQ—See Publicis Groupe S.A.; *Int'l*, pg. 6112
STARCOM WW—See Publicis Groupe S.A.; *Int'l*, pg. 6112
STARCON, INC.; *U.S. Private*, pg. 3786
STAR CONSTRUCTION, INC.—See MidOcean Partners, LLP; *U.S. Private*, pg. 2717
STAR CONSTRUCTION, LLC—See Dycom Industries, Inc.; *U.S. Public*, pg. 699
STARCORE INTERNATIONAL MINES LTD.; *Int'l*, pg. 7176
STAR COURIER—See Gannett Co., Inc.; *U.S. Public*, pg. 904
STAR & CRESCENT BOAT COMPANY; *U.S. Private*, pg. 3784
STARCREST EDUCATION LIMITED; *Int'l*, pg. 7176
STARCREST OF CALIFORNIA—See Starcrest Products of California; *U.S. Private*, pg. 3786
STARCREST PRODUCTS OF CALIFORNIA; *U.S. Private*, pg. 3786
STAR CRUISES (HK) LIMITED—See Genting Hong Kong Limited; *Int'l*, pg. 2929
STARC SYSTEMS, INC.; *U.S. Private*, pg. 3786
STAR CUTTER COMPANY - ELK RAPIDS ENGINEERING DIVISION—See Star Cutter Company; *U.S. Private*, pg. 3784
STAR CUTTER COMPANY; *U.S. Private*, pg. 3784
STAR DELTA TRANSFORMERS LIMITED; *Int'l*, pg. 7173
STARDEV, S.R.O.—See PrismaStar Limited; *Int'l*, pg. 5982
STAR DIALYSIS, LLC—See DaVita Inc.; *U.S. Public*, pg. 643
STAR DIAMOND CORPORATION; *Int'l*, pg. 7174
STAR DISTRIBUTION SYSTEMS INC.; *U.S. Private*, pg. 3784
STAR DODGE CHRYSLER JEEP HYUNDAI; *U.S. Private*, pg. 3784

STAR DUNKIN', LP—See Roark Capital Group Inc.; *U.S. Private*, pg. 3455
STARDUST TRANSPORTATION; *U.S. Private*, pg. 3786
STARDYNE TECHNOLOGIES INC.; *Int'l*, pg. 7176
STAR EAGLE HOLDINGS LIMITED—See Genting Berhad; *Int'l*, pg. 2929
STAR ELECTRICITY, INC.—See Constellation Energy Corporation; *U.S. Public*, pg. 572
STAR ELECTRONICS CO., LTD.—See SATORI ELECTRIC CO., LTD.; *Int'l*, pg. 6587
STAR ENERGY GEOTHERMAL ("SEG") PTE. LTD.—See PT Barito Pacific Tbk; *Int'l*, pg. 6028
STAR ENERGY GROUP LTD.—See Star Energy Group plc; *Int'l*, pg. 7174
STAR ENERGY GROUP PLC; *Int'l*, pg. 7174
STAR ENERGY INTERNATIONAL CORPORATION; *U.S. Private*, pg. 3784
STAR ENERGY RESOURCES LTD.—See Marquard & Bahls AG; *Int'l*, pg. 4700
STAR ENERGY; *Int'l*, pg. 7174
STAR ENERGY—See Growmark, Inc.; *U.S. Private*, pg. 1795
STARENSIER INC.; *U.S. Private*, pg. 3786
THE STAR ENTERTAINMENT GROUP LIMITED; *Int'l*, pg. 7688
STAR ENTERTAINMENT (UNIVERSE) LIMITED—See Neway Group Holdings Limited; *Int'l*, pg. 5232
STARENT NETWORKS BEIJING CO., LTD.—See Cisco Systems, Inc.; *U.S. Public*, pg. 500
STARENT NETWORKS, CORP.—See Cisco Systems, Inc.; *U.S. Public*, pg. 500
STAR ENVIROTECH, INC.—See Harbour Group Industries, Inc.; *U.S. Private*, pg. 1860
STAR EQUIPMENT, LTD.; *U.S. Private*, pg. 3784
STAR EQUITY HOLDINGS, INC.; *U.S. Public*, pg. 1937
STAR ESTATE SRL—See Africa Israel Investments Ltd.; *Int'l*, pg. 190
STAR EVENTS LIMITED—See Altrad Investment Authority SAS; *Int'l*, pg. 398
STAR EXHIBITS & ENVIRONMENTS, INC.; *U.S. Private*, pg. 3784
STAR FABRICATORS—See The Stellar Group Inc.; *U.S. Private*, pg. 4121
STAR FARM PAKISTAN PVT. LTD.—See Metro AG; *Int'l*, pg. 4859
STAR FARM (SHANGHAI) AGRICULTURE INFORMATION CONSULTING COMPANY LIMITED—See Metro AG; *Int'l*, pg. 4858
STAR FASHION CULTURE HOLDINGS LIMITED; *Int'l*, pg. 7174
STAR FEEDMILLS (M) SDN. BHD.—See Charoen Pokphand Foods Public Company Limited; *Int'l*, pg. 1453
STAR FERRO & CEMENT LIMITED; *Int'l*, pg. 7174
THE STAR FERRY COMPANY LIMITED—See Wheelock & Company Limited; *Int'l*, pg. 8397
STAR FIBERGLASS HARBIN CO., LTD.—See NOV, Inc.; *U.S. Public*, pg. 1546
STARFIELD TECHNOLOGIES, INC.—See KKR & Co. Inc.; *U.S. Public*, pg. 1252
STARFIELD TECHNOLOGIES, INC.—See Silver Lake Group, LLC; *U.S. Private*, pg. 3657
STARFIELD TECHNOLOGIES, INC.—See TCMI, Inc.; *U.S. Private*, pg. 3943
STAR FINANCIAL BANK—See STAR Financial Group Inc.; *U.S. Public*, pg. 1937
STAR FINANCIAL GROUP INC.; *U.S. Public*, pg. 1937
STAR FINE FOODS-BORGES USA—See Aceites Borges Pont, S.A.; *Int'l*, pg. 95
STARFIRE DIRECT, INC.—See Blackford Capital LLC; *U.S. Public*, pg. 574
STARFIRE MINERALS INC.; *Int'l*, pg. 7176
STARFIRE SYSTEMS, INC.—See The Riverside Company; *U.S. Private*, pg. 4108
STARFISH CAYO SANTA MARIA—See Sunwing Travel Group, Inc.; *Int'l*, pg. 7332
STARFISH CUARTO PALMAS—See Sunwing Travel Group, Inc.; *Int'l*, pg. 7332
STARFISH DISCOVERY BAY RESORT—See Sunwing Travel Group, Inc.; *Int'l*, pg. 7332
STAR FISHERIES INC.; *U.S. Private*, pg. 3784
THE STARFISH FOUNDATION; *U.S. Private*, pg. 4121
STARFISH HALCYON COVE RESORT—See Sunwing Travel Group, Inc.; *Int'l*, pg. 7332
STARFISH JOLLY BEACH RESORT—See Sunwing Travel Group, Inc.; *Int'l*, pg. 7332
STARFISH LAS PALMAS—See Sunwing Travel Group, Inc.; *Int'l*, pg. 7332
STARFISH MONTEHABANA—See Sunwing Travel Group, Inc.; *Int'l*, pg. 7332
STARFISH ST. LUCIA—See Sunwing Travel Group, Inc.; *Int'l*, pg. 7332
STARFISH TOBAGO—See Sunwing Travel Group, Inc.; *Int'l*, pg. 7332
STARFISH TROPICAL—See Sunwing Travel Group, Inc.; *Int'l*, pg. 7332
STARFISH VARADERO—See Sunwing Travel Group, Inc.; *Int'l*, pg. 7332
STARFLEX CO., LTD.; *Int'l*, pg. 7176

COMPANY NAME INDEX

STARFLEX PUBLIC COMPANY LIMITED; *Int'l*, pg. 7176
THE STARFLO CORPORATION—See The Wm. Powell Company; *U.S. Private*, pg. 4138
THE STARFLO CORPORATION—See The Wm. Powell Company; *U.S. Private*, pg. 4138
STARFLOWER ESSENTIALS ORGANIC SKIN CARE; *U.S. Private*, pg. 3786
STAR FLYER INC.; *Int'l*, pg. 7174
STARFOOD FINLAND OY—See Deutsche Lufthansa AG; *Int'l*, pg. 2067
STAR FOOD PRODUCTS, INC., *U.S. Private*, pg. 3784
STAR FOODS BULGARIA EOOD—See PepsiCo, Inc.; *U.S. Public*, pg. 1672
STAR FORD; *U.S. Private*, pg. 3784
STAR FORGE, LLC—See CE Star Holdings, LLC; *U.S. Private*, pg. 803
STAR FORMING MANUFACTURING, LLC - ORANGE PLANT—See CE Star Holdings, LLC; *U.S. Private*, pg. 803
STAR FORMING MANUFACTURING, LLC—See CE Star Holdings, LLC; *U.S. Private*, pg. 803
STARFOTO BV—See Ifolor AG; *Int'l*, pg. 3599
STAR FURNITURE COMPANY; *U.S. Private*, pg. 3784
STAR FURNITURE COMPANY—See Berkshire Hathaway Inc.; *U.S. Public*, pg. 316
STARGAMES AUSTRALIA PTY LIMITED—See Light & Wonder, Inc.; *U.S. Public*, pg. 1315
STARGARAGE AG—See CTS Eventim AG & Co. KGAA; *Int'l*, pg. 1873
STAR GAS CORPORATION—See Star Group, L.P.; *U.S. Public*, pg. 1938
STARGATE CAPITAL GMBH; *Int'l*, pg. 7176
STARGATE INDUSTRIES LLC; *U.S. Private*, pg. 3786
STARGATE TELECOM INC.; *U.S. Private*, pg. 3786
STARGAZE ENTERTAINMENT GROUP, INC.; *U.S. Public*, pg. 1939
STAR-GAZETTE—See Gannett Co., Inc.; *U.S. Public*, pg. 899
STARGAZE WINDOWS LIMITED—See Emerson Developments (Holdings) Limited; *Int'l*, pg. 2380
STARGEL OFFICE SYSTEMS, INC.; *U.S. Private*, pg. 3786
STAR-GLO INDUSTRIES LLC; *U.S. Private*, pg. 3786
STARGLORY HOLDINGS COMPANY LIMITED; *Int'l*, pg. 7176
THE STAR GOLD COAST—See The Star Entertainment Group Limited; *Int'l*, pg. 7688
STAR GOLD CORP.; *U.S. Public*, pg. 1937
STAR GRANITE CO., INC.—See Matthews International Corporation; *U.S. Public*, pg. 1401
STAR GRAPHICS, INC.; *U.S. Private*, pg. 3784
STAR GROUP COMPANY LIMITED; *Int'l*, pg. 7174
THE STAR GROUP, INC.—See Mauna N.V.; *Int'l*, pg. 4732
STAR GROUP, L.P.; *U.S. Public*, pg. 1937
STAR GROUP NEWSPAPERS—See Alden Global Capital LLC; *U.S. Private*, pg. 156
STAR GROUP PVT. LTD.—See Atlantic China Welding Consumables, Inc.; *Int'l*, pg. 674
STARGUIDE GROUP, INC.; *Int'l*, pg. 7177
STAR GUIDE LIMITED—See Integer Holdings Corporation; *U.S. Public*, pg. 1135
STAR HEADLIGHT AND LANTERN CO., INC.; *U.S. Private*, pg. 3784
STAR HEALTH & ALLIED INSURANCE CO. LTD.; *Int'l*, pg. 7174
STARHEDGE S.A.; *Int'l*, pg. 7177
STARHILL GLOBAL REIT; *Int'l*, pg. 7177
STAR HOLDINGS, INC.; *U.S. Public*, pg. 1938
STAR HOLIDAY MART PTE LTD—See JTB Corp.; *Int'l*, pg. 4016
STARHOME MACH GMBH—See Vista Equity Partners, LLC; *U.S. Private*, pg. 4402
STARHOME MACH—See Vista Equity Partners, LLC; *U.S. Private*, pg. 4402
STAR HOUSING FINANCE LTD.; *Int'l*, pg. 7174
STARHUB LTD.; *Int'l*, pg. 7177
STARI DERAM A.D.; *Int'l*, pg. 7177
STARI GRAD A.D.; *Int'l*, pg. 7177
STARI GRAD A.D.; *Int'l*, pg. 7177
STARI GRAD GP A.D.; *Int'l*, pg. 7177
STAR INDIA PRIVATE LIMITED—See National Amusements, Inc.; *U.S. Private*, pg. 2844
STAR INDIA PRIVATE LIMITED—See Reliance - ADA Group Limited; *Int'l*, pg. 6263
STAR INDUSTRIES INC.; *U.S. Private*, pg. 3784
STAR INDUSTRIES INC.; *U.S. Private*, pg. 3784
STAR INFO TECH CO., LTD.—See Daido Steel Co., Ltd.; *Int'l*, pg. 1923
STARIN MARKETING, INC.—See Midwich Group Plc; *Int'l*, pg. 4488
STAR INTERNATIONAL, INC.; *U.S. Private*, pg. 3784
STAR INTERNATIONAL SAINT-PETERSBURG LLC—See GHW International; *Int'l*, pg. 2960
STARI TAMIS A.D.; *Int'l*, pg. 7177
STARIZON, INC.; *U.S. Private*, pg. 3786
STARJET AIR INC.—See Royal Street Corporation; *U.S. Private*, pg. 3493
STAR JETS INTERNATIONAL, INC.; *U.S. Public*, pg. 1938

THE STAR-JOURNAL PUBLISHING CORP.; *U.S. Private*, pg. 4121
STAR JOY SDN. BHD.—See Oriental Holdings Berhad; *Int'l*, pg. 5625
STARK AEROSPACE, INC.—See Israel Aerospace Industries Ltd.; *Int'l*, pg. 3822
STARK AMBULATORY SURGERY CENTER, LLC—See Tenet Healthcare Corporation; *U.S. Public*, pg. 2007
STARKAR INSURANCE COMPANY—See Ster Group; *Int'l*, pg. 7208
STARK AUTOMOTIVE GROUP; *U.S. Private*, pg. 3786
STARK BANK GROUP LTD.; *U.S. Private*, pg. 3786
STARK BROTHERS NURSERIES & ORCHARDS CO.; *U.S. Private*, pg. 3786
STARK CAPITAL MANAGEMENT LLC—See Atlantic Capital Group, Inc.; *U.S. Public*, pg. 372
STARK CARPET CORPORATION; *U.S. Private*, pg. 3786
STARK COMMUNITY FOUNDATION, INC.; *U.S. Private*, pg. 3787
STARK CORPORATION PUBLIC COMPANY LIMITED; *Int'l*, pg. 7177
STARK DANMARK A/S—See Lone Star Global Acquisitions, LLC; *U.S. Private*, pg. 2489
STARK DEUTSCHLAND GMBH—See Lone Star Global Acquisitions, LLC; *U.S. Private*, pg. 2489
STARKE ARVID AB—See Indutrade AB; *Int'l*, pg. 3681
STARKE ASIA SDN. BHD.—See UMS Holdings Limited; *Int'l*, pg. 8027
STARKE COUNTY FARM BUREAU COOPERATIVE ASSOCIATION; *U.S. Private*, pg. 3787
STARKEN AAC SDN BHD—See Chin Hin Group Berhad; *Int'l*, pg. 1480
STARKEN DRYMIX SOLUTIONS SDN BHD—See Chin Hin Group Berhad; *Int'l*, pg. 1480
STARKEN PAINT SDN BHD—See Chin Hin Group Berhad; *Int'l*, pg. 1480
STARKE SINGAPORE PTE LTD.—See UMS Holdings Limited; *Int'l*, pg. 8027
STARK EXCAVATING INC.; *U.S. Private*, pg. 3787
STARKEY, INC.; *U.S. Private*, pg. 3787
STARKEY LABORATORIES, INC.; *U.S. Private*, pg. 3787
STARK FILM AB—See Shortcut Media AB; *Int'l*, pg. 6860
STARK FOCUS GROUP INC.; *Int'l*, pg. 7177
STARK GROUP A/S—See CVC Capital Partners SICAV-FIS S.A.; *Int'l*, pg. 1884
STARKIST CO.—See Dongwon Enterprise Co., Ltd.; *Int'l*, pg. 2171
STARK METAL SALES, INC.—See Pennsylvania Steel Company, Inc; *U.S. Private*, pg. 3137
STARK (NINGBO) TECHNOLOGY INC.—See Stark Technology, Inc.; *Int'l*, pg. 7177
STARKOT CORP.; *Int'l*, pg. 7177
STARK & ROTH, INC.; *U.S. Private*, pg. 3786
STARKS DIALYSIS, LLC—See DaVita Inc.; *U.S. Public*, pg. 643
STARK SERVICES; *U.S. Private*, pg. 3787
STARKS FINANCIAL GROUP INC.—See Genstar Capital, LLC; *U.S. Private*, pg. 1677
STARKS FINANCIAL GROUP INC.—See Keystone Group, L.P.; *U.S. Private*, pg. 2298
STARKS PLUMBING & HEATING LTD.; *Int'l*, pg. 7177
STARKSTROM-GERATEBAU GMBH—See BC Partners LLP; *Int'l*, pg. 925
STARK SUOMI OY—See Lone Star Global Acquisitions, LLC; *U.S. Private*, pg. 2489
STARK TALENT; *U.S. Private*, pg. 3787
STARK TECHNOLOGY INC.—See Stark Technology, Inc.; *Int'l*, pg. 7177
STARK TECHNOLOGY, INC.; *Int'l*, pg. 7177
STARK VERLAGSGESELLSCHAFT MBH & CO KG—See Pearson plc; *Int'l*, pg. 5778
STARK VERWALTUNGSGESELLSCHAFT MBH—See Pearson plc; *Int'l*, pg. 5778
STARKVILLE LP GAS INC—See Ergon, Inc.; *U.S. Private*, pg. 1418
STARKWEATHER & SHEPLEY INSURANCE BROKERAGE, INC.; *U.S. Private*, pg. 3787
STARLAB FRANCE S.A.R.L—See Eppendorf AG; *Int'l*, pg. 2464
STARLAB INTERNATIONAL GMBH—See Eppendorf AG; *Int'l*, pg. 2464
STARLAB S.R.L.—See Eppendorf AG; *Int'l*, pg. 2464
STARLAB (UK) LIMITED—See Eppendorf AG; *Int'l*, pg. 2464
STAR LAKE BIOSCIENCE CO., INC.; *Int'l*, pg. 7174
STAR LEASING CO.—See I Squared Capital Advisors (US) LLC; *U.S. Private*, pg. 2026
STARLECS INC.—See Sunstar Suisse S.A.; *Int'l*, pg. 7323
THE STAR-LEDGER—See Advance Publications, Inc.; *U.S. Private*, pg. 87
STARLIGHT ADVERTISING PTE. LTD.; *Int'l*, pg. 7177
STARLIGHT ENERGY CORP.; *U.S. Public*, pg. 1939
STARLIGHT EXPRESS TRANSPORT CO., LTD.—See Sri Trang Agro-Industry Public Company Limited; *Int'l*, pg. 7151
STARLIGHT INTERNATIONAL LTD, LP; *U.S. Private*, pg. 3787
STARLIGHT INVESTMENTS LTD.; *Int'l*, pg. 7177

STAR MEDIA NETWORK

STARLIGHT U.S. MULTI-FAMILY (NO. 5) CORE FUND—See Blackstone Inc.; *U.S. Public*, pg. 352
STARLIMS ASIA PACIFIC LIMITED—See Abbott Laboratories; *U.S. Public*, pg. 20
STARLIMS CORPORATION—See Abbott Laboratories; *U.S. Public*, pg. 20
STARLIMS FRANCE S.A.S.—See Abbott Laboratories; *U.S. Public*, pg. 20
STARLIMS GERMANY GMBH—See Abbott Laboratories; *U.S. Public*, pg. 20
STARLIMS IBERICA, S.A.—See Abbott Laboratories; *U.S. Public*, pg. 20
STARLIMS ISRAEL LTD.—See Abbott Laboratories; *U.S. Public*, pg. 20
STARLIMS NETHERLANDS B.V.—See Abbott Laboratories; *U.S. Public*, pg. 20
STARLIMS (SEA) PTE. LTD.—See Abbott Laboratories; *U.S. Public*, pg. 21
STARLIMS TECHNOLOGIES LTD.—See Abbott Laboratories; *U.S. Public*, pg. 20
STARLIMS THAILAND CO., LTD.—See Abbott Laboratories; *U.S. Public*, pg. 20
STARLINE HOLDINGS LLC—See Legrand S.A.; *Int'l*, pg. 4446
STARLINE PRINTING COMPANY, LLLP—See Gannett Co., Inc.; *U.S. Public*, pg. 906
STARLINEPS ENTERPRISES LTD.; *Int'l*, pg. 7177
STARLINGER & CO. GMBH - FACTORY 1—See Starlinger & Co. GmbH; *Int'l*, pg. 7178
STARLINGER & CO. GMBH - FACTORY 2—See Starlinger & Co. GmbH; *Int'l*, pg. 7178
STARLINGER & CO. GMBH; *Int'l*, pg. 7178
STARLINGER DO BRASIL LTDA.—See Starlinger & Co. GmbH; *Int'l*, pg. 7178
STARLINGER EXPORT GMBH—See Starlinger & Co. GmbH; *Int'l*, pg. 7178
STARLINGER PLASTICS MACHINERY (TAICANG) CO., LTD.—See Starlinger & Co. GmbH; *Int'l*, pg. 7178
STARLINGER SOUTHERN AFRICA (PTY) LTD—See Starlinger & Co. GmbH; *Int'l*, pg. 7178
STARLINK AVIATION INC.; *Int'l*, pg. 7178
STARLITE COMPONENTS LTD.; *Int'l*, pg. 7178
STARLITE ENTERPRISE (SHANGHAI) INC.—See Starlite Holdings Limited; *Int'l*, pg. 7178
STARLITE FERRIES, INC.—See Chelsea Logistics and Infrastructure Holdings Corp.; *Int'l*, pg. 1460
STARLITE HOLDINGS LIMITED; *Int'l*, pg. 7178
STARLITE PRINTERS (FAR EAST) PTE LTD—See Starlite Holdings Limited; *Int'l*, pg. 7178
STARLITE PRINTERS LIMITED—See Starlite Holdings Limited; *Int'l*, pg. 7178
STARLITE PRINTERS (SHENZHEN) CO., LTD.—See Starlite Holdings Limited; *Int'l*, pg. 7178
STARLITE PRINTERS (SUZHOU) CO., LTD.—See Starlite Holdings Limited; *Int'l*, pg. 7178
STARLITE RECOVERY CENTER, LLC—See Acadia Healthcare Company, Inc.; *U.S. Public*, pg. 30
STARLITE ROECHLING AUTOMOTIVE CO., LTD.—See Rochling SE & Co. KG; *Int'l*, pg. 6378
STARLITE SERVICES, INC.—See Distribution 2000 Inc.; *U.S. Private*, pg. 1239
STARLIT POWER SYSTEMS LTD; *Int'l*, pg. 7178
STAR LOCAL MEDIA—See 10/13 Communications LLC; *U.S. Private*, pg. 2
STARLOG ENTERPRISES LIMITED; *Int'l*, pg. 7178
STARLO VENTURES LTD.; *Int'l*, pg. 7178
STAR LUMBER & SUPPLY COMPANY, INC.; *U.S. Private*, pg. 3785
STAR MAGAZINE—See Chatham Asset Management, LLC; *U.S. Private*, pg. 860
STARMANN SP. Z O.O.—See LKQ Corporation; *U.S. Public*, pg. 1336
STAR MANUFACTURING INTERNATIONAL, INC.—See The Middleby Corporation; *U.S. Public*, pg. 2115
STAR MANUFACTURING, L.L.C.—See Sheldons' Inc.; *U.S. Public*, pg. 3631
STARMARK CABINETRY—See MasterBrand, Inc.; *U.S. Public*, pg. 1394
STAR MARKETING LTD.—See Health and Plant Protein Group Limited; *Int'l*, pg. 3303
STAR MARKETING SERVICES—See Omnicom Group Inc.; *U.S. Public*, pg. 1594
STAR MARKETS COMPANY, INC.—See Cerberus Capital Management, L.P.; *U.S. Private*, pg. 836
STARMARK GLOBAL, INC.—See MARC USA, LLC; *U.S. Private*, pg. 2571
STARMARK INTERNATIONAL, INC.; *U.S. Private*, pg. 3787
STARMARK MANAGEMENT HOLDINGS LLC; *U.S. Private*, pg. 3787
STARMARK—See Trustmark Mutual Holding Company; *U.S. Private*, pg. 4251
STARMAX ASSETS LIMITED—See Henderson Land Development Co. Ltd.; *Int'l*, pg. 3344
STAR MEDIA GROUP BERHAD; *Int'l*, pg. 7174
STAR MEDIA NETWORK; *U.S. Private*, pg. 3785
STARMEDTEC GMBH—See Boston Scientific Corporation; *U.S. Public*, pg. 375

STAR MEDIA NETWORK / CORPORATE AFFILIATIONS

STARMER PACKAGING PTY. LTD.—See Bischof + Klein GmbH & Co. KG; *Int'l*, pg. 1049

STAR METAL COMPANY—See Star Micronics Co Ltd; *Int'l*, pg. 7174

STARMET VENTURES INC.; *Int'l*, pg. 7178

STAR MICA ASSET PARTNERS CO., LTD.—See Star Mica Holdings Co., Ltd.; *Int'l*, pg. 7174

STAR MICA CO., LTD.; *Int'l*, pg. 7174

STAR MICA HOLDINGS CO., LTD.; *Int'l*, pg. 7174

STAR MICA PROPERTY CO., LTD.—See Star Mica Holdings Co., Ltd.; *Int'l*, pg. 7174

STAR MICA RESIDENCE CO., LTD.—See Star Mica Holdings Co., Ltd.; *Int'l*, pg. 7174

STAR MICRONICS AG—See Star Micronics Co Ltd; *Int'l*, pg. 7175

STAR MICRONICS CO LTD; *Int'l*, pg. 7174

STAR MICRONICS GMBH—See Star Micronics Co Ltd; *Int'l*, pg. 7175

STAR MICRONICS MANUFACTURING (THAILAND) CO., LTD.—See Star Micronics Co Ltd; *Int'l*, pg. 7175

STAR MICRONICS PRECISION (THAILAND) CO., LTD.—See Star Micronics Co Ltd; *Int'l*, pg. 7175

STAR MICRONICS PTY. LTD.—See Star Micronics Co Ltd; *Int'l*, pg. 7175

STAR MICRONICS SOUTHEAST ASIA CO., LTD.—See Star Micronics Co Ltd; *Int'l*, pg. 7175

STAR MICROWAVE, INC.—See Electro Technik Industries; *U.S. Private*, pg. 1354

STAR MIDDLE EAST FZ-LLC—See National Amusements, Inc.; *U.S. Private*, pg. 2844

STAR MIDDLE EAST FZ-LLC—See Reliance - ADA Group Limited; *Int'l*, pg. 6263

STAR MILLING COMPANY INC—See Mountaire Corporation; *U.S. Private*, pg. 2801

STARMINE CORPORATION—See Thomson Reuters Corporation; *Int'l*, pg. 7716

STAR MINERALS LIMITED; *Int'l*, pg. 7175

STAR MONEY PUBLIC COMPANY LIMITED; *Int'l*, pg. 7175

STAR MOTORS, LLC—See AutoNation, Inc.; *U.S. Public*, pg. 237

STAR MOTORS, LLC—See AutoNation, Inc.; *U.S. Public*, pg. 237

STAR MOUNTAIN RESOURCES, INC.; *U.S. Public*, pg. 1938

STARMOUNT CO.—See Koch Industries, Inc.; *U.S. Private*, pg. 2331

STARMOUNT LIFE INSURANCE COMPANY; *U.S. Private*, pg. 3787

STAR MULTI CARE SERVICES INC.; *U.S. Private*, pg. 3785

STAR MULTI CARE SERVICES OF FLORIDA, INC—See Star Multi Care Services Inc.; *U.S. Private*, pg. 3785

STAR NAVIGATION SYSTEMS GROUP LTD.; *Int'l*, pg. 7175

STAR NAVIGATION SYSTEMS INC.—See Star Navigation Systems Group Ltd.; *Int'l*, pg. 7175

STARNBERGER KLINIKEN GMBH; *Int'l*, pg. 7175

STARNET CO., LTD.—See Sapporo Holdings Limited; *Int'l*, pg. 6573

STARNET INSURANCE COMPANY—See W.R. Berkley Corporation; *U.S. Public*, pg. 2318

STARNETONE GMBH—See Hubert Burda Media Holding Kommanditgesellschaft; *Int'l*, pg. 3520

STAR NETWORKS, INC.—See Fiserv, Inc.; *U.S. Public*, pg. 851

STAR NURSERY INC.; *U.S. Private*, pg. 3785

STAR NUTRITION, INC.; *U.S. Public*, pg. 1938

STAR OF INDIA FASHIONS, INC.; *U.S. Private*, pg. 3785

STAR OF THE WEST MILLING CO.; *U.S. Private*, pg. 3785

STAR ONE CREDIT UNION; *U.S. Private*, pg. 3785

STAR ONE S.A.—See SES S.A.; *Int'l*, pg. 6728

STAR PACIFIC LOGISTICS LTD.—See Beijing Sports & Entertainment Industry Group Limited; *Int'l*, pg. 957

STAR PACKAGING CORP.—See Nicolet Capital Partners, LLC; *U.S. Private*, pg. 2926

STAR PAPER INTERNATIONAL CO., LTD.—See Charoen Aksorn Holding Group Co. Ltd.; *Int'l*, pg. 1451

STAR PAPER MILLS LIMITED; *Int'l*, pg. 7175

STAR PAVING CO.; *U.S. Private*, pg. 3785

STARPET INC.—See Indorama Ventures Public Company Limited; *Int'l*, pg. 3658

STAR/PETRO, INC.—See Star Group, L.P.; *U.S. Public*, pg. 1938

STAR PETROLEUM REFINING PUBLIC CO., LTD.—See Chevron Corporation; *U.S. Public*, pg. 488

STAR PETROTECH PTE. LTD.—See Petro-King Oilfield Services Limited; *Int'l*, pg. 5826

STAR PHARMACEUTICAL LIMITED; *Int'l*, pg. 7175

STARPHARMA HOLDINGS LIMITED; *Int'l*, pg. 7178

STARPHARMA PTY. LTD.—See Starpharma Holdings Limited; *Int'l*, pg. 7178

STAR PHOENIX GROUP LTD; *Int'l*, pg. 7175

STAR PHOENIX GROUP UK LIMITED—See Star Phoenix Group Ltd; *Int'l*, pg. 7175

THE STARPHOENIX—See Chatham Asset Management, LLC; *U.S. Private*, pg. 861

STAR PHYSICAL THERAPY, LIMITED PARTNERSHIP—See U.S. Physical Therapy, Inc.; *U.S. Public*, pg. 2216

STAR PLANNING CO., LTD.—See Tsunagu Group Holdings Inc.; *Int'l*, pg. 7957

STARPOINT GENERAL CORPORATION; *U.S. Private*, pg. 3787

STARPOINT; *U.S. Private*, pg. 3787

STAR PORTFOLIO CORP.; *Int'l*, pg. 7175

STARPOWER COMMUNICATIONS, LLC—See Stonepeak Partners L.P.; *U.S. Private*, pg. 3829

STARPOWER SEMICONDUCTOR LTD.; *Int'l*, pg. 7178

THE STAR PRESS—See Gannett Co., Inc.; *U.S. Public*, pg. 900

STAR PRINTING & SUPPLY CO., INC.—See Yellowstone Communications; *U.S. Private*, pg. 4588

STAR PRODUCE LTD.; *Int'l*, pg. 7175

THE STAR PTY LIMITED—See The Star Entertainment Group Limited; *Int'l*, pg. 7688

STAR PUBLICATIONS (SINGAPORE) PTE. LTD.—See Star Media Group Berhad; *Int'l*, pg. 7174

STAR PUBLISHING COMPANY—See Lee Enterprises, Incorporated; *U.S. Public*, pg. 1300

STARPURI DEVELOPMENT SDN BHD—See Wing Tai Holdings Limited; *Int'l*, pg. 8427

STARRAG AG—See Starrag Group Holding AG; *Int'l*, pg. 7179

STARRAG GMBH—See Starrag Group Holding AG; *Int'l*, pg. 7179

STARRAG GROUP HOLDING AG; *Int'l*, pg. 7179

STARRAG INDIA PRIVATE LIMITED—See Starrag Group Holding AG; *Int'l*, pg. 7179

STARRAG ITALIA SRL—See Starrag Group Holding AG; *Int'l*, pg. 7179

STARRAG RU LTD.—See Starrag Group Holding AG; *Int'l*, pg. 7179

STARRAG S.A.S.—See Starrag Group Holding AG; *Int'l*, pg. 7179

STARRAG (SHANGHAI) CO. LTD.—See Starrag Group Holding AG; *Int'l*, pg. 7179

STARRAG UK LTD.—See Starrag Group Holding AG; *Int'l*, pg. 7179

STARRAG USA INC.—See Starrag Group Holding AG; *Int'l*, pg. 7179

STARRAG VUADENS SA—See Starrag Group Holding AG; *Int'l*, pg. 7179

STARRCO COMPANY INC.; *U.S. Private*, pg. 3787

STAR READY MIX INC.; *U.S. Private*, pg. 3785

STAR RECORDING, INC.—See Lopez, Inc.; *Int'l*, pg. 4556

STAR REEFERS AS—See Siem Industries Inc.; *Int'l*, pg. 6886

STAR REEFERS LTD—See Siem Industries Inc.; *Int'l*, pg. 6886

STARR ELECTRIC CO. INC.—See Comfort Systems USA, Inc.; *U.S. Public*, pg. 544

STARR ELECTRIC COMPANY—See Comfort Systems USA, Inc.; *U.S. Public*, pg. 544

STAR REPUBLIC AB—See DBAY Advisors Limited; *Int'l*, pg. 1987

STARRETT (ASIA) PTE. LTD.—See MiddleGround Management, LP; *U.S. Private*, pg. 2713

STARRETT BYTEWISE DEVELOPMENT, INC.—See MiddleGround Management, LP; *U.S. Private*, pg. 2713

STARRETT CORPORATION; *U.S. Private*, pg. 3787

STARRETT GMBH—See MiddleGround Management, LP; *U.S. Private*, pg. 2713

STARRETT GRANITE SURFACE PLATE DIVISION—See MiddleGround Management, LP; *U.S. Private*, pg. 2713

STARRETT INDUSTRIA E COMERCIO LTDA.—See MiddleGround Management, LP; *U.S. Private*, pg. 2713

STARRETT KINEMETRIC ENGINEERING, INC.—See MiddleGround Management, LP; *U.S. Private*, pg. 2713

STARRETT (NEW ZEALAND) LIMITED—See MiddleGround Management, LP; *U.S. Private*, pg. 2713

STARRETT PRECISION OPTICAL LIMITED—See MiddleGround Management, LP; *U.S. Private*, pg. 2713

STARRETT TOOLS (SUZHOU) CO. LTD.—See MiddleGround Management, LP; *U.S. Private*, pg. 2713

STARREX INTERNATIONAL LTD.; *Int'l*, pg. 7179

STARREZ INC.; *U.S. Private*, pg. 3787

STARR FARM PARTNERSHIP—See Apollo Global Management, Inc.; *U.S. Public*, pg. 157

STARRFOAM MANUFACTURING INC.; *U.S. Private*, pg. 3788

STARR INVESTMENT HOLDINGS LLC—See C.V. Starr & Co., Inc.; *U.S. Private*, pg. 709

STAR RISK SERVICES INC.—See Deutsche Lufthansa AG; *Int'l*, pg. 2070

STARR PEAK MINING LTD.; *Int'l*, pg. 7179

STARRTECH INTERACTIVE; *U.S. Private*, pg. 3788

STARR TINCUP; *U.S. Private*, pg. 3787

STARR TRANSIT CO. INC.; *U.S. Private*, pg. 3787

STARRY GROUP HOLDINGS, INC.; *U.S. Public*, pg. 1939

STAR SALES CO., INC.; *U.S. Private*, pg. 3785

STAR SALES & DISTRIBUTING; *U.S. Private*, pg. 3785

STARS ALLIANCE, LLC—See Ameren Corporation; *U.S. Public*, pg. 94

STAR SANITARYWARE (THAILAND) CO., LTD.; *Int'l*, pg. 7175

STAR SCHOOLS (PTY) LTD.—See ADvTECH Limited; *Int'l*, pg. 169

STARSEED MEDICINAL INC.—See Entourage Health Corp.; *Int'l*, pg. 2452

STARSEM—See Airbus SE; *Int'l*, pg. 246

THE STARS GROUP INC.—See Flutter Entertainment plc; *Int'l*, pg. 2715

STAR SHINE GLOBAL TRADING SDN. BHD.—See BlueScope Steel Limited; *Int'l*, pg. 1074

STAR SHINE INDUSTRIES SDN. BHD.—See BlueScope Steel Limited; *Int'l*, pg. 1074

STAR SHINE MARKETING SDN. BHD.—See BlueScope Steel Limited; *Int'l*, pg. 1073

STAR SHINE STEEL PRODUCTS SDN. BHD.—See BlueScope Steel Limited; *Int'l*, pg. 1074

STARS MICROELECTRONICS (THAILAND) PUBLIC COMPANY LIMITED; *Int'l*, pg. 7179

STARS MICROELECTRONICS USA, INC.—See Stars Microelectronics (Thailand) Public Company Limited; *Int'l*, pg. 7179

THE STAR—See Gannett Co., Inc.; *U.S. Public*, pg. 906

STAR SPORTS LNDIA PRIVATE LIMITED—See National Amusements, Inc.; *U.S. Private*, pg. 2844

STAR SPORTS LNDIA PRIVATE LIMITED—See Reliance - ADA Group Limited; *Int'l*, pg. 6263

STAR STABILIANTO ALIMENTARE S.P.A.—See Danone; *Int'l*, pg. 1968

STAR STAINLESS SCREW CO.; *U.S. Private*, pg. 3785

STARS TECHNOLOGIES INDUSTRIAL LIMITED—See Mitsuboshi Belting Ltd.; *Int'l*, pg. 4972

STARSTONE INSURANCE SERVICES LIMITED—See Enstar Group Limited; *Int'l*, pg. 2449

STARSTONE INSURANCE SE—See Enstar Group Limited; *Int'l*, pg. 2449

STARSTONE NATIONAL INSURANCE COMPANY—See Enstar Group Limited; *Int'l*, pg. 2449

STARSTONE SPECIALTY INSURANCE COMPANY—See Enstar Group Limited; *Int'l*, pg. 2449

STAR STRUCK/PROTEAM, INC.—See Kynetic LLC; *U.S. Private*, pg. 2360

STAR SU FEDERAL DE MEXICO S.A. DE C.V—See Star Cutter Company; *U.S. Private*, pg. 3784

STAR-SU LLC.—See Star Gutter Company; *U.S. Private*, pg. 3784

START AD—See Monbat AD; *Int'l*, pg. 5025

START:BAUSPARKASSE AG—See BAWAG Group AG; *Int'l*, pg. 900

START:BAUSPARKASSE AG—See BAWAG Group AG; *Int'l*, pg. 900

STAR TEAMS INC.—See XVIVO Perfusion AB; *Int'l*, pg. 8541

STARTEC GLOBAL COMMUNICATIONS CORPORATION—See Platinum Equity, LLC; *U.S. Private*, pg. 3208

STARTECH.COM LTD.; *Int'l*, pg. 7179

STARTECH.COM USA LLP; *U.S. Private*, pg. 3788

STARTECH LABS, INC.; *U.S. Public*, pg. 1939

STARTECK FINANCE LIMITED; *Int'l*, pg. 7179

STARTEK AUSTRALIA PTY LTD—See StarTek, Inc.; *U.S. Private*, pg. 3788

STARTEK CANADA SERVICES, LTD.—See StarTek, Inc.; *U.S. Private*, pg. 3788

STARTEK HEALTH SERVICES, INC.—See StarTek, Inc.; *U.S. Private*, pg. 3788

STARTEK, INC.; *U.S. Private*, pg. 3788

STARTEL CORPORATION; *U.S. Private*, pg. 3788

STAR-TELEGRAM, INC.—See Chatham Asset Management, LLC; *U.S. Private*, pg. 867

STAR TELEPHONE MEMBERSHIP CORP.; *U.S. Private*, pg. 3785

STARTENGINE CROWDFUNDING, INC.; *U.S. Private*, pg. 3788

THE STARTERPACK COMPANY (PTY) LTD.—See Lesaka Technologies, Inc.; *Int'l*, pg. 4469

STARTEX CHEMICAL, LLC—See Apollo Global Management, Inc.; *U.S. Public*, pg. 165

STARTEX RUBBER CORPORATION LIMITED—See Sri Trang Agro-Industry Public Company Limited; *Int'l*, pg. 7151

STARTIA HOLDINGS, INC.; *Int'l*, pg. 7179

STARTIA SHANGHAI INC.; *Int'l*, pg. 7179

START.IO, INC; *U.S. Private*, pg. 3788

START MEDIA LLC—See Dalian Wanda Group Corporation Ltd.; *Int'l*, pg. 1953

STARTMONDAY TECHNOLOGY CORP.; *Int'l*, pg. 7179

START MORTGAGES LIMITED—See Lone Star Global Acquisitions, LLC; *U.S. Private*, pg. 2489

STAR TOUR A/S—See TUI AG; *Int'l*, pg. 7966

STAR TOUR HOLDING A/S—See TUI AG; *Int'l*, pg. 7966

STARTOUR-STJERNEREISER AS—See TUI AG; *Int'l*, pg. 7966

STAR TOWER S.A.L.—See Al-Massaleh Real Estate Company K.S.C.C.; *Int'l*, pg. 287

START PEOPLE BV—See Recruit Holdings Co., Ltd.; *Int'l*, pg. 6240

START PEOPLE NV—See Recruit Holdings Co., Ltd.; *Int'l*, pg. 6240

START PEORLE SAS—See Recruit Holdings Co., Ltd.; *Int'l*, pg. 6240

COMPANY NAME INDEX

STAR TRAC - IRVINE—See Core Health & Fitness LLC; *U.S. Private*, pg. 1048

STAR TRACK EXPRESS PTY. LTD.—See Australian Postal Corporation; *Int'l*, pg. 722

STARTRAK INFORMATION TECHNOLOGIES, LLC—See ORBCOMM, Inc.; *U.S. Public*, pg. 1614

STARTRAK PRODUCTS, INC.; *U.S. Private*, pg. 3788

STAR TRANSPORTATION, LLC—See Covenant Logistics Group, Inc.; *U.S. Public*, pg. 588

STAR TRAVEL SERVICES, INC.—See Cook Group Incorporated; *U.S. Private*, pg. 1038

THE STAR TRIBUNE COMPANY—See Star Tribune Media Company LLC; *U.S. Private*, pg. 3785

STAR TRIBUNE MEDIA COMPANY LLC; *U.S. Private*, pg. 3785

START-RITE SHOES LTD.—See James Southall & Company Ltd.; *Int'l*, pg. 3878

STARTRONICS—See STG International Ltd; *Int'l*, pg. 7213

STAR TRUCK RENTALS INC.—See Mitsui & Co., Ltd.; *Int'l*, pg. 4980

STAR TRUCK RENTALS INC.—See Penske Automotive Group, Inc.; *U.S. Public*, pg. 1666

STAR TRUCK RENTALS INC.—See Penske Corporation; *U.S. Private*, pg. 3139

STARTS AMENITY CORPORATION—See Starts Corporation, Inc.; *Int'l*, pg. 7180

STARTS CAM CO., LTD.—See Starts Corporation, Inc.; *Int'l*, pg. 7180

STARTS CONSTRUCTION & ASSET MANAGEMENT CO. LTD.—See Starts Corporation, Inc.; *Int'l*, pg. 7180

STARTS CORPORATION, INC.; *Int'l*, pg. 7179

STARTS DEVELOPMENT CORPORATION—See Starts Corporation, Inc.; *Int'l*, pg. 7180

STARTS GUAM GOLF RESORT INC.—See Starts Corporation, Inc.; *Int'l*, pg. 7180

STARTS (GUANGZHOU) CONSULTING SERVICE CO., LTD.—See Starts Corporation, Inc.; *Int'l*, pg. 7180

STARTS INTERNATIONAL AUSTRALIA PTY., LTD.—See Starts Corporation, Inc.; *Int'l*, pg. 7180

STARTS INTERNATIONAL HAWAII, INC.—See Starts Corporation, Inc.; *Int'l*, pg. 7180

STARTS INTERNATIONAL MALAYSIA SDN. BHD.—See Starts Corporation, Inc.; *Int'l*, pg. 7180

STARTS INTERNATIONAL (THAILAND) CO., LTD.—See Starts Corporation, Inc.; *Int'l*, pg. 7180

STARTS INTERNATIONAL VIETNAM CO., LTD.—See Starts Corporation, Inc.; *Int'l*, pg. 7180

STARTS NEW YORK REALTY LLC—See Starts Corporation, Inc.; *Int'l*, pg. 7180

STARTS PACIFIC INC.—See Starts Corporation, Inc.; *Int'l*, pg. 7180

STARTS PROCEED INVESTMENT CORPORATION; *Int'l*, pg. 7180

STARTS REAL ESTATE CONSULTANTS (SHANGHAI) CO., LTD.—See Starts Corporation, Inc.; *Int'l*, pg. 7180

STARTS SECURITIES CO., LTD.—See Starts Corporation, Inc.; *Int'l*, pg. 7180

STARTS SINGAPORE PTE. LTD.—See Starts Corporation, Inc.; *Int'l*, pg. 7180

START TREATMENT & RECOVERY CENTERS; *U.S. Private*, pg. 3788

START TRUCKING, INC.; *U.S. Private*, pg. 3788

STARTUP300 AG; *Int'l*, pg. 7180

STARTUP HEALTH HOLDINGS, INC.; *U.S. Private*, pg. 3788

STAR UNION DAI-ICHI LIFE INSURANCE COMPANY LIMITED—See Dai-ichi Life Holdings, Inc.; *Int'l*, pg. 1918

STAR UNIVERSAL NETWORK PUBLIC COMPANY LIMITED; *Int'l*, pg. 7175

STAR-USA LLC; *U.S. Private*, pg. 3786

STARVAGGI INDUSTRIES, INC.; *U.S. Private*, pg. 3788

STARVEST PLC; *Int'l*, pg. 7180

STARVING STUDENTS MOVING COMPANY; *U.S. Private*, pg. 3788

STARVIN MARVIN, INC.—See Marathon Petroleum Corporation; *U.S. Public*, pg. 1364

STARVISION HONG KONG LIMITED—See National Amusements, Inc.; *U.S. Private*, pg. 2844

STARVISION HONG KONG LIMITED—See Reliance - ADA Group Limited; *Int'l*, pg. 6263

STARVISION, INC.—See Star Telephone Membership Corp.; *U.S. Private*, pg. 3785

STARVR CORP.—See Starbreeze AB; *Int'l*, pg. 7176

STARWARD INDUSTRIES S.A.; *Int'l*, pg. 7180

STARWAY BIO-TECHNOLOGY CO., LTD. - QINGXI I FACTORY—See INKON Life Technology Co., Ltd.; *Int'l*, pg. 3705

STARWAY BIO-TECHNOLOGY CO., LTD. - SHAOGUAN FACTORY—See INKON Life Technology Co., Ltd.; *Int'l*, pg. 3705

STAR WEALTH GROUP INC.; *Int'l*, pg. 7175

STAR WEALTH MANAGEMENT INC—See STAR Financial Group Inc.; *U.S. Public*, pg. 1937

STARWEAR INC.; *U.S. Private*, pg. 3788

STAR WERKS INC.; *U.S. Private*, pg. 3785

STAR WEST SATELLITE INC.; *U.S. Private*, pg. 3785

STAR WEST SATELLITE—See Star West Satellite Inc.; *U.S. Private*, pg. 3785

STAR WEST SATELLITE—See Star West Satellite Inc.; *U.S. Private*, pg. 3785

STAR WHEELS ELECTRONIC SDN. BHD.—See GUH Holdings Berhad; *Int'l*, pg. 3173

STARWIN PRODUCTS LIMITED; *Int'l*, pg. 7180

STARWOOD ASIA PACIFIC HOTELS & RESORTS PTE LTD.—See Marriott International, Inc.; *U.S. Public*, pg. 1371

STARWOOD CAPITAL EUROPE ADVISERS, LLP—See Starwood Capital Group Global I, LLC; *U.S. Private*, pg. 3789

STARWOOD CAPITAL GROUP EUROPEAN SARL—See Starwood Capital Group Global I, LLC; *U.S. Private*, pg. 3789

STARWOOD CAPITAL GROUP GLOBAL I, LLC; *U.S. Private*, pg. 3789

STARWOOD EUROPEAN REAL ESTATE FINANCE LIMITED; *Int'l*, pg. 7180

STARWOOD HOTELS & RESORTS WORLDWIDE, LLC—See Marriott International, Inc.; *U.S. Public*, pg. 1371

STARWOOD ITALIA S.R.L.—See Marriott International, Inc.; *U.S. Public*, pg. 1372

STARWOOD MORTGAGE CAPITAL LLC—See Starwood Property Trust, Inc.; *U.S. Public*, pg. 1940

STARWOOD PROPERTY TRUST, INC.; *U.S. Public*, pg. 1939

STARWOOD REAL ESTATE INCOME TRUST, INC.; *U.S. Private*, pg. 3789

STARWOOD REAL ESTATE SECURITIES, LLC—See Starwood Capital Group Global I, LLC; *U.S. Private*, pg. 3789

STARWORLD HOTEL COMPANY LIMITED—See Galaxy Entertainment Group Limited; *Int'l*, pg. 2871

STARWORTH INFRASTRUCTURE & CONSTRUCTION LIMITED—See Puravankara Ltd.; *Int'l*, pg. 6121

STARYNSKA BREEDING FARM AGRICULTURAL LLC—See OJSC Myronivsky Hliboproduct; *Int'l*, pg. 5541

STARZ ACQUISITION LLC—See Lions Gate Entertainment Corp.; *Int'l*, pg. 4521

STARZEN COMPANY LIMITED; *Int'l*, pg. 7180

STARZ ENTERTAINMENT, LLC—See Lions Gate Entertainment Corp.; *Int'l*, pg. 4521

STARZ, LLC—See Lions Gate Entertainment Corp.; *Int'l*, pg. 4521

STARZ MEDIA, LLC—See Lions Gate Entertainment Corp.; *Int'l*, pg. 4521

STARZ POWER PRODUCTIONS, LLC—See Lions Gate Entertainment Corp.; *Int'l*, pg. 4521

STASCO MECHANICAL CONTRACTORS; *U.S. Private*, pg. 3790

STASH FINANCIAL, INC.; *U.S. Private*, pg. 3790

STASON PHARMACEUTICALS,INC.—See Standard Chem. & Pharm. Co., Ltd.; *Int'l*, pg. 7168

S.T.A. S.R.L.—See Aega ASA; *Int'l*, pg. 173

STASSEN EXPORTS LTD.; *Int'l*, pg. 7180

S.T.A.S.—See Schindler Holding AG; *Int'l*, pg. 6619

STASZAK COMMUNICATIONS; *U.S. Private*, pg. 3790

STATCO ENGINEERING & FABRICATORS INC.; *U.S. Private*, pg. 3790

STATCORP MEDICAL—See OSI Systems, Inc.; *U.S. Public*, pg. 1621

STATCO SIX LIMITED—See E.ON SE; *Int'l*, pg. 2256

STATCOUNTER LTD.; *Int'l*, pg. 7180

STAT CREW SOFTWARE, INC.—See National Amusements, Inc.; *U.S. Private*, pg. 2843

STATE ALARM, INC.—See Redwire LLC; *U.S. Private*, pg. 3380

STATE ATOMIC ENERGY CORPORATION ROSATOM; *Int'l*, pg. 7180

STATE AUTO FINANCIAL CORPORATION—See State Automobile Mutual Insurance Company; *U.S. Private*, pg. 3791

STATE AUTO INSURANCE COMPANY—See State Automobile Mutual Insurance Company; *U.S. Private*, pg. 3791

STATE AUTOMOBILE MUTUAL INSURANCE COMPANY; *U.S. Private*, pg. 3790

STATE AUTO P & C—See State Automobile Mutual Insurance Company; *U.S. Private*, pg. 3791

STATE AUTO PROPERTY AND CASUALTY INSURANCE COMPANY—See State Automobile Mutual Insurance Company; *U.S. Private*, pg. 3791

THE STATE BANK AND TRUST COMPANY—See SB Financial Group, Inc.; *U.S. Public*, pg. 1842

STATE BANK FINANCIAL—See First Bancorporation Inc.; *U.S. Public*, pg. 1513

STATE BANK OF ARCADIA, INC.—See Treynor Bancshares, Inc.; *U.S. Private*, pg. 4219

STATE BANK OF CHILTON—See Calumet Bancorporation, Inc.; *U.S. Private*, pg. 724

STATE BANK OF COUNTRYSIDE INC.; *U.S. Private*, pg. 3791

STATE BANK OF CROSS PLAINS—See S.B.C.P. Bancorp, Inc.; *U.S. Public*, pg. 1832

STATE BANK OF FOX LAKE—See Farmers State Bank; *U.S. Private*, pg. 1479

STATE EQUIPMENT INC.

STATE BANK OF INDIA-CHICAGO BRANCH—See State Bank of India; *Int'l*, pg. 7181

STATE BANK OF INDIA; *Int'l*, pg. 7181

STATE BANK OF INDIA (UK) LIMITED—See State Bank of India; *Int'l*, pg. 7181

STATE BANK OF LINCOLN CORP.; *U.S. Private*, pg. 3791

STATE BANK OF LISMORE—See First Western Bank & Trust; *U.S. Private*, pg. 1530

STATE BANK OF LIZTON—See Lizton Financial Corporation; *U.S. Private*, pg. 2474

STATE BANK OF MAURITIUS LTD.; *Int'l*, pg. 7181

STATE BANK OF MYSORE—See State Bank of India; *Int'l*, pg. 7181

STATE BANK OF PAKISTAN; *Int'l*, pg. 7181

STATE BANK OF SOUTHERN UTAH; *U.S. Private*, pg. 3791

STATE BANK OF TEXAS—See SBT Bancshares, Inc.; *U.S. Private*, pg. 3560

STATE BANK OF THE LAKES, N.A.—See Wintrust Financial Corporation; *U.S. Public*, pg. 2375

STATE BANK OPERATIONS SUPPORT SERVICES PVT. LTD.—See State Bank of India; *Int'l*, pg. 7181

STATE BANKSHARES, INC.; *U.S. Private*, pg. 3791

THE STATE BANK—See Fentura Financial, Inc.; *U.S. Public*, pg. 829

STATE BANK—See Wonder Bancorp, Inc.; *U.S. Private*, pg. 4556

STATE BANK—See Everly Bancorporation; *U.S. Private*, pg. 1440

STATE BANK & TRUST COMPANY; *U.S. Private*, pg. 3791

STATE BANK & TRUST CO.—See Ames National Corporation; *U.S. Public*, pg. 116

STATE BEAUTY SUPPLY OF ST. LOUIS; *U.S. Private*, pg. 3791

STATE BUILDING GROUP, INC.—See State Utility Contractors Inc.; *U.S. Private*, pg. 3793

STATE CAPITAL INVESTMENT CORPORATION; *Int'l*, pg. 7182

STATE CENTER FINANCIAL, INC.; *U.S. Private*, pg. 3791

STATE CENTRAL BANK; *U.S. Private*, pg. 3791

STATE CHEMICAL SALES COMPANY INTERNATIONAL INC.—See State Industrial Products Corporation; *U.S. Private*, pg. 3792

STA TECHNOLOGIES INC.—See SICPA Holding SA; *Int'l*, pg. 6882

STATECH SLOVAKIA S.R.O.—See Group Thermote & Vanhalst; *Int'l*, pg. 3089

STATECH S.R.O.—See Group Thermote & Vanhalst; *Int'l*, pg. 3090

STATE CLEANING SOLUTIONS—See State Industrial Products Corporation; *U.S. Private*, pg. 3792

STATE COLLEGE SPIKES BASEBALL CLUB—See Greenberg Sports Group Inc.; *U.S. Private*, pg. 1775

STATE CONTRACT MANUFACTURING—See State Industrial Products Corporation; *U.S. Private*, pg. 3792

STATE ELECTRIC SUPPLY COMPANY—See Arthur's Enterprises, Inc.; *U.S. Private*, pg. 342

STATE ELECTRIC SUPPLY COMPANY—See Arthur's Enterprises, Inc.; *U.S. Private*, pg. 342

STATE ELECTRIC SUPPLY CO.—See Arthur's Enterprises, Inc.; *U.S. Private*, pg. 342

STATE ELECTRIC SUPPLY CO.—See Arthur's Enterprises, Inc.; *U.S. Private*, pg. 342

STATE EMPLOYEES CREDIT UNION OF MARYLAND, INC.; *U.S. Private*, pg. 3791

STATE EMPLOYEES' CREDIT UNION; *U.S. Private*, pg. 3791

STATE EMPLOYEES CREDIT UNION; *U.S. Private*, pg. 3791

STATE ENERGY GROUP INTERNATIONAL ASSETS HOLDINGS LIMITED; *Int'l*, pg. 7182

STATE EQUIPMENT INC.; *U.S. Private*, pg. 3791

STATE FARM ANNUITY & LIFE INSURANCE CO.—See State Farm Mutual Automobile Insurance Company; *U.S. Private*, pg. 3792

STATE FARM BANK, F.S.B.—See State Farm Mutual Automobile Insurance Company; *U.S. Private*, pg. 3792

STATE FARM FIRE & CASUALTY CO.—See State Farm Mutual Automobile Insurance Company; *U.S. Private*, pg. 3792

STATE FARM FLORIDA INSURANCE COMPANY—See State Farm Mutual Automobile Insurance Company; *U.S. Private*, pg. 3792

STATE FARM GENERAL INSURANCE COMPANY—See State Farm Mutual Automobile Insurance Company; *U.S. Private*, pg. 3792

STATE FARM GUARANTY INSURANCE COMPANY—See State Farm Mutual Automobile Insurance Company; *U.S. Private*, pg. 3792

STATE FARM INDEMNITY COMPANY—See State Farm Mutual Automobile Insurance Company; *U.S. Private*, pg. 3792

STATE FARM INSURANCE CO.—See State Farm Mutual Automobile Insurance Company; *U.S. Private*, pg. 3792

STATE FARM INSURANCE CO.—See State Farm Mutual Automobile Insurance Company; *U.S. Private*, pg. 3792

STATE EQUIPMENT INC.
CORPORATE AFFILIATIONS

STATE FARM INVESTMENT MANAGEMENT CORP.—See State Farm Mutual Automobile Insurance Company; *U.S. Private*, pg. 3792

STATE FARM LIFE & ACCIDENT ASSURANCE CO.—See State Farm Mutual Automobile Insurance Company; *U.S. Private*, pg. 3792

STATE FARM LLOYDS, INC.—See State Farm Mutual Automobile Insurance Company; *U.S. Private*, pg. 3792

STATE FARM MUTUAL AUTOMOBILE INSURANCE COMPANY; *U.S. Private*, pg. 3791

STATE FARM MUTUAL AUTOMOBILE INSURANCE COMPANY—See Mouvement des caisses Desjardins; *Int'l*, pg. 5058

STATE FISH COMPANY INC.; *U.S. Private*, pg. 3792

STATE FUND MUTUAL INSURANCE CO.; *U.S. Private*, pg. 3792

STATE GAS LIMITED; *Int'l*, pg. 7182

STATE GAS & OIL, LLC; *U.S. Private*, pg. 3792

STATE GRID CORPORATION OF CHINA; *Int'l*, pg. 7182

STATE GRID INFORMATION & COMMUNICATION CO LTD; *Int'l*, pg. 7183

STATE GRID INTERNATIONAL DEVELOPMENT LIMITED—See State Grid Corporation of China; *Int'l*, pg. 7183

STATE GRID YINGDA CO., LTD.; *Int'l*, pg. 7183

STATE GUARANTY BANK—See First Keyes Bancshares, Inc.; *U.S. Private*, pg. 1520

STATEHOUSE HOLDINGS INC.; *Int'l*, pg. 7184

STATE INDUSTRIAL PRODUCTS CORPORATION; *U.S. Private*, pg. 3792

STATE INDUSTRIES, LLC; *U.S. Private*, pg. 3792

THE STATE JOURNAL-REGISTER—See Gannett Co., Inc.; *U.S. Public*, pg. 905

STATEK BLATINY, S.R.O.—See CPI Property Group, S.A.; *Int'l*, pg. 1825

STATEK STANZEREI TECHNIK GMBH—See NORMA Group SE; *Int'l*, pg. 5431

STATE LINE BUILDING SUPPLY INC.—See GMS Inc.; *U.S. Public*, pg. 948

STATELINE COOPERATIVE INC.; *U.S. Private*, pg. 3793

STATELINE COPY PRODUCTS, INC.—See Stan's - LPS Midwest; *U.S. Private*, pg. 3777

THE STATE MEDIA COMPANY—See Chatham Asset Management, LLC; *U.S. Private*, pg. 868

STATE MUTUAL INSURANCE CO., INC.—See Concord General Mu; *U.S. Private*, pg. 1010

STATE NARROW FABRICS INC.; *U.S. Private*, pg. 3792

STATE NATIONAL COMPANIES, INC.—See Markel Group Inc.; *U.S. Public*, pg. 1369

STATEN ISLAND ADVANCE—See Advance Publications, Inc.; *U.S. Private*, pg. 87

STATEN ISLAND BOAT SALES INC.; *U.S. Private*, pg. 3793

STATEN ISLAND MENTAL HEALTH SOCIETY, INC.; *U.S. Private*, pg. 3793

STATEN ISLAND NISSAN; *U.S. Private*, pg. 3793

STATEN ISLAND YACHT CLUB, INC.—See Germain Motor Company; *U.S. Private*, pg. 1687

STATE OF FRANKLIN HEALTHCARE ASSOCIATES PLLC; *U.S. Private*, pg. 3792

STATE OF NEW YORK MORTGAGE AGENCY; *U.S. Private*, pg. 3792

STATE OIL CO. OF AZERBAIJAN REPUBLIC; *Int'l*, pg. 7184

STATE OIL FUND OF THE REPUBLIC OF AZERBAIJAN; *Int'l*, pg. 7184

STATE OIL LIMITED; *Int'l*, pg. 7184

STATE PIPE & SUPPLY INC.—See SeAH Holdings Corp.; *Int'l*, pg. 6664

STATE POWER INVESTMENT CORPORATION; *Int'l*, pg. 7184

STATE POWER RIXIN TECH. CO., LTD.; *Int'l*, pg. 7184

STATE PROPERTY FUND OF UKRAINE; *Int'l*, pg. 7184

STATERA BIOPHARMA, INC.; *U.S. Public*, pg. 1941

STATERA, INC.—See Boathouse Capital Management, LLC; *U.S. Private*, pg. 603

STATER BELGIUM N.V. / S.A.—See Infosys Limited; *Int'l*, pg. 3696

STATER BROS DEVELOPMENT INC—See La Cadena Investments; *U.S. Private*, pg. 2368

STATER BROS. MARKETS—See La Cadena Investments; *U.S. Private*, pg. 2368

STATER BROTHERS HOLDINGS—See La Cadena Investments; *U.S. Private*, pg. 2368

THE STATE-RECORD COMPANY—See Chatham Asset Management, LLC; *U.S. Private*, pg. 867

STATER N.V.—See Infosys Limited; *Int'l*, pg. 3696

STATESBORO COCA-COLA BOTTLING COMPANY—See Coca-Cola Bottling Co. United, Inc.; *U.S. Private*, pg. 959

STATESBORO HMA, INC.—See Community Health Systems, Inc.; *U.S. Public*, pg. 557

STATE SERVICE CO. INC.; *U.S. Private*, pg. 3792

STATE SERVICES ORGANIZATION, INC.; *U.S. Private*, pg. 3792

STATESERV MEDICAL, LLC; *U.S. Private*, pg. 3793

STATES INDUSTRIES, LLC—See Renovo Capital, LLC; *U.S. Private*, pg. 3399

STATES INDUSTRIES, LLC—See The Rosewood Corporation; *U.S. Private*, pg. 4112

STATESMAN JOURNAL—See Gannett Co., Inc.; *U.S. Public*, pg. 899

STATE STEEL SUPPLY CO; *U.S. Private*, pg. 3793

STATES TITLE HOLDING, INC.—See Doma Holdings, Inc.; *U.S. Public*, pg. 673

STATES TITLE, INC.—See Doma Holdings, Inc.; *U.S. Public*, pg. 673

STATE STREET AUSTRALIA LTD.—See State Street Corporation; *U.S. Public*, pg. 1940

STATE STREET BANK EUROPE LIMITED—See State Street Corporation; *U.S. Public*, pg. 1940

STATE STREET BANK GMBH - BRUSSELS BRANCH—See State Street Corporation; *U.S. Public*, pg. 1940

STATE STREET BANK GMBH—See State Street Corporation; *U.S. Public*, pg. 1940

STATE STREET BANK GMBH - ZURICH BRANCH—See State Street Corporation; *U.S. Public*, pg. 1940

STATE STREET BANK LUXEMBOURG S.A.—See State Street Corporation; *U.S. Public*, pg. 1940

STATE STREET BANK S.P.A.—See State Street Corporation; *U.S. Public*, pg. 1940

STATE STREET BANK & TRUST COMPANY - HONG KONG—See State Street Corporation; *U.S. Public*, pg. 1940

STATE STREET BANK & TRUST COMPANY - LONDON—See State Street Corporation; *U.S. Public*, pg. 1940

STATE STREET BANK & TRUST COMPANY - SEOUL—See State Street Corporation; *U.S. Public*, pg. 1940

STATE STREET BANK & TRUST COMPANY - SINGAPORE—See State Street Corporation; *U.S. Public*, pg. 1940

STATE STREET BANK & TRUST COMPANY—See State Street Corporation; *U.S. Public*, pg. 1940

STATE STREET BANK & TRUST COMPANY - TAIPEI—See State Street Corporation; *U.S. Public*, pg. 1940

STATE STREET BANK & TRUST COMPANY - TOKYO—See State Street Corporation; *U.S. Public*, pg. 1940

STATE STREET CALIFORNIA, INC.—See State Street Corporation; *U.S. Public*, pg. 1940

STATE STREET CAPITAL REALTY, LLC; *U.S. Private*, pg. 3793

STATE STREET CORPORATION; *U.S. Public*, pg. 1940

STATE STREET EUROPE LIMITED—See State Street Corporation; *U.S. Public*, pg. 1941

STATE STREET FINANCIAL SERVICES—See State Street Corporation; *U.S. Public*, pg. 1941

STATE STREET FUND SERVICES IRELAND LTD—See State Street Corporation; *U.S. Public*, pg. 1941

STATE STREET FUND SERVICES TORONTO—See State Street Corporation; *U.S. Public*, pg. 1941

STATE STREET GLOBAL ADVISORS AG—See State Street Corporation; *U.S. Public*, pg. 1941

STATE STREET GLOBAL ADVISORS ASIA LIMITED—See State Street Corporation; *U.S. Public*, pg. 1941

STATE STREET GLOBAL ADVISORS AUSTRALIA LTD.—See State Street Corporation; *U.S. Public*, pg. 1941

STATE STREET GLOBAL ADVISORS GMBH—See State Street Corporation; *U.S. Public*, pg. 1941

STATE STREET GLOBAL ADVISORS, INC.—See State Street Corporation; *U.S. Public*, pg. 1941

STATE STREET GLOBAL ADVISORS IRELAND LIMITED—See State Street Corporation; *U.S. Public*, pg. 1941

STATE STREET GLOBAL ADVISORS LIMITED—See State Street Corporation; *U.S. Public*, pg. 1941

STATE STREET GLOBAL ADVISORS SA/NV—See State Street Corporation; *U.S. Public*, pg. 1941

STATE STREET GLOBAL ADVISORS SINGAPORE LIMITED—See State Street Corporation; *U.S. Public*, pg. 1941

STATE STREET GLOBAL ADVISORS—See State Street Corporation; *U.S. Public*, pg. 1941

STATE STREET GLOBAL MARKETS, LLC—See State Street Corporation; *U.S. Public*, pg. 1941

STATE STREET INTERNATIONAL IRELAND LIMITED—See State Street Corporation; *U.S. Public*, pg. 1941

STATE STREET MASSACHUSETTS SECURITIES CORPORATION—See State Street Corporation; *U.S. Public*, pg. 1941

STATE STREET TRUST COMPANY CANADA—See State Street Corporation; *U.S. Public*, pg. 1941

STATES UNLIMITED; *U.S. Private*, pg. 3793

STATESVILLE AUTO AUCTION—See Cox Enterprises, Inc.; *U.S. Private*, pg. 1077

STATESVILLE HMA, INC.—See Community Health Systems, Inc.; *U.S. Public*, pg. 557

STATE TEACHERS RETIREMENT SYSTEM OF OHIO; *U.S. Private*, pg. 3793

STATE TIRE & SERVICE—See Complete General Construction Co. Inc.; *U.S. Private*, pg. 1000

STATE TOOL & MANUFACTURING CO.; *U.S. Private*, pg. 3793

STATE TRADING CORPORATION OF BHUTAN LTD.—See Bridgestone Corporation; *Int'l*, pg. 1160

STATE TRADING CORPORATION OF INDIA LTD; *Int'l*, pg. 7184

STATE TRADING ORGANIZATION PLC—See Maldives Transport & Contracting Company Plc; *Int'l*, pg. 4662

STATE TRANSPORT LEASING COMPANY PJSC; *Int'l*, pg. 7184

STATE UNIVERSITY RAILROAD CO.—See Norfolk Southern Corporation; *U.S. Public*, pg. 1536

STATE UTILITY CONTRACTORS INC.; *U.S. Private*, pg. 3793

STATE VOLUNTEER MUTUAL INSURANCE CO.; *U.S. Private*, pg. 3793

STATEWIDE DISASTER RESTORATION, INC.; *U.S. Private*, pg. 3793

STATEWIDE INDEPENDENT WHOLESALERS LIMITED—See Woolworths Group Limited; *Int'l*, pg. 8452

STATEWIDE INSULATION, INC.—See Installed Building Products, Inc.; *U.S. Public*, pg. 1133

STATE-WIDE INSURANCE COMPANY—See MAPFRE S.A.; *Int'l*, pg. 4684

STATEWIDE MORTGAGE, LLC; *U.S. Private*, pg. 3793

STATEWIDE REMODELING, INC.—See Florida Home Improvement Associates Inc.; *U.S. Private*, pg. 1549

STATEWIDE ROLLINS PTY LTD—See Rollins, Inc.; *U.S. Public*, pg. 1809

STATEWIDE SERVICES, INC.—See Compass Group PLC; *Int'l*, pg. 1752

STATEWIDE TIRE DISTRIBUTORS; *U.S. Private*, pg. 3793

STATEWIDE TYRE DISTRIBUTION PTY LTD—See National Tyre & Wheel Limited; *Int'l*, pg. 5164

STATEWIDE WHOLESALE, INC.—See Beacon Roofing Supply, Inc.; *U.S. Public*, pg. 287

STATEWOOD INCORPORATED; *U.S. Private*, pg. 3793

STATEX PETROLEUM I, L.P.; *U.S. Private*, pg. 3793

STAT HEALTH, LLC—See Teladoc Health, Inc.; *U.S. Public*, pg. 1992

STATHMOI PANTECHNIKI SA—See ELLAKTOR S.A.; *Int'l*, pg. 2365

STATHOLDING AS—See Equinor ASA; *Int'l*, pg. 2485

STATIA TERMINALS, INC.—See Sunoco LP; *U.S. Public*, pg. 1965

STATIC CONTROL COMPONENTS, INC.—See Zhuhai Seine Technology Co., Ltd.; *Int'l*, pg. 8678

STATIC SYSTEMS GROUP LIMITED—See Halma plc; *Int'l*, pg. 3233

STATICWORX, INC; *U.S. Private*, pg. 3793

STATIM FINANCE LIMITED—See McKesson Corporation; *U.S. Public*, pg. 1408

STATION A LLC—See NRG Energy, Inc.; *U.S. Public*, pg. 1551

STATION CASINOS LLC—See Red Rock Resorts, Inc.; *U.S. Public*, pg. 1769

STATIONERS, INC.—See Champion Industries, Inc.; *U.S. Public*, pg. 478

THE STATIONERY OFFICE ENTERPRISES LIMITED—See Deutsche Post AG; *Int'l*, pg. 2082

THE STATIONERY OFFICE LIMITED—See Advent International Corporation; *U.S. Private*, pg. 107

STATIONONE S.A.S.—See Alstom S.A.; *Int'l*, pg. 383

STATION PLACE ON MONMOUTH, LLC—See First Real Estate Investment Trust New Jersey Co.; *U.S. Public*, pg. 847

STATIONSERV HOLDINGS, LLC—See The Rosewood Corporation; *U.S. Private*, pg. 4112

STATISTA GMBH—See Stroer SE & Co. KGaA; *Int'l*, pg. 7242

STATISTA INC.—See Stroer SE & Co. KGaA; *Int'l*, pg. 7242

STATISTA LTD.—See Stroer SE & Co. KGaA; *Int'l*, pg. 7242

STATISTA PTE. LTD.—See Stroer SE & Co. KGaA; *Int'l*, pg. 7242

STATISTA S.A.R.L.—See Stroer SE & Co. KGaA; *Int'l*, pg. 7242

STATISTICS COLLABORATIVE, INC.—See Leonard Green & Partners, L.P.; *U.S. Private*, pg. 2430

STATISTICS.COM, LLC—See Elder Research Inc.; *U.S. Private*, pg. 1351

STATIT SOFTWARE, INC.—See Xerox Holdings Corporation; *U.S. Public*, pg. 2388

STATKING CONSULTING, INC.—See Genesis Biotechnology Group, LLC; *U.S. Private*, pg. 1669

STATKRAFT AS; *Int'l*, pg. 7184

STATKRAFT BRASIL AS—See Statkraft AS; *Int'l*, pg. 7185

STATKRAFT CHILE INVERSIONES ELECTRICAS LTD.—See Statkraft AS; *Int'l*, pg. 7185

STATKRAFT ENERGIA DO BRASIL LTDA.—See Statkraft AS; *Int'l*, pg. 7185

STATKRAFT ENERJI A.S.—See Statkraft AS; *Int'l*, pg. 7185

COMPANY NAME INDEX

STATKRAFT FINANCIAL ENERGY AB—See Statkraft AS; *Int'l*, pg. 7185
STATKRAFT FRANCE SAS—See Statkraft AS; *Int'l*, pg. 7185
STATKRAFT INDIA PVT. LTD.—See Statkraft AS; *Int'l*, pg. 7185
STATKRAFT MARKETS BV—See Statkraft AS; *Int'l*, pg. 7185
STATKRAFT MARKETS GMBH—See Statkraft AS; *Int'l*, pg. 7185
STATKRAFT NORFUND POWER INVEST AS—See Statkraft AS; *Int'l*, pg. 7185
STATKRAFT ROMANIA SRL—See Statkraft AS; *Int'l*, pg. 7185
STATKRAFT SODRA VINDKRAFT AB—See Statkraft AS; *Int'l*, pg. 7185
STATKRAFT SOUTH EAST EUROPE EOOD—See Statkraft AS; *Int'l*, pg. 7185
STATKRAFT SUOMI OY—See Statkraft AS; *Int'l*, pg. 7185
STATKRAFT SVERIGE AB—See Statkraft AS; *Int'l*, pg. 7185
STATKRAFT SVERIGE VATTENDEL 3 AB—See Statkraft AS; *Int'l*, pg. 7185
STATKRAFT TREASURY CENTRE SA—See Statkraft AS; *Int'l*, pg. 7185
STATKRAFT UK LTD.—See Statkraft AS; *Int'l*, pg. 7185
STATKRAFT VARME AB—See Statkraft AS; *Int'l*, pg. 7185
STATKRAFT VARME AS—See Statkraft AS; *Int'l*, pg. 7185
STATKRAFT WESTERN BALKANS D.O.O.—See Statkraft AS; *Int'l*, pg. 7185
STATLAB MEDICAL PRODUCTS, LLC—See Audax Group, Limited Partnership; *U.S. Private*, pg. 389
STATLAND MEDICAL GROUP, LLC—See HCA Healthcare, Inc.; *U.S. Public*, pg. 1010
STATLAND MEDICAL GROUP, LLC—See HCA Healthcare, Inc.; *U.S. Public*, pg. 1010
STATLINK SYSTEMS LLC; *U.S. Private*, pg. 3793
STATMINDS LLC—See Alten S.A.; *Int'l*, pg. 391
STATMON TECHNOLOGIES CORP.; *U.S. Private*, pg. 3793
STAT NURSING SERVICES INC.; *U.S. Private*, pg. 3790
STATOIL FUEL & RETAIL ASA—See FUCHS SE; *Int'l*, pg. 2804
STATOMAT SPECIAL MACHINES (INDIA) PVT. LTD.—See INA-Holding Schaeffler GmbH & Co. KG; *Int'l*, pg. 3642
STATON WHOLESALE INC.; *U.S. Private*, pg. 3793
STATPRO ASIA LTD.—See TA Associates, Inc.; *U.S. Private*, pg. 3915
STATPRO AUSTRALIA PTY LTD.—See TA Associates, Inc.; *U.S. Private*, pg. 3915
STATPRO (DEUTSCHLAND) GMBH—See TA Associates, Inc.; *U.S. Private*, pg. 3915
STATPRO FRANCE SARL—See TA Associates, Inc.; *U.S. Private*, pg. 3915
STATPRO GROUP LIMITED—See TA Associates, Inc.; *U.S. Private*, pg. 3915
STATPRO INC.—See TA Associates, Inc.; *U.S. Private*, pg. 3915
STATPRO ITALIA SRL—See TA Associates, Inc.; *U.S. Private*, pg. 3915
STATPRO S.A.—See TA Associates, Inc.; *U.S. Private*, pg. 3915
STATPRO SOUTH AFRICA PTY LTD.—See TA Associates, Inc.; *U.S. Private*, pg. 3915
STATRAD; *U.S. Private*, pg. 3794
STA TRAVEL (HOLDINGS) PTE LTD—See Diethelm Keller Holding Limited; *Int'l*, pg. 2117
STA TRAVEL, INC—See Diethelm Keller Holding Limited; *Int'l*, pg. 2117
STA TRAVEL LTD.—See Diethelm Keller Holding Limited; *Int'l*, pg. 2117
STA TRAVEL PTY LTD—See Diethelm Keller Holding Limited; *Int'l*, pg. 2117
STAT RESOURCE GROUP, INC.—See The Alesco Group, LLC; *U.S. Private*, pg. 3983
STATRON AG; *Int'l*, pg. 7185
STATRON B.V.—See Statron AG; *Int'l*, pg. 7185
STATRON GMBH—See Statron AG; *Int'l*, pg. 7186
STATRON MIDDLE EAST FZCO—See Statron AG; *Int'l*, pg. 7186
STATRON (UK) LTD.—See Statron AG; *Int'l*, pg. 7185
STATS ASIA PACIFIC PTE. LTD.—See Eurofins Scientific S.E.; *Int'l*, pg. 2552
STATS CHIPPAC INC.—See Temasek Holdings (Private) Limited; *Int'l*, pg. 7551
STATS CHIPPAC KOREA LTD.—See Temasek Holdings (Private) Limited; *Int'l*, pg. 7551
STATS CHIPPAC PTE. LTD.—See Temasek Holdings (Private) Limited; *Int'l*, pg. 7551
STATS CHIPPAC SEMICONDUCTOR (JIANGYIN) CO., LTD.—See JCET Group Co., Ltd.; *Int'l*, pg. 3923
STATS CHIPPAC SHANGHAI CO., LTD—See Temasek Holdings (Private) Limited; *Int'l*, pg. 7551
STATS LLC—See Vista Equity Partners, LLC; *U.S. Private*, pg. 4401
STATSOFT, INC.—See Dell Technologies Inc.; *U.S. Public*, pg. 650
STATS PERFORM—See Vista Equity Partners, LLC; *U.S. Private*, pg. 4401

STATSPIN, INC.—See Danaher Corporation; *U.S. Public*, pg. 625
STATSURE DIAGNOSTIC SYSTEMS, INC.; *U.S. Public*, pg. 1941
STAT TECH SERVICES, LLC—See CMC Consulting Boston, Inc.; *U.S. Private*, pg. 950
STATURE ELECTRIC, INC.—See Allient Inc.; *U.S. Public*, pg. 80
STATUS BUILDING SERVICES LTD.—See Kazera Global plc; *Int'l*, pg. 4103
STATUS ELECTRICAL SERVICES LTD.—See Kazera Global plc; *Int'l*, pg. 4103
STATUS PRODUCE LIMITED—See BayWa AG; *Int'l*, pg. 919
STATUS VERMOGENSVERWALTUNG GMBH—See UniCredit S.p.A.; *Int'l*, pg. 8039
STAUB ELECTRONICS LTD.—See Resideo Technologies, Inc.; *U.S. Public*, pg. 1790
STAUBER CALIFORNIA, INC.—See Hawkins, Inc.; *U.S. Public*, pg. 989
STAUBER NEW YORK, INC.—See Hawkins, Inc.; *U.S. Public*, pg. 989
STAUBER PERFORMANCE INGREDIENTS, INC.—See Hawkins, Inc.; *U.S. Public*, pg. 989
STAUB METALS CORPORATION; *U.S. Private*, pg. 3794
STAUBO ELEKTRO MASKIN AS—See Addtech AB; *Int'l*, pg. 135
STAUCH VETROMILE & MITCHELL ADVERTISING, INC.; *U.S. Private*, pg. 3794
STAUFEN GMBH & CO. KG; *Int'l*, pg. 7186
STAUFF CORPORATION; *U.S. Private*, pg. 3794
STAUFFER GLOVE & SAFETY; *U.S. Private*, pg. 3794
STAUFFERS OF KISSEL HILL—See SKH Management Co. Inc.; *U.S. Private*, pg. 3681
STAUFFERS OF KISSEL HILL—See SKH Management Co. Inc.; *U.S. Private*, pg. 3681
STAUFFERS OF ROHRERSTOWN INC.—See SKH Management Co. Inc.; *U.S. Private*, pg. 3681
ST. AUGSTINE SIGHTSEEING TRAINS—See The Jim Pattison Group; *Int'l*, pg. 7660
ST. AUGUSTINE ENDOSCOPY CENTER, LLC—See Tenet Healthcare Corporation; *U.S. Public*, pg. 2007
ST. AUGUSTINE GOLD AND COPPER LIMITED; *Int'l*, pg. 7158
THE ST. AUGUSTINE RECORD—See Gannett Co., Inc.; *U.S. Public*, pg. 905
STAUNTON CAPITAL, INC.; *U.S. Private*, pg. 3794
ST. AUSTELL BREWERY COMPANY LIMITED; *Int'l*, pg. 7158
ST AUSTELL VETS4PETS LIMITED—See Pets at Home Group Plc; *Int'l*, pg. 5834
S&T AUSTRIA GMBH—See Kontron AG; *Int'l*, pg. 4277
ST AUTOMOTIVE INDUSTRIAL PTE LTD.—See Temasek Holdings (Private) Limited; *Int'l*, pg. 7551
ST AUTOMOTIVE INSPECTION PTE. LTD.—See Temasek Holdings (Private) Limited; *Int'l*, pg. 7551
ST AUTOMOTIVE INSPECTION PTE LTD.—See Temasek Holdings (Private) Limited; *Int'l*, pg. 7551
STAVANGER MEKANISKE AS—See IKM Gruppen AS; *Int'l*, pg. 3612
STAVANGER STAAL SVENSKA AB—See Scana ASA; *Int'l*, pg. 6611
STAVANGER STORSENTER AS—See BNP Paribas SA; *Int'l*, pg. 1092
STAVBY MOSTOV SLOVAKIA A.S.—See VINCI S.A.; *Int'l*, pg. 8234
STAVE ASSOCIATES INTERNATIONAL, INC.—See Isco Holding Company Inc.; *U.S. Private*, pg. 2143
STAVE ISLAND LTD. PARTNERSHIP; *U.S. Private*, pg. 3794
STAVELY MINERALS LIMITED; *Int'l*, pg. 7186
ST AVIATION SERVICES CO. PTE LTD.—See Temasek Holdings (Private) Limited; *Int'l*, pg. 7552
STAVOLA CONTRACTING CO. INC.; *U.S. Private*, pg. 3794
STAVOLT NON STOP POWER GMBH—See Statron AG; *Int'l*, pg. 7185
STAVROPOLENERGOSBYT OJSC; *Int'l*, pg. 7186
STAVROS CENTER FOR INDEPENDENT LIVING, INC.; *U.S. Private*, pg. 3794
STAX TRADE CENTRES PLC; *Int'l*, pg. 7186
STAY AS—See QuMei Home Furnishings Group Co., Ltd.; *Int'l*, pg. 6166
STAYBRIDGE SUITES - TORRANCE/REDONDO BEACH HOTEL—See InterContinental Hotels Group PLC; *Int'l*, pg. 3738
STAYFRIENDS GMBH—See Stroer SE & Co. KGaA; *Int'l*, pg. 7242
STAY-GREEN, INC.; *U.S. Private*, pg. 3794
STAY-LITE LIGHTING, INC.—See Orion Energy Systems, Inc.; *U.S. Public*, pg. 1618
STAYSAFE RESEARCH SYSTEMS LTD.; *U.S. Private*, pg. 3794
STAYSURE.CO.UK LIMITED; *Int'l*, pg. 7186
STAYTOP SYSTEMS INC—See AION-TECH Solutions Limited; *Int'l*, pg. 234
THE STAYWELL COMPANY, LLC—See KKR & Co. Inc.; *U.S. Public*, pg. 1254
STAYWELL HEALTH CARE, INC.; *U.S. Private*, pg. 3794

ST. CLOUD CAPITAL, LLC

STAYWELL HOLDINGS PTY. LTD.—See Seibu Holdings Inc.; *Int'l*, pg. 6685
STAZIONI MARITIME S.P.A.—See Carnival Corporation; *U.S. Public*, pg. 438
STAZ SINGAPORE PTE. LTD.—See Daehan Steel Co., Ltd.; *Int'l*, pg. 1907
STAZ USA INC.—See Daehan Steel Co., Ltd.; *Int'l*, pg. 1907
STAZ VIETNAM CO. LTD.—See Daehan Steel Co., Ltd.; *Int'l*, pg. 1907
S&T BANCORP, INC.; *U.S. Public*, pg. 1832
S&T BANK—See S&T Bancorp, Inc.; *U.S. Public*, pg. 1832
ST BARBARA LIMITED; *Int'l*, pg. 7157
ST. BARNABAS INC.; *U.S. Private*, pg. 3770
ST. BARTH PROPERTIES, INC.; *U.S. Private*, pg. 3771
ST. BERNARDINE MEDICAL CENTER—See Catholic Health Initiatives; *U.S. Private*, pg. 789
ST. BERNARDS HEALTHCARE, INC.; *U.S. Private*, pg. 3771
S&T BH D.O.O—See Kontron AG; *Int'l*, pg. 4277
S&T BILISIM COZUMLERI ANONIM SIRKETI—See Kontron AG; *Int'l*, pg. 4277
ST BRIDES PARTNERS LTD.—See Fandango Holdings Plc; *Int'l*, pg. 2613
STB SERVICOS TELEMATICOS E BIOMEDICOS UNIPESSOAL LDA—See Permira Advisers LLP; *Int'l*, pg. 5808
STB TEXTILES INDUSTRY CO., LTD.—See Toyota Boshoku Corporation; *Int'l*, pg. 7864
S&T BULGARIA E.O.O.D.—See Kontron AG; *Int'l*, pg. 4277
S.T. BUNN CONSTRUCTION COMPANY; *U.S. Private*, pg. 3519
S.T. BUSINESS SUPPORT CO., LTD.—See S.T. CORPORATION; *Int'l*, pg. 6457
S T B - WOLTJEN GMBH—See Per Aarsleff Holding A/S; *Int'l*, pg. 5796
ST. CAMILLUS CENTER—See Formation Capital, LLC; *U.S. Private*, pg. 1571
STC ASSOCIATES; *U.S. Private*, pg. 3794
THE ST. CATHARINES STANDARD—See Torstar Corporation; *Int'l*, pg. 7831
ST. CATHERINE LABOURE MANOR, INC.—See Ascension Health Alliance; *U.S. Private*, pg. 348
ST. CATHERINE OF SIENA MEDICAL CENTER—See Catholic Health Services of Long Island; *U.S. Private*, pg. 791
ST. CATHERINE OF SIENA NURSING & REHABILITATION CARE CENTER—See Catholic Health Services of Long Island; *U.S. Private*, pg. 791
STC BAHRAIN B.S.C.—See Saudi Telecom Company; *Int'l*, pg. 6595
STC CONCRETE PRODUCT PUBLIC COMPANY LIMITED; *Int'l*, pg. 7186
STC DIP SPIN—See Prab, Inc.; *U.S. Private*, pg. 3241
S&T CEE HOLDING S.R.O.—See Kontron AG; *Int'l*, pg. 4277
STC GROUP INC.; *U.S. Private*, pg. 3794
ST. CHARLES BANK & TRUST COMPANY—See Wintrust Financial Corporation; *U.S. Public*, pg. 2375
ST. CHARLES GLASS & GLAZING, INC.; *U.S. Private*, pg. 3771
ST. CHARLES HOSPITAL—See Catholic Health Services of Long Island; *U.S. Private*, pg. 791
ST. CHARLES TOWNE PLAZA, LLC—See Washington Prime Group Inc.; *U.S. Public*, pg. 4449
ST. CHRISTOPHER'S HOSPITAL FOR CHILDREN, LLC—See Drexel University; *U.S. Private*, pg. 1276
ST. CHRISTOPHER'S HOSPITAL FOR CHILDREN, LLC—See Tower Health; *U.S. Private*, pg. 4193
ST. CHRISTOPHER'S, INC.; *U.S. Private*, pg. 3771
ST. CHRISTOPHER'S Pediatric URGENT CARE CENTER, L.L.C.—See Drexel University; *U.S. Private*, pg. 1276
ST. CHRISTOPHER'S Pediatric URGENT CARE CENTER, L.L.C.—See Tower Health; *U.S. Private*, pg. 4193
ST. CLAIR APPAREL, INC.; *U.S. Private*, pg. 3771
ST. CLAIR DARDEN HEALTH SYSTEM; *U.S. Private*, pg. 3770
ST. CLAIR DIE CASTING, LLC; *U.S. Private*, pg. 3771
ST. CLAIRE GROUP; *U.S. Private*, pg. 3771
ST. CLAIRE PLASTICS CO.; *U.S. Private*, pg. 3771
ST. CLAIR FOODS; *U.S. Private*, pg. 3771
ST. CLAIR SERVICE CO.; *U.S. Private*, pg. 3771
ST. CLAIR SHORES MI OPHTHALMOLOGY ASC, LLC—See KKR & Co. Inc.; *U.S. Public*, pg. 1246
ST. CLAIR SQUARE LIMITED PARTNERSHIP—See CBL & Associates Properties, Inc.; *U.S. Public*, pg. 459
ST. CLEMENT VINEYARDS—See Treasury Wine Estates Limited; *Int'l*, pg. 7909
STCL LIMITED—See State Trading Corporation of India Ltd; *Int'l*, pg. 7184
ST. CLOUD CAPITAL, LLC; *U.S. Private*, pg. 3771
THE ST. CLOUD MN OPHTHALMOLOGY ASC, LLC—See KKR & Co. Inc.; *U.S. Public*, pg. 1248
ST. CLOUD PHYSICIAN MANAGEMENT, LLC—See Community Health Systems, Inc.; *U.S. Public*, pg. 557
ST. CLOUD SURGICAL CENTER, LLC—See UnitedHealth Group Incorporated; *U.S. Public*, pg. 2250

ST. CLOUD CAPITAL, LLC

Company Index

ST. CLOUD TIMES—See Gannett Co., Inc.; *U.S. Public*, pg. 899
ST. CLOUD TOYOTA INC.; *U.S. Private*, pg. 3771
ST. CLOUD TRUCK SALES INC.; *U.S. Private*, pg. 3771
STC NICCA CO., LTD.—See Nicca Chemical Co., Ltd.; *Int'l*, pg. 5264
STC NICCA CO., LTD. - TAIBAN FACTORY—See Nicca Chemical Co., Ltd.; *Int'l*, pg. 5264
ST. CONSTANTINE AND HELENA HOLDING JSC; *Int'l*, pg. 7158
S&T CONSULTING HUNGARY KFT.—See Kontron AG; *Int'l*, pg. 4278
S&T CORPORATION LIMITED; *Int'l*, pg. 6445
S&T CORPORATION—See SNT Holdings Co., Ltd.; *Int'l*, pg. 7029
S.T. CORPORATION; *Int'l*, pg. 6457
ST. COUSAIR CO., LTD.; *Int'l*, pg. 7158
ST. COUSAIR, INC.—See St. Cousair Co., Ltd.; *Int'l*, pg. 7159
STC PRODUCTS SERVICE CENTER CO., LTD.—See Panasonic Holdings Corporation; *Int'l*, pg. 5723
S&T CRNA GORA D.O.O.—See Kontron AG; *Int'l*, pg. 4278
ST. CROIX PRESS, INC.; *U.S. Private*, pg. 3771
ST. CROIX SOLUTIONS, INC.—See Pinnacle Business Systems, Inc.; *U.S. Private*, pg. 3184
ST. CROIX TREE SERVICE, INC.; *U.S. Private*, pg. 3771
STC SWITZERLAND TRAVEL CENTRE AG—See Schweizerische Bundesbahnen SBB AG; *Int'l*, pg. 6646
STC SWITZERLAND TRAVEL CENTRE LTD.—See Schweizerische Bundesbahnen SBB AG; *Int'l*, pg. 6646
STC TRANSPORTATION INC.—See Myers Container, LLC; *U.S. Private*, pg. 2824
STCUBE, INC.; *Int'l*, pg. 7186
STCUBE PHARMACEUTICALS, INC.—See STCube, Inc.; *Int'l*, pg. 7186
S&T CZ S.R.O.—See Kontron AG; *Int'l*, pg. 4278
ST DAVID'S CARDIFF HOTEL OPCO LIMITED—See InterContinental Hotels Group PLC; *Int'l*, pg. 3739
ST. DAVID'S CARDIOLOGY, PLLC—See HCA Healthcare, Inc.; *U.S. Public*, pg. 1010
ST. DAVID'S GEORGETOWN HOSPITAL—See HCA Healthcare, Inc.; *U.S. Public*, pg. 1010
ST. DAVID'S MEDICAL CENTER—See HCA Healthcare, Inc.; *U.S. Public*, pg. 1010
ST. DAVID'S NORTH AUSTIN MEDICAL CENTER—See HCA Healthcare, Inc.; *U.S. Public*, pg. 1010
ST. DAVID'S ROUND ROCK MEDICAL CENTER—See HCA Healthcare, Inc.; *U.S. Public*, pg. 1010
ST. DAVID'S SOUTH AUSTIN MEDICAL CENTER—See HCA Healthcare, Inc.; *U.S. Public*, pg. 1010
ST. DAVID'S SPECIALIZED WOMENS SERVICES, PLLC—See HCA Healthcare, Inc.; *U.S. Public*, pg. 1010
ST. DAVIS'S SOUTH AUSTIN MEDICAL CENTER—See HCA Healthcare, Inc.; *U.S. Public*, pg. 1010
STD PHARMACEUTICAL PRODUCTS LIMITED—See Merit Medical Systems, Inc.; *U.S. Public*, pg. 1425
S.T.DUPONT DEUTSCHLAND GMBH—See ST Dupont S.A.; *Int'l*, pg. 7158
S.T.DUPONT ITALIA S.P.A.—See ST Dupont S.A.; *Int'l*, pg. 7158
S.T.DUPONT LTD.—See ST Dupont S.A.; *Int'l*, pg. 7158
S.T.DUPONT (MALAYSIA) SDN BHD—See ST Dupont S.A.; *Int'l*, pg. 7158
S.T. DUPONT MARKETING LIMITED—See ST Dupont S.A.; *Int'l*, pg. 7158
S.T.DUPONT MARKETING LTD.—See ST Dupont S.A.; *Int'l*, pg. 7158
ST DUPONT S.A.; *Int'l*, pg. 7157
STEADFAST APARTMENT REIT, INC.—See Independence Realty Trust, Inc.; *U.S. Public*, pg. 1116
STEADFAST BRAND, INC.; *U.S. Private*, pg. 3794
STEADFAST CAPITAL MARKETS GROUP, LLC—See Steadfast Companies; *U.S. Private*, pg. 3794
STEADFAST COMPANIES; *U.S. Private*, pg. 3794
STEADFAST DISTRIBUTION SERVICES PTE LTD.—See Steadfast Group Limited; *Int'l*, pg. 7187
STEADFAST GROUP LIMITED; *Int'l*, pg. 7187
STEADFAST INCOME REIT, INC.—See Steadfast Companies; *U.S. Private*, pg. 3794
STEADFAST INSURANCE COMPANY—See Zurich Insurance Group Limited; *Int'l*, pg. 8699
STEADFAST INTERNATIONAL LIMITED—See Content Ventures Limited; *Int'l*, pg. 1779
STEADFAST MARINE TBK; *Int'l*, pg. 7187
STEADFAST NZ LTD.—See Steadfast Group Limited; *Int'l*, pg. 7187
STEADFAST PLACEMENT SOLUTIONS UK LTD.—See Steadfast Group Limited; *Int'l*, pg. 7187
STEADFAST PROPERTIES & DEVELOPMENT, INC.—See Steadfast Companies; *U.S. Private*, pg. 3794
STEADFAST TASWIDE INSURANCE BROKERS PTY LTD—See Steadfast Group Limited; *Int'l*, pg. 7188
STEADFAST TELEVISION LIMITED—See Content Ventures Limited; *Int'l*, pg. 1779
STEADFAST UNDERWRITING AGENCIES HOLDINGS PTY LTD—See Steadfast Group Limited; *Int'l*, pg. 7188

STEADLINK ASSET MANAGEMENT PTE LTD.—See Colour Life Services Group Co., Ltd.; *Int'l*, pg. 1704
STEAD MCALPIN & COMPANY LIMITED—See Sandown & Bourne; *Int'l*, pg. 6526
STEADRIGHT CRITICAL MINERALS INC; *Int'l*, pg. 7188
STEADYMED LTD.—See United Therapeutics Corporation; *U.S. Public*, pg. 2238
STEADYMED THERAPEUTICS, INC.—See United Therapeutics Corporation; *U.S. Public*, pg. 2238
STEADY SAFE TBK; *Int'l*, pg. 7188
STEADY STUDY LTD.—See Sunny Side Up Group Inc.; *Int'l*, pg. 7319
STEAG ELECTRONIC SYSTEMS SPOL S.R.O.—See Singulus Technologies AG; *Int'l*, pg. 6944
STEAG ENERGY SERVICES DO BRASIL LTDA.—See Asterion Industrial Partners SGEIC SA; *Int'l*, pg. 654
STEAG ENERGY SERVICES GMBH—See Asterion Industrial Partners SGEIC SA; *Int'l*, pg. 654
STEAG ENERGY SERVICES (INDIA) PVT. LTD.—See Asterion Industrial Partners SGEIC SA; *Int'l*, pg. 654
STEAG FERNWARME GMBH—See Asterion Industrial Partners SGEIC SA; *Int'l*, pg. 654
STEAG GMBH—See Asterion Industrial Partners SGEIC SA; *Int'l*, pg. 654
STEAG KETEK IT GMBH—See Asterion Industrial Partners SGEIC SA; *Int'l*, pg. 654
STEAG NEW ENERGIES GMBH—See Asterion Industrial Partners SGEIC SA; *Int'l*, pg. 654
STEAG POWER MINERALS GMBH—See Energeticky a Prumyslovy Holding, a.s.; *Int'l*, pg. 2420
STEAG POWER SAAR GMBH—See Asterion Industrial Partners SGEIC SA; *Int'l*, pg. 654
STEAG SCR-TECH, INC.—See Energy Capital Partners Management, LP; *U.S. Private*, pg. 1394
STEAG SOLAR ENERGY SOLUTIONS GMBH—See Asterion Industrial Partners SGEIC SA; *Int'l*, pg. 654
STEAG TECHNISCHER SERVICE GMBH—See Asterion Industrial Partners SGEIC SA; *Int'l*, pg. 654
STEAK GROUP LTD.—See Dentsu Group Inc.; *Int'l*, pg. 2038
STEAK GROUP; *Int'l*, pg. 7188
STEAKHOLDER FOODS LTD.; *Int'l*, pg. 7188
STEAK N SHAKE ALAMO RANCH, LLC—See Biglari Holdings Inc.; *U.S. Public*, pg. 331
STEAK N SHAKE ENTERPRISES, INC.—See Biglari Holdings Inc.; *U.S. Public*, pg. 331
STEAK N SHAKE, LLC—See Biglari Holdings Inc.; *U.S. Public*, pg. 331
STEAK N SHAKE OPERATIONS, INC.—See Biglari Holdings Inc.; *U.S. Public*, pg. 331
STEAK RANCHES INTERNATIONAL BV—See Spur Corporation; *Int'l*, pg. 7146
STEAK—See Steak Group; *Int'l*, pg. 7188
STEAK—See Steak Group; *Int'l*, pg. 7188
STEAL NETWORK, LLC.; *U.S. Private*, pg. 3794
STEALS N DEALS—See Digital Air Strike Inc.; *U.S. Private*, pg. 1230
STEALTH AEROSPACE, INC.—See Audax Group, Limited Partnership; *U.S. Private*, pg. 388
STEALTH BIOTHERAPEUTICS CORP.; *Int'l*, pg. 7188
STEALTHBITS TECHNOLOGIES, INC.—See TA Associates, Inc.; *U.S. Private*, pg. 3916
STEALTHCO, INC.—See Wellness Center USA, Inc.; *U.S. Public*, pg. 2343
STEALTH COMPOSITES, LLC—See Patient Square Capital, L.P.; *U.S. Private*, pg. 3107
STEALTHCOM SOLUTIONS INC.; *U.S. Private*, pg. 3795
STEALTHGAS INC.; *U.S. Public*, pg. 3795
STEALTH GLOBAL HOLDINGS LTD.; *Int'l*, pg. 7188
STEALTH-ISS GROUP INC.; *U.S. Private*, pg. 3795
STEALTH MAYFLOWER INC.—See UniGroup, Inc.; *U.S. Private*, pg. 4283
STEALTH MINERALS LIMITED; *Int'l*, pg. 7188
STEALTH VENTURES INC.; *Int'l*, pg. 7188
STEAMATIC, INC.—See Johns Lyng Group Limited; *Int'l*, pg. 3984
STEAMATIC OF NASHVILLE, LLC—See Johns Lyng Group Limited; *Int'l*, pg. 3984
STEAMBOAT MOTORS, L.L.C.; *U.S. Private*, pg. 3795
STEAMBOAT PILOT & TODAY—See The World Company; *U.S. Private*, pg. 4139
STEAMBOAT SKI & RESORT CORPORATION—See KSL Capital Partners, LLC; *U.S. Private*, pg. 2354
STEAMBOAT VENTURES ASIA, L.P.—See The Walt Disney Company; *U.S. Public*, pg. 2139
STEAM & CONTROL SYSTEMS, INC.; *U.S. Private*, pg. 3795
S-TEAM ELEKTRONIK GMBH—See Koch Industries, Inc.; *U.S. Private*, pg. 2334
STEAM ENGINEERING, INC.—See BHS Specialty Chemicals; *U.S. Private*, pg. 549
STEAM FRANCE SA; *Int'l*, pg. 7188
STEAM PLANT SQUARE, LLC—See Avista Corporation; *U.S. Public*, pg. 249
THE STEAMSHIP AUTHORITY; *U.S. Private*, pg. 4121
STEAMSHIPS TRADING COMPANY LIMITED; *Int'l*, pg. 7188
STE APOSTROPHE; *Int'l*, pg. 7186
STEARMAN RESOURCES INC.; *Int'l*, pg. 7189

CORPORATE AFFILIATIONS

STEARNS BANK HOLDINGFORD N.A.—See Stearns Financial Services, Inc.; *U.S. Private*, pg. 3795
STEARNS BANK N.A.—See Stearns Financial Services, Inc.; *U.S. Private*, pg. 3795
STEARNS BANK UPSALA N.A.—See Stearns Financial Services, Inc.; *U.S. Private*, pg. 3795
STEARNS DIALYSIS, LLC—See DaVita Inc.; *U.S. Public*, pg. 643
STEARNS ELECTRIC ASSOCIATION; *U.S. Private*, pg. 3795
STEARNS FINANCIAL SERVICES, INC.; *U.S. Private*, pg. 3795
STEARNS HOLDINGS, LLC—See Blackstone Inc.; *U.S. Public*, pg. 358
STEARNS LENDING, LLC—See Blackstone Inc.; *U.S. Public*, pg. 358
STEARNS PACKAGING CORPORATION; *U.S. Private*, pg. 3795
STEARNS PLUMBING INC—See Wiseway Supply Inc.; *U.S. Private*, pg. 4550
STEARNS PRODUCTS INC.; *U.S. Private*, pg. 3795
STEAR S.A.—See Industria de Diseno Textil, S.A.; *Int'l*, pg. 3667
STEATITE LIMITED—See Solid State plc; *Int'l*, pg. 7072
STEATITE LTD - EMBEDDED DIVISION—See Solid State plc; *Int'l*, pg. 7072
STEATITE LTD - RUGGED DIVISION—See Solid State plc; *Int'l*, pg. 7072
STEAUA ELECTRICA S.A.; *Int'l*, pg. 7189
STEBA AG—See ThyssenKrupp AG; *Int'l*, pg. 7726
STEBBINS ENGINEERING & MANUFACTURING COMPANY; *U.S. Private*, pg. 3795
STEBBINS ENGINEERING & MANUFACTURING CO. - PORT ALLEN—See Stebbins Engineering & Manufacturing Company; *U.S. Private*, pg. 3795
STEBBINS ENGINEERING & MANUFACTURING CO. - SEATTLE—See Stebbins Engineering & Manufacturing Company; *U.S. Private*, pg. 3795
STEBBINS ENTERPRISES INC.; *U.S. Private*, pg. 3795
STE CANANGA SARL.—See Takasago International Corporation; *Int'l*, pg. 7433
STEC CO., LTD.—See Senshu Electric Co., Ltd.; *Int'l*, pg. 6713
S-TEC CORPORATION—See Advent International Corporation; *U.S. Private*, pg. 100
STECE FJADRAR AB—See Beijer Alma AB; *Int'l*, pg. 943
S-TECH JAPAN CO., LTD.—See Tera Science Co., Ltd.; *Int'l*, pg. 7563
S-TECH RESOURCE CO., LTD.—See Starts Corporation, Inc.; *Int'l*, pg. 7180
S&TECHS (HONG KONG) LIMITED—See STO Building Group Inc.; *U.S. Private*, pg. 3814
S&TECHS (JAPAN) LIMITED—See STO Building Group Inc.; *U.S. Private*, pg. 3814
S&TECHS (TAIWAN) LIMITED—See STO Building Group Inc.; *U.S. Private*, pg. 3814
STECK ELECTRIC SA—See Schneider Electric SE; *Int'l*, pg. 6635
STECK WHOLESALE FOODS, INC.—See Tennessee Bun Company, LLC; *U.S. Private*, pg. 3967
STECO, LLC—See KNL Holdings, LLC; *U.S. Private*, pg. 2322
STE COOP AGRIC PERIGORD TABAC; *Int'l*, pg. 7186
STEC SHANGHAI CITY BUILDING MATERIAL CO., LTD.—See Shanghai Tunnel Engineering Co., Ltd.; *Int'l*, pg. 6780
STEC SHANGHAI CONSTRUCTION PROPERTY DEVELOPMENT CO., LTD.—See Shanghai Tunnel Engineering Co., Ltd.; *Int'l*, pg. 6780
STEC SHANGHAI GAS ENGINEERING DESIGN & RESEARCH CO., LTD.—See Shanghai Tunnel Engineering Co., Ltd.; *Int'l*, pg. 6780
STEC SHANGHAI INFRASTRUCTURE CONSTRUCTION & DEVELOPMENT CO., LTD.—See Shanghai Tunnel Engineering Co., Ltd.; *Int'l*, pg. 6780
STEC SHANGHAI MUNICIPAL ENGINEERING MATERIAL COMPANY—See Shanghai Tunnel Engineering Co., Ltd.; *Int'l*, pg. 6780
STEC SHANGHAI MUNICIPAL MAINTENANCE & MANAGEMENT CO., LTD.—See Shanghai Tunnel Engineering Co., Ltd.; *Int'l*, pg. 6780
STEC SHANGHAI NO. 1 GAS PIPELINE ENGINEERING CO., LTD.—See Shanghai Tunnel Engineering Co., Ltd.; *Int'l*, pg. 6780
STEC SHANGHAI NO. 2 GAS PIPELINE ENGINEERING CO., LTD.—See Shanghai Tunnel Engineering Co., Ltd.; *Int'l*, pg. 6780
STEC SHANGHAI PUDONG WATER SUPPLY & DRAINAGE CONSTRUCTION CO., LTD.—See Shanghai Tunnel Engineering Co., Ltd.; *Int'l*, pg. 6780
STEC SHANGHAI ROAD & BRIDGE (GROUP) CO., LTD.—See Shanghai Tunnel Engineering Co., Ltd.; *Int'l*, pg. 6780
STEC SHANGHAI TAP WATER PIPELINE ENGINEERING CO., LTD.—See Shanghai Tunnel Engineering Co., Ltd.; *Int'l*, pg. 6780
STEC SHANGHAI UNDERGROUND SPACE DEVELOPMENT COMPANY—See Shanghai Tunnel Engineering Co., Ltd.; *Int'l*, pg. 6780

COMPANY NAME INDEX

STEC SHANGHAI URBAN CONSTRUCTION INVESTMENT & DEVELOPMENT CO., LTD.—See Shanghai Tunnel Engineering Co., Ltd.; *Int'l*, pg. 6780
STEC SHANGHAI URBAN CONSTRUCTION MUNICIPAL ENGINEERING (GROUP) CO., LTD.—See Shanghai Tunnel Engineering Co., Ltd.; *Int'l*, pg. 6780
STEC SHANGHAI WATER CONSTRUCTION & ENGINEERING CO., LTD.—See Shanghai Tunnel Engineering Co., Ltd.; *Int'l*, pg. 6780
STEC SUCG INTERNATIONAL ENGINEERING CO., LTD.—See Shanghai Tunnel Engineering Co., Ltd.; *Int'l*, pg. 6780
STEC THE OPERATION MANAGEMENT CO., LTD.—See Shanghai Tunnel Engineering Co., Ltd.; *Int'l*, pg. 6780
STEDDI PAYMENTS AS—See Elmera Group ASA; *Int'l*, pg. 2367
STE DE DISTRIBUTION DU DON; *Int'l*, pg. 7186
STE DES PETROLES SHELL SAS—See Shell plc; *Int'l*, pg. 6799
STE: DES TRANSPORTS RAPIDES BRETONS—See SNCF; *Int'l*, pg. 7025
STE DE TRANSPORT NEGOCE AUTOMOBILE; *Int'l*, pg. 7186
STE D'INDUSTRIEE PHARMACEUTIQUE IBN AL BAYTAR—See Hikma Pharmaceuticals PLC; *Int'l*, pg. 3390
STEDMAN MACHINE COMPANY; *U.S. Private*, pg. 3795
ST EDOUARD S.A.R.L—See Heidelberg Materials AG; *Int'l*, pg. 3319
STE DU GRAND GARAGE DES CHANTIERS; *Int'l*, pg. 7186
STE DU PIPELINE SUD-EUROPEEN; *Int'l*, pg. 7186
ST. EDWARD HOME; *U.S. Private*, pg. 3771
STEEB ANWENDUNGSSYSTEME GMBH—See Unternehmens Invest AG; *Int'l*, pg. 8085
STE ECONOMIE MIXTE LOGEMENT DE EURE; *Int'l*, pg. 7186
STEED CONSTRUCTION, INC.; *U.S. Private*, pg. 3795
STE EDIT ARTISTES PEIGNANT BOUCHE PIED; *Int'l*, pg. 7186
STEED ORIENTAL (HOLDINGS) COMPANY LIMITED; *Int'l*, pg. 7189
STEED TIMBER CO. INC.; *U.S. Private*, pg. 3795
STEEGER USA, LLC—See Forsyth Capital Investors LLC; *U.S. Private*, pg. 1574
STEEL ALLIANCE SERVICE CENTER CO., LTD.—See JFE Holdings, Inc.; *Int'l*, pg. 3937
STEEL & ALLOY UTILITY PRODUCTS, INC.; *U.S. Private*, pg. 3795
STEEL AND SOLAR ROOF COMPANY LIMITED—See SPCG Public Company Limited; *Int'l*, pg. 7128
STEELARIS PTE. LTD.—See AYS Ventures Berhad; *Int'l*, pg. 776
STEELASIA MANUFACTURING CORPORATION; *Int'l*, pg. 7190
STEELASTIC COMPANY, LLC—See The Heico Companies, L.L.C.; *U.S. Private*, pg. 4051
STEEL AUTHORITY OF INDIA LIMITED - IISCO STEEL PLANT—See Steel Authority of India Limited; *Int'l*, pg. 7189
STEEL AUTHORITY OF INDIA LIMITED - SAIL REFRACTORY UNIT—See Steel Authority of India Limited; *Int'l*, pg. 7189
STEEL AUTHORITY OF INDIA LIMITED; *Int'l*, pg. 7189
STEEL AUTHORITY OF INDIA LIMITED - VISVESVARAYA IRON AND STEEL PLANT—See Steel Authority of India Limited; *Int'l*, pg. 7189
STEEL BAR—See Reliance Steel & Aluminum Co.; *U.S. Public*, pg. 1781
STEELBLAST COATINGS AND PAINTING INC.—See HTC Purenergy Inc.; *Int'l*, pg. 3508
STEEL BRANDING; *U.S. Private*, pg. 3795
STEELBRO INTERNATIONAL CO. INC.; *U.S. Private*, pg. 3796
STEELBUILDING.COM, INC.—See Clayton, Dubilier & Rice, LLC; *U.S. Private*, pg. 921
STEELBUY LIMITED—See ThyssenKrupp AG; *Int'l*, pg. 7726
STEEL CANADA LTD.; *Int'l*, pg. 7189
STEELCASE AG—See Steelcase Inc.; *U.S. Public*, pg. 1944
STEELCASE AUSTRALIA PTY. LTD.—See Steelcase Inc.; *U.S. Public*, pg. 1944
STEELCASE CANADA LIMITED—See Steelcase Inc.; *U.S. Public*, pg. 1944
STEELCASE CZECH REPUBLIC S.R.O.—See Steelcase Inc.; *U.S. Public*, pg. 1944
STEELCASE DE MEXICO, S. DE R.L. DE C.V.,—See Steelcase Inc.; *U.S. Public*, pg. 1944
STEELCASE FINANCIAL SERVICES, INC.—See Steelcase Inc.; *U.S. Public*, pg. 1944
STEELCASE FURNITURE (DONGGUAN) COMPANY LIMITED—See Steelcase Inc.; *U.S. Public*, pg. 1944
STEELCASE HEALTH—See Steelcase Inc.; *U.S. Public*, pg. 1944
STEELCASE HONG KONG LTD.—See Steelcase Inc.; *U.S. Public*, pg. 1944
STEELCASE INC.; *U.S. Public*, pg. 1943

STEELCASE INC.—See Steelcase Inc.; *U.S. Public*, pg. 1944
STEELCASE JAPAN, K.K.—See Steelcase Inc.; *U.S. Public*, pg. 1944
STEELCASE JERAISY LTD.—See Jeraisy Group; *Int'l*, pg. 3931
STEELCASE PLC—See Steelcase Inc.; *U.S. Public*, pg. 1944
STEELCASE S.A.—See Steelcase Inc.; *U.S. Public*, pg. 1944
STEELCASE SAS—See Steelcase Inc.; *U.S. Public*, pg. 1944
STEELCASE WERNDL AG—See Steelcase Inc.; *U.S. Public*, pg. 1944
STEELCAST LTD - MANUFACTURING PLANT—See Steelcast Ltd; *Int'l*, pg. 7190
STEELCAST LTD; *Int'l*, pg. 7190
STEELCELL OF NORTH AMERICA, INC.; *U.S. Private*, pg. 3796
STEEL CENTER EUROPE, S.R.O.—See Sumitomo Corporation; *Int'l*, pg. 7271
STEEL CENTRE MALAYSIA SDN. BHD.—See Sumitomo Corporation; *Int'l*, pg. 7271
STEEL CITY CORPORATION; *U.S. Private*, pg. 3795
STEEL CITY PRODUCTS, INC.—See Sterling Infrastructure, Inc.; *U.S. Public*, pg. 1947
STEEL CITY SECURITIES LIMITED; *Int'l*, pg. 7189
STEELCLOUD LLC; *U.S. Private*, pg. 3796
STEELCO GUJARAT LTD.; *Int'l*, pg. 7190
STEELCOM FITTINGS S.R.L.—See Acciaierie Valbruna S.p.A.; *Int'l*, pg. 89
STEEL CONNECT, INC.; *U.S. Public*, pg. 1941
STEEL CONSTRUCTION SYSTEMS—See CEMEX, S.A.B. de C.V.; *Int'l*, pg. 1399
STEELCO S.P.A.—See Miele & Cie KG; *Int'l*, pg. 4889
STEEL CRAFT CORP—See MiddleGround Management, LP; *U.S. Private*, pg. 2712
STEEL CRAFT DOOR PRODUCTS LTD.; *Int'l*, pg. 7189
STEELCRAFT ERECTION SERVICES LIMITED—See Severfield Plc; *Int'l*, pg. 6735
STEELCRAFT MANUFACTURING COMPANY—See Ingersoll Rand Inc.; *U.S. Public*, pg. 1122
STEEL CRAFTS EUROPA S.R.L.—See Ni Hsin Group Berhad; *Int'l*, pg. 5259
STEEL OUNTAIN INDUSTRIES, LLC; *U.S. Private*, pg. 3796
STEEL DYNAMICS COLUMBUS, LLC—See Steel Dynamics, Inc.; *U.S. Public*, pg. 1942
STEEL DYNAMICS HEARTLAND, LLC—See Steel Dynamics, Inc.; *U.S. Public*, pg. 1942
STEEL DYNAMICS, INC.; *U.S. Public*, pg. 1942
STEEL DYNAMICS ROANOKE BAR DIVISION—See Steel Dynamics, Inc.; *U.S. Public*, pg. 1942
STEELE CREEK CAPITAL CORPORATION; *U.S. Private*, pg. 3796
STE ELECTRIQUE DE L'OUR SA; *Int'l*, pg. 7186
STEELE FORD LINCOLN; *Int'l*, pg. 7190
STEELE HOLDINGS, INC.; *U.S. Private*, pg. 3796
STEEL ENCOUNTERS INC.; *U.S. Private*, pg. 3796
STEELE OCEANIC CORP; *U.S. Public*, pg. 1944
STEELER INC.; *U.S. Private*, pg. 3796
STEELE SOLUTIONS, INC.—See Wellspring Capital Management LLC; *U.S. Private*, pg. 4477
STEELE+; *U.S. Private*, pg. 3796
STEEL ETC., LLP; *U.S. Private*, pg. 3796
STEELE VOLKSWAGEN LIMITED; *Int'l*, pg. 7190
STEELE WINES, INC.—See Shannon Ridge, Inc.; *U.S. Private*, pg. 3625
STEEL EXCEL INC.—See Steel Partners Holdings L.P.; *U.S. Public*, pg. 1943
STEEL EXCHANGE INDIA LTD.; *Int'l*, pg. 7189
STEELFAB INC. OF ALABAMA—See Steelfab Inc.; *U.S. Private*, pg. 3797
STEELFAB INC. OF SOUTH CAROLINA—See Steelfab Inc.; *U.S. Private*, pg. 3797
STEELFAB INC. OF VIRGINIA—See Steelfab Inc.; *U.S. Private*, pg. 3797
STEEL FAB., INC.—See Samuel, Son & Co., Limited; *Int'l*, pg. 6516
STEELFAB INC.; *U.S. Private*, pg. 3796
STEEL FABRICATION DIVISION—See NOV, Inc.; *U.S. Public*, pg. 1544
STEELFAB TEXAS, INC.; *U.S. Private*, pg. 3797
STEEL FLOWER CO., LTD. - JINYOUNG PLANT—See Steel Flower Co., Ltd.; *Int'l*, pg. 7190
STEEL FLOWER CO., LTD. - POHANG PLANT—See Steel Flower Co., Ltd.; *Int'l*, pg. 7190
STEEL FLOWER CO., LTD.; *Int'l*, pg. 7190
STEELFORM AB—See Ratos AB; *Int'l*, pg. 6220
STEELHEAD FINANCE, LLC—See Peoples Bank of Commerce; *U.S. Private*, pg. 3141
STEELHEAD PETROLEUM LTD.; *Int'l*, pg. 7190
THE STEEL INDEX LIMITED—See S&P Global Inc.; *U.S. Public*, pg. 1832
STEEL INDUSTRIES INC.—See Arlington Capital Partners LLC; *U.S. Private*, pg. 327
STEEL INGENIERIA, S.A.—See Ferrovial S.A.; *Int'l*, pg. 2645
STEEL KING INDUSTRIES INC.; *U.S. Private*, pg. 3796

STEEL-LINE GARAGE DOORS—See Crescent Capital Partners Ltd.; *Int'l*, pg. 1839
STEEL, LLC; *U.S. Private*, pg. 3796
STEEL & MACHINERY TRANSPORTATION; *U.S. Private*, pg. 3795
STEELMAG INTERNATIONAL S.A.S.—See Lingyi iTech (Guangdong) Company; *Int'l*, pg. 4512
STEELMAN-DUFF INC.; *U.S. Private*, pg. 3797
STEELMAN TELECOM PRIVATE LIMITED; *Int'l*, pg. 7190
STEELMAN TRANSPORTATION, INC.—See Daseke, Inc.; *U.S. Private*, pg. 1162
STEELMART, INC.; *U.S. Private*, pg. 3797
STEELMASTER BUILDINGS, INC.; *U.S. Private*, pg. 3797
STEELMATIC WIRE INC.—See Martinrea International, Inc.; *Int'l*, pg. 4704
STEELMATIC WIRE USA, INC.—See Martinrea International, Inc.; *Int'l*, pg. 4704
STEEL MEDIA INC.—See SRAX, Inc.; *U.S. Public*, pg. 1922
STEELMET ROMANIA S.A—See Viohalco SA/NV; *Int'l*, pg. 8244
STEELMET S.A—See Viohalco SA/NV; *Int'l*, pg. 8244
STEELO AB—See Lagercrantz Group AB; *Int'l*, pg. 4395
STEEL & O'BRIEN MANUFACTURING, INC.—See Edgewater Services, LLC; *U.S. Private*, pg. 1335
STEEL OF WEST VIRGINIA, INC.—See Steel Dynamics, Inc.; *U.S. Public*, pg. 1942
STEEL PARK INTERNATIONAL PTE. LTD.—See BRC Asia Limited; *Int'l*, pg. 1143
STEEL PARK RESOURCES PTE. LTD.—See BRC Asia Limited; *Int'l*, pg. 1143
STEEL PARTNERS HOLDINGS GP INC.—See Steel Partners Holdings L.P.; *U.S. Public*, pg. 1943
STEEL PARTNERS HOLDINGS L.P.; *U.S. Public*, pg. 1942
STEEL PARTNERS LLC—See Steel Partners Holdings L.P.; *U.S. Public*, pg. 1943
STEEL PARTS MANUFACTURING, INC.—See Monomoy Capital Partners LLC; *U.S. Private*, pg. 2772
STEEL PIER CAPITAL ADVISORS LLC; *U.S. Private*, pg. 3796
STEEL & PIPES INC.; *U.S. Private*, pg. 3795
STEEL & PIPE SUPPLY COMPANY INC.; *U.S. Private*, pg. 3795
STEEL PLATE & SECTIONS LTD—See Stemcor Holdings Limited; *Int'l*, pg. 7206
STEEL PLUS LIMITED—See AIP, LLC; *U.S. Private*, pg. 134
STEEL PLUS LIMITED—See Placements CMI Inc.; *Int'l*, pg. 5887
STEELPOINT CAPITAL PARTNERS, LP; *U.S. Private*, pg. 3797
THE STEEL PUBLIC COMPANY LIMITED; *Int'l*, pg. 7688
STEELRIVER INFRASTRUCTURE PARTNERS LP; *U.S. Private*, pg. 3797
STEEL ROLLING EQUIPMENT SUB-CO.—See Taiyuan Heavy Industry Co., Ltd.; *Int'l*, pg. 7427
STEEL ROLLING MILLS LTD.—See Alam Group of Companies; *Int'l*, pg. 289
STEEL ROOF COMPANY LIMITED—See SPCG Public Company Limited; *Int'l*, pg. 7128
STEELSCAPE INC.—See BlueScope Steel Limited; *Int'l*, pg. 1073
STEELSERIES APS; *Int'l*, pg. 7190
STEEL SERVICE CORPORATION; *U.S. Private*, pg. 3796
STEEL SERVICE OILFIELD TUBULAR, INC.—See Kanematsu Corporation; *Int'l*, pg. 4069
STEEL SERVICES INCORPORATED; *U.S. Private*, pg. 3796
STEEL SPORTS INC.—See Steel Partners Holdings L.P.; *U.S. Public*, pg. 1943
STEEL STORAGE SYSTEMS, INC.; *U.S. Private*, pg. 3796
STEEL STRIPS & TUBES LTD.—See Steel Strips Wheels Ltd.; *Int'l*, pg. 7190
STEEL STRIPS WHEELS LTD.; *Int'l*, pg. 7190
STEEL STRUCTURE MANUFACTURE JOINT STOCK COMPANY; *Int'l*, pg. 7190
STEELSUMMIT HOLDINGS, INC.—See Sumitomo Corporation; *Int'l*, pg. 7273
STEEL SUMMIT INTERNATIONAL, INC.—See Sumitomo Corporation; *Int'l*, pg. 7273
STEEL SUMMIT OHIO; *U.S. Private*, pg. 3796
STEEL SYSTEMS INC.—See Clayton, Dubilier & Rice, LLC; *U.S. Private*, pg. 921
STEEL TANK & FABRICATING CORPORATION—See Kennedy Tank & Manufacturing Company, Inc.; *U.S. Private*, pg. 2285
STEELTEC AG—See Swiss Steel Holding AG; *Int'l*, pg. 7373
STEELTECH INDUSTRIAL FABRICATING CORPORATION—See J Fitzgibbons LLC; *U.S. Private*, pg. 2153
STEELTECH INDUSTRIES PTE. LTD.—See Tiong Seng Holdings Limited; *Int'l*, pg. 7755
STEEL TECHNOLOGIES DE MEXICO, S.A. DE C.V.—See Mitsui & Co., Ltd.; *Int'l*, pg. 4975
STEEL TECHNOLOGIES INC.—See Mitsui & Co., Ltd.; *Int'l*, pg. 4975

STEEL SUMMIT OHIO

STEEL TECHNOLOGIES INC.—See Mitsui & Co., Ltd.; *Int'l*, pg. 4975
STEEL TECHNOLOGIES INC.—See Mitsui & Co., Ltd.; *Int'l*, pg. 4975
STEEL TECHNOLOGIES LLC—See Mitsui & Co., Ltd.; *Int'l*, pg. 4975
STEEL TECHNOLOGIES, LLC—See Helen of Troy Limited; *Int'l*, pg. 3329
STEEL TECHNOLOGY, LLC—See Helen of Troy Limited; *Int'l*, pg. 3329
STEEL TESTING LABORATORY; *U.S. Private*, pg. 3796
STEEL TEST (PROPRIETARY) LTD.—See I Squared Capital Advisors (US) LLC; *U.S. Private*, pg. 2023
STEEL TEST (PROPRIETARY) LTD.—See TDR Capital LLP; *Int'l*, pg. 7493
STEELTOWN FORD SALES; *Int'l*, pg. 7190
STEEL & TUBE HOLDINGS LIMITED; *Int'l*, pg. 7189
STEEL WAREHOUSE OF WISCONSIN, INC.; *U.S. Private*, pg. 3796
STEELWELD—See VDL Groep B.V.; *Int'l*, pg. 8141
STEELWIND NORDENHAM GMBH—See AG der Dillinger Huttenwerke; *Int'l*, pg. 197
THE STEELWORKS CORPORATION—See Acme Manufacturing Company Inc.; *U.S. Private*, pg. 61
STEENKIST RECA NEDERLAND B.V.—See Wurth Verwaltungsgesellschaft mbH; *Int'l*, pg. 8508
STEEN MACEK PAPER CO. INC.; *U.S. Private*, pg. 3797
STEEN RIVER OIL & GAS LTD.; *Int'l*, pg. 7190
STEENSMA B.V.—See Alberco Holding B.V.; *Int'l*, pg. 294
STEEN & STROM AS—See Klepierre SA; *Int'l*, pg. 4200
STEEN & STROM DANEMARK A/S—See Klepierre SA; *Int'l*, pg. 4200
STEEN & STROM HOLDING AB—See BNP Paribas SA; *Int'l*, pg. 1092
STEEP & BREW, INC.—See Coffee Holding Company, Inc.; *U.S. Public*, pg. 522
STEEP GMBH; *Int'l*, pg. 7190
STEEP HILL INC.; *Int'l*, pg. 7190
STEEPLETON TIRE CO.; *U.S. Private*, pg. 3797
STE EQUIPEMENT DU DEPART MAINE ET LOIRE; *Int'l*, pg. 7186
STEER DAVIES & GLEAVE LIMITED; *Int'l*, pg. 7190
STEERE HOUSE; *U.S. Private*, pg. 3797
STEERING HOLDINGS LTD.; *Int'l*, pg. 7190
STEERS (PROPRIETARY) LIMITED—See Famous Brands Limited; *Int'l*, pg. 2612
STE ESSARTAISE DE DISTRIBUTION; *Int'l*, pg. 7186
STEET-PONTE FORD; *U.S. Private*, pg. 3797
STE EUROPEENNE LOGISTIQUE INTERNATIONALE; *Int'l*, pg. 7186
STE EXPLOITATION MATERIELS MARTIN BAKER; *Int'l*, pg. 7186
STEFANEL POLONIA SP. Z O.O.—See Stefanel S.p.A.; *Int'l*, pg. 7192
STEFANEL ROMANIA S.R.L.—See Stefanel S.p.A.; *Int'l*, pg. 7192
STEFANEL S.P.A.; *Int'l*, pg. 7192
STEFANINI CONSULTORIA E ASSESSORIA EM INFORMATICA, LTDA.; *Int'l*, pg. 7192
STEFANINI INTERNATIONAL CORP.—See Stefanini Consultoria E Assessoria Em Informatica, Ltda.; *Int'l*, pg. 7192
STEFANINI TECHTEAM AKELA SRL—See Stefanini Consultoria E Assessoria Em Informatica, Ltda.; *Int'l*, pg. 7192
STEFANINI TECHTEAM GLOBAL GMBH—See Stefanini Consultoria E Assessoria Em Informatica, Ltda.; *Int'l*, pg. 7192
STEFANINI TECHTEAM GLOBAL LTD.—See Stefanini Consultoria E Assessoria Em Informatica, Ltda.; *Int'l*, pg. 7192
STEFANINI TECHTEAM GLOBAL NV/SA—See Stefanini Consultoria E Assessoria Em Informatica, Ltda.; *Int'l*, pg. 7192
STEFANINI TECHTEAM GLOBAL SRL—See Stefanini Consultoria E Assessoria Em Informatica, Ltda.; *Int'l*, pg. 7192
STEFANOBI S.R.L.—See LVMH Moet Hennessy Louis Vuitton SE; *Int'l*, pg. 4603
STEFANO FOODS, INC.—See WH Group Limited; *Int'l*, pg. 8395
STEFANO'S PRINTING, INC.—See Ford Business Machines, Inc.; *U.S. Private*, pg. 1564
STEFANO'S PRINTING, INC.—See Unity Printing Co., Inc.; *U.S. Private*, pg. 4303
STEFANO TOSELLI SAS—See What's Cooking Group NV; *Int'l*, pg. 8396
STEFAN SYDOR OPTICS, INC.; *U.S. Private*, pg. 3797
STEFAN TAGESSON—See Bischof + Klein GmbH & Co. KG; *Int'l*, pg. 1049
STEFANUTTI STOCKS BOTSWANA (PTY) LIMITED—See Stefanutti Stocks Holdings Limited; *Int'l*, pg. 7192
STEFANUTTI STOCKS BUILDING BOTSWANA (PTY) LTD—See Stefanutti Stocks Holdings Limited; *Int'l*, pg. 7192
STEFANUTTI STOCKS BUILDING BUSINESS UNIT - STEFANUTTI STOCKS BUILDING MAJOR PROJECTS DIVISION—See Stefanutti Stocks Holdings Limited; *Int'l*, pg. 7193

STEFANUTTI STOCKS BUILDING GAUTENG (PTY) LIMITED—See Stefanutti Stocks Holdings Limited; *Int'l*, pg. 7192
STEFANUTTI STOCKS BUILDING KZN (PTY) LTD—See Stefanutti Stocks Holdings Limited; *Int'l*, pg. 7192
STEFANUTTI STOCKS BUILDING (PTY) LTD—See Stefanutti Stocks Holdings Limited; *Int'l*, pg. 7192
STEFANUTTI STOCKS BUILDING W CAPE (PTY) LIMITED—See Stefanutti Stocks Holdings Limited; *Int'l*, pg. 7192
STEFANUTTI STOCKS CIVILS GAUTENG (PTY) LIMITED—See Stefanutti Stocks Holdings Limited; *Int'l*, pg. 7192
STEFANUTTI STOCKS CIVILS KZN (PTY) LIMITED—See Stefanutti Stocks Holdings Limited; *Int'l*, pg. 7192
STEFANUTTI STOCKS CIVILS (PTY) LTD—See Stefanutti Stocks Holdings Limited; *Int'l*, pg. 7192
STEFANUTTI STOCKS CONSTRUCOES (MOCAMBIQUE) LDA—See Stefanutti Stocks Holdings Limited; *Int'l*, pg. 7192
STEFANUTTI STOCKS EARTHWORKS (PTY) LTD—See Stefanutti Stocks Holdings Limited; *Int'l*, pg. 7192
STEFANUTTI STOCKS GEOTECHNICAL (PTY) LIMITED—See Stefanutti Stocks Holdings Limited; *Int'l*, pg. 7192
STEFANUTTI STOCKS GULF FZE—See Stefanutti Stocks Holdings Limited; *Int'l*, pg. 7192
STEFANUTTI STOCKS HOLDINGS LIMITED; *Int'l*, pg. 7192
STEFANUTTI STOCKS HOLDINGS LIMITED - STEFANUTTI STOCKS BUILDING BUSINESS UNIT—See Stefanutti Stocks Holdings Limited; *Int'l*, pg. 7193
STEFANUTTI STOCKS HOLDINGS LIMITED - STEFANUTTI STOCKS BUILDING WESTERN CAPE DIVISION—See Stefanutti Stocks Holdings Limited; *Int'l*, pg. 7193
STEFANUTTI STOCKS HOLDINGS LIMITED - STEFANUTTI STOCKS ELECTRICAL & INSTRUMENTATION DIVISION—See Stefanutti Stocks Holdings Limited; *Int'l*, pg. 7193
STEFANUTTI STOCKS HOLDINGS LIMITED - STEFANUTTI STOCKS HOUSING DIVISION—See Stefanutti Stocks Holdings Limited; *Int'l*, pg. 7193
STEFANUTTI STOCKS HOLDINGS LIMITED - STEFANUTTI STOCKS MECHANICAL DIVISION—See Stefanutti Stocks Holdings Limited; *Int'l*, pg. 7193
STEFANUTTI STOCKS HOLDINGS LIMITED - STEFANUTTI STOCKS NORTH WEST DIVISION—See Stefanutti Stocks Holdings Limited; *Int'l*, pg. 7193
STEFANUTTI STOCKS HOLDINGS LIMITED - STEFANUTTI STOCKS POWER DIVISION—See Stefanutti Stocks Holdings Limited; *Int'l*, pg. 7193
STEFANUTTI STOCKS HOLDINGS LIMITED - STEFANUTTI STOCKS ROADS & EARTHWORKS UNIT—See Stefanutti Stocks Holdings Limited; *Int'l*, pg. 7193
STEFANUTTI STOCKS HOUSING (PTY) LIMITED—See Stefanutti Stocks Holdings Limited; *Int'l*, pg. 7192
STEFANUTTI STOCKS INTERNATIONAL HOLDINGS (PTY) LIMITED—See Stefanutti Stocks Holdings Limited; *Int'l*, pg. 7193
STEFANUTTI STOCKS MATERIAL HANDLING (PTY) LIMITED—See Stefanutti Stocks Holdings Limited; *Int'l*, pg. 7193
STEFANUTTI STOCKS MECHANICAL & ELECTRICAL—See Stefanutti Stocks Holdings Limited; *Int'l*, pg. 7193
STEFANUTTI STOCKS MIDDLE EAST FZE—See Stefanutti Stocks Holdings Limited; *Int'l*, pg. 7193
STEFANUTTI STOCKS PROPERTY & CONCESSIONS (PTY) LTD—See Stefanutti Stocks Holdings Limited; *Int'l*, pg. 7193
STEFANUTTI STOCKS—See Stefanutti Stocks Holdings Limited; *Int'l*, pg. 7193
STEFANUTTI STOCKS SWAZILAND (PTY) LIMITED—See Stefanutti Stocks Holdings Limited; *Int'l*, pg. 7192
STEFANUTTI STOCKS WORKSHOPS (PTY) LIMITED—See Stefanutti Stocks Holdings Limited; *Int'l*, pg. 7193
STEF BODEGRAVEN BV—See STEF SA; *Int'l*, pg. 7190
STEF EUROFRISCHFRACHT SASU—See STEF SA; *Int'l*, pg. 7191
STEFFEN, INC.—See Americold Realty Trust, Inc.; *U.S. Public*, pg. 113
STEFFEN MIDWEST INC.—See Americold Realty Trust, Inc.; *U.S. Public*, pg. 113
STEFFES CORPORATION; *U.S. Private*, pg. 3797
STEFFNER COMMERCIAL REAL ESTATE, LLC—See BGC Group, Inc.; *U.S. Public*, pg. 330
STEF LOGISTICS COURCELLES SA—See STEF SA; *Int'l*, pg. 7191
STEF LOGISTICS SAINTES SA—See STEF SA; *Int'l*, pg. 7191
STEF LOGISTIQUE AULNAY-SOUS-BOIS SA—See STEF SA; *Int'l*, pg. 7191
STEF LOGISTIQUE AURICE SAS—See STEF SA; *Int'l*, pg. 7191
STEF LOGISTIQUE DARVAULT SAS—See STEF SA; *Int'l*, pg. 7191

CORPORATE AFFILIATIONS

STEF LOGISTIQUE FUVEAU SA—See STEF SA; *Int'l*, pg. 7191
STEF LOGISTIQUE GIVORS SA—See STEF SA; *Int'l*, pg. 7191
STEF LOGISTIQUE LE PLESSIS BELLEVILLE SAS—See STEF SA; *Int'l*, pg. 7191
STEF LOGISTIQUE LE PLESSIS-PATE SA—See STEF SA; *Int'l*, pg. 7191
STEF LOGISTIQUE LESQUIN SA—See STEF SA; *Int'l*, pg. 7191
STEF LOGISTIQUE MIONS SAS—See STEF SA; *Int'l*, pg. 7191
STEF LOGISTIQUE MOULINS LES METZ SA—See STEF SA; *Int'l*, pg. 7191
STEF LOGISTIQUE NEMOURS SA—See STEF SA; *Int'l*, pg. 7191
STEF LOGISTIQUE NIORT SAS—See STEF SA; *Int'l*, pg. 7191
STEF LOGISTIQUE PESSAC SA—See STEF SA; *Int'l*, pg. 7191
STEF LOGISTIQUE PLOUENAN EFL—See STEF SA; *Int'l*, pg. 7191
STEF LOGISTIQUE ST PIERRE DES CORPS SA—See STEF SA; *Int'l*, pg. 7191
STEF LOGISTIQUE TIGERY SAS—See STEF SA; *Int'l*, pg. 7191
STEF LOGISTIQUE TOUSSIEU SASU—See STEF SA; *Int'l*, pg. 7191
STEF LOGISTIQUE VENISSIEUX SA—See STEF SA; *Int'l*, pg. 7191
STEFRRAHA S.R.O.—See Stefanel S.p.A.; *Int'l*, pg. 7192
STEF SA; *Int'l*, pg. 7190
STEF TRANSPORT ANGERS SASU—See STEF SA; *Int'l*, pg. 7191
STEF TRANSPORT AVIGNON SAS—See STEF SA; *Int'l*, pg. 7191
STEF TRANSPORT BORDEAUX BEGLES SAS—See STEF SA; *Int'l*, pg. 7191
STEF TRANSPORT BOULOGNE SAS—See STEF SA; *Int'l*, pg. 7191
STEF TRANSPORT CHAULNES SAS—See STEF SA; *Int'l*, pg. 7191
STEF TRANSPORT CLERMONT-FERRAND SA—See STEF SA; *Int'l*, pg. 7191
STEF TRANSPORT DIJON SA—See STEF SA; *Int'l*, pg. 7191
STEF TRANSPORT LANDIVISIAU SAS—See STEF SA; *Int'l*, pg. 7191
STEF TRANSPORT LANGRES SA—See STEF SA; *Int'l*, pg. 7191
STEF TRANSPORT LAVAL SA—See STEF SA; *Int'l*, pg. 7191
STEF TRANSPORT LE MANS SAS—See STEF SA; *Int'l*, pg. 7191
STEF TRANSPORT LESQUIN SAS—See STEF SA; *Int'l*, pg. 7191
STEF TRANSPORT LIMOGES SASU—See STEF SA; *Int'l*, pg. 7191
STEF TRANSPORT MACON SA—See STEF SA; *Int'l*, pg. 7191
STEF TRANSPORT MARSEILLE SA—See STEF SA; *Int'l*, pg. 7191
STEF TRANSPORT MONTPELLIER SA—See STEF SA; *Int'l*, pg. 7191
STEF TRANSPORT MULHOUSE SA—See STEF SA; *Int'l*, pg. 7191
STEF TRANSPORT NANTES CARQUEFOU SA—See STEF SA; *Int'l*, pg. 7191
STEF TRANSPORT NIORT 1 LA CRECHE SA—See STEF SA; *Int'l*, pg. 7191
STEF TRANSPORT NIORT 2 LA CRECHE SA—See STEF SA; *Int'l*, pg. 7191
STEF TRANSPORT ORLEANS SA—See STEF SA; *Int'l*, pg. 7191
STEF TRANSPORT PARIS RUNGIS SA—See STEF SA; *Int'l*, pg. 7191
STEF TRANSPORT REIMS SA—See STEF SA; *Int'l*, pg. 7191
STEF TRANSPORT ROUEN SAS—See STEF SA; *Int'l*, pg. 7191
STEF TRANSPORT SAINT-BRIEUC SA—See STEF SA; *Int'l*, pg. 7191
STEF TRANSPORT SAINT-SEVER SA—See STEF SA; *Int'l*, pg. 7191
STEF TRANSPORT ST-ETIENNE SASU—See STEF SA; *Int'l*, pg. 7191
STEF TRANSPORT TOULOUSE SA—See STEF SA; *Int'l*, pg. 7191
STEF TSA ORLEANS NORD SAS—See STEF SA; *Int'l*, pg. 7191
STE GARAGE MOISON; *Int'l*, pg. 7186
STEGDOC GMBH—See ManpowerGroup Inc.; *U.S. Public*, pg. 1362
STEGEMAN B.V.—See ALFA, S.A.B. de C.V.; *Int'l*, pg. 314
STEG ENTREPRENOR AS—See Per Aarsleff Holding A/S; *Int'l*, pg. 5796
STEGGLES FOODS; *Int'l*, pg. 7193
STEGMANN PERSONALDIENSTLEISTUNG GMBH—See ManpowerGroup Inc.; *U.S. Public*, pg. 1362

COMPANY NAME INDEX

STEGPLUS PERSONAL GMBH—See ManpowerGroup Inc.; *U.S. Public*, pg. 1362
STE GRAND GARAGE DU BOULEVARD; *Int'l*, pg. 7186
STEICO INDUSTRIES, INC.—See Senior plc; *Int'l*, pg. 6709
STEICO SE—See Kingspan Group PLC; *Int'l*, pg. 4179
STEIERMARKISCHE BANK UND SPARKASSEN AG—See Erste Group Bank AG; *Int'l*, pg. 2499
STEIERMARKISCHE MEDIZINARCHIV GESMBH—See Siemens Aktiengesellschaft; *Int'l*, pg. 6901
STEIER OIL FIELD SERVICE INC.—See Apollo Global Management, Inc.; *U.S. Public*, pg. 167
STEIGENBERGER HOTELS AKTIENGESELLSCHAFT—See H World Group Limited; *Int'l*, pg. 3191
STEIGENBERGER SPA GMBH—See H World Group Limited; *Int'l*, pg. 3191
STEIGER PARTICIPATIONS SA—See Ningbo Cixing Co., Ltd.; *Int'l*, pg. 5301
STEIJN VASTGOED B.V.—See Smurfit Kappa Group plc; *Int'l*, pg. 7018
STEILMANN-BOECKER FASHION POINT GMBH & CO. KG—See Steilmann Holding AG; *Int'l*, pg. 7193
STEILMANN HOLDING AG; *Int'l*, pg. 7193
STEILMANN OSTEUROPA GMBH & CO. KG—See Steilmann Holding AG; *Int'l*, pg. 7193
STEILMANN SE; *Int'l*, pg. 7193
STEINBACH DODGE CHRYSLER LTD.; *Int'l*, pg. 7193
STEINBEIS PAPIER GLUCKSTADT GMBH & CO. KG; *Int'l*, pg. 7193
STEINBEIS TEMMING PAPIER GMBH & CO.—See Steinbeis Papier Gluckstadt GmbH & Co. KG; *Int'l*, pg. 7193
STEINBERG MEDIA TECHNOLOGIES GMBH—See Yamaha Corporation; *Int'l*, pg. 8549
STEINBERG MFG. CO. INC.—See Heik Holding Company Inc.; *U.S. Private*, pg. 1904
STEIN BROS INC.; *U.S. Private*, pg. 3797
STEINBRUCH AG VORBERG BOZINGEN—See Vicat S.A.; *Int'l*, pg. 8186
STEIN DISTRIBUTING INC.—See C. Stein, Inc.; *U.S. Private*, pg. 705
STEINEL (UK) LTD.—See ADCURAM Group AG; *Int'l*, pg. 128
STEINEL VERTRIED GMBH—See ADCURAM Group AG; *Int'l*, pg. 128
STEINER-ATLANTIC CORP—See EVI Industries, Inc.; *U.S. Public*, pg. 803
STEINER EDUCATION GROUP, INC.—See Catterton Management Company, LLC; *U.S. Private*, pg. 794
STEINER ELECTRIC COMPANY - CHICAGO—See Steiner Electric Company; *U.S. Private*, pg. 3798
STEINER ELECTRIC COMPANY; *U.S. Private*, pg. 3798
STEINER EQUITIES GROUP LLC; *U.S. Private*, pg. 3798
STEINER HOPS LIMITED—See S.S. Steiner Inc.; *U.S. Private*, pg. 3518
STEINER HYGIENE MONTAGUE GARDENS (PTY) LIMITED—See The Bidvest Group Limited; *Int'l*, pg. 7626
STEINER HYGIENE (PTY) LIMITED—See The Bidvest Group Limited; *Int'l*, pg. 7626
STEINER HYGIENE SWAZILAND (PTY) LIMITED—See The Bidvest Group Limited; *Int'l*, pg. 7626
STEINER INDUSTRIES, INC.—See Bunzl plc; *Int'l*, pg. 1218
STEINER LEISURE LIMITED—See Catterton Management Company, LLC; *U.S. Private*, pg. 794
STEINER SPORTS MARKETING—See Omnicom Group Inc.; *U.S. Public*, pg. 1594
STEINER STUDIOS LLC—See Steiner Equities Group LLC; *U.S. Private*, pg. 3798
STEINFELS CLEANING SYSTEMS—See Coop-Gruppe Genossenschaft; *Int'l*, pg. 1790
STEIN FIBERS LTD.; *U.S. Private*, pg. 3797
STEIN GARDEN CENTERS, INC.; *U.S. Private*, pg. 3797
STEINGOLD VOLVO; *U.S. Private*, pg. 3798
STEINHAFEL'S INC.; *U.S. Private*, pg. 3798
STEINHAGEN OIL COMPANY, INC.; *U.S. Private*, pg. 3798
STEINHOFF AFRICA HOLDINGS (PROPRIETARY) LIMITED—See Steinhoff International Holdings N.V.; *Int'l*, pg. 7195
STEINHOFF ASIA PACIFIC HOLDINGS PROPRIETARY LIMITED—See Steinhoff International Holdings N.V.; *Int'l*, pg. 7195
STEINHOFF ASIA PACIFIC LIMITED—See Freedom Group Limited; *Int'l*, pg. 2769
STEINHOFF EUROPE AG—See Steinhoff International Holdings N.V.; *Int'l*, pg. 7195
STEINHOFF FINANCE HOLDING GMBH—See Steinhoff International Holdings N.V.; *Int'l*, pg. 7195
STEINHOFF INTERNATIONAL HOLDINGS LIMITED—See Steinhoff International Holdings N.V.; *Int'l*, pg. 7194
STEINHOFF INTERNATIONAL HOLDINGS N.V.; *Int'l*, pg. 7194
STEINHOFF INVESTMENT HOLDINGS LIMITED—See Steinhoff International Holdings N.V.; *Int'l*, pg. 7194
STEINHOFF SERVICE GMBH—See Steinhoff International Holdings N.V.; *Int'l*, pg. 7195

STEINHOFF UK RETAIL LIMITED—See Steinhoff International Holdings N.V.; *Int'l*, pg. 7195
STEINHOUSE SUPPLY CO INC—See Southern Pipe & Supply Co., Inc.; *U.S. Private*, pg. 3734
STEINIGKE SHOWTECHNIC GMBH; *Int'l*, pg. 7195
STEIN INDUSTRIES, INC.; *U.S. Private*, pg. 3797
STEIN INVESTMENT GROUP; *U.S. Private*, pg. 3798
STEINKAMP WAREHOUSES, INC.; *U.S. Private*, pg. 3798
STEIN, LLC—See The Pritzker Organization, LLC; *U.S. Private*, pg. 4100
STEINMAN PARK RESTAURANT INC—See Lancaster Newspapers Inc.; *U.S. Private*, pg. 2381
STEIN MART BUYING CORP.—See Stein Mart, Inc.; *U.S. Private*, pg. 3798
STEIN MART INC. (ALABAMA)—See Stein Mart, Inc.; *U.S. Private*, pg. 3798
STEIN MART, INC. (CALIFORNIA)—See Stein Mart, Inc.; *U.S. Private*, pg. 3798
STEIN MART, INC. (FLORIDA)—See Stein Mart, Inc.; *U.S. Private*, pg. 3798
STEIN MART, INC. (NORTH CAROLINA)—See Stein Mart, Inc.; *U.S. Private*, pg. 3798
STEIN MART, INC.; *U.S. Private*, pg. 3798
STEIN MART, INC. (SOUTH CAROLINA)—See Stein Mart, Inc.; *U.S. Private*, pg. 3798
STEIN MART, INC. (TENNESSEE)—See Stein Mart, Inc.; *U.S. Private*, pg. 3798
STEIN MART, INC. (TEXAS)—See Stein Mart, Inc.; *U.S. Private*, pg. 3798
STEINMUELLER BABCOCK ENGINEERING CO., LTD.—See Nippon Steel Corporation; *Int'l*, pg. 5336
STEINMUELLER BABCOCK ENVIRONMENT GMBH—See Nippon Steel Corporation; *Int'l*, pg. 5335
STEINMULLER AFRICA (PTY) LTD.—See Bilfinger SE; *Int'l*, pg. 1027
STEINMULLER ENGINEERING GMBH—See IHI Corporation; *Int'l*, pg. 3606
STEINMULLER ENGINEERING SERVICES (PTY) LTD.—See Bilfinger SE; *Int'l*, pg. 1029
STEIN + PARTNERS BRAND ACTIVATION; *U.S. Private*, pg. 3797
STEINREICH COMMUNICATIONS, LLC; *U.S. Private*, pg. 3798
STEIN ROGAN + PARTNERS; *U.S. Private*, pg. 3798
STEIN SEAL COMPANY; *U.S. Private*, pg. 3798
STE INSULAIRE AUTOMOBILES; *Int'l*, pg. 7186
STEINWALL, INC.; *U.S. Private*, pg. 3798
STEINWAY AUTO PARTS INC.—See Advance Auto Parts, Inc.; *U.S. Public*, pg. 45
STEINWAY CHILD AND FAMILY SERVICES, INC.; *U.S. Private*, pg. 3798
STEINWAY HAUS DUSSELDORF GMBH—See Paulson & Co. Inc.; *U.S. Private*, pg. 3114
STEINWAY MUSICAL INSTRUMENTS HOLDINGS, INC.; *U.S. Private*, pg. 3798
STEINWAY MUSICAL INSTRUMENTS, INC.—See Paulson & Co. Inc.; *U.S. Private*, pg. 3114
STEINWAY RETAIL DEUTSCHLAND GMBH—See Paulson & Co. Inc.; *U.S. Private*, pg. 3114
STEINWAY & SONS—See Paulson & Co. Inc.; *U.S. Private*, pg. 3114
STEINWEG KUNSTSTOFFFOLIEN GMBH—See KAP Beteiligungs-AG; *Int'l*, pg. 4076
STEIN WORLD OPERATING CO.—See ELK Group International, Inc.; *U.S. Private*, pg. 1362
STEINY & COMPANY, INC.; *U.S. Private*, pg. 3799
STEINY & COMPANY INC.—See Steiny & Company, Inc.; *U.S. Private*, pg. 3799
STEINZENTRALE NORD LEEUWIS GMBH—See Wienerberger AG; *Int'l*, pg. 8406
STEINZEUG-KERAMO GMBH—See Wienerberger AG; *Int'l*, pg. 8406
STEINZEUG-KERAMO N.V.—See Wienerberger AG; *Int'l*, pg. 8406
STEINZEUG KERAMO S R.O.—See Wienerberger AG; *Int'l*, pg. 8406
STE JOSEPH HUWER; *Int'l*, pg. 7186
S-TEK INC.; *U.S. Private*, pg. 3514
STEKLARNA ROGASKA D.O.O.—See Fiskars Oyj Abp; *Int'l*, pg. 2694
STELAR INC.; *U.S. Private*, pg. 3799
STELAR METALS LIMITED; *Int'l*, pg. 7195
STELCO HOLDINGS, INC.—See Cleveland-Cliffs, Inc.; *U.S. Public*, pg. 514
STELCO INC.—See Bedrock Industries GP, LLC; *U.S. Private*, pg. 512
ST ELECTRONICS (INFO-COMM SYSTEMS) PTE. LTD.—See Temasek Holdings (Private) Limited; *Int'l*, pg. 7552
ST ELECTRONICS (INFO-SOFTWARE SYSTEMS) PTE. LTD.—See Temasek Holdings (Private) Limited; *Int'l*, pg. 7552
ST ELECTRONICS (TRAINING & SIMULATION SYSTEMS) PTE. LTD.—See Temasek Holdings (Private) Limited; *Int'l*, pg. 7552
STELFAST, INC.—See Nautic Partners, LLC; *U.S. Private*, pg. 2871
STELFORM PIPING SYSTEMS PTY LTD—See RCR Tomlinson Ltd.; *Int'l*, pg. 6229

STELLAR RECOVERY, INC.

STEL HOLDINGS LIMITED; *Int'l*, pg. 7195
STELIOS KANAKIS INDUSTRIAL AND COMMERCIAL SA—See Orkla ASA; *Int'l*, pg. 5638
ST. ELISABETH-KRANKENHAUS GMBH—See Fresenius SE & Co. KGaA; *Int'l*, pg. 2779
ST. ELIZABETH COMMUNITY HOSPITAL—See Catholic Health Initiatives; *U.S. Private*, pg. 789
STELKO ELECTRIC, INC.—See Motor City Electric Co., Inc.; *U.S. Private*, pg. 2797
STELKOM D.O.O.—See Elektro Slovenia d.o.o.; *Int'l*, pg. 2357
STELLA CHEMIFA CORPORATION - IZUMI FACTORY—See Stella Chemifa Corporation; *Int'l*, pg. 7195
STELLA CHEMIFA CORPORATION - KITAKYUSHU FACTORY—See Stella Chemifa Corporation; *Int'l*, pg. 7195
STELLA CHEMIFA CORPORATION - SANPO FACTORY—See Stella Chemifa Corporation; *Int'l*, pg. 7195
STELLA CHEMIFA CORPORATION; *Int'l*, pg. 7195
STELLA CHEMIFA SINGAPORE PTE. LTD.—See Hitachi, Ltd.; *Int'l*, pg. 3424
STELLA & CHEWY'S; *U.S. Private*, pg. 3799
STELLA & DOT LLC; *U.S. Private*, pg. 3799
STELLA EXPRESS (SINGAPORE) PTE LTD.—See Stella Chemifa Corporation; *Int'l*, pg. 7195
STELLA GROUP PTY LTD.—See CVC Capital Partners SICAV-FIS S.A.; *Int'l*, pg. 1885
STELLA HOLDINGS BERHAD; *Int'l*, pg. 7195
STELLA INTERNATIONAL HOLDINGS LIMITED; *Int'l*, pg. 7195
STELLA-JONES CANADA, INC.—See Stella-Jones, Inc.; *Int'l*, pg. 7196
STELLA-JONES CORP. - BANGOR—See Stella-Jones, Inc.; *Int'l*, pg. 7196
STELLA-JONES CORP. - ELOY—See Stella-Jones, Inc.; *Int'l*, pg. 7196
STELLA-JONES CORP. - LIVINGSTON—See Stella-Jones, Inc.; *Int'l*, pg. 7196
STELLA-JONES CORP. - MONTEVALLO—See Stella-Jones, Inc.; *Int'l*, pg. 7196
STELLA-JONES, INC.; *Int'l*, pg. 7196
STELLA MARIS INC.; *U.S. Private*, pg. 3799
STELLA MCCARTNEY AMERICA INC.—See Stella McCartney Limited; *Int'l*, pg. 7196
STELLA MCCARTNEY FRANCE SAS—See Stella McCartney Limited; *Int'l*, pg. 7196
STELLA MCCARTNEY ITALIA SRL—See Stella McCartney Limited; *Int'l*, pg. 7196
STELLA MCCARTNEY LIMITED; *Int'l*, pg. 7196
STELLANA AB—See HEXPOL AB; *Int'l*, pg. 3372
STELLANA DEUTSCHLAND GMBH—See HEXPOL AB; *Int'l*, pg. 3372
STELLANA (QINGDAO) CO., LTD.—See HEXPOL AB; *Int'l*, pg. 3372
STELLANA U.S. INC.—See HEXPOL AB; *Int'l*, pg. 3372
STELLANTIS N.V.; *Int'l*, pg. 7196
STELLANT SECURITIES (INDIA) LIMITED; *Int'l*, pg. 7196
STELLA ORTON HOME CARE AGENCY; *U.S. Private*, pg. 3799
STELLA PERFORMANCE LIMITED—See TRISTEL PLC; *Int'l*, pg. 7928
STELLA PHARMA CORPORATION—See Stella Chemifa Corporation; *Int'l*, pg. 7195
STELLA POINT CAPITAL, LP; *U.S. Private*, pg. 3799
STELLAR AFRICAGOLD INC.; *Int'l*, pg. 7204
STELLAR BANCORP, INC.; *U.S. Public*, pg. 1944
STELLAR CALL CENTRES PTY. LIMITED; *Int'l*, pg. 7204
STELLAR CAPITAL PARTNERS LIMITED; *Int'l*, pg. 7204
STELLAR CAPITAL SERVICES LIMITED; *Int'l*, pg. 7204
STELLAR COLLECTIONS LIMITED—See Geneva Finance Limited; *Int'l*, pg. 2922
STELLAR DEVELOPMENT, INC.; *U.S. Private*, pg. 3799
STELLAR DIAMONDS LIMITED—See Newfield Resources Limited; *Int'l*, pg. 5234
STELLAR DISTRIBUTION LLC; *U.S. Private*, pg. 3799
STELLAR ENERGY AMERICAS, INC.—See The Stellar Group Inc.; *U.S. Private*, pg. 4121
STELLAR ENERGY ASIA—See The Stellar Group Inc.; *U.S. Private*, pg. 4121
STELLAR ENERGY MENA—See The Stellar Group Inc.; *U.S. Private*, pg. 4121
THE STELLAR GROUP INC.; *U.S. Private*, pg. 4121
STELLAR INDUSTRIAL SUPPLY LLC; *U.S. Private*, pg. 3799
STELLAR INDUSTRIES INC.; *U.S. Private*, pg. 3799
STELLARIS GROWTH ACQUISITION CORP.; *Int'l*, pg. 7204
STELLARIS, LLC—See Primoris Services Corporation; *U.S. Public*, pg. 1719
STELLAR IT SOLUTIONS, INC.; *U.S. Private*, pg. 3799
STELLAR IT SOLUTIONS, LLC; *U.S. Private*, pg. 3799
STELLAR MANAGEMENT GROUP, INC.; *U.S. Private*, pg. 3799
STELLAR PARTNERS INC.—See Avolta AG; *Int'l*, pg. 749
STELLAR PRINTING INC.—See Family Federation for World Peace & Unification; *U.S. Private*, pg. 1470
STELLAR RECOVERY, INC.; *U.S. Private*, pg. 3799

STELLAR RESOURCES LIMITED

CORPORATE AFFILIATIONS

STELLAR RESOURCES LIMITED; *Int'l*, pg. 7204
STELLAR SOLUTIONS INC.; *U.S. Private*, pg. 3799
STELLAR STRUCTURES LLC; *U.S. Private*, pg. 3799
STELLAR VALUE CHAIN SOLUTIONS PVT. LTD.—See CMA CGM S.A.; *Int'l*, pg. 1667
STELLAS CO., LTD.—See NSD CO., LTD.; *Int'l*, pg. 5477
STELLASERVICE, INC.—See Thoma Bravo, L.P.; *U.S. Private*, pg. 4149
STELLA TRAVEL SERVICES (AUSTRALIA) PTY LTD—See Helloworld Travel Limited; *Int'l*, pg. 3337
STELLA TRAVEL SERVICES (UK) LIMITED—See The Emirates Group; *Int'l*, pg. 7639
STELLENBOSCH ACADEMY OF SPORT PROPRIETARY LIMITED—See Remgro Limited; *Int'l*, pg. 6271
STELLENBOSCH FOOTBALL CLUB PROPRIETARY LIMITED—See Remgro Limited; *Int'l*, pg. 6271
STELLE S.R.L.—See Gismondi 1754 S.p.A.; *Int'l*, pg. 2979
STELLEX CAPITAL MANAGEMENT LP; *U.S. Private*, pg. 3800
STELLINE SERVIZI IMMOBILIARI S.P.A.—See Credito Valtellinese Societa Cooperativa; *Int'l*, pg. 1837
STELLUS CAPITAL INVESTMENT CORPORATION—See Stellus Capital Management, LLC; *U.S. Private*, pg. 3801
STELLUS CAPITAL MANAGEMENT, LLC; *U.S. Private*, pg. 3801
STELMET SA; *Int'l*, pg. 7204
STELMINE CANADA LTD.—See Stellar AfricaGold Inc.; *Int'l*, pg. 7204
ST ELMO VETERINARY CLINIC LIMITED—See CVS Group Plc; *Int'l*, pg. 1890
STELOTEC GMBH—See Mercedes-Benz Group AG; *Int'l*, pg. 4829
STELRAD GROUP PLC; *Int'l*, pg. 7204
STEL S.R.L.—See KONE Oyj; *Int'l*, pg. 4250
STELTECH STRUCTURAL LTD.—See BlueScope Steel Limited; *Int'l*, pg. 1074
STELUX HOLDINGS INTERNATIONAL LIMITED; *Int'l*, pg. 7204
STELUX PROPERTIES LIMITED—See Stelux Holdings International Limited; *Int'l*, pg. 7205
STELUX TRADING (INTERNATIONAL) LTD—See Stelux Holdings International Limited; *Int'l*, pg. 7205
STELUX WATCH LIMITED—See Stelux Holdings International Limited; *Int'l*, pg. 7205
STELZER RUHRTECHNIK INTERNATIONAL GMBH—See Lone Star Funds; *U.S. Private*, pg. 2486
STEMACO USA, INC.; *U.S. Private*, pg. 3801
STEMA METALLEICHTBAU GMBH; *Int'l*, pg. 7205
STEMA SHIPPING A/S—See Heidelberg Materials AG; *Int'l*, pg. 3319
STEMA SHIPPING FRANCE S.A.S.—See Heidelberg Materials AG; *Int'l*, pg. 3319
STEMA SNC—See Carrefour SA; *Int'l*, pg. 1346
S&T EMBEDDED GMBH—See Kontron AG; *Int'l*, pg. 4278
STEM CELL AUTHORITY, LTD.; *U.S. Public*, pg. 1944
STEMCELL HOLDINGS, INC.; *Int'l*, pg. 7205
STEM CELLS BANK SA—See MedLife S.A.; *Int'l*, pg. 4785
STEMCELL TECHNOLOGIES CANADA INC.; *Int'l*, pg. 7205
STEMCELL TECHNOLOGIES INC—See STEMCELL Technologies Canada Inc.; *Int'l*, pg. 7205
STEMCELL UNITED LIMITED; *Int'l*, pg. 7205
STEMCO CREWSON, LLC—See Enpro Inc.; *U.S. Public*, pg. 775
STEMCO INC.—See Enpro Inc.; *U.S. Public*, pg. 775
STEMCO KAISER—See Enpro Inc.; *U.S. Public*, pg. 775
STEMCO LP—See Enpro Inc.; *U.S. Public*, pg. 775
STEMCO, LTD.—See Toray Industries, Inc.; *Int'l*, pg. 7823
STEMCO PRODUCTS, INC.—See Enpro Inc.; *U.S. Public*, pg. 775
STEMCOR AG—See Stemcor Holdings Limited; *Int'l*, pg. 7205
STEMCOR ARCHITECTURAL—See Stemcor Holdings Limited; *Int'l*, pg. 7206
STEMCOR AUSTRALIA PTY. LTD.—See Stemcor Holdings Limited; *Int'l*, pg. 7205
STEMCOR BANGKOK—See Stemcor Holdings Limited; *Int'l*, pg. 7205
STEMCOR BIELEFELD—See Stemcor Holdings Limited; *Int'l*, pg. 7205
STEMCOR BUCHAREST—See Stemcor Holdings Limited; *Int'l*, pg. 7205
STEMCOR BUDAPEST LTD.—See Stemcor Holdings Limited; *Int'l*, pg. 7205
STEMCOR CHILE SPA—See Stemcor Holdings Limited; *Int'l*, pg. 7205
STEMCOR (CONTISTAHL) BEIJING LTD.—See Stemcor Holdings Limited; *Int'l*, pg. 7205
STEMCOR DE MEXICO, S.A. DE C.V.—See Stemcor Holdings Limited; *Int'l*, pg. 7206
STEMCOR DEUTSCHLAND HOLDING GMBH—See Stemcor Holdings Limited; *Int'l*, pg. 7205
STEMCOR DIS TICARET LTD. STI—See Stemcor Holdings Limited; *Int'l*, pg. 7205
STEMCOR DNEPROPETROVSK—See Stemcor Holdings Limited; *Int'l*, pg. 7205
STEMCOR EGYPT—See Stemcor Holdings Limited; *Int'l*, pg. 7205
STEMCOR FLACHSTAHL GMBH—See Stemcor Holdings Limited; *Int'l*, pg. 7205
STEMCOR FRANCE SAS—See Stemcor Holdings Limited; *Int'l*, pg. 7205
STEMCOR GDANSK—See Stemcor Holdings Limited; *Int'l*, pg. 7205
STEMCOR GMBH—See Stemcor Holdings Limited; *Int'l*, pg. 7205
STEMCOR HAMBURG—See Stemcor Holdings Limited; *Int'l*, pg. 7205
STEMCOR HANOI—See Stemcor Holdings Limited; *Int'l*, pg. 7205
STEMCOR HELLAS LTD—See Stemcor Holdings Limited; *Int'l*, pg. 7205
STEMCOR HOLDINGS LIMITED; *Int'l*, pg. 7205
STEMCOR HONG KONG LTD.—See Stemcor Holdings Limited; *Int'l*, pg. 7205
STEMCOR INDIA PVT LTD—See Stemcor Holdings Limited; *Int'l*, pg. 7205
STEMCOR ITALIA S.R.L.—See Stemcor Holdings Limited; *Int'l*, pg. 7205
STEMCOR JAPAN LTD.—See Stemcor Holdings Limited; *Int'l*, pg. 7205
STEMCOR KIEV—See Stemcor Holdings Limited; *Int'l*, pg. 7205
STEMCOR KRAKOW—See Stemcor Holdings Limited; *Int'l*, pg. 7205
STEMCOR LAHORE—See Stemcor Holdings Limited; *Int'l*, pg. 7205
STEMCOR MESA DMCC—See Stemcor Holdings Limited; *Int'l*, pg. 7205
STEMCOR MOROCCO SARL—See Stemcor Holdings Limited; *Int'l*, pg. 7206
STEMCOR MOSCOW—See Stemcor Holdings Limited; *Int'l*, pg. 7206
STEMCOR NEW ZEALAND—See Stemcor Holdings Limited; *Int'l*, pg. 7206
STEMCOR NORWAY AS—See Stemcor Holdings Limited; *Int'l*, pg. 7206
STEMCOR ODESSA—See Stemcor Holdings Limited; *Int'l*, pg. 7206
STEMCOR SA—See Stemcor Holdings Limited; *Int'l*, pg. 7206
STEMCOR (S.E.A.) PTE LTD.—See Stemcor Holdings Limited; *Int'l*, pg. 7205
STEMCOR SECTIONS—See Stemcor Holdings Limited; *Int'l*, pg. 7206
STEMCOR SHANGHAI LTD.—See Stemcor Holdings Limited; *Int'l*, pg. 7206
STEMCOR SKOPJE—See Stemcor Holdings Limited; *Int'l*, pg. 7206
STEMCOR SOUTH AFRICA (PROPRIETARY) LTD.—See Stemcor Holdings Limited; *Int'l*, pg. 7206
STEMCOR SPECIAL STEELS GULF FZE—See Stemcor Holdings Limited; *Int'l*, pg. 7206
STEMCOR SPECIAL STEELS LLC—See Stemcor Holdings Limited; *Int'l*, pg. 7206
STEMCOR SPECIAL STEELS LTD—See Stemcor Holdings Limited; *Int'l*, pg. 7206
STEMCOR SPECIAL STEELS PTE LTD—See Stemcor Holdings Limited; *Int'l*, pg. 7206
STEMCOR STAINLESS UK—See Stemcor Holdings Limited; *Int'l*, pg. 7206
STEMCOR STEEL, S.L.—See Stemcor Holdings Limited; *Int'l*, pg. 7206
STEMCOR TUBES—See Stemcor Holdings Limited; *Int'l*, pg. 7206
STEMCOR UK LTD.—See Stemcor Holdings Limited; *Int'l*, pg. 7206
STEMCOR USA INC.—See Stemcor Holdings Limited; *Int'l*, pg. 7206
STEMCOR VIETNAM CO.—See Stemcor Holdings Limited; *Int'l*, pg. 7206
STEMCO VEHICLE TECHNOLOGY (SHANGHAI) CO. LTD.—See Enpro Inc.; *U.S. Public*, pg. 775
STEMCYTE, INC.; *U.S. Private*, pg. 3801
STEMEDICA CELL TECHNOLOGIES, INC.—See Jiuzhitang Co., Ltd.; *Int'l*, pg. 3971
STE MEDICEF—See Hikma Pharmaceuticals PLC; *Int'l*, pg. 3349
STEMGENT, INC.; *U.S. Private*, pg. 3801
STEM HOLDINGS, INC.; *U.S. Public*, pg. 1944
STE. MICHELLE WINE ESTATES, LLC—See Altria Group, Inc.; *U.S. Public*, pg. 89
STEMILT GROWERS INC.; *U.S. Private*, pg. 3801
STEM, INC.; *U.S. Public*, pg. 1945
STEM, INC—See Stem, Inc.; *U.S. Public*, pg. 1945
STEMLAB, INC.; *Int'l*, pg. 7206
STEMLIFE BERHAD—See Cordlife Group Limited; *Int'l*, pg. 1796
STEMLINE THERAPEUTICS, INC.—See A Menarini Industrie Farmaceutiche Riunite Srl; *Int'l*, pg. 18
STEMMANN POLSKA SP ZOO—See Westinghouse Air Brake Technologies Corporation; *U.S. Public*, pg. 2359
STEMMANN TECHNIK FRANCE SAS—See Westinghouse Air Brake Technologies Corporation; *U.S. Public*, pg. 2359
STEMMANN-TECHNIK GMBH—See Westinghouse Air Brake Technologies Corporation; *U.S. Public*, pg. 2358
STEMMANN TECHNIK NEDERLAND BV—See Westinghouse Air Brake Technologies Corporation; *U.S. Public*, pg. 2359
STEMMANN TECHNIK NETHERLANDS BV—See Westinghouse Air Brake Technologies Corporation; *U.S. Public*, pg. 2358
STEMMANN TECHNIK POLSKA SP ZOO—See Westinghouse Air Brake Technologies Corporation; *U.S. Public*, pg. 2359
STEM MED PTE. LTD.—See Talkmed Group Limited; *Int'l*, pg. 7447
STEMMER GMBH—See Bechtle AG; *Int'l*, pg. 938
STEMMER IMAGING AB—See MiddleGround Management, LP; *U.S. Private*, pg. 2712
STEMMER IMAGING AG—See MiddleGround Management, LP; *U.S. Private*, pg. 2713
STEMMER IMAGING AG—See MiddleGround Management, LP; *U.S. Private*, pg. 2712
STEMMER IMAGING A/S—See MiddleGround Management, LP; *U.S. Private*, pg. 2712
STEMMER IMAGING B.V.—See MiddleGround Management, LP; *U.S. Private*, pg. 2713
STEMMER IMAGING GES.M.B.H.—See MiddleGround Management, LP; *U.S. Private*, pg. 2713
STEMMER IMAGING LTD.—See MiddleGround Management, LP; *U.S. Private*, pg. 2713
STEMMER IMAGING OY—See MiddleGround Management, LP; *U.S. Private*, pg. 2713
STEMMER IMAGING S.A.S.—See MiddleGround Management, LP; *U.S. Private*, pg. 2713
STEMMER IMAGING SP.Z O.O.—See MiddleGround Management, LP; *U.S. Private*, pg. 2713
STEMMER IMAGING S.R.L.—See MiddleGround Management, LP; *U.S. Private*, pg. 2713
STE MONTOISE DU BOIS; *Int'l*, pg. 7187
STEMRIM, INC.; *Int'l*, pg. 7206
STEMSATION USA, INC.; *U.S. Public*, pg. 1945
STEMTECH CORPORATION; *Int'l*, pg. 7206
STEMTECH INTERNATIONAL, INC.; *U.S. Private*, pg. 3801
STEMTECH INTERNATIONAL SDN. BHD.—See Cryocord Holdings Sdn. Bhd.; *Int'l*, pg. 1859
STE MULHOUSIENNE DES CITES OUVRIERES; *Int'l*, pg. 7187
STENA AB; *Int'l*, pg. 7206
STENA ADACTUM AB—See STENA AB; *Int'l*, pg. 7206
STENA BULK AB—See STENA AB; *Int'l*, pg. 7206
STENA DRILLING (HOLDINGS) LTD—See STENA AB; *Int'l*, pg. 7207
STENA FASTIGHETER AB—See STENA AB; *Int'l*, pg. 7207
STENA HOLDING (CYPRUS) LTD—See STENA AB; *Int'l*, pg. 7207
STENA INTERNATIONAL S.A.—See STENA AB; *Int'l*, pg. 7207
STENA LINE AB—See STENA AB; *Int'l*, pg. 7207
STENA LINE (BELFAST)—See STENA AB; *Int'l*, pg. 7207
STENA LINE (DUN LAOGHAIRE)—See STENA AB; *Int'l*, pg. 7207
STENA LINE (FISHGUARD)—See STENA AB; *Int'l*, pg. 7207
STENA LINE (FREDERIKSHAVN)—See STENA AB; *Int'l*, pg. 7207
STENA LINE FREIGHT—See STENA AB; *Int'l*, pg. 7207
STENA LINE (GRENA)—See STENA AB; *Int'l*, pg. 7207
STENA LINE (HARWICH)—See STENA AB; *Int'l*, pg. 7207
STENA LINE (HOEK VAN HOLLAND)—See STENA AB; *Int'l*, pg. 7207
STENA LINE (KARLSKRONA)—See STENA AB; *Int'l*, pg. 7207
STENA LINE (KIEL)—See STENA AB; *Int'l*, pg. 7207
STENA LINE (ROSSLARE)—See STENA AB; *Int'l*, pg. 7207
STENA LINE SCANDIC HOTEL FREDERIKSHAVN—See STENA AB; *Int'l*, pg. 7207
STENA LINE (STRANRAER)—See STENA AB; *Int'l*, pg. 7207
STENA LINE UK—See STENA AB; *Int'l*, pg. 7207
STENA MARITIME AG—See STENA AB; *Int'l*, pg. 7207
STENA METALL AB—See STENA AB; *Int'l*, pg. 7207
STENA REALTY B.V.—See STENA AB; *Int'l*, pg. 7207
STENA RECYCLING AB—See STENA AB; *Int'l*, pg. 7207
STENA RECYCLING SP. Z O.O—See REISSWOLF International AG; *Int'l*, pg. 6258
STENA REDERI AB—See STENA AB; *Int'l*, pg. 7207
STENA RENEWABLE AB—See STENA AB; *Int'l*, pg. 7206
STENA ROPAX LTD—See STENA AB; *Int'l*, pg. 7207
STENCOR COMPANY, LLC; *U.S. Private*, pg. 3801
STENDER AG; *Int'l*, pg. 7207
STENDORREN FASTIGHETER AB—See EQT AB; *Int'l*, pg. 2481
STENENTREPRENADER I HESSLEHOLM AB—See Volati AB; *Int'l*, pg. 8301
STENERSON BROS LUMBER COMPANY; *U.S. Private*, pg. 3801
STENFLEX RUDOLF STENDER GMBH; *Int'l*, pg. 7207
STENFLEX S.A.R.L.—See STENFLEX Rudolf Stender GmbH; *Int'l*, pg. 7207

COMPANY NAME INDEX

STENFLEX S.A.—See STENFLEX Rudolf Stender GmbH; *Int'l*, pg. 7207
STENGEL HILL ARCHITECTURE, INC—See Godspeed Capital Management LP; *U.S. Private*, pg. 1725
STENHAM LTD—See Peregrine Holdings Limited; *Int'l*, pg. 5797
STENHOUSE PUBLISHERS—See Highlights for Children, Inc.; *U.S. Private*, pg. 1940
STENHUS FASTIGHETER I NORDEN AB; *Int'l*, pg. 7207
STENI AS—See Accent Equity Partners AS; *Int'l*, pg. 81
STENIEL MANUFACTURING CORPORATION; *Int'l*, pg. 7207
S. TEN NINES KYOTO CO., LTD.—See Screen Holdings Co., Ltd.; *Int'l*, pg. 6655
STENOCARE A/S; *Int'l*, pg. 7208
STENO DIABETES CENTER—See Novo Nordisk Fonden; *Int'l*, pg. 5465
STENOGRAPH LLC—See The Heico Companies, L.L.C.; *U.S. Private*, pg. 4051
STENSTROM COMPANIES LTD.; *U.S. Private*, pg. 3801
STENSTROM EXCAVATION & BLACKTOP GROUP—See Stenstrom Companies Ltd.; *U.S. Private*, pg. 3801
STENSTROM GENERAL CONTRACTOR-DESIGN BUILD GROUP—See Stenstrom Companies Ltd.; *U.S. Private*, pg. 3801
STENSTROM PETROLEUM SERVICES—See Stenstrom Companies Ltd.; *U.S. Private*, pg. 3801
STENSTROM SAND & GRAVEL GROUP—See Stenstrom Companies Ltd.; *U.S. Private*, pg. 3801
STENTA FILMS (MALAYSIA) SENDIRIAN BERHAD—See Mehran Sugar Mills Limited; *Int'l*, pg. 4797
STENTECH, INC.—See Align Capital Partners, LLC; *U.S. Private*, pg. 167
STENTEKNIK I KARLSTAD AB—See Volati AB; *Int'l*, pg. 8301
STENTEN'S GOLF CART ACCESSORIES, INC.; *U.S. Private*, pg. 3801
STENTORIUS; *Int'l*, pg. 7208
STENTYS S.A.; *Int'l*, pg. 7208
STENUNGS TORG FASTIGHETS AB—See Citycon Oyj; *Int'l*, pg. 1629
STENVALLS TRA AB; *Int'l*, pg. 7208
STE OBCHODNI SLUZBY SPOL, S R O.—See CEZ, a.s.; *Int'l*, pg. 1428
THE STEP2 COMPANY LLC—See Aterian Investment Management, L.P.; *U.S. Private*, pg. 367
STEPAC BRASIL LTDA—See Johnson Matthey PLC; *Int'l*, pg. 3993
STEPAC L.A. LIMITED—See Johnson Matthey PLC; *Int'l*, pg. 3993
STEPAN ASIA PTE. LTD.—See Stepan Company; *U.S. Public*, pg. 1945
STEPAN CANADA, INC.—See Stepan Company; *U.S. Public*, pg. 1945
STEPAN COLOMBIA S.A.S.—See Stepan Company; *U.S. Public*, pg. 1945
STEPAN COMPANY - ELWOOD POLYMER & SURFACTANT PLANT—See Stepan Company; *U.S. Public*, pg. 1945
STEPAN COMPANY; *U.S. Public*, pg. 1945
STEPAN DEUTSCHLAND GMBH—See Stepan Company; *U.S. Public*, pg. 1945
STEPAN EUROPE S.A.—See Stepan Company; *U.S. Public*, pg. 1945
STEPAN MEXICO, S.A. DE C.V.—See Stepan Company; *U.S. Public*, pg. 1945
STEPAN POLSKA SP. Z O.O.—See Stepan Company; *U.S. Public*, pg. 1945
STEPAN QUIMICA LTDA.—See Stepan Company; *U.S. Public*, pg. 1945
STEPAN UK LIMITED—See Stepan Company; *U.S. Public*, pg. 1945
STEP BY STEP, INC.; *U.S. Private*, pg. 3801
STEP CO., LTD.; *Int'l*, pg. 7208
STEP D.D.; *Int'l*, pg. 7208
STEP ENERGY SERVICES LTD.; *Int'l*, pg. 7208
STEPGRADES MOTOR ACCESSORIES LTD.—See Halfords Group plc; *Int'l*, pg. 3229
STEPHAN & BRADY, INC.; *U.S. Private*, pg. 3801
STEPHAN, COLE & ASSOCIATES, LLC; *U.S. Private*, pg. 3802
THE STEPHAN COMPANY; *U.S. Public*, pg. 2132
STEPHANIE CHURCHILL PR—See Clayton, Dubilier & Rice, LLC; *U.S. Private*, pg. 925
STEPHANIE ODEGARD COLLECTION; *U.S. Private*, pg. 3802
STEPHANIE TIRE CORP.; *U.S. Private*, pg. 3802
STEPHAN MACHINERY GMBH—See Capvis AG; *Int'l*, pg. 1318
STEPHANOTIS FINANCE LIMITED; *Int'l*, pg. 7208
STEPHEN DAVID ENTERTAINMENT—See LOV Group Invest SAS; *Int'l*, pg. 4564
THE STEPHEN GOULD CORPORATION—See Stephen Gould Corporation; *U.S. Private*, pg. 3802
STEPHEN GOULD CORPORATION; *U.S. Private*, pg. 3802
STEPHEN GOULD CORP—See Stephen Gould Corporation; *U.S. Private*, pg. 3802

STEPHEN GOULD, INC./LA—See Stephen Gould Corporation; *U.S. Private*, pg. 3802
STEPHEN GOULD OF ALABAMA, INC.—See Stephen Gould Corporation; *U.S. Private*, pg. 3802
STEPHEN GOULD OF ARIZONA, INC.—See Stephen Gould Corporation; *U.S. Private*, pg. 3802
STEPHEN GOULD OF CAROLINA, INC./CHARLOTTE DIV.—See Stephen Gould Corporation; *U.S. Private*, pg. 3802
STEPHEN GOULD OF CAROLINA, INC.—See Stephen Gould Corporation; *U.S. Private*, pg. 3802
STEPHEN GOULD OF COLORADO, INC.—See Stephen Gould Corporation; *U.S. Private*, pg. 3802
STEPHEN GOULD OF CONNECTICUT CORP.—See Stephen Gould Corporation; *U.S. Private*, pg. 3802
STEPHEN GOULD OF ILLINOIS, INC.—See Stephen Gould Corporation; *U.S. Private*, pg. 3802
STEPHEN GOULD OF INDIANA, INC.—See Stephen Gould Corporation; *U.S. Private*, pg. 3802
STEPHEN GOULD OF MARYLAND, INC.—See Stephen Gould Corporation; *U.S. Private*, pg. 3802
STEPHEN GOULD OF MICHIGAN, INC.—See Stephen Gould Corporation; *U.S. Private*, pg. 3802
STEPHEN GOULD OF NEW ENGLAND, INC.—See Stephen Gould Corporation; *U.S. Private*, pg. 3802
STEPHEN GOULD OF OHIO, CORP.—See Stephen Gould Corporation; *U.S. Private*, pg. 3802
STEPHEN GOULD OF OHIO, CORP.—See Stephen Gould Corporation; *U.S. Private*, pg. 3802
STEPHEN GOULD OF PENNSYLVANIA CORP.—See Stephen Gould Corporation; *U.S. Private*, pg. 3802
STEPHEN GOULD OF PUERTO RICO, INC.—See Stephen Gould Corporation; *U.S. Private*, pg. 3802
STEPHEN GOULD OF ROCHESTER—See Stephen Gould Corporation; *U.S. Private*, pg. 3802
STEPHEN GOULD OF TENNESSEE, INC.—See Stephen Gould Corporation; *U.S. Private*, pg. 3802
STEPHEN GOULD OF TEXAS, INC.—See Stephen Gould Corporation; *U.S. Private*, pg. 3802
STEPHEN GOULD PAPER CO., INC.—See Stephen Gould Corporation; *U.S. Private*, pg. 3802
STEPHEN GROSS & SONS INC.; *U.S. Private*, pg. 3802
STEPHEN IMPORTS INC.; *U.S. Private*, pg. 3802
STEPHEN JAMES ASSOCIATES, INC.—See Allegis Group, Inc.; *U.S. Private*, pg. 177
STEPHEN L. LAFRANCE PHARMACY, INC.—See Walgreens Boots Alliance, Inc.; *U.S. Public*, pg. 2323
STEPHEN PASTURE SEEDS PTY LIMITED—See Agria Corporation; *Int'l*, pg. 216
STEPHEN PONTIAC-CADILLAC, INC.; *U.S. Private*, pg. 3802
STEPHEN R. HAKY FUNERAL HOME, INC.—See Axar Capital Management L.P.; *U.S. Private*, pg. 412
STEPHENS & ASSOCIATES ADVERTISING, INC.; *U.S. Private*, pg. 3803
STEPHENS CAPITAL PARTNERS LLC—See SF Holding Corp.; *U.S. Private*, pg. 3621
STEPHENS FLOOR COVERING CO. INC.; *U.S. Private*, pg. 3803
THE STEPHENS GROUP, LLC; *U.S. Private*, pg. 4121
STEPHENS, INC.—See SF Holding Corp.; *U.S. Private*, pg. 3621
STEPHENS MEDIA GROUP MANAGEMENT, LLC; *U.S. Private*, pg. 3803
STEPHENS MEDIA GROUP-WATERTOWN, LLC—See Stephens Media Group Management, LLC; *U.S. Private*, pg. 3803
STEPHENSON EQUIPMENT, INC.; *U.S. Private*, pg. 3803
STEPHENSON GOBIN LTD—See British Engines Ltd.; *Int'l*, pg. 1171
STEPHENSON GROUP; *U.S. Private*, pg. 3803
STEPHENSON GROUP—See Stephenson Group; *U.S. Private*, pg. 3803
STEPHENSON LASER CENTER, L.L.C.—See HCA Healthcare, Inc.; *U.S. Public*, pg. 1010
STEPHENSON LUMBER COMPANY; *U.S. Private*, pg. 3803
STEPHENSON MARKETING COOPERATIVE, INC.; *U.S. Private*, pg. 3803
STEPHENSON MILLWORK CO. INC.; *U.S. Private*, pg. 3803
STEPHENSON NATIONAL BANK & TRUST; *U.S. Private*, pg. 3803
STEPHENSON OIL CO., INC.; *U.S. Private*, pg. 3803
STEPHENSON PARK (WALLSEND) RESIDENTS MANAGEMENT COMPANY LIMITED—See Persimmon plc; *Int'l*, pg. 5817
STEPHENSON PRINTING, INC.; *U.S. Private*, pg. 3803
STEPHENSON WHOLESALE COMPANY INC.; *U.S. Private*, pg. 3803
STEPHENS PIPE & STEEL INC.; *U.S. Private*, pg. 3803
STEPHENS PRODUCTION COMPANY—See SF Holding Corp.; *U.S. Private*, pg. 3621
STEPHENS PROPERTIES SDN BHD—See Berjaya Corporation Berhad; *Int'l*, pg. 984
STEPHENS & SMITH CONSTRUCTION CO. INC; *U.S. Private*, pg. 3803
STEPHEN WADE AUTO CENTER; *U.S. Private*, pg. 3802
THE STEPHENZ GROUP, INC.; *U.S. Private*, pg. 4121

STEPHERSON INCORPORATED; *U.S. Private*, pg. 3803
STEP KIDS EDUCATION GMBH—See AcadeMedia AB; *Int'l*, pg. 77
STEP KIDS KITAS GMBH—See AcadeMedia AB; *Int'l*, pg. 77
STEP NEXUS LTD—See Thales S.A.; *Int'l*, pg. 7600
STEP OILTOOLS AS—See Akastor ASA; *Int'l*, pg. 260
STEP OILTOOLS (AUSTRALIA) PTY LTD—See Akastor ASA; *Int'l*, pg. 260
STEP OILTOOLS GMBH—See Akastor ASA; *Int'l*, pg. 260
STEP OILTOOLS LLC—See Akastor ASA; *Int'l*, pg. 260
STEP OILTOOLS LLP—See Akastor ASA; *Int'l*, pg. 260
STEP OILTOOLS PTE LTD—See Akastor ASA; *Int'l*, pg. 260
STEP OILTOOLS (THAILAND) LTD.—See Akastor ASA; *Int'l*, pg. 260
STEP OILTOOLS (UK) LTD.—See Akastor ASA; *Int'l*, pg. 260
STEP ONE CLOTHING LIMITED; *Int'l*, pg. 7208
STEPPE CEMENT LTD.; *Int'l*, pg. 7208
STEPPE GOLD LTD.; *Int'l*, pg. 7208
STEPP EQUIPMENT COMPANY—See H.I.G. Capital, LLC; *U.S. Private*, pg. 1833
STEPPER FRANCE—See Arts Optical International Holdings Ltd; *Int'l*, pg. 586
STEPPER SOUTH AFRICA (PROPRIETARY) LIMITED—See Arts Optical International Holdings Ltd; *Int'l*, pg. 586
STEPPING STONES HEALTHCARE SERVICES, LLC—See Rothschild & Co SCA; *Int'l*, pg. 6403
STEP SIGRINER ELEKTRONIK GMBH—See Shanghai STEP Electric Corporation; *Int'l*, pg. 6779
STEPSTONE DEUTSCHLAND GMBH—See Axel Springer SE; *Int'l*, pg. 767
STEPSTONE GESTAO DE RECURSOS LTDA.—See StepStone Group Inc.; *U.S. Public*, pg. 1945
STEPSTONE GMBH—See Axel Springer SE; *Int'l*, pg. 766
STEPSTONE GROUP (CHINA) LIMITED—See StepStone Group Inc.; *U.S. Public*, pg. 1945
STEPSTONE GROUP EUROPE ALTERNATIVE INVESTMENTS LIMITED—See StepStone Group Inc.; *U.S. Public*, pg. 1945
STEPSTONE GROUP (HK) LIMITED—See StepStone Group Inc.; *U.S. Public*, pg. 1945
STEPSTONE GROUP INC.; *U.S. Public*, pg. 1945
STEPSTONE GROUP LP; *U.S. Private*, pg. 3803
STEPSTONE GROUP REAL ESTATE LP—See StepStone Group LP; *U.S. Private*, pg. 3804
STEPSTONE, INC.; *U.S. Private*, pg. 3804
STEPSTONE NV—See Axel Springer SE; *Int'l*, pg. 767
STEPSTONE OSTERREICH GMBH—See Axel Springer SE; *Int'l*, pg. 767
STEPSTONE PL SP. Z O.O.—See Axel Springer SE; *Int'l*, pg. 767
STEPSTONE SERVICES SP. Z O.O.—See Axel Springer SE; *Int'l*, pg. 767
STEP-TEC AG—See Mikron Holding AG; *Int'l*, pg. 4893
STEPTOE & JOHNSON LLP; *U.S. Private*, pg. 3804
STEP TWO CORPORATION LIMITED; *Int'l*, pg. 7208
STEP UP FOR STUDENTS, INC.; *U.S. Private*, pg. 3801
STEP-UP PRODUCTIONS, INC.—See Lions Gate Entertainment Corp.; *U.S. Private*, pg. 4521
ST EQUIPMENT & TECHNOLOGY LLC—See Titan Cement Company S.A.; *Int'l*, pg. 7759
ST EQUIPMENT & TECHNOLOGY LLC—See Titan Cement Company S.A.; *Int'l*, pg. 7759
STER CINEMAS A.E.—See AVE S.A.; *Int'l*, pg. 737
STER COMPANY—See Ster Group; *Int'l*, pg. 7208
STEREAU SAS—See Ardian SAS; *Int'l*, pg. 556
STEREAU SAS—See Caisse des Depots et Consignations; *Int'l*, pg. 1258
STEREN ELECTRONICS INTERNATIONAL LLC; *U.S. Private*, pg. 3804
STEREOCARTO, S.L.—See Airtificial Intelligence Structures SA; *Int'l*, pg. 249
STEREO OPTICAL CO. INC.—See EssilorLuxottica SA; *Int'l*, pg. 2514
STEREO SDN BHD—See Balchem Corporation; *U.S. Public*, pg. 266
STEREOTAXIS, INC.; *U.S. Public*, pg. 1945
STEREO VISION ENTERTAINMENT, INC.; *U.S. Public*, pg. 1945
STER GROUP; *Int'l*, pg. 7208
STERIA MUMMERT CONSULTING GMBH—See Sopra Steria Group S.A.; *Int'l*, pg. 7110
STERICARE ROMANIA—See Waste Management, Inc.; *U.S. Public*, pg. 2332
STERICYCLE COMMUNICATION SOLUTIONS, INC.—See Infomedia Group Inc; *U.S. Private*, pg. 2072
STERICYCLE ENVIRONMENTAL SOLUTIONS, INC.—See Enviri Corporation; *U.S. Public*, pg. 781
STERICYCLE HOKKAIDO GK—See Waste Management, Inc.; *U.S. Public*, pg. 2332
STERICYCLE, INC.—See Waste Management, Inc.; *U.S. Public*, pg. 2332
STERICYCLE INC.—See Waste Management, Inc.; *U.S. Public*, pg. 2332
STERICYCLE INTERNATIONAL, LLC—See Waste Management, Inc.; *U.S. Public*, pg. 2332

STER GROUP

STERICYCLE JAPAN CO. LTD.—See Waste Management, Inc.; *U.S. Public*, pg. 2332
STERICYCLE KOREA CO LTD.—See Waste Management, Inc.; *U.S. Public*, pg. 2332
STERICYCLE PORTUGAL—See Waste Management, Inc.; *U.S. Public*, pg. 2332
STERICYCLE ROMANIA, SRL—See Waste Management, Inc.; *U.S. Public*, pg. 2332
STERICYCLE SPECIALTY WASTE SOLUTIONS, INC.—See Waste Management, Inc.; *U.S. Public*, pg. 2332
STERICYCLE ULC—See Waste Management, Inc.; *U.S. Public*, pg. 2332
STERIDOSE SALES AB—See IDEX Corp; *U.S. Public*, pg. 1092
STERIDOSE SALES INC.—See IDEX Corp; *U.S. Public*, pg. 1092
STERIFAST STERILIZATION & DISINFECTION SYSTEMS, LDA.—See Metall Zug AG; *Int'l*, pg. 4846
STERIFAST STERILIZATION & DISINFECTION SYSTEMS, LDA.—See Miele & Cie KG; *Int'l*, pg. 4890
STERIFLOW SAS—See Groupe SFPI SA; *Int'l*, pg. 3111
STERIFX, INC.—See Synergy Technologies, Inc.; *U.S. Private*, pg. 3904
STERIGENICS INTERNATIONAL LLC - SHARED SERVICES CENTER—See Warburg Pincus LLC; *U.S. Private*, pg. 4439
STERIGENICS U.S., LLC—See Warburg Pincus LLC; *U.S. Private*, pg. 4439
STERIHEALTH LIMITED; *Int'l*, pg. 7208
STERIHEALTH SERVICES PTY. LTD.—See SteriHealth Limited; *Int'l*, pg. 7208
ST. ERIKS HISS AB—See Sdiptech AB; *Int'l*, pg. 6659
STERILE SERVICES SDN BHD—See KPJ Healthcare Berhad; *Int'l*, pg. 4297
STERILIN LIMITED—See Thermo Fisher Scientific Inc.; *U.S. Public*, pg. 2152
STERILITE CORPORATION; *U.S. Private*, pg. 3804
STERILIZATION SERVICES OF GEORGIA—See Altair Corporation; *U.S. Public*, pg. 86
STERILIZATION SERVICES OF TENNESSEE—See Altair Corporation; *U.S. Public*, pg. 86
STERILIZATION SERVICES OF VIRGINIA—See Altair Corporation; *U.S. Public*, pg. 86
STERILMED, INC.—See Johnson & Johnson; *U.S. Public*, pg. 1200
STERILSYSTEMS GMBH—See Dr. Honle AG; *Int'l*, pg. 2192
STERILUMEN, INC.—See Applied UV, Inc.; *U.S. Public*, pg. 173
STERIMEDIX LIMITED—See Bausch Health Companies Inc.; *U.S. Public*, pg. 897
STERI-MED PHARMA INC.—See LSL Pharma Group Inc.; *Int'l*, pg. 4570
STERIMED SRL—See SOL S.p.A.; *Int'l*, pg. 7068
STERIPAC GMBH—See Eurofins Scientific S.E.; *Int'l*, pg. 2552
STERIPACK ASIA SDN BHD—See Inflexion Private Equity Partners LLP; *Int'l*, pg. 3689
STERIPACK GROUP LTD.—See Inflexion Private Equity Partners LLP; *Int'l*, pg. 3689
STERIPACK MEDICAL POLAND SP. Z O.O.—See Inflexion Private Equity Partners LLP; *Int'l*, pg. 3689
STERIPACK USA LLC—See Inflexion Private Equity Partners LLP; *Int'l*, pg. 3689
STERIPLUS AG—See Die Schweizerische Post AG; *Int'l*, pg. 2113
STERIS-AUSTAR PHARMACEUTICAL SYSTEMS HONG KONG LIMITED—See STERIS plc; *Int'l*, pg. 7211
STERIS BARRIER PRODUCTS SOLUTIONS, INC.—See STERIS plc; *Int'l*, pg. 7210
STERIS BRASIL SERVICOS ADMINISTRATIVOS LTDA.—See STERIS plc; *Int'l*, pg. 7210
STERIS CANADA CORPORATION—See STERIS plc; *Int'l*, pg. 7210
STERIS CANADA, INC.—See STERIS plc; *Int'l*, pg. 7210
STERIS CORPORATION - MONTGOMERY PLANT—See STERIS plc; *Int'l*, pg. 7210
STERIS CORPORATION—See STERIS plc; *Int'l*, pg. 7209
STERIS DEUTSCHLAND GMBH—See STERIS plc; *Int'l*, pg. 7210
STERIS FINN-AQUA—See STERIS plc; *Int'l*, pg. 7210
STERIS GMBH—See STERIS plc; *Int'l*, pg. 7210
STERISIL, INC.—See Avista Capital Partners, L.P.; *U.S. Private*, pg. 409
STERIS (INDIA) PRIVATE LIMITED—See STERIS plc; *Int'l*, pg. 7210
STERIS JAPAN, INC.—See STERIS plc; *Int'l*, pg. 7210
STERIS LIMITED—See STERIS plc; *Int'l*, pg. 7210
STERIS NV—See STERIS plc; *Int'l*, pg. 7211
STERIS PLC; *Int'l*, pg. 7208
STERIS SAS—See STERIS plc; *Int'l*, pg. 7211
STERIS SINGAPORE PTE. LTD.—See STERIS plc; *Int'l*, pg. 7211
STERIS SOLUTIONS LIMITED—See STERIS plc; *Int'l*, pg. 7210
STERIS SPRL/BVRA—See STERIS plc; *Int'l*, pg. 7211
STERIS S.R.L.—See STERIS plc; *Int'l*, pg. 7211
STERIS USA DISTRIBUTION CORPORATION—See STERIS plc; *Int'l*, pg. 7211
THE STERITECH GROUP, INC.—See Rentokil Initial plc; *Int'l*, pg. 6289
STERITEC PRODUCTS MFG. CO., INC.—See Getinge AB; *Int'l*, pg. 2952
STER-KINEKOR THEATRES—See Primedia Limited; *Int'l*, pg. 5979
STERKOVNY A PISKOVNY BRNO A.S.—See Heidelberg Materials AG; *Int'l*, pg. 3310
STERKS SUPER FOODS INC.; *U.S. Private*, pg. 3804
STERLING ABRASIVES LTD—See The Murugappa Group, Ltd.; *Int'l*, pg. 7668
STERLING ACCEPTANCE CORP.; *U.S. Private*, pg. 3804
STERLING ACCESS CC—See Haulotte Group SA; *Int'l*, pg. 3285
STERLING ACQUISTION CORP—See Omega Healthcare Investors, Inc.; *U.S. Public*, pg. 1572
STERLING ADVERTISING CO.; *U.S. Private*, pg. 3804
STERLING ADVISORS—See Truist Financial Corporation; *U.S. Public*, pg. 2201
STERLING AIRLINES A/S; *Int'l*, pg. 7211
STERLING AIR SERVICES, LLC—See Brookfield Corporation; *Int'l*, pg. 1188
STERLING AMERICAN PROPERTY INC.; *U.S. Private*, pg. 3804
STERLING AND WILSON PVT. LTD.—See Shapoorji Pallonji & Co. Ltd.; *Int'l*, pg. 6788
STERLING-ASHTON-SCHWAB FUNERAL HOME, INC.—See Service Corporation International; *U.S. Public*, pg. 1871
STERLING-ASHTON-SCHWAB-WITZKE FUNERAL HOME OF CATONSVILLE, INC.—See Service Corporation International; *U.S. Public*, pg. 1871
STERLING AVIATION, INC.; *U.S. Private*, pg. 3804
STERLING BANCORP, INC.; *U.S. Public*, pg. 1946
STERLING BANCORP; *U.S. Public*, pg. 1946
STERLING BANCSHARES, INC.; *U.S. Private*, pg. 3804
STERLING BANK PLC; *Int'l*, pg. 7211
STERLING BANK—See Sterling Bancshares, Inc.; *U.S. Private*, pg. 3804
STERLING BANK & TRUST, FSB—See Sterling Bancorp, Inc.; *U.S. Public*, pg. 1946
STERLING BIOTECH LTD.; *Int'l*, pg. 7211
STERLING-BM, LLC—See Lithia Motors, Inc.; *U.S. Public*, pg. 1326
STERLING BOILER & MECHANICAL INC.; *U.S. Private*, pg. 3804
STERLING BRANDS—See Omnicom Group Inc.; *U.S. Public*, pg. 1594
STERLING BUILDING SYSTEMS, INC.—See Wausau Homes, Inc.; *U.S. Public*, pg. 4457
STERLING BUSINESS FORMS INC.; *U.S. Private*, pg. 3804
STERLING CAPITAL MANAGEMENT LLC—See Guardian Capital Group Limited; *Int'l*, pg. 3170
STERLING CAPITAL MANAGEMENT LLC—See Guardian Capital Group Limited; *Int'l*, pg. 3170
STERLING CAPITAL MANAGEMENT LLC - WASHINGTON—See Guardian Capital Group Limited; *Int'l*, pg. 3170
STERLING CASUALTY INSURANCE COMPANY INC.—See H&H Agency, Inc.; *U.S. Private*, pg. 1822
STERLING CAVIAR LLC—See Stolt-Nielsen Limited; *Int'l*, pg. 7221
STERLING CHECK CORP.; *U.S. Public*, pg. 1946
STERLING COMMERCIAL CREDIT; *U.S. Private*, pg. 3804
STERLING COMMUNICATIONS; *U.S. Private*, pg. 3804
STERLING COMPUTERS; *U.S. Private*, pg. 3805
STERLING CONSOLIDATED CORP.; *U.S. Public*, pg. 1946
STERLING CONSTRUCTION COMPANY; *U.S. Private*, pg. 3805
STERLING CONTROLS, INC.—See DNS Capital, LLC; *U.S. Private*, pg. 1249
STERLING CORPORATION; *U.S. Private*, pg. 3805
THE STERLING CORPORATION—See Lambert & Co.; *U.S. Private*, pg. 2380
STERLING CRANE - CONTRACT LIFTING DIVISION—See Berkshire Hathaway Inc.; *U.S. Public*, pg. 309
STERLING CRANE - RENTALS DIVISION—See Berkshire Hathaway Inc.; *U.S. Public*, pg. 309
STERLING CRANE—See Berkshire Hathaway Inc.; *U.S. Public*, pg. 309
STERLING CUT GLASS COMPANY, INC.; *U.S. Private*, pg. 3805
STERLING ELECTRIC, INC.; *U.S. Private*, pg. 3805
STERLING-ENERGY LLC—See Commerzbank AG; *Int'l*, pg. 1719
STERLING ENERGY RESOURCES INC.; *U.S. Public*, pg. 1946
STERLING ENERGY (UK) LIMITED—See Afentra plc; *Int'l*, pg. 185
STERLING ENGINEERING CORPORATION—See Air Industries Group; *U.S. Public*, pg. 64
STERLING ENGINEERING, INC.; *U.S. Private*, pg. 3805
STERLING ENTERTAINMENT ENTERPRISES, LLC—See Sterling Equities, Inc.; *U.S. Private*, pg. 3805
STERLING EQUITIES, INC.; *U.S. Private*, pg. 3805
STERLING FACTORS CORPORATION—See Sterling Bancorp; *U.S. Public*, pg. 1946
STERLING FEDERAL BANK FSB; *U.S. Public*, pg. 3805
STERLING FINANCE COMPANY—See Mathes Management Enterprises; *U.S. Private*, pg. 2610
STERLING FLUID SYSTEMS (AUSTRIA) GMBH—See Flowserve Corporation; *U.S. Public*, pg. 857
STERLING FLUID SYSTEMS (CZECH REPUBLIC) S.R.O.—See Flowserve Corporation; *U.S. Public*, pg. 857
STERLING FLUID SYSTEMS (HUNGARIA) KFT.—See Flowserve Corporation; *U.S. Public*, pg. 857
STERLING FLUID SYSTEMS (ITALY) S.P.A.—See Flowserve Corporation; *U.S. Public*, pg. 857
STERLING FLUID SYSTEMS (POLASKA) SP.ZO.O.—See Flowserve Corporation; *U.S. Public*, pg. 857
STERLING FLUID SYSTEMS (POLSKA) SP.ZQ.O.—See Flowserve Corporation; *U.S. Public*, pg. 857
STERLING FLUID SYSTEMS (ROMANIA) S.R.L.—See Flowserve Corporation; *U.S. Public*, pg. 857
STERLING FLUID SYSTEMS (UK) LIMITED—See TBG Holdings NV; *Int'l*, pg. 7479
STERLING FOODS, LLC—See Cotton Creek Capital Management LLC; *U.S. Private*, pg. 1063
STERLING FORD SALES (OTTAWA) INC.; *Int'l*, pg. 7211
STERLING FURNITURE CO; *U.S. Private*, pg. 3805
STERLING GLOBAL OPERATIONS, INC.; *U.S. Private*, pg. 3805
STERLING GOLD MINING CORPORATION—See Imperial Metals Corporation; *Int'l*, pg. 3635
STERLING GREENWOODS LTD.; *Int'l*, pg. 7211
STERLING GROUP HOLDINGS LIMITED; *Int'l*, pg. 7211
THE STERLING GROUP, L.P.; *U.S. Private*, pg. 4121
STERLING GROUP SERVICES PTY LTD—See CityWide Service Solutions Pty Ltd; *Int'l*, pg. 1630
STERLING GROUP VENTURES, INC.; *Int'l*, pg. 7211
STERLING GUARANTY & FINANCE LTD.; *Int'l*, pg. 7211
STERLING HAWAII ASPHALT, LLC—See Sterling Infrastructure, Inc.; *U.S. Public*, pg. 1947
STERLING HEALTHCARE SERVICES, INC.—See CVS Health Corporation; *U.S. Public*, pg. 616
STERLING HEIGHTS DODGE, INC.; *U.S. Private*, pg. 3805
STERLING HOLDINGS INC.; *U.S. Private*, pg. 3805
STERLING HOLIDAY RESORTS (INDIA) LIMITED—See Fairfax Financial Holdings Limited; *Int'l*, pg. 2608
STERLING HOUSING LLC; *U.S. Private*, pg. 3805
STERLING, INC.—See Harbour Group Industries, Inc.; *U.S. Private*, pg. 1860
STERLING INDUSTRIES LTD.—See Caledonia Investments plc; *Int'l*, pg. 1262
STERLING INDUSTRY CONSULT GMBH—See Flowserve Corporation; *U.S. Public*, pg. 857
STERLING INFOSYSTEMS, INC.—See Caisse de Depot et Placement du Quebec; *Int'l*, pg. 1255
STERLING INFOSYSTEMS, INC.—See The Goldman Sachs Group, Inc.; *U.S. Public*, pg. 2080
STERLING INFRASTRUCTURE, INC.; *U.S. Public*, pg. 1946
STERLING INSTRUMENT DIV.—See Designatronics, Inc.; *U.S. Private*, pg. 1214
STERLING INTERNATIONAL ENTERPRISES LIMITED; *Int'l*, pg. 7211
STERLING INTERNATIONAL, INC.—See A. Arnold Moving Company, Inc.; *U.S. Private*, pg. 22
STERLING INTERNATIONAL INC.; *U.S. Private*, pg. 3805
STERLING INVESTMENT PARTNERS, L.P.; *U.S. Private*, pg. 3805
STERLING JEWELERS, INC.—See Signet Jewelers Limited; *Int'l*, pg. 6911
STERLING LIFE INSURANCE COMPANY—See Munchener Ruckversicherungs AG; *Int'l*, pg. 5091
STERLING LOGISTICS, LLC—See Neste Oyj; *Int'l*, pg. 5202
STERLING-LOHJA LTD.—See UPM-Kymmene Corporation; *Int'l*, pg. 8091
STERLING LUMBER COMPANY; *U.S. Private*, pg. 3806
STERLING LUMBER & INVESTMENT CO.; *U.S. Private*, pg. 3806
STERLING MACHINERY CO., INC.—See KONE Oyj; *Int'l*, pg. 4249
STERLING MARKING PRODUCTS LTD.; *Int'l*, pg. 7211
STERLING MCCALL CADILLAC—See Group 1 Automotive, Inc.; *U.S. Public*, pg. 972
STERLING MCCALL HONDA—See Group 1 Automotive, Inc.; *U.S. Public*, pg. 972
STERLING MCCALL TOYOTA GROUP—See Group 1 Automotive, Inc.; *U.S. Public*, pg. 972
STERLING METALS CORP.; *Int'l*, pg. 7212
STERLING METS, L.P.—See Sterling Equities, Inc.; *U.S. Private*, pg. 3805
STERLING MOTOR PROPERTIES LIMITED—See General Motors Company; *U.S. Public*, pg. 928
STERLING NATIONAL BANK—See Sterling Bancorp; *U.S. Public*, pg. 1946

COMPANY NAME INDEX STEVES CHEVROLET-BUICK, INC.

Company Index

STERLING NATIONAL INSURANCE AGENCY INC—See QBE Insurance Group Limited; *Int'l*, pg. 6137
STERLING NATIONAL MORTGAGE COMPANY, INC.—See Sterling Bancorp; *U.S. Public*, pg. 1946
STERLING ORGANIZATION; *U.S. Private*, pg. 3806
STERLING PAPER COMPANY; *U.S. Private*, pg. 3806
STERLING PAPER CO.; *U.S. Private*, pg. 3806
STERLING PARTNERS - CHICAGO OFFICE—See Sterling Partners; *U.S. Private*, pg. 3806
STERLING PARTNERS; *U.S. Private*, pg. 3806
STERLING PAYMENT TECHNOLOGIES, INC.—See EVO Payments International, LLC; *U.S. Private*, pg. 1442
STERLING PHARMA SOLUTIONS LTD.—See GHO Capital Partners LLP; *Int'l*, pg. 2959
STERLING PIPE & TUBE INC.; *U.S. Private*, pg. 3807
STERLING PLANNERS PTY. LTD.—See Azimut Holding SpA; *Int'l*, pg. 779
STERLING PLANTATIONS LIMITED; *Int'l*, pg. 7212
STERLING PLUMBING, INC.—See Kohler Company; *U.S. Private*, pg. 2340
STERLING PONTIAC BUICK GMC INC.; *U.S. Private*, pg. 3807
STERLING POWERGENSYS LIMITED; *Int'l*, pg. 7212
STERLING PRIMARY CARE ASSOCIATES, LLC—See HCA Healthcare, Inc.; *U.S. Public*, pg. 1010
STERLING PRODUCTS LIMITED—See Edward B. Beharry & Co. Ltd.; *Int'l*, pg. 2316
STERLING PUBLISHING CO., INC.—See Elliott Management Corporation; *U.S. Private*, pg. 1365
STERLING PUMPS PTY LIMITED—See WPIL Limited; *Int'l*, pg. 8462
STERLING QUAIL CREEK, LLC—See Sterling Real Estate Trust; *U.S. Private*, pg. 3807
STERLING REAL ESTATE TRUST; *U.S. Private*, pg. 3807
STERLING REALTY ORGANIZATION CO.; *U.S. Private*, pg. 3807
STERLING RE INC.—See Swiss Re Ltd.; *Int'l*, pg. 7372
STERLING RESOURCE FUNDING CORP.—See Sterling Bancorp; *U.S. Public*, pg. 1946
STERLING RICE GROUP; *U.S. Private*, pg. 3807
STERLING RIDGE MEDICAL CENTER LLC—See Adeptus Health Inc.; *U.S. Private*, pg. 78
STERLING-RLM, LLC—See Lithia Motors, Inc.; *U.S. Public*, pg. 1326
STERLING SEAL & SUPPLY, INC.—See Sterling Consolidated Corp.; *U.S. Public*, pg. 1946
STERLING SERVICE INC.; *U.S. Private*, pg. 3807
STERLING SIHI BULGARIA EOOD—See Flowserve Corporation; *U.S. Public*, pg. 857
STERLING SIHI GMBH—See TBG Holdings NV; *Int'l*, pg. 7479
STERLING SIHI (NETHERLANDS) B.V.—See Flowserve Corporation; *U.S. Public*, pg. 857
STERLING SOFTWARE (NETHERLANDS) IV B.V.—See Broadcom Inc.; *U.S. Public*, pg. 390
STERLING SOFTWARE PRIVATE LIMITED—See Computer Age Management Services Limited; *Int'l*, pg. 1759
STERLING SOLUTIONS, LLC—See Where Food Comes From, Inc.; *U.S. Public*, pg. 2366
STERLING SPRING LLC; *U.S. Private*, pg. 3807
STERLING STEEL COMPANY, LLC—See Leggett & Platt, Incorporated; *U.S. Public*, pg. 1303
STERLING & STERLING, INC.—See Ontario Teachers' Pension Plan; *Int'l*, pg. 5590
STERLING SUGARS INC.—See M.A. Patout & Son Limited; *U.S. Private*, pg. 2528
STERLING SUPPLY CO. INC.; *U.S. Private*, pg. 3807
STERLINGTECH, INC.—See Ampersand Management LLC; *U.S. Private*, pg. 265
STERLING THERMAL TECHNOLOGY LIMITED—See Caledonia Investments plc; *Int'l*, pg. 1262
STERLING TOOLS LIMITED; *Int'l*, pg. 7212
STERLING TRADE CAPITAL—See Sterling Bancorp; *U.S. Public*, pg. 1946
STERLING TRADER, INC.—See Professional Trading Solutions, Inc.; *U.S. Private*, pg. 3276
STERLING TRUST COMPANY—See Equity Trust Company; *U.S. Private*, pg. 1416
STERLING TRUST PROFESSIONAL (SHEFFIELD) LIMITED—See Kingswood Holdings Ltd.; *Int'l*, pg. 4180
STERLING VALLEY SYSTEMS, INC.—See EagleTree Capital, LP; *U.S. Private*, pg. 1312
STERLING-VELCON FILTERS CORP.—See Parker Hannifin Corporation; *U.S. Public*, pg. 1649
STERLING VINEYARDS—See Treasury Wine Estates Limited; *Int'l*, pg. 7909
STERLING WHITE HALIBUT AS; *Int'l*, pg. 7212
STERLING & WILSON SOLAR LIMITED; *Int'l*, pg. 7211
STERLITECH CORPORATION; *U.S. Private*, pg. 3807
STERLITE CONDUSPAR INDUSTRIAL LTDA—See Sterlite Technologies Limited; *Int'l*, pg. 7212
STERLITE TECHNOLOGIES DMCC—See Sterlite Technologies Limited; *Int'l*, pg. 7212
STERLITE TECHNOLOGIES LIMITED; *Int'l*, pg. 7212
STERLITE TECHNOLOGIES S.P.A—See Sterlite Technologies Limited; *Int'l*, pg. 7212
STERMEDIA SP. Z O.O.—See Work Service S.A.; *Int'l*, pg. 8455
STERN APOTHEKE AG—See CSL Limited; *Int'l*, pg. 1866
STERN + ASSOCIATES—See Stern Strategy Group; *U.S. Private*, pg. 3807
STERNBERG CHRYSLER PLYMOUTH; *U.S. Private*, pg. 3807
STERN CARDIOVASCULAR FOUNDATION; *U.S. Private*, pg. 3807
STERN.DE GMBH—See Bertelsmann SE & Co. KGaA; *Int'l*, pg. 997
STERNE ACURA; *Int'l*, pg. 7212
STERN ENERGY LTD.—See Encavis AG; *Int'l*, pg. 2401
STERN ENERGY S.P.A.—See Encavis AG; *Int'l*, pg. 2401
STERN IMMOBILIEN AG; *Int'l*, pg. 7212
STERN INTERNATIONAL LTD.—See Shantivijay Jewels Ltd.; *Int'l*, pg. 6785
STERN INVESTOR RELATIONS, INC.—See Precision Medicine Group, Inc.; *U.S. Private*, pg. 3245
STERN METALS, INC.—See Berkshire Hathaway Inc.; *U.S. Public*, pg. 316
STERN OIL COMPANY INC.; *U.S. Private*, pg. 3807
STERNO PRODUCTS, LLC—See Compass Diversified Holdings; *U.S. Public*, pg. 560
STERN PARTNERS INC.; *Int'l*, pg. 7212
STERN & STERN INDUSTRIES INC.; *U.S. Private*, pg. 3807
STERN STEWART CAPITAL GMBH—See Stern Stewart & Co. GmbH; *Int'l*, pg. 7212
STERN STEWART & CO. GMBH; *Int'l*, pg. 7212
STERN STRATEGY GROUP; *U.S. Private*, pg. 3807
STERNVENT CO., INC.—See Durex Inc.; *U.S. Private*, pg. 1293
STER PETROLEUM LLC—See Ster Group; *Int'l*, pg. 7208
STERR & EDER INDUSTRIESERVICE GMBH—See Quaker Chemical Corporation; *U.S. Public*, pg. 1747
STERRX, LLC—See Nichi-Iko Pharmaceutical Co., Ltd.; *Int'l*, pg. 5266
STER SECURITY—See Ster Group; *Int'l*, pg. 7208
STE SACEM TRAINING SA—See Kuwait Projects Company (Holding) K.S.C.P.; *Int'l*, pg. 4347
STESA—See Thales S.A.; *Int'l*, pg. 7601
STESA—See Thales S.A.; *Int'l*, pg. 7601
STESSA, INC.—See Roofstock, Inc.; *U.S. Private*, pg. 3479
STET HOLLAND B.V.—See HZPC Holland B.V.; *Int'l*, pg. 3561
STETSON BUILDING PRODUCTS, LLC—See The Sterling Group, L.P.; *U.S. Private*, pg. 4122
STETSON ENGINEERING, INC.—See HDR, Inc.; *U.S. Private*, pg. 1890
STETSON HAT CO.—See Pro Equine Products Inc.; *U.S. Private*, pg. 3269
STETSON MOTORS 2000 LTD; *Int'l*, pg. 7212
STETTIN BAY LUMBER CO. LTD.—See Sojitz Corporation; *Int'l*, pg. 7065
STEUART INVESTMENT COMPANY; *U.S. Private*, pg. 3807
STEUART-KRET HOMES—See Steuart Investment Company; *U.S. Private*, pg. 3807
STEUBEN FOODS INC.; *U.S. Private*, pg. 3807
STEUBEN GAS STORAGE COMPANY—See Crestwood Equity Partners LP; *U.S. Public*, pg. 594
STEUBENVILLE TRUCK CENTER, INC.—See American Securities LLC; *U.S. Private*, pg. 248
STEUER-FACHSCHULE DR. ENDRISS GMBH & CO. KG—See Amadeus Fire AG; *Int'l*, pg. 405
STEVANATO GROUP S.P.A.; *Int'l*, pg. 7212
STEVA OY—See Lone Star Funds; *U.S. Private*, pg. 2486
STEVE BARRY BUICK INC.; *U.S. Private*, pg. 3807
STEVE CASEY MOTORS INC.; *U.S. Private*, pg. 3808
STEVE CONNOLLY SEAFOODS CO; *U.S. Private*, pg. 3808
STEVE COURY BUICK PONTIAC GMC; *U.S. Private*, pg. 3808
STEVE DEYOUNG'S BIG TOP MARKET; *U.S. Private*, pg. 3808
STEVEDORING SERVICES LTD.; *Int'l*, pg. 7213
STEVE FOLEY CADILLAC; *U.S. Private*, pg. 3808
STEVE HENDERSON LOGGING INC.; *U.S. Private*, pg. 3808
STEVE HOPKINS INC.; *U.S. Private*, pg. 3808
ST. EVE INTERNATIONAL, INC.—See Komar Company; *U.S. Private*, pg. 2341
STEVE LEUNG DESIGNERS (BEIJING) LIMITED—See Steve Leung Design Group Ltd.; *Int'l*, pg. 7213
STEVE LEUNG DESIGN GROUP LTD.; *Int'l*, pg. 7213
STEVE LEUNG EXCHANGE LIMITED—See Steve Leung Design Group Ltd.; *Int'l*, pg. 7213
STEVE MARSHALL FORD LINCOLN; *Int'l*, pg. 7213
STEVE MARSHALL GROUP LTD.; *Int'l*, pg. 7213
STEVE MOORE CHEVROLET DELRAY, LLC—See AutoNation, Inc.; *U.S. Public*, pg. 237
STEVE MOORE CHEVROLET, LLC—See AutoNation, Inc.; *U.S. Public*, pg. 237
STEVEN DOUGLAS ASSOCIATES, INC.; *U.S. Private*, pg. 3808
STEVEN ENGINEERING, INC.; *U.S. Private*, pg. 3808
STEVEN FELLER P.E., PL—See Yenni Capital, Inc.; *U.S. Private*, pg. 4588
STEVENIN NOLLEVAUX FORGES ET ESTAMPAGE—See Capital Grand Est SAS; *Int'l*, pg. 1311
STEVEN LABEL CORPORATION; *U.S. Private*, pg. 3808
STEVEN MADDEN, LTD.; *U.S. Public*, pg. 1947
STEVEN MARSHALL BUILDING SUPPLIES LIMITED—See Fletcher Building Limited; *Int'l*, pg. 2701
STEVEN MOTOR GROUP; *U.S. Private*, pg. 3808
STEVEN ROBERTS ORIGINAL DESSERTS LLC.; *U.S. Private*, pg. 3808
STEVENS ADVERTISING; *U.S. Private*, pg. 3809
STEVENS AVIATION INC.; *U.S. Private*, pg. 3809
STEVENS COMMUNICATIONS INC.; *U.S. Private*, pg. 3809
STEVENS COMMUNICATIONS, LLC—See Dycom Industries, Inc.; *U.S. Public*, pg. 699
STEVENS COMMUNITY MEDICAL CENTER; *U.S. Private*, pg. 3809
STEVENS CONSTRUCTION CORP; *U.S. Private*, pg. 3809
STEVENS CONSTRUCTION, INC.; *U.S. Private*, pg. 3809
STEVENS CREEK LUXURY IMPORTS, INC.—See AutoNation, Inc.; *U.S. Public*, pg. 237
STEVENS CREEK MOTORS, INC.—See AutoNation, Inc.; *U.S. Public*, pg. 237
STEVENS CREEK QUARRY INC.; *U.S. Private*, pg. 3809
STEVENS CREEK VOLKSWAGEN; *U.S. Private*, pg. 3809
STEVENS' CYCLE SALES INC.; *U.S. Private*, pg. 3810
STEVENS EGAN JOHNSTON PTY. LTD.—See Nutrien Ltd.; *Int'l*, pg. 5493
STEVENS ENGINEERS & CONSTRUCTORS; *U.S. Private*, pg. 3809
STEVENS FILTERITE LIMITED—See Skellerup Holdings Limited; *Int'l*, pg. 6980
STEVENS FKM PUBLIC RELATIONS—See The Company of Others; *U.S. Private*, pg. 4013
STEVENS FORWARDERS INC.—See Stevens Group, Inc.; *U.S. Private*, pg. 3809
STEVENS GROUP, INC.; *U.S. Private*, pg. 3809
STEVENS INDUSTRIES, INC.; *U.S. Private*, pg. 3809
STEVENS KOENIG REPORTING; *U.S. Private*, pg. 3809
THE STEVENS & LEE COMPANIES, LLC; *U.S. Private*, pg. 4123
STEVENS & LEE, P.C.—See The Stevens & Lee Companies, LLC; *U.S. Private*, pg. 4123
STEVENS MANUFACTURING COMPANY INCORPORATED—See Essex Industries, Inc.; *U.S. Private*, pg. 1428
STEVENS MARINE INC.; *U.S. Private*, pg. 3810
STEVENS MATTRESS MFG., INC.—See Restonic Mattress Corporation; *U.S. Private*, pg. 3409
STEVENS MATTRESS OF IOWA, INC.—See Restonic Mattress Corporation; *U.S. Private*, pg. 3409
STEVENS MOTORS LTD—See The Colonial Motor Company Limited; *Int'l*, pg. 7635
STEVENS OFFICE INTERIORS; *U.S. Private*, pg. 3810
THE STEVENSON COLOR COMPANY, INC.—See HPS Investment Partners, LLC; *U.S. Private*, pg. 1997
STEVENSON LOGISTICS PTY. LTD.; *Int'l*, pg. 7213
STEVENSON THE COLOR COMPANY; *U.S. Private*, pg. 3810
STEVENS PASS MOUNTAIN RESORT, LLC—See Vail Resorts, Inc.; *U.S. Public*, pg. 2271
STEVENS POINT JOURNAL—See Gannett Co., Inc.; *U.S. Public*, pg. 899
STEVENS POINT SENIOR LIVING, INC.—See The Ensign Group, Inc.; *U.S. Public*, pg. 2070
STEVENS & STEVENS BUSINESS RECORDS MANAGEMENT, INC.; *U.S. Private*, pg. 3809
STEVENS STRATEGIC COMMUNICATIONS, INC.; *U.S. Private*, pg. 3810
STEVENS TRANSPORTATION CO. INC.—See Stevens Group, Inc.; *U.S. Private*, pg. 3809
STEVENS TRANSPORT INC.; *U.S. Private*, pg. 3810
THE STEVEN STYLE GROUP; *U.S. Private*, pg. 4123
STEVENS VAN LINES INC.—See Stevens Group, Inc.; *U.S. Private*, pg. 3809
STEVENS & WILKINSON GA, INC.—See SSOE Group; *U.S. Private*, pg. 3769
STEVENS & WILKINSON, INC.—See SSOE Group; *U.S. Private*, pg. 3769
STEVENS & WILKINSON SC, INC.—See SSOE Group; *U.S. Private*, pg. 3769
STEVEN TOYOTA SCION; *U.S. Private*, pg. 3808
STEVEN TOYS—See EXX Inc.; *U.S. Private*, pg. 1453
STEVEN WALKER COMMUNITIES, INC; *U.S. Private*, pg. 3809
STEVEN WINTER ASSOCIATES, INC.; *U.S. Private*, pg. 3809
STEVE PADIS JEWELRY PLUS ENTERPRISES; *U.S. Private*, pg. 3808
STEVE PLATZ REALTY INC.; *U.S. Private*, pg. 3808
STEVE P. RADOS, INC.—See The Rados Companies; *U.S. Private*, pg. 4102
STEVE RAYMAN CHEVROLET, LLC—See ZT Corporate; *U.S. Private*, pg. 4609
S&T-EVERGREEN INSURANCE, LLC—See S&T Bancorp, Inc.; *U.S. Public*, pg. 1832
STEVERSON & COMPANY, INC.—See Hamilton-Ryker Company; *U.S. Private*, pg. 1848
STEVES CHEVROLET-BUICK, INC.; *U.S. Private*, pg. 3810

STEVE'S CHEVROLET OF CHOWCHILL, LLC.; *U.S. Private,* pg. 3808
STEVE SCHMITT INC.—See Carriage Corporation; *U.S. Private,* pg. 772
STEVE SELVIN ASSOCIATE INC; *U.S. Private,* pg. 3808
STEVE'S EQUIPMENT SERVICE, INC.; *U.S. Private,* pg. 3808
STEVE SHANNON TIRE COMPANY; *U.S. Private,* pg. 3808
STEVES & SONS, INC.; *U.S. Private,* pg. 3810
STEVE WARD & ASSOCIATES INC.; *U.S. Private,* pg. 3808
STEVE WHITE MOTORS, INC.; *U.S. Private,* pg. 3808
STEVIA CORP.; *U.S. Public,* pg. 1947
STEVIA NUTRA CORP.; *Int'l,* pg. 7213
STEVINSON AUTOMOTIVE INC.; *U.S. Private,* pg. 3810
STEVINSON CHEVROLET-WEST INC—See Stevinson Automotive Inc.; *U.S. Private,* pg. 3810
STEVINSON IMPORTS INC—See Stevinson Automotive Inc.; *U.S. Private,* pg. 3810
STEVINSON LEXUS OF LAKEWOOD—See Stevinson Automotive Inc.; *U.S. Private,* pg. 3810
STEVINSON TOYOTA EAST SCION INC.—See Stevinson Automotive Inc.; *U.S. Private,* pg. 3810
STEVINSON TOYOTA-WEST INC—See Stevinson Automotive Inc.; *U.S. Private,* pg. 3810
STEVVA CORPORATION; *U.S. Private,* pg. 3810
STEWARD CONSTRUCTION SERVICES, LLC; *U.S. Private,* pg. 3810
STEWARD CONSULTING INC.—See Bcs Prosoft; *U.S. Private,* pg. 500
STEWARD EASTON HOSPITAL, INC.—See Steward Health Care System LLC; *U.S. Private,* pg. 3810
STEWARD HEALTH CARE SYSTEM LLC; *U.S. Private,* pg. 3810
STEWARD HILLSIDE REHABILITATION HOSPITAL, INC.—See Steward Health Care System LLC; *U.S. Private,* pg. 3810
STEWARD MARKETING, LLC; *U.S. Private,* pg. 3811
STEWARD MELBOURNE HOSPITAL, INC.—See Steward Health Care System LLC; *U.S. Private,* pg. 3810
STEWARD PARTNERS GLOBAL ADVISORY, LLC; *U.S. Private,* pg. 3811
STEWARD PARTNERS INVESTMENT SOLUTIONS, LLC—See Steward Partners Global Advisory, LLC; *U.S. Private,* pg. 3811
STEWARD ROCKLEDGE HOSPITAL, INC.—See Steward Health Care System LLC; *U.S. Private,* pg. 3810
STEWARD SEBASTIAN RIVER MEDICAL CENTER, INC.—See Steward Health Care System LLC; *U.S. Private,* pg. 3810
STEWARD SHARON REGIONAL HEALTH SYSTEM, INC.—See Steward Health Care System LLC; *U.S. Private,* pg. 3810
STEWARDSHIP FINANCIAL CORPORATION—See Columbia Financial, Inc.; *U.S. Public,* pg. 534
STEWARD STEEL INC.; *U.S. Private,* pg. 3811
STEWARD TRUMBULL MEMORIAL HOSPITAL, INC.—See Steward Health Care System LLC; *U.S. Private,* pg. 3810
STEWART, BRIMNER, PETERS & COMPANY, INC.—See Arthur J. Gallagher & Co.; *U.S. Public,* pg. 207
STEWART BROS INC.; *U.S. Private,* pg. 3811
STEWART BUILDERS LTD; *U.S. Private,* pg. 3811
STEWART BUILDING & ROOFING SUPPLY, INC.—See Leonard Green & Partners, L.P.; *U.S. Private,* pg. 2429
STEWART BUSINESS SYSTEMS, LLC—See Xerox Holdings Corporation; *U.S. Public,* pg. 2388
STEWART BUSINESS SYTEMS—See Xerox Holdings Corporation; *U.S. Public,* pg. 2388
STEWART CAPITAL ADVISORS, LLC—See S&T Bancorp, Inc.; *U.S. Public,* pg. 1832
STEWART CAPITAL PARTNERS LLC; *U.S. Private,* pg. 3811
STEWART C MILLER & CO. INC.; *U.S. Private,* pg. 3811
STEWART CORPORATION; *U.S. Private,* pg. 3811
STEWART DIALYSIS, LLC—See DaVita Inc.; *U.S. Public,* pg. 643
STEWART ENTERPRISES, INC.—See Service Corporation International; *U.S. Public,* pg. 1871
STEWART FILMSCREEN CORPORATION - OHIO—See Stewart Filmscreen Corporation; *U.S. Private,* pg. 3811
STEWART FILMSCREEN CORPORATION; *U.S. Private,* pg. 3811
STEWART FINANCIAL SERVICES, INC.—See Stewart Information Services Corporation; *U.S. Public,* pg. 1948
STEWART GRAIN CO. INC.; *U.S. Private,* pg. 3811
STEWART-HUNT INC.—See AEA Investors LP; *U.S. Private,* pg. 115
STEWART INFORMATION SERVICES CORPORATION; *U.S. Public,* pg. 1947
STEWART INVESTMENT & FINANCIAL PRIVATE LIMITED; *Int'l,* pg. 7213
STEWART MANAGEMENT GROUP INC.; *U.S. Private,* pg. 3811
STEWART MILLER MCCULLOCH & CO. LIMITED—See White Mountains Insurance Group, Ltd.; *U.S. Public,* pg. 2369

STEWART OF ALABAMA, INC.—See Xerox Holdings Corporation; *U.S. Public,* pg. 2388
STEWART PAKISTAN (PRIVATE) LIMITED—See Stewart Information Services Corporation; *U.S. Public,* pg. 1948
STEWART P. WILSON INC.; *U.S. Private,* pg. 3811
STEWART-RICHEY CONSTRUCTION, INC.—See Houchens Industries, Inc.; *U.S. Private,* pg. 1990
STEWART'S CLASSICS, INC.—See Lithia Motors, Inc.; *U.S. Public,* pg. 1326
STEWART'S CLASSICS OF COLORADO LLC—See Lithia Motors, Inc.; *U.S. Public,* pg. 1326
STEWART SENTER INC.; *U.S. Private,* pg. 3811
STEWART'S FOOD STORE INC.; *U.S. Private,* pg. 3811
STEWARTS & LLOYDS OF INDIA LTD; *Int'l,* pg. 7213
STEWART'S PRIVATE BLEND FOODS INC.; *U.S. Private,* pg. 3811
STEWART'S PROCESSING CORP; *U.S. Private,* pg. 3812
STEWART'S SHOPS CORPORATION; *U.S. Private,* pg. 3811
STEWART'S SLEEP CENTER INC.; *U.S. Private,* pg. 3811
STEWART STAINLESS SUPPLY INC.; *U.S. Private,* pg. 3811
STEWART STAMPING CORP.—See UBS Group AG; *Int'l,* pg. 8006
STEWART & STEVENSON DE LAS AMERICAS COLOMBIA LTDA.—See Kirby Corporation; *U.S. Public,* pg. 1236
STEWART & STEVENSON FDDA LLC—See Kirby Corporation; *U.S. Public,* pg. 1236
STEWART & STEVENSON, LLC—See Kirby Corporation; *U.S. Public,* pg. 1236
STEWART & STEVENSON POWER PRODUCTS, LLC—See Kirby Corporation; *U.S. Public,* pg. 1236
STEWART & STEVENSON SERVICES, INC.—See BAE Systems plc; *Int'l,* pg. 796
STEWART SUPERABSORBENTS, LLC—See KKR & Co. Inc.; *U.S. Public,* pg. 1243
STEWART SYSTEMS BAKING, LLC—See The Middleby Corporation; *U.S. Public,* pg. 2115
STEWART & TATE, INC.; *U.S. Private,* pg. 3811
STEWART TITLE COMPANY - KISSIMMEE—See Stewart Information Services Corporation; *U.S. Public,* pg. 1948
STEWART TITLE COMPANY—See Stewart Information Services Corporation; *U.S. Public,* pg. 1948
STEWART TITLE GROUP, LLC—See Stewart Information Services Corporation; *U.S. Public,* pg. 1948
STEWART TITLE GUARANTY COMPANY—See Stewart Information Services Corporation; *U.S. Public,* pg. 1948
STEWART TITLE INSURANCE AGENCY OF UTAH, INC.—See Stewart Information Services Corporation; *U.S. Public,* pg. 1948
STEWART TITLE INSURANCE COMPANY—See Stewart Information Services Corporation; *U.S. Public,* pg. 1948
STEWART TITLE INSURANCE CORP. - UPSTATE CORPORATE OFFICE—See Stewart Information Services Corporation; *U.S. Public,* pg. 1948
STEWART TITLE LTD.—See Stewart Information Services Corporation; *U.S. Public,* pg. 1948
STEWART TITLE OF ALABAMA, LLC—See Stewart Information Services Corporation; *U.S. Public,* pg. 1948
STEWART TITLE OF ALBUQUERQUE, LLC—See Stewart Information Services Corporation; *U.S. Public,* pg. 1948
STEWART TITLE OF ARKANSAS, LLC—See Stewart Information Services Corporation; *U.S. Public,* pg. 1948
STEWART TITLE OF CALIFORNIA, INC.—See Stewart Information Services Corporation; *U.S. Public,* pg. 1948
STEWART TITLE OF CAMERON COUNTY, INC.—See Stewart Information Services Corporation; *U.S. Public,* pg. 1948
STEWART TITLE OF LUBBOCK, INC.—See Stewart Information Services Corporation; *U.S. Public,* pg. 1948
STEWART TITLE OF MINNESOTA, INC.—See Stewart Information Services Corporation; *U.S. Public,* pg. 1948
STEWART TITLE OF MONTGOMERY COUNTY INC.—See Howard Hughes Holdings Inc.; *U.S. Public,* pg. 1060
STEWART TITLE OF NEVADA HOLDINGS, INC.—See Stewart Information Services Corporation; *U.S. Public,* pg. 1948
STEWART TITLE OF OKLAHOMA, INC.—See Stewart Information Services Corporation; *U.S. Public,* pg. 1948
STEWART TITLE PUERTO RICO, INC.—See Stewart Information Services Corporation; *U.S. Public,* pg. 1948
STEWART TITLE S.R.O.—See Stewart Information Services Corporation; *U.S. Public,* pg. 1948
STEWART TITLE & TRUST OF TUCSON—See Stewart Information Services Corporation; *U.S. Public,* pg. 1948
STEWART TUBULAR PRODUCTS, INC.—See Pelican Energy Partners LP; *U.S. Private,* pg. 3130
STEWART WARNER CORPORATION OF CANADA—See SKF AB; *Int'l,* pg. 6985
STEWART WARNER CORPORATION—See Schneider Electric SE; *Int'l,* pg. 6635
STEWART & WIGHT PLC; *Int'l,* pg. 7213
STEW HANSEN HYUNDAI; *U.S. Private,* pg. 3810
STEW LEONARD'S; *U.S. Private,* pg. 3810
STEYR CENTER NORD GMBH—See CNH Industrial N.V.; *Int'l,* pg. 1676

STEYERMUHL SAGEWERKSGESELLSCHAFT M.B.H. NFG KG—See Heinzel Holding GmbH; *Int'l,* pg. 3325
STEYR MOTORS BETRIEBS GMBH—See Mutares SE & Co. KGaA; *Int'l,* pg. 5106
STEYR MOTORS CO., LTD.; *Int'l,* pg. 7213
STF AGRICULTURE SDN BHD—See Lay Hong Berhad; *Int'l,* pg. 4427
STF CO., LTD.—See The Furukawa Electric Co., Ltd.; *Int'l,* pg. 7646
STF ENERJI LIMITED—See STF S.p.A; *Int'l,* pg. 7213
STF PRECISION TECHNOLOGIES & TOOLS, INC.—See L Squared Capital Management LP; *U.S. Private,* pg. 2362
ST. FRANCIS AFFILIATED SERVICES, LLC—See Apollo Global Management, Inc.; *U.S. Public,* pg. 158
ST. FRANCIS FOUNDATION—See Catholic Health Initiatives; *U.S. Private,* pg. 790
ST. FRANCIS HEALTH, LLC—See Apollo Global Management, Inc.; *U.S. Public,* pg. 159
ST. FRANCIS HOSPITAL—See Catholic Health Services of Long Island; *U.S. Private,* pg. 791
ST. FRANCIS MEDICAL CENTER—See Daughters of Charity Health System; *U.S. Private,* pg. 1167
ST. FRANCIS PHYSICIAN PRACTICES, LLC—See Apollo Global Management, Inc.; *U.S. Public,* pg. 159
STF SLOVAKIA S.R.O.—See STF S.p.A; *Int'l,* pg. 7213
STF S.P.A; *Int'l,* pg. 7213
STF SVENSKA TEXTILFILTER AB—See Daikin Industries, Ltd.; *Int'l,* pg. 1936
ST. GABRIEL CC COMPANY, LLC—See Eastman Chemical Company; *U.S. Public,* pg. 706
ST. GALLER KANTONALBANK AG; *Int'l,* pg. 7159
ST. GALLER KANTONALBANK GERMANY LTD.—See St. Galler Kantonalbank AG; *Int'l,* pg. 7159
ST. GALLER TAGBLATT AG—See NZZ-Mediengruppe; *Int'l,* pg. 5502
STG CO., LTD.; *Int'l,* pg. 7213
STG ENGINEERING LLC—See PJSC Stroytransgaz; *Int'l,* pg. 5885
ST. GEORGE BANK LIMITED—See Westpac Banking Corporation; *Int'l,* pg. 8391
ST GEORGE CENTRAL LONDON LIMITED—See The Berkeley Group Holdings plc; *Int'l,* pg. 7621
ST. GEORGE ENDOSCOPY CENTER, LLC—See KKR & Co. Inc.; *U.S. Public,* pg. 1246
ST GEORGE LOGISTICS CORP.—See Wind Point Advisors LLC; *U.S. Private,* pg. 4535
ST GEORGE MINING LIMITED; *Int'l,* pg. 7158
ST. GEORGE MOTOR FINANCE LIMITED—See Westpac Banking Corporation; *Int'l,* pg. 8392
ST GEORGE PLC—See The Berkeley Group Holdings plc; *Int'l,* pg. 7621
ST-GEORGES ECO-MINING CORP.; *Int'l,* pg. 7158
ST GEORGE SOUTH LONDON LIMITED—See The Berkeley Group Holdings plc; *Int'l,* pg. 7621
ST. GEORGE WAREHOUSE TRUCKING OF CALIFORNIA; *U.S. Private,* pg. 3771
ST. GEORGE WAREHOUSE TRUCKING OF TEXAS INC.—See St. George Warehouse Trucking of California; *U.S. Private,* pg. 3771
ST GEORGE WEST LONDON LIMITED—See The Berkeley Group Holdings plc; *Int'l,* pg. 7621
ST. GERMAIN'S GLASS CO.—See Brin Northwestern Glass Company Inc.; *U.S. Private,* pg. 654
S&T GERMANY GMBH—See Kontron AG; *Int'l,* pg. 4278
STG GROUP, INC.; *U.S. Public,* pg. 1948
STGI INC.; *U.S. Private,* pg. 3812
ST. GILES-THE TUSCANY HOTEL; *U.S. Private,* pg. 3771
STG, INC.—See STG Group, Inc.; *U.S. Public,* pg. 1949
STG INTERNATIONAL LTD; *Int'l,* pg. 7213
STG LIFECARE LIMITED; *Int'l,* pg. 7213
S+T GMBH & CO. KG—See Matthews International Corporation; *U.S. Public,* pg. 1399
S.T. GOOD INSURANCE, INC.—See Aquiline Capital Partners LLC; *U.S. Private,* pg. 305
STG PARTNERS, LLC—See Symphony Technology Group, LLC; *U.S. Private,* pg. 3901
ST GREGORY SPA PTE LTD—See UOL Group Limited; *Int'l,* pg. 8086
ST GROUP FOOD INDUSTRIES HOLDINGS LIMITED; *Int'l,* pg. 7158
S&T GULF CO., LTD.—See SNT Holdings Co., Ltd.; *Int'l,* pg. 7029
STHALER LIMITED; *Int'l,* pg. 7213
STHEALTH CAPITAL INVESTMENT CORP.; *U.S. Private,* pg. 3812
ST HEALTHCARE PTE. LTD.—See Japan Post Holdings Co., Ltd.; *Int'l,* pg. 3901
ST HELENA HOSPITAL PROPRIETARY LIMITED—See Sibanye-Stillwater Limited; *Int'l,* pg. 6876
ST. HELENS PRIVATE HOSPITAL—See Brookfield Corporation; *Int'l,* pg. 1176
THE ST. HENRY BANK; *U.S. Private,* pg. 4120
ST. HENRY TILE CO. INC.; *U.S. Private,* pg. 3770
ST. HILAIRE AG INSURANCE, INC.—See CHS INC.; *U.S. Public,* pg. 492
ST HITEC LTD.—See HKS CO., LTD.; *Int'l,* pg. 3429
STHREE BELGIUM NV—See SThree Plc.; *Int'l,* pg. 7214
STHREE GMBH—See SThree Plc.; *Int'l,* pg. 7214

COMPANY NAME INDEX

STHREE LLC—See SThree Plc.; *Int'l*, pg. 7214
STHREE PLC.; *Int'l*, pg. 7214
STHREE PTE. LTD.—See SThree Plc.; *Int'l*, pg. 7214
STHREE S.A R.L—See SThree Plc.; *Int'l*, pg. 7214
STHREE SAS—See SThree Plc.; *Int'l*, pg. 7214
S&T HRVATSKA D.O.O.—See Kontron AG; *Int'l*, pg. 4278
STH SRI BULATAN SDN. BHD.—See Wah Seong Corporation Berhad; *Int'l*, pg. 8329
ST. HUBERT SAS—See Beijing Capital Agribusiness Group Co., Ltd.; *Int'l*, pg. 946
ST. HUBERT SAS—See Fosun International Limited; *Int'l*, pg. 2752
STIAOS TECHNOLOGIES INC.—See ObjectOne Information Systems Limited; *Int'l*, pg. 5511
ST IBERICA LDA.—See Freudenberg SE; *Int'l*, pg. 2790
STICHD B.V.—See Kering S.A.; *Int'l*, pg. 4136
STICHD GERMANY GMBH—See Kering S.A.; *Int'l*, pg. 4136
STICHD GROUP B.V.—See Puma SE; *Int'l*, pg. 6118
STICHD ITALY SRL—See Puma SE; *Int'l*, pg. 6118
STICHD SOUTHEAST ASIA SDN. BHD.—See Puma SE; *Int'l*, pg. 6118
STICHD TRADING (SHANGHAI) CO., LTD.—See Puma SE; *Int'l*, pg. 6118
STICHTING BEHEER SNS REAAL; *Int'l*, pg. 7214
STICHTING CRYO-SAVE—See Esperite N.V.; *Int'l*, pg. 2506
STICHTING DELTA ZEELAND FONDS—See Delta N.V.; *Int'l*, pg. 2019
STICHTING INGKA FOUNDATION; *Int'l*, pg. 7214
STICHTING SURF; *Int'l*, pg. 7215
STIC INVESTMENT, INC.—See Stick Investment Co., Ltd.; *Int'l*, pg. 7215
STICK INVESTMENT CO., LTD.; *Int'l*, pg. 7215
STICKIT TECHNOLOGIES INC.; *Int'l*, pg. 7215
STICKLER CONSTRUCTION LLC; *U.S. Private*, pg. 3812
STICKS YARRA VALLEY PTY. LTD.—See BRAND NEW VINTAGE LIMITED; *Int'l*, pg. 1139
STI CO. LTD.; *Int'l*, pg. 7214
STI CONTROLS, L.P.—See AMETEK, Inc.; *U.S. Public*, pg. 121
STIDHAM TRUCKING INC.; *U.S. Private*, pg. 3812
STIEBEL ELTRON GMBH & CO. KG; *Int'l*, pg. 7215
STI EDUCATION SERVICES GROUP, INC.—See STI Education Systems Holdings Inc.; *Int'l*, pg. 7214
STI EDUCATION SYSTEMS HOLDINGS INC.; *Int'l*, pg. 7214
STIEFEL GMBH & CO. KG—See GSK plc; *Int'l*, pg. 3149
STIEFEL INDIA PRIVATE LIMITED—See GSK plc; *Int'l*, pg. 3149
STIEFEL LABORATORIES, INC.—See GSK plc; *Int'l*, pg. 3149
STIEFEL LABORATORIES (IRELAND) LIMITED—See GSK plc; *Int'l*, pg. 3149
STIEFEL LABORATORIES (U.K.) LTD.—See GSK plc; *Int'l*, pg. 3149
STIEGLER, WELLS, BRUNSWICK & ROTH, INC.; *U.S. Private*, pg. 3812
STI ELECTRONICS, INC.; *U.S. Private*, pg. 3812
STIERLEN GMBH—See Ali Holding S.r.l; *Int'l*, pg. 321
STIFEL BANK—See Stifel Financial Corp.; *U.S. Public*, pg. 1950
STIFEL BANK & TRUST—See Stifel Financial Corp.; *U.S. Public*, pg. 1950
STIFEL EUROPE ADVISORY GMBH—See Stifel Financial Corp.; *U.S. Public*, pg. 1950
STIFEL EUROPE BANK AG—See Stifel Financial Corp.; *U.S. Public*, pg. 1950
STIFEL FINANCIAL CORP.; *U.S. Public*, pg. 1949
STIFEL INDEPENDENT ADVISORS, LLC—See Stifel Financial Corp.; *U.S. Public*, pg. 1950
STIFEL, NICOLAUS & COMPANY, INCORPORATED—See Stifel Financial Corp.; *U.S. Public*, pg. 1950
STIFEL NICOLAUS EUROPE LIMITED—See Stifel Financial Corp.; *U.S. Public*, pg. 1950
STIFEL NICOLAUS INSURANCE AGENCY, INCORPORATED—See Stifel Financial Corp.; *U.S. Public*, pg. 1950
STIFEL SCHWEIZ AG—See Stifel Financial Corp.; *U.S. Public*, pg. 1950
STIFEL TRUST COMPANY, NATIONAL ASSOCIATION—See Stifel Financial Corp.; *U.S. Public*, pg. 1950
STIFEL VENTURE CORP.—See Stifel Financial Corp.; *U.S. Public*, pg. 1950
STIF FRANCE SAS; *Int'l*, pg. 7215
STI FOODS HOLDINGS, INC.; *Int'l*, pg. 7214
STI FRANCE SAS—See Arbonia AG; *Int'l*, pg. 538
STIFTUNG DEUTSCHE KLINIK FUR DIAGNOSTIK GMBH—See Fresenius SE & Co. KGaA; *Int'l*, pg. 2779
STIGAB AB—See Addtech AB; *Int'l*, pg. 135
STIGAB OY—See Addtech AB; *Int'l*, pg. 135
STIGA SPORTS AB—See Escalade, Incorporated; *U.S. Public*, pg. 793
STIG GP A.D.; *Int'l*, pg. 7215
STIG JIANGSU LIGHT & TEXTILE IMP. & EXP. CO., LTD—See Jiangsu Sainty Corp., Ltd.; *Int'l*, pg. 3953
STIGMA PARTICIPACOES S.A.—See BTG Pactual Holding S.A.; *Int'l*, pg. 1204

STI GROUP; *U.S. Public*, pg. 1949
STIG WAHLSTROM AUTOMATIK AB—See Addtech AB; *Int'l*, pg. 135
STIG WAHLSTROM HYDRAULIK AB—See Addtech AB; *Int'l*, pg. 135
STIG WAHLSTROM OY—See Addtech AB; *Int'l*, pg. 135
STI HARTCHROM AG—See Arbonia AG; *Int'l*, pg. 538
STI HARTCHROM INC.—See Arbonia AG; *Int'l*, pg. 538
STIHLER ELECTRONIC GMBH—See Gentherm Incorporated; *U.S. Public*, pg. 932
STIHL, INC.—See Andreas Stihl AG & Co.; *Int'l*, pg. 451
STIHL LTD—See Andreas Stihl AG & Co.; *Int'l*, pg. 451
STIHL PARTS, INC.—See Andreas Stihl AG & Co.; *Int'l*, pg. 451
STI HOLDINGS INC.—See Seaboard Corporation; *U.S. Public*, pg. 1850
STI IMMOBILIEN (DEUTSCHLAND) GMBH—See Arbonia AG; *Int'l*, pg. 538
STI INDIA LIMITED—See Bombay Rayon Fashions Limited; *Int'l*, pg. 1104
STILA CORP.—See Patriarch Partners, LLC; *U.S. Private*, pg. 3109
STILES CORPORATION; *U.S. Private*, pg. 3812
STILES CUSTOM METAL, INC.—See ASSA ABLOY AB; *Int'l*, pg. 640
STILES MACHINERY, INC.—See Durr AG; *Int'l*, pg. 2232
STILES ROAD IMAGING LLC—See HCA Healthcare, Inc.; *U.S. Public*, pg. 1010
STILES TRUCK LINE INC.; *U.S. Private*, pg. 3812
STILETTO TOOL COMPANY—See Techtronic Industries Co., Ltd.; *Int'l*, pg. 7513
STILL AG—See KKR & Co. Inc.; *U.S. Public*, pg. 1255
STILL AG—See The Goldman Sachs Group, Inc.; *U.S. Public*, pg. 2079
STILLCANNA INC.; *Int'l*, pg. 7215
STILL CR, SPOL. S R.O.—See KKR & Co. Inc.; *U.S. Public*, pg. 1255
STILL CR, SPOL. S R.O.—See The Goldman Sachs Group, Inc.; *U.S. Public*, pg. 2079
STILL DANMARK A/S—See KKR & Co. Inc.; *U.S. Public*, pg. 1255
STILL DANMARK A/S—See The Goldman Sachs Group, Inc.; *U.S. Public*, pg. 2079
STILLE AB; *Int'l*, pg. 7215
STILLFRONT GROUP AB; *Int'l*, pg. 7215
STILL GESELLSCHAFT M.B.H.—See KKR & Co. Inc.; *U.S. Public*, pg. 1255
STILL GESELLSCHAFT M.B.H.—See The Goldman Sachs Group, Inc.; *U.S. Public*, pg. 2079
STILL GMBH—See KKR & Co. Inc.; *U.S. Public*, pg. 1255
STILL GMBH—See The Goldman Sachs Group, Inc.; *U.S. Public*, pg. 2079
STILL INTERN TRANSPORT B.V.—See KKR & Co. Inc.; *U.S. Public*, pg. 1255
STILL INTERN TRANSPORT B.V.—See The Goldman Sachs Group, Inc.; *U.S. Public*, pg. 2079
STILL ITALIA S.P.A.—See KKR & Co. Inc.; *U.S. Public*, pg. 1255
STILL ITALIA S.P.A.—See The Goldman Sachs Group, Inc.; *U.S. Public*, pg. 2079
STILL LUMBER CO. INC.—See Spahn & Rose Lumber Co., Inc.; *U.S. Private*, pg. 3744
STILLMAN BANCCORP N.A.; *U.S. Private*, pg. 3812
STILLMAN BANK—See Stillman BancCorp N.A.; *U.S. Private*, pg. 3812
STILL MATERIALS HANDLING LTD.—See KKR & Co. Inc.; *U.S. Public*, pg. 1255
STILL MATERIALS HANDLING LTD.—See The Goldman Sachs Group, Inc.; *U.S. Public*, pg. 2079
STILL N.V.—See KKR & Co. Inc.; *U.S. Public*, pg. 1255
STILL N.V.—See The Goldman Sachs Group, Inc.; *U.S. Public*, pg. 2080
STILL S.A.—See KKR & Co. Inc.; *U.S. Public*, pg. 1255
STILL S.A.—See The Goldman Sachs Group, Inc.; *U.S. Public*, pg. 2080
STILL S.A.S—See KKR & Co. Inc.; *U.S. Public*, pg. 1255
STILL S.A.S—See The Goldman Sachs Group, Inc.; *U.S. Public*, pg. 2080
STILL WAGNER GMBH & CO. KG—See KKR & Co. Inc.; *U.S. Public*, pg. 1255
STILL WAGNER GMBH & CO. KG—See The Goldman Sachs Group, Inc.; *U.S. Public*, pg. 2080
STILLWATER CENTRAL RAILROAD, LLC—See Kinder Morgan, Inc.; *U.S. Public*, pg. 1233
STILLWATER CRITICAL MINERALS CORP.; *Int'l*, pg. 7215
STILLWATER DESIGNS & AUDIO; *U.S. Private*, pg. 3812
STILLWATER FASTENERS INC.—See Vertex Distribution; *U.S. Private*, pg. 4369
STILLWATER INVESTMENT MANAGEMENT, LLC—See Dakota Wealth Management LLC; *U.S. Private*, pg. 1148
STILLWATER MILLING COMPANY INC.; *U.S. Private*, pg. 3812
STILL WATERS DESIGN/BUILD GROUP; *U.S. Private*, pg. 3812
STILLWATER TECHNOLOGIES, LLC—See Brixey & Meyer, Inc.; *U.S. Private*, pg. 658
STILLWELL ENTERPRISES, INC.; *U.S. Private*, pg. 3812

STILLWELL HANSEN INC.; *U.S. Private*, pg. 3812
STILLWELL MOTOR GROUP—See Autosports Group Limited; *Int'l*, pg. 732
STILLWELL TRUCKS PTY LTD—See Eagers Automotive Limited; *Int'l*, pg. 2263
STILO CORPORATION—See Stilo International Plc; *Int'l*, pg. 7215
STILO ENERGY S.A.; *Int'l*, pg. 7215
STILOG I.S.T.—See Industrielle De Controle Et D Equipement; *Int'l*, pg. 3675
STILO INTERNATIONAL PLC; *Int'l*, pg. 7215
STILO TECHNOLOGY LIMITED—See Stilo International Plc; *Int'l*, pg. 7215
STILTON GATE MANAGEMENT COMPANY LIMITED—See Bellway plc; *Int'l*, pg. 968
STIM-AIR INC.—See Stimson Lumber Company; *U.S. Private*, pg. 3812
S.T.I.M.A. S.A.R.L.—See BASF SE; *Int'l*, pg. 884
STIMAS ENGINEERING S.R.L.—See Durr AG; *Int'l*, pg. 2233
STIMAS S.R.L.—See Durr AG; *Int'l*, pg. 2233
STIMET SA; *Int'l*, pg. 7215
STIMIT AG—See Draegerwerk AG & Co. KGaA; *Int'l*, pg. 2198
STIM-LAB, INC.—See Core Laboratories N.V.; *Int'l*, pg. 1798
STIMSOL CANADA INC.—See Western Energy Services Corp.; *Int'l*, pg. 8388
STIMSON LUMBER COMPANY; *U.S. Private*, pg. 3812
STIMSON LUMBER TILLAMOOK—See Stimson Lumber Company; *U.S. Private*, pg. 3812
STIMULAN B.V.—See ForFarmers Group B.V.; *Int'l*, pg. 2733
STIMULANT; *U.S. Private*, pg. 3812
STIMUL-T OOO—See PetroNeft Resources plc; *Int'l*, pg. 5831
STINAG STUTTGART INVEST AG; *Int'l*, pg. 7215
S-T INDUSTRIES, INC.; *U.S. Private*, pg. 3514
STINE INC.; *U.S. Private*, pg. 3812
STINE LUMBER COMPANY; *U.S. Private*, pg. 3813
STINE & LUMBER INC.—See Stine Inc.; *U.S. Private*, pg. 3813
STINES DIALYSIS, LLC—See DaVita Inc.; *U.S. Public*, pg. 643
STINE SEED COMPANY; *U.S. Private*, pg. 3813
STING ALARM INC.; *U.S. Private*, pg. 3813
STINGER GHAFFARIAN TECHNOLOGIES INC.—See KBR, Inc.; *U.S. Public*, pg. 1216
STINGER LOGISTICS, INC.—See Celadon Group, Inc.; *U.S. Public*, pg. 464
STINGER WELLHEAD PROTECTION (CANADA) INCORPORATED—See Oil States International, Inc.; *U.S. Public*, pg. 1565
STINGL GMBH—See VINCI S.A.; *Int'l*, pg. 8226
STINGRAY GROUP INC.; *Int'l*, pg. 7215
STINGRAY MUSIC USA INC.—See Stingray Group Inc.; *Int'l*, pg. 7216
STINGRAY OPTICS, LLC—See Gooch & Housego PLC; *Int'l*, pg. 3038
STINKAL—See Eiffage S.A.; *Int'l*, pg. 2331
STINKER STORES, INC.; *U.S. Private*, pg. 3813
ST INNOVATION GMBH—See The Swatch Group Ltd.; *Int'l*, pg. 7692
STINS COMAN INCORPORATED; *Int'l*, pg. 7216
STINSON LEONARD STREET LLP - MINNEAPOLIS—See Stinson Leonard Street LLP; *U.S. Private*, pg. 3813
STINSON LEONARD STREET LLP; *U.S. Private*, pg. 3813
ST INSTRUMENTS B.V.; *Int'l*, pg. 7158
S&T INSURANCE GROUP, LLC—See S&T Bancorp, Inc.; *U.S. Public*, pg. 1832
ST INTERNATIONAL HOLDINGS CO., LTD.; *Int'l*, pg. 7158
S&T INTERNATIONAL—See Kontron AG; *Int'l*, pg. 4278
STI OPTRONICS, INC.; *U.S. Private*, pg. 3812
STI PACIFIC PTE. LTD.—See Samchully Co., Ltd.; *Int'l*, pg. 6503
STI PREPAID, LLC—See Marcatel S.A. de C.V.; *Int'l*, pg. 4688
STI PRODUCTS INDIA LTD.; *Int'l*, pg. 7214
STIR ADVERTISING & INTEGRATED MARKETING; *U.S. Private*, pg. 3813
STIR FOODS, LLC—See Wind Point Advisors LLC; *U.S. Private*, pg. 4536
STIRILAB S.R.O.—See Dominique Dutscher SAS; *Int'l*, pg. 2161
STIRISTA, LLC; *U.S. Private*, pg. 3813
STIRLING CAPITAL PROPERTIES, LLC—See Prologis, Inc.; *U.S. Public*, pg. 1726
STIRLING HOTELS & RESORTS, INC.; *U.S. Private*, pg. 3813
STIRLING INSTITUTE OF AUSTRALIA PTY. LTD.—See MAXIMUS, Inc.; *U.S. Public*, pg. 1402
STIRLING PARK LLP—See Capita plc; *Int'l*, pg. 1309
STIRLING PRODUCTS LIMITED; *Int'l*, pg. 7216
STIRLING PROPERTIES, INC.—See Maurin-Ogden Properties; *U.S. Private*, pg. 2615
STIRLING SQUARE CAPITAL PARTNERS LLP; *Int'l*, pg. 7216

STIRLING SQUARE CAPITAL PARTNERS LLP

Company Index

STIRRAT COAL COMPANY—See Alpha Natural Resources, Inc.; *U.S. Private*, pg. 198
STIRRINGS LLC—See Diageo plc; *Int'l*, pg. 2103
STIRRINGS—See Nantucket Harvest Co., Inc.; *U.S. Private*, pg. 2833
STI-SAN ANTONIO TERMINAL INTERNACIONAL—See Carrix, Inc.; *U.S. Private*, pg. 773
STI SANOH INDIA LTD. - BANGALORE PLANT—See Sanoh Industrial Co., Ltd.; *Int'l*, pg. 6552
STI SANOH INDIA LTD.—See Sanoh Industrial Co., Ltd.; *Int'l*, pg. 6552
STI SANYO, INC.—See STI Foods Holdings, Inc.; *Int'l*, pg. 7214
STI S.R.L.—See IMI plc; *Int'l*, pg. 3626
STI SURFACE TECHNOLOGIES INTERNATIONAL HOLDING AG—See Arbonia AG; *Int'l*, pg. 538
STITCHER INC.—See Liberty Media Corporation; *U.S. Public*, pg. 1311
STITCH FIX, INC.; *U.S. Public*, pg. 1950
STITCH LABS, INC.—See Block, Inc.; *U.S. Public*, pg. 362
STITCH TECHNOLOGIES (THAILAND) CO., LTD.—See Tajima Industries Ltd.; *Int'l*, pg. 7428
STIT CO., LTD.—See STP&I Public Company Limited; *Int'l*, pg. 7229
STI TECHNOLOGIES LIMITED—See IQVIA Holdings Inc.; *U.S. Public*, pg. 1170
STITZ & ASSOCIATES, INC.—See Heffernan Insurance Brokers; *U.S. Private*, pg. 1904
STIVERS SUBARU; *U.S. Private*, pg. 3813
STIVERS TEMPORARY PERSONNEL INC.; *U.S. Private*, pg. 3813
ST. IVES BLACKBURN LIMITED—See Kin and Carta plc; *Int'l*, pg. 4164
ST. IVES BURNLEY LIMITED—See Kin and Carta plc; *Int'l*, pg. 4164
ST. IVES DIRECT LEEDS LIMITED—See Kin and Carta plc; *Int'l*, pg. 4164
ST. IVES GOLD MINING COMPANY PTY LIMITED—See Gold Fields Limited; *Int'l*, pg. 3024
ST. IVES LABORATORIES, INC.—See Unilever PLC; *Int'l*, pg. 8048
ST. IVES WESTERHAM PRESS LTD.—See Kin and Carta plc; *Int'l*, pg. 4164
STIVO—See Regie Autonome des Transports Parisiens; *Int'l*, pg. 6253
STI WEST NEGROS UNIVERSITY, INC.—See STI Education Systems Holdings Inc.; *Int'l*, pg. 7214
STIWEX - FLUGGER SWEDEN AB—See Flugger Group A/S; *Int'l*, pg. 2712
STIWEX SRL—See Flugger Group A/S; *Int'l*, pg. 2712
STIX HOLDINGS, LLC—See West Coast Capital LLC; *U.S. Private*, pg. 4484
STIZO INDUSTRIAL SERVICES S.R.L.—See VINCI S.A.; *Int'l*, pg. 8238
STIZO NUCLEAR SA—See VINCI S.A.; *Int'l*, pg. 8229
ST JACOBS ANIMAL BREEDING CORP.—See Genus Plc; *Int'l*, pg. 2931
ST. JAKOB-APOTHEKE AG—See CSL Limited; *Int'l*, pg. 1866
ST JAMES CORPORATE SERVICES LIMITED—See Gold Fields Limited; *Int'l*, pg. 3024
ST. JAMES GOLD CORP.; *Int'l*, pg. 7159
ST. JAMES GROUP LIMITED—See The Berkeley Group Holdings plc; *Int'l*, pg. 7621
ST. JAMES INSURANCE GROUP, INC.; *U.S. Private*, pg. 3771
THE ST. JAMES PTE LTD—See Perennial Real Estate Holdings Limited; *Int'l*, pg. 5797
ST. JAMES'S PLACE PLC; *Int'l*, pg. 7159
ST. JAMES'S PLACE WEALTH MANAGEMENT GROUP LIMITED—See St. James's Place plc; *Int'l*, pg. 7159
ST. JAMES VOLKSWAGEN LTD.; *Int'l*, pg. 7159
STJENIK A.D.; *Int'l*, pg. 7216
ST. JOE CLUB & RESORTS VACATION RENTALS, LLC—See The St. Joe Company; *U.S. Public*, pg. 2131
THE ST. JOE COMPANY; *U.S. Public*, pg. 2131
ST. JOE PETROLEUM CO.; *U.S. Private*, pg. 3771
ST. JOE TIMBERLAND COMPANY OF DELAWARE, L.L.C.—See The St. Joe Company; *U.S. Public*, pg. 2131
ST. JOHN CONNER CREEK VILLAGE—See Ascension Health Alliance; *U.S. Private*, pg. 347
ST. JOHN ENCOMPASS HEALTH REHABILITATION HOSPITAL, LLC—See Encompass Health Corporation; *U.S. Public*, pg. 759
ST. JOHN HEALTH SYSTEM INC.; *U.S. Private*, pg. 3771
ST. JOHN HOLDINGS INC.; *U.S. Private*, pg. 3771
ST. JOHN HOSPITAL & MEDICAL CENTER—See Ascension Health Alliance; *U.S. Private*, pg. 347
ST. JOHN KNITS INTERNATIONAL, INC.—See Vestar/Gray Investors LLC; *U.S. Private*, pg. 4373
ST. JOHN MACOMB HOSPITAL—See Ascension Health Alliance; *U.S. Private*, pg. 347
ST. JOHN NISSAN 7198; *U.S. Private*, pg. 3772
ST. JOHN OAKLAND HOSPITAL—See Ascension Health Alliance; *U.S. Private*, pg. 347
ST. JOHN OF GOD RETIREMENT AND CARE CENTER; *U.S. Private*, pg. 3770
ST. JOHN & PARTNERS; *U.S. Private*, pg. 3771

ST. JOHN PROVIDENCE HEALTH SYSTEM—See Ascension Health Alliance; *U.S. Private*, pg. 347
ST. JOHN RIVER DISTRICT HOSPITAL—See Ascension Health Alliance; *U.S. Private*, pg. 347
ST. JOHNS BUILDING LIMITED—See The Hongkong and Shanghai Hotels Limited; *Int'l*, pg. 7653
ST. JOHN'S HOSPITAL OF THE HOSPITAL SISTERS OF THE THIRD ORDER OF ST. FRANCIS-SPRINGFIELD—See Hospital Sisters Health System; *U.S. Private*, pg. 1987
ST. JOHN'S ICECAPS HOCKEY CLUB—See True North Sports & Entertainment Limited; *Int'l*, pg. 7941
ST. JOHN'S MANCHESTER LIMITED—See Henry Boot PLC; *Int'l*, pg. 3355
ST. JOHN'S MERCY HEALTH CARE—See Sisters of Mercy Health System; *U.S. Private*, pg. 3676
S.T. JOHNSON CO.; *U.S. Private*, pg. 3519
ST. JOHNS PACKAGING (KUNSHAN) LTD.—See St. Johns Packaging Ltd.; *Int'l*, pg. 7159
ST. JOHNS PACKAGING LTD.; *Int'l*, pg. 7159
ST. JOHN'S PLEASANT VALLEY HOSPITAL—See Catholic Health Initiatives; *U.S. Private*, pg. 789
ST. JOHN'S REGIONAL IMAGING CENTER, LLC—See Catholic Health Initiatives; *U.S. Private*, pg. 790
ST. JOHN'S REGIONAL MEDICAL CENTER—See Catholic Health Initiatives; *U.S. Private*, pg. 789
ST. JOHNS SHIP BUILDING, INC.—See Libra Group Limited; *Int'l*, pg. 4486
ST. JOHN'S SPORTS & ENTERTAINMENT—See True North Sports & Entertainment Limited; *Int'l*, pg. 7941
ST. JOSEPH COMMUNICATIONS INC.; *Int'l*, pg. 7159
ST. JOSEPH COUNTY HIGHWAY DEPARTMENT; *U.S. Private*, pg. 3772
ST. JOSEPH ENCOMPASS HEALTH REHABILITATION HOSPITAL, LLC—See Encompass Health Corporation; *U.S. Public*, pg. 759
ST. JOSEPH HEALTH SYSTEM—See Providence St. Joseph Health; *U.S. Private*, pg. 3295
ST JOSEPH HOMES LIMITED—See The Berkeley Group Holdings plc; *Int'l*, pg. 7621
ST. JOSEPH HOSPITAL—See Catholic Health Services of Long Island; *U.S. Private*, pg. 791
ST. JOSEPH, INC.; *U.S. Private*, pg. 3772
ST. JOSEPH MANOR HEALTH CARE INC.; *U.S. Private*, pg. 3772
ST. JOSEPH MEDIA INC.—See St. Joseph Communications Inc.; *Int'l*, pg. 7159
ST. JOSEPH MEDICAL CENTER—See Prime Healthcare Services, Inc.; *U.S. Private*, pg. 3262
ST. JOSEPH MERCY OAKLAND—See Trinity Health Corporation; *U.S. Private*, pg. 4234
ST. JOSEPH MERCY PORT HURON—See Trinity Health Corporation; *U.S. Private*, pg. 4234
ST. JOSEPH PRINT INC.—See St. Joseph Communications Inc.; *Int'l*, pg. 7159
ST JOSEPH REGIONAL HEALTH NETWORK—See Penn State Health; *U.S. Private*, pg. 3134
ST. JOSEPH REGIONAL MEDICAL CENTER—See Ascension Health Alliance; *U.S. Private*, pg. 347
ST. JOSEPH'S-BAPTIST HEALTH CARE—See BayCare Health System Inc.; *U.S. Private*, pg. 495
ST. JOSEPH'S BEHAVIORAL HEALTH CENTER—See Catholic Health Initiatives; *U.S. Private*, pg. 790
ST. JOSEPH'S/CANDLER; *U.S. Private*, pg. 3772
ST. JOSEPH'S CENTER—See Formation Capital, LLC; *U.S. Private*, pg. 1571
ST. JOSEPH'S CENTER; *U.S. Private*, pg. 3772
ST. JOSEPH'S CHILDREN'S HOSPITAL—See BayCare Health System Inc.; *U.S. Private*, pg. 496
ST. JOSEPH'S HEALTH CENTRE—See Laboratory Corporation of America Holdings; *U.S. Public*, pg. 1287
ST. JOSEPH'S HOSPITAL & MEDICAL CENTER—See Catholic Health Initiatives; *U.S. Private*, pg. 790
ST. JOSEPH'S HOSPITAL-NORTH—See BayCare Health System Inc.; *U.S. Private*, pg. 496
ST. JOSEPH'S HOSPITAL—See Ascension Health Alliance; *U.S. Private*, pg. 347
ST. JOSEPH'S HOSPITAL—See BayCare Health System Inc.; *U.S. Private*, pg. 496
ST. JOSEPHS MEDICAL CENTER—See Catholic Health Initiatives; *U.S. Private*, pg. 790
ST. JOSEPH'S OUTPATIENT SURGERY CENTER, LLC—See Tenet Healthcare Corporation; *U.S. Public*, pg. 2013
ST. JOSEPH'S REHABILITATION & RESIDENCE; *U.S. Private*, pg. 3772
ST. JOSEPH'S SURGERY CENTER, L.P.—See Tenet Healthcare Corporation; *U.S. Public*, pg. 2013
ST. JOSEPH'S WOMEN'S HOSPITAL—See BayCare Health System Inc.; *U.S. Private*, pg. 496
ST. JOSEPH TV, LLC—See Heartland Media, LLC; *U.S. Private*, pg. 1900
ST JSC GOLOIL—See RussNeft PJSC; *Int'l*, pg. 6432
ST. JUDE CHILDREN'S RESEARCH HOSPITAL; *U.S. Private*, pg. 3772
ST. JUDE COLLEGE, INC.—See PHINMA Corporation; *Int'l*, pg. 5848
ST. JUDE MEDICAL BRASIL, LTDA.—See Abbott Laboratories; *U.S. Public*, pg. 21

CORPORATE AFFILIATIONS

ST. JUDE MEDICAL, LLC—See Abbott Laboratories; *U.S. Public*, pg. 20
STK ATLANTA, LLC—See The ONE Group Hospitality, Inc.; *U.S. Public*, pg. 2118
STK CHICAGO, LLC—See The ONE Group Hospitality, Inc.; *U.S. Public*, pg. 2118
STK DC, LLC—See The ONE Group Hospitality, Inc.; *U.S. Public*, pg. 2118
STK DEKRA RYCHNOV S.R.O.—See DEKRA e.V.; *Int'l*, pg. 2009
STK IBIZA, LLC—See The ONE Group Hospitality, Inc.; *U.S. Public*, pg. 2118
ST. KITTS-NEVIS-ANGUILLA NATIONAL BANK LIMITED; *Int'l*, pg. 7159
ST. KITTS NEVIS ANGUILLA TRADING & DEVELOPMENT CO., LTD.; *Int'l*, pg. 7159
ST. KITTS-NEVIS FINANCE COMPANY LTD.—See St. Kitts Nevis Anguilla Trading & Development Co., Ltd.; *Int'l*, pg. 7159
ST. KITTS-NEVIS MORTGAGE & INVESTMENT CO., LTD.—See St. Kitts-Nevis-Anguilla National Bank Limited; *Int'l*, pg. 7160
STK-LA, LLC—See The ONE Group Hospitality, Inc.; *U.S. Public*, pg. 2118
STK-LAS VEGAS, LLC—See The ONE Group Hospitality, Inc.; *U.S. Public*, pg. 2118
STK MIAMI, LLC—See The ONE Group Hospitality, Inc.; *U.S. Public*, pg. 2118
STK MIDTOWN, LLC—See The ONE Group Hospitality, Inc.; *U.S. Public*, pg. 2118
STK NASHVILLE, LLC—See The ONE Group Hospitality, Inc.; *U.S. Public*, pg. 2118
STK ORLANDO, LLC—See The ONE Group Hospitality, Inc.; *U.S. Public*, pg. 2118
STK SLAVKOV S.R.O.—See DEKRA e.V.; *Int'l*, pg. 2009
STK - STANICE TECHNICKO KOITROLY S.R.O.—See DEKRA e.V.; *Int'l*, pg. 2009
STK TECHNO CORPORATION—See MIRAIT ONE Corporation; *Int'l*, pg. 4918
ST. LANDRY EXTENDED CARE HOSPITAL, LLC—See UnitedHealth Group Incorporated; *U.S. Public*, pg. 2247
ST. LANDRY HOMESTEAD FEDERAL SAVINGS BANK; *U.S. Private*, pg. 3772
ST.LA. S.R.L.—See LCI Industries; *U.S. Public*, pg. 1296
ST. LAURENT FUNERAL HOME, INC.—See Service Corporation International; *U.S. Public*, pg. 1870
ST LAURENT VOLVO; *Int'l*, pg. 7158
ST. LAWRENCE & ATLANTIC RAILROAD COMPANY—See Brookfield Infrastructure Partners L.P.; *Int'l*, pg. 1192
ST. LAWRENCE & ATLANTIC RAILROAD COMPANY—See GIC Pte. Ltd.; *Int'l*, pg. 2967
ST. LAWRENCE & ATLANTIC RAILROAD (QUEBEC) INC.—See Brookfield Infrastructure Partners L.P.; *Int'l*, pg. 1191
ST. LAWRENCE & ATLANTIC RAILROAD (QUEBEC) INC.—See Brookfield Infrastructure Partners L.P.; *Int'l*, pg. 1193
ST. LAWRENCE & ATLANTIC RAILROAD (QUEBEC) INC.—See GIC Pte. Ltd.; *Int'l*, pg. 2966
ST. LAWRENCE & ATLANTIC RAILROAD (QUEBEC) INC.—See GIC Pte. Ltd.; *Int'l*, pg. 2967
ST. LAWRENCE GAS COMPANY, INC.—See Algonquin Power & Utilities Corp.; *Int'l*, pg. 319
ST. LAWRENCE HOMES INC.; *U.S. Private*, pg. 3772
ST. LAWRENCE-LEWIS BOCES; *U.S. Private*, pg. 3772
THE ST. LAWRENCE SEAWAY MANAGEMENT CORPORATION; *Int'l*, pg. 7688
ST. LAWRENCE ZING COMPANY LLC—See HudBay Minerals Inc.; *Int'l*, pg. 3521
ST. LEON WIND ENERGY LP—See Algonquin Power & Utilities Corp.; *Int'l*, pg. 319
STL GLOBAL LTD.; *Int'l*, pg. 7216
STLLR GOLD INC.; *Int'l*, pg. 7216
ST LOGISTICS (AUSTRALIA) PTY LTD—See Japan Post Holdings Co., Ltd.; *Int'l*, pg. 3901
ST LOGISTICS PTE. LTD.—See Japan Post Holdings Co., Ltd.; *Int'l*, pg. 3901
S&T LOGISTICS (SHANGHAI) CO., LTD.—See Kokuyo Co., Ltd.; *Int'l*, pg. 4232
ST. LOUIS ARC, INC.; *U.S. Private*, pg. 3772
ST. LOUIS AREA FOODBANK, INC.; *U.S. Private*, pg. 3772
ST. LOUIS AUTO AUCTION—See Cox Enterprises, Inc.; *U.S. Private*, pg. 1077
ST. LOUIS BLUES HOCKEY CLUB, LLC—See SCP Worldwide; *U.S. Private*, pg. 3579
ST. LOUIS BOILER SUPPLY, INC.; *U.S. Private*, pg. 3770
ST. LOUIS BRIDGE CONSTRUCTION CO.; *U.S. Private*, pg. 3772
ST. LOUIS BUSINESS JOURNAL CORPORATION—See Advance Publications, Inc.; *U.S. Private*, pg. 85
ST. LOUIS COLD DRAWN LLC—See Nucor Corporation; *U.S. Public*, pg. 1554
ST. LOUIS COUNTIAN—See The Dolan Company; *U.S. Private*, pg. 4022
ST. LOUIS CYBERKNIFE, LLC—See Akumin, Inc.; *U.S. Public*, pg. 70

2608

COMPANY NAME INDEX

ST. LOUIS GAMING VENTURES, LLC—See PENN Entertainment, Inc.; *U.S. Public*, pg. 1662
ST. LOUIS METALLIZING CO.—See CIC Group, Inc.; *U.S. Private*, pg. 896
ST. LOUIS-METRO ELECTRICAL SUPPLY, INC.—See Graybar Electric Company, Inc.; *U.S. Private*, pg. 1760
ST. LOUIS METRO ELECTRIC SUPPLY; *U.S. Private*, pg. 3772
THE ST. LOUIS MO ORTHOPAEDIC ASC, LLC—See KKR & Co. Inc.; *U.S. Public*, pg. 1248
ST. LOUIS MUNICIPAL FINANCE CORPORATION; *U.S. Private*, pg. 3770
ST. LOUIS MUSIC, INC.—See U.S. Band & Orchestra Supplies, Inc.; *U.S. Private*, pg. 4270
ST. LOUIS PARKING COMPANY INC.; *U.S. Private*, pg. 3772
ST. LOUIS PIPE & SUPPLY, INC.; *U.S. Private*, pg. 3772
ST. LOUIS POST-DISPATCH LLC—See Lee Enterprises, Incorporated; *U.S. Public*, pg. 1300
ST. LOUIS RIVERPORT HOLDING COMPANY, INC.; *U.S. Private*, pg. 3770
ST. LOUIS SPECIALTY SURGICAL CENTER, LLC—See UnitedHealth Group Incorporated; *U.S. Public*, pg. 2250
ST. LOUIS SURGICAL CENTER, LC—See Tenet Healthcare Corporation; *U.S. Public*, pg. 2013
ST. LOUIS TELECOMMUNICATIONS; *U.S. Private*, pg. 3772
ST. LOUIS URGENT CARE #2, L.L.C.—See Tenet Healthcare Corporation; *U.S. Public*, pg. 2005
ST. LOUIS WOMEN'S SURGERY CENTER, LLC—See Bain Capital, LP; *U.S. Private*, pg. 446
STL TECHNOLOGY CO., LTD.; *Int'l*, pg. 7216
STL TECHNOLOGY SIP CO., LTD.—See STL Technology Co., Ltd.; *Int'l*, pg. 7216
ST. LUCIA ELECTRICITY SERVICES LTD.; *Int'l*, pg. 7160
ST. LUCIE BATTERY & TIRE INC.; *U.S. Private*, pg. 3772
ST. LUCIE HOSPITALISTS, LLC—See HCA Healthcare, Inc.; *U.S. Public*, pg. 1010
ST. LUCIE MEDICAL CENTER—See HCA Healthcare, Inc.; *U.S. Public*, pg. 1010
ST. LUCIE MEDICAL SPECIALISTS, LLC—See HCA Healthcare, Inc.; *U.S. Public*, pg. 1010
ST. LUKE'S CATARACT & LASER INSTITUTE; *U.S. Private*, pg. 3772
ST. LUKE'S CORNWALL HOSPITAL—See Montefiore Medical Center; *U.S. Private*, pg. 2776
ST. LUKE'S DES PERES HOSPITAL—See St. Luke's Hospital; *U.S. Private*, pg. 3773
ST. LUKE'S FREE MEDICAL CLINIC; *U.S. Private*, pg. 3772
ST. LUKE'S HEALTH NETWORK, INC.; *U.S. Private*, pg. 3773
ST. LUKE'S HEALTH SYSTEM, INC.—See UnityPoint Health; *U.S. Private*, pg. 4303
ST. LUKE'S HOSPITAL; *U.S. Private*, pg. 3773
ST. LUKE'S PATHOLOGY ASSOCIATES, P.A.—See Quest Diagnostics, Inc.; *U.S. Public*, pg. 1756
ST. LUKE'S PHYSICIAN GROUP, INC.—See St. Luke's Health Network, Inc.; *U.S. Private*, pg. 3773
ST. LUKE'S REHABILITATION HOSPITAL, LLC—See Apollo Global Management, Inc.; *U.S. Public*, pg. 157
S&T MACEDONIA DOOEL—See Kontron AG; *Int'l*, pg. 4278
S&T MANUFACTURING CO.; *U.S. Private*, pg. 3514
ST. MARGARET'S AT MERCY; *U.S. Private*, pg. 3773
ST. MARIEN KRANKENHAUS LAMPERTHEIM GMBH—See Eurofins Scientific S.E.; *Int'l*, pg. 2551
ST. MARIES RIVER RAILROAD COMPANY—See Williams Group LLC; *U.S. Private*, pg. 4526
ST MARK HOMES PLC; *Int'l*, pg. 7158
ST. MARK'S HOSPITAL—See HCA Healthcare, Inc.; *U.S. Public*, pg. 1010
ST. MARKS PHYSICIAN BILLING, LLC—See HCA Healthcare, Inc.; *U.S. Public*, pg. 1010
ST. MARKS POWDER, INC.—See General Dynamics Corporation; *U.S. Public*, pg. 914
ST. MARTINS PRESS, INC.—See Verlagsgruppe Georg von Holtzbrinck GmbH; *Int'l*, pg. 8171
ST. MARY BANANA ESTATES LIMITED—See PanJam Investment Limited; *Int'l*, pg. 5728
ST. MARY CATHOLIC HOUSING CORPORATION—See Catholic Health Initiatives; *U.S. Private*, pg. 790
ST. MARY LAND & EXPLORATION CO. - SHREVEPORT—See SM Energy Company; *U.S. Public*, pg. 1895
ST. MARY MEDICAL CENTER—See Catholic Health Initiatives; *U.S. Private*, pg. 789
ST. MARY'S AMBULATORY SURGERY CENTER, LLC—See Tenet Healthcare Corporation; *U.S. Public*, pg. 2013
ST. MARY'S BANK; *U.S. Private*, pg. 3773
ST. MARYS CEMENT INC.—See Votorantim S.A.; *Int'l*, pg. 8310
ST. MARY'S CREDIT UNION; *U.S. Private*, pg. 3773
ST. MARY'S HEALTH CARE SYSTEM; *U.S. Private*, pg. 3773
ST. MARY'S HOSPITAL—See Ascension Health Alliance; *U.S. Private*, pg. 347
ST. MARY'S HOSPITAL—See Ascension Health Alliance; *U.S. Private*, pg. 347
ST. MARY'S MANOR—See Ascension Health Alliance; *U.S. Private*, pg. 347
ST. MARY'S MEDICAL CENTER HOME HEALTH SERVICES, LLC—See UnitedHealth Group Incorporated; *U.S. Public*, pg. 2247
ST. MARY'S MEDICAL CENTER, INC.—See Cabell Huntington Hospital, Inc.; *U.S. Private*, pg. 710
ST. MARY'S MEDICAL CENTER, INC.—See Tenet Healthcare Corporation; *U.S. Public*, pg. 2008
ST. MARY'S MEDICAL CENTER—See Catholic Health Initiatives; *U.S. Private*, pg. 790
ST. MARY'S MEDICAL CENTER—See Prime Healthcare Services, Inc.; *U.S. Private*, pg. 3262
ST. MARY'S MEDICAL PARK PHARMACY, INC.—See Select Medical Holdings Corporation; *U.S. Public*, pg. 1861
ST. MARYS PAPER CORP.; *Int'l*, pg. 7160
ST. MARY'S PROPERTIES, INC.—See Omega Healthcare Investors, Inc.; *U.S. Public*, pg. 1571
ST. MARYS SAND COMPANY, LLC—See Martin Marietta Materials, Inc.; *U.S. Public*, pg. 1389
ST. MARY'S SURGICAL CENTER, LLC—See Tenet Healthcare Corporation; *U.S. Public*, pg. 2013
ST. MARY'S TITLE SERVICES, LLC—See Anywhere Real Estate Inc.; *U.S. Public*, pg. 142
ST. MARY'S/WESTSIDE FOOD BANK ALLIANCE; *U.S. Private*, pg. 3773
STM AUTOMOTIVE; *U.S. Private*, pg. 3813
ST MEDIA HOLDINGS, LLC—See Chicago Public Media, Inc.; *U.S. Private*, pg. 879
S&T MEDTECH S.R.L.—See Kontron AG; *Int'l*, pg. 4278
STMEM, A.S.—See CEZ, a.s.; *Int'l*, pg. 1428
STM GROUP PLC; *Int'l*, pg. 7216
ST MICHAELS PLACE (COLCHESTER) RESIDENTS MANAGEMENT COMPANY LIMITED—See Persimmon plc; *Int'l*, pg. 5817
ST MICHAEL'S SUPPORT & CARE LIMITED—See Sheikh Holdings Group (Investments) Limited; *Int'l*, pg. 6794
ST MICHAELS WAY (SOUTH RYHOPE) RESIDENTS MANAGEMENT COMPANY LIMITED—See Persimmon plc; *Int'l*, pg. 5817
STMICROELECTRONICS (CHINA) INVESTMENT CO. LTD.—See STMicroelectronics N.V.; *Int'l*, pg. 7218
STMICROELECTRONICS (GRENOBLE 2) SAS—See STMicroelectronics N.V.; *Int'l*, pg. 7218
STMICROELECTRONICS AB—See STMicroelectronics N.V.; *Int'l*, pg. 7217
STMICROELECTRONICS-AMK6—See STMicroelectronics N.V.; *Int'l*, pg. 7217
STMICROELECTRONICS-AMK8—See STMicroelectronics N.V.; *Int'l*, pg. 7217
STMICROELECTRONICS ASIA PACIFIC PTE. LTD.—See STMicroelectronics N.V.; *Int'l*, pg. 7217
STMICROELECTRONICS (CANADA), INC.—See STMicroelectronics N.V.; *Int'l*, pg. 7217
STMICROELECTRONICS (CHINA) INVESTMENT CO. LTD.—See STMicroelectronics N.V.; *Int'l*, pg. 7217
STMICROELECTRONICS (CROLLES 2) SAS—See STMicroelectronics N.V.; *Int'l*, pg. 7218
STMICROELECTRONICS DESIGN AND APPLICATION S.R.O.—See STMicroelectronics N.V.; *Int'l*, pg. 7217
STMICROELECTRONICS - EUROPE MANUFACTURING & DESIGN—See STMicroelectronics N.V.; *Int'l*, pg. 7218
STMICROELECTRONICS GMBH—See STMicroelectronics N.V.; *Int'l*, pg. 7217
STMICROELECTRONICS (GRENOBLE 2) SAS—See STMicroelectronics N.V.; *Int'l*, pg. 7217
STMICROELECTRONICS, INC.—See STMicroelectronics N.V.; *Int'l*, pg. 7218
STMICROELECTRONICS K.K. - JAPAN REGIONAL WAREHOUSE—See STMicroelectronics N.V.; *Int'l*, pg. 7218
STMICROELECTRONICS K.K.—See STMicroelectronics N.V.; *Int'l*, pg. 7217
STMICROELECTRONICS LIMITED—See STMicroelectronics N.V.; *Int'l*, pg. 7218
STMICROELECTRONICS LTDA—See STMicroelectronics N.V.; *Int'l*, pg. 7217
STMICROELECTRONICS LTD.—See STMicroelectronics N.V.; *Int'l*, pg. 7217
STMICROELECTRONICS (MALTA) LTD.—See STMicroelectronics N.V.; *Int'l*, pg. 7217
STMICROELECTRONICS MARKETING, S. DE R.L. DE C.V.—See STMicroelectronics N.V.; *Int'l*, pg. 7218
STMICROELECTRONICS MARKETING SDN BHD—See STMicroelectronics N.V.; *Int'l*, pg. 7218
STMICROELECTRONICS (NORTH AMERICA) HOLDING, INC.—See STMicroelectronics N.V.; *Int'l*, pg. 7217
STMICROELECTRONICS N.V.; *Int'l*, pg. 7217
STMICROELECTRONICS PTE. LTD.-AMK5—See STMicroelectronics N.V.; *Int'l*, pg. 7217
STMICROELECTRONICS PTY LTD—See STMicroelectronics N.V.; *Int'l*, pg. 7218
STMICROELECTRONICS PVT. LTD.—See STMicroelectronics N.V.; *Int'l*, pg. 7217

STOCKADE COMPANIES, INC.

STMICROELECTRONICS (R&D) LTD. - BRISTOL—See STMicroelectronics N.V.; *Int'l*, pg. 7218
STMICROELECTRONICS (R&D) LTD. - EDINBURGH—See STMicroelectronics N.V.; *Int'l*, pg. 7218
STMICROELECTRONICS - RENNES INDUSTRIAL & DESIGN CENTER—See STMicroelectronics N.V.; *Int'l*, pg. 7218
STMICROELECTRONICS ROUSSET SAS—See STMicroelectronics N.V.; *Int'l*, pg. 7218
STMICROELECTRONICS S.A.—See STMicroelectronics N.V.; *Int'l*, pg. 7218
STMICROELECTRONICS SA—See STMicroelectronics N.V.; *Int'l*, pg. 7218
STMICROELECTRONICS SDN BHD—See STMicroelectronics N.V.; *Int'l*, pg. 7217
STMICROELECTRONICS (SHANGHAI) CO., LTD.—See STMicroelectronics N.V.; *Int'l*, pg. 7217
STMICROELECTRONICS (SHANGHAI) R&D CO. LTD—See STMicroelectronics N.V.; *Int'l*, pg. 7217
STMICROELECTRONICS (SHENZHEN) CO. LTD.—See STMicroelectronics N.V.; *Int'l*, pg. 7217
STMICROELECTRONICS (SHENZHEN) R&D CO. LTD.—See STMicroelectronics N.V.; *Int'l*, pg. 7217
STMICROELECTRONICS SOFTWARE AB—See STMicroelectronics N.V.; *Int'l*, pg. 7218
STMICROELECTRONICS S.R.L. - CASTELLETTO PLANT—See STMicroelectronics N.V.; *Int'l*, pg. 7218
STMICROELECTRONICS S.R.L. - CATANIA PLANT—See STMicroelectronics N.V.; *Int'l*, pg. 7218
STMICROELECTRONICS S.R.L. - INCARD DIVISION—See STMicroelectronics N.V.; *Int'l*, pg. 7218
STMICROELECTRONICS S.R.L. - NAPOLI PLANT—See STMicroelectronics N.V.; *Int'l*, pg. 7218
STMICROELECTRONICS S.R.L.—See STMicroelectronics N.V.; *Int'l*, pg. 7218
STMICROELECTRONICS S.R.O.—See STMicroelectronics N.V.; *Int'l*, pg. 7218
STMICROELECTRONICS (THAILAND) LTD—See STMicroelectronics N.V.; *Int'l*, pg. 7217
STMICROELECTRONICS TOURS SAS—See STMicroelectronics N.V.; *Int'l*, pg. 7218
STM INDUSTRIES, INC.; *U.S. Private*, pg. 3813
STM LOTTERY SDN. BHD.—See Berjaya Corporation Berhad; *Int'l*, pg. 984
STM NUMMOS LIFE S.L.—See STM Group Plc; *Int'l*, pg. 7217
ST. MODWEN DEVELOPMENTS LIMITED—See Blackstone Inc.; *U.S. Public*, pg. 358
ST. MODWEN PROPERTIES PLC—See Blackstone Inc.; *U.S. Public*, pg. 358
ST. MODWEN VENTURES LIMITED—See Blackstone Inc.; *U.S. Public*, pg. 358
S&T MOLDOVA S.R.L.—See Kontron AG; *Int'l*, pg. 4278
S&T MOLD SRL—See Kontron AG; *Int'l*, pg. 4278
ST. MORITZ SECURITY SERVICES, INC.; *U.S. Private*, pg. 3773
STM PACKAGING GROUP LTD.—See DPG Media Group NV; *Int'l*, pg. 2189
STM SWISS AG—See STM Group Plc; *Int'l*, pg. 7217
S&T MUTUAL SAVINGS BANK—See SNT Holdings Co., Ltd.; *Int'l*, pg. 7029
STNET, INCORPORATED—See Shikoku Electric Power Co., Incorporated; *Int'l*, pg. 6830
ST. NICHOLAS HUMAN SUPPORT CORPORATION; *U.S. Private*, pg. 3770
ST.NICKS ALLIANCE; *U.S. Private*, pg. 3774
STN SCHIFFSELEKTRIK VERWALTUNGS GMBH—See L3Harris Technologies, Inc.; *U.S. Public*, pg. 1284
STOBA PRAZISIONSTECHNIK GMBH & CO. KG—See Berndorf AG; *Int'l*, pg. 987
STOBA PRAZISIONSTECHNIK UK LTD.—See Berndorf AG; *Int'l*, pg. 987
STOBART AIR (UK) LIMITED—See Esken Limited; *Int'l*, pg. 2503
STOBART (IRELAND) LIMITED—See DBAY Advisors Limited; *Int'l*, pg. 1986
STOBART RAIL FREIGHT LIMITED—See DBAY Advisors Limited; *Int'l*, pg. 1986
STOBART RAIL LIMITED—See BAVARIA Industries Group AG; *Int'l*, pg. 899
STOBA SONDERMASCHINEN GMBH—See Berndorf AG; *Int'l*, pg. 987
STO BRASIL REVESTIMENTOS E FACHADAS LTDA.—See Sto SE & Co. KGaA; *Int'l*, pg. 7219
STOBRNO A.S.—See L'Arche Green N.V.; *Int'l*, pg. 4377
STO BUILDING GROUP INC.; *U.S. Private*, pg. 3813
STO CANADA LTD.—See Sto SE & Co. KGaA; *Int'l*, pg. 7219
STOCAR A.D.; *Int'l*, pg. 7219
STOCCAGGI GAS ITALIA S.P.A.—See Eni S.p.A.; *Int'l*, pg. 2438
STOCK3 AG; *Int'l*, pg. 7219
STOCKADE BUILDINGS, INC.; *U.S. Private*, pg. 3814
STOCKADE COMPANIES, INC.; *U.S. Private*, pg. 3814
STOCK AMERICA, LLC—See Leonard Green & Partners, L.P.; *U.S. Private*, pg. 2428
STOCKBREST S.A.—See Rubis SCA; *Int'l*, pg. 6423

2609

STOCKADE COMPANIES, INC.

STOCKBROKERS MALAWI LIMITED—See National Bank of Malawi; *Int'l*, pg. 5154
STOCK BUILDING SUPPLY OF ARKANSAS, LLC—See Builders FirstSource, Inc.; *U.S. Public*, pg. 409
STOCK BUILDING SUPPLY; *U.S. Private*, pg. 3814
STOCK BUILDING SUPPLY—See Builders FirstSource, Inc.; *U.S. Public*, pg. 409
STOCK BUILDING SUPPLY—See Builders FirstSource, Inc.; *U.S. Public*, pg. 409
STOCK BUILDING SUPPLY—See Builders FirstSource, Inc.; *U.S. Public*, pg. 409
STOCK BUILDING SUPPLY—See Builders FirstSource, Inc.; *U.S. Public*, pg. 409
STOCK BUILDING SUPPLY—See Builders FirstSource, Inc.; *U.S. Public*, pg. 409
THE STOCK COMPANY MOSKABEL-FUJIKURA—See Fujikura Ltd.; *Int'l*, pg. 2829
STOCK CONSTRUCTION—See Stock Development, LLC; *U.S. Private*, pg. 3814
STOCKCROSS FINANCIAL SERVICES, INC; *U.S. Private*, pg. 3814
STOCKCUBE PLC; *Int'l*, pg. 7219
STOCKCUBE RESEARCH LIMITED—See Stockcube Plc; *Int'l*, pg. 7219
STOCKDALE—See Tennessee Farmers Cooperative; *U.S. Private*, pg. 3967
STOCK DEVELOPMENT, LLC; *U.S. Private*, pg. 3814
STOCK DRIVE PRODUCTS DIV.—See Designatronics, Inc.; *U.S. Private*, pg. 1214
STOCK DRIVE PRODUCTS—See Designatronics, Inc.; *U.S. Private*, pg. 1214
STOCKELL CONSULTING INC.; *U.S. Private*, pg. 3814
STOCK EQUIPMENT COMPANY INC.—See Blackstone Inc.; *U.S. Public*, pg. 360
STOCKERTOWN CONSTRUCTION MATERIALS—See Haines & Kibblehouse Inc.; *U.S. Private*, pg. 1841
THE STOCK EXCHANGE OF HONG KONG LIMITED—See Hong Kong Exchanges & Clearing Limited; *Int'l*, pg. 3466
THE STOCK EXCHANGE OF MAURITIUS; *Int'l*, pg. 7688
THE STOCK EXCHANGE OF THAILAND; *Int'l*, pg. 7688
THE STOCK EXCHANGE (PROPERTIES) LTD—See London Stock Exchange Group plc; *Int'l*, pg. 4548
STOCK FAIRFIELD CORPORATION—See Blackstone Inc.; *U.S. Public*, pg. 360
STOCK FINANCIAL—See Stock Development, LLC; *U.S. Private*, pg. 3814
STOCKFISH GEORGE FORD SALES (1987) LTD.; *Int'l*, pg. 7220
STOCKHAM CONSTRUCTION, INC.; *U.S. Private*, pg. 3815
STOCKHAM VALVES & FITTINGS, INC.—See Crane NXT, Co.; *U.S. Public*, pg. 590
STOCKHOLM ARRHYTHMIA CENTER AB—See Apax Partners LLP; *Int'l*, pg. 502
STOCKHOLM ENTREPRENAD AB—See Peab AB; *Int'l*, pg. 5773
STOCKHOLM GAS AB—See Fortum Oyj; *Int'l*, pg. 2741
STOCKHOLM HISS & ELTEKNIK AB—See Sdiptech AB; *Int'l*, pg. 6659
STOCKHOLM LUFTKOMPETENS AB—See Instalco AB; *Int'l*, pg. 3722
STOCKHOLMRADIO AB—See Sdiptech AB; *Int'l*, pg. 6659
STOCKHOLMS FISKAUKTION AB—See Sysco Corporation; *U.S. Public*, pg. 1975
STOCKHOLMS GEOMEKANISKA AB—See Indutrade AB; *Int'l*, pg. 3681
STOCKHOLMS INTERNATIONELLA HANDELSSKOLA AB—See Storskogen Group AB; *Int'l*, pg. 7228
STOCKHOLM SKAVSTA FLYGPLATS AB—See ACS, Actividades de Construccion y Servicios, S.A.; *Int'l*, pg. 112
STOCKHOLMS STADS UTREDNINGS- OCH STATISTIKKONTOR AB—See Sweco AB; *Int'l*, pg. 7363
STOCK & INFO LTDA.—See EVERTEC, Inc.; *U.S. Public*, pg. 802
STOCK JOURNAL PUBLISHERS PTY LTD—See Nine Entertainment Co. Holdings Limited; *Int'l*, pg. 5299
STOCKLAND CORPORATION LTD.; *Int'l*, pg. 7220
STOCKLAND GRAIN COMPANY INC.; *U.S. Private*, pg. 3815
STOCKLINK DISTRIBUTION LTD.—See Wickliffe Ltd.; *Int'l*, pg. 8401
STOCKLIN LOGISTIK AG; *Int'l*, pg. 7220
STOCKMAN ASSET MANAGEMENT, INC.—See Stockman Financial Corp.; *U.S. Private*, pg. 3815
STOCKMAN BANK OF MONTANA—See Stockman Financial Corp.; *U.S. Private*, pg. 3815
STOCKMAN FINANCIAL CORP.; *U.S. Private*, pg. 3815
STOCKMAN INSURANCE INC.—See Stockman Financial Corp.; *U.S. Private*, pg. 3815
STOCKMANN OYJ ABP; *Int'l*, pg. 7220
STOCKMANN PLC - DEPARTMENT STORE DIVISION—See Stockmann plc; *Int'l*, pg. 7220
STOCKMANN PLC; *Int'l*, pg. 7220
STOCKMAN OIL COMPANY; *U.S. Private*, pg. 3815
STOCKMANS BANK; *U.S. Private*, pg. 3815
STOCKMAN'S CASINO—See Full House Resorts, Inc.; *U.S. Public*, pg. 892

STOCKMEIER CHEMIE AUSTRIA GMBH—See Stockmeier Holding GmbH; *Int'l*, pg. 7220
STOCKMEIER CHEMIE BVBA—See Stockmeier Holding GmbH; *Int'l*, pg. 7220
STOCKMEIER CHEMIE DILLENBURG GMBH & CO. KG—See Stockmeier Holding GmbH; *Int'l*, pg. 7220
STOCKMEIER CHEMIE EILENBURG GMBH & CO. KG—See Stockmeier Holding GmbH; *Int'l*, pg. 7220
STOCKMEIER CHEMIE POLEN SP Z O.O.—See Stockmeier Holding GmbH; *Int'l*, pg. 7220
STOCKMEIER FOOD GMBH & CO. KG—See Stockmeier Holding GmbH; *Int'l*, pg. 7220
STOCKMEIER HOLDING GMBH; *Int'l*, pg. 7220
STOCKMEIER URETHANES FRANCE S.A.—See Stockmeier Holding GmbH; *Int'l*, pg. 7220
STOCKMEIER URETHANES GMBH & CO. KG—See Stockmeier Holding GmbH; *Int'l*, pg. 7220
STOCKMEIER URETHANES UK LTD—See Stockmeier Holding GmbH; *Int'l*, pg. 7220
STOCKMEIER URETHANES USA, INC.—See Stockmeier Holding GmbH; *Int'l*, pg. 7220
STOCKMENS FINANCIAL CORPORATION; *U.S. Private*, pg. 3815
STOCKMEN'S SUPPLY, INC.—See Animart Inc.; *U.S. Private*, pg. 283
STOCK MUST GO LIMITED—See SK Inc.; *Int'l*, pg. 6972
STOCKNER'S NURSERY, INC.; *U.S. Private*, pg. 3815
STOCKNET—See The Hearst Corporation; *U.S. Private*, pg. 4045
STOCKO CONTACT EURL—See Wieland Holding GmbH; *Int'l*, pg. 8402
STOCKO CONTACT GMBH & CO. KG - HELLENTHAL FACTORY—See Wieland Holding GmbH; *Int'l*, pg. 8402
STOCKO CONTACT GMBH & CO. KG—See Wieland Holding GmbH; *Int'l*, pg. 8402
STOCKO DO BRASIL LTDA.—See Wieland Holding GmbH; *Int'l*, pg. 8402
STOCK & OPTION SOLUTIONS, INC.; *U.S. Private*, pg. 3814
STOCK PLUS AD; *U.S. Public*, pg. 1950
STOCK POINT, INC.—See Credit Saison Co., Ltd.; *Int'l*, pg. 1836
STOCKPOT INC.—See Campbell Soup Company; *U.S. Public*, pg. 427
STOCK REDLER LIMITED—See Blackstone Inc.; *U.S. Public*, pg. 360
STOCK ROOFING COMPANY, LLC—See Atlas Partners LP; *Int'l*, pg. 386
STOCK SPIRITS GROUP PLC—See CVC Capital Partners SICAV-FIS S.A.; *Int'l*, pg. 1888
STOCKTON 12 AUTOMOTIVE, INC.; *U.S. Private*, pg. 3815
STOCKTON DELTA RESORT, LLC—See Sun Communities, Inc.; *U.S. Public*, pg. 1963
STOCKTON DIALYSIS, LLC—See DaVita Inc.; *U.S. Public*, pg. 643
STOCKTON FURTHER PROCESSING—See Zacky Farms, Inc.; *U.S. Private*, pg. 4597
STOCKTON NEWSPAPERS INC.—See Lee Enterprises, Incorporated; *U.S. Public*, pg. 1299
STOCKTON OIL COMPANY; *U.S. Private*, pg. 3815
STOCKTON OUTPATIENT SURGERY CENTER, LLC—See Tenet Healthcare Corporation; *U.S. Public*, pg. 2013
STOCKTON TELECOMMUNICATIONS; *U.S. Private*, pg. 3815
STOCK TRANSPORTATION LIMITED—See Mobico Group PLC.; *Int'l*, pg. 5009
STOCK TRANSPORT INC.; *U.S. Private*, pg. 3814
STOCK TREND CAPITAL INC.; *Int'l*, pg. 7219
STOCK USA EXECUTION SERVICES INC; *U.S. Private*, pg. 3814
STOCKVANTAGE INC.—See Morgan Stanley; *U.S. Public*, pg. 1475
STOCKWELL COMMODITIES LIMITED—See Southeast Asia Properties & Finance Limited; *Int'l*, pg. 7117
STOCKWELL SECURITIES LIMITED—See Southeast Asia Properties & Finance Limited; *Int'l*, pg. 7117
STOCKWIK FORVALTNING AB; *Int'l*, pg. 7220
STOCK YARDS BANCORP, INC.; *U.S. Public*, pg. 1950
STOCK YARDS BANK & TRUST COMPANY—See Stock Yards Bancorp, Inc.; *U.S. Public*, pg. 1951
STOCK YARDS MEAT PACKING COMPANY—See US Foods Holding Corp.; *U.S. Public*, pg. 2266
STOCK YARDS PACKING CO., INC.—See US Foods Holding Corp.; *U.S. Public*, pg. 2266
STO COLOMBIA S.A.S.—See Sto SE & Co. KGaA; *Int'l*, pg. 7219
STO CO., LTD.; *Int'l*, pg. 7218
STO CORPORATION; *U.S. Private*, pg. 3814
STO-CPH PRODUKTION AB—See The Walt Disney Company; *U.S. Public*, pg. 2141
STOCRETEC FLOORING AS—See Sto SE & Co. KGaA; *Int'l*, pg. 7219
STOCRETEC GMBH—See Sto SE & Co. KGaA; *Int'l*, pg. 7219
STOCZEK NATURA SP. Z O.O.—See Makarony Polskie S.A.; *Int'l*, pg. 4655

CORPORATE AFFILIATIONS

STOCZNIA GDANSKA GRUPA STOCZNI GDYNIA S.A.—See Stocznia Gdynia S.A.; *Int'l*, pg. 7220
STOCZNIA GDYNIA S.A.; *Int'l*, pg. 7220
STO DANMARK A/S—See Sto SE & Co. KGaA; *Int'l*, pg. 7219
STODDARD BAPTIST GLOBAL CARE, INC.; *U.S. Private*, pg. 3815
STODDARD NLA, LLC; *U.S. Private*, pg. 3815
STODOLA-MAAS CONSTRUCTION INC.; *U.S. Private*, pg. 3815
STOEGER INDUSTRIES—See Fabbrica d'Armi Pietro Beretta S.p.A.; *Int'l*, pg. 2598
STOEL RIVES LLP; *U.S. Private*, pg. 3815
STOELTING CO.; *U.S. Private*, pg. 3815
STOELZLE GLASS LLC—See CAG Holding GmbH; *Int'l*, pg. 1250
STOELZLE MASNIERES SAS—See CAG Holding GmbH; *Int'l*, pg. 1250
STO EPITOANYAG KFT.—See Sto SE & Co. KGaA; *Int'l*, pg. 7219
STO EXPRESS CO., LTD.; *Int'l*, pg. 7218
STOFA A/S—See Sydvest Energi AmbA; *Int'l*, pg. 7378
STOFFEL EQUIPMENT COMPANY, INC.—See Toyota Industries Corporation; *Int'l*, pg. 7869
S&T OFFICE PRODUCTS, INC.; *U.S. Private*, pg. 3514
STO FINEXTER OY—See Sto SE & Co. KGaA; *Int'l*, pg. 7219
STOFNFISKUR HF.—See Benchmark Holdings Plc; *Int'l*, pg. 970
STO GES.M.B.H.—See Sto SE & Co. KGaA; *Int'l*, pg. 7219
STOHLMAN AND ROGERS INC.; *U.S. Private*, pg. 3816
STOHLMAN AUTOMOTIVE FAMILY; *U.S. Private*, pg. 3816
STOIC HOLDINGS LLC; *U.S. Private*, pg. 3816
STOILENSKY GOK—See Novolipetski Metallurgicheski Komb OAO; *Int'l*, pg. 5466
STO ISONED B.V.—See Sto SE & Co. KGaA; *Int'l*, pg. 7219
STO ITALIA SRL—See Sto SE & Co. KGaA; *Int'l*, pg. 7219
STOKE-ON-TRENT REGENERATION LIMITED—See Blackstone Inc.; *U.S. Public*, pg. 358
THE STOKE ON TRENT & STAFFORDSHIRE SAFER COMMUNITIES COMMUNITY INTEREST COMPANY—See Bilfinger SE; *Int'l*, pg. 1029
STOKER OSTLER WEALTH ADVISORS, INC.—See Bank of Montreal; *Int'l*, pg. 846
STOKERS TENDEREX FARMS INC.; *U.S. Private*, pg. 3816
STOKES APPLIANCE PARTS—See SKS Technologies Group Limited; *Int'l*, pg. 6991
STOKES APPLIANCE PARTS—See SKS Technologies Group Limited; *Int'l*, pg. 6991
STOKES AUTOMOTIVE, INC.; *U.S. Private*, pg. 3816
STOKES BROWN TOYOTA OF HILTON HEAD—See Stokes Automotive, Inc.; *U.S. Private*, pg. 3816
STOKES CHEVROLET, INC.; *U.S. Private*, pg. 3816
STOKES-CRAVEN AUTOMOTIVE—See Stokes Automotive, Inc.; *U.S. Private*, pg. 3816
STOKES DISTRIBUTING CO. INC.; *U.S. Private*, pg. 3816
STOKES ELECTRIC COMPANY; *U.S. Private*, pg. 3816
STOKES FORGINGS DUDLEY LIMITED—See Mahindra & Mahindra Limited; *Int'l*, pg. 4646
STOKES GROUP LIMITED—See Mahindra & Mahindra Limited; *Int'l*, pg. 4646
STOKES MECHANICAL CONTRACTORS INC; *U.S. Private*, pg. 3816
STOKES & SPIEHLER INC.; *U.S. Private*, pg. 3816
STOKE THERAPEUTICS, INC.; *U.S. Public*, pg. 1951
STOKKAN LYS; *Int'l*, pg. 7221
STOKROTKA SP.Z.O.O—See Emperia Holding S.A; *Int'l*, pg. 2386
STOKVIS CELIX PORTUGAL UNIPESSOAL LDA—See Illinois Tool Works Inc.; *U.S. Public*, pg. 1110
STOKVIS DANMARK AS—See Illinois Tool Works Inc.; *U.S. Public*, pg. 1110
STOKVIS NIG PLC.; *Int'l*, pg. 7221
STOKVIS TAPE GROUP B.V.—See Illinois Tool Works Inc.; *U.S. Public*, pg. 1110
STOKVIS TAPES (BEIJING) CO. LTD.—See Illinois Tool Works Inc.; *U.S. Public*, pg. 1110
STOKVIS TAPES BENELUX B.V.—See Illinois Tool Works Inc.; *U.S. Public*, pg. 1110
STOKVIS TAPES BVBA—See Illinois Tool Works Inc.; *U.S. Public*, pg. 1110
STOKVIS TAPES DEUTSCHLAND GMBH—See Illinois Tool Works Inc.; *U.S. Public*, pg. 1110
STOKVIS TAPES ESTONIA OU—See Illinois Tool Works Inc.; *U.S. Public*, pg. 1110
STOKVIS TAPES FRANCE SAS—See Illinois Tool Works Inc.; *U.S. Public*, pg. 1111
STOKVIS TAPES ITALIA S.R.L.—See Illinois Tool Works Inc.; *U.S. Public*, pg. 1111
STOKVIS TAPES LIMITED LIABILITY COMPANY—See Illinois Tool Works Inc.; *U.S. Public*, pg. 1111
STOKVIS TAPES MAGYARORSZAG KFT—See Illinois Tool Works Inc.; *U.S. Public*, pg. 1111
STOKVIS TAPES NORGE AS—See Illinois Tool Works Inc.; *U.S. Public*, pg. 1111

COMPANY NAME INDEX

STOKVIS TAPES OY—See Illinois Tool Works Inc.; *U.S. Public*, pg. 1111
STOKVIS TAPES (SHANGHAI) CO. LTD.—See Illinois Tool Works Inc.; *U.S. Public*, pg. 1110
STOKVIS TAPES (SHENZHEN) CO. LTD.—See Illinois Tool Works Inc.; *U.S. Public*, pg. 1110
STOKVIS TAPES SVERIGE AB—See Illinois Tool Works Inc.; *U.S. Public*, pg. 1111
STOKVIS TAPES (TAIWAN) CO. LTD.—See Illinois Tool Works Inc.; *U.S. Public*, pg. 1110
STOKVIS TAPES (TIANJIN) CO. LTD.—See Illinois Tool Works Inc.; *U.S. Public*, pg. 1110
STOLECZNE PRZEDSIEBIORSTWO ENERGETYKI CIEPLNEJ S.A.—See Veolia Environnement S.A.; *Int'l*, pg. 8157
STOLLE ASIA PACIFIC CO., LTD.—See Toyo Seikan Group Holdings, Ltd.; *Int'l*, pg. 7857
STOLLE EMS PRECISION LIMITED—See Toyo Seikan Group Holdings, Ltd.; *Int'l*, pg. 7857
STOLLE EUROPEAN MANUFACTURING SOLUTIONS LIMITED—See Toyo Seikan Group Holdings, Ltd.; *Int'l*, pg. 7857
STOLLE EUROPE LTD.—See Toyo Seikan Group Holdings, Ltd.; *Int'l*, pg. 7857
STOLLE MACHINERY COMPANY - CANTON—See Toyo Seikan Group Holdings, Ltd.; *Int'l*, pg. 7857
STOLLE MACHINERY COMPANY - CONTAINER MACHINERY—See Toyo Seikan Group Holdings, Ltd.; *Int'l*, pg. 7857
STOLLE MACHINERY COMPANY - END & METAL FORMING—See Toyo Seikan Group Holdings, Ltd.; *Int'l*, pg. 7857
STOLLE MACHINERY COMPANY, LLC—See Toyo Seikan Group Holdings, Ltd.; *Int'l*, pg. 7857
STOLLE MACHINERY DO BRASIL INDUSTRIA E COMERCIO EQUIPAMENTOS LTDA.—See Toyo Seikan Group Holdings, Ltd.; *Int'l*, pg. 7857
STOLLE MACHINERY (GUANGDONG) CO., LTD.—See Toyo Seikan Group Holdings, Ltd.; *Int'l*, pg. 7857
STOLLE MACHINERY (SHANGHAI) CO., LTD.—See Toyo Seikan Group Holdings, Ltd.; *Int'l*, pg. 7857
STOLLE MILK BIOLOGICS INC.—See Spencer Trask & Co.; *U.S. Private*, pg. 3755
STOLLER ARGENTINA—See Corteva, Inc.; *U.S. Public*, pg. 584
STOLLER AUSTRALIA PTY. LTD.—See Corteva, Inc.; *U.S. Public*, pg. 584
STOLLER CHEMICAL COMPANY OF CANADA LTD.—See Corteva, Inc.; *U.S. Public*, pg. 584
STOLLER COLOMBIA S.A.—See Corteva, Inc.; *U.S. Public*, pg. 584
STOLLER DE CHILE, S.A.—See Corteva, Inc.; *U.S. Public*, pg. 584
STOLLER DO BRASIL, LTDA.—See Corteva, Inc.; *U.S. Public*, pg. 584
STOLLER ENTERPRISES DE MEXICO, SA DE CV—See Corteva, Inc.; *U.S. Public*, pg. 584
STOLLER ENTERPRISES, INC.—See Corteva, Inc.; *U.S. Public*, pg. 584
STOLLER ENTERPRISES, INC.—See Corteva, Inc.; *U.S. Public*, pg. 584
STOLLER EUROPE, S.L.U.—See Corteva, Inc.; *U.S. Public*, pg. 584
STOLLER GROUP, INC.—See Corteva, Inc.; *U.S. Public*, pg. 584
THE STOLLER GROUP; *U.S. Private*, pg. 4123
STOLLER IBERICA, S.L.—See Corteva, Inc.; *U.S. Public*, pg. 584
STOLLER INTERNATIONAL INC.; *U.S. Private*, pg. 3816
STOLLER MEXICO S.A. DE C.V.—See Corteva, Inc.; *U.S. Public*, pg. 584
STOLLER NEWPORT NEWS NUCLEAR, INC.—See Huntington Ingalls Industries, Inc.; *U.S. Public*, pg. 1072
STOLLER - PERU S.A.—See Corteva, Inc.; *U.S. Public*, pg. 584
STOLLER PHILLIPINNES, INC.—See Corteva, Inc.; *U.S. Public*, pg. 584
STOLLER SOUTH AFRICA (PTY) LTD.—See Corteva, Inc.; *U.S. Public*, pg. 584
STOLLER TURKEY ORGANIK TARIM SANAYI TICARET A.S.—See Corteva, Inc.; *U.S. Public*, pg. 584
STOLLER USA, INC.—See Corteva, Inc.; *U.S. Public*, pg. 585
STOLLER WHOLESALE WINE & SPIRITS; *U.S. Private*, pg. 3816
STOLL KEENON OGDEN PLLC; *U.S. Private*, pg. 3816
STOLLREFLEX GMBH—See SWARCO AG; *Int'l*, pg. 7361
STOLLWERCK GMBH - SAALFELD—See Sweet Products Logistics NV; *Int'l*, pg. 7366
STOLLWERCK GMBH—See Sweet Products Logistics NV; *Int'l*, pg. 7366
STOLLWERCK ITALIA S.P.A.—See Sweet Products Logistics NV; *Int'l*, pg. 7366
STOLTE INSURANCE AGENCY, INC.—See Ewing-Leavitt Insurance Agency, Inc.; *U.S. Private*, pg. 1444
STOLTENBERG CONSULTING, INC.; *U.S. Private*, pg. 3816
STOLTHAVEN HOUSTON INC.—See Stolt-Nielsen Limited; *Int'l*, pg. 7221

STOLTHAVEN NEW ORLEANS LLC—See Stolt-Nielsen Limited; *Int'l*, pg. 7221
STOLTHAVEN SINGAPORE PTE. LTD.—See Stolt-Nielsen Limited; *Int'l*, pg. 7221
STOLTHAVEN (WESTPORT) SDN BHD—See Kuala Lumpur Kepong Berhad; *Int'l*, pg. 4319
STOLT-NIELSEN ARGENTINA S.A.—See Stolt-Nielsen Limited; *Int'l*, pg. 7221
STOLT-NIELSEN AUSTRALIA PTY LTD.—See Stolt-Nielsen Limited; *Int'l*, pg. 7221
STOLT-NIELSEN BRASIL LTDA.—See Stolt-Nielsen Limited; *Int'l*, pg. 7221
STOLT-NIELSEN JAPAN CO., LTD.—See Stolt-Nielsen Limited; *Int'l*, pg. 7221
STOLT-NIELSEN LIMITED; *Int'l*, pg. 7221
STOLT-NIELSEN MEXICO S.A. DE C.V.—See Stolt-Nielsen Limited; *Int'l*, pg. 7221
STOLT-NIELSEN PHILIPPINES, INC.—See Stolt-Nielsen Limited; *Int'l*, pg. 7221
STOLT-NIELSEN SINGAPORE PTE. LTD.—See Stolt-Nielsen Limited; *Int'l*, pg. 7221
STOLT-NIELSEN SWITZERLAND AG—See Stolt-Nielsen Limited; *Int'l*, pg. 7221
STOLT-NIELSEN TRANSPORTATION (SHANGHAI) LTD.—See Stolt-Nielsen Limited; *Int'l*, pg. 7221
STOLT-NIELSEN USA INC.—See Stolt-Nielsen Limited; *Int'l*, pg. 7221
STOLT-NIELSEN USA INC.—See Stolt-Nielsen Limited; *Int'l*, pg. 7221
STOLT SEA FARM AMERICAS—See Stolt-Nielsen Limited; *Int'l*, pg. 7221
STOLT SEA FARM HOLDINGS LTD—See Stolt-Nielsen Limited; *Int'l*, pg. 7221
STOLT SEA FARM INC.—See Stolt-Nielsen Limited; *Int'l*, pg. 7221
STOLT SEA FARM S.A.—See Stolt-Nielsen Limited; *Int'l*, pg. 7221
STOLT SEA FARM TAIWAN—See Stolt-Nielsen Limited; *Int'l*, pg. 7221
STOLT TANK CONTAINERS BV—See Stolt-Nielsen Limited; *Int'l*, pg. 7221
STOLT TANK CONTAINERS FRANCE S.A.S.—See Stolt-Nioloon Limitad; *Int'l*, pg. 7221
STOLT TANK CONTAINERS ITALY SRL—See Stolt-Nielsen Limited; *Int'l*, pg. 7221
STOLT TANK CONTAINERS SAUDI ARABIA LTD.—See Stolt-Nielsen Limited; *Int'l*, pg. 7221
STOLT TANKERS B.V. & MIDDLE EAST SERVICE LTD.—See Stolt-Nielsen Limited; *Int'l*, pg. 7221
STOLT TANKERS B.V.—See Stolt-Nielsen Limited; *Int'l*, pg. 7221
STOLT TANKERS SINGAPORE PTE. LTD.—See Stolt-Nielsen Limited; *Int'l*, pg. 7221
STOLTZ MARKETING GROUP; *U.S. Private*, pg. 3816
STOLZLE CZESTOCHOWA SP. Z O.O.—See CAG Holding GmbH; *Int'l*, pg. 1250
STOLZLE FLACONNAGE LTD.—See CAG Holding GmbH; *Int'l*, pg. 1250
STOLZLE FRANCE SAS—See CAG Holding GmbH; *Int'l*, pg. 1251
STOLZLE GLASS USA, INC.—See CAG Holding GmbH; *Int'l*, pg. 1251
STOLZLE LAUSITZ GMBH—See CAG Holding GmbH; *Int'l*, pg. 1250
STOLZLE-OBERGLAS GMBH—See CAG Holding GmbH; *Int'l*, pg. 1250
STOLZLE-UNION S.R.O—See CAG Holding GmbH; *Int'l*, pg. 1251
STOLZ S.A.S.—See Alfa Laval AB; *Int'l*, pg. 312
STOLZ SEQUIPAG S.A.S.—See Alfa Laval AB; *Int'l*, pg. 312
STOMANA INDUSTRY SA—See Viohalco SA/NV; *Int'l*, pg. 8243
STOMET SP. Z.O.O.—See Sanockie Zaklady Przemyslu Gumowego Stomil Sanok S.A.; *Int'l*, pg. 6547
STO MEXICO S. DE R.L. DE C.V.—See Sto SE & Co. KGaA; *Int'l*, pg. 7219
STOMIL EAST SP. Z O.O.—See Sanockie Zaklady Przemyslu Gumowego Stomil Sanok S.A.; *Int'l*, pg. 6547
STOMIL SANOK-DYSTRYBUCJA SP. Z O.O.—See Sanockie Zaklady Przemyslu Gumowego Stomil Sanok S.A.; *Int'l*, pg. 6547
STOMIL SANOK RUS SP. Z O.O.—See Sanockie Zaklady Przemyslu Gumowego Stomil Sanok S.A.; *Int'l*, pg. 6547
STOMIL SANOK UKRAINA SP. Z O.O.—See Sanockie Zaklady Przemyslu Gumowego Stomil Sanok S.A.; *Int'l*, pg. 6547
STONCOR AFRICA PTY. LTD.—See RPM International Inc.; *U.S. Public*, pg. 1819
STONCOR BENELUX B.V.—See RPM International Inc.; *U.S. Public*, pg. 1819
STONCOR CORROSION SPECIALISTS GROUP LTDA.—See RPM International Inc.; *U.S. Public*, pg. 1819
STONCOR (DEUTSCHLAND) GMBH—See RPM International Inc.; *U.S. Public*, pg. 1819

STONCOR ESPANA SL—See RPM International Inc.; *U.S. Public*, pg. 1819
STONCOR GROUP, INC.—See RPM International Inc.; *U.S. Public*, pg. 1818
STONCOR SOUTH CONE S.A.—See RPM International Inc.; *U.S. Public*, pg. 1819
STONE ADVANCE TECHNOLOGY LIMITED—See Stone Group Holdings Limited; *Int'l*, pg. 7222
STONE AGE EQUIPMENT, INC.—See adidas AG; *Int'l*, pg. 146
STONEAGE, INC.; *U.S. Private*, pg. 3827
STONE APPLE CONSULTING CO., LTD.—See Hitachi, Ltd.; *Int'l*, pg. 3424
STONE APPLE MALAYSIA SDN BHD.—See Hitachi, Ltd.; *Int'l*, pg. 3424
STONE APPLE SOLUTIONS PTE. LTD.—See Hitachi, Ltd.; *Int'l*, pg. 3424
STONE ARCH CAPITAL, LLC; *U.S. Private*, pg. 3816
STONE ASSET MANAGEMENT, INC.—See Avidian Wealth Solutions, LLC; *U.S. Private*, pg. 407
STONE BELT FREIGHT LINES INC.; *U.S. Private*, pg. 3816
STONE BOAT MINING CORP.; *Int'l*, pg. 7221
STONE BOY INC.—See Northern Star Resources Ltd; *Int'l*, pg. 5444
STONE BREWING CO.; *U.S. Private*, pg. 3817
STONEBRIDGE CASUALTY INSURANCE COMPANY—See Aegon N.V.; *Int'l*, pg. 174
STONE BRIDGE CELLARS, INC.; *U.S. Private*, pg. 3817
STONEBRIDGE CROSSING RETIREMENT COMMUNITY INC.—See Extendicare Inc.; *Int'l*, pg. 2591
STONEBRIDGE HEALTHCARE, INC—See The Ensign Group, Inc.; *U.S. Public*, pg. 2072
STONEBRIDGE INC.—See AIP, LLC; *U.S. Private*, pg. 134
STONEBRIDGE INC.—See Placements CMI Inc.; *Int'l*, pg. 5887
STONEBRIDGE INVESTMENTS BV—See Timeless Investments BV; *Int'l*, pg. 7751
STONEBRIDGE INVESTMENTS—See Timeless Investments BV; *Int'l*, pg. 7751
STONEBRIDGE PARTNERS, LLC; *U.S. Private*, pg. 3827
STONEBRIDGE REALTY ADVISORS, INC.; *U.S. Private*, pg. 3827
STONEBRIDGE RESOURCES EXPLORATIONS LTD.; *Int'l*, pg. 7222
STONEBRIDGE; *U.S. Private*, pg. 3827
STONEBRIDGE VENTURES INC.; *Int'l*, pg. 7222
STONEBROOKE ENGINEERING, INC.; *U.S. Private*, pg. 3827
STONEBURNER COMPANIES, LLC; *U.S. Private*, pg. 3827
STONECALIBRE, LLC; *U.S. Private*, pg. 3827
STONE CANYON INDUSTRIES, LLC; *U.S. Private*, pg. 3817
STONE CAPITAL GROUP INC.; *U.S. Private*, pg. 3818
STONE CENTER—See SiteOne Landscape Supply, Inc.; *U.S. Public*, pg. 1889
STONE & CLADDING INTERNATIONAL (SCI)—See Zeidler & Wimmel Verwaltungs-GmbH; *Int'l*, pg. 8631
STONECO LTD.; *Int'l*, pg. 7222
STONE & COMPANY; *U.S. Private*, pg. 3816
STONE COMPANY SPILIT; *Int'l*, pg. 7221
STONECOURT CAPITAL LP; *U.S. Private*, pg. 3828
STONE CREEK APARTMENTS COLORADO, LLC—See RAIT Financial Trust; *U.S. Public*, pg. 3349
STONECREEK CAPITAL, INC.; *U.S. Private*, pg. 3828
STONE CREEK FURNITURE INC.; *U.S. Private*, pg. 3818
STONECREST AT DOUBLE OAK MOUNTAIN; *U.S. Private*, pg. 3828
STONECREST MEDICAL GROUP - FAMILY PRACTICE OF MURFREESBORO, LLC—See HCA Healthcare, Inc.; *U.S. Public*, pg. 1010
STONECUTTER MILLS CORP.; *U.S. Private*, pg. 3828
STONE DEVELOPEMENTS LIMITED—See Sicon Ltd.; *Int'l*, pg. 6882
STONE EAGLE ELECTRICAL SUPPLY LIMITED PARTNERSHIP—See WESCO International, Inc.; *U.S. Public*, pg. 2351
STONEEAGLE F&I, INC.; *U.S. Private*, pg. 3828
STONEEAGLE, INC.—See StoneEagle F&I, Inc.; *U.S. Private*, pg. 3828
STONEFIRE GRILL INC.—See Goode Partners, LLC; *U.S. Private*, pg. 1739
STONE FREE CO., LTD.—See SUS Co., Ltd.; *Int'l*, pg. 7346
STONEGATE PUB COMPANY LIMITED; *Int'l*, pg. 7222
STONEGATE SURGERY CENTER, L.P.—See UnitedHealth Group Incorporated; *U.S. Public*, pg. 2250
STONE GLACIER, INC.; *U.S. Private*, pg. 3818
STONE-GOFF PARTNERS, LLC; *U.S. Private*, pg. 3826
STONE GOLD INC.; *Int'l*, pg. 7221
STONE GROUP HOLDINGS LIMITED; *Int'l*, pg. 7221
THE STONE GROUP, INC.; *U.S. Private*, pg. 4123
STONEHAGE FLEMING FAMILY & PARTNERS LIMITED; *Int'l*, pg. 7222
STONEHAGE FLEMING INVESTMENT MANAGEMENT (SUISSE) AG—See Stonehage Fleming Family & Partners Limited; *Int'l*, pg. 7222
STONEHAM BANK; *U.S. Private*, pg. 3828

**STONEHAM MOTOR CO. INC.; ** *U.S. Private,* pg. 3828
STONEHAM SUN—See Gannett Co., Inc.; *U.S. Public,* pg. 903
STONE HARBOR EMERGING MARKETS INCOME FUND; *U.S. Public,* pg. 1951
STONE HARBOR EMG MKTS TOTAL INCOME FUND; *U.S. Public,* pg. 1951
STONEHENGE CAPITAL CORP.; *U.S. Private,* pg. 3828
STONEHENGE COMPANY LIMITED—See Stonehenge Inter PCL; *Int'l,* pg. 7222
STONEHENGE GROWTH EQUITY PARTNERS—See Stonehenge Capital Corp.; *U.S. Private,* pg. 3828
STONEHENGE INTER PCL; *Int'l,* pg. 7222
STONEHENGE PARTNERS, INC.; *U.S. Private,* pg. 3828
STONEHILL ENVIRONMENTAL, INC.—See Comprehensive Environmental Assessments, Inc.; *U.S. Private,* pg. 1003
STONE HILL WINERY; *U.S. Private,* pg. 3818
STONE HORN RIDGE, LLC—See Cook Inlet Region, Inc.; *U.S. Private,* pg. 1038
STONEHOUSE NOV DOWNHOLE EURASIA LIMITED—See NOV, Inc.; *U.S. Public,* pg. 1546
STONE INDUSTRIAL—See Auxo Investment Partners, LLC; *U.S. Private,* pg. 402
STONELEIGH RECOVERY ASSOCIATES LLC; *U.S. Private,* pg. 3828
STONE MARKETING INTERNATIONAL; *U.S. Private,* pg. 3818
STONEMARKET LIMITED—See Marshalls plc; *Int'l,* pg. 4702
STONEMARTIN PLC; *Int'l,* pg. 7222
STONE MASTER CORPORATION BERHAD; *Int'l,* pg. 7222
STONE MASTER DESIGN & BUILD SDN. BHD.—See Stone Master Corporation Berhad; *Int'l,* pg. 7222
STONEMOR CEMETERY PRODUCTS LLC—See Axar Capital Management L.P.; *U.S. Private,* pg. 412
STONEMOR INC.—See Axar Capital Management L.P.; *U.S. Private,* pg. 411
STONEMOR PARTNERS L.P.—See Axar Capital Management L.P.; *U.S. Private,* pg. 411
STONEMOR PENNSYLVANIA SUBSIDIARY LLC—See Axar Capital Management L.P.; *U.S. Private,* pg. 412
STONEMOR PUERTO RICO LLC—See Axar Capital Management L.P.; *U.S. Private,* pg. 412
STONE MOTORS INC.; *U.S. Private,* pg. 3818
STONE MOUNTAIN SCHOOL, INC.—See Acadia Healthcare Company, Inc.; *U.S. Public,* pg. 30
STONE OAK SURGICENTER, LLC—See HCA Healthcare, Inc.; *U.S. Public,* pg. 1010
STONE ORCHARD SOFTWARE INC.—See StarDyne Technologies Inc.; *Int'l,* pg. 7176
STONE PANELS, INC.—See Thompson Street Capital Manager LLC; *U.S. Private,* pg. 4161
STONEPEAK PARTNERS L.P.; *U.S. Private,* pg. 3828
STONE PLUS, INC.—See SiteOne Landscape Supply, Inc.; *U.S. Public,* pg. 1889
STONE POINT CAPITAL LLC; *U.S. Private,* pg. 3818
STONE POINT CREDIT CORPORATION; *U.S. Private,* pg. 3826
STONE POINTE, LLC; *U.S. Private,* pg. 3826
STONEPOINT MATERIALS, LLC—See Sun Capital Partners, Inc.; *U.S. Private,* pg. 3861
STONE PRODUCTS INC.—See The Beaver Excavating Company, Inc.; *U.S. Private,* pg. 3992
STONER BUNTING ADVERTISING; *U.S. Private,* pg. 3830
STONER & CO., INC.; *U.S. Private,* pg. 3830
STONER ELECTRIC INC.; *U.S. Private,* pg. 3830
STONERIDGE APARTMENTS, INC.—See Deutsche Bank Aktiengesellschaft; *Int'l,* pg. 2062
STONERIDGE ASIA PACIFIC ELECTRONICS (SUZHOU) CO. LTD.—See Stoneridge, Inc.; *U.S. Public,* pg. 1951
STONERIDGE CONTROL DEVICES, INC.—See Standard Motor Products, Inc.; *U.S. Public,* pg. 1929
STONERIDGE ELECTRONICS AB—See Stoneridge, Inc.; *U.S. Public,* pg. 1951
STONERIDGE ELECTRONICS AB—See Stoneridge, Inc.; *U.S. Public,* pg. 1951
STONERIDGE ELECTRONICS AB—See Stoneridge, Inc.; *U.S. Public,* pg. 1951
STONERIDGE ELECTRONICS AB—See Stoneridge, Inc.; *U.S. Public,* pg. 1951
STONERIDGE ELECTRONICS, INC.—See Stoneridge, Inc.; *U.S. Public,* pg. 1951
STONERIDGE ELECTRONICS LTD.—See Stoneridge, Inc.; *U.S. Public,* pg. 1951
STONERIDGE FARMS HUNT CLUB, LLC—See Blackstone Inc.; *U.S. Public,* pg. 351
STONERIDGE GOLF COURSE, LLC—See Pinnacle West Capital Corporation; *U.S. Public,* pg. 1692
STONERIDGE, INC.; *U.S. Public,* pg. 1951
STONERIDGE NORDIC AB—See Stoneridge, Inc.; *U.S. Public,* pg. 1951
STONERIDGE - PRESCOTT VALLEY LLC—See Pinnacle West Capital Corporation; *U.S. Public,* pg. 1692
STONER INC.; *U.S. Private,* pg. 3830
STONERISE HEALTHCARE LLC; *U.S. Private,* pg. 3830

STONE RIVER CAPITAL PARTNERS, LLC; *U.S. Private,* pg. 3826
STONERIVER INC.—See Sapiens International Corporation N.V.; *Int'l,* pg. 6571
STONERIVER, INC.—See Sapiens International Corporation N.V.; *Int'l,* pg. 6571
STONESET EQUITY DEVELOPMENT CORP.; *Int'l,* pg. 7222
STONESIFER & KELLEY, P.C.—See Barley Snyder LLC; *U.S. Private,* pg. 476
STONE & SIMONS ADVERTISING; *U.S. Private,* pg. 3816
STONE'S, INC.—See Clyde Companies Inc.; *U.S. Private,* pg. 949
STONE'S, INC.; *U.S. Private,* pg. 3826
STONE & SOIL DEPOT INC.—See SiteOne Landscape Supply, Inc.; *U.S. Public,* pg. 1889
STONE SOURCE LLC—See Platinum Equity, LLC; *U.S. Private,* pg. 3206
STONES TOWN & COUNTRY MOTORS; *U.S. Private,* pg. 3830
STONE STRAW LIMITED—See Wentworth Technologies Co. Ltd.; *Int'l,* pg. 8377
STONESTREET & STONESTREET; *U.S. Private,* pg. 3830
STONESTREET WINERY—See Jackson Family Wines, Inc.; *U.S. Private,* pg. 2176
STONE TRANSPORT INC.; *U.S. Private,* pg. 3826
STONE TRUSS COMPANY, INC.—See Building Industry Partners LLC; *U.S. Private,* pg. 683
STONEWALL CONTRACTING CORP; *U.S. Private,* pg. 3830
STONEWALL KITCHEN LLC—See TA Associates, Inc.; *U.S. Private,* pg. 3918
STONE WARD; *U.S. Private,* pg. 3826
STONEWAY ELECTRIC SUPPLY INC.—See Crescent Electric Supply Company; *U.S. Private,* pg. 1093
STONEWAY ROOFING SUPPLY; *U.S. Private,* pg. 3830
STONEWEG SA; *Int'l,* pg. 7222
STONE WHEEL INC.; *U.S. Private,* pg. 3826
STONEWQOD INSURANCE COMPANY—See D. E. Shaw & Co., L.P.; *U.S. Private,* pg. 1139
STONEWOOD INSURANCE SERVICES, INC.—See Stone Point Capital LLC; *U.S. Private,* pg. 3819
STONEWORKS TECHNOLOGIES, INC.—See Fulcrum IT Partners; *Int'l,* pg. 2841
STONE WORLD SDN BHD—See Major Team Holdings Berhad; *Int'l,* pg. 4655
STONEX BANCO DE CAMBIO S.A.—See StoneX Group Inc.; *U.S. Public,* pg. 1953
STONEX COLOMBIA S.A.—See StoneX Group Inc.; *U.S. Public,* pg. 1953
STONEX COMMODITIES DMCC—See StoneX Group Inc.; *U.S. Public,* pg. 1953
STONEX DIGITAL INTERNATIONAL LIMITED—See StoneX Group Inc.; *U.S. Public,* pg. 1953
STONEX DTVM LTDA.—See StoneX Group Inc.; *U.S. Public,* pg. 1953
STONEX EUROPE LTD.—See StoneX Group Inc.; *U.S. Public,* pg. 1953
STONEX FINANCIAL EUROPE S.A.—See StoneX Group Inc.; *U.S. Public,* pg. 1953
STONEX FINANCIAL GMBH—See StoneX Group Inc.; *U.S. Public,* pg. 1953
STONEX GROUP INC.; *U.S. Public,* pg. 1951
STONEX INVESTIMENTOS LTDA.—See StoneX Group Inc.; *U.S. Public,* pg. 1953
STONEX POLAND SP. Z O.O.—See StoneX Group Inc.; *U.S. Public,* pg. 1953
STONEX SECURITIES S.A.—See StoneX Group Inc.; *U.S. Public,* pg. 1953
STONEX (SHANGHAI) TRADING CO., LTD.—See StoneX Group Inc.; *U.S. Public,* pg. 1953
STONEYBROOK GOLF CLUB, INC.—See Lennar Corporation; *U.S. Public,* pg. 1307
STONEY CREEK FURNITURE; *Int'l,* pg. 7222
STONEY HILL HEALTHCARE, INC.—See The Ensign Group, Inc.; *U.S. Public,* pg. 2071
STONE & YOUNGBERG LLC—See Stifel Financial Corp.; *U.S. Public,* pg. 1950
STONEY RIVER, LLC—See SoftBank Group Corp.; *Int'l,* pg. 7054
STONEY ROAD PRODUCTION INC.; *U.S. Private,* pg. 3830
STONHARD NEDERLAND B.V.—See RPM International Inc.; *U.S. Public,* pg. 1819
STONHARD S.A.S.—See RPM International Inc.; *U.S. Public,* pg. 1819
STONHARD (U.K.) LIMITED—See RPM International Inc.; *U.S. Public,* pg. 1819
STONINGTON FERTILIZER INC.; *U.S. Private,* pg. 3830
STONITE COIL CORPORATION; *U.S. Private,* pg. 3830
STO NORGE AS—See Sto SE & Co. KGaA; *Int'l,* pg. 7219
STONTRONICS LIMITED—See TT Electronics plc; *Int'l,* pg. 7959
STO N.V.—See Sto SE & Co. KGaA; *Int'l,* pg. 7219
STONY CREEK WF HOLDCO, LLC—See E.ON SE; *Int'l,* pg. 2259
STONY CREEK WIND FARM, LLC—See E.ON SE; *Int'l,* pg. 2259

STONYFIELD FARM, INC.—See Groupe Lactalis SA; *Int'l,* pg. 3106
STONY HILL VINEYARD—See Long Meadow Ranch Winery & Farmstead; *U.S. Private,* pg. 2491
STONY POINT FASHION PARK ASSOCIATES, LLC—See Simon Property Group, Inc.; *U.S. Public,* pg. 1881
STONY POINT GROUP, INC.; *U.S. Private,* pg. 3830
STOODY COMPANY—See Enovis Corporation; *U.S. Public,* pg. 771
STOOL & DINETTE FACTORY INC.; *U.S. Private,* pg. 3830
STOOPS AUTOMOTIVE GROUP, INC.; *U.S. Private,* pg. 3830
STOOPS BUICK, INC.—See Stoops Automotive Group, Inc.; *U.S. Private,* pg. 3830
STOOPS FREIGHTLINER QUALITY TRAILER; *U.S. Private,* pg. 3830
STOOPS NATIONALEASE INC—See Stoops Freightliner Quality Trailer; *U.S. Private,* pg. 3830
STOP AGING NOW, LLC—See The Clorox Company; *U.S. Public,* pg. 2062
STOPANSKA BANKA AD-SKOPJE—See National Bank of Greece S.A.; *Int'l,* pg. 5153
STOPAQ B.V.—See Berry Global Group, Inc; *U.S. Public,* pg. 325
STOP CHOC LIMITED—See TotalEnergies SE; *Int'l,* pg. 7837
STOPINC AG—See RHI Magnesita N.V.; *Int'l,* pg. 6326
STOP IN FOOD STORES, INC.—See CrossAmerica Partners LP; *U.S. Public,* pg. 596
STOPLIFT, INC.—See NCR Voyix Corporation.; *U.S. Public,* pg. 1503
STOP-N-GO OF MADISON INC.—See Kwik Trip Inc.; *U.S. Private,* pg. 2359
STOP N SAVE, INC.—See Kapoor Enterprises; *U.S. Private,* pg. 2261
THE STOP & SHOP SUPERMARKET COMPANY—See Koninklijke Ahold Delhaize N.V.; *Int'l,* pg. 4260
STOP START TRANSPORT LTD.—See Storskogen Group AB; *Int'l,* pg. 7228
STORADIO AB—See Sdiptech AB; *Int'l,* pg. 6659
STORADIO AERO AB—See Sdiptech AB; *Int'l,* pg. 6659
STORA ENSO AB—See Stora Enso Oyj; *Int'l,* pg. 7223
STORA ENSO AMSTERDAM B.V.—See Stora Enso Oyj; *Int'l,* pg. 7223
STORA ENSO ARGENTINA S.A.—See Stora Enso Oyj; *Int'l,* pg. 7223
STORA ENSO AUSTRIA GMBH—See Stora Enso Oyj; *Int'l,* pg. 7223
STORA ENSO BAIENFURT GMBH—See Pyroll Group Oy; *Int'l,* pg. 6128
STORA ENSO BASE INDUSTRIES GROUP—See Stora Enso Oyj; *Int'l,* pg. 7223
STORA ENSO BELGIUM NV—See Stora Enso Oyj; *Int'l,* pg. 7223
STORA ENSO BIOENERGI AB—See Stora Enso Oyj; *Int'l,* pg. 7223
STORA ENSO BRASIL LTDA—See Stora Enso Oyj; *Int'l,* pg. 7223
STORA ENSO CORBEHEM SAS—See Stora Enso Oyj; *Int'l,* pg. 7224
STORA ENSO DEUTSCHLAND GMBH—See Stora Enso Oyj; *Int'l,* pg. 7223
STORA ENSO EESTI AS—See Stora Enso Oyj; *Int'l,* pg. 7224
STORA ENSO ESPANA S.A.U.—See Stora Enso Oyj; *Int'l,* pg. 7224
STORA ENSO FINE PAPER AB—See Stora Enso Oyj; *Int'l,* pg. 7223
STORA ENSO FOREST—See Stora Enso Oyj; *Int'l,* pg. 7223
STORA ENSO FOREST—See Stora Enso Oyj; *Int'l,* pg. 7223
STORA ENSO FORS AB—See Stora Enso Oyj; *Int'l,* pg. 7223
STORA ENSO FRANCE SAS—See Stora Enso Oyj; *Int'l,* pg. 7224
STORA ENSO GRAFIC S.A.U.—See Stora Enso Oyj; *Int'l,* pg. 7224
STORA ENSO (HK) LIMITED—See Stora Enso Oyj; *Int'l,* pg. 7223
STORA ENSO HOLDINGS UK LTD—See Stora Enso Oyj; *Int'l,* pg. 7224
STORA ENSO HUNGARY KFT—See Stora Enso Oyj; *Int'l,* pg. 7224
STORA ENSO HYLTE AB—See Stora Enso Oyj; *Int'l,* pg. 7223
STORA ENSO INGEROIS OY—See Stora Enso Oyj; *Int'l,* pg. 7224
STORA ENSO INTERNATIONAL LTD.—See Stora Enso Oyj; *Int'l,* pg. 7224
STORA ENSO ITALIA SRL—See Stora Enso Oyj; *Int'l,* pg. 7224
STORA ENSO JAPAN K.K.—See Stora Enso Oyj; *Int'l,* pg. 7224
STORA ENSO KABEL GMBH & CO. KG—See Stora Enso Oyj; *Int'l,* pg. 7223
STORA ENSO KABEL VERWALTUNGS GMBH—See Stora Enso Oyj; *Int'l,* pg. 7223

STORA ENSO KOREA CO., LTD.—See Stora Enso Oyj; *Int'l*, pg. 7224
STORA ENSO KVARNSVEDEN AB—See Stora Enso Oyj; *Int'l*, pg. 7223
STORA ENSO LANGERBRUGGE N.V.—See Stora Enso Oyj; *Int'l*, pg. 7224
STORA ENSO LAOS CO. LTD—See Stora Enso Oyj; *Int'l*, pg. 7225
STORA ENSO LATVIA A/S—See Stora Enso Oyj; *Int'l*, pg. 7224
STORA ENSO LOGISTICS AB—See Stora Enso Oyj; *Int'l*, pg. 7223
STORA ENSO LOGISTICS GMBH—See Stora Enso Oyj; *Int'l*, pg. 7223
STORA ENSO LUMBER TRADING GMBH—See Stora Enso Oyj; *Int'l*, pg. 7223
STORA ENSO MAGAZINE PAPER—See Stora Enso Oyj; *Int'l*, pg. 7223
STORA ENSO MAXAU GMBH—See Stora Enso Oyj; *Int'l*, pg. 7224
STORA ENSO MEXICO S.A.—See Stora Enso Oyj; *Int'l*, pg. 7224
STORA ENSO MIDDLE EAST JLT—See Stora Enso Oyj; *Int'l*, pg. 7224
STORA ENSO NAREW SP. Z.O.O—See Stora Enso Oyj; *Int'l*, pg. 7224
STORA ENSO NEWSPRINT SACHSEN MILL—See Stora Enso Oyj; *Int'l*, pg. 7223
STORA ENSO NORTH AMERICA—See Stora Enso Oyj; *Int'l*, pg. 7224
STORA ENSO NYMOLLA AB—See Stora Enso Oyj; *Int'l*, pg. 7223
STORA ENSO OULU HOLDING OY—See Stora Enso Oyj; *Int'l*, pg. 7224
STORA ENSO OYJ; *Int'l*, pg. 7222
STORA ENSO PACKAGENT OY—See Stora Enso Oyj; *Int'l*, pg. 7224
STORA ENSO PACKAGING AB—See Stora Enso Oyj; *Int'l*, pg. 7224
STORA ENSO PACKAGING AS—See Stora Enso Oyj; *Int'l*, pg. 7224
STORA ENSO PACKAGING BOARDS GROUP—See Stora Enso Oyj; *Int'l*, pg. 7224
STORA ENSO PACKAGING KFT—See Stora Enso Oyj; *Int'l*, pg. 7224
STORA ENSO PACKAGING - LAHTI MILL—See Stora Enso Oyj; *Int'l*, pg. 7224
STORA ENSO PACKAGING OY—See Stora Enso Oyj; *Int'l*, pg. 7224
STORA ENSO PACKAGING SIA—See Stora Enso Oyj; *Int'l*, pg. 7224
STORA ENSO POLSKA S.A.—See Stora Enso Oyj; *Int'l*, pg. 7224
STORA ENSO PRAHA S.R.O.—See Stora Enso Oyj; *Int'l*, pg. 7224
STORA ENSO PUBLICATION PAPER OY LTD.—See Stora Enso Oyj; *Int'l*, pg. 7225
STORA ENSO PUBLICATION PAPER OY LTD. - VEITSILUOTO MILL—See Stora Enso Oyj; *Int'l*, pg. 7225
STORA ENSO PUBLICATION PAPER—See Stora Enso Oyj; *Int'l*, pg. 7223
STORA ENSO PULP—See Stora Enso Oyj; *Int'l*, pg. 7223
STORA ENSO RESEARCH—See Stora Enso Oyj; *Int'l*, pg. 7223
STORA ENSO SACHSEN GMBH—See Stora Enso Oyj; *Int'l*, pg. 7223
STORA ENSO (SCHWEIZ) AG—See Stora Enso Oyj; *Int'l*, pg. 7225
STORA ENSO SINGAPORE PTE LTD.-MALAYSIAN OFFICE—See Stora Enso Oyj; *Int'l*, pg. 7225
STORA ENSO SINGAPORE—See Stora Enso Oyj; *Int'l*, pg. 7225
STORA ENSO SKOG AB—See Stora Enso Oyj; *Int'l*, pg. 7223
STORA ENSO SKOGHALL AB—See Stora Enso Oyj; *Int'l*, pg. 7223
STORA ENSO SOUTH EAST ASIA PTE LTD—See Stora Enso Oyj; *Int'l*, pg. 7225
STORA ENSO SOUTH EAST ASIA—See Stora Enso Oyj; *Int'l*, pg. 7225
STORA ENSO SOUTHERN AFRICA LTD.—See Stora Enso Oyj; *Int'l*, pg. 7225
STORA ENSO TIMBER AB—See Stora Enso Oyj; *Int'l*, pg. 7223
STORA ENSO TIMBER (DEUTSCHLAND)—See Stora Enso Oyj; *Int'l*, pg. 7223
STORA ENSO TIMBER D.O.O—See Stora Enso Oyj; *Int'l*, pg. 7225
STORA ENSO TIMBER JAPAN K.K.—See Stora Enso Oyj; *Int'l*, pg. 7225
STORA ENSO TIMBER SP. Z.O.O.—See Stora Enso Oyj; *Int'l*, pg. 7225
STORA ENSO TIMBER UK LTD—See Stora Enso Oyj; *Int'l*, pg. 7224
STORA ENSO TRANSPORT GMBH—See Stora Enso Oyj; *Int'l*, pg. 7224
STORA ENSO UK LTD.—See Stora Enso Oyj; *Int'l*, pg. 7224
STORA ENSO WOOD PRODUCTS GMBH—See Stora Enso Oyj; *Int'l*, pg. 7225
STORA ENSO WOOD PRODUCTS OY LTD—See Stora Enso Oyj; *Int'l*, pg. 7225
STORA ENSO WOOD PRODUCTS ZDIREC S.R.O.—See Stora Enso Oyj; *Int'l*, pg. 7225
STORA ENSO WP BAD ST LEONHARD GMBH—See Stora Enso Oyj; *Int'l*, pg. 7225
STORA ENSO WP HOLZVERARBEITUNGS GMBH—See Stora Enso Oyj; *Int'l*, pg. 7225
STORA ENSO WP HV S.R.O.—See Stora Enso Oyj; *Int'l*, pg. 7225
STORA FASAD AB—See Balco Group AB; *Int'l*, pg. 807
STORAGECRAFT TECHNOLOGY CORPORATION—See Marlin Equity Partners, LLC; *U.S. Private*, pg. 2583
STORAGE DROP; *Int'l*, pg. 7225
STORAGE EXPRESS MANAGEMENT, LLC—See Extra Space Storage, Inc.; *U.S. Public*, pg. 813
STORAGEFLEX, INC.; *Int'l*, pg. 7225
STORAGEMART PARTNERS L.L.C.—See TKG-StorageMart Partners Portfolio, LLC; *U.S. Private*, pg. 4178
STORAGE PLUS CORP.—See Warburg Pincus LLC; *U.S. Private*, pg. 4439
STOR-AGE PROPERTY REIT LTD.; *Int'l*, pg. 7222
STORAGE RENTALS OF AMERICA—See Benjamin Macfarland Company, LLC; *U.S. Private*, pg. 526
STORAGE SOLUTION IBERICA S.L.—See Kardex Holding AG; *Int'l*, pg. 4080
STORAGE SOLUTIONS INC.—See Merit Capital Partners; *U.S. Private*, pg. 2674
STORAGE SOLUTIONS INC.—See MFG Partners LLC; *U.S. Private*, pg. 2693
STORAGE SYSTEMS MIDWEST; *U.S. Private*, pg. 3831
STORAGE SYSTEMS UNLIMITED, INC.—See Cme Corporation; *U.S. Private*, pg. 950
STORAGE & TRANSPORTATION CO., INC.; *U.S. Private*, pg. 3831
STORAGE TREASURES LLC—See OpenTech Alliance, Inc.; *U.S. Private*, pg. 3031
STORAGEVAULT CANADA INC.; *Int'l*, pg. 7225
STORAKERS MCCANN—See The Interpublic Group of Companies, Inc.; *U.S. Public*, pg. 2102
STORANESET 12 AS—See Orkla ASA; *Int'l*, pg. 5639
STORCENTRIC, INC.; *U.S. Private*, pg. 3831
STORCK ADRIA D.O.O.—See Storck GmbH & Co.; *Int'l*, pg. 7225
STORCK ASIA PACIFIC PTE LTD—See Storck GmbH & Co.; *Int'l*, pg. 7225
STORCK B.V.B.A.—See Storck GmbH & Co.; *Int'l*, pg. 7225
STORCK B.V.—See Storck GmbH & Co.; *Int'l*, pg. 7225
STORCK CANADA INC.—See Storck GmbH & Co.; *Int'l*, pg. 7225
STORCK CESKA REPUBLIKA, S.R.O.—See Storck GmbH & Co.; *Int'l*, pg. 7226
STORCK CROATIA D.O.O.—See Storck GmbH & Co.; *Int'l*, pg. 7226
STORCK DANMARK A/S—See Storck GmbH & Co.; *Int'l*, pg. 7226
STORCK GES.M.B.H.—See Storck GmbH & Co.; *Int'l*, pg. 7226
STORCK GMBH & CO.; *Int'l*, pg. 7225
STORCK HUNGARIA KFT.—See Storck GmbH & Co.; *Int'l*, pg. 7226
STORCK IBERICA, S.L.U.—See Storck GmbH & Co.; *Int'l*, pg. 7226
STORCK MIDDLE EAST & AFRICA FZ-LLC—See Storck GmbH & Co.; *Int'l*, pg. 7226
STORCK (SCHWEIZ) GMBH—See Storck GmbH & Co.; *Int'l*, pg. 7226
STORCK SP. Z O.O.—See Storck GmbH & Co.; *Int'l*, pg. 7226
STORCK SVERIGE AB—See Storck GmbH & Co.; *Int'l*, pg. 7226
STORCK TRAVEL RETAIL LTD—See Storck GmbH & Co.; *Int'l*, pg. 7226
STORCK UK LTD.—See Storck GmbH & Co.; *Int'l*, pg. 7226
STORCK USA, L.P.—See Storck GmbH & Co.; *Int'l*, pg. 7226
STORD, INC.; *U.S. Private*, pg. 3831
STORD INTERNATIONAL A.S.—See Putsch GmbH & Co. KG; *Int'l*, pg. 6124
STOREBOARD MEDIA LLC—See Leonard Green & Partners, L.P.; *U.S. Private*, pg. 2423
STOREBRAND ASA; *Int'l*, pg. 7226
STOREBRAND BANK ASA—See Storebrand ASA; *Int'l*, pg. 7226
STOREBRAND EIENDOM AS—See Storebrand ASA; *Int'l*, pg. 7226
STOREBRAND EIENDOM HOLDING AS—See Storebrand ASA; *Int'l*, pg. 7226
STOREBRAND FINANS AS—See Storebrand ASA; *Int'l*, pg. 7226
STOREBRAND FONDER AB—See Storebrand ASA; *Int'l*, pg. 7226
STOREBRAND HELSEFORSIKRING AS—See Munchener Ruckversicherungs AG; *Int'l*, pg. 5087
STOREBRAND HELSEFORSIKRING AS—See Storebrand ASA; *Int'l*, pg. 7226
STOREBRAND I AS—See Storebrand ASA; *Int'l*, pg. 7226
STOREBRAND KAPITALFORVALTNING—See Storebrand ASA; *Int'l*, pg. 7226
STOREBRAND LEIEFORVALTNING AS—See Storebrand ASA; *Int'l*, pg. 7226
STOREBRAND LIVSFORSIKRING AS—See Storebrand ASA; *Int'l*, pg. 7226
STOREBRAND—See Storebrand ASA; *Int'l*, pg. 7226
STORE CAPITAL CORPORATION—See Blue Owl Capital Inc.; *U.S. Public*, pg. 364
STORE CAPITAL CORPORATION—See GIC Pte. Ltd.; *Int'l*, pg. 2964
THE STORE CORPORATION BERHAD; *Int'l*, pg. 7689
STORE DESIGN SERVICES—See United Natural Foods, Inc.; *U.S. Public*, pg. 2232
STORED VALUE SOLUTIONS INTERNATIONAL B.V.—See Corpay, Inc.; *U.S. Public*, pg. 580
STOREFEEDER LTD.—See International Distributions Services plc; *Int'l*, pg. 3748
STORE FINANCIAL SERVICES, LLC—See EML Payments Limited; *Int'l*, pg. 2384
STOREFRONT FOR ART & ARCHITECTURE; *U.S. Private*, pg. 3831
THE STORE HOLDINGS SDN. BHD.—See The Store Corporation Berhad; *Int'l*, pg. 7689
THE STORE HOUSE LIMITED—See Singapore Post Limited; *Int'l*, pg. 6942
STORE KRAFT MANUFACTURING CO; *U.S. Private*, pg. 3831
THE STORE (MALAYSIA) SDN. BHD.—See The Store Corporation Berhad; *Int'l*, pg. 7689
STORE MASTER FUNDING I, LLC—See Blue Owl Capital Inc.; *U.S. Public*, pg. 364
STORE MASTER FUNDING I, LLC—See GIC Pte. Ltd.; *Int'l*, pg. 2964
STORENEXT LTD.—See NCR Voyix Corporation.; *U.S. Public*, pg. 1502
STORENGY DEUTSCHLAND GMBH—See ENGIE SA; *Int'l*, pg. 2435
STORENGY SA—See ENGIE SA; *Int'l*, pg. 2435
STORENGY UK LTD—See ENGIE SA; *Int'l*, pg. 2435
STORE OPENING SOLUTIONS, INC.—See Berkshire Hathaway Inc.; *U.S. Public*, pg. 311
STORER EQUIPMENT COMPANY LTD.; *U.S. Private*, pg. 3831
STOREROOM SOLUTIONS COSTA RICA CORP.—See RS Group plc; *Int'l*, pg. 6418
STOREROOM SOLUTIONS PUERTO RICO CORP.—See RS Group plc; *Int'l*, pg. 6418
STOREROOM SOLUTIONS—See RS Group plc; *Int'l*, pg. 6418
STOREROTICA MAGAZINE, INC.—See RCI Hospitality Holdings, Inc.; *U.S. Public*, pg. 1767
STORES GROUP LIMITED—See Morrison (Wm) Supermarkets PLC; *Int'l*, pg. 5049
STORES SPECIALISTS, INC.—See SSI Group, Inc.; *Int'l*, pg. 7156
STORE SUPPLY WAREHOUSE, LLC.; *U.S. Private*, pg. 3831
THE STORE TAIPING WISMA DATO' TOH ENG HOE—See The Store Corporation Berhad; *Int'l*, pg. 7689
STOREWEAVER GMBH—See Fujitsu Limited; *Int'l*, pg. 2837
STOREWELL MEDIA MANUFACTURING LTD.—See Shinvest Holding Limited; *Int'l*, pg. 6849
STOREY-KENWORTHY COMPANY; *U.S. Private*, pg. 3831
STOREY PARK CLUB, LLC—See Lennar Corporation; *U.S. Public*, pg. 1307
STORHUB MANAGEMENT PTE LTD—See Warburg Pincus LLC; *U.S. Private*, pg. 4439
STORIA TELEVISION SAS—See Mediawan SA; *Int'l*, pg. 4774
STORIS INC.; *U.S. Private*, pg. 3831
STORITVENO PODJETJE LASKO D.O.O.—See EVN AG; *Int'l*, pg. 2571
STORIX INC.—See Cristie Software Limited; *Int'l*, pg. 1850
STORK AVENUE, INC.; *U.S. Private*, pg. 3831
STORK B.V.—See Fluor Corporation; *U.S. Public*, pg. 859
STORKE A/S—See Ratos AB; *Int'l*, pg. 6220
STORK - ELECTRIC EQUIPMENT SERVICES - REGENSBURG—See Fluor Corporation; *U.S. Public*, pg. 860
STORK - ESLOO—See Fluor Corporation; *U.S. Public*, pg. 860
STORK FOOD & DAIRY SYSTEMS B.V.—See John Bean Technologies Corporation; *U.S. Public*, pg. 1192
STORK GEARS & SERVICES ASIA PTE. LTD.—See Fluor Corporation; *U.S. Public*, pg. 859
STORK GEARS & SERVICES B.V.—See Fluor Corporation; *U.S. Public*, pg. 860
STORK GERMAN HOLDING GMBH—See Fluor Corporation; *U.S. Public*, pg. 860
STORK H & E TURBO BLADING; *U.S. Private*, pg. 3831
STORK HOLDING B.V.—See Fluor Corporation; *U.S. Public*, pg. 859

STORK PLASTICS MACHINERY B.V.—See Fluor Corporation; *U.S. Public*, pg. 860
STORK POWER SERVICES & TECHNOLOGY BEIJING LIMITED—See Fluor Corporation; *U.S. Public*, pg. 860
STORK RAILWAY SERVICES—See Fluor Corporation; *U.S. Public*, pg. 860
STORK TECHNICAL SERVICES BELGIUM N.V.—See Fluor Corporation; *U.S. Public*, pg. 860
STORK TECHNICAL SERVICES HOLDCO B.V.—See Fluor Corporation; *U.S. Public*, pg. 860
STORK TECHNICAL SERVICES LIMITED—See Fluor Corporation; *U.S. Public*, pg. 860
STORK TECHNICAL SERVICES (STS) LTD—See Fluor Corporation; *U.S. Public*, pg. 860
STORK - THERMEQ - HENGELO—See Fluor Corporation; *U.S. Public*, pg. 860
STORK TITAN B.V.—See Marel hf; *Int'l*, pg. 4691
STORK TURBO BLADING B.V.—See Fluor Corporation; *U.S. Public*, pg. 860
STORK - TURBO BLADING - SNEEK—See Fluor Corporation; *U.S. Public*, pg. 860
STORK TURBO SERVICE B V.—See Fluor Corporation; *U.S. Public*, pg. 860
STORK USA, INC.—See Fluor Corporation; *U.S. Public*, pg. 860
STORM8, INC.—See Stillfront Group AB; *Int'l*, pg. 7215
STORMANS INC.; *U.S. Private*, pg. 3831
STORMAN SOFTWARE, INC.—See Global Payments Inc.; *U.S. Public*, pg. 944
STORMAN SOFTWARE LIMITED—See Global Payments Inc.; *U.S. Public*, pg. 944
STORMAN SOFTWARE PTY LTD.—See Global Payments Inc.; *U.S. Public*, pg. 944
STORM CAPITAL MANAGEMENT LTD.; *Int'l*, pg. 7226
STORM EXPLORATION INC; *Int'l*, pg. 7226
STORMFRONT RETAIL LIMITED—See Compu B Ltd.; *Int'l*, pg. 1754
STORMGEO AB—See Alfa Laval AB; *Int'l*, pg. 312
STORMGEO AS—See Alfa Laval AB; *Int'l*, pg. 312
STORMGEO AS—See EQT AB; *Int'l*, pg. 2481
STORMGEO BRASIL AS—See Alfa Laval AB; *Int'l*, pg. 312
STORMGEO DENMARK A/S—See Alfa Laval AB; *Int'l*, pg. 312
STORMGEO DO BRASIL—See Alfa Laval AB; *Int'l*, pg. 312
STORMGEO FZ LLC—See Alfa Laval AB; *Int'l*, pg. 312
STORMGEO GERMANY—See Alfa Laval AB; *Int'l*, pg. 312
STORMGEO JAPAN KK—See Alfa Laval AB; *Int'l*, pg. 312
STORMGEO KOREA—See Alfa Laval AB; *Int'l*, pg. 312
STORMGEO LIMITED—See Alfa Laval AB; *Int'l*, pg. 312
STORMGEO PH INC.—See Alfa Laval AB; *Int'l*, pg. 312
STORMGEO PTE. LTD.—See Alfa Laval AB; *Int'l*, pg. 312
STORMGEO SINGAPORE—See Alfa Laval AB; *Int'l*, pg. 312
STORM HOLDING NORWAY AS—See BNP Paribas SA; *Int'l*, pg. 1092
STORM INDUSTRIES, INC.; *U.S. Private*, pg. 3831
STORM MANUFACTURING GROUP, INC.—See Storm Industries, Inc.; *U.S. Private*, pg. 3831
STORM MASTER CO., INC.—See Installed Building Products, Inc.; *U.S. Public*, pg. 1133
STORM MODEL MANAGEMENT LTD.—See Apollo Global Management, Inc.; *U.S. Public*, pg. 148
STORMNET INFORMATION TECHNOLOGY (SHANGHAI) CO., LTD.—See NetEase, Inc.; *Int'l*, pg. 5214
STORMONT CARE HOME BLAIRGOWRIE—See Balhousie Holdings Limited; *Int'l*, pg. 808
STORM REPLY INC.—See Reply S.p.A.; *Int'l*, pg. 6291
STORM REPLY ROMA S.R.L.—See Reply S.p.A.; *Int'l*, pg. 6291
STORM RESOURCES LTD.; *Int'l*, pg. 7226
STORM SEAFOOD, INC.—See Norsk Sjomat AS; *Int'l*, pg. 5437
STORM SMART BUILDING SYSTEMS, INC.; *U.S. Private*, pg. 3831
STORMS MOTORS, INC.; *U.S. Private*, pg. 3831
STORMSOURCE LLC—See Independence Capital Partners, LLC; *U.S. Private*, pg. 2056
STORMSOURCE LLC—See PCP Enterprise, L.P.; *U.S. Private*, pg. 3121
STORMTECH LLC—See Advanced Drainage Systems, Inc.; *U.S. Public*, pg. 46
STORM TECHNOLOGIES, INC.—See Xurpas Inc.; *Int'l*, pg. 8540
STORMTECH PERFORMANCE APPAREL LTD.; *Int'l*, pg. 7227
STORM VULCAN MATTONI; *U.S. Private*, pg. 3831
STORM-WESTERN DEVELOPMENT CORP.—See Storm Industries, Inc.; *U.S. Private*, pg. 3831
STORNOWAY DIAMOND CORPORATION; *Int'l*, pg. 7227
STORNOWAY GAZETTE LTD—See JPIMedia Holdings Limited; *Int'l*, pg. 4006
STORO BLIKKENSLAGERVERKSTED AS—See AF Gruppen ASA; *Int'l*, pg. 184
STORRIE DIALYSIS, LLC—See DaVita Inc.; *U.S. Public*, pg. 643
STORR OFFICE ENVIRONMENTS, INC.; *U.S. Private*, pg. 3831

STORR OFFICE ENVIRONMENTS OF FLORIDA, INC.—See Storr Office Environments, Inc.; *U.S. Private*, pg. 3832
STORR TRACTOR CO.; *U.S. Private*, pg. 3832
STORSACK PVT LTD.—See Greif Inc.; *U.S. Public*, pg. 967
STORSACK SHENZEN CO., LTD.—See Greif Inc.; *U.S. Public*, pg. 967
STORSACK VIETNAM LTD.—See Greif Inc.; *U.S. Public*, pg. 967
STORSKOGEN GROUP AB; *Int'l*, pg. 7227
STORT DOONWEG B.V.—See Mayr-Melnhof Karton AG; *Int'l*, pg. 4747
STORTECH ELECTRONICS LTD.—See discoverIE Group plc; *Int'l*, pg. 2133
STORTERCHILDS PRINTING CO., INC.—See Chatham Asset Management, LLC; *U.S. Private*, pg. 865
STORTER CHILDS PRINTING COMPANY, INC.—See Chatham Asset Management, LLC; *U.S. Private*, pg. 863
STORTPLAATS KOEGORSPOLDER B.V.—See Delta N.V.; *Int'l*, pg. 2019
STORTPLAATS NOORD EN MIDDEN ZEELAND B.V.—See Delta N.V.; *Int'l*, pg. 2019
STORY(ATION) PTY LIMITED—See News Corporation; *U.S. Public*, pg. 1521
STORYBOOK COTTAGE DAYCARE CENTER, LLC; *U.S. Private*, pg. 3832
STORY CONSTRUCTION CO; *U.S. Private*, pg. 3832
STORY DISTRIBUTING CO.; *U.S. Private*, pg. 3832
STORY HOUSE PRODUCTION, INC.; *U.S. Private*, pg. 3832
STORY HOUSE PRODUCTIONS GMBH—See SPIEGEL-Verlag Rudolf Augstein GmbH & Co.; *Int'l*, pg. 7136
STORY HOUSE PRODUCTIONS GMBH—See STORY HOUSE Production, Inc.; *U.S. Private*, pg. 3832
STORY-I LIMITED; *Int'l*, pg. 7228
STORYLINE STRATEGIES LLC—See Stagwell, Inc.; *U.S. Public*, pg. 1928
STORYTEL AB; *Int'l*, pg. 7228
STORY TELECOM LTD.; *Int'l*, pg. 7228
STORYTOYS LIMITED—See Team17 Group plc; *Int'l*, pg. 7500
STORY UK LTD—See The Mission Group Public Limited Company; *Int'l*, pg. 7667
STORYWIZ CO., LTD.—See KT Corporation; *Int'l*, pg. 4315
STORY WORLDWIDE, LLC - LONDON—See Next 15 Group plc; *Int'l*, pg. 5246
STORY WORLDWIDE, LLC—See Next 15 Group plc; *Int'l*, pg. 5246
STORZ ENDOSKOP PRODUKTIONS GMBH—See Karl Storz GmbH & Co.; *Int'l*, pg. 4083
STO S.A.S.—See Sto SE & Co. KGaA; *Int'l*, pg. 7219
STO SCANDINAVIA AB—See Sto SE & Co. KGaA; *Int'l*, pg. 7219
STO SDF IBERICA S.L.U.—See Sto SE & Co. KGaA; *Int'l*, pg. 7219
STO SEA PTE. LTD.—See Sto SE & Co. KGaA; *Int'l*, pg. 7219
STO SEA SDN. BHD.—See Sto SE & Co. KGaA; *Int'l*, pg. 7219
STO SE & CO. KGAA; *Int'l*, pg. 7219
STO SLOVENSKO S.R.O.—See Sto SE & Co. KGaA; *Int'l*, pg. 7219
STO SP. Z O.O.—See Sto SE & Co. KGaA; *Int'l*, pg. 7219
STO S.R.O.—See Sto SE & Co. KGaA; *Int'l*, pg. 7219
STOTEKS A.D.; *Int'l*, pg. 7228
STOTHERT & PITT LTD—See Langley Holdings Plc; *Int'l*, pg. 4410
STOTT & DAVIS MOTOR EXPRESS; *U.S. Private*, pg. 3832
STOTTECOMPAGNIET APS—See Humana AB; *Int'l*, pg. 3530
STOUDT ADVISORS, INC.—See GTCR LLC; *U.S. Private*, pg. 1804
STOUGHTON JOURNAL—See Gannett Co., Inc.; *U.S. Public*, pg. 903
STOUGHTON SENIOR LIVING, INC.—See The Ensign Group, Inc.; *U.S. Public*, pg. 2070
STOUGHTON TRAILERS, INC.; *U.S. Private*, pg. 3832
S-TOURISMUSFONDS MANAGEMENT AKTIENGESELLSCHAFT—See Erste Group Bank AG; *Int'l*, pg. 2499
STOUT RISIUS ROSS, INC.; *U.S. Private*, pg. 3832
STOUT ROOFING INC.; *U.S. Private*, pg. 3832
STOVAX GROUP LTD.—See NIBE Industrier AB; *Int'l*, pg. 5262
STOVAX LTD.—See NIBE Industrier AB; *Int'l*, pg. 5262
STOVEC INDUSTRIES LTD.—See Investcorp Holdings B.S.C.; *Int'l*, pg. 3776
STOVE KRAFT LIMITED; *Int'l*, pg. 7228
STOVESAND AUTO GROUP; *U.S. Private*, pg. 3832
STOVNER SENTER AS—See BNP Paribas SA; *Int'l*, pg. 1092
STOWASSER BUICK GMC, INC.; *U.S. Private*, pg. 3832
STOW AUSTRIA GMBH—See Blackstone Inc.; *U.S. Public*, pg. 348

STOW CESKA REPUBLIKA S.R.O—See Blackstone Inc.; *U.S. Public*, pg. 348
STOW DEUTSCHLAND GMBH—See Blackstone Inc.; *U.S. Public*, pg. 348
STOWE AREA ASSOCIATION AGENCY; *U.S. Private*, pg. 3832
STOWE GROUP HEALTHCARE, LLC—See ManpowerGroup Inc.; *U.S. Public*, pg. 1362
STOWE-PHARR MILLS, INC. - PHARR PALOMAR PLANT—See Stowe-Pharr Mills, Inc.; *U.S. Private*, pg. 3832
STOWE-PHARR MILLS, INC.; *U.S. Private*, pg. 3832
STOWERS CONTAINMENT SOLUTIONS LTD.—See Pact Group Holdings Ltd.; *Int'l*, pg. 5693
STOWERS FURNITURE COMPANIES LTD; *U.S. Private*, pg. 3832
STOWERS MACHINERY CORP; *U.S. Private*, pg. 3832
STOWERS RESOURCE MANAGEMENT, INC.; *U.S. Private*, pg. 3832
STOWE WOODWARD FINLAND OY—See ANDRITZ AG; *Int'l*, pg. 457
STOWE WOODWARD LLC—See ANDRITZ AG; *Int'l*, pg. 457
STOW FRANCE S.A.S.—See Blackstone Inc.; *U.S. Public*, pg. 348
STOW INTERNATIONAL NV—See Blackstone Inc.; *U.S. Public*, pg. 348
STOW NEDERLAND BV—See Blackstone Inc.; *U.S. Public*, pg. 348
STOW POLSKA SP. Z O.O.—See Blackstone Inc.; *U.S. Public*, pg. 348
STOW U.K. CO. LTD—See Kardex Holding AG; *Int'l*, pg. 4080
STOW (UK) LIMITED—See Blackstone Inc.; *U.S. Public*, pg. 348
STOXX LTD.—See Deutsche Borse AG; *Int'l*, pg. 2064
STO YAPI SISTEMLERI SANAYI VE TIGARET A.S.—See Sto SE & Co. KGaA; *Int'l*, pg. 7219
STO-ZAP SP. Z O.O.—See Grupa Azoty S.A.; *Int'l*, pg. 3116
ST PAE HOLDINGS PTY LTD.—See Temasek Holdings (Private) Limited; *Int'l*, pg. 7551
ST PAPER - DULUTH MILL—See Sofidel S.p.A.; *Int'l*, pg. 7050
ST. PAPER, LLC; *U.S. Private*, pg. 3770
ST. PATRICK CENTER; *U.S. Private*, pg. 3773
ST. PATRICKS HOME; *U.S. Private*, pg. 3773
ST. PATRICK'S MANOR SKILLED NURSING AND SHORT TERM REHABILITATION CENTER; *U.S. Private*, pg. 3773
ST. PATRICK'S RESIDENCE; *U.S. Private*, pg. 3773
ST. PAUL FIRE AND MARINE INSURANCE COMPANY—See The Travelers Companies, Inc.; *U.S. Public*, pg. 2136
ST. PAUL FIRE & MARINE INSURANCE COMPANY—See The Travelers Companies, Inc.; *U.S. Public*, pg. 2136
ST. PAUL MERCURY INSURANCE COMPANY—See The Travelers Companies, Inc.; *U.S. Public*, pg. 2136
ST. PAUL PARK REFINING CO. LLC—See Marathon Petroleum Corporation; *U.S. Public*, pg. 1363
ST. PAUL SURPLUS LINES INSURANCE COMPANY—See The Travelers Companies, Inc.; *U.S. Public*, pg. 2136
ST. PAUL TOWER, L.L.C.—See Northeast Communications of Wisconsin Incorporated; *U.S. Private*, pg. 2949
STP & DIN CHEMICALS SP. Z O.O.—See Air Products & Chemicals, Inc.; *U.S. Public*, pg. 67
STP DISTRIBUTORS (M) SDN BHD—See Thai Beverage Public Company Limited; *Int'l*, pg. 7590
STP ELBUD SP. Z O.O.—See Stalprodukt S.A.; *Int'l*, pg. 7164
ST. PETE AUTO AUCTION—See Cox Enterprises, Inc.; *U.S. Private*, pg. 1077
ST PETER PORT CAPITAL LIMITED; *Int'l*, pg. 7158
THE ST. PETERSBURG FREE CLINIC, INC.; *U.S. Private*, pg. 4120
ST. PETERSBURG GENERAL HOSPITAL—See HCA Healthcare, Inc.; *U.S. Public*, pg. 1010
ST. PETERSBURG KIDNEY CARE SOUTH, LLC—See Nautic Partners, LLC; *U.S. Private*, pg. 2871
THE ST. PETERSBURG TIMES—See Novamedia Group; *Int'l*, pg. 5455
ST. PETER'S HEALTH PARTNERS; *U.S. Private*, pg. 3773
ST PHARM CO., LTD.—See Dong-A Socio Holdings Co., Ltd.; *Int'l*, pg. 2165
STPI ESPANOLA S.L.—See STPI Group; *Int'l*, pg. 7229
STPI GROUP; *Int'l*, pg. 7229
STP INVESTMENT SERVICES; *U.S. Private*, pg. 3832
STP&I PUBLIC COMPANY LIMITED - CHONBURI FABRICATION FACILITY—See STP&I Public Company Limited; *Int'l*, pg. 7229
STP&I PUBLIC COMPANY LIMITED - LAEM CHABANG YARD FACILITY—See STP&I Public Company Limited; *Int'l*, pg. 7229
STP&I PUBLIC COMPANY LIMITED - RAYONG FABRICATION FACILITY—See STP&I Public Company Limited; *Int'l*, pg. 7229
STP&I PUBLIC COMPANY LIMITED; *Int'l*, pg. 7228

COMPANY NAME INDEX

STP&I PUBLIC COMPANY LIMITED - SRIRACHA FABRICATION FACILITY—See STP&I Public Company Limited; *Int'l*, pg. 7229
S&T PLUS S.R.O.—See Kontron AG; *Int'l*, pg. 4278
S&T POLAND SP. Z O.O.—See Kontron AG; *Int'l*, pg. 4278
STP PUBLICATIONS LIMITED PARTNERSHIP—See GVIC Communications Corp.; *Int'l*, pg. 3189
STP SCHMIEDETECHNIK PLETTENBERG GMBH & CO.; *Int'l*, pg. 7228
STRABAG AG—See STRABAG SE; *Int'l*, pg. 7233
STRABAG AG—See STRABAG SE; *Int'l*, pg. 7232
STRABAG ALTALANOS EPITO KFT.—See STRABAG SE; *Int'l*, pg. 7233
STRABAG ASFALT S.R.O.—See STRABAG SE; *Int'l*, pg. 7233
STRABAG A.S.—See STRABAG SE; *Int'l*, pg. 7233
STRABAG ASZFALT KFT.—See STRABAG SE; *Int'l*, pg. 7232
STRABAG BAU GMBH—See STRABAG SE; *Int'l*, pg. 7232
STRABAG BEOGRAD D.O.O.—See STRABAG SE; *Int'l*, pg. 7232
STRABAG BETON GMBH & CO. KG—See STRABAG SE; *Int'l*, pg. 7232
STRABAG BUILDING & INDUSTRIAL SERVICES GMBH—See STRABAG SE; *Int'l*, pg. 7233
STRABAG BV—See Orascom Construction PLC; *Int'l*, pg. 5612
STRABAG DEVELOPMENT BELGIUM NV—See STRABAG SE; *Int'l*, pg. 7233
STRABAG D.O.O.—See STRABAG SE; *Int'l*, pg. 7233
STRABAG D.O.O.—See STRABAG SE; *Int'l*, pg. 7233
STRABAG EAD—See STRABAG SE; *Int'l*, pg. 7232
STRABAG EPITO ZARTKORUEN MUKODO RESZVENYTARSASAG—See STRABAG SE; *Int'l*, pg. 7233
STRABAG FACILITY MANAGEMENT GMBH—See STRABAG SE; *Int'l*, pg. 7232
STRABAG GMBH—See STRABAG SE; *Int'l*, pg. 7232
STRABAG GRADBENE STORITVE D.O.O—See STRABAG SE; *Int'l*, pg. 7232
STRABAG GROSSPROJEKTE GMBH—See STRABAG SE; *Int'l*, pg. 7233
STRABAG IMOBILIJA-AGENCIJA ZA POSREDNISTVO V PROMETU Z NEPRE MIONINAMI D.O.O.—See STRABAG SE; *Int'l*, pg. 7232
STRABAG INC.—See STRABAG SE; *Int'l*, pg. 7233
STRABAG INFRASTRUCTURE & SAFETY SOLUTIONS GMBH—See STRABAG SE; *Int'l*, pg. 7233
STRABAG INTERNATIONAL GMBH—See STRABAG SE; *Int'l*, pg. 7232
STRABAG KIESERLING FLOORING SYSTEMS GMBH—See STRABAG SE; *Int'l*, pg. 7233
STRABAG-MML KFT.—See STRABAG SE; *Int'l*, pg. 7232
STRABAG OFF-SHORE WIND GMBH—See STRABAG SE; *Int'l*, pg. 7232
STRABAG OMAN L.L.C.—See STRABAG SE; *Int'l*, pg. 7233
STRABAG PFS POLSKA SP. Z O.O.—See STRABAG SE; *Int'l*, pg. 7232
STRABAG PIPELINE- UND ROHRLEITUNGSBAU GMBH—See STRABAG SE; *Int'l*, pg. 7232
STRABAG POZEMNI A INZENYRSKE STAVITELSTVI S.R.O.—See STRABAG SE; *Int'l*, pg. 7232
STRABAG PROJEKTENTWICKLUNG GMBH—See STRABAG SE; *Int'l*, pg. 7232
STRABAG PROPERTY AND FACILITY SERVICES GMBH—See STRABAG SE; *Int'l*, pg. 7232
STRABAG PROPERTY AND FACILITY SERVICES GMBH—See STRABAG SE; *Int'l*, pg. 7232
STRABAG QATAR W.L.L.—See STRABAG SE; *Int'l*, pg. 7233
STRABAG RAIL A.S.—See STRABAG SE; *Int'l*, pg. 7233
STRABAG RAIL FAHRLEITUNGEN GMBH—See STRABAG SE; *Int'l*, pg. 7232
STRABAG RAIL GMBH—See STRABAG SE; *Int'l*, pg. 7232
STRABAG REAL ESTATE GMBH—See STRABAG SE; *Int'l*, pg. 7232
STRABAG SE; *Int'l*, pg. 7229
STRABAG SIA—See STRABAG SE; *Int'l*, pg. 7233
STRABAG SPORTSTATTENBAU GMBH—See STRABAG SE; *Int'l*, pg. 7232
STRABAG SP.Z O.O.—See STRABAG SE; *Int'l*, pg. 7232
STRABAG SRL—See STRABAG SE; *Int'l*, pg. 7233
STRABAG S.R.O.—See STRABAG SE; *Int'l*, pg. 7232
STRABAG STRASSENBAU UND BETON AG—See STRABAG SE; *Int'l*, pg. 7233
STRABAG SVERIGE AB—See STRABAG SE; *Int'l*, pg. 7233
STRABAG UK LIMITED—See STRABAG SE; *Int'l*, pg. 7233
STRABAG UMWELTTECHNIK GMBH—See STRABAG SE; *Int'l*, pg. 7232
STRABAG UNTERSTUTZUNGSKASSE GMBH—See STRABAG SE; *Int'l*, pg. 7232
STRABAG WASSERBAU GMBH—See STRABAG SE; *Int'l*, pg. 7233

STRABAG - ZIPP DEVELOPMENT S.R.O.—See STRABAG SE; *Int'l*, pg. 7232
STRABENS HALL (HONG KONG) LIMITED—See Realord Group Holdings Limited; *Int'l*, pg. 6234
STRAB IL STRABAG BILDUNG IM LAUENBURGISCHEN GMBH—See STRABAG SE; *Int'l*, pg. 7232
STRABIL STRABAG BILDUNG IM LAUENBURGISCHEN GMBH—See STRABAG SE; *Int'l*, pg. 7232
STRACHAN & LIVINGSTON LTD—See JPIMedia Holdings Limited; *Int'l*, pg. 4007
STRACK GMBH—See SKion GmbH; *Int'l*, pg. 6988
STRACO CORPORATION, LTD.; *Int'l*, pg. 7234
STRACO LEISURE PTE LTD—See Straco Corporation, Ltd.; *Int'l*, pg. 7234
STRACON GYM S.A.—See Ashmore Group plc; *Int'l*, pg. 608
STRADA AUTO PASSION; *Int'l*, pg. 7234
STRADA CAPITAL, CORP.; *U.S. Private*, pg. 3832
STRADAL ENVIRONNEMENT—See Compagnie de Saint-Gobain SA; *Int'l*, pg. 1737
STRADAL SAS—See CRH plc; *Int'l*, pg. 1844
STRADA SERVICES, LLC; *U.S. Private*, pg. 3832
STRADAVERSE SDN. BHD.—See Chin Hin Group Berhad; *Int'l*, pg. 1480
STRAD CONTROLS LTD—See Strad Energy Services Ltd.; *Int'l*, pg. 7234
STRAD DOWNHOLE SERVICES LTD.—See Strad Energy Services Ltd.; *Int'l*, pg. 7234
STRAD ENERGY SERVICES LTD.; *Int'l*, pg. 7234
STRAD ENERGY SERVICES USA LTD.—See Strad Energy Services Ltd.; *Int'l*, pg. 7234
STRADIM-ESPACE FINANCE SA; *Int'l*, pg. 7234
STRADIVARIUS BH, D.O.O.—See Industria de Diseno Textil, S.A.; *Int'l*, pg. 3667
STRADIVARIUS CESKA REPUBLIKA, S.R.O—See Industria de Diseno Textil, S.A.; *Int'l*, pg. 3667
STRADIVARIUS CIS LTD.—See Industria de Diseno Textil, S.A.; *Int'l*, pg. 3667
STRADIVARIUS COMMERCIAL SHANGAI CO, LTD—See Industria de Diseno Textil, S.A.; *Int'l*, pg. 3667
STRADIVARIUS DISENO, S.L.—See Industria de Diseno Textil, S.A.; *Int'l*, pg. 3667
STRADIVARIUS ESPANA, S.A—See Industria de Diseno Textil, S.A.; *Int'l*, pg. 3667
STRADIVARIUS FRANCE S.A.H.L.—See Industria de Diseno Textil, S.A.; *Int'l*, pg. 3667
STRADIVARIUS HELLAS, S.A.—See Industria de Diseno Textil, S.A.; *Int'l*, pg. 3667
STRADIVARIUS HONG KONG, LTD—See Industria de Diseno Textil, S.A.; *Int'l*, pg. 3667
STRADIVARIUS IRELAND LIMITED—See Industria de Diseno Textil, S.A.; *Int'l*, pg. 3667
STRADIVARIUS LOGISTICA S.A.—See Industria de Diseno Textil, S.A.; *Int'l*, pg. 3667
STRADIVARIUS MAGYAROSZAG KFT.—See Industria de Diseno Textil, S.A.; *Int'l*, pg. 3667
STRADIVARIUS NEDERLAND, B.V.—See Industria de Diseno Textil, S.A.; *Int'l*, pg. 3667
STRADIVARIUS POLSKA SP ZO.O.—See Industria de Diseno Textil, S.A.; *Int'l*, pg. 3667
STRADIVARIUS PORTUGAL, CONF. UNIP. LDA.—See Industria de Diseno Textil, S.A.; *Int'l*, pg. 3667
STRADIVARIUS SLOVAKIA, S.R.O.—See Industria de Diseno Textil, S.A.; *Int'l*, pg. 3667
STRAD MANUFACTURING INC—See Strad Energy Services Ltd.; *Int'l*, pg. 7234
STRAD OILFIELD RENTALS LTD—See Strad Energy Services Ltd.; *Int'l*, pg. 7234
STRAFFIC CO,. LTD.; *Int'l*, pg. 7234
STRAFFORD PUBLICATIONS, INC.—See Francisco Partners Management, LP; *U.S. Private*, pg. 1588
STRAHMAN VALVES, INC.—See Audax Group, Limited Partnership; *U.S. Private*, pg. 388
STRAIGHT ARROW PRODUCTS, INC.; *U.S. Private*, pg. 3833
STRAIGHT FLIGHT, INC.—See Sierra Nevada Corporation; *U.S. Private*, pg. 3647
STRAIGHT INTERNATIONAL SECURITY BV—See Live Nation Entertainment, Inc.; *U.S. Public*, pg. 1330
STRAIGHT LINE METAL BUILDINGS, INC.—See Ambassador Enterprises, LLC; *U.S. Private*, pg. 217
STRAIGHT LTD—See Madison Dearborn Partners, LLC; *U.S. Private*, pg. 2541
STRAIGHT NORTH LLC; *U.S. Private*, pg. 3833
STRAIGHT PATH COMMUNICATIONS INC.—See Verizon Communications Inc.; *U.S. Public*, pg. 2285
STRAINRITE INC.; *U.S. Private*, pg. 3833
STRAINSFORPAINS, INC.; *U.S. Public*, pg. 1953
STRAINSTALL AS—See James Fisher & Sons Public Limited Company; *Int'l*, pg. 3876
STRAINSTALL GROUP LTD.—See James Fisher & Sons Public Limited Company; *Int'l*, pg. 3876
STRAINSTALL MALAYSIA SDN BHD—See James Fisher & Sons Public Limited Company; *Int'l*, pg. 3877
STRAINSTALL SINGAPORE PTE. LTD.—See James Fisher & Sons Public Limited Company; *Int'l*, pg. 3877
STRAINSTALL UK LIMITED—See James Fisher & Sons Public Limited Company; *Int'l*, pg. 3877

STRAITFLEX CORPORATION—See Worthington Industries, Inc.; *U.S. Public*, pg. 2382
STRAIT INNOVATION INTERNET CO., LTD.; *Int'l*, pg. 7234
STRAIT & LAMP LUMBER CO. INC.; *U.S. Private*, pg. 3833
STRAIT LANE CAPITAL PARTNERS, LLC; *U.S. Private*, pg. 3833
STRAITS CORPORATION; *U.S. Private*, pg. 3833
STRAITS ENERGY RESOURCES BERHAD; *Int'l*, pg. 7234
STRAITS FINANCIAL GROUP PTE LTD—See CWT International Limited; *Int'l*, pg. 1891
STRAITS FINANCIAL LLC—See CWT International Limited; *Int'l*, pg. 1891
STRAITS-KMP RESORT DEVELOPMENT PTE LTD—See Keppel Corporation Limited; *Int'l*, pg. 4132
STRAITS MANSFIELD PROPERTY MARKETING PTE LTD—See Keppel Corporation Limited; *Int'l*, pg. 4132
STRAITS MARINE SERVICES PTE LTD—See Straits Energy Resources Berhad; *Int'l*, pg. 7234
STRAITS MINING PTY LTD—See Aeris Resources Limited; *Int'l*, pg. 180
STRAITS ORGANIZATION PTE. LTD.—See Katrina Group Ltd.; *Int'l*, pg. 4092
STRAITS PODIATRY PTE. LTD.—See OUE Limited; *Int'l*, pg. 5666
STRAITS STEEL & WIRE COMPANY—See Trive Capital Inc.; *U.S. Private*, pg. 4240
STRAITS TIMES PRESS PTE LTD—See Singapore Press Holdings Ltd.; *Int'l*, pg. 6943
THE STRAITS TRADING COMPANY LIMITED—See Tecity Group; *Int'l*, pg. 7514
STRAKAN INTERNATIONAL LTD—See Kirin Holdings Company, Limited; *Int'l*, pg. 4189
STRAKER GERMANY GMBH—See Straker Limited; *Int'l*, pg. 7235
STRAKER LIMITED; *Int'l*, pg. 7235
STRAKER LINGOTEK LLC—See Straker Limited; *Int'l*, pg. 7235
STRAKER TRANSLATIONS AUSTRALIA PTY LIMITED—See Straker Limited; *Int'l*, pg. 7235
STRAKER TRANSLATIONS UK LIMITED—See Straker Limited; *Int'l*, pg. 7235
STRALFORS AB—See PostNord AB; *Int'l*, pg. 5940
STRALFORS AG—See PostNord AB; *Int'l*, pg. 5940
STRALFORS AS—See PostNord AB; *Int'l*, pg. 5940
STRALFORS A/S—See PostNord AB; *Int'l*, pg. 5940
STRALFORS DEUTSCHLAND GMBH & CO. KG—See PostNord AB; *Int'l*, pg. 5941
STRALFORS FINANCE SAS—See PostNord AB; *Int'l*, pg. 5941
STRALFORS FRANCE S.A.—See PostNord AB; *Int'l*, pg. 5941
STRALFORS GOTEBORG AB—See PostNord AB; *Int'l*, pg. 5941
STRALFORS INFORMATION LOGISTICS A/S—See PostNord AB; *Int'l*, pg. 5941
STRALFORS INFORMATION LOGISTICS OY—See PostNord AB; *Int'l*, pg. 5941
STRALFORS MAILA NORDIC AB—See PostNord AB; *Int'l*, pg. 5941
STRALFORS MEDIGRAFIK A/S—See PostNord AB; *Int'l*, pg. 5941
STRALFORS NV—See PostNord AB; *Int'l*, pg. 5941
STRALFORS OY—See PostNord AB; *Int'l*, pg. 5941
STRALFORS PLC—See PostNord AB; *Int'l*, pg. 5941
STRALFORS PLC—See PostNord AB; *Int'l*, pg. 5941
STRALFORS SAS—See PostNord AB; *Int'l*, pg. 5941
STRALFORS SP.Z.O.O—See PostNord AB; *Int'l*, pg. 5941
STRALFORS SVENSKA AB—See PostNord AB; *Int'l*, pg. 5941
STRALFORS TANDSBYN AB—See PostNord AB; *Int'l*, pg. 5941
STRAMIT CORPORATION PTY LIMITED—See Fletcher Building Limited; *Int'l*, pg. 2701
STRAMIT INDUSTRIES LTD.—See Eleco Plc; *Int'l*, pg. 2348
STRAMIT PTY LIMITED—See Fletcher Building Limited; *Int'l*, pg. 2701
STRAN & COMPANY, INC.; *U.S. Public*, pg. 1953
STRAND AEROSPACE MALAYSIA—See Stress Analysis and Design Engineering Ltd.; *Int'l*, pg. 7240
STRAND ASSOCIATES, INC.; *U.S. Private*, pg. 3833
STRANDBAGS GROUP PTY. LTD.; *Int'l*, pg. 7235
STRAND BOOK STORE INC.; *U.S. Private*, pg. 3833
STRAND BROTHERS SERVICE EXPERTS HEATING & AIR CONDITIONING—See Service Experts LLC; *U.S. Private*, pg. 3615
STRANDHERD MONTESSORI DAYCARE INC.—See Ontario Teachers' Pension Plan; *Int'l*, pg. 5587
STRAND I JONKOPING AB—See Storskogen Group AB; *Int'l*, pg. 7228
STRAND LIFE SCIENCES PVT. LTD.—See Quadria Capital Investment Management Pte Ltd; *Int'l*, pg. 6150
STRAND LIGHTING, INC.—See Signify N.V.; *Int'l*, pg. 6912
STRANDLINE RESOURCES LIMITED; *Int'l*, pg. 7235

STRAND-TECH MARTIN INCORPORATED—See Insteel Industries, Inc.; *U.S. Public*, pg. 1134
STRANGBETONG AB—See Bain Capital, LP; *U.S. Private*, pg. 438
STRANG CORPORATION; *U.S. Private*, pg. 3833
STRANGE'S FLORIST & GREENHOUSES; *U.S. Private*, pg. 3833
STRAN LOYALTY SOLUTIONS, LLC—See Stran & Company, Inc.; *U.S. Public*, pg. 1953
STRAN TECHNOLOGIES INC.—See Corning Incorporated; *U.S. Public*, pg. 579
STRAPACK INC.; *U.S. Private*, pg. 3833
STRAPEX AUSTRIA GES. MBH—See Illinois Tool Works Inc.; *U.S. Public*, pg. 1111
STRAPEX EMBALAGEM L.D.A.—See Illinois Tool Works Inc.; *U.S. Public*, pg. 1111
STRAPEX GMBH—See Illinois Tool Works Inc.; *U.S. Public*, pg. 1111
STRAPEX GMBH—See Illinois Tool Works Inc.; *U.S. Public*, pg. 1111
STRAPEX HOLDING GMBH—See Crown Holdings, Inc.; *U.S. Public*, pg. 600
STRAPEX S.A.S.—See Illinois Tool Works Inc.; *U.S. Public*, pg. 1111
STRAPEX S.P.R.L.—See Illinois Tool Works Inc.; *U.S. Public*, pg. 1111
STRAPEX SRL—See Illinois Tool Works Inc.; *U.S. Public*, pg. 1111
STRAPTECH AE—See M.J. Maillis S.A.; *Int'l*, pg. 4616
STRAP TRANSPORT S.A.S.—See Derichebourg S.A.; *Int'l*, pg. 2042
STRASBURGER ENTERPRISES, INC.; *U.S. Private*, pg. 3833
STRASBURGER & PRICE, LLP; *U.S. Private*, pg. 3833
STRATABOLT (PTY) LIMITED—See Orica Limited; *Int'l*, pg. 5621
STRATABOUND MINERALS CORP.; *Int'l*, pg. 7235
STRATACACHE INC.; *U.S. Private*, pg. 3833
STRATACOMM LLC - DETROIT OFFICE—See Omnicom Group Inc.; *U.S. Public*, pg. 1585
STRATACOMM LLC—See Omnicom Group Inc.; *U.S. Public*, pg. 1585
STRATA CORPORATION; *U.S. Private*, pg. 3833
STRATACUITY STAFFING PARTNERS, INC.—See ASGN Incorporated; *U.S. Public*, pg. 211
STRATA DECISION TECHNOLOGY INDIA PRIVATE LIMITED—See Roper Technologies, Inc.; *U.S. Public*, pg. 1813
STRATA DECISION TECHNOLOGY, L.L.C.—See Roper Technologies, Inc.; *U.S. Public*, pg. 1813
STRATA DECISION TECHNOLOGY LLC—See Roper Technologies, Inc.; *U.S. Public*, pg. 1813
STRATAGENE CORP.—See Agilent Technologies, Inc.; *U.S. Public*, pg. 62
STRATAGEN SYSTEMS, INC.—See DDS Wireless International Inc.; *Int'l*, pg. 1994
STRATAGOLD GUYANA INC.—See Alicanto Minerals Limited; *Int'l*, pg. 327
STRATA GRAPHICS, INC.; *U.S. Private*, pg. 3833
STRATA INFORMATION TECHNOLOGY INC.—See GoodSuite; *U.S. Private*, pg. 1740
STRATA MANUFACTURING PJSC—See Mubadala Investment Company PJSC; *Int'l*, pg. 5076
STRATA MARKETING, INC.; *U.S. Private*, pg. 3833
STRATA MATERIALS, LLC—See Arcosa, Inc.; *U.S. Public*, pg. 186
STRATA MINERALS PTY LTD.—See Revival Gold Inc.; *Int'l*, pg. 6313
STRATA NIAGA SDN. BHD.—See Muhibbah Engineering (M) Bhd.; *Int'l*, pg. 5079
STRATA POWER CORPORATION; *Int'l*, pg. 7235
STRATA PRODUCTS LIMITED—See Chiltern Capital LLP; *Int'l*, pg. 1479
STRATA PROPERTIES, LLC—See UDR, Inc.; *U.S. Public*, pg. 2218
STRATASAN, LLC—See Roper Technologies, Inc.; *U.S. Public*, pg. 1813
STRATASHOPS LLC; *U.S. Private*, pg. 3834
STRATA SKIN SCIENCES, INC.; *U.S. Public*, pg. 1953
STRATASOFT, INC.—See Vector Capital Management, L.P.; *U.S. Private*, pg. 4350
STRATA SOLICITORS LTD.—See Arthur J. Gallagher & Co.; *U.S. Public*, pg. 205
STRATASYS DIRECT, INC. - BELTON PLANT—See The Lamarjean Group, Inc.; *U.S. Private*, pg. 4067
STRATASYS DIRECT, INC. - DETROIT PLANT—See The Lamarjean Group, Inc.; *U.S. Private*, pg. 4067
STRATASYS DIRECT, INC.—See The Lamarjean Group, Inc.; *U.S. Private*, pg. 4067
STRATASYS GMBH—See Stratasys Ltd.; *Int'l*, pg. 7235
STRATASYS, INC—See Stratasys Ltd.; *Int'l*, pg. 7235
STRATASYS LTD.; *Int'l*, pg. 7235
STRATA-TAC, INC.—See OpenGate Capital Management, LLC; *U.S. Private*, pg. 3030
STRATA TILES LIMITED—See Topps Tiles Plc; *Int'l*, pg. 7820
STRATATURE, INC.—See Microsoft Corporation; *U.S. Public*, pg. 1441

STRATAVEST SDN. BHD.—See Eden Inc. Berhad; *Int'l*, pg. 2306
STRATAWIDE MANAGEMENT PTY LIMITED—See Metroland Australia Limited; *Int'l*, pg. 4862
STRATCO B.V.; *Int'l*, pg. 7235
STRATEBAU GMBH—See STRABAG SE; *Int'l*, pg. 7233
STRATEC BIOMEDICAL DATA MANAGEMENT SYSTEMS—See Stratec SE; *Int'l*, pg. 7235
STRATEC BIOMEDICAL INC.—See Stratec SE; *Int'l*, pg. 7235
STRATECH AEROSPACE, INC.—See The Stratech Group Limited; *Int'l*, pg. 7689
THE STRATECH GROUP LIMITED; *Int'l*, pg. 7689
STRATEC MEDICAL LDA.—See Johnson & Johnson; *U.S. Public*, pg. 1195
STRATEC MEDICAL MEDIZINTECHNIK GMBH—See Johnson & Johnson; *U.S. Public*, pg. 1195
STRATEC MEDICAL S.P.A.—See Johnson & Johnson; *U.S. Public*, pg. 1195
STRATEC MOLECULAR GMBH—See Stratec SE; *Int'l*, pg. 7235
STRATEC NEWGEN GMBH—See Stratec SE; *Int'l*, pg. 7235
STRATECO RESOURCES INC.; *Int'l*, pg. 7236
STRATEC SE; *Int'l*, pg. 7235
STRATEGAS RESEARCH PARTNERS, LLC; *U.S. Private*, pg. 3834
STRATEGEM CAPITAL CORPORATION; *Int'l*, pg. 7236
STRATEGEX GROUP CHARTERED PROFESSIONAL ACCOUNTANTS; *Int'l*, pg. 7236
STRATEGEX, INC.; *U.S. Private*, pg. 3834
STRATEGIA ITALIA SGR SPA—See Agenzia Nazionale per l'Attrazione degli Investimenti e lo Sviluppo d'Impresa SpA; *Int'l*, pg. 206
STRATEGIC ACQUISITIONS, INC.; *U.S. Public*, pg. 1953
STRATEGIC ADVISORY GROUP INC.—See Jones Lang LaSalle Incorporated; *U.S. Public*, pg. 1206
STRATEGIC AMERICA; *U.S. Private*, pg. 3834
STRATEGIC ANALYSIS INC.; *U.S. Private*, pg. 3834
STRATEGIC AR; *U.S. Private*, pg. 3834
STRATEGIC ASSET LEASING, INC.—See Redwoods Acquisition Corp.; *U.S. Public*, pg. 1771
STRATEGIC ASSET MANAGEMENT GROUP ADVISORS, INC.; *U.S. Private*, pg. 3834
STRATEGIC ASSET MANAGEMENT, INC.; *U.S. Private*, pg. 3834
STRATEGIC ASSET MANAGERS LIMITED—See Kingswood Holdings Ltd.; *Int'l*, pg. 4180
STRATEGIC BCP, INC.—See EQT AB; *Int'l*, pg. 2471
STRATEGIC BUSINESS SYSTEMS, INC.; *U.S. Private*, pg. 3834
STRATEGIC CAPITAL HOLDINGS, LLC; *U.S. Private*, pg. 3834
STRATEGICCLAIM; *U.S. Private*, pg. 3836
STRATEGIC COMMUNICATIONS, LLC.; *U.S. Private*, pg. 3834
STRATEGIC COMMUNICATIONS—See FTI Consulting, Inc.; *U.S. Public*, pg. 890
STRATEGIC CONSULTING SOLUTIONS, INC.; *U.S. Private*, pg. 3834
STRATEGIC CRISIS ADVISORS LLC—See AIP, LLC; *U.S. Private*, pg. 137
STRATEGIC DATA MANAGEMENT PTY LTD—See DWS Limited; *Int'l*, pg. 2236
STRATEGIC DATA SYSTEMS; *U.S. Private*, pg. 3834
STRATEGIC DECISIONS GROUP INTERNATIONAL LLC; *U.S. Private*, pg. 3834
STRATEGIC DELIVERY SOLUTIONS LLC—See HCI Equity Management, L.P.; *U.S. Private*, pg. 1889
STRATEGIC DIGITAL SERVICES INC.; *U.S. Private*, pg. 3834
STRATEGIC DISTRIBUTION, INC.—See Independence Capital Partners, LLC; *U.S. Private*, pg. 2056
STRATEGIC DISTRIBUTION, INC.—See Pouschine Cook Capital Management LLC; *U.S. Private*, pg. 3236
STRATEGIC DISTRIBUTION MARKETING DE MEXICO, S.A. DE C.V.—See Independence Capital Partners, LLC; *U.S. Private*, pg. 2056
STRATEGIC DISTRIBUTION MARKETING DE MEXICO, S.A. DE C.V.—See Pouschine Cook Capital Management LLC; *U.S. Private*, pg. 3236
STRATEGIC DISTRIBUTION SERVICES DE MEXICO, S.A. DE C.V.—See Independence Capital Partners, LLC; *U.S. Private*, pg. 2056
STRATEGIC DISTRIBUTION SERVICES DE MEXICO, S.A. DE C.V.—See Pouschine Cook Capital Management LLC; *U.S. Private*, pg. 3236
STRATEGIC EDGE COMMUNCIATIONS, INC.—See MD On-Line Inc.; *U.S. Private*, pg. 2646
STRATEGIC EDUCATION, INC.; *U.S. Public*, pg. 1953
STRATEGIC ELEMENTS LTD.; *Int'l*, pg. 7236
STRATEGIC ENERGY RESOURCES LIMITED; *Int'l*, pg. 7236
STRATEGIC ENVIRONMENTAL & ENERGY RESOURCES, INC.; *U.S. Public*, pg. 1954
STRATEGIC EQUIPMENT & SUPPLY CORP.—See Warburg Pincus LLC; *U.S. Private*, pg. 4440
STRATEGIC EQUITY CAPITAL PLC; *Int'l*, pg. 7236
STRATEGIC FEEDBACK INC.; *U.S. Private*, pg. 3835

STRATEGIC FINANCIAL SOLUTIONS, LLC—See Nasdaq, Inc.; *U.S. Public*, pg. 1492
STRATEGIC FOCUS; *U.S. Private*, pg. 3835
STRATEGIC FULFILLMENT GROUP LLC—See Dynamic Resource Group, Inc.; *U.S. Private*, pg. 1299
STRATEGIC FUNDRAISING, INC.; *U.S. Private*, pg. 3835
STRATEGIC GOVERNMENT RESOURCES INC.; *U.S. Private*, pg. 3835
STRATEGIC HEALTHCARE PROGRAMS, LLC—See Roper Technologies, Inc.; *U.S. Public*, pg. 1813
STRATEGIC HOLDINGS, INC.—See Lennar Corporation; *U.S. Public*, pg. 1307
STRATEGIC HOSPITALITY EXTENDABLE FREEHOLD & LEASEHOLD REIT; *Int'l*, pg. 7236
STRATEGIC INCOME ALLOCATION FUND—See Fiera Capital Corporation; *Int'l*, pg. 2660
STRATEGIC INDUSTRIES, LLC; *U.S. Private*, pg. 3835
STRATEGIC INSIGHT, INC.—See Genstar Capital, LLC; *U.S. Private*, pg. 1675
STRATEGIC INTELLIGENCE GROUP LLC—See D.C. Capital Partners, LLC; *U.S. Private*, pg. 1141
STRATEGIC INTERNET INVESTMENTS, INCORPORATED; *Int'l*, pg. 7236
STRATEGIC INTERNET MARKETING PARTNERS, INC.—See Reputation.com, Inc.; *U.S. Private*, pg. 3403
STRATEGIC INVESTMENT GROUP—See Northill Capital LLP; *Int'l*, pg. 5445
STRATEGIC INVESTMENTS A/S; *Int'l*, pg. 7236
STRATEGIC INVESTMENTS & HOLDING INC.; *U.S. Private*, pg. 3835
STRATEGIC INVESTORS FUND V-B, L.P.—See SVB Financial Group; *U.S. Public*, pg. 1968
STRATEGIC INVESTORS FUND VII, L.P.—See SVB Financial Group; *U.S. Public*, pg. 1968
STRATEGIC INVESTORS GROUP, INC.; *Int'l*, pg. 7236
STRATEGIC MANAGEMENT DECISIONS LLC—See Ares Management Corporation; *U.S. Public*, pg. 190
STRATEGIC MANAGEMENT DECISIONS LLC—See Leonard Green & Partners, L.P.; *U.S. Private*, pg. 2427
STRATEGIC MANAGEMENT & OPPORTUNITY CORP.; *U.S. Public*, pg. 1954
STRATEGIC MARINE (S) PTE. LTD.—See TRIYARDS Holdings Limited; *Int'l*, pg. 7937
STRATEGIC MARINE (V) CO., LTD.—See TRIYARDS Holdings Limited; *Int'l*, pg. 7937
STRATEGIC MATERIALS, INC.—See Littlejohn & Co., LLC; *U.S. Private*, pg. 2471
STRATEGIC MATERIALS PTY LTD.—See Strategic Elements Ltd.; *Int'l*, pg. 7236
STRATEGIC MEDIA, INC.; *U.S. Private*, pg. 3835
STRATEGIC METALS LTD.; *Int'l*, pg. 7236
STRATEGIC MICRO SYSTEMS OF NJ, LLC.; *U.S. Private*, pg. 3835
STRATEGIC MINERALS CORPORATION NL; *Int'l*, pg. 7236
STRATEGIC MINERALS EUROPE LTD.—See Gunsynd plc; *Int'l*, pg. 3185
STRATEGIC MINERALS PLC; *Int'l*, pg. 7236
STRATEGIC MOBILITY GROUP; *U.S. Private*, pg. 3835
STRATEGIC NATURAL RESOURCES PLC; *Int'l*, pg. 7236
STRATEGIC NURSE STAFFING, INC.; *U.S. Private*, pg. 3835
STRATEGIC OIL & GAS LTD.; *Int'l*, pg. 7236
STRATEGIC OUTSOURCING, INC.—See General Atlantic Service Company, L.P.; *U.S. Private*, pg. 1663
STRATEGIC PARTNERS CO., LTD.—See CRE, Inc.; *Int'l*, pg. 1830
STRATEGIC PARTNERS, INC.—See New Mountain Capital, LLC; *U.S. Private*, pg. 2903
STRATEGIC PUBLICATIONS, LLC; *U.S. Private*, pg. 3835
STRATEGIC PUBLIC RELATIONS GROUP LIMITED; *Int'l*, pg. 7236
STRATEGIC PUBLIC RELATIONS—See Strategic Public Relations Group Limited; *Int'l*, pg. 7236
STRATEGIC PUBLIC RELATIONS—See Strategic Public Relations Group Limited; *Int'l*, pg. 7236
STRATEGIC PUBLIC RELATIONS—See Strategic Public Relations Group Limited; *Int'l*, pg. 7236
STRATEGIC PUBLIC RELATIONS—See Strategic Public Relations Group Limited; *Int'l*, pg. 7236
STRATEGIC PUBLIC RELATIONS—See Strategic Public Relations Group Limited; *Int'l*, pg. 7236
STRATEGIC REALTY CAPITAL, LLC; *U.S. Private*, pg. 3835
STRATEGIC REALTY TRUST, INC.; *U.S. Private*, pg. 3835
STRATEGIC RESOURCE ALTERNATIVES—See Arena Investors, LP; *U.S. Private*, pg. 318
STRATEGIC RESOURCE COMPANY—See CVS Health Corporation; *U.S. Public*, pg. 615
STRATEGIC RESOURCES INC.; *Int'l*, pg. 7236
STRATEGIC RESOURCES INTERNATIONAL, INC.—See Peraton Government Communications, Inc.; *U.S. Private*, pg. 3146
STRATEGIC RETAIL ADVISORS, INC.; *U.S. Private*, pg. 3835
STRATEGIC RISK SOLUTIONS INC.—See Strategic Risk Solutions Inc.; *U.S. Private*, pg. 3835

COMPANY NAME INDEX

STRATEGIC RISK SOLUTIONS INC.; *U.S. Private*, pg. 3835
STRATEGIC SERVICE CONSULTING GMBH—See Serviceware SE; *Int'l*, pg. 6726
STRATEGIC SIMULATION & ANALYSIS LTD.—See Addnode Group AB; *Int'l*, pg. 130
STRATEGIC STAFFING SOLUTIONS INC.; *U.S. Private*, pg. 3835
STRATEGIC STUDENT & SENIOR HOUSING TRUST, INC.—See Strategic Capital Holdings, LLC; *U.S. Private*, pg. 3834
STRATEGIC SYSTEMS, INC.; *U.S. Private*, pg. 3835
STRATEGIC SYSTEMS & TECHNOLOGY CORPORATION; *U.S. Private*, pg. 3835
STRATEGIC TECHNOLOGY ENTERPRISE, INC.—See STERIS plc; *Int'l*, pg. 7211
STRATEGIC TELECOM SOLUTIONS; *U.S. Private*, pg. 3835
STRATEGIC VALUE PARTNERS, LLC; *U.S. Private*, pg. 3835
STRATEGIC WEALTH ADVISORY LLC—See Informed Family Financial Services, Inc.; *U.S. Private*, pg. 2073
STRATEGIES, A MARKETING COMMUNICATIONS CORPORATION; *U.S. Private*, pg. 3836
STRATEGIQUE SANTE—See IQVIA Holdings Inc.; *U.S. Public*, pg. 1170
STRATEGIS; *U.S. Private*, pg. 3836
STRATEGX ELEMENTS CORP.; *Int'l*, pg. 7236
STRATEGY ANALYTICS GMBH—See CVC Capital Partners SICAV-FIS S.A.; *Int'l*, pg. 1888
STRATEGY ANALYTICS GMBH—See Oakley Capital Limited; *Int'l*, pg. 5504
STRATEGY ANALYTICS, INC.—See CVC Capital Partners SICAV-FIS S.A.; *Int'l*, pg. 1888
STRATEGY ANALYTICS INC.—See CVC Capital Partners SICAV-FIS S.A.; *Int'l*, pg. 1888
STRATEGY ANALYTICS INC.—See CVC Capital Partners SICAV-FIS S.A.; *Int'l*, pg. 1888
STRATEGY ANALYTICS INC.—See CVC Capital Partners SICAV-FIS S.A.; *Int'l*, pg. 1888
STRATEGY ANALYTICS, INC.—See Oakley Capital Limited; *Int'l*, pg. 5504
STRATEGY ANALYTICS INC.—See Oakley Capital Limited; *Int'l*, pg. 5504
STRATEGY ANALYTICS INC.—See Oakley Capital Limited; *Int'l*, pg. 5504
STRATEGY ANALYTICS INC.—See Oakley Capital Limited; *Int'l*, pg. 5504
STRATEGY ANALYTICS LTD.—See CVC Capital Partners SICAV-FIS S.A.; *Int'l*, pg. 1888
STRATEGY ANALYTICS LTD.—See Oakley Capital Limited; *Int'l*, pg. 5504
STRATEGY ANALYTICS—See CVC Capital Partners SICAV-FIS S.A.; *Int'l*, pg. 1888
STRATEGY ANALYTICS—See Oakley Capital Limited; *Int'l*, pg. 5504
STRATEGY COMMUNICATIONS; *U.S. Private*, pg. 3836
STRATEGY INTERNATIONAL INSURANCE GROUP, INC.; *Int'l*, pg. 7237
STRATEGY PARTNERS GROUP JSC—See OJSC Sberbank of Russia; *Int'l*, pg. 5542
STRATEGY TO REVENUE INC.—See LevelBlox, Inc.; *U.S. Public*, pg. 1308
STRATEGYWISE, LLC—See Align Capital Partners, LLC; *U.S. Private*, pg. 167
STRATEJIC SOLUTIONS S.A. DE C.V.—See Maritz Holdings Inc.; *U.S. Private*, pg. 2577
STRATES ENTERPRISES INC.; *U.S. Private*, pg. 3836
STRATES HOLDING CORP—See Strates Enterprises Inc.; *U.S. Private*, pg. 3837
STRATE TECHNOLOGIE FUR ABWASSER GMBH—See Triton Advisers Limited; *Int'l*, pg. 7934
STRATEVIC FINANCE GROUP AB; *Int'l*, pg. 7237
STRATE WELDING SUPPLY CO. INC.; *U.S. Private*, pg. 3834
STRATEX EXPLORATION LIMITED—See Oriole Resources PLC; *Int'l*, pg. 5631
STRATEX MADENCILIK SANAYI VE TICARET LTD. STI—See Oriole Resources PLC; *Int'l*, pg. 5631
STRATFORD BANCSHARES, INC.; *U.S. Private*, pg. 3837
THE STRATFORD-CAMBRIDGE GROUP CO.; *U.S. Private*, pg. 4123
STRATFORD CONSULTING LLC—See Creative Planning, LLC; *U.S. Private*, pg. 1090
STRATFORD HOMES LP; *U.S. Private*, pg. 3837
STRATFORD INSURANCE COMPANY—See American International Group, Inc.; *U.S. Public*, pg. 107
STRATFORD MOTOR PRODUCTS; *Int'l*, pg. 7237
STRATFOR ENTERPRISES, LLC—See Risk Assistance Network + Exchange Network, Inc.; *U.S. Private*, pg. 3440
STRATHALLEN CAPITAL CORP.; *Int'l*, pg. 7237
STRATHAM TIRE INC.; *U.S. Private*, pg. 3837
STRATHCLYDE INNOVATION FUND LP—See Braveheart Investment Group Plc; *Int'l*, pg. 1141
STRATHCONA RESOURCES LTD.—See Waterous Energy Fund; *Int'l*, pg. 8358

STRATHMANN GMBH & CO. KG—See Dermapharm Holding SE; *Int'l*, pg. 2043
STRATHMORE ARTIST PAPERS—See F.I.L.A. - Fabbrica Italiana Lapis ed Affini S.p.A.; *Int'l*, pg. 2596
STRATHMORE COLLEGE LIMITED—See Acadia Healthcare Company, Inc.; *U.S. Public*, pg. 30
STRATHMORE PLUS URANIUM CORP; *Int'l*, pg. 7237
STRATHMORE PRODUCTS INC.—See CSW Industrials, Inc.; *U.S. Public*, pg. 602
STRATHSPEY CROWN LLC—See ALPHAEON Corporation; *U.S. Private*, pg. 200
STRATICELL SA/NV—See Plant Advanced Technologies SA; *Int'l*, pg. 5890
STRATIM CLOUD ACQUISITION CORP.; *U.S. Public*, pg. 1954
STRATIVA, INC.—See Avasant LLC; *U.S. Private*, pg. 404
STRATIVIA LLC; *U.S. Private*, pg. 3837
STRATIVITY GROUP, LLC—See Tailwind Capital Group, LLC; *U.S. Private*, pg. 3924
STRATIX CORPORATION—See Independence Capital Partners, LLC; *U.S. Private*, pg. 2056
STRATMAR RETAIL SERVICES; *U.S. Private*, pg. 3837
STRATMONT INDUSTRIES LIMITED; *Int'l*, pg. 7237
STRATO AG—See United Internet AG; *Int'l*, pg. 8069
STRAT-O-MATIC MEDIA, LLC; *U.S. Private*, pg. 3833
STRATON BUSINESS SOLUTIONS PRIVATE LIMITED—See Variman Global Enterprises Ltd.; *Int'l*, pg. 8133
STRATOS INTERNATIONAL, INC.—See Emerson Electric Co.; *U.S. Public*, pg. 752
STRATOS MANAGEMENT SYSTEMS, INC.—See Calian Group Ltd.; *Int'l*, pg. 1264
STRATOS OFFSHORE SERVICES COMPANY—See ViaSat, Inc.; *U.S. Public*, pg. 2292
STRATOSPHERE COMMUNICATIONS PTY LTD—See PepsiCo, Inc.; *U.S. Public*, pg. 1672
STRATOSPHERE GAMING LLC—See Golden Entertainment, Inc.; *U.S. Public*, pg. 950
STRATOSPHERE LLC—See Golden Entertainment, Inc.; *U.S. Public*, pg. 950
STRATOSPHERE QUALITY, LLC—See Sojitz Corporation; *Int'l*, pg. 7064
STRATSTONE LIMITED—See Pinewood Technologies Group PLC; *Int'l*, pg. 5869
STRATTAM CAPITAL, LLC; *U.S. Private*, pg. 3837
STRATTEC DE MEXICO S.A. DE C.V.—See Strattec Security Corporation; *U.S. Public*, pg. 1954
STRATTEC POWER ACCESS LLC—See Strattec Security Corporation; *U.S. Public*, pg. 1954
STRATTEC SECURITY CORPORATION; *U.S. Public*, pg. 1954
STRATTON AGENCY—See ABRY Partners, LLC; *U.S. Private*, pg. 42
STRATTON & BRATT LANDSCAPES, LLC; *U.S. Private*, pg. 3837
THE STRATTON CORPORATION—See KSL Capital Partners, LLC; *U.S. Private*, pg. 2354
STRATTON EQUITY CO-OPERATIVE COMPANY INC.; *U.S. Private*, pg. 3837
STRATUM OY; *Int'l*, pg. 7237
STRATUM OY - STRATUM TUUSULA UNIT—See Stratum Oy; *Int'l*, pg. 7237
STRATUM OY - STRATUM VANTAA UNIT—See Stratum Oy; *Int'l*, pg. 7237
STRATUM PORI—See Stratum Oy; *Int'l*, pg. 7237
STRATUS BUILDING SOLUTIONS; *U.S. Private*, pg. 3837
STRATUS CAPITAL CORP.; *U.S. Public*, pg. 1954
STRATUS CONSULTING, INC.—See Abt Associates Inc.; *U.S. Private*, pg. 45
STRATUS GESTAO DE CARTEIRAS LTDA.; *Int'l*, pg. 7237
STRATUS GROUP LLC—See Unity Partners LP; *U.S. Public*, pg. 2253
STRATUS INVESTMENTS, LLC—See Stratus Properties, Inc.; *U.S. Public*, pg. 1954
STRATUS PROPERTIES, INC.; *U.S. Public*, pg. 1954
STRATUS TECHNOLOGIES BERMUDA LTD.—See Siris Capital Group, LLC; *U.S. Private*, pg. 3674
STRATUS TECHNOLOGIES GROUP, S.A.—See Siris Capital Group, LLC; *U.S. Private*, pg. 3674
STRATUS TECHNOLOGIES, INC.—See Penguin Solutions, Inc.; *U.S. Public*, pg. 1661
STRATUS TECHNOLOGIES INTERNATIONAL S.A.R.L.—See Siris Capital Group, LLC; *U.S. Private*, pg. 3674
STRATUS TECHNOLOGIES IRELAND LIMITED—See Penguin Solutions, Inc.; *U.S. Public*, pg. 1661
STRATUS VIDEO, LLC—See Kinderhook Industries, LLC; *U.S. Private*, pg. 2306
STRAUB DISTRIBUTING CO. LTD; *U.S. Private*, pg. 3837
STRAUBE CENTER LLC; *U.S. Private*, pg. 3837
STRAUB INTERNATIONAL INC.—See KanEquip, Inc.; *U.S. Private*, pg. 2260
STRAUB MOTORS, INC.; *U.S. Private*, pg. 3837
STRAUB WERKE AG—See Aliaxis S.A./N.V.; *Int'l*, pg. 325
STRAUMANN AB—See Straumann Holding AG; *Int'l*, pg. 7237
STRAUMANN AS—See Straumann Holding AG; *Int'l*, pg. 7237

STRAUSS MEDIA STRATEGIES, INC.

STRAUMANN AUSTRALIA P/L—See Straumann Holding AG; *Int'l*, pg. 7237
STRAUMANN (BEIJING) MEDICAL DEVICE CONSULTING CO., LTD.—See Straumann Holding AG; *Int'l*, pg. 7238
STRAUMANN BELGIUM—See Straumann Holding AG; *Int'l*, pg. 7237
STRAUMANN BIOLOGICS DIVISION—See Straumann Holding AG; *Int'l*, pg. 7237
STRAUMANN BRASIL LTDA—See Straumann Holding AG; *Int'l*, pg. 7237
STRAUMANN B.V.—See Straumann Holding AG; *Int'l*, pg. 7237
STRAUMANN CADCAM GMBH—See Straumann Holding AG; *Int'l*, pg. 7238
STRAUMANN CANADA LIMITED—See Straumann Holding AG; *Int'l*, pg. 7238
STRAUMANN DANMARK APS—See Straumann Holding AG; *Int'l*, pg. 7238
STRAUMANN DENTAL INDIA LLP—See Straumann Holding AG; *Int'l*, pg. 7238
STRAUMANN DENTAL KOREA INC—See Straumann Holding AG; *Int'l*, pg. 7238
STRAUMANN DENTAL S.R.L.—See Straumann Holding AG; *Int'l*, pg. 7238
STRAUMANN DIGITAL PLANNING SERVICES (PRIVATE) LTD.—See Straumann Holding AG; *Int'l*, pg. 7238
STRAUMANN GMBH—See Straumann Holding AG; *Int'l*, pg. 7237
STRAUMANN GROUP ADRIATIC D.O.O.—See Straumann Holding AG; *Int'l*, pg. 7238
STRAUMANN GROUP & CLEAR CORRECT SINGAPORE PTE. LTD.—See Straumann Holding AG; *Int'l*, pg. 7238
STRAUMANN GROUP COSTA RICA S.A.—See Straumann Holding AG; *Int'l*, pg. 7238
STRAUMANN GROUP PERU SA—See Straumann Holding AG; *Int'l*, pg. 7238
STRAUMANN GROUP SDN. BHD.—See Straumann Holding AG; *Int'l*, pg. 7238
STRAUMANN GROUP SOUTH AFRICA (PTY) LTD.—See Straumann Holding AG; *Int'l*, pg. 7238
STRAUMANN GROUP (TAIWAN) CO. LTD.—See Straumann Holding AG; *Int'l*, pg. 7238
STRAUMANN GROUP (THAILAND) LIMITED—See Straumann Holding AG; *Int'l*, pg. 7238
STRAUMANN HOLDING AG; *Int'l*, pg. 7237
STRAUMANN HOLDING DEUTSCHLAND GMBH—See Straumann Holding AG; *Int'l*, pg. 7238
STRAUMANN ITALIA SRL—See Straumann Holding AG; *Int'l*, pg. 7238
STRAUMANN JAPAN KK—See Straumann Holding AG; *Int'l*, pg. 7238
STRAUMANN LATVIA SIA—See Straumann Holding AG; *Int'l*, pg. 7238
STRAUMANN LITHUANIA UAB—See Straumann Holding AG; *Int'l*, pg. 7238
STRAUMANN LTD—See Straumann Holding AG; *Int'l*, pg. 7237
STRAUMANN MEXICO SA DE C V—See Straumann Holding AG; *Int'l*, pg. 7238
STRAUMANN MIDDLE EAST PJS—See Straumann Holding AG; *Int'l*, pg. 7238
STRAUMANN OY—See Straumann Holding AG; *Int'l*, pg. 7238
STRAUMANN PTY. LTD.—See Straumann Holding AG; *Int'l*, pg. 7238
STRAUMANN SA—See Straumann Holding AG; *Int'l*, pg. 7238
STRAUMANN SINGAPORE PTE LTD—See Straumann Holding AG; *Int'l*, pg. 7238
STRAUMANN SRO—See Straumann Holding AG; *Int'l*, pg. 7238
STRAUMANN USA, LLC—See Straumann Holding AG; *Int'l*, pg. 7238
STRAUMANN VILLERET SA—See Straumann Holding AG; *Int'l*, pg. 7238
STRAUS, ITZKOWITZ & LECOMPTE INSURANCE AGENCY, INC.—See Towne Bank; *U.S. Public*, pg. 2166
STRAUSS CAFE POLAND SP. Z O.O.—See Strauss Group Ltd.; *Int'l*, pg. 7238
STRAUSS COFFEE B.V.—See Strauss Group Ltd.; *Int'l*, pg. 7238
STRAUSS COMMODITIES AG—See Strauss Group Ltd.; *Int'l*, pg. 7238
STRAUSSER INSURANCE AGENCY, INC.; *U.S. Private*, pg. 3837
STRAUSS FEEDS—See Strauss Veal Feeds Inc.; *U.S. Private*, pg. 7238
STRAUSS GROUP LTD.; *Int'l*, pg. 7238
STRAUSS INNOVATION GMBH; *Int'l*, pg. 7239
STRAUSS MEDIA STRATEGIES, INC.; *U.S. Private*, pg. 3837
STRAUSS MEDIA STRATEGIES, INC.—See Strauss Media Strategies, Inc.; *U.S. Private*, pg. 3837
STRAUSS PAPER CO., INC.—See Bain Capital, LP; *U.S. Private*, pg. 440
STRAUSS & PARTNER DEVELOPMENT GMBH—See PORR AG; *Int'l*, pg. 5925

STRAUSS PROPERTY MANAGEMENT GMBH—See PORR AG; *Int'l*, pg. 5925
STRAUSS RUSSIA LLC—See Strauss Group Ltd.; *Int'l*, pg. 7239
STRAUSS VEAL FEEDS INC.; *U.S. Private*, pg. 3837
STRAWBEAR ENTERTAINMENT GROUP; *Int'l*, pg. 7239
STRAWBERRY FIELDS REIT, INC.; *U.S. Public*, pg. 1954
STRAWBERRYFROG—See APCO Worldwide; *U.S. Private*, pg. 291
STRAW HAT RESTAURANTS, INC.; *U.S. Private*, pg. 3837
THE STRAWHECKER GROUP, LLC; *U.S. Private*, pg. 4123
STRAWSER PAVING CO., INC.; *U.S. Private*, pg. 3837
STRAX AB; *Int'l*, pg. 7239
STRAX AMERICAS, INC.—See Strax AB; *Int'l*, pg. 7239
STRAX ASIA LTD.—See Strax AB; *Int'l*, pg. 7239
STRAX FRANCE SARL—See Strax AB; *Int'l*, pg. 7239
STRAX GERMANY GMBH—See Strax AB; *Int'l*, pg. 7239
STRAX NORWAY S.A.—See Strax AB; *Int'l*, pg. 7239
STRAX SHENZHEN LIMITED—See Strax AB; *Int'l*, pg. 7239
STRAX SP. Z O.O.—See Strax AB; *Int'l*, pg. 7239
STRAX (UK) LTD.—See Strax AB; *Int'l*, pg. 7239
STRAYER UNIVERSITY—See Strategic Education, Inc.; *U.S. Public*, pg. 1954
STR COLUMBIA SAS—See CoStar Group, Inc.; *U.S. Public*, pg. 586
STREACKER TRACTOR SALES INC.; *U.S. Private*, pg. 3838
STREAKSAI PLC; *Int'l*, pg. 7239
STREAMAX TECHNOLOGY CO., LTD.; *Int'l*, pg. 7239
STREAM CO., LTD.; *Int'l*, pg. 7239
STREAM COMPANIES; *U.S. Private*, pg. 3838
STREAM ENERGY ILLINOIS, LLC—See NRG Energy, Inc.; *U.S. Public*, pg. 1551
STREAM ENERGY MARYLAND, LLC—See NRG Energy, Inc.; *U.S. Public*, pg. 1551
STREAM ENERGY NEW JERSEY, LLC—See NRG Energy, Inc.; *U.S. Public*, pg. 1551
STREAM ENERGY NEW YORK, LLC—See NRG Energy, Inc.; *U.S. Public*, pg. 1551
STREAM ENVIRONMENT SDN. BHD.—See AWC Berhad; *Int'l*, pg. 752
STREAM ENVIRONMENT SDN. BHD.—See AWC Berhad; *Int'l*, pg. 752
STREAM ENVIRONMENT (S) PTE. LTD.—See AWC Berhad; *Int'l*, pg. 752
STREAM GLOBAL SERVICES - AZ, INC.—See Concentrix Corporation; *U.S. Public*, pg. 565
STREAM GLOBAL SERVICES EL SALVADOR, S.A. DE C.V.—See Concentrix Corporation; *U.S. Public*, pg. 565
STREAM GLOBAL SERVICES HONDURAS, S.A.—See Concentrix Corporation; *U.S. Public*, pg. 565
STREAM GLOBAL SERVICES NICARAGUA, S.A.—See Concentrix Corporation; *U.S. Public*, pg. 565
STREAM IDEAS GROUP LTD.; *Int'l*, pg. 7239
STREAMINGEDGE.COM INC.—See Viel & Compagnie SA; *Int'l*, pg. 8192
STREAMING MEDIA, INC.—See Information Today Inc.; *U.S. Private*, pg. 2073
STREAM INTERNATIONAL CANADA ULC—See Concentrix Corporation; *U.S. Public*, pg. 565
STREAM INTERNATIONAL COSTA RICA S.A.—See Concentrix Corporation; *U.S. Public*, pg. 565
STREAM INTERNATIONAL SP. Z.O.O.—See Concentrix Corporation; *U.S. Public*, pg. 565
STREAMLIGHT INC.; *U.S. Private*, pg. 3838
STREAMLINE CAPITAL, INC.; *U.S. Private*, pg. 3838
STREAMLINE COPPER & BRASS LTD.—See Mueller Industries, Inc.; *U.S. Public*, pg. 1485
STREAMLINE DEFENSE, LLC; *U.S. Private*, pg. 3838
STREAMLINE DEVELOPMENT, LLC—See Siris Capital Group, LLC; *U.S. Private*, pg. 3673
STREAMLINE ENVIRONMENTAL, INC.; *U.S. Private*, pg. 3838
STREAMLINE HEALTH SOLUTIONS, INC.; *U.S. Public*, pg. 1954
STREAMLINE MARKETING, LLC—See Mountaingate Capital Management, L.P.; *U.S. Private*, pg. 2801
STREAMLINE PRODUCTION SYSTEMS, INC.—See First Reserve Management, L.P.; *U.S. Private*, pg. 1526
STREAMLINE TECHNICAL SERVICES, INC.; *U.S. Private*, pg. 3838
STREAMLINEVENTS INC.; *U.S. Private*, pg. 3838
STREAM MEDIA CORPORATION—See Keyeast Co., LTD; *Int'l*, pg. 4145
STREAM NEW YORK INC—See Concentrix Corporation; *U.S. Public*, pg. 565
STREAMPLAY STUDIO LIMITED; *Int'l*, pg. 7239
STREAM REALTY PARTNERS, L.P.; *U.S. Private*, pg. 3838
STREAMSERVE OY—See Open Text Corporation; *Int'l*, pg. 5598
STREAMSERVE SARL.B.V.—See Open Text Corporation; *Int'l*, pg. 5598
STREAMSETS, INC.—See Silver Lake Group, LLC; *U.S. Private*, pg. 3660

STREAM SOLUTIONS (HOLDINGS) PTY LTD—See Japan Post Holdings Co., Ltd.; *Int'l*, pg. 3901
STREAM TUNISIE, S.A.R.L.—See Concentrix Corporation; *U.S. Public*, pg. 565
STREAMWARE CORPORATION—See Crane NXT, Co.; *U.S. Public*, pg. 591
STREAMWEAVER, INC.—See KKR & Co. Inc.; *U.S. Public*, pg. 1241
STREAMWIDE, INC.—See Streamwide S.A.; *Int'l*, pg. 7239
STREAMWIDE PTE. LTD.—See Streamwide S.A.; *Int'l*, pg. 7239
STREAMWIDE ROMANIA S.R.L.—See Streamwide S.A.; *Int'l*, pg. 7239
STREAMWIDE S.A.; *Int'l*, pg. 7239
STREAMWIDE TUNISIA SARL—See Streamwide S.A.; *Int'l*, pg. 7239
STREAMWORKS LLC; *U.S. Private*, pg. 3838
STREATER, INC.—See Berkshire Hathaway Inc.; *U.S. Public*, pg. 311
STREATOR INDUSTRIAL HANDLING, INC.; *U.S. Private*, pg. 3838
STRECKFUSS SYSTEMS GMBH & CO. KG; *Int'l*, pg. 7239
STRECK LABORATORIES INC.; *U.S. Private*, pg. 3838
STREDOCESKA ENERGETICKA, A.S.—See CEZ, a.s.; *Int'l*, pg. 1428
STREDOSLOVENSKA ENERGETIKA, A.S.; *Int'l*, pg. 7239
STREDOSLOVENSKA ENERGETIKA - DISTRIBUCIA, A. S.—See Stredoslovenska Energetika, A.S.; *Int'l*, pg. 7239
STREETACCOUNT LLC—See FactSet Research Systems Inc.; *U.S. Public*, pg. 820
STREET CANCE MARKETING COMMUNICATIONS; *U.S. Private*, pg. 3838
STREET CAPITAL GROUP INC.—See RFA Capital Holdings Inc.; *U.S. Private*, pg. 6318
STREETER ASSOCIATES INC.; *U.S. Private*, pg. 3838
STREETERVILLE CAPITAL LLC; *U.S. Private*, pg. 3838
STREET FURNITURE (NSW) PTY LTD.—See iHeartMedia, Inc.; *U.S. Public*, pg. 1096
STREETINSIDER.COM, INC.—See Fusion Media Ltd.; *Int'l*, pg. 2849
STREETLINE, INC.—See Kapsch-Group Beteiligungs GmbH; *Int'l*, pg. 4077
STREETLINKS LLC—See Novation Companies, Inc.; *U.S. Public*, pg. 1548
STREETMAN HOMES CORP.—See Lennar Corporation; *U.S. Public*, pg. 1305
STREET MODA FOOTWEAR; *U.S. Private*, pg. 3838
STREET MOTOR SALES LTD.; *Int'l*, pg. 7239
STREET ONE GMBH; *Int'l*, pg. 7239
STREET RESOURCE GROUP, INC.—See Stone Point Capital LLC; *U.S. Private*, pg. 3825
STREET RETAIL, INC.—See Federal Realty Investment Trust; *U.S. Public*, pg. 826
STREET RETAIL WEST 6, L.P.—See Federal Realty Investment Trust; *U.S. Public*, pg. 826
STREETSCOOTER GMBH—See Deutsche Post AG; *Int'l*, pg. 2082
STREETSENSE, INC.; *U.S. Private*, pg. 3839
STREETS ICE CREAM PTY. LTD.—See Unilever PLC; *Int'l*, pg. 8045
STREET SMART OUTDOOR CORP.—See Sun Pacific Holding Corp; *U.S. Public*, pg. 1963
STREET & SMITH SPORTS GROUP—See Advance Publications, Inc.; *U.S. Public*, pg. 85
STREET TOYOTA, INC.; *U.S. Private*, pg. 3838
STREETWISE MAPS, INC.—See Compagnie Generale des Etablissements Michelin SCA; *Int'l*, pg. 1744
STREETWISE REPORTS; *U.S. Private*, pg. 3839
STREGA COMPANY LIMITED—See Triton Holding Public Company Limited; *Int'l*, pg. 7936
THE ST. REGIS ASPEN RESORT—See Marriott International, Inc.; *U.S. Public*, pg. 1372
THE ST. REGIS HOTEL - HOUSTON—See Marriott International, Inc.; *U.S. Public*, pg. 1372
THE ST. REGIS - NEW YORK—See Marriott International, Inc.; *U.S. Public*, pg. 1372
ST. REGIS PAPER COMPANY LIMITED—See DS Smith Plc; *Int'l*, pg. 2209
ST. REGIS SAADIYAT ISLAND RESORT - ABU DHABI—See Alpha Dhabi Holding PJSC; *Int'l*, pg. 368
ST. REGIS SAN FRANCISCO HOTEL LLC—See Marriott International, Inc.; *U.S. Public*, pg. 1371
STREHL, LLC—See Knight-Swift Transportation Holdings Inc.; *U.S. Public*, pg. 1269
STREIF BAULOGISTIK GMBH—See ACS, Actividades de Construccion y Servicios, S.A.; *Int'l*, pg. 114
STREIF GMBH; *Int'l*, pg. 7240
STREIF GMBH—See Streif GmbH; *Int'l*, pg. 7240
STREIF UK LTD—See Streif GmbH; *Int'l*, pg. 7240
STREIT MECANIQUE SA; *Int'l*, pg. 7240
STREM CHEMICALS, INC.—See Wind Point Advisors LLC; *U.S. Private*, pg. 4534
STREMICKS HERITAGE FOODS LLC; *U.S. Private*, pg. 3839
STRENESSE NEW GMBH; *Int'l*, pg. 7240

STRENGTH CAPITAL PARTNERS, LLC; *U.S. Private*, pg. 3839
STRESCON LIMITED - PRECAST PLANT—See OSCO Construction Group; *Int'l*, pg. 5648
STRESCON LIMITED—See OSCO Construction Group; *Int'l*, pg. 5648
STRESS ANALYSIS AND DESIGN ENGINEERING LTD.; *Int'l*, pg. 7240
STRESSCON CORPORATION; *U.S. Private*, pg. 3839
STRESS CON INDUSTRIES INC.; *U.S. Private*, pg. 3839
STRESS-TEK, INC.—See Vishay Precision Group, Inc.; *U.S. Public*, pg. 2303
STRETCH ASSOCIATES, INC.; *U.S. Private*, pg. 3839
STRETCH ISLAND FRUIT SALES L.L.C.—See Ferrero International S.A.; *Int'l*, pg. 2641
STRETCHTAPE, INC.—See Akoya Capital LLC; *U.S. Private*, pg. 146
STRETCH WRAP PACKAGING INDUSTRIES LLC; *U.S. Private*, pg. 3839
STRETCH ZONE FRANCHISING, LLC; *U.S. Private*, pg. 3839
STR HOLDINGS, INC.; *U.S. Public*, pg. 1953
STRIA, INC.; *U.S. Private*, pg. 3839
STRIA LITHIUM INC.; *Int'l*, pg. 7240
STRIATA, INC.—See GI Manager L.P.; *U.S. Private*, pg. 1692
STRIBBONS INC.; *U.S. Private*, pg. 3839
STRIBLING EQUIPMENT LLC—See GS&L Enterprises Incorporated; *U.S. Private*, pg. 1800
STRICK CORPORATION; *U.S. Private*, pg. 3839
STRICK CORPORATION—See Strick Corporation; *U.S. Private*, pg. 3839
STRICKLAND COMPANIES, INC.; *U.S. Private*, pg. 3839
STRICKLAND FIRE PROTECTION, INC.—See Pye-Barker Fire & Safety, LLC; *U.S. Private*, pg. 3309
STRICKLAND INSURANCE BROKERS INC.—See Strickland Insurance Group Inc.; *U.S. Private*, pg. 3840
STRICKLAND INSURANCE GROUP INC.; *U.S. Private*, pg. 3839
STRICKLAND METALS LIMITED; *Int'l*, pg. 7240
STRICKLAND RANCH AND EXPORTS, INC.; *U.S. Private*, pg. 3840
STRIC-LAN COMPANIES CORP; *U.S. Private*, pg. 3839
STRIDE & ASSOCIATES INC.; *U.S. Private*, pg. 3840
STRIDE CONSULTING LLC; *U.S. Private*, pg. 3840
STRIDE GAMING PLC—See The Rank Group Plc; *Int'l*, pg. 7678
STRIDE, INC.; *U.S. Private*, pg. 3840
STRIDE, INC.; *U.S. Public*, pg. 1954
STRIDE MANAGEMENT CORP.—See Jumbo Interactive Limited; *Int'l*, pg. 4026
STRIDE ONLINE TUTORING, INC.—See Stride, Inc.; *U.S. Public*, pg. 1955
STRIDE RITE CHILDREN'S GROUP, INC.—See Wolverine World Wide, Inc.; *U.S. Public*, pg. 2377
THE STRIDE RITE CORPORATION—See Wolverine World Wide, Inc.; *U.S. Public*, pg. 2377
STRIDERS CORPORATION; *Int'l*, pg. 7240
STRIDES ARCOLAB (FA) LTD.—See Strides Pharma Science Limited; *Int'l*, pg. 7240
STRIDES ARCOLAB POLSKA SP.Z O.O—See Strides Pharma Science Limited; *Int'l*, pg. 7241
STRIDES CHEMICALS PRIVATE LIMITED—See Strides Pharma Science Limited; *Int'l*, pg. 7241
STRIDES PHARMA., INC.—See Strides Pharma Science Limited; *Int'l*, pg. 7241
STRIDES PHARMA SCIENCE LIMITED; *Int'l*, pg. 7240
STRIDES PHARMA UK LIMITED—See Strides Pharma Science Limited; *Int'l*, pg. 7241
STRIDES SINGAPORE PTE LTD.—See Strides Pharma Science Limited; *Int'l*, pg. 7241
STRIDE TOGETHER LIMITED—See The Rank Group Plc; *Int'l*, pg. 7678
STRIDE TOOL INC.—See Partners Group Holding AG; *Int'l*, pg. 5749
STRIDE WELL SERVICE—See Hamm Management Co.; *U.S. Public*, pg. 1849
STRIEBEL & JOHN FRANCE S.A.R.L.—See ABB Ltd.; *Int'l*, pg. 50
STRIEBEL & JOHN GMBH & CO. KG—See ABB Ltd.; *Int'l*, pg. 50
STRIGLOS COMPANIES INC.; *U.S. Private*, pg. 3840
STRIHL SCANDINAVIA AB—See Indutrade AB; *Int'l*, pg. 3681
STRIKE CO., LTD.; *Int'l*, pg. 7241
STRIKEDECK, INC.—See Thoma Bravo, L.P.; *U.S. Private*, pg. 4149
STRIKE ENERGY LIMITED; *Int'l*, pg. 7241
STRIKEFORCE MINING & RESOURCES LTD—See En+ Group Ltd.; *Int'l*, pg. 2395
STRIKE HOLDINGS LLC—See Bowlero Corp; *U.S. Public*, pg. 376
STRIKEIRON, LLC—See Canada Pension Plan Investment Board; *Int'l*, pg. 1280
STRIKEIRON, LLC—See Permira Advisers LLP; *Int'l*, pg. 5806
STRIKE KING LURE CO.—See BDT Capital Partners, LLC; *U.S. Private*, pg. 503
STRIKE LIMITED; *Int'l*, pg. 7241

COMPANY NAME INDEX

STRIKE LLC—See AIP, LLC; *U.S. Private*, pg. 137
STRIKE LUCKY GAMES LTD—See DM plc; *Int'l*, pg. 2142
STRIKE MEDIA (PTY) LTD.—See WPP plc; *Int'l*, pg. 8488
STRIKE MINERALS INC.; *Int'l*, pg. 7241
STRIKEPOINT GOLD INC.; *Int'l*, pg. 7241
STRIKE RESOURCES LIMITED; *Int'l*, pg. 7241
STRIKER OIL & GAS, INC.; *U.S. Private*, pg. 3840
STRIKES UNLIMITED, INC.—See Bowlero Corp; *U.S. Public*, pg. 376
STRIKEWELL ENERGY CORP.; *Int'l*, pg. 7241
STRIKOWESTOFEN GMBH—See BPE Unternehmens beteiligungen GmbH; *Int'l*, pg. 1131
STR INC.—See STR Holdings, Inc.; *U.S. Public*, pg. 1953
STR, INC.—See CoStar Group, Inc.; *U.S. Public*, pg. 586
STRINE PRINTING COMPANY INC.—See Menasha Corporation; *U.S. Private*, pg. 2665
STRINGERS INTERNATIONAL INC.; *U.S. Private*, pg. 3840
STRINGFELLOW LUMBER COMPANY LLC; *U.S. Private*, pg. 3840
STRINGFELLOW TECHNOLOGY GROUP INC.; *U.S. Private*, pg. 3840
STRIONAIR, INC.—See Carrier Global Corporation; *U.S. Public*, pg. 442
THE STRIP DEVELOPMENT, INC.; *U.S. Private*, pg. 4123
STRIPE-A-ZONE, INC.—See The Sterling Group, L.P.; *U.S. Private*, pg. 4123
STRIPE, INC.; *U.S. Private*, pg. 3840
STRIPES LLC—See Sunoco LP; *U.S. Public*, pg. 1965
STRIPESTAR LIMITED—See Pinewood Technologies Group PLC; *Int'l*, pg. 5869
STRIPING TECHNOLOGY L.P.; *U.S. Private*, pg. 3840
STRIP TINNING HOLDINGS PLC; *Int'l*, pg. 7241
STRIP TINNING LIMITED—See Strip Tinning Holdings Plc; *Int'l*, pg. 7241
STRITEX LLC—See Investment AB Latour; *Int'l*, pg. 3784
STRITT & PRIEBE, INC.; *U.S. Private*, pg. 3840
STRIVE CAPITAL LLP; *Int'l*, pg. 7241
THE STRIVE GROUP LLC—See Menasha Corporation; *U.S. Private*, pg. 2665
STRIVE LOGISTICS, LLC—See AEA Investors LP; *U.S. Private*, pg. 115
STRIX DRAMA AB—See Modern Times Group MTG AB; *Int'l*, pg. 5014
STRIX GROUP PLC; *Int'l*, pg. 7241
STRIX GUANGZHOU LTD.—See Strix Group Plc; *Int'l*, pg. 7241
STRIX HONG KONG LTD.—See Strix Group Plc; *Int'l*, pg. 7241
STRIX INTERNATIONAL—See Modern Times Group MTG AB; *Int'l*, pg. 5015
STRIX LIMITED—See Strix Group Plc; *Int'l*, pg. 7241
STRIX TELEVISION AB—See Modern Times Group MTG AB; *Int'l*, pg. 5015
STRIX TELEVISION A/S DANMARK—See Modern Times Group MTG AB; *Int'l*, pg. 5014
STRIX TELEVISION BV—See Modern Times Group MTG AB; *Int'l*, pg. 5015
STRIX TELEVISJON AS—See Modern Times Group MTG AB; *Int'l*, pg. 5014
STRIX (U.K.) LIMITED—See Strix Group Plc; *Int'l*, pg. 7241
STR LABORATUAR HIZMETLERI A.S.—See STR Holdings, Inc.; *U.S. Public*, pg. 1953
STR MECHANICAL, LLC—See SkyKnight Capital LLC; *U.S. Private*, pg. 3685
STROBELGASSE WERBEAGENTUR GMBH; *Int'l*, pg. 7241
STROBES-R-US, INC.—See The Shyft Group, Inc.; *U.S. Public*, pg. 2130
STROBIC AIR CORPORATION—See Dominus Capital, L.P.; *U.S. Private*, pg. 1257
STROC INDUSTRIE; *Int'l*, pg. 7241
STROEHMANN BAKERIES, L.C.—See Grupo Bimbo, S.A.B. de C.V.; *Int'l*, pg. 3122
STROEHMANN BAKERIES—See Grupo Bimbo, S.A.B. de C.V.; *Int'l*, pg. 3122
STROER DIALOG GROUP GMBH—See Stroer SE & Co. KGaA; *Int'l*, pg. 7242
STROER DIGITAL MEDIA GMBH—See Stroer SE & Co. KGaA; *Int'l*, pg. 7242
STROER DIGITAL PUBLISHING GMBH—See Stroer SE & Co. KGaA; *Int'l*, pg. 7242
STROER MEDIA BRANDS APPS D.O.O.—See Stroer SE & Co. KGaA; *Int'l*, pg. 7242
STROER MEDIA BRANDS GMBH—See Stroer SE & Co. KGaA; *Int'l*, pg. 7242
STROER MEDIA SP. Z.O.O.—See Stroer SE & Co. KGaA; *Int'l*, pg. 7242
STROER MOBILE MEDIA GMBH—See Stroer SE & Co. KGaA; *Int'l*, pg. 7242
STROER SE & CO. KGAA; *Int'l*, pg. 7241
STROFI SA—See Carrefour SA; *Int'l*, pg. 1346
STROH CORPORATION—See MMC Corp.; *U.S. Private*, pg. 2754
STROH DIE CASTING CO.; *U.S. Private*, pg. 3840
STROHER GMBH—See Sto SE & Co. KGaA; *Int'l*, pg. 7219
STROHMEYER & ARPE COMPANY; *U.S. Private*, pg. 3840
STROHM HOLDING B.V.—See Sumitomo Corporation; *Int'l*, pg. 7271
STROHWIG INDUSTRIES, INC.; *U.S. Private*, pg. 3840
STROLID, INC.; *U.S. Private*, pg. 3840
STROLL; *U.S. Private*, pg. 3840
STROMAG DESSAU GMBH—See Regal Rexnord Corporation; *U.S. Public*, pg. 1772
STROMAG FRANCE SAS—See Regal Rexnord Corporation; *U.S. Public*, pg. 1772
STROMAG GMBH—See Regal Rexnord Corporation; *U.S. Public*, pg. 1772
STROMA GROUP LTD.—See Lloyds Banking Group plc; *Int'l*, pg. 4538
ST. ROMAIN OIL CO. INC.; *U.S. Private*, pg. 3773
S&T ROMANIA S.R.L.—See Kontron AG; *Int'l*, pg. 4278
STROM AS—See Altia Oyj; *Int'l*, pg. 392
STROMBERG METAL WORKS, INC.; *U.S. Private*, pg. 3840
STROMBERG SHEET METAL WORKS INC.—See Metals Inc.; *U.S. Private*, pg. 2682
STROMBERG'S UNLIMITED, INC.—See Grey Mountain Partners, LLC; *U.S. Private*, pg. 1784
STROMEK EMIRATES FOUNDATIONS LLC—See Dubai Investments PJSC; *Int'l*, pg. 2219
STROM GERMERING GMBH—See E.ON SE; *Int'l*, pg. 2259
STROM GUNDERSEN AS—See AF Gruppen ASA; *Int'l*, pg. 184
STROM GUNDERSEN VESTFOLD AS—See AF Gruppen ASA; *Int'l*, pg. 184
STROM MANUFACTURING INC.—See Compass Precision LLC; *U.S. Private*, pg. 999
STROMNETZ BERLIN GMBH—See Vattenfall AB; *Int'l*, pg. 8137
STROMNETZGESELLSCHAFT HERRENBERG MBH & CO. KG—See EnBW Energie Baden-Wurttemberg AG; *Int'l*, pg. 2400
STROMNETZ HAMBURG GMBH—See HGV Hamburger Gesellschaft fur Vermogens- und Beteiligungsmanagement mbH; *Int'l*, pg. 3378
STROMPILEN AB—See Citycon Oyj; *Int'l*, pg. 1629
STROM PRODUCTS LTD.; *U.S. Private*, pg. 3840
STROMQUIST & COMPANY INC.; *U.S. Private*, pg. 3840
STROMSHOLMEN AB—See Barnes Group Inc.; *U.S. Public*, pg. 277
STROMVERSORGUNG AHRENSBURG GMBH—See E.ON SE; *Int'l*, pg. 2259
STROMVERSORGUNG RUHPOLDING GESELLSCHAFT MIT BESCHRANKTER HAFTUNG—See E.ON SE; *Int'l*, pg. 2259
THE STRONACH GROUP INC.; *Int'l*, pg. 7689
STRONG ADVISORY GROUP, INC.—See Arthur J. Gallagher & Co.; *U.S. Public*, pg. 207
STRONG AUDI; *U.S. Private*, pg. 3840
STRONGBAR (UK) LIMITED—See RotoPrecision Inc.; *Int'l*, pg. 6405
STRONGBRIDGE BIOPHARMA LIMITED—See Xeris Biopharma Holdings, Inc.; *U.S. Public*, pg. 2386
STRONG-BRIDGE CONSULTING LLC.; *U.S. Private*, pg. 3840
STRONGBRIDGE CORPORATION; *U.S. Private*, pg. 3841
STRONGCO CORPORATION—See Nors S.A.; *Int'l*, pg. 5432
STRONG CONSTRUCTION MACHINERY CO., LTD—See Shandong Heavy Industry Group Co., Ltd.; *Int'l*, pg. 6753
STRONG GLOBAL ENTERTAINMENT, INC.—See Kingsway Financial Services Inc.; *U.S. Public*, pg. 1234
STRONGHOLD DIGITAL MINING, INC.; *U.S. Public*, pg. 1955
STRONGHOLD ENGINEERING, INC.; *U.S. Private*, pg. 3841
STRONGHOLD, LTD.—See Quanta Services, Inc.; *U.S. Public*, pg. 1753
STRONGLED LIGHTING SYSTEM (CAYMAN) CO., LTD.; *Int'l*, pg. 7243
STRONGLED LIGHTING SYSTEMS (CAYON) CO., LTD.—See StrongLED Lighting System (Cayman) Co., Ltd.; *Int'l*, pg. 7243
STRONGLED SMART LIGHTING (SUZHOU) CO., LTD.—See StrongLED Lighting System (Cayman) Co., Ltd.; *Int'l*, pg. 7243
STRONGMAIL SYSTEMS, INC.; *U.S. Private*, pg. 3841
STRONGMAIL SYSTEMS UK LTD—See StrongMail Systems, Inc.; *U.S. Private*, pg. 3841
STRONG/MDI SCREEN SYSTEMS, INC.—See Saltire Capital Ltd.; *Int'l*, pg. 6495
STRONG MIXED CONCRETE SDN BHD—See IJM Corporation Berhad; *Int'l*, pg. 3609
STRONG PACK CO., LTD.—See Thanachart Capital PCL; *Int'l*, pg. 7607
STRONG PETROCHEMICAL HOLDINGS LIMITED; *Int'l*, pg. 7243
STRONG PETROCHEMICAL LIMITED—See Strong Petrochemical Holdings Limited; *Int'l*, pg. 7243
STRONGPOINT ASA; *Int'l*, pg. 7243
STRONGPOINT CUB AB—See StrongPoint ASA; *Int'l*, pg. 7243
STRONGPOINT UAB—See StrongPoint ASA; *Int'l*, pg. 7243
STRONG PRECISION TECHNOLOGIES, INC.—See Tricor Pacific Capital, Inc.; *Int'l*, pg. 7920
STRONGROOM SOLUTIONS, LLC—See AvidXchange Holdings, Inc.; *U.S. Public*, pg. 246
STRONG SOLUTIONS, INC.; *U.S. Public*, pg. 1955
THE STRONG; *U.S. Private*, pg. 4123
STRONGSVILLE AUTOMOTIVE COATINGS—See PPG Industries, Inc.; *U.S. Public*, pg. 1710
STRONGSVILLE DIALYSIS, LLC—See DaVita Inc.; *U.S. Public*, pg. 643
STRONG SYSTEMS INTERNATIONAL, INC.—See RAF Industries, Inc.; *U.S. Private*, pg. 3345
STRONG TECHNICAL SERVICES, INC.—See Kingsway Financial Services Inc.; *U.S. Public*, pg. 1234
STRONG TOWER COMMUNICATIONS, LLC—See Squan Construction Services LLC; *U.S. Private*, pg. 3766
STRONG VOLKSWAGON; *U.S. Private*, pg. 3840
STRONG WAY INTERNATIONAL LIMITED—See Golden Century International Holdings Group Limited; *Int'l*, pg. 3028
STRONG WAY INVESTMENT LIMITED—See Dynamic Holdings Limited; *Int'l*, pg. 2240
STRONGWELL CORPORATION; *U.S. Private*, pg. 3841
STRONGWOOD INSURANCE HOLDINGS CORP.; *U.S. Private*, pg. 3841
STRONTIUM PLC; *Int'l*, pg. 7243
STROOCK & STROOCK & LAVAN LLP; *U.S. Private*, pg. 3841
ST. ROSE DOMINICAN HOSPITAL—See Catholic Health Initiatives; *U.S. Private*, pg. 790
STROTHMANN MACHINES & HANDLING GMBH—See G. Siempelkamp GmbH & Co. KG; *Int'l*, pg. 2865
STROTHMANN (SHANGHAI) CO. LTD.—See G. Siempelkamp GmbH & Co. KG; *Int'l*, pg. 2865
STROTHMANN SPIRITUOSEN VERWALTUNG GMBH—See Berentzen-Gruppe AG; *Int'l*, pg. 978
STROTOG GMBH—See E.ON SE; *Int'l*, pg. 2259
STROTTMAN INTERNATIONAL INC.; *U.S. Private*, pg. 3841
STROUD DESIGN, INC.; *U.S. Private*, pg. 3841
STROUD MALL LLC—See CBL & Associates Properties, Inc.; *U.S. Public*, pg. 459
STROUD RESOURCES LTD.; *Int'l*, pg. 7243
STROUD RILEY (PTY) LTD—See Chargeurs SA; *Int'l*, pg. 1449
STROUHAL'S TIRE RECAPPING PLANT INC.; *U.S. Private*, pg. 3841
STROUM JEWISH COMMUNITY CENTER; *U.S. Private*, pg. 3841
STROYINVEST HOLDING AD; *Int'l*, pg. 7243
STROYNOVATSIYA, LLC—See Summa Group; *Int'l*, pg. 7300
STROZ FRIEDBERG, LLC—See Aon plc; *Int'l*, pg. 493
STR TESTING & INSPECTION AG—See STR Holdings, Inc.; *U.S. Public*, pg. 1953
STRUCSURE HOME WARRANTY, LLC—See Milestone Partners Ltd.; *U.S. Private*, pg. 2729
STRUCT CO., LTD.—See ZIGExN Co., Ltd.; *Int'l*, pg. 8682
STRUCT-CON CONSTRUCTION LTD.; *Int'l*, pg. 7243
STRUCTHERM HOLDINGS LIMITED—See Heidelberg Materials AG; *Int'l*, pg. 3319
STRUCTHERM LIMITED—See Heidelberg Materials AG; *Int'l*, pg. 3319
STRUCTIL SASU—See Hexcel Corporation; *U.S. Public*, pg. 1033
STRUCTURA INC; *U.S. Private*, pg. 3841
STRUCTURA, INC.; *U.S. Private*, pg. 3841
STRUCTURAL COMPONENT SYSTEMS INC; *U.S. Private*, pg. 3841
STRUCTURAL COMPOSITES, INC.—See Patrick Industries, Inc.; *U.S. Public*, pg. 1653
STRUCTURAL COMPOSITES INDUSTRIES LLC—See Luxfer Holdings PLC; *Int'l*, pg. 4589
STRUCTURAL COMPOSITES OF INDIANA, INC.—See Patrick Industries, Inc.; *U.S. Public*, pg. 1653
STRUCTURAL CONCEPTS CORPORATION—See Mason Wells, Inc.; *U.S. Private*, pg. 2602
STRUCTURAL ENGINEERING ASSOCIATES, INC.—See Johnson, Mirmiran & Thompson, Inc.; *U.S. Private*, pg. 2229
STRUCTURAL GRAPHICS, LLC; *U.S. Private*, pg. 3841
STRUCTURAL GROUP, INC.; *U.S. Private*, pg. 3841
STRUCTURAL INDUSTRIES, INC.; *U.S. Private*, pg. 3842
STRUCTURAL INTEGRITY ASSOCIATES, INC.—See Munchener Ruckversicherungs AG; *Int'l*, pg. 5090
STRUCTURAL MAINTENANCE SYSTEMS, INC.—See Structural Group, Inc.; *U.S. Private*, pg. 3841
STRUCTURAL MATERIALS CO., INC.—See Beacon Roofing Supply, Inc.; *U.S. Public*, pg. 287
STRUCTURAL MONITORING SYSTEMS LTD.—See Structural Monitoring Systems Plc; *Int'l*, pg. 7243
STRUCTURAL MONITORING SYSTEMS PLC; *Int'l*, pg. 7243
STRUCTURAL PRESERVATION SYSTEMS, INC.—See Structural Group, Inc.; *U.S. Private*, pg. 3841

STRUCTURAL STEEL HOLDING INC.

CORPORATE AFFILIATIONS

STRUCTURAL STEEL HOLDING INC.; *U.S. Private,* pg. 3842
STRUCTURAL STEEL OF CAROLINA, LLC—See Rodgers Metal Craft, Inc.; *U.S. Private,* pg. 3470
STRUCTURAL & STEEL PRODUCTS, INC.—See Race Rock GP, L.L.C; *U.S. Private,* pg. 3341
STRUCTURAL STEEL SERVICES INC—See Structural Steel Holding Inc.; *U.S. Private,* pg. 3842
STRUCTURED ASSET MANAGEMENT INC—See Apella Capital LLC; *U.S. Private,* pg. 291
STRUCTURED COMMUNICATION SYSTEMS, INC.; *U.S. Private,* pg. 3842
STRUCTURED CONNECTIVITY SOLUTIONS (PTY) LTD—See Stellar Capital Partners Limited; *Int'l,* pg. 7204
STRUCTURED EMPLOYMENT ECONOMIC DEVELOPMENT CORPORATION; *U.S. Private,* pg. 3842
STRUCTURED INVEST SOCIETE ANONYME—See Uni-Credit S.p.A.; *Int'l,* pg. 8033
STRUCTURED PRODUCTS CORP.—See Citigroup Inc.; *U.S. Public,* pg. 503
STRUCTUREDWEB, INC.; *U.S. Private,* pg. 3842
STRUCTURE HOUSE, LLC—See Acadia Healthcare Company, Inc.; *U.S. Public,* pg. 30
STRUCTURES ILE-DE-FRANCE SAS—See VINCI S.A.; *Int'l,* pg. 8235
STRUCTURES UNLIMITED, INC.; *U.S. Private,* pg. 3842
STRUCTURE THERAPEUTICS INC.; *U.S. Public,* pg. 1955
STRUCTURE TONE, INC. - BOSTON—See STO Building Group Inc.; *U.S. Private,* pg. 3814
STRUCTURE TONE INC.-HAMILTON—See STO Building Group Inc.; *U.S. Private,* pg. 3814
STRUCTURE TONE INC.-PHILADELPHIA—See STO Building Group Inc.; *U.S. Private,* pg. 3814
STRUCTURE TONE, INC.—See STO Building Group Inc.; *U.S. Private,* pg. 3814
STRUCTURE TONE, INC.—See STO Building Group Inc.; *U.S. Private,* pg. 3814
STRUCTURE TONE, INC.—See STO Building Group Inc.; *U.S. Private,* pg. 3814
STRUCTURE TONE LIMITED—See STO Building Group Inc.; *U.S. Private,* pg. 3814
STRUCTURE TONE, LLC—See STO Building Group Inc.; *U.S. Private,* pg. 3814
STRUCTURE TONE SOUTHWEST—See STO Building Group Inc.; *U.S. Private,* pg. 3814
STRUCTURE TONE UK—See STO Building Group Inc.; *U.S. Private,* pg. 3814
STRUCTURE VENTURES LLC; *U.S. Private,* pg. 3842
STRUCTURE WORKS, INC.—See Wind Point Advisors LLC; *U.S. Private,* pg. 4535
STRUCTURGRUPPEN AB—See NIBE Industrier AB; *Int'l,* pg. 5262
STRUCTURLAM PRODUCTS LTD.; *Int'l,* pg. 7243
STRUERS A/S—See Roper Technologies, Inc.; *U.S. Public,* pg. 1813
STRUERS GMBH—See Roper Technologies, Inc.; *U.S. Public,* pg. 1813
STRUERS INC.—See Roper Technologies, Inc.; *U.S. Public,* pg. 1813
STRUERS LTD.—See Roper Technologies, Inc.; *U.S. Public,* pg. 1813
STRUERS SARL—See Roper Technologies, Inc.; *U.S. Public,* pg. 1813
STRUEVER BROS. ECCLES & ROUSE INC.; *U.S. Private,* pg. 3842
STRUIK FOODS DEUTSCHLAND GMBH—See Struik Holding N.V.; *Int'l,* pg. 7243
STRUIK FOODS EUROPE N.V.—See Struik Holding N.V.; *Int'l,* pg. 7243
STRUIK FOODS GROUP MOSCOW—See Struik Holding N.V.; *Int'l,* pg. 7243
STRUIK HOLDING N.V.; *Int'l,* pg. 7243
STRUKMYER, LLC; *U.S. Private,* pg. 3842
STRUKTOL COMPANY OF AMERICA—See Schill + Seilacher AG; *Int'l,* pg. 6618
STRUKTON BOUW B.V.—See Centric Holding B.V.; *Int'l,* pg. 1412
STRUKTON CIVIEL B.V.—See Centric Holding B.V.; *Int'l,* pg. 1412
STRUKTON GROEP N.V.—See Centric Holding B.V.; *Int'l,* pg. 1412
STRUKTON INTEGRALE PROJECTEN B.V.—See Centric Holding B.V.; *Int'l,* pg. 1412
STRUKTON RAILINFRA N.V.—See Centric Holding B.V.; *Int'l,* pg. 1412
STRUKTON RAIL SHORT LINE BV—See Centric Holding B.V.; *Int'l,* pg. 1412
STRUKTON SYSTEMS B.V.—See Centric Holding B.V.; *Int'l,* pg. 1413
STRUKTON WORKSPHERE B.V.—See Centric Holding B.V.; *Int'l,* pg. 1413
STRUMENTI SCIENTIFICI CINEL S.R.L.—See SAES Getters S.p.A.; *Int'l,* pg. 6467
STRUMICA TABAK AD; *Int'l,* pg. 7243
STRUST CO., LTD.; *Int'l,* pg. 7243
STRUTHERS ELECTRONICS CORPORATION; *U.S. Private,* pg. 3842

STRUWE & PARTNER AGENTUR KOMMUNKATION GMBH; *Int'l,* pg. 7243
STRUXTURE ARCHITECTS, P.L.C.; *U.S. Private,* pg. 3842
STRUXURE OUTDOOR, INC.; *U.S. Private,* pg. 3842
STRUYK VERWO GROEP B.V.—See CRH plc; *Int'l,* pg. 1848
STRYKER AB—See Stryker Corporation; *U.S. Public,* pg. 1956
STRYKER AUSTRALIA PTY. LTD.—See Stryker Corporation; *U.S. Public,* pg. 1956
STRYKER BENELUX—See Stryker Corporation; *U.S. Public,* pg. 1956
STRYKER BIOTECH LLC—See Stryker Corporation; *U.S. Public,* pg. 1956
STRYKER B.V.—See Stryker Corporation; *U.S. Public,* pg. 1956
STRYKER CANADA HOLDING COMPANY—See Stryker Corporation; *U.S. Public,* pg. 1956
STRYKER CANADA INC.—See Stryker Corporation; *U.S. Public,* pg. 1956
STRYKER CHINA LIMITED—See Stryker Corporation; *U.S. Public,* pg. 1956
STRYKER COLOMBIA SAS—See Stryker Corporation; *U.S. Public,* pg. 1956
STRYKER COMMUNICATIONS LIMITED—See Digital Barriers plc; *Int'l,* pg. 2120
STRYKER CORPORATION; *U.S. Public,* pg. 1955
STRYKER EMEA SUPPLY CHAIN SERVICES BV—See Stryker Corporation; *U.S. Public,* pg. 1957
STRYKER ENDOSCOPY—See Stryker Corporation; *U.S. Public,* pg. 1956
STRYKER FRANCE S.A.-LEIBINGER MEDSURG DIVISION—See Stryker Corporation; *U.S. Public,* pg. 1956
STRYKER FRANCE SAS—See Stryker Corporation; *U.S. Public,* pg. 1956
STRYKER GMBH & CO. KG—See Stryker Corporation; *U.S. Public,* pg. 1956
STRYKER GMBH & CO. KG—See Stryker Corporation; *U.S. Public,* pg. 1956
STRYKER GMBH—See Stryker Corporation; *U.S. Public,* pg. 1956
STRYKER GMBH—See Stryker Corporation; *U.S. Public,* pg. 1956
STRYKER GRUNDSTUCKS GMBH & CO KG—See Stryker Corporation; *U.S. Public,* pg. 1956
STRYKER HOLDINGS BV—See Stryker Corporation; *U.S. Public,* pg. 1957
STRYKER IBERIA, S.L.—See Stryker Corporation; *U.S. Public,* pg. 1957
STRYKER INDIA PRIVATE LIMITED—See Stryker Corporation; *U.S. Public,* pg. 1957
STRYKER INSTRUMENTS IRELAND LIMITED—See Stryker Corporation; *U.S. Public,* pg. 1957
STRYKER ITALIA SRL—See Stryker Corporation; *U.S. Public,* pg. 1957
STRYKER JAPAN HOLDING KK—See Stryker Corporation; *U.S. Public,* pg. 1957
STRYKER JAPAN HOLDINGS BV—See Stryker Corporation; *U.S. Public,* pg. 1957
STRYKER JAPAN K.K.—See Stryker Corporation; *U.S. Public,* pg. 1957
STRYKER KOREA LTD.—See Stryker Corporation; *U.S. Public,* pg. 1957
STRYKER LEIBINGER GMBH & CO. KG—See Stryker Corporation; *U.S. Public,* pg. 1957
STRYKER LEIBINGER INC.—See Stryker Corporation; *U.S. Public,* pg. 1957
STRYKER MEXICO, S.A. DE C.V.—See Stryker Corporation; *U.S. Public,* pg. 1957
STRYKER NEDERLAND BV—See Stryker Corporation; *U.S. Public,* pg. 1957
STRYKER NETHERLANDS BV—See Stryker Corporation; *U.S. Public,* pg. 1957
STRYKER NEW ZEALAND LIMITED—See Stryker Corporation; *U.S. Public,* pg. 1957
STRYKER OSTEONICS AG—See Stryker Corporation; *U.S. Public,* pg. 1957
STRYKER OSTEONICS ROMANIA S.R.L.—See Stryker Corporation; *U.S. Public,* pg. 1957
STRYKER-OSTEONICS SA—See Stryker Corporation; *U.S. Public,* pg. 1957
STRYKER PACIFIC LIMITED—See Stryker Corporation; *U.S. Public,* pg. 1957
STRYKER POLSKA SP. ZO.O.—See Stryker Corporation; *U.S. Public,* pg. 1957
STRYKER PORTUGAL PRODUTOS MEDICOS, LDA—See Stryker Corporation; *U.S. Public,* pg. 1957
STRYKER PORTUGAL - PRODUTOS MEDICOS UNIPESSOAL, LDA.—See Stryker Corporation; *U.S. Public,* pg. 1957
STRYKER PUERTO RICO, LTD—See Stryker Corporation; *U.S. Public,* pg. 1957
STRYKER ROMANIA SRL—See Stryker Corporation; *U.S. Public,* pg. 1957
STRYKER S.A.-EUROPEAN HEADQUARTERS—See Stryker Corporation; *U.S. Public,* pg. 1957

STRYKER SALES CORPORATION—See Stryker Corporation; *U.S. Public,* pg. 1957
STRYKER (SHANGHAI) HEALTHCARE PRODUCTS CO., LTD.—See Stryker Corporation; *U.S. Public,* pg. 1956
STRYKER SINGAPORE PRIVATE LIMITED—See Stryker Corporation; *U.S. Public,* pg. 1957
STRYKER SONOMA—See Foley Family Wines Holdings Inc; *U.S. Private,* pg. 1558
STRYKER SOUTH AFRICA (PROPRIETARY) LIMITED—See Stryker Corporation; *U.S. Public,* pg. 1957
STRYKER SPINE SA—See Stryker Corporation; *U.S. Public,* pg. 1957
STRYKER SPINE SAS—See Stryker Corporation; *U.S. Public,* pg. 1957
STRYKER SPINE—See Stryker Corporation; *U.S. Public,* pg. 1957
STRYKER SUSTAINABILITY SOLUTIONS, INC.—See Stryker Corporation; *U.S. Public,* pg. 1957
STRYKER (SUZHOU) MEDICAL TECHNOLOGY CO LTD.—See Stryker Corporation; *U.S. Public,* pg. 1956
STRYKER (THAILAND) LIMITED—See Stryker Corporation; *U.S. Public,* pg. 1956
STRYKER TRAUMA GMBH—See Stryker Corporation; *U.S. Public,* pg. 1957
STRYKER UK LTD.—See Stryker Corporation; *U.S. Public,* pg. 1957
STRYVE ADVISORS—See Tectonic LLC; *U.S. Private,* pg. 3957
STRYVE FOODS, INC.; *U.S. Public,* pg. 1958
STS ACOUSTICS S.P.A.—See Adler Plastic SpA; *Int'l,* pg. 150
STS AVIATION GROUP; *U.S. Private,* pg. 3842
STS COMPONENT SOLUTIONS, LLC—See STS Aviation Group; *U.S. Private,* pg. 3842
STS ELECTRONICS RECYCLING, INC.; *U.S. Private,* pg. 3842
S&T SERBIA D.O.O.—See Kontron AG; *Int'l,* pg. 4278
ST SERVICES CO., LTD.—See Seikitokyu Kogyo Co., Ltd.; *Int'l,* pg. 6686
S T SERVICES LTD.; *Int'l,* pg. 6444
S&T SERVICES POLSKA SP. Z O.O.—See Kontron AG; *Int'l,* pg. 4278
STSE TECHNOLOGIES MARINE LTD—See Temasek Holdings (Private) Limited; *Int'l,* pg. 7552
STS EVERMEDIA CORP.; *U.S. Public,* pg. 1958
STS GEMS JAPAN LIMITED—See Vaibhav Global Limited; *Int'l,* pg. 8108
STS GEMS LIMITED—See Vaibhav Global Limited; *Int'l,* pg. 8108
STS GEMS THAI LIMITED—See Vaibhav Global Limited; *Int'l,* pg. 8108
STS GLOBAL INCOME & GROWTH TRUST PLC; *Int'l,* pg. 7243
STS GROUP AG—See Adler Plastic SpA; *Int'l,* pg. 150
ST SHINE OPTICAL CO., LTD.; *Int'l,* pg. 7158
STS HOLDINGS, INC.; *U.S. Private,* pg. 3842
STSI-INTEGRIRANI TEHNICKI SERVISI D.O.O.—See INA-Industrija Nafte, d.d.; *Int'l,* pg. 3643
STS INTERNATIONAL, INC.; *U.S. Private,* pg. 3842
STS JEWELS INC.—See Vaibhav Global Limited; *Int'l,* pg. 8108
S.T.S., LLC—See Dycom Industries, Inc.; *U.S. Public,* pg. 699
S&T SLOVAKIA S.R.O.—See Kontron AG; *Int'l,* pg. 4278
S&T SLOVENIJA D.D.—See Kontron AG; *Int'l,* pg. 4278
STS MEDICAL GROUP SARL—See Monitor Clipper Partners, LLC; *U.S. Private,* pg. 2771
STS MEDIC INC.—See System Support, Inc.; *Int'l,* pg. 7390
S&T SOFTWARE DEVELOPMENT SP. Z O.O.—See Kontron AG; *Int'l,* pg. 4278
ST SOFTWARE S.R.O.—See The Swatch Group Ltd.; *Int'l,* pg. 7692
S&T SOLUTION CO., LTD.—See SNT Holdings Co., Ltd.; *Int'l,* pg. 7029
STS OPERATING INC.—See Clayton, Dubilier & Rice, LLC; *U.S. Private,* pg. 926
S.T. SPECIALTY FOODS, INC.—See TreeHouse Foods, Inc.; *U.S. Public,* pg. 2187
ST SPORTSERVICE GMBH—See The Swatch Group Ltd.; *Int'l,* pg. 7692
STS PRODUCTS FZE—See Sara SAE Pvt. Ltd.; *Int'l,* pg. 6575
STS PRODUCTS INC.—See Sara SAE Pvt. Ltd.; *Int'l,* pg. 6575
STS PRODUCTS (S) PTE. LTD.—See Sara SAE Pvt. Ltd.; *Int'l,* pg. 6575
STS SERVICES, INC.—See STS Holdings, Inc.; *U.S. Private,* pg. 3842
STS SHENZHEN TESTING SERVICE LIMITED—See Li & Fung Limited; *Int'l,* pg. 4480
S & T STAINLESS LIMITED—See STEEL & TUBE Holdings Limited; *Int'l,* pg. 7189
STS TECHNICAL SERVICES LLC—See STS Aviation Group; *U.S. Private,* pg. 3842
ST. STEPHENS SHOPPING CENTRE LIMITED—See The British Land Company PLC; *Int'l,* pg. 7628

COMPANY NAME INDEX

STS TRACER SERVICES, LTD.—See NCS Multistage Holdings, Inc.; *U.S. Public*, pg. 1503
STS TRAFFIC SOLUTIONS GMBH—See VINCI S.A.; *Int'l*, pg. 8226
STS TRUCK EQUIPMENT; *U.S. Private*, pg. 3842
STS TURBO, INC.; *U.S. Private*, pg. 3843
ST. SUPERY, INC.—See Chanel S.A.; *Int'l*, pg. 1441
STT ENVIRO CORP.—See Carmeuse Holding SA; *Int'l*, pg. 1342
ST. THOMAS DEVELOPMENTS INCORPORATED—See National Electronics Holdings Limited; *Int'l*, pg. 5156
ST THOMAS FORD LINCOLN SALES LIMITED; *Int'l*, pg. 7158
ST TRINITY LIMITED—See LSL Property Services plc; *Int'l*, pg. 4571
ST TROPEZ HOLDINGS LTD—See PZ Cussons Plc; *Int'l*, pg. 6128
ST TROPEZ INC—See PZ Cussons Plc; *Int'l*, pg. 6128
STUART ALEXANDER & CO., PTY. LTD.; *Int'l*, pg. 7244
STUART ANDERSON'S BLACK ANGUS & CATTLE COMPANY RESTAURANTS—See American Restaurant Group, Inc.; *U.S. Private*, pg. 246
STUART & ASSOCIATES, INC.; *U.S. Private*, pg. 3843
STUART-BOWMAN AUTO CENTER; *U.S. Private*, pg. 3843
STUART C. IRBY COMPANY—See Sonepar S.A.; *Int'l*, pg. 7093
STUART CONKLIN BUICK INC—See Conklin Fangman Investment Co.; *U.S. Private*, pg. 1014
STUART-DEAN CO. INC.; *U.S. Private*, pg. 3843
STUART KIA LTD; *Int'l*, pg. 7244
STUART KING CAPITAL CORP.; *U.S. Private*, pg. 3843
STUART KITCHENS INC.; *U.S. Private*, pg. 3843
STUART M. PERRY INC.; *U.S. Private*, pg. 3843
THE STUART NEWS—See Gannett Co., Inc.; *U.S. Public*, pg. 898
STUART NISSAN, LLC—See AutoNation, Inc.; *U.S. Public*, pg. 237
STUART OLSON DOMINION CONSTRUCTION LTD.—See Bird Construction Inc.; *Int'l*, pg. 1047
STUART OLSON INC.—See Bird Construction Inc.; *Int'l*, pg. 1046
STUART POWELL FORD INC.; *U.S. Private*, pg. 3843
STUARTS' PETROLEUM INC.; *U.S. Private*, pg. 3843
STUART SPORTS SPECIALTIES, INC.; *U.S. Private*, pg. 3843
STUART WEITZMAN, LLC—See Tapestry, Inc.; *U.S. Public*, pg. 1981
STUBB'S AUSTIN RESTAURANT COMPANY, LC—See Live Nation Entertainment, Inc.; *U.S. Public*, pg. 1330
STUBBS OIL COMPANY INC.; *U.S. Private*, pg. 3843
STUBHUB, INC.—See viagogo AG; *Int'l*, pg. 8183
STUCKI DE MEXICO S DE RL DE C.V.—See Stone Canyon Industries, LLC; *U.S. Private*, pg. 3817
STUCKI DO BRASIL LTDA—See Stone Canyon Industries, LLC; *U.S. Private*, pg. 3817
STUDEC; *Int'l*, pg. 7244
STUDEN & CO. HOLDING GMBH; *Int'l*, pg. 7244
STUDEN & CO LTD—See Studen & Co. Holding GmbH; *Int'l*, pg. 7244
STUDENT ACHIEVEMENT PARTNERS; *U.S. Private*, pg. 3843
STUDENT ADVANTAGE LLC—See Roper Technologies, Inc.; *U.S. Public*, pg. 1813
STUDENT ALTERNATIVE PROGRAM, INC.; *U.S. Private*, pg. 3843
STUDENTBOSTADER I NORDEN AB; *Int'l*, pg. 7244
STUDENTCITY.COM INC.; *U.S. Private*, pg. 3843
STUDENT FACTORY SAS—See VINCI S.A.; *Int'l*, pg. 8229
STUDENT MARKETING GROUP, INC.—See Nelnet, Inc.; *U.S. Public*, pg. 1504
STUDENTPAINTERS.NET; *U.S. Private*, pg. 3843
STUDENTS BOOK CORPORATION; *U.S. Private*, pg. 3843
STUDENTSCOUT, LLC—See TrueBlue, Inc.; *U.S. Public*, pg. 2199
STUDENT SKIING LIMITED—See TUI AG; *Int'l*, pg. 7968
STUDENT TRANSPORTATION INC.—See Caisse de Depot et Placement du Quebec; *Int'l*, pg. 1255
STUDENT TRANSPORTATION INC.—See Ullico Inc.; *U.S. Private*, pg. 4276
STUDENT TRANSPORTATION OF AMERICA, INC.—See Caisse de Depot et Placement du Quebec; *Int'l*, pg. 1255
STUDENT TRANSPORTATION OF AMERICA, INC.—See Ullico Inc.; *U.S. Private*, pg. 4276
STUDENT TRANSPORTATION OF CANADA, INC.—See Caisse de Depot et Placement du Quebec; *Int'l*, pg. 1255
STUDENT TRANSPORTATION OF CANADA, INC.—See Ullico Inc.; *U.S. Private*, pg. 4276
STUDER DEUTSCHLAND GMBH—See Evertz Microsystems Limited; *Int'l*, pg. 2569
THE STUDER GROUP, LLC—See Huron Consulting Group Inc.; *U.S. Public*, pg. 1076
STUDER HOLDINGS, INC.—See Huron Consulting Group Inc.; *U.S. Public*, pg. 1076

STUDER PROFESSIONAL AUDIO GMBH—See Evertz Microsystems Limited; *Int'l*, pg. 2569
STUDERTEC K.K.—See United Grinding Group AG; *Int'l*, pg. 8067
STUDIO 100 ANIMATION SAS—See Studio 100 NV; *Int'l*, pg. 7244
STUDIO 100 MEDIA GMBH—See Studio 100 NV; *Int'l*, pg. 7244
STUDIO 100 NV; *Int'l*, pg. 7244
STUDIO41—See Logan Square Aluminum Supply, Inc.; *U.S. Private*, pg. 2481
STUDIO 71 GMBH—See ProSiebenSat.1 Media SE; *Int'l*, pg. 6001
STUDIO 89 SAS—See Metropole Television SA; *Int'l*, pg. 4863
STUDIO 921 SALON & DAY SPA; *U.S. Private*, pg. 3843
STUDIO 951—See Shive-Hattery Group Inc.; *U.S. Private*, pg. 3638
STUDIO98, LLC; *U.S. Private*, pg. 3844
STUDIO A INC.—See Cheng Eui Precision Industry Co., Ltd.; *Int'l*, pg. 1465
STUDIO ALFA S.P.A.—See Iren S.p.A.; *Int'l*, pg. 3808
STUDIO ALICE CO., LTD.; *Int'l*, pg. 7244
STUDIO ALTA CO., LTD.—See Isetan Mitsukoshi Holdings Ltd.; *Int'l*, pg. 3815
STUDIO ATAO CO., LTD.; *Int'l*, pg. 7244
STUDIO A TECHNOLOGY LIMITED—See Cheng Eui Precision Industry Co., Ltd.; *Int'l*, pg. 1465
STUDIO AUDIO & VIDEO LTD—See Prism Sound Limited; *Int'l*, pg. 5982
STUDIO BLUE SPIRIT CANADA INC.—See Television Francaise 1 S.A.; *Int'l*, pg. 7543
STUDIO CALICO; *U.S. Private*, pg. 3843
STUDIOCANAL SA—See Vivendi SE; *Int'l*, pg. 8266
STUDIO CITY INC.—See StealthGas Inc.; *Int'l*, pg. 7188
STUDIO CITY INTERNATIONAL HOLDINGS LIMITED; *Int'l*, pg. 7244
STUDIODRAGON CORP.—See CJ Corporation; *Int'l*, pg. 1632
STUDIOFARMA S.R.L.—See CompuGroup Medical SE & Co. KGaA; *Int'l*, pg. 1756
STUDIO FIESCHI & SOCI S.R.L.—See Tinexta S.p.A.; *Int'l*, pg. 7753
STUDIO FOUR DESIGN INC.—See Michael Graves & Associates, Inc.; *U.S. Private*, pg. 2698
STUDIOINSITE LLC—See Confluence; *U.S. Private*, pg. 1013
STUDIO LICO CORP.—See NAVER Corporation; *Int'l*, pg. 5174
STUDIO MARKETING KOMUNIKACIJE D. O. O. ZAGREB—See WPP plc; *Int'l*, pg. 8481
STUDIO MARKETING LJUBLJANA, D. O. O.—See WPP plc; *Int'l*, pg. 8481
STUDIONOW, INC.; *U.S. Private*, pg. 3844
STUDIO ONE NETWORKS INC.—See CHR Group LLC; *U.S. Private*, pg. 889
STUDIO PLUS ARCHITECTURE CORP.; *U.S. Private*, pg. 3843
STUDIO PONTE S.R.L.—See Piovan SpA; *Int'l*, pg. 5873
STUDIO PRESS NIGERIA PLC.; *Int'l*, pg. 7244
STUDIO RETAIL GROUP PLC—See Frasers Group plc; *Int'l*, pg. 2765
STUDIO RK SALON; *U.S. Private*, pg. 3843
STUDIO RTA; *U.S. Private*, pg. 3843
STUDIO SANTA CLAUS ENTERTAINMENT CO., LTD.; *Int'l*, pg. 7244
STUDIO SBV, INC.; *U.S. Private*, pg. 3844
STUDIO SERENISSIMA SRL—See Clariane SE; *Int'l*, pg. 1645
STUDIO SOCIO INC.—See Calbee, Inc.; *Int'l*, pg. 1262
STUDIOUL CINEMATOGRAFIC ANIMAFILM SA; *Int'l*, pg. 7244
STUDIO ZET SP. Z O.O.—See Vivendi SE; *Int'l*, pg. 8275
STUDSVIK AB; *Int'l*, pg. 7244
STUDSVIK ENGINEERING TECHNOLOGY (BEIJING) CO., LTD.—See Studsvik AB; *Int'l*, pg. 7244
STUDSVIK GERMANY GMBH—See Studsvik AB; *Int'l*, pg. 7244
STUDSVIK GMBH & CO. KG—See Studsvik AB; *Int'l*, pg. 7244
STUDSVIK JAPAN LTD—See Studsvik AB; *Int'l*, pg. 7245
STUDSVIK NUCLEAR AB—See Studsvik AB; *Int'l*, pg. 7245
STUDSVIK SAS—See Studsvik AB; *Int'l*, pg. 7245
STUDSVIK SCANDPOWER GMBH—See Studsvik AB; *Int'l*, pg. 7245
STUDSVIK SCANDPOWER, INC—See Studsvik AB; *Int'l*, pg. 7245
STUDSVIK SCANDPOWER SUISSE GMBH—See Studsvik AB; *Int'l*, pg. 7245
STUDSVIK UK LTD—See Studsvik AB; *Int'l*, pg. 7245
THE STUDY ABROAD FOUNDATION; *U.S. Private*, pg. 4123
STUDYFLIX GMBH—See Bertelsmann SE & Co. KGaA; *Int'l*, pg. 996
STUDY GROUP AUSTRALIA PTY. LIMITED—See Providence Equity Partners L.L.C.; *U.S. Private*, pg. 3293
STUDY GROUP PTY. LIMITED—See Providence Equity Partners L.L.C.; *U.S. Private*, pg. 3293

STU SEGALL PRODUCTIONS INC.

STUDY GROUP UK LIMITED—See Ardian SAS; *Int'l*, pg. 556
STUDY GROUP USA, INC.—See Providence Equity Partners L.L.C.; *U.S. Private*, pg. 3293
STUDY OVERSEAS GLOBAL PVT LTD.—See Navitas Limited; *Int'l*, pg. 5177
STUDY OVERSEAS INDIA PVT LTD.—See Navitas Limited; *Int'l*, pg. 5177
STUDYPOINT, INC.; *U.S. Private*, pg. 3844
STUDYRAMA; *Int'l*, pg. 7245
STU EMMERT CHEVROLET-BUICK-CADILLAC, INC.; *U.S. Private*, pg. 3843
STUHINI EXPLORATION LTD.; *Int'l*, pg. 7245
S&T UKRAINE—See Kontron AG; *Int'l*, pg. 4278
STULLER, INC.; *U.S. Private*, pg. 3844
STULL TECHNOLOGIES INC.—See Irving Place Capital Management, L.P.; *U.S. Private*, pg. 2142
STULTZ, INC.; *U.S. Private*, pg. 3844
STULZ-SICKLES STEEL CO., INC.; *U.S. Private*, pg. 3844
STUMBLEUPON, INC.; *U.S. Private*, pg. 3844
STUMP CREEK INC—See Symmco Group Inc.; *U.S. Private*, pg. 3899
STUMP-HYDROBUDOWA SPOLKA Z OGRANICZONA ODPOWIEDZIALNOSCIA—See PORR AG; *Int'l*, pg. 5925
STUMPP+SCHULE GMBH—See Beijer Alma AB; *Int'l*, pg. 943
STUN CREATIVE, LLC—See Known Global LLC; *U.S. Private*, pg. 2324
STUPA HEIZWERK FRANKFURT (ODER) NORD BETEILIGUNGSGESELLSCHAFT MBH—See Deutsche Bank Aktiengesellschaft; *Int'l*, pg. 2062
STUPP BRIDGE COMPANY—See Stupp Bros., Inc.; *U.S. Private*, pg. 3844
STUPP BROS., INC.; *U.S. Private*, pg. 3844
STUPP COATINGS, LLC—See Stupp Bros., Inc.; *U.S. Private*, pg. 3844
STUPP CORPORATION—See Stupp Bros., Inc.; *U.S. Private*, pg. 3844
STUPPY INCORPORATED; *U.S. Private*, pg. 3844
STUP VRSAC A.D.; *Int'l*, pg. 7245
STURDELL INDUSTRIES INC.—See voestalpine AG; *Int'l*, pg. 8291
STURDELL INDUSTRIES, INC.—See voestalpine AG; *Int'l*, pg. 8291
STURDEVANTS INC.; *U.S. Private*, pg. 3844
STURDY CORPORATION; *U.S. Private*, pg. 3844
STURDY INDUSTRIES LTD.; *Int'l*, pg. 7245
STURDY MEMORIAL HOSPITAL; *U.S. Private*, pg. 3844
STURDY OIL COMPANY; *U.S. Private*, pg. 3844
STURDY SAVINGS BANK; *U.S. Private*, pg. 3844
STURGE INDUSTRIES—See Bead Industries Inc.; *U.S. Private*, pg. 505
STURGEON & BECK INC.; *U.S. Private*, pg. 3844
STURGEON ELECTRIC CALIFORNIA, LLC—See MYR Group Inc.; *U.S. Public*, pg. 1489
STURGEON ELECTRIC COMPANY INC. - OREGON—See MYR Group Inc.; *U.S. Public*, pg. 1489
STURGEON ELECTRIC COMPANY—See MYR Group Inc.; *U.S. Public*, pg. 1489
STURGEON & SON INCORPORATED; *U.S. Private*, pg. 3844
THE STURGESS COMPANY; *U.S. Private*, pg. 4123
STURGIS BANCORP, INC.; *U.S. Public*, pg. 1958
STURGIS BANK & TRUST COMPANY—See Sturgis Bancorp, Inc.; *U.S. Public*, pg. 1958
STURGIS FOUNDRY CORP.—See Armstrong International, Inc.; *U.S. Private*, pg. 332
STURGIS MOTORCYCLE INC.; *U.S. Private*, pg. 3844
STURMAN & LARKIN FORD INC.; *U.S. Private*, pg. 3845
THE STURM FINANCIAL GROUP, INC.; *U.S. Private*, pg. 4124
STURM FOODS, INC.—See TreeHouse Foods, Inc.; *U.S. Public*, pg. 2188
STURM, RUGER & CO., INC.-PRESCOTT FIREARMS DIVISION—See Sturm, Ruger & Company, Inc.; *U.S. Public*, pg. 1958
STURM, RUGER & CO., INC.—See Sturm, Ruger & Company, Inc.; *U.S. Public*, pg. 1958
STURM, RUGER & COMPANY, INC.; *U.S. Public*, pg. 1958
STURM, RUGER-NEWPORT PLANT—See Sturm, Ruger & Company, Inc.; *U.S. Public*, pg. 1958
STURTEVANT AUTO PARTS INC.; *U.S. Private*, pg. 3845
STURTEVANT INC.; *U.S. Private*, pg. 3845
ST USA HOLDING CORP.—See Fox Factory Holding Corp.; *U.S. Public*, pg. 877
STU SEGALL PRODUCTIONS INC.; *U.S. Private*, pg. 3843
STUSSER ELECTRIC COMPANY—See Blackfriars Corp.; *U.S. Private*, pg. 574
STUTE LOGISTICS (AG & CO.) KG—See Kuehne + Nagel International AG; *Int'l*, pg. 4325
STUTZMAN REFUSE DISPOSAL, INC.—See Waste Connections, Inc.; *Int'l*, pg. 8354
STUURGROEP FLEET (NETHERLANDS) B.V.—See Hertz Global Holdings, Inc.; *U.S. Public*, pg. 1029

STU SEGALL PRODUCTIONS INC.

STUYVESANT ENVIRONMENTAL CONTRACTING, LLC—See HAL Trust N.V.; *Int'l*, pg. 3227
STV ARCHITECTS, INC.—See STV Group, Inc.; *U.S. Private*, pg. 3845
S&T VARIAS S.R.O.—See Kontron AG; *Int'l*, pg. 4278
STV CENTRAL LIMITED—See STV Group plc; *Int'l*, pg. 7245
STV CONSTRUCTION SERVICES, INC.—See STV Group, Inc.; *U.S. Private*, pg. 3846
STV ENERGY SERVICES—See STV Group, Inc.; *U.S. Private*, pg. 3845
STV ENVIRONMENTAL, INC.—See STV Group, Inc.; *U.S. Private*, pg. 3846
STVE PTE LTD—See Goldbell Corporation; *Int'l*, pg. 3027
STV GROUP, INC.; *U.S. Private*, pg. 3845
STV GROUP PLC; *Int'l*, pg. 7245
STV/GWD INC—See STV Group, Inc.; *U.S. Private*, pg. 3846
STV/GWD—See STV Group, Inc.; *U.S. Private*, pg. 3846
ST. VINCENT DE PAUL OF SEATTLE/KING COUNTY; *U.S. Private*, pg. 3773
ST. VINCENT DE PAUL SOCIETY OF LANE COUNTY, INC.; *U.S. Private*, pg. 3773
ST. VINCENT DE PAUL VILLAGE, INC.; *U.S. Private*, pg. 3773
ST. VINCENT HOSPITAL; *U.S. Private*, pg. 3773
ST. VINCENT MEDICAL CENTER—See The Chan Soon-Shiong Family Foundation; *U.S. Private*, pg. 4007
ST. VINCENT'S HEALTHCARE FOUNDATION—See Ascension Health Alliance; *U.S. Private*, pg. 348
ST. VINCENT'S HEALTHCARE—See Ascension Health Alliance; *U.S. Private*, pg. 347
ST. VINCENT'S MEDICAL CENTER RIVERSIDE—See Ascension Health Alliance; *U.S. Private*, pg. 348
ST. VINCENT'S MEDICAL CENTER SOUTHSIDE—See Ascension Health Alliance; *U.S. Private*, pg. 348
STV INC/RALPH WHITEHEAD ASSOCIATES—See STV Group, Inc.; *U.S. Private*, pg. 3846
STV INC.—See STV Group, Inc.; *U.S. Private*, pg. 3845
STV INC.—See STV Group, Inc.; *U.S. Private*, pg. 3845
STV INC.—See STV Group, Inc.; *U.S. Private*, pg. 3845
STV INC.—See STV Group, Inc.; *U.S. Private*, pg. 3845
STV INC.—See STV Group, Inc.; *U.S. Private*, pg. 3845
STV INC.—See STV Group, Inc.; *U.S. Private*, pg. 3845
STV INC.—See STV Group, Inc.; *U.S. Private*, pg. 3845
STV INC.—See STV Group, Inc.; *U.S. Private*, pg. 3845
STV INC.—See STV Group, Inc.; *U.S. Private*, pg. 3845
STV INC.—See STV Group, Inc.; *U.S. Private*, pg. 3845
STV INC.—See STV Group, Inc.; *U.S. Private*, pg. 3845
STV INC.—See STV Group, Inc.; *U.S. Private*, pg. 3845
STV INC—See STV Group, Inc.; *U.S. Private*, pg. 3845
STV, INC.—See STV Group, Inc.; *U.S. Private*, pg. 3845
STV INC.—See STV Group, Inc.; *U.S. Private*, pg. 3845
STV INC.—See STV Group, Inc.; *U.S. Private*, pg. 3845
STV INC.—See STV Group, Inc.; *U.S. Private*, pg. 3845
STV INC.—See STV Group, Inc.; *U.S. Private*, pg. 3845
STVI SAS—See Compagnie des Alpes S.A.; *Int'l*, pg. 1738
STV NORTH LIMITED—See STV Group plc; *Int'l*, pg. 7245
STV PRODUCTIONS LIMITED—See STV Group plc; *Int'l*, pg. 7245
STV/RALPH WHITEHEAD ASSOCIATES—See STV Group, Inc.; *U.S. Private*, pg. 3846
STV/RALPH WHITEHEAD ASSOCIATES—See STV Group, Inc.; *U.S. Private*, pg. 3846
STV/RALPH WHITEHEAD ASSOCIATES—See STV Group, Inc.; *U.S. Private*, pg. 3846
STV/RALPH WHITEHEAD ASSOCIATES—See STV Group, Inc.; *U.S. Private*, pg. 3846
STV/RALPH WHITEHEAD ASSOCIATES—See STV Group, Inc.; *U.S. Private*, pg. 3846
STV/RALPH WHITEHEAD ASSOCIATES—See STV Group, Inc.; *U.S. Private*, pg. 3846
STV/RALPH WHITEHEAD ASSOCIATES—See STV Group, Inc.; *U.S. Private*, pg. 3846
STV SV TELE & VIDEO KONSULT AB—See Lagercrantz Group AB; *Int'l*, pg. 4395
STV VIDEO DATA AB—See Lagercrantz Group AB; *Int'l*, pg. 4395
STWB INC.—See Bayer Aktiengesellschaft; *Int'l*, pg. 902
STWC HOLDINGS, INC.; *U.S. Public*, pg. 1958
STW FIXED INCOME MANAGEMENT LLC—See Schroders plc; *Int'l*, pg. 6640
S.T. WOOTEN CORPORATION; *U.S. Private*, pg. 3519
STX ARCHITECTURAL DESIGN CO., LTD.—See STX Corporation; *Int'l*, pg. 7245
STX BRAZIL OFFSHORE SA—See STX Corporation; *Int'l*, pg. 7245
STX CORPORATION; *Int'l*, pg. 7245
STX ENGINE CO., LTD.—See STX Corporation; *Int'l*, pg. 7245

STX GLOBAL LOGIX CO., LTD—See STX Corporation; *Int'l*, pg. 7245
STX HEAVY INDUSTRY CO., LTD.—See Dalian Huarui Heavy Industry Group Co., Ltd.; *Int'l*, pg. 1952
STX JAPAN CORPORATION—See STX Corporation; *Int'l*, pg. 7245
STX, LLC—See Wm T. Burnett & Co.; *U.S. Private*, pg. 4552
STX MARINE SERVICE CO., LTD.—See STX Corporation; *Int'l*, pg. 7245
STX METAL CO., LTD.—See STX Corporation; *Int'l*, pg. 7245
STX MIDDLE EAST FZE—See STX Corporation; *Int'l*, pg. 7245
STX OFFSHORE & SHIPBUILDING CO. LTD.—See STX Corporation; *Int'l*, pg. 7245
STX PRECISION (JB) SDN. BHD.—See STG Co., Ltd.; *Int'l*, pg. 7213
STX SERVICES B.V.—See Ekwienox Limited; *Int'l*, pg. 2340
STX SERVICES—See Ekwienox Limited; *Int'l*, pg. 2340
STX SOLAR CO., LTD.—See STX Corporation; *Int'l*, pg. 7245
S. TYGESEN ENERGI A/S—See Addtech AB; *Int'l*, pg. 135
STYKEMAIN BUICK GMC, LTD.; *U.S. Private*, pg. 3846
STYLAM INDUSTRIES LIMITED; *Int'l*, pg. 7245
STYLAND HOLDINGS LIMITED; *Int'l*, pg. 7245
STYLECRAFT LIMITED; *Int'l*, pg. 7246
STYLECRAFT PRINTING, CO.—See Ennis, Inc.; *U.S. Public*, pg. 769
STYLE CREST, INC.; *U.S. Private*, pg. 3846
STYLEFRUITS GMBH—See Stroer SE & Co. KGaA; *Int'l*, pg. 7243
STYLEHAUL, INC.—See Bertelsmann SE & Co. KGaA; *Int'l*, pg. 991
STYLE HAUL INC—See Bertelsmann SE & Co. KGaA; *Int'l*, pg. 995
STYLE INDUSTRIES LIMITED—See Godrej & Boyce Mfg. Co. Ltd.; *Int'l*, pg. 3021
STYLE-LINE FURNITURE INC.; *U.S. Private*, pg. 3846
STYLES LOGISTICS, INC.—See Carl Marks & Co., Inc.; *U.S. Private*, pg. 763
STYLESPOT, INC.; *U.S. Private*, pg. 3846
STYLES & WOOD GROUP PLC; *Int'l*, pg. 7246
STYLES & WOOD LIMITED—See 7FC LLP; *Int'l*, pg. 15
STYLE WEEKLY INC.—See Irish Times; *U.S. Private*, pg. 2139
STYLEWEST; *U.S. Private*, pg. 3846
STYLEX AUTO PRODUCTS LTD.—See Rubicon Partners Limited; *Int'l*, pg. 6422
STYLIGHT GMBH—See ProSiebenSat.1 Media SE; *Int'l*, pg. 6001
STYLINE BROKERAGE SERVICE INC.—See Styline Industries Inc.; *U.S. Private*, pg. 3846
STYLINE DIESEL SERVICE CENTER INC.—See Styline Industries Inc.; *U.S. Private*, pg. 3846
STYLINE INDUSTRIES INC.; *U.S. Private*, pg. 3846
STYLINE TRANSPORTATION INC.—See Styline Industries Inc.; *U.S. Private*, pg. 3846
STYLINGLIFE HOLDINGS INC.—See TBS Holdings, Inc.; *Int'l*, pg. 7481
STYLMARK, INC.; *U.S. Private*, pg. 3846
STYLUTION INT'L CORP.—See Restonic Mattress Corporation; *U.S. Private*, pg. 3409
STYLUTION INT'L CORP.—See Restonic Mattress Corporation; *U.S. Private*, pg. 3409
STYLUTION JAPAN INC.—See Restonic Mattress Corporation; *U.S. Private*, pg. 3409
STYNER+BIENZ FORMTECH LTD.—See Adval Tech Holding AG; *Int'l*, pg. 155
STYROLUTION AMERICA LLC—See INEOS Limited; *Int'l*, pg. 3683
STYROLUTION AMERICA LLC—See INEOS Limited; *Int'l*, pg. 3683
STYROLUTION AMERICA LLC—See INEOS Limited; *Int'l*, pg. 3683
STYROLUTION GMBH—See INEOS Limited; *Int'l*, pg. 3683
STYROLUTION GROUP GMBH—See INEOS Limited; *Int'l*, pg. 3683
STYROLUTION INDIA PVT. LTD.—See INEOS Limited; *Int'l*, pg. 3683
STYROLUTION INTERNATIONAL S.A.—See INEOS Limited; *Int'l*, pg. 3683
STYROLUTION KOLN GMBH—See INEOS Limited; *Int'l*, pg. 3683
STYROLUTION MEXICANA S.A. DE C.V.—See BASF SE; *Int'l*, pg. 885
STYROLUTION (THAILAND) CO., LTD.—See INEOS Limited; *Int'l*, pg. 3683
STYROMATIC A/S; *Int'l*, pg. 7246
STYROMATIC (THAILAND) CO., LTD.—See Styromatic A/S; *Int'l*, pg. 7246
STYRON DEUTSCHLAND ANLAGENGESELLSCHAFT MBH—See Bain Capital, LP; *U.S. Private*, pg. 449
STYRON DEUTSCHLAND GMBH—See Bain Capital, LP; *U.S. Private*, pg. 449

CORPORATE AFFILIATIONS

STYRON DO BRASIL COMERCIO DE PRODUTOS QUIMICOS LTDA.—See Bain Capital, LP; *U.S. Private*, pg. 449
STYRON FRANCE SAS—See Bain Capital, LP; *U.S. Private*, pg. 449
STYRON HOLDINGS ASIA PTE LTD.—See Bain Capital, LP; *U.S. Private*, pg. 449
STYRON (HONG KONG) LIMITED—See Bain Capital, LP; *U.S. Private*, pg. 449
STYRON ITALIA S.R.L.—See Bain Capital, LP; *U.S. Private*, pg. 449
STYRON KOREA LTD.—See Bain Capital, LP; *U.S. Private*, pg. 449
STYRON LLC—See Bain Capital, LP; *U.S. Private*, pg. 449
STYRON SPAIN, S.L.—See Bain Capital, LP; *U.S. Private*, pg. 449
STYRON SVERIGE AB—See Bain Capital, LP; *U.S. Private*, pg. 449
STYROPEK DO BRASIL LTD.—See ALFA, S.A.B. de C.V.; *Int'l*, pg. 314
STYROPEK MEXICO, S. A. DE C. V.—See ALFA, S.A.B. de C.V.; *Int'l*, pg. 314
STYROPEK S. A.—See ALFA, S.A.B. de C.V.; *Int'l*, pg. 314
STYX & LEO BURNETT—See Publicis Groupe S.A.; *Int'l*, pg. 6102
SUAB CO., LTD.—See Denso Corporation; *Int'l*, pg. 2032
SUALAB CO., LTD.—See Cognex Corporation; *U.S. Public*, pg. 523
SUALAB (SUZHOU) CO., LTD.—See Cognex Corporation; *U.S. Public*, pg. 523
SUANPLU BHIMAN LIMITED—See Oriental Holdings Berhad; *Int'l*, pg. 5625
SUAREZ CORPORATION INDUSTRIES; *U.S. Private*, pg. 3846
SUAREZ MANUFACTURING INDUSTRIES—See Suarez Corporation Industries; *U.S. Private*, pg. 3847
SUASHISH DIAMONDS (BOTSWANA) (PTY.) LTD.—See Suashish Diamonds Ltd.; *Int'l*, pg. 7246
SUASHISH DIAMONDS (HK) LIMITED—See Suashish Diamonds Ltd.; *Int'l*, pg. 7246
SUASHISH DIAMONDS LTD.; *Int'l*, pg. 7246
SUASHISH JEWELRY INDIA LTD.—See Suashish Diamonds Ltd.; *Int'l*, pg. 7246
SUASHISH JEWELS CANADA INC.—See Suashish Diamonds Ltd.; *Int'l*, pg. 7246
SUASHISH JEWELS INC.—See Suashish Diamonds Ltd.; *Int'l*, pg. 7246
SUAY ENERGY SERVICES LLP—See Imdex Limited; *Int'l*, pg. 3623
SUB60—See Freightways Group Limited; *Int'l*, pg. 2772
SUBA ENGINEERING PTY. LTD.—See Komax Holding AG; *Int'l*, pg. 4241
SUBARU ACCEPTANCE CORPORATION—See Subaru Corporation; *Int'l*, pg. 7248
SUBARU (AUSTRALIA) PTY LIMITED—See Inchcape plc; *Int'l*, pg. 3647
SUBARU AUTO ACCESSORY CO.,LTD.—See Subaru Corporation; *Int'l*, pg. 7247
SUBARU CANADA, INC.—See Subaru Corporation; *Int'l*, pg. 7247
SUBARU CO., LTD.; *Int'l*, pg. 7246
SUBARU CORPORATION; *Int'l*, pg. 7246
SUBARU DISTRIBUTOR CORP.—See Subaru Corporation; *Int'l*, pg. 7247
SUBARU ENTERPRISE CO., LTD.; *Int'l*, pg. 7248
SUBARU EUROPE N.V./S.A.—See Subaru Corporation; *Int'l*, pg. 7247
SUBARU FINANCE CO., LTD.—See Subaru Corporation; *Int'l*, pg. 7247
SUBARU FINANCIAL SERVICES, INC.—See Subaru Corporation; *Int'l*, pg. 7248
SUBARU ITALIA S.P.A.—See Subaru Corporation; *Int'l*, pg. 7247
SUBARU IT CREATIONS CORPORATION—See Subaru Corporation; *Int'l*, pg. 7247
SUBARU KOHSAN CO., LTD.—See Subaru Corporation; *Int'l*, pg. 7247
SUBARU KOSAN CO., LTD.—See Subaru Corporation; *Int'l*, pg. 7247
SUBARU LEASING CORPORATION—See Subaru Corporation; *Int'l*, pg. 7248
SUBARU LIVING SERVICE CO.,LTD.—See Subaru Corporation; *Int'l*, pg. 7247
SUBARU LOGISTICS CO.,LTD.—See Subaru Corporation; *Int'l*, pg. 7247
SUBARU MONTREAL; *Int'l*, pg. 7248
SUBARU MOTOR LLC—See Sojitz Corporation; *Int'l*, pg. 7065
SUBARU OF AMERICA, INC. - CENTRAL REGION—See Subaru Corporation; *Int'l*, pg. 7248
SUBARU OF AMERICA, INC.—See Subaru Corporation; *Int'l*, pg. 7248
SUBARU OF AMERICA NORTHWEST REGION—See Subaru Corporation; *Int'l*, pg. 7248
SUBARU OF AMERICA SOUTHEAST REGION—See Subaru Corporation; *Int'l*, pg. 7248

COMPANY NAME INDEX

SUBARU OF CHINA, INC.—See Subaru Corporation; *Int'l*, pg. 7248
SUBARU OF INDIANA AUTOMOTIVE, INC.—See Isuzu Motors Limited; *Int'l*, pg. 3826
SUBARU OF INDIANA AUTOMOTIVE, INC.—See Subaru Corporation; *Int'l*, pg. 7248
SUBARU OF NEW ENGLAND, INC.—See Subaru Corporation; *Int'l*, pg. 7248
SUBARU RESEARCH & DEVELOPMENT, INC.—See Subaru Corporation; *Int'l*, pg. 7247
SUBARU RESEARCH & DEVELOPMENT—See Subaru Corporation; *Int'l*, pg. 7247
SUBARU ROBIN POWER PRODUCTS—See Subaru Corporation; *Int'l*, pg. 7248
SUBARU STEEL CO., LTD.—See Hanwa Co., Ltd.; *Int'l*, pg. 3263
SUBARU TECNICA INTERNATIONAL INC.—See Subaru Corporation; *Int'l*, pg. 7248
SUBARU TEST & DEVELOPMENT CENTER IN EUROPE—See Subaru Corporation; *Int'l*, pg. 7248
SUBARU VEHICLE DISTRIBUTION BV—See Subaru Corporation; *Int'l*, pg. 7248
SUBARU WESTERN REGION, INC.—See Subaru Corporation; *Int'l*, pg. 7248
SUBA SEEDS COMPANY SRL; *Int'l*, pg. 7246
SUBAYE, INC.; *Int'l*, pg. 7248
SUBCO FOODS, INC.; *U.S. Private*, pg. 3847
SUBCO FOODS OF WISCONSIN—See Subco Foods, Inc.; *U.S. Private*, pg. 3847
SUBCO INC.; *U.S. Private*, pg. 3847
SUB-CONTRACTORS INC—See Walz Harman Huffman Companies; *U.S. Private*, pg. 4435
SUBENSAMBLES INTERNACIONALES SA DE CV—See Apollo Global Management, Inc.; *U.S. Public*, pg. 162
SUBEX (ASIA PACIFIC) PTE. LIMITED—See Subex Ltd; *Int'l*, pg. 7248
SUBEX INC.—See Subex Ltd; *Int'l*, pg. 7248
SUBEX LTD; *Int'l*, pg. 7248
SUBEX TECHNOLOGIES INC.—See Subex Ltd; *Int'l*, pg. 7248
SUBEX (UK) LIMITED—See Subex Ltd; *Int'l*, pg. 7248
SUBHASH SILK MILLS LTD.; *Int'l*, pg. 7248
SUBIC BAY INTERNATIONAL TERMINAL CORP.—See International Container Terminal Services, Inc.; *Int'l*, pg. 3746
SUBIC BAY INTERNATIONAL TERMINAL HOLDINGS, INC.—See International Container Terminal Services, Inc.; *Int'l*, pg. 3746
SUBIC TELECOMMUNICATIONS COMPANY, INC.—See PLDT Inc.; *Int'l*, pg. 5896
SUBIC WATER & SEWERAGE COMPANY INC.—See DMCI Holdings, Inc.; *Int'l*, pg. 2143
SUBIC WATER & SEWERAGE COMPANY INC.—See Sembcorp Industries Ltd.; *Int'l*, pg. 6704
SUBJEX CORPORATION; *U.S. Private*, pg. 3847
SUBLETTE COOPERATIVE INC.; *U.S. Private*, pg. 3847
SUBLETTE ENTERPRISES INC.; *U.S. Private*, pg. 3847
SUBLIME CHINA INFORMATION CO., LTD.; *Int'l*, pg. 7248
SUBLIME TECHNOLOGY (FRANCE) S.A.R.L.—See Team Internet Group plc; *Int'l*, pg. 7500
SUBMARINO VIAGENS LTDA—See CVC Brasil Operadora e Agencia de Viagens S.A.; *Int'l*, pg. 1881
SUBMITTABLE HOLDINGS, INC.; *U.S. Private*, pg. 3847
SUBOR BORU SANAYI VE TICARET A.S.—See Saudi Arabian Amiantit Company; *Int'l*, pg. 6588
SUBOR BORU SANAYI VE TICARET A.S.—See Yapi Merkezi Holding A.S.; *Int'l*, pg. 8566
SUB PERMPOON 8 CO., LTD.—See Thai Beverage Public Company Limited; *Int'l*, pg. 7592
SUB POP LTD.; *U.S. Private*, pg. 3847
SUBRENTA IMMOBILIENVERWALTUNGSGESELL-SCHAFT MBH—See Tengelmann Warenhandelsgesellschaft KG; *Int'l*, pg. 7560
SUBROS LTD; *Int'l*, pg. 7248
SUBSCRIBACAR PTY. LTD.—See The Market Herald Limited; *Int'l*, pg. 7665
SUBSCRIBERMAIL, LLC—See MacAndrews & Forbes Incorporated; *U.S. Private*, pg. 2532
SUBSEA 7 ASIA PACIFIC SDN. BHD.—See Subsea 7 S.A.; *Int'l*, pg. 7249
SUBSEA 7 AUSTRALIA PTY. LTD.—See Subsea 7 S.A.; *Int'l*, pg. 7249
SUBSEA 7 BLUE SPACE LIMITED—See Subsea 7 S.A.; *Int'l*, pg. 7249
SUBSEA 7 BRASIL S.A.—See Subsea 7 S.A.; *Int'l*, pg. 7249
SUBSEA 7 B.V.—See Subsea 7 S.A.; *Int'l*, pg. 7249
SUBSEA 7 CANADA INC.—See Subsea 7 S.A.; *Int'l*, pg. 7249
SUBSEA 7 CONTRACTING (NORWAY) AS—See Subsea 7 S.A.; *Int'l*, pg. 7249
SUBSEA 7 DO BRASIL SERVICOS LTDA—See Subsea 7 S.A.; *Int'l*, pg. 7249
SUBSEA 7 (GOM) INC.—See Subsea 7 S.A.; *Int'l*, pg. 7249
SUBSEA 7 I-TECH MEXICO S. DE R.L. DE C.V.—See Subsea 7 S.A.; *Int'l*, pg. 7249
SUBSEA 7 I-TECH NORWAY AS—See Subsea 7 S.A.; *Int'l*, pg. 7249
SUBSEA 7 I-TECH US INC.—See Subsea 7 S.A.; *Int'l*, pg. 7249
SUBSEA 7 - I-TECH & VERIPOS DIVISIONS—See Subsea 7 S.A.; *Int'l*, pg. 7249
SUBSEA 7 MOCAMBIQUE LDA—See Subsea 7 S.A.; *Int'l*, pg. 7249
SUBSEA 7 PIPELINE PRODUCTION LIMITED—See Subsea 7 S.A.; *Int'l*, pg. 7249
SUBSEA 7 PORTUGAL, LIMITADA—See Subsea 7 S.A.; *Int'l*, pg. 7249
SUBSEA 7 S.A.; *Int'l*, pg. 7248
SUBSEA 7 SHIPPING AS—See Subsea 7 S.A.; *Int'l*, pg. 7249
SUBSEA 7 (SINGAPORE) PTE. LTD.—See Subsea 7 S.A.; *Int'l*, pg. 7249
SUBSEA 7 (UK)—See Subsea 7 S.A.; *Int'l*, pg. 7249
SUBSEA 7 (US) LLC—See Subsea 7 S.A.; *Int'l*, pg. 7249
SUBSEA 7 (VESSEL COMPANY) LIMITED—See Subsea 7 S.A.; *Int'l*, pg. 7249
SUBSEA GLOBAL SOLUTIONS LLC—See GenNx360 Capital Partners, L.P.; *U.S. Private*, pg. 1672
SUBSEA STABILISATION INDONESIA—See MTQ Corporation Limited; *Int'l*, pg. 5072
SUBSEA TECHNOLOGIES LIMITED—See Helix Energy Solutions Group, Inc.; *U.S. Public*, pg. 1024
SUBSIDIUM HEALTHCARE, LLC; *U.S. Private*, pg. 3847
SUBSIDIUM TECHNOLOGIES INC.—See UPSTACK, Inc.; *U.S. Private*, pg. 4313
SUBSPLIT SERVICES GROUP, L.P.; *U.S. Private*, pg. 3847
SUBSRITHAI PUBLIC COMPANY LIMITED; *Int'l*, pg. 7249
SUBSTANTIAL INC.; *U.S. Private*, pg. 3847
SUBSTRA NEDERLAND B.V.—See ROCKWOOL A/S; *Int'l*, pg. 6381
SUBSTRATE AL SPAIN, S.L.—See Substrate Artificial Inteligence SA; *Int'l*, pg. 7249
SUBSTRATE ARTIFICIAL INTELIGENCE SA; *Int'l*, pg. 7249
SUB SURFACE TOOLS, LLC—See Superior Energy Services, Inc.; *U.S. Private*, pg. 3877
SUBSURFACE UTILITY IMAGING, LLC—See USIC, LLC; *U.S. Private*, pg. 4323
SUBSYSTEM TECHNOLOGIES, INC.; *U.S. Private*, pg. 3847
SUBTYPE PTY. LTD.—See Accent Group Limited; *Int'l*, pg. 81
SUBURBAN ADULT SERVICES INC.; *U.S. Private*, pg. 3847
SUBURBAN AIR FREIGHT INC.—See AE Industrial Partners, LP; *U.S. Private*, pg. 111
SUBURBAN ANN ARBOR, LLC—See Suburban Motors Company, LLC; *U.S. Private*, pg. 3848
SUBURBAN CADILLAC OF LANSING, LLC—See Sonic Automotive, Inc.; *U.S. Public*, pg. 1903
SUBURBAN CARTING CORPORATION; *U.S. Private*, pg. 3848
SUBURBAN CHRYSLER JEEP DODGE, INC.—See Suburban Motors Company, LLC; *U.S. Private*, pg. 3848
SUBURBAN DEVELOPMENTS INC.—See Wimmer Brothers Realty Inc.; *U.S. Private*, pg. 4532
SUBURBAN ELEVATOR COMPANY—See KONE Oyj; *Int'l*, pg. 4249
SUBURBAN ENDOSCOPY CENTER, LLC—See Tenet Healthcare Corporation; *U.S. Public*, pg. 2013
SUBURBAN FORD OF FERNDALE, LLC—See Suburban Motors Company, LLC; *U.S. Private*, pg. 3848
SUBURBAN FRANCHISING, LLC—See Suburban Propane Partners, L.P.; *U.S. Public*, pg. 1958
SUBURBAN HAGGERTY IMPORTED CARS, LLC—See Suburban Motors Company, LLC; *U.S. Private*, pg. 3848
SUBURBAN IMPORTS OF TROY, INC.—See Suburban Motors Company, LLC; *U.S. Private*, pg. 3848
SUBURBAN INSULATION, INC.—See Installed Building Products, Inc.; *U.S. Public*, pg. 1133
SUBURBAN JOURNALS OF GREATER ST. LOUIS LLC—See Lee Enterprises, Incorporated; *U.S. Public*, pg. 1300
SUBURBAN LAWN & GARDEN INC.; *U.S. Private*, pg. 3848
SUBURBAN MANUFACTURING, CO.—See Thor Industries, Inc.; *U.S. Public*, pg. 2156
SUBURBAN MINERALS CORP.; *Int'l*, pg. 7249
SUBURBAN MORTGAGE INC.; *U.S. Private*, pg. 3848
SUBURBAN MOTORS COMPANY, LLC; *U.S. Private*, pg. 3848
SUBURBAN NATURAL GAS COMPANY; *U.S. Private*, pg. 3848
SUBURBAN NEWSPAPERS OF GREATER ST. LOUIS—See Lee Enterprises, Incorporated; *U.S. Public*, pg. 1300
SUBURBAN OF WEST MICHIGAN, LLC—See Suburban Motors Company, LLC; *U.S. Private*, pg. 3848
THE SUBURBAN PAVILION, LLC—See Omega Healthcare Investors, Inc.; *U.S. Public*, pg. 1572
SUBURBAN PAVILION INC.—See Omega Healthcare Investors, Inc.; *U.S. Public*, pg. 1572
SUBURBAN PLASTICS CO; *U.S. Private*, pg. 3848
SUBURBAN PROPANE GROUP, INC.—See Suburban Propane Partners, L.P.; *U.S. Public*, pg. 1959
SUBURBAN PROPANE, L.P.—See Suburban Propane Partners, L.P.; *U.S. Public*, pg. 1959
SUBURBAN PROPANE, L.P.—See Suburban Propane Partners, L.P.; *U.S. Public*, pg. 1959
SUBURBAN PROPANE, L.P.—See Suburban Propane Partners, L.P.; *U.S. Public*, pg. 1959
SUBURBAN PROPANE PARTNERS, L.P.; *U.S. Public*, pg. 1958
SUBURBAN STEEL SUPPLY CO.; *U.S. Private*, pg. 3848
SUBURBAN SURGICAL CO.; *U.S. Private*, pg. 3848
SUBURBAN TIRE COMPANY; *U.S. Private*, pg. 3848
SUBURBAN WATER SYSTEMS—See JPMorgan Chase & Co.; *U.S. Public*, pg. 1207
SUBURBAN WATER SYSTEMS—See Water Asset Management, LLC; *U.S. Private*, pg. 4451
SUBURBIA ADVERTISING - DELTA—See Suburbia Advertising; *Int'l*, pg. 7250
SUBURBIA ADVERTISING; *Int'l*, pg. 7250
SUBUR TIASA HOLDINGS BERHAD; *Int'l*, pg. 7249
SUBUR TIASA PARTICLEBOARD SDN. BHD.—See Subur Tiasa Holdings Berhad; *Int'l*, pg. 7249
SUBWAY FINANCE & INVESTMENT COMPANY LIMITED; *Int'l*, pg. 7250
SUBWAY JAPAN INC.—See Suntory Holdings Limited; *Int'l*, pg. 7326
SUBWAY REAL ESTATE CORP.—See Doctor's Associates Inc.; *U.S. Private*, pg. 1251
SUBWAY RESTAURANTS—See Doctor's Associates Inc.; *U.S. Private*, pg. 1251
SUBY, VON HADEN & ASSOCIATES, S.C.; *U.S. Private*, pg. 3848
SUBZERO CONSTRUCTORS, INC.; *U.S. Private*, pg. 3848
SUB-ZERO FREEZER CO., INC.; *U.S. Private*, pg. 3847
SUB-ZERO GROUP EAST LLC; *U.S. Private*, pg. 3847
SUBZERO GROUP LIMITED; *Int'l*, pg. 7250
SUB ZERO ICE CREAM INC.; *U.S. Private*, pg. 3847
SUB-ZERO WOLF SOUTHEAST, INC.—See Sub-Zero Freezer Co., Inc.; *U.S. Private*, pg. 3847
SUBZI-MANDI—See House of Spices India Inc.; *U.S. Private*, pg. 1991
SUCCEED CORPORATION; *U.S. Private*, pg. 3848
SUCCEED MANAGEMENT SOLUTIONS, LLC—See Providence Equity Partners L.L.C.; *U.S. Private*, pg. 3293
SUCCESS 4 KIDS & FAMILIES, INC.; *U.S. Private*, pg. 3848
SUCCESS ACQUISITION CORPORATION—See Acadia Healthcare Company, Inc.; *U.S. Public*, pg. 30
SUCCESS ADVERTISING; *U.S. Private*, pg. 3848
SUCCESS ADVERTISING—See Success Advertising; *U.S. Private*, pg. 3848
SUCCESS ADVERTISING—See Success Advertising; *U.S. Private*, pg. 3848
SUCCESS ADVERTISING—See Success Advertising; *U.S. Private*, pg. 3848
SUCCESS ADVERTISING—See Success Advertising; *U.S. Private*, pg. 3848
SUCCESS ADVERTISING—See Success Advertising; *U.S. Private*, pg. 3848
SUCCESS BASE ENGINEERING LIMITED—See Superland Group Holdings Limited; *Int'l*, pg. 7338
SUCCESS CENTURY SDN BHD—See Emerging Glory Sdn Bhd; *Int'l*, pg. 2379
SUCCESS COMMUNICATIONS GROUP—See Success Advertising; *U.S. Private*, pg. 3848
SUCCESS DRAGON INTERNATIONAL HOLDINGS LIMITED; *Int'l*, pg. 7250
SUCCESS DRAGON KINGBOX LIMITED—See Success Dragon International Holdings Limited; *Int'l*, pg. 7250
SUCCESS ELECTRONICS & TRANSFORMER MANUFACTURER SDN. BHD.—See Success Transformer Corporation Berhad; *Int'l*, pg. 7250
SUCCESSFACTORS, INC.—See SAP SE; *Int'l*, pg. 6568
SUCCESSFUL FARMING MAGAZINE—See Meredith Corporation; *U.S. Public*, pg. 1423
SUCCESS GLOBAL MEDIA LIMITED; *Int'l*, pg. 7250
SUCCESS HOLDINGS CO., LTD.—See LIKE Co., Ltd.; *Int'l*, pg. 4498
SUCCESSION CAPITAL PARTNERS; *U.S. Private*, pg. 3849
SUCCESSION RESOURCE GROUP, INC.; *U.S. Private*, pg. 3849
SUCCESSMORE BEING PUBLIC COMPANY LIMITED; *Int'l*, pg. 7250
SUCCESSORIES.COM LLC—See TWS Partnership LLC; *U.S. Private*, pg. 4267
SUCCESS PRIME CORPORATION; *Int'l*, pg. 7250
SUCCESS RESOURCES PTE. LTD.—See Success Global Media Limited; *Int'l*, pg. 7250
SUCCESS RESOURCES SDN. BHD.—See Success Global Media Limited; *Int'l*, pg. 7250
SUCCESS RESOURCES UK LTD.—See Success Global Media Limited; *Int'l*, pg. 7250
SUCCESS TRADE, INC.; *U.S. Private*, pg. 3849
SUCCESS TRADE SECURITIES, INC.—See Success Trade, Inc.; *U.S. Private*, pg. 3849

SUCCESS TRANSFORMER CORPORATION BERHAD; *Int'l*, pg. 7250
SUCCESS TRANSFORMER PTE. LTD.—See Success Transformer Corporation Berhad; *Int'l*, pg. 7250
SUCCESS UNIVERSE GROUP LIMITED; *Int'l*, pg. 7250
SUCESORES DE RIVADENEYRA SA; *Int'l*, pg. 7250
SUCHERMAN CONSULTING GROUP, INC.—See RFE Investment Partners; *U.S. Private*, pg. 3420
SUCHUANG GAS CORPORATION LIMITED; *Int'l*, pg. 7250
SUCOCITRICO CUTRALE LTDA.; *Int'l*, pg. 7251
SUCROGEN LTD.—See Wilmar International Limited; *Int'l*, pg. 8421
SUCROS LTD.—See Nordzucker AG; *Int'l*, pg. 5427
SUDAC AIR SERVICES—See L'Air Liquide S.A.; *Int'l*, pg. 4376
SUDACO INC.; *U.S. Private*, pg. 3849
SUDAL INDUSTRIES LTD.; *Int'l*, pg. 7251
SUDAMERICANA, AGENCIAS AEREAS Y MARITIMAS S.A.—See Compania Sudamericana de Vapores, S.A.; *Int'l*, pg. 1749
SUDAMIN FRANCE S.A.S—See AMG Critical Materials N.V.; *Int'l*, pg. 426
SUDAMIN HOLDING SPRL—See AMG Critical Materials N.V.; *Int'l*, pg. 426
SUDAMIN HOLDINGS SA—See AMG Critical Materials N.V.; *Int'l*, pg. 426
SUDAMIN SPRL—See AMG Critical Materials N.V.; *Int'l*, pg. 426
THE SU-DAN CORPORATION; *U.S. Private*, pg. 4124
SUDANESE EGYPTIAN ELECTRIC INDUSTRIES COMPANY LTD—See El Sewedy Electric Company; *Int'l*, pg. 2341
SUDANESE FRENCH BANK; *Int'l*, pg. 7251
SUDANESE ISLAMIC BANK; *Int'l*, pg. 7251
SUDARSHAN CHEMICAL INDUSTRIES LTD.; *Int'l*, pg. 7251
SUDARSHAN EUROPE B.V.—See Sudarshan Chemical Industries Ltd.; *Int'l*, pg. 7251
SUDARSHAN PHARMA INDUSTRIES LIMITED; *Int'l*, pg. 7251
SUDARSHAN POLYFAB PRIVATE LTD.—See Yash Management & Satellite Ltd.; *Int'l*, pg. 8568
SUDARSHAN TELECOM—See West Coast Paper Mills Ltd.; *Int'l*, pg. 8383
SUDATEL TELECOM GROUP LIMITED; *Int'l*, pg. 7251
SUDBAYERISCHES PORTLAND-ZEMENTWERK GEBR. WIESBOCK & CO. GMBH—See Rohrdorfer Gruppe; *Int'l*, pg. 6386
SUD BETEILIGUNGEN GMBH—See Landesbank Baden-Wurttemberg; *Int'l*, pg. 4406
SUD - BETON - SOCIETE DE FABRICATION DE BETON DU SUD—See SODIM, SGPS, SA; *Int'l*, pg. 7049
SUDBURY AUTO AUCTION LTD.—See RB Global, Inc.; *Int'l*, pg. 6226
SUDBURY AVALON, INC.—See AvalonBay Communities, Inc.; *U.S. Public*, pg. 240
SUDBURY LUMBER COMPANY, INC.—See Arlington Coal & Lumber Co. Inc.; *U.S. Private*, pg. 329
THE SUDBURY STAR—See Chatham Asset Management, LLC; *U.S. Private*, pg. 861
THE SUDBURY TOWN CRIER—See Gannett Co., Inc.; *U.S. Public*, pg. 903
SUD-CHEMIE INC.-AIR PURIFICATION—See Clariant AG; *Int'l*, pg. 1647
SUD-CHEMIE INDIA PVT. LTD.—See Clariant AG; *Int'l*, pg. 1648
SUD COMOE CAOUTCHOUC SCC S.A.—See Societe Financiere des Caoutchoucs SA; *Int'l*, pg. 7038
THE SUDDATH COMPANIES; *U.S. Private*, pg. 4124
SUDDATH GLOBAL LOGISTICS, LLC—See The Suddath Companies; *U.S. Private*, pg. 4124
SUDDATH RELOCATION SYSTEMS INC—See The Suddath Companies; *U.S. Private*, pg. 4124
SUDDATH RELOCATION SYSTEMS OF ARIZONA LLC—See The Suddath Companies; *U.S. Private*, pg. 4124
SUDDATH RELOCATION SYSTEMS OF ARIZONA - PHOENIX—See The Suddath Companies; *U.S. Private*, pg. 4124
SUDDATH RELOCATION SYSTEMS OF ATLANTA, INC.—See The Suddath Companies; *U.S. Private*, pg. 4124
SUDDATH RELOCATION SYSTEMS OF CHARLOTTE, LLC—See The Suddath Companies; *U.S. Private*, pg. 4124
SUDDATH RELOCATION SYSTEMS OF FT. LAUDERDALE, INC.—See The Suddath Companies; *U.S. Private*, pg. 4124
SUDDATH RELOCATION SYSTEMS OF HOUSTON, INC.—See The Suddath Companies; *U.S. Private*, pg. 4124
SUDDATH RELOCATION SYSTEMS OF MARYLAND, INC.—See The Suddath Companies; *U.S. Private*, pg. 4124
SUDDATH RELOCATION SYSTEMS OF MILWAUKEE, LLC—See The Suddath Companies; *U.S. Private*, pg. 4124

SUDDATH RELOCATION SYSTEMS OF MINNESOTA, LLC—See The Suddath Companies; *U.S. Private*, pg. 4124
SUDDATH RELOCATION SYSTEMS OF NORTHERN CALIFORNIA, INC.—See The Suddath Companies; *U.S. Private*, pg. 4124
SUDDATH RELOCATION SYSTEMS OF OREGON LLC—See The Suddath Companies; *U.S. Private*, pg. 4124
SUDDATH RELOCATION SYSTEMS OF ORLANDO, INC.—See The Suddath Companies; *U.S. Private*, pg. 4124
SUDDATH RELOCATION SYSTEMS OF ST. PETERSBURG, INC.—See The Suddath Companies; *U.S. Private*, pg. 4124
SUDDATH RELOCATION SYSTEMS OF TEXAS, INC.—See The Suddath Companies; *U.S. Private*, pg. 4124
SUDDATH RELOCATION SYSTEMS OF THE TWIN CITIES, LLC—See The Suddath Companies; *U.S. Private*, pg. 4124
SUDDATH TRANSPORTATION SERVICES, INC.—See The Suddath Companies; *U.S. Private*, pg. 4125
SUDDATH VAN LINES, INC. - KENT—See The Suddath Companies; *U.S. Private*, pg. 4124
SUDDATH VAN LINES INC.—See The Suddath Companies; *U.S. Private*, pg. 4124
SUDDEN IMPACT MARKETING INC.; *U.S. Private*, pg. 3849
SUDDENLY SLENDER INTERNATIONAL, INC.; *U.S. Private*, pg. 3849
SUDDEUTSCHE EMULSIONS-CHEMIE GMBH—See MUNZING Chemie GmbH; *Int'l*, pg. 5095
SUDDEUTSCHER VERLAG GMBH—See Sudwestdeutsche Medienholding GmbH; *Int'l*, pg. 7252
SUDDEUTSCHE VERMOGENSVERWALTUNG GESELLSCHAFT MIT BESCHRANKTER HAFTUNG—See Deutsche Bank Aktiengesellschaft; *Int'l*, pg. 2062
SUDDEUTSCHE WOHNUNGSBAU GMBH—See ACS, Actividades de Construccion y Servicios, S.A.; *Int'l*, pg. 114
SUDDEUTSCHE ZUCKERRUBEN-VERWERTUNGS-GENOSSENSCHAFT EG; *Int'l*, pg. 7252
SUD ENGINEERING S.R.L.—See Rai Way S.p.A.; *Int'l*, pg. 6182
SUDESTE S.A.; *Int'l*, pg. 7252
SUD EST TRAITEUR SAS—See Compass Group PLC; *Int'l*, pg. 1752
SU DEVELOPMENT CO., LLC—See Energy Transfer LP; *U.S. Public*, pg. 763
SUDFACTORING GMBH—See Landesbank Baden-Wurttemberg; *Int'l*, pg. 4406
SUD-FASSADEN GMBH—See BayernLB Holding AG; *Int'l*, pg. 914
SUDHARSANAM INVESTMENTS LIMITED—See Ramco Industries Limited; *Int'l*, pg. 6198
SUDHAUS AN DER KUNSTHALLE WURTH—See Wurth Verwaltungsgesellschaft mbH; *Int'l*, pg. 8506
SUDHAUS GMBH & CO. KG; *Int'l*, pg. 7252
SU DISTRIBUIDORA SUL TU. CORPO, S.L.—See Van de Velde N.V.; *Int'l*, pg. 8125
SUDITI INDUSTRIES LIMITED; *Int'l*, pg. 7252
SUDKURIER GMBH—See Presse-Druck- und Verlags-GmbH; *Int'l*, pg. 5965
SUDLEASING SUISSE AG—See Landesbank Baden-Wurttemberg; *Int'l*, pg. 4406
SUDLER & HENNESSEY EUROPEAN HEADQUARTERS—See WPP plc; *Int'l*, pg. 8492
SUDLER & HENNESSEY FRANKFURT—See WPP plc; *Int'l*, pg. 8492
SUDLER & HENNESSEY LTD. - LONDON—See WPP plc; *Int'l*, pg. 8492
SUDLER & HENNESSEY MILAN—See WPP plc; *Int'l*, pg. 8492
SUDLER & HENNESSEY NEW YORK/WORLDWIDE HEADQUARTERS—See WPP plc; *Int'l*, pg. 8492
SUDLER & HENNESSEY ONTARIO—See WPP plc; *Int'l*, pg. 8492
SUDLER & HENNESSEY PARIS—See WPP plc; *Int'l*, pg. 8492
SUDLER & HENNESSEY—See WPP plc; *Int'l*, pg. 8492
SUDLER & HENNESSEY SYDNEY—See WPP plc; *Int'l*, pg. 8492
SUDMO HOLDING GMBH—See Pentair plc; *Int'l*, pg. 5791
SUDMO NORTH AMERICA, INC.—See Pentair plc; *Int'l*, pg. 5791
SUDMO (UK) LTD.—See Pentair plc; *Int'l*, pg. 5791
SUDPARK HOLDING GMBH—See Unibail-Rodamco-Westfield SE; *Int'l*, pg. 8030
SUDPROGETTI S.P.A.—See Techint S.p.A.; *Int'l*, pg. 7504
SUDRAD GMBH RADTECHNIK—See Crestview Partners, L.P.; *U.S. Private*, pg. 1097
SUDRENTING ESPANA, S.A.—See Landesbank Baden-Wurttemberg; *Int'l*, pg. 4405
SUD-TREBER GMBH—See BayWa AG; *Int'l*, pg. 919
SUDU TRADING HONG KONG LIMITED; *Int'l*, pg. 7252
SUDWASSER GMBH—See E.ON SE; *Int'l*, pg. 2259
SUDWESTDEUTSCHE MEDIENHOLDING GMBH; *Int'l*, pg. 7252

SUDWESTDEUTSCHE ROHRLEITUNGSBAU GMBH—See ACS, Actividades de Construccion y Servicios, S.A.; *Int'l*, pg. 114
SUDWESTFALEN ENERGIE UND WASSER AG; *Int'l*, pg. 7252
SUDWEST LACKE & FARBEN GMBH & CO. KG—See Buzzi SpA; *Int'l*, pg. 1231
SUDWEST MOBIL GMBH—See Deutsche Bahn AG; *Int'l*, pg. 2054
SUDWESTSACHSISCHE NETZ GMBH—See RWE AG; *Int'l*, pg. 6435
SUDZUCKER AG—See Suddeutsche Zuckerruben-Verwertungs-Genossenschaft eG; *Int'l*, pg. 7252
SUDZUCKER AG - ZEITZ PLANT—See Suddeutsche Zuckerruben-Verwertungs-Genossenschaft eG; *Int'l*, pg. 7252
SUEDBAU PROJEKTENTWICKLUNG UND BAUMANAGEMENT GMBH—See Landesbank Baden-Wurttemberg; *Int'l*, pg. 4406
SUED FACTORING GMBH—See Landesbank Baden-Wurttemberg; *Int'l*, pg. 4406
SUED-KAPITALBETEILIGUNGS-GESELLSCHAFT MBH—See Landesbank Baden-Wurttemberg; *Int'l*, pg. 4406
SUEDLEASING BERLINDRESDENLEIPZIG GMBH—See Landesbank Baden-Wurttemberg; *Int'l*, pg. 4406
SUEDLEASING GMBH—See Landesbank Baden-Wurttemberg; *Int'l*, pg. 4406
SUEDWEST-WOHNUNGSPRIVATISIERUNGSGESELLSCHAFT MBH—See Landesbank Baden-Wurttemberg; *Int'l*, pg. 4406
SUEDWESTDEUTSCHE SALZWERKE AG; *Int'l*, pg. 7252
SUEHIRO CONFECTIONERY CO., LTD—See Yamazaki Baking Co., Ltd.; *Int'l*, pg. 8556
SUEHIRO SANGYO CO., LTD.—See Kobayashi Pharmaceutical Co., Ltd.; *Int'l*, pg. 4216
SUEK AG—See SUEK LTD; *Int'l*, pg. 7253
SUEK LTD; *Int'l*, pg. 7253
SUELOPETROL C.A. S.A.C.A.; *Int'l*, pg. 7253
SUELOPETROL CORP.—See Suelopetrol C.A. S.A.C.A.; *Int'l*, pg. 7253
SUEMATSU KYUKI CO., LTD.—See Yaskawa Electric Corporation; *Int'l*, pg. 8569
SUER LLC—See M2I Corporation; *Int'l*, pg. 4617
SUERYAA KNITWEAR LIMITED; *Int'l*, pg. 7253
SUE & SAM CO. INC.; *U.S. Private*, pg. 3849
SUES, YOUNG & BROWN INC.; *U.S. Private*, pg. 3849
SUE VALVE SCIENCE AND TECHNOLOGY INDUSTRIAL CO., LTD.—See SUFA Technology Industry Co., Ltd., CNNC; *Int'l*, pg. 7253
SUEYOSHI KOGYO CO., LTD.—See Fukoku Co., Ltd.; *Int'l*, pg. 2839
SUEZ ASIA HOLDINGS PTE. LTD.; *Int'l*, pg. 7253
SUEZ BAGS COMPANY S.A.E.—See Mondi plc; *Int'l*, pg. 5027
SUEZ CANAL BANK SAE; *Int'l*, pg. 7253
SUEZ CANAL COMPANY FOR TECHNOLOGY SETTLING; *Int'l*, pg. 7253
SUEZ CANAL CONTAINER TERMINAL SAE—See A.P. Moller-Maersk A/S; *Int'l*, pg. 28
SUEZ CEMENT COMPANY (S.A.E.)—See Heidelberg Materials AG; *Int'l*, pg. 3320
SUEZ COMPANY FOR MINERALS—See Gruppo Minerali Maffei S.p.A.; *Int'l*, pg. 3140
SUEZ ENVIRONNEMENT SAS—See Veolia Environnement S.A.; *Int'l*, pg. 8154
SUEZ ENVIRONNEMENT SPAIN, S.L.—See Veolia Environnement S.A.; *Int'l*, pg. 8155
SUEZ GULF POWER S.A.E.—See Tanjong Plc; *Int'l*, pg. 7459
SUEZ INDUSTRIAL DEVELOPMENT COMPANY—See Orascom Construction PLC; *Int'l*, pg. 5613
SUEZ INTERNATIONAL NITRATE COMPANY—See Saudi Chemical Holding Company; *Int'l*, pg. 6593
SUEZ NEDERLAND HOLDING B.V.—See Veolia Environnement S.A.; *Int'l*, pg. 8155
SUEZ NORTH AMERICA INC.—See Veolia Environnement S.A.; *Int'l*, pg. 8155
SUEZ NWS R&R (HONG KONG) LIMITED—See Veolia Environnement S.A.; *Int'l*, pg. 8156
SUEZ POLSKA SP. Z O.O.—See Veolia Environnement S.A.; *Int'l*, pg. 8156
SUEZ RECYCLING AB—See Veolia Environnement S.A.; *Int'l*, pg. 8156
SUEZ RECYCLING AND RECOVERY HOLDINGS UK LTD.—See Veolia Environnement S.A.; *Int'l*, pg. 8156
SUEZ SA—See Veolia Environnement S.A.; *Int'l*, pg. 8154
SUEZ-TRACTEBEL SA—See ENGIE SA; *Int'l*, pg. 2431
SUEZ TREATMENT SOLUTIONS INC.—See Veolia Environnement S.A.; *Int'l*, pg. 8155
SUEZ WATER IDAHO INC.—See Veolia Environnement S.A.; *Int'l*, pg. 8155
SUEZ WATER INC.—See Veolia Environnement S.A.; *Int'l*, pg. 8155
SUEZ WATER NEW JERSEY INC.—See Veolia Environnement S.A.; *Int'l*, pg. 8155
SUEZ WATER NEW YORK INC.—See Veolia Environnement S.A.; *Int'l*, pg. 8156

COMPANY NAME INDEX

SUEZ WATER PENNSYLVANIA INC.—See Veolia Environnement S.A.; *Int'l*, pg. 8156
SUEZ WATER RHODE ISLAND INC.—See Veolia Environnement S.A.; *Int'l*, pg. 8156
SUEZ WATER TECHNOLOGIES & SOLUTIONS—See Veolia Environnement S.A.; *Int'l*, pg. 8156
SUEZ WATER TOMS RIVER INC.—See Veolia Environnement S.A.; *Int'l*, pg. 8156
SUEZ WATER WESTCHESTER INC.—See Veolia Environnement S.A.; *Int'l*, pg. 8156
SUFA TECHNOLOGY INDUSTRY CO., LTD, CNNC; *Int'l*, pg. 7253
SUFFIELD POULTRY INC.; *U.S. Private*, pg. 3849
SUFFOLK CONSTRUCTION COMPANY, INC.; *U.S. Private*, pg. 3849
SUFFOLK JEWELERS INC.; *U.S. Private*, pg. 3849
SUFFOLK LEASING, INC.—See Mercedes-Benz Group AG; *Int'l*, pg. 4829
SUFFOLK REGIONAL OFF-TRACK BETTING; *U.S. Private*, pg. 3849
SUFFOLK-ROEL—See Suffolk Construction Company, Inc.; *U.S. Private*, pg. 3849
SUFRIN HOLDINGS LTD.; *Int'l*, pg. 7253
SUGACH SOCAPI; *Int'l*, pg. 7253
SUGA DIGITAL TECHNOLOGY LIMITED—See Suga International Holdings Limited; *Int'l*, pg. 7253
SUGA ELECTRONICS LIMITED—See Suga International Holdings Limited; *Int'l*, pg. 7253
SUGA ELECTRONICS (SHENZHEN) CO. LTD.—See Suga International Holdings Limited; *Int'l*, pg. 7253
SUGAI CHEMICAL IND. CO., LTD.; *Int'l*, pg. 7253
SUGAI CHEMICAL IND. CO., LTD. - WAKAYAMA NISHI FACTORY—See Sugai Chemical Ind. Co., Ltd.; *Int'l*, pg. 7253
SUGA INTERNATIONAL HOLDINGS LIMITED; *Int'l*, pg. 7253
SUGAKIKAI KOGYO CO., LTD.—See Kanamoto Co., Ltd.; *Int'l*, pg. 4064
SUGAL CHILE LIMITADA—See Sugalidal Industrias de Alimentacao SA; *Int'l*, pg. 7253
SUGAL CHILE LIMITADA TILCOCO FACTORY—See Sugalidal Industrias de Alimentacao SA; *Int'l*, pg. 7254
SUGAL & DAMANI SHARE BROKERS LTD; *Int'l*, pg. 7253
SUGALIDAL INDUSTRIAS DE ALIMENTACAO SA; *Int'l*, pg. 7253
SUGA NETWORKS HONG KONG LIMITED—See Suga International Holdings Limited; *Int'l*, pg. 7253
SUGANUMA SANGYO K.K.—See Koike Sanso Kogyo Co., Ltd.; *Int'l*, pg. 4230
SUGAR & ALLIED INDUSTRIES LIMITED—See Alam Group of Companies; *Int'l*, pg. 289
SUGARBUD CRAFT GROWERS CORP.—See Servus Credit Union; *Int'l*, pg. 6726
SUGARCANE ECOWARE CO., LTD.—See Buriram Sugar Public Company Limited; *Int'l*, pg. 1224
SUGAR CANE GROWERS COOPERATIVE OF FLORIDA; *U.S. Private*, pg. 3849
SUGAR CREEK FINANCIAL CORP.; *U.S. Private*, pg. 3849
SUGAR CREEK FOODS INTERNATIONAL, INC.; *U.S. Private*, pg. 3849
SUGAR CREEK PACKING CO.; *U.S. Private*, pg. 3849
SUGARCRM DEUTSCHLAND GMBH—See Accel Partners L.P.; *U.S. Private*, pg. 49
SUGARCRM DEUTSCHLAND GMBH—See KKR & Co. Inc.; *U.S. Public*, pg. 1238
SUGARCRM, INC.—See Accel Partners L.P.; *U.S. Private*, pg. 48
SUGARCRM, INC.—See KKR & Co. Inc.; *U.S. Public*, pg. 1238
SUGARCRM SWEDEN—See Accel Partners L.P.; *U.S. Private*, pg. 49
SUGARCRM SWEDEN—See KKR & Co. Inc.; *U.S. Public*, pg. 1238
SUGARCRM UK—See Accel Partners L.P.; *U.S. Private*, pg. 49
SUGARCRM UK—See KKR & Co. Inc.; *U.S. Public*, pg. 1238
SUGARDALE FOOD SERVICE—See Fresh Mark, Inc.; *U.S. Private*, pg. 1610
SUGARDALE FOODS INC.—See Fresh Mark, Inc.; *U.S. Private*, pg. 1610
SUGAR FARMS INC.—See Florida Crystals Corporation; *U.S. Private*, pg. 1548
SUGAR FOODS CORPORATION—See The Pritzker Group - Chicago, LLC; *U.S. Private*, pg. 4099
SUGAR HELSINKI OY—See Adelis Equity Partners AB; *Int'l*, pg. 142
SUGAR HILL RECORDS, INC.—See Massachusetts Mutual Life Insurance Company; *U.S. Private*, pg. 2605
SUGARITE DIALYSIS, LLC—See DaVita Inc.; *U.S. Public*, pg. 643
SUGARLAND SHOPPING CENTRE PTY LIMITED—See AMP Limited; *Int'l*, pg. 433
SUGAR LAND SURGERY CENTER, LTD.—See HCA Healthcare, Inc.; *U.S. Public*, pg. 1011
SUGARLOAF DIALYSIS, LLC—See DaVita Inc.; *U.S. Public*, pg. 643

SUGAR LOAF FORD; *U.S. Private*, pg. 3849
SUGARLOAF/USA—See Boyne USA Resorts Inc.; *U.S. Private*, pg. 629
SUGARMADE, INC.; *U.S. Public*, pg. 1959
SUGAR MAPLE SOLAR, LLC—See The AES Corporation; *U.S. Public*, pg. 2032
SUGAR NAGHSHE JAHAN COMPANY; *Int'l*, pg. 7254
SUGAR RIVER SAVINGS BANK; *U.S. Private*, pg. 3849
SUGAR STORES INC.; *U.S. Private*, pg. 3849
SUGAR TERMINALS LIMITED; *Int'l*, pg. 7254
SUGARTOWN WORLDWIDE LLC—See Oxford Industries, Inc.; *U.S. Public*, pg. 1629
SUGARWORLD LIMITED—See Terra Mauricia Limited; *Int'l*, pg. 7567
SUGA STEEL CO., LTD.; *Int'l*, pg. 7254
SUG ENERGY, LLC—See Energy Transfer LP; *U.S. Public*, pg. 763
SUGENTECH INC.; *Int'l*, pg. 7254
SUGG LIGHTING LIMITED—See F.W. Thorpe plc; *Int'l*, pg. 2597
SUGI HOLDINGS CO., LTD.; *Int'l*, pg. 7254
SUGIKO GROUP HOLDINGS CO., LTD.; *Int'l*, pg. 7254
SUGIMOTO & CO., LTD.; *Int'l*, pg. 7254
SUGIMURA SEIKO CO., LTD.; *Int'l*, pg. 7254
SUGIMURA WAREHOUSE CO., LTD.; *Int'l*, pg. 7254
SUGITA ACE CO., LTD.; *Int'l*, pg. 7254
SUGIURA CO., LTD.—See MatsukiyoCocokara & Co.; *Int'l*, pg. 4730
SUGIYAMA INDUSTRIES CO., LTD.—See Toyota Industries Corporation; *Int'l*, pg. 7866
SUGIYAMAKANKOUSETUBI CO., LTD.—See Chudenko Corporation; *Int'l*, pg. 1594
SUGOI PERFORMANCE APPAREL LIMITED PARTNERSHIP—See Dorel Industries, Inc.; *Int'l*, pg. 2176
SU GROUP HOLDINGS LIMITED; *Int'l*, pg. 7246
SUHAIL BAHWAN AUTOMOTIVE GROUP—See Suhail Bahwan Group (Holding) LLC; *Int'l*, pg. 7254
SUHAIL BAHWAN GROUP (HOLDING) LLC; *Int'l*, pg. 7254
SUHAIL JUTE MILLS LIMITED; *Int'l*, pg. 7254
SUHEUNG-AMERICA CORPORATION—See Suheung Co., Ltd.; *Int'l*, pg. 7255
SUHEUNG CO., LTD.; *Int'l*, pg. 7254
SUHEUNG VEITNAM CO., LTD.—See Suheung Co., Ltd.; *Int'l*, pg. 7255
SUHM SPRING WORKS INC.; *U.S. Private*, pg. 3849
SU-HOLDINGS CO.,LTD.; *Int'l*, pg. 7246
SUHOR INDUSTRIES INC.; *U.S. Private*, pg. 3850
SUHRBIER COMPANY; *U.S. Private*, pg. 3850
SUIC WORLDWIDE HOLDINGS LTD.; *U.S. Public*, pg. 1959
SUIDO KIKO KAISHA, LTD.—See Toray Industries, Inc.; *Int'l*, pg. 7823
SUIKER UNIE B.V.—See Royal Cosun U.A.; *Int'l*, pg. 6412
SUI NORTHERN GAS PIPELINES LTD.; *Int'l*, pg. 7255
SUIR ENGINEERING LTD.—See Duke Street Capital Limited; *Int'l*, pg. 2224
SUIRYO PLASTICS CO., LTD.—See Mitsubishi Motors Corporation; *Int'l*, pg. 4967
SUISAN CO. LTD; *U.S. Private*, pg. 3850
SUISAN RYUTSU CO., LTD—See Nissui Corporation; *Int'l*, pg. 5379
SUISHO PETROCHEMICAL INDUSTRY CO., LTD.—See Niitaka Co., Ltd.; *Int'l*, pg. 5289
SUI SOUTHERN GAS COMPANY LIMITED; *Int'l*, pg. 7255
SUISSE DE REASSURANCES (FRANCE)—See Swiss Re Ltd.; *Int'l*, pg. 7371
SUI TAI & ASSOCIATES LIMITED—See Heng Tai Consumables Group Limited; *Int'l*, pg. 3345
SUITE EXPERIENCE GROUP LLC; *U.S. Private*, pg. 3850
SUITEY, INC.—See The Agency; *U.S. Private*, pg. 3983
SUIT-KOTE CORP.; *U.S. Private*, pg. 3850
SUITO TRAVEL CO., LTD.—See Seino Holdings Co., Ltd.; *Int'l*, pg. 6691
SUIWAH CORPORATION BERHAD; *Int'l*, pg. 7255
SUIZA DE RESEGUROS VENEZUELA C.A.—See Swiss Re Ltd.; *Int'l*, pg. 7371
SUIZA RE MEXICO, S.A. DE C.V.—See Swiss Re Ltd.; *Int'l*, pg. 7371
SUIZHOU TAIHUA ELECTRONIC TECHNOLOGY CO., LTD.—See TKD Science And Technology Co., Ltd.; *Int'l*, pg. 7762
SUJALA TRADING & HOLDINGS LTD.; *Int'l*, pg. 7255
SUJANA UNIVERSAL INDUSTRIES LIMITED; *Int'l*, pg. 7255
SUJAN BARRE THOMAS AVS PRIVATE LIMITED—See Cooper-Standard Holdings Inc.; *U.S. Public*, pg. 574
SUKARI GOLD MINES—See Centamin plc; *Int'l*, pg. 1402
SUKARI INVESTMENT COMPANY LIMITED—See Alteo Limited; *Int'l*, pg. 391
SUKARTIK CLOTHING PRIVATE LIMITED—See Garnet International Limited; *Int'l*, pg. 2885
SUKEGAWA ELECTRIC CO., LTD.; *Int'l*, pg. 7255
SUKGYUNG AT CO., LTD.; *Int'l*, pg. 7255
SUKHATASANA CO.—See Saha Pathanapibul Public Company Limited; *Int'l*, pg. 6479
SUKHJIT MEGA FOOD PARK & INFRA LTD.—See Sukhjit Starch & Chemicals Ltd.; *Int'l*, pg. 7255

SUKHJIT STARCH & CHEMICALS LTD.; *Int'l*, pg. 7255
SUKHOI COMPANY (JSC)—See PJSC United Aircraft Corporation; *Int'l*, pg. 5885
SUKI INTERNATIONAL GESMBH—See Serafin Unternehmensgruppe GmbH; *Int'l*, pg. 6720
SUKI.INTERNATIONAL GMBH—See Serafin Unternehmensgruppe GmbH; *Int'l*, pg. 6720
SUKI SUSHI PTE LTD.; *Int'l*, pg. 7255
SUK KUNSTSTOFFRECHNIK GMBH—See Luxshare Precision Industry Co., Ltd.; *Int'l*, pg. 4589
SUKLE ADVERTISING, INC.; *U.S. Private*, pg. 3850
SUKOON INSURANCE PJSC—See Mashreqbank P.S.C; *Int'l*, pg. 4721
SUKOON TAKAFUL PJSC—See Mashreqbank P.S.C; *Int'l*, pg. 4721
SUKSAWAT TERMINAL CO., LTD.—See PT Nusantara Pelabuhan Handal Tbk; *Int'l*, pg. 6061
SUKUP MANUFACTURING CO; *U.S. Private*, pg. 3850
SUKUT CONSTRUCTION INC.; *U.S. Private*, pg. 3850
SUL 116 PARTICIPACOES S.A.; *Int'l*, pg. 7255
SULAAN SOLUTIONS INC.; *U.S. Private*, pg. 3850
SULAIBIYHA FACTORIES GROUP—See National Industries Group Holding S.A.K.; *Int'l*, pg. 5159
SULAKE OY—See Azerion Group N.V.; *Int'l*, pg. 778
SUL AMERICA S.A.—See Rede D'Or Sao Luiz SA; *Int'l*, pg. 6246
SULA SYSTEMS LTD.—See Jacobs Engineering Group, Inc.; *U.S. Public*, pg. 1186
SULA VINEYARDS LIMITED; *Int'l*, pg. 7255
SULI CO., LTD; *Int'l*, pg. 7255
SULI PHARMACEUTICAL TECHNOLOGY JIANGYIN CO., LTD.—See Suli Co., Ltd; *Int'l*, pg. 7255
SULIRAN CORPORATION; *Int'l*, pg. 7255
SULLAIR ARGENTINA S.A.—See Hitachi, Ltd.; *Int'l*, pg. 3417
SULLAIR ASIA PTE. LTD.—See Hitachi, Ltd.; *Int'l*, pg. 3424
SULLAIR AUSTRALIA PTY LTD—See Hitachi, Ltd.; *Int'l*, pg. 3417
SULLAIR OF HOUSTON, INC.—See HOLT Texas, LTD.; *U.S. Private*, pg. 1969
SULLAIR TAIWAN LLC—See Hitachi, Ltd.; *Int'l*, pg. 3417
SULLIDEN MINING CAPITAL INC.; *Int'l*, pg. 7255
SULLIVAN AND MERRITT INC.; *U.S. Private*, pg. 3851
SULLIVAN & ARMSTRONG BUILDING SUPPLIES LIMITED—See Fletcher Building Limited; *Int'l*, pg. 2701
SULLIVAN BANK—See Mid-Missouri Holding Company, Inc.; *U.S. Private*, pg. 2708
SULLIVAN, BRUYETTE, SPEROS & BLAYNEY, LLC—See Creative Planning, LLC; *U.S. Private*, pg. 1090
SULLIVAN BUICK GMC, INC.; *U.S. Private*, pg. 3851
SULLIVAN BUICK GMC—See Sullivan Cadillac; *U.S. Private*, pg. 3851
SULLIVAN CADILLAC; *U.S. Private*, pg. 3851
SULLIVAN & COGLIANO DESIGNERS INC., RHODE ISLAND—See Sullivan & Cogliano Designers Inc.; *U.S. Private*, pg. 3850
SULLIVAN & COGLIANO DESIGNERS INC.; *U.S. Private*, pg. 3850
SULLIVAN & COGLIANO—See Sullivan & Cogliano Designers Inc.; *U.S. Private*, pg. 3850
SULLIVAN & COGLIANO TRAINING CENTER INC.—See Sullivan & Cogliano Designers Inc.; *U.S. Private*, pg. 3850
SULLIVAN & COGLIANO TRAINING CENTERS INC.—See Sullivan & Cogliano Designers Inc.; *U.S. Private*, pg. 3850
SULLIVAN & COMPANY; *U.S. Private*, pg. 3850
SULLIVAN & COZART INC.; *U.S. Private*, pg. 3850
SULLIVAN CREATIVE SERVICES, LTD.; *U.S. Private*, pg. 3851
SULLIVAN CREATIVE—See Sullivan Creative Services, Ltd.; *U.S. Private*, pg. 3851
SULLIVAN & CROMWELL LLP; *U.S. Private*, pg. 3850
SULLIVANCURTISMONROE INSURANCE SERVICES, LLC; *U.S. Private*, pg. 3852
SULLIVAN DATA MANAGEMENT, INC.—See The Riverside Company; *U.S. Private*, pg. 4109
SULLIVAN ENGINEERING, LLC—See Rimkus Consulting Group, Inc.; *U.S. Private*, pg. 3437
SULLIVAN HIGDON & SINK INCORPORATED; *U.S. Private*, pg. 3851
SULLIVAN HIGDON & SINK INCORPORATED—See Sullivan Higdon & Sink Incorporated; *U.S. Private*, pg. 3851
SULLIVAN HIGDON & SINK INCORPORATED—See Sullivan Higdon & Sink Incorporated; *U.S. Private*, pg. 3851
SULLIVAN, INC.; *U.S. Private*, pg. 3852
SULLIVAN INTERNATIONAL GROUP, INC.; *U.S. Private*, pg. 3851
SULLIVAN INVESTMENT CO. INC.—See Sullivan Tire Co. Inc.; *U.S. Private*, pg. 3852
SULLIVAN INVESTMENT CORPORATION; *U.S. Private*, pg. 3851
SULLIVAN & MANN LUMBER CO., INC.; *U.S. Private*, pg. 3851
SULLIVAN & MCLAUGHLIN COMPANIES, INC.; *U.S. Private*, pg. 3851
SULLIVAN MOVING AND STORAGE CO; *U.S. Private*, pg. 3851

SULLIVAN MOVING AND STORAGE CO — CORPORATE AFFILIATIONS

SULLIVAN NICOLAIDES PATHOLOGY—See Sonic Healthcare Limited; *Int'l*, pg. 7098
SULLIVAN NICOLAIDES PTY LIMITED—See Sonic Healthcare Limited; *Int'l*, pg. 7098
SULLIVAN OIL COMPANY; *U.S. Private*, pg. 3851
SULLIVAN PAPER COMPANY; *U.S. Private*, pg. 3851
SULLIVAN PERKINS; *U.S. Private*, pg. 3851
SULLIVAN PETROLEUM COMPANY LLC; *U.S. Private*, pg. 3851
SULLIVAN ROOFING, INC.; *U.S. Private*, pg. 3851
SULLIVAN'S - AUSTIN, L.P.—See Catterton Management Company, LLC; *U.S. Private*, pg. 793
SULLIVAN'S OF ARIZONA, INC.—See Catterton Management Company, LLC; *U.S. Private*, pg. 793
SULLIVAN'S OF DELAWARE, INC.—See Catterton Management Company, LLC; *U.S. Private*, pg. 793
SULLIVAN'S OF ILLINOIS, INC.—See Catterton Management Company, LLC; *U.S. Private*, pg. 793
SULLIVAN'S OF KANSAS, INC.—See Catterton Management Company, LLC; *U.S. Private*, pg. 793
SULLIVAN'S OF NORTH CAROLINA, INC.—See Catterton Management Company, LLC; *U.S. Private*, pg. 793
SULLIVAN'S OF OHIO, INC.—See Catterton Management Company, LLC; *U.S. Private*, pg. 793
SULLIVAN'S OF WASHINGTON, LLC—See Catterton Management Company, LLC; *U.S. Private*, pg. 793
SULLIVAN SOLAR POWER; *U.S. Private*, pg. 3851
SULLIVAN'S RESTAURANTS OF NEBRASKA, INC.—See Catterton Management Company, LLC; *U.S. Private*, pg. 793
SULLIVAN STREET PARTNERS LIMITED; *Int'l*, pg. 7256
SULLIVAN TIRE CO. INC.; *U.S. Private*, pg. 3852
SULLIVAN WELDING—See Quanta Services, Inc.; *U.S. Public*, pg. 1751
SULLIVAN & WORCESTER LLP; *U.S. Private*, pg. 3851
SULNOX FUEL FUSIONS LTD.—See SulNOx Group Plc; *Int'l*, pg. 7256
SULNOX GROUP PLC; *Int'l*, pg. 7256
SULPACO WEST—See Sullivan Paper Company; *U.S. Private*, pg. 3851
SULPHCO, INC.; *U.S. Private*, pg. 3852
SULPHUR CARRIERS, INC.—See AIP, LLC; *U.S. Private*, pg. 136
SULPHURIC ACID TRADING CO.; *U.S. Private*, pg. 3852
SULPHUR SPRINGS VALLEY ELECTRIC COOPERATIVE INC.; *U.S. Private*, pg. 3852
SULTANA DISTRIBUTION SERVICES INC.; *U.S. Private*, pg. 3852
SULTAN CENTER FOOD PRODUCTS CO. KSCC; *Int'l*, pg. 7256
SULTAN RESOURCES LIMITED; *Int'l*, pg. 7256
SULTAN & SONS INC.; *U.S. Private*, pg. 3852
SULTAN SUSHI B.V.—See ProSiebenSat.1 Media SE; *Int'l*, pg. 6001
SULTAN SUSHI CVBA—See ProSiebenSat.1 Media SE; *Int'l*, pg. 6001
SULZER BOMBAS CHILE LTDA.—See Sulzer Ltd.; *Int'l*, pg. 7256
SULZER BRASIL S.A. (CHEMTECH)—See Sulzer Ltd.; *Int'l*, pg. 7258
SULZER BRASIL S.A.—See Sulzer Ltd.; *Int'l*, pg. 7258
SULZER CHEMTECH AG (BUCHS)—See Sulzer Ltd.; *Int'l*, pg. 7256
SULZER CHEMTECH AG—See Sulzer Ltd.; *Int'l*, pg. 7256
SULZER CHEMTECH CANADA INC.—See Sulzer Ltd.; *Int'l*, pg. 7256
SULZER CHEMTECH (FRANCE) SASU—See Sulzer Ltd.; *Int'l*, pg. 7256
SULZER CHEMTECH GMBH (NEUENKIRCHEN)—See Sulzer Ltd.; *Int'l*, pg. 7256
SULZER CHEMTECH GMBH—See Sulzer Ltd.; *Int'l*, pg. 7256
SULZER CHEMTECH ITALIA S.R.L.—See Sulzer Ltd.; *Int'l*, pg. 7256
SULZER CHEMTECH NEDERLAND B.V.—See Sulzer Ltd.; *Int'l*, pg. 7256
SULZER CHEMTECH, S. DE R.L. DE C.V.—See Sulzer Ltd.; *Int'l*, pg. 7257
SULZER CHEMTECH TOWER FIELD SERVICES (INDIA) PVT. LTD.—See Sulzer Ltd.; *Int'l*, pg. 7256
SULZER CHEMTECH (UK) LTD.—See Sulzer Ltd.; *Int'l*, pg. 7256
SULZER CHEMTECH (UK) LTD.—See Sulzer Ltd.; *Int'l*, pg. 7256
SULZER CHEMTECH USA, INC.—See Sulzer Ltd.; *Int'l*, pg. 7256
SULZER CHEMTECH USA, INC.—See Sulzer Ltd.; *Int'l*, pg. 7256
SULZER DAIICHI K.K.—See Daiichi Jitsugyo Co. Ltd.; *Int'l*, pg. 1927
SULZER DAIICHI K.K.—See Sulzer Ltd.; *Int'l*, pg. 7258
SULZER DALIAN PUMPS & COMPRESSORS LTD.—See Sulzer Ltd.; *Int'l*, pg. 7258
SULZER DE VENEZUELA S.A.—See Sulzer Ltd.; *Int'l*, pg. 7257
SULZER ELECTRO MECHANICAL SERVICES (UK) LIMITED—See Sulzer Ltd.; *Int'l*, pg. 7257
SULZER EMS INC.—See Sulzer Ltd.; *Int'l*, pg. 7257

SULZER ENSIVAL MORET FRANCE SASU—See Sulzer Ltd.; *Int'l*, pg. 7257
SULZER INDIA LTD.—See Sulzer Ltd.; *Int'l*, pg. 7257
SULZER INNOTEC AG—See Sulzer Ltd.; *Int'l*, pg. 7257
SULZER ITALY S.R.L.—See Sulzer Ltd.; *Int'l*, pg. 7257
SULZER KOREA LTD.—See Sulzer Ltd.; *Int'l*, pg. 7258
SULZER LTD.; *Int'l*, pg. 7256
SULZER MANAGEMENT AG—See Sulzer Ltd.; *Int'l*, pg. 7257
SULZER MARKETS AND TECHNOLOGY AG—See Sulzer Ltd.; *Int'l*, pg. 7257
SULZER MIXPAC AG—See Sulzer Ltd.; *Int'l*, pg. 7257
SULZER MIXPAC (UK) LTD.—See Sulzer Ltd.; *Int'l*, pg. 7257
SULZER NETHERLANDS HOLDING B.V.—See Sulzer Ltd.; *Int'l*, pg. 7257
SULZER POMPA COZUMLERI LTD. STI.—See Sulzer Ltd.; *Int'l*, pg. 7258
SULZER POMPES FRANCE S.A., MANTES-LA-JOLIE, FRANCE—See Sulzer Ltd.; *Int'l*, pg. 7258
SULZER POMPES PROCESS S.A.—See Sulzer Ltd.; *Int'l*, pg. 7258
SULZER PORTUGAL LDA.—See Sulzer Ltd.; *Int'l*, pg. 7257
SULZER PUMPEN AG—See Sulzer Ltd.; *Int'l*, pg. 7257
SULZER PUMPEN (DEUTSCHLAND) GMBH—See Sulzer Ltd.; *Int'l*, pg. 7258
SULZER PUMPEN (DEUTSCHLAND) GMBH—See Sulzer Ltd.; *Int'l*, pg. 7258
SULZER PUMPEN GMBH—See Sulzer Ltd.; *Int'l*, pg. 7258
SULZER PUMPEN OESTERREICH GMBH—See Sulzer Ltd.; *Int'l*, pg. 7258
SULZER PUMPS (ANZ) PTY LTD.—See Sulzer Ltd.; *Int'l*, pg. 7258
SULZER PUMPS ASIA PACIFIC PTE LTD.—See Sulzer Ltd.; *Int'l*, pg. 7258
SULZER PUMPS BENELUX B.V.—See Sulzer Ltd.; *Int'l*, pg. 7258
SULZER PUMPS CANADA INCORPORATED—See Sulzer Ltd.; *Int'l*, pg. 7258
SULZER PUMPS CANADA—See Sulzer Ltd.; *Int'l*, pg. 7258
SULZER PUMPS (CHINA) LTD.—See Sulzer Ltd.; *Int'l*, pg. 7258
SULZER PUMPS COLOMBIA S.A.S.—See Sulzer Ltd.; *Int'l*, pg. 7259
SULZER PUMPS DENMARK A/S—See Sulzer Ltd.; *Int'l*, pg. 7258
SULZER PUMPS FINLAND OY—See Sulzer Ltd.; *Int'l*, pg. 7259
SULZER PUMPS INC.—See Sulzer Ltd.; *Int'l*, pg. 7259
SULZER PUMPS INDIA LTD.—See Sulzer Ltd.; *Int'l*, pg. 7259
SULZER PUMPS MEXICO, S.A. DE C.V.—See Sulzer Ltd.; *Int'l*, pg. 7259
SULZER PUMPS (NIGERIA) LTD.—See Sulzer Ltd.; *Int'l*, pg. 7259
SULZER PUMPS NORWAY A/S—See Sulzer Ltd.; *Int'l*, pg. 7259
SULZER PUMP SOLUTIONS AB—See Sulzer Ltd.; *Int'l*, pg. 7258
SULZER PUMP SOLUTIONS FINLAND OY—See Sulzer Ltd.; *Int'l*, pg. 7258
SULZER PUMP SOLUTIONS GERMANY GMBH—See Sulzer Ltd.; *Int'l*, pg. 7258
SULZER PUMP SOLUTIONS IRELAND LTD.—See Sulzer Ltd.; *Int'l*, pg. 7258
SULZER PUMP SOLUTIONS NORDMALING AB—See Sulzer Ltd.; *Int'l*, pg. 7258
SULZER PUMP SOLUTIONS SWEDEN AB - ARLOV—See Sulzer Ltd.; *Int'l*, pg. 7258
SULZER PUMP SOLUTIONS SWEDEN AB—See Sulzer Ltd.; *Int'l*, pg. 7258
SULZER PUMP SOLUTIONS (US) INC.—See Sulzer Ltd.; *Int'l*, pg. 7258
SULZER PUMP SOLUTIONS VADSTENA AB—See Sulzer Ltd.; *Int'l*, pg. 7258
SULZER PUMPS RUS LLC—See Sulzer Ltd.; *Int'l*, pg. 7259
SULZER PUMPS SOLUTIONS INC.—See Sulzer Ltd.; *Int'l*, pg. 7259
SULZER PUMPS (SOUTH AFRICA) (PTY) LTD.—See Sulzer Ltd.; *Int'l*, pg. 7258
SULZER PUMPS SPAIN S.A.—See Sulzer Ltd.; *Int'l*, pg. 7259
SULZER PUMPS SUZHOU LTD.—See Sulzer Ltd.; *Int'l*, pg. 7259
SULZER PUMPS SWEDEN AB—See Sulzer Ltd.; *Int'l*, pg. 7259
SULZER PUMPS (UK) LTD.—See Sulzer Ltd.; *Int'l*, pg. 7258
SULZER PUMPS (UK) LTD.—See Sulzer Ltd.; *Int'l*, pg. 7258
SULZER PUMPS (US) INC.—See Sulzer Ltd.; *Int'l*, pg. 7258
SULZER PUMPS US, INC.—See Sulzer Ltd.; *Int'l*, pg. 7259

SULZER PUMPS (VENEZUELA) S.A.—See Sulzer Ltd.; *Int'l*, pg. 7258
SULZER PUMPS WASTEWATER ASIA PACIFIC PTE LTD.—See Sulzer Ltd.; *Int'l*, pg. 7259
SULZER PUMPS WASTEWATER AUSTRIA GMBH—See Sulzer Ltd.; *Int'l*, pg. 7259
SULZER PUMPS WASTEWATER BELGIUM NV/SA—See Sulzer Ltd.; *Int'l*, pg. 7259
SULZER PUMPS WASTEWATER BRASIL LTDA.—See Sulzer Ltd.; *Int'l*, pg. 7259
SULZER PUMPS WASTEWATER FRANCE SAS—See Sulzer Ltd.; *Int'l*, pg. 7259
SULZER PUMPS WASTEWATER GERMANY GMBH—See Sulzer Ltd.; *Int'l*, pg. 7259
SULZER PUMPS WASTEWATER HUNGARY KFT.—See Sulzer Ltd.; *Int'l*, pg. 7259
SULZER PUMPS WASTEWATER MALAYSIA SDN. BHD.—See Sulzer Ltd.; *Int'l*, pg. 7259
SULZER PUMPS WASTEWATER NETHERLANDS B.V.—See Sulzer Ltd.; *Int'l*, pg. 7259
SULZER PUMPS WASTEWATER NORWAY AS—See Sulzer Ltd.; *Int'l*, pg. 7259
SULZER PUMPS WASTEWATER POLAND SP. Z O.O.—See Sulzer Ltd.; *Int'l*, pg. 7259
SULZER PUMPS WASTEWATER SPAIN S.A.—See Sulzer Ltd.; *Int'l*, pg. 7259
SULZER PUMPS WASTEWATER UK LIMITED—See Sulzer Ltd.; *Int'l*, pg. 7259
SULZER SHANGHAI ENGINEERING & MACHINERY WORKS LIMITED—See Sulzer Ltd.; *Int'l*, pg. 7257
SULZER SINGAPORE PTE. LTD.—See Sulzer Ltd.; *Int'l*, pg. 7259
SULZER SISTEMAS E INSTALACIONES (CHILE) S.A.—See Sulzer Ltd.; *Int'l*, pg. 7257
SULZER (SOUTH AFRICA) HOLDINGS (PTY) LTD.—See Sulzer Ltd.; *Int'l*, pg. 7256
SULZER (SOUTH AFRICA) LTD.—See Sulzer Ltd.; *Int'l*, pg. 7258
SULZER TURBO SERVICES ARGENTINA S.A.—See Sulzer Ltd.; *Int'l*, pg. 7257
SULZER TURBO SERVICES CANADA LTD.—See Sulzer Ltd.; *Int'l*, pg. 7257
SULZER TURBO SERVICES HOUSTON INC.—See Sulzer Ltd.; *Int'l*, pg. 7257
SULZER TURBO SERVICES NEW ORLEANS INC.—See Sulzer Ltd.; *Int'l*, pg. 7257
SULZER TURBO SERVICES ROTTERDAM B.V.—See Sulzer Ltd.; *Int'l*, pg. 7257
SULZER TURBO SERVICES RUS LLC—See Sulzer Ltd.; *Int'l*, pg. 7259
SULZER TURBO SERVICES VENLO B.V.—See Sulzer Ltd.; *Int'l*, pg. 7257
SULZER (UK) HOLDINGS LTD.—See Sulzer Ltd.; *Int'l*, pg. 7256
SULZER ZAMBIA LTD.—See Sulzer Ltd.; *Int'l*, pg. 7259
SUMACHEM LLC—See Sealed Air Corporation; *U.S. Public*, pg. 1855
SUMADIJA A.D.; *Int'l*, pg. 7259
SUMADIJA TRANSPORT A.D.; *Int'l*, pg. 7259
SUMA (ESPOSENDE) - SERVICOS URBANOS E MEIO AMBIENTE, LDA.—See Mota-Engil SGPS, S.A.; *Int'l*, pg. 5052
SUMAINOTOSHOKAN, LTD—See Sekisui House, Ltd.; *Int'l*, pg. 6698
SUMA (PORTO) - SERVICOS URBANOS E MEIO AMBIENTE, S.A.—See Mota-Engil SGPS, S.A.; *Int'l*, pg. 5052
SUMAPROJEKT D.D. SARAJEVO; *Int'l*, pg. 7259
SUMARIA GROUP; *Int'l*, pg. 7259
SU-MARKETI A.D; *Int'l*, pg. 7246
SUMAR REALTORS; *U.S. Private*, pg. 3852
SUMARSTVO PRENJ D.D. KONJIC; *Int'l*, pg. 7260
SUMA - SERVICOS URBANOS E MEIO AMBIENTE, S.A.—See Mota-Engil SGPS, S.A.; *Int'l*, pg. 5052
SUMAS SUNI TAHTA VE MOBILYA SANAYI A.S.; *Int'l*, pg. 7260
SUMATERIALS CO., LTD.—See UBE Corporation; *Int'l*, pg. 8001
SUMATRA BIOSCIENCE PTE., LTD.—See PT PP London Sumatra Indonesia Tbk; *Int'l*, pg. 6066
SUMATRA COPPER & GOLD PLC; *Int'l*, pg. 7260
SUMATRA PULP CORPORATION—See Marubeni Corporation; *Int'l*, pg. 4710
SUMAVISION TECHNOLOGIES CO., LTD.; *Int'l*, pg. 7260
SUMBER DORONGAN SDN. BHD.—See Sunway Berhad; *Int'l*, pg. 7328
SUMCO CORPORATION - CHITOSE PLANT—See SUMCO Corporation; *Int'l*, pg. 7260
SUMCO CORPORATION - IMARI FACTORY—See SUMCO Corporation; *Int'l*, pg. 7260
SUMCO CORPORATION - KANSAI FACTORY (AMAGASAKI)—See SUMCO Corporation; *Int'l*, pg. 7260
SUMCO CORPORATION - SAGA FACTORY—See SUMCO Corporation; *Int'l*, pg. 7260
SUMCO CORPORATION; *Int'l*, pg. 7260
SUMCO CORPORATION - YONEZAWA PLANT—See SUMCO Corporation; *Int'l*, pg. 7260

COMPANY NAME INDEX — SUMIDA CORPORATION

SUMCO EUROPE SALES PLC—See SUMCO Corporation; *Int'l*, pg. 7260
SUMCO INSURANCE SERVICE CORP.—See SUMCO Corporation; *Int'l*, pg. 7260
SUMCO KOREA CORPORATION—See SUMCO Corporation; *Int'l*, pg. 7260
SUMCO, LLC; *U.S. Private*, pg. 3852
SUMCO PHOENIX CORPORATION—See SUMCO Corporation; *Int'l*, pg. 7260
SUMCO SERVICE CORPORATION—See SUMCO Corporation; *Int'l*, pg. 7260
SUMCO SHANGHAI CORPORATION—See SUMCO Corporation; *Int'l*, pg. 7260
SUMCO SINGAPORE PTE. LTD.—See SUMCO Corporation; *Int'l*, pg. 7260
SUMCO SOLAR CORPORATION—See SUMCO Corporation; *Int'l*, pg. 7260
SUMCO SOUTHWEST CORPORATION—See SUMCO Corporation; *Int'l*, pg. 7260
SUMCO SUPPORT CORP.—See SUMCO Corporation; *Int'l*, pg. 7260
SUMCO TAIWAN TECHNOLOGY CORPORATION—See SUMCO Corporation; *Int'l*, pg. 7260
SUMCO TECHNOLOGY CORPORATION—See SUMCO Corporation; *Int'l*, pg. 7260
SUMCO TECHXIV CORPORATION—See SUMCO Corporation; *Int'l*, pg. 7260
SUMCO TECHXIV EUROPE NV—See SUMCO Corporation; *Int'l*, pg. 7260
SUMEC CORPORATION LIMITED—See China National Machinery Industry Corporation; *Int'l*, pg. 1531
SUMEDHA FISCAL SERVICES LTD.; *Int'l*, pg. 7260
SUMEEKO INDUSTRIES CO., LTD.; *Int'l*, pg. 7261
SUMEET INDUSTRIES LTD; *Int'l*, pg. 7261
SUM EFFECT SOFTWARE, INC.; *U.S. Private*, pg. 3852
SUMER COMMERICAL BANK; *Int'l*, pg. 7261
SUMER FAKTORING A.S.; *Int'l*, pg. 7261
SUMERU EQUITY PARTNERS LLC; *U.S. Private*, pg. 3852
SUMER VARLIK YONETIMI A.S.; *Int'l*, pg. 7261
SUME TK D.D. KLADANJ; *Int'l*, pg. 7260
SUM HITECHS CO., LTD.—See Thai Stanley Electric Public Company Limited; *Int'l*, pg. 7595
SUMI AGRO EUROPE LIMITED—See Sumitomo Corporation; *Int'l*, pg. 7271
SUMIBE KOREA CO., LTD.—See Sumitomo Bakelite Co., Ltd.; *Int'l*, pg. 7263
SUMI (CAMBODIA) WIRING SYSTEMS CO., LTD.—See Sumitomo Electric Industries, Ltd.; *Int'l*, pg. 7281
SUMICO LUBRICANT CO., LTD.—See Sumitomo Metal Mining Co., Ltd.; *Int'l*, pg. 7291
SUMI-CYCLO DRIVE INDIA PRIVATE LIMITED—See Sumitomo Heavy Industries, Ltd.; *Int'l*, pg. 7288
SUMIDA AG—See Sumida Corporation; *Int'l*, pg. 7262
SUMIDA AMERICA COMPONENTS INC.—See Sumida Corporation; *Int'l*, pg. 7261
SUMIDA AUSTRIA GMBH—See Sumida Corporation; *Int'l*, pg. 7262
SUMIDA COMPONENTS & MODULES GMBH—See Sumida Corporation; *Int'l*, pg. 7262
SUMIDA CORPORATE SERVICE COMPANY LIMITED—See Sumida Corporation; *Int'l*, pg. 7261
SUMIDA CORPORATE SERVICE INCORPORATED—See Sumida Corporation; *Int'l*, pg. 7261
SUMIDA CORPORATION - ELECTRIC FACTORY—See Sumida Corporation; *Int'l*, pg. 7261
SUMIDA CORPORATION; *Int'l*, pg. 7261
SUMIDA ELECTRIC (CHANGDE) CO., LTD.—See Sumida Corporation; *Int'l*, pg. 7261
SUMIDA ELECTRIC CO., LTD. - AOMORI FACTORY—See Sumida Corporation; *Int'l*, pg. 7261
SUMIDA ELECTRIC CO., LTD. (OSAKA)—See Sumida Corporation; *Int'l*, pg. 7261
SUMIDA ELECTRIC CO., LTD.—See Sumida Corporation; *Int'l*, pg. 7261
SUMIDA ELECTRIC (GUANGXI) CO., LTD.—See Sumida Corporation; *Int'l*, pg. 7261
SUMIDA ELECTRIC (H.K.) COMPANY LIMITED—See Sumida Corporation; *Int'l*, pg. 7261
SUMIDA ELECTRIC (INDIA) PRIVATE LIMITED—See Sumida Corporation; *Int'l*, pg. 7261
SUMIDA ELECTRIC (JI'AN) CO., LTD.—See Sumida Corporation; *Int'l*, pg. 7261
SUMIDA ELECTRIC (THAILAND) CO., LTD.—See Sumida Corporation; *Int'l*, pg. 7261
SUMIDA ELECTRONIC COMPONENTS CO., LTD.—See Sumida Corporation; *Int'l*, pg. 7261
SUMIDA ELECTRONIC QUANG NGAI CO., LTD.—See Sumida Corporation; *Int'l*, pg. 7261
SUMIDA ELECTRONIC SHANGHAI CO., LTD.—See Sumida Corporation; *Int'l*, pg. 7262
SUMIDA ELECTRONIC SUQIAN CO., LTD.—See Sumida Corporation; *Int'l*, pg. 7261
SUMIDA ELECTRONIC VIETNAM CO., LTD.—See Sumida Corporation; *Int'l*, pg. 7261
SUMIDA EMS GMBH—See Sumida Corporation; *Int'l*, pg. 7261
SUMIDA EUROPE GMBH—See Sumida Corporation; *Int'l*, pg. 7261
SUMIDA POWER ELECTRONICS CO., LTD.—See Sumida Corporation; *Int'l*, pg. 7262
SUMIDA POWER TECHNOLOGY CO., LTD.—See Sumida Corporation; *Int'l*, pg. 7262
SUMIDA ROMANIA S.R.L.—See Sumida Corporation; *Int'l*, pg. 7262
SUMIDA SERVICE COMPANY LIMITED—See Sumida Corporation; *Int'l*, pg. 7261
SUMIDA SERVICE COMPANY LIMITED—See Sumida Corporation; *Int'l*, pg. 7261
SUMIDA SLOVENIJA D.O.O—See Sumida Corporation; *Int'l*, pg. 7262
SUMIDA TRADING COMPANY LIMITED—See Sumida Corporation; *Int'l*, pg. 7261
SUMIDA TRADING (KOREA) COMPANY LIMITED—See Sumida Corporation; *Int'l*, pg. 7261
SUMIDA TRADING PTE LTD.—See Sumida Corporation; *Int'l*, pg. 7261
SUMIDA TRADING (SHANGHAI) COMPANY LIMITED - GUANGZHOU PANYU SUMIDA KOU SHUI HENG ELECTRIC FACTORY—See Sumida Corporation; *Int'l*, pg. 7262
SUMIDA TRADING (SHANGHAI) COMPANY LIMITED (SHENZHEN)—See Sumida Corporation; *Int'l*, pg. 7262
SUMIDA TRADING (SHANGHAI) COMPANY LIMITED—See Sumida Corporation; *Int'l*, pg. 7261
SUMIDEN ASIA (SHENZHEN) CO., LTD.—See Sumitomo Electric Industries, Ltd.; *Int'l*, pg. 7281
SUMIDEN CARBIDE MANUFACTURING (TIANJIN) CO., LTD.—See Sumitomo Electric Industries, Ltd.; *Int'l*, pg. 7281
SUMIDEN COMMUNICATION ENGINEERING CO., LTD.—See Sumitomo Electric Industries, Ltd.; *Int'l*, pg. 7281
SUMIDEN DENGYO CO., LTD.—See Sumitomo Electric Industries, Ltd.; *Int'l*, pg. 7281
SUMIDEN DEVICE INNOVATIONS VIETNAM CO., LTD.—See Sumitomo Electric Industries, Ltd.; *Int'l*, pg. 7281
SUMIDEN ELECTRONIC MATERIALS (M) SDN. BHD.—See Sumitomo Electric Industries, Ltd.; *Int'l*, pg. 7281
SUMIDEN FINE CONDUCTORS CO., LTD. - HIMEJIMA PLANT—See Sumitomo Electric Industries, Ltd.; *Int'l*, pg. 7201
SUMIDEN FINE CONDUCTORS CO., LTD. - MAEBASHI PLANT—See Sumitomo Electric Industries, Ltd.; *Int'l*, pg. 7281
SUMIDEN FINE CONDUCTORS CO., LTD.—See Sumitomo Electric Industries, Ltd.; *Int'l*, pg. 7281
SUMIDEN FRIEND, LTD.—See Sumitomo Electric Industries, Ltd.; *Int'l*, pg. 7281
SUMIDEN HITACHI CABLE LTD.—See Sumitomo Electric Industries, Ltd.; *Int'l*, pg. 7281
SUMIDEN HYOSUNG STEEL CORD (THAILAND) CO., LTD.—See Hyosung Corporation; *Int'l*, pg. 3552
SUMIDEN INTERNATIONAL TRADING (SHANGHAI) CO., LTD.—See Sumitomo Electric Industries, Ltd.; *Int'l*, pg. 7281
SUMIDEN INTERNATIONAL TRADING (VIETNAM) CO., LTD.—See Sumitomo Electric Industries, Ltd.; *Int'l*, pg. 7281
SUMIDEN LIGHT ALLOY (CHANGZHOU) CO., LTD.—See Sumitomo Electric Industries, Ltd.; *Int'l*, pg. 7281
SUMIDEN OPCOM, LTD.—See Sumitomo Electric Industries, Ltd.; *Int'l*, pg. 7281
SUMIDEN POWDER METALLURGY (WUXI) CO., LTD.—See Sumitomo Electric Industries, Ltd.; *Int'l*, pg. 7281
SUMIDEN SEMICONDUCTOR MATERIALS CO., LTD.—See Sumitomo Electric Industries, Ltd.; *Int'l*, pg. 7281
SUMIDEN SHOJI CO., LTD.—See Sumitomo Electric Industries, Ltd.; *Int'l*, pg. 7281
SUMIDEN SHOJI (THAILAND) CO., LTD.—See Sumitomo Electric Industries, Ltd.; *Int'l*, pg. 7281
SUMIDEN SIZAI KAKOU CO., LTD.—See Sumitomo Electric Industries, Ltd.; *Int'l*, pg. 7281
SUMIDENSO AUTOMOTIVE TECHNOLOGIES ASIA CORPORATION—See Sumitomo Electric Industries, Ltd.; *Int'l*, pg. 7284
SUMIDENSO DO BRASIL INDUSTRIAS ELECTRICAS LTDA.—See Sumitomo Electric Industries, Ltd.; *Int'l*, pg. 7282
SUMIDENSO DO BRASIL INDUSTRIAS ELETRICAS LTDA.—See Sumitomo Electric Industries, Ltd.; *Int'l*, pg. 7282
SUMIDENSO MEDIATECH (HUIZHOU)LTD.—See Sumitomo Electric Industries, Ltd.; *Int'l*, pg. 7282
SUMIDENSO MEDIATECH SUZHOU CO., LTD.—See Sumitomo Electric Industries, Ltd.; *Int'l*, pg. 7282
SUMIDENSO PLATECH, LTD.—See Sumitomo Electric Industries, Ltd.; *Int'l*, pg. 7282
SUMIDENSO SERVICE, LTD.—See Sumitomo Electric Industries, Ltd.; *Int'l*, pg. 7282
SUMIDENSO VIETNAM CO., LTD.—See Sumitomo Electric Industries, Ltd.; *Int'l*, pg. 7282
SUMIDEN STEEL WIRE (THAILAND) CO., LTD.—See Sumitomo Electric Industries, Ltd.; *Int'l*, pg. 7281
SUMIDEN TRANSMISSION & DISTRIBUTION SYSTEM PRODUCTS, LTD.—See Sumitomo Electric Industries, Ltd.; *Int'l*, pg. 7281
SUMIDEN VIETNAM AUTOMOTIVE WIRE CO., LTD.—See Sumitomo Electric Industries, Ltd.; *Int'l*, pg. 7281
SUMIDEN WIRE PRODUCTS CORPORATION—See Sumitomo Electric Industries, Ltd.; *Int'l*, pg. 7281
SUMIDEN WIRE PRODUCTS CORPORATION—See Sumitomo Electric Industries, Ltd.; *Int'l*, pg. 7282
SUMIDUREZ SINGAPORE PTE. LTD.—See Sumitomo Bakelite Co., Ltd.; *Int'l*, pg. 7263
SUMIFERT SDN. BHD.—See Sumitomo Corporation; *Int'l*, pg. 7271
SUMIFRU CORPORATION—See Sumitomo Corporation; *Int'l*, pg. 7271
SUMIGOMUSANGYO, LTD.—See Sumitomo Rubber Industries, Ltd.; *Int'l*, pg. 7299
SUMIGOMU TAKASAGO INTEGRATE, LTD.—See Sumitomo Rubber Industries, Ltd.; *Int'l*, pg. 7299
SUMI-HANEL WIRING SYSTEMS CO., LTD.—See Sumitomo Electric Industries, Ltd.; *Int'l*, pg. 7284
SUMIHATSU CO., LTD.—See NHK Spring Co., Ltd.; *Int'l*, pg. 5258
SUMIJU BUSINESS, LTD—See Sumitomo Heavy Industries, Ltd.; *Int'l*, pg. 7288
SUMIJU ENVIRONMENTAL ENGINEERING, INC.—See Sumitomo Heavy Industries, Ltd.; *Int'l*, pg. 7288
SUMIJU ENVIRONMENTAL TECHNOLOGIES, LTD.—See Sumitomo Heavy Industries, Ltd.; *Int'l*, pg. 7288
SUMIJU LOGITECH CO., LTD.—See Sumitomo Heavy Industries, Ltd.; *Int'l*, pg. 7288
SUMIJU MAGNET (KUNSHAN) CO., LTD.—See Sumitomo Heavy Industries, Ltd.; *Int'l*, pg. 7288
SUMIJU PLANT ENGINEERING CO., LTD. - NIIHAMA WORKS—See Sumitomo Heavy Industries, Ltd.; *Int'l*, pg. 7288
SUMIJU PLANT ENGINEERING CO., LTD.—See Sumitomo Heavy Industries, Ltd.; *Int'l*, pg. 7288
SUMIJU PLATEC CO., LTD—See Sumitomo Heavy Industries, Ltd.; *Int'l*, pg. 7289
SUMIJU PRECISION FORGING CO., LTD.—See Sumitomo Heavy Industries, Ltd.; *Int'l*, pg. 7289
SUMIJU SCE (XIAMEN) CONSTRUCTION MACHINERY CO., LTD.—See Sumitomo Heavy Industries, Ltd.; *Int'l*, pg. 7289
SUMIJU TOKKI SERVICE CO., LTD.—See Sumitomo Heavy Industries, Ltd.; *Int'l*, pg. 7289
SUMIJU YOKOSUKA KOGYO CO., LTD.—See Sumitomo Heavy Industries, Ltd.; *Int'l*, pg. 7289
SUMIKA ACRYL CO., LTD—See Sumitomo Chemical Company, Limited; *Int'l*, pg. 7264
SUMIKA AGRO MANUFACTURING CO., LTD.—See Sumitomo Chemical Company, Limited; *Int'l*, pg. 7264
SUMIKA AGROTECH CO., LTD.—See Sumitomo Chemical Company, Limited; *Int'l*, pg. 7265
SUMIKA ALCHEM CO., LTD.—See Sumitomo Chemical Company, Limited; *Int'l*, pg. 7265
SUMIKA ASSEMBLY TECHNO CO., LTD.—See Sumitomo Chemical Company, Limited; *Int'l*, pg. 7265
SUMIKA BAYER URETHANE CO., LTD.—See Bayer Aktiengesellschaft; *Int'l*, pg. 910
SUMIKA CHEMICAL ANALYSIS SERVICE, LTD.—See Sumitomo Chemical Company, Limited; *Int'l*, pg. 7265
SUMIKA CHEMTEX CO., LTD—See Sumitomo Chemical Company, Limited; *Int'l*, pg. 7265
SUMIKA COLOR CO., LTD.—See Sumitomo Chemical Company, Limited; *Int'l*, pg. 7265
SUMIKA DX ACCENT CO., LTD.—See Sumitomo Chemical Company, Limited; *Int'l*, pg. 7265
SUMIKA ELECTRONIC MATERIALS (CHANGZHOU) CO., LTD.—See Sumitomo Chemical Company, Limited; *Int'l*, pg. 7265
SUMIKA ELECTRONIC MATERIALS (CHENGDU) CO., LTD.—See Sumitomo Chemical Company, Limited; *Int'l*, pg. 7265
SUMIKA ELECTRONIC MATERIALS (CHONGQING) CO., LTD.—See Sumitomo Chemical Company, Limited; *Int'l*, pg. 7265
SUMIKA ELECTRONIC MATERIALS (HEFEI) CO., LTD.—See Sumitomo Chemical Company, Limited; *Int'l*, pg. 7265
SUMIKA ELECTRONIC MATERIALS POLAND SP. ZO.O.—See Sumitomo Chemical Company, Limited; *Int'l*, pg. 7265
SUMIKA ELECTRONIC MATERIALS (SHANGHAI) CO., LTD.—See Sumitomo Chemical Company, Limited; *Int'l*, pg. 7265
SUMIKA ELECTRONIC MATERIALS (SHENZHEN) CO., LTD.—See Sumitomo Chemical Company, Limited; *Int'l*, pg. 7265
SUMIKA ELECTRONIC MATERIALS (WUXI) CO., LTD.—See Sumitomo Chemical Company, Limited; *Int'l*, pg. 7265
SUMIKA ELECTRONIC MATERIALS (XI'AN) CO., LTD.—See Sumitomo Chemical Company, Limited; *Int'l*, pg. 7265
SUMIKA ENVIRO-SCIENCE CO., LTD—See Sumitomo Chemical Company, Limited; *Int'l*, pg. 7265

SUMIDA CORPORATION
CORPORATE AFFILIATIONS
Company Index

SUMIKA FARM IBARAKI CO., LTD.—See Sumitomo Chemical Company, Limited; *Int'l*, pg. 7265
SUMIKA FARM MIE CO., LTD.—See Sumitomo Chemical Company, Limited; *Int'l*, pg. 7265
SUMIKA FARM OITA CO., LTD.—See Sumitomo Chemical Company, Limited; *Int'l*, pg. 7265
SUMIKA FINANCE CO., LTD—See Sumitomo Chemical Company, Limited; *Int'l*, pg. 7265
SUMIKA GREEN CO., LTD.—See Sumitomo Chemical Company, Limited; *Int'l*, pg. 7265
SUMIKA HIGH-PURITY GAS COMPANY—See Sumitomo Chemical Company, Limited; *Int'l*, pg. 7265
SUMIKA HUABEI ELECTRONIC MATERIALS (BEIJING) CO., LTD.—See Sumitomo Chemical Company, Limited; *Int'l*, pg. 7265
SUMIKA-KAKOUSHI CO., LTD.—See Sumitomo Chemical Company, Limited; *Int'l*, pg. 7265
SUMIKA LIFE TECH CO., LTD.—See Sumitomo Chemical Company, Limited; *Int'l*, pg. 7265
SUMIKA LOGISTICS CO., LTD.—See Sumitomo Chemical Company, Limited; *Int'l*, pg. 7265
SUMIKA PLASTECH CO., LTD.—See Sumitomo Chemical Company, Limited; *Int'l*, pg. 7265
SUMIKA POLYCARBONATE LIMITED—See Sumitomo Chemical Company, Limited; *Int'l*, pg. 7265
SUMIKA POLYMER COMPOUNDS AMERICA, INC.—See Sumitomo Chemical Company, Limited; *Int'l*, pg. 7266
SUMIKA POLYMER COMPOUNDS DALIAN CO., LTD.—See Sumitomo Chemical Company, Limited; *Int'l*, pg. 7265
SUMIKA POLYMER COMPOUNDS EUROPE LTD.—See Sumitomo Chemical Company, Limited; *Int'l*, pg. 7265
SUMIKA POLYMER COMPOUNDS (THAILAND) CO., LTD.—See Toyo Ink SC Holdings Co., Ltd.; *Int'l*, pg. 7854
SUMIKA POLYMERS NORTH AMERICA LLC—See Sumitomo Chemical Company, Limited; *Int'l*, pg. 7265
SUMIKA REAL ESTATE CO., LTD—See Sumitomo Chemical Company, Limited; *Int'l*, pg. 7265
SUMIKA SEKISUI FILM CO., LTD.—See Sumitomo Chemical Company, Limited; *Int'l*, pg. 7265
SUMIKA STYRON POLYCARBONATE LIMITED—See Bain Capital, LP; *U.S. Private*, pg. 449
SUMIKA STYRON POLYCARBONATE LIMITED—See Sumitomo Chemical Company, Limited; *Int'l*, pg. 7265
SUMIKA TECHNICAL INFORMATION SERVICE, INC.—See Sumitomo Chemical Company, Limited; *Int'l*, pg. 7265
SUMIKA TECHNOLOGY CO., LTD.—See Sumitomo Chemical Company, Limited; *Int'l*, pg. 7265
SUMIKA TECHNOSERVICE CORPORATION1989—See Sumitomo Chemical Company, Limited; *Int'l*, pg. 7265
SUMIKAWA ADD CO., LTD.—See A.D.Works Group Co., Ltd.; *Int'l*, pg. 23
SUMIKEI-NIKKEI ENGINEERING CO., LTD.—See Nippon Light Metal Holdings Company, Ltd.; *Int'l*, pg. 5324
SUMIKEN MITSUI ROAD CO., LTD.—See Mitsui & Co., Ltd.; *Int'l*, pg. 4980
SUMIKIN BUSSAN BUSINESS SUPPORT CORP.—See Nippon Steel Corporation; *Int'l*, pg. 5339
SUMIKIN BUSSAN INDIA PVT. LTD.—See Nippon Steel Corporation; *Int'l*, pg. 5339
SUMIKIN BUSSAN INTERNATIONAL (HK) LTD.—See Nippon Steel Corporation; *Int'l*, pg. 5339
SUMIKIN BUSSAN INTERNATIONAL (KOREA) CO., LTD.—See Nippon Steel Corporation; *Int'l*, pg. 5339
SUMIKIN BUSSAN INTERNATIONAL (M) SDN. BHD.—See Nippon Steel Corporation; *Int'l*, pg. 5339
SUMIKIN BUSSAN INTERNATIONAL (THAILAND) LTD.—See Nippon Steel Corporation; *Int'l*, pg. 5339
SUMIKIN BUSSAN KENZAI CORP.—See Nippon Steel Corporation; *Int'l*, pg. 5339
SUMIKIN BUSSAN MATEX CORP.—See Nippon Steel Corporation; *Int'l*, pg. 5339
SUMIKIN BUSSAN OCEANIA PTY LTD—See Nippon Steel Corporation; *Int'l*, pg. 5339
SUMIKIN BUSSAN REAL ESTATE CO., LTD.—See Nippon Steel Corporation; *Int'l*, pg. 5339
SUMIKIN BUSSAN SPECIAL STEEL CO., LTD.—See Nippon Steel Corporation; *Int'l*, pg. 5339
SUMIKO CONSULTANTS CO., LTD.—See Sumitomo Metal Mining Co., Ltd.; *Int'l*, pg. 7291
SUMIKO ELECTRONICS SUZHOU CO., LTD.—See Sumitomo Metal Mining Co., Ltd.; *Int'l*, pg. 7291
SUMIKO ELECTRONICS TAIWAN CO., LTD.—See Sumitomo Metal Mining Co., Ltd.; *Int'l*, pg. 7292
SUMIKO KUNITOMI DENSHI CO., LTD.—See Sumitomo Metal Mining Co., Ltd.; *Int'l*, pg. 7292
SUMIKO LEADFRAME CHENGDU CO., LTD.—See Sumitomo Metal Mining Co., Ltd.; *Int'l*, pg. 7292
SUMIKO LEADFRAME SINGAPORE PTE LTD—See Sumitomo Metal Mining Co., Ltd.; *Int'l*, pg. 7292
SUMIKO LEADFRAME (THAILAND) CO., LTD.—See Sumitomo Metal Mining Co., Ltd.; *Int'l*, pg. 7292
SUMIKO LOGISTICS CO., LTD.—See Sumitomo Metal Mining Co., Ltd.; *Int'l*, pg. 7292
SUMIKO PLANTECH CO., LTD.—See Sumitomo Metal Mining Co., Ltd.; *Int'l*, pg. 7292
SUMIKO RESOURCES EXPLORATION & DEVELOPMENT CO., LTD.—See Sumitomo Metal Mining Co., Ltd.; *Int'l*, pg. 7292
SUMIKO TEC CO., LTD.—See Sumitomo Metal Mining Co., Ltd.; *Int'l*, pg. 7292
SUMIKO TECHNICAL SERVICE CO., LTD.—See Sumitomo Metal Mining Co., Ltd.; *Int'l*, pg. 7292
SUMIKO TECHNO-RESEARCH CO., LTD.—See Sumitomo Metal Mining Co., Ltd.; *Int'l*, pg. 7292
SUMIKURAKOUZAI CO., LTD.—See Toami Corporation; *Int'l*, pg. 7770
SUMIKYO CO., LTD.—See Sumitomo Forestry Co., Ltd.; *Int'l*, pg. 7286
SUMIKYO WINTEC CO., LTD.—See Sumitomo Forestry Co., Ltd.; *Int'l*, pg. 7286
SUMILAB, S.A DE C.V.—See HORIBA Ltd; *Int'l*, pg. 3478
SUMILAB S.A.—See HORIBA Ltd; *Int'l*, pg. 3478
SUMIMEC ENGINEERING INC.—See Sumitomo Heavy Industries, Ltd.; *Int'l*, pg. 7289
SUMIMETAL MINING CO., LTD—See Nippon Steel Corporation; *Int'l*, pg. 5339
SUMINET COMMUNICATION TECHNOLOGIES (SHANGHAI) CO., LTD.—See Sumitomo Electric Industries, Ltd.; *Int'l*, pg. 7282
SUMINISTRO DE LUZ Y FUERZA SL—See Enel S.p.A.; *Int'l*, pg. 2414
SUMINISTROS FRANQUESA S.A.—See Interpump Group S.p.A.; *Int'l*, pg. 3757
SUMINISTROS, IMPORTACIONES Y MANTENIMIENTOS ELECTRONICOS, S.A.—See ACS, Actividades de Construccion y Servicios, S.A.; *Int'l*, pg. 116
SUMINISTROS LOINAZ S.A.—See Klockner & Co. SE; *Int'l*, pg. 4202
SUMINOE CO., LTD.—See Suminoe Textile Co., Ltd.; *Int'l*, pg. 7262
SUMINOE LOGISTICS CO., LTD.—See Suminoe Textile Co., Ltd.; *Int'l*, pg. 7262
SUMINOE TECHNO CO., LTD. - SHIGA FACTORY—See Suminoe Textile Co., Ltd.; *Int'l*, pg. 7262
SUMINOE TECHNO CO., LTD.—See Suminoe Textile Co., Ltd.; *Int'l*, pg. 7262
SUMINOE TEIJIN TECHNO KRISHNA INDIA PVT. LTD.—See Suminoe Textile Co., Ltd.; *Int'l*, pg. 7262
SUMINOE TEXTILE CO., LTD.; *Int'l*, pg. 7262
SUMINOE TEXTILE DE MEXICO, S.A. DE C.V.—See Suminoe Textile Co., Ltd.; *Int'l*, pg. 7262
SUMINOE TEXTILE OF AMERICA CORPORATION—See Suminoe Textile Co., Ltd.; *Int'l*, pg. 7262
SUMINOE TEXTILE SHANGHAI CO., LTD.—See Suminoe Textile Co., Ltd.; *Int'l*, pg. 7262
SUMINOE WORKS CO., LTD.—See Suminoe Textile Co., Ltd.; *Int'l*, pg. 7262
SUMI-PAC CONSTRUCTION CO., LTD.—See Sumitomo Electric Industries, Ltd.; *Int'l*, pg. 7281
SUMI-PAC CORPORATION—See Sumitomo Electric Industries, Ltd.; *Int'l*, pg. 7281
SUMI-PAC ELECTRO-CHEMICAL CORPORATION—See Sumitomo Electric Industries, Ltd.; *Int'l*, pg. 7281
SUMIPAR, S.A.—See ACS, Actividades de Construccion y Servicios, S.A.; *Int'l*, pg. 116
SUMIPEX TECHSHEET CO., LTD.—See Sumitomo Chemical Company, Limited; *Int'l*, pg. 7265
SUMIPEX (THAILAND) CO., LTD.—See Sumitomo Chemical Company, Limited; *Int'l*, pg. 7265
SUMI PHILIPPINES WIRING SYSTEMS CORPORATION—See Sumitomo Electric Industries, Ltd.; *Int'l*, pg. 7281
SUMIPUTEH STEEL CENTRE SDN. BHD.—See Sumitomo Corporation; *Int'l*, pg. 7271
SUMIRE AGENCY, INC.—See H2O Retailing Corp.; *Int'l*, pg. 3201
SUMIRIKO AVS GERMANY GMBH—See Sumitomo Riko Company Limited; *Int'l*, pg. 7298
SUMIRIKO AVS RUS LLC—See Sumitomo Riko Company Limited; *Int'l*, pg. 7298
SUMIRIKO AVS SPAIN S.A.U.—See Sumitomo Riko Company Limited; *Int'l*, pg. 7298
SUMIRIKO EASTERN RUBBER (THAILAND) LTD.—See Sumitomo Riko Company Limited; *Int'l*, pg. 7298
SUMIRIKO OHIO, INC.—See Sumitomo Riko Company Limited; *Int'l*, pg. 7298
SUMIRIKO RUBBER COMPOUNDING FRANCE S.A.S.—See Sumitomo Riko Company Limited; *Int'l*, pg. 7298
SUMIRIKO SOUTH AFRICA (PTY) LTD.—See Sumitomo Riko Company Limited; *Int'l*, pg. 7298
SUMIRIKO TENNESSEE, INC.—See Sumitomo Riko Company Limited; *Int'l*, pg. 7298
SUMIRIKO YAMAGATA COMPANY LIMITED—See Sumitomo Riko Company Limited; *Int'l*, pg. 7298
SUMIRIN CARE LIFE CO., LTD.—See Kobe Steel, Ltd.; *Int'l*, pg. 4221
SUMIRIN ENTERPRISES CO., LTD.—See Sumitomo Forestry Co., Ltd.; *Int'l*, pg. 7286
SUMIRIN SASH CO., LTD.—See Sumitomo Forestry Co., Ltd.; *Int'l*, pg. 7286
SUMIRUBBER INDUSTRIES (MALAYSIA) SDN. BHD.—See Sumitomo Rubber Industries, Ltd.; *Int'l*, pg. 7299
SUMIRUBBER MALAYSIA SDN. BHD.—See Sumitomo Rubber Industries, Ltd.; *Int'l*, pg. 7299
SUMIRUBBER VIETNAM, LTD.—See Sumitomo Rubber Industries, Ltd.; *Int'l*, pg. 7299
SUMI'SACCS CORP.—See Nippon Steel Corporation; *Int'l*, pg. 5339
SUMISEI BUSINESS SERVICE CO., LTD.—See Sumitomo Life Insurance Company; *Int'l*, pg. 7291
SUMISEI CHEMICAL COMPANY LIMITED—See Sumitomo Seika Chemicals Company Limited; *Int'l*, pg. 7300
SUMISEI ENGINEERING CO., LTD.—See Sumitomo Corporation; *Int'l*, pg. 7275
SUMISEI HYDRAULIC SYSTEMS CO., LTD.—See Sumitomo Corporation; *Int'l*, pg. 7275
SUMISEI INSURANCE SERVICE CORPORATION—See Sumitomo Life Insurance Company; *Int'l*, pg. 7291
SUMISEI SANGYO CO., LTD.—See Sumitomo Corporation; *Int'l*, pg. 7275
SUMISEI SERVICE CO., LTD.—See Sumitomo Corporation; *Int'l*, pg. 7275
SUMISEI-SUPPORT & CONSULTING CO., LTD.—See Sumitomo Life Insurance Company; *Int'l*, pg. 7291
SUMISEI TAIWAN TECHNOLOGY CO., LTD.—See Sumitomo Seika Chemicals Company Limited; *Int'l*, pg. 7300
SUMISEI TECHNO SERVICE CO., LTD.—See Sumitomo Corporation; *Int'l*, pg. 7275
SUMISE KENZAI CO., LTD.—See Sumitomo Osaka Cement Co Ltd; *Int'l*, pg. 7297
SUMISEKI HOLDINGS, INC.; *Int'l*, pg. 7262
SUMISETSU CHINA CO., LTD.—See Sumitomo Densetsu Co., Ltd.; *Int'l*, pg. 7277
SUMISETSU PHILIPPINES, INC.—See Sumitomo Densetsu Co., Ltd.; *Int'l*, pg. 7277
SUMISETSU TECHNO CO., LTD.—See Sumitomo Electric Industries, Ltd.; *Int'l*, pg. 7282
SUMISETSU VIETNAM CO., LTD.—See Sumitomo Densetsu Co., Ltd.; *Int'l*, pg. 7277
SUMISHIN LIFE CARD COMPANY, LIMITED—See AIFUL Corporation; *Int'l*, pg. 232
SUMISHO ADMINISTRATION SERVICES CO., LTD.—See Sumitomo Corporation; *Int'l*, pg. 7271
SUMISHO AERO-SYSTEMS CORPORATION—See Sumitomo Corporation; *Int'l*, pg. 7271
SUMISHO AIRBAG SYSTEMS CO., LTD.—See Sumitomo Corporation; *Int'l*, pg. 7271
SUMISHO AIRCRAFT ASSET MANAGEMENT B.V.—See Sumitomo Corporation; *Int'l*, pg. 7271
SUMISHO BUILDING MANAGEMENT CO., LTD.—See Sumitomo Corporation; *Int'l*, pg. 7271
SUMISHO CAPITAL MANAGEMENT (SINGAPORE) PTE. LTD.—See Sumitomo Corporation; *Int'l*, pg. 7271
SUMISHO GLOBAL LOGISTICS (CHINA) CO., LTD.—See Sumitomo Corporation; *Int'l*, pg. 7271
SUMISHO GLOBAL LOGISTICS CO., LTD.—See Sumitomo Corporation; *Int'l*, pg. 7271
SUMISHO GLOBAL LOGISTICS EUROPE GMBH—See Sumitomo Corporation; *Int'l*, pg. 7271
SUMISHO GLOBAL LOGISTICS EUROPE S.R.O.—See Sumitomo Corporation; *Int'l*, pg. 7271
SUMISHO GLOBAL LOGISTICS (SHANGHAI) CO., LTD.—See Sumitomo Corporation; *Int'l*, pg. 7271
SUMISHO GLOBAL LOGISTICS SOUTH CHINA CO., LTD.—See Sumitomo Corporation; *Int'l*, pg. 7271
SUMISHO GLOBAL LOGISTICS (THAILAND) CO., LTD.—See Sumitomo Corporation; *Int'l*, pg. 7271
SUMISHO GLOBAL LOGISTICS (USA) CORPORATION—See Sumitomo Corporation; *Int'l*, pg. 7273
SUMISHO INAX CORPORATION—See Sumitomo Corporation; *Int'l*, pg. 7271
SUMISHO INTERIOR INTERNATIONAL INC.—See Sumitomo Corporation; *Int'l*, pg. 7271
SUMISHO MACHINERY TRADE CORPORATION—See Sumitomo Corporation; *Int'l*, pg. 7271
SUMISHO MARINE CO., LTD.—See Sumitomo Corporation; *Int'l*, pg. 7271
SUMISHO MATERIALS CORPORATION—See Sumitomo Corporation; *Int'l*, pg. 7271
SUMISHO METALEX CORPORATION—See Sumitomo Corporation; *Int'l*, pg. 7271
SUMISHO MONTBLANC CO., LTD.—See Sumitomo Corporation; *Int'l*, pg. 7271
SUMISHO MOTOR FINANCE CORPORATION—See Sumitomo Corporation; *Int'l*, pg. 7271
SUMISHO PAPER CO., LTD.—See Sumitomo Corporation; *Int'l*, pg. 7272
SUMISHO REALTY MANAGEMENT CO., LTD.—See Sumitomo Corporation; *Int'l*, pg. 7272
SUMISHO STEEL SHEETS WORKS CO., LTD.—See Sumitomo Corporation; *Int'l*, pg. 7272
SUMISHO TATEMONO CO., LTD.—See Sumitomo Corporation; *Int'l*, pg. 7271
SUMISHO TEKKO HANBAI CO., LTD.—See Sumitomo Corporation; *Int'l*, pg. 7272
SUMISO INTERNATIONAL LOGISTICS (GUANGZHOU) CO., LTD.—See The Sumitomo Warehouse Co. Ltd.; *Int'l*, pg. 7690
SUMISO INTERNATIONAL LOGISTICS (QINGDAO) CO., LTD.—See Nippon Steel Corporation; *Int'l*, pg. 5339

COMPANY NAME INDEX

SUMISO (LAEM CHABANG) CO., LTD.—See The Sumitomo Warehouse Co. Ltd.; *Int'l*, pg. 7690
SUMISO (MALAYSIA) SDN. BHD.—See The Sumitomo Warehouse Co. Ltd.; *Int'l*, pg. 7690
SUMISO REAL ESTATE SERVICES CO., LTD.—See The Sumitomo Warehouse Co. Ltd.; *Int'l*, pg. 7690
SUMISO (TAIWAN) CO., LTD.—See The Sumitomo Warehouse Co. Ltd.; *Int'l*, pg. 7690
SUMISO (THAILAND) CO., LTD.—See The Sumitomo Warehouse Co. Ltd.; *Int'l*, pg. 7690
SUMITA OPTICAL GLASS EUROPE GMBH—See Sumita Optical Glass, Inc.; *Int'l*, pg. 7262
SUMITA OPTICAL GLASS, INC.; *Int'l*, pg. 7262
SUMITA OPTICAL GLASS, INC. - TAJIMA FACTORY—See Sumita Optical Glass, Inc.; *Int'l*, pg. 7262
SUMITEC CO., LTD.—See Sumitomo Osaka Cement Co Ltd; *Int'l*, pg. 7297
SUMITECH ENGINEERING SOLUTIONS LTD.—See UNI-MECH Group Berhad; *Int'l*, pg. 8049
SUMITEC INTERNATIONAL, LTD.—See Sumitomo Corporation; *Int'l*, pg. 7272
SUMI TEXAS WIRE, INC.—See Sumitomo Electric Industries, Ltd.; *Int'l*, pg. 7281
SUMITEX HONG KONG LIMITED—See Sumitomo Corporation; *Int'l*, pg. 7272
SUMITEX INTERNATIONAL CO., LTD.—See Sumitomo Corporation; *Int'l*, pg. 7272
SUMI-THAI INTERNATIONAL LIMITED—See Sumitomo Corporation; *Int'l*, pg. 7271
SUMITMO WAREHOUSE (EUROPE) GMBH—See The Sumitomo Warehouse Co. Ltd.; *Int'l*, pg. 7690
SUMITOMO 3M LIMITED—See 3M Company; *U.S. Public*, pg. 8
SUMITOMO AUSTRALIA PTY LTD—See Sumitomo Corporation; *Int'l*, pg. 7272
SUMITOMO BAKELITE CO., LTD.; *Int'l*, pg. 7262
SUMITOMO BAKELITE (DONGGUAN) CO., LTD.—See Sumitomo Bakelite Co., Ltd.; *Int'l*, pg. 7263
SUMITOMO BAKELITE EUROPE (BARCELONA), S.L.U.—See Sumitomo Bakelite Co., Ltd.; *Int'l*, pg. 7263
SUMITOMO BAKELITE EUROPE N.V.—See Sumitomo Bakelite Co., Ltd.; *Int'l*, pg. 7263
SUMITOMO BAKELITE HONG KONG CO., LTD.—See Sumitomo Bakelite Co., Ltd.; *Int'l*, pg. 7263
SUMITOMO BAKELITE MACAU CO., LTD.—See Sumitomo Bakelite Co., Ltd.; *Int'l*, pg. 7263
SUMITOMO BAKELITE (NANTONG) CO., LTD.—See Sumitomo Bakelite Co., Ltd.; *Int'l*, pg. 7263
SUMITOMO BAKELITE NORTH AMERICA HOLDING, INC.—See Sumitomo Bakelite Co., Ltd.; *Int'l*, pg. 7263
SUMITOMO BAKELITE NORTH AMERICA INC—See Sumitomo Bakelite Co., Ltd.; *Int'l*, pg. 7264
SUMITOMO BAKELITE (SHANGHAI) CO., LTD.—See Sumitomo Bakelite Co., Ltd.; *Int'l*, pg. 7263
SUMITOMO BAKELITE SINGAPORE PTE. LTD.—See Sumitomo Bakelite Co., Ltd.; *Int'l*, pg. 7263
SUMITOMO BAKELITE (SUZHOU) CO., LTD.—See Sumitomo Bakelite Co., Ltd.; *Int'l*, pg. 7263
SUMITOMO BAKELITE (TAIWAN) CORPORATION LIMITED—See ChangChun Group; *Int'l*, pg. 1442
SUMITOMO BAKELITE (TAIWAN) CORPORATION LIMITED—See Sumitomo Bakelite Co., Ltd.; *Int'l*, pg. 7263
SUMITOMO BAKELITE (THAILAND) CO., LTD.—See Sumitomo Bakelite Co., Ltd.; *Int'l*, pg. 7263
SUMITOMO BENELUX S.A./N.V.—See Sumitomo Corporation; *Int'l*, pg. 7272
SUMITOMO CANADA LTD.—See Sumitomo Corporation; *Int'l*, pg. 7272
SUMITOMO CEMENT COMPUTER SYSTEMS CO., LTD.—See Sumitomo Osaka Cement Co Ltd; *Int'l*, pg. 7297
SUMITOMO CHEMICAL ADVANCED TECHNOLOGIES—See Sumitomo Chemical Company, Limited; *Int'l*, pg. 7266
SUMITOMO CHEMICAL AGRO EUROPE S.A.S.—See Sumitomo Chemical Company, Limited; *Int'l*, pg. 7266
SUMITOMO CHEMICAL AGRO SEOUL, LTD.—See Sumitomo Chemical Company, Limited; *Int'l*, pg. 7265
SUMITOMO CHEMICAL AMERICA, INC.—See Sumitomo Chemical Company, Limited; *Int'l*, pg. 7265
SUMITOMO CHEMICAL ARGENTINA S.A.—See Sumitomo Chemical Company, Limited; *Int'l*, pg. 7266
SUMITOMO CHEMICAL ASIA PTE. LTD.—See Sumitomo Chemical Company, Limited; *Int'l*, pg. 7266
SUMITOMO CHEMICAL AUSTRALIA PTY. LTD.—See Sumitomo Chemical Company, Limited; *Int'l*, pg. 7266
SUMITOMO CHEMICAL COLOMBIA S.A.S.—See Sumitomo Chemical Company, Limited; *Int'l*, pg. 7266
SUMITOMO CHEMICAL COMPANY, LIMITED; *Int'l*, pg. 7264
SUMITOMO CHEMICAL COMPANY, LTD. - CHIBA WORKS—See Sumitomo Chemical Company, Limited; *Int'l*, pg. 7266
SUMITOMO CHEMICAL COMPANY, LTD. - EHIME WORKS—See Sumitomo Chemical Company, Limited; *Int'l*, pg. 7266
SUMITOMO CHEMICAL COMPANY, LTD. - GIFU PLANT—See Sumitomo Chemical Company, Limited; *Int'l*, pg. 7266
SUMITOMO CHEMICAL COMPANY, LTD. - MISAWA WORKS—See Sumitomo Chemical Company, Limited; *Int'l*, pg. 7266
SUMITOMO CHEMICAL COMPANY, LTD. - OHE WORKS—See Sumitomo Chemical Company, Limited; *Int'l*, pg. 7266
SUMITOMO CHEMICAL COMPANY, LTD. - OITA WORKS—See Sumitomo Chemical Company, Limited; *Int'l*, pg. 7266
SUMITOMO CHEMICAL COMPANY, LTD. - OKAYAMA PLANT—See Sumitomo Chemical Company, Limited; *Int'l*, pg. 7266
SUMITOMO CHEMICAL COMPANY, LTD. - OSAKA WORKS—See Sumitomo Chemical Company, Limited; *Int'l*, pg. 7266
SUMITOMO CHEMICAL ENGINEERING CO., LTD.—See Sumitomo Chemical Company, Limited; *Int'l*, pg. 7266
SUMITOMO CHEMICAL ENVIRO-AGRO ASIA PACIFIC SDN. BHD.—See Sumitomo Chemical Company, Limited; *Int'l*, pg. 7266
SUMITOMO CHEMICAL EUROPE S.A./N.V.—See Sumitomo Chemical Company, Limited; *Int'l*, pg. 7266
SUMITOMO CHEMICAL GARDEN PRODUCTS CO., LTD.—See Sumitomo Chemical Company, Limited; *Int'l*, pg. 7266
SUMITOMO CHEMICAL INDIA PRIVATE LIMITED—See Sumitomo Chemical Company, Limited; *Int'l*, pg. 7266
SUMITOMO CHEMICAL INTELLECTUAL PROPERTY SERVICE, LTD.—See Sumitomo Chemical Company, Limited; *Int'l*, pg. 7266
SUMITOMO CHEMICAL ITALIA S.R.L.—See Sumitomo Chemical Company, Limited; *Int'l*, pg. 7266
SUMITOMO CHEMICAL NEDERLAND B.V.—See Sumitomo Chemical Company, Limited; *Int'l*, pg. 7266
SUMITOMO CHEMICAL PHILIPPINES, INC.—See Sumitomo Chemical Company, Limited; *Int'l*, pg. 7266
SUMITOMO CHEMICAL SHANGHAI CO., LTD.—See Sumitomo Chemical Company, Limited; *Int'l*, pg. 7266
SUMITOMO CHEMICAL SINGAPORE PTE. LTD.—See Sumitomo Chemical Company, Limited; *Int'l*, pg. 7266
SUMITOMO CHEMICAL SYSTEM SERVICE CO., LTD.—See Sumitomo Chemical Company, Limited; *Int'l*, pg. 7267
SUMITOMO CHEMICAL TAIWAN CO., LTD.—See Sumitomo Chemical Company, Limited; *Int'l*, pg. 7267
SUMITOMO CHEMICAL (U.K.) PLC—See Sumitomo Chemical Company, Limited; *Int'l*, pg. 7266
SUMITOMO CHEMICAL VIETNAM CO., LTD.—See Sumitomo Chemical Company, Limited; *Int'l*, pg. 7267
SUMITOMO CONSTRUCTION MACHINERY CO., LTD.—See Sumitomo Heavy Industries, Ltd.; *Int'l*, pg. 7289
SUMITOMO CONSTRUCTION MACHINERY SALES CO., LTD.—See Sumitomo Heavy Industries, Ltd.; *Int'l*, pg. 7289
SUMITOMO CORPORATION ANDES S.A.S.—See Sumitomo Corporation; *Int'l*, pg. 7272
SUMITOMO CORPORATION ARGENTINA S.A.—See Sumitomo Corporation; *Int'l*, pg. 7272
SUMITOMO CORPORATION ASIA & OCEANIA PTE. LTD.—See Sumitomo Corporation; *Int'l*, pg. 7272
SUMITOMO CORPORATION ASIA PTE. LTD.—See Sumitomo Corporation; *Int'l*, pg. 7272
SUMITOMO CORPORATION CAPITAL EUROPE PLC—See Sumitomo Corporation; *Int'l*, pg. 7272
SUMITOMO CORPORATION (CENTRAL EURASIA) LLC—See Sumitomo Corporation; *Int'l*, pg. 7272
SUMITOMO CORPORATION (CHILE) LIMITADA—See Sumitomo Corporation; *Int'l*, pg. 7272
SUMITOMO CORPORATION (CHINA) HOLDING LTD.—See Sumitomo Corporation; *Int'l*, pg. 7272
SUMITOMO CORPORATION COLOMBIA S.A.—See Sumitomo Corporation; *Int'l*, pg. 7272
SUMITOMO CORPORATION DEL ECUADOR S.A.—See Sumitomo Corporation; *Int'l*, pg. 7273
SUMITOMO CORPORATION DEL PERU S.A.—See Sumitomo Corporation; *Int'l*, pg. 7273
SUMITOMO CORPORATION DE MEXICO S.A. DE C.V.—See Sumitomo Corporation; *Int'l*, pg. 7273
SUMITOMO CORPORATION DIS TICARET A.S.—See Sumitomo Corporation; *Int'l*, pg. 7272
SUMITOMO CORPORATION DO BRASIL S.A.—See Sumitomo Corporation; *Int'l*, pg. 7273
SUMITOMO CORPORATION EQUITY ASIA LIMITED—See Sumitomo Corporation; *Int'l*, pg. 7272
SUMITOMO CORPORATION ESPANA S.A.—See Sumitomo Corporation; *Int'l*, pg. 7272
SUMITOMO CORPORATION EUROPE HOLDING LIMITED—See Sumitomo Corporation; *Int'l*, pg. 7272
SUMITOMO CORPORATION EUROPE LIMITED—See Sumitomo Electric Industries, Ltd.; *Int'l*, pg. 7282
SUMITOMO CORPORATION GLOBAL COMMODITIES LIMITED—See Sumitomo Corporation; *Int'l*, pg. 7272
SUMITOMO CORPORATION GLOBAL RESEARCH CO. LTD.—See Sumitomo Corporation; *Int'l*, pg. 7272

SUMITOMO DENSETSU CO., LTD.

SUMITOMO CORPORATION (GUANGZHOU) LTD.—See Sumitomo Corporation; *Int'l*, pg. 7272
SUMITOMO CORPORATION HOKKAIDO CO., LTD.—See Sumitomo Corporation; *Int'l*, pg. 7272
SUMITOMO CORPORATION (HONG KONG) LIMITED—See Sumitomo Corporation; *Int'l*, pg. 7272
SUMITOMO CORPORATION INDIA PRIVATE LIMITED—See Sumitomo Corporation; *Int'l*, pg. 7272
SUMITOMO CORPORATION IRAN, LTD.—See Sumitomo Corporation; *Int'l*, pg. 7272
SUMITOMO CORPORATION ITALIA S.P.A.—See Sumitomo Corporation; *Int'l*, pg. 7272
SUMITOMO CORPORATION KOREA LTD.—See Sumitomo Corporation; *Int'l*, pg. 7272
SUMITOMO CORPORATION KYUSHU CO., LTD.—See Sumitomo Corporation; *Int'l*, pg. 7272
SUMITOMO CORPORATION MIDDLE EAST FZE—See Sumitomo Corporation; *Int'l*, pg. 7272
SUMITOMO CORPORATION OF AMERICA—See Sumitomo Corporation; *Int'l*, pg. 7274
SUMITOMO CORPORATION OF AMERICA—See Sumitomo Corporation; *Int'l*, pg. 7273
SUMITOMO CORPORATION OF THE PHILIPPINES—See Sumitomo Corporation; *Int'l*, pg. 7274
SUMITOMO CORPORATION - OSAKA OFFICE—See Sumitomo Corporation; *Int'l*, pg. 7272
SUMITOMO CORPORATION (QINGDAO) LTD.—See Sumitomo Corporation; *Int'l*, pg. 7272
SUMITOMO CORPORATION SAUDI ARABIA LTD.—See Sumitomo Corporation; *Int'l*, pg. 7272
SUMITOMO CORPORATION (SHANGHAI) LIMITED—See Sumitomo Corporation; *Int'l*, pg. 7272
SUMITOMO CORPORATION; *Int'l*, pg. 7268
SUMITOMO CORPORATION THAILAND, LTD.—See Sumitomo Corporation; *Int'l*, pg. 7272
SUMITOMO CORPORATION (TIANJIN) LTD.—See Sumitomo Corporation; *Int'l*, pg. 7272
SUMITOMO CORPORATION TOHOKU CO., LTD.—See Sumitomo Corporation; *Int'l*, pg. 7273
SUMITOMO CORPORATION VIETNAM LLC—See Sumitomo Corporation; *Int'l*, pg. 7273
SUMITOMO DAINIPPON PHARMA ONCOLOGY, INC.—See Sumitomo Chemical Company, Limited; *Int'l*, pg. 7267
SUMITOMO DENSETSU CO., LTD.; *Int'l*, pg. 7276
SUMITOMO DEUTSCHLAND GMBH—See Sumitomo Corporation; *Int'l*, pg. 7274
SUMITOMO EATON NOVA CORPORATION—See Axcelis Technologies, Inc.; *U.S. Public*, pg. 255
SUMITOMO EATON NOVA CORPORATION—See Sumitomo Heavy Industries, Ltd.; *Int'l*, pg. 7289
SUMITOMO ELECTRIC ASIA, LTD.—See Sumitomo Electric Industries, Ltd.; *Int'l*, pg. 7282
SUMITOMO ELECTRIC ASIA PACIFIC PTE. LTD.—See Sumitomo Electric Industries, Ltd.; *Int'l*, pg. 7282
SUMITOMO ELECTRIC AUTOMOTIVE PRODUCTS (SINGAPORE) PTE., LTD.—See Sumitomo Electric Industries, Ltd.; *Int'l*, pg. 7282
SUMITOMO ELECTRIC BORDNETZE GMBH—See Sumitomo Electric Industries, Ltd.; *Int'l*, pg. 7282
SUMITOMO ELECTRIC CARBIDE, INC.—See Sumitomo Electric Industries, Ltd.; *Int'l*, pg. 7282
SUMITOMO ELECTRIC CARBIDE MANUFACTURING, INC.—See Sumitomo Electric Industries, Ltd.; *Int'l*, pg. 7282
SUMITOMO ELECTRIC DEVICE INNOVATIONS, INC.—See Sumitomo Electric Industries, Ltd.; *Int'l*, pg. 7282
SUMITOMO ELECTRIC DEVICE INNOVATIONS INC. - YAMANASHI PLANT—See Sumitomo Electric Industries, Ltd.; *Int'l*, pg. 7282
SUMITOMO ELECTRIC DEVICE INNOVATIONS U.S.A., INC.—See Sumitomo Electric Industries, Ltd.; *Int'l*, pg. 7282
SUMITOMO ELECTRIC EUROPE LTD.—See Sumitomo Electric Industries, Ltd.; *Int'l*, pg. 7282
SUMITOMO ELECTRIC EUROPE LTD.—See Sumitomo Electric Industries, Ltd.; *Int'l*, pg. 7282
SUMITOMO ELECTRIC FINANCE U.K. LTD.—See Sumitomo Electric Industries, Ltd.; *Int'l*, pg. 7282
SUMITOMO ELECTRIC FINANCE U.S.A., INC.—See Sumitomo Electric Industries, Ltd.; *Int'l*, pg. 7282
SUMITOMO ELECTRIC FINE POLYMER, INC.—See Sumitomo Electric Industries, Ltd.; *Int'l*, pg. 7282
SUMITOMO ELECTRIC FINE POLYMER (SUZHOU) LTD.—See Sumitomo Electric Industries, Ltd.; *Int'l*, pg. 7282
SUMITOMO ELECTRIC HARDMETAL ASIA PACIFIC PTE LTD—See Sumitomo Electric Industries, Ltd.; *Int'l*, pg. 7282
SUMITOMO ELECTRIC HARDMETAL CORP.—See Sumitomo Electric Industries, Ltd.; *Int'l*, pg. 7282
SUMITOMO ELECTRIC HARDMETAL DE MEXICO, S.A. DE C.V.—See Sumitomo Electric Industries, Ltd.; *Int'l*, pg. 7283
SUMITOMO ELECTRIC HARDMETAL LTD.—See Sumitomo Electric Industries, Ltd.; *Int'l*, pg. 7282

SUMITOMO DENSETSU CO., LTD.

CORPORATE AFFILIATIONS

SUMITOMO ELECTRIC HARDMETAL MANUFACTURING (CHANGZHOU) CO., LTD.—See Sumitomo Electric Industries, Ltd.; *Int'l*, pg. 7282
SUMITOMO ELECTRIC HARDMETAL MANUFACTURING INDIA PVT. LTD.—See Sumitomo Electric Industries, Ltd.; *Int'l*, pg. 7282
SUMITOMO ELECTRIC HARDMETAL MANUFACTURING (THAILAND), LTD.—See Sumitomo Electric Industries, Ltd.; *Int'l*, pg. 7282
SUMITOMO ELECTRIC HARDMETAL TRADING (SHANGHAI) CO., LTD.—See Sumitomo Electric Industries, Ltd.; *Int'l*, pg. 7282
SUMITOMO ELECTRIC HARTMETAL GMBH—See Sumitomo Electric Industries, Ltd.; *Int'l*, pg. 7283
SUMITOMO ELECTRIC HARTMETALLFABRIK GMBH—See Sumitomo Electric Industries, Ltd.; *Int'l*, pg. 7283
SUMITOMO ELECTRIC INDUSTRIAL WIRE & CABLE INC.—See Sumitomo Electric Industries, Ltd.; *Int'l*, pg. 7283
SUMITOMO ELECTRIC INDUSTRIES, LTD. - ITAMI WORKS—See Sumitomo Electric Industries, Ltd.; *Int'l*, pg. 7283
SUMITOMO ELECTRIC INDUSTRIES, LTD. - OSAKA WORKS—See Sumitomo Electric Industries, Ltd.; *Int'l*, pg. 7283
SUMITOMO ELECTRIC INDUSTRIES, LTD.—See Sumitomo Electric Industries, Ltd.; *Int'l*, pg. 7283
SUMITOMO ELECTRIC INDUSTRIES, LTD.; *Int'l*, pg. 7277
SUMITOMO ELECTRIC INDUSTRIES, LTD. - YOKOHAMA WORKS—See Sumitomo Electric Industries, Ltd.; *Int'l*, pg. 7283
SUMITOMO ELECTRIC INFORMATION SYSTEMS CO., LTD.—See Sumitomo Electric Industries, Ltd.; *Int'l*, pg. 7283
SUMITOMO ELECTRIC INTELLECTUAL PROPERTY & TECHNOLOGY CENTER, LTD.—See Sumitomo Electric Industries, Ltd.; *Int'l*, pg. 7283
SUMITOMO ELECTRIC INTERCONNECT HONG KONG LTD—See Sumitomo Electric Industries, Ltd.; *Int'l*, pg. 7283
SUMITOMO ELECTRIC INTERCONNECT PRODUCTS (HONG KONG), LTD.—See Sumitomo Electric Industries, Ltd.; *Int'l*, pg. 7283
SUMITOMO ELECTRIC INTERCONNECT PRODUCTS INC.—See Sumitomo Electric Industries, Ltd.; *Int'l*, pg. 7283
SUMITOMO ELECTRIC INTERCONNECT PRODUCTS (M) SDN. BHD.—See Sumitomo Electric Industries, Ltd.; *Int'l*, pg. 7283
SUMITOMO ELECTRIC INTERCONNECT PRODUCTS (SHANGHAI), LTD.—See Sumitomo Electric Industries, Ltd.; *Int'l*, pg. 7283
SUMITOMO ELECTRIC INTERCONNECT PRODUCTS (SHENZHEN), LTD.—See Sumitomo Electric Industries, Ltd.; *Int'l*, pg. 7283
SUMITOMO ELECTRIC INTERCONNECT PRODUCTS (SINGAPORE) PTE., LTD.—See Sumitomo Electric Industries, Ltd.; *Int'l*, pg. 7283
SUMITOMO ELECTRIC INTERCONNECT PRODUCTS (SUZHOU), LTD.—See Sumitomo Electric Industries, Ltd.; *Int'l*, pg. 7283
SUMITOMO ELECTRIC INTERCONNECT PRODUCTS (VIETNAM), LTD.—See Sumitomo Electric Industries, Ltd.; *Int'l*, pg. 7283
SUMITOMO ELECTRIC INTERNATIONAL (SINGAPORE) PTE. LTD.—See Sumitomo Electric Industries, Ltd.; *Int'l*, pg. 7283
SUMITOMO ELECTRIC (KOREA) ELECTRONICS, LTD.—See Sumitomo Electric Industries, Ltd.; *Int'l*, pg. 7282
SUMITOMO ELECTRIC LIGHTWAVE CORP.—See Sumitomo Electric Industries, Ltd.; *Int'l*, pg. 7283
SUMITOMO ELECTRIC MAGNET WIRE (M) SDN. BHD.—See Sumitomo Electric Industries, Ltd.; *Int'l*, pg. 7283
SUMITOMO ELECTRIC MANAGEMENT (SHANGHAI) CO., LTD.—See Sumitomo Electric Industries, Ltd.; *Int'l*, pg. 7283
SUMITOMO ELECTRIC OPTICAL COMPONENTS (WUXI) CO., LTD.—See Sumitomo Electric Industries, Ltd.; *Int'l*, pg. 7283
SUMITOMO ELECTRIC OPTIFRONTIER CO., LTD.—See Sumitomo Electric Industries, Ltd.; *Int'l*, pg. 7283
SUMITOMO ELECTRIC PHOTO-ELECTRONICS COMPONENTS (SUZHOU), LTD.—See Sumitomo Electric Industries, Ltd.; *Int'l*, pg. 7283
SUMITOMO ELECTRIC PRINTED CIRCUITS, INC.—See Sumitomo Electric Industries, Ltd.; *Int'l*, pg. 7283
SUMITOMO ELECTRIC SCHRUMPF-PRODUKTE GMBH—See Sumitomo Electric Industries, Ltd.; *Int'l*, pg. 7282
SUMITOMO ELECTRIC SEMICONDUCTOR MATERIALS, INC.—See Sumitomo Electric Industries, Ltd.; *Int'l*, pg. 7283
SUMITOMO ELECTRIC (SHANGHAI) ELECTRONICS, LTD.—See Sumitomo Electric Industries, Ltd.; *Int'l*, pg. 7282

SUMITOMO ELECTRIC SINTERED ALLOY LTD.—See Sumitomo Electric Industries, Ltd.; *Int'l*, pg. 7283
SUMITOMO ELECTRIC SINTERED COMPONENTS (GERMANY) GMBH—See Sumitomo Electric Industries, Ltd.; *Int'l*, pg. 7283
SUMITOMO ELECTRIC SINTERED COMPONENTS (M) SDN. BHD.—See Sumitomo Electric Industries, Ltd.; *Int'l*, pg. 7283
SUMITOMO ELECTRIC SINTERED COMPONENTS (THAILAND) CO., LTD.—See Sumitomo Electric Industries, Ltd.; *Int'l*, pg. 7283
SUMITOMO ELECTRIC SYSTEM SOLUTIONS CO., LTD. - KONOHANA WORKS—See Sumitomo Electric Industries, Ltd.; *Int'l*, pg. 7283
SUMITOMO ELECTRIC SYSTEM SOLUTIONS CO., LTD.—See Sumitomo Electric Industries, Ltd.; *Int'l*, pg. 7283
SUMITOMO ELECTRIC TECHNICAL SOLUTIONS, INC.—See Sumitomo Electric Industries, Ltd.; *Int'l*, pg. 7283
SUMITOMO ELECTRIC (THAILAND) LTD.—See Sumitomo Electric Industries, Ltd.; *Int'l*, pg. 7282
SUMITOMO ELECTRIC (THAILAND) LTD.—See Sumitomo Electric Industries, Ltd.; *Int'l*, pg. 7282
SUMITOMO ELECTRIC (THAILAND), LTD.—See Sumitomo Electric Industries, Ltd.; *Int'l*, pg. 7284
SUMITOMO ELECTRIC TOCHIGI CO., LTD.—See Sumitomo Electric Industries, Ltd.; *Int'l*, pg. 7283
SUMITOMO ELECTRIC TOOL NET, INC.—See Sumitomo Electric Industries, Ltd.; *Int'l*, pg. 7283
SUMITOMO ELECTRIC TOYAMA CO., LTD.—See Sumitomo Electric Industries, Ltd.; *Int'l*, pg. 7283
SUMITOMO ELECTRIC U.S.A. HOLDINGS, INC.—See Sumitomo Electric Industries, Ltd.; *Int'l*, pg. 7278
SUMITOMO ELECTRIC U.S.A., INC.—See Sumitomo Electric Industries, Ltd.; *Int'l*, pg. 7283
SUMITOMO ELECTRIC WINDTECH AMERICA, INC.—See Sumitomo Electric Industries, Ltd.; *Int'l*, pg. 7284
SUMITOMO ELECTRIC WINTEC AMERICA, INC.—See Sumitomo Electric Industries, Ltd.; *Int'l*, pg. 7284
SUMITOMO ELECTRIC WINTEC, INC.—See Sumitomo Electric Industries, Ltd.; *Int'l*, pg. 7284
SUMITOMO ELECTRIC WINTEC (MALAYSIA) SDN. BHD.—See Sumitomo Electric Industries, Ltd.; *Int'l*, pg. 7284
SUMITOMO ELECTRIC WINTEC (SINGAPORE) PTE LTD—See Sumitomo Electric Industries, Ltd.; *Int'l*, pg. 7284
SUMITOMO ELECTRIC WINTEC (THAILAND) CO., LTD.—See Sumitomo Electric Industries, Ltd.; *Int'l*, pg. 7284
SUMITOMO ELECTRIC WINTEC (WUXI) CO., LTD.—See Sumitomo Electric Industries, Ltd.; *Int'l*, pg. 7284
SUMITOMO ELECTRIC WIRING SYSTEMS (EUROPE) LTD.—See Sumitomo Electric Industries, Ltd.; *Int'l*, pg. 7284
SUMITOMO ELECTRIC WIRING SYSTEMS, INC.—See Sumitomo Electric Industries, Ltd.; *Int'l*, pg. 7284
SUMITOMO ELECTRIC WIRING SYSTEMS - NASHVILLE DISTRIBUTION CENTER—See Sumitomo Electric Industries, Ltd.; *Int'l*, pg. 7284
SUMITOMO ELECTRIC WIRING SYSTEMS (SLOVAKIA) LTD.—See Sumitomo Electric Industries, Ltd.; *Int'l*, pg. 7284
SUMITOMO ELECTRIC WIRING SYSTEMS (THAILAND), LTD.—See Sumitomo Electric Industries, Ltd.; *Int'l*, pg. 7284
SUMITOMO FORESTRY AMERICA, INC.—See Sumitomo Forestry Co., Ltd.; *Int'l*, pg. 7286
SUMITOMO FORESTRY ARCHI TECHNO CO., LTD.—See Sumitomo Forestry Co., Ltd.; *Int'l*, pg. 7286
SUMITOMO FORESTRY AUSTRALIA PTY. LTD.—See Sumitomo Forestry Co., Ltd.; *Int'l*, pg. 7286
SUMITOMO FORESTRY CO., LTD.; *Int'l*, pg. 7285
SUMITOMO FORESTRY CREST CO., LTD.—See Sumitomo Forestry Co., Ltd.; *Int'l*, pg. 7286
SUMITOMO FORESTRY (DALIAN) LTD.—See Sumitomo Forestry Co., Ltd.; *Int'l*, pg. 7286
SUMITOMO FORESTRY HOME ENGINEERING CO., LTD.—See Sumitomo Forestry Co., Ltd.; *Int'l*, pg. 7286
SUMITOMO FORESTRY HOME SERVICE CO., LTD.—See Sumitomo Forestry Co., Ltd.; *Int'l*, pg. 7286
SUMITOMO FORESTRY INDIA PVT. LTD.—See Sumitomo Forestry Co., Ltd.; *Int'l*, pg. 7286
SUMITOMO FORESTRY INFORMATION SYSTEMS CO., LTD.—See Sumitomo Forestry Co., Ltd.; *Int'l*, pg. 7286
SUMITOMO FORESTRY LANDSCAPING CO., LTD.—See Sumitomo Forestry Co., Ltd.; *Int'l*, pg. 7286
SUMITOMO FORESTRY RESIDENTIAL CO., LTD.—See Sumitomo Forestry Co., Ltd.; *Int'l*, pg. 7286
SUMITOMO FORESTRY (SINGAPORE) LTD.—See Sumitomo Forestry Co., Ltd.; *Int'l*, pg. 7286
SUMITOMO FRANCE S.A.S.—See Sumitomo Corporation; *Int'l*, pg. 7274
SUMITOMO FUDOSAN BELLESALLE CO., LTD.—See Sumitomo Realty & Development Co., Ltd.; *Int'l*, pg. 7297

SUMITOMO FUDOSAN ESFORTA CO., LTD.—See Sumitomo Realty & Development Co., Ltd.; *Int'l*, pg. 7297
SUMITOMO FUDOSAN FINANCE CO., LTD.—See Sumitomo Realty & Development Co., Ltd.; *Int'l*, pg. 7297
SUMITOMO FUDOSAN REFORM CO., LTD.—See Sumitomo Realty & Development Co., Ltd.; *Int'l*, pg. 7297
SUMITOMO FUDOSAN SYSCON CO., LTD.—See Sumitomo Realty & Development Co., Ltd.; *Int'l*, pg. 7297
SUMITOMO FUDOSAN TATEMONO SERVICE CO., LTD.—See Sumitomo Realty & Development Co., Ltd.; *Int'l*, pg. 7297
SUMITOMO FUDOSAN VILLA FONTAINE CO., LTD.—See Sumitomo Realty & Development Co., Ltd.; *Int'l*, pg. 7297
SUMITOMO HEAVY INDUSTRIES BUSINESS ASSOCIATES, LTD.—See Sumitomo Heavy Industries, Ltd.; *Int'l*, pg. 7289
SUMITOMO HEAVY INDUSTRIES (CHINA), LTD.—See Sumitomo Heavy Industries, Ltd.; *Int'l*, pg. 7289
SUMITOMO HEAVY INDUSTRIES CONSTRUCTION CRANES CO., LTD.—See Sumitomo Heavy Industries, Ltd.; *Int'l*, pg. 7289
SUMITOMO HEAVY INDUSTRIES ENGINEERING AND SERVICES CO., LTD.—See Sumitomo Heavy Industries, Ltd.; *Int'l*, pg. 7289
SUMITOMO HEAVY INDUSTRIES ENGINEERING & SERVICES CO., LTD. - NIIHAMA WORKS—See Sumitomo Heavy Industries, Ltd.; *Int'l*, pg. 7289
SUMITOMO HEAVY INDUSTRIES ENVIRONMENT CO., LTD.—See Sumitomo Heavy Industries, Ltd.; *Int'l*, pg. 7289
SUMITOMO HEAVY INDUSTRIES FINETECH, LTD.—See Sumitomo Heavy Industries, Ltd.; *Int'l*, pg. 7289
SUMITOMO HEAVY INDUSTRIES GEARBOX CO., LTD.—See Sumitomo Heavy Industries, Ltd.; *Int'l*, pg. 7290
SUMITOMO HEAVY INDUSTRIES HIMATEX CO., LTD.—See Sumitomo Heavy Industries, Ltd.; *Int'l*, pg. 7290
SUMITOMO HEAVY INDUSTRIES ION TECHNOLOGY CO., LTD.—See Sumitomo Heavy Industries, Ltd.; *Int'l*, pg. 7290
SUMITOMO HEAVY INDUSTRIES, LTD. - CHIBA WORKS—See Sumitomo Heavy Industries, Ltd.; *Int'l*, pg. 7290
SUMITOMO HEAVY INDUSTRIES, LTD. - ENGINEERING AND SALES DIVISION—See Sumitomo Heavy Industries, Ltd.; *Int'l*, pg. 7290
SUMITOMO HEAVY INDUSTRIES, LTD. - MECHATRONICS DIVISION—See Sumitomo Heavy Industries, Ltd.; *Int'l*, pg. 7290
SUMITOMO HEAVY INDUSTRIES, LTD. - NAGOYA WORKS—See Sumitomo Heavy Industries, Ltd.; *Int'l*, pg. 7290
SUMITOMO HEAVY INDUSTRIES, LTD. - NIIHAMA PLANT—See Sumitomo Heavy Industries, Ltd.; *Int'l*, pg. 7290
SUMITOMO HEAVY INDUSTRIES, LTD. - OKAYAMA WORKS—See Sumitomo Heavy Industries, Ltd.; *Int'l*, pg. 7290
SUMITOMO HEAVY INDUSTRIES, LTD. - POWER TRANSMISSION & CONTROLS DIVISION—See Sumitomo Heavy Industries, Ltd.; *Int'l*, pg. 7290
SUMITOMO HEAVY INDUSTRIES, LTD. - QUANTUM EQUIPMENT DIVISION—See Sumitomo Heavy Industries, Ltd.; *Int'l*, pg. 7290
SUMITOMO HEAVY INDUSTRIES, LTD. - SAIJO PLANT—See Sumitomo Heavy Industries, Ltd.; *Int'l*, pg. 7290
SUMITOMO HEAVY INDUSTRIES, LTD.; *Int'l*, pg. 7286
SUMITOMO HEAVY INDUSTRIES, LTD. - TANASHI WORKS—See Sumitomo Heavy Industries, Ltd.; *Int'l*, pg. 7290
SUMITOMO HEAVY INDUSTRIES, LTD. - YOKOSUKA WORKS—See Sumitomo Heavy Industries, Ltd.; *Int'l*, pg. 7290
SUMITOMO HEAVY INDUSTRIES MARINE & ENGINEERING CO., LTD.—See Sumitomo Heavy Industries, Ltd.; *Int'l*, pg. 7290
SUMITOMO HEAVY INDUSTRIES MATERIAL HANDLING SYSTEMS CO., LTD.—See Sumitomo Heavy Industries, Ltd.; *Int'l*, pg. 7290
SUMITOMO HEAVY INDUSTRIES MECHATRONICS, LTD.—See Sumitomo Heavy Industries, Ltd.; *Int'l*, pg. 7290
SUMITOMO HEAVY INDUSTRIES MODERN, LTD. - FUTTSU PLANT—See Sumitomo Heavy Industries, Ltd.; *Int'l*, pg. 7290
SUMITOMO HEAVY INDUSTRIES MODERN, LTD.—See Sumitomo Heavy Industries, Ltd.; *Int'l*, pg. 7290
SUMITOMO HEAVY INDUSTRIES PROCESS EQUIPMENT CO., LTD.—See Sumitomo Heavy Industries, Ltd.; *Int'l*, pg. 7290
SUMITOMO HEAVY INDUSTRIES PTC SALES CO., LTD.—See Sumitomo Heavy Industries, Ltd.; *Int'l*, pg. 7290
SUMITOMO HEAVY INDUSTRIES (TANGSHAN), LTD.—See Sumitomo Heavy Industries, Ltd.; *Int'l*, pg. 7289

COMPANY NAME INDEX

SUMITOMO HEAVY INDUSTRIES TECHNO-FORT CO., LTD.—See Sumitomo Heavy Industries, Ltd.; *Int'l*, pg. 7290
SUMITOMO HEAVY INDUSTRIES (USA), INC.—See Sumitomo Heavy Industries, Ltd.; *Int'l*, pg. 7289
SUMITOMO HEAVY INDUSTRIES (VIETNAM) CO., LTD.—See Sumitomo Heavy Industries, Ltd.; *Int'l*, pg. 7289
SUMITOMO INDUSTRIAS PESADAS DO BRASIL LTDA.—See Sumitomo Heavy Industries, Ltd.; *Int'l*, pg. 7290
SUMITOMO JOINT ELECTRIC POWER CO., LTD.—See Sumitomo Chemical Company, Limited; *Int'l*, pg. 7267
SUMITOMO LIFE INSURANCE COMPANY - NEW YORK—See Sumitomo Life Insurance Company; *Int'l*, pg. 7291
SUMITOMO LIFE INSURANCE COMPANY; *Int'l*, pg. 7291
SUMITOMO MACHINERY CORPORATION OF AMERICA—See Sumitomo Heavy Industries, Ltd.; *Int'l*, pg. 7290
SUMITOMO METAL MINING AMERICA INC.—See Sumitomo Metal Mining Co., Ltd.; *Int'l*, pg. 7292
SUMITOMO METAL MINING ARIZONA INC.—See Sumitomo Metal Mining Co., Ltd.; *Int'l*, pg. 7292
SUMITOMO METAL MINING ASIA PACIFIC PTE. LTD.—See Sumitomo Metal Mining Co., Ltd.; *Int'l*, pg. 7292
SUMITOMO METAL MINING BRASS AND COPPER CO., LTD.—See Sumitomo Metal Mining Co., Ltd.; *Int'l*, pg. 7292
SUMITOMO METAL MINING CANADA LTD.—See Sumitomo Metal Mining Co., Ltd.; *Int'l*, pg. 7292
SUMITOMO METAL MINING CHILE LTDA.—See Sumitomo Metal Mining Co., Ltd.; *Int'l*, pg. 7292
SUMITOMO METAL MINING CO., LTD. - BESSHI-NIIHAMA DISTRICT DIVISION—See Sumitomo Metal Mining Co., Ltd.; *Int'l*, pg. 7292
SUMITOMO METAL MINING CO., LTD. - ENERGY & ENVIRONMENT BUSINESS DIV. RESEARCH & DEVELOPMENT CENTER—See Sumitomo Metal Mining Co., Ltd.; *Int'l*, pg. 7292
SUMITOMO METAL MINING CO., LTD. - HARIMA DISTRICT DIVISION—See Sumitomo Metal Mining Co., Ltd.; *Int'l*, pg. 7292
SUMITOMO METAL MINING CO., LTD. - HARIMA SMELTER FACILITY—See Sumitomo Metal Mining Co., Ltd.; *Int'l*, pg. 7292
SUMITOMO METAL MINING CO., LTD. - ICHIKAWA RESEARCH LABORATORY—See Sumitomo Metal Mining Co., Ltd.; *Int'l*, pg. 7292
SUMITOMO METAL MINING CO., LTD. - ISOURA PLANT—See Sumitomo Metal Mining Co., Ltd.; *Int'l*, pg. 7292
SUMITOMO METAL MINING CO., LTD. - KUNITOMI DISTRICT DIVISION—See Sumitomo Metal Mining Co., Ltd.; *Int'l*, pg. 7292
SUMITOMO METAL MINING CO., LTD. - NIIHAMA NICKEL REFINERY FACILITY—See Sumitomo Metal Mining Co., Ltd.; *Int'l*, pg. 7292
SUMITOMO METAL MINING CO., LTD. - NIIHAMA RESEARCH LABORATORY—See Sumitomo Metal Mining Co., Ltd.; *Int'l*, pg. 7292
SUMITOMO METAL MINING CO., LTD. - OME DISTRICT DIVISION—See Sumitomo Metal Mining Co., Ltd.; *Int'l*, pg. 7292
SUMITOMO METAL MINING CO., LTD. - SAGAMI PLANT—See Sumitomo Metal Mining Co., Ltd.; *Int'l*, pg. 7292
SUMITOMO METAL MINING CO., LTD.; *Int'l*, pg. 7291
SUMITOMO METAL MINING CO., LTD. - TOYO SMELTER & REFINERY FACILITY—See Sumitomo Metal Mining Co., Ltd.; *Int'l*, pg. 7292
SUMITOMO METAL MINING DO BRASIL LTDA.—See Sumitomo Metal Mining Co., Ltd.; *Int'l*, pg. 7292
SUMITOMO METAL MINING ELECTRONICS PARTS PTE. LTD.—See Sumitomo Metal Mining Co., Ltd.; *Int'l*, pg. 7292
SUMITOMO METAL MINING ENGINEERING CO., LTD.—See Sumitomo Metal Mining Co., Ltd.; *Int'l*, pg. 7292
SUMITOMO METAL MINING OCEANIA PTY. LTD.—See Sumitomo Metal Mining Co., Ltd.; *Int'l*, pg. 7292
SUMITOMO METAL MINING PERU S.A.—See Sumitomo Metal Mining Co., Ltd.; *Int'l*, pg. 7292
SUMITOMO METAL MINING SIPOREX CO., LTD.—See Sumitomo Metal Mining Co., Ltd.; *Int'l*, pg. 7292
SUMITOMO MITSUI ASSET MANAGEMENT CO., LTD.—See Sumitomo Mitsui Financial Group, Inc.; *Int'l*, pg. 7293
SUMITOMO MITSUI ASSET MANAGEMENT (HONG KONG) LIMITED—See Sumitomo Mitsui Financial Group, Inc.; *Int'l*, pg. 7293
SUMITOMO MITSUI ASSET MANAGEMENT (NEW YORK) INC.—See Sumitomo Mitsui Financial Group, Inc.; *Int'l*, pg. 7293
SUMITOMO MITSUI AUTO LEASING & SERVICE (THAILAND) CO., LTD.—See Sumitomo Corporation; *Int'l*, pg. 7275

SUMITOMO MITSUI AUTO LEASING & SERVICE (THAILAND) CO., LTD.—See Sumitomo Mitsui Financial Group, Inc.; *Int'l*, pg. 7295
SUMITOMO MITSUI AUTO SERVICE COMPANY, LIMITED—See Sumitomo Corporation; *Int'l*, pg. 7274
SUMITOMO MITSUI AUTO SERVICE COMPANY, LIMITED—See Sumitomo Mitsui Financial Group, Inc.; *Int'l*, pg. 7293
SUMITOMO MITSUI BANKING CORPORATION - BAHRAIN—See Sumitomo Mitsui Financial Group, Inc.; *Int'l*, pg. 7295
SUMITOMO MITSUI BANKING CORPORATION - BANGKOK—See Sumitomo Mitsui Financial Group, Inc.; *Int'l*, pg. 7295
SUMITOMO MITSUI BANKING CORPORATION (CHINA) LIMITED—See Sumitomo Mitsui Financial Group, Inc.; *Int'l*, pg. 7294
SUMITOMO MITSUI BANKING CORPORATION - DUSSELDORF—See Sumitomo Mitsui Financial Group, Inc.; *Int'l*, pg. 7295
SUMITOMO MITSUI BANKING CORPORATION EUROPE LIMITED—See Sumitomo Mitsui Financial Group, Inc.; *Int'l*, pg. 7295
SUMITOMO MITSUI BANKING CORPORATION - HONG KONG—See Sumitomo Mitsui Financial Group, Inc.; *Int'l*, pg. 7295
SUMITOMO MITSUI BANKING CORPORATION OF CANADA—See Sumitomo Mitsui Financial Group, Inc.; *Int'l*, pg. 7295
SUMITOMO MITSUI BANKING CORPORATION—See Sumitomo Mitsui Financial Group, Inc.; *Int'l*, pg. 7293
SUMITOMO MITSUI CARD CO., LTD.—See Sumitomo Mitsui Financial Group, Inc.; *Int'l*, pg. 7293
SUMITOMO MITSUI CONSTRUCTION CO., LTD.—See Mitsui & Co., Ltd.; *Int'l*, pg. 4980
SUMITOMO MITSUI DS ASSET MANAGEMENT COMPANY, LIMITED—See Daiwa Securities Group Inc.; *Int'l*, pg. 1949
SUMITOMO MITSUI DS ASSET MANAGEMENT COMPANY, LIMITED—See Sumitomo Mitsui Financial Group, Inc.; *Int'l*, pg. 7295
SUMITOMO MITSUI FINANCE AUSTRALIA LIMITED—See Sumitomo Mitsui Financial Group, Inc.; *Int'l*, pg. 7295
SUMITOMO MITSUI FINANCE & LEASING (CHINA) CO., LTD. - SHANGHAI BRANCH—See Sumitomo Corporation; *Int'l*, pg. 7275
SUMITOMO MITSUI FINANCE & LEASING (CHINA) CO., LTD. - SHANGHAI BRANCH—See Sumitomo Mitsui Financial Group, Inc.; *Int'l*, pg. 7295
SUMITOMO MITSUI FINANCE & LEASING (CHINA) CO., LTD.—See Sumitomo Corporation; *Int'l*, pg. 7275
SUMITOMO MITSUI FINANCE & LEASING (CHINA) CO., LTD.—See Sumitomo Mitsui Financial Group, Inc.; *Int'l*, pg. 7295
SUMITOMO MITSUI FINANCE & LEASING CO., LTD.—See Sumitomo Corporation; *Int'l*, pg. 7274
SUMITOMO MITSUI FINANCE & LEASING CO., LTD.—See Sumitomo Mitsui Financial Group, Inc.; *Int'l*, pg. 7295
SUMITOMO MITSUI FINANCE & LEASING (HONG KONG) LTD.—See Sumitomo Corporation; *Int'l*, pg. 7275
SUMITOMO MITSUI FINANCE & LEASING (HONG KONG) LTD.—See Sumitomo Mitsui Financial Group, Inc.; *Int'l*, pg. 7295
SUMITOMO MITSUI FINANCE & LEASING (SINGAPORE) PTE. LTD.—See Sumitomo Corporation; *Int'l*, pg. 7275
SUMITOMO MITSUI FINANCE & LEASING (SINGAPORE) PTE. LTD.—See Sumitomo Mitsui Financial Group, Inc.; *Int'l*, pg. 7295
SUMITOMO MITSUI FINANCIAL GROUP, INC.; *Int'l*, pg. 7293
SUMITOMO MITSUI TRUST BANK, LIMITED—See Sumitomo Mitsui Trust Holdings, Inc.; *Int'l*, pg. 7296
SUMITOMO MITSUI TRUST BANK, LTD. - SINGAPORE BRANCH—See Sumitomo Mitsui Trust Holdings, Inc.; *Int'l*, pg. 7296
SUMITOMO MITSUI TRUST BANK, LTD. - USA BRANCH—See Sumitomo Mitsui Trust Holdings, Inc.; *Int'l*, pg. 7296
SUMITOMO MITSUI TRUST BANK (LUXEMBOURG) S.A.—See Sumitomo Mitsui Trust Holdings, Inc.; *Int'l*, pg. 7296
SUMITOMO MITSUI TRUST CLUB CO., LTD.—See Sumitomo Mitsui Trust Holdings, Inc.; *Int'l*, pg. 7296
SUMITOMO MITSUI TRUST HOLDINGS, INC.; *Int'l*, pg. 7296
SUMITOMO MITSUI TRUST (HONG KONG) LIMITED—See Sumitomo Mitsui Trust Holdings, Inc.; *Int'l*, pg. 7296
SUMITOMO MITSUI TRUST INTERNATIONAL LIMITED—See Sumitomo Mitsui Trust Holdings, Inc.; *Int'l*, pg. 7296
SUMITOMO MITSUI TRUST (IRELAND) LIMITED—See Sumitomo Mitsui Trust Holdings, Inc.; *Int'l*, pg. 7296
SUMITOMO MITSUI TRUST (UK) LIMITED—See Sumitomo Mitsui Trust Holdings, Inc.; *Int'l*, pg. 7296

SUMITOMO NAACO MATERIALS HANDLING CO., LTD.—See Hyster-Yale Materials Handling, Inc.; *U.S. Public*, pg. 1080
SUMITOMO NAACO MATERIALS HANDLING CO., LTD.—See Sumitomo Heavy Industries, Ltd.; *Int'l*, pg. 7290
SUMITOMO NACCO FORKLIFT CO., LTD.—See Sumitomo Heavy Industries, Ltd.; *Int'l*, pg. 7290
SUMITOMO NACCO MATERIALS HANDLING SALES CO., LTD.—See Hyster-Yale Materials Handling, Inc.; *U.S. Public*, pg. 1080
SUMITOMO NACCO MATERIALS HANDLING SALES CO., LTD.—See Sumitomo Heavy Industries, Ltd.; *Int'l*, pg. 7290
SUMITOMO OSAKA CEMENT CO LTD; *Int'l*, pg. 7296
SUMITOMO PHARMA AMERICA HOLDINGS, INC.—See Sumitomo Chemical Company, Limited; *Int'l*, pg. 7266
SUMITOMO PHARMACEUTICALS ASIA PACIFIC PTE. LTD.—See Sumitomo Chemical Company, Limited; *Int'l*, pg. 7267
SUMITOMO PHARMACEUTICALS(SUZHOU)CO., LTD.—See Sumitomo Chemical Company, Limited; *Int'l*, pg. 7267
SUMITOMO PHARMACEUTICALS (THAILAND) CO., LTD.—See Sumitomo Chemical Company, Limited; *Int'l*, pg. 7267
SUMITOMO PHARMA (CHINA) CO., LTD.—See Sumitomo Chemical Company, Limited; *Int'l*, pg. 7267
SUMITOMO PHARMA CO., LTD.—See Sumitomo Chemical Company, Limited; *Int'l*, pg. 7267
SUMITOMO PHARMA CO., LTD.—See Sumitomo Chemical Company, Limited; *Int'l*, pg. 7267
SUMITOMO PHARMA MALAYSIA SDN. BHD.—See Sumitomo Chemical Company, Limited; *Int'l*, pg. 7267
SUMITOMO PHARMA TAIWAN CO., LTD.—See Sumitomo Chemical Company, Limited; *Int'l*, pg. 7267
SUMITOMO PLASTICS AMERICA, INC.—See Sumitomo Bakelite Co., Ltd.; *Int'l*, pg. 7263
SUMITOMO PRECISION PRODUCTS CO., LTD. - SHIGA PLANT—See Sumitomo Corporation; *Int'l*, pg. 7275
SUMITOMO PRECISION PRODUCTS CO., LTD.—See Sumitomo Corporation; *Int'l*, pg. 7275
SUMITOMO PRECISION PRODUCTS CO., LTD. - WAKAYAMA PLANT—See Sumitomo Corporation; *Int'l*, pg. 7275
SUMITOMO PRECISION SHANGHAI CO., LTD.—See Sumitomo Corporation; *Int'l*, pg. 7275
SUMITOMO PRECISION USA, INC.—See Sumitomo Corporation; *Int'l*, pg. 7275
SUMITOMO REAL ESTATE SALES CO., LTD.—See Sumitomo Realty & Development Co., Ltd.; *Int'l*, pg. 7297
SUMITOMO REAL ESTATE SALES (N.Y) INC—See Sumitomo Realty & Development Co., Ltd.; *Int'l*, pg. 7297
SUMITOMO REALTY & DEVELOPMENT CO., LTD.; *Int'l*, pg. 7297
SUMITOMO RIKO AMERICA, INC.—See Sumitomo Riko Company Limited; *Int'l*, pg. 7298
SUMITOMO RIKO COMPANY LIMITED; *Int'l*, pg. 7297
SUMITOMO RIKO HOSETEX, LTD.—See Sumitomo Riko Company Limited; *Int'l*, pg. 7298
SUMITOMO RUBBER AKO LASTIK SANAYI VE TICARET A.S.—See Sumitomo Rubber Industries, Ltd.; *Int'l*, pg. 7299
SUMITOMO RUBBER ASIA (TYRE) PTE, LTD.—See Sumitomo Rubber Industries, Ltd.; *Int'l*, pg. 7299
SUMITOMO RUBBER (CHANGSHU) CO., LTD.—See Sumitomo Rubber Industries, Ltd.; *Int'l*, pg. 7299
SUMITOMO RUBBER INDUSTRIES, LTD. - CHANGSHU FACTORY—See Sumitomo Rubber Industries, Ltd.; *Int'l*, pg. 7299
SUMITOMO RUBBER INDUSTRIES, LTD. - INDONESIA FACTORY—See Sumitomo Rubber Industries, Ltd.; *Int'l*, pg. 7299
SUMITOMO RUBBER INDUSTRIES, LTD. - IZUMIOHTSU FACTORY—See Sumitomo Rubber Industries, Ltd.; *Int'l*, pg. 7299
SUMITOMO RUBBER INDUSTRIES, LTD. - KAKOGAWA FACTORY—See Sumitomo Rubber Industries, Ltd.; *Int'l*, pg. 7299
SUMITOMO RUBBER INDUSTRIES, LTD. - MIYAZAKI FACTORY—See Sumitomo Rubber Industries, Ltd.; *Int'l*, pg. 7299
SUMITOMO RUBBER INDUSTRIES, LTD. - NAGOYA FACTORY—See Sumitomo Rubber Industries, Ltd.; *Int'l*, pg. 7299
SUMITOMO RUBBER INDUSTRIES, LTD. - SHIRAKAWA FACTORY—See Sumitomo Rubber Industries, Ltd.; *Int'l*, pg. 7299
SUMITOMO RUBBER INDUSTRIES, LTD.; *Int'l*, pg. 7298
SUMITOMO RUBBER INDUSTRIES, LTD. - SPORTS BUSINESS—See Sumitomo Rubber Industries, Ltd.; *Int'l*, pg. 7299
SUMITOMO RUBBER MIDDLE EAST FZE—See Sumitomo Rubber Industries, Ltd.; *Int'l*, pg. 7300
SUMITOMO RUBBER NORTH AMERICA, INC.—See Sumitomo Rubber Industries, Ltd.; *Int'l*, pg. 7300

SUMITOMO RUBBER INDUSTRIES, LTD.

CORPORATE AFFILIATIONS

SUMITOMO RUBBER SOUTH AFRICA (PTY) LIMITED—See Sumitomo Rubber Industries, Ltd.; pg. 7300
SUMITOMO RUBBER (THAILAND) CO., LTD.—See Sumitomo Rubber Industries, Ltd.; Int'l, pg. 7299
SUMITOMO RUBBER USA, LLC—See Sumitomo Rubber Industries, Ltd.; Int'l, pg. 7300
SUMITOMO (SEI) ELECTRONIC WIRE, INC.—See Sumitomo Electric Industries, Ltd.; Int'l, pg. 7282
SUMITOMO SEIKA AMERICA, INC.—See Sumitomo Seika Chemicals Company Limited; Int'l, pg. 7300
SUMITOMO SEIKA ASIA PACIFIC PTE. LTD.—See Sumitomo Seika Chemicals Company Limited; Int'l, pg. 7300
SUMITOMO SEIKA CHEMICALS COMPANY LIMITED; Int'l, pg. 7300
SUMITOMO SEIKA EUROPE S.A./N.V.—See Sumitomo Seika Chemicals Company Limited; Int'l, pg. 7300
SUMITOMO SEIKA SINGAPORE PTE. LTD.—See Sumitomo Seika Chemicals Company Limited; Int'l, pg. 7300
SUMITOMO (SEI) STEEL WIRE CORP.—See Sumitomo Electric Industries, Ltd.; Int'l, pg. 7282
SUMITOMO (S.H.I.) CONSTRUCTION MACHINERY CO., LTD.—See Sumitomo Heavy Industries, Ltd.; Int'l, pg. 7289
SUMITOMO (S.H.I.) CONSTRUCTION MACHINERY SALES CO., LTD.—See Sumitomo Heavy Industries, Ltd.; Int'l, pg. 7289
SUMITOMO (S.H.I.) CONSTRUCTION MACHINERY (TANGSHAN) CO., LTD.—See Sumitomo Heavy Industries, Ltd.; Int'l, pg. 7289
SUMITOMO (SHI) CRYOGENICS KOREA CO., LTD.—See Sumitomo Heavy Industries, Ltd.; Int'l, pg. 7289
SUMITOMO (SHI) CRYOGENICS OF AMERICA, INC.—See Sumitomo Heavy Industries, Ltd.; Int'l, pg. 7287
SUMITOMO (SHI) CRYOGENICS OF AMERICA, INC.—See Sumitomo Heavy Industries, Ltd.; Int'l, pg. 7287
SUMITOMO (SHI) CRYOGENICS OF EUROPE GMBH—See Sumitomo Heavy Industries, Ltd.; Int'l, pg. 7287
SUMITOMO (SHI) CRYOGENICS OF EUROPE, LTD.—See Sumitomo Heavy Industries, Ltd.; Int'l, pg. 7287
SUMITOMO (SHI) CRYOGENICS SHANGHAI, LTD.—See Sumitomo Heavy Industries, Ltd.; Int'l, pg. 7289
SUMITOMO (SHI) CRYOGENICS TAIWAN CO., LTD.—See Sumitomo Heavy Industries, Ltd.; Int'l, pg. 7289
SUMITOMO (SHI) CYCLO DRIVE ASIA PACIFIC PTE. LTD.—See Sumitomo Heavy Industries, Ltd.; Int'l, pg. 7289
SUMITOMO (SHI) CYCLO DRIVE CHINA, LTD.—See Sumitomo Heavy Industries, Ltd.; Int'l, pg. 7289
SUMITOMO (SHI) CYCLO DRIVE GERMANY GMBH—See Sumitomo Heavy Industries, Ltd.; Int'l, pg. 7289
SUMITOMO (SHI) CYCLO DRIVE KOREA, LTD.—See Sumitomo Heavy Industries, Ltd.; Int'l, pg. 7289
SUMITOMO (SHI) CYCLO DRIVE LOGISTICS, LTD.—See Sumitomo Heavy Industries, Ltd.; Int'l, pg. 7289
SUMITOMO (SHI) CYCLO DRIVE SHANGHAI, LTD.—See Sumitomo Heavy Industries, Ltd.; Int'l, pg. 7289
SUMITOMO (SHI) DEMAG PLASTICS MACHINERY ESPANA S.L.—See Sumitomo Heavy Industries, Ltd.; Int'l, pg. 7289
SUMITOMO (SHI) DEMAG PLASTICS MACHINERY (FRANCE) S.A.S.—See Sumitomo Heavy Industries, Ltd.; Int'l, pg. 7289
SUMITOMO (SHI) DEMAG PLASTICS MACHINERY GMBH—See Sumitomo Heavy Industries, Ltd.; Int'l, pg. 7289
SUMITOMO (SHI) DEMAG PLASTICS MACHINERY HUNGARIA KFT.—See Sumitomo Heavy Industries, Ltd.; Int'l, pg. 7289
SUMITOMO (SHI) DEMAG PLASTICS MACHINERY (ITALIA) S.R.L.—See Sumitomo Heavy Industries, Ltd.; Int'l, pg. 7289
SUMITOMO (SHI) DEMAG PLASTICS MACHINERY NORTH AMERICA, INC.—See Sumitomo Heavy Industries, Ltd.; Int'l, pg. 7289
SUMITOMO (SHI) DEMAG PLASTICS MACHINERY SP. Z O.O.—See Sumitomo Heavy Industries, Ltd.; Int'l, pg. 7289
SUMITOMO (SHI) DEMAG PLASTICS MACHINERY (UK) LTD.—See Sumitomo Heavy Industries, Ltd.; Int'l, pg. 7289
SUMITOMO SHI FW BRAZIL MANAGEMENT LTDA.—See Sumitomo Heavy Industries, Ltd.; Int'l, pg. 7290
SUMITOMO SHI FW ENERGI AKTIEBOLAG—See Sumitomo Heavy Industries, Ltd.; Int'l, pg. 7290
SUMITOMO SHI FW ENERGIA OY—See Sumitomo Heavy Industries, Ltd.; Int'l, pg. 7290
SUMITOMO SHI FW ENERGIA POLSKA SP. Z O.O.—See Sumitomo Heavy Industries, Ltd.; Int'l, pg. 7290
SUMITOMO SHI FW ENERGIE B.V.—See Sumitomo Heavy Industries, Ltd.; Int'l, pg. 7290
SUMITOMO SHI FW ENERGIE GMBH—See Sumitomo Heavy Industries, Ltd.; Int'l, pg. 7290
SUMITOMO SHI FW ENERGY FAKOP SP. Z O.O.—See Sumitomo Heavy Industries, Ltd.; Int'l, pg. 7290
SUMITOMO SHI FW ENERGY MANAGEMENT (SHANGHAI) CO., LTD.—See Sumitomo Heavy Industries, Ltd.; Int'l, pg. 7290
SUMITOMO SHI FW POWER GROUP ASIA LTD.—See Sumitomo Heavy Industries, Ltd.; Int'l, pg. 7290
SUMITOMO SHI FW POWER SERVICE PHILIPPINE CORPORATION—See Sumitomo Heavy Industries, Ltd.; Int'l, pg. 7290
SUMITOMO SHI FW POWER VIETNAM LTD.—See Sumitomo Heavy Industries, Ltd.; Int'l, pg. 7290
SUMITOMO SHI FW SERVICE (THAILAND) LTD.—See Sumitomo Heavy Industries, Ltd.; Int'l, pg. 7291
SUMITOMO (SHI) HANSEN AUSTRALIA PTY. LTD.—See Sumitomo Heavy Industries, Ltd.; Int'l, pg. 7289
SUMITOMO SHOJI CHEMICALS CO., LTD.—See Sumitomo Corporation; Int'l, pg. 7275
SUMITOMO SHOJI FINANCIAL MANAGEMENT CO., LTD.—See Sumitomo Corporation; Int'l, pg. 7275
SUMITOMO SHOJI MACHINEX CO., LTD.—See Sumitomo Corporation; Int'l, pg. 7275
SUMITOMO WAREHOUSE (CHINA) LTD.—See The Sumitomo Warehouse Co. Ltd.; Int'l, pg. 7690
THE SUMITOMO WAREHOUSE CO. LTD.; Int'l, pg. 7689
SUMITOMO WAREHOUSE (EUROPE) GMBH—See The Sumitomo Warehouse Co. Ltd.; Int'l, pg. 7690
SUMITOMO WAREHOUSE (EUROPE) GMBH—See The Sumitomo Warehouse Co. Ltd.; Int'l, pg. 7690
SUMITOMO WAREHOUSE (HONG KONG) LTD.—See The Sumitomo Warehouse Co. Ltd.; Int'l, pg. 7690
SUMITOMO WAREHOUSE KYUSHU CO., LTD.—See The Sumitomo Warehouse Co. Ltd.; Int'l, pg. 7690
SUMITOMO WAREHOUSE (SHANGHAI) LTD.—See The Sumitomo Warehouse Co. Ltd.; Int'l, pg. 7690
SUMITOMO WAREHOUSE (SHENZHEN) LTD.—See The Sumitomo Warehouse Co. Ltd.; Int'l, pg. 7690
SUMITOMO WAREHOUSE (SINGAPORE) PTE. LTD.—See The Sumitomo Warehouse Co. Ltd.; Int'l, pg. 7690
SUMITOMO WAREHOUSE (U.S.A.) INC.- FREIGHT FORWARDING DIVISION—See The Sumitomo Warehouse Co. Ltd.; Int'l, pg. 7690
SUMITOMO WAREHOUSE (U.S.A.) INC.- PARTS CENTER DIVISION—See The Sumitomo Warehouse Co. Ltd.; Int'l, pg. 7690
SUMITOMO WAREHOUSE (U.S.A.) INC.—See The Sumitomo Warehouse Co. Ltd.; Int'l, pg. 7690
SUMITOMO WAREHOUSE (VIETNAM) CO., LTD.—See The Sumitomo Warehouse Co. Ltd.; Int'l, pg. 7690
SUMITOMO WIRING SYSTEMS, LTD. - IBARAKI AUTOMOTIVE WIRE WORKS—See Sumitomo Electric Industries, Ltd.; Int'l, pg. 7284
SUMITOMO WIRING SYSTEMS, LTD. - KAMEYAMA WORKS—See Sumitomo Electric Industries, Ltd.; Int'l, pg. 7284
SUMITOMO WIRING SYSTEMS, LTD.—See Sumitomo Electric Industries, Ltd.; Int'l, pg. 7284
SUMITOMO WIRING SYSTEMS, LTD. - SUZUKA PLANT—See Sumitomo Electric Industries, Ltd.; Int'l, pg. 7284
SUMITOMO WIRING SYSTEMS, LTD. - TSU PLANT—See Sumitomo Electric Industries, Ltd.; Int'l, pg. 7284
SUMITOMO WIRING SYSTEMS (U.S.A.) INC.—See Sumitomo Electric Industries, Ltd.; Int'l, pg. 7284
SUMITOVANT BIOPHARMA LTD.—See Sumitomo Chemical Company, Limited; Int'l, pg. 7267
SUMITRONICS CORPORATION—See Sumitomo Corporation; Int'l, pg. 7275
SUMITRONICS HONG KONG LTD—See Sumitomo Corporation; Int'l, pg. 7275
SUMITRONICS PHILIPPINES, INC.—See Sumitomo Corporation; Int'l, pg. 7275
SUMITRONICS SHANGHAI CO., LTD.—See Sumitomo Corporation; Int'l, pg. 7275
SUMITRONICS (SHENZHEN) LTD—See Sumitomo Corporation; Int'l, pg. 7275
SUMITRONICS TAIWAN CO., LTD.—See Sumitomo Corporation; Int'l, pg. 7275
SUMITRONICS (THAILAND) CO., LTD.—See Sumitomo Corporation; Int'l, pg. 7275
SUMIT WOODS LIMITED; Int'l, pg. 7262
SUMI VIETNAM WIRING SYSTEM CO., LTD.—See Sumitomo Electric Industries, Ltd.; Int'l, pg. 7281
SUMIX CORPORATION—See C.Uyemura & Co., Ltd.; Int'l, pg. 1244
SUMMA GROUP; Int'l, pg. 7300
SUMMA HOLDINGS, INC.; U.S. Private, pg. 3852
SUMMA KUMAGAI, INC.—See Kumagai Gumi Co., Ltd.; Int'l, pg. 4329
SUMMA SILVER CORP.; Int'l, pg. 7300
SUMMA TELECOM LLC—See Summa Group; Int'l, pg. 7300
SUMMA TRADING COMPANY INC.; U.S. Private, pg. 3853
SUMMER BAY RESORT; U.S. Private, pg. 3853
SUMMERDAYS FESTIVAL AG—See CTS Eventim AG & Co. KGAA; Int'l, pg. 1873
SUMMER ENERGY HOLDINGS, INC.; U.S. Public, pg. 1959
SUMMER FRESH SALADS INC.; Int'l, pg. 7300
SUMMERHILL VENTURE PARTNERS; Int'l, pg. 7300
SUMMERILL TUBE CORP.—See Sandvik AB; Int'l, pg. 6535
SUMMER INFANT, INC.—See Kids2, Inc.; U.S. Private, pg. 2303
SUMMERLIN DEVELOPMENT, LLC—See Howard Hughes Holdings Inc.; U.S. Public, pg. 1060
SUMMERLIN HOSPITAL MEDICAL CENTER LLC—See Universal Health Services, Inc.; U.S. Public, pg. 2259
SUMMERLIN LAS VEGAS BASEBALL CLUB, LLC—See Howard Hughes Holdings Inc.; U.S. Public, pg. 1060
SUMMER RANGE SDN. BHD.—See Gromutual Berhad; Int'l, pg. 3088
SUMMERSDALE PUBLISHERS LTD.—See Vivendi SE; Int'l, pg. 8278
SUMMERSET GROUP HOLDINGS LIMITED; Int'l, pg. 7300
SUMMERSET PROFESSIONAL GRILLS; U.S. Private, pg. 3853
SUMMERSET VILLAGES (AOTEA) LIMITED—See Summerset Group Holdings Limited; Int'l, pg. 7300
SUMMERSET VILLAGES (AVONHEAD) LIMITED—See Summerset Group Holdings Limited; Int'l, pg. 7300
SUMMERSET VILLAGES (BELL BLOCK) LIMITED—See Summerset Group Holdings Limited; Int'l, pg. 7300
SUMMERSET VILLAGES (BLENHEIM) LIMITED—See Summerset Group Holdings Limited; Int'l, pg. 7300
SUMMERSET VILLAGES (CAMBRIDGE) LIMITED—See Summerset Group Holdings Limited; Int'l, pg. 7300
SUMMERSET VILLAGES (DUNEDIN) LIMITED—See Summerset Group Holdings Limited; Int'l, pg. 7301
SUMMERSET VILLAGES (ELLERSLIE) LIMITED—See Summerset Group Holdings Limited; Int'l, pg. 7301
SUMMERSET VILLAGES (HALF MOON BAY) LIMITED—See Summerset Group Holdings Limited; Int'l, pg. 7301
SUMMERSET VILLAGES (HAMILTON) LIMITED—See Summerset Group Holdings Limited; Int'l, pg. 7301
SUMMERSET VILLAGES (HASTINGS) LIMITED—See Summerset Group Holdings Limited; Int'l, pg. 7301
SUMMERSET VILLAGES (HAVELOCK NORTH) LIMITED—See Summerset Group Holdings Limited; Int'l, pg. 7301
SUMMERSET VILLAGES (HOBSONVILLE) LIMITED—See Summerset Group Holdings Limited; Int'l, pg. 7301
SUMMERSET VILLAGES (KARAKA) LIMITED—See Summerset Group Holdings Limited; Int'l, pg. 7301
SUMMERSET VILLAGES (KATIKATI) LIMITED—See Summerset Group Holdings Limited; Int'l, pg. 7301
SUMMERSET VILLAGES (KENEPURU) LIMITED—See Summerset Group Holdings Limited; Int'l, pg. 7301
SUMMERSET VILLAGES (LEVIN) LIMITED—See Summerset Group Holdings Limited; Int'l, pg. 7301
SUMMERSET VILLAGES (LOWER HUTT) LIMITED—See Summerset Group Holdings Limited; Int'l, pg. 7301
SUMMERSET VILLAGES (MANUKAU) LIMITED—See Summerset Group Holdings Limited; Int'l, pg. 7301
SUMMERSET VILLAGES (NAPIER) LIMITED—See Summerset Group Holdings Limited; Int'l, pg. 7301
SUMMERSET VILLAGES (NELSON) LIMITED—See Summerset Group Holdings Limited; Int'l, pg. 7301
SUMMERSET VILLAGES (NEW PLYMOUTH) LIMITED—See Summerset Group Holdings Limited; Int'l, pg. 7301
SUMMERSET VILLAGES (PALMERSTON NORTH) LIMITED—See Summerset Group Holdings Limited; Int'l, pg. 7301
SUMMERSET VILLAGES (PAPAMOA) LIMITED—See Summerset Group Holdings Limited; Int'l, pg. 7301
SUMMERSET VILLAGES (PARAPARAUMU) LIMITED—See Summerset Group Holdings Limited; Int'l, pg. 7301
SUMMERSET VILLAGES (PARNELL) LIMITED—See Summerset Group Holdings Limited; Int'l, pg. 7301
SUMMERSET VILLAGES (RANGIORA) LIMITED—See Summerset Group Holdings Limited; Int'l, pg. 7301
SUMMERSET VILLAGES (ROTOTUNA) LIMITED—See Summerset Group Holdings Limited; Int'l, pg. 7301
SUMMERSET VILLAGES (ST JOHNS) LIMITED—See Summerset Group Holdings Limited; Int'l, pg. 7301
SUMMERSET VILLAGES (TAUPO) LIMITED—See Summerset Group Holdings Limited; Int'l, pg. 7301
SUMMERSET VILLAGES (TE AWA) LIMITED—See Summerset Group Holdings Limited; Int'l, pg. 7301
SUMMERSET VILLAGES (TRENTHAM) LIMITED—See Summerset Group Holdings Limited; Int'l, pg. 7301
SUMMERSET VILLAGES (WANGANUI) LIMITED—See Summerset Group Holdings Limited; Int'l, pg. 7301
SUMMERSET VILLAGES (WARKWORTH) LIMITED—See Summerset Group Holdings Limited; Int'l, pg. 7301
SUMMERSET VILLAGES (WHANGAREI) LIMITED—See Summerset Group Holdings Limited; Int'l, pg. 7301
SUMMERS MANUFACTURING CO. INC.; U.S. Private, pg. 3853
SUMMERS RUBBER CO. INC.—See AEA Investors LP; U.S. Private, pg. 115

COMPANY NAME INDEX — SUMMIT PET PRODUCTS DISTRIBUTORS, INC.

SUMMERS-TAYLOR INC.; *U.S. Private,* pg. 3853
SUMMERS THOMPSON LOWRY, INC.—See Aquiline Capital Partners LLC; *U.S. Private,* pg. 305
SUMMER STREET CAPITAL PARTNERS LLC; *U.S. Private,* pg. 3853
SUMMERSVILLE REGIONAL MEDICAL CENTER; *U.S. Private,* pg. 3853
SUMMERTIME INTERNATIONAL LTD.—See TUI AG; *Int'l,* pg. 7966
SUMMER TIMES LTD.—See TUI AG; *Int'l,* pg. 7966
SUMMERVILLE AT NORTH HILLS LLC—See Brookdale Senior Living Inc.; *U.S. Public,* pg. 395
SUMMERVILLE AT OUTLOOK MANOR LLC—See Brookdale Senior Living Inc.; *U.S. Public,* pg. 395
SUMMERVILLE AT PRINCE WILLIAM, INC.—See Brookdale Senior Living Inc.; *U.S. Public,* pg. 395
SUMMERVILLE AT RIDGEWOOD GARDENS LLC—See Brookdale Senior Living Inc.; *U.S. Public,* pg. 395
SUMMERVILLE AT ROSEVILLE GARDENS LLC—See Brookdale Senior Living Inc.; *U.S. Public,* pg. 395
SUMMERVILLE AT STAFFORD, LLC—See Brookdale Senior Living Inc.; *U.S. Public,* pg. 395
SUMMERVILLE AT VOORHEES, LLC—See Brookdale Senior Living Inc.; *U.S. Public,* pg. 395
SUMMERVILLE AT WEKIWA SPRINGS LLC—See Brookdale Senior Living Inc.; *U.S. Public,* pg. 395
SUMMERVILLE AT WESTMINSTER, LLC—See Brookdale Senior Living Inc.; *U.S. Public,* pg. 395
SUMMERVILLE COMMUNICATIONS, INC.—See Evening Post Publishing Co.; *U.S. Private,* pg. 1436
SUMMERWINDS GARDEN CENTERS INC.; *U.S. Private,* pg. 3853
SUMMERWINDS GARDEN CENTERS INC.—See Summerwinds Garden Centers Inc.; *U.S. Private,* pg. 3853
SUMMERWINDS GARDEN CENTERS OF CALIFORNIA INC.—See Summerwinds Garden Centers Inc.; *U.S. Private,* pg. 3853
SUMMERWOOD MEDICAL CENTER LLC—See Adeptus Health Inc.; *U.S. Private,* pg. 78
SUMMI (FUJIAN) FOOD CO. LIMITED—See Summi (Group) Holdings Limited; *Int'l,* pg. 7301
SUMMI (GROUP) HOLDINGS LIMITED; *Int'l,* pg. 7301
SUMMIT2SEA CONSULTING, LLC—See Bluestone Investment Partners, LLC; *U.S. Private,* pg. 590
SUMMIT 7 SYSTEMS, LLC; *U.S. Private,* pg. 3853
SUMMIT AEROSPACE USA INC.—See Plaintree Systems Inc.; *Int'l,* pg. 5888
SUMMIT AG INVESTORS, LLC—See Summit Agricultural Group, LLC; *U.S. Private,* pg. 3853
SUMMIT AGRI-BUSINESS CORPORATION—See Sumitomo Corporation; *Int'l,* pg. 7275
SUMMIT AGRICULTURAL GROUP, LLC; *U.S. Private,* pg. 3853
SUMMIT AGRO CHINA CO., LTD.—See Sumitomo Corporation; *Int'l,* pg. 7275
SUMMIT AGRO INTERNATIONAL, LTD.—See Sumitomo Corporation; *Int'l,* pg. 7275
SUMMIT ALLIANCE PORT EAST GATEWAY INDIA PVT LTD.—See Summit Alliance Port Limited; *Int'l,* pg. 7301
SUMMIT ALLIANCE PORT LIMITED; *Int'l,* pg. 7301
SUMMIT AMBULATORY SURGICAL CENTER, L.L.C.—See Tenet Healthcare Corporation; *U.S. Public,* pg. 2007
SUMMIT AMUSEMENT & DISTRIBUTING LTD.—See AMCON Distributing Company; *U.S. Public,* pg. 93
SUMMIT ASCENT HOLDINGS LIMITED; *Int'l,* pg. 7301
SUMMIT AUTO LEASE AUSTRALIA PTY LIMITED—See Sumitomo Corporation; *Int'l,* pg. 7275
SUMMIT AUTOMOTIVE PARTNERS, LLC—See Booth Creek Management Corporation; *U.S. Private,* pg. 616
SUMMIT AUTO POLAND SP. Z.O.O.—See Sumitomo Corporation; *Int'l,* pg. 7276
SUMMIT AUTO TRADE FACILITIES—See Sumitomo Corporation; *Int'l,* pg. 7276
SUMMIT AVIATION, INC.—See TransMedics Group, Inc.; *U.S. Public,* pg. 2183
SUMMIT BANK; *U.S. Private,* pg. 3853
SUMMIT BHC SEVIERVILLE, LLC—See FFL Partners, LLC; *U.S. Private,* pg. 1500
SUMMIT BHC SEVIERVILLE, LLC—See Lee Equity Partners LLC; *U.S. Private,* pg. 2412
SUMMIT BREWING CO.; *U.S. Private,* pg. 3853
SUMMIT BROADBAND INC.—See Cable Bahamas Ltd.; *Int'l,* pg. 1246
SUMMIT BROKERAGE SERVICES, INC.—See RCAP Holdings, LLC; *U.S. Private,* pg. 3361
SUMMIT BUSINESS MEDIA, LLC; *U.S. Private,* pg. 3853
SUMMIT CAPITAL LEASING CO., LTD.—See Sumitomo Corporation; *Int'l,* pg. 7276
SUMMIT CD MANUFACTURE PTE LTD—See Centurion Corporation Limited; *Int'l,* pg. 1417
SUMMIT COLMO, INC.—See Sumitomo Corporation; *Int'l,* pg. 7276
SUMMIT COMMERCIAL FINANCE COMPANY—See Mintaka Financial, LLC; *U.S. Private,* pg. 2745
SUMMIT COMMUNITY BANK, INC.—See Summit Financial Group, Inc.; *U.S. Public,* pg. 1959
SUMMIT CONSTRUCTION CORP.; *U.S. Private,* pg. 3854

SUMMIT CONSULTING, LLC—See American Financial Group, Inc.; *U.S. Public,* pg. 103
SUMMIT CONTAINER CORPORATION; *U.S. Private,* pg. 3854
SUMMIT CONTRACTING LLC—See Irex Corporation; *U.S. Private,* pg. 2138
SUMMIT CORPORATION OF AMERICA; *U.S. Private,* pg. 3854
SUMMIT COSMETICS CORPORATION—See Sumitomo Corporation; *Int'l,* pg. 7276
SUMMIT CREATIONS PTE. LTD.—See Centurion Corporation Limited; *Int'l,* pg. 1417
SUMMIT CRM, LTD.—See Sumitomo Corporation; *Int'l,* pg. 7276
SUMMIT DEVELOPMENT CORPORATION SDN. BHD.—See Hexza Corporation Berhad; *Int'l,* pg. 3373
SUMMIT DIALYSIS CENTER, L.P.—See DaVita Inc.; *U.S. Public,* pg. 643
SUMMIT DIGITEL INFRASTRUCTURE PRIVATE LIMITED—See Data Infrastructure Trust; *Int'l,* pg. 1976
SUMMIT DISPOSAL INC.—See Waste Management, Inc.; *U.S. Public,* pg. 2332
SUMMITECH ENGINEERING, INC.—See Tempo International Group Ltd.; *Int'l,* pg. 7556
SUMMIT ELECTRIC SUPPLY COMPANY - MARINE DIVISION—See Summit Electric Supply Company; *U.S. Public,* pg. 3854
SUMMIT ELECTRIC SUPPLY COMPANY; *U.S. Private,* pg. 3854
SUMMIT ENERGY INTERNATIONAL BVBA—See Schneider Electric SE; *Int'l,* pg. 6635
SUMMIT ENERGY LLC; *U.S. Private,* pg. 3854
SUMMIT ENERGY SERVICES BV—See Schneider Electric SE; *Int'l,* pg. 6635
SUMMIT ENERGY SERVICES, INC.—See Schneider Electric SE; *Int'l,* pg. 6634
SUMMIT ENGINEERING, LABORATORY & TESTING, P.C.—See Universal Engineering Sciences, LLC; *U.S. Private,* pg. 4304
SUMMIT ENTERTAINMENT, LLC—See Lions Gate Entertainment Corp.; *Int'l,* pg. 4521
SUMMIT ENVIRONMENTAL TECHNOLOGIES, INC.—See Morgan Stanley; *U.S. Public,* pg. 1474
SUMMIT EQUITY GROUP, LLC; *U.S. Private,* pg. 3854
SUMMIT EXPLORATION & PRODUCTION LIMITED—See Sumitomo Corporation; *Int'l,* pg. 7276
SUMMIT FARMS SOLAR, LLC—See Dominion Energy, Inc.; *U.S. Public,* pg. 674
SUMMIT FINANCE GROUP, LLC—See Summit Materials, Inc.; *U.S. Public,* pg. 1959
SUMMIT FINANCE SLOVAKIA S.R.O.—See Sumitomo Corporation; *Int'l,* pg. 7276
SUMMIT FINANCIAL GROUP, INC.; *U.S. Public,* pg. 1959
SUMMIT FINANCIAL SERVICES GROUP, INC.—See RCAP Holdings, LLC; *U.S. Private,* pg. 3361
SUMMIT FIRE PROTECTION CO.—See BlackRock, Inc.; *U.S. Public,* pg. 346
SUMMIT FIRE & SECURITY—See BlackRock, Inc.; *U.S. Public,* pg. 346
SUMMIT FLEET—See Kaizen Automotive Group; *Int'l,* pg. 4053
SUMMIT FOOD INDUSTRIES CO., LTD.—See Kanematsu Corporation; *Int'l,* pg. 4069
SUMMIT FOOD SERVICE DISTRIBUTORS, INC.—See Flanagan Foodservice, Inc.; *Int'l,* pg. 2698
SUMMIT FOREST PRODUCTS INC.; *Int'l,* pg. 7302
SUMMIT FUNDING GROUP INC.; *U.S. Private,* pg. 3854
SUMMIT GAS RESOURCES, INC.—See The Bank of Nova Scotia; *Int'l,* pg. 7617
SUMMIT GERMANY LIMITED—See Summit Real Estate Holdings Ltd.; *Int'l,* pg. 7302
SUMMIT GROUP, INC.—See Retirement, LLC - Series Two; *U.S. Private,* pg. 3412
SUMMIT GROUP INC.; *U.S. Private,* pg. 3854
SUMMIT GROUP SOFTWARE; *U.S. Private,* pg. 3854
SUMMIT HANDLING SYSTEMS INC.; *U.S. Private,* pg. 3854
SUMMIT HEALTHCARE ACQUISITION CORP.; *Int'l,* pg. 7302
SUMMIT HEALTHCARE, INC.—See The Ensign Group, Inc.; *U.S. Public,* pg. 2072
SUMMIT HEALTHCARE MANAGEMENT, LLC—See FFL Partners, LLC; *U.S. Private,* pg. 1500
SUMMIT HEALTHCARE MANAGEMENT, LLC—See Lee Equity Partners LLC; *U.S. Private,* pg. 2412
SUMMIT HEALTHCARE REIT, INC.; *U.S. Private,* pg. 3854
SUMMIT HEALTH, INC.—See Quest Diagnostics, Inc.; *U.S. Public,* pg. 1756
SUMMIT HELICOPTERS, INC.—See Ledcor Group of Companies; *Int'l,* pg. 4438
SUMMIT HILL FOODS, INC.—See EagleTree Capital, LP; *U.S. Private,* pg. 1312
SUMMIT HI-TECH PTE LTD—See Centurion Corporation Limited; *Int'l,* pg. 1417
SUMMIT HOLDING SOUTHEAST, INC.—See American Financial Group, Inc.; *U.S. Public,* pg. 103
SUMMIT HOME MORTGAGE, LLC—See Rithm Capital Corp.; *U.S. Public,* pg. 1800

SUMMIT HOMES GROUP; *Int'l,* pg. 7302
SUMMIT HOSTING LLC; *U.S. Private,* pg. 3854
SUMMIT HOTEL PROPERTIES, INC.; *U.S. Public,* pg. 1959
SUMMIT IMAGING, LLC; *U.S. Private,* pg. 3854
SUMMIT, INC.—See Sumitomo Corporation; *Int'l,* pg. 7276
SUMMIT INDUSTRIAL INCOME REIT—See Dream Unlimited Corp.; *Int'l,* pg. 2203
SUMMIT INDUSTRIAL INCOME REIT—See GIC Pte. Ltd.; *Int'l,* pg. 2968
SUMMIT INDUSTRIES, INC. - LEXOL DIVISION—See Summit Industries, Inc.; *U.S. Private,* pg. 3854
SUMMIT INDUSTRIES, INC.; *U.S. Private,* pg. 3854
SUMMIT INDUSTRIES, INC.; *U.S. Private,* pg. 3854
SUMMIT INSURANCE SERVICES, LLC—See ABRY Partners, LLC; *U.S. Private,* pg. 43
SUMMIT INTERCONNECT, INC.; *U.S. Private,* pg. 3855
SUMMIT LABORATORIES INC.; *U.S. Private,* pg. 3855
SUMMIT LAGHUBITTA BITTIYA SANSTHA LTD.—See National Laghubitta Bittiya Sanstha Limited; *Int'l,* pg. 5161
SUMMIT LEARNING SERVICES; *U.S. Private,* pg. 3855
SUMMIT LEASING SLOVENIJA D.O.O.—See Nova Ljubljanska banka d.d.; *Int'l,* pg. 5451
SUMMIT LINE CONSTRUCTION, INC.—See Quanta Services, Inc.; *U.S. Public,* pg. 1753
SUMMIT LUBRICANTS, INC.—See Quaker Chemical Corporation; *U.S. Public,* pg. 1747
SUMMIT MACHINE, LLC—See Berkshire Hathaway Inc.; *U.S. Public,* pg. 315
SUMMIT MACHINE TOOL MANUFACTURING LLC—See LSB Industries, Inc.; *U.S. Public,* pg. 1344
SUMMIT MANUFACTURING LLC—See Array Marketing Group Inc.; *Int'l,* pg. 578
SUMMIT MARKETING GROUP—See Summit Marketing; *U.S. Private,* pg. 3855
SUMMIT MARKETING; *U.S. Private,* pg. 3855
SUMMIT MARKETING—See Summit Marketing; *U.S. Private,* pg. 3855
SUMMIT MARKETING—See Summit Marketing; *U.S. Private,* pg. 3855
SUMMIT MARKETING—See Summit Marketing; *U.S. Private,* pg. 3855
SUMMIT MARKETING—See Summit Marketing; *U.S. Private,* pg. 3855
SUMMIT MARKETING—See Summit Marketing; *U.S. Private,* pg. 3855
SUMMIT MARKETING—See Summit Marketing; *U.S. Private,* pg. 3855
SUMMIT MATERIALS FINANCE CORP.—See Summit Materials, Inc.; *U.S. Public,* pg. 1959
SUMMIT MATERIALS, INC.; *U.S. Public,* pg. 1959
SUMMIT MATERIALS, LLC—See Summit Materials, Inc.; *U.S. Public,* pg. 1959
SUMMIT MEDICAL CENTER—See HCA Healthcare, Inc.; *U.S. Public,* pg. 1012
SUMMIT MEDICAL GROUP LIMITED—See Apposite Capital LLP; *Int'l,* pg. 522
SUMMIT MEDICAL, INC.—See The Graham Group, Inc.; *U.S. Private,* pg. 4037
SUMMIT MEDICAL LIMITED—See Apposite Capital LLP; *Int'l,* pg. 522
SUMMIT MIDSTREAM FINANCE CORP.—See Summit Midstream Partners, LP; *U.S. Public,* pg. 1960
SUMMIT MIDSTREAM PARTNERS, LP; *U.S. Public,* pg. 1960
SUMMIT MINERALS GMBH—See Sumitomo Corporation; *Int'l,* pg. 7276
SUMMIT MORTGAGE CORPORATION; *U.S. Private,* pg. 3855
SUMMIT MORTGAGE, INC.—See Northwest Bancshares, Inc.; *U.S. Public,* pg. 1541
SUMMIT MORTGAGE; *U.S. Private,* pg. 3855
SUMMIT MOTORS LJUBLJANA D.O.O.—See Sumitomo Corporation; *Int'l,* pg. 7276
SUMMIT MOTORS POLAND SP. Z.O.O.—See Sumitomo Corporation; *Int'l,* pg. 7276
SUMMIT MOTORS SLOVAKIA, SPOL. S R. O.—See Sumitomo Corporation; *Int'l,* pg. 7276
SUMMIT NATIONAL BANK—See Hulett Bancorp; *U.S. Private,* pg. 2005
SUMMIT NATURAL GAS OF MAINE, INC.—See Summit Utilities Inc.; *U.S. Public,* pg. 3857
SUMMIT NATURAL GAS OF MISSOURI, INC.—See Summit Utilities Inc.; *U.S. Public,* pg. 3857
SUMMIT NETWORKS INC.; *Int'l,* pg. 7302
SUMMIT OAKS HOSPITAL, INC.—See Universal Health Services, Inc.; *U.S. Public,* pg. 2259
SUMMIT OIL MILL CO., LTD.—See Sumitomo Corporation; *Int'l,* pg. 7276
SUMMIT (OXFORD) LIMITED—See Summit Therapeutics Inc.; *U.S. Public,* pg. 1961
SUMMIT PACKAGING SYSTEMS INC.; *U.S. Private,* pg. 3855
SUMMIT PARTNERS LIMITED—See Summit Partners, L.P.; *U.S. Private,* pg. 3856
SUMMIT PARTNERS, L.P. - PALO ALTO OFFICE—See Summit Partners, L.P.; *U.S. Private,* pg. 3856
SUMMIT PARTNERS, L.P.; *U.S. Private,* pg. 3855
SUMMIT PET PRODUCTS DISTRIBUTORS, INC.; *U.S. Private,* pg. 3856

SUMMIT PET PRODUCTS DISTRIBUTORS, INC.

Company Index

SUMMIT PHARMACEUTICALS CHINA LIMITED—See Sumitomo Corporation; *Int'l*, pg. 7276
SUMMIT PHARMACEUTICALS EUROPE SRL—See Sumitomo Corporation; *Int'l*, pg. 7276
SUMMIT PHARMACEUTICALS INTERNATIONAL CORPORATION—See Sumitomo Corporation; *Int'l*, pg. 7276
SUMMIT PIPELINE SERVICES LTD.; *Int'l*, pg. 7302
SUMMIT PLASTIC CO.; *U.S. Private*, pg. 3856
SUMMIT PLASTICS, INC.—See LongueVue Capital, LLC; *U.S. Private*, pg. 2493
SUMMIT POLYMERS INC.; *U.S. Private*, pg. 3856
SUMMIT POWER HOLDINGS LIMITED—See Sumitomo Corporation; *Int'l*, pg. 7276
SUMMIT POWER LTD.; *Int'l*, pg. 7302
SUMMIT PRINTING (AUSTRALIA) PTY LIMITED—See Centurion Corporation Limited; *Int'l*, pg. 1417
SUMMIT PRODUCTS, INC.—See Propel Equity Partners, LLC; *U.S. Private*, pg. 3285
SUMMIT REAL ESTATE HOLDINGS LTD.; *Int'l*, pg. 7302
SUMMIT RESEARCH NETWORK, INC.—See KKR & Co. Inc.; *U.S. Public*, pg. 1252
SUMMIT RESOURCES, INC.—See Paramount Resources Ltd.; *Int'l*, pg. 5738
SUMMIT RESOURCES LIMITED—See Paladin Energy Ltd.; *Int'l*, pg. 5705
SUMMIT RESOURCES LLC; *U.S. Private*, pg. 3856
SUMMIT RIDGE CORPORATION; *U.S. Private*, pg. 3857
SUMMIT RURAL (WA) PTY LIMITED—See Sumitomo Corporation; *Int'l*, pg. 7276
SUMMIT SECURITIES LTD.; *Int'l*, pg. 7302
SUMMIT SECURITY SERVICES INC.; *U.S. Private*, pg. 3857
SUMMIT SHIPPING AGENCIES LTD.—See The Sumitomo Warehouse Co. Ltd.; *Int'l*, pg. 7690
SUMMIT SHOWA ALUMINUM LTD.—See Asahi Seiren Co., Ltd.; *Int'l*, pg. 598
SUMMIT SHOWA MANUFACTURING CO., LTD.—See Hitachi Astemo, Ltd.; *Int'l*, pg. 3410
SUMMIT SOFTWARE, INC.—See F.W. Davison & Company, Inc.; *U.S. Private*, pg. 1457
SUMMIT SOLUTIONS, INC.—See FedCap Partners, LLC; *U.S. Private*, pg. 1486
SUMMIT SPORTS, INC.; *U.S. Private*, pg. 3857
SUMMIT STAINLESS—See Sumitomo Corporation; *Int'l*, pg. 7274
SUMMIT STAINLESS STEEL, LLC—See Sumitomo Corporation; *Int'l*, pg. 7274
SUMMIT STATE BANK—See Summit State Bank; *U.S. Public*, pg. 1961
SUMMIT STATE BANK; *U.S. Public*, pg. 1960
SUMMIT STEEL CORPORATION—See Sumitomo Corporation; *Int'l*, pg. 7276
SUMMIT STEEL & MANUFACTURING INC.—See Lorraine Capital LLC; *U.S. Private*, pg. 2496
SUMMIT STEEL (M.E.) FZCO—See Sumitomo Corporation; *Int'l*, pg. 7276
SUMMIT STEEL OITA CO., LTD.—See Sumitomo Corporation; *Int'l*, pg. 7276
SUMMIT STRATEGIES INC.; *U.S. Private*, pg. 3857
SUMMIT SUNRISE ENERGY CO., LTD.—See Sumitomo Corporation; *Int'l*, pg. 7276
SUMMIT SURGERY CENTER, L.P.—See HCA Healthcare, Inc.; *U.S. Public*, pg. 1011
SUMMIT SYSTEMS AND DESIGN, LLC—See NEWTEKONE, INC.; *U.S. Public*, pg. 1521
SUMMIT SYSTEMS, INC.—See Vista Equity Partners, LLC; *U.S. Private*, pg. 4397
SUMMIT SYSTEMS SA—See Vista Equity Partners, LLC; *U.S. Private*, pg. 4397
SUMMIT TECH CONSULTING; *U.S. Private*, pg. 3857
SUMMIT TECHNICAL SERVICES, INC.; *U.S. Private*, pg. 3857
SUMMIT TECHNICAL SOLUTIONS, LLC; *U.S. Private*, pg. 3857
SUMMIT TECHNOLOGY AUSTRALIA PTY LTD—See Centurion Corporation Limited; *Int'l*, pg. 1417
SUMMIT TECHNOLOGY, LLC; *U.S. Private*, pg. 3857
SUMMIT TERMINAL, LLC—See HALLADOR ENERGY COMPANY; *U.S. Public*, pg. 980
SUMMIT FORESTS INC.; *U.S. Private*, pg. 3857
SUMMIT THERAPEUTICS INC.; *U.S. Public*, pg. 1961
SUMMIT THERAPEUTICS LIMITED—See Summit Therapeutics Inc.; *U.S. Public*, pg. 1961
SUMMIT TIRES NORTHEAST, LLC—See TPG Capital, L.P.; *U.S. Public*, pg. 2166
SUMMIT TOOL COMPANY; *U.S. Private*, pg. 3857
SUMMIT TOOLING INC.—See CORE Industrial Partners, LLC; *U.S. Private*, pg. 1049
SUMMIT TREESTANDS, LLC—See EBSCO Industries, Inc.; *U.S. Private*, pg. 1325
SUMMIT TRUCKING, INC.; *U.S. Private*, pg. 3857
SUMMIT TUBULARS CORP.—See Sumitomo Corporation; *Int'l*, pg. 7276
SUMMIT UTILITIES INC.; *U.S. Private*, pg. 3857
SUMMIT UTILITY STRUCTURES, LLC—See Nucor Corporation; *U.S. Public*, pg. 1554

SUMMIT VALVE & CONTROLS INC.—See Endress+Hauser (International) Holding AG; *Int'l*, pg. 2409
SUMMITVIEW CAPITAL MANAGEMENT LTD.; *Int'l*, pg. 7302
SUMMIT VIEW SURGERY CENTER, LLC—See Tenet Healthcare Corporation; *U.S. Public*, pg. 2013
SUMMITVILLE TILES, INC.; *U.S. Private*, pg. 3857
SUMMIT WALK-IN CLINIC, LLC—See HCA Healthcare, Inc.; *U.S. Public*, pg. 1011
SUMMIT WOOL SPINNERS LIMITED—See Sumitomo Corporation; *Int'l*, pg. 7276
SUMMUS SOLUTIONS N.V.; *Int'l*, pg. 7302
SUMNER BANK & TRUST—See Edmonton Bancshares Inc.; *U.S. Private*, pg. 1337
SUMNER COMMUNICATIONS INC.; *U.S. Private*, pg. 3857
SUMNER-COWLEY ELECTRIC COOPERATIVE, INC.; *U.S. Private*, pg. 3857
SUMNER FINANCIAL CORPORATION; *U.S. Private*, pg. 3857
SUMNER GROUP HEALTH LIMITED; *Int'l*, pg. 7302
SUMNER GROUP INC.; *U.S. Private*, pg. 3857
SUMNER MANUFACTURING CO., INC.—See Southwire Company, LLC; *U.S. Private*, pg. 3742
SUMNER REGIONAL MEDICAL CENTER, LLC—See Apollo Global Management, Inc.; *U.S. Public*, pg. 159
SUMO DIGITAL LTD.—See Perwyn LLP; *Int'l*, pg. 5822
SUMO GROUP PLC; *Int'l*, pg. 7302
SUMOL+COMPAL - POMBAL FACTORY—See Sumol+Compal; *Int'l*, pg. 7302
SUMOL+COMPAL; *Int'l*, pg. 7302
SUMO LOGIC, INC.—See Francisco Partners Management, LP; *U.S. Public*, pg. 1592
SUMO RESOURCES PLC; *Int'l*, pg. 7302
SUMO SERVICES LTD—See Franchise Concepts Limited; *Int'l*, pg. 2760
SUMO SERVICES LTD—See Pipehawk Plc; *Int'l*, pg. 5873
SUMOTEXT CORP.—See Cisco Systems, Inc.; *U.S. Public*, pg. 499
SUMOTO S.R.L.—See Ebara Corporation; *Int'l*, pg. 2284
SUMRIDGE PARTNERS, LLC—See Raymond James Financial, Inc.; *U.S. Public*, pg. 1765
SUMTEC SERVICE CORPORATION—See SUMCO Corporation; *Int'l*, pg. 7260
SUMTER ELECTRIC COOPERATIVE INC.; *U.S. Private*, pg. 3857
SUMTER ELECTRIC MEMBERSHIP CORPORATION; *U.S. Private*, pg. 3858
SUMTER PACKAGING CORPORATION—See Hood Container Corporation; *U.S. Private*, pg. 1977
SUMTER TIMBER COMPANY, LLC—See McElroy Truck Lines Inc.; *U.S. Private*, pg. 2633
SUMTER UTILITIES, INC.—See Quanta Services, Inc.; *U.S. Public*, pg. 1753
SUMTOTAL SYSTEMS LLC—See Clearlake Capital Group, L.P.; *U.S. Private*, pg. 934
SUMTOTAL SYSTEMS - PARSIPPANY—See Clearlake Capital Group, L.P.; *U.S. Private*, pg. 934
SUMTOTAL SYSTEMS - WEST DES MOINES—See Clearlake Capital Group, L.P.; *U.S. Private*, pg. 934
SUMUKA AGRO INDUSTRIES LIMITED; *Int'l*, pg. 7302
SUMUP PAYMENTS LIMITED; *Int'l*, pg. 7303
SUMUR CAHAYA SDN. BHD.—See Sumitomo Corporation; *Int'l*, pg. 7276
SUN 108 CO., LTD.—See Saha Pathanapibul Public Company Limited; *Int'l*, pg. 6479
SUNABON LIMITED PARTNERSHIP; *U.S. Private*, pg. 3864
SUNAC CHINA HOLDINGS LIMITED; *Int'l*, pg. 7309
SUN-A CORPORATION—See Kuriyama Holdings Corporation; *Int'l*, pg. 4342
SUNAC SERVICES HOLDINGS LIMITED; *Int'l*, pg. 7309
SUN ACTION TRACKERS LLC—See Paru Co., Ltd.; *Int'l*, pg. 5751
SUN-AD COMPANY LIMITED—See Suntory Holdings Limited; *Int'l*, pg. 7326
SUN-AG INC.; *U.S. Private*, pg. 3864
SUN AGRO COMPANY LIMITED—See Nissan Chemical Corporation; *Int'l*, pg. 5367
SUNAIM INCORPORATED—See Sanix Incorporated; *Int'l*, pg. 6540
SUN A. KAKEN CO., LTD.; *Int'l*, pg. 7303
SUN ALLOMER LTD. - KAWASAKI PLANT—See Resonac Holdings Corporation; *Int'l*, pg. 6301
SUN ALLOMER LTD. - OITA PLANT—See Resonac Holdings Corporation; *Int'l*, pg. 6301
SUN ALLOMER LTD.—See Resonac Holdings Corporation; *Int'l*, pg. 6301
SUN ALLOYS CO., LTD.—See Mitsui Chemicals, Inc.; *Int'l*, pg. 4984
SUNAM CO., LTD.; *Int'l*, pg. 7310
SUNAMERICA ASSET MANAGEMENT, LLC—See American International Group, Inc.; *U.S. Public*, pg. 105
SUNAMERICA CAPITAL SERVICES, INC.—See American International Group, Inc.; *U.S. Public*, pg. 105
THE SUNAPEE DIFFERENCE LLC—See Vail Resorts, Inc.; *U.S. Public*, pg. 2271

CORPORATE AFFILIATIONS

SUNAPEE MUTUAL FIRE INSURANCE CO., INC.—See Concord General Mu; *U.S. Private*, pg. 1010
SUNAQUA TOTO LTD.—See Toto Ltd.; *Int'l*, pg. 7845
SUN ARROW KASEI CO., LTD.—See Tokuyama Corporation; *Int'l*, pg. 7787
SUN ART RETAIL GROUP LIMITED—See Alibaba Group Holding Limited; *Int'l*, pg. 326
SUNAUTAS CORPORATION; *Int'l*, pg. 7310
SUN AUTOMOTIVE, INC.—See Morgan Auto Group, LLC; *U.S. Private*, pg. 2783
SUN AUTO TIRE & SERVICE, INC.—See Greenbriar Equity Group, L.P.; *U.S. Private*, pg. 1776
SUN AVIATION, INC.; *U.S. Private*, pg. 3858
SUNBEAM AMERICAS HOLDINGS, LLC—See Newell Brands Inc.; *U.S. Public*, pg. 1515
SUNBEAM CORPORATION PTY LTD—See Newell Brands Inc.; *U.S. Public*, pg. 1515
SUNBEAM COUNTRY HEARTH THRIFT STORE; *U.S. Private*, pg. 3864
SUNBEAM DEVELOPMENT CORPORATION—See Sunbeam Television Corporation; *U.S. Private*, pg. 3864
SUN BEAM INFOTECH LTD.—See Parle Industries Ltd.; *Int'l*, pg. 5745
SUNBEAM PRODUCTS, INC.—See Newell Brands Inc.; *U.S. Public*, pg. 1515
SUNBEAM SOLAR, LLC—See National Grid plc; *Int'l*, pg. 5158
SUNBEAM TELEVISION CORPORATION; *U.S. Private*, pg. 3864
SUN BELLE INC.; *U.S. Private*, pg. 3858
SUNBELT ASPHALT SURFACES, INC—See Construction Partners, Inc.; *U.S. Public*, pg. 572
SUNBELT BUSINESS ADVISORS NETWORK, LLC—See Merrymeeting, Inc.; *U.S. Private*, pg. 2677
SUN BELT COATING, LLC—See Aalberts N.V.; *Int'l*, pg. 34
THE SUN BELT CONFERENCE; *U.S. Private*, pg. 4125
SUNBELT CONSTRUCTION INC.; *U.S. Private*, pg. 3864
SUNBELT CREDIT INC.—See Continental Holding Company; *U.S. Private*, pg. 1030
SUN BELT FOOD COMPANY, INC.; *U.S. Private*, pg. 3858
SUNBELT FOREST PRODUCTS CORPORATION—See UFP Industries, Inc.; *U.S. Public*, pg. 2219
SUNBELT FURNITURE XPRESS, INC.—See Anderson Trucking Service Inc.; *U.S. Private*, pg. 277
SUNBELT GOLF CORPORATION; *U.S. Private*, pg. 3864
SUNBELT GROUP L.P.—See Russel Metals Inc.; *Int'l*, pg. 6430
SUNBELT HEALTH AND REHAB CENTER APOPKA; *U.S. Private*, pg. 3865
SUN BELT INC.—See Platte River Ventures, LLC; *U.S. Private*, pg. 3211
SUNBELT MARKETING INC.—See Sunbelt Marketing Investment Corp.; *U.S. Private*, pg. 3865
SUNBELT MARKETING INVESTMENT CORP. - DEERFIELD BEACH—See Sunbelt Marketing Investment Corp.; *U.S. Private*, pg. 3865
SUNBELT MARKETING INVESTMENT CORP.; *U.S. Private*, pg. 3865
SUNBELT MATERIAL HANDLING INC.; *U.S. Private*, pg. 3865
SUNBELT MODULAR, INC.—See Littlejohn & Co., LLC; *U.S. Private*, pg. 2471
SUNBELT OUTDOOR PRODUCTS INC.—See Deere & Company; *U.S. Public*, pg. 647
SUNBELT PACKAGING, LLC—See Kelso & Company, L.P.; *U.S. Public*, pg. 2279
SUNBELT PACKAGING, LLC—See Warburg Pincus LLC; *U.S. Private*, pg. 4436
SUNBELT POWER CONTROLS INC.—See Innovative IDM LLC; *U.S. Private*, pg. 2082
SUNBELT RENTALS CLIMATE CONTROL SERVICES—See Ashtead Group Plc; *Int'l*, pg. 609
SUNBELT RENTALS, INC.—See Ashtead Group Plc; *Int'l*, pg. 609
SUNBELT SOLOMON SERVICES, LLC—See Trilantic Capital Management L.P.; *U.S. Private*, pg. 4231
SUNBELT SUPPLY CO.—See Clearlake Capital Group, L.P.; *U.S. Public*, pg. 937
SUNBELT TELECOMMUNICATIONS INC.; *U.S. Private*, pg. 3865
SUNBELT TRANSPORT, LLC—See Cypress Truck Lines, Inc.; *U.S. Private*, pg. 1135
SUNBELT-TURRET STEEL, INC.—See Ryerson Holding Corporation; *U.S. Public*, pg. 1829
SUNBILT LTD.—See Goddard Enterprises Limited; *Int'l*, pg. 3019
SUNBILT SOLAR PRODUCTS BY SUSSMAN, INC.—See J. Sussman, Inc.; *U.S. Private*, pg. 2157
SUNBIO, INC.; *Int'l*, pg. 7310
SUN BIOMASS, INC.; *U.S. Private*, pg. 3858
SUNBLASTER HOLDINGS ULC—See Hydrofarm Holdings Group, Inc.; *U.S. Public*, pg. 1079
SUN BLAZING STAR LLC—See Sun Communities, Inc.; *U.S. Public*, pg. 1963
SUNBLOCK SYSTEMS, INC.; *U.S. Private*, pg. 3865
SUNBOSS CHEMICALS CORP.—See AirBoss of America Corp.; *Int'l*, pg. 241

COMPANY NAME INDEX

SUN BRANDING SOLUTIONS LTD.—See DIC Corporation; *Int'l*, pg. 2109
SUNBRIDGE BRITTANY REHABILITATION CENTER, INC.—See Formation Capital, LLC; *U.S. Private*, pg. 1570
SUNBRIDGE CARE ENTERPRISES WEST, INC.—See Formation Capital, LLC; *U.S. Private*, pg. 1570
SUNBRIDGE CARMICHAEL REHABILITATION CENTER, INC.—See Formation Capital, LLC; *U.S. Private*, pg. 1570
SUNBRIDGE GROUP LIMITED; *Int'l*, pg. 7310
SUNBRIDGE HALLMARK HEALTH SERVICES, INC.—See Formation Capital, LLC; *U.S. Private*, pg. 1570
SUN-BRITE FOODS INC.; *Int'l*, pg. 7309
SUNBRITETV LLC; *U.S. Private*, pg. 3865
SUN BROADCAST GROUP—See Gen Media Partners LLC; *U.S. Private*, pg. 1660
SUN BROTHERS DEVELOPMENT CO., LTD.; *Int'l*, pg. 7303
SUN BROTHERS LLC; *U.S. Private*, pg. 3858
SUN BULB COMPANY, INC.; *U.S. Private*, pg. 3858
SUNBURST CONTEMPORARY HOMES INC.; *U.S. Private*, pg. 3865
SUNBURST FOODS INC.; *U.S. Private*, pg. 3865
SUNBURST HOSPITALITY CORPORATION; *U.S. Private*, pg. 3865
SUNBURST SEED COMPANY; *U.S. Private*, pg. 3865
SUNBURY CLINIC COMPANY, LLC—See Quorum Health Corporation; *U.S. Private*, pg. 3330
SUNBURY MOTOR COMPANY; *U.S. Private*, pg. 3865
SUNBURY TEXTILES MILLS, INC.—See Glen Raven, Inc.; *U.S. Private*, pg. 1709
SUN BUS LIMITED—See Transport International Holdings Limited; *Int'l*, pg. 7905
SUNCADIA WATER COMPANY, LLC—See Northwest Natural Holding Company; *U.S. Public*, pg. 1542
SUNCALL CO., (H.K.) LTD.—See Suncall Corporation; *Int'l*, pg. 7310
SUNCALL CORPORATION - HIROSE PLANT—See Suncall Corporation; *Int'l*, pg. 7310
SUNCALL CORPORATION; *Int'l*, pg. 7310
SUNCALL CORPORATION - SUNCALL BUJI NAN LING FACTORY—See Suncall Corporation; *Int'l*, pg. 7310
SUNCALL ENGINEERING CORP.—See Suncall Corporation; *Int'l*, pg. 7310
SUNCALL (GUANGZHOU) CO., LTD.—See Suncall Corporation; *Int'l*, pg. 7310
SUNCALL (GUANGZHOU) TRADING CO., LTD.—See Suncall Corporation; *Int'l*, pg. 7310
SUNCALL HIGH PRECISION (THAILAND) LTD.—See Suncall Corporation; *Int'l*, pg. 7310
SUNCALL KIKUCHI CORP.—See Suncall Corporation; *Int'l*, pg. 7310
SUNCALL TECHNOLOGIES MEXICO, S.A. DE C.V.—See Suncall Corporation; *Int'l*, pg. 7310
SUNCALL TECHNOLOGIES (SZ) CO., LTD.—See Suncall Corporation; *Int'l*, pg. 7310
SUNCALL TECHNOLOGY VIETNAM CO., LTD.—See Suncall Corporation; *Int'l*, pg. 7310
SUNCALL (TIANJIN) CO., LTD.—See Suncall Corporation; *Int'l*, pg. 7310
SUN CAMELOT VILLA LLC—See Sun Communities, Inc.; *U.S. Public*, pg. 1963
SUN CAN INTERNATIONAL LTD. - SINYON PLASTIC & MOULD FACTORY—See COXON Precise Industrial Co., Ltd.; *Int'l*, pg. 1823
SUN CAPITAL ADVISERS, LLC—See Guggenheim Partners, LLC; *U.S. Private*, pg. 1813
SUN CAPITAL PARTNERS, INC.; *U.S. Private*, pg. 3858
SUN CAPITAL PARTNERS JAPAN K.K.—See Sun Capital Partners, Inc.; *U.S. Private*, pg. 3861
SUN CAPITAL PARTNERS SOURCING, LLC—See Sun Capital Partners, Inc.; *U.S. Private*, pg. 3861
SUNCARE TRADERS LTD.; *Int'l*, pg. 7310
SUNCAR TECHNOLOGY GROUP INC; *Int'l*, pg. 7310
SUN CAST CO., LTD.—See Nagano Keiki Co., Ltd.; *Int'l*, pg. 5125
SUNCAST SOLAR ENERGY, INC.; *U.S. Public*, pg. 1963
SUN CHAIN TECHNOLOGY CORP.—See Arrow Electronics, Inc.; *U.S. Public*, pg. 200
SUNCHANGITS CO., LTD.—See SUN&L Co., Ltd.; *Int'l*, pg. 7309
SUNCHASE HOLDINGS, INC.; *U.S. Private*, pg. 3865
SUNCHA TECHNOLOGY CO., LTD.; *Int'l*, pg. 7310
SUN CHEMICAL AB—See DIC Corporation; *Int'l*, pg. 2110
SUN CHEMICAL AG—See DIC Corporation; *Int'l*, pg. 2110
SUN CHEMICAL AG—See DIC Corporation; *Int'l*, pg. 2110
SUN CHEMICAL ALBANIA SHPK—See DIC Corporation; *Int'l*, pg. 2110
SUN CHEMICAL A/S—See DIC Corporation; *Int'l*, pg. 2109
SUN CHEMICAL A/S—See DIC Corporation; *Int'l*, pg. 2109
SUN CHEMICAL B.V.—See DIC Corporation; *Int'l*, pg. 2110
SUN CHEMICAL CHILE S.A.—See DIC Corporation; *Int'l*, pg. 2110
SUN CHEMICAL CORPORATION OF MICHIGAN—See DIC Corporation; *Int'l*, pg. 2110
SUN CHEMICAL CORPORATION, PIGMENTS DIVISION—See DIC Corporation; *Int'l*, pg. 2110

SUN CHEMICAL CORPORATION—See DIC Corporation; *Int'l*, pg. 2109
SUN CHEMICAL DE CENTRO AMERICA, S.A. DE C.V.—See DIC Corporation; *Int'l*, pg. 2110
SUN CHEMICAL DE PANAMA, S.A.—See DIC Corporation; *Int'l*, pg. 2110
SUN CHEMICAL DO BRASIL LTDA.—See DIC Corporation; *Int'l*, pg. 2110
SUN CHEMICAL, D.O.O.—See DIC Corporation; *Int'l*, pg. 2111
SUN CHEMICAL DRUCKFARBEN GMBH—See DIC Corporation; *Int'l*, pg. 2110
SUN CHEMICAL ECP S.A./N.V.—See DIC Corporation; *Int'l*, pg. 2110
SUN CHEMICAL GROUP COOPERATIEF U.A.—See DIC Corporation; *Int'l*, pg. 2110
SUN CHEMICAL GROUP S.P.A—See DIC Corporation; *Int'l*, pg. 2110
SUN CHEMICAL, INC. S.A.—See DIC Corporation; *Int'l*, pg. 2111
SUN CHEMICAL, INC. S.A.—See DIC Corporation; *Int'l*, pg. 2111
SUN CHEMICAL INDUSTRY CO., LTD.—See TS Tech Co Ltd; *Int'l*, pg. 7948
SUN CHEMICAL INKS A/S—See DIC Corporation; *Int'l*, pg. 2110
SUN CHEMICAL INKS LTD.—See DIC Corporation; *Int'l*, pg. 2110
SUN CHEMICAL INK—See DIC Corporation; *Int'l*, pg. 2110
SUN CHEMICAL INKS S.A.—See DIC Corporation; *Int'l*, pg. 2110
SUN CHEMICAL LASFELDE GMBH—See DIC Corporation; *Int'l*, pg. 2110
SUN CHEMICAL LIMITED—See DIC Corporation; *Int'l*, pg. 2110
SUN CHEMICAL LTD.—See DIC Corporation; *Int'l*, pg. 2109
SUN CHEMICAL LTD.—See DIC Corporation; *Int'l*, pg. 2110
SUN CHEMICAL MATBAA MUREKKEPLERI VE GERECLERI SANAYII VE TICARET A.S.—See DIC Corporation; *Int'l*, pg. 2110
SUN CHEMICAL MOSCOW—See DIC Corporation; *Int'l*, pg. 2110
SUN CHEMICAL N.V./S.A.—See DIC Corporation; *Int'l*, pg. 2110
SUN CHEMICAL NYOMDAFESTEK KERESKEDELMI ES GYARTO KFT—See DIC Corporation; *Int'l*, pg. 2110
SUN CHEMICAL OSTERODE DRUCKFARBEN GMBH—See DIC Corporation; *Int'l*, pg. 2110
SUN CHEMICAL OY—See DIC Corporation; *Int'l*, pg. 2110
SUN CHEMICAL PIGMENTS S.L.—See DIC Corporation; *Int'l*, pg. 2110
SUN CHEMICAL PORTUGAL TINTAS GRAFICAS UNIPESSOAL, LTDA.—See DIC Corporation; *Int'l*, pg. 2110
SUN CHEMICAL PRINTING INK D.O.O.—See DIC Corporation; *Int'l*, pg. 2110
SUN CHEMICAL S.A. DE C.V.—See DIC Corporation; *Int'l*, pg. 2110
SUN CHEMICAL S.A.—See DIC Corporation; *Int'l*, pg. 2110
SUN CHEMICAL S.A.S.—See DIC Corporation; *Int'l*, pg. 2110
SUN CHEMICAL S.P.A.—See DIC Corporation; *Int'l*, pg. 2110
SUN CHEMICAL SP. ZO.O.—See DIC Corporation; *Int'l*, pg. 2110
SUN CHEMICAL S.R.L.—See DIC Corporation; *Int'l*, pg. 2110
SUN CHEMICAL S.R.O.—See DIC Corporation; *Int'l*, pg. 2111
SUN CHEMICAL S.R.O.—See DIC Corporation; *Int'l*, pg. 2111
SUN CHEMICALS S.A.-PIGMENTS INTERNATIONAL—See DIC Corporation; *Int'l*, pg. 2111
SUN CHEMICALS—See DIC Corporation; *Int'l*, pg. 2111
SUN CHEMICAL TRADING (SHANGHAI) CO., LTD.—See DIC Corporation; *Int'l*, pg. 2111
SUN CHEMICAL ZAO—See DIC Corporation; *Int'l*, pg. 2110
SUNCHEMI CO., LTD.—See Miura Co., Ltd.; *Int'l*, pg. 4995
SUN CHEONG CREATIVE DEVELOPMENT HOLDINGS LIMITED; *Int'l*, pg. 7303
SUNCHIP TECHNOLOGY, INC.; *U.S. Private*, pg. 3865
SUNCHIRIN AUTOPARTS INDIA PVT. LTD.—See Sunrise Industry Co., Ltd.; *Int'l*, pg. 7321
SUNCHIRIN INDUSTRIES (MALAYSIA) BERHAD—See Sunrise Industry Co., Ltd.; *Int'l*, pg. 7321
SUNCHIRIN INDUSTRY (THAILAND) LTD.—See Sunrise Industry Co., Ltd.; *Int'l*, pg. 7321
SUN CITIES INDEPENDENT—See Independent Newspapers, Inc.; *U.S. Private*, pg. 2060
SUNCITI MANUFACTURERS LTD.—See Citizen Watch Co., Ltd.; *Int'l*, pg. 1625
SUNCITI PVD (JIANGMEN) LTD.—See Citizen Watch Co., Ltd.; *Int'l*, pg. 1625
SUN CITY DIALYSIS CENTER, LLC—See DaVita Inc.; *U.S. Public*, pg. 643

SUNCITY ENERGY S.R.L.—See A2A S.p.A.; *Int'l*, pg. 29
SUN CITY HILTON HEAD—See PulteGroup, Inc.; *U.S. Public*, pg. 1737
SUN CITY HUNTLEY—See PulteGroup, Inc.; *U.S. Public*, pg. 1737
SUN CITY RV, INC.; *U.S. Private*, pg. 3862
SUNCITY SYNTHETICS LTD.; *Int'l*, pg. 7310
SUN CITY TEXAS—See PulteGroup, Inc.; *U.S. Public*, pg. 1737
SUN CITY WEST DIALYSIS CENTER LLC—See DaVita Inc.; *U.S. Public*, pg. 643
SUNCLASS AIRLINES A/S—See Thomas Cook Northern Europe AB; *Int'l*, pg. 7713
SUNCLEAR SRL—See Arkema S.A.; *Int'l*, pg. 571
SUNCOAL INDUSTRIES GMBH—See UPM-Kymmene Corporation; *Int'l*, pg. 8090
SUNCOAST ASPHALT PTY. LTD.—See Heidelberg Materials AG; *Int'l*, pg. 3320
SUNCOAST BAKERIES, INC.—See Shoreline Equity Partners, LLC; *U.S. Private*, pg. 3641
SUNCOAST BEVERAGE SALES, LLLP; *U.S. Private*, pg. 3865
SUNCOAST CENTER INC.; *U.S. Private*, pg. 3865
SUNCOAST CREDIT UNION; *U.S. Private*, pg. 3865
SUNCOAST DIGITAL PRESS INC.; *U.S. Private*, pg. 3865
THE SUNCOAST ENDOSCOPY ASC, L.P.—See KKR & Co. Inc.; *U.S. Public*, pg. 1248
SUNCOAST FORMS & SYSTEMS, INC.; *U.S. Private*, pg. 3865
SUN COAST INDUSTRIES, LLC—See Berry Global Group, Inc; *U.S. Public*, pg. 321
SUN COAST MEDIA GROUP, INC.; *U.S. Private*, pg. 3862
SUN COAST NURSING CENTERS INC; *U.S. Private*, pg. 3862
SUNCOAST OIL CO. OF FLORIDA INC.; *U.S. Private*, pg. 3866
SUNCOAST ORTHOTICS & PROSTHETICS, INC.—See Patient Square Capital, L.P.; *U.S. Private*, pg. 3107
SUN COAST PARTNERS, LLC; *U.S. Private*, pg. 3862
SUNCOAST PORSCHE—See Sunset Automotive Group; *U.S. Private*, pg. 3871
SUNCOAST POST-TENSION LTD.—See Keller Group plc; *Int'l*, pg. 4121
SUN COAST RESOURCES INC.—See AIP, LLC; *U.S. Private*, pg. 136
SUNCOAST RHIO, INC.; *U.S. Private*, pg. 3866
SUNCOAST SIGN SHOP, INC.; *U.S. Private*, pg. 3866
SUNCOAST SITRA PTE LTD—See Sitra Holdings International Limited; *Int'l*, pg. 6965
SUNCOAST SPECIALTY SURGERY CENTER, LLLP—See Bain Capital, LP; *U.S. Private*, pg. 446
SUNCO BUILDERS & DEVELOPERS LIMITED; *Int'l*, pg. 7310
SUNCO CARRIERS, INC.—See Watkins Associated Industries Inc.; *U.S. Private*, pg. 4455
SUNCOKE ENERGY, INC.; *U.S. Public*, pg. 1963
SUNCOKE ENERGY PARTNERS, L.P.—See SunCoke Energy, Inc.; *U.S. Public*, pg. 1964
SUNCOKE LOGISTICS LLC—See SunCoke Energy, Inc.; *U.S. Public*, pg. 1964
SUN COMMUNITIES, INC.; *U.S. Public*, pg. 1961
SUN COMPANY, INC.—See Energy Transfer LP; *U.S. Public*, pg. 764
SUN COMPANY, INC.; *U.S. Private*, pg. 3862
SUNCOM TECHNOLOGY CORPORATION—See COMSYS Holdings Corporation; *Int'l*, pg. 1762
SUN CONTRACTORS LTD; *Int'l*, pg. 7303
SUNCORE, INC.; *Int'l*, pg. 7311
SUNCOR ENERGY GERMANY GMBH—See Suncor Energy Inc.; *Int'l*, pg. 7311
SUNCOR ENERGY INC.; *Int'l*, pg. 7310
SUNCOR ENERGY MARKETING INC.—See Suncor Energy Inc.; *Int'l*, pg. 7311
SUNCOR ENERGY OIL (NORTH AFRICA) GMBH—See Suncor Energy Inc.; *Int'l*, pg. 7311
SUNCOR ENERGY UK LIMITED—See Suncor Energy Inc.; *Int'l*, pg. 7311
SUNCOR ENERGY (U.S.A.) INC.—See Suncor Energy Inc.; *Int'l*, pg. 7311
SUNCORP CUSTODIAN SERVICES PTY LTD—See Suncorp Group Limited; *Int'l*, pg. 7311
SUNCORP GROUP HOLDINGS PTY LIMITED—See Suncorp Group Limited; *Int'l*, pg. 7311
SUNCORP GROUP LIMITED; *Int'l*, pg. 7311
SUNCORP GROUP LIMITED; *Int'l*, pg. 7311
SUNCORP INSURANCE SERVICES LIMITED—See Suncorp Group Limited; *Int'l*, pg. 7311
SUN CORPORATION; *Int'l*, pg. 7303
SUNCORP SECURITIES LIMITED—See SunCorp Technologies Limited; *Int'l*, pg. 7311
SUNCORP TECHNOLOGIES LIMITED; *Int'l*, pg. 7311
SUNCO SPRING COMPANY, LTD.—See Kyokuto Boeki Kaisha, Ltd.; *Int'l*, pg. 4362
SUN COUNTRY AIRLINES HOLDINGS, INC.; *U.S. Public*, pg. 1963
SUN COUNTRY, INC.—See Sun Country Airlines Holdings, Inc.; *U.S. Public*, pg. 1963
SUN COUNTRY INDUSTRIES LLC—See McNally Industries, LLC; *U.S. Private*, pg. 2643

SUN COUNTRY AIRLINES HOLDINGS, INC.   CORPORATE AFFILIATIONS

SUN COUNTRY MATERIALS, LLC—See Waste Connections, Inc.; *Int'l*, pg. 8354
SUN COUNTRY RESTORATION, LLC; *U.S. Private*, pg. 3863
SUN COUNTRY TOYOTA; *Int'l*, pg. 7303
SUNCRAFT TECHNOLOGIES INC.; *U.S. Private*, pg. 3866
SUNCREST FARMS COUNTRY HAMS, INC.; *U.S. Private*, pg. 3866
SUNCREST HEALTHCARE, INC.—See UnitedHealth Group Incorporated; *U.S. Public*, pg. 2244
SUN CURRENT/SUN NEWSPAPERS—See Adams Publishing Group, LLC; *U.S. Private*, pg. 75
SUN CYPRESS SHIPPING CO. LTD—See Israel Corporation Ltd.; *Int'l*, pg. 3823
SUNDA ENERGY PLC; *Int'l*, pg. 7311
SUNDAGARDAR LTD.—See Norske Skog ASA; *Int'l*, pg. 5438
SUNDANCE BEHAVIORAL HEALTHCARE SYSTEM; *U.S. Private*, pg. 3866
SUNDANCE BUICK, GMC, INC.—See Sundance Chevrolet, Inc.; *U.S. Private*, pg. 3866
SUNDANCE CATALOG CO., LTD.—See Brentwood Associates; *U.S. Private*, pg. 646
SUNDANCE CHEVROLET, INC.; *U.S. Private*, pg. 3866
SUNDANCE ENERGY AUSTRALIA LIMITED; *U.S. Public*, pg. 1964
SUNDANCE ENERGY INC.—See KKR & Co. Inc.; *U.S. Public*, pg. 1244
SUNDANCE HELICOPTERS, INC.—See American Securities LLC; *U.S. Private*, pg. 247
SUNDANCE MARINE, INC.; *U.S. Private*, pg. 3866
SUNDANCE MARINE NORTH, INC.—See OneWater Marine Holdings LLC; *U.S. Private*, pg. 3026
SUNDANCE PUBLISHING—See Carolrhoda Books, Inc.; *U.S. Private*, pg. 769
SUNDANCE RESOURCES LIMITED; *Int'l*, pg. 7311
SUNDANCE SERVICES CORPORATION—See Formation Capital, LLC; *U.S. Private*, pg. 1570
SUNDANCE STRATEGIES, INC.; *U.S. Public*, pg. 1964
SUNDANCE VACATIONS; *U.S. Private*, pg. 3866
SUNDARAM ALTERNATE ASSETS LIMITED—See Sundaram Finance Ltd; *Int'l*, pg. 7312
SUNDARAM ASSET MANAGEMENT COMPANY LIMITED—See Sundaram Finance Ltd; *Int'l*, pg. 7312
SUNDARAM ASSET MANAGEMENT SINGAPORE PTE. LIMITED—See Sundaram Finance Ltd; *Int'l*, pg. 7312
SUNDARAM AUTO COMPONENTS LIMITED—See TVS Motor Company Ltd.; *Int'l*, pg. 7989
SUNDARAM BRAKE LININGS LIMITED - PADI PLANT—See Sundaram Brake Linings Limited; *Int'l*, pg. 7312
SUNDARAM BRAKE LININGS LIMITED - PLANT 4 & 5—See Sundaram Brake Linings Limited; *Int'l*, pg. 7312
SUNDARAM BRAKE LININGS LIMITED; *Int'l*, pg. 7311
SUNDARAM BUSINESS SERVICES LIMITED—See Sundaram Finance Holdings Limited; *Int'l*, pg. 7312
SUNDARAM CLAYTON LTD. - CHENNAI PLANT—See Sundaram Clayton Ltd.; *Int'l*, pg. 7312
SUNDARAM CLAYTON LTD. - KANCHIPURAM PLANT—See Sundaram Clayton Ltd.; *Int'l*, pg. 7312
SUNDARAM CLAYTON LTD.; *Int'l*, pg. 7312
SUNDARAM-CLAYTON (USA) LIMITED—See Sundaram Clayton Ltd.; *Int'l*, pg. 7312
SUNDARAM FINANCE HOLDINGS LIMITED; *Int'l*, pg. 7312
SUNDARAM FINANCE LTD; *Int'l*, pg. 7312
SUNDARAM INDUSTRIES PRIVATE LIMITED—See TVS Electronics Limited; *Int'l*, pg. 7989
SUNDARAM MOTORS PVT. LTD.—See TV Sundram Iyengar & Sons Limited; *Int'l*, pg. 7987
SUNDARAM MULTI PAP LIMITED; *Int'l*, pg. 7312
SUNDARAM TEXTILES LIMITED—See Sundaram Brake Linings Limited; *Int'l*, pg. 7312
SUNDART ENGINEERING & CONTRACTING(BEIJING) LIMITED—See Rykadan Capital Limited; *Int'l*, pg. 6439
SUNDART ENGINEERING SERVICES(MACAU) LIMITED—See Rykadan Capital Limited; *Int'l*, pg. 6439
SUNDART HOLDINGS LIMITED; *Int'l*, pg. 7312
SUNDART TIMBER PRODUCTS COMPANY LIMITED—See Rykadan Capital Limited; *Int'l*, pg. 6439
SUNDAY CO., LTD.—See AEON Co., Ltd.; *Int'l*, pg. 178
SUNDAY GMBH—See Bertelsmann SE & Co. KGaA; *Int'l*, pg. 996
SUNDAY NEWSPAPERS LIMITED—See Mediahuis Partners NV; *Int'l*, pg. 4772
SUNDAY NEWSPAPERS LIMITED—See VP Exploitatie N.V.; *Int'l*, pg. 8311
SUNDAY PAINT CO., LTD.—See Dai Nippon Toryo Co., Ltd.; *Int'l*, pg. 1916
SUNDAY RIVER SKI RESORT; *U.S. Private*, pg. 3866
SUNDAY RIVER SKIWAY CORP.—See Boyne USA Resorts Inc.; *U.S. Private*, pg. 629
SUNDAYSKY INC.—See Clearhaven Partners LP; *U.S. Private*, pg. 933
SUNDAYSKY ISRAEL—See Clearhaven Partners LP; *U.S. Private*, pg. 933
THE SUNDAY TIMES LIMITED—See News Corporation; *U.S. Public*, pg. 1521

SUND BIRSTA AB—See Danieli & C. Officine Meccaniche S.p.A.; *Int'l*, pg. 1963
SUNDBYVESTERHUS A/S—See Jyske Bank A/S; *Int'l*, pg. 4037
SUNDE AS; *Int'l*, pg. 7312
SUN-DELICA CO., LTD.—See Yamazaki Baking Co., Ltd.; *Int'l*, pg. 8556
SUNDERLAND BROTHERS COMPANY; *U.S. Private*, pg. 3866
SUN DESERT DIALYSIS, LLC—See DaVita Inc.; *U.S. Public*, pg. 643
SUN DEVIL AUTO PARTS INC.—See Greenbriar Equity Group, L.P.; *U.S. Private*, pg. 1776
SUNDEX CO., LTD.—See FTGroup Co Ltd.; *Int'l*, pg. 2800
SUNDIA CORPORATION; *U.S. Private*, pg. 3866
SUNDIAL BEACH AND GOLF RESORT—See CoreStates Capital Advisors, LLC; *U.S. Private*, pg. 1049
SUNDIAL BRANDS LLC—See Unilever PLC; *Int'l*, pg. 8048
SUNDIAL & CO.—See Sun Ling & Company; *Int'l*, pg. 7306
SUNDIAL MARINE TUG & BARGE WORKS INC.—See Tidewater Holdings, Inc.; *U.S. Private*, pg. 4168
SUNDIC INC.—See DIC Corporation; *Int'l*, pg. 2109
SUNDIN ASSOCIATES, INC.; *U.S. Private*, pg. 3866
SUNDIRO HOLDING CO., LTD.; *Int'l*, pg. 7312
SUNDIRO SANLORENZO YACHT MANUFACTURING CO., LTD.—See Sundiro Holding Co., Ltd.; *Int'l*, pg. 7313
SUNDOG INTERACTIVE, INC.—See EQT AB; *Int'l*, pg. 2483
SUNDOG; *U.S. Private*, pg. 3866
SUNDO INDUSTRIAL CO., LTD.—See Pungguk Alcohol Industrial Co., Ltd; *Int'l*, pg. 6119
SUNDOLITT LIMITED—See Sunde AS; *Int'l*, pg. 7312
SUNDOWN FOODS U.S.A., INC.—See A.V.O.D. Kurutulmus Gida ve Tarim Urunleri San. Tic. A.S.; *Int'l*, pg. 28
SUNDOWN M RANCH; *U.S. Private*, pg. 3866
SUNDQUIST COMPONENTS AB—See Axel Johnson Gruppen AB; *Int'l*, pg. 763
SUNDQUIST HOMES LLC—See Century Communities, Inc.; *U.S. Public*, pg. 475
SUN DRAGON IMPORT, INC.; *U.S. Private*, pg. 3863
SUNDRAM FASTENERS LTD.—See TV Sundram Iyengar & Sons Limited; *Int'l*, pg. 7987
SUN DREAMS S.A.—See Sun International Limited; *Int'l*, pg. 7304
SUNDRE FOREST PRODUCTS LTD.—See West Fraser Timber Co., Ltd.; *Int'l*, pg. 8384
SUN DRILLING PRODUCTS CORP; *U.S. Private*, pg. 3863
SUNDS MDF TECHNOLOGIES AB—See Dieffenbacher Holding GmbH & Co. KG; *Int'l*, pg. 2114
SUNDSVALLS STAL AB—See SSAB AB; *Int'l*, pg. 7155
THE SUNDT COMPANIES, INC.; *U.S. Private*, pg. 4125
SUNDT CONSTRUCTION, INC. - IRVINE OFFICE—See The Sundt Companies, Inc.; *U.S. Private*, pg. 4125
SUNDT CONSTRUCTION, INC. - SACRAMENTO OFFICE—See The Sundt Companies, Inc.; *U.S. Private*, pg. 4125
SUNDT CONSTRUCTION, INC. - SAN ANTONIO OFFICE—See The Sundt Companies, Inc.; *U.S. Private*, pg. 4125
SUNDT CONSTRUCTION, INC. - SAN DIEGO OFFICE—See The Sundt Companies, Inc.; *U.S. Private*, pg. 4125
SUNDT CONSTRUCTION, INC.—See The Sundt Companies, Inc.; *U.S. Private*, pg. 4125
SUNDURANCE ENERGY, LLC; *U.S. Private*, pg. 3866
SUNDWIGER MESSINGWERK GMBH & CO. KG—See Deutsche Invest Capital Partners GmbH; *Int'l*, pg. 2066
SUNDY LAND INVESTMENT CO., LTD.; *Int'l*, pg. 7313
SUNDYNE, LLC—See BC Partners LLP; *Int'l*, pg. 922
SUNDYNE, LLC—See The Carlyle Group Inc.; *U.S. Public*, pg. 2044
SUNDYNE NIKKISO COMPANY—See Nikkiso Co., Ltd.; *Int'l*, pg. 5291
SUNDY SERVICE GROUP CO., LTD.; *Int'l*, pg. 7313
SUNEARTH, INC.—See Solaray Corporation; *U.S. Private*, pg. 3707
SUN ECO THERMAL CO., LTD.—See Tsukishima Holdings Co., Ltd.; *Int'l*, pg. 7956
SUNEDISON ENERGY INDIA PVT. LTD.—See SunEdison, Inc.; *U.S. Private*, pg. 3867
SUNEDISON HOLDINGS CORPORATION—See SunEdison, Inc.; *U.S. Private*, pg. 3867
SUNEDISON, INC.; *U.S. Private*, pg. 3866
SUNEDISON LLC—See SunEdison, Inc.; *U.S. Private*, pg. 3867
SUNEDISON SEMICONDUCTOR BV—See SunEdison, Inc.; *U.S. Private*, pg. 3867
SUNEDISON SEMICONDUCTOR LIMITED—See Sino-American Silicon Products Inc.; *Int'l*, pg. 6948
SUNEDISON SEMICONDUCTOR, LLC—See Sino-American Silicon Products Inc.; *Int'l*, pg. 6948
SUNEDISON SEMICONDUCTOR TECHNOLOGY (SHANGHAI) LTD.—See Sino-American Silicon Products Inc.; *Int'l*, pg. 6948

SUN-EIGHT TRADING CO., LTD.—See Kamei Corporation; *Int'l*, pg. 4062
SUN-ELECTRIC AUSTRIA GESELLSCHAFT M.B.H—See Snap-on Incorporated; *U.S. Public*, pg. 1899
SUN ELECTRIC HEATER COMPANY—See NIBE Industrier AB; *Int'l*, pg. 5260
SUN ELECTRIC SERVICES, INC.—See Primoris Services Corporation; *U.S. Public*, pg. 1719
SUN ENERGY HIRONO CO., LTD.—See Japan Pulp and Paper Company Limited; *Int'l*, pg. 3904
SUN ENERGY SOLUTIONS; *U.S. Private*, pg. 3863
SUN ENTERPRISES INCORPORATED—See Sun Powersports Investments, LLC; *U.S. Private*, pg. 3863
SUNERA LLC; *U.S. Private*, pg. 3867
SUNERGY, INC.; *U.S. Private*, pg. 3867
SUNESIS CONSTRUCTION COMPANY, INC.; *U.S. Private*, pg. 3867
SUNESYS, LLC—See Quanta Services, Inc.; *U.S. Public*, pg. 1751
SUNETRIC; *U.S. Private*, pg. 3867
SUN EUROPEAN PARTNERS GMBH—See Sun Capital Partners, Inc.; *U.S. Private*, pg. 3862
SUN EUROPEAN PARTNERS, LLP—See Sun Capital Partners, Inc.; *U.S. Private*, pg. 3861
SUN EUROPEAN PARTNERS, SAS—See Sun Capital Partners, Inc.; *U.S. Private*, pg. 3862
SUNEVISION HOLDINGS LTD.—See Sun Hung Kai Properties Limited; *Int'l*, pg. 7304
SUNEX SA; *Int'l*, pg. 7313
SUNEXT TECHNOLOGY CO., LTD.—See Sunplus Technology Co., Ltd.; *Int'l*, pg. 7320
SUN FAIR ELECTRIC WIRE & CABLE (HK) COMPANY LIMITED—See Century Energy International Holdings Limited; *Int'l*, pg. 1418
SUNFAR COMPUTER CO., LTD.; *Int'l*, pg. 7313
SUN FARMACEUTICA DO BRASIL LTDA.—See Sun Pharmaceutical Industries Ltd.; *Int'l*, pg. 7307
SUN-FARM SP. Z O.O.—See Dermapharm Holding SE; *Int'l*, pg. 2043
SUN FAVORITE CO., LTD.—See Cheng Loong Corp.; *Int'l*, pg. 1466
SUNFCO LTD.; *Int'l*, pg. 7313
SUNFED PRODUCE LLC—See GrubMarket, Inc.; *U.S. Private*, pg. 1797
SUNFELT CO., LTD.—See Chiyoda Integre Co., Ltd.; *Int'l*, pg. 1575
SUNFIELD HOMES MISSISSAUGA LIMITED; *Int'l*, pg. 7313
SUNFIELD INTERNET CO., LTD—See MITSUBA Corporation; *Int'l*, pg. 4929
SUNFIELD RESOURCES PTY. LIMITED—See China Coal Energy Company Limited; *Int'l*, pg. 1490
SUN FINANCE COMPANY LIMITED—See Imperium Financial Group Limited; *Int'l*, pg. 3635
SUN FINANCE COMPANY, LLC; *U.S. Private*, pg. 3863
SUNFIRE ACQUISITION CORP LIMITED; *U.S. Public*, pg. 1964
SUNFLAG IRON AND STEEL COMPANY LIMITED; *Int'l*, pg. 7313
SUNFLAME ENTERPRISES PRIVATE LIMITED—See V-Guard Industries Ltd.; *Int'l*, pg. 8105
SUNFLEX ELECTRONIC (SHENZHEN) CO., LTD.—See Sunflex Tech Co., Ltd.; *Int'l*, pg. 7313
SUNFLEX TECH CO., LTD.; *Int'l*, pg. 7313
SUNFLOWER BANK, NATIONAL ASSOCIATION—See FirstSun Capital Bancorp; *U.S. Public*, pg. 850
SUNFLOWER ELECTRIC POWER CORPORATION; *U.S. Private*, pg. 3867
SUNFLOWER ELECTRIC POWER HOLCOMB STATION—See Sunflower Electric Power Corporation; *U.S. Private*, pg. 3867
THE SUNFLOWER GROUP; *U.S. Private*, pg. 4125
THE SUNFLOWER GROUP—See The Sunflower Group; *U.S. Private*, pg. 4125
THE SUNFLOWER GROUP—See The Sunflower Group; *U.S. Private*, pg. 4125
THE SUNFLOWER GROUP—See The Sunflower Group; *U.S. Private*, pg. 4125
SUNFLOWER MANUFACTURING INC.—See AGCO Corporation; *U.S. Public*, pg. 59
SUNFLOWER MARKETING—See M-C Industries Inc.; *U.S. Private*, pg. 2525
SUNFLOWER MEDICAL LTD.—See Indutrade AB; *Int'l*, pg. 3681
SUNFLOWER PHARMACEUTICAL GROUP CO., LTD.; *Int'l*, pg. 7313
SUNFLOWER SUSTAINABLE INVESTMENTS LTD.; *Int'l*, pg. 7313
SUNFLOWER SYSTEMS—See CGI Inc.; *Int'l*, pg. 1432
SUNFLOWER SYSTEMS—See CGI Inc.; *Int'l*, pg. 1432
SUNFLOWER TELEPHONE CO.—See Consolidated Communications Holdings, Inc.; *U.S. Public*, pg. 570
SUNFLY INTELLIGENT TECHNOLOGY CO., LTD.; *Int'l*, pg. 7313
SUNFLY SOLAR ENERGY SOLUTIONS, INC.—See Xxentria Technology Materials Co., Ltd.; *Int'l*, pg. 8541
SUNFON CONSTRUCTION CO., LTD.; *Int'l*, pg. 7313
SUNFONDA GROUP HOLDINGS LIMITED; *Int'l*, pg. 7313

COMPANY NAME INDEX

SUN FOODS INC.—See PepsiCo, Inc.; *U.S. Public*, pg. 1672
SUNFOODS LLC—See Ricegrowers Limited; *Int'l*, pg. 6329
SUN FOOK KONG GROUP; *Int'l*, pg. 7303
SUNF PU TECHNOLOGY CO., LTD.; *Int'l*, pg. 7313
SUNF PU TECHNOLOGY (DONG-GUAN) CO., LTD.—See SUNF PU TECHNOLOGY CO., Ltd.; *Int'l*, pg. 7313
SUNFRESH AGRO INDUSTRIES PRIVATE LIMITED—See Prabhat Dairy Limited; *Int'l*, pg. 5952
SUNFRESH PRODUCE, INC.; *U.S. Private*, pg. 3867
SUN FRONTIER COMMUNITY ARRANGEMENT CO., LTD.—See Sun Frontier Fudousan Co. Ltd.; *Int'l*, pg. 7303
SUN FRONTIER FUDOUSAN CO. LTD.; *Int'l*, pg. 7303
SUN FRONTIER SADO CO., LTD.—See Sun Frontier Fudousan Co. Ltd.; *Int'l*, pg. 7303
SUN FRONTIER SPACE MANAGEMENT CO., LTD.—See Sun Frontier Fudousan Co. Ltd.; *Int'l*, pg. 7303
SUNFUN (HK) INTERNATIONAL CO., LTD.—See Shifeng Cultural Development Co., Ltd.; *Int'l*, pg. 6828
SUNFUN INFO CO., LTD.; *Int'l*, pg. 7313
SUNGAI HARMONI SDN. BHD.—See Taliworks Corporation Berhad; *Int'l*, pg. 7447
SUNGAI LONG INDUSTRIES SDN BHD—See Bina Puri Holdings Bhd; *Int'l*, pg. 1032
SUNGAME CORPORATION; *U.S. Private*, pg. 3867
SUNGARD AVAILABILITY SERVICES CAPITAL, INC.; *U.S. Private*, pg. 3867
SUNGARD AVAILABILITY SERVICES (FRANCE) SA—See SunGard Availability Services Capital, Inc.; *U.S. Private*, pg. 3867
SUNGARD AVAILABILITY SERVICES LP—See SunGard Availability Services Capital, Inc.; *U.S. Private*, pg. 3867
SUNGARD AVAILABILITY SERVICES - MISSISSAUGA—See SunGard Availability Services Capital, Inc.; *U.S. Private*, pg. 3867
SUNGARD AVAILABILITY SERVICES - SAN RAMON—See SunGard Availability Services Capital, Inc.; *U.S. Private*, pg. 3867
SUNGARD AVAILABILITY SERVICES (UK) LIMITED—See SunGard Availability Services Capital, Inc.; *U.S. Private*, pg. 3867
SUNGARNER ENERGIES LIMITED; *Int'l*, pg. 7314
SUN-GAZETTE COMPANY INC.—See The Nutting Company, Inc.; *U.S. Private*, pg. 4086
SUNGBO CHEMICAL CO., LTD.; *Int'l*, pg. 7314
SUNGCHANG AUTOTECH CO., LTD. - ASAN PLANT—See Sungchang Autotech Co., Ltd.; *Int'l*, pg. 7314
SUNGCHANG AUTOTECH CO., LTD.; *Int'l*, pg. 7314
SUNGCHANG ENTERPRISE BOARD LIMITED—See Sungchang Enterprise Holdings Limited; *Int'l*, pg. 7314
SUNGCHANG ENTERPRISE HOLDINGS LIMITED; *Int'l*, pg. 7314
SUNGDO E&C (CHINA) CO., LTD—See Sungdo Engineering & Construction Co., Ltd.; *Int'l*, pg. 7314
SUNGDO ENG HUNGARY KFT; *Int'l*, pg. 7314
SUNGDO ENGINEERING & CONSTRUCTION CO., LTD.; *Int'l*, pg. 7314
SUNGDO ENGINEERING&CONSTRUCTION PVT LTD—See Sungdo Engineering & Construction Co., Ltd.; *Int'l*, pg. 7314
SUNGDOENG USA; *U.S. Private*, pg. 3867
SUNGDO PHILIPPINES CONSTRUCTION INC—See Sungdo Engineering & Construction Co., Ltd.; *Int'l*, pg. 7314
SUNGEAR, INC.—See Hicks Holdings, LLC; *U.S. Private*, pg. 1934
SUNGEAR, INC.—See The Riverside Company; *U.S. Private*, pg. 4108
SUNGEAR, INC.—See Weinberg Capital Group, Inc.; *U.S. Private*, pg. 4471
SUNGEI BAGAN RUBBER COMPANY (MALAYA) BERHAD; *Int'l*, pg. 7314
SUNGEI WAY OCEAN JOINT VENTURE LTD—See Sunway Berhad; *Int'l*, pg. 7328
SUNGENE GMBH—See BASF SE; *Int'l*, pg. 877
SUNGEN INTERNATIONAL LIMITED—See Anwell Technologies Ltd.; *Int'l*, pg. 486
SUNG-EUM MUSIC CO., LTD.; *Int'l*, pg. 7314
SUNGEVITY, INC.—See Hercules Capital, Inc.; *U.S. Public*, pg. 1028
SUNGEVITY, INC.—See Northern Pacific Group; *U.S. Private*, pg. 2954
SUNG GANG CORP LTD.; *Int'l*, pg. 7314
SUNG HO ELECTRONICS CORP. - CHINA (WEIHAI) FACTORY—See Sung Ho Electronics Corp.; *Int'l*, pg. 7314
SUNG HO ELECTRONICS CORP. - CHINA (ZHUHAI) FACTORY—See Sung Ho Electronics Corp.; *Int'l*, pg. 7314
SUNG HO ELECTRONICS CORP.; *Int'l*, pg. 7314
SUNGJEE CONSTRUCTION CO., LTD.; *Int'l*, pg. 7314
SUNGJI TRADING CO., LTD.; *Int'l*, pg. 7314
SUNGKWANG BEND CO., LTD.; *Int'l*, pg. 7314

SUNGMOON ELECTRONICS CO., LTD. - 1ST FACTORY—See Sungmoon Electronics Co., Ltd.; *Int'l*, pg. 7315
SUNGMOON ELECTRONICS CO., LTD. - 2ND FACTORY—See Sungmoon Electronics Co., Ltd.; *Int'l*, pg. 7315
SUNGMOON ELECTRONICS CO., LTD.; *Int'l*, pg. 7315
SUNGOLD CAPITAL LIMITED; *Int'l*, pg. 7315
SUNGOLD FOOD INC.—See ACOMO N.V.; *Int'l*, pg. 108
SUNGOLD INTERNATIONAL HOLDINGS CORP; *Int'l*, pg. 7315
SUNGOLD MEDIA & ENTERTAINMENT LTD.; *Int'l*, pg. 7315
SUNGOURMET CORPORATION—See Maruha Nichiro Corporation; *Int'l*, pg. 4712
SUNGRACE PHARMA PRIVATE LIMITED—See Medico Intercontinental Limited; *Int'l*, pg. 4776
SUNGRAIN, LTD.—See Suntory Holdings Limited; *Int'l*, pg. 7326
SUN GRANITE EXPORT LIMITED; *Int'l*, pg. 7303
SUN GRAPHICS INC.; *U.S. Private*, pg. 3863
SUN GRAPHICS PRINTING, INC.; *U.S. Private*, pg. 3863
SUN GRAPHIC TECHNOLOGIES, INC.; *U.S. Private*, pg. 3863
SUNGRID SOLUTIONS, INC.—See Hull Street Energy, LLC; *U.S. Private*, pg. 2005
SUN GRO HORTICULTURE DISTRIBUTION, INC.—See IKO Enterprises Ltd.; *Int'l*, pg. 3612
SUN GRO HORTICULTURE, INC.—See IKO Enterprises Ltd.; *Int'l*, pg. 3612
SUNGROW CANADA INC.—See Sungrow Power Supply Co., Ltd.; *Int'l*, pg. 7315
SUNGROW LANDSCAPE SERVICES; *U.S. Private*, pg. 3867
SUNGROW POWER AUSTRALIA PTY LTD.—See Sungrow Power Supply Co., Ltd.; *Int'l*, pg. 7315
SUNGROW POWER SUPPLY CO., LTD.; *Int'l*, pg. 7315
SUNG SAN COMPANY, LTD.—See General Motors Company; *U.S. Public*, pg. 929
SUNGSHIN CEMENT CO., LTD.; *Int'l*, pg. 7315
SUNGSHIN VINA CO., LTD.—See Sungshin Cement Co., Ltd.; *Int'l*, pg. 7315
SUNG WOO ELECTRONICS CO., LTD. - ESTECH GWANG.IU FACTORY—See Sung Woo Electronics Co., Ltd.; *Int'l*, pg. 7314
SUNG WOO ELECTRONICS CO., LTD.; *Int'l*, pg. 7314
SUNGWOO HITECH AUTOMOBILE COMPONENTS (YANCHENG) CO., LTD.—See Sungwoo Hitech Co., Ltd.; *Int'l*, pg. 7315
SUNGWOO HITECH CO., LTD. - DADAE FACTORY—See Sungwoo Hitech Co., Ltd.; *Int'l*, pg. 7315
SUNGWOO HITECH CO., LTD. - JEONGGWAN FACTORY—See Sungwoo Hitech Co., Ltd.; *Int'l*, pg. 7315
SUNGWOO HITECH CO., LTD. - JISA FACTORY—See Sungwoo Hitech Co., Ltd.; *Int'l*, pg. 7315
SUNGWOO HITECH CO., LTD. - JUNGKWAN FACTORY—See Sungwoo Hitech Co., Ltd.; *Int'l*, pg. 7315
SUNGWOO HITECH CO., LTD. - JUNGKWAN NO.2 FACTORY—See Sungwoo Hitech Co., Ltd.; *Int'l*, pg. 7315
SUNGWOO HITECH CO., LTD. - SEOCHANG FACTORY—See Sungwoo Hitech Co., Ltd.; *Int'l*, pg. 7315
SUNGWOO HITECH CO., LTD.; *Int'l*, pg. 7315
SUNGWOO HITECH INDIA LTD.—See Sungwoo Hitech Co., Ltd.; *Int'l*, pg. 7315
SUNGWOO HITECH SLOVAKIA S.R.O—See Sungwoo Hitech Co., Ltd.; *Int'l*, pg. 7315
SUNGWOO HITECH S.R.O—See Sungwoo Hitech Co., Ltd.; *Int'l*, pg. 7315
SUNGWOO HITECH WMU—See Sungwoo Hitech Co., Ltd.; *Int'l*, pg. 7315
SUNGWOO HITECH WUXI CO., LTD.—See Sungwoo Hitech Co., Ltd.; *Int'l*, pg. 7315
SUNGWOO MOLD CO., LTD.—See Sungwoo Hitech Co., Ltd.; *Int'l*, pg. 7315
SUNGWOO NIT, INC—See Sung Woo Electronics Co., Ltd.; *Int'l*, pg. 7314
SUNGWOO TECHRON CO., LTD.; *Int'l*, pg. 7315
SUNGY MOBILE LIMITED; *Int'l*, pg. 7316
SUN HEALTHCARE (M) SDN. BHD.—See Southern Capital Group Pte. Ltd.; *Int'l*, pg. 7118
SUN HEALTH SERVICES; *U.S. Private*, pg. 3863
THE SUN HERALD—See Chatham Asset Management, LLC; *U.S. Private*, pg. 867
THE SUN-HERALD—See Nine Entertainment Co. Holdings Limited; *Int'l*, pg. 5299
SUNHILL FOOD OF VERMONT, INC.—See Danish Crown AmbA; *Int'l*, pg. 1965
SUNHILLO CORPORATION; *U.S. Private*, pg. 3867
SUN HING PAPER COMPANY, LIMITED—See Hung Hing Printing Group Limited; *Int'l*, pg. 3535
SUN HING POSH HOLDINGS LIMITED—See MillerKnoll, Inc.; *U.S. Public*, pg. 1448
SUN HING PRINTING HOLDINGS LIMITED; *Int'l*, pg. 7303

SUN.KING TECHNOLOGY GROUP LIMITED

SUN HING VISION GROUP HOLDINGS LIMITED; *Int'l*, pg. 7303
SUN HONG OPTRONICS LTD.—See Wah Hong Industrial Corp.; *Int'l*, pg. 8328
SUNHOTELS LTD.—See Webjet Limited; *Int'l*, pg. 8366
SUN HOUSE FOODS CORPORATION—See House Foods Group Inc.; *Int'l*, pg. 3490
SUN HUNG KAI & CO. LIMITED—See Allied Group Limited; *Int'l*, pg. 357
SUN HUNG KAI CREDIT LIMITED—See Allied Group Limited; *Int'l*, pg. 357
SUN HUNG KAI DEVELOPMENT (CHINA) LIMITED—See Sun Hung Kai Properties Limited; *Int'l*, pg. 7304
SUN HUNG KAI INVESTMENT SERVICES LIMITED - MACAU BRANCH—See Allied Group Limited; *Int'l*, pg. 357
SUN HUNG KAI INVESTMENT SERVICES LIMITED - SHENZHEN BRANCH—See Allied Group Limited; *Int'l*, pg. 357
SUN HUNG KAI PROPERTIES INSURANCE LTD.—See Sun Hung Kai Properties Limited; *Int'l*, pg. 7304
SUN HUNG KAI PROPERTIES LIMITED; *Int'l*, pg. 7304
SUN HYDRAULICS CHINA CO., LTD.—See Helios Technologies, Inc.; *U.S. Public*, pg. 1023
SUN HYDRAULICS KOREA CORPORATION—See Helios Technologies, Inc.; *U.S. Public*, pg. 1024
SUN HYDRAULICS LIMITED—See Helios Technologies, Inc.; *U.S. Public*, pg. 1024
SUN HYDRAULIK GMBH—See Helios Technologies, Inc.; *U.S. Public*, pg. 1024
SUNHYDROGEN, INC.; *U.S. Public*, pg. 1964
SUNIC SYSTEM CO., LTD.; *Int'l*, pg. 7316
SUNIL AGRO FOODS LIMITED; *Int'l*, pg. 7316
SUNILAN PUHDISTAMO OY—See Stora Enso Oyj; *Int'l*, pg. 7225
SUNIL HEALTHCARE LIMITED; *Int'l*, pg. 7316
SUNIL INDUSTRIES LIMITED; *Int'l*, pg. 7316
SUNIL SFS INTEC AUTOMOTIVE PARTS (TIANJIN) CO., LTD.—See SFS Group AG; *Int'l*, pg. 6739
SUNING.COM CO., LTD.—See Suning Holdings Group Co., Ltd.; *Int'l*, pg. 7316
SUNING HOLDINGS GROUP CO., LTD.; *Int'l*, pg. 7316
SUNING UNIVERSAL CO., LTD.; *Int'l*, pg. 7316
SUN INSTRUMENTS, INC.—See YKT CORPORATION; *Int'l*, pg. 8589
SUN INTERNATIONAL INDUSTRIAL LTD.—See WT Microelectronics Co., Ltd.; *Int'l*, pg. 8498
SUN INTERNATIONAL LIMITED; *Int'l*, pg. 7304
SUN INTERNATIONAL MANAGEMENT LIMITED—See Sun International Limited; *Int'l*, pg. 7304
SUN INTERNATIONAL SECURITIES LIMITED—See Imperium Financial Group Limited; *Int'l*, pg. 3635
SUN INTERNATIONAL (SOUTH AFRICA) LIMITED—See Sun International Limited; *Int'l*, pg. 7304
SUN INTERNATIONAL TRAVEL (PTY) LIMITED—See Sun International Limited; *Int'l*, pg. 7304
SUNION TECHNOLOGY CO., LTD.—See Taiwan Fu Hsing Industrial Co., Ltd.; *Int'l*, pg. 7420
SUNITY ONLINE ENTERTAINMENT LTD.; *Int'l*, pg. 7316
SUNIVA, INC.—See Shunfeng International Clean Energy Ltd.; *Int'l*, pg. 6870
SUNJET COMPONENTS CORP.—See EDOM Technology Co., Ltd.; *Int'l*, pg. 2313
SUNJIN BEAUTY SCIENCE CO., LTD.; *Int'l*, pg. 7316
SUNJIN CHENGDU FEED CO., LTD.—See SUNJIN CO., LTD.; *Int'l*, pg. 7316
SUNJIN CO., LTD.; *Int'l*, pg. 7316
SUNJIN FARMSCO CO., LTD.—See SUNJIN CO., LTD.; *Int'l*, pg. 7316
SUNJIN GENETICS CORPORATION—See SUNJIN CO., LTD.; *Int'l*, pg. 7316
SUNJIN MOTORS CO. LTD.—See Kukdong Oil & Chemical Co., Ltd.; *Int'l*, pg. 4327
SUNJIN PHILIPPINES INC.—See SUNJIN CO., LTD.; *Int'l*, pg. 7316
SUNJIN VINA CO., LTD.—See SUNJIN CO., LTD.; *Int'l*, pg. 7316
SUNJIN VINA MEKONG CO., LTD.—See SUNJIN CO., LTD.; *Int'l*, pg. 7316
SUN JOURNAL—See Gannett Co., Inc.; *U.S. Public*, pg. 906
SUNJUICE HOLDINGS CO., LTD.; *Int'l*, pg. 7316
SUNJUICE LIMITED—See PanJam Investment Limited; *Int'l*, pg. 5728
SUN KAKO CO., LTD.—See Kurita Water Industries Ltd.; *Int'l*, pg. 4341
SUNKAR RESOURCES PLC; *Int'l*, pg. 7317
SUNKEN STONE INC.; *U.S. Private*, pg. 3867
SUN-KIMURAYA CO., LTD—See Yamazaki Baking Co., Ltd.; *Int'l*, pg. 8556
SUN.KING TECHNOLOGY GROUP LIMITED; *Int'l*, pg. 7309
SUNKIST (FAR EAST) PROMOTION, LTD.—See Sunkist Growers, Inc.; *U.S. Private*, pg. 3867
SUNKIST GROWERS, INC.-CENTRAL DIVISION—See Sunkist Growers, Inc.; *U.S. Private*, pg. 3867
SUNKIST GROWERS, INC.-EASTERN DIVISION—See Sunkist Growers, Inc.; *U.S. Private*, pg. 3867

SUNKIST GROWERS, INC. - PROCESSED PRODUCTS—See Sunkist Growers, Inc.; *U.S. Private*, pg. 3867
SUNKIST GROWERS, INC.; *U.S. Private*, pg. 3867
SUNKIST GROWERS, INC.-SOUTHERN DIVISION—See Sunkist Growers, Inc.; *U.S. Private*, pg. 3868
SUNKIST GROWERS, INC.-WESTERN DIVISION—See Sunkist Growers, Inc.; *U.S. Private*, pg. 3868
SUNKO INK CO., LTD.; *Int'l*, pg. 7317
SUN KONG HOLDINGS LTD.; *Int'l*, pg. 7304
SUN KWANG CO., LTD. - CONTAINER DIVISION—See Sun Kwang Co., Ltd.; *Int'l*, pg. 7304
SUN KWANG CO., LTD. - LOGISTICS DIVISION—See Sun Kwang Co., Ltd.; *Int'l*, pg. 7304
SUN KWANG CO., LTD. - SEA SAND DIVISION—See Sun Kwang Co., Ltd.; *Int'l*, pg. 7304
SUN KWANG CO., LTD.; *Int'l*, pg. 7304
SUN KWANG LOGISTICS CO., LTD—See Sun Kwang Co., Ltd.; *Int'l*, pg. 7305
SUN KWANG NEW CONTAINER TERMINAL CO., LTD.—See Sun Kwang Co., Ltd.; *Int'l*, pg. 7305
SUNKWAN PROPERTIES GROUP LIMITED; *Int'l*, pg. 7317
SUNLABZ LLC—See Aterian, Inc.; *U.S. Public*, pg. 221
SUNLAKE CO., LTD.—See SK Engineering & Construction Co., Ltd.; *Int'l*, pg. 6970
SUN LAKES MARKETING LP; *U.S. Private*, pg. 3863
SUNLAND ASPHALT & CONSTRUCTION, LLC—See Huron Capital Partners LLC; *U.S. Private*, pg. 2012
SUNLAND BUILDERS; *U.S. Private*, pg. 3868
SUNLAND CONSTRUCTION INC.; *U.S. Private*, pg. 3868
SUNLAND GROUP LIMITED; *Int'l*, pg. 7317
SUNLAND INTERNATIONAL, LLC—See CRU Data Security Group, LLC; *U.S. Private*, pg. 1113
SUNLAND OPTICAL COMPANY INC.; *U.S. Private*, pg. 3868
SUNLAND PARK MALL, LLC—See Washington Prime Group Inc.; *U.S. Private*, pg. 4449
SUNLANDS TECHNOLOGY GROUP; *Int'l*, pg. 7317
SUNLAND VOLONTE AGENCY SDN. BHD.—See EA Holdings Berhad; *Int'l*, pg. 2261
SUN&L CO., LTD.; *Int'l*, pg. 7308
SUN LEE INC.; *U.S. Private*, pg. 3863
SUNLESS INC.—See Castle Harlan, Inc.; *U.S. Private*, pg. 785
SUNLEX CO., LTD—See Mitsubishi Heavy Industries, Ltd.; *Int'l*, pg. 4961
SUNLEY M&E ENGINEERING PTE. LTD.—See CNQC International Holdings Ltd.; *Int'l*, pg. 1678
SUN LIFE ASSURANCE COMPANY OF CANADA—See Sun Life Financial Inc.; *Int'l*, pg. 7305
SUN LIFE ASSURANCE COMPANY OF CANADA (U.K.) LIMITED—See Sun Life Financial Inc.; *Int'l*, pg. 7305
SUN LIFE ASSURANCE COMPANY OF CANADA - U.S. OPERATIONS HOLDINGS, INC.—See Guggenheim Partners, LLC; *U.S. Private*, pg. 1812
SUN LIFE ASSURANCE—See Sun Life Financial Inc.; *Int'l*, pg. 7305
SUN LIFE ASSURANCE—See Sun Life Financial Inc.; *Int'l*, pg. 7305
SUN LIFE CO., LTD.—See Sumitomo Mitsui Financial Group, Inc.; *Int'l*, pg. 7294
SUN LIFE CORPORATION; *Int'l*, pg. 7305
SUNLIFE CREATION CO., LTD.—See Mitsui Fudosan Co., Ltd.; *Int'l*, pg. 4988
SUN LIFE EVERBRIGHT LIFE INSURANCE COMPANY LIMITED—See Anshan Iron & Steel Group Corporation; *Int'l*, pg. 479
SUN LIFE EVERBRIGHT LIFE INSURANCE COMPANY LIMITED—See China Everbright Group Limited; *Int'l*, pg. 1501
SUN LIFE EVERBRIGHT LIFE INSURANCE COMPANY LIMITED—See China North Industries Group Corporation; *Int'l*, pg. 1536
SUN LIFE EVERBRIGHT LIFE INSURANCE COMPANY LIMITED—See Sun Life Financial Inc.; *Int'l*, pg. 7305
SUN LIFE FINANCIAL EMPLOYEE BENEFITS GROUP—See Guggenheim Partners, LLC; *U.S. Private*, pg. 1813
SUN LIFE FINANCIAL INC.; *Int'l*, pg. 7305
SUN LIFE FINANCIAL INSURANCE—See Sun Life Financial Inc.; *Int'l*, pg. 7305
SUN LIFE FINANCIAL INVESTMENTS (BERMUDA) LTD.—See Sun Life Financial Inc.; *Int'l*, pg. 7305
SUN LIFE FINANCIAL INVESTMENT SERVICES (CANADA) INC.—See Sun Life Financial Inc.; *Int'l*, pg. 7305
SUN LIFE FINANCIAL OF CANADA TRUSTEE LIMITED—See Sun Life Financial Inc.; *Int'l*, pg. 7306
SUN LIFE FINANCIAL OF CANADA (U.K.) LIMITED—See Sun Life Financial Inc.; *Int'l*, pg. 7306
SUN LIFE FINANCIAL PLANS, INC.—See Sun Life Financial Inc.; *Int'l*, pg. 7306
SUN LIFE FINANCIAL REINSURANCE (BARBADOS) LIMITED—See Sun Life Financial Inc.; *Int'l*, pg. 7305
SUN LIFE FINANCIAL TRUST INC.—See Sun Life Financial Inc.; *Int'l*, pg. 7305
SUN LIFE GLOBAL INVESTMENTS (CANADA) INC.—See Sun Life Financial Inc.; *Int'l*, pg. 7306

SUN LIFE GREPA FINANCIAL, INC.—See Sun Life Financial Inc.; *Int'l*, pg. 7306
SUN LIFE GREPA FINANCIAL, INC.—See Yuchengco Group of Companies; *Int'l*, pg. 8610
SUN LIFE HOLDING CO., LTD.; *Int'l*, pg. 7306
SUN LIFE INDIA SERVICE CENTRE PRIVATE LIMITED—See Sun Life Financial Inc.; *Int'l*, pg. 7306
SUN LIFE INFORMATION SERVICES CANADA, INC.—See Sun Life Financial Inc.; *Int'l*, pg. 7305
SUN LIFE INFORMATION SERVICES IRELAND LIMITED—See Sun Life Financial Inc.; *Int'l*, pg. 7305
SUN LIFE INSURANCE & ANNUITY COMPANY OF NEW YORK—See Guggenheim Partners, LLC; *U.S. Private*, pg. 1813
SUNLIFE INSURANCE COMPANY LTD.; *Int'l*, pg. 7317
SUN LIFE MALAYSIA ASSURANCE BERHAD—See Khazanah Nasional Berhad; *Int'l*, pg. 4153
SUN LIFE MALAYSIA ASSURANCE BERHAD—See Sun Life Financial Inc.; *Int'l*, pg. 7306
SUN LIFE MALAYSIA TAKAFUL BERHAD—See Khazanah Nasional Berhad; *Int'l*, pg. 4153
SUN LIFE MALAYSIA TAKAFUL BERHAD—See Sun Life Financial Inc.; *Int'l*, pg. 7306
SUN LIFE OF CANADA UNIT MANAGERS LIMITED—See Sun Life Financial Inc.; *Int'l*, pg. 7306
SUN LIFE OF CANADA (U.S.) HOLDINGS, INC.—See Sun Life Financial Inc.; *Int'l*, pg. 7306
SUN LIFE STADIUM—See Dolphins Enterprises, LLC; *U.S. Private*, pg. 1255
SUNLIGHT (1977) HOLDINGS LTD.; *Int'l*, pg. 7317
SUNLIGHT ELECTRICAL PTE LTD—See Chint Group Corporation; *Int'l*, pg. 1571
SUNLIGHT ELECTRICAL (VIETNAM) CO., LTD.—See Chint Group Corporation; *Int'l*, pg. 1571
SUNLIGHTEN, INC.; *U.S. Private*, pg. 3868
SUNLIGHT FINANCIAL HOLDINGS INC.; *U.S. Public*, pg. 1964
SUNLIGHT FINANCIAL LLC—See Sunlight Financial Holdings Inc.; *U.S. Public*, pg. 1964
SUNLIGHT GMBH—See Thor Industries, Inc.; *U.S. Public*, pg. 2157
SUNLIGHT GROUP ENERGY STORAGE SYSTEMS INDUSTRIAL AND COMMERCIAL SINGLEMEMBER SOCIETE ANONYME; *Int'l*, pg. 7317
SUN LIGHT & POWER; *U.S. Private*, pg. 3863
SUNLIGHT ROMANIA S.R.L. FILIALA—See Hellenic Telecommunications Organization S.A.; *Int'l*, pg. 3333
SUNLIGHT RUBBER PRODUCTS (SHANG HAI) CO., LTD.—See TPR Co., Ltd.; *Int'l*, pg. 7884
SUNLIGHT SWITCHGEAR SDN. BHD.—See Chint Group Corporation; *Int'l*, pg. 1571
SUN LIMITED; *Int'l*, pg. 7306
SUNLINE DIRECT MAIL LTD.—See CEPS PLC; *Int'l*, pg. 1420
SUNLINE HOLDING (HK) LIMITED—See Shenzhen Sunline Tech Co., Ltd.; *Int'l*, pg. 6821
SUNLINE TECHNOLOGY (MALAYSIA) SDN BHD—See Shenzhen Sunline Tech Co., Ltd.; *Int'l*, pg. 6821
SUNLINE TECHNOLOGY (THAILAND) LIMITED—See Shenzhen Sunline Tech Co., Ltd.; *Int'l*, pg. 6821
SUN LING & COMPANY; *Int'l*, pg. 7306
SUNLINK HEALTHCARE LLC—See SunLink Health Systems, Inc.; *U.S. Public*, pg. 1964
SUNLINK HEALTHCARE PROFESSIONAL PROPERTY, LLC—See SunLink Health Systems, Inc.; *U.S. Public*, pg. 1964
SUNLINK HEALTH SYSTEMS, INC.; *U.S. Public*, pg. 1964
SUN LOGISTICS CO., LTD—See Yamazaki Baking Co., Ltd.; *Int'l*, pg. 8556
SUNLORD ELECTRONICS JAPAN LLC—See Shenzhen Sunlord Electronics Co., Ltd.; *Int'l*, pg. 6822
SUNLORD ELECTRONICS TAIWAN, INC.—See Shenzhen Sunlord Electronics Co., Ltd.; *Int'l*, pg. 6822
SUNLORD ELECTRONICS USA, INC.—See Shenzhen Sunlord Electronics Co., Ltd.; *Int'l*, pg. 6822
SUNLOUR PIGMENT CO., LTD.; *Int'l*, pg. 7317
SUNLOUR PIGMENT TAIXING CITY CO., LTD.—See Sunlour Pigment Co., Ltd.; *Int'l*, pg. 7317
SUNLOVER HOLIDAYS PTY LTD—See Helloworld Travel Limited; *Int'l*, pg. 3337
SUNLUX MEDITERRANEAN—See Sunlux; *Int'l*, pg. 7317
SUNLUX; *Int'l*, pg. 7317
SUNMAC HAWAII, LTD.—See Sunkist Growers, Inc.; *U.S. Private*, pg. 3867
SUN MACHINERY CO., LTD.; *Int'l*, pg. 7306
SUN-MAID GROWERS OF CALIFORNIA; *U.S. Private*, pg. 3864
S.U.N. MANAGEMENT CO., LTD—See Sansiri pcl; *Int'l*, pg. 6557
SUN MANSFIELD MANUFACTURING (DONGGUAN) COMPANY LIMITED—See InnoTek Limited; *Int'l*, pg. 3711
SUNMAR CORPORATION—See Proroute Marumitsu Co., Ltd.; *Int'l*, pg. 5999
SUN MARKETING & COMMUNICATIONS LTD./SOLEIL COMMUNICATIONS-MARKETING LTEE; *Int'l*, pg. 7306
SUN MARK LIMITED; *Int'l*, pg. 7306

SUNMAR SHIPPING, INC.; *U.S. Private*, pg. 3868
SUNMART HOLDINGS LIMITED; *Int'l*, pg. 7317
SUN MARUKO CO., LTD.—See O-Well Corporation; *Int'l*, pg. 5503
SUNMASTER LIMITED—See The Emirates Group; *Int'l*, pg. 7639
SUN MATERIALS TECHNOLOGY CO., LTD.—See China Ruyi Holdings Limited; *Int'l*, pg. 1549
SUN MAX TECH LTD.; *Int'l*, pg. 7306
SUN MECHANICAL CONTRACTING INC.; *U.S. Private*, pg. 3863
SUNMED CLINICS SDN. BHD.—See Sunway Berhad; *Int'l*, pg. 7328
SUNMEDIA TECHNOLOGY CO., LTD—See Sunplus Technology Co., Ltd.; *Int'l*, pg. 7320
SUNMEDICAL CO., LTD.—See Toho Holdings Co., Ltd.; *Int'l*, pg. 7776
SUN MEDICAL INC.; *U.S. Private*, pg. 3863
SUN MEDICAL TECHNOLOGY RESEARCH CORP.—See Hi-Lex Corporation; *Int'l*, pg. 3381
SUN-MED, LLC—See HCA Healthcare, Inc.; *U.S. Public*, pg. 1011
SUNMERGE SYSTEMS INC.; *U.S. Private*, pg. 3868
SUN MESSE CO., LTD. - NAKA FACTORY—See Sun Messe Co., Ltd.; *Int'l*, pg. 7306
SUN MESSE CO., LTD. - NISHI FACTORY—See Sun Messe Co., Ltd.; *Int'l*, pg. 7306
SUN MESSE CO., LTD.; *Int'l*, pg. 7306
SUN MESSE (THAIIAND) CO., LTD.—See Sun Messe Co., Ltd.; *Int'l*, pg. 7306
SUN METAL CO., LTD.—See Sanwa Holdings Corporation; *Int'l*, pg. 6561
SUN METAL CORPORATION PTY LTD.—See Korea Zinc Company, Ltd.; *Int'l*, pg. 4288
SUN METALS CORP.—See NorthWest Copper Corp.; *Int'l*, pg. 5446
SUN MICROSTAMPING TECHNOLOGIES—See E.S. Investments, LLC; *U.S. Private*, pg. 1307
SUN MICROSYSTEMS AUSTRALIA PTY. LTD.—See Oracle Corporation; *U.S. Public*, pg. 1611
SUN MICROSYSTEMS DE CHILE S.A.—See Oracle Corporation; *U.S. Public*, pg. 1611
SUN MICROSYSTEMS DE MEXICO, S.A. DE C.V.—See Oracle Corporation; *U.S. Public*, pg. 1611
SUN MICROSYSTEMS DO BRASIL INDUSTRIA E COMERCIO LTDA.—See Oracle Corporation; *U.S. Public*, pg. 1611
SUN MICROSYSTEMS FRANCE, S.A.—See Oracle Corporation; *U.S. Public*, pg. 1611
SUN MICROSYSTEMS KOREA, LTD.—See Oracle Corporation; *U.S. Public*, pg. 1611
SUN MICROSYSTEMS LUXEMBOURG SARL—See Oracle Corporation; *U.S. Public*, pg. 1611
SUN MICROSYSTEMS NEDERLAND, B.V.—See Oracle Corporation; *U.S. Public*, pg. 1611
SUNMIRROR AG; *Int'l*, pg. 7317
SUNMOON FOOD COMPANY LIMITED; *Int'l*, pg. 7317
SUN MOTORS BMW; *U.S. Private*, pg. 3863
SUN MOUNTAIN LUMBER, INC.; *U.S. Private*, pg. 3863
SUN MOUNTAIN SPORTS INC.—See Solace Capital Partners, LLC; *U.S. Private*, pg. 3706
SUN MURPHY INTERNATIONAL TRADING (SHANGHAI) CO., LTD—See Helios Technologies, Inc.; *U.S. Public*, pg. 1024
SUN MYUNG AHAM LOGISTICS CO., LTD—See Sun Kwang Co., Ltd.; *Int'l*, pg. 7305
SUNNAP CO., LTD.—See Toyo Seikan Group Holdings, Ltd.; *Int'l*, pg. 7857
SUNNDAL SPAREBANK; *Int'l*, pg. 7317
SUNNEN AG—See Sunnen Products Company; *U.S. Private*, pg. 3868
SUNNEN PRODUCTS COMPANY; *U.S. Private*, pg. 3868
SUNNEN PRODUCTS LIMITED—See Sunnen Products Company; *U.S. Private*, pg. 3868
SUNNEN SAS—See Sunnen Products Company; *U.S. Private*, pg. 3868
SUNNEN S.R.O.—See Sunnen Products Company; *U.S. Private*, pg. 3868
THE SUN NEWS—See Chatham Asset Management, LLC; *U.S. Private*, pg. 866
SUNNEX EQUIPMENT AB—See Amplex AB; *Int'l*, pg. 434
SUNNEX EQUIPMENT SARL—See Amplex AB; *Int'l*, pg. 435
SUNNEXTA GROUP INC.; *Int'l*, pg. 7317
SUN NGAI PLASTIC PRODUCTS FACTORY LIMITED—See K & P International Holdings Limited; *Int'l*, pg. 4037
SUNNIC TECHNOLOGY & MERCHANDISE, INC.; *Int'l*, pg. 7317
SUNNILAND CORPORATION; *U.S. Private*, pg. 3868
SUNNILAND CORP.—See Leonard Green & Partners, L.P.; *U.S. Private*, pg. 2429
SUNNINGDALE PRECISION INDUSTRIES LTD.—See Sunningdale Tech Ltd; *Int'l*, pg. 7318
SUNNINGDALE PRECISION INDUSTRIES (SHANGHAI) CO., LTD.—See Sunningdale Tech Ltd; *Int'l*, pg. 7318
SUNNINGDALE PRECISION MOLD INDUSTRIES (TIANJIN) CO., LTD.—See Sunningdale Tech Ltd; *Int'l*, pg. 7318

COMPANY NAME INDEX

SUNNINGDALE TECH INC.—See Sunningdale Tech Ltd; *Int'l*, pg. 7318
SUNNINGDALE TECH LTD; *Int'l*, pg. 7317
SUNNINGDALE TECH (MALAYSIA) SDN BHD—See Sunningdale Tech Ltd; *Int'l*, pg. 7318
SUNNINGDALE TECHNOLOGIES S.A. DE C.V.—See Sunningdale Tech Ltd; *Int'l*, pg. 7318
SUNNIVA DRIKKER AS—See TINE SA; *Int'l*, pg. 7753
SUNNIVA, INC.; *Int'l*, pg. 7318
SUNNOVA ENERGY INTERNATIONAL INC.; *U.S. Public*, pg. 1964
SUN NUCLEAR CORPORATION—See Mirion Technologies, Inc.; *U.S. Public*, pg. 1450
SUNNY BUILDING AND DECORATION MATERIALS COMPANY LIMITED—See E. Bon Holdings Ltd; *Int'l*, pg. 2250
SUNNY CREEK FARM, LLC.; *U.S. Private*, pg. 3868
SUNNY DAY AD-VARNA; *Int'l*, pg. 7318
SUNNY DELIGHT BEVERAGES CO.—See Brynwood Partners Management LLC; *U.S. Private*, pg. 674
SUNNY DESIGN INC.; *U.S. Private*, pg. 3868
SUNNY ELECTRONICS CORP.; *Int'l*, pg. 7318
SUNNY FARMS, INC.; *U.S. Private*, pg. 3868
SUNNY FLORIDA DAIRY INC.; *U.S. Private*, pg. 3868
SUNNY FOODS CO., LTD.—See Mitsubishi Corporation; *Int'l*, pg. 4940
SUNNY FOOTWEAR CO., LTD.—See Fulgent Sun International (Holding) Co., Ltd.; *Int'l*, pg. 2842
SUNNY FRIEND ENVIRONMENTAL TECHNOLOGY CO., LTD.; *Int'l*, pg. 7318
SUNNY HILL ENERGY; *Int'l*, pg. 7318
SUNNYHILL, INC.; *U.S. Private*, pg. 3868
SUNNY I/E CO., LTD—See Zhejiang Orient Financial Holdings Group Co., Ltd.; *Int'l*, pg. 8661
SUNNY INSTRUMENTS SINGAPORE PTE. LTD.—See Sunny Optical Technology (Group) Company Limited; *Int'l*, pg. 7319
SUNNY JAPAN CO., LTD.—See Sunny Optical Technology (Group) Company Limited; *Int'l*, pg. 7319
SUNNY LOAN TOP CO., LTD.; *Int'l*, pg. 7318
SUNNY MAIZE CO., LTD.—See Oenon Holdings Inc; *Int'l*, pg. 5529
SUNNY MARINE TRANSPORT CO., LTD.—See Kamigumi Co., Ltd.; *Int'l*, pg. 4063
SUNNY METAL CORP.—See Rever Holdings Corporation; *Int'l*, pg. 6313
SUNNY MODE SDN. BHD.—See Hua Yang Berhad; *Int'l*, pg. 3510
SUNNY MORNING FOODS INC.; *U.S. Private*, pg. 3868
SUNNYNOOK SOLAR ENERGY INC.—See Westbridge Renewable Energy Corp.; *Int'l*, pg. 8387
SUNNY OPOTECH NORTH AMERICA INC—See Sunny Optical Technology (Group) Company Limited; *Int'l*, pg. 7319
SUNNY OPTICAL TECHNOLOGY (GROUP) COMPANY LIMITED; *Int'l*, pg. 7318
SUNNY OPTICS (ZHONGSHAN) CO., LTD.—See Sunny Optical Technology (Group) Company Limited; *Int'l*, pg. 7319
SUNNY QUEEN PTY LTD; *Int'l*, pg. 7319
SUNNYSIDE AUTOMOTIVE INC.; *U.S. Private*, pg. 3868
SUNNYSIDE AUTO PARTS; *U.S. Private*, pg. 3868
SUNNYSIDE FEDERAL SAVINGS & LOAN ASSOCIATION OF IRVINGTON—See Vecta Inc.; *U.S. Private*, pg. 4349
SUNNY SIDE UP GROUP INC.; *Int'l*, pg. 7319
SUNNY SIGN COMPANY PTY LTD—See Traffic Technologies Ltd.; *Int'l*, pg. 7889
SUNNY SKY PRODUCTS, LLC—See The Jordan Company, LP.; *U.S. Private*, pg. 4062
SUNNYTECH INC.; *U.S. Private*, pg. 3869
SUNNYTECH INC.—See Sunnytech Inc.; *U.S. Private*, pg. 3869
SUNNYVALE LUMBER INC.; *U.S. Private*, pg. 3869
SUNNYVILLE NURSING HOME (1996) PTE LTD—See China Healthcare Limited; *Int'l*, pg. 1507
SUNNYWAY FOODS INC.; *U.S. Private*, pg. 3869
SUNNY WORLD (SHAOXING) GREEN LIGHTING CO., LTD.—See Siemens Aktiengesellschaft; *Int'l*, pg. 6901
SUNOCO INC. - MARCUS HOOK REFINERY—See Energy Transfer LP; *U.S. Public*, pg. 764
SUNOCO INC. - PHILADELPHIA REFINERY—See Energy Transfer LP; *U.S. Public*, pg. 764
SUNOCO INC. (R&M)—See Energy Transfer LP; *U.S. Public*, pg. 764
SUNOCO, INC.—See Energy Transfer LP; *U.S. Public*, pg. 763
SUNOCO LOGISTIC PARTNERS L.P.—See Energy Transfer LP; *U.S. Public*, pg. 764
SUNOCO LOGISTICS PARTNERS GP LLC—See Energy Transfer LP; *U.S. Public*, pg. 764
SUNOCO LP; *U.S. Public*, pg. 1964
SUNOCO MASCOT, INC.—See Energy Transfer LP; *U.S. Public*, pg. 764
SUNOCO SARNIA REFINERY—See Suncor Energy Inc.; *Int'l*, pg. 7311
SUN OFFICE SERVICE, INC.—See Aramark; *U.S. Public*, pg. 178
SUNOIL LTD.; *Int'l*, pg. 7319

SUNON CORPORATION—See Sunonwealth Electric Machine Industry Company Limited; *Int'l*, pg. 7319
SUNON (HONG KONG) INTERNATIONAL CO., LTD.—See Shenzhen Energy Group Co., Ltd.; *Int'l*, pg. 6809
SUNON INC.—See Sunonwealth Electric Machine Industry Company Limited; *Int'l*, pg. 7319
SUNON SAS—See Sunonwealth Electric Machine Industry Company Limited; *Int'l*, pg. 7319
SUNONWEALTH ELECTRIC MACHINE INDUSTRY COMPANY LIMITED; *Int'l*, pg. 7319
SUNOPTA ASEPTIC, INC.—See SunOpta Inc.; *Int'l*, pg. 7319
SUNOPTA CONSUMER PRODUCTS GROUP - SUNOPTA FOOD SOLUTIONS DIVISION—See SunOpta Inc.; *Int'l*, pg. 7319
SUNOPTA FOOD (DALIAN) CO., LTD.—See SunOpta Inc.; *Int'l*, pg. 7320
SUNOPTA FOOD GROUP LLC—See SunOpta Inc.; *Int'l*, pg. 7319
SUNOPTA FOODS EUROPE B.V.—See SunOpta Inc.; *Int'l*, pg. 7319
SUNOPTA FOODS INC.—See SunOpta Inc.; *Int'l*, pg. 7319
SUNOPTA GLOBAL ORGANIC INGREDIENTS, INC.—See SunOpta Inc.; *Int'l*, pg. 7319
SUNOPTA GRAINS AND FOODS INC.—See SunOpta Inc.; *Int'l*, pg. 7319
SUNOPTA GRAINS & FOODS INC. - CROOKSTON—See SunOpta Inc.; *Int'l*, pg. 7319
SUNOPTA INC.; *Int'l*, pg. 7319
SUNOPTA INGREDIENTS, INC.—See SunOpta Inc.; *Int'l*, pg. 7319
SUNORA ENERGY SOLUTIONS LIMITED PARTNERSHIP—See NRG Energy, Inc.; *U.S. Public*, pg. 1551
SUNORA FOODS INC.; *Int'l*, pg. 7320
SUN ORCHARD FRUIT COMPANY, INC.; *U.S. Private*, pg. 3863
SUN ORCHARD INCORPORATED—See Centre Partners Management LLC; *U.S. Private*, pg. 828
SUN ORCHARD OF FLORIDA INC—See Centre Partners Management LLC; *U.S. Private*, pg. 828
SUNOVION PHARMACEUTICALS EUROPE LTD.—See Sumitomo Chemical Company, Limited; *Int'l*, pg. 7267
SUNOVION—See Sumitomo Chemical Company, Limited; *Int'l*, pg. 7267
SUN PACIFIC ENERGY; *U.S. Private*, pg. 3863
SUN PACIFIC FARMING CO., INC.; *U.S. Private*, pg. 3863
SUN PACIFIC HOLDING CORP; *U.S. Public*, pg. 1963
SUN PACIFIC POWER CORP.—See Sun Pacific Holding Corp; *U.S. Public*, pg. 1963
SUN PACKING, INC.; *U.S. Private*, pg. 3863
SUN PAINTS & COATINGS, INC.; *U.S. Private*, pg. 3863
SUN PAPER AND BOARD LIMITED—See Suzano Holding S.A.; *Int'l*, pg. 7348
SUNPARADISE ALUTECHNIK VERTRIEBS GMBH—See Nordstjernan AB; *Int'l*, pg. 5426
SUNPARADISE EST.—See Nordstjernan AB; *Int'l*, pg. 5426
SUN PEAK METALS CORP.; *Int'l*, pg. 7306
SUN PET, LTD.—See Central Garden & Pet Company; *U.S. Public*, pg. 473
SUN PHARMA ADVANCED RESEARCH COMPANY LTD; *Int'l*, pg. 7306
SUN PHARMA ANZ PTY. LTD.—See Sun Pharmaceutical Industries Ltd.; *Int'l*, pg. 7307
SUN PHARMACEUTICAL (BANGLADESH) LIMITED—See Sun Pharmaceutical Industries Ltd.; *Int'l*, pg. 7307
SUN PHARMACEUTICAL INDUSTRIES (AUSTRALIA) PTY. LTD.—See Sun Pharmaceutical Industries Ltd.; *Int'l*, pg. 7307
SUN PHARMACEUTICAL INDUSTRIES EUROPE B.V—See Sun Pharmaceutical Industries Ltd.; *Int'l*, pg. 7307
SUN PHARMACEUTICAL INDUSTRIES, INC.—See Sun Pharmaceutical Industries Ltd.; *Int'l*, pg. 7307
SUN PHARMACEUTICAL INDUSTRIES LTD.; *Int'l*, pg. 7307
SUN PHARMACEUTICAL INDUSTRIES S.A.C.—See Sun Pharmaceutical Industries Ltd.; *Int'l*, pg. 7307
SUN PHARMACEUTICAL SDN. BHD.—See Sunway Berhad; *Int'l*, pg. 7328
SUN PHARMACEUTICALS FRANCE—See Sun Pharmaceutical Industries Ltd.; *Int'l*, pg. 7308
SUN PHARMACEUTICALS GERMANY GMBH—See Sun Pharmaceutical Industries Ltd.; *Int'l*, pg. 7308
SUN PHARMACEUTICALS ITALIA S.R.L.—See Sun Pharmaceutical Industries Ltd.; *Int'l*, pg. 7308
SUN PHARMACEUTICALS MOROCCO LLC—See Sun Pharmaceutical Industries Ltd.; *Int'l*, pg. 7307
SUN PHARMACEUTICALS SPAIN, SL—See Sun Pharmaceutical Industries Ltd.; *Int'l*, pg. 7308
SUN PHARMACEUTICAL UK LIMITED—See Sun Pharmaceutical Industries Ltd.; *Int'l*, pg. 7308
SUN PHARMA DE MEXICO S.A. DE C.V.—See Sun Pharmaceutical Industries Ltd.; *Int'l*, pg. 7307
SUN PHARMA EXPORTS LTD—See Sun Pharmaceutical Industries Ltd.; *Int'l*, pg. 7307

SUN REALTY USA, INC.

SUN PHARMA JAPAN LTD.—See Sun Pharmaceutical Industries Ltd.; *Int'l*, pg. 7307
SUN PHARMA LABORATORIOS, S.L.U.—See Sun Pharmaceutical Industries Ltd.; *Int'l*, pg. 7307
SUN PHOENIX MEXICO S.A. DE C.V.—See Sanyo Trading Co., Ltd.; *Int'l*, pg. 6565
SUN PIPE LINE COMPANY OF DELAWARE LLC—See Energy Transfer LP; *U.S. Public*, pg. 764
SUNPLANET CO., LTD.—See Eisai Co., Ltd.; *Int'l*, pg. 2335
SUN PLANNING CO., LTD.—See Janome Sewing Machine Co., Ltd.; *Int'l*, pg. 3880
SUN PLANT CO., LTD.—See Takuma Co., Ltd.; *Int'l*, pg. 7442
SUN PLASTECH INC.—See Asahi Kasei Corporation; *Int'l*, pg. 597
SUNPLAY.COM; *U.S. Private*, pg. 3869
SUN PLAZA HOME CO., LTD.—See Iida Group Holdings Co., Ltd.; *Int'l*, pg. 3607
SUNPLUS CORE TECHNOLOGY CO., LTD—See Sunplus Technology Co., Ltd.; *Int'l*, pg. 7320
SUNPLUS INNOVATION TECHNOLOGY INC.—See Sunplus Technology Co., Ltd.; *Int'l*, pg. 7320
SUNPLUS MMOBILE INC.—See Sunplus Technology Co., Ltd.; *Int'l*, pg. 7320
SUNPLUS PROF-TEK TECHNOLOGY (SHENZHEN) CO., LTD.—See Sunplus Technology Co., Ltd.; *Int'l*, pg. 7320
SUNPLUS TECHNOLOGY CO., LTD.; *Int'l*, pg. 7320
SUNPLUS TECHNOLOGY (H.K.) CO., LTD—See Sunplus Technology Co., Ltd.; *Int'l*, pg. 7320
SUNPORCH STRUCTURES INC.; *U.S. Private*, pg. 3869
THE SUNPORK GROUP; *Int'l*, pg. 7691
SUN PORTS INTERNATIONAL INC.; *U.S. Private*, pg. 3863
SUNPOWER CLEAN ENERGY INVESTMENT (JIANGSU) CO., LTD.—See Sunpower Group Ltd.; *Int'l*, pg. 7320
SUNPOWER CORPORATION-EAST COAST REGIONAL OFFICE—See SunPower Corporation; *U.S. Public*, pg. 1965
SUNPOWER CORPORATION; *U.S. Public*, pg. 1965
SUNPOWER CORPORATION—See Enphase Energy, Inc.; *U.S. Public*, pg. 774
SUNPOWER CORPORATION, SYSTEMS—See SunPower Corporation; *U.S. Public*, pg. 1965
SUNPOWER ENERGY SYSTEMS-KOREA—See SunPower Corporation; *U.S. Public*, pg. 1965
SUNPOWER ENERGY SYSTEMS SPAIN, S.L.—See SunPower Corporation; *U.S. Public*, pg. 1965
SUNPOWER GROUP LTD.; *Int'l*, pg. 7320
SUNPOWER, INC.—See AMETEK, Inc.; *U.S. Public*, pg. 118
SUNPOWER MALAYSIA MANUFACTURING SDN. BHD.—See SunPower Corporation; *U.S. Public*, pg. 1965
SUN POWERSPORTS INVESTMENTS, LLC; *U.S. Private*, pg. 3863
SUNPOWER SYSTEMS SARL—See SunPower Corporation; *U.S. Public*, pg. 1965
SUN PRINTING INC.; *U.S. Private*, pg. 3863
SUN PROCESS CONVERTING COMPANY, INC.; *U.S. Private*, pg. 3864
SUNPRO CORPORATION—See Clyde Companies Inc.; *U.S. Private*, pg. 949
SUNPRO, INC.—See Savage Services Corporation; *U.S. Private*, pg. 3555
SUN PUBLISHING COMPANY, INC.—See Chatham Asset Management, LLC; *U.S. Private*, pg. 866
SUNQUEST INFORMATION SYSTEMS (EUROPE) LIMITED—See Roper Technologies, Inc.; *U.S. Public*, pg. 1813
SUNQUEST INFORMATION SYSTEMS, INC.—See Roper Technologies, Inc.; *U.S. Public*, pg. 1813
SUNQUEST INFORMATION SYSTEMS (INDIA) PRIVATE LIMITED—See Roper Technologies, Inc.; *U.S. Public*, pg. 1813
SUN RACE STURMEY-ARCHER EUROPE BV—See Sun Race Sturmey-Archer Inc.; *Int'l*, pg. 7308
SUN RACE STURMEY-ARCHER INC.; *Int'l*, pg. 7308
SUN RACE STURMEY ARCHER USA INC.—See Sun Race Sturmey-Archer Inc.; *Int'l*, pg. 7308
SUN RADIOPHARMA COMPANY—See Sun Pharmaceutical Industries Ltd.; *Int'l*, pg. 7308
SUNRAJ DIAMOND EXPORTS LIMITED; *Int'l*, pg. 7320
SUNRAY CO-OP. INC.; *U.S. Private*, pg. 3869
SUNRAY ELECTRIC SUPPLY CO., INC.; *U.S. Private*, pg. 3869
SUNRAY ENGINEERING GROUP LIMITED; *Int'l*, pg. 7320
SUNRAY ENTERPRISE INC.; *U.S. Private*, pg. 3869
SUNRAY MACAO COMMERCIAL OFFSHORE LIMITED—See Texhong Textile Group Limited; *Int'l*, pg. 7584
SUN RAY MANUFACTORY, LIMITED—See China International Development Corporation Limited; *Int'l*, pg. 1510
SUNRAY REINETSU CO., LTD.—See Sumitomo Electric Industries, Ltd.; *Int'l*, pg. 7284
SUN REALTY & AUCTION SERVICE, LLC; *U.S. Private*, pg. 3864
SUN REALTY USA, INC.; *U.S. Private*, pg. 3864

Company Index

SUN REALTY USA, INC.

CORPORATE AFFILIATIONS

SUN REFORM CO., LTD.—See Pan Pacific International Holdings Corporation; *Int'l*, pg. 5715
SUN RESIDENTIAL REAL ESTATE INVESTMENT TRUST; *Int'l*, pg. 7308
SUNRESIN NEW MATERIALS CO., LTD.; *Int'l*, pg. 7320
SUN RETAIL LTD.; *Int'l*, pg. 7308
SUNREX INDUSTRY CO., LTD.—See Mitsui Chemicals, Inc.; *Int'l*, pg. 4984
SUNREX TECHNOLOGY CORPORATION; *Int'l*, pg. 7320
SUN RHINE ENTERPRISES LTD.—See Advent International Corporation; *U.S. Private*, pg. 106
SUN RHINE ENTERPRISES LTD.—See Cinven Limited; *Int'l*, pg. 1614
SUN RHINE ENTERPRISES LTD.—See RAG-Stiftung; *Int'l*, pg. 6179
SUNRICE TRADING PTY LTD—See Ricegrowers Limited; *Int'l*, pg. 6329
SUN RICH ENTERPRISES LTD.—See ThyssenKrupp AG; *Int'l*, pg. 7726
SUN RICH FRESH FOODS, INC. - NORTHEAST FRESH FACILITY—See Kainos Capital, LLC; *U.S. Private*, pg. 2255
SUN RICH FRESH FOODS, INC.—See Kainos Capital, LLC; *U.S. Private*, pg. 2255
SUN RICH FRESH FOODS (USA) INC. - EASTERN FRESH FACILITY—See Kainos Capital, LLC; *U.S. Private*, pg. 2255
SUN RICH FRESH FOODS (USA) INC.—See Kainos Capital, LLC; *U.S. Private*, pg. 2255
SUNRICH INTEGRATED SDN. BHD—See ecoWise Holdings Limited; *Int'l*, pg. 2300
SUNRICH LLC—See SunOpta Inc.; *Int'l*, pg. 7319
SUNRICH MARKETING SDN. BHD—See ecoWise Holdings Limited; *Int'l*, pg. 2300
SUNRICH MODE INC.—See Toray Industries, Inc.; *Int'l*, pg. 7823
SUNRICH TYRE & AUTO PRODUCTS SDN BHD—See ecoWise Holdings Limited; *Int'l*, pg. 2300
THE SUNRIDER CORPORATION; *U.S. Private*, pg. 4125
SUNRIDGE CANYON, LLC—See Pinnacle West Capital Corporation; *U.S. Public*, pg. 1692
SUNRIDGE INTERNATIONAL, INC.; *U.S. Public*, pg. 1965
SUNRIDGE PARTNERS (UK), LLP; *Int'l*, pg. 7321
SUNRIDGE PROPERTIES INC.; *U.S. Private*, pg. 3869
SUNRIGHT LIMITED; *Int'l*, pg. 7321
SUNRISE ACQUISITION CORP.; *U.S. Private*, pg. 3869
SUNRISE ADVERTISING; *U.S. Private*, pg. 3869
SUNRISE ADVISORS, INC.—See Creative Planning, LLC; *U.S. Private*, pg. 1090
SUNRISE AG COOPERATIVE; *U.S. Private*, pg. 3869
SUNRISE AMBULATORY SURGICAL CENTER, LLC—See KKR & Co. Inc.; *U.S. Public*, pg. 1246
SUNRISE ASIAN LTD; *Int'l*, pg. 7321
SUNRISE BAKING CO. LLC.; *U.S. Private*, pg. 3869
SUNRISE BANCSHARES, INC.; *U.S. Private*, pg. 3869
SUNRISE BANK—See Sunrise Bancshares, Inc.; *U.S. Private*, pg. 3869
SUNRISE BEACH CORPORATION—See The Day & Zimmermann Group, Inc.; *U.S. Private*, pg. 4019
SUNRISE BRANDS, LLC—See Sunrise Acquisition Corp.; *U.S. Private*, pg. 3869
SUNRISE BROADCASTING OF NEW YORK, INC.; *U.S. Private*, pg. 3869
SUNRISE BROKERS (HONG KONG) LTD.—See BGC Group, Inc.; *U.S. Public*, pg. 330
SUNRISE BROKERS, LLC—See BGC Group, Inc.; *U.S. Public*, pg. 330
SUNRISE BROKERS LLP—See BGC Group, Inc.; *U.S. Public*, pg. 330
SUNRISE BUICK-PONTIAC-GMC-HUMMER WOLFCHASE; *U.S. Private*, pg. 3869
SUNRISE CAPITAL PARTNERS LP; *U.S. Private*, pg. 3869
SUNRISE CHEVROLET—See Garber Management Group Inc.; *U.S. Private*, pg. 1642
SUNRISE COAL LLC—See HALLADOR ENERGY COMPANY; *U.S. Public*, pg. 980
SUNRISE CO., LTD.—See Kurimoto Ltd; *Int'l*, pg. 4340
SUNRISE COMMUNICATIONS GROUP AG—See Liberty Global plc; *Int'l*, pg. 4485
SUNRISE COMMUNITY, INC.; *U.S. Private*, pg. 3869
SUNRISE CONSTRUCTION INC.; *U.S. Private*, pg. 3869
SUNRISE COOPERATIVE, INC.; *U.S. Private*, pg. 3869
SUNRISE DAIRY—See Hy-Vee, Inc.; *U.S. Private*, pg. 2016
SUNRISE DETOX; *U.S. Private*, pg. 3869
SUNRISE DIGITAL; *U.S. Private*, pg. 3870
SUNRISE EFFICIENT MARKETING LIMITED; *Int'l*, pg. 7321
SUNRISE ELEVATOR CO., INC.—See Aldine Capital Partners, Inc.; *U.S. Private*, pg. 159
SUNRISE ELEVATOR CO., INC.—See Stoic Holdings LLC; *U.S. Private*, pg. 3816
SUNRISE ENERGY, LLC—See HALLADOR ENERGY COMPANY; *U.S. Public*, pg. 980
SUNRISE ENERGY METALS LIMITED; *Int'l*, pg. 7321
SUNRISE EXPLORATION PTY LTD—See Pelican Resources Limited; *Int'l*, pg. 5782
SUNRISE FARM SAIJO CO., LTD.—See Sumitomo Chemical Company, Limited; *Int'l*, pg. 7267
SUNRISE FARMS, INC.—See Eli Lilly & Company; *U.S. Public*, pg. 734
SUNRISE FARM TOYOTA CO., LTD.—See Sumitomo Chemical Company, Limited; *Int'l*, pg. 7267
SUNRISE FIBERGLASS LLC.—See North Central Equity LLC; *U.S. Private*, pg. 2943
SUNRISE FLOOR SYSTEMS LLC; *U.S. Private*, pg. 3870
SUNRISE FORD SALES; *Int'l*, pg. 7321
SUNRISE FRANCE S.A.S.—See Vestar Capital Partners, LLC; *U.S. Private*, pg. 4372
SUNRISE FRESH PRODUCE, LLC—See Performance Food Group Company; *U.S. Public*, pg. 1676
SUNRISE FS—See Growmark, Inc.; *U.S. Private*, pg. 1795
SUNRISE GLOBAL SOLAR ENERGY CO., LTD.; *Int'l*, pg. 7321
SUNRISE GOLF DEVELOPMENT CORP.—See CMC Realty Inc.; *U.S. Private*, pg. 950
SUNRISE GREETINGS—See Hallmark Cards, Inc.; *U.S. Private*, pg. 1845
SUNRISE GROUP COMPANY LIMITED; *Int'l*, pg. 7321
SUNRISE GROWERS, INC.—See SunOpta Inc.; *Int'l*, pg. 7319
SUNRISE HANDICAP TRANSPORT CORP.—See KKR & Co. Inc.; *U.S. Public*, pg. 1251
SUNRISE HOMES; *U.S. Private*, pg. 3870
SUNRISE HOSPITAL AND MEDICAL CENTER, LLC—See HCA Healthcare, Inc.; *U.S. Public*, pg. 1011
SUNRISE HOSPITAL & MEDICAL CENTER—See HCA Healthcare, Inc.; *U.S. Public*, pg. 1011
SUNRISE IDENTITY; *U.S. Private*, pg. 3870
SUNRISE INC.—See Phoenix Capital Co., Ltd.; *Int'l*, pg. 5849
SUNRISE INDUSTRIAL TRADERS LIMITED; *Int'l*, pg. 7321
SUNRISE INDUSTRY CO., LTD.; *Int'l*, pg. 7321
SUNRISE LAND COMPANY, LLC—See HALLADOR ENERGY COMPANY; *U.S. Public*, pg. 980
SUNRISE LANDSCAPE, INC.; *U.S. Private*, pg. 3870
SUNRISE MANNER SDN. BHD.—See Mayu Global Group Berhad; *Int'l*, pg. 4747
SUNRISE MEDICAL AB—See Vestar Capital Partners, LLC; *U.S. Private*, pg. 4372
SUNRISE MEDICAL AG—See Vestar Capital Partners, LLC; *U.S. Private*, pg. 4372
SUNRISE MEDICAL AS—See Vestar Capital Partners, LLC; *U.S. Private*, pg. 4372
SUNRISE MEDICAL BENELUS—See Vestar Capital Partners, LLC; *U.S. Private*, pg. 4372
SUNRISE MEDICAL CANADA INC.—See Vestar Capital Partners, LLC; *U.S. Private*, pg. 4372
SUNRISE MEDICAL GMBH—See Vestar Capital Partners, LLC; *U.S. Private*, pg. 4372
SUNRISE MEDICAL GROUP II, L.L.C.—See Tenet Healthcare Corporation; *U.S. Public*, pg. 2004
SUNRISE MEDICAL GROUP I, L.L.C.—See Tenet Healthcare Corporation; *U.S. Public*, pg. 2004
SUNRISE MEDICAL INC.—See Vestar Capital Partners, LLC; *U.S. Private*, pg. 4372
SUNRISE MEDICAL INC.—See Vestar Capital Partners, LLC; *U.S. Private*, pg. 4372
SUNRISE MEDICAL JAPAN CO., LTD.—See Mikuni Corporation; *Int'l*, pg. 4893
SUNRISE MEDICAL LABORATORIES, INC.—See Sonic Healthcare Limited; *Int'l*, pg. 7098
SUNRISE MEDICAL LABORATORIES—See Sonic Healthcare Limited; *Int'l*, pg. 7098
SUNRISE MEDICAL LONG TERM CARE—See Vestar Capital Partners, LLC; *U.S. Private*, pg. 4372
SUNRISE MEDICAL LTD.—See Vestar Capital Partners, LLC; *U.S. Private*, pg. 4372
SUNRISE MEDICAL MOBILITY PRODUCTS—See Vestar Capital Partners, LLC; *U.S. Private*, pg. 4372
SUNRISE MEDICAL PTY. LTD.—See Vestar Capital Partners, LLC; *U.S. Private*, pg. 4372
SUNRISE MEDICAL S.R.L.—See Vestar Capital Partners, LLC; *U.S. Private*, pg. 4372
SUNRISE MUSIC PUBLISHING CO., LTD.—See BANDAI NAMCO Holdings Inc.; *Int'l*, pg. 829
SUNRISE NATIONAL DISTRIBUTORS; *U.S. Private*, pg. 3870
SUNRISE NEW ENERGY CO., LTD.; *Int'l*, pg. 7321
SUNRISE OF CUPERTINO PROPCO, LLC—See Welltower Inc.; *U.S. Public*, pg. 2349
SUNRISE OF OCEANSIDE CA PROPCO, LLC—See Welltower Inc.; *U.S. Public*, pg. 2349
SUNRISE OF PHILADELPHIA; *U.S. Private*, pg. 3870
SUNRISE OF REDMOND PROPCO, LLC—See Welltower Inc.; *U.S. Public*, pg. 2349
SUNRISE OILFIELD SUPPLY, INC.—See Wingate Partners, LLP; *U.S. Private*, pg. 4541
SUNRISE PACKAGING INC.; *U.S. Private*, pg. 3870
SUNRISE PLAZA TRANSPORTATION OF NEVADA, CO.—See JTB Corp.; *Int'l*, pg. 4015
SUNRISE POULTRY PROCESSORS LTD.; *Int'l*, pg. 7322
SUNRISE PUBLICATIONS, INC.—See GameStop Corp.; *U.S. Public*, pg. 896
SUNRISE REAL ESTATE GROUP, INC.; *Int'l*, pg. 7322
SUNRISE RESOURCES LTD.; *Int'l*, pg. 7322
SUNRISE RESOURCES PLC; *Int'l*, pg. 7322
SUNRISE SANITATION SERVICE, INC.—See Republic Services, Inc.; *U.S. Public*, pg. 1787
SUNRISE SENIOR LIVING LIMITED—See Public Sector Pension Investment Board; *Int'l*, pg. 6097
SUNRISE SENIOR LIVING, LLC—See Public Sector Pension Investment Board; *Int'l*, pg. 6096
SUNRISE SENIOR LIVING MANAGEMENT, INC.—See Public Sector Pension Investment Board; *Int'l*, pg. 6096
SUNRISE SHARES HOLDINGS LTD.; *Int'l*, pg. 7322
SUNRISE SHOP RITE INC.; *U.S. Private*, pg. 3870
SUNRISE SOYA FOODS; *Int'l*, pg. 7322
SUNRISE SPAIN (URIBARRI)—See Vestar Capital Partners, LLC; *U.S. Private*, pg. 4372
SUNRISE SPORTS & ENTERTAINMENT LLLP; *U.S. Private*, pg. 3870
SUNRISE STORES, LLC—See Foster Blue Water Oil, LLC; *U.S. Private*, pg. 1578
SUNRISE TECHNOLOGIES, INC.—See Electro Switch Corporation; *U.S. Private*, pg. 1354
SUNRISE TECH PARK CO. LLC—See Brookfield Corporation; *Int'l*, pg. 1186
SUNRISE TOYOTA ABBOTSFORD; *Int'l*, pg. 7322
SUNRISE TRAUMA SERVICES, LLC—See HCA Healthcare, Inc.; *U.S. Public*, pg. 1011
SUNRISE UPC GMBH—See Liberty Global plc; *Int'l*, pg. 4485
SUNRISE VIEW WIND FARM, LLC—See Edison International; *U.S. Public*, pg. 719
SUNRISE WINDOWS LTD.—See Koch Industries, Inc.; *U.S. Private*, pg. 2332
SUN RIVER CO., LTD.—See Toyota Industries Corporation; *Int'l*, pg. 7866
SUNRIVER ENVIRONMENTAL LLC—See Northwest Natural Holding Company; *U.S. Public*, pg. 1542
SUNRIVER RESORT LIMITED PARTNERSHIP; *U.S. Private*, pg. 3870
SUNRIVER UTILITIES COMPANY INC.—See Sunriver Resort Limited Partnership; *U.S. Private*, pg. 3870
SUNRIVER WATER LLC—See Northwest Natural Holding Company; *U.S. Public*, pg. 1542
SUNROAD HOLDING CORPORATION; *U.S. Private*, pg. 3870
SUNROC CORPORATION—See Clyde Companies Inc.; *U.S. Private*, pg. 949
SUNROOM CONCEPTS—See MacArthur Co.; *U.S. Private*, pg. 2534
SUN RUBBER INDUSTRY SDN. BHD—See ecoWise Holdings Limited; *Int'l*, pg. 2300
SUNRUN INC.; *U.S. Public*, pg. 1965
SUNRX, INC.; *U.S. Private*, pg. 3870
SUN-RYPE PRODUCTS LTD.—See Lassonde Industries, Inc.; *Int'l*, pg. 4422
SUNSAIL HELLAS MEPE—See TUI AG; *Int'l*, pg. 7966
SUNSAIL INTERNATIONAL B.V.—See TUI AG; *Int'l*, pg. 7966
SUNSAIL LIMITED—See TUI AG; *Int'l*, pg. 7968
SUNSAIL SAS—See TUI AG; *Int'l*, pg. 7966
SUNSAIL WORLDWIDE SAILING LIMITED—See TUI AG; *Int'l*, pg. 7966
SUN SAVINGS BANK INC.; *Int'l*, pg. 7308
SUNSEA AIOT TECHNOLOGY CO., LTD.; *Int'l*, pg. 7322
SUN-SEA CONSTRUCTION CO., LTD.; *Int'l*, pg. 7309
SUNSEAP ENTERPRISES PTE LTD.—See SUNSET Energietechnik GmbH; *Int'l*, pg. 7322
SUNSEEKER ENERGY HOLDING AG; *Int'l*, pg. 7322
SUN-SENTINEL COMPANY—See Tribune Publishing Company; *U.S. Private*, pg. 4228
SUNSET AIR INCORPORATED; *U.S. Private*, pg. 3871
SUNSET AUTO COMPANY INC.; *U.S. Private*, pg. 3871
SUNSET AUTOMOTIVE GROUP; *U.S. Private*, pg. 3871
SUNSET BEACH CLUB S.A.—See Farmer Business Developments plc; *Int'l*, pg. 2619
SUNSET CHEVROLET, INC.—See Sunset Automotive Group; *U.S. Private*, pg. 3871
SUNSET CITY, LLC—See Pebblebrook Hotel Trust; *U.S. Public*, pg. 1660
SUNSET COMMUNITY HEALTH CENTER; *U.S. Private*, pg. 3871
SUNSET COMUNICACAO—See Omnicom Group Inc.; *U.S. Public*, pg. 1585
SUNSET DIALYSIS, LLC—See DaVita Inc.; *U.S. Public*, pg. 643
SUNSET ENERGIETECHNIK GMBH; *Int'l*, pg. 7322
SUNSET FINANCIAL SERVICES, INC.—See Reverence Capital Partners LLC; *U.S. Private*, pg. 3415
SUNSET FOOD MART INC.; *U.S. Private*, pg. 3871
SUNSET GARBAGE COLLECTION, INC.—See Arakelian Enterprises, Inc.; *U.S. Private*, pg. 307
SUNSET HEALTHCARE SOLUTIONS; *U.S. Private*, pg. 3871
SUNSET ISLAND GROUP, INC.; *U.S. Public*, pg. 1966
SUNSET LABORATORY, INC.—See Hebei Sailhero Environmental Protection High-Tech Co., Ltd.; *Int'l*, pg. 3306
SUNSET LIFE INSURANCE COMPANY—See Kansas City Life Insurance Company; *U.S. Public*, pg. 1214
SUNSET MEMORIAL PARK CEMETERY TRUST—See Service Corporation International; *U.S. Public*, pg. 1870

COMPANY NAME INDEX

SUNSET MEMORIAL PARK COMPANY—See Service Corporation International; *U.S. Public*, pg. 1871
SUNSET MEMORIAL PARK INC.—See Axar Capital Management L.P.; *U.S. Private*, pg. 412
SUNSET MOULDING CO., INC.; *U.S. Private*, pg. 3871
SUNSET PACIFIC PETROLEUM LTD.; *Int'l*, pg. 7322
SUNSET PACIFIC TRANSPORTATION, INC.—See Granite Creek Capital Partners, LLC; *U.S. Private*, pg. 1755
SUNSET PACIFIC TRANSPORTATION, INC.—See Red Arts Capital, LLC; *U.S. Private*, pg. 3373
SUNSET POINT CARE & REHABILITATION CENTER - CLEARWATER—See Formation Capital, LLC; *U.S. Private*, pg. 1571
SUNSET PROPERTIES, LLC—See GCC, S.A.B. de C.V.; *Int'l*, pg. 2895
SUNSET PROPERTY SERVICES, INC.—See Warburg Pincus LLC; *U.S. Private*, pg. 4440
SUNSET PUBLISHING CORPORATION—See Regent, L.P.; *U.S. Private*, pg. 3388
SUNSET RETIREMENT COMMUNITIES; *U.S. Private*, pg. 3871
SUNSET SUITS HOLDINGS, INC.; *Int'l*, pg. 7322
SUNSETTER PRODUCTS, LP—See AEA Investors LP; *U.S. Private*, pg. 115
SUNSETTER PRODUCTS, LP—See British Columbia Investment Management Corp.; *Int'l*, pg. 1170
SUNSET TRANSPORTATION, LLC—See Armada Group, Ltd.; *U.S. Private*, pg. 329
SUNSET+VINE INTERNATIONAL LTD.—See Vitruvian Partners LLP; *Int'l*, pg. 8263
SUNSHIELD CHEMICALS LTD.—See Indus Petrochem Limited; *Int'l*, pg. 3664
SUNSHINE 100 CHINA HOLDINGS LIMITED; *Int'l*, pg. 7322
SUNSHINE100 CO LTD; *Int'l*, pg. 7323
SUNSHINE ACE HARDWARE INC.; *U.S. Private*, pg. 3871
SUNSHINE AGRI-TECH INC.; *Int'l*, pg. 7322
SUNSHINE ANSWERING SERVICE, INC.—See ECI Partners LLP; *Int'l*, pg. 2289
SUNSHINE AVIONICS LLC—See HEICO Corporation; *U.S. Public*, pg. 1020
SUNSHINE BIOPHARMA, INC.; *Int'l*, pg. 7322
SUNSHINE BOTTLING, CO.; *U.S. Private*, pg. 3871
SUNSHINE BOUQUET COMPANY INC.; *U.S. Private*, pg. 3871
SUNSHINE BS CORPORATION—See Mitsubishi Estate Co., Ltd.; *Int'l*, pg. 4947
SUNSHINE CAPITAL LTD.; *Int'l*, pg. 7322
SUNSHINE CINEMAS PTY LIMITED—See Event Hospitality & Entertainment Limited; *Int'l*, pg. 2562
SUNSHINE CIRCUITS USA, LLC—See Sunshine Global Circuits Co., Ltd.; *Int'l*, pg. 7322
SUNSHINE CITY CORPORATION—See Mitsubishi Estate Co., Ltd.; *Int'l*, pg. 4947
SUNSHINE COAST COMMUNITY FINANCIAL SERVICES LIMITED—See Bendigo & Adelaide Bank Ltd.; *Int'l*, pg. 971
SUNSHINE COAST RADIOLOGY PTY. LTD.—See Integral Diagnostics Limited; *Int'l*, pg. 3730
SUNSHINE COAST REPORTER PARTNERSHIP—See GVIC Communications Corp.; *Int'l*, pg. 3189
SUNSHINE CO., LTD.—See Teikoku Tsushin Kogyo Co., Ltd.; *Int'l*, pg. 7524
SUNSHINE COMPUTERS & SOFTWARE; *U.S. Private*, pg. 3871
SUNSHINE CONCRETE & MATERIALS, INC.—See Union Andina de Cementos S.A.A.; *Int'l*, pg. 8050
SUNSHINE.CO.UK LIMITED—See On the Beach Group plc; *Int'l*, pg. 5573
SUNSHINE DAIRY FOODS INC.; *U.S. Private*, pg. 3871
SUNSHINE DAIRY INC.—See Sunshine Dairy Foods Inc.; *U.S. Private*, pg. 3871
SUNSHINE DRAPERY & INTERIOR FASHIONS; *U.S. Private*, pg. 3871
SUNSHINE ENTERPRISE CORPORATION—See Mitsubishi Estate Co., Ltd.; *Int'l*, pg. 4947
SUNSHINE EQUIPMENT CO., INC.; *U.S. Private*, pg. 3871
SUNSHINE GLOBAL CIRCUITS CO., LTD.; *Int'l*, pg. 7322
THE SUNSHINE GROUP, LTD.—See Anywhere Real Estate Inc.; *U.S. Public*, pg. 142
SUNSHINE GROUP PTY. LIMITED—See Peter Warren Automotive Holdings Ltd.; *Int'l*, pg. 5824
SUNSHINE GUOJIAN PHARMACEUTICALS (SHANGHAI) CO., LTD.—See 3SBio Inc.; *Int'l*, pg. 9
SUNSHINE GUOJIAN PHARMACEUTICALS (SHANGHAI) CO., LTD.—See 3SBio Inc.; *Int'l*, pg. 9
SUNSHINE HARDWARE INC.; *U.S. Private*, pg. 3871
SUNSHINE HELICOPTERS, INC.; *U.S. Private*, pg. 3871
SUNSHINE HOMES INC.—See Sunshine Mills Inc.; *U.S. Private*, pg. 3872
SUNSHINE INDUSTRIES LTD—See Associated Brands Industries Limited; *Int'l*, pg. 648
SUNSHINE INSURANCE GROUP COMPANY LIMITED; *Int'l*, pg. 7323
SUNSHINE KAIDI NEW ENERGY GROUP CO., LTD.; *Int'l*, pg. 7323
SUNSHINE KUREHA CO., LTD.—See Kureha Corporation; *Int'l*, pg. 4339
SUNSHINE MANUFACTURING PTE LTD—See Lippo Limited; *Int'l*, pg. 4522
SUNSHINE MEDIA GROUP, INC—See Gladstone Management Corporation; *U.S. Public*, pg. 1705
SUNSHINE MILLS INC. - HALIFAX DIVISION—See Sunshine Mills Inc.; *U.S. Private*, pg. 3872
SUNSHINE MILLS INC.; *U.S. Private*, pg. 3871
SUNSHINE MILLS INC. - TUPELO DIVISION—See Sunshine Mills Inc.; *U.S. Private*, pg. 3872
SUNSHINE MILLS OF VIRGINIA INC.—See Sunshine Mills Inc.; *U.S. Private*, pg. 3872
SUNSHINE MINTING INC.; *U.S. Private*, pg. 3872
SUNSHINE NEWPAPER PRINTING—See Independent Newspapers, Inc.; *U.S. Private*, pg. 2060
SUNSHINE OILSANDS LTD.; *Int'l*, pg. 7323
SUNSHINE OJI (SHOUGUANG) SPECIALTY PAPER LTD.—See Oji Holdings Corporation; *Int'l*, pg. 5538
SUNSHINE PAPER LLC; *U.S. Private*, pg. 3872
SUNSHINE PCB GMBH—See Sunshine Global Circuits Co., Ltd.; *Int'l*, pg. 7323
SUNSHINE PHARMACY, INC.; *U.S. Private*, pg. 3872
SUNSHINE PLUMBING HEATING AIR LLC; *U.S. Private*, pg. 3872
SUNSHINE RAISIN CORPORATION; *U.S. Private*, pg. 3872
SUNSHINE REFUELLERS PTY. LTD.—See Rivet Pty. Ltd.; *Int'l*, pg. 6353
SUNSHINE RENTALS, INC.; *U.S. Private*, pg. 3872
SUNSHINE RESTAURANT PARTNERS, LLC; *U.S. Private*, pg. 3872
SUNSHINE ROOMS, INC.; *U.S. Private*, pg. 3872
SUNSHINE SANITATION, LLC—See Macquarie Group Limited; *Int'l*, pg. 4628
SUNSHINE SECURITY INSURANCE AGENCY, INC.—See The Progressive Corporation; *U.S. Public*, pg. 2124
SUNSHINE SILVER MINES CORPORATION; *U.S. Private*, pg. 3872
SUNSHINE STATE DAIRY FARMS—See Southeast Milk, Inc.; *U.S. Private*, pg. 3726
SUNSHINE STATE HEALTH PLAN, INC.—See Centene Corporation; *U.S. Public*, pg. 470
SUNSHINE SUPPLY CO., INC.; *U.S. Private*, pg. 3872
SUNSHINE TOURS—See Abu Dhabi National Hotels PJSC; *Int'l*, pg. 72
SUNSHINE TOYOTA INC.; *U.S. Private*, pg. 3872
SUN & SKIN CARE RESEARCH, LLC.; *U.S. Private*, pg. 3858
SUNS LEGACY PARTNERS, LLC; *U.S. Private*, pg. 3870
SUNSOFT TECHNOLOGIES, INC.; *U.S. Private*, pg. 3872
THE SUN—See Alden Global Capital LLC; *U.S. Public*, pg. 156
THE SUN—See Alden Global Capital LLC; *U.S. Public*, pg. 159
THE SUN—See Independent Newspapers, Inc.; *U.S. Private*, pg. 2060
THE SUN—See News Corporation; *U.S. Public*, pg. 1521
SUN SOUGOU MAINTENANCE CO., LTD.—See Pan Pacific International Holdings Corporation; *Int'l*, pg. 5715
SUN SOURCE (INDIA) LIMITED; *Int'l*, pg. 7308
SUNSOUTH BANCSHARES, INC.; *U.S. Private*, pg. 3872
SUNSOUTH BANK—See SunSouth Bancshares, Inc.; *U.S. Private*, pg. 3872
SUNSOUTH - BLAKELY—See SunSouth LLC; *U.S. Private*, pg. 3872
SUNSOUTH - DOTHAN—See SunSouth LLC; *U.S. Private*, pg. 3872
SUNSOUTH LLC; *U.S. Private*, pg. 3872
SUNSOUTH - SAMSON—See SunSouth LLC; *U.S. Private*, pg. 3873
SUNSOUTH - TUSCALOOSA—See SunSouth LLC; *U.S. Private*, pg. 3873
SUNSPORTS, INC.; *U.S. Private*, pg. 3873
SUNSPRING AMERICA, INC.—See Sunspring Metal Corporation; *Int'l*, pg. 7323
SUNSPRING METAL CORPORATION; *Int'l*, pg. 7323
SUNSPRING NORTH AMERICA, LLC—See Sunspring Metal Corporation; *Int'l*, pg. 7323
SUN STAFF, INC.—See Toyota Industries Corporation; *Int'l*, pg. 7866
SUNSTAGE CO., LTD.—See BELLUNA CO. LTD.; *Int'l*, pg. 967
SUNSTAR AMERICAS INC.—See Sunstar Suisse S.A.; *Int'l*, pg. 7323
SUNSTAR AMERICAS INC.—See Sunstar Suisse S.A.; *Int'l*, pg. 7323
SUNSTAR AMERICAS, MEXICO S. DE R.L. DE C.V.—See Sunstar Suisse S.A.; *Int'l*, pg. 7323
SUNSTAR BENELUX B.V.—See Sunstar Suisse S.A.; *Int'l*, pg. 7323
SUNSTAR CHEMICAL (THAILAND) CO., LTD.—See Sunstar Suisse S.A.; *Int'l*, pg. 7323
SUNSTAR CHEM & PHARM, CORP.—See Standard Chem. & Pharm. Co., Ltd.; *Int'l*, pg. 7168
SUNSTAR CO., LTD.—See Sunstar Suisse S.A.; *Int'l*, pg. 7323
SUNSTAR DEUTSCHLAND GMBH—See Sunstar Suisse S.A.; *Int'l*, pg. 7323
SUNSTAR DO BRAZIL LTDA.—See Sunstar Suisse S.A.; *Int'l*, pg. 7323
SUNSTAR ENGINEERING AMERICAS INC.—See Sunstar Suisse S.A.; *Int'l*, pg. 7323
SUNSTAR ENGINEERING EUROPE GMBH—See Sunstar Suisse S.A.; *Int'l*, pg. 7323
SUNSTAR ENGINEERING INC. - SHIGA PLANT—See Sunstar Suisse S.A.; *Int'l*, pg. 7323
SUNSTAR ENGINEERING INC.—See Sunstar Suisse S.A.; *Int'l*, pg. 7323
SUNSTAR ENGINEERING INC. - YAMANASHI PLANT—See Sunstar Suisse S.A.; *Int'l*, pg. 7323
SUNSTAR ENGINEERING ITALY S.R.L.—See Sunstar Suisse S.A.; *Int'l*, pg. 7323
SUNSTAR ENGINEERING (THAILAND) CO., LTD.—See Sunstar Suisse S.A.; *Int'l*, pg. 7323
SUNSTAR EUROPE SA—See Sunstar Suisse S.A.; *Int'l*, pg. 7323
SUNSTAR EUROPE S.A.—See Sunstar Suisse S.A.; *Int'l*, pg. 7323
SUNSTAR FRANCE S.A.S.—See Sunstar Suisse S.A.; *Int'l*, pg. 7323
SUNSTAR GUANGZHOU LTD.—See Sunstar Suisse S.A.; *Int'l*, pg. 7323
SUNSTAR IBERIA S.L.U.—See Sunstar Suisse S.A.; *Int'l*, pg. 7323
SUNSTAR, INC.—See Sunstar Suisse S.A.; *Int'l*, pg. 7324
SUNSTAR, INC. - TOKUSHIMA PLANT—See Sunstar Suisse S.A.; *Int'l*, pg. 7324
SUNSTAR INSURANCE GROUP, LLC—See Reverence Capital Partners LLC; *U.S. Private*, pg. 3415
SUNSTAR INTERBROS GMBH—See Sunstar Suisse S.A.; *Int'l*, pg. 7324
SUNSTAR ITALIANA SRL—See Sunstar Suisse S.A.; *Int'l*, pg. 7324
SUNSTAR PHARMACEUTICAL, INC.—See Sunstar Suisse S.A.; *Int'l*, pg. 7323
SUNSTAR REALTY DEVELOPMENT LIMITED; *Int'l*, pg. 7323
SUNSTAR SINGAPORE PTE. LTD.—See Sunstar Suisse S.A.; *Int'l*, pg. 7324
SUN-STAR STATIONERY CO., LTD.—See BANDAI NAMCO Holdings Inc.; *Int'l*, pg. 829
SUNSTAR SUISSE S.A.; *Int'l*, pg. 7323
SUNSTAR SVERIGE AB—See Sunstar Suisse S.A.; *Int'l*, pg. 7324
SUN STATE COMPONENTS OF NEVADA; *U.S. Private*, pg. 3864
SUNSTATE EQUIPMENT CO. LLC—See Sumitomo Corporation; *Int'l*, pg. 7273
SUN STATE FORD INC.; *U.S. Private*, pg. 3864
SUN STATE INTERNATIONAL TRUCKS, LLC; *U.S. Private*, pg. 3864
SUN STEEL CO.—See Esmark Incorporated; *U.S. Private*, pg. 1426
SUNSTOCK, INC.; *U.S. Public*, pg. 1966
SUNSTONE ASSURANCE, LLC; *U.S. Private*, pg. 3873
SUNSTONE DEVELOPMENT CO., LTD.; *Int'l*, pg. 7324
SUNSTONE HOTEL INVESTORS, INC.; *U.S. Public*, pg. 1966
SUNSTONE IMPORTS INC.; *U.S. Private*, pg. 3873
SUNSTONE METALS LTD; *Int'l*, pg. 7324
SUNSTONE PARTNERS MANAGEMENT LLC; *U.S. Private*, pg. 3873
SUNSTONE REALTY ADVISORS INC.; *Int'l*, pg. 7324
SUNSTONE SAINT CLAIR LESSEE, INC.—See Sunstone Hotel Investors, Inc.; *U.S. Public*, pg. 1966
SUNSTONE SAINT CLAIR, LLC—See Sunstone Hotel Investors, Inc.; *U.S. Public*, pg. 1966
SUNSTONE (TANGSHAN) PHARMACEUTICAL CO., LTD.—See Sanofi; *Int'l*, pg. 6552
SUNSTREAM, INC.; *U.S. Private*, pg. 3873
SUN STUD PTY. LIMITED—See Imperium Financial Group Limited; *Int'l*, pg. 3635
SUN SUMMIT MINERALS CORP.; *Int'l*, pg. 7308
SUN SUN TRADING CO. INC.; *U.S. Private*, pg. 3864
SUN SUPPLY CORPORATION—See House Foods Group Inc.; *Int'l*, pg. 3490
SUN SUPPLY INC.; *U.S. Private*, pg. 3864
SUNSURIA BERHAD; *Int'l*, pg. 7324
SUNSWEET DRYERS—See Sunsweet Growers, Inc.; *U.S. Private*, pg. 3873
SUNSWEET GROWERS, INC.; *U.S. Private*, pg. 3873
SUNSWEET PCL; *Int'l*, pg. 7324
SUNSYSTEM DEVELOPMENT CORPORATION; *U.S. Private*, pg. 3873
SUNTAK TECHNOLOGY CO., LTD.; *Int'l*, pg. 7324
SUN TAN CITY; *U.S. Private*, pg. 3864
SUNTAR ECO-CITY LIMITED; *Int'l*, pg. 7324
SUNTAR ENVIRONMENTAL TECHNOLOGY CO., LTD.; *Int'l*, pg. 7324
SUNTAR MEMBRANE TECHNOLOGY (SINGAPORE) PTE LTD—See CDH China Management Company Limited; *Int'l*, pg. 1370
SUNTAR MEMBRANE TECHNOLOGY (XIAMEN) CO., LTD.—See CDH China Management Company Limited; *Int'l*, pg. 1370
SUNTEC BUSINESS SOLUTIONS FZE—See SunTec Business Solutions Pvt. Ltd.; *Int'l*, pg. 7324

SUNTAR ENVIRONMENTAL TECHNOLOGY CO., LTD. CORPORATE AFFILIATIONS

SUNTEC BUSINESS SOLUTIONS GMBH—See SunTec Business Solutions Pvt. Ltd.; *Int'l*, pg. 7324
SUNTEC BUSINESS SOLUTIONS INC—See SunTec Business Solutions Pvt. Ltd.; *Int'l*, pg. 7324
SUNTEC BUSINESS SOLUTIONS LTD.—See SunTec Business Solutions Pvt. Ltd.; *Int'l*, pg. 7324
SUNTEC BUSINESS SOLUTIONS PVT. LTD.; *Int'l*, pg. 7324
SUNTEC BUSINESS SOLUTIONS SINGAPORE PTE LTD.—See SunTec Business Solutions Pvt. Ltd.; *Int'l*, pg. 7324
SUNTEC CORPORATION—See TBK Co. Ltd.; *Int'l*, pg. 7480
SUNTECH AMERICA, INC.—See Suntech Power Holdings Co., Ltd.; *Int'l*, pg. 7325
SUNTECH ARIZONA, INC.—See Suntech Power Holdings Co., Ltd.; *Int'l*, pg. 7325
SUNTECH AUSTRALIA PTY LTD—See Suntech Power Holdings Co., Ltd.; *Int'l*, pg. 7325
SUNTECH BUILDING SYSTEMS INC.; *U.S. Private*, pg. 3873
SUNTECH CO., LTD.; *Int'l*, pg. 7324
SUNTECH MEDICAL DEVICES (SHENZHEN) CO. LTD.—See Halma plc; *Int'l*, pg. 3233
SUNTECH MEDICAL, INC.—See Halma plc; *Int'l*, pg. 3233
SUN TECHNICAL SERVICES, INC.—See Bernhard Capital Partners Management, LP; *U.S. Private*, pg. 537
SUNTECHNICS FABRISOLAR AG—See Elektrizitatswerk der Stadt Zurich; *Int'l*, pg. 2356
SUN TECHNOLOGIES CO., LTD.; *Int'l*, pg. 7308
SUNTECH OPTICS INC.—See EssilorLuxottica SA; *Int'l*, pg. 2514
SUNTECH POWER AUSTRALIA PTY LTD—See Suntech Power Holdings Co., Ltd.; *Int'l*, pg. 7325
SUNTECH POWER DEUTSCHLAND GMBH—See Suntech Power Holdings Co., Ltd.; *Int'l*, pg. 7325
SUNTECH POWER HOLDINGS CO., LTD.; *Int'l*, pg. 7324
SUNTECH POWER INTERNATIONAL LTD—See Suntech Power Holdings Co., Ltd.; *Int'l*, pg. 7325
SUNTECH POWER ITALY CO., SRL—See Suntech Power Holdings Co., Ltd.; *Int'l*, pg. 7325
SUNTECH POWER JAPAN CORPORATION—See Suntech Power Holdings Co., Ltd.; *Int'l*, pg. 7325
SUNTECH R&D AUSTRALIA PTY LTD—See Suntech Power Holdings Co., Ltd.; *Int'l*, pg. 7325
SUNTEC INDUSTRIES INC.; *U.S. Private*, pg. 3873
SUNTEC INFO SYSTEMS PVT. LTD.—See SunTec Business Solutions Pvt. Ltd.; *Int'l*, pg. 7324
SUNTEC INTERNATIONAL CONVENTION & EXHIBITION SERVICES PTE. LTD.—See ESR Group Limited; *Int'l*, pg. 2508
SUNTECK INFRACON PRIVATE LIMITED—See Sunteck Realty Limited; *Int'l*, pg. 7325
SUNTECK REALTY LIMITED; *Int'l*, pg. 7325
SUNTECK TRANSPORT GROUP, INC.—See Comvest Group Holdings LLC; *U.S. Private*, pg. 1007
SUNTEC REAL ESTATE INVESTMENT TRUST; *Int'l*, pg. 7324
SUNTEC SINGAPORE INTERNATIONAL CONVENTION & EXHIBITION SERVICES PTE. LTD.—See ESR Group Limited; *Int'l*, pg. 2508
SUN TECTRO, LTD.—See The Japan Steel Works, Ltd.; *Int'l*, pg. 7659
SUNTEK AUSTRALIA PTY. LTD.—See Eastman Chemical Company; *U.S. Public*, pg. 706
SUNTEK EUROPE GMBH—See Eastman Chemical Company; *U.S. Public*, pg. 706
SUNTEK FILMS CANADA, INC.—See Eastman Chemical Company; *U.S. Public*, pg. 706
SUNTEK UK LIMITED—See Eastman Chemical Company; *U.S. Public*, pg. 706
SUNTELEPHONE CO., LTD.—See NITTO KOGYO CORPORATION; *Int'l*, pg. 5387
SUNTEN ELECTRIC EQUIPMENT CO., LTD.—See Schneider Electric SE; *Int'l*, pg. 6635
SUN TEN (SINGAPORE) PRIVATE LIMITED—See Y.S.P. Southeast Asia Holding Berhad; *Int'l*, pg. 8544
SUNTEX MARINAS INVESTORS LLC—See Centerbridge Partners, L.P.; *U.S. Private*, pg. 815
THE SUN TIMES—See Chatham Asset Management, LLC; *U.S. Private*, pg. 861
THE SUN-TIMES—See Gannett Co., Inc.; *U.S. Public*, pg. 905
SUN TIN LUN GARMENT ACCESSORIES (HUIZHOU) COMPANY LIMITED—See Reach New Holdings Limited; *Int'l*, pg. 6231
SUNTIVA, LLC; *U.S. Private*, pg. 3873
SUNTONE TECHNOLOGY COMPANY LIMITED—See Jinhua Chunguang Technology Co., Ltd.; *Int'l*, pg. 3968
SUN TONG SENG MOULD-TECH SDN. BHD.—See SKP Resources Bhd; *Int'l*, pg. 6991
SUNTOOL CO., LTD.—See Eson Precision Ind. Co., Ltd.; *Int'l*, pg. 2504
SUNTORY ALLIED LTD.—See Pernod Ricard S.A.; *Int'l*, pg. 5811
SUNTORY ALLIED LTD.—See Suntory Holdings Limited; *Int'l*, pg. 7326
SUNTORY (AUST.) PTY. LTD.—See Suntory Holdings Limited; *Int'l*, pg. 7326

SUNTORY BEVERAGE & FOOD EUROPE LTD.—See Suntory Holdings Limited; *Int'l*, pg. 7326
SUNTORY BEVERAGE & FOOD LIMITED—See Suntory Holdings Limited; *Int'l*, pg. 7326
SUNTORY (CHINA) HOLDING CO., LTD.—See Suntory Holdings Limited; *Int'l*, pg. 7326
SUNTORY F&B INTERNATIONAL (H.K.) CO., LTD.—See Suntory Holdings Limited; *Int'l*, pg. 7327
SUNTORY F&B INTERNATIONAL (SHA) CO., LTD.—See Suntory Holdings Limited; *Int'l*, pg. 7327
SUNTORY FLOWERS LTD.—See Suntory Holdings Limited; *Int'l*, pg. 7327
SUNTORY FOODS, LTD.—See Suntory Holdings Limited; *Int'l*, pg. 7327
SUNTORY HOLDINGS LIMITED; *Int'l*, pg. 7325
SUNTORY INTERNATIONAL CORP.—See Suntory Holdings Limited; *Int'l*, pg. 7327
SUNTORY INVESTMENT & DEVELOPMENT LTD.—See Suntory Holdings Limited; *Int'l*, pg. 7327
SUNTORY LOGISTICS LTD.—See Suntory Holdings Limited; *Int'l*, pg. 7327
SUNTORY MEXICANA, S.A. DE C.V.—See Suntory Holdings Limited; *Int'l*, pg. 7327
SUNTORY PUBLICITY SERVICE CO., LTD.—See Suntory Holdings Limited; *Int'l*, pg. 7327
SUNTORY SERVICE LTD.—See Suntory Holdings Limited; *Int'l*, pg. 7327
SUNTORY (SHANGHAI) FOODS CO., LTD.—See Suntory Holdings Limited; *Int'l*, pg. 7326
SUNTORY (SHANGHAI) FOODS MARKETING CO., LTD.—See Suntory Holdings Limited; *Int'l*, pg. 7326
SUNTORY SHOPPING CLUB, LTD.—See Suntory Holdings Limited; *Int'l*, pg. 7327
SUNTORY SPIRITS LTD.—See Suntory Holdings Limited; *Int'l*, pg. 7327
SUNTORY SPORTS SYSTEM, LTD.—See Suntory Holdings Limited; *Int'l*, pg. 7327
SUNTORY TRADING HONG KONG LTD.—See Suntory Holdings Limited; *Int'l*, pg. 7327
SUNTORY U.K. LTD.—See Suntory Holdings Limited; *Int'l*, pg. 7327
SUNTORY WELLNESS LTD.—See Suntory Holdings Limited; *Int'l*, pg. 7327
SUN TOX CO., LTD.—See Rengo Co., Ltd.; *Int'l*, pg. 6281
SUN TOYOTA LTD; *Int'l*, pg. 7308
SUNTRADE EXPORT SERVICES; *U.S. Private*, pg. 3873
SUN TRADING CO., LTD.—See Asahi Kasei Corporation; *Int'l*, pg. 597
SUNTREAT PACKING & SHIPPING CO.; *U.S. Private*, pg. 3874
SUNTRON CORPORATION—See Blum Capital Partners, L.P.; *U.S. Private*, pg. 599
SUNTRON CORPORATION—See HCI Equity Management, L.P.; *U.S. Private*, pg. 1889
SUNTRON GULF COAST OPERATIONS—See Blum Capital Partners, L.P.; *U.S. Private*, pg. 599
SUNTRON GULF COAST OPERATIONS—See HCI Equity Management, L.P.; *U.S. Private*, pg. 1889
SUNTRON INVESTMENTS LIMITED—See CJ Corporation; *Int'l*, pg. 1634
SUNTRON NORTHEAST EXPRESS—See Blum Capital Partners, L.P.; *U.S. Private*, pg. 599
SUNTRON NORTHEAST EXPRESS—See HCI Equity Management, L.P.; *U.S. Private*, pg. 1889
SUNTRON NORTHEAST OPERATIONS—See Blum Capital Partners, L.P.; *U.S. Private*, pg. 599
SUNTRON NORTHEAST OPERATIONS—See HCI Equity Management, L.P.; *U.S. Private*, pg. 1889
SUNTRONT TECHNOLOGY CO., LTD.; *Int'l*, pg. 7327
SUNTRUP BUICK-PONTIAC-GMC TRUCK, INC.—See Southland Imports, Inc.; *U.S. Private*, pg. 3737
SUNTRUP FORD KIRKWOOD—See Southland Imports, Inc.; *U.S. Private*, pg. 3737
SUNTRUP VOLKSWAGEN—See Southland Imports, Inc.; *U.S. Private*, pg. 3737
SUNTRUST BANK, CENTRAL FLORIDA DIVISION HEADQUARTERS—See Truist Financial Corporation; *U.S. Public*, pg. 2199
SUNTRUST BANK, EAST TENNESSEE REGION HEADQUARTERS—See Truist Financial Corporation; *U.S. Public*, pg. 2199
SUNTRUST BANK, GEORGIA REGION HEADQUARTERS—See Truist Financial Corporation; *U.S. Public*, pg. 2199
SUNTRUST BANK HOLDING COMPANY—See Truist Financial Corporation; *U.S. Public*, pg. 2199
SUNTRUST BANK, MID-ATLANTIC DIVISION HEADQUARTERS—See Truist Financial Corporation; *U.S. Public*, pg. 2199
SUNTRUST BANK, NASHVILLE REGION HEADQUARTERS—See Truist Financial Corporation; *U.S. Public*, pg. 2199
SUNTRUST BANKS, INC.—See Truist Financial Corporation; *U.S. Public*, pg. 2199
SUNTRUST BANK—See Truist Financial Corporation; *U.S. Public*, pg. 2199
SUNTRUST BANK, SOUTH FLORIDA DIVISION HEADQUARTERS—See Truist Financial Corporation; *U.S. Public*, pg. 2199

SUNTRUST BANK, SOUTHWEST FLORIDA REGION HEADQUARTERS—See Truist Financial Corporation; *U.S. Public*, pg. 2200
SUNTRUST BANK, TAMPA REGION HEADQUARTERS—See Truist Financial Corporation; *U.S. Public*, pg. 2200
SUNTRUST DELAWARE TRUST COMPANY—See Truist Financial Corporation; *U.S. Public*, pg. 2200
SUNTRUST INSURANCE COMPANY—See Truist Financial Corporation; *U.S. Public*, pg. 2200
SUNTRUST INVESTMENT SERVICES, INC.—See Truist Financial Corporation; *U.S. Public*, pg. 2200
SUNTRUST MORTGAGE INC.—See Truist Financial Corporation; *U.S. Public*, pg. 2200
SUNTRUST PROPERTIES, INC.—See Alliance Global Group, Inc.; *Int'l*, pg. 339
SUNTRUST RESORT HOLDINGS, INC.; *Int'l*, pg. 7327
SUNTURF INC.; *U.S. Private*, pg. 3874
SUN TV NETWORK LIMITED; *Int'l*, pg. 7308
SUN TV NETWORK LIMITED - SUN-PICTURES—See Sun TV Network Limited; *Int'l*, pg. 7308
SUNTX CAPITAL PARTNERS, L.P.; *U.S. Private*, pg. 3874
SUNTY DEVELOPMENT CO., LTD.; *Int'l*, pg. 7327
SUN TYRE INDUSTRIES SDN. BHD—See ecoWise Holdings Limited; *Int'l*, pg. 2300
SUN TZU CORP.; *U.S. Public*, pg. 1963
SUNU ASSURANCES NIGERIA PLC; *Int'l*, pg. 7327
SUNU HEALTH NIGERIA LIMITED—See Sunu Assurances Nigeria Plc; *Int'l*, pg. 7327
SUN-UP RECYCLING CO., LTD.—See Air Water Inc.; *Int'l*, pg. 240
THE SUN US, INC.—See News Corporation; *U.S. Public*, pg. 1521
SUN VALLEY AVIATION, INC.—See Macquarie Group Limited; *Int'l*, pg. 4627
SUN VALLEY COMPANY—See HF Sinclair Corporation; *U.S. Public*, pg. 1034
SUN VALLEY FILM WASH, INC.—See PyroPure, Inc.; *U.S. Private*, pg. 3310
SUN VALLEY GOLD LLC; *U.S. Private*, pg. 3864
SUN VALLEY HEALTH, LLC—See Empower Clinics Inc.; *Int'l*, pg. 2388
SUN VALLEY INC.—See Toyota Industries Corporation; *Int'l*, pg. 7866
SUN VALLEY LTD.; *Int'l*, pg. 7308
SUN VALLEY MASONRY INC.; *U.S. Private*, pg. 3864
SUNVALLEY SOLAR, INC.; *U.S. Public*, pg. 1966
SUNVAULT ENERGY, INC.; *Int'l*, pg. 7327
SUN VERTEX CO., LTD.—See Taiyo Yuden Company Ltd.; *Int'l*, pg. 7427
SUNVESTA COSTA RICA LIMITADA—See SunVesta, Inc.; *Int'l*, pg. 7328
SUNVESTA HOLDING AG—See SunVesta, Inc.; *Int'l*, pg. 7328
SUNVESTA, INC.; *Int'l*, pg. 7327
SUNVEST CORPORATION LIMITED; *Int'l*, pg. 7327
SUNVIC CHEMICAL HOLDINGS LIMITED; *Int'l*, pg. 7328
SUNVIC TECHNOLOGY CO., LTD.; *Int'l*, pg. 7328
SUN VIEW IMAGING, L.L.C.—See Tenet Healthcare Corporation; *U.S. Public*, pg. 2004
SUNVIEW NIRMAN PRIVATE LIMITED—See Gretex Corporate Services Ltd; *Int'l*, pg. 3082
SUNVIEW SOFTWARE INC.—See Serviceaide, Inc.; *U.S. Private*, pg. 3616
SUNVIM GROUP CO., LTD.; *Int'l*, pg. 7328
SUNWAH INTERNATIIONAL LIMITED; *Int'l*, pg. 7328
SUNWAH KINGSWAY CAPITAL HOLDINGS LIMITED—See Sunwah Internatiional Limited; *Int'l*, pg. 7328
SUNWA-LOGISTIC CORPORATION—See Sun-Wa Technos Corporation; *Int'l*, pg. 7309
SUNWARD EUROPE HEAVY INDUSTRY NV—See Sunward Intelligent Equipment Co., Ltd.; *Int'l*, pg. 7328
SUNWARD INTELLIGENT EQUIPMENT CO., LTD.; *Int'l*, pg. 7328
SUN-WA TECHNOS AMERICA, INC.—See Sun-Wa Technos Corporation; *Int'l*, pg. 7309
SUN-WA TECHNOS ASIA (THAILAND) CO, LTD.—See Sun-Wa Technos Corporation; *Int'l*, pg. 7309
SUN-WA TECHNOS CORPORATION; *Int'l*, pg. 7309
SUN-WA TECHNOS (EUROPE) GMBH—See Sun-Wa Technos Corporation; *Int'l*, pg. 7309
SUN-WA TECHNOS (EUROPE) GMBH—See Sun-Wa Technos Corporation; *Int'l*, pg. 7309
SUN-WA TECHNOS EUROPE GMBH—See Sun-Wa Technos Corporation; *Int'l*, pg. 7309
SUN-WA TECHNOS (HONG KONG) CO. LTD.—See Sun-Wa Technos Corporation; *Int'l*, pg. 7309
SUN-WA TECHNOS (MALAYSIA) SDN. BHD.—See Sun-Wa Technos Corporation; *Int'l*, pg. 7309
SUN-WA TECHNOS MEXICO S.A. DE C.V.—See Sun-Wa Technos Corporation; *Int'l*, pg. 7309
SUN-WA TECHNOS (PHILIPPINES), INC.—See Sun-Wa Technos Corporation; *Int'l*, pg. 7309
SUN-WA TECHNOS (SHENZHEN) CO., LTD—See Sun-Wa Technos Corporation; *Int'l*, pg. 7309
SUN-WA TECHNOS (SINGAPORE) PTE LTD—See Sun-Wa Technos Corporation; *Int'l*, pg. 7309

COMPANY NAME INDEX

SUN-WA TECHNOS TAIWAN CO. LTD.—See Sun-Wa Technos Corporation; *Int'l*, pg. 7309
SUN-WA TECHNOS (VIETNAM) CO., LTD.—See Sun-Wa Technos Corporation; *Int'l*, pg. 7309
SUN-WA TRINITY CORPORATION—See Sun-Wa Technos Corporation; *Int'l*, pg. 7309
SUNWAVE COMMUNICATIONS CO., LTD.; *Int'l*, pg. 7328
SUNWAVE GAS & POWER INC.—See ONEnergy Inc.; *Int'l*, pg. 5576
SUNWAVE HOME COMFORT INC.—See Cricket Energy Holdings, Inc.; *Int'l*, pg. 1849
SUNWAVE KITCHEN TECHNO CORP.—See Tenpos Holdings, Inc.; *Int'l*, pg. 7561
SUNWAY AVILA SDN. BHD.—See Sunway Berhad; *Int'l*, pg. 7328
SUNWAY BANGI SDN BHD—See Sunway Berhad; *Int'l*, pg. 7331
SUNWAY (BENELUX) B.V.—See 3G Capital Partners L.P.; *U.S. Private*, pg. 13
SUNWAY BERHAD - BATANG KALI FACTORY—See Sunway Berhad; *Int'l*, pg. 7328
SUNWAY BERHAD - NIBONG TEBAL FACTORY—See Sunway Berhad; *Int'l*, pg. 7328
SUNWAY BERHAD - SENAI FACTORY—See Sunway Berhad; *Int'l*, pg. 7328
SUNWAY BERHAD; *Int'l*, pg. 7328
SUNWAY BIG BOX SDN. BHD.—See Sunway Co., Ltd.; *Int'l*, pg. 7331
SUNWAY BINTANG SDN. BHD.—See Sunway Berhad; *Int'l*, pg. 7328
SUNWAY BUILDERS SDN BHD—See Sunway Berhad; *Int'l*, pg. 7329
SUNWAY CAVITY WALL PANEL SDN BHD—See Sunway Berhad; *Int'l*, pg. 7330
SUNWAY CAVITY WALL PANEL (S) PTE LTD—See Sunway Berhad; *Int'l*, pg. 7330
SUNWAY CITY (IPOH) SDN. BHD.—See Sunway Berhad; *Int'l*, pg. 7328
SUNWAY CITY (JB) SDN. BHD.—See Sunway Berhad; *Int'l*, pg. 7328
SUNWAY CITY (S'PORE) PTE. LTD.—See Sunway Berhad; *Int'l*, pg. 7328
SUNWAY COATING SOLUTIONS SDN. BHD.—See Sunway Berhad; *Int'l*, pg. 7329
SUNWAY CO., LTD.; *Int'l*, pg. 7331
SUNWAY CONCRETE PRODUCTS (M) SDN. BHD.—See Sunway Berhad; *Int'l*, pg. 7329
SUNWAY CONCRETE PRODUCTS (S) PTE LTD—See Sunway Berhad; *Int'l*, pg. 7329
SUNWAY CONSTRUCTION INDIA PVT. LTD.—See Sunway Berhad; *Int'l*, pg. 7329
SUNWAY CONSTRUCTION SDN BHD—See Sunway Berhad; *Int'l*, pg. 7329
SUNWAY CREATIVE STONES SDN BHD—See Sunway Berhad; *Int'l*, pg. 7329
SUNWAY CREATIVE STONES (XIAMEN) CO., LTD.—See Sunway Berhad; *Int'l*, pg. 7329
SUNWAY CREDIT SDN. BHD.—See Sunway Berhad; *Int'l*, pg. 7329
SUNWAY DAECHANG FORGING (ANHUI) CO. LTD.—See Sunway Berhad; *Int'l*, pg. 7329
SUNWAY DAMANSARA SDN. BHD.—See Sunway Berhad; *Int'l*, pg. 7329
SUNWAY DESIGN SDN. BHD.—See Sunway Berhad; *Int'l*, pg. 7329
SUNWAY DESTINY SDN. BHD.—See Sunway Berhad; *Int'l*, pg. 7329
SUNWAY DEVELOPMENTS PTE. LTD.—See Sunway Berhad; *Int'l*, pg. 7329
SUNWAY DIMENSION STONES SDN BHD—See Sunway Berhad; *Int'l*, pg. 7329
SUNWAY EASTWOOD SDN. BHD.—See Sunway Berhad; *Int'l*, pg. 7331
SUNWAY ENGINEERING SDN BHD—See Sunway Berhad; *Int'l*, pg. 7329
SUNWAY ENTERPRISE (1988) SDN BHD—See Sunway Berhad; *Int'l*, pg. 7329
SUNWAY FACILITY MANAGEMENT SDN. BHD.—See Sunway Berhad; *Int'l*, pg. 7329
SUNWAY GD PILING SDN BHD—See Sunway Berhad; *Int'l*, pg. 7329
SUNWAY GEOTECHNICS (M) SDN BHD—See Sunway Berhad; *Int'l*, pg. 7329
SUNWAY GIZA MALL SDN. BHD.—See Sunway Berhad; *Int'l*, pg. 7329
SUNWAY GIZA PARKING SDN. BHD.—See Sunway Berhad; *Int'l*, pg. 7329
SUNWAY GLOBAL INC.; *Int'l*, pg. 7331
SUNWAY GREENVIEW SDN BHD—See Sunway Berhad; *Int'l*, pg. 7331
SUNWAY GUANGHAO REAL ESTATE (JIANGYIN) CO. LTD.—See Sunway Berhad; *Int'l*, pg. 7329
SUNWAY HEALTHY LIFESTYLE SDN. BHD.—See Sunway Berhad; *Int'l*, pg. 7329
SUNWAY HOSE CENTRE SDN BHD—See Sunway Berhad; *Int'l*, pg. 7329
SUNWAY HOTEL HANOI LIABILITY LIMITED COMPANY—See Sunway Berhad; *Int'l*, pg. 7329
SUNWAY HOTEL (PENANG) SDN. BHD.—See Sunway Berhad; *Int'l*, pg. 7329
SUNWAY HOTEL PHNOM PENH LTD.—See Sunway Berhad; *Int'l*, pg. 7330
SUNWAY HOTEL (SEBERANG JAYA) SDN. BHD.—See Sunway Berhad; *Int'l*, pg. 7329
SUNWAY HYDRAULIC INDUSTRIES SDN BHD—See Sunway Berhad; *Int'l*, pg. 7329
SUNWAY HYDRAULIC INDUSTRIES (WUHU) CO. LTD.—See Sunway Berhad; *Int'l*, pg. 7329
SUNWAY IFM SDN. BHD.—See Sunway Berhad; *Int'l*, pg. 7329
SUNWAY INTEGRATED PROPERTIES SDN. BHD.—See Sunway Berhad; *Int'l*, pg. 7329
SUNWAY INTERNATIONAL HOLDINGS LIMITED; *Int'l*, pg. 7331
SUNWAY INTERNATIONAL HOTELS & RESORTS SDN. BHD.—See Sunway Berhad; *Int'l*, pg. 7330
SUNWAY INTERNATIONAL TRADING (TIANJIN) PTE. LTD.—See Sunway Berhad; *Int'l*, pg. 7330
SUNWAY INTERNATIONAL VACATION CLUB BERHAD—See Sunway Berhad; *Int'l*, pg. 7330
SUNWAY INVESTMENT MANAGEMENT CONSULTANCY (SHANGHAI) CO. LTD.—See Sunway Berhad; *Int'l*, pg. 7329
SUNWAY ISKANDAR SDN. BHD.—See Sunway Berhad; *Int'l*, pg. 7330
SUNWAY KERAMO SDN BHD—See Sunway Berhad; *Int'l*, pg. 7330
SUNWAY KORDIS (SHANGHAI) LIMITED—See Hengan International Group Co. Ltd.; *Int'l*, pg. 3346
SUNWAY LAGOON CLUB BERHAD—See Sunway Berhad; *Int'l*, pg. 7330
SUNWAY LAGOON SDN. BHD.—See Sunway Berhad; *Int'l*, pg. 7330
SUNWAY LEASING SDN. BHD.—See Sunway Berhad; *Int'l*, pg. 7330
SUNWAY LEISURE SERVICES SDN. BHD.—See Sunway Berhad; *Int'l*, pg. 7330
SUNWAY LOST WORLD HOTEL SDN. BHD.—See Sunway Berhad; *Int'l*, pg. 7330
SUNWAY LOST WORLD WATER PARK SDN. BHD.—See Sunway Berhad; *Int'l*, pg. 7328
SUNWAY MACHINERIES SERVICES SDN BHD—See Sunway Berhad; *Int'l*, pg. 7329
SUNWAY MACHINERY SDN BHD—See Sunway Berhad; *Int'l*, pg. 7329
SUNWAY MARKETING (EAST MALAYSIA) SDN BHD—See Sunway Berhad; *Int'l*, pg. 7330
SUNWAY MARKETING SDN. BHD.—See Sunway Berhad; *Int'l*, pg. 7330
SUNWAY MARKETING (SHANGHAI) PTE LTD—See Sunway Berhad; *Int'l*, pg. 7330
SUNWAY MARKETING (S) PTE LTD—See Sunway Berhad; *Int'l*, pg. 7330
SUNWAY MARKETING (THAILAND) LTD.—See Sunway Berhad; *Int'l*, pg. 7330
SUNWAY MARKETING (VIETNAM) CO., LTD.—See Sunway Berhad; *Int'l*, pg. 7330
SUNWAYMAS SDN BHD—See Sunway Berhad; *Int'l*, pg. 7331
SUNWAY MEDICAL CENTRE BERHAD—See Sunway Berhad; *Int'l*, pg. 7330
SUNWAY MEDICAL CENTRE (SINGAPORE) PTE. LTD.—See Sunway Co., Ltd.; *Int'l*, pg. 7331
SUNWAY MELAWATI SDN. BHD.—See Sunway Berhad; *Int'l*, pg. 7330
SUNWAY MONTEREZ SDN. BHD.—See Sunway Berhad; *Int'l*, pg. 7329
SUNWAY NEXIS PARKING SDN. BHD.—See Sunway Berhad; *Int'l*, pg. 7330
SUNWAY PALS LOYALTY SDN. BHD.—See Sunway Berhad; *Int'l*, pg. 7328
SUNWAY PAVING SOLUTIONS SDN BHD—See Sunway Berhad; *Int'l*, pg. 7330
SUNWAY PHARMA SDN BHD—See Sunway Berhad; *Int'l*, pg. 7328
SUNWAY PIPEPLUS TECHNOLOGY SDN BHD—See Sunway Berhad; *Int'l*, pg. 7330
SUNWAY PUTRA HOTEL SDN. BHD.—See Sunway Berhad; *Int'l*, pg. 7330
SUNWAY PYRAMID DEVELOPMENT SDN. BHD.—See Sunway Berhad; *Int'l*, pg. 7330
SUNWAY QUARRY INDUSTRIES (CARIBBEAN) LIMITED—See Sunway Berhad; *Int'l*, pg. 7330
SUNWAY QUARRY INDUSTRIES (MELAKA) SDN. BHD.—See Sunway Berhad; *Int'l*, pg. 7330
SUNWAY QUARRY INDUSTRIES (MELAKA) SDN. BHD.—See Sunway Berhad; *Int'l*, pg. 7330
SUNWAY QUARRY INDUSTRIES (S) SDN. BHD.—See Sunway Berhad; *Int'l*, pg. 7330
SUNWAY RAHMAN PUTRA SDN. BHD.—See Sunway Berhad; *Int'l*, pg. 7330
SUNWAY REAL ESTATE INVESTMENT TRUST; *Int'l*, pg. 7331
SUNWAY RISK MANAGEMENT SDN BHD—See Sunway Berhad; *Int'l*, pg. 7330
SUNWAY SAF-T-QUIP SDN. BHD.—See Sunway Berhad; *Int'l*, pg. 7331
SUNWAY SEMENYIH SDN. BHD.—See Sunway Berhad; *Int'l*, pg. 7330
SUNWAY SHARED SERVICES CENTRE SDN BHD—See Sunway Berhad; *Int'l*, pg. 7330
SUNWAY SOUTH QUAY SDN. BHD.—See Sunway Berhad; *Int'l*, pg. 7330
SUNWAY SPUN PILE (ZHUHAI) CO. LTD.—See Sunway Berhad; *Int'l*, pg. 7330
SUNWAY SUBANG SDN. BHD.—See Sunway Berhad; *Int'l*, pg. 7330
SUNWAY TECHTRONIC COMMUNICATION TECHNOLOGY (BEIJING) CO LTD—See Shenzhen Sunway Communication Co., Ltd.; *Int'l*, pg. 6822
SUNWAY (TIANJIN) MANAGEMENT CONSULTANCY CO. LTD.—See Sunway Berhad; *Int'l*, pg. 7330
SUNWAY TOTALRUBBER SERVICES FRANCHISING PTY. LTD.—See Sunway Berhad; *Int'l*, pg. 7330
SUNWAY TRADING (SHANGHAI) PTE. LTD.—See Sunway Berhad; *Int'l*, pg. 7330
SUNWAY TRAVEL SDN. BHD.—See Sunway Berhad; *Int'l*, pg. 7330
SUNWAY TUNAS SDN. BHD.—See Sunway Berhad; *Int'l*, pg. 7331
SUNWAY UNITED STAR SDN. BHD.—See Sunway Berhad; *Int'l*, pg. 7331
SUNWAY VELOCITY HOTEL SDN. BHD.—See Sunway Berhad; *Int'l*, pg. 7331
SUNWAY VELOCITY MALL SDN. BHD.—See Sunway Berhad; *Int'l*, pg. 7331
SUNWAY WINSTAR SDN. BHD.—See Sunway Berhad; *Int'l*, pg. 7331
SUNWAY XIN LONG (ANHUI) HYDRAULIC CO. LTD.—See Sunway Berhad; *Int'l*, pg. 7331
SUN WELL SERVICE, INC.—See Steel Partners Holdings L.P.; *U.S. Public*, pg. 1943
SUNWEST AUTO CENTRE LTD; *Int'l*, pg. 7331
SUNWEST BANCORP, INC.; *U.S. Private*, pg. 3874
SUNWEST BANK—See Sunwest Bancorp, Inc.; *U.S. Private*, pg. 3874
SUN WEST COMMUNICATIONS, INC.; *U.S. Private*, pg. 3864
SUNWEST ELECTRIC, INC.; *U.S. Private*, pg. 3874
SUNWEST FOODS INC.; *U.S. Private*, pg. 3874
SUNWEST INTERNATIONAL (PTY) LIMITED—See Sun International Limited; *Int'l*, pg. 7304
SUNWEST MANAGEMENT, INC.; *U.S. Private*, pg. 3874
SUNWEST MILLING COMPANY, INC.; *U.S. Private*, pg. 3874
SUN WEST OIL COMPANY LLC; *U.S. Private*, pg. 3864
SUN WEST RESTAURANT CONCEPTS; *U.S. Private*, pg. 3864
SUNWING JETS—See Sunwing Travel Group, Inc.; *Int'l*, pg. 7332
SUNWING TRAVEL GROUP, INC.; *Int'l*, pg. 7331
SUNWING VACATIONS INC.—See Sunwing Travel Group, Inc.; *Int'l*, pg. 7333
SUNWIN SERVICES GROUP, LIMITED—See NCR Voyix Corporation.; *U.S. Public*, pg. 1501
SUNWIN STEVIA INTERNATIONAL, INC.; *Int'l*, pg. 7331
SUNWIZE TECHNOLOGIES, INC.—See Mitsui & Co., Ltd.; *Int'l*, pg. 4976
SUNWODA ELECTRONICS CO., LTD.; *Int'l*, pg. 7333
SUNWOOD CORPORATION; *Int'l*, pg. 7333
SUNWORKS, INC.; *U.S. Public*, pg. 1966
SUN WORLD INTERNATIONAL LLC—See Renewable Resources Group Inc.; *U.S. Private*, pg. 3398
SUN WORLD INTERNATIONAL LLC—See Vision Ridge Partners, LLC; *U.S. Private*, pg. 4391
SUN YAD CONSTRUCTION CO., LTD.; *Int'l*, pg. 7308
SUNYARD TECHNOLOGY CO., LTD.; *Int'l*, pg. 7333
SUNY CELLULAR COMMUNICATION LTD.—See Suny Electronics Ltd.; *Int'l*, pg. 7333
SUN YEE GODOWN&TRANSPORTATION CO. LTD—See China Merchants Group Limited; *Int'l*, pg. 1523
SUNY ELECTRONICS LTD.; *Int'l*, pg. 7333
SUN-YOU CORP.—See MITSUBA Corporation; *Int'l*, pg. 4929
SUNZEN BIOTECH BERHAD; *Int'l*, pg. 7333
SUNZEN CORPORATION SDN. BHD.—See Sunzen Biotech Berhad; *Int'l*, pg. 7333
SUNZ INSURANCE COMPANY; *U.S. Private*, pg. 3874
SUOFEIYA HOME COLLECTION CO., LTD.; *Int'l*, pg. 7333
SUOMALAINEN KIRJAKAUPPA OY—See Otava Ltd.; *Int'l*, pg. 5656
SUOMALAINEN LEHTITAINO OY—See Alma Media Corporation; *Int'l*, pg. 362
SUOMEN 3M OY—See 3M Company; *U.S. Public*, pg. 8
SUOMEN ASIAKASTIETO OY—See Enento Group Plc; *Int'l*, pg. 2415
SUOMEN BUSINESS VIESTINTA SBV OY—See Alma Media Corporation; *Int'l*, pg. 362
SUOMEN EUROMASTER OY—See Compagnie Generale des Etablissements Michelin SCA; *Int'l*, pg. 1745
SUOMEN HELASTO OY—See Panostaja Oyj; *Int'l*, pg. 5729
SUOMEN HIIVA OY—See Lallemand, Inc.; *Int'l*, pg. 4400
SUOMEN JOUSTAVA OY—See Multitude SE; *Int'l*, pg. 5084

SUOMEN KARBONAATTI OY—See SigmaRoc Plc; *Int'l*, pg. 6909
SUOMEN KERAYSTUOTE OY—See Lassila & Tikanoja plc; *Int'l*, pg. 4421
SUOMEN KIINNIKEKESKUS OY—See Panostaja Oyj; *Int'l*, pg. 5729
SUOMEN LISARAVINNE OY—See Celsius Holdings, Inc.; *U.S. Public*, pg. 466
SUOMEN NESTLE OY—See Nestle S.A.; *Int'l*, pg. 5211
SUOMEN OSUUSKAUPPOJEN KESKUSKUNTA; *Int'l*, pg. 7333
SUOMEN PAIKALLISSANOMAT OY—See Alma Media Corporation; *Int'l*, pg. 362
SUOMEN RADER OY—See Wulff-Group Plc; *Int'l*, pg. 8502
SUOMEN RAKENNUSLEHTI OY—See DPG Media Group NV; *Int'l*, pg. 2188
SUOMEN TEOLLISUUSSIJOITUS OY; *Int'l*, pg. 7333
SUOMEN TRANSVAL OY—See Posti Group Oyj; *Int'l*, pg. 5940
SUOMEN TUKKUAUTOT OY—See Alma Media Corporation; *Int'l*, pg. 362
SUOMEN TURVAKAMERA OY—See Teleste Corporation; *Int'l*, pg. 7541
SUOMEN TUULILEIJONA OY—See Nordic Fibreboard AS; *Int'l*, pg. 5422
SUOMEN UNIPOL OY—See Algol Oy; *Int'l*, pg. 318
SUOMINEN OYJ; *Int'l*, pg. 7333
SUOMINEN US HOLDING, INC.—See Suominen Oyj; *Int'l*, pg. 7333
SUORAMARKKINOINTI MEGA OY—See Alma Media Corporation; *Int'l*, pg. 361
SUOSDEY FINANCE PLC—See Thitikorn Public Company Limited; *Int'l*, pg. 7711
SUPALAI PUBLIC COMPANY LIMITED; *Int'l*, pg. 7334
SUPAMA FOREX PRIVATE LIMITED—See Arvog; *Int'l*, pg. 588
SUPARA COMPANY LIMITED—See M.P. Evans Group PLC; *Int'l*, pg. 4616
SUPECO INVESTMENT SRL—See Carrefour SA; *Int'l*, pg. 1346
SUPELCO, INC.—See Merck KGaA; *Int'l*, pg. 4832
SUPER 10 S.A.—See SMU S.A.; *Int'l*, pg. 7017
SUPER 1 FOODS; *U.S. Private*, pg. 3874
SUPER 8 MOTEL TIMMINS—See Clarke Inc.; *Int'l*, pg. 1650
SUPER ABASTOS CENTRALES Y COMERCIALES, S.A. DE C.V.—See Desarrolladora Homex, S.A. de C.V.; *Int'l*, pg. 2044
SUPERACTIVE GROUP COMPANY LIMITED; *Int'l*, pg. 7336
SUPER A FOODS INCORPORATED; *U.S. Private*, pg. 3874
SUPERALLOY INDUSTRIAL CO., LTD.; *Int'l*, pg. 7336
SUPER AMERICA; *U.S. Private*, pg. 3874
SUPERAUTO24.COM SP. Z O.O.—See Wirtualna Polska Holding S.A.; *Int'l*, pg. 8434
SUPER BABYLON NEDERLAND B.V.—See Jumbo Supermarkten B.V.; *Int'l*, pg. 4026
SUPERBAG CO., LTD.; *Int'l*, pg. 7336
SUPER BAKERS (INDIA) LTD.; *Int'l*, pg. 7334
SUPERB INDUSTRIES, INC.; *U.S. Private*, pg. 3875
SUPERB INTERNET CORP—See CherryRoad Technologies Inc.; *U.S. Private*, pg. 874
SUPERBLOOM FESTIVAL GMBH & CO. KG—See Live Nation Entertainment, Inc.; *U.S. Public*, pg. 1330
SUPERBOLT INC.—See Investment AB Latour; *Int'l*, pg. 3783
SUPERBOWL DEVELOPMENT PTE. LTD.—See SuperBowl Holdings Limited; *Int'l*, pg. 7336
SUPERBOWL HOLDINGS LIMITED; *Int'l*, pg. 7336
SUPERBREAK MINI HOLIDAYS GROUP LTD.—See Cox & Kings Limited; *Int'l*, pg. 1823
SUPERBREAK MINI-HOLIDAYS LIMITED—See Cox & Kings Limited; *Int'l*, pg. 1823
SUPER BROADBAND NETWORK CO., LTD.—See Advanced Info Service Plc; *Int'l*, pg. 160
SUPERB SOUND CLARKSVILLE INC—See Superb Sound Inc.; *U.S. Private*, pg. 3875
SUPERB SOUND INC.; *U.S. Private*, pg. 3875
SUPERB SUMMIT INTERNATIONAL GROUP LIMITED; *Int'l*, pg. 7336
SUPER CAMPARICO PITUSA; *U.S. Private*, pg. 3874
SUPER CARE INC.; *U.S. Private*, pg. 3874
SUPERCART AUSTRALIA (PTY.) LTD.—See Supercart Plc; *Int'l*, pg. 7336
SUPERCART EUROPE LIMITED (GERMANY)—See Supercart Plc; *Int'l*, pg. 7336
SUPERCART PLC; *Int'l*, pg. 7336
SUPERCART SOUTH AFRICA (PTY.) LTD.—See Supercart Plc; *Int'l*, pg. 7336
SUPERCASE INTERNATIONAL CORPORATION—See Solytech Enterprise Corporation; *Int'l*, pg. 7083
THE SUPERCAT FAST FERRY CORPORATION—See SM Investments Corporation; *Int'l*, pg. 6998
SUPERCELL OY—See SoftBank Group Corp.; *Int'l*, pg. 7054
SUPER CENTER CONCEPTS INC.; *U.S. Private*, pg. 3874

SUPER CENTURY INVESTMENTS LIMITED; *Int'l*, pg. 7334
SUPER CERTAIN PTY. LTD.—See Kelly Partners Group Holdings Limited; *Int'l*, pg. 4121
SUPER CHANCE PROPERTIES PTE LTD—See Second Chance Properties Ltd.; *Int'l*, pg. 6672
SUPER CHEAP AUTO (NEW ZEALAND) PTY. LTD.—See Super Retail Group Limited; *Int'l*, pg. 7335
SUPER CHEAP AUTO PTY LTD.—See Super Retail Group Limited; *Int'l*, pg. 7335
SUPERCHECK GMBH—See Allianz SE; *Int'l*, pg. 351
SUPERCITY REALTY DEVELOPMENT CORPORATION; *Int'l*, pg. 7336
SUPERCLEAN BRANDS, LLC—See Wakefield Canada Inc.; *Int'l*, pg. 8332
SUPERCLICK, INC.—See AT&T Inc.; *U.S. Public*, pg. 220
SUPER CLUBS INTERNATIONAL LTD.; *Int'l*, pg. 7334
SUPER C MART INC.; *U.S. Private*, pg. 3874
SUPERCOMAL ADVANCED CABLE SDN. BHD.—See Supercomnet Technologies Berhad; *Int'l*, pg. 7336
SUPERCOMAL MEDICAL PRODUCTS SDN. BHD.—See Supercomnet Technologies Berhad; *Int'l*, pg. 7336
SUPERCOM LTD.; *Int'l*, pg. 7336
SUPERCOM LTD.—See SuperCom Ltd.; *Int'l*, pg. 7336
SUPERCOMM INC—See The Walt Disney Company; *U.S. Public*, pg. 2139
SUPERCOMNET TECHNOLOGIES BERHAD; *Int'l*, pg. 7336
SUPERCOR, S.A.—See El Corte Ingles, S.A.; *Int'l*, pg. 2340
SUPERCO SPECIALTY PRODUCTS—See Momar, Inc.; *U.S. Private*, pg. 2768
SUPERCO S.R.O.; *Int'l*, pg. 7336
SUPER CROP SAFE LIMITED; *Int'l*, pg. 7334
SUPERCUTS CORPORATE SHOPS, INC.—See Regis Corporation; *U.S. Public*, pg. 1777
SUPERCUTS, INC.—See Regis Corporation; *U.S. Public*, pg. 1777
SUPER DERIVATIVES INC.—See Intercontinental Exchange, Inc.; *U.S. Public*, pg. 1143
SUPERDIMENSION, INC.—See Medtronic plc; *Int'l*, pg. 4787
SUPER D, INC.; *U.S. Private*, pg. 3874
SUPERDIS SA—See Carrefour SA; *Int'l*, pg. 1346
SUPER DOLLAR DISCOUNT FOODS—See K-VA-T Food Stores, Inc.; *U.S. Private*, pg. 2251
SUPER-DRAGON ENGINEERING PLASTICS CO., LTD.; *Int'l*, pg. 7336
SUPER DRAGON TECHNOLOGY CO., LTD.; *Int'l*, pg. 7334
SUPERDRUG STORES PLC—See CK Hutchison Holdings Limited; *Int'l*, pg. 1636
SUPERDRY GERMANY GMBH—See Superdry PLC; *Int'l*, pg. 7337
SUPERDRY NORWAY A/S—See Superdry PLC; *Int'l*, pg. 7337
SUPERDRY PLC; *Int'l*, pg. 7337
SUPERDRY SWEDEN AB—See Superdry PLC; *Int'l*, pg. 7337
SUPER-ELECTRIC CONSTRUCTION CO.; *U.S. Private*, pg. 3875
SUPER ENERGY CORPORATION PUBLIC COMPANY LIMITED; *Int'l*, pg. 7334
SUPERFAST DEKA MC.—See Attica Group; *Int'l*, pg. 696
SUPER FASTENING SYSTEM (SHANGHAI) CO., LTD.; *Int'l*, pg. 7334
SUPERFAST FERRIES SINGLE MEMBER MARITIME S.A.—See Attica Group; *Int'l*, pg. 696
SUPER FINE KNITTERS LIMITED; *Int'l*, pg. 7334
SUPERFLEX, LTD.—See Alexander Forbes Group Holdings Limited; *Int'l*, pg. 307
SUPER-FLITE OIL CO. INC.; *U.S. Private*, pg. 3875
SUPERFLOORS INC.; *U.S. Private*, pg. 3875
SUPERFLOW TECHNOLOGIES GROUP; *U.S. Private*, pg. 3875
SUPERFLY MANUFACTURING CO.; *U.S. Private*, pg. 3875
SUPER FRESH COMPANY—See The Great Atlantic & Pacific Tea Company, Inc.; *U.S. Private*, pg. 4038
SUPERFRIO ARMAZENS GERIAS S.A.—See Americold Realty Trust, Inc.; *U.S. Public*, pg. 113
SUPERFUND GOLD, L.P.; *Int'l*, pg. 7337
SUPERFUND GREEN, L.P.; *Int'l*, pg. 7337
SUPER FUNWORLD PTE LTD—See Hiap Hoe Limited; *Int'l*, pg. 3382
SUPERGARANT VERZEKERINGEN B.V.—See ASR Nederland N.V.; *Int'l*, pg. 632
SUPER GARDEN CENTERS, INC.; *U.S. Private*, pg. 3874
SUPERGASBRAS DISTRIBUIDORA DE GAS S.A.—See SHV Holdings N.V.; *Int'l*, pg. 6873
SUPER GAS COMPANY LIMITED—See Siamgas and Petrochemicals Public Company Limited; *Int'l*, pg. 6876
SUPERGAS ENERGY LTD.; *Int'l*, pg. 7337
SUPERGAS ISRAEL GAS DISTRIBUTION CO. LTD—See Azrieli Group Ltd.; *Int'l*, pg. 781
SUPER GENERAL TRADING CO. LLC—See Bhatia Brothers Group; *Int'l*, pg. 1014
SUPERGLASS DAMMSTOFFE GMBH—See Compagnie de Saint-Gobain SA; *Int'l*, pg. 1726

SUPERGLASS INSULATION LTD.—See Inflection Management Corporation Limited; *Int'l*, pg. 3688
SUPERGLASS S.A.—See CRH plc; *Int'l*, pg. 1848
SUPER GLUE CORPORATION—See AC MARCA, S.A; *Int'l*, pg. 74
SUPERGREEN SOLUTIONS SDN. BHD.—See Selangor Dredging Berhad; *Int'l*, pg. 6699
SUPER GRIP CORPORATION—See TVS Srichakra Ltd; *Int'l*, pg. 7989
SUPERGROS A/S—See NorgesGruppen ASA; *Int'l*, pg. 5427
SUPERGROUP INTERNET LIMITED—See Superdry PLC; *Int'l*, pg. 7337
SUPER GROUP LIMITED; *Int'l*, pg. 7334
SUPER GROUP LTD.—See JAB Holding Company S.a.r.l.; *Int'l*, pg. 3863
SUPERGROUP RETAIL IRELAND LIMITED—See Superdry PLC; *Int'l*, pg. 7337
SUPERHERO CHEESECAKE B.V.—See S4 Capital plc; *Int'l*, pg. 6458
SUPERHEROSTUFF.COM—See eMerchandise Group LLC; *U.S. Private*, pg. 1380
SUPERHOME CENTER (DIY) LTD—See N.K. Shacolas (Holdings) Ltd.; *Int'l*, pg. 5116
SUPERHOUSE GMBH—See Superhouse Limited; *Int'l*, pg. 7337
SUPERHOUSE LIMITED - ACCESSORIES FACTORY NO.1—See Superhouse Limited; *Int'l*, pg. 7337
SUPERHOUSE LIMITED - BREECHES DIVISION—See Superhouse Limited; *Int'l*, pg. 7337
SUPERHOUSE LIMITED - FINISHED LEATHER FACILITY—See Superhouse Limited; *Int'l*, pg. 7337
SUPERHOUSE LIMITED - FOOTWEAR DIVISION - III—See Superhouse Limited; *Int'l*, pg. 7337
SUPERHOUSE LIMITED - FOOTWEAR DIVISION - I—See Superhouse Limited; *Int'l*, pg. 7337
SUPERHOUSE LIMITED - LEATHER GARMENT DIVISION - I—See Superhouse Limited; *Int'l*, pg. 7337
SUPERHOUSE LIMITED - SAFETY FOOTWEAR DIVISION - I—See Superhouse Limited; *Int'l*, pg. 7337
SUPERHOUSE LIMITED; *Int'l*, pg. 7337
SUPERHOUSE MIDDLE EAST FZC—See Superhouse Limited; *Int'l*, pg. 7337
SUPERHOUSE (U.K.) LTD.—See Superhouse Limited; *Int'l*, pg. 7337
SUPERHOUSE (USA) INTERNATIONAL INC.—See Superhouse Limited; *Int'l*, pg. 7337
SUPERIA N.V.—See Proventus AB; *Int'l*, pg. 6007
SUPERIA RADIATOREN, N.V.—See Vaessen Industries nv; *Int'l*, pg. 8108
SUPERINOX PIPE INDUSTRY SDN. BHD.—See Ingenieur Gudang Berhad; *Int'l*, pg. 3701
SUPERION PUBLIC SECTOR, LLC—See Vista Equity Partners, LLC; *U.S. Private*, pg. 4395
SUPERIOR ACCESS INSURANCE SERVICES, INC.—See CVC Capital Partners SICAV-FIS S.A.; *Int'l*, pg. 1885
SUPERIOR ADSORBENTS, INC.—See Oxbow Corporation; *U.S. Private*, pg. 3056
SUPERIOR AG RESOURCES CO-OP, INC.; *U.S. Private*, pg. 3875
SUPERIOR AG RESOURCES CO-OP—See Superior Ag Resources Co-op, Inc.; *U.S. Private*, pg. 3875
SUPERIOR AG RESOURCES CO-OP—See Superior Ag Resources Co-op, Inc.; *U.S. Private*, pg. 3875
SUPERIOR AG RESOURCES CO-OP—See Superior Ag Resources Co-op, Inc.; *U.S. Private*, pg. 3875
SUPERIOR AG RESOURCES CO-OP—See Superior Ag Resources Co-op, Inc.; *U.S. Private*, pg. 3875
SUPERIOR AIR HANDLING CORPORATION—See Harris Companies; *U.S. Private*, pg. 1869
SUPERIOR AIR PARTS INC.; *U.S. Private*, pg. 3875
SUPERIOR ALLOY TECHNOLOGY CO; *Int'l*, pg. 7337
SUPERIOR AMBULANCE SERVICE, INC.; *U.S. Private*, pg. 3875
SUPERIOR ASPHALT INC.—See W.G. Yates & Sons Construction Company; *U.S. Private*, pg. 4420
SUPERIOR AUTO GROUP; *U.S. Private*, pg. 3876
SUPERIOR AUTO, INC.—See Parallel Investment Partners LLC; *U.S. Private*, pg. 3092
SUPERIOR AUTO MALL—See Superior Auto Group; *U.S. Private*, pg. 3876
SUPERIOR AUTOMATIC SPRINKLER CO.; *U.S. Private*, pg. 3876
SUPERIOR AUTOMOTIVE; *U.S. Private*, pg. 3876
SUPERIOR BOWEN ASPHALT COMPANY—See Clarkson Construction Company; *U.S. Private*, pg. 915
SUPERIOR BULK LOGISTICS, INC.—See Heniff Transportation Systems Inc.; *U.S. Private*, pg. 1916
SUPERIOR CABINETS.; *Int'l*, pg. 7337
SUPERIOR CABLES USA LTD.—See The Alpine Group, Inc.; *U.S. Private*, pg. 3984
SUPERIOR CAKE PRODUCTS, INC.—See KKR & Co. Inc.; *U.S. Public*, pg. 1263
SUPERIOR CANS & PAILS CONTAINERS (PUNE) PRIVATE LIMITED—See Crown Holdings, Inc.; *U.S. Public*, pg. 599
SUPERIOR CAPITAL PARTNERS LLC; *U.S. Private*, pg. 3876
SUPERIOR CARE PHARMACY, INC.—See CVS Health Corporation; *U.S. Public*, pg. 616

COMPANY NAME INDEX

SUPERIOR CARRIERS, INC.—See Heniff Transportation Systems Inc.; *U.S. Private*, pg. 1916
SUPERIOR (CHENGDU) MULTI-PACKAGING CO., LTD.—See Crown Holdings, Inc.; *U.S. Public*, pg. 599
SUPERIOR CHOICE CREDIT UNION; *U.S. Private*, pg. 3876
SUPERIOR COMMUNICATIONS PRODUCTS; *U.S. Private*, pg. 3876
SUPERIOR COMPANIES INC.; *U.S. Private*, pg. 3876
SUPERIOR COMPANIES-MANUFACTURING DIVISION—See Superior Companies Inc.; *U.S. Private*, pg. 3876
SUPERIOR CONCRETE FENCE OF TEXAS; *U.S. Private*, pg. 3876
SUPERIOR CONCRETE MATERIALS, INC.—See Vulcan Materials Company; *U.S. Public*, pg. 2314
SUPERIOR CONSTRUCTION CO., INC.; *U.S. Private*, pg. 3876
SUPERIOR CONTROLS, INC.—See The Graham Group, Inc.; *U.S. Private*, pg. 4036
SUPERIOR CONTROLS, INC.—See Lincoln Electric Holdings, Inc.; *U.S. Public*, pg. 1318
SUPERIOR DAIRY, INC.; *U.S. Private*, pg. 3876
SUPERIOR DATA SOLUTIONS INC.—See Recast Software Inc.; *U.S. Private*, pg. 3370
SUPERIOR DENTAL CARE ALLIANCE, INC.; *U.S. Private*, pg. 3876
SUPERIOR DESHLER INC.; *U.S. Private*, pg. 3876
SUPERIOR DESIGN INTERNATIONAL, INC.; *U.S. Private*, pg. 3876
SUPERIOR DIE SET CORP.; *U.S. Private*, pg. 3876
SUPERIOR DIGITAL DISPLAYS, LLC—See PennantPark Investment Corporation; *U.S. Public*, pg. 1663
SUPERIOR DISTRIBUTING CO., INC.; *U.S. Private*, pg. 3876
SUPERIOR DISTRIBUTION COMPANY—See Leonard Green & Partners, L.P.; *U.S. Private*, pg. 2429
SUPERIOR DISTRIBUTION OF INDIANAPOLIS; *U.S. Private*, pg. 3876
SUPERIOR DISTRIBUTORS OF CHICAGO—See Superior Distribution of Indianapolis; *U.S. Private*, pg. 3876
SUPERIOR DOCUMENT SERVICE INC.—See Pivotal Acquisition Corp.; *U.S. Private*, pg. 3192
SUPERIOR DRILLING PRODUCTS, INC.—See Drilling Tools International Corp.; *U.S. Public*, pg. 688
SUPERIOR DRILLING SOLUTIONS, LLC—See Drilling Tools International Corp.; *U.S. Public*, pg. 688
SUPERIOR DRILLPIPE MANUFACTURING—See Texas Steel Conversion, Inc.; *U.S. Private*, pg. 3977
SUPERIOR EAST, INC.—See Superior Products Distributors Inc.; *U.S. Private*, pg. 3880
SUPERIOR ECONOMIC MED PRODUCTS CO.; *U.S. Private*, pg. 3876
SUPERIOR ELECTRIC HOLDING GROUP LLC—See Fortive Corporation; *U.S. Public*, pg. 872
SUPERIOR ENERGY MANAGEMENT ELECTRICITY LP—See Superior Plus Corp.; *Int'l*, pg. 7338
SUPERIOR ENERGY SERVICES (AUSTRALIA) PTY. LTD.—See Superior Energy Services, Inc.; *U.S. Private*, pg. 3877
SUPERIOR ENERGY SERVICES DO BRASIL—See Superior Energy Services, Inc.; *U.S. Private*, pg. 3877
SUPERIOR ENERGY SERVICES, INC.; *U.S. Private*, pg. 3877
SUPERIOR ENERGY SERVICES—See Superior Energy Services, Inc.; *U.S. Private*, pg. 3877
SUPERIOR ENERGY SERVICES (SPN) B.V.—See Superior Energy Services, Inc.; *U.S. Private*, pg. 3877
SUPERIOR ENGINEERED PRODUCTS CORP—See Kenner & Company, Inc.; *U.S. Private*, pg. 2285
SUPERIOR ENGINEERED PRODUCTS CORP.—See North Cove Partners; *U.S. Private*, pg. 2944
SUPERIOR ENVIRONMENTAL SOLUTIONS, LLC—See Palladium Equity Partners, LLC; *U.S. Private*, pg. 3078
SUPERIOR EQUIPMENT PTY LTD—See Alamo Group Inc.; *U.S. Public*, pg. 71
SUPERIOR EQUIPMENT SALES INC.; *U.S. Private*, pg. 3877
SUPERIOR EQUIPMENT SOLUTIONS; *U.S. Private*, pg. 3877
SUPERIOR ESSEX, INC.—See LS Corp.; *Int'l*, pg. 4569
SUPERIOR ESSEX INTERNATIONAL LP—See LS Corp.; *Int'l*, pg. 4569
SUPERIOR FABRICATION COMPANY, LLC—See Reserve Group Management Company; *U.S. Private*, pg. 3405
SUPERIOR FABRICATION, INC.; *U.S. Private*, pg. 3878
SUPERIOR FABRICATION, INC.—See First Reserve Management, L.P.; *U.S. Private*, pg. 1526
SUPERIOR FABRICS, INC.; *U.S. Private*, pg. 3878
SUPERIOR FELT & FILTRATION LLC; *U.S. Private*, pg. 3878
SUPERIOR FINANCE COMPANY—See Arvest Bank Group, Inc.; *U.S. Private*, pg. 344
SUPERIOR FINANCIAL SERVICES, INC.—See First Horizon Corporation; *U.S. Public*, pg. 844
SUPERIOR FINLEASE LIMITED; *Int'l*, pg. 7337
SUPERIOR FOOD GROUP PTY LTD—See Quadrant Private Equity Pty. Ltd.; *Int'l*, pg. 6149

SUPERIOR FOODS COMPANY INC.; *U.S. Private*, pg. 3878
SUPERIOR FOODS INTERNATIONAL, LLC—See Viru SA; *Int'l*, pg. 8249
SUPERIOR FORGE & STEEL CORPORATION - NEW CASTLE—See Superior Forge & Steel Corporation; *U.S. Private*, pg. 3878
SUPERIOR FORGE & STEEL CORPORATION; *U.S. Private*, pg. 3878
SUPERIOR FREIGHT SERVICES INC.; *U.S. Private*, pg. 3878
SUPERIOR FUEL COMPANY; *U.S. Private*, pg. 3878
SUPERIOR FUELS, INC.; *U.S. Private*, pg. 3878
SUPERIOR FURNITURE SOLUTIONS, INC.—See One80 Intermediaries LLC; *U.S. Private*, pg. 3024
SUPERIOR GAS LIQUIDS PARTNERSHIP—See Superior Plus Corp.; *Int'l*, pg. 7338
SUPERIOR GENERAL PARTNER INC.—See Superior Plus Corp.; *Int'l*, pg. 7338
SUPERIOR GOLD, INC.—See Catalyst Metals Limited; *Int'l*, pg. 1358
SUPERIOR GRAPHITE CO.; *U.S. Private*, pg. 3878
SUPERIOR GRAPHITE EUROPE, LTD.—See Superior Graphite Co.; *U.S. Private*, pg. 3878
SUPERIOR GROUP, INC.; *U.S. Private*, pg. 3878
SUPERIOR GROUP OF COMPANIES, INC.; *U.S. Public*, pg. 1966
SUPERIOR GROUP; *U.S. Private*, pg. 3878
SUPERIOR GUNITE INCORPORATED; *U.S. Private*, pg. 3878
SUPERIOR HARDWOODS INC.—See J.T. Shannon Lumber Inc.; *U.S. Private*, pg. 2171
SUPERIOR HEALTH LINENS, LLC.—See York Capital Management Global Advisors, LLC; *U.S. Private*, pg. 4590
SUPERIOR HEALTHPLAN COMMUNITY SOLUTIONS, INC.—See Centene Corporation; *U.S. Public*, pg. 470
SUPERIOR HEALTHPLAN INC.—See Centene Corporation; *U.S. Public*, pg. 470
SUPERIOR HOLDING CORP; *U.S. Private*, pg. 3878
SUPERIOR HONDA OF OMAHA; *U.S. Private*, pg. 3878
SUPERIOR IMAGING GROUP, INC.—See Vomela Specialty Company; *U.S. Private*, pg. 4412
SUPERIOR INDUSTRIAL ENTERPRISES LIMITED; *Int'l*, pg. 7337
SUPERIOR INDUSTRIAL MAINTENANCE COMPANY, LLC—See Warren Equity Partners, LLC; *U.S. Private*, pg. 4443
SUPERIOR INDUSTRIES AUTOMOTIVE GERMANY GMBH—See SUPERIOR INDUSTRIES INTERNATIONAL INC; *U.S. Public*, pg. 1967
SUPERIOR INDUSTRIES DE MEXICO, S.A. DE C.V.—See SUPERIOR INDUSTRIES INTERNATIONAL INC; *U.S. Public*, pg. 1967
SUPERIOR INDUSTRIES EUROPE AG—See SUPERIOR INDUSTRIES INTERNATIONAL INC; *U.S. Public*, pg. 1967
SUPERIOR INDUSTRIES-FAYETTEVILLE—See SUPERIOR INDUSTRIES INTERNATIONAL INC; *U.S. Public*, pg. 1967
SUPERIOR INDUSTRIES, INC.; *U.S. Private*, pg. 3878
SUPERIOR INDUSTRIES INTERNATIONAL INC; *U.S. Public*, pg. 1966
SUPERIOR INDUSTRIES INTERNATIONAL KANSAS, LLC—See SUPERIOR INDUSTRIES INTERNATIONAL INC; *U.S. Public*, pg. 1967
SUPERIOR INDUSTRIES INTERNATIONAL MICHIGAN, LLC—See SUPERIOR INDUSTRIES INTERNATIONAL INC; *U.S. Public*, pg. 1967
SUPERIOR INDUSTRIES LEICHTMETALLRADER GERMANY GMBH—See SUPERIOR INDUSTRIES INTERNATIONAL INC; *U.S. Public*, pg. 1967
SUPERIOR INDUSTRIES PRODUCTION GERMANY GMBH—See SUPERIOR INDUSTRIES INTERNATIONAL INC; *U.S. Public*, pg. 1967
SUPERIOR INDUSTRIES-SOUTHFIELD—See SUPERIOR INDUSTRIES INTERNATIONAL INC; *U.S. Public*, pg. 1967
SUPERIOR INSULATION, LLC—See Installed Building Products, Inc.; *U.S. Public*, pg. 1133
SUPERIOR INSULATION SERVICES, LLC—See Installed Building Products, Inc.; *U.S. Public*, pg. 1133
SUPERIOR INTERNATIONAL INDUSTRIES INC.—See Pfingsten Partners, LLC; *U.S. Private*, pg. 3164
SUPERIOR INTERNET SOLUTIONS; *U.S. Private*, pg. 3878
SUPERIOR INVESTMENT HOLDINGS PTE. LTD.—See Crown Holdings, Inc.; *U.S. Public*, pg. 599
SUPERIOR INVESTMENTS HOLDINGS PTE LTD—See Crown Holdings, Inc.; *U.S. Public*, pg. 599
SUPERIOR IRON WORKS INC.; *U.S. Private*, pg. 3878
SUPERIOR KILNS, INC.—See Midwest Hardwood Corporation; *U.S. Private*, pg. 2721
SUPERIOR (LANGFANG) MULTI-PACKAGING CO., LTD.—See Crown Holdings, Inc.; *U.S. Public*, pg. 599
SUPERIOR LINEN SERVICE INC.; *U.S. Private*, pg. 3878
SUPERIOR LOGISTICS SOLUTIONS LLC; *U.S. Private*, pg. 3878

SUPERIOR PRODUCTS, LLC.

SUPERIOR LUBRICANTS COMPANY; *U.S. Private*, pg. 3878
SUPERIOR MACHINE COMPANY DIVISION—See Woodings Industrial Corporation; *U.S. Private*, pg. 4558
SUPERIOR MACHINE COMPANY OF SOUTH CAROLINA, INC.—See Woodings Industrial Corporation; *U.S. Private*, pg. 4558
SUPERIOR MANUFACTURING GROUP EUROPE BV—See Audax Group, Limited Partnership; *U.S. Private*, pg. 387
SUPERIOR MATERIALS, INC.—See Vulcan Materials Company; *U.S. Public*, pg. 2314
SUPERIOR MATERIALS, INC.; *U.S. Private*, pg. 3879
SUPERIOR MECHANICAL SYSTEMS, INC.; *U.S. Private*, pg. 3879
SUPERIOR MEDIA SOLUTIONS LLC; *U.S. Private*, pg. 3879
SUPERIOR METAL FINISHING, INC.—See Aterian Investment Management, L.P.; *U.S. Private*, pg. 367
SUPERIOR METAL PRINTING (HUIYANG) CO., LTD.—See Crown Holdings, Inc.; *U.S. Public*, pg. 599
SUPERIOR METAL PRODUCTS CO.; *U.S. Private*, pg. 3879
SUPERIOR MIDSTREAM, LLC; *U.S. Private*, pg. 3879
SUPERIOR MINERALS COMPANY—See Carmeuse Holding SA; *Int'l*, pg. 1342
SUPERIOR MINING INTERNATIONAL CORPORATION; *Int'l*, pg. 7337
SUPERIOR MOTORS INC.; *U.S. Private*, pg. 3879
SUPERIOR MULTI-PACKAGING LIMITED—See Crown Holdings, Inc.; *U.S. Public*, pg. 599
SUPERIOR MULTI-PACKAGING (VIETNAM) CO., LTD—See Crown Holdings, Inc.; *U.S. Public*, pg. 599
SUPERIOR NATIONAL BANK & TRUST COMPANY; *U.S. Private*, pg. 3879
SUPERIOR NATURAL GAS CORP.; *U.S. Private*, pg. 3879
SUPERIOR NUT AND CANDY CO.; *U.S. Private*, pg. 3879
SUPERIOR OIL CO., INC. - CINCINNATI PLANT—See Superior Oil Co., Inc.; *U.S. Private*, pg. 3879
SUPERIOR OIL CO., INC. - COWPENS PLANT—See Superior Oil Co., Inc.; *U.S. Private*, pg. 3879
SUPERIOR OIL CO., INC. - EFFINGHAM PLANT—See Superior Oil Co., Inc.; *U.S. Private*, pg. 3879
SUPERIOR OIL CO., INC. - ELKHART PLANT—See Superior Oil Co., Inc.; *U.S. Private*, pg. 3879
SUPERIOR OIL CO., INC. - INDIANAPOLIS PLANT—See Superior Oil Co., Inc.; *U.S. Private*, pg. 3879
SUPERIOR OIL CO., INC. - LOUISVILLE PLANT—See Superior Oil Co., Inc.; *U.S. Private*, pg. 3879
SUPERIOR OIL CO., INC. - NASHVILLE PLANT—See Superior Oil Co., Inc.; *U.S. Private*, pg. 3879
SUPERIOR OIL CO., INC.; *U.S. Private*, pg. 3879
SUPERIOR OIL CO., INC. - SPRINGFIELD PLANT—See Superior Oil Co., Inc.; *U.S. Private*, pg. 3879
SUPERIOR OIL CO., INC. - ST. LOUIS PLANT—See Superior Oil Co., Inc.; *U.S. Private*, pg. 3879
SUPERIOR OIL FIELD SERVICES L.L.C.—See Gulf Petroleum Investment Co. S.A.K.C.; *Int'l*, pg. 3182
SUPERIOR ORTHOTICS & PROSTHETICS, LLC—See Patient Square Capital, L.P.; *U.S. Private*, pg. 3107
SUPERIOR PACKAGING INC.; *U.S. Private*, pg. 3879
SUPERIOR PACKAGING INC.; *U.S. Private*, pg. 3879
SUPERIOR PACKAGING SOLUTIONS; *U.S. Private*, pg. 3879
SUPERIOR PETROLEUM COMPANY; *U.S. Private*, pg. 3879
SUPERIOR PLATING TECHNOLOGY CO., LTD.; *Int'l*, pg. 7337
SUPERIOR PLUS CORP.; *Int'l*, pg. 7337
SUPERIOR PLUS ENERGY SERVICES INC.—See Superior Plus Corp.; *Int'l*, pg. 7338
SUPERIOR PLUS LP—See Superior Plus Corp.; *Int'l*, pg. 7338
SUPERIOR PLUS PROPANE—See Superior Plus Corp.; *Int'l*, pg. 7338
SUPERIOR POOL PRODUCTS, INC.—See Pool Corporation; *U.S. Public*, pg. 1702
SUPERIOR POOLS OF SOUTHWEST FLORIDA INC.; *U.S. Private*, pg. 3879
SUPERIOR PRESS, INC.; *U.S. Private*, pg. 3879
SUPERIOR PRINT & EXHIBIT, INC.; *U.S. Private*, pg. 3879
SUPERIOR PRINTING INK COMPANY INCORPORATED; *U.S. Private*, pg. 3880
SUPERIOR PROCESSING SERVICE CORPORATION—See Superior Natural Gas Corp.; *U.S. Private*, pg. 3879
SUPERIOR PRODUCTION LLC; *U.S. Private*, pg. 3880
SUPERIOR PRODUCTION LLC - STAMPING DIVISION—See Superior Production LLC; *U.S. Private*, pg. 3880
SUPERIOR PRODUCTS DISTRIBUTORS INC.; *U.S. Private*, pg. 3880
SUPERIOR PRODUCTS, LLC.; *U.S. Private*, pg. 3880
SUPERIOR PROPANE INC.—See Superior Plus Corp.; *Int'l*, pg. 7338
SUPERIOR PUBLISHING, INC.—See American Consolidated Media LP; *U.S. Private*, pg. 228

SUPERIOR PRODUCTS, LLC.

SUPERIOR READY MIX CONCRETE LP - AGUANGA PLANT—See Superior Ready Mix Concrete LP; *U.S. Private*, pg. 3880
SUPERIOR READY MIX CONCRETE LP - CARROLL CANYON PLANT—See Superior Ready Mix Concrete LP; *U.S. Private*, pg. 3880
SUPERIOR READY MIX CONCRETE LP - COACHELLA PLANT—See Superior Ready Mix Concrete LP; *U.S. Private*, pg. 3880
SUPERIOR READY MIX CONCRETE LP - EL CENTRO PLANT—See Superior Ready Mix Concrete LP; *U.S. Private*, pg. 3880
SUPERIOR READY MIX CONCRETE LP - FALLBROOK PLANT—See Superior Ready Mix Concrete LP; *U.S. Private*, pg. 3880
SUPERIOR READY MIX CONCRETE LP - HEMET (BCC) PLANT—See Superior Ready Mix Concrete LP; *U.S. Private*, pg. 3880
SUPERIOR READY MIX CONCRETE LP - OCEANSIDE PLANT—See Superior Ready Mix Concrete LP; *U.S. Private*, pg. 3880
SUPERIOR READY MIX CONCRETE LP - RAMONA PLANT—See Superior Ready Mix Concrete LP; *U.S. Private*, pg. 3880
SUPERIOR READY MIX CONCRETE LP; *U.S. Private*, pg. 3880
SUPERIOR READY MIX CONCRETE LP - SOUTHLAND PLANT—See Superior Ready Mix Concrete LP; *U.S. Private*, pg. 3880
SUPERIOR RESOURCE GROUP, INC.—See NSC Technologies, Inc.; *U.S. Private*, pg. 2970
SUPERIOR RESOURCES LIMITED; *Int'l*, pg. 7338
SUPERIOR ROLL FORMING CO., INC.; *U.S. Private*, pg. 3880
SUPERIOR'S BRAND MEATS—See Fresh Mark, Inc.; *U.S. Private*, pg. 1610
SUPERIOR SEWING MACHINE & SUPPLY LLC; *U.S. Private*, pg. 3880
SUPERIOR SIGNALS, INC.—See Group Thermote & Vanhalst; *Int'l*, pg. 3090
SUPERIOR SPECIALTIES, INC.—See The Van Hoof Companies; *U.S. Private*, pg. 4130
SUPERIOR SPRING COMPANY—See Illinois Tool Works Inc.; *U.S. Public*, pg. 1111
SUPERIOR STEEL INC.; *U.S. Private*, pg. 3880
SUPERIOR STORAGE LIMITED—See Iron Mountain Incorporated; *U.S. Public*, pg. 1174
SUPERIOR SUPPLY CO., INC.—See Kelso & Company, L.P.; *U.S. Private*, pg. 2279
SUPERIOR SUPPLY CO., INC.—See Warburg Pincus LLC; *U.S. Private*, pg. 4437
SUPERIOR SUPPLY & STEEL; *U.S. Private*, pg. 3880
SUPERIOR SUPPORT RESOURCES, INC.; *U.S. Private*, pg. 3880
SUPERIOR SYSTEMS & TECHNOLOGIES, LLP.—See Mission Critical Group; *U.S. Private*, pg. 2747
SUPERIOR TANK CO., INC.; *U.S. Private*, pg. 3880
SUPERIOR TECHNICAL CERAMICS CORP.—See Artemis Capital Partners Management Co., LLC; *U.S. Private*, pg. 341
SUPERIOR TECHNOLOGY CORP; *U.S. Private*, pg. 3880
SUPERIOR (TIANJIN) MULTI-PACKAGING CO., LTD.—See Crown Holdings, Inc.; *U.S. Public*, pg. 599
SUPERIOR TIRE SERVICE INC.; *U.S. Private*, pg. 3880
SUPERIOR TOOL CORPORATION; *U.S. Private*, pg. 3880
SUPERIOR TRAVELLERS SERVICES LIMITED—See King Fook Holdings Limited; *Int'l*, pg. 4168
SUPERIOR TRIM & DOOR, INC.; *U.S. Private*, pg. 3880
SUPERIOR TRUCKING SERVICES—See First Reserve Management, L.P.; *U.S. Private*, pg. 1526
SUPERIOR TRUSS SYSTEMS, LLC.; *U.S. Private*, pg. 3880
SUPERIOR TUBE COMPANY INC.—See AMETEK, Inc.; *U.S. Public*, pg. 116
SUPERIOR TUBING TESTERS, LLC—See Forbes Energy Services Ltd.; *U.S. Public*, pg. 864
SUPERIOR UNIFORM GROUP, INC. - MARTIN'S UNIFORMS DIVISION—See Superior Group Of Companies, Inc.; *U.S. Public*, pg. 1966
SUPERIOR UNIFORM GROUP, INC. - SHANE UNIFORMS DIVISION—See Superior Group Of Companies, Inc.; *U.S. Public*, pg. 1966
SUPERIOR UNIFORM GROUP, INC. - WORKLON DIVISION—See Superior Group Of Companies, Inc.; *U.S. Public*, pg. 1966
SUPERIOR URANIUM PTY. LTD.—See Deep Yellow Limited; *Int'l*, pg. 2002
SUPERIOR VAN & MOBILITY, LLC.; *U.S. Private*, pg. 3881
SUPERIOR VISION OF NEW JERSEY, INC.—See MetLife, Inc.; *U.S. Public*, pg. 1431
SUPERIOR VISION SERVICES, INC.—See Centerbridge Partners, L.P.; *U.S. Private*, pg. 816
SUPERIOR WASHER & GASKET CORP.; *U.S. Private*, pg. 3881
SUPERIOR WASTE INDUSTRIES LLC; *U.S. Private*, pg. 3881
SUPERIOR WATER, LIGHT & POWER COMPANY—See ALLETE, Inc.; *U.S. Public*, pg. 79

SUPERIOR-WILD WELL ENERGY SERVICES LIMITED—See Superior Energy Services, Inc.; *U.S. Private*, pg. 3877
SUPERIOR WOOD TREATING—See Manke Lumber Company, Inc.; *U.S. Private*, pg. 2564
SUPER JUMBO CORPORATION—See Kimura-Unity Co., Ltd.; *Int'l*, pg. 4164
SUPER KIAN HOLDINGS SDN. BHD.—See Harvest Miracle Capital Berhad; *Int'l*, pg. 3281
SUPER-KRETE PRODUCTS—See Audax Group, Limited Partnership; *U.S. Private*, pg. 388
SUPERLAND GROUP HOLDINGS LIMITED; *Int'l*, pg. 7338
SUPER LAUNDRY EQUIPMENT CORP.—See Pamplona Capital Management LLP; *Int'l*, pg. 5711
SUPER LEAGUE ENTERPRISE, INC.; *U.S. Public*, pg. 1966
SUPERLIFE LIMITED—See NZX Limited; *Int'l*, pg. 5502
SUPERLINK LOGISTICS (SHENZHEN) CO., LTD.—See Jardine Matheson Holdings Limited; *Int'l*, pg. 3908
SUPERLON HOLDINGS BERHAD; *Int'l*, pg. 7338
SUPERLON WORLDWIDE SDN BHD.—See Superlon Holdings Berhad; *Int'l*, pg. 7338
SUPERLOOP LIMITED; *Int'l*, pg. 7338
SUPER LOW FOODS—See Wayfield Foods Inc.; *U.S. Private*, pg. 4459
SUPERMAN RESOURCES INC; *Int'l*, pg. 7338
SUPERMAP JAPAN CO., LTD.—See SuperMap Software Co., Ltd.; *Int'l*, pg. 7338
SUPERMAP SOFTWARE CO., LTD.; *Int'l*, pg. 7338
SUPERMARKET DISTRIBUTORS OF AMERICA; *U.S. Private*, pg. 3881
SUPERMARKET ENVIRONMENTAL SERVICES CO.; *U.S. Private*, pg. 3881
SUPERMARKET INCOME REIT PLC; *Int'l*, pg. 7339
SUPERMARKET MANAGEMENT INC.; *U.S. Private*, pg. 3881
SUPERMARKET NEWS—See Informa plc; *Int'l*, pg. 3692
SUPERMARKET OPERATIONS INC.; *U.S. Private*, pg. 3881
SUPERMARKET OPERATORS OF AMERICA INC.—See United Natural Foods, Inc.; *U.S. Public*, pg. 2232
SUPERMARKET SOURCE; *U.S. Private*, pg. 3881
SUPERMASSA DO BRASIL LTDA.—See Sika AG; *Int'l*, pg. 6918
SUPERMAX CORPORATION BERHAD; *Int'l*, pg. 7339
SUPERMAX GLOBAL (HK) LIMITED—See Supermax Corporation Berhad; *Int'l*, pg. 7339
SUPERMAX HEALTHCARE CANADA INCORPORATED—See Supermax Corporation Berhad; *Int'l*, pg. 7339
SUPERMAX HEALTHCARE INCORPORATED—See Supermax Corporation Berhad; *Int'l*, pg. 7339
SUPERMAX HEALTHCARE LIMITED—See Supermax Corporation Berhad; *Int'l*, pg. 7339
SUPERMEC MIDDLE EAST FZE—See Rotary Engineering Pte. Ltd.; *Int'l*, pg. 6402
SUPERMEC (M) SDN. BHD.—See Rotary Engineering Pte. Ltd.; *Int'l*, pg. 6402
SUPERMEC PROIZVODNJA IN PRODAJA ELEKTRONIKE D.O.O.—See Rotary Engineering Pte. Ltd.; *Int'l*, pg. 6402
SUPERMEC PTE. LTD.—See Rotary Engineering Pte. Ltd.; *Int'l*, pg. 6402
SUPERMEC VIETNAM CO. LTD.—See Rotary Engineering Pte. Ltd.; *Int'l*, pg. 6402
SUPERMERCADO AGUEYBANA INC.; *U.S. Private*, pg. 3881
SUPERMERCADO CONCHITA HATO REY; *U.S. Private*, pg. 3881
SUPERMERCADO FACUNDO INC.; *U.S. Private*, pg. 3881
SUPERMERCADO PLAZA GUAYAMA; *U.S. Private*, pg. 3881
SUPERMERCADOS DEL ESTE INC.; *U.S. Private*, pg. 3881
SUPERMERCADOS LA FAVORITA C.A.; *Int'l*, pg. 7339
SUPER MICRO COMPUTER B.V.—See Super Micro Computer, Inc.; *U.S. Public*, pg. 1966
SUPER MICRO COMPUTER, INC.; *U.S. Public*, pg. 1966
SUPER MICRO COMPUTER TAIWAN INC.—See Super Micro Computer, Inc.; *U.S. Public*, pg. 1966
SUPERMICRO KK—See Super Micro Computer, Inc.; *U.S. Public*, pg. 1966
SUPERMICRO TECHNOLOGY (BEIJING) CO., LTD.—See Super Micro Computer, Inc.; *U.S. Public*, pg. 1966
SUPERMIX, INC.; *U.S. Private*, pg. 3881
SUPERM&N UG—See Stroer SE & Co. KGaA; *Int'l*, pg. 7242
SUPERMOON HOLDINGS LTD.—See Sonepar S.A.; *Int'l*, pg. 7094
SUPERMOON LTD—See Sonepar S.A.; *Int'l*, pg. 7091
SUPERNAIL—See American International Industries Company; *U.S. Private*, pg. 238
SUPERNET E-SOLUTIONS (PVT.) LIMITED—See TELECARD LIMITED; *Int'l*, pg. 7529
SUPERNET INFRASTRUCTURE SOLUTIONS (PVT.) LTD.—See TELECARD LIMITED; *Int'l*, pg. 7529

CORPORATE AFFILIATIONS

SUPERNET LIMITED—See TELECARD LIMITED; *Int'l*, pg. 7529
SUPERNOVA ADVERTISING LIMITED; *Int'l*, pg. 7339
SUPERNOVA ENERGY, INC.; *U.S. Private*, pg. 3881
SUPERNOVA METALS, CORP.; *Int'l*, pg. 7339
SUPERNOVA PERFORMANCE TECHNOLOGIES LTD.—See Sparta Capital Ltd.; *Int'l*, pg. 7127
SUPERNUS PHARMACEUTICALS, INC.; *U.S. Public*, pg. 1967
SUPERONE CO., LTD.—See Al Co., Ltd.; *Int'l*, pg. 226
SUPEROXYGEN, INC.; *U.S. Private*, pg. 3881
SUPERPAK AMBALAJ SANAYI VE TICARET ANONIM SIRKETI—See Mayr-Melnhof Karton AG; *Int'l*, pg. 4747
SUPER PALLET RECYCLING CORP.; *U.S. Private*, pg. 3874
SUPERPETZ, LLC—See Weis Markets, Inc.; *U.S. Public*, pg. 2342
SUPERPHARM LIMITED—See Agostini's Limited; *Int'l*, pg. 213
SUPER PLUS ACQUISITION CORPORATION; *U.S. Private*, pg. 3874
SUPERPOLO S.A.—See Marcopolo S.A.; *Int'l*, pg. 4690
SUPER PRODUCTS LLC—See Alamo Group Inc.; *U.S. Public*, pg. 71
SUPER QUIK INC.; *U.S. Private*, pg. 3875
SUPERQUINN LTD.—See Musgrave Group plc; *Int'l*, pg. 5102
SUPER RADIATOR COILS LTD.; *U.S. Private*, pg. 3875
SUPER REGIONAL, INC.—See Shimizu Corporation; *Int'l*, pg. 6836
SUPER RELIGARE LABORATORIES INTERNATIONAL FZ LLC—See Fortis Healthcare Limited; *Int'l*, pg. 2739
SUPERRE SOLUTION S.R.L.—See Sesa S.p.A.; *Int'l*, pg. 6729
SUPER RETAIL GROUP LIMITED; *Int'l*, pg. 7335
SUPER RIFLE S.P.A.; *Int'l*, pg. 7335
SUPERROBOTICS HOLDINGS LTD.; *Int'l*, pg. 7339
SUPERROBOTICS LIMITED; *Int'l*, pg. 7339
SUPER RUNNERS SHOP, INC.—See Surefoot Inc; *U.S. Private*, pg. 3883
SUPER SALES INDIA LIMITED - MARKETING DIVISION—See Super Sales India Limited; *Int'l*, pg. 7335
SUPER SALES INDIA LIMITED; *Int'l*, pg. 7335
SUPERSCAPES, INC.—See Crux Capital Ltd; *U.S. Private*, pg. 1114
SUPER-SENSITIVE MUSICAL STRING CO.; *U.S. Private*, pg. 3875
SUPER-SERVER, LLC—See Sourcepass, Inc.; *U.S. Private*, pg. 3719
SUPER SERVICE HOLDINGS, LLC—See Wayzata Investment Partners LLC; *U.S. Private*, pg. 4461
SUPER SERVICE, LLC - KENTUCKY OFFICE—See Wayzata Investment Partners LLC; *U.S. Private*, pg. 4461
SUPER SERVICE, LLC—See Wayzata Investment Partners LLC; *U.S. Private*, pg. 4461
SUPERSHAKTI METALIKS LIMITED; *Int'l*, pg. 7339
SUPERSHIP HOLDINGS CO., LTD.—See Dentsu Group Inc.; *Int'l*, pg. 2039
SUPERSHUTTLE INTERNATIONAL, INC.—See Caisse des Depots et Consignations; *Int'l*, pg. 1258
SUPERSIGNS POLSKA SP ZO.O.—See iHeartMedia, Inc.; *U.S. Public*, pg. 1096
SUPER SKY PRODUCTS ENTERPRISES, LLC—See Trulite Glass & Aluminum Solutions, LLC; *U.S. Private*, pg. 4249
SUPERSONIC CAR WASH INC.; *U.S. Private*, pg. 3881
SUPERSONIC CAR WASH—See Supersonic Car Wash Inc.; *U.S. Private*, pg. 3881
SUPERSONIC IMAGINE, GMBH—See SuperSonic Imagine SA; *Int'l*, pg. 7339
SUPERSONIC IMAGINE LTD.—See SuperSonic Imagine SA; *Int'l*, pg. 7339
SUPERSONIC IMAGINE SA; *Int'l*, pg. 7339
SUPERSONIC IMAGINE (SHANGHAI) MEDICAL DEVICES CO. LTD.—See SuperSonic Imagine SA; *Int'l*, pg. 7339
SUPER SORGHUM ASIA HOLDINGS PTE. LTD.—See Sorghum Japan Holdings Corp.; *Int'l*, pg. 7112
SUPER SORGHUM MEXICO S.A. DE C.V.—See Sorghum Japan Holdings Corp.; *Int'l*, pg. 7112
SUPER SPINNING MILLS LTD; *Int'l*, pg. 7335
SUPER SPINNING MILLS LTD - UNIT SARA APPAREL & FASHION—See Super Spinning Mills Ltd; *Int'l*, pg. 7335
SUPER SPINNING MILLS LTD - UNIT SUPER A—See Super Spinning Mills Ltd; *Int'l*, pg. 7335
SUPER SPINNING MILLS LTD - UNIT SUPER B—See Super Spinning Mills Ltd; *Int'l*, pg. 7335
SUPER SPINNING MILLS LTD - UNIT SUPER C—See Super Spinning Mills Ltd; *Int'l*, pg. 7335
SUPERSPORT INTERNATIONAL (PTY) LIMITED—See Naspers Limited; *Int'l*, pg. 5149
SUPERSTAR HOLIDAYS LTD—See El Al Airlines Ltd.; *Int'l*, pg. 2340
SUPERSTAR PRODUCTIONS USA INC.—See National Amusements, Inc.; *U.S. Private*, pg. 2843

COMPANY NAME INDEX

SUPERSTATION INC.—See Warner Bros. Discovery, Inc.; *U.S. Public*, pg. 2328
SUPER STEEL LLC; *U.S. Private*, pg. 3875
SUPERSTITION CRUSHING LLC; *U.S. Private*, pg. 3881
SUPER STORAGE TECHNOLOGY CORPORATION—See Phison Electronics Corporation; *Int'l*, pg. 5848
SUPER STORE INDUSTRIES - FAIRFIELD DAIRY DIVISION—See Super Store Industries; *U.S. Private*, pg. 3875
SUPER STORE INDUSTRIES; *U.S. Private*, pg. 3875
SUPER STORE INDUSTRIES - TURLOCK DAIRY DIVISION—See Super Store Industries; *U.S. Private*, pg. 3875
SUPERSTREAM INC.—See Canon Inc.; *Int'l*, pg. 1296
SUPER STRONG HOLDINGS LIMITED; *Int'l*, pg. 7335
SUPERSTYLE FURNITURE LTD.; *Int'l*, pg. 7339
SUPER SYNCOTEX (INDIA) LTD.; *Int'l*, pg. 7335
SUPER TANNERY LIMITED; *Int'l*, pg. 7335
SUPER TELECOM CO., LTD.; *Int'l*, pg. 7335
SUPERTEST OIL COMPANY INC.; *U.S. Private*, pg. 3881
SUPERTEX INDUSTRIES LTD.; *Int'l*, pg. 7339
SUPER TIENDAS LA TAPCHULTECA; *U.S. Private*, pg. 3875
SUPERTIME DEVELOPMENT COMPANY LIMITED—See GDH Limited; *Int'l*, pg. 2896
SUPER TOOL CO., LTD.; *Int'l*, pg. 7335
SUPERTRANSPORT - TRAFFIC CENTER KONTICH—See Carrefour SA; *Int'l*, pg. 1344
SUPERTRANSPORT - TRAFFIC CENTER NORD (KDC)—See Carrefour SA; *Int'l*, pg. 1344
SUPERTRANSPORT - TRAFFIC CENTER SUD—See Carrefour SA; *Int'l*, pg. 1344
SUPERTRANSPORT - TRAFFIC CENTER VILVOORDE—See Carrefour SA; *Int'l*, pg. 1344
SUPERTRAPP INDUSTRIES, INC.—See Dreison International, Inc.; *U.S. Private*, pg. 1276
SUPERTURBO TECHNOLOGIES—See Woodward, Inc.; *U.S. Public*, pg. 2377
SUPERTUR-IMOBILIARIA, COMERCIO E TURISMO, S.A.—See Jeronimo Martins SGPS SA; *Int'l*, pg. 3931
SUPER TURTLE PUBLIC COMPANY LIMITED; *Int'l*, pg. 7336
SUPERUNION LIMITED—See WPP plc; *Int'l*, pg. 8466
SUPER VALUE CO., LTD.; *Int'l*, pg. 7336
SUPER VALUE FOOD STORES LIMITED; *Int'l*, pg. 7336
SUPERVALU FOUNDATION—See United Natural Foods, Inc.; *U.S. Public*, pg. 2232
SUPERVALU, INC. - ANNISTON DISTRIBUTION CENTER—See United Natural Foods, Inc.; *U.S. Public*, pg. 2232
SUPERVALU, INC. - BILLINGS DISTRIBUTION CENTER—See United Natural Foods, Inc.; *U.S. Public*, pg. 2232
SUPERVALU, INC., BISMARCK DIVISION—See United Natural Foods, Inc.; *U.S. Public*, pg. 2232
SUPERVALU, INC. - CHAMPAIGN DISTRIBUTION CENTER—See United Natural Foods, Inc.; *U.S. Public*, pg. 2232
SUPERVALU, INC. - EASTERN REGION—See United Natural Foods, Inc.; *U.S. Public*, pg. 2232
SUPERVALU, INC. - EASTON DISTRIBUTION CENTER—See United Natural Foods, Inc.; *U.S. Public*, pg. 2232
SUPERVALU, INC., FARGO DISTRIBUTION DIVISION—See United Natural Foods, Inc.; *U.S. Public*, pg. 2232
SUPERVALU, INC., FOOD MARKETING DIVISION—See United Natural Foods, Inc.; *U.S. Public*, pg. 2232
SUPERVALU, INC. - GREEN BAY DISTRIBUTION CENTER—See United Natural Foods, Inc.; *U.S. Public*, pg. 2232
SUPERVALU, INC., HARRISBURG DIVISION—See United Natural Foods, Inc.; *U.S. Public*, pg. 2232
SUPERVALU, INC., LEWIS GROCER DIVISION—See United Natural Foods, Inc.; *U.S. Public*, pg. 2232
SUPERVALU, INC. - MIDWEST REGION—See United Natural Foods, Inc.; *U.S. Public*, pg. 2232
SUPERVALU, INC., MILTON DIVISION—See United Natural Foods, Inc.; *U.S. Public*, pg. 2232
SUPERVALU, INC., MINNEAPOLIS DIVISION—See United Natural Foods, Inc.; *U.S. Public*, pg. 2232
SUPERVALU, INC., OHIO VALLEY DIVISION—See United Natural Foods, Inc.; *U.S. Public*, pg. 2232
SUPERVALU, INC., PITTSBURGH DIVISION—See United Natural Foods, Inc.; *U.S. Public*, pg. 2232
SUPERVALU, INC., QUINCY DIVISION—See United Natural Foods, Inc.; *U.S. Public*, pg. 2232
SUPERVALU INC.—See United Natural Foods, Inc.; *U.S. Public*, pg. 2231
SUPERVALU, INC., SPOKANE DIVISION—See United Natural Foods, Inc.; *U.S. Public*, pg. 2232
SUPERVALU, INC. - ST. LOUIS DISTRIBUTION CENTER—See United Natural Foods, Inc.; *U.S. Public*, pg. 2232
SUPERVALU, INC., TACOMA DIVISION—See United Natural Foods, Inc.; *U.S. Public*, pg. 2232
SUPERVALU INTERNATIONAL—See United Natural Foods, Inc.; *U.S. Public*, pg. 2232

SUPERVALU PHARMACIES, INC.—See United Natural Foods, Inc.; *U.S. Public*, pg. 2232
SUPERVALU TRANSPORTATION INC.—See United Natural Foods, Inc.; *U.S. Public*, pg. 2232
SUPERVIELLE SEGUROS S.A.—See Grupo Supervielle S.A.; *Int'l*, pg. 3135
SUPERVISION OPTIMAX SDN. BHD.—See Supermax Corporation Berhad; *Int'l*, pg. 7339
SUPER VISTA SDN BHD—See Hotel Properties Limited; *Int'l*, pg. 3488
SUPERVITAMINS SDN. BHD.—See Keck Seng (Malaysia) Berhad; *Int'l*, pg. 4114
SUPER WAREHOUSE; *U.S. Private*, pg. 3875
SUPER WASH INC.; *U.S. Private*, pg. 3875
SUPERWINCH, LLC—See Kinderhook Industries, LLC; *U.S. Private*, pg. 2307
SUPERWINCH LTD.—See Kinderhook Industries, LLC; *U.S. Private*, pg. 2307
SUPER WIN ELECTRONICS LIMITED—See IDT International Limited; *Int'l*, pg. 3597
SUPERWORLD ELECTRONICS (HK) LIMITED—See Tai-Tech Advanced Electronics (S) Pte Ltd.; *Int'l*, pg. 7410
SUPERWORLD ELECTRONICS (S) PTE LTD.—See Tai-Tech Advanced Electronics (S) Pte Ltd.; *Int'l*, pg. 7410
SUPER YACHT MANAGEMENT S.A.S.—See MarineMax, Inc.; *U.S. Public*, pg. 1367
SUPER YAMAZAKI CO., LTD.—See Yamazaki Baking Co., Ltd.; *Int'l*, pg. 8556
SUPFINA GRIESHABER GMBH & CO. KG—See Grieshaber Holding GmbH; *Int'l*, pg. 3083
SUPFINA MACHINE CO., INC.—See Grieshaber Holding GmbH; *Int'l*, pg. 3083
S&U PLC; *Int'l*, pg. 6445
SUPORT LOGISTIC BUCURESTI SA; *Int'l*, pg. 7339
SUPOR (VIETNAM) CO. LTD.—See SEB S.A.; *Int'l*, pg. 6668
SUPOTANT CO., LTD.—See Cross Marketing Group Inc.; *Int'l*, pg. 1856
SUPPES FORD; *U.S. Private*, pg. 3881
SUPPLAY SAS—See ManpowerGroup Inc.; *U.S. Public*, pg. 1360
SUPPLEMENTAL HEALTH CARE SERVICES, INC.; *U.S. Private*, pg. 3881
SUPPLEMENT HUNT, INC.—See Aytu BioPharma, Inc.; *U.S. Public*, pg. 257
SUPPLIER.IO, INC.; *U.S. Private*, pg. 3882
SUPPLIER MANAGEMENT SOLUTIONS, INC.—See Ardian SAS; *Int'l*, pg. 556
SUPPLIER SOCIEDADE DE CREDITO DIRETO S.A.—See TOTVS S.A.; *Int'l*, pg. 7846
SUPPLIES DISTRIBUTORS S.A.—See GXO Logistics, Inc.; *U.S. Public*, pg. 976
SUPPLIVA GMBH—See AlzChem Group AG; *Int'l*, pg. 402
SUPPLY CHAIN COACH, INC.—See AEA Investors LP; *U.S. Private*, pg. 115
THE SUPPLYCHAIN LIMITED—See Woolworths Group Limited; *Int'l*, pg. 8452
SUPPLY CHAIN SERVICES INTERNATIONAL, INC—See Ardian SAS; *Int'l*, pg. 556
SUPPLY CHAIN SERVICES, LLC—See Sole Source Capital LLC; *U.S. Private*, pg. 3708
SUPPLY CHAIN SOFTWARE NV—See Mannai Corporation QPSC; *Int'l*, pg. 4675
SUPPLY CHAIN SOLUTIONS, INC. - HOLLAND OFFICE—See Supply Chain Solutions, Inc.; *U.S. Private*, pg. 3882
SUPPLY CHAIN SOLUTIONS, INC.; *U.S. Private*, pg. 3882
SUPPLY CHAIN SOLUTIONS LLC; *U.S. Private*, pg. 3882
SUPPLYCORE INC.; *U.S. Private*, pg. 3882
SUPPLY DESK LIMITED—See Sovereign Capital Partners LLP; *Int'l*, pg. 7121
SUPPLY DESK LIMITED - TEACH IN DIVISION—See Sovereign Capital Partners LLP; *Int'l*, pg. 7121
SUPPLY DIRECT PTY. LTD.—See Perenti Global Limited; *Int'l*, pg. 5798
SUPPLY DIRECT SOUTH AFRICA PTY. LTD.—See Perenti Global Limited; *Int'l*, pg. 5798
SUPPLY DYNAMICS LLC—See Exiger LLC; *U.S. Private*, pg. 1449
SUPPLY FORCE INTERNATIONAL PTE LTD—See Capital Limited; *Int'l*, pg. 1311
SUPPLY@ME CAPITAL PLC; *Int'l*, pg. 7340
SUPPLY NETWORK LIMITED; *Int'l*, pg. 7339
SUPPLY NEW ENGLAND INC.; *U.S. Private*, pg. 3882
SUPPLYON AG; *Int'l*, pg. 7340
SUPPLYON CONSULTING (SHANGHAI) CO., LTD.—See SupplyOn AG; *Int'l*, pg. 7340
SUPPLYONE CLEVELAND, INC.—See Wellspring Capital Management LLC; *U.S. Private*, pg. 4478
SUPPLYONE HOLDINGS COMPANY, INC.—See Meridian Venture Partners; *U.S. Private*, pg. 2673
SUPPLYONE, INC. - DALLAS PLANT—See Wellspring Capital Management LLC; *U.S. Private*, pg. 4478
SUPPLYONE, INC.—See Wellspring Capital Management LLC; *U.S. Private*, pg. 4477
SUPPLYONE TUCSON, INC. - ALBUQUERQUE PLANT—See Wellspring Capital Management LLC; *U.S. Private*, pg. 4478

SUPREME BEVERAGE CO. INC.

SUPPLYONE TUCSON, INC.—See Wellspring Capital Management LLC; *U.S. Private*, pg. 4478
SUPPLYONE WEYERS CAVE, INC. - CHESAPEAKE PLANT—See Wellspring Capital Management LLC; *U.S. Private*, pg. 4478
SUPPLYONE WEYERS CAVE, INC.—See Wellspring Capital Management LLC; *U.S. Private*, pg. 4478
SUPPLYONE WISCONSIN, LLC—See Wellspring Capital Management LLC; *U.S. Private*, pg. 4478
SUPPLYON NORTH AMERICA INC.—See SupplyOn AG; *Int'l*, pg. 7340
SUPPLY PLUS LIMITED—See Lagercrantz Group AB; *Int'l*, pg. 4395
SUPPLYPRO INC.; *U.S. Private*, pg. 3882
SUPPLY PRO INC.—See Bunzl plc; *Int'l*, pg. 1218
THE SUPPLY ROOM COMPANIES INC.; *U.S. Private*, pg. 4125
SUPPLYSOURCE INC.; *U.S. Private*, pg. 3882
SUPPLY TECHNOLOGIES COMPANY OF CANADA—See Park-Ohio Holdings Corp.; *U.S. Public*, pg. 1640
SUPPLY TECHNOLOGIES COMPANY OF PUERTO RICO—See Park-Ohio Holdings Corp.; *U.S. Public*, pg. 1640
SUPPLY TECHNOLOGIES CR S.R.O.—See Park-Ohio Holdings Corp.; *U.S. Public*, pg. 1640
SUPPLY TECHNOLOGIES (INDIA) PRIVATE LIMITED—See Park-Ohio Holdings Corp.; *U.S. Public*, pg. 1640
SUPPLY TECHNOLOGIES KFT—See Park-Ohio Holdings Corp.; *U.S. Public*, pg. 1640
SUPPLY TECHNOLOGIES LIMITED—See Park-Ohio Holdings Corp.; *U.S. Public*, pg. 1640
SUPPLY TECHNOLOGIES LIMITED—See Park-Ohio Holdings Corp.; *U.S. Public*, pg. 1640
SUPPLY TECHNOLOGIES LLC—See Park-Ohio Holdings Corp.; *U.S. Public*, pg. 1640
SUPPLY TECHNOLOGIES PTE. LTD.—See Park-Ohio Holdings Corp.; *U.S. Public*, pg. 1640
SUPPLY TECHNOLOGIES—See Park-Ohio Holdings Corp.; *U.S. Public*, pg. 1640
SUPPLY TECHNOLOGIES—See Park-Ohio Holdings Corp.; *U.S. Public*, pg. 1640
SUPPLY VISION, INC.—See The Descartes Systems Group Inc.; *Int'l*, pg. 7636
SUPPLYWORKS—See The Home Depot, Inc.; *U.S. Public*, pg. 2089
SUPPORT-A LTD.—See Persol Holdings Co., Ltd.; *Int'l*, pg. 5819
SUPPORT BITTIYA SANSTHA LIMITED; *Int'l*, pg. 7340
SUPPORT.COM, INC.—See RealDefense LLC; *U.S. Private*, pg. 3368
SUPPORT.COM INDIA PVT LTD—See RealDefense LLC; *U.S. Private*, pg. 3368
THE SUPPORTING CAST, INC.; *U.S. Private*, pg. 4125
SUPPORTING FAMILIES TOGETHER ASSOCIATION; *U.S. Private*, pg. 3882
SUPPORTINGSMALLBUSINESS, INC.; *Int'l*, pg. 7340
SUPPORT LOGISTIC SERVICES S.R.L.—See Cassa Depositi e Prestiti S.p.A.; *Int'l*, pg. 1355
SUPPORT OUR TROOPS, INC.; *U.S. Private*, pg. 3882
SUPPORT PRODUTOS NUTRICIONAIS LTDA.—See Danone; *Int'l*, pg. 1967
SUPPORT SYSTEM CO., LTD.—See UT Group Co., Ltd.; *Int'l*, pg. 8100
SUPPORT SYSTEMS ASSOCIATES, INC.; *U.S. Private*, pg. 3882
SUPPORT SYSTEMS INTERNATIONAL INC.; *U.S. Private*, pg. 3882
SUPPRO CO LTD; *Int'l*, pg. 7340
SUPRA AGROCHEMIA SP. Z O.O.—See Grupa Azoty S.A.; *Int'l*, pg. 3116
SUPRAJIT ENGINEERING LIMITED; *Int'l*, pg. 7340
SUPRAJIT EUROPE LIMITED—See Suprajit Engineering Limited; *Int'l*, pg. 7340
SUPRALON PRODUKTIONS UND VERTRIEBS GMBH—See Viscofan SA; *Int'l*, pg. 8250
SUPRA PACIFIC FINANCIAL SERVICES LTD.; *Int'l*, pg. 7340
SUPRA SA—See Taurus Group; *Int'l*, pg. 7476
SUPRA SP. Z O.O.—See Zaklady Chemiczne POLICE S.A.; *Int'l*, pg. 8621
SUPRA TRENDS LIMITED; *Int'l*, pg. 7340
SUPRE INC.; *U.S. Private*, pg. 3882
SUPREMA EUROPE S.A.R.L.—See Suprema HQ Inc.; *Int'l*, pg. 7340
SUPREMA HQ INC.; *Int'l*, pg. 7340
SUPREMA MIDDLE EAST FZCO—See Suprema HQ Inc.; *Int'l*, pg. 7340
SUPREM ASSOCIATES PARTNERSHIP FIRM—See Precot Ltd.; *Int'l*, pg. 5958
SUPREMA SYSTEMS JAPAN LTD.—See Suprema HQ Inc.; *Int'l*, pg. 7340
SUPREMA SYSTEMS UK LTD.—See Suprema HQ Inc.; *Int'l*, pg. 7340
SUPREMEAIR (PTY) LIMITED—See Johnson Controls International plc; *Int'l*, pg. 3986
SUPREME BEVERAGE CO. INC.; *U.S. Private*, pg. 3882
SUPREME BUILDING PRODUCTS, INC.—See Beacon Roofing Supply, Inc.; *U.S. Public*, pg. 286

THE SUPREME CANNABIS COMPANY, INC.—See Canopy Growth Corporation; *Int'l*, pg. 1298
SUPREME CHEVROLET, INC.; *U.S. Private*, pg. 3882
SUPREME CONCRETE BLOCK INC.—See CRH plc; *Int'l*, pg. 1846
SUPREME CONCRETE LIMITED—See Ibstock plc; *Int'l*, pg. 3577
SUPREME CORPORATION OF TEXAS—See WABASH NATIONAL CORPORATION; *U.S. Public*, pg. 2320
SUPREME COUNCIL OF THE ROYAL ARCANUM; *U.S. Private*, pg. 3882
SUPREME DEVELOPMENT CO., LTD.—See Sojitz Corporation; *Int'l*, pg. 7066
SUPREME EDUCATION LTD.—See Randstad N.V.; *Int'l*, pg. 6205
SUPREME ELASTIC CORP; *U.S. Private*, pg. 3882
SUPREME ELECTRONICS CO., LTD.; *Int'l*, pg. 7340
SUPREME ENERGY, INC.; *U.S. Private*, pg. 3882
SUPREME ENGINEERING LIMITED; *Int'l*, pg. 7340
SUPREME FOODS PROCESSING COMPANY LTD.—See Dabbagh Group Holding Company Ltd.; *Int'l*, pg. 1903
SUPREME GROUP BV; *Int'l*, pg. 7341
SUPREME GROUP; *Int'l*, pg. 7340
SUPREME GROUP - SUPREME STEEL BRIDGE DIVISION—See Supreme Group; *Int'l*, pg. 7341
SUPREME HOLDINGS & HOSPITALITY (INDIA) LTD.; *Int'l*, pg. 7341
SUPREME IMPORTS LTD.; *Int'l*, pg. 7341
SUPREME INDUSTRIES, INC.—See WABASH NATIONAL CORPORATION; *U.S. Public*, pg. 2320
THE SUPREME INDUSTRIES LIMITED; *Int'l*, pg. 7691
THE SUPREME INDUSTRIES OVERSEAS FZE—See The Supreme Industries Limited; *Int'l*, pg. 7691
SUPREME INFRASTRUCTURE INDIA LIMITED; *Int'l*, pg. 7341
SUPREME INTEGRATED TECHNOLOGY, INC.—See Employee Owned Holdings, Inc.; *U.S. Private*, pg. 1386
SUPREME MACHINED PRODUCTS COMPANY, INC.; *U.S. Private*, pg. 3882
SUPREME MID-ATLANTIC CORPORATION—See WABASH NATIONAL CORPORATION; *U.S. Public*, pg. 2320
SUPREME NURSING GLOBAL PTY LTD—See PeopleIn Limited; *Int'l*, pg. 5794
SUPREME OFFICE PRODUCTS LIMITED; *Int'l*, pg. 7341
SUPREME OIL COMPANY INC.; *U.S. Private*, pg. 3882
SUPREME OIL COMPANY INC.; *U.S. Private*, pg. 3882
SUPREME PAPER SUPPLIES LLC—See Bain Capital, LP; *U.S. Private*, pg. 441
SUPREME PETROCHEM LIMITED; *Int'l*, pg. 7341
SUPREME PLC; *Int'l*, pg. 7341
SUPREME POULTRY (PTY) LIMITED—See Country Bird Holdings Limited; *Int'l*, pg. 1818
SUPREME POWER EQUIPMENT LIMITED; *Int'l*, pg. 7341
SUPREME RESOURCES, INC.; *U.S. Private*, pg. 3883
SUPREME SECURITY SYSTEMS, INC.—See Securitas AB; *Int'l*, pg. 6676
SUPREMESOFT CORPORATION—See Kellton Tech Solutions Ltd.; *Int'l*, pg. 4121
SUPREME SPRING HOLDINGS LTD.—See Metair Investments Limited; *Int'l*, pg. 4844
SUPREME STEEL SASKATOON—See Supreme Group; *Int'l*, pg. 7341
SUPREME STEEL WINNIPEG—See Supreme Group; *Int'l*, pg. 7341
SUPREME TELECOM SYSTEMS INC.; *U.S. Private*, pg. 3883
SUPREME TEX MART LIMITED; *Int'l*, pg. 7341
SUPREME TRUCK BODIES OF CALIFORNIA, INC.—See WABASH NATIONAL CORPORATION; *U.S. Public*, pg. 2320
SUPREME UPFIT SOLUTIONS & SERVICE, INC.—See WABASH NATIONAL CORPORATION; *U.S. Public*, pg. 2320
SUPREME VENTURES FINANCIAL SERVICES LIMITED—See Supreme Ventures Limited; *Int'l*, pg. 7341
SUPREME VENTURES LIMITED; *Int'l*, pg. 7341
SUPREME VENTURES LOTTERIES LIMITED—See Supreme Ventures Limited; *Int'l*, pg. 7341
SUPREME VOYAGER PTE. LTD.—See Hoe Leong Corporation Ltd.; *Int'l*, pg. 3439
SUPREME WINDOWS (CALGARY) INC.; *Int'l*, pg. 7341
SUPREMEX INC.; *Int'l*, pg. 7341
SUPRIYA LIFESCIENCE LTD.; *Int'l*, pg. 7341
SUP SANTE S.A.R.L.—See Gift SAS; *Int'l*, pg. 2970
SUQIAN CNG ELECTRONIC GLASS COMPANY LIMITED—See China Glass Holdings Limited; *Int'l*, pg. 1504
SUQIAN CNG NEW MATERIALS COMPANY LIMITED—See China Glass Holdings Limited; *Int'l*, pg. 1504
SUQIAN LINTONG NEW MATERIAL CO., LTD.—See DIC India Ltd; *Int'l*, pg. 2111
SUQIAN LINTONG NEW MATERIALS CO., LTD.—See DIC Corporation; *Int'l*, pg. 2111
SUQIAN YOUNG TOP GARMENTS CO., LTD.—See Fountain Set (Holdings) Limited; *Int'l*, pg. 2754

SUQUASH COAL LTD.—See Electra Stone Ltd.; *Int'l*, pg. 2348
SURACHAI (1997) CO., LTD.—See Energy Absolute Public Company Limited; *Int'l*, pg. 2422
SURA DEVELOPMENT & INVESTMENT PLC; *Int'l*, pg. 7342
SURAHAMMAR BRUKS AB—See Tata Sons Limited; *Int'l*, pg. 7472
SURAHAMMARS BRUKS AB—See Tata Sons Limited; *Int'l*, pg. 7471
SURAJ COTTON MILLS LIMITED; *Int'l*, pg. 7342
SU-RAJ DIAMONDS AND JEWELLERY DMCC—See Winsome Diamonds & Jewellery Ltd.; *Int'l*, pg. 8430
SU-RAJ DIAMONDS AND JEWELRY USA, INC.—See Winsome Diamonds & Jewellery Ltd.; *Int'l*, pg. 8430
SU-RAJ DIAMONDS N.V.—See Winsome Diamonds & Jewellery Ltd.; *Int'l*, pg. 8430
SURAJ ESTATE DEVELOPERS LIMITED; *Int'l*, pg. 7342
SURAJ GHEE INDUSTRIES LIMITED; *Int'l*, pg. 7342
SURAJ INDUSTRIES LTD.; *Int'l*, pg. 7342
SURAJ LTD.; *Int'l*, pg. 7342
SURAJ PRODUCTS LIMITED; *Int'l*, pg. 7342
SURALA NET CO., LTD.; *Int'l*, pg. 7342
SURANA INDUSTRIES LTD.; *Int'l*, pg. 7342
SURANA MINES AND MINERALS LIMITED—See Surana Industries Ltd.; *Int'l*, pg. 7342
SURANA SOLAR LIMITED; *Int'l*, pg. 7342
SURANA TELECOM AND POWER LIMITED; *Int'l*, pg. 7342
SURANI STEEL TUBES LIMITED; *Int'l*, pg. 7342
SURA PISET THIPPARAT CO., LTD.—See Thai Beverage Public Company Limited; *Int'l*, pg. 7592
SURAPON AQUACULTURE CO., LTD.—See Surapon Foods Public Company Limited; *Int'l*, pg. 7342
SURAPON FOODS PUBLIC COMPANY LIMITED - FACTORY 1—See Surapon Foods Public Company Limited; *Int'l*, pg. 7342
SURAPON FOODS PUBLIC COMPANY LIMITED; *Int'l*, pg. 7342
SURAPON NICHIREI FOODS CO., INC.—See Nichirei Corporation; *Int'l*, pg. 5270
SURAPON NICHIREI FOODS CO., INC.—See Surapon Foods Public Company Limited; *Int'l*, pg. 7342
SUR ASISTENCIA S.A.—See MAPFRE S.A.; *Int'l*, pg. 4684
SURASSUR SA—See MAPFRE S.A.; *Int'l*, pg. 4683
SURAT SEAFOODS COMPANY LIMITED—See Surapon Foods Public Company Limited; *Int'l*, pg. 7342
SURAT TEXTILE MILLS LIMITED; *Int'l*, pg. 7342
SURATWWALA BUSINESS GROUP LTD.; *Int'l*, pg. 7342
SURBANA JURONG PRIVATE LIMITED—See Temasek Holdings (Private) Limited; *Int'l*, pg. 7554
SURBHI INDUSTRIES LIMITED; *Int'l*, pg. 7343
SURCO LOG, INC.; *U.S. Private*, pg. 3883
SURCON, LTD.—See Helmerich & Payne, Inc.; *U.S. Public*, pg. 1024
SURCO PRODUCTS, INC.; *U.S. Private*, pg. 3883
SURDEX CORP.—See Bowman Consulting Group Ltd.; *U.S. Public*, pg. 377
SURE/ARC WELDING SUPPLY (1977) LTD.—See Linde plc; *Int'l*, pg. 4510
SURECLEAN LIMITED—See Republic Services, Inc.; *U.S. Public*, pg. 1788
SURECLICK PROMOTIONS, LLC; *U.S. Private*, pg. 3883
SUREDO AB—See Schibsted ASA; *Int'l*, pg. 6617
SUREFIL LLC; *U.S. Private*, pg. 3883
SUREFIRE, LLC; *U.S. Private*, pg. 3883
SUREFIRE MANAGEMENT SERVICES LTD.—See Berger Paints India Limited; *Int'l*, pg. 980
SUREFIRE RESOURCES NL; *Int'l*, pg. 7343
SURE FIT INC.—See Centre Lane Partners, LLC; *U.S. Private*, pg. 827
SUREFLEX, INC.—See The Eastern Company; *U.S. Public*, pg. 2069
SURE FOOD PTE. LTD.—See Soup Holdings Limited; *Int'l*, pg. 7115
SUREFOOT INC; *U.S. Private*, pg. 3883
SURE (GUERNSEY) LIMITED—See Bahrain Telecommunications Company BSC; *Int'l*, pg. 801
SUREHAND, INC.—See Stanley Black & Decker, Inc.; *U.S. Public*, pg. 1936
SUREHARVEST, INC.—See Where Food Comes From, Inc.; *U.S. Public*, pg. 2366
SUREHARVEST SERVICES, LLC—See Where Food Comes From, Inc.; *U.S. Public*, pg. 2366
SURELAND INDUSTRIAL FIRE SAFETY LIMITED—See Bain Capital, LP; *U.S. Private*, pg. 437
SURE LINK LOGISTICS (SHENZHEN) CO., LTD.—See KS Energy Limited; *Int'l*, pg. 4310
SURE LINK TRANSPORTATION CO., LTD.—See KS Energy Limited; *Int'l*, pg. 4310
SURE - LOC HARDWARE, INC.—See ASSA ABLOY AB; *Int'l*, pg. 640
SURE MAINTENANCE LIMITED—See Cap10 Partners LLP; *Int'l*, pg. 1301
SUREPAYROLL, INC.—See Paychex, Inc.; *U.S. Public*, pg. 1656
SUREPHOUSE GMBH—See Superhouse Limited; *Int'l*, pg. 7337

SUREPHOUSE (UK) LTD.—See Superhouse Limited; *Int'l*, pg. 7337
SURE POWER, INC.—See Eaton Corporation plc; *Int'l*, pg. 2282
SURE PREP LEARNING LLC; *U.S. Private*, pg. 3883
SURE PROMISE LIMITED—See Hanison Construction Holdings Limited; *Int'l*, pg. 3252
SUREPURE, INC.; *U.S. Public*, pg. 1967
SURERUS MURPHY JV—See J. Murphy & Sons Limited; *Int'l*, pg. 3856
SURERUS PIPELINE INC.; *Int'l*, pg. 7343
SURE-SEAL LLC—See CSW Industrials, Inc.; *U.S. Public*, pg. 601
SURESERVE FIRE & ELECTRICAL LIMITED—See Cap10 Partners LLP; *Int'l*, pg. 1301
SURESERVE GROUP PLC—See Cap10 Partners LLP; *Int'l*, pg. 1301
SURESNES IMMOBILIER S.A.—See Assicurazioni Generali S.p.A.; *Int'l*, pg. 645
SURESTAFF, LLC—See Owner Resource Group, LLC; *U.S. Private*, pg. 3055
SURETANK GROUP LTD.—See HitecVision AS; *Int'l*, pg. 3426
SURETEC; *U.S. Private*, pg. 3883
SURE TRACE SECURITY CORP.; *U.S. Private*, pg. 3883
SURETY BONDING COMPANY OF AMERICA—See Loews Corporation; *U.S. Public*, pg. 1340
SURETY HOLDINGS CORP.; *U.S. Public*, pg. 1967
SURETY SOLUTIONS INSURANCE SERVICES INC.—See GTCR LLC; *U.S. Public*, pg. 1804
SURETY SOLUTIONS, LLC—See Arthur J. Gallagher & Co.; *U.S. Public*, pg. 207
SURETY SUPPORT SERVICES, LLC—See Boston Omaha Corporation; *U.S. Public*, pg. 372
SURETY SYSTEMS, INC.; *U.S. Private*, pg. 3883
SURE VENTURES PLC; *Int'l*, pg. 7343
SUREWAY INTERNATIONAL INC; *Int'l*, pg. 7343
SUREWERX INC.—See Partners Group Holding AG; *Int'l*, pg. 5750
SUREWEST COMMUNICATIONS—See Consolidated Communications Holdings, Inc.; *U.S. Public*, pg. 570
SUREWEST DIRECTORIES—See Gannett Co., Inc.; *U.S. Public*, pg. 906
SUREWEST KANSAS, INC.—See Consolidated Communications Holdings, Inc.; *U.S. Public*, pg. 570
SUREWEST LONG DISTANCE COMPANY—See Consolidated Communications Holdings, Inc.; *U.S. Public*, pg. 570
SUREWEST TELEPHONE—See Consolidated Communications Holdings, Inc.; *U.S. Public*, pg. 570
SURE WIN INC. LIMITED—See Talent Property Group Limited; *Int'l*, pg. 7446
SURE WINNER FOODS INC.; *U.S. Private*, pg. 3883
SURFACE COMBUSTION, INC.; *U.S. Private*, pg. 3883
SURFACECYCLE, INC.; *U.S. Private*, pg. 3884
SURFACE INSPECTION GRADE TWO LIMITED—See Sacmi Imola S.C.A.R.L.; *Int'l*, pg. 6464
SURFACE MATERIAL SALES INC.; *U.S. Private*, pg. 3883
SURFACE MATERIALS IKI OY—See Fletcher Building Limited; *Int'l*, pg. 2701
SURFACE MOUNT DISTRIBUTION; *U.S. Private*, pg. 3884
SURFACE MOUNT TECHNOLOGY CORPORATION; *U.S. Private*, pg. 3884
SURFACE MOUNT TECHNOLOGY (HOLDINGS) LIMITED; *Int'l*, pg. 7343
SURFACE MOUNT TECHNOLOGY (JAPAN) COMPANY LIMITED—See Surface Mount Technology (Holdings) Limited; *Int'l*, pg. 7343
SURFACE MOUNT TECHNOLOGY LIMITED—See Surface Mount Technology (Holdings) Limited; *Int'l*, pg. 7343
SURFACE ONCOLOGY, INC.—See Coherus BioSciences, Inc.; *U.S. Public*, pg. 529
SURFACE PREPARATION TECHNOLOGIES, INC.—See Dominus Capital, L.P.; *U.S. Private*, pg. 1257
SURFACEPREP MOBILE LLC—See Nautic Partners, LLC; *U.S. Private*, pg. 2871
SURFACE PROJECT PTE. LTD.—See Hap Seng Consolidated Berhad; *Int'l*, pg. 3268
SURFACES & FINITIONS S.A.S.—See Graco, Inc.; *U.S. Public*, pg. 954
SURFACE STONE PTE. LTD.—See Hap Seng Consolidated Berhad; *Int'l*, pg. 3268
SURFACE TECHNOLOGIES CORP; *U.S. Private*, pg. 3884
SURFACE TECHNOLOGIES, INC.—See Facility Concepts Inc.; *U.S. Private*, pg. 1459
SURFACE TECHNOLOGY ABERDEEN LTD.—See Quaker Chemical Corporation; *U.S. Public*, pg. 1747
SURFACE TECHNOLOGY AUSTRALIA—See Quaker Chemical Corporation; *U.S. Public*, pg. 1747
SURFACE TECHNOLOGY (COVENTRY) LTD.—See Quaker Chemical Corporation; *U.S. Public*, pg. 1747
SURFACE TECHNOLOGY (EAST KILBRIDE) LTD.—See Quaker Chemical Corporation; *U.S. Public*, pg. 1747
SURFACE TECHNOLOGY (LEEDS) LTD.—See Quaker Chemical Corporation; *U.S. Public*, pg. 1747

COMPANY NAME INDEX SURGICAL STAFF, INC.

Company Index

SURFACE TECHNOLOGY SYSTEMS PLC—See Sumitomo Corporation; *Int'l*, pg. 7275
SURFACE TRANSFORMS PLC; *Int'l*, pg. 7343
SURFACE TREATMENT COMPANY N.V.—See Gimv NV; *Int'l*, pg. 2976
SURFACTANTS INTERNATIONAL LLC—See Galaxy Surfactants Limited; *Int'l*, pg. 2872
SURF AIR INC.—See Surf Air Mobility Inc.; *U.S. Public*, pg. 1967
SURF AIR MOBILITY INC.; *U.S. Public*, pg. 1967
SURF ASSOCIATES, INC.; *U.S. Private*, pg. 3883
SURF CITY GARAGE, LLC; *U.S. Private*, pg. 3883
SURFCOMBER HOTEL—See InterContinental Hotels Group PLC; *Int'l*, pg. 3738
SURF COMMUNICATION SOLUTIONS, LTD.; *Int'l*, pg. 7343
SURFECT HOLDINGS, INC.; *U.S. Private*, pg. 3884
SURFER MAGAZINE—See TEN: The Enthusiast Network, Inc.; *U.S. Private*, pg. 3964
SURF HARDWARE INTERNATIONAL EUROPE SARL—See Gowing Brothers Limited; *Int'l*, pg. 3044
SURF HARDWARE INTERNATIONAL USA INC.—See Gowing Brothers Limited; *Int'l*, pg. 3045
SURFILM SAS; *Int'l*, pg. 7343
SURFILTER NETWORK TECHNOLOGY CO., LTD.; *Int'l*, pg. 7343
SURF INVESTMENTS, LTD.—See E-Waste Systems, Inc.; *U.S. Private*, pg. 1303
SURF JAPAN, KK.—See Surf Communication Solutions, Ltd.; *Int'l*, pg. 7343
SUR-FLO PLASTICS & ENGINEERING INC.; *U.S. Private*, pg. 3883
SURFMARKET BV—See Stichting SURF; *Int'l*, pg. 7215
SURFNET BV—See Stichting SURF; *Int'l*, pg. 7215
SUR-FORM CORPORATION—See Andrew W. Byrd & Co., LLC; *U.S. Private*, pg. 280
SURFRIDER FOUNDATION; *U.S. Private*, pg. 3884
SURFSARA BV—See Stichting SURF; *Int'l*, pg. 7215
SURF S.R.L.—See Gruppo MutuiOnline S.p.A; *Int'l*, pg. 3141
SURFSTITCH GROUP LIMITED; *Int'l*, pg. 7343
SURGAID MEDICAL (XIAMEN) CO., LTD.—See Double Medical Technology Inc.; *Int'l*, pg. 2181
SURGALIGN HOLDINGS, INC.; *U.S. Public*, pg. 1967
SURGCENTER AT PARADISE VALLEY, LLC—See Tenet Healthcare Corporation; *U.S. Public*, pg. 2007
SURGCENTER CAMELBACK, LLC—See Tenet Healthcare Corporation; *U.S. Public*, pg. 2007
SURGCENTER DEVELOPMENT; *U.S. Private*, pg. 3884
SURGCENTER NORTHEAST, LLC—See Tenet Healthcare Corporation; *U.S. Public*, pg. 2007
SURGCENTER OF GLEN BURNIE, LLC—See Tenet Healthcare Corporation; *U.S. Public*, pg. 2007
SURGCENTER OF GREATER JACKSONVILLE, LLC—See Tenet Healthcare Corporation; *U.S. Public*, pg. 2007
SURGCENTER OF NORTHERN BALTIMORE, LLC—See Tenet Healthcare Corporation; *U.S. Public*, pg. 2007
SURGCENTER OF PALM BEACH GARDENS, LLC—See Tenet Healthcare Corporation; *U.S. Public*, pg. 2007
SURGCENTER OF PLANO, LLC—See Tenet Healthcare Corporation; *U.S. Public*, pg. 2007
SURGCENTER OF SILVER SPRING, LLC—See Tenet Healthcare Corporation; *U.S. Public*, pg. 2007
SURGCENTER OF SOUTHERN MARYLAND, LLC—See Tenet Healthcare Corporation; *U.S. Public*, pg. 2007
SURGCENTER OF ST. LUCIE, LLC—See Tenet Healthcare Corporation; *U.S. Public*, pg. 2007
SURGCENTER OF THE POTOMAC, LLC—See Tenet Healthcare Corporation; *U.S. Public*, pg. 2007
SURGCENTER OF WHITE MARSH, LLC—See Tenet Healthcare Corporation; *U.S. Public*, pg. 2007
SURGCENTER PINELLAS, LLC—See Tenet Healthcare Corporation; *U.S. Public*, pg. 2007
SURGCENTER TUCSON, LLC—See Tenet Healthcare Corporation; *U.S. Public*, pg. 2007
SURGE BATTERY METALS INC.; *Int'l*, pg. 7343
SURGE CENTER OF GLEN BURNIE LLC—See Tenet Healthcare Corporation; *U.S. Public*, pg. 2007
SURGE COMMUNICATIONS; *Int'l*, pg. 7343
SURGE COMPONENTS, INC.; *U.S. Public*, pg. 1967
SURGE COPPER CORP.; *Int'l*, pg. 7343
SURGE ENERGY INC.; *Int'l*, pg. 7343
SURGE GLOBAL ENERGY, INC.; *U.S. Private*, pg. 3884
SURGE/LELON LLC—See Lelon Electronics Corp.; *Int'l*, pg. 4447
SURGE LLC; *U.S. Private*, pg. 3884
SURGENOR NATIONAL LEASING LTD.; *Int'l*, pg. 7343
SURGENOR PONTIAC BUICK LIMITED; *Int'l*, pg. 7343
SURGENT HOLDING CORP—See Moelis Asset Management LP; *U.S. Private*, pg. 2764
SURGEPAYS INC.; *U.S. Public*, pg. 1967
SURGE PRIVATE EQUITY LLC; *U.S. Private*, pg. 3884
SURGE RESOURCES INC.—See GPB Capital Holdings, LLC; *U.S. Private*, pg. 1748
SURGERY ASSOCIATES OF NTX, PLLC—See HCA Healthcare, Inc.; *U.S. Public*, pg. 1011
SURGERY CENTER AT CHERRY CREEK, LLC—See UnitedHealth Group Incorporated; *U.S. Public*, pg. 2250
SURGERY CENTER AT COTTONWOOD, LLC—See UnitedHealth Group Incorporated; *U.S. Public*, pg. 2250
THE SURGERY CENTER AT JENSEN BEACH, LLC—See Tenet Healthcare Corporation; *U.S. Public*, pg. 2009
SURGERY CENTER AT KISSING CAMELS, LLC—See UnitedHealth Group Incorporated; *U.S. Public*, pg. 2250
SURGERY CENTER AT ST. ANDREWS—See HCA Healthcare, Inc.; *U.S. Public*, pg. 1011
SURGERY CENTER AT UNIVERSITY PARK, LLC—See Tenet Healthcare Corporation; *U.S. Public*, pg. 2013
THE SURGERY CENTER AT WILLIAMSON, LLC—See Tenet Healthcare Corporation; *U.S. Public*, pg. 2013
THE SURGERY CENTER, L.L.C.—See Bain Capital, LP; *U.S. Private*, pg. 447
THE SURGERY CENTER, LLC—See Bain Capital, LP; *U.S. Private*, pg. 447
SURGERY CENTER OF ALLENTOWN, LLC—See KKR & Co. Inc.; *U.S. Public*, pg. 1247
SURGERY CENTER OF ATHENS, LLC—See UnitedHealth Group Incorporated; *U.S. Public*, pg. 2250
SURGERY CENTER OF ATLANTA, LLC—See Tenet Healthcare Corporation; *U.S. Public*, pg. 2013
SURGERY CENTER OF AVENTURA, LTD.—See HCA Healthcare, Inc.; *U.S. Public*, pg. 1011
SURGERY CENTER OF CANFIELD, LLC—See Tenet Healthcare Corporation; *U.S. Public*, pg. 2013
SURGERY CENTER OF CHATTANOOGA, L.P.—See HCA Healthcare, Inc.; *U.S. Public*, pg. 1011
SURGERY CENTER OF CLARKSVILLE, L.P.—See UnitedHealth Group Incorporated; *U.S. Public*, pg. 2250
SURGERY CENTER OF COLUMBIA, L.P.—See Tenet Healthcare Corporation; *U.S. Public*, pg. 2013
SURGERY CENTER OF DES MOINES, LLC—See UnitedHealth Group Incorporated; *U.S. Public*, pg. 2250
SURGERY CENTER OF FORT COLLINS, LLC—See UnitedHealth Group Incorporated; *U.S. Public*, pg. 2250
SURGERY CENTER OF FREMONT, LLC—See Bain Capital, LP; *U.S. Private*, pg. 446
SURGERY CENTER OF GILBERT, L.L.C.—See Tenet Healthcare Corporation; *U.S. Public*, pg. 2013
SURGERY CENTER OF KALAMAZOO, LLC—See Bain Capital, LP; *U.S. Private*, pg. 446
SURGERY CENTER OF KEY WEST, LLC—See Community Health Systems, Inc.; *U.S. Public*, pg. 557
SURGERY CENTER OF LANCASTER, LLC—See Nueterra Capital Management, LLC; *U.S. Private*, pg. 2972
SURGERY CENTER OF LEBANON, LP—See Bain Capital, LP; *U.S. Private*, pg. 446
SURGERY CENTER OF LEXINGTON, LLC—See UnitedHealth Group Incorporated; *U.S. Public*, pg. 2250
THE SURGERY CENTER OF MIDDLE TENNESSEE, LLC—See KKR & Co. Inc.; *U.S. Public*, pg. 1248
SURGERY CENTER OF MIDWEST CITY, LLC—See Community Health Systems, Inc.; *U.S. Public*, pg. 557
SURGERY CENTER OF NORTHEAST TEXAS, LLC—See KKR & Co. Inc.; *U.S. Public*, pg. 1247
THE SURGERY CENTER OF OCALA, LLC—See Bain Capital, LP; *U.S. Private*, pg. 447
SURGERY CENTER OF OKEECHOBEE, LLC—See Tenet Healthcare Corporation; *U.S. Public*, pg. 2005
SURGERY CENTER OF PEMBROKE PINES, L.L.C.—See Tenet Healthcare Corporation; *U.S. Public*, pg. 2005
SURGERY CENTER OF PEORIA, L.L.C.—See Tenet Healthcare Corporation; *U.S. Public*, pg. 2013
SURGERY CENTER OF PORT CHARLOTTE, LTD.—See HCA Healthcare, Inc.; *U.S. Public*, pg. 1011
SURGERY CENTER OF ROCKVILLE, LLC—See UnitedHealth Group Incorporated; *U.S. Public*, pg. 2250
SURGERY CENTER OF ROME, L.P.—See HCA Healthcare, Inc.; *U.S. Public*, pg. 1011
SURGERY CENTER OF SCOTTSDALE, LLC—See Tenet Healthcare Corporation; *U.S. Public*, pg. 2013
SURGERY CENTER OF SOUTH CENTRAL KANSAS—See KKR & Co. Inc.; *U.S. Public*, pg. 1247
SURGERY CENTER OF TEMPE, LLC—See Tenet Healthcare Corporation; *U.S. Public*, pg. 2013
SURGERY CENTER OF THE ROCKIES, LLC—See HCA Healthcare, Inc.; *U.S. Public*, pg. 1011
SURGERY CENTER OF VOLUSIA, LLC—See KKR & Co. Inc.; *U.S. Public*, pg. 1247
SURGERY CENTER PARTNERS, LLC—See Bain Capital, LP; *U.S. Private*, pg. 446
SURGERY CENTERS OF DES MOINES, LTD.—See UnitedHealth Group Incorporated; *U.S. Public*, pg. 2250
SURGERY CENTRE OF SW FLORIDA, LLC—See Tenet Healthcare Corporation; *U.S. Public*, pg. 2007
SURGERY PARTNERS HOLDINGS LLC—See Bain Capital, LP; *U.S. Private*, pg. 446
SURGERY PARTNERS, INC.—See Bain Capital, LP; *U.S. Private*, pg. 444
SURGERY PARTNERS OF PARK PLACE, LLC—See Bain Capital, LP; *U.S. Private*, pg. 447
SURGERY SPECIALISTS OF BROWARD, INC.—See KKR & Co. Inc.; *U.S. Public*, pg. 1247
SURGERY SPECIALTY HOSPITALS OF AMERICA (SSHA)—See Dynacq Healthcare, Inc.; *U.S. Private*, pg. 1297
SURGE VENTURES, LLC; *U.S. Private*, pg. 3884
SURGICAL AND MEDICAL SUPPLIES PTY. LTD.—See EBOS Group Limited; *Int'l*, pg. 2286
SURGICAL APPLIANCE INDUSTRIES, INC. - PCP-CHAMPION DIVISION—See Surgical Appliance Industries, Inc.; *U.S. Private*, pg. 3884
SURGICAL APPLIANCE INDUSTRIES, INC.; *U.S. Private*, pg. 3884
SURGICAL ASSOCIATES OF THE NEW RIVER VALLEY, LLC—See HCA Healthcare, Inc.; *U.S. Public*, pg. 1011
SURGICAL CARE AFFILIATES, LLC—See UnitedHealth Group Incorporated; *U.S. Public*, pg. 2250
SURGICAL CENTER AT MILLBURN, LLC—See KKR & Co. Inc.; *U.S. Public*, pg. 1250
SURGICAL CENTER OF EL PASO—See HCA Healthcare, Inc.; *U.S. Public*, pg. 1011
SURGICAL CENTER OF SOUTH JERSEY, LIMITED PARTNERSHIP—See UnitedHealth Group Incorporated; *U.S. Public*, pg. 2251
THE SURGICAL CENTER OF THE TREASURE COAST, LLC—See UnitedHealth Group Incorporated; *U.S. Public*, pg. 2251
SURGICAL DIRECTIONS, LLC—See MEDNAX, Inc.; *U.S. Public*, pg. 1413
SURGICAL ELITE OF AVONDALE, L.L.C.—See Tenet Healthcare Corporation; *U.S. Public*, pg. 2005
SURGICAL EYE EXPEDITIONS INTERNATIONAL; *U.S. Private*, pg. 3884
SURGICAL HOSPITAL OF AUSTIN, L.P.—See Bain Capital, LP; *U.S. Private*, pg. 447
SURGICAL HOSPITAL OF OKLAHOMA, LLC—See UnitedHealth Group Incorporated; *U.S. Public*, pg. 2251
SURGICAL INFORMATION SYSTEMS, LLC—See Wells Fargo & Company; *U.S. Public*, pg. 2344
SURGICAL INNOVATIONS GROUP PLC; *Int'l*, pg. 7344
SURGICAL INNOVATIONS LIMITED—See Surgical Innovations Group Plc; *Int'l*, pg. 7344
SURGICAL INSTITUTE OF READING, LLC—See Tenet Healthcare Corporation; *U.S. Public*, pg. 2013
SURGICAL PARK CENTER, LTD.—See HCA Healthcare, Inc.; *U.S. Public*, pg. 1011
SURGICAL PRINCIPALS, INC.; *U.S. Private*, pg. 3884
SURGICAL PROCESS INSTITUTE DEUTSCHLAND GMBH—See Johnson & Johnson; *U.S. Public*, pg. 1200
SURGICAL PRODUCT SOLUTIONS LLC—See Shore Capital Partners, LLC; *U.S. Private*, pg. 3641
SURGICAL SCIENCE SWEDEN AB; *Int'l*, pg. 7344
SURGICAL SITE SOLUTIONS, INC.—See Becton, Dickinson & Company; *U.S. Public*, pg. 292
SURGICAL SOLUTIONS, LLC; *U.S. Private*, pg. 3884
SURGICAL SPECIALISTS AT PRINCETON, LLC—See Tenet Healthcare Corporation; *U.S. Public*, pg. 2013
SURGICAL SPECIALISTS OF CLEAR LAKE, PLLC—See HCA Healthcare, Inc.; *U.S. Public*, pg. 1011
SURGICAL SPECIALTIES CORPORATION—See GTCR LLC; *U.S. Private*, pg. 1804
SURGICAL SPECIALTY CENTER OF MID-ATLANTIC, LLC—See Tenet Healthcare Corporation; *U.S. Public*, pg. 2007
SURGICAL SPECIALTY CENTER OF NORTHEASTERN PENNSYLVANIA, LLC—See KKR & Co. Inc.; *U.S. Public*, pg. 1250
SURGICAL STAFF, INC.; *U.S. Private*, pg. 3885
SURGICAL TABLES INC.—See ADDvise Group AB; *Int'l*, pg. 136
SURGICAL TECHNOLOGIES BV—See Permira Advisers LLP; *Int'l*, pg. 5808
SURGI-CARE, INC.—See Enovis Corporation; *U.S. Public*, pg. 773
SURGICARE OF CENTRAL JERSEY, LLC—See UnitedHealth Group Incorporated; *U.S. Public*, pg. 2251
SURGICARE OF CENTRAL PARK SURGERY CENTER, LLC—See HCA Healthcare, Inc.; *U.S. Public*, pg. 1011
SURGICARE OF CLARKSVILLE, LLC—See HCA Healthcare, Inc.; *U.S. Public*, pg. 1011
SURGICARE OF CORPUS CHRISTI, LLC—See HCA Healthcare, Inc.; *U.S. Public*, pg. 1011
SURGICARE OF COUNTRYSIDE, INC.—See HCA Healthcare, Inc.; *U.S. Public*, pg. 1011
SURGICARE OF DENVER MID-TOWN, INC.—See HCA Healthcare, Inc.; *U.S. Public*, pg. 1011
SURGICARE OF JACKSON, LLC—See UnitedHealth Group Incorporated; *U.S. Public*, pg. 2251
SURGICARE OF MIRAMAR, L.L.C.—See Tenet Healthcare Corporation; *U.S. Public*, pg. 2008
SURGICARE OF MOBILE, LLC—See UnitedHealth Group Incorporated; *U.S. Public*, pg. 2251
SURGICARE OF SALEM, LLC—See HCA Healthcare, Inc.; *U.S. Public*, pg. 1011
SURGICARE OF SOUTH AUSTIN, INC.—See HCA Healthcare, Inc.; *U.S. Public*, pg. 1011
SURGICARE OF SOUTH AUSTIN—See HCA Healthcare, Inc.; *U.S. Public*, pg. 1011
SURGICARE OF SOUTHERN HILLS, INC.—See HCA Healthcare, Inc.; *U.S. Public*, pg. 1011

SURGICAL STAFF, INC.

SURGICARE OF WASATCH FRONT, LLC—See HCA Healthcare, Inc.; *U.S. Public*, pg. 1011
SURGICARE OF WICHITA, LLC—See HCA Healthcare, Inc.; *U.S. Public*, pg. 1011
SURGICARE OUTPATIENT CENTER OF LAKE CHARLES, INC.—See Community Health Systems, Inc.; *U.S. Public*, pg. 557
SURGICARE - UNIDADES DE SAUDE, S.A.—See Fosun International Limited; *Int'l*, pg. 2751
SURGICENTER OF BALTIMORE, LLP—See Tenet Healthcare Corporation; *U.S. Public*, pg. 2013
SURGICENTER OF JOHNSON COUNTY, LTD.—See HCA Healthcare, Inc.; *U.S. Public*, pg. 1011
SURGICENTER OF JOHNSON COUNTY—See HCA Healthcare, Inc.; *U.S. Public*, pg. 1003
SURGICENTER OF KANSAS CITY, L.L.C.—See HCA Healthcare, Inc.; *U.S. Public*, pg. 1011
SURGIQUEST, INC.—See CONMED Corporation; *U.S. Public*, pg. 567
SUR GRO PLANT FOOD CO., INC.; *U.S. Private*, pg. 3883
SURGUTGAZPROM—See PJSC Gazprom; *Int'l*, pg. 5880
SURGUTNEFTEGAS OAO; *Int'l*, pg. 7344
SURIA BUMIRIA SDN. BHD.—See Suria Capital Holdings Berhad; *Int'l*, pg. 7344
SURIA CAPITAL HOLDINGS BERHAD; *Int'l*, pg. 7344
SURINAME ALCHOLIC BEVERAGES N.V.—See Angostura Holdings Limited; *Int'l*, pg. 463
SURINAME ALUMINUM COMPANY, L.L.C.—See Alcoa Corporation; *U.S. Public*, pg. 74
SURINAME CABLE AND COMMUNICATION NETWORK N.V.—See Rudisa Holdingmaatschappij N.V.; *Int'l*, pg. 6424
SURINAME GOLD COMPANY, LLC—See Newmont Corporation; *U.S. Public*, pg. 1517
SURINAME HOUT & HOUTVERWERKING INDUSTRIE N.V.—See Rudisa Holdingmaatschappij N.V.; *Int'l*, pg. 6424
SURINT OMYA (VIETNAM) CO., LTD.—See Omya (Schweiz) AG; *Int'l*, pg. 5572
SURKOREA CORPORATION—See KODI Co., Ltd.; *Int'l*, pg. 4226
SUR LA TABLE INC.—See Investcorp Holdings B.S.C.; *Int'l*, pg. 3776
SURLEAN MEAT CO.—See L&H Packing Company; *U.S. Private*, pg. 2362
SURLY BREWING CO.; *U.S. Private*, pg. 3885
SURMA HOLDINGS B.V.—See Cementos Molins S.A.; *Int'l*, pg. 1398
SURMA HOLDINGS B.V.—See Holcim Ltd.; *Int'l*, pg. 3449
SURMODICS, INC.; *U.S. Public*, pg. 1967
SURMODICS IVD, INC.—See SurModics, Inc.; *U.S. Public*, pg. 1967
SURMODICS MD, LLC—See SurModics, Inc.; *U.S. Public*, pg. 1967
SURO CAPITAL CORP.; *U.S. Public*, pg. 1967
SURONGO SA; *Int'l*, pg. 7344
SURPLUS ACQUISITION VENTURE, LLC—See Liquidity Services, Inc.; *U.S. Public*, pg. 1321
SURPLUS CENTER—See Burden Sales Company; *U.S. Private*, pg. 686
SURPLUS DIABETIC, INC.—See ADDvise Group AB; *Int'l*, pg. 136
SURPLUSGLOBAL, INC.; *Int'l*, pg. 7344
SURPRISE INDEPENDENT—See Independent Newspapers, Inc.; *U.S. Private*, pg. 2060
SURPRO GMBH; *Int'l*, pg. 7344
SURREY BANCORP—See First Community Bankshares, Inc.; *U.S. Public*, pg. 842
SURREY & BERKSHIRE MEDIA LIMITED—See Reach PLC; *Int'l*, pg. 6231
SURREY ENVELOPES LTD—See Bong AB; *Int'l*, pg. 1107
SURREY HONDA; *Int'l*, pg. 7344
SURREY MOTORS LIMITED—See Panther Securities PLC; *Int'l*, pg. 5731
SURREY SATELLITE SERVICES LTD.—See Airbus SE; *Int'l*, pg. 245
SURREY SATELLITE TECHNOLOGY LTD.—See Airbus SE; *Int'l*, pg. 245
SURROZEN, INC.; *U.S. Public*, pg. 1968
SURSCHISTE, S.A.—See E.ON SE; *Int'l*, pg. 2259
SUR-SEAL, INC.; *U.S. Private*, pg. 3883
SUR-SEAL LLC; *U.S. Private*, pg. 3883
SURTEC ADRIA D.O.O.—See Freudenberg SE; *Int'l*, pg. 2790
SURTEC BENELUX B.V.—See Freudenberg SE; *Int'l*, pg. 2790
SURTEC CACAK D.O.O.—See Freudenberg SE; *Int'l*, pg. 2790
SURTEC CHEMICALS INDIA PVT. LTD.—See Freudenberg SE; *Int'l*, pg. 2790
SURTEC CR S.R.O.—See Freudenberg SE; *Int'l*, pg. 2790
SURTEC DEUTSCHLAND GMBH—See Freudenberg SE; *Int'l*, pg. 2790
SURTEC DO BRASIL LTDA.—See Freudenberg SE; *Int'l*, pg. 2790
SURTEC D.O.O.—See Freudenberg SE; *Int'l*, pg. 2790
SURTEC FRANCE S.A.S.—See Freudenberg SE; *Int'l*, pg. 2790

SURTECH SYSTEMS PTY LTD.—See Orica Limited; *Int'l*, pg. 5621
SURTEC, INC.—See Freudenberg SE; *Int'l*, pg. 2790
SURTEC INTERNATIONAL GMBH—See Freudenberg SE; *Int'l*, pg. 2790
SURTEC KOREA CO., LTD.—See Freudenberg SE; *Int'l*, pg. 2790
SURTEC METAL SURFACE TREATMENT TECHNOLOGY CO. LTD.—See Freudenberg SE; *Int'l*, pg. 2790
SURTEC MMC JAPAN KK—See Freudenberg SE; *Int'l*, pg. 2790
SURTECO ART GMBH—See Surteco Group SE; *Int'l*, pg. 7345
SURTECO AUSTRALIA PTY. LTD.—See Surteco Group SE; *Int'l*, pg. 7345
SURTECO CANADA LTD.—See Surteco Group SE; *Int'l*, pg. 7345
SURTECO DECORATIVE MATERIAL CO. LTD.—See Surteco Group SE; *Int'l*, pg. 7345
SURTECO DEKOR A.S.—See Surteco Group SE; *Int'l*, pg. 7345
SURTECO FRANCE S.A.S.—See Surteco Group SE; *Int'l*, pg. 7345
SURTECO GMBH—See Surteco Group SE; *Int'l*, pg. 7345
SURTECO GROUP SE; *Int'l*, pg. 7344
SURTECO IBERIA S.L.—See Surteco Group SE; *Int'l*, pg. 7345
SURTECO NORTH AMERICA INC.—See Surteco Group SE; *Int'l*, pg. 7345
SURTECO PTE. LTD.—See Surteco Group SE; *Int'l*, pg. 7345
SURTECO UK LTD.—See Surteco Group SE; *Int'l*, pg. 7345
SURTECO USA INC.—See Surteco Group SE; *Int'l*, pg. 7345
SURTEC POLSKA SP. Z O.O.—See Freudenberg SE; *Int'l*, pg. 2790
SURTEC PRODUKTE UND SYSTEME FUR DIE OBERFLACHENBEHANDLUNG GESMBH—See Freudenberg SE; *Int'l*, pg. 2790
SURTEC ROMANIA S.R.L.—See Freudenberg SE; *Int'l*, pg. 2790
SURTEC SCANDINAVIA APS—See Freudenberg SE; *Int'l*, pg. 2790
SURTEC SK S.R.O.—See Freudenberg SE; *Int'l*, pg. 2790
SURTEC SOUTH AFRICA PTY. LTD.—See Freudenberg SE; *Int'l*, pg. 2790
SURTEC VIET NAM CO., LTD.—See Freudenberg SE; *Int'l*, pg. 2790
SURTIGAS S.A. E.S.P.—See Grupo Aval Acciones y Valores S.A.; *Int'l*, pg. 3121
SURTRON TECHNOLOGIES PTY LTD.—See Kinetic Consolidated Pty Ltd; *Int'l*, pg. 4167
SURUGA BANK LTD.; *Int'l*, pg. 7345
SURUGA CARD CO., LTD.—See Suruga Bank Ltd.; *Int'l*, pg. 7345
SURUGA COMPUTER SERVICE CO., LTD.—See Suruga Bank Ltd.; *Int'l*, pg. 7345
SURUGA INDIA PVT. LTD.—See MISUMI Group Inc.; *Int'l*, pg. 4922
SURUGA KOREA CO., LTD.—See MISUMI Group Inc.; *Int'l*, pg. 4922
SURUGA POLSKA SP. Z O.O.—See MISUMI Group Inc.; *Int'l*, pg. 4922
SURUGA PRODUCTION PLATFORM CO., LTD.—See MISUMI Group Inc.; *Int'l*, pg. 4922
SURUGA SEIKI CO., LTD. - KANSAI PLANT—See MISUMI Group Inc.; *Int'l*, pg. 4922
SURUGA SEIKI (GUANGZHOU) CO., LTD.—See MISUMI Group Inc.; *Int'l*, pg. 4922
SURUGA SEIKI (NANTONG) CO., LTD.—See MISUMI Group Inc.; *Int'l*, pg. 4922
SURUGA SEIKI SALES & TRADING (SHANGHAI) CO., LTD.—See MISUMI Group Inc.; *Int'l*, pg. 4922
SURUGA SEIKI (SHANGHAI) CO.,LTD.—See MISUMI Group Inc.; *Int'l*, pg. 4922
SURUGA (THAILAND) CO., LTD.—See MISUMI Group Inc.; *Int'l*, pg. 4922
SURUGA TOYO KAISHA, LTD.—See Toyo Suisan Kaisha, Ltd.; *Int'l*, pg. 7858
SURUGA USA CORP.—See MISUMI Group Inc.; *Int'l*, pg. 4922
SURU GROUP LTD.—See Haldane McCall PLC; *Int'l*, pg. 3227
SURU HOMES LTD—See Haldane McCall PLC; *Int'l*, pg. 3227
SURVEILLANCE AUSTRALIA PTY LIMITED—See Advent International Corporation; *U.S. Private*, pg. 100
SURVEYCONNECT INC.—See Orcus Technologies, Inc.; *U.S. Private*, pg. 3039
SURVEYING AND MAPPING, LLC; *U.S. Private*, pg. 3885
SURVEYING & MAPPING, LLC—See Peak Rock Capital LLC; *U.S. Private*, pg. 3124
SURVEYMONKEY.COM LLC; *U.S. Private*, pg. 3885
SURVEYVITALS, INC.; *U.S. Private*, pg. 3885
SURVIAL S.A.—See Aenza S.A.A.; *Int'l*, pg. 176
SURVIRN ENGINEERING LTD.—See Harlow Aerostructures, LLC; *U.S. Private*, pg. 1865

CORPORATE AFFILIATIONS

SURVITEC GROUP LIMITED—See ONEX Corporation; *Int'l*, pg. 5580
SURVITEC SERVICE & DISTRIBUTION B.V.—See ONEX Corporation; *Int'l*, pg. 5580
SURVITEC SERVICE & DISTRIBUTION GMBH—See ONEX Corporation; *Int'l*, pg. 5580
SURVITEC SERVICE & DISTRIBUTION LIMITED—See ONEX Corporation; *Int'l*, pg. 5580
SURVITEC SERVICE & DISTRIBUTION N.V.—See ONEX Corporation; *Int'l*, pg. 5580
SURVIVAL INSURANCE, INC.—See Stone Point Capital LLC; *U.S. Private*, pg. 3819
SURVIVAL MEDIA LLC; *U.S. Private*, pg. 3885
SURVIVAL-ONE LIMITED—See ONEX Corporation; *Int'l*, pg. 5580
SURYAAMBA SPINNING MILLS LIMITED; *Int'l*, pg. 7345
SURYACHAKRA POWER CORPORATION LTD; *Int'l*, pg. 7345
SURYA INC.; *U.S. Private*, pg. 3885
SURYA INDIA LTD.; *Int'l*, pg. 7345
SURYAJYOTI LIFE INSURANCE COMPANY LTD.; *Int'l*, pg. 7345
SURYAJYOTI SPINNING MILLS LIMITED; *Int'l*, pg. 7345
SURYAKIRAN INTERNATIONAL LTD—See Suryalakshmi Cotton Mills Limited; *Int'l*, pg. 7345
SURYALAKSHMI COTTON MILLS LIMITED; *Int'l*, pg. 7345
SURYALATA SPINNING MILLS LIMITED; *Int'l*, pg. 7345
SURYA PHARMACEUTICAL LIMITED; *Int'l*, pg. 7345
SURYA ROSHNI LED LIGHTING PROJECTS LIMITED—See Surya Roshni Limited; *Int'l*, pg. 7345
SURYA ROSHNI LIMITED; *Int'l*, pg. 7345
SURYAVANSHI SPINNING MILLS LIMITED; *Int'l*, pg. 7346
SURYA VIDYUT LIMITED—See Torrent Power Limited; *Int'l*, pg. 7831
SURYODAYA INVESTMENT & TRADING COMPANY LIMITED; *Int'l*, pg. 7346
SURYODAY ALLO-METALS POWDERS LIMITED; *Int'l*, pg. 7346
SURYODAYA WOMI LAGHUBITTA BITTIYA SANSTHA LTD; *Int'l*, pg. 7346
SURYODAY SMALL FINANCE BANK LTD.; *Int'l*, pg. 7346
SURYO FOODS & INDUSTRIES LIMITED; *Int'l*, pg. 7346
S.USA LIFE INSURANCE COMPANY, INC.—See Prosperity Group Holdings, LP; *U.S. Private*, pg. 3289
SUSAN DAVIS INTERNATIONAL; *U.S. Private*, pg. 3885
SUSAN SCHEIN AUTOMOTIVE; *U.S. Private*, pg. 3885
SUS CO., LTD.; *Int'l*, pg. 7346
SUSCO PUBLIC COMPANY LIMITED; *Int'l*, pg. 7346
SUSCRIPCIONES ESPANA—See ADLPartner SA; *Int'l*, pg. 151
SUSE LINUX GMBH—See EQT AB; *Int'l*, pg. 2481
SUSE S.A.—See EQT AB; *Int'l*, pg. 2479
SUSGLOBAL ENERGY BELLEVILLE LTD.—See SusGlobal Energy Corp.; *Int'l*, pg. 7346
SUSGLOBAL ENERGY CORP.; *Int'l*, pg. 7346
SUSHI BAR ATARI-YA LIMITED—See JFLA Holdings Inc.; *Int'l*, pg. 3939
SUSHI GUANGBO ENVIRONMENT & RELIABILITY TECHNOLOGY (CHONGQING) CO., LTD.—See Suzhou Sushi Testing Group Co., Ltd.; *Int'l*, pg. 7352
SUSHI GUANGBO ENVIRONMENT & RELIABILITY TECHNOLOGY (NANJING) CO., LTD—See Suzhou Sushi Testing Group Co., Ltd.; *Int'l*, pg. 7352
SUSHI KING SDN. BHD.—See Texchem Resources Bhd.; *Int'l*, pg. 7583
SUSHI LYON 64 SAS—See AmRest Holdings SE; *Int'l*, pg. 437
SUSHIRO KOREA, INC.—See Food & Life Companies Ltd.; *Int'l*, pg. 2727
SUSHI SHOP AMIENS SARL—See AmRest Holdings SE; *Int'l*, pg. 437
SUSHI SHOP ANGERS SARL—See AmRest Holdings SE; *Int'l*, pg. 437
SUSHI SHOP CAEN SARL—See AmRest Holdings SE; *Int'l*, pg. 437
SUSHI SHOP CAUDERAN SAS—See AmRest Holdings SE; *Int'l*, pg. 437
SUSHI SHOP COURCELLES SARL—See AmRest Holdings SE; *Int'l*, pg. 437
SUSHI SHOP GENEVE SA—See AmRest Holdings SE; *Int'l*, pg. 437
SUSHI SHOP LA ROCHELLE SARL—See AmRest Holdings SE; *Int'l*, pg. 437
SUSHI SHOP LAUSANNE SARL—See AmRest Holdings SE; *Int'l*, pg. 437
SUSHI SHOP LE MANS SARL—See AmRest Holdings SE; *Int'l*, pg. 437
SUSHI SHOP LEPIC SARL—See AmRest Holdings SE; *Int'l*, pg. 438
SUSHI SHOP LEVALLOIS SARL—See AmRest Holdings SE; *Int'l*, pg. 437
SUSHI SHOP LILLE CENTRE SAS—See AmRest Holdings SE; *Int'l*, pg. 438
SUSHI SHOP LOUISE SA—See AmRest Holdings SE; *Int'l*, pg. 438
SUSHI SHOP MARTYRS SARL—See AmRest Holdings SE; *Int'l*, pg. 438

COMPANY NAME INDEX

SUSHI SHOP NYON SARL—See AmRest Holdings SE; *Int'l*, pg. 438
SUSHI SHOP RENNES NEMOURS SARL—See AmRest Holdings SE; *Int'l*, pg. 438
SUSHI SHOP ROUEN SAS—See AmRest Holdings SE; *Int'l*, pg. 438
SUSHI SHOP SECRETAN SARL—See AmRest Holdings SE; *Int'l*, pg. 438
SUSHI SHOP ST DOMINIQUE SARL—See AmRest Holdings SE; *Int'l*, pg. 438
SUSHI SHOP TOULOUSE 3 SARL—See AmRest Holdings SE; *Int'l*, pg. 438
SUSHI SHOP TOURS SARL—See AmRest Holdings SE; *Int'l*, pg. 438
SUSHI SHOP VINCENNES SARL—See AmRest Holdings SE; *Int'l*, pg. 438
SUSHI SHOP ZURICH GMBH—See AmRest Holdings SE; *Int'l*, pg. 438
SUSHI ZHONGBO ENVIRONMENT & RELIABILITY TECHNOLOGY (CHONGQING) CO., LTD—See Suzhou Sushi Testing Group Co., Ltd.; *Int'l*, pg. 7352
SUSI PARTNERS AG; *Int'l*, pg. 7346
SUSMED, INC.; *Int'l*, pg. 7346
SUSPA COMPART ASIA PTE. LTD.—See Andlinger & Company, Inc.; *U.S. Private*, pg. 279
SUSPA GMBH—See Andlinger & Company, Inc.; *U.S. Private*, pg. 279
SUSPA, INC.—See Andlinger & Company, Inc.; *U.S. Private*, pg. 279
SUSPA NANJING CO. LTD.—See Andlinger & Company, Inc.; *U.S. Private*, pg. 279
SUSPA PNEUMATICS INDIA PVT. LTD.—See Andlinger & Company, Inc.; *U.S. Private*, pg. 279
SUSPA TEC AG—See Andlinger & Company, Inc.; *U.S. Private*, pg. 279
SUSPA UK LTD.—See Andlinger & Company, Inc.; *U.S. Private*, pg. 279
SUSPA VERTRIEBSGESELLSCHAFT MBH—See Andlinger & Company, Inc.; *U.S. Private*, pg. 279
SUSPECT DETECTION SYSTEMS INC.; *U.S. Private*, pg. 3885
SUSPECT DETECTION SYSTEMS LTD.—See Suspect Detection Systems Inc.; *U.S. Private*, pg. 3885
SUSQUEHANNA COMMUNITY FINANCIAL, INC.; *U.S. Public*, pg. 1968
SUSQUEHANNA GROWTH EQUITY, LLC—See Susquehanna International Group, LLP; *U.S. Private*, pg. 3885
SUSQUEHANNA INTERNATIONAL GROUP, LLP; *U.S. Private*, pg. 3885
SUSQUEHANNA INTERNATIONAL SECURITIES, LTD.—See Susquehanna International Group, LLP; *U.S. Private*, pg. 3885
SUSQUEHANNA PRIVATE CAPITAL, LLC—See Susquehanna International Group, LLP; *U.S. Private*, pg. 3885
SUSQUEHANNA PROPERTIES, INC.—See Delaware Otsego Corp.; *U.S. Private*, pg. 1195
SUSQUEHANNA VALLEY WATER CONDITIONING CO.—See Culligan Soft Water Service Co.; *U.S. Private*, pg. 1121
SUSQUE-VIEW HOME, INC.; *U.S. Private*, pg. 3885
SUSSER ENERGY SERVICES LLC—See Energy Transfer LP; *U.S. Public*, pg. 764
SUSSER HOLDINGS CORPORATION—See Sunoco LP; *U.S. Public*, pg. 1965
SUSSER PETROLEUM COMPANY—See Sunoco LP; *U.S. Public*, pg. 1965
SUSSER PETROLEUM OPERATING COMPANY LLC—See Sunoco LP; *U.S. Public*, pg. 1965
SUSSEX HALL APARTMENTS—See Revona Properties; *U.S. Private*, pg. 3417
SUSSEX INSURANCE AGENCY INCORPORATED; *Int'l*, pg. 7347
SUSSEX INSURANCE COMPANY—See Enstar Group Limited; *Int'l*, pg. 2449
SUSSEX NEWSPAPERS LTD—See JPIMedia Holdings Limited; *Int'l*, pg. 4007
SUSSEX POST—See Independent Newspapers, Inc.; *U.S. Private*, pg. 2060
SUSSEX PUBLISHERS, LLC; *U.S. Private*, pg. 3886
SUSSEX RURAL ELECTRIC COOPERATIVE; *U.S. Private*, pg. 3886
SUSSEX WIRE, INC.—See Argosy Capital Group, LLC; *U.S. Private*, pg. 321
SUS(SINGAPORE) PTE. LTD.—See SUS Co., Ltd.; *Int'l*, pg. 7346
SUSSMAN SALES COMPANY; *U.S. Private*, pg. 3886
SUSS MICROTEC COMPANY LTD—See SUSS MicroTec SE; *Int'l*, pg. 7346
SUSS MICROTEC, INC.—See SUSS MicroTec SE; *Int'l*, pg. 7347
SUSS MICROTEC KK—See SUSS MicroTec SE; *Int'l*, pg. 7346
SUSS MICROTEC KOREA CO. LTD—See SUSS MicroTec SE; *Int'l*, pg. 7347
SUSS MICROTEC LITHOGRAPHY GMBH—See SUSS MicroTec SE; *Int'l*, pg. 7346
SUSS MICROTEC LITHOGRAPHY GMBH—See SUSS MicroTec SE; *Int'l*, pg. 7346
SUSS MICROTEC LTD.—See SUSS MicroTec SE; *Int'l*, pg. 7346
SUSS MICROTEC PHOTOMASK EQUIPMENT GMBH & CO. KG—See SUSS MicroTec SE; *Int'l*, pg. 7346
SUSS MICROTEC REMAN GMBH—See SUSS MicroTec SE; *Int'l*, pg. 7346
SUSS MICROTEC S.A.R.L.—See SUSS MicroTec SE; *Int'l*, pg. 7347
SUSS MICROTEC S.A.S—See SUSS MicroTec SE; *Int'l*, pg. 7347
SUSS MICROTEC SE; *Int'l*, pg. 7346
SUSS MICROTEC (SINGAPORE) PTE. LTD.—See SUSS MicroTec SE; *Int'l*, pg. 7346
SUSS MICROTEC (TAIWAN) CO., LTD—See SUSS MicroTec SE; *Int'l*, pg. 7346
SUSTAINABLE COMFORT, INC.; *U.S. Private*, pg. 3886
SUSTAINABLE ENERGY EUROPA SL—See Eguana Technologies Inc.; *Int'l*, pg. 2327
SUSTAINABLE ENERGY SOLUTIONS, INC.—See Chart Industries, Inc.; *U.S. Public*, pg. 482
SUSTAINABLE ENERGY SYSTEMS INC—See Eguana Technologies Inc.; *Int'l*, pg. 2327
SUSTAINABLE FIBRE SOLUTIONS (PTY) LTD—See Industrial Development Corporation of South Africa, Ltd.; *Int'l*, pg. 3672
SUSTAINABLE GREEN TEAM LTD.; *U.S. Public*, pg. 1968
SUSTAINABLE GROWTH ADVISERS, LP—See Virtus Investment Partners, Inc.; *U.S. Public*, pg. 2301
SUSTAINABLE HARVEST COFFEE IMPORTERS; *U.S. Private*, pg. 3886
SUSTAINABLE INNOVATIONS, LLC; *U.S. Private*, pg. 3886
SUSTAINABLE PRODUCT STEWARDS PTY. LTD.—See SK Inc.; *Int'l*, pg. 6973
SUSTAINABLE PROJECTS GROUP INC.; *U.S. Public*, pg. 1968
SUSTAINABLE RESOURCES MANAGEMENT, LLC—See Quest Resource Holding Corporation; *U.S. Public*, pg. 1756
SUSTAINALYTICS JAPAN INC.—See Morningstar, Inc.; *U.S. Public*, pg. 1477
SUSTAINALYTICS UK LIMITED—See Morningstar, Inc.; *U.S. Public*, pg. 1477
SUSTAINALYTICS U.S. INC.—See Morningstar, Inc.; *U.S. Public*, pg. 1477
SUSTAINED INFRASTRUCTURE HOLDING COMPANY SJSC; *Int'l*, pg. 7347
SUSTAINED QUALITY LLC—See Groupe Crit, S.A.; *Int'l*, pg. 3101
SUSTAINSERV, INC.; *U.S. Private*, pg. 3886
SUSTAIN TECHNOLOGIES, INC.—See Daily Journal Corporation; *U.S. Public*, pg. 620
SUSTINERE HOLDINGS, INC.; *U.S. Private*, pg. 3886
SUSU LEMBU ASLI (JOHORE) SDN. BHD.—See Asahi Group Holdings Ltd.; *Int'l*, pg. 593
SUSU LEMBU ASLI MARKETING SDN. BHD.—See Asahi Group Holdings Ltd.; *Int'l*, pg. 593
SUSY CARD GMBH—See Pelikan International Corporation Berhad; *Int'l*, pg. 5783
SUTARIA SERVICES INC.—See Elisa Corporation; *Int'l*, pg. 2361
SUTEKI EUROPE NV—See Nice Corporation; *Int'l*, pg. 5264
SUTERA HARBOUR RESORT SDN BHD—See GSH Corporation Limited; *Int'l*, pg. 3144
SUTERRA LLC—See The Wonderful Company LLC; *U.S. Private*, pg. 4138
SUT GLOBAL COMPANY LIMITED—See Hydrotek Public Company Limited; *Int'l*, pg. 3548
SUTHERLAND BUILDING MATERIAL COMPANY; *U.S. Private*, pg. 3886
SUTHERLAND CARE CENTER—See AlerisLife Inc.; *U.S. Private*, pg. 162
SUTHERLAND CONSULTING LIMITED—See Capgemini SE; *Int'l*, pg. 1305
SUTHERLAND GLOBAL SERVICES EGYPT, LLC—See Sutherland Global Services, Inc.; *U.S. Private*, pg. 3886
SUTHERLAND GLOBAL SERVICES, INC.; *U.S. Private*, pg. 3886
SUTHERLAND GLOBAL SERVICES JLT—See Sutherland Global Services, Inc.; *U.S. Private*, pg. 3886
SUTHERLAND LUMBER CO.; *U.S. Private*, pg. 3886
SUTHERLAND LUMBER & HOME CENTER INC.; *U.S. Private*, pg. 3886
SUTHERLAND MANAGEMENT COMPANY; *U.S. Private*, pg. 3886
SUTHERLAND PRINTING, INC.—See Nationwide Argosy Solutions, LLC; *U.S. Private*, pg. 2865
SUTHERLAND'S FOODSERVICE, INC.; *U.S. Private*, pg. 3886
SUTHERLAND (SUZHOU) INFORMATION CONSULTING CO., LTD.—See Sutherland Global Services, Inc.; *U.S. Private*, pg. 3886
SUTHERLIN AUTOMOTIVE GROUP, LLC; *U.S. Private*, pg. 3886
SUTHERLIN H. IMPORTS, LLC—See AutoNation, Inc.; *U.S. Public*, pg. 237
SUTHERLIN H. IMPORTS, LLC—See AutoNation, Inc.; *U.S. Public*, pg. 237
SUTHERLIN IMPORTS, LLC—See AutoNation, Inc.; *U.S. Public*, pg. 237
SUTHERLIN NISSAN, LLC—See AutoNation, Inc.; *U.S. Public*, pg. 238
SUTHERLIN OPTICAL COMPANY—See EssilorLuxottica SA; *Int'l*, pg. 2514
SUTIMCO INTERNATIONAL, INC.—See AURI, Inc.; *U.S. Public*, pg. 227
SUTLEJ TEXTILES & INDUSTRIES LTD - RAJASTHAN TEXTILE MILLS—See K.K. Birla Group; *Int'l*, pg. 4044
SUTLEJ TEXTILES & INDUSTRIES LTD.—See K.K. Birla Group; *Int'l*, pg. 4044
SUTL ENTERPRISE LIMITED; *Int'l*, pg. 7347
SUTLIFF AUTO GROUP; *U.S. Private*, pg. 3887
SUTLIFF BUICK GMC CADILLAC—See Sutliff Auto Group; *U.S. Private*, pg. 3887
SUTLIFF CHEVROLET CO.—See Sutliff Auto Group; *U.S. Private*, pg. 3887
SUTLIFF TOBACCO COMPANY, LLC—See Skandinavisk Holding A/S; *Int'l*, pg. 6976
SUTOR TECHNOLOGY GROUP LTD.; *Int'l*, pg. 7347
THE SUTPHEN CORPORATION; *U.S. Private*, pg. 4125
SUTRANS N.V.—See REWE-Zentral-Aktiengesellschaft; *Int'l*, pg. 6315
SUTRA SOFTWARE PRIVATE LIMITED—See SecMark Consultancy Limited; *Int'l*, pg. 6670
SUTRO BIOPHARMA, INC.; *U.S. Public*, pg. 1968
SUTRON CORPORATION—See Danaher Corporation; *U.S. Public*, pg. 627
SUTRON ELECTRONIC GMBH—See PHOENIX CONTACT GmbH & Co. KG; *Int'l*, pg. 5850
SUTRO TOWER, INC.—See Nexstar Media Group, Inc.; *U.S. Public*, pg. 1524
SUT SAWMILL (3064) SDN. BHD.—See W T K Holdings Berhad; *Int'l*, pg. 8320
SUTTER ALHAMBRA SURGERY CENTER, L.P.—See UnitedHealth Group Incorporated; *U.S. Public*, pg. 2251
SUTTER AMADOR HOSPITAL—See Sutter Health; *U.S. Private*, pg. 3887
SUTTER DAVIS HOSPITAL—See Sutter Health; *U.S. Private*, pg. 3887
SUTTER DELTA MEDICAL CENTER—See Sutter Health; *U.S. Private*, pg. 3887
SUTTER GOLD MINING, INC.; *U.S. Public*, pg. 1968
SUTTER HEALTH; *U.S. Private*, pg. 3887
SUTTER INSURANCE COMPANY; *U.S. Private*, pg. 3887
SUTTER LAKESIDE HOSPITAL—See Sutter Health; *U.S. Private*, pg. 3887
SUTTER, MCLELLAN & GILBREATH, INC.—See Genstar Capital, LLC; *U.S. Private*, pg. 1675
SUTTER MEDICAL CENTER FOUNDATION—See Sutter Health; *U.S. Private*, pg. 3887
SUTTER MEDICAL CENTER, SACRAMENTO—See Sutter Health; *U.S. Private*, pg. 3887
SUTTER ROOFING COMPANY OF FLORIDA; *U.S. Private*, pg. 3887
SUTTER SECURITIES, INC.—See Flashfunders, Inc.; *U.S. Private*, pg. 1540
SUTTER'S PLACE INC.; *U.S. Private*, pg. 3887
SUTTLE APPARATUS CORPORATION—See Pineapple Energy Inc.; *U.S. Public*, pg. 1691
SUTTLE EQUIPMENT INC.; *U.S. Private*, pg. 3887
SUTTLE, INC.—See Pineapple Energy Inc.; *U.S. Public*, pg. 1691
SUTTLE MOTOR CORP.; *U.S. Private*, pg. 3887
SUTTLE-STRAUS INC.—See Telephone & Data Systems, Inc.; *U.S. Public*, pg. 1997
SUTTLES TRUCK LEASING INC.—See Dana Transport Inc.; *U.S. Private*, pg. 1152
SUTTON CORPORATION; *U.S. Private*, pg. 3887
SUTTON FERNERIES, INC.; *U.S. Private*, pg. 3887
SUTTON HARBOUR COMPANY—See Sutton Harbour Group PLC; *Int'l*, pg. 7347
SUTTON HARBOUR DEVELOPMENT LIMITED—See Sutton Harbour Group PLC; *Int'l*, pg. 7347
SUTTON HARBOUR GROUP PLC; *Int'l*, pg. 7347
SUTTON HARBOUR SERVICES LIMITED—See Sutton Harbour Group PLC; *Int'l*, pg. 7347
SUTTON JAMES INCORPORATED—See Optisure Risk Partners, LLC; *U.S. Private*, pg. 3035
SUTTONS AND ROBERTSONS LIMITED—See Lone Star Global Acquisitions, LLC; *U.S. Private*, pg. 2487
SUTTONS CONSUMER PRODUCTS LIMITED; *Int'l*, pg. 7347
SUTTONS INTERNATIONAL FREIGHT FORWARDING (SHANGHAI) CO., LTD—See Suttons Transport Group Ltd.; *Int'l*, pg. 7347
SUTTONS INTERNATIONAL GMBH—See Suttons Transport Group Ltd.; *Int'l*, pg. 7347
SUTTONS INTERNATIONAL JAPAN KK—See Suttons Transport Group Ltd.; *Int'l*, pg. 7347
SUTTONS INTERNATIONAL N.A. INC.—See Suttons Transport Group Ltd.; *Int'l*, pg. 7347
SUTTONS INTERNATIONAL NV—See Suttons Transport Group Ltd.; *Int'l*, pg. 7347

SUTTONS INTERNATIONAL SINGAPORE PTE LTD—See Suttons Transport Group Ltd.; *Int'l*, pg. 7347
SUTTONS LIMITED—See Bord na Mona Plc; *Int'l*, pg. 1113
SUTTONS MALAYSIA—See Suttons Transport Group Ltd.; *Int'l*, pg. 7347
SUTTONS MOTORS; *Int'l*, pg. 7347
SUTTONS OIL LIMITED—See Bord na Mona Plc; *Int'l*, pg. 1113
SUTTONS TRANSPORT GROUP LTD.; *Int'l*, pg. 7347
SUTTON'S WESTERN WHOLESALE FLOORING; *U.S. Private*, 3887
SUTUREX & RENODEX S.A.S.—See B. Braun Melsungen AG; *Int'l*, pg. 788
SUUMAYA CORPORATION LTD.; *Int'l*, pg. 7347
SUUNNITTELUTOIMISTO TTNK HELSINKI OY—See Alma Media Corporation; *Int'l*, pg. 362
SUUNTO OY—See ANTA Sports Products Limited; *Int'l*, pg. 481
SUUR-HELSINGIN HISSIHUOLTO OY—See KONE Oyj; *Int'l*, pg. 4250
SUVANZA; *U.S. Private*, pg. 3887
SUVARNABHUMI AIRPORT HOTEL COMPANY LIMITED—See Airports of Thailand Public Company Limited; *Int'l*, pg. 248
SUVARNABHUMI ENVIRONMENT CARE CO., LTD.—See Samart Corporation Public Company Limited; *Int'l*, pg. 6502
SUVEN LIFE SCIENCES LTD.; *Int'l*, pg. 7348
SUVEN NEUROSCIENCES INC.—See Suven Life Sciences Ltd.; *Int'l*, pg. 7348
SUVEN PHARMACEUTICALS LIMITED—See Advent International Corporation; *U.S. Private*, pg. 105
SUVIC OY—See Dovre Group Plc; *Int'l*, pg. 2182
SUVIDHAA INFOSERVE LIMITED; *Int'l*, pg. 7348
SUVIDHA INFRAESTATE CORPORATION LIMITED; *Int'l*, pg. 7348
SUVITECH CO., LTD.—See Axiata Group Berhad; *Int'l*, pg. 768
SUWA DAIICHI TRAFFIC LTD.—See Daiichi Koutsu Sangyo Co., Ltd.; *Int'l*, pg. 1929
SUWAG ENERGIE AG—See RWE AG; *Int'l*, pg. 6435
SUWAG NETZ GMBH—See RWE AG; *Int'l*, pg. 6436
SUWAKO HIGH TRUST CO., LTD.—See Takuma Co., Ltd.; *Int'l*, pg. 7442
SUWANNEE AMERICAN CEMENT CO INC—See Anderson Columbia Co. Inc.; *U.S. Private*, pg. 276
SUWANNEE LUMBER COMPANY LLC—See Conifex Timber Inc.; *Int'l*, pg. 1768
SUWANNEE RIVER RENDEZVOUS RESORT & CAMPGROUND; *U.S. Private*, pg. 3887
SUWANNEE VALLEY ELECTRIC COOPERATIVE, INC.; *U.S. Private*, pg. 3887
SUWARY S.A.—See PTS Plast-Box S.A.; *Int'l*, pg. 6091
SUWEN ELECTRIC ENERGY TECHNOLOGY CO., LTD.; *Int'l*, pg. 7348
SUWS OF THE CAROLINAS, INC.—See Acadia Healthcare Company, Inc.; *U.S. Public*, pg. 30
SUXIN JOYFUL LIFE SERVICES CO., LTD.; *Int'l*, pg. 7348
SUYASH LABORATORIES LTD.—See Aarti Drugs Ltd.; *Int'l*, pg. 38
SUYASH SOFTWARE PVT. LTD.—See Solventum Corporation; *U.S. Public*, pg. 1902
SUYOG GURBAXANI FUNICULAR ROPEWAYS LTD.; *Int'l*, pg. 7348
SUYOG TELEMATICS LIMITED; *Int'l*, pg. 7348
SUZANNE EVANS COACHING LLC; *U.S. Private*, pg. 3887
SUZANO HOLDING S.A.; *Int'l*, pg. 7348
SUZANO PULP AND PAPER AMERICA INC.—See Suzano Holding S.A.; *Int'l*, pg. 7348
SUZANO PULP AND PAPER ASIA S.A.—See Suzano Holding S.A.; *Int'l*, pg. 7348
SUZANO PULP AND PAPER EUROPE S.A.—See Suzano Holding S.A.; *Int'l*, pg. 7348
SUZANO S.A.—See Suzano Holding S.A.; *Int'l*, pg. 7348
SUZHOU 1000VIDEO VISIUAL TECHNOLOGY CO., LTD.—See PCI Technology Group Co., Ltd; *Int'l*, pg. 5768
SUZHOU AICHI TECHNOLOGY CO., LTD.—See Aichi Electric Co., Ltd.; *Int'l*, pg. 229
SUZHOU AIR WATER TRADING CO., LTD.—See Air Water Inc.; *Int'l*, pg. 240
SUZHOU AKCOME PHOTOVOLTAICS SYSTEM CO., LTD.—See Zhejiang Akcome New Energy Technology Co.,Ltd.; *Int'l*, pg. 8648
SUZHOU ALLIED TECH CO., LTD.—See Allied Technologies Ltd.; *Int'l*, pg. 358
SUZHOU ALTON ELECTRICAL & MECHANICAL INDUSTRY CO., LTD.; *Int'l*, pg. 7348
SUZHOU ANCHI CONTROL SYSTEM CO., LTD.—See Shenzhen Megmeet Electrical Co.,Ltd; *Int'l*, pg. 6817
SUZHOU ANJIE TECHNOLOGY CO., LTD.; *Int'l*, pg. 7348
SUZHOU ANTAI AIR TECH CO., LTD.—See AIRTECH JAPAN, LTD.; *Int'l*, pg. 249
SUZHOU ANZHIXING AUTOMOBILE SALES SERVICES CO., LTD.—See China ZhengTong Auto Services Holdings Limited; *Int'l*, pg. 1567

SUZHOU ASEN SEMICONDUCTORS CO., LTD.; *Int'l*, pg. 7349
SUZHOU ASIAN MICRO RECOVERY TECHNOLOGY CO LTD—See Asian Micro Holdings Ltd.; *Int'l*, pg. 618
SUZHOU AUCHAN HYPERMARKETS CO., LTD.—See Alibaba Group Holding Limited; *Int'l*, pg. 326
SUZHOU BAOFORGING CO., LTD.—See Jiangsu Hongtian Technology Co., Ltd.; *Int'l*, pg. 3948
SUZHOU BAOMING REFRACTORIES CO., LTD.—See Puyang Refractories Group Co., Ltd.; *Int'l*, pg. 6124
SUZHOU BASECARE MEDICAL CORPORATION LIMITED; *Int'l*, pg. 7349
SUZHOU BEAUTY STAR CO., LTD.—See Shenzhen Leaguer Co., Ltd.; *Int'l*, pg. 6816
SUZHOU BOE CHATANI ELECTRONICS CO., LTD.—See BOE Technology Group Co., Ltd.; *Int'l*, pg. 1099
SUZHOU BONDEX NISSHIN LOGISTIC CO., LTD.—See KKR & Co. Inc.; *U.S. Public*, pg. 1259
SUZHOU BORDNETZE ELECTRICAL SYSTEMS LTD.—See Sumitomo Electric Industries, Ltd.; *Int'l*, pg. 7284
SUZHOU BUCHER HYDRAULICS CO. LTD—See Bucher Industries AG; *Int'l*, pg. 1207
SUZHOU CABLEPLUS TECHNOLOGIES CO., LTD.—See Jiangsu Zhongli Group Co., Ltd.; *Int'l*, pg. 3957
SUZHOU CAERI AUTOMOBILE TEST & DEVELOPMENT CO., LTD.—See China Automotive Engineering Research Institute Co., Ltd.; *Int'l*, pg. 1484
SUZHOU CAPSUGEL LTD.—See Pfizer Inc.; *U.S. Public*, pg. 1683
SUZHOU CENTRAL MIN LAI SOLAR POWER CO., LTD.—See Jolywood Suzhou Sunwatt Co., Ltd.; *Int'l*, pg. 3997
SUZHOU CENTRAL PHOTOVOLTAIC NEW MATERIAL LIMITED—See Jolywood Suzhou Sunwatt Co., Ltd.; *Int'l*, pg. 3997
SUZHOU CHANGHE INVESTMENT & DEVELOPMENT CO., LTD.—See Tiong Seng Holdings Limited; *Int'l*, pg. 7755
SUZHOU CHEERSSON PRECISION METAL FORMING CO., LTD.; *Int'l*, pg. 7349
SUZHOU CHENG LOONG PAPER CO., LTD.—See Cheng Loong Corp.; *Int'l*, pg. 1466
SUZHOU CHIALIN PRECISION INDUSTRIAL CO., LTD.—See CHIALIN Precision Industrial Co., Ltd.; *Int'l*, pg. 1475
SUZHOU CHUANGYI PLASTIC CO., LTD—See Shenzhen Tongyi Industry Co., Ltd.; *Int'l*, pg. 6823
SUZHOU CHUNQIU ELECTRONIC TECHNOLOGY CO., LTD.; *Int'l*, pg. 7349
SUZHOU CHUNXING PRECISION MECHANICAL CO., LTD.; *Int'l*, pg. 7349
SUZHOU CICOR TECHNOLOGY CO., LTD.—See Cicor Technologies Ltd.; *Int'l*, pg. 1603
SUZHOU CMB MACHINERY CO., LTD.—See China Metal Products Co., Ltd.; *Int'l*, pg. 1523
SUZHOU CMR ELECTRONIC DEVICES CO., LTD.—See Amphenol Corporation; *U.S. Public*, pg. 132
SUZHOU CMS MACHINERY CO., LTD.—See China Metal Products Co., Ltd.; *Int'l*, pg. 1523
SUZHOU COMFORT TAXI CO., LTD.—See ComfortDelGro Corporation Limited; *Int'l*, pg. 1713
SUZHOU CORPORATION; *Int'l*, pg. 7349
SUZHOU CRESTEC PRINTING CO., LTD.—See Crestec Inc.; *Int'l*, pg. 1841
SUZHOU CTI TESTING TECHNOLOGY CO., LTD.—See Centre Testing International Corporation; *Int'l*, pg. 1411
SUZHOU CUIZHUO DIANZI LTD.—See Adtec Plasma Technology Co., Ltd.; *Int'l*, pg. 154
SUZHOU DAWNRAYS PHARMACEUTICAL CO., LTD.—See Dawnrays Pharmaceutical (Holdings) Ltd; *Int'l*, pg. 1984
SUZHOU DELTA PLUS PERSONAL PROTECTION—See Delta Plus Group; *Int'l*, pg. 2020
SUZHOU DIVA LAB. INC.—See Diva Laboratories Ltd.; *Int'l*, pg. 2137
SUZHOU DMD BIOMED CO., LTD.—See Shanxi C&Y Pharmaceutical Group Co., Ltd.; *Int'l*, pg. 6786
SUZHOU DONGSHAN PRECISION MANUFACTURING CO., LTD.; *Int'l*, pg. 7349
SUZHOU DONGWU CEMENT CO., LTD.—See Dongwu Cement International Limited; *Int'l*, pg. 2171
SUZHOU DOUSON VALVE CO., LTD.—See Jiangsu Hongtian Technology Co., Ltd.; *Int'l*, pg. 3948
SUZHOU DRAKA CABLE CO. LTD.—See Prysmian S.p.A.; *Int'l*, pg. 6013
SUZHOU DSG-CANUSA POLYMER TECHNOLOGIES CO. LTD.—See ShawCor Ltd.; *Int'l*, pg. 6791
SUZHOU DUNLOP SRIXON SPORTS CO., LTD.—See Sumitomo Rubber Industries, Ltd.; *Int'l*, pg. 7300
SUZHOU EBRAIN ELECTRONICS CO., LTD.—See Ebrains, Inc.; *Int'l*, pg. 2286
SUZHOU EKA TRADE CO. LTD—See Akzo Nobel N.V.; *Int'l*, pg. 275
SUZHOU ELECTRICAL APPARATUS SCIENCE ACADEMY CO., LTD.; *Int'l*, pg. 7349
SUZHOU ENABLENCE PHOTONIC TECHNOLOGIES CO., LTD.—See Enablence Technologies Inc.; *Int'l*, pg. 2395

SUZHOU EPILEDS CO., LTD.—See Epileds Technologies, Inc.; *Int'l*, pg. 2460
SUZHOU EPSON CO., LTD.—See Seiko Epson Corporation; *Int'l*, pg. 6688
SUZHOU ESCA STEP CO. LTD.—See Schindler Holding AG; *Int'l*, pg. 6620
SUZHOU ETRON TECHNOLOGIES CO., LTD.; *Int'l*, pg. 7349
SUZHOU EVERFORUTNE IMPORT & EXPORT, LTD.—See Sinochem Corporation; *Int'l*, pg. 6951
SUZHOU FEILI SUPPLY CHAIN MANAGEMENT CO., LTD.—See Jiangsu Feiliks International Logistics Inc.; *Int'l*, pg. 3946
SUZHOU FIRMENICH AROMATICS CO. LTD.—See Firmenich International SA; *Int'l*, pg. 2681
SUZHOU FIRST PHARMACEUTICAL CO., LTD.—See China NT Pharma Group Company Limited; *Int'l*, pg. 1536
SUZHOU FULFIL ELECTRONICS CO., LTD.—See Syncmold Enterprise Corp.; *Int'l*, pg. 7382
SUZHOU FURUKAWA POWER OPTIC CABLE CO., LTD.—See The Furukawa Electric Co., Ltd.; *Int'l*, pg. 7647
SUZHOU FURUN MEAT PROCESSING CO., LTD.—See China Yurun Food Group Limited; *Int'l*, pg. 1566
SUZHOU FUSHILAI PHARMACEUTICAL CO., LTD.; *Int'l*, pg. 7349
SUZHOU GEM OPTO-ELECTRONICS TERMINAL CO., LTD.—See Gem Terminal Ind. Co., Ltd.; *Int'l*, pg. 2915
SUZHOU GIGA SOLAR MATERIALS CORP.—See Giga Solar Materials Corp.; *Int'l*, pg. 2971
SUZHOU GOLDENGREEN TECHNOLOGIES LTD; *Int'l*, pg. 7350
SUZHOU GOLD MANTIS CONSTRUCTION DECORATION CO., LTD.; *Int'l*, pg. 7350
SUZHOU GOLD MANTIS CURTAIN WALL CO. LTD.—See Suzhou Gold Mantis Construction Decoration Co., Ltd.; *Int'l*, pg. 7350
SUZHOU GOLD MANTIS FURNITURE DESIGN & MANUFACTURING CO., LTD.—See Suzhou Gold Mantis Construction Decoration Co., Ltd.; *Int'l*, pg. 7350
SUZHOU GOLD MANTIS LANDSCAPE CO. LTD.—See Suzhou Gold Mantis Construction Decoration Co., Ltd.; *Int'l*, pg. 7350
SUZHOU GOOD-ARK ELECTRONICS CO., LTD.; *Int'l*, pg. 7350
SUZHOU GOOD-ARK NEW ENERGY TECHNOLOGY CO., LTD. - SUZHOU FACTORY—See Suzhou Good-Ark Electronics Co., Ltd.; *Int'l*, pg. 7350
SUZHOU GYZ ELECTRONIC TECHNOLOGY CO., LTD.; *Int'l*, pg. 7350
SUZHOU HAILU HEAVY INDUSTRY CO., LTD.; *Int'l*, pg. 7350
SUZHOU HAISHUN PACKAGING MATERIAL CO., LTD.—See Shanghai Haishun New Pharmaceutical Packaging Co., Ltd.; *Int'l*, pg. 6769
SUZHOU HAIXING AUTOMOBILE SALES & SERVICES CO., LTD.—See Zhongsheng Group Holdings Limited; *Int'l*, pg. 8674
SUZHOU HANCHUAN INTELLIGENT TECHNOLOGY CO., LTD.; *Int'l*, pg. 7350
SUZHOU HAPPYNARAE CO., LTD.—See SK hynix Inc.; *Int'l*, pg. 6971
SUZHOU HEKEDA LIQUID CRYSTAL EQUIPMENT CO., LTD.—See Shenzhen Hekeda Precision Cleaning Equipment Co., Ltd.; *Int'l*, pg. 6811
SUZHOU HEKEDA WATER TREATMENT TECHNOLOGY LIMITED—See Shenzhen Hekeda Precision Cleaning Equipment Co., Ltd.; *Int'l*, pg. 6811
SUZHOU HENGMINGDA ELECTRONIC TECHNOLOGY CO., LTD.; *Int'l*, pg. 7350
SUZHOU HESHENG SPECIAL MATERIAL CO., LTD.; *Int'l*, pg. 7350
SUZHOU HIDRIA DIESEL COLD START TECHNOLOGIES CO., LTD.—See Hidria d.o.o.; *Int'l*, pg. 3384
SUZHOU HONGDA ENZYME CO., LTD.—See Novonesis A/S; *Int'l*, pg. 5469
SUZHOU HUALI ENVIRONMENTAL PACKAGING TECHNOLOGY CO., LTD—See Overseas Chinese Town (Asia) Holdings Limited; *Int'l*, pg. 5672
SUZHOU HUAXIN INTERNATIONAL PROPERTY MANAGEMENT CO., LTD; *Int'l*, pg. 7350
SUZHOU HUAYA INTELLIGENCE TECHNOLOGY CO., LTD.; *Int'l*, pg. 7350
SUZHOU HUIYE CHEMICAL & LIGHT INDUSTRY CO., LTD.—See Dynamic Colours Limited; *Int'l*, pg. 2240
SUZHOU HUIYE PLASTIC INDUSTRY CO., LTD.—See Dynamic Colours Limited; *Int'l*, pg. 2240
SUZHOU HYCAN HOLDINGS CO., LTD.; *Int'l*, pg. 7350
SUZHOU HYC TECHNOLOGY CO., LTD.; *Int'l*, pg. 7350
SUZHOU IL JEONG CO., LTD—See Il Jeong Industrial Co., Ltd; *Int'l*, pg. 3613
SUZHOU ILLINOIS MEDICARE ROBOT CO., LTD.—See Suzhou Alton Electrical & Mechanical Industry Co., Ltd.; *Int'l*, pg. 7348
SUZHOU INAX BUILDING MATERIALS CO., LTD.—See LIXIL Group Corporation; *Int'l*, pg. 4534
SUZHOU INDUSTRIAL PARK HESHUN ELECTRIC CO., LTD.; *Int'l*, pg. 7350

COMPANY NAME INDEX

SUZHOU INOAC ELASTOMER CO., LTD.—See INOAC Corporation; *Int'l*, pg. 3714
SUZHOU INOAC TRADING CORPORATION—See INOAC Corporation; *Int'l*, pg. 3714
SUZHOU INOAC ZHONGDING OFFICE MACHINE PRODUCTS CO., LTD.—See INOAC Corporation; *Int'l*, pg. 3715
SUZHOU INOVANCE AUTOMOTIVE CO., LTD.—See Shenzhen Inovance Technology Co., Ltd.; *Int'l*, pg. 6813
SUZHOU INSTITUTE OF BUILDING SCIENCE GROUP CO., LTD.; *Int'l*, pg. 7351
SUZHOU IRON TECHNOLOGY CO., LTD.; *Int'l*, pg. 7351
SUZHOU IWATANI METAL PRODUCTS CO.,LTD—See Iwatani Corporation; *Int'l*, pg. 3850
SUZHOU JDI DEVICES INC.—See Japan Display Inc.; *Int'l*, pg. 3888
SUZHOU JDI ELECTRONICS INC.—See Suzhou Dongshan Precision Manufacturing Co., Ltd.; *Int'l*, pg. 7349
SUZHOU JIAHUA BIOCHEMISTRY CO.—See JAB Holding Company S.a.r.l.; *Int'l*, pg. 3861
SUZHOU JINFU TECHNOLOGY CO., LTD.; *Int'l*, pg. 7351
SUZHOU JINHONG GAS CO., LTD.; *Int'l*, pg. 7351
SUZHOU JIN HONG SHUN AUTO PARTS CO., LTD.; *Int'l*, pg. 7351
SUZHOU JIUFU ELECTRONIC CO.,LTD—See Suzhou Jinfu Technology Co., Ltd.; *Int'l*, pg. 7351
SUZHOU JIUHONG ELECTRON CO.—See JUIC International Corp.; *Int'l*, pg. 4022
SUZHOU JUNMENG BIOSCIENCES CO.—See Shanghai Junshi Biosciences Co., Ltd.; *Int'l*, pg. 6773
SUZHOU KAIMEI ELECTRONICS CO., LTD.—See Kaiemei Electronic Corp.; *Int'l*, pg. 4051
SUZHOU KANSAI PAINT CO., LTD.—See Kansai Paint Co., Ltd.; *Int'l*, pg. 4073
SUZHOU KEDA TECHNOLOGY CO., LTD.; *Int'l*, pg. 7351
SUZHOU KELIDA BUILDING & DECORATION CO., LTD.; *Int'l*, pg. 7351
SUZHOU KEYANG PHOTOELECTRICITY TECHNOLOGY CO., LTD.—See Huizhou Speed Wireless Technology Co., Ltd.; *Int'l*, pg. 3527
SUZHOU K&H RUBBER & PLASTIC CO., LTD.—See Jinhua Chunguang Technology Co., Ltd.; *Int'l*, pg. 3968
SUZHOU KINGCWOOD EDUCATION TECHNOLOGY CO., LTD.; *Int'l*, pg. 7351
SUZHOU KINSEI MATEC CO., LTD.—See Iwatani Corporation; *Int'l*, pg. 3850
SUZHOU KOBE COPPER TECHNOLOGY CO., LTD.—See Kobe Steel, Ltd.; *Int'l*, pg. 4220
SUZHOU KOHOKU OPTO-ELECTRONICS CO., LTD.—See Kohoku Kogyo Co., Ltd.; *Int'l*, pg. 4229
SUZHOU KULTHORN MAGNET WIRE COMPANY LIMITED—See Kulthorn Kirby Public Co., Ltd.; *Int'l*, pg. 4329
SUZHOU KUNLENE FILM INDUSTRIES CO., LTD.—See PT Indopoly Swakarsa Industry Tbk; *Int'l*, pg. 6046
SUZHOU LANLIAN-FUJI INSTRUMENTS CO., LTD.—See Fuji Electric Co., Ltd.; *Int'l*, pg. 2813
SUZHOU LARGAN CO., LTD.—See Largan Precision Co., Ltd.; *Int'l*, pg. 4418
SUZHOU LIANPENG AUTOMATION EQUIPMENT CO., LTD.—See Shenzhen Liande Automation Equipment Co.,Ltd.; *Int'l*, pg. 6816
SUZHOU LINK WAYS TECH CO., LTD.—See ViTrox Corporation Berhad; *Int'l*, pg. 8262
SUZHOU LINTONG CHEMICAL SCIENCE CORP.—See DIC Corporation; *Int'l*, pg. 2111
SUZHOU LONGJIE SPECIAL FIBER CO., LTD.; *Int'l*, pg. 7351
SUZHOU MAXWELL TECHNOLOGIES CO., LTD.; *Int'l*, pg. 7351
SUZHOU MEIRUIDE BUILDING DECORATION CO., LTD.—See Suzhou Gold Mantis Construction Decoration Co., Ltd.; *Int'l*, pg. 7350
SUZHOU MICROPORT ORTHOPEDICS SCIENTIFIC (GROUP) CO., LTD.—See MicroPort Scientific Corporation; *Int'l*, pg. 4881
SUZHOU MI EQUIPMENT CO., LTD.—See Mi Technovation Berhad; *Int'l*, pg. 4873
SUZHOU MIGATRONIC WELDING TECHNOLOGY CO., LTD.—See Svejsemaskinefabrikken Migatronic A/S; *Int'l*, pg. 7356
SUZHOU MINGDE ALUMINIUM CO.—See ZYF Lopsking Material Technology Co Ltd; *Int'l*, pg. 8701
SUZHOU MINGZHI TECHNOLOGY CO., LTD.; *Int'l*, pg. 7351
SUZHOU MITSUBOSHI BELTING CO., LTD.—See Mitsuboshi Belting Ltd.; *Int'l*, pg. 4972
SUZHOU MOBYDATA SMART SYSTEM CO. LTD.—See Datalogic S.p.A.; *Int'l*, pg. 1978
SUZHOU MONARCH CONTROL TECHNOLOGY CO., LTD.—See Shenzhen Inovance Technology Co., Ltd.; *Int'l*, pg. 6813
SUZHOU MRC OPTO-DEVICE CO., LTD.—See Mitsubishi Chemical Group Corporation; *Int'l*, pg. 4934
SUZHOU MYS ENVIRONMENTAL PROTECTION & TECHNOLOGY COMPANY LTD.—See MYS Group Co., Ltd.; *Int'l*, pg. 5114

SUZHOU NDK CO., LTD.—See NIHON DEMPA KOGYO Co Ltd; *Int'l*, pg. 5283
SUZHOU NDK TRADING CO., LTD.—See NIHON DEMPA KOGYO Co Ltd; *Int'l*, pg. 5283
SUZHOU NEW DISTRICT HI-TECH INDUSTRIAL CO., LTD.; *Int'l*, pg. 7351
SUZHOU NICHIAS INDUSTRIAL PRODUCTS CO., LTD.—See Nichias Corporation; *Int'l*, pg. 5267
SUZHOU NIKKU SUNTEC ELECTROMECHANICAL TECHNOLOGY CO., LTD.—See Nippon Air conditioning Services Co., Ltd.; *Int'l*, pg. 5310
SUZHOU NIPPON PAINT YASHILI CO., LTD.—See Nippon Paint Holdings Co., Ltd.; *Int'l*, pg. 5326
SUZHOU NITTO MATEX ELECTRONICS CO., LTD.—See Nitto Denko Corporation; *Int'l*, pg. 5387
SUZHOU NOVARTIS PHARMA TECHNOLOGY CO. LTD.—See Novartis AG; *Int'l*, pg. 5459
SUZHOU NOVARTIS TECHNICAL DEVELOPMENT CO., LTD.—See Novartis AG; *Int'l*, pg. 5460
SUZHOU NSK BEARINGS CO., LTD.—See NSK Ltd.; *Int'l*, pg. 5480
SUZHOU OJI PACKAGING CO., LTD.—See Oji Holdings Corporation; *Int'l*, pg. 5538
SUZHOU OKAMOTO TRADING CO., LTD.—See Okamoto Glass Co., Ltd; *Int'l*, pg. 5544
SUZHOU OTSUKA PHARMACEUTICAL CO., LTD.—See Otsuka Holdings Co., Ltd.; *Int'l*, pg. 5661
SUZHOU PACIFIC MILLENNIUM PACKAGING & PAPER INDUSTRIES CO., LTD.—See Pacific Millennium Packaging Group Corporation; *Int'l*, pg. 5691
SUZHOU PARSUN POWER MACHINE CO., LTD.; *Int'l*, pg. 7351
SUZHOU PILLAR INDUSTRY CO., LTD.—See Nippon Pillar Packing Co., Ltd.; *Int'l*, pg. 5328
SUZHOU RAKEN TECHNOLOGY CO., LTD.—See AmTRAN Technology; *Int'l*, pg. 442
SUZHOU SCHLEMMER AUTOMOTIVE PARTS CO., LTD.—See Ningbo Huaxiang Electronic Co., Ltd.; *Int'l*, pg. 5302
SUZHOU SEAH PRECISION METAL CO., LTD.—See SeAH Holdings Corp.; *Int'l*, pg. 6664
SUZHOU SECOTE PRECISION ELECTRONIC CO., LTD.; *Int'l*, pg. 7351
SUZHOU SEKSUN TECHNOLOGY CO., LTD.—See Suzhou Anjie Technology Co., Ltd.; *Int'l*, pg. 7349
SUZHOU SEOYON DIE CASTING LTD—See Mobase Co., Ltd.; *Int'l*, pg. 5007
SUZHOU SEOYON ELECTRONICS LTD.—See Mobase Co., Ltd.; *Int'l*, pg. 5007
SUZHOU SHAGANG MATERIALS TRADE CO., LTD.—See Jiangsu Shagang Group Ltd.; *Int'l*, pg. 3954
SUZHOU SHIHLIN ELECTRIC & ENGINEERING CO., LTD.—See Shihlin Electric & Engineering Corp.; *Int'l*, pg. 6829
SUZHOU SHIHUA NEW MATERIAL TECHNOLOGY CO., LTD.; *Int'l*, pg. 7351
SUZHOU SHIJIA SCIENCE & TECHNOLOGY INC; *Int'l*, pg. 7351
SUZHOU SHIJING ENVIRONMENTAL TECHNOLOGY CO., LTD.; *Int'l*, pg. 7352
SUZHOU SHIN-ETSU POLYMER CO., LTD.—See Shin-Etsu Chemical Co. Ltd.; *Int'l*, pg. 6841
SUZHOU SHINKO-SHOJI MATERIAL CO., LTD.—See Kobe Steel, Ltd.; *Int'l*, pg. 4221
SUZHOU SHINSUNG CO., LTD.—See Shinsung E&G Co., Ltd.; *Int'l*, pg. 6849
SUZHOU SH PRECISION CO., LTD.—See Jih Lin Technology Co., Ltd.; *Int'l*, pg. 3963
SUZHOU SLAC PRECISION EQUIPMENT COMPANY LIMITED; *Int'l*, pg. 7352
SUZHOU SNAKE MEDICAL TECHNOLOGY CONSULTING SERVICE CO., LTD.—See B. Braun Melsungen AG; *Int'l*, pg. 788
SUZHOU SODICK HIGHTECH CO., LTD.—See Sodick Co., Ltd.; *Int'l*, pg. 7048
SUZHOU SODICK SPECIAL EQUIPMENT CO., LTD.—See Sodick Co., Ltd.; *Int'l*, pg. 7048
SUZHOU SOKEN CHEMICAL CO.—See Soken Chemical & Engineering Co., Ltd.; *Int'l*, pg. 7066
SUZHOU SONAVOX ELECTRONICS CO., LTD.; *Int'l*, pg. 7352
SUZHOU STANLEY ELECTRIC CO, LTD.—See Stanley Electric Co., Ltd.; *Int'l*, pg. 7171
SUZHOU STANLEY LED LIGHTING TECHNOLOGY CO., LTD.—See Stanley Electric Co., Ltd.; *Int'l*, pg. 7171
SUZHOU SUMIDEN AUTOMOTIVE WIRE CO., LTD.—See Sumitomo Electric Industries, Ltd.; *Int'l*, pg. 7284
SUZHOU SUMIDEN ELECTRONIC MATERIALS CO., LTD.—See Sumitomo Electric Industries, Ltd.; *Int'l*, pg. 7284
SUZHOU SUMINOE KOIDE AUTOMOTIVE ACCESSORIES CO., LTD.—See Suminoe Textile Co., Ltd.; *Int'l*, pg. 7262
SUZHOU SUMINOE TEXTILES CO., LTD.—See Suminoe Textile Co., Ltd.; *Int'l*, pg. 7262
SUZHOU SUNMUN TECHNOLOGY CO.,LTD.; *Int'l*, pg. 7352

SUZHOU SUNTONE TECHNOLOGY MANUFACTURING CO., LTD.—See Jinhua Chunguang Technology Co., Ltd.; *Int'l*, pg. 3968
SUZHOU SUPER PILLAR AUTOMATION EQUIPMENT CO., LTD.—See ACE PILLAR Co., Ltd; *Int'l*, pg. 94
SUZHOU SUSHI TESTING GROUP CO., LTD.; *Int'l*, pg. 7352
SUZHOU TAISOL ELECTRONICS CO., LTD.—See TaiSol Electronics Co., Ltd.; *Int'l*, pg. 7418
SUZHOU TAIYO NIPPON SANSO GAS CO., LTD—See Mitsubishi Chemical Group Corporation; *Int'l*, pg. 4937
SUZHOU TALANT OPTRONLICS TECHNOLOGY CO., LTD.—See Talant Optronics (suzhou) Co., Ltd.; *Int'l*, pg. 7443
SUZHOU TALESUN SOLAR TECHNOLOGY CO., LTD.—See Jiangsu Zhongli Group Co., Ltd.; *Int'l*, pg. 3958
SUZHOU TANJI ELECTRONIC TECHNOLOGY CO., LTD.—See Jiangsu Feiliks International Logistics Inc.; *Int'l*, pg. 3946
SUZHOU TAXAN KAGA TRADING CO., LTD.—See Kaga Electronics Co., Ltd.; *Int'l*, pg. 4049
SUZHOU TEMPSTAFF DATA CO., LTD.—See Persol Holdings Co., Ltd.; *Int'l*, pg. 5819
SUZHOU TFC OPTICAL COMMUNICATION CO., LTD.; *Int'l*, pg. 7352
SUZHOU THVOW TECHNOLOGY CO., LTD.; *Int'l*, pg. 7352
SUZHOU TIANSHAN CEMENT CO.,LTD.—See China National Materials; *Int'l*, pg. 1532
SUZHOU TONSAN ADHESIVE CO., LTD.—See H.B. Fuller Company; *U.S. Public*, pg. 978
SUZHOU TOX PRESSOTECHNIK CO. LTD.—See TOX Pressotechnik GmbH & Co. KG; *Int'l*, pg. 7851
SUZHOU TOYO ALUMINIUM EKCO HOUSEHOLD PRODUCTS CO., LTD.—See Nippon Light Metal Holdings Company, Ltd.; *Int'l*, pg. 5324
SUZHOU TZTEK TECHNOLOGY CO., LTD.; *Int'l*, pg. 7352
SUZHOU UIGREEN MICRO & NANO TECHNOLOGIES CO., LTD.; *Int'l*, pg. 7352
SUZHOU UNION BIOPHARM BIOSCIENCES CO., LTD.—See Shanghai Junshi Biosciences Co., Ltd.; *Int'l*, pg. 6773
SUZHOU UNION BIOPHARM CO., LTD.—See Shanghai Junshi Biosciences Co., Ltd.; *Int'l*, pg. 6773
SUZHOU U-WISH JOINT MEDICAL DEVICES CO., LTD.—See LEAD DATA INC.; *Int'l*, pg. 4432
SUZHOU VEICHI ELECTRIC CO., LTD.; *Int'l*, pg. 7352
SUZHOU VICTOR MEDICAL EQUIPMENT CO., LTD.—See Cefla S.C.; *Int'l*, pg. 1390
SUZHOU VICTORY PRECISION MANUFACTURE CO., LTD.; *Int'l*, pg. 7352
SUZHOU WALSIN TECHNOLOGY ELECTRONICS CO., LTD.—See Walsin Technology Corporation; *Int'l*, pg. 8335
SUZHOU WANSHEN FLOUR PRODUCTS CO., LTD.; *Int'l*, pg. 7352
SUZHOU WANSHIH ELECTRONIC ELEMENT CO., LTD.—See Wanshih Electronics Co., Ltd.; *Int'l*, pg. 8342
SUZHOU WANSHIH OPTICAL COMMUNICATION CO., LTD.—See Wanshih Electronics Co., Ltd.; *Int'l*, pg. 8342
SUZHOU WANXIANG TECHNOLOGY CO., LTD.; *Int'l*, pg. 7352
SUZHOU WEISIDONGSHAN ELECTRONIC TECHNOLOGY CO., LTD.—See Suzhou Anjie Technology Co., Ltd.; *Int'l*, pg. 7349
SUZHOU WEIZHIXIANG FOOD CO., LTD.; *Int'l*, pg. 7353
SUZHOU WINMAX TECHNOLOGY CORP.—See Acter Co., Ltd.; *Int'l*, pg. 117
SUZHOU WSDS ELECTRONIC TECHNOLOGY CO., LTD.—See Suzhou Anjie Technology Co., Ltd.; *Int'l*, pg. 7349
SUZHOU WUFANG PHOTOELECTRIC MATERIAL CO., LTD.—See Hubei W Olf Photoelectric Technology Co., Ltd.; *Int'l*, pg. 3518
SUZHOU WUTONG INTELLIGENT ELECTRONICS CO., LTD.—See Wutong Holding Group Co., Ltd.; *Int'l*, pg. 8514
SUZHOU XIANGLOU NEW MATERIAL CO., LTD.; *Int'l*, pg. 7353
SUZHOU XIDIAN CO. LTD.—See Rexel, S.A.; *Int'l*, pg. 6317
SUZHOU XINGYE MATERIAL & TECHNOLOGY CO., LTD.; *Int'l*, pg. 7353
SUZHOU YANGTZE NEW MATERIALS CO., LTD.; *Int'l*, pg. 7353
SUZHOU YOKOGAWA METER COMPANY—See Yokogawa Electric Corporation; *Int'l*, pg. 8592
SUZHOU YOUNGTEK MICRO-ELECTRONICS CO., LTD.—See Youngtek Electronics Co., Ltd.; *Int'l*, pg. 8604
SUZHOU YOURBEST NEW-TYPE MATERIALS CO., LTD.; *Int'l*, pg. 7353
SUZHOU ZELGEN BIOPHARMACEUTICALS CO., LTD.; *Int'l*, pg. 7353

SUZHOU ZELGEN BIOSCIENCES CO. LTD.—See Suzhou Zelgen Biopharmaceuticals Co., Ltd.; *Int'l*, pg. 7353
SUZHOU ZHI SHENG INFORMATION TECHNOLOGY CO., LTD.—See Yum China Holdings, Inc.; *U.S. Public*, pg. 2399
SUZHOU ZHIWEI PRECISION DRIVE CONTROL TECHNOLOGY CO., LTD.—See Shenzhen Megmeet Electrical Co.,Ltd.; *Int'l*, pg. 6817
SUZLON BLADE TECHNOLOGY B.V.—See Suzlon Energy Ltd.; *Int'l*, pg. 7353
SUZLON ENERGY A/S—See Suzlon Energy Ltd.; *Int'l*, pg. 7353
SUZLON ENERGY AUSTRALIA PTY. LTD.—See Suzlon Energy Ltd.; *Int'l*, pg. 7353
SUZLON ENERGY GMBH—See Suzlon Energy Ltd.; *Int'l*, pg. 7353
SUZLON ENERGY LTD.; *Int'l*, pg. 7353
SUZLON ENERGY (TIANJIN) LIMITED—See Suzlon Energy Ltd.; *Int'l*, pg. 7353
SUZLON GENERATORS LIMITED—See Suzlon Energy Ltd.; *Int'l*, pg. 7353
SUZLON INFRASTRUCTURE SERVICES LIMITED—See Suzlon Energy Ltd.; *Int'l*, pg. 7353
SUZLON POWER INFRASTRUCTURE PVT. LTD.—See Suzlon Energy Ltd.; *Int'l*, pg. 7353
SUZLON ROTOR CORPORATION—See Suzlon Energy Ltd.; *Int'l*, pg. 7353
SUZLON STRUCTURES LIMITED—See Suzlon Energy Ltd.; *Int'l*, pg. 7353
SUZLON TOWERS AND STRUCTURES LIMITED—See Suzlon Energy Ltd.; *Int'l*, pg. 7353
SUZLON WIND ENERGY CORPORATION—See Suzlon Energy Ltd.; *Int'l*, pg. 7353
SUZLON WIND ENERGY ESPANA, S.L—See Suzlon Energy Ltd.; *Int'l*, pg. 7353
SUZO-HAPP GROUP AMERICAS (AR) S.R.L.—See ACON Investments, LLC; *U.S. Private*, pg. 63
SUZO-HAPP GROUP DO BRASIL LTDA—See ACON Investments, LLC; *U.S. Private*, pg. 63
SUZO-HAPP GROUP GMBH—See ACON Investments, LLC; *U.S. Private*, pg. 63
SUZO-HAPP GROUP (NL) BV—See ACON Investments, LLC; *U.S. Private*, pg. 63
SUZO-HAPP GROUP—See ACON Investments, LLC; *U.S. Private*, pg. 62
SUZO-HAPP GROUP SP. ZO.O—See ACON Investments, LLC; *U.S. Private*, pg. 63
SUZO-HAPP GROUP TECHNICAL COMPONENTS ESPANA, SAU—See ACON Investments, LLC; *U.S. Private*, pg. 63
SUZO-HAPP GROUP (UK) LTD.—See ACON Investments, LLC; *U.S. Private*, pg. 63
SUZORITE MICA PRODUCTS, INC.—See Cementos Pacasmayo S.A.A.; *Int'l*, pg. 1398
SUZUDEN CORP.; *Int'l*, pg. 7353
SUZUKA CIRCUITLAND CO., LTD.—See Honda Motor Co., Ltd.; *Int'l*, pg. 3464
SUZUKA ENGINEERING CO., LTD.—See Sanwa Holdings Corporation; *Int'l*, pg. 6561
SUZUKA FUJI XEROX CO., LTD.—See FUJIFILM Holdings Corporation; *Int'l*, pg. 2826
SUZUKA ROBO CARE CENTER CO., LTD.—See Cyberdyne Inc.; *Int'l*, pg. 1893
SUZUKEN CO., LTD.; *Int'l*, pg. 7353
SUZUKI AKITA AUTO PARTS MANUFACTURING CO., LTD.—See Suzuki Motor Corporation; *Int'l*, pg. 7354
SUZUKI ASSEMBLERS MALAYSIA SDN. BHD.—See Suzuki Motor Corporation; *Int'l*, pg. 7354
SUZUKI AUSTRALIA PTY. LTD.—See Suzuki Motor Corporation; *Int'l*, pg. 7354
SUZUKI AUSTRIA AUTOMOBIL HANDELS GMBH—See Suzuki Motor Corporation; *Int'l*, pg. 7354
SUZUKI BUSINESS CO., LTD.—See Suzuki Motor Corporation; *Int'l*, pg. 7354
SUZUKI CANADA, INC.—See Suzuki Motor Corporation; *Int'l*, pg. 7354
SUZUKI CO., LTD.; *Int'l*, pg. 7354
SUZUKI CO., LTD.—See NIPPN Corporation; *Int'l*, pg. 5310
SUZUKI CONSTRUCTION CO., LTD.—See Suzuki Motor Corporation; *Int'l*, pg. 7354
SUZUKI EGYPT S.A.E.—See Suzuki Motor Corporation; *Int'l*, pg. 7354
SUZUKI FINANCE CO., LTD.—See Suzuki Motor Corporation; *Int'l*, pg. 7354
SUZUKI FRANCE S.A.—See Suzuki Motor Corporation; *Int'l*, pg. 7354
SUZUKI GB PLC—See Suzuki Motor Corporation; *Int'l*, pg. 7354
SUZUKI GIKEN CO., LTD.—See Fujikura Ltd.; *Int'l*, pg. 2829
SUZUKIGUMI CO., LTD.—See Sala Corporation; *Int'l*, pg. 6490
SUZUKI INTERNATIONAL EUROPE GMBH—See Suzuki Motor Corporation; *Int'l*, pg. 7354
SUZUKI ITALIA S.P.A.—See Suzuki Motor Corporation; *Int'l*, pg. 7354

SUZUKI KASEI CO.,LTD.—See Suzuki Motor Corporation; *Int'l*, pg. 7354
SUZUKI MARINA, HAMANAKO, CO., LTD.—See Suzuki Motor Corporation; *Int'l*, pg. 7354
SUZUKI MARINE CO., LTD.—See Suzuki Motor Corporation; *Int'l*, pg. 7354
SUZUKI METAL INDUSTRY CO., LTD.—See Nippon Steel Corporation; *Int'l*, pg. 5340
SUZUKI MOTOR CORPORATION; *Int'l*, pg. 7354
SUZUKI MOTOR CORPORATION—See Suzuki Motor Corporation; *Int'l*, pg. 7354
SUZUKI MOTORCYCLE INDIA PRIVATE LIMITED—See Suzuki Motor Corporation; *Int'l*, pg. 7354
SUZUKI MOTOR DE COLOMBIA S.A.—See Suzuki Motor Corporation; *Int'l*, pg. 7354
SUZUKI MOTOR ESPANA, S.A.—See Suzuki Motor Corporation; *Int'l*, pg. 7354
SUZUKI MOTOR IBERICA, S.A.U.—See Suzuki Motor Corporation; *Int'l*, pg. 7354
SUZUKI MOTORLU ARACLAR PAZARLAMA A.S.; *Int'l*, pg. 7355
SUZUKI MOTOR POLAND Z.O.O.—See Suzuki Motor Corporation; *Int'l*, pg. 7354
SUZUKI MOTOR SALES KINKI INC.—See Suzuki Motor Corporation; *Int'l*, pg. 7354
SUZUKI MOTOR (THAILAND) CO., LTD.—See Suzuki Motor Corporation; *Int'l*, pg. 7354
SUZUKI NEW ZEALAND LTD.—See Suzuki Motor Corporation; *Int'l*, pg. 7355
SUZUKI OF LAKE WALES, INC.; *U.S. Private*, pg. 3887
SUZUKI PHILIPPINES, INC.—See Suzuki Motor Corporation; *Int'l*, pg. 7355
SUZUKI SHUTTER CORPORATION—See Sanwa Holdings Corporation; *Int'l*, pg. 6561
SUZUKI SOLAR TECHNO CORP.—See Takashima & Co., Ltd.; *Int'l*, pg. 7435
SUZUKI SPECIAL PRODUCTS MANUFACTURING CO., LTD.—See Suzuki Motor Corporation; *Int'l*, pg. 7355
SUZUKI-SUMIDEN STAINLESS WIRE CO., LTD.—See Sumitomo Electric Industries, Ltd.; *Int'l*, pg. 7284
SUZUKI TOYAMA AUTO PARTS MFG CO., LTD.—See Suzuki Motor Corporation; *Int'l*, pg. 7355
SUZUKYU YAKUHIN CO., LTD.—See Qol Holdings Co., Ltd.; *Int'l*, pg. 6147
SUZUMO INTERNATIONAL CORPORATION—See Suzumo Machinery Company Limited; *Int'l*, pg. 7355
SUZUMO MACHINERY COMPANY LIMITED; *Int'l*, pg. 7355
SUZUMO SINGAPORE CORPORATION PTE. LTD.—See Suzumo Machinery Company Limited; *Int'l*, pg. 7355
SUZUNUI CORPORATION; *Int'l*, pg. 7355
SUZUTAMI PRECISION INDUSTRY CO., LTD.—See Juki Corporation; *Int'l*, pg. 4024
SUZUYO SHINWART CORPORATION; *Int'l*, pg. 7355
SVABO KAROSS & HYDRAULSERVICE AB—See Heidelberg Materials AG; *Int'l*, pg. 3320
SVADS HOLDINGS SA—See Strides Pharma Science Limited; *Int'l*, pg. 7240
SVA (GROUP) CO., LTD.; *Int'l*, pg. 7355
SVAGSTROMSINSTALLATIONER I NORRKOPING AB—See Bravida Holding AB; *Int'l*, pg. 1142
SVA INDIA LIMITED; *Int'l*, pg. 7355
SVA INFORMATION INDUSTRY CO., LTD.—See SVA (Group) Co., Ltd.; *Int'l*, pg. 7355
S.V.A. JEAN ROZE; *Int'l*, pg. 6457
SVALOEF WEIBULL AB—See BASF SE; *Int'l*, pg. 871
SVALOEF WEIBULL AB—See Lantmannen ek for; *Int'l*, pg. 4414
SVAM, INDIA-NORTH SHORE TECHNOLOGIES—See SVAM International, Inc.; *U.S. Private*, pg. 3888
SVAM INTERNATIONAL, INC.; *U.S. Private*, pg. 3888
SVAM SOFTWARE LIMITED; *Int'l*, pg. 7355
SVAN CARE AB—See AddLife AB; *Int'l*, pg. 130
S-VANCE LTD.—See Sanko Gosei Ltd.; *Int'l*, pg. 6541
SVANEHOJ DANMARK A/S—See ITT Inc.; *U.S. Public*, pg. 1178
SVARAJ TRADING & AGENCIES LIMITED; *Int'l*, pg. 7355
SVARNIM TRADE UDYOG LIMITED; *Int'l*, pg. 7355
SVAROG ASSET MANAGEMENT LLC; *Int'l*, pg. 7355
SVAS BIOSANA S.P.A.; *Int'l*, pg. 7355
SVATON SA—See ASSA ABLOY AB; *Int'l*, pg. 638
SVA VERKEHRSSICHERUNGS-ANLAGEN GESELLSCHAFT MIT BESCHRANKTER HAFTUNG—See Bilfinger SE; *Int'l*, pg. 1028
SVB ANALYTICS, INC.—See SVB Financial Group; *U.S. Public*, pg. 1968
SVB ASSET MANAGEMENT—See Federal Deposit Insurance Corporation; *U.S. Private*, pg. 1487
SVB BUSINESS PARTNERS (BEIJING) CO. LTD.—See SVB Financial Group; *U.S. Public*, pg. 1968
SVB FINANCIAL GROUP; *U.S. Public*, pg. 1968
SVB FOOD & BEVERAGE CO.; *U.S. Private*, pg. 3888
SVB GLOBAL FINANCIAL, INC.—See SVB Financial Group; *U.S. Public*, pg. 1968
SVB ISRAEL ADVISORS, LTD.—See SVB Financial Group; *U.S. Public*, pg. 1968
SVB&T CORPORATION; *U.S. Private*, pg. 3888
SVB WEALTH ADVISORY, INC.—See SVB Financial Group; *U.S. Public*, pg. 1968

SVC INDUSTRIES LIMITED; *Int'l*, pg. 7355
SVC RESOURCES LTD.; *Int'l*, pg. 7355
S.V.D.P. MANAGEMENT, INC.; *U.S. Private*, pg. 3519
SVEAFASTIGHETER BOSTAD VAXHOLM AB—See Samhallsbyggnadsbolaget I Norden AB; *Int'l*, pg. 6504
SVEA MASKINER AS—See Smalandsstenars Mekaniska Verkstad - SMV Industrier AB; *Int'l*, pg. 7000
SVEASKOG AB; *Int'l*, pg. 7355
SVEASKOG BALTFOR SIA—See Sveaskog AB; *Int'l*, pg. 7356
SVEASKOG FORVALTNINGS AB—See Sveaskog AB; *Int'l*, pg. 7356
SVEBA-DAHLEN BALTIC OU—See The Middleby Corporation; *U.S. Public*, pg. 2115
SVEBA-DAHLEN ESPANA—See The Middleby Corporation; *U.S. Public*, pg. 2115
SVEBA-DAHLEN GROUP AB—See The Middleby Corporation; *U.S. Public*, pg. 2115
SVEBA DAHLEN RUS. LTD.—See The Middleby Corporation; *U.S. Public*, pg. 2115
SVEDBERGS CERAMICS AS—See Svedbergs i Dalstorp AB; *Int'l*, pg. 7356
SVEDBERGS I DALSTORP AB; *Int'l*, pg. 7356
SVEDBERGS OY—See Svedbergs i Dalstorp AB; *Int'l*, pg. 7356
SVEDEA AB—See Talanx AG; *Int'l*, pg. 7445
SVEJSEMASKINEFABRIKKEN MIGATRONIC A/S; *Int'l*, pg. 7356
SVENDBORG BRAKES APS—See Regal Rexnord Corporation; *U.S. Public*, pg. 1772
SVENDBORG BRAKES PERU S.A.C.—See Regal Rexnord Corporation; *U.S. Public*, pg. 1772
SVENDSEN'S BOAT WORKS, INC.—See Bay Ship & Yacht Co; *U.S. Private*, pg. 494
SVENHARD'S SWEDISH BAKERY INC.; *U.S. Private*, pg. 3888
SVENSKA BATTERIPOOLEN AB—See OEM International AB; *Int'l*, pg. 5528
SVENSKA BLOUNT AB—See American Securities LLC; *U.S. Private*, pg. 247
SVENSKA BLOUNT AB—See P2 Capital Partners, LLC; *U.S. Private*, pg. 3062
SVENSKA CELLULOSA AKTIEBOLAGET SCA; *Int'l*, pg. 7356
SVENSKA DAGBLADET ANNONS AB—See Schibsted ASA; *Int'l*, pg. 6617
SVENSKA DAGBLADET DIGITALA MEDIER AB—See Schibsted ASA; *Int'l*, pg. 6617
SVENSKA DAGBLADET DISTRIBUTION AB—See Schibsted ASA; *Int'l*, pg. 6617
SVENSKA DAGBLADET HOLDING AB—See Schibsted ASA; *Int'l*, pg. 6618
SVENSKA DAGBLADETS AB—See Schibsted ASA; *Int'l*, pg. 6617
SVENSK ADRESSANDRING AB—See PostNord AB; *Int'l*, pg. 5941
SVENSKA EINHELL AB—See Einhell Germany AG; *Int'l*, pg. 2334
SVENSKA FONSTER AB—See VKR Holding A/S; *Int'l*, pg. 8281
SVENSKA GEOTECH AB—See Indutrade AB; *Int'l*, pg. 3681
SVENSKA GRINDMATRISER AB—See Storskogen Group AB; *Int'l*, pg. 7228
SVENSKA HANDELSBANKEN AB; *Int'l*, pg. 7357
SVENSKA HANDELSBANKEN FRANCE—See Svenska Handelsbanken AB; *Int'l*, pg. 7358
SVENSKA HANDELSBANKEN—See Svenska Handelsbanken AB; *Int'l*, pg. 7358
SVENSKA HANDELSBANKEN—See Svenska Handelsbanken AB; *Int'l*, pg. 7358
SVENSKA HARDI AB—See Exel Industries SA; *Int'l*, pg. 2582
SVENSKA HELAG AB—See OEM International AB; *Int'l*, pg. 5528
SVENSKA INDUSTRIBORSTAR I VASTERAS AB—See Lagercrantz Group AB; *Int'l*, pg. 4395
SVENSK AIRBAG AB—See Autoliv, Inc.; *Int'l*, pg. 728
SVENSKA KAOLIN AB—See Barclays PLC; *Int'l*, pg. 863
SVENSKA MCDONALD'S AB—See McDonald's Corporation; *U.S. Public*, pg. 1406
SVENSKA MEDIA I LJUSDAL AB—See Byggfakta Group Nordic HoldCo AB; *Int'l*, pg. 1235
SVENSKA NYHETSBREV AB—See Ratos AB; *Int'l*, pg. 6218
SVENSKA ORIENT LINIEN AB; *Int'l*, pg. 7358
SVENSKA PROPERTY NOMINEES LIMITED—See Svenska Handelsbanken AB; *Int'l*, pg. 7358
SVENSK ARBETSHYGIEN AB—See Eurofins Scientific S.E.; *Int'l*, pg. 2552
SVENSKA ROTOR MASKINER AB—See Fujian Snowman Co., Ltd.; *Int'l*, pg. 2819
SVENSKA SKOGSPLANTOR AB—See Sveaskog AB; *Int'l*, pg. 7356
SVENSKA STADSNAT AB—See Telia Company AB; *Int'l*, pg. 7544
SVENSKA STADSNAT PERSPEKTIV AB—See Telia Company AB; *Int'l*, pg. 7544

COMPANY NAME INDEX

SVENSKA TEKNISK BYRA AB—See Axel Johnson Gruppen AB; *Int'l*, pg. 765
SVENSKA VANADIN AB—See Tricorona AB; *Int'l*, pg. 7920
SVENSKA VOLKSWAGEN AB—See Porsche Automobil Holding SE; *Int'l*, pg. 5929
SVENSK DOS AB—See Oriola Corporation; *Int'l*, pg. 5631
SVENSK FASTIGHETSFORMEDLING AB—See DNB Bank ASA; *Int'l*, pg. 2148
SVENSK FILMINDUSTRI, AB—See Telia Company AB; *Int'l*, pg. 7544
SVENSK FORM I KOSTA AB—See New Wave Group AB; *Int'l*, pg. 5230
SVENSK INSTALLATIONSPARTNER AB—See BHG Group AB; *Int'l*, pg. 1014
SVENSK KARNBRANSLEHANTERING AB—See Vattenfall AB; *Int'l*, pg. 8136
SVENSK KRAFTMAKLING AB—See Tricorona AB; *Int'l*, pg. 7920
SVENSK PETROLEUM FORVALTNING AB—See Preem AB; *Int'l*, pg. 5958
SVENSK SPECIALGRAFIT AB—See Tokai Carbon Co., Ltd.; *Int'l*, pg. 7778
SVENSK STALINREDNING AB—See Lagercrantz Group AB; *Int'l*, pg. 4395
SVE PORTABLE ROADWAY SYSTEMS, INC.—See Audax Group, Limited Partnership; *U.S. Private*, pg. 387
SVERICA CAPITAL MANAGEMENT LP; *U.S. Private*, pg. 3888
SVERICA INTERNATIONAL (BOSTON) LLC—See Sverica Capital Management LP; *U.S. Private*, pg. 3888
SVERICA INTERNATIONAL (SAN FRANCISCO) LLC—See Sverica Capital Management LP; *U.S. Private*, pg. 3888
SVERIGES RIKSBANK; *Int'l*, pg. 7358
SVERULL AB—See Axel Johnson Gruppen AB; *Int'l*, pg. 763
SVETLINA PLC—See Synergon Holding PLC; *Int'l*, pg. 7384
SVETOFOR GROUP PJSC; *Int'l*, pg. 7358
SVF HOLDCO (UK) LIMITED—See SoftBank Group Corp.; *Int'l*, pg. 7052
SVF INVESTMENT CORP.; *U.S. Public*, pg. 1968
SVG GROUP CO., LTD.; *Int'l*, pg. 7358
6 V GLOBAL MILL LIMITED; *Int'l*, pg. 6444
SVG MEDIA PVT. LTD.—See Dentsu Group Inc.; *Int'l*, pg. 2037
SVG STEINWERDER VERWALTUNGSGESELLSCHAFT MBH—See ThyssenKrupp AG; *Int'l*, pg. 7725
SV HEALTH INVESTORS, LLP; *U.S. Private*, pg. 3887
SVH HANDELS-GMBH—See Wurth Verwaltungsgesellschaft mbH; *Int'l*, pg. 8507
SVI (AEC) COMPANY LIMITED—See SVI Public Co., Ltd.; *Int'l*, pg. 7358
SVI (AUSTRIA) GMBH—See SVI Public Co., Ltd.; *Int'l*, pg. 7359
SVIAZ-BANK; *Int'l*, pg. 7359
SVI ELECTRONICS (USA) LLC—See SVI Public Co., Ltd.; *Int'l*, pg. 7359
SVI ELECTRONIC (TIANJIN) LIMITED—See SVI Public Co., Ltd.; *Int'l*, pg. 7358
SVI (HKG) LIMITED—See SVI Public Co., Ltd.; *Int'l*, pg. 7358
SVI HUNGARY KFT.—See SVI Public Co., Ltd.; *Int'l*, pg. 7359
SVILOSA AD; *Int'l*, pg. 7359
SVILUPPO ITALIA ABRUZZO S.P.A.—See Agenzia Nazionale per l'Attrazione degli Investimenti e lo Svillupo d'Impresa SpA; *Int'l*, pg. 206
SVILUPPO ITALIA CAMPANIA SPA—See Agenzia Nazionale per l'Attrazione degli Investimenti e lo Svillupo d'Impresa SpA; *Int'l*, pg. 206
SVILUPPO ITALIA MARCHE SPA—See Agenzia Nazionale per l'Attrazione degli Investimenti e lo Svillupo d'Impresa SpA; *Int'l*, pg. 206
SVILUPPO ITALIA MOLISE SPA—See Agenzia Nazionale per l'Attrazione degli Investimenti e lo Svillupo d'Impresa SpA; *Int'l*, pg. 206
SVILUPPO ITALIA PUGLIA SPA—See Agenzia Nazionale per l'Attrazione degli Investimenti e lo Svillupo d'Impresa SpA; *Int'l*, pg. 206
SVINECOMPLEX NIKOLOVO AD; *Int'l*, pg. 7359
SVININ & PARTNERS MANAGEMENT COMPANY; *Int'l*, pg. 7359
S&V INSURANCE SERVICES LLC; *U.S. Private*, pg. 3514
SV INVESTMENT CORPORATION; *Int'l*, pg. 7355
SV INVESTMENT PARTNERS; *U.S. Private*, pg. 3888
SVI PUBLIC CO., LTD.; *Int'l*, pg. 7358
SVI PUBLIC (HK) LIMITED—See SVI Public Co., Ltd.; *Int'l*, pg. 7359
SVITZER A/S—See A.P. Moller-Maersk A/S; *Int'l*, pg. 27
SVITZER AUSTRALASIA—See A.P. Moller-Maersk A/S; *Int'l*, pg. 27
SVITZER AUSTRALIA PTY LTD.—See A.P. Moller-Maersk A/S; *Int'l*, pg. 28
S V J ENTERPRISES LIMITED; *Int'l*, pg. 6444
SVJETLOSTKOMERC D.D. SARAJEVO; *Int'l*, pg. 7359
SVJETLOST-SARS D.D.; *Int'l*, pg. 7359
SVK SYSTEMS; *U.S. Private*, pg. 3889

SV LABS CORPORATION—See San Francisco Equity Partners; *U.S. Private*, pg. 3540
SV-LIDCO CONSTRUCCIONES GENERALES S.A.—See Sacyr, S.A.; *Int'l*, pg. 6466
SV LIGHTING—See Revolution Lighting Technologies, Inc.; *U.S. Public*, pg. 1793
S&V MANAGEMENT CONSULTANTS NV—See Mahindra & Mahindra Limited; *Int'l*, pg. 4647
SVM ASSET MANAGEMENT LIMITED—See AssetCo plc; *Int'l*, pg. 643
SVM, LP—See P2 Capital Partners, LLC; *U.S. Private*, pg. 3061
SVM, LP—See Silver Lake Group, LLC; *U.S. Private*, pg. 3656
SVM SERVICES CANADA, LTD.—See Rentokil Initial plc; *Int'l*, pg. 6289
SVO ACCESS GMBH—See E.ON SE; *Int'l*, pg. 2259
SVOA PUBLIC COMPANY LIMITED; *Int'l*, pg. 7359
SVOBODA CAPITAL PARTNERS LLC; *U.S. Private*, pg. 3889
SVO ECO-INDUSTRIES—See Groupe Seche SAS; *Int'l*, pg. 3110
SVOGL OIL GAS AND ENERGY LIMITED; *Int'l*, pg. 7359
SVOLDER AB; *Int'l*, pg. 7359
SVO MANAGEMENT, INC.—See Marriott International, Inc.; *U.S. Public*, pg. 1372
SVO VERTRIEB GMBH—See E.ON SE; *Int'l*, pg. 2259
SVOX AG—See Microsoft Corporation; *U.S. Public*, pg. 1442
SVP BUILDERS INDIA LTD.; *Int'l*, pg. 7359
SVP CANADA INC.—See Platinum Equity, LLC; *U.S. Private*, pg. 3207
SVP EUROPE SPA—See Platinum Equity, LLC; *U.S. Private*, pg. 3207
SVP GLOBAL TEXTILES LIMITED; *Int'l*, pg. 7359
SV PROBE, INC.—See Nidec Corporation; *Int'l*, pg. 5279
SV PROBE PTE. LTD.—See Nidec Corporation; *Int'l*, pg. 5279
SV PROBE (SIP) CO., LTD—See Nidec Corporation; *Int'l*, pg. 5279
SV PROBE TECH. TAIWAN CO. LTD—See Nidec Corporation; *Int'l*, pg. 5279
SV PROBE VIETNAM CO., LTD—See Nidec Corporation; *Int'l*, pg. 5279
SVP WORLDWIDE, LLC—See Platinum Equity, LLC; *U.S. Private*, pg. 3207
SVRC INDUSTRIES, INC.; *U.S. Private*, pg. 3889
SVS GROUP INC.; *U.S. Private*, pg. 3889
SVS VENTURES LIMITED; *Int'l*, pg. 7359
SVS VISION, INC—See Fielmann Group AG; *Int'l*, pg. 2659
SVS-VISTEK GMBH—See TKH Group N.V.; *Int'l*, pg. 7764
SVS-VISTEK INC.—See TKH Group N.V.; *Int'l*, pg. 7764
SVS-VISTEK K.K.—See TKH Group N.V.; *Int'l*, pg. 7764
SVT APAC PTE. LTD.—See Gesco AG; *Int'l*, pg. 2946
SVT FLEET, LLC—See Velocity Vehicle Group; *U.S. Private*, pg. 4355
SVT GMBH—See Groupe Bruxelles Lambert SA; *Int'l*, pg. 3099
SVT GMBH—See Parcom Capital Management B.V.; *Int'l*, pg. 5739
SVTI-SAN VICENTE TERMINAL INTERNACIONAL—See Carrix, Inc.; *U.S. Private*, pg. 773
SV TRADING & AGENCIES LIMITED; *Int'l*, pg. 7355
SV VISION LIMITED; *Int'l*, pg. 7355
SVYAZMONTAZH HOLDING LLP; *Int'l*, pg. 7359
SVYAZTRANSNEFT, JSC—See OAO AK Transneft; *Int'l*, pg. 5505
SVZ ESPANA S.A—See Royal Cosun U.A.; *Int'l*, pg. 6412
SVZ FRANCE SA—See Royal Cosun U.A.; *Int'l*, pg. 6412
SVZ INTERNATIONAL B.V.—See Royal Cosun U.A.; *Int'l*, pg. 6412
SVZ KARCZMISKA SP. Z O.O.—See Royal Cosun U.A.; *Int'l*, pg. 6412
SVZ ASIA S.A.—See Royal Cosun U.A.; *Int'l*, pg. 6412
SVZ POLAND SP. Z O.O.—See Royal Cosun U.A.; *Int'l*, pg. 6412
SVZ RIJKEVORSEL NV—See Royal Cosun U.A.; *Int'l*, pg. 6412
SVZ UK LTD.—See Royal Cosun U.A.; *Int'l*, pg. 6412
SVZ-USA, INC—See Royal Cosun U.A.; *Int'l*, pg. 6412
SW34 GASTRO GMBH—See GFT Technologies SE; *Int'l*, pg. 2957
SWADESHI INDUSTRIES & LEASING LIMITED; *Int'l*, pg. 7359
SWADESHI POLYTEX LIMITED; *Int'l*, pg. 7359
THE SWAEN B.V.—See Asahi Group Holdings Ltd.; *Int'l*, pg. 594
SWAFFORD WAREHOUSING, INC.—See Peoples Services Inc.; *U.S. Private*, pg. 3142
SWAGELINING LIMITED—See Subsea 7 S.A.; *Int'l*, pg. 7249
SWAGELOK BAKU—See Swagelok Company; *U.S. Private*, pg. 3889
SWAGELOK CAPITAL PROJECTS COMPANY—See Swagelok Company; *U.S. Private*, pg. 3889
SWAGELOK COMPANY; *U.S. Private*, pg. 3889
SWAGELOK HY-LEVEL—See Swagelok Company; *U.S. Private*, pg. 3889

SWANSON GROUP INC.

SWAGELOK KAZAKHSTAN—See Swagelok Company; *U.S. Private*, pg. 3889
SWAGGART BROTHERS INC.—See John Wood Group PLC; *Int'l*, pg. 3983
SWAGGART LOGGING & EXCAVATION LLC—See John Wood Group PLC; *Int'l*, pg. 3984
SWAG PROMO, INC.; *U.S. Private*, pg. 3889
SWAGTAM TRADING & SERVICES LTD.; *Int'l*, pg. 7359
SWAIM INC.; *U.S. Private*, pg. 3889
SWAIM LOGISTICS LLC; *U.S. Private*, pg. 3889
SWAINSBORO DIALYSIS CLINIC, LLC—See Nautic Partners, LLC; *U.S. Private*, pg. 2871
SWAJAS AIR CHARTERS LTD; *Int'l*, pg. 7359
SWAL CORPORATION LIMITED—See UPL Limited; *Int'l*, pg. 8089
SWALLOW CONSTRUCTION CORPORATION; *U.S. Private*, pg. 3889
SWALLOW HOTELS GROUP; *Int'l*, pg. 7360
SWALLOW OIL CO.; *U.S. Private*, pg. 3889
SWALLOWS & AMAZONS PTE. LTD.—See Chip Eng Seng Corporation Ltd.; *Int'l*, pg. 1572
S. WALTER PACKAGING CORP.—See LMP Management Group, Inc.; *U.S. Private*, pg. 2476
SWAMP MATS INC—See Dexterra Group Inc.; *Int'l*, pg. 2093
THE SWAMPSCOTT REPORTER—See Gannett Co., Inc.; *U.S. Public*, pg. 903
SWANBERG CONSTRUCTION, INC.; *U.S. Private*, pg. 3889
SWAN CO., LTD.—See Yamato Holdings Co., Ltd.; *Int'l*, pg. 8554
SWANCOR ADVANCED MATERIALS CO., LTD.; *Int'l*, pg. 7360
SWANCOR IND. CO., LTD.; *Int'l*, pg. 7360
SWANCOR (TIANJIN) WIND BLADE MATERIALS CO., LTD.—See Swancor Ind. Co., Ltd.; *Int'l*, pg. 7360
SWANDER PACE CAPITAL, LLC; *U.S. Private*, pg. 3889
S.W. ANDERSON COMPANY, INC.; *U.S. Private*, pg. 3519
S.W. ANDERSON SALES CORP.—See Ferguson plc; *Int'l*, pg. 2638
SWAN ELECTRIC COMPANY INC.; *U.S. Private*, pg. 3889
SWAN ENERGY LTD.; *Int'l*, pg. 7360
SWANER HARDWOOD COMPANY, INC.; *U.S. Private*, pg. 3890
SWAN FIBER CO., LTD.—See China Hi-Tech Group Corporation; *Int'l*, pg. 1508
SWANG CHAI CHUAN LIMITED; *Int'l*, pg. 7360
SWAN GENERAL LTD.; *Int'l*, pg. 7360
SWAN HILL MILK DISTRIBUTORS PTY. LTD.—See Groupe Lactalis SA; *Int'l*, pg. 3106
SWAN HOME HEALTH, LLC—See TPG Capital, L.P.; *U.S. Public*, pg. 2168
SWAN HOSE—See Jacobson Partners; *U.S. Private*, pg. 2180
SWAN HYGIENE SERVICES LTD.—See Savills plc; *Int'l*, pg. 6600
SWANILLON, INC.; *U.S. Private*, pg. 3890
SWANK ASSOCIATED COMPANIES INC.; *U.S. Private*, pg. 3890
SWANK CAPITAL, LLC; *U.S. Private*, pg. 3890
SWANKE HAYDEN CONNELL LTD; *U.S. Private*, pg. 3890
SWANKE HAYDEN CONNELL MIMARLIK AS—See Aukett Swanke Group Plc; *Int'l*, pg. 704
SWANK ENTERPRISES INC.; *U.S. Private*, pg. 3890
SWANK, INC.—See Randa Corp.; *U.S. Private*, pg. 3353
THE SWANK SHOP (BEIJING) LIMITED—See ENM Holdings Limited; *Int'l*, pg. 2442
THE SWANK SHOP LIMITED—See ENM Holdings Limited; *Int'l*, pg. 2442
SWANKTEK, INC.; *U.S. Private*, pg. 3890
SWAN LIFE LTD.—See SWAN General Ltd.; *Int'l*, pg. 7360
SWAN MILL PAPER COMPANY LTD.; *Int'l*, pg. 7360
SWAN NET GUNDRY LTD.—See Hampidjan hf; *Int'l*, pg. 3239
SWANN INSURANCE (AUST) PTY LTD.—See Insurance Australia Group Limited; *Int'l*, pg. 3725
SWAN PARK (DAWLISH) MANAGEMENT COMPANY LIMITED—See Persimmon plc; *Int'l*, pg. 5817
SWAN POINT YACHT & COUNTRY CLUB INC—See United States Steel Corporation; *U.S. Public*, pg. 2236
SWAN REAL ESTATE PLC; *Int'l*, pg. 7360
SWAN RETAIL INC.; *U.S. Private*, pg. 3889
SWANSEA BUILDING SOCIETY; *Int'l*, pg. 7360
SWANSON-ANAHEIM CORP—See Swanson Systems, Inc.; *U.S. Private*, pg. 3891
SWANSON BARK & WOOD PRODUCTS, INC.—See Denali Water Solutions LLC; *U.S. Private*, pg. 1204
SWANSON BUILDING MATERIALS; *U.S. Private*, pg. 3890
SWANSON-ERIE CORPORATION—See Swanson Systems, Inc.; *U.S. Private*, pg. 3891
SWANSON-FAHRNEY FORD SALES; *U.S. Private*, pg. 3891
SWANSON-FLOSYSTEMS CO.; *U.S. Private*, pg. 3891
SWANSON GROUP INC.; *U.S. Private*, pg. 3891
SWANSON HEALTH PRODUCTS—See Swander Pace Capital, LLC; *U.S. Private*, pg. 3890

SWANSON GROUP INC.

SWANSON-JAPAN LTD—See Swanson Systems, Inc.; *U.S. Private*, pg. 3891
SWANSON ORTHOTIC AND PROSTHETIC CENTER, INC.—See Select Medical Holdings Corporation; *U.S. Public*, pg. 1861
SWANSON RUSSELL ASSOCIATES; *U.S. Private*, pg. 3891
SWANSON RUSSELL ASSOCIATES—See Swanson Russell Associates; *U.S. Private*, pg. 3891
SWANSON SERVICES CORPORATION—See H.I.G. Capital, LLC; *U.S. Private*, pg. 1832
SWANSONS FOOD OF ABERDEEN; *U.S. Private*, pg. 3891
SWANSON SYSTEMS, INC.; *U.S. Private*, pg. 3891
SWANSON VINEYARDS & WINERY—See Vintage Wine Estates, Inc.; *U.S. Public*, pg. 2298
SWANSON & YOUNGDALE INC.; *U.S. Private*, pg. 3890
SWAN STONE CORPORATION; *U.S. Private*, pg. 3889
SWAN SUPER CLEANERS INC.; *U.S. Private*, pg. 3889
SWANSWAY GARAGES LTD.; *Int'l*, pg. 7360
SWANTAK INC.—See Tym Corporation; *Int'l*, pg. 7995
SWAN TAXIS PTY. LTD.—See ComfortDelGro Corporation Limited; *Int'l*, pg. 1713
SWANTEX ASIA LIMITED—See Swan Mill Paper Company Ltd.; *Int'l*, pg. 7360
SWANTON WELDING & MACHINING CO, INC.; *U.S. Private*, pg. 3891
SWAPDRIVE, INC.—See Gen Digital Inc.; *U.S. Public*, pg. 910
SWAP FINANCIAL GROUP LLC—See GoldenTree Asset Management LP; *U.S. Private*, pg. 1734
SWARAJ ENGINES LTD—See Mahindra & Mahindra Limited; *Int'l*, pg. 4646
SWARAJ SUITING LIMITED; *Int'l*, pg. 7360
SWARAJ TECHNOCRAFT PVT. LTD.—See Rajratan Global Wire Limited; *Int'l*, pg. 6194
SWARCO AG; *Int'l*, pg. 7360
SWARCO ALBANIA SHPK—See SWARCO AG; *Int'l*, pg. 7361
SWARCO AMERICA INC.—See SWARCO AG; *Int'l*, pg. 7361
SWARCO ASIA LTD.—See SWARCO AG; *Int'l*, pg. 7361
SWARCO BULGARIA LTD.—See SWARCO AG; *Int'l*, pg. 7360
SWARCO CENTRAL SERVICES GMBH—See SWARCO AG; *Int'l*, pg. 7361
SWARCO DANMARK AS—See SWARCO AG; *Int'l*, pg. 7361
SWARCO FINLAND OY—See SWARCO AG; *Int'l*, pg. 7361
SWARCO FUELCELL SYSTEMS GMBH—See SWARCO AG; *Int'l*, pg. 7361
SWARCO FUTURIT VERKEHRSSIGNALSYSTEME GESMBH—See SWARCO AG; *Int'l*, pg. 7361
SWARCO HEOSCONT STRASSENMARKIERUNGEN GESMBH—See SWARCO AG; *Int'l*, pg. 7361
SWARCO INDUSTRIES INC—See SWARCO AG; *Int'l*, pg. 7361
SWARCO LEA D.O.O.—See SWARCO AG; *Int'l*, pg. 7360
SWARCO LIMBURGER LACKFABRIK GMBH—See SWARCO AG; *Int'l*, pg. 7361
SWARCO MEXICO S.A. DE C.V.—See SWARCO AG; *Int'l*, pg. 7361
SWARCO MIZAR AB—See SWARCO AG; *Int'l*, pg. 7361
SWARCO MIZAR S.P.A—See SWARCO AG; *Int'l*, pg. 7361
SWARCO NEDERLAND B.V.—See SWARCO AG; *Int'l*, pg. 7361
SWARCO NORGE AS—See SWARCO AG; *Int'l*, pg. 7361
SWARCO RECYCLING GMBH—See SWARCO AG; *Int'l*, pg. 7361
SWARCO REFLEX INC.—See SWARCO AG; *Int'l*, pg. 7361
SWARCO ROMANIA SRL—See SWARCO AG; *Int'l*, pg. 7361
SWARCO SAUDIA LLC—See SWARCO AG; *Int'l*, pg. 7361
SWARCO SERVICE ITALIA S.R.L.—See SWARCO AG; *Int'l*, pg. 7361
SWARCO SVERIGE AB—See SWARCO AG; *Int'l*, pg. 7361
SWARCO TECHNOLOGY APS—See SWARCO AG; *Int'l*, pg. 7361
SWARCO TRAFFIC AUSTRIA GMBH—See SWARCO AG; *Int'l*, pg. 7361
SWARCO TRAFFIC BRASIL LTDA.—See SWARCO AG; *Int'l*, pg. 7361
SWARCO TRAFFIC CZ S.R.O.—See SWARCO AG; *Int'l*, pg. 7361
SWARCO TRAFFIC HOLDING AG—See SWARCO AG; *Int'l*, pg. 7361
SWARCO TRAFFIC HUNGARIA KFT.—See SWARCO AG; *Int'l*, pg. 7361
SWARCO TRAFFIC LIMITED—See SWARCO AG; *Int'l*, pg. 7361
SWARCO TRAFFIC MANAGEMENT INC.—See SWARCO AG; *Int'l*, pg. 7361
SWARCO TRAFFIC POLSKA SP. Z.O.O.—See SWARCO AG; *Int'l*, pg. 7361

SWARCO TRAFFIC SWITZERLAND GMBH—See SWARCO AG; *Int'l*, pg. 7361
SWARCO TRAFFIC SYSTEMS GMBH—See SWARCO AG; *Int'l*, pg. 7361
SWARCO UKRAINE LLC—See SWARCO AG; *Int'l*, pg. 7361
SWARCO VESTGLAS GMBH—See SWARCO AG; *Int'l*, pg. 7361
SWARCO VICAS S.A.—See SWARCO AG; *Int'l*, pg. 7361
SWARCO V.S.M. GMBH—See SWARCO AG; *Int'l*, pg. 7361
THE SWARM AGENCY, INC.; *U.S. Private*, pg. 4125
SWARNAJYOTHI AGROTECH & POWER LIMITED; *Int'l*, pg. 7362
SWARNA SECURITIES LIMITED; *Int'l*, pg. 7361
SWARNSARITA JEWELS INDIA LTD.; *Int'l*, pg. 7362
SWAROJGAR LAGHUBITTA BITTIYA SANSTHA LTD; *Int'l*, pg. 7362
SWAROVSKI CONSUMER GOODS LTD.—See Swarovski & Co.; *Int'l*, pg. 7362
SWAROVSKI & CO.; *Int'l*, pg. 7362
SWAROVSKI LIGHTING PARTS—See Swarovski & Co.; *Int'l*, pg. 7362
SWAROVSKI NORTH AMERICA LIMITED INC.—See Swarovski & Co.; *Int'l*, pg. 7362
SWAROVSKI OPTIK NORTH AMERICA LIMITED—See Swarovski & Co.; *Int'l*, pg. 7362
SWAROVSKI U.K. LTD.—See Swarovski & Co.; *Int'l*, pg. 7362
SWARTH GROUP; *Int'l*, pg. 7362
THE SWARTHMORE GROUP, INC.; *U.S. Private*, pg. 4125
SWARTWOUT DIVISION—See Canada Pension Plan Investment Board; *Int'l*, pg. 1282
SWA SARL—See Sarama Resources Ltd.; *Int'l*, pg. 6576
SWASCAN S.R.L.—See Tinexta S.p.A.; *Int'l*, pg. 7753
SWASTIKA INVESTMART LTD.; *Int'l*, pg. 7362
SWASTIK ENTERPRISES PRIVATE LIMITED; *Int'l*, pg. 7362
SWASTIK SAFE DEPOSIT & INVESTMENTS LIMITED; *Int'l*, pg. 7362
SWASTI VINAYAKA ART & HERITAGE CORPORATION LIMITED; *Int'l*, pg. 7362
SWASTI VINAYAKA SYNTHETICS LIMITED; *Int'l*, pg. 7362
THE SWATCH GROUP ASSEMBLY SA—See The Swatch Group Ltd.; *Int'l*, pg. 7693
THE SWATCH GROUP (AUSTRALIA) PTY LTD—See The Swatch Group Ltd.; *Int'l*, pg. 7692
THE SWATCH GROUP (BELGIUM) SA—See The Swatch Group Ltd.; *Int'l*, pg. 7692
SWATCH GROUP BELGIUM S.A.—See The Swatch Group Ltd.; *Int'l*, pg. 7692
THE SWATCH GROUP (CANADA) LTD.—See The Swatch Group Ltd.; *Int'l*, pg. 7692
THE SWATCH GROUP (CHINA) LTD—See The Swatch Group Ltd.; *Int'l*, pg. 7692
THE SWATCH GROUP CUSTOMER SERVICE (EUROPE) GMBH—See The Swatch Group Ltd.; *Int'l*, pg. 7693
THE SWATCH GROUP (DEUTSCHLAND) GMBH—See The Swatch Group Ltd.; *Int'l*, pg. 7692
THE SWATCH GROUP (DEUTSCHLAND) LES BOUTIQUES GMBH—See The Swatch Group Ltd.; *Int'l*, pg. 7692
SWATCH GROUP DO BRAZIL—See The Swatch Group Ltd.; *Int'l*, pg. 7692
THE SWATCH GROUP (ESPANA) SA—See The Swatch Group Ltd.; *Int'l*, pg. 7692
SWATCH GROUP ESPANA S.A.—See The Swatch Group Ltd.; *Int'l*, pg. 7692
THE SWATCH GROUP FINANCE (LUXEMBOURG) S.A.—See The Swatch Group Ltd.; *Int'l*, pg. 7693
THE SWATCH GROUP (FRANCE) LES BOUTIQUES, SAS—See The Swatch Group Ltd.; *Int'l*, pg. 7692
THE SWATCH GROUP (FRANCE) S.A.—See The Swatch Group Ltd.; *Int'l*, pg. 7692
THE SWATCH GROUP (GREECE) SA—See The Swatch Group Ltd.; *Int'l*, pg. 7692
THE SWATCH GROUP (HONG KONG) LTD.—See The Swatch Group Ltd.; *Int'l*, pg. 7693
THE SWATCH GROUP IMMEUBLES SA—See The Swatch Group Ltd.; *Int'l*, pg. 7693
SWATCH GROUP (INDIA) PRIVATE LTD—See The Swatch Group Ltd.; *Int'l*, pg. 7692
THE SWATCH GROUP (ITALIA) S.P.A.—See The Swatch Group Ltd.; *Int'l*, pg. 7693
THE SWATCH GROUP (JAPAN) KK—See The Swatch Group Ltd.; *Int'l*, pg. 7693
THE SWATCH GROUP (KOREA) LTD.—See The Swatch Group Ltd.; *Int'l*, pg. 7693
THE SWATCH GROUP LES BOUTIQUES SA—See The Swatch Group Ltd.; *Int'l*, pg. 7693
THE SWATCH GROUP LTD.; *Int'l*, pg. 7691
THE SWATCH GROUP LTD.—See The Swatch Group Ltd.; *Int'l*, pg. 7693
THE SWATCH GROUP (MALAYSIA) SDN. BHD.—See The Swatch Group Ltd.; *Int'l*, pg. 7693
THE SWATCH GROUP MANAGEMENT SERVICES SA—See The Swatch Group Ltd.; *Int'l*, pg. 7693

CORPORATE AFFILIATIONS

THE SWATCH GROUP MEXICO S.A DE C.V—See The Swatch Group Ltd.; *Int'l*, pg. 7693
THE SWATCH GROUP (NETHERLANDS) BV—See The Swatch Group Ltd.; *Int'l*, pg. 7693
THE SWATCH GROUP (NORDIC) AB—See The Swatch Group Ltd.; *Int'l*, pg. 7693
THE SWATCH GROUP (OESTERREICH) GMBH—See The Swatch Group Ltd.; *Int'l*, pg. 7693
THE SWATCH GROUP (OSTERREICH) GMBH—See The Swatch Group Ltd.; *Int'l*, pg. 7693
THE SWATCH GROUP PANAMA SA—See The Swatch Group Ltd.; *Int'l*, pg. 7693
THE SWATCH GROUP (POLSKA) SP. Z.O.O.—See The Swatch Group Ltd.; *Int'l*, pg. 7693
THE SWATCH GROUP RECHERCHE ET DEVELOPPEMENT SA—See The Swatch Group Ltd.; *Int'l*, pg. 7693
THE SWATCH GROUP RE (LUXEMBOURG) SA—See The Swatch Group Ltd.; *Int'l*, pg. 7693
THE SWATCH GROUP (RUS) OOO—See The Swatch Group Ltd.; *Int'l*, pg. 7693
THE SWATCH GROUP S.E.A. (S) PTE. LTD.—See The Swatch Group Ltd.; *Int'l*, pg. 7693
THE SWATCH GROUP SERVICES LTD.—See The Swatch Group Ltd.; *Int'l*, pg. 7693
THE SWATCH GROUP (SOUTH AFRICA) (PROPRIETARY) LTD—See The Swatch Group Ltd.; *Int'l*, pg. 7693
THE SWATCH GROUP (TAIWAN) LTD—See The Swatch Group Ltd.; *Int'l*, pg. 7693
THE SWATCH GROUP TRADING (THAILAND) LTD—See The Swatch Group Ltd.; *Int'l*, pg. 7693
THE SWATCH GROUP TURKEY SAAT TICARET LIMITED SIRKETI—See The Swatch Group Ltd.; *Int'l*, pg. 7693
THE SWATCH GROUP (UK) LES BOUTIQUES—See The Swatch Group Ltd.; *Int'l*, pg. 7693
THE SWATCH GROUP (UK) LTD—See The Swatch Group Ltd.; *Int'l*, pg. 7693
THE SWATCH GROUP (U.S.) INC.—See The Swatch Group Ltd.; *Int'l*, pg. 7693
SWATCH RETAIL AG—See The Swatch Group Ltd.; *Int'l*, pg. 7692
SWATCH S.A.—See The Swatch Group Ltd.; *Int'l*, pg. 7692
SWATCH WATCH U.S.A.—See The Swatch Group Ltd.; *Int'l*, pg. 7693
SWAT ENVIRONMENTAL INC.; *U.S. Private*, pg. 3891
SWAT FAME INC.; *U.S. Private*, pg. 3891
SWATI ENTERPRISES INC.; *U.S. Private*, pg. 3891
SWATY D.D.—See Avtotehna, d.d.; *Int'l*, pg. 751
SW AUTOMATIK AB—See Addtech AB; *Int'l*, pg. 135
SWAVELLE/MILL CREEK FABRICS, INC.; *U.S. Private*, pg. 3891
SWAZI GASES (PTY.) LIMITED—See L'Air Liquide S.A.; *Int'l*, pg. 4376
SWAZILAND FRUIT CANNERS (PTY.) LTD.—See Nestle S.A.; *Int'l*, pg. 5211
SWAZILAND POSTS & TELECOMMUNICATIONS CORPORATION; *Int'l*, pg. 7362
SWAZILAND PROPERTY INVESTMENT LIMITED; *Int'l*, pg. 7362
SWAZI MTN LTD.—See MTN Group Limited; *Int'l*, pg. 5071
SWAZI POST—See Swaziland Posts & Telecommunications Corporation; *Int'l*, pg. 7362
SWAZISPA HOLDINGS LIMITED—See Sun International Limited; *Int'l*, pg. 7304
SWAZI TELECOM—See Swaziland Posts & Telecommunications Corporation; *Int'l*, pg. 7362
SWB BELEUCHTUNG GMBH—See EWE Aktiengesellschaft; *Int'l*, pg. 2576
SWB ENTSORGUNG GMBH & CO. KG—See EWE Aktiengesellschaft; *Int'l*, pg. 2576
SWB ERZEUGUNG GMBH & CO. KG—See EWE Aktiengesellschaft; *Int'l*, pg. 2576
SWB GASUMSTELLUNG GMBH—See EWE Aktiengesellschaft; *Int'l*, pg. 2576
SWB MESSUNG UND ABRECHNUNG GMBH—See EWE Aktiengesellschaft; *Int'l*, pg. 2576
SWB SERVICES AG & CO. KG—See EWE Aktiengesellschaft; *Int'l*, pg. 2576
SWB VERTRIEB BREMEN GMBH—See EWE Aktiengesellschaft; *Int'l*, pg. 2576
SWB VERTRIEB BREMERHAVEN GMBH & CO. KG—See EWE Aktiengesellschaft; *Int'l*, pg. 2576
SWB YANKEES, LLC—See Mandalay Entertainment Group; *U.S. Private*, pg. 2562
SWB YANKEES, LLC—See New York Yankees Partnership; *U.S. Private*, pg. 2912
SWB YANKEES, LLC—See Seaport Capital, LLC; *U.S. Private*, pg. 3586
SWCC CORPORATION; *Int'l*, pg. 7362
SWCC SHOWA CABLE SYSTEMS CO., LTD.—See SWCC Corporation; *Int'l*, pg. 7363
SWCC SHOWA (H.K.) CO., LTD.—See SWCC Corporation; *Int'l*, pg. 7363
SWCC SHOWA (SHANGHAI) CO., LTD.—See SWCC Corporation; *Int'l*, pg. 7363
SWCC SHOWA (S) PTE. LTD.—See SWCC Corporation; *Int'l*, pg. 7363

COMPANY NAME INDEX

S & W CONTRACTING COMPANY INC.; *U.S. Private,* pg. 3512
S&W CONTRACTING OF WNY, INC.; *U.S. Private,* pg. 3514
S&W CORPORATION - SECOND FACTORY—See S&W Corporation; *Int'l,* pg. 6446
S&W CORPORATION; *Int'l,* pg. 6446
SWC TRADING INC.—See Sibanye-Stillwater Limited; *Int'l,* pg. 6876
SWD CORPORATION; *U.S. Private,* pg. 3891
SWEA ENERGI AB—See DCC plc; *Int'l,* pg. 1991
SWE-CHICK AB—See Lantmannen ek for; *Int'l,* pg. 4414
SWECO AB; *Int'l,* pg. 7363
SWECO ARCHITECTS A/S—See Sweco AB; *Int'l,* pg. 7363
SWECO ARCHITEKCI SP. Z O.O.—See Sweco AB; *Int'l,* pg. 7363
SWECO BELGIUM NV—See Sweco AB; *Int'l,* pg. 7364
SWECO CENTRAL EASTERN EUROPE AB—See Sweco AB; *Int'l,* pg. 7363
SWECO CONNECT AB—See Sweco AB; *Int'l,* pg. 7363
SWECO CONSULTING SP. Z O.O.—See Sweco AB; *Int'l,* pg. 7364
SWECO DANMARK A/S—See Sweco AB; *Int'l,* pg. 7364
SWECO EASTERN EUROPE AB—See Sweco AB; *Int'l,* pg. 7363
SWECO ELEKTRONIK AB—See Inission AB; *Int'l,* pg. 3704
SWECO ENERGOPROEKT JSC—See Sweco AB; *Int'l,* pg. 7363
SWECO ENERGUIDE AB—See Sweco AB; *Int'l,* pg. 7363
SWECO ENVIRONMENT AB—See Sweco AB; *Int'l,* pg. 7363
SWECO EST OU—See Sweco AB; *Int'l,* pg. 7363
SWECO EUROFUTURES AB—See Sweco AB; *Int'l,* pg. 7363
SWECO EUROPE S.A.—See Schlumberger Limited; *U.S. Public,* pg. 1846
SWECO FAB, INC.—See Piping Technology & Products Inc.; *U.S. Private,* pg. 3190
SWECO FINLAND OY—See Sweco AB; *Int'l,* pg. 7363
SWECO GMBH—See Sweco AB; *Int'l,* pg. 7364
SWECO HYDROPROJEKT A.S.—See Sweco AB; *Int'l,* pg. 7364
SWECO INDUSTRY AB—See Sweco AB; *Int'l,* pg. 7364
SWECO INFRASTRUCTURE AB—See Sweco AB; *Int'l,* pg. 7364
SWECO INTERNATIONAL AB—See Sweco AB; *Int'l,* pg. 7364
SWECO INTERNATIONAL EXPORT AB—See Sweco AB; *Int'l,* pg. 7364
SWECO MANAGEMENT AB—See Sweco AB; *Int'l,* pg. 7364
SWECO MEC AS—See Sweco AB; *Int'l,* pg. 7364
SWECON ANLAEGGNINGSMASKINER AB—See Lantmannen ek for; *Int'l,* pg. 4414
SWECO NEDERLAND B.V.—See Sweco AB; *Int'l,* pg. 7364
SWECO NIPI TRTI—See Sweco AB; *Int'l,* pg. 7364
SWECO NORGE AS—See Sweco AB; *Int'l,* pg. 7364
SWECO PAATELA ARCHITECTS OY—See Sweco AB; *Int'l,* pg. 7364
SWECO PM OY—See Sweco AB; *Int'l,* pg. 7364
SWECO POLSKA SP.Z O.O.—See Sweco AB; *Int'l,* pg. 7363
SWECO POSITION AB—See Sweco AB; *Int'l,* pg. 7364
SWECO PROJEKT AS—See Sweco AB; *Int'l,* pg. 7363
SWECO RUSSIA AB—See Sweco AB; *Int'l,* pg. 7364
SWECO—See Schlumberger Limited; *U.S. Public,* pg. 1846
SWECO STRUCTURES AB—See Sweco AB; *Int'l,* pg. 7364
SWECO UK LIMITED—See Sweco AB; *Int'l,* pg. 7364
SWEDA CANADA INC.—See Sweda Corporation; *U.S. Private,* pg. 3891
SWEDA CORPORATION; *U.S. Private,* pg. 3891
SWEDA INTERNATIONAL LTD.—See Sweda Corporation; *U.S. Private,* pg. 3891
SWEDBANK AB; *Int'l,* pg. 7364
SWEDBANK AS—See Swedbank AB; *Int'l,* pg. 7364
SWEDBANK FASTIGHETSBYRA AB—See Swedbank AB; *Int'l,* pg. 7364
SWEDBANK FINANS AB—See Swedbank AB; *Int'l,* pg. 7364
SWEDBANK FIRST SECURITIES LLC—See Swedbank AB; *Int'l,* pg. 7364
SWEDBANK (LITHUANIA) AB—See Swedbank AB; *Int'l,* pg. 7364
SWEDBANK (LUXEMBOURG) S.A.—See Swedbank AB; *Int'l,* pg. 7364
SWEDBANK MANAGEMENT COMPANY S.A.—See Swedbank AB; *Int'l,* pg. 7364
SWEDBANK MARKETS—See Swedbank AB; *Int'l,* pg. 7364
SWEDE ENERGY POWER SOLUTIONS AB—See SolTech Energy Sweden AB; *Int'l,* pg. 7076
SWEDEGAS AB; *Int'l,* pg. 7364
SWEDELTACO AB—See DistIT AB; *Int'l,* pg. 2136
SWEDEN BUYERSCLUB AB; *Int'l,* pg. 7365
SWEDENCARE AB; *Int'l,* pg. 7365
SWEDENCARE BUCCOSANTE SARL—See Swedencare AB; *Int'l,* pg. 7365
SWEDENCARE IRELAND LTD.—See Swedencare AB; *Int'l,* pg. 7365
SWEDENCARE SPAIN SLU—See Swedencare AB; *Int'l,* pg. 7365
SWEDENCARE UK LTD.—See Swedencare AB; *Int'l,* pg. 7365
SWEDENCARE USA INC.—See Swedencare AB; *Int'l,* pg. 7365
SWEDEN HOUSE CO., LTD.—See Tomoku Co., Ltd.; *Int'l,* pg. 7802
SWEDEN HOUSE REFORM CO., LTD.—See Tomoku Co., Ltd.; *Int'l,* pg. 7802
SWEDEN RECYCLING AB—See Rentokil Initial plc; *Int'l,* pg. 6289
SWEDEN RENT A CAR AB—See Avis Budget Group, Inc.; *U.S. Public,* pg. 249
SWEDEN ROCK FESTIVAL AB—See Live Nation Entertainment, Inc.; *U.S. Public,* pg. 1331
SWEDISHAMERICAN HEALTH SYSTEM; *U.S. Private,* pg. 3891
SWEDISH LOGISTIC PROPERTY AB; *Int'l,* pg. 7365
SWEDISH MATCH AB—See Philip Morris International Inc.; *U.S. Public,* pg. 1687
SWEDISH MATCH DISTRIBUTION AB—See Philip Morris International Inc.; *U.S. Public,* pg. 1687
SWEDISH MATCH DO BRASIL S/A—See Philip Morris International Inc.; *U.S. Public,* pg. 1687
SWEDISH MATCH DOMINICANA S.A.—See Philip Morris International Inc.; *U.S. Public,* pg. 1687
SWEDISH MATCH INDUSTRIES AB—See Philip Morris International Inc.; *U.S. Public,* pg. 1687
SWEDISH MATCH LIGHTERS BV—See Philip Morris International Inc.; *U.S. Public,* pg. 1687
SWEDISH MATCH NORGE AS—See Philip Morris International Inc.; *U.S. Public,* pg. 1687
SWEDISH MATCH NORTH AMERICA INC.—See Philip Morris International Inc.; *U.S. Public,* pg. 1687
SWEDISH MATCH NORTH EUROPE AB—See Philip Morris International Inc.; *U.S. Public,* pg. 1687
SWEDISH MEDICAL CENTER—See HCA Healthcare, Inc.; *U.S. Public,* pg. 998
SWEDISH MICROWAVE AB—See Beijer Alma AB; *Int'l,* pg. 943
SWEDISH MOTOR ASSEMBLIES SDN BHD—See Zhejiang Geely Holding Group Co., Ltd.; *Int'l,* pg. 8653
SWEDISH ORPHAN BIOVITRUM AB; *Int'l,* pg. 7365
SWEDISH ORPHAN BIOVITRUM AG—See Swedish Orphan Biovitrum AB; *Int'l,* pg. 7365
SWEDISH ORPHAN BIOVITRUM A/S—See Swedish Orphan Biovitrum AB; *Int'l,* pg. 7365
SWEDISH ORPHAN BIOVITRUM AS—See Swedish Orphan Biovitrum AB; *Int'l,* pg. 7365
SWEDISH ORPHAN BIOVITRUM GMBH—See Swedish Orphan Biovitrum AB; *Int'l,* pg. 7365
SWEDISH ORPHAN BIOVITRUM INTERNATIONAL AB—See Swedish Orphan Biovitrum AB; *Int'l,* pg. 7365
SWEDISH ORPHAN BIOVITRUM LTD—See Swedish Orphan Biovitrum AB; *Int'l,* pg. 7365
SWEDISH ORPHAN BIOVITRUM MANUFACTURING AB—See Swedish Orphan Biovitrum AB; *Int'l,* pg. 7365
SWEDISH ORPHAN BIOVITRUM SARL—See Swedish Orphan Biovitrum AB; *Int'l,* pg. 7365
SWEDISH ORPHAN BIOVITRUM S.L.—See Swedish Orphan Biovitrum AB; *Int'l,* pg. 7365
SWEDISH ORPHAN BIOVITRUM (SOBI) CANADA, INC.—See Swedish Orphan Biovitrum AB; *Int'l,* pg. 7365
SWEDISH ORPHAN BIOVITRUM S.R.L.—See Swedish Orphan Biovitrum AB; *Int'l,* pg. 7365
SWEDISH ORPHAN BIOVITRUM S.R.O—See Swedish Orphan Biovitrum AB; *Int'l,* pg. 7366
SWEDISH ORPHAN BIOVITRUM SVERIGE AB—See Swedish Orphan Biovitrum AB; *Int'l,* pg. 7365
SWEDISH SAW BLADES AB—See Duroc AB; *Int'l,* pg. 2230
SWEDISH SPACE CORPORATION—See GomSpace Group AB; *Int'l,* pg. 3037
SWEDOL AB—See Nordstjernan AB; *Int'l,* pg. 5425
SWEDRIVE AB—See Nordstjernan AB; *Int'l,* pg. 5425
SWEDSPAN INTERNATIONAL S.R.O.—See Stichting INGKA Foundation; *Int'l,* pg. 7214
SWEDTEL ARABIA LTD—See Al-Hejailan Group; *Int'l,* pg. 286
SWEDTEL INTERNATIONAL AB—See Al-Hejailan Group; *Int'l,* pg. 286
SWEDTEL INTERNATIONAL CO.—See Al-Hejailan Group; *Int'l,* pg. 286
SWEDTEL SEA SDN. BHD—See Al-Hejailan Group; *Int'l,* pg. 286
SWEDWIRE AB—See Lagercrantz Group AB; *Int'l,* pg. 4395
SWEDWISE AB—See Storskogen Group AB; *Int'l,* pg. 7228
SWEEGEN, INC.; *U.S. Public,* pg. 1968
SWEENEY BROTHERS TRACTOR CO.; *U.S. Private,* pg. 3891
SWEENEY HARDWOODS, INC.—See R.E. Sweeney Company Inc.; *U.S. Private,* pg. 3335
SWEENEY; *U.S. Private,* pg. 3891
SWEENEY—See SWEENEY; *U.S. Private,* pg. 3891
SWEENEY STEEL SERVICE CORP; *U.S. Private,* pg. 3891
SWEEPING CORPORATION OF AMERICA, INC.—See Warburg Pincus LLC; *U.S. Private,* pg. 4439
SWEEPING SOUTH, INC.—See Warburg Pincus LLC; *U.S. Private,* pg. 4440
SWEEPSTER ATTACHMENTS LLC; *U.S. Private,* pg. 3891
SWEET ACQUISITIONS CA3, LLC—See Hilton Grand Vacations Inc.; *U.S. Public,* pg. 1039
SWEET ACQUISITONS UT1—See Hilton Grand Vacations Inc.; *U.S. Public,* pg. 1039
SWEET BABY RAY'S BARBECUE WOOD DALE LLC—See SBR Events Group; *U.S. Private,* pg. 3560
SWEET CANDY COMPANY; *U.S. Private,* pg. 3892
SWEET CORN PRODUCTS COMPANY LIMITED—See Agripure Holdings Company Limited; *Int'l,* pg. 218
SWEET EARTH HOLDINGS CORPORATION; *Int'l,* pg. 7366
SWEETENERS PLUS LLC—See Graycliff Partners LP; *U.S. Private,* pg. 1761
SWEETEN REAL ESTATE DEVELOPMENT CO., LTD.; *Int'l,* pg. 7366
SWEETEN TRUCK CENTER; *U.S. Private,* pg. 3892
SWEET FLAVOR OF FLORIDA LLC; *U.S. Private,* pg. 3892
SWEETFROG ENTERPRISES, LLC—See MTY Food Group Inc.; *Int'l,* pg. 5073
SWEET GARDEN CO., LTD.—See Fujiya Co., Ltd.; *Int'l,* pg. 2838
SWEET GREEN FIELDS CO., LIMITED—See Tate & Lyle PLC; *Int'l,* pg. 7474
SWEET GREEN FIELDS USA LLC—See Tate & Lyle PLC; *Int'l,* pg. 7474
SWEETGREEN, INC.; *U.S. Public,* pg. 1968
SWEET HARVEST FOODS CO.—See Peak Rock Capital LLC; *U.S. Private,* pg. 3124
SWEETHEART CUP COMPANY INC.—See Dart Container Corporation; *U.S. Private,* pg. 1160
SWEETIQ ANALYTICS CORP.—See uberall GmbH; *Int'l,* pg. 8002
THE SWEET LAKE LAND & OIL CO. LLC; *U.S. Private,* pg. 4125
SWEET LEAF TEA CO.—See Nestle S.A.; *Int'l,* pg. 5210
THE SWEET LIFE ENTERPRISES; *U.S. Private,* pg. 4125
SWEETMAN CONSTRUCTION CO.—See MDU Resources Group, Inc.; *U.S. Public,* pg. 1411
SWEET NATURAL TRADING CO. LIMITED; *Int'l,* pg. 7366
SWEET POISON SPIRITS INC; *Int'l,* pg. 7366
SWEET PRODUCTIONS LTD.; *U.S. Private,* pg. 3892
SWEET PRODUCTS LOGISTICS NV; *Int'l,* pg. 7366
THE SWEET SHOP USA; *U.S. Private,* pg. 4125
SWEET SISTERS, INC.; *U.S. Private,* pg. 3892
THE SWEETS MIX COMPANY, INC.—See Tootsie Roll Industries, Inc.; *U.S. Public,* pg. 2163
SWEETS OF OMAN S.A.O.G; *Int'l,* pg. 7366
SWEET SPARKMAN ARCHITECTS, INC.; *U.S. Private,* pg. 3892
SWEET SPOT DIGITAL (MALAYSIA) SDN BHD—See Berjaya Corporation Berhad; *Int'l,* pg. 984
SWEET STREET DESSERTS INC.; *U.S. Private,* pg. 3892
SWEETVIEW PARTNERS, INC.; *U.S. Private,* pg. 3892
SWEETWATER BREWING COMPANY, LLC; *U.S. Private,* pg. 3892
SWEETWATER DEVELOPMENT LLC—See Duke Energy Corporation; *U.S. Public,* pg. 691
SWEETWATER HOSPITAL ASSOCIATION; *U.S. Private,* pg. 3892
SWEETWATER LANDING—See Bonita Bay Properties, Inc.; *U.S. Private,* pg. 614
SWEETWATER LLC; *U.S. Private,* pg. 3892
SWEETWATER ORGANIC COMMUNITY FARM, INC.; *U.S. Private,* pg. 3892
SWEETWATER SECURITY SYSTEMS LLC; *U.S. Private,* pg. 3892
SWEETWATER SOUND INC.; *U.S. Private,* pg. 3892
SWEETWATER STEEL CO., INC.; *U.S. Private,* pg. 3892
SWEETWATER TELEVISION COMPANY—See Novacap Management Inc.; *Int'l,* pg. 5453
SWEETWATER VALLEY OIL CO.; *U.S. Private,* pg. 3892
SWEETWORKS, INC.; *U.S. Private,* pg. 3892
SWEFOUR GSM AB—See Tele2 AB; *Int'l,* pg. 7529
SWEGON AB—See Investment AB Latour; *Int'l,* pg. 3783
SWEGON AG—See Investment AB Latour; *Int'l,* pg. 3784
SWEGON AS—See Investment AB Latour; *Int'l,* pg. 3783
SWEGON A/S—See Investment AB Latour; *Int'l,* pg. 3783
SWEGON BELGIUM S.A.—See Investment AB Latour; *Int'l,* pg. 3783
SWEGON BLUE BOX PRIVATE LIMITED—See Investment AB Latour; *Int'l,* pg. 3784
SWEGON BV—See Investment AB Latour; *Int'l,* pg. 3783
SWEGON CLIMATE SYSTEMS GERMANY GMBH—See Investment AB Latour; *Int'l,* pg. 3783

SWEETWORKS, INC.

SWEGON EESTI OU—See Investment AB Latour; *Int'l*, pg. 3783
SWEGON GERMANY GMBH—See Investment AB Latour; *Int'l*, pg. 3784
SWEGON GMBH—See Investment AB Latour; *Int'l*, pg. 3783
SWEGON GMBH—See Investment AB Latour; *Int'l*, pg. 3783
SWEGON ILTO OY—See Investment AB Latour; *Int'l*, pg. 3784
SWEGON INDOOR CLIMATE S.A.—See Investment AB Latour; *Int'l*, pg. 3783
SWEGON LIDKOPING AB—See Investment AB Latour; *Int'l*, pg. 3784
SWEGON LTD—See Investment AB Latour; *Int'l*, pg. 3783
SWEGON NORTH AMERICA INC.—See Investment AB Latour; *Int'l*, pg. 3784
SWEGON OPERATIONS BELGIUM S.A.—See Investment AB Latour; *Int'l*, pg. 3784
SWEGON OPERATIONS S.R.L.—See Investment AB Latour; *Int'l*, pg. 3784
SWEGON S.A.R.L.—See Investment AB Latour; *Int'l*, pg. 3783
SWEGON SA—See Investment AB Latour; *Int'l*, pg. 3783
SWEGON SP.Z O.O—See Investment AB Latour; *Int'l*, pg. 3783
SWEGON S.R.O.—See Investment AB Latour; *Int'l*, pg. 3784
SWEKIP SWEDEN AB—See Volati AB; *Int'l*, pg. 8301
SWELDX AB—See Illinois Tool Works Inc.; *U.S. Public*, pg. 1111
SWELECT ENERGY SYSTEMS LTD.; *Int'l*, pg. 7366
SWELECT ENERGY SYSTEMS PTE LIMITED—See SWELECT Energy Systems Ltd.; *Int'l*, pg. 7366
SWELECT HHV SOLAR PHOTOVOLTAICS PRIVATE LIMITED—See SWELECT Energy Systems Ltd.; *Int'l*, pg. 7366
SWELEX AB—See Addtech AB; *Int'l*, pg. 135
SWELL ENERGY INC; *U.S. Private*, pg. 3892
SWELL INTERNATIONAL INC; *U.S. Private*, pg. 3892
SWELL-MARUI (GUANGZHOU) AUTOMOBILE PARTS CO.,LTD.—See Guangdong Hongtu Technology (Holdings) Co., Ltd.; *Int'l*, pg. 3156
SWENEX - SWISS ENERGY EXCHANGE LTD.; *Int'l*, pg. 7366
SWENSEN'S OF SINGAPORE PTE. LTD.—See ABR Holdings, Ltd.; *Int'l*, pg. 67
SWENSON GRANITE COMPANY LLC—See TorQuest Partners Inc.; *Int'l*, pg. 7830
SWENSON GROUP INC.; *U.S. Private*, pg. 3892
SWENSON SPREADER LLC—See Aebi Schmidt Holding AG; *Int'l*, pg. 170
SWENSON TECHNOLOGY, INC.—See GK Enterprises, Inc.; *U.S. Private*, pg. 1703
SWEPCO TUBE CORPORATION; *U.S. Private*, pg. 3892
SWEP GERMANY GMBH—See Dover Corporation; *U.S. Public*, pg. 682
SWEPI LP—See ConocoPhillips; *U.S. Public*, pg. 569
SWEP INTERNATIONAL AB—See Dover Corporation; *U.S. Public*, pg. 679
SWEQUIPOS, S.A. DE C.V.—See Schlumberger Limited; *U.S. Public*, pg. 1846
SWERDLOW GROUP; *U.S. Private*, pg. 3892
SWEROCK AB—See Peab AB; *Int'l*, pg. 5773
SWEROCK OY—See Peab AB; *Int'l*, pg. 5773
SWESAFE AB—See ASSA ABLOY AB; *Int'l*, pg. 640
SWESPAR AB—See Multitude SE; *Int'l*, pg. 5084
SWETS INFORMATION SERVICES B.V.—See Gilde Buy Out Partners B.V.; *Int'l*, pg. 2975
SWETS INFORMATION SERVICES, INC.—See Gilde Buy Out Partners B.V.; *Int'l*, pg. 2975
THE SWETT & CRAWFORD GROUP, INC.—See Lightyear Capital LLC; *U.S. Private*, pg. 2454
SWETZ OIL CO. INC.; *U.S. Private*, pg. 3893
SW FINANCIAL—See Live Ventures Incorporated; *U.S. Public*, pg. 1332
SWF KRANTECHNIK CO., LTD.—See Konecranes Plc; *Int'l*, pg. 4252
SWF KRANTECHNIK GMBH—See Konecranes Plc; *Int'l*, pg. 4253
SWG FRANCE SARL—See Wurth Verwaltungsgesellschaft mbH; *Int'l*, pg. 8507
SWG SCHRAUBENWERK GAISBACH GMBH—See Wurth Verwaltungsgesellschaft mbH; *Int'l*, pg. 8507
SWG SCREWS IBERIA S.L.U.—See Wurth Verwaltungsgesellschaft mbH; *Int'l*, pg. 8507
SWH FREDERICK MARYLAND, INC.—See Holding Le Duff SA; *Int'l*, pg. 3450
SWH HOLDINGS, INC.—See Centene Corporation; *U.S. Public*, pg. 469
SWH HOWARD MARYLAND, INC.—See Holding Le Duff SA; *Int'l*, pg. 3450
SWH MIMI'S CAFE, LLC—See Holding Le Duff SA; *Int'l*, pg. 3450
SWH SOFTWAREHAUS HEIDER GMBH—See MEDIQON Group AG; *Int'l*, pg. 4780
S.W.H. SUPPLY COMPANY; *U.S. Private*, pg. 3519
SWIAT ZDROWIA S.A.—See NEUCA S.A.; *Int'l*, pg. 5218

SWIBER CORPORATE SERVICES PTE LTD.—See Swiber Holdings Limited; *Int'l*, pg. 7366
SWIBER ENGINEERING PTE LTD.—See Swiber Holdings Limited; *Int'l*, pg. 7366
SWIBER HOLDINGS LIMITED; *Int'l*, pg. 7366
SWIBER MARINE PTE LTD.—See Swiber Holdings Limited; *Int'l*, pg. 7366
SWIBER OFFSHORE (B) SDN BHD.—See Swiber Holdings Limited; *Int'l*, pg. 7366
SWIBER OFFSHORE CONSTRUCTION PTE LTD—See Swiber Holdings Limited; *Int'l*, pg. 7366
SWIBER OFFSHORE (INDIA) PVT. LTD.—See Swiber Holdings Limited; *Int'l*, pg. 7366
SWIBER OFFSHORE MARINE PTE LTD—See Swiber Holdings Limited; *Int'l*, pg. 7367
SWIBER OFFSHORE MIDDLE EAST (FZE)—See Swiber Holdings Limited; *Int'l*, pg. 7367
SWIBER OFFSHORE PTE LTD.—See Swiber Holdings Limited; *Int'l*, pg. 7367
SWICK MINING SERVICES LTD.—See Perenti Global Limited; *Int'l*, pg. 5798
SWICORP; *Int'l*, pg. 7367
SWICORP (UAE) LIMITED—See SwiCorp; *Int'l*, pg. 7367
SWIDERSKI EQUIPMENT, INC.; *U.S. Private*, pg. 3893
SWIETELSKY BAUGESELLSCHAFT M.B.H.; *Int'l*, pg. 7367
SWIETELSKY BAUGESELLSCHAFT MBH.—See Swietelsky Baugesellschaft m.b.H.; *Int'l*, pg. 7367
SWIETELSKY BAUTRAGER GES.M.B.H.—See Swietelsky Baugesellschaft m.b.H.; *Int'l*, pg. 7367
SWIETELSKY CONSTRUCTII SRL—See Swietelsky Baugesellschaft m.b.H.; *Int'l*, pg. 7367
SWIETELSKY CONSTRUCTION COMPANY LTD.—See Swietelsky Baugesellschaft m.b.H.; *Int'l*, pg. 7367
SWIETELSKY D.O.O—See Swietelsky Baugesellschaft m.b.H.; *Int'l*, pg. 7367
SWIETELSKY EPITO KFT.—See Swietelsky Baugesellschaft m.b.H.; *Int'l*, pg. 7367
SWIETELSKY GRADBENO D.O.O.—See Swietelsky Baugesellschaft m.b.H.; *Int'l*, pg. 7367
SWIETELSKY MAGYARORSZAG KFT.—See Swietelsky Baugesellschaft m.b.H.; *Int'l*, pg. 7367
SWIETELSKY RAIL (AUSTRALIA) PTY LTD—See Swietelsky Baugesellschaft m.b.H.; *Int'l*, pg. 7367
SWIETELSKY RAIL BENELUX B.V.—See Swietelsky Baugesellschaft m.b.H.; *Int'l*, pg. 7367
SWIETELSKY RAIL NORWAY AS—See Swietelsky Baugesellschaft m.b.H.; *Int'l*, pg. 7367
SWIETELSKY RAIL POLSKA SPOLKA Z O.O.—See Swietelsky Baugesellschaft m.b.H.; *Int'l*, pg. 7367
SWIETELSKY RAIL SRB D.O.O.—See Swietelsky Baugesellschaft m.b.H.; *Int'l*, pg. 7367
SWIETELSKY SLOVAKIA SPOL. S.R.O—See Swietelsky Baugesellschaft m.b.H.; *Int'l*, pg. 7367
SWIETELSKY SPOLKA Z.O.O—See Swietelsky Baugesellschaft m.b.H.; *Int'l*, pg. 7367
SWIETELSKY STAVEBNI S.R.O.—See Swietelsky Baugesellschaft m.b.H.; *Int'l*, pg. 7367
SWIFF-TRAIN COMPANY INC.—See The Belknap White Group, LLC; *U.S. Private*, pg. 3993
SWIFT AIR INC.—See iAero Group; *U.S. Private*, pg. 2027
SWIFTAIR S.A.; *Int'l*, pg. 7368
SWIFT BIOSCIENCES, INC.—See Danaher Corporation; *U.S. Public*, pg. 627
SWIFT COMMUNICATIONS, INC.; *U.S. Private*, pg. 3893
SWIFT CRAFTED LTD; *Int'l*, pg. 7367
SWIFTECH COMPANY LIMITED—See China Oral Industry Group Holdings Limited; *Int'l*, pg. 1538
SWIFTECH INTERNATIONAL LIMITED—See China Oral Industry Group Holdings Limited; *Int'l*, pg. 1538
SWIFTEL COMMUNICATIONS INC.; *U.S. Private*, pg. 3893
SWIFT ELECTRICAL SUPPLY CO.; *U.S. Private*, pg. 3893
SWIFT ENERGY OPERATING, LLC—See KKR & Co. Inc.; *U.S. Public*, pg. 1244
SWIFT FINANCIAL, LLC—See PayPal Holdings, Inc.; *U.S. Public*, pg. 1657
SWIFT GALEY—See Patriarch Partners, LLC; *U.S. Private*, pg. 3109
S.W.I.F.T. GERMANY GMBH—See S.W.I.F.T. SCRL; *Int'l*, pg. 6457
THE SWIFT GROUP, LLC; *U.S. Private*, pg. 4126
SWIFT HAULAGE SDN. BHD.; *Int'l*, pg. 7368
SWIFT INDUSTRIAL POWER INC.; *U.S. Private*, pg. 3893
SWIFT INSTRUMENTS, INC.-TECHNICAL INSTRUMENTS DIV.—See Swift Optical Instruments, Inc.; *U.S. Private*, pg. 3893
SWIFT JAPAN LTD.—See S.W.I.F.T. SCRL; *Int'l*, pg. 6457
SWIFT LEASING CO., LLC—See Knight-Swift Transportation Holdings Inc.; *U.S. Public*, pg. 1269
SWIFT LEVIC MAGNETS—See Compass Diversified Holdings; *U.S. Public*, pg. 560
SWIFT LOGISTICS, LLC—See Knight-Swift Transportation Holdings Inc.; *U.S. Public*, pg. 1269
SWIFTMERGE ACQUISITION CORP.; *Int'l*, pg. 7368
SWIFTNET LIMITED; *Int'l*, pg. 7368
SWIFT NETWORKS GROUP LIMITED; *Int'l*, pg. 7368

CORPORATE AFFILIATIONS

S.W.I.F.T. NORDIC AB—See S.W.I.F.T. SCRL; *Int'l*, pg. 6457
SWIFT OPTICAL INSTRUMENTS, INC.; *U.S. Private*, pg. 3893
S.W.I.F.T. PAN-AMERICAS, INC.—See S.W.I.F.T. SCRL; *Int'l*, pg. 6457
SWIFT PREPAID SOLUTIONS, INC.—See Bain Capital, LP; *U.S. Private*, pg. 436
SWIFT PREPAID SOLUTIONS, INC.—See Silversmith Management, L.P.; *U.S. Private*, pg. 3664
SWIFTREACH NETWORKS, INC.—See Motorola Solutions, Inc.; *U.S. Public*, pg. 1479
SWIFT REFRIGERATED SERVICE, LLC—See Knight-Swift Transportation Holdings Inc.; *U.S. Public*, pg. 1269
SWIFT RENT-A-CAR LIMITED—See ZIGUP plc; *Int'l*, pg. 8682
SWIFT RIVER ACADEMY, L.L.C.—See Acadia Healthcare Company, Inc.; *U.S. Public*, pg. 30
S.W.I.F.T. SCRL; *Int'l*, pg. 6457
S.W.I.F.T. SECURENET LTD.—See S.W.I.F.T. SCRL; *Int'l*, pg. 6457
S.W.I.F.T. SERVICES AUSTRALIA PTY. LTD.—See S.W.I.F.T. SCRL; *Int'l*, pg. 6457
SWIFTS SUPERSTORE; *U.S. Private*, pg. 3893
SWIFTSTACK, INC.—See NVIDIA Corporation; *U.S. Public*, pg. 1558
SWIFT SUPPLY, INC.; *U.S. Private*, pg. 3893
SWIFTSURE CAPITAL LLC; *U.S. Private*, pg. 3893
SWIFT SYSTEMS, INC.—See Tonka Bay Equity Partners LLC; *U.S. Private*, pg. 4185
S.W.I.F.T. TERMINAL SERVICES (PTE) LTD.—See S.W.I.F.T. SCRL; *Int'l*, pg. 6457
SWIFT TEXTILE METALIZING LLC—See Arcline Investment Management LP; *U.S. Private*, pg. 314
SWIFT TRADE INC.; *Int'l*, pg. 7368
SWIFT TRANSPORTATION CO., LLC—See Knight-Swift Transportation Holdings Inc.; *U.S. Public*, pg. 1269
SWIFT TRANSPORTATION SERVICES, LLC—See Knight-Swift Transportation Holdings Inc.; *U.S. Public*, pg. 1269
SWIFTTRIP, LLC—See Altour International, Inc.; *U.S. Private*, pg. 210
SWIFT WORLDWIDE RESOURCES; *Int'l*, pg. 7368
SWIFTY GLOBAL; *U.S. Public*, pg. 1968
SWIFTY OIL, LLC; *U.S. Private*, pg. 3893
SWIGER COIL SYSTEMS - A WABTEC COMPANY—See Westinghouse Air Brake Technologies Corporation; *U.S. Public*, pg. 2359
SWIM ACROSS AMERICA INC.; *U.S. Private*, pg. 3893
SWIMART (NZ) LTD—See Waterco Limited; *Int'l*, pg. 8357
SWIMC, INC.—See The Sherwin-Williams Company; *U.S. Public*, pg. 2128
SWIMKIDS SWIM SCHOOLS; *U.S. Private*, pg. 3893
SWIM & SWEAT, INC.—See ALPHAGILITY LLC; *U.S. Private*, pg. 200
SWIMWAYS CORPORATION—See Spin Master Corp.; *Int'l*, pg. 7136
SWIMWEAR ANYWHERE, INC.; *U.S. Private*, pg. 3893
SWINDELL DRESSLER INTERNATIONAL CO.; *U.S. Private*, pg. 3893
SWINDOLL, JANZEN, HAWK & LLOYD, LLC; *U.S. Private*, pg. 3893
SWINDON PRESSINGS LIMITED—See Bayerische Motoren Werke Aktiengesellschaft; *Int'l*, pg. 913
SWINDON SILICON SYSTEMS LIMITED—See Sensata Technologies Holding plc; *U.S. Public*, pg. 1866
SWINEFORD NATIONAL BANK—See Fulton Financial Corporation; *U.S. Public*, pg. 892
SWINE GENETICS INTERNATIONAL, LTD.—See Prima Meat Packers Ltd.; *Int'l*, pg. 5975
SWINE GRAPHICS ENTERPRISES LP; *U.S. Private*, pg. 3893
SWINERTON BUILDERS—See Swinerton Incorporated; *U.S. Private*, pg. 3894
SWINERTON INCORPORATED; *U.S. Private*, pg. 3893
SWING BAKERY CO., LTD.—See Showa Sangyo Co., Ltd.; *Int'l*, pg. 6862
SWING CITY PTY. LIMITED—See Mulpha International Bhd; *Int'l*, pg. 5081
SWING CORPORATION—See Ebara Corporation; *Int'l*, pg. 2284
SWINGER INTERNATIONAL SPA; *Int'l*, pg. 7368
SWING KINGDOM LLC—See PennSpring Capital, LLC; *U.S. Private*, pg. 3136
SWINGLE, INC.—See Apax Partners LLP; *Int'l*, pg. 506
SWING MEDIA; *U.S. Private*, pg. 3894
SWING STAGING LLC—See Brand Industrial Services, Inc.; *U.S. Private*, pg. 637
SWING TRANSPORT INC.; *U.S. Private*, pg. 3894
SWINTON GROUP LTD.—See The Ardonagh Group Limited; *Int'l*, pg. 7614
SWIPEDON LIMITED—See Smartspace Software Plc; *Int'l*, pg. 7003
SWIRE (BEIJING) AIR SERVICE LIMITED—See John Swire & Sons Limited; *Int'l*, pg. 3981
SWIRE COCA-COLA, USA—See John Swire & Sons Limited; *Int'l*, pg. 3981

COMPANY NAME INDEX

SWIRE COLD STORAGE PTY., LTD.—See John Swire & Sons Limited; *Int'l*, pg. 3980
SWIRE COLD STORAGE VIETNAM CO., LTD.—See John Swire & Sons Limited; *Int'l*, pg. 3981
SWIRE GROUP TAIWAN—See John Swire & Sons Limited; *Int'l*, pg. 3980
SWIRE INTERNATIONAL(SHANGHAI)AIR SERVICE LTD.—See John Swire & Sons Limited; *Int'l*, pg. 3981
SWIRE INTERNATIONAL TRAVEL SERVICES LTD.—See John Swire & Sons Limited; *Int'l*, pg. 3980
SWIRE OILFIELD SERVICES A/S—See John Swire & Sons Limited; *Int'l*, pg. 3980
SWIRE OILFIELD SERVICES DO BRASIL LTDA—See John Swire & Sons Limited; *Int'l*, pg. 3980
SWIRE OILFIELD SERVICES INDIA PRIVATE LTD.—See John Swire & Sons Limited; *Int'l*, pg. 3980
SWIRE OILFIELD SERVICES L.L.C—See John Swire & Sons Limited; *Int'l*, pg. 3980
SWIRE OILFIELD SERVICES LTD.—See John Swire & Sons Limited; *Int'l*, pg. 3980
SWIRE OILFIELD SERVICES PTE LTD.—See John Swire & Sons Limited; *Int'l*, pg. 3980
SWIRE OILFIELD SERVICES PTY LTD.—See John Swire & Sons Limited; *Int'l*, pg. 3980
SWIRE PACIFIC LIMITED—See John Swire & Sons Limited; *Int'l*, pg. 3980
SWIRE PROPERTIES LIMITED—See John Swire & Sons Limited; *Int'l*, pg. 3981
SWIRE RESOURCES (SHANGHAI) TRADING COMPANY LIMITED—See John Swire & Sons Limited; *Int'l*, pg. 3981
SWIRE SHIPPING PTE LTD—See John Swire & Sons Limited; *Int'l*, pg. 3981
SWIRE TRAVEL LTD.—See John Swire & Sons Limited; *Int'l*, pg. 3981
SWIRE WASTE MANAGEMENT LIMITED—See Waste Management, Inc.; *U.S. Public*, pg. 2332
SWIRIDOFF VERLAG GMBH & CO. KG—See Wurth Verwaltungsgesellschaft mbH; *Int'l*, pg. 8508
SWIRL CORPORATION—See Nestle S.A.; *Int'l*, pg. 5211
SWISH BUILDING PRODUCTS LIMITED—See Epwin Group Plc; *Int'l*, pg. 2466
SWISHER COUNTY CATTLE CO.—See Friona Industries, LP; *U.S. Private*, pg. 1612
SWISHER ELECTRIC COOPERATIVE, INC.; *U.S. Private*, pg. 3894
SWISHER HYGIENE FRANCHISE CORP.—See Ecolab Inc.; *U.S. Public*, pg. 716
SWISHER HYGIENE INC.; *U.S. Private*, pg. 3894
SWISHER HYGIENE USA OPERATIONS, INC.—See Swisher Hygiene Inc.; *U.S. Private*, pg. 3894
SWISHER HYGIENE USA OPERATIONS, INC.—See Ecolab Inc.; *U.S. Public*, pg. 716
SWISHER INTERNATIONAL, INC.—See Hay Island Holding Corporation; *U.S. Private*, pg. 1884
SWISHER MAIDS, INC.—See Swisher Hygiene Inc.; *U.S. Private*, pg. 3894
SWISH WHITE RIVER LTD.; *U.S. Private*, pg. 3894
SWISH WHITE RIVER LTD.—See Kelso & Company, L.P.; *U.S. Private*, pg. 2279
SWISH WHITE RIVER LTD.—See Warburg Pincus LLC; *U.S. Private*, pg. 4437
SWISS ADVISORY GROUP S.A.—See UBS Group AG; *Int'l*, pg. 8007
SWISS ALERTIS AG—See Johnson Controls International plc; *Int'l*, pg. 3987
SWISSALP SA—See Compagnie des Alpes S.A.; *Int'l*, pg. 1738
SWISS AMERICAN CDMO, LLC; *U.S. Private*, pg. 3894
SWISS-AMERICAN PRODUCTS, INC.; *U.S. Private*, pg. 3894
SWISSAM PRODUCTS LIMITED—See Movado Group, Inc.; *U.S. Public*, pg. 1480
SWISS-AM REASSURANCE COMPANY—See Swiss Re Ltd.; *Int'l*, pg. 7372
SWISS AVIATION SOFTWARE AG—See Deutsche Lufthansa AG; *Int'l*, pg. 2070
SWISSBILLING AG—See Cembra Money Bank AG; *Int'l*, pg. 1396
SWISS BIO PHARMA SDN BHD.—See Vita Life Sciences Limited; *Int'l*, pg. 8257
SWISSBIT AG; *Int'l*, pg. 7373
SWISSBORING & CO. LLC—See Trevi Finanziaria Industriale SpA.; *Int'l*, pg. 7917
SWISSBORING OVERSEAS PILING CORP. LTD.—See Trevi Finanziaria Industriale SpA.; *Int'l*, pg. 7917
SWISSBORING QATAR WLL—See Trevi Finanziaria Industriale SpA.; *Int'l*, pg. 7917
SWISSCANTO ASSET MANAGEMENT INTERNATIONAL S.A.—See Zurcher Kantonalbank; *Int'l*, pg. 8697
SWISSCANTO ASSET MANAGEMENT LTD.—See Zurcher Kantonalbank; *Int'l*, pg. 8697
SWISSCANTO HOLDING SA—See Zurcher Kantonalbank; *Int'l*, pg. 8697
SWISSCANTO PENSIONS LTD.—See Zurcher Kantonalbank; *Int'l*, pg. 8697
SWISS CAPS AG—See BC Partners LLP; *Int'l*, pg. 923
SWISSCARD AECS AG—See American Express Company; *U.S. Public*, pg. 101
SWISSCARD AECS AG—See UBS Group AG; *Int'l*, pg. 8007
SWISSCARD AECS GMBH—See American Express Company; *U.S. Public*, pg. 102
SWISSCARD AECS GMBH—See UBS Group AG; *Int'l*, pg. 8007
SWISS CHALET FINE FOODS INC.; *U.S. Private*, pg. 3894
SWISSCO HOLDINGS LIMITED; *Int'l*, pg. 7373
SWISS COLONY DATA CENTER INC.; *U.S. Private*, pg. 3894
SWISSCOM AG INNOVATIONS—See Swisscom AG; *Int'l*, pg. 7374
SWISSCOM AG; *Int'l*, pg. 7373
SWISSCO MANUFACTURING LIMITED—See Temasek Holdings (Private) Limited; *Int'l*, pg. 7550
SWISSCOM BELGIUM N.V.—See Swisscom AG; *Int'l*, pg. 7374
SWISSCOM BROADCAST LTD—See Swisscom AG; *Int'l*, pg. 7374
SWISSCOM CLOUD LAB LTD.—See Swisscom AG; *Int'l*, pg. 7374
SWISSCOM DIRECTORIES LTD—See Swisscom AG; *Int'l*, pg. 7374
SWISSCOM EVENT & MEDIA SOLUTIONS LTD—See Swisscom AG; *Int'l*, pg. 7374
SWISSCOM FIXNET LTD—See Swisscom AG; *Int'l*, pg. 7374
SWISSCOM IMMOBILIEN LTD—See Swisscom AG; *Int'l*, pg. 7374
SWISSCOM IT SERVICES AG—See Swisscom AG; *Int'l*, pg. 7374
SWISSCOM IT SERVICES ENTERPRISE SOLUTIONS LTD—See Swisscom AG; *Int'l*, pg. 7374
SWISSCOM IT SERVICES FINANCE LTD—See Swisscom AG; *Int'l*, pg. 7374
SWISSCOM IT SERVICES SOURCING LTD—See Swisscom AG; *Int'l*, pg. 7374
SWISSCOM MOBILE LTD—See Swisscom AG; *Int'l*, pg. 7374
SWISSCOM SOLUTIONS LTD—See Swisscom AG; *Int'l*, pg. 7374
SWISSCOM TRUST SERVICES LTD.—See Swisscom AG; *Int'l*, pg. 7374
SWISSCO SERVICES AG—See BC Partners LLP; *Int'l*, pg. 923
SWISS E-MOBILITY GROUP (SCHWEIZ) AG—See TVS Motor Company Ltd.; *Int'l*, pg. 7989
SWISS EUROPEAN AIR LINES AG—See Deutsche Lufthansa AG; *Int'l*, pg. 2070
SWISSE WELLNESS PTY LTD—See Health and Happiness (H&H) International Holdings Limited; *Int'l*, pg. 3303
SWISSE WELLNESS PTY LTD—See Health and Happiness (H&H) International Holdings Limited; *Int'l*, pg. 3303
SWISS FARMS PRODUCTS, INC.—See The Scotts Miracle-Gro Company; *U.S. Public*, pg. 2127
SWISSFEX AG—See Swiss Life Holding; *Int'l*, pg. 7370
SWISS GADGET ENTERTAINMENT AG—See CTS Eventim AG & Co. KGAA; *Int'l*, pg. 1873
SWISS-GARDEN INTERNATIONAL SDN. BHD.—See OSK Holdings Berhad; *Int'l*, pg. 5651
SWISSHAUS AG—See swisspor Management AG; *Int'l*, pg. 7374
SWISS HEALTHCARE PROPERTIES AG—See AEVIS VICTORIA SA; *Int'l*, pg. 183
SWISS HELVETIA FUND, INC.; *U.S. Public*, pg. 1968
SWISSINSO HOLDING INC.; *U.S. Private*, pg. 3894
SWISS INSULATING WORKS LTD.—See SKion GmbH; *Int'l*, pg. 6987
SWISS INTERBANK CLEARING AG—See Schweizerische Nationalbank; *Int'l*, pg. 6646
SWISS INTERNATIONAL AIR LINES AG—See Deutsche Lufthansa AG; *Int'l*, pg. 2070
SWISSI PROCESS SAFETY GMBH—See TUV SUD AG; *Int'l*, pg. 7984
SWISSLAB GMBH—See Roche Holding AG; *Int'l*, pg. 6376
SWISS LACK THELER PERREN AG—See Bystronic AG; *Int'l*, pg. 1236
SWISSLASTIC AG—See Salzmann AG; *Int'l*, pg. 6499
SWISS LEARNING HUB AG—See Constellation Software Inc.; *Int'l*, pg. 1772
SWISS LIFE ASSET MANAGEMENT AG—See Swiss Life Holding; *Int'l*, pg. 7369
SWISS LIFE ASSET MANAGEMENT (FRANCE)—See Swiss Life Holding; *Int'l*, pg. 7369
SWISS LIFE ASSET MANAGEMENT GMBH—See Swiss Life Holding; *Int'l*, pg. 7369
SWISS LIFE ASSET MANAGERS DEUTSCHLAND GMBH—See Swiss Life Holding; *Int'l*, pg. 7369
SWISS LIFE ASSET MANAGERS FRANCE S.A.S—See Swiss Life Holding; *Int'l*, pg. 7369
SWISS LIFE ASSET MANAGERS LUXEMBOURG SA—See Swiss Life Holding; *Int'l*, pg. 7369
SWISS LIFE ASSET MANAGERS NORDIC AS—See Swiss Life Holding; *Int'l*, pg. 7369
SWISS LIFE ASSURANCE ET PATRIMOINE S.A.—See Swiss Life Holding; *Int'l*, pg. 7369
SWISS LIFE ASSURANCES DE BIENS S.A.—See Swiss Life Holding; *Int'l*, pg. 7369
SWISS LIFE ASSURANCE SOLUTIONS S.A.—See Swiss Life Holding; *Int'l*, pg. 7369
SWISS LIFE BANQUE PRIVEE S.A.—See Swiss Life Holding; *Int'l*, pg. 7369
SWISS LIFE BETEILIGUNGS GMBH—See Swiss Life Holding; *Int'l*, pg. 7369
SWISS LIFE CAPITAL HOLDING AG—See Swiss Life Holding; *Int'l*, pg. 7369
SWISS LIFE DEUTSCHLAND HOLDING GMBH—See Swiss Life Holding; *Int'l*, pg. 7369
SWISS LIFE DEUTSCHLAND VERTRIEBSHOLDING AG—See Swiss Life Holding; *Int'l*, pg. 7369
SWISS LIFE FRANCE S.A.—See Swiss Life Holding; *Int'l*, pg. 7370
SWISS LIFE FUND MANAGEMENT (LUX) S.A.—See Swiss Life Holding; *Int'l*, pg. 7370
SWISS LIFE HOLDING; *Int'l*, pg. 7370
SWISS LIFE INTELLECTUAL PROPERTY MANAGEMENT AG—See Swiss Life Holding; *Int'l*, pg. 7370
SWISS LIFE INTERNATIONAL HOLDING AG—See Swiss Life Holding; *Int'l*, pg. 7370
SWISS LIFE INVEST GMBH—See Swiss Life Holding; *Int'l*, pg. 7370
SWISS LIFE INVESTMENT MANAGEMENT HOLDING AG—See Swiss Life Holding; *Int'l*, pg. 7370
SWISS LIFE (ITALIA) INFORTUNI E MALATTIE—See Swiss Life Holding; *Int'l*, pg. 7369
SWISS LIFE (ITALIA)—See Swiss Life Holding; *Int'l*, pg. 7369
SWISS LIFE KAPITALVERWALTUNGSGESELLSCHAFT MBH—See Swiss Life Holding; *Int'l*, pg. 7370
SWISS LIFE (LIECHTENSTEIN) AG—See Swiss Life Holding; *Int'l*, pg. 7369
SWISS LIFE (LIECHTENSTEIN) SERVICES AG—See Swiss Life Holding; *Int'l*, pg. 7369
SWISS LIFE (LUXEMBOURG) S.A.—See Swiss Life Holding; *Int'l*, pg. 7369
SWISS LIFE OSTERREICH AG—See Swiss Life Holding; *Int'l*, pg. 7370
SWISS LIFE PARTNER SERVICE- UND FINANZVERMITTLUNGS GMBH—See Swiss Life Holding; *Int'l*, pg. 7370
SWISS LIFE PENSION SERVICES AG—See Swiss Life Holding; *Int'l*, pg. 7370
SWISS LIFE PENSIONSFONDS AG—See Swiss Life Holding; *Int'l*, pg. 7370
SWISS LIFE PENSIONSKASSE AG—See Swiss Life Holding; *Int'l*, pg. 7370
SWISS LIFE PORTFOLIO MANAGEMENT—See Swiss Life Holding; *Int'l*, pg. 7370
SWISS LIFE PREVOYANCE ET SANTE S.A.—See Swiss Life Holding; *Int'l*, pg. 7370
SWISS LIFE PRIVATE EQUITY PARTNERS AG—See Swiss Life Holding; *Int'l*, pg. 7370
SWISS LIFE PRIVATE PLACEMENT (MIDDLE EAST) LIMITED—See Swiss Life Holding; *Int'l*, pg. 7370
SWISS LIFE PROPERTY MANAGEMENT AG—See Swiss Life Holding; *Int'l*, pg. 7370
SWISS LIFE SELECT CESKA REPUBLIKA S.R.O.—See Swiss Life Holding; *Int'l*, pg. 7370
SWISS LIFE SELECT DEUTSCHLAND GMBH—See Swiss Life Holding; *Int'l*, pg. 7370
SWISS LIFE SELECT OSTERREICH GMBH—See Swiss Life Holding; *Int'l*, pg. 7370
SWISS LIFE SELECT SCHWEIZ AG—See Swiss Life Holding; *Int'l*, pg. 7370
SWISS LIFE SELECT SLOVENSKO, A.S.—See Swiss Life Holding; *Int'l*, pg. 7370
SWISS LIFE SERVICE GMBH—See Swiss Life Holding; *Int'l*, pg. 7370
SWISS LIFE (SINGAPORE) PTE. LTD.—See Swiss Life Holding; *Int'l*, pg. 7369
SWISS LIFE—See Swiss Life Holding; *Int'l*, pg. 7369
SWISSLINK CARRIER AG—See IQSTEL Inc.; *U.S. Public*, pg. 1167
SWISS LION AG—See Bucherer AG; *Int'l*, pg. 1209
SWISSLION INDUSTRIJA ALATA A.D.; *Int'l*, pg. 7374
SWISSLION MILODUH A.D.; *Int'l*, pg. 7374
SWISSLOG AB—See Midea Group Co., Ltd.; *Int'l*, pg. 4885
SWISSLOG-ACCALON AB—See Midea Group Co., Ltd.; *Int'l*, pg. 4885
SWISSLOG AG—See Midea Group Co., Ltd.; *Int'l*, pg. 4885
SWISSLOG AS—See Midea Group Co., Ltd.; *Int'l*, pg. 4885
SWISSLOG AUSTRALIA PTY. LTD.—See Midea Group Co., Ltd.; *Int'l*, pg. 4885
SWISSLOG B.V.—See Midea Group Co., Ltd.; *Int'l*, pg. 4885
SWISSLOG ERGOTRANS B.V.—See Midea Group Co., Ltd.; *Int'l*, pg. 4885
SWISSLOG EVOMATIC GMBH—See Midea Group Co., Ltd.; *Int'l*, pg. 4885
SWISSLOG FRANCE SA—See Midea Group Co., Ltd.; *Int'l*, pg. 4885

SWISSLOG GMBH—See Midea Group Co., Ltd.; *Int'l*, pg. 4885
SWISSLOG GMBH—See Midea Group Co., Ltd.; *Int'l*, pg. 4885
SWISSLOG HEALTHCARE CANADA—See Midea Group Co., Ltd.; *Int'l*, pg. 4885
SWISSLOG HEALTHCARE NORTH AMERICA—See Midea Group Co., Ltd.; *Int'l*, pg. 4885
SWISSLOG HOLDING AG—See Midea Group Co., Ltd.; *Int'l*, pg. 4885
SWISSLOG ITALIA S.P.A.—See Midea Group Co., Ltd.; *Int'l*, pg. 4885
SWISSLOG LOGISTICS, INC.—See Midea Group Co., Ltd.; *Int'l*, pg. 4885
SWISSLOG LOGISTICS N.V.—See Midea Group Co., Ltd.; *Int'l*, pg. 4885
SWISSLOG LOGISTICS (SHANGHAI) CO., LTD.—See Midea Group Co., Ltd.; *Int'l*, pg. 4885
SWISSLOG MALAYSIA SDN BHD—See Midea Group Co., Ltd.; *Int'l*, pg. 4885
SWISSLOG ROHRPOSTSYSTEME GMBH—See Midea Group Co., Ltd.; *Int'l*, pg. 4885
SWISSLOG SINGAPORE PTE. LTD.—See Midea Group Co., Ltd.; *Int'l*, pg. 4885
SWISSLOG (UK) LTD.—See Midea Group Co., Ltd.; *Int'l*, pg. 4885
SWISSMA BUILDING TECHNOLOGIES SDN. BHD.—See Nam Fatt Corporation Berhad; *Int'l*, pg. 5133
SWISSMED CENTRUM ZDROWIA SA; *Int'l*, pg. 7374
SWISS MEDICAL CENTERS NETWORK S.A.—See AEVIS VICTORIA SA; *Int'l*, pg. 183
SWISS MEDICAL NETWORK SA—See AEVIS VICTORIA SA; *Int'l*, pg. 183
SWISSMED PTE. LTD.—See EBOS Group Limited; *Int'l*, pg. 2286
SWISSMED SDN. BHD.—See EBOS Group Limited; *Int'l*, pg. 2286
SWISSMETAL EAST ASIA LTD.—See Baoshida International Holding Group Co., Ltd.; *Int'l*, pg. 856
SWISSNOVACHEM LTD.—See Clariant AG; *Int'l*, pg. 1648
SWISSOIL DEL ECUADOR S.A.; *Int'l*, pg. 7374
SWISSOPTIC AG—See Jenoptik AG; *Int'l*, pg. 3929
SWISSOPTIC (WUHAN) CO., LTD.—See Jenoptik AG; *Int'l*, pg. 3929
SWISSPARTNERS ADVISORS LTD.—See Liechtensteinische Landesbank AG; *Int'l*, pg. 4492
SWISSPARTNERS INSURANCE COMPANY SPC LTD.—See Liechtensteinische Landesbank AG; *Int'l*, pg. 4492
SWISSPARTNERS VERSICHERUNG AG—See Liechtensteinische Landesbank AG; *Int'l*, pg. 4492
SWISSPEARL GROUP AG—See swisspor Management AG; *Int'l*, pg. 7375
SWISSPLAKAT AG—See APG/SGA SA; *Int'l*, pg. 513
SWISSPOR DEUTSCHLAND GMBH—See swisspor Management AG; *Int'l*, pg. 7375
SWISSPOR MANAGEMENT AG; *Int'l*, pg. 7374
SWISSPOR OSTERREICH GMBH & CO. KG—See swisspor Management AG; *Int'l*, pg. 7375
SWISSPOR POLSKA SP. Z O.O.—See swisspor Management AG; *Int'l*, pg. 7375
SWISSPOR ROMANDIE SA—See swisspor Management AG; *Int'l*, pg. 7375
SWISSPORT AMSTERDAM B.V.—See Hainan Traffic Administration Holding Co., Ltd.; *Int'l*, pg. 3216
SWISSPORT BELGIUM N. V.—See Hainan Traffic Administration Holding Co., Ltd.; *Int'l*, pg. 3216
SWISSPORT CANADA HANDLING INC.—See Hainan Traffic Administration Holding Co., Ltd.; *Int'l*, pg. 3216
SWISSPORT CARGO SERVICES, L.P.—See Hainan Traffic Administration Holding Co., Ltd.; *Int'l*, pg. 3216
SWISSPORT CHILE—See Hainan Traffic Administration Holding Co., Ltd.; *Int'l*, pg. 3216
SWISSPORT DENMARK—See Hainan Traffic Administration Holding Co., Ltd.; *Int'l*, pg. 3216
SWISSPORT FINLAND OY—See Hainan Traffic Administration Holding Co., Ltd.; *Int'l*, pg. 3216
SWISSPORT FUELING, INC.—See Hainan Traffic Administration Holding Co., Ltd.; *Int'l*, pg. 3216
SWISSPORT INTERNATIONAL LTD.—See Hainan Traffic Administration Holding Co., Ltd.; *Int'l*, pg. 3216
SWISSPORT PORTUGAL—See Hainan Traffic Administration Holding Co., Ltd.; *Int'l*, pg. 3216
SWISSPORT TANZANIA PLC.—See Hainan Traffic Administration Holding Co., Ltd.; *Int'l*, pg. 3216
SWISSPORT TRINIDAD & TOBAGO—See Hainan Traffic Administration Holding Co., Ltd.; *Int'l*, pg. 3216
SWISSPORT USA, INC.—See Hainan Traffic Administration Holding Co., Ltd.; *Int'l*, pg. 3216
SWISS POSTER RESEARCH PLUS AG—See APG/SGA SA; *Int'l*, pg. 513
SWISS POST INTERNATIONAL HOLDING AG—See Die Schweizerische Post AG; *Int'l*, pg. 2113
SWISS POST INTERNATIONAL MANAGEMENT AG—See Die Schweizerische Post AG; *Int'l*, pg. 2113
SWISS POST SOLUTIONS AG—See Die Schweizerische Post AG; *Int'l*, pg. 2113
SWISS POST SOLUTIONS GMBH, PRIEN—See Die Schweizerische Post AG; *Int'l*, pg. 2113

SWISS POST SOLUTIONS GMBH, PULSNITZ—See Die Schweizerische Post AG; *Int'l*, pg. 2113
SWISS POST SOLUTIONS GMBH—See Die Schweizerische Post AG; *Int'l*, pg. 2113
SWISS POST SOLUTIONS GMBH—See Die Schweizerische Post AG; *Int'l*, pg. 2113
SWISS POST SOLUTIONS HOLDING PTE. LTD.—See Die Schweizerische Post AG; *Int'l*, pg. 2113
SWISS POST SOLUTIONS INC.—See Die Schweizerische Post AG; *Int'l*, pg. 2113
SWISS POST SOLUTIONS LTD—See Die Schweizerische Post AG; *Int'l*, pg. 2113
SWISS POST SOLUTIONS SAS—See Die Schweizerische Post AG; *Int'l*, pg. 2113
SWISS POST SOLUTIONS SINGAPORE—See Die Schweizerische Post AG; *Int'l*, pg. 2113
SWISS POST SOLUTIONS S.P.A.—See Die Schweizerische Post AG; *Int'l*, pg. 2113
SWISS POST SOLUTIONS S.R.O—See Die Schweizerische Post AG; *Int'l*, pg. 2113
SWISS PRECISION INSTRUMENTS, INC.—See MSC Industrial Direct Co., Inc.; *U.S. Public*, pg. 1483
SWISS PREMIUM DAIRY, LLC—See Dean Foods Company; *U.S. Private*, pg. 1184
SWISS PRESTIGE UHREN HANDEL GMBH—See The Swatch Group Ltd.; *Int'l*, pg. 7692
SWISS PRIME SITE AG; *Int'l*, pg. 7370
SWISS PRIME SITE IMMOBILIEN AG—See Swiss Prime Site AG; *Int'l*, pg. 7370
SWISS PRIME SITE SOLUTIONS AG—See Swiss Prime Site AG; *Int'l*, pg. 7370
SWISS PRIVATE AVIATION AG—See Deutsche Lufthansa AG; *Int'l*, pg. 2070
SWISS PROPERTIES INVEST A/S; *Int'l*, pg. 7371
SWISSQUOTE ASIA LTD.—See Swissquote Group Holding Ltd.; *Int'l*, pg. 7375
SWISSQUOTE BANK EUROPE S.A.—See Swissquote Group Holding Ltd.; *Int'l*, pg. 7375
SWISSQUOTE FINANCIAL SERVICES (MALTA) LTD.—See Swissquote Group Holding Ltd.; *Int'l*, pg. 7375
SWISSQUOTE GROUP HOLDING LTD.; *Int'l*, pg. 7375
SWISSQUOTE LTD.—See Swissquote Group Holding Ltd.; *Int'l*, pg. 7375
SWISSQUOTE MEA LTD.—See Swissquote Group Holding Ltd.; *Int'l*, pg. 7375
SWISSQUQTE PTE. LTD.—See Swissquote Group Holding Ltd.; *Int'l*, pg. 7375
SWISSRAY INTERNATIONAL, INC.—See S&S Healthcare Holding Ltd; *Int'l*, pg. 6445
SWISSRAY MEDICAL AG—See S&S Healthcare Holding Ltd; *Int'l*, pg. 6445
SWISSRE ADVISERS TALLINN—See Swiss Re Ltd.; *Int'l*, pg. 7372
SWISS RE AMERICA HOLDING CORP.—See Swiss Re Ltd.; *Int'l*, pg. 7371
SWISS RE ASIA PTE. LTD.—See Swiss Re Ltd.; *Int'l*, pg. 7371
SWISS RE ATRIUM CORPORATION—See Swiss Re Ltd.; *Int'l*, pg. 7371
SWISS RE AUSTRALIA LTD.—See Swiss Re Ltd.; *Int'l*, pg. 7372
SWISS RE BRASIL RESSEGUROS S.A.—See Swiss Re Ltd.; *Int'l*, pg. 7371
SWISS RE BRASIL SERVICOS E PARTICIPACOES LTDA—See Swiss Re Ltd.; *Int'l*, pg. 7372
SWISS RE CAPITAL MARKETS CORPORATION—See Swiss Re Ltd.; *Int'l*, pg. 7371
SWISS RE CAPITAL MARKETS LIMITED—See Swiss Re Ltd.; *Int'l*, pg. 7372
SWISS RE CORPORATE SOLUTIONS BRASIL SEGUROS S.A.—See Swiss Re Ltd.; *Int'l*, pg. 7371
SWISS RE CORPORATE SOLUTIONS INSURANCE CHINA LTD.—See Swiss Re Ltd.; *Int'l*, pg. 7371
SWISS RE CORPORATE SOLUTIONS PREMIER INSURANCE CORPORATION—See Swiss Re Ltd.; *Int'l*, pg. 7372
SWISS RE DENMARK SERVICES A/S—See Swiss Re Ltd.; *Int'l*, pg. 7372
SWISS RE EUROPE HOLDINGS S.A.—See Swiss Re Ltd.; *Int'l*, pg. 7372
SWISS RE EUROPE S.A.—See Swiss Re Ltd.; *Int'l*, pg. 7372
SWISS RE EUROPE, S.A.—See Swiss Re Ltd.; *Int'l*, pg. 7372
SWISSRE FINANCE (BERMUDA) LTD.—See Swiss Re Ltd.; *Int'l*, pg. 7372
SWISS RE FINANCE (LUXEMBOURG) S.A.—See Swiss Re Ltd.; *Int'l*, pg. 7373
SWISS RE FINANCE (UK) PLC—See Swiss Re Ltd.; *Int'l*, pg. 7371
SWISS RE FINANCIAL PRODUCTS CORPORATION—See Swiss Re Ltd.; *Int'l*, pg. 7371
SWISS RE GLOBAL BUSINESS SOLUTIONS INDIA PRIVATE LIMITED—See Swiss Re Ltd.; *Int'l*, pg. 7372
SWISS RE HOLDINGS (CANADA) INC.—See Swiss Re Ltd.; *Int'l*, pg. 7372
SWISS REINSURANCE AMERICA—See Swiss Re Ltd.; *Int'l*, pg. 7372

SWISS REINSURANCE AMERICA—See Swiss Re Ltd.; *Int'l*, pg. 7372
SWISS REINSURANCE AMERICA—See Swiss Re Ltd.; *Int'l*, pg. 7372
SWISS REINSURANCE AMERICA—See Swiss Re Ltd.; *Int'l*, pg. 7371
SWISS REINSURANCE AMERICA—See Swiss Re Ltd.; *Int'l*, pg. 7372
SWISS REINSURANCE COMPANY CANADA—See Swiss Re Ltd.; *Int'l*, pg. 7372
SWISS REINSURANCE COMPANY LTD.—See Swiss Re Ltd.; *Int'l*, pg. 7371
SWISS REINSURANCE COMPANY—See Swiss Re Ltd.; *Int'l*, pg. 7372
SWISS REINSURANCE COMPANY—See Swiss Re Ltd.; *Int'l*, pg. 7372
SWISS REINSURANCE COMPANY UK LTD.—See Swiss Re Ltd.; *Int'l*, pg. 7372
SWISS REINSURANCE—See Swiss Re Ltd.; *Int'l*, pg. 7371
SWISS RE INTERNATIONAL SE—See Swiss Re Ltd.; *Int'l*, pg. 7372
SWISS RE (ISRAEL) LTD.—See Swiss Re Ltd.; *Int'l*, pg. 7371
SWISS RE ITALIA S.P.A.—See Swiss Re Ltd.; *Int'l*, pg. 7372
SWISS RE LIFE & HEALTH AFRICA LTD.—See Swiss Re Ltd.; *Int'l*, pg. 7372
SWISS RE LIFE & HEALTH AMERICA HOLDING COMPANY—See Swiss Re Ltd.; *Int'l*, pg. 7372
SWISS RE LIFE & HEALTH AMERICA, INC.—See Swiss Re Ltd.; *Int'l*, pg. 7372
SWISS RE LIFE & HEALTH AUSTRALIA LIMITED—See Swiss Re Ltd.; *Int'l*, pg. 7372
SWISS RE LTD.; *Int'l*, pg. 7371
SWISS RE MANAGEMENT LTD.—See Swiss Re Ltd.; *Int'l*, pg. 7371
SWISS RE SOLUTIONS HOLDING CORPORATION—See Swiss Re Ltd.; *Int'l*, pg. 7371
SWISS RE TREASURY (HUNGARY) GROUP FINANCING LIMITED LIABILITY COMPANY—See Swiss Re Ltd.; *Int'l*, pg. 7372
SWISS RE TREASURY (US) CORPORATION—See Swiss Re Ltd.; *Int'l*, pg. 7371
SWISSSIGN AG—See Die Schweizerische Post AG; *Int'l*, pg. 2113
SWISSSIGN GROUP AG—See Die Schweizerische Post AG; *Int'l*, pg. 2114
SWISS SIMTEC AG—See Rheinmetall AG; *Int'l*, pg. 6324
SWISS SINGAPORE CANADA PTE. LTD.—See The Aditya Birla Group; *Int'l*, pg. 7612
SWISS SINGAPORE OVERSEAS ENTERPRISES PTE LIMITED—See The Aditya Birla Group; *Int'l*, pg. 7612
SWISS STEEL AG—See Swiss Steel Holding AG; *Int'l*, pg. 7373
SWISS STEEL HOLDING AG; *Int'l*, pg. 7372
SWISS-TECH, LLC—See News-Press & Gazette Company; *U.S. Private*, pg. 2917
SWISS TECHNOLOGY PRODUCTION SA—See Fossil Group, Inc.; *U.S. Public*, pg. 875
SWISSTEC SOURCING VIETNAM JOINT STOCK COMPANY—See Einhell Germany AG; *Int'l*, pg. 2334
SWISSTEK ALUMINIUM LTD.—See Lanka Walltile PLC; *Int'l*, pg. 4412
SWISSTEK (CEYLON) PLC; *Int'l*, pg. 7375
SWISS TEKNIK LLC; *U.S. Private*, pg. 3894
SWISSTEX COMPANY; *U.S. Private*, pg. 3894
SWISSTEX INC.—See Bystronic Inc.; *Int'l*, pg. 1236
SWISS TIMING LTD.—See The Swatch Group Ltd.; *Int'l*, pg. 7692
SWISS TIMING—See The Swatch Group Ltd.; *Int'l*, pg. 7692
SWISS TOOL SYSTEMS AG—See RBC Bearings Incorporated; *U.S. Public*, pg. 1766
SWISSTRAX CORPORATION—See Sentinel Capital Partners, L.L.C.; *U.S. Private*, pg. 3609
SWISSTRONICS CONTRACT MANUFACTURING AG—See Cicor Technologies Ltd.; *Int'l*, pg. 1603
SWISS TXT AG—See SRG SSR Idee Suisse; *Int'l*, pg. 7149
SWISS VALLEY FARMS CO.—See Prairie Farms Dairy, Inc.; *U.S. Private*, pg. 3242
SWISS VALLEY OIL CO.—See Ullman Oil, Inc; *U.S. Private*, pg. 4277
SWISSVOICE SA; *Int'l*, pg. 7375
SWISS WATCH INTERNATIONAL INC.; *U.S. Private*, pg. 3894
SWISS WATER DECAFFEINATED COFFEE COMPANY, INC.; *U.S. Public*, pg. 7373
SWISS WATER DECAFFEINATED COFFEE INC.; *Int'l*, pg. 7373
SWISSWINDOWS AG - DULLIKEN WORKS—See swisspor Management AG; *Int'l*, pg. 7375
SWISSWINDOWS AG—See swisspor Management AG; *Int'l*, pg. 7375
SWISS WORLDCARGO (INDIA) PRIVATE LIMITED—See Deutsche Lufthansa AG; *Int'l*, pg. 2070
SWITCHBACK GROUP, INC.—See MPAC Group PLC; *Int'l*, pg. 5060

COMPANY NAME INDEX

SWITCH CONCEPT SDN. BHD.—See PT Erajaya Swasembada Tbk; *Int'l*, pg. 6038
SWITCH CONCEPTS LIMITED; *Int'l*, pg. 7375
SWITCHCRAFT FAR EAST COMPANY, LTD.—See HEICO Corporation; *U.S. Public*, pg. 1021
SWITCHCRAFT INC.—See HEICO Corporation; *U.S. Public*, pg. 1020
SWITCHDIGITAL (LONDON) LIMITED—See News Corporation; *U.S. Public*, pg. 1520
SWITCHED RELUCTANCE DRIVES LIMITED—See Nidec Corporation; *Int'l*, pg. 5277
THE SWITCH ENGINEERING OY—See Yaskawa Electric Corporation; *Int'l*, pg. 8569
THE SWITCH ENTERPRISES, LLC—See Tata Sons Limited; *Int'l*, pg. 7469
SWITCHES PLUS, INC.—See EAO AG; *Int'l*, pg. 2267
SWITCHFAST TECHNOLOGIES LLC; *U.S. Private*, pg. 3894
SWITCHGEAR AB—See Addtech AB; *Int'l*, pg. 135
SWITCHGRASS HOLDINGS, LLC—See BOK Financial Corporation; *U.S. Public*, pg. 367
SWITCH, INC.—See DigitalBridge Group, Inc.; *U.S. Public*, pg. 665
SWITCH, INC.—See Industry Super Holdings Pty. Ltd.; *Int'l*, pg. 3676
SWITCHING TECHNOLOGIES GUNTHER LIMITED; *Int'l*, pg. 7375
SWITCH IT SOLUTIONS B.V.—See Dustin Group AB; *Int'l*, pg. 2235
SWITCH NORDIC GREEN AB—See Elmera Group ASA; *Int'l*, pg. 2367
SWITCHPLACE; *U.S. Private*, pg. 3894
SWITCH TECHNIQUE KZN PROPRIETARY LIMITED—See Mobicon Group Limited; *Int'l*, pg. 5010
SWITLIK PARACHUTE COMPANY INC.; *U.S. Private*, pg. 3894
SWITZER ASSET MANAGEMENT PTY. LIMITED—See WCM Global Long Short Limited; *Int'l*, pg. 8361
SWITZERLAND BOSSARD AG—See Bossard Holding AG; *Int'l*, pg. 1118
SWITZERLAND CHEESE MARKETING AG; *Int'l*, pg. 7375
SWITZERLAND GLOBAL ENTERPRISE LAUSANNE—See Switzerland Global Enterprise; *Int'l*, pg. 7375
SWITZERLAND GLOBAL ENTERPRISE; *Int'l*, pg. 7375
SWIVELIER CO., INC.; *U.S. Private*, pg. 3894
SWIX SPORT AS—See Ferd AS; *Int'l*, pg. 2636
SWIX SPORT JAPAN K.K.—See Ferd AS; *Int'l*, pg. 2636
SWIX SPORT USA INC.—See Ferd AS; *Int'l*, pg. 2636
SWK HOLDINGS CORPORATION—See Carlson Capital, L.P.; *U.S. Private*, pg. 764
SWKIEL NETZ GMBH—See MVV Energie AG; *Int'l*, pg. 5109
SWKIEL SERVICE GMBH—See MVV Energie AG; *Int'l*, pg. 5109
SWKIEL SPEICHER GMBH—See MVV Energie AG; *Int'l*, pg. 5109
SWK TECHNOLOGIES, INC.—See QXO, Inc.; *U.S. Public*, pg. 1758
SWLA CENTER FOR HEALTH SERVICES, INC.; *U.S. Private*, pg. 3895
S&W MANUFACTURING—See Smead Manufacturing Company; *U.S. Private*, pg. 3693
SWMBRD SPORTS INC.; *Int'l*, pg. 7375
S&W METAL PRODUCTS; *U.S. Private*, pg. 3514
SWM INTERNATIONAL - MASSACHUSETTS—See Mativ Holdings, Inc.; *U.S. Public*, pg. 1396
SWN COMMUNICATIONS, INC.—See BC Partners LLP; *Int'l*, pg. 924
SWN RESOURCES CANADA, INC.—See Expand Energy Corporation; *U.S. Public*, pg. 808
SWN WELL SERVICES, LLC—See Expand Energy Corporation; *U.S. Public*, pg. 809
S WOHNBAUBANK AG—See Erste Group Bank AG; *Int'l*, pg. 2499
S WOHNFINANZIERUNG BERATUNGS GMBH—See Erste Group Bank AG; *Int'l*, pg. 2499
SWOOP HOLDINGS LIMITED; *Int'l*, pg. 7375
SWOPE HEALTH SERVICES; *U.S. Private*, pg. 3895
SWOPE VENTURES, INC.; *U.S. Private*, pg. 3895
SWORD CHARTERIS LIMITED—See Sword Group SE; *Int'l*, pg. 7376
SWORD CONNECT SAS—See Sword Group SE; *Int'l*, pg. 7376
SWORD CREATION INFORMATIQUE LTD.—See Sword Group SE; *Int'l*, pg. 7376
SWORD-EDGE COMMERCIALS LIMITED; *Int'l*, pg. 7376
SWORDFISH COMMUNICATIONS; *U.S. Private*, pg. 3895
SWORDFISH VENTURES CORPORATION; *Int'l*, pg. 7376
SWORD GENERAL PARTNERS LTD.—See Sword Group SE; *Int'l*, pg. 7376
SWORD GLOBAL INDIA PVT. LTD.—See Sword Group SE; *Int'l*, pg. 7376
SWORD GRC INC.—See Sword Group SE; *Int'l*, pg. 7376
SWORD GRC LTD.—See TA Associates, Inc.; *U.S. Private*, pg. 3918
SWORD GRC PTY LTD.—See Sword Group SE; *Int'l*, pg. 7376

SWORD GROUP SE; *Int'l*, pg. 7375
SWORD, INC.—See Sword Group SE; *Int'l*, pg. 7376
SWORD INTEGRA SA—See Sword Group SE; *Int'l*, pg. 7376
SWORD IT SOLUTIONS LTD.—See Sword Group SE; *Int'l*, pg. 7376
SWORD LEBANON—See Sword Group SE; *Int'l*, pg. 7376
SWORD MIDDLE EAST FZ LLC—See Sword Group SE; *Int'l*, pg. 7376
SWORD MIDDLE EAST SOFTWARE SOLUTIONS LLC—See Sword Group SE; *Int'l*, pg. 7376
SWORD SERVICES SA—See Sword Group SE; *Int'l*, pg. 7376
SWORD SOLUTIONS INC.—See Sword Group SE; *Int'l*, pg. 7376
SWORD SOUTH AFRICA (PTY) LTD.; *Int'l*, pg. 7376
SWORD TECHNOLOGIES LTD.—See Sword Group SE; *Int'l*, pg. 7376
SWORD TECHNOLOGY SOLUTIONS LTD.—See Sword Group SE; *Int'l*, pg. 7376
SWP ASSET MANAGEMENT CO., LTD.—See Srisawad Corporation Public Company Limited; *Int'l*, pg. 7151
SW PECAS DE FIXACAO LTDA.—See Wurth Verwaltungsgesellschaft mbH; *Int'l*, pg. 8513
SWP GROUP LIMITED; *Int'l*, pg. 7376
SWP N.Z. LIMITED—See Lincoln Electric Holdings, Inc.; *U.S. Public*, pg. 1318
SW POST BEHEER B.V.—See Deutsche Post AG; *Int'l*, pg. 2082
SW RADIODIFFUSION SAS—See NRJ Group SA; *Int'l*, pg. 5474
S&W READY MIX CONCRETE CO.—See Titan Cement Company S.A.; *Int'l*, pg. 7760
SW RESOURCES, INC.—See Goodwill Industries of Kanawha Valley, Inc.; *U.S. Private*, pg. 1740
S.W. RODGERS COMPANY INC.; *U.S. Private*, pg. 3519
SWRVE NEW MEDIA INC.—See Long Ridge Equity Partners, LLC; *U.S. Private*, pg. 2492
SWS AUSTRALIA PTY., LTD.—See Sumitomo Electric Industries, Ltd.; *Int'l*, pg. 7281
SWS CAPITAL BERHAD; *Int'l*, pg. 7376
SWS CHINA LTD—See Sumitomo Electric Industries, Ltd.; *Int'l*, pg. 7281
SWS DO BRASIL COMERCIAL LTDA.—See Sumitomo Electric Industries, Ltd.; *Int'l*, pg. 7281
SWS EAST JAPAN, LTD.—See Sumitomo Electric Industries, Ltd.; *Int'l*, pg. 7281
S&W SEED COMPANY AUSTRALIA PTY LTD—See S&W Seed Co.; *U.S. Public*, pg. 1832
S&W SEED CO.; *U.S. Public*, pg. 1832
SWS ENVIRONMENTAL SERVICES; *U.S. Private*, pg. 3895
S&W SERVICES, INC.; *U.S. Private*, pg. 3514
SWSH DALEY MFG, INC.—See Ecolab Inc.; *U.S. Public*, pg. 716
SWS INDIA MANAGEMENT SUPPORT & SERVICE PVT, LTD.—See Sumitomo Electric Industries, Ltd.; *Int'l*, pg. 7281
SWS KOREA CO., LTD.—See Sumitomo Electric Industries, Ltd.; *Int'l*, pg. 7281
SWS LOGISTICS & MARKETING (THAILAND) CO., LTD.—See Sumitomo Electric Industries, Ltd.; *Int'l*, pg. 7281
SWS MANAGEMENT SUPPORT, LTD.—See Sumitomo Electric Industries, Ltd.; *Int'l*, pg. 7281
SWS MU FUND MANAGEMENT CO., LTD.—See Shenwan Hongyuan Group Co., Ltd.; *Int'l*, pg. 6803
SWS RE-DISTRIBUTION COMPANY, INC.; *U.S. Private*, pg. 3895
SWS RESEARCH CO., LTD.—See Shenwan Hongyuan Group Co., Ltd.; *Int'l*, pg. 6803
SWS SALES & MARKETING (THAILAND) CO., LTD.—See Sumitomo Electric Industries, Ltd.; *Int'l*, pg. 7281
SWS S.R.O.—See MOL Magyar Olaj- es Gazipari Nyrt.; *Int'l*, pg. 5021
SWS WEST JAPAN, LTD.—See Sumitomo Electric Industries, Ltd.; *Int'l*, pg. 7281
SWT HOLDINGS B.V.—See Illinois Tool Works Inc.; *U.S. Public*, pg. 1110
SWT SERSA WELDING TEAM GMBH—See Rhomberg Sersa Rail Holding GmbH; *Int'l*, pg. 6327
SWTS PTE LTD—See Siemens Aktiengesellschaft; *Int'l*, pg. 6888
SW UMWELTTECHNIK OSTERREICH GMBH—See SW Umwelttechnik Stoiser & Wolschner AG; *Int'l*, pg. 7359
SW UMWELTTECHNIK ROMANIA S.R.L.—See SW Umwelttechnik Stoiser & Wolschner AG; *Int'l*, pg. 7359
SW UMWELTTECHNIK STOISER & WOLSCHNER AG; *Int'l*, pg. 7359
SWVL HOLDINGS CORP.; *Int'l*, pg. 7376
SWWC UTILITIES, INC.,—See JPMorgan Chase & Co.; *U.S. Public*, pg. 1207
SWWC UTILITIES, INC.,—See Water Asset Management, LLC; *U.S. Private*, pg. 4451
SWYFT, INC.; *U.S. Private*, pg. 3895
SWYPE, INC.—See Microsoft Corporation; *U.S. Public*, pg. 1443
SW ZOLL-BERATUNG GMBH—See Deutsche Bahn AG; *Int'l*, pg. 2052

SYCAMORE PARTNERS MANAGEMENT, LP

SX ENVIRONMENTAL SUPPLIES LIMITED—See Lloyds Banking Group plc; *Int'l*, pg. 4537
SX ENVIRONMENTAL SUPPLIES LIMITED—See Pelsis Holding (UK) Limited; *Int'l*, pg. 5784
SXF INC.—See SIGMAXYZ Holdings Inc.; *Int'l*, pg. 6909
SXR MEDICAL, LLC—See KKR & Co. Inc.; *U.S. Public*, pg. 1250
SYAN HOLDINGS LIMITED—See Xerox Holdings Corporation; *U.S. Public*, pg. 2388
SYAPPS LLC; *U.S. Private*, pg. 3895
SYAR CONCRETE LLC - FAIRFIELD READYMIX PLANT—See Syar Industries, Inc.; *U.S. Private*, pg. 3895
SYAR CONCRETE LLC—See Syar Industries, Inc.; *U.S. Private*, pg. 3895
SYARIKAT AIR TERENGGANU SDN BHD—See Terengganu Incorporated Sdn. Bhd.; *Int'l*, pg. 7564
SYARIKAT BEKALAN AIR SELANGOR SDN. BHD.—See Puncak Niaga Holdings Berhad; *Int'l*, pg. 6118
SYARIKAT BUKIT GRANITE SDN. BHD.—See AbleGroup Berhad; *Int'l*, pg. 63
SYARIKAT CHENG SUN QUARRY SDN. BHD.—See Mega First Corporation Berhad; *Int'l*, pg. 4792
SYARIKAT KAYU WANGI BERHAD; *Int'l*, pg. 7377
SYARIKAT KIA LIM KILANG BATU BATA SDN. BHD.—See Kia Lim Berhad; *Int'l*, pg. 4157
SYARIKAT MINHO KILNING SDN BHD—See Minho (M) Berhad; *Int'l*, pg. 4910
SYARIKAT ORIENTAL CREDIT BERHAD—See Oriental Holdings Berhad; *Int'l*, pg. 5625
SYARIKAT PENANAMAN BUKIT SENORANG SDN. BHD.—See United Malacca Berhad; *Int'l*, pg. 8070
SYARIKAT PENGANGKUTAN MAJU BERHAD—See Johor Corporation; *Int'l*, pg. 3994
SYARIKAT PERNIAGAAN BINGEL (M) SDN. BHD.—See Teo Guan Lee Corporation Berhad; *Int'l*, pg. 7562
SYARIKAT PERNIAGAAN LEKO SDN. BHD.—See Watta Holding Berhad; *Int'l*, pg. 8358
SYARIKAT PERNIAGAAN SELANGOR SDN. BHD.—See MPHB Capital Berhad; *Int'l*, pg. 5062
SYARIKAT SEE WIDE LETRIK SDN BHD—See KVC Industrial Supplies Sdn. Bhd.; *Int'l*, pg. 4349
SYARIKAT SIN KWANG PLASTIC INDUSTRIES SDN. BHD.—See SKP Resources Bhd; *Int'l*, pg. 6991
SYARIKAT TAKAFUL MALAYSIA KELUARGA BERHAD—See Lembaga Tabung Haji; *Int'l*, pg. 4449
SYARIKAT TENAGA SAHABAT SDN. BHD.—See Global Oriental Berhad; *Int'l*, pg. 3000
SYARIKAT THONG GUAN TRADING SDN. BHD.—See Thong Guan Industries Berhad; *Int'l*, pg. 7717
SYARIKAT TUNAS PANTAI SDN. BHD.—See Khazanah Nasional Berhad; *Int'l*, pg. 4152
SYARIKAT U.D. TRADING CORPORATION SDN. BHD.—See SWS Capital Berhad; *Int'l*, pg. 7376
SYARIKAT VINCO TIMBER INDUSTRIES SDN. BHD.—See Minho (M) Berhad; *Int'l*, pg. 4910
SYAR INDUSTRIES, INC. - HEALDSBURG PLANT—See Syar Industries, Inc.; *U.S. Private*, pg. 3895
SYAR INDUSTRIES, INC.; *U.S. Private*, pg. 3895
SYAR INDUSTRIES, INC. - TODD ROAD PLANT—See Syar Industries, Inc.; *U.S. Private*, pg. 3895
SYBARIS CLUBS INTERNATIONAL INC.; *U.S. Private*, pg. 3895
SYBASE DO BRASIL SOFTWARE LTDA.—See SAP SE; *Int'l*, pg. 6570
SYBASE LUXEMBOURG S.A.R.L.—See SAP SE; *Int'l*, pg. 6570
SYBER; *Int'l*, pg. 7377
SYBIT GMBH—See Nippon Telegraph & Telephone Corporation; *Int'l*, pg. 5355
SYBLEU INC.; *U.S. Public*, pg. 1968
SYBLY INDUSTRIES LTD.; *Int'l*, pg. 7377
SYBRIDGE TECHNOLOGIES, INC.—See Crestview Partners, L.P.; *U.S. Private*, pg. 1099
SYBRON CANADA LP—See Danaher Corporation; *U.S. Public*, pg. 631
SYBRON DENTAL SPECIALTIES, INC.—See Danaher Corporation; *U.S. Public*, pg. 631
SYCAL BERHAD—See Sycal Ventures Berhad; *Int'l*, pg. 7377
SYCAL KULAI SDN BHD—See Sycal Ventures Berhad; *Int'l*, pg. 7377
SYCALLAND DEVELOPMENT SDN. BHD.—See Sycal Ventures Berhad; *Int'l*, pg. 7377
SYCAL PROPERTIES SDN. BHD.—See Sycal Ventures Berhad; *Int'l*, pg. 7377
SYCAL RESORTS SDN. BHD.—See Sycal Ventures Berhad; *Int'l*, pg. 7377
SYCAL VENTURES BERHAD; *Int'l*, pg. 7377
SYCAMORE ENGINEERING; *U.S. Private*, pg. 3895
SYCAMORE ENTERTAINMENT GROUP, INC.; *Int'l*, pg. 7377
SYCAMORE LAKE, INC.—See Vail Resorts, Inc.; *U.S. Public*, pg. 2271
SYCAMORE LANDFILL, INC.—See Republic Services, Inc.; *U.S. Public*, pg. 1787
SYCAMORE PARTNERS MANAGEMENT, LP; *U.S. Private*, pg. 3895

SYCAMORE PARTNERS MANAGEMENT, LP

SYCAMORE SHOALS HOSPITAL, INC.—See HCA Healthcare, Inc.; *U.S. Public*, pg. 1011
SYCAMORE SYSTEMS, INC.—See Lyon & Dittrich Holding Company; *U.S. Private*, pg. 2522
SYCAMORE VENTURES PTE. LTD.; *Int'l*, pg. 7377
SYCAMORE VILLAGE MOBILE HOME PARK, LLC—See Sun Communities, Inc.; *U.S. Public*, pg. 1963
SYCARPHA BOLTON, LLC—See The AES Corporation; *U.S. Public*, pg. 2032
SYCHIP ELECTRONIC TECHNOLOGY (SHANGHAI) LTD.—See Murata Manufacturing Co., Ltd.; *Int'l*, pg. 5098
SYCHIP INC.—See Murata Manufacturing Co., Ltd.; *Int'l*, pg. 5098
SYCLEF HOLDING SAS—See Ardian SAS; *Int'l*, pg. 556
SYCLE, LLC—See Cochlear Limited; *Int'l*, pg. 1687
SYCLOPE ELECTRONIQUE—See ProMinent Dosiertechnik GmbH; *Int'l*, pg. 5994
SY CO., LTD.; *Int'l*, pg. 7377
SY COMING CO, LTD.—See SY Co., Ltd.; *Int'l*, pg. 7377
SYCOMORE ASSET MANAGEMENT S.A.—See Assicurazioni Generali S.p.A.; *Int'l*, pg. 648
SYCOM TECHNOLOGIES, L.L.C.—See Huron Capital Partners LLC; *U.S. Private*, pg. 2012
SYCOM TECHNOLOGIES, L.L.C.—See MidOcean Partners, LLP; *U.S. Private*, pg. 2716
SYCOR AMERICAS INC.—See Ottobock Holding GmbH & Co. KG; *Int'l*, pg. 5665
SYCOR ASIA PTE LTD.—See Ottobock Holding GmbH & Co. KG; *Int'l*, pg. 5665
SYCOR AUSTRIA GMBH—See Ottobock Holding GmbH & Co. KG; *Int'l*, pg. 5665
SYCOR GMBH—See Ottobock Holding GmbH & Co. KG; *Int'l*, pg. 5665
SYCOR SHANGHAI CO., LTD.—See Ottobock Holding GmbH & Co. KG; *Int'l*, pg. 5665
SYCOTEC GMBH & CO. KG—See Fukuda Corporation; *Int'l*, pg. 2839
SYC SETTLEMENT SERVICES, INC.—See Orrstown Financial Services, Inc.; *U.S. Public*, pg. 1619
SYDAC LTD.—See Sogeclair; *Int'l*, pg. 7058
SYDAC PTY. LTD.—See Knorr-Bremse AG; *Int'l*, pg. 4212
SYDAMI; *Int'l*, pg. 7377
SYDBANK A/S; *Int'l*, pg. 7377
SYDBELAGGNINGAR AB—See Veidekke ASA; *Int'l*, pg. 8148
SYDEK CORPORATION BINAN FACTORY—See Sydek Corporation; *Int'l*, pg. 7377
SYDEK CORPORATION SENDAI FACTORY—See Sydek Corporation; *Int'l*, pg. 7377
SYDEK CORPORATION; *Int'l*, pg. 7377
SYDEK HANG FUNG PRECISE PACKAGE (SHANGHAI) CO., LTD.—See Hang Fung International Industrial Co., Ltd.; *Int'l*, pg. 3244
SYDEK HANG FUNG PRECISE PACKAGE (SHANGHAI) CO., LTD.—See Sydek Corporation; *Int'l*, pg. 7377
SYDEK HANG FUNG PRECISION (SUZHOU) CO., LTD.—See Hang Fung International Industrial Co., Ltd.; *Int'l*, pg. 3244
SYDEK HANG FUNG PRECISION (SUZHOU) CO., LTD.—See Sydek Corporation; *Int'l*, pg. 7378
SYDEK HANG FUNG TRADING CO., LTD.—See Hang Fung International Industrial Co., Ltd.; *Int'l*, pg. 3244
SYDEK HANG FUNG TRADING CO., LTD.—See Sydek Corporation; *Int'l*, pg. 7377
SYDEK PRECISION (ZHONGSHAN) CO., LTD.—See Sydek Corporation; *Int'l*, pg. 7378
SYDELL GROUP LTD.—See Hilton Worldwide Holdings Inc.; *U.S. Public*, pg. 1041
SYDENSTRICKERS FARM & LAWN; *U.S. Private*, pg. 3898
SYDEX FLOW LTDA.—See Gevelot S.A.; *Int'l*, pg. 2954
SYDEX SINGAPORE LTD.—See Gevelot S.A.; *Int'l*, pg. 2955
SYDEX SRL—See Gevelot S.A.; *Int'l*, pg. 2954
SYDEX USA LLC—See Gevelot S.A.; *Int'l*, pg. 2955
SYDFACTORING A/S—See Sydbank A/S; *Int'l*, pg. 7377
SYDKRAFT AB—See Fortum Oyj; *Int'l*, pg. 2742
SYDKRAFT EC SLUPSK SP. Z O.O.—See E.ON SE; *Int'l*, pg. 2259
SYDKRAFT FORSAKRING AB—See Fortum Oyj; *Int'l*, pg. 2742
SYDKRAFT HYDROPOWER AB—See Fortum Oyj; *Int'l*, pg. 2742
SYDKRAFT NUCLEAR POWER AB—See Fortum Oyj; *Int'l*, pg. 2742
SYDKRAFT POLEN AB—See E.ON SE; *Int'l*, pg. 2259
SYDKRAFT TERM SP. Z O.O.—See E.ON SE; *Int'l*, pg. 2259
SYDKRAFT THERMAL POWER AB—See Fortum Oyj; *Int'l*, pg. 2742
SYDKRAFT ZLOTOW SP. Z O.O.—See E.ON SE; *Int'l*, pg. 2259
SYDLEASING A/S—See Sydbank A/S; *Int'l*, pg. 7377
SYDNEY AIRPORT CORPORATION LIMITED—See Sydney Airport Holdings Pty Ltd; *Int'l*, pg. 7378
SYDNEY AIRPORT FINANCE COMPANY PTY. LTD.—See Sydney Airport Holdings Pty Ltd; *Int'l*, pg. 7378
SYDNEY AIRPORT HOLDINGS PTY LTD; *Int'l*, pg. 7378

SYDNEY BREAST CLINIC PTY LIMITED; *Int'l*, pg. 7378
SYDNEY COAL RAILWAY INC.—See Blue Wolf Capital Partners LLC; *U.S. Private*, pg. 595
SYDNEY EURO-CENTER PTY. LTD.—See Munchener Ruckversicherungs AG; *Int'l*, pg. 5091
SYDNEY FISH MARKET PTY LTD; *Int'l*, pg. 7378
SYDNEY INSTITUTE OF BUSINESS AND TECHNOLOGY PTY LTD.—See Navitas Limited; *Int'l*, pg. 5177
SYDNEY MARKETS LTD; *Int'l*, pg. 7378
SYDNEY METROPOLITAN PIPELINE PTY LTD—See Ampol Limited; *Int'l*, pg. 437
THE SYDNEY MORNING HERALD—See Nine Entertainment Co. Holdings Limited; *Int'l*, pg. 5299
SYDNEY NORTH SHORE AUTOMOTIVE PTY. LIMITED—See Peter Warren Automotive Holdings Ltd.; *Int'l*, pg. 5824
SYDNEY OPERA HOUSE; *Int'l*, pg. 7378
SYDNOR HYDRO INC.; *U.S. Private*, pg. 3898
SYDSVENSKA ELANLAGGNINGAR AB—See Instalco AB; *Int'l*, pg. 3722
SYDSVENSKA HEM AB; *Int'l*, pg. 7378
SYDVEST ENERGI AMBA; *Int'l*, pg. 7378
SYDYS CORPORATION; *U.S. Private*, pg. 3898
SYENSQO SA; *Int'l*, pg. 7378
SYFADIS SAS—See ManpowerGroup Inc.; *U.S. Public*, pg. 1360
SYFAN MANUFACTURING CORP.; *U.S. Private*, pg. 3898
SYFON SYSTEMS PTY LTD—See EVZ Limited; *Int'l*, pg. 2574
SYFRETS SECURITIES LIMITED—See Nedbank Group Limited; *Int'l*, pg. 5188
SYFY LLC—See Comcast Corporation; *U.S. Public*, pg. 540
SYGECO LIMITED—See ENL Limited; *Int'l*, pg. 2442
SYGIC, A.S.—See W.A.G Payment Solutions Plc; *Int'l*, pg. 8321
SYG INC.—See AOYAMA TRADING Co. Ltd.; *Int'l*, pg. 499
SY GLOBAL SOUTHEAST VINA CO., LTD.—See Korea Electric Terminal Co., Ltd.; *Int'l*, pg. 4284
THE SYGMA NETWORK, INC.—See Sysco Corporation; *U.S. Public*, pg. 1977
THE SYGMA NETWORK, INC.—See Sysco Corporation; *U.S. Public*, pg. 1977
THE SYGMA NETWORK OF PENNSYLVANIA—See Sysco Corporation; *U.S. Public*, pg. 1977
SYGNETICS INCORPORATED; *U.S. Private*, pg. 3898
SYGNIA LIMITED; *Int'l*, pg. 7378
SYGNIS BIOSCIENCE GMBH & CO. KG—See 2invest AG; *Int'l*, pg. 5
SYGNITY S.A.—See Constellation Software Inc.; *Int'l*, pg. 1774
SY HOLDINGS GROUP LIMITED; *Int'l*, pg. 7377
SYI CO., LTD.—See SYS Holdings Co., Ltd.; *Int'l*, pg. 7388
SY INNOVATION CO., LTD.; *Int'l*, pg. 7377
SYKATEC SYSTEME, KOMPONENTEN, ANWENDUNGSTECHNOLOGIE GMBH & CO. KG—See Siemens Aktiengesellschaft; *Int'l*, pg. 6888
SYKEL ENTERPRISES INC.; *U.S. Private*, pg. 3898
SYKES ASIA, INC.—See Creadev SAS; *Int'l*, pg. 1831
SYKES ASSISTANCE SERVICES CORPORATION—See Creadev SAS; *Int'l*, pg. 1831
SYKES DATASVAR SUPPORT AB—See Creadev SAS; *Int'l*, pg. 1831
SYKES EL SALVADOR, LTDA—See Creadev SAS; *Int'l*, pg. 1831
SYKES ENTERPRISES BERLIN GMBH & CO. KG—See Creadev SAS; *Int'l*, pg. 1831
SYKES ENTERPRISES BOCHUM GMBH & CO. KG—See Creadev SAS; *Int'l*, pg. 1831
SYKES ENTERPRISES DENMARK APS—See Creadev SAS; *Int'l*, pg. 1831
SYKES ENTERPRISES EASTERN EUROPE S.R.L.—See Creadev SAS; *Int'l*, pg. 1831
SYKES ENTERPRISES, INCORPORATED—See Creadev SAS; *Int'l*, pg. 1831
SYKES ENTERPRISES (INDIA) PVT LTD—See Creadev SAS; *Int'l*, pg. 1831
SYKES ENTERPRISES MANAGEMENT GMBH—See Creadev SAS; *Int'l*, pg. 1831
SYKES ENTERPRISES NORWAY AS—See Creadev SAS; *Int'l*, pg. 1831
SYKES GLOBAL SERVICES LTD.—See Creadev SAS; *Int'l*, pg. 1831
SYKES KOZEP-EUROPA KFT—See Creadev SAS; *Int'l*, pg. 1831
SYKES LATIN AMERICA, S.A.—See Creadev SAS; *Int'l*, pg. 1831
SYKES REALTY, INC.—See Creadev SAS; *Int'l*, pg. 1831
SYKES (SHANGHAI) CO. LTD—See Creadev SAS; *Int'l*, pg. 1831
SYKES SLOVAKIA SRO—See Creadev SAS; *Int'l*, pg. 1831
SYKES SWEDEN AB—See Creadev SAS; *Int'l*, pg. 1831
SYLA TECHNOLOGIES CO., LTD.; *Int'l*, pg. 7378
SYLENTIS, S.A.—See Zeltia, S.A.; *Int'l*, pg. 8632
SYLHAN LLC; *U.S. Private*, pg. 3898
SYLINT GROUP INC.; *U.S. Private*, pg. 3898
SYLIOS CORP.; *U.S. Public*, pg. 1969
SYLLA GOLD CORP.; *Int'l*, pg. 7378

CORPORATE AFFILIATIONS

SYLLA GOLD MINING S.A.R.L.—See Sylla Gold Corp.; *Int'l*, pg. 7378
SYLOGIST LTD.; *Int'l*, pg. 7378
SYLOG OST AB—See Adecco Group AG; *Int'l*, pg. 140
SYLOG SVERIGE AB—See Adecco Group AG; *Int'l*, pg. 140
SYLOG SYSTEMS AB—See Adecco Group AG; *Int'l*, pg. 140
SYLPHID INC.—See Daiki Axis Co., Ltd.; *Int'l*, pg. 1932
SYLPH TECHNOLOGIES LIMITED; *Int'l*, pg. 7378
SYLVA INDUSTRIES LIMITED—See Gold Peak Technology Group Limited; *Int'l*, pg. 3026
SYLVAMO CORPORATION; *U.S. Public*, pg. 1969
SYLVAMO SWEDEN AB—See Sylvamo Corporation; *U.S. Public*, pg. 1969
SYLVANIA EUROPE HOLDING CO. LTD. (GERMAN BRANCH)—See Havell's India Ltd.; *Int'l*, pg. 3286
SYLVANIA LIGHTING SERVICES CORP.—See WESCO International, Inc.; *U.S. Public*, pg. 2352
SYLVANIA LIGHTING SERVICES—See WESCO International, Inc.; *U.S. Public*, pg. 2352
SYLVANIA N.V.—See Havell's India Ltd.; *Int'l*, pg. 3286
SYLVANIA PLATINUM LIMITED; *Int'l*, pg. 7378
SYLVANIA SOUTH AFRICA (PTY) LTD.—See Sylvania Platinum Limited; *Int'l*, pg. 7378
SYLVANIA TELEPHONE—See Gannett Co., Inc.; *U.S. Public*, pg. 904
SYLVAN INC.—See The Snyder Group, Inc.; *U.S. Private*, pg. 4119
SYLVAN LEARNING, INC.—See Sterling Partners; *U.S. Private*, pg. 3807
SYLVESTRE ENERGIES SAS—See VINCI S.A.; *Int'l*, pg. 8229
SYLVESTRE FRERES INC.; *Int'l*, pg. 7379
SYLVIA MARKETING & PUBLIC RELATIONS, LLC; *U.S. Private*, pg. 3898
SYLVIA WOODS, INC.; *U.S. Private*, pg. 3898
SYLVIN TECHNOLOGIES, INC.—See Grupo Empresarial Kaluz S.A. de C.V.; *Int'l*, pg. 3128
SYLVITE SALES (USA); *U.S. Private*, pg. 3898
SYMAG SASU—See BNP Paribas SA; *Int'l*, pg. 1093
SYMANTEC CORPORATION - MIAMI—See Gen Digital Inc.; *U.S. Public*, pg. 911
SYMANTEC CORPORATION - OREM—See Gen Digital Inc.; *U.S. Public*, pg. 911
SYMANTEC CORPORATION - WALTHAM—See Gen Digital Inc.; *U.S. Public*, pg. 911
SYMANTEC GMBH—See Gen Digital Inc.; *U.S. Public*, pg. 911
SYMANTEC INDIA PRIVATE LIMITED—See Gen Digital Inc.; *U.S. Public*, pg. 911
SYMANTEC INTERNATIONAL LTD.—See Gen Digital Inc.; *U.S. Public*, pg. 911
SYMANTEC JAPAN, INC.—See Gen Digital Inc.; *U.S. Public*, pg. 911
SYMANTEC LIMITED—See Gen Digital Inc.; *U.S. Public*, pg. 911
SYMANTEC LTD.—See Gen Digital Inc.; *U.S. Public*, pg. 911
SYMANTEC SECURITY (UK) LIMITED—See Gen Digital Inc.; *U.S. Public*, pg. 911
SYMANTEC—See Gen Digital Inc.; *U.S. Public*, pg. 910
SYMANTEC SRL—See Gen Digital Inc.; *U.S. Public*, pg. 911
SYMANTEC (SWITZERLAND) SARL—See Gen Digital Inc.; *U.S. Public*, pg. 910
SYMANTEC TECHNOLOGIES (IRELAND) LIMITED—See Gen Digital Inc.; *U.S. Public*, pg. 911
SYMANTEC (UK) LTD. - READING—See Gen Digital Inc.; *U.S. Public*, pg. 911
SYMANTEC (UK) LTD.—See Gen Digital Inc.; *U.S. Public*, pg. 910
SYMAP SAS; *Int'l*, pg. 7379
SYMAX LIFT (HOLDING) CO. LTD.; *Int'l*, pg. 7379
SYMBEO, INC.—See CorVel Corporation; *U.S. Public*, pg. 585
SYMBIA LOGISTICS; *U.S. Private*, pg. 3898
SYMBIENT PRODUCT DEVELOPMENT, LLC—See Sverica Capital Management LP; *U.S. Private*, pg. 3888
SYMBILITY SOLUTIONS CORP.—See Insight Venture Management, LLC; *U.S. Private*, pg. 2089
SYMBILITY SOLUTIONS CORP.—See Stone Point Capital LLC; *U.S. Private*, pg. 3823
SYMBILITY SOLUTIONS GMBH—See Insight Venture Management, LLC; *U.S. Private*, pg. 2089
SYMBILITY SOLUTIONS GMBH—See Stone Point Capital LLC; *U.S. Private*, pg. 3823
SYMBILITY SOLUTIONS, INC.—See Insight Venture Management, LLC; *U.S. Private*, pg. 2089
SYMBILITY SOLUTIONS, INC.—See Stone Point Capital LLC; *U.S. Private*, pg. 3823
SYMBILITY SOLUTIONS INC.—See Insight Venture Management, LLC; *U.S. Private*, pg. 2089
SYMBILITY SOLUTIONS INC.—See Stone Point Capital LLC; *U.S. Private*, pg. 3823
SYMBILITY SOLUTIONS LIMITED—See Insight Venture Management, LLC; *U.S. Private*, pg. 2089

COMPANY NAME INDEX

SYMBILITY SOLUTIONS LIMITED—See Stone Point Capital LLC; *U.S. Private*, pg. 3823
SYMBIO (APAC) CO., LTD.—See Symbio, LLC; *U.S. Private*, pg. 3899
SYMBIO FINLAND OY - OULU—See Bain Capital, LP; *U.S. Private*, pg. 451
SYMBIO FINLAND OY—See Bain Capital, LP; *U.S. Private*, pg. 451
SYMBIO HOLDINGS LIMITED—See Aussie Broadband Ltd.; *Int'l*, pg. 716
SYMBIO, LLC; *U.S. Private*, pg. 3898
SYMBION PTY LTD—See EBOS Group Limited; *Int'l*, pg. 2286
SYMBIONT, INC.; *U.S. Private*, pg. 3899
SYMBIONT SERVICE CORP.; *U.S. Private*, pg. 3899
SYMBIO PHARMACEUTICALS LIMITED; *Int'l*, pg. 7379
SYMBIOSIS PHARMA PVT LTD; *Int'l*, pg. 7379
SYMBIOSYS, INC.; *U.S. Private*, pg. 3899
SYMBIOTIX, LLC—See Vivendi SE; *Int'l*, pg. 8267
SYMBIOX INVESTMENT & TRADING COMPANY LTD.; *Int'l*, pg. 7379
SYMBOLARTS, LLC; *U.S. Private*, pg. 3899
SYMBOL HEALTHCARE, INC.—See The Ensign Group, Inc.; *U.S. Public*, pg. 2072
SYMBOL HEALTH SOLUTIONS, LLC.—See Community Health Systems, Inc.; *U.S. Public*, pg. 557
SYMBOLIC LOGIC, INC.—See CCUR Holdings Inc.; *U.S. Public*, pg. 461
SYMBOL MATTRESS OF NEW ENGLAND INC.—See Eastern Sleep Products Company Inc.; *U.S. Private*, pg. 1321
SYMBOL MATTRESS OF WISCONSIN, INC.—See Eastern Sleep Products Company Inc.; *U.S. Private*, pg. 1321
SYMBOL TECHNOLOGIES CZECH REPUBLIC S.R.O.—See Zebra Technologies Corporation; *U.S. Public*, pg. 2401
SYMBOL TECHNOLOGIES HOLDINGS DO BRASIL LTDA.—See Zebra Technologies Corporation; *U.S. Public*, pg. 2401
SYMBOL TOWER DEVELOPMENT CO., LTD.—See Taisei Corporation; *Int'l*, pg. 7416
SYMBORG CHILE, SPA—See Corteva, Inc.; *U.S. Public*, pg. 585
SYMBORG, INC.—See Corteva, Inc.; *U.S. Public*, pg. 585
SYMBORG PARTICIPACOES LTDA.—See Corteva, Inc.; *U.S. Public*, pg. 585
SYMBORG PERU S.A.C.—See Corteva, Inc.; *U.S. Public*, pg. 585
SYMBORG (SHANGHAI) TRADING CO., LTD.—See Corteva, Inc.; *U.S. Public*, pg. 585
SYMBORG, S.L.U.—See Corteva, Inc.; *U.S. Public*, pg. 585
SYMBORG TURKEY TARIM A.S.—See Corteva, Inc.; *U.S. Public*, pg. 585
SYMBOTIC, INC.; *U.S. Public*, pg. 1969
SYMBOTIC LLC—See Symbotic, Inc.; *U.S. Public*, pg. 1969
SYMBRIO AB—See Carl Bennet AB; *Int'l*, pg. 1332
SYMBRIO AS—See Carl Bennet AB; *Int'l*, pg. 1332
SYMCOR INC.; *Int'l*, pg. 7379
SYMDON CHEVROLET; *U.S. Private*, pg. 3899
SY.MED DEVELOPMENT, INC.—See HealthStream, Inc.; *U.S. Public*, pg. 1017
SYMEO GMBH—See Analog Devices, Inc.; *U.S. Public*, pg. 136
SYMEO SP. Z O.O.—See Analog Devices, Inc.; *U.S. Public*, pg. 136
SYMERES BV—See Keensight Capital SAS; *Int'l*, pg. 4115
SYMES CADILLAC, INC.; *U.S. Private*, pg. 3899
SYMETA HYBRID NV—See Colruyt Group N.V.; *Int'l*, pg. 1705
SYMETAL SA - OINOFYTA PLANT—See Viohalco SA/NV; *Int'l*, pg. 8243
SYMETAL SA—See Viohalco SA/NV; *Int'l*, pg. 8243
SYMETA N.V.—See Colruyt Group N.V.; *Int'l*, pg. 1705
SYMETIS SA—See Boston Scientific Corporation; *U.S. Public*, pg. 375
SYMETRA FINANCIAL CORPORATION—See Sumitomo Life Insurance Company; *Int'l*, pg. 7291
SYMETRA INVESTMENT SERVICES, INC.—See Manulife Financial Corporation; *Int'l*, pg. 4678
SYMETRA LIFE INSURANCE COMPANY—See Sumitomo Life Insurance Company; *Int'l*, pg. 7291
SYMETRI AB—See Addnode Group AB; *Int'l*, pg. 130
SYMETRI A/S—See Addnode Group AB; *Int'l*, pg. 131
SYMETRI AS—See Addnode Group AB; *Int'l*, pg. 131
SYMETRI LTD.—See Addnode Group AB; *Int'l*, pg. 131
SYMETRI OY—See Addnode Group AB; *Int'l*, pg. 131
SYMETRIX SARL—See Scientific Brain Training SA; *Int'l*, pg. 6648
SYMINGTON'S LTD.—See Newlat Food S.p.A.; *Int'l*, pg. 5235
SYMITAR SYSTEMS, INC.—See Jack Henry & Associates, Inc.; *U.S. Public*, pg. 1183
SYMMCO GROUP INC.; *U.S. Private*, pg. 3899
SYMMCO REALTY INC—See Symmco Group Inc.; *U.S. Private*, pg. 3899

SYMMEDRX, LLC—See Premier, Inc.; *U.S. Public*, pg. 1715
SYMMES LIFE CARE INC.; *U.S. Private*, pg. 3899
SYMMES MAINI & MCKEE ASSOCIATES, INC.; *U.S. Private*, pg. 3899
SYMMETRI MARKETING GROUP, LLC; *U.S. Private*, pg. 3899
SYMMETRY CREATIVE PRODUCTION; *U.S. Private*, pg. 3899
SYMMETRY ELECTRONICS CORP.—See Berkshire Hathaway Inc.; *U.S. Public*, pg. 316
SYMMETRY GLOBAL, LLC; *U.S. Private*, pg. 3899
SYMMETRY, LLC—See Nippon Telegraph & Telephone Corporation; *Int'l*, pg. 5345
SYMMETRY SURGICAL INC.—See Audax Group, Limited Partnership; *U.S. Private*, pg. 386
SYMMONS INDUSTRIES, INC.; *U.S. Private*, pg. 3899
SYMONS AMBULANCE; *U.S. Private*, pg. 3899
SYMONS CORPORATION—See Dayton Superior Corporation; *U.S. Private*, pg. 1178
SYMONS INTERNATIONAL GROUP, INC.—See Goran Capital Inc.; *Int'l*, pg. 3042
SYMOTION GMBH—See Symrise AG; *Int'l*, pg. 7380
SYMPATICO—See BCE Inc.; *Int'l*, pg. 927
SYMPHOGEN A/S—See Les Laboratoires Servier SAS; *Int'l*, pg. 4468
SYMPHOGEN INC.—See Les Laboratoires Servier SAS; *Int'l*, pg. 4468
SYMPHONIC SOFTWARE LIMITED—See Thoma Bravo, L.P.; *U.S. Public*, pg. 4150
SYMPHONY ASIA HOLDINGS PTE LTD—See Symphony International Holdings Limited; *Int'l*, pg. 7379
SYMPHONY ASIA LIMITED—See Symphony International Holdings Limited; *Int'l*, pg. 7379
SYMPHONY ASSET MANAGEMENT, LLC—See Teachers Insurance Association - College Retirement Fund; *U.S. Private*, pg. 3947
SYMPHONY ASSETS SDN. BHD.—See Ranhill Utilities Berhad; *Int'l*, pg. 6207
SYMPHONY AU PTY. LIMITED—See Symphony Limited; *Int'l*, pg. 7379
SYMPHONY CLINICAL RESEARCH SP. Z O.O.—See ICON plc; *Int'l*, pg. 3586
SYMPHONY COMMUNICATION PUBLIC COMPANY LIMITED; *Int'l*, pg. 7379
SYMPHONY CORPORATEHOUSE SDN. BHD.—See Ranhill Utilities Berhad; *Int'l*, pg. 6207
SYMPHONY CORP.; *U.S. Private*, pg. 3899
SYMPHONY CREATIVE SOLUTIONS PTE. LTD.—See Nippon Yusen Kabushiki Kaisha; *Int'l*, pg. 5359
SYMPHONY ENERGY LIMITED—See Symphony Environmental Technologies Plc; *Int'l*, pg. 7379
SYMPHONY ENVIRONMENTAL LIMITED—See Symphony Environmental Technologies Plc; *Int'l*, pg. 7379
SYMPHONY ENVIRONMENTAL TECHNOLOGIES PLC; *Int'l*, pg. 7379
SYMPHONYEYC D.O.O.—See Symphony Technology Group, LLC; *U.S. Private*, pg. 3902
SYMPHONYEYC FRANCE S.A.S.—See Symphony Technology Group, LLC; *U.S. Private*, pg. 3902
SYMPHONYEYC GMBH—See Symphony Technology Group, LLC; *U.S. Private*, pg. 3902
SYMPHONYEYC SOLUTION UK LTD.—See Symphony Technology Group, LLC; *U.S. Private*, pg. 3902
SYMPHONYEYC—See Symphony Technology Group, LLC; *U.S. Private*, pg. 3902
SYMPHONYEYC—See Symphony Technology Group, LLC; *U.S. Private*, pg. 3902
SYMPHONY FABRICS CORP.; *U.S. Private*, pg. 3899
SYMPHONY FLOATING RATE SENIOR LOAN FUND—See Brompton Funds Limited; *Int'l*, pg. 1173
SYMPHONY HEALTH SOLUTIONS CORPORATION—See ICON plc; *Int'l*, pg. 3585
SYMPHONY HOLDINGS LIMITED; *Int'l*, pg. 7379
SYMPHONY INNOVATION, LLC; *U.S. Private*, pg. 3899
SYMPHONY INTERNATIONAL HOLDINGS LIMITED; *Int'l*, pg. 7379
SYMPHONY LIFE BERHAD; *Int'l*, pg. 7379
SYMPHONY LIMITED - SEZ UNIT—See Symphony Limited; *Int'l*, pg. 7379
SYMPHONY LIMITED; *Int'l*, pg. 7379
SYMPHONY PERFORMANCE HEALTH, INC.—See Ares Management Corporation; *U.S. Public*, pg. 190
SYMPHONY PERFORMANCE HEALTH, INC.—See Leonard Green & Partners, L.P.; *U.S. Private*, pg. 2427
SYMPHONY RESOURCES LIMITED—See Symphony Holdings Limited; *Int'l*, pg. 7379
SYMPHONY TECHNOLOGY GROUP, LLC; *U.S. Private*, pg. 3900
SYMPHONY USA INC.—See Symphony Limited; *Int'l*, pg. 7379
SYMPLE CANADA FINANCIAL GROUP LIMITED—See Latitude Group Holdings Limited; *Int'l*, pg. 4423
SYMPLESOFT SDN. BHD.—See Citra Nusa Holdings Berhad; *Int'l*, pg. 1626
SYMPLICIT PTY LTD—See DWS Limited; *Int'l*, pg. 2236
SYMPLICITY CORPORATION—See H.I.G. Capital, LLC; *U.S. Private*, pg. 1831
SYMPLIFIED INC.; *U.S. Private*, pg. 3902

SYNAPTICS INCORPORATED

SYMPOINT COMMUNICATIONS; *U.S. Private*, pg. 3902
SYMPOZ, LLC—See Apple Leisure Group; *U.S. Private*, pg. 297
SYMPRES CO., LTD.—See EQT AB; *Int'l*, pg. 2467
SYMPRO, INC.—See Constellation Software Inc.; *Int'l*, pg. 1772
SYMQUEST GROUP, INC.—See Konica Minolta, Inc.; *Int'l*, pg. 4259
SYMRISE AG; *Int'l*, pg. 7380
SYMRISE AROMAS E FRAGRANCIAS LTDA.—See Symrise AG; *Int'l*, pg. 7380
SYMRISE ASIA PACIFIC PTE LTD.—See Symrise AG; *Int'l*, pg. 7380
SYMRISE ASIA PACIFIC PTE LTD—See Symrise AG; *Int'l*, pg. 7380
SYMRISE BIOACTIVES GMBH—See Symrise AG; *Int'l*, pg. 7380
SYMRISE B.V.—See Symrise AG; *Int'l*, pg. 7380
SYMRISE C.A.—See Symrise AG; *Int'l*, pg. 7380
SYMRISE CORPORATION—See Symrise AG; *Int'l*, pg. 7381
SYMRISE GMBH—See Symrise AG; *Int'l*, pg. 7380
SYMRISE HOLDING PTE LTD—See Symrise AG; *Int'l*, pg. 7380
SYMRISE IBERICA S.L.—See Symrise AG; *Int'l*, pg. 7380
SYMRISE, INC.—See Symrise AG; *Int'l*, pg. 7381
SYMRISE INC—See Symrise AG; *Int'l*, pg. 7380
SYMRISE ITALY—See Symrise AG; *Int'l*, pg. 7380
SYMRISE KIMYA SANAYI VE TICARET LTD—See Symrise AG; *Int'l*, pg. 7381
SYMRISE K.K.—See Symrise AG; *Int'l*, pg. 7380
SYMRISE LTDA.—See Symrise AG; *Int'l*, pg. 7381
SYMRISE LTDA.—See Symrise AG; *Int'l*, pg. 7381
SYMRISE LTD—See Symrise AG; *Int'l*, pg. 7381
SYMRISE LTD—See Symrise AG; *Int'l*, pg. 7381
SYMRISE LTD—See Symrise AG; *Int'l*, pg. 7381
SYMRISE MIDDLE EAST LIMITED—See Symrise AG; *Int'l*, pg. 7381
SYMRISE PARSIAN PJS CO.—See Symrise AG; *Int'l*, pg. 7381
SYMRISE PTY. LTD.—See Symrise AG; *Int'l*, pg. 7381
SYMRISE (PTY) LTD—See Symrise AG; *Int'l*, pg. 7381
SYMRISE PVT LTD—See Symrise AG; *Int'l*, pg. 7381
SYMRISE S.A. DE C.V.—See Symrise AG; *Int'l*, pg. 7381
SYMRISE S.A.E.—See Symrise AG; *Int'l*, pg. 7381
SYMRISE S.A.R.L.—See Symrise AG; *Int'l*, pg. 7381
SYMRISE SA—See Symrise AG; *Int'l*, pg. 7381
SYMRISE SDN BHD—See Symrise AG; *Int'l*, pg. 7381
SYMRISE SHANGHAI LIMITED—See Symrise AG; *Int'l*, pg. 7381
SYMRISE—See Symrise AG; *Int'l*, pg. 7380
SYMRISE S.R.L.—See Symrise AG; *Int'l*, pg. 7381
SYMRISE S.R.L.—See Symrise AG; *Int'l*, pg. 7381
SYMRISE VERTRIEBS GMBH—See Symrise AG; *Int'l*, pg. 7381
SYM SAS—See Steilmann Holding AG; *Int'l*, pg. 7193
SYMTEK AUTOMATION ASIA CO., LTD.; *Int'l*, pg. 7381
SYMVIONICS, INC.; *U.S. Private*, pg. 3902
SYNABIZ CO., LTD.—See Aucfan Co., Ltd.; *Int'l*, pg. 699
SYNACOR, INC.—See Centre Lane Partners, LLC; *U.S. Private*, pg. 827
SYNACT PHARMA AB; *Int'l*, pg. 7381
SYNAGEX, INC; *U.S. Private*, pg. 3902
SYNA GMBH—See RWE AG; *Int'l*, pg. 6436
SYNAGRI LP—See Cargill, Inc.; *U.S. Private*, pg. 758
SYNAGRI LP—See Yara International ASA; *Int'l*, pg. 8566
SYNAGRI—See Cargill, Inc.; *U.S. Private*, pg. 758
SYNAGRI—See Yara International ASA; *Int'l*, pg. 8566
SYNAGRO TECHNOLOGIES, INC.—See EQT AB; *Int'l*, pg. 2481
SYNAIRGEN PLC; *Int'l*, pg. 7381
SYNAIRGEN RESEARCH LIMITED—See Synairgen Plc; *Int'l*, pg. 7381
SYNALIA; *Int'l*, pg. 7381
SYNAMEDIA LTD.—See Permira Advisers LLP; *Int'l*, pg. 5808
SYNAPSE GROUP, INC.—See Meredith Corporation; *U.S. Public*, pg. 1423
SYNAPSENSE CORPORATION—See Vigilent Corporation; *U.S. Public*, pg. 4382
SYNAPSE PRODUCT DEVELOPMENT, INC.—See Capgemini SE; *Int'l*, pg. 1305
SYNAPSE SERVICES, LLC—See IAC Inc.; *U.S. Public*, pg. 1083
SYNAPSE STUDIOS, LLC; *U.S. Private*, pg. 3902
SYNAPSE WIRELESS INC.—See McWane, Inc.; *U.S. Private*, pg. 2645
SYNAPSIS ARGENTINA LTDA—See Enel S.p.A.; *Int'l*, pg. 2412
SYNAPSYS LIMITED—See DFCC Bank PLC; *Int'l*, pg. 2094
SYNAPTIC DIGITAL, INC.—See DMA Media Ltd.; *Int'l*, pg. 2142
SYNAPTICORE; *U.S. Private*, pg. 3902
SYNAPTICS EUROPE SARL—See Synaptics Incorporated; *U.S. Public*, pg. 1969
SYNAPTICS HONG KONG LTD.—See Synaptics Incorporated; *U.S. Public*, pg. 1969
SYNAPTICS INCORPORATED; *U.S. Public*, pg. 1969

2663

SYNAPTICS INCORPORATED

SYNAPTICS INTERNATIONAL INC.—See Synaptics Incorporated; *U.S. Public*, pg. 1969
SYNAPTICS JAPAN GK—See Synaptics Incorporated; *U.S. Public*, pg. 1969
SYNAPTICS JAPAN (K.K.) LIMITED—See Synaptics Incorporated; *U.S. Public*, pg. 1969
SYNAPTIC SOLUTIONS, INC.—See Carl Marks & Co., Inc.; *U.S. Private*, pg. 763
SYNAPTOGENIX, INC.; *U.S. Public*, pg. 1969
SYNAPTOGENIX, INC.; *U.S. Public*, pg. 1969
SYNAQ (PTY.) LTD.—See Nippon Telegraph & Telephone Corporation; *Int'l*, pg. 5355
SYNATEC GMBH—See Atlas Copco AB; *Int'l*, pg. 684
SYNATOM SA—See ENGIE SA; *Int'l*, pg. 2435
SYNBIOTICS CORPORATION—See Zoetis, Inc.; *U.S. Public*, pg. 2409
SYNBIOTIC SE; *Int'l*, pg. 7381
SYNBIOTICS EUROPE S.A.S.—See Zoetis, Inc.; *U.S. Public*, pg. 2409
SYNBIOTICS LTD.—See Ambalal Sarabhai Enterprises Ltd.; *Int'l*, pg. 413
SYNCADA EUROPE BVBA—See U.S. Bancorp; *U.S. Public*, pg. 2212
SYNCARDIA SYSTEMS LLC—See Hunniwell Lake Ventures LLC; *U.S. Private*, pg. 2008
SYNCFUSION, INC; *U.S. Private*, pg. 3902
SYNCHRO FOOD CO., LTD.; *Int'l*, pg. 7381
SYNCHROGENIX INFORMATION STRATEGIES INC.—See Certara, Inc.; *U.S. Public*, pg. 476
SYNCHRONISED SOFTWARE PTY LIMITED—See Mitsubishi UFJ Financial Group, Inc.; *Int'l*, pg. 4972
SYNCHRONOSS TECHNOLOGIES, INC.; *U.S. Public*, pg. 1969
SYNCHRONY ASSET MANAGEMENT SA—See Banque Cantonale de Geneve S.A.; *Int'l*, pg. 852
SYNCHRONY BANK—See Synchrony Financial; *U.S. Public*, pg. 1970
SYNCHRONY FINANCIAL CANADA—See Synchrony Financial; *U.S. Public*, pg. 1970
SYNCHRONY FINANCIAL; *U.S. Public*, pg. 1970
SYNCHRONY, INC.—See Johnson Controls International plc; *Int'l*, pg. 3986
SYNCHROSERV INC.—See Sun Life Financial Inc.; *Int'l*, pg. 7306
SYNCHROSOUND STUDIO SDN. BHD.—See Media Prima Berhad; *Int'l*, pg. 4771
SYNCH-SOLUTIONS; *U.S. Private*, pg. 3902
SYNCIER GMBH—See Allianz SE; *Int'l*, pg. 356
SYNCLAYER INC.; *Int'l*, pg. 7382
SYNCMOLD ENTERPRISE CORP.; *Int'l*, pg. 7382
SYNCO (H.K.) LIMITED—See Eu Yan Sang International Ltd.; *Int'l*, pg. 2525
SYNCOM FORMULATIONS (INDIA) LIMITED.; *Int'l*, pg. 7382
SYNCOM HEALTHCARE LIMITED; *Int'l*, pg. 7382
SYNCOMM CORPORATION LTD.—See Alcor Micro Corporation Ltd.; *Int'l*, pg. 303
SYNCOMM TECHNOLOGY CORP.; *Int'l*, pg. 7382
SYNCONA INVESTMENT MANAGEMENT LIMITED—See Syncona Ltd.; *Int'l*, pg. 7382
SYNCONA LTD.; *Int'l*, pg. 7382
SYNCORA GUARANTEE INC.—See GoldenTree Asset Management LP; *U.S. Private*, pg. 1734
SYNCORDIA TECHNOLOGIES AND HEALTHCARE SOLUTIONS CORP.; *Int'l*, pg. 7382
SYNCORDIS FRANCE SARL—See Larsen & Toubro Limited; *Int'l*, pg. 4419
SYNCORDIS LIMITED—See Larsen & Toubro Limited; *Int'l*, pg. 4419
SYNCORDIS SOFTWARE SERVICES INDIA PRIVATE LIMITED—See Larsen & Toubro Limited; *Int'l*, pg. 4419
SYNCORE BIOTECHNOLOGY CO., LTD.; *Int'l*, pg. 7382
SYNCORE TECHNOLOGIES AB—See Etteplan Oyj; *Int'l*, pg. 2525
SYNCOT PLASTICS, INC.—See Vinmar International Limited; *U.S. Private*, pg. 4385
SYNCPLICITY LLC—See Axway Software SA; *Int'l*, pg. 772
SYNCREON DUBLIN—See syncreon International Group; *U.S. Private*, pg. 3903
SYNCREON INTERNATIONAL GROUP; *U.S. Private*, pg. 3903
SYNCREST INC.—See Yokogawa Electric Corporation; *Int'l*, pg. 8592
SYNCROFLO, INC.—See Kirloskar Brothers Limited; *Int'l*, pg. 4191
SYNCROLIFT AS—See Nekkar ASA; *Int'l*, pg. 5192
SYNCROMATICS CORP.—See Grupo Tecnologico e Industrial GMV, S.A.; *Int'l*, pg. 3135
SYNCRONESS, INC.; *U.S. Private*, pg. 3903
SYNCRUDE CANADA LTD.—See Suncor Energy Inc.; *Int'l*, pg. 7311
SYNDAVER LABS INC.; *U.S. Private*, pg. 3903
SYNDAX PHARMACEUTICALS, INC.; *U.S. Public*, pg. 1970
SYNDBANK SERVICES LIMITED—See Canara Bank; *Int'l*, pg. 1287
SYNDERO, INC.; *U.S. Private*, pg. 3903

SYNDIAL SERVIZI AMBIENTALI S.P.A.—See Eni S.p.A.; *Int'l*, pg. 2438
SYNDICATE BANK LTD.—See Canara Bank; *Int'l*, pg. 1287
SYNDICATED RESORTS ASSOCIATION, INC.; *U.S. Private*, pg. 3903
SYNDICATED SERVICES COMPANY INC—See R&Q Insurance Holdings Ltd.; *Int'l*, pg. 6168
SYNDICATE SALES INC.; *U.S. Private*, pg. 3903
SYNDICATION, INC.; *U.S. Private*, pg. 3903
SYNDIGO LLC—See Summit Partners, L.P.; *U.S. Private*, pg. 3856
SYNDIGO LLC—See The Jordan Company, L.P.; *U.S. Private*, pg. 4062
SYNEAR FOOD HOLDINGS LIMITED; *Int'l*, pg. 7382
SYNECHRON INC.; *U.S. Private*, pg. 3903
SYNECHRON IT TOWERS—See Synechron Inc.; *U.S. Private*, pg. 3903
SYNECHRON LIMITED—See Synechron Inc.; *U.S. Private*, pg. 3903
SYNECHRON—See Synechron Inc.; *U.S. Private*, pg. 3903
SYNECO INC.—See Envipro Holdings Inc.; *Int'l*, pg. 2454
SYNECO TEC GMBH—See CEZ, a.s.; *Int'l*, pg. 1428
SYNECTIC ENGINEERING, INC.—See Mack Molding Company Inc.; *U.S. Private*, pg. 2536
SYNECTIC RESEARCH & ANALYSIS, INC.—See Avion Solutions, Inc.; *U.S. Private*, pg. 407
SYNECTICS INDUSTRIAL SYSTEMS LTD.—See Synectics plc; *Int'l*, pg. 7383
SYNECTICS PLC; *Int'l*, pg. 7382
SYNECTICS SECURITY NETWORKS LTD—See Synectics plc; *Int'l*, pg. 7383
SYNECTIC SYSTEMS (ASIA) PTE LIMITED—See Synectics plc; *Int'l*, pg. 7383
SYNECTIC SYSTEMS GMBH—See Synectics plc; *Int'l*, pg. 7383
SYNECTIC SYSTEMS GROUP LIMITED—See Synectics plc; *Int'l*, pg. 7382
SYNECTIC SYSTEMS, INC—See Synectics plc; *Int'l*, pg. 7383
SYNECTIC SYSTEMS (MACAU) LIMITED—See Synectics plc; *Int'l*, pg. 7383
SYNECTIVE LABS AB—See Addtech AB; *Int'l*, pg. 135
SYNEGEX HOLDINGS PTY. LTD.—See Perenti Global Limited; *Int'l*, pg. 5798
SYNEGRA EMS LIMITED—See Smartlink Holdings Limited; *Int'l*, pg. 7002
SYNEKTIK S.A.; *Int'l*, pg. 7383
SYNEL MLL PAYWAY LTD.; *Int'l*, pg. 7383
SYNEO, LLC—See Arcline Investment Management LP; *U.S. Private*, pg. 315
SYNEOS HEALTH CLINICAL, LLC—See Elliott Management Corporation; *U.S. Private*, pg. 1365
SYNEOS HEALTH CLINICAL, LLC—See Patient Square Capital, L.P.; *U.S. Private*, pg. 3108
SYNEOS HEALTH CLINICAL, LLC—See Veritas Capital Fund Management, LLC; *U.S. Private*, pg. 4365
SYNEOS HEALTH CLINICAL, LLC—See Elliott Management Corporation; *U.S. Private*, pg. 1365
SYNEOS HEALTH CLINICAL, LLC—See Patient Square Capital, L.P.; *U.S. Private*, pg. 3108
SYNEOS HEALTH CLINICAL, LLC—See Veritas Capital Fund Management, LLC; *U.S. Private*, pg. 4365
SYNEOS HEALTH COMMUNICATIONS, INC.—See Elliott Management Corporation; *U.S. Private*, pg. 1366
SYNEOS HEALTH COMMUNICATIONS, INC.—See Patient Square Capital, L.P.; *U.S. Private*, pg. 3108
SYNEOS HEALTH COMMUNICATIONS, INC.—See Veritas Capital Fund Management, LLC; *U.S. Private*, pg. 4365
SYNEOS HEALTH CONSULTING, INC.—See Elliott Management Corporation; *U.S. Private*, pg. 1365
SYNEOS HEALTH CONSULTING, INC.—See Patient Square Capital, L.P.; *U.S. Private*, pg. 3108
SYNEOS HEALTH CONSULTING, INC.—See Veritas Capital Fund Management, LLC; *U.S. Private*, pg. 4365
SYNEOS HEALTH GERMANY GMBH—See Elliott Management Corporation; *U.S. Private*, pg. 1365
SYNEOS HEALTH GERMANY GMBH—See Patient Square Capital, L.P.; *U.S. Private*, pg. 3108
SYNEOS HEALTH GERMANY GMBH—See Veritas Capital Fund Management, LLC; *U.S. Private*, pg. 4365
SYNEOS HEALTH, INC.—See Elliott Management Corporation; *U.S. Private*, pg. 1365
SYNEOS HEALTH, INC.—See Patient Square Capital, L.P.; *U.S. Private*, pg. 3108
SYNEOS HEALTH, INC.—See Veritas Capital Fund Management, LLC; *U.S. Private*, pg. 4365
SYNEOS HEALTH ITALY S.R.L.—See Elliott Management Corporation; *U.S. Private*, pg. 1365
SYNEOS HEALTH ITALY S.R.L.—See Patient Square Capital, L.P.; *U.S. Private*, pg. 3108
SYNEOS HEALTH ITALY S.R.L.—See Veritas Capital Fund Management, LLC; *U.S. Private*, pg. 4365
SYNEOS HEALTH IVH UK LIMITED—See Elliott Management Corporation; *U.S. Private*, pg. 1365
SYNEOS HEALTH IVH UK LIMITED—See Patient Square Capital, L.P.; *U.S. Private*, pg. 3108

CORPORATE AFFILIATIONS

SYNEOS HEALTH IVH UK LIMITED—See Veritas Capital Fund Management, LLC; *U.S. Private*, pg. 4365
SYNEOS HEALTH, LLC—See Elliott Management Corporation; *U.S. Private*, pg. 1365
SYNEOS HEALTH, LLC—See Patient Square Capital, L.P.; *U.S. Private*, pg. 3108
SYNEOS HEALTH, LLC—See Veritas Capital Fund Management, LLC; *U.S. Private*, pg. 4365
SYNEOS HEALTH NETHERLANDS B.V.—See Elliott Management Corporation; *U.S. Private*, pg. 1365
SYNEOS HEALTH NETHERLANDS B.V.—See Patient Square Capital, L.P.; *U.S. Private*, pg. 3108
SYNEOS HEALTH NETHERLANDS B.V.—See Veritas Capital Fund Management, LLC; *U.S. Private*, pg. 4365
SYNEOS HEALTH US, INC.—See Elliott Management Corporation; *U.S. Private*, pg. 1365
SYNEOS HEALTH US, INC.—See Patient Square Capital, L.P.; *U.S. Private*, pg. 3108
SYNEOS HEALTH US, INC.—See Veritas Capital Fund Management, LLC; *U.S. Private*, pg. 4365
SYNERAIL SAS—See VINCI S.A.; *Int'l*, pg. 8229
SYNERDYNE INC.—See P-Duke Technology Co., Ltd.; *Int'l*, pg. 5682
SYNERFAC TECHNICAL STAFFING; *U.S. Private*, pg. 3903
SYNERGEN CONSULTING INTERNATIONAL LLC—See Cobepa S.A.; *Int'l*, pg. 1683
SYNERGERP LIMITED - DWC LCC—See Alviva Holdings Limited; *Int'l*, pg. 402
SYNERGETIC AUTO PERFORMANCE PCL; *Int'l*, pg. 7383
SYNERGETIC, INC.; *U.S. Private*, pg. 3903
SYNERGETIC INFORMATION SYSTEMS INC.; *U.S. Private*, pg. 3903
SYNERGETICS DCS INC.; *U.S. Private*, pg. 3903
SYNERGETICS, INC.—See Bausch Health Companies Inc.; *Int'l*, pg. 897
SYNERGEYES UK LTD.—See The Cooper Companies, Inc.; *U.S. Public*, pg. 2066
SYNERGIA ENERGY LTD; *Int'l*, pg. 7383
SYNERGIA LIFE SCIENCES PVT. LTD.—See Novonesis A/S; *Int'l*, pg. 5469
SYNERGIC SOLUTIONS, INC.; *U.S. Private*, pg. 3903
SYNERGIE CAD GERMANY GMBH—See Synergie CAD Group; *Int'l*, pg. 7383
SYNERGIE CAD GROUP; *Int'l*, pg. 7383
SYNERGIE CAD LTD.—See Synergie CAD Group; *Int'l*, pg. 7383
SYNERGIE CAD MAROCCO—See Synergie CAD Group; *Int'l*, pg. 7383
SYNERGIE CAD PHILIPPINES—See Synergie CAD Group; *Int'l*, pg. 7383
SYNERGIE CAD PSC—See Synergie CAD Group; *Int'l*, pg. 7383
SYNERGIE CAD SOUTH KOREA—See Synergie CAD Group; *Int'l*, pg. 7383
SYNERGIE CAD TEST—See Synergie CAD Group; *Int'l*, pg. 7383
SYNERGIE CAD USA INC—See Synergie CAD Group; *Int'l*, pg. 7383
SYNERGIE FORMATION S.A.R.L.—See Synergie SA; *Int'l*, pg. 7383
SYNERGIE HUMAN RESOURCES B.V.—See Synergie SA; *Int'l*, pg. 7383
SYNERGIE SA; *Int'l*, pg. 7383
SYNERGIE SLOVAKIA S.R.O.—See Synergie SA; *Int'l*, pg. 7383
SYNERGIE TT ETT SA—See Synergie SA; *Int'l*, pg. 7384
SYNERGIS CAPITAL PLC—See Octagonal plc; *Int'l*, pg. 5521
SYNERGIS PROPERTY MANAGEMENT (SHENZHEN) CO., LIMITED—See ISP Holdings Limited; *Int'l*, pg. 3821
SYNERGIS; *U.S. Private*, pg. 3903
SYNERGIS TECHNOLOGIES GROUP; *U.S. Private*, pg. 3903
SYNERGISTIC INTERNATIONAL LLC—See Harvest Partners L.P.; *U.S. Private*, pg. 1877
SYNERGISTICS, INC.; *U.S. Private*, pg. 3903
SYNERGISTICS LLC—See Tomra Systems ASA; *Int'l*, pg. 7803
SYNERGISTIX, INC.; *U.S. Private*, pg. 3903
SYNERGIZE CONSULTING LTD.; *Int'l*, pg. 7384
SYNERGON CARD SERVICE LTD.—See Synergon Holding PLC; *Int'l*, pg. 7384
SYNERGON ENERGY LTD.—See Synergon Holding PLC; *Int'l*, pg. 7384
SYNERGON HOLDING PLC; *Int'l*, pg. 7384
SYNERGON HOTELS PLC—See Synergon Holding PLC; *Int'l*, pg. 7384
SYNERGON PETROLEUM LTD.—See Synergon Holding PLC; *Int'l*, pg. 7384
SYNERGON TRANSPORT LTD.—See Synergon Holding PLC; *Int'l*, pg. 7384
SYNERGO SGR S.P.A.; *Int'l*, pg. 7384
SYNERGY ABSTRACT, LP—See Banco Santander, S.A.; *Int'l*, pg. 827
SYNERGY AROMAS LTDA—See Carbery Group; *Int'l*, pg. 1320

COMPANY NAME INDEX

SYNERGY ASSOCIATES LLC; *U.S. Private*, pg. 3904
SYNERGY BANCSHARES INC.; *U.S. Private*, pg. 3904
SYNERGY BANK—See Synergy Bancshares Inc.; *U.S. Private*, pg. 3904
SYNERGY BOARD SYSTEMS USA, INC.—See Synergie CAD Group; *Int'l*, pg. 7383
SYNERGY BUSINESS SOLUTIONS AUSTRALIA PTY. LTD.—See Kingston Resources Limited; *Int'l*, pg. 4180
SYNERGY BUSINESS SOLUTIONS INC—See Velosio, LLC; *U.S. Private*, pg. 4355
SYNERGY CABLES GMBH—See The Alpine Group, Inc.; *U.S. Private*, pg. 3984
SYNERGY CABLES LTD.—See The Alpine Group, Inc.; *U.S. Private*, pg. 3984
SYNERGY CARDS SDN. BHD.—See Advance Synergy Berhad; *Int'l*, pg. 157
SYNERGY CHC CORP.; *U.S. Public*, pg. 1970
SYNERGY COMMUNICATIONS MANAGEMENT; *U.S. Private*, pg. 3904
SYNERGY COMPUTERS & COMMUNICATIONS LIMITED—See BoardWare Intelligence Technology Limited; *Int'l*, pg. 1094
SYNERGY CONSORTIUM SERVICES, LLC; *U.S. Private*, pg. 3904
SYNERGY CONSULTING CO., LTD—See J-Holdings Corp.; *Int'l*, pg. 3854
SYNERGY (CORBY) LTD—See Carbery Group; *Int'l*, pg. 1320
SYNERGY CORE LLC; *U.S. Private*, pg. 3904
SYNERGY DIRECT MORTGAGE, INC.; *U.S. Private*, pg. 3904
SYNERGY ECP, LLC—See Falfurrias Capital Partners, LP; *U.S. Private*, pg. 1467
SYNERGY EMPIRE LIMITED; *Int'l*, pg. 7384
SYNERGY ESCO (MALAYSIA) SDN. BHD.—See Unity Group Holdings International Limited; *Int'l*, pg. 8076
SYNERGY FINANCE LIMITED; *Int'l*, pg. 7384
SYNERGY FLAVORS, INC.—See Carbery Group; *Int'l*, pg. 1320
SYNERGY FLAVORS (NY) COMPANY, LLC—See Carbery Group; *Int'l*, pg. 1320
SYNERGY FLAVORS (OH). LLC—See Carbery Group; *Int'l*, pg. 1320
SYNERGY FLAVORS (OH), LLC—See Carbery Group; *Int'l*, pg. 1320
SYNERGY FLAVOURS (THAILAND) LTD—See Carbery Group; *Int'l*, pg. 1320
SYNERGY GLOBAL SOLUTIONS; *U.S. Private*, pg. 3904
SYNERGY GREEN INDUSTRIES LTD.; *Int'l*, pg. 7384
SYNERGY GRID & DEVELOPMENT PHILIPPINES INC.; *Int'l*, pg. 7384
SYNERGY GROUP; *Int'l*, pg. 7384
SYNERGY HEALTH ALLERSHAUSEN GMBH—See STERIS plc; *Int'l*, pg. 7210
SYNERGY HEALTH AMERICAS—See STERIS plc; *Int'l*, pg. 7210
SYNERGY HEALTH AMSTERDAM B.V.—See STERIS plc; *Int'l*, pg. 7210
SYNERGY HEALTH AST, LLC—See STERIS plc; *Int'l*, pg. 7210
SYNERGY HEALTH DANIKEN AG—See STERIS plc; *Int'l*, pg. 7210
SYNERGY HEALTH EDE B.V.—See STERIS plc; *Int'l*, pg. 7211
SYNERGY HEALTH HOORN B.V.—See STERIS plc; *Int'l*, pg. 7211
SYNERGY HEALTH INVESTMENTS LIMITED—See STERIS plc; *Int'l*, pg. 7210
SYNERGY HEALTH IRELAND LIMITED—See STERIS plc; *Int'l*, pg. 7210
SYNERGY HEALTH LIMITED—See STERIS plc; *Int'l*, pg. 7210
SYNERGY HEALTH MANAGED SERVICES LIMITED—See STAR Capital Partners Limited; *Int'l*, pg. 7173
SYNERGY HEALTH MARSEILLE SAS—See STERIS plc; *Int'l*, pg. 7210
SYNERGY HEALTH NEDERLAND B.V.—See STERIS plc; *Int'l*, pg. 7210
SYNERGY HEALTH OUTSOURCING SOLUTIONS, INC.—See STERIS plc; *Int'l*, pg. 7210
SYNERGY HEALTH RADEBERG GMBH—See STERIS plc; *Int'l*, pg. 7211
SYNERGY HEALTH STERILISATION UK LIMITED—See STERIS plc; *Int'l*, pg. 7211
SYNERGY HEALTH (SUZHOU) LIMITED—See STERIS plc; *Int'l*, pg. 7210
SYNERGY HEALTH (SUZHOU) STERILIZATION TECHNOLOGIES LIMITED—See STERIS plc; *Int'l*, pg. 7210
SYNERGY HEALTH (THAILAND) LIMITED—See STERIS plc; *Int'l*, pg. 7210
SYNERGY HEALTH UTRECHT B.V.—See STERIS plc; *Int'l*, pg. 7211
SYNERGY (HIGH WYCOMBE) LTD—See Carbery Group; *Int'l*, pg. 1320
SYNERGY HOME CARE CAPITOL REGION, INC.—See Apollo Global Management, Inc.; *U.S. Public*, pg. 157
SYNERGY HOME CARE CENTRAL REGION, INC.—See Apollo Global Management, Inc.; *U.S. Public*, pg. 157
SYNERGY HOMECARE FRANCHISING LLC; *U.S. Private*, pg. 3904
SYNERGY HOME CARE NORTHEASTERN REGION, INC.—See Apollo Global Management, Inc.; *U.S. Public*, pg. 157
SYNERGY HOME CARE NORTHSHORE REGION, INC.—See Apollo Global Management, Inc.; *U.S. Public*, pg. 158
SYNERGY HOME CARE NORTHWESTERN REGION, INC.—See Apollo Global Management, Inc.; *U.S. Public*, pg. 158
SYNERGY HOME CARE SOUTHEASTERN REGION, INC.—See Apollo Global Management, Inc.; *U.S. Public*, pg. 158
SYNERGY HOME MORTGAGE, LLC—See Rithm Capital Corp.; *U.S. Public*, pg. 1800
SYNERGY HOUSE BERHAD; *Int'l*, pg. 7385
SYNERGY INNOVATION CO., LTD.; *Int'l*, pg. 7385
SYNERGY IRELAND—See Carbery Group; *Int'l*, pg. 1320
SYNERGY LTD.—See Cyberlinks Co., Ltd.; *Int'l*, pg. 1893
SYNERGY MARKETING, INC.—See SoftBank Group Corp.; *Int'l*, pg. 7052
SYNERGY MEDICAL BRG INC.—See Becton, Dickinson & Company; *U.S. Public*, pg. 292
SYNERGY MEDICAL EUROPE LTD.—See Becton, Dickinson & Company; *U.S. Public*, pg. 292
SYNERGY NETWORKS GMBH—See freenet AG; *Int'l*, pg. 2770
SYNERGY PACKAGING PTY. LIMITED—See Berry Global Group, Inc; *U.S. Public*, pg. 325
SYNERGY PARTNERS CO., LTD.; *Int'l*, pg. 7385
SYNERGY PETROLEUM LLC; *U.S. Private*, pg. 3904
SYNERGY PHARMACEUTICALS, INC.—See Bausch Health Companies Inc.; *Int'l*, pg. 898
SYNERGYPLUS GMBH—See ecotel communication ag; *Int'l*, pg. 2300
SYNERGY PROJECTS LTD.; *Int'l*, pg. 7385
SYNERGY RADIOLOGY ASSOCIATES, P.A.—See MEDNAX, Inc.; *U.S. Public*, pg. 1413
SYNERGY RECYCLING, LLC—See Clean Harbors, Inc.; *U.S. Public*, pg. 510
SYNERGY RELOCATIONS INC.; *U.S. Private*, pg. 3904
SYNERGY SCIENTECH CORP.; *Int'l*, pg. 7385
SYNERGY SPONSORSHIP—See The Engine Group; *Int'l*, pg. 7640
SYNERGY STERILISATION KULIM (M) SDN BHD—See STERIS plc; *Int'l*, pg. 7211
SYNERGY STERILISATION (M) SDN BHD—See STERIS plc; *Int'l*, pg. 7210
SYNERGY STERILISATION RAWANG (M) SDN BHD—See STERIS plc; *Int'l*, pg. 7211
SYNERGY STERILISATION SOUTH AFRICA (PTY) LIMITED—See STERIS plc; *Int'l*, pg. 7210
SYNERGYST RESEARCH GROUP; *U.S. Private*, pg. 3904
SYNERGY SYSTEMS, INC.—See Sealaska Corporation; *U.S. Private*, pg. 3585
SYNERGY TECHNOLOGIES, INC.; *U.S. Private*, pg. 3904
SYNERGY TELECOM, INC.—See Digerati Technologies, Inc.; *U.S. Public*, pg. 661
SYNERGY TOURS SDN. BHD.2002—See Advance Synergy Berhad; *Int'l*, pg. 157
SYNERGY TOURS SDN. BHD.—See Advance Synergy Berhad; *Int'l*, pg. 157
SYNERGY WORLDWIDE AUSTRALIA PTY LTD.—See Nature's Sunshine Products, Inc.; *U.S. Public*, pg. 1499
SYNERGY WORLDWIDE INC.—See Nature's Sunshine Products, Inc.; *U.S. Public*, pg. 1499
SYNERGY WORLDWIDE ITALY S.R.L.—See Nature's Sunshine Products, Inc.; *U.S. Public*, pg. 1499
SYNERGY WORLDWIDE MARKETING SDN BHD—See Nature's Sunshine Products, Inc.; *U.S. Public*, pg. 1499
SYNERGY WORLDWIDE NEW ZEALAND, ULC—See Nature's Sunshine Products, Inc.; *U.S. Public*, pg. 1500
SYNERGY WORLDWIDE PHILIPPINES DISTRIBUTION INC.—See Nature's Sunshine Products, Inc.; *U.S. Public*, pg. 1500
SYNERGY WORLDWIDE (S) PTE LTD.—See Nature's Sunshine Products, Inc.; *U.S. Public*, pg. 1499
SYNERON CANDELA CANADA—See Apax Partners LLP; *Int'l*, pg. 506
SYNERON CANDELA CO., LTD.—See Apax Partners LLP; *Int'l*, pg. 506
SYNERON CANDELA CORPORATION AUSTRALIA PTY LTD—See Apax Partners LLP; *Int'l*, pg. 506
SYNERON CANDELA S.A.—See Apax Partners LLP; *Int'l*, pg. 506
SYNERON CANDELA (UK) LIMITED—See Apax Partners LLP; *Int'l*, pg. 506
SYNERON MEDICAL (HK) LTD.—See Apax Partners LLP; *Int'l*, pg. 506
SYNERON MEDICAL LTD.—See Apax Partners LLP; *Int'l*, pg. 506
SYNERTEC CORPORATION LIMITED; *Int'l*, pg. 7385
SYNERTEC PTY. LTD.—See Synertec Corporation Limited; *Int'l*, pg. 7385
SYNERTONE COMMUNICATION CORPORATION; *Int'l*, pg. 7385
SYNER TRADE S.A.—See Econocom Group SA; *Int'l*, pg. 2298
SYNERZIP; *U.S. Private*, pg. 3904
SYNESSO, INC.—See The Middleby Corporation; *U.S. Public*, pg. 2115
SYNETRIX LIMITED—See Capita plc; *Int'l*, pg. 1309
SYNEVO BULGARIA LTD.—See Medicover Holding S.A.; *Int'l*, pg. 4776
SYNEVO MEDICAL (POLAND) SP.Z O.O—See Medicover Holding S.A.; *Int'l*, pg. 4776
SYNEVO MOLDOVA—See Medicover Holding S.A.; *Int'l*, pg. 4776
SYNEVO UKRAINE—See Medicover Holding S.A.; *Int'l*, pg. 4776
SYNEX ENERGY RESOURCES LTD.—See Synex Renewable Energy Corporation; *Int'l*, pg. 7385
SYNEXMED (HONG KONG) LIMITED—See Japan Lifeline Co.; *Int'l*, pg. 3898
SYNEX RENEWABLE ENERGY CORPORATION; *Int'l*, pg. 7385
SYNEXS GMBH—See ACS, Actividades de Construccion y Servicios, S.A.; *Int'l*, pg. 116
SYNEXUS CLINICAL RESEARCH LIMITED—See Lloyds Banking Group plc; *Int'l*, pg. 4538
SYNEXUS CLINICAL RESEARCH SOUTH AFRICA (PTY.) LIMITED—See Thermo Fisher Scientific Inc.; *U.S. Public*, pg. 2152
SYNEXUS CZECH S.R.O.—See Thermo Fisher Scientific Inc.; *U.S. Public*, pg. 2152
SYNEXUS POLSKA SP. Z O.O.—See Thermo Fisher Scientific Inc.; *U.S. Public*, pg. 2152
SYNFORM CO., LTD.—See EQT AB; *Int'l*, pg. 2467
SYNGEN BIOTECH INTERNATIONAL SDN. BHD.—See Standard Chem. & Pharm. Co., Ltd.; *Int'l*, pg. 7168
SYNGENE INTERNATIONAL LIMITED—See Biocon Ltd.; *Int'l*, pg. 1036
SYNGENTA AGRO AG—See China National Chemical Corporation; *Int'l*, pg. 1529
SYNGENTA AGRO D.O.O.—See China National Chemical Corporation; *Int'l*, pg. 1529
SYNGENTA AGRO GMBH—See China National Chemical Corporation; *Int'l*, pg. 1529
SYNGENTA AGRO, S.A. DE C.V.—See China National Chemical Corporation; *Int'l*, pg. 1529
SYNGENTA AGRO S.A—See China National Chemical Corporation; *Int'l*, pg. 1529
SYNGENTA AGRO SERVICES AG—See China National Chemical Corporation; *Int'l*, pg. 1529
SYNGENTA AG—See China National Chemical Corporation; *Int'l*, pg. 1529
SYNGENTA ASIA PACIFIC PTE. LTD.—See China National Chemical Corporation; *Int'l*, pg. 1529
SYNGENTA BANGLADESH LIMITED—See China National Chemical Corporation; *Int'l*, pg. 1529
SYNGENTA BULGARIA EOOD—See China National Chemical Corporation; *Int'l*, pg. 1529
SYNGENTA CANADA INC.—See China National Chemical Corporation; *Int'l*, pg. 1529
SYNGENTA (CHINA) INVESTMENT COMPANY LIMITED—See China National Chemical Corporation; *Int'l*, pg. 1529
SYNGENTA CORPORATION—See China National Chemical Corporation; *Int'l*, pg. 1529
SYNGENTA CROP PROTECTION AG—See China National Chemical Corporation; *Int'l*, pg. 1530
SYNGENTA CROP PROTECTION A/S—See China National Chemical Corporation; *Int'l*, pg. 1530
SYNGENTA CROP PROTECTION B.V.—See China National Chemical Corporation; *Int'l*, pg. 1530
SYNGENTA CROP PROTECTION - FINLAND OFFICE—See China National Chemical Corporation; *Int'l*, pg. 1530
SYNGENTA CROP PROTECTION, INC.—See China National Chemical Corporation; *Int'l*, pg. 1529
SYNGENTA CROP PROTECTION LIMITED—See China National Chemical Corporation; *Int'l*, pg. 1530
SYNGENTA CROP PROTECTION, LLC—See China National Chemical Corporation; *Int'l*, pg. 1529
SYNGENTA CROP PROTECTION MONTHEY SA—See China National Chemical Corporation; *Int'l*, pg. 1530
SYNGENTA CROP PROTECTION MUNCHWILEN AG—See China National Chemical Corporation; *Int'l*, pg. 1530
SYNGENTA CROP PROTECTION S.A.—See China National Chemical Corporation; *Int'l*, pg. 1530
SYNGENTA CROP PROTECTION SDN BHD—See China National Chemical Corporation; *Int'l*, pg. 1530
SYNGENTA CZECH S.R.O.—See China National Chemical Corporation; *Int'l*, pg. 1530
SYNGENTA FINANCE N.V.—See China National Chemical Corporation; *Int'l*, pg. 1530
SYNGENTA GRANGEMOUTH—See China National Chemical Corporation; *Int'l*, pg. 1530
SYNGENTA IRELAND LIMITED—See China National Chemical Corporation; *Int'l*, pg. 1530
SYNGENTA JAPAN CO., LTD.—See China National Chemical Corporation; *Int'l*, pg. 1530
SYNGENTA LAN—See China National Chemical Corporation; *Int'l*, pg. 1530

SYNGENTA LTD.—See China National Chemical Corporation; *Int'l*, pg. 1530
SYNGENTA POLSKA SP. Z O.O—See China National Chemical Corporation; *Int'l*, pg. 1529
SYNGENTA POLSKA SP. Z O.O—See China National Chemical Corporation; *Int'l*, pg. 1529
SYNGENTA POLSKA SP. Z O.O.—See China National Chemical Corporation; *Int'l*, pg. 1530
SYNGENTA PROTECAO DE CULTIVOS LTDA.—See China National Chemical Corporation; *Int'l*, pg. 1530
SYNGENTA S.A.—See China National Chemical Corporation; *Int'l*, pg. 1530
SYNGENTA SEEDCO (PTY) LIMITED—See China National Chemical Corporation; *Int'l*, pg. 1530
SYNGENTA SEEDS A/S—See China National Chemical Corporation; *Int'l*, pg. 1530
SYNGENTA SEEDS B.V.—See China National Chemical Corporation; *Int'l*, pg. 1530
SYNGENTA SEEDS CO. LTD.—See China National Chemical Corporation; *Int'l*, pg. 1530
SYNGENTA SEEDS GMBH—See China National Chemical Corporation; *Int'l*, pg. 1530
SYNGENTA SEEDS, LLC—See China National Chemical Corporation; *Int'l*, pg. 1530
SYNGENTA SEEDS N.V.—See China National Chemical Corporation; *Int'l*, pg. 1530
SYNGENTA SLOVAKIA S.R.O.—See China National Chemical Corporation; *Int'l*, pg. 1530
SYNGENTA SOUTH AFRICA (PTY) LIMITED—See China National Chemical Corporation; *Int'l*, pg. 1530
SYNGENTA TAIWAN LTD—See China National Chemical Corporation; *Int'l*, pg. 1530
SYNGENTA TREASURY N.V.—See China National Chemical Corporation; *Int'l*, pg. 1530
SYNGENTA UK LIMITED—See China National Chemical Corporation; *Int'l*, pg. 1530
SYNGROUP MANAGEMENT CONSULTING GMBH; *Int'l*, pg. 7385
SYN HF; *Int'l*, pg. 7381
SYNISE TECHNOLOGIES LTD—See Kalyani Group; *Int'l*, pg. 4059
SYNIVERSE HOLDINGS, INC.—See The Carlyle Group Inc.; *U.S. Public*, pg. 2054
SYNIVERSE TECHNOLOGIES LIMITED—See The Carlyle Group Inc.; *U.S. Public*, pg. 2054
SYNIVERSE TECHNOLOGIES, LLC—See The Carlyle Group Inc.; *U.S. Public*, pg. 2054
SYNKEM S.A.S.—See International Chemical Investors S.E.; *Int'l*, pg. 3745
SYNLAB HOLDING DEUTSCHLAND GMBH—See Cinven Limited; *Int'l*, pg. 1614
SYNLAB INTERNATIONAL GMBH—See Cinven Limited; *Int'l*, pg. 1614
SYNLAB LABORATORY SERVICES LIMITED—See Cinven Limited; *Int'l*, pg. 1614
SYNLAIT MILK LIMITED; *Int'l*, pg. 7385
SYNLOGIC, INC; *U.S. Public*, pg. 1970
SYN MUN KONG INSURANCE PUBLIC COMPANY LIMITED; *Int'l*, pg. 7381
SYNNEFO TECHNOLOGY SOLUTIONS, INC.—See CDW Corporation; *U.S. Public*, pg. 463
SYNNEX AUSTRALIA PTY. LTD.—See Synnex Technology International Corporation; *Int'l*, pg. 7385
SYNNEX CANADA LTD.—See TD Synnex Corp; *U.S. Public*, pg. 1984
SYNNEX CO., LTD.—See TD Synnex Corp; *U.S. Public*, pg. 1984
SYNNEX DE MEXICO, S.A. DE C.V.—See TD Synnex Corp; *U.S. Public*, pg. 1984
SYNNEX INFORMATION TECHNOLOGIES (BEIJING) LTD.—See TD Synnex Corp; *U.S. Public*, pg. 1984
SYNNEX INFOTEC CORPORATION—See TD Synnex Corp; *U.S. Public*, pg. 1984
SYNNEX TECHNOLOGY INTERNATIONAL CORPORATION; *Int'l*, pg. 7385
SYNNEX TECHNOLOGY INTERNATIONAL (HK) LTD—See Synnex Technology International Corporation; *Int'l*, pg. 7385
SYNNEX (THAILAND) PUBLIC CO., LTD.; *Int'l*, pg. 7385
SYNNOVIA PLC; *Int'l*, pg. 7385
SYNOKEM PHARMACEUTICALS LTD.—See TA Associates, Inc.; *U.S. Private*, pg. 3918
SYNOPEX INC.; *Int'l*, pg. 7386
SYNOPEX VIETNAM CO., LTD.—See Synopex Inc.; *Int'l*, pg. 7386
SYNOPSE SAS—See Econocom Group SA; *Int'l*, pg. 2298
SYNOPSYS ARMENIA CJSC—See Synopsys, Inc.; *U.S. Public*, pg. 1971
SYNOPSYS DENMARK APS—See Synopsys, Inc.; *U.S. Public*, pg. 1971
SYNOPSYS EMULATION AND VERIFICATION S.A.S.—See Synopsys, Inc.; *U.S. Public*, pg. 1971
SYNOPSYS GLOBAL KFT.—See Synopsys, Inc.; *U.S. Public*, pg. 1971
SYNOPSYS GMBH—See Synopsys, Inc.; *U.S. Public*, pg. 1971
SYNOPSYS HARDWARE PLATFORMS GROUP AB—See Synopsys, Inc.; *U.S. Public*, pg. 1971
SYNOPSYS, INC.; *U.S. Public*, pg. 1970

SYNOPSYS (INDIA) PRIVATE LIMITED—See Synopsys, Inc.; *U.S. Public*, pg. 1970
SYNOPSYS INTERNATIONAL LIMITED—See Synopsys, Inc.; *U.S. Public*, pg. 1971
SYNOPSYS ITALIA S.R.L.—See Synopsys, Inc.; *U.S. Public*, pg. 1971
SYNOPSYS KOREA INC.—See Synopsys, Inc.; *U.S. Public*, pg. 1971
SYNOPSYS LLC—See Synopsys, Inc.; *U.S. Public*, pg. 1971
SYNOPSYS (NORTHERN EUROPE) LTD.—See Synopsys, Inc.; *U.S. Public*, pg. 1971
SYNOPSYS SARL—See Synopsys, Inc.; *U.S. Public*, pg. 1971
SYNOPSYS (SINGAPORE) PTE. LTD.—See Synopsys, Inc.; *U.S. Public*, pg. 1970
SYNOPSYS SOFTWARE SCIENCE AND TECHNOLOGY (SHANGHAI) CO., LTD.—See Synopsys, Inc.; *U.S. Public*, pg. 1971
SYNOPSYS SPB LLC—See Synopsys, Inc.; *U.S. Public*, pg. 1971
SYNOPSYS SWITZERLAND LLC—See Synopsys, Inc.; *U.S. Public*, pg. 1971
SYNOPSYS TAIWAN CO., LTD.—See Synopsys, Inc.; *U.S. Public*, pg. 1971
SYNOPSYS TAIWAN CO., LTD.—See Synopsys, Inc.; *U.S. Public*, pg. 1971
SYNOPTEK, LLC—See Sverica Capital Management LP; *U.S. Private*, pg. 3888
SYNOVA CAPITAL LLP; *Int'l*, pg. 7386
SYNOVA, INC.; *U.S. Private*, pg. 3904
SYNOVATE HOLDINGS BV—See Ipsos S.A.; *Int'l*, pg. 3802
SYNOVATE K.K.—See Ipsos S.A.; *Int'l*, pg. 3802
SYNOVATE-MAHWAH—See Ipsos S.A.; *Int'l*, pg. 3800
SYNOVATE-NEW YORK—See Ipsos S.A.; *Int'l*, pg. 3800
SYNOVATE PTY. LTD.—See Ipsos S.A.; *Int'l*, pg. 3802
SYNOVIA PHARMA PLC.—See Beximco Pharmaceuticals Limited; *Int'l*, pg. 1005
SYNOVIA SOLUTIONS LLC—See CalAmp Corp.; *U.S. Public*, pg. 422
SYNOVIS LIFE TECHNOLOGIES, INC.—See Baxter International Inc.; *U.S. Public*, pg. 281
SYNOVIS MICRO COMPANIES ALLIANCE, INC.—See Baxter International Inc.; *U.S. Public*, pg. 281
SYNOVOS, INC.—See RS Group plc; *Int'l*, pg. 6418
SYNOVUS BANK—See Synovus Financial Corp.; *U.S. Public*, pg. 1971
SYNOVUS BANK—See Synovus Financial Corp.; *U.S. Public*, pg. 1971
SYNOVUS BANK—See Synovus Financial Corp.; *U.S. Public*, pg. 1971
SYNOVUS BANK—See Synovus Financial Corp.; *U.S. Public*, pg. 1971
SYNOVUS FINANCIAL CORP.; *U.S. Public*, pg. 1971
SYNOVUS MORTGAGE CORP.—See Synovus Financial Corp.; *U.S. Public*, pg. 1971
SYNOVUS MORTGAGE CORP.—See Synovus Financial Corp.; *U.S. Public*, pg. 1971
SYNOVUS SECURITIES, INC.—See Synovus Financial Corp.; *U.S. Public*, pg. 1972
SYNOVUS TRUST COMPANY, NATIONAL ASSOCIATION—See Synovus Financial Corp.; *U.S. Public*, pg. 1971
SYNOVUS TRUST COMPANY, NATIONAL ASSOCIATION—See Synovus Financial Corp.; *U.S. Public*, pg. 1972
SYNPAC-KINGDOM PHARMACEUTICAL CO., LTD.—See China Synthetic Rubber Corporation; *Int'l*, pg. 1557
SYNPLICITY, LLC—See Synopsys, Inc.; *U.S. Public*, pg. 1971
SYNPOWER CO., LTD.—See Sungwoo Techron Co., Ltd.; *Int'l*, pg. 7316
SYNPRODO BV—See BEWi ASA; *Int'l*, pg. 1004
SYN PROP E TECH SA; *Int'l*, pg. 7381
SYNQOR INC.; *U.S. Private*, pg. 3904
SYNQUEST LABORATORIES, INC.—See Central Glass Co., Ltd.; *Int'l*, pg. 1407
SYNRAD, INC.—See Novanta Inc.; *U.S. Public*, pg. 1548
SYNRES-ALMOCO B.V.—See PMC Capital Partners, LLC; *U.S. Private*, pg. 3217
SYNSAM AB; *Int'l*, pg. 7386
SYNSAM GROUP AB—See Synsam AB; *Int'l*, pg. 7386
SYNSAM GROUP FINLAND OY—See Synsam AB; *Int'l*, pg. 7386
SYNSAM GROUP NORWAY AS—See Synsam AB; *Int'l*, pg. 7386
SYNSAM GROUP SWEDEN AB—See Synsam AB; *Int'l*, pg. 7386
SYNSEAL EXTRUSIONS LIMITED—See H.I.G. Capital, LLC; *U.S. Private*, pg. 1828
SYNSOR CORPORATION; *U.S. Private*, pg. 3904
SYNSPEC B.V.—See Focused Photonics (Hangzhou), Inc.; *Int'l*, pg. 2720
SYN STRAND INC.—See Voith GmbH & Co. KGaA; *Int'l*, pg. 8298
SYNSTREAM ENERGY CORP.; *Int'l*, pg. 7386
SYNTACOLL GMBH—See Gurnet Point Capital LLC; *U.S. Private*, pg. 1819

SYNTACTX, LLC—See ArchiMed SAS; *Int'l*, pg. 549
SYNTAGMA CAPITAL MANAGEMENT SA; *Int'l*, pg. 7386
SYN TAI HUNG (CAMBODIA) CO. LTD.—See Wah Seong Corporation Berhad; *Int'l*, pg. 8329
SYN TAI HUNG CORPORATION SDN. BHD.—See Wah Seong Corporation Berhad; *Int'l*, pg. 8329
SYN TAI HUNG TRADING SDN. BHD.—See Wah Seong Corporation Berhad; *Int'l*, pg. 8329
SYNTAX SOFT-TECH PVT. LTD.—See UCA Group Component Specialty Inc.; *U.S. Private*, pg. 4273
SYNTEC BIOFUEL, INC.; *Int'l*, pg. 7386
SYNTEC CONSTRUCTION PUBLIC COMPANY LIMITED; *Int'l*, pg. 7386
SYNTECH CHEMICALS, INC.—See Standard Chem. & Pharm. Co., Ltd.; *Int'l*, pg. 7168
SYN-TECH CHEM & PHARM CO., LTD.; *Int'l*, pg. 7381
SYNTECH DEVELOPMENT & MANUFACTURING, INC.; *U.S. Private*, pg. 3904
SYNTECH DISTRIBUTORS LTD.—See INDUS Holding AG; *Int'l*, pg. 3664
SYNTECH RESEARCH, INC.; *U.S. Private*, pg. 3904
SYNTEC INDUSTRIES INC.; *U.S. Private*, pg. 3904
SYNTEC, LLC—See Solmax International, Inc.; *Int'l*, pg. 7074
SYNTEC OPTICS HOLDING, INC.; *U.S. Public*, pg. 1972
SYNTEC OPTICS, INC.—See Syntec Optics Holding, Inc.; *U.S. Public*, pg. 1972
SYN TEC SEATING SOLUTIONS, LLC—See Indiana Mills & Manufacturing, Inc.; *U.S. Private*, pg. 2062
SYNTEEN & LUCKENHAUS GMBH—See KAP Beteiligungs-AG; *Int'l*, pg. 4076
SYNTEGON TECHNOLOGY GMBH—See CVC Capital Partners SICAV-FIS S.A.; *Int'l*, pg. 1884
SYNTEGRA CAPITAL INVESTORS LIMITED; *Int'l*, pg. 7386
SYNTEKABIO, INC.; *Int'l*, pg. 7386
SYNTEL DEUTSCHLAND GMBH—See Atos SE; *Int'l*, pg. 692
SYNTEL EUROPE LTD.—See Atos SE; *Int'l*, pg. 692
SYNTEL, INC.—See Atos SE; *Int'l*, pg. 692
SYNTEL INTERNATIONAL PVT. LTD.—See Atos SE; *Int'l*, pg. 692
SYNTELLECT, INC.—See Enghouse Systems Limited; *Int'l*, pg. 2428
SYNTELLECT LTD—See Enghouse Systems Limited; *Int'l*, pg. 2428
SYNTELLECT TECHNOLOGY CORP.—See Enghouse Systems Limited; *Int'l*, pg. 2428
SYNTELLIS PERFORMANCE SOLUTIONS, LLC—See Roper Technologies, Inc.; *U.S. Public*, pg. 1813
SYNTELLIX AG; *Int'l*, pg. 7386
SYNTEL LTD.—See Atos SE; *Int'l*, pg. 692
SYNTEL PRIVATE LIMITED—See Atos SE; *Int'l*, pg. 692
SYNTEL TELECOM LIMITED—See Lalbhai Group; *Int'l*, pg. 4399
SYNTEMA I VAGGERYD AB—See The Sherwin-Williams Company; *U.S. Public*, pg. 2129
SYNTERACT CORP.—See Elliott Management Corporation; *U.S. Private*, pg. 1366
SYNTERACT CORP.—See Patient Square Capital, L.P.; *U.S. Private*, pg. 3108
SYNTERACT CORP.—See Veritas Capital Fund Management, LLC; *U.S. Private*, pg. 4365
SYNTERACTHCR BENELUX NV—See Elliott Management Corporation; *U.S. Private*, pg. 1366
SYNTERACTHCR BENELUX NV—See Patient Square Capital, L.P.; *U.S. Private*, pg. 3108
SYNTERACTHCR BENELUX NV—See Veritas Capital Fund Management, LLC; *U.S. Private*, pg. 4365
SYNTERACTHCR DEUTSCHLAND GMBH—See Elliott Management Corporation; *U.S. Private*, pg. 1366
SYNTERACTHCR DEUTSCHLAND GMBH—See Patient Square Capital, L.P.; *U.S. Private*, pg. 3108
SYNTERACTHCR DEUTSCHLAND GMBH—See Veritas Capital Fund Management, LLC; *U.S. Private*, pg. 4365
SYNTERACTHCR EASTERN EUROPE FORSCHUNGSGESELLSCHAFT M.B.H.—See Elliott Management Corporation; *U.S. Private*, pg. 1366
SYNTERACTHCR EASTERN EUROPE FORSCHUNGSGESELLSCHAFT M.B.H.—See Patient Square Capital, L.P.; *U.S. Private*, pg. 3108
SYNTERACTHCR EASTERN EUROPE FORSCHUNGSGESELLSCHAFT M.B.H.—See Veritas Capital Fund Management, LLC; *U.S. Private*, pg. 4365
SYNTERACTHCR FRANCE SAS—See Elliott Management Corporation; *U.S. Private*, pg. 1366
SYNTERACTHCR FRANCE SAS—See Patient Square Capital, L.P.; *U.S. Private*, pg. 3108
SYNTERACTHCR FRANCE SAS—See Veritas Capital Fund Management, LLC; *U.S. Private*, pg. 4365
SYNTERACTHCR IBERICA, SL—See Elliott Management Corporation; *U.S. Private*, pg. 1366
SYNTERACTHCR IBERICA, SL—See Patient Square Capital, L.P.; *U.S. Private*, pg. 3108
SYNTERACTHCR IBERICA, SL—See Veritas Capital Fund Management, LLC; *U.S. Private*, pg. 4365
SYNTERACTHCR LIMITED—See Elliott Management Corporation; *U.S. Private*, pg. 1366

COMPANY NAME INDEX

SYNTERACTHCR LIMITED—See Patient Square Capital, L.P.; *U.S. Private*, pg. 3109
SYNTERACTHCR LIMITED—See Veritas Capital Fund Management, LLC; *U.S. Private*, pg. 4365
SYNTERACTHCR S.R.L.—See Elliott Management Corporation; *U.S. Private*, pg. 1366
SYNTERACTHCR S.R.L.—See Patient Square Capital, L.P.; *U.S. Private*, pg. 3109
SYNTERACTHCR S.R.L.—See Veritas Capital Fund Management, LLC; *U.S. Private*, pg. 4365
SYNTERACTHCR SWEDEN AB—See Elliott Management Corporation; *U.S. Private*, pg. 1366
SYNTERACTHCR SWEDEN AB—See Patient Square Capital, L.P.; *U.S. Private*, pg. 3109
SYNTERACTHCR SWEDEN AB—See Veritas Capital Fund Management, LLC; *U.S. Private*, pg. 4365
SYNTERACTIVE; *U.S. Private*, pg. 3905
SYNTERAS, LLC—See Nana Regional Corporation, Inc.; *U.S. Private*, pg. 2832
SYNTERRA CORP.; *U.S. Private*, pg. 3905
SYNTER RESOURCE GROUP, LLC; *U.S. Private*, pg. 3905
SYNTHANE-TAYLOR (CANADA) LIMITED—See Dunes Point Capital, LLC; *U.S. Private*, pg. 1289
SYNTHANE-TAYLOR (CANADA) LTD. - STE. THERESE FACILITY—See Dunes Point Capital, LLC; *U.S. Private*, pg. 1289
SYNTHAX INC.—See Transition Evergreen; *Int'l*, pg. 7901
SYNTHES AB—See Johnson & Johnson; *U.S. Public*, pg. 1195
SYNTHES ARGENTINA S.A.—See Johnson & Johnson; *U.S. Public*, pg. 1195
SYNTHES AUSTRALIA PTY LTD—See Johnson & Johnson; *U.S. Public*, pg. 1200
SYNTHES (CANADA) LTD.—See Johnson & Johnson; *U.S. Public*, pg. 1200
SYNTHES COLOMBIA LTDA—See Johnson & Johnson; *U.S. Public*, pg. 1195
SYNTHES, GMBH - EUROPEAN HEADQUARTERS—See Johnson & Johnson; *U.S. Public*, pg. 1195
SYNTHES GMBH—See Johnson & Johnson; *U.S. Public*, pg. 1195
SYNTHESIA, A.S.—See Agrofert Holding, a.s.; *Int'l*, pg. 219
SYNTHES, INC.—See Johnson & Johnson; *U.S. Public*, pg. 1195
SYNTHES IND. COM. LTDA.—See Johnson & Johnson; *U.S. Public*, pg. 1195
SYNTHES INDUSTRIA E COMERCIO LTDA.—See Johnson & Johnson; *U.S. Public*, pg. 1200
SYNTHESIO, INC.—See Ipsos S.A.; *Int'l*, pg. 3802
SYNTHESIO PARIS—See Ipsos S.A.; *Int'l*, pg. 3802
SYNTHESIO SINGAPORE—See Ipsos S.A.; *Int'l*, pg. 3802
SYNTHESIO UK—See Ipsos S.A.; *Int'l*, pg. 3802
SYNTHESIS ELECTRONIC TECHNOLOGY CO., LTD.; *Int'l*, pg. 7386
SYNTHESIS ENERGY SYSTEMS, INC. - SHANGHAI—See Synthesis Energy Systems, Inc.; *U.S. Public*, pg. 1972
SYNTHESIS ENERGY SYSTEMS, INC.; *U.S. Public*, pg. 1972
SYNTHESIS ENERGY SYSTEMS, INC. - ZAOZHUANG—See Synthesis Energy Systems, Inc.; *U.S. Public*, pg. 1972
SYNTHESIS INTERNATIONAL LIMITED—See Kiri Industries Ltd.; *Int'l*, pg. 4186
SYNTHESIS SOFTWARE TECHNOLOGIES PROPRIETARY LIMITED—See Capital Appreciation Ltd.; *Int'l*, pg. 1309
SYNTHESIS TECHNOLOGY CORP.—See Blue Horizon Software Holdings LLC; *U.S. Private*, pg. 589
SYNTHES LTD.—See Johnson & Johnson; *U.S. Public*, pg. 1195
SYNTHES MEDICAL IMMOBILIEN GMBH—See Johnson & Johnson; *U.S. Public*, pg. 1195
SYNTHES MEDICAL KFT.—See Johnson & Johnson; *U.S. Public*, pg. 1195
SYNTHES PRODUKTIONS GMBH—See Johnson & Johnson; *U.S. Public*, pg. 1200
SYNTHES (SHANGHAI) MEDICAL TRADING CO., LTD.—See Johnson & Johnson; *U.S. Public*, pg. 1200
SYNTHES S.R.O.—See Johnson & Johnson; *U.S. Public*, pg. 1195
SYNTHES STRATEC—See Johnson & Johnson; *U.S. Public*, pg. 1195
SYNTHES (SUZHOU) MEDICAL CO., LTD.—See Johnson & Johnson; *U.S. Public*, pg. 1200
SYNTHES TUTTLINGEN GMBH—See Johnson & Johnson; *U.S. Public*, pg. 1200
SYNTHES USA, LLC—See Johnson & Johnson; *U.S. Public*, pg. 1200
SYNTHETICA AD; *Int'l*, pg. 7387
SYNTHETIC GENOMICS, INC.; *U.S. Private*, pg. 3905
THE SYNTHETIC LATEX CO (PTY) LTD—See Karbochem (Pty) Limited; *Int'l*, pg. 4079
SYNTHETIC MATERIALS LLC—See Seven Group Holdings Limited; *Int'l*, pg. 6733
SYNTHETIC ORGANIC CHEMICAL MANUFACTURERS ASSOCIATION; *U.S. Private*, pg. 3905

SYNTHETIC PACKAGING LTD—See Thrace Plastics Holding and Commercial S.A.; *Int'l*, pg. 7720
SYNTHETIC PRODUCTS ENTERPRISES LIMITED; *Int'l*, pg. 7386
SYNTHEXIM SAS—See Argos Wityu S.A.; *Int'l*, pg. 563
SYNTHIKO FOILS LIMITED; *Int'l*, pg. 7387
SYNTHOMER BV—See Synthomer plc; *Int'l*, pg. 7387
SYNTHOMER CHEMICALS (PTY) LTD—See Synthomer plc; *Int'l*, pg. 7387
SYNTHOMER FINLAND OY—See Synthomer plc; *Int'l*, pg. 7387
SYNTHOMER GMBH—See Synthomer plc; *Int'l*, pg. 7387
SYNTHOMER PLC; *Int'l*, pg. 7387
SYNTHOMER SA—See Synthomer plc; *Int'l*, pg. 7387
SYNTHOMER SDN BHD—See Synthomer plc; *Int'l*, pg. 7387
SYNTHOMER (UK) LTD.—See Synthomer plc; *Int'l*, pg. 7387
SYNTHOMER VIETNAM CO. LTD.—See Synthomer plc; *Int'l*, pg. 7387
SYNTHORX, INC.—See Sanofi; *Int'l*, pg. 6552
SYNTHOS DWORY 2 SP. Z O.O.—See Synthos S.A.; *Int'l*, pg. 7387
SYNTHOS DWORY SP. Z O.O.—See Synthos S.A.; *Int'l*, pg. 7387
SYNTHOS KRALUPY A.S.—See Synthos S.A.; *Int'l*, pg. 7387
SYNTHOS S.A.; *Int'l*, pg. 7387
SYNTOM METAL RECYCLING SP. Z O.O.—See Elemental Holding S.A.; *Int'l*, pg. 2358
SYNTONIC LIMITED; *Int'l*, pg. 7387
SYNTONICS LLC—See Ironwave Technologies LLC; *U.S. Private*, pg. 2140
SYNTRANS, LLC—See Ascent Industries Co.; *U.S. Public*, pg. 210
SYNTREND CREATIVE PARK CO., LTD.—See Hon Hai Precision Industry Co., Ltd.; *Int'l*, pg. 3459
SYNTRIO, INC.—See Ontario Teachers' Pension Plan; *Int'l*, pg. 5586
SYNTROL CORP.; *U.S. Public*, pg. 1972
SYNTRON MATERIAL HANDLING GROUP, LLC—See Kadant, Inc.; *U.S. Public*, pg. 1212
SYNTRUS ACHMEA PENSIOENBEHEER N.V.—See Achmea B.V.; *Int'l*, pg. 104
SYNTRUS ACHMEA REAL ESTATE & FINANCE B.V.—See Achmea B.V.; *Int'l*, pg. 104
SYNTURN (M) SDN. BHD.—See Spindex Industries Limited; *Int'l*, pg. 7137
SYNUTRA, INC.—See Synutra International, Inc.; *U.S. Private*, pg. 3905
SYNUTRA INTERNATIONAL, INC.; *U.S. Private*, pg. 3905
SYNVASIVE TECHNOLOGY, INC.—See Zimmer Biomet Holdings, Inc.; *U.S. Public*, pg. 2406
SYNVENTIVE MOLDING SOLUTIONS BV—See Barnes Group Inc.; *U.S. Public*, pg. 277
SYNVENTIVE MOLDING SOLUTIONS GMBH—See Barnes Group Inc.; *U.S. Public*, pg. 278
SYNVENTIVE MOLDING SOLUTIONS, INC.—See Barnes Group Inc.; *U.S. Public*, pg. 278
SYNVENTIVE MOLDING SOLUTIONS JBJ PRIVATE LIMITED—See Barnes Group Inc.; *U.S. Public*, pg. 277
SYNVENTIVE MOLDING SOLUTIONS K.K.—See Barnes Group Inc.; *U.S. Public*, pg. 277
SYNVENTIVE MOLDING SOLUTIONS LDA—See Barnes Group Inc.; *U.S. Public*, pg. 277
SYNVENTIVE MOLDING SOLUTIONS LIMITED—See Barnes Group Inc.; *U.S. Public*, pg. 278
SYNVENTIVE MOLDING SOLUTIONS LTDA—See Barnes Group Inc.; *U.S. Public*, pg. 278
SYNVENTIVE MOLDING SOLUTIONS PTE LTD.—See Barnes Group Inc.; *U.S. Public*, pg. 278
SYNVENTIVE MOLDING SOLUTIONS SAS—See Barnes Group Inc.; *U.S. Public*, pg. 278
SYNVENTIVE MOLDING SOLUTIONS SL—See Barnes Group Inc.; *U.S. Public*, pg. 278
SYNVENTIVE MOLDING SOLUTIONS S.R.L.—See Barnes Group Inc.; *U.S. Public*, pg. 278
SYNVENTIVE MOLDING SOLUTIONS S.R.O.—See Barnes Group Inc.; *U.S. Public*, pg. 278
SYNVENTIVE MOLDING SOLUTIONS (SUZHOU) CO., LTD.—See Barnes Group Inc.; *U.S. Public*, pg. 277
SYNVIA ENERGY GMBH—See Vonovia SE; *Int'l*, pg. 8305
SYNVIA MEDIA GMBH—See Deutsche Wohnen SE; *Int'l*, pg. 2085
SYNXIS CORPORATION; *U.S. Private*, pg. 3905
SYNYGY, INC.; *U.S. Private*, pg. 3905
SYNZTEC CO., LTD - KUKI PLANT—See NOK Corporation; *Int'l*, pg. 5403
SYNZTEC CO., LTD - YOKOSUKA PLANT A—See NOK Corporation; *Int'l*, pg. 5403
SYNZTEC CO., LTD - YOKOSUKA PLANT B—See NOK Corporation; *Int'l*, pg. 5403
SYNZTEC (H.K.) CO., LIMITED—See NOK Corporation; *Int'l*, pg. 5403
SYNZTEC (MALAYSIA) SDN. BHD.—See NOK Corporation; *Int'l*, pg. 5403
SYNZTEC PRECISION PARTS (SHANGHAI) CO., LTD.—See NOK Corporation; *Int'l*, pg. 5403

SYNZTEC PRECISION PARTS (SHENZHEN) CO., LTD.—See NOK Corporation; *Int'l*, pg. 5403
SYNZTEC SINGAPORE PTE LTD.—See NOK Corporation; *Int'l*, pg. 5403
SYNZTEC VIETNAM CO., LTD.—See NOK Corporation; *Int'l*, pg. 5403
SYOEI CO., LTD.—See Gakken Holdings Co., Ltd.; *Int'l*, pg. 2869
SYOUNG GROUP CO., LTD.; *Int'l*, pg. 7387
SY PANEL NEPAL PVT. LTD.—See SY Co., Ltd.; *Int'l*, pg. 7377
SYP BUILDING GLASS CO., LTD.—See Shanghai Yaohua Pilkington Glass Group Co., Ltd.; *Int'l*, pg. 6782
SYPHERMEDIA INTERNATIONAL, INC.—See Verimatrix SA; *Int'l*, pg. 8169
SYP KANGQIAO AUTOGLASS CO., LTD.—See Shanghai Yaohua Pilkington Glass Group Co., Ltd.; *Int'l*, pg. 6782
SYPRIS ELECTRONICS, LLC—See Sypris Solutions, Inc.; *U.S. Public*, pg. 1972
SYPRIS SOLUTIONS, INC.; *U.S. Public*, pg. 1972
SYPRIS TECHNOLOGIES, INC.—See Sypris Solutions, Inc.; *U.S. Public*, pg. 1972
SYPRIS TECHNOLOGIES, INC. - TUBE TURNS FACILITY—See Sypris Solutions, Inc.; *U.S. Public*, pg. 1972
SYPRIS TECHNOLOGIES TOLUCA, S.A. DE C.V.—See Sypris Solutions, Inc.; *U.S. Public*, pg. 1972
S.Y. PROMOTION CO., LTD.—See Kewpie Corporation; *Int'l*, pg. 4144
SYQWEST, LLC—See CTS Corporation; *U.S. Public*, pg. 603
SYRACUSE BRICK HOUSE, INC.; *U.S. Private*, pg. 3905
SYRACUSE COMMUNITY HEALTH CENTER, INC.; *U.S. Private*, pg. 3905
SYRACUSE ENERGY CORPORATION—See ENGIE SA; *Int'l*, pg. 2433
SYRACUSE OFFICE EQUIPMENT; *U.S. Private*, pg. 3905
SYRACUSE PLASTICS OF NORTH CAROLINA, INC.—See Nordstjernan AB; *Int'l*, pg. 5426
SYRACUSE'S SAUSAGE COMPANY—See Standard Meat Company; *U.S. Private*, pg. 3781
SYRACUSE SYMPHONY ORCHESTRA; *U.S. Private*, pg. 3905
SYRACUSE TRAILER SALES; *U.S. Private*, pg. 3905
SYRACUSE UNIVERSITY PRESS; *U.S. Private*, pg. 3905
SYRA HEALTH CORP.; *U.S. Public*, pg. 1972
SYRAH GLOBAL DMCC—See Syrah Resources Limited; *Int'l*, pg. 7387
SYRAH RESOURCES LIMITED; *Int'l*, pg. 7387
SYRAINFOTEK LLC; *U.S. Private*, pg. 3905
SYRAL BELGIUM N.V.—See Tereos; *Int'l*, pg. 7564
SYRAL S.A.S.—See Tereos; *Int'l*, pg. 7564
SYREMAT SA—See Softimat SA; *Int'l*, pg. 7055
SYRIA GULF BANK S.A.; *Int'l*, pg. 7387
SYRIA INTERNATIONAL INSURANCE COMPANY—See BLOM Bank, S.A.L.; *Int'l*, pg. 1064
SYRIA INTERNATIONAL ISLAMIC BANK; *Int'l*, pg. 7387
SYRIAN COMBINED GROUP CONTRACTING CO. W.L.L.—See Combined Group Contracting Company KSCC; *Int'l*, pg. 1709
SYRIAN-FINNISH COMPANY FOR DAIRY PRODUCTS—See MAS Economic Group; *Int'l*, pg. 4718
SYRIAN-FINNISH COMPANY FOR DAIRY PRODUCTS—See Valio Ltd.; *Int'l*, pg. 8116
SYRIAN KUWAITI INSURANCE COMPANY—See Fairfax Financial Holdings Limited; *Int'l*, pg. 2607
SYRIAN MEAT PROCESSING COMPANY—See MAS Economic Group; *Int'l*, pg. 4718
SYRIA SHELL PETROLEUM DEVELOPMENT BV—See Shell plc; *Int'l*, pg. 6799
SYRINIX LIMITED—See Badger Meter, Inc.; *U.S. Public*, pg. 264
SYRINX CONSULTING CORPORATION—See New Heritage Capital LLC; *U.S. Private*, pg. 2896
SYRMA SGS TECHNOLOGY LIMITED; *Int'l*, pg. 7387
SYROS PHARMACEUTICALS, INC.; *U.S. Public*, pg. 1972
SYRP, INC.—See Videndum plc; *Int'l*, pg. 8191
SYRP LIMITED—See Videndum plc; *Int'l*, pg. 8191
SY RUBBER (THAILAND) CO., LTD.—See Sankyo Kasei Corporation; *Int'l*, pg. 6543
SYSARMY SDN BHD—See Systech Bhd; *Int'l*, pg. 7390
SYSCHEM (INDIA) LIMITED; *Int'l*, pg. 7388
SYSCO ALBANY, LLC—See Sysco Corporation; *U.S. Public*, pg. 1975
SYSCO ARIZONA, INC.—See Sysco Corporation; *U.S. Public*, pg. 1975
SYSCO ARIZONA LEASING, INC.—See Sysco Corporation; *U.S. Public*, pg. 1975
SYSCO ARKANSAS—See Sysco Corporation; *U.S. Public*, pg. 1975
SYSCO ASIAN FOODS, INC.—See Sysco Corporation; *U.S. Public*, pg. 1975
SYSCO ATLANTA, LLC—See Sysco Corporation; *U.S. Public*, pg. 1975
SYSCO ATLANTIC CANADA—See Sysco Corporation; *U.S. Public*, pg. 1975

SYSCO AUSTIN, INC.—See Sysco Corporation; *U.S. Public*, pg. 1975
SYSCO BALTIMORE, LLC—See Sysco Corporation; *U.S. Public*, pg. 1975
SYSCO BARABOO, LLC—See Sysco Corporation; *U.S. Public*, pg. 1975
SYSCO BOSTON LLC—See Sysco Corporation; *U.S. Public*, pg. 1975
SYSCO CALGARY—See Sysco Corporation; *U.S. Public*, pg. 1975
SYSCO CANADA, INC.—See Sysco Corporation; *U.S. Public*, pg. 1975
SYSCO CENTRAL ALABAMA, INC.—See Sysco Corporation; *U.S. Public*, pg. 1975
SYSCO CENTRAL CALIFORNIA, INC.—See Sysco Corporation; *U.S. Public*, pg. 1975
SYSCO CENTRAL FLORIDA, INC.—See Sysco Corporation; *U.S. Public*, pg. 1975
SYSCO CENTRAL ILLINOIS, INC.—See Sysco Corporation; *U.S. Public*, pg. 1975
SYSCO CENTRAL ONTARIO, INC.—See Sysco Corporation; *U.S. Public*, pg. 1975
SYSCO CENTRAL PENNSYLVANIA, LLC—See Sysco Corporation; *U.S. Public*, pg. 1975
SYSCO CENTRAL TEXAS, INC.—See Sysco Corporation; *U.S. Public*, pg. 1975
SYSCO CHARLOTTE, LLC—See Sysco Corporation; *U.S. Public*, pg. 1975
SYSCO CHICAGO, INC.—See Sysco Corporation; *U.S. Public*, pg. 1975
SYSCO CINCINNATI, LLC—See Sysco Corporation; *U.S. Public*, pg. 1975
SYSCO CLEVELAND, INC.—See Sysco Corporation; *U.S. Public*, pg. 1975
SYSCO COLUMBIA, LLC—See Sysco Corporation; *U.S. Public*, pg. 1975
SYSCO CONNECTICUT, LLC—See Sysco Corporation; *U.S. Public*, pg. 1975
SYSCO CORPORATION; *U.S. Public*, pg. 1972
SYSCO DALLAS, INC.—See Sysco Corporation; *U.S. Public*, pg. 1976
SYSCO DENVER, INC.—See Sysco Corporation; *U.S. Public*, pg. 1976
SYSCO DETROIT, LLC—See Sysco Corporation; *U.S. Public*, pg. 1976
SYSCO EASTERN MARYLAND, LLC—See Sysco Corporation; *U.S. Public*, pg. 1976
SYSCO EASTERN WISCONSIN, LLC—See Sysco Corporation; *U.S. Public*, pg. 1976
SYSCO EAST TEXAS, LLC—See Sysco Corporation; *U.S. Public*, pg. 1976
SYSCO FRANCE SAS—See Sysco Corporation; *U.S. Public*, pg. 1976
SYSCO GRAND RAPIDS, LLC—See Sysco Corporation; *U.S. Public*, pg. 1976
SYSCO GUEST SUPPLY CANADA INC.—See Sysco Corporation; *U.S. Public*, pg. 1976
SYSCO GUEST SUPPLY EUROPE LIMITED—See Sysco Corporation; *U.S. Public*, pg. 1976
SYSCO GUEST SUPPLY, LLC - HAWAII DISTRIBUTION CENTER—See Sysco Corporation; *U.S. Public*, pg. 1976
SYSCO GUEST SUPPLY, LLC—See Sysco Corporation; *U.S. Public*, pg. 1976
SYSCO GULF COAST, INC.—See Sysco Corporation; *U.S. Public*, pg. 1976
SYSCO HAMPTON ROADS, INC.—See Sysco Corporation; *U.S. Public*, pg. 1976
SYSCO HAWAII, INC.—See Sysco Corporation; *U.S. Public*, pg. 1976
SYSCO HOUSTON, INC.—See Sysco Corporation; *U.S. Public*, pg. 1976
SYSCO IDAHO, INC.—See Sysco Corporation; *U.S. Public*, pg. 1976
SYSCO INDIANAPOLIS, LLC—See Sysco Corporation; *U.S. Public*, pg. 1976
SYSCO INDUSTRIES LIMITED; *Int'l*, pg. 7388
SYSCO INTERMOUNTAIN, INC.—See Sysco Corporation; *U.S. Public*, pg. 1976
SYSCO INTERNATIONAL FOOD GROUP, INC.—See Sysco Corporation; *U.S. Public*, pg. 1976
SYSCO IOWA, INC.—See Sysco Corporation; *U.S. Public*, pg. 1976
SYSCO JACKSON, LLC—See Sysco Corporation; *U.S. Public*, pg. 1976
SYSCO JACKSONVILLE, INC.—See Sysco Corporation; *U.S. Public*, pg. 1976
SYSCO KANSAS CITY, INC.—See Sysco Corporation; *U.S. Public*, pg. 1976
SYSCO KELOWNA, LTD.—See Sysco Corporation; *U.S. Public*, pg. 1976
SYSCO KNOXVILLE, LLC—See Sysco Corporation; *U.S. Public*, pg. 1976
SYSCO LABS PVT. LTD.—See Sysco Corporation; *U.S. Public*, pg. 1976
SYSCO LABS TECHNOLOGIES (PRIVATE) LIMITED—See Sysco Corporation; *U.S. Public*, pg. 1976
SYSCO LAS VEGAS, INC.—See Sysco Corporation; *U.S. Public*, pg. 1976
SYSCO LINCOLN, INC.—See Sysco Corporation; *U.S. Public*, pg. 1976
SYSCO LINCOLN TRANSPORTATION COMPANY, INC.—See Sysco Corporation; *U.S. Public*, pg. 1976
SYSCO LOS ANGELES, INC.—See Sysco Corporation; *U.S. Public*, pg. 1976
SYSCO LOUISVILLE, INC.—See Sysco Corporation; *U.S. Public*, pg. 1976
SYSCOM AS—See DXC Technology Company; *U.S. Public*, pg. 697
SYSCOM COMPUTER ENGINEERING COMPANY; *Int'l*, pg. 7388
SYSCOM COMPUTER(THAILAND) CO., LTD.—See SYSCOM Computer Engineering Company; *Int'l*, pg. 7388
SYSCOM EMIRATES LLC—See Dubai Investments PJSC; *Int'l*, pg. 2219
SYSCO MEMPHIS, LLC—See Sysco Corporation; *U.S. Public*, pg. 1976
SYSCO METRO NEW YORK, LLC—See Sysco Corporation; *U.S. Public*, pg. 1976
SYSCOM INC.; *U.S. Private*, pg. 3906
SYSCO MINNESOTA, INC.—See Sysco Corporation; *U.S. Public*, pg. 1976
SYSCO MONTANA, INC.—See Sysco Corporation; *U.S. Public*, pg. 1976
SYSCOMP BIOCHEMISCHE DIENSTLEISTUNGEN GMBH—See Sonic Healthcare Limited; *Int'l*, pg. 7099
SYSCOM TECHNOLOGIES; *U.S. Private*, pg. 3906
SYSCOM (USA) INC.; *U.S. Private*, pg. 3905
SYSCO NASHVILLE, LLC—See Sysco Corporation; *U.S. Public*, pg. 1976
SYSCO NEW MEXICO, LLC—See Sysco Corporation; *U.S. Public*, pg. 1976
SYSCO NEW ORLEANS, LLC—See Sysco Corporation; *U.S. Public*, pg. 1977
SYSCO NEWPORT MEAT COMPANY—See Sysco Corporation; *U.S. Public*, pg. 1977
SYSCON JUSTICE SYSTEMS, INC.—See Constellation Software Inc.; *Int'l*, pg. 1774
SYS-CON MEDIA, INC.; *U.S. Private*, pg. 3905
SYSCO NORTH DAKOTA, INC.—See Sysco Corporation; *U.S. Public*, pg. 1977
SYSCO NORTHERN NEW ENGLAND, INC.—See Sysco Corporation; *U.S. Public*, pg. 1977
SYSCO OKLAHOMA—See Sysco Corporation; *U.S. Public*, pg. 1977
SYSCO PHILADELPHIA, LLC—See Sysco Corporation; *U.S. Public*, pg. 1977
SYSCO PITTSBURGH, LLC—See Sysco Corporation; *U.S. Public*, pg. 1977
SYSCO PORTLAND, INC.—See Sysco Corporation; *U.S. Public*, pg. 1977
SYSCO PRODUCE MARKETING & MERCHANDISING SERVICES—See Sysco Corporation; *U.S. Public*, pg. 1977
SYSCO QUEBEC—See Sysco Corporation; *U.S. Public*, pg. 1975
SYSCO RALEIGH, LLC—See Sysco Corporation; *U.S. Public*, pg. 1977
SYSCOR CONTROLS & AUTOMATION INC.—See Enbridge Inc.; *Int'l*, pg. 2397
SYSCO SACRAMENTO, INC.—See Sysco Corporation; *U.S. Public*, pg. 1977
SYSCO SAN DIEGO, INC.—See Sysco Corporation; *U.S. Public*, pg. 1977
SYSCO SAN FRANCISCO, INC.—See Sysco Corporation; *U.S. Public*, pg. 1977
SYSCO SEATTLE, INC.—See Sysco Corporation; *U.S. Public*, pg. 1977
SYSCO SOUTHEAST FLORIDA, LLC—See Sysco Corporation; *U.S. Public*, pg. 1977
SYSCO SOUTH FLORIDA, INC.—See Sysco Corporation; *U.S. Public*, pg. 1977
SYSCO SPOKANE, INC.—See Sysco Corporation; *U.S. Public*, pg. 1977
SYSCO ST. LOUIS, LLC—See Sysco Corporation; *U.S. Public*, pg. 1977
SYSCO SYRACUSE, LLC—See Sysco Corporation; *U.S. Public*, pg. 1977
SYSCO TORONTO—See Sysco Corporation; *U.S. Public*, pg. 1975
SYSCO VANCOUVER—See Sysco Corporation; *U.S. Public*, pg. 1975
SYSCO VENTURA, INC.—See Sysco Corporation; *U.S. Public*, pg. 1977
SYSCO VICTORIA, INC.—See Sysco Corporation; *U.S. Public*, pg. 1977
SYSCO VIRGINIA, LLC—See Sysco Corporation; *U.S. Public*, pg. 1977
SYSCO WEST COAST FLORIDA, INC.—See Sysco Corporation; *U.S. Public*, pg. 1977
SYSCO WESTERN MINNESOTA, INC.—See Sysco Corporation; *U.S. Public*, pg. 1977
SYSCO WESTERN MINNESOTA—See Sysco Corporation; *U.S. Public*, pg. 1977
SYSENG (S) PTE LTD—See Tritech Group Limited; *Int'l*, pg. 7928
SYS - ENTERPRISE SOLUTIONS DIVISION—See Kratos Defense & Security Solutions, Inc.; *U.S. Public*, pg. 1277
SYSGRATION LTD.; *Int'l*, pg. 7388
SYSGROUP PLC; *Int'l*, pg. 7388
SYS HOLDINGS CO., LTD.; *Int'l*, pg. 7387
SYS INC.—See H.I.S. Co., Ltd.; *Int'l*, pg. 3196
SYSINT AS—See MilDef Group AB; *Int'l*, pg. 4894
SYS - INTEGRATED & INFORMATION SOLUTIONS GROUP—See Kratos Defense & Security Solutions, Inc.; *U.S. Public*, pg. 1277
SYSKA HENNESSY GROUP INC.; *U.S. Private*, pg. 3906
SYSKEN CORPORATION—See COMSYS Holdings Corporation; *Int'l*, pg. 1762
SYSKONNECT INC.—See Marvell Technology Group Ltd.; *Int'l*, pg. 4717
SYSKOPLAN REPLY LLC—See Reply S.p.A.; *Int'l*, pg. 6291
SYSKOPLAN REPLY S.R.L.—See Reply S.p.A.; *Int'l*, pg. 6291
SYSKRON GMBH—See Krones AG; *Int'l*, pg. 4306
SYSKRON X GMBH—See Krones AG; *Int'l*, pg. 4306
SYS-MAC AUTOMATION ENGINEERING PTE. LTD.—See Zicom Group Limited; *Int'l*, pg. 8681
SYSMA HOLDINGS LIMITED; *Int'l*, pg. 7388
SYSMEX AMERICA, INC.—See Sysmex Corporation; *Int'l*, pg. 7388
SYSMEX ASIA PACIFIC PTE. LTD.—See Sysmex Corporation; *Int'l*, pg. 7388
SYSMEX AUSTRALIA PTY LTD.—See Sysmex Corporation; *Int'l*, pg. 7389
SYSMEX AUSTRIA GMBH—See Sysmex Corporation; *Int'l*, pg. 7389
SYSMEX BELGIUM N.V.—See Sysmex Corporation; *Int'l*, pg. 7389
SYSMEX CANADA, INC.—See Sysmex Corporation; *Int'l*, pg. 7389
SYSMEX CHILE SPA—See Sysmex Corporation; *Int'l*, pg. 7389
SYSMEX CNA CO., LTD.—See Sysmex Corporation; *Int'l*, pg. 7389
SYSMEX COLOMBIA SAS—See Sysmex Corporation; *Int'l*, pg. 7389
SYSMEX CORPORATION - KAKOGAWA FACTORY—See Sysmex Corporation; *Int'l*, pg. 7389
SYSMEX CORPORATION; *Int'l*, pg. 7388
SYSMEX CZ S.R.O.—See Sysmex Corporation; *Int'l*, pg. 7389
SYSMEX DEUTSCHLAND GMBH—See Sysmex Corporation; *Int'l*, pg. 7389
SYSMEX DIAGNOSTICOS MEXICO, S. DE R.L. DE C.V.—See Sysmex Corporation; *Int'l*, pg. 7389
SYSMEX DIGITANA AG—See Sysmex Corporation; *Int'l*, pg. 7389
SYSMEX DO BRASIL INDUSTRIA E COMERCIO LTDA.—See Sysmex Corporation; *Int'l*, pg. 7390
SYSMEX ESPANA S.L.—See Sysmex Corporation; *Int'l*, pg. 7389
SYSMEX EUROPE GMBH—See Sysmex Corporation; *Int'l*, pg. 7389
SYSMEX FRANCE S.A.R.L.—See Sysmex Corporation; *Int'l*, pg. 7389
SYSMEX HONG KONG LIMITED—See Sysmex Corporation; *Int'l*, pg. 7389
SYSMEX HUNGARIA KFT.—See Sysmex Corporation; *Int'l*, pg. 7389
SYSMEX INDIA PVT. LTD.—See Sysmex Corporation; *Int'l*, pg. 7388
SYSMEX INOSTICS GMBH—See Sysmex Corporation; *Int'l*, pg. 7389
SYSMEX INOSTICS, INC.—See Sysmex Corporation; *Int'l*, pg. 7389
SYSMEX INTERNATIONAL REAGENTS CO., LTD. - ONO FACTORY—See Sysmex Corporation; *Int'l*, pg. 7389
SYSMEX INTERNATIONAL REAGENTS CO., LTD—See Sysmex Corporation; *Int'l*, pg. 7389
SYSMEX LOGISTICS CO., LTD.—See Sysmex Corporation; *Int'l*, pg. 7389
SYSMEX LOGISTICS UK LTD.—See Sysmex Corporation; *Int'l*, pg. 7389
SYSMEX (MALAYSIA) SDN BHD—See Sysmex Corporation; *Int'l*, pg. 7388
SYSMEX MEDICA CO., LTD.—See Sysmex Corporation; *Int'l*, pg. 7389
SYSMEX MIDDLE EAST FZ-LLC—See Sysmex Corporation; *Int'l*, pg. 7389
SYSMEX NEDERLAND B.V.—See Sysmex Corporation; *Int'l*, pg. 7389
SYSMEX NEW ZEALAND LIMITED—See Sysmex Corporation; *Int'l*, pg. 7389
SYSMEX NORDIC APS—See Sysmex Corporation; *Int'l*, pg. 7389
SYSMEX NORDIC APS—See Sysmex Corporation; *Int'l*, pg. 7389
SYSMEX NORGE AS—See Sysmex Corporation; *Int'l*, pg. 7389
SYSMEX PARTEC BURKINA FASO SARL—See Sysmex Corporation; *Int'l*, pg. 7389

COMPANY NAME INDEX

SYSMEX PARTEC GMBH—See Sysmex Corporation; *Int'l*, pg. 7389
SYSMEX PARTEC ITALIA S.R.L—See Sysmex Corporation; *Int'l*, pg. 7389
SYSMEX PHILIPPINES INC.—See Sysmex Corporation; *Int'l*, pg. 7389
SYSMEX POLSKA S.P.Z O.O—See Sysmex Corporation; *Int'l*, pg. 7389
SYSMEX RA CO., LTD—See Sysmex Corporation; *Int'l*, pg. 7389
SYSMEX R&D CENTER EUROPE GMBH—See Sysmex Corporation; *Int'l*, pg. 7389
SYSMEX REAGENTS AMERICA, INC.—See Sysmex Corporation; *Int'l*, pg. 7389
SYSMEX RUS LLC—See Sysmex Corporation; *Int'l*, pg. 7389
SYSMEX SAN TUNG CO., LTD.—See Sysmex Corporation; *Int'l*, pg. 7389
SYSMEX SHANGHAI LTD.—See Sysmex Corporation; *Int'l*, pg. 7389
SYSMEX SLOVAKIA S.R.O.—See Sysmex Corporation; *Int'l*, pg. 7389
SYSMEX SOUTH AFRICA (PTY) LTD.—See Sysmex Corporation; *Int'l*, pg. 7389
SYSMEX TAIWAN CO., LTD.—See Sysmex Corporation; *Int'l*, pg. 7390
SYSMEX (THAILAND) CO., LTD.—See Sysmex Corporation; *Int'l*, pg. 7388
SYSMEX TMC CO., LTD.—See Sysmex Corporation; *Int'l*, pg. 7390
SYSMEX TRANSASIA SERVICES PVT. LTD.—See Sysmex Corporation; *Int'l*, pg. 7390
SYSMEX TURKEY DIAGNOSTIK SISTEMLERI LTD. STI.—See Sysmex Corporation; *Int'l*, pg. 7390
SYSMEX UK LIMITED—See Sysmex Corporation; *Int'l*, pg. 7390
SYSMEX VIETNAM COMPANY LIMITED—See Sysmex Corporation; *Int'l*, pg. 7390
SYSMEX WEST & CENTRAL AFRICA LTD.—See Sysmex Corporation; *Int'l*, pg. 7390
SYSMEX WUXI CO., LTD.—See Sysmex Corporation; *Int'l*, pg. 7390
SYSMIND LLC; *U.S. Private*, pg. 3906
SYSNET TECHNOLOGY SOLUTIONS, INC.—See ASTIR IT Solutions, Inc.; *U.S. Private*, pg. 360
SYSOCO SAS—See VINCI S.A.; *Int'l*, pg. 8229
SYSOMOS INC.—See Meltwater News US Inc.; *U.S. Private*, pg. 2663
SYSOP TOOLS, INC.; *U.S. Private*, pg. 3906
SYSOREX, INC.; *U.S. Public*, pg. 1977
SYSPRO IMPACT SOFTWARE INC.; *U.S. Private*, pg. 3906
SYS - SYSTEMS ENGINEERING & MANAGEMENT DIVISION—See Kratos Defense & Security Solutions, Inc.; *U.S. Public*, pg. 1277
SYSTAG, SYSTEM TECHNIK AG—See Dottikon ES Holding AG; *Int'l*, pg. 2180
SYSTAIN CONSULTING GMBH—See Otto GmbH & Co. KG; *Int'l*, pg. 5663
SYSTAR SA—See Axway Software SA; *Int'l*, pg. 772
SYSTAT SOFTWARE GMBH—See Cranes Software International Limited; *Int'l*, pg. 1828
SYSTEA S.P.A.—See Focused Photonics (Hangzhou), Inc.; *Int'l*, pg. 2720
SYSTECH BHD; *Int'l*, pg. 7390
SYSTECH CHILE LTDA.—See Searchlight Capital Partners, L.P.; *U.S. Private*, pg. 3590
SYSTECH CORPORATION; *U.S. Private*, pg. 3906
SYSTECH ENVIRONMENTAL CORPORATION—See Holcim Ltd.; *Int'l*, pg. 3449
SYS-TECH, INC.—See Jack Henry & Associates, Inc.; *U.S. Public*, pg. 1183
SYS TECHNOLOGIES, INC.—See Kratos Defense & Security Solutions, Inc.; *U.S. Public*, pg. 1277
SYSTECH PERUANA SRL—See Searchlight Capital Partners, L.P.; *U.S. Private*, pg. 3590
SYSTECH SOLUTIONS, INC.—See Dover Corporation; *U.S. Public*, pg. 682
SYSTECON LLC—See ENGIE SA; *Int'l*, pg. 2429
SYSTEC SISTEM TEKNOLOJILERI A.S.—See BOWE SYSTEC AG; *Int'l*, pg. 1123
SYSTEK INFORMATION (SHANGHAI) LTD.—See SYSTEX Corporation; *Int'l*, pg. 7393
SYSTEL BUSINESS EQUIPMENT CO. INC.; *U.S. Private*, pg. 3906
SYSTELCOM SAS—See VINCI S.A.; *Int'l*, pg. 8229
SYSTEL SA—See Cicor Technologies Ltd.; *Int'l*, pg. 1603
SYSTEM1 GROUP PLC; *Int'l*, pg. 7390
SYSTEM1, INC.; *U.S. Public*, pg. 1977
SYSTEM1 RESEARCH B.V.—See System1 Group PLC; *Int'l*, pg. 7390
SYSTEM1 RESEARCH FRANCE SARL—See System1 Group PLC; *Int'l*, pg. 7390
SYSTEM1 RESEARCH GMBH—See System1 Group PLC; *Int'l*, pg. 7390
SYSTEM1 RESEARCH SARL—See System1 Group PLC; *Int'l*, pg. 7390
SYSTEM 3 INC.—See Renewable Energy Systems Ltd; *Int'l*, pg. 6278

SYSTEM 3R AG—See Georg Fischer AG; *Int'l*, pg. 2935
SYSTEM 3R CZECH S.R.O.—See Georg Fischer AG; *Int'l*, pg. 2935
SYSTEM 3R EUROPE GMBH—See Georg Fischer AG; *Int'l*, pg. 2937
SYSTEM 3R FAR EAST PTE LTD.—See Georg Fischer AG; *Int'l*, pg. 2935
SYSTEM 3R FRANCE S.A.S.—See Georg Fischer AG; *Int'l*, pg. 2935
SYSTEM 3R INTERNATIONAL AB—See Georg Fischer AG; *Int'l*, pg. 2935
SYSTEM 3R ITALIA SRL—See Georg Fischer AG; *Int'l*, pg. 2935
SYSTEM 3R JAPAN CO., LTD.—See Georg Fischer AG; *Int'l*, pg. 2935
SYSTEM 3R SHANGHAI CO LTD—See Georg Fischer AG; *Int'l*, pg. 2935
SYSTEM 3R (UK) LTD.—See Georg Fischer AG; *Int'l*, pg. 2935
SYSTEM 3R USA INC.—See Georg Fischer AG; *Int'l*, pg. 2935
SYSTEMA AS—See WiseTech Global Limited; *Int'l*, pg. 8437
SYSTEMA HIS HUMAN INFORMATION SYSTEMS GESELLSCHAFT MBH—See CompuGroup Medical SE & Co. KGaA; *Int'l*, pg. 1755
SYSTEMAIR AB; *Int'l*, pg. 7390
SYSTEMAIR AC SAS—See Systemair AB; *Int'l*, pg. 7391
SYSTEMAIR A/S—See Systemair AB; *Int'l*, pg. 7391
SYSTEMAIR AS—See Systemair AB; *Int'l*, pg. 7391
SYSTEMAIR AS—See Systemair AB; *Int'l*, pg. 7391
SYSTEMAIR B.V.—See Systemair AB; *Int'l*, pg. 7391
SYSTEMAIR CO LTD—See Systemair AB; *Int'l*, pg. 7391
SYSTEMAIR D.O.O.—See Systemair AB; *Int'l*, pg. 7392
SYSTEMAIR D.O.O.—See Systemair AB; *Int'l*, pg. 7392
SYSTEMAIR D.O.O.—See Systemair AB; *Int'l*, pg. 7392
SYSTEMAIR EOOD—See Systemair AB; *Int'l*, pg. 7391
SYSTEMAIR FANS & SPARES LTD—See Systemair AB; *Int'l*, pg. 7391
SYSTEMAIR GMBH—See Systemair AB; *Int'l*, pg. 7391
SYSTEMAIR GMBH—See Systemair AB; *Int'l*, pg. 7391
SYSTEMAIR HAV. EKIP. SAN.VE TIC. LTD STI.—See Systemair AB; *Int'l*, pg. 7391
SYSTEMAIR HELLAS S.A.—See Systemair AB; *Int'l*, pg. 7391
SYSTEMAIR HONG KONG LTD.—See Systemair AB; *Int'l*, pg. 7391
SYSTEMAIR HSK HAV. EKIP. SAN. VE TIC. LTD.—See Systemair AB; *Int'l*, pg. 7391
SYSTEMAIR HSK—See Systemair AB; *Int'l*, pg. 7391
SYSTEMAIR HVAC S.L.U.—See Systemair AB; *Int'l*, pg. 7391
SYSTEMAIR INDIA PVT. LTD.—See Systemair AB; *Int'l*, pg. 7391
SYSTEMAIR IOOO—See Systemair AB; *Int'l*, pg. 7391
SYSTEMAIR ITALY S.R.L.—See Systemair AB; *Int'l*, pg. 7391
SYSTEMAIR LTD—See Systemair AB; *Int'l*, pg. 7391
SYSTEMAIR LTD—See Systemair AB; *Int'l*, pg. 7392
SYSTEMAIR MAROC SARL—See Systemair AB; *Int'l*, pg. 7392
SYSTEMAIR MFG INC.—See Systemair AB; *Int'l*, pg. 7392
SYSTEMAIR MIDDLE EAST LLC—See Systemair AB; *Int'l*, pg. 7392
SYSTEMAIR NV—See Systemair AB; *Int'l*, pg. 7392
SYSTEMAIR OOO—See Systemair AB; *Int'l*, pg. 7392
SYSTEMAIR OY—See Systemair AB; *Int'l*, pg. 7392
SYSTEMAIR PERU SAC—See Systemair AB; *Int'l*, pg. 7392
SYSTEMAIR (PTY) LTD—See Systemair AB; *Int'l*, pg. 7391
SYSTEMAIR RT—See Systemair AB; *Int'l*, pg. 7392
SYSTEMAIR SA—See Systemair AB; *Int'l*, pg. 7392
SYSTEMAIR SA—See Systemair AB; *Int'l*, pg. 7392
SYSTEMAIR SA—See Systemair AB; *Int'l*, pg. 7392
SYSTEMAIR SAS—See Systemair AB; *Int'l*, pg. 7392
SYSTEMAIR SDN BHD—See Systemair AB; *Int'l*, pg. 7392
SYSTEMAIR (SEA) PTE LTD—See Systemair AB; *Int'l*, pg. 7391
SYSTEMAIR SIA—See Systemair AB; *Int'l*, pg. 7392
SYSTEMAIR SPA—See Systemair AB; *Int'l*, pg. 7392
SYSTEMAIR S.P.A.—See Systemair AB; *Int'l*, pg. 7392
SYSTEMAIR SUISSE AG—See Systemair AB; *Int'l*, pg. 7392
SYSTEMAIR SVERIGE AB—See Systemair AB; *Int'l*, pg. 7392
SYSTEMAIR TOO—See Systemair AB; *Int'l*, pg. 7392
SYSTEMAIR TOV—See Systemair AB; *Int'l*, pg. 7392
SYSTEMAIR TRADING LLC—See Systemair AB; *Int'l*, pg. 7392
SYSTEMAIR UAB—See Systemair AB; *Int'l*, pg. 7392
SYSTEM AND APPLICATION TECHNOLOGIES INC.; *Int'l*, pg. 7390
SYSTEMA S.R.L.—See Cellularline SpA; *Int'l*, pg. 1395
SYSTEMAT BELGIUM NV—See Softimat SA; *Int'l*, pg. 7055
SYSTEMAT BELGIUM SA - CHARLEROI—See Softimat SA; *Int'l*, pg. 7055

SYSTEMATECH TECHNICAL MANAGEMENT SERVICES, INC.—See Kinderhook Industries, LLC; *U.S. Private*, pg. 2306
SYSTEMATICA DISTRIBUTION SRL—See SoftwareONE Holding AG; *Int'l*, pg. 7058
SYSTEMATICA INVESTMENTS LIMITED—See Affiliated Managers Group, Inc.; *U.S. Public*, pg. 56
SYSTEMATICA INVESTMENTS US LLC—See Affiliated Managers Group, Inc.; *U.S. Public*, pg. 56
SYSTEMATIC FINANCIAL MANAGEMENT, L.P.—See Affiliated Managers Group, Inc.; *U.S. Public*, pg. 56
SYSTEMATIC FLUID POWER LTD.—See Proax Technologies Ltd.; *Int'l*, pg. 5986
SYSTEMATIC POWER MANUFACTURING, LLC—See Systematic Power Solutions, LLC; *U.S. Private*, pg. 3907
SYSTEMATIC POWER SOLUTIONS, LLC; *U.S. Private*, pg. 3907
SYSTEMATIX CORPORATE SERVICES LTD.; *Int'l*, pg. 7392
SYSTEMATIX SECURITIES LTD.; *Int'l*, pg. 7392
SYSTEMAT LUXEMBOURG S.A.—See Softimat SA; *Int'l*, pg. 7055
SYSTEMAX BUSINESS SERVICES K.F.T.—See Global Industrial Company; *U.S. Public*, pg. 942
SYSTEMAX MANUFACTURING CO.—See Global Industrial Company; *U.S. Public*, pg. 942
SYSTEMAX PTY LTD—See Carrier Global Corporation; *U.S. Public*, pg. 444
SYSTEM BEE D.O.O.—See DHH SpA; *Int'l*, pg. 2099
SYSTEMCARE PRODUCTS LIMITED—See Illinois Tool Works Inc.; *U.S. Public*, pg. 1111
SYSTEM C HEALTHCARE LTD.—See Symphony Technology Group, LLC; *U.S. Private*, pg. 3902
SYSTEMCORP ENERGY PTY LTD—See PESTECH International Berhad; *Int'l*, pg. 5823
SYSTEM CREATIVE CO., LTD—See Core Corporation; *Int'l*, pg. 1797
SYSTEM DESIGN ADVANTAGE LLC; *U.S. Private*, pg. 3906
SYSTEM DESIGN DEVELOPMENT CO., LTD.—See Broadmedia Corporation; *Int'l*, pg. 1172
SYSTEM DESIGN GMBH—See Mercedes-Benz Group AG; *Int'l*, pg. 4829
SYSTEM DEVELOPMENT.INTEGRATION LLC; *U.S. Private*, pg. 3906
SYSTEMD INC.; *Int'l*, pg. 7392
SYSTEM DYNAMICS INTERNATIONAL INC.; *U.S. Private*, pg. 3906
SYSTEM DYNAMIX CORPORATION—See GSS Infotech Limited; *Int'l*, pg. 3150
SYSTEM ELECTRIC CO.; *U.S. Private*, pg. 3906
SYSTEM ENERGY RESOURCES, INC.—See Entergy Corporation; *U.S. Public*, pg. 777
SYSTEM ENGINEERING CO., LTD.—See Densan System Co., Ltd.; *Int'l*, pg. 2028
SYSTEM ENHANCEMENT RESOURCES & TECHNOLOGIES SDN. BHD.—See Destini Berhad; *Int'l*, pg. 2046
SYSTEMES EQUIPEMENTS TABLEAUX BASSE TENSION SAS—See Schneider Electric SE; *Int'l*, pg. 6635
SYSTEMEXE VIET NAM CO., LTD.; *Int'l*, pg. 7392
SYSTEMFARMA B.V.—See Advent International Corporation; *U.S. Private*, pg. 104
SYSTEM FREIGHT INC.; *U.S. Private*, pg. 3906
SYSTEM FRUGT A/S—See Midsona AB; *Int'l*, pg. 4887
SYSTEM GENERAL CORPORATION—See ON Semiconductor Corporation; *U.S. Public*, pg. 1601
SYSTEM HOUSE R & C CO., LTD.—See Nissei Build Kogyo Co., Ltd.; *Int'l*, pg. 5370
SYSTEMHOUSE SOLUTIONS AB—See Bravida Holding AB; *Int'l*, pg. 1142
SYSTEM IC CO., LTD.—See Densan System Co., Ltd.; *Int'l*, pg. 2028
SYSTEM INFORMATION CO., LTD.; *Int'l*, pg. 7390
SYSTEM IN FRONTIER INC.—See JEOL Ltd.; *Int'l*, pg. 3930
SYSTEM INTEGRATOR CORP.; *Int'l*, pg. 7390
SYSTEM INTEGRATORS, L.L.C.; *U.S. Private*, pg. 3906
SYSTEM IO CO., LTD.—See MIT Holdings Co., Ltd.; *Int'l*, pg. 4923
SYSTEM K CORPORATION—See SAXA Holdings Inc.; *Int'l*, pg. 6603
SYSTEM KEISOKU CO., LTD.—See NIHON DENKEI CO., LTD.; *Int'l*, pg. 5284
SYSTEM KIKOU CO., LTD.—See Daiseki Co. Ltd.; *Int'l*, pg. 1941
SYSTEM LAND, INC.—See KYOCERA Corporation; *Int'l*, pg. 4360
SYSTEM LOCATION CO., LTD.; *Int'l*, pg. 7390
SYSTEMLOG DE MEXICO S.A. DE C.V.—See Krones AG; *Int'l*, pg. 4306
SYSTEM LOGISTICS ASIA CO. LTD.—See Krones AG; *Int'l*, pg. 4306
SYSTEM LOGISTICS CORPORATION—See Krones AG; *Int'l*, pg. 4306
SYSTEM LOGISTICS GMBH—See Krones AG; *Int'l*, pg. 4306
SYSTEM LOGISTICS S.P.A.—See Krones AG; *Int'l*, pg. 4306

SYSTEM LOCATION CO., LTD.

SYSTEM MANAGEMENT GROUP—See Cruise America, Inc.; *U.S. Private*, pg. 1114
SYSTEMMETRICS CORPORATION—See Macquarie Group Limited; *Int'l*, pg. 4628
SYSTEM NORTHERN EUROPE AB—See Krones AG; *Int'l*, pg. 4306
SYSTEM ONE CONTROL—See Peoples Electric Contractor, Inc.; *U.S. Private*, pg. 3142
SYSTEM ONE HOLDINGS, LLC; *U.S. Private*, pg. 3906
SYSTEMONE TECHNOLOGIES INC.; *U.S. Private*, pg. 3907
SYSTEM PAVERS INC.; *U.S. Public*, pg. 3907
SYSTEM PLANNING CORPORATION; *U.S. Private*, pg. 3907
SYSTEM PLAST GMBH—See Emerson Electric Co.; *U.S. Public*, pg. 752
SYSTEM PLAST, LLC—See Emerson Electric Co.; *U.S. Public*, pg. 752
SYSTEM PLAST S.R.L.—See Emerson Electric Co.; *U.S. Public*, pg. 752
SYSTEMPLUS LOGISTICS SERVICES NV—See Mainfreight Ltd.; *Int'l*, pg. 4651
SYSTEM PROPERTY DEVELOPMENT COMPANY, INC.; *U.S. Private*, pg. 3907
SYSTEM REPAIR CENTER GMBH—See Philion SE; *Int'l*, pg. 5845
SYSTEM RESEARCH CO., LTD.; *Int'l*, pg. 7390
SYSTEMS 3, INC.—See Gallant Capital Partners, LLC; *U.S. Public*, pg. 1639
SYSTEMS ALLIANCE, INC.; *U.S. Private*, pg. 3907
SYSTEMS ALTERNATIVES INTERNATIONAL LLC—See Brady plc; *Int'l*, pg. 1135
SYSTEMS AND METHODS INC.; *U.S. Private*, pg. 3907
SYSTEMS APPLICATIONS PRODUCTS AFRICA (PTY.) LTD.—See SAP SE; *Int'l*, pg. 6570
SYSTEMS APPLICATIONS PRODUCTS AFRICA REGION (PTY.) LTD.—See SAP SE; *Int'l*, pg. 6570
SYSTEMS APPLICATIONS PRODUCTS NIGERIA LIMITED—See SAP SE; *Int'l*, pg. 6570
SYSTEMS APPLICATIONS PRODUCTS SOUTH AFRICA (PROPRIETARY) LIMITED—See SAP SE; *Int'l*, pg. 6570
SYSTEMS BUILDING CONTRACTING LTD.—See Ireland Blyth Limited; *Int'l*, pg. 3807
SYSTEM SCALE CORPORATION; *U.S. Private*, pg. 3907
SYSTEMS CONNECTION OF MARYLAND; *U.S. Private*, pg. 3907
SYSTEMS CONSULTANTS SERVICES LIMITED—See Cohort plc; *Int'l*, pg. 1696
SYSTEMS CONTRACTING CORP; *U.S. Private*, pg. 3907
SYSTEMS DEPOT; *U.S. Private*, pg. 3907
SYSTEMS DESIGN CO., LTD.; *Int'l*, pg. 7392
SYSTEMS DESIGN ENGINEERING, INC. (SDE); *U.S. Private*, pg. 3907
SYSTEMS DESIGN GROUP LLC—See Pye-Barker Fire & Safety, LLC; *U.S. Private*, pg. 3309
SYSTEMS ELECTRONICS, INC.—See Wind Point Advisors LLC; *U.S. Private*, pg. 4535
SYSTEMS ENGINEERING & ASSESSMENT LTD.—See Cohort plc; *Int'l*, pg. 1696
SYSTEMS ENGINEERING CONSULTANTS CO., LTD.; *Int'l*, pg. 7392
SYSTEMS ENGINEERING GROUP, INC.—See Griffon Corporation; *U.S. Public*, pg. 969
SYSTEMS ENGINEERING & MANAGEMENT, CO.—See The O'Neil Group Company, LLC; *U.S. Private*, pg. 4087
SYSTEMS ENGINEERING SERVICES; *U.S. Private*, pg. 3907
SYSTEM SENSOR CANADA—See Honeywell International Inc.; *U.S. Public*, pg. 1049
SYSTEM SENSOR EUROPE—See Honeywell International Inc.; *U.S. Public*, pg. 1049
SYSTEM SENSOR—See Honeywell International Inc.; *U.S. Public*, pg. 1049
SYSTEMS FINANCE GROUP INC.; *U.S. Private*, pg. 3907
SYSTEMS FORMULATIONS AND INTEGRATIONS INCORPORATED—See FUJISOFT INCORPORATED; *Int'l*, pg. 2830
SYSTEMS HARDWARE INC.; *U.S. Private*, pg. 3907
SYSTEMS INTEGRATION AND DEVELOPMENT, INC.; *U.S. Private*, pg. 3907
SYSTEMS INTEGRATION, INC.—See Rimhub, Inc.; *U.S. Private*, pg. 3437
SYSTEMS INTEGRATION SOLUTIONS INC.; *U.S. Private*, pg. 3907
SYSTEMS LIMITED; *Int'l*, pg. 7392
SYSTEMSLINK 2000 LIMITED—See Inspired PLC; *Int'l*, pg. 3720
SYSTEMS MACHINE AUTOMATION COMPONENTS; *U.S. Private*, pg. 3907
SYSTEMS MADE SIMPLE, INC.—See Lockheed Martin Corporation; *U.S. Public*, pg. 1339
SYSTEMS MANAGEMENT PLANNING, INC. (SMP); *U.S. Private*, pg. 3908
SYSTEMS MISSILES & SPACE LTD.—See Israel Aerospace Industries Ltd.; *Int'l*, pg. 3822
SYSTEMSOFT CORPORATION; *Int'l*, pg. 7392

SYSTEM SOFT S.A.—See Marfin Investment Group Holdings S.A.; *Int'l*, pg. 4692
SYSTEM SOLUTIONS CO., LTD.—See ON Semiconductor Corporation; *U.S. Public*, pg. 1601
SYSTEMS PLANNING AND ANALYSIS, INC.—See Arlington Capital Partners LLC; *U.S. Private*, pg. 328
SYSTEMS PRODUCTS AND SOLUTIONS, INC.; *U.S. Private*, pg. 3908
SYSTEMS PRODUCTS INTERNATIONAL, INC.—See Kingsway Financial Services Inc.; *U.S. Public*, pg. 1235
SYSTEMS SERVICES OF AMERICA, INC.—See US Foods Holding Corp.; *U.S. Public*, pg. 2266
SYSTEMS & SOFTWARE SERVICE INC.—See Mullins & Associates Inc.; *U.S. Private*, pg. 2812
SYSTEMS SOLUTION INC.—See Vitruvian Partners LLP; *Int'l*, pg. 8263
SYSTEMS SOURCE, INC.; *U.S. Private*, pg. 3908
SYSTEMS SPECIALTIES COMPANY; *U.S. Private*, pg. 3908
SYSTEMS TECHNOLOGY ASSOCIATES, INC.—See Sagewind Capital LLC; *U.S. Private*, pg. 3528
SYSTEMS TECHNOLOGY ASSOCIATES INC.; *U.S. Private*, pg. 3908
SYSTEMS TECHNOLOGY GROUP, INC.; *U.S. Private*, pg. 3908
SYSTEMS TECHNOLOGY, INC.; *U.S. Private*, pg. 3908
SYSTEM SUPPORT, INC.; *Int'l*, pg. 7390
SYSTEMS@WORK PTE. LTD.—See Wirecard AG; *Int'l*, pg. 8434
SYSTEM TECHNIK GMBH—See Cabka N.V.; *Int'l*, pg. 1246
SYSTEM TM A/S—See Durr AG; *Int'l*, pg. 2233
SYSTEMTRANSPORT A/S; *Int'l*, pg. 7393
SYSTEM TRANSPORT INC.—See Trans-System Inc.; *U.S. Private*, pg. 4206
SYSTEM TRANSPORT ZOO—See Systemtransport A/S; *Int'l*, pg. 7393
SYSTEMWARE, INC.; *U.S. Private*, pg. 3908
SYSTENA AMERICA INC.—See Systena Corporation; *Int'l*, pg. 7393
SYSTENA CORPORATION; *Int'l*, pg. 7393
SYSTENO GMBH—See Helaba Landesbank Hessen-Thuringen; *Int'l*, pg. 3328
SYSTERRA COMPUTER GMBH—See Addtech AB; *Int'l*, pg. 135
SYSTEST LABORATORIES INC.; *U.S. Private*, pg. 3908
SYSTEX CORPORATION; *Int'l*, pg. 7393
SYSTEX INFORMATION (H.K.) LTD.—See SYSTEX Corporation; *Int'l*, pg. 7393
SYSTEX JAPAN INC.—See Denso Corporation; *Int'l*, pg. 2032
SYSTEX PRODUCTS ARKANSAS COMPANY—See Denso Corporation; *Int'l*, pg. 2033
SYSTEX SOFTWARE & SERVICE CORP.—See SYSTEX Corporation; *Int'l*, pg. 7393
SYSTIMA TECHNOLOGIES, INC.—See Trive Capital Inc.; *U.S. Private*, pg. 4240
SYSTIME COMPUTER SYSTEMS (I) LTD.—See CMS Computers Ltd.; *Int'l*, pg. 1672
SYSTIME—See CMS Computers Ltd.; *Int'l*, pg. 1672
SYSTM BRANDS, LLC; *U.S. Private*, pg. 3908
SYSTM FOODS INC.—See SYSTM Brands, LLC; *U.S. Private*, pg. 3908
SYSTRA LTD.; *Int'l*, pg. 7393
SYSTRAN FINANCIAL SERVICES CORP.—See Textron Inc.; *U.S. Public*, pg. 2029
SYSTRAN INTERNATIONAL CO., LTD.; *Int'l*, pg. 7393
SYSTRAN S.A.—See CHAPS Holding SAS; *Int'l*, pg. 1448
SYSTRAN SOFTWARE, INC.—See CHAPS Holding SAS; *Int'l*, pg. 1448
SYSTRA—See Regie Autonome des Transports Parisiens; *Int'l*, pg. 6253
SYSTRA—See SNCF; *Int'l*, pg. 7027
SYSTRON-DONNER CORPORATION—See EMCORE Corporation; *U.S. Public*, pg. 739
SYSTRONICS DEPOT—See Systronics Inc.; *U.S. Private*, pg. 3908
SYSTRONICS INC.; *U.S. Private*, pg. 3908
SYSTRONICS (INDIA) LTD.—See Ambalal Sarabhai Enterprises Ltd.; *Int'l*, pg. 413
SYSTRONICS S.R.L.—See Cicor Technologies Ltd.; *Int'l*, pg. 1603
SYSU INTERNATIONAL, INC.; *Int'l*, pg. 7393
SYSWARE SINGAPORE PTE. LTD.—See SYSTEX Corporation; *Int'l*, pg. 7393
SYSWARE (THAILAND) CO., LTD.—See SYSTEX Corporation; *Int'l*, pg. 7393
SYSWIN INC.; *Int'l*, pg. 7394
SYSWORK CO., LTD.; *Int'l*, pg. 7394
SYSYSTEM CO., LTD.—See SYS Holdings Co., Ltd.; *Int'l*, pg. 7388
SYTECH—See Cummins Inc.; *U.S. Public*, pg. 609
SYTNER CARS LIMITED—See Penske Automotive Group, Inc.; *U.S. Public*, pg. 1666
SYTNER COVENTRY LIMITED—See Penske Automotive Group, Inc.; *U.S. Public*, pg. 1666
SYTNER FINANCE LIMITED—See Penske Automotive Group, Inc.; *U.S. Public*, pg. 1666

CORPORATE AFFILIATIONS

SYTNER GROUP LIMITED—See Penske Automotive Group, Inc.; *U.S. Public*, pg. 1666
SYTNER LIMITED—See Penske Automotive Group, Inc.; *U.S. Public*, pg. 1666
SYTNER OF LEICESTER LIMITED—See Penske Automotive Group, Inc.; *U.S. Public*, pg. 1666
SYTNER RETAIL LIMITED—See Penske Automotive Group, Inc.; *U.S. Public*, pg. 1666
SYTNER SHEFFIELD LIMITED—See Penske Automotive Group, Inc.; *U.S. Public*, pg. 1666
SYUPPIN CO., LTD.; *Int'l*, pg. 7394
SYVANTIS TECHNOLOGIES, INC.; *U.S. Private*, pg. 3908
SYVECO S.A.—See Thermador Groupe; *Int'l*, pg. 7707
SYVERSON TILE INC.; *U.S. Private*, pg. 3908
SYWEST MEDICAL TECHNOLOGIES INC.—See Merry X-Ray Corporation; *U.S. Private*, pg. 2676
SYY NETHERLANDS C.V.—See Sysco Corporation; *U.S. Public*, pg. 1975
SYZ ASSET MANAGEMENT (SUISSE) SA—See Financiere SYZ & CO SA; *Int'l*, pg. 2669
SYZYGY AG; *Int'l*, pg. 7394
SZAIDEL COSMETIC GMBH; *Int'l*, pg. 7394
SZAL-AGRO KFT.—See Tym Corporation; *Int'l*, pg. 7995
SZAM-ERT KFT.—See Betonut Szolgaltato es Epito Rt.; *Int'l*, pg. 1003
SZAMITO- ES UGYVITELI KOZPONT KORLATOLT FELELOSSEGU TARSASAG—See STRABAG SE; *Int'l*, pg. 7233
SZANCA SOLUTIONS, INC.; *U.S. Private*, pg. 3908
SZCZECINSKA ENERGETYKA CIEPLNA SP. Z O.O.—See E.ON SE; *Int'l*, pg. 2259
SZ DESIGN SRL—See Autoline Industries Limited; *Int'l*, pg. 728
SZEGED PLAZA KFT.—See BNP Paribas SA; *Int'l*, pg. 1093
SZENTESI VASUTEPITO KFT.—See STRABAG SE; *Int'l*, pg. 7233
SZEPVOLGYI BUSINESS PARK KFT.—See Immofinanz AG; *Int'l*, pg. 3628
SZ HANBANG TECHNOLOGY CO., LTD.—See Beijing Hanbang Technology Corp.; *Int'l*, pg. 951
SZ - INFRASTRUKTURA, D. O. O.—See Slovenske zeleznice, d.o.o.; *Int'l*, pg. 6998
SZOLNOK PLAZA KFT.—See BNP Paribas SA; *Int'l*, pg. 1093
SZOTT M-59 CHRYSLER JEEP; *U.S. Private*, pg. 3908
SZPITAL POLOZNICZO - GINEKOLOGICZNY UJASTEK SP. Z O.O—See Innova Capital Sp. z o.o.; *Int'l*, pg. 3711
SZR COLUMBIA LLC—See Ventas, Inc.; *U.S. Public*, pg. 2278
SZ-REISEN GMBH—See Bertelsmann SE & Co. KGaA; *Int'l*, pg. 996
SZR NORTH HILLS LLC—See Ventas, Inc.; *U.S. Public*, pg. 2278
SZR OLD TAPPAN ASSISTED LIVING, L.L.C.—See Ventas, Inc.; *U.S. Public*, pg. 2278
SZR SAN MATEO LLC—See Ventas, Inc.; *U.S. Public*, pg. 2278
SZS PRECISION ELECTRONICS CO., LTD.—See Shin Zu Shing Co., Ltd.; *Int'l*, pg. 6838
SZ - TOVORNI PROMET, D. O. O.—See Slovenske zeleznice, d.o.o.; *Int'l*, pg. 6998
SZ-ZELEZNISKI ZDRAVSTVENI DOM LJUBLJANA—See Slovenske zeleznice, d.o.o.; *Int'l*, pg. 6998
SZ-ZIP, STORITVE, D. O. O.—See Slovenske zeleznice, d.o.o.; *Int'l*, pg. 6998
SZZT ELECTRONICS CO., LTD.; *Int'l*, pg. 7394

T

T0.COM, INC.—See Beyond, Inc.; *U.S. Public*, pg. 327
T1T LAB, LLC—See Enerfund, LLC; *U.S. Private*, pg. 1393
T2 BIOSYSTEMS, INC.; *U.S. Public*, pg. 1978
T2 CONSTRUCTION, LLC—See Lennar Corporation; *U.S. Public*, pg. 1305
T2 INTERNATIONAL LLC; *U.S. Private*, pg. 3913
T2 OPTIMISE PTY. LTD.—See Allegis Group, Inc.; *U.S. Private*, pg. 177
T2 OPTIMISE PTY. LTD.—See Morgan & Banks Investments Pty. Ltd.; *Int'l*, pg. 5041
T2 PARTNERS GROUP, LLC; *U.S. Private*, pg. 3913
T2 PARTNERS MANAGEMENT, LP—See T2 Partners Group, LLC; *U.S. Private*, pg. 3913
T 2 SOFTWARE S.A.—See Antares Vision SpA; *Int'l*, pg. 482
T2 SYSTEMS CANADA INC.—See Verra Mobility Corporation; *U.S. Public*, pg. 2287
T2 SYSTEMS, INC.—See Verra Mobility Corporation; *U.S. Public*, pg. 2287
T2 TOKYO K.K.—See Allegis Group, Inc.; *U.S. Private*, pg. 177
T2 TOKYO K.K.—See Morgan & Banks Investments Pty. Ltd.; *Int'l*, pg. 5041
T3 COMMUNICATIONS, INC.—See Digerati Technologies, Inc.; *U.S. Public*, pg. 661
T3 CORPORATION; *U.S. Private*, pg. 3913
T3EX GLOBAL HOLDINGS CORP.; *Int'l*, pg. 7398
T3 LIVE LLC; *U.S. Private*, pg. 3913

COMPANY NAME INDEX

T3MEDIA, INC.; *U.S. Private,* pg. 3913
T3 MOTION, INC.; *U.S. Private,* pg. 3913
T4B LTD.—See Attard & Co. Ltd.; *Int'l,* pg. 696
T4C CO., LTD.—See System Support, Inc.; *Int'l,* pg. 7390
T4F ENTRETENIMENTO S.A.; *Int'l,* pg. 7398
T4G LIMITED; *Int'l,* pg. 7398
T4 SCIENCE SA—See Eurazeo SE; *Int'l,* pg. 2528
T5 CORP.; *U.S. Private,* pg. 3913
T7 GASTEC SDN BHD—See T7 Global Berhad; *Int'l,* pg. 7398
T7 GLOBAL BERHAD; *Int'l,* pg. 7398
T7 KILGOUR SDN BHD—See T7 Global Berhad; *Int'l,* pg. 7398
T7 WENMAX SDN BHD—See T7 Global Berhad; *Int'l,* pg. 7398
T8 GALLERY PTE. LTD.—See Tan Chong International Limited; *Int'l,* pg. 7453
T8 SOFTWARE CONSULTING LIMITED—See True Partner Capital Holding Limited; *Int'l,* pg. 7941
TA AEROSPACE CO.—See TransDigm Group Incorporated; *U.S. Public,* pg. 2181
TAAGEER FINANCE COMPANY SAOG; *Int'l,* pg. 7400
TAAL DISTRIBUTED INFORMATION TECHNOLOGIES INC.; *Int'l,* pg. 7400
TAAL ENTERPRISES LTD.; *Int'l,* pg. 7400
TAALERI BIOINDUSTRY LTD.—See Taaleri Oyj; *Int'l,* pg. 7401
TAALERI ENERGIA LTD.—See Taaleri Oyj; *Int'l,* pg. 7401
TAALERI KAPITAALI LTD.—See Taaleri Oyj; *Int'l,* pg. 7401
TAALERI OYJ; *Int'l,* pg. 7401
TAALERI PORTFOY YONETIMI A.S.—See Taaleri Oyj; *Int'l,* pg. 7401
TAALERI REAL ESTATE LTD.—See Taaleri Oyj; *Int'l,* pg. 7401
TAAMEER HOSPITALITY FOR HOTEL MANAGEMENT S.A.—See Al-Massaleh Real Estate Company K.S.C.C.; *Int'l,* pg. 287
TAAMEER HOSPITALITY-S.A.L.—See Al-Massaleh Real Estate Company K.S.C.C.; *Int'l,* pg. 287
TAAMEER HOTEL MANAGEMENT COMPANY & CONSULTANCY S.A.—See Al-Massaleh Real Estate Company K.S.C.C.; *Int'l,* pg. 287
TAAMEER LEBANON HOLDING COMPANY-S.A.L.—See Al-Massaleh Real Estate Company K.S.C.C.; *Int'l,* pg. 287
TAAMEER REAL ESTATE INVESTMENT CO. KSCC—See Al-Massaleh Real Estate Company K.S.C.C.; *Int'l,* pg. 287
T.A. AMERICA CORPORATION—See Sumitomo Electric Industries, Ltd.; *Int'l,* pg. 7285
TA ANN HOLDINGS BERHAD; *Int'l,* pg. 7398
TA ANN PLYWOOD SDN. BHD.—See Ta Ann Holdings Berhad; *Int'l,* pg. 7399
TA ANN TASMANIA PTY. LTD.—See Ta Ann Holdings Berhad; *Int'l,* pg. 7399
TA AN PRECISION CO., LTD.—See Ta Ya Electric Wire & Cable Co., Ltd.; *Int'l,* pg. 7400
TAASINGE ELEMENTER A/S—See Kingspan Group PLC; *Int'l,* pg. 4179
TA ASSET MANAGEMENT SDN BHD—See TA Enterprise Berhad; *Int'l,* pg. 7399
TA ASSOCIATES ADVISORY PVT. LTD.—See TA Associates, Inc.; *U.S. Private,* pg. 3918
TA ASSOCIATES ASIA PACIFIC LTD.—See TA Associates, Inc.; *U.S. Private,* pg. 3918
TA ASSOCIATES, INC.; *U.S. Private,* pg. 3913
TA ASSOCIATES LTD.—See TA Associates, Inc.; *U.S. Private,* pg. 3918
TA ASSOCIATES MANAGEMENT, L.P.—See TA Associates, Inc.; *U.S. Private,* pg. 3918
TA ASSOCIATES (UK), LLP—See TA Associates, Inc.; *U.S. Private,* pg. 3918
TAAT GLOBAL ALTERNATIVES INC.; *Int'l,* pg. 7401
TA AUTOMOTIVE PARTS (THAILAND) CO., LTD.—See Sumitomo Electric Industries, Ltd.; *Int'l,* pg. 7285
TAAV BIOMANUFACTURING SOLUTIONS, S.L.U.—See Bayer Aktiengesellschaft; *Int'l,* pg. 910
TAAVURA HOLDINGS, LTD.; *Int'l,* pg. 7401
TAAZA INTERNATIONAL LTD.; *Int'l,* pg. 7401
TABACALERA HONDURENA SA—See British American Tobacco plc; *Int'l,* pg. 1168
TABACALERA ISTMENA SA—See British American Tobacco plc; *Int'l,* pg. 1168
TABACALERA NICARAGUENSE S.A.—See British American Tobacco plc; *Int'l,* pg. 1168
TABADOM HOLDING INC.—See Oettinger IMEX AG; *Int'l,* pg. 5530
TABATCHNICK FINE FOODS, INC.; *U.S. Private,* pg. 3919
TABBLER GMBH—See Bertelsmann SE & Co. KGaA; *Int'l,* pg. 996
TAB CANADA—See H.S. Morgan Limited Partnership; *U.S. Private,* pg. 1835
TABC, INC.—See Toyota Motor Corporation; *Int'l,* pg. 7874
TABCOM, LLC; *U.S. Private,* pg. 3919
TAB CONTRACTORS INC.—See New-Com Inc.; *U.S. Private,* pg. 2913
TABCORP HOLDINGS LIMITED; *Int'l,* pg. 7401
TABC—See Toyota Motor Corporation; *Int'l,* pg. 7874

TAB DATA FILE—See H.S. Morgan Limited Partnership; *U.S. Private,* pg. 1835
TABELEC FORCE ET COMMANDES S.A.—See Burkhalter Holding AG; *Int'l,* pg. 1226
TABER CRANE CONSTRUCTION SERVICES CORP.; *U.S. Private,* pg. 3919
TABER EXTRUSIONS LP—See Tang Industries Inc.; *U.S. Private,* pg. 3930
TABERNA CAPITAL MANAGEMENT, LLC—See RAIT Financial Trust; *U.S. Private,* pg. 3349
TABERNUS EUROPE LIMITED—See Francisco Partners Management, LP; *U.S. Private,* pg. 1589
TABERNUS LLC—See Francisco Partners Management, LP; *U.S. Private,* pg. 1588
TABICT, INC.—See Robot Home, Inc.; *Int'l,* pg. 6371
TABIKOBO CO., LTD.; *Int'l,* pg. 7401
TABIMADO CO., LTD—See Rakuten Group, Inc.; *Int'l,* pg. 6195
TABIMED GESTION DE PROYECTOS, S.L.—See Banco de Sabadell, S.A.; *Int'l,* pg. 821
TAB INDIA GRANITES PVT. LTD. - NORTH PLANT—See Tab India Granites Pvt. Ltd.; *Int'l,* pg. 7401
TAB INDIA GRANITES PVT. LTD.; *Int'l,* pg. 7401
TAB INDIA GRANITES PVT. LTD. - SOUTH PLANT—See Tab India Granites Pvt. Ltd.; *Int'l,* pg. 7401
TABIO CORPORATION; *Int'l,* pg. 7402
TABIO EUROPE LIMITED—See Tabio Corporation; *Int'l,* pg. 7402
TABIO FRANCE SAS—See Tabio Corporation; *Int'l,* pg. 7402
TABIO NARA CO., LTD.—See Tabio Corporation; *Int'l,* pg. 7402
TABLABS INC.—See Philip Morris International Inc.; *U.S. Public,* pg. 1687
TABLEAU ASIA PACIFIC PTE. LTD.—See Salesforce, Inc.; *U.S. Public,* pg. 1838
TABLEAU (CHINA) CO., LTD.—See Salesforce, Inc.; *U.S. Public,* pg. 1838
TABLEAU FRANCE S.A.S.—See Salesforce, Inc.; *U.S. Public,* pg. 1838
TABLEAU GERMANY GMBH—See Salesforce, Inc.; *U.S. Public,* pg. 1838
TABLEAU JAPAN K.K.—See Salesforce, Inc.; *U.S. Public,* pg. 1000
TABLEAU SOFTWARE, INC.—See Salesforce, Inc.; *U.S. Public,* pg. 1838
TABLEAU SOFTWARE UK—See Salesforce, Inc.; *U.S. Public,* pg. 1838
TABLECRAFT PRODUCTS CO., INC.; *U.S. Private,* pg. 3920
TABLEMARK CO., LTD.—See Japan Tobacco Inc.; *Int'l,* pg. 3907
TABLE TENNIS PRO EUROPE LTD.—See Frasers Group plc; *Int'l,* pg. 2765
TABLET, INC.—See Compagnie Generale des Etablissements Michelin SCA; *Int'l,* pg. 1745
TABLE TO TABLE; *U.S. Private,* pg. 3920
TABLE TRAC, INC.; *U.S. Public,* pg. 1978
TABLE TRENDS INC.—See Lee's Curtain Co., Inc.; *U.S. Private,* pg. 2414
TABLE & VINE, INC.—See Big Y Foods, Inc.; *U.S. Private,* pg. 555
TABLEX MILLER, S.A. DE C.V.—See Grupo La Moderna, S.A.B. de C.V.; *Int'l,* pg. 3131
TABOOLA.COM LTD.; *U.S. Public,* pg. 1978
TABOOLA.COM LTD.—See Nexstar Media Group, Inc.; *U.S. Public,* pg. 1524
TABO OTOMOTIV AS—See Cofle SpA; *Int'l,* pg. 1693
TABOR CITY LUMBER COMPANY INCORPORATED; *U.S. Private,* pg. 3920
TABOR COMMUNICATIONS, INC.; *U.S. Private,* pg. 3920
TABOR MACHINE COMPANY—See Brookfield Corporation; *Int'l,* pg. 1181
TAB PRODUCTS CO. LLC—See H.S. Morgan Limited Partnership; *U.S. Private,* pg. 1835
TAB PRODUCTS EUROPE B.V.—See H.S. Morgan Limited Partnership; *U.S. Private,* pg. 1835
TABREED OMAN SAOC—See National Central Cooling Company PJSC; *Int'l,* pg. 5155
TAB REFRACTORY CONSTRUCTION & MAINTENANCE CO.—See Pyrotek Incorporated; *U.S. Private,* pg. 3311
TABREWER CONSULTING, INC.—See General Atlantic Service Company, L.P.; *U.S. Private,* pg. 1662
TABREWER CONSULTING, INC.—See HgCapital Trust plc; *Int'l,* pg. 3376
TABRIZ PETROCHEMICAL CO.—See Parsian Oil & Gas Development Co.; *Int'l,* pg. 5747
TABS ANALYTICS, INC.—See TELUS CORPORATION; *Int'l,* pg. 7546
TABUA INVESTMENTS LIMITED—See Hong Leong Investment Holdings Pte. Ltd.; *Int'l,* pg. 3468
TABUCHI ELECTRIC CO., LTD.—See Diamond Electric Mfg. Co., Ltd.; *Int'l,* pg. 2105
TABUCHI ELECTRIC COMPANY OF AMERICA—See Diamond Electric Mfg. Co., Ltd.; *Int'l,* pg. 2105
TABUCHI ELECTRIC U.K. LTD.—See Diamond Electric Mfg. Co., Ltd.; *Int'l,* pg. 2105

TACHIKAWA CORPORATION

TABUK AGRICULTURE DEVELOPMENT COMPANY; *Int'l,* pg. 7402
TABUK CEMENT COMPANY; *Int'l,* pg. 7402
TABUK PHARMACEUTICAL MANUFACTURING COMPANY—See ASTRA INDUSTRIAL GROUP COMPANY; *Int'l,* pg. 657
TABUK PHARMACEUTICALS LTD.—See ASTRA INDUSTRIAL GROUP COMPANY; *Int'l,* pg. 657
TABULA, INC.; *U.S. Private,* pg. 3920
TABULA RASA HEALTHCARE, INC.—See Nautic Partners, LLC; *U.S. Private,* pg. 2871
TACA INTERNATIONAL AIRLINES, S.A.—See Synergy Group; *Int'l,* pg. 7384
TACA INTERNATIONAL AIRLINES, S.A.—See Synergy Group; *Int'l,* pg. 7384
TACALA, LLC; *U.S. Private,* pg. 3920
TACALA LLC—See Altamont Capital Partners; *U.S. Private,* pg. 205
TA CAPITAL SDN BHD—See TA Enterprise Berhad; *Int'l,* pg. 7399
TACBRIGHT OPTRONICS CORP.—See Shin Kong Group; *Int'l,* pg. 6837
TACC CONSTRUCTION LTD.; *Int'l,* pg. 7402
T.A.C. CERAMIC TILE CO.—See Littlejohn & Co., LLC; *U.S. Private,* pg. 2470
T.A.C. CERAMIC TILE CO.—See Platinum Equity, LLC; *U.S. Private,* pg. 3205
TAC COAT CO.,LTD—See Sigma Koki Co., Ltd.; *Int'l,* pg. 6908
TAC CO., LTD.; *Int'l,* pg. 7402
T.A.C. CONSUMER PCL; *Int'l,* pg. 7396
TAC (DALIAN) CO., LTD.—See TAC Co., Ltd.; *Int'l,* pg. 7402
TAC ENERGY—See Truman Arnold Companies; *U.S. Private,* pg. 7402
TA CENTRE BERHAD—See TA Enterprise Berhad; *Int'l,* pg. 7399
TAC GOLD CORPORATION; *Int'l,* pg. 7402
TACHAN SECURITIES CO., LTD.; *Int'l,* pg. 7402
TAC HEALTHCARE GROUP LTD.; *Int'l,* pg. 7402
TA CHEN (BOYE) PRECISION CASTING CO., LTD.—See Ta Chen Stainless Pipe, Ltd.; *Int'l,* pg. 7399
TA CHEN (CHANGSHU) MACHINERY CO., LTD.—See Ta Chen Stainless Pipe, Ltd.; *Int'l,* pg. 7399
TA-CHEN CONSTRUCTION & ENGINEERING CORP.—See Prince Housing & Development Corp.; *Int'l,* pg. 5980
TA CHEN INTERNATIONAL INC; *U.S. Private,* pg. 3919
TA CHEN STAINLESS PIPE, LTD.; *Int'l,* pg. 7399
TACHIA YUNG HO MACHINE INDUSTRY CO., LTD.; *Int'l,* pg. 7402
TACHIBANA CREATE LTD—See Tachibana Eletech Co., Ltd.; *Int'l,* pg. 7403
TACHIBANA DEVICE COMPONENT CO., LTD.—See Tachibana Eletech Co., Ltd.; *Int'l,* pg. 7403
TACHIBANA ELECTRONIC SOLUTIONS CO., LTD.—See Tachibana Eletech Co., Ltd.; *Int'l,* pg. 7403
TACHIBANA ELETECH CO., LTD.; *Int'l,* pg. 7402
TACHIBANA ENTERPRISES, LLC—See JTB Corp.; *Int'l,* pg. 4015
TACHIBANA ES LTD—See Tachibana Eletech Co., Ltd.; *Int'l,* pg. 7403
TACHIBANA KOUWA SYSTEM SERVICE CO., LTD.—See Tachibana Eletech Co., Ltd.; *Int'l,* pg. 7403
TACHIBANA MANAGEMENT SERVICE LTD.—See Tachibana Eletech Co., Ltd.; *Int'l,* pg. 7403
TACHIBANA METAL MANUFACTURING CO., LTD.—See Mitsubishi Materials Corporation; *Int'l,* pg. 4965
TACHIBANA METAL MFG CO., LTD.—See Mitsubishi Materials Corporation; *Int'l,* pg. 4965
TACHIBANA OVERSEAS HOLDINGS LTD.—See Tachibana Eletech Co., Ltd.; *Int'l,* pg. 7403
TACHIBANA SALES BANGKOK CO., LTD.—See Tachibana Eletech Co., Ltd.; *Int'l,* pg. 7403
TACHIBANA SALES (H.K.) LTD.—See Tachibana Eletech Co., Ltd.; *Int'l,* pg. 7403
TACHIBANA SALES (KOREA) LTD.—See Tachibana Eletech Co., Ltd.; *Int'l,* pg. 7403
TACHIBANA SALES (MALAYSIA) SDN. BHD.—See Tachibana Eletech Co., Ltd.; *Int'l,* pg. 7403
TACHIBANA SALES (SHANGHAI) LTD.—See Tachibana Eletech Co., Ltd.; *Int'l,* pg. 7403
TACHIBANA SALES (SINGAPORE) PTE. LTD.—See Tachibana Eletech Co., Ltd.; *Int'l,* pg. 7403
TACHIBANA SALES (S) PTE., LTD—See Tachibana Eletech Co., Ltd.; *Int'l,* pg. 7403
TACHIBANA SALES TAIWAN LTD.—See Tachibana Eletech Co., Ltd.; *Int'l,* pg. 7403
TACHIBANA SOLUTIONS PLAZA LTD.—See Tachibana Eletech Co., Ltd.; *Int'l,* pg. 7403
TACHIKARA COMPANY, LTD.; *Int'l,* pg. 7403
TACHIKARA USA INC.—See Tachikara Company, Ltd.; *Int'l,* pg. 7403
TACHIKAWA BUS CO., LTD—See Odakyu Electric Railway Co., Ltd.; *Int'l,* pg. 5524
TACHIKAWA CORPORATION; *Int'l,* pg. 7403
TACHIKAWA DANBORU KOGYO CO., LTD.—See Rengo Co., Ltd.; *Int'l,* pg. 6281

TACHIKAWA CORPORATION

TACHIKAWA TRADING CO., LTD.—See Tachikawa Corporation; *Int'l*, pg. 7403
TACHI-S AUTOMOTIVE SEATING (THAILAND) CO LTD.—See Tachi-S Co., Ltd.; *Int'l*, pg. 7402
TACHI-S BRASIL INDUSTRIA DE ASSENTOS AUTOMOTIVOS LTDA.—See Tachi-S Co., Ltd.; *Int'l*, pg. 7402
TACHI-S CO., LTD.; *Int'l*, pg. 7402
TACHI-S ENGINEERING U.S.A., INC.—See Tachi-S Co., Ltd.; *Int'l*, pg. 7402
TACHI-S H&P CO., LTD.—See Tachi-S Co., Ltd.; *Int'l*, pg. 7402
TACHI-S SERVICE CO., LTD.—See Tachi-S Co., Ltd.; *Int'l*, pg. 7402
TACHIYA CO., LTD.—See Valor Holdings Co., Ltd.; *Int'l*, pg. 8122
TAC HOLDINGS LLC—See Tredegar Corporation; *U.S. Public*, pg. 2187
TA CHONG BANK, LTD.—See Yuanta Financial Holding Co., Ltd.; *Int'l*, pg. 8608
TACIRLER YATIRIM MENKUL DEGERLER A.S.; *Int'l*, pg. 7403
TACISA TRANSITARIA S.L.—See DSV A/S; *Int'l*, pg. 2216
TACIT KNOWLEDGE, INC.—See Grid Dynamics Holdings, Inc.; *U.S. Public*, pg. 969
TACIT KNOWLEDGE LTD.—See Grid Dynamics Holdings, Inc.; *U.S. Public*, pg. 969
TACLE AUTOMOTIVE INDIA PRIVATE LIMITED—See Lear Corporation; *U.S. Public*, pg. 1298
TAC MANUFACTURING, INC.—See Tokai Rika Co., Ltd.; *Int'l*, pg. 7780
TACMIC CO., LTD.—See Tenma Corporation; *Int'l*, pg. 7560
TACMINA CORPORATION; *Int'l*, pg. 7403
TACMINA USA CORPORATION—See Tacmina Corporation; *Int'l*, pg. 7403
TACO ALOHA, INC.—See Grupo Finaccess S.A.P.I. de C.V.; *Int'l*, pg. 3129
TACOBA CONSULTANT FORESTRY N.V—See China International Marine Containers (Group) Co., Ltd.; *Int'l*, pg. 1512
TACO BELL CORP.—See Yum! Brands, Inc.; *U.S. Public*, pg. 2400
TACO BUENO RESTAURANTS, L.P.—See TPG Capital, L.P.; *U.S. Public*, pg. 2177
TACO CABANA, INC.—See Yadav Enterprises, Inc.; *U.S. Private*, pg. 4584
TACO (CANADA) LTD.—See Taco Incorporated; *U.S. Private*, pg. 3920
TACO CO., LTD.—See Azbil Corporation; *Int'l*, pg. 777
TACO DEL MAR FRANCHISING CORP.; *U.S. Private*, pg. 3920
TACO ELECTRONIC SOLUTIONS, INC.—See Taco Incorporated; *U.S. Private*, pg. 3920
TACO INCORPORATED; *U.S. Private*, pg. 3920
TACO JOHN'S INTERNATIONAL, INC.; *U.S. Private*, pg. 3920
TACOMA ELECTRIC SUPPLY, INC.; *U.S. Private*, pg. 3921
TACOMA ELECTRIC SUPPLY INC.—See Winsupply, Inc.; *U.S. Private*, pg. 4545
TACOMA GOODWILL INDUSTRIES, INC.—See Goodwill Industries International, Inc.; *U.S. Private*, pg. 1740
TACOMA INC.; *U.S. Private*, pg. 3921
TACOMA LUTHERAN RETIREMENT COMMUNITY; *U.S. Private*, pg. 3921
TACOMA NEWS, INC.—See Chatham Asset Management, LLC; *U.S. Private*, pg. 867
TACOMA PUBLIC UTILITIES; *U.S. Private*, pg. 3921
TACOMA RECYCLING COMPANY, INC.—See Waste Connections, Inc.; *Int'l*, pg. 8354
TACOMA SCREW PRODUCTS, INC.; *U.S. Private*, pg. 3921
TACO MAYO FRANCHISE SYSTEMS, INC.; *U.S. Private*, pg. 3920
TACO METALS INC.; *U.S. Private*, pg. 3920
TACONICARTEMIS GMBH—See Taconic Farms, Inc.; *U.S. Private*, pg. 3921
TACONIC EUROPE A/S—See Taconic Farms, Inc.; *U.S. Private*, pg. 3921
TACONIC FARMS, INC.; *U.S. Private*, pg. 3921
TACONY CORPORATION; *U.S. Private*, pg. 3921
TACONY MANUFACTURING—See Tacony Corporation; *U.S. Private*, pg. 3921
TACORI ENTERPRISES; *U.S. Private*, pg. 3921
TA CORPORATION LTD.; *Int'l*, pg. 7399
TACO TRUCK CREATIVE, LLC; *U.S. Private*, pg. 3920
TAC PARTNERS, INC.; *U.S. Private*, pg. 3920
TAC PROPERTY CO., LTD.—See Charoen Pokphand Group Co., Ltd.; *Int'l*, pg. 1453
TACTAIR FLUID CONTROLS INC—See TransDigm Group Incorporated; *U.S. Public*, pg. 2183
TACT GROUP LIMITED—See Matthews International Corporation; *U.S. Public*, pg. 1401
TACT HOLDING—See Aldi Einkauf SE & Co. oHG; *Int'l*, pg. 304
TACT HOME CO., LTD.—See Iida Group Holdings Co., Ltd.; *Int'l*, pg. 3607
TACTICAL COMMAND INDUSTRIES, INC.—See Kanders & Company, Inc.; *U.S. Private*, pg. 2259

TACTICAL COMMUNICATIONS GROUP, LLC—See Curtiss-Wright Corporation; *U.S. Public*, pg. 612
TACTICAL MEDICAL SOLUTIONS, INC.—See CNL Strategic Capital Management LLC; *U.S. Private*, pg. 952
TACTICAL PRODUCTS GROUP, INC.; *U.S. Private*, pg. 3921
TACTICAL RELIEF, LLC—See Allied Corp.; *Int'l*, pg. 357
TACTICAL RESOURCES CORP.; *Int'l*, pg. 7403
TACTICAL SUPPORT EQUIPMENT INC.; *U.S. Private*, pg. 3921
TACTICO, LTD.—See Takaoka Toko Co., Ltd.; *Int'l*, pg. 7431
TACTICS GROUP; *Int'l*, pg. 7403
TACTILE LIMITED—See Advent International Corporation; *U.S. Private*, pg. 97
TACTILE LIMITED—See Centerbridge Partners, L.P.; *U.S. Private*, pg. 813
TACTILE SYSTEMS TECHNOLOGY, INC.; *U.S. Public*, pg. 1978
TACTRON ELEKTRONIK GMBH & CO. KG—See GigaLane Co., Ltd.; *Int'l*, pg. 2971
TACTUS TECHNOLOGY, INC.—See General Motors Company; *U.S. Public*, pg. 929
TACTY CORPORATION—See Meiji Shipping Co., Ltd.; *Int'l*, pg. 4802
TAC WORLDWIDE COMPANIES—See American Crystal Holdings, Inc.; *U.S. Private*, pg. 229
TADA ELECTRIC CO., LTD. - HEAT EXCHANGER WORKS—See Mitsubishi Electric Corporation; *Int'l*, pg. 4946
TADA ELECTRIC CO., LTD.—See Mitsubishi Electric Corporation; *Int'l*, pg. 4946
TADAKIKO CO., LTD.—See Hitachi, Ltd.; *Int'l*, pg. 3424
TADANO AMERICA CORPORATION—See Tadano Ltd.; *Int'l*, pg. 7404
TADANO ASIA PTE. LTD.—See Tadano Ltd.; *Int'l*, pg. 7404
TADANO (BEIJING) LTD.—See Tadano Ltd.; *Int'l*, pg. 7403
TADANO BELGIUM BV—See Tadano Ltd.; *Int'l*, pg. 7404
TADANO BRASIL EQUIPAMENTOS DE ELEVACAO LTDA.—See Tadano Ltd.; *Int'l*, pg. 7404
TADANO CHILE SPA—See Tadano Ltd.; *Int'l*, pg. 7404
TADANO DEMAG ESPANA, S.A.—See Tadano Ltd.; *Int'l*, pg. 7404
TADANO DEMAG FRANCE SA—See Tadano Ltd.; *Int'l*, pg. 7404
TADANO DEMAG GMBH—See Tadano Ltd.; *Int'l*, pg. 7404
TADANO DEMAG SCANDINAVIA AB—See Tadano Ltd.; *Int'l*, pg. 7404
TADANO DEMAG UK LIMITED—See Tadano Ltd.; *Int'l*, pg. 7404
TADANO ESCORTS INDIA PVT. LTD.—See Tadano Ltd.; *Int'l*, pg. 7404
TADANO FAUN GMBH—See Tadano Ltd.; *Int'l*, pg. 7404
TADANO FAUN HOLLAND B.V.—See Tadano Ltd.; *Int'l*, pg. 7404
TADANO FRANCE SAS—See Tadano Ltd.; *Int'l*, pg. 7404
TADANO IMES LTD.—See Tadano Ltd.; *Int'l*, pg. 7404
TADANO ITALTHAI CO., LTD.—See Tadano Ltd.; *Int'l*, pg. 7404
TADANO KOREA CO LTD.—See Tadano Ltd.; *Int'l*, pg. 7404
TADANO LTD.; *Int'l*, pg. 7403
TADANO MANTIS CORPORATION—See Tadano Ltd.; *Int'l*, pg. 7403
TADANO ME LIFTING EQUIPMENT TRADING L.L.C—See Tadano Ltd.; *Int'l*, pg. 7404
TADANO NEDERLAND B.V.—See Tadano Ltd.; *Int'l*, pg. 7404
TADANO OCEANIA PTY LTD—See Tadano Ltd.; *Int'l*, pg. 7404
TADANO SOUTH CHINA COMPANY LTD.—See Tadano Ltd.; *Int'l*, pg. 7404
TADANO (THAILAND) CO., LTD.—See Tadano Ltd.; *Int'l*, pg. 7403
TADANO UK LTD.—See Tadano Ltd.; *Int'l*, pg. 7404
TADA-SMITH COMPANY, LTD.—See Noritz Corporation; *Int'l*, pg. 5430
TADBIK GROUP; *Int'l*, pg. 7404
TADBIK PACK SA—See Tadbik Group; *Int'l*, pg. 7404
TADDIKEN TREE COMPANY—See Apax Partners LLP; *Int'l*, pg. 506
TADHAMON INTERNATIONAL ISLAMIC BANK; *Int'l*, pg. 7404
TAD INOX SERVICE BV—See ERG S.p.A.; *Int'l*, pg. 2491
TAD INOX SERVICE GMBH—See ERG S.p.A.; *Int'l*, pg. 2491
TADIRAN BATTERIES GMBH—See TotalEnergies SE; *Int'l*, pg. 7838
TADIRAN BATTERIES LTD—See TotalEnergies SE; *Int'l*, pg. 7838
TADIRAN GROUP LTD.; *Int'l*, pg. 7404
TADIR-GAN (PRECISION PRODUCTS) 1993 LTD.; *Int'l*, pg. 7404
TADLOCK PIPE & EQUIPMENT INC.; *U.S. Private*, pg. 3921
TAD PHARMA GMBH—See Krka, d.d., Novo Mesto; *Int'l*, pg. 4303
TADVEST LTD.; *Int'l*, pg. 7404

CORPORATE AFFILIATIONS

TAE-A INDUSTRY CO., LTD.—See KT&G Corporation; *Int'l*, pg. 4316
TAE AVIATION PTY LIMITED—See Air New Zealand Limited; *Int'l*, pg. 238
T.A. E-FURNISHINGS SDN. BHD.—See TAFI Industries Berhad; *Int'l*, pg. 7406
TAE GAS TURBINES PTY LIMITED—See Air New Zealand Limited; *Int'l*, pg. 238
TAEGU BROADCASTING CORPORATION; *Int'l*, pg. 7404
TAEGUTEC LTD—See Berkshire Hathaway Inc.; *U.S. Public*, pg. 308
TAEKWANG FINE CHEMICAL CO., LTD.—See Miwon Commercial Co., Ltd.; *Int'l*, pg. 4995
TAEKWANG INDUSTRIAL CO., LTD. - BANEYO FACTORY—See Taekwang Industrial Co., Ltd.; *Int'l*, pg. 7405
TAEKWANG INDUSTRIAL CO., LTD. - BUSAN FACTORY—See Taekwang Industrial Co., Ltd.; *Int'l*, pg. 7405
TAEKWANG INDUSTRIAL CO., LTD. - DAEGU FACTORY—See Taekwang Industrial Co., Ltd.; *Int'l*, pg. 7405
TAEKWANG INDUSTRIAL CO., LTD. - GYEONGJU FACTORY—See Taekwang Industrial Co., Ltd.; *Int'l*, pg. 7405
TAEKWANG INDUSTRIAL CO., LTD. - PETROCHEMICAL 1 PLANT—See Taekwang Industrial Co., Ltd.; *Int'l*, pg. 7405
TAEKWANG INDUSTRIAL CO., LTD. - PETROCHEMICAL 2 PLANT—See Taekwang Industrial Co., Ltd.; *Int'l*, pg. 7405
TAEKWANG INDUSTRIAL CO., LTD. - PETROCHEMICAL 3 PLANT—See Taekwang Industrial Co., Ltd.; *Int'l*, pg. 7405
TAEKWANG INDUSTRIAL CO., LTD. - SNIPYEONG FACTORY—See Taekwang Industrial Co., Ltd.; *Int'l*, pg. 7405
TAEKWANG INDUSTRIAL CO., LTD.; *Int'l*, pg. 7404
TAEKWANG INDUSTRIAL CO., LTD. - ULSAN PLANT—See Taekwang Industrial Co., Ltd.; *Int'l*, pg. 7405
TAEKWANG INDUSTRIAL CO., LTD. - UNGSANG FACTORY—See Taekwang Industrial Co., Ltd.; *Int'l*, pg. 7405
TAEKWANG INDUSTRIAL GAESEONG CO., LTD.—See Taekwang Industrial Co., Ltd.; *Int'l*, pg. 7405
TAEKWANG SYNTHETIC FIBER (CHANGSHU) CO., LTD.—See Taekwang Industrial Co., Ltd.; *Int'l*, pg. 7405
TAEKYONG ELECTRONICS CORP.—See Arlitech Electronic Corp.; *Int'l*, pg. 573
TAEKYUNG BK CO., LTD.; *Int'l*, pg. 7405
TAEKYUNG CHEMICAL CO., LTD.—See Taekyung BK Co., Ltd.; *Int'l*, pg. 7405
TAEKYUNG INDUSTRIAL CO., LTD.; *Int'l*, pg. 7405
TAEMA—See L'Air Liquide S.A.; *Int'l*, pg. 4374
TA ENTERPRISE BERHAD; *Int'l*, pg. 7399
TAE PTY LIMITED—See Air New Zealand Limited; *Int'l*, pg. 238
TAESANG CO. LTD—See Taewoong Co., Ltd.; *Int'l*, pg. 7405
TAESAN LCD CO., LTD.; *Int'l*, pg. 7405
TAESUNG CO., LTD.; *Int'l*, pg. 7405
TAEUBER & CORSSEN SWA PROPRIETARY LIMITED—See The Bidvest Group Limited; *Int'l*, pg. 7626
TAE WON MULSAN CO., LTD. - INCHEON MACHINERY FACTORY—See Tae Won Mulsan Co., Ltd.; *Int'l*, pg. 7404
TAE WON MULSAN CO., LTD.; *Int'l*, pg. 7404
TAE WON MULSAN CO., LTD. - ULSAN GYPSUM FACTORY—See Tae Won Mulsan Co., Ltd.; *Int'l*, pg. 7404
TAEWOO CO., LTD.—See Seowon Co., Ltd.; *Int'l*, pg. 6717
TAEWOONG CO., LTD.; *Int'l*, pg. 7405
TAEWOONG LOGISTICS CO., LTD.; *Int'l*, pg. 7405
TAEWOONG MANUFACTURING & MACHINING DIVISION CO., LTD. - FACTORY 2—See Taewoong Co., Ltd.; *Int'l*, pg. 7405
TAEWOONG MANUFACTURING & MACHINING DIVISION CO., LTD.—See Taewoong Co., Ltd.; *Int'l*, pg. 7405
TAEWOONG P & C—See Taewoong Co., Ltd.; *Int'l*, pg. 7405
TAEWOONG STEEL MATERIALS TRADING DIVISION CO., LTD.—See Taewoong Co., Ltd.; *Int'l*, pg. 7405
TAEYANG CORPORATION; *Int'l*, pg. 7406
TAEYANG ELECTRONICS CO., LTD. - WAEGWAN FACTORY—See GenNBio Inc.; *Int'l*, pg. 2925
TAEYANG METAL INDUSTRIAL CO., LTD; *Int'l*, pg. 7406
TAEYANG METAL (ZHANGJIAGANG) CO., LTD.—See Taeyang Metal Industrial Co., Ltd.; *Int'l*, pg. 7406
TAEYOUNG ENGINEERING & CONSTRUCTION CO., LTD.; *Int'l*, pg. 7406
TAEYOUNG GRAIN TERMINAL CORPORATION—See TAEYOUNG Engineering & Construction Co., Ltd.; *Int'l*, pg. 7406
TAFEL MOTORS INCORPORATED; *U.S. Private*, pg. 3921

COMPANY NAME INDEX

TAFI INDUSTRIES BERHAD; *Int'l*, pg. 7406
TA FIRST CREDIT SDN. BHD—See TA Enterprise Berhad; *Int'l*, pg. 7399
TAFONCO A.S.—See Tatra, a.s.; *Int'l*, pg. 7474
TAFORGE A.S.—See Tatra, a.s.; *Int'l*, pg. 7474
TAFT ENGINEERING, INC.—See Watts Water Technologies, Inc.; *U.S. Public*, pg. 2337
TAFT PRODUCTION COMPANY—See Oil-Dri Corporation of America; *U.S. Public*, pg. 1566
TAFT RECYCLING, INC.—See Waste Connections, Inc.; *Int'l*, pg. 8354
TAFT STETTINIUS & HOLLISTER LLP - CHICAGO—See Taft Stettinius & Hollister LLP; *U.S. Private*, pg. 3922
TAFT STETTINIUS & HOLLISTER LLP; *U.S. Private*, pg. 3921
T.A. FURNITURE INDUSTRIES SDN. BHD.—See TAFI Industries Berhad; *Int'l*, pg. 7406
TA FUTURES SDN BHD—See TA Enterprise Berhad; *Int'l*, pg. 7399
TAG-1 CO., LTD.—See Zensho Holdings Co., Ltd.; *Int'l*, pg. 8634
TAGANITO HPAL NICKEL CORPORATION—See Sumitomo Metal Mining Co., Ltd.; *Int'l*, pg. 7292
TAGANITO MINING CORPORATION—See Nickel Asia Corporation; *Int'l*, pg. 5271
TAGANROGSKIY KOMB ZAVOD AO; *Int'l*, pg. 7407
TAG AVIATION ASIA LTD.—See TAG Aviation S.A.; *Int'l*, pg. 7406
TAG AVIATION AUSTRALIA PTY LTD.—See TAG Aviation S.A.; *Int'l*, pg. 7406
TAG AVIATION ESPANA S.L.—See TAG Aviation S.A.; *Int'l*, pg. 7406
TAG AVIATION EUROPE S.A.—See TAG Aviation S.A.; *Int'l*, pg. 7406
TAG AVIATION MIDDLE-EAST WLL—See TAG Aviation S.A.; *Int'l*, pg. 7406
TAG AVIATION S.A.; *Int'l*, pg. 7406
TAG AVIATION (UK) LTD—See TAG Aviation S.A.; *Int'l*, pg. 7406
TAG AVIATION USA, INC.—See TAG Aviation S.A.; *Int'l*, pg. 7406
TAGAWA GREENHOUSES, INC.; *U.S. Private*, pg. 3922
TAGAYTAY HIGHLANDS INTERNATIONAL GOLF CLUB, INC.—See Belle Corporation; *Int'l*, pg. 066
TAGAYTAY MIDLANDS GOLF CLUB, INC.—See Belle Corporation; *Int'l*, pg. 966
TAGBLATT DER STADT ZURICH AG—See TX Group AG; *Int'l*, pg. 7992
TAG COMPOSITES & CARPETS GMBH—See Jagenberg AG; *Int'l*, pg. 3870
TAG CONSULTING; *U.S. Private*, pg. 3922
TAG CREATIVE LIMITED—See Dentsu Group Inc.; *Int'l*, pg. 2039
TAG D.D. GORAZDE; *Int'l*, pg. 7406
TAG ELECTRIC COMPANY; *U.S. Private*, pg. 3922
TAG EMPLOYER SERVICES, LLC; *U.S. Private*, pg. 3922
TAG ENVIRONMENTAL INC.—See Leggett & Platt, Incorporated; *U.S. Public*, pg. 1303
TAG EUROPE LIMITED—See Dentsu Group Inc.; *Int'l*, pg. 2039
TAG FASTENERS SDN. BHD.—See Illinois Tool Works Inc.; *U.S. Public*, pg. 1111
TAGGARTS MOTOR GROUP LTD.—See Lookers plc; *Int'l*, pg. 4555
TAGGED, INC.; *U.S. Private*, pg. 3922
TAG GERMANY GMBH—See Dentsu Group Inc.; *Int'l*, pg. 2039
TAGG LOGISTICS, LLC—See Hub Group, Inc.; *U.S. Public*, pg. 1066
TAG HEUER CANADA LTD.—See LVMH Moet Hennessy Louis Vuitton SE; *Int'l*, pg. 4603
TAG HEUER S.A.—See LVMH Moet Hennessy Louis Vuitton SE; *Int'l*, pg. 4603
TAGHLEEF INDUSTRIES CANADA INC.—See Al Ghurair Group; *Int'l*, pg. 277
TAGHLEEF INDUSTRIES GMBH—See Al Ghurair Group; *Int'l*, pg. 277
TAGHLEEF INDUSTRIES INC.—See Al Ghurair Group; *Int'l*, pg. 277
TAGHLEEF INDUSTRIES KFT—See Al Ghurair Group; *Int'l*, pg. 278
TAGHLEEF INDUSTRIES L.L.C.—See Al Ghurair Group; *Int'l*, pg. 277
TAGHLEEF INDUSTRIES PTY. LTD.—See Al Ghurair Group; *Int'l*, pg. 277
TAGHLEEF INDUSTRIES S.A.E.—See Al Ghurair Group; *Int'l*, pg. 277
TAGHLEEF INDUSTRIES S.A.O.C.—See Al Ghurair Group; *Int'l*, pg. 278
TAGHLEEF INDUSTRIES S.L.U.—See Al Ghurair Group; *Int'l*, pg. 278
TAGHLEEF INDUSTRIES S.L.U.—See Al Ghurair Group; *Int'l*, pg. 278
TAGHLEEF INDUSTRIES S.P.A.—See Al Ghurair Group; *Int'l*, pg. 278
TAG HOLDINGS, LLC; *U.S. Private*, pg. 3922
TAG IDEA REVOLUTION; *Int'l*, pg. 7406
TAG IMMOBILIEN AG; *Int'l*, pg. 7406
TAG INDIA PRIVATE LIMITED—See Dentsu Group Inc.; *Int'l*, pg. 2039
TAG-IT PACIFIC (HK) LTD—See Talon International, Inc.; *U.S. Public*, pg. 1980
TAG LEIPZIG-IMMOBILIEN GMBH—See TAG Immobilien AG; *Int'l*, pg. 7407
TAGLIAFERRI ELECTRIC ARC FURNACES—See Techint S.p.A.; *Int'l*, pg. 7504
TAGLICH BROTHERS, INC.; *U.S. Private*, pg. 3922
TAGLICH BROTHERS, INC.—See Taglich Brothers, Inc.; *U.S. Private*, pg. 3922
TAGLICH PRIVATE EQUITY LLC; *U.S. Private*, pg. 3922
TA GLOBAL BERHAD—See TA Enterprise Berhad; *Int'l*, pg. 7399
TAG LOGISTIK IMMOBILIEN GMBH & CO. KG—See TAG Immobilien AG; *Int'l*, pg. 7407
TAG MAGDEBURG-IMMOBILIEN GMBH—See TAG Immobilien AG; *Int'l*, pg. 7407
TAG MAINTENANCE SERVICES FARNBOROUGH LTD.—See TAG Aviation S.A.; *Int'l*, pg. 7406
TAGMAN, INC.—See Ensighten, Inc.; *U.S. Private*, pg. 1402
TAGMAN LIMITED—See Ensighten, Inc.; *U.S. Private*, pg. 1402
TAG MANUFACTURING, INC.; *U.S. Private*, pg. 3922
TAGMASTER AB; *Int'l*, pg. 7407
TAG MENA FZE—See Dentsu Group Inc.; *Int'l*, pg. 2039
TAGMET PAO—See PAO TMK; *Int'l*, pg. 5733
TAG NEWCO LIMITED—See Dentsu Group Inc.; *Int'l*, pg. 2039
TAG OIL LTD.; *Int'l*, pg. 7407
TAG ONE, INC.—See AE Industrial Partners, LP; *U.S. Private*, pg. 111
TAG PAC LIMITED—See Deutsche Post AG; *Int'l*, pg. 2082
TAG POTSDAM-IMMOBILIEN GMBH—See TAG Immobilien AG; *Int'l*, pg. 7407
TAG PRINT SERVICES LIMITED—See Dentsu Group Inc.; *Int'l*, pg. 2039
TAG RESOURCES LLC—See Aegon N.V.; *Int'l*, pg. 174
TAG RESPONSE LIMITED—See Dentsu Group Inc.; *Int'l*, pg. 2039
TAGROS D.O.O.—See Cargotec Corporation; *Int'l*, pg. 1329
TAG SAO PAULO SERVICO DE CONSULTORIA LTDA.—See Dentsu Group Inc.; *Int'l*, pg. 2039
TAGS & LABELS—See Heartwood Partners, LLC; *U.S. Private*, pg. 1901
TAG SOLUTIONS, LLC—See Charge Enterprises, Inc.; *U.S. Public*, pg. 479
TAG STADTHAUS AM ANGER GMBH—See TAG Immobilien AG; *Int'l*, pg. 7407
TAG SYSTEMS SMART SOLUTIONS S.L.U.—See Austriacard Holdings AG; *Int'l*, pg. 724
TAG TRUCK CENTER; *U.S. Private*, pg. 3922
TAGUE LUMBER INC.; *U.S. Private*, pg. 3922
TAGUS - SOCIEDADE DE TITULARIZACAO DE CREDITOS, S.A.—See Deutsche Bank Aktiengesellschaft; *Int'l*, pg. 2062
TAG WOHNEN & SERVICE GMBH—See TAG Immobilien AG; *Int'l*, pg. 7407
TAG WOHNEN & SERVICE GMBH—See TAG Immobilien AG; *Int'l*, pg. 7407
TAG WOHNIMMOBILIEN HALLE GMBH & CO. KG—See TAG Immobilien AG; *Int'l*, pg. 7407
TAG WOLFSBURG-IMMOBILIEN GMBH—See TAG Immobilien AG; *Int'l*, pg. 7407
TAG WORLDWIDE AUSTRALIA PTY LTD.—See Dentsu Group Inc.; *Int'l*, pg. 2039
TAG WORLDWIDE GROUP LIMITED—See Dentsu Group Inc.; *Int'l*, pg. 2039
TAG WORLDWIDE HOLDINGS LIMITED—See Dentsu Group Inc.; *Int'l*, pg. 2039
TAG WORLDWIDE (SHANGHAI) CO LTD.—See Dentsu Group Inc.; *Int'l*, pg. 2039
TAG WORLDWIDE (SINGAPORE) PTE. LTD.—See Dentsu Group Inc.; *Int'l*, pg. 2039
TAG WORLDWIDE (USA) INC.—See Dentsu Group Inc.; *Int'l*, pg. 2039
TAHAL CONSULTING ENGINEERS LTD.—See Kardan N.V.; *Int'l*, pg. 4079
TAHAL GROUP ASSETS B.V.—See Kardan N.V.; *Int'l*, pg. 4079
TAHAL GROUP B.V.—See Kardan N.V.; *Int'l*, pg. 4079
TAHAL GROUP INTERNATIONAL B.V.—See Kardan N.V.; *Int'l*, pg. 4079
TAHARA MACHINERY LTD.—See The Japan Steel Works, Ltd.; *Int'l*, pg. 7659
TAHA SPINNING MILLS LIMITED; *Int'l*, pg. 7407
TA HEIMEIER GMBH—See IMI plc; *Int'l*, pg. 3626
TA HENG ELECTRIC WIRE & CABLE CO., LTD.—See Ta Ya Electric Wire & Cable Co., Ltd.; *Int'l*, pg. 7400
TAHER INC; *U.S. Private*, pg. 3922
TAH HSIN INDUSTRIAL CORPORATION; *Int'l*, pg. 7407
TAH HSIN INDUSTRIAL CORPORATION - TAICHUNG PLANT—See Tah Hsin Industrial Corporation; *Int'l*, pg. 7407
TAHITIAN NONI INTERNATIONAL—See NewAge, Inc.; *U.S. Public*, pg. 1513

TAI CHEUNG HOLDINGS LIMITED

TAHITI MOTOR YET SING—See Toyota Tsusho Corporation; *Int'l*, pg. 7876
TAHITI PHARM (FRENCH POLYNESIA) S.A—See Toyota Tsusho Corporation; *Int'l*, pg. 7876
TAH KONG CHEMICAL INDUSTRIAL CORP.; *Int'l*, pg. 7407
TAH KONG FINE CHEMICAL (KUN-SHAN) CO., LTD.—See Tah Kong Chemical Industrial Corp.; *Int'l*, pg. 7407
TAHLEQUAH CABLE TELEVISION INC.—See Wehco Media, Inc.; *U.S. Private*, pg. 4469
TAHLEQUAH PUBLIC WORKS AUTHORITY; *U.S. Private*, pg. 3923
TAHMAR ENTERPRISES LIMITED; *Int'l*, pg. 7408
TAHMOOR COAL PTY. LIMITED—See GFG Alliance Limited; *Int'l*, pg. 2956
TAHOCO LOGISTICS, INC.—See Thompson, Ahern & Co. Ltd.; *Int'l*, pg. 7714
TAHOE DONNER ASSOCIATION; *U.S. Private*, pg. 3923
TAHOE GROUP CO., LTD.—See Tahoe Investment Group Co., Ltd.; *Int'l*, pg. 7408
TAHOE INVESTMENT GROUP CO., LTD.; *Int'l*, pg. 7408
TAHOE JOE'S FAMOUS STEAKHOUSE, INC.—See Food Management Partners, Inc.; *U.S. Private*, pg. 1561
TAHOE LIFE INSURANCE CO., LTD.—See Tahoe Investment Group Co., Ltd.; *Int'l*, pg. 7408
TAHO ENGINEERING CO., LTD.—See The Furukawa Electric Co., Ltd.; *Int'l*, pg. 7647
TAHOE PARTNERS, LLC; *U.S. Private*, pg. 3923
TAHOE RESOURCES INC.—See Pan American Silver Corp.; *Int'l*, pg. 5713
TAHOE SAND & GRAVEL INC.—See Trilantic Capital Management L.P.; *U.S. Private*, pg. 4231
TAHOKA FIRST BANCORP INC.; *U.S. Private*, pg. 3923
TA HOLDINGS LIMITED—See Masawara PLC; *Int'l*, pg. 4719
TAHSIN INDUSTRIAL CORP—See Tah Hsin Industrial Corporation; *Int'l*, pg. 7407
TAHSIN SHOJI CO.,LTD—See Tah Hsin Industrial Corporation; *Int'l*, pg. 7407
TAH TONG TEXTILE CO., LTD. - CHUNGLI MILL—See Tah Tong Textile Co., Ltd.; *Int'l*, pg. 7407
TAH TONG TEXTILE CO., LTD.; *Int'l*, pg. 7407
TAH TONG TEXTILE CO., LTD. - TAICHUNG MILL—See Tah Tong Textile Co., Ltd.; *Int'l*, pg. 7407
TA HYDRONICS AS—See IMI plc; *Int'l*, pg. 3626
TAHZOO LLC; *U.S. Private*, pg. 3923
TAIAN AGS PIPELINE CONSTRUCTION CO., LTD.—See Halcyon Coast Investment (Canada) Ltd.; *Int'l*, pg. 3227
TAIAN HAOHUA PLASTIC CO., LTD—See China National Chemical Corporation; *Int'l*, pg. 1527
TAIAN HAVAY GROUP CO., LTD.—See GHW International; *Int'l*, pg. 2960
TAIAN-JAYA ELECTRIC SDN. BHD.—See Teco Electric & Machinery Co., Ltd.; *Int'l*, pg. 7518
TAIAN (SUBIC) ELECTRIC CO., INC.—See Teco Electric & Machinery Co., Ltd.; *Int'l*, pg. 7518
TAI-AN TECHNOLOGY (WUXI) CO., LTD.—See Teco Electric & Machinery Co., Ltd.; *Int'l*, pg. 7518
TAIBA INVESTMENTS COMPANY; *Int'l*, pg. 7410
TAICANG ALPINE ELECTRONICS CO., LTD.—See Alps Alpine Co., Ltd.; *Int'l*, pg. 376
TAICANG BAOZEN AUTOMOBILE SALES AND SERVICES CO., LTD.—See China Yongda Automobiles Services Holdings Limited; *Int'l*, pg. 1565
TAICANG BONDEX-NISSHIN LOGISTICS CO., LTD.; *Int'l*, pg. 7410
TAICANG CIMC CONTAINERS CO., LTD.—See China International Marine Containers (Group) Co., Ltd.; *Int'l*, pg. 1512
TAICANG CONET ELECTRONICS CO., LTD.—See IDEC Corporation; *Int'l*, pg. 3590
TAICANG KLH COOLING SYSTEMS CO. LTD.—See Technotrans AG; *Int'l*, pg. 7511
TAICANG ONWARD HIGH FASHION CO., LTD.—See Onward Holdings Co., Ltd.; *Int'l*, pg. 5593
TAICANG PACIFIC MILLENNIUM PACKAGING & PAPER INDUSTRIES CO., LTD.—See Pacific Millennium Packaging Group Corporation; *Int'l*, pg. 5691
TAICANG SEJONG INDUSTRIAL CO., LTD.—See SJG Sejong Co., Ltd.; *Int'l*, pg. 6969
TAICANG T&W ELECTRONICS CO., LTD.—See Shenzhen Gongjin Electronics Co., Ltd.; *Int'l*, pg. 6810
TAICANG VAN OERLE ALBERTON SHENDA SPECIAL TYPE TEXTILE PRODUCTS CO., LTD.—See Autoliv, Inc.; *Int'l*, pg. 730
TAICANG ZHONGSHENG STAR AUTOMOBILE SALES & SERVICE CO., LTD.—See Zhongsheng Group Holdings Limited; *Int'l*, pg. 8674
TAICERA ENTERPRISE COMPANY; *Int'l*, pg. 7410
TAICHA MEDICAL CORP.—See Hi-Clearance, Inc.; *Int'l*, pg. 3380
TAICHEM MATERIALS CO., LTD.—See Taiflex Scientific Co., Ltd.; *Int'l*, pg. 7410
TAI CHEUNG HOLDINGS LIMITED; *Int'l*, pg. 7408
TAI CHIN CHEMICAL INDUSTRY CO., LTD.—See Dainichiseika Color & Chemicals Mfg. Co., Ltd.; *Int'l*, pg. 1939

TAICHUNG COMMERCIAL BANK CO., LTD.

TAICHUNG COMMERCIAL BANK CO., LTD.; *Int'l*, pg. 7410
TAICHUNG PHOTRONICS PHOTOMASK CO., LTD.—See Photronics, Inc.; *U.S. Public*, pg. 1689
TAICIN SY CO., LTD.—See Daikin Industries, Ltd.; *Int'l*, pg. 1936
TAI CORPORATION; *U.S. Private*, pg. 3923
TAIC- SAN DIEGO, INC.—See Dream Center Foundation, a California Nonprofit Corp.; *U.S. Private*, pg. 1274
TAIC- SAN FRANCISCO, INC.—See Dream Center Foundation, a California Nonprofit Corp.; *U.S. Private*, pg. 1274
TAIDEN ENVIRONTECH CO., LTD.—See Takuma Co., Ltd.; *Int'l*, pg. 7442
TAIDOC TECHNOLOGY CORP.; *Int'l*, pg. 7410
TAIEI SANGYO CO., LTD.—See Marubeni Corporation; *Int'l*, pg. 4710
TAIER HEAVY INDUSTRY CO., LTD.; *Int'l*, pg. 7410
TAIF-INVEST OOO—See PSC TAIF; *Int'l*, pg. 6016
TAIFLEX GREEN POWER CO., LTD.—See Taiflex Scientific Co., Ltd.; *Int'l*, pg. 7410
TAIFLEX SCIENTIFIC CO., LTD.; *Int'l*, pg. 7410
TAIFLEX SCIENTIFIC JAPAN CO., LTD.—See Taiflex Scientific Co., Ltd.; *Int'l*, pg. 7410
TAIFLEX SCIENTIFIC (THAILAND) CO., LTD.—See Taiflex Scientific Co., Ltd.; *Int'l*, pg. 7410
TAIFLEX USA CORPORATION—See Taiflex Scientific Co., Ltd.; *Int'l*, pg. 7410
TAIF-NK—See PSC TAIF; *Int'l*, pg. 6016
TAIFON COMPUTER CO., LTD.—See SYSTEX Corporation; *Int'l*, pg. 7393
TAI FOONG INTERNATIONAL LTD.; *Int'l*, pg. 7408
TAIFUN-COLLECTION GERRY WEBER FASHION GMBH—See GERRY WEBER International AG; *Int'l*, pg. 2945
TAI FUNG BANK LIMITED—See Bank of China, Ltd.; *Int'l*, pg. 842
TAI FUNG COACH COMPANY LIMITED—See KWOON CHUNG BUS HOLDINGS LIMITED; *Int'l*, pg. 4351
TAIGA BUILDING PRODUCTS LTD.—See Avarga Limited; *Int'l*, pg. 737
TAIGA BUILDING PRODUCTS USA LTD.—See Avarga Limited; *Int'l*, pg. 737
TAIGEN BIOPHARMACEUTICALS HOLDINGS LTD.; *Int'l*, pg. 7410
TAIGMARKS INC.; *U.S. Private*, pg. 3923
TAIHAN CABLE & SOLUTION CO., LTD.; *Int'l*, pg. 7410
TAIHAN ELECTRIC USA, LTD.—See Taihan Cable & Solution Co., Ltd.; *Int'l*, pg. 7410
TAIHAN ELECTRIC WIRE CO., LTD. - DANGJIN PLANT—See Taihan Cable & Solution Co., Ltd.; *Int'l*, pg. 7410
TAIHAN FIBEROPTICS CO., LTD.; *Int'l*, pg. 7410
TAIHAN PRECISION TECHNOLOGY CO., LTD.; *Int'l*, pg. 7411
TAIHAN TEXTILE CO., LTD. - DAEGU PLANT—See Taihan Textile Co., Ltd.; *Int'l*, pg. 7411
TAIHAN TEXTILE CO., LTD. - JEONJU PLANT—See Taihan Textile Co., Ltd.; *Int'l*, pg. 7411
TAIHAN TEXTILE CO., LTD.; *Int'l*, pg. 7411
TAIHAN TEXTILE(SHANGHAI)CO., LTD.—See Taihan Textile Co., Ltd.; *Int'l*, pg. 7411
TAIHE GROUP, INC.; *U.S. Public*, pg. 1978
TAIHEI BUTSURYU CO., LTD.—See Takara Holdings, Inc.; *Int'l*, pg. 7432
TAIHEI CHEMICALS LIMITED - KAWAGUCHI FACTORY—See Tosoh Corporation; *Int'l*, pg. 7833
TAIHEI CHEMICALS LIMITED—See Tosoh Corporation; *Int'l*, pg. 7833
TAIHEI CHEMICALS LIMITED - SOUKA FACTORY—See Tosoh Corporation; *Int'l*, pg. 7833
TAIHEI COMPUTER CO., LTD.—See Hirata Corporation; *Int'l*, pg. 3404
TAIHEI DENGYO KAISHA LTD.; *Int'l*, pg. 7411
TAIHEI ELECTRIC CO., LTD.—See TOYO DENKI SEIZO K.K.; *Int'l*, pg. 7852
TAIHEI HOUSING CO., LTD.—See Taihei Machinery Works, Ltd.; *Int'l*, pg. 7411
TAIHEI MACHINERY WORKS, LTD. - OSAKA PLANT—See Taihei Machinery Works, Ltd.; *Int'l*, pg. 7411
TAIHEI MACHINERY WORKS, LTD.; *Int'l*, pg. 7411
TAIHEI METAL INDUSTRY CO., LTD.—See Sumitomo Metal Mining Co., Ltd.; *Int'l*, pg. 7293
TAIHEI PRINTING LTD.—See Takara Holdings, Inc.; *Int'l*, pg. 7432
TAIHEI REAL ESTATE CORPORATION—See Senko Group Holdings Co., Ltd.; *Int'l*, pg. 6710
TAIHEI SANGYO CO., LTD.—See Dynic Corporation; *Int'l*, pg. 2243
TAIHEI (SHANGHAI) CO., LTD.—See Tosoh Corporation; *Int'l*, pg. 7833
TAIHEI TECHNOS CO., LTD.—See Hirata Corporation; *Int'l*, pg. 3404
TAIHEIYO ACCOUNTING & FINANCIAL SERVICES CORPORATION—See Taiheiyo Cement Corporation; *Int'l*, pg. 7412
TAIHEIYO CEMENT (CHINA) INVESTMENT CO., LTD.—See Taiheiyo Cement Corporation; *Int'l*, pg. 7412

TAIHEIYO CEMENT CORPORATION; *Int'l*, pg. 7411
TAIHEIYO CEMENT PHILIPPINES, INC.—See Taiheiyo Cement Corporation; *Int'l*, pg. 7412
TAIHEIYO CEMENT U.S.A., INC.—See Taiheiyo Cement Corporation; *Int'l*, pg. 7412
TAIHEIYO CLUB, INC.—See Maruhan Corporation; *Int'l*, pg. 4712
TAIHEIYO COAL MINING CO., LTD.—See Taiheiyo Kouhatsu Incorporated; *Int'l*, pg. 7412
TAIHEIYO COAL SERVICE & TRANSPORTATION CO., LTD.—See Taiheiyo Kouhatsu Incorporated; *Int'l*, pg. 7412
TAIHEIYO ENGINEERING CORPORATION—See Taiheiyo Cement Corporation; *Int'l*, pg. 7412
TAIHEIYO GOLF SERVICE, K.K.—See Maruhan Corporation; *Int'l*, pg. 4712
TAIHEIYO GOLF SQUARE, INC.—See Maruhan Corporation; *Int'l*, pg. 4712
TAIHEIYO KISEN KAISHA, LTD.—See Nippon Yusen Kabushiki Kaisha; *Int'l*, pg. 5359
TAIHEIYO KOSAN CO., LTD.—See Pacific Metals Co., Ltd.; *Int'l*, pg. 5690
TAIHEIYO KOUHATSU INCORPORATED; *Int'l*, pg. 7412
TAIHEIYO MATERIALS CORPORATION—See Taiheiyo Cement Corporation; *Int'l*, pg. 7412
TAIHEIYO PRECAST CONCRETE INDUSTRY CO., LTD.—See Taiheiyo Cement Corporation; *Int'l*, pg. 7412
TAIHEIYO REAL ESTATE CO., LTD.—See Taiheiyo Cement Corporation; *Int'l*, pg. 7412
TAIHEIYO SANGYO CO., LTD.—See PACIFIC INDUSTRIAL CO. LTD.; *Int'l*, pg. 5690
TAIHEIYO SEISAKUSHO INC.—See Taiheiyo Kouhatsu Incorporated; *Int'l*, pg. 7412
TAIHEIYO SILVER SERVICE CO., LTD.—See Taiheiyo Kouhatsu Incorporated; *Int'l*, pg. 7412
TAIHEIYO SILVER SERVICE HOKKAIDO CO., LTD.—See Taiheiyo Kouhatsu Incorporated; *Int'l*, pg. 7412
TAIHEIYO SINGAPORE PTE. LTD.—See Taiheiyo Cement Corporation; *Int'l*, pg. 7412
TAIHEIYO UNYU INC.—See Taiheiyo Kouhatsu Incorporated; *Int'l*, pg. 7412
TAI HING GROUP HOLDINGS LIMITED; *Int'l*, pg. 7408
TAI HING PAPER PRODUCTS COMPANY, LIMITED—See Hung Hing Printing Group Limited; *Int'l*, pg. 3535
TAIHO CORPORATION OF AMERICA—See Taiho Kogyo Co., Ltd; *Int'l*, pg. 7413
TAIHO CORPORATION OF EUROPE KFT.—See Taiho Kogyo Co., Ltd; *Int'l*, pg. 7413
TAIHO CORPORATION OF KOREA—See Taiho Kogyo Co., Ltd; *Int'l*, pg. 7413
TAIHO KOGYO CO., LTD - MAIN PLANT—See Taiho Kogyo Co., Ltd; *Int'l*, pg. 7413
TAIHO KOGYO CO., LTD; *Int'l*, pg. 7412
TAIHO KOGYO CORPORATION OF YANTAI—See Taiho Kogyo Co., Ltd; *Int'l*, pg. 7413
TAIHO MARINE CO., LTD.—See Iino Kaiun Kaisha Ltd.; *Int'l*, pg. 3608
TAI HONG CIRCUIT IND. CO., LTD.—See ChangChun Group; *Int'l*, pg. 1442
TAI HONG CIRCUIT IND. CO., LTD.—See Mitsubishi Gas Chemical Company, Inc.; *Int'l*, pg. 4950
TAIHO PAPER CO., LTD.—See Japan Pulp and Paper Company Limited; *Int'l*, pg. 3905
TAIHO PHARMACEUTICAL CO., LTD.—See Otsuka Holdings Co., Ltd.; *Int'l*, pg. 5661
TAIHO PHARMACEUTICAL OF BEIJING CO., LTD.—See Otsuka Holdings Co., Ltd.; *Int'l*, pg. 5661
TAIHO PHARMA U.S.A., INC.—See Otsuka Holdings Co., Ltd.; *Int'l*, pg. 5661
TAIHO SANGYO CORPORATION—See OSG Corporation; *Int'l*, pg. 5649
TAIHO TOOL MFG. CO., LTD.—See OSG Corporation; *Int'l*, pg. 5649
TAIHO TRANSPORTATION CO., LTD.; *Int'l*, pg. 7413
TAI HUA CARBURETER CO., LTD.—See NIKKI CO. LTD.; *Int'l*, pg. 5290
TAIHUA SHIPPING (BEJING) LIMITED—See Pacific Basin Shipping Limited; *Int'l*, pg. 5686
TAI-I COPPER (GUANGZHOU) CO., LTD.—See Tai-I Electric Wire & Cable Co., Ltd.; *Int'l*, pg. 7409
TAI-I ELECTRIC WIRE & CABLE CO., LTD. - GUANYIN PLANT—See Tai-I Electric Wire & Cable Co., Ltd.; *Int'l*, pg. 7409
TAI-I ELECTRIC WIRE & CABLE CO., LTD. - HSINCHU PLANT—See Tai-I Electric Wire & Cable Co., Ltd.; *Int'l*, pg. 7409
TAI-I ELECTRIC WIRE & CABLE CO., LTD.; *Int'l*, pg. 7409
TAI-I JIANG CORP (GUANGZHOU) CO., LTD.—See Tai-I Electric Wire & Cable Co., Ltd.; *Int'l*, pg. 7409
TAI INDUSTRIES LIMITED; *Int'l*, pg. 7408
TAIJI COMPUTER CORPORATION LIMITED; *Int'l*, pg. 7413
TAIJI SEMICONDUCTOR (SUZHOU) CO., LTD.—See Wuxi Taiji Industry Co., Ltd.; *Int'l*, pg. 8516
TAIJU LIFE INSURANCE COMPANY LIMITED—See Nippon Life Insurance Company; *Int'l*, pg. 5323
TAIJU LIFE & I TECHNOLOGY LTD.—See Nippon Life Insurance Company; *Int'l*, pg. 5323

CORPORATE AFFILIATIONS

TAI KAM HOLDINGS LIMITED; *Int'l*, pg. 7408
TAIKANG INSURANCE GROUP CO., LTD.; *Int'l*, pg. 7413
TAIKISHA (CAMBODIA) CO., LTD.—See Taikisha Ltd.; *Int'l*, pg. 7413
TAIKISHA CANADA INC.—See Taikisha Ltd.; *Int'l*, pg. 7413
TAIKISHA DO BRASIL LTDA.—See Taikisha Ltd.; *Int'l*, pg. 7413
TAIKISHA ENGINEERING INDIA LTD.—See Taikisha Ltd.; *Int'l*, pg. 7414
TAIKISHA ENGINEERING INDIA PVT. LTD. - MANUFACTURING PLANT—See Taikisha Ltd.; *Int'l*, pg. 7414
TAIKISHA ENGINEERING (M) SDN. BHD.—See Taikisha Ltd.; *Int'l*, pg. 7414
TAIKISHA KOREA LTD.—See Taikisha Ltd.; *Int'l*, pg. 7414
TAIKISHA LAO CO., LTD.—See Taikisha Ltd.; *Int'l*, pg. 7414
TAIKISHA LTD.; *Int'l*, pg. 7413
TAIKISHA MYANMAR CO., LTD.—See Taikisha Ltd.; *Int'l*, pg. 7414
TAIKISHA PHILIPPINES INC.—See Taikisha Ltd.; *Int'l*, pg. 7414
TAIKISHA (SINGAPORE) PTE. LTD.—See Taikisha Ltd.; *Int'l*, pg. 7413
TAIKISHA (TAIWAN) LTD.—See Taikisha Ltd.; *Int'l*, pg. 7413
TAIKISHA (THAILAND) CO., LTD. - PAINT FINISHING DIVISION—See Taikisha Ltd.; *Int'l*, pg. 7414
TAIKISHA (THAILAND) CO., LTD.—See Taikisha Ltd.; *Int'l*, pg. 7413
TAIKISHA TRADING (THAILAND) CO., LTD.—See Taikisha Ltd.; *Int'l*, pg. 7414
TAIKISHA VIETNAM ENGINEERING INC.—See Taikisha Ltd.; *Int'l*, pg. 7414
THE TAIKO BANK, LTD.; *Int'l*, pg. 7693
TAIKO ELECTRIC WORK, LTD.—See Oki Electric Industry Co., Ltd.; *Int'l*, pg. 5549
TAIKO ENVIRONMENTALTECHNOLOGIES(SHANGHAI) CO., LTD.—See Taiko Pharmaceutical Co., Ltd.; *Int'l*, pg. 7414
TAIKOH TRANSPORTATION CO., LTD.—See Toyota Industries Corporation; *Int'l*, pg. 7866
TAIKO PAPER MFG., LTD.—See Rengo Co., Ltd.; *Int'l*, pg. 6281
TAIKO PHARMACEUTICAL (ASIA PACIFIC) CO., LTD.—See Taiko Pharmaceutical Co., Ltd.; *Int'l*, pg. 7414
TAIKO PHARMACEUTICAL CO., LTD.; *Int'l*, pg. 7414
TAIKO PHARMACEUTICAL (SHENZHEN) CO., LTD.—See Taiko Pharmaceutical Co., Ltd.; *Int'l*, pg. 7414
TAIKO PLANTATIONS SDN BHD—See Kuala Lumpur Kepong Berhad; *Int'l*, pg. 4319
TAIKO SHOJI LTD.—See BASF SE; *Int'l*, pg. 885
TAIKO TRADING CO., LTD.—See Kajima Corporation; *Int'l*, pg. 4055
TAI KUN (DG) ELECTRONICS HARDWARE CO., LIMITED—See Jess-Link Products Co., Ltd.; *Int'l*, pg. 3932
TAILAM TECH CONSTRUCTION HOLDINGS LIMITED; *Int'l*, pg. 7414
TAILIM CO., LTD. - CHEONGWON FACTORY—See Tailim Co., Ltd.; *Int'l*, pg. 7414
TAILIM CO., LTD. - GWANGJU FACTORY—See Tailim Co,. Ltd.; *Int'l*, pg. 7414
TAILIM CO., LTD. - IKSAN FACTORY—See Tailim Co., Ltd.; *Int'l*, pg. 7414
TAILIM CO,. LTD. - KUMI FACTORY—See Tailim Co,. Ltd.; *Int'l*, pg. 7414
TAILIM CO,. LTD. - POCHEON FACTORY—See Tailim Co,. Ltd.; *Int'l*, pg. 7414
TAILIM CO,. LTD.; *Int'l*, pg. 7414
TAILIM CO,. LTD. - YANGJU FACTORY—See Tailim Co,. Ltd.; *Int'l*, pg. 7414
TAILIM PAPER CO., LTD.; *Int'l*, pg. 7414
TAIL INC.; *U.S. Private*, pg. 3923
TAI-LING BIOTECH, INC.—See Taiwan Tea Corporation; *Int'l*, pg. 7425
TAI LIN INVESTMENT COMPANY—See Taiwan Tea Corporation; *Int'l*, pg. 7425
TAILORED ADJUSTMENT SERVICES, INC.—See Global Risk Solutions, Inc.; *U.S. Private*, pg. 1717
TAILORED BRANDS, INC.; *U.S. Public*, pg. 1978
TAILORED FOAM OF FLORIDA, INC.—See SEI Group, Inc.; *U.S. Private*, pg. 3599
TAILORED LABEL PRODUCTS, INC.; *U.S. Private*, pg. 3923
TAILORED MANAGEMENT, INC.; *U.S. Private*, pg. 3923
TAILOR MADE COMPOUNDING, LLC; *U.S. Private*, pg. 3923
TAILOR WELDED BLANKS OF CANADA, INC.—See Worthington Industries, Inc.; *U.S. Public*, pg. 2382
TAILORWELL INC.—See Cambia Health Solutions, Inc.; *U.S. Private*, pg. 726
TAIL TARGET TECNOLOGIA DE INFORMACAO LTD.—See TOTVS S.A.; *Int'l*, pg. 7846
TAILWATER CAPITAL LLC; *U.S. Private*, pg. 3923
TAILWIND CAPITAL GROUP, LLC; *U.S. Private*, pg. 3923
TAILWIND ENERGY LTD.; *Int'l*, pg. 7414
TAILWIND INTERNATIONAL ACQUISITION CORP.; *U.S. Private*, pg. 3924

COMPANY NAME INDEX

TAILWIND MANAGEMENT LP—See Tailwind Capital Group, LLC; *U.S. Private*, pg. 3924
TAILWINDS DEVELOPMENT, LLC; *U.S. Private*, pg. 3924
TAILWIND TECHNOLOGIES INC.; *U.S. Private*, pg. 3924
TAILYN TECHNOLOGIES, INC.; *Int'l*, pg. 7414
TAIMED BIOLOGICS INC.; *Int'l*, pg. 7415
TAIMED BIOLOGICS USA CORP.—See TaiMed Biologics Inc.; *Int'l*, pg. 7415
TAI MEI FOOD INDUSTRIAL CORP.—See Nissui Corporation; *Int'l*, pg. 5379
TAIMEN TRANSPORT, LLC; *U.S. Private*, pg. 3924
TAIMIDE TECH. INC.; *Int'l*, pg. 7415
TAIMING ASSURANCE BROKER CO., LTD.; *Int'l*, pg. 7415
TAI MING GREEN POWER CO., LTD.—See Taiwan Surface Mounting Technology Corp.; *Int'l*, pg. 7424
TAINAHONG TRADING LIMITED—See TT International Limited; *Int'l*, pg. 7960
TAINAN ENTERPRISE (CAYMAN) CO., LTD.—See Tainan Enterprises Co., Ltd.; *Int'l*, pg. 7415
TAINAN ENTERPRISES CO., LTD.; *Int'l*, pg. 7415
TAINAN ENTERPRISES CO., LTD. - TAIWAN FACTORY—See Tainan Enterprises Co., Ltd.; *Int'l*, pg. 7415
TAINAN SPINNING CO. LTD.—See Tainan Spinning Company Limited; *Int'l*, pg. 7415
TAINAN SPINNING COMPANY LIMITED - RENDE PLANT & FIBER PLANT—See Tainan Spinning Company Limited; *Int'l*, pg. 7415
TAINAN SPINNING COMPANY LIMITED - SINSHIH PLANT—See Tainan Spinning Company Limited; *Int'l*, pg. 7415
TAINAN SPINNING COMPANY LIMITED; *Int'l*, pg. 7415
TAINAN SPINNING COMPANY LIMITED - TAIZI PLANT—See Tainan Spinning Company Limited; *Int'l*, pg. 7415
TAINAN TEXTILE CO., LTD.—See Tainan Spinning Company Limited; *Int'l*, pg. 7415
T&A INDUSTRIAL LTD; *U.S. Private*, pg. 3909
TA INDUSTRIES INC.—See CSW Industrials, Inc.; *U.S. Public*, pg. 602
TAINERGY TECH CO., LTD.; *Int'l*, pg. 7415
TAINERGY TECHNOLOGY (KUNSHAN) CO., LTD—See Tainergy Tech Co., Ltd.; *Int'l*, pg. 7415
TAINET COMMUNICATION SYSTEM CORP.; *Int'l*, pg. 7415
TAINOL, S.A.—See American CyberSystems, Inc.; *U.S. Private*, pg. 230
TA INSTRUMENTS JAPAN—See Waters Corporation; *U.S. Public*, pg. 2335
TA INSTRUMENTS LTD.—See Waters Corporation; *U.S. Public*, pg. 2335
TA INSTRUMENTS-WATERS LLC—See Waters Corporation; *U.S. Public*, pg. 2335
TA INSTRUMENTS - WATERS TECHNOLOGIES (SHANGHAI) LIMITED—See Waters Corporation; *U.S. Public*, pg. 2335
TA INVESTMENT MANAGEMENT BERHAD—See TA Enterprise Berhad; *Int'l*, pg. 7399
TAINWALA CHEMICALS AND PLASTICS (INDIA) LIMITED; *Int'l*, pg. 7415
TA-I OHMELECTRONICS (M) SDN.BHD.—See Ta-I Technology Co., Ltd.; *Int'l*, pg. 7400
TAI PAN LAUNDRY & DRY CLEANING SERVICES, LIMITED—See The Hongkong and Shanghai Hotels Limited; *Int'l*, pg. 7653
TAIPEI EXCHANGE; *Int'l*, pg. 7415
TAIPEI FUBON COMMERCIAL BANK CO., LTD.—See Fubon Financial Holding Co. Ltd.; *Int'l*, pg. 2802
TAIPEI HOKURIKU CO., LTD.—See Hokuriku Electric Industry Co., Ltd.; *Int'l*, pg. 3445
TAIPEI HOKURIKU ELECTRIC INDUSTRY CO., LTD.—See Hokuriku Electric Industry Co., Ltd.; *Int'l*, pg. 3445
TAIPEI TAKASHIMAYA INTERNATIONAL CO., LTD.—See Takashimaya Company, Limited; *Int'l*, pg. 7435
TAIPEI WESTMINSTER TRAVEL LIMITED (TAIWAN)—See Corporate Travel Management Limited; *Int'l*, pg. 1806
TAIPE TRANCOSO EMPREENDIMENTOS S.A.; *Int'l*, pg. 7415
TAI PING CARPETS AMERICAS, INC.—See Tai Ping Carpets International Limited; *Int'l*, pg. 7408
TAI PING CARPETS EUROPE SAS—See Tai Ping Carpets International Limited; *Int'l*, pg. 7408
TAI PING CARPETS INDIA PRIVATE LIMITED—See Tai Ping Carpets International Limited; *Int'l*, pg. 7408
TAI PING CARPETS INTERIEUR GMBH—See Tai Ping Carpets International Limited; *Int'l*, pg. 7408
TAI PING CARPETS INTERNATIONAL LIMITED; *Int'l*, pg. 7408
TAI PING CARPETS LATIN AMERICA S.A.—See Tai Ping Carpets International Limited; *Int'l*, pg. 7408
TAI PING CARPETS LIMITED—See Tai Ping Carpets International Limited; *Int'l*, pg. 7408
TAI PING CARPETS (S) PTE. LIMITED—See Tai Ping Carpets International Limited; *Int'l*, pg. 7408
TAI PING CARPETS UK LIMITED—See Tai Ping Carpets International Limited; *Int'l*, pg. 7408

TAIPING FINANCIAL HOLDINGS COMPANY LIMITED—See China Taiping Insurance Holdings Company Limited; *Int'l*, pg. 1557
TAIPING FUND MANAGEMENT COMPANY LIMITED—See China Taiping Insurance Holdings Company Limited; *Int'l*, pg. 1557
TAIPING REINSURANCE BROKERS LIMITED—See China Taiping Insurance Holdings Company Limited; *Int'l*, pg. 1557
TAIPING REINSURANCE (CHINA) COMPANY LIMITED—See China Taiping Insurance Holdings Company Limited; *Int'l*, pg. 1557
TAIPING REINSURANCE COMPANY LIMITED—See China Taiping Insurance Holdings Company Limited; *Int'l*, pg. 1557
TAIROUN PRODUCTS CO., LTD.; *Int'l*, pg. 7415
TAI RUNG DEVELOPMENT CO., LTD.—See China Chemical & Pharmaceutical Co., Ltd.; *Int'l*, pg. 1488
TAIRX, INC.—See Formosa Laboratories, Inc.; *Int'l*, pg. 2735
TAI SANG LAND DEVELOPMENT LTD; *Int'l*, pg. 7408
TAI-SAW TECHNOLOGY CO., LTD.; *Int'l*, pg. 7409
TAISEI BUILDING MANAGEMENT CO., LTD.—See Nippon Life Insurance Company; *Int'l*, pg. 5323
TAISEI CONSTRUCTION CORPORATION—See Taisei Corporation; *Int'l*, pg. 7416
TAISEI CORPORATION; *Int'l*, pg. 7415
TAISEI CORPORATION—See Taisei Corporation; *Int'l*, pg. 7416
TAISEI (DEUTSCHLAND) GMBH—See Taisei Corporation; *Int'l*, pg. 7416
TAISEI HOUSING CORPORATION—See Taisei Corporation; *Int'l*, pg. 7416
THE TAISEI KAIUN KAISHA, LTD.—See The Sumitomo Warehouse Co. Ltd.; *Int'l*, pg. 7690
TAISEI KOGYO CORPORATION—See JFE Holdings, Inc.; *Int'l*, pg. 3937
TAISEI KOKI CO., LTD.—See Fair Friend Group; *Int'l*, pg. 2605
TAISEI LAMICK CO., LTD. - MACHINE FACTORY—See Taisei Lamick Co., Ltd.; *Int'l*, pg. 7416
TAISEI LAMICK CO., LTD. - SHIRAOKA FACTORY 2—See Taisei Lamick Co., Ltd.; *Int'l*, pg. 7416
TAISEI LAMICK CO., LTD. - SHIRAOKA FACTORY 3—See Taisei Lamick Co., Ltd.; *Int'l*, pg. 7416
TAISEI LAMICK CO., LTD.; *Int'l*, pg. 7416
TAISEI LAMICK USA, INC.—See Taisei Lamick Co., Ltd.; *Int'l*, pg. 7416
TAISEI ONCHO CO., LTD.; *Int'l*, pg. 7416
TAISEI ONCHO HAWAII INC.—See Taisei Oncho Co., Ltd.; *Int'l*, pg. 7416
TAISEI ONCHO (HONG KONG) CO., LTD—See Taisei Oncho Co., Ltd.; *Int'l*, pg. 7416
TAISEI ONCHO INDIA PVT., LTD—See Taisei Oncho Co., Ltd.; *Int'l*, pg. 7416
TAISEI ONCHO (SHANGHAI) CO., LTD—See Taisei Oncho Co., Ltd.; *Int'l*, pg. 7416
TAISEI PAPER CORPORATION—See Daio Paper Corporation; *Int'l*, pg. 1940
TAISEI PHILIPPINE CONSTRUCTION INC.—See Taisei Corporation; *Int'l*, pg. 7416
TAISEI ROTEC CORPORATION—See Taisei Corporation; *Int'l*, pg. 7416
TAISEI SAUDI ARABIA CO., LTD.—See Taisei Corporation; *Int'l*, pg. 7416
TAISEI SETSUBI CO., LTD.—See Taisei Corporation; *Int'l*, pg. 7416
TAISEI (THAILAND) CO., LTD—See Taisei Corporation; *Int'l*, pg. 7416
TAISEI U. LEC CO., LTD—See Taisei Corporation; *Int'l*, pg. 7416
TAISEI (WEST AFRICA) LTD.—See Taisei Corporation; *Int'l*, pg. 7416
TAISEI-YURAKU REAL ESTATE CO., LTD.—See Taisei Corporation; *Int'l*, pg. 7416
TAISETSU NO KURA CO., LTD.—See Oenon Holdings Inc; *Int'l*, pg. 5529
TAI SHAN COMMUNICATIONS, INC.; *Int'l*, pg. 7408
TAISHAN FIBERGLASS INC.—See China National Materials; *Int'l*, pg. 1532
TAISHAN FIBERGLASS ZOUCHENG CO., LTD.—See China National Materials; *Int'l*, pg. 1532
TAISHIN FINANCIAL HOLDING CO., LTD.; *Int'l*, pg. 7416
TAI SHING ELECTRONICS COMPONENTS CORP.; *Int'l*, pg. 7408
TAI SHING INTERNATIONAL (HOLDINGS) LIMITED; *Int'l*, pg. 7408
TAISHIN INTERNATIONAL BANK CO., LTD.—See Taishin Financial Holding Co., Ltd.; *Int'l*, pg. 7416
TAISHO ACTIVE HEALTH CO., LTD.—See Taisho Pharmaceutical Holdings Co., Ltd; *Int'l*, pg. 7417
TAISHO (AUSTRALIA) PTY. LTD.—See Taisho Pharmaceutical Holdings Co., Ltd; *Int'l*, pg. 7417
TAISHOBOSEKI INDUSTRIES LTD.—See Kurabo Industries Ltd.; *Int'l*, pg. 4336
TAISHO BUSINESS RESEARCH INSTITUTE CO., LTD.—See Taisho Pharmaceutical Holdings Co., Ltd; *Int'l*, pg. 7417

TAITIEN ELECTRONICS CO., LTD.

TAISHO GUAN SHENG YUAN CO., LTD. SHANGHAI—See Taisho Pharmaceutical Holdings Co., Ltd; *Int'l*, pg. 7417
TAISHO HIZON MANUFACTURING, INC.—See Taisho Pharmaceutical Holdings Co., Ltd; *Int'l*, pg. 7417
TAISHO KOGYO CORPORATION—See Takamatsu Construction Group Co., Ltd.; *Int'l*, pg. 7430
TAISHO M.T.C. CO., LTD.—See Taisho Pharmaceutical Holdings Co., Ltd; *Int'l*, pg. 7417
TAISHO OKINAWA CO., LTD.—See Taisho Pharmaceutical Holdings Co., Ltd; *Int'l*, pg. 7417
TAISHO PHARMACEUTICAL CALIFORNIA INC.—See Taisho Pharmaceutical Holdings Co., Ltd; *Int'l*, pg. 7417
TAISHO PHARMACEUTICAL CO., LTD.—See Taisho Pharmaceutical Holdings Co., Ltd; *Int'l*, pg. 7417
TAISHO PHARMACEUTICAL CO., LTD. - THE HANYU FACTORY—See Taisho Pharmaceutical Holdings Co., Ltd; *Int'l*, pg. 7417
TAISHO PHARMACEUTICAL CO., LTD. - THE OKAYAMA FACTORY—See Taisho Pharmaceutical Holdings Co., Ltd; *Int'l*, pg. 7417
TAISHO PHARMACEUTICAL CO., LTD. - THE OMIYA FACTORY—See Taisho Pharmaceutical Holdings Co., Ltd; *Int'l*, pg. 7417
TAISHO PHARMACEUTICAL HOLDINGS CO., LTD; *Int'l*, pg. 7417
TAISHO PHARMACEUTICAL INDUSTRIES, LTD.—See Teva Pharmaceutical Industries, Ltd.; *Int'l*, pg. 7579
TAISHO PHARMACEUTICAL LOGISTICS CO., LTD.—See Taisho Pharmaceutical Holdings Co., Ltd; *Int'l*, pg. 7417
TAISHO PHARMACEUTICAL (M) SDN. BHD.—See Taisho Pharmaceutical Holdings Co., Ltd; *Int'l*, pg. 7417
TAISHO PHARMACEUTICAL R&D INC.—See Taisho Pharmaceutical Holdings Co., Ltd; *Int'l*, pg. 7417
TAISHO PHARMACEUTICAL SINGAPORE PRIVATE LIMITED—See Taisho Pharmaceutical Holdings Co., Ltd; *Int'l*, pg. 7418
TAISHO PHARMACEUTICALS PHILIPPINES INC.—See Taisho Pharmaceutical Holdings Co., Ltd; *Int'l*, pg. 7417
TAISHO PHARMACEUTICAL (TAIWAN) CO., LTD.—See Taisho Pharmaceutical Holdings Co., Ltd; *Int'l*, pg. 7417
TAISHO PHARMA CO., LTD.—See Taisho Pharmaceutical Holdings Co., Ltd; *Int'l*, pg. 7417
TAISHO TOYAMA PHARMACEUTICAL CO., LTD.—See FUJIFILM Holdings Corporation; *Int'l*, pg. 2826
TAISHO TOYAMA PHARMACEUTICAL CO., LTD.—See Taisho Pharmaceutical Holdings Co., Ltd; *Int'l*, pg. 7417
TAISHO VIETNAM CO., LTD.—See Taisho Pharmaceutical Holdings Co., Ltd; *Int'l*, pg. 7417
TAI-SHUO ELECTRONICS, INC.—See TaiSol Electronics Co., Ltd.; *Int'l*, pg. 7418
TAISIL ELECTRONIC MATERIALS CORP.—See Sino-American Silicon Products Inc.; *Int'l*, pg. 6948
TAI SIN ELECTRIC CABLES (MALAYSIA) SDN BHD—See Tai Sin Electric Limited; *Int'l*, pg. 7409
TAI SIN ELECTRIC CABLES (VN) COMPANY LIMITED—See Tai Sin Electric Limited; *Int'l*, pg. 7409
TAI SIN ELECTRIC LIMITED; *Int'l*, pg. 7409
TAI SIN POWER DISTRIBUTION PTE. LTD.—See Tai Sin Electric Limited; *Int'l*, pg. 7409
TAISO COMMERCE, INC.—See Ajinomoto Company, Inc.; *Int'l*, pg. 257
TAISOL ELECTRONICS CO., LTD.; *Int'l*, pg. 7418
TAISOL ELECTRONICS JAPAN CO., LTD.—See TaiSol Electronics Co., Ltd.; *Int'l*, pg. 7418
TAISUN ENTERPRISE CO., LTD.; *Int'l*, pg. 7418
TAISUN INT'L (HOLDING) CORP; *Int'l*, pg. 7418
TAITA CHEMICAL COMPANY LIMITED - CUBIC PRINTING—See Taita Chemical Company Limited; *Int'l*, pg. 7418
TAITA CHEMICAL COMPANY LIMITED; *Int'l*, pg. 7418
TAITA CHEMICAL COMPANY LIMITED - TOUFEN PLANT—See Taita Chemical Company Limited; *Int'l*, pg. 7418
TAI TAK PAPER CO., LTD.—See Japan Pulp and Paper Company Limited; *Int'l*, pg. 3904
TAI TAK PAPER (SHENZHEN) CO., LTD.—See Japan Pulp and Paper Company Limited; *Int'l*, pg. 3904
TAI TAK TAKEO FINE PAPER CO., LTD.—See Japan Pulp and Paper Company Limited; *Int'l*, pg. 3904
TAITBOUT PARTICIPATION 3 SNC—See BNP Paribas SA; *Int'l*, pg. 1093
TAI-TECH ADVANCED ELECTRONICS CO., LTD.; *Int'l*, pg. 7410
TAI-TECH ADVANCED ELECTRONICS (S) PTE LTD.; *Int'l*, pg. 7409
TA-I TECHNOLOGY CO., LTD.; *Int'l*, pg. 7400
TA-I TECHNOLOGY (SUZHOU)CO., LTD.—See Ta-I Technology Co., Ltd.; *Int'l*, pg. 7400
TAIT ELECTRONICS LTD.; *Int'l*, pg. 7418
TAITIEN ELECTRONICS CO., LTD.; *Int'l*, pg. 7418
TAITIEN ELECTRONICS (NANJING) CO., LTD.—See Taitien Electronics Co., Ltd.; *Int'l*, pg. 7418
TAITIEN ELECTRONICS (SHENZHEN) CO., LTD.—See Taitien Electronics Co., Ltd.; *Int'l*, pg. 7418
TAI TIEN PHARMACEUTICALS CO., LTD.—See Mitsubishi Chemical Group Corporation; *Int'l*, pg. 4935
TAITIEN U.S.A. INC.—See Taitien Electronics Co., Ltd.; *Int'l*, pg. 7418

TAITIEN ELECTRONICS CO., LTD. CORPORATE AFFILIATIONS

TAITONG FOOD LIMITED COMPANY—See Ottogi Corporation; *Int'l*, pg. 5665
TAITRON COMPONENTS INCORPORATED E REPRESENTACOES DO BRASIL LTDA—See Taitron Components Incorporated; *U.S. Public*, pg. 1979
TAITRON COMPONENTS INCORPORATED; *U.S. Public*, pg. 1979
TAITRON COMPONENTS INCORPORATED TAIWAN—See Taitron Components Incorporated; *U.S. Public*, pg. 1979
TAITRON COMPONENTS MEXICO, S.A. DE C.V.—See Taitron Components Incorporated; *U.S. Public*, pg. 1979
TAITTINGER SA; *Int'l*, pg. 7418
TAIT TOWERS INC.; *U.S. Private*, pg. 3925
TAI TUNG COMMUNICATION CO., LTD. - ANHUI FACTORY—See Tai Tung Communication Co., Ltd.; *Int'l*, pg. 7409
TAI TUNG COMMUNICATION CO., LTD.; *Int'l*, pg. 7409
TAI TUNG COMMUNICATION CO., LTD. - TAOYUAN FACTORY—See Tai Tung Communication Co., Ltd.; *Int'l*, pg. 7409
TAI TWUN ENTERPRISE CO., LTD.; *Int'l*, pg. 7409
TAI UNITED HOLDINGS LIMITED; *Int'l*, pg. 7409
TAIVAS OGILVY—See WPP plc; *Int'l*, pg. 8464
TAIVAS—See WPP plc; *Int'l*, pg. 8488
TAIVEX THERAPEUTICS INC.—See China Petrochemical Development Corp.; *Int'l*, pg. 1540
TAIWANABRATOR CO., LTD.—See Sintokogio Ltd.; *Int'l*, pg. 6959
TAIWAN ADVANCE BIO-PHARMACEUTICAL, INC.; *Int'l*, pg. 7418
TAIWAN AHOKU ELECTRONIC COMPANY—See Ahoku Electronic Company; *Int'l*, pg. 225
TAIWAN AICA KOGYO CO., LTD.—See AICA Kogyo Company, Limited; *Int'l*, pg. 229
TAIWAN AIR CARGO TERMINAL LTD.—See China Airlines Ltd.; *Int'l*, pg. 1482
TAIWAN AIRCRAFT MAINTENANCE & ENGINEERING CO., LTD.—See China Airlines Ltd.; *Int'l*, pg. 1482
TAIWAN AIR WATER MACH TECH. CO., LTD.—See Air Water Inc.; *Int'l*, pg. 241
TAIWAN ALLIED CONTAINER TERMINAL CORP; *Int'l*, pg. 7418
TAIWAN ALPHA ELECTRONIC CO., LTD.; *Int'l*, pg. 7418
TAIWAN ARAKAWA CHEMICAL INDUSTRIES, LTD.—See Arakawa Chemical Industries, Ltd.; *Int'l*, pg. 535
TAIWAN ARIAKE FOODS CO., LTD.—See ARIAKE JAPAN Co., Ltd.; *Int'l*, pg. 564
TAIWAN ASAHI DIAMOND INDUSTRIAL CO., LTD.—See Asahi Diamond Industrial Co. Ltd.; *Int'l*, pg. 593
TAIWAN AUTOMATED SYSTEMS LTD.—See Beijing Teamsun Technology Co., Ltd.; *Int'l*, pg. 958
TAIWAN BILLS FINANCE CO., LTD.—See Taishin Financial Holding Co., Ltd.; *Int'l*, pg. 7416
TAIWAN BIOMATEIRAL CO., LTD.; *Int'l*, pg. 7419
TAIWAN BROTHER INDUSTRIES, LTD.—See Brother Industries, Ltd.; *Int'l*, pg. 1198
TAIWAN BUSINESS BANK LTD.; *Int'l*, pg. 7419
TAIWAN CELLULAR CO., LTD.—See Taiwan Mobile Co., Ltd.; *Int'l*, pg. 7422
TAIWAN CEMEDINE CO., LTD.—See Kaneka Corporation; *Int'l*, pg. 4066
TAIWAN CEMENT CORPORATION; *Int'l*, pg. 7419
TAIWAN CENTRAL GLASS CO., LTD.—See Central Glass Co., Ltd.; *Int'l*, pg. 1407
TAIWAN CHELIC CORP. LTD.; *Int'l*, pg. 7419
TAIWAN CHEMI-CON CORP.—See Nippon Chemi-Con Corporation; *Int'l*, pg. 5313
TAIWAN CHINSAN ELECTRONIC INDUSTRIAL CO., LTD.; *Int'l*, pg. 7419
TAIWAN CHLORINE INDUSTRIES LTD.—See China Petrochemical Development Corp.; *Int'l*, pg. 1540
TAIWAN CHLORINE INDUSTRIES LTD.—See Westlake Corporation; *U.S. Public*, pg. 2360
TAIWAN CHORI MERCHANDISE COOPERATION LTD.—See Chori Co., Ltd.; *Int'l*, pg. 1583
TAIWAN CHUGAI RO CO., LTD.—See Chugai Ro Co., Ltd.; *Int'l*, pg. 1594
TAIWAN CHUHATSU FACTORY CO., LTD.—See Chuo Spring Co., Ltd.; *Int'l*, pg. 1599
TAIWAN CKD CORPORATION—See CKD Corporation; *Int'l*, pg. 1639
TAIWAN COGENERATION CORPORATION - ACHEM COGENERATION PLANT—See Taiwan Cogeneration Corporation; *Int'l*, pg. 7419
TAIWAN COGENERATION CORPORATION - KUAN-TIEN COGENERATION PLANT—See Taiwan Cogeneration Corporation; *Int'l*, pg. 7419
TAIWAN COGENERATION CORPORATION; *Int'l*, pg. 7419
TAIWAN CONTEC CO., LTD.—See Daifuku Co., Ltd.; *Int'l*, pg. 1925
TAIWAN COOPERATIVE BANK CO., LTD.—See Taiwan Cooperative Financial Holding Co., Ltd.; *Int'l*, pg. 7419
TAIWAN COOPERATIVE BILLS FINANCE CO., LTD.—See Taiwan Cooperative Financial Holding Co., Ltd.; *Int'l*, pg. 7419

TAIWAN COOPERATIVE BILLS FINANCE CORPORATION—See Taiwan Cooperative Financial Holding Co., Ltd.; *Int'l*, pg. 7419
TAIWAN COOPERATIVE FINANCIAL HOLDING CO., LTD.; *Int'l*, pg. 7419
TAIWAN COOPERATIVE SECURITIES CO., LTD.—See Taiwan Cooperative Financial Holding Co., Ltd.; *Int'l*, pg. 7419
TAIWAN COOPERATIVE SECURITIES INVESTMENT TRUST CO., LTD.—See Taiwan Cooperative Financial Holding Co., Ltd.; *Int'l*, pg. 7419
TAIWAN COOPERATIVE VENTURE CAPITAL CO., LTD.—See Taiwan Cooperative Financial Holding Co., Ltd.; *Int'l*, pg. 7420
TAIWAN CORPORATION—See Shian Yih Electronic Industry Co., Ltd.; *Int'l*, pg. 6827
TAIWAN CUMMINS SALES & SERVICES CO. LTD.—See Cummins Inc.; *U.S. Public*, pg. 609
TAIWAN DAEJOO ELECTRONIC MATERIALS CO., LTD.—See Daejoo Electronic Materials Co., Ltd.; *Int'l*, pg. 1907
TAIWAN DAIFUKU CO., LTD.—See Daifuku Co., Ltd.; *Int'l*, pg. 1926
TAIWAN DAIFUKU CO., LTD. - TAICHUNG PLANT—See Daifuku Co., Ltd.; *Int'l*, pg. 1926
TAIWAN DAIKIN ADVANCED CHEMICALS, INC.—See Daikin Industries, Ltd.; *Int'l*, pg. 1936
TAIWAN DAIMARU KOGYO, LTD.—See J. Front Retailing Co., Ltd.; *Int'l*, pg. 3855
TAIWAN DAIOHS CO., LTD.—See Daiohs Corporation; *Int'l*, pg. 1940
TAIWAN DAISO CHEMICAL CO., LTD.—See Osaka Soda Co., Ltd.; *Int'l*, pg. 5646
TAIWAN DAIWA HOUSE CONSTRUCTION CO., LTD.—See Daiwa House Industry Co., Ltd.; *Int'l*, pg. 1947
TAIWAN DENKEI SOLUTION CO., LTD.—See NIHON DENKEI CO., LTD.; *Int'l*, pg. 5284
TAIWAN DISPLAY INC.—See Japan Display Inc.; *Int'l*, pg. 3888
TAIWAN DISTRIBUTION CENTER CO., LTD.—See ITOCHU Corporation; *Int'l*, pg. 3841
TAIWAN DONGJIN SEMICHEM CO., LTD.—See Dongjin Semichem Co., Ltd.; *Int'l*, pg. 2168
TAIWAN ELECTRO-MATERIALS CO., LTD.—See Japan Pulp and Paper Company Limited; *Int'l*, pg. 3905
TAIWAN E&M SYSTEM INC.—See TOPCO Scientific Co., Ltd.; *Int'l*, pg. 7814
TAIWAN ENVIRONMENT SCIENTIFIC CO LTD.; *Int'l*, pg. 7420
TAIWAN EXPRESS (HK) CO., LTD.—See T3EX Global Holdings Corp.; *Int'l*, pg. 7398
TAIWAN FANUC CORPORATION—See FANUC Corporation; *Int'l*, pg. 2615
TAIWAN FANUC ROBOTICS CORPORATION—See FANUC Corporation; *Int'l*, pg. 2615
TAIWAN FELT CO., LTD.—See Nippon Felt Co., Ltd.; *Int'l*, pg. 5317
TAIWAN FERTILIZER CO., LTD.; *Int'l*, pg. 7420
TAIWAN FIRE & MARINE INSURANCE CO., LTD.; *Int'l*, pg. 7420
TAIWAN FIXED NETWORK CO., LTD.—See Taiwan Mobile Co., Ltd.; *Int'l*, pg. 7422
TAIWAN FU HSING INDUSTRIAL CO., LTD. - CHANGHUA FACTORY—See Taiwan Fu Hsing Industrial Co., Ltd.; *Int'l*, pg. 7420
TAIWAN FU HSING INDUSTRIAL CO., LTD.; *Int'l*, pg. 7420
TAIWAN FUKUSIMA INTERNATIONAL CO., LTD.—See Fukushima Galilei Co. Ltd.; *Int'l*, pg. 2841
TAIWAN FURUKAWA ELECTRIC CO., LTD.—See The Furukawa Electric Co., Ltd.; *Int'l*, pg. 7647
TAIWAN FUTABA ELECTRONICS CORPORATION—See Futaba Corporation; *Int'l*, pg. 2851
TAIWAN GLASS INDUSTRY CORPORATION; *Int'l*, pg. 7420
TAIWAN GOOD COM CO., LTD.—See Good Com Asset Co., Ltd.; *Int'l*, pg. 3038
TAIWAN GREEN ENVIRONMENT TECHNOLOGY INC.; *Int'l*, pg. 7420
TAIWAN GREEN POINT ENTERPRISES CO., LTD—See Jabil Inc.; *U.S. Public*, pg. 1182
TAIWAN HAKUHODO MEDIA INC.—See Hakuhodo DY Holdings Incorporated; *Int'l*, pg. 3222
TAIWAN HANWA KOGYO CO., LTD.—See Hanwa Co., Ltd.; *Int'l*, pg. 3263
TAIWAN HEWTECH CORP.—See Hirakawa Hewtech Corp.; *Int'l*, pg. 3403
TAIWAN HIGH SPEED RAIL CORPORATION; *Int'l*, pg. 7420
TAIWAN HIRATA CORPORATION—See Hirata Corporation; *Int'l*, pg. 3404
TAIWAN HITACHI CO., LTD.—See Hitachi, Ltd.; *Int'l*, pg. 3424
TAIWAN HON CHUAN ENTERPRISE CO., LTD. - ANHUI CHUZHOU PLANT—See Taiwan Hon Chuan Enterprise Co., Ltd.; *Int'l*, pg. 7421

TAIWAN HON CHUAN ENTERPRISE CO., LTD. - ANHUI LIUAN PLANT—See Taiwan Hon Chuan Enterprise Co., Ltd.; *Int'l*, pg. 7421
TAIWAN HON CHUAN ENTERPRISE CO., LTD. - CAMBODIA HONLY PLANT—See Taiwan Hon Chuan Enterprise Co., Ltd.; *Int'l*, pg. 7421
TAIWAN HON CHUAN ENTERPRISE CO., LTD. - HENAN ANYANG PLANT—See Taiwan Hon Chuan Enterprise Co., Ltd.; *Int'l*, pg. 7421
TAIWAN HON CHUAN ENTERPRISE CO., LTD. - HON CHUAN CHANGSHA PLANT—See Taiwan Hon Chuan Enterprise Co., Ltd.; *Int'l*, pg. 7421
TAIWAN HON CHUAN ENTERPRISE CO., LTD. - HON CHUAN GUANGDONG PLANT—See Taiwan Hon Chuan Enterprise Co., Ltd.; *Int'l*, pg. 7421
TAIWAN HON CHUAN ENTERPRISE CO., LTD. - HON CHUAN JINAN PLANT—See Taiwan Hon Chuan Enterprise Co., Ltd.; *Int'l*, pg. 7421
TAIWAN HON CHUAN ENTERPRISE CO., LTD. - HON CHUAN KUNMING (PEPSI) PLANT—See Taiwan Hon Chuan Enterprise Co., Ltd.; *Int'l*, pg. 7421
TAIWAN HON CHUAN ENTERPRISE CO., LTD. - HON CHUAN KUNMING PLANT—See Taiwan Hon Chuan Enterprise Co., Ltd.; *Int'l*, pg. 7421
TAIWAN HON CHUAN ENTERPRISE CO., LTD. - HON CHUAN SUZHOU PLANT—See Taiwan Hon Chuan Enterprise Co., Ltd.; *Int'l*, pg. 7421
TAIWAN HON CHUAN ENTERPRISE CO., LTD. - HON CHUAN TAIYUAN PLANT—See Taiwan Hon Chuan Enterprise Co., Ltd.; *Int'l*, pg. 7421
TAIWAN HON CHUAN ENTERPRISE CO., LTD. - HON CHUAN XIAN (COCA COLA) PLANT—See Taiwan Hon Chuan Enterprise Co., Ltd.; *Int'l*, pg. 7421
TAIWAN HON CHUAN ENTERPRISE CO., LTD. - HON CHUAN ZHENGZHOU PLANT—See Taiwan Hon Chuan Enterprise Co., Ltd.; *Int'l*, pg. 7421
TAIWAN HON CHUAN ENTERPRISE CO., LTD. - HON CHUNA FD PLANT—See Taiwan Hon Chuan Enterprise Co., Ltd.; *Int'l*, pg. 7421
TAIWAN HON CHUAN ENTERPRISE CO., LTD. - HUBEI XIANTAO PLANT—See Taiwan Hon Chuan Enterprise Co., Ltd.; *Int'l*, pg. 7421
TAIWAN HON CHUAN ENTERPRISE CO., LTD. - INDONESIA (ABC) PLANT—See Taiwan Hon Chuan Enterprise Co., Ltd.; *Int'l*, pg. 7421
TAIWAN HON CHUAN ENTERPRISE CO., LTD. - INDONESIA (FUTAMI) PLANT—See Taiwan Hon Chuan Enterprise Co., Ltd.; *Int'l*, pg. 7421
TAIWAN HON CHUAN ENTERPRISE CO., LTD. - INDONESIA PLANT—See Taiwan Hon Chuan Enterprise Co., Ltd.; *Int'l*, pg. 7421
TAIWAN HON CHUAN ENTERPRISE CO., LTD. - INDONESIA SURABAYA PLANT—See Taiwan Hon Chuan Enterprise Co., Ltd.; *Int'l*, pg. 7421
TAIWAN HON CHUAN ENTERPRISE CO., LTD. - MOZAMBIQUE SHIMADA PLANT—See Taiwan Hon Chuan Enterprise Co., Ltd.; *Int'l*, pg. 7421
TAIWAN HON CHUAN ENTERPRISE CO., LTD. - MYANMAR (KH) PLANT—See Taiwan Hon Chuan Enterprise Co., Ltd.; *Int'l*, pg. 7421
TAIWAN HON CHUAN ENTERPRISE CO., LTD. - MYANMAR (LOIHEIN) PLANT—See Taiwan Hon Chuan Enterprise Co., Ltd.; *Int'l*, pg. 7421
TAIWAN HON CHUAN ENTERPRISE CO., LTD. - MYANMAR PLANT—See Taiwan Hon Chuan Enterprise Co., Ltd.; *Int'l*, pg. 7421
TAIWAN HON CHUAN ENTERPRISE CO., LTD.; *Int'l*, pg. 7420
TAIWAN HON CHUAN ENTERPRISE CO., LTD. - SUZHOU HON HSING BEVERAGE PLANT—See Taiwan Hon Chuan Enterprise Co., Ltd.; *Int'l*, pg. 7421
TAIWAN HON CHUAN ENTERPRISE CO., LTD. - THAILAND (FOODSTAR) PLANT—See Taiwan Hon Chuan Enterprise Co., Ltd.; *Int'l*, pg. 7421
TAIWAN HON CHUAN ENTERPRISE CO., LTD. - THAILAND PLANT—See Taiwan Hon Chuan Enterprise Co., Ltd.; *Int'l*, pg. 7421
TAIWAN HON CHUAN ENTERPRISE CO., LTD. - THAILAND (UNI-PRESIDENT) PLANT—See Taiwan Hon Chuan Enterprise Co., Ltd.; *Int'l*, pg. 7421
TAIWAN HON CHUAN ENTERPRISE CO., LTD. - VIETNAM PLANT—See Taiwan Hon Chuan Enterprise Co., Ltd.; *Int'l*, pg. 7421
TAIWAN HON CHUAN ENTERPRISE CO., LTD. - VIETNAM (TRIBECO) PLANT—See Taiwan Hon Chuan Enterprise Co., Ltd.; *Int'l*, pg. 7421
TAIWAN HON CHUAN ENTERPRISE CO., LTD. - ZHANGZHOU ASEPTIC-FILLING PLANT—See Taiwan Hon Chuan Enterprise Co., Ltd.; *Int'l*, pg. 7421
TAIWAN HOPAX CHEMICALS MFG CO., LTD.; *Int'l*, pg. 7421
TAIWAN HOSIDEN CO., LTD.—See Hosiden Corporation; *Int'l*, pg. 3485
TAIWAN INABATA SANGYO CO., LTD.—See Inabata & Co. Ltd.; *Int'l*, pg. 3644
TAIWAN INAX CORPORATION—See LIXIL Group Corporation; *Int'l*, pg. 4534
TAIWAN INOAC POLYMER CORPORATION—See INOAC Corporation; *Int'l*, pg. 3715

COMPANY NAME INDEX

TAIWAN INPAQ ELECTRONIC CO., LTD.—See Inpaq Technology Co., Ltd.; *Int'l*, pg. 3716
TAIWAN I-O DATA DEVICE, INC.—See I-O DATA DEVICE, INC.; *Int'l*, pg. 3563
TAIWAN ISUZU MOTORS CO., LTD.—See Isuzu Motors Limited; *Int'l*, pg. 3826
TAIWAN ISUZU MOTORS CO., LTD.—See Isuzu Motors Limited; *Int'l*, pg. 3826
TAIWAN JSP CHEMICAL CO., LTD.—See Mitsubishi Gas Chemical Company, Inc.; *Int'l*, pg. 4948
TAIWAN JTEKT CO., LTD.—See JTEKT Corporation; *Int'l*, pg. 4019
TAIWAN JUKEN CO. LTD.—See EMNI Co., Ltd; *Int'l*, pg. 2385
TAIWAN KAGOME CO., LTD.—See Kagome Co., Ltd.; *Int'l*, pg. 4050
TAIWAN KAI YIH INDUSTRIAL COMPANY LTD.—See Tong Yang Industry Co., Ltd.; *Int'l*, pg. 7806
TAIWAN KANEBO COSMETICS CO., LTD.—See Kao Corporation; *Int'l*, pg. 4074
TAIWAN KANSAI PAINT CO., LTD.—See Kansai Paint Co., Ltd.; *Int'l*, pg. 4073
TAIWAN KANTO DENKA CO., LTD.—See Kanto Denka Kogyo Co., Ltd.; *Int'l*, pg. 4073
TAIWAN KAWATA CO., LTD.—See KAWATA MFG CO., LTD.; *Int'l*, pg. 4101
TAIWAN KEIHHIN CARBURETOR CO., LTD. - CHINGSHUI FACTORY—See Hitachi Astemo, Ltd.; *Int'l*, pg. 3409
TAIWAN KEIHHIN CARBURETOR CO., LTD.—See Hitachi Astemo, Ltd.; *Int'l*, pg. 3409
TAIWAN KEIWA INC.—See Keiwa Incorporated; *Int'l*, pg. 4118
TAIWAN KEY COFFEE INC.—See Key Coffee Inc.; *Int'l*, pg. 4145
TAIWAN KIRIN CO., LTD.—See Kirin Holdings Company, Limited; *Int'l*, pg. 4187
TAIWAN KONG KING CO., LIMITED—See Wong's Kong King International (Holdings) Limited; *Int'l*, pg. 8447
TAIWAN KOSE CO., LTD.—See KOSE Corporation; *Int'l*, pg. 4290
TAIWAN KOSTER PRODUCTS CO., LTD.—See Koster Bauchemie AG; *Int'l*, pg. 4291
TAIWAN KUMAGAI CO., LTD.—See Kumagai Gumi Co., Ltd.; *Int'l*, pg. 4329
TAIWAN KUOTOONG INTERNATIONAL CO., LTD.—See Xinjiang Guotong Pipeline Co., Ltd.; *Int'l*, pg. 8531
TAIWAN KURE GRINDING WHEEL CO., LTD.—See Kure Grinding Wheel Co., Ltd.; *Int'l*, pg. 4338
TAIWAN KUREHA CO., LTD.—See Shinih Enterprise Co., Ltd.; *Int'l*, pg. 6845
TAIWAN KYOSAN CO., LTD.—See Kyosan Electric Manufacturing Co., Ltd.; *Int'l*, pg. 4365
TAIWAN KYUSYUYA CO., LTD.—See Air Water Inc.; *Int'l*, pg. 241
TAIWAN LAND DEVELOPMENT CORPORATION; *Int'l*, pg. 7421
TAIWAN LIFE INSURANCE CO., LTD.—See CTBC Financial Holding Co., Ltd.; *Int'l*, pg. 1869
TAIWAN LINE TEK ELECTRONIC CO., LTD.; *Int'l*, pg. 7422
TAIWAN LIPOSOME COMPANY, LTD.; *Int'l*, pg. 7422
TAIWAN LIPOSOME COMPANY - US—See Taiwan Liposome Company, Ltd.; *Int'l*, pg. 7422
TAIWAN LOTTERY CO., LTD.—See CTBC Financial Holding Co., Ltd.; *Int'l*, pg. 1869
TAIWAN LOTTERY CORPORATION—See CTBC Financial Holding Co., Ltd.; *Int'l*, pg. 1869
TAIWAN LUBCON LUBRICANTS CO., LTD.—See LUBRICANT CONSULT GMBH; *Int'l*, pg. 4573
TAIWAN MAIN FINE INTERNATIONAL CO., LTD—See Main Fine International Ltd.; *Int'l*, pg. 4650
TAIWAN MARINE ELECTRIC CO., LTD.—See Allis Electric Co., Ltd.; *Int'l*, pg. 359
TAIWAN MARKETING & TRANSPORTATION DIVISION—See CPC Corporation; *Int'l*, pg. 1824
TAIWAN MARUWA CO LTD—See Maruwa Co., Ltd.; *Int'l*, pg. 4715
TAIWAN MASK CORPORATION; *Int'l*, pg. 7422
TAIWAN MATERIAL TECHNOLOGY CO., LTD.—See Japan Material Co., Ltd.; *Int'l*, pg. 3899
TAIWAN MESCO CO., LTD.—See MESCO Inc; *Int'l*, pg. 4840
TAIWAN MICHAEL PAGE INTERNATIONAL CO., LTD.—See PageGroup plc; *Int'l*, pg. 5699
TAIWAN MITACHI CO., LTD.—See MITACHI Co., Ltd.; *Int'l*, pg. 4924
TAIWAN MITSUBISHI ELEVATOR CO., LTD.—See Mitsubishi Electric Corporation; *Int'l*, pg. 4946
TAIWAN MITSUI CHEMICALS, INC.—See Mitsui Chemicals, Inc.; *Int'l*, pg. 4984
TAIWAN MITSUMI CO., LTD.—See Minebea Mitsumi Inc.; *Int'l*, pg. 4904
TAIWAN MJC CO., LTD.—See MICRONICS JAPAN CO., LTD.; *Int'l*, pg. 4880
TAIWAN MOBILE CO., LTD.; *Int'l*, pg. 7422
TAIWAN MORINAGA CO., LTD.—See Morinaga & Co., Ltd.; *Int'l*, pg. 5046

TAIWAN MORINAGA NUTRITIONAL FOODS INC.—See Morinaga Milk Industry Co., Ltd.; *Int'l*, pg. 5046
TAIWAN MOTOR IMAGE CO.—See Tan Chong International Limited; *Int'l*, pg. 7453
TAIWAN MURATA ELECTRONICS CO., LTD.—See Murata Manufacturing Co., Ltd.; *Int'l*, pg. 5098
TAIWAN NABTESCO SERVICE CO., LTD.—See Nabtesco Corporation; *Int'l*, pg. 5121
TAIWAN NAME PLATE CO., LTD.; *Int'l*, pg. 7422
TAIWAN NAVIGATION CO., LTD.; *Int'l*, pg. 7422
TAIWAN NEXSTGO LIMITED—See Alco Holdings Limited; *Int'l*, pg. 301
TAIWAN NGK SPARK PLUG CO., LTD.—See Niterra Co., Ltd.; *Int'l*, pg. 5381
TAIWAN NICCA CHEMICAL CO., LTD.—See Nicca Chemical Co., Ltd.; *Int'l*, pg. 5264
TAIWAN NICCA CHEMICAL CO., LTD. - TAOYUAN FACTORY—See Nicca Chemical Co., Ltd.; *Int'l*, pg. 5264
TAIWAN NICHINETU CO., LTD.—See Air Water Inc.; *Int'l*, pg. 241
TAIWAN NICKEL REFINING CORPORATION—See Vale S.A.; *Int'l*, pg. 8112
TAIWAN NIHON NOHYAKU CO., LTD.—See Adeka Corporation; *Int'l*, pg. 142
TAIWAN NIKKISO CO., LTD.—See Nikkiso Co., Ltd.; *Int'l*, pg. 5291
TAIWAN NIPPON KAYAKU CO., LTD.—See Nippon Kayaku Co., Ltd.; *Int'l*, pg. 5321
TAIWAN NIPPON STEEL TRADING CO., LTD.—See Nippon Steel Corporation; *Int'l*, pg. 5339
TAIWAN NISSEI DISPLAY SYSTEM CO., LTD.—See Nippon Seiki Co., Ltd.; *Int'l*, pg. 5330
TAIWAN NISSEI MACHINERY CORPORATION—See Nissei Plastic Industrial Co., Ltd.; *Int'l*, pg. 5371
TAIWAN NISSEKI CO., LTD.—See ENEOS Holdings, Inc.; *Int'l*, pg. 2417
TAIWAN NISSHA CO., LTD.—See Nissha Co., Ltd.; *Int'l*, pg. 5372
TAIWAN NISSHINBO PHOTOVOLTAIC CO., LTD.—See Nisshinbo Holdings Inc.; *Int'l*, pg. 5375
TAIWAN NISSHIN SHOKAI CO., LTD.—See The Nisshin OilliO Group, Ltd.; *Int'l*, pg. 7671
TAIWAN NITTA FILTER CO., LTD. - PINCHEN FACTORY—See Nitta Corporation; *Int'l*, pg. 5382
TAIWAN NITTA FILTER CO., LTD.—See Nitta Corporation; *Int'l*, pg. 5382
TAIWAN NITTAN INDUSTRIAL CO., LTD.—See NITTAN Corporation; *Int'l*, pg. 5383
TAIWAN NITTO CORPORATION—See Nitto Denko Corporation; *Int'l*, pg. 5387
TAIWAN NITTOKU ADVANCED CO., LTD.—See Nittoku Co., Ltd.; *Int'l*, pg. 5389
TAIWAN NITTO OPTICAL CO., LTD.—See Nitto Denko Corporation; *Int'l*, pg. 5387
TAIWAN NJC CORPORATION—See New Japan Chemical Co., Ltd.; *Int'l*, pg. 5225
TAIWAN NOBLE ELECTRONIC CO., LTD.—See Teikoku Tsushin Kogyo Co., Ltd.; *Int'l*, pg. 7524
TAIWAN NSK PRECISION CO., LTD.—See NSK Ltd.; *Int'l*, pg. 5480
TAIWAN NSK TECHNOLOGY CO., LTD.—See NSK Ltd.; *Int'l*, pg. 5480
TAIWAN OASIS TECHNOLOGY CO., LTD.; *Int'l*, pg. 7422
TAIWAN OBAYASHI CORPORATION—See Obayashi Corporation; *Int'l*, pg. 5509
TAIWAN OILES INDUSTRY COMPANY LIMITED—See Oiles Corporation; *Int'l*, pg. 5535
TAIWAN OPLINK COMMUNICATIONS, INC.—See Koch Industries, Inc.; *U.S. Private*, pg. 2335
TAIWAN OPTICAL PLATFORM CO., LTD.; *Int'l*, pg. 7422
TAIWAN ORBIS INC.—See Pola Orbis Holdings Inc.; *Int'l*, pg. 5905
TAIWAN ORIENTAL MOTOR CO., LTD.—See Oriental Motor Co., Ltd.; *Int'l*, pg. 5626
TAIWAN OSTOR CORPORATION; *Int'l*, pg. 7422
TAIWAN OTSUKA PHARMACEUTICAL CO., LTD.—See Otsuka Holdings Co., Ltd.; *Int'l*, pg. 5661
TAIWAN PAIHO LIMITED; *Int'l*, pg. 7422
TAIWAN PAIHO LIMITED - TAIWAN FACTORY—See Taiwan Paiho Limited; *Int'l*, pg. 7423
TAIWAN PARK24 PARKING CO., LTD.—See PARK24 Co. Ltd.; *Int'l*, pg. 5743
TAIWANPAY CORPORATION—See SYSTEX Corporation; *Int'l*, pg. 7393
TAIWAN PCB TECHVEST CO., LTD.; *Int'l*, pg. 7423
TAIWAN PELICAN EXPRESS CO., LTD.; *Int'l*, pg. 7423
TAIWAN PILLAR INDUSTRY CO., LTD.—See Nippon Pillar Packing Co., Ltd.; *Int'l*, pg. 5328
TAIWAN PLA MATELS CORPORATION—See Sojitz Corporation; *Int'l*, pg. 7065
TAIWAN PLUS CORPORATION—See PLUS Corporation; *Int'l*, pg. 5899
TAIWAN POWER COMPANY; *Int'l*, pg. 7423
TAIWAN PROSPERITY CHEMICAL CORPORATION—See Taiwan Cement Corporation; *Int'l*, pg. 7419
TAIWAN PULP & PAPER CORPORATION - HSINGYING MILL—See Taiwan Pulp & Paper Corporation; *Int'l*, pg. 7423

TAIWAN PULP & PAPER CORPORATION; *Int'l*, pg. 7423
TAIWAN PYROLYSIS & ENERGY REGENERATION CORP.—See Hota Industrial Mfg. Co., Ltd.; *Int'l*, pg. 3487
TAIWAN RATINGS CORPORATION—See S&P Global Inc.; *U.S. Public*, pg. 1832
TAIWAN RIVER CO., LTD.—See River Eletec Corporation; *Int'l*, pg. 6352
TAIWAN RYOSHO CO., LTD.—See Ryoden Corporation; *Int'l*, pg. 6441
TAIWAN SAKATA INX CORP.—See Sakata INX Corporation; *Int'l*, pg. 6488
TAIWAN SAKURA CORPORATION; *Int'l*, pg. 7423
TAIWAN SAN-ETSU CO., LTD.—See CK SAN-ETSU Co., Ltd.; *Int'l*, pg. 1639
TAIWAN SANKEN ELECTRIC CO., LTD.—See Sanken Electric Co., Ltd.; *Int'l*, pg. 6541
TAIWAN SANOH ELECTRIC CO., LTD.—See Sanoh Industrial Co., Ltd.; *Int'l*, pg. 6553
TAIWAN SANSHIN ELECTRONICS CO., LTD.—See Sanshin Electronics Co., Ltd.; *Int'l*, pg. 6556
TAIWAN SANTEN PHARMACEUTICAL CO. LTD.—See Santen Pharmaceutical Co., Ltd.; *Int'l*, pg. 6558
TAIWAN SANYO ELECTRIC CO., LTD.; *Int'l*, pg. 7423
TAIWAN SATORI CO., LTD.—See SATORI ELECTRIC CO., LTD.; *Int'l*, pg. 6587
TAIWAN SECOM COMPANY LTD.; *Int'l*, pg. 7423
TAIWAN SEKISUI CENTEX CO., LTD.—See Sekisui Kasei Co., Ltd.; *Int'l*, pg. 6698
TAIWAN SEKISUI YUNCHU CO., LTD.—See Sekisui Kasei Co., Ltd.; *Int'l*, pg. 6698
TAIWAN SEMBA CO., LTD.—See SEMBA Corporation; *Int'l*, pg. 6702
TAIWAN SEMICONDUCTOR CO., LTD.; *Int'l*, pg. 7423
TAIWAN SEMICONDUCTOR EUROPE GMBH—See Taiwan Semiconductor Co., Ltd.; *Int'l*, pg. 7423
TAIWAN SEMICONDUCTOR (H.K.) CO., LTD.—See Taiwan Semiconductor Co., Ltd.; *Int'l*, pg. 7423
TAIWAN SEMICONDUCTOR JAPAN LTD.—See Taiwan Semiconductor Co., Ltd.; *Int'l*, pg. 7423
TAIWAN SEMICONDUCTOR MANUFACTURING COMPANY LTD.; *Int'l*, pg. 7423
TAIWAN SHINKO ELECTRONICS CO., LTD.—See Fujitsu Limited; *Int'l*, pg. 2838
TAIWAN SHIN KONG COMMERCIAL BANK CO., LTD.—See Shin Kong Group; *Int'l*, pg. 6837
TAIWAN SHIN KONG SECURITY CO., LTD.; *Int'l*, pg. 7424
TAIWAN SHINMAYWA INDUSTRIES CO., LTD.—See ShinMaywa Industries, Ltd.; *Int'l*, pg. 6847
TAIWAN SHIONOGI & CO., LTD.—See Shionogi & Co., Ltd.; *Int'l*, pg. 6851
TAIWAN SHISEIDO CO., LTD.—See Shiseido Company, Limited; *Int'l*, pg. 6854
TAIWAN SHOWA CHEMICALS MANUFACTURING CO., LTD.—See Resonac Holdings Corporation; *Int'l*, pg. 6301
TAIWAN SHOWA DENKO ELECTRONICS CO., LTD.—See Resonac Holdings Corporation; *Int'l*, pg. 6301
TAIWAN SINKO KOGYO CO., LTD.—See Sinko Industries Ltd.; *Int'l*, pg. 6946
TAIWAN SINTONG MACHINERY CO., LTD.—See Sintokogio Ltd.; *Int'l*, pg. 6959
TAIWAN SKYLARK CO., LTD.—See Bain Capital, LP; *U.S. Private*, pg. 444
TAIWAN SOSHIN ELECTRIC CO., LTD.—See NGK Insulators, Ltd.; *Int'l*, pg. 5255
TAIWAN SRU CO., LTD.—See The Furukawa Electric Co., Ltd.; *Int'l*, pg. 7647
TAIWAN STOCK EXCHANGE CORPORATION; *Int'l*, pg. 7424
TAIWAN STYRENE MONOMER CORPORATION - KAOHSIUNG PLANT—See Taiwan Styrene Monomer Corporation; *Int'l*, pg. 7424
TAIWAN STYRENE MONOMER CORPORATION; *Int'l*, pg. 7424
TAIWAN STYRON LIMITED—See Bain Capital, LP; *U.S. Private*, pg. 450
TAIWAN SUMIDA TRADING COMPANY LIMITED—See Sumida Corporation; *Int'l*, pg. 7261
TAIWAN SUMIKO MATERIALS CO., LTD.—See Sumitomo Metal Mining Co., Ltd.; *Int'l*, pg. 7293
TAIWAN SUPERCRITICAL TECHNOLOGY CO., LTD.—See Tex-Ray Industrial Co., Ltd.; *Int'l*, pg. 7582
TAIWAN SURFACE MOUNTING TECHNOLOGY CORP.; *Int'l*, pg. 7424
TAIWAN TADANO LTD.—See Tadano Ltd.; *Int'l*, pg. 7404
TAIWAN TAFFETA FABRIC CO., LTD.; *Int'l*, pg. 7424
TAIWAN TAIKO PHARMACEUTICAL CO., LTD.—See Taiko Pharmaceutical Co., Ltd.; *Int'l*, pg. 7414
TAIWAN TAIYO INK CO., LTD.—See TAIYO HOLDINGS CO., LTD.; *Int'l*, pg. 7425
TAIWAN TAIYOKOGYO INC.—See Taiyo Kogyo Corporation; *Int'l*, pg. 7426
TAIWAN TAIYO YUDEN COMPANY LTD.—See Taiyo Yuden Company Ltd.; *Int'l*, pg. 7427
TAIWAN TAMURA TECHNOLOGY CO., LTD.—See Tamura Corporation; *Int'l*, pg. 7451

TAIWAN TAFFETA FABRIC CO., LTD.

TAIWAN TANABE SEIYAKU CO., LTD.—See Mitsubishi Chemical Group Corporation; *Int'l*, pg. 4935
TAIWAN TANAKA KIKINZOKU KOGYO CO., LTD.—See Tanaka Holdings Co., Ltd.; *Int'l*, pg. 7455
TAIWAN TAOMEE CO., LTD.—See Taomee Holdings Limited; *Int'l*, pg. 7461
TAIWAN TAXI CO., LTD.; *Int'l*, pg. 7424
TAIWAN TEAC CORPORATION—See Evolution Capital Management LLC; *U.S. Private*, pg. 1443
TAIWAN TEA CORPORATION; *Int'l*, pg. 7424
TAIWAN TEIKOKU PUMP CO.,LTD.—See Teikoku Electric Mfg. Co., Ltd.; *Int'l*, pg. 7524
TAIWAN TERMINAL SERVICE CORPORATION LTD.—See Evergreen Marine Corporation (Taiwan) Ltd.; *Int'l*, pg. 2567
TAIWAN THICK-FILM INDUSTRIES CORP.; *Int'l*, pg. 7425
TAIWAN TOAGOSEI CO., LTD.—See Toagosei Co. Ltd.; *Int'l*, pg. 7770
TAIWAN TOBACCO & LIQUOR CORPORATION; *Int'l*, pg. 7425
TAIWAN TOCOS ELECTRIC CO., LTD—See Tokyo Cosmos Electric Co., Ltd.; *Int'l*, pg. 7790
TAIWAN TOHCELLO FUNCTIONAL SHEET, INC.—See Mitsui Chemicals, Inc.; *Int'l*, pg. 4984
TAIWAN TOKUYAMA CORPORATION—See Tokuyama Corporation; *Int'l*, pg. 7787
TAIWAN TOPLINE, INC.—See Topline Imports, Inc.; *U.S. Private*, pg. 4187
TAIWAN TOSHIBA INTERNATIONAL PROCUREMENT CORP.—See Japan Industrial Partners, Inc.; *Int'l*, pg. 3891
TAIWAN TOTAL MANAGEMENT CONSULTING LTD.—See EPS Holdings, Inc.; *Int'l*, pg. 2465
TAIWAN TOTO CO., LTD.—See Toto Ltd.; *Int'l*, pg. 7846
TAIWAN TRINITY INDUSTRIAL CORP.—See Trinity Industrial Corporation; *Int'l*, pg. 7924
TAIWAN TSUBAKIMOTO COMPANY—See Tsubakimoto Chain Co.; *Int'l*, pg. 7953
TAIWAN UNION TOOL CORP.—See Union Tool Co.; *Int'l*, pg. 8054
TAIWAN UNITED MEDICAL INC.—See Taiwan Styrene Monomer Corporation; *Int'l*, pg. 7424
TAIWAN UNITED VENTURE CAPITAL CORP.—See USI Corporation; *Int'l*, pg. 8099
TAIWAN USHIO LIGHTING, INC.—See Ushio, Inc.; *Int'l*, pg. 8097
TAIWAN UYEMURA CO., LTD.—See C.Uyemura & Co., Ltd.; *Int'l*, pg. 1244
TAIWAN VALQUA ENGINEERING INTERNATIONAL, LTD.—See VALQUA, LTD.; *Int'l*, pg. 8122
TAIWAN VALQUA INDUSTRIES LTD.—See VALQUA, LTD.; *Int'l*, pg. 8122
TAIWAN VALVE CO., LTD—See Emerson Electric Co.; *U.S. Public*, pg. 751
TAIWAN VMWARE INFORMATION TECHNOLOGY LLC—See Broadcom Inc.; *U.S. Public*, pg. 390
TAIWAN WACOAL CO., LTD.—See Wacoal Holdings Corp.; *Int'l*, pg. 8326
TAIWAN WAX COMPANY LTD.; *Int'l*, pg. 7425
TAIWAN WEB SERVICE CORPORATION—See ASUSTeK Computer Inc.; *Int'l*, pg. 664
TAIWAN WKK DISTRIBUTION CO., LTD.—See Wong's Kong King International (Holdings) Limited; *Int'l*, pg. 8447
TAIWAN YAMAHA MUSICAL INSTRUMENT MANUFACTURING CO., LTD.—See Yamaha Corporation; *Int'l*, pg. 8549
TAIWAN YAMATO INTERNATIONAL LOGISTICS INC.—See Yamato Holdings Co., Ltd.; *Int'l*, pg. 8555
TAIWAN YAZAKI CORPORATION—See Yazaki Corporation; *Int'l*, pg. 8572
TAIWAN YES DEEP OCEAN WATER CO., LTD.—See Taiwan Fertilizer Co., Ltd.; *Int'l*, pg. 7420
TAIWAN YUASA BATTERY CO., LTD.—See GS Yuasa Corporation; *Int'l*, pg. 3143
TAIWAY INDUSTRY CO., LTD.—See Dana Incorporated; *U.S. Public*, pg. 623
TAIWAY INDUSTRY CO., LTD.—See GKN plc; *Int'l*, pg. 2986
TAIWAY INDUSTRY CO., LTD.—See NTN Corporation; *Int'l*, pg. 5482
TAIW FRUCTOSE CO., LTD.; *Int'l*, pg. 7418
TAI WO TONG COMPANY LIMITED—See Hin Sang Group (International) Holding Co. Ltd.; *Int'l*, pg. 3397
TAIXIANG VEHICLE REPLACE PARTS (SHENZHEN) CO., LTD.—See Robert Bosch GmbH; *Int'l*, pg. 6368
TAIXIN FIBER PRODUCTS (SUZHOU) CO., LTD.—See Shinih Enterprise Co., Ltd.; *Int'l*, pg. 6845
TAIXING LINGSU SPECIALTY MATERIALS CO., LTD.—See Mitsubishi Gas Chemical Company, Inc.; *Int'l*, pg. 4950
TAIXING MGC LINGSU CO., LTD.—See Mitsubishi Gas Chemical Company, Inc.; *Int'l*, pg. 4950
TAIXING SUNKE CHEMICALS CO.—See Arkema S.A.; *Int'l*, pg. 571
TAIXING XIN XIN RESOURCES RECYCLING COMPANY LIMITED—See New Universe Environmental Group Limited; *Int'l*, pg. 5228
TAIXING YONGDA ZHONGCHENG AUTOMOBILE SALES & SERVICES CO., LTD.—See China Yongda Automobiles Services Holdings Limited; *Int'l*, pg. 1565
TAIYA(QUANZHOU) SHOES CO.,LTD.—See Kingnet Network Co., Ltd.; *Int'l*, pg. 4174
TAIYEN BIOTECH CO., LTD.; *Int'l*, pg. 7425
TAIYO A&F CO., LTD.—See Maruha Nichiro Corporation; *Int'l*, pg. 4712
TAIYO AMERICA, INC.—See Parker Hannifin Corporation; *U.S. Public*, pg. 1649
TAIYO BIRDAIR DO BRASIL LTDA.—See Taiyo Kogyo Corporation; *Int'l*, pg. 7426
TAIYO BUSSAN KAISHA LTD; *Int'l*, pg. 7425
TAIYO CHEMICAL CO., LTD.—See Japan Waste Corporation; *Int'l*, pg. 3908
TAIYO CHEMICAL INDUSTRY CO., LTD.—See Sojitz Corporation; *Int'l*, pg. 7066
TAIYO-CO. INC.—See Sala Corporation; *Int'l*, pg. 6490
TAIYO CO., LTD.; *Int'l*, pg. 7425
TAIYO CREDIT GUARANTEE CO., LTD—See T&D Holdings, Inc.; *Int'l*, pg. 7395
TAIYO DAIICHI TRAFFIC CO., LTD.—See Daiichi Koutsu Sangyo Co., Ltd.; *Int'l*, pg. 1929
TAIYO ELEC CO., LTD.—See Sega Sammy Holdings, Inc.; *Int'l*, pg. 6681
TAIYO ELECTRIC MFG. CO., LTD.—See NITTO KOGYO CORPORATION; *Int'l*, pg. 5387
TAIYO EUROPE GMBH—See Taiyo Kogyo Corporation; *Int'l*, pg. 7426
TAIYO GMBH—See Taiyo Kagaku Co., Ltd.; *Int'l*, pg. 7425
TAIYO GREEN POWER CO., LTD.—See Taiyo Kagaku Co., Ltd.; *Int'l*, pg. 7425
TAIYO HOLDINGS CO., LTD.; *Int'l*, pg. 7425
TAIYO INDUSTRIAL CO., LTD. - KYUSHU PLANT.—See Taiyo Technolex Co.,Ltd.; *Int'l*, pg. 7426
TAIYO INDUSTRY CO., LTD.—See Ochi Holdings Co., Ltd.; *Int'l*, pg. 5519
TAIYO INK INTERNATIONAL (HK) LTD.—See TAIYO HOLDINGS CO., LTD.; *Int'l*, pg. 7425
TAIYO INK INTERNATIONAL (SINGAPORE) PTE. LTD.—See TAIYO HOLDINGS CO., LTD.; *Int'l*, pg. 7425
TAIYO INK MFG. CO., LTD.—See TAIYO HOLDINGS CO., LTD.; *Int'l*, pg. 7425
TAIYO INK (SUZHOU) CO., LTD.—See TAIYO HOLDINGS CO., LTD.; *Int'l*, pg. 7425
TAIYO INTER KOREA LIMITED—See Taiyo Kagaku Co., Ltd.; *Int'l*, pg. 7425
TAIYO INTERNATIONAL, INC.—See Taiyo Kagaku Co., Ltd.; *Int'l*, pg. 7425
TAIYO KAGAKU CHINA CO., LTD.—See Taiyo Kagaku Co., Ltd.; *Int'l*, pg. 7425
TAIYO KAGAKU CO., LTD.; *Int'l*, pg. 7425
TAIYO KAGAKU INDIA PVT. LTD.—See Taiyo Kagaku Co., Ltd.; *Int'l*, pg. 7425
TAIYO KAIHATSU CO., LTD.—See Hisamitsu Pharmaceutical Co., Inc.; *Int'l*, pg. 3406
TAIYOKENKI RENTAL CO., LTD.—See Mitsui & Co., Ltd.; *Int'l*, pg. 4980
TAIYO KISEN CO., LTD.—See Sumitomo Osaka Cement Co Ltd; *Int'l*, pg. 7297
TAIYO KISOKOGYO CO., LTD.; *Int'l*, pg. 7425
TAIYO KOGYO CORPORATION; *Int'l*, pg. 7425
TAIYO KOGYO(THAILAND) CO.,LTD.—See Taiyo Kogyo Corporation; *Int'l*, pg. 7426
TAIYO KOKI CO., LTD.—See DMG MORI Co., Ltd.; *Int'l*, pg. 2145
TAIYO KOKO CO LTD; *Int'l*, pg. 7426
TAIYOKOZAI CO., LTD.—See Hanwa Co., Ltd.; *Int'l*, pg. 3263
THE TAIYO LIFE INSURANCE COMPANY—See T&D Holdings, Inc.; *Int'l*, pg. 7395
TAIYO, LTD.—See Parker Hannifin Corporation; *U.S. Public*, pg. 1649
TAIYO MEMBRANE CORPORATION PTY LTD—See Taiyo Kogyo Corporation; *Int'l*, pg. 7426
TAIYO MEMBRANE INDIA PVT LTD—See Taiyo Kogyo Corporation; *Int'l*, pg. 7426
TAIYO MICRONESIA CORPORATION—See Maruha Nichiro Corporation; *Int'l*, pg. 4712
TAIYO MIDDLE EAST LLC—See Taiyo Kogyo Corporation; *Int'l*, pg. 7426
TAIYO NAMIBIA (PTY) LTD.—See Maruha Nichiro Corporation; *Int'l*, pg. 4712
TAIYONIC LTD-(TAIYO)—See Northern Technologies International Corporation; *U.S. Public*, pg. 1538
TAIYO NIPPON KISEN CO., LTD.—See Kawasaki Kisen Kaisha, Ltd.; *Int'l*, pg. 4101
TAIYO NIPPON SANSO TAIWAN, INC.—See Mitsubishi Chemical Group Corporation; *Int'l*, pg. 4937
TAIYO NIPPON SANSO TRADING (SHANGHAI) CO., LTD.—See Mitsubishi Chemical Group Corporation; *Int'l*, pg. 4937
TAIYO PARKER FLUIDPOWER (SHANGHAI) CO., LTD.—See Parker Hannifin Corporation; *U.S. Public*, pg. 1650
TAIYO PLASTIC CORPORATION OF THE PHILIPPINES—See Toyo Seikan Group Holdings, Ltd.; *Int'l*, pg. 7857
TAIYO PLASTICS CO., LTD.—See Inabata & Co., Ltd.; *Int'l*, pg. 3644
TAIYO PORK CORP.—See Itoham Yonekyu Holdings Inc.; *Int'l*, pg. 3843
TAIYO SHEARING CO., LTD.—See Nippon Steel Corporation; *Int'l*, pg. 5339
TAIYO SHIGYO CO., LTD.—See Rengo Co., Ltd.; *Int'l*, pg. 6281
TAIYO SHIPPING CO., LTD.—See Sumitomo Osaka Cement Co Ltd; *Int'l*, pg. 7297
TAIYO SHOKAI CO., LTD—See Tachibana Eletech Co., Ltd.; *Int'l*, pg. 7403
TAIYO SHOKUHIN CO., LTD.—See Maruha Nichiro Corporation; *Int'l*, pg. 4712
TAIYO TECH CO., LTD.—See Parker Hannifin Corporation; *U.S. Public*, pg. 1650
TAIYO TECHNOLEX CO.,LTD.; *Int'l*, pg. 7426
TAIYO TECHNOLEX (SHANGHAI) CO., LTD.—See Taiyo Technolex Co.,Ltd.; *Int'l*, pg. 7426
TAIYO TECHNOLEX (THAILAND) CO., LTD.—See Taiyo Technolex Co.,Ltd.; *Int'l*, pg. 7426
TAIYO TECHNO, LTD.—See Parker Hannifin Corporation; *U.S. Public*, pg. 1649
TAIYO TECHNO RESEARCH LTD.—See Eurofins Scientific S.E.; *Int'l*, pg. 2552
TAIYOUGIKEN CO., LTD.—See Uchida Yoko Co., Ltd.; *Int'l*, pg. 8012
TAI YOUNG CHEMICAL CO., LTD.—See Mitsubishi Chemical Group Corporation; *Int'l*, pg. 4934
TAI-YOUNG FILM CO., LTD.—See Mitsubishi Chemical Group Corporation; *Int'l*, pg. 4934
TAI YOUNG HIGH TECH CO., LTD.—See Mitsubishi Chemical Group Corporation; *Int'l*, pg. 4934
TAI-YOUNG NYLON CO. LTD.—See Koninklijke DSM N.V.; *Int'l*, pg. 4263
TAIYOUNG SANKYU INTERNATIONAL LOGISTICS CO., LTD.—See Sankyu, Inc.; *Int'l*, pg. 6545
TAIYO VINYL CORPORATION—See Tosoh Corporation; *Int'l*, pg. 7833
TAIYO VINYL CORPORATION - YOKKAICHI PLANT—See Tosoh Corporation; *Int'l*, pg. 7833
TAIYO YUDEN (CHANGZHOU) CO., LTD.—See Taiyo Yuden Company Ltd.; *Int'l*, pg. 7427
TAIYO YUDEN (CHINA) CO., LTD.—See Taiyo Yuden Company Ltd.; *Int'l*, pg. 7427
TAIYO YUDEN COMPANY LTD. - ANECHOIC CHAMBER TEST FACILITY—See Taiyo Yuden Company Ltd.; *Int'l*, pg. 7427
TAIYO YUDEN COMPANY LTD. - NAKANOJO PLANT—See Taiyo Yuden Company Ltd.; *Int'l*, pg. 7427
TAIYO YUDEN COMPANY LTD.; *Int'l*, pg. 7426
TAIYO YUDEN COMPANY LTD. - YAWATABARA PLANT—See Taiyo Yuden Company Ltd.; *Int'l*, pg. 7427
TAIYO YUDEN ENERGY DEVICE CO., LTD.—See Taiyo Yuden Company Ltd.; *Int'l*, pg. 7427
TAIYO YUDEN EUROPE GMBH—See Taiyo Yuden Company Ltd.; *Int'l*, pg. 7427
TAIYO YUDEN (GUANGDONG) CO., LTD.—See Taiyo Yuden Company Ltd.; *Int'l*, pg. 7427
TAIYO YUDEN (MALAYSIA) SDN BHD—See Taiyo Yuden Company Ltd.; *Int'l*, pg. 7427
TAIYO YUDEN MOBILE TECHNOLOGY CO., LTD.—See Taiyo Yuden Company Ltd.; *Int'l*, pg. 7427
TAIYO YUDEN (PHILIPPINES) INC.—See Taiyo Yuden Company Ltd.; *Int'l*, pg. 7427
TAIYO YUDEN (SARAWAK) SDN BHD—See Taiyo Yuden Company Ltd.; *Int'l*, pg. 7427
TAIYO YUDEN (SHANGHAI) TRADING CO., LTD.—See Taiyo Yuden Company Ltd.; *Int'l*, pg. 7427
TAIYO YUDEN (SHENZHEN) ELECTRONICS TRADING CO., LTD.—See Taiyo Yuden Company Ltd.; *Int'l*, pg. 7427
TAIYO YUDEN (SINGAPORE) PTE LTD—See Taiyo Yuden Company Ltd.; *Int'l*, pg. 7427
TAIYO YUDEN (SUZHOU) CO., LTD.—See Taiyo Yuden Company Ltd.; *Int'l*, pg. 7427
TAIYO YUDEN TECHNO SOLUTIONS CO., LTD.—See Taiyo Yuden Company Ltd.; *Int'l*, pg. 7427
TAIYO YUDEN (TIANJIN) ELECTRONICS CO., LTD.—See Taiyo Yuden Company Ltd.; *Int'l*, pg. 7427
TAIYO YUDEN (U.S.A.), INC.—See Taiyo Yuden Company Ltd.; *Int'l*, pg. 7427
TAIYO YUDEN (U.S.A.), INC—See Taiyo Yuden Company Ltd.; *Int'l*, pg. 7427
TAIYO YUSHI CORPORATION—See Kaneka Corporation; *Int'l*, pg. 4067
TAIYUAN BAOZEN AUTOMOBILE SALES AND SERVICES CO., LTD.—See China Yongda Automobiles Services Holdings Limited; *Int'l*, pg. 1565
TAIYUAN DAHAO YIDA ELECTRONIC CO., LTD.—See Beijing Dahao Technology Corporation Limited; *Int'l*, pg. 948
TAI-YUAN GARMENTS CO., LTD.—See Eclat Textile Co., Ltd.; *Int'l*, pg. 2291
TAIYUAN HEAVY INDUSTRY CO., LTD.; *Int'l*, pg. 7427
TAIYUAN RAILWAY ROLLING STOCK CO., LTD.—See CRRC Corporation Limited; *Int'l*, pg. 1859

COMPANY NAME INDEX

TAIYUAN ZHONGFU IN-LINE CONTAINER CO., LTD—See Zhuhai Zhongfu Enterprise Co., Ltd.; *Int'l*, pg. 8679
TAI YU & CO., LTD.—See CHINO Corporation; *Int'l*, pg. 1571
TAI-YUE RUBBER INDUSTRIAL CO., LTD.—See Toyoda Gosei Co., Ltd.; *Int'l*, pg. 7862
TAIZHOU AUCHAN HYPERMARKETS CO., LTD.—See Alibaba Group Holding Limited; *Int'l*, pg. 326
TAIZHOU BAOZEN AUTOMOBILE SALES AND SERVICES CO., LTD.—See China Yongda Automobiles Services Holdings Limited; *Int'l*, pg. 1565
TAIZHOU MINGXIN MICROELECTRONICS CO., LTD.—See Daheng New Epoch Technology, Inc.; *Int'l*, pg. 1913
TAIZHOU NEW UNIVERSE SOLID WASTE DISPOSAL COMPANY LIMITED—See New Universe Environmental Group Limited; *Int'l*, pg. 5229
TAIZHOU POLY GRAND THEATRE MANAGEMENT CORPORATION LIMITED—See Poly Culture Group Corporation Limited; *Int'l*, pg. 5914
TAIZHOU SHAGANG MATERIALS TRADE CO., LTD.—See Jiangsu Shagang Group Ltd.; *Int'l*, pg. 3954
TAIZHOU SHIMGE MACHINERY & ELECTRONIC CO., LTD.; *Int'l*, pg. 7427
TAIZHOU TIGERMED-JYTON MEDICAL TECH. CO., LTD.—See Hangzhou Tigermed Consulting Co., Ltd.; *Int'l*, pg. 3251
TAIZHOU TON YI INDUSTRIAL CO., LTD.—See Uni-President Enterprises Corporation; *Int'l*, pg. 8029
TAIZHOU TOPCUT-BULLMER MECHANICAL & ELECTRICAL CO., LTD.—See Jack Technology Co., Ltd.; *Int'l*, pg. 3864
TAIZHOU WATER GROUP COMPANY LIMTED; *Int'l*, pg. 7428
TAIZHOU YONGDA AOCHENG AUTOMOBILE SALES AND SERVICES CO., LTD.—See China Yongda Automobiles Services Holdings Limited; *Int'l*, pg. 1565
TAIZHOU ZHONG LAI PHOTOELECTRIC TECHNOLOGY CO., LTD.—See Jolywood Suzhou Sunwatt Co., Ltd.; *Int'l*, pg. 3997
TAI ZI CAPITAL LIMITED; *Int'l*, pg. 7409
TAJBA, A.S.—See Agrofert Holding, a.s.; *Int'l*, pg. 219
TAJGVK HOTELS & RESORTS LTD; *Int'l*, pg. 7428
TA JIANG CO., LTD.; *Int'l*, pg. 7400
TAJIMA AMERICA CORPORATION—See Tajima Industries Ltd.; *Int'l*, pg. 7428
TAJIMA ASIA PTE LTD.—See Tajima Industries Ltd.; *Int'l*, pg. 7428
TAJIMA AUSTRALIA PTY. LTD.—See Tajima Industries Ltd.; *Int'l*, pg. 7428
TAJIMA COLOMBO (PTE) LTD—See Tajima Industries Ltd.; *Int'l*, pg. 7428
TAJIMA DO BRASIL—See Tajima Industries Ltd.; *Int'l*, pg. 7428
TAJIMA EMBROIDERY MACHINES (CHINA) CO. LTD.—See Tajima Industries Ltd.; *Int'l*, pg. 7428
TAJIMA EMBROIDERY MACHINES LTD.—See Tajima Industries Ltd.; *Int'l*, pg. 7428
TAJIMA EUROPE S.A.R.L—See Tajima Industries Ltd.; *Int'l*, pg. 7428
TAJIMA GOSEN CO., LTD.—See GSI Creos Corporation; *Int'l*, pg. 3145
TAJIMA-HIRSCH INCORPORATED—See Hirsch International Corp.; *U.S. Private*, pg. 1951
TAJIMA INDUSTRIES LTD.; *Int'l*, pg. 7428
TAJIMA METALWORK CO., LTD.—See Sanwa Holdings Corporation; *Int'l*, pg. 6561
TAJIMA METALWORK KANSAI CO., LTD.—See Sanwa Holdings Corporation; *Int'l*, pg. 6561
TAJIMA SERVICE LTD.—See Tajima Industries Ltd.; *Int'l*, pg. 7428
TAJIMA SHOKUHIN KOGYO CO., LTD.—See Nippon Shinyaku Co., Ltd.; *Int'l*, pg. 5332
TAJIMA USA, INC.—See Hirsch International Corp.; *U.S. Private*, pg. 1950
TAJIMA USA, INC.—See Tajima Industries Ltd.; *Int'l*, pg. 7428
TAJIMI DYNAPAC CO., LTD.—See Dynapac Co., Ltd.; *Int'l*, pg. 2241
TAJIRI RESOURCES CORP.; *Int'l*, pg. 7428
TAJ MEDIA, LLC—See AAC Holdings, Inc.; *U.S. Private*, pg. 31
TAJO S. COOP.—See Mondragon Corporation; *Int'l*, pg. 5031
TAJ TECHNOLOGIES INC.; *U.S. Private*, pg. 3925
TAJ TELEVISION LTD.—See Essel Corporate Resources Pvt. Ltd.; *Int'l*, pg. 2510
TAJ TEXTILE MILLS LIMITED—See Nishat Chunian Limited; *Int'l*, pg. 5363
TAJ TV LIMITED—See Essel Corporate Resources Pvt. Ltd.; *Int'l*, pg. 2509
TAJ TV LIMITED—See Essel Corporate Resources Pvt. Ltd.; *Int'l*, pg. 2510
TAKACHIHO CO., LTD.; *Int'l*, pg. 7428
TAKACHIHO FIRE, SECURITY & SERVICES (THAILAND) LTD.—See Takachiho Koheki Co., Ltd.; *Int'l*, pg. 7429
TAKACHIHO KOHEKI CO., LTD.; *Int'l*, pg. 7428

TAKACHIHO KOHEKI (H.K.) LTD.—See Takachiho Koheki Co., Ltd.; *Int'l*, pg. 7429
TAKACHIHO TRADING (SHANGHAI) CO., LTD.—See Takachiho Koheki Co., Ltd.; *Int'l*, pg. 7429
TAKADA CORPORATION ASIA LTD.—See Takada Corporation; *Int'l*, pg. 7429
TAKADA CORPORATION; *Int'l*, pg. 7429
TAKADAKIKO (STEEL CONSTRUCTION) CO., LTD.; *Int'l*, pg. 7429
TAKAFUL EMARAT - INSURANCE (PSC); *Int'l*, pg. 7429
TAKAFUL IKHLAS FAMILY BERHAD—See MNRB Holdings Berhad; *Int'l*, pg. 5006
TAKAFUL IKHLAS GENERAL BERHAD—See MNRB Holdings Berhad; *Int'l*, pg. 5006
TAKAFUL IKHLAS SDN. BHD.—See MNRB Holdings Berhad; *Int'l*, pg. 5006
TAKAFUL INTERNATIONAL COMPANY B.S.C—See Fairfax Financial Holdings Limited; *Int'l*, pg. 2607
TAKAFUL ISLAMI INSURANCE LIMITED; *Int'l*, pg. 7429
TAKAFUL OMAN INSURANCE SAOG; *Int'l*, pg. 7429
TAKAFUL RE LIMITED—See Arab Insurance Group B.S.C.; *Int'l*, pg. 530
TAKAGI AUTO PARTS (FOSHAN) CO., LTD.—See Takagi Seiko Corporation; *Int'l*, pg. 7429
TAKAGI CHOKOKU CO., LTD.; *Int'l*, pg. 7429
TAKAGI CO., LTD.; *Int'l*, pg. 7429
TAKAGI CO., LTD.—See Tachibana Eletech Co., Ltd.; *Int'l*, pg. 7403
TAKAGI KOGYO TRANSPORT CO., LTD.—See Yasuda Logistics Corporation; *Int'l*, pg. 8570
TAKAGI SEIKO CORPORATION; *Int'l*, pg. 7429
TAKAGI SEIKO (H.K.) LIMITED—See Takagi Seiko Corporation; *Int'l*, pg. 7429
TAKAGI VIETNAM CO., LTD.—See Takagi Co., Ltd.; *Int'l*, pg. 7429
TAKAHAGI NICHIHA CORPORATION—See Nichiha Corporation; *Int'l*, pg. 5269
TAKAHASHI CURTAIN WALL CORPORATION; *Int'l*, pg. 7429
TAKAHASHI WORKS U.S.A., INC.—See Komatsu Ltd.; *Int'l*, pg. 4239
TAKAHATA CO., LTD.—See Sojitz Corporation; *Int'l*, pg. 7066
T.A. KAISER HEATING & AIR, INC.—See NRG Energy, Inc.; *U.S. Public*, pg. 1549
TAKA JEWELLERY HOLDINGS LIMITED; *Int'l*, pg. 7428
TAKAKITA CO., LTD.; *Int'l*, pg. 7429
TAKAKO AMERICA CO., INC.—See KYB Corporation; *Int'l*, pg. 4354
TAKAKO INDUSTRIES, INC.—See KYB Corporation; *Int'l*, pg. 4354
TAKAKO VIETNAM CO., LTD.—See KYB Corporation; *Int'l*, pg. 4354
TAKAMASAMUNE CO LTD—See Coca-Cola Bottlers Japan Holdings Inc.; *Int'l*, pg. 1684
TAKAMATSU CONSTRUCTION GROUP CO., LTD.; *Int'l*, pg. 7429
TAKAMATSU ESTATE CO., LTD.—See Takamatsu Construction Group Co., Ltd.; *Int'l*, pg. 7430
TAKAMATSU HOUSE CO., LTD.—See Takamatsu Construction Group Co., Ltd.; *Int'l*, pg. 7430
TAKAMATSU MACHINERY CO., LTD.; *Int'l*, pg. 7430
TAKAMATSU MACHINERY (THAILAND) CO., LTD.—See Takamatsu Machinery Co., Ltd.; *Int'l*, pg. 7430
TAKAMATSU MACHINERY U.S.A., INC.—See Takamatsu Machinery Co., Ltd.; *Int'l*, pg. 7430
TAKAMATSU MITSUKOSHI LTD.—See Isetan Mitsukoshi Holdings Ltd.; *Int'l*, pg. 3815
TAKAMATSU TECHNO SERVICE CO., LTD.—See Takamatsu Construction Group Co., Ltd.; *Int'l*, pg. 7430
TAKAMAZ MACHINERY EUROPE GMBH—See Takamatsu Machinery Co., Ltd.; *Int'l*, pg. 7430
TAKAMISAWA CO., LTD.; *Int'l*, pg. 7430
TAKAMISAWA CYBERNETICS CO., LTD.; *Int'l*, pg. 7430
TAKAMISAWA MEX CO., LTD.—See TAKAMISAWA CYBERNETICS CO., LTD.; *Int'l*, pg. 7430
TAKAMISAWA SERVICE CORPORATION—See TAKAMISAWA CYBERNETICS CO., LTD.; *Int'l*, pg. 7430
TAKAMISAWA SOLUTIONS CO., LTD.—See TAKAMISAWA CYBERNETICS CO., LTD.; *Int'l*, pg. 7430
TAKAMIYA CO., LTD.; *Int'l*, pg. 7430
TAKAMUL INVESTMENT CO. S.A.O.C—See OQ S.A.O.C.; *Int'l*, pg. 5607
TAKANASHI MILK OCEANIA PTY.LTD.—See Takanashi Milk Products Co., Ltd.; *Int'l*, pg. 7430
TAKANASHI MILK PRODUCTS CO., LTD.; *Int'l*, pg. 7430
TAKANASHI MILK PRODUCTS SALES CO., LTD—See Takanashi Milk Products Co., Ltd.; *Int'l*, pg. 7430
TAKANET SERVICE CO., LTD.; *Int'l*, pg. 7431
TAKANO CO., LTD. - INA FACTORY—See Takano Co., Ltd.; *Int'l*, pg. 7431
TAKANO CO., LTD. - MINAMIDAIRA FACTORY—See Takano Co., Ltd.; *Int'l*, pg. 7431
TAKANO CO., LTD. - SHIMOJIMA FACTORY—See Takano Co., Ltd.; *Int'l*, pg. 7431
TAKANO CO., LTD.; *Int'l*, pg. 7431
TAKANO MACHINERY CO., LTD.—See Takano Co., Ltd.; *Int'l*, pg. 7431

TAKANO MACHINERY WORKS CO., LTD.—See Senko Group Holdings Co., Ltd.; *Int'l*, pg. 6712
TAKAOKA CHEMICAL CO., LTD.—See Takaoka Toko Co., Ltd.; *Int'l*, pg. 7431
TAKAOKA DENSETSU CO., LTD.—See Takaoka Toko Co., Ltd.; *Int'l*, pg. 7431
TAKAOKA ELECTRIC MFG. CO., LTD.—See Takaoka Toko Co., Ltd.; *Int'l*, pg. 7431
TAKAOKA ELECTRONICS CO., LTD.—See Hamamatsu Photonics K.K.; *Int'l*, pg. 3235
TAKAOKA ENGINEERING CO., LTD.—See Takaoka Toko Co., Ltd.; *Int'l*, pg. 7431
TAKAOKA LIOHO INDUSTRY CO.,LTD.—See Universal Cement Corporation; *Int'l*, pg. 8078
TAKAOKA LIOHO (TIANJIN) INDUSTRIES CO., LTD—See AISIN Corporation; *Int'l*, pg. 253
TAKAOKA TOKO CO., LTD.; *Int'l*, pg. 7431
TAKA-Q CO., LTD.; *Int'l*, pg. 7428
TAKARA ASSET MANAGEMENT CO., LTD.—See Mirarth Holdings, Inc.; *Int'l*, pg. 4918
TAKARA BELMONT CORPORATION MARBLE PRODUCTS DIV.—See Takara Belmont Corporation; *Int'l*, pg. 7431
TAKARA BELMONT CORPORATION; *Int'l*, pg. 7431
TAKARA BELMONT (KOREA) CORPORATION—See Takara Belmont Corporation; *Int'l*, pg. 7431
TAKARA BELMONT PARA AMERICA DO SUL INDUSTRIA E COMERCIO DE MOVEIS LTDA.—See Takara Belmont Corporation; *Int'l*, pg. 7431
TAKARA BELMONT (SHANGHAI) CORPORATION—See Takara Belmont Corporation; *Int'l*, pg. 7431
TAKARA BELMONT (TAIWAN) CORP.—See Takara Belmont Corporation; *Int'l*, pg. 7431
TAKARA BELMONT(U.K.)LTD.—See Takara Belmont Corporation; *Int'l*, pg. 7431
TAKARA BELMONT U.S.A., INC.—See Takara Belmont Corporation; *Int'l*, pg. 7432
TAKARA BIO EUROPE S.A.S.—See Takara Holdings, Inc.; *Int'l*, pg. 7432
TAKARA BIO, INC.—See Takara Holdings, Inc.; *Int'l*, pg. 7432
TAKARA BIOMEDICAL TECHNOLOGY (BEIJING) CO., LTD.—See Takara Holdings, Inc.; *Int'l*, pg. 7432
TAKARA BIOTECHNOLOGY (DALIAN) CO., LTD.—See Takara Holdings, Inc.; *Int'l*, pg. 7432
TAKARA BIO USA HOLDINGS INC.—See Takara Holdings, Inc.; *Int'l*, pg. 7432
TAKARA BIO USA, INC.—See Takara Holdings, Inc.; *Int'l*, pg. 7432
TAKARA BUILDING MAINTENANCE CO., LTD.—See Sinanen Holdings Co., Ltd.; *Int'l*, pg. 6936
TAKARA BUSSAN CO., LTD.—See Takara Holdings, Inc.; *Int'l*, pg. 7432
TAKARA BUTSURYU SYSTEM CO., LTD.—See Takara Holdings, Inc.; *Int'l*, pg. 7432
TAKARA CHOUJN CO., LTD—See Aspirant Group, Inc.; *Int'l*, pg. 631
TAKARA COMPAGNIE PARIS S.A.R.L.—See Takara Belmont Corporation; *Int'l*, pg. 7432
TAKARA COMPANY,CANADA,LTD.—See Takara Belmont Corporation; *Int'l*, pg. 7432
TAKARA COMPANY EUROPE GMBH—See Takara Belmont Corporation; *Int'l*, pg. 7432
TAKARA & COMPANY LTD.; *Int'l*, pg. 7431
TAKARA HOLDINGS, INC.; *Int'l*, pg. 7432
TAKARAJIMA LTD.—See Zensho Holdings Co., Ltd.; *Int'l*, pg. 8634
TAKARA KOREA BIOMEDICAL, INC.—See Takara Holdings, Inc.; *Int'l*, pg. 7432
TAKARA LEBEN INFRASTRUCTURE FUND, INC.; *Int'l*, pg. 7433
TAKARA LEBEN REAL ESTATE INVESTMENT CORPORATION; *Int'l*, pg. 7433
TAKARA LEBEN REALNET CO., LTD.—See Mirarth Holdings, Inc.; *Int'l*, pg. 4918
TAKARA NETWORK SYSTEM CO., LTD.—See Takara Holdings, Inc.; *Int'l*, pg. 7432
TAKARA PAG REAL ESTATE ADVISORY LTD.—See Mirarth Holdings, Inc.; *Int'l*, pg. 4918
TAKARA SAKE USA INC.—See Takara Holdings, Inc.; *Int'l*, pg. 7432
TAKARA SANGYO CO., LTD.—See Sumitomo Electric Industries, Ltd.; *Int'l*, pg. 7284
TAKARA SHUZO ASIA PACIFIC PTE. LTD.—See Takara Holdings, Inc.; *Int'l*, pg. 7432
TAKARA SHUZO CO., LTD—See Takara Holdings, Inc.; *Int'l*, pg. 7432
TAKARA SHUZO FOODS CO., LTD.—See Takara Holdings, Inc.; *Int'l*, pg. 7433
TAKARA SHUZO INTERNATIONAL CO., LTD.—See Takara Holdings, Inc.; *Int'l*, pg. 7433
TAKARA STANDARD CO., LTD.—See Takara Belmont Corporation; *Int'l*, pg. 7432
TAKARA YOKI CO., LTD.—See Takara Holdings, Inc.; *Int'l*, pg. 7432
TAKARAZUKA CREATIVE ARTS CO., LTD.—See Hankyu Hanshin Holdings Inc.; *Int'l*, pg. 3255
TAKARAZUKA STAGE CO., LTD.—See Hankyu Hanshin Holdings Inc.; *Int'l*, pg. 3255

TAKARA LEBEN REAL ESTATE INVESTMENT CORPORATION

CORPORATE AFFILIATIONS

TAKASAGO CONSTRUCTORS AND ENGINEERS (CHINA) CO., LTD.—See Takasago Thermal Engineering Co., Ltd.; *Int'l*, pg. 7434
TAKASAGO CONSTRUCTORS & ENGINEERS (BEIJING) CO., LTD.—See Takasago Thermal Engineering Co., Ltd.; *Int'l*, pg. 7434
TAKASAGO DE CENTROAMERICA S.A.—See Takasago International Corporation; *Int'l*, pg. 7433
TAKASAGO DE MEXICO S.A. DE C.V.—See Takasago International Corporation; *Int'l*, pg. 7433
TAKASAGO ELECTRIC INDUSTRY CO., LTD. - MIE FACTORY—See Konami Group Corporation; *Int'l*, pg. 4245
TAKASAGO ELECTRIC INDUSTRY CO., LTD.—See Konami Group Corporation; *Int'l*, pg. 4245
TAKASAGO ENGINEERING MEXICO, S.A. DE C.V.—See Takasago Thermal Engineering Co., Ltd.; *Int'l*, pg. 7434
TAKASAGO EUROPE G.M.B.H.—See Takasago International Corporation; *Int'l*, pg. 7433
TAKASAGO EUROPE G.M.B.H.—See Takasago International Corporation; *Int'l*, pg. 7433
TAKASAGO EUROPE PERFUMERY LABORATORY S.A.R.L. - SAINT-OUEN L'AUMONE FACTORY—See Takasago International Corporation; *Int'l*, pg. 7433
TAKASAGO EUROPE PERFUMERY LABORATORY S.A.R.L.—See Takasago International Corporation; *Int'l*, pg. 7433
TAKASAGO EUROPE PERFUMERY LABORATORY S.A.R.L.—See Takasago International Corporation; *Int'l*, pg. 7433
TAKASAGO FRAGRANCIAS E AROMAS LTDA.—See Takasago International Corporation; *Int'l*, pg. 7433
TAKASAGO IMPORT AND EXPORT (THAILAND) LTD.—See Takasago International Corporation; *Int'l*, pg. 7433
TAKASAGO INTERNATIONAL CHEMICALS (EUROPE) S.A.—See Takasago International Corporation; *Int'l*, pg. 7434
TAKASAGO INTERNATIONAL CORP. - FLAVOR FACTORY—See Takasago International Corporation; *Int'l*, pg. 7434
TAKASAGO INTERNATIONAL CORP. - HARRIMAN FRAGRANCE FACTORY—See Takasago International Corporation; *Int'l*, pg. 7434
TAKASAGO INTERNATIONAL CORP. - NORTHVALE FRAGRANCE FACTORY—See Takasago International Corporation; *Int'l*, pg. 7434
TAKASAGO INTERNATIONAL CORPORATION—See Takasago International Corporation; *Int'l*, pg. 7434
TAKASAGO INTERNATIONAL CORPORATION—See Takasago International Corporation; *Int'l*, pg. 7434
TAKASAGO INTERNATIONAL CORPORATION; *Int'l*, pg. 7433
TAKASAGO INTERNATIONAL CORPORATION SOUTH AFRICA (PTY) LTD.—See Takasago International Corporation; *Int'l*, pg. 7434
TAKASAGO INTERNATIONAL CORP.—See Takasago International Corporation; *Int'l*, pg. 7434
TAKASAGO INTERNATIONAL (DEUTSCHLAND) G.M.B.H.—See Takasago International Corporation; *Int'l*, pg. 7433
TAKASAGO INTERNATIONAL (ESPANA) S.R.L.—See Takasago International Corporation; *Int'l*, pg. 7433
TAKASAGO INTERNATIONAL (GUANGZHOU) CO., LTD.—See Takasago International Corporation; *Int'l*, pg. 7433
TAKASAGO INTERNATIONAL (INDIA) PVT. LTD.—See Takasago International Corporation; *Int'l*, pg. 7433
TAKASAGO INTERNATIONAL (ITALIA) S.R.L.—See Takasago International Corporation; *Int'l*, pg. 7433
TAKASAGO INTERNATIONAL (MALAYSIA) SDN. BHD.—See Takasago International Corporation; *Int'l*, pg. 7434
TAKASAGO INTERNATIONAL (PHILIPPINES), INC.—See Takasago International Corporation; *Int'l*, pg. 7434
TAKASAGO INTERNATIONAL (SHANGHAI) CO., LTD.—See Takasago International Corporation; *Int'l*, pg. 7434
TAKASAGO INTERNATIONAL (SINGAPORE) PTE. LTD.—See Takasago International Corporation; *Int'l*, pg. 7434
TAKASAGO INTERNATIONAL (SINGAPORE) PTE. LTD.—See Takasago International Corporation; *Int'l*, pg. 7434
TAKASAGO INTERNATIONAL (SINGAPORE) PTE. LTD.—See Takasago International Corporation; *Int'l*, pg. 7434
TAKASAGO INTERNATIONAL (SINGAPORE) PTE. LTD.—See Takasago International Corporation; *Int'l*, pg. 7434
TAKASAGO INTERNATIONAL TURKEY ESANS VE AROMA SAN. TIC. A.S.—See Takasago International Corporation; *Int'l*, pg. 7434
TAKASAGO MADAGASCAR S.A.—See Takasago International Corporation; *Int'l*, pg. 7434
TAKASAGO MARUSEI ENGINEERING SERVICE CO., LTD.—See Takasago Thermal Engineering Co., Ltd.; *Int'l*, pg. 7435

TAKASAGO MOROCCO (SOCIETE CANANGA S.A.R.L.)—See Takasago International Corporation; *Int'l*, pg. 7434
TAKASAGO SINGAPORE PTE. LTD.—See Takasago Thermal Engineering Co., Ltd.; *Int'l*, pg. 7435
TAKASAGO STEEL CO., LTD.—See Takasago Tekko K.K.; *Int'l*, pg. 7434
TAKASAGO TEKKO K.K.; *Int'l*, pg. 7434
TAKASAGO THERMAL ENGINEERING CO., LTD.—See Takasago Thermal Engineering Co., Ltd.; *Int'l*, pg. 7435
TAKASAGO THERMAL ENGINEERING CO., LTD.; *Int'l*, pg. 7434
TAKASAGO THERMAL ENGINEERING (HONG KONG) CO., LTD.—See Takasago Thermal Engineering Co., Ltd.; *Int'l*, pg. 7435
TAKASAGO (U.K.) LTD.—See Takasago International Corporation; *Int'l*, pg. 7433
TAKASAGO VIETNAM CO., LTD.—See Takasago Thermal Engineering Co., Ltd.; *Int'l*, pg. 7435
TAKASAKI DAIICHI TRAFFIC CO., LTD.—See Daiichi Koutsu Sangyo Co., Ltd.; *Int'l*, pg. 1929
TAKASE ADD SYSTEM, INC.—See TAKASE CORPORATION; *Int'l*, pg. 7435
TAKASE ADD SYSTEM (SHANGHAI) INC.—See TAKASE CORPORATION; *Int'l*, pg. 7435
TAKASE CORPORATION; *Int'l*, pg. 7435
TAKASHIMA & CO., LTD.; *Int'l*, pg. 7435
(TAKASHIMA) DAIICHI TRAFFIC LTD.—See Daiichi Koutsu Sangyo Co., Ltd.; *Int'l*, pg. 1928
TAKASHIMA GIKEN CO., LTD.—See IHI Corporation; *Int'l*, pg. 3606
TAKASHIMA HOME SERVICE CORP.—See Takashima & Co., Ltd.; *Int'l*, pg. 7435
TAKASHIMA MITSUGI PF (THAILAND) CO., LTD.—See Takashima & Co., Ltd.; *Int'l*, pg. 7435
TAKASHIMA (U.S.A.), INC.—See Takashima & Co., Ltd.; *Int'l*, pg. 7435
TAKASHIMAYA COMPANY, LIMITED; *Int'l*, pg. 7435
TAKASHIMAYA CREDIT CO. LTD.—See Credit Saison Co., Ltd.; *Int'l*, pg. 1836
TAKASHIMAYA ENTERPRISES, INC. (SHIRO OF JAPAN)—See Takashimaya Company, Limited; *Int'l*, pg. 7435
TAKASHIMAYA FINANCIAL PARTNERS CO., LTD.—See Takashimaya Company, Limited; *Int'l*, pg. 7435
TAKASHIMAYA (FRANCE) S.A.—See Takashimaya Company, Limited; *Int'l*, pg. 7435
TAKASHIMAYA HONG KONG ENTERPRISES LIMITED—See Takashimaya Company, Limited; *Int'l*, pg. 7435
TAKASHIMAYA SERVICE CO., LTD.—See Takashimaya Company, Limited; *Int'l*, pg. 7435
TAKASHIMAYA SINGAPORE LTD.—See Takashimaya Company, Limited; *Int'l*, pg. 7435
TAKASHIMAYA TRANSCOSMOS INTERNATIONAL COMMERCE PTE. LTD.—See Transcosmos Inc.; *Int'l*, pg. 7898
TAKASHIMAYA VIETNAM LTD.—See Takashimaya Company, Limited; *Int'l*, pg. 7435
TAKASHO AUSTRALASIA PTY LTD.—See Takasho Co.,Ltd.; *Int'l*, pg. 7436
TAKASHO CO.,LTD.; *Int'l*, pg. 7436
TAKASHO GARDEN LIVING INDIA PTE. LTD.—See Takasho Co.,Ltd.; *Int'l*, pg. 7436
TAKASO RUBBER PRODUCTS SDN. BHD.—See OCR Group Berhad; *Int'l*, pg. 5520
TAKATA ASIA PTE. LTD.—See Ningbo Joyson Electronic Corp.; *Int'l*, pg. 5304
TAKATA AUTOMOTIVE ELECTRONICS (SHANGHAI) CO., LTD.—See Ningbo Joyson Electronic Corp.; *Int'l*, pg. 5304
TAKATA CORPORATION—See Ningbo Joyson Electronic Corp.; *Int'l*, pg. 5303
TAKATA GLOBAL GROUP; *U.S. Private*, pg. 3925
TAKATA INDIA PRIVATE LIMITED—See Ningbo Joyson Electronic Corp.; *Int'l*, pg. 5304
TAKATA-PETRI (SACHSEN) GMBH—See Ningbo Joyson Electronic Corp.; *Int'l*, pg. 5304
TAKATA (SHANGHAI) AUTOMOTIVE COMPONENT CO., LTD.—See Ningbo Joyson Electronic Corp.; *Int'l*, pg. 5304
TAKATECH CO., LTD.—See Toyota Boshoku Corporation; *Int'l*, pg. 7864
TAKATETSU LIFE CO., LTD.—See Takasago Tekko K.K.; *Int'l*, pg. 7434
TAKATOKU CO., LTD.—See Ledax Co., Ltd.; *Int'l*, pg. 4438
TAKATORI CORPORATION; *Int'l*, pg. 7436
TAKATSUKI KASEI CORPORATION—See Tigers Polymer Corporation; *Int'l*, pg. 7747
TAKAUD SAVINGS & PENSIONS B.S.C.—See Kuwait Projects Company (Holding) K.S.C.P.; *Int'l*, pg. 4347
TAKAYA SIIX ELECTRONICS (SHANGHAI) CO., LTD.—See SIIX CORPORATION; *Int'l*, pg. 6914
TAKBO GROUP HOLDINGS LIMITED; *Int'l*, pg. 7436
TAK CO.—See Ibiden Co., Ltd.; *Int'l*, pg. 3576
TAK CONSTRUCTION, INC.; *U.S. Private*, pg. 3925
TAK DEVELOPMENT, INC.—See Takenaka Corporation; *Int'l*, pg. 7441

TAKE2 CONSULTING, LLC; *U.S. Private*, pg. 3925
TAKE 5 OIL CHANGE, LLC—See Roark Capital Group Inc.; *U.S. Private*, pg. 3454
TAKE AND GIVE. ARTS CO., LTD.—See TAKE AND GIVE. NEEDS Co. Ltd.; *Int'l*, pg. 7436
TAKE AND GIVE. NEEDS CO. LTD.; *Int'l*, pg. 7436
TAKEBACK LIMITED—See Restore plc; *Int'l*, pg. 6304
TAKEBE TEKKOSHO CO., LTD.—See Toyota Motor Corporation; *Int'l*, pg. 7872
TAKEBISHI CORPORATION; *Int'l*, pg. 7436
TAKEBISHI ELECTRIC SALES HONG KONG LIMITED—See Takebishi Corporation; *Int'l*, pg. 7436
TAKEBISHI ELECTRIC SALES SHANGHAI LIMITED—See Takebishi Corporation; *Int'l*, pg. 7437
TAKEBISHI EUROPE B.V.—See Takebishi Corporation; *Int'l*, pg. 7437
TAKEBISHI (THAILAND) CO., LTD.—See Takebishi Corporation; *Int'l*, pg. 7436
TAKEBISHI VIETNAM CO., LTD.—See Takebishi Corporation; *Int'l*, pg. 7437
TAKE CARE HEALTH SYSTEMS, LLC—See Walgreens Boots Alliance, Inc.; *U.S. Public*, pg. 2324
TAKECARE INSURANCE COMPANY INC.; *U.S. Private*, pg. 3925
TAKE CARE PRIVATE DUTY HOME HEALTH CARE; *U.S. Private*, pg. 3925
TAKEDA AMERICA HOLDINGS, INC.—See Takeda Pharmaceutical Company Limited; *Int'l*, pg. 7439
TAKEDA AS—See Takeda Pharmaceutical Company Limited; *Int'l*, pg. 7439
TAKEDA AUSTRIA GMBH—See Takeda Pharmaceutical Company Limited; *Int'l*, pg. 7439
TAKEDA BELGIUM SCA/CVA—See Takeda Pharmaceutical Company Limited; *Int'l*, pg. 7439
TAKEDA BIO DEVELOPMENT CENTER LIMITED—See Takeda Pharmaceutical Company Limited; *Int'l*, pg. 7439
TAKEDA CAMBRIDGE LIMITED—See Takeda Pharmaceutical Company Limited; *Int'l*, pg. 7439
TAKEDA CANADA, INC.—See Takeda Pharmaceutical Company Limited; *Int'l*, pg. 7439
TAKEDA CHEMICAL INDUSTRIES (TAIWAN), LTD.—See Takeda Pharmaceutical Company Limited; *Int'l*, pg. 7439
TAKEDA (CHINA) HOLDINGS CO., LTD.—See Takeda Pharmaceutical Company Limited; *Int'l*, pg. 7439
TAKEDA CLINICAL RESEARCH SINGAPORE PRIVATE LIMITED—See Takeda Pharmaceutical Company Limited; *Int'l*, pg. 7439
TAKEDA DEVELOPMENT CENTER ASIA, PTE. LTD.—See Takeda Pharmaceutical Company Limited; *Int'l*, pg. 7439
TAKEDA DEVELOPMENT CENTRE EUROPE LTD.—See Takeda Pharmaceutical Company Limited; *Int'l*, pg. 7439
TAKEDA DISTRIBUIDORA LTDA.—See Takeda Pharmaceutical Company Limited; *Int'l*, pg. 7439
TAKEDA EUROPE HOLDINGS B.V.—See Takeda Pharmaceutical Company Limited; *Int'l*, pg. 7439
TAKEDA FARMACEUTICA ESPANA S.A.—See Takeda Pharmaceutical Company Limited; *Int'l*, pg. 7439
TAKEDA FARMACEUTICA ESPANA S.A.U.—See Takeda Pharmaceutical Company Limited; *Int'l*, pg. 7439
TAKEDA FARMACEUTICOS PORTUGAL UNIPESSOAL LDA—See Takeda Pharmaceutical Company Limited; *Int'l*, pg. 7439
TAKEDA FRANCE S.A.S.—See Takeda Pharmaceutical Company Limited; *Int'l*, pg. 7439
TAKEDA GLOBAL RESEARCH & DEVELOPMENT CENTRE EUROPE LTD.—See Takeda Pharmaceutical Company Limited; *Int'l*, pg. 7439
TAKEDA GMBH - ORANIENBURG—See Takeda Pharmaceutical Company Limited; *Int'l*, pg. 7439
TAKEDA GMBH—See Takeda Pharmaceutical Company Limited; *Int'l*, pg. 7439
TAKEDA HEALTHCARE PRODUCTS CO., LTD.—See Takeda Pharmaceutical Company Limited; *Int'l*, pg. 7439
TAKEDA ILACLARI TIC. LTD. STI.—See Takeda Pharmaceutical Company Limited; *Int'l*, pg. 7439
TAKEDA IP HOLDINGS CO.,LTD.; *Int'l*, pg. 7437
TAKEDA IRELAND LTD.—See Takeda Pharmaceutical Company Limited; *Int'l*, pg. 7439
TAKEDA ITALIA FARMACEUTICI S.P.A.—See Takeda Pharmaceutical Company Limited; *Int'l*, pg. 7439
TAKEDA ITALIA S.P.A.—See Takeda Pharmaceutical Company Limited; *Int'l*, pg. 7439
TAKEDA MACHINERY CO., LTD.; *Int'l*, pg. 7437
TAKEDA MEXICO S.A. DE C.V.—See Takeda Pharmaceutical Company Limited; *Int'l*, pg. 7439
TAKEDA NEDERLAND BV—See Takeda Pharmaceutical Company Limited; *Int'l*, pg. 7439
TAKEDA NYCOMED AS—See Takeda Pharmaceutical Company Limited; *Int'l*, pg. 7440
TAKEDA PHARMA AG—See Takeda Pharmaceutical Company Limited; *Int'l*, pg. 7440
TAKEDA PHARMA A/S—See Takeda Pharmaceutical Company Limited; *Int'l*, pg. 7439

COMPANY NAME INDEX

TAKEDA PHARMACEUTICAL (CHINA) COMPANY LIMITED—See Takeda Pharmaceutical Company Limited; *Int'l*, pg. 7439
TAKEDA PHARMACEUTICAL CO., LTD. - HIKARI PLANT—See Takeda Pharmaceutical Company Limited; *Int'l*, pg. 7439
TAKEDA PHARMACEUTICAL CO., LTD. - OSAKA PLANT—See Takeda Pharmaceutical Company Limited; *Int'l*, pg. 7439
TAKEDA PHARMACEUTICAL COMPANY LIMITED; *Int'l*, pg. 7437
TAKEDA PHARMACEUTICALS ASIA PRIVATE LIMITED—See Takeda Pharmaceutical Company Limited; *Int'l*, pg. 7440
TAKEDA PHARMACEUTICALS BENELUX BVBA—See Takeda Pharmaceutical Company Limited; *Int'l*, pg. 7440
TAKEDA PHARMACEUTICALS CZECH REPUBLIC S.R.O.—See Takeda Pharmaceutical Company Limited; *Int'l*, pg. 7440
TAKEDA PHARMACEUTICALS INTERNATIONAL GMBH—See Takeda Pharmaceutical Company Limited; *Int'l*, pg. 7439
TAKEDA PHARMACEUTICALS INTERNATIONAL, INC.—See Takeda Pharmaceutical Company Limited; *Int'l*, pg. 7439
TAKEDA PHARMACEUTICALS KOREA CO., LTD—See Takeda Pharmaceutical Company Limited; *Int'l*, pg. 7440
TAKEDA PHARMACEUTICALS LIMITED LIABILITY COMPANY—See Takeda Pharmaceutical Company Limited; *Int'l*, pg. 7440
TAKEDA PHARMACEUTICALS MEXICO, S.A. DE C.V—See Takeda Pharmaceutical Company Limited; *Int'l*, pg. 7440
TAKEDA PHARMACEUTICALS NORDICS AB—See Takeda Pharmaceutical Company Limited; *Int'l*, pg. 7440
TAKEDA PHARMACEUTICALS (PHILIPPINES), INC.—See Takeda Pharmaceutical Company Limited; *Int'l*, pg. 7440
TAKEDA PHARMACEUTICALS SLOVAKIA S.R.O.—See Takeda Pharmaceutical Company Limited; *Int'l*, pg. 7440
TAKEDA PHARMACEUTICALS TAIWAN—See Takeda Pharmaceutical Company Limited; *Int'l*, pg. 7440
TAKEDA PHARMACEUTICALS U.S.A, INC.—See Takeda Pharmaceutical Company Limited; *Int'l*, pg. 7439
TAKEDA PHARMA GES.M.B.H.—See Takeda Pharmaceutical Company Limited; *Int'l*, pg. 7440
TAKEDA PHARMA GMBH—See Takeda Pharmaceutical Company Limited; *Int'l*, pg. 7440
TAKEDA PHARMA LTDA.—See Takeda Pharmaceutical Company Limited; *Int'l*, pg. 7440
TAKEDA PHARMA S.A.—See Takeda Pharmaceutical Company Limited; *Int'l*, pg. 7440
TAKEDA PHARMA SP. Z.O.O.—See Takeda Pharmaceutical Company Limited; *Int'l*, pg. 7440
TAKEDA SAN DIEGO, INC—See Takeda Pharmaceutical Company Limited; *Int'l*, pg. 7439
TAKEDA SEIKI CO., LTD.—See Takeda Machinery Co., Ltd.; *Int'l*, pg. 7437
TAKEDASHIKI CO., LTD.—See Rengo Co., Ltd.; *Int'l*, pg. 6282
TAKEDA SHOJI CO., LTD.—See Meiwa Corporation; *Int'l*, pg. 4805
TAKEDA SUNTECH CO., LTD.—See Koito Manufacturing Co., Ltd.; *Int'l*, pg. 4231
TAKEDA (THAILAND), LTD.—See Takeda Pharmaceutical Company Limited; *Int'l*, pg. 7439
TAKEDA UK LIMITED—See Takeda Pharmaceutical Company Limited; *Int'l*, pg. 7440
TAKEEI CORPORATION; *Int'l*, pg. 7440
TAKEEI GREEN RECYCLING CO., LTD.—See Takeei Corporation; *Int'l*, pg. 7440
TAKEEI METAL CO., LTD.—See Takeei Corporation; *Int'l*, pg. 7440
TAKEFUJI CORPORATION; *Int'l*, pg. 7440
TAKEHARA ZEON (SHANGHAI) CO., LTD.—See Zeon Corporation; *Int'l*, pg. 8635
TAKEMOTO & COMPANY LIMITED—See Seika Corporation; *Int'l*, pg. 6685
TAKEMOTO NETHERLANDS B.V.—See Takemoto Yohki Co., Ltd.; *Int'l*, pg. 7440
TAKEMOTO PACKAGING (THAILAND) CO., LTD.—See Takemoto Yohki Co., Ltd.; *Int'l*, pg. 7440
TAKEMOTO YOHKI CO., LTD.; *Int'l*, pg. 7440
TAKEMOTO YOHKI (KUNSHAN) CO., LTD—See Takemoto Yohki Co., Ltd.; *Int'l*, pg. 7440
TAKENAKA (CHINA) CONSTRUCTION CO.,LTD.—See Takenaka Corporation; *Int'l*, pg. 7441
TAKENAKA CIVIL ENGINEERING & CONSTRUCTION CO., LTD.—See Takenaka Corporation; *Int'l*, pg. 7441
TAKENAKA CORPORATION; *Int'l*, pg. 7440
TAKENAKA CORPORATION USA—See Takenaka Corporation; *Int'l*, pg. 7441
TAKENAKA CORPORATION USA—See Takenaka Corporation; *Int'l*, pg. 7441

TAKENAKA EUROPE GMBH, BELGIUM—See Takenaka Corporation; *Int'l*, pg. 7441
TAKENAKA EUROPE GMBH, FRANKFURT—See Takenaka Corporation; *Int'l*, pg. 7441
TAKENAKA EUROPE GMBH, ITALY—See Takenaka Corporation; *Int'l*, pg. 7441
TAKENAKA EUROPE GMBH—See Takenaka Corporation; *Int'l*, pg. 7441
TAKENAKA EUROPE GMBH, SPAIN—See Takenaka Corporation; *Int'l*, pg. 7441
TAKENAKA EUROPE—See Takenaka Corporation; *Int'l*, pg. 7441
TAKENAKA HUNGARIA KFT—See Takenaka Corporation; *Int'l*, pg. 7441
TAKENAKA INDIA PRIVATE LIMITED—See Takenaka Corporation; *Int'l*, pg. 7441
TAKENAKA (MALAYSIA) SDN. BHD.—See Takenaka Corporation; *Int'l*, pg. 7441
TAKENAKA PARTNERS, LLC—See YAMADA Consulting Group Co., Ltd.; *Int'l*, pg. 8547
TAKENAKA RESEARCH & DEVELOPMENT INSTITUTE—See Takenaka Corporation; *Int'l*, pg. 7441
TAKENAKA (U.K.) LTD.—See Takenaka Corporation; *Int'l*, pg. 7441
TAK ENGINEERING OSAKA, INC.—See Takenaka Corporation; *Int'l*, pg. 7441
TAKE OFF S.P.A.; *Int'l*, pg. 7436
TAKEONE CO., LTD.—See Takefuji Corporation; *Int'l*, pg. 7440
TAKES CO., LTD.—See ISB Corporation; *Int'l*, pg. 3812
TAKE SHAPE FOR LIFE, INC—See Medifast, Inc.; *U.S. Public*, pg. 1412
TAKE SOLUTIONS, INC.—See TAKE Solutions Limited; *Int'l*, pg. 7436
TAKE SOLUTIONS LIMITED; *Int'l*, pg. 7436
TAKESYSTEMS CO., LTD.—See TV Asahi Holdings Corporation; *Int'l*, pg. 7987
TAKE-TWO INTERACTIVE BENELUX B.V.—See Take-Two Interactive Software, Inc.; *U.S. Public*, pg. 1979
TAKE-TWO INTERACTIVE SOFTWARE EUROPE LIMITED—See Take-Two Interactive Software, Inc.; *U.S. Public*, pg. 1979
TAKE-TWO INTERACTIVE SOFTWARE, INC.; *U.S. Public*, pg. 1979
TAKEUCHI FRANCE S.A.S.—See Takeuchi Mfg. Co., Ltd.; *Int'l*, pg. 7441
TAKEUCHI INDUSTRIAL EQUIPMENT MANUFACTURING CO., LTD.—See Toyota Industries Corporation; *Int'l*, pg. 7866
TAKEUCHI MFG. CO., LTD.; *Int'l*, pg. 7441
TAKEUCHI MFG. CO., LTD. - TOGURA PLANT—See Takeuchi Mfg. Co., Ltd.; *Int'l*, pg. 7441
TAKEUCHI MFG. (U.K.) LTD.—See Takeuchi Mfg. Co., Ltd.; *Int'l*, pg. 7441
TAKEUCHI MFG. (U.S.), LTD.—See Takeuchi Mfg. Co., Ltd.; *Int'l*, pg. 7441
TAKEUCHI PRESS INDUSTRIES COMPANY LIMITED—See Alucon Public Company Limited; *Int'l*, pg. 400
TAKEUCHI QINGDAO MFG. CO., LTD.—See Takeuchi Mfg. Co., Ltd.; *Int'l*, pg. 7441
TAKE UNITED SDN BHD—See TAKE Solutions Limited; *Int'l*, pg. 7436
TAKEX CO., LTD.—See TOA Corporation; *Int'l*, pg. 7768
TAK GREEN SERVICE CO., LTD.—See Takashima & Co., Ltd.; *Int'l*, pg. 7435
TAK HAWAII, INC.—See Takenaka Corporation; *Int'l*, pg. 7441
TAK HOW INVESTMENT LIMITED—See InterContinental Hotels Group PLC; *Int'l*, pg. 3739
TAKI CHEMICAL CO., LTD.; *Int'l*, pg. 7441
THE TAKIGAMI STEEL CONSTRUCTION CO., LTD.; *Int'l*, pg. 7694
TAKIHOUSE CO., LTD.—See VT Holdings Co., Ltd.; *Int'l*, pg. 8315
TAKIHYO CO., LTD.; *Int'l*, pg. 7441
TAKIHYO (H.K.) CO., LTD.—See Takihyo Co., Ltd.; *Int'l*, pg. 7441
TAKIHYO KEMICA CO., LTD.—See Takihyo Co., Ltd.; *Int'l*, pg. 7441
TAKIHYO OPERATION PLAZA CO., LTD.—See Takihyo Co., Ltd.; *Int'l*, pg. 7441
TAKIMOTO CO., LTD.—See Nippon Steel Corporation; *Int'l*, pg. 5339
TAKIR GRUNDSTUCKS-VERMIETUNGSGESELLSCHAFT MBH—See Deutsche Bank Aktiengesellschaft; *Int'l*, pg. 2062
TAKIRON ENGINEERING CO., LTD.—See ITOCHU Corporation; *Int'l*, pg. 3835
TAKIRON KC HOME IMPROVEMENT CO., LTD.—See ITOCHU Corporation; *Int'l*, pg. 3835
TAKIRON MATEX CO., LTD.—See ITOCHU Corporation; *Int'l*, pg. 3835
TAKIRON POLYMER CO., LTD.—See ITOCHU Corporation; *Int'l*, pg. 3835
TAKIRON PROTECH CO., LTD.—See ITOCHU Corporation; *Int'l*, pg. 3835

TALBERT MANUFACTURING INC.

TAKIRON-ROWLAND LIMITED—See ITOCHU Corporation; *Int'l*, pg. 3835
TAKISAWA MACHINE TOOL CO. LTD. - SHIMOSHO FACTORY—See Nidec Corporation; *Int'l*, pg. 5280
TAKISAWA MACHINE TOOL CO., LTD.—See Nidec Corporation; *Int'l*, pg. 5280
TAKISAWA (SHANGHI) CO., LTD.—See Nidec Corporation; *Int'l*, pg. 5280
TAKISAWA TECHNO SERVICE INC.—See Nidec Corporation; *Int'l*, pg. 5280
TAKITIMU COAL LIMITED—See Galilee Energy Limited; *Int'l*, pg. 2873
TAKIZAWA HAM CO., LTD.; *Int'l*, pg. 7441
TAKKO MODEMARKT GMBH & CO KG—See Apax Partners LLP; *Int'l*, pg. 507
TAKKT AG—See Franz Haniel & Cie. GmbH; *Int'l*, pg. 2763
TAK LEE MACHINERY COMPANY LIMITED—See Tak Lee Machinery Holdings Limited; *Int'l*, pg. 7428
TAK LEE MACHINERY HOLDINGS LIMITED; *Int'l*, pg. 7428
TAKMOR LLC—See WHP Global; *U.S. Private*, pg. 4515
TAKORADI LIMITED; *Int'l*, pg. 7442
TAKOR GROUP LTD; *Int'l*, pg. 7442
TAKOVO A.D.; *Int'l*, pg. 7442
TAKOVO OSIGURANJE A.D.; *Int'l*, pg. 7442
TAKOVO TRANSPORT A.D.; *Int'l*, pg. 7442
TAKRAF GMBH—See Techint S.p.A.; *Int'l*, pg. 7504
TAKRAF TENOVA MINING TECHNOLOGIES (BEIJING) CO. LTD.—See Techint S.p.A.; *Int'l*, pg. 7505
TAKRAF USA INC.—See Techint S.p.A.; *Int'l*, pg. 7505
TAKSHEEL SOLUTIONS LTD; *Int'l*, pg. 7442
TAK SHUN TECHNOLOGY GROUP LIMITED; *Int'l*, pg. 7428
TAKSIM OTELCILIK AS—See Turkiye Vakiflar Bankasi T.A.O.; *Int'l*, pg. 7977
TAK SYSTEMS CORPORATION—See Takenaka Corporation; *Int'l*, pg. 7441
TAK TAI ENVIROSCAPE LIMITED—See Baguio Green Group Limited; *Int'l*, pg. 799
TAKT SYSTEMS, INC.—See Comture Corporation; *Int'l*, pg. 1763
TAKUMA CO., LTD. - HARIMA FACTORY—See Takuma Co., Ltd.; *Int'l*, pg. 7442
TAKUMA CO., LTD.; *Int'l*, pg. 7442
TAKUMA ENERGY CO., LTD.—See Takuma Co., Ltd.; *Int'l*, pg. 7442
TAKUMA ENGINEERING CO., LTD.—See Takuma Co., Ltd.; *Int'l*, pg. 7442
TAKUMA PLANT CO., LTD.—See Takuma Co., Ltd.; *Int'l*, pg. 7442
TAKUMA PLANT SERVICE CO., LTD.—See Takuma Co., Ltd.; *Int'l*, pg. 7442
TAKUMA SEINO TRANSPORTATION CO., LTD.—See Seino Holdings Co., Ltd.; *Int'l*, pg. 6691
TAKUMA SYSTEM CONTROL CO., LTD.—See Takuma Co., Ltd.; *Int'l*, pg. 7442
TAKUMA TECHNOS CO., LTD.—See Takuma Co., Ltd.; *Int'l*, pg. 7443
TAKUMA TECHNOS HOKKAIDO CO., LTD.—See Takuma Co., Ltd.; *Int'l*, pg. 7443
TAKUMI CORPORATION—See Sanshin Electronics Co., Ltd.; *Int'l*, pg. 6556
TAKUMI MACHINERY CO., LTD.—See Liberty Diversified International Inc.; *U.S. Private*, pg. 2444
TAKUMI PRECISION CO., LTD.—See Hurco Companies, Inc.; *U.S. Public*, pg. 1076
TAKUNG ART CO., LTD.; *Int'l*, pg. 7443
TAKUNI GROUP PUBLIC COMPANY LIMITED; *Int'l*, pg. 7443
TAKUNI (THAILAND) COMPANY LIMITED—See Takuni Group Public Company Limited; *Int'l*, pg. 7443
TAKU SEIMO CO., LTD.—See Nitto Seimo Co., Ltd.; *Int'l*, pg. 5388
TAKWEEN ADVANCED INDUSTRIES; *Int'l*, pg. 7443
TALAAT MOUSTAFA GROUP HOLDING COMPANY; *Int'l*, pg. 7443
TALABAT ELECTRONIC & DELIVERY SERVICES LLC—See Delivery Hero SE; *Int'l*, pg. 2013
TALABAT GENERAL TRADING & CONTRACTING COMPANY W.L.L—See Delivery Hero SE; *Int'l*, pg. 2013
TALABAT SERVICES COMPANY L.L.C.—See Delivery Hero SE; *Int'l*, pg. 2013
TALAM TRANSFORM BERHAD; *Int'l*, pg. 7443
TALAN PRODUCTS, INC.; *U.S. Private*, pg. 3925
TALANT OPTRONICS (SUZHOU) CO., LTD.; *Int'l*, pg. 7443
TALANX AG; *Int'l*, pg. 7443
TALANX DEUTSCHLAND AG—See Talanx AG; *Int'l*, pg. 7445
TALANX REINSURANCE BROKER GMBH—See Talanx AG; *Int'l*, pg. 7445
TALASCEND, LLC; *U.S. Private*, pg. 3925
TALAWAKELLE TEA ESTATES PLC; *Int'l*, pg. 7445
TALBERT HOUSE; *U.S. Private*, pg. 3925
TALBERT MANUFACTURING INC.; *U.S. Private*, pg. 3925
TALBOOM B.V.—See Clarins S.A.; *Int'l*, pg. 1649

TALBOT ADVANCED TECHNOLOGIES LIMITED—See Skellerup Holdings Limited; *Int'l*, pg. 6980
TALBOT HOLDINGS INC.; *U.S. Private*, pg. 3925
TALBOT INDUSTRIES, INC.—See Leggett & Platt, Incorporated; *U.S. Private*, pg. 1303
TALBOT RISK SERVICES (LABUAN) PTE. LTD.—See American International Group, Inc.; *U.S. Public*, pg. 107
TALBOT RISK SERVICES PTE LTD.—See American International Group, Inc.; *U.S. Public*, pg. 107
THE TALBOTS, INC.—See Sycamore Partners Management, LP; *U.S. Private*, pg. 3898
TALBOTS PRODUCT DEVELOPMENT CENTER—See Sycamore Partners Management, LP; *U.S. Private*, pg. 3898
TALBOTT VINEYARDS—See E. & J. Gallo Winery; *U.S. Private*, pg. 1303
TALBOT UNDERWRITING (LATAM) S.A—See American International Group, Inc.; *U.S. Public*, pg. 107
TALBOT UNDERWRITING (LATAM) S.A—See American International Group, Inc.; *U.S. Public*, pg. 107
TALBOT UNDERWRITING LTD.—See American International Group, Inc.; *U.S. Public*, pg. 107
TALBOT UNDERWRITING (MENA) LTD.—See American International Group, Inc.; *U.S. Public*, pg. 107
TALBOT UNDERWRITING RISK SERVICES LTD.—See American International Group, Inc.; *U.S. Public*, pg. 107
TALBOT UNDERWRITING SERVICES, LTD.—See American International Group, Inc.; *U.S. Public*, pg. 107
TALBOT UNDERWRITING SERVICES (US), LTD.—See American International Group, Inc.; *U.S. Public*, pg. 107
TALBROS AUTOMOTIVE COMPONENTS LIMITED - GASKET DIVISION—See Talbros Automotive Components Limited; *Int'l*, pg. 7446
TALBROS AUTOMOTIVE COMPONENTS LIMITED; *Int'l*, pg. 7445
TALBROS ENGINEERING LIMITED; *Int'l*, pg. 7446
TALCASOFT AUSTRALIA PTY. LTD.—See Zoom2u Technologies Limited; *Int'l*, pg. 8689
TALC DE LUZENAC S.A.—See Rio Tinto plc; *Int'l*, pg. 6347
TALCE SIA—See VINCI S.A.; *Int'l*, pg. 8229
TAL CONSOLIDATED INC.; *U.S. Private*, pg. 3925
TALCO PLASTICS INC.; *U.S. Private*, pg. 3925
TALCOTT RESOLUTION LIFE INSURANCE COMPANY—See Sixth Street Specialty Lending, Inc.; *U.S. Public*, pg. 1891
TALCOTT RESOLUTION LIFE INSURANCE COMPANY—See Sixth Street Specialty Lending, Inc.; *U.S. Public*, pg. 1891
TALC S.R.O.—See Tulikivi Corporation; *Int'l*, pg. 7969
TAL DAI-ICHI LIFE AUSTRALIA PTY LTD.—See Dai-ichi Life Holdings, Inc.; *Int'l*, pg. 1918
TALDE GESTION, S.G.E.I.C., S.A; *Int'l*, pg. 7446
TAL DIRECT PTY LIMITED—See Dai-ichi Life Holdings, Inc.; *Int'l*, pg. 1918
TALDOR COMPUTER SYSTEMS (1986) LTD.; *Int'l*, pg. 7446
TALEA GROUP S.P.A.; *Int'l*, pg. 7446
TALE, A.S.—See Zeleziarne Podbrezova a.s.; *Int'l*, pg. 8631
TALEB GROUP; *Int'l*, pg. 7446
TALEB MEDICAL COMPANY—See Taleb Group; *Int'l*, pg. 7446
TALEB TRADING CO. W.L.L—See Taleb Group; *Int'l*, pg. 7446
TALECH, INC.—See U.S. Bancorp; *U.S. Public*, pg. 2212
TAL EDUCATION GROUP; *Int'l*, pg. 7443
TALENCE GESTION SAS; *Int'l*, pg. 7446
TALEND BEIJNG TECHNOLOGY CO., LTD.—See Thoma Bravo, L.P.; *U.S. Private*, pg. 4154
TALEND GMBH—See Thoma Bravo, L.P.; *U.S. Private*, pg. 4154
TALEND GMBH—See Thoma Bravo, L.P.; *U.S. Private*, pg. 4154
TALEND GMBH—See Thoma Bravo, L.P.; *U.S. Private*, pg. 4154
TALEND GMBH—See Thoma Bravo, L.P.; *U.S. Private*, pg. 4154
TALEND INC.—See Thoma Bravo, L.P.; *U.S. Private*, pg. 4154
TALEND KK—See Thoma Bravo, L.P.; *U.S. Private*, pg. 4154
TALEND LTD—See Thoma Bravo, L.P.; *U.S. Private*, pg. 4154
TALEND SA—See Thoma Bravo, L.P.; *U.S. Private*, pg. 4154
TALEN ENERGY CORPORATION—See Riverstone Holdings LLC; *U.S. Private*, pg. 3447
TALEN ENERGY MARKETING, LLC—See Riverstone Holdings LLC; *U.S. Private*, pg. 3447
TALEN ENERGY SUPPLY, LLC—See Riverstone Holdings LLC; *U.S. Private*, pg. 3447
TALEN NUCLEAR DEVELOPMENT, LLC—See Riverstone Holdings LLC; *U.S. Private*, pg. 3447
TALENOM OY; *Int'l*, pg. 7446
TALENS MARINE & FUEL INC.; *U.S. Private*, pg. 3926
TALENT2 INTERNATIONAL LIMITED—See Allegis Group, Inc.; *U.S. Private*, pg. 177
TALENT2 INTERNATIONAL LIMITED—See Morgan & Banks Investments Pty. Ltd.; *Int'l*, pg. 5040
TALENT2 K.K.—See Allegis Group, Inc.; *U.S. Private*, pg. 177
TALENT2 K.K.—See Morgan & Banks Investments Pty. Ltd.; *Int'l*, pg. 5041
TALENT2 NZ LIMITED—See Allegis Group, Inc.; *U.S. Private*, pg. 177
TALENT2 NZ LIMITED—See Morgan & Banks Investments Pty. Ltd.; *Int'l*, pg. 5041
TALENT2 PTY LIMITED—See Allegis Group, Inc.; *U.S. Private*, pg. 177
TALENT2 PTY LIMITED—See Morgan & Banks Investments Pty. Ltd.; *Int'l*, pg. 5041
TALENT2 SINGAPORE PTE. LTD.—See Allegis Group, Inc.; *U.S. Private*, pg. 177
TALENT2 SINGAPORE PTE. LTD.—See Morgan & Banks Investments Pty. Ltd.; *Int'l*, pg. 5041
TALENT2 UK EXECUTIVE LIMITED—See Allegis Group, Inc.; *U.S. Private*, pg. 177
TALENT2 UK EXECUTIVE LIMITED—See Morgan & Banks Investments Pty. Ltd.; *Int'l*, pg. 5041
TALENT2 WORKS LIMITED—See Allegis Group, Inc.; *U.S. Private*, pg. 177
TALENT2 WORKS LIMITED—See Morgan & Banks Investments Pty. Ltd.; *Int'l*, pg. 5041
TALENT2 WORKS PTY. LTD.—See Allegis Group, Inc.; *U.S. Private*, pg. 177
TALENT2 WORKS PTY. LTD.—See Morgan & Banks Investments Pty. Ltd.; *Int'l*, pg. 5041
THE TALENT ADVISORS, LLC—See International Resources Group Ltd.; *Int'l*, pg. 3752
TALENT-ASIA HOLDINGS CO. LIMITED—See Link-Asia International MedTech Group Limited; *Int'l*, pg. 4514
TALENT BANG LIMITED—See Emperor Culture Group Limited; *Int'l*, pg. 2386
TALENT BRIDGE, LLC; *U.S. Private*, pg. 3926
TALENTBURST, INC; *U.S. Private*, pg. 3926
TALENTBURST—See TalentBurst, Inc.; *U.S. Private*, pg. 3926
TALENT CONNECTIONS, LLC; *U.S. Private*, pg. 3926
TALENT CURVE SOLUTIONS LLC; *U.S. Private*, pg. 3926
TALENTED IT INC.; *U.S. Private*, pg. 3926
TALENTFIRST LLC; *U.S. Private*, pg. 3926
TALENTFORT (PVT.) LTD.—See Sri Lanka Telecom PLC; *Int'l*, pg. 7150
TALENTHOUSE AG; *Int'l*, pg. 7446
TALENT, INC.; *U.S. Private*, pg. 3926
TALENT KEEPERS, INC.—See Quantum Market Research, Inc.; *U.S. Private*, pg. 3323
TALENTMINE LLC—See Webster Equity Partners, LLC; *U.S. Private*, pg. 4467
TALENTO GREY PUBLICIDAD—See WPP plc; *Int'l*, pg. 8472
TALENTOZ SDN BHD—See SMRT Holdings Berhad; *Int'l*, pg. 7014
TALENT PARTNERS (DUBAI) LLC—See Allegis Group, Inc.; *U.S. Private*, pg. 177
TALENT PARTNERS (DUBAI) LLC—See Morgan & Banks Investments Pty. Ltd.; *Int'l*, pg. 5041
TALENT PARTNERS; *U.S. Private*, pg. 3926
TALENT PARTNERS—See Talent Partners; *U.S. Private*, pg. 3926
TALENT PLUS INC.; *U.S. Private*, pg. 3926
TALENT PROPERTY GROUP LIMITED; *Int'l*, pg. 7446
TALENTQUEST INC.; *U.S. Private*, pg. 3926
TALENTREEF, INC.—See Ontario Teachers' Pension Plan; *Int'l*, pg. 5586
TALENTSCALE, LLC—See SCST, Inc.; *U.S. Private*, pg. 3581
TALENT TECH LABS, LLC—See Allegis Group, Inc.; *U.S. Private*, pg. 177
TALENTUM HR AB—See Wise Group AB; *Int'l*, pg. 8436
TALESIS LIMITED—See HM International Holdings Limited; *Int'l*, pg. 3431
TALESOL S.A.—See Dana Incorporated; *U.S. Public*, pg. 623
TALEX S.A.; *Int'l*, pg. 7446
TALGA ADVANCED MATERIALS GMBH—See Talga Group Ltd; *Int'l*, pg. 7446
TALGA GROUP LTD; *Int'l*, pg. 7446
TALGE DESCARTAVEIS DO BRASIL LTDA.—See Bunzl plc; *Int'l*, pg. 1219
TALGER-ELEKTROTEHNIKA OSAUHING—See Wurth Verwaltungsgesellschaft mbH; *Int'l*, pg. 8509
TALGO BH D.O.O—See Patentes Talgo S.L.; *Int'l*, pg. 5756
TALGO (DEUTSCHLAND) GMBH—See Patentes Talgo S.L.; *Int'l*, pg. 5756
TALGO, INC.—See Patentes Talgo S.L.; *Int'l*, pg. 5756
TALGO S.A.; *Int'l*, pg. 7446
TALGO UK LTD.—See Talgo S.A.; *Int'l*, pg. 7446
TALHADO FISHING ENTERPRISES PROPRIETARY LIMITED—See African Equity Empowerment Investmts Limited; *Int'l*, pg. 191
TALHER, S.A.—See ACS, Actividades de Construccion y Servicios, S.A.; *Int'l*, pg. 116
TAL HOLDINGS LLC; *U.S. Private*, pg. 3925
TA LIANG TECHNOLOGY CO., LTD.; *Int'l*, pg. 7400
TALICO, S.A. DE C.V.—See Japan Pulp and Paper Company Limited; *Int'l*, pg. 3905
TALI DIGITAL LIMITED; *Int'l*, pg. 7446
TAL INTERNATIONAL GROUP, INC—See Brookfield Infrastructure Partners L.P.; *U.S. Public*, pg. 1190
TALIS ADVISORY SERVICES LLC—See Generational Equity Group, Inc.; *U.S. Private*, pg. 1668
TALIS BIOMEDICAL CORPORATION; *U.S. Public*, pg. 1979
TALIS CAPITAL LIMITED; *Int'l*, pg. 7446
TALIS CLINICAL LLC—See Getinge AB; *Int'l*, pg. 2952
TALIS DEUTSCHLAND GMBH & CO, KG—See Triton Advisers Limited; *Int'l*, pg. 7934
TALISKER CORPORATION; *Int'l*, pg. 7447
TALISKER RESOURCES LTD.; *Int'l*, pg. 7447
TALIS MANAGEMENT HOLDING GMBH—See Triton Advisers Limited; *Int'l*, pg. 7934
TALISMAN (ASIA) LIMITED—See Repsol, S.A.; *Int'l*, pg. 6293
TALISMAN CAPITAL PARTNERS LLC; *U.S. Private*, pg. 3926
TALISMAN (COLOMBIA) OIL & GAS LTD.—See Repsol, S.A.; *Int'l*, pg. 6293
TALISMAN COMPANY—See Terryberry Company LLC; *U.S. Private*, pg. 3972
TALISMAN ENERGY NORWAY AS—See Repsol, S.A.; *Int'l*, pg. 6293
TALISMAN ENERGY SWEDEN AB—See Repsol, S.A.; *Int'l*, pg. 6293
TALISMAN GLOBAL ASSET MANAGEMENT LIMITED—See The William Pears Group of Companies Limited; *Int'l*, pg. 7701
TALISMAN HOLDING INTERNATIONAL SARL—See Repsol, S.A.; *Int'l*, pg. 6293
TALISMAN INDONESIA LTD.—See Repsol, S.A.; *Int'l*, pg. 6293
TALISMAN INTERNATIONAL, LLC—See Brookfield Corporation; *Int'l*, pg. 1182
TALISMAN (JAMBI) LIMITED—See Repsol, S.A.; *Int'l*, pg. 6293
TALISMAN (JAMBI MERANG) LIMITED—See Repsol, S.A.; *Int'l*, pg. 6293
TALISMAN MINING LIMITED; *Int'l*, pg. 7447
TALISMAN (SAGERI) LTD.—See Repsol, S.A.; *Int'l*, pg. 6293
TALISMAN SOFTWARE (BENELUX) BV—See Randstad N.V.; *Int'l*, pg. 6205
TALISMAN SYSTEMS GROUP, INC.—See Perspecta LLC; *U.S. Private*, pg. 3156
TALISMAN UK (SOUTH EAST SUMATRA) LIMITED—See Repsol, S.A.; *Int'l*, pg. 6293
TALISMAN WILD RIVER PARTNERSHIP—See Repsol, S.A.; *Int'l*, pg. 6293
TALISMARK; *U.S. Private*, pg. 3926
TALISON LITHIUM PTY. LTD.—See Albemarle Corporation; *U.S. Public*, pg. 73
TALISON LITHIUM PTY. LTD.—See Chengdu Tianqi Industry (Group) Co., Ltd.; *Int'l*, pg. 1469
TALIS POLSKA SP. Z.O.O.—See Triton Advisers Limited; *Int'l*, pg. 7934
TALIUS GROUP LIMITED; *Int'l*, pg. 7447
TALIWORKS CORPORATION BERHAD; *Int'l*, pg. 7447
TALIWORKS (LANGKAWI) SDN. BHD.—See Taliworks Corporation Berhad; *Int'l*, pg. 7447
TALIX, INC.—See Edifecs, Inc.; *U.S. Private*, pg. 1336
TALK2REP, INC.; *U.S. Private*, pg. 3926
TALK-A-PHONE CO.; *U.S. Private*, pg. 3926
TALKBACK THAMES—See Bertelsmann SE & Co. KGaA; *Int'l*, pg. 994
TALKH CHIKHER JSC; *Int'l*, pg. 7447
TALK, INC.; *U.S. Private*, pg. 3926
TALKING MEDICINES LIMITED—See Tern PLC; *Int'l*, pg. 7565
TALKING STICK COMMUNICATIONS, LLC—See Federated Media Inc.; *U.S. Private*, pg. 1492
TALKLINE GMBH—See freenet AG; *Int'l*, pg. 2770
TALKMED GROUP LIMITED; *Int'l*, pg. 7447
TALKMOBILE LIMITED—See Vodafone Group Plc; *Int'l*, pg. 8285
TAL KNITS LTD.—See Toray Industries, Inc.; *Int'l*, pg. 7823
TALKPOINT EMEA—See Siris Capital Group, LLC; *U.S. Private*, pg. 3674
TALKPOINT HOLDINGS, L.L.C.—See Siris Capital Group, LLC; *U.S. Private*, pg. 3674
TALKPOOL AG; *Int'l*, pg. 7447
TALKPOOL NV—See TalkPool AG; *Int'l*, pg. 7447
TALK PR—See M&C Saatchi plc; *Int'l*, pg. 4611
TALK RADIO NETWORK; *U.S. Private*, pg. 3926
TALKSPACE, INC.; *U.S. Public*, pg. 1979
TALKSPORT LIMITED—See News Corporation; *U.S. Public*, pg. 1521
TALK SYSTEM CORPORATION—See THK CO., LTD.; *Int'l*, pg. 7712
TALKTALK AG—See mobilezone holding ag; *Int'l*, pg. 5011
TALKTALK COMMUNICATIONS LIMITED—See Old Oak Holdings Limited; *Int'l*, pg. 5552
TALKTALK TELECOM GROUP PLC—See Old Oak Holdings Limited; *Int'l*, pg. 5552

COMPANY NAME INDEX

TALKTALK TELECOM LIMITED—See Old Oak Holdings Limited; *Int'l*, pg. 5552
TALKWEB INFORMATION SYSTEM INC.; *Int'l*, pg. 7447
TALLADEGA MACHINERY & SUPPLY CO., INC.; *U.S. Private*, pg. 3926
TALLADEGA SUPERSPEEDWAY, LLC—See National Association for Stock Car Auto Racing, Inc.; *U.S. Private*, pg. 2846
TALLAHASSEE AUTOMOTIVE, LLC; *U.S. Private*, pg. 3926
TALLAHASSEE DEMOCRAT—See Gannett Co., Inc.; *U.S. Public*, pg. 899
TALLAHASSEE LAND COMPANY, INC.; *U.S. Private*, pg. 3927
TALLAHASSEE MEDICAL CENTER, INC.—See HCA Healthcare, Inc.; *U.S. Public*, pg. 1011
TALLAHASSEE MEMORIAL HEALTHCARE; *U.S. Private*, pg. 3927
TALLAHASSEE OUTPATIENT SURGERY CENTER—See HCA Healthcare, Inc.; *U.S. Public*, pg. 1011
TALLAHASSEE STATE BANK—See Synovus Financial Corp.; *U.S. Public*, pg. 1971
TALLAHASSEE STATE BANK—See Synovus Financial Corp.; *U.S. Public*, pg. 1972
TALLAHATCHIE VALLEY ELECTRIC POWER ASSOCIATION; *U.S. Private*, pg. 3927
TALLAN INC.; *U.S. Private*, pg. 3927
TAL LANKA HOTELS PLC; *Int'l*, pg. 7443
TALLAPOOSA RIVER ELECTRIC CO-OP; *U.S. Private*, pg. 3927
TALLEGA SOFTWARE, LLC—See InStream, LLC; *U.S. Private*, pg. 2094
TALLER DE EDITORES, S.A.—See Vocento, S.A.; *Int'l*, pg. 8284
TALLER DONGGUAN ELECTRONICS COMPONENTS LTD—See Taller GmbH; *Int'l*, pg. 7447
TALLERES DEL AGUA SL—See Fluidra SA; *Int'l*, pg. 2714
TALLER GMBH; *Int'l*, pg. 7447
TALLEUR GMBH—See MPC Munchmeyer Petersen & Co. GmbH; *Int'l*, pg. 5061
TALLEY INC.; *U.S. Private*, pg. 3927
TALLEY MACHINERY CORPORATION—See Tingue, Brown & Co.; *U.S. Private*, pg. 4173
TALLEY METALS TECHNOLOGY, INC—See Carpenter Technology Corporation; *U.S. Public*, pg. 439
TALLGRASS ENERGY, LP—See Blackstone Inc.; *U.S. Public*, pg. 359
TALLGRASS ENERGY PARTNERS, LP—See Blackstone Inc.; *U.S. Public*, pg. 359
TALLGRASS MIDSTREAM, LLC—See Blackstone Inc.; *U.S. Public*, pg. 359
TALLGRASS MLP OPERATIONS, LLC—See Blackstone Inc.; *U.S. Public*, pg. 359
TALLIENCE LLC—See Steven Douglas Associates, Inc.; *U.S. Private*, pg. 3808
TAL LIFE LIMITED—See Dai-ichi Life Holdings, Inc.; *Int'l*, pg. 1918
TAL LIMITED-VICTORIA—See Dai-ichi Life Holdings, Inc.; *Int'l*, pg. 1918
TALLINK LATVIJA AS—See AS Infortar; *Int'l*, pg. 590
TALLINK SILJA AB—See AS Infortar; *Int'l*, pg. 590
TALLINK SILJA GMBH—See AS Infortar; *Int'l*, pg. 590
TALLINK SILJA OY—See AS Infortar; *Int'l*, pg. 590
TALLINNA KAUBAMAJA AS; *Int'l*, pg. 7447
TALLINNA KUTE—See Veolia Environnement S.A.; *Int'l*, pg. 8158
TALLINNA SADAM AS; *Int'l*, pg. 7448
TALLO LLC—See Stride, Inc.; *U.S. Public*, pg. 1955
TALL TREE FOODS, INC.—See Altamont Capital Partners; *U.S. Private*, pg. 205
TALLWOODS INTERNATIONAL GOLF RESORT PTY. LIMITED; *Int'l*, pg. 7448
TALLY ENERGY SERVICES—See RedBird Capital Partners L.P.; *U.S. Private*, pg. 3377
TALLY LTD.; *Int'l*, pg. 7448
TALLYSMAN WIRELESS INC.—See Calian Group Ltd.; *Int'l*, pg. 1264
TALLY-UNION GMBH & CO. KG—See Addicks & Kreye Holding GmbH; *Int'l*, pg. 128
TALMA TRAVEL AND TOURS LTD.; *Int'l*, pg. 7448
TALMORA DIAMOND INC.; *Int'l*, pg. 7448
TALOCA CAFE LTDA.—See Mondelez International, Inc.; *U.S. Public*, pg. 1463
TALOCA GMBH—See Mondelez International, Inc.; *U.S. Public*, pg. 1463
TALOKAIVO OY—See Wienerberger AG; *Int'l*, pg. 8406
TALOMA FARMERS GRAIN COMPANY; *U.S. Private*, pg. 3927
TALON AIR, INC.; *U.S. Private*, pg. 3927
TALON ENERGY LTD.—See Strike Energy Limited; *Int'l*, pg. 7241
TALON FIRST TRUST, LLC—See Talon Real Estate Holding Corp.; *U.S. Public*, pg. 1980
TALON GROUP LLC; *U.S. Private*, pg. 3927
TALON INTERNATIONAL, INC.; *U.S. Public*, pg. 1979
TALON LLC; *U.S. Private*, pg. 3927
TALON/LPE; *U.S. Private*, pg. 3927
TALON METALS CORP.; *Int'l*, pg. 7448

TALON OP, L.P.—See Talon Real Estate Holding Corp.; *U.S. Public*, pg. 1980
TALON PROFESSIONAL SERVICES, LLC; *U.S. Private*, pg. 3927
TALON REAL ESTATE HOLDING CORP.; *U.S. Public*, pg. 1980
TALON TEST LABORATORIES INCORPORATED—See I Squared Capital Advisors (US) LLC; *U.S. Public*, pg. 2023
TALON TEST LABORATORIES INCORPORATED—See TDR Capital LLP; *Int'l*, pg. 7492
TALON TEST LABORATORIES (PHOENIX) INC.—See I Squared Capital Advisors (US) LLC; *U.S. Public*, pg. 2023
TALON TEST LABORATORIES (PHOENIX) INC.—See TDR Capital LLP; *Int'l*, pg. 7492
TALON ZIPPER (SHENZHEN) CO. LTD.—See Talon International, Inc.; *U.S. Public*, pg. 1980
TALOON YHTIOT OY—See BHG Group AB; *Int'l*, pg. 1015
TALOS ENERGY INC.; *U.S. Public*, pg. 1980
TALOS ENERGY LLC—See Talos Energy Inc.; *U.S. Public*, pg. 1980
TALOUSSANOMAT OY—See Sanoma Oyj; *Int'l*, pg. 6553
T.A. LOVING COMPANY; *U.S. Private*, pg. 3927
TALPA GERMANY GMBH & CO KG—See ITV plc; *Int'l*, pg. 3845
TALPA HOLDING B.V.; *Int'l*, pg. 7448
TALPA MEDIA B.V.—See ITV plc; *Int'l*, pg. 3845
TALPA RADIO B.V.—See Talpa Holding B.V.; *Int'l*, pg. 7448
TALPA TV—See Talpa Holding B.V.; *Int'l*, pg. 7448
TALPHERA, INC.; *U.S. Public*, pg. 1980
TALQUIN ELECTRIC COOPERATIVE, INC.; *U.S. Private*, pg. 3927
TAL SERVICES LIMITED—See Dai-ichi Life Holdings, Inc.; *Int'l*, pg. 1918
TALUM D.D.—See Elektro Slovenia d.o.o.; *Int'l*, pg. 2357
TALUS MANUFACTURING, LTD.—See Lam Research Corporation; *U.S. Public*, pg. 1290
TALWALKARS BETTER VALUE FITNESS LIMITED; *Int'l*, pg. 7448
TALX CORPORATION—See Equifax Inc.; *U.S. Public*, pg. 786
TALYST, INC.; *U.S. Private*, pg. 3927
TAMA AD.CO., LTD.—See Tama Home Co., Ltd.; *Int'l*, pg. 7448
TAMA-BENTON COOPERATIVE CO.; *U.S. Private*, pg. 3928
TAMA CHEMICALS CO., LTD.; *Int'l*, pg. 7448
TAMACHI BUILDING CO., LTD.—See Mitsubishi Heavy Industries, Ltd.; *Int'l*, pg. 4961
TAMA FINANCE CO., LTD.—See Tama Home Co., Ltd.; *Int'l*, pg. 7448
TAMAGAWA ELECTRONICS CO., LTD.—See Tamagawa Holdings Co., Ltd.; *Int'l*, pg. 7449
TAMAGAWA ENGINEERING CO., LTD.—See Mitsubishi Materials Corporation; *Int'l*, pg. 4965
TAMAGAWA HOLDINGS CO., LTD.; *Int'l*, pg. 7448
TAMA HOME (CAMBODIA) LTD.—See Tama Home Co., Ltd.; *Int'l*, pg. 7448
TAMA HOME CO., LTD.; *Int'l*, pg. 7448
TAMAI KASEI CO., LTD.—See Kaneka Corporation; *Int'l*, pg. 4067
TAMAI-MISO CO., LTD.—See Marusan-Ai Co., Ltd.; *Int'l*, pg. 4715
TAMAI STEAMSHIP CO., LTD.; *Int'l*, pg. 7449
TAMA KAGAKU KOGYO CO., LTD.—See Mitani Sangyo Co., Ltd.; *Int'l*, pg. 4925
TAMA KAKO CO., LTD.—See TOPPAN Holdings Inc.; *Int'l*, pg. 7817
TAMA LIVING CO., LTD.—See Tama Home Co., Ltd.; *Int'l*, pg. 7448
TAMALPAIS GROUP INC.; *U.S. Private*, pg. 3928
TA MANAGEMENT LIMITED—See TA Enterprise Berhad; *Int'l*, pg. 7399
TAMANDA HOLDINGS USA INC.; *U.S. Private*, pg. 3928
TAMAN EQUINE (M) SDN. BHD.—See Global Oriental Berhad; *Int'l*, pg. 3000
TAMAN GUNONG HIJAU SDN BHD—See S P Setia Berhad; *Int'l*, pg. 6444
TAMANO ENGINEERING CO., LTD.—See Mitsui E&S Holdings Co., Ltd.; *Int'l*, pg. 4986
TAMANO REFINERY, HIBI KYODO SMELTING CO., LTD.—See Nittetsu Mining Co., Ltd.; *Int'l*, pg. 5383
TAMAPOLY CO., LTD.—See TOPPAN Holdings Inc.; *Int'l*, pg. 7817
TAMARAC, INC.—See Bain Capital, LP; *U.S. Private*, pg. 439
TAMARACK CELLARS—See Vintage Wine Estates, Inc.; *U.S. Public*, pg. 2298
TAMARACK MATERIALS, INC.—See GMS Inc.; *U.S. Public*, pg. 948
TAMARACK PACKAGING LIMITED—See Channellock, Inc.; *U.S. Private*, pg. 849
TAMARACK VALLEY ENERGY LTD.; *Int'l*, pg. 7449
TAMARAC SURGERY CENTER, LLC—See Tenet Healthcare Corporation; *U.S. Public*, pg. 2013
TAMARES GROUP; *Int'l*, pg. 7449
TAMAR FOODS LIMITED—See Samworth Brothers Ltd.; *Int'l*, pg. 6519

TAMARI INDUSTRY CO., LTD.—See NADEX CO., LTD.; *Int'l*, pg. 5124
TAMARIND CONSOLIDATED, INC.—See Crowley Maritime Corporation; *U.S. Private*, pg. 1110
TAMARIND MANAGEMENT SDN. BHD.; *Int'l*, pg. 7449
TAMARIND NEW ZEALAND PTY. LIMITED—See Tamarind Management Sdn. Bhd.; *Int'l*, pg. 7449
TAMARIND TARANAKI LIMITED—See Tamarind Management Sdn. Bhd.; *Int'l*, pg. 7449
TAMARIND TOURS PRIVATE LIMITED—See Crest Ventures Limited; *Int'l*, pg. 1841
TAMARIND TRADING (SHANGHAI) LIMITED—See Daohe Global Group Limited; *Int'l*, pg. 1970
TAMARIND VILLAGE CO., LTD.—See Premier Marketing Public Company Limited; *Int'l*, pg. 5961
TAMARIS INDUSTRIES SAS—See CVC Capital Partners SICAV-FIS S.A.; *Int'l*, pg. 1887
TAMARKIN CO., INC.—See Giant Eagle, Inc.; *U.S. Private*, pg. 1694
TAMAROFF LEASING CO.—See Tamaroff Motors, Inc.; *U.S. Private*, pg. 3928
TAMAROFF MOTORS, INC.; *U.S. Private*, pg. 3928
TAMAR PETROLEUM LTD.; *Int'l*, pg. 7449
TAMA TRADING COMPANY; *U.S. Private*, pg. 3927
TAMAULIGAS S.A. DE C.V.—See ENGIE SA; *Int'l*, pg. 2434
TAMAWOOD LIMITED; *Int'l*, pg. 7449
TAMAWOOD REALTY PTY LTD.—See TAMAWOOD LIMITED; *Int'l*, pg. 7449
TAMAYA TECHNICS INC.—See Kyowa Electronic Instruments Co., Ltd.; *Int'l*, pg. 4366
TAMAZEN CO., LTD.—See Tomoku Co., Ltd.; *Int'l*, pg. 7802
TAMBANKULU ESTATES LIMITED—See Tongaat Hulett Limited; *Int'l*, pg. 7807
TAMBLA LIMITED; *Int'l*, pg. 7449
TAMBOLI CASTINGS LIMITED—See Tamboli Industries Limited; *Int'l*, pg. 7449
TAMBOLI INDUSTRIES LIMITED; *Int'l*, pg. 7449
TAMBORAN RESOURCES LIMITED; *Int'l*, pg. 7449
TAMBOURAH METALS LTD.; *Int'l*, pg. 7449
TAMBOUR LIMITED—See The Kusto Group Inc.; *Int'l*, pg. 7663
TAMBOV ENERGOSBYT COMPANY; *Int'l*, pg. 7449
TAMBOVSKY BACON—See Gruppa Kompaniy Rusagro OOO; *Int'l*, pg. 3140
TAMBUN INDAH LAND BERHAD; *Int'l*, pg. 7449
TAMBURI INVESTMENT PARTNERS S.P.A; *Int'l*, pg. 7450
TAM BUSINESS SYSTEMS INC.; *U.S. Private*, pg. 3927
TAM CERAMICS GROUP OF NY, LLC; *U.S. Private*, pg. 3927
TAM CERAMICS LLC—See TAM Ceramics Group of NY, LLC; *U.S. Private*, pg. 3927
TAMCO ELECTRICAL INDUSTRIES AUSTRALIA PTY LIMITED—See Schneider Electric SE; *Int'l*, pg. 6635
TAMCO HOLDINGS, LLC; *U.S. Private*, pg. 3928
TAM CONSULTANTS, INC.—See Terracon Consultants, Inc.; *U.S. Private*, pg. 3971
TAMCO STEEL, INC.—See Metalurgica Gerdau S.A.; *Int'l*, pg. 4850
TAMCO SWITCHGEAR (MALAYSIA) SDN. BHD.—See Schneider Electric SE; *Int'l*, pg. 6635
TAMDEEN REAL ESTATE COMPANY K.S.C.C.; *Int'l*, pg. 7450
TAM DEVELOPMENT COMPANY; *Int'l*, pg. 7448
TAMDOWN GROUP LIMITED—See Nexus Infrastructure plc; *Int'l*, pg. 5251
TAMEDIA PUBLICATIONS ROMANDES SA—See TX Group AG; *Int'l*, pg. 7992
TAMEER REAL ESTATE AGENCIES WLL—See Inovest BSC; *Int'l*, pg. 3715
TAMENY INC.; *U.S. Private*, pg. 7450
TAMERICA PRODUCTS INC.—See Tah Hsin Industrial Corporation; *Int'l*, pg. 7407
TAMER MEDIA, LLC; *U.S. Private*, pg. 3928
TAMEX OBIEKTY SPORTOWE SA; *Int'l*, pg. 7450
TAM FAKTORING A.S.; *Int'l*, pg. 7448
TAMIL MURASU LTD—See Singapore Press Holdings Ltd.; *Int'l*, pg. 6943
TAMIL NADU INDUSTRIAL DEVELOPMENT CORPORATION LTD.; *Int'l*, pg. 7450
TAMILNADU JAI BHARATH MILLS LIMITED; *Int'l*, pg. 7450
TAMIL NADU NEWSPRINT & PAPERS LTD; *Int'l*, pg. 7450
TAMILNADU PETROPRODUCTS LIMITED; *Int'l*, pg. 7450
TAMILNADU STEEL TUBES LIMITED; *Int'l*, pg. 7450
TAMILNADU TELECOMMUNICATION LIMITED; *Int'l*, pg. 7450
TAMIL NADU WATER INVESTMENT COMPANY LIMITED—See Infrastructure Leasing & Financial Services Limited; *Int'l*, pg. 3698
TAMIMI PHARMACY LLC; *U.S. Private*, pg. 3928
TAMIMI POWER AND INDUSTRIAL GROUP—See Ali Abdullah Al Tamimi Company; *Int'l*, pg. 319
TAMIMI & SAIHAITI TRANSPORT CO.—See Ali Abdullah Al Tamimi Company; *Int'l*, pg. 319
TAMIMI TAPE MANUFACTURING CO. LTD—See Ali Abdullah Al Tamimi Company; *Int'l*, pg. 320

TAMIMI PHARMACY LLC / CORPORATE AFFILIATIONS

Company Index

TAMINCO ARGENTINA SA—See Eastman Chemical Company; *U.S. Public*, pg. 706

TAMINCO BVBA—See Eastman Chemical Company; *U.S. Public*, pg. 706

TAMINCO CHOLINE CHLORIDE (SHANGHAI) CO., LTD.—See Eastman Chemical Company; *U.S. Public*, pg. 706

TAMINCO DO BRASIL COMERCIO E INDUSTRIA DE AMINAS LTDA.—See Eastman Chemical Company; *U.S. Public*, pg. 706

TAMINCO DO BRAZIL PRODUTOS QUIMICOS LTDA.—See Eastman Chemical Company; *U.S. Public*, pg. 706

TAMINCO FINLAND OY—See Eastman Chemical Company; *U.S. Public*, pg. 706

TAMINCO GERMANY GMBH—See Eastman Chemical Company; *U.S. Public*, pg. 706

TAMINCO GLOBAL CHEMICAL CORPORATION—See Eastman Chemical Company; *U.S. Public*, pg. 706

TAMINCO UK LIMITED—See Eastman Chemical Company; *U.S. Public*, pg. 706

TAM INC.—See Casella Waste Systems, Inc.; *U.S. Public*, pg. 446

TAMINI TRASFORMATORI S.R.L.—See Terna S.p.A. - Rete Elettrica Nazionale; *Int'l*, pg. 7566

TAMINO MINERALS, INC.; *Int'l*, pg. 7450

TAMIN PETROLEUM & PETROCHEMICAL INVESTMENT CO.; *Int'l*, pg. 7450

TAM INTERNATIONAL INC.; *U.S. Private*, pg. 3927

TAMIR ENGINEERING & DEVELOPMENT LTD.—See Komax Holding AG; *Int'l*, pg. 4241

TAMKEEN HOLDING CO; *Int'l*, pg. 7451

TAMKEEN LEASING COMPANY—See Invest Bank; *Int'l*, pg. 3775

TAMKIN FOULAD ASANBAR CO.—See Schindler Holding AG; *Int'l*, pg. 6621

TAMKO ROOFING PRODUCTS INC.; *U.S. Private*, pg. 3928

TAM LINHAS AEREAS S.A.—See LATAM Airlines Group S.A.; *Int'l*, pg. 4422

TAMLYN SHIPPING LIMITED—See World Kinect Corporation; *U.S. Public*, pg. 2381

TAM MERCOSUR S.A.—See LATAM Airlines Group S.A.; *Int'l*, pg. 4422

TAMMERMATIC GROUP OY—See Sentica Partners Oy; *Int'l*, pg. 6715

TAMMERMATIC OY—See Sentica Partners Oy; *Int'l*, pg. 6715

TAMMY LYNN OUTDOOR, LLC—See Boston Omaha Corporation; *U.S. Public*, pg. 372

TAMNAVAPUT A.D.; *Int'l*, pg. 7451

TAMPA ARMATURE WORKS INC.; *U.S. Private*, pg. 3928

TAMPA BANKING CO.; *U.S. Private*, pg. 3928

TAMPA BAY BUSINESS JOURNAL—See Advance Publications, Inc.; *U.S. Private*, pg. 85

TAMPA BAY & CO.; *U.S. Private*, pg. 3928

TAMPA BAY FISHERIES, INC.—See Red Chamber Co.; *U.S. Private*, pg. 3373

TAMPA BAY INNOVATION CENTER; *U.S. Private*, pg. 3928

TAMPA BAY JOINT & SPINE, LLC—See Tenet Healthcare Corporation; *U.S. Public*, pg. 2007

TAMPA BAY MAGAZINE—See Tampa Bay Publications, Inc.; *U.S. Private*, pg. 3929

TAMPA BAY NEWSPAPERS, INC.—See Times Holding Co.; *U.S. Private*, pg. 4172

TAMPA BAY ORTHOPAEDIC SPECIALISTS, PA; *U.S. Private*, pg. 3929

THE TAMPA BAY PALM—See Palm Restaurant Group; *U.S. Private*, pg. 3080

TAMPA BAY PARTNERSHIP FOR REGIONAL ECONOMIC DEVELOPMENT, INC.; *U.S. Private*, pg. 3929

TAMPA BAY PUBLICATIONS, INC.; *U.S. Private*, pg. 3929

TAMPA BAY RAYS BASEBALL, LTD.; *U.S. Private*, pg. 3929

TAMPA BAY SPORTS & ENTERTAINMENT LLC; *U.S. Private*, pg. 3929

TAMPA BAY STEEL CORPORATION—See Russel Metals Inc.; *Int'l*, pg. 6430

TAMPA BAY SYSTEMS SALES INC.; *U.S. Private*, pg. 3929

TAMPA BAY TIMES—See Times Holding Co.; *U.S. Private*, pg. 4172

THE TAMPA BAY TRUST COMPANY—See The Sanibel Captiva Trust Company; *U.S. Private*, pg. 4114

TAMPA BAY WATER-REGIONAL WATER SUPPLY AUTHORITY; *U.S. Private*, pg. 3929

TAMPA BAY WORKFORCE ALLIANCE; *U.S. Private*, pg. 3929

TAMPA BRASS & ALUMINUM CORP.; *U.S. Private*, pg. 3929

THE TAMPA CLUB; *U.S. Private*, pg. 4126

TAMPA DIGITAL STUDIOS, INC.; *U.S. Private*, pg. 3929

TAMPA DOWNTOWN PARTNERSHIP, INC.; *U.S. Private*, pg. 3929

TAMPA ELECTRIC COMPANY—See Emera, Inc.; *Int'l*, pg. 2377

TAMPA EYE & SPECIALTY SURGERY CENTER—See HCA Healthcare, Inc.; *U.S. Public*, pg. 1011

TAMPA FORK LIFT INC.; *U.S. Private*, pg. 3929

TAMPA HOUSING AUTHORITY; *U.S. Private*, pg. 3929

TAMPA INTERNATIONAL FOREST PRODUCTS, LLC—See Forest City Trading Group, LLC; *U.S. Private*, pg. 1566

TAMPA INTERNATIONAL JET CENTER—See Sheltair Aviation Center, LLC; *U.S. Private*, pg. 3631

TAMPA LENNAR DIVISION—See Lennar Corporation; *U.S. Public*, pg. 1306

TAMPA MICROWAVE, INC.—See Thales S.A.; *Int'l*, pg. 7606

TAMPA PAIN RELIEF CENTER, INC.—See Bain Capital, LP; *U.S. Private*, pg. 447

TAMPA PALMS TRAVELWORLD; *U.S. Private*, pg. 3929

TAMPA PAVEMENT CONSTRUCTORS, INC.—See VINCI S.A.; *Int'l*, pg. 8220

TAMPA PAVEMENT CONSTRUCTORS, INC. - TPC ASPHALT PLANT—See VINCI S.A.; *Int'l*, pg. 8220

TAMPA PORT AUTHORITY INC.; *U.S. Private*, pg. 3929

TAMPA SPORTS AUTHORITY; *U.S. Private*, pg. 3930

TAMPA STEEL ERECTING COMPANY; *U.S. Private*, pg. 3930

TAMPA TANK & WELDING INC.—See TTI Holdings Inc.; *U.S. Private*, pg. 4254

TAMPA THEATRE, INC.; *U.S. Private*, pg. 3930

TAMP AUTO PARTS INDUSTRIAL CO., LTD.—See Hitachi, Ltd.; *Int'l*, pg. 3424

TAMPEREEN LANSIKESKUS OY—See Kesko Corporation; *Int'l*, pg. 4143

TAMPEREEN SAHKOPALVELU OY—See Addtech AB; *Int'l*, pg. 135

TAMPEREEN SUVANTOKATU KOY—See Citycon Oyj; *Int'l*, pg. 1629

TAMPEREEN TIETOVERKKO OY—See Elisa Corporation; *Int'l*, pg. 2361

TAMPICO BEVERAGES, INC.—See Houchens Industries, Inc.; *U.S. Private*, pg. 1990

TAMRAC INC.; *U.S. Private*, pg. 3930

TAMRO AB—See PHOENIX Pharmahandel GmbH & Co. KG; *Int'l*, pg. 5854

TAMRO AB—See PHOENIX Pharmahandel GmbH & Co. KG; *Int'l*, pg. 5854

TAMRO BALTICS—See PHOENIX Pharmahandel GmbH & Co. KG; *Int'l*, pg. 5855

TAMRO EESTI OU—See PHOENIX Pharmahandel GmbH & Co. KG; *Int'l*, pg. 5855

TAMRON CO., LTD. - HIROSAKI PLANT—See Tamron Co. Ltd.; *Int'l*, pg. 7451

TAMRON CO. LTD. - NAMIOKA PLANT—See Tamron Co. Ltd.; *Int'l*, pg. 7451

TAMRON CO., LTD. - OWANI PLANT—See Tamron Co. Ltd.; *Int'l*, pg. 7451

TAMRON CO. LTD.; *Int'l*, pg. 7451

TAMRON EUROPE GMBH—See Tamron Co. Ltd.; *Int'l*, pg. 7451

TAMRON FRANCE EURL—See Tamron Co. Ltd.; *Int'l*, pg. 7451

TAMRON INDIA PRIVATE LIMITED—See Tamron Co. Ltd.; *Int'l*, pg. 7451

TAMRON INDUSTRIES (HONG KONG) LIMITED—See Tamron Co. Ltd.; *Int'l*, pg. 7451

TAMRON OPTICAL (FOSHAN) CO., LTD.—See Tamron Co. Ltd.; *Int'l*, pg. 7451

TAMRON OPTICAL (SHANGHAI) CO., LTD.—See Tamron Co. Ltd.; *Int'l*, pg. 7451

TAMRON OPTICAL (VIETNAM) CO., LTD.—See Tamron Co. Ltd.; *Int'l*, pg. 7451

TAMRON (RUSSIA) LLC—See Tamron Co. Ltd.; *Int'l*, pg. 7451

TAMRON USA INC.—See Tamron Co. Ltd.; *Int'l*, pg. 7451

TAMRO OYJ—See PHOENIX Pharmahandel GmbH & Co. KG; *Int'l*, pg. 5854

TAMRO SIA—See PHOENIX Pharmahandel GmbH & Co. KG; *Int'l*, pg. 5855

TAMROTOR KOMPRESSORIT OY—See Ingersoll Rand Inc.; *U.S. Public*, pg. 1120

TAMROTOR MARINE COMPRESSORS AS—See Ingersoll Rand Inc.; *U.S. Public*, pg. 1120

TAM S.A.—See LATAM Airlines Group S.A.; *Int'l*, pg. 4422

TAM-TAM/TBWA—See Omnicom Group Inc.; *U.S. Public*, pg. 1598

TAMTAS YAPI MALZEMELERI SANAYI VE TICARET AS—See Vicat S.A.; *Int'l*, pg. 8186

TAMTRON GROUP OYJ; *Int'l*, pg. 7451

TAM TRUCK & TRAILER SERVICES LLC—See American Securities LLC; *U.S. Private*, pg. 248

TAMURA CHEMICAL KOREA CO., LTD.—See Tamura Corporation; *Int'l*, pg. 7451

TAMURA CORPORATION - IRUMA FACTORY—See Tamura Corporation; *Int'l*, pg. 7451

TAMURA CORPORATION - KODAMA FACTORY—See Tamura Corporation; *Int'l*, pg. 7451

TAMURA CORPORATION OF AMERICA—See Tamura Corporation; *Int'l*, pg. 7451

TAMURA CORPORATION OF CHINA LIMITED—See Tamura Corporation; *Int'l*, pg. 7451

TAMURA CORPORATION OF HONG KONG LIMITED—See Tamura Corporation; *Int'l*, pg. 7451

TAMURA CORPORATION OF KOREA—See Tamura Corporation; *Int'l*, pg. 7451

TAMURA CORPORATION - SAKADO FACTORY—See Tamura Corporation; *Int'l*, pg. 7451

TAMURA CORPORATION - SAYAMA FACTORY—See Tamura Corporation; *Int'l*, pg. 7451

TAMURA CORPORATION SINGAPORE PTE. LTD.—See Tamura Corporation; *Int'l*, pg. 7451

TAMURA CORPORATION; *Int'l*, pg. 7451

TAMURA CORPORATION VIETNAM CO., LTD.—See Tamura Corporation; *Int'l*, pg. 7451

TAMURA ELCOMPONICS TECHNOLOGIES PRIVATE LIMITED—See Tamura Corporation; *Int'l*, pg. 7451

TAMURA ELECTRONIC MATERIAL (TIANJIN) CO., LTD.—See Tamura Corporation; *Int'l*, pg. 7452

TAMURA ELECTRONICS (H.K.) CO., LTD.—See Tamura Corporation; *Int'l*, pg. 7452

TAMURA ELECTRONICS (HUI ZHOU) CO., LTD.—See Tamura Corporation; *Int'l*, pg. 7452

TAMURA ELECTRONICS (M) SDN. BHD.—See Tamura Corporation; *Int'l*, pg. 7452

TAMURA ELECTRONICS (SHANGHAI) CO., LTD.—See Tamura Corporation; *Int'l*, pg. 7452

TAMURA ELECTRONICS (SUZHOU) CO., LTD.—See Tamura Corporation; *Int'l*, pg. 7452

TAMURA ELECTRONICS (S.Z.) CO., LTD.—See Tamura Corporation; *Int'l*, pg. 7452

TAMURA ELECTRONICS (THAILAND) CO., LTD.—See Tamura Corporation; *Int'l*, pg. 7452

TAMURA ELSOLD GMBH—See Tamura Corporation; *Int'l*, pg. 7452

TAMURA EUROPE LIMITED—See Tamura Corporation; *Int'l*, pg. 7452

TAMURA FA SYSTEM (SUZHOU) CO., LTD.—See Tamura Corporation; *Int'l*, pg. 7452

TAMURA KAKEN CORPORATION U.S.A.—See Tamura Corporation; *Int'l*, pg. 7451

TAMURA KAKEN (DONGGUAN) LTD.—See Tamura Corporation; *Int'l*, pg. 7452

TAMURA KAKEN (M) SDN. BHD.—See Tamura Corporation; *Int'l*, pg. 7452

TAMURA KAKEN TECH CO., LTD.—See Tamura Corporation; *Int'l*, pg. 7452

TAMURA KAKEN (U.K.) LTD.—See Tamura Corporation; *Int'l*, pg. 7452

TAMURA MACHINERY (THAILAND) CO., LTD.—See Tamura Corporation; *Int'l*, pg. 7452

TAMURA MAGNETIC ENGINEERING S.R.L.—See Tamura Corporation; *Int'l*, pg. 7452

TAMURA POWER TECHNOLOGIES DE MEXICO, S.A. DE C.V.—See Tamura Corporation; *Int'l*, pg. 7452

TAMURA POWER TECHNOLOGY CO., LTD.—See Tamura Corporation; *Int'l*, pg. 7452

TAMURA SUPERETTE INC.; *U.S. Private*, pg. 3930

TAMURA THERMAL DEVICE CORPORATION—See Tamura Corporation; *Int'l*, pg. 7452

TAMURA THERMAL DEVICE (H.K.) CO., LTD.—See Tamura Corporation; *Int'l*, pg. 7452

TAMWEEL MORTGAGE FINANCE COMPANY S.A.E.; *Int'l*, pg. 7452

TAMWEEL PJSC—See Dubai Islamic Bank PSJ; *Int'l*, pg. 2220

TANABE CO., LTD.—See Maruha Nichiro Corporation; *Int'l*, pg. 4712

TANABE CONSULTING CO., LTD.—See Tanabe Consulting Group Co., Ltd.; *Int'l*, pg. 7454

TANABE CONSULTING GROUP CO., LTD.; *Int'l*, pg. 7454

TANABE ENGINEERING CORPORATION; *Int'l*, pg. 7454

TANABE ENGINEERING SINGAPORE PTE. LTD.—See Tanabe Engineering Corporation; *Int'l*, pg. 7454

TANABE R&D SERVICE CO., LTD.—See Mitsubishi Chemical Group Corporation; *Int'l*, pg. 4935

TANABE RESEARCH LABORATORIES U.S.A., INC.—See Mitsubishi Chemical Group Corporation; *Int'l*, pg. 4935

TANABE SEIYAKU CO., LTD.—See Mitsubishi Chemical Group Corporation; *Int'l*, pg. 4935

TANABE SEIYAKU (MALAYSIA) SDN. BHD.—See Mitsubishi Chemical Group Corporation; *Int'l*, pg. 4935

TANABE TOTAL SERVICE CO., LTD.—See Mitsubishi Chemical Group Corporation; *Int'l*, pg. 4935

TANABE U.S.A., INC.—See Mitsubishi Chemical Group Corporation; *Int'l*, pg. 4935

TANABE U.S.A.—See Mitsubishi Chemical Group Corporation; *Int'l*, pg. 4935

TANAC AUTOMATION CO., LTD.; *Int'l*, pg. 7454

TANACHIRA GROUP; *Int'l*, pg. 7454

TANACK SEIKI (MALAYSIA) SDN. BHD—See Tanac Automation Co., Ltd.; *Int'l*, pg. 7454

TANADGUSIX CORP.; *U.S. Private*, pg. 3930

TANA ENGINEERING PLC—See Schindler Holding AG; *Int'l*, pg. 6621

TANAGER, INC.; *U.S. Private*, pg. 3930

TANAGURA DEVELOPMENT CO., LTD.—See Topy Industries, Ltd.; *Int'l*, pg. 7822

TANAHEAD SENDIRIAN BERHAD—See Ta Ann Holdings Berhad; *Int'l*, pg. 7399

COMPANY NAME INDEX

TANAH MERAH QUARRY SDN BHD—See Heidelberg Materials AG; *Int'l*, pg. 3320
TANAIS LLC—See Onexim Group Limited; *Int'l*, pg. 5581
TANAKA CHEMICAL CORPORATION—See Sumitomo Chemical Company, Limited; *Int'l*, pg. 7267
TANAKA CO., LTD.; *Int'l*, pg. 7454
TANAKA CO., LTD.; *Int'l*, pg. 7454
TANAKA DENSHI KOGYO K.K.—See Tanaka Holdings Co., Ltd.; *Int'l*, pg. 7455
TANAKA ELECTRONICS (HANGZHOU) CO., LTD.—See Tanaka Holdings Co., Ltd.; *Int'l*, pg. 7455
TANAKA ELECTRONICS MALAYSIA SDN. BHD.—See Tanaka Holdings Co., Ltd.; *Int'l*, pg. 7455
TANAKA ELECTRONICS SINGAPORE PTE. LTD.—See Tanaka Holdings Co., Ltd.; *Int'l*, pg. 7455
TANAKA ENGINEERING CO., LTD.—See Tanaka Seimitsu Kogyo Co., Ltd.; *Int'l*, pg. 7456
TANAKA HOLDINGS CO., LTD.; *Int'l*, pg. 7455
TANAKA KIKINZOKU HANBAI K.K.—See Tanaka Holdings Co., Ltd.; *Int'l*, pg. 7455
TANAKA KIKINZOKU INTERNATIONAL (AMERICA) INC.—See Tanaka Holdings Co., Ltd.; *Int'l*, pg. 7455
TANAKA KIKINZOKU INTERNATIONAL (EUROPE) GMBH—See Tanaka Holdings Co., Ltd.; *Int'l*, pg. 7456
TANAKA KIKINZOKU INTERNATIONAL K.K.—See Tanaka Holdings Co., Ltd.; *Int'l*, pg. 7455
TANAKA KIKINZOKU INTERNATIONAL (SHANGHAI) CO.,LTD.—See Tanaka Holdings Co., Ltd.; *Int'l*, pg. 7456
TANAKA KIKINZOKU INTERNATIONAL (THAILAND)CO.,LTD.—See Tanaka Holdings Co., Ltd.; *Int'l*, pg. 7456
TANAKA KIKINZOKU JEWELRY K.K.—See Tanaka Holdings Co., Ltd.; *Int'l*, pg. 7456
TANAKA KIKINZOKU KOGYO K.K.—See Tanaka Holdings Co., Ltd.; *Int'l*, pg. 7456
TANAKA KIKINZOKU (SUZHOU) CO., LTD.—See Tanaka Holdings Co., Ltd.; *Int'l*, pg. 7455
TANAKA OF TOKYO RESTAURANTS; *U.S. Private*, pg. 3930
TANAKA PRECISION (THAILAND) CO., LTD.—See Tanaka Seimitsu Kogyo Co., Ltd.; *Int'l*, pg. 7456
TANAKA PRECISION VIETNAM CO., LTD.—See Tanaka Seimitsu Kogyo Co., Ltd.; *Int'l*, pg. 7456
TANAKA SEIMITSU KOGYO CO., LTD. - FUCHU FACTORY—See Tanaka Seimitsu Kogyo Co., Ltd.; *Int'l*, pg. 7456
TANAKA SEIMITSU KOGYO CO., LTD. - KUREHA FACTORY—See Tanaka Seimitsu Kogyo Co., Ltd.; *Int'l*, pg. 7456
TANAKA SEIMITSU KOGYO CO., LTD. - NAMERIKAWA FACTORY—See Tanaka Seimitsu Kogyo Co., Ltd.; *Int'l*, pg. 7456
TANAKA SEIMITSU KOGYO CO., LTD. - NYUZEN FACTORY—See Tanaka Seimitsu Kogyo Co., Ltd.; *Int'l*, pg. 7456
TANAKA SEIMITSU KOGYO CO., LTD.; *Int'l*, pg. 7456
TANAKA STEEL TRADING CO., LTD.—See Hanwa Co., Ltd.; *Int'l*, pg. 3263
TANAKEN KK; *Int'l*, pg. 7456
TANAMI EXPLORATION NL—See Tanami Gold NL; *Int'l*, pg. 7456
TANAMI GOLD NL; *Int'l*, pg. 7456
TANA RESOURCES CORP.; *Int'l*, pg. 7454
TANASEYBERT; *U.S. Private*, pg. 3930
TANASIO INDUSTRIAL GASES CYF—See Air Products & Chemicals, Inc.; *U.S. Public*, pg. 67
TANATEX CHEMICALS ARGENTINA SA—See Transfar Group Co., Ltd.; *Int'l*, pg. 7899
TANATEX CHEMICALS BV—See Transfar Group Co., Ltd.; *Int'l*, pg. 7899
TANATEX CHEMICALS HONG KONG LIMITED—See Transfar Group Co., Ltd.; *Int'l*, pg. 7899
TANATEX CHEMICALS IBERICA, S.L.U.—See Transfar Group Co., Ltd.; *Int'l*, pg. 7899
TANATEX CHEMICALS INDIA PRIVATE LIMITED—See Transfar Group Co., Ltd.; *Int'l*, pg. 7899
TANATEX CHEMICALS JAPAN K.K.—See Transfar Group Co., Ltd.; *Int'l*, pg. 7899
TANATEX CHEMICALS (THAILAND) CO., LTD.—See Transfar Group Co., Ltd.; *Int'l*, pg. 7899
TANATEX CHEMICALS TRADING (SHANGHAI) CO., LTD.—See Transfar Group Co., Ltd.; *Int'l*, pg. 7899
TANAUD INTERNATIONAL BV—See Takeda Pharmaceutical Company Limited; *Int'l*, pg. 7438
TAN BINH IMPORT-EXPORT JOINT STOCK CORPORATION; *Int'l*, pg. 7452
TAN BOOKS & PUBLISHERS—See Saint Benedict Press; *U.S. Private*, pg. 3529
TANBRIDGE CORPORATION; *Int'l*, pg. 7456
TAN CANG - CAI MEP INTERNATIONAL TERMINAL CO., LTD.—See Mitsui O.S.K. Lines, Ltd.; *Int'l*, pg. 4991
TAN CANG - CAI MEP TOWAGE SERVICES CO., LTD.—See Mitsui O.S.K. Lines, Ltd.; *Int'l*, pg. 4991
TAN CANG HAI PHONG INTERNATIONAL CONTAINER TERMINAL CO., LTD.—See Mitsui O.S.K. Lines, Ltd.; *Int'l*, pg. 4991
TAN CANG LOGISTICS AND STEVEDORING JOINT STOCK COMPANY; *Int'l*, pg. 7452

TAN CHONG APPARELS MANUFACTURER SDN BHD—See Warisan TC Holdings Berhad; *Int'l*, pg. 8345
TAN CHONG CREDIT PTE LTD—See Tan Chong International Limited; *Int'l*, pg. 7453
TAN CHONG EDUCATION SERVICES SDN. BHD.—See Tan Chong Motor Holdings Berhad; *Int'l*, pg. 7454
TAN CHONG EKSPRES AUTO SERVIS SDN. BHD.—See Tan Chong Motor Holdings Berhad; *Int'l*, pg. 7454
TAN CHONG INDUSTRIAL EQUIPMENT (SABAH) SDN. BHD.—See Tan Chong Motor Holdings Berhad; *Int'l*, pg. 7454
TAN CHONG INDUSTRIAL EQUIPMENT SDN. BHD.—See Tan Chong Motor Holdings Berhad; *Int'l*, pg. 7454
TAN CHONG INDUSTRIAL MACHINERY (PTE) LTD—See Tan Chong International Limited; *Int'l*, pg. 7453
TAN CHONG INDUSTRIAL TRADING (SHANGHAI) LTD—See Tan Chong International Limited; *Int'l*, pg. 7453
TAN CHONG INTERNATIONAL LIMITED; *Int'l*, pg. 7452
TAN CHONG LAND COMPANY PTE LTD—See Tan Chong International Limited; *Int'l*, pg. 7453
TAN CHONG MOTOR ASSEMBLIES SDN. BHD.—See Nissan Motor Co., Ltd.; *Int'l*, pg. 5369
TAN CHONG MOTOR (CAMBODIA) CO., LTD.—See Nissan Motor Co., Ltd.; *Int'l*, pg. 5369
TAN CHONG MOTOR HOLDINGS BERHAD; *Int'l*, pg. 7453
TAN CHONG MOTOR (LAO) SOLE CO., LTD.—See Nissan Motor Co., Ltd.; *Int'l*, pg. 5369
TAN CHONG MOTOR SALES PTE LTD—See Tan Chong International Limited; *Int'l*, pg. 7453
TAN CHONG MOTOR SALES—See Tan Chong International Limited; *Int'l*, pg. 7453
TAN CHONG REALTY (PRIVATE) LIMITED—See Tan Chong International Limited; *Int'l*, pg. 7453
TAN CHONG & SONS MOTOR COMPANY SDN. BHD.—See Tan Chong Motor Holdings Berhad; *Int'l*, pg. 7454
TAN CHONG & SONS MOTOR CO (S) PTE LTD—See Tan Chong International Limited; *Int'l*, pg. 7453
TAN CHONG TRADING (MALAYSIA) SDN. BHD.—See Tan Chong Motor Holdings Berhad; *Int'l*, pg. 7454
TAN CHONG (VIETNAM) INDUSTRIAL MACHINERY CO., LTD—See Tan Chong International Limited; *Int'l*, pg. 7453
TANCOAL ENERGY LIMITED—See Intra Energy Corporation Limited; *Int'l*, pg. 3767
TANCO HOLDINGS BERHAD; *Int'l*, pg. 7456
TANCO LUMBER, L.L.C.—See Bain Capital, LP; *U.S. Private*, pg. 450
TANCO RESORTS BERHAD—See Tanco Holdings Berhad; *Int'l*, pg. 7456
TANCSOS UND BINDER GESELLSCHAFT M.B.H.—See PORR AG; *Int'l*, pg. 5925
TANCY INSTRUMENT GROUP CO., LTD.—See Goldcard Smart Group Co., Ltd.; *Int'l*, pg. 3027
TAN DAI HUNG PLASTIC J.S CO.; *Int'l*, pg. 7454
TANDBERG ASA—See Cisco Systems, Inc.; *U.S. Public*, pg. 500
TANDBERG DATA GMBH—See Cyrus Capital Partners, L.P.; *U.S. Private*, pg. 1135
TANDBERG DATA (JAPAN) INC.—See Cyrus Capital Partners, L.P.; *U.S. Private*, pg. 1135
TANDBERG DATA NORGE AS—See Cyrus Capital Partners, L.P.; *U.S. Private*, pg. 1135
TANDBERG DATA—See Cyrus Capital Partners, L.P.; *U.S. Private*, pg. 1135
TANDBERG TELEVISION JAPAN—See Telefonaktiebolaget LM Ericsson; *Int'l*, pg. 7532
TANDE CO., LTD.; *Int'l*, pg. 7456
TANDEL SYSTEMS, INC.—See AE Industrial Partners, LP; *U.S. Private*, pg. 111
TANDEM ADVISORY SDN. BHD.—See Mindtell Technology Limited; *Int'l*, pg. 4902
TANDEM COMMUNICATIONS GMBH—See Vivendi SE; *Int'l*, pg. 8266
TANDEM DIABETES CANADA—See Tandem Diabetes Care, Inc.; *U.S. Public*, pg. 1980
TANDEM DIABETES CARE, INC.; *U.S. Public*, pg. 1980
TANDEM FINANCE INC.—See Chesswood Group Limited; *Int'l*, pg. 1472
TANDEM GLOBAL LOGISTICS (HK) LIMITED—See Azuma Shipping Co., Ltd.; *Int'l*, pg. 782
TANDEM GLOBAL LOGISTICS (INDIA) PVT. LTD.—See Azuma Shipping Co., Ltd.; *Int'l*, pg. 782
TANDEM GLOBAL LOGISTICS JAPAN CO., LTD.—See Azuma Shipping Co., Ltd.; *Int'l*, pg. 782
TANDEM GLOBAL LOGISTICS NETHERLANDS B.V.—See Azuma Shipping Co., Ltd.; *Int'l*, pg. 782
TANDEM GLOBAL LOGISTICS (SHANGHAI) CO., LTD.—See Azuma Shipping Co., Ltd.; *Int'l*, pg. 782
TANDEM GROUP CYCLES LIMITED—See Tandem Group PLC; *Int'l*, pg. 7456
TANDEM GROUP PLC; *Int'l*, pg. 7456
TANDEM HR, INC.; *U.S. Private*, pg. 3930
TANDEM INC.; *U.S. Private*, pg. 3930

TANGERINE BEACH HOTELS PLC

TANDEM INNOVATIVE PAYMENT SOLUTIONS LLC—See Independence Capital Partners, LLC; *U.S. Private*, pg. 2056
TANDEM LABS, INC.—See Laboratory Corporation of America Holdings; *U.S. Public*, pg. 1287
TANDEM PUBLISHING GROUP, INC.; *U.S. Private*, pg. 3930
TANDEMSEVEN, INC.—See Genpact Limited; *Int'l*, pg. 2927
TANDEM; *U.S. Private*, pg. 3930
TANDEM TIRE & AUTO SERVICE; *U.S. Private*, pg. 3930
TANDEM TRANSPORT INC.—See Prolog Services; *U.S. Private*, pg. 3282
TANDET INDUSTRIAL INC.—See Tandet Management Inc.; *Int'l*, pg. 7456
TANDET MANAGEMENT INC.; *Int'l*, pg. 7456
TANDLIANWALA SUGAR MILLS LTD.; *Int'l*, pg. 7456
TANDO BUILDING PRODUCTS—See Clearview Capital, LLC; *U.S. Private*, pg. 939
TANDOM METALLURGICAL GROUP LTD.; *Int'l*, pg. 7457
TANDOM METALLURGICAL (MIDLANDS) LTD—See Tandom Metallurgical Group Ltd.; *Int'l*, pg. 7457
TANDUAY DISTILLERS, INC.—See LT Group, Inc.; *Int'l*, pg. 4571
TANDUS GROUP, INC.—See Tarkett S.A.; *Int'l*, pg. 7463
TANDY LEATHER FACTORY, INC.; *U.S. Public*, pg. 1980
TANDYM GROUP, LLC—See Great Mill Rock LLC; *U.S. Private*, pg. 1766
TANEHASHI KIKAI CO., LTD.; *Int'l*, pg. 7457
TANEJA AEROSPACE & AVIATION LIMITED; *Int'l*, pg. 7457
TANENBAUM HARBER OF FLORIDA, LLC—See Kelso & Company, L.P.; *U.S. Private*, pg. 2280
TANETY ZINA SARL—See Brainchip Holdings Ltd.; *Int'l*, pg. 1137
THE TANEY CORPORATION; *U.S. Private*, pg. 4126
TANFAC INDUSTRIES LIMITED—See Tamil Nadu Industrial Development Corporation Ltd.; *Int'l*, pg. 7450
TANFAC INDUSTRIES LIMITED—See The Aditya Birla Group; *Int'l*, pg. 7611
TANFEETH LLC—See Emirates NBD PJSC; *Int'l*, pg. 2382
TANFIELD ENGINEERING SYSTEMS LTD.—See Tanfield Group Plc; *Int'l*, pg. 7457
TANFIELD ENGINEERING SYSTEMS (US), INC.—See Tanfield Group Plc; *Int'l*, pg. 7457
TANFIELD GROUP PLC; *Int'l*, pg. 7457
TANGANDA TEA COMPANY—See Meikles Limited; *Int'l*, pg. 4802
TANG CITY PROPERTIES PTE LIMITED.—See Far East Consortium International Limited; *Int'l*, pg. 2615
TANGEL CULTURE CO., LTD.; *Int'l*, pg. 7457
TANGELO GAMES CORP.; *Int'l*, pg. 7457
TANG ENG IRON WORKS CO., LTD.—See China Steel Corporation; *Int'l*, pg. 1556
TANGENT COMMUNICATIONS PLC; *Int'l*, pg. 7457
TANGENT COMPUTER INC.; *U.S. Private*, pg. 3930
TANGENT ENERGY SOLUTIONS, INC.—See Caterpillar, Inc.; *U.S. Public*, pg. 454
TANGENT FUND MANAGEMENT LLC; *U.S. Private*, pg. 3930
TANGENT GERMANY—See Tangent International Group Plc; *Int'l*, pg. 7457
TANGENT INDUSTRIES LTD.—See Esquire Radio & Electronics Inc.; *U.S. Private*, pg. 1427
TANGENT INNOVATION—See Tangent International Group Plc; *Int'l*, pg. 7457
TANGENT INTERNATIONAL GROUP PLC; *Int'l*, pg. 7457
TANGENT INTERNATIONAL LIMITED—See Tangent International Group Plc; *Int'l*, pg. 7457
TANGENT INTERNATIONAL LIMITED—See Tangent International Group Plc; *Int'l*, pg. 7457
TANGENT INTERNATIONAL PTY LIMITED—See Tangent International Group Plc; *Int'l*, pg. 7457
TANGENT ON DEMAND—See Tangent Communications PLC; *Int'l*, pg. 7457
TANGENT SNOWBALL—See Tangent Communications PLC; *Int'l*, pg. 7457
TANGENT TECHNOLOGIES, LLC; *U.S. Private*, pg. 3930
TANGENZIALE DI NAPOLI SPA—See Edizione S.r.l.; *Int'l*, pg. 2312
TANGER BRANSON, LLC—See Tanger Inc.; *U.S. Public*, pg. 1980
TANGER CHARLESTON, LLC—See Tanger Inc.; *U.S. Public*, pg. 1980
TANGER DAYTONA, LLC—See Tanger Inc.; *U.S. Public*, pg. 1980
TANGER FORT WORTH, LLC—See Tanger Inc.; *U.S. Public*, pg. 1980
TANGER GRAND RAPIDS, LLC—See Tanger Inc.; *U.S. Public*, pg. 1980
TANGER INC.; *U.S. Public*, pg. 1980
TANGERINE BEACH HOTELS PLC; *Int'l*, pg. 7457
TANGERINE COMPANY LIMITED—See Yip In Tsoi & Co., Ltd.; *Int'l*, pg. 8585
TANGERINE CONFECTIONERY LTD. - LION CONFECTIONARY DIVISION—See CapVest Limited; *Int'l*, pg. 1318
TANGERINE CONFECTIONERY LTD.—See CapVest Limited; *Int'l*, pg. 1318

TANGERINE HOLDINGS, INC.

CORPORATE AFFILIATIONS

TANGERINE HOLDINGS, INC.; *U.S. Private,* pg. 3930
TANGERINE PENSIONS LIMITED—See AXA S.A.; *Int'l,* pg. 757
TANGER JEFFERSONVILLE, LLC—See Tanger Inc.; *U.S. Public,* pg. 1981
TANGER OUTLETS DEER PARK, LLC—See Tanger Inc.; *U.S. Public,* pg. 1981
TANGER PROPERTIES LIMITED PARTNERSHIP—See Tanger Inc.; *U.S. Public,* pg. 1981
TANGER RIVERHEAD, LLC—See Tanger Inc.; *U.S. Public,* pg. 1981
TANGER TERRELL, LLC—See Tanger Inc.; *U.S. Public,* pg. 1981
TANGER WISCONSIN DELLS, LLC—See Tanger Inc.; *U.S. Public,* pg. 1981
TANGIAMO TOUCH TECHNOLOGY AB; *Int'l,* pg. 7457
TANGIBLE GROUP LIMITED—See Arsenal Capital Management LP; *U.S. Private,* pg. 338
TANGIBLE MEDIA, INC.; *U.S. Private,* pg. 3930
TANGIERS GROUP PLC; *Int'l,* pg. 7458
TANG INDUSTRIES INC.; *U.S. Private,* pg. 3930
TANGKO PRIMA PT—See CHINO Corporation; *Int'l,* pg. 1571
TANGLEWOOD INVESTMENTS INC.; *U.S. Private,* pg. 3931
TANGLEWOOD PARK—See Peabody Properties, Inc.; *U.S. Private,* pg. 3122
TANGLIN PLACE DEVELOPMENT PTE LTD—See Allgreen Properties Ltd.; *Int'l,* pg. 338
TANGNEY INVESTMENTS (PROPRIETARY) LIMITED—See Hosken Consolidated Investments Limited; *Int'l,* pg. 3485
TANGO CARD, INC.—See Financial Technology Ventures Management Co. LLC; *U.S. Private,* pg. 1508
TANGO COMUNICACION ESTRATEGICA, S.L.—See Vocento, S.A.; *Int'l,* pg. 8284
TANGOE (CHINA) CO., LTD.—See Marlin Equity Partners, LLC; *U.S. Private,* pg. 2583
TANGOE EUROPE LIMITED—See Marlin Equity Partners, LLC; *U.S. Private,* pg. 2584
TANGOE, INC.—See Marlin Equity Partners, LLC; *U.S. Private,* pg. 2583
TANGOE INDIA SOFTEK SERVICES PRIVATE LIMITED—See Marlin Equity Partners, LLC; *U.S. Private,* pg. 2584
TANGO INDUSTRIES LTD.; *U.S. Private,* pg. 3931
TANGO KINGDOM BREWERY INC.—See Pasona Group Inc.; *Int'l,* pg. 5754
TANGOKURA INC.—See Pasona Group Inc.; *Int'l,* pg. 5754
TANGO MANAGEMENT CONSULTING, LLC; *U.S. Private,* pg. 3931
TANGOME, INC.; *U.S. Private,* pg. 3931
TANGO MOBILE SA—See Proximus PLC; *Int'l,* pg. 6008
TANGO S.A.—See Proximus PLC; *Int'l,* pg. 6008
TANGO SA—See Proximus PLC; *Int'l,* pg. 6008
TANGO SUPPLIES, INC.; *U.S. Private,* pg. 3931
TANGO SYSTEM LLC—See Applied Materials, Inc.; *U.S. Public,* pg. 172
TANGO TECHNOLOGY PTY. LTD.—See Comms Group Ltd; *Int'l,* pg. 1720
TANGO TELECOM LIMITED—See CSG Systems International, Inc.; *U.S. Public,* pg. 601
TANGO THERAPEUTICS, INC.; *U.S. Public,* pg. 1981
TANG PALACE (CHINA) HOLDINGS LTD.; *Int'l,* pg. 7457
TANGQUAN HOTEL OF HUANGSHAN TOURISM DEVELOPMENT CO., LTD.—See Huangshan Tourism Development Co., Ltd.; *Int'l,* pg. 3513
TANGRENSHEN GROUP CO., LTD.; *Int'l,* pg. 7458
TANGSHAN AISIN AUTOMOTIVE PARTS CO., LTD—See AISIN Corporation; *Int'l,* pg. 254
TANGSHAN AISIN GEAR CO., LTD.—See AISIN Corporation; *Int'l,* pg. 254
TANGSHAN COSCO SHIPPING LINES LOGISTICS CO., LTD.—See China COSCO Shipping Corporation Limited; *Int'l,* pg. 1494
TANGSHAN DBT MACHINERY CO., LTD.—See Caterpillar, Inc.; *U.S. Public,* pg. 454
TANGSHAN HIGH VOLTAGE PORCELAIN INSULATOR WORKS CO., LTD.—See BBMG Corporation; *Int'l,* pg. 921
TANGSHAN JIA YUAN REAL ESTATE DEVELOPMENT CO., LTD.; *Int'l,* pg. 7458
TANGSHAN JIDONG CEMENT CO., LTD.; *Int'l,* pg. 7458
TANGSHAN JIDONG DEVELOPMENT YAN DONG CONSTRUCTION CO., LTD.—See BBMG Corporation; *Int'l,* pg. 921
TANGSHAN JIDONG EQUIPMENT EQUIPMENT CO., LTD.; *Int'l,* pg. 7458
TANGSHAN PORT GROUP CO., LTD.; *Int'l,* pg. 7458
TANGSHAN SANNVHE AIRPORT CO., LTD.—See Hainan Traffic Administration Holding Co., Ltd.; *Int'l,* pg. 3216
TANGSHAN SANYOU CHEMICAL INDUSTRIES CO., LTD.; *Int'l,* pg. 7458
TANGSHAN SENPU MINE EQUIPMENT CO., LTD.—See China National Building Material Group Co., Ltd.; *Int'l,* pg. 1526
TANGSHAN SUNFAR SILICON INDUSTRIES CO., LTD.; *Int'l,* pg. 7459

TANGSHAN VANKE REAL ESTATE DEVELOPMENT COMPANY LIMITED—See China Vanke Co., Ltd.; *Int'l,* pg. 1562
TANGSHAN YIAN BIOLOGICAL ENGINEERING CO., LTD.—See Sinovac Biotech Ltd.; *Int'l,* pg. 6956
TANGSTEEL COMPANY LTD.—See HBIS Group Co., Ltd.; *Int'l,* pg. 3296
TANGXIAN JIDONG CEMENT CO., LTD.—See Tangshan Jidong Cement Co., Ltd.; *Int'l,* pg. 7458
TANHAY CO., LTD.; *Int'l,* pg. 7459
TAN HOLDINGS CORPORATION—See Shangtex Holding Co., Ltd.; *Int'l,* pg. 6784
TANICO INC.; *Int'l,* pg. 7459
TANIKAWA YUKA KOGYO CO., LTD. - KANAZAWA FACTORY—See SPK Corporation; *Int'l,* pg. 7140
TANIKAWA YUKA KOGYO CO., LTD.—See SPK Corporation; *Int'l,* pg. 7140
TANIMURA & ANTLE INC.; *U.S. Private,* pg. 3931
TANIN ELNA CO., LTD.—See Taiyo Yuden Company Ltd.; *Int'l,* pg. 7426
TANINTCO INC.—See Tangent International Group Plc; *Int'l,* pg. 7457
TANI PAZARLAMA VE ILETISIM HIZMETLERI A.S.—See Koc Holding A.S.; *Int'l,* pg. 4224
TANJONG MANAGEMENT SERVICES SDN BHD.—See Tanjong Plc; *Int'l,* pg. 7459
TANJONG MANIS HOLDINGS SDN BHD—See Ta Ann Holdings Berhad; *Int'l,* pg. 7399
TANJONG PLC; *Int'l,* pg. 7459
TANJONG PUTERI GOLF RESORT BERHAD—See Keck Seng (Malaysia) Berhad; *Int'l,* pg. 4114
TANJUNG DIGITAL SDN BHD—See Axiata Group Berhad; *Int'l,* pg. 768
TANJUNG LANGSAT PORT SDN BHD—See Johor Corporation; *Int'l,* pg. 3994
TANJUNG TUAN HOTEL SDN BHD—See Johor Corporation; *Int'l,* pg. 3994
TANKE BIOSCIENCES CORPORATION; *Int'l,* pg. 7459
TANKE, INC.; *U.S. Public,* pg. 1981
TANKERSKA NEXT GENERATION D.D; *Int'l,* pg. 7459
TANKERSKA PLOVIDBA D.D; *Int'l,* pg. 7459
TANK HOLDING CORP.—See Olympus Partners; *U.S. Private,* pg. 3013
TANKLINK CORPORATION—See AMETEK, Inc.; *U.S. Public,* pg. 122
TANKNOLOGY CANADA INC.—See Colliers International Group Inc.; *Int'l,* pg. 1701
TANKNOLOGY INC; *U.S. Private,* pg. 3931
TANKNOLOGY/NDE CORPORATION—See Tanknology Inc; *U.S. Private,* pg. 3931
TANKNOLOGY OHIO VALLEY REGION—See Tanknology Inc; *U.S. Private,* pg. 3931
TANKSHIPS INVESTMENT HOLDINGS INC.; *Int'l,* pg. 7459
TANKSTAR USA, INC.; *U.S. Private,* pg. 3931
TANK SYSTEMS BV—See Tailwind Capital Group, LLC; *U.S. Private,* pg. 3924
TAN KY CONSTRUCTION REAL ESTATE TRADING CORPORATION; *Int'l,* pg. 7454
TANLA MOBILE ASIA PACIFIC PTE LTD.—See Tanla Platforms Limited; *Int'l,* pg. 7459
TANLA MOBILE SOUTH AFRICA PROPRIETARY LTD—See Tanla Platforms Limited; *Int'l,* pg. 7459
TANLA MOBILE (UK) LTD.—See Tanla Platforms Limited; *Int'l,* pg. 7459
TANLA PLATFORMS LIMITED; *Int'l,* pg. 7459
TANLA SOLUTIONS (UK) LTD—See Tanla Platforms Limited; *Int'l,* pg. 7459
TANMIAH COMMERCIAL GROUP LTD.—See Dabbagh Group Holding Company Ltd.; *Int'l,* pg. 1903
TANMIAH FOOD GROUP—See Dabbagh Group Holding Company Ltd.; *Int'l,* pg. 1903
TANNAHILL ADVERTISING; *U.S. Private,* pg. 3931
TANNEHILL INTERNATIONAL INDUSTRIES; *U.S. Private,* pg. 3931
TANNENHOF SCHWARZWALDER FLEISCHWAREN GMBH & CO. KG; *Int'l,* pg. 7459
TANNER COMPANIES, LP; *U.S. Private,* pg. 3931
TANNER HOME & ENERGY; *U.S. Private,* pg. 3931
TANNERIE REMY CARRIAT; *Int'l,* pg. 7459
TANNERIES DUPIRE SA; *Int'l,* pg. 7459
TANNER INDUSTRIES INC.; *U.S. Private,* pg. 3931
TANNER MATERIALS COMPANY LLC; *U.S. Private,* pg. 3932
TANNER SERVICES, LLC; *U.S. Private,* pg. 3932
TANNER SERVICES - TIMBER DIVISION—See Tanner Services, LLC; *U.S. Private,* pg. 3932
TANN GERMANY GMBH—See Mayr-Melnhof Karton AG; *Int'l,* pg. 4747
TANNIN CORPORATION; *U.S. Private,* pg. 3932
TANNING RESEARCH LABORATORIES, LLC—See Edgewell Personal Care Company; *U.S. Public,* pg. 718
TANN LONGYOU LTD.—See Mayr-Melnhof Karton AG; *Int'l,* pg. 4747
TANN PAPER LIMITED—See Mayr-Melnhof Karton AG; *Int'l,* pg. 4747
TANNPAPIER GMBH—See Mayr-Melnhof Karton AG; *Int'l,* pg. 4747

TANN PHILIPPINES, INC.—See Mayr-Melnhof Karton AG; *Int'l,* pg. 4747
TANN SHANGHAI CO., LTD.—See Mayr-Melnhof Karton AG; *Int'l,* pg. 4747
TAN PHU VIET NAM JSC; *Int'l,* pg. 7454
TANPOPO CO., LTD.—See VITAL KSK HOLDINGS, INC.; *Int'l,* pg. 8258
TANQUE VERDE ENTERPRISES, INC.—See United Flea Markets; *U.S. Private,* pg. 4292
TANQUISADO - TERMINAIS MARITIMOS, S.A.—See Galp Energia SGPS, S.A.; *Int'l,* pg. 2876
TANRICH ASSET MANAGEMENT LIMITED—See Southwest Securities Co., Ltd.; *Int'l,* pg. 7121
TANSEI BUSINESS CO., LTD.—See TANSEISHA CO. LTD.; *Int'l,* pg. 7459
TANSEI CO., LTD.—See TANSEISHA CO. LTD.; *Int'l,* pg. 7459
TANSEI CREATIVE DESIGN CONSULTING CO., LTD.—See TANSEISHA CO. LTD.; *Int'l,* pg. 7459
TANSEI DISPLAY CO., LTD.—See TANSEISHA CO. LTD.; *Int'l,* pg. 7459
TANSEI HUMANET CO., LTD.—See TANSEISHA CO. LTD.; *Int'l,* pg. 7459
TANSEI INSTITUTE CO., LTD.—See TANSEISHA CO. LTD.; *Int'l,* pg. 7459
TANSEISHA CO. LTD.; *Int'l,* pg. 7459
TANSEI TDC CO., LTD.—See TANSEISHA CO. LTD.; *Int'l,* pg. 7459
TANSHIN BUILDING SERVICES CO., LTD.—See Mitsui O.S.K. Lines, Ltd.; *Int'l,* pg. 4989
TANSKY'S SALES INC.; *U.S. Private,* pg. 3932
TANSKY'S SAWMILL TOYOTA INC.; *U.S. Private,* pg. 3932
TANSUN TECHNOLOGY CO., LTD.; *Int'l,* pg. 7460
TANTALEX LITHIUM RESOURCES CORPORATION; *Int'l,* pg. 7460
TANTALEX SAU S.A.R.L.—See Tantalex Lithium Resources Corporation; *Int'l,* pg. 7460
TANTALIZERS PLC; *Int'l,* pg. 7460
TANTAL PJSC; *Int'l,* pg. 7460
TANTALUM CORPORATION LIMITED; *Int'l,* pg. 7460
TANTALUM MINING CORPORATION OF CANADA LIMITED—See Sinomine Resource Group Co., Ltd.; *Int'l,* pg. 6953
TANTALUS MEDIA PTY. LIMITED—See Canada Pension Plan Investment Board; *Int'l,* pg. 1280
TANTALUS MEDIA PTY. LIMITED—See EQT AB; *Int'l,* pg. 2483
TANTALUS MEDIA PTY. LIMITED—See Temasek Holdings (Private) Limited; *Int'l,* pg. 7548
TANTALUS RARE EARTHS AG; *Int'l,* pg. 7460
TANTALUS SYSTEMS CORP.—See Tantalus Systems Holding Inc.; *Int'l,* pg. 7460
TANTALUS SYSTEMS HOLDING INC.; *Int'l,* pg. 7460
TANTALUS SYSTEMS INC.—See Tantalus Systems Holding Inc.; *Int'l,* pg. 7460
TAN & TAN DEVELOPMENTS BERHAD—See IGB Berhad; *Int'l,* pg. 3601
TANTARA SERVICES INC.—See Tantara Transportation Group; *U.S. Private,* pg. 3932
TANTARA TRANSPORTATION GROUP; *U.S. Private,* pg. 3932
TANTECH HOLDINGS LTD.; *Int'l,* pg. 7460
T. ANTHONY LTD.; *U.S. Private,* pg. 3911
TANTIA CONSTRUCTIONS LTD.; *Int'l,* pg. 7460
TAN TIEN PLASTIC PACKAGING JOINT STOCK COMPANY; *Int'l,* pg. 7454
TANTOR MEDIA, INC.—See Shamrock Holdings, Inc.; *U.S. Private,* pg. 3624
TANTRA INFOSOLUTIONS PVT. LTD.—See UCA Group Component Specialty Inc.; *U.S. Private,* pg. 4273
TANTUR TURIZM SEYAHAT LTD.—See TUI AG; *Int'l,* pg. 7968
TANTUS TECHNOLOGIES, INC.; *U.S. Private,* pg. 3932
TANVI FOODS (INDIA) LIMITED; *Int'l,* pg. 7460
TANXIA SYSTEM, INC.; *U.S. Public,* pg. 1981
TANYUAN TECHNOLOGY CO LTD; *Int'l,* pg. 7460
TANZANIA BREWERIES LIMITED—See Anheuser-Busch InBev SA/NV; *Int'l,* pg. 465
TANZANIA MINERALS CORP.; *Int'l,* pg. 7460
TANZANIA PORTLAND CEMENT COMPANY LTD.—See Heidelberg Materials AG; *Int'l,* pg. 3315
TANZANITEONE LIMITED—See Lexington Gold Ltd.; *Int'l,* pg. 4472
TANZANITE ONE MINING LIMITED—See Lexington Gold Ltd.; *Int'l,* pg. 4472
TANZARA INTERNATIONAL INC.; *U.S. Private,* pg. 3932
TANZOIL NL—See Aminex PLC; *Int'l,* pg. 428
TAOBAO—See Alibaba Group Holding Limited; *Int'l,* pg. 326
TAODUE S.R.L.—See Mediaset S.p.A.; *Int'l,* pg. 4773
TAOGLAS LTD.—See The Graham Group, Inc.; *U.S. Private,* pg. 4037
TAO HEUNG HOLDINGS LIMITED; *Int'l,* pg. 7460
TAOKA CHEMICAL CO., LTD.—See Sumitomo Chemical Company, Limited; *Int'l,* pg. 7267
TAO KAE NOI CARE COMPANY LIMITED—See Taokaenoi Food & Marketing Public Company, Limited; *Int'l,* pg. 7460

COMPANY NAME INDEX

TAOKAENOI FOOD & MARKETING PUBLIC COMPANY LIMITED; *Int'l*, pg. 7460
TAO KAE NOI RESTAURANT & FRANCHISE COMPANY LIMITED—See Taokaenoi Food & Marketing Public Company Limited; *Int'l*, pg. 7460
TAOKAENOI USA INC.—See Taokaenoi Food & Marketing Public Company Limited; *Int'l*, pg. 7460
TAOMEE HOLDINGS LIMITED; *Int'l*, pg. 7460
TA OPERATING LLC—See BP plc; *Int'l*, pg. 1127
TAOPING INC.; *Int'l*, pg. 7461
TAOS - FL, LLC—See The Procter & Gamble Company; *U.S. Public*, pg. 2123
TAOS MOUNTAIN LLC—See International Business Machines Corporation; *U.S. Public*, pg. 1151
TAOSOFTWARE CO., LTD.—See sMedio Inc.; *Int'l*, pg. 7007
TAOS SKI & BOOT COMPANY—See Taos Ski Valley, Inc.; *U.S. Private*, pg. 3932
TAOS SKI VALLEY, INC.; *U.S. Private*, pg. 3932
TAOYUAN TAISOL ELECTRONICS CO., LTD.—See TaiSol Electronics Co., Ltd.; *Int'l*, pg. 7418
TAPACO PUBLIC COMPANY LIMITED; *Int'l*, pg. 7461
TAPAD, INC.—See Experian plc; *Int'l*, pg. 2588
TAPARIA TOOLS LIMITED; *Int'l*, pg. 7461
TAPCO CREDIT UNION; *U.S. Private*, pg. 3932
TAPCOENPRO UK LIMITED—See KKR & Co. Inc.; *U.S. Public*, pg. 1242
TAPCO INTERNATIONAL INC.—See Curtiss-Wright Corporation; *U.S. Public*, pg. 612
TAPCO UNDERWRITERS, INC.—See Truist Financial Corporation; *U.S. Public*, pg. 2200
TAPECOAT COMPANY—See KKR & Co. Inc.; *U.S. Public*, pg. 1243
TAPE CRAFT CORPORATION—See YKK Corporation; *Int'l*, pg. 8588
TAPE INDUSTRIAL SALES INC.—See Genstar Capital, LLC; *U.S. Private*, pg. 1678
T.A. PELSUE COMPANY; *U.S. Private*, pg. 3911
TAPEL WILLAMETTE INC. S.A.—See The Willamette Valley Company; *Int'l*, pg. 4136
TAPEMARK, INC.—See dievini Hopp BioTech holding GmbH & Co. KG; *Int'l*, pg. 2117
TAP ENTERPRISES INC.; *U.S. Private*, pg. 3932
TAPE PRODUCTS COMPANY INC.; *U.S. Private*, pg. 3932
TAPER-LOK CORP.—See First Reserve Management, L.P.; *U.S. Private*, pg. 1525
TAPE; *U.S. Private*, pg. 3932
TAPESTRY, INC.; *U.S. Public*, pg. 1981
TAPESTRY MANAGEMENT LLC—See Hilton Worldwide Holdings Inc.; *U.S. Public*, pg. 1041
TAPESTRY PARTNERS—See Publicis Groupe S.A.; *Int'l*, pg. 6112
TAPESTRY PARTNERS—See Publicis Groupe S.A.; *Int'l*, pg. 6112
TAPESTRY SOLUTIONS, INC.—See The Boeing Company; *U.S. Public*, pg. 2040
TAPESTRY SOLUTIONS—See The Boeing Company; *U.S. Public*, pg. 2040
TAPESTRY TECHNOLOGIES, INC.—See The Carlyle Group Inc.; *U.S. Public*, pg. 2049
TAPEX INC.; *Int'l*, pg. 7461
TAPEX MEXICANA S.A. DE C.V.—See Toyoda Gosei Co., Ltd.; *Int'l*, pg. 7862
TAPFIN LLC—See ManpowerGroup Inc.; *U.S. Public*, pg. 1362
TAPFIN SARL—See ManpowerGroup Inc.; *U.S. Public*, pg. 1360
TAPHANDLES INC.; *U.S. Private*, pg. 3932
TAPIA BROS. CO.; *U.S. Private*, pg. 3932
TAPIA SEGURIDAD, S.L.—See Prosegur Compania de Seguridad S.A.; *Int'l*, pg. 5999
TAPINATOR, INC.; *U.S. Public*, pg. 1981
TAPINGO, INC.—See Just Eat Takeaway.com N.V.; *Int'l*, pg. 4030
TAPIO GMBH—See Durr AG; *Int'l*, pg. 2233
TAPI S.P.A.—See Wise Equity SGR S.p.A.; *Int'l*, pg. 8435
TAPJOY, INC.; *U.S. Private*, pg. 3932
TAPLEN COMMERCIAL CONSTRUCTION INC.; *Int'l*, pg. 7461
TAP MANUFACTURING, LLC—See Polaris, Inc.; *U.S. Public*, pg. 1701
TAP-MANUTENCAO E ENGENHARIA BRASIL, S.A.—See TAP-Transportes Aereos Portugueses, SGPS, S.A.; *Int'l*, pg. 7461
TAP OIL LIMITED; *Int'l*, pg. 7461
TAP-ON-IT, LLC—See Gannett Co., Inc.; *U.S. Public*, pg. 906
TAPOUT LLC—See Leonard Green & Partners, L.P.; *U.S. Private*, pg. 2429
TAPPER'S; *U.S. Private*, pg. 3932
TAPPERS STAL & METALLER AB—See SSAB AB; *Int'l*, pg. 7155
TAPPER TRANSPORT LIMITED—See Port of Tauranga Limited; *Int'l*, pg. 5933
TAP PLASTICS INC.; *U.S. Private*, pg. 3932
TAPPLE, INC.—See CyberAgent, Inc.; *Int'l*, pg. 1892

TAP PORTUGAL - US REPRESENTATIVE OFFICE—See TAP-Transportes Aereos Portugueses, SGPS, S.A.; *Int'l*, pg. 7461
TAPPS B.V.—See GlobalData Plc; *Int'l*, pg. 3003
TAPP'S SUPERMARKETS INC.; *U.S. Private*, pg. 3932
TAPRITE-FASSCO MFG., INC.—See Aalberts N.V.; *Int'l*, pg. 36
TA PROPERTIES (CANADA) LTD—See TA Enterprise Berhad; *Int'l*, pg. 7399
TA PROPERTIES SDN BHD—See TA Enterprise Berhad; *Int'l*, pg. 7399
TAPS DIRECT LTD.—See Norcros plc; *Int'l*, pg. 5415
TAPSTONE ENERGY INC.; *U.S. Private*, pg. 3932
TAP-TRANSPORTES AEREOS PORTUGUESES, SGPS, S.A.; *Int'l*, pg. 7461
TAP WORLDWIDE, LLC—See Polaris, Inc.; *U.S. Public*, pg. 1701
TAQA ENERGY B.V.—See Abu Dhabi Water & Electricity Authority; *Int'l*, pg. 73
TAQA MOROCCO SA; *Int'l*, pg. 7461
TAQA NORTH LTD.—See Abu Dhabi Water & Electricity Authority; *Int'l*, pg. 73
T.A.Q.S TOYOTSU AUTOMOTIVE QUALITY SUPPORT CENTER—See Toyota Tsusho Corporation; *Int'l*, pg. 7879
TAQUA LLC—See Ribbon Communications Inc.; *U.S. Public*, pg. 1797
TAQUIPNEU; *Int'l*, pg. 7461
TARAASHNA FINANCIAL SERVICES LIMITED—See Satin Creditcare Network Limited; *Int'l*, pg. 6584
TARA CHAND LOGISTIC SOLUTIONS LTD.; *Int'l*, pg. 7461
TARACHI GOLD CORP; *Int'l*, pg. 7461
TARADEL, LLC; *U.S. Private*, pg. 3933
TARA ENERGY—See Just Energy Group Inc.; *Int'l*, pg. 4031
TARA FOODS—See The Kroger Co.; *U.S. Public*, pg. 2109
TARA GOLF & COUNTRY CLUB; *U.S. Private*, pg. 3933
TARAH ASPHALT PRODUCTS; *U.S. Private*, pg. 3933
TARA HEALTH FOODS LTD.; *Int'l*, pg. 7461
TARAI FOODS LIMITED - RUDRAPUR FACTORY—See TARAI FOODS LIMITED; *Int'l*, pg. 7461
TARAI FOODS LIMITED; *Int'l*, pg. 7461
TARA IMMOBILIENGESELLSCHAFT MBH—See Commerzbank AG; *Int'l*, pg. 1718
TARA IMMOBILIENPROJEKTE GMBH—See Commerzbank AG; *Int'l*, pg. 1718
TARA MATERIALS INC.; *U.S. Private*, pg. 3933
TARAMAX SA—See LVMH Moet Hennessy Louis Vuitton SE; *Int'l*, pg. 4596
TARAMAX USA INC—See LVMH Moet Hennessy Louis Vuitton SE; *Int'l*, pg. 4596
TARAMI CORPORATION—See DyDo Group Holdings, Inc.; *Int'l*, pg. 2238
TARANAKI NEWSPAPERS LIMITED—See Nine Entertainment Co. Holdings Limited; *Int'l*, pg. 5298
TARANIS RESOURCES INC.; *Int'l*, pg. 7461
TARANTO CRUISE PORT S.R.L.—See Global Yatirim Holding A.S.; *Int'l*, pg. 3003
TARANTULA CORPORATION—See Davoil Inc.; *U.S. Private*, pg. 1175
TARANTULA MERCANTILE CORPORATION—See Davoil Inc.; *U.S. Private*, pg. 1175
TARA PICTURE FRAMES—See Tara Materials Inc.; *U.S. Private*, pg. 3933
TARA PLASTICS CORPORATION—See Alpha Industries, Inc.; *U.S. Private*, pg. 197
TARA PROPERTY MANAGEMENT GMBH—See Commerzbank AG; *Int'l*, pg. 1719
TARAPUR TRANSFORMERS LIMITED—See Bilpower Limited; *Int'l*, pg. 1031
TARA SPA THERAPY, INC.—See Branford Castle, Inc.; *U.S. Private*, pg. 639
TARA TILES PVT. LTD.—See The Ugar Sugar Works Limited; *Int'l*, pg. 7697
TARA TOY CORP.—See Just Play Products, LLC; *U.S. Private*, pg. 2245
TARATRANS A.D.; *Int'l*, pg. 7461
TARAY INTERNATIONAL CORPORATION; *U.S. Private*, pg. 3933
TARBELL FINANCIAL CORPORATION; *U.S. Private*, pg. 3933
TARBELL REALTORS—See Tarbell Financial Corporation; *U.S. Private*, pg. 3933
TARBELL REALTORS—See Tarbell Financial Corporation; *U.S. Private*, pg. 3933
TARC LIMITED; *Int'l*, pg. 7462
TARCO INC.; *U.S. Private*, pg. 3933
TARCO OF TEXAS, INC.—See Tarco Inc.; *U.S. Private*, pg. 3933
TARCZYNSKI S.A.; *Int'l*, pg. 7462
TARDIEU TECHNICAL SUPPORT LTD.—See Forges Tardieu Ltd; *Int'l*, pg. 2733
TA REALTY LLC—See Mitsubishi Estate Co., Ltd.; *Int'l*, pg. 4947
TA REGULATOR D.O.O—See IMI plc; *Int'l*, pg. 3626
TA RESOURCES MYANMAR COMPANY LIMITED—See TA Corporation Ltd.; *Int'l*, pg. 7399

TARGA CANADA LIQUIDS INC.—See Targa Resources Corp.; *U.S. Public*, pg. 1981
TARGA DOWNSTREAM LLC—See Targa Resources Corp.; *U.S. Public*, pg. 1982
TARGA ENERGY LP—See Targa Resources Corp.; *U.S. Public*, pg. 1981
TARGA EXPLORATION CORP.; *Int'l*, pg. 7462
TARGA GAS MARKETING LLC—See Targa Resources Corp.; *U.S. Public*, pg. 1982
TARGA INTRASTATE PIPELINE LLC—See Targa Resources Corp.; *U.S. Public*, pg. 1982
TARGA LIQUIDS MARKETING & TRADE LLC—See Targa Resources Corp.; *U.S. Public*, pg. 1982
TARGA LOUISIANA INTRASTATE LLC—See Targa Resources Corp.; *U.S. Public*, pg. 1982
TARGA MIDSTREAM SERVICES LLC - CAMERON—See Targa Resources Corp.; *U.S. Public*, pg. 1982
TARGA MIDSTREAM SERVICES LLC—See Targa Resources Corp.; *U.S. Public*, pg. 1982
TARGA PIPELINE MID-CONTINENT LLC—See Targa Resources Corp.; *U.S. Public*, pg. 1982
TARGA PIPELINE PARTNERS GP LLC—See Targa Resources Corp.; *U.S. Public*, pg. 1982
TARGA PIPELINE PARTNERS LP—See Targa Resources Corp.; *U.S. Public*, pg. 1982
TARGA RESOURCES CORP.; *U.S. Public*, pg. 1981
TARGA RESOURCES FINANCE CORP.—See Targa Resources Corp.; *U.S. Public*, pg. 1981
TARGA RESOURCES GP LLC—See Targa Resources Corp.; *U.S. Public*, pg. 1981
TARGA RESOURCES LLC—See Targa Resources Corp.; *U.S. Public*, pg. 1981
TARGA RESOURCES OPERATING LLC—See Targa Resources Corp.; *U.S. Public*, pg. 1982
TARGA RESOURCES PARTNERS LP—See Targa Resources Corp.; *U.S. Public*, pg. 1981
TARGENS GMBH—See Landesbank Baden-Wurttemberg; *Int'l*, pg. 4406
TARGETABLE MARKETING SERVICES LLC; *U.S. Private*, pg. 3933
TARGET ADVERTISING AGENCY LIMITED; *Int'l*, pg. 7462
TARGET AUSTRALIA PTY. LTD.—See Wesfarmers Limited; *Int'l*, pg. 8382
TARGETBASE CLAYDON HEELEY—See Omnicom Group Inc.; *U.S. Public*, pg. 1599
TARGETBASE - GREENSBORO—See Omnicom Group Inc.; *U.S. Public*, pg. 1599
TARGETBASE—See Omnicom Group Inc.; *U.S. Public*, pg. 1599
TARGET COMMERCIAL INTERIORS, INC. - GREEN BAY—See HNI Corporation; *U.S. Public*, pg. 1043
TARGET CORPORATION INDIA PRIVATE LIMITED—See Target Corporation; *U.S. Public*, pg. 1982
TARGET CORPORATION; *U.S. Public*, pg. 1982
TARGET DATA, INC.—See ARS Advertising, LLC; *U.S. Private*, pg. 337
TARGETED CELL THERAPIES, LLC; *U.S. Private*, pg. 3933
TARGETED JOB FAIRS, INC.—See DHI Group, Inc.; *U.S. Public*, pg. 658
TARGETED MEDICAL PHARMA, INC.; *U.S. Public*, pg. 1982
TARGETED MICROWAVE SOLUTIONS, INC.; *Int'l*, pg. 7462
TARGET ENERGY LIMITED; *Int'l*, pg. 7462
TARGET ENGINEERING CONSTRUCTION COMPANY LLC—See Arabtec Holding PJSC; *Int'l*, pg. 534
TARGET ENTERPRISES LTD.; *U.S. Private*, pg. 3933
TARGET FREIGHT MANAGEMENT; *U.S. Private*, pg. 3933
TARGET GROUP, INC.; *Int'l*, pg. 7462
TARGET HEALTHCARE REIT PLC; *Int'l*, pg. 7462
TARGET:HEALTH—See WPP plc; *Int'l*, pg. 8475
TARGET HOSPITALITY CORP.—See TDR Capital LLP; *Int'l*, pg. 7493
TARGETING GROUP—See The Company of Others; *U.S. Private*, pg. 4013
TARGET INSURANCE COMPANY, LIMITED—See Target Insurance (Holdings) Limited; *Int'l*, pg. 7462
TARGET INSURANCE (HOLDINGS) LIMITED; *Int'l*, pg. 7462
TARGET INSURANCE SERVICES INC.—See Ash Brokerage Corp.; *U.S. Private*, pg. 349
TARGET INTERSTATE SYSTEMS INC.; *U.S. Private*, pg. 3933
TARGET LOGISTICS MANAGEMENT LLC—See TDR Capital LLP; *Int'l*, pg. 7493
TARGET MARKETING COMMUNICATIONS; *Int'l*, pg. 7462
TARGET MARKETING GROUP—See Banyan Technologies Group, LLC; *U.S. Public*, pg. 470
TARGET MARKETING MAINE; *U.S. Private*, pg. 3933
TARGET MEDIA PARTNERS—See Digital Air Strike Inc.; *U.S. Private*, pg. 1230
TARGET OMAHA MARKETING, INC.; *U.S. Private*, pg. 3933
TARGET PEST CONTROL, INC.—See Rollins, Inc.; *U.S. Public*, pg. 1809

TARGET OMAHA MARKETING, INC.

CORPORATE AFFILIATIONS

TARGET PRECAST INDUSTRIES SDN. BHD.—See SK Target Group Limited; *Int'l*, pg. 6975
TARGET PRINT & MAIL; *U.S. Private*, pg. 3933
TARGET PROFESSIONAL PROGRAMS—See Truist Financial Corporation; *U.S. Public*, pg. 2200
TARGET PROGRAMS, LLC—See W.R. Berkley Corporation; *U.S. Public*, pg. 2318
TARGET + RESPONSE INC.; *U.S. Private*, pg. 3933
TARGET ROOFING INC.—See Altas Partners LP; *Int'l*, pg. 386
TARGETS/LEO BURNETT ADVERTISING—See Publicis Groupe S.A.; *Int'l*, pg. 6102
TARGETS/LEO BURNETT—See Publicis Groupe S.A.; *Int'l*, pg. 6102
TARGET STORES, INC.—See Target Corporation; *U.S. Public*, pg. 1982
TARGETTI-MLE S.A.—See 3F Filippi SpA; *Int'l*, pg. 7
TARGETTI POULSEN POLAND SP. Z O.O.—See 3F Filippi SpA; *Int'l*, pg. 7
TARGETTI SANKEY S.P.A.—See 3F Filippi SpA; *Int'l*, pg. 7
TARGETX.COM LLC—See Liaison International, Inc.; *U.S. Private*, pg. 2442
TARGIT GMBH—See TAMBURI INVESTMENT PARTNERS S.p.A; *Int'l*, pg. 7450
TARGOBANK AG & CO. KGAA—See Confederation Nationale du Credit Mutuel; *Int'l*, pg. 1767
TARGO COMMERCIAL FINANCE AG—See Confederation Nationale du Credit Mutuel; *Int'l*, pg. 1767
TARGO LEASING GMBH—See Confederation Nationale du Credit Mutuel; *Int'l*, pg. 1767
TARGRAY TECHNOLOGY INTERNATIONAL INC.; *Int'l*, pg. 7462
TARGUS ASIA PACIFIC LIMITED—See Targus Group International, Inc.; *U.S. Private*, pg. 3934
TARGUS ASIA PACIFIC PTE. LTD.—See Targus Group International, Inc.; *U.S. Private*, pg. 3934
TARGUS AUSTRALIA PTY. LTD.—See Targus Group International, Inc.; *U.S. Private*, pg. 3934
TARGUS CANADA LTD.—See Targus Group International, Inc.; *U.S. Private*, pg. 3934
TARGUS GROUP INTERNATIONAL, INC.; *U.S. Private*, pg. 3933
TARGUS INDIA PVT. LTD.—See Targus Group International, Inc.; *U.S. Private*, pg. 3934
TARGUS JAPAN LTD.—See Targus Group International, Inc.; *U.S. Private*, pg. 3934
TARGUS KOREA CO., LTD.—See Targus Group International, Inc.; *U.S. Private*, pg. 3934
TAR HEEL BASEMENT SYSTEMS LLC—See JES Construction, LLC; *U.S. Private*, pg. 2203
TARHEEL BILLBOARD, INC.; *U.S. Private*, pg. 3934
TAR HEEL CAPITAL CORPORATION NO. 2; *U.S. Private*, pg. 3933
TAR HEEL HOUSING CENTER INC.; *U.S. Private*, pg. 3933
TARHEEL PAPER & SUPPLY CO.; *U.S. Private*, pg. 3934
TARIC S.A.U.—See WiseTech Global Limited; *Int'l*, pg. 8437
TARIC TRANS S.L.—See WiseTech Global Limited; *Int'l*, pg. 8437
TARIFOLD S.A.—See ACCO Brands Corporation; *U.S. Public*, pg. 33
TARIM KREDI HOLDING A.S.; *Int'l*, pg. 7462
TARINGA 24 HOUR MEDICAL CENTRE PTY LIMITED—See Sonic Healthcare Limited; *Int'l*, pg. 7099
TARINI INTERNATIONAL LTD; *Int'l*, pg. 7462
TARINNET COMPANY—See Ster Group; *Int'l*, pg. 7208
TARIQ AL GHANIM—See Sodexo S.A.; *Int'l*, pg. 7047
TARIQ CORPORATION LIMITED; *Int'l*, pg. 7462
TARIQ GLASS INDUSTRIES LTD; *Int'l*, pg. 7462
TARKETT AB—See Tarkett S.A.; *Int'l*, pg. 7463
TARKETT ASIA PACIFIC LTD.—See Tarkett S.A.; *Int'l*, pg. 7463
TARKETT ASIA PACIFIC LTD.—See Tarkett S.A.; *Int'l*, pg. 7463
TARKETT ASIA PACIFIC (SHANGHAI) MANAGEMENT CO. LTD.—See Tarkett S.A.; *Int'l*, pg. 7463
TARKETT ASPEN ZEMIN AS—See Tarkett S.A.; *Int'l*, pg. 7463
TARKETT A/S—See Tarkett S.A.; *Int'l*, pg. 7462
TARKETT AS—See Tarkett S.A.; *Int'l*, pg. 7463
TARKETT AUSTRALIA PTY. LTD.—See Tarkett S.A.; *Int'l*, pg. 7463
TARKETT BENELUX B.V.—See Tarkett S.A.; *Int'l*, pg. 7463
TARKETT BRASIL REVESTIMENTOS LTDA—See Tarkett S.A.; *Int'l*, pg. 7463
TARKETT BV—See Tarkett S.A.; *Int'l*, pg. 7463
TARKETT FLOORING INDIA PRIVATE LTD.—See Tarkett S.A.; *Int'l*, pg. 7463
TARKETT FLOORS S.L.—See Tarkett S.A.; *Int'l*, pg. 7463
TARKETT FRANCE SAS—See Tarkett S.A.; *Int'l*, pg. 7463
TARKETT GES.M.B.H.—See Tarkett S.A.; *Int'l*, pg. 7463
TARKETT HOLDING GMBH—See Tarkett S.A.; *Int'l*, pg. 7463
TARKETT HONG KONG LTD.—See Tarkett S.A.; *Int'l*, pg. 7463
TARKETT INC.—See Tarkett S.A.; *Int'l*, pg. 7463
TARKETT, INC.—See Tarkett S.A.; *Int'l*, pg. 7463

TARKETT LIMITED—See Tarkett S.A.; *Int'l*, pg. 7463
TARKETT MIDDLE EAST—See Tarkett S.A.; *Int'l*, pg. 7463
TARKETT MONOPROSOPI LTD.—See Tarkett S.A.; *Int'l*, pg. 7463
TARKETT NV—See Tarkett S.A.; *Int'l*, pg. 7463
TARKETT OY—See Tarkett S.A.; *Int'l*, pg. 7463
TARKETT POLSKA SP.Z.O.O.—See Tarkett S.A.; *Int'l*, pg. 7463
TARKETT S.A.; *Int'l*, pg. 7462
TARKETT S.P.A.—See Tarkett S.A.; *Int'l*, pg. 7463
TARKETT SPORTS S.A.—See Tarkett S.A.; *Int'l*, pg. 7463
TARKETT SP. Z O.O.—See Tarkett S.A.; *Int'l*, pg. 7463
TARKETT SVERIGE AB—See Tarkett S.A.; *Int'l*, pg. 7463
TARKETT USA INC.—See Tarkett S.A.; *Int'l*, pg. 7463
TARKU RESOURCES LTD.; *Int'l*, pg. 7463
TARKUS INTERIORS PTE. LTD.—See Itoki Corporation; *Int'l*, pg. 3844
TARLTON CORPORATION; *U.S. Private*, pg. 3934
TARMAC AGGREGATES LIMITED—See CRH plc; *Int'l*, pg. 1848
TARMAC AMERICA—See Titan Cement Company S.A.; *Int'l*, pg. 7760
TARMAC BUILDING PRODUCTS LIMITED—See CRH plc; *Int'l*, pg. 1848
TARMAC CEMENT & LIME LIMITED—See CRH plc; *Int'l*, pg. 1848
TARMAC HOLDINGS LIMITED—See CRH plc; *Int'l*, pg. 1848
TARMAC TRADING LIMITED—See CRH plc; *Int'l*, pg. 1848
TARMAC TRADING LIMITED—See CRH plc; *Int'l*, pg. 1848
TARMAT LTD.; *Int'l*, pg. 7463
TARNAISE DES PANNEAUX SAS; *Int'l*, pg. 7464
TARNAVA UG—See S.C. Tarnava S.A.; *Int'l*, pg. 6455
TAROKO CO., LTD.; *Int'l*, pg. 7464
TAROKO (HONG KONG) LTD.—See Taroko Co., Ltd.; *Int'l*, pg. 7464
TAROLIT A.D.; *Int'l*, pg. 7464
TARONG COAL LTD—See ACS, Actividades de Construccion y Servicios, S.A.; *Int'l*, pg. 113
TARONG COAL LTD—See Elliott Management Corporation; *U.S. Private*, pg. 1365
TARO PHARMACEUTICAL INDUSTRIES LTD.—See Sun Pharmaceutical Industries Ltd.; *Int'l*, pg. 7308
TARO PHARMACEUTICALS, INC.—See Sun Pharmaceutical Industries Ltd.; *Int'l*, pg. 7308
TARO PHARMACEUTICALS U.S.A. INC.—See Sun Pharmaceutical Industries Ltd.; *Int'l*, pg. 7308
TARO PLAST S.P.A.; *Int'l*, pg. 7464
TAROS CAPITAL GMBH—See Taros Capital Netherlands B.V.; *Int'l*, pg. 7464
TAROS CAPITAL NETHERLANDS B.V.; *Int'l*, pg. 7464
T-AROUND CO., LTD.—See Iida Group Holdings Co., Ltd.; *Int'l*, pg. 3607
TARPON COVE YACHT AND RACQUET CLUB—See Escalante Golf, Inc.; *U.S. Private*, pg. 1424
TARPON ENERGY SERVICES LLC—See PTW Energy Services Ltd.; *Int'l*, pg. 6093
TARPON ENERGY SERVICES LTD.—See PTW Energy Services Ltd.; *Int'l*, pg. 6093
TARPON INTERNATIONAL ENERGY SERVICES LLC—See PTW Energy Services Ltd.; *Int'l*, pg. 6093
TARPON INVESTIMENTOS S.A.; *Int'l*, pg. 7464
TARPON LANDING MARINA—See East Lake, LLC; *U.S. Private*, pg. 1316
TARP WORLDWIDE EUROPE—See TARP Worldwide; *U.S. Private*, pg. 3934
TARP WORLDWIDE; *U.S. Private*, pg. 3934
TARRAGONA POWER, S.L.—See Iberdrola, S.A.; *Int'l*, pg. 3574
TARRAGUE A.G.—See Grupo Televisa, S.A.B.; *Int'l*, pg. 3136
TARRANT COMPANY LIMITED—See Sunrise Acquisition Corp.; *U.S. Private*, pg. 3869
TARRANT CONCRETE COMPANY, INC.—See Holcim Ltd.; *Int'l*, pg. 3449
TARRANT COUNTY CONCESSIONS, LLC—See Aramark; *U.S. Public*, pg. 178
TARRANT COUNTY INDIGENT CARE CORPORATION; *U.S. Private*, pg. 3934
TARRANT COUNTY REHABILITATION HOSPITAL, INC.—See Encompass Health Corporation; *U.S. Public*, pg. 759
TARRANT COUNTY SURGERY CENTER, L.P.—See HCA Healthcare, Inc.; *U.S. Public*, pg. 1011
TARRANT SERVICE, INC.; *U.S. Private*, pg. 3934
TARR LLC; *U.S. Private*, pg. 3934
TARR WHITMAN GROUP, LLC—See HanmiGlobal Co., LTD.; *Int'l*, pg. 3257
TARSADIA INVESTMENTS, LLC; *U.S. Private*, pg. 3934
TARSIER LTD.; *U.S. Public*, pg. 1982
TARSIN MOBILE, INC.; *U.S. Public*, pg. 1982
TARSONS PRODUCTS LIMITED; *Int'l*, pg. 7464
TARSUS EXPOSITIONS INC—See Charterhouse Capital Partners LLP; *Int'l*, pg. 1456
TARSUS FRANCE—See Charterhouse Capital Partners LLP; *Int'l*, pg. 1456

TARSUS GROUP PLC—See Charterhouse Capital Partners LLP; *Int'l*, pg. 1456
TARSUS MEDICAL INC.—See Integra LifeSciences Holdings Corporation; *U.S. Public*, pg. 1136
TARSUS PHARMACEUTICALS, INC.; *U.S. Public*, pg. 1982
TARTAN MARKETING; *U.S. Private*, pg. 3934
TARTAN TEXTILE SERVICES, INC.—See Dover Corporation; *U.S. Public*, pg. 683
TARTARIC CHEMICALS CORPORATION; *U.S. Private*, pg. 3934
TARTE, INC.—See KOSE Corporation; *Int'l*, pg. 4290
TARTER GATE COMPANY, LLC—See Platinum Equity, LLC; *U.S. Private*, pg. 3208
TARTISAN NICKEL CORP.; *Int'l*, pg. 7464
TARTISAN NICKEL CORP.; *Int'l*, pg. 7464
TARTOUS INTERNATIONAL CONTAINER TERMINAL JSC—See International Container Terminal Services, Inc.; *Int'l*, pg. 3747
T-ARTS KOREA COMPANY, LTD.—See Tomy Company, Ltd.; *Int'l*, pg. 7804
TART S.R.O—See Sealed Air Corporation; *U.S. Public*, pg. 1855
TARTU POSTIMEES—See UP Invest OU; *Int'l*, pg. 8086
TARUGA MINERALS LIMITED; *Int'l*, pg. 7464
TARUI CO., LTD.—See SAN Holdings, Inc.; *Int'l*, pg. 6521
TARUMI GOLF CO., LTD.—See Mitsubishi Heavy Industries, Ltd.; *Int'l*, pg. 4961
TARUS PRODUCTS INC.; *U.S. Private*, pg. 3934
TARUTANI INDUSTRIAL PACKAGING CORPORATION—See Rengo Co., Ltd.; *Int'l*, pg. 6282
TARUTIN KESTER CO., LTD.—See Illinois Tool Works Inc.; *U.S. Public*, pg. 1111
TARYN GOLD MINING COMPANY, CJSC—See OJSC Vysochaishy; *Int'l*, pg. 5543
TASACIONES HIPOTECARIAS SA—See BNP Paribas SA; *Int'l*, pg. 1093
TASAKA TEKKO KENSETSU CO., LTD.—See RAIZNEXT Corporation; *Int'l*, pg. 6192
TASAKI CHINA CO., LTD—See MBK Partners Ltd.; *Int'l*, pg. 4754
TASAKI & CO., LTD.—See MBK Partners Ltd.; *Int'l*, pg. 4753
TASAKI FRANCE S.A.S.—See MBK Partners Ltd.; *Int'l*, pg. 4754
TASAKI JEWELLERY (SHANGHAI) CO., LTD—See MBK Partners Ltd.; *Int'l*, pg. 4754
TASAKI KOREA CO., LTD.—See MBK Partners Ltd.; *Int'l*, pg. 4754
TASAKI TAIWAN CO., LTD.—See MBK Partners Ltd.; *Int'l*, pg. 4754
TAS AMERICAS LTD.—See Tas Tecnologia Avanzata Dei Sistemi Spa; *Int'l*, pg. 7464
TAS ASSEKURANZ SERVICE GMBH—See Munchener Ruckversicherungs AG; *Int'l*, pg. 5091
TASCA LINCOLN MERCURY, INC.; *U.S. Private*, pg. 3934
TASCO BERHAD; *Int'l*, pg. 7464
TASCO INLAND AUSTRALIA PTY LTD; *Int'l*, pg. 7464
TASCO INSURANCE COMPANY LIMITED—See Tasco JSC; *Int'l*, pg. 7465
TASCO JSC; *Int'l*, pg. 7464
TAS COMMERCIAL CONCRETE CONSTRUCTION, L.P.—See Orion Group Holdings, Inc.; *U.S. Public*, pg. 1618
T.A.S. COMMERCIAL CONCRETE SOLUTIONS, LLC—See Orion Group Holdings, Inc.; *U.S. Public*, pg. 1618
TAS CONCRETE CONSTRUCTION, LLC—See Orion Group Holdings, Inc.; *U.S. Public*, pg. 1618
TASCON, INC.; *U.S. Private*, pg. 3934
TASCOR SERVICES LIMITED—See Capita plc; *Int'l*, pg. 1309
TASCOSA OFFICE MACHINES, INC.; *U.S. Private*, pg. 3934
TASC TECHNICAL SERVICES LLC; *U.S. Private*, pg. 3934
TAS EASTERN EUROPE D.O.O—See Nexi SpA; *Int'l*, pg. 5244
TASECO AIR SERVICES JSC; *Int'l*, pg. 7465
TA SECURITIES HOLDING BERHAD—See TA Enterprise Berhad; *Int'l*, pg. 7399
TASEK CONCRETE SDN. BHD.—See Hong Leong Investment Holdings Pte. Ltd.; *Int'l*, pg. 3469
TASEK CORPORATION BERHAD - IPOH FACTORY—See Hong Leong Investment Holdings Pte. Ltd.; *Int'l*, pg. 3469
TASEK CORPORATION BERHAD—See Hong Leong Investment Holdings Pte. Ltd.; *Int'l*, pg. 3469
TASEKO MINES LIMITED; *Int'l*, pg. 7465
TAS ENERGY, INC.—See Comfort Systems USA, Inc.; *U.S. Public*, pg. 544
TAS ENVIRONMENTAL SERVICES, L.P.; *U.S. Private*, pg. 3934
TA SERVICES, INC.—See P&S Transportation, Inc.; *U.S. Private*, pg. 3059
TASETO CO., LTD.—See Kobe Steel, Ltd.; *Int'l*, pg. 4221
TASFIYE HALINDE ARAKLI DOGALGAZ URETIM SANAYI VE TICARET A.S.—See Ayen Enerji AS; *Int'l*, pg. 775
TASFOODS LIMITED; *Int'l*, pg. 7465

TAS FRANCE SASU—See Tas Tecnologia Avanzata Dei Sistemi Spa; *Int'l*, pg. 7464
TAS GROUP LLC; *Int'l*, pg. 7464
TASHCO INDUSTRIES, INC.—See Andersen Corporation; *U.S. Private*, pg. 275
TASHEELAT AUTOMOTIVE COMPANY WLL—See Bahrain Commercial Facilities Company BSC; *Int'l*, pg. 800
TASHEELAT CAR LEASING COMPANY W.L.L.—See Bahrain Commercial Facilities Company BSC; *Int'l*, pg. 800
TASHEEL HOLDING GROUP; *Int'l*, pg. 7465
T.A. SHEETS GENERAL CONTRACTORS, INC.; *U.S. Private*, pg. 3911
TASHI INDIA LIMITED; *Int'l*, pg. 7465
TASHIMA DEVELOPMENT SDN BHD—See EcoFirst Consolidated Bhd; *Int'l*, pg. 2295
TASHIN HOLDING BERHAD; *Int'l*, pg. 7465
TASHIN STEEL SDN. BHD.—See Prestar Resources Berhad; *Int'l*, pg. 5966
TASHKENT PALACE NEW LLC—See National Bank for Foreign Economic Activity of the Republic of Uzbekistan; *Int'l*, pg. 5151
TAS IBERIA SLU—See Tas Tecnologia Avanzata Dei Sistemi Spa; *Int'l*, pg. 7464
THE TASI GROUP; *U.S. Private*, pg. 4126
TAS INTERNATIONAL SA—See Tas Tecnologia Avanzata Dei Sistemi Spa; *Int'l*, pg. 7464
TASJA DEVELOPMENT SDN. BHD.—See Astral Asia Berhad; *Int'l*, pg. 658
TASK CO,. LTD.—See TAKARA & COMPANY LTD.; *Int'l*, pg. 7431
TASK CONSTRUCTION MANAGEMENT INC.—See Fayolle et Fils; *Int'l*, pg. 2626
TASK FORCE FOR GLOBAL HEALTH, INC.; *U.S. Private*, pg. 3934
TASK FORCE TIPS LLC—See John S. Frey Enterprises; *U.S. Private*, pg. 2224
TASK GROUP HOLDINGS LIMITED; *Int'l*, pg. 7465
TASK SOURCE INC.; *U.S. Private*, pg. 3935
TASK TECHNOLOGIES, INC.; *U.S. Private*, pg. 3935
TASKUS, INC.; *U.S. Public*, pg. 1982
TASKUS; *U.S. Private*, pg. 3935
TASKUS—See TaskUS; *U.S. Private*, pg. 3935
TASK WATER B.V.—See Kardan N.V.; *Int'l*, pg. 4079
TASLER INC.; *U.S. Private*, pg. 3935
TAS LOGISTICS CO., LTD. See SBS Holdings Inc.; *Int'l*, pg. 6607
TASLY EUROPE CO., LTD.—See Tasly Pharmaceutical Group Co., Ltd.; *Int'l*, pg. 7465
TASLYHEALTHPAC INTEGRATIVE MEDICINE PTY. LTD.—See Tasly Pharmaceutical Group Co., Ltd.; *Int'l*, pg. 7465
TASLY INTERNATIONAL VIETNAM CO., LTD.—See Tasly Pharmaceutical Group Co., Ltd.; *Int'l*, pg. 7465
TASLY JAPAN CO., LTD.—See Tasly Pharmaceutical Group Co., Ltd.; *Int'l*, pg. 7465
TASLY (MALAYSIA) SDN. BHD.—See Tasly Pharmaceutical Group Co., Ltd.; *Int'l*, pg. 7465
TASLY PHARMACEUTICAL GROUP CO., LTD.; *Int'l*, pg. 7465
TASLY PHARMACEUTICAL INTERNATIONAL CO., LTD.—See Tasly Pharmaceutical Group Co., Ltd.; *Int'l*, pg. 7465
TASLY PHARMACEUTICALS, INC.—See Tasly Pharmaceutical Group Co., Ltd.; *Int'l*, pg. 7465
TASLY SOUTH AFRICA (PTY) LTD.—See Tasly Pharmaceutical Group Co., Ltd.; *Int'l*, pg. 7465
TASLY WORLD (RUSSIA) CO. LTD.—See Tasly Pharmaceutical Group Co., Ltd.; *Int'l*, pg. 7465
TASMAN ASSET MANAGEMENT LIMITED—See Sumitomo Mitsui Trust Holdings, Inc.; *Int'l*, pg. 7296
TASMAN BUILDING PRODUCTS PTY LIMITED—See Fletcher Building Limited; *Int'l*, pg. 2701
TASMAN CAPITAL PARTNERS PTY. LIMITED; *Int'l*, pg. 7465
TASMANIA FARM EQUIPMENT PTY. LTD.—See Nutrien Ltd.; *Int'l*, pg. 5493
TASMANIA FEEDLOT PTY. LTD.—See AEON Co., Ltd.; *Int'l*, pg. 178
TASMANIA MINES LIMITED; *Int'l*, pg. 7465
TASMANIAN ADVANCED MINERALS PTY. LTD.—See Sumitomo Corporation; *Int'l*, pg. 7276
TASMANIAN ALKALOIDS PTY. LTD.—See SK Capital Partners, LP; *U.S. Private*, pg. 3680
TASMANIAN BANKING SERVICES LIMITED—See Bendigo & Adelaide Bank Ltd.; *Int'l*, pg. 971
TASMANIAN ELECTRO METALLURGICAL COMPANY PTY. LTD.—See GFG Alliance Limited; *Int'l*, pg. 2956
TASMANIAN OPTICAL CY PTY LTD—See EssilorLuxottica SA; *Int'l*, pg. 2516
TASMAN INDUSTRIES INC.; *U.S. Private*, pg. 3935
TASMAN INSULATION NEW ZEALAND LIMITED—See Fletcher Building Limited; *Int'l*, pg. 2701
TASMAN LIQUOR COMPANY LIMITED—See Metcash Limited; *Int'l*, pg. 4852
TASMAN RESOURCES LIMITED; *Int'l*, pg. 7465
TASMAN SINKWARE PTY LIMITED—See Fletcher Building Limited; *Int'l*, pg. 2701
TAS OFFSHORE BERHAD; *Int'l*, pg. 7464
T.A. SOLBERG CO., INC.; *U.S. Private*, pg. 3911

TAS PLAN, INC.—See Taisei Corporation; *Int'l*, pg. 7416
TASQ TECHNOLOGY, INC.—See Fiserv, Inc.; *U.S. Public*, pg. 851
TASSAL GROUP LIMITED; *Int'l*, pg. 7465
TASSAL OPERATIONS PTY LTD—See Tassal Group Limited; *Int'l*, pg. 7466
TASS INTERNATIONAL B.V.—See Siemens Aktiengesellschaft; *Int'l*, pg. 6901
TASTE BUDS, INC.; *U.S. Private*, pg. 3935
TAS TECNOLOGIA AVANZATA DEI SISTEMI SPA; *Int'l*, pg. 7464
TASTEE FREEZ LLC—See Galardi Group, Inc.; *U.S. Private*, pg. 1636
TASTEFULLY SIMPLE INC.; *U.S. Private*, pg. 3935
TASTE GOURMET GROUP LIMITED; *Int'l*, pg. 7466
TASTE, INC.—See Vivendi SE; *Int'l*, pg. 8276
TASTE MAKER COMPANY LIMITED—See Nawarat Patanakarn Public Company Limited; *Int'l*, pg. 5177
TASTEPOINT, INC.—See International Flavors & Fragrances Inc.; *U.S. Public*, pg. 1154
TASTEPOINT INC.—See International Flavors & Fragrances Inc.; *U.S. Public*, pg. 1154
TASTER FOOD PTE LTD—See BreadTalk Group Pte Ltd.; *Int'l*, pg. 1143
TASTI D-LITE LLC—See Kahala Corp.; *U.S. Private*, pg. 2254
TAS TOURISTIK ASSEKURANZMAKLER UND SERVICE GMBH—See Munchener Ruckversicherungs AG; *Int'l*, pg. 5090
TAS TOURISTIK ASSEKURANZ SERVICE INTERNATIONAL GMBH—See Munchener Ruckversicherungs AG; *Int'l*, pg. 5091
TASTY BAKING COMPANY—See Flowers Foods, Inc.; *U.S. Public*, pg. 854
TASTY BAKING OXFORD, INC.—See Flowers Foods, Inc.; *U.S. Public*, pg. 854
TASTY BITE EATABLES LTD.—See Mars, Incorporated; *U.S. Private*, pg. 2590
TASTY BLEND FOODS, INC.; *U.S. Private*, pg. 3935
TASTY CATERING, INC.; *U.S. Private*, pg. 3935
TASTY CONCEPTS HOLDING LTD.; *Int'l*, pg. 7466
TASTY DAIRY SPECIALITIES LTD.; *Int'l*, pg. 7466
TASTY FOODS S.A.—See PepsiCo, Inc.; *U.S. Public*, pg. 1672
TASTY FRIES, INC.; *U.S. Public*, pg. 1983
TASTY PLC; *Int'l*, pg. 7466
TASTY PURE FOOD CO. INC.; *U.S. Private*, pg. 3935
TASTY SEAFOOD CO. INC.; *U.S. Private*, pg. 3935
TASTY-TOPPINGS, INC.; *U.S. Private*, pg. 3935
TASUKI CORPORATION; *Int'l*, pg. 7466
T&A SUPPLY CO. INC.; *U.S. Private*, pg. 3909
T.A. SYSTEMS FURNITURE INDUSTRIES SDN. BHD.—See TAFI Industries Berhad; *Int'l*, pg. 7406
TASZ, INC.; *U.S. Private*, pg. 3935
TASZ, INC.—See TASZ, Inc.; *U.S. Private*, pg. 3935
TATA ADVANCED MATERIALS LTD—See Tata Motors Limited; *Int'l*, pg. 7467
TATA AFRICA HOLDINGS (GHANA) LIMITED—See Tata Sons Limited; *Int'l*, pg. 7470
TATA AFRICA HOLDINGS (KENYA) LIMITED—See Tata Sons Limited; *Int'l*, pg. 7470
TATA AFRICA HOLDINGS (SA) PTY. LTD.—See Tata Motors Limited; *Int'l*, pg. 7467
TATA AFRICA HOLDINGS (TANZANIA) LIMITED—See Tata Sons Limited; *Int'l*, pg. 7470
TATA AFRICA (SENEGAL) SARL—See Tata Sons Limited; *Int'l*, pg. 7470
TATA AFRICA SERVICES (NIGERIA) LIMITED—See Tata Sons Limited; *Int'l*, pg. 7470
TATA AMERICA INTERNATIONAL CORPORATION—See Tata Sons Limited; *Int'l*, pg. 7469
TATA ASSET MANAGEMENT COMPANY LTD.—See Tata Sons Limited; *Int'l*, pg. 7468
TATA AUTOCOMP SYSTEMS LIMITED; *Int'l*, pg. 7466
TATA BP SOLAR INDIA LIMITED—See Tata Sons Limited; *Int'l*, pg. 7468
TATA CAPITAL LIMITED—See Tata Sons Limited; *Int'l*, pg. 7468
TATA CERAMICS LIMITED—See Tata Motors Limited; *Int'l*, pg. 7467
TATA CHEMICALS EUROPE—See Tata Sons Limited; *Int'l*, pg. 7469
TATA CHEMICALS LIMITED - MAGADI PLANT—See Tata Sons Limited; *Int'l*, pg. 7469
TATA CHEMICALS LIMITED—See Tata Sons Limited; *Int'l*, pg. 7468
TATA CHEMICALS LIMITED - TATA CHEMICALS NORTH AMERICA PLANT—See Tata Sons Limited; *Int'l*, pg. 7469
TATA CHEMICALS MAGADI LTD—See Tata Motors Limited; *Int'l*, pg. 7467
TATA CHEMICALS NORTH AMERICA INC.—See Tata Motors Limited; *Int'l*, pg. 7467
TATA CHEMICALS (SODA ASH) PARTNERS, INC.—See Tata Sons Limited; *Int'l*, pg. 7469
TATA CHEMICALS SOUTH AFRICA (PROPRIETARY) LIMITED—See Tata Sons Limited; *Int'l*, pg. 7469
TATA COFFEE—See Tata Sons Limited; *Int'l*, pg. 7470

TATA COMMUNICATIONS (AMERICA) INC.—See Tata Sons Limited; *Int'l*, pg. 7469
TATA COMMUNICATIONS DEUTSCHLAND GMBH—See Tata Sons Limited; *Int'l*, pg. 7469
TATA COMMUNICATIONS FRANCE SAS—See Tata Sons Limited; *Int'l*, pg. 7469
TATA COMMUNICATIONS HONG KONG LTD.—See Tata Sons Limited; *Int'l*, pg. 7469
TATA COMMUNICATIONS INTERNATIONAL PTE. LTD.—See Tata Sons Limited; *Int'l*, pg. 7469
TATA COMMUNICATIONS LIMITED—See Tata Sons Limited; *Int'l*, pg. 7469
TATA COMMUNICATIONS LTD—See Tata Sons Limited; *Int'l*, pg. 7469
TATA CONSULTANCY SERVICES ARGENTINA S.A.—See Tata Sons Limited; *Int'l*, pg. 7469
TATA CONSULTANCY SERVICES ASIA PACIFIC PTE LTD.—See Tata Sons Limited; *Int'l*, pg. 7469
TATA CONSULTANCY SERVICES BELGIUM S.A.—See Tata Sons Limited; *Int'l*, pg. 7470
TATA CONSULTANCY SERVICES CHILE S.A.—See Tata Sons Limited; *Int'l*, pg. 7470
TATA CONSULTANCY SERVICES (CHINA) CO., LTD.—See Tata Sons Limited; *Int'l*, pg. 7469
TATA CONSULTANCY SERVICES DE ESPANA S.A.—See Tata Sons Limited; *Int'l*, pg. 7470
TATA CONSULTANCY SERVICES DE MEXICO S.A., DE C.V.—See Tata Sons Limited; *Int'l*, pg. 7470
TATA CONSULTANCY SERVICES DEUTSCHLAND GMBH—See Tata Sons Limited; *Int'l*, pg. 7470
TATA CONSULTANCY SERVICES DO BRASIL LTDA—See Tata Sons Limited; *Int'l*, pg. 7470
TATA CONSULTANCY SERVICES FRANCE SAS—See Tata Sons Limited; *Int'l*, pg. 7470
TATA CONSULTANCY SERVICES JAPAN LTD—See Tata Sons Limited; *Int'l*, pg. 7470
TATA CONSULTANCY SERVICES LTD.—See Tata Sons Limited; *Int'l*, pg. 7469
TATA CONSULTANCY SERVICES LUXEMBOURG S.A.—See Tata Sons Limited; *Int'l*, pg. 7470
TATA CONSULTANCY SERVICES MALAYSIA SDN BHD—See Tata Sons Limited; *Int'l*, pg. 7469
TATA CONSULTANCY SERVICES NETHERLANDS BV—See Tata Sons Limited; *Int'l*, pg. 7470
TATA CONSULTANCY SERVICES (PHILIPPINES) INC.—See Tata Sons Limited; *Int'l*, pg. 7469
TATA CONSULTANCY SERVICES PORTUGAL UNIPESSOAL LIMITADA—See Tata Sons Limited; *Int'l*, pg. 7470
TATA CONSULTANCY SERVICES (SOUTH AFRICA) (PTY) LIMITED—See Tata Sons Limited; *Int'l*, pg. 7469
TATA CONSULTANCY SERVICES SVERIGE AB—See Tata Sons Limited; *Int'l*, pg. 7470
TATA CONSULTANCY SERVICES SWITZERLAND LTD.—See Tata Sons Limited; *Int'l*, pg. 7470
TATA CONSULTANCY SERVICES (THAILAND) LIMITED—See Tata Sons Limited; *Int'l*, pg. 7469
TATA CONSUMER PRODUCTS LIMITED—See Tata Sons Limited; *Int'l*, pg. 7470
TATA DAEWOO COMMERCIAL VEHICLE CO. LTD.—See Tata Motors Limited; *Int'l*, pg. 7467
TATA ELXSI INCORPORATED—See Tata Elxsi Limited; *Int'l*, pg. 7466
TATA ELXSI LIMITED; *Int'l*, pg. 7466
TATA GLOBAL BEVERAGES AUSTRALIA PTY LTD—See Tata Sons Limited; *Int'l*, pg. 7470
TATA GLOBAL BEVERAGES CANADA INC—See Tata Sons Limited; *Int'l*, pg. 7470
TATA GLOBAL BEVERAGES GB LTD—See Tata Sons Limited; *Int'l*, pg. 7470
TATA GLOBAL BEVERAGES POLSKA SP.ZO.O—See Tata Sons Limited; *Int'l*, pg. 7470
TATA GLOBAL BEVERAGES—See Tata Sons Limited; *Int'l*, pg. 7470
TATA GROUP OF COMPANIES LTD.; *Int'l*, pg. 7466
TATA HEALTH INTERNATIONAL HOLDINGS LTD.; *Int'l*, pg. 7466
TATA HISPANO MOTORS CARROCERA S.A.—See Tata Motors Limited; *Int'l*, pg. 7467
TATA HITACHI CONSTRUCTION MACHINERY COMPANY PRIVATE LIMITED—See Hitachi, Ltd.; *Int'l*, pg. 3424
TATA HOLDINGS MOCAMBIQUE LIMITADA—See Tata Sons Limited; *Int'l*, pg. 7471
TATA HOUSING DEVELOPMENT CO. LTD—See Tata Sons Limited; *Int'l*, pg. 7468
TATA INC.—See Tata Sons Limited; *Int'l*, pg. 7470
TATA INDUSTRIAL SERVICES LIMITED—See Tata Sons Limited; *Int'l*, pg. 7470
TATA INTERACTIVE SYSTEMS LIMITED—See Tata Sons Limited; *Int'l*, pg. 7470
TATA INTERNATIONAL AG—See Tata Sons Limited; *Int'l*, pg. 7471
TATA INTERNATIONAL LIMITED—See Tata Sons Limited; *Int'l*, pg. 7470
TATA INTERNATIONAL METALS AMERICAS—See Tata Sons Limited; *Int'l*, pg. 7471
TATA INTERNATIONAL METALS (ASIA) LIMITED—See Tata Sons Limited; *Int'l*, pg. 7471

TATA HEALTH INTERNATIONAL HOLDINGS LTD. CORPORATE AFFILIATIONS

TATA INTERNATIONAL SINGAPORE PTE LIMITED—See Tata Sons Limited; *Int'l*, pg. 7471
TATA INTERNATIONAL TRADING BRAZIL LIMITADA—See Tata Sons Limited; *Int'l*, pg. 7471
TATA INVESTMENT CORPORATION LIMITED—See Tata Sons Limited; *Int'l*, pg. 7471
TATA LIMITED—See Tata Sons Limited; *Int'l*, pg. 7471
TATA MARCOPOLO MOTORS LTD.—See Tata Motors Limited; *Int'l*, pg. 7467
TATA METALIKS LTD; *Int'l*, pg. 7466
TATA MOTORS EUROPEAN TECHNICAL CENTRE PLC—See Tata Motors Limited; *Int'l*, pg. 7467
TATA MOTORS FINANCE LTD.—See Tata Motors Limited; *Int'l*, pg. 7467
TATA MOTORS INSURANCE BROKING AND ADVISORY SERVICES LTD.—See Tata Motors Limited; *Int'l*, pg. 7467
TATA MOTORS LIMITED; *Int'l*, pg. 7466
TATANGO, INC.; *U.S. Private*, pg. 3935
TATA NYK SHIPPING PTE. LTD.—See Nippon Yusen Kabushiki Kaisha; *Int'l*, pg. 5359
TATA PETRODYNE LTD.; *Int'l*, pg. 7468
TATA POWER COMPANY LIMITED; *Int'l*, pg. 7468
TATA POWER DELHI DISTRIBUTION LTD.—See Tata Power Company Limited; *Int'l*, pg. 7468
TATA POWER INTERNATIONAL PTE. LTD.—See Tata Power Company Limited; *Int'l*, pg. 7468
TATA POWER RENEWABLE ENERGY LTD.—See Tata Power Company Limited; *Int'l*, pg. 7468
TATA POWER SOLAR SYSTEMS LIMITED—See Tata Power Company Limited; *Int'l*, pg. 7468
TATA POWER TRADING CO. LTD.—See Tata Power Company Limited; *Int'l*, pg. 7468
TATA PROJECTS LIMITED—See Artson Engineering Ltd; *Int'l*, pg. 586
TATA QUALITY MANAGEMENT SERVICES—See Tata Sons Limited; *Int'l*, pg. 7471
TATA REALTY AND INFRASTRUCTURE LIMITED—See Tata Sons Limited; *Int'l*, pg. 7471
TAT-ARKA LLP—See Caspian Services, Inc.; *U.S. Public*, pg. 446
TATA RYERSON LTD.—See Tata Sons Limited; *Int'l*, pg. 7471
TATA'S NATURAL ALCHEMY, LLC—See Amorepacific Corp.; *Int'l*, pg. 430
TATASOLUTION CENTER S.A—See Tata Sons Limited; *Int'l*, pg. 7469
TATA SONS LIMITED; *Int'l*, pg. 7468
TATA SOUTH-EAST ASIA (CAMBODIA) LIMITED—See Tata Sons Limited; *Int'l*, pg. 7471
TATA SOUTH-EAST ASIA LTD—See Tata Sons Limited; *Int'l*, pg. 7471
TATA STARBUCKS PRIVATE LIMITED—See Starbucks Corporation; *U.S. Public*, pg. 1939
TATA STEEL ASIA (HONG KONG) LTD.—See Tata Sons Limited; *Int'l*, pg. 7472
TATA STEEL BELGIUM PACKAGING STEELS N.V.—See Tata Sons Limited; *Int'l*, pg. 7472
TATA STEEL BELGIUM SERVICES N.V.—See Tata Sons Limited; *Int'l*, pg. 7472
TATA STEEL BSL LTD.—See Tata Sons Limited; *Int'l*, pg. 7471
TATA STEEL DENMARK BYGGSYSTEMER A/S—See Tata Sons Limited; *Int'l*, pg. 7472
TATA STEEL - DISTRIBUTION UK & IRELAND, STEELPARK—See Tata Sons Limited; *Int'l*, pg. 7473
TATA STEEL EUROPE LIMITED—See Tata Sons Limited; *Int'l*, pg. 7471
TATA STEEL FRANCE BATIMENT ET SYSTEMES SAS—See Tata Sons Limited; *Int'l*, pg. 7472
TATA STEEL FRANCE RAIL SA—See Tata Sons Limited; *Int'l*, pg. 7472
TATA STEEL HOLDINGS PTE. LTD.—See Tata Sons Limited; *Int'l*, pg. 7473
TATA STEEL IJMUIDEN B.V.—See Tata Sons Limited; *Int'l*, pg. 7472
TATA STEEL INTERNATIONAL (AMERICAS) INC.—See Tata Sons Limited; *Int'l*, pg. 7473
TATA STEEL INTERNATIONAL (BENELUX) BV—See Tata Sons Limited; *Int'l*, pg. 7472
TATA STEEL INTERNATIONAL (DENMARK) A/S—See Tata Sons Limited; *Int'l*, pg. 7472
TATA STEEL INTERNATIONAL (FINLAND) OY—See Tata Sons Limited; *Int'l*, pg. 7472
TATA STEEL INTERNATIONAL (ITALIA) S.R.L.—See Tata Sons Limited; *Int'l*, pg. 7472
TATA STEEL INTERNATIONAL (JAPAN) LTD.—See Tata Sons Limited; *Int'l*, pg. 7473
TATA STEEL INTERNATIONAL (POLAND) SP Z.O.O.—See Tata Sons Limited; *Int'l*, pg. 7472
TATA STEEL INTERNATIONAL (SWEDEN) AB—See Tata Sons Limited; *Int'l*, pg. 7472
TATA STEEL ISTANBUL METAL SANAYI VE TICARET AS—See Tata Sons Limited; *Int'l*, pg. 7472
TATA STEEL (KZN) (PTY) LTD—See Tata Sons Limited; *Int'l*, pg. 7472
TATA STEEL LIMITED—See Tata Sons Limited; *Int'l*, pg. 7471

TATA STEEL LOGISTICS & SHIPPING B.V.—See Tata Sons Limited; *Int'l*, pg. 7472
TATA STEEL LONG PRODUCTS LTD.; *Int'l*, pg. 7473
TATA STEEL NEDERLAND B.V.—See Tata Sons Limited; *Int'l*, pg. 7472
TATA STEEL NEDERLAND TUBES B.V. - ARNHEM PLANT—See Tata Sons Limited; *Int'l*, pg. 7472
TATA STEEL NEDERLAND TUBES B.V.—See Tata Sons Limited; *Int'l*, pg. 7472
TATA STEEL NETHERLANDS HOLDINGS B.V—See Tata Sons Limited; *Int'l*, pg. 7472
TATA STEEL STRIP PRODUCTS IJMUIDEN—See Tata Sons Limited; *Int'l*, pg. 7472
TATA STEEL (THAILAND) PUBLIC CO., LTD.—See Tata Sons Limited; *Int'l*, pg. 7472
TATA STEEL TUBES EUROPE—See Tata Sons Limited; *Int'l*, pg. 7472
TATA STEEL UK LIMITED—See Tata Sons Limited; *Int'l*, pg. 7472
TATA STEEL USA INC.—See Tata Sons Limited; *Int'l*, pg. 7473
TATA STRATEGIC MANAGEMENT GROUP—See Tata Sons Limited; *Int'l*, pg. 7473
TATA TECHNOLOGIES COVENTRY—See Tata Motors Limited; *Int'l*, pg. 7467
TATA TECHNOLOGIES DE MEXICO, S.A. DE C.V.—See Tata Motors Limited; *Int'l*, pg. 7467
TATA TECHNOLOGIES GMBH—See Tata Motors Limited; *Int'l*, pg. 7467
TATA TECHNOLOGIES, INC.—See Tata Motors Limited; *Int'l*, pg. 7467
TATA TECHNOLOGIES LTD.—See Tata Motors Limited; *Int'l*, pg. 7467
TATA TECHNOLOGIES PTE. LTD.—See Tata Motors Limited; *Int'l*, pg. 7467
TATA TELESERVICES LIMITED—See Tata Sons Limited; *Int'l*, pg. 7473
TATA TELESERVICES (MAHARASHTRA) LTD.—See Tata Sons Limited; *Int'l*, pg. 7468
TATA TEXTILE MILLS LIMITED—See Tata Group of Companies Ltd.; *Int'l*, pg. 7466
TATA UGANDA LIMITED—See Tata Sons Limited; *Int'l*, pg. 7471
TATA WEST ASIA FZE—See Tata Sons Limited; *Int'l*, pg. 7471
TATA ZAMBIA LIMITED—See Tata Sons Limited; *Int'l*, pg. 7471
TATCHA, LLC—See Unilever PLC; *Int'l*, pg. 8048
TAT CHUN PRINTED CIRCUIT BOARD COMPANY LIMITED—See China Silver Technology; *Int'l*, pg. 1552
TATE ACCESS FLOORS, INC.—See Kingspan Group PLC; *Int'l*, pg. 4179
TATE ASP ACCESS FLOORS INC—See Kingspan Group PLC; *Int'l*, pg. 4179
TATEAUSTINHAHN; *U.S. Private*, pg. 3936
TATE AUTOMOTIVE GROUP; *U.S. Private*, pg. 3935
TATE CAPITAL REAL ESTATE SOLUTIONS, LLC; *U.S. Private*, pg. 3935
TATE CHEVROLET—See Tate Automotive Group; *U.S. Private*, pg. 3935
TA TECHNOLOGY (SHANGHAI) CO., LTD.—See Eurofins Scientific S.E.; *Int'l*, pg. 2552
TATE DODGE CHRYSLER JEEP, INC.; *U.S. Private*, pg. 3935
TAT EE METROLOGY SDN BHD—See Chien Wei Precise Technology Co., Ltd.; *Int'l*, pg. 1477
TATE ENGINEERING SYSTEMS INC.; *U.S. Private*, pg. 3936
TATEHO CHEMICAL DALIAN CO., LTD.—See Air Water Inc.; *Int'l*, pg. 241
TATEHO CHEMICAL INDUSTRIES CO., LTD.—See Air Water Inc.; *Int'l*, pg. 241
TATEHO OZARK TECHNICAL CERAMICS, INC.—See Air Water Inc.; *Int'l*, pg. 241
TATE & LYLE ACUCARES PORTUGAL—See Tate & Lyle PLC; *Int'l*, pg. 7474
TATE & LYLE ANZ PTY LIMITED—See Tate & Lyle PLC; *Int'l*, pg. 7474
TATE & LYLE CUSTOM INGREDIENTS LLC—See Tate & Lyle PLC; *Int'l*, pg. 7474
TATE & LYLE DO BRASIL SERVICOS E PARTICIPACOES LTDA.—See Tate & Lyle PLC; *Int'l*, pg. 7474
TATE & LYLE EUROPE—See Tate & Lyle PLC; *Int'l*, pg. 7474
TATE & LYLE HOLDINGS LIMITED—See Tate & Lyle PLC; *Int'l*, pg. 7474
TATE & LYLE INDUSTRIES LIMITED—See Tate & Lyle PLC; *Int'l*, pg. 7474
TATE & LYLE INGREDIENTS AMERICAS, LLC—See Tate & Lyle PLC; *Int'l*, pg. 7474
TATE & LYLE INGREDIENTS FRANCE S.A.S.—See Tate & Lyle PLC; *Int'l*, pg. 7474
TATE & LYLE INSURANCE (GILBRALTAR) LIMITED—See Tate & Lyle PLC; *Int'l*, pg. 7474
TATE & LYLE INTERNATIONAL FINANCE LIMITED—See Tate & Lyle PLC; *Int'l*, pg. 7474
TATE & LYLE INVESTMENTS LIMITED—See Tate & Lyle PLC; *Int'l*, pg. 7474
TATE & LYLE LLC—See Tate & Lyle PLC; *Int'l*, pg. 7474

TATE & LYLE LTD—See Tate & Lyle PLC; *Int'l*, pg. 7474
TATE & LYLE MANAGEMENT & FINANCE LTD—See Tate & Lyle PLC; *Int'l*, pg. 7474
TATE & LYLE NETHERLANDS BV—See Tate & Lyle PLC; *Int'l*, pg. 7474
TATE & LYLE NORTH AMERICAN SUGARS INC.—See Florida Crystals Corporation; *U.S. Private*, pg. 1548
TATE & LYLE PLC; *Int'l*, pg. 7473
TATE & LYLE REINSURANCE LTD.—See Tate & Lyle PLC; *Int'l*, pg. 7474
TATE & LYLE SERVICES BELGIUM NV—See Tate & Lyle PLC; *Int'l*, pg. 7474
TATE & LYLE SINGAPORE PTE LTD—See Tate & Lyle PLC; *Int'l*, pg. 7474
TATE & LYLE—See Tate & Lyle PLC; *Int'l*, pg. 7474
TATE & LYLE SOUTH AFRICA (PTY) LIMITED—See Tate & Lyle PLC; *Int'l*, pg. 7474
TATE & LYLE SUCRALOSE LLC—See Tate & Lyle PLC; *Int'l*, pg. 7474
TATE & LYLE SUGAR QUAY INVESTMENTS LTD—See Tate & Lyle PLC; *Int'l*, pg. 7474
TATE & LYLE TRADING (SHANGHAI) LIMITED—See Tate & Lyle PLC; *Int'l*, pg. 7474
TATERKA—See Publicis Groupe S.A.; *Int'l*, pg. 6112
T/A TERMINALS, INC.—See Trammo, Inc.; *U.S. Private*, pg. 4204
TATE'S AUTO CENTER; *U.S. Private*, pg. 3936
TATE'S BAKE SHOP—See Mondelez International, Inc.; *U.S. Public*, pg. 1464
TATEX INC.—See Taylor Corporation; *U.S. Private*, pg. 3939
TATEYAMAADVANCE-COMPANY—See Sankyo Tateyama Inc.; *Int'l*, pg. 6543
TAT HONG EQUIPMENT (CHINA) PTE. LTD.—See Affirma Capital Limited; *Int'l*, pg. 187
TAT HONG EQUIPMENT SERVICE CO., LTD.—See Affirma Capital Limited; *Int'l*, pg. 187
TAT HONG HEAVY EQUIPMENT (HONG KONG) LIMITED—See Affirma Capital Limited; *Int'l*, pg. 187
TAT HONG HEAVY EQUIPMENT (PTE.) LTD.—See Affirma Capital Limited; *Int'l*, pg. 187
TAT HONG HEAVYLIFT PTE LTD—See Affirma Capital Limited; *Int'l*, pg. 187
TAT HONG HOLDINGS LTD.—See Affirma Capital Limited; *Int'l*, pg. 187
TAT HONG MACHINERY PTE LTD—See Affirma Capital Limited; *Int'l*, pg. 187
TAT HONG PLANT LEASING PTE LTD—See Affirma Capital Limited; *Int'l*, pg. 187
TAT HONG TRAINING SERVICES PTE. LTD.; *Int'l*, pg. 7466
TAT HONG (VIETNAM) CO., LTD.—See Affirma Capital Limited; *Int'l*, pg. 187
TAT HONG (V.N.) PTE LTD—See Affirma Capital Limited; *Int'l*, pg. 187
TATIA GLOBAL VENTURE LTD.; *Int'l*, pg. 7474
TATIARA MEAT COMPANY PTY. LTD.—See JBS S.A.; *Int'l*, pg. 3918
TATIL LIFE ASSURANCE LIMITED—See ANSA McAl Limited; *Int'l*, pg. 477
TATI NICKEL MINING COMPANY (PTY) LTD.—See BCL Limited; *Int'l*, pg. 928
TATINVESTBANK ZAO—See Chimimport AD; *Int'l*, pg. 1479
TATITNEFT LLC—See PJSC Tatneft; *Int'l*, pg. 5885
TAT KONSERVE SAN. AS—See Koç Holding A.S.; *Int'l*, pg. 4224
TATNEFT-AZS CENTER LLC—See PJSC Tatneft; *Int'l*, pg. 5885
TATNEFT- AZS - TASHKENT LLC—See PJSC Tatneft; *Int'l*, pg. 5885
TATNEFT-AZS-UKRAINE LLC—See PJSC Tatneft; *Int'l*, pg. 5885
TATNEFT-AZS -ZAPAD LLC—See PJSC Tatneft; *Int'l*, pg. 5885
TATNEFT-ENERGOSBYT LLC—See PJSC Tatneft; *Int'l*, pg. 5885
TATNEFT-NAO LLC—See PJSC Tatneft; *Int'l*, pg. 5885
TATNEFT-NEFTEKHIMSERVIS LLC—See PJSC Tatneft; *Int'l*, pg. 5885
TATNEFT-SAMARA LLC—See PJSC Tatneft; *Int'l*, pg. 5885
TATNEFT-TRANS LLC—See PJSC Tatneft; *Int'l*, pg. 5885
TATNUCK BOOKSELLERS INC.; *U.S. Private*, pg. 3936
TAT PETROLEUM (HK) PTE LIMITED—See BRENNTAG SE; *Int'l*, pg. 1150
TAT PETROLEUM PTE. LTD.—See BRENNTAG SE; *Int'l*, pg. 1150
TAT PETROLEUM (VIETNAM) CO., LTD.—See BRENNTAG SE; *Int'l*, pg. 1150
TATRA, A.S.; *Int'l*, pg. 7474
TATRA BANKA, A.S.—See Raiffeisen Bank International AG; *Int'l*, pg. 6184
TATRA HOLDINGS S.R.O.; *Int'l*, pg. 7474
TATRA LEASING BROKER, S.R.O.—See Raiffeisen Bank International AG; *Int'l*, pg. 6184
TATRA ROTALAC LIMITED—See Coral Products PLC; *Int'l*, pg. 1795
TATRA SPRING POLSKA Z.O.O.—See Intercos S.p.A.; *Int'l*, pg. 3739

COMPANY NAME INDEX

TATRAVAGONKA A.S.—See Optifin Invest s.r.o.; *Int'l*, pg. 5603
TA TRIUMPH-ADLER AG—See KYOCERA Corporation; *Int'l*, pg. 4358
TATRO CAPITAL LLC—See Warburg Pincus LLC; *U.S. Private*, pg. 4439
TATRO & WHEELER CORP.; *U.S. Private*, pg. 3936
TATRY MOUNTAIN RESORTS A.S.; *Int'l*, pg. 7474
TAT SENG PACKAGING GROUP LTD.—See PSC Corporation Ltd.; *Int'l*, pg. 6015
TAT SENG PACKAGING (SUZHOU) CO., LTD—See PSC Corporation Ltd.; *Int'l*, pg. 6015
TAT SERVICES SASU; *Int'l*, pg. 7466
TATS - TRAVEL AGENCY TECHNOLOGIES & SERVICES GMBH—See Deutsche Lufthansa AG; *Int'l*, pg. 2070
TATSUMI CO., LTD.—See Takamiya Co., Ltd.; *Int'l*, pg. 7430
TATSUMI CORPORATION—See MITSUBA Corporation; *Int'l*, pg. 4929
TATSUMI PLANNING CO., LTD.—See Takamatsu Construction Group Co., Ltd.; *Int'l*, pg. 7430
TATSUNO CHEMICAL INDUSTRIES, INC.—See Shin-Etsu Chemical Co. Ltd.; *Int'l*, pg. 6841
TATSUTA CHEMICAL CO., LTD.—See Kaneka Corporation; *Int'l*, pg. 4067
TATSUTA ELECTRIC WIRE & CABLE CO., LTD. - KYOTO WORKS—See ENEOS Holdings, Inc.; *Int'l*, pg. 2416
TATSUTA ELECTRIC WIRE & CABLE CO., LTD.—See ENEOS Holdings, Inc.; *Int'l*, pg. 2416
TATSUTA ELECTRONIC MATERIALS MALAYSIA SDN. BHD.—See ENEOS Holdings, Inc.; *Int'l*, pg. 2416
TATSUTA ENVIRONMENTAL ANALYSIS CENTER CO., LTD.—See ENEOS Holdings, Inc.; *Int'l*, pg. 2416
TATSUTA KOGYO CO., LTD.—See Nichias Corporation; *Int'l*, pg. 5267
TATTARANG PTY. LTD.; *Int'l*, pg. 7474
TAT TECHNOLOGIES LTD.—See First Israel Mezzanine Investors Ltd.; *Int'l*, pg. 2685
TATTELEKOM; *Int'l*, pg. 7475
TATTERSALL COMPANIES, LLC; *U.S. Private*, pg. 3936
TATT GIAP HARDWARE SDN. BHD.—See Ingenieur Gudang Berhad; *Int'l*, pg. 3701
TAT THE ASTONISHING TRIBE AB; *Int'l*, pg. 7466
TATTON ASSET MANAGEMENT PLC; *Int'l*, pg. 7475
TATTON INVESTMENT MANAGEMENT LIMITED See Tatton Asset Management plc; *Int'l*, pg. 7475
TATTOODO APS—See Thornico A/S; *Int'l*, pg. 7720
TATTOOED CHEF, INC.; *U.S. Public*, pg. 1983
TATTORI SANYO ELECTRIC (HONG KONG) LIMITED—See Panasonic Holdings Corporation; *Int'l*, pg. 5725
TATUM - AUSTIN/SAN ANTONIO—See Randstad N.V.; *Int'l*, pg. 6205
TATUM - CHARLOTTE—See Randstad N.V.; *Int'l*, pg. 6205
TATUM - CHICAGO—See Randstad N.V.; *Int'l*, pg. 6205
TATUM DEVELOPMENT CORP.; *U.S. Private*, pg. 3936
TATUM - HOUSTON—See Randstad N.V.; *Int'l*, pg. 6205
TATUM, LLC—See Randstad N.V.; *Int'l*, pg. 6205
TATUM - LOS ANGELES—See Randstad N.V.; *Int'l*, pg. 6205
TATUM - MID-ATLANTIC—See Randstad N.V.; *Int'l*, pg. 6205
TATUM - MINNEAPOLIS—See Randstad N.V.; *Int'l*, pg. 6205
TATUM - NEW ENGLAND—See Randstad N.V.; *Int'l*, pg. 6205
TATUM - ORANGE COUNTY—See Randstad N.V.; *Int'l*, pg. 6205
TATUM - PHILADELPHIA—See Randstad N.V.; *Int'l*, pg. 6205
TATUM - PORTLAND—See Randstad N.V.; *Int'l*, pg. 6206
TATUM - SEATTLE—See Randstad N.V.; *Int'l*, pg. 6206
TATUM - TAMPA—See Randstad N.V.; *Int'l*, pg. 6206
TATUNG COATINGS (KUNSHAN) CO., LTD.—See Tatung Company; *Int'l*, pg. 7475
TATUNG COMPANY OF AMERICA—See Tatung Company; *Int'l*, pg. 7475
TATUNG COMPANY; *Int'l*, pg. 7475
TATUNG COMPANY - TATUNG HEAVY ELECTRIC BUSINESS UNIT—See Tatung Company; *Int'l*, pg. 7475
TATUNG CONSUMER PRODUCTS (TAIWAN) CO. LTD.—See Tatung Company; *Int'l*, pg. 7475
TATUNG CZECH S.R.O—See Tatung Company; *Int'l*, pg. 7475
TATUNG DIE CASTING CO., LTD.—See Tatung Company; *Int'l*, pg. 7475
TATUNG ELECTRIC CO. OF AMERICA, INC.—See Tatung Company; *Int'l*, pg. 7475
TATUNG ELECTRONICS (SINGAPORE) PTE. LTD.—See Tatung Company; *Int'l*, pg. 7475
TATUNG-FANUC ROBOTICS COMPANY—See FANUC Corporation; *Int'l*, pg. 2615
TATUNG-FANUC ROBOTICS COMPANY—See Tatung Company; *Int'l*, pg. 7476
TATUNG FINE CHEMICALS CO., LTD.; *Int'l*, pg. 7476
TATUNG INFOCOMM CO., LTD.—See Vee Time Corp.; *Int'l*, pg. 8146
TATUNG INFORMATION (SINGAPORE) PTE. LTD.—See Tatung Company; *Int'l*, pg. 7475

TATUNG INFORMATION TECHNOLOGY (JIANGSU) CO., LTD.—See Tatung Company; *Int'l*, pg. 7475
TATUNG MEDICAL HEALTHCARE TECHNOLOGIES CO., LTD.—See Tatung Company; *Int'l*, pg. 7475
TATUNG OF JAPAN, INC.—See Tatung Company; *Int'l*, pg. 7476
TATUNG-OKUMA CO., LTD.—See Okuma Corporation; *Int'l*, pg. 5551
TATUNG (SHANGHAI) CO., LTD.—See Tatung Company; *Int'l*, pg. 7475
TATUNG SYSTEM TECHNOLOGIES, INC.; *Int'l*, pg. 7476
TATUNG TELECOM CORP.—See Tatung Company; *Int'l*, pg. 7475
TATUNG (THAILAND) CO., LTD.—See Tatung Company; *Int'l*, pg. 7475
TATUNG UK LTD.—See Tatung Company; *Int'l*, pg. 7475
TATUNG WIRE AND CABLE (THAILAND) CO., LTD.—See Tatung Company; *Int'l*, pg. 7475
TATUNG WIRE AND CABLE (WUJIANG) CO., LTD.—See Tatung Company; *Int'l*, pg. 7476
TATURA MILK INDUSTRIES PTY LTD—See Bega Cheese Ltd.; *Int'l*, pg. 940
TATVA CHINTAN PHARMA CHEM LIMITED; *Int'l*, pg. 7476
TATWAH SMARTECH CO., LTD.; *Int'l*, pg. 7476
TATWEER DUBAI LLC—See Dubai Holding LLC; *Int'l*, pg. 2218
TAU ATLANTIC, LLC—See Realty Income Corporation; *U.S. Public*, pg. 1768
TAUBATKOMPANIET AS; *Int'l*, pg. 7476
TAUBENPOST, INC.; *U.S. Private*, pg. 3936
TAUBENPOST MAILING, INC.—See Taubenpost, Inc.; *U.S. Private*, pg. 3936
TAUBENSEE STEEL & WIRE COMPANY INC.; *U.S. Private*, pg. 3936
TAUBER OIL COMPANY; *U.S. Private*, pg. 3936
TAUBMAN ASIA LIMITED—See Simon Property Group, Inc.; *U.S. Public*, pg. 1882
TAUBMAN CENTERS, INC.—See Simon Property Group, Inc.; *U.S. Public*, pg. 1881
TAUBMAN CHERRY CREEK SHOPPING CENTER, L.L.C.—See Simon Property Group, Inc.; *U.S. Public*, pg. 1882
THE TAUBMAN COMPANY LLC—See Simon Property Group, Inc.; *U.S. Public*, pg. 1882
TAUBMAN (HONG KONG) LIMITED—See Simon Property Group, Inc.; *U.S. Public*, pg. 1882
TAUBMAN PRESTIGE OUTLETS OF CHESTERFIELD LLC—See Simon Property Group, Inc.; *U.S. Public*, pg. 1882
TAUBMAN REALTY GROUP LIMITED PARTNERSHIP—See Simon Property Group, Inc.; *U.S. Public*, pg. 1882
TAU CAPITAL PLC; *Int'l*, pg. 7476
TAULIA GMBH—See SAP SE; *Int'l*, pg. 6570
TAULIA INC.—See SAP SE; *Int'l*, pg. 6570
TAULIA UK LTD.—See SAP SE; *Int'l*, pg. 6570
TAUNG GOLD INTERNATIONAL LIMITED; *Int'l*, pg. 7476
TAUNG GOLD LIMITED—See Taung Gold International Limited; *Int'l*, pg. 7476
THE TAUNTON GAZETTE—See Gannett Co., Inc.; *U.S. Public*, pg. 903
TAUNTON HEALTHCARE CLINIC, LLC—See Nautic Partners, LLC; *U.S. Private*, pg. 2871
TAUNTON, INC.; *U.S. Private*, pg. 3936
TAUNTON MUNICIPAL LIGHTING PLANT INC.; *U.S. Private*, pg. 3936
THE TAUNTON PRESS, INC.—See Active Interest Media, Inc.; *U.S. Private*, pg. 69
TAUNTON TRUSS, INC.; *U.S. Private*, pg. 3936
TAUNUS-AUTO-VERKAUFS GMBH—See Mercedes-Benz Group AG; *Int'l*, pg. 4829
TAUNUS PRINTING (HESHAN) COMPANY LIMITED—See Q P Group Holdings Limited; *Int'l*, pg. 6129
TAURA NATURAL INGREDIENTS LTD.—See International Flavors & Fragrances Inc.; *U.S. Public*, pg. 1154
TAURA NATURAL INGREDIENTS (NORTH AMERICA) INC.—See International Flavors & Fragrances Inc.; *U.S. Public*, pg. 1154
TAURA NATURAL INGREDIENTS NV—See International Flavors & Fragrances Inc.; *U.S. Public*, pg. 1154
TAUREX DRILL BITS LLC—See Intervale Capital, LLC; *U.S. Private*, pg. 2127
TAURIGA SCIENCES, INC.; *U.S. Public*, pg. 1983
TAURISSON S.A.; *Int'l*, pg. 7476
TAURON CIEPLO S.A.—See Tauron Polska Energia S.A.; *Int'l*, pg. 7476
TAURON CZECH ENERGY S.R.O.—See Tauron Polska Energia S.A.; *Int'l*, pg. 7476
TAURON DYSTRYBUCJA POMIARY SP. Z O.O.—See Tauron Polska Energia S.A.; *Int'l*, pg. 7476
TAURON EKOENERGIA SP. Z O.O.—See Tauron Polska Energia S.A.; *Int'l*, pg. 7476
TAURON POLSKA ENERGIA S.A.; *Int'l*, pg. 7476
TAURON SERWIS GZE SP. Z O.O.—See Tauron Polska Energia S.A.; *Int'l*, pg. 7476
TAURON WYTWARZANIE S.A.—See Tauron Polska Energia S.A.; *Int'l*, pg. 7476
TAURUS ARMAS S.A.; *Int'l*, pg. 7476

TAWOOS LLC

TAURUS ENERGY AB; *Int'l*, pg. 7476
TAURUS GOLD CORP.; *Int'l*, pg. 7476
TAURUS GROUP; *Int'l*, pg. 7476
TAURUS INVESTMENTS LLC—See Goff Capital, Inc.; *U.S. Private*, pg. 1726
TAURUS MINERAL LIMITED—See China Development Bank Corporation; *Int'l*, pg. 1497
TAURUS MINERAL LIMITED—See China Guangdong Nuclear Power Holding Co., Ltd.; *Int'l*, pg. 1506
TAURUS SECURITIES LIMITED—See State Bank of Pakistan; *Int'l*, pg. 7182
TAURUS SERVICE INC.—See Livestock Improvement Corporation Limited; *Int'l*, pg. 4531
TAURUS SP. Z O.O.—See SELENA FM S.A.; *Int'l*, pg. 6700
TAURUS SYSTEMS GMBH—See Saab AB; *Int'l*, pg. 6459
TAURUS TOOL & ENGINEERING INC.—See L Squared Capital Management LP; *U.S. Private*, pg. 2362
TAURUS TRADE FINANCE PTY LTD—See Suncorp Group Limited; *Int'l*, pg. 7311
TAUTACHROME INC.; *U.S. Public*, pg. 1983
TAUTECH AB—See Veidekke ASA; *Int'l*, pg. 8148
TAUW GROUP B.V.; *Int'l*, pg. 7476
TAVAC CO., LTD.—See TOEI ANIMATION CO., LTD.; *Int'l*, pg. 7773
TAV AKADEMI EGITIM VE DANISMANLIK HIZMETLERI A.S.—See TAV Havalimanlari Holding A.S.; *Int'l*, pg. 7477
TAVANT TECHNOLOGIES, INC.; *U.S. Private*, pg. 3936
TAVA ORGANICS, LTD.; *U.S. Private*, pg. 3936
TAVE & ASSOCIATES, LLC—See Arthur J. Gallagher & Co.; *U.S. Public*, pg. 207
TAVENS CONTAINER INCORPORATED; *U.S. Private*, pg. 3936
TAVERNIER LIMITED—See City of London Group PLC; *Int'l*, pg. 1627
TAVERNIER RESOURCES LTD.; *Int'l*, pg. 7477
TAVERN ON THE GREEN LP; *U.S. Private*, pg. 3936
TAV HAVALIMANLARI HOLDING A.S.; *Int'l*, pg. 7477
TAVIGATOR, INC.—See SoftBank Group Corp.; *Int'l*, pg. 7054
TAVISTOCK GROUP, INC.; *U.S. Private*, pg. 3937
TAVISTOCK HOUSE DAY NURSERY LIMITED—See Mid Counties Co-operative; *Int'l*, pg. 4882
TAVISTOCK INVESTMENTS PLC; *Int'l*, pg. 7477
THE TAVISTOCK PARTNERSHIP LIMITED—See Tavistock Investments PLC; *Int'l*, pg. 7477
TAVISTOCK PARTNERS LIMITED—See Saltus Partners LLP; *Int'l*, pg. 6495
TAVISTOCK PARTNERS (UK) LTD.—See Tavistock Investments PLC; *Int'l*, pg. 7477
TAVISTOCK PRIVATE CLIENT LIMITED—See Tavistock Investments PLC; *Int'l*, pg. 7477
TAVISTOCK RESTAURANTS, LLC—See Tavistock Group, Inc.; *U.S. Private*, pg. 3937
TAV JCS; *Int'l*, pg. 7477
T.A. VOLLMER ESPANA S.L.—See Vollmer Werke Maschinenfabrik GmbH; *Int'l*, pg. 8302
TAVVE SOFTWARE COMPANY—See Defiance Ventures LLC; *U.S. Private*, pg. 1191
TAWA ASSOCIATES LTD.—See Financiere Pinault SCA; *Int'l*, pg. 2669
TAWADA LIMITED—See SICPA Holding SA; *Int'l*, pg. 6882
TAWA MANAGEMENT LTD.—See Financiere Pinault SCA; *Int'l*, pg. 2669
TAWAM MOLECULAR IMAGING CENTRE LLC—See Mubadala Investment Company PJSC; *Int'l*, pg. 5076
TAWANA CONTAINER CO., LTD.—See Rengo Co., Ltd.; *Int'l*, pg. 6282
TAWA SUPERMARKET INC.; *U.S. Private*, pg. 3937
TAWEELAH ASIA POWER COMPANY—See Abu Dhabi Water & Electricity Authority; *Int'l*, pg. 73
TAWESCO S.R.O—See Promet Froup a.s.; *Int'l*, pg. 5993
TAWIL ASSOCIATES INC.; *U.S. Private*, pg. 3937
TAW INC.—See Tampa Armature Works Inc.; *U.S. Private*, pg. 3928
TA WIN HOLDINGS BERHAD; *Int'l*, pg. 7400
TA WIN INDUSTRIES (M) SDN. BHD.—See Ta Win Holdings Berhad; *Int'l*, pg. 7400
TAW MACON SERVICE CTR—See Tampa Armature Works Inc.; *U.S. Private*, pg. 3928
TAWOOS AGRICULTURAL SYSTEMS LLC—See Tawoos LLC; *Int'l*, pg. 7477
TAWOOS AGRICULTURE (UAE) LLC—See Tawoos LLC; *Int'l*, pg. 7477
TAWOOS DESCON ENGINEERING LLC—See Tawoos LLC; *Int'l*, pg. 7477
TAWOOS LLC—See Tawoos LLC; *Int'l*, pg. 7477
TAWOOS LLC; *Int'l*, pg. 7477
TAWOOS OILFIELD SUPPLY COMPANY LLC—See Tawoos LLC; *Int'l*, pg. 7477
TAWOOS POWER & TELECOMMUNICATIONS LLC—See Tawoos LLC; *Int'l*, pg. 7477
TAWOW RESOURCES INC.—See Vertex Resource Group Ltd.; *Int'l*, pg. 8174
TAW—See Tampa Armature Works Inc.; *U.S. Private*, pg. 3928
TAXACT, INC.—See Genstar Capital, LLC; *U.S. Private*, pg. 1676

2691

TAX AIRFREIGHT INC.

TAX AIRFREIGHT INC.; *U.S. Private*, pg. 3937
TAXAMETER CENTRALE B.V.—See Waysis BV; *Int'l*, pg. 8361
TAX ANALYSTS; *U.S. Private*, pg. 3937
TAXAN MEXICO S.A. DE C.V.—See Kaga Electronics Co., Ltd.; *Int'l*, pg. 4049
TAXBREAK LLC; *U.S. Private*, pg. 3937
TAXBRIEFS LIMITED—See Centaur Media plc; *Int'l*, pg. 1402
TAX CARE S.A.—See Getin Holding S.A.; *Int'l*, pg. 2947
TAX COMPLIANCE, INC.—See Corporation Service Company; *U.S. Private*, pg. 1058
TAXGROUP PARTNERS INC.—See Cherry Bekaert LLP; *U.S. Private*, pg. 874
TAX GUARD, INC.—See Bertram Capital Management, LLC; *U.S. Private*, pg. 540
TAXI 2—See WPP plc; *Int'l*, pg. 8493
TAXI COMBINED SERVICES PTY LTD—See ComfortDelGro Corporation Limited; *Int'l*, pg. 1712
TAXI NEW YORK—See WPP plc; *Int'l*, pg. 8492
TAXIPOST SA/NV—See bpost NV/SA; *Int'l*, pg. 1133
TAXI RADIO BRUXELLOIS S.A.—See s.a. D'leteren n.v.; *Int'l*, pg. 6448
TAXIRAMA SAS—See G7 Entreprises; *Int'l*, pg. 2867
TAXI—See WPP plc; *Int'l*, pg. 8492
TAXI—See WPP plc; *Int'l*, pg. 8492
TAXI VANCOUVER—See WPP plc; *Int'l*, pg. 8492
TAX MANAGEMENT, INC.—See Bloomberg L.P.; *U.S. Private*, pg. 584
TAXOPS LLC; *U.S. Private*, pg. 3937
TAX PLANNING SEMINARS INC.—See Allianz SE; *Int'l*, pg. 347
TAX SYSTEMS PLC—See Bowmark Capital LLP; *Int'l*, pg. 1124
TAX TRILOGY, LLC; *U.S. Private*, pg. 3937
TAXUS PHARMACEUTICALS HOLDINGS, INC.; *U.S. Private*, pg. 3937
TAXWORKS, INC.—See Thomson Reuters Corporation; *Int'l*, pg. 7715
TAYA CO. LTD.; *Int'l*, pg. 7478
TA YA ELECTRIC WIRE & CABLE CO., LTD.; *Int'l*, pg. 7400
TAYA INVESTMENT COMPANY LTD.; *Int'l*, pg. 7478
TAYANGAN UNGGUL SDN. BHD.—See Astro All Asia Networks plc; *Int'l*, pg. 662
TA YANG GROUP HOLDINGS LIMITED - DONGGUAN FACTORY—See Ta Yang Group Holdings Limited; *Int'l*, pg. 7400
TA YANG GROUP HOLDINGS LIMITED - HUZHOU FACTORY—See Ta Yang Group Holdings Limited; *Int'l*, pg. 7400
TA YANG GROUP HOLDINGS LIMITED; *Int'l*, pg. 7400
TA YA VENTURE CAPITAL CO., LTD.—See Ta Ya Electric Wire & Cable Co., Ltd.; *Int'l*, pg. 7400
TA YA (VIETNAM) ELECTRIC WIRE & CABLE CO., LTD.—See Ta Ya Electric Wire & Cable Co., Ltd.; *Int'l*, pg. 7400
TAYA (VIETNAM) ELECTRIC WIRE & CABLE JOINT STOCK COMPANY; *Int'l*, pg. 7478
TAYBURN LTD.; *Int'l*, pg. 7478
TAYCA CORPORATION; *Int'l*, pg. 7478
TAYCOR LLC; *U.S. Private*, pg. 3937
TAYGANPOINT CONSULTING GROUP, INC.—See Grant Thornton LLP - USA; *U.S. Private*, pg. 1757
TA YIH INDUSTRIAL CO., LTD.—See Koito Manufacturing Co., Ltd.; *Int'l*, pg. 4231
TAYIH KENMOS AUTO PARTS CO.; *Int'l*, pg. 7478
TA YI PLASTIC CO., LTD—See Ta Ya Electric Wire & Cable Co., Ltd.; *Int'l*, pg. 7400
TAYLEK DRUGS COMPANY LIMITED—See Sandoz Group AG; *Int'l*, pg. 6527
TAYLOR AIR CENTER—See Atlas Copco AB; *Int'l*, pg. 684
TAYLOR & ASSOCIATES BENEFITS—See Aquiline Capital Partners LLC; *U.S. Private*, pg. 805
TAYLOR ASSOCIATES/COMMUNICATIONS, INC.—See Clearlake Capital Group, L.P.; *U.S. Private*, pg. 934
TAYLOR & ASSOCIATES LAW GROUP, PLLC; *U.S. Private*, pg. 3937
TAYLOR ASSOCIATES; *U.S. Private*, pg. 3937
TAYLOR BROS. CONSTRUCTION CO., INC.—See Harmon Group; *U.S. Private*, pg. 1866
TAYLOR BROTHERS LUMBER COMPANY—See The Lester Group Inc.; *U.S. Private*, pg. 4069
TAYLOR BUILDING CORPORATION OF AMERICA; *U.S. Private*, pg. 3937
TAYLOR & CARLS, P.A.—See Becker & Poliakoff, P.A.; *U.S. Private*, pg. 510
TAYLOR CHEVROLET COMPANY, INC.; *U.S. Private*, pg. 3937
TAYLOR COMMERCIAL, INC.; *U.S. Private*, pg. 3937
TAYLOR COMMUNICATIONS, INC.—See Taylor Corporation; *U.S. Private*, pg. 3939
TAYLOR COMPANY—See The Middleby Corporation; *U.S. Public*, pg. 2115
TAYLOR CONSULTING INC.; *U.S. Private*, pg. 1983
TAYLOR CORPORATION; *U.S. Private*, pg. 3937
TAYLOR COTTON & RIDLEY INC.; *U.S. Private*, pg. 3939
TAYLOR CUTLERY CO. LLC; *U.S. Private*, pg. 3939
TAYLOR DEVICES, INC.; *U.S. Public*, pg. 1983

TAYLOR DIALYSIS, LLC—See DaVita Inc.; *U.S. Public*, pg. 643
TAYLOR-DUNN MANUFACTURING COMPANY—See Polaris, Inc.; *U.S. Public*, pg. 1701
TAYLOR DYNAMOMETER, INC.; *U.S. Private*, pg. 3939
TAYLORED SERVICES INC.—See Nippon Yusen Kabushiki Kaisha; *Int'l*, pg. 5360
TAYLOR ELECTRIC CO-OPERATIVE; *U.S. Private*, pg. 3939
TAYLOR ELECTRIC COOPERATIVE—See Touchstone Energy Cooperative, Inc.; *U.S. Private*, pg. 4192
TAYLOR ENERGY COMPANY; *U.S. Private*, pg. 3939
TAYLOR ENERGY, LLC; *U.S. Private*, pg. 3939
TAYLOR ENGINEERING & PLASTICS LIMITED; *Int'l*, pg. 7478
TAYLOR FARMS CALIFORNIA INC.—See Taylor Fresh Foods Inc.; *U.S. Private*, pg. 3940
TAYLOR FARMS FLORIDA INC.—See Taylor Fresh Foods Inc.; *U.S. Private*, pg. 3940
TAYLOR FARMS; *U.S. Private*, pg. 3939
TAYLOR FORD SALES LTD; *Int'l*, pg. 7478
TAYLOR FORGE ENGINEERED SYSTEMS INC.; *U.S. Private*, pg. 3939
TAYLOR-FOSTER HARDWARE, INC.—See Tyndale Advisors, LLC; *U.S. Private*, pg. 4268
TAYLOR & FRANCIS GROUP LIMITED—See Informa plc; *Int'l*, pg. 3693
TAYLOR & FRANCIS GROUP LLC—See Informa plc; *Int'l*, pg. 3693
TAYLOR & FRANCIS LIMITED—See Informa plc; *Int'l*, pg. 3693
TAYLOR & FRANCIS (S) PTE. LTD.—See Informa plc; *Int'l*, pg. 3693
TAYLOR FREEZER OF MICHIGAN; *U.S. Private*, pg. 3940
TAYLOR FREEZERS SALES CO., INC.; *U.S. Private*, pg. 3940
TAYLOR FRESH FOODS INC.; *U.S. Private*, pg. 3940
TAYLOR GARBAGE SERVICE, INC.—See Casella Waste Systems, Inc.; *U.S. Public*, pg. 446
TAYLOR GLOBAL INC.; *U.S. Private*, pg. 3940
TAYLOR GLOBAL INC.—See Taylor Global Inc.; *U.S. Private*, pg. 3940
TAYLOR HEATING, INC.—See Brookfield Corporation; *Int'l*, pg. 1188
TAYLOR & HILL, INC.; *U.S. Private*, pg. 3937
TAYLOR HOBSON HOLDINGS LTD.—See AMETEK, Inc.; *U.S. Public*, pg. 118
TAYLOR HOBSON LTD.—See AMETEK, Inc.; *U.S. Public*, pg. 122
TAYLOR HOME HEALTH INC.—See Rotech Healthcare, Inc.; *U.S. Private*, pg. 3486
TAYLOR HOPKINSON CORPORATION—See Brunel International N.V.; *Int'l*, pg. 1200
TAYLOR HOPKINSON LIMITED—See Brunel International N.V.; *Int'l*, pg. 1200
TAYLOR HOPKINSON PTE. LTD.—See Brunel International N.V.; *Int'l*, pg. 1200
TAYLOR INDUSTRIES, LLC—See Basic Energy Services Inc.; *U.S. Public*, pg. 279
TAYLOR (INSURANCE BROKERS) LIMITED—See Taylor Wimpey plc; *Int'l*, pg. 7478
TAYLOR INTERNATIONAL CO. INC.; *U.S. Private*, pg. 3940
TAYLOR-LISTUG INC.; *U.S. Private*, pg. 3941
TAYLOR MADE CUSTOM PRODUCTS—See LCI Industries; *U.S. Public*, pg. 1295
TAYLOR MADE GLASS OHIO, INC.—See LCI Industries; *U.S. Public*, pg. 1295
TAYLOR MADE GLASS & SYSTEMS LIMITED—See LCI Industries; *U.S. Public*, pg. 1295
TAYLOR MADE GOLF COMPANY, INC.; *U.S. Private*, pg. 3940
TAYLOR MADE GOLF LIMITED—See Taylor Made Golf Company, Inc.; *U.S. Private*, pg. 3940
TAYLOR MADE GROUP, LLC—See LCI Industries; *U.S. Public*, pg. 1295
TAYLOR MADE KOREA LTD.—See adidas AG; *Int'l*, pg. 146
TAYLOR MADE LABELS—See Ares Management Corporation; *U.S. Public*, pg. 191
TAYLOR MADE PRODUCTS—See LCI Industries; *U.S. Public*, pg. 1295
TAYLORMADE RENEWABLES LTD.; *Int'l*, pg. 7478
TAYLOR MADE SYSTEMS - INDIANA FACILITY—See LCI Industries; *U.S. Public*, pg. 1295
TAYLOR MADE SYSTEMS—See LCI Industries; *U.S. Public*, pg. 1295
TAYLOR-MADE TRANSPORTATION INC.; *U.S. Private*, pg. 3941
TAYLOR MARINE CENTER, INC.—See OneWater Marine Inc.; *U.S. Public*, pg. 1604
TAYLOR MARITIME INVESTMENTS LIMITED; *Int'l*, pg. 7478
TAYLOR & MARTIN ENTERPRISES INC.; *U.S. Private*, pg. 3937
TAYLOR & MARTIN INC.—See Taylor & Martin Enterprises Inc.; *U.S. Private*, pg. 3937
TAYLOR & MATHIS, INC.; *U.S. Private*, pg. 3937

CORPORATE AFFILIATIONS

TAYLOR MORRISON HOME CORPORATION—See Brookfield Corporation; *Int'l*, pg. 1183
TAYLOR MORRISON, INC.—See Brookfield Corporation; *Int'l*, pg. 1183
TAYLOR MORRISON OF CALIFORNIA, LLC—See Brookfield Corporation; *Int'l*, pg. 1183
TAYLOR MORRISON OF FLORIDA, INC.—See Brookfield Corporation; *Int'l*, pg. 1183
TAYLOR MORRISON OF TEXAS, INC. - HOUSTON DIVISION—See Brookfield Corporation; *Int'l*, pg. 1183
TAYLOR MORRISON OF TEXAS, INC.—See Brookfield Corporation; *Int'l*, pg. 1183
TAYLOR & MURPHY CONSTRUCTION CO.; *U.S. Private*, pg. 3937
TAYLOR NELSON SOFRES AUSTRALIA PTY. LTD.—See Bain Capital, LP; *U.S. Private*, pg. 448
TAYLOR NELSON SOFRES GROUP HOLDINGS LTD—See Bain Capital, LP; *U.S. Private*, pg. 448
TAYLOR NELSON SOFRES S.A.—See Bain Capital, LP; *U.S. Private*, pg. 448
TAYLOR NELSON SOFRES—See Bain Capital, LP; *U.S. Private*, pg. 448
TAYLOR OIL CO., INC.; *U.S. Private*, pg. 3940
TAYLOR OIL COMPANY INCORPORATED; *U.S. Private*, pg. 3940
TAYLOR OIL CO. OF WASHINGTON NC; *U.S. Private*, pg. 3940
TAYLOR OIL INC.; *U.S. Private*, pg. 3940
TAYLOR PALLETS & RECYCLING , INC—See Audax Group, Limited Partnership; *U.S. Private*, pg. 386
TAYLOR-PANSING INC.; *U.S. Private*, pg. 3941
TAYLOR POWER SYSTEMS, INC.; *U.S. Private*, pg. 3940
TAYLOR PRECISION PRODUCTS, INC. - LAS CRUCES—See Lifetime Brands, Inc.; *U.S. Public*, pg. 1313
TAYLOR PRECISION PRODUCTS, INC.—See Lifetime Brands, Inc.; *U.S. Public*, pg. 1313
TAYLOR PRODUCTS; *U.S. Private*, pg. 3940
TAYLOR PUBLISHING CO.—See Fenway Partners, LLC; *U.S. Private*, pg. 1495
TAYLOR RAFFERTY ASSOCIATES, INC.; *U.S. Private*, pg. 3940
TAYLOR RENTAL—See ACON Investments, LLC; *U.S. Private*, pg. 63
TAYLOR'S AUTO MAX; *U.S. Private*, pg. 3941
TAYLOR SHELLFISH FARMS—See Taylor United Inc.; *U.S. Private*, pg. 3940
TAYLOR'S INDUSTRIAL SERVICES, L.L.C.; *U.S. Private*, pg. 3941
TAYLOR SMITH GROUP; *Int'l*, pg. 7478
TAYLOR'S OF NEWCASTLE—See The Bidvest Group Limited; *Int'l*, pg. 7622
TAYLOR STEEL INC.; *Int'l*, pg. 7478
TAYLOR STEEL INC.—See Taylor Steel Inc.; *Int'l*, pg. 7478
TAYLOR STUDIOS, INC.; *U.S. Private*, pg. 3940
TAYLOR UNITED INC.; *U.S. Private*, pg. 3940
TAYLOR-WHARTON AMERICA INC.—See Air Water Inc.; *Int'l*, pg. 241
TAYLOR-WHARTON AUSTRALIA PTY. LTD.—See Wind Point Advisors LLC; *U.S. Private*, pg. 4536
TAYLOR-WHARTON (BEIJING) CRYOGENIC EQUIPMENT CO.,LTD.—See Wind Point Advisors LLC; *U.S. Private*, pg. 4536
TAYLOR-WHARTON CRYOGENICS, LLC—See Wind Point Advisors LLC; *U.S. Private*, pg. 4536
TAYLOR-WHARTON GERMANY GMBH—See Wind Point Advisors LLC; *U.S. Private*, pg. 4536
TAYLOR-WHARTON INTERNATIONAL LLC—See Wind Point Advisors LLC; *U.S. Private*, pg. 4536
TAYLOR-WHARTON SLOVAKIA S.R.O.—See Wind Point Advisors LLC; *U.S. Private*, pg. 4536
TAYLOR WHITE SPECIALIZED STAFFING SERVICES, INC.; *U.S. Private*, pg. 3940
TAYLOR WIMPEY DE ESPANA S.A.U—See Taylor Wimpey plc; *Int'l*, pg. 7478
TAYLOR WIMPEY LOGISTICS—See Taylor Wimpey plc; *Int'l*, pg. 7478
TAYLOR WIMPEY PLC; *Int'l*, pg. 7478
TAYLOR WIMPEY (SOLIHULL) LIMITED—See Taylor Wimpey plc; *Int'l*, pg. 7478
TAYLOR WIMPEY UK LIMITED—See Taylor Wimpey plc; *Int'l*, pg. 7478
TAYLOR WINCH (COFFEE) LIMITED—See ED&F Man Holdings Limited; *Int'l*, pg. 2303
TAYLOR WINCH (TANZANIA) LIMITED—See ED&F Man Holdings Limited; *Int'l*, pg. 2303
THE TAYLOR-WINFIELD CORPORATION—See Olympus Partners; *U.S. Private*, pg. 3014
TAYLOR WOODROW HOMES - SOUTHWEST FLORIDA DIVISION, LLC—See Brookfield Corporation; *Int'l*, pg. 1183
TAYMAN INDUSTRIES, INC.—See Republic Services, Inc.; *U.S. Public*, pg. 1787
TAYMARK, INC.—See Taylor Corporation; *U.S. Private*, pg. 3939
TAY NGUYEN ELECTRICITY INVESTMENT JOINT STOCK COMPANY; *Int'l*, pg. 7477

COMPANY NAME INDEX

TAY NINH CABLE CAR TOUR JOINT-STOCK COMPANY; *Int'l*, pg. 7477
TAY NINH RUBBER JOINT STOCK COMPANY; *Int'l*, pg. 7477
TAY NINH TOURIST-TRADING JOINT STOCK COMPANY; *Int'l*, pg. 7477
TAY NINH WATER SUPPLY SEWERAGE JOINT STOCK COMPANY—See DongNai Plastic JSC; *Int'l*, pg. 2169
TAYO ROLLS LTD.—See Sojitz Corporation; *Int'l*, pg. 7066
TAYO ROLLS LTD.—See Tata Sons Limited; *Int'l*, pg. 7473
TAY PAPER RECYCLING PTE. LTD; *Int'l*, pg. 7477
TAYSEB - TOROS ADANA YUMURTALIK FREE TRADE ZONE FOUNDER AND OPERATING CO., INC.—See Tekfen Holding A.S.; *Int'l*, pg. 7527
TAYSE INTERNATIONAL TRADING, INC.; *U.S. Private*, pg. 3941
TAYSHA GENE THERAPIES, INC.; *U.S. Public*, pg. 1983
TAYSIDE PUBLIC TRANSPORT CO LIMITED—See Mobico Group PLC; *Int'l*, pg. 5009
TAY TWO CO., LTD.; *Int'l*, pg. 7477
TA-YUAN COGEN CO., LTD.—See Taiwan Cogeneration Corporation; *Int'l*, pg. 7419
TA-YUAN COGENERATION CO., LTD.; *Int'l*, pg. 7400
TAZAKI FOODS LIMITED—See Takara Holdings, Inc.; *Int'l*, pg. 7433
TAZE KURU GIDA SANAYI VE TICARET A.S.; *Int'l*, pg. 7478
TAZEWELL & PEORIA RAILROAD, INC.—See Brookfield Infrastructure Partners L.P.; *Int'l*, pg. 1192
TAZEWELL & PEORIA RAILROAD, INC.—See GIC Pte. Ltd.; *Int'l*, pg. 2967
TAZMO CO., LTD. - PLANT NO.2—See Tazmo Co., Ltd.; *Int'l*, pg. 7479
TAZMO CO., LTD. - PLANT NO.3—See Tazmo Co., Ltd.; *Int'l*, pg. 7479
TAZMO CO., LTD. - PLANT NO.5—See Tazmo Co., Ltd.; *Int'l*, pg. 7479
TAZMO CO., LTD.; *Int'l*, pg. 7479
TAZMO CO., LTD. - TAMASHIMA PLANT—See Tazmo Co., Ltd.; *Int'l*, pg. 7479
TAZMO INC.—See Tazmo Co., Ltd.; *Int'l*, pg. 7479
TAZMO VIETNAM CO., LTD.—See Tazmo Co., Ltd.; *Int'l*, pg. 7479
TAZO TEA COMPANY—See Unilever PLC; *Int'l*, pg. 8048
TBA COMMUNICATIONS—See The Brand Agency Pty. Ltd.; *Int'l*, pg. 7627
TBA CREATIVE NETWORK GROUP—See Pico Far East Holdings Limited; *Int'l*, pg. 5861
TBA DONCASTER LIMITED—See Konecranes Plc; *Int'l*, pg. 4253
TBA GLOBAL, LLC - CHICAGO—See TBA Global, LLC; *U.S. Private*, pg. 3941
TBA GLOBAL, LLC - NASHVILLE—See TBA Global, LLC; *U.S. Private*, pg. 3941
TBA GLOBAL, LLC; *U.S. Private*, pg. 3941
TBA INSURANCE INC.; *U.S. Private*, pg. 3941
TBAI POLAND SP. Z O.O.—See Toyota Boshoku Corporation; *Int'l*, pg. 7864
T. BAIRD McILVAIN CO.; *U.S. Private*, pg. 3911
TBA LEICESTER LIMITED—See Konecranes Plc; *Int'l*, pg. 4251
T BANCSHARES, INC.—See Tectonic Financial, Inc.; *U.S. Public*, pg. 1989
T BANK, N.A.—See Tectonic Financial, Inc.; *U.S. Public*, pg. 1989
T BANK S.A.—See Eurobank Ergasias Services and Holdings S.A.; *Int'l*, pg. 2533
TBA ROMANIA S.R.L.—See Terex Corporation; *U.S. Public*, pg. 2019
TBA STUDIO ARCHITECTURE, A PROFESSIONAL CORPORATION; *U.S. Private*, pg. 3941
TBB (CAMBODIA) MICROFINANCE INSTITUTION PLC—See Taiwan Business Bank Ltd.; *Int'l*, pg. 7419
TBB GLOBAL LOGISTICS INC.; *U.S. Private*, pg. 3941
TBB GLOBAL LOGISTICS INC., TRUCKLOAD DIVISION—See TBB Global Logistics Inc.; *U.S. Private*, pg. 3941
TBC BANK GROUP PLC; *Int'l*, pg. 7479
TBC CAPITAL LLC—See TBC Bank Group PLC; *Int'l*, pg. 7479
TBC CORPORATION—See Sumitomo Corporation; *Int'l*, pg. 7274
TBC DIRECT, INC.—See TBC Inc.; *U.S. Private*, pg. 3941
TBC FINANCIAL SERVICES, INC.—See Flowers Foods, Inc.; *U.S. Public*, pg. 854
TBC INC.; *U.S. Private*, pg. 3941
TBC INC.—See TBC Inc.; *U.S. Private*, pg. 3941
TBC INTERNATIONAL LLC—See BoxUnion Holdings LLC; *U.S. Private*, pg. 627
TBC KREDIT LLC—See TBC Bank Group PLC; *Int'l*, pg. 7479
TBC LEASING JSC—See TBC Bank Group PLC; *Int'l*, pg. 7479
TBC NET INC.; *U.S. Private*, pg. 3941
TB CO., LTD—See Takara Holdings, Inc.; *Int'l*, pg. 7432
TB CORPORATE SERVICE CORPORATION—See Toyota Boshoku Corporation; *Int'l*, pg. 7864
TBC PRIVATE BRANDS—See Sumitomo Corporation; *Int'l*, pg. 7274

TBC PUBLIC RELATIONS—See TBC Inc.; *U.S. Private*, pg. 3941
TBC PUBLIC RELATIONS—See Ted Barkus Company, Inc.; *U.S. Private*, pg. 3957
TB CREATE STAFF CORPORATION—See Toyota Boshoku Corporation; *Int'l*, pg. 7864
TBC SALES PROMOTION—See Ted Barkus Company, Inc.; *U.S. Private*, pg. 3957
TBC—See Golden Gate Capital Management II, LLC; *U.S. Private*, pg. 1731
TBC TELETHEATRE B.C. LTD.—See Great Canadian Gaming Corporation; *Int'l*, pg. 3063
TB DE MEXICO, S.A. DE C.V.—See Toyota Boshoku Corporation; *Int'l*, pg. 7864
TBD NETWORKS, INC.—See MetricStream, Inc.; *U.S. Private*, pg. 2685
TBEA CO., LTD.; *Int'l*, pg. 7479
TBEA ENERGY (INDIA) PVT. LTD.—See TBEA Co., Ltd.; *Int'l*, pg. 7479
TBEA HENGYANG TRANSFORMER CO., LTD.—See TBEA Co., Ltd.; *Int'l*, pg. 7479
TBEA SHANDONG LUNENG TAISHAN CABLE CO., LTD.—See TBEA Co., Ltd.; *Int'l*, pg. 7479
TBEA SHENYANG TRANSFORMER GROUP CO., LTD.—See TBEA Co., Ltd.; *Int'l*, pg. 7479
TBEA TIANJIN TRANSFORMER CO., LTD.—See TBEA Co., Ltd.; *Int'l*, pg. 7479
TBEA XIAN ELECTRIC TECHNOLOGY CO.,LTD.—See TBEA Co., Ltd.; *Int'l*, pg. 7479
TBEA XINJIANG CABLE CO., LTD.—See TBEA Co., Ltd.; *Int'l*, pg. 7479
TBEA XINJIANG SUNOASIS CO., LTD.—See TBEA Co., Ltd.; *Int'l*, pg. 7479
TBE-CONSTRUCTION OY—See SRV Group Plc; *Int'l*, pg. 7153
TB ENGINEERING CORPORATION—See Toyota Boshoku Corporation; *Int'l*, pg. 7864
TBF MALAISIE—See Compagnie de Saint-Gobain SA; *Int'l*, pg. 1737
TB FRASHION GERRY WEBER GMBH—See GERRY WEBER International AG; *Int'l*, pg. 2945
TBG BAK S.R.O.—See Heidelberg Materials AG; *Int'l*, pg. 3320
TBG BETONMIX A. S.—See Heidelberg Materials AG; *Int'l*, pg. 3320
TBG BETONPUMPY MORAVA S.R.O.—See Heidelberg Materials AG; *Int'l*, pg. 3320
TBG DIAGNOSTICS LIMITED; *Int'l*, pg. 7479
TB GERMANY GMBH—See Turtle Beach Corporation; *U.S. Public*, pg. 2205
TBG HOLDINGS CORP.; *U.S. Private*, pg. 3941
TBG HOLDINGS NV; *Int'l*, pg. 7479
TBG ILM-BETON GMBH & CO. KG—See Heidelberg Materials AG; *Int'l*, pg. 3320
TB GROUP INC.; *Int'l*, pg. 7479
TBG SECURITY INC.—See Kelso & Company, L.P.; *U.S. Private*, pg. 2278
TBG TRANSPORTBETON ELSTER-SPREE VERWALTUNGS-GMBH—See Heidelberg Materials AG; *Int'l*, pg. 3320
TBG TRANSPORTBETON FRANKEN GESCHAFTSFUHRUNG GMBH—See Heidelberg Materials AG; *Int'l*, pg. 3320
TBG TRANSPORTBETON GMBH & CO. KG—See Heidelberg Materials AG; *Int'l*, pg. 3320
TBG TRANSPORTBETON KURPFALZ GMBH & CO. KG—See Heidelberg Materials AG; *Int'l*, pg. 3320
TBG TRANSPORTBETON MAINFRANKEN GESCHAFTSFUHRUNGS GMBH—See Heidelberg Materials AG; *Int'l*, pg. 3320
TBG TRANSPORTBETON REICHENBACH GMBH & CO. KG—See Heidelberg Materials AG; *Int'l*, pg. 3320
TBG TRANSPORTBETON REICHENBACH VERWALTUNGS-GMBH—See Heidelberg Materials AG; *Int'l*, pg. 3320
TBG TRANSPORTBETON SAALFELD VERWALTUNGS-GMBH—See Heidelberg Materials AG; *Int'l*, pg. 3320
TBG TRANSPORTBETON SCHWARZENBERG VERWALTUNGS-GMBH—See Heidelberg Materials AG; *Int'l*, pg. 3320
TBG TREUHAND PARTNER AG; *Int'l*, pg. 7479
TBG WIKA-BETON VERWALTUNGS-GMBH—See Heidelberg Materials AG; *Int'l*, pg. 3320
TBG ZNOJMO S. R. O.—See Heidelberg Materials AG; *Int'l*, pg. 3320
TBH GLOBAL CO., LTD.; *Int'l*, pg. 7480
TBH HONGKONG LIMITED—See TBH Global Co., Ltd.; *Int'l*, pg. 7480
TBH INGENIEUR GMBH—See BKW AG; *Int'l*, pg. 1056
TBH TRANSPORTBETON HAMBURG GMBH & CO. KG—See Heidelberg Materials AG; *Int'l*, pg. 3320
TBH TRANSPORTBETON HAMBURG VERWALTUNGS-GMBH—See Heidelberg Materials AG; *Int'l*, pg. 3320
TBI AIRPORT MANAGEMENT INC.—See ACS, Actividades de Construccion y Servicios, S.A.; *Int'l*, pg. 112
TBI BANK EAD—See 4finance Holding S.A.; *Int'l*, pg. 11
TBI CARGO INC.—See ACS, Actividades de Construccion y Servicios, S.A.; *Int'l*, pg. 112

TBIH FINANCIAL SERVICES GROUP N.V.—See Vienna Insurance Group AG Wiener Versicherung Gruppe; *Int'l*, pg. 8195
TBI INC.; *U.S. Private*, pg. 3941
TBI INDUSTRIES GMBH—See Enovis Corporation; *U.S. Public*, pg. 773
TBI INDUSTRIES S.R.O.—See Enovis Corporation; *U.S. Public*, pg. 773
TBI INFO EOOD—See Vienna Insurance Group AG Wiener Versicherung Gruppe; *Int'l*, pg. 8195
TBI LEASING IFN S.A.—See 4finance Holding S.A.; *Int'l*, pg. 12
TBILVINO JOINT STOCK COMPANY; *Int'l*, pg. 7480
TBI MOTION INTELLIGENCE CO., LTD.—See TBI Motion Technology Co., Ltd.; *Int'l*, pg. 7480
TBI MOTION TECHNOLOGY CO., LTD.; *Int'l*, pg. 7480
TBI MOTION TECHNOLOGY (SUZHOU) CO., LTD.—See TBI Motion Technology Co., Ltd.; *Int'l*, pg. 7480
TBI MOTION TECHONOLOGY (SUZHOU) CO., LTD.—See TBI Motion Technology Co., Ltd.; *Int'l*, pg. 7480
TBI PLC—See ACS, Actividades de Construccion y Servicios, S.A.; *Int'l*, pg. 112
T-BIRD RESTAURANT GROUP, INC.—See H.I.G. Capital, LLC; *U.S. Private*, pg. 1831
TBJ BEHAVIORAL CENTER, LLC—See Universal Health Services, Inc.; *U.S. Public*, pg. 2259
TBK AMERICA INC.—See TBK Co. Ltd.; *Int'l*, pg. 7480
TBK AUTOMATISIERUNG UND MESSTECHNIK GMBH—See SMS Holding GmbH; *Int'l*, pg. 7016
TB KAWASHIMA CO., LTD.—See Toyota Boshoku Corporation; *Int'l*, pg. 7864
TB KAWASHIMA USA, INC.—See Toyota Boshoku Corporation; *Int'l*, pg. 7864
TBK BANK, SSB—See Triumph Financial, Inc.; *U.S. Public*, pg. 2196
TBK CHINA CO., LTD.—See TBK Co. Ltd.; *Int'l*, pg. 7480
TBK CO. LTD. - FUKUSHIMA NO. 1 PLANT—See TBK Co. Ltd.; *Int'l*, pg. 7480
TBK CO. LTD. - FUKUSHIMA NO. 2 PLANT—See TBK Co. Ltd.; *Int'l*, pg. 7480
TBK CO. LTD.; *Int'l*, pg. 7480
TBK INDIA PRIVATE LTD.—See TBK Co. Ltd.; *Int'l*, pg. 7480
TBKK (THAILAND) CO., LTD—See TBK Co. Ltd.; *Int'l*, pg. 7480
TBK SALES CO., LTD.—See TBK Co. Ltd.; *Int'l*, pg. 7480
TBK & SONS HOLDINGS LIMITED; *Int'l*, pg. 7480
TBL GROUP, INC.; *U.S. Private*, pg. 3941
TBL NETWORKS, INC.; *U.S. Private*, pg. 3941
TB LOGISTICS CORPORATION—See Toyota Boshoku Corporation; *Int'l*, pg. 7864
TBMC (2) LIMITED—See Paragon Banking Group PLC; *Int'l*, pg. 5736
TBMECA POLAND SP. Z O.O.—See Denso Corporation; *Int'l*, pg. 2029
TBMECA POLAND SP. Z O.O.—See Equistone Partners Europe Limited; *Int'l*, pg. 2487
TBMECA POLAND SP. Z O.O.—See Toyota Boshoku Corporation; *Int'l*, pg. 7864
TBM TRANSPORTBETON-GESELLSCHAFT MBH MARIENFELD & CO. KG—See Heidelberg Materials AG; *Int'l*, pg. 3320
TBM TRANSPORTBETON-GESELLSCHAFT MIT BESCHRANKTER HAFTUNG MARIENFELD—See Heidelberg Materials AG; *Int'l*, pg. 3320
TBN ASSOCIATES INC.—See Thomas Rawlings Group Inc.; *U.S. Private*, pg. 4157
TBO-HAGLINDS AB—See Balco Group AB; *Int'l*, pg. 807
TBO OIL & GAS, LLC—See Mexco Energy Corporation; *U.S. Public*, pg. 1433
TBP ELECTRONICS BELGIUM—See tbp electronics BV; *Int'l*, pg. 7480
TBP ELECTRONICS BV; *Int'l*, pg. 7480
TB PROPRIETARY CORP.—See Toll Brothers, Inc.; *U.S. Public*, pg. 2162
TBR CO., LTD.—See TBK Co. Ltd.; *Int'l*, pg. 7480
T&B RETAIL CONSUMER PRODUCTS—See ABB Ltd.; *Int'l*, pg. 52
T BROKER CO., LTD.—See Thanachart Capital PCL; *Int'l*, pg. 7607
T. BROWN CONSTRUCTORS INC.; *U.S. Private*, pg. 3911
T. BRUCE SALES, INC.; *U.S. Private*, pg. 3911
TB SA ACQUISITION CORP.; *Int'l*, pg. 7479
TBS BE TELEMATIC & BIOMEDICAL SERVICES BVBA—See Permira Advisers LLP; *Int'l*, pg. 5808
TBS DENIZCILIK VE PETROL URUNLERI DIS TICARET AS—See Koc Holding A.S.; *Int'l*, pg. 4223
TB SEWTECH KYUSHU CORPORATION—See Toyota Boshoku Corporation; *Int'l*, pg. 7864
TB SEWTECH TOHOKU CORPORATION—See Toyota Boshoku Corporation; *Int'l*, pg. 7864
TBS FR TELEMATIC & BIOMEDICAL SERVICES SARL—See Permira Advisers LLP; *Int'l*, pg. 5808
TBS GB TELEMATIC & BIOMEDICAL SERVICES LTD—See Permira Advisers LLP; *Int'l*, pg. 5808
TBSG, LLC—See Builders FirstSource, Inc.; *U.S. Public*, pg. 409

TB SA ACQUISITION CORP. CORPORATE AFFILIATIONS

TBS GROUP SPA—See Permira Advisers LLP; *Int'l*, pg. 5808
TBS HOLDINGS, INC.; *Int'l*, pg. 7480
TBS INDIA TELEMATIC & BIOMEDICAL SERVICES PVT LTD.—See Permira Advisers LLP; *Int'l*, pg. 5808
TBS INTERNATIONAL PLC; *Int'l*, pg. 7481
TBS KIKAKU CO., LTD.—See TBS Holdings, Inc.; *Int'l*, pg. 7481
TBS MEDIA RESEARCH INSTITUTE INC.—See TBS Holdings, Inc.; *Int'l*, pg. 7481
TBS MINING SOLUTIONS PTY LTD.—See Aquirian Limited; *Int'l*, pg. 528
TBS RADIO & COMMUNICATIONS, INC—See TBS Holdings, Inc.; *Int'l*, pg. 7481
TBS SERVICE, INC—See TBS Holdings, Inc.; *Int'l*, pg. 7481
TBS SHIPPING SERVICES, INC.—See TBS INTERNATIONAL PLC; *Int'l*, pg. 7481
TBS SOEST B.V.—See Triacta BV; *Int'l*, pg. 7918
TBS SPECIALTIES DIRECT INC.—See ITR Industries Inc.; *U.S. Private*, pg. 2150
TBS SUNWORK, INC—See TBS Holdings, Inc.; *Int'l*, pg. 7481
TBS TEAM 24 PODJETJE ZA STORITVENE DEJAVNOSTI IN TRGOVINO D.O.O.—See Pozavarovalnica Sava, d.d.; *Int'l*, pg. 5949
TB SUPPLY BASE SDN BHD—See Ahmad Zaki Resources Berhad; *Int'l*, pg. 225
TBS VISION, INC—See TBS Holdings, Inc.; *Int'l*, pg. 7481
TBS WORKFORCE PTY LTD.—See Aquirian Limited; *Int'l*, pg. 528
TB TECHNOGREEN CORPORATION—See Toyota Boshoku Corporation; *Int'l*, pg. 7864
T & B TUBE COMPANY; *U.S. Private*, pg. 3908
T-BULL SA; *Int'l*, pg. 7396
TB UNIFASHION CORPORATION—See Toyota Boshoku Corporation; *Int'l*, pg. 7864
TBWA ADRIATIC REGION—See Omnicom Group Inc.; *U.S. Public*, pg. 1594
TBWA/ALIF—See Omnicom Group Inc.; *U.S. Public*, pg. 1597
TBWA AME MED—See Omnicom Group Inc.; *U.S. Public*, pg. 1597
TBWA ASIA PACIFIC—See Omnicom Group Inc.; *U.S. Public*, pg. 1595
TBWA ATHENS—See Omnicom Group Inc.; *U.S. Public*, pg. 1594
TBWA/AUSTRALIA—See Omnicom Group Inc.; *U.S. Public*, pg. 1595
TBWA & BBDO A/S—See Omnicom Group Inc.; *U.S. Public*, pg. 1577
TBWA BELARUS—See Omnicom Group Inc.; *U.S. Public*, pg. 1594
TBWA BRUSSELS—See Omnicom Group Inc.; *U.S. Public*, pg. 1596
TBWA BUDAPEST—See Omnicom Group Inc.; *U.S. Public*, pg. 1594
TBWA CALIFORNIA—See Omnicom Group Inc.; *U.S. Public*, pg. 1598
TBWA CENTRAL ASIA—See Omnicom Group Inc.; *U.S. Public*, pg. 1596
TBWA/CHIAT/DAY LOS ANGELES INC.—See Omnicom Group Inc.; *U.S. Public*, pg. 1598
TBWA CHIAT DAY LOS ANGELES—See Omnicom Group Inc.; *U.S. Public*, pg. 1598
TBWA CHIAT DAY NEW YORK—See Omnicom Group Inc.; *U.S. Public*, pg. 1598
TBWA/CHIAT/DAY—See Omnicom Group Inc.; *U.S. Public*, pg. 1597
TBWA/COLOMBIA SUIZA DE PUBLICIDAD LTDA—See Omnicom Group Inc.; *U.S. Public*, pg. 1599
TBWA/COMPACT—See Omnicom Group Inc.; *U.S. Public*, pg. 1596
TBWA COMPANY GROUP—See Omnicom Group Inc.; *U.S. Public*, pg. 1596
TBWA CONCEPT UNIT—See Omnicom Group Inc.; *U.S. Public*, pg. 1596
TBWA COPENHAGEN—See Omnicom Group Inc.; *U.S. Public*, pg. 1595
TBWA CORPORATE—See Omnicom Group Inc.; *U.S. Public*, pg. 1596
TBWA COSTA RICA—See Omnicom Group Inc.; *U.S. Public*, pg. 1599
TBWA (DEUTSCHLAND) HOLDING GMBH—See Omnicom Group Inc.; *U.S. Public*, pg. 1594
TBWA/DUBLIN—See Omnicom Group Inc.; *U.S. Public*, pg. 1597
TBWA DURBAN—See Omnicom Group Inc.; *U.S. Public*, pg. 1597
TBWA/EL SALVADOR—See Omnicom Group Inc.; *U.S. Public*, pg. 1599
TBWA EMCG—See Omnicom Group Inc.; *U.S. Public*, pg. 1595
TBWA ESTONIA—See Omnicom Group Inc.; *U.S. Public*, pg. 1595
TBWA EUROPE—See Omnicom Group Inc.; *U.S. Public*, pg. 1596
TBWA FKGB—See Omnicom Group Inc.; *U.S. Public*, pg. 1596
TBWA FRANCE—See Omnicom Group Inc.; *U.S. Public*, pg. 1596
TBWA FREDERICK—See Omnicom Group Inc.; *U.S. Public*, pg. 1597
TBWA/G1—See Omnicom Group Inc.; *U.S. Public*, pg. 1596
TBWA GREATER CHINA—See Omnicom Group Inc.; *U.S. Public*, pg. 1595
TBWA/GROUP GERMANY—See Omnicom Group Inc.; *U.S. Public*, pg. 1595
TBWA GROUP POLAND—See Omnicom Group Inc.; *U.S. Public*, pg. 1595
TBWA GROUP—See Omnicom Group Inc.; *U.S. Public*, pg. 1596
TBWA/ GROUP VIETNAM—See Omnicom Group Inc.; *U.S. Public*, pg. 1595
TBWA/GUATEMALA—See Omnicom Group Inc.; *U.S. Public*, pg. 1599
TBWA/HAKUHODO; *Int'l*, pg. 7481
TBWA HEALTH A.G.—See Omnicom Group Inc.; *U.S. Public*, pg. 1595
TBWA HONG KONG LIMITED—See Omnicom Group Inc.; *U.S. Public*, pg. 1595
TBWA HUNT LASCARIS (CAPE TOWN) PROPRIETARY LIMITED—See Omnicom Group Inc.; *U.S. Public*, pg. 1597
TBWA HUNT LASCARIS (DURBAN) PTY. LTD.—See Omnicom Group Inc.; *U.S. Public*, pg. 1597
TBWA HUNT LASCARIS (JOHANNESBURG) PTY. LTD.—See Omnicom Group Inc.; *U.S. Public*, pg. 1597
TBWA INDIA CORPORATE—See Omnicom Group Inc.; *U.S. Public*, pg. 1597
TBWA INDIA—See Omnicom Group Inc.; *U.S. Public*, pg. 1595
TBWA INDIA—See Omnicom Group Inc.; *U.S. Public*, pg. 1597
TBWA INDIA—See Omnicom Group Inc.; *U.S. Public*, pg. 1597
TBWA INDIA—See Omnicom Group Inc.; *U.S. Public*, pg. 1597
TBWA INTERACTIVE—See Omnicom Group Inc.; *U.S. Public*, pg. 1595
TBWA ISC MALAYSIA—See Omnicom Group Inc.; *U.S. Public*, pg. 1595
TBWA ISTANBUL—See Omnicom Group Inc.; *U.S. Public*, pg. 1595
TBWA ITALIA—See Omnicom Group Inc.; *U.S. Public*, pg. 1595
TBWA/JAIMEURIBE—See Omnicom Group Inc.; *U.S. Public*, pg. 1599
TBWA KOREA—See Omnicom Group Inc.; *U.S. Public*, pg. 1595
TBWA LATVIJA—See Omnicom Group Inc.; *U.S. Public*, pg. 1595
TBWA LISBON—See Omnicom Group Inc.; *U.S. Public*, pg. 1597
TBWA/LONDON LIMITED—See Omnicom Group Inc.; *U.S. Public*, pg. 1597
TBWA/MANCHESTER—See Omnicom Group Inc.; *U.S. Public*, pg. 1597
TBWA/MEDIA ARTS LAB—See Omnicom Group Inc.; *U.S. Public*, pg. 1598
TBWA MERLIN—See Omnicom Group Inc.; *U.S. Public*, pg. 1595
TBWA MOSCOW—See Omnicom Group Inc.; *U.S. Public*, pg. 1595
TBWA NEBOKO—See Omnicom Group Inc.; *U.S. Public*, pg. 1596
TBWA OSLO—See Omnicom Group Inc.; *U.S. Public*, pg. 1597
TBWA PALING WALTERS—See Omnicom Group Inc.; *U.S. Public*, pg. 1597
TBWA/PARAGON—See Omnicom Group Inc.; *U.S. Public*, pg. 1599
TBWA PARIS—See Omnicom Group Inc.; *U.S. Public*, pg. 1596
TBWA PERU—See Omnicom Group Inc.; *U.S. Public*, pg. 1599
TBWA PHS—See Omnicom Group Inc.; *U.S. Public*, pg. 1595
TBWA PRAHA—See Omnicom Group Inc.; *U.S. Public*, pg. 1595
TBWA PR—See Omnicom Group Inc.; *U.S. Public*, pg. 1595
TBWA RAAD—See Omnicom Group Inc.; *U.S. Public*, pg. 1597
TBWA ROMA—See Omnicom Group Inc.; *U.S. Public*, pg. 1595
TBWA SANTIAGO MANGADA PUNO—See Omnicom Group Inc.; *U.S. Public*, pg. 1595
TBWA SHANGHAI—See Omnicom Group Inc.; *U.S. Public*, pg. 1595
TBWA SINGAPORE—See Omnicom Group Inc.; *U.S. Public*, pg. 1595
TBWA SOFIA—See Omnicom Group Inc.; *U.S. Public*, pg. 1595
TBWA SOUTH AFRICA GROUP—See Omnicom Group Inc.; *U.S. Public*, pg. 1597
TBWA STOCKHOLM—See Omnicom Group Inc.; *U.S. Public*, pg. 1597
TBWA SWITZERLAND A.G.—See Omnicom Group Inc.; *U.S. Public*, pg. 1595
TBWA TANGO/ HELSINKI—See Omnicom Group Inc.; *U.S. Public*, pg. 1597
TBWA THAILAND—See Omnicom Group Inc.; *U.S. Public*, pg. 1595
TBWA TORONTO—See Omnicom Group Inc.; *U.S. Public*, pg. 1598
TBWA UK GROUP LIMITED—See Omnicom Group Inc.; *U.S. Public*, pg. 1597
TBWA UKRAINE—See Omnicom Group Inc.; *U.S. Public*, pg. 1595
TBWA UNITED—See Omnicom Group Inc.; *U.S. Public*, pg. 1597
TBWA VANCOUVER—See Omnicom Group Inc.; *U.S. Public*, pg. 1598
TBWA VENEZUELA—See Omnicom Group Inc.; *U.S. Public*, pg. 1597
TBWA VILNIUS—See Omnicom Group Inc.; *U.S. Public*, pg. 1595
TBWA WARSZAWA—See Omnicom Group Inc.; *U.S. Public*, pg. 1595
TBWA WHYBIN LIMITED—See Omnicom Group Inc.; *U.S. Public*, pg. 1597
TBWA WIEN—See Omnicom Group Inc.; *U.S. Public*, pg. 1595
TBWA WORLDHEALTH CHICAGO INC.—See Omnicom Group Inc.; *U.S. Public*, pg. 1599
TBWA/WORLDHEALTH NEW YORK—See Omnicom Group Inc.; *U.S. Public*, pg. 1599
TBWA/WORLDHEALTH—See Omnicom Group Inc.; *U.S. Public*, pg. 1598
TBWA WORLDWIDE INC.—See Omnicom Group Inc.; *U.S. Public*, pg. 1594
TBWA ZAGREB—See Omnicom Group Inc.; *U.S. Public*, pg. 1595
T & B WHITWOOD HOLDINGS LIMITED—See Deutsche Post AG; *Int'l*, pg. 2082
TB WOOD'S CORPORATION—See Regal Rexnord Corporation; *U.S. Public*, pg. 1772
TB WOOD'S INCORPORATED—See Regal Rexnord Corporation; *U.S. Public*, pg. 1772
TC3 GROUP HOLDINGS LLC—See JTC PLC; *Int'l*, pg. 4017
TC3 HEALTH, INC.—See McKesson Corporation; *U.S. Public*, pg. 1407
TC3 TELECOM INC.; *U.S. Private*, pg. 3942
TCAA; *U.S. Private*, pg. 3942
TCA FINANCIAL, LLC; *U.S. Private*, pg. 3942
TC AGENCY CORPORATION—See Tokyo Century Corporation; *Int'l*, pg. 7789
TCA HOLDINGS, LLC; *U.S. Private*, pg. 3942
TCA/HORIBA SISTEMAS DE TESTES AUTOMOTIVOS LTDA.—See HORIBA Ltd; *Int'l*, pg. 3478
TC ALUMINIUM CASTINGS SDN. BHD.—See APM Automotive Holdings Berhad; *Int'l*, pg. 516
TC/AMERICAN CRANE COMPANY—See Orion Financial Corp.; *U.S. Private*, pg. 3043
TC/AMERICAN CRANE COMPANY—See Stewart Capital Partners LLC; *U.S. Private*, pg. 3811
T CAPITAL PARTNERS CO., LTD.; *Int'l*, pg. 7394
TCAP PTE LTD—See Thakral Corp. Ltd.; *Int'l*, pg. 7598
T CARD & MARKETING CO., LTD.—See Culture Convenience Club Co., Ltd.; *Int'l*, pg. 1877
TCA - TECNOLOGIA EM COMPONENTES AUTOMOTIVOS. SA.—See Stellantis N.V.; *Int'l*, pg. 7203
TC AUTOCLINIC PTE LTD—See Tan Chong International Limited; *Int'l*, pg. 7453
TC AUTOHUB (THAILAND) CO., LTD.—See Tan Chong International Limited; *Int'l*, pg. 7453
TC AUTO TOOLING SDN. BHD.—See Tan Chong Motor Holdings Berhad; *Int'l*, pg. 7453
TC BALKANA A.D.; *Int'l*, pg. 7481
TC BANCSHARES, INC.; *U.S. Public*, pg. 1983
TCB-ARROW LTD - CABLE PLANT—See TCB-Arrow Ltd; *Int'l*, pg. 7482
TCB-ARROW LTD; *Int'l*, pg. 7482
TCB AVGIDIS AUTOMATION SA—See Yokogawa Electric Corporation; *Int'l*, pg. 8592
TCB CORPORATION—See Prodigy Ventures, Inc.; *Int'l*, pg. 5988
T-CBC (TAIWAN) CO., LTD.—See CBC Co., Ltd.; *Int'l*, pg. 1365
TC BEFEKTETESI NYILVANOSAN MUKODO RESZVENYTARSASAG; *Int'l*, pg. 7481
TCB ENTERPRISES, LLC.—See NFI Group Inc.; *Int'l*, pg. 5252
TC BIOPHARM (HOLDINGS) PLC; *Int'l*, pg. 7481
T&C BIO TECHNOLOGY—See Dentium Co., Ltd; *Int'l*, pg. 2034
TCB LAND SDN. BHD.—See Tradewinds Corporation Berhad; *Int'l*, pg. 7888
TCBN COMPANY LIMITED—See Pico (Thailand) Public Company Limited; *Int'l*, pg. 5860

COMPANY NAME INDEX

TC BOY MARKETING SDN. BHD.—See Tropical Canning (Thailand) Public Company Limited; *Int'l*, pg. 7939
TC BUSINESS EXPERTS CORPORATION—See Tokyo Century Corporation; *Int'l*, pg. 7789
TC BUSINESS SERVICE CORPORATION—See Tokyo Century Corporation; *Int'l*, pg. 7789
TCBY SYSTEMS, LLC—See Capricorn Holdings, Inc.; *U.S. Private*, pg. 745
TCC AGROCHEMICAL CO., LTD—See Thai Central Chemical Public Company Limited; *Int'l*, pg. 7592
TCC AMERICA CORP.—See TCC STEEL CORP.; *Int'l*, pg. 7483
TC CAPITAL RESOURCES SDN. BHD.—See Tan Chong Motor Holdings Berhad; *Int'l*, pg. 7453
TCC ASSETS (THAILAND) COMPANY LIMITED; *Int'l*, pg. 7483
TCC CEMENT CORP.—See Taiwan Cement Corporation; *Int'l*, pg. 7419
T.C.C. COMMERCIAL PROPERTY MANAGEMENT CO., LTD.—See Asset World Corp Public Company Limited; *Int'l*, pg. 643
TCC CONCEPTS LTD; *Int'l*, pg. 7483
TCC ENGINEERING CORPORATION—See TCC STEEL CORP.; *Int'l*, pg. 7483
TCC HANJIN CORPORATION—See TCC STEEL CORP.; *Int'l*, pg. 7483
TCC INS CORPORATION—See TCC STEEL CORP.; *Int'l*, pg. 7483
TCC INTERNATIONAL HOLDINGS LIMITED—See Taiwan Cement Corporation; *Int'l*, pg. 7419
TCC INVESTMENT CORP.—See Technical Communications Corporation; *U.S. Public*, pg. 1988
TCC KOREA INC.—See SingAsia Holdings Limited; *Int'l*, pg. 6943
TCC LOGIS CORPORATION—See TCC STEEL CORP.; *Int'l*, pg. 7483
TCC METAL CORPORATION—See TCC STEEL CORP.; *Int'l*, pg. 7483
TC CONTACT CENTRE SERVICES SDN. BHD.—See Tan Chong Motor Holdings Berhad; *Int'l*, pg. 7453
T & C CONTRACTING INC.; *U.S. Private*, pg. 3908
TC CORPORATE SUPPORT PROPRIETARY LIMITED—See Transaction Capital Limited; *Int'l*, pg. 7094
TCC PROPERTIES INC.; *U.S. Private*, pg. 3942
TCC SERVICE COMPANY LIMITED—See KKR & Co. Inc.; *U.S. Public*, pg. 1259
TCC STEEL CORP.; *Int'l*, pg. 7483
TCC TRADING CORPORATION—See TCC STEEL CORP.; *Int'l*, pg. 7483
TCDC, INC.—See Target Corporation; *U.S. Public*, pg. 1982
T-C DISTRIBUTION COMPANY; *U.S. Private*, pg. 3910
TCE CASTING SDN. BHD.—See UNIMECH Group Berhad; *Int'l*, pg. 8049
TCECUR SWEDEN AB; *Int'l*, pg. 7483
TCE, INCORPORATED; *U.S. Private*, pg. 3942
T-CELLULAR, INC.; *U.S. Private*, pg. 3910
TC ENERGY CORPORATION; *Int'l*, pg. 7482
TC ENTERTAINMENT, INC.—See TBS Holdings, Inc.; *Int'l*, pg. 7481
TCE QSTP-LLC—See Tata Sons Limited; *Int'l*, pg. 7468
TC EURO CARS SDN. BHD.—See Tan Chong Motor Holdings Berhad; *Int'l*, pg. 7453
TC FARMING UKRAINE LTD.—See Agromino A/S; *Int'l*, pg. 220
TCFC FINANCE LTD; *Int'l*, pg. 7483
TCF COMMERCIAL FINANCE CANADA, INC.—See Huntington Bancshares Incorporated; *U.S. Public*, pg. 1071
TCFCW, LLC—See Aquiline Capital Partners LLC; *U.S. Private*, pg. 304
TCFCW, LLC—See Genstar Capital, LLC; *U.S. Private*, pg. 1675
TCF FOUNDATION—See Huntington Bancshares Incorporated; *U.S. Public*, pg. 1071
TCF, INC.—See Taylor Power Systems, Inc.; *U.S. Private*, pg. 3940
TC FLEXIBLE PACKAGING CO., LTD.—See The Siam Cement Public Company Limited; *Int'l*, pg. 7685
TC FORUM CORP.—See Tokyu Fudosan Holdings Corporation; *Int'l*, pg. 7798
TCF VZDUCHOTECHNIKA LTD.—See Twin City Fan Companies, Ltd.; *U.S. Private*, pg. 4265
TCG DEVELOPMENTS INDIA PVT. LTD.—See Vornado Realty Trust; *U.S. Public*, pg. 2309
TCG GROWTH OPPORTUNITIES CORP.; *U.S. Public*, pg. 1983
TCG HOLDINGS, S.A.—See Telefonica, S.A.; *Int'l*, pg. 7535
TCG INTERESTS, LTD.—See Elm Creek Partners; *U.S. Private*, pg. 1375
TC GLOBAL, INC.; *U.S. Private*, pg. 3942
TCG MERCHANT GROUP, INC.; *Int'l*, pg. 7483
TCG REAL ESTATE INVESTMENT MANAGEMENT COMPANY PVT. LTD.—See Vornado Realty Trust; *U.S. Public*, pg. 2309
TC GROUP, LLC - LOS ANGELES—See The Carlyle Group Inc.; *U.S. Public*, pg. 2055

TC GROUP, LLC - NEW YORK—See The Carlyle Group Inc.; *U.S. Public*, pg. 2055
TC GROUP, LLC - SAN FRANCISCO—See The Carlyle Group Inc.; *U.S. Public*, pg. 2055
TC GROUP, LLC—See The Carlyle Group Inc.; *U.S. Public*, pg. 2054
TCG; *U.S. Private*, pg. 3942
TCHAIKAPHARMA HIGHQUALITY MEDICINES AD; *Int'l*, pg. 7483
T-CHAMBER CO., LTD.—See Thanulux Public Company Limited; *Int'l*, pg. 7608
T. C. HARRISON GROUP LIMITED; *Int'l*, pg. 7396
T C H DE ANGELI; *Int'l*, pg. 7394
TC HEARTLAND LLC; *U.S. Private*, pg. 3942
TCHIBO BUDAPEST KFT.—See maxingvest ag; *Int'l*, pg. 4741
TCHIBO CIS LLC—See maxingvest ag; *Int'l*, pg. 4741
TCHIBO COFFEE INTERNATIONAL LTD.—See maxingvest ag; *Int'l*, pg. 4741
TCHIBO COFFEE NEDERLAND B.V.—See maxingvest ag; *Int'l*, pg. 4741
TCHIBO COFFEE SERVICE POLSKA SP.Z O.O.—See maxingvest ag; *Int'l*, pg. 4741
TCHIBO GMBH—See maxingvest ag; *Int'l*, pg. 4741
TCHIBO KAHVE MAMULLERI DAGITIM VE PAZARLAMA TICARET LIMITED—See maxingvest ag; *Int'l*, pg. 4741
TCHIBO MANUFACTURING (AUSTRIA) GMBH—See maxingvest ag; *Int'l*, pg. 4741
TCHIBO MANUFACTURING POLAND SP.Z O.O.—See maxingvest ag; *Int'l*, pg. 4741
TCHIBO MERCHANDISING HONGKONG LP—See maxingvest ag; *Int'l*, pg. 4741
TCHIBO PRAHA SPOL. S.R.O.—See maxingvest ag; *Int'l*, pg. 4741
TCHIBO (SCHWEIZ) AG—See maxingvest ag; *Int'l*, pg. 4741
TCHIBO SLOVENSKO SPOL. S R.O.—See maxingvest ag; *Int'l*, pg. 4742
TCH INDUSTRIES INC.; *U.S. Private*, pg. 3942
T&C HOLDING LTD; *U.S. Private*, pg. 3909
TCHO VENTURES, INC.—See Ezaki Glico Co., Ltd.; *Int'l*, pg. 2593
TCH RESTAURANT GROUP INC.; *U.S. Private*, pg. 3942
T.C.H. SUMINOE CO., LTD.—See Suminoe Textile Co., Ltd.; *Int'l*, pg. 7262
TCHUGUNOLEENE JSC; *Int'l*, pg. 7483
TCI ARCHITECTS ENGINEERS CONTRACTORS INC.; *U.S. Private*, pg. 3942
TCI BANGLADESH LTD.—See Transport Corporation of India Ltd.; *Int'l*, pg. 7904
TCI CERAMICS—See National Magnetics Group, Inc.; *U.S. Private*, pg. 2859
TCI COLD CHAIN SOLUTIONS LTD.—See Transport Corporation of India Ltd.; *Int'l*, pg. 7904
TCI-CONCOR MULTIMODAL SOLUTIONS PVT. LTD.—See Transport Corporation of India Ltd.; *Int'l*, pg. 7904
TCI CONTRACTING, LLC—See Installed Building Products, Inc.; *U.S. Public*, pg. 1133
TCI CONTRACTING OF HILTON HEAD, LLC—See Installed Building Products, Inc.; *U.S. Public*, pg. 1133
TCI DEVELOPERS LIMITED—See Transport Corporation of India Ltd.; *Int'l*, pg. 7904
TCIE VIETNAM PTE. LTD.—See Tan Chong Motor Holdings Berhad; *Int'l*, pg. 7454
TCI EXPRESS LIMITED; *Int'l*, pg. 7483
TCI FINANCE LTD.; *Int'l*, pg. 7483
TCI FREIGHT—See Transport Corporation of India Ltd.; *Int'l*, pg. 7904
TCI GLOBAL (HKG) LTD.—See Transport Corporation of India Ltd.; *Int'l*, pg. 7904
TCI GLOBAL LOGISTIK GMBH—See Transport Corporation of India Ltd.; *Int'l*, pg. 7904
TCI GLOBAL PTE LTD.—See Transport Corporation of India Ltd.; *Int'l*, pg. 7904
TCI GLOBAL (SANGHAI) CO., LTD.—See Transport Corporation of India Ltd.; *Int'l*, pg. 7904
TCI GLOBAL (THAILAND) CO., LTD.—See Transport Corporation of India Ltd.; *Int'l*, pg. 7904
TCI HOLDING COMPANY; *U.S. Private*, pg. 3942
TCI, INC.—See RPM International Inc.; *U.S. Public*, pg. 1819
TCI INDUSTRIES LTD; *Int'l*, pg. 7483
TCI INTERNATIONAL, INC.—See SPX Technologies, Inc.; *U.S. Public*, pg. 1922
TCI, LLC—See Allient Inc.; *U.S. Public*, pg. 80
TCIM SDN BHD—See Warisan TC Holdings Berhad; *Int'l*, pg. 8345
TCIM SERVICES INC.; *U.S. Private*, pg. 3942
TCI NEPAL PVT. LTD.—See Transport Corporation of India Ltd.; *Int'l*, pg. 7904
TC INFRASTRUCTURE SERVICES LTD.—See Quanta Services, Inc.; *U.S. Public*, pg. 1753
T C INTERNATIONAL TRADING CO., LTD—See CNlight Co., Ltd.; *Int'l*, pg. 1677
TCI POWDER COATING CANADA INC.—See RPM International Inc.; *U.S. Public*, pg. 1820

TCL TECHNOLOGY GROUP CORP.

TCI POWDER COATINGS DE MEXICO, S.A. DE C.V.—See RPM International Inc.; *U.S. Public*, pg. 1820
TCI PRECISION METALS, INC.; *U.S. Private*, pg. 3942
TCI RENEWABLES LTD.—See Service Stream Limited; *Int'l*, pg. 6725
TCI SANMAR CHEMICALS LLC—See Sanmar Holdings Ltd.; *Int'l*, pg. 6546
TCI SANMAR CHEMICALS S.A.E. - PORT SAID PLANT—See Sanmar Holdings Ltd.; *Int'l*, pg. 6546
TCI SEAWAYS—See Transport Corporation of India Ltd.; *Int'l*, pg. 7904
TCI SERVICES, INC.—See Team, Inc.; *U.S. Public*, pg. 1988
TCI SUPPLY CHAIN SOLUTIONS—See Transport Corporation of India Ltd.; *Int'l*, pg. 7904
T&C ITALIA S.R.L.—See Carlsberg A/S; *Int'l*, pg. 1341
TC ITECH SDN. BHD.—See Tan Chong Motor Holdings Berhad; *Int'l*, pg. 7454
TCI TIRE CENTERS, LLC—See Compagnie Generale des Etablissements Michelin SCA; *Int'l*, pg. 1744
TCI TIRE CENTERS—See Compagnie Generale des Etablissements Michelin SCA; *Int'l*, pg. 1744
T CITY (IPOH) SDN. BHD.—See Goodland Group Limited; *Int'l*, pg. 3040
TCI XPS—See Transport Corporation of India Ltd.; *Int'l*, pg. 7904
T.C. JACOBY & COMPANY, INC.; *U.S. Private*, pg. 3911
T.C.J. ASIA PUBLIC COMPANY LIMITED; *Int'l*, pg. 7397
TCJC INC.—See Charisma Brands, LLC; *U.S. Private*, pg. 850
TCK SHANGHAI CO., LTD.—See Toray Industries, Inc.; *Int'l*, pg. 7824
TCK WORKSHOP CO., LTD.—See Nippon Parking Development Co., Ltd.; *Int'l*, pg. 5328
TCLAD EUROPE GMBH—See Polytronics Technology Corp.; *Int'l*, pg. 5917
TCLAD INC.—See Polytronics Technology Corp.; *Int'l*, pg. 5917
TCLAD TECHNOLOGY CO., LTD.—See Polytronics Technology Corp.; *Int'l*, pg. 5917
TCL & ALCATEL REPAIR & DISTRIBUTION CENTRE (SUZHOU)—See mDR Limited; *Int'l*, pg. 4762
TCLANDSCAPES LTD.—See idverde UK Ltd.; *Int'l*, pg. 3597
T. CLARKE (BRISTOL) LIMITED—See Regent Gas Holdings Limited; *Int'l*, pg. 6252
TCLARKE LEEDS—See Regent Gas Holdings Limited; *Int'l*, pg. 6252
T.CLARKE (MIDLANDS) LIMITED—See Regent Gas Holdings Limited; *Int'l*, pg. 6252
T.CLARKE MIDLANDS LTD.—See Regent Gas Holdings Limited; *Int'l*, pg. 6252
T. CLARKE PLC - FALKIRK—See Regent Gas Holdings Limited; *Int'l*, pg. 6252
T. CLARKE PLC - HUNTINGDON—See Regent Gas Holdings Limited; *Int'l*, pg. 6252
TCLARKE PLC—See Regent Gas Holdings Limited; *Int'l*, pg. 6252
TCLARKE—See Regent Gas Holdings Limited; *Int'l*, pg. 6252
TCL CHINA STAR OPTOELECTRONICS TECHNOLOGY CO., LTD.—See TCL Technology Group Corp.; *Int'l*, pg. 7483
TCL COMMUNICATION TECHNOLOGY HOLDINGS LIMITED—See TCL Technology Group Corp.; *Int'l*, pg. 7484
TCL DIGI TRADE SRO—See SoftwareONE Holding AG; *Int'l*, pg. 7058
TCL ELECTRONICS HOLDINGS LIMITED—See TCL Technology Group Corp.; *Int'l*, pg. 7483
TCL HOFMANN PTY. LTD.—See BERICAP GmbH & Co. KG; *Int'l*, pg. 981
TCL HUNT LIMITED—See BERICAP GmbH & Co. KG; *Int'l*, pg. 981
TCL LABOR-HIRE COMPANY (PRIVATE) LIMITED—See Treet Corporation Limited; *Int'l*, pg. 7910
TCL MANUFACTURING LTD.—See Fortune Brands Innovations, Inc.; *U.S. Public*, pg. 873
TCL MOBILE COMMUNICATION (HK) COMPANY LIMITED—See TCL Technology Group Corp.; *Int'l*, pg. 7484
TCL MOBILE COMMUNICATION (HOHHOT) CO., LTD.—See TCL Technology Group Corp.; *Int'l*, pg. 7484
TCL MOKA MANUFACTURING S.A. DE C.V.—See TCL Technology Group Corp.; *Int'l*, pg. 7484
TCL PONSA MANUFACTURING LIMITED (TPM)—See CEMEX, S.A.B. de C.V.; *Int'l*, pg. 1400
TCL RECHI (HUIZHOU) REFRIGERATION EQUIPMENT LTD.—See Rechi Precision Co., Ltd.; *Int'l*, pg. 6235
TCL RESEARCH—See Thirumalai Chemicals Ltd; *Int'l*, pg. 7710
TCL SUPPLY CHAIN (CANADA) INC.—See Deutsche Post AG; *Int'l*, pg. 2082
TCL TANKER RENTAL LTD.—See Turner & Co. (Glasgow) Limited; *Int'l*, pg. 7978
TCL TECHNOLOGY GROUP CORP.; *Int'l*, pg. 7483

TCL TECHNOLOGY GROUP CORP. CORPORATE AFFILIATIONS

TCL TRADING LIMITED—See CEMEX, S.A.B. de C.V.; *Int'l*, pg. 1400
TCL ZHONGHUAN RENEWABLE ENERGY TECHNOLOGY CO.,LTD.; *Int'l*, pg. 7484
T.C. MANAGEMENT, INC.—See Yadav Enterprises, Inc.; *U.S. Private*, pg. 4584
TC MANUFACTURING CO., INC.; *U.S. Private*, pg. 3942
T. & C. MANUFACTURING CO. PTE. LTD.—See The Nisshin OilliO Group, Ltd.; *Int'l*, pg. 7671
T&C MARKETS IRON MOUNTAIN INC.; *U.S. Private*, pg. 3909
TCM BIOSCIENCES, INC.—See BL PharmTech Corp; *Int'l*, pg. 1056
TCM BIOTECH INTERNATIONAL CORP.; *Int'l*, pg. 7484
TCM COMPANY; *U.S. Private*, pg. 3942
TCM CORPORATION PUBLIC COMPANY LIMITED; *Int'l*, pg. 7484
TCM FISHERY CO., LTD.—See Thai Union Group Public Company Limited; *Int'l*, pg. 7596
TCM FRANCE S.A.S.—See Hitachi, Ltd.; *Int'l*, pg. 3416
TCM GROUP A/S; *Int'l*, pg. 7484
TCM HEALTHCARE PRIVATE LIMITED—See TCM Limited; *Int'l*, pg. 7484
TCMI, INC.; *U.S. Private*, pg. 3942
TCM LIMITED; *Int'l*, pg. 7484
TC MOTORS (SARAWAK) SDN. BHD.—See Tan Chong Motor Holdings Berhad; *Int'l*, pg. 7454
TC MOTOR VIETNAM CO. LTD.—See Tan Chong Motor Holdings Berhad; *Int'l*, pg. 7454
TCM SOLAR PRIVATE LIMITED—See TCM Limited; *Int'l*, pg. 7484
TCM STAMPING PRODUCTS SDN. BHD.—See Tan Chong Motor Holdings Berhad; *Int'l*, pg. 7454
TCM TRADING & SERVICE COMPANY LIMITED—See Astena Holdings Co., Ltd.; *Int'l*, pg. 653
TCN ANTIBES S.A.R.L.—See MarineMax, Inc.; *U.S. Public*, pg. 1367
TCN CHANNEL NINE PTY. LIMITED—See Nine Entertainment Co. Holdings Limited; *Int'l*, pg. 5299
TCN, INC.; *U.S. Private*, pg. 3943
TCNS CLOTHING CO., LTD.; *Int'l*, pg. 7484
TC NU-STAR, INC.; *U.S. Private*, pg. 3942
TCO HOLDINGS JOINT STOCK COMPANY; *Int'l*, pg. 7484
T-C OIL COMPANY INC.; *U.S. Private*, pg. 3910
TCOM, L.P.; *U.S. Private*, pg. 3943
T-CONN PRECISION CO., LTD.—See SINBON Electronics Co., Ltd.; *Int'l*, pg. 6937
TCOOMBS & ASSOCIATES LLC; *U.S. Private*, pg. 3943
TCOR INSURANCE MANAGEMENT, LTD.—See Stone Point Capital LLC; *U.S. Private*, pg. 3819
TCORP NOMINEES PTY LIMITED—See New South Wales Treasury Corporation; *Int'l*, pg. 5228
TC PACIFIC CONSTRUCTION, LLC—See Tokura Construction Co., Ltd.; *Int'l*, pg. 7786
TCP INTERNATIONAL HOLDINGS LTD.—See Q L Light Source Company Limited; *Int'l*, pg. 6129
TC PIPELINES, LP—See TC Energy Corporation; *Int'l*, pg. 7482
TCP LIMITED; *Int'l*, pg. 7485
TCPL PACKAGING LIMITED - GOA FACTORY—See TCPL PACKAGING LIMITED; *Int'l*, pg. 7485
TCPL PACKAGING LIMITED - HARIDWAR PLANT—See TCPL PACKAGING LIMITED; *Int'l*, pg. 7485
TCPL PACKAGING LIMITED - SILVASSA FACTORY—See TCPL PACKAGING LIMITED; *Int'l*, pg. 7485
TCPL PACKAGING LIMITED; *Int'l*, pg. 7485
TCP RELIABLE MANUFACTURING, INC.—See Integreon Global; *U.S. Private*, pg. 2102
TCP SOLUTIONS B.V.—See Q L Light Source Company Limited; *Int'l*, pg. 6129
TCP-TBWA INDONESIA—See Omnicom Group Inc.; *U.S. Public*, pg. 1595
TCP-TERMINAL DE CONTEINERES DE PARANAGUA S.A.; *Int'l*, pg. 7485
TCR2 THERAPEUTICS, INC.; *U.S. Public*, pg. 1983
TCR BUSINESS SYSTEMS, INC.—See NCR Voyix Corporation.; *U.S. Public*, pg. 1503
TCR CAPITAL SAS; *Int'l*, pg. 7485
TCR CORPORATION; *U.S. Private*, pg. 3943
TCR INDUSTRIES, INC.; *U.S. Private*, pg. 3943
TCRS RESTAURANTS SDN. BHD.—See Zensho Holdings Co., Ltd.; *Int'l*, pg. 8635
TCS AMERICA—See Tata Sons Limited; *Int'l*, pg. 7469
TCS (ASIA) CO. LTD.—See TCS TurControlSysteme AG; *Int'l*, pg. 7486
TCS COMMUNICATIONS, LLC—See Dycom Industries, Inc.; *U.S. Public*, pg. 699
TCS CONTRACTING CORPORATION; *U.S. Private*, pg. 3943
TCS SERVICES, INC.—See US 1 Industries, Inc.; *U.S. Private*, pg. 4317
TCS E-SERVE AMERICA, INC.—See Tata Sons Limited; *Int'l*, pg. 7469
TCS FREEHOLD INVESTMENTS LIMITED—See Town Centre Securities Plc; *Int'l*, pg. 7851
TCS GROUP HOLDING BERHAD; *Int'l*, pg. 7485
TCS GROUP HOLDING PLC; *Int'l*, pg. 7485
TCS HOLDINGS CO., LTD.; *Int'l*, pg. 7485

TCS HOLDINGS LIMITED—See Town Centre Securities Plc; *Int'l*, pg. 7851
TC SIGLO 21 S.A.A.; *Int'l*, pg. 7482
TCS, INC.—See L3Harris Technologies, Inc.; *U.S. Public*, pg. 1284
TCS INTELLIGENT BUILDING TECHNOLOGY (SHANGHAI) CO. LTD.—See TCS TurControlSysteme AG; *Int'l*, pg. 7486
TCS INTERNATIONAL, INC.—See Guardian Capital Group Limited; *Int'l*, pg. 3170
TC SISTEMA SERVIZI SPA; *Int'l*, pg. 7482
TCS ITALIA SRL—See Tata Sons Limited; *Int'l*, pg. 7470
TCSI/TRANSLAND INC.; *U.S. Private*, pg. 3943
TCS KAPI ILETISIMI VE BINA OTOMATIZASYON TIC. LTD. STI—See TCS TurControlSysteme AG; *Int'l*, pg. 7486
TCS MEDIA, INC.; *U.S. Private*, pg. 3943
TCS MEDIA NORTH; *Int'l*, pg. 7485
TCS (MILL HILL) LIMITED—See Town Centre Securities Plc; *Int'l*, pg. 7851
TCS PACIFIC PTY LTD.—See TCS TurControlSysteme AG; *Int'l*, pg. 7486
TCS SASU; *Int'l*, pg. 7485
T&C STAMPING INC.; *U.S. Private*, pg. 3909
TCST BUILDING SOLUTIONS INDIA PVT. LTD.—See TCS TurControlSysteme AG; *Int'l*, pg. 7486
TCS TRUSTEES LIMITED—See Town Centre Securities Plc; *Int'l*, pg. 7851
TCS STUDIOS, LLC; *U.S. Private*, pg. 3942
TCS TURCONTROLSYSTEME AG; *Int'l*, pg. 7485
TCS TURCONTROLSYSTEME GMBH—See TCS TurControlSysteme AG; *Int'l*, pg. 7486
T&C SURF DESIGNS—See T&C Holding Ltd; *U.S. Private*, pg. 3909
TCS URUGUAY S. A.—See Tata Sons Limited; *Int'l*, pg. 7469
TCT COMPUTING GROUP, INC.—See 10Pearls LLC; *U.S. Private*, pg. 2
TC-TERTIA PROJEKTVERWALTUNGSGESELLSCHAFT MBH—See UniCredit S.p.A.; *Int'l*, pg. 8035
TCTFAMERICA, INC.—See The Walt Disney Company; *U.S. Public*, pg. 2141
TCT MINISTRIES, INC.; *U.S. Private*, pg. 3943
TCTM KIDS IT EDUCATION INC.; *Int'l*, pg. 7486
T.C. TOPLU KONUT IDARESI BASKANLIGI; *Int'l*, pg. 7396
TCT STAINLESS STEEL INC—See ERG S.p.A.; *Int'l*, pg. 2491
TCT STAINLESS STEEL OF NASHVILLE INC—See ERG S.p.A.; *Int'l*, pg. 2491
T-CUBE GLOBAL LOGISTICS CO., LTD.—See T8EX Global Holdings Corp.; *Int'l*, pg. 7398
TCU UNTERHALTUNGSELEKTRONIK AG; *Int'l*, pg. 7482
TCV ACQUISITION CORP.; *U.S. Public*, pg. 1983
TCVS-ASHLAND PLANT—See Terumo Corporation; *Int'l*, pg. 7569
TCV STEVEDORING COMPANY, S.A.—See Mitsubishi Corporation; *Int'l*, pg. 4943
TCW ASSET MANAGEMENT CO., INC.—See The Carlyle Group Inc.; *U.S. Public*, pg. 2056
TCW CAPITAL INVESTMENT CORPORATION—See The Carlyle Group Inc.; *U.S. Public*, pg. 2056
TCW DIRECT LENDING LLC; *U.S. Private*, pg. 3943
TCW FUNDS MANAGEMENT, INC.—See The Carlyle Group Inc.; *U.S. Public*, pg. 2056
THE TCW GROUP, INC.—See The Carlyle Group Inc.; *U.S. Public*, pg. 2055
T&C WHOLESALE LLC—See Sunoco LP; *U.S. Public*, pg. 1965
TCW SPECIAL PURPOSE ACQUISITION CORP.; *U.S. Public*, pg. 1983
TCW STRATEGIC INCOME FUND, INC.; *U.S. Public*, pg. 1983
TCX, LLC—See Delta Apparel, Inc.; *U.S. Public*, pg. 652
T.C. ZIRAAT BANKASI A.S.; *Int'l*, pg. 7397
TDA ADVERTISING & DESIGN; *U.S. Private*, pg. 3944
TDA ARMEMENTS S.A.S.—See Thales S.A.; *Int'l*, pg. 7601
TDA GROUP, LLC—See The Marketing Group Plc; *Int'l*, pg. 7605
TDA INDUSTRIES, INC.; *U.S. Private*, pg. 3944
TD AMERITRADE ASIA PTE. LTD.—See The Charles Schwab Corporation; *U.S. Public*, pg. 2058
TD AMERITRADE CLEARING, INC.—See The Charles Schwab Corporation; *U.S. Public*, pg. 2058
TD AMERITRADE FUTURES & FOREX LLC—See The Charles Schwab Corporation; *U.S. Public*, pg. 2058
TD AMERITRADE HOLDING CORPORATION—See The Charles Schwab Corporation; *U.S. Public*, pg. 2058
TD AMERITRADE HONG KONG LIMITED—See The Charles Schwab Corporation; *U.S. Public*, pg. 2058
TD AMERITRADE, INC.—See The Charles Schwab Corporation; *U.S. Public*, pg. 2058
TD AMERITRADE INC.—See The Toronto-Dominion Bank; *Int'l*, pg. 7695
TD AMERITRADE SERVICES COMPANY, INC.—See The Charles Schwab Corporation; *U.S. Public*, pg. 2058
TD AMERITRADE SINGAPORE PTE. LTD.—See The Charles Schwab Corporation; *U.S. Public*, pg. 2058

TD AMERITRADE TRUST COMPANY—See The Charles Schwab Corporation; *U.S. Public*, pg. 2058
T DAMLA DENIZCILIK A.S.—See Koc Holding A.S.; *Int'l*, pg. 4224
TDAM USA INC.—See The Toronto-Dominion Bank; *Int'l*, pg. 7696
T D A NOYON; *Int'l*, pg. 7394
T'DASH G.K.—See eREX Co., Ltd.; *Int'l*, pg. 2490
TDA; *Int'l*, pg. 7486
T&D ASSET MANAGEMENT CO., LTD.—See T&D Holdings, Inc.; *Int'l*, pg. 7395
TDATA CORPORATION (MALAYSIA) SDN. BHD.—See Teradata Corporation; *U.S. Public*, pg. 2016
TD AUTO FINANCE LLC—See The Toronto-Dominion Bank; *Int'l*, pg. 7695
TD AUTO FINANCE SERVICES INC.—See The Toronto-Dominion Bank; *Int'l*, pg. 7695
TD AUTOMOTIVE COMPRESSOR GEORGIA, LLC—See Toyota Industries Corporation; *Int'l*, pg. 7869
TD AUTOMOTIVE COMPRESSOR KUNSHAN CO., LTD.—See Toyota Industries Corporation; *Int'l*, pg. 7866
TD BANK, N.A.—See The Toronto-Dominion Bank; *Int'l*, pg. 7695
TD BANK US HOLDING COMPANY - CHERRY HILL—See The Toronto-Dominion Bank; *Int'l*, pg. 7695
TD BANK US HOLDING COMPANY—See The Toronto-Dominion Bank; *Int'l*, pg. 7695
TDB AUTOMOBILES SA; *Int'l*, pg. 7486
TDBBS LLC.—See Central Garden & Pet Company; *U.S. Public*, pg. 473
TDB CREDIT INFORMATION KOREA, LTD.—See Teikoku Databank, Ltd.; *Int'l*, pg. 7524
TDB FUSION CORP.—See Teikoku Databank, Ltd.; *Int'l*, pg. 7524
TDB SPLIT CORP.—See Quadravest Capital Management Inc.; *Int'l*, pg. 6150
TDC AIRLINES SERVICES LTD.—See St. Kitts Nevis Anguilla Trading & Development Co., Ltd.; *Int'l*, pg. 7159
TD CANADA TRUST—See The Toronto-Dominion Bank; *Int'l*, pg. 7695
TDC AS—See Telia Company AB; *Int'l*, pg. 7544
TDC COLOMBIA LIMITADA—See Teradata Corporation; *U.S. Public*, pg. 2016
TDC HOLDING A/S—See Arbejdsmarkedets Tillaegspension; *Int'l*, pg. 537
TDC HOLDING A/S—See Macquarie Group Limited; *Int'l*, pg. 4626
TDC HOLDING A/S—See PFA Holding A/S; *Int'l*, pg. 5835
TDC HOLDING A/S—See PKA A/S; *Int'l*, pg. 5887
TDCI, INC.—See Koch Industries, Inc.; *U.S. Private*, pg. 2331
TDC NEVIS LTD.—See St. Kitts Nevis Anguilla Trading & Development Co., Ltd.; *Int'l*, pg. 7159
T & D CONCRETE INC.; *U.S. Private*, pg. 3908
T&D CONFIRM LTD.—See T&D Holdings, Inc.; *Int'l*, pg. 7395
TD CONSTRUCTION SERVICES, LLC—See Teixeira Duarte SA; *Int'l*, pg. 7525
TDC PETS, LLC—See Summit Partners, L.P.; *U.S. Private*, pg. 3855
TDC RENTALS LTD.—See St. Kitts Nevis Anguilla Trading & Development Co., Ltd.; *Int'l*, pg. 7159
TDC RENTALS (NEVIS) LTD.—See St. Kitts Nevis Anguilla Trading & Development Co., Ltd.; *Int'l*, pg. 7159
TDC SHIPPING LTD.—See St. Kitts Nevis Anguilla Trading & Development Co., Ltd.; *Int'l*, pg. 7159
TDC SOFT INC.; *Int'l*, pg. 7486
TDC SOLUTIONS A/S—See Arbejdsmarkedets Tillaegspension; *Int'l*, pg. 537
TDC SOLUTIONS A/S—See Macquarie Group Limited; *Int'l*, pg. 4626
TDC SOLUTIONS A/S—See PFA Holding A/S; *Int'l*, pg. 5835
TDC SOLUTIONS A/S—See PKA A/S; *Int'l*, pg. 5887
TDC SYSTEMS INTEGRATION; *U.S. Private*, pg. 3944
T&D CUSTOMER SERVICES CO., LTD.—See T&D Holdings, Inc.; *Int'l*, pg. 7395
TDCX INC.; *Int'l*, pg. 7486
TDCX INFORMATION CONSULTING (SHANGHAI) CO., LTD.—See TDCX Inc.; *Int'l*, pg. 7486
TDCX JAPAN KK—See TDCX Inc.; *Int'l*, pg. 7486
TD DEUTSCHE KLIMAKOMPRESSOR GMBH—See Toyota Industries Corporation; *Int'l*, pg. 7867
TD DRIVE MANUFACTURING CO., LTD.—See TOYO DENKI SEIZO K.K.; *Int'l*, pg. 7852
TDE CO LTD—See Toho Zinc Co., Ltd.; *Int'l*, pg. 7776
TD-EC, S.A.—See Teixeira Duarte SA; *Int'l*, pg. 7525
TD-EC, S.A.—See Teixeira Duarte SA; *Int'l*, pg. 7525
TD-EC, S.A.—See Teixeira Duarte SA; *Int'l*, pg. 7525
TD-EC, S.A.—See Teixeira Duarte SA; *Int'l*, pg. 7525
TD-EC, S.A.—See Teixeira Duarte SA; *Int'l*, pg. 7525
TD-EC, S.A.—See Teixeira Duarte SA; *Int'l*, pg. 7525
TDE - TRANS DATA ELEKTRONIK GMBH; *Int'l*, pg. 7486
TDF CORPORATION—See SPARX Group Co., Ltd.; *Int'l*, pg. 7128
T&D FINANCIAL LIFE INSURANCE COMPANY—See T&D Holdings, Inc.; *Int'l*, pg. 7395

COMPANY NAME INDEX

TD FINANCING SERVICE INC.—See The Toronto-Dominion Bank; *Int'l*, pg. 7695
TDF, INC.—See Fluor Corporation; *U.S. Public*, pg. 859
TD FOOD GROUP, INC.—See Grupo Finaccess S.A.P.I. de C.V.; *Int'l*, pg. 3129
TDF S.A.S.—See Arcus Infrastructure Partners LLP; *Int'l*, pg. 553
TDF S.A.S.—See Brookfield Infrastructure Partners L.P.; *Int'l*, pg. 1190
TDF S.A.S.—See Public Sector Pension Investment Board; *Int'l*, pg. 6097
TD GENERAL INSURANCE COMPANY—See The Toronto-Dominion Bank; *Int'l*, pg. 7695
TDG GERMANY GMBH—See TransDigm Group Incorporated; *U.S. Public*, pg. 2183
TDG HOLDING CO., LTD.; *Int'l*, pg. 7486
TDGI, LTDA.—See Teixeira Duarte SA; *Int'l*, pg. 7525
TDG INC.; *U.S. Private*, pg. 3944
TDGI, S.A.—See Teixeira Duarte SA; *Int'l*, pg. 7525
TDGI, S.A.—See Teixeira Duarte SA; *Int'l*, pg. 7525
TDGI, SL—See Teixeira Duarte SA; *Int'l*, pg. 7525
TD GLOBAL FINANCE—See The Toronto-Dominion Bank; *Int'l*, pg. 7695
TDG OPERATIONS, LLC—See The Dixie Group, Inc.; *U.S. Public*, pg. 2067
TDG ORION SHANGHAI—See Transnational Diversified Group of Companies; *Int'l*, pg. 7902
TDG TOKYO—See Transnational Diversified Group of Companies; *Int'l*, pg. 7902
TDH HOLDINGS, INC.; *Int'l*, pg. 7486
T&D HOLDINGS, INC.; *Int'l*, pg. 7394
TD HOME AND AUTO INSURANCE COMPANY—See The Toronto-Dominion Bank; *Int'l*, pg. 7695
TDI ADVANCED CONVERSION PRODUCTS—See TDI Power Systems; *U.S. Private*, pg. 3944
TDI-CIRCUITEK—See TDI Power Systems; *U.S. Private*, pg. 3944
T.D.I. CO., LTD.; *Int'l*, pg. 7397
TDI-ENTERPRISE POWER SYSTEMS—See TDI Power Systems; *U.S. Private*, pg. 3944
TD INDUSTRIES, INC.; *U.S. Private*, pg. 3943
T&D INFORMATION SYSTEM LTD.—See T&D Holdings, Inc.; *Int'l*, pg. 7395
T&D INVEST NV—See TINC Comm. VA; *Int'l*, pg. 7753
TDI POWER SYSTEMS - COMMERCIAL PRODUCTS DIVISION—See TDI Power Systems; *U.S. Private*, pg. 3944
TDI POWER SYSTEMS - DYNALOAD DIVISION—See TDI Power Systems; *U.S. Private*, pg. 3944
TDI POWER SYSTEMS; *U.S. Private*, pg. 3944
TD IRELAND UNLIMITED COMPANY—See The Toronto-Dominion Bank; *Int'l*, pg. 7695
T.D.I SAS—See Tessi S.A.; *Int'l*, pg. 7574
T DISTRIBUTION; *U.S. Private*, pg. 3908
TDI TERRAPLAN DEVELOPMENT; *U.S. Private*, pg. 3944
TDJ S.A.; *Int'l*, pg. 7486
TDK AUSTRIA GESMBH—See TDK Corporation; *Int'l*, pg. 7488
TDK CHINA CO., LTD.—See TDK Corporation; *Int'l*, pg. 7488
TDK CIS LLC—See TDK Corporation; *Int'l*, pg. 7488
TDK COMPONENTS PTE. LTD.—See TDK Corporation; *Int'l*, pg. 7488
TDK COMPONENTS TAIWAN CO., LTD.—See TDK Corporation; *Int'l*, pg. 7488
TDK COMPONENTS U.S.A., INC—See TDK Corporation; *Int'l*, pg. 7489
TDK CONSTRUCTION CO. INC.; *U.S. Private*, pg. 3944
TDK CORPORATION OF AMERICA—See TDK Corporation; *Int'l*, pg. 7489
TDK CORPORATION; *Int'l*, pg. 7487
TDK CZECH S.R.O.—See TDK Corporation; *Int'l*, pg. 7488
TDK DA AMAZONIA IMPORTACAO E COMERCIO LTDA.—See TDK Corporation; *Int'l*, pg. 7489
TDK DALIAN CORPORATION—See TDK Corporation; *Int'l*, pg. 7488
TDK DESIGN INC.—See TDK Corporation; *Int'l*, pg. 7488
TDK DO BRASIL ELECTRONIC COMPONENTS LTDA.—See TDK Corporation; *Int'l*, pg. 7489
TDK DO BRASIL IND. E COM. LTDA.—See TDK Corporation; *Int'l*, pg. 7489
TDK ELECTRONICS AG—See TDK Corporation; *Int'l*, pg. 7488
TDK ELECTRONICS DO BRASIL LTDA.—See TDK Corporation; *Int'l*, pg. 7488
TDK ELECTRONICS EUROPE GMBH—See TDK Corporation; *Int'l*, pg. 7488
TDK ELECTRONICS FRANCE—See TDK Corporation; *Int'l*, pg. 7488
TDK ELECTRONICS ITALY—See TDK Corporation; *Int'l*, pg. 7488
TDK ELECTRONICS KOREA CORPORATION—See TDK Corporation; *Int'l*, pg. 7488
TDK ELECTRONICS NORDIC—See TDK Corporation; *Int'l*, pg. 7488
TDK ELECTRONICS PHILIPPINES CORPORATION—See TDK Corporation; *Int'l*, pg. 7488
TDK ELECTRONICS S.R.O.—See TDK Corporation; *Int'l*, pg. 7488

TDK-EPC AG & CO. KG—See TDK Corporation; *Int'l*, pg. 7487
TDK-EPC CORPORATION—See TDK Corporation; *Int'l*, pg. 7489
TDK-EPC HONG KONG LTD.—See TDK Corporation; *Int'l*, pg. 7489
TDK EUROPE S.A.—See TDK Corporation; *Int'l*, pg. 7488
TDK FERRITES CORPORATION—See TDK Corporation; *Int'l*, pg. 7489
TDK FOIL ICELAND EHF.—See TDK Corporation; *Int'l*, pg. 7488
TDK (GUANGZHOU) CO., LTD.—See TDK Corporation; *Int'l*, pg. 7488
TDK HONG KONG CO., LTD.—See TDK Corporation; *Int'l*, pg. 7488
TDK INNOVETA INC.—See TDK Corporation; *Int'l*, pg. 7489
TDK ITALY S.R.L.—See TDK Corporation; *Int'l*, pg. 7488
TDK KOFU CORPORATION—See TDK Corporation; *Int'l*, pg. 7488
TDK-LAMBDA AMERICAS (CANADA)—See TDK Corporation; *Int'l*, pg. 7489
TDK-LAMBDA AMERICAS INC.—See TDK Corporation; *Int'l*, pg. 7489
TDK-LAMBDA AMERICAS INC.—See TDK Corporation; *Int'l*, pg. 7489
TDK-LAMBDA CORPORATION—See TDK Corporation; *Int'l*, pg. 7489
TDK-LAMBDA FRANCE SAS—See TDK Corporation; *Int'l*, pg. 7489
TDK-LAMBDA GERMANY GMBH—See TDK Corporation; *Int'l*, pg. 7489
TDK-LAMBDA HIGH POWER DIVISION—See TDK Corporation; *Int'l*, pg. 7489
TDK-LAMBDA MALAYSIA SDN. BHD. - KUANTAN FACTORY—See TDK Corporation; *Int'l*, pg. 7489
TDK-LAMBDA MALAYSIA SDN. BHD. - SENAI FACTORY—See TDK Corporation; *Int'l*, pg. 7489
TDK-LAMBDA MALAYSIA SDN. BHD.—See TDK Corporation; *Int'l*, pg. 7489
TDK-LAMBDA UK LTD.—See TDK Corporation; *Int'l*, pg. 7489
TDK (MALAYSIA) SDN. BHD.—See TDK Corporation; *Int'l*, pg. 7487
TDK MANAGEMENT SERVICES GMBH—See TDK Corporation; *Int'l*, pg. 7488
TDK-MCC CORPORATION—See TDK Corporation; *Int'l*, pg. 7489
TDK-MICRONAS GMBH—See TDK Corporation; *Int'l*, pg. 7489
TDK-MICRONAS K.K.—See TDK Corporation; *Int'l*, pg. 7489
TDK PHILIPPINES CORPORATION—See TDK Corporation; *Int'l*, pg. 7488
TDK PRECISION TOOL CORPORATION—See TDK Corporation; *Int'l*, pg. 7488
TDK RF SOLUTIONS INC.—See TDK Corporation; *Int'l*, pg. 7489
TDK SERVICE CORPORATION—See TDK Corporation; *Int'l*, pg. 7488
TDK (SHANGHAI) INTERNATIONAL TRADING CO., LTD.—See TDK Corporation; *Int'l*, pg. 7488
TDK (SHANGHAI) INVESTMENT LTD.—See TDK Corporation; *Int'l*, pg. 7487
TDK SINGAPORE (PTE.) LTD.—See TDK Corporation; *Int'l*, pg. 7488
TDK (SUZHOU) CO., LTD.—See TDK Corporation; *Int'l*, pg. 7488
TDK TAIWAN CORPORATION—See TDK Corporation; *Int'l*, pg. 7488
TDK TECHNO CORPORATION—See TDK Corporation; *Int'l*, pg. 7488
TDK TECHNOLOGIES, LLC; *U.S. Private*, pg. 3944
TDK (THAILAND) CO., LTD.—See TDK Corporation; *Int'l*, pg. 7488
TDK UGO CORPORATION—See TDK Corporation; *Int'l*, pg. 7489
TDK UJO CORPORATION—See TDK Corporation; *Int'l*, pg. 7489
TDK UK LIMITED—See TDK Corporation; *Int'l*, pg. 7489
TDK U.S.A. CORPORATION—See TDK Corporation; *Int'l*, pg. 7488
TDK (XIAMEN) ELECTRONICS CO., LTD.—See TDK Corporation; *Int'l*, pg. 7488
TDK (XIAOGAN) CO., LTD.—See TDK Corporation; *Int'l*, pg. 7488
TDK YURIHONJO CORPORATION—See TDK Corporation; *Int'l*, pg. 7489
TDK (ZHUHAI FTZ) CO., LTD.—See TDK Corporation; *Int'l*, pg. 7488
T&D LEASE CO., LTD—See T&D Holdings, Inc.; *Int'l*, pg. 7395
TDL EQUIPMENT LTD—See Ballyvesey Holdings Limited; *Int'l*, pg. 809
TD MAKOSPED AD; *Int'l*, pg. 7486
TDM BERHAD; *Int'l*, pg. 7489
T&D METAL PRODUCTS LLC; *U.S. Private*, pg. 3909
TD MOBILE CORPORATION—See Denso Corporation; *Int'l*, pg. 2033

TDM SYSTEMS GMBH—See Sandvik AB; *Int'l*, pg. 6535
TDM SYSTEMS, INC.—See Sandvik AB; *Int'l*, pg. 6535
TDMY TECHNOLOGY GROUP, INC.; *U.S. Public*, pg. 1987
TDN FINANS AS—See Infront ASA; *Int'l*, pg. 3699
TD POWER SYSTEMS LIMITED; *Int'l*, pg. 7486
TD RAKHAT-SHYMKENT LTD—See Lotte Co., Ltd.; *Int'l*, pg. 4560
TDR CAPITAL LLP; *Int'l*, pg. 7490
TDR D.O.O., BEOGRAD—See British American Tobacco plc; *Int'l*, pg. 1168
TDR D.O.O., BLAZUJ—See British American Tobacco plc; *Int'l*, pg. 1168
TDR D.O.O., ROVINJ—See British American Tobacco plc; *Int'l*, pg. 1168
TDRE INVESTMENTS, LLC—See Teixeira Duarte SA; *Int'l*, pg. 7525
TD REPLY GMBH—See Reply S.p.A.; *Int'l*, pg. 6291
TDR ROVITA D.O.O.—See British American Tobacco plc; *Int'l*, pg. 1168
TDR SKOPJE DOOEL—See British American Tobacco plc; *Int'l*, pg. 1168
TDS AUTOMATION, INC.—See Doerfer Corporation; *U.S. Private*, pg. 1253
TDS BAJA BROADBAND LLC—See Telephone & Data Systems, Inc.; *U.S. Public*, pg. 1997
TDSC, INC.—See Henry Schein, Inc.; *U.S. Public*, pg. 1027
TDS CO., LTD.—See Japan Asia Group Limited; *Int'l*, pg. 3885
TDS CONSTRUCTION INC.; *U.S. Private*, pg. 3944
TDS CORPORATE SERVICES LLC—See ITT Inc.; *U.S. Public*, pg. 1179
TD SEARCH—See TradeDoubler AB; *Int'l*, pg. 7887
TD SECURITIES AUSTRALIA LTD.—See The Toronto-Dominion Bank; *Int'l*, pg. 7696
TD SECURITIES INC.—See The Toronto-Dominion Bank; *Int'l*, pg. 7695
TD SECURITIES JAPAN INC.—See The Toronto-Dominion Bank; *Int'l*, pg. 7696
TD SECURITIES (SINGAPORE) LIMITED—See The Toronto-Dominion Bank; *Int'l*, pg. 7696
TD SECURITIES (UNITED KINGDOM) LTD.—See The Toronto-Dominion Bank; *Int'l*, pg. 7696
TD SECURITIES (USA) LLC - CHICAGO—See The Toronto-Dominion Bank; *Int'l*, pg. 7696
TD SECURITIES (USA) LLC - HOUSTON—See The Toronto-Dominion Bank; *Int'l*, pg. 7696
TD SECURITIES (USA) LLC—See The Toronto-Dominion Bank; *Int'l*, pg. 7696
TDS METRO-COM—See Telephone & Data Systems, Inc.; *U.S. Public*, pg. 1997
TDS METROCOM—See Telephone & Data Systems, Inc.; *U.S. Public*, pg. 1997
TD SPLIT INC.; *Int'l*, pg. 7486
TDS TECHNOLOGY (S) PTE LTD—See ISDN Holdings Limited; *Int'l*, pg. 3813
TDS TELECOMMUNICATIONS CORPORATION—See Telephone & Data Systems, Inc.; *U.S. Public*, pg. 1998
TDS TELECOM—See Telephone & Data Systems, Inc.; *U.S. Public*, pg. 1997
TDS TELECOM—See Telephone & Data Systems, Inc.; *U.S. Public*, pg. 1997
TDS TELECOM—See Telephone & Data Systems, Inc.; *U.S. Public*, pg. 1997
TDS TELECOM—See Telephone & Data Systems, Inc.; *U.S. Public*, pg. 1997
TDS TELECOM—See Telephone & Data Systems, Inc.; *U.S. Public*, pg. 1997
TDS TELECOM—See Telephone & Data Systems, Inc.; *U.S. Public*, pg. 1997
TDS TELECOM—See Telephone & Data Systems, Inc.; *U.S. Public*, pg. 1997
TDS TELECOM—See Telephone & Data Systems, Inc.; *U.S. Public*, pg. 1997
TDS TELECOM—See Telephone & Data Systems, Inc.; *U.S. Public*, pg. 1997
TDS TELECOM—See Telephone & Data Systems, Inc.; *U.S. Public*, pg. 1997
TDS TELECOM—See Telephone & Data Systems, Inc.; *U.S. Public*, pg. 1997
TDS TELECOM—See Telephone & Data Systems, Inc.; *U.S. Public*, pg. 1997
TDS TELECOM—See Telephone & Data Systems, Inc.; *U.S. Public*, pg. 1997
TDS TELECOM—See Telephone & Data Systems, Inc.; *U.S. Public*, pg. 1997
TDS TELECOM—See Telephone & Data Systems, Inc.; *U.S. Public*, pg. 1997

TDS TELECOM—See Telephone & Data Systems, Inc.; U.S. Public, pg. 1997
TDS TELECOM—See Telephone & Data Systems, Inc.; U.S. Public, pg. 1997
TDS TELECOM—See Telephone & Data Systems, Inc.; U.S. Public, pg. 1997
TDS TELECOM—See Telephone & Data Systems, Inc.; U.S. Public, pg. 1997
TDS TELECOM—See Telephone & Data Systems, Inc.; U.S. Public, pg. 1997
TDS TELECOM—See Telephone & Data Systems, Inc.; U.S. Public, pg. 1997
TDS TELECOM—See Telephone & Data Systems, Inc.; U.S. Public, pg. 1998
TDS TELECOM—See Telephone & Data Systems, Inc.; U.S. Public, pg. 1997
TDS TELECOM—See Telephone & Data Systems, Inc.; U.S. Public, pg. 1997
TDS TELECOM—See Telephone & Data Systems, Inc.; U.S. Public, pg. 1998
TDS TELECOM—See Telephone & Data Systems, Inc.; U.S. Public, pg. 1997
TDS TELECOM—See Telephone & Data Systems, Inc.; U.S. Public, pg. 1997
TD SYNNEX AS CZECH S.R.O.—See TD Synnex Corp; U.S. Public, pg. 1984
TD SYNNEX AUSTRIA GMBH—See TD Synnex Corp; U.S. Public, pg. 1984
TD SYNNEX CANADA ULC—See TD Synnex Corp; U.S. Public, pg. 1984
TD SYNNEX CORP; U.S. Public, pg. 1983
TD SYNNEX CROATIA D.O.O.—See TD Synnex Corp; U.S. Public, pg. 1984
TD SYNNEX CZECH S.R.O.—See TD Synnex Corp; U.S. Public, pg. 1984
TD SYNNEX EUROPE GMBH—See TD Synnex Corp; U.S. Public, pg. 1984
TD SYNNEX FINLAND OY—See TD Synnex Corp; U.S. Public, pg. 1984
TD SYNNEX FRANCE S.A.S.—See TD Synnex Corp; U.S. Public, pg. 1984
TD SYNNEX GERMANY GMBH & CO. OHG—See TD Synnex Corp; U.S. Public, pg. 1984
TD SYNNEX HUNGARY KFT—See TD Synnex Corp; U.S. Public, pg. 1984
TD SYNNEX IRELAND LIMITED—See TD Synnex Corp; U.S. Public, pg. 1984
TD SYNNEX ITALY S.R.L.—See TD Synnex Corp; U.S. Public, pg. 1984
TD SYNNEX KFT—See TD Synnex Corp; U.S. Public, pg. 1984
TD SYNNEX K.K.—See TD Synnex Corp; U.S. Public, pg. 1985
TD SYNNEX NETHERLANDS B.V.—See TD Synnex Corp; U.S. Public, pg. 1984
TD SYNNEX NORWAY AS—See TD Synnex Corp; U.S. Public, pg. 1985
TD SYNNEX POLAND SP. Z O.O.—See TD Synnex Corp; U.S. Public, pg. 1985
TD SYNNEX PORTUGAL, LDA—See TD Synnex Corp; U.S. Public, pg. 1985
TD SYNNEX SPAIN, S.L.U.—See TD Synnex Corp; U.S. Public, pg. 1985
TD SYNNEX SWEDEN AB—See TD Synnex Corp; U.S. Public, pg. 1985
TD SYNNEX SWITZERLAND GMBH—See TD Synnex Corp; U.S. Public, pg. 1985
TD SYNNEX UK LIMITED—See TD Synnex Corp; U.S. Public, pg. 1985
T&D TAIYO DAIDO LEASE CO., LTD.—See T&D Holdings, Inc.; Int'l, pg. 7395
TD TECH DATA AB—See TD Synnex Corp; U.S. Public, pg. 1986
TD TECH DATA PORTUGAL LDA—See TD Synnex Corp; U.S. Public, pg. 1986
T&D UNITED CAPITAL CO., LTD.—See T&D Holdings, Inc.; Int'l, pg. 7395
TDV DENTAL LTDA.—See Septodont Inc.; U.S. Private, pg. 3612
TD WATERHOUSE BANK—See The Toronto-Dominion Bank; Int'l, pg. 7695
TD WATERHOUSE CANADA INC.—See The Toronto-Dominion Bank; Int'l, pg. 7696
TD WATERHOUSE INVESTOR SERVICES, INC.—See The Toronto-Dominion Bank; Int'l, pg. 7695
TD WATERHOUSE PRIVATE INVESTMENT COUNSEL INC.—See The Toronto-Dominion Bank; Int'l, pg. 7696
TDW-GESELLSCHAFT FUR VERTEIDIGUNGSTECHNISCHE WIRKSYSTEME GMBH—See Airbus SE; Int'l, pg. 247
TDW-GESELLSCHAFT FUR VERTEIDIGUNGSTECHNISCHE WIRKSYSTEME GMBH—See BAE Systems plc; Int'l, pg. 798
TDW-GESELLSCHAFT FUR VERTEIDIGUNGSTECHNISCHE WIRKSYSTEME GMBH—See Leonardo S.p.A.; Int'l, pg. 4460

T.D. WILLIAMSON ASIA PACIFIC PTY LTD.—See T.D. Williamson, Inc.; U.S. Private, pg. 3911
T.D. WILLIAMSON, INC.; U.S. Private, pg. 3911
TDW, INC.—See T.D. Williamson, Inc.; U.S. Private, pg. 3911
TDW INC.; U.S. Private, pg. 3944
TDW OFFSHORE SERVICES—See T.D. Williamson, Inc.; U.S. Private, pg. 3911
TDW PIGGING PRODUCTS—See T.D. Williamson, Inc.; U.S. Private, pg. 3911
TDW SERVICES, INC.—See T.D. Williamson, Inc.; U.S. Private, pg. 3911
TDX GROUP LIMITED—See Equifax Inc.; U.S. Public, pg. 786
TDX INDIGO IBERIA S.L.U—See Equifax Inc.; U.S. Public, pg. 786
TEA AVENUE (PRIVATE) LIMITED—See Food Empire Holdings Limited; Int'l, pg. 2727
TEAC AMERICA, INC.—See Evolution Capital Management LLC; U.S. Private, pg. 1443
TEAC AUDIO (CHINA) CO., LTD.—See Evolution Capital Management LLC; U.S. Private, pg. 1443
TEAC CANADA LTD.—See Evolution Capital Management LLC; U.S. Private, pg. 1443
TEAC CORPORATION—See Evolution Capital Management LLC; U.S. Private, pg. 1442
TEAC DEUTSCHLAND GMBH—See Evolution Capital Management LLC; U.S. Private, pg. 1443
TEAC ELECTRONICS (M) SDN. BHD.—See Evolution Capital Management LLC; U.S. Private, pg. 1443
TEAC EUROPE GMBH.—See Evolution Capital Management LLC; U.S. Private, pg. 1443
TEACHANYWHERE LTD—See Randstad N.V.; Int'l, pg. 6206
TEACHERBOARDS (1985) LIMITED—See Havelock Europa PLC; Int'l, pg. 3287
TEACHER RETIREMENT SYSTEM OF TEXAS; U.S. Private, pg. 3944
TEACHERS BUILDING SOCIETY; Int'l, pg. 7499
TEACHERS CREDIT UNION; U.S. Private, pg. 3944
TEACHERS INSURANCE & ANNUITY ASSOCIATION OF AMERICA—See Teachers Insurance Association - College Retirement Fund; U.S. Private, pg. 3945
TEACHERS INSURANCE ASSOCIATION - COLLEGE RETIREMENT FUND; U.S. Private, pg. 3945
TEACHERS INSURANCE COMPANY—See Horace Mann Educators Corporation; U.S. Public, pg. 1053
TEACHERS OF TOMORROW LLC—See Gauge Capital LLC; U.S. Private, pg. 1652
TEACHERS ON CALL, INC.—See Kelly Services, Inc.; U.S. Public, pg. 1220
TEACHERS' PRIVATE CAPITAL—See Ontario Teachers' Pension Plan; Int'l, pg. 5586
TEACHFORALL, INC.; U.S. Private, pg. 3948
TEACH FOR AMERICA; U.S. Private, pg. 3944
TEACHING PERSONNEL LTD.—See Intermediate Capital Group plc; Int'l, pg. 3742
TEACHING RESOURCE CENTER LLC; U.S. Private, pg. 3948
TEACHING STRATEGIES, LLC—See Summit Partners, L.P.; U.S. Private, pg. 3856
TEAC MANUFACTURING SOLUTIONS CORPORATION—See Evolution Capital Management LLC; U.S. Private, pg. 1443
TEAC MANUFACTURING SOLUTIONS CORPORATION—See Evolution Capital Management LLC; U.S. Private, pg. 1443
TEAC MEXICO S.A. DE C.V.—See Evolution Capital Management LLC; U.S. Private, pg. 1443
TEAC NEDERLAND B.V.—See Evolution Capital Management LLC; U.S. Private, pg. 1443
TEA COLLECTION; U.S. Private, pg. 3944
TEACRATE LIMITED—See The Bidvest Group Limited; Int'l, pg. 7622
TEAC SYSTEM CREATE CORPORATION—See Evolution Capital Management LLC; U.S. Private, pg. 1443
TEAC UK LTD.—See Evolution Capital Management LLC; U.S. Private, pg. 1443
TEA FORTE, INC.—See JAB Holding Company S.a.r.l.; Int'l, pg. 3863
TEAGUE ELECTRIC CONSTRUCTION; U.S. Private, pg. 3948
TEAGUE LUMBER COMPANY INC.; U.S. Private, pg. 3948
TEA HOUSE LLP—See Food Empire Holdings Limited; Int'l, pg. 2727
TEAK HOLZ HANDELS- UND VERARBEITUNGS GMBH—See Teak Holz International AG; Int'l, pg. 7499
TEAK HOLZ INTERNATIONAL AG; Int'l, pg. 7499
TEAKWOOD CAPITAL, L.P.; U.S. Private, pg. 3948
TEAL AD; Int'l, pg. 7499
TEAL CONSTRUCTION COMPANY; U.S. Private, pg. 3948
TEA LIFE CO., LTD.; Int'l, pg. 7499
TEALIUM INC.; U.S. Private, pg. 3948
TEALL CAPITAL PARTNERS, LLC; U.S. Private, pg. 3948
TEALS EXPRESS INC.; U.S. Private, pg. 3949
TEAL; U.S. Private, pg. 3948

TEALSTONE COMMERCIAL, INC.—See Sterling Infrastructure, Inc.; U.S. Public, pg. 1947
TEAM17 GROUP PLC; Int'l, pg. 7500
TEAM 2015 SRL—See Vivaticket; Int'l, pg. 8265
TEAM24 LIMITED—See Capita plc; Int'l, pg. 1309
TEAM2VENTURE GMBH—See Randstad N.V.; Int'l, pg. 6206
TEAM ACCESSORIES LIMITED—See Moog Inc.; U.S. Public, pg. 1471
TEAM ACQUISITION CORPORATION; U.S. Private, pg. 3949
TEAM AQUATIC INC.—See Clearford Water Systems Inc.; Int'l, pg. 1657
TEAM/ATHENS—See Omnicom Group Inc.; U.S. Public, pg. 1573
TEAMAX SMART CITY TECHNOLOGY CORPORATION LIMITED; Int'l, pg. 7501
TEAMBANK AG—See DZ BANK AG Deutsche Zentral-Genossenschaftsbank; Int'l, pg. 2245
TEAMBONDING; U.S. Private, pg. 3951
THE TEAM BRAND COMMUNICATION CONSULTANTS LIMITED—See Writtle Holdings Limited; Int'l, pg. 8495
TEAM BUILDERS PLUS; U.S. Private, pg. 3949
TEAM CHEVROLET BUICK GMC CADILLAC; U.S. Private, pg. 3949
TEAM COMPANIES; U.S. Private, pg. 3949
TEAM CONCEPTS PRIVATE LIMITED—See Varroc Engineering Ltd.; Int'l, pg. 8133
TEAM CONSTRUCTION MANAGEMENT COMPANY LIMITED—See Team Consulting Engi; Int'l, pg. 7500
TEAM CONSULTING ENGINEERING & MANAGEMENT PCL; Int'l, pg. 7499
TEAM CONVEYANCING LIMITED—See First American Financial Corporation; U.S. Public, pg. 838
TEAM COSMO ZURICH AG—See WPP plc; Int'l, pg. 8482
TEAM-CRUCIBLE, LLC; U.S. Private, pg. 3950
TEAM DES MOINES PARTNERS, LLC—See Telephone & Data Systems, Inc.; U.S. Public, pg. 1998
TEAM DRIVE-AWAY, INC.—See The Carlyle Group Inc.; U.S. Public, pg. 2056
TEAM EDITION APPAREL, INC.—See Foot Locker, Inc.; U.S. Public, pg. 864
TEAM ENERGY RESOURCES LTD.—See Buckthorn Partners LLP; Int'l, pg. 1210
TEAM ENERGY RESOURCES LTD.—See OEP Capital Advisors, L.P.; U.S. Private, pg. 2997
TEAM ENTERPRISES, INC.—See Stagwell, Inc.; U.S. Public, pg. 1928
TEAM EPIPHANY—See Stagwell, Inc.; U.S. Public, pg. 1928
TEAM EXPRESS DISTRIBUTING, LLC; U.S. Private, pg. 3949
TEAM FITZ GRAPHICS, LLC; U.S. Private, pg. 3949
TEAM FORD LINCOLN; U.S. Private, pg. 3949
TEAM GLASS ENGINEERING PTE. LTD.—See Chasen Holdings Limited; Int'l, pg. 1457
TEAM GREYHOUNDS (BROUGH PARK) LIMITED—See William Hill Plc; Int'l, pg. 8413
TEAM HEALTH HOLDINGS, INC.—See Blackstone Inc.; U.S. Public, pg. 359
TEAM HEALTH, LLC—See Blackstone Inc.; U.S. Public, pg. 359
TEAM, INC.; U.S. Public, pg. 1987
TEAM INDIA MANAGERS LTD.; Int'l, pg. 7500
TEAM INDUSTRIAL SERVICES ASIA PRIVATE LTD.—See Team, Inc.; U.S. Public, pg. 1988
TEAM INDUSTRIAL SERVICES BELGIUM—See Team, Inc.; U.S. Public, pg. 1988
TEAM INDUSTRIAL SERVICES, INC.—See Team, Inc.; U.S. Public, pg. 1988
TEAM INDUSTRIAL SERVICES MALAYSIA SDN BHD—See Team, Inc.; U.S. Public, pg. 1988
TEAM INDUSTRIAL SERVICES—See Team, Inc.; U.S. Public, pg. 1988
TEAM INDUSTRIAL SERVICES (UK) LIMITED—See Team, Inc.; U.S. Public, pg. 1988
TEAM INDUSTRIES ANDREWS, INC.—See TEAM Industries, Inc.; U.S. Private, pg. 3949
TEAM INDUSTRIES - AUDUBON—See TEAM Industries, Inc.; U.S. Private, pg. 3949
TEAM INDUSTRIES BAGLEY-AUDUBON, INC.—See TEAM Industries, Inc.; U.S. Private, pg. 3949
TEAM INDUSTRIES - DETROIT LAKES—See TEAM Industries, Inc.; U.S. Private, pg. 3949
TEAM INDUSTRIES, INC.; U.S. Private, pg. 3949
TEAM INDUSTRIES, INC.; U.S. Private, pg. 3949
TEAM INDUSTRIES - PARK RAPIDS—See TEAM Industries, Inc.; U.S. Private, pg. 3949
TEAM INFORMATION SERVICES; U.S. Private, pg. 3949
TEAM INTEGRATED ENGINEERING, INC.; U.S. Private, pg. 3949
TEAM INTERNET GROUP PLC; Int'l, pg. 7500
TEAMINVEST PRIVATE GROUP LIMITED; Int'l, pg. 7501
TEAMINVEST PTY. LTD.—See Teaminvest Private Group Limited; Int'l, pg. 7501
TEAM IP.COM; U.S. Private, pg. 3949
TEAM JO-ANN STORES, INC.—See Leonard Green & Partners, L.P.; U.S. Public, pg. 2426
TEAM KALORIK GROUP NV; Int'l, pg. 7500

COMPANY NAME INDEX

TEAM LAB INC.—See Transcosmos Inc.; *Int'l*, pg. 7898
TEAMLEASE EDTECH LIMITED—See TeamLease Services Ltd.; *Int'l*, pg. 7501
TEAMLEASE E-HIRE PRIVATE LIMITED—See TeamLease Services Ltd.; *Int'l*, pg. 7501
TEAMLEASE REGTECH PRIVATE LIMITED—See TeamLease Services Ltd.; *Int'l*, pg. 7501
TEAMLEASE SERVICES LTD.; *Int'l*, pg. 7501
TEAM LEGAL—See Apax Partners LLP; *Int'l*, pg. 503
TEAM LENDING CONCEPTS LLC; *U.S. Private*, pg. 3949
TEAMLINE, LTD.—See Bain Capital, LP; *U.S. Private*, pg. 451
TEAM LTD.—See Malam-Team Ltd.; *Int'l*, pg. 4659
TEAM MARKETING AG—See Highlight Communications AG; *Int'l*, pg. 3388
TEAMMATES COMMERCIAL INTERIORS; *U.S. Private*, pg. 3951
TEAM MOTO PTY. LTD.—See Archer Capital Pty. Ltd.; *Int'l*, pg. 547
TEAM MOTOR SPORTS INC.; *U.S. Private*, pg. 3949
TEAM NATIONAL; *U.S. Private*, pg. 3949
TEAM NISSAN INC.; *U.S. Private*, pg. 3949
TEAM NURSE, INC.—See Searchlight Capital Partners, L.P.; *U.S. Private*, pg. 3587
TEAM OIL TOOLS, LLC; *U.S. Private*, pg. 3950
TEAM OIL TOOLS LP—See Intervale Capital, LLC; *U.S. Private*, pg. 2127
TEAM ONE ADVERTISING—See Publicis Groupe S.A.; *Int'l*, pg. 6110
TEAM ONE ADVERTISING—See Publicis Groupe S.A.; *Int'l*, pg. 6110
TEAM ONE ADVERTISING—See Publicis Groupe S.A.; *Int'l*, pg. 6110
TEAM ONE ADVERTISING—See Publicis Groupe S.A.; *Int'l*, pg. 6110
TEAM ONE GM AUTO MALL; *U.S. Private*, pg. 3950
TEAM ONE PLASTICS INC.; *U.S. Private*, pg. 3950
TEAM ONE—See Publicis Groupe S.A.; *Int'l*, pg. 6110
TEAM-ONE STAFFING SERVICES; *U.S. Private*, pg. 3950
TEAM-PACK GMBH—See Arla Foods amba; *Int'l*, pg. 573
TEAM PRECISION PUBLIC COMPANY LIMITED - PRACHINBURI FACTORY—See Team Precision Public Company Limited; *Int'l*, pg. 7500
TEAM PRECISION PUBLIC COMPANY LIMITED - RANGSIT FACTORY—See Team Precision Public Company Limited; *Int'l*, pg. 7500
TEAM PRECISION PUBLIC COMPANY LIMITED; *Int'l*, pg. 7500
TEAM RAHAL OF MECHANICSBURG, INC.; *U.S. Private*, pg. 3950
TEAM RELOCATIONS; *Int'l*, pg. 7500
TEAM RETAIL SOLUTIONS LLC—See Teall Capital Partners, LLC; *U.S. Private*, pg. 3949
TEAM SAATCHI/SAATCHI & SAATCHI HEALTHCARE—See Publicis Groupe S.A.; *Int'l*, pg. 6110
TEAM SAATCHI—See Publicis Groupe S.A.; *Int'l*, pg. 6109
TEAMSALES LIMITED—See Empresaria Group Plc; *Int'l*, pg. 2389
TEAM SA—See Advent International Corporation; *U.S. Private*, pg. 99
TEAM SA—See Advent International Corporation; *U.S. Private*, pg. 100
TEAM SCHIERL COMPANIES; *U.S. Private*, pg. 3950
TEAM SERVICES, INC.; *U.S. Private*, pg. 3950
TEAMSHARES INC.; *U.S. Private*, pg. 3951
TEAM SLEDD, LLC—See AMCON Distributing Company; *U.S. Public*, pg. 93
TEAMSNAP, INC.—See Waud Capital Partners LLC; *U.S. Private*, pg. 4457
TEAMSOFT, INC.—See Groupe Crit, S.A.; *Int'l*, pg. 3101
TEAM SOFTWARE, INC.—See Accel Partners L.P.; *U.S. Private*, pg. 49
TEAM SOFTWARE, INC.—See KKR & Co. Inc.; *U.S. Public*, pg. 1238
TEAM SOLUTIONS GROUP, INC.; *U.S. Private*, pg. 3950
TEAM SOLUTIONS PROJECT GROUP, INC.; *U.S. Private*, pg. 3950
TEAMSON DESIGN CORP.; *U.S. Private*, pg. 3951
TEAMSOURCE INC.; *U.S. Private*, pg. 3951
TEAMSPIRIT, INC.; *Int'l*, pg. 7501
TEAMSPIRIT LIMITED—See Providence Equity Partners L.L.C.; *U.S. Private*, pg. 3292
TEAM SUPERSTORES OF VALLEJO; *U.S. Private*, pg. 3950
TEAM TANKERS INTERNATIONAL LTD.; *U.S. Private*, pg. 3950
TEAM TANKERS MANAGEMENT AS—See Team Tankers International Ltd.; *U.S. Private*, pg. 3950
TEAM TANKERS MANAGEMENT A/S—See Team Tankers International Ltd.; *U.S. Private*, pg. 3950
TEAM TANKERS MANAGEMENT LLC—See Team Tankers International Ltd.; *U.S. Private*, pg. 3950
TEAM TANKERS MANAGEMENT PTE. LTD.—See Team Tankers International Ltd.; *U.S. Private*, pg. 3950
TEAM TANKERS MANAGEMENT S.A.—See Team Tankers International Ltd.; *U.S. Private*, pg. 3950
TEAM TANKERS (USA) LLC—See Team Tankers International Ltd.; *U.S. Private*, pg. 3950

TEAM TECHNICAL SCHOOL, LLC—See Team, Inc.; *U.S. Public*, pg. 1988
TEAMTECHNIK AUTOMATION GMBH—See Durr AG; *Int'l*, pg. 2233
TEAMTECHNIK MASCHINEN UND ANLAGEN GMBH—See Durr AG; *Int'l*, pg. 2233
TEAM TECHNOLOGIES, INC.—See Clearlake Capital Group, L.P.; *U.S. Private*, pg. 937
TEAMTEK WHOLESALE; *U.S. Private*, pg. 3951
TEAM TELECOMMUNICATIONS GROUP LTD.; *Int'l*, pg. 7500
TEAM TERMINAL BV—See Saudi Arabian Oil Company; *Int'l*, pg. 6589
TEAM TRACTOR AND EQUIPMENT CORP.—See Tym Corporation; *Int'l*, pg. 7995
TEAM TRIDENT LLC; *U.S. Private*, pg. 3950
TEAM TUBE—See Reliance Steel & Aluminum Co.; *U.S. Public*, pg. 1781
TEAM TURBO MACHINES JSC—See Hiolle Industries S.A.; *Int'l*, pg. 3401
TEAMULTRA LIMITED—See Computacenter plc; *Int'l*, pg. 1758
TEAMUNIFY, LLC—See Comcast Corporation; *U.S. Public*, pg. 540
TEAMUP, INC.—See Slogan Inc.; *Int'l*, pg. 6997
TEAMUP TECHNOLOGIES, INC.—See Autodesk, Inc.; *U.S. Public*, pg. 229
TEAM VALVE AND ROTATING SERVICES LIMITED—See Team, Inc.; *U.S. Public*, pg. 1988
TEAM VELOCITY MARKETING LLC; *U.S. Private*, pg. 3950
TEAM VOLKSWAGEN OF HAYWARD; *U.S. Private*, pg. 3950
TEAM WASHINGTON, INC.; *U.S. Private*, pg. 3950
TEAMWAY FINANCE LIMITED—See Teamway International Group Holdings Limited; *Int'l*, pg. 7501
TEAMWAY INTERNATIONAL GROUP HOLDINGS LIMITED; *Int'l*, pg. 7501
TEAM WENDY, LLC—See Dan T. Moore Co.; *U.S. Private*, pg. 1151
TEAMWORKNET INC.; *U.S. Private*, pg. 3951
TEAMWORK SAUDI ARABIA LTD.—See Ali Zaid Al-Quraishi & Brothers Co.; *Int'l*, pg. 323
TEAMWORLD INC.; *U.S. Private*, pg. 3951
TEAM WORLDWIDE; *U.S. Private*, pg. 3950
TEAM YOKOHAMA MOTORSPORT FRANCE—See The Yokohama Rubber Co., Ltd.; *Int'l*, pg. 7702
TEAM YOUN BIO MEDICINE INTERNATIONAL CORP. LIMITED; *Int'l*, pg. 7500
TEAMYOUNG TECHNOLOGY CO., LTD.; *Int'l*, pg. 7501
TEAM/Y&R AMMAN—See WPP plc; *Int'l*, pg. 8493
TEAM/Y&R JEDDAH—See WPP plc; *Int'l*, pg. 8493
TEA PARTY PATRIOTS, INC.; *U.S. Private*, pg. 3944
TEAPIGS LTD—See Tata Sons Limited; *Int'l*, pg. 7470
TEAPO DONGGUAN ELECTRONIC CORP.—See Kaiemei Electronic Corp.; *Int'l*, pg. 4051
TEAPO ELECTRONICS DONGGUAN CO., LTD.—See Kaiemei Electronic Corp.; *Int'l*, pg. 4051
TEAPO SUZHOU ELECTRONIC CORP.—See Kaiemei Electronic Corp.; *Int'l*, pg. 4051
TEAR CORP.; *Int'l*, pg. 7501
TEA REGION PARISIENNE; *Int'l*, pg. 7499
TEARLAB CORP.—See Accelmed Partners II Management, LLC; *U.S. Private*, pg. 50
TEARLACH RESOURCES LIMITED; *Int'l*, pg. 7501
TEARSCIENCE, INC.—See Johnson & Johnson; *U.S. Public*, pg. 1200
TEASDALE FOODS, INC.—See TruArc Partners, L.P.; *U.S. Private*, pg. 4245
TEA SMALLHOLDER FACTORIES PLC; *Int'l*, pg. 7499
TEA TIME LIMITED; *Int'l*, pg. 7499
TEATIME TASTIES LIMITED—See Kitwave Group Plc; *Int'l*, pg. 4196
TEATRO DE LOS INSURGENTES, S.A. DE C.V.—See Grupo Televisa, S.A.B.; *Int'l*, pg. 3136
TEATRO MANZONI SPA—See Fininvest S.p.A.; *Int'l*, pg. 2675
TEATRO VILLAGEMALL LTDA.—See Multiplan Empreendimentos Imobiliarios S.A.; *Int'l*, pg. 5084
TEAVANA CANADA, INC.—See Starbucks Corporation; *U.S. Public*, pg. 1939
TEAVANA CORPORATION—See Starbucks Corporation; *U.S. Public*, pg. 1939
TEAVANA HOLDINGS, INC.—See Starbucks Corporation; *U.S. Public*, pg. 1939
TEBARCO MECHANICAL CORP.—See Modigent LLC; *U.S. Public*, pg. 2763
TEB ARVAL ARAC FILO KIRALAMA AS—See BNP Paribas SA; *Int'l*, pg. 1093
TEB BANCORP, INC.; *U.S. Public*, pg. 1988
TEB CETELEM TUKETICI FINANSMANI A.S.—See BNP Paribas SA; *Int'l*, pg. 1093
TEBECON BV—See VINCI S.A.; *Int'l*, pg. 8229
TEB FAKTORING INC.—See BNP Paribas SA; *Int'l*, pg. 1093
TEB HOLDING ANONIM SIRKETI—See BNP Paribas SA; *Int'l*, pg. 1093
TEB INVESTMENT SECURITIES, INC—See BNP Paribas SA; *Int'l*, pg. 1093

TEC EQUIPMENT, INC.

TEB LEASING INC—See BNP Paribas SA; *Int'l*, pg. 1093
TEBODIN PETERS ENGINEERING FRANCE SARL—See Bilfinger SE; *Int'l*, pg. 1029
TEBODIN PETERS ENGINEERING GMBH—See Bilfinger SE; *Int'l*, pg. 1029
TEBRA MESSEN INDUSTRIE B.V.—See Indutrade AB; *Int'l*, pg. 3681
TEBRAU BAY CONSTRUCTION SDN. BHD.—See Iskandar Waterfront City Berhad; *Int'l*, pg. 3819
TEBRAU BAY SDN. BHD.—See Iskandar Waterfront City Berhad; *Int'l*, pg. 3819
TEB TUKETICI FINANSMAN AS—See BNP Paribas SA; *Int'l*, pg. 1093
TEB YATIRIM MENKUL DEGERLER AS—See BNP Paribas SA; *Int'l*, pg. 1093
TEC5 AG—See Nynomic AG; *Int'l*, pg. 5501
TEC5 TECHNOLOGY CO. LTD.—See Nynomic AG; *Int'l*, pg. 5501
TEC5 USA INC.—See Nynomic AG; *Int'l*, pg. 5501
TEC ACCOUNTING & CONSULTING, LTD.—See Toyo Engineering Corporation; *Int'l*, pg. 7853
TEC-AIR INC.; *U.S. Private*, pg. 3951
TEC AIR SERVICE CORPORATION—See Toyo Engineering Corporation; *Int'l*, pg. 7853
TECALEMIT FLOW OY—See Indutrade AB; *Int'l*, pg. 3681
TECALLIANCE GMBH—See Aptiv PLC; *Int'l*, pg. 525
TECAN ASIA (PTE.) LTD.—See Tecan Group AG; *Int'l*, pg. 7502
TECAN AUSTRALIA PTY LTD—See Tecan Group AG; *Int'l*, pg. 7502
TECAN AUSTRIA GMBH—See Tecan Group AG; *Int'l*, pg. 7502
TECAN BENELUX B.V.B.A.—See Tecan Group AG; *Int'l*, pg. 7502
TECAN DEUTSCHLAND GMBH—See Tecan Group AG; *Int'l*, pg. 7502
TECAN GENOMICS, INC.—See Tecan Group AG; *Int'l*, pg. 7502
TECAN GROUP AG; *Int'l*, pg. 7501
TECAN IBERICA INSTRUMENTACION S.L.U—See Tecan Group AG; *Int'l*, pg. 7502
TECAN ITALIA S.R.L.—See Tecan Group AG; *Int'l*, pg. 7502
TECAN JAPAN CO., LTD.—See Tecan Group AG; *Int'l*, pg. 7502
TECAN KOREA LTD.—See Tecan Group AG; *Int'l*, pg. 7502
TECAN NORDIC AB—See Tecan Group AG; *Int'l*, pg. 7502
TECAN SALES AUSTRIA GMBH—See Tecan Group AG; *Int'l*, pg. 7502
TECAN SALES SWITZERLAND AG—See Tecan Group AG; *Int'l*, pg. 7502
TECAN SCHWEIZ AG—See Tecan Group AG; *Int'l*, pg. 7502
TECAN (SHANGHAI) LABORATORY EQUIPMENT CO., LTD.—See Tecan Group AG; *Int'l*, pg. 7502
TECAN (SHANGHAI) TRADING CO., LTD.—See Tecan Group AG; *Int'l*, pg. 7502
TECAN SOFTWARE COMPETENCE CENTER GMBH—See Tecan Group AG; *Int'l*, pg. 7502
TECAN SP, INC.—See Tecan Group AG; *Int'l*, pg. 7502
TECAN SYSTEMS, INC.—See Tecan Group AG; *Int'l*, pg. 7502
TECAN TRADING AG—See Tecan Group AG; *Int'l*, pg. 7502
TECAN UK LTD.—See Tecan Group AG; *Int'l*, pg. 7502
TECAN US, INC.—See Tecan Group AG; *Int'l*, pg. 7502
TECARENA+ GMBH—See Bayer Aktiengesellschaft; *Int'l*, pg. 910
TEC ARTEC GMBH—See AVK Holding A/S; *Int'l*, pg. 748
TEC ARTEC VALVES GMBH & CO. KG I.L.—See PCC SE; *Int'l*, pg. 5767
T & E CATTLE COMPANY; *U.S. Private*, pg. 3908
TECBLU TECELAGEM BLUMENAU S.A.; *Int'l*, pg. 7502
TEC BRITE TECHNOLOGY CO., LTD.—See Nippon Filcon Co., Ltd.; *Int'l*, pg. 5318
TEC BUILDING SERVICES (NORTH WEST) CO., LTD.; *Int'l*, pg. 7501
TEC BUSINESS SERVICES CORPORATION—See Toyo Engineering Corporation; *Int'l*, pg. 7853
TECCA AB—See Volati AB; *Int'l*, pg. 8301
TECCO GMBH—See Ilford Imaging Switzerland GmbH; *Int'l*, pg. 3614
TEC COMMUNICATIONS CO., LTD.—See Screen Holdings Co., Ltd.; *Int'l*, pg. 6656
TEC CORP.; *U.S. Private*, pg. 3951
TECCWEB INC.—See Alan Allman Associates SA; *Int'l*, pg. 290
TEC D DISTRIBUTION (MALAYSIA) SDN. BHD.—See TD Synnex Corp; *U.S. Public*, pg. 1985
TEC DIRECT MEDIA, INC.; *U.S. Private*, pg. 3951
TEC ELECTRONICA, S.A. DE C.V.—See Japan Industrial Partners, Inc.; *Int'l*, pg. 3897
TEC ELEVATOR, INC.—See 3Phase Elevator Corp; *U.S. Private*, pg. 14
TEC EQUIPMENT, INC.; *U.S. Private*, pg. 3951
TECFRESH SAC—See HORIBA Ltd; *Int'l*, pg. 3478
TECH 21 ENGINEERING SOLUTIONS LIMITED—See Weatherford International plc; *U.S. Public*, pg. 2339

TECH21 LIMITED

TECH21 LIMITED; *Int'l*, pg. 7503
TECH3 SOLUTIONS SDN. BHD.—See TFP Solutions Berhad; *Int'l*, pg. 7587
TECH ADVANCED COMPUTERS INC.; *U.S. Private*, pg. 3951
TECH AGRICULTURAL, INC.; *U.S. Private*, pg. 3951
TECH AIR, INCORPORATED—See L'Air Liquide S.A.; *Int'l*, pg. 4372
TECH AIR OF NEW YORK, INC.—See CI Capital Partners LLC; *U.S. Private*, pg. 895
TECH AIRPORT HOLDING SAS—See The Swatch Group Ltd.; *Int'l*, pg. 7692
TECH AIRPORT ORLY SAS—See The Swatch Group Ltd.; *Int'l*, pg. 7692
TECHALLOY CO., INC.—See Lincoln Electric Holdings, Inc.; *U.S. Public*, pg. 1318
TECHALTEN PORTUGAL, LDA—See Alten S.A.; *Int'l*, pg. 391
TECH AMERICAS USA, INC.; *U.S. Private*, pg. 3951
TE CHANG CONSTRUCTION CO., LTD.; *Int'l*, pg. 7494
TECHAPP SOLUTIONS, INC.; *U.S. Private*, pg. 3952
TECHAU'S INC.; *U.S. Private*, pg. 3952
TECH-BANK FOOD CO., LTD.; *Int'l*, pg. 7502
TECHBARN.COM, INC.; *U.S. Private*, pg. 3952
TECHBASE INDUSTRIES BERHAD; *Int'l*, pg. 7503
TECHBOND GROUP BERHAD; *Int'l*, pg. 7503
TECHBOND MANUFACTURING SDN. BHD.—See Techbond Group Berhad; *Int'l*, pg. 7503
TECHBOND MFG (VIETNAM) CO., LTD.—See Techbond Group Berhad; *Int'l*, pg. 7503
TECHBOND (SABAH) SDN. BHD.—See Techbond Group Berhad; *Int'l*, pg. 7503
TECHBOND (VIETNAM) CO. LTD.—See Techbond Group Berhad; *Int'l*, pg. 7503
TECHCENTIAL INTERNATIONAL LTD.; *Int'l*, pg. 7503
TECH CENTRAL INC.; *U.S. Public*, pg. 1988
TECHCESS SOLUTIONS INC—See Konica Minolta, Inc.; *Int'l*, pg. 4258
TECHCHEFS SOFTWARE PRIVATE LIMITED—See EQT AB; *Int'l*, pg. 2472
TECH CIRCUITS INC.—See IGP Industries, LLC; *U.S. Private*, pg. 2039
TECHCOM, INC.; *Int'l*, pg. 7503
TECHCOMP (CHINA) LIMITED—See Yunnan Energy International Co. Ltd.; *Int'l*, pg. 8615
TECHCOMP (MACAO COMMERCIAL OFFSHORE) LIMITED—See Yunnan Energy International Co. Ltd.; *Int'l*, pg. 8615
TECHCOMP (SINGAPORE) PTE. LTD.—See Yunnan Energy International Co. Ltd.; *Int'l*, pg. 8615
TECHCOMP (TIANJIN) LTD.—See Yunnan Energy International Co. Ltd.; *Int'l*, pg. 8615
TECH-COM (SHANGHAI) COMPUTER CO., LTD.—See Quanta Computer, Inc.; *Int'l*, pg. 6153
TECHCOM VIETNAM REIT FUND; *Int'l*, pg. 7503
TECH CON CZECH REPUBLIC S.R.O.—See THK CO., LTD.; *Int'l*, pg. 7713
TECH CON HUNGARIA KFT—See THK CO., LTD.; *Int'l*, pg. 7713
TECH CON INDUSTRY SRL—See THK CO., LTD.; *Int'l*, pg. 7713
TECHCONN HOLDING GROUP CO., LTD.; *Int'l*, pg. 7503
TECH-CON POLAND SP. Z.O.O.—See THK CO., LTD.; *Int'l*, pg. 7713
TECH-COR, LLC—See The Allstate Corporation; *U.S. Public*, pg. 2034
TECHCOTE INDUSTRIAL COATING, LTD.—See Tailwind Capital Group, LLC; *U.S. Private*, pg. 3924
TECH CREDIT UNION CORPORATION; *U.S. Private*, pg. 3951
TECHCXO; *U.S. Private*, pg. 3952
TECH DATA ADVANCED PRIVATE LIMITED—See TD Synnex Corp; *U.S. Public*, pg. 1985
TECH DATA ADVANCED SOLUTIONS (ANZ) LIMITED—See TD Synnex Corp; *U.S. Public*, pg. 1985
TECH DATA ADVANCED SOLUTIONS (ANZ) LIMITED—See TD Synnex Corp; *U.S. Public*, pg. 1986
TECH DATA ADVANCED SOLUTIONS (INDIA) PRIVATE LIMITED—See TD Synnex Corp; *U.S. Public*, pg. 1985
TECH DATA ADVANCED SOLUTIONS (MALAYSIA) SDN. BHD.—See TD Synnex Corp; *U.S. Public*, pg. 1985
TECH DATA ADVANCED SOLUTIONS NV—See TD Synnex Corp; *U.S. Public*, pg. 1985
TECH DATA ADVANCED SOLUTIONS (SINGAPORE) PTE. LTD.—See TD Synnex Corp; *U.S. Public*, pg. 1986
TECH DATA ADVANCED SOLUTIONS (SINGAPORE) PTE. LTD.—See TD Synnex Corp; *U.S. Public*, pg. 1985
TECH DATA ADVANCED SOLUTIONS (THAILAND) LIMITED—See TD Synnex Corp; *U.S. Public*, pg. 1986
TECH DATA ADVANCED SOLUTIONS (VIETNAM) COMPANY LIMITED—See TD Synnex Corp; *U.S. Public*, pg. 1986
TECH DATA AS CZECH S.R.O.—See TD Synnex Corp; *U.S. Public*, pg. 1985
TECH DATA AS KFT—See TD Synnex Corp; *U.S. Public*, pg. 1985
TECH DATA AUSTRIA GMBH—See TD Synnex Corp; *U.S. Public*, pg. 1985
TECH DATA BILGISAYAR SISTEMLERI A.S.—See TD Synnex Corp; *U.S. Public*, pg. 1985
TECH DATA BRASIL, LTDA—See TD Synnex Corp; *U.S. Public*, pg. 1986
TECH DATA BVBA/SPRL—See TD Synnex Corp; *U.S. Public*, pg. 1986
TECH DATA CANADA CORPORATION—See TD Synnex Corp; *U.S. Public*, pg. 1986
TECH DATA COLOMBIA S.A.S.—See TD Synnex Corp; *U.S. Public*, pg. 1986
TECH DATA COMPUTER SERVICE (HONG KONG) LIMITED—See TD Synnex Corp; *U.S. Public*, pg. 1986
TECH DATA COMPUTER SERVICE (MACAU) LIMITED—See TD Synnex Corp; *U.S. Public*, pg. 1986
TECH DATA CORPORATION—See TD Synnex Corp; *U.S. Public*, pg. 1985
TECH DATA CROATIA D.O.O.—See TD Synnex Corp; *U.S. Public*, pg. 1986
TECH DATA DELAWARE, INC.—See TD Synnex Corp; *U.S. Public*, pg. 1986
TECH DATA DENMARK APS—See TD Synnex Corp; *U.S. Public*, pg. 1986
TECH DATA DEUTSCHLAND GMBH—See TD Synnex Corp; *U.S. Public*, pg. 1986
TECH DATA DISTRIBUTION CROATIA D.O.O.—See TD Synnex Corp; *U.S. Public*, pg. 1986
TECH DATA DISTRIBUTION (HONG KONG) LIMITED—See TD Synnex Corp; *U.S. Public*, pg. 1987
TECH DATA DISTRIBUTION IRELAND—See TD Synnex Corp; *U.S. Public*, pg. 1985
TECH DATA DISTRIBUTION (SINGAPORE) PTE. LTD.—See TD Synnex Corp; *U.S. Public*, pg. 1987
TECH DATA DISTRIBUTION S.R.O.—See TD Synnex Corp; *U.S. Public*, pg. 1986
TECH DATA ESPANA S.L.U.—See TD Synnex Corp; *U.S. Public*, pg. 1986
TECH DATA EUROPEAN MANAGEMENT GMBH—See TD Synnex Corp; *U.S. Public*, pg. 1986
TECH DATA EUROPE GMBH—See TD Synnex Corp; *U.S. Public*, pg. 1986
TECH DATA FRANCE SAS—See TD Synnex Corp; *U.S. Public*, pg. 1986
TECH DATA GMBH & CO. OHG—See TD Synnex Corp; *U.S. Public*, pg. 1986
TECH DATA GMBH & CO. OHG—See TD Synnex Corp; *U.S. Public*, pg. 1986
TECH DATA GMBH & CO. OHG—See TD Synnex Corp; *U.S. Public*, pg. 1985
TECH DATA GMBH & CO OHG—See TD Synnex Corp; *U.S. Public*, pg. 1986
TECH DATA HUNGARY KFT.—See TD Synnex Corp; *U.S. Public*, pg. 1986
TECH DATA LATIN AMERICA, INC.—See TD Synnex Corp; *U.S. Public*, pg. 1986
TECH DATA LIMITED—See TD Synnex Corp; *U.S. Public*, pg. 1986
TECH DATA LTD.—See TD Synnex Corp; *U.S. Public*, pg. 1985
TECH DATA MEXICO S. DE R. L. DE C. V.—See TD Synnex Corp; *U.S. Public*, pg. 1986
TECH DATA MOBILE ACQUISITION LIMITED—See TD Synnex Corp; *U.S. Public*, pg. 1986
TECH DATA MOBILE BELGIUM, BVBA—See TD Synnex Corp; *U.S. Public*, pg. 1986
TECH DATA MOBILE LIMITED—See TD Synnex Corp; *U.S. Public*, pg. 1986
TECH DATA MOBILE NETHERLANDS B.V.—See TD Synnex Corp; *U.S. Public*, pg. 1987
TECH DATA NEDERLAND B.V.—See TD Synnex Corp; *U.S. Public*, pg. 1985
TECH DATA NORGE AS—See TD Synnex Corp; *U.S. Public*, pg. 1987
TECH DATA OSTERREICH GMBH—See TD Synnex Corp; *U.S. Public*, pg. 1985
TECH DATA OSTERREICH GMBH—See TD Synnex Corp; *U.S. Public*, pg. 1987
TECH DATA POLSKA SP. Z.O.O.—See TD Synnex Corp; *U.S. Public*, pg. 1987
TECH DATA (SCHWEIZ) GMBH—See TD Synnex Corp; *U.S. Public*, pg. 1986
TECH DATA (SINGAPORE) PTE. LTD.—See TD Synnex Corp; *U.S. Public*, pg. 1986
TECHDEMOCRACY LLC; *U.S. Private*, pg. 3952
TECHDEPOT—See The ODP Corporation; *U.S. Public*, pg. 2117
TECH DEVELOPMENT INC.—See General Electric Company; *U.S. Public*, pg. 919
TECHDEVICE LLC—See TE Connectivity Ltd.; *Int'l*, pg. 7496
TECHDIGITAL CORP.; *U.S. Private*, pg. 3952
TECHE ACTION BOARD INC; *U.S. Private*, pg. 3952
TECHEAD; *U.S. Private*, pg. 3952
TECHEDGE S.P.A.; *Int'l*, pg. 7503
TECHE ELECTRIC SUPPLY INC.—See Rexel, S.A.; *Int'l*, pg. 6317
TECH ELECTRONICS, INC.—See Tronicom Corp.; *U.S. Private*, pg. 4241

CORPORATE AFFILIATIONS

TECH ELECTRONICS OF COLORADO, LLC—See Tronicom Corp.; *U.S. Private*, pg. 4241
TECH ELECTRONICS OF COLUMBIA, INC.—See Tronicom Corp.; *U.S. Private*, pg. 4242
TECH ELECTRONICS OF ILLINOIS, LLC—See Tronicom Corp.; *U.S. Private*, pg. 4242
TECH ELECTRONICS OF INDIANA, LLC—See Tronicom Corp.; *U.S. Private*, pg. 4242
TECH ELEVATOR INC.—See Stride, Inc.; *U.S. Public*, pg. 1955
TECHEM DANMARK A/S—See Caisse de Depot et Placement du Quebec; *Int'l*, pg. 1255
TECHEM DANMARK A/S—See Ontario Teachers' Pension Plan; *Int'l*, pg. 5590
TECHEM DANMARK A/S—See Partners Group Holding AG; *Int'l*, pg. 5751
TECHEM DO BRASIL SERVICOS DE MEDICAO DE AGUA LTDA.—See Caisse de Depot et Placement du Quebec; *Int'l*, pg. 1255
TECHEM DO BRASIL SERVICOS DE MEDICAO DE AGUA LTDA.—See Ontario Teachers' Pension Plan; *Int'l*, pg. 5590
TECHEM DO BRASIL SERVICOS DE MEDICAO DE AGUA LTDA.—See Partners Group Holding AG; *Int'l*, pg. 5751
TECHEM ENERGY METERING SERVICE GMBH & CO. KG; *Int'l*, pg. 7503
TECHEM ENERGY SERVICES B.V.—See Caisse de Depot et Placement du Quebec; *Int'l*, pg. 1255
TECHEM ENERGY SERVICES B.V.—See Ontario Teachers' Pension Plan; *Int'l*, pg. 5590
TECHEM ENERGY SERVICES B.V.—See Partners Group Holding AG; *Int'l*, pg. 5751
TECHEM ENERGY SERVICES MIDDLE EAST FZCO—See Caisse de Depot et Placement du Quebec; *Int'l*, pg. 1255
TECHEM ENERGY SERVICES MIDDLE EAST FZCO—See Ontario Teachers' Pension Plan; *Int'l*, pg. 5590
TECHEM ENERGY SERVICES MIDDLE EAST FZCO—See Partners Group Holding AG; *Int'l*, pg. 5751
TECHEM ENERGY SERVICES S.R.L.—See Caisse de Depot et Placement du Quebec; *Int'l*, pg. 1255
TECHEM ENERGY SERVICES S.R.L.—See Ontario Teachers' Pension Plan; *Int'l*, pg. 5590
TECHEM ENERGY SERVICES S.R.L.—See Partners Group Holding AG; *Int'l*, pg. 5751
TECHEM ENERJI HIZMETLERI SANAYI VE TICARET LIMITED SIRKETI—See Caisse de Depot et Placement du Quebec; *Int'l*, pg. 1255
TECHEM ENERJI HIZMETLERI SANAYI VE TICARET LIMITED SIRKETI—See Ontario Teachers' Pension Plan; *Int'l*, pg. 5590
TECHEM ENERJI HIZMETLERI SANAYI VE TICARET LIMITED SIRKETI—See Partners Group Holding AG; *Int'l*, pg. 5751
TECHEM GMBH—See Caisse de Depot et Placement du Quebec; *Int'l*, pg. 1255
TECHEM GMBH—See Ontario Teachers' Pension Plan; *Int'l*, pg. 5590
TECHEM GMBH—See Partners Group Holding AG; *Int'l*, pg. 5750
TECHEM NORGE A/S—See Caisse de Depot et Placement du Quebec; *Int'l*, pg. 1255
TECHEM NORGE A/S—See Ontario Teachers' Pension Plan; *Int'l*, pg. 5590
TECHEM NORGE A/S—See Partners Group Holding AG; *Int'l*, pg. 5751
TECHEM SAS—See Caisse de Depot et Placement du Quebec; *Int'l*, pg. 1255
TECHEM SAS—See Ontario Teachers' Pension Plan; *Int'l*, pg. 5590
TECHEM SAS—See Partners Group Holding AG; *Int'l*, pg. 5751
TECHEM (SCHWEIZ) AG—See Caisse de Depot et Placement du Quebec; *Int'l*, pg. 1255
TECHEM (SCHWEIZ) AG—See Ontario Teachers' Pension Plan; *Int'l*, pg. 5590
TECHEM (SCHWEIZ) AG—See Partners Group Holding AG; *Int'l*, pg. 5751
TECHEM SERVICES E.O.O.D.—See Caisse de Depot et Placement du Quebec; *Int'l*, pg. 1255
TECHEM SERVICES E.O.O.D.—See Ontario Teachers' Pension Plan; *Int'l*, pg. 5590
TECHEM SERVICES E.O.O.D.—See Partners Group Holding AG; *Int'l*, pg. 5751
TECHEM SPOL. S. R. O.—See Caisse de Depot et Placement du Quebec; *Int'l*, pg. 1255
TECHEM SPOL. S. R. O.—See Caisse de Depot et Placement du Quebec; *Int'l*, pg. 1255
TECHEM SPOL. S. R. O.—See Ontario Teachers' Pension Plan; *Int'l*, pg. 5590
TECHEM SPOL. S. R. O.—See Ontario Teachers' Pension Plan; *Int'l*, pg. 5590
TECHEM SPOL. S. R. O.—See Partners Group Holding AG; *Int'l*, pg. 5751
TECHEM SPOL. S. R. O.—See Partners Group Holding AG; *Int'l*, pg. 5751

COMPANY NAME INDEX

TECHEM S.R.L.—See Caisse de Depot et Placement du Quebec; *Int'l*, pg. 1255
TECHEM S.R.L.—See Ontario Teachers' Pension Plan; *Int'l*, pg. 5590
TECHEM S.R.L.—See Partners Group Holding AG; *Int'l*, pg. 5751
TECHEM SVERIGE AB—See Caisse de Depot et Placement du Quebec; *Int'l*, pg. 1255
TECHEM SVERIGE AB—See Ontario Teachers' Pension Plan; *Int'l*, pg. 5590
TECHEM SVERIGE AB—See Partners Group Holding AG; *Int'l*, pg. 5751
TECHEM TECHNIKI POMIAROWE SP. Z O.O.—See Caisse de Depot et Placement du Quebec; *Int'l*, pg. 1255
TECHEM TECHNIKI POMIAROWE SP. Z O.O.—See Ontario Teachers' Pension Plan; *Int'l*, pg. 5590
TECHEM TECHNIKI POMIAROWE SP. Z O.O.—See Partners Group Holding AG; *Int'l*, pg. 5751
TECHEN CO., LTD.; *Int'l*, pg. 7503
TECH & ENERGY TRANSITION CORPORATION; *U.S. Public*, pg. 1988
TECH ENTERPRISES, INC.; *U.S. Private*, pg. 3951
TECHE REGIONAL PHYSICIAN PRACTICES, LLC—See Apollo Global Management, Inc.; *U.S. Public*, pg. 159
TECH-ETCH INC.; *U.S. Private*, pg. 3952
TECHEX—See INNOVARO, Inc.; *U.S. Private*, pg. 2081
TECHFAITH INTELLIGENT HANDSET TECHNOLOGY LIMITED—See China TechFaith Wireless Communication Technology Limited; *Int'l*, pg. 1557
TECHFAITH (SHANGHAI)—See China TechFaith Wireless Communication Technology Limited; *Int'l*, pg. 1557
TECHFAITH (SHENZHEN)—See China TechFaith Wireless Communication Technology Limited; *Int'l*, pg. 1557
TECH. FINANCE CO., LLC—See Kingsbridge Holdings LLC; *U.S. Private*, pg. 2311
TECHFINANCIALS, INC.; *Int'l*, pg. 7503
TECHFINO LLC; *U.S. Private*, pg. 3952
TECHFIRM HOLDINGS, INC.; *Int'l*, pg. 7503
TECHFLEX PACKAGING, LLC—See H.I.G. Capital, LLC; *U.S. Private*, pg. 1834
TECH-FLO CONSULTING, LLC—See RedBird Capital Partners L.P.; *U.S. Private*, pg. 3377
TECHFLUID NORD S.A.S.—See Atlas Copco AB; *Int'l*, pg. 684
TECHFORCE PERSONNEL PTY. LTD.—See PeopleIn Limited; *Int'l*, pg. 5794
TECHFORM INDUSTRIAL CO., LTD.—See Taiwan Fu Hsing Industrial Co., Ltd.; *Int'l*, pg. 7420
TECH-FRONT (CHONGQING) COMPUTER CO., LTD.—See Quanta Computer, Inc.; *Int'l*, pg. 6153
TECH-FRONT (SHANGHAI) COMPUTER CO., LTD.—See Quanta Computer, Inc.; *Int'l*, pg. 6153
TECH-FULL (CHANGSHU) COMPUTER CO., LTD.—See Quanta Computer, Inc.; *Int'l*, pg. 6153
TECH-FULL COMPUTER (CHANGSHU) CO., LTD.—See Quanta Computer, Inc.; *Int'l*, pg. 6153
TECHFUN—See Montagne et Neige Developpement SA; *Int'l*, pg. 5035
TECH GATE VIENNA WISSENSCHAFTS- UND TECHNOLOGIEPARK GMBH—See STRABAG SE; *Int'l*, pg. 7233
TECHGEN CONSULTING, INC.—See Teal; *U.S. Private*, pg. 3948
TECH GROUP EUROPE LIMITED—See West Pharmaceutical Services, Inc.; *U.S. Public*, pg. 2352
TECH GROUP GRAND RAPIDS, INC.—See West Pharmaceutical Services, Inc.; *U.S. Public*, pg. 2352
TECH GROUP MEDICAL PRODUCTS—See Valley Capital Corporation; *U.S. Private*, pg. 4333
TECH GROUP NORTH AMERICA, INC.—See West Pharmaceutical Services, Inc.; *U.S. Public*, pg. 2352
TECH GROUP PHOENIX, INC.—See West Pharmaceutical Services, Inc.; *U.S. Public*, pg. 2352
TECH GROUP PUERTO RICO—See West Pharmaceutical Services, Inc.; *U.S. Public*, pg. 2352
TECH GROUP—See West Pharmaceutical Services, Inc.; *U.S. Public*, pg. 2352
TECH GROUP TEMPE—See West Pharmaceutical Services, Inc.; *U.S. Public*, pg. 2352
TECHHEALTH, INC.—See Apax Partners LLP; *Int'l*, pg. 505
TECHHOUSE INTEGRATED INFORMATION SYSTEM SOLUTIONS, INC.; *U.S. Private*, pg. 3952
TECH & HOUSE S.A.—See Aiphone Co., Ltd.; *Int'l*, pg. 235
TECH IMAGE—See SmithBucklin Corporation; *U.S. Private*, pg. 3697
TECH IMPACT; *U.S. Private*, pg. 3951
TECHINDIA NIRMAN LIMITED; *Int'l*, pg. 7503
TECHINFORMSERVICE, LLC—See Weatherford International plc; *U.S. Public*, pg. 2339
TECHINSIGHTS INC.—See CVC Capital Partners SICAV-FIS S.A.; *Int'l*, pg. 1888
TECHINSIGHTS INC.—See Oakley Capital Limited; *Int'l*, pg. 5504
TECHINT CHILE S.A.—See Techint S.p.A.; *Int'l*, pg. 7504
TECHINT CIMIMONTUBI NIGERIA LTD—See Techint S.p.A.; *Int'l*, pg. 7504

TECHINT - COMPAGNIA TECNICA INTERNAZIONALE S.P.A.—See Techint S.p.A.; *Int'l*, pg. 7504
TECH IN TECH CO., LTD.—See Screen Holdings Co., Ltd.; *Int'l*, pg. 6656
TECHINT ENGENHARIA E CONSTRUCAO S/A—See Techint S.p.A.; *Int'l*, pg. 7504
TECHINT IBERIA, S.L.—See Techint S.p.A.; *Int'l*, pg. 7504
TECHINT INDIA PVT.LTD.—See Techint S.p.A.; *Int'l*, pg. 7504
TECHINT INDUSTRIAL TECHNOLOGIES (BEIJING) CO. LTD.—See Techint S.p.A.; *Int'l*, pg. 7504
TECHINT-ITALIMPIANTI—See Techint S.p.A.; *Int'l*, pg. 7504
TECHINT S.A.C.—See Techint S.p.A.; *Int'l*, pg. 7504
TECHINT S.A. DE C.V.—See Techint S.p.A.; *Int'l*, pg. 7504
TECHINT S.P.A.; *Int'l*, pg. 7503
TECHLAB, INC.—See Adelis Equity Partners AB; *Int'l*, pg. 142
TECHLAM S.A.—See TotalEnergies SE; *Int'l*, pg. 7837
TECHLANTIC LTD.; *Int'l*, pg. 7505
TECHLAW HOLDINGS, INC.; *U.S. Private*, pg. 3952
TECHLAW INC.—See TechLaw Holdings, Inc.; *U.S. Private*, pg. 3952
TECHLAW SOLUTIONS, INC.—See Fronteo, Inc.; *Int'l*, pg. 2794
TECH-LEAD (SHANGHAI) COMPUTER CO., LTD.—See Quanta Computer, Inc.; *Int'l*, pg. 6153
TECHLIGHTENMENT LIMITED—See Experian plc; *Int'l*, pg. 2588
TECH LIGHTING L.L.C.—See AEA Investors LP; *U.S. Private*, pg. 114
TECHLINE INC.; *U.S. Private*, pg. 3952
TECH LINK CONSTRUCTION ENGINEERING LIMITED—See Sunray Engineering Group Limited; *Int'l*, pg. 7320
TECHLINK, INC.—See Great Mill Rock LLC; *U.S. Private*, pg. 1766
TECH-LINK STORAGE ENGINEERING PTE LTD.; *Int'l*, pg. 7502
TECHLINK SYSTEMS, INC.; *U.S. Private*, pg. 3952
TECH LONG EUROPE GMBH—See Guangzhou Tech-Long Packaging Machinery Co., Ltd.; *Int'l*, pg. 3168
TECH-LONG INC.—See Guangzhou Tech-Long Packaging Machinery Co., Ltd.; *Int'l*, pg. 3168
TECHMA CORPORATION—See Denso Corporation; *Int'l*, pg. 2033
TECHMAGIC; *Int'l*, pg. 7505
TECH MAHINDRA (AMERICAS), INC.—See Mahindra & Mahindra Limited; *Int'l*, pg. 4647
TECH MAHINDRA BPO LIMITED—See Mahindra & Mahindra Limited; *Int'l*, pg. 4647
TECH MAHINDRA FOUNDATION—See Mahindra & Mahindra Limited; *Int'l*, pg. 4647
TECH MAHINDRA GMBH—See Mahindra & Mahindra Limited; *Int'l*, pg. 4647
TECH MAHINDRA LIMITED—See Mahindra & Mahindra Limited; *Int'l*, pg. 4647
TECH MAHINDRA LTD—See Mahindra & Mahindra Limited; *Int'l*, pg. 4647
TECH MAHINDRA (R&D SERVICES) INC.—See Mahindra & Mahindra Limited; *Int'l*, pg. 4647
TECH MAHINDRA (R&D SERVICES) LIMITED—See Mahindra & Mahindra Limited; *Int'l*, pg. 4647
TECH MAHINDRA (SINGAPORE) PTE. LIMITED—See Mahindra & Mahindra Limited; *Int'l*, pg. 4647
TECHMAN ELECTRONICS (THAILAND) CO., LTD.—See Quanta Computer, Inc.; *Int'l*, pg. 6153
TECHMAN ENGINEERING LIMITED—See Schoeller-Bleckmann Oilfield Equipment AG; *Int'l*, pg. 6638
TECHMAN ROBOT INC.—See Quanta Computer, Inc.; *Int'l*, pg. 6153
TECHMAN ROBOT (SHANGHAI) LTD.—See Quanta Computer, Inc.; *Int'l*, pg. 6153
TECH MANUFACTURING, LLC—See Onward Capital LLC; *U.S. Private*, pg. 3028
TECH MANUFACTURING, LLC—See Thompson Street Capital Manager LLC; *U.S. Private*, pg. 4161
TECHMATION ELECTRIC & CONTROLS LTD.; *Int'l*, pg. 7505
TECHMATRIX CORPORATION; *Int'l*, pg. 7505
TECH MECHANICAL INC.—See Ares Management Corporation; *U.S. Public*, pg. 189
TECH MECHANICAL SYSTEMS LTD; *Int'l*, pg. 7502
TECH-MEDI DEVELOPMENT LIMITED—See Meilleure Health International Industry Group Limited; *Int'l*, pg. 4803
TECHMER ENGINEERED SOLUTIONS, LLC—See SK Capital Partners, LP; *U.S. Private*, pg. 3680
TECHMER PM, LLC; *U.S. Private*, pg. 3952
TECHMER PVT. LTD.—See Mer Group; *Int'l*, pg. 4818
TECHMETALS, INC.; *U.S. Private*, pg. 3953
TECHMETA SA—See Bodycote plc; *Int'l*, pg. 1098
TECHMIRE—See Partners Group Holding AG; *Int'l*, pg. 5749
TECH MOLD, INC.; *U.S. Private*, pg. 3952
TECHNA CO. LTD.—See Hitachi, Ltd.; *Int'l*, pg. 3424
TECHNA GLASS, INC.; *U.S. Private*, pg. 3953
TECHNATOMY CORPORATION; *U.S. Private*, pg. 3953
TECHNA-X BERHAD; *Int'l*, pg. 7506

TECHNICAL MARKETING ASSOCIATES

TECHNEGLAS, INC.—See Nippon Electric Glass Co., Ltd.; *Int'l*, pg. 5314
TECHNEGLAS LLC—See Nippon Electric Glass Co., Ltd.; *Int'l*, pg. 5314
TECHNESIS, INC.—See Sepialine, Inc.; *U.S. Private*, pg. 3611
TECHNETICS GROUP DAYTONA, INC.—See Enpro Inc.; *U.S. Public*, pg. 775
TECHNETICS GROUP JAPAN LTD.—See Enpro Inc.; *U.S. Public*, pg. 775
TECHNETICS GROUP LLC—See Enpro Inc.; *U.S. Public*, pg. 775
TECHNETICS GROUP OXFORD, INC.—See Enpro Inc.; *U.S. Public*, pg. 775
TECHNETICS GROUP SINGAPORE PTE. LTD.—See Enpro Inc.; *U.S. Public*, pg. 775
TECHNETICS GROUP—See Enpro Inc.; *U.S. Public*, pg. 775
TECHNETICS GROUP U.K. LTD.—See Enpro Inc.; *U.S. Public*, pg. 775
TECHNETICS UK LIMITED—See Enpro Inc.; *U.S. Public*, pg. 775
TECHNET RESOURCES, INC.; *U.S. Private*, pg. 3953
TECH NH INC.; *U.S. Private*, pg. 3952
TECHNIA AB—See Addnode Group AB; *Int'l*, pg. 131
TECHNIA AS—See Addnode Group AB; *Int'l*, pg. 131
TECHNIA B.V.—See Addnode Group AB; *Int'l*, pg. 131
TECHNIA INC.—See Addnode Group AB; *Int'l*, pg. 131
TECHNIA K.K.—See Addnode Group AB; *Int'l*, pg. 131
TECHNIA LTD.—See Addnode Group AB; *Int'l*, pg. 131
TECHNIA PLM OY—See Addnode Group AB; *Int'l*, pg. 131
TECHNIA S.A.S.—See Addnode Group AB; *Int'l*, pg. 131
TECHNIA SLOVAKIA S.R.O.—See Addnode Group AB; *Int'l*, pg. 131
TECHNI BHARATHI PRIVATE LIMITED—See IGC Pharma, Inc.; *U.S. Public*, pg. 1095
TECHNIBUS, INC.—See IES Holdings, Inc.; *U.S. Public*, pg. 1094
TECHNICA CO., LTD.—See Kawasaki Heavy Industries, Ltd.; *Int'l*, pg. 4098
TECHNICA CORPORATION; *U.S. Private*, pg. 3953
TECHNICAL ADHESIVES LIMITED; *Int'l*, pg. 7506
TECHNICAL AIRBORNE COMPONENTS INDUSTRIES SPRL—See TransDigm Group Incorporated; *U.S. Public*, pg. 2183
TECHNICAL AND PROJECT ENGINEERING, LLC; *U.S. Private*, pg. 3953
TECHNICAL APPLICATIONS ASSOCIATES, INC.; *U.S. Private*, pg. 3953
TECHNICAL ASSOCIATES OF GEORGIA INC.; *U.S. Private*, pg. 3953
TECHNICAL ASSOCIATES SERVICES P. LTD.—See Endress+Hauser (International) Holding AG; *Int'l*, pg. 2409
TECHNICAL CAREER INSTITUTES, INC.—See EVCI Career Colleges Holding Corp.; *U.S. Private*, pg. 1436
TECHNICAL CHEMICAL COMPANY INC.; *U.S. Private*, pg. 3953
TECHNICAL COMMUNICATIONS CORPORATION; *U.S. Public*, pg. 1988
TECHNICAL COMMUNITIES, INC.; *U.S. Private*, pg. 3953
TECHNICAL CONSUMER PRODUCTS, INC.—See Q L Light Source Company Limited; *Int'l*, pg. 6129
TECHNICAL DESIGN SERVICES, INC—See NV5 Global, Inc.; *U.S. Public*, pg. 1558
TECHNICAL DEVICES CO.; *U.S. Private*, pg. 3954
TECHNICAL DRILLING AND BLASTING CO. LLC—See Al Fajar Al Alamia Company SAOG; *Int'l*, pg. 277
TECHNICAL EDUCATION RESEARCH CENTERS, INC.; *U.S. Private*, pg. 3954
TECHNICAL EQUIPMENT CO., INC.—See JCI Industries Inc.; *U.S. Private*, pg. 2194
TECHNICAL EQUIPMENT SALES COMPANY—See Morris Group, Inc.; *U.S. Private*, pg. 2787
TECHNICAL FIBER PRODUCTS INC—See James Cropper Plc; *Int'l*, pg. 3875
TECHNICAL FIBRE PRODUCTS LIMITED—See James Cropper Plc; *Int'l*, pg. 3875
TECHNICAL FOUNDATIONS INC.; *U.S. Private*, pg. 3954
TECHNICAL GAS PRODUCTS, INC.; *U.S. Private*, pg. 3954
TECHNICAL GLASS PRODUCTS DMCC—See Allegion Public Limited Company; *Int'l*, pg. 335
TECHNICAL GLASS PRODUCTS, INC.—See Allegion Public Limited Company; *Int'l*, pg. 335
TECHNICAL IMAGE PRODUCTS, INC.; *U.S. Private*, pg. 3954
TECHNICAL INNOVATION, LLC—See Diversified Specialties, Inc.; *U.S. Private*, pg. 1243
TECHNICAL INSPECTION & CORROSION CONTROL CO; *Int'l*, pg. 7506
TECHNICAL INSTRUMENTS SAN FRANCISCO; *U.S. Private*, pg. 3954
TECHNICAL LINKS DESIGN CO., LTD.—See Toyota Boshoku Corporation; *Int'l*, pg. 7864
TECHNICAL MARKETING ASSOCIATES; *U.S. Private*, pg. 3954
TECHNICAL MARKETING MANUFACTURING INC.—See Hamilton Robinson LLC; *U.S. Private*, pg. 1848

TECHNICAL MARKETING ASSOCIATES / CORPORATE AFFILIATIONS

TECHNICAL MATERIALS, INC.—See Materion Corporation; *U.S. Public*, pg. 1396
TECHNICAL OLYMPIC SA; *Int'l*, pg. 7506
TECHNICAL PARTS COMPANY INDIA PVT LTD.—See Bhatia Brothers Group; *Int'l*, pg. 1014
TECHNICAL PARTS COMPANY LLC—See Bhatia Brothers Group; *Int'l*, pg. 1014
TECHNICAL PARTS ESTABLISHMENT—See Bhatia Brothers Group; *Int'l*, pg. 1014
TECHNICAL PERSPECTIVES, INC.—See Computer Automation Systems, Inc.; *U.S. Private*, pg. 1004
TECHNICAL PLASTIC SYSTEMS GMBH—See L. Possehl & Co. mbH; *Int'l*, pg. 4385
TECHNICAL PLASTIC SYSTEMS S. DE R.L. DE C.V.—See L. Possehl & Co. mbH; *Int'l*, pg. 4385
TECHNICAL POLYMERS, LLC—See Domo NV; *Int'l*, pg. 2162
TECHNICAL PROSPECTS LLC—See NMS Capital Services, LLC; *U.S. Private*, pg. 2931
TECHNICAL RESOURCE GROUP, INC—See White Wolf Capital LLC; *U.S. Private*, pg. 4510
TECHNICAL RESOURCES INTERNATIONAL, INC.; *U.S. Private*, pg. 3954
TECHNICAL RESPONSE PLANNING CORP.—See Gryphon Investors, LLC; *U.S. Private*, pg. 1798
TECHNICAL RUBBER COMPANY, INC.; *U.S. Private*, pg. 3954
TECHNICAL SAFETY SERVICES, LLC—See Levine Leichtman Capital Partners, LLC; *U.S. Private*, pg. 2436
TECHNICAL SALES INTERNATIONAL, LLC (TSI); *U.S. Private*, pg. 3954
TECHNICAL SEAL COMPANY LTD.—See Zamil Group Holding Company; *Int'l*, pg. 8623
TECHNICAL SERVICES BUREAU CO.—See Endress+Hauser (International) Holding AG; *Int'l*, pg. 2409
TECHNICAL SERVICES CO. LIMITED (TECHSERV)—See Mannai Corporation QPSC; *Int'l*, pg. 4675
TECHNICAL SERVICES HUNGARIA KFT.—See OBB-Holding AG; *Int'l*, pg. 5510
TECHNICAL SERVICES, INC.—See SkyKnight Capital LLC; *U.S. Private*, pg. 3685
TECHNICAL SERVICES SLOVAKIA, S.R.O.—See OBB-Holding AG; *Int'l*, pg. 5510
TECHNICAL SOLUTIONS, LLC.; *U.S. Private*, pg. 3954
TECHNICAL STAFFING DIVISION—See Resilience Capital Partners, LLC; *U.S. Private*, pg. 3405
TECHNICAL STAFFING RESOURCES, LLC—See KBR, Inc.; *U.S. Public*, pg. 1216
TECHNICAL SUPPORT CO.,LTD.—See Kumagai Gumi Co., Ltd.; *Int'l*, pg. 4329
TECHNICAL TEXTILE SERVICES LIMITED—See Ecolab Inc.; *U.S. Public*, pg. 716
TECHNICAL TRADING COMPANY LTD.—See The Olayan Group; *Int'l*, pg. 7672
TECHNICAL TRAFFIC CONSULTANTS CORP.—See PKF O'Connor Davies, LLP; *U.S. Private*, pg. 3193
TECHNICAL TRANSPORTATION INC.; *U.S. Private*, pg. 3954
TECHNICAL YOUTH LLC.; *U.S. Private*, pg. 3954
TECHNI-CAR INC.; *U.S. Private*, pg. 3953
TECHNIC ASIA-PACIFIC PTE LTD.—See Technic Incorporated; *U.S. Private*, pg. 3953
TECHNIC ASIA-PACIFIC SDN. BHD.—See Technic Incorporated; *U.S. Private*, pg. 3953
TECHNICA TOMOEGAWA CO., LTD.—See Tomoegawa Co., Ltd.; *Int'l*, pg. 7801
TECHNIC AUTOMATION SAS—See VINCI S.A.; *Int'l*, pg. 8229
TECHNIC CANADA—See Technic Incorporated; *U.S. Private*, pg. 3953
TECHNIC (CHINA-HK) LTD.—See Technic Incorporated; *U.S. Private*, pg. 3953
TECHNIC FRANCE—See Technic Incorporated; *U.S. Private*, pg. 3953
TECHNICHE LIMITED; *Int'l*, pg. 7506
TECHNIC INCORPORATED - CHALON PLANT—See Technic Incorporated; *U.S. Private*, pg. 3953
TECHNIC INCORPORATED-EQUIPMENT DIV.—See Technic Incorporated; *U.S. Private*, pg. 3953
TECHNIC INCORPORATED; *U.S. Private*, pg. 3953
TECHNIC INCORPORATED - TECHNIC ADVANCED TECHNOLOGY DIVISION—See Technic Incorporated; *U.S. Private*, pg. 3953
TECHNIC INCORPORATED - TECHNIC ENGINEERED POWDERS DIVISION—See Technic Incorporated; *U.S. Private*, pg. 3953
TECHNIC INNOVATIVE SURFACE TECHNOLOGIES FACILITY—See Technic Incorporated; *U.S. Private*, pg. 3953
TECHNICIS SAS—See Groupe BPCE; *Int'l*, pg. 3095
TECHNIC JAPAN, INC.—See Technic Incorporated; *U.S. Private*, pg. 3953
TECHNICKE PLASTOVE SYSTEMY S.R.O.—See L. Possehl & Co. mbH; *Int'l*, pg. 4385
TECHNICO AGRI SCIENCES LIMITED—See ITC Limited; *Int'l*, pg. 3832
TECHNI-COAT GERMANY GMBH—See Akzo Nobel N.V.; *Int'l*, pg. 275

TECHNI-COAT INTERNATIONAL N.V.—See Akzo Nobel N.V.; *Int'l*, pg. 275
TECHNICO HORTICULTURAL (KUNMING) CO. LIMITED—See ITC Limited; *Int'l*, pg. 3832
TECHNICO INDUSTRIES LTD. - BAWAL WORKS—See Technico Industries Ltd.; *Int'l*, pg. 7506
TECHNICO INDUSTRIES LTD.; *Int'l*, pg. 7506
TECHNICOLOR BRASIL MIDIA EENTRETENIMENTO LTDA.—See Vantiva SA; *Int'l*, pg. 8131
TECHNICOLOR CANADA INC.—See Vantiva SA; *Int'l*, pg. 8131
TECHNICOLOR CREATIVE SERVICES CANADA INC.—See Vantiva SA; *Int'l*, pg. 8131
TECHNICOLOR CREATIVE SERVICES CANADA INC. - TORONTO—See Vantiva SA; *Int'l*, pg. 8131
TECHNICOLOR CREATIVE SERVICES—See Vantiva SA; *Int'l*, pg. 8131
TECHNICOLOR CREATIVE STUDIOS UK LTD.—See Vantiva SA; *Int'l*, pg. 8130
TECHNICOLOR DIGITAL CINEMA INC.—See Vantiva SA; *Int'l*, pg. 8131
TECHNICOLOR DISC SERVICES INTERNATIONAL LTD.—See Vantiva SA; *Int'l*, pg. 8131
TECHNICOLOR ENTERTAINMENT SERVICES, S.L.—See Vantiva SA; *Int'l*, pg. 8130
TECHNICOLOR ENTERTAINMENT SERVICES—See Vantiva SA; *Int'l*, pg. 8131
TECHNICOLOR HOME ENTERTAINMENT SERVICES, INC.—See Vantiva SA; *Int'l*, pg. 8131
TECHNICOLOR, INC.—See Vantiva SA; *Int'l*, pg. 8131
TECHNICOLOR INDIA PVT LTD.—See Vantiva SA; *Int'l*, pg. 8130
TECHNICOLOR INTERNATIONAL SAS—See Vantiva SA; *Int'l*, pg. 8130
TECHNICOLOR JAPAN KK—See Vantiva SA; *Int'l*, pg. 8130
TECHNICOLOR LABORATORY CANADA, INC.—See Vantiva SA; *Int'l*, pg. 8131
TECHNICOLOR LIMITED—See Vantiva SA; *Int'l*, pg. 8130
TECHNICOLOR MEXICANA, S DE R.L. DE C.V.—See Vantiva SA; *Int'l*, pg. 8131
TECHNICOLOR POLSKA.—See Vantiva SA; *Int'l*, pg. 8131
TECHNICOLOR PTY LTD.—See Vantiva SA; *Int'l*, pg. 8131
TECHNICOLOR R&D FRANCE SNC—See Vantiva SA; *Int'l*, pg. 8131
TECHNICOLOR S.P.A.—See Vantiva SA; *Int'l*, pg. 8131
TECHNICOLOR TRADEMARK MANAGEMENT SASU—See Vantiva SA; *Int'l*, pg. 8131
TECHNICOLOR USA INC.—See Vantiva SA; *Int'l*, pg. 8131
TECHNICOLOR VIDEOCASSETTE OF MICHIGAN, INC.—See Vantiva SA; *Int'l*, pg. 8131
TECHNI-CON CONTAINER SURVEY LIMITED—See Eng Kong Holdings Pte Ltd.; *Int'l*, pg. 2426
TECHNICON DESIGN CORP.—See Segula Technologies SA; *Int'l*, pg. 6683
TECHNICO PTY LIMITED—See ITC Limited; *Int'l*, pg. 3831
TECHNICORP INTERNATIONAL II; *U.S. Private*, pg. 3954
TECHNICO TECHNOLOGIES INC.—See ITC Limited; *Int'l*, pg. 3832
TECHNICOTE INC.; *U.S. Private*, pg. 3954
TECHNICS OFFSHORE ENGINEERING PTE LTD—See Technics Oil & Gas Limited; *Int'l*, pg. 7506
TECHNICS OIL & GAS LIMITED; *Int'l*, pg. 7506
TECHNICS PLASMA GMBH PLASMA- UND LONENSTRAHLSYSTEME—See Robert Bosch GmbH; *Int'l*, pg. 6368
TECHNIC (SUZHOU) SEMICONDUCTOR ENGINEERING CO., LTD—See Technic Incorporated; *U.S. Private*, pg. 3953
TECHNIC TAIWAN CO., LTD.—See Technic Incorporated; *U.S. Private*, pg. 3953
TECHNIC UK—See Technic Incorporated; *U.S. Private*, pg. 3953
TECHNICUM GMBH—See Recruit Holdings Co., Ltd.; *Int'l*, pg. 6240
TECHNICUM NEDERLAND—See Recruit Holdings Co., Ltd.; *Int'l*, pg. 6240
TECHNIDATA BCS GMBH—See SAP SE; *Int'l*, pg. 6570
TECHNIDATA IT-SERVICE GMBH—See SAP SE; *Int'l*, pg. 6571
TECHNIFAB PRODUCTS, INC.—See Crane Company; *U.S. Public*, pg. 589
TECHNIFAX CORPORATION; *U.S. Private*, pg. 3954
TECHNIFORM METAL CURVING INC.; *U.S. Private*, pg. 3954
TECHNIFORM METAL CURVING OF TEXAS—See Techniform Metal Curving Inc.; *U.S. Private*, pg. 3954
TECHNIGRAPHICS, INC—See CACI International Inc.; *U.S. Public*, pg. 418
TECHNIK CENTER ALPEN GMBH—See AGRAVIS Raiffeisen AG; *Int'l*, pg. 215
TECHNIKCENTER GRIMMA GMBH—See BayWa AG; *Int'l*, pg. 919
TECHNIK LIMITED—See Writtle Holdings Limited; *Int'l*, pg. 8495

TECHNIKS INDUSTRIES—See Audax Group, Limited Partnership; *U.S. Private*, pg. 389
TECHNIKS, LLC—See Z Capital Group, LLC; *U.S. Private*, pg. 4595
TECHNI-LAB SARL—See HORIBA Ltd; *Int'l*, pg. 3478
TECHNILAMP PROPRIETARY LIMITED—See The Bidvest Group Limited; *Int'l*, pg. 7626
TECHNILINE SA; *Int'l*, pg. 7506
TECHNIMARK LLC—See The Pritzker Group - Chicago, LLC; *U.S. Private*, pg. 4099
TECHNIMOLD, S.R.L.—See Stratasys Ltd.; *Int'l*, pg. 7235
TECHNIP ABU DHABI—See TechnipFMC plc; *Int'l*, pg. 7508
TECHNIPAK; *U.S. Private*, pg. 3954
TECHNIPAQ, INC.; *U.S. Private*, pg. 3954
TECHNIP BEIJING—See TechnipFMC plc; *Int'l*, pg. 7508
TECHNIP BENELUX B.V.—See TechnipFMC plc; *Int'l*, pg. 7508
TECHNIP BRAZIL—See TechnipFMC plc; *Int'l*, pg. 7508
TECHNIP CANADA LIMITED—See TechnipFMC plc; *Int'l*, pg. 7508
TECHNIP E&C LIMITED—See TechnipFMC plc; *Int'l*, pg. 7508
TECHNIP ENERGIES INDIA LIMITED—See Technip Energies N.V.; *Int'l*, pg. 7507
TECHNIP ENERGIES N.V.; *Int'l*, pg. 7506
TECHNIP ENGINEERING (B) SDN BHD—See TechnipFMC plc; *Int'l*, pg. 7508
TECHNIP ENGINEERING CONSULTANT (SHANGHAI) CO. LTD.—See TechnipFMC plc; *Int'l*, pg. 7508
TECHNIP-EPG B.V.—See TechnipFMC plc; *Int'l*, pg. 7509
TECHNIP EUROCASH SNC—See TechnipFMC plc; *Int'l*, pg. 7508
TECHNIPFMC CANADA LIMITED—See TechnipFMC plc; *Int'l*, pg. 7509
TECHNIPFMC GUYANA INC.—See TechnipFMC plc; *Int'l*, pg. 7509
TECHNIPFMC NIGERIA LIMITED—See TechnipFMC plc; *Int'l*, pg. 7509
TECHNIPFMC PLC; *Int'l*, pg. 7507
TECHNIPFMC UMBILICALS LTD—See TechnipFMC plc; *Int'l*, pg. 7509
TECHNIP FRANCE—See TechnipFMC plc; *Int'l*, pg. 7508
TECHNIP HOLDING BENELUX BV—See TechnipFMC plc; *Int'l*, pg. 7508
TECHNIP IBERIA—See TechnipFMC plc; *Int'l*, pg. 7508
TECHNIP INDIA LTD—See TechnipFMC plc; *Int'l*, pg. 7508
TECHNIP ITALY S.P.A.—See TechnipFMC plc; *Int'l*, pg. 7508
TECHNIP KT INDIA LTD.—See TechnipFMC plc; *Int'l*, pg. 7508
TECHNIPLAS, LLC; *U.S. Private*, pg. 3954
TECHNIPLUS S.A.R.L.—See Hili Ventures Ltd; *Int'l*, pg. 3391
TECHNIP MALAYSIA—See TechnipFMC plc; *Int'l*, pg. 7508
TECHNIP MARITIME UK LTD—See TechnipFMC plc; *Int'l*, pg. 7508
TECHNIP NORGE AS-ORKANGER SPOOLBASE—See TechnipFMC plc; *Int'l*, pg. 7508
TECHNIP NORGE AS—See TechnipFMC plc; *Int'l*, pg. 7508
TECHNIP NORGE AS—See TechnipFMC plc; *Int'l*, pg. 7508
TECHNIP OCEANIA PTY LTD—See TechnipFMC plc; *Int'l*, pg. 7508
TECHNIP OFFSHORE FINLAND OY—See TechnipFMC plc; *Int'l*, pg. 7508
TECHNIP OFFSHORE, INC.—See TechnipFMC plc; *Int'l*, pg. 7509
TECHNIP OFFSHORE INTERNATIONAL S.A.—See TechnipFMC plc; *Int'l*, pg. 7508
TECHNIP OIL AND GAS B.V.—See TechnipFMC plc; *Int'l*, pg. 7508
TECHNIP POLSKA SP. Z O.O.—See TechnipFMC plc; *Int'l*, pg. 7508
TECHNIP RUSSIA—See TechnipFMC plc; *Int'l*, pg. 7508
TECHNIP S.A.—See TechnipFMC plc; *Int'l*, pg. 7507
TECHNIP SERVICIOS DE MEXICO—See TechnipFMC plc; *Int'l*, pg. 7508
TECHNIP SHIPS (NETHERLANDS) B.V.—See TechnipFMC plc; *Int'l*, pg. 7508
TECHNIP SINGAPORE PTE LTD—See TechnipFMC plc; *Int'l*, pg. 7508
TECHNIP—See TechnipFMC plc; *Int'l*, pg. 7508
TECHNIP SOUTH AFRICA LIMITED—See TechnipFMC plc; *Int'l*, pg. 7508
TECHNIP THAILAND—See TechnipFMC plc; *Int'l*, pg. 7508
TECHNIP TIANCHEN CHEMICAL ENGINEERING (TIANJIN) CO., LTD.—See TechnipFMC plc; *Int'l*, pg. 7508
TECHNIP TPS LYON—See WSP Global, Inc.; *Int'l*, pg. 8497
TECHNIP TPS SAS—See WSP Global, Inc.; *Int'l*, pg. 8497
TECHNIP TPS TOULOUSE—See WSP Global, Inc.; *Int'l*, pg. 8497
TECHNIP UK LIMITED—See TechnipFMC plc; *Int'l*, pg. 7508
TECHNIP USA, INC.—See TechnipFMC plc; *Int'l*, pg. 7508
TECHNIQUE DE L'EMBELLAGE EN CARTON—See Poulina Group Holding S.A.; *Int'l*, pg. 5942

COMPANY NAME INDEX

TECHNIQUES LLC—See Kirkwood Holding, Inc.; *U.S. Private*, pg. 2315

TECHNISAND, INC.—See Covia Holdings Corporation; *U.S. Private*, pg. 1072

TECHNISCAN, INC.; *U.S. Private*, pg. 3954

TECHNISCHE GASE UND GASETECHNIK GMBH—See DCC plc; *Int'l*, pg. 1991

TECHNISCHE INDUSTRIE VDS BV—See VDL Groep B.V.; *Int'l*, pg. 8141

TECHNISCHES BURO SEPP STEHRER BAUSTOFF-GROBHANDLUNG GESELLSCHAFT M.B.H—See PORR AG; *Int'l*, pg. 5925

TECHNISCHE UNIE—See Sonepar S.A.; *Int'l*, pg. 7092

TECHNISCH SERVICE CENTRUM RHENOY B.V.—See LKQ Corporation; *U.S. Public*, pg. 1336

TECHNIS, INC.; *U.S. Private*, pg. 3954

TECHNIS INTERNATIONAL PLC; *Int'l*, pg. 7509

TECHNISONIC SAS—See Gerard Perrier Industrie S.A.; *Int'l*, pg. 2942

TECHNISUB S.P.A.—See L'Air Liquide S.A.; *Int'l*, pg. 4375

TECHNI-TOOL INC.—See Distribution Solutions Group, Inc.; *U.S. Public*, pg. 669

TECHNIVAP SAS—See Rentokil Initial plc; *Int'l*, pg. 6289

TECHNIWELD CORPORATION; *Int'l*, pg. 7509

TECHNO5, INC.—See ManpowerGroup Inc.; *U.S. Public*, pg. 1362

TECHNO-AGRICULTURAL SUPPLYING JOINT STOCK COMPANY; *Int'l*, pg. 7509

TECHNO-AID CO., LTD.—See Aohata Corporation; *Int'l*, pg. 487

TECHNO ALPHA CO., LTD.; *Int'l*, pg. 7509

TECHNOALPIN AUSTRIA GMBH—See TechnoAlpin S.p.A.; *Int'l*, pg. 7509

TECHNOALPIN DEUTSCHLAND GMBH—See TechnoAlpin S.p.A.; *Int'l*, pg. 7509

TECHNOALPIN EAST EUROPE S.R.O.—See TechnoAlpin S.p.A.; *Int'l*, pg. 7509

TECHNOALPIN FRANCE SAS—See TechnoAlpin S.p.A.; *Int'l*, pg. 7509

TECHNOALPIN NORDIC AB—See TechnoAlpin S.p.A.; *Int'l*, pg. 7509

TECHNOALPIN ROMANIA SRL—See TechnoAlpin S.p.A.; *Int'l*, pg. 7509

TECHNOALPIN SCHWEIZ A.G.—See TechnoAlpin S.p.A.; *Int'l*, pg. 7510

TECHNOALPIN SNOW MAKING EQUIPMENT (SANHE) CO., LTD.—See TechnoAlpin S.p.A.; *Int'l*, pg. 7510

TECHNOALPIN S.P.A.; *Int'l*, pg. 7509

TECHNOALPIN USA, INC.—See TechnoAlpin S.p.A.; *Int'l*, pg. 7510

TECHNO ASSOCIE CO., LTD.—See Sumitomo Electric Industries, Ltd.; *Int'l*, pg. 7284

TECHNO ASSOCIE CZECH S.R.O.—See Sumitomo Electric Industries, Ltd.; *Int'l*, pg. 7285

TECHNO ASSOCIE (DALIAN F.T.Z.) CO., LTD.—See Sumitomo Electric Industries, Ltd.; *Int'l*, pg. 7285

TECHNO ASSOCIE DE MEXICO, S.A. DE C.V. - AGUASCALIENTES FACILITY—See Sumitomo Electric Industries, Ltd.; *Int'l*, pg. 7285

TECHNO ASSOCIE DE MEXICO, S.A. DE C.V. - MONTERREY FACILITY—See Sumitomo Electric Industries, Ltd.; *Int'l*, pg. 7285

TECHNO ASSOCIE DE MEXICO, S.A. DE C.V. - TIJUANA FACILITY—See Sumitomo Electric Industries, Ltd.; *Int'l*, pg. 7285

TECHNO ASSOCIE (GUANGZHOU) CO., LTD.—See Sumitomo Electric Industries, Ltd.; *Int'l*, pg. 7285

TECHNO ASSOCIE HONG KONG CO., LTD.—See Sumitomo Electric Industries, Ltd.; *Int'l*, pg. 7285

TECHNO ASSOCIE SHANGHAI CO., LTD.—See Sumitomo Electric Industries, Ltd.; *Int'l*, pg. 7285

TECHNO ASSOCIE SINGAPORE PTE. LTD.—See Sumitomo Electric Industries, Ltd.; *Int'l*, pg. 7285

TECHNO ASSOCIE TAIWAN CO., LTD.—See Sumitomo Electric Industries, Ltd.; *Int'l*, pg. 7285

TECHNO ASSOCIE (THAILAND) CO., LTD.—See Sumitomo Electric Industries, Ltd.; *Int'l*, pg. 7285

TECHNOCAST, S.A. DE C.V.—See TUPY S.A.; *Int'l*, pg. 7973

TECHNOCELL DEKOR SHANGHAI—See Felix Schoeller Holding GmbH & Co. KG; *Int'l*, pg. 2633

TECHNOCELL DEKOR USA—See Felix Schoeller Holding GmbH & Co. KG; *Int'l*, pg. 2633

TECHNOCELL INC.—See Felix Schoeller Holding GmbH & Co. KG; *Int'l*, pg. 2633

TECHNOCHEM ENVIRONMENTAL COMPLEX PTE. LTD.—See Dowa Holdings Co., Ltd.; *Int'l*, pg. 2184

TECHNO CHUBU CO., LTD.—See Chubu Electric Power Co., Inc.; *Int'l*, pg. 1593

TECHNO COATINGS INC.; *U.S. Private*, pg. 3954

TECHNOCOM SYSTEMS SDN BHD—See Venture Corporation Limited; *Int'l*, pg. 8151

TECHNO CONSTRUCTION CO., LTD.—See Zensho Holdings Co., Ltd.; *Int'l*, pg. 8635

TECHNOCONTACT S.A.—See TransDigm Group Incorporated; *U.S. Public*, pg. 2181

TECHNOCOVER LIMITED—See Threesixty Investments Limited; *Int'l*, pg. 7721

TECHNOCRAFT AUSTRALIA PTY LTD—See Technocraft Industries India Limited; *Int'l*, pg. 7510

TECHNOCRAFT (HUNGARY) KFT—See Technocraft Industries India Limited; *Int'l*, pg. 7510

TECHNOCRAFT INDUSTRIES INDIA LIMITED; *Int'l*, pg. 7510

TECHNOCRAFT INTERNATIONAL LTD—See Technocraft Industries India Limited; *Int'l*, pg. 7510

TECHNOCRAFT NZ LIMITED—See Technocraft Industries India Limited; *Int'l*, pg. 7510

TECHNOCRAFT TRADING SPOLKA Z O.O.—See Technocraft Industries India Limited; *Int'l*, pg. 7510

TECHNO-CREATE CORPORATION—See Kanaden Corporation; *Int'l*, pg. 4063

TECHNO DAI-ICHI CO., LTD—See I-PEX Inc.; *Int'l*, pg. 3564

TECHNO DATA ENGINEERING CO., LTD.—See Mitsubishi Heavy Industries, Ltd.; *Int'l*, pg. 4961

TECHNO DESIGN GMBH—See PDS Limited; *Int'l*, pg. 5771

TECHNODEX BERHAD; *Int'l*, pg. 7510

TECHNODINAMIKA—See Russian Technologies State Corporation; *Int'l*, pg. 6432

TECHNO DIV.—See Designatronics, Inc.; *U.S. Private*, pg. 1214

TECHNODYNE INTERNATIONAL LIMITED—See China International Marine Containers (Group) Co., Ltd.; *Int'l*, pg. 1512

TECHNO EARTH CORPORATION—See K&O Energy Group Inc.; *Int'l*, pg. 4038

TECHNO EIGHT CO., LTD.—See Yashima Denki Co., Ltd.; *Int'l*, pg. 8568

TECHNO ELECTRIC & ENGINEERING COMPANY LTD. - POWER PLANT & ELECTRIC DIVISION—See Techno Electric & Engineering Company Ltd.; *Int'l*, pg. 7509

TECHNO ELECTRIC & ENGINEERING COMPANY LTD.; *Int'l*, pg. 7509

TECHNOFAB ENGINEERING LIMITED; *Int'l*, pg. 7510

TECHNOFAN INC.—See Safran SA; *Int'l*, pg. 6476

TECHNOFAN SA—See Safran SA; *Int'l*, pg. 6476

TECHNO FIBRE AUSTRALIA PTY. LTD.—See Destini Berhad; *Int'l*, pg. 2047

TECHNO FIBRE MIDDLE EAST MARINE SERVICES FZE—See Destini Berhad; *Int'l*, pg. 2047

TECHNO FIBRE (S) PTE. LTD.—See Destini Berhad; *Int'l*, pg. 2046

TECHNOFINE CO., LTD.—See Mochida Pharmaceutical Co., Ltd.; *Int'l*, pg. 5012

TECHNOFIRST SA; *Int'l*, pg. 7510

TECHNOFLEX CORPORATION; *Int'l*, pg. 7510

TECHNOFLEX SA; *Int'l*, pg. 7510

TECHNOFLEX (SHANGHAI) INC.—See Technoflex Corporation; *Int'l*, pg. 7510

TECHNOFOAM CHINA CO., LTD.—See INOAC Corporation; *Int'l*, pg. 3715

TECHNOGAS SP. Z O.O.—See Linde plc; *Int'l*, pg. 4510

TECHNOGENETICS S.R.L.—See Shanghai Kehua Bioengineering Co., Ltd.; *Int'l*, pg. 6773

TECHNO-GRAPHICS & TRANSLATIONS, INC.; *U.S. Private*, pg. 3955

TECHNOGYM ASIA LTD.—See Technogym SpA; *Int'l*, pg. 7510

TECHNOGYM FRANCE SAS—See Technogym SpA; *Int'l*, pg. 7510

TECHNOGYM GERMANY GMBH—See Technogym SpA; *Int'l*, pg. 7510

TECHNOGYM JAPAN LTD.—See Technogym SpA; *Int'l*, pg. 7510

TECHNOGYM SHANGHAI INT. TRADING CO. LTD.—See Technogym SpA; *Int'l*, pg. 7510

TECHNOGYM SPA; *Int'l*, pg. 7510

TECHNOGYM ZAO—See Technogym SpA; *Int'l*, pg. 7510

TECHNO-HOKUETSU, LTD.—See Hokuetsu Corporation; *Int'l*, pg. 3444

TECHNO HORIZON CO., LTD.; *Int'l*, pg. 7509

TECHNO HVAC SYSTEM LTD.—See Daikin Industries, Ltd.; *Int'l*, pg. 1936

TECHNO IKEGAMI CO., LTD—See Ikegami Tsushinki Co., Ltd.; *Int'l*, pg. 3610

TECHNO INDAH SDN BHD—See Malaysia Marine and Heavy Engineering Holdings Berhad; *Int'l*, pg. 4662

TECHNOJET CONSULTANTS LIMITED; *Int'l*, pg. 7510

TECHNOKAR S.A.—See AUTOHELLAS S.A.; *Int'l*, pg. 727

TECHNO LABO CO., LTD.—See KOSE Corporation; *Int'l*, pg. 4290

TECHNOLAMP—See A.A.G. STUCCHI s.r.l.; *Int'l*, pg. 23

TECHNOLEASING LLP; *Int'l*, pg. 7510

TECHNO LIKE US CO., LTD.—See Alten S.A.; *Int'l*, pg. 391

TECHNOLINES S.R.L.—See EMC Limited; *Int'l*, pg. 2376

TECHNO LINKS INC.—See Takuma Co., Ltd.; *Int'l*, pg. 7443

TECHNOLOGIA CORPORATION—See Response Informatics Limited; *Int'l*, pg. 6302

TECHNOLOGIA INTERCONTINENETAL S.A. DE C.V.—See Empresas Publicas de Medellin ESP; *Int'l*, pg. 2391

TECHNOLOGIA MEXICANA S.A. DE C.V.—See CTS Corporation; *U.S. Public*, pg. 603

TECHNOLOGY SERVICES CORP.

TECHNOLOGICAL DEVELOPMENT & AUTOMATION LTD.; *Int'l*, pg. 7511

TECHNOLOGICAL LABORATORY FURNITURE MANUFACTURER (LABTEC)—See Dubai Investments PJSC; *Int'l*, pg. 2219

TECHNOLOGIE & ART PTE. LTD.—See New Mountain Capital, LLC; *U.S. Private*, pg. 2900

TECHNOLOGIEPARK TENINGEN GMBH—See Ascom Holding AG; *Int'l*, pg. 603

THE TECHNOLOGIES ALLIANCE, INC.—See Dril-Quip, Inc.; *U.S. Public*, pg. 688

TECHNOLOGIES AND INNOVATIONS CORPORATION SAEDINENIE PLC; *Int'l*, pg. 7511

TECHNOLOGIES FOR WATER SERVICES S.P.A.—See ACEA S.p.A.; *Int'l*, pg. 95

TECHNOLOGIES IBEX R&D INC.—See Novo Nordisk Fonden; *Int'l*, pg. 5463

TECHNOLOGIES LANKA INC.—See Knorr-Bremse AG; *Int'l*, pg. 4212

TECHNOLOGIES NTER INC—See Loto-Quebec; *Int'l*, pg. 4559

TECHNOLOGIES RESEARCH CORPORATION—See National Center for Manufacturing Sciences Inc.; *U.S. Private*, pg. 2850

TECHNOLOGIE TWORZYW SZTUCNYCH SPOL. ZOO.—See Aurelius Equity Opportunities SE & Co. KGaA; *Int'l*, pg. 709

TECHNOLOG LIMITED—See Roper Technologies, Inc.; *U.S. Public*, pg. 1813

TECHNOLOGUE—See The Hearst Corporation; *U.S. Private*, pg. 4045

TECHNOLOGY AND PRODUCTION CENTER SWITZERLAND AG—See SRG SSR Idee Suisse; *Int'l*, pg. 7149

TECHNOLOGY ASSOCIATES EC INC.; *U.S. Private*, pg. 3955

TECHNOLOGY & BUSINESS INTEGRATORS INC.; *U.S. Private*, pg. 3955

TECHNOLOGY CONCEPTS & DESIGN, INC.; *U.S. Private*, pg. 3955

TECHNOLOGY CONSULTING S.R.L.—See Sesa S.p.A.; *Int'l*, pg. 6729

TECHNOLOGY CONTAINER CORP.—See Connecticut Container Corporation; *U.S. Private*, pg. 1625

TECHNOLOGY CROSSOVER VENTURES L.P. - MILLBURN—See TCMI, Inc.; *U.S. Private*, pg. 3943

TECHNOLOGY DESIGN LIMITED—See Oceaneering International, Inc.; *U.S. Public*, pg. 1563

TECHNOLOGY DYNAMICS, INC.; *U.S. Private*, pg. 3955

TECHNOLOGY FINANCE PARTNERS INC.; *U.S. Private*, pg. 3955

TECHNOLOGY FOR BUSINESS CORP.—See Fusion Connect, Inc.; *U.S. Private*, pg. 1625

TECHNOLOGY FOR ENERGY CORPORATION; *U.S. Private*, pg. 3955

TECHNOLOGY GENERAL CORP.; *U.S. Public*, pg. 1988

TECHNOLOGY INSURANCE ASSOCIATES, LLC; *U.S. Private*, pg. 3955

TECHNOLOGY INVESTMENT PARTNERS, LLC—See Pathward Financial, Inc.; *U.S. Public*, pg. 1652

TECHNOLOGY MANAGEMENT ASSOCIATES INC.—See SAP SE; *Int'l*, pg. 6571

TECHNOLOGY MANAGEMENT CORP.—See The Carlyle Group Inc.; *U.S. Public*, pg. 2049

TECHNOLOGY METALS AUSTRALIA LIMITED—See Australian Vanadium Limited; *Int'l*, pg. 723

TECHNOLOGY MINERALS PLC; *Int'l*, pg. 7511

TECHNOLOGY OF ENERGY & CONTROLS CO., LTD.—See Aiphone Co., Ltd.; *Int'l*, pg. 235

TECHNOLOGY ONE CORPORATION SDN. BHD.—See TECHNOLOGYONE LIMITED; *Int'l*, pg. 7511

TECHNOLOGYONE LIMITED; *Int'l*, pg. 7511

TECHNOLOGY ONE LIMITED—See TECHNOLOGYONE LIMITED; *Int'l*, pg. 7511

TECHNOLOGY ONE NEW ZEALAND LTD.—See TECHNOLOGYONE LIMITED; *Int'l*, pg. 7511

TECHNOLOGY ONE; *U.S. Private*, pg. 3955

TECHNOLOGY PARTNERS, INC.; *U.S. Private*, pg. 3955

TECHNOLOGY PARTNERS INC.; *U.S. Private*, pg. 3955

TECHNOLOGY PLUS INC.; *U.S. Private*, pg. 3955

TECHNOLOGY RECOVERY GROUP LTD.; *U.S. Private*, pg. 3955

TECHNOLOGY REPLY S.R.L.—See Reply S.p.A.; *Int'l*, pg. 6291

TECHNOLOGY RESEARCH CORPORATION—See Southwire Company, LLC; *U.S. Private*, pg. 3742

TECHNOLOGY RESOURCE CENTER OF AMERICA, LLC (TRCA); *U.S. Private*, pg. 3955

TECHNOLOGY RESOURCE COMPANY LIMITED—See Aleator Energy Limited; *Int'l*, pg. 305

TECHNOLOGY RESOURCES INDUSTRIES—See Axiata Group Berhad; *Int'l*, pg. 768

TECHNOLOGY SECURITY ASSOCIATES, INC.—See JHNA, Inc.; *U.S. Private*, pg. 2208

TECHNOLOGY SERVICE CORPORATION; *U.S. Private*, pg. 3955

TECHNOLOGY SERVICE PARTNERS, INC.—See DXC Technology Company; *U.S. Public*, pg. 696

TECHNOLOGY SERVICES CORP.; *U.S. Private*, pg. 3955

TECHNOLOGY SERVICES CORP.

TECHNOLOGY SOLUTIONS PROVIDER INC.—See Abt Associates Inc.; *U.S. Private*, pg. 45
TECHNOLOGY STAFFING ON CALL; *U.S. Private*, pg. 3955
THE TECHNOLOGY STORE, INC.—See Scandium International Mining Corp; *U.S. Public*, pg. 1843
TECHNOLOGY SUPPORT, INC.; *U.S. Private*, pg. 3955
TECHNOLOGY & TELECOMMUNICATION ACQUISITION CORPORATION; *Int'l*, pg. 7511
TECHNOLOGY TRANSFER INSTITUTE/VANGUARD; *U.S. Private*, pg. 3956
TECHNOLOGY UNLIMITED INC.; *U.S. Private*, pg. 3956
TECHNOLOGY VENTURES, INC; *U.S. Private*, pg. 3956
TECHNOL SEVEN CO., LTD.—See TCS Holdings Co., Ltd.; *Int'l*, pg. 7485
TECHNOMARINE YACHTS, INC.; *U.S. Private*, pg. 3956
TECHNOMATERIAL CORPORATION—See Daiwa House Industry Co., Ltd.; *Int'l*, pg. 1946
TECHNO MATHEMATICAL CO., LTD.; *Int'l*, pg. 7509
TECHNOMAT S.A.—See TCS TurControlSysteme AG; *Int'l*, pg. 7486
TECHNOMAX, INC.—See TV TOKYO Holdings Corporation; *Int'l*, pg. 7987
TECHNOMAX LLC; *U.S. Private*, pg. 3956
TECHNOMECA AEROSPACE SA; *Int'l*, pg. 7511
TECHNO MEDICA CO., LTD.; *Int'l*, pg. 7509
TECHNO MEDICAL PCL; *Int'l*, pg. 7509
TECHNOMIC INC.—See Informa plc; *Int'l*, pg. 3694
TECHNOMILE LLC; *U.S. Private*, pg. 3956
TECHNOMINE AFRICA SARL—See Trigon Metals, Inc.; *Int'l*, pg. 7922
TECHNONET CO., LTD.—See Mochida Pharmaceutical Co., Ltd.; *Int'l*, pg. 5012
TECHNOPACK POLYMERS LIMITED; *Int'l*, pg. 7511
TECHNOPAL CO., LTD.—See Rentracks Co., Ltd.; *Int'l*, pg. 6289
TECHNOPARK IMMOBILIEN AG—See AXA S.A.; *Int'l*, pg. 758
TECHNO PARTS CO., LTD.—See Rinnai Corporation; *Int'l*, pg. 6345
TECHNO-PATH (DISTRIBUTION) LIMITED—See Diploma PLC; *Int'l*, pg. 2129
TECHNOPIA (THAILAND) LTD.—See Fumakilla Limited; *Int'l*, pg. 2844
TECHNOPIA (THAILAND) LTD.—See Texchem Resources Bhd.; *Int'l*, pg. 7583
TECHNOPIA VIETNAM PTE. LTD.—See Texchem Resources Bhd.; *Int'l*, pg. 7583
TECHNOPLUS INDUSTRIES SAS; *Int'l*, pg. 7511
TECHNOPLUS VENTURES LTD.; *Int'l*, pg. 7511
TECHNOPOLIS PLC; *Int'l*, pg. 7511
TECHNO POLYMER GUANGZHOU CO., LTD.—See JSR Corp.; *Int'l*, pg. 4014
TECHNO POLYMER SHANGHAI TECHNICAL DEVELOPMENT CO., LTD.—See JSR Corp.; *Int'l*, pg. 4014
TECHNOPORT INC.—See TOKYO KEIKI, INC.; *Int'l*, pg. 7792
TECHNOPROBE ASIA PTE. LTD.—See Technoprobe S.p.A.; *Int'l*, pg. 7511
TECHNOPROBE FRANCE S.A.S.—See Technoprobe S.p.A.; *Int'l*, pg. 7511
TECHNOPROBE GERMANY GMBH—See Technoprobe S.p.A.; *Int'l*, pg. 7511
TECHNOPROBE KOREA CO. LTD.—See Technoprobe S.p.A.; *Int'l*, pg. 7511
TECHNOPROBE S.P.A.; *Int'l*, pg. 7511
TECHNOPROBE US HOLDING LLC—See Technoprobe S.p.A.; *Int'l*, pg. 7511
TECHNOPROBE WUXI CO. LTD.—See Technoprobe S.p.A.; *Int'l*, pg. 7511
TECHNOPRO ENGINEERING INC.—See CVC Capital Partners SICAV-FIS S.A.; *Int'l*, pg. 1885
TECHNOPRO HOLDINGS, INC.—See CVC Capital Partners SICAV-FIS S.A.; *Int'l*, pg. 1885
TECHNOPRO SMILE, INC.—See CVC Capital Partners SICAV-FIS S.A.; *Int'l*, pg. 1885
TECHNO QUARTZ INC.—See GL Sciences Inc.; *Int'l*, pg. 2986
TECHNO RUBBER COMPANY—See Dubai Investments PJSC; *Int'l*, pg. 2219
TECHNO RYOWA LTD.; *Int'l*, pg. 7509
TECHNO SCIENCE, INC.—See DIC Corporation; *Int'l*, pg. 2111
TECHNOSCIENT HUSSEIN NAGUI & CO.—See Sartorius AG; *Int'l*, pg. 6581
TECHNOS CO., LTD.—See Kumagai Gumi Co., Ltd.; *Int'l*, pg. 4329
TECHNOS DA AMAZONIA INDUSTRIA E COMERCIO S.A.—See TECHNOS S.A.; *Int'l*, pg. 7511
TECHNO-SEAWAYS INC.—See Mitsui E&S Holdings Co., Ltd.; *Int'l*, pg. 4986
TECHNOSERVE CO., INC.—See JGC Holdings Corporation; *Int'l*, pg. 3940
TECHNOSERVICEDRIVE LTD.—See SEMIKRON International GmbH; *Int'l*, pg. 6705
TECHNOSKRUV I VARNAMO AB—See Indutrade AB; *Int'l*, pg. 3681
TECHNO SMART CORP. - SHIGA FACTORY—See Techno Smart Corp.; *Int'l*, pg. 7509

TECHNO SMART CORP.; *Int'l*, pg. 7509
TECHNO SOFT CO., LTD.—See Kuraray Co., Ltd.; *Int'l*, pg. 4338
TECHNOSOFT ENGINEERING INC.—See Technocraft Industries India Limited; *Int'l*, pg. 7510
TECHNOSOFT ENGINEERING PROJECTS LIMITED—See Technocraft Industries India Limited; *Int'l*, pg. 7510
TECHNOSOFT ENGINEERING UK LIMITED—See Technocraft Industries India Limited; *Int'l*, pg. 7510
TECHNOSOFT GMBH—See Technocraft Industries India Limited; *Int'l*, pg. 7510
TECHNOSOFT INFORMATION TECHNOLOGIES (INDIA) LTD.—See Technocraft Industries India Limited; *Int'l*, pg. 7510
TECHNOSOFT SA—See Shanghai Moons' Electric Co., Ltd.; *Int'l*, pg. 6775
TECHNOSOFT SERVICES INC.—See Technocraft Industries India Limited; *Int'l*, pg. 7510
TECHNO SOLUTIONS PRIVATE LIMITED—See Endress+Hauser (International) Holding AG; *Int'l*, pg. 2409
TECHNO-SPACE CREATES CO.,LTD.—See Kumagai Gumi Co., Ltd.; *Int'l*, pg. 4329
TECHNO SPECIALS N.V.—See TKH Group N.V.; *Int'l*, pg. 7765
TECHNOSPRING KFT.—See Hutter & Schrantz PMS Ges.m.b.H; *Int'l*, pg. 3540
TECHNOS S.A.; *Int'l*, pg. 7511
TECHNO STEEL PROCESSING DE MEXICO S.A. DE C.V.—See Toyota Tsusho Corporation; *Int'l*, pg. 7878
TECHNO-STEP GMBH—See Durr AG; *Int'l*, pg. 2233
TECHNO SUPPORT CO., LTD.—See Yahagi Construction Co., Ltd.; *Int'l*, pg. 8546
TECHNO SUPPORT CO., LTD.—See Tokushu Tokai Paper Co., Ltd.; *Int'l*, pg. 7786
TECHNOSYSTEMS CONSOLIDATED CORPORATION; *U.S. Private*, pg. 3956
TECHNO SYSTEMS INC.—See Sala Corporation; *Int'l*, pg. 6490
TECHNO TAR ENGINEERING COMPANY; *Int'l*, pg. 7509
TECHNO TEST S.R.L.—See Endress+Hauser (International) Holding AG; *Int'l*, pg. 2409
TECHNO TOPPAN FORMS CO., LTD.—See TOPPAN Holdings Inc.; *Int'l*, pg. 7817
TECHNOTRANS AG; *Int'l*, pg. 7511
TECHNOTRANS AMERICA INC.—See Technotrans AG; *Int'l*, pg. 7512
TECHNOTRANS AMERICA LATINA LTDA—See Technotrans AG; *Int'l*, pg. 7512
TECHNOTRANS CHINA LTD.—See Technotrans AG; *Int'l*, pg. 7512
TECHNOTRANS FRANCE S.A.R.L.—See Technotrans AG; *Int'l*, pg. 7512
TECHNOTRANS GRAPHICS LIMITED—See Technotrans AG; *Int'l*, pg. 7512
TECHNOTRANS INDIA PVT.LTD—See Technotrans AG; *Int'l*, pg. 7512
TECHNOTRANS ITALIA S.R.L.—See Technotrans AG; *Int'l*, pg. 7512
TECHNOTRANS JAPAN K.K.—See Technotrans AG; *Int'l*, pg. 7512
TECHNOTRANS MIDDLE EAST FZ-LLC—See Technotrans AG; *Int'l*, pg. 7512
TECHNOTRANS PRINTING EQUIPMENT (BEIJING) COMPANY LTD.—See Technotrans AG; *Int'l*, pg. 7512
TECHNOTRANS SCANDINAVIA AB—See Technotrans AG; *Int'l*, pg. 7512
TECHNOTRANS TECHNOLOGIES PTE. LTD.—See Technotrans AG; *Int'l*, pg. 7512
TECHNOTRIM DE MEXICO, S. DE R.L. DE C.V.—See Adient plc; *Int'l*, pg. 148
TECHNO-UMG AMERICA, INC.—See JSR Corp.; *Int'l*, pg. 4014
TECHNO-UMG AMERICA, INC.—See Mitsubishi Chemical Group Corporation; *Int'l*, pg. 4934
TECHNO-UMG AMERICA, INC.—See UBE Corporation; *Int'l*, pg. 8001
TECHNO-UMG ASIA CO., LTD.—See JSR Corp.; *Int'l*, pg. 4014
TECHNO-UMG ASIA CO., LTD.—See Mitsubishi Chemical Group Corporation; *Int'l*, pg. 4934
TECHNO-UMG ASIA CO., LTD.—See UBE Corporation; *Int'l*, pg. 8001
TECHNO-UMG CO., LTD.—See JSR Corp.; *Int'l*, pg. 4014
TECHNO-UMG CO., LTD.—See Mitsubishi Chemical Group Corporation; *Int'l*, pg. 4934
TECHNO-UMG CO., LTD.—See UBE Corporation; *Int'l*, pg. 8001
TECHNO-UMG EUROPE GMBH—See JSR Corp.; *Int'l*, pg. 4014
TECHNO-UMG HONG KONG CO., LTD.—See JSR Corp.; *Int'l*, pg. 4014
TECHNO-UMG HONG KONG CO., LTD.—See Mitsubishi Chemical Group Corporation; *Int'l*, pg. 4934
TECHNO-UMG HONG KONG CO., LTD.—See UBE Corporation; *Int'l*, pg. 8001
TECHNO-UMG (SHANGHAI) CO., LTD.—See JSR Corp.; *Int'l*, pg. 4014

CORPORATE AFFILIATIONS

TECHNO-UMG (SHANGHAI) CO., LTD.—See Mitsubishi Chemical Group Corporation; *Int'l*, pg. 4934
TECHNO-UMG (SHANGHAI) CO., LTD.—See UBE Corporation; *Int'l*, pg. 8001
TECHNO-UMG SHANGHAI TECHNICAL CENTER CO., LTD.—See JSR Corp.; *Int'l*, pg. 4014
TECHNO-UMG SHANGHAI TECHNICAL CENTER CO., LTD.—See Mitsubishi Chemical Group Corporation; *Int'l*, pg. 4934
TECHNO-UMG SHANGHAI TECHNICAL CENTER CO., LTD.—See UBE Corporation; *Int'l*, pg. 8001
TECHNOVA, INC.—See AISIN Corporation; *Int'l*, pg. 254
TECHNOVATIVE GROUP, INC.; *Int'l*, pg. 7512
TECHNOVATOR INTERNATIONAL LIMITED; *Int'l*, pg. 7512
TECHNUM-TRACTEBEL ENGINEERING N.V.—See ENGIE SA; *Int'l*, pg. 2432
TECHNVISION VENTURES LIMITED; *Int'l*, pg. 7512
TECHNYX EURO SERVICES S.R.L.—See AIP, LLC; *U.S. Private*, pg. 134
TECHNYX EURO SERVICES S.R.L.—See Placements CMI Inc.; *Int'l*, pg. 5887
TECHO, A. S.—See HAL Trust N.V.; *Int'l*, pg. 3223
TECH OPTICS FIRST COMPANY LTD.—See Hexatronic Group AB; *Int'l*, pg. 3371
TECH OPTICS LTD.—See Hexatronic Group AB; *Int'l*, pg. 3371
TECHORBIT, INC.—See Brightcom Group Ltd.; *Int'l*, pg. 1162
TECH ORD—See National Presto Industries, Inc; *U.S. Public*, pg. 1497
TECH PACK S.A.—See Quinenco S.A.; *Int'l*, pg. 6164
TECH-PAK—See President Container Group, Inc.; *U.S. Private*, pg. 3254
TECH PEOPLE AS—See Adecco Group AG; *Int'l*, pg. 140
TECH PHARMACY SERVICES, INC.—See Partners Pharmacy, LLC; *U.S. Private*, pg. 3103
TECHPLAY MARKETING LTD—See Playtech plc; *Int'l*, pg. 5894
TECHPOINT GROUP LTD.—See Literacy Capital Plc; *Int'l*, pg. 4526
TECHPOINT, INC.; *U.S. Public*, pg. 1988
TECHPOWER SOLUTIONS INC.; *U.S. Private*, pg. 3956
TECHPRECISION CORPORATION; *U.S. Public*, pg. 1988
TECH-PRO INC.; *U.S. Private*, pg. 3952
TECHPRO POWER GROUP, INC.; *U.S. Private*, pg. 3956
TECH PRO TECHNOLOGY DEVELOPMENT LIMITED; *Int'l*, pg. 7502
TECHPRO TRADING LIMITED—See E. Bon Holdings Ltd; *Int'l*, pg. 2250
TECH-R2; *U.S. Private*, pg. 3952
TECHRADIUM, INC.; *U.S. Private*, pg. 3956
TECH RENTALS (MALAYSIA) SDN. BHD.—See Vp PLC; *Int'l*, pg. 8312
TECH RESOURCES, INC.; *U.S. Private*, pg. 3952
TECHSAFE AUSTRALIA PTY. LTD.—See Service Stream Limited; *Int'l*, pg. 6725
TECH SEMICONDUCTORS CO., LTD.; *Int'l*, pg. 7502
TECH SEMICONDUCTOR SINGAPORE PTE. LTD.—See Canon Inc.; *Int'l*, pg. 1296
TECHSHINE ELECTRONICS CO., LTD.; *Int'l*, pg. 7512
TECHSHOT, INC.—See Redwire Corporation; *U.S. Public*, pg. 1771
TECHSKILLS, LLC; *U.S. Private*, pg. 3956
TECHSKILLS RESOURCES LIMITED—See Bain Capital, LP; *U.S. Private*, pg. 434
TECHSMITH CORPORATION; *U.S. Private*, pg. 3956
TECHSOL4U, INC.; *U.S. Private*, pg. 3956
TECHSOUP GLOBAL; *U.S. Private*, pg. 3956
TECH SOURCE, INC.—See EIZO Corporation; *Int'l*, pg. 2337
TECHSOURCE, INC.; *U.S. Private*, pg. 3956
TECHSOURCE LLC—See Dubai Investments PJSC; *Int'l*, pg. 2219
TECHSPAN SYSTEMS—See Hill & Smith PLC; *Int'l*, pg. 3392
TECHSPIRE CO., LTD.—See Argo Graphics Inc.; *Int'l*, pg. 562
TECH SPRAY, L.P.—See Illinois Tool Works Inc.; *U.S. Public*, pg. 1111
TECHSTACKERY, INC.; *U.S. Private*, pg. 3956
TECHSTAR ACQUISITION CORPORATION; *Int'l*, pg. 7512
TECHSTAR GROUP, INC.; *U.S. Private*, pg. 3956
TECH-STEEL INC.; *U.S. Private*, pg. 3952
TECHSTEP ASA; *Int'l*, pg. 7512
TECH SYN CORPORATION; *U.S. Private*, pg. 3952
TECHTARGET GERMANY GMBH—See TechTarget, Inc.; *U.S. Public*, pg. 1989
TECHTARGET, INC.; *U.S. Public*, pg. 1988
TECHTARGET LIMITED—See TechTarget, Inc.; *U.S. Public*, pg. 1989
TECHTARGET (SINGAPORE) PTE. LTD.—See TechTarget, Inc.; *U.S. Public*, pg. 1989
TECHTEX GMBH VLIESSTOFFE MITTWEIDA—See Hoftex Group AG; *Int'l*, pg. 3440
TECH TOEI CO., LTD.—See TS Tech Co Ltd; *Int'l*, pg. 7948

COMPANY NAME INDEX

TECHTRACKER, INC.—See National Amusements, Inc.; *U.S. Private*, pg. 2840
TECHTRAN GROUP LIMITED—See IP Group plc; *Int'l*, pg. 3795
TECHTRAN LENSES INC.—See Techtran Ophthalmics Pvt Ltd.; *Int'l*, pg. 7512
TECHTRAN OPHTHALMICS PVT LTD.; *Int'l*, pg. 7512
TECH-TREND (SHANGHAI) COMPUTER CO., LTD.—See Quanta Computer, Inc.; *Int'l*, pg. 6153
TECHTRENDS, INC.—See Nuvera Communications, Inc.; *U.S. Public*, pg. 1556
TECHTRONIC CORDLESS GP—See Techtronic Industries Co., Ltd.; *Int'l*, pg. 7513
TECHTRONIC INDUSTRIES ARGENTINA, S.R.L.—See Techtronic Industries Co., Ltd.; *Int'l*, pg. 7513
TECHTRONIC INDUSTRIES AUSTRALIA PTY. LIMITED—See Techtronic Industries Co., Ltd.; *Int'l*, pg. 7513
TECHTRONIC INDUSTRIES CANADA, INC—See Techtronic Industries Co., Ltd.; *Int'l*, pg. 7513
TECHTRONIC INDUSTRIES CENTRAL EUROPE B.E.—See Techtronic Industries Co., Ltd.; *Int'l*, pg. 7513
TECHTRONIC INDUSTRIES CENTRAL EUROPE GMBH—See Techtronic Industries Co., Ltd.; *Int'l*, pg. 7513
TECHTRONIC INDUSTRIES CO., LTD.; *Int'l*, pg. 7512
TECHTRONIC INDUSTRIES COM FERRAM DO BRASIL LTDA.—See Techtronic Industries Co., Ltd.; *Int'l*, pg. 7513
TECHTRONIC INDUSTRIES DO BRASIL LTDA—See Techtronic Industries Co., Ltd.; *Int'l*, pg. 7513
TECHTRONIC INDUSTRIES (DONGGUAN) CO. LTD—See Techtronic Industries Co., Ltd.; *Int'l*, pg. 7513
TECHTRONIC INDUSTRIES ELC GMBH—See Techtronic Industries Co., Ltd.; *Int'l*, pg. 7513
TECHTRONIC INDUSTRIES FRANCE SAS—See Techtronic Industries Co., Ltd.; *Int'l*, pg. 7513
TECHTRONIC INDUSTRIES GERMANY HOLDING GMBH—See Techtronic Industries Co., Ltd.; *Int'l*, pg. 7513
TECHTRONIC INDUSTRIES GMBH—See Techtronic Industries Co., Ltd.; *Int'l*, pg. 7513
TECHTRONIC INDUSTRIES NORDIC A/S—See Techtronic Industries Co., Ltd.; *Int'l*, pg. 7513
TECHTRONIC INDUSTRIES NORTH AMERICA, INC.—See Techtronic Industries Co., Ltd.; *Int'l*, pg. 4148
TECHTRONIC INDUSTRIES N.Z. LIMITED—See Techtronic Industries Co., Ltd.; *Int'l*, pg. 7513
TECHTRONIC INDUSTRIES (SUZHOU) CO., LTD.—See Techtronic Industries Co., Ltd.; *Int'l*, pg. 7513
TECHTRONIC INDUSTRIES (TAIWAN) CO. LTD—See Techtronic Industries Co., Ltd.; *Int'l*, pg. 7513
TECHTRONIC INDUSTRIES (UK) LTD—See Techtronic Industries Co., Ltd.; *Int'l*, pg. 7513
TECHTRONIC POWER TOOLS TECHNOLOGY LIMITED—See Techtronic Industries Co., Ltd.; *Int'l*, pg. 7513
TECHTRONIC TRADING LIMITED—See Techtronic Industries Co., Ltd.; *Int'l*, pg. 7513
TECHTUIT CO., LTD.—See Techtuit Holdings Co., Ltd.; *Int'l*, pg. 7513
TECHTUIT HOLDINGS CO., LTD.; *Int'l*, pg. 7513
TECHTURN, INC.—See Arrow Electronics, Inc.; *U.S. Public*, pg. 200
TECHUM-TRACTABEL ENGINEERING N.V.—See ENGIE SA; *Int'l*, pg. 2432
TECH USA INC.; *U.S. Private*, pg. 3952
TECH VALUE IBERICA SRL—See Sesa S.p.A.; *Int'l*, pg. 6729
TECH-VALUE S.P.A.; *Int'l*, pg. 7503
TECHWAN SA—See Thoma Bravo, L.P.; *U.S. Private*, pg. 4148
TECHWAVE CONSULTING INC.; *U.S. Private*, pg. 3956
TECHWAVE MEDIA SERVICES PTE LTD—See Teckwah Industrial Corporation Ltd; *Int'l*, pg. 7515
TECHWAX LIMITED—See Ashland Inc.; *U.S. Public*, pg. 213
TECHWELL ENGINEERING LTD.—See China CGame, Inc.; *Int'l*, pg. 1488
TECHWING INC.; *Int'l*, pg. 7513
TECHWIN OPTO-ELECTRONICS CO., LTD.—See CHIA-LIN Precision Industrial Co., Ltd.; *Int'l*, pg. 1476
TECHWISE CIRCUITS COMPANY LIMITED—See Kingboard Holdings Limited; *Int'l*, pg. 4171
TECHWISE SHIRAI (FOGANG) CIRCUITS LIMITED—See Kingboard Holdings Limited; *Int'l*, pg. 4171
TECHXTEND, INC.—See Climb Global Solutions, Inc.; *U.S. Public*, pg. 515
TEC, INC.; *U.S. Private*, pg. 3951
TECIS FINANZDIENSTLEISTUNGEN AG—See Swiss Life Holding; *Int'l*, pg. 7369
TECITY GROUP; *Int'l*, pg. 7514
TECK ADVANCED MATERIALS INCORPORATED—See Teck Resources Limited; *Int'l*, pg. 7514
TECK ALASKA INCORPORATED—See Teck Resources Limited; *Int'l*, pg. 7514
TECK AMERICAN INCORPORATED—See Teck Resources Limited; *Int'l*, pg. 7514
TECK AUSTRALIA PTY LTD.—See Teck Resources Limited; *Int'l*, pg. 7514
TECK BASE METALS LTD.—See Teck Resources Limited; *Int'l*, pg. 7514
TECK CHIANG REALTY PRIVATE LIMITED—See LTC Corporation Limited; *Int'l*, pg. 4571
TECK COAL LIMITED—See Teck Resources Limited; *Int'l*, pg. 7514
TECK CONSTRUCTION LLP; *Int'l*, pg. 7514
TECKENTRUP B.V.—See Teckentrup GmbH & Co. KG; *Int'l*, pg. 7514
TECKENTRUP FRANCE SAS—See Teckentrup GmbH & Co. KG; *Int'l*, pg. 7514
TECKENTRUP GMBH & CO. KG GROSSZOBERITZ PLANT—See Teckentrup GmbH & Co. KG; *Int'l*, pg. 7514
TECKENTRUP GMBH & CO. KG; *Int'l*, pg. 7514
TECKENTRUP SCANDINAVIA AB—See Teckentrup GmbH & Co. KG; *Int'l*, pg. 7514
TECKENTRUP SCHWEIZ AG—See Teckentrup GmbH & Co. KG; *Int'l*, pg. 7514
TECKENTRUP SP. Z O.O.—See Teckentrup GmbH & Co. KG; *Int'l*, pg. 7514
TECKENTRUP UK LTD.—See Teckentrup GmbH & Co. KG; *Int'l*, pg. 7514
TECK GUAN PERDANA BERHAD; *Int'l*, pg. 7514
TECK HIGHLAND VALLEY COPPER PARTNERSHIP—See Teck Resources Limited; *Int'l*, pg. 7514
TECK IRELAND LTD.—See Teck Resources Limited; *Int'l*, pg. 7514
TECK MADENCILIK SANAYI TICARET A.S.—See Teck Resources Limited; *Int'l*, pg. 7514
TECK METALS LTD. - APPLIED RESEARCH TECHNOLOGY—See Teck Resources Limited; *Int'l*, pg. 7514
TECK METALS LTD.—See Teck Resources Limited; *Int'l*, pg. 7514
TECK METALS LTD. - TRAIL OPERATIONS—See Teck Resources Limited; *Int'l*, pg. 7514
TECK NAMIBIA LIMITED—See Teck Resources Limited; *Int'l*, pg. 7514
TECKON INDUSTRIAL CORPORATION—See COXON Precise Industrial Co., Ltd.; *Int'l*, pg. 1823
TECK PERU S.A.—See Teck Resources Limited; *Int'l*, pg. 7514
TECK RESOURCES CHILE LIMITADA—See Teck Resources Limited; *Int'l*, pg. 7514
TECK RESOURCES LIMITED; *Int'l*, pg. 7514
TECK SEE PLASTICS SDN. BHD—See Oriental Holdings Berhad; *Int'l*, pg. 5625
TECKWAH INDUSTRIAL CORPORATION LTD; *Int'l*, pg. 7515
TECKWAH LOGISTICS (INDIA) PRIVATE LIMITED—See Teckwah Industrial Corporation Ltd; *Int'l*, pg. 7515
TECKWAH LOGISTICS PTE LTD—See Teckwah Industrial Corporation Ltd; *Int'l*, pg. 7515
TECKWAH PACKAGING SYSTEMS (SHANGHAI) CO LTD—See Teckwah Industrial Corporation Ltd; *Int'l*, pg. 7515
TECKWAH TRADING (SHANGHAI) CO., LTD.—See Teckwah Industrial Corporation Ltd; *Int'l*, pg. 7515
TECKWAH VALUE CHAIN (JAPAN) CO LTD—See Teckwah Industrial Corporation Ltd; *Int'l*, pg. 7515
TECKWAH VALUE CHAIN PTE LTD—See Teckwah Industrial Corporation Ltd; *Int'l*, pg. 7515
TECKWAH VALUE CHAIN PTY LTD—See Teckwah Industrial Corporation Ltd; *Int'l*, pg. 7515
TECKWAH VALUE CHAIN SDN. BHD.—See Teckwah Industrial Corporation Ltd; *Int'l*, pg. 7515
TECKWAH VALUE CHAIN (SHANGHAI) CO., LTD—See Teckwah Industrial Corporation Ltd; *Int'l*, pg. 7515
TECKWAH VALUE CHAIN (THAILAND) CO LTD—See Teckwah Industrial Corporation Ltd; *Int'l*, pg. 7515
TEC LABORATORIES, INC.—See Promus Holdings, LLC; *U.S. Private*, pg. 3284
TECMAG, INC.—See Avingtrans plc; *Int'l*, pg. 744
TECMAG JAPAN CO.—See Tecnomagnete SpA; *Int'l*, pg. 7516
TECMA GROUP, LLC; *U.S. Private*, pg. 3956
TEC MARITSA 3 AD; *Int'l*, pg. 7501
TECMARKET SERVIZI S.P.A.—See Banco BPM S.p.A.; *Int'l*, pg. 819
TECMAR TRANSPORTES LTDA.—See Log-In Logistica Intermodal S.A.; *Int'l*, pg. 4541
TECMA SOLUTIONS S.P.A.; *Int'l*, pg. 7515
TEC-MASTERS INC.; *U.S. Private*, pg. 3951
TECMAT SERVICE; *Int'l*, pg. 7515
TECMED MAROC, S.A.R.L.—See ACS, Actividades de Construccion y Servicios, S.A.; *Int'l*, pg. 116
TECMO ARABIA LTD—See A.H. Algosaibi & Bros.; *Int'l*, pg. 24
TECMO CO., LTD.—See Press Kogyo Co., Ltd.; *Int'l*, pg. 5965
TEC MOTION CO., LTD.—See T3EX Global Holdings Corp.; *Int'l*, pg. 7398
TECMOTIVE GMBH—See Hella GmbH & Co. KGaA; *Int'l*, pg. 3332
TECNAIR LV S.P.A.—See LU-VE SpA; *Int'l*, pg. 4572
TECNANDINA S.A.—See Grunenthal GmbH; *Int'l*, pg. 3115
TECNA SRL—See Eurofins Scientific S.E.; *Int'l*, pg. 2552
TECNATOM FRANCE S.A.S.—See Enel S.p.A.; *Int'l*, pg. 2414
TECNATOM S.A.—See Enel S.p.A.; *Int'l*, pg. 2414
TECNAU AB—See Tecnau Srl; *Int'l*, pg. 7515
TECNAU INC.—See Tecnau Srl; *Int'l*, pg. 7515
TECNAU LTD.—See Tecnau Srl; *Int'l*, pg. 7515
TECNAU PTE LTD—See Tecnau Srl; *Int'l*, pg. 7515
TECNAU SRL; *Int'l*, pg. 7515
TECNEIRA, S.A.—See ACS, Actividades de Construccion y Servicios, S.A.; *Int'l*, pg. 116
TECNEL ELEVADORES, LDA—See Schindler Holding AG; *Int'l*, pg. 6621
TECNEL S.R.L.—See Antares Vision SpA; *Int'l*, pg. 482
TECNET INC.—See Tachibana Eletech Co., Ltd.; *Int'l*, pg. 7403
TECNICA DEL FUTURO S.A.—See HORIBA Ltd; *Int'l*, pg. 3478
TECNICARTON FRANCE S.A.S.—See DS Smith Plc; *Int'l*, pg. 2209
TECNICARTON PORTUGAL UNIPESSOAL LDA—See DS Smith Plc; *Int'l*, pg. 2209
TECNICAS AUTOCONTROL, S.L.U.—See KONE Oyj; *Int'l*, pg. 4250
TECNICAS DE DESALINIZACION DE AGUAS, S.A.—See ACS, Actividades de Construccion y Servicios, S.A.; *Int'l*, pg. 116
TECNICAS DE ENTIBACION, S.A.U.—See Duro Felguera, S.A.; *Int'l*, pg. 2229
TECNICAS E IMAGEN CORPORATIVA, S.L.—See ACS, Actividades de Construccion y Servicios, S.A.; *Int'l*, pg. 116
TECNICAS E INGENIERIA DE PROTECCION, S.A.U.—See Kuriyama Holdings Corporation; *Int'l*, pg. 4342
TECNICAS REUNIDAS CHILE LTDA.—See Tecnicas Reunidas, S.A.; *Int'l*, pg. 7515
TECNICAS REUNIDAS DE CONSTRUCAO UNIP. LDA—See Tecnicas Reunidas, S.A.; *Int'l*, pg. 7516
TECNICAS REUNIDAS GULF LTD.—See Tecnicas Reunidas, S.A.; *Int'l*, pg. 7515
TECNICAS REUNIDAS MEXICO INGENIERIA Y CONSTRUCCION DE R.L. DE C.V.—See Tecnicas Reunidas, S.A.; *Int'l*, pg. 7516
TECNICAS REUNIDAS OMAN LLC—See Tecnicas Reunidas, S.A.; *Int'l*, pg. 7516
TECNICAS REUNIDAS PERU INGENIERIA Y CONSTRUCCION, S.A.C.—See Tecnicas Reunidas, S.A.; *Int'l*, pg. 7516
TECNICAS REUNIDAS, S.A. - MADRID PLANT—See Tecnicas Reunidas, S.A.; *Int'l*, pg. 7516
TECNICAS REUNIDAS, S.A.; *Int'l*, pg. 7515
TECNICAS REUNIDAS, S.A. - WOODLANDS BRANCH—See Tecnicas Reunidas, S.A.; *Int'l*, pg. 7516
TECNICAS REUNIDAS TEC LTDA.—See Tecnicas Reunidas, S.A.; *Int'l*, pg. 7516
TECNICA Y PROYECTOS S.A.; *Int'l*, pg. 7515
TECNICENTROS MUNDIAL INC.—See Icahn Enterprises L.P.; *U.S. Public*, pg. 1084
TECNICO CORPORATION—See American Maritime Holdings, Inc.; *U.S. Private*, pg. 240
TECNICOS EN LA ALTA PRODUCCION S.A. DE C.V.—See Corpfin Capital SA; *Int'l*, pg. 1802
TECNIDATA BMT BUSINESS MANAGEMENT TECNOLOGIES, S.A.—See Reditus SGPS S.A.; *Int'l*, pg. 6248
TECNIDATA IF INVESTIMENTOS FINANCEIROS SGPS, S.A.—See Reditus SGPS S.A.; *Int'l*, pg. 6248
TECNIDOORS S.P.A.—See Tecnolama S.A.; *Int'l*, pg. 7516
TECNILUZ S.A.—See A.A.G. STUCCHI s.r.l.; *Int'l*, pg. 23
TECNIMONT CIVIL CONSTRUCTION—See Maire Tecnimont S.p.A.; *Int'l*, pg. 4652
TECNIMONT ICB PVT. LTD.—See Maire Tecnimont S.p.A.; *Int'l*, pg. 4652
TECNIMONT ICB QATAR WLL.—See Maire Tecnimont S.p.A.; *Int'l*, pg. 4652
TECNIMONT MEXICO SA DE CV—See Maire Tecnimont S.p.A.; *Int'l*, pg. 4652
TECNIMONT NIGERIA LTD.—See Maire Tecnimont S.p.A.; *Int'l*, pg. 4652
TECNIMONT PHILIPPINES INC.—See Maire Tecnimont S.p.A.; *Int'l*, pg. 4652
TECNIMONT PRIVATE LIMITED—See Maire Tecnimont S.p.A.; *Int'l*, pg. 4652
TECNIMONT RUSSIA—See Maire Tecnimont S.p.A.; *Int'l*, pg. 4652
TECNIQ, INC.; *U.S. Private*, pg. 3957
TECNIQUIMIA MEXICANA S.A. DE C.V.—See Quaker Chemical Corporation; *U.S. Public*, pg. 1747
TECNISA S.A.; *Int'l*, pg. 7516
TECNISCO LTD.; *Int'l*, pg. 7516
TECNISEGUROS, SOCIEDAD DE AGENCIA DE SEGUROS, S.A.—See Grupo Catalana Occidente, S.A.; *Int'l*, pg. 3124
TECNIWELL S.R.L.—See Granite Construction Incorporated; *U.S. Public*, pg. 958

TECNO ACCION S.A.—See INTRALOT S.A.; *Int'l*, pg. 3768
TECNOAMBIENTAL S.A.S.—See WSP Global, Inc.; *Int'l*, pg. 8497
TECNOAMERICA IND. E COMERCIO LTDA.—See Tecnolama S.A.; *Int'l*, pg. 7516
TECNO ARASAT SERVICIOS DE MANTENIMIENTO S.L.—See Brookfield Corporation; *Int'l*, pg. 1189
TECNO ART RESEARCH CO., LTD.—See Toyoda Gosei Co., Ltd.; *Int'l*, pg. 7862
TECNO BOGA COMERCIAL LIMITADA—See Bunzl plc; *Int'l*, pg. 1219
TECNOCAP EURL—See Tecnocap S.p.A.; *Int'l*, pg. 7516
TECNOCAP GMBH—See Tecnocap S.p.A.; *Int'l*, pg. 7516
TECNOCAP LLC—See Tecnocap S.p.A.; *Int'l*, pg. 7516
TECNOCAP-MET S.l.—See Tecnocap S.p.A.; *Int'l*, pg. 7516
TECNOCAP S.P.A.; *Int'l*, pg. 7516
TECNOCAP S.R.O.—See Tecnocap S.p.A.; *Int'l*, pg. 7516
TECNOCAP UA—See Tecnocap S.p.A.; *Int'l*, pg. 7516
TECNOCONSULT S A—See Fluor Corporation; *U.S. Public*, pg. 859
TECNOCONTROL CHILE LTDA.—See Grupo Empresarial San Jose, S.A.; *Int'l*, pg. 3128
TECNOCONTROL SERVICIOS, S.A.U.—See Grupo Empresarial San Jose, S.A.; *Int'l*, pg. 3128
TECNOCRAM S.R.L.—See KONE Oyj; *Int'l*, pg. 4250
TECNOCREDIT, S.A.—See Banco de Sabadell, S.A.; *Int'l*, pg. 822
TECNOCRETO, S.A.—See Grupo Lamosa S.A. de C.V.; *Int'l*, pg. 3132
TECNO DIAGNOSTICA—See Abbott Laboratories; *U.S. Public*, pg. 20
TECNODIESEL S.A.S.—See Aiphone Co., Ltd.; *Int'l*, pg. 235
TECNO DOORS PVT. LTD.—See Tecnolama S.A.; *Int'l*, pg. 7516
TECNOELASTOMERI S.R.L.—See Huntsman Corporation; *U.S. Public*, pg. 1075
TECNOFARMA, S.A. DE C.V.—See Bausch Health Companies Inc.; *Int'l*, pg. 898
TECNO FAST SA; *Int'l*, pg. 7516
TECNOFISIL, CONSULTORES DE ENGENHARIA, S.A.—See Tecnica Y Proyectos S.A.; *Int'l*, pg. 7515
TECNOGAS S/A—See Linde plc; *Int'l*, pg. 4510
TECNO GAS S.R.L.—See L'Air Liquide S.A.; *Int'l*, pg. 4373
TECNOGLASS INC.; *Int'l*, pg. 7516
TECNOGLOBAL SA—See SONDA S.A.; *Int'l*, pg. 7089
TECNOLAB S.R.L.—See ViTrox Corporation Berhad; *Int'l*, pg. 8262
TECNOLAMA, S.A.—See Tecnolama S.A.; *Int'l*, pg. 7516
TECNOLAMA S.A.; *Int'l*, pg. 7516
TECNO-LECHE S.A.—See GEA Group Aktiengesellschaft; *Int'l*, pg. 2903
TECNOLINES OU; *Int'l*, pg. 7516
TECNOLOGIA AUTOELECTRONICA DE DURANGO, S. DE R.L. DE C.V.—See Yazaki Corporation; *Int'l*, pg. 8572
TECNOLOGIA & DESIGN S.C.A.R.L.—See Solid World S.p.A.; *Int'l*, pg. 7072
TECNOLOGIA MARITIMA, S.A.—See Emera, Inc.; *Int'l*, pg. 2377
TECNOLOGIA MODIFICADA, S.A. DE C.V.—See Caterpillar, Inc.; *U.S. Public*, pg. 454
TECNOLOGIAS DE INFORMACION EN SALUD S.A.—See UnitedHealth Group Incorporated; *U.S. Public*, pg. 2251
TECNOLOGIE DIESEL E SISTEMI FRENANTI S.P.A.—See Robert Bosch GmbH; *Int'l*, pg. 6368
TECNOLOGIE DIESEL S.P.A.—See Robert Bosch GmbH; *Int'l*, pg. 6368
TECNOMAGNETE GMBH—See Tecnomagnete SpA; *Int'l*, pg. 7516
TECNOMAGNETE, INC.—See Tecnomagnete SpA; *Int'l*, pg. 7516
TECNOMAGNETE SARL—See Tecnomagnete SpA; *Int'l*, pg. 7516
TECNOMAGNETE SPA; *Int'l*, pg. 7516
TECNOMA TECHNOLOGIES SAS—See Exel Industries SA; *Int'l*, pg. 2583
TECNO MATIC EUROPE S.R.O.—See Ingersoll Rand Inc.; *U.S. Public*, pg. 1122
TECNOMEN GMBH—See Tecnotree Corporation; *Int'l*, pg. 7517
TECNOMEN RUSSIA—See Tecnotree Corporation; *Int'l*, pg. 7517
TECNOMETAL—See Arcline Investment Management LP; *U.S. Private*, pg. 313
TECNON ELECTRONICS CO., LTD.; *Int'l*, pg. 7517
TECNONET S.A.—See Ascom Holding AG; *Int'l*, pg. 603
TECNON (GUANGDONG) LIGHTING TECHNOLOGY CO., LTD.—See Tecnon Electronics Co., Ltd.; *Int'l*, pg. 7517
TECNON SMART DISPLAY TECHNOLOGY (SHENZHEN) CO., LTD.—See Tecnon Electronics Co., Ltd.; *Int'l*, pg. 7517
TECNONUCLEAR S.A.—See Eckert & Ziegler Strahlen- und Medizintechnik AG; *Int'l*, pg. 2290

TECNON (XIAMEN) LIGHTING APPLIANCE SALES SERVICE CO., LTD.—See Tecnon Electronics Co., Ltd.; *Int'l*, pg. 7517
TECNOPACKING, S.L.U.—See Bunzl plc; *Int'l*, pg. 1219
TECNOPOL DE SISTEMAS SL—See Mapei SpA; *Int'l*, pg. 4683
TECNO POULTRY EQUIPMENT S.P.A.—See AGCO Corporation; *U.S. Public*, pg. 59
TECNORD S.R.L.—See Delta Power Co.; *U.S. Private*, pg. 1201
TECNOR MACCHINE S.P.A.—See Quaser Machine Tools, Inc.; *Int'l*, pg. 6157
TECNOSAGOT S.A.—See Endress+Hauser (International) Holding AG; *Int'l*, pg. 2409
TECNOS DATA SCIENCE ENGINEERING, INC.; *Int'l*, pg. 7517
TECNOSERVIZI AMBIENTALI S.R.L.—See Linde plc; *Int'l*, pg. 4510
TECNOS GLOBAL COMPANY OF AMERICA, INC.—See Tecnos Japan Inc.; *Int'l*, pg. 7517
TECNOS INTERNATIONAL CONSULTANT CO., LTD.—See Teco Electric & Machinery Co., Ltd.; *Int'l*, pg. 7518
TECNOS JAPAN INC.; *Int'l*, pg. 7517
TECNOSOLO ENGENHARIA SA; *Int'l*, pg. 7517
TECNO-STAR DUE S.R.L.—See Cremonini S.p.A.; *Int'l*, pg. 1838
TECNOSULFUR SISTEMA DE TRATAMENTO DE METAIS LIQUIDOS S/A—See SKW Stahl-Metallurgie Holding AG; *Int'l*, pg. 6992
TECNOSUR S.A.—See Kimberly-Clark Corporation; *U.S. Public*, pg. 1231
TECNO TEAM SRL—See TXT e-Solutions S.p.A.; *Int'l*, pg. 7993
TECNOTEL CLIMA, S.L.—See ACS, Actividades de Construccion y Servicios, S.A.; *Int'l*, pg. 116
TECNOTREE B.V.—See Tecnotree Corporation; *Int'l*, pg. 7517
TECNOTREE CONVERGENCE PRIVATE LIMITED—See Tecnotree Corporation; *Int'l*, pg. 7517
TECNOTREE CORPORATION; *Int'l*, pg. 7517
TECNOTREE LATIN AMERICA—See Tecnotree Corporation; *Int'l*, pg. 7517
TECNOTREE LTD.—See Tecnotree Corporation; *Int'l*, pg. 7517
TECNOTREE MEA—See Tecnotree Corporation; *Int'l*, pg. 7517
TECNOTREE (M) SDN BHD—See Tecnotree Corporation; *Int'l*, pg. 7517
TECNOTREE SISTEMAS DE TELECOMMUNICACAO LTDA—See Tecnotree Corporation; *Int'l*, pg. 7517
TECNOTREE SPAIN S.L.—See Tecnotree Corporation; *Int'l*, pg. 7517
TECNOVENT SA—See Lindab International AB; *Int'l*, pg. 4504
TECO 2030 ASA; *Int'l*, pg. 7517
TECO 2030 PTE. LTD.—See Teco 2030 ASA; *Int'l*, pg. 7517
TECO COATING SERVICES AS—See TECO Group AS; *Int'l*, pg. 7518
TECO DIVERSIFIED, INC.—See Emera, Inc.; *Int'l*, pg. 2377
TECO ELECTRIC EUROPE LIMITED—See Teco Electric & Machinery Co., Ltd.; *Int'l*, pg. 7518
TECO ELECTRIC & MACHINERY CO., LTD.; *Int'l*, pg. 7517
TECO ELECTRO DEVICES CO., LTD.—See Teco Electric & Machinery Co., Ltd.; *Int'l*, pg. 7518
TECO ELECTRONICS AS—See TECO Group AS; *Int'l*, pg. 7518
TECO ELEKTRIK TURKEY A.S.—See Teco Electric & Machinery Co., Ltd.; *Int'l*, pg. 7518
TECO ENERGY, INC.—See Emera, Inc.; *Int'l*, pg. 2377
TECOFI SAS; *Int'l*, pg. 7518
TEC-OF JACKSON INC.—See Telephone Electronics Corporation; *U.S. Private*, pg. 3961
TECOGEN INC.; *U.S. Public*, pg. 1989
TECO GROUP AS; *Int'l*, pg. 7518
TECO GUATEMALA, INC.—See Emera, Inc.; *Int'l*, pg. 2377
TECOLOCO EL SALVADOR S.A. DE C.V.—See Axel Springer SE; *Int'l*, pg. 767
TECOLOTE RESEARCH INC.; *U.S. Private*, pg. 3957
TECOLOTE RESOURCES, INC.—See Owl Companies; *U.S. Private*, pg. 3055
TECO MARITIME ASA—See TECO Group AS; *Int'l*, pg. 7518
TECO MARITIME AS—See TECO Group AS; *Int'l*, pg. 7518
TECO MARITIME BENELUX B.V.—See TECO Group AS; *Int'l*, pg. 7518
TECO MARITIME FAR EAST PTE LTD.—See TECO Group AS; *Int'l*, pg. 7518
TECO MARITIME HOLDING AS—See TECO Group AS; *Int'l*, pg. 7518
TECO MARITIME HOUSTON, INC.—See TECO Group AS; *Int'l*, pg. 7518
TECO MARITIME POLAND SP. Z O.O.—See TECO Group AS; *Int'l*, pg. 7518

TECOM CO., LTD.; *Int'l*, pg. 7518
TECOMEC S.R.L.—See Emak S.p.A.; *Int'l*, pg. 2373
TECOMET INC.—See Charlesbank Capital Partners, LLC; *U.S. Private*, pg. 856
TECOM INDUSTRIES, INC.—See Smiths Group plc; *Int'l*, pg. 7012
TECOM INVESTMENTS LLC—See Dubai Holding LLC; *Int'l*, pg. 2218
TE-COM TELEKOMMUNIKATIONS-TECHNIK GMBH—See Alpiq Holding AG; *Int'l*, pg. 372
TECON BIOLOGY CO., LTD.; *Int'l*, pg. 7519
TECON CORPORATION; *U.S. Private*, pg. 3957
TECO (NEW ZEALAND) LIMITED—See Teco Electric & Machinery Co., Ltd.; *Int'l*, pg. 7518
TE CONNECTIVITY AMP ESPANA S.L.U.—See TE Connectivity Ltd.; *Int'l*, pg. 7496
TE CONNECTIVITY AMP ITALIA S.R.L.—See TE Connectivity Ltd.; *Int'l*, pg. 7496
TE CONNECTIVITY COLOMBIA S.A.S.—See TE Connectivity Ltd.; *Int'l*, pg. 7496
TE CONNECTIVITY (DENMARK) APS—See TE Connectivity Ltd.; *Int'l*, pg. 7496
TE CONNECTIVITY GERMANY GMBH—See TE Connectivity Ltd.; *Int'l*, pg. 7496
TE CONNECTIVITY HK LIMITED—See TE Connectivity Ltd.; *Int'l*, pg. 7496
TE CONNECTIVITY INC.—See TE Connectivity Ltd.; *Int'l*, pg. 7497
TE CONNECTIVITY INDIA PRIVATE LIMITED—See TE Connectivity Ltd.; *Int'l*, pg. 7496
TE CONNECTIVITY LIMERICK—See TE Connectivity Ltd.; *Int'l*, pg. 7496
TE CONNECTIVITY LTD.; *Int'l*, pg. 7494
TE CONNECTIVITY - MEASUREMENT SPECIALTIES - CHATSWORTH—See TE Connectivity Ltd.; *Int'l*, pg. 7495
TE CONNECTIVITY NEDERLAND B.V.—See TE Connectivity Ltd.; *Int'l*, pg. 7496
TE CONNECTIVITY NEDERLAND B.V.—See TE Connectivity Ltd.; *Int'l*, pg. 7496
TE CONNECTIVITY NETWORKS, INC.—See TE Connectivity Ltd.; *Int'l*, pg. 7497
TE CONNECTIVITY PHOENIX OPTIX INC.—See TE Connectivity Ltd.; *Int'l*, pg. 7496
TE CONNECTIVITY SENSORS GERMANY GMBH—See TE Connectivity Ltd.; *Int'l*, pg. 7496
TE CONNECTIVITY - SENSOR SOLUTIONS - FREMONT—See TE Connectivity Ltd.; *Int'l*, pg. 7495
TE CONNECTIVITY SERVICES INDIA PRIVATE LIMITED—See TE Connectivity Ltd.; *Int'l*, pg. 7496
TE CONNECTIVITY SOLUTIONS GMBH—See TE Connectivity Ltd.; *Int'l*, pg. 7496
TE CONNECTIVITY SPAIN, S.A.U.—See TE Connectivity Ltd.; *Int'l*, pg. 7496
TE CONNECTIVITY UK LIMITED—See TE Connectivity Ltd.; *Int'l*, pg. 7496
TE CONNECTIVITY UK LTD—See TE Connectivity Ltd.; *Int'l*, pg. 7496
TE CONNECTIVITY ULC—See TE Connectivity Ltd.; *Int'l*, pg. 7496
TE CONNECTIVITY (WUXI) COMPANY LIMITED—See TE Connectivity Ltd.; *Int'l*, pg. 7496
TECON RIO GRANDE S.A.—See Ocean Wilsons Holdings Limited; *Int'l*, pg. 5517
TECON SALVADOR S.A.—See Ocean Wilsons Holdings Limited; *Int'l*, pg. 5517
TECON SERVICES INC.; *U.S. Private*, pg. 3957
TECON S.R.L.—See Rosetti Marino S.p.A.; *Int'l*, pg. 6400
TECON SUAPE, S.A.—See International Container Terminal Services, Inc.; *Int'l*, pg. 3747
TECO PARTNERS, INC.—See Emera, Inc.; *Int'l*, pg. 2377
TECO PEOPLES GAS—See Emera, Inc.; *Int'l*, pg. 2377
TECO SMART TECHNOLOGIES CO., LTD.—See Teco Electric & Machinery Co., Ltd.; *Int'l*, pg. 7518
TECO SOLUTIONS, INC.—See Emera, Inc.; *Int'l*, pg. 2377
TECO TECHNOLOGY & MARKETING CENTER CO., LTD.—See Teco Electric & Machinery Co., Ltd.; *Int'l*, pg. 7518
TECO TECHNOLOGY (VIETNAM) CO., LTD.—See Teco Electric & Machinery Co., Ltd.; *Int'l*, pg. 7518
TECO (THAI) CO.—See Teco Electric & Machinery Co., Ltd.; *Int'l*, pg. 7518
TECO (VIETNAM) ELECTRIC & MACHINERY COMPANY LTD.—See Teco Electric & Machinery Co., Ltd.; *Int'l*, pg. 7518
TECO WESTINGHOUSE MOTOR COMPANY—See Teco Electric & Machinery Co., Ltd.; *Int'l*, pg. 7518
TECPETROL DEL PERU—See Techint S.p.A.; *Int'l*, pg. 7504
TECPETROL DE VENEZUELA S.A.—See Techint S.p.A.; *Int'l*, pg. 7504
TECPETROL INTERNATIONAL S.A.—See Techint S.p.A.; *Int'l*, pg. 7504
TECPETROL S.A.—See Techint S.p.A.; *Int'l*, pg. 7504
TECPLOT, INC.—See Constellation Software Inc.; *Int'l*, pg. 1774
TEC PROJECT SERVICES CORPORATION—See Toyo Engineering Corporation; *Int'l*, pg. 7853
TECPRO SYSTEMS LIMITED; *Int'l*, pg. 7519

COMPANY NAME INDEX

TECPROTEC ASIA PRIVATE LIMITED—See Stone Point Capital LLC; *U.S. Private*, pg. 3821
TECPROTEC SDN BHD—See Stone Point Capital LLC; *U.S. Private*, pg. 3821
TECRA INTERNATIONAL PTY. LTD.—See 3M Company; *U.S. Public*, pg. 5
TECRESA PROTECCION PASIVA, S.L.—See Mercor S.A.; *Int'l*, pg. 4833
TECSA EMPRESA CONSTRUCTORA, S.A.—See ACS, Actividades de Construccion y Servicios, S.A.; *Int'l*, pg. 116
TEC-SAN CO., LTD.—See Topy Industries, Ltd.; *Int'l*, pg. 7822
TECSEFIN GUATEMALA—See Aon plc; *Int'l*, pg. 495
TEC SERVICES, INC.—See Telephone Electronics Corporation; *U.S. Private*, pg. 3961
TECSIS FAR EAST PTE. LTD.—See tecsis GmbH; *Int'l*, pg. 7519
TECSIS GMBH; *Int'l*, pg. 7519
TECSIS INSTRUMENTS (INDIA) PVT. LTD.—See tecsis GmbH; *Int'l*, pg. 7519
TECSIS LP—See tecsis GmbH; *Int'l*, pg. 7519
TECSIS (SHANGHAI) INDUSTRIAL MEASUREMENT TECHNOLOGY CO., LTD.—See tecsis GmbH; *Int'l*, pg. 7519
TECSIS (SHENZHEN) SENSORS CO., LTD.—See tecsis GmbH; *Int'l*, pg. 7519
TECSIT S.R.L.—See CAD IT S.p.A.; *Int'l*, pg. 1247
TECSOUND (QLD) PTY. LTD.—See Azure Healthcare Limited; *Int'l*, pg. 782
TECSOUND (VIC) PTY. LTD.—See Azure Healthcare Limited; *Int'l*, pg. 782
TECSOUND (WEST AUSTRALIA) PTY. LTD.—See Azure Healthcare Limited; *Int'l*, pg. 782
TECSTAR MFG. GROUP, INC.—See MGS Manufacturing Group, Inc.; *U.S. Private*, pg. 2695
TECSTAR TECHNOLOGY CO., LTD.; *Int'l*, pg. 7519
TECSUR S.A.—See China Three Gorges Corporation; *Int'l*, pg. 1559
TECSYS A/S—See TECSYS, Inc.; *Int'l*, pg. 7519
TECSYS, INC.; *Int'l*, pg. 7519
TEC SYSTEMS—See VINCI S.A.; *Int'l*, pg. 8234
TECSYS US INC.—See TECSYS, Inc.; *Int'l*, pg. 7519
TECTA AMERICA ARIZONA, LLC—See Altas Partners LP; *Int'l*, pg. 386
TECTA AMERICA CAROLINAS, LLC—See Altas Partners LP; *Int'l*, pg. 386
TECTA AMERICA COLORADO, LLC—See Altas Partners LP; *Int'l*, pg. 386
TECTA AMERICA CORP.—See Altas Partners LP; *Int'l*, pg. 386
TECTA AMERICA DAKOTAS, LLC - JAMESTOWN—See Altas Partners LP; *Int'l*, pg. 387
TECTA AMERICA DAKOTAS, LLC—See Altas Partners LP; *Int'l*, pg. 386
TECTA AMERICA EAST LLC - FRUITLAND—See Altas Partners LP; *Int'l*, pg. 387
TECTA AMERICA EAST LLC - GLEN ROCK—See Altas Partners LP; *Int'l*, pg. 387
TECTA AMERICA EAST LLC - JESSUP—See Altas Partners LP; *Int'l*, pg. 387
TECTA AMERICA EAST LLC—See Altas Partners LP; *Int'l*, pg. 387
TECTA AMERICA ILLINOIS ROOFING, LLC—See Altas Partners LP; *Int'l*, pg. 387
TECTA AMERICA METRO NEW YORK, LLC—See Altas Partners LP; *Int'l*, pg. 387
TECTA AMERICA NEW ENGLAND, LLC—See Altas Partners LP; *Int'l*, pg. 387
TECTA AMERICA SACRAMENTO INC.—See Altas Partners LP; *Int'l*, pg. 387
TECTA AMERICA SOUTHERN CALIFORNIA, INC.—See Altas Partners LP; *Int'l*, pg. 387
TECTA AMERICA SOUTH FLORIDA, LLC—See Altas Partners LP; *Int'l*, pg. 387
TECTA AMERICA WEST FLORIDA, LLC—See Altas Partners LP; *Int'l*, pg. 387
TECTA AMERICA ZERO COMPANY LLC - COLUMBUS—See Altas Partners LP; *Int'l*, pg. 387
TECTA AMERICA ZERO COMPANY LLC - LOUISVILLE—See Altas Partners LP; *Int'l*, pg. 387
TECTA AMERICA ZERO COMPANY LLC—See Altas Partners LP; *Int'l*, pg. 387
TECT AEROSPACE, INC.—See UCA Holdings Inc.; *U.S. Private*, pg. 4273
TECT AEROSPACE—See Stony Point Group, Inc.; *U.S. Private*, pg. 3830
TECT AEROSPACE—See Stony Point Group, Inc.; *U.S. Private*, pg. 3830
TECTAREAL PROPERTY MANAGEMENT GMBH—See Vincitag Investment Management AG; *Int'l*, pg. 8240
TECT HOLDINGS LIMITED; *Int'l*, pg. 7519
TECTIA, INC.—See SSH Communications Security Corporation; *Int'l*, pg. 7156
TECTIA LTD.—See SSH Communications Security Corporation; *Int'l*, pg. 7156
TECTIA OPERATIONS LTD.—See SSH Communications Security Corporation; *Int'l*, pg. 7156

TECTO CYPRUS LIMITED—See Exmar N.V.; *Int'l*, pg. 2585
TECTONA LTD; *Int'l*, pg. 7519
TECTON ENGINEERING GMBH—See ISG PLC; *Int'l*, pg. 3816
TECTONIC ADVISORS, LLC—See Tectonic Financial, Inc.; *U.S. Public*, pg. 1989
TECTONIC ELEMENTS LTD.—See FLAT Audio Technologies, LLC; *U.S. Private*, pg. 1541
TECTONIC ENGINEERING AND SURVEYING CONSULTANTS P.C.; *U.S. Private*, pg. 3957
TECTONIC FINANCIAL, INC.; *U.S. Public*, pg. 1989
TECTONIC GOLD PLC; *Int'l*, pg. 7519
TECTONIC LLC; *U.S. Private*, pg. 3957
TECTONIC METALS, INC.; *Int'l*, pg. 7519
TECTONIC THERAPEUTIC, INC.; *U.S. Public*, pg. 1989
TECTOWELD INC.—See Hicks Lightning Protection, Inc.; *U.S. Private*, pg. 1934
TECTRA LTD.—See WAMGROUP S.p.A.; *Int'l*, pg. 8338
TECTRION GMBH—See Bayer Aktiengesellschaft; *Int'l*, pg. 910
TECTUM, INC.—See Armstrong World Industries, Inc.; *U.S. Public*, pg. 194
TECTURA CORPORATION; *U.S. Private*, pg. 3957
TECUM CAPITAL PARTNERS, LLC; *U.S. Private*, pg. 3957
TECUMSEH DO BRASIL, LTDA.—See Atlas Holdings, LLC; *U.S. Private*, pg. 378
TECUMSEH DO BRASIL, LTDA.—See Mueller Industries, Inc.; *U.S. Public*, pg. 1485
TECUMSEH EURO-MALAYSIA SDN. BHD—See Atlas Holdings, LLC; *U.S. Private*, pg. 378
TECUMSEH EURO-MALAYSIA SDN. BHD—See Mueller Industries, Inc.; *U.S. Public*, pg. 1485
TECUMSEH EUROPE SA—See Atlas Holdings, LLC; *U.S. Private*, pg. 378
TECUMSEH EUROPE SA—See Mueller Industries, Inc.; *U.S. Public*, pg. 1485
TECUMSEH PACKAGING SOLUTIONS—See Akers Packaging Service Inc.; *U.S. Private*, pg. 145
TECUMSEH POULTRY LLC—See Tyson Foods, Inc.; *U.S. Public*, pg. 2210
TECUMSEH POWER COMPANY—See Platinum Equity, LLC; *U.S. Private*, pg. 3208
TECUMSEH POWER COMPANY—See Platinum Equity, LLC; *U.S. Private*, pg. 3208
TECUMSEH PRODUCTS COMPANY LLC—See Atlas Holdings, LLC; *U.S. Private*, pg. 378
TECUMSEH PRODUCTS COMPANY LLC—See Mueller Industries, Inc.; *U.S. Public*, pg. 1485
TECUMSEH PRODUCTS COMPANY-PARIS DIVISION—See Atlas Holdings, LLC; *U.S. Private*, pg. 378
TECUMSEH PRODUCTS COMPANY-PARIS DIVISION—See Mueller Industries, Inc.; *U.S. Public*, pg. 1485
TECUMSEH PRODUCTS INDIA PVT. LTD.—See Atlas Holdings, LLC; *U.S. Private*, pg. 378
TECUMSEH PRODUCTS INDIA PVT. LTD.—See Mueller Industries, Inc.; *U.S. Public*, pg. 1485
TECUNI, S.A.—See VINCI S.A.; *Int'l*, pg. 8229
TECUOS CO., LTD.—See Toyo Construction Co., Ltd.; *Int'l*, pg. 7852
TEC UTILITIES SUPPLY INC.; *U.S. Private*, pg. 3951
TECVIS GMBH—See AGRAVIS Raiffeisen AG; *Int'l*, pg. 215
TECVOX OEM SOLUTIONS, LLC—See Amphenol Corporation; *U.S. Public*, pg. 132
T. E. C. WELL SERVICE, INC.; *U.S. Private*, pg. 3911
TECWORLD LIMITED—See Nippon Telegraph & Telephone Corporation; *Int'l*, pg. 5351
TECXO FARBEN PRODUKTIONSGESELLSCHAFT MBH—See Farbchemie Braun KG; *Int'l*, pg. 2618
TEDA CO., LTD.—See Samart Corporation Public Company Limited; *Int'l*, pg. 6502
TEDAGUA INTERNACIONAL, S.L.—See ACS, Actividades de Construccion y Servicios, S.A.; *Int'l*, pg. 116
TEDAN SURGICAL INNOVATIONS, INC—See Halma plc; *Int'l*, pg. 3233
THE TED ARISON FAMILY FOUNDATION (ISRAEL) A PUBLIC BENEFIT COMPANY LTD.—See Arison Holdings (1998) Ltd.; *Int'l*, pg. 566
TE DATA JORDAN SAE—See Telecom Egypt; *Int'l*, pg. 7530
TE DATA S.A.E.—See Telecom Egypt; *Int'l*, pg. 7530
TED BAKER (FRANCE) SARL—See Leonard Green & Partners, L.P.; *U.S. Private*, pg. 2425
TED BAKER INTERNATIONAL LTD—See Leonard Green & Partners, L.P.; *U.S. Private*, pg. 2425
TED BAKER LIMITED—See Leonard Green & Partners, L.P.; *U.S. Private*, pg. 2425
TED BAKER NETHERLANDS B.V.—See Leonard Green & Partners, L.P.; *U.S. Private*, pg. 2425
TED BAKER PLC—See Leonard Green & Partners, L.P.; *U.S. Private*, pg. 2425
TED BARKUS COMPANY, INC.; *U.S. Private*, pg. 3957
TED BERRY COMPANY LLC—See Vortex Company, LLC; *U.S. Private*, pg. 4413
TED BRITT FORD SALES INC.; *U.S. Private*, pg. 3957

TEEL CONSTRUCTION INC.

TED BROWN MUSIC COMPANY, INC.; *U.S. Private*, pg. 3957
TED DE MEXICO S.A. DE C.V.—See Stoneridge, Inc.; *U.S. Public*, pg. 1951
TEDD ENGINEERING LTD.—See Metso Oyj; *Int'l*, pg. 4868
TEDDIES CHILDCARE PROVISION LIMITED—See Bain Capital, LP; *U.S. Private*, pg. 437
TEDD WOOD, INC.—See Executive Cabinetry,LLC; *U.S. Private*, pg. 1447
TEDDY BEAR AND FRIENDS MAGAZINES—See BeBop Channel Corporation; *U.S. Public*, pg. 288
TEDDY'S TRANSPORTATION SYSTEM, INC.; *U.S. Private*, pg. 3957
TEDDY'S TRANSPORT; *U.S. Private*, pg. 3957
TEDEC-MEIJI FARMA S.A.—See Meiji Holdings Co., Ltd.; *Int'l*, pg. 4801
TEDERIC MACHINERY CO., LTD.; *Int'l*, pg. 7519
TEDESCHI FOOD SHOPS, INC.; *U.S. Private*, pg. 3957
TEDESCHI VINEYARDS, LTD.; *U.S. Private*, pg. 3957
TED HARPER BUILDING SUPPLIES LIMITED—See Fletcher Building Limited; *Int'l*, pg. 2701
TEDI TRANSLOGIC EXPRESS DEDICATED INC.—See Deutsche Post AG; *Int'l*, pg. 2082
TEDRIVE STEERING SYSTEMS GMBH - PLANT 2—See Knorr-Bremse AG; *Int'l*, pg. 4212
TEDRIVE STEERING SYSTEMS GMBH—See Knorr-Bremse AG; *Int'l*, pg. 4212
TEDRIVE YONLENDIRME SISTEMLERI SAN.VE TIC.LTD. STI.—See Knorr-Bremse AG; *Int'l*, pg. 4212
TEDRO & ASSOCIATES, INC.—See Water Street Healthcare Partners, LLC; *U.S. Private*, pg. 4452
TED RUSSELL ENTERPRISES INC.; *U.S. Private*, pg. 3957
TED'S CAMERA STORES (VIC) PTY LTD; *Int'l*, pg. 7519
TED'S & FRED'S INC.; *U.S. Private*, pg. 3957
TED TODD INSURANCE, INC.; *U.S. Private*, pg. 3957
TED WIENS TIRE & AUTO CENTERS; *U.S. Private*, pg. 3957
TEEBA INVESTMENT FOR DEVELOPED FOOD PROCESSING COMPANY—See Almarai Company Ltd.; *Int'l*, pg. 363
TEEC HOLDINGS LIMITED—See Triple Point Energy Transition Plc; *Int'l*, pg. 7927
TEECO PRODUCTS INC.; *U.S. Private*, pg. 3958
TEE DEVELOPMENT PTE LTD—See TEE International Limited; *Int'l*, pg. 7519
TEE E&C (MALAYSIA) SDN. BHD.—See TEE International Limited; *Int'l*, pg. 7519
TEEG AUSTRALIA PTY. LTD.—See Quadrant Private Equity Pty. Ltd.; *Int'l*, pg. 6149
TEE GROUP FILMS; *U.S. Private*, pg. 3957
TEE HAI CHEM PTE. LTD.—See BRENNTAG SE; *Int'l*, pg. 1150
TEE HONG KONG LIMITED; *Int'l*, pg. 7519
TEE INTERNATIONAL LIMITED; *Int'l*, pg. 7519
TEEJAY INDIA (PRIVATE) LIMITED—See Teejay Lanka PLC; *Int'l*, pg. 7520
TEEJAY LANKA PLC; *Int'l*, pg. 7520
TEEJAY LANKA PRINTS (PRIVATE) LIMITED—See Teejay Lanka PLC; *Int'l*, pg. 7520
TEEKANNE GMBH; *Int'l*, pg. 7520
TEEKAY CORPORATION; *Int'l*, pg. 7520
TEEKAY NAVION OFFSHORE LOADING PTE LTD.—See Teekay Corporation; *Int'l*, pg. 7520
TEEKAY NETHERLANDS EUROPEAN HOLDINGS B.V.—See Teekay Corporation; *Int'l*, pg. 7520
TEEKAY NORWAY AS—See Nordic American Tankers Limited; *Int'l*, pg. 5419
TEEKAY PETROJARL PRODUCAO PETROLIFERADO BRASIL LTDA.—See Teekay Corporation; *Int'l*, pg. 7520
TEEKAY SHIPPING (AUSTRALIA) PTY. LTD.—See Teekay Corporation; *Int'l*, pg. 7520
TEEKAY SHIPPING (CANADA) LTD.—See Teekay Corporation; *Int'l*, pg. 7520
TEEKAY SHIPPING (GLASGOW) LTD.—See Teekay Corporation; *Int'l*, pg. 7520
TEEKAY SHIPPING (INDIA) PVT. LTD.—See Teekay Corporation; *Int'l*, pg. 7520
TEEKAY SHIPPING (JAPAN) LTD.—See Teekay Corporation; *Int'l*, pg. 7520
TEEKAY SHIPPING (LATVIA)—See Teekay Corporation; *Int'l*, pg. 7520
TEEKAY SHIPPING NORWAY AS—See Teekay Corporation; *Int'l*, pg. 7520
TEEKAY SHIPPING PHILIPPINES, INC.—See Teekay Corporation; *Int'l*, pg. 7520
TEEKAY SHIPPING (SINGAPORE) PTE. LTD.—See Teekay Corporation; *Int'l*, pg. 7520
TEEKAY SHIPPING SPAIN, S.L.—See Teekay Corporation; *Int'l*, pg. 7520
TEEKAY SHIPPING (UK) LTD.—See Teekay Corporation; *Int'l*, pg. 7520
TEEKAY SHIPPING (USA) INC.—See Teekay Corporation; *Int'l*, pg. 7520
TEEKAY TANKERS LTD.—See Teekay Corporation; *Int'l*, pg. 7520
TEEL CONSTRUCTION INC.; *U.S. Private*, pg. 3958

TEEL CONSTRUCTION INC. — CORPORATE AFFILIATIONS

TEEL PLASTICS INC.—See JLS Investment Group LLC; *U.S. Private*, pg. 2213
TEE MANAGEMENT PTE LTD—See TEE International Limited; *Int'l*, pg. 7519
TEEMA SOLUTIONS GROUP INC.; *U.S. Private*, pg. 3958
TEENESS ASA—See Sandvik AB; *Int'l*, pg. 6535
TEE OFF, LLC—See adidas AG; *Int'l*, pg. 146
TEE PEE CONTRACTORS INC.; *U.S. Private*, pg. 3957
TEE PEE OLIVES, INC./ ITALICA IMPORTS; *U.S. Private*, pg. 3957
TEE PROPERTY PTE. LTD.—See TEE International Limited; *Int'l*, pg. 7519
TEERAG-ASDAG AG—See PORR AG; *Int'l*, pg. 5925
TEERAG-ASDAG AKTIENGESELLSCHAFT—See PORR AG; *Int'l*, pg. 5925
TEERAG-ASDAG HOCHBAU BURGENLAND GMBH—See PORR AG; *Int'l*, pg. 5925
TEERAG-ASDAG POLSKA SPOLKA Z OGRANICZONA ODPOWIEDZIALNOSCIA—See PORR AG; *Int'l*, pg. 5925
TEERAG-ASDAG SLOVAKIA S.R.O.—See PORR AG; *Int'l*, pg. 5925
TEERA-MONGKOL INDUSTRY CO., LTD.; *Int'l*, pg. 7520
TEE REALTY PTE LTD—See TEE International Limited; *Int'l*, pg. 7520
TEESSIDE LEISURE PARK LIMITED—See The British Land Company PLC; *Int'l*, pg. 7628
TEESTA AGRO INDUSTRIES LIMITED; *Int'l*, pg. 7520
TEES VALLEY LITHIUM LIMITED—See Alkemy Capital Investments Plc; *Int'l*, pg. 331
TEETER IRRIGATION INC.; *U.S. Private*, pg. 3958
TEEVER ACHLAL JOINT STOCK COMPANY; *Int'l*, pg. 7520
TEEWINOT LIFE SCIENCES CORPORATION; *U.S. Private*, pg. 3958
TEFAG AG—See Sulzer Ltd.; *Int'l*, pg. 7259
TEFAHOT INSURANCE AGENCY (1989) LTD.—See Mizrahi Tefahot Bank Ltd.; *Int'l*, pg. 4997
TEFAL INDIA HOUSEHOLD APPLIANCES PVT. LTD.—See SEB S.A.; *Int'l*, pg. 6668
TEFAL S.A.S.—See SEB S.A.; *Int'l*, pg. 6668
T.E. FINANCIAL CONSULTANTS LTD.—See iA Financial Corporation Inc.; *Int'l*, pg. 3567
TEFRON CANADA INC.—See Tefron Ltd.; *Int'l*, pg. 7520
TEFRON LTD.; *Int'l*, pg. 7520
TEFRON TRADING (SHANGHAI) COMPANY LIMITED—See Tefron Ltd.; *Int'l*, pg. 7520
TEFRON USA, INC.—See Tefron Ltd.; *Int'l*, pg. 7521
TEGA INDUSTRIES AFRICA PROPRIETARY LIMITED—See Tega Industries Limited; *Int'l*, pg. 7521
TEGA INDUSTRIES AUSTRALIA PTY. LTD.—See Tega Industries Limited; *Int'l*, pg. 7521
TEGA INDUSTRIES LIMITED; *Int'l*, pg. 7521
TEGA INDUSTRIES PERU SAC—See Tega Industries Limited; *Int'l*, pg. 7521
TEGAM, INC.—See Advanced Energy Industries, Inc.; *U.S. Public*, pg. 47
TEGA-TECHNISCHE GASE UND GASETECHNIK GMBH—See DCC plc; *Int'l*, pg. 1991
TEGEL FOODS LIMITED—See Affinity Equity Partners (HK) Ltd.; *Int'l*, pg. 186
TEGES GRUNDSTUCKS-VERMIETUNGSGESELLSCHAFT MBH—See Landesbank Saar; *Int'l*, pg. 4406
TEGILE SYSTEMS PRIVATE LIMITED—See Western Digital Corporation; *U.S. Public*, pg. 2355
TEGIWA IMPORTS LTD.—See WEDS CO., LTD.; *Int'l*, pg. 8367
TEGMA CARGAS ESPECIAIS LTDA.—See Tegma Gestao Logistica S.A.; *Int'l*, pg. 7521
TEGMA GESTAO LOGISTICA S.A.; *Int'l*, pg. 7521
TEGNA BROADCASTING GROUP—See TEGNA Inc.; *U.S. Public*, pg. 1990
TEGNA INC.; *U.S. Public*, pg. 1989
TEGNER HERMANSSON AB; *Int'l*, pg. 7521
TEGO CYBER INC.; *U.S. Public*, pg. 1991
TEGOMETALL FRANCE SARL—See Tegometall International Sales GmbH; *Int'l*, pg. 7521
TEGOMETALL INTERNATIONAL SALES GMBH; *Int'l*, pg. 7521
TEGOMETALL INZENIRING D.O.O.—See Tegometall International Sales GmbH; *Int'l*, pg. 7521
TEGOMETALL LIMITED—See Tegometall International Sales GmbH; *Int'l*, pg. 7521
TEGOMETALL OPREMA, D.O.O.—See Tegometall International Sales GmbH; *Int'l*, pg. 7521
TEGOMETALL POLCSZERKEZET GJARTO KFT.—See Tegometall International Sales GmbH; *Int'l*, pg. 7521
TEGOMETALL WYPOSAZENIE SKLEPOW PNIEWY SP. Z O.O.—See Tegometall International Sales GmbH; *Int'l*, pg. 7521
TEGO MULTIFIL SDN BHD—See Kuok Brothers Sdn. Bhd.; *Int'l*, pg. 4334
TEGO SCIENCE INC.; *Int'l*, pg. 7521
TEGO SDN BHD—See Kuok Brothers Sdn. Bhd.; *Int'l*, pg. 4334
TEGRA CORPORATION; *U.S. Private*, pg. 3958
TEGRAL HOLDINGS LTD.—See Etex SA/NV; *Int'l*, pg. 2523

TEGRA MEDICAL COSTA RICA S.A.—See SFS Group AG; *Int'l*, pg. 6739
TEGRA MEDICAL, LLC—See SFS Group AG; *Int'l*, pg. 6739
TEGRANT ALLOYD BRANDS, INC.—See Sonoco Products Company; *U.S. Public*, pg. 1905
TEGRATON LIMITED—See Hang Lung Group Limited; *Int'l*, pg. 3245
TEGREL LIMITED—See Hill & Smith PLC; *Int'l*, pg. 3392
TEGRIA HOLDINGS LLC—See Providence St. Joseph Health; *U.S. Private*, pg. 3295
TEGRIS LLC—See LionTree LLC; *U.S. Private*, pg. 2464
TEGRITY, INC.—See Platinum Equity, LLC; *U.S. Private*, pg. 3206
TEGRO AG—See Deutsche Bahn AG; *Int'l*, pg. 2054
TEHMAG FOODS CORPORATION SDN. BHD.—See Tehmag Foods Corp.; *Int'l*, pg. 7521
TEHMAG FOODS CORP.; *Int'l*, pg. 7521
TEHNICKI REMONTNI ZAVOD HADZICI D.D.; *Int'l*, pg. 7521
TEHNIKA A.D.; *Int'l*, pg. 7521
TEHNIKA D.D.; *Int'l*, pg. 7521
TEHNOBIRO D.O.O.—See Unifiedpost Group SA; *Int'l*, pg. 8043
TEHNOGRADNJA A.D.; *Int'l*, pg. 7521
TEHNOHEMIJA A.D.; *Int'l*, pg. 7521
TEHNOHEMIJA A.D.; *Int'l*, pg. 7521
TEHNOMETAL-VARDAR AD SKOPJE; *Int'l*, pg. 7521
TEHNOPROMET A.D.; *Int'l*, pg. 7521
TEHNORADIONICA A.D.; *Int'l*, pg. 7521
TEHNOSERVIS A.D.; *Int'l*, pg. 7522
TEHNOUNION 1 D.O.O.—See Doppelmayr Group; *Int'l*, pg. 2175
TEHNOUNION D.O.O.; *Int'l*, pg. 7522
TEHO DEVELOPMENT PTE. LTD.—See Teho International Inc. Ltd.; *Int'l*, pg. 7522
TEHO ENGINEERING PTE. LTD.—See Teho International Inc. Ltd.; *Int'l*, pg. 7522
TEHO EUROPE B.V.—See Teho International Inc. Ltd.; *Int'l*, pg. 7522
TEHO INTERNATIONAL INC. LTD.; *Int'l*, pg. 7522
TEHO INTERNATIONAL (USA), LLC—See Teho International Inc. Ltd.; *Int'l*, pg. 7522
TE HOLDING SARL—See Repsol, S.A.; *Int'l*, pg. 6293
TEHOMET OY—See Valmont Industries, Inc.; *U.S. Public*, pg. 2274
TEHO ROPES KOREA CO., LTD.—See Teho International Inc. Ltd.; *Int'l*, pg. 7522
TEHO ROPES & SUPPLIES PTE. LTD.—See Teho International Inc. Ltd.; *Int'l*, pg. 7522
TEHO (SHANGHAI) CO., LTD.—See Teho International Inc. Ltd.; *Int'l*, pg. 7522
TEHO WATER & ENVIROTEC PTE. LTD.—See Teho International Inc. Ltd.; *Int'l*, pg. 7522
TEHRAN CEMENT COMPANY; *Int'l*, pg. 7522
TEHRAN CHEMIE PHARMACEUTICAL COMPANY; *Int'l*, pg. 7522
TEHRAN DAROU PHARMACUTICAL CO.; *Int'l*, pg. 7522
TEHRAN STOCK EXCHANGE; *Int'l*, pg. 7522
T.E. IBBERSON COMPANY—See Peter Kiewit Sons', Inc.; *U.S. Private*, pg. 3158
TEI BIOSCIENCES INC—See Integra LifeSciences Holdings Corporation; *U.S. Public*, pg. 1136
TEICHERT, INC.; *U.S. Private*, pg. 3958
TEICHERT LAND CO.—See Teichert, Inc.; *U.S. Private*, pg. 3958
TEICHIKU ENTERTAINMENT, INC.—See Brother Industries, Ltd.; *Int'l*, pg. 1198
TEICHIKU MUSIC, INC.—See Brother Industries, Ltd.; *Int'l*, pg. 1198
TEICHIKU RECORDS CO., LTD.—See Panasonic Holdings Corporation; *Int'l*, pg. 5725
TEI CONSTRUCTION SERVICES INC.—See Babcock Power, Inc.; *U.S. Private*, pg. 422
TEIGLINGSWERK DOMMITZSCH GMBH—See Vandemoortele N.V.; *Int'l*, pg. 8129
TEIJIN AMERICA, INC.—See Teijin Limited; *Int'l*, pg. 7522
TEIJIN ARAMID ASIA CO LTD—See Teijin Limited; *Int'l*, pg. 7522
TEIJIN ARAMID B.V.—See Teijin Limited; *Int'l*, pg. 7522
TEIJIN ARAMID GMBH—See Teijin Limited; *Int'l*, pg. 7522
TEIJIN ARAMID USA INC.—See Teijin Limited; *Int'l*, pg. 7522
TEIJIN AUTOMOTIVE TECHNOLOGIES, INC.—See Teijin Limited; *Int'l*, pg. 7522
TEIJIN AUTOMOTIVE TECHNOLOGIES NA HOLDINGS CORP.—See Teijin Limited; *Int'l*, pg. 7522
TEIJIN AUTOMOTIVE TECHNOLOGIES—See Teijin Limited; *Int'l*, pg. 7523
TEIJIN CARBON SHANGHAI CO., LTD.—See Teijin Limited; *Int'l*, pg. 7523
TEIJIN (CHINA) INVESTMENT CO.—See Teijin Limited; *Int'l*, pg. 7522
TEIJIN CREATIVE STAFF CO LTD—See Teijin Limited; *Int'l*, pg. 7523
TEIJIN DUPONT FILMS JAPAN LIMITED—See DuPont de Nemours, Inc.; *U.S. Public*, pg. 692
TEIJIN DUPONT FILMS JAPAN LIMITED—See Teijin Limited; *Int'l*, pg. 7523

TEIJIN ENGINEERING LIMITED—See Teijin Limited; *Int'l*, pg. 7523
TEIJIN ENTECH CO LTD—See Teijin Limited; *Int'l*, pg. 7523
TEIJIN FRONTIER CO., LTD.—See Teijin Limited; *Int'l*, pg. 7523
TEIJIN FRONTIER EUROPE GMBH—See Teijin Limited; *Int'l*, pg. 7523
TEIJIN FRONTIER (SHANGHAI) CO., LTD.—See Teijin Limited; *Int'l*, pg. 7523
TEIJIN FRONTIER (THAILAND) CO., LTD.—See Teijin Limited; *Int'l*, pg. 7523
TEIJIN FRONTIER (U.S.A.), INC.—See Teijin Limited; *Int'l*, pg. 7523
TEIJIN GROUP CHINA MANAGEMENT LIMITED—See Teijin Limited; *Int'l*, pg. 7523
TEIJIN HOLDINGS NETHERLANDS B.V.—See Teijin Limited; *Int'l*, pg. 7523
TEIJIN HOLDINGS USA INC—See Teijin Limited; *Int'l*, pg. 7523
TEIJIN HOME HEALTHCARE CO LTD—See Teijin Limited; *Int'l*, pg. 7523
TEIJIN INDIA PRIVATE LIMITED—See Teijin Limited; *Int'l*, pg. 7523
TEIJIN INTELLECTUAL PROPERTY CENTER LIMITED—See Teijin Limited; *Int'l*, pg. 7523
TEIJIN KASEI AMERICA, INC—See Teijin Limited; *Int'l*, pg. 7523
TEIJIN KASEI EUROPE B.V—See Teijin Limited; *Int'l*, pg. 7523
TEIJIN KASEI MALAYSIA SDN. BHD.—See Teijin Limited; *Int'l*, pg. 7523
TEIJIN KASEI TAIWAN CO., LTD.—See Teijin Limited; *Int'l*, pg. 7523
TEIJIN LIMITED - IWAKUNI FACTORY—See Teijin Limited; *Int'l*, pg. 7523
TEIJIN LIMITED - MATSUYAMA FACTORY—See Teijin Limited; *Int'l*, pg. 7523
TEIJIN LIMITED; *Int'l*, pg. 7522
TEIJIN LIMITED - TOKYO HEADQUARTERS—See Teijin Limited; *Int'l*, pg. 7523
TEIJIN LOGISTICS CO LTD—See Teijin Limited; *Int'l*, pg. 7523
TEIJIN PHARMA LIMITED—See Teijin Limited; *Int'l*, pg. 7523
TEIJIN PHARMA (SHANGHAI) CONSULTING CO., LTD—See Teijin Limited; *Int'l*, pg. 7523
TEIJIN POLYCARBONATE CHINA LTD—See Teijin Limited; *Int'l*, pg. 7523
TEIJIN POLYCARBONATE SINGAPORE PTE LTD—See Teijin Limited; *Int'l*, pg. 7523
TEIJIN POLYESTER (THAILAND) LIMITED; *Int'l*, pg. 7524
TEIJIN PRODUCT DEVELOPMENT CHINA CO., LTD.—See Teijin Limited; *Int'l*, pg. 7523
TEIJIN TECHNO PRODUCTS LIMITED—See Teijin Limited; *Int'l*, pg. 7523
TEIKAMETRICS LLC; *U.S. Private*, pg. 3958
TEIKA-PRECISION CO.—See FP Corporation; *Int'l*, pg. 2756
TEIKOKU DATABANK AMERICA, INC.—See Teikoku Databank, Ltd.; *Int'l*, pg. 7524
TEIKOKU DATABANK AXIS, LTD.—See Teikoku Databank, Ltd.; *Int'l*, pg. 7524
TEIKOKU DATABANK BUSINESS SERVICES, LTD.—See Teikoku Databank, Ltd.; *Int'l*, pg. 7524
TEIKOKU DATABANK, LTD.; *Int'l*, pg. 7524
TEIKOKU ELECTRIC GMBH—See Teikoku Electric Mfg. Co., Ltd.; *Int'l*, pg. 7524
TEIKOKU ELECTRIC MFG. CO., LTD.; *Int'l*, pg. 7524
TEIKOKU KOREA CO.,LTD—See Teikoku Electric Mfg. Co., Ltd.; *Int'l*, pg. 7524
TEIKOKU OIL ALGERIA CO., LTD.—See INPEX CORPORATION; *Int'l*, pg. 3717
TEIKOKU OIL (CABINDA) CO., LTD.—See INPEX CORPORATION; *Int'l*, pg. 3717
TEIKOKU OIL ECUADOR—See INPEX CORPORATION; *Int'l*, pg. 3717
TEIKOKU OIL NILE NQR CO., LTD.—See INPEX CORPORATION; *Int'l*, pg. 3717
TEIKOKU OIL (NORTH AMERICA) CO.,LTD.—See INPEX CORPORATION; *Int'l*, pg. 3717
TEIKOKU OIL (SURINAME) CO., LTD.—See INPEX CORPORATION; *Int'l*, pg. 3717
TEIKOKU OIL (VENEZUELA) CO., LTD.—See INPEX CORPORATION; *Int'l*, pg. 3717
TEIKOKU PISTON RING CO. LTD. - GIFU PLANT—See TPR Co., Ltd.; *Int'l*, pg. 7884
TEIKOKU PISTON RING CO. LTD. - NAGANO PLANT—See TPR Co., Ltd.; *Int'l*, pg. 7884
TEIKOKU SEN-I CO., LTD.; *Int'l*, pg. 7524
TEIKOKU SOUTH ASIA PTE LTD—See Teikoku Electric Mfg. Co., Ltd.; *Int'l*, pg. 7524
TEIKOKU TAPING SYSTEM CO., LTD.—See Nippon Kayaku Co., Ltd.; *Int'l*, pg. 5321
TEIKOKU TAPING SYSTEM,INC.—See Nippon Kayaku Co., Ltd.; *Int'l*, pg. 5321
TEIKOKU TAPING SYSTEM(SINGAPORE) PTE. LTD.—See Nippon Kayaku Co., Ltd.; *Int'l*, pg. 5321
TEIKOKU TSUSHIN KOGYO CO., LTD.; *Int'l*, pg. 7524

COMPANY NAME INDEX

TEIKOKU USA, INC.—See Teikoku Electric Mfg. Co., Ltd.; *Int'l*, pg. 7524
TEIKOKU YOGYO CO., LTD.—See Shinagawa Refractories Co., Ltd.; *Int'l*, pg. 6841
TEIKURO CORPORATION; *U.S. Private*, pg. 3958
TEILSA SERVICIOS, S.L.—See Emerson Electric Co.; *U.S. Public*, pg. 752
TEIMO CO., LTD.; *Int'l*, pg. 7524
TEIN FAR EAST INTERNATIONAL TRADE COMPANY OF CHINA—See TEIN, INC.; *Int'l*, pg. 7525
TEIN HONG KONG LIMITED—See TEIN, INC.; *Int'l*, pg. 7525
TEIN, INC.; *Int'l*, pg. 7525
TEIN UK LIMITED—See TEIN, INC.; *Int'l*, pg. 7525
TEIN U.S.A., INC.—See TEIN, INC.; *Int'l*, pg. 7525
T.E. INVESTMENT COUNSEL INC.—See iA Financial Corporation Inc.; *Int'l*, pg. 3567
TEIPI ALTEC CO., LTD.—See TPR Co., Ltd.; *Int'l*, pg. 7884
TEIPI BUSINESS CO., LTD.—See TPR Co., Ltd.; *Int'l*, pg. 7884
TEIPI ENGINEERING CO., LTD.—See TPR Co., Ltd.; *Int'l*, pg. 7884
TEIPI INDUSTRIES CO., LTD.—See TPR Co., Ltd.; *Int'l*, pg. 7884
TEIPI KOSAN CO., LTD.—See TPR Co., Ltd.; *Int'l*, pg. 7884
TEIPI PREMEC CO., LTD.—See TPR Co., Ltd.; *Int'l*, pg. 7884
TEIPI SALES CO., LTD.—See TPR Co., Ltd.; *Int'l*, pg. 7884
TEISEKI DRILLING CO., LTD.—See INPEX CORPORATION; *Int'l*, pg. 3717
TEISEKI PIPELINE CO., LTD.—See INPEX CORPORATION; *Int'l*, pg. 3717
TEISEKI REAL ESTATE CO., LTD.—See INPEX CORPORATION; *Int'l*, pg. 3717
TEISEN TECHNO CO., LTD.—See Teikoku Sen-I Co., Ltd.; *Int'l*, pg. 7524
TEISHIN ELECTRIC MFG. CO., LTD.—See Teikoku Electric Mfg. Co., Ltd.; *Int'l*, pg. 7524
TEISSEIRE FRANCE SAS—See Britvic plc; *Int'l*, pg. 1171
TEISSEIRE SAS—See Britvic plc; *Int'l*, pg. 1171
TEI STRUCTURE WELLS—See Babcock Power, Inc.; *U.S. Private*, pg. 422
TEITELBAUM CONCRETE—See Fred Teitelbaum Construction Co. Inc.; *U.S. Private*, pg. 1601
TEITSU DENSHI KENKYUSHO CO., LTD.—See Teikoku Tsushin Kogyo Co., Ltd.; *Int'l*, pg. 7524
TEITSU ENGINEERING CO., LTD.—See Teikoku Tsushin Kogyo Co., Ltd.; *Int'l*, pg. 7524
TEIWA ENGINEERING CO., LTD.—See Teikoku Electric Mfg. Co., Ltd.; *Int'l*, pg. 7524
TEIXEIRA DUARTE - ENGENHARIA E CONSTRUCOES, S.A.—See Teixeira Duarte SA; *Int'l*, pg. 7525
TEIXEIRA DUARTE SA; *Int'l*, pg. 7525
TEIXEIRA FARMS INC.; *U.S. Private*, pg. 3958
TEJAS AMERICAN GENERAL AGENCY, LLC—See Arthur J. Gallagher & Co.; *U.S. Public*, pg. 207
TEJAS COMMUNICATION (NIGERIA) LIMITED—See Tejas Networks Limited; *Int'l*, pg. 7525
TEJAS COMMUNICATION PTE. LTD.—See Tejas Networks Limited; *Int'l*, pg. 7525
TEJAS COMMUNICATION PTE. LTD.—See Tejas Networks Limited; *Int'l*, pg. 7525
TEJAS COMMUNICATION PTE. LTD.—See Tejas Networks Limited; *Int'l*, pg. 7525
TEJAS INDUSTRIES; *U.S. Private*, pg. 3958
TEJAS MATERIALS, INC.—See GMS Inc.; *U.S. Public*, pg. 948
TEJAS NETWORKS LIMITED; *Int'l*, pg. 7525
TEJAS NETWORKS LTD.—See Tejas Networks Limited; *Int'l*, pg. 7525
TEJAS NETWORKS LTD.—See Tejas Networks Limited; *Int'l*, pg. 7525
TEJAS NETWORKS LTD.—See Tejas Networks Limited; *Int'l*, pg. 7525
TEJAS PB DISTRIBUTING, INC.—See Utz Brands, Inc.; *U.S. Public*, pg. 2268
TEJAS TOYOTA INC.; *U.S. Private*, pg. 3958
TEJNAKSH HEALTHCARE LIMITED; *Int'l*, pg. 7525
TEJON AGRICULTURAL CORP.—See Tejon Ranch Company; *U.S. Public*, pg. 1991
TEJON HOUNDS, LLC.—See Tejon Ranch Company; *U.S. Public*, pg. 1991
TEJON MOUNTAIN VILLAGE, LLC.—See Tejon Ranch Company; *U.S. Public*, pg. 1991
TEJON RANCH COMPANY; *U.S. Public*, pg. 1991
TEKAB CO. LTD.—See GIBCA Limited; *Int'l*, pg. 2963
TEKADOOR GMBH—See Systemair AB; *Int'l*, pg. 7392
TEKA INTERCONNECTION SYSTEMS, INC.—See Blackstone Inc.; *U.S. Public*, pg. 355
TEK-AIR SYSTEMS, INC.—See Desco Corporation; *U.S. Private*, pg. 1211
TEKALA CORPORATION BERHAD; *Int'l*, pg. 7526
TEK-ART INSAAT TICARET TURIZM SANAYI VE YATIRIMLAR A.S.; *Int'l*, pg. 7526
TEKA - TECELAGEM KUEHNRICH S.A.; *Int'l*, pg. 7526
TEKBRANDS LLC—See WILsquare Capital LLC; *U.S. Private*, pg. 7526
TEKCAPITAL LLC—See Tekcapital plc; *Int'l*, pg. 7526
TEKCAPITAL PLC; *Int'l*, pg. 7526
TEKCHEM, S.A.B. DE C.V.; *Int'l*, pg. 7526
TEKCOM RESOURCES, INC.; *U.S. Private*, pg. 3958
TEKCON ELECTRONICS CORPORATION—See Pan-International Industrial Corporation; *Int'l*, pg. 5716
TEKCORE CO., LTD.; *Int'l*, pg. 7526
TEKDATA INTERCONNECTIONS LIMITED—See Avnet, Inc.; *U.S. Public*, pg. 254
TEKEGLDMPIRE, INC.; *U.S. Public*, pg. 1991
TEKEYAN CULTURAL ASSOCIATION INC.; *U.S. Private*, pg. 3958
TEKFALT BINDERS (PTY) LTD.—See Wilson Bayly Holmes-Ovcon Limited; *Int'l*, pg. 8423
TEKFEN CONSTRUCTION & INSTALLATION CO., INC.—See Tekfen Holding A.S.; *Int'l*, pg. 7526
TEKFEN EMLAK GELISTIRME YATIRIM VE TICARET A.S.—See Tekfen Holding A.S.; *Int'l*, pg. 7526
TEKFEN ENDUSTRI VE TICARET A.S.—See Tekfen Holding A.S.; *Int'l*, pg. 7526
TEKFEN ENGINEERING CO., INC.—See Tekfen Holding A.S.; *Int'l*, pg. 7526
TEKFEN GAYRIMENKUL YATIRIM A.S.—See Tekfen Holding A.S.; *Int'l*, pg. 7526
TEKFEN HOLDING A.S.; *Int'l*, pg. 7526
TEKFEN INDUSTRY & TRADE CO., INC.—See Tekfen Holding A.S.; *Int'l*, pg. 7526
TEKFEN INSURANCE BROKERAGE SERVICES CO., INC.—See Tekfen Holding A.S.; *Int'l*, pg. 7526
TEKFEN SIGORTA ARACILIK HIZMETLERI A.S.—See Tekfen Holding A.S.; *Int'l*, pg. 7526
TEKFEN TARIMSAL ARASTIRMA URETIM VE PAZARLAMA A.S.—See Tekfen Holding A.S.; *Int'l*, pg. 7526
TEKFEN TURIZM VE ISLETMECILIK A.S.—See Tekfen Holding A.S.; *Int'l*, pg. 7526
TEKFEN VENTURES L.P.—See Tekfen Holding A.S.; *Int'l*, pg. 7526
TEKFOR INC—See Amtek Auto Limited; *Int'l*, pg. 441
TEKFOR SERVICES GMBH—See Amtek Auto Limited; *Int'l*, pg. 441
TEKFOR SERVICES INC.—See Amtek Auto Limited; *Int'l*, pg. 441
TEKGARD, INC.—See Advanced Cooling Technologies, Inc.; *U.S. Private*, pg. 88
TEK INDIA - PRODUCTRONICS—See Hanmi Semiconductor Co., Ltd.; *Int'l*, pg. 3256
TEK INDIA—See Hanmi Semiconductor Co., Ltd.; *Int'l*, pg. 3256
TEK INDUSTRIES INC.; *U.S. Private*, pg. 3958
TEKIS AB—See Addnode Group AB; *Int'l*, pg. 131
TEKI SOLUTIONS AS; *Int'l*, pg. 7527
TEKKEN CORPORATION; *Int'l*, pg. 7527
TEKKEN INDUSTRY COMPANY—See Hanwa Co., Ltd.; *Int'l*, pg. 3263
TEKKIS SDN. BHD.—See HeiTech Padu Berhad; *Int'l*, pg. 3326
TEKKORP DIGITAL ACQUISITION CORP.; *U.S. Public*, pg. 1991
TEK LABEL AND PRINTING, INC.—See Ares Management Corporation; *U.S. Public*, pg. 191
TEKLA CORPORATION—See Trimble, Inc.; *U.S. Public*, pg. 2191
TEKLA GMBH—See Trimble, Inc.; *U.S. Public*, pg. 2191
TEKLA INC.—See Trimble, Inc.; *U.S. Public*, pg. 2191
TEKLA INDIA PRIVATE LIMITED—See Trimble, Inc.; *U.S. Public*, pg. 2191
TEKLA KK—See Trimble, Inc.; *U.S. Public*, pg. 2191
TEKLA KOREA—See Trimble, Inc.; *U.S. Public*, pg. 2191
TEKLA OYJ—See Trimble, Inc.; *U.S. Public*, pg. 2191
TEKLA SARL—See Trimble, Inc.; *U.S. Public*, pg. 2191
TEKLA (SEA) PTE. LTD.—See Trimble, Inc.; *U.S. Public*, pg. 2191
TEKLA SOFTWARE AB—See Trimble, Inc.; *U.S. Public*, pg. 2191
TEKLA SOFTWARE (SHANGHAI) CO., LTD.—See Trimble, Inc.; *U.S. Public*, pg. 2191
TEKLA (UK) LTD.—See Trimble, Inc.; *U.S. Public*, pg. 2191
TEKLINK INTERNATIONAL INC.—See Hinduja Global Solutions Ltd.; *Int'l*, pg. 3398
TEKLOS TEKNOLOJI LOJISTIK HIZMETLERI A.S.—See Indeks Bilgisayar Sistemleri Muhendislik Sanayi ve Ticaret A.S.; *Int'l*, pg. 3649
TEKMANNI EESTI OU—See YIT Corporation; *Int'l*, pg. 8586
TEKMANNI OY—See YIT Corporation; *Int'l*, pg. 8587
TEKMANNI POHJANMAA OY—See YIT Corporation; *Int'l*, pg. 8587
TEKMANNI RUSSERVICE OY—See YIT Corporation; *Int'l*, pg. 8587
TEKMAR ENERGY LIMITED—See Tekmar Group plc; *Int'l*, pg. 7527
TEKMAR GMBH—See Tekmar Group plc; *Int'l*, pg. 7527
TEKMAR GROUP PLC; *Int'l*, pg. 7527
TEKMARK GLOBAL SOLUTIONS LLC—See OEP Capital Advisors, L.P.; *U.S. Private*, pg. 2999
TEKMASTERS LLC—See Godspeed Capital Management LP; *U.S. Private*, pg. 1725
TEKMATE, LLC—See ATN International, Inc.; *U.S. Public*, pg. 224
TEKMATE, LLC—See Freedom 3 Capital, LLC; *U.S. Private*, pg. 1603
TEKNA INC.—See Arendals Fossekompani ASA; *Int'l*, pg. 559
TEKNA PLASMA EUROPE SAS—See Arendals Fossekompani ASA; *Int'l*, pg. 559
TEKNA SEAL LLC—See Aptiv PLC; *Int'l*, pg. 526
TEKNA SYSTEMES PLASMA INC—See Arendals Fossekompani ASA; *Int'l*, pg. 559
TEKNEK (CHINA) LIMITED—See Illinois Tool Works Inc.; *U.S. Public*, pg. 1111
TEKNEK (JAPAN) LIMITED—See Illinois Tool Works Inc.; *U.S. Public*, pg. 1111
TEKNEK LIMITED—See Illinois Tool Works Inc.; *U.S. Public*, pg. 1111
TEKNETEX INC.; *U.S. Private*, pg. 3958
TEKNETIX INC.; *U.S. Private*, pg. 3958
TEKNICKS LLC; *U.S. Private*, pg. 3958
TEKNIK I MEDIA DATACENTER STOCKHOLM AB—See Addnode Group AB; *Int'l*, pg. 131
TEKNIK MUHENDISLIK VE MUSAVIRLIK A.S.—See Dogus Holding AS; *Int'l*, pg. 2155
TEKNIKPRODUKTER NORDIC AB—See Addtech AB; *Int'l*, pg. 135
TEKNIK TRADING INC.—See Clover Systems Inc.; *U.S. Private*, pg. 947
TEKNION CORPORATION; *Int'l*, pg. 7527
TEKNION EUROPE LIMITED—See Teknion Corporation; *Int'l*, pg. 7527
TEKNION FURNITURE SYSTEMS LIMITED—See Teknion Corporation; *Int'l*, pg. 7527
TEKNION INTERNATIONAL—See Teknion Corporation; *Int'l*, pg. 7527
TEKNION LLC—See Teknion Corporation; *Int'l*, pg. 7527
TEKNI-PLEX, INC.—See Genstar Capital, LLC; *U.S. Private*, pg. 1678
TEKNISK AGENTUR A/S—See REHAU Verwaltungszentrale AG; *Int'l*, pg. 6256
TEKNISK VENTILASJON AS—See Instalco AB; *Int'l*, pg. 3722
TEKNO BOOKS—See NovelStem International Corp.; *U.S. Public*, pg. 1549
TEKNOFOAM HELLAS E.P.E.—See Recticel S.A.; *Int'l*, pg. 6242
TEKNOFOAM IZOLASYON SANAYI VE TICARET A.S.—See Recticel S.A.; *Int'l*, pg. 6242
TEKNOL INC.; *U.S. Private*, pg. 3958
TEKNOLUXION CONSULTING LLC—See NewSpring Capital LLC; *U.S. Private*, pg. 2917
TEKNOMINING PLC; *Int'l*, pg. 7527
TEKNON CORPORATION—See LINX LLLP; *U.S. Private*, pg. 2463
TEKNOR APEX ASIA PACIFIC PTE. LTD.—See Teknor Apex Company; *U.S. Private*, pg. 3958
TEKNOR APEX B.V.—See Teknor Apex Company; *U.S. Private*, pg. 3958
TEKNOR APEX COMPANY; *U.S. Private*, pg. 3958
TEKNOR APEX COMPANY - THERMOPLASTIC ELASTOMER DIVISION—See Teknor Apex Company; *U.S. Private*, pg. 3958
TEKNOR APEX ELASTOMERS, INC.—See Teknor Apex Company; *U.S. Private*, pg. 3958
TEKNOR APEX (SUZHOU) ADVANCED POLYMER COMPOUNDS CO. PTE LTD.—See Teknor Apex Company; *U.S. Private*, pg. 3958
TEKNOR APEX VERMONT COMPANY—See Teknor Apex Company; *U.S. Private*, pg. 3959
TEKNOR COLOR CO.—See Teknor Apex Company; *U.S. Private*, pg. 3959
TEKNOS AB—See Teknos Group Oy; *Int'l*, pg. 7527
TEKNOSA IC VE DIS TICARET A.S.—See Haci Omer Sabanci Holding A.S.; *Int'l*, pg. 3204
TEKNO S.A. - INDUSTRIA E COMERCIO; *Int'l*, pg. 7527
TEKNOS A/S—See Teknos Group Oy; *Int'l*, pg. 7527
TEKNOS COATINGS TRADING (SHANGHAI) CO., LTD—See Teknos Group Oy; *Int'l*, pg. 7527
TEKNOS DEUTSCHLAND GMBH—See Arbonia AG; *Int'l*, pg. 537
TEKNOS DEUTSCHLAND GMBH—See Teknos Group Oy; *Int'l*, pg. 7527
TEKNOS D.O.O.—See Teknos Group Oy; *Int'l*, pg. 7527
TEKNOSER A.S.—See Hitay Investment Holdings A.S.; *Int'l*, pg. 3425
TEKNOSERV ENGINEERING SDN. BHD.—See GUH Holdings Berhad; *Int'l*, pg. 3173
TEKNOS FEYCO AG—See Arbonia AG; *Int'l*, pg. 538
TEKNOS GROUP OY; *Int'l*, pg. 7527
TEKNOS IRELAND LIMITED—See Teknos Group Oy; *Int'l*, pg. 7527
TEKNOS LLC—See Teknos Group Oy; *Int'l*, pg. 7527
TEKNOS NORGE AS—See Teknos Group Oy; *Int'l*, pg. 7527
TEKNOS OHTEK OOO—See Teknos Group Oy; *Int'l*, pg. 7527

TEKNOS GROUP OY / CORPORATE AFFILIATIONS

TEKNOS OLIVA SP. Z O.O.—See Teknos Group Oy; *Int'l*, pg. 7527
TEKNOS OOO—See Teknos Group Oy; *Int'l*, pg. 7527
TEKNOS SCOTLAND LIMITED—See Teknos Group Oy; *Int'l*, pg. 7527
TEKNOS SP. Z O.O.—See Teknos Group Oy; *Int'l*, pg. 7527
TEKNOS (UK) LIMITED—See Teknos Group Oy; *Int'l*, pg. 7527
TEKNOS US, INC.—See Arbonia AG; *Int'l*, pg. 538
TEKNO-TIP ANALITIK SISTEMLER LTD. STI.; *Int'l*, pg. 7527
TEKNO TUBI S.R.L.—See Interpump Group S.p.A.; *Int'l*, pg. 3757
TEKNOWEB CONVERTING S.R.L.—See I.M.A. Industria Macchine Automatiche S.p.A.; *Int'l*, pg. 3566
TEKNOWEB N.A. LLC—See I.M.A. Industria Macchine Automatiche S.p.A.; *Int'l*, pg. 3566
TEKOM A.D.; *Int'l*, pg. 7527
TEKOM TECHNOLOGIES, INC.; *Int'l*, pg. 7528
TEKONTROL INC.; *U.S. Private*, pg. 3959
TEKOTO MOTORLU TASTLAR ANKARA—See Stellantis N.V.; *Int'l*, pg. 7203
TEKOTO MOTORLU TASTLAR ISTAMBUL—See Stellantis N.V.; *Int'l*, pg. 7203
TEKPARTNERS—See P2P Staffing Corp.; *U.S. Private*, pg. 3062
TEKPRO SERVICES, LLC—See Bristol Bay Native Corporation; *U.S. Private*, pg. 656
TEKPROS INC.; *U.S. Private*, pg. 3959
TEKRA - EAST COAST DIVISION—See Audax Group, Limited Partnership; *U.S. Private*, pg. 387
TEKRA, LLC—See Audax Group, Limited Partnership; *U.S. Private*, pg. 387
TEKRAN INSTRUMENTS CORPORATION—See TSI Incorporated; *U.S. Private*, pg. 4253
TE KRONOS GMBH—See Helaba Landesbank Hessen-Thuringen; *Int'l*, pg. 3328
TEKSAVERS, INC.; *U.S. Private*, pg. 3959
TEKSCAN, INC.—See Artemis Capital Partners Management Co., LLC; *U.S. Private*, pg. 341
TEKSCAPE; *U.S. Private*, pg. 3959
TEKSELL, INC.; *U.S. Private*, pg. 3959
TEK SENG HOLDINGS BERHAD; *Int'l*, pg. 7526
TEK SENG SDN. BHD.—See Tek Seng Holdings Berhad; *Int'l*, pg. 7526
TEKSID ALUMINUM S.R.L.—See Stellantis N.V.; *Int'l*, pg. 7203
TEKSID HIERRO DE MEXICO S.A. DE C.V.—See Stellantis N.V.; *Int'l*, pg. 7203
TEKSID INC.—See Stellantis N.V.; *Int'l*, pg. 7203
TEKSID IRON POLAND SP. Z O.O.—See Stellantis N.V.; *Int'l*, pg. 7203
TEKSID S.P.A.—See Stellantis N.V.; *Int'l*, pg. 7203
TEKSTAR CABLEVISION INC.—See Arvig Enterprises, Inc.; *U.S. Private*, pg. 345
TEKSTIL A.D.; *Int'l*, pg. 7528
TEKSTIL A.D.; *Int'l*, pg. 7528
TEKSTIL FAKTORING A.S.—See GSD Holding A.S.; *Int'l*, pg. 3144
TEKSTILPROMET D.D; *Int'l*, pg. 7528
TEKSTINA TEKSTILNA INDUSTRIJA D.O.O.; *Int'l*, pg. 7528
TEKSTURE CORAP SAN. VE TIC. A.S.; *Int'l*, pg. 7528
TEKSYSTEMS GLOBAL SERVICES, LLC—See Allegis Group, Inc.; *U.S. Private*, pg. 177
TEKSYSTEMS, INC.—See Allegis Group, Inc.; *U.S. Private*, pg. 177
TEKTRONIX GMBH—See Fortive Corporation; *U.S. Public*, pg. 872
TEKTRONIX, INC.—See Fortive Corporation; *U.S. Public*, pg. 872
TEKTRONIX INDIA PRIVATE LIMITED—See Fortive Corporation; *U.S. Public*, pg. 872
TEKTRONIX INTERNATIONAL SALES GMBH—See Fortive Corporation; *U.S. Public*, pg. 872
TEKTRONIX JAPAN, LTD.—See Fortive Corporation; *U.S. Public*, pg. 872
TEKTRONIX SAS—See Fortive Corporation; *U.S. Public*, pg. 872
TEKTRONIX SOUTHEAST ASIA PTE LTD—See Fortive Corporation; *U.S. Public*, pg. 872
TEKTRONIX UK LTD.—See Fortive Corporation; *U.S. Public*, pg. 872
TEKUN ASAS SDN. BHD.—See Ewein Berhad; *Int'l*, pg. 2576
TEKUN ASAS SDN BHD (TASB)—See Ewein Berhad; *Int'l*, pg. 2576
TEKUNI EOOD—See Komax Holding AG; *Int'l*, pg. 4241
TEKWIND CO., LTD.—See MCJ Co., Ltd.; *Int'l*, pg. 4759
TEKYAR TEKNIK YARDIM A. S.—See Akzo Nobel N.V.; *Int'l*, pg. 275
TELA BIO, INC.; *U.S. Public*, pg. 1991
TEL-AD JERUSALEM STUDIO LTD.—See The Israel Land Development Co.; *Int'l*, pg. 7657
TELADOC HEALTH BRASIL - SERVICOS DE CONSULTORIA EM SAUDE LTDA—See Teladoc Health, Inc.; *U.S. Public*, pg. 1992
TELADOC HEALTH, INC.; *U.S. Public*, pg. 1991

TELADOC HEALTH PORTUGAL, S.A.—See Teladoc Health, Inc.; *U.S. Public*, pg. 1992
TELAG AG—See Capita plc; *Int'l*, pg. 1309
TELAID INDUSTRIES, INC.; *U.S. Private*, pg. 3959
TELAIR INTERNATIONAL AB—See TransDigm Group Incorporated; *U.S. Public*, pg. 2183
TELAIR INTERNATIONAL GMBH—See TransDigm Group Incorporated; *U.S. Public*, pg. 2183
TELAIR INTERNATIONAL SERVICES PTE. LTD.—See TransDigm Group Incorporated; *U.S. Public*, pg. 2183
TELALASKA INC.; *U.S. Private*, pg. 3959
TELAL RESORT LLC—See Alpha Dhabi Holding PJSC; *Int'l*, pg. 368
TELAMO MUSIK & UNTERHALTUNG GMBH—See Bertelsmann SE & Co. KGaA; *Int'l*, pg. 996
TELAMON CONSTRUCTION INC.—See Mosser Construction Inc.; *U.S. Private*, pg. 2795
TELAMON CORPORATION; *U.S. Private*, pg. 3959
TELAMON INTERNATIONAL CORP.—See Telamon Corporation; *U.S. Private*, pg. 3959
TELAMON TECHNOLOGIES CORP—See Telamon Corporation; *U.S. Private*, pg. 3959
TELAPEX INC.; *U.S. Private*, pg. 3959
TELARIA BRAZIL PUBLICIDADE LTDA.—See Magnite, Inc.; *U.S. Public*, pg. 1354
TELARIA, INC.—See Magnite, Inc.; *U.S. Public*, pg. 1354
TELARIX, INC.—See Vista Equity Partners, LLC; *U.S. Private*, pg. 4402
TELARUS PTY LTD—See Over the Wire Holdings Limited; *Int'l*, pg. 5671
TELASI JSC—See JSC INTER RAO UES; *Int'l*, pg. 4009
TELATHENA SYSTEMS—See Pacific Equity Partners Pty. Limited; *Int'l*, pg. 5689
TELAURUS COMMUNICATIONS LLC—See SpeedCast International Limited; *Int'l*, pg. 7133
TEL AVIV HILTON LIMITED—See Hilton Worldwide Holdings Inc.; *U.S. Public*, pg. 1041
TEL AVIV STOCK EXCHANGE LTD.; *Int'l*, pg. 7528
TELCA 2000—See ENGIE SA; *Int'l*, pg. 2434
TELCAGE AS—See Telenor ASA; *Int'l*, pg. 7539
TELCARE MEDICAL SUPPLY, LLC—See Koninklijke Philips N.V.; *U.S. Public*, pg. 4267
TELCAT KOMMUNIKATIONS-TECHNIK GMBH—See Salzgitter AG; *Int'l*, pg. 6499
TELCAT MULTICOM GMBH—See Salzgitter AG; *Int'l*, pg. 6499
TELCEL, C.A.—See Telefonica, S.A.; *Int'l*, pg. 7535
TELCITE—See Regie Autonome des Transports Parisiens; *Int'l*, pg. 6253
TELCOBRIDGES INC.; *Int'l*, pg. 7528
TELCOBUY.COM LLC—See World Wide Technology Holding Co., LLC; *U.S. Private*, pg. 4568
TELCO CUBA, INC.; *U.S. Public*, pg. 1992
TELCO DATA SYSTEMS, INC.—See Chickasaw Holding Company; *U.S. Private*, pg. 880
TELCO EXPERTS LLC—See Alpine Investors; *U.S. Private*, pg. 201
TELCOIQ, INC.; *U.S. Private*, pg. 3959
TELCO LUBLIN SP ZOO—See Liberty Global plc; *Int'l*, pg. 4485
TELCOM CONSTRUCTION, INC.—See Dycom Industries, Inc.; *U.S. Public*, pg. 699
TELCON RF PHARMACEUTICAL, INC.; *Int'l*, pg. 7528
TELCO PROPERTIES—See Telalaska Inc.; *U.S. Private*, pg. 3959
TELCO PRO SERVICES, A. S.—See CEZ, a.s.; *Int'l*, pg. 1428
TELCO SUPPLY COMPANY—See Chickasaw Holding Company; *U.S. Private*, pg. 880
TELCO SYSTEMS—See BATM Advanced Communications Ltd.; *Int'l*, pg. 890
TELCOWARE CO LTD; *Int'l*, pg. 7528
TELDATA; *U.S. Private*, pg. 3959
TELDIG SYSTEMS, INC.—See Caisse de Depot et Placement du Quebec; *Int'l*, pg. 1256
TELDON MEDIA GROUP, INC.—See CARDON Group Inc.; *Int'l*, pg. 1323
TELDOR CABLES & SYSTEMS LTD.; *Int'l*, pg. 7528
TEL DRUG, INC.—See The Cigna Group; *U.S. Public*, pg. 2061
TEL DRUG OF PENNSYLVANIA, LLC—See The Cigna Group; *U.S. Public*, pg. 2061
TELE2 AB; *Int'l*, pg. 7529
TELE 2 AB—See Modern Times Group MTG AB; *Int'l*, pg. 5015
TELE2 A/S—See Tele2 AB; *Int'l*, pg. 7529
TELE2BUTIKERNA AB—See Tele2 AB; *Int'l*, pg. 7529
TELE2 EESTI AS—See Tele2 AB; *Int'l*, pg. 7529
TELE2 FINANCE BELGIUM SA—See Tele2 AB; *Int'l*, pg. 7529
TELE2 HOLDING AS—See Tele2 AB; *Int'l*, pg. 7529
TELE2 NETHERLANDS B.V.—See Deutsche Telekom AG; *Int'l*, pg. 2084
TELE2 NETHERLANDS HOLDING B.V.—See Tele2 AB; *Int'l*, pg. 7529
TELE2 NORGE AS—See Telia Company AB; *Int'l*, pg. 7544
TELE2 RUSSIA—See PJSC VTB Bank; *Int'l*, pg. 5886
TELE2 SVERIGE AB—See Tele2 AB; *Int'l*, pg. 7529

TELE2 SWEDEN SA—See Tele2 AB; *Int'l*, pg. 7529
TELE2 TREASURY AB—See Tele2 AB; *Int'l*, pg. 7529
TELE2VISION AB—See Tele2 AB; *Int'l*, pg. 7529
TELE AG—See Deutsche Wohnen SE; *Int'l*, pg. 2085
TELEALLIANCE—See De Agostini S.p.A.; *Int'l*, pg. 1995
TELEASSETS CO., LTD.—See Charoen Pokphand Group Co., Ltd.; *Int'l*, pg. 1453
TELEATENTO DEL PERU, S.A.C.—See Telefonica, S.A.; *Int'l*, pg. 7536
TELE ATLAS BV—See TomTom N.V.; *Int'l*, pg. 7804
TELE ATLAS DATAS—See TomTom N.V.; *Int'l*, pg. 7804
TELE ATLAS GERMANY—See TomTom N.V.; *Int'l*, pg. 7804
TELE ATLAS MALAYSIA SDN. BHD—See TomTom N.V.; *Int'l*, pg. 7804
TELE ATLAS POLSKA SP. Z O.O.—See TomTom N.V.; *Int'l*, pg. 7804
TELE ATLAS RUSSIA—See TomTom N.V.; *Int'l*, pg. 7804
TELE ATLAS SURVEY B.V.—See TomTom N.V.; *Int'l*, pg. 7804
TELE ATLAS TAIWAN CO. LTD—See TomTom N.V.; *Int'l*, pg. 7804
TELE ATLAS UK—See TomTom N.V.; *Int'l*, pg. 7804
TELEBEC LIMITED PARTNERSHIP—See BCE Inc.; *Int'l*, pg. 926
TELEBEEP WIRELESS—See JAB Wireless, Inc.; *U.S. Private*, pg. 2172
TELEBT SP.ZO.O.—See Impel S.A.; *Int'l*, pg. 3632
TELEBYTE, INC.; *U.S. Private*, pg. 3960
TELECANOR GLOBAL LIMITED; *Int'l*, pg. 7529
TELECARD LIMITED; *Int'l*, pg. 7529
TELECARD NETWORK, L.L.C.—See IDT Corporation; *U.S. Public*, pg. 1094
TELECATS B.V.—See Concentrix Corporation; *U.S. Public*, pg. 565
TELEC BRASILEIRAS S.A. TELEBRAS; *Int'l*, pg. 7529
TELECEL GROUP LTD.; *Int'l*, pg. 7529
TELECENTER PANAMERICANA LTDA.—See AT&T Inc.; *U.S. Public*, pg. 220
TELE-CENTRE SERVICES PTE. LTD.—See Hai Leck Holdings Limited; *Int'l*, pg. 3208
TELECHECK SERVICES CANADA INC.—See Fiserv, Inc.; *U.S. Public*, pg. 851
TELECHECK SERVICES, INC.—See Fiserv, Inc.; *U.S. Public*, pg. 851
TELECHIPS INC.; *Int'l*, pg. 7529
TELECHIPS SHANGHAI CO., LTD.—See Telechips Inc.; *Int'l*, pg. 7529
TELECHIPS SHENZHEN CO., LTD.—See Telechips Inc.; *Int'l*, pg. 7529
TELECHIPS USA INC.—See Telechips Inc.; *Int'l*, pg. 7529
TELECHOICE INTERNATIONAL LIMITED—See Temasek Holdings (Private) Limited; *Int'l*, pg. 7554
TELECLOUD, LLC; *U.S. Private*, pg. 3960
TELECO GMBH COTTBUS TELEKOMMUNIKATION—See Morgan Stanley; *U.S. Public*, pg. 1473
TELECO INC.; *U.S. Private*, pg. 3960
TELECOISE; *Int'l*, pg. 7530
TELE COLUMBUS AG—See Morgan Stanley; *U.S. Public*, pg. 1472
TELECOLUMBUS GMBH; *Int'l*, pg. 7530
TELECOM ANIMATION FILM CO., LTD.—See Sega Sammy Holdings, Inc.; *Int'l*, pg. 6681
TELECOM ARGENTINA S.A.—See Cablevision Holding S.A.; *Int'l*, pg. 1246
TELECOM COOK ISLANDS LIMITED—See Fiji National Provident Fund; *Int'l*, pg. 2661
TELECOM COTE D'IVOIRE—See Orange S.A.; *Int'l*, pg. 5611
TELECOM DECISION MAKERS, INC; *U.S. Private*, pg. 3960
TELECOM DESIGN; *Int'l*, pg. 7530
TELECOM DEVELOPMENT COMPANY AFGHANISTAN LTD—See Aga Khan Development Network; *Int'l*, pg. 199
TELECOM DIGITAL HOLDINGS LIMITED; *Int'l*, pg. 7530
TELECOM EGYPT; *Int'l*, pg. 7530
TELECOM ENTERPRISES INC.; *U.S. Private*, pg. 3960
TELECOM EQUIPMENT PTE LTD—See Temasek Holdings (Private) Limited; *Int'l*, pg. 7554
TELECOMET TECHNOSERVICE, INC.—See KDDI Corporation; *Int'l*, pg. 4111
TELECOM EXPRESS CO., LTD.—See SoftBank Group Corp.; *Int'l*, pg. 7054
TELECOM FIJI LTD.—See Fiji National Provident Fund; *Int'l*, pg. 2661
TELECOM IBERICA DE INVERSIONES, S.L.—See EQT AB; *Int'l*, pg. 2479
TELECOM IBERICA DE INVERSIONES, S.L.—See Public Sector Pension Investment Board; *Int'l*, pg. 6096
TELECOM ITALIA CAPITAL S.A.—See TIM S.p.A.; *Int'l*, pg. 7749
TELECOM ITALIA FINANCE S.A.—See TIM S.p.A.; *Int'l*, pg. 7749
TELECOM ITALIA LAB—See TIM S.p.A.; *Int'l*, pg. 7750
TELECOM ITALIA MEDIA BROADCASTING S.R.L.—See TIM S.p.A.; *Int'l*, pg. 7750
TELECOM ITALIA SPAIN SL—See TIM S.p.A.; *Int'l*, pg. 7750

COMPANY NAME INDEX

TELEFLEX INCORPORATED

Company Index

TELECOM ITALIA SPARKLE OF NORTH AMERICA, INC.—See TIM S.p.A.; *Int'l*, pg. 7750
TELECOM ITALIA SPARKLE SINGAPORE PTE. LTD.—See TIM S.p.A.; *Int'l*, pg. 7750
TELECOM ITALIA SPARKLE S.P.A.—See TIM S.p.A.; *Int'l*, pg. 7750
TELECOM ITALIA WIRELINE—See TIM S.p.A.; *Int'l*, pg. 7750
TELECOM LIECHTENSTEIN AG; *Int'l*, pg. 7530
TELECOM LIFESTYLE FASHION B.V.—See Strax AB; *Int'l*, pg. 7239
TELECOMMUNICATIONS DEVELOPMENT CORPORATION; *U.S. Private*, pg. 3960
TELECOMMUNICATIONS INDUSTRY ASSOCIATION; *U.S. Private*, pg. 3960
TELECOMMUNICATIONS MANAGEMENT LIMITED—See Telecom Plus Plc; *Int'l*, pg. 7530
TELECOMMUNICATIONS MANAGEMENT, LLC—See Cable One, Inc.; *U.S. Public*, pg. 416
TELECOMMUNICATIONS ON DEMAND, INC.; *U.S. Private*, pg. 3960
TELECOMMUNICATIONS SERVICES OF TRINIDAD & TOBAGO LIMITED; *Int'l*, pg. 7530
TELECOMMUNICATION SUPPORT SERVICES, INC.—See Acorn Growth Companies, LC; *U.S. Private*, pg. 63
TELECOMMUNICATION TECHNICAL SERVICE JOINT STOCK COMPANY; *Int'l*, pg. 7530
TELECOM NEW ZEALAND USA LIMITED—See Spark New Zealand Limited; *Int'l*, pg. 7126
TELECOMODA, S.A. DE C.V.—See America Movil, S.A.B. de C.V.; *Int'l*, pg. 421
TELECOM PLUS PLC; *Int'l*, pg. 7530
TELECOMPUTING SWEDEN AB—See IK Investment Partners Limited; *Int'l*, pg. 3610
TELECOM SERVICE CO., LTD.—See Hikari Tsushin, Inc.; *Int'l*, pg. 3390
TELECOM SERVICE ONE HOLDINGS LIMITED; *Int'l*, pg. 7530
TELECOM SOUND INC—See TBS Holdings, Inc.; *Int'l*, pg. 7481
TELECOM TECHNICIANS INC.—See Motor City Electric Co., Inc.; *U.S. Private*, pg. 2797
TELECOMUNICACION, ELECTRONICA Y COMUNICACION S.A.—See Siemens Aktiengesellschaft; *Int'l*, pg. 6901
TELECOMUNICACION, ELECTRONICA Y CONMUTACION S.A.—See Siemens Aktiengesellschaft; *Int'l*, pg. 6901
TELECOMUNICACIONES Y SERVICIOS CONOSUR LTDA.—See ITOCHU Corporation; *Int'l*, pg. 3841
TELECOMUNICACOES BRASILEIRAS S.A.; *Int'l*, pg. 7530
TELECOM VANUATU LIMITED—See Fiji National Provident Fund; *Int'l*, pg. 2661
TELECOM VASTGOED, B.V.—See EQT AB; *Int'l*, pg. 2479
TELECOM VASTGOED, B.V.—See Public Sector Pension Investment Board; *Int'l*, pg. 6096
TELECONCEPTS, INC.—See AbleNet, Inc.; *U.S. Private*, pg. 39
TELE-CONSULTANTS, INC.; *U.S. Private*, pg. 3959
TELECONSULT AUSTRIA GMBH—See OHB SE; *Int'l*, pg. 5532
TELECONTACT CENTER S.P.A.—See TIM S.p.A.; *Int'l*, pg. 7750
TELECONTROL AG; *Int'l*, pg. 7530
TELECOR, S.A.—See El Corte Ingles, S.A.; *Int'l*, pg. 2340
TELECT DE MEXICO S. DE R.L. DE C.V.—See Amphenol Corporation; *U.S. Public*, pg. 132
TELECTRONICS SA—See Proximus PLC; *Int'l*, pg. 6008
TELECUBE, INC.—See V-cube, Inc.; *Int'l*, pg. 8104
TELEDATA INFORMATICS LTD.—See Agnite Education Limited; *Int'l*, pg. 212
TELEDATA MARINE SOLUTIONS LTD; *Int'l*, pg. 7530
TELEDEPORTES S.A.—See Grupo Clarin S.A.; *Int'l*, pg. 3125
TELEDESIC LLC; *U.S. Private*, pg. 3960
TELEDEX CORPORATION; *U.S. Private*, pg. 3960
TELEDIFUSORA BAHIENSE S.A.—See Grupo Clarin S.A.; *Int'l*, pg. 3125
TELEDIGITAL D.D.; *Int'l*, pg. 7530
TELEDIRECT HONG KONG LIMITED—See TDCX Inc.; *Int'l*, pg. 7486
TELEDIRECT TELECOMMERCE (THAILAND) LIMITED—See TDCX Inc.; *Int'l*, pg. 7486
TELEDISTAL SA—See Liberty Global plc; *Int'l*, pg. 4485
TELEDU APOLLO CYFYNGEDIG—See Boomerang Plus plc; *Int'l*, pg. 1110
TELEDYNAMIC COMMUNICATIONS INC.—See BCT Consulting, Inc.; *U.S. Private*, pg. 500
TELE DYNAMICS GLOBAL COM SDN. BHD—See Japan Industrial Partners, Inc.; *Int'l*, pg. 3897
TELEDYNE BENTHOS, INC.—See Teledyne Technologies Incorporated; *U.S. Public*, pg. 1992
TELEDYNE BLUEVIEW, INC.—See Teledyne Technologies Incorporated; *U.S. Public*, pg. 1993
TELEDYNE BROWN ENGINEERING, INC.—See Teledyne Technologies Incorporated; *U.S. Public*, pg. 1993
TELEDYNE CARIS, INC.—See Teledyne Technologies Incorporated; *U.S. Public*, pg. 1993
TELEDYNE CARIS USA, INC.—See Teledyne Technologies Incorporated; *U.S. Public*, pg. 1993
TELEDYNE CDL, INC.—See Teledyne Technologies Incorporated; *U.S. Public*, pg. 1993
TELEDYNE CETAC TECHNOLOGIES—See Teledyne Technologies Incorporated; *U.S. Public*, pg. 1994
TELEDYNE COLLABORX, INC.—See Teledyne Technologies Incorporated; *U.S. Public*, pg. 1993
TELEDYNE CONTROLS—See Teledyne Technologies Incorporated; *U.S. Public*, pg. 1993
TELEDYNE COUGAR—See Teledyne Technologies Incorporated; *U.S. Public*, pg. 1993
TELEDYNE DALSA, INC.—See Teledyne Technologies Incorporated; *U.S. Public*, pg. 1993
TELEDYNE DALSA, INC.—See Teledyne Technologies Incorporated; *U.S. Public*, pg. 1993
TELEDYNE DEFENSE ELECTRONICS, LLC—See Teledyne Technologies Incorporated; *U.S. Public*, pg. 1993
TELEDYNE E2V, INC.—See Teledyne Technologies Incorporated; *U.S. Public*, pg. 1995
TELEDYNE E2V LIMITED—See Teledyne Technologies Incorporated; *U.S. Public*, pg. 1995
TELEDYNE E2V SEMICONDUCTORS SAS—See Teledyne Technologies Incorporated; *U.S. Public*, pg. 1995
TELEDYNE E2V (UK) LIMITED—See Teledyne Technologies Incorporated; *U.S. Public*, pg. 1995
TELEDYNE E2V US, INC.—See Teledyne Technologies Incorporated; *U.S. Public*, pg. 1995
TELEDYNE FLIR, LLC—See Teledyne Technologies Incorporated; *U.S. Public*, pg. 1993
TELEDYNE FRANCE SAS—See Teledyne Technologies Incorporated; *U.S. Public*, pg. 1993
TELEDYNE GAVIA EHF.—See Teledyne Technologies Incorporated; *U.S. Public*, pg. 1993
TELEDYNE GERMANY GMBH—See Teledyne Technologies Incorporated; *U.S. Public*, pg. 1993
TELEDYNE IMPULSE- PDM LTD.—See Teledyne Technologies Incorporated; *U.S. Public*, pg. 1993
TELEDYNE INSTRUMENTS, INC.—See Teledyne Technologies Incorporated; *U.S. Public*, pg. 1993
TELEDYNE ISCO—See Teledyne Technologies Incorporated; *U.S. Public*, pg. 1994
TELEDYNE ISRAEL COMPOSITE LTD.—See ATI Inc.; *U.S. Public*, pg. 222
TELEDYNE ITALY—See ATI Inc.; *U.S. Public*, pg. 222
TELEDYNE JUDSON TECHNOLOGIES—See Teledyne Technologies Incorporated; *U.S. Public*, pg. 1995
TELEDYNE LABTECH LIMITED—See Teledyne Technologies Incorporated; *U.S. Public*, pg. 1994
TELEDYNE LABTECH LTD. - MILTON KEYNES PLANT—See Teledyne Technologies Incorporated; *U.S. Public*, pg. 1994
TELEDYNE LECROY (BEIJING) TRADING CO., LTD.—See Teledyne Technologies Incorporated; *U.S. Public*, pg. 1994
TELEDYNE LECROY GMBH—See Teledyne Technologies Incorporated; *U.S. Public*, pg. 1994
TELEDYNE LECROY, INC. - PROTOCOL SOLUTIONS GROUP—See Teledyne Technologies Incorporated; *U.S. Public*, pg. 1994
TELEDYNE LECROY, INC.—See Teledyne Technologies Incorporated; *U.S. Public*, pg. 1994
TELEDYNE LECROY INDIA TRADING PRIVATE LTD.—See Teledyne Technologies Incorporated; *U.S. Public*, pg. 1994
TELEDYNE LECROY JAPAN CORPORATION—See Teledyne Technologies Incorporated; *U.S. Public*, pg. 1994
TELEDYNE LECROY KOREA, LTD.—See Teledyne Technologies Incorporated; *U.S. Public*, pg. 1994
TELEDYNE LECROY, S.A.R.L—See Teledyne Technologies Incorporated; *U.S. Public*, pg. 1994
TELEDYNE LECROY, S.A.—See Teledyne Technologies Incorporated; *U.S. Public*, pg. 1994
TELEDYNE LECROY SINGAPORE PTE. LTD.—See Teledyne Technologies Incorporated; *U.S. Public*, pg. 1994
TELEDYNE LECROY, S.R.L.—See Teledyne Technologies Incorporated; *U.S. Public*, pg. 1994
TELEDYNE LECROY XENA APS.—See Teledyne Technologies Incorporated; *U.S. Public*, pg. 1994
TELEDYNE LEEMAN LABS—See Teledyne Technologies Incorporated; *U.S. Public*, pg. 1994
TELEDYNE LTD.—See Teledyne Technologies Incorporated; *U.S. Public*, pg. 1994
TELEDYNE MICRALYNE, INC.—See Teledyne Technologies Incorporated; *U.S. Public*, pg. 1994
TELEDYNE MICROELECTRONIC TECHNOLOGIES—See Teledyne Technologies Incorporated; *U.S. Public*, pg. 1994
TELEDYNE MONITOR LABS, INC.—See Teledyne Technologies Incorporated; *U.S. Public*, pg. 1994
TELEDYNE OIL & GAS—See Teledyne Technologies Incorporated; *U.S. Public*, pg. 1994
TELEDYNE OLDHAM SIMTRONICS SAS—See Teledyne Technologies Incorporated; *U.S. Public*, pg. 1994
TELEDYNE OPTECH INCORPORATED—See Teledyne Technologies Incorporated; *U.S. Public*, pg. 1994
TELEDYNE PARADISE DATACOM LIMITED—See Teledyne Technologies Incorporated; *U.S. Public*, pg. 1994
TELEDYNE PARADISE DATACOM, LLC—See Teledyne Technologies Incorporated; *U.S. Public*, pg. 1994
TELEDYNE RAD-ICON IMAGING CORP.—See Teledyne Technologies Incorporated; *U.S. Public*, pg. 1995
TELEDYNE RD INSTRUMENTS, INC.—See Teledyne Technologies Incorporated; *U.S. Public*, pg. 1994
TELEDYNE RD TECHNOLOGIES (SHANGHAI) CO., LTD.—See Teledyne Technologies Incorporated; *U.S. Public*, pg. 1994
TELEDYNE REAL TIME SYSTEMS INC.—See Teledyne Technologies Incorporated; *U.S. Public*, pg. 1995
TELEDYNE RESON A/S—See Teledyne Technologies Incorporated; *U.S. Public*, pg. 1994
TELEDYNE RESON B.V.—See Teledyne Technologies Incorporated; *U.S. Public*, pg. 1995
TELEDYNE RESON GMBH—See Teledyne Technologies Incorporated; *U.S. Public*, pg. 1995
TELEDYNE RESON, INC.—See Teledyne Technologies Incorporated; *U.S. Public*, pg. 1995
TELEDYNE REYNOLDS INC.—See Teledyne Technologies Incorporated; *U.S. Public*, pg. 1995
TELEDYNE REYNOLDS UK—See Teledyne Technologies Incorporated; *U.S. Public*, pg. 1995
TELEDYNE RISI, INC.—See Teledyne Technologies Incorporated; *U.S. Public*, pg. 1995
TELEDYNE SCIENTIFIC & IMAGING, LLC—See Teledyne Technologies Incorporated; *U.S. Public*, pg. 1995
TELEDYNE SEABOTIX INC.—See Teledyne Technologies Incorporated; *U.S. Public*, pg. 1995
TELEDYNE SIGNAL PROCESSING DEVICES SWEDEN AB—See Teledyne Technologies Incorporated; *U.S. Public*, pg. 1995
TELEDYNE STORM CABLE—See Teledyne Technologies Incorporated; *U.S. Public*, pg. 1995
TELEDYNE TAPTONE—See Teledyne Technologies Incorporated; *U.S. Public*, pg. 1993
TELEDYNE TECHNOLOGIES INCORPORATED; *U.S. Public*, pg. 1992
TELEDYNE TEKMAR—See Teledyne Technologies Incorporated; *U.S. Public*, pg. 1995
TELEDYNE TSS LIMITED—See Teledyne Technologies Incorporated; *U.S. Public*, pg. 1995
TELEDYNE VARISYSTEMS, INC.—See Teledyne Technologies Incorporated; *U.S. Public*, pg. 1995
TELEFACT S.A.—See Orange S.A.; *Int'l*, pg. 5611
TELEFERICOS DOPPELMAYR BOLIVIA S.A.—See Doppelmayr Group; *Int'l*, pg. 2175
TELEFIELD INC. - SEONGNAM FACTORY—See TELEFIELD Inc.; *Int'l*, pg. 7530
TELEFIELD INC.; *Int'l*, pg. 7530
TELEFIELD LIMITED—See Link-Asia International MedTech Group Limited; *Int'l*, pg. 4514
TELEFIELD NA, INC.—See Link-Asia International MedTech Group Limited; *Int'l*, pg. 4514
TELEFLEX FUNDING CORPORATION—See Teleflex Incorporated; *U.S. Public*, pg. 1995
TELEFLEX GRUNDSTUCKS GMBH & CO. KG—See Teleflex Incorporated; *U.S. Public*, pg. 1995
TELEFLEX INCORPORATED - LIMERICK—See Teleflex Incorporated; *U.S. Public*, pg. 1995
TELEFLEX INCORPORATED; *U.S. Public*, pg. 1995
TELEFLEX MEDICAL ASIA PTE LTD.—See Teleflex Incorporated; *U.S. Public*, pg. 1996
TELEFLEX MEDICAL AUSTRALIA PTY LTD—See Teleflex Incorporated; *U.S. Public*, pg. 1995
TELEFLEX MEDICAL BV—See Teleflex Incorporated; *U.S. Public*, pg. 1996
TELEFLEX MEDICAL CANADA INC.—See Teleflex Incorporated; *U.S. Public*, pg. 1996
TELEFLEX MEDICAL COLOMBIA SAS—See Teleflex Incorporated; *U.S. Public*, pg. 1995
TELEFLEX MEDICAL DE MEXICO, S. DE R.L. DE C.V.—See Teleflex Incorporated; *U.S. Public*, pg. 1996
TELEFLEX MEDICAL EDC BVBA—See Teleflex Incorporated; *U.S. Public*, pg. 1996
TELEFLEX MEDICAL EUROPE LIMITED—See Teleflex Incorporated; *U.S. Public*, pg. 1996
TELEFLEX MEDICAL GMBH—See Teleflex Incorporated; *U.S. Public*, pg. 1995
TELEFLEX MEDICAL GROUP—See Teleflex Incorporated; *U.S. Public*, pg. 1995
TELEFLEX MEDICAL HELLAS A.E.E.—See Teleflex Incorporated; *U.S. Public*, pg. 1996
TELEFLEX MEDICAL IBERIA S.A.—See Teleflex Incorporated; *U.S. Public*, pg. 1996
TELEFLEX MEDICAL INCORPORATED—See Teleflex Incorporated; *U.S. Public*, pg. 1996
TELEFLEX MEDICAL JAPAN, LTD.—See Teleflex Incorporated; *U.S. Public*, pg. 1996
TELEFLEX MEDICAL PRIVATE LIMITED—See Teleflex Incorporated; *U.S. Public*, pg. 1996
TELEFLEX MEDICAL (PROPRIETARY) LIMITED—See Teleflex Incorporated; *U.S. Public*, pg. 1996
TELEFLEX MEDICAL SAS—See Teleflex Incorporated; *U.S. Public*, pg. 1996
TELEFLEX MEDICAL S.R.L.—See Teleflex Incorporated; *U.S. Public*, pg. 1996

TELEFLEX INCORPORATED

TELEFLEX MEDICAL, S.R.O.—See Teleflex Incorporated; *U.S. Public*, pg. 1996
TELEFLEX MEDICAL, S.R.O.—See Teleflex Incorporated; *U.S. Public*, pg. 1996
TELEFLEX MEDICAL TUTTLINGEN GMBH—See Teleflex Incorporated; *U.S. Public*, pg. 1996
TELEFLEX SWISS HOLDING GMBH—See Teleflex Incorporated; *U.S. Public*, pg. 1996
TELEFLIGHT LIMITED—See International Consolidated Airlines Group S.A.; *Int'l*, pg. 3746
TELEFLORA LLC—See The Wonderful Company LLC; *U.S. Private*, pg. 4138
TELEFON AB LM ERICSSON LIBYA BRANCH—See Telefonaktiebolaget LM Ericsson; *Int'l*, pg. 7534
TELEFON AB LM ERICSSON—See Telefonaktiebolaget LM Ericsson; *Int'l*, pg. 7534
TELEFON AB LM ERICSSON—See Telefonaktiebolaget LM Ericsson; *Int'l*, pg. 7534
TELEFONAKTIEBOLAGET LM ERICSSON; *Int'l*, pg. 7530
TELEFONBAU MARIENFELD GMBH & CO. KG—See Salzgitter AG; *Int'l*, pg. 6499
TELEFONIA DIALOG S.A.—See Cyfrowy Polsat S.A.; *Int'l*, pg. 1895
TELEFONICA BRASIL S.A.—See Telefonica, S.A.; *Int'l*, pg. 7535
TELEFONICA CHILE S.A.—See Telefonica, S.A.; *Int'l*, pg. 7535
TELEFONICA DE ARGENTINA S.A.—See Telefonica, S.A.; *Int'l*, pg. 7536
TELEFONICA DE ESPANA, S.A.U.—See Telefonica, S.A.; *Int'l*, pg. 7536
TELEFONICA DE ESPANA, S.A.U. - TERRA NETWORKS GROUP—See Telefonica, S.A.; *Int'l*, pg. 7536
TELEFONICA DEL PERU S.A.A.—See Telefonica, S.A.; *Int'l*, pg. 7536
TELEFONICA DEUTSCHLAND HOLDING AG—See Telefonica, S.A.; *Int'l*, pg. 7535
TELEFONICA DIGITAL LIMITED—See Telefonica, S.A.; *Int'l*, pg. 7535
TELEFONICA ENGENHARIA DE SEGURANCA—See Telefonica, S.A.; *Int'l*, pg. 7535
TELEFONICA EUROPE, B.V.—See Telefonica, S.A.; *Int'l*, pg. 7535
TELEFONICA EUROPE PLC—See Telefonica, S.A.; *Int'l*, pg. 7535
TELEFONICA FINANZAS, S.A.U.—See Telefonica, S.A.; *Int'l*, pg. 7536
TELEFONICA GERMANY GMBH & CO. OHG—See Telefonica, S.A.; *Int'l*, pg. 7535
TELEFONICA HOLDING DE ARGENTINA S.A.—See Telefonica, S.A.; *Int'l*, pg. 7536
TELEFONICA INSURANCE S.A.—See Telefonica, S.A.; *Int'l*, pg. 7535
TELEFONICA INTERNACIONAL INTERNACIONAL S.A.U.—See Telefonica, S.A.; *Int'l*, pg. 7536
TELEFONICA INTERNATIONAL WHOLESALE SERVICES AMERICA, S.A.—See Telefonica, S.A.; *Int'l*, pg. 7536
TELEFONICA INTERNATIONAL WHOLESALE SERVICES ARGENTINA, S.A.—See Telefonica, S.A.; *Int'l*, pg. 7536
TELEFONICA INTERNATIONAL WHOLESALE SERVICES BRASIL PARTICIPACOES, LTD.—See Telefonica, S.A.; *Int'l*, pg. 7536
TELEFONICA INTERNATIONAL WHOLESALE SERVICES PERU, S.A.C.—See Telefonica, S.A.; *Int'l*, pg. 7536
TELEFONICA INTERNATIONAL WHOLESALE SERVICES USA, INC.—See Telefonica, S.A.; *Int'l*, pg. 7536
TELEFONICA INVESTIGACION Y DESARROLLO, S.A.—See Telefonica, S.A.; *Int'l*, pg. 7536
TELEFONICA LEARNING SERVICES, S.L.—See Telefonica, S.A.; *Int'l*, pg. 7536
TELEFONICA MOVILES GUATEMALA, S.A.—See America Movil, S.A.B. de C.V.; *Int'l*, pg. 421
TELEFONICA MOVILES MEXICO, S.A. DE C.V.—See Telefonica, S.A.; *Int'l*, pg. 7536
TELEFONICA MOVILES PANAMA, S.A.—See Telefonica, S.A.; *Int'l*, pg. 7536
TELEFONICA MOVILES SOLUCIONES Y APLICACIONES, S.A.—See Telefonica, S.A.; *Int'l*, pg. 7535
TELEFONICA, S.A.; *Int'l*, pg. 7535
TELEFONICA SERVICIOS AUDIOVISUALES, S.A.U.—See Telefonica, S.A.; *Int'l*, pg. 7535
TELEFONICA SERVICOS EMPRESARIAIS DO BRASIL, LTDA.—See Telefonica, S.A.; *Int'l*, pg. 7535
TELEFONICA SOLUCIONES SECTORIALES, S.A.U.—See Telefonica, S.A.; *Int'l*, pg. 7536
TELEFONICA TECH S.L.U.—See Telefonica, S.A.; *Int'l*, pg. 7536
TELEFONICA TECH UK LIMITED—See Telefonica, S.A.; *Int'l*, pg. 7536
TELEFONICA TELECOMUNICACIONES PUBLICAS, S.A.U.—See Telefonica, S.A.; *Int'l*, pg. 7536
TELEFONICA UK LIMITED—See Liberty Global plc; *Int'l*, pg. 4485
TELEFONICA UK LIMITED—See Telefonica, S.A.; *Int'l*, pg. 7536
TELEFONICA USA INC.—See Telefonica, S.A.; *Int'l*, pg. 7536

TELEFONIJA BRCKO D.O.O.—See P.S. Telefonija a.d. Beograd; *Int'l*, pg. 5682
TELE-FONIKA CABLE AMERICAS CORPORATION—See TELE-FONIKA Kable Sp. z o.o. S.K.A.; *Int'l*, pg. 7528
TELE-FONIKA FRANCE SA—See TELE-FONIKA Kable Sp. z o.o. S.K.A.; *Int'l*, pg. 7528
TELE-FONIKA KABELY CZ S.R.O.—See TELE-FONIKA Kable Sp. z o.o. S.K.A.; *Int'l*, pg. 7528
TELE-FONIKA KABLE GMBH—See TELE-FONIKA Kable Sp. z o.o. S.K.A.; *Int'l*, pg. 7528
TELE-FONIKA KABLE HANDEL S.A.—See TELE-FONIKA Kable Sp. z o.o. S.K.A.; *Int'l*, pg. 7528
TELE FONIKA KABLE S.A. - BYDGOSZCZ FACTORY—See TELE-FONIKA Kable Sp. z o.o. S.K.A.; *Int'l*, pg. 7528
TELE FONIKA KABLE S.A. - CHERNIHIV FACTORY—See TELE-FONIKA Kable Sp. z o.o. S.K.A.; *Int'l*, pg. 7528
TELE FONIKA KABLE S.A. - KRAKOW-BIEZANOW FACTORY—See TELE-FONIKA Kable Sp. z o.o. S.K.A.; *Int'l*, pg. 7529
TELE FONIKA KABLE S.A. - KRAKOW-WIELICKA FACTORY—See TELE-FONIKA Kable Sp. z o.o. S.K.A.; *Int'l*, pg. 7529
TELE FONIKA KABLE S.A. - MYSLENICE FACTORY—See TELE-FONIKA Kable Sp. z o.o. S.K.A.; *Int'l*, pg. 7529
TELE FONIKA KABLE S.A. - TOW TF KABEL UKRAINE PLANT—See TELE-FONIKA Kable Sp. z o.o. S.K.A.; *Int'l*, pg. 7529
TELE FONIKA KABLE S.A. - ZAJECAR FACTORY—See TELE-FONIKA Kable Sp. z o.o. S.K.A.; *Int'l*, pg. 7529
TELE-FONIKA KABLE SP. Z O.O. S.K.A.; *Int'l*, pg. 7528
TELEFONKABL A.D.; *Int'l*, pg. 7537
TELEFONKATALOGENS GULE SIDER AS—See Eniro Group AB; *Int'l*, pg. 2439
TELEFONOS DE MEXICO S.A.B. DE C.V.—See America Movil, S.A.B. de C.V.; *Int'l*, pg. 421
TELEFON-SERVICEGESELLSCHAFT DER DEUTSCHEN BANK MBH—See Deutsche Bank Aktiengesellschaft; *Int'l*, pg. 2062
TELEFUNKEN RADIO COMMUNICATIONS SYSTEMS GMBH—See Elbit Systems Limited; *Int'l*, pg. 2345
TELEFUUSIO OY—See Instalco AB; *Int'l*, pg. 3722
TELEGAMES INC.; *U.S. Private*, pg. 3960
TELEGENIA, S.L—See LOV Group Invest SAS; *Int'l*, pg. 4565
TELEGENIX INC.—See Indel, Inc.; *U.S. Private*, pg. 2055
TELEGESIS (UK) LIMITED—See Silicon Laboratories Inc.; *U.S. Public*, pg. 1880
TELEGRAAF MEDIA NEDERLAND—See Mediahuis Partners NV; *Int'l*, pg. 4772
TELEGRAAF MEDIA NEDERLAND—See VP Exploitatie N.V.; *Int'l*, pg. 8312
TELEGRAPH HILL PARTNERS MANAGEMENT COMPANY, LLC; *U.S. Private*, pg. 3960
TELE GREENLAND A/S; *Int'l*, pg. 7528
TELE GREENLAND INTERNATIONAL A/S—See TELE Greenland A/S; *Int'l*, pg. 7528
TELE GROUP CORP.; *U.S. Public*, pg. 1992
TELEGUAM HOLDINGS, LLC—See Huntsman Family Investments, LLC; *U.S. Private*, pg. 2011
TELEHOUSE BEIJING CO. LTD.—See KDDI Corporation; *Int'l*, pg. 4112
TELEHOUSE INTERNATIONAL CORP OF AMERICA—See KDDI Corporation; *Int'l*, pg. 4112
TELEHOUSE INTERNATIONAL CORPORATION OF EUROPE LTD.—See KDDI Corporation; *Int'l*, pg. 4112
TELE-IMAGES INC.—See Gonzales Consulting Services, Inc.; *U.S. Private*, pg. 1737
TELEINFO MEDIA PUBLIC COMPANY LIMITED—See Advanced Info Service Plc; *Int'l*, pg. 160
TELEINFORMATICA Y COMUNICACIONES, S.A.—See Telefonica, S.A.; *Int'l*, pg. 7536
TELEINVENTION SP. Z O.O.—See Unima 2000 Systemy Teleinformatyczne S.A.; *Int'l*, pg. 8048
TELEION CONSULTING LLC; *U.S. Private*, pg. 3960
TELEKOM APPLIED BUSINESS SDN. BHD.—See Telekom Malaysia Berhad; *Int'l*, pg. 7537
TELEKOM AUSTRIA AG—See America Movil, S.A.B. de C.V.; *Int'l*, pg. 421
TELEKOM AUSTRIA TA AKTIENGESELLSCHAFT—See America Movil, S.A.B. de C.V.; *Int'l*, pg. 421
TELEKOM DEUTSCHLAND GMBH—See Deutsche Telekom AG; *Int'l*, pg. 2084
TELEKOM FINANZMANAGEMENT GMBH—See America Movil, S.A.B. de C.V.; *Int'l*, pg. 421
TELEKOM INTERNATIONAL (L) LTD.—See Telekom Malaysia Berhad; *Int'l*, pg. 7537
TELEKOM MALAYSIA (AUSTRALIA) PTY. LTD.—See Telekom Malaysia Berhad; *Int'l*, pg. 7537
TELEKOM MALAYSIA BERHAD; *Int'l*, pg. 7537
TELEKOM MALAYSIA DMCC—See Telekom Malaysia Berhad; *Int'l*, pg. 7537
TELEKOM MALAYSIA (HONG KONG) LIMITED—See Telekom Malaysia Berhad; *Int'l*, pg. 7537
TELEKOM MALAYSIA INTERNATIONAL (CAMBODIA) CO. LTD.—See Axiata Group Berhad; *Int'l*, pg. 768
TELEKOM MALAYSIA (S) PTE LTD—See Telekom Malaysia Berhad; *Int'l*, pg. 7537

CORPORATE AFFILIATIONS

TELEKOM MALAYSIA (UK) LIMITED—See Telekom Malaysia Berhad; *Int'l*, pg. 7537
TELEKOM MALAYSIA (USA) INC—See Telekom Malaysia Berhad; *Int'l*, pg. 7537
TELEKOM NETWORKS MALAWI LIMITED—See Telekom Malaysia Berhad; *Int'l*, pg. 7537
TELEKOM PROJEKTENTWICKLUNGS GMBH—See America Movil, S.A.B. de C.V.; *Int'l*, pg. 421
TELEKOM RESEARCH AND DEVELOPMENT SDN BHD—See Telekom Malaysia Berhad; *Int'l*, pg. 7537
TELEKOM SALES & SERVICES SDN. BHD.—See Telekom Malaysia Berhad; *Int'l*, pg. 7537
TELEKOM SLOVENIJE, D.D.; *Int'l*, pg. 7537
TELEKOM SRBIJA AD; *Int'l*, pg. 7538
TELEKOM SRPSKE A.D.; *Int'l*, pg. 7538
TELEKOMUNIKACIJE REPUBLIKE SRPSKE A.D.; *Int'l*, pg. 7538
TELEKOMUNIKACJA POLSKA—See Orange S.A.; *Int'l*, pg. 5611
TELEKOMUNIKASI INDONESIA INTERNATIONAL AUSTRALIA PTY. LTD.—See Perusahaan Perseroan Indonesia Tbk; *Int'l*, pg. 5822
TELEKOMUNIKASI INDONESIA INTERNATIONAL INC.—See Perusahaan Perseroan Indonesia Tbk; *Int'l*, pg. 5822
TELEKOMUNIKASI INDONESIA INTERNATIONAL LTD.—See Perusahaan Perseroan Indonesia Tbk; *Int'l*, pg. 5822
TELEKOMUNIKASI INDONESIA INTERNATIONAL (MALAYSIA) SDN. BHD.—See Perusahaan Perseroan Indonesia Tbk; *Int'l*, pg. 5822
TELEKOMUNIKASI INDONESIA INTERNATIONAL S.A.—See Perusahaan Perseroan Indonesia Tbk; *Int'l*, pg. 5822
TELEKOMUNIKASI INDONESIA INTL (MALAYSIA) SDN. BHD.—See Perusahaan Perseroan Indonesia Tbk; *Int'l*, pg. 5822
TELELANGUAGE INC.—See Leonard Green & Partners, L.P.; *U.S. Private*, pg. 2428
TELELANGUAGE INC.—See TTCP Management Services, LLC; *U.S. Private*, pg. 4254
TELELATINO NETWORK INC.—See Corus Entertainment Inc.; *Int'l*, pg. 1809
TELELEASING S.P.A.—See Mediobanca-Banca de Credito Finanziario S.p.A.; *Int'l*, pg. 4778
TELELINK SERVICES INC.—See FirstService Corporation; *Int'l*, pg. 2691
TELE M1 AG—See BT Holding AG; *Int'l*, pg. 1204
TELEMA & BERGER RESISTORS, INC.—See Telema S.p.A; *Int'l*, pg. 7538
TELEMAC, S.A.—See Nova Ventures Group Corp.; *U.S. Private*, pg. 2966
TELEMANTENIMIENTO DE ALTA TENSION, SL—See Schneider Electric SE; *Int'l*, pg. 6635
TELEMARKETING ASIA (SINGAPORE) PTE LTD—See Teleperformance SE; *Int'l*, pg. 7540
TELEMARKETING CO., INC.—See TTC Marketing Solutions; *U.S. Private*, pg. 4254
TELEMARKETING (TMS)—See Vivendi SE; *Int'l*, pg. 8274
TELEMARKET SIA—See Alma Media Corporation; *Int'l*, pg. 361
TELEMAR NORTE LESTE S.A.—See Oi S.A.; *Int'l*, pg. 5533
TELEMA S.P.A; *Int'l*, pg. 7538
TELEMASTERS HOLDINGS LIMITED; *Int'l*, pg. 7538
TELEMAST NORDIC OY—See NRJ Group SA; *Int'l*, pg. 5474
TELEMATCH BV—See Koninklijke KPN N.V.; *Int'l*, pg. 4267
TELEMATIC SOLUTIONS S.R.L.—See VINCI S.A.; *Int'l*, pg. 8229
TELE-MEDIA CORPORATION; *U.S. Private*, pg. 3959
TELEMEDIA FREE ZONE LIMITED—See Belize Telecommunications Limited; *Int'l*, pg. 965
TELEMED ONLINE SERVICE FUR HEILBERUFE GMBH—See CompuGroup Medical SE & Co. KGaA; *Int'l*, pg. 1757
TELEMEDX CORP.—See Ancor Holdings, L.P.; *U.S. Private*, pg. 275
TELEMESSAGING SERVICES INC.; *U.S. Private*, pg. 3960
TELEMETRY INC—See Telemetry Ltd.; *Int'l*, pg. 7538
TELEMETRY LTD.; *Int'l*, pg. 7538
TELEMOS CAPITAL; *Int'l*, pg. 7538
TELE MUNCHEN FERNSEH GMBH + CO. PRODUKTIONSGESELLSCHAFT; *Int'l*, pg. 7528
TELEMUNDO 314 REDWOOD LLC—See Comcast Corporation; *U.S. Public*, pg. 541
TELEMUNDO LAS VEGAS LLC—See Comcast Corporation; *U.S. Public*, pg. 541
TELEMUNDO NETWORK LLC—See Comcast Corporation; *U.S. Public*, pg. 540
TELEMUNDO OF ARIZONA LLC—See Comcast Corporation; *U.S. Public*, pg. 542
TELEMUNDO OF CHICAGO LLC—See Comcast Corporation; *U.S. Public*, pg. 542
TELEMUNDO OF DENVER LLC—See Comcast Corporation; *U.S. Public*, pg. 542

COMPANY NAME INDEX

TELEMUNDO OF FRESNO LLC—See Comcast Corporation; *U.S. Public*, pg. 542
TELEMUNDO OF NEW ENGLAND LLC—See Comcast Corporation; *U.S. Public*, pg. 542
TELEMUNDO OF NEW MEXICO LLC—See Comcast Corporation; *U.S. Public*, pg. 542
TELEMUNDO OF NORTHERN CALIFORNIA LLC—See Comcast Corporation; *U.S. Public*, pg. 542
TELEMUNDO OF PUERTO RICO LLC—See Comcast Corporation; *U.S. Public*, pg. 542
TELEMUNDO OF SAN DIEGO LLC—See Comcast Corporation; *U.S. Public*, pg. 542
TELEMUNDO RIO GRANDE VALLEY, LLC—See Comcast Corporation; *U.S. Public*, pg. 541
TELEMUS CAPITAL PARTNERS, LLC—See Clayton, Dubilier & Rice, LLC; *U.S. Private*, pg. 923
TELEMUS CAPITAL PARTNERS, LLC—See Stone Point Capital LLC; *U.S. Private*, pg. 3824
TELENAV DO BRASIL SERVICOS DE LOCALIZACAO LTDA.—See Telenav, Inc.; *U.S. Private*, pg. 3960
TELENAV GMBH—See Telenav, Inc.; *U.S. Private*, pg. 3960
TELENAV, INC.; *U.S. Private*, pg. 3960
TELENAV KOREA, LIMITED—See Telenav, Inc.; *U.S. Private*, pg. 3961
TELENERGIA S.R.L.—See TIM S.p.A.; *Int'l*, pg. 7750
TELENE S.A.S.—See Zeon Corporation; *Int'l*, pg. 8635
TELENET BVBA—See Liberty Global plc; *Int'l*, pg. 4485
TELENET GROUP HOLDING NV—See Liberty Global plc; *Int'l*, pg. 4485
TELENET GROUP PLLC—See Liberty Global plc; *Int'l*, pg. 4485
TELENET MOBILE NV—See Liberty Global plc; *Int'l*, pg. 4485
TELENET NV—See Liberty Global plc; *Int'l*, pg. 4485
TELENEXT MEDIA—See Publicis Groupe S.A.; *Int'l*, pg. 6112
TELENIA S.R.L.—See Retelit S.p.A.; *Int'l*, pg. 6306
TELENOR AB—See Telenor ASA; *Int'l*, pg. 7539
TELENOR ASA; *Int'l*, pg. 7538
TELENOR BROADCAST HOLDING AS—See Telenor ASA; *Int'l*, pg. 7539
TELENOR CONNEXION AB—See Telenor ASA; *Int'l*, pg. 7539
TELENOR DENMARK HOLDING A/S—See Telenor ASA; *Int'l*, pg. 7539
TELENOR EIENDOM FORNEBU KVARTAL 3 AS—See Telenor ASA; *Int'l*, pg. 7539
TELENOR INTERNATIONAL AS—See Telenor ASA; *Int'l*, pg. 7539
TELENOR KAPITALFORVALTNING ASA—See Telenor ASA; *Int'l*, pg. 7539
TELENOR LINX AS—See Telenor ASA; *Int'l*, pg. 7539
TELENOR MARITIME AS—See Telenor ASA; *Int'l*, pg. 7539
TELENOR MOBIL AS—See Telenor ASA; *Int'l*, pg. 7539
TELENOR NETT AS—See Telenor ASA; *Int'l*, pg. 7539
TELENOR OBJECTS AS—See Telenor ASA; *Int'l*, pg. 7539
TELENOR PLUS AS—See Telenor ASA; *Int'l*, pg. 7539
TELENOR PROGRAMVARE AS—See Telenor ASA; *Int'l*, pg. 7539
TELENOR SATELLITE AS—See Space Norway AS; *Int'l*, pg. 7123
TELENOR SATELLITE—See Telenor ASA; *Int'l*, pg. 7539
TELENOR SVERIGE AB—See Telenor ASA; *Int'l*, pg. 7539
TELENOR TRAXION AB—See Telenor ASA; *Int'l*, pg. 7539
TELENOR UK LTD.—See Telenor ASA; *Int'l*, pg. 7539
TELENOR VENTURE VI AS—See Telenor ASA; *Int'l*, pg. 7539
TELENOR VENTURE VII AS—See Telenor ASA; *Int'l*, pg. 7539
TELENT GMBH—See Zech Group SE; *Int'l*, pg. 8628
TELENT LIMITED; *Int'l*, pg. 7539
TELENT—See Telent Limited; *Int'l*, pg. 7539
TELEO CAPITAL MANAGEMENT, LLC; *U.S. Private*, pg. 3961
TELEON SURGICAL VERTRIEBS GMBH—See Gaush Meditech Ltd.; *Int'l*, pg. 2891
TELE-OPTICS INC.; *U.S. Private*, pg. 3960
TELEPAK NETWORKS, INC.—See Telapex Inc.; *U.S. Private*, pg. 3959
TELE-PAPER (M) SDN. BHD.—See Oji Holdings Corporation; *Int'l*, pg. 5538
TELEPART TAMURA INDUSTRIA E COMERCIO LTDA—See Tamura Corporation; *Int'l*, pg. 7452
TELEPASS PAY SPA—See Edizione S.r.l.; *Int'l*, pg. 2312
TELEPAYROLL, INC.—See Asure Software, Inc.; *U.S. Public*, pg. 218
TELEPERFORMANCE CRM SA—See Teleperformance SE; *Int'l*, pg. 7540
TELEPERFORMANCE CZ, A. S.—See Teleperformance SE; *Int'l*, pg. 7540
TELEPERFORMANCE DANEMARK AS—See Teleperformance SE; *Int'l*, pg. 7540
TELEPERFORMANCE DEBTORS INFORMATION SERVICES—See Teleperformance SE; *Int'l*, pg. 7540
TELEPERFORMANCE DENMARK A/S—See Teleperformance SE; *Int'l*, pg. 7540

TELEPERFORMANCE EMEA—See Teleperformance SE; *Int'l*, pg. 7540
TELEPERFORMANCE FINLAND OY—See Teleperformance SE; *Int'l*, pg. 7540
TELEPERFORMANCE FRANCE SAS—See Teleperformance SE; *Int'l*, pg. 7540
TELEPERFORMANCE GROUP INC.—See Teleperformance SE; *Int'l*, pg. 7540
TELEPERFORMANCE LEBANON SAL—See Teleperformance SE; *Int'l*, pg. 7540
TELEPERFORMANCE NORDIC AB—See Teleperformance SE; *Int'l*, pg. 7540
TELEPERFORMANCE NORGE AS—See Teleperformance SE; *Int'l*, pg. 7540
TELEPERFORMANCE POLSKA—See Teleperformance SE; *Int'l*, pg. 7540
TELEPERFORMANCE RUSSIA—See Teleperformance SE; *Int'l*, pg. 7541
TELEPERFORMANCE SE; *Int'l*, pg. 7539
TELEPERFORMANCE UK LTD—See Teleperformance SE; *Int'l*, pg. 7541
TELEPERFORMANCE UNTERNEHMUNGSBEATUNG GMBH—See Teleperformance SE; *Int'l*, pg. 7541
TELEPERFORMANCE USA—See Teleperformance SE; *Int'l*, pg. 7541
TELEPHARM, LLC—See Cardinal Health, Inc.; *U.S. Public*, pg. 434
TELEPHONE CABLES LTD.; *Int'l*, pg. 7541
THE TELEPHONE CENTRE, INC.; *U.S. Private*, pg. 4126
TELEPHONE & DATA SYSTEMS, INC.; *U.S. Public*, pg. 1996
TELEPHONE ELECTRONICS CORPORATION; *U.S. Private*, pg. 3961
TELEPHONE INDUSTRIES OF PAKISTAN (PVT) LTD.—See Pakistan Telecommunication Company Limited; *Int'l*, pg. 5705
TELEPHONE SERVICE CO.; *U.S. Private*, pg. 3961
TELEPHONE SERVICES INC.; *U.S. Private*, pg. 3961
TELEPHONE USA OF WISCONSIN, LLC—See Lumen Technologies, Inc.; *U.S. Public*, pg. 1348
TELEPHONICS CORPORATION—See TTM Technologies, Inc.; *U.S. Public*, pg. 2203
TELEPHONICS SWEDEN AB—See TTM Technologies, Inc.; *U.S. Public*, pg. 2203
TELEPHONY PARTNERS LLC; *U.S. Private*, pg. 3961
TELEPICTURES PRODUCTION INC.—See Warner Bros. Discovery, Inc.; *U.S. Public*, pg. 2328
TELEPIZZA GROUP SA; *Int'l*, pg. 7541
TELEPLAN CENTRAL EUROPE HOLDING B.V.—See Clover Wireless; *U.S. Private*, pg. 948
TELEPLAN COLCHESTER LTD.—See Clover Wireless; *U.S. Private*, pg. 948
TELEPLAN COMMUNICATIONS B.V.—See Clover Wireless; *U.S. Private*, pg. 948
TELEPLAN COMMUNICATIONS HOLDING B.V.—See Clover Wireless; *U.S. Private*, pg. 948
TELEPLAN ELECTRONIC TECHNOLOGY (SHANGHAI) CO. LTD.—See Clover Wireless; *U.S. Private*, pg. 948
TELEPLAN GERMANY GMBH—See Clover Wireless; *U.S. Private*, pg. 948
TELEPLAN INTERNATIONAL N.V.—See Clover Wireless; *U.S. Private*, pg. 947
TELEPLAN POLSKA SP. Z O.O.—See Clover Wireless; *U.S. Private*, pg. 948
TELEPLAN RHEIN-MAIN GMBH—See Clover Wireless; *U.S. Private*, pg. 948
TELEPLAN TECHNOLOGY SERVICES SDN BHD—See Clover Wireless; *U.S. Private*, pg. 948
TELEPLAN VIDEOCOM SOLUTIONS, INC.—See Clover Wireless; *U.S. Private*, pg. 948
TELEPLAN & WHITE ELECTRONICS B.V.—See Clover Wireless; *U.S. Private*, pg. 947
TELE PLASTIC, C.A.; *Int'l*, pg. 7528
TELEPOOL GMBH; *Int'l*, pg. 7541
TELEPORT COMMUNICATIONS AMERICA, LLC—See AT&T Inc.; *U.S. Public*, pg. 220
TELEPRO PTY LIMITED—See Seven West Media Limited; *Int'l*, pg. 6734
TELEPROVIDERS INC.; *U.S. Private*, pg. 3961
TELEQUALITY COMMUNICATIONS LLC—See ZelnickMedia Corp.; *U.S. Private*, pg. 4600
TELEQUERY.NET, INC.; *U.S. Private*, pg. 3961
TELEQUOTE DATA INTERNATIONAL LIMITED—See Frontier Services Group Limited; *Int'l*, pg. 2796
TELEREACH, INC.—See Aquiline Capital Partners LLC; *U.S. Private*, pg. 305
TELEREAL SERVICES LIMITED—See The William Pears Group of Companies Limited; *Int'l*, pg. 7701
TELE RED IMAGEN S.A.—See Grupo Clarin S.A.; *Int'l*, pg. 3125
TELERENT LEASING CORPORATION—See ITOCHU Corporation; *Int'l*, pg. 3839
TELEREP, LLC—See Apollo Global Management, Inc.; *U.S. Public*, pg. 164
TELERESOURCES CONSULTANCY LTD.—See Randstad N.V.; *Int'l*, pg. 6205
TELE RESOURCES, INC.; *U.S. Private*, pg. 3959
TELERESOURCES (PTY) LTD.—See Workforce Holdings Ltd.; *Int'l*, pg. 8456

TELESTE CORPORATION

TELEREX NEDERLAND B.V.—See P-Duke Technology Co., Ltd.; *Int'l*, pg. 5682
TELEREX N.V.—See P-Duke Technology Co., Ltd.; *Int'l*, pg. 5682
TELERHYTHMICS, LLC—See G Medical Innovations Holdings Ltd.; *Int'l*, pg. 2861
TELERIK INDIA PRIVATE LIMITED—See Progress Software Corporation; *U.S. Public*, pg. 1726
TELERIK UK LTD.—See Progress Software Corporation; *U.S. Public*, pg. 1725
TELEROBOT LABS SRL—See Danieli & C. Officine Meccaniche S.p.A.; *Int'l*, pg. 1963
TELERX MARKETING, INC.—See HCL Technologies Ltd.; *Int'l*, pg. 3299
TELESAFE SDN. BHD.—See Telekom Malaysia Berhad; *Int'l*, pg. 7537
TELESAT CANADA—See Telesat Corporation; *Int'l*, pg. 7541
TELESAT CORPORATION; *Int'l*, pg. 7541
TELESAT PARTNERSHIP LP—See Telesat Corporation; *Int'l*, pg. 7541
TELESCIENCES (PTY) LTD.—See Jasco Electronics Holdings Limited; *Int'l*, pg. 3911
TELESCOPE CASUAL FURNITURE INC.; *U.S. Private*, pg. 3961
TELESCOPE UK LTD.—See Bally's Corporation; *U.S. Public*, pg. 268
TELESEARCH INC.; *U.S. Private*, pg. 3961
TELESENSORY CORPORATION—See Telesensory (S) Pte. Ltd.; *Int'l*, pg. 7541
TELESENSORY EUROPE LTD.—See Telesensory (S) Pte. Ltd.; *Int'l*, pg. 7541
TELESENSORY (S) PTE. LTD.; *Int'l*, pg. 7541
TELESERVICES DIRECT—See Career Horizons, Inc.; *U.S. Private*, pg. 752
TELESERVICES (MAURITIUS) LTD.—See Mauritius Telecom Ltd.; *Int'l*, pg. 4732
TELESIA S.P.A.—See Class Editori S.p.A.; *Int'l*, pg. 1652
TELESIGN CORPORATION—See Proximus PLC; *Int'l*, pg. 6008
TELESIS BIO, INC.; *U.S. Public*, pg. 1998
TELESIS CORPORATION; *U.S. Private*, pg. 3961
TELESIS TECHNOLOGIES INC.—See Bertram Capital Management, LLC; *U.S. Private*, pg. 540
TELESIS TECHNOLOGIES INC.—See Crimson Investment; *U.S. Private*, pg. 1100
TELESITES, S.A.B. DE C.V.; *Int'l*, pg. 7541
TELESOFT CORP.—See Sumeru Equity Partners LLC; *U.S. Private*, pg. 3852
TELESOFT TECHNOLOGIES INC.—See Telesoft Technologies Limited; *Int'l*, pg. 7541
TELESOFT TECHNOLOGIES LIMITED; *Int'l*, pg. 7541
TELESOFT TECHNOLOGIES LTD—See Telesoft Technologies Limited; *Int'l*, pg. 7541
TELESOURCE, INC.; *U.S. Private*, pg. 3961
TELESPAN NETWORK SERVICES, LLC—See Byers Engineering Company; *U.S. Private*, pg. 700
TELESPAZIO ARGENTINA S.A.—See Leonardo S.p.A.; *Int'l*, pg. 4461
TELESPAZIO DEUTSCHLAND GMBH—See Leonardo S.p.A.; *Int'l*, pg. 4461
TELESPAZIO IBERICA S.L.—See Leonardo S.p.A.; *Int'l*, pg. 4461
TELESPAZIO SPA—See Leonardo S.p.A.; *Int'l*, pg. 4461
TELESPAZIO VEGA DEUTSCHLAND GMBH—See Leonardo S.p.A.; *Int'l*, pg. 4461
TELESPAZIO VEGA UK LTD.—See Leonardo S.p.A.; *Int'l*, pg. 4461
TELESPHERE NETWORKS LTD.—See Telefonaktiebolaget LM Ericsson; *Int'l*, pg. 7534
TELESPHERE; *U.S. Private*, pg. 3961
TELESPHERE—See Telesphere; *U.S. Private*, pg. 3962
TELESPREE COMMUNICATIONS—See CCUR Holdings Inc.; *U.S. Public*, pg. 461
TELES PROPERTIES; *U.S. Private*, pg. 3961
TELESTACK, LIMITED—See Astec Industries, Inc.; *U.S. Public*, pg. 216
TELESTE CORPORATION; *Int'l*, pg. 7541
TELESTE D.O.O.—See Teleste Corporation; *Int'l*, pg. 7542
TELESTE GMBH—See Teleste Corporation; *Int'l*, pg. 7541
TELESTE INTERCEPT, LLC—See Teleste Corporation; *Int'l*, pg. 7542
TELESTE LLC—See Teleste Corporation; *Int'l*, pg. 7542
TELESTE NETWORKS SERVICES S.A.—See Teleste Corporation; *Int'l*, pg. 7542
TELESTE NETWORKS SP. Z O.O.—See Teleste Corporation; *Int'l*, pg. 7542
TELESTE NORGE A/S—See Teleste Corporation; *Int'l*, pg. 7542
TELESTE OYJ—See Teleste Corporation; *Int'l*, pg. 7542
TELESTEPS AB—See Investment AB Latour; *Int'l*, pg. 3784
TELESTE SERVICES GMBH—See Teleste Corporation; *Int'l*, pg. 7542
TELESTE SP. Z O.O.—See Teleste Corporation; *Int'l*, pg. 7542
TELESTE S.R.O.—See Teleste Corporation; *Int'l*, pg. 7542
TELESTE SWEDEN AB—See Teleste Corporation; *Int'l*, pg. 7542

TELESTE CORPORATION

Company Index

TELESTE SYSTEMS GMBH—See Teleste Corporation; *Int'l*, pg. 7542
TELESTE UK LTD—See Teleste Corporation; *Int'l*, pg. 7542
TELESTE VIDEO NETWORKS SP. Z O.O.—See Teleste Corporation; *Int'l*, pg. 7542
TELESTO COMMUNICATIONS (PTY) LTD—See Jasco Electronics Holdings Limited; *Int'l*, pg. 3911
TELESTO GROUP LLC; *U.S. Private*, pg. 3962
TELESTONE TECHNOLOGIES CORPORATION; *Int'l*, pg. 7542
TELESTREAM, LLC—See Genstar Capital, LLC; *U.S. Private*, pg. 1679
TELE-SYSTEM HARZ GMBH—See Morgan Stanley; *U.S. Public*, pg. 1473
TELETALK BANGLADESH LIMITED; *Int'l*, pg. 7542
TELE-TEC CONTRACTORS, INC.—See Frontier Communications Parent, Inc.; *U.S. Public*, pg. 887
TELETECH CUSTOMER CARE MANAGEMENT COSTA RICA, S.A.—See TTEC Holdings, Inc.; *U.S. Public*, pg. 2203
TELETECH GOVERNMENT SOLUTIONS, LLC—See TTEC Holdings, Inc.; *U.S. Public*, pg. 2203
TELETECH INTERNATIONAL PTY LTD—See TTEC Holdings, Inc.; *U.S. Public*, pg. 2203
TELETECH NORTH AMERICA—See TTEC Holdings, Inc.; *U.S. Public*, pg. 2203
TELE-TECTOR OF MARYLAND, INC.—See GTOR LLC; *U.S. Private*, pg. 1802
TELETEXT LIMITED—See Daily Mail & General Trust plc; *Int'l*, pg. 1938
TELE TIPS DIGITAL, S.A. DE C.V.—See Grupo Televisa, S.A.B.; *Int'l*, pg. 3136
TELETRACKING TECHNOLOGIES, INC.; *U.S. Private*, pg. 3962
TELETRACK, LLC—See Equifax Inc.; *U.S. Public*, pg. 787
TELETRAC NAVMAN—See Vontier Corporation; *U.S. Public*, pg. 2309
TELETRAC NAVMAN (UK) LTD.—See Vontier Corporation; *U.S. Public*, pg. 2309
TELETRAC NAVMAN US LTD.—See Vontier Corporation; *U.S. Public*, pg. 2309
TELETRANS SA—See CNTEE TRANSELECTRICA SA; *Int'l*, pg. 1679
TELETRONIC SERVICES INC.; *U.S. Private*, pg. 3962
TELETRONICS TECHNOLOGY CORP.—See Curtiss-Wright Corporation; *U.S. Public*, pg. 612
TELETYPOS S.A.; *Int'l*, pg. 7542
TELEVAS HOLDINGS SDN. BHD.—See FSBM Holdings Berhad; *Int'l*, pg. 2798
TELEVERBIER SA; *Int'l*, pg. 7542
TELEVICENTRO OF PUERTO RICO, LLC—See Hemisphere Media Group, Inc.; *U.S. Private*, pg. 1913
TELEVIMEX, S.A. DE C.V.—See Grupo Televisa, S.A.B.; *Int'l*, pg. 3136
TELEVISA CONSUMER PRODUCTS USA, LLC—See Grupo Televisa, S.A.B.; *Int'l*, pg. 3136
TELEVISA CORPORACION, S.A. DE C.V.—See Grupo Televisa, S.A.B.; *Int'l*, pg. 3137
TELEVISA ENTRETENIMIENTO, S.A. DE C.V.—See Grupo Televisa, S.A.B.; *Int'l*, pg. 3137
TELEVISA INTERNACIONAL, LLC—See Grupo Televisa, S.A.B.; *Int'l*, pg. 3137
TELEVISAT, S.A. DE C.V.—See Grupo Televisa, S.A.B.; *Int'l*, pg. 3137
TELEVISION AIRTIME SERVICES SDN. BHD.—See Pertama Digital Berhad; *Int'l*, pg. 5821
TELEVISION BROADCASTS LIMITED; *Int'l*, pg. 7542
TELEVISION FRANCAISE 1 S.A.; *Int'l*, pg. 7542
TELEVISION HOKKAIDO BROADCASTING CO., LTD.—See Nikkei Inc.; *Int'l*, pg. 5290
TELEVISION JAMAICA LIMITED—See Radio Jamaica Limited; *Int'l*, pg. 6176
TELEVISION OSAKA, INC.—See Nikkei Inc.; *Int'l*, pg. 5290
TELEVISIONSAKTIEBOLAGET TV8 AB—See Modern Times Group MTG AB; *Int'l*, pg. 5015
TELEVISION SATELITAL CODIFICADA S.A.—See AT&T Inc.; *U.S. Public*, pg. 220
TELEVISION TOKYO CHANNEL 12 LTD.—See Nikkei Inc.; *Int'l*, pg. 5290
TELEVISIONWEEK—See Crain Communications, Inc.; *U.S. Private*, pg. 1084
TELEVISORA DE MEXICALI, S.A. DE C.V.—See Grupo Televisa, S.A.B.; *Int'l*, pg. 3137
TELEVISORA DE OCCIDENTE, S.A. DE C.V.—See Grupo Televisa, S.A.B.; *Int'l*, pg. 3137
TELEVISORA PENINSULAR, S.A. DE C.V.—See Grupo Televisa, S.A.B.; *Int'l*, pg. 3137
TELEVISTA S.A.—See Warner Bros. Discovery, Inc.; *U.S. Public*, pg. 2327
TELEVIZIJA LESKOVAC A.D.; *Int'l*, pg. 7543
TELEVORGU AS—See Tele2 AB; *Int'l*, pg. 7529
TELEWARE PLC; *Int'l*, pg. 7543
TELEWIG; *Int'l*, pg. 7543
TELEWIZJA KABLOWA BRODNICA SP. Z O.O.—See Vectra S.A.; *Int'l*, pg. 8145
TELEWORLD SOLUTIONS, INC.—See Samsung Group; *Int'l*, pg. 6513

TELEZURI AG—See BT Holding AG; *Int'l*, pg. 1204
TELEZYGOLOGY, INC.—See TZ LIMITED; *Int'l*, pg. 7996
TELFA AB—See OEM International AB; *Int'l*, pg. 5528
TELFER OIL COMPANIES; *U.S. Private*, pg. 3962
TELFISA GLOBAL, B.V.—See Telefonica, S.A.; *Int'l*, pg. 7535
TELFORCEONE S.A.; *Int'l*, pg. 7543
TELFORD FOODS LTD.—See Brand Partnership Ltd.; *Int'l*, pg. 1139
TELFORD HOMES PLC—See CBRE Group, Inc.; *U.S. Public*, pg. 460
TELFORD INDUSTRIES PTE. LTD.—See ASTI Holdings Limited; *Int'l*, pg. 655
TELFORD SERVICE (MELAKA) SDN. BHD.—See ASTI Holdings Limited; *Int'l*, pg. 655
TELFORD SERVICE SDN. BHD.—See ASTI Holdings Limited; *Int'l*, pg. 655
TELFORDS (PORTLAOISE) LIMITED—See Grafton Group plc; *Int'l*, pg. 3051
TELFORD SVC. PHILS., INC.—See ASTI Holdings Limited; *Int'l*, pg. 655
TELFORD TECHNOLOGIES (SHANGHAI) PTE LTD—See ASTI Holdings Limited; *Int'l*, pg. 655
TELGIAN INC.; *U.S. Private*, pg. 3962
TELHIO CREDIT UNION; *U.S. Private*, pg. 3962
TELIA A/S—See Telia Company AB; *Int'l*, pg. 7544
TELIA CARRIER AB—See Fjarde AP-fonden; *Int'l*, pg. 2697
TELIA CARRIER AB—See Forsta AP-fonden; *Int'l*, pg. 2737
TELIA CARRIER AB—See Tredje AP-fonden; *Int'l*, pg. 7909
TELIA CARRIER CZECH REPUBLIC A.S.—See Telia Company AB; *Int'l*, pg. 7544
TELIA CARRIER DENMARK A/S—See Telia Company AB; *Int'l*, pg. 7544
TELIA CARRIER GERMANY GMBH—See Telia Company AB; *Int'l*, pg. 7544
TELIA CARRIER HUNGARY KFT—See Telia Company AB; *Int'l*, pg. 7544
TELIA CARRIER ITALY S.P.A.—See Telia Company AB; *Int'l*, pg. 7544
TELIA CARRIER NETHERLANDS B.V.—See Telia Company AB; *Int'l*, pg. 7544
TELIA CARRIER POLAND SP.Z.O.O.—See Telia Company AB; *Int'l*, pg. 7544
TELIA CARRIER U.S. INC.—See Telia Company AB; *Int'l*, pg. 7544
TELIA COMPANY AB; *Int'l*, pg. 7543
TELIA CYGATE OY—See Telia Company AB; *Int'l*, pg. 7544
TELIA INTERNATIONAL HOLDINGS AB—See Telia Company AB; *Int'l*, pg. 7544
TELIA NATTJANSTER NORDEN AB—See Telia Company AB; *Int'l*, pg. 7544
TELIANI TRADING UKRAINE LTD.—See Bank of Georgia Group PLC; *Int'l*, pg. 843
TELIA NORGE AS—See Telia Company AB; *Int'l*, pg. 7544
TELIA & PAVLA BBDO—See Omnicom Group Inc.; *U.S. Public*, pg. 1577
TELIASONERA ASSET FINANCE AB—See Telia Company AB; *Int'l*, pg. 7544
TELIASONERA CHESS HOLDING AS—See Telia Company AB; *Int'l*, pg. 7544
TELIASONERA DANMARK A/S—See Telia Company AB; *Int'l*, pg. 7544
TELIASONERA FINANS AB—See Telia Company AB; *Int'l*, pg. 7544
TELIASONERA FINLAND—See Telia Company AB; *Int'l*, pg. 7544
TELIASONERA FORSAKRING AB—See Telia Company AB; *Int'l*, pg. 7544
TELIASONERA INTERNATIONAL CARRIER AUSTRIA GMBH—See Telia Company AB; *Int'l*, pg. 7544
TELIASONERA INTERNATIONAL CARRIER FINLAND OY—See Telia Company AB; *Int'l*, pg. 7544
TELIASONERA INTERNATIONAL CARRIER FRANCE S.A.S.—See Telia Company AB; *Int'l*, pg. 7544
TELIASONERA INTERNATIONAL CARRIER GERMANY GMBH—See Telia Company AB; *Int'l*, pg. 7544
TELIASONERA INTERNATIONAL CARRIER HUNGARIA TAVKOZLESI KFT.—See Telia Company AB; *Int'l*, pg. 7544
TELIASONERA INTERNATIONAL CARRIER, INC.—See Telia Company AB; *Int'l*, pg. 7544
TELIASONERA INTERNATIONAL CARRIER ITALY S.P.A—See Telia Company AB; *Int'l*, pg. 7544
TELIASONERA INTERNATIONAL CARRIER LATVIA SIA—See Telia Company AB; *Int'l*, pg. 7544
TELIASONERA INTERNATIONAL CARRIER NETHERLANDS B.V.—See Telia Company AB; *Int'l*, pg. 7544
TELIASONERA INTERNATIONAL CARRIER POLAND SP. Z.O.O.—See Telia Company AB; *Int'l*, pg. 7544
TELIASONERA MOBILE NETWORKS AB—See Telia Company AB; *Int'l*, pg. 7544
TELIASONERA NETWORK SALES AB—See Telia Company AB; *Int'l*, pg. 7544
TELIASONERA SKANOVA ACCESS AB—See Telia Company AB; *Int'l*, pg. 7544

CORPORATE AFFILIATIONS

TELIASONERA SKANOVA ACCESS AB—See Telia Company AB; *Int'l*, pg. 7544
TELIASONERA SVERIGE AB—See Telia Company AB; *Int'l*, pg. 7544
TELIASONERA SVERIGE NET FASTIGHETER AB—See Telia Company AB; *Int'l*, pg. 7545
TELIASONERA SWEDEN—See Telia Company AB; *Int'l*, pg. 7545
TELIA TELECOMMUNICATIONS INTERNATIONAL B.V.—See Telia Company AB; *Int'l*, pg. 7544
TELIDYNE INC.; *U.S. Public*, pg. 1998
TELIGENTEMS, LLC—See Prime Technological Services, LLC; *U.S. Private*, pg. 3262
TELIGENT, INC.; *U.S. Public*, pg. 1998
TELINDUS BV—See Proximus PLC; *Int'l*, pg. 6008
TELINDUS FRANCE SA—See Proximus PLC; *Int'l*, pg. 6008
TELINDUS INTERNATIONAL BV—See Proximus PLC; *Int'l*, pg. 6008
TELINDUS LIMITED—See Proximus PLC; *Int'l*, pg. 6008
TELINDUS PSF SA—See Proximus PLC; *Int'l*, pg. 6008
TELINDUS SA—See Proximus PLC; *Int'l*, pg. 6008
TEL-INSTRUMENT ELECTRONICS CORP.; *U.S. Public*, pg. 1991
TELINVEST S.A.; *Int'l*, pg. 7545
TELIO IP SERVICES BV—See Kistefos AS; *Int'l*, pg. 4193
TELIO NETHERLANDS BV—See Kistefos AS; *Int'l*, pg. 4193
TELIO SA—See Kistefos AS; *Int'l*, pg. 4193
TELIO TELECOM AS—See Kistefos AS; *Int'l*, pg. 4193
TELIPHONE CORP.; *Int'l*, pg. 7545
TELISIMO INTERNATIONAL CORPORATION; *U.S. Private*, pg. 3962
TELIT COMMUNICATIONS PLC—See DBAY Advisors Limited; *Int'l*, pg. 1987
TELIT COMMUNICATIONS S.P.A.—See DBAY Advisors Limited; *Int'l*, pg. 1988
TELITI INTERNATIONAL LTD; *Int'l*, pg. 7545
TELIT WIRELESS SOLUTIONS CO., LTD.—See DBAY Advisors Limited; *Int'l*, pg. 1988
TELIT WIRELESS SOLUTIONS INC.—See DBAY Advisors Limited; *Int'l*, pg. 1988
TELIT WIRELESS SOLUTIONS LTD.—See DBAY Advisors Limited; *Int'l*, pg. 1988
TELIT WIRELESS SOLUTIONS (PTY) LTD.—See DBAY Advisors Limited; *Int'l*, pg. 1988
TELIX PHARMACEUTICALS LIMITED; *Int'l*, pg. 7545
TELKO DENMARK A/S—See Aspo Oyj; *Int'l*, pg. 631
TELKO ESTONIA OU—See Aspo Oyj; *Int'l*, pg. 631
TELKO LATVIA SIA—See Aspo Oyj; *Int'l*, pg. 631
TELKO LIETUVA UAB—See Aspo Oyj; *Int'l*, pg. 631
TELKO LTD.—See Aspo Oyj; *Int'l*, pg. 631
TELKOM KENYA LIMITED—See Helios Investment Partners LLP; *Int'l*, pg. 3330
TELKOM SA SOC LIMITED; *Int'l*, pg. 7545
TELKONET COMMUNICATIONS, INC.—See TELKONET, INC.; *U.S. Public*, pg. 1999
TELKONET, INC.; *U.S. Public*, pg. 1999
TELKO NORWAY AS—See Aspo Oyj; *Int'l*, pg. 631
TELKOOR POWER SUPPLIES LTD.—See Telkoor Telecom Ltd.; *Int'l*, pg. 7545
TELKOOR TELECOM LTD.; *Int'l*, pg. 7545
TELKO OY—See Aspo Oyj; *Int'l*, pg. 631
TELKO-POLAND SP. Z O.O.—See Aspo Oyj; *Int'l*, pg. 631
TELKO ROMANIA SRL—See Aspo Oyj; *Int'l*, pg. 631
TELKO SHANGHAI LTD.—See Aspo Oyj; *Int'l*, pg. 631
TELKO SOLUTION LLC—See Aspo Oyj; *Int'l*, pg. 631
TELKO SWEDEN AB—See Aspo Oyj; *Int'l*, pg. 631
TELKO UAB—See Aspo Oyj; *Int'l*, pg. 631
TELKWA COAL LIMITED—See Allegiance Coal Limited; *Int'l*, pg. 334
TELLABS AB—See Marlin Equity Partners, LLC; *U.S. Private*, pg. 2585
TELLABS COMMUNICATIONS INTERNATIONAL LIMITED—See Marlin Equity Partners, LLC; *U.S. Private*, pg. 2585
TELLABS COMMUNICATIONS (MALAYSIA) SDN. BHD.—See Marlin Equity Partners, LLC; *U.S. Private*, pg. 2585
TELLABS DEUTSCHLAND GMBH—See Marlin Equity Partners, LLC; *U.S. Private*, pg. 2585
TELLABS DO BRASIL, LTDA.—See Marlin Equity Partners, LLC; *U.S. Private*, pg. 2585
TELLABS, INC.—See Marlin Equity Partners, LLC; *U.S. Private*, pg. 2585
TELLABS INDIA PRIVATE LIMITED—See Marlin Equity Partners, LLC; *U.S. Private*, pg. 2585
TELLABS OPERATIONS, INC.—See Marlin Equity Partners, LLC; *U.S. Private*, pg. 2585
TELLABS OY—See Marlin Equity Partners, LLC; *U.S. Private*, pg. 2585
TELLABS PTY LIMITED—See Marlin Equity Partners, LLC; *U.S. Private*, pg. 2585
TELLABS SANTA CLARA—See Marlin Equity Partners, LLC; *U.S. Private*, pg. 2585
TELLABS SOUTH AFRICA (PROPRIETARY) LIMITED—See Marlin Equity Partners, LLC; *U.S. Private*, pg. 2585
TELLAGO INC.; *U.S. Private*, pg. 3962

COMPANY NAME INDEX

TELLA, INC.; *Int'l*, pg. 7545
TELLA TOOL & MANUFACTURING COMPANY; *U.S. Private*, pg. 3962
TELLENGER, INC.—See WaveDancer, Inc.; *U.S. Public*, pg. 2338
TELLENNIUM, INC.; *U.S. Private*, pg. 3962
TELLEPSEN BUILDERS LP; *U.S. Private*, pg. 3962
TELLGEN CORPORATION; *Int'l*, pg. 7545
TELLHOW GROUP CO., LTD.; *Int'l*, pg. 7545
TELLHOW SCI-TECH CO., LTD.—See Tellhow Group Co., Ltd.; *Int'l*, pg. 7545
TELLING TELECOM HOLDING CO., LTD.; *Int'l*, pg. 7545
TELLIO APS—See Kistefos AS; *Int'l*, pg. 4193
TELL MANUFACTURING, INC.—See Spectrum Brands Holdings, Inc.; *U.S. Public*, pg. 1917
TELL TOOL, INC.—See Arlington Capital Partners LLC; *U.S. Private*, pg. 327
TELLUMAT (PTY) LTD.—See Stellar Capital Partners Limited; *Int'l*, pg. 7204
TELLURIAN INC.—See Woodside Energy Group Ltd; *Int'l*, pg. 8450
TELLURIAN INVESTMENTS LLC—See Woodside Energy Group Ltd; *Int'l*, pg. 8450
TELLURIDE HEALTH COMPANY—See American Cannabis Innovations Conglomerated; *U.S. Private*, pg. 226
TELLURIDE SKI & GOLF COMPANY LLP; *U.S. Private*, pg. 3962
TELLUS IGNIS S.L.—See NIBE Industrier AB; *Int'l*, pg. 5262
TELLUS INSTITUTE INC.; *U.S. Private*, pg. 3962
TELLUS, LLC—See TA Associates, Inc.; *U.S. Private*, pg. 3917
TELLZA INC.; *U.S. Public*, pg. 1999
TEL MAGNETIC SOLUTIONS LTD.—See Tokyo Electron Limited; *Int'l*, pg. 7790
TEL MANUFACTURING AND ENGINEERING OF AMERICA, INC.—See Tokyo Electron Limited; *Int'l*, pg. 7791
TELMAR (ASIA) LTD.—See Splashlight LLC; *U.S. Private*, pg. 3759
TELMAR COMMUNICATIONS LIMITED—See Splashlight LLC; *U.S. Private*, pg. 3759
TELMA RETARDER DEUTSCHLAND GMBH—See Valeo S.A.; *Int'l*, pg. 8113
TELMA RETARDER DIVISION—See Valeo S.A.; *Int'l*, pg. 8113
TELMA RETARDER, INC.—See Valeo S.A.; *Int'l*, pg. 8113
TELMA RETARDER LTD.—See Valeo S.A.; *Int'l*, pg. 8113
TELMAR GROUP INC.—See Splashlight LLC; *U.S. Private*, pg. 3759
TELMAR-HET MEDIA INSTITUUT BV—See Splashlight LLC; *U.S. Private*, pg. 3759
TELMAR HMS LTD.—See Splashlight LLC; *U.S. Private*, pg. 3759
TELMAR INFORMATION SERVICES CORP.—See Splashlight LLC; *U.S. Private*, pg. 3759
TELMAR INTERNATIONAL INC.—See Splashlight LLC; *U.S. Private*, pg. 3759
TELMAR MEDIA SYSTEMS (PTY) LIMITED—See Splashlight LLC; *U.S. Private*, pg. 3759
TELMAR NETWORK TECHNOLOGY B.V.—See Jabil Inc.; *U.S. Public*, pg. 1182
TELMAR NETWORK TECHNOLOGY CO., LTD.—See Jabil Inc.; *U.S. Public*, pg. 1182
TELMAR NETWORK TECHNOLOGY-COUNCIL BLUFFS—See Jabil Inc.; *U.S. Public*, pg. 1182
TELMAR NETWORK TECHNOLOGY INC.—See Jabil Inc.; *U.S. Public*, pg. 1182
TELMAR NETWORK TECHNOLOGY SDN BHD—See Jabil Inc.; *U.S. Public*, pg. 1182
TELMAR NETWORK TECHNOLOGY S.R.L.—See Jabil Inc.; *U.S. Public*, pg. 1182
TELMAR PEAKTIME B.V.—See Splashlight LLC; *U.S. Private*, pg. 3759
TELMAR PEAKTIME S.A.S.—See Splashlight LLC; *U.S. Private*, pg. 3759
TELMAR POLSKA SP ZOO—See Splashlight LLC; *U.S. Private*, pg. 3759
TELMAR SOFTWARE (SHANGHAI) LTD.—See Splashlight LLC; *U.S. Private*, pg. 3759
TELMETRICS CORPORATION—See Marchex, Inc.; *U.S. Public*, pg. 1365
TELMEX COLOMBIA, S.A.—See America Movil, S.A.B. de C.V.; *Int'l*, pg. 422
TELMEX INTERNACIONAL, S.A.B. DE C.V.—See America Movil, S.A.B. de C.V.; *Int'l*, pg. 422
TELMEX PERU, S.A.—See America Movil, S.A.B. de C.V.; *Int'l*, pg. 421
TELMIC CORP.—See Sansei Technologies Inc.; *Int'l*, pg. 6555
TELMIC CORP. - YOSHIKAWA FACTORY—See Sansei Technologies Inc.; *Int'l*, pg. 6555
TELMIL ELECTRONICS, INC.—See Avnet, Inc.; *U.S. Public*, pg. 254
TELNET CORP.—See Guest-Tek Interactive Entertainment Ltd.; *Int'l*, pg. 3172
TEL NEXX, INC.—See ASM INTERNATIONAL N.V.; *Int'l*, pg. 626

TELNITE CO., LTD.—See INPEX CORPORATION; *Int'l*, pg. 3717
TEL-NT BRAZIL COMERCIO DE EQUIPAMENTOS DE TELECOMUNICAOES LTDA.—See Jabil Inc.; *U.S. Public*, pg. 1182
TELO GENOMICS CORP.; *Int'l*, pg. 7545
TELOGIA POWER LLC—See Leaf Clean Energy Company; *Int'l*, pg. 4434
TELOGICA LIMITED; *Int'l*, pg. 7545
TELOG INSTRUMENTS, INC.—See Trimble, Inc.; *U.S. Public*, pg. 2191
TELOGY NETWORKS, INC.—See Texas Instruments Incorporated; *U.S. Public*, pg. 2026
TELOK ANSON HOTEL SDN BERHAD—See MHC Plantations Bhd; *Int'l*, pg. 4872
TELOMIR PHARMACEUTICALS, INC.; *U.S. Public*, pg. 1999
TELOS CORPORATION; *U.S. Public*, pg. 1999
TELPAR, INC.—See Sole Source Capital LLC; *U.S. Private*, pg. 3708
TELPRO INC.; *U.S. Private*, pg. 3962
TELRAD CHILE S.A.—See EcoCash Holdings Zimbabwe Limited; *Int'l*, pg. 2295
TELRAD NET D.O.O.—See Telekomunikacije Republike Srpske a.d.; *Int'l*, pg. 7538
TELRAD NETWORKS LTD.—See EcoCash Holdings Zimbabwe Limited; *Int'l*, pg. 2295
TELREPCO INC.; *U.S. Private*, pg. 3962
TELRITE CORPORATION—See Telrite Holdings, Inc.; *U.S. Private*, pg. 3962
TELRITE HOLDINGS, INC.; *U.S. Private*, pg. 3962
TELSA INSTALACIONES DE TELECOMUNICACIONES Y ELECTRICIDAD, S.A.—See ACS, Actividades de Construccion y Servicios, S.A.; *Int'l*, pg. 116
TELSCO INDUSTRIES, INC.; *U.S. Private*, pg. 3962
TELSEON INCORPORATED; *U.S. Private*, pg. 3962
TELSIS GMBH—See Gamma Communications PLC; *Int'l*, pg. 2878
TEL SOLAR AG—See Tokyo Electron Limited; *Int'l*, pg. 7790
TEL SOLAR-LAB SA—See Tokyo Electron Limited; *Int'l*, pg. 7790
TEL SOLAR (SHANGHAI) LTD.—See Tokyo Electron Limited; *Int'l*, pg. 7790
TEL SOLAR SWITZERLAND AG—See Tokyo Electron Limited; *Int'l*, pg. 7790
TEL SOLAR TAIWAN LTD.—See Tokyo Electron Limited; *Int'l*, pg. 7790
TELSTAR CO., LTD.—See Sankyu, Inc.; *Int'l*, pg. 6545
TELSTAR INDUSTRIAL, S.L.—See Azbil Corporation; *Int'l*, pg. 777
TELSTAR INSTRUMAT, S.L.—See Azbil Corporation; *Int'l*, pg. 777
TELSTAR LIFE SCIENCE SOLUTIONS—See Azbil Corporation; *Int'l*, pg. 777
TELSTRA BROADCAST SERVICES PTY. LTD.—See Telstra Group Limited; *Int'l*, pg. 7546
TELSTRA GROUP LIMITED; *Int'l*, pg. 7545
TELSTRA INTERNATIONAL LIMITED—See Telstra Group Limited; *Int'l*, pg. 7546
TELSTRA INTERNATIONAL PHILIPPINES, INC.—See Telstra Group Limited; *Int'l*, pg. 7546
TELSTRA SUPER FINANCIAL PLANNING PTY LTD.—See Telstra Group Limited; *Int'l*, pg. 7546
TELSTRAT, INC.—See Marlin Equity Partners, LLC; *U.S. Private*, pg. 2585
TELSY ELETTRONICA E TELECOMUNICAZIONI S.P.A.—See TIM S.p.A.; *Int'l*, pg. 7750
TELSYS LTD.; *Int'l*, pg. 7546
TELSY S.P.A.—See TIM S.p.A.; *Int'l*, pg. 7750
TELSYS SA—See Orange S.A.; *Int'l*, pg. 5609
TELTEC CO., LTD.—See Nippon Telegraph & Telephone Corporation; *Int'l*, pg. 5355
TELTECH COMMUNICATIONS, LLC; *U.S. Private*, pg. 3962
TEL TECHNOLOGY CENTER, AMERICA, LLC—See Tokyo Electron Limited; *Int'l*, pg. 7791
TELTECH SYSTEMS, INC.—See IAC Inc.; *U.S. Public*, pg. 1083
TELTEC SIKOKU CO.,LTD.—See Nippon Telegraph & Telephone Corporation; *Int'l*, pg. 5355
TELTRONIC INC.; *U.S. Private*, pg. 3963
TELTRONIC S.A.U.—See Hytera Communications Corporation Limited; *Int'l*, pg. 3555
TELULAR CORPORATION—See AMETEK, Inc.; *U.S. Public*, pg. 122
TELUS COMMUNICATIONS COMPANY—See TELUS CORPORATION; *Int'l*, pg. 7546
TELUS COMMUNICATIONS (QUEBEC) INC.—See TELUS CORPORATION; *Int'l*, pg. 7546
TELUS CORPORATION; *Int'l*, pg. 7546
TELUS CORPORATION - TELUS BUSINESS SOLUTIONS DIVISION—See TELUS CORPORATION; *Int'l*, pg. 7546
TELUS INTEGRATED COMMUNICATIONS—See TELUS CORPORATION; *Int'l*, pg. 7546
TELUS INTERNATIONAL (CDA) INC.—See TELUS CORPORATION; *Int'l*, pg. 7546

TELUS INTERNATIONAL PHILIPPINES, INC.—See TELUS CORPORATION; *Int'l*, pg. 7546
TELUS MOBILITY—See TELUS CORPORATION; *Int'l*, pg. 7546
TELUS QUEBEC, INC.—See TELUS CORPORATION; *Int'l*, pg. 7546
TELUS SERVICES INC.—See TELUS CORPORATION; *Int'l*, pg. 7546
TELVENT AUSTRALIA PTY. LIMITED—See TBG Treuhand Partner AG; *Int'l*, pg. 7480
TELVENT FARRADYNE ENGINEERING, PC—See Schneider Electric SE; *Int'l*, pg. 6634
TELVENT GIT, S.A.—See TBG Treuhand Partner AG; *Int'l*, pg. 7480
TELVENT USA INC.—See TBG Treuhand Partner AG; *Int'l*, pg. 7480
TELVETIA S.A.—See SRG SSR Idee Suisse; *Int'l*, pg. 7149
TELVISTA COMPANY; *U.S. Private*, pg. 3963
TELVUE CORPORATION; *U.S. Private*, pg. 3963
TELWAY AS—See Telenor ASA; *Int'l*, pg. 7539
TELWEL EAST JAPAN CORPORATION—See Nippon Telegraph & Telephone Corporation; *Int'l*, pg. 5354
TELWEL WEST NIPPON CORPORATION—See Nippon Telegraph & Telephone Corporation; *Int'l*, pg. 5355
TELX - DALLAS, LLC—See Digital Realty Trust, Inc.; *U.S. Public*, pg. 663
TELXIUS TELECOM SA—See Telefonica, S.A.; *Int'l*, pg. 7536
TELXON CORPORATION—See Zebra Technologies Corporation; *U.S. Public*, pg. 2401
TEMACON ENGINEERING SDN. BHD.—See Sumitomo Densetsu Co., Ltd.; *Int'l*, pg. 7277
TEMA CONTENEUR TERMINAL LTD.—See Financiere de L'Odet; *Int'l*, pg. 2668
TEM AGENCIES CC—See Stonepeak Partners L.P.; *U.S. Private*, pg. 3829
TEMAIRAZU, INC.; *Int'l*, pg. 7546
TEMAMED MEDIZINTECHNISCHE DIENSTLEISTUNGS GMBH—See Fresenius SE & Co. KGaA; *Int'l*, pg. 2781
TE-MAPOL POLIMER PLASTIK VE INSAAT TICARET SANAYI A.S.; *Int'l*, pg. 7499
TEMA SAS—See VINCI S.A.; *Int'l*, pg. 8229
TEMASEK BRASIL CONSULTORIA E PARTICIPACOES LTDA.—See Temasek Holdings (Private) Limited; *Int'l*, pg. 7554
TEMASEK HOLDINGS ADVISORS (BEIJING) CO., LTD—See Temasek Holdings (Private) Limited; *Int'l*, pg. 7554
TEMASEK HOLDINGS ADVISORS INDIA PVT. LTD—See Temasek Holdings (Private) Limited; *Int'l*, pg. 7554
TEMASEK HOLDINGS CONSULTING (SHANGHAI) COMPANY LIMITED—See Temasek Holdings (Private) Limited; *Int'l*, pg. 7554
TEMASEK HOLDINGS (HK) LIMITED—See Temasek Holdings (Private) Limited; *Int'l*, pg. 7554
TEMASEK HOLDINGS (PRIVATE) LIMITED; *Int'l*, pg. 7546
TEMASEK INTERNATIONAL (EUROPE) LIMITED—See Temasek Holdings (Private) Limited; *Int'l*, pg. 7554
TEMASEK INTERNATIONAL (USA) LLC—See Temasek Holdings (Private) Limited; *Int'l*, pg. 7554
TEMASEK LIFE SCIENCES LABORATORY LIMITED—See Temasek Holdings (Private) Limited; *Int'l*, pg. 7554
TEMAS RESOURCES CORP.; *Int'l*, pg. 7546
TEMASYA DEVELOPMENT CO. SDN. BHD.—See S P Setia Berhad; *Int'l*, pg. 6444
T-EMBALLAGE FORPACKNING AB—See Volati AB; *Int'l*, pg. 8301
T-EMBALLAGE THURESON AKTIEBOLAG—See Volati AB; *Int'l*, pg. 8301
TEMBEC INC. - MATANE HIGH-YIELD PULP MILL—See Sappi Limited; *Int'l*, pg. 6573
TEMBO GLOBAL INDUSTRIES LTD.; *Int'l*, pg. 7554
TEMBO GOLD CORP.; *Int'l*, pg. 7554
TEMBO GOLD (T) LTD.—See Tembo Gold Corp.; *Int'l*, pg. 7554
TEMBR-BANK JSC; *Int'l*, pg. 7554
TEMC CO., LTD.; *Int'l*, pg. 7554
TEMCO CORPORATION—See Toyota Tsusho Corporation; *Int'l*, pg. 7877
TEMCO SERVICE INDUSTRIES, INC.—See ATALIAN Global Services; *Int'l*, pg. 665
THE TEMECULA CA ENDOSCOPY CENTER ASC, L.P.—See KKR & Co. Inc.; *U.S. Public*, pg. 1248
TEMECULA CA UNITED SURGERY, L.P.—See KKR & Co. Inc.; *U.S. Public*, pg. 1247
TEMECULA VALLEY HOSPITAL, INC.—See Universal Health Services, Inc.; *U.S. Public*, pg. 2259
TEM ELECTRONICS (JIANGMEN) CO LTD—See TEM Holdings Limited; *Int'l*, pg. 7546
TEM ELECTRONICS (M) SDN. BHD.—See Solartech International Holdings Limited; *Int'l*, pg. 7070
TEMENOS AFRICA (PTY) LIMITED—See Temenos AG; *Int'l*, pg. 7554
TEMENOS AG; *Int'l*, pg. 7554
TEMENOS AUSTRALIA FINANCIAL PTY LTD.—See Temenos AG; *Int'l*, pg. 7555

TEMENOS AG

TEMENOS AUSTRALIA PTY LIMITED—See Temenos AG; *Int'l*, pg. 7554
TEMENOS AUSTRALIA SERVICES PTY LIMITED—See Temenos AG; *Int'l*, pg. 7555
TEMENOS BELGIUM SA—See Temenos AG; *Int'l*, pg. 7555
TEMENOS CANADA INC.—See Temenos AG; *Int'l*, pg. 7555
TEMENOS COLOMBIA S.A.S.—See Temenos AG; *Int'l*, pg. 7555
TEMENOS DENMARK APS—See Temenos AG; *Int'l*, pg. 7555
TEMENOS DEUTSCHLAND GMBH—See Temenos AG; *Int'l*, pg. 7554
TEMENOS EAST AFRICA LIMITED—See Temenos AG; *Int'l*, pg. 7555
TEMENOS ECUADOR SA—See Temenos AG; *Int'l*, pg. 7554
TEMENOS EGYPT LLC—See Temenos AG; *Int'l*, pg. 7555
TEMENOS FRANCE SAS—See Temenos AG; *Int'l*, pg. 7555
TEMENOS HEADQUARTERS SA—See Temenos AG; *Int'l*, pg. 7555
TEMENOS HELLAS SA—See Temenos AG; *Int'l*, pg. 7555
TEMENOS HISPANIA SA—See Temenos AG; *Int'l*, pg. 7555
TEMENOS HOLDINGS FRANCE SAS—See Temenos AG; *Int'l*, pg. 7555
TEMENOS HOLLAND BV—See Temenos AG; *Int'l*, pg. 7555
TEMENOS HONG KONG LIMITED—See Temenos AG; *Int'l*, pg. 7555
TEMENOS INDIA PRIVATE LIMITED—See Temenos AG; *Int'l*, pg. 7555
TEMENOS ISRAEL LIMITED—See Temenos AG; *Int'l*, pg. 7555
TEMENOS JAPAN KK—See Temenos AG; *Int'l*, pg. 7555
TEMENOS KAZAKHSTAN LLP—See Temenos AG; *Int'l*, pg. 7555
TEMENOS KOREA LIMITED—See Temenos AG; *Int'l*, pg. 7555
TEMENOS LUXEMBOURG SA—See Temenos AG; *Int'l*, pg. 7555
TEMENOS MALAYSIA SDN BHD—See Temenos AG; *Int'l*, pg. 7555
TEMENOS MEXICO SA DE CV—See Temenos AG; *Int'l*, pg. 7555
TEMENOS MIDDLE EAST LIMITED—See Temenos AG; *Int'l*, pg. 7555
TEMENOS NORTH AFRICA LLC—See Temenos AG; *Int'l*, pg. 7555
TEMENOS PHILIPPINES, INC.—See Temenos AG; *Int'l*, pg. 7555
TEMENOS POLSKA SP. ZO.O—See Temenos AG; *Int'l*, pg. 7555
TEMENOS ROMANIA SRL—See Temenos AG; *Int'l*, pg. 7555
TEMENOS SINGAPORE FT PTE LIMITED—See Temenos AG; *Int'l*, pg. 7555
TEMENOS SINGAPORE PTE LIMITED—See Temenos AG; *Int'l*, pg. 7555
TEMENOS SOFTWARE BRASIL LIMITADA—See Temenos AG; *Int'l*, pg. 7555
TEMENOS SOFTWARE CANADA LIMITED—See Temenos AG; *Int'l*, pg. 7555
TEMENOS SOFTWARE LUXEMBOURG SA—See Temenos AG; *Int'l*, pg. 7555
TEMENOS SOFTWARE SHANGHAI CO LIMITED—See Temenos AG; *Int'l*, pg. 7555
TEMENOS (THAILAND) CO. LIMITED—See Temenos AG; *Int'l*, pg. 7555
TEMENOS UK LTD—See Temenos AG; *Int'l*, pg. 7555
TEMENOS USA, INC.—See Temenos AG; *Int'l*, pg. 7555
TEMENOS VIETNAM COMPANY LIMITED—See Temenos AG; *Int'l*, pg. 7555
TEM ENTERPRISES; *U.S. Private*, pg. 3963
TEM EQUIPMENT MANAGEMENT GMBH—See Stonepeak Partners L.P.; *U.S. Private*, pg. 3829
TEMETRA LIMITED—See Itron, Inc.; *U.S. Public*, pg. 1176
TEMET USA LLC—See Temet Oy; *Int'l*, pg. 7556
TEM (H.K.) LIMITED—See Stonepeak Partners L.P.; *U.S. Private*, pg. 3829
TEM HOLDINGS LIMITED; *Int'l*, pg. 7546
TEMIR CORP.; *Int'l*, pg. 7556
TEMIRTAU ELECTRO-METALLURGY PLANT JSC; *Int'l*, pg. 7556
TEMIS CONSEIL & FORMATION—See The Brink's Company; *U.S. Public*, pg. 2043
TEMISIS THERAPEUTICS SA—See Plant Advanced Technologies SA; *Int'l*, pg. 5890
TEMIS S.R.L.—See Avio S.p.A.; *Int'l*, pg. 744
TEMKIN INTERNATIONAL INC.—See GTCR LLC; *U.S. Private*, pg. 1806
TEMKIN & TEMKIN; *U.S. Private*, pg. 3963
TEMMLER IRELAND LTD.—See BC Partners LLP; *Int'l*, pg. 923
TEMMLER ITALIA S.R.L.—See BC Partners LLP; *Int'l*, pg. 923

TEMMLER PHARMA GMBH & CO. KG—See BC Partners LLP; *Int'l*, pg. 923
TEMMLER WERKE GMBH—See BC Partners LLP; *Int'l*, pg. 923
TEMO INC.; *U.S. Private*, pg. 3963
TEMONA, INC.; *Int'l*, pg. 7556
TEMP-AIR, INC.; *U.S. Private*, pg. 3963
TEMPBROS CO., LTD.—See Persol Holdings Co., Ltd.; *Int'l*, pg. 5819
TEMPCO ELECTRIC HEATER CORP; *U.S. Private*, pg. 3963
TEMPCOLD SP. Z O. O.—See Ahlsell AB; *Int'l*, pg. 223
TEMP-CONTROL MECHANICAL CORP.; *U.S. Private*, pg. 3963
TEMPEARL INDUSTRIAL CO LTD—See The Chugoku Electric Power Co., Inc.; *Int'l*, pg. 7632
TEMPEFF NORTH AMERICA LTD.—See NIBE Industrier AB; *Int'l*, pg. 5262
TEMPEL BURLINGTON—See Worthington Industries, Inc.; *U.S. Public*, pg. 2383
TEMPEL CANADA CORPORATION—See Worthington Industries, Inc.; *U.S. Public*, pg. 2382
TEMPEL (CHANGZHOU) PRECISION METAL PRODUCTS CO. LTD.—See Worthington Industries, Inc.; *U.S. Public*, pg. 2383
TEMPE LIFE CARE VILLAGE INC; *U.S. Private*, pg. 3963
TEMPEL PRECISION METAL PRODUCTS INDIA PVT. LTD.—See Worthington Industries, Inc.; *U.S. Public*, pg. 2382
TEMPEL STEEL COMPANY—See Worthington Industries, Inc.; *U.S. Public*, pg. 2382
TEMPERATURE CONTROL SYSTEMS, INC.—See The Stephens Group, LLC; *U.S. Private*, pg. 4121
TEMPERATURE ELECTRONICS LTD.—See Sdiptech AB; *Int'l*, pg. 6659
TEMPERATURE EQUIPMENT CORPORATION - MELROSE PARK—See Carrier Global Corporation; *U.S. Public*, pg. 444
TEMPERATURE EQUIPMENT CORPORATION - MELROSE PARK—See Watsco, Inc.; *U.S. Public*, pg. 2336
TEMPERATURE EQUIPMENT CORPORATION—See Carrier Global Corporation; *U.S. Public*, pg. 444
TEMPERATURE EQUIPMENT CORPORATION—See Watsco, Inc.; *U.S. Public*, pg. 2336
TEMPERATURE SERVICE COMPANY, INC.; *U.S. Private*, pg. 3963
TEMPERATURE SYSTEMS, INC.; *U.S. Private*, pg. 3963
TEMPERED PRODUCTS, INC.—See Masco Corporation; *U.S. Public*, pg. 1392
TEMPER ENERGY INTERNATIONAL, SOCIEDAD LIMITADA—See Boer Power Holdings Limited; *Int'l*, pg. 1099
TEMPERFORM, LLC—See Oakland Standard Co., LLC; *U.S. Private*, pg. 2985
TEMPERPACK TECHNOLOGIES, INC.; *U.S. Private*, pg. 3963
TEMPEST DEVELOPMENT GROUP INC.—See StarDyne Technologies Inc.; *Int'l*, pg. 7176
TEMPEST MINERALS LIMITED; *Int'l*, pg. 7556
TEMPEST TELECOM SOLUTIONS, LLC; *U.S. Private*, pg. 3963
TEMPEST THERAPEUTICS, INC.; *U.S. Public*, pg. 1999
TEMPIL, INC.—See Illinois Tool Works Inc.; *U.S. Public*, pg. 1111
TEMPLAR ESSEX INC—See International Paper Company; *U.S. Public*, pg. 1158
TEMPLAR HUMAN SEARCH INC—See Adecco Group AG; *Int'l*, pg. 139
TEMPLAR INTERNATIONAL CONSULTANTS LIMITED-GUANGZHOU—See Adecco Group AG; *Int'l*, pg. 139
TEMPLAR INTERNATIONAL CONSULTANTS LIMITED—See Adecco Group AG; *Int'l*, pg. 139
TEMPLE ASSOCIATES INC.—See CenterOak Partners LLC; *U.S. Private*, pg. 816
TEMPLE BAR INVESTMENT TRUST PLC; *Int'l*, pg. 7556
TEMPLE BOTTLING COMPANY LTD; *U.S. Private*, pg. 3963
THE TEMPLE FOUNDATION; *U.S. Private*, pg. 4126
TEMPLE HOTELS INC.—See Morguard Corporation; *Int'l*, pg. 5045
TEMPLE-INLAND INC.—See International Paper Company; *U.S. Public*, pg. 1158
TEMPLE-INLAND RESOURCE COMPANY—See International Paper Company; *U.S. Public*, pg. 1158
TEMPLE LIFTS LIMITED—See Rcapital Partners LLP; *Int'l*, pg. 6227
TEMPLE SQUARE HOSPITALITY CORPORATION—See Deseret Management Corporation; *U.S. Private*, pg. 1212
TEMPLE & TEMPLE EXCAVATING & PAVING, INC.; *U.S. Private*, pg. 3963
TEMPLETON AND PARTNERS B.V.—See Templeton and Partners Ltd; *Int'l*, pg. 7556
TEMPLETON AND PARTNERS LTD; *Int'l*, pg. 7556
TEMPLETON ASSET MANAGEMENT LTD.—See Franklin Resources, Inc.; *U.S. Public*, pg. 883
TEMPLETON COAL COMPANY, INC.; *U.S. Private*, pg. 3963

CORPORATE AFFILIATIONS

TEMPLETON CONSTRUCTION CO.; *U.S. Private*, pg. 3963
TEMPLETON DO BRASIL LTDA.—See Franklin Resources, Inc.; *U.S. Public*, pg. 883
TEMPLETON DRAGON FUND, INC.; *U.S. Public*, pg. 1999
TEMPLETON EMERGING MARKETS FUND; *Int'l*, pg. 7556
TEMPLETON EMERGING MARKETS INVESTMENT TRUST PLC; *Int'l*, pg. 7556
TEMPLETON GLOBAL ADVISORS LIMITED—See Franklin Resources, Inc.; *U.S. Public*, pg. 883
TEMPLETON GLOBAL INCOME FUND; *U.S. Public*, pg. 1999
TEMPLETON IMAGING, INC.—See Adventist Health System; *U.S. Private*, pg. 108
TEMPLETON INTERNATIONAL, INC.—See Franklin Resources, Inc.; *U.S. Public*, pg. 883
TEMPLETON INVESTMENT COUNSEL, LLC—See Franklin Resources, Inc.; *U.S. Public*, pg. 883
TEMPLETON LPA LIMITED—See LSL Property Services plc; *Int'l*, pg. 4571
TEMPLETON SANTA BARBARA, LLC—See Limoneira Company; *U.S. Public*, pg. 1316
TEMPLETON WORLDWIDE, INC.—See Franklin Resources, Inc.; *U.S. Public*, pg. 883
TEMPLE & WEBSTER PTY LTD.; *Int'l*, pg. 7556
TEMPO AUTOMATION HOLDINGS, INC.; *U.S. Public*, pg. 1999
TEMPO BANK—See Scott Credit Union; *U.S. Private*, pg. 3576
TEMPO BEVERAGES CYPRUS LTD.—See Tempo Beverages Ltd.; *Int'l*, pg. 7556
TEMPO BEVERAGES LTD.; *Int'l*, pg. 7556
TEMPO COMMUNICATIONS, INC.—See Emerson Electric Co.; *U.S. Public*, pg. 742
TEMPO COMMUNICATIONS, INC.—See Emerson Electric Co.; *U.S. Public*, pg. 750
TEMPO EUROPE LIMITED—See Emerson Electric Co.; *U.S. Public*, pg. 742
TEMPO EUROPE LIMITED—See Emerson Electric Co.; *U.S. Public*, pg. 750
TEMPOGRAPHICS INC.; *U.S. Private*, pg. 3964
TEMPO INDUSTRIES INC.; *U.S. Private*, pg. 3964
TEMPO INTERNATIONAL GROUP LTD.; *Int'l*, pg. 7556
TEMPO INTI MEDIA TBK; *Int'l*, pg. 7556
TEMPO PARTICIPACOES S.A.—See The Carlyle Group Inc.; *U.S. Public*, pg. 2055
TEMPORAL POWER LTD.—See Enbridge Inc.; *Int'l*, pg. 2397
TEMPORARY ACCOMMODATIONS, INC.—See The Carlyle Group Inc.; *U.S. Public*, pg. 2054
TEMPORARY HOUSING DIRECTORY, INC.; *U.S. Private*, pg. 3964
TEMPORARY SOLUTIONS INC.—See Employment Enterprises Inc.; *U.S. Private*, pg. 1387
TEMPORARY SYSTEMS INC.—See Meador Staffing Services Inc.; *U.S. Private*, pg. 2647
TEMPOS21 S.A.—See Atos SE; *Int'l*, pg. 691
TEMPO SCAN PACIFIC TBK; *Int'l*, pg. 7556
TEMPO SOFTWARE, INC.; *U.S. Private*, pg. 3964
TEMPOSONICS GMBH & CO. KG—See Amphenol Corporation; *U.S. Public*, pg. 132
TEMPO-TEAM GMBH—See Randstad N.V.; *Int'l*, pg. 6206
TEMPO-TEAM GROUP B.V.—See Randstad N.V.; *Int'l*, pg. 6206
TEMPO-TEAM HR SERVICES SA—See Randstad N.V.; *Int'l*, pg. 6206
TEMPO-TEAM IT-FLEX—See Randstad N.V.; *Int'l*, pg. 6205
TEMPO-TEAM MANAGEMENT HOLDING GMBH—See Randstad N.V.; *Int'l*, pg. 6206
TEMPO-TEAM NV—See Randstad N.V.; *Int'l*, pg. 6206
TEMPO-TEAM PERSONEELSDIENSTEN—See Randstad N.V.; *Int'l*, pg. 6205
TEMPO-TEAM PROJECTEN—See Randstad N.V.; *Int'l*, pg. 6205
TEMPO-TEAM SA—See Randstad N.V.; *Int'l*, pg. 6206
TEMPO-TEAM—See Randstad N.V.; *Int'l*, pg. 6206
TEMPO-TEAM UITZENDEN—See Randstad N.V.; *Int'l*, pg. 6205
TEMPOTEL, EMPRESA DE TRABAJO TEMPORAL, S.A.—See Telefonica, S.A.; *Int'l*, pg. 7536
TEMP-POWER, INC.—See Herc Holdings Inc.; *U.S. Public*, pg. 1028
TEMPRA EHF.—See Berry Global Group, Inc; *U.S. Public*, pg. 325
TEMP RESEARCH INSTITUTE CO., LTD.—See Persol Holdings Co., Ltd.; *Int'l*, pg. 5819
TEMPRESS SYSTEMS B.V.—See Amtech Systems, Inc.; *U.S. Public*, pg. 134
TEMPRESS SYSTEMS, INC.—See Amtech Systems, Inc.; *U.S. Public*, pg. 134
TEMPRESS TECHNOLOGIES INC.—See Oil States International, Inc.; *U.S. Public*, pg. 1565
TEMP-RITE INTERNATIONAL GMBH—See Ali Holding S.r.l; *Int'l*, pg. 321
TEMP-RITE INTERNATIONAL HOLDING B.V.—See Ali Holding S.r.l; *Int'l*, pg. 322

TEMP-RITE INTERNATIONAL KFT.—See Ali Holding S.r.l; *Int'l*, pg. 322
TEMPSTAFF CAREER CO., LTD.—See Persol Holdings Co., Ltd.; *Int'l*, pg. 5820
TEMPSTAFF CAREER TRANSITION CO., LTD.—See Persol Holdings Co., Ltd.; *Int'l*, pg. 5820
TEMPSTAFF CREATIVE CO., LTD—See Persol Holdings Co., Ltd.; *Int'l*, pg. 5819
TEMPSTAFF CROSS CO., LTD.—See Persol Holdings Co., Ltd.; *Int'l*, pg. 5819
TEMPSTAFF DATA CO., LTD.—See Persol Holdings Co., Ltd.; *Int'l*, pg. 5820
TEMPSTAFF FAMILIE CO., LTD.—See Persol Holdings Co., Ltd.; *Int'l*, pg. 5819
TEMPSTAFF FORUM CO., LTD.—See Persol Holdings Co., Ltd.; *Int'l*, pg. 5819
TEMPSTAFF FRONTIER CO., LTD.—See Persol Holdings Co., Ltd.; *Int'l*, pg. 5819
TEMPSTAFF FUKUOKA CO., LTD.—See Persol Holdings Co., Ltd.; *Int'l*, pg. 5819
TEMPSTAFF GROW CO., LTD.—See Persol Holdings Co., Ltd.; *Int'l*, pg. 5819
TEMPSTAFF GUANGZHOU LTD.—See Persol Holdings Co., Ltd.; *Int'l*, pg. 5819
TEMPSTAFF (HONG KONG) LIMITED—See Kelly Services, Inc.; *U.S. Public*, pg. 1219
TEMPSTAFF (HONG KONG) LIMITED—See Persol Holdings Co., Ltd.; *Int'l*, pg. 5820
TEMPSTAFF INDONESIA CO., LTD.—See Persol Holdings Co., Ltd.; *Int'l*, pg. 5819
TEMPSTAFF INTEGRATION CO., LTD.—See Persol Holdings Co., Ltd.; *Int'l*, pg. 5819
TEMPSTAFF KAMEI CORPORATION—See Persol Holdings Co., Ltd.; *Int'l*, pg. 5819
TEMPSTAFF KOREA CO., LTD.—See Persol Holdings Co., Ltd.; *Int'l*, pg. 5819
TEMPSTAFF LEARNING CO., LTD.—See Persol Holdings Co., Ltd.; *Int'l*, pg. 5819
TEMPSTAFF MEDICAL CO., LTD.—See Persol Holdings Co., Ltd.; *Int'l*, pg. 5820
TEMPSTAFF PLUS CO., LTD.—See Persol Holdings Co., Ltd.; *Int'l*, pg. 5819
TEMPSTAFF SHANGHAI CO., LTD.—See Persol Holdings Co., Ltd.; *Int'l*, pg. 5819
TEMPSTAFF SP CO., LTD.—See Persol Holdings Co., Ltd.; *Int'l*, pg. 5820
TEMPSTAFF TAIWAN CO., LTD.—See Persol Holdings Co., Ltd.; *Int'l*, pg. 5819
TEMPSTAFF TECHNOLOGIES CO., LTD.—See Persol Holdings Co., Ltd.; *Int'l*, pg. 5819
TEMPSTAFF WELFARE CO., LTD.—See Persol Holdings Co., Ltd.; *Int'l*, pg. 5819
TEMPSTAFF WISH CO., LTD.—See Poppins Corp.; *Int'l*, pg. 5921
TEMPTATION FOODS LTD; *Int'l*, pg. 7556
TEMPTIME CORP.—See Zebra Technologies Corporation; *U.S. Public*, pg. 2401
TEMPTRONIC CORPORATION—See inTEST Corporation; *U.S. Public*, pg. 1159
TEMPTRONIC GMBH—See inTEST Corporation; *U.S. Public*, pg. 1159
TEMPUR AUSTRALIA PTY. LTD.—See Tempur Sealy International, Inc.; *U.S. Public*, pg. 2000
TEMPUR BENELUX B.V.—See Tempur Sealy International, Inc.; *U.S. Public*, pg. 2000
TEMPUR DANMARK A/S—See Tempur Sealy International, Inc.; *U.S. Public*, pg. 2000
TEMPUR DEUTSCHLAND GMBH—See Tempur Sealy International, Inc.; *U.S. Public*, pg. 2000
TEMPUR FRANCE SARL—See Tempur Sealy International, Inc.; *U.S. Public*, pg. 2000
TEMPUR NORGE AS—See Tempur Sealy International, Inc.; *U.S. Public*, pg. 2000
TEMPUR-PEDIC AMERICA, LLC—See Tempur Sealy International, Inc.; *U.S. Public*, pg. 2000
TEMPUR PRODUCTION USA, LLC—See Tempur Sealy International, Inc.; *U.S. Public*, pg. 2000
TEMPUR SCHWEIZ AG—See Tempur Sealy International, Inc.; *U.S. Public*, pg. 2000
TEMPUR SEALY BENELUX B.V.—See Tempur Sealy International, Inc.; *U.S. Public*, pg. 2000
TEMPUR SEALY DACH GMBH—See Tempur Sealy International, Inc.; *U.S. Public*, pg. 2000
TEMPUR SEALY DEUTSCHLAND GMBH—See Tempur Sealy International, Inc.; *U.S. Public*, pg. 2000
TEMPUR SEALY ESPANA S.A.—See Tempur Sealy International, Inc.; *U.S. Public*, pg. 2000
TEMPUR SEALY FRANCE SAS—See Tempur Sealy International, Inc.; *U.S. Public*, pg. 2000
TEMPUR SEALY INTERNATIONAL, INC.; *U.S. Public*, pg. 1999
TEMPUR SEALY JAPAN YUGEN KAISHA, LTD.—See Tempur Sealy International, Inc.; *U.S. Public*, pg. 2000
TEMPUR SINGAPORE PTE LTD.—See Tempur Sealy International, Inc.; *U.S. Public*, pg. 2000
TEMPUR SUOMI OY—See Tempur Sealy International, Inc.; *U.S. Public*, pg. 2000
TEMPUR SVERIGE AB—See Tempur Sealy International, Inc.; *U.S. Public*, pg. 2000

TEMPUR UK LIMITED—See Tempur Sealy International, Inc.; *U.S. Public*, pg. 2000
TEMPUS AI, INC.; *U.S. Public*, pg. 2000
TEMPUS APPLIED SOLUTIONS HOLDINGS, INC.; *U.S. Public*, pg. 2000
TEMPUS APPLIED SOLUTIONS, LLC—See Tempus Applied Solutions Holdings, Inc.; *U.S. Public*, pg. 2000
TEMPUS CAPITAL, INC.; *Int'l*, pg. 7556
TEMPUS GLOBAL BUSINESS SERVICE GROUP HOLDING LTD.; *Int'l*, pg. 7556
TEMPUS HOLDINGS LIMITED; *Int'l*, pg. 7557
TEMPUS INC.; *U.S. Private*, pg. 3964
TEMPUS IT STAFFING; *U.S. Private*, pg. 3964
TEMPUS JETS INC.—See Tempus Applied Solutions Holdings, Inc.; *U.S. Public*, pg. 2000
TEMPUS NOVA, INC.—See Investcorp Holdings B.S.C.; *Int'l*, pg. 3776
TEMPUS TRAINING SOLUTIONS LLC—See Tempus Applied Solutions Holdings, Inc.; *U.S. Public*, pg. 2000
TEMPUS WEALTH GROUP PTY. LTD.—See Azimut Holding SpA; *Int'l*, pg. 779
TEMPWISE, INC.—See The Reserves Network Inc.; *U.S. Private*, pg. 4105
TEMSA EUROPE NV—See Haci Omer Sabanci Holding A.S.; *Int'l*, pg. 3204
TEMSA GLOBAL SANAYI VE TICARET A.S. - ADANA PLANT—See Haci Omer Sabanci Holding A.S.; *Int'l*, pg. 3204
TEMSA GLOBAL SANAYI VE TICARET A.S.—See Haci Omer Sabanci Holding A.S.; *Int'l*, pg. 3204
TEMSA IS MAKINALARI IMALAT PAZARLAMA VE SATIS A.S.—See Marubeni Corporation; *Int'l*, pg. 4710
TEMSYS SA—See Societe Generale S.A.; *Int'l*, pg. 7042
TEM SYSTEMS, INC.; *U.S. Private*, pg. 3963
TEMTCO STEEL, LLC—See Klockner & Co. SE; *Int'l*, pg. 4203
TEN-8 FIRE EQUIPMENT INC.; *U.S. Private*, pg. 3964
TENA A.D.; *Int'l*, pg. 7557
TENABLE HOLDINGS, INC.; *U.S. Public*, pg. 2000
TENABLE NETWORK SECURITY, INC.; *U.S. Private*, pg. 3964
TENAGA CABLE INDUSTRIES SDN. BHD.—See Tenaga Nasional Berhad; *Int'l*, pg. 7558
TENAGA NASIONAL BERHAD; *Int'l*, pg. 7557
TENAGA SWITCHGEAR SDN BHD (TSG)—See Tenaga Nasional Berhad; *Int'l*, pg. 7558
TEN ALLIED CO., LTD.; *Int'l*, pg. 7557
TEN ALPS TV LIMITED—See Zinc Media Group plc; *Int'l*, pg. 8684
TENANTS FIRST HOUSING CO-OPERATIVE LIMITED—See Sanctuary Housing Association; *Int'l*, pg. 6524
TENARIS GLOBAL SERVICES DE BOLIVIA S.R.L.—See Techint S.p.A.; *Int'l*, pg. 7504
TENARIS GLOBAL SERVICES FAR EAST PTE. LTD.—See Techint S.p.A.; *Int'l*, pg. 7504
TENARIS GLOBAL SERVICES NIGERIA LTD.—See Techint S.p.A.; *Int'l*, pg. 7504
TENARIS GLOBAL SERVICES (U.S.A.) CORPORATION—See Techint S.p.A.; *Int'l*, pg. 7504
TENARIS NIGERIA LTD.—See Techint S.p.A.; *Int'l*, pg. 7504
TENARIS S.A.—See Techint S.p.A.; *Int'l*, pg. 7504
TENART—See TCS TurControlSysteme AG; *Int'l*, pg. 7486
TENASKA BIOFUELS, LLC—See Tenaska, Inc.; *U.S. Private*, pg. 3965
TENASKA CAPITAL MANAGEMENT, LLC—See Tenaska, Inc.; *U.S. Private*, pg. 3965
TENASKA, INC.; *U.S. Private*, pg. 3964
TENASKA MARKETING CANADA—See Tenaska, Inc.; *U.S. Private*, pg. 3965
TENASKA MARKETING VENTURES—See Tenaska, Inc.; *U.S. Private*, pg. 3965
TENASKA POWER SERVICES CO.—See Tenaska, Inc.; *U.S. Private*, pg. 3965
T.EN AUSTRALIA AND NEW ZEALAND PTY. LTD.—See Technip Energies N.V.; *Int'l*, pg. 7506
TENAX CORPORATION—See Tenax International BV; *Int'l*, pg. 7558
TENAX INTERNATIONAL BV; *Int'l*, pg. 7558
TENAX INTERNATIONAL S.P.A.; *Int'l*, pg. 7558
TENAX KUNSTSTOFFE GMBH—See Tenax International BV; *Int'l*, pg. 7558
TENAX MANUFACTURING ALABAMA—See Tenax International BV; *Int'l*, pg. 7558
TENAX SARL—See Tenax International BV; *Int'l*, pg. 7558
TENAX SPA—See Tenax International BV; *Int'l*, pg. 7558
TENAX THERAPEUTICS, INC.; *U.S. Public*, pg. 2001
TENAX UK LTD.—See Tenax International BV; *Int'l*, pg. 7558
TENAX USA; *U.S. Private*, pg. 3965
TENAYA ACQUISITIONS COMPANY; *U.S. Private*, pg. 3965
TENAYA CAPITAL, LLC; *U.S. Private*, pg. 3965
TENAYA GROUP INC.; *Int'l*, pg. 7558
TENAYA THERAPEUTICS, INC.; *U.S. Public*, pg. 2001
TENAZ ENERGY CORP.; *Int'l*, pg. 7558
TEN BROECK TAMPA, LLC—See Acadia Healthcare Company, Inc.; *U.S. Public*, pg. 30

TENCARVA MACHINERY COMPANY, LLC - ALCOA—See Tencarva Machinery Company, LLC; *U.S. Private*, pg. 3965
TENCARVA MACHINERY COMPANY, LLC - BROOKHAVEN—See Tencarva Machinery Company, LLC; *U.S. Private*, pg. 3965
TENCARVA MACHINERY COMPANY, LLC - CHARLOTTE—See Tencarva Machinery Company, LLC; *U.S. Private*, pg. 3965
TENCARVA MACHINERY COMPANY, LLC - CHATTANOOGA—See Tencarva Machinery Company, LLC; *U.S. Private*, pg. 3965
TENCARVA MACHINERY COMPANY, LLC - CHESAPEAKE—See Tencarva Machinery Company, LLC; *U.S. Private*, pg. 3965
TENCARVA MACHINERY COMPANY, LLC - COLUMBIA—See Tencarva Machinery Company, LLC; *U.S. Private*, pg. 3965
TENCARVA MACHINERY COMPANY, LLC - GREENVILLE—See Tencarva Machinery Company, LLC; *U.S. Private*, pg. 3965
TENCARVA MACHINERY COMPANY, LLC - JACKSON—See Tencarva Machinery Company, LLC; *U.S. Private*, pg. 3965
TENCARVA MACHINERY COMPANY, LLC - JOHNSON CITY—See Tencarva Machinery Company, LLC; *U.S. Private*, pg. 3965
TENCARVA MACHINERY COMPANY, LLC - LITTLE ROCK—See Tencarva Machinery Company, LLC; *U.S. Private*, pg. 3965
TENCARVA MACHINERY COMPANY, LLC - MEMPHIS—See Tencarva Machinery Company, LLC; *U.S. Private*, pg. 3965
TENCARVA MACHINERY COMPANY, LLC - NASHVILLE—See Tencarva Machinery Company, LLC; *U.S. Private*, pg. 3965
TENCARVA MACHINERY COMPANY, LLC - NORTH CHARLESTON—See Tencarva Machinery Company, LLC; *U.S. Private*, pg. 3965
TENCARVA MACHINERY COMPANY, LLC - RICHMOND—See Tencarva Machinery Company, LLC; *U.S. Private*, pg. 3965
TENCARVA MACHINERY COMPANY, LLC - SALEM—See Tencarva Machinery Company, LLC; *U.S. Private*, pg. 3965
TENCARVA MACHINERY COMPANY, LLC; *U.S. Private*, pg. 3965
TENCARVA MACHINERY COMPANY, LLC - WILMINGTON—See Tencarva Machinery Company, LLC; *U.S. Private*, pg. 3965
TEN CATE ADVANCED ARMOR USA INC.—See Toray Industries, Inc.; *Int'l*, pg. 7824
TEN CATE ADVANCED ARMOUR DANMARK A/S—See ABN AMRO Group N.V.; *Int'l*, pg. 64
TEN CATE ADVANCED ARMOUR DANMARK A/S—See Gilde Buy Out Partners B.V.; *Int'l*, pg. 2974
TEN CATE ADVANCED ARMOUR DANMARK A/S—See Parcom Capital Management B.V.; *Int'l*, pg. 5740
TENCATE ADVANCED ARMOUR SASU—See ABN AMRO Group N.V.; *Int'l*, pg. 64
TENCATE ADVANCED ARMOUR SASU—See Gilde Buy Out Partners B.V.; *Int'l*, pg. 2974
TENCATE ADVANCED ARMOUR SASU—See Parcom Capital Management B.V.; *Int'l*, pg. 5740
TEN CATE ADVANCED ARMOUR UK LIMITED—See ABN AMRO Group N.V.; *Int'l*, pg. 64
TEN CATE ADVANCED ARMOUR UK LIMITED—See Gilde Buy Out Partners B.V.; *Int'l*, pg. 2974
TEN CATE ADVANCED ARMOUR UK LIMITED—See Parcom Capital Management B.V.; *Int'l*, pg. 5740
TEN CATE ADVANCED TEXTILES BV—See ABN AMRO Group N.V.; *Int'l*, pg. 64
TEN CATE ADVANCED TEXTILES BV—See Gilde Buy Out Partners B.V.; *Int'l*, pg. 2974
TEN CATE ADVANCED TEXTILES BV—See Parcom Capital Management B.V.; *Int'l*, pg. 5740
TEN CATE DANMARK A/S—See ABN AMRO Group N.V.; *Int'l*, pg. 64
TEN CATE DANMARK A/S—See Gilde Buy Out Partners B.V.; *Int'l*, pg. 2974
TEN CATE DANMARK A/S—See Parcom Capital Management B.V.; *Int'l*, pg. 5740
TENCATE FRANCE SASU—See ABN AMRO Group N.V.; *Int'l*, pg. 64
TENCATE FRANCE SASU—See Gilde Buy Out Partners B.V.; *Int'l*, pg. 2974
TENCATE FRANCE SASU—See Parcom Capital Management B.V.; *Int'l*, pg. 5740
TENCATE GEOSYNTHETICS ASIA SDN. BHD.—See ABN AMRO Group N.V.; *Int'l*, pg. 64
TENCATE GEOSYNTHETICS ASIA SDN. BHD.—See Gilde Buy Out Partners B.V.; *Int'l*, pg. 2975
TENCATE GEOSYNTHETICS ASIA SDN. BHD.—See Parcom Capital Management B.V.; *Int'l*, pg. 5740
TENCATE GEOSYNTHETICS AUSTRIA GES.M.B.H—See ABN AMRO Group N.V.; *Int'l*, pg. 64
TENCATE GEOSYNTHETICS AUSTRIA GES.M.B.H—See Gilde Buy Out Partners B.V.; *Int'l*, pg. 2975

TENCARVA MACHINERY COMPANY, LLC CORPORATE AFFILIATIONS

TENCATE GEOSYNTHETICS AUSTRIA GES.M.B.H—See Parcom Capital Management B.V.; *Int'l*, pg. 5740
TENCATE GEOSYNTHETICS FRANCE S.A.S.—See ABN AMRO Group N.V.; *Int'l*, pg. 64
TENCATE GEOSYNTHETICS FRANCE S.A.S.—See Gilde Buy Out Partners B.V.; *Int'l*, pg. 2975
TENCATE GEOSYNTHETICS FRANCE S.A.S.—See Parcom Capital Management B.V.; *Int'l*, pg. 5740
TENCATE GEOSYNTHETICS MALAYSIA SDN BHD—See ABN AMRO Group N.V.; *Int'l*, pg. 64
TENCATE GEOSYNTHETICS MALAYSIA SDN BHD—See Gilde Buy Out Partners B.V.; *Int'l*, pg. 2975
TENCATE GEOSYNTHETICS MALAYSIA SDN BHD—See Parcom Capital Management B.V.; *Int'l*, pg. 5740
TENCATE GEOSYNTHETICS NETHERLANDS B.V.—See ABN AMRO Group N.V.; *Int'l*, pg. 64
TENCATE GEOSYNTHETICS NETHERLANDS B.V.—See Gilde Buy Out Partners B.V.; *Int'l*, pg. 2975
TENCATE GEOSYNTHETICS NETHERLANDS B.V.—See Parcom Capital Management B.V.; *Int'l*, pg. 5740
TEN CATE GEOSYNTHETICS NORTH AMERICA INC.—See Solmax International, Inc.; *Int'l*, pg. 7074
TENCATE GEOSYNTHETICS (THAILAND) LTD—See ABN AMRO Group N.V.; *Int'l*, pg. 64
TENCATE GEOSYNTHETICS (THAILAND) LTD—See Gilde Buy Out Partners B.V.; *Int'l*, pg. 2975
TENCATE GEOSYNTHETICS (THAILAND) LTD—See Parcom Capital Management B.V.; *Int'l*, pg. 5740
TEN CATE GEOSYNTHETICS (UK) LIMITED—See ABN AMRO Group N.V.; *Int'l*, pg. 64
TEN CATE GEOSYNTHETICS (UK) LIMITED—See Gilde Buy Out Partners B.V.; *Int'l*, pg. 2974
TEN CATE GEOSYNTHETICS (UK) LIMITED—See Parcom Capital Management B.V.; *Int'l*, pg. 5740
TENCATE GRASS HOLDING BV—See Crestview Partners, L.P.; *U.S. Private*, pg. 1099
TENCATE INDUSTRIAL ZHUHAI CO. LTD.—See ABN AMRO Group N.V.; *Int'l*, pg. 65
TENCATE INDUSTRIAL ZHUHAI CO. LTD.—See Gilde Buy Out Partners B.V.; *Int'l*, pg. 2975
TENCATE INDUSTRIAL ZHUHAI CO. LTD.—See Parcom Capital Management B.V.; *Int'l*, pg. 5740
TENCATE PROTECTIVE FABRICS HOLDING BV—See ABN AMRO Group N.V.; *Int'l*, pg. 65
TENCATE PROTECTIVE FABRICS HOLDING BV—See Gilde Buy Out Partners B.V.; *Int'l*, pg. 2975
TENCATE PROTECTIVE FABRICS HOLDING BV—See Parcom Capital Management B.V.; *Int'l*, pg. 5740
TENCATE PROTECTIVE FABRICS USA INC.—See ABN AMRO Group N.V.; *Int'l*, pg. 65
TENCATE PROTECTIVE FABRICS USA INC.—See Gilde Buy Out Partners B.V.; *Int'l*, pg. 2975
TENCATE PROTECTIVE FABRICS USA INC.—See Parcom Capital Management B.V.; *Int'l*, pg. 5740
TEN CATE THIOBAC BV—See ABN AMRO Group N.V.; *Int'l*, pg. 64
TEN CATE THIOBAC BV—See Gilde Buy Out Partners B.V.; *Int'l*, pg. 2974
TEN CATE THIOBAC BV—See Parcom Capital Management B.V.; *Int'l*, pg. 5740
TEN CATE THIOLON B.V.—See Crestview Partners, L.P.; *U.S. Private*, pg. 1099
TEN CATE THIOLON USA INC.—See Crestview Partners, L.P.; *U.S. Private*, pg. 1099
TENCENT HOLDINGS LIMITED; *Int'l*, pg. 7558
TENCENT LIMITED—See Tencent Holdings Limited; *Int'l*, pg. 7559
TENCENT MUSIC ENTERTAINMENT GROUP; *Int'l*, pg. 7559
TENCENT TECHNOLOGY (BEIJING) COMPANY LIMITED—See Tencent Holdings Limited; *Int'l*, pg. 7559
TENCENT TECHNOLOGY (SHENZHEN) CO., LTD—See Tencent Holdings Limited; *Int'l*, pg. 7559
TENCO INC.—See Alamo Group Inc.; *U.S. Public*, pg. 71
TENCO INDUSTRIES, INC.—See Alamo Group Inc.; *U.S. Public*, pg. 71
TENCO INDUSTRIES, INC.—See Alamo Group Inc.; *U.S. Public*, pg. 71
TENCO INDUSTRIES SDN BHD—See Jiankun International Berhad; *Int'l*, pg. 3961
T.EN COLOMBIA S.A.—See Technip Energies N.V.; *Int'l*, pg. 7506
TENCO SERVICES, INC.; *U.S. Private*, pg. 3965
TENCO (USA), INC.—See Alamo Group Inc.; *U.S. Public*, pg. 71
TEN CUE PRODUCTIONS—See Opus Solutions, LLC; *U.S. Private*, pg. 3036
TENDA CO., LTD.; *Int'l*, pg. 7559
TENDANCES ECO GROUP SA; *Int'l*, pg. 7559
TENDELE COAL MINING (PTY) LTD—See Petmin Limited; *Int'l*, pg. 5824
TEN D. ENTERPRISES, INC.; *U.S. Private*, pg. 3964
TENDENZ HARLEIE AS—See Validus AS; *Int'l*, pg. 8116
TENDERCARE, INC.—See Extendicare Inc.; *Int'l*, pg. 2591
TENDER CO., LTD.—See TOKAI Holdings Corporation; *Int'l*, pg. 7779
TENDER CORPORATION; *U.S. Private*, pg. 3966

TENDERCUT MEATS LTD—See Argent Group Europe Limited; *Int'l*, pg. 560
TENDER LOVING CARE HEALTH CARE SERVICES OF ERIE NIAGARA, LLC—See Amedisys, Inc.; *U.S. Public*, pg. 94
TENDER LOVING CARE HEALTH CARE SERVICES OF GEORGIA, LLC—See Amedisys, Inc.; *U.S. Public*, pg. 94
TENDER LOVING CARE HEALTH CARE SERVICES OF LONG ISLAND, LLC—See Amedisys, Inc.; *U.S. Public*, pg. 94
TENDER LOVING CARE OF DULUTH—See Centerbridge Partners, L.P.; *U.S. Private*, pg. 814
TENDER LOVING THINGS INC.; *U.S. Private*, pg. 3966
THE TENDIT GROUP, LLC—See Osceola Capital Management, LLC; *U.S. Private*, pg. 3047
TENDON SYSTEMS, LLC—See Commercial Metals Company; *U.S. Public*, pg. 547
TENDO SYSTEMS INC.; *U.S. Private*, pg. 3966
TENDYNE HOLDINGS, INC.—See Abbott Laboratories; *U.S. Public*, pg. 21
TENDYNE MEDICAL, INC.—See Abbott Laboratories; *U.S. Public*, pg. 21
T.EN E&C LIMITED—See Technip Energies N.V.; *Int'l*, pg. 7507
TENEDORA AGNICO EAGLE MEXICO S.A. DE C.V.—See Agnico Eagle Mines Limited; *Int'l*, pg. 212
TENEDORA DE EMPRESAS SA DE CV; *Int'l*, pg. 7559
TENEI SEAL INDUSTRY CORPORATION—See NOK Corporation; *Int'l*, pg. 5403
TENENBAUM RECYCLING GROUP, LLC—See Alter Trading Corporation; *U.S. Private*, pg. 207
TEN ENTERTAINMENT GROUP PLC—See Trive Capital Inc.; *U.S. Private*, pg. 4240
TENEO AI AB; *Int'l*, pg. 7559
TENEO BLUE RUBICON LIMITED—See CVC Capital Partners SICAV-FIS S.A.; *Int'l*, pg. 1889
TENEO BLUE RUBICON - SINGAPORE—See CVC Capital Partners SICAV-FIS S.A.; *Int'l*, pg. 1889
TENEO HOLDINGS LLC—See CVC Capital Partners SICAV-FIS S.A.; *Int'l*, pg. 1888
TENEO SAS—See Sealed Air Corporation; *U.S. Public*, pg. 1855
TENERE INC.—See CORE Industrial Partners, LLC; *U.S. Private*, pg. 1048
TENERIFE SOL, S.A.—See Melia Hotels International, S.A.; *Int'l*, pg. 4810
TENERITY, INC.; *U.S. Private*, pg. 3966
TENET COMPUTER GROUP INC.; *Int'l*, pg. 7559
TENET FINTECH GROUP INC; *Int'l*, pg. 7559
TENET FLORIDA, INC.—See Tenet Healthcare Corporation; *U.S. Public*, pg. 2004
TENET FLORIDA PHYSICIAN SERVICES III, L.L.C.—See Tenet Healthcare Corporation; *U.S. Public*, pg. 2004
TENET FLORIDA PHYSICIAN SERVICES, L.L.C.—See Tenet Healthcare Corporation; *U.S. Public*, pg. 2004
TENET FRISCO, LTD—See Tenet Healthcare Corporation; *U.S. Public*, pg. 2004
TENET HEALTHCARE CORPORATION; *U.S. Public*, pg. 2001
TENET HEALTHSYSTEM HAHNEMANN, LLC—See Paladin Healthcare Capital, LLC; *U.S. Public*, pg. 3076
TENET HEALTHSYSTEM MEDICAL, INC.—See Tenet Healthcare Corporation; *U.S. Public*, pg. 2007
TENET HILTON HEAD HEART, L.L.C.—See Tenet Healthcare Corporation; *U.S. Public*, pg. 2008
TENET MEDICAL ENGINEERING INC.—See Smith & Nephew plc; *Int'l*, pg. 7009
TENET SOMPO INSURANCE PTE. LTD.—See Sompo Holdings, Inc.; *Int'l*, pg. 7087
TENET SOUTH CAROLINA ISLAND MEDICAL, L.L.C.—See Tenet Healthcare Corporation; *U.S. Public*, pg. 2008
TENET SOUTH CAROLINA LOWCOUNTRY OB/GYN, L.L.C.—See Tenet Healthcare Corporation; *U.S. Public*, pg. 2008
TENET UNIFOUR URGENT CARE CENTER, L.L.C.—See Tenet Healthcare Corporation; *U.S. Public*, pg. 2004
TENEX CAPITAL MANAGEMENT, L.P.; *U.S. Private*, pg. 3966
TENEX CORPORATION; *U.S. Private*, pg. 3966
TENEX HEALTH INC.—See Trice Medical, Inc; *U.S. Private*, pg. 4229
TEN FEET WRIGHT INC.—See Seika Corporation; *Int'l*, pg. 6685
TENFU (CAYMAN) HOLDINGS COMPANY LIMITED; *Int'l*, pg. 7559
TENGASCO PIPELINE CORPORATION—See Riley Exploration Permian, Inc.; *U.S. Public*, pg. 1798
TENGCO INC.; *U.S. Private*, pg. 3967
TENGDA CONSTRUCTION GROUP CO., LTD.; *Int'l*, pg. 7559
TENGELMANN WARENHANDELSGESELLSCHAFT KG; *Int'l*, pg. 7559
T ENGINEERING CORPORATION PUBLIC COMPANY LIMITED; *Int'l*, pg. 7394
TENGJUN BIOTECHNOLOGY CORP.; *U.S. Public*, pg. 2015
TENGOINTERNET; *U.S. Private*, pg. 3967

TENGRAM CAPITAL PARTNERS, LIMITED PARTNERSHIP; *U.S. Private*, pg. 3967
TENGRI CA SAATCHI & SAATCHI—See Publicis Groupe S.A.; *Int'l*, pg. 6109
TENGRI RESOURCES LIMITED—See Stanhill Operations Ltd.; *Int'l*, pg. 7169
TEN GROUP AUSTRALIA PTY. LIMITED—See Ten Lifestyle Group PLC; *Int'l*, pg. 7557
TEN GROUP BELGIUM BVBA—See Ten Lifestyle Group PLC; *Int'l*, pg. 7557
TEN GROUP JAPAN K.K.—See Ten Lifestyle Group PLC; *Int'l*, pg. 7557
TEN GROUP (RUS) LLC—See Ten Lifestyle Group PLC; *Int'l*, pg. 7557
TEN GROUP SINGAPORE PTE. LIMITED—See Ten Lifestyle Group PLC; *Int'l*, pg. 7557
TENGZHOU EASTERN STEEL CORD CO., LTD.—See Shougang Century Holdings Limited; *Int'l*, pg. 6860
TEN & HAN TRADING PTE LTD—See Old Chang Kee Ltd; *Int'l*, pg. 5552
TENIBAC-GRAPHION INC.; *U.S. Private*, pg. 3967
TENIK CO.,LTD.—See Nippon Telegraph & Telephone Corporation; *Int'l*, pg. 5355
T.EN INGENIERIE REGIONALE POUR INDUSTRIES S.A.S.—See Technip Energies N.V.; *Int'l*, pg. 7507
TENIR INVESTMENTS INC.; *U.S. Private*, pg. 3967
TENIX AUSTRALIA PTY LTD.—See Tenix Group Pty Ltd.; *Int'l*, pg. 7560
TENIX GROUP PTY. LTD.; *Int'l*, pg. 7560
TENIX SOLUTIONS PTY LTD—See Tenix Group Pty Ltd.; *Int'l*, pg. 7560
TENKAY RESOURCES INC.—See Hunting Plc; *Int'l*, pg. 3537
TEN LAKES CENTER, LLC—See Acadia Healthcare Company, Inc.; *U.S. Public*, pg. 30
TEN LIFESTYLE GROUP PLC; *Int'l*, pg. 7557
TEN LIFESTYLE MANAGEMENT AFRICA (PTY.) LIMITED—See Ten Lifestyle Group PLC; *Int'l*, pg. 7557
TEN LIFESTYLE MANAGEMENT (ASIA) LIMITED—See Ten Lifestyle Group PLC; *Int'l*, pg. 7557
TEN LIFESTYLE MANAGEMENT (CANADA) ULC—See Ten Lifestyle Group PLC; *Int'l*, pg. 7557
TEN LIFESTYLE MANAGEMENT LIMITED S DE RL DE CV—See Ten Lifestyle Group PLC; *Int'l*, pg. 7557
TEN LIFESTYLE MANAGEMENT LIMITED—See Ten Lifestyle Group PLC; *Int'l*, pg. 7557
TEN LIFESTYLE MANAGEMENT SWITZERLAND, GMBH—See Ten Lifestyle Group PLC; *Int'l*, pg. 7557
TEN LIFESTYLE MANAGEMENT USA INC.—See Ten Lifestyle Group PLC; *Int'l*, pg. 7557
T.EN LOADING SYSTEMS S.A.S.—See Technip Energies N.V.; *Int'l*, pg. 7507
TENMA CORPORATION - HACHINOHE FACTORY—See Tenma Corporation; *Int'l*, pg. 7561
TENMA CORPORATION - HIROSAKI FACTORY—See Tenma Corporation; *Int'l*, pg. 7561
TENMA CORPORATION - NODA FACTORY—See Tenma Corporation; *Int'l*, pg. 7561
TENMA CORPORATION - SHIGA FACTORY—See Tenma Corporation; *Int'l*, pg. 7561
TENMA CORPORATION - SHIN-SHIRAKAWA FACTORY—See Tenma Corporation; *Int'l*, pg. 7561
TENMA CORPORATION; *Int'l*, pg. 7560
TENMA CORPORATION - YAMAGUCHI FACTORY—See Tenma Corporation; *Int'l*, pg. 7561
TENMA PLASTIC MEXICO, SA DE CV—See Tenma Corporation; *Int'l*, pg. 7561
TENMA PRECISION (SHENZHEN) CO., LTD.—See Tenma Corporation; *Int'l*, pg. 7561
TENMA PRECISION (ZHONGSHAN) CO., LTD.—See Tenma Corporation; *Int'l*, pg. 7561
TENMAST SOFTWARE CO.; *U.S. Private*, pg. 3967
TENMA (THAILAND) CO., LTD. - PRACHINBURI FACTORY—See Tenma Corporation; *Int'l*, pg. 7560
TENMA (THAILAND) CO., LTD.—See Tenma Corporation; *Int'l*, pg. 7560
TENMA VIETNAM CO., LTD. - HA NOI FACTORY—See Tenma Corporation; *Int'l*, pg. 7560
TENMA VIETNAM CO., LTD. - HOCHIMINH FACTORY—See Tenma Corporation; *Int'l*, pg. 7560
TENMA VIETNAM CO., LTD.—See Tenma Corporation; *Int'l*, pg. 7560
TENMAYA STORE CO.; *Int'l*, pg. 7561
TENNANT AUSTRALIA—See Tennant Company; *U.S. Public*, pg. 2016
TENNANT CEE GMBH—See Tennant Company; *U.S. Public*, pg. 2016
TENNANT CLEANING SYSTEM & EQUIPMENT CO. LTD.—See Tennant Company; *U.S. Public*, pg. 2016
TENNANT COMPANY COMMERCIAL, USA—See Tennant Company; *U.S. Public*, pg. 2016
TENNANT COMPANY; *U.S. Public*, pg. 2015
TENNANT EUROPE B.V.—See Tennant Company; *U.S. Public*, pg. 2016
TENNANT EUROPE N.V.—See Tennant Company; *U.S. Public*, pg. 2016
TENNANT GMBH & CO. KG—See Tennant Company; *U.S. Public*, pg. 2016
TENNANT GROUP LTD.; *Int'l*, pg. 7561

COMPANY NAME INDEX

TENNANT HOLDING B.V.—See Tennant Company; *U.S. Public*, pg. 2016
TENNANT HOLDINGS—See Tennant Group Ltd.; *Int'l*, pg. 7561
TENNANT MINERALS NL; *Int'l*, pg. 7561
TENNANT N.V.—See Tennant Company; *U.S. Public*, pg. 2016
TENNANT SALES AND SERVICE COMPANY—See Tennant Company; *U.S. Public*, pg. 2016
TENNANT SALES & SERVICE SPAIN S.A.—See Tennant Company; *U.S. Public*, pg. 2016
TENNANT S.A.—See Tennant Company; *U.S. Public*, pg. 2016
TENNECO AUTOMOTIVE DEUTSCHLAND GMBH—See Apollo Global Management, Inc.; *U.S. Public*, pg. 162
TENNECO AUTOMOTIVE EASTERN EUROPE SP. Z0.0.—See Apollo Global Management, Inc.; *U.S. Public*, pg. 162
TENNECO AUTOMOTIVE EUROPE COORDINATION CENTER BVBA—See Apollo Global Management, Inc.; *U.S. Public*, pg. 162
TENNECO AUTOMOTIVE EUROPE, LTD.—See Apollo Global Management, Inc.; *U.S. Public*, pg. 162
TENNECO AUTOMOTIVE HOLDINGS SOUTH AFRICA PTY. LTD—See Apollo Global Management, Inc.; *U.S. Public*, pg. 163
TENNECO AUTOMOTIVE ITALIA S.R.L.—See Apollo Global Management, Inc.; *U.S. Public*, pg. 163
TENNECO AUTOMOTIVE OPERATING COMPANY INC—See Apollo Global Management, Inc.; *U.S. Public*, pg. 163
TENNECO AUTOMOTIVE POLSKA SP. Z.O.O.—See Apollo Global Management, Inc.; *U.S. Public*, pg. 163
TENNECO AUTOMOTIVE PORT ELIZABETH (PTY) LIMITED—See Apollo Global Management, Inc.; *U.S. Public*, pg. 163
TENNECO AUTOMOTIVE SVERIGE A.B.—See Apollo Global Management, Inc.; *U.S. Public*, pg. 163
TENNECO AUTOMOTIVE WALKER—See Apollo Global Management, Inc.; *U.S. Public*, pg. 163
TENNECO CANADA INC—See Apollo Global Management, Inc.; *U.S. Public*, pg. 163
TENNECO, INC.—See Apollo Global Management, Inc.; *U.S. Public*, pg. 160
TENNECO MARZOCCHI ASIA LTD.—See Apollo Global Management, Inc.; *U.S. Public*, pg. 163
TENNECO MARZOCCHI S.R.L.—See Apollo Global Management, Inc.; *U.S. Public*, pg. 163
TENNECO ZWICKAU GMBH—See Apollo Global Management, Inc.; *U.S. Public*, pg. 163
TENNENBAUM CAPITAL PARTNERS, LLC—See BlackRock, Inc.; *U.S. Public*, pg. 347
THE TENNESSEAN—See Gannett Co., Inc.; *U.S. Public*, pg. 900
TENNESSEE, ALABAMA & GEORGIA RAILWAY CO.—See Norfolk Southern Corporation; *U.S. Public*, pg. 1536
TENNESSEE ALUMINUM PROCESSORS; *U.S. Private*, pg. 3967
TENNESSEE AMERICAN WATER—See American Water Works Company, Inc.; *U.S. Public*, pg. 112
TENNESSEE APPAREL CORP.; *U.S. Private*, pg. 3967
TENNESSEE BLOOD SERVICES CORP.—See BioIVT, LLC; *U.S. Private*, pg. 562
TENNESSEE BOOK COMPANY LLC—See Ingram Industries, Inc.; *U.S. Private*, pg. 2076
TENNESSEE BUN COMPANY, LLC - DICKSON PLANT—See Tennessee Bun Company, LLC; *U.S. Private*, pg. 3967
TENNESSEE BUN COMPANY, LLC; *U.S. Private*, pg. 3967
TENNESSEE CLINICAL SCHOOLS, LLC—See Universal Health Services, Inc.; *U.S. Public*, pg. 2259
TENNESSEE COMMERCIAL WAREHOUSE INC.; *U.S. Private*, pg. 3967
THE TENNESSEE CREDIT UNION; *U.S. Private*, pg. 4126
TENNESSEE EASTMAN DIVISION—See Eastman Chemical Company; *U.S. Public*, pg. 706
TENNESSEE FARMERS COOPERATIVE; *U.S. Private*, pg. 3967
TENNESSEE FOOTBALL, INC.; *U.S. Private*, pg. 3967
TENNESSEE GAS PIPELINE COMPANY, L.L.C.—See Kinder Morgan, Inc.; *U.S. Public*, pg. 1233
TENNESSEE HEALTHCARE MANAGEMENT, INC.—See HCA Healthcare, Inc.; *U.S. Public*, pg. 1011
TENNESSEE HOSPITAL ASSOCIATION; *U.S. Private*, pg. 3968
TENNESSEE INDUSTRIAL ELECTRONICS, LLC—See Diploma PLC; *Int'l*, pg. 2129
TENNESSEE IN-HOME PARTNER-II, LLC—See UnitedHealth Group Incorporated; *U.S. Public*, pg. 2247
TENNESSEE PACKAGING—See Buckeye Corrugated Inc.; *U.S. Private*, pg. 677
TENNESSEE PRESS SERVICE, INC; *U.S. Private*, pg. 3968
TENNESSEE RAILWAY CO.—See Norfolk Southern Corporation; *U.S. Public*, pg. 1536
TENNESSEE RAND, INC.—See Lincoln Electric Holdings, Inc.; *U.S. Public*, pg. 1318
TENNESSEE STATE BANK; *U.S. Private*, pg. 3968
TENNESSEE STEEL HAULERS, INC.—See Daseke, Inc.; *U.S. Private*, pg. 1161
TENNESSEE STEELSUMMIT—See Sumitomo Corporation; *Int'l*, pg. 7274
TENNESSEE TRACTOR, LLC - JACKSON—See Charter Communications, Inc.; *U.S. Public*, pg. 483
TENNESSEE TUBEBENDING INC.—See Morris Coupling Company; *U.S. Private*, pg. 2787
TENNESSEE VALLEY AUTHORITY; *U.S. Public*, pg. 2016
TENNESSEE VALLEY DIALYSIS CENTER, LLC—See DaVita Inc.; *U.S. Public*, pg. 643
TENNESSEE VALLEY ELECTRIC COOPERATIVE; *U.S. Private*, pg. 3968
TENNESSEE VALLEY FINANCIAL HOLDINGS, INC.; *U.S. Public*, pg. 2016
TENNESSEE VALLEY HAM CO., INC.; *U.S. Private*, pg. 3968
TENNESSEE VALLEY PRINTING CO.; *U.S. Private*, pg. 3968
TENNESSEE VALLEY RECYCLING LLC; *U.S. Private*, pg. 3968
TENNESSEE VALLEY SIGN & PRINTING, INC.; *U.S. Private*, pg. 3968
T.EN NETHERLANDS B.V.—See Technip Energies N.V.; *Int'l*, pg. 7507
TEN NETWORK HOLDINGS LIMITED—See National Amusements, Inc.; *U.S. Private*, pg. 2844
TENNEY TELEPHONE COMPANY—See Telephone & Data Systems, Inc.; *U.S. Public*, pg. 1998
TENNIER INDUSTRIES INC.; *U.S. Private*, pg. 3968
THE TENNIS CHANNEL, INC.—See Sinclair, Inc.; *U.S. Public*, pg. 1888
TENNIS EXPRESS, LP—See SIGNA Sports United N.V.; *Int'l*, pg. 6910
TENNIS MAGAZINE—See Miller Publishing Group, LLC; *U.S. Private*, pg. 2735
TENNOJI STATION BUILDING CO., LTD—See West Japan Railway Company; *Int'l*, pg. 8385
TENNOJI TERMINAL BUILDING CO., LTD.—See West Japan Railway Company; *Int'l*, pg. 8385
TENNOR HOLDING BV; *Int'l*, pg. 7561
TENNSCO CORPORATION - PLANT 2—See Tennsco Corporation; *U.S. Private*, pg. 3968
TENNSCO CORPORATION; *U.S. Private*, pg. 3968
TENNYSON CHEVROLET; *U.S. Private*, pg. 3968
TEN OAKS GROUP; *U.S. Private*, pg. 3964
TENO.HOLDINGS COMPANY LIMITED.; *Int'l*, pg. 7561
TENOLD TRANSPORTATION LIMITED PARTNERSHIP—See Mullen Group Ltd.; *Int'l*, pg. 5080
TENON MEDICAL, INC.; *U.S. Public*, pg. 2016
TENON TOURS; *U.S. Private*, pg. 3968
TENON USA, INC—See Hardwoods Distribution Inc.; *Int'l*, pg. 3273
TENOVA AUSTRALIA PTY. LTD.—See Techint S.p.A.; *Int'l*, pg. 7505
TENOVA CHILE S.P.A—See Techint S.p.A.; *Int'l*, pg. 7505
TENOVA DO BRASIL LTDA—See Techint S.p.A.; *Int'l*, pg. 7505
TENOVA EAST EUROPE LLC—See Techint S.p.A.; *Int'l*, pg. 7505
TENOVA GOODFELLOW INC.—See Techint S.p.A.; *Int'l*, pg. 7505
TENOVA HYPERTHERM PVT LTD—See Techint S.p.A.; *Int'l*, pg. 7505
TENOVA INC.—See Techint S.p.A.; *Int'l*, pg. 7505
TENOVA INDUSTRIAL TECHNOLOGY CO., LTD—See Techint S.p.A.; *Int'l*, pg. 7505
TENOVA MINERALS (PTY) LTD—See Techint S.p.A.; *Int'l*, pg. 7505
TENOVA MINING & MINERALS USA INC—See Techint S.p.A.; *Int'l*, pg. 7505
TENOVA POMINI—See Techint S.p.A.; *Int'l*, pg. 7505
TENOVA RE ENERGY GMBH—See Techint S.p.A.; *Int'l*, pg. 7504
TENOVA S.P.A.—See Techint S.p.A.; *Int'l*, pg. 7504
TENOWO DE MEXIKO S. DE R.L. DE C.V.—See Hoftex Group AG; *Int'l*, pg. 3441
TENOWO HUZHOU NEW MATERIALS CO., LTD.—See Hoftex Group AG; *Int'l*, pg. 3440
TENOWO REICHENBACH GMBH—See Hoftex Group AG; *Int'l*, pg. 3441
TENOX ASIA COMPANY LIMITED—See TENOX CO., LTD.; *Int'l*, pg. 7561
TENOX CO., LTD.; *Int'l*, pg. 7561
TENOX GIKEN CO., LTD.—See TENOX CO., LTD.; *Int'l*, pg. 7561
TENPAL CO., LTD.—See Bunka Shutter Co., Ltd.; *Int'l*, pg. 1216
TEN PAO GROUP HOLDINGS LIMITED; *Int'l*, pg. 7557
TEN PAO INTERNATIONAL CO., LTD.—See TEN PAO GROUP HOLDINGS LIMITED; *Int'l*, pg. 7557
TENPO INNOVATION CO., LTD.—See Crops Corporation; *Int'l*, pg. 1855
TENPO RYUTSUU NET, INC.—See Hurxley Corporation; *Int'l*, pg. 3538
TENPOS HOLDINGS, INC.; *Int'l*, pg. 7561
TEN PRINS PLC—See Clariane SE; *Int'l*, pg. 1645
T.EN PROCESS TECHNOLOGY, INC.—See Technip Energies N.V.; *Int'l*, pg. 7507
TEN REN TEA CO., LTD.; *Int'l*, pg. 7557
TENRYU AERO COMPONENT CO., LTD.—See ShinMaywa Industries, Ltd.; *Int'l*, pg. 6847
TENRYU AMERICA, INC.—See Tenryu Saw Mfg. Co., Ltd.; *Int'l*, pg. 7561
TENRYU (CHINA) SAW MFG. CO., LTD.—See Tenryu Saw Mfg. Co., Ltd.; *Int'l*, pg. 7561
TENRYU EUROPE GMBH—See Tenryu Saw Mfg. Co., Ltd.; *Int'l*, pg. 7561
TENRYU SANGYO CO., LTD.—See F.C.C. Co., Ltd.; *Int'l*, pg. 2596
TENRYU SAW DE MEXICO, S.A. DE C.V.—See Tenryu Saw Mfg. Co., Ltd.; *Int'l*, pg. 7561
TENRYU SAW INDIA PRIVATE LIMITED—See Tenryu Saw Mfg. Co., Ltd.; *Int'l*, pg. 7561
TENRYU SAW MFG. CO., LTD. - GIKEN FACTORY—See Tenryu Saw Mfg. Co., Ltd.; *Int'l*, pg. 7561
TENRYU SAW MFG. CO., LTD.; *Int'l*, pg. 7561
TENRYU SAW (THAILAND) CO., LTD.—See Tenryu Saw Mfg. Co., Ltd.; *Int'l*, pg. 7561
TENSAR CORPORATION, LLC—See Commercial Metals Company; *U.S. Public*, pg. 547
TENSAR GEOSYNTHETICS (CHINA) LIMITED—See Commercial Metals Company; *U.S. Public*, pg. 547
TENSAR INTERNATIONAL B.V.—See Commercial Metals Company; *U.S. Public*, pg. 547
TENSAR INTERNATIONAL GMBH—See Commercial Metals Company; *U.S. Public*, pg. 547
TENSAR INTERNATIONAL LIMITED—See Commercial Metals Company; *U.S. Public*, pg. 547
TENSAR INTERNATIONAL SARL—See Commercial Metals Company; *U.S. Public*, pg. 547
TENSATOR INC.—See Tensator Ltd.; *Int'l*, pg. 7562
TENSATOR LTD.; *Int'l*, pg. 7562
TEN SERVICOS DE CONCIERGE DO BRASIL LIMITED—See Ten Lifestyle Group PLC; *Int'l*, pg. 7557
TENSHO AMERICA CORPORATION—See Tensho Electric Industries Co., Ltd.; *Int'l*, pg. 7562
TENSHO ELECTRIC INDUSTRIES CO., LTD. - FUKUSHIMA PLANT—See Tensho Electric Industries Co., Ltd.; *Int'l*, pg. 7562
TENSHO ELECTRIC INDUSTRIES CO., LTD. - GUNMA PLANT—See Tensho Electric Industries Co., Ltd.; *Int'l*, pg. 7562
TENSHO ELECTRIC INDUSTRIES CO., LTD. - MIE PLANT—See Tensho Electric Industries Co., Ltd.; *Int'l*, pg. 7562
TENSHO ELECTRIC INDUSTRIES CO., LTD. - SAITAMA PLANT—See Tensho Electric Industries Co., Ltd.; *Int'l*, pg. 7562
TENSHO ELECTRIC INDUSTRIES CO., LTD.; *Int'l*, pg. 7562
TENSHO ELECTRIC INDUSTRIES CO., LTD. - YABUKI PLANT—See Tensho Electric Industries Co., Ltd.; *Int'l*, pg. 7562
TENSHO MEXICO CORPORATION S.A. DE C.V.—See Tensho Electric Industries Co., Ltd.; *Int'l*, pg. 7562
TENSHO PLASTIC (CHANGZHOU) CO., LTD.—See Tensho Electric Industries Co., Ltd.; *Int'l*, pg. 7562
TENSHO POLAND CORPORATION SP. Z O.O.—See Tensho Electric Industries Co., Ltd.; *Int'l*, pg. 7562
TENSILKUT ENGINEERING—See Sieburg International, Inc.; *U.S. Private*, pg. 3646
TENSILKUT INTL. CORP.—See Sieburg International, Inc.; *U.S. Private*, pg. 3646
TENSION ENVELOPE CORPORATION; *U.S. Private*, pg. 3968
TENSITRON, INC.—See Main Line Equity Partners, LLC; *U.S. Private*, pg. 2551
TEN SIXTY FOUR LIMITED; *Int'l*, pg. 7557
TENSOL RAIL LTD.—See TrackNet Holding; *Int'l*, pg. 7886
TEN SQUARE GAMES SA; *Int'l*, pg. 7557
TENSTREET LLC—See Providence Equity Partners L.L.C.; *U.S. Private*, pg. 3293
T ENTERPRISES, INC.; *U.S. Private*, pg. 3909
TENTH AVENUE HOLDINGS LLC; *U.S. Private*, pg. 3968
TENTH AVENUE PETROLEUM CORP.; *Int'l*, pg. 7562
TENTH & BLAKE BEER COMPANY—See Molson Coors Beverage Company; *U.S. Public*, pg. 1459
TEN: THE ENTHUSIAST NETWORK, INC.; *U.S. Private*, pg. 3964
TEN: THE ENTHUSIAST NETWORK, LLC—See TEN: The Enthusiast Network, Inc.; *U.S. Private*, pg. 3964
TENTHOREY S.A.; *Int'l*, pg. 7562
TEN THOUSAND VILLAGES; *U.S. Private*, pg. 3964
TENTH STREET CAPITAL, LLC; *U.S. Private*, pg. 3968
TEN THURINGER ENERGIENETZE GMBH—See E.ON SE; *Int'l*, pg. 2259
TENTHWAVE DIGITAL, LLC—See Wire Stone, LLC; *U.S. Private*, pg. 4546
TENTIWALA METAL PRODUCTS LIMITED; *Int'l*, pg. 7562
TEN TRANSMISSION COMPANY—See Iberdrola, S.A.; *Int'l*, pg. 3571
TENUTA DI CASTELFALFI S.P.A.—See TUI AG; *Int'l*, pg. 7968
TENUTE RUFFINO S.R.L.—See Constellation Brands, Inc.; *U.S. Public*, pg. 571

TENVISION, LLC—See Avista Capital Partners, L.P.; *U.S. Private*, pg. 409
TENWOW INTERNATIONAL HOLDINGS LIMITED; *Int'l*, pg. 7562
TEN-X, LLC—See CoStar Group, Inc.; *U.S. Public*, pg. 586
T.EN ZIMMER GMBH—See Technip Energies N.V.; *Int'l*, pg. 7507
TENZING PRIVATE EQUITY LLP; *Int'l*, pg. 7562
TEOCO CORPORATION; *U.S. Private*, pg. 3968
TEO FOODS INC.; *Int'l*, pg. 7562
TEO GUAN LEE CORPORATION BERHAD; *Int'l*, pg. 7562
TEO GUAN LEE (K.L.) SDN. BHD.—See Teo Guan Lee Corporation Berhad; *Int'l*, pg. 7562
TEO HONG PHAISAN CO., LTD.—See Aiphone Co., Ltd.; *Int'l*, pg. 235
T&E OIL COMPANY INC.; *U.S. Private*, pg. 3909
TEOLLISUUDEN VOIMA OYJ; *Int'l*, pg. 7562
TEORA HEALTH LTD.—See Aequus Pharmaceuticals Inc.; *Int'l*, pg. 179
TEO SENG CAPITAL BERHAD—See Emerging Glory Sdn Bhd; *Int'l*, pg. 2379
TEO SENG FARMING SDN BHD—See Emerging Glory Sdn Bhd; *Int'l*, pg. 2379
TEO SENG FEEDMILL SDN BHD—See Emerging Glory Sdn Bhd; *Int'l*, pg. 2379
TEO SENG PAPER PRODUCTS SDN BHD—See Emerging Glory Sdn Bhd; *Int'l*, pg. 2379
TEO TECHNOLOGIES; *U.S. Private*, pg. 3968
TEO TRAINING LIMITED—See Financial Index Australia Pty Ltd.; *Int'l*, pg. 2665
TEPAC ENTREPRENAD AB—See Storskogen Group AB; *Int'l*, pg. 7228
TEPAK MARKETING SDN BHD—See Johor Corporation; *Int'l*, pg. 3994
TEPCO FINTECH, INC.—See Tokyo Electric Power Company Holdings, Incorporated; *Int'l*, pg. 7790
TEPCO FUEL & POWER, INC.—See Tokyo Electric Power Company Holdings, Incorporated; *Int'l*, pg. 7790
TEPCO HOMETECH, INC.—See Tokyo Electric Power Company Holdings, Incorporated; *Int'l*, pg. 7790
TEPCO HUMMING WORK CO., LTD.—See Tokyo Electric Power Company Holdings, Incorporated; *Int'l*, pg. 7790
TEPCO LIFE SERVICE, INC.—See Tokyo Electric Power Company Holdings, Incorporated; *Int'l*, pg. 7790
TEPCO LOGISTICS CO. LTD.—See Tokyo Electric Power Company Holdings, Incorporated; *Int'l*, pg. 7790
TEPCO OPTICAL NETWORK ENGINEERING INC.—See Tokyo Electric Power Company Holdings, Incorporated; *Int'l*, pg. 7790
TEPCO RENEWABLE POWER, INC.—See Tokyo Electric Power Company Holdings, Incorporated; *Int'l*, pg. 7790
TEPCO SOLUTION ADVANCE CO., LTD.—See Tokyo Electric Power Company Holdings, Incorporated; *Int'l*, pg. 7790
TEPCO TOWN PLANNING CO., LTD.—See Tokyo Electric Power Company Holdings, Incorporated; *Int'l*, pg. 7790
TEPCO VENTURES, INC.—See Tokyo Electric Power Company Holdings, Incorporated; *Int'l*, pg. 7790
TEPE INTERNATIONAL HEALTH INFORMATION SYSTEMS A.S.—See CompuGroup Medical SE & Co. KGaA; *Int'l*, pg. 1757
TEPELNE HOSPODARSTVI MESTA USTI NAD LABEM S.R.O.—See CEZ, a.s.; *Int'l*, pg. 1428
TEPE SANITARY SUPPLY, INC.—See Bain Capital, LP; *U.S. Private*, pg. 441
TEPHA, INC.; *U.S. Private*, pg. 3969
TEPLARNA KYJOV, A.S.—See E.ON SE; *Int'l*, pg. 2259
TEPLARNA LIBEREC A.S.—See Groupe BPCE; *Int'l*, pg. 3094
TEPLARNA OTROKOVICE A.S.—See E.ON SE; *Int'l*, pg. 2256
TEPLARNA TABOR, A.S.—See Carpaterra Capital Partners sro; *Int'l*, pg. 1343
TEPLARNA TRMICE, A.S.—See CEZ, a.s.; *Int'l*, pg. 1428
TEPLO KLASTEREC S.R.O.—See CEZ, a.s.; *Int'l*, pg. 1429
TEPLOPROGRESS OJSC—See Enel S.p.A.; *Int'l*, pg. 2414
TEPLOVI NASOSY LTD—See NIBE Industrier AB; *Int'l*, pg. 5262
TEPPAN RESTAURANTS LTD.—See TPG Capital, L.P.; *U.S. Public*, pg. 2168
TEPPER AUFZUGE GMBH—See ThyssenKrupp AG; *Int'l*, pg. 7726
TEPPITAK SEAFOOD CO., LTD.—See Kiang Huat Sea Gull Trading Frozen Food Public Company Limited; *Int'l*, pg. 4157
TEPRO METAL AG—See Viohalco SA/NV; *Int'l*, pg. 8244
TEQNION AB; *Int'l*, pg. 7562
TEQUILA AUSTRIA—See Omnicom Group Inc.; *U.S. Public*, pg. 1598
TEQUILA BELGIUM—See Omnicom Group Inc.; *U.S. Public*, pg. 1598
TEQUILA BR—See Omnicom Group Inc.; *U.S. Public*, pg. 1598
TEQUILA CHINA—See Omnicom Group Inc.; *U.S. Public*, pg. 1598

TEQUILA COMMUNICATION & MARKETING INC.; *Int'l*, pg. 7562
TEQUILA DIGITAL—See Omnicom Group Inc.; *U.S. Public*, pg. 1598
TEQUILA DURBAN MARKETING SERVICES—See Omnicom Group Inc.; *U.S. Public*, pg. 1598
TEQUILA ESECE—See Omnicom Group Inc.; *U.S. Public*, pg. 1598
TEQUILA FRANCE—See Omnicom Group Inc.; *U.S. Public*, pg. 1598
TEQUILA GUATEMALA—See Omnicom Group Inc.; *U.S. Public*, pg. 1598
TEQUILA HONG KONG—See Omnicom Group Inc.; *U.S. Public*, pg. 1598
TEQUILA INDIA—See Omnicom Group Inc.; *U.S. Public*, pg. 1598
TEQUILA IRELAND—See Omnicom Group Inc.; *U.S. Public*, pg. 1598
TEQUILA ITALIA—See Omnicom Group Inc.; *U.S. Public*, pg. 1598
TEQUILA ITALIA—See Omnicom Group Inc.; *U.S. Public*, pg. 1598
TEQUILA JOHANNESBURG—See Omnicom Group Inc.; *U.S. Public*, pg. 1598
TEQUILA LONDON—See Omnicom Group Inc.; *U.S. Public*, pg. 1598
TEQUILA MANILA—See Omnicom Group Inc.; *U.S. Public*, pg. 1598
TEQUILA MYALO—See Omnicom Group Inc.; *U.S. Public*, pg. 1598
TEQUILA PARTIDA DE MEXICO, S.A. DE C.V.—See Partida Tequila, LLC; *U.S. Private*, pg. 3101
TEQUILA POLSKA SP ZOO—See Omnicom Group Inc.; *U.S. Public*, pg. 1598
TEQUILA PORTUGAL—See Omnicom Group Inc.; *U.S. Public*, pg. 1598
TEQUILA RAAD—See Omnicom Group Inc.; *U.S. Public*, pg. 1598
TEQUILA SINGAPORE—See Omnicom Group Inc.; *U.S. Public*, pg. 1598
TEQUILA SWITZERLAND AG—See Omnicom Group Inc.; *U.S. Public*, pg. 1598
TEQUITY AB; *Int'l*, pg. 7563
TERA AUTOTECH CORP.; *Int'l*, pg. 7563
TERA BALKANIKA D.O.O.—See Terra Balcanica Resources Corporation; *Int'l*, pg. 7566
TERABO CO., LTD.—See Unitika Ltd.; *Int'l*, pg. 8074
TERABYTE NET SOLUTION PUBLIC COMPANY LIMITED—See Nex Point Public Company Limited; *Int'l*, pg. 5239
TERABYTE PLUS PUBLIC CO., LTD.—See Nex Point Public Company Limited; *Int'l*, pg. 5239
TERACENT CORPORATION—See Alphabet Inc.; *U.S. Public*, pg. 84
TERACO DATA ENVIRONMENTS PROPRIETARY LIMITED—See Digital Realty Trust, Inc.; *U.S. Public*, pg. 663
TERACOMM RO SRL—See Link Mobility Group Holding ASA; *Int'l*, pg. 4514
TERACORE, INC. (MID-ATLANTIC REGION)—See Teracore, Inc.; *U.S. Private*, pg. 3969
TERACORE, INC.; *U.S. Private*, pg. 3969
TERACT SA; *Int'l*, pg. 7563
TERADATA ASTER DATA—See Teradata Corporation; *U.S. Public*, pg. 2017
TERADATA AUSTRALIA PTY. LTD.—See Teradata Corporation; *U.S. Public*, pg. 2016
TERADATA AUSTRIA GMBH—See Teradata Corporation; *U.S. Public*, pg. 2017
TERADATA BELGIUM SNC—See Teradata Corporation; *U.S. Public*, pg. 2017
TERADATA BILISIM SISTEMLERI LTD. STI.—See Teradata Corporation; *U.S. Public*, pg. 2017
TERADATA CANADA ULC—See Teradata Corporation; *U.S. Public*, pg. 2017
TERADATA CESKA REPUBLIKA SPOL. S R.O.—See Teradata Corporation; *U.S. Public*, pg. 2017
TERADATA CHILE TECNOLOGIAS DE INFORMACION LIMITADA—See Teradata Corporation; *U.S. Public*, pg. 2017
TERADATA CORPORATION; *U.S. Public*, pg. 2016
TERADATA CZECH REPUBLIC, SPOL. S R.O.—See Teradata Corporation; *U.S. Public*, pg. 2017
TERADATA DANMARK APS—See Teradata Corporation; *U.S. Public*, pg. 2017
TERADATA DE ARGENTINA S.R.L.—See Teradata Corporation; *U.S. Public*, pg. 2017
TERADATA DE MEXICO, S. DE R.L. DE C.V.—See Teradata Corporation; *U.S. Public*, pg. 2017
TERADATA EGYPT WLL—See Teradata Corporation; *U.S. Public*, pg. 2017
TERADATA FINLAND OY—See Teradata Corporation; *U.S. Public*, pg. 2017
TERADATA FRANCE SAS—See Teradata Corporation; *U.S. Public*, pg. 2017
TERADATA GMBH—See Teradata Corporation; *U.S. Public*, pg. 2017
TERADATA GOVERNMENT SYSTEMS LLC—See Teradata Corporation; *U.S. Public*, pg. 2017

TERADATA IBERIA SLU—See Teradata Corporation; *U.S. Public*, pg. 2017
TERADATA INDIA PRIVATE LIMITED—See Teradata Corporation; *U.S. Public*, pg. 2017
TERADATA INFORMATION SYSTEMS (BEIJING) LIMITED—See Teradata Corporation; *U.S. Public*, pg. 2017
TERADATA IRELAND LIMITED—See Teradata Corporation; *U.S. Public*, pg. 2017
TERADATA ITALIA S.R.L.—See Teradata Corporation; *U.S. Public*, pg. 2017
TERADATA JAPAN LTD.—See Teradata Corporation; *U.S. Public*, pg. 2017
TERADATA LLC—See Teradata Corporation; *U.S. Public*, pg. 2017
TERADATA MAGYARORSZAG KFT—See Teradata Corporation; *U.S. Public*, pg. 2017
TERADATA NETHERLANDS B.V.—See Teradata Corporation; *U.S. Public*, pg. 2017
TERADATA NORGE AS—See Teradata Corporation; *U.S. Public*, pg. 2017
TERADATA (NZ) CORPORATION—See Teradata Corporation; *U.S. Public*, pg. 2016
TERADATA OPERATIONS, INC.—See Teradata Corporation; *U.S. Public*, pg. 2017
TERADATA PAKISTAN LIMITED—See Teradata Corporation; *U.S. Public*, pg. 2017
TERADATA PHILIPPINES LLC, MANILA BRANCH—See Teradata Corporation; *U.S. Public*, pg. 2017
TERADATA POLSKA SP. Z O.O—See Teradata Corporation; *U.S. Public*, pg. 2017
TERADATA SAUDI ARABIA LLC—See Teradata Corporation; *U.S. Public*, pg. 2017
TERADATA SCHWEIZ GMBH—See Teradata Corporation; *U.S. Public*, pg. 2017
TERADATA (SINGAPORE) PTE. LTD.—See Teradata Corporation; *U.S. Public*, pg. 2016
TERADATA SWEDEN AB—See Teradata Corporation; *U.S. Public*, pg. 2017
TERADATA TAIWAN LLC—See Teradata Corporation; *U.S. Public*, pg. 2017
TERADATA (THAILAND) CO LTD—See Teradata Corporation; *U.S. Public*, pg. 2016
TERADATA UK LIMITED—See Teradata Corporation; *U.S. Public*, pg. 2017
TERADEK, LLC—See Videndum plc; *Int'l*, pg. 8191
TERADICI CORPORATION—See HP Inc.; *U.S. Public*, pg. 1065
TERA D.P. S.R.L.—See Vista Equity Partners, LLC; *U.S. Private*, pg. 4399
TERADYNE GMBH—See Teradyne, Inc.; *U.S. Public*, pg. 2018
TERADYNE, INC.-ASSEMBLY TEST DIVISION—See Teradyne, Inc.; *U.S. Public*, pg. 2018
TERADYNE, INC.-INTEGRA TEST DIVISION—See Teradyne, Inc.; *U.S. Public*, pg. 2018
TERADYNE, INC.-MEMORY TEST DIVISION—See Teradyne, Inc.; *U.S. Public*, pg. 2018
TERADYNE, INC.; *U.S. Public*, pg. 2017
TERADYNE, K.K.—See Teradyne, Inc.; *U.S. Public*, pg. 2018
TERADYNE KOREA LTD.—See Teradyne, Inc.; *U.S. Public*, pg. 2018
TERADYNE ROBOTS (GERMANY) GMBH—See Teradyne, Inc.; *U.S. Public*, pg. 2018
TERADYNE (SHANGHAI) CO., LTD—See Teradyne, Inc.; *U.S. Public*, pg. 2018
TERADYNE TAIWAN LTD.—See Teradyne, Inc.; *U.S. Public*, pg. 2018
TERA ENERGY DEVELOPMENT CO., LTD.—See United Microelectronics Corporation; *Int'l*, pg. 8070
TERAFLEX, INC.—See Clearlake Capital Group, L.P.; *U.S. Private*, pg. 938
TERAGLASS BISTRITA SRL—See Teraplast S.A.; *Int'l*, pg. 7563
TERAGO INC.; *Int'l*, pg. 7563
TERAGREN; *U.S. Private*, pg. 3969
TERAHERTZ TECHNOLOGIES INC.—See Trend Networks Limited; *Int'l*, pg. 7916
TERAI TEA COMPANY LIMITED; *Int'l*, pg. 7563
TERAJOULE ENERGY GMBH; *Int'l*, pg. 7563
TERAKEET, LLC; *U.S. Private*, pg. 3969
TERALIGHT LTD.; *Int'l*, pg. 7563
TERALOGICS LLC—See Elliott Management Corporation; *U.S. Private*, pg. 1368
TERALOGICS LLC—See Veritas Capital Fund Management, LLC; *U.S. Private*, pg. 4362
TER ALP; *Int'l*, pg. 7563
TERALTA—See CRH plc; *Int'l*, pg. 1849
TERAMECS CO., LTD.—See TERASAKI ELECTRIC CO.,LTD; *Int'l*, pg. 7564
TERANGA GOLD CORPORATION—See Endeavour Mining plc.; *Int'l*, pg. 2402
TERANG NUSA (MALAYSIA) SDN. BHD.—See Southern Capital Group Pte. Ltd.; *Int'l*, pg. 7118
TERAN TBWA—See Omnicom Group Inc.; *U.S. Public*, pg. 1599
TERAOKA SEIKO CO., LTD.; *Int'l*, pg. 7563

COMPANY NAME INDEX

TERAOKA SEISAKUSHO CO., LTD. - IBARAKI FACTORY—See TERAOKA SEISAKUSHO Co Ltd; *Int'l*, pg. 7563
TERAOKA SEISAKUSHO CO., LTD. - SANO FACTORY—See TERAOKA SEISAKUSHO Co Ltd; *Int'l*, pg. 7563
TERAOKA SEISAKUSHO CO LTD; *Int'l*, pg. 7563
TERAOKA SEISAKUSHO (HONG KONG) CO., LTD.—See TERAOKA SEISAKUSHO Co Ltd; *Int'l*, pg. 7563
TERAOKA SEISAKUSHO (SHANGHAI) CO., LTD.—See TERAOKA SEISAKUSHO Co Ltd; *Int'l*, pg. 7563
TERAON CO., LTD.—See SK Inc.; *Int'l*, pg. 6973
TERAPIA SA—See Sun Pharmaceutical Industries Ltd.; *Int'l*, pg. 7308
TERAPLAST S.A.; *Int'l*, pg. 7563
TERAPOWER TECHNOLOGY, INC.—See Powertech Technology Inc.; *Int'l*, pg. 5948
TERA PROBE, INC.—See Powertech Technology Inc.; *Int'l*, pg. 5948
TERARECON, INC.—See Symphony Innovation, LLC; *U.S. Private*, pg. 3900
TERAS 336 PTE LTD—See Ezion Holdings Limited; *Int'l*, pg. 2594
TERASAKI CIRCUIT BREAKERS (S) PTE. LTD.—See TERASAKI ELECTRIC CO.,LTD; *Int'l*, pg. 7564
TERASAKI DO BRASIL LTDA.—See TERASAKI ELECTRIC CO.,LTD; *Int'l*, pg. 7564
TERASAKI ELECTRIC (CHINA) LTD.—See TERASAKI ELECTRIC CO.,LTD; *Int'l*, pg. 7564
TERASAKI ELECTRIC CO. FAR EAST PTE. LTD.—See TERASAKI ELECTRIC CO.,LTD; *Int'l*, pg. 7564
TERASAKI ELECTRIC CO.,LTD; *Int'l*, pg. 7563
TERASAKI ELECTRIC (EUROPE) LTD.—See TERASAKI ELECTRIC CO.,LTD; *Int'l*, pg. 7564
TERASAKI ELECTRIC (M) SDN. BHD.—See TERASAKI ELECTRIC CO.,LTD; *Int'l*, pg. 7564
TERASAKI ELECTRIC (SHANGHAI) CO., LTD.—See TERASAKI ELECTRIC CO.,LTD; *Int'l*, pg. 7564
TERASAKI ELECTRIC TRADING & SERVICES (M) SDN. BHD.—See TERASAKI ELECTRIC CO.,LTD; *Int'l*, pg. 7564
TERASAKI SKANDINAVISKA AB.—See TERASAKI ELECTRIC CO.,LTD; *Int'l*, pg. 7564
TERAS CARGO TRANSPORT (AMERICA) LLC—See Ezion Holdings Limited; *Int'l*, pg. 2594
TERA SCIENCE CO., LTD.; *Int'l*, pg. 7563
TERAS CONQUEST 2 PTE LTD—See Ezion Holdings Limited; *Int'l*, pg. 2594
TERAS ECO SDN. BHD.—See Axteria Group Berhad; *Int'l*, pg. 772
TERAS OFFSHORE PTE LTD—See Ezion Holdings Limited; *Int'l*, pg. 2594
TERA SOFTWARE LTD.; *Int'l*, pg. 7563
TERAS RESOURCES INC.; *Int'l*, pg. 7563
TERASTEEL S.A.—See Teraplast S.A.; *Int'l*, pg. 7563
TERAS TEKNOLOGI SDN BHD—See Khazanah Nasional Berhad; *Int'l*, pg. 4153
TERATECH CO., LTD.; *Int'l*, pg. 7564
TERA TECHNOLOGIES, INC.; *U.S. Private*, pg. 3969
TERATEC LTD.—See TERASAKI ELECTRIC CO.,LTD; *Int'l*, pg. 7564
TERATEC (USA) INC.—See TERASAKI ELECTRIC CO.,LTD; *Int'l*, pg. 7564
TERATHINK CORPORATION; *U.S. Private*, pg. 3969
TERATRON GMBH—See TXT e-Solutions S.p.A.; *Int'l*, pg. 7993
TERAUCHI CO., LTD.—See Senko Group Holdings Co., Ltd.; *Int'l*, pg. 6712
TERAVIEW LTD.; *Int'l*, pg. 7564
TERAWAREHOUSE KOREA CO., LTD.—See Teradata Corporation; *U.S. Public*, pg. 2016
TERAWULF INC.; *U.S. Public*, pg. 2018
TERAX ENERGY, INC.; *U.S. Public*, pg. 2018
TERAXION, INC.; *Int'l*, pg. 7564
TERA YATIRIM MENKUL DEGERLER A.S.; *Int'l*, pg. 7563
TER BEKE FRANCE SA—See What's Cooking Group NV; *Int'l*, pg. 8396
TERBEKE-PLUMA NEDERLAND BV—See What's Cooking Group NV; *Int'l*, pg. 8397
TERBEKE-PLUMA NV—See What's Cooking Group NV; *Int'l*, pg. 8397
TER BEKE VLEESWARENPRODUKTIE NV—See What's Cooking Group NV; *Int'l*, pg. 8397
TERENEO SAS—See Nexity SA; *Int'l*, pg. 5244
TERENGGANU INCORPORATED SDN. BHD.; *Int'l*, pg. 7564
TEREOS INTERNATIONAL—See Tereos; *Int'l*, pg. 7564
TEREOS; *Int'l*, pg. 7564
TEREOS STARCH & SWEETENERS EUROPE SAS—See Tereos; *Int'l*, pg. 7564
TEREOS SUCRE FRANCE SE—See Tereos; *Int'l*, pg. 7564
TEREOS UK LTD—See Tereos; *Int'l*, pg. 7564
TERESOFT AS—See HitecVision AS; *Int'l*, pg. 3426
TERETNI TRANSPORT BOR U RESTRUKTURIRANJU A.D.; *Int'l*, pg. 7564
TEREX ADVANCE MIXER, INC.—See Terex Corporation; *U.S. Public*, pg. 2018

TEREX AERIAL WORK PLATFORMS—See Terex Corporation; *U.S. Public*, pg. 2019
TEREX BETIM EQUIPAMENTO LTDA—See Terex Corporation; *U.S. Public*, pg. 2019
TEREX COMPACT EQUIPMENT—See Terex Corporation; *U.S. Public*, pg. 2019
TEREX CONSTRUCTION AMERICAS—See Terex Corporation; *U.S. Public*, pg. 2019
TEREX CONSTRUCTION—See Terex Corporation; *U.S. Public*, pg. 2019
TEREX CORPORATION; *U.S. Public*, pg. 2018
TEREX CRANES HUNGARY KFT.—See Terex Corporation; *U.S. Public*, pg. 2019
TEREX CRANES, INC.—See Terex Corporation; *U.S. Public*, pg. 2019
TEREX CRANES KOREA CO., LTD.—See Terex Corporation; *U.S. Public*, pg. 2019
TEREX CRANES PTY. LTD.—See Terex Corporation; *U.S. Public*, pg. 2019
TEREX CRANES WILMINGTON, INC.—See Terex Corporation; *U.S. Public*, pg. 2019
TEREX DEUTSCHLAND BAU-BETEILIGUNGEN GMBH—See Terex Corporation; *U.S. Public*, pg. 2019
TEREX DISTRIBUTION LIMITED—See Terex Corporation; *U.S. Public*, pg. 2020
TEREX EQUIPMENT LIMITED—See AB Volvo; *Int'l*, pg. 43
TEREX GB LIMITED—See Terex Corporation; *U.S. Public*, pg. 2019
TEREX GERMANY GMBH & CO. K.G.—See Terex Corporation; *U.S. Public*, pg. 2020
TEREX INDIA PRIVATE LIMITED—See Terex Corporation; *U.S. Public*, pg. 2020
TEREX ITALIA S.R.L.—See Terex Corporation; *U.S. Public*, pg. 2019
TEREX LATIN AMERICA EQUIPAMENTOS LTDA.—See Terex Corporation; *U.S. Public*, pg. 2020
TEREX LIFTING AUSTRALIA PTY. LTD.—See Terex Corporation; *U.S. Public*, pg. 2019
TEREX LIFTING U.K. LIMITED—See Terex Corporation; *U.S. Public*, pg. 2019
TEREXLIFT S.R.L.—See Terex Corporation; *U.S. Public*, pg. 2019
TEREX LIGHT CONSTRUCTION—See Terex Corporation; *U.S. Public*, pg. 2019
TEREX MALAYSIA SDN BHD—See Terex Corporation; *U.S. Public*, pg. 2020
TEREX MATERIAL HANDLING AG—See Terex Corporation; *U.S. Public*, pg. 2020
TEREX MATERIAL HANDLING A/S—See Terex Corporation; *U.S. Public*, pg. 2020
TEREX MATERIAL HANDLING GMBH—See Terex Corporation; *U.S. Public*, pg. 2020
TEREX MATERIAL HANDLING SPOL. S.R.O.—See Terex Corporation; *U.S. Public*, pg. 2020
TEREX MATERIAL HANDLING SP. Z O.O.—See Terex Corporation; *U.S. Public*, pg. 2020
TEREX MATERIALS PROCESSING & MINING—See Terex Corporation; *U.S. Public*, pg. 2020
TEREX MHPS GMBH—See Konecranes Plc; *Int'l*, pg. 4253
TEREX MINERALS PROCESSING SYSTEMS—See Terex Corporation; *U.S. Public*, pg. 2020
TEREX NFLG (QUANZHOU) MOBILE PROCESSING EQUIPMENT CO LTD—See Terex Corporation; *U.S. Public*, pg. 2020
TEREX REDRILL—See Terex Corporation; *U.S. Public*, pg. 2020
TEREX SOUTH DAKOTA, INC.—See Terex Corporation; *U.S. Public*, pg. 2020
TEREX-TELELECT, INC.—See Terex Corporation; *U.S. Public*, pg. 2020
TEREX UTILITIES, INC.—See Terex Corporation; *U.S. Public*, pg. 2020
TEREX UTILITIES SOUTH—See Terex Corporation; *U.S. Public*, pg. 2020
TEREX UTILITIES WEST—See Terex Corporation; *U.S. Public*, pg. 2020
TEREX VERWALTUNGS GMBH—See Terex Corporation; *U.S. Public*, pg. 2020
TERGENE BIOTECH PRIVATE LIMITED—See Aurobindo Pharma Ltd.; *Int'l*, pg. 713
TERGO GRUNDSTUCKS-VERMIETUNGSGESELLSCHAFT MBH—See Deutsche Bank Aktiengesellschaft; *Int'l*, pg. 2062
TERICO; *U.S. Private*, pg. 3969
TERILOGY CO., LTD.; *Int'l*, pg. 7565
TERILOGY SERVICEWARE CORPORATION—See Terilogy Co., Ltd.; *Int'l*, pg. 7565
TERILOGY WORX CORPORATION—See Terilogy Co., Ltd.; *Int'l*, pg. 7565
TERIS—See Veolia Environnement S.A.; *Int'l*, pg. 8155
THE TERLATO WINE GROUP; *U.S. Private*, pg. 4126
TERLATO WINES INTERNATIONAL INC.—See The Terlato Wine Group; *U.S. Private*, pg. 4126
TERLATO WINES—See The Terlato Wine Group; *U.S. Private*, pg. 4126
TERLINDEN TEXTILPFLEGE AG; *Int'l*, pg. 7565
TERLYN INDUSTRIES, INC.; *U.S. Private*, pg. 3969
TERMAS DE PUYEHUE SA; *Int'l*, pg. 7565

TERMINAL GARAGEM MENEZES CORTES S.A.

TERMATECH A/S—See NIBE Industrier AB; *Int'l*, pg. 5262
TERMAX CORPORATION—See LISI S.A.; *Int'l*, pg. 4524
TERMBRAY INDUSTRIES INTERNATIONAL (HOLDINGS) LIMITED; *Int'l*, pg. 7565
TERM COMMODITIES INC.—See Raizen S.A.; *Int'l*, pg. 6192
TERME 3000 MORAVSKE TOPLICE D.D.—See Sava d.d.; *Int'l*, pg. 6596
TERME BANCORP, INC.; *U.S. Public*, pg. 2020
TERME CATEZ, D.D.; *Int'l*, pg. 7565
TERME DOBRNA D.D.; *Int'l*, pg. 7565
TERME KRKA, D. O. O.—See Krka, d.d., Novo Mesto; *Int'l*, pg. 4303
TERME LENDAVA D.D.O.—See Sava d.d.; *Int'l*, pg. 6596
TERMELTFOODS CO., LTD.—See Kobe Bussan Co., Ltd.; *Int'l*, pg. 4217
TERME MARIBOR D.D.—See NFD Holding d.d.; *Int'l*, pg. 5252
TERME PTUJ D.O.O.—See Sava d.d.; *Int'l*, pg. 6596
TERME RADENCI D.O.O.—See Sava d.d.; *Int'l*, pg. 6596
TERM HOLDINGS, LLC—See Blackstone Inc.; *U.S. Public*, pg. 349
TERM HOLDINGS, LLC—See Five Point Energy LLC; *U.S. Private*, pg. 1537
TERMICA COLLEFERRO SPA—See Enel S.p.A.; *Int'l*, pg. 2414
TERMIKA A.D.; *Int'l*, pg. 7565
TERMIKA A.D.; *Int'l*, pg. 7565
TERMIMESH, LLC—See Nippon Filcon Co., Ltd.; *Int'l*, pg. 5318
TERMI-MESH SINGAPORE PTE LTD—See Nippon Filcon Co., Ltd.; *Int'l*, pg. 5318
TERMIMESH VIETNAM—See Nippon Filcon Co., Ltd.; *Int'l*, pg. 5318
TERMINAL 4 S.A.—See A.P. Moller-Maersk A/S; *Int'l*, pg. 28
TERMINAL ALPTRANSIT S.R.L.—See Ferrovie dello Stato Italiane S.p.A.; *Int'l*, pg. 2645
TERMINAL BAHIA BLANCA S.A.—See Bunge Limited; *U.S. Public*, pg. 412
TERMINALCARE SUPPORT INSTITUTE, INC.; *Int'l*, pg. 7565
TERMINAL CERROS DE VALPARAISO, S.A.—See Industry Super Holdings Pty. Ltd.; *Int'l*, pg. 3676
TERMINAL CONSOLIDATION CO. INC.; *U.S. Private*, pg. 3969
TERMINAL CONSTRUCTION CORPORATION; *U.S. Private*, pg. 3969
TERMINAL CONTAINER RAVENNA S.P.A.—See EUROKAI GmbH & Co. KGaA; *Int'l*, pg. 2553
TERMINAL CORPORATION; *U.S. Private*, pg. 3969
TERMINAL DE ALTAMIRA DE S. DE R.L. DE C.V.—See Koninklijke Vopak N.V.; *Int'l*, pg. 4272
TERMINAL DE CARGAS ARGENTINA—See Corporacion America S.A.; *Int'l*, pg. 1803
TERMINAL DE CARGAS URUGUAY S.A.—See Corporacion America S.A.; *Int'l*, pg. 1803
TERMINAL DE CARVAO—See Companhia Siderurgica Nacional; *Int'l*, pg. 1748
TERMINAL DE CONTENEDORES DE ALGECIRAS, S.A.—See Acciona, S.A.; *Int'l*, pg. 90
TERMINAL DE CONTENEDORES DE TENERIFE, S.A—See Grupo Villar Mir, S.A.U.; *Int'l*, pg. 3139
TERMINAL DE FERTILIZANTES ARGENTINOS SA—See Bunge Limited; *U.S. Public*, pg. 412
TERMINALE GNL ADRIATICO S.R.L—See Exxon Mobil Corporation; *U.S. Public*, pg. 817
TERMINALES MARITIMAS DEL SURESTE, S.A.—See Industry Super Holdings Pty. Ltd.; *Int'l*, pg. 3676
TERMINAL ESPECIALIZADA DE CONTENEDORES—See Grupo TMM, S.A.B.; *Int'l*, pg. 3138
TERMINALES RIO DE LA PLATA SA—See Dubai World Corporation; *Int'l*, pg. 2222
TERMINAL EXPORTADOR DE SANTOS S.A.—See Louis Dreyfus Company B.V.; *Int'l*, pg. 4562
TERMINAL FOREST PRODUCTS - LANGDALE DIVISION—See Terminal Forest Products Ltd.; *Int'l*, pg. 7565
TERMINAL FOREST PRODUCTS LTD.; *Int'l*, pg. 7565
TERMINAL FOREST PRODUCTS - MAINLAND DIVISION—See Terminal Forest Products Ltd.; *Int'l*, pg. 7565
TERMINAL FREEZERS, INC.—See Bay Grove Capital LLC; *U.S. Private*, pg. 493
TERMINAL GARAGEM MENEZES CORTES S.A.; *Int'l*, pg. 7565
TERMINAL GRANELES DEL NORTE S.A.—See Ultramar Ltda.; *Int'l*, pg. 8019
TERMINAL INTERNACIONAL DEL SUR S.A.—See Grupo Romero; *Int'l*, pg. 3135
TERMINAL MANUFACTURING CO.—See Crane NXT, Co.; *U.S. Public*, pg. 592
TERMINAL MARITIMA DE TUXPAN S.A. DE C.V.—See International Container Terminal Services, Inc.; *Int'l*, pg. 3747
TERMINAL MARITIMA MAZATLAN S.A. DE C.V.—See Quinenco S.A.; *Int'l*, pg. 6164
TERMINAL NAPOLI S.P.A.—See Carnival Corporation; *U.S. Public*, pg. 438

TERMINAL GARAGEM MENEZES CORTES S.A.   CORPORATE AFFILIATIONS

TERMINAL PACIFICO SUR VALPARAISO S.A.—See Ultramar Ltda.; *Int'l*, pg. 8019
TERMINAL PUERTO ARICA S.A.—See Empresa Constructora Belfi SA; *Int'l*, pg. 2388
TERMINAL PUERTO ARICA S.A.—See Ultramar Ltda.; *Int'l*, pg. 8018
TERMINAL QUIMICO DE ARATU S.A. - TEQUIMAR—See Ultrapar Participacoes S.A.; *Int'l*, pg. 8019
TERMINAL RAILROAD ASSOCIATION; *U.S. Private*, pg. 3969
TERMINALS AND TANKS PETROCHEMICAL CO.—See Petrochemical Transportation Engineering Co.; *Int'l*, pg. 5826
TERMINALS NEW ZEALAND LTD.—See Ampol Limited; *Int'l*, pg. 437
TERMINALS PTY. LTD—See Sunoco LP; *U.S. Public*, pg. 1965
TERMINAL SUPPLY INC.; *U.S. Private*, pg. 3969
TERMINAL TRANSPORT INC.; *U.S. Private*, pg. 3969
TERMINAL WAREHOUSE, INC.—See Peoples Services Inc.; *U.S. Private*, pg. 3142
TERMINAL X ONLINE LTD.; *Int'l*, pg. 7565
TERMINIX GLOBAL HOLDINGS, INC.—See Rentokil Initial plc; *Int'l*, pg. 6289
THE TERMINIX INTERNATIONAL COMPANY LIMITED PARTNERSHIP—See Roark Capital Group Inc.; *U.S. Private*, pg. 3456
TERMINIX SERVICE, INC., *U.S. Private*, pg. 3969
TERMINIX U.K. LIMITED—See Rentokil Initial plc; *Int'l*, pg. 6289
TERMINUS CAPITAL PARTNERS, LLC; *U.S. Private*, pg. 3969
TERMINUS ENERGY, INC., *U.S. Public*, pg. 2020
TERMINUS SOFTWARE, INC.—See Demand Science Group, LLC; *U.S. Private*, pg. 2549
TERMIZO A.S.—See MVV Energie AG; *Int'l*, pg. 5109
TERMO DECIN A.S.—See MVV Energie AG; *Int'l*, pg. 5109
TERMOELECTRICA JOSE DE SAN MARTIN S.A.—See Enel S.p.A.; *Int'l*, pg. 2415
TERMOMONTAZA AD BANJA LUKA; *Int'l*, pg. 7565
TERMONT MONTREAL INC.—See Blue Wolf Capital Partners LLC; *U.S. Private*, pg. 595
TERMOPERNAMBUCO S.A.—See Iberdrola, S.A.; *Int'l*, pg. 3573
TERMOPOMPENI SISTEMI LTD.—See NIBE Industrier AB; *Int'l*, pg. 5262
TERMORAD SPOLKA Z.O.O.—See NIBE Industrier AB; *Int'l*, pg. 5262
TERMO-REX S.A.; *Int'l*, pg. 7565
TERMOSOLAR ALVARADO, S.L.—See ContourGlobal Limited; *Int'l*, pg. 1785
TERMOSOLAR MAJADAS, S.L.—See ContourGlobal Limited; *Int'l*, pg. 1785
TERMOSOLAR PALMA SAETILLA, S.L.—See ContourGlobal Limited; *Int'l*, pg. 1785
TERMOTEC DE CHIHUAHUA, S.A. DE C.V.—See Emerson Electric Co.; *U.S. Public*, pg. 752
TERMOTEK GMBH—See Technotrans AG; *Int'l*, pg. 7512
TERMOVENT KOMERC D.O.O.—See Arbonia AG; *Int'l*, pg. 538
TERMOVENT SC D.O.O.; *Int'l*, pg. 7565
TERNA BAHRAIN HOLDING W.L.L.—See Gek Terna Societe Anonyme Holdings Real Estate Constructions; *Int'l*, pg. 2913
TERNA ENERGY FINANCE S.A.—See TERNA ENERGY SOCIETE ANONYME INDUSTRIAL COMMERCIAL TECHNICAL COMPANY S.A.; *Int'l*, pg. 7566
TERNA ENERGY SA—See Gek Terna Societe Anonyme Holdings Real Estate Constructions; *Int'l*, pg. 2913
TERNA ENERGY SOCIETE ANONYME INDUSTRIAL COMMERCIAL TECHNICAL COMPANY S.A.; *Int'l*, pg. 7566
TERNA ENERGY SOLUTIONS S.R.L.—See Terna S.p.A. - Rete Elettrica Nazionale; *Int'l*, pg. 7566
TERNA GMBH—See Allgeier SE; *Int'l*, pg. 337
TERNA ILIAKI PELOPONNISOU S.A.—See TERNA ENERGY SOCIETE ANONYME INDUSTRIAL COMMERCIAL TECHNICAL COMPANY S.A.; *Int'l*, pg. 7566
TERNA MAG SA—See Gek Terna Societe Anonyme Holdings Real Estate Constructions; *Int'l*, pg. 2913
TERNA PLUS S.R.L.—See Terna S.p.A. - Rete Elettrica Nazionale; *Int'l*, pg. 7566
TERNA S.A.—See Gek Terna Societe Anonyme Holdings Real Estate Constructions; *Int'l*, pg. 2913
TERNA S.P.A. - CAGLIARI—See Terna S.p.A. - Rete Elettrica Nazionale; *Int'l*, pg. 7566
TERNA S.P.A. - RETE ELETTRICA NAZIONALE; *Int'l*, pg. 7566
TERNA S.P.A. - TORINO—See Terna S.p.A. - Rete Elettrica Nazionale; *Int'l*, pg. 7566
TERNEFTEGAZ JSC—See TotalEnergies SE; *Int'l*, pg. 7839
TERNIAN INSURANCE GROUP, LLC—See AXIS Capital Holdings Limited; *Int'l*, pg. 770
TERNIENERGIA S.P.A.; *Int'l*, pg. 7566
TERNIGREEN S.P.A.—See TerniEnergia S.p.A.; *Int'l*, pg. 7566
TERNINOX S.P.A.—See ThyssenKrupp AG; *Int'l*, pg. 7726

TERNITZ DRUCKGUSS GMBH—See Schindler Holding AG; *Int'l*, pg. 6621
TERNIUM BRASIL LTDA.—See Techint S.p.A.; *Int'l*, pg. 7505
TERNIUM HYLSA S.A. DE C.V.—See Techint S.p.A.; *Int'l*, pg. 7505
TERNIUM MEXICO S.A. DE C.V.—See Techint S.p.A.; *Int'l*, pg. 7505
TERNIUM S.A.—See Techint S.p.A.; *Int'l*, pg. 7505
TERN PLC; *Int'l*, pg. 7565
TERNPRO INC.—See Smartsheet Inc.; *U.S. Public*, pg. 1896
TERN PROPERTIES COMPANY LIMITED; *Int'l*, pg. 7565
TERNS PHARMACEUTICALS, INC.; *U.S. Public*, pg. 2020
TERPAC PLASTICS INTERNATIONAL INC.; *Int'l*, pg. 7566
TERPHANE INC.—See Oben Holding Group SAC; *Int'l*, pg. 5510
TERPHANE, LTDA.—See Oben Holding Group SAC; *Int'l*, pg. 5510
TERPIN COMMUNICATIONS GROUP; *U.S. Private*, pg. 3970
TERRA ARMADA LTDA—See VINCI S.A.; *Int'l*, pg. 8233
TERRA ARMADA LTDA—See VINCI S.A.; *Int'l*, pg. 8233
TERRA ARMATA S.R.L.—See VINCI S.A.; *Int'l*, pg. 8233
TERRA BALCANICA RESOURCES CORPORATION; *Int'l*, pg. 7566
TERRABANK NA; *U.S. Private*, pg. 3970
TERRABAU GMBH—See CR Capital Real Estate AG; *Int'l*, pg. 1827
TERRABIOGEN TECHNOLOGIES INC.; *Int'l*, pg. 7567
TERRA BRANDS LTD.—See Terra Mauricia Limited; *Int'l*, pg. 7567
TERRA CANIS GMBH—See Nestle S.A.; *Int'l*, pg. 5211
TERRA CAPITAL PLC; *Int'l*, pg. 7566
TERRACARE ASSOCIATES, LLC—See One Rock Capital Partners, LLC; *U.S. Private*, pg. 3023
TERRACE COURT SENIOR LIVING, INC.—See The Ensign Group, Inc.; *U.S. Public*, pg. 2070
TERRACE FORD LINCOLN SALES INC; *Int'l*, pg. 7567
TERRACE GLOBAL, INC.; *Int'l*, pg. 7567
TERRACE HEARING CLINIC LTD.—See Amplifon S.p.A.; *Int'l*, pg. 436
TERRACE HOTEL (OPERATIONS) PTY LTD—See Stamford Land Corporation Ltd.; *Int'l*, pg. 7165
TERRACE INSURANCE BROKERS PTY. LTD.—See AUB Group Limited; *Int'l*, pg. 698
THE TERRACES AT BONITA SPRINGS—See SantaFe Healthcare, Inc.; *U.S. Private*, pg. 3548
TERRACE TOTEM FORD SALES LTD.; *Int'l*, pg. 7567
TERRA COASTAL ESCROW, INC.—See Anywhere Real Estate Inc.; *U.S. Public*, pg. 143
TERRACO GOLD CORP.—See Sailfish Royalty Corp.; *Int'l*, pg. 6483
TERRACOM LIMITED; *Int'l*, pg. 7567
TERRACON CONSULTANTS, INC. - AMES—See Terracon Consultants, Inc.; *U.S. Private*, pg. 3971
TERRACON CONSULTANTS, INC. - BIRMINGHAM—See Terracon Consultants, Inc.; *U.S. Private*, pg. 3971
TERRACON CONSULTANTS, INC. - CINCINNATI—See Terracon Consultants, Inc.; *U.S. Private*, pg. 3971
TERRACON CONSULTANTS, INC. - DALLAS—See Terracon Consultants, Inc.; *U.S. Private*, pg. 3971
TERRACON CONSULTANTS, INC. - SIOUX CITY—See Terracon Consultants, Inc.; *U.S. Private*, pg. 3971
TERRACON CONSULTANTS, INC; *U.S. Private*, pg. 3970
TERRACON CONSULTANTS, INC.; *U.S. Private*, pg. 3970
TERRACON CONSULTANTS, INC. - TAMPA—See Terracon Consultants, Inc.; *U.S. Private*, pg. 3971
TERRACON CONSULTANTS, INC. - WEST FARGO—See Terracon Consultants, Inc.; *U.S. Private*, pg. 3971
TERRACON CORPORATION—See Chargepoint Technology Ltd.; *Int'l*, pg. 1448
TERRA CONTRACTING SERVICES, LLC—See Great Lakes Dredge & Dock Corporation; *U.S. Public*, pg. 962
TERRACOTTA, INC.—See Silver Lake Group, LLC; *U.S. Private*, pg. 3660
TERRACYCLE INC.; *U.S. Private*, pg. 3971
TERRADATUM, INC.—See Lone Wolf Real Estate Technologies Inc.; *Int'l*, pg. 4548
TERRADEK LIGHTING INC.—See Great Plains Companies, Inc.; *U.S. Private*, pg. 1766
TERRA DEVELOPMENT MARKETING, LLC—See Halstead Property, LLC; *U.S. Private*, pg. 1846
TERRA DRIVE SYSTEMS, INC.—See HCI Equity Management, L.P.; *U.S. Private*, pg. 1889
TERRADYNE ENGINEERING, INC.; *U.S. Private*, pg. 3971
TERRA ENERGIA—See Grupo Terra S.A. de C.V.; *Int'l*, pg. 3137
TERRA ENERGY PARTNERS LLC—See Kayne Anderson Capital Advisors, L.P.; *U.S. Private*, pg. 2267
TERRA ENERGY PARTNERS LLC—See Warburg Pincus LLC; *U.S. Private*, pg. 4440
TERRA ENERGY & RESOURCE TECHNOLOGIES, INC.; *U.S. Public*, pg. 2020
TERRA ESTIVAL 2002 S.A.; *Int'l*, pg. 7566
TERRAFAME GROUP OY; *Int'l*, pg. 7567

TERRAFAME OY—See Terrafame Group Oy; *Int'l*, pg. 7567
TERRA FIRMA CAPITAL CORPORATION—See GM Capital Corp; *Int'l*, pg. 3011
TERRA FIRMA CAPITAL MANAGEMENT LIMITED—See Terra Firma Capital Partners Ltd.; *Int'l*, pg. 7566
TERRA FIRMA CAPITAL PARTNERS LTD.; *Int'l*, pg. 7566
TERRA FIRMA FERTILISERS PTY LIMITED—See Nutrien Ltd.; *Int'l*, pg. 5493
TERRAFIRMA GMBH—See Terra Firma Capital Partners Ltd.; *Int'l*, pg. 7566
TERRAFIRMA ROADWAYS LIMITED—See Newpark Resources, Inc.; *U.S. Public*, pg. 1518
TERRAFIX GEOSYNTHETICS INC.—See Leggett & Platt, Incorporated; *U.S. Public*, pg. 1303
TERRA FLUID MANAGEMENT, LLC—See Great Lakes Dredge & Dock Corporation; *U.S. Public*, pg. 962
TERRAFORM GLOBAL, INC.—See Brookfield Corporation; *Int'l*, pg. 1189
TERRAFORM POWER, INC.—See Brookfield Corporation; *Int'l*, pg. 1189
TERRAFOUNDATIONS S.A.—See Echeverria Izquierdo S.A.; *Int'l*, pg. 2289
TERRA FRUCTI S.A.S.—See CBC Co., Ltd.; *Int'l*, pg. 1365
TERRAFUGIA, INC.—See Zhejiang Geely Holding Group Co., Ltd.; *Int'l*, pg. 8652
TERRAGEN HOLDINGS LIMITED; *Int'l*, pg. 7567
TERRAGEN LTD.—See Terra Mauricia Limited; *Int'l*, pg. 7567
TERRA-GEN OPERATING CO., LLC—See ArcLight Capital Holdings, LLC; *U.S. Private*, pg. 312
TERRA-GEN OPERATING COMPANY, LLC—See ArcLight Capital Holdings, LLC; *U.S. Private*, pg. 312
TERRA-GEN POWER, LLC—See ArcLight Capital Holdings, LLC; *U.S. Private*, pg. 312
TERRAGRI LTD.—See Terra Mauricia Limited; *Int'l*, pg. 7567
TERRA GROUP; *U.S. Private*, pg. 3970
TERRAHEALTH INC.; *U.S. Private*, pg. 3971
TERRAIN-AKTIENGESELLSCHAFT HERZOGPARK—See Advent International Corporation; *U.S. Private*, pg. 97
TERRAIN-AKTIENGESELLSCHAFT HERZOGPARK—See Centerbridge Partners, L.P.; *U.S. Private*, pg. 813
TERRA INFORMATION GROUP, INC (TIG)—See HR Path SAS; *Int'l*, pg. 3501
TERRAIN MINERALS LTD; *Int'l*, pg. 7567
TERRA INVENTIONS CORP.; *U.S. Private*, pg. 3970
TERRAKOMP GMBH—See E.ON SE; *Int'l*, pg. 2259
THE TERRALIGN GROUP, INC.—See Salesforce, Inc.; *U.S. Public*, pg. 1837
TERRALINK HORTICULTURE INC. - DELTA DIVISION—See Stern Partners Inc.; *Int'l*, pg. 7212
TERRALINK HORTICULTURE INC. - GROTEC EQUIPMENT DIVISION—See Stern Partners Inc.; *Int'l*, pg. 7212
TERRALINK HORTICULTURE INC.—See Stern Partners Inc.; *Int'l*, pg. 7212
TERRAL RIVERSERVICE, INC.; *U.S. Private*, pg. 3971
TERRAL SEED, INC.—See Corteva, Inc.; *U.S. Public*, pg. 583
TERRAMAR CAPITAL LLC; *U.S. Private*, pg. 3971
TERRAMARE OY—See HAL Trust N.V.; *Int'l*, pg. 3227
TERRAMAR RETAIL CENTERS, LLC; *U.S. Private*, pg. 3971
TERRA MAURICIA LIMITED; *Int'l*, pg. 7567
TERRA MEDITERRANEA D.D.; *Int'l*, pg. 7567
TERRAM GEOSYNTHETICS PRIVATE LIMITED—See Berry Global Group, Inc; *U.S. Public*, pg. 325
TERRA MILLENIUM CORPORATION; *U.S. Private*, pg. 3970
TERRAMIN AUSTRALIA LIMITED; *Int'l*, pg. 7567
TERRAM LIMITED—See Berry Global Group, Inc; *U.S. Public*, pg. 321
TERRAMOR HOMES, INC.—See D.R. Horton, Inc.; *U.S. Public*, pg. 620
TERRANAVIGATOR, LLC—See Ameresco, Inc.; *U.S. Public*, pg. 95
TERRANET AB; *Int'l*, pg. 7567
TERRANETS BW GMBH—See EnBW Energie Baden-Wurttemberg AG; *Int'l*, pg. 2401
TERRA NETWORKS ARGENTINA, S.A.—See Telefonica, S.A.; *Int'l*, pg. 7536
TERRA NETWORKS BRASIL, S.A.—See Telefonica, S.A.; *Int'l*, pg. 7535
TERRA NETWORKS MEXICO, S.A. DE C.V.—See Telefonica, S.A.; *Int'l*, pg. 7536
TERRA NETWORKS PERU, S.A.—See Telefonica, S.A.; *Int'l*, pg. 7536
TERRANEXT L.L.C.; *U.S. Private*, pg. 3971
TERRA NITROGEN COMPANY, L.P.—See CF Industries Holdings, Inc.; *U.S. Public*, pg. 477
TERRANIX CO., LTD.—See Korea Circuit Co Ltd; *Int'l*, pg. 4282
TERRANOR A/S—See Mutares SE & Co. KGaA; *Int'l*, pg. 5106
TERRAN ORBITAL CORPORATION—See Lockheed Martin Corporation; *U.S. Public*, pg. 1339
TERRANOR OY—See Mutares SE & Co. KGaA; *Int'l*, pg. 5106

2722

COMPANY NAME INDEX

TERRA NOVA MOTORS LTD.; *Int'l*, pg. 7567
TERRANOVA PAPERS, S.A.—See Miquel y Costas & Miquel, S.A.; *Int'l*, pg. 4915
TERRANOVA PARTNERS, L.P.; *Int'l*, pg. 7567
TERRA NOVA STEEL & IRON INC. - ALBERTA PLANT—See Terra Nova Steel & Iron Inc.; *Int'l*, pg. 7567
TERRA NOVA STEEL & IRON INC.; *Int'l*, pg. 7567
TERRA NOVA TECHNOLOGIES, INC.—See Murray & Roberts Holdings Ltd.; *Int'l*, pg. 5100
TERRANUEVA CORPORATION—See Goldflare Exploration Inc.; *Int'l*, pg. 3033
TERRA PACIFIC LANDSCAPE, INC.—See Gothic Landscape, Inc.; *U.S. Private*, pg. 1745
TERRAPASS INC.—See Just Energy Group Inc.; *Int'l*, pg. 4031
TERRAPHASE ENGINEERING INC.; *U.S. Private*, pg. 3972
TERRAPIN 3 ACQUISITION CORPORATION; *U.S. Private*, pg. 3972
TERRAPIN 4 ACQUISITION CORPORATION; *U.S. Private*, pg. 3972
TERRAPIN ASSET MANAGEMENT, LLC—See Terrapin Partners LLC; *U.S. Private*, pg. 3972
TERRAPIN BEER COMPANY, LLC—See Tilray Brands, Inc.; *Int'l*, pg. 7748
TERRAPIN PARTNERS LLC; *U.S. Private*, pg. 3972
TERRAPIN RIDGE FARMS, LLC; *U.S. Private*, pg. 3972
TERRAPIN UTILITY SERVICES, INC.—See American States Water Company; *U.S. Public*, pg. 110
TERRAPOINTE LLC—See Rayonier Inc.; *U.S. Public*, pg. 1765
TERRAPRIME, INC.—See Lopez, Inc.; *Int'l*, pg. 4557
TERRA PROPERTY TRUST, INC.; *U.S. Public*, pg. 2020
TERRAQUEST SOLUTIONS LIMITED—See Apse Capital Ltd.; *Int'l*, pg. 523
TERRA REAL ESTATE ADVISORS—See Terra Group; *U.S. Private*, pg. 3970
TERRA RECYCLING SP. Z O.O.SP.K.—See Elemental Holding S.A.; *Int'l*, pg. 2358
TERRA SANTA AGRO S.A.—See SLC Agricola S.A.; *Int'l*, pg. 6996
TERRASCEND CORP.; *Int'l*, pg. 7567
TERRA SEARCH PARTNERS, LLC—See RFE Investment Partners; *U.S. Private*, pg. 3420
TERRA SECURED INCOME TRUST, INC.; *U.S. Private*, pg. 3970
TERRASEM CO., LTD.; *Int'l*, pg. 7568
TERRASIM, INC.—See BAE Systems plc; *Int'l*, pg. 798
TERRASKY CO., LTD.; *Int'l*, pg. 7568
TERRASKY INC.—See TerraSky Co., Ltd.; *Int'l*, pg. 7568
TERRASMART, LLC—See Gibraltar Industries, Inc.; *U.S. Public*, pg. 936
TERRA SOLAR NORTH AMERICA, INC.—See China Solar Energy Holdings Limited; *Int'l*, pg. 1552
TERRASOURCE GLOBAL CIS LIMITED LIABILITY COMPANY—See Hillenbrand, Inc.; *U.S. Public*, pg. 1037
TERRASOURCE GLOBAL CORPORATION - DUNCAN—See Hillenbrand, Inc.; *U.S. Public*, pg. 1037
TERRASOURCE GLOBAL CORPORATION—See Hillenbrand, Inc.; *U.S. Public*, pg. 1037
TERRASSA CONCRETE INDUSTRIES; *U.S. Private*, pg. 3972
TERRASSEMENTS ET CANALISATIONS; *Int'l*, pg. 7568
TERRA STRUCTURES—See Haines & Kibblehouse Inc.; *U.S. Private*, pg. 1841
TERRASURE DEVELOPMENT, LLC—See OceanSound Partners, LP; *U.S. Private*, pg. 2991
TERRATEC AS; *Int'l*, pg. 7568
TERRATEC ELECTRONIC GMBH; *Int'l*, pg. 7568
TERRATECH ENGINEERS, INC.—See NV5 Global, Inc.; *U.S. Public*, pg. 1558
TERRATEC SWEDEN AB—See Terratec AS; *Int'l*, pg. 7568
TERRATHERM, INC.—See TruArc Partners, L.P.; *U.S. Private*, pg. 4245
TERRA TIMBERS PTY LTD—See Brickworks Limited; *Int'l*, pg. 1152
TERRA TRITECH ENGINEERING (M) SDN BHD—See Tritech Group Limited; *Int'l*, pg. 7928
TERRA UNIVERSAL INC.; *U.S. Private*, pg. 3970
TERRA URANIUM LIMITED; *Int'l*, pg. 7567
TERRA VERDE GROUP, LLC; *U.S. Private*, pg. 3970
TERRAVEST INDUSTRIES, INC.; *Int'l*, pg. 7568
TERRAVICI DRILLING SOLUTIONS, INC.—See Helmerich & Payne, Inc.; *U.S. Public*, pg. 1024
TERRAVIS GMBH—See AGRAVIS Raiffeisen AG; *Int'l*, pg. 215
TERRA VITRIS EMPREENDIMENTOS IMOBILIARIOS LTDA.—See Even Construtora e Incorporadora S.A.; *Int'l*, pg. 2562
TERREAL S.A.—See LBO France S.a.r.l.; *Int'l*, pg. 4429
TERRE ARMEE B.V.—See VINCI S.A.; *Int'l*, pg. 8233
TERRE ARMEE INTERNATIONALE SAS—See VINCI S.A.; *Int'l*, pg. 8233
TERRE ARMEE K K—See VINCI S.A.; *Int'l*, pg. 8229
TERRE ARMEE MAROC—See VINCI S.A.; *Int'l*, pg. 8233
TERRE D'AZUR SAS—See VINCI S.A.; *Int'l*, pg. 8229

TERRE HAUTE REGIONAL HOSPITAL—See HCA Healthcare, Inc.; *U.S. Public*, pg. 1011
TERRE HAUTE SURGICAL CENTER, LLC—See Tenet Healthcare Corporation; *U.S. Public*, pg. 2013
TERRE HAUTE TV, LLC—See Entertainment Studios, Inc.; *U.S. Private*, pg. 1405
TERRE HILL COMPOSITES, INC.—See Terre Hill Concrete Products, Inc.; *U.S. Private*, pg. 3972
TERRE HILL CONCRETE PRODUCTS, INC.; *U.S. Private*, pg. 3972
TERRE HILL CONCRETE PRODUCTS, INC. - TERRE HILL STORMWATER SYSTEMS DIVISION—See Terre Hill Concrete Products, Inc.; *U.S. Private*, pg. 3972
TERREIS; *Int'l*, pg. 7568
TERRELL IRON & METAL INC.—See M. Lipsitz & Co., Ltd.; *U.S. Private*, pg. 2527
TERRELL'S OFFICE MACHINES, INC.—See Fisher's Document Systems, Inc.; *U.S. Private*, pg. 1535
TERREMARK WORLDWIDE, INC.-MIAMI—See Verizon Communications Inc.; *U.S. Public*, pg. 2285
TERRENO 3601 PENNSY LLC—See Terreno Realty Corporation; *U.S. Public*, pg. 2021
TERRENO AIRGATE LLC—See Terreno Realty Corporation; *U.S. Public*, pg. 2021
TERRENO GRUNDSTUCKSVERWALTUNG GMBH—See UniCredit S.p.A.; *Int'l*, pg. 8038
TERRENO REALTY CORPORATION; *U.S. Public*, pg. 2020
TERRENO RESOURCES CORP.; *Int'l*, pg. 7568
TERRES AGENTUR GMBH—See AGRAVIS Raiffeisen AG; *Int'l*, pg. 215
TERRES MARKETING- UND CONSULTING GMBH—See AGRAVIS Raiffeisen AG; *Int'l*, pg. 216
TERRESTAR CORPORATION; *U.S. Private*, pg. 3972
TERRESTRIAL RF LICENSING, INC.—See iHeartMedia, Inc.; *U.S. Public*, pg. 1096
TERRIER MEDIA BUYER, INC.—See Apollo Global Management, Inc.; *U.S. Public*, pg. 163
TERRIER SECURITY SERVICES (INDIA) PRIVATE LIMITED—See Quess Corp Limited; *Int'l*, pg. 6160
TERRIN LTD.—See PJSC Concern Galnaftogaz; *Int'l*, pg. 5878
TERRIO THERAPY-FITNESS, INC.; *U.S. Private*, pg. 3972
TERRI SCHEER INSURANCE PTY LTD—See Suncorp Group Limited; *Int'l*, pg. 7311
TERRI'S CONSIGN & DESIGN HOLDING; *U.S. Private*, pg. 3972
TERRITOIRES ENERGIES NOUVELLES—See Rubis SCA; *Int'l*, pg. 6423
TERRITORIAL BANCORP INC.; *U.S. Public*, pg. 2021
TERRITORIAL GENERATING CO NO.14 OAO; *Int'l*, pg. 7568
TERRITORIAL GENERATING CO NO 1 PJSC; *Int'l*, pg. 7568
TERRITORIAL SAVINGS BANK—See Territorial Bancorp Inc.; *U.S. Public*, pg. 2021
THE TERRITORY AHEAD—See Qurate Retail, Inc.; *U.S. Public*, pg. 1758
TERRITORY EMBRACE GMBH—See Bertelsmann SE & Co. KGaA; *Int'l*, pg. 996
TERRITORY GMBH—See Bertelsmann SE & Co. KGaA; *Int'l*, pg. 996
TERRITORY INFLUENCE GMBH—See Bertelsmann SE & Co. KGaA; *Int'l*, pg. 996
TERRITORY RURAL MCPHERSON PTY. LTD.—See Nutrien Ltd.; *Int'l*, pg. 5493
TERRITORY TELEVISION PTY. LIMITED—See Nine Entertainment Co. Holdings Limited; *Int'l*, pg. 5300
TERROIRS DISTILLERS; *Int'l*, pg. 7568
TERROS INC.; *U.S. Private*, pg. 3972
TERRUS GRUNDSTUCKS-VERMIETUNGSGESELLSCHAFT MBH & CO. OBJEKT BERNBACH KG—See Deutsche Bank Aktiengesellschaft; *Int'l*, pg. 2062
TERRUS GRUNDSTUCKS-VERMIETUNGSGESELLSCHAFT MBH—See Deutsche Bank Aktiengesellschaft; *Int'l*, pg. 2062
TERRUZZI FERCALX ENERGY SRL—See Terruzzi Fercalx SpA; *Int'l*, pg. 7568
TERRUZZI FERCALX ENGINEERING PVT LTD—See Terruzzi Fercalx SpA; *Int'l*, pg. 7568
TERRUZZI FERCALX INDIA LTD.—See Terruzzi Fercalx SpA; *Int'l*, pg. 7568
TERRUZZI FERCALX SPA; *Int'l*, pg. 7568
TERRYBERRY COMPANY LLC; *U.S. Private*, pg. 3972
TERRY ENVIRONMENTAL SERVICES, INC.; *U.S. Private*, pg. 3972
TERRY HUNT CONSTRUCTION; *U.S. Private*, pg. 3972
TERRY MELLSOP BUILDING SUPPLIES LIMITED—See Fletcher Building Limited; *Int'l*, pg. 2701
TERRYN HOUT NV—See VINCI S.A.; *Int'l*, pg. 8229
TERRY'S ELECTRIC INC.; *U.S. Private*, pg. 3972
TERRY SHIELDS PTY. LTD.; *Int'l*, pg. 7568
TERRY SLIGH AUTOMOTIVE, INC.; *U.S. Private*, pg. 3972
TERRY'S LINCOLN MERCURY; *U.S. Private*, pg. 3972
TERRY'S MACHINE & MANUFACTURING, INC.—See Loar Group, Inc.; *U.S. Private*, pg. 2477

TERUMO CORPORATION

TERRY'S TIRE TOWN INC.—See TPG Capital, L.P.; *U.S. Public*, pg. 2166
TERRY WYNTER AUTO SERVICE CENTER, INC.; *U.S. Private*, pg. 3972
TERRY YORK MOTOR CARS, LTD.—See AutoNation, Inc.; *U.S. Public*, pg. 238
TERRY YORK MOTOR CARS, LTD.—See AutoNation, Inc.; *U.S. Public*, pg. 238
TERTIANUM AG—See Swiss Prime Site AG; *Int'l*, pg. 7371
TERTIANUM ROMANDIE MANAGEMENT SA—See Swiss Prime Site AG; *Int'l*, pg. 7371
TERTIARY GOLD LIMITED—See Tertiary Minerals plc; *Int'l*, pg. 7569
TERTIARY MINERALS PLC; *Int'l*, pg. 7568
TERTIUM S.P.R.L.—See A.A.G. STUCCHI s.r.l.; *Int'l*, pg. 23
TERTRE ROUGE ASSETS PLC; *Int'l*, pg. 7569
TERUBE LTD.—See Seven & i Holdings Co., Ltd.; *Int'l*, pg. 6731
TERUMO AMERICAS HOLDING, INC.—See Terumo Corporation; *Int'l*, pg. 7569
TERUMO ASIA HOLDINGS PTE. LTD.—See Terumo Corporation; *Int'l*, pg. 7569
TERUMO AUSTRALIA PTY LIMITED—See Terumo Corporation; *Int'l*, pg. 7569
TERUMO BCT ASIA PTE. LTD.—See Terumo Corporation; *Int'l*, pg. 7569
TERUMO BCT AUSTRALIA PTY. LTD.—See Terumo Corporation; *Int'l*, pg. 7569
TERUMO BCT (CANADA), INC.—See Terumo Corporation; *Int'l*, pg. 7569
TERUMO BCT CHILE S.A.—See Terumo Corporation; *Int'l*, pg. 7569
TERUMO BCT COLOMBIA S.A.—See Terumo Corporation; *Int'l*, pg. 7569
TERUMO BCT EUROPE N.V.—See Terumo Corporation; *Int'l*, pg. 7569
TERUMO BCT EUROPE N.V.—See Terumo Corporation; *Int'l*, pg. 7569
TERUMO BCT (HONG KONG) LTD.—See Terumo Corporation; *Int'l*, pg. 7569
TERUMO BCT, INC.—See Terumo Corporation; *Int'l*, pg. 7569
TERUMO BCT JAPAN, INC.—See Terumo Corporation; *Int'l*, pg. 7569
TERUMO BCT LATIN AMERICA S.A.—See Terumo Corporation; *Int'l*, pg. 7569
TERUMO BCT, LTD.—See Terumo Corporation; *Int'l*, pg. 7570
TERUMO BCT MEDICAL PRODUCT TRADING (SHANGHAI) LTD.—See Terumo Corporation; *Int'l*, pg. 7569
TERUMO BCT MEXICO S.A. DE C.V.—See Terumo Corporation; *Int'l*, pg. 7569
TERUMO BCT PERU S.A.C.—See Terumo Corporation; *Int'l*, pg. 7569
TERUMO BCT TECNOLOGIA MEDICA LTDA.—See Terumo Corporation; *Int'l*, pg. 7569
TERUMO BCT URUGUAY S.A.—See Terumo Corporation; *Int'l*, pg. 7569
TERUMO BCT VENEZUELA, C.A.—See Terumo Corporation; *Int'l*, pg. 7569
TERUMO BCT VIETNAM CO., LTD.—See Terumo Corporation; *Int'l*, pg. 7569
TERUMO BUSINESS SUPPORT CORP.—See Terumo Corporation; *Int'l*, pg. 7570
TERUMO CARDIOVASCULAR SYSTEMS CORPORATION—See Terumo Corporation; *Int'l*, pg. 7570
TERUMO CARDIOVASCULAR SYSTEMS EUROPE, GMBH—See Terumo Corporation; *Int'l*, pg. 7570
TERUMO CHILE LTDA.—See Terumo Corporation; *Int'l*, pg. 7570
TERUMO (CHINA) HOLDING CO., LTD.—See Terumo Corporation; *Int'l*, pg. 7569
TERUMO CHINA (HONG KONG) LTD.—See Terumo Corporation; *Int'l*, pg. 7570
TERUMO CLINICAL SUPPLY CO., LTD.—See Terumo Corporation; *Int'l*, pg. 7570
TERUMO COLOMBIA ANDINA S.A.S.—See Terumo Corporation; *Int'l*, pg. 7570
TERUMO CORPORATION-AUSTRALIA—See Terumo Corporation; *Int'l*, pg. 7570
TERUMO CORPORATION BEIJING OFFICE—See Terumo Corporation; *Int'l*, pg. 7570
TERUMO CORPORATION GUANGZHOU OFFICE—See Terumo Corporation; *Int'l*, pg. 7570
TERUMO CORPORATION SHANGHAI OFFICE—See Terumo Corporation; *Int'l*, pg. 7570
TERUMO CORPORATION; *Int'l*, pg. 7569
TERUMO (DEUTSCHLAND) G.M.B.H.—See Terumo Corporation; *Int'l*, pg. 7570
TERUMO EUROPE ESPANA SL—See Terumo Corporation; *Int'l*, pg. 7570
TERUMO EUROPE N.V. BENELUX SALES DIVISION—See Terumo Corporation; *Int'l*, pg. 7570
TERUMO EUROPE N.V.—See Terumo Corporation; *Int'l*, pg. 7570

TERUMO CORPORATION

TERUMO FRANCE S.A.S.—See Terumo Corporation; *Int'l*, pg. 7570
TERUMO HEART, INC.—See Terumo Corporation; *Int'l*, pg. 7570
TERUMO HUMAN CREATE CORP.—See Terumo Corporation; *Int'l*, pg. 7570
TERUMO INDIA PRIVATE LIMITED—See Terumo Corporation; *Int'l*, pg. 7570
TERUMO ITALIA SRL—See Terumo Corporation; *Int'l*, pg. 7570
TERUMO KOREA CORP.—See Terumo Corporation; *Int'l*, pg. 7570
TERUMO LATIN AMERICA CORP.—See Terumo Corporation; *Int'l*, pg. 7570
TERUMO LEASE CO., LTD.—See Terumo Corporation; *Int'l*, pg. 7570
TERUMO MALAYSIA SDN. BHD.—See Terumo Corporation; *Int'l*, pg. 7570
TERUMO MARKETING PHILIPPINES, INC—See Terumo Corporation; *Int'l*, pg. 7570
TERUMO MEDICAL CANADA INC.—See Terumo Corporation; *Int'l*, pg. 7570
TERUMO MEDICAL CORPORATION DO BRASIL LTDA.—See Terumo Corporation; *Int'l*, pg. 7570
TERUMO MEDICAL CORPORATION—See Terumo Corporation; *Int'l*, pg. 7570
TERUMO MEDICAL CORPORATION—See Terumo Corporation; *Int'l*, pg. 7570
TERUMO MEDICAL DE MEXICO S.A. DE C.V.—See Terumo Corporation; *Int'l*, pg. 7570
TERUMO MEDICAL DO BRASIL LTDA.—See Terumo Corporation; *Int'l*, pg. 7570
TERUMO MEDICAL PHOENIX DISTRIBUTION CENTER—See Terumo Corporation; *Int'l*, pg. 7570
TERUMO MEDICAL PRODUCTS (HANGZHOU) CO., LTD.—See Terumo Corporation; *Int'l*, pg. 7570
TERUMO MEDICAL (SHANGHAI) CO., LTD.—See Terumo Corporation; *Int'l*, pg. 7570
TERUMO MEDICAL-TORONTO—See Terumo Corporation; *Int'l*, pg. 7570
TERUMO MIDDLE EAST FZE—See Terumo Corporation; *Int'l*, pg. 7570
TERUMO PENPOL LIMITED—See Terumo Corporation; *Int'l*, pg. 7570
TERUMO (PHILIPPINES) CORPORATION—See Terumo Corporation; *Int'l*, pg. 7569
TERUMO PUERTO RICO LLC—See Terumo Corporation; *Int'l*, pg. 7570
TERUMO RUSSIA LLC—See Terumo Corporation; *Int'l*, pg. 7570
TERUMO SEQUENT—See Terumo Corporation; *Int'l*, pg. 7569
TERUMO SINGAPORE PTE. LTD.—See Terumo Corporation; *Int'l*, pg. 7570
TERUMO SWEDEN AB—See Terumo Corporation; *Int'l*, pg. 7570
TERUMO TAIWAN MEDICAL CO., LTD.—See Terumo Corporation; *Int'l*, pg. 7571
TERUMO (THAILAND) CO., LTD.—See Terumo Corporation; *Int'l*, pg. 7569
TERUMO UK LTD.—See Terumo Corporation; *Int'l*, pg. 7571
TERUMO VIETNAM CO., LTD.—See Terumo Corporation; *Int'l*, pg. 7571
TERUMO VIETNAM MEDICAL EQUIPMENT CO., LTD.—See Terumo Corporation; *Int'l*, pg. 7571
TERUMO YAMAGUCHI CORPORATION—See Terumo Corporation; *Int'l*, pg. 7571
TERUMO YAMAGUCHI D&D CORPORATION—See Terumo Corporation; *Int'l*, pg. 7571
TERUYA BROS., LTD.; *U.S. Private*, pg. 3972
TERVAKOSKI OY—See delfortgroup AG; *Int'l*, pg. 2013
TERVEYSTALO PLC; *Int'l*, pg. 7571
TERVIS TUMBLER COMPANY; *U.S. Private*, pg. 3972
TERVITA CORPORATION—See Secure Energy Services Inc.; *Int'l*, pg. 6674
TERVITA, LLC—See Republic Services, Inc.; *U.S. Public*, pg. 1787
TERZA, S.A. DE C.V.—See ALFA, S.A.B. de C.V.; *Int'l*, pg. 314
TERZA, S.A. DE C.V.—See Berkshire Hathaway Inc.; *U.S. Public*, pg. 316
TERZ Z IMMOBILIEN LEASING GESELLSCHAFT M.B.H.—See UniCredit S.p.A.; *Int'l*, pg. 8037
TESA AB—See maxingvest ag; *Int'l*, pg. 4740
TESA A/S—See maxingvest ag; *Int'l*, pg. 4740
TESA AS—See maxingvest ag; *Int'l*, pg. 4740
TESA BANT SANAYI VE TICARET A.S.—See maxingvest ag; *Int'l*, pg. 4740
TESAB ENGINEERING LTD.—See Metso Oyj; *Int'l*, pg. 4868
TESA BRASIL LTDA.—See maxingvest ag; *Int'l*, pg. 4740
TESA BV—See maxingvest ag; *Int'l*, pg. 4740
TESA CONVERTING CENTER GMBH—See maxingvest ag; *Int'l*, pg. 4740
TESAC SHINKO WIREROPE CO., LTD.—See Kobelco Wire Co Ltd; *Int'l*, pg. 4221
TESAC SHINKO WIREROPE CONSULTING (SHANGHAI) CO., LTD.—See Kobelco Wire Co Ltd; *Int'l*, pg. 4221

TESAC WIREROPE CO., LTD.—See Kobelco Wire Co Ltd; *Int'l*, pg. 4221
TESA LABTEC GMBH—See maxingvest ag; *Int'l*, pg. 4740
TES-AMM JAPAN K.K.—See SK Inc.; *Int'l*, pg. 6973
TES-AMM (SINGAPORE) PTE. LTD.—See SK Inc.; *Int'l*, pg. 6973
TESAN S.P.A—See Permira Advisers LLP; *Int'l*, pg. 5808
TESAN TELEVITA S.R.L—See Permira Advisers LLP; *Int'l*, pg. 5808
TESA OY—See maxingvest ag; *Int'l*, pg. 4740
TESA PLANT (SINGAPORE) PTE. LTD.—See maxingvest ag; *Int'l*, pg. 4740
TESA PLANT SUZHOU CO. LTD.—See maxingvest ag; *Int'l*, pg. 4740
TESA PORTUGAL, LDA—See maxingvest ag; *Int'l*, pg. 4740
TESARO BIO SPAIN, S.L.U.—See GSK plc; *Int'l*, pg. 3149
TESARO, INC.—See GSK plc; *Int'l*, pg. 3149
TESA SA-NV—See maxingvest ag; *Int'l*, pg. 4741
TESA S.A.S.—See maxingvest ag; *Int'l*, pg. 4741
TESA SCRIBOS GMBH—See maxingvest ag; *Int'l*, pg. 4741
TESA SE—See maxingvest ag; *Int'l*, pg. 4740
TESA SPA - CONCAGNO PLANT—See maxingvest ag; *Int'l*, pg. 4740
TESA SPA—See maxingvest ag; *Int'l*, pg. 4740
TESA TALLERES DE ESCORIAZA S.A.U.—See ASSA ABLOY AB; *Int'l*, pg. 640
TESA TAPE AE—See maxingvest ag; *Int'l*, pg. 4741
TESA TAPE ARGENTINA S.R.L.—See maxingvest ag; *Int'l*, pg. 4741
TESA TAPE ASIA PACIFIC PTE. LTD.—See maxingvest ag; *Int'l*, pg. 4741
TESA TAPE AUSTRALIA PTY. LTD.—See maxingvest ag; *Int'l*, pg. 4740
TESA TAPE CENTRO AMERICA S.A.—See maxingvest ag; *Int'l*, pg. 4741
TESA TAPE CHILE SA—See maxingvest ag; *Int'l*, pg. 4741
TESA TAPE COLOMBIA LTDA—See maxingvest ag; *Int'l*, pg. 4740
TESA TAPE (HONG KONG) LIMITED—See maxingvest ag; *Int'l*, pg. 4740
TESA TAPE INC.—See maxingvest ag; *Int'l*, pg. 4740
TESA TAPE KFT.—See maxingvest ag; *Int'l*, pg. 4741
TESA TAPE K.K.—See maxingvest ag; *Int'l*, pg. 4740
TESA TAPE KOREA LTD.—See maxingvest ag; *Int'l*, pg. 4741
TESA TAPE (MALAYSIA) SDN. BHD.—See maxingvest ag; *Int'l*, pg. 4740
TESA TAPE MEXICO SRL DE CV—See maxingvest ag; *Int'l*, pg. 4740
TESA TAPE POSREDNISTVO IN TRGOVINA D.O.O.—See maxingvest ag; *Int'l*, pg. 4741
TESA TAPE SCHWEIZ AG—See maxingvest ag; *Int'l*, pg. 4741
TESA TAPE (SHANGHAI) CO., LTD.—See maxingvest ag; *Int'l*, pg. 4741
TESA TAPES (INDIA) PVT. LTD.—See maxingvest ag; *Int'l*, pg. 4740
TESA TAPE SP. Z.O.O.—See maxingvest ag; *Int'l*, pg. 4741
TESA TAPE SRL—See maxingvest ag; *Int'l*, pg. 4741
TESA TAPE S.R.O.—See maxingvest ag; *Int'l*, pg. 4741
TESA TAPE (THAILAND) LIMITED—See maxingvest ag; *Int'l*, pg. 4741
TESA TECHNOLOGY UK LTD—See Hexagon AB; *Int'l*, pg. 3369
TESAT-SPACECOM GESCHAFTSFUHRUNG GMBH—See Airbus SE; *Int'l*, pg. 243
TESAT-SPACECOM GMBH & CO. KG—See Airbus SE; *Int'l*, pg. 243
TESA U.K. LIMITED—See maxingvest ag; *Int'l*, pg. 4740
TESA WERK HAMBURG GMBH—See maxingvest ag; *Int'l*, pg. 4740
TESA WERK OFFENBURG GMBH—See maxingvest ag; *Int'l*, pg. 4741
TESA WESTERN EUROPE B.V.—See maxingvest ag; *Int'l*, pg. 4747
TESCA INGENIERIA DEL ECUADOR, S.A.—See ACS, Actividades de Construccion y Servicios, S.A.; *Int'l*, pg. 116
TESC CONTRACTING COMPANY LTD.; *Int'l*, pg. 7571
TESCHGLOBAL LLC; *U.S. Private*, pg. 3973
TESCO AKADEMIA KEPZESI ES FEJLESZTESI KORA-TOLT FELELOSSEGU TARSASAG—See Tesco PLC; *Int'l*, pg. 7572
TESCO BENGALURU PRIVATE LIMITED—See Tesco PLC; *Int'l*, pg. 7572
TESCO CO., LTD.—See Shin Maint Holdings Co., Ltd.; *Int'l*, pg. 6837
TESCO INSURANCE LTD.—See Tesco PLC; *Int'l*, pg. 7572
TESCO INTERNATIONAL SOURCING LIMITED—See Tesco PLC; *Int'l*, pg. 7572
TESCO IRELAND LIMITED—See Tesco PLC; *Int'l*, pg. 7572
TES CO., LTD.; *Int'l*, pg. 7571

CORPORATE AFFILIATIONS

TESCOM CORPORATION—See Emerson Electric Co.; *U.S. Public*, pg. 752
TESCOM EUROPE GMBH & CO. KG—See Emerson Electric Co.; *U.S. Public*, pg. 752
TESCOM EUROPE MANAGEMENT GMBH—See Emerson Electric Co.; *U.S. Public*, pg. 752
TESCO MOBILE IRELAND LIMITED—See Tesco PLC; *Int'l*, pg. 7572
TESCOM SOFTWARE SYSTEMS TESTING LTD.—See One Software Technologies Ltd.; *Int'l*, pg. 5575
TESCOM USA—See One Software Technologies Ltd.; *Int'l*, pg. 5575
TES CONSUMER SOLUTIONS LTD.—See SK Inc.; *Int'l*, pg. 6973
TESCO PERSONAL FINANCE LIMITED—See NatWest Group plc; *Int'l*, pg. 5172
TESCO PERSONAL FINANCE LIMITED—See Tesco PLC; *Int'l*, pg. 7572
TESCO PLC; *Int'l*, pg. 7571
TESCO POLSKA SP. Z O.O.—See Kobmand Herman Sallings Fond; *Int'l*, pg. 4222
TESCO PROPERTY HOLDINGS LTD.—See Tesco PLC; *Int'l*, pg. 7572
TESCOR, INC.; *U.S. Private*, pg. 3973
TESCO STORES LTD.—See Tesco PLC; *Int'l*, pg. 7572
TESCO STORES (MALAYSIA) SDN BHD—See Tesco PLC; *Int'l*, pg. 7572
TESCO STORES SR, A.S.—See Tesco PLC; *Int'l*, pg. 7572
TESC TEST SOLUTION CENTER GMBH—See Kudelski S.A.; *Int'l*, pg. 4323
TESEC CHINA (SHANGHAI) CO., LTD.—See TESEC Corporation; *Int'l*, pg. 7572
TESEC CORPORATION; *Int'l*, pg. 7572
TESEC, INC.—See TESEC Corporation; *Int'l*, pg. 7572
TESEC (M) SDN. BHD.—See TESEC Corporation; *Int'l*, pg. 7572
TESEI PETROLEUM INC.; *U.S. Private*, pg. 3973
TES ENGINEERING; *U.S. Private*, pg. 3973
TESEQ AG—See AMETEK, Inc.; *U.S. Public*, pg. 119
TESEQ COMPANY LTD.—See AMETEK, Inc.; *U.S. Public*, pg. 119
TESEQ GMBH—See AMETEK, Inc.; *U.S. Public*, pg. 119
TESEQ HOLDING AG—See AMETEK, Inc.; *U.S. Public*, pg. 119
TESEQ INC.—See AMETEK, Inc.; *U.S. Public*, pg. 119
TESEQ K.K.—See AMETEK, Inc.; *U.S. Public*, pg. 119
TESEQ (TAIWAN) LTD.—See AMETEK, Inc.; *U.S. Public*, pg. 119
TESERA CO., LTD.—See Mitani Sangyo Co., Ltd.; *Int'l*, pg. 4925
T.E.S. FILER CITY STATION LIMITED PARTNERSHIP—See CMS Energy Corporation; *U.S. Public*, pg. 519
TESGAS S.A.; *Int'l*, pg. 7572
TES GLOBAL LIMITED—See ONEX Corporation; *Int'l*, pg. 5580
TESHMONT CONSULTANTS LP—See John Wood Group PLC; *Int'l*, pg. 3982
TESI DE MEXICO S.A. DE C.V.—See GPI S.p.A.; *Int'l*, pg. 3046
TESINC LLC—See Dycom Industries, Inc.; *U.S. Public*, pg. 699
TESIS BIOSCIENCES, INC.; *U.S. Private*, pg. 3973
TESI S.P.A.—See GPI S.p.A.; *Int'l*, pg. 3046
TESI SRL TECNOLOGIA & SICUREZZA—See SOL S.p.A.; *Int'l*, pg. 7068
TESIUM GMBH—See Symrise AG; *Int'l*, pg. 7381
TESKED AB—See Schibsted ASA; *Int'l*, pg. 6618
TESLA AUTOMATION GMBH—See Tesla, Inc.; *U.S. Public*, pg. 2021
TESLA CANADA LP—See Tesla, Inc.; *U.S. Public*, pg. 2021
TESLA CONSULTING S.R.L.—See TAMBURI INVESTMENT PARTNERS S.p.A; *Int'l*, pg. 7450
TESLA CZECH REPUBLIC S.R.O.—See Tesla, Inc.; *U.S. Public*, pg. 2021
TESLA FRANCE S.A.R.L.—See Tesla, Inc.; *U.S. Public*, pg. 2021
TESLA GROHMANN AUTOMATION GMBH—See Tesla, Inc.; *U.S. Public*, pg. 2021
TESLA HUNGARY KFT.—See Tesla, Inc.; *U.S. Public*, pg. 2021
TESLA, INC.; *U.S. Public*, pg. 2021
TESLA ITALY S.R.L.—See Tesla, Inc.; *U.S. Public*, pg. 2021
TESLA MOTORS AUSTRALIA, PTY LTD—See Tesla, Inc.; *U.S. Public*, pg. 2021
TESLA MOTORS AUSTRIA GMBH—See Tesla, Inc.; *U.S. Public*, pg. 2021
TESLA MOTORS BELGIUM SPRL—See Tesla, Inc.; *U.S. Public*, pg. 2021
TESLA MOTORS ICELAND EHF.—See Tesla, Inc.; *U.S. Public*, pg. 2021
TESLA MOTORS LUXEMBOURG S.A.R.L.—See Tesla, Inc.; *U.S. Public*, pg. 2021
TESLA MOTORS UT, INC.—See Tesla, Inc.; *U.S. Public*, pg. 2021

COMPANY NAME INDEX

TESLA NORWAY AS—See Tesla, Inc.; *U.S. Public*, pg. 2021
TESLA POLAND SP. Z O.O.—See Tesla, Inc.; *U.S. Public*, pg. 2021
TESLA SWITZERLAND GMBH—See Tesla, Inc.; *U.S. Public*, pg. 2021
TESLIC PREVOZ A.D.; *Int'l*, pg. 7572
TESMEC AUSTRALIA (PTY) LTD.—See TESMEC S.p.A.; *Int'l*, pg. 7572
TESMEC AUTOMATION S.R.L.—See TESMEC S.p.A.; *Int'l*, pg. 7572
TESMEC GUINEE SARLU—See TESMEC S.p.A.; *Int'l*, pg. 7572
TESMEC NEW TECHNOLOGY BEIJING LTD.—See TESMEC S.p.A.; *Int'l*, pg. 7572
TESMEC RAIL S.R.L.—See TESMEC S.p.A.; *Int'l*, pg. 7572
TESMEC SA (PTY) LTD.—See TESMEC S.p.A.; *Int'l*, pg. 7572
TESMEC SAUDI ARABIA LLC—See TESMEC S.p.A.; *Int'l*, pg. 7572
TESMEC S.p.A.; *Int'l*, pg. 7572
TESMEC USA, INC.—See TESMEC S.p.A.; *Int'l*, pg. 7572
TESM LIMITED—See DXC Technology Company; *U.S. Public*, pg. 697
TESM/NL B.V.—See DXC Technology Company; *U.S. Public*, pg. 697
TESNA INC. - ANSEONG FACTORY—See Doosan Tesna Inc; *Int'l*, pg. 2174
TESNET SOFTWARE TESTING, LTD.—See Amanet Management & Systems Ltd.; *Int'l*, pg. 410
TESONA GMBH & CO. KG—See Shanghai Baolong Automotive Corporation; *Int'l*, pg. 6762
TESORO ALASKA CO LLC—See Marathon Petroleum Corporation; *U.S. Public*, pg. 1363
TESORO ALASKA PIPELINE CO. LLC—See Marathon Petroleum Corporation; *U.S. Public*, pg. 1363
TESORO COMPANIES, INC.—See Marathon Petroleum Corporation; *U.S. Public*, pg. 1363
TESORO GOLD LTD; *Int'l*, pg. 7572
TESORO HIGH PLAINS PIPELINE COMPANY LLC—See Marathon Petroleum Corporation; *U.S. Public*, pg. 1364
TESORO LOGISTICS OPERATIONS LLC—See Marathon Petroleum Corporation; *U.S. Public*, pg. 1364
TESORO MINERALS CORP.; *Int'l*, pg. 7572
TESORO REFINING & MARKETING COMPANY LLC—See Marathon Petroleum Corporation; *U.S. Public*, pg. 1363
TES PHILIPPINES, INC.—See Mitsubishi Heavy Industries, Ltd.; *Int'l*, pg. 4961
TESSA CONSTRUCTION & TECH COMPANY LLC.; *U.S. Private*, pg. 3973
TESS AGRO PLC; *Int'l*, pg. 7573
TESSCO TECHNOLOGIES, INC.—See Lee Equity Partners LLC; *U.S. Private*, pg. 2412
TESSCO TECHNOLOGIES, INC.—See Twin Point Capital, LLC; *U.S. Private*, pg. 4265
TESSELLIS S.P.A.—See Jefferies Financial Group Inc.; *U.S. Public*, pg. 1189
TESSENDERLO AGROCHEM TARIM VE KIMYA SAN. VE TIC. LTD.—See Tessenderlo Group NV; *Int'l*, pg. 7574
TESSENDERLO CHEMIE ROTTERDAM B.V.—See Tessenderlo Group NV; *Int'l*, pg. 7574
TESSENDERLO FINANCE N.V.—See Tessenderlo Group NV; *Int'l*, pg. 7574
TESSENDERLO FINE CHEMICALS LTD.—See Tessenderlo Group NV; *Int'l*, pg. 7574
TESSENDERLO GROUP NV; *Int'l*, pg. 7573
TESSENDERLO HOLDING UK LTD.—See Tessenderlo Group NV; *Int'l*, pg. 7574
TESSENDERLO KERLEY, INC.—See Tessenderlo Group NV; *Int'l*, pg. 7574
TESSENDERLO KERLEY LATINOAMERICANA S.A.—See Tessenderlo Group NV; *Int'l*, pg. 7574
TESSENDERLO KERLEY MEXICO S.A. DE C.V.—See Tessenderlo Group NV; *Int'l*, pg. 7574
TESSENDERLO NL HOLDING B.V.—See Tessenderlo Group NV; *Int'l*, pg. 7574
TESSENDERLO SCHWEIZ AG—See Tessenderlo Group NV; *Int'l*, pg. 7574
TESSENDERLO TRADING SHANGHAI CO.,LTD.—See Tessenderlo Group NV; *Int'l*, pg. 7574
TESSENDERLO U.S.A. INC.—See Tessenderlo Group NV; *Int'l*, pg. 7574
TESSENDORF MECHANICAL SERVICES, INC.—See Partners Group Holding AG; *Int'l*, pg. 5750
TESS ENGINEERING CO., LTD.—See Tess Holdings Co., Ltd.; *Int'l*, pg. 7573
TESSERACT CORPORATION WEATHERFORD LABORATORIES—See Weatherford International plc; *U.S. Public*, pg. 2339
TESSERA, INC. - YOKOHAMA FACILITY—See Adeia Inc.; *U.S. Public*, pg. 41
TESSERENT LIMITED—See Thales S.A.; *Int'l*, pg. 7601
TES-SERVICE CO., LTD.—See Toei Co., Ltd.; *Int'l*, pg. 7774
TES SERVICES INC.—See Total Energy Services Inc.; *Int'l*, pg. 7835
TESS HOLDINGS CO., LTD.; *Int'l*, pg. 7573

TESSI DOCUMENT SOLUTIONS (GERMANY) GMBH—See Tessi S.A.; *Int'l*, pg. 7574
TESSI DOCUMENT SOLUTIONS SWITZERLAND GMBH—See Tessi S.A.; *Int'l*, pg. 7574
TESSIER'S, INC.—See APi Group Corporation; *Int'l*, pg. 514
TESSI GESTIONA SAS—See Tessi S.A.; *Int'l*, pg. 7574
TESSILFORM S.P.A.; *Int'l*, pg. 7575
TESSIN NORDIC HOLDING AB; *Int'l*, pg. 7575
TESSI S.A.; *Int'l*, pg. 7574
TESSON HOLDINGS LIMITED; *Int'l*, pg. 7575
TESSU SYSTEMS B.V.—See Absolent Air Care Group AB; *Int'l*, pg. 70
TESSUTICA NV—See Beaulieu International Group NV; *Int'l*, pg. 934
TESSY AUTOMATION, LLC—See Tessy Plastics Corp; *U.S. Private*, pg. 3973
TESSY PLASTICS CORP; *U.S. Private*, pg. 3973
TESTAMERICA BUFFALO—See H.I.G. Capital, LLC; *U.S. Private*, pg. 1831
TESTAMERICA DENVER—See H.I.G. Capital, LLC; *U.S. Private*, pg. 1831
TESTAMERICA DRILLING CORP.—See H.I.G. Capital, LLC; *U.S. Private*, pg. 1831
TESTAMERICA LABORATORIES, INC.—See H.I.G. Capital, LLC; *U.S. Private*, pg. 1831
TESTA PRODUCE INC—See Wind Point Advisors LLC; *U.S. Private*, pg. 4534
TESTAR ELECTRONIC CORPORATION—See Chroma ATE Inc.; *Int'l*, pg. 1588
TESTAR ELECTRONICS CORPORATION—See Chroma ATE Inc.; *Int'l*, pg. 1588
TEST DEVICES INC.—See Durr AG; *Int'l*, pg. 2233
TESTEK, LLC—See Odyssey Investment Partners, LLC; *U.S. Private*, pg. 2995
TEST EQUIPMENT DISTRIBUTORS, LLC—See X-Ray Industries Inc.; *U.S. Private*, pg. 4579
TESTEQUITY LLC—See Distribution Solutions Group, Inc.; *U.S. Public*, pg. 669
TESTIAN, INC.—See UniTest Inc.; *Int'l*, pg. 8074
TESTING INSPECTION & SOLUTION PTE. LTD.—See PEC Ltd.; *Int'l*, pg. 5779
TESTING MACHINES INC.; *U.S. Private*, pg. 3973
TESTING TECHNOLOGIES IST GMBH—See Spirent Communications plc; *Int'l*, pg. 7140
TEST & INNOVATION LAB S.R.L.—See Kering S.A.; *Int'l*, pg. 4136
TEST INTERNATIONAL—See Schlumberger Limited; *U.S. Public*, pg. 1844
TEST IO GMBH—See EPAM Systems, Inc.; *U.S. Public*, pg. 783
TEST IO, INC.—See EPAM Systems, Inc.; *U.S. Public*, pg. 783
TESTMASTERS EDUCATIONAL SERVICES, INC.; *U.S. Private*, pg. 3973
THE TESTOR CORPORATION—See RPM International Inc.; *U.S. Public*, pg. 1817
TES TOUCH EMBEDDED SOLUTIONS (XIAMEN) CO., LTD.; *Int'l*, pg. 7571
TESTOUT CORP.—See Computing Technology Industry Association; *U.S. Private*, pg. 1006
TESTPLANT UK LIMITED—See Keysight Technologies, Inc.; *U.S. Public*, pg. 1227
TESTPOWER AB—See Yokogawa Electric Corporation; *Int'l*, pg. 8592
TEST RESEARCH INC.; *Int'l*, pg. 7575
TEST RESEARCH INNOVATION THAILAND COMPANY LIMITED—See Test Research Inc.; *Int'l*, pg. 7575
TEST RESEARCH USA INC.—See Test Research Inc.; *Int'l*, pg. 7575
TEST RITE BUSINESS DEVELOPMENT CORPORATION (CHINA) CO., LTD.—See Test-Rite International Co., Ltd.; *Int'l*, pg. 7575
TEST-RITE INTERNATIONAL CO., LTD.; *Int'l*, pg. 7575
TESTRITE INTERNATIONAL CO, LTD.—See Test-Rite International Co., Ltd.; *Int'l*, pg. 7575
TEST RITE INTL (AUSTRALIA) PTY. LTD.—See Test-Rite International Co., Ltd.; *Int'l*, pg. 7575
TEST-RITE INT'L. (CANADA) LTD.—See Test-Rite International Co., Ltd.; *Int'l*, pg. 7575
TEST RITE INT'L (GERMANY) GMBH—See Test-Rite International Co., Ltd.; *Int'l*, pg. 7575
TEST RITE INT'L (U.K.) LTD.—See Test-Rite International Co., Ltd.; *Int'l*, pg. 7575
TEST-RITE PRODUCTS CORP.—See Test-Rite International Co., Ltd.; *Int'l*, pg. 7575
TEST RITE PRODUCTS (HONG KONG) LTD.—See Test-Rite International Co., Ltd.; *Int'l*, pg. 7575
TEST RITE PTE. LTD.—See Test-Rite International Co., Ltd.; *Int'l*, pg. 7575
TEST-RITE PTE. LTD.—See Test-Rite International Co., Ltd.; *Int'l*, pg. 7575
TEST RITE RETAIL CO., LTD.—See Test-Rite International Co., Ltd.; *Int'l*, pg. 7575
TEST-RITE (UK) LTD.—See Test-Rite International Co., Ltd.; *Int'l*, pg. 7575
TEST-RITE VIETNAM CO., LTD.—See Test-Rite International Co., Ltd.; *Int'l*, pg. 7575

TETRALOGIC PHARMACEUTICALS CORPORATION

TESTRONIC LABORATORIES LTD—See NorthEdge Capital LLP; *Int'l*, pg. 5442
TEST-SERV INC.—See Sigurd Microelectronics Corp.; *Int'l*, pg. 6913
TEST SOLUTION SERVICES, INC.—See YAMAICHI ELECTRONICS Co Ltd; *Int'l*, pg. 8552
TEST VE MUHENDISLIK A.S.—See Yokogawa Electric Corporation; *Int'l*, pg. 8592
TETA BI CENTER SP. Z O.O.—See UNIT4 N.V.; *Int'l*, pg. 8063
TETA HR CENTER SP. Z O.O.—See UNIT4 N.V.; *Int'l*, pg. 8063
TETC, LLC—See Energy Transfer LP; *U.S. Public*, pg. 764
TETCO, INC.; *U.S. Private*, pg. 3973
TETEKS AD; *Int'l*, pg. 7575
TETEL SA DE CV—See Concentrix Corporation; *U.S. Public*, pg. 565
TETERS FLORAL PRODUCTS, INC.; *U.S. Private*, pg. 3973
TETHERS UNLIMITED, INC.—See Amergint Technologies, Inc.; *U.S. Private*, pg. 219
TETHIS LABS INC.—See Genextra S.p.A.; *Int'l*, pg. 2923
TETHIS S.P.A.—See Genextra S.p.A.; *Int'l*, pg. 2923
TETHYAN RESOURCES PLC; *Int'l*, pg. 7575
TETHYS BIOSCIENCE, INC.; *U.S. Private*, pg. 3973
TETHYS INVEST SAS; *Int'l*, pg. 7575
TETHYS MINING LLC—See Vale S.A.; *Int'l*, pg. 8112
TETHYS OIL AB; *Int'l*, pg. 7576
TETHYS OIL MIDDLE EAST NORTH AFRICA BV—See Tethys Oil AB; *Int'l*, pg. 7576
TETLEY USA INC.—See Tata Sons Limited; *Int'l*, pg. 7470
TE-TO AD; *Int'l*, pg. 7499
TETON ADVISORS, INC.; *U.S. Public*, pg. 2021
TETON AUTO GROUP; *U.S. Private*, pg. 3973
TETON BUILDINGS LLC; *U.S. Private*, pg. 3973
TETON HEALTHCARE, INC.—See The Ensign Group, Inc.; *U.S. Public*, pg. 2072
TETON HERITAGE BUILDERS INC.; *U.S. Private*, pg. 3973
TETON INDUSTRIAL CONSTRUCTION, INC.—See PCL Employees Holdings Ltd.; *Int'l*, pg. 5769
TETON OUTFITTERS, LLC—See Polaris, Inc.; *U.S. Public*, pg. 1701
TETON OUTPATIENT SERVICES, LLC—See Tenet Healthcare Corporation; *U.S. Public*, pg. 2013
TETON STEEL CO.—See Dalco Industries Inc.; *U.S. Private*, pg. 1148
TETON TRUST COMPANY—See Truist Financial Corporation; *U.S. Public*, pg. 2199
TETON VALLEY HEALTH CARE, INC.; *U.S. Private*, pg. 3973
TETRA APPLIED HOLDING COMPANY—See TETRA Technologies, Inc.; *U.S. Public*, pg. 2024
TETRA BIO-PHARMA INC.; *Int'l*, pg. 7576
TETRA CHEMICALS EUROPE AB—See TETRA Technologies, Inc.; *U.S. Public*, pg. 2024
TETRA CHEMICALS EUROPE OY—See TETRA Technologies, Inc.; *U.S. Public*, pg. 2024
TETRA CONCEPTS LLC—See Carl Marks & Co., Inc.; *U.S. Private*, pg. 763
TETRAD ELECTRONICS INC.; *U.S. Private*, pg. 3973
TETRA-DUR KUNSTSTOFF-PRODUKTION GMBH—See LyondellBasell Industries N.V.; *Int'l*, pg. 4608
TETRADYNE, LLC—See Neogen Corporation; *U.S. Public*, pg. 1505
TETRA ENERGIE TECHNOLOGIE TRANSFER GMBH—See PJSC EnergoMashinostroitelny Alliance; *Int'l*, pg. 5878
TETRA FINANCIAL SERVICES, INC.—See TETRA Technologies, Inc.; *U.S. Public*, pg. 2024
TETRAG AUTOMATION AG—See swenex - swiss energy exchange Ltd.; *Int'l*, pg. 7366
TETRAGENETICS, INC.—See AbCellera Biologics Inc.; *Int'l*, pg. 57
TETRA GMBH—See Spectrum Brands Holdings, Inc.; *U.S. Public*, pg. 1917
TETRAGON FINANCIAL GROUP LIMITED; *Int'l*, pg. 7578
TETRA - IBI GROUP ARCHITECTURE PLANNING—See ARCADIS N.V.; *Int'l*, pg. 542
TETRA IRELAND COMMUNICATIONS LIMITED—See eircom Holdings (Ireland) Limited; *Int'l*, pg. 2334
TETRA JAPAN K.K.—See Spectrum Brands Holdings, Inc.; *U.S. Public*, pg. 1917
TETRA LAVAL INTERNATIONAL S.A.; *Int'l*, pg. 7576
TETRALENE, INC.—See Freudenberg SE; *Int'l*, pg. 2790
TETRALOGIC PHARMACEUTICALS CORPORATION; *U.S. Public*, pg. 2024
TETRA MEDIA STUDIO SAS—See ITV plc; *Int'l*, pg. 3845
TETRANED VOF—See Koninklijke KPN N.V.; *Int'l*, pg. 4267
TETRA PAK AMERICA LATINA—See Tetra Laval International S.A.; *Int'l*, pg. 7577
TETRA PAK A/O—See Tetra Laval International S.A.; *Int'l*, pg. 7577
TETRA PAK A/S—See Tetra Laval International S.A.; *Int'l*, pg. 7577
TETRA PAK A.S.—See Tetra Laval International S.A.; *Int'l*, pg. 7578

TETRALOGIC PHARMACEUTICALS CORPORATION

CORPORATE AFFILIATIONS

TETRA PAK BALTIC STATES—See Tetra Laval International S.A.; *Int'l*, pg. 7577
TETRA PAK B.V.—See Tetra Laval International S.A.; *Int'l*, pg. 7577
TETRA PAK CHINA LTD.—See Tetra Laval International S.A.; *Int'l*, pg. 7577
TETRA PAK CIA. LTDA—See Tetra Laval International S.A.; *Int'l*, pg. 7577
TETRA PAK DAIRY & BEVERAGE AB—See Tetra Laval International S.A.; *Int'l*, pg. 7577
TETRA PAK DANMARK A/S—See Tetra Laval International S.A.; *Int'l*, pg. 7577
TETRA PAK DE CHILE COMERCIAL LTDA.—See Tetra Laval International S.A.; *Int'l*, pg. 7578
TETRA PAK EXPORT SA—See Tetra Laval International S.A.; *Int'l*, pg. 7577
TETRA PAK FRANCE—See Tetra Laval International S.A.; *Int'l*, pg. 7577
TETRA PAK GMBH & CO. KG.—See Tetra Laval International S.A.; *Int'l*, pg. 7577
TETRA PAK HUNGARY LTD.—See Tetra Laval International S.A.; *Int'l*, pg. 7577
TETRA PAK IMPORTS PTY LTD—See Tetra Laval International S.A.; *Int'l*, pg. 7577
TETRA PAK INC.—See Tetra Laval International S.A.; *Int'l*, pg. 7577
TETRA PAK INC. - VERNON HILLS OFFICE—See Tetra Laval International S.A.; *Int'l*, pg. 7577
TETRA PAK INTERNATIONAL S.A.—See Tetra Laval International S.A.; *Int'l*, pg. 7577
TETRA PAK IRAN—See Tetra Laval International S.A.; *Int'l*, pg. 7578
TETRA PAK IRELAND LTD.—See Tetra Laval International S.A.; *Int'l*, pg. 7578
TETRA PAK ITALIANA S.P.A.—See Tetra Laval International S.A.; *Int'l*, pg. 7578
TETRA PAK LTDA.—See Tetra Laval International S.A.; *Int'l*, pg. 7578
TETRA PAK LTD.—See Tetra Laval International S.A.; *Int'l*, pg. 7578
TETRA PAK MALAYSIA SDN BHD—See Tetra Laval International S.A.; *Int'l*, pg. 7578
TETRA PAK MANUFACTURING LIMITED—See Tetra Laval International S.A.; *Int'l*, pg. 7578
TETRA PAK MANUFACTURING LTD—See Tetra Laval International S.A.; *Int'l*, pg. 7578
TETRA PAK MOULDING PACKAGING SYSTEMS LTD.—See Tetra Laval International S.A.; *Int'l*, pg. 7578
TETRA PAK NEW ZEALAND LIMITED—See Tetra Laval International S.A.; *Int'l*, pg. 7578
TETRA PAK OY—See Tetra Laval International S.A.; *Int'l*, pg. 7578
TETRA PAK PHILIPPINES, INC.—See Tetra Laval International S.A.; *Int'l*, pg. 7578
TETRA PAK PROCESSING EQUIPMENT INC.—See Tetra Laval International S.A.; *Int'l*, pg. 7578
TETRA PAK PROCESSING GMBH—See Tetra Laval International S.A.; *Int'l*, pg. 7578
TETRA PAK PROCESSING SNC—See Tetra Laval International S.A.; *Int'l*, pg. 7578
TETRA PAK RESEARCH GMBH—See Tetra Laval International S.A.; *Int'l*, pg. 7578
TETRA PAK S.A.—See Tetra Laval International S.A.; *Int'l*, pg. 7578
TETRA PAK SCANIMA A/S—See Tetra Laval International S.A.; *Int'l*, pg. 7578
TETRA PAK SCHWEIZ AG—See Tetra Laval International S.A.; *Int'l*, pg. 7578
TETRA PAK SOUTH EAST ASIA PTE LTD—See Tetra Laval International S.A.; *Int'l*, pg. 7578
TETRA PAK TAIWAN LTD—See Tetra Laval International S.A.; *Int'l*, pg. 7578
TETRA PAK (THAILAND) LTD.—See Tetra Laval International S.A.; *Int'l*, pg. 7577
TETRAPHASE PHARMACEUTICALS, INC.; *U.S. Public*, pg. 2025
TETRA TECH BAS, INC.—See Tetra Tech, Inc.; *U.S. Public*, pg. 2023
TETRA TECH CANADA INC.—See Tetra Tech, Inc.; *U.S. Public*, pg. 2023
TETRA TECH CAPE CANAVERAL, LLC—See Tetra Tech, Inc.; *U.S. Public*, pg. 2023
TETRA TECH COFFEY PTY. LTD.—See Tetra Tech, Inc.; *U.S. Public*, pg. 2023
TETRA TECH CONSULTORIA LTDA—See Tetra Tech, Inc.; *U.S. Public*, pg. 2023
TETRA TECH CONTINGENCY CONSTRUCTORS, LLC—See Tetra Tech, Inc.; *U.S. Public*, pg. 2023
TETRA TECH EC, INC.—See Tetra Tech, Inc.; *U.S. Public*, pg. 2023
TETRA TECH EMC, INC.—See Tetra Tech, Inc.; *U.S. Public*, pg. 2023
TETRA TECH EM INC.—See Tetra Tech, Inc.; *U.S. Public*, pg. 2023
TETRA TECH EM INC.—See Tetra Tech, Inc.; *U.S. Public*, pg. 2023
TETRA TECH ENGINEERING & ARCHITECTURE SERVICES—See Tetra Tech, Inc.; *U.S. Public*, pg. 2023

TETRA TECH FHC, INC.—See Tetra Tech, Inc.; *U.S. Public*, pg. 2023
TETRA TECH HEI, INC.—See Tetra Tech, Inc.; *U.S. Public*, pg. 2023
TETRA TECH, INC. - ANN ARBOR—See Tetra Tech, Inc.; *U.S. Public*, pg. 2024
TETRA TECH, INC. - BRECKENRIDGE—See Tetra Tech, Inc.; *U.S. Public*, pg. 2024
TETRA TECH, INC. - BURLINGTON—See Tetra Tech, Inc.; *U.S. Public*, pg. 2024
TETRA TECH, INC. - FRAMINGHAM—See Tetra Tech, Inc.; *U.S. Public*, pg. 2024
TETRA TECH, INC. - LEXINGTON—See Tetra Tech, Inc.; *U.S. Public*, pg. 2024
TETRA TECH, INC. - MADISON—See Tetra Tech, Inc.; *U.S. Public*, pg. 2024
TETRA TECH, INC.; *U.S. Public*, pg. 2021
TETRA TECH INDIA LIMITED—See Tetra Tech, Inc.; *U.S. Public*, pg. 2023
TETRA TECH/KCM, INC.—See Tetra Tech, Inc.; *U.S. Public*, pg. 2023
TETRA TECHNOLOGIES DE MEXICO, S.A. DE C.V.—See TETRA Technologies, Inc.; *U.S. Public*, pg. 2024
TETRA TECHNOLOGIES DO BRASIL, LIMITADA—See TETRA Technologies, Inc.; *U.S. Public*, pg. 2024
TETRA TECHNOLOGIES, INC.; *U.S. Public*, pg. 2024
TETRA TECHNOLOGIES UK LIMITED—See TETRA Technologies, Inc.; *U.S. Public*, pg. 2024
TETRA TECH NUCLEAR—See Tetra Tech, Inc.; *U.S. Public*, pg. 2023
TETRA TECH NUS, INC.—See Tetra Tech, Inc.; *U.S. Public*, pg. 2023
TETRA TECH OGD INC.—See Tetra Tech, Inc.; *U.S. Public*, pg. 2024
TETRA TECH RMC, INC.—See Tetra Tech, Inc.; *U.S. Public*, pg. 2024
TETRA TECH TESORO, INC.—See Tetra Tech, Inc.; *U.S. Public*, pg. 2024
TETRA (UK) LIMITED—See Spectrum Brands Holdings, Inc.; *U.S. Public*, pg. 1917
TETRIS DESIGN AND BUILD (PTY) LTD.—See Jones Lang LaSalle Incorporated; *U.S. Public*, pg. 1206
TETRIS DESIGN AND BUILD SARL—See Jones Lang LaSalle Incorporated; *U.S. Public*, pg. 1206
TETRIS DESIGN AND BUILD S.R.L.—See Jones Lang LaSalle Incorporated; *U.S. Public*, pg. 1206
TETRIS DESIGN & BUILD BV—See Jones Lang LaSalle Incorporated; *U.S. Public*, pg. 1206
TETRIS DESIGN & BUILD SARL—See Jones Lang LaSalle Incorporated; *U.S. Public*, pg. 1206
TETRIS DESIGN & BUILD SPRL—See Jones Lang LaSalle Incorporated; *U.S. Public*, pg. 1206
TETRIS MEDIA LIMITED; *Int'l*, pg. 7578
TETRIS PHARMA LTD.—See Arecor Therapeutics Plc; *Int'l*, pg. 557
TETRIS PROJECTS GMBH—See Jones Lang LaSalle Incorporated; *U.S. Public*, pg. 1206
TETRIS SAS—See Jones Lang LaSalle Incorporated; *U.S. Public*, pg. 1206
TETRIS; *Int'l*, pg. 7578
TETRON SICHERHEITSNETZ ERRICHTUNGS UND BETRIEBSGMBH—See Motorola Solutions, Inc.; *U.S. Public*, pg. 1479
TETROSYL LTD.; *Int'l*, pg. 7578
TETRYS S.A.; *Int'l*, pg. 7578
TETSUJIN INC.; *Int'l*, pg. 7578
TETSUSHO KAYABA CORP.—See Nippon Steel Corporation; *Int'l*, pg. 5339
TETSUSO BUTSURYU CO., LTD.—See Okaya & Co., Ltd.; *Int'l*, pg. 5547
TEUCRIUM AGRICULTURAL FUND; *U.S. Public*, pg. 2025
TEUCRIUM CORN FUND; *U.S. Public*, pg. 2025
TEUCRIUM NATURAL GAS FUND; *U.S. Private*, pg. 3974
TEUCRIUM SOYBEAN FUND; *U.S. Public*, pg. 2025
TEUCRIUM SUGAR FUND; *U.S. Public*, pg. 2025
TEUCRIUM TRADING, LLC—See BGC Group, Inc.; *U.S. Public*, pg. 330
TEUCRIUM WHEAT FUND; *U.S. Public*, pg. 2025
TEUDELOFF GMBH & CO. KG—See Wurth Verwaltungsgesellschaft mbH; *Int'l*, pg. 8508
TEUFEL HOLLY FARMS, INC.—See Teufel Landscape, Inc.; *U.S. Private*, pg. 3974
TEUFEL LANDSCAPE, INC.; *U.S. Private*, pg. 3974
TEUFEL NURSERY INC.—See Teufel Landscape, Inc.; *U.S. Private*, pg. 3974
TEUFELSBAD FACHKLINIK BLANKENBURG GMBH—See MK-Kliniken AG; *Int'l*, pg. 5002
TEUFELSBAD RESIDENZ BLANKENBURG GMBH—See MK-Kliniken AG; *Int'l*, pg. 5002
TEULING STAAL B.V.—See Van Leeuwen Pipe & Tube Group B.V.; *Int'l*, pg. 8127
TEUPEN MASCHINENBAU GMBH—See Altec Industries Inc.; *U.S. Public*, pg. 206
TEUREMA SL—See EUROLLS S.p.A.; *Int'l*, pg. 2553
TEUSCHER KUNSTSTOFF-TECHNIK LTD—See Adval Tech Holding AG; *Int'l*, pg. 155
TEUTEBERG INCORPORATED; *U.S. Private*, pg. 3974

TEUTECH INDUSTRIES INC.—See Hi-Tech Gears Ltd; *Int'l*, pg. 3381
TEUTONIA FRACHT- UND ASSEKURANZKONTOR GMBH—See L. Possehl & Co. mbH; *Int'l*, pg. 4385
TEUTONIA KINDERWAGENFABRIK GMBH—See Newell Brands Inc.; *U.S. Public*, pg. 1515
TEUTON RESOURCES CORP.; *Int'l*, pg. 7578
TEUWEN ONE IMAGE, INC.—See Evins Communications, Ltd.; *U.S. Private*, pg. 1442
TEUZA-A FAIRCHILD TECHNOLOGY VENTURE LTD.; *Int'l*, pg. 7578
TEVA API B.V.—See Teva Pharmaceutical Industries, Ltd.; *Int'l*, pg. 7579
TEVA API, INC.—See Teva Pharmaceutical Industries, Ltd.; *Int'l*, pg. 7581
TEVA API INTERNATIONAL SPAIN—See Teva Pharmaceutical Industries, Ltd.; *Int'l*, pg. 7580
TEVA BELGIUM SA/NV—See Teva Pharmaceutical Industries, Ltd.; *Int'l*, pg. 7580
TEVA BIOPHARMACEUTICALS USA—See Teva Pharmaceutical Industries, Ltd.; *Int'l*, pg. 7581
TEVA BULGARIA D.O.O.—See Teva Pharmaceutical Industries, Ltd.; *Int'l*, pg. 7580
TEVA CANADA LIMITED—See Teva Pharmaceutical Industries, Ltd.; *Int'l*, pg. 7579
TEVA CLASSICS FRANCE—See Teva Pharmaceutical Industries, Ltd.; *Int'l*, pg. 7580
TEVA CZECH INDUSTRIES S.R.O.—See Teva Pharmaceutical Industries, Ltd.; *Int'l*, pg. 7579
TEVA DENMARK A/S—See Teva Pharmaceutical Industries, Ltd.; *Int'l*, pg. 7579
TEVA EUROPE B.V.—See Teva Pharmaceutical Industries, Ltd.; *Int'l*, pg. 7579
TEVA FARMACEUTICA LTDA.—See Teva Pharmaceutical Industries, Ltd.; *Int'l*, pg. 7579
TEVA GENERICS SPAIN—See Teva Pharmaceutical Industries, Ltd.; *Int'l*, pg. 7580
TEVA GMBH—See Teva Pharmaceutical Industries, Ltd.; *Int'l*, pg. 7580
TEVA-HANDOK PHARMA CO., LTD.—See Teva Pharmaceutical Industries, Ltd.; *Int'l*, pg. 7581
TEVA HUNGARY LTD.—See Teva Pharmaceutical Industries, Ltd.; *Int'l*, pg. 7580
TEVA ILACLARI SANAYI VE TICARET A.S.—See Teva Pharmaceutical Industries, Ltd.; *Int'l*, pg. 7579
TEVA INDIA PVT LTD.—See Teva Pharmaceutical Industries, Ltd.; *Int'l*, pg. 7579
TEVA ITALIA S.R.L.—See Teva Pharmaceutical Industries, Ltd.; *Int'l*, pg. 7580
TEVAK S.R.O.—See Atlas Copco AB; *Int'l*, pg. 684
TEVA LIMITED LIABILITY COMPANY—See Teva Pharmaceutical Industries, Ltd.; *Int'l*, pg. 7579
TEVA MOSCOW—See Teva Pharmaceutical Industries, Ltd.; *Int'l*, pg. 7580
TEVA NEDERLAND B.V.—See Teva Pharmaceutical Industries, Ltd.; *Int'l*, pg. 7579
TEVA NORWAY AS—See Teva Pharmaceutical Industries, Ltd.; *Int'l*, pg. 7579
TEVANO SYSTEMS HOLDINGS INC.; *Int'l*, pg. 7581
TEVA OPERATIONS POLAND SP. Z O.O.—See Teva Pharmaceutical Industries, Ltd.; *Int'l*, pg. 7579
TEVA PERU S.A.—See Teva Pharmaceutical Industries, Ltd.; *Int'l*, pg. 7579
TEVA PHARMA AG—See Teva Pharmaceutical Industries, Ltd.; *Int'l*, pg. 7579
TEVA PHARMA AUSTRALIA PTY. LTD.—See Teva Pharmaceutical Industries, Ltd.; *Int'l*, pg. 7579
TEVA PHARMA BELGIUM N.V.—See Teva Pharmaceutical Industries, Ltd.; *Int'l*, pg. 7579
TEVA PHARMACETICALS CR SRO—See Teva Pharmaceutical Industries, Ltd.; *Int'l*, pg. 7580
TEVA PHARMACEUTICAL FINE CHEMICALS SRL—See Teva Pharmaceutical Industries, Ltd.; *Int'l*, pg. 7580
TEVA PHARMACEUTICAL HONG KONG LIMITED—See Teva Pharmaceutical Industries, Ltd.; *Int'l*, pg. 7579
TEVA PHARMACEUTICAL INDUSTRIES, LTD.; *Int'l*, pg. 7578
TEVA PHARMACEUTICAL INFORMATION CONSULTING (SHANGHAI) CO., LTD.—See Teva Pharmaceutical Industries, Ltd.; *Int'l*, pg. 7580
TEVA PHARMACEUTICAL INVESTMENTS SINGAPORE PTE. LTD.—See Teva Pharmaceutical Industries, Ltd.; *Int'l*, pg. 7580
TEVA PHARMACEUTICAL KK—See Teva Pharmaceutical Industries, Ltd.; *Int'l*, pg. 7580
TEVA PHARMACEUTICAL LTD.—See Teva Pharmaceutical Industries, Ltd.; *Int'l*, pg. 7580
TEVA PHARMACEUTICAL PTE LTD—See Teva Pharmaceutical Industries, Ltd.; *Int'l*, pg. 7580
TEVA PHARMACEUTICALS CR S.R.O.—See Teva Pharmaceutical Industries, Ltd.; *Int'l*, pg. 7580
TEVA PHARMACEUTICALS CURACAO NV—See Teva Pharmaceutical Industries, Ltd.; *Int'l*, pg. 7580
TEVA PHARMACEUTICALS EUROPE B.V.—See Teva Pharmaceutical Industries, Ltd.; *Int'l*, pg. 7580
TEVA PHARMACEUTICALS HELLAS S.A.—See Teva Pharmaceutical Industries, Ltd.; *Int'l*, pg. 7580

COMPANY NAME INDEX

TEVA PHARMACEUTICALS INTERNATIONAL GMBH—See Teva Pharmaceutical Industries, Ltd.; *Int'l*, pg. 7580
TEVA PHARMACEUTICALS IRELAND—See Teva Pharmaceutical Industries, Ltd.; *Int'l*, pg. 7580
TEVA PHARMACEUTICAL SLOVAKIA SRO—See Teva Pharmaceutical Industries, Ltd.; *Int'l*, pg. 7580
TEVA PHARMACEUTICALS MEXICO—See Teva Pharmaceutical Industries, Ltd.; *Int'l*, pg. 7580
TEVA PHARMACEUTICALS MEXICO—See Teva Pharmaceutical Industries, Ltd.; *Int'l*, pg. 7580
TEVA PHARMACEUTICALS POLSKA SP. Z O.O.—See Teva Pharmaceutical Industries, Ltd.; *Int'l*, pg. 7580
TEVA PHARMACEUTICALS (PTY) LTD—See Teva Pharmaceutical Industries, Ltd.; *Int'l*, pg. 7580
TEVA PHARMACEUTICALS ROMANIA S.R.L—See Teva Pharmaceutical Industries, Ltd.; *Int'l*, pg. 7580
TEVA PHARMACEUTICALS USA, INC. - SALT LAKE CITY—See Teva Pharmaceutical Industries, Ltd.; *Int'l*, pg. 7581
TEVA PHARMACEUTICALS USA, INC.—See Teva Pharmaceutical Industries, Ltd.; *Int'l*, pg. 7580
TEVA PHARMACEUTICAL WORKS LTD.—See Teva Pharmaceutical Industries, Ltd.; *Int'l*, pg. 7580
TEVA PHARMACHEMIE B.V.—See Teva Pharmaceutical Industries, Ltd.; *Int'l*, pg. 7581
TEVA PHARMA ISRAEL—See Teva Pharmaceutical Industries, Ltd.; *Int'l*, pg. 7579
TEVA PHARMA JAPAN INC.—See Teva Pharmaceutical Industries, Ltd.; *Int'l*, pg. 7579
TEVA PHARMA (NEW ZEALAND) LIMITED—See Teva Pharmaceutical Industries, Ltd.; *Int'l*, pg. 7580
TEVA PHARMA PORTUGAL LTD.—See Teva Pharmaceutical Industries, Ltd.; *Int'l*, pg. 7580
TEVA PHARMA - PRODUTOS FARMACEUTICOS, LDA—See Teva Pharmaceutical Industries, Ltd.; *Int'l*, pg. 7579
TEVA PHARMA, S.L.U.—See Teva Pharmaceutical Industries, Ltd.; *Int'l*, pg. 7579
TEVA POLSKA SP. Z O.O.—See Teva Pharmaceutical Industries, Ltd.; *Int'l*, pg. 7580
TEVA ROMANIA SRL—See Teva Pharmaceutical Industries, Ltd.; *Int'l*, pg. 7580
TEVA RUNCORN—See Teva Pharmaceutical Industries, Ltd.; *Int'l*, pg. 7580
TEVA SANTE SAS—See Teva Pharmaceutical Industries, Ltd.; *Int'l*, pg. 7581
TEVA SERBIA LTD.—See Teva Pharmaceutical Industries, Ltd.; *Int'l*, pg. 7579
TEVASON INVESTMENTS (PVT) LTD—See Innscor Africa Ltd.; *Int'l*, pg. 3713
TEVA SWEDEN AB—See Teva Pharmaceutical Industries, Ltd.; *Int'l*, pg. 7580
TEVA TAKEDA PHARMA LTD.—See Teva Pharmaceutical Industries, Ltd.; *Int'l*, pg. 7581
TEVA-TUTEUR S.A.C.I.F.A.—See Teva Pharmaceutical Industries, Ltd.; *Int'l*, pg. 7581
TEVA UK LTD.—See Teva Pharmaceutical Industries, Ltd.; *Int'l*, pg. 7580
TEVA UKRAINE LLC—See Teva Pharmaceutical Industries, Ltd.; *Int'l*, pg. 7581
TEVA URUGUAY S.A.—See Teva Pharmaceutical Industries, Ltd.; *Int'l*, pg. 7581
TEVA WOMEN'S HEALTH, INC. - CINCINNATI—See Teva Pharmaceutical Industries, Ltd.; *Int'l*, pg. 7581
TEVA WOMEN'S HEALTH, INC.—See Teva Pharmaceutical Industries, Ltd.; *Int'l*, pg. 7581
TEVCO ENTERPRISES, INC.—See RPM International Inc.; *U.S. Public*, pg. 1820
TEVET, LLC; *U.S. Private*, pg. 3974
TEVIS-AGENCIJA ZA KADRE, D.O.O.—See Iskra, d.d.; *Int'l*, pg. 3819
TEVO LOKOMO OY—See Tevo Oy; *Int'l*, pg. 7581
TEVO OY; *Int'l*, pg. 7581
TEVVA MOTORS LIMITED; *Int'l*, pg. 7581
TEWE BAUCHEMIEGESELLSCHAFT MBH—See Dortmunder Gussasphalt GmbH & Co. KG; *Int'l*, pg. 2180
TEWE ENERGIEVERSORGUNGSGESELLSCHAFT MBH—See EWE Aktiengesellschaft; *Int'l*, pg. 2575
TEWELL WARREN PRINTING COMPANY—See Chatham Asset Management, LLC; *U.S. Private*, pg. 863
TEW ENGINEERING LIMITED—See L.B. Foster Company; *U.S. Public*, pg. 1279
TE WIRE & CABLE LLC—See Berkshire Hathaway Inc.; *U.S. Public*, pg. 310
TEWKSBURY ADVOCATE—See Gannett Co., Inc.; *U.S. Public*, pg. 903
TEWOO GROUP CO., LTD.; *Int'l*, pg. 7581
TEWOO (H.K) LIMITED—See Tewoo Group Co., Ltd.; *Int'l*, pg. 7581
TEWOO HOPERAY (SINGAPORE) PTE. LTD.—See Tewoo Group Co., Ltd.; *Int'l*, pg. 7581
TEWOO INTERNATIONAL TRADE CO., LTD.—See Tewoo Group Co., Ltd.; *Int'l*, pg. 7581
TEWOO METALS INTERNATIONAL TRADE CO., LTD.—See Tewoo Group Co., Ltd.; *Int'l*, pg. 7581
TEWOO USA, INC—See Tewoo Group Co., Ltd.; *Int'l*, pg. 7581

TEW PLUS LIMITED—See L.B. Foster Company; *U.S. Public*, pg. 1279
TEXADIAN ENERGY CANADA LIMITED—See Par Pacific Holdings, Inc.; *U.S. Public*, pg. 1636
TEXADIA SYSTEMS LLC; *U.S. Private*, pg. 3974
TEXAF SA; *Int'l*, pg. 7582
TEXAN AMBULATORY SURGERY CENTER, L.P.—See Tenet Healthcare Corporation; *U.S. Public*, pg. 2013
TEXAN FORD, INC.—See AutoNation, Inc.; *U.S. Public*, pg. 238
TEXAN FORD SALES, LTD.—See AutoNation, Inc.; *U.S. Public*, pg. 238
TEXAN FORD SALES, LTD.—See AutoNation, Inc.; *U.S. Public*, pg. 238
TEXANLAB LABORATORIES PVT. LTD.—See Kiri Industries Ltd.; *Int'l*, pg. 4186
TEXAN MARKETS INC.; *U.S. Private*, pg. 3974
TEXANS CREDIT UNION; *U.S. Private*, pg. 3974
TEXANS CUSO SERVICES—See Texans Credit Union; *U.S. Private*, pg. 3974
TEXARKANA BEHAVIORAL ASSOCIATES, L.C.—See Acadia Healthcare Company, Inc.; *U.S. Public*, pg. 30
TEXARKANA GAZETTE—See Wehco Media, Inc.; *U.S. Private*, pg. 4470
TEXARKANA NEWSPAPER INC.—See Wehco Media, Inc.; *U.S. Private*, pg. 4469
TEXARKANA SURGERY CENTER GP, LLC—See Bain Capital, LP; *U.S. Private*, pg. 447
TEXARKANA WATER UTILITIES; *U.S. Private*, pg. 3974
TEXAS ADVANCED OPTOELECTRONIC SOLUTIONS, INC.—See ams AG; *Int'l*, pg. 440
TEXAS AIR COMPOSITES, INC.—See JLL Partners, LLC; *U.S. Private*, pg. 2212
TEXAS ALLIED CHEMICALS INC.—See Texas Allied Holdings Inc.; *U.S. Private*, pg. 3974
TEXAS ALLIED HOLDINGS INC.; *U.S. Private*, pg. 3974
TEXAS ALL RISK GENERAL AGENCY, INC.—See Brown & Brown, Inc.; *U.S. Public*, pg. 401
TEXAS AMERICAN RESOURCES I, LLC—See Venado Oil & Gas, LLC; *U.S. Private*, pg. 4355
TEXAS AMERICAN RESOURCES OPERATING COMPANY—See Venado Oil & Gas, LLC; *U.S. Private*, pg. 4355
TEXAS AMERICAN TITLE COMPANY—See Anywhere Real Estate Inc.; *U.S. Public*, pg. 142
TEXAS BANKERS ASSOCIATION; *U.S. Private*, pg. 3974
TEXAS BANKERS INSURANCE AGENCY, INC.—See Texas Bankers Association; *U.S. Private*, pg. 3974
TEXAS BANK HOLDING COMPANY—See Doss, Ltd.; *U.S. Private*, pg. 1264
TEXAS BANK—See Doss, Ltd.; *U.S. Private*, pg. 1264
TEXAS BANK & TRUST COMPANY—See Overton Financial Corporation; *U.S. Private*, pg. 3054
TEXAS BARCODE SYSTEMS INC.; *U.S. Private*, pg. 3974
TEXAS BAY AREA CREDIT UNION; *U.S. Private*, pg. 3974
TEXAS BEEF LTD.; *U.S. Private*, pg. 3974
TEXAS BIOMEDICAL RESEARCH INSTITUTE; *U.S. Private*, pg. 3975
TEXAS BOOK COMPANY INC.—See BibliU Ltd.; *Int'l*, pg. 1018
TEXAS BRINE COMPANY LLC—See United Salt Corporation; *U.S. Private*, pg. 4297
TEXAS BUILDERS INSURANCE COMPANY—See Hallmark Financial Services, Inc.; *U.S. Public*, pg. 981
TEXAS BUTYLENE CHEMICAL CORPORATION—See First Reserve Management, L.P.; *U.S. Private*, pg. 1526
TEXAS BUTYLENE CHEMICAL CORPORATION—See SK Capital Partners, LP; *U.S. Private*, pg. 3680
TEXAS CABLE NEWS—See TEGNA Inc.; *U.S. Public*, pg. 1991
TEXAS CAPITAL BANCSHARES, INC.; *U.S. Public*, pg. 2025
TEXAS CAPITAL BANK, N.A.—See Texas Capital Bancshares, Inc.; *U.S. Public*, pg. 2025
TEXAS CAR-MART, INC.—See America's Car-Mart, Inc.; *U.S. Public*, pg. 95
TEXAS CITIZENS BANCORP, INC.—See Business First Bancshares, Inc.; *U.S. Public*, pg. 413
TEXAS CITIZENS BANK, N.A.—See Business First Bancshares, Inc.; *U.S. Public*, pg. 413
TEXAS CMT INC.—See Gee Consultants, Inc.; *U.S. Private*, pg. 1655
TEXAS COMMERCIAL WASTE—See M. Lipsitz & Co., Ltd.; *U.S. Private*, pg. 2527
TEXAS COMMUNITY BANCSHARES, INC.; *U.S. Public*, pg. 2025
TEXAS COMMUNITY MEDIA LLC; *U.S. Private*, pg. 3975
TEXAS CRUSHED STONE CO.; *U.S. Private*, pg. 3975
TEXAS CUSTOM POOLS INC.; *U.S. Private*, pg. 3975
TEXAS CYPRESS CREEK HOSPITAL, L.P.—See Universal Health Services, Inc.; *U.S. Public*, pg. 2259
TEXAS DE FRANCE; *Int'l*, pg. 7583
TEXAS DIGITAL SYSTEMS, INC.—See NCR Voyix Corporation.; *U.S. Public*, pg. 1503
TEXAS DIRECT AUTO—See Vroom, Inc.; *U.S. Public*, pg. 2312

TEXAS HOLDINGS LTD.

TEXAS DIRECTORS LIFE INSURANCE COMPANY INC.—See Directors Investment Group Inc.; *U.S. Private*, pg. 1236
TEXAS DISPOSAL SYSTEMS INC.; *U.S. Private*, pg. 3975
TEXAS DODGE; *U.S. Private*, pg. 3975
TEXAS DOW EMPLOYEES CREDIT UNION; *U.S. Private*, pg. 3975
TEXAS EGG PRODUCTS, LLC—See Cal-Maine Foods, Inc.; *U.S. Public*, pg. 421
TEXAS ELECTRIC COOPERATIVES, INC.; *U.S. Private*, pg. 3975
TEXAS ELECTRIC COOPERATIVES, INC. - TEC POLE MANUFACTURING PLANT—See Texas Electric Cooperatives, Inc.; *U.S. Private*, pg. 3975
TEXAS EMERGENCY CARE CENTERS, LLC—See Family ER + Urgent Care; *U.S. Private*, pg. 1469
TEXAS ENDOSCOPY CENTERS, LLC—See Tenet Healthcare Corporation; *U.S. Public*, pg. 2008
TEXAS ENERGY AGGREGATION—See O2 Investment Partners, LLC; *U.S. Private*, pg. 2982
TEXAS ENERGY HOLDINGS INC.; *U.S. Private*, pg. 3975
TEXAS ENGINEERING EXT SERVICE; *U.S. Private*, pg. 3975
TEXAS ENGINEERING & MAPPING CO.—See McKim & Creed, Inc.; *U.S. Private*, pg. 2638
TEXAS ENTERPRISES INC.; *U.S. Private*, pg. 3975
TEXAS ESCROW COMPANY, INC.—See First American Financial Corporation; *U.S. Public*, pg. 838
TEXAS EXCAVATION SAFETY; *U.S. Private*, pg. 3975
TEXAS FAMILY FITNESS LLC—See Topspin Partners, L.P.; *U.S. Private*, pg. 4188
TEXAS FARM BUREAU MUTUAL INSURANCE; *U.S. Private*, pg. 3975
TEXAS FARM PRODUCTS COMPANY; *U.S. Private*, pg. 3975
TEXAS FIRE & SAFETY—See Highview Capital, LLC; *U.S. Private*, pg. 1942
TEXAS FIRST BANK—See Preferred Bancshares, Inc.; *U.S. Private*, pg. 3247
TEXAS FIRST NATIONAL BANK; *U.S. Private*, pg. 3975
TEXAS FOAM, INC.—See Wynnchurch Capital, L.P.; *U.S. Private*, pg. 4577
TEXAS FRENCH BREAD INC.; *U.S. Private*, pg. 3975
TEXAS GAS SERVICE CO.—See ONEOK, Inc.; *U.S. Public*, pg. 1603
TEXAS GAS TRANSMISSION, LLC—See Loews Corporation; *U.S. Public*, pg. 1339
TEXAS GROUP PLC—See Texas Holdings Ltd.; *Int'l*, pg. 7583
TEXAS GULF ENERGY, INCORPORATED; *U.S. Public*, pg. 2025
TEXAS HEALTH CARE GROUP, LLC—See UnitedHealth Group Incorporated; *U.S. Public*, pg. 2247
TEXAS HEALTH RESOURCES; *U.S. Private*, pg. 3975
TEXAS HEALTH SURGERY CENTER CHISHOLM TRAIL, LLC—See UnitedHealth Group Incorporated; *U.S. Public*, pg. 2251
TEXAS HERITAGE BANK—See Southwestern Bancorp, Inc.; *U.S. Private*, pg. 3741
TEXAS HERITAGE NATIONAL BANK—See Daingerfield Holding Company; *U.S. Private*, pg. 1145
TEXAS HOLDINGS LTD.; *Int'l*, pg. 7583
TEXAS HONING, INC.—See Berkshire Hathaway Inc.; *U.S. Public*, pg. 314
TEXAS HYDRAULICS, INC.—See Wynnchurch Capital, L.P.; *U.S. Private*, pg. 4578
TEXAS - IBI GROUP, INC.—See ARCADIS N.V.; *Int'l*, pg. 542
TEXAS INDEPENDENT BANCSHARES, INC.—See Preferred Bancshares, Inc.; *U.S. Private*, pg. 3247
TEXAS INDUSTRIES, INC.—See Martin Marietta Materials, Inc.; *U.S. Public*, pg. 1389
TEXAS INSTITUTE OF MEDICINE & SURGERY—See HCA Healthcare, Inc.; *U.S. Public*, pg. 1011
TEXAS INSTITUTE OF PEDIATRICS, PLLC—See HCA Healthcare, Inc.; *U.S. Public*, pg. 1011
TEXAS INSTRUMENTS AUSTIN INCORPORATED—See Texas Instruments Incorporated; *U.S. Public*, pg. 2026
TEXAS INSTRUMENTS AUSTRALIA PTY LIMITED—See Texas Instruments Incorporated; *U.S. Public*, pg. 2026
TEXAS INSTRUMENTS BELGIUM SA—See Texas Instruments Incorporated; *U.S. Public*, pg. 2026
TEXAS INSTRUMENTS BROADBAND COMMUNICATIONS GROUP—See Texas Instruments Incorporated; *U.S. Public*, pg. 2026
TEXAS INSTRUMENTS BUSINESS EXPANSION GMBH—See Texas Instruments Incorporated; *U.S. Public*, pg. 2026
TEXAS INSTRUMENTS CANADA LIMITED—See Texas Instruments Incorporated; *U.S. Public*, pg. 2026
TEXAS INSTRUMENTS CHINA TRADING LIMITED—See Texas Instruments Incorporated; *U.S. Public*, pg. 2026
TEXAS INSTRUMENTS DENMARK A/S—See Texas Instruments Incorporated; *U.S. Public*, pg. 2026
TEXAS INSTRUMENTS DEUTSCHLAND GMBH—See Texas Instruments Incorporated; *U.S. Public*, pg. 2026
TEXAS INSTRUMENTS ESPANA, S.A.—See Texas Instruments Incorporated; *U.S. Public*, pg. 2026

TEXAS HOLDINGS LTD. CORPORATE AFFILIATIONS

Company Index

TEXAS INSTRUMENTS FINLAND OY—See Texas Instruments Incorporated; *U.S. Public*, pg. 2026
TEXAS INSTRUMENTS FRANCE SA—See Texas Instruments Incorporated; *U.S. Public*, pg. 2026
TEXAS INSTRUMENTS HONG KONG LTD.—See Texas Instruments Incorporated; *U.S. Public*, pg. 2026
TEXAS INSTRUMENTS INCORPORATED - PLUG & POWER—See Texas Instruments Incorporated; *U.S. Public*, pg. 2026
TEXAS INSTRUMENTS INCORPORATED; *U.S. Public*, pg. 2025
TEXAS INSTRUMENTS (INDIA) PRIVATE LIMITED—See Texas Instruments Incorporated; *U.S. Public*, pg. 2026
TEXAS INSTRUMENTS INTERNATIONAL TRADE CORPORATION—See Texas Instruments Incorporated; *U.S. Public*, pg. 2026
TEXAS INSTRUMENTS ISRAEL LTD.—See Texas Instruments Incorporated; *U.S. Public*, pg. 2026
TEXAS INSTRUMENTS ITALIA S.P.A.—See Texas Instruments Incorporated; *U.S. Public*, pg. 2026
TEXAS INSTRUMENTS ITALIA S.R.L.—See Texas Instruments Incorporated; *U.S. Public*, pg. 2026
TEXAS INSTRUMENTS JAPAN LTD.—See Texas Instruments Incorporated; *U.S. Public*, pg. 2026
TEXAS INSTRUMENTS JAPAN SEMICONDUCTOR LIMITED—See Texas Instruments Incorporated; *U.S. Public*, pg. 2026
TEXAS INSTRUMENTS LIMITED—See Texas Instruments Incorporated; *U.S. Public*, pg. 2026
TEXAS INSTRUMENTS MALAYSIA SDN. BHD.—See Texas Instruments Incorporated; *U.S. Public*, pg. 2026
TEXAS INSTRUMENTS MARKETING & FINANCE GMBH & CO. KG—See Texas Instruments Incorporated; *U.S. Public*, pg. 2026
TEXAS INSTRUMENTS MELBOURNE INCORPORATED—See Texas Instruments Incorporated; *U.S. Public*, pg. 2026
TEXAS INSTRUMENTS NORWAY AS—See Texas Instruments Incorporated; *U.S. Public*, pg. 2026
TEXAS INSTRUMENTS PALO ALTO INCORPORATED—See Texas Instruments Incorporated; *U.S. Public*, pg. 2026
TEXAS INSTRUMENTS RUSSIA SALES OOO—See Texas Instruments Incorporated; *U.S. Public*, pg. 2026
TEXAS INSTRUMENTS SEMICONDUCTOR GROUP—See Texas Instruments Incorporated; *U.S. Public*, pg. 2026
TEXAS INSTRUMENTS SEMICONDUCTOR MANUFACTURING (CHENGDU) CO., LTD.—See Texas Instruments Incorporated; *U.S. Public*, pg. 2026
TEXAS INSTRUMENTS SEMICONDUCTOR TECHNOLOGIES (SHANGHAI) CO., LTD.—See Texas Instruments Incorporated; *U.S. Public*, pg. 2026
TEXAS INSTRUMENTS SINGAPORE (PTE.) LTD.—See Texas Instruments Incorporated; *U.S. Public*, pg. 2026
TEXAS INSTRUMENTS SOUTHEAST ASIA PTE. LTD.—See Texas Instruments Incorporated; *U.S. Public*, pg. 2026
TEXAS INSTRUMENTS SUNNYVALE INCORPORATED—See Texas Instruments Incorporated; *U.S. Public*, pg. 2026
TEXAS INSTRUMENTS TUCSON CORPORATION—See Texas Instruments Incorporated; *U.S. Public*, pg. 2026
TEXAS INSTRUMENTS (UK) LIMITED—See Diodes Incorporated; *U.S. Public*, pg. 667
TEXAS INSURANCE MANAGERS, INC.—See Arthur J. Gallagher & Co.; *U.S. Public*, pg. 207
TEXAS INTERNAL PIPE COATING, LLC—See Hilong Holding Limited; *Int'l*, pg. 3393
TEXAS INTERNATIONAL GAS & OIL CO., INC.; *U.S. Private*, pg. 3975
TEXAS IRON WORKS INC.—See Dril-Quip, Inc.; *U.S. Public*, pg. 688
TEXAS JASMINE; *U.S. Private*, pg. 3976
TEXAS JOINT INSTITUTE, PLLC—See HCA Healthcare, Inc.; *U.S. Public*, pg. 1011
TEXAS KEYSTONE INC.; *U.S. Private*, pg. 3976
TEXAS LAND & CATTLE; *U.S. Private*, pg. 3976
TEXAS LAND & CATTLE STEAKHOUSE—See Day Star Restaurant Holdings, LLC; *U.S. Private*, pg. 1176
TEXAS LAUREL RIDGE HOSPITAL, L.P.—See Universal Health Services, Inc.; *U.S. Public*, pg. 2259
TEXAS LEHIGH CEMENT COMPANY LP—See Eagle Materials Inc.; *U.S. Public*, pg. 702
TEXAS LEHIGH CEMENT COMPANY LP—See Heidelberg Materials AG; *Int'l*, pg. 3313
TEXAS LIFE INSURANCE COMPANY—See Vestar Capital Partners, LLC; *U.S. Private*, pg. 4373
TEXAS LIGHTING SALES INCORPORATED; *U.S. Private*, pg. 3976
TEXAS LIME COMPANY—See United States Lime & Minerals, Inc.; *U.S. Public*, pg. 2236
TEXAS LINEN COMPANY; *U.S. Private*, pg. 3976
TEXAS LONE STAR AUTO AUCTION LUBBOCK—See Huron Capital Partners LLC; *U.S. Private*, pg. 2012
TEXAS LOTTERY COMMISSION; *U.S. Private*, pg. 3976
TEXAS LPG STORAGE CO. INC.; *U.S. Private*, pg. 3976
TEXAS MARKET RESEARCH GROUP LLC; *U.S. Private*, pg. 3976
TEXAS MEDICAL CENTER CORP.; *U.S. Private*, pg. 3976
TEXAS METAL WORKS—See First Reserve Management, L.P.; *U.S. Private*, pg. 1525
THE TEXAS MEXICAN RAILWAY COMPANY—See Canadian Pacific Kansas City Limited; *Int'l*, pg. 1285
TEXAS MINERAL RESOURCES CORP.; *U.S. Public*, pg. 2026
TEXAS MOLECULAR, LLC; *U.S. Private*, pg. 3976
TEXAS MONTHLY, INC.; *U.S. Private*, pg. 3976
TEXAS MOTOR SPEEDWAY—See Sonic Financial Corporation; *U.S. Private*, pg. 3713
TEXAS MOVING COMPANY INC.—See Willis Permian Movers, Inc.; *U.S. Private*, pg. 4528
TEXAS MUNICIPAL POWER AGENCY; *U.S. Private*, pg. 3976
TEXAS MUTUAL INSURANCE COMPANY; *U.S. Private*, pg. 3976
TEXAS-NEW MEXICO NEWSPAPERS, LLC—See Gannett Co., Inc.; *U.S. Public*, pg. 899
TEXAS-NEW MEXICO POWER COMPANY—See TXNM Energy, Inc.; *U.S. Public*, pg. 2208
TEXAS-NEW MEXICO RAILROAD—See Iowa Pacific Holdings, LLC; *U.S. Private*, pg. 2135
TEXAS NHI INVESTORS, LLC—See National Health Investors, Inc.; *U.S. Public*, pg. 1495
TEXAS NICUSA, LLC—See Tyler Technologies, Inc.; *U.S. Public*, pg. 2209
TEXAS NORTHEASTERN RAILROAD—See Brookfield Infrastructure Partners L.P.; *Int'l*, pg. 1191
TEXAS NORTHEASTERN RAILROAD—See GIC Pte. Ltd.; *Int'l*, pg. 2965
TEXAS & NORTHERN RAILWAY COMPANY—See United States Steel Corporation; *U.S. Public*, pg. 2236
TEXAS OIL & MINERALS, INC.; *U.S. Public*, pg. 2027
TEXAS OILPATCH SERVICES, LLC—See Applied Industrial Technologies, Inc.; *U.S. Public*, pg. 171
TEXAS & OKLAHOMA COAL COMPANY LTD—See Advance Metals Limited; *Int'l*, pg. 156
TEXAS & OKLAHOMA COAL COMPANY (USA) LLC—See Advance Metals Limited; *Int'l*, pg. 156
TEXAS ONCOLOGY, PA; *U.S. Private*, pg. 3976
TEXAS ONCOLOGY - SAN ANTONIO NORTHEAST—See Texas Oncology, PA; *U.S. Private*, pg. 3976
TEXAS ORGAN SHARING ALLIANCE; *U.S. Private*, pg. 3976
TEXAS ORTHOPEDIC HOSPITAL—See HCA Healthcare, Inc.; *U.S. Public*, pg. 1011
TEXAS ORTHOPEDIC HOSPITAL—See HCA Healthcare, Inc.; *U.S. Public*, pg. 1011
TEXAS ORTHOPEDICS SURGERY CENTER, LLC—See Tenet Healthcare Corporation; *U.S. Public*, pg. 2013
TEXAS PACIFIC LAND CORP.; *U.S. Public*, pg. 2027
TEXAS PANHANDLE CLINICAL PARTNERS ACO, LLC—See Universal Health Services, Inc.; *U.S. Public*, pg. 2259
TEXAS PARIMUTUEL MANAGEMENT INC.—See Greene Group Inc.; *U.S. Private*, pg. 1776
TEXAS PARTNERS BANK—See Southwest Bancshares, Inc.; *U.S. Private*, pg. 3738
TEXAS PEOPLES NATIONAL BANCSHARES, INC.; *U.S. Private*, pg. 3976
TEXAS PETROLEUM INVESTMENT CO.; *U.S. Private*, pg. 3976
TEXAS PHYSICAL THERAPY SPECIALISTS; *U.S. Private*, pg. 3976
TEXAS PIPE & SUPPLY COMPANY LTD.; *U.S. Private*, pg. 3976
TEXAS PIPE WORKS INC.; *U.S. Private*, pg. 3976
TEXAS PNEUMATIC SYSTEMS, INC.—See JLL Partners, LLC; *U.S. Private*, pg. 2212
TEXAS POS, INC.—See NCR Voyix Corporation.; *U.S. Public*, pg. 1503
TEXAS PRESS ASSOCIATION; *U.S. Private*, pg. 3977
TEXAS PROCESS EQUIPMENT CO.; *U.S. Private*, pg. 3977
TEXAS PROPERTY & CASUALTY INSURANCE GUARANTY ASSOCIATION; *U.S. Private*, pg. 3977
TEXAS RECREATION CORPORATION; *U.S. Private*, pg. 3977
TEXAS REFINERY CORP. - LUBRICANTS DIVISION—See Texas Refinery Corp.; *U.S. Private*, pg. 3977
TEXAS REFINERY CORP OF CANADA LIMITED—See Texas Refinery Corp.; *U.S. Private*, pg. 3977
TEXAS REFINERY CORP. - PROTECTIVE COATINGS DIVISION—See Texas Refinery Corp.; *U.S. Private*, pg. 3977
TEXAS REFINERY CORP.; *U.S. Private*, pg. 3977
TEXAS REGIONAL BANK—See Texas State Bankshares, Inc.; *U.S. Private*, pg. 3977
TEXAS REPUBLIC BANK, N.A.—See TXRB Holdings, Inc.; *U.S. Private*, pg. 4267
TEXAS REPUBLIC CAPITAL CORPORATION; *U.S. Private*, pg. 3977
TEXAS REPUBLIC LIFE INSURANCE COMPANY—See Texas Republic Capital Corporation; *U.S. Private*, pg. 3977
TEXAS REPUBLIC LIFE SOLUTIONS—See Texas Republic Capital Corporation; *U.S. Private*, pg. 3977
TEXAS ROADHOUSE DELAWARE LLC—See Texas Roadhouse, Inc.; *U.S. Public*, pg. 2027
TEXAS ROADHOUSE HOLDINGS LLC—See Texas Roadhouse, Inc.; *U.S. Public*, pg. 2027
TEXAS ROADHOUSE, INC.; *U.S. Public*, pg. 2027
TEXAS ROADHOUSE OF AUSTIN, LTD.—See Texas Roadhouse, Inc.; *U.S. Public*, pg. 2027
TEXAS ROADHOUSE OF AUSTIN-NORTH, LTD.—See Texas Roadhouse, Inc.; *U.S. Public*, pg. 2027
TEXAS ROADHOUSE OF BAKERSFIELD, LLC—See Texas Roadhouse, Inc.; *U.S. Public*, pg. 2027
TEXAS ROADHOUSE OF BAYTOWN, TX, LLC—See Texas Roadhouse, Inc.; *U.S. Public*, pg. 2027
TEXAS ROADHOUSE OF CEDAR FALLS, LLC—See Texas Roadhouse, Inc.; *U.S. Public*, pg. 2027
TEXAS ROADHOUSE OF CHEYENNE, LLC—See Texas Roadhouse, Inc.; *U.S. Public*, pg. 2027
TEXAS ROADHOUSE OF CONWAY, INC.—See Texas Roadhouse, Inc.; *U.S. Public*, pg. 2027
TEXAS ROADHOUSE OF CORONA, CA LLC—See Texas Roadhouse, Inc.; *U.S. Public*, pg. 2027
TEXAS ROADHOUSE OF ELYRIA, LLC—See Texas Roadhouse, Inc.; *U.S. Public*, pg. 2027
TEXAS ROADHOUSE OF FORT WAYNE, LLC—See Texas Roadhouse, Inc.; *U.S. Public*, pg. 2027
TEXAS ROADHOUSE OF GRAND JUNCTION, LLC—See Texas Roadhouse, Inc.; *U.S. Public*, pg. 2027
TEXAS ROADHOUSE OF HENDERSONVILLE, DE NOVO, LLC—See Texas Roadhouse, Inc.; *U.S. Public*, pg. 2027
TEXAS ROADHOUSE OF HUBER HEIGHTS, LLC—See Texas Roadhouse, Inc.; *U.S. Public*, pg. 2027
TEXAS ROADHOUSE OF JACKSONVILLE, NC, LLC—See Texas Roadhouse, Inc.; *U.S. Public*, pg. 2027
TEXAS ROADHOUSE OF KANSAS, LLC—See Texas Roadhouse, Inc.; *U.S. Public*, pg. 2027
TEXAS ROADHOUSE OF LANCASTER, LLC—See Texas Roadhouse, Inc.; *U.S. Public*, pg. 2027
TEXAS ROADHOUSE OF LANCASTER OH, LLC—See Texas Roadhouse, Inc.; *U.S. Public*, pg. 2027
TEXAS ROADHOUSE OF LANSING, LLC—See Texas Roadhouse, Inc.; *U.S. Public*, pg. 2027
TEXAS ROADHOUSE OF LYNCHBURG, LLC—See Texas Roadhouse, Inc.; *U.S. Public*, pg. 2027
TEXAS ROADHOUSE OF MANSFIELD, LTD.—See Texas Roadhouse, Inc.; *U.S. Public*, pg. 2027
TEXAS ROADHOUSE OF MENIFEE, CA, LLC—See Texas Roadhouse, Inc.; *U.S. Public*, pg. 2027
TEXAS ROADHOUSE OF PARKER, LLC—See Texas Roadhouse, Inc.; *U.S. Public*, pg. 2027
TEXAS ROADHOUSE OF RENO, NV, LLC—See Texas Roadhouse, Inc.; *U.S. Public*, pg. 2027
TEXAS ROADHOUSE OF RICHMOND, LLC—See Texas Roadhouse, Inc.; *U.S. Public*, pg. 2027
TEXAS ROADHOUSE OF ROSEVILLE, LLC—See Texas Roadhouse, Inc.; *U.S. Public*, pg. 2027
TEXAS ROADHOUSE OF STILLWATER, OK, LLC—See Texas Roadhouse, Inc.; *U.S. Public*, pg. 2027
TEXAS ROADHOUSE OF WARWICK, LLC—See Texas Roadhouse, Inc.; *U.S. Public*, pg. 2027
TEXAS RUBBER SUPPLY, INC.—See AEA Investors LP; *U.S. Private*, pg. 115
TEXAS SAN MARCOS TREATMENT CENTER, L.P.—See Universal Health Services, Inc.; *U.S. Public*, pg. 2259
TEXAS SCENIC COMPANY INC.; *U.S. Private*, pg. 3977
TEXAS SCOTTISH RITE HOSPITAL FOR CHILDREN; *U.S. Private*, pg. 3977
TEXAS SECURITY GENERAL INSURANCE AGENCY, INC.—See Brown & Brown, Inc.; *U.S. Public*, pg. 402
TEXAS SOUTH-EASTERN RAILROAD COMPANY—See International Paper Company; *U.S. Public*, pg. 1158
TEXAS SOUTH ENERGY, INC.; *U.S. Private*, pg. 3977
TEXAS SPINE AND JOINT HOSPITAL, LLC—See Tenet Healthcare Corporation; *U.S. Public*, pg. 2009
TEXAS STAR BANK; *U.S. Private*, pg. 3977
TEXAS STAR EXPRESS—See EPES Carriers Inc.; *U.S. Private*, pg. 1412
TEXAS STATE BANKSHARES, INC.; *U.S. Private*, pg. 3977
TEXAS STEEL CONVERSION, INC.; *U.S. Private*, pg. 3977
TEXAS STERLING CONSTRUCTION CO.—See Sterling Infrastructure, Inc.; *U.S. Public*, pg. 1947
TEXAS SUBS; *U.S. Private*, pg. 3977
TEXAS TACO CABANA, L.P.—See Restaurant Brands International Inc.; *Int'l*, pg. 6304
TEXAS TIMBERJACK, INC.—See TreeCon Resources, Inc.; *U.S. Public*, pg. 2187
TEXAS TOOL DISTRIBUTORS INC.; *U.S. Private*, pg. 3977
TEXAS TRAILER CORP.—See Markel Group Inc.; *U.S. Public*, pg. 1369
TEXAS TRANSEASTERN INC.; *U.S. Private*, pg. 3977
TEXAS TRIBUNE INC.; *U.S. Private*, pg. 3978
TEXAS TRUST CREDIT UNION; *U.S. Private*, pg. 3978
TEXAS TUBULAR PRODUCTS—See Friedman Industries, Inc.; *U.S. Public*, pg. 886

COMPANY NAME INDEX

TEXAS UNITED CHEMICAL COMPANY LLC—See United Salt Corporation; *U.S. Private*, pg. 4297
TEXAS UNITED SUPPLY COMPANY INC.—See United Salt Corporation; *U.S. Private*, pg. 4297
TEXAS VET LAB INC.—See Bimeda, Inc.; *U.S. Private*, pg. 560
TEXAS VISITING NURSE LTD.; *U.S. Private*, pg. 3978
TEXASWEET CITRUS MARKETING INC.; *U.S. Private*, pg. 3978
TEXAS WEST BOP SALES & SERVICE LLC—See Meyer Service, Inc.; *U.S. Private*, pg. 2692
TEXAS WESTMORELAND COAL COMPANY—See Westmoreland Coal Company; *U.S. Private*, pg. 4499
TEXAS WILSON OFFICE FURNITURE & SERVICES; *U.S. Private*, pg. 3978
TEX A.T.C. LIMITED—See Tex Holdings Plc; *Int'l*, pg. 7582
TEXATRONICS INC.; *U.S. Private*, pg. 3978
TEX-BEST TRAVEL CENTERS INC.; *U.S. Private*, pg. 3974
TEXCAN DIVISION—See Sonepar S.A.; *Int'l*, pg. 7091
TEX-CAP ELECTRIC INC.—See McCarty Corporation; *U.S. Private*, pg. 2628
TEXCHEM CORPORATION SDN. BHD.—See Texchem Resources Bhd.; *Int'l*, pg. 7583
TEXCHEM FOOD MATERIALS (VIETNAM) CO. LTD.—See Texchem Resources Bhd.; *Int'l*, pg. 7583
TEXCHEM LIFE SCIENCES SDN. BHD.—See Texchem Resources Bhd.; *Int'l*, pg. 7583
TEXCHEM MALAYSIA SDN. BERHAD—See Texchem Resources Bhd.; *Int'l*, pg. 7583
TEXCHEM MATERIALS SDN. BHD.—See Texchem Resources Bhd.; *Int'l*, pg. 7583
TEXCHEM MATERIALS (THAILAND) LTD.—See Texchem Resources Bhd.; *Int'l*, pg. 7583
TEXCHEM MATERIALS (VIETNAM) CO., LTD.—See Texchem Resources Bhd.; *Int'l*, pg. 7583
TEXCHEM-PACK (JOHOR) SDN. BHD.—See Texchem Resources Bhd.; *Int'l*, pg. 7583
TEXCHEM-PACK (M) SDN. BHD.—See Texchem Resources Bhd.; *Int'l*, pg. 7583
TEXCHEM-PACK (THAILAND) CO., LTD.—See Texchem Resources Bhd.; *Int'l*, pg. 7583
TEXCHEM-PACK (VIETNAM) CO., LTD.—See Texchem Resources Bhd.; *Int'l*, pg. 7583
TEXCHEM POLYMER ENGINEERING SDN. BHD.—See Texchem Resources Bhd.; *Int'l*, pg. 7583
TEXCHEM POLYMERS SDN. BHD.—See Texchem Resources Bhd.; *Int'l*, pg. 7583
TEXCHEM RESOURCES BHD.; *Int'l*, pg. 7583
TEXCHEM RISK MANAGEMENT SDN. BHD.—See Texchem Resources Bhd.; *Int'l*, pg. 7583
TEXCHEM SINGAPORE PRIVATE LIMITED—See Texchem Resources Bhd.; *Int'l*, pg. 7583
TEXCOM BENNETT ENVIRONMENTAL SERVICES, LLC—See Texcom, Inc.; *U.S. Public*, pg. 2027
TEXCOM ENVIRONMENTAL SERVICES, LLC—See Texcom, Inc.; *U.S. Public*, pg. 2027
TEXCOM, INC.; *U.S. Public*, pg. 2027
TEXCOM PEAK ENVIRONMENTAL SERVICES, LLC—See Texcom, Inc.; *U.S. Public*, pg. 2027
TEXCOTE TECHNOLOGY (INTERNATIONAL) LIMITED—See Fullsun International Holdings Group Co., Limited; *Int'l*, pg. 2843
TEX CYCLE (P2) SDN. BHD.—See Tex Cycle Technology (M) Berhad; *Int'l*, pg. 7582
TEX CYCLE TECHNOLOGY (M) BERHAD; *Int'l*, pg. 7582
TEXECOM LIMITED—See Lloyds Banking Group plc; *Int'l*, pg. 4538
TEXEL GEOSOL INC.—See Lydall, Inc.; *U.S. Public*, pg. 1350
TEXEL INDUSTRIES LIMITED; *Int'l*, pg. 7583
TEXELL CREDIT UNION; *U.S. Private*, pg. 3978
TEXEL TECHNICAL MATERIALS, INC.—See Lydall, Inc.; *U.S. Public*, pg. 1350
TEXEN - CEICA—See PSB Industries SA; *Int'l*, pg. 6015
TEX ENGINEERING LIMITED—See Tex Holdings Plc; *Int'l*, pg. 7582
TEXEN GROUP—See PSB Industries SA; *Int'l*, pg. 6014
TEXEN SERVICES—See PSB Industries SA; *Int'l*, pg. 6015
TEXET AB—See New Wave Group AB; *Int'l*, pg. 5230
TEXET BENELUX N.V.—See New Wave Group AB; *Int'l*, pg. 5230
TEXET DENMARK A/S—See New Wave Group AB; *Int'l*, pg. 5230
TEXET DEUTCHLAND GMBH—See New Wave Group AB; *Int'l*, pg. 5230
TEXET FRANCE SAS—See New Wave Group AB; *Int'l*, pg. 5230
TEXET GMBH—See New Wave Group AB; *Int'l*, pg. 5229
TEXET NORGE A/S—See New Wave Group AB; *Int'l*, pg. 5230
TEXET POLAND LTD—See New Wave Group AB; *Int'l*, pg. 5230
TEXET POLAND SP. Z O.O.—See New Wave Group AB; *Int'l*, pg. 5231
TEX HOLDINGS PLC; *Int'l*, pg. 7582
TEXHOMA ENERGY, INC.; *U.S. Private*, pg. 3978
TEXHOMA WHEAT GROWERS INC.; *U.S. Private*, pg. 3978
TEXHONG (CHINA) INVESTMENT CO., LTD.—See Texhong Textile Group Limited; *Int'l*, pg. 7584
TEXHONG TEXTILE GROUP LIMITED; *Int'l*, pg. 7583
TEX HUNGARY KFT.—See CTS Eventim AG & Co. KGAA; *Int'l*, pg. 1873
TEXIM BANK AD; *Int'l*, pg. 7584
TEXIM EUROPE BVBA—See TKH Group N.V.; *Int'l*, pg. 7765
TEXIM EUROPE B.V.—See TKH Group N.V.; *Int'l*, pg. 7765
TEXIM EUROPE GMBH—See TKH Group N.V.; *Int'l*, pg. 7765
TEX INDUSTRIALISED CONSTRUCTION SYSTEMS LIMITED—See Tex Holdings Plc; *Int'l*, pg. 7582
TEX INDUSTRIAL PLASTICS LIMITED—See Tex Holdings Plc; *Int'l*, pg. 7582
TEXIO TECHNOLOGY CORPORATION—See Good Will Instrument Co., Ltd.; *Int'l*, pg. 3039
TEX ISLE SUPPLY INC.; *U.S. Private*, pg. 3974
TEX-LA ELECTRIC COOPERATIVE OF TEXAS INC; *U.S. Private*, pg. 3974
TEXMAC, INC.—See ITOCHU Corporation; *Int'l*, pg. 3839
TEXMACO INFRASTRUCTURE & HOLDINGS LIMITED—See Adventz Group; *Int'l*, pg. 167
TEXMACO RAIL & ENGINEERING LTD.—See Adventz Group; *Int'l*, pg. 167
TEXMARK CHEMICALS, INC.—See Chemical Exchange Industries, Inc.; *U.S. Private*, pg. 871
TEXMO PIPES AND PRODUCTS LIMITED; *Int'l*, pg. 7584
TEXNIL LIMITED—See Hayleys PLC; *Int'l*, pg. 3291
TEXNOLOGY NANO TEXTILE (CHINA) LIMITED—See Fullsun International Holdings Group Co., Limited; *Int'l*, pg. 2843
TEXNORTE INDUSTRIAL LIMITED—See Li & Fung Limited; *Int'l*, pg. 4481
TEXOMACARE—See Universal Health Services, Inc.; *U.S. Public*, pg. 2259
TEXOMACARE SPECIALTY PHYSICIANS—See Universal Health Services, Inc.; *U.S. Public*, pg. 2259
TEXOMA PEANUT COMPANY; *U.S. Private*, pg. 3978
TEXOMA PEANUT INN—See Texoma Peanut Company; *U.S. Private*, pg. 3978
TEXON CO., LTD—See SeoJin System Co., Ltd.; *Int'l*, pg. 6716
TEXON COMPONENTS GMBH—See Navis Capital Partners Limited; *Int'l*, pg. 5176
TEXON FRANCE SA—See Navis Capital Partners Limited; *Int'l*, pg. 5176
TEXON INDIA PVT. LTD—See Navis Capital Partners Limited; *Int'l*, pg. 5176
TEXON INTERNATIONAL (ASIA) LTD—See Navis Capital Partners Limited; *Int'l*, pg. 5176
TEXON INTERNATIONAL GROUP LTD.—See Coats Group plc; *Int'l*, pg. 1682
TEXON ITALIA S.P.A.—See Navis Capital Partners Limited; *Int'l*, pg. 5176
TEXON LP; *U.S. Private*, pg. 3978
TEXON MANAGEMENT LTD—See Coats Group plc; *Int'l*, pg. 1682
TEXON MATERIALES, S.L.—See Navis Capital Partners Limited; *Int'l*, pg. 5176
TEXON MOCKMUHL GMBH—See Navis Capital Partners Limited; *Int'l*, pg. 5176
TEXON OESTERREICH G.M.B.H—See Navis Capital Partners Limited; *Int'l*, pg. 5176
TEXON OZ PTY LTD—See Navis Capital Partners Limited; *Int'l*, pg. 5176
TEXON POLYMER GROUP, INC.—See Myers Industries, Inc.; *U.S. Public*, pg. 1488
TEXON USA CO., LTD.—See SeoJin System Co., Ltd.; *Int'l*, pg. 6716
TEXOR PETROLEUM COMPANY—See World Kinect Corporation; *U.S. Public*, pg. 2381
TEXOZ E&P I, INC.—See Strike Energy Limited; *Int'l*, pg. 7241
TEXPA MASCHINENBAU; *Int'l*, pg. 7584
TEXPAR ENERGY INC.; *U.S. Private*, pg. 3978
TEX PLASTIC PRODUCTS LIMITED—See Tex Holdings Plc; *Int'l*, pg. 7582
TEXPLORE CO., LTD.—See The Siam Cement Public Company Limited; *Int'l*, pg. 7685
TEXPLOR OF DALLAS, INC.—See Terracon Consultants, Inc; *U.S. Private*, pg. 3970
TEX-RAY INDUSTRIAL CO., LTD.; *Int'l*, pg. 7582
TEXSA LTD.—See Texsa Systems, SL.U.; *Int'l*, pg. 7584
TEXSA PORTUGAL S.A.—See Texsa Systems, SL.U.; *Int'l*, pg. 7584
TEXSA S.A.S.—See Texsa Systems, SL.U.; *Int'l*, pg. 7584
TEXSA SYSTEMS, SL.U.; *Int'l*, pg. 7584
TEX SPECIAL PROJECTS LIMITED—See Tex Holdings Plc; *Int'l*, pg. 7582
TEXSTAR ENTERPRISES, INC.—See Dycom Industries, Inc.; *U.S. Public*, pg. 699
TEXSTAR INSURANCE SERVICES, INC.—See Inszone Insurance Services, LLC; *U.S. Public*, pg. 2096
TEXSTAR PHYSICAL THERAPY, LIMITED PARTNERSHIP—See U.S. Physical Therapy, Inc.; *U.S. Public*, pg. 2216
TEXSTARS LLC—See PPG Industries, Inc.; *U.S. Public*, pg. 1710
TEXSTRIP MANUFACTURING SDN. BHD.—See PRG Holdings Berhad; *Int'l*, pg. 5969
TEXSUN SWIMMING POOLS & SPAS, INC.; *U.S. Private*, pg. 3978
TEXT 100 AB—See Next 15 Group plc; *Int'l*, pg. 5246
TEXT 100 AMSTERDAM BV—See Next 15 Group plc; *Int'l*, pg. 5246
TEXT 100 BEIJING—See Next 15 Group plc; *Int'l*, pg. 5246
TEXT 100 BOSTON CORP.—See Next 15 Group plc; *Int'l*, pg. 5246
TEXT 100 COPENHAGEN—See Next 15 Group plc; *Int'l*, pg. 5246
TEXT 100 FRANCE—See Next 15 Group plc; *Int'l*, pg. 5246
TEXT 100 HELSINKI—See Next 15 Group plc; *Int'l*, pg. 5246
TEXT 100 HONG KONG—See Next 15 Group plc; *Int'l*, pg. 5246
TEXT 100 HONG KONG—See Next 15 Group plc; *Int'l*, pg. 5247
TEXT 100 INDIA-BANGALORE—See Next 15 Group plc; *Int'l*, pg. 5247
TEXT 100 INDIA PVT. LTD.—See Next 15 Group plc; *Int'l*, pg. 5247
TEXT 100 ITALY SRL—See Next 15 Group plc; *Int'l*, pg. 5246
TEXT 100 JAPAN K.K.—See Next 15 Group plc; *Int'l*, pg. 5247
TEXT 100 JOHANNESBURG PTY. LTD.—See Next 15 Group plc; *Int'l*, pg. 5247
TEXT 100 LIMITED—See Next 15 Group plc; *Int'l*, pg. 5246
TEXT 100 LONDON LTD.—See Next 15 Group plc; *Int'l*, pg. 5247
TEXT 100 MADRID S.L.—See Next 15 Group plc; *Int'l*, pg. 5247
TEXT 100 MILAN S.R.L.—See Next 15 Group plc; *Int'l*, pg. 5247
TEXT 100 MUMBAI—See Next 15 Group plc; *Int'l*, pg. 5247
TEXT 100 MUNICH GMBH—See Next 15 Group plc; *Int'l*, pg. 5247
TEXT 100 NEW YORK CORP.—See Next 15 Group plc; *Int'l*, pg. 5247
TEXT 100 NEW ZEALAND—See Next 15 Group plc; *Int'l*, pg. 5247
TEXT 100 OSLO—See Next 15 Group plc; *Int'l*, pg. 5247
TEXT 100 PTY LIMITED—See Next 15 Group plc; *Int'l*, pg. 5246
TEXT 100 (PTY) LIMITED—See Next 15 Group plc; *Int'l*, pg. 5246
TEXT 100 PUBLIC RELATIONS—See Next 15 Group plc; *Int'l*, pg. 5246
TEXT 100 ROCHESTER CORP.—See Next 15 Group plc; *Int'l*, pg. 5247
TEXT 100 SHANGHAI—See Next 15 Group plc; *Int'l*, pg. 5247
TEXT 100 SINGAPORE PVT. LTD.—See Next 15 Group plc; *Int'l*, pg. 5247
TEXT 100 SL—See Next 15 Group plc; *Int'l*, pg. 5247
TEXT 100 STOCKHOLM—See Next 15 Group plc; *Int'l*, pg. 5247
TEXT 100 SUNNY RELATIONS—See Next 15 Group plc; *Int'l*, pg. 5247
TEXT 100 SYDNEY—See Next 15 Group plc; *Int'l*, pg. 5247
TEXT 100 TAIPEI—See Next 15 Group plc; *Int'l*, pg. 5247
TEXTAINER EQUIPMENT MANAGEMENT—See Stonepeak Partners L.P.; *U.S. Private*, pg. 3829
TEXTAINER EQUIPMENT MANAGEMENT (U.S.) LIMITED—See Stonepeak Partners L.P.; *U.S. Private*, pg. 3829
TEXTAINER EQUIPMENT RESALE—See Stonepeak Partners L.P.; *U.S. Private*, pg. 3829
TEXTAINER EQUIPMENT—See Stonepeak Partners L.P.; *U.S. Private*, pg. 3829
TEXTAINER GROUP HOLDINGS LIMITED—See Stonepeak Partners L.P.; *U.S. Private*, pg. 3829
TEXTAINER JAPAN LIMITED—See Stonepeak Partners L.P.; *U.S. Private*, pg. 3829
TEXTAINER MARINE CONTAINERS LTD.—See BNP Paribas SA; *Int'l*, pg. 1093
TEX TAN WESTERN LEATHER COMPANY—See Action Company; *U.S. Private*, pg. 67
TEXTAPE, INC.; *U.S. Private*, pg. 3978
TEXTBOOK PRINTING JSC IN HOCHIMINH CITY; *Int'l*, pg. 7584
TEX-TECH INDUSTRIES, INC.—See Arlington Capital Partners LLC; *U.S. Private*, pg. 328
TEXTERITY INC.—See Godengo, Inc.; *U.S. Private*, pg. 1724
TEXT HUNDRED INDIA PRIVATE LIMITED—See Next 15 Group plc; *Int'l*, pg. 5247

TEXTILCORD STEINFORT S.A.—See CAG Holding GmbH; *Int'l*, pg. 1251
TEXTILE CARE SERVICES, INC.; *U.S. Private*, pg. 3978
TEXTILE CARE SERVICES, INC.; *U.S. Private*, pg. 3978
TEXTILE IMPORT LLC; *U.S. Private*, pg. 3978
TEXTILE RUBBER & CHEMICAL CO., INC. - COATINGS & ADHESIVES DIVISION—See Textile Rubber & Chemical Co., Inc.; *U.S. Private*, pg. 3978
TEXTILE RUBBER & CHEMICAL CO., INC.; *U.S. Private*, pg. 3978
TEXTILES FROM EUROPE INC.; *U.S. Private*, pg. 3978
TEXTILE SYSTEMS, INC.—See Ascension Health Alliance; *U.S. Private*, pg. 347
TEXTILIA TVATT & TEXTILSERVICE AB—See Accent Equity Partners AB; *Int'l*, pg. 81
TEXTIL MANUEL GONCALVES, SGPS, S.A.; *Int'l*, pg. 7584
TEXTIL RENAUXVIEW S.A.; *Int'l*, pg. 7584
TEXTLOCAL LTD.—See Cisco Systems, Inc.; *U.S. Public*, pg. 500
TEXTON PROPERTY FUND LTD.; *Int'l*, pg. 7584
TEX TRACING CO., LTD—See Tokai Senko K.K.; *Int'l*, pg. 7781
TEXTRAIL, INC. - FITZGERALD—See Bain Capital, LP; *U.S. Private*, pg. 436
TEXTRAIL, INC. - FLORIDA—See Bain Capital, LP; *U.S. Private*, pg. 436
TEXTRAIL, INC. - GEORGIA—See Bain Capital, LP; *U.S. Private*, pg. 436
TEXTRAIL, INC. - HOUSTON—See Bain Capital, LP; *U.S. Private*, pg. 436
TEXTRAIL, INC. - IDAHO—See Bain Capital, LP; *U.S. Private*, pg. 436
TEXTRAIL, INC. - ODESSA—See Bain Capital, LP; *U.S. Private*, pg. 436
TEXTRAIL, INC.—See Bain Capital, LP; *U.S. Private*, pg. 436
TEXTRON ACQUISITION LIMITED—See Textron Inc.; *U.S. Public*, pg. 2028
TEXTRON ATLANTIC HOLDING GMBH—See Textron Inc.; *U.S. Public*, pg. 2028
TEXTRON AVIATION DEFENSE LLC—See Textron Inc.; *U.S. Public*, pg. 2029
TEXTRON AVIATION DEFENSE LLC—See Textron Inc.; *U.S. Public*, pg. 2028
TEXTRON CAPITAL B.V.—See Textron Inc.; *U.S. Public*, pg. 2029
TEXTRON FINANCIAL CORPORATION—See Textron Inc.; *U.S. Public*, pg. 2029
TEXTRON FINANCIAL INVESTMENT CORPORATION—See Textron Inc.; *U.S. Public*, pg. 2029
TEXTRON GERMANY HOLDING GMBH—See Textron Inc.; *U.S. Public*, pg. 2028
TEXTRONICS, INC.—See adidas AG; *Int'l*, pg. 146
TEXTRON INC.; *U.S. Public*, pg. 2027
TEXTRON INTERNATIONAL MEXICO, S DE RL DE CV—See Textron Inc.; *U.S. Public*, pg. 2029
TEXTRON LYCOMING—See Textron Inc.; *U.S. Public*, pg. 2029
TEXTRON MARINE & LAND SYSTEMS—See Textron Inc.; *U.S. Public*, pg. 2029
TEXTRON SYSTEMS AUSTRALIA PTY LTD.—See Textron Inc.; *U.S. Public*, pg. 2029
TEXTRON SYSTEMS CANADA INC.—See Textron Inc.; *U.S. Public*, pg. 2029
TEXTRON SYSTEMS CORPORATION—See Textron Inc.; *U.S. Public*, pg. 2029
TEXTRON SYSTEMS ELECTRONIC SYSTEMS UK (HOLDINGS) LIMITED—See Textron Inc.; *U.S. Public*, pg. 2029
TEXTRON VERWALTUNGS-GMBH—See Textron Inc.; *U.S. Public*, pg. 2028
TEX-TRUDE LP; *U.S. Private*, pg. 3974
TEXT S.A.; *Int'l*, pg. 7584
TEXTUEL LA MINE—See Omnicom Group Inc.; *U.S. Public*, pg. 1597
TEXTUEL—See Omnicom Group Inc.; *U.S. Public*, pg. 1597
TEXWINCA ENTERPRISES LIMITED—See Texwinca Holdings Limited; *Int'l*, pg. 7584
TEXWINCA HOLDINGS LIMITED; *Int'l*, pg. 7584
TEX YEAR EUROPE SP. Z O. O.—See Tex Year Industries Inc.; *Int'l*, pg. 7582
TEX YEAR FINE CHEMICAL CO., LTD.—See Tex Year Industries Inc.; *Int'l*, pg. 7582
TEX YEAR (HONG KONG) LTD.—See Tex Year Industries Inc.; *Int'l*, pg. 7582
TEX YEAR INDUSTRIAL ADHESIVES PVT. LTD.—See Tex Year Industries Inc.; *Int'l*, pg. 7582
TEX YEAR INDUSTRIES INC.; *Int'l*, pg. 7582
TEX YEAR MINIMA TECHNOLOGY INC.—See Tex-Year Industries Inc.; *Int'l*, pg. 7582
TEX YEAR TECHNOLOGY (JIANGSU) CO., LTD.—See Tex Year Industries Inc.; *Int'l*, pg. 7582
TEX YEAR VIETNAM CO., LTD.—See Tex Year Industries Inc.; *Int'l*, pg. 7582
TEYI PHARMACEUTICAL GROUP CO., LTD.; *Int'l*, pg. 7584

TEYLOR AG; *Int'l*, pg. 7584
TEYS AUSTRALIA PTY LTD.; *Int'l*, pg. 7585
TEYSEER SERVICES COMPANY—See Sodexo S.A.; *Int'l*, pg. 7047
TEYS (USA) INC.—See Teys Australia Pty Ltd.; *Int'l*, pg. 7585
TEZAK HEAVY EQUIPMENT CO., INC.—See Holcim Ltd.; *Int'l*, pg. 3447
TEZAO S.R.O.—See Aiphone Co., Ltd.; *Int'l*, pg. 235
TF1 DROITS AUDIOVISUELS S.A.S.—See Television Francaise 1 S.A.; *Int'l*, pg. 7543
TF1 FILMS PRODUCTION S.A.S.—See Television Francaise 1 S.A.; *Int'l*, pg. 7543
TF1 PUBLICITE SAS—See Television Francaise 1 S.A.; *Int'l*, pg. 7543
T-FAL CORPORATION—See SEB S.A.; *Int'l*, pg. 6668
TF BANK AB; *Int'l*, pg. 7585
TFB, INC—See H.U. Group Holdings, Inc.; *Int'l*, pg. 3196
TF CABLE JSC—See TELE-FONIKA Kable Sp. z o.o. S.K.A.; *Int'l*, pg. 7528
TFC ASSOCIATES, LLC; *U.S. Private*, pg. 3978
TFC CO., LTD.—See Tomoegawa Co., Ltd.; *Int'l*, pg. 7801
TFC CO., LTD.—See Zeon Corporation; *Int'l*, pg. 8635
TFCHEM S.A.S—See Sirona Biochem Corp.; *Int'l*, pg. 6962
TFC HOLLAND B.V.—See BayWa AG; *Int'l*, pg. 919
T.F. COLLETTE COMPANIES, INC.; *U.S. Private*, pg. 3912
T.F. COMPANY, LTD.—See TOPPAN Holdings Inc.; *Int'l*, pg. 7818
TFC SOUTH AMERICA S.A.—See Amphenol Corporation; *U.S. Public*, pg. 132
TFC ZAHIDTRANSSERVICE LIMITED—See Intereuropa d.d.; *Int'l*, pg. 3740
TFE CO., LTD.; *Int'l*, pg. 7585
TFE GROUP INC.—See International Management Services Company; *U.S. Private*, pg. 2118
TFE TEXTIL GMBH—See Getzner Textil AG; *Int'l*, pg. 2954
TFF PHARMACEUTICALS, INC.; *U.S. Public*, pg. 2029
TFG INTERNATIONAL GROUP LIMITED; *Int'l*, pg. 7585
TFG TRANSFRACHT GMBH—See Deutsche Bahn AG; *Int'l*, pg. 2054
TFH PUBLICATIONS, INC.—See Central Garden & Pet Company; *U.S. Public*, pg. 473
T.F. HUDGINS, INC.—See Shell plc; *Int'l*, pg. 6796
TFI ALLIANZ POLSKA S.A.—See Allianz SE; *Int'l*, pg. 356
TFI BNP PARIBAS POLSKA SA—See BNP Paribas SA; *Int'l*, pg. 1084
T-FIELDTEC COMPANY, LTD.—See Tomy Company, Ltd.; *Int'l*, pg. 7804
TFI/EPI LLC; *U.S. Private*, pg. 3979
TFI INC.; *U.S. Private*, pg. 3978
TFI INTERNATIONAL INC.; *Int'l*, pg. 7585
TFI TAB GIDA YATIRIMLARI A.S.; *Int'l*, pg. 7587
TFI TELEMARK—See APT, Inc.; *U.S. Private*, pg. 302
T-FIT INSULATION SOLUTIONS INDIA PRIVATE LIMITED—See Zotefoams plc; *Int'l*, pg. 8690
TF KABEL LIMITED LIABILITY COMPANY—See TELE-FONIKA Kable Sp. z o.o. S.K.A.; *Int'l*, pg. 7528
TFK CORP.—See Temasek Holdings (Private) Limited; *Int'l*, pg. 7550
T.F. KINNEALEY & CO., INC.—See Performance Food Group Company; *U.S. Private*, pg. 1676
T.F. KURK INC.; *U.S. Private*, pg. 3912
TF LAND SDN. BHD.—See Multi-Usage Holdings Berhad; *Int'l*, pg. 5083
T-FLEX TECHVEST PCB CO., LTD.; *Int'l*, pg. 7396
T.F. LOUDERBACK, INC.—See Reyes Holdings, LLC; *U.S. Private*, pg. 3418
TFMC HOLDINGS (PROPRIETARY) LIMITED—See The Bidvest Group Limited; *Int'l*, pg. 7625
TF-METAL CO., LTD.—See Tachi-S Co., Ltd.; *Int'l*, pg. 7402
TF-METAL GUANGZHOU CO., LTD.—See Tachi-S Co., Ltd.; *Int'l*, pg. 7402
TF-METAL HIGASHI MIKAWA CO., LTD.—See Tachi-S Co., Ltd.; *Int'l*, pg. 7402
TF-METAL IWATA CO., LTD.—See Tachi-S Co., Ltd.; *Int'l*, pg. 7402
TF-METAL KYUSHU CO., LTD.—See Tachi-S Co., Ltd.; *Int'l*, pg. 7402
TF-METAL USA LLC—See Tachi-S Co., Ltd.; *Int'l*, pg. 7402
TFML LIMITED—See BlackWall Limited; *Int'l*, pg. 1062
TFM RADIO—See Heinrich Bauer Verlag KG; *Int'l*, pg. 3324
TFQ AMERICA INC.—See Taihan Fiberoptics Co., Ltd.; *Int'l*, pg. 7411
T-FORCE GROUP; *U.S. Private*, pg. 3910
TFP CORPORATION; *U.S. Private*, pg. 3979
TFP DATA SYSTEMS—See Taylor Corporation; *U.S. Private*, pg. 3939
TFPD CORPORATION—See Japan Industrial Partners, Inc.; *Int'l*, pg. 3891
TFPL LIMITED—See Progility plc; *Int'l*, pg. 5990
TFP SOLUTIONS BERHAD; *Int'l*, pg. 7587
TFS CURRENCIES PTE LTD.—See Viel & Compagnie SA; *Int'l*, pg. 8192
TFS CURRENCY OPTIONS LTD—See Viel & Compagnie SA; *Int'l*, pg. 8192

TFS DUBAI LTD—See Viel & Compagnie SA; *Int'l*, pg. 8193
TFS ENERGY FUTURES LLC—See Viel & Compagnie SA; *Int'l*, pg. 8193
TFS ENERGY, LLC—See Viel & Compagnie SA; *Int'l*, pg. 8193
TFS ENERGY (S) PTE LTD—See Viel & Compagnie SA; *Int'l*, pg. 8193
TFS FINANCIAL CORPORATION; *U.S. Public*, pg. 2029
TFS-ICAP HOLDINGS LLC—See CME Group, Inc.; *U.S. Public*, pg. 518
TFS-ICAP HOLDINGS LLC—See Viel & Compagnie SA; *Int'l*, pg. 8193
TFS-ICAP LIMITED—See CME Group, Inc.; *U.S. Public*, pg. 517
TFS-ICAP LIMITED—See Viel & Compagnie SA; *Int'l*, pg. 8193
TFS-ICAP LLC—See CME Group, Inc.; *U.S. Public*, pg. 518
TFS-ICAP LLC—See Viel & Compagnie SA; *Int'l*, pg. 8193
TFS LLC—See Thermo Fisher Scientific Inc.; *U.S. Public*, pg. 2152
TFS LOGISTICS PTE. LTD.—See Transocean Holdings Bhd.; *Int'l*, pg. 7902
TFS, LTD.—See Southfield Capital Advisors, LLC; *U.S. Private*, pg. 3736
TFSUPPLEMENTS; *U.S. Private*, pg. 3979
TF VARLIK KIRALAMA A.S.; *Int'l*, pg. 7585
TF VICTOR, S.A. DE C.V.—See Grupo Kuo, S.A.B. de C.V.; *Int'l*, pg. 3131
TFW INC.; *U.S. Private*, pg. 3979
TFX GROUP LIMITED—See Teleflex Incorporated; *U.S. Public*, pg. 1995
TFX MEDICAL OEM—See Teleflex Incorporated; *U.S. Public*, pg. 1996
TFX MEDICAL WIRE PRODUCTS, INC.—See Teleflex Incorporated; *U.S. Public*, pg. 1996
TGA CO., LTD; *Int'l*, pg. 7587
TGA DEUTSCHLAND GMBH—See Fortive Corporation; *U.S. Public*, pg. 872
T-GAIA CORP.; *Int'l*, pg. 7396
T-GAIA (SHANGHAI) CORPORATION—See T-Gaia Corp.; *Int'l*, pg. 7396
TGA INDUSTRIES LIMITED—See Danaher Corporation; *U.S. Public*, pg. 631
TGAP CO., LTD.—See Toyoda Gosei Co., Ltd.; *Int'l*, pg. 7862
TGAS ADVISORS, LLC—See Kohlberg & Company, LLC; *U.S. Private*, pg. 2339
TGA SCIENCES, INC.—See Pharmaron Beijing Co., Ltd.; *Int'l*, pg. 5841
TGA UTBILDNING AB—See AcadeMedia AB; *Int'l*, pg. 77
TG AUTOMOTIVE SEALING KENTUCKY, LLC—See Toyoda Gosei Co., Ltd.; *Int'l*, pg. 7862
T.G. BATTERY CO. (CHINA) LTD.—See Gold Peak Technology Group Limited; *Int'l*, pg. 3026
TGB BANQUETS & HOTELS LIMITED; *Int'l*, pg. 7587
TGB TECHNISCHES GEMEINSCHAFTSBURO GMBH—See Siemens Aktiengesellschaft; *Int'l*, pg. 6901
TG CHANGJIANG GLASS CO., LTD.—See Taiwan Glass Industry Corporation; *Int'l*, pg. 7420
TGC HOMES—See Tomasz General Contracting Ltd.; *Int'l*, pg. 7799
TG CONCEPT SAS—See VINCI S.A.; *Int'l*, pg. 8229
TG CONCEPT SUISSE SA—See VINCI S.A.; *Int'l*, pg. 8229
TG CONSTRUCTION INC.; *U.S. Private*, pg. 3979
T&G CORPORATION; *U.S. Private*, pg. 3909
TG CORPORATION—See Toagosei Co. Ltd.; *Int'l*, pg. 7770
T&G CORP.—See GEO Holdings Corporation; *Int'l*, pg. 2932
TG DONGHAI GLASS CO., LTD.—See Taiwan Glass Industry Corporation; *Int'l*, pg. 7420
TG ECOMMERCE SDN. BHD.—See Top Glove Corporation Bhd.; *Int'l*, pg. 7812
T. GEDDES GRANT (BARBADOS) LIMITED—See Massy Holdings Ltd.; *Int'l*, pg. 4724
TGE GAS ENGINEERING GMBH—See China International Marine Containers (Group) Co., Ltd.; *Int'l*, pg. 1512
T. GERDING CONSTRUCTION CO. (TGCC); *U.S. Private*, pg. 3911
TG FLUID SYSTEMS USA CORPORATION—See Toyoda Gosei Co., Ltd.; *Int'l*, pg. 7862
TG FUND MANAGEMENT BV—See KBL European Private Bankers S.A.; *Int'l*, pg. 4107
TGF UNIQUE LTD—See Unique Logistics International Inc.; *U.S. Public*, pg. 2227
TGG ACCOUNTING; *U.S. Private*, pg. 3979
T&G GLOBAL LIMITED—See BayWa AG; *Int'l*, pg. 919
TGH (AP) PTE. LTD.—See Forum Energy Technologies, Inc.; *U.S. Public*, pg. 874
TG HOLDING AG; *Int'l*, pg. 7587
TG HOLDINGS YEMEN INC.—See VAALCO Energy, Inc.; *U.S. Public*, pg. 2270
TG HUANAN GLASS CO., LTD.—See Taiwan Glass Industry Corporation; *Int'l*, pg. 7420

COMPANY NAME INDEX

T.G.I. FRIDAY'S INC.—See Carlson Companies Inc.; *U.S. Private*, pg. 765
T&G INDUSTRIES INC.; *U.S. Private*, pg. 3909
TGI SOLAR POWER GROUP INC.; *U.S. Public*, pg. 2030
TGI SYSTEMS CORP—See Quadrant Private Equity Pty. Ltd.; *Int'l*, pg. 6149
TGK-2; *Int'l*, pg. 7587
TGK A.D.—See SOL S.p.A.; *Int'l*, pg. 7068
TG KENTUCKY, LLC—See Toyoda Gosei Co., Ltd.; *Int'l*, pg. 7862
T.G.K. SOFIA AD—See SOL S.p.A.; *Int'l*, pg. 7068
TGL CHILE S.A.—See Taewoong Logistics Co., Ltd.; *Int'l*, pg. 7405
TGL COLOMBIA LTDA—See Taewoong Logistics Co., Ltd.; *Int'l*, pg. 7405
TGL HUNGARY KFT.—See Taewoong Logistics Co., Ltd.; *Int'l*, pg. 7405
TGL INDONESIA. PT—See Taewoong Logistics Co., Ltd.; *Int'l*, pg. 7405
TGL JAPAN CO., LTD.—See Taewoong Logistics Co., Ltd.; *Int'l*, pg. 7405
TGL MALAYSIA SDN. BHD.—See Taewoong Logistics Co., Ltd.; *Int'l*, pg. 7405
TG LOGISTICS CO., LTD.—See Toyoda Gosei Co., Ltd.; *Int'l*, pg. 7861
TGL QINGDAO CO., LTD.—See Taewoong Logistics Co., Ltd.; *Int'l*, pg. 7406
TGL RUS LLC—See Taewoong Logistics Co., Ltd.; *Int'l*, pg. 7406
TGL SHANGHAI CO., LTD.—See Taewoong Logistics Co., Ltd.; *Int'l*, pg. 7406
TGL SHENZHEN CO., LTD.—See Taewoong Logistics Co., Ltd.; *Int'l*, pg. 7406
TGLT S.A.; *Int'l*, pg. 7587
TGL USA INC.—See Taewoong Logistics Co., Ltd.; *Int'l*, pg. 7406
TG MADISON; *U.S. Private*, pg. 3979
TG MAINTENANCE INC.—See Toyoda Gosei Co., Ltd.; *Int'l*, pg. 7861
TG MEDICAL SDN. BHD. - FACTORY 14—See Top Glove Corporation Bhd.; *Int'l*, pg. 7812
TG MEDICAL SDN. BHD.—See Top Glove Corporation Bhd.; *Int'l*, pg. 7812
TG MEDICAL (U.S.A.) INC.—See Top Glove Corporation Bhd.; *Int'l*, pg. 7812
T. G. MERCER CONSULTING SERVICES, INC.—See Quanta Services, Inc.; *U.S. Public*, pg. 1753
TG METALS LIMITED; *Int'l*, pg. 7587
TGMGROUP LIMITED—See I Squared Capital Advisors (US) LLC; *U.S. Private*, pg. 2025
TGM GROUP PTY LTD—See Cardno Limited; *Int'l*, pg. 1323
TG MINTO CORPORATION—See Toyoda Gosei Co., Ltd.; *Int'l*, pg. 7861
TG MISSOURI CORPORATION—See Toyoda Gosei Co., Ltd.; *Int'l*, pg. 7862
TG NATURAL RESOURCES LLC—See Tokyo Gas Co., Ltd.; *Int'l*, pg. 7791
TGOOD AFRICA (PTY) LTD.—See Qingdao TGOOD Electric Co., Ltd.; *Int'l*, pg. 6144
TGOOD AUSTRALIA PTY LTD—See Qingdao TGOOD Electric Co., Ltd.; *Int'l*, pg. 6144
TGOOD CENTRAL ASIA LLP—See Qingdao TGOOD Electric Co., Ltd.; *Int'l*, pg. 6144
TGOOD GERMANY GMBH—See Qingdao TGOOD Electric Co., Ltd.; *Int'l*, pg. 6144
TGOOD LATIN AMERICA SAS—See Qingdao TGOOD Electric Co., Ltd.; *Int'l*, pg. 6144
TGOOD MIDDLE EAST GENERAL TRADING LLC—See Qingdao TGOOD Electric Co., Ltd.; *Int'l*, pg. 6144
TGOOD NORTH AMERICA INC.—See Qingdao TGOOD Electric Co., Ltd.; *Int'l*, pg. 6144
TGOOD RUSSIA LTD.—See Qingdao TGOOD Electric Co., Ltd.; *Int'l*, pg. 6144
TG OPSEED CO., LTD.—See Toyoda Gosei Co., Ltd.; *Int'l*, pg. 7861
TGP CANADA ENTERPRISES, ULC—See Allegion Public Limited Company; *Int'l*, pg. 335
TGP INVESTMENTS, LLC; *U.S. Private*, pg. 3979
TGP MARKETING SDN. BHD.—See Thong Guan Industries Berhad; *Int'l*, pg. 7717
TG POWER WRAP SDN. BHD.—See Thong Guan Industries Berhad; *Int'l*, pg. 7717
TGP PLASPACK (SUZHOU) CO., LTD.—See Thong Guan Industries Berhad; *Int'l*, pg. 7717
TGR BIOSCIENCES PTY LTD.—See 2invest AG; *Int'l*, pg. 5
TG RESIDENTIAL VALUE PROPERTIES LTD.; *Int'l*, pg. 7587
TGR FINANCIAL INC.; *U.S. Private*, pg. 3979
TGRP SOLUTIONS LLC; *U.S. Private*, pg. 3979
TGR TECHNICAL CENTER, LLC—See Toyoda Gosei Co., Ltd.; *Int'l*, pg. 7862
T.G.S. AD—See SOL S.p.A.; *Int'l*, pg. 7068
TGS AP INVESTMENTS AS—See TGS ASA; *Int'l*, pg. 7588
TGS ASA; *Int'l*, pg. 7587
TGS CANADA CORP.—See TGS ASA; *Int'l*, pg. 7588
TGS DIS TICARET A.S.; *Int'l*, pg. 7588

TGS DO BRASIL LTDA.—See TGS ASA; *Int'l*, pg. 7588
TGS ESPORTS, INC.; *Int'l*, pg. 7588
TGS FASTIGHETER NR 2 AB—See Peab AB; *Int'l*, pg. 5773
TGSH PLASTIC INDUSTRIES SDN. BHD.—See Thong Guan Industries Berhad; *Int'l*, pg. 7717
TGS INTERNATIONAL LTD.; *Int'l*, pg. 7588
TGS-NOPEC GEOPHYSICAL COMPANY L.P.—See TGS ASA; *Int'l*, pg. 7588
TGS-NOPEC GEOPHYSICAL COMPANY PTY. LTD.—See TGS ASA; *Int'l*, pg. 7588
TGS-NOPEC GEOPHYSICAL COMPANY—See TGS ASA; *Int'l*, pg. 7588
TGS-NOPEC GEOPHYSICAL COMPANY—See TGS ASA; *Int'l*, pg. 7588
TGS-NOPEC GEOPHYSICAL COMPANY (UK) LIMITED—See TGS ASA; *Int'l*, pg. 7588
TG SPORTS CO., LTD.—See Toyoda Gosei Co., Ltd.; *Int'l*, pg. 7861
T&G SRL—See FOS S.p.A.; *Int'l*, pg. 2748
TGT A.D.—See SOL S.p.A.; *Int'l*, pg. 7068
TG-TECHNO CO., LTD.—See Toyoda Gosei Co., Ltd.; *Int'l*, pg. 7862
TG THERAPEUTICS, INC.; *U.S. Public*, pg. 2030
TG TIANJIN GLASS CO., LTD.—See Taiwan Glass Industry Corporation; *Int'l*, pg. 7420
TGT SPECIAL STEEL COMPANY LIMITED—See Tiangong International Company Limited; *Int'l*, pg. 7738
T.G.U.S. CORP.—See Taiwan Glass Industry Corporation; *Int'l*, pg. 7420
TG VALENTINE, LLC; *U.S. Private*, pg. 3979
TGV CINEMAS SDN BHD—See Tanjong Plc; *Int'l*, pg. 7459
TG VENTURE ACQUISITION CORP.; *U.S. Public*, pg. 2030
TGV SRAAC LIMITED; *Int'l*, pg. 7588
TG WELFARE CO., LTD.—See Toyoda Gosei Co., Ltd.; *Int'l*, pg. 7861
TGW-ERMANCO, INC.—See TGW Transportgerate GmbH; *Int'l*, pg. 7588
TGW IBERICA SISTEMAS LOGISTICOS S.L.—See TGW Transportgerate GmbH; *Int'l*, pg. 7588
TGW ITALIA SRL—See TGW Transportgerate GmbH; *Int'l*, pg. 7588
TGW TRANSPORTGERATE GMBH; *Int'l*, pg. 7588
TGX MEDICAL SYSTEMS, LLC—See Integra LifeSciences Holdings Corporation; *U.S. Public*, pg. 1136
TG YUEDA SOLAR MIRROR CO., LTD.—See Taiwan Glass Industry Corporation; *Int'l*, pg. 7420
THAAI TECH SOLUTIONS PVT. LTD.—See A-TECH Solution Co., Ltd.; *Int'l*, pg. 21
THABASCO—See Omnicom Group Inc.; *U.S. Public*, pg. 1597
THAC BA HYDROPOWER JOINT STOCK COMPANY—See Refrigeration Electrical Engineering Corporation; *Int'l*, pg. 6250
THACHANG GREEN ENERGY PUBLIC COMPANY LIMITED; *Int'l*, pg. 7588
THACKER & COMPANY LIMITED; *Int'l*, pg. 7589
THAD ZIEGLER GLASS LTD.; *U.S. Private*, pg. 3979
T H AGRI-CHEMICALS, INC.; *U.S. Private*, pg. 3909
THAI ABS CO., LTD—See IRPC Public Company Limited; *Int'l*, pg. 3811
THAI ACRYLIC FIBRE COMPANY LIMITED—See The Aditya Birla Group; *Int'l*, pg. 7612
THAI AGRO ENERGY PUBLIC CO., LTD.—See Lanna Resources pcl; *Int'l*, pg. 4413
THAI AHRESTY DIE CO., LTD.—See Ahresty Corporation; *Int'l*, pg. 225
THAI AHRESTY ENGINEERING CO., LTD.—See Ahresty Corporation; *Int'l*, pg. 226
THAI AIRWAYS INTERNATIONAL LTD.—See Thai Airways International Public Company Limited; *Int'l*, pg. 7589
THAI AIRWAYS INTERNATIONAL PUBLIC COMPANY LIMITED; *Int'l*, pg. 7589
THAI-AMADEUS SOUTHEAST ASIA CO., LTD.—See Thai Airways International Public Company Limited; *Int'l*, pg. 7589
THAI ANBAO PAPER PRODUCTS CO., LTD.—See Thai President Foods Public Company Limited; *Int'l*, pg. 7594
THAI ASAHI KASEI SPANDEX CO., LTD. - AMPHUR SRIRACHA FACTORY—See Asahi Kasei Corporation; *Int'l*, pg. 597
THAI ASAHI KASEI SPANDEX CO., LTD.—See Asahi Kasei Corporation; *Int'l*, pg. 597
THAI ASSET ENFORCEMENT AND RECOVERY ASSET MANAGEMENT COMPANY LIMITED—See Deutsche Bank Aktiengesellschaft; *Int'l*, pg. 2062
THAI AUTOMOTIVE & APPLIANCES LTD.—See IFB Industries Limited; *Int'l*, pg. 3598
THAI AUTO PRESSPARTS CO., LTD.—See Thai Rung Union Car Public Company Limited; *Int'l*, pg. 7595
THAI AVIATION REFUELLING COMPANY LIMITED—See Bangkok Aviation Fuel Services Public Company Limited; *Int'l*, pg. 832
THAI BAUER CO.LTD.—See BAUER Aktiengesellschaft; *Int'l*, pg. 894

THAI EASTERN GROUP HOLDINGS PUBLIC COMPANY LIMITED

THAI BEVERAGE BRANDS CO., LTD.—See Thai Beverage Public Company Limited; *Int'l*, pg. 7592
THAI BEVERAGE CAN LTD.—See Ball Corporation; *U.S. Public*, pg. 268
THAI BEVERAGE ENERGY CO., LTD.—See Thai Beverage Public Company Limited; *Int'l*, pg. 7592
THAI BEVERAGE MARKETING CO., LTD.—See Thai Beverage Public Company Limited; *Int'l*, pg. 7592
THAI BEVERAGE PUBLIC COMPANY LIMITED; *Int'l*, pg. 7589
THAI BEVERAGE RECYCLE CO., LTD.—See Thai Beverage Public Company Limited; *Int'l*, pg. 7592
THAI BEVERAGE TRAINING CO., LTD.—See Thai Beverage Public Company Limited; *Int'l*, pg. 7592
THAI BINH CEMENT JSC; *Int'l*, pg. 7592
THAI BINH PETROVIETNAM OIL JSC—See Vietnam Oil and Gas Group; *Int'l*, pg. 8203
THAI BRIDGESTONE CO., LTD. - NONG KHAE PLANT—See Bridgestone Corporation; *Int'l*, pg. 1160
THAI BRIDGESTONE CO., LTD. - RANGSIT PLANT—See Bridgestone Corporation; *Int'l*, pg. 1160
THAI BRIDGESTONE CO., LTD.—See Bridgestone Corporation; *Int'l*, pg. 1160
THAI BUNKA FASHION CO., LTD.—See Saha Pathanapibul Public Company Limited; *Int'l*, pg. 6479
THAI BUSINESS SOLUTION CO., LTD.—See KCE Electronics Public Company Limited; *Int'l*, pg. 4109
THAI CANE PAPER PUBLIC COMPANY LIMITED—See The Siam Cement Public Company Limited; *Int'l*, pg. 7685
THAI CAPITAL CORPORATION PUBLIC COMPANY LIMITED; *Int'l*, pg. 7592
THAI CENTRAL CHEMICAL PUBLIC COMPANY LIMITED - NAKHON LUANG PLANT—See Thai Central Chemical Public Company Limited; *Int'l*, pg. 7592
THAI CENTRAL CHEMICAL PUBLIC COMPANY LIMITED - PHRAPRADAENG PLANT SITE—See Thai Central Chemical Public Company Limited; *Int'l*, pg. 7592
THAI CENTRAL CHEMICAL PUBLIC COMPANY LIMITED; *Int'l*, pg. 7592
THAI CERAMIC CO., LTD.—See The Siam Cement Public Company Limited; *Int'l*, pg. 7683
THAI CERAMIC ROOF TILE CO., LTD.—See The Siam Cement Public Company Limited; *Int'l*, pg. 7684
THAI CHEMICAL TERMINAL CO., LTD.—See Toyota Tsusho Corporation; *Int'l*, pg. 7878
THAI CHORI CO., LTD.—See Chori Co., Ltd.; *Int'l*, pg. 1583
THAI COATED STEEL SHEET CO., LTD.—See JFE Holdings, Inc.; *Int'l*, pg. 3938
THAI COATING INDUSTRIAL PUBLIC COMPANY LIMITED; *Int'l*, pg. 7592
THAI COMPRESSOR MANUFACTURING CO., LTD.—See Mitsubishi Heavy Industries, Ltd.; *Int'l*, pg. 4962
THAI CONTAINERS GROUP CO., LTD.—See Rengo Co., Ltd.; *Int'l*, pg. 6282
THAI CONTAINERS GROUP CO., LTD.—See The Siam Cement Public Company Limited; *Int'l*, pg. 7684
THAI CONTAINERS INDUSTRY CO., LTD.—See The Siam Cement Public Company Limited; *Int'l*, pg. 7685
THAI CONTAINERS KHONKAEN CO., LTD.—See The Siam Cement Public Company Limited; *Int'l*, pg. 7685
THAI CONTAINERS RATCHABURI (1989) CO., LTD.—See The Siam Cement Public Company Limited; *Int'l*, pg. 7685
THAI CONTAINERS RAYONG CO., LTD.—See The Siam Cement Public Company Limited; *Int'l*, pg. 7685
THAI CONTRACTING & ENTERPRISES CO., LTD.—See Tiong Woon Corporation Holding Ltd.; *Int'l*, pg. 7755
THAI COOPERAGE CO., LTD.—See Thai Beverage Public Company Limited; *Int'l*, pg. 7592
THAI CORP INTERNATIONAL CO., LTD.—See Berli Jucker Public Co. Ltd.; *Int'l*, pg. 985
THAI CORP INTERNATIONAL (VIETNAM) CO. LTD.—See Berli Jucker Public Co. Ltd.; *Int'l*, pg. 985
THAI CRT CO., LTD.—See The Siam Cement Public Company Limited; *Int'l*, pg. 7682
THAI CUBIC TECHNOLOGY CO., LTD.—See Cubic Korea INC.; *Int'l*, pg. 1875
THAI CUBIC TECHNOLOGY CO., LTD. - SRIRACHA FACTORY—See Cubic Korea INC.; *Int'l*, pg. 1875
THAI DAIHO COMPANY LIMITED—See DAIHO CORPORATION; *Int'l*, pg. 1927
THAI DAI-ICHI SEIKO CO., LTD - THAI PLANT—See I-PEX Inc.; *Int'l*, pg. 3564
THAI DECAL CO., LTD.—See NIPPON CARBIDE INDUSTRIES CO., INC.; *Int'l*, pg. 5311
THAI DELMAR CO., LTD.—See Nissui Corporation; *Int'l*, pg. 5379
THAIDEN MARITIME CO., LTD.—See BIO GREEN ENERGY TECH PUBLIC COMPANY LIMITED; *Int'l*, pg. 1035
THAI DNT PAINT MANUFACTURING CO., LTD.—See Dai Nippon Toryo Co., Limited; *Int'l*, pg. 1917
THAI DRINKS CO., LTD.—See Thai Beverage Public Company Limited; *Int'l*, pg. 7592
THAI EASTERN GROUP HOLDINGS PUBLIC COMPANY LIMITED; *Int'l*, pg. 7592

THAI EASTERN GROUP HOLDINGS PUBLIC COMPANY LIMITED

CORPORATE AFFILIATIONS

THAIEKALUCK POWER CO., LTD.—See Kaset Thai International Sugar Corporation Public Company Limited; *Int'l*, pg. 4087

THAI ENGER HOLDING PCL; *Int'l*, pg. 7592

THAI ENGINEERING PRODUCTS CO., LTD.—See The Siam Cement Public Company Limited; *Int'l*, pg. 7682

THAI ENVIRONMENTAL TECHNIC CO., LTD.—See Eurofins Scientific S.E.; *Int'l*, pg. 2552

THAI ESCORP LTD.—See Kobe Steel, Ltd.; *Int'l*, pg. 4221

THAI ETHANOLAMINES CO., LTD.—See PTT Global Chemical Public Company Limited; *Int'l*, pg. 6091

THAI ETHOXYLATE COMPANY LIMITED—See BASF SE; *Int'l*, pg. 885

THAI FARM INTERNATIONAL LIMITED—See Flour Mills of Nigeria Plc.; *Int'l*, pg. 2709

THAI FASHION PLASTICS IND CO., LTD.—See Pacific Equity Partners Pty. Limited; *Int'l*, pg. 5688

THAI FIBER OPTICS CO., LTD.—See Loxley Public Company Limited; *Int'l*, pg. 4567

THAI FILM INDUSTRIES PUBLIC COMPANY LIMITED - RAYONG FACTORY—See Thai Future Incorporation Public Company Limited; *Int'l*, pg. 7593

THAI FIN CO., LTD.—See Tirathai Public Company Limited; *Int'l*, pg. 7756

THAI FINE SINTER CO., LTD.—See Fine Sinter Co., Ltd.; *Int'l*, pg. 2673

THAI FLAVOR & FRAGRANCE COMPANY LIMITED—See R&B Food Supply Public Company Limited; *Int'l*, pg. 6168

THAI FLEXIBLE CO., LTD.—See NPPG (Thailand) Public Company Limited; *Int'l*, pg. 5473

THAIFOODS GROUP PUBLIC COMPANY LIMITED; *Int'l*, pg. 7598

THAI FUJI SEIKI CO., LTD.—See Fuji Seiki Co., Ltd.; *Int'l*, pg. 2817

THAI FUJI XEROX CO., LTD.—See FUJIFILM Holdings Corporation; *Int'l*, pg. 2826

THAI FUKOKU CO., LTD.—See Fukoku Co., Ltd.; *Int'l*, pg. 2839

THAIFUKOKU PANAPLUS FOUNDRY CO., LTD.—See Fukoku Co., Ltd.; *Int'l*, pg. 2839

THAI FURUKAWA UNICOMM CONSTRUCTION CO., LTD.—See The Furukawa Electric Co., Ltd.; *Int'l*, pg. 7647

THAI FURUKAWA UNICOMM ENGINEERING CO., LTD.—See The Furukawa Electric Co., Ltd.; *Int'l*, pg. 7647

THAI FUTURE INCORPORATION PUBLIC COMPANY LIMITED; *Int'l*, pg. 7593

THAI GALLERY SRL—See Graphex Group Limited; *Int'l*, pg. 3060

THAI GAS CORPORATION COMPANY LIMITED—See WP Energy PCL; *Int'l*, pg. 8460

THAI GATEWAY CO. LTD.—See Loxley Public Company Limited; *Int'l*, pg. 4567

THAI GCI RESITOP CO., LTD.—See Gun Ei Chemical Industry Co., Ltd.; *Int'l*, pg. 3183

THAI-GERMAN CERAMIC INDUSTRY PUBLIC COMPANY LIMITED; *Int'l*, pg. 7598

THAI-GERMAN PRODUCTS PUBLIC COMPANY LIMITED - RAYONG FACTORY—See Thai-German Products Public Company Limited; *Int'l*, pg. 7598

THAI-GERMAN PRODUCTS PUBLIC COMPANY LIMITED; *Int'l*, pg. 7598

THAIGERTEC CO., LTD.—See KPIT Technologies Ltd; *Int'l*, pg. 4296

THAI GLICO CO., LTD.—See Ezaki Glico Co., Ltd.; *Int'l*, pg. 2593

THAI GMB INDUSTRY CO., LTD—See GMB Corp.; *Int'l*, pg. 3012

THAI GROUP HOLDINGS PUBLIC COMPANY LIMITED; *Int'l*, pg. 7593

THAI GUNZE CO., LTD.—See Saha Pathanapibul Public Company Limited; *Int'l*, pg. 6479

THAI GYPSUM PRODUCTS PCL.—See Compagnie de Saint-Gobain SA; *Int'l*, pg. 1727

THAI HACHIBAN CO., LTD.—See HACHI-BAN CO., LTD.; *Int'l*, pg. 3203

THAI HA PUBLIC COMPANY LIMITED; *Int'l*, pg. 7593

THAI HERRICK CO., LTD.—See The Herrick Corporation; *U.S. Private*, pg. 4052

THAI HERRICK CO., LTD. - THAI HERRICK PRACHINBURI PLANT—See The Herrick Corporation; *U.S. Private*, pg. 4052

THAI HERRICK CO., LTD. - THAI HERRICK RAYONG PLANT—See The Herrick Corporation; *U.S. Private*, pg. 4052

THAI HITACHI ENAMEL WIRE CO., LTD.—See Proterial, Ltd.; *Int'l*, pg. 6006

THAI HOA INTERNATIONAL HOSPITAL JSC—See VinaCapital Vietnam Opportunity Fund, Ltd.; *Int'l*, pg. 8209

THAI HOA VIET NAM GROUP JOINT STOCK COMPANY; *Int'l*, pg. 7593

THAI HONDA MANUFACTURING CO., LTD.—See Honda Motor Co., Ltd.; *Int'l*, pg. 3464

THAI HOOVER INDUSTRY CO., LTD.—See Saha Pathanapibul Public Company Limited; *Int'l*, pg. 6479

THAI HOUGHTON 1993 CO., LTD.—See Quaker Chemical Corporation; *U.S. Public*, pg. 1746

THAI HOYA LENS LTD.—See Hoya Corporation; *Int'l*, pg. 3496

THAI HUNG TRADING JSC; *Int'l*, pg. 7593

THAI HYGIENIC PRODUCTS CO., LTD.; *Int'l*, pg. 7593

THAI IDENTITY SUGAR FACTORY CO., LTD.—See Kaset Thai International Sugar Corporation Public Company Limited; *Int'l*, pg. 4087

THAI INDO KORDSA CO., LTD.—See PT Indo Kordsa Tbk; *Int'l*, pg. 6045

THAI INOAC MOLD CO., LTD.—See INOAC Corporation; *Int'l*, pg. 3715

THAI INTERMODAL SYSTEMS CO., LTD.—See Mitsui O.S.K. Lines, Ltd.; *Int'l*, pg. 4991

THAI INTERNATIONAL DIE MAKING CO., LTD. (TDI)—See Isuzu Motors Limited; *Int'l*, pg. 3826

THAI ITOKIN CO., LTD.—See Saha Pathanapibul Public Company Limited; *Int'l*, pg. 6479

THAI KABAYA INDUSTRIES CO., LTD.—See KYB Corporation; *Int'l*, pg. 4354

THAI KAJIMA CO., LTD.—See Kajima Corporation; *Int'l*, pg. 4055

THAI KAMAYA CO., LTD.—See Kamaya Kagaku Kogyo Co. Ltd.; *Int'l*, pg. 4060

THAI KAMEDA CO., LTD.—See Kameda Seika Co., Ltd.; *Int'l*, pg. 4061

THAI-KAMI COMPANY LIMITED—See King Wai Group (Thailand) Public Company Limited; *Int'l*, pg. 4170

THAI KANDENKO CO., LTD.—See Kandenko Co., Ltd.; *Int'l*, pg. 4065

THAI KANSAI PAINT CO., LTD.—See Kansai Paint Co., Ltd.; *Int'l*, pg. 4073

THAI KAWANISHI LTD.—See Kawanishi Warehouse Co., Ltd.; *Int'l*, pg. 4094

THAI KEC SALES CO., LTD.—See KEC Holdings Co., Ltd.; *Int'l*, pg. 4113

THAIKEN MAINTENANCE & SERVICE CO., LTD.—See Taikisha Ltd.; *Int'l*, pg. 7414

THAI KOBE WELDING CO., LTD.—See Kobe Steel, Ltd.; *Int'l*, pg. 4221

THAI KOKUSAI CO., LTD.—See KOKUSAI CO., LTD; *Int'l*, pg. 4231

THAI KRAFT PAPER INDUSTRY CO., LTD.—See The Siam Cement Public Company Limited; *Int'l*, pg. 7685

THAI KURABO CO., LTD.—See Mitsubishi Corporation; *Int'l*, pg. 4943

THAI LAMINATE MANUFACTURER CO., LTD.—See KCE Electronics Public Company Limited; *Int'l*, pg. 4109

THAILAND CLEARING HOUSE CO., LTD.—See The Stock Exchange of Thailand; *Int'l*, pg. 7689

THAILAND COMPUTER CENTER LIMITED—See Yip In Tsoi & Co., Ltd.; *Int'l*, pg. 8585

THAILAND FUTURES EXCHANGE PCL—See The Stock Exchange of Thailand; *Int'l*, pg. 7689

THAILAND IRON WORKS PUBLIC COMPANY LIMITED; *Int'l*, pg. 7598

THAILAND PRIME PROPERTY FREEHOLD & LEASEHOLD REAL ESTATE INVESTMENT TRUST; *Int'l*, pg. 7598

THAILAND SECURITIES DEPOSITORY COMPANY LIMITED—See The Stock Exchange of Thailand; *Int'l*, pg. 7689

THAILAND SMELTING & REFINING CO LTD—See Amalgamated Metal Corporation PLC; *Int'l*, pg. 409

THAILAND WEI AN CO., LTD.—See China Security Co., Ltd.; *Int'l*, pg. 1550

THAI LIFE INSURANCE PUBLIC COMPANY LIMITED; *Int'l*, pg. 7593

THAI LNG COMPANY LIMITED—See Krung Thai Bank Public Company Limited; *Int'l*, pg. 4308

THAI LOGISTICS SERVICE CO., LTD.—See Kamigumi Co., Ltd.; *Int'l*, pg. 4063

THAI LONG DISTANCE TELECOMMUNICATIONS CO., LTD.—See Jasmine International Public Company Limited; *Int'l*, pg. 3912

THAI LOTTE CO., LTD. - AMATANAKORN FACTORY—See Lotte Co., Ltd.; *Int'l*, pg. 4560

THAI LOTTE CO., LTD.—See Lotte Co., Ltd.; *Int'l*, pg. 4560

THAI LOTTE CO., LTD. - SRIRACHA FACTORY—See Lotte Co., Ltd.; *Int'l*, pg. 4560

THAI LUBE BASE PUBLIC CO., LTD.—See Thai Oil Public Company Limited; *Int'l*, pg. 7594

THAI-LYSAGHT CO., LTD.—See Univentures Public Company Limited; *Int'l*, pg. 8077

THAI MAEDA CORPORATION—See Maeda Corporation; *Int'l*, pg. 4635

THAI MALAYA GLASS CO., LTD.—See Berli Jucker Public Co. Ltd.; *Int'l*, pg. 985

THAI MARBLE CORP., LTD.—See Golden Lime Public Company Limited; *Int'l*, pg. 3030

THAI MARINE DEVELOPMENT PRODUCTS CO LTD.—See Thai Union Group Public Company Limited; *Int'l*, pg. 7596

THAI MARSOL CO., LTD.—See Rengo Co., Ltd.; *Int'l*, pg. 6282

THAI MARUJUN CO., LTD.—See J-MAX Co., Ltd.; *Int'l*, pg. 3854

THAI MARUKEN CO., LTD.—See Italian-Thai Development pcl; *Int'l*, pg. 3829

THAI MATTO NS CO., LTD.—See Nippon Seiki Co., Ltd.; *Int'l*, pg. 5330

THAI MC COMPANY LTD.—See Mitsubishi Corporation; *Int'l*, pg. 4943

THAI MEDICAL CENTER PCL.—See Bangkok Dusit Medical Services Public Company Limited; *Int'l*, pg. 834

THAI MEIDENSHA CO., LTD.—See Meidensha Corporation; *Int'l*, pg. 4798

THAI MEIDENSHA CO., LTD.—See Meidensha Corporation; *Int'l*, pg. 4798

THAI MEIJI FOOD CO., LTD.—See Meiji Holdings Co., Ltd.; *Int'l*, pg. 4801

THAI MEIJI PHARMACEUTICAL CO., LTD.—See Meiji Holdings Co., Ltd.; *Int'l*, pg. 4801

THAI MEIWA TRADING CO., LTD.—See Meiwa Corporation; *Int'l*, pg. 4805

THAI METAL DRUM MFG. PUBLIC CO., LTD. - CHACHOENGSAO PLANT—See Thai Metal Drum Mfg. Public Co., Ltd.; *Int'l*, pg. 7593

THAI METAL DRUM MFG. PUBLIC CO., LTD.; *Int'l*, pg. 7593

THAI METAL PROCESSING CO., LTD.—See Yazaki Corporation; *Int'l*, pg. 8572

THAI METROPOLE ZURICH INSURANCE CO. LTD.—See Zurich Insurance Group Limited; *Int'l*, pg. 8697

THAI MITCHI CORPORATION LTD.—See Mitsuchi Corporation; *Int'l*, pg. 4973

THAI MITSUI SPECIALTY CHEMICALS CO., LTD.—See Mitsui Chemicals, Inc.; *Int'l*, pg. 4984

THAI MITSUWA PUBLIC COMPANY LIMITED—See Mitsuwa Electric Industry Co., Ltd.; *Int'l*, pg. 4994

THAI MIZUNO CO., LTD.—See Mizuno Corporation; *Int'l*, pg. 5000

THAI MMA CO., LTD.—See Mitsubishi Chemical Group Corporation; *Int'l*, pg. 4934

THAI MOLASSES CO., LTD.—See Thai Beverage Public Company Limited; *Int'l*, pg. 7592

THAI MONSTER CO., LTD.—See Saha Pathanapibul Public Company Limited; *Int'l*, pg. 6479

THAI MUI CORPORATION PUBLIC COMPANY LIMITED; *Int'l*, pg. 7593

THAI MURATA ELECTRONICS TRADING, LTD.—See Murata Manufacturing Co., Ltd.; *Int'l*, pg. 5098

THAI NAKANO CO., LTD.—See Nakano Corporation; *Int'l*, pg. 5133

THAI NAKARIN HOSPITAL PCL; *Int'l*, pg. 7593

THAINAK INDUSTRIES CO., LTD.—See Nisshin Seifun Group, Inc.; *Int'l*, pg. 5372

THAI NAM PLASTIC (PUBLIC) COMPANY LIMITED; *Int'l*, pg. 7593

THAI NAN PAO RESINS CHEMICAL., LTD—See Nan Pao Resins Chemical Co., Ltd.; *Int'l*, pg. 5138

THAI NATIONAL POWER CO., LTD.—See ENGIE SA; *Int'l*, pg. 2433

THAI NATIONAL PRODUCT CO., LTD—See Rich Asia Corporation Public Company Limited; *Int'l*, pg. 6329

THAI NGUYEN IRON AND STEEL CORPORATION - PHAN ME COAL MINE FACTORY—See Thai Nguyen Iron and Steel Corporation; *Int'l*, pg. 7593

THAI NGUYEN IRON AND STEEL CORPORATION; *Int'l*, pg. 7593

THAI NGUYEN IRON AND STEEL CORPORATION - TRAI CAU IRON ORE MINE FACTORY—See Thai Nguyen Iron and Steel Corporation; *Int'l*, pg. 7593

THAI NICHIAS ENGINEERING CO., LTD.—See Nichias Corporation; *Int'l*, pg. 5267

THAI NICHIAS INTERNATIONAL CO., LTD.—See Nichias Corporation; *Int'l*, pg. 5267

THAI NIKKEI TRADING CO., LTD.—See Nippon Light Metal Holdings Company, Ltd.; *Int'l*, pg. 5324

THAI NIPPON FOODS CO., LTD.—See NH Foods Ltd.; *Int'l*, pg. 5257

THAI NIPPON MEAT PACKERS CO., LTD.—See NH Foods Ltd.; *Int'l*, pg. 5257

THAI NIPPON ROAD CO., LTD.—See Shimizu Corporation; *Int'l*, pg. 6836

THAI NIPPON RUBBER INDUSTRY CO., LTD. - SI RACHA FACTORY—See Charoen Aksorn Holding Group Co. Ltd.; *Int'l*, pg. 1451

THAI NIPPON SEIKI CO., LTD.—See Nippon Seiki Co., Ltd.; *Int'l*, pg. 5330

THAI NIPPON STEEL ENGINEERING & CONSTRUCTION CORPORATION CO., LTD.—See GJ Steel Public Company Limited; *Int'l*, pg. 2982

THAI NIPPON STEEL & SUMIKIN ENGINEERING & CONSTRUCTION CORP., LTD.—See Nippon Steel Corporation; *Int'l*, pg. 5336

THAI NISHIMATSU CONSTRUCTION CO., LTD.—See Nishimatsu Construction Co., Ltd.; *Int'l*, pg. 5365

THAI NITRATE CO.,LTD—See TPI Polene Public Company Limited; *Int'l*, pg. 7883

THAI NITTO SEIKO MACHINERY CO., LTD.—See Nitto Seiko Co., Ltd.; *Int'l*, pg. 5388

THAI NJR CO., LTD.—See Nisshinbo Holdings Inc.; *Int'l*, pg. 5375

THAI NOK CO., LTD.—See NOK Corporation; *Int'l*, pg. 5403

COMPANY NAME INDEX

THAI NONDESTRUCTIVE TESTING PUBLIC COMPANY LIMITED; *Int'l*, pg. 7593
THAI NS SOLUTIONS CO., LTD.—See Nippon Steel Corporation; *Int'l*, pg. 5335
THAI NVDR COMPANY LIMITED—See The Stock Exchange of Thailand; *Int'l*, pg. 7688
THAI NYLON CO., LTD.—See Unitika Ltd.; *Int'l*, pg. 8074
THAI OBAYASHI CORPORATION LIMITED—See Obayashi Corporation; *Int'l*, pg. 5509
THAIOIL ENERGY CO., LTD.—See Thai Oil Public Company Limited; *Int'l*, pg. 7594
THAIOIL ENERGY SOLUTIONS CO., LTD—See Thai Oil Public Company Limited; *Int'l*, pg. 7594
THAIOIL ETHANOL CO., LTD.—See Thai Oil Public Company Limited; *Int'l*, pg. 7594
THAIOIL MARINE CO., LTD.—See Prima Marine PCL; *Int'l*, pg. 5975
THAIOIL POWER CO., LTD.—See Thai Oil Public Company Limited; *Int'l*, pg. 7594
THAI OIL PUBLIC COMPANY LIMITED; *Int'l*, pg. 7593
THAIOIL SOLVENT COMPANY LIMITED—See Thai Oil Public Company Limited; *Int'l*, pg. 7594
THAI OKK MACHINERY CO., LTD.—See OKK Corporation; *Int'l*, pg. 5550
THAI OLEOCHEMICALS COMPANY LIMITED—See PTT Global Chemical Public Company Limited; *Int'l*, pg. 6091
THAI O PP PCL; *Int'l*, pg. 7593
THAI O.P.P. PUBLIC COMPANY LIMITED; *Int'l*, pg. 7593
THAI OPTICAL COMPANY LIMITED—See Thai Optical Group Public Company Limited; *Int'l*, pg. 7594
THAI OPTICAL GROUP PUBLIC COMPANY LIMITED; *Int'l*, pg. 7594
THAI ORIX LEASING CO., LTD.—See ORIX Corporation; *Int'l*, pg. 5636
THAI OTSUKA PHARMACEUTICAL CO., LTD.—See Otsuka Holdings Co., Ltd.; *Int'l*, pg. 5661
THAI PACKAGING & PRINTING PUBLIC COMPANY LIMITED, pg. 7594
THAI PAPAYA OY—See NoHo Partners Plc; *Int'l*, pg. 5400
THAI PAPER CO., LTD.—See The Siam Cement Public Company Limited; *Int'l*, pg. 7685
THAI PARAXYLENE CO., LTD—See Thai Oil Public Company Limited; *Int'l*, pg. 7594
THAI PARKERIZING CO., LTD. - HEAT & SURFACE TREATMENT FACTORY—See Nihon Parkerizing Co., Ltd.; *Int'l*, pg. 5287
THAI PARKERIZING CO., LTD. - HEAT TREATMENT FACTORY—See Nihon Parkerizing Co., Ltd.; *Int'l*, pg. 5287
THAI PARKERIZING CO., LTD.—See Nihon Parkerizing Co., Ltd.; *Int'l*, pg. 5287
THAI PET RESIN CO., LTD.—See Mitsui Chemicals, Inc.; *Int'l*, pg. 4984
THAI PET RESIN CO., LTD.—See The Siam Cement Public Company Limited; *Int'l*, pg. 7684
THAI PET RESIN CO., LTD.—See Toray Industries, Inc.; *Int'l*, pg. 7823
THAI PEX CO., LTD.—See Japan Pulp and Paper Company Limited; *Int'l*, pg. 3905
THAI PIGEON CO., LTD.—See Pigeon Corporation; *Int'l*, pg. 5865
THAI PIPELINE NETWORK COMPANY LIMITED—See Power Solution Technologies Public Company Limited; *Int'l*, pg. 5946
THAI PLASPAC PUBLIC COMPANY LIMITED; *Int'l*, pg. 7594
THAI PLASTIC & CHEMICALS PUBLIC COMPANY LIMITED—See The Siam Cement Public Company Limited; *Int'l*, pg. 7685
THAI PLASTIC INDUSTRIAL (1994) PCL; *Int'l*, pg. 7594
THAI POLYACETAL CO., LTD.—See Mitsubishi Gas Chemical Company, Inc.; *Int'l*, pg. 4950
THAI POLY ACRYLIC PUBLIC COMPANY LTD.—See EAC Invest AS; *Int'l*, pg. 2262
THAI POLYCARBONATE CO., LTD.—See Mitsubishi Gas Chemical Company, Inc.; *Int'l*, pg. 4950
THAI POLYCONS PUBLIC COMPANY LIMITED; *Int'l*, pg. 7594
THAI POLYETHYLENE (1993) CO., LTD.—See The Siam Cement Public Company Limited; *Int'l*, pg. 7684
THAI POLYETHYLENE CO., LTD.—See The Siam Cement Public Company Limited; *Int'l*, pg. 7684
THAI POLYPROPYLENE (1994) CO., LTD.—See The Siam Cement Public Company Limited; *Int'l*, pg. 7684
THAI PRESIDENT FOODS PUBLIC COMPANY LIMITED - LUMPHUN FACTORY—See Thai President Foods Public Company Limited; *Int'l*, pg. 7594
THAI PRESIDENT FOODS PUBLIC COMPANY LIMITED - RAYONG FACTORY—See Thai President Foods Public Company Limited; *Int'l*, pg. 7594
THAI PRESIDENT FOODS PUBLIC COMPANY LIMITED; *Int'l*, pg. 7594
THAI PRESIDENT FOODS PUBLIC COMPANY LIMITED - SRI RACHA FACTORY—See Thai President Foods Public Company Limited; *Int'l*, pg. 7595
THAI PREX ENGINEERING CO., LTD.—See L.K. Technology Holdings Limited; *Int'l*, pg. 4386

THAI PRIDE CEMENT CO., LTD. - FACTORY—See Italian-Thai Development pcl; *Int'l*, pg. 3829
THAI PRIDE CEMENT CO., LTD.—See Italian-Thai Development pcl; *Int'l*, pg. 3829
THAI PROPERTY PUBLIC COMPANY LIMITED; *Int'l*, pg. 7595
THAI QIAN HU COMPANY LIMITED—See Qian Hu Corporation Limited; *Int'l*, pg. 6140
THAI RAYON PUBLIC COMPANY LIMITED—See The Aditya Birla Group; *Int'l*, pg. 7612
THAI REINSURANCE PUBLIC CO., LTD.; *Int'l*, pg. 7595
THAIRE LIFE ASSURANCE PUBLIC COMPANY LIMITED—See Thai Reinsurance Public Co., Ltd.; *Int'l*, pg. 7595
THAIRE SERVICES CO. LTD.—See Thai Reinsurance Public Co., Ltd.; *Int'l*, pg. 7595
THAI ROTARY ENGINEERING PUBLIC COMPANY LIMITED—See Rotary Engineering Pte. Ltd.; *Int'l*, pg. 6402
THAI RUBBER ENTERPRISE CO., LTD.—See Saha-Union Public Company Limited; *Int'l*, pg. 6480
THAI RUBBER LAND AND PLANTATION CO., LTD.—See Thai Rubber Latex Group Public Company Limited; *Int'l*, pg. 7595
THAI RUBBER LATEX GROUP PUBLIC COMPANY LIMITED; *Int'l*, pg. 7595
THAI RUNG TEXTILE CO., LTD.—See Thai Textile Industry Public Company Limited; *Int'l*, pg. 7595
THAI RUNG UNION CAR PUBLIC COMPANY LIMITED; *Int'l*, pg. 7595
THAI SAMSUNG ELECTRONICS CO., LTD.—See Samsung Group; *Int'l*, pg. 6514
THAI SANKO CO., LTD.—See Sanko Co., Ltd.; *Int'l*, pg. 6541
THAI SATORI CO., LTD.—See SATORI ELECTRIC CO., LTD.; *Int'l*, pg. 6587
THAI-SCANDIC STEEL COMPANY LIMITED—See Berli Jucker Public Co. Ltd.; *Int'l*, pg. 985
THAI SEAT BELT CO LTD—See Tokai Rika Co., Ltd.; *Int'l*, pg. 7780
THAI SEISEN CO., LTD.—See Daido Steel Co., Ltd.; *Int'l*, pg. 1923
THAI SEKISUI FOAM CO., LTD.—See Sekisui Chemical Co., Ltd.; *Int'l*, pg. 6696
THAI SEMCON CO., LTD.—See Sumitomo Densetsu Co., Ltd.; *Int'l*, pg. 7277
THE THAI SETAKIJ INSURANCE PUBLIC COMPANY LIMITED; *Int'l*, pg. 7694
THAI SHIBAURA DENSHI CO., LTD.—See Shibaura Electronics Co., Ltd.; *Int'l*, pg. 6827
THAI SHIKIBO CO., LTD.—See Shikibo Ltd.; *Int'l*, pg. 6829
THAI SHIMIZU CO., LTD.—See Shimizu Corporation; *Int'l*, pg. 6836
THAI SHINMAYWA CO., LTD.—See ShinMaywa Industries, Ltd.; *Int'l*, pg. 6847
THAI SINTERED MESH CO., LTD.—See Nippon Filcon Co., Ltd.; *Int'l*, pg. 5318
THAI SINTOKOGIO CO., LTD.—See Sintokogio Ltd.; *Int'l*, pg. 6959
THAI SI, S.R.L.—See Istrabenz, holdinska druzba, d.d.; *Int'l*, pg. 3824
THAI-SK SECURITY INTERNATIONAL CO., LTD.—See Taiwan Shin Kong Security Co., Ltd.; *Int'l*, pg. 7424
THAI SKYLARK CO., LTD.—See Bain Capital, LP; *U.S. Private*, pg. 444
THAI SMART CARD CO., LTD.—See C.P. All Public Company Limited; *Int'l*, pg. 1244
THAI SMILE AIRWAYS CO., LTD.—See Thai Airways International Public Company Limited; *Int'l*, pg. 7589
THAI SOFTWARE ENGINEERING CO., LTD.—See SYS Holdings Co., Ltd.; *Int'l*, pg. 7388
THAI SOLAR ENERGY PUBLIC COMPANY LIMITED; *Int'l*, pg. 7595
THAI SPECIAL WIRE CO., LTD.—See Nippon Steel Corporation; *Int'l*, pg. 5340
THAI STAFLEX CO., LTD.—See Saha Pathanapibul Public Company Limited; *Int'l*, pg. 6479
THAI STANLEY ELECTRIC PUBLIC COMPANY LIMITED; *Int'l*, pg. 7595
THAI STAR SHIPPING CO—See Israel Corporation Ltd.; *Int'l*, pg. 3823
THAI STEEL CABLE PUBLIC COMPANY LIMITED; *Int'l*, pg. 7595
THAI STEEL SERVICE CENTER LTD.—See Sumitomo Corporation; *Int'l*, pg. 7276
THAI STEWARD SERVICES COMPANY LIMITED—See Peerapat Technology Public Company Limited; *Int'l*, pg. 5779
THAI STICK HERB CO., LTD.—See Gunkul Engineering Co., Ltd.; *Int'l*, pg. 3184
THAI SUGAR TERMINAL PUBLIC COMPANY LIMITED; *Int'l*, pg. 7595
THAI SUMIDEN ENGINEERING AND CONSTRUCTION CO., LTD.—See Proterial, Ltd.; *Int'l*, pg. 6006
THAI SUMIDEN ENGINEERING AND CONSTRUCTION CO., LTD.—See Sumitomo Electric Industries, Ltd.; *Int'l*, pg. 7278
THAI SUMMIT MITSUBA ELECTRIC MANUFACTURING CO., LTD.—See MITSUBA Corporation; *Int'l*, pg. 4929

THAI UNIQUE COIL CENTER PUBLIC COMPANY LIMITED

THAI SUMMIT PK CORPORATION LTD.—See Press Kogyo Co., Ltd.; *Int'l*, pg. 5965
THAI SUMMIT PKK BANGPAKONG CO., LTD.—See Press Kogyo Co., Ltd.; *Int'l*, pg. 5965
THAI SUMMIT PKK CO., LTD.—See Press Kogyo Co., Ltd.; *Int'l*, pg. 5965
THAI SUN FOODS CO., LTD.—See Thai President Foods Public Company Limited; *Int'l*, pg. 7595
THAI SUPER SORGHUM CO., LTD—See Sorghum Japan Holdings Corp.; *Int'l*, pg. 7112
THAI SUZUKI MOTOR CO., LTD.—See Suzuki Motor Corporation; *Int'l*, pg. 7355
THAI SYNTHETIC RUBBERS CO., LTD.—See UBE Corporation; *Int'l*, pg. 8001
THAI TAIYO TENT CO.,LTD.—See Taiyo Kogyo Corporation; *Int'l*, pg. 7426
THAI TAKAGI SEIKO CO., LTD.—See Takagi Seiko Corporation; *Int'l*, pg. 7429
THAI TAKASAGO CO., LTD.—See Takasago Thermal Engineering Co., Ltd.; *Int'l*, pg. 7435
THAI TAKENAKA INTERNATIONAL LTD.—See Takenaka Corporation; *Int'l*, pg. 7441
THAI TANK TERMINAL LIMITED—See Koninklijke Vopak N.V.; *Int'l*, pg. 4272
THAI TANK TERMINAL LIMITED—See PTT Global Chemical Public Company Limited; *Int'l*, pg. 6091
THAI TECH RUBBER CORPORATION LIMITED—See Sri Trang Agro-Industry Public Company Limited; *Int'l*, pg. 7151
THAITEX CBD SMARTFARMCO., LTD.—See Thai Rubber Latex Group Public Company Limited; *Int'l*, pg. 7595
THAI TEXTILE DEVELOPMENT & FINISHING CO., LTD.—See Kurabo Industries Ltd.; *Int'l*, pg. 4336
THAI TEXTILE INDUSTRY PUBLIC COMPANY LIMITED; *Int'l*, pg. 7595
THAI THEPAROS FOOD PRODUCTS PUBLIC COMPANY LIMITED; *Int'l*, pg. 7596
THAI THUM DISTILLERY CO., LTD.—See Thai Beverage Public Company Limited; *Int'l*, pg. 7592
THAI TICKET MAJOR CO., LTD.—See BEC World Public Company Limited; *Int'l*, pg. 936
THAI TODA CORPORATION LTD.—See Toda Corporation; *Int'l*, pg. 7773
THAI TOKAI CARBON PRODUCT COMPANY LTD.—See Tokai Carbon Co., Ltd.; *Int'l*, pg. 7778
THAI TORAY SYNTHETIC CO., LTD.—See Toray Industries, Inc.; *Int'l*, pg. 7823
THAI TORAY TEXTILE MILLS PUBLIC COMPANY LIMITED—See Toray Industries, Inc.; *Int'l*, pg. 7827
THAI TOSHIBA ELECTRIC INDUSTRIES CO., LTD.—See Japan Industrial Partners, Inc.; *Int'l*, pg. 3891
THAI TRADE NET CO., LTD.—See Samart Corporation Public Company Limited; *Int'l*, pg. 6502
THAI TRINITY CO, LTD.—See Trinity Industrial Corporation; *Int'l*, pg. 7924
THAI TRUST FUND MANAGEMENT CO., LTD—See The Stock Exchange of Thailand; *Int'l*, pg. 7689
THAI ULTIMATE CAR CO. LTD.—See Thai Rung Union Car Public Company Limited; *Int'l*, pg. 7595
THAI UNION CHINA CO., LTD.—See Thai Union Group Public Company Limited; *Int'l*, pg. 7596
THAI UNION EUROPE S.A.S.—See Thai Union Group Public Company Limited; *Int'l*, pg. 7597
THAI UNION EUROP SAS—See Thai Union Group Public Company Limited; *Int'l*, pg. 7596
THAI UNION FEEDMILL CO LTD.—See Thai Union Group Public Company Limited; *Int'l*, pg. 7597
THAI UNION GERMANY GMBH—See Thai Union Group Public Company Limited; *Int'l*, pg. 7597
THAI UNION GRAPHIC CO LTD.—See Thai Union Group Public Company Limited; *Int'l*, pg. 7597
THAI UNION GROUP PUBLIC COMPANY LIMITED; *Int'l*, pg. 7596
THAI UNION HATCHERY CO., LTD—See Thai Union Group Public Company Limited; *Int'l*, pg. 7597
THAI UNION INVESTMENT HOLDING CO., LTD.—See Thai Union Group Public Company Limited; *Int'l*, pg. 7597
THAI UNION MANUFACTURING COMPANY LIMITED—See Thai Union Group Public Company Limited; *Int'l*, pg. 7597
THAI UNION MARINE NUTRIENTS GMBH—See Thai Union Group Public Company Limited; *Int'l*, pg. 7597
THAI UNION NORTH AMERICA, INC.—See Thai Union Group Public Company Limited; *Int'l*, pg. 7597
THAI UNION ONLINE SHOP CO., LTD.—See Thai Union Group Public Company Limited; *Int'l*, pg. 7597
THAI UNION PAPER PUBLIC COMPANY LIMITED—See The Siam Cement Public Company Limited; *Int'l*, pg. 7685
THAI UNION POLAND S.P. Z O.O.—See Thai Union Group Public Company Limited; *Int'l*, pg. 7597
THAI UNION SEAFOOD CO LTD—See Thai Union Group Public Company Limited; *Int'l*, pg. 7597
THAI UNION TRADING EUROPE B.V.—See Thai Union Group Public Company Limited; *Int'l*, pg. 7597
THAI UNIQUE COIL CENTER PUBLIC COMPANY LIMITED; *Int'l*, pg. 7597

THAI UNITED AWA PAPER CO., LTD.—See Awa Paper & Technological Company Inc.; *Int'l*, pg. 751
THAI UNITIKA SPUNBOND CO., LTD.—See Unitika Ltd.; *Int'l*, pg. 8074
THAI USUI CO., LTD.; *Int'l*, pg. 7597
THAI VEGETABLE OIL PUBLIC COMPANY LIMITED - NAKORN CHAISRI FACTORY—See Thai Vegetable Oil Public Company Limited; *Int'l*, pg. 7597
THAI VEGETABLE OIL PUBLIC COMPANY LIMITED; *Int'l*, pg. 7597
THAI VIET SWINE LINE JOINT STOCK COMPANY LIMITED—See Thaifoods Group Public Company Limited; *Int'l*, pg. 7598
THAI VILLAGE RESTAURANT LTD.; *Int'l*, pg. 7597
THAI VILLAGE RESTAURANT PTE. LTD.—See Thai Village Restaurant Ltd.; *Int'l*, pg. 7597
THAI VILLAGE SHARKSFIN RESTAURANT (YUNNAN) CO., LTD.—See Thai Village Restaurant Ltd.; *Int'l*, pg. 7597
THAI VIRAWAT CO., LTD.; *Int'l*, pg. 7597
THAIVIVAT INSURANCE PUBLIC COMPANY LIMITED; *Int'l*, pg. 7598
THAI V.P. AUTO SERVICE CO., LTD.—See Thai Rung Union Car Public Company Limited; *Int'l*, pg. 7595
THAI WACOAL PUBLIC CO., LTD.—See Wacoal Holdings Corp.; *Int'l*, pg. 8326
THAI WAH PLAZA LIMITED—See Banyan Tree Holdings Ltd.; *Int'l*, pg. 855
THAI WAH PUBLIC COMPANY LIMITED; *Int'l*, pg. 7597
THAI WAH STARCH PUBLIC COMPANY LIMITED; *Int'l*, pg. 7597
THAI WATER OPERATIONS COMPANY LIMITED - BANG LEN WATER TREATMENT PLANT—See TTW Public Company Limited; *Int'l*, pg. 7961
THAI WATER OPERATIONS COMPANY LIMITED—See TTW Public Company Limited; *Int'l*, pg. 7961
THAI WIRE & CABLE SERVICES CO., LTD.—See Hayakawa Densen Kogyo Co., Ltd.; *Int'l*, pg. 3289
THAI WIRE PRODUCTS PUBLIC COMPANY LIMITED - MAP TA PHUT PLANT—See Thai Wire Products Public Company Limited; *Int'l*, pg. 7598
THAI WIRE PRODUCTS PUBLIC COMPANY LIMITED; *Int'l*, pg. 7597
THAI WONDERFUL WIRE CABLE CO., LTD.—See Wonderful Hi-Tech Co., Ltd.; *Int'l*, pg. 8446
THAI WOO REE ENGINEERING CO., LTD.—See SK Engineering & Construction Co., Ltd.; *Int'l*, pg. 6970
THAI YAMAZAKI CO., LTD.—See Yamazaki Baking Co., Ltd.; *Int'l*, pg. 8556
THAI YOKOREI CO., LTD.—See Yokorei Co.,Ltd.; *Int'l*, pg. 8595
THAI-ZINC OXIDE COMPANY LIMITED—See Univentures Public Company Limited; *Int'l*, pg. 8077
THAKKERS DEVELOPERS LIMITED; *Int'l*, pg. 7598
THAKRAL BROTHERS LIMITED—See Thakral Corp. Ltd.; *Int'l*, pg. 7598
THAKRAL BROTHERS PTE LTD—See Thakral Corp. Ltd.; *Int'l*, pg. 7598
THAKRAL CAPITAL AUSTRALIA PTY LTD—See Thakral Corp. Ltd.; *Int'l*, pg. 7598
THAKRAL CHINA LTD.—See Thakral Corp. Ltd.; *Int'l*, pg. 7598
THAKRAL CORP. LTD.; *Int'l*, pg. 7598
THAKRAL CORPORATION (HK) LIMITED—See Thakral Corp. Ltd.; *Int'l*, pg. 7598
THAKRAL ELECTRONICS (SHANGHAI) LTD.—See Thakral Corp. Ltd.; *Int'l*, pg. 7598
THAKRAL (INDO-CHINA) PTE. LTD—See Thakral Corp. Ltd.; *Int'l*, pg. 7598
THAKRAL LIFESTYLE PTE LTD—See Thakral Corp. Ltd.; *Int'l*, pg. 7598
THAKRAL SERVICES INDIA LIMITED; *Int'l*, pg. 7598
THALANGA COPPER MINES PTY LIMITED—See Vedanta Resources Ltd; *Int'l*, pg. 8146
THALASSO N 1; *Int'l*, pg. 7598
THAL ENGINEERING—See House of Habib; *Int'l*, pg. 3491
THALER MACHINE COMPANY INC.; *U.S. Private*, pg. 3979
THALER OIL COMPANY, INC.; *U.S. Private*, pg. 3979
THALES AEROSPACE ASIA PTE LTD—See Thales S.A.; *Int'l*, pg. 7601
THALES AEROSPACE DIVISION—See Thales S.A.; *Int'l*, pg. 7606
THALES AFV SYSTEMS LTD—See Thales S.A.; *Int'l*, pg. 7605
THALES AIRBORNE SYSTEMS CANADA—See Thales S.A.; *Int'l*, pg. 7601
THALES AIR DEFENCE LTD—See Thales S.A.; *Int'l*, pg. 7601
THALES AIR DEFENCE—See Thales S.A.; *Int'l*, pg. 7601
THALES AIR SYSTEMS GMBH—See Thales S.A.; *Int'l*, pg. 7601
THALES AIR SYSTEMS LTD—See Thales S.A.; *Int'l*, pg. 7601
THALES AIR SYSTEMS SA—See Thales S.A.; *Int'l*, pg. 7601
THALES AIR SYSTEMS—See Thales S.A.; *Int'l*, pg. 7601
THALES ALENIA SPACE ESPANA—See Thales S.A.; *Int'l*, pg. 7601
THALES ALENIA SPACE FRANCE SAS—See Thales S.A.; *Int'l*, pg. 7601
THALES ALENIA SPACE NORTH AMERICA, INC.—See Thales S.A.; *Int'l*, pg. 7601
THALES ALENIA SPACE SAS—See Thales S.A.; *Int'l*, pg. 7601
THALES ALENIA SPACE—See Thales S.A.; *Int'l*, pg. 7601
THALES ANGENIEUX SA—See Thales S.A.; *Int'l*, pg. 7605
THALES ASIA PTE LTD—See Thales S.A.; *Int'l*, pg. 7601
THALES ATM GMBH—See Thales S.A.; *Int'l*, pg. 7601
THALES ATM LTD—See Thales S.A.; *Int'l*, pg. 7601
THALES ATM PTY LTD.—See Thales S.A.; *Int'l*, pg. 7601
THALES ATM S.A.—See Thales S.A.; *Int'l*, pg. 7601
THALES AUSTRALIA CENTRE-AIR OPERATIONS—See Thales S.A.; *Int'l*, pg. 7602
THALES AUSTRALIA - CIVIL—See Thales S.A.; *Int'l*, pg. 7601
THALES AUSTRALIA - DEFENCE SERVICES & AEROSPACE—See Thales S.A.; *Int'l*, pg. 7602
THALES AUSTRALIA - LAND—See Thales S.A.; *Int'l*, pg. 7602
THALES AUSTRALIA LTD. - ARMAMENTS DIVISION—See Thales S.A.; *Int'l*, pg. 7602
THALES AUSTRALIA LTD. - MARITIME & AEROSPACE DIVISION—See Thales S.A.; *Int'l*, pg. 7602
THALES AUSTRALIA LTD. - NATIONAL SECURITY & C4I DIVISION—See Thales S.A.; *Int'l*, pg. 7602
THALES AUSTRALIA LTD. - PROTECTED VEHICLES DIVISION—See Thales S.A.; *Int'l*, pg. 7602
THALES AUSTRALIA LTD. - TRANSPORT DIVISION—See Thales S.A.; *Int'l*, pg. 7602
THALES AUSTRALIA PTY. LTD.—See Thales S.A.; *Int'l*, pg. 7601
THALES AUSTRIA GMBH—See Thales S.A.; *Int'l*, pg. 7602
THALES AVIONICS ASIA PTE LTD—See Thales S.A.; *Int'l*, pg. 7602
THALES AVIONICS CANADA, INC.—See Thales S.A.; *Int'l*, pg. 7602
THALES AVIONICS ELECTRICAL MOTORS SA—See Safran SA; *Int'l*, pg. 6474
THALES AVIONICS, INC.—See Thales S.A.; *Int'l*, pg. 7602
THALES AVIONICS LCD SA—See Safran SA; *Int'l*, pg. 6474
THALES AVIONICS LTD—See Thales S.A.; *Int'l*, pg. 7602
THALES AVIONICS SA—See Thales S.A.; *Int'l*, pg. 7602
THALES AVIONICS—See Thales S.A.; *Int'l*, pg. 7602
THALES AVIONICS S.A—See Thales S.A.; *Int'l*, pg. 7602
THALES AVIONICS SA—See Thales S.A.; *Int'l*, pg. 7602
THALES AVIONICS—See Thales S.A.; *Int'l*, pg. 7602
THALES AVIONICS—See Thales S.A.; *Int'l*, pg. 7602
THALES AVIONICS SPA—See Thales S.A.; *Int'l*, pg. 7602
THALES AVS FRANCE SAS—See Thales S.A.; *Int'l*, pg. 7601
THALES CANADA INC.-OPTOMETRIC DIVISION—See Thales S.A.; *Int'l*, pg. 7605
THALES CANADA, SYSTEMS DIVISION—See Thales S.A.; *Int'l*, pg. 7602
THALES CANADA SYSTEMS—See Thales S.A.; *Int'l*, pg. 7606
THALES (CHINA) ENTERPRISES MANAGEMENT CO. LTD.—See Thales S.A.; *Int'l*, pg. 7601
THALES COMMUNICATIONS BELGIUM S.A—See Thales S.A.; *Int'l*, pg. 7602
THALES COMMUNICATIONS B.V—See Thales S.A.; *Int'l*, pg. 7602
THALES COMMUNICATIONS-MASSY—See Thales S.A.; *Int'l*, pg. 7602
THALES COMMUNICATIONS S.A—See Thales S.A.; *Int'l*, pg. 7602
THALES COMMUNICATIONS & SECURITY SA—See Thales S.A.; *Int'l*, pg. 7602
THALES COMMUNICATIONS S.P.A—See Thales S.A.; *Int'l*, pg. 7602
THALES COMMUNICATIONS UK LTD—See Thales S.A.; *Int'l*, pg. 7602
THALES COMPONENTS CORP—See Thales S.A.; *Int'l*, pg. 7606
THALES COMPUTERS FRANCE—See Thales S.A.; *Int'l*, pg. 7603
THALES CONSULTING & ENGINEERING—See Thales S.A.; *Int'l*, pg. 7603
THALES CORPORATE SERVICES LTD—See Thales S.A.; *Int'l*, pg. 7603
THALES CORPORATE VENTURES—See Thales S.A.; *Int'l*, pg. 7603
THALES CRITICAL INFORMATION SYSTEMS—See Thales S.A.; *Int'l*, pg. 7603
THALES CRYOGENICS B.V—See Thales S.A.; *Int'l*, pg. 7604
THALES CRYOGENIE S.A—See Thales S.A.; *Int'l*, pg. 7605
THALES DEFENCE DEUTSCHLAND GMBH—See Thales S.A.; *Int'l*, pg. 7603
THALES DEFENCE DEUTSCHLAND—See Thales S.A.; *Int'l*, pg. 7603
THALES DEFENCE & SECURITY SYSTEMS GMBH—See Thales S.A.; *Int'l*, pg. 7603
THALES DEFENSE & SECURITY, INC.—See Thales S.A.; *Int'l*, pg. 7606
THALES DEUTSCHLAND GMBH—See Thales S.A.; *Int'l*, pg. 7603
THALES ELECTRON DEVICES GMBH—See Thales S.A.; *Int'l*, pg. 7603
THALES ELECTRON DEVICES S.A. - RF & MICROWAVE SOURCES—See Thales S.A.; *Int'l*, pg. 7603
THALES ELECTRON DEVICES S.A—See Thales S.A.; *Int'l*, pg. 7603
THALES ELECTRON DEVICES S.A. - XRIS—See Thales S.A.; *Int'l*, pg. 7603
THALES ELECTRON DEVICES—See Thales S.A.; *Int'l*, pg. 7603
THALES ELECTRONIC SYSTEMS GMBH—See Thales S.A.; *Int'l*, pg. 7602
THALES ELECTRONIC SYSTEMS S.A.—See Thales S.A.; *Int'l*, pg. 7603
THALES ELECTRO OPTICS PTE. LTD.—See Thales S.A.; *Int'l*, pg. 7605
THALES E-SECURITY (ASIA) LTD.—See Thales S.A.; *Int'l*, pg. 7603
THALES E-SECURITY, INC.—See Thales S.A.; *Int'l*, pg. 7602
THALES E-SECURITY LTD—See Thales S.A.; *Int'l*, pg. 7602
THALES E-SECURITY LTD—See Thales S.A.; *Int'l*, pg. 7602
THALES ESPANA GRP, SAU—See Thales S.A.; *Int'l*, pg. 7603
THALES FIELD SERVICES INTERNATIONAL LIMITED (TFSI LTD)—See Thales S.A.; *Int'l*, pg. 7605
THALES HOLDINGS UK PLC—See Thales S.A.; *Int'l*, pg. 7603
THALES IDENTIFICATION SYSTEMS—See Thales S.A.; *Int'l*, pg. 7603
THALES IDENTIFICATION SYSTEMS—See Thales S.A.; *Int'l*, pg. 7603
THALES INDIA PVT LTD—See Thales S.A.; *Int'l*, pg. 7603
THALES INDIA PVT. LTD.—See Thales S.A.; *Int'l*, pg. 7603
THALES INDUSTRIAL SERVICES SA—See Thales S.A.; *Int'l*, pg. 7605
THALES INDUSTRIAL SERVICES S.A—See Thales S.A.; *Int'l*, pg. 7605
THALES INFORMATION SYSTEMS SA/NV—See Thales S.A.; *Int'l*, pg. 7606
THALES INFORMATION SYSTEMS—See Thales S.A.; *Int'l*, pg. 7606
THALES INFORMATION SYSTEMS—See Thales S.A.; *Int'l*, pg. 7606
THALES INFORMATION SYSTEMS—See Thales S.A.; *Int'l*, pg. 7606
THALES INFORMATION SYSTEMS SPA—See Thales S.A.; *Int'l*, pg. 7606
THALES INSURANCE & RISK MANAGEMENT S.A.—See Thales S.A.; *Int'l*, pg. 7603
THALES INTELLECTUAL PROPERTY—See Thales S.A.; *Int'l*, pg. 7603
THALES INTERNATIONAL BRASIL LTDA—See Thales S.A.; *Int'l*, pg. 7604
THALES INTERNATIONAL BV—See Thales S.A.; *Int'l*, pg. 7604
THALES INTERNATIONAL CHILE LTDA—See Thales S.A.; *Int'l*, pg. 7604
THALES INTERNATIONAL - CHINA—See Thales S.A.; *Int'l*, pg. 7604
THALES INTERNATIONAL DEUTSCHLAND GMBH—See Thales S.A.; *Int'l*, pg. 7604
THALES INTERNATIONAL EUROPE B.V.—See Thales S.A.; *Int'l*, pg. 7604
THALES INTERNATIONAL GREECE S.A.—See Thales S.A.; *Int'l*, pg. 7604
THALES INTERNATIONAL JAPAN KK—See Thales S.A.; *Int'l*, pg. 7604
THALES INTERNATIONAL MIDDLE EAST FZE—See Thales S.A.; *Int'l*, pg. 7604
THALES INTERNATIONAL NEDERLAND B.V.—See Thales S.A.; *Int'l*, pg. 7604
THALES INTERNATIONAL OFFSETS SAS—See Thales S.A.; *Int'l*, pg. 7604
THALES INTERNATIONAL PACIFIC HOLDINGS—See Thales S.A.; *Int'l*, pg. 7604
THALES INTERNATIONAL POLSKA SP. Z O.O.—See Thales S.A.; *Int'l*, pg. 7604
THALES INTERNATIONAL PVT LTD.—See Thales S.A.; *Int'l*, pg. 7604
THALES INTERNATIONAL S.A.S.—See Thales S.A.; *Int'l*, pg. 7604
THALES INTERNATIONAL—See Thales S.A.; *Int'l*, pg. 7603
THALES INTERNATIONAL—See Thales S.A.; *Int'l*, pg. 7604
THALES INTERNATIONAL—See Thales S.A.; *Int'l*, pg. 7601
THALES INTERNATIONAL—See Thales S.A.; *Int'l*, pg. 7603

COMPANY NAME INDEX

THALES INTERNATIONAL—See Thales S.A.; *Int'l*, pg. 7603
THALES INTERNATIONAL—See Thales S.A.; *Int'l*, pg. 7604
THALES INTERNATIONAL—See Thales S.A.; *Int'l*, pg. 7604
THALES INTERNATIONAL SVERIGE AB—See Thales S.A.; *Int'l*, pg. 7604
THALES INTERNATIONAL TAIWAN COMPANY LIMITED—See Thales S.A.; *Int'l*, pg. 7604
THALES INTERNATIONAL TURKIYE—See Thales S.A.; *Int'l*, pg. 7604
THALES INTERNATIONAL VENEZUELA—See Thales S.A.; *Int'l*, pg. 7604
THALES ITALIA SPA - AIR OPERATIONS DIVISION—See Thales S.A.; *Int'l*, pg. 7604
THALES ITALIA SPA - AVIONICS DIVISION—See Thales S.A.; *Int'l*, pg. 7604
THALES ITALIA SPA - COMPONENTS DIVISION—See Thales S.A.; *Int'l*, pg. 7603
THALES JAPAN K.K.—See Thales S.A.; *Int'l*, pg. 7604
THALES KOREA LTD—See Thales S.A.; *Int'l*, pg. 7604
THALES LAND & JOINT SYSTEMS UK—See Thales S.A.; *Int'l*, pg. 7604
THALES LASER K.K—See Thales S.A.; *Int'l*, pg. 7605
THALES LTD—See Thales S.A.; *Int'l*, pg. 7604
THALES MACKAY RADIO, INC—See Thales S.A.; *Int'l*, pg. 7606
THALES MALAYSIA SDN BHD—See Thales S.A.; *Int'l*, pg. 7604
THALES MICROELECTRONICS S.A—See Thales S.A.; *Int'l*, pg. 7604
THALES MICROWAVE S.A—See Thales S.A.; *Int'l*, pg. 7604
THALES MISSILE ELECTRONICS LTD—See Thales S.A.; *Int'l*, pg. 7604
THALES MISSIONS & CONSEIL—See Thales S.A.; *Int'l*, pg. 7601
THALES MUNITRONICS BV—See Thales S.A.; *Int'l*, pg. 7604
THALES NAVAL GMBH—See Thales S.A.; *Int'l*, pg. 7603
THALES NAVAL LTD—See Thales S.A.; *Int'l*, pg. 7603
THALES NAVAL SA—See Thales S.A.; *Int'l*, pg. 7604
THALES NEDERLAND B.V.—See Thales S.A.; *Int'l*, pg. 7604
THALES NEDERLAND TRANPORTATION—See Thales S.A.; *Int'l*, pg. 7604
THALES NEW ZEALAND LIMITED—See Thales S.A.; *Int'l*, pg. 7604
THALES NORWAY A/S—See Thales S.A.; *Int'l*, pg. 7603
THALES NORWAY AS—See Thales S.A.; *Int'l*, pg. 7604
THALES OPTRONICS BV—See Thales S.A.; *Int'l*, pg. 7605
THALES OPTRONICS (GLASGOW) LTD—See Thales S.A.; *Int'l*, pg. 7605
THALES OPTRONICS (STAINES) LTD—See Thales S.A.; *Int'l*, pg. 7605
THALES OPTRONICS (TAUNTON) LTD—See Thales S.A.; *Int'l*, pg. 7605
THALES OPTRONICS (VINTEN) LTD—See Thales S.A.; *Int'l*, pg. 7605
THALES OPTRONIQUE ITALIA SRL—See Thales S.A.; *Int'l*, pg. 7605
THALES OPTRONIQUE SA—See Thales S.A.; *Int'l*, pg. 7605
THALES PARKING SYSTEMS SA—See Thales S.A.; *Int'l*, pg. 7605
THALES POLSKA SP. Z O.O.—See Thales S.A.; *Int'l*, pg. 7605
THALES PORTUGAL S.A.—See Thales S.A.; *Int'l*, pg. 7605
THALES PROPERTIES LTD—See Thales S.A.; *Int'l*, pg. 7605
THALES RAIL SIGNALING SOLUTIONS—See Thales S.A.; *Int'l*, pg. 7601
THALES RAIL SIGNALLING SOLUTIONS AG—See Thales S.A.; *Int'l*, pg. 7605
THALES-RAYTHEON SYSTEMS COMPANY LLC—See RTX Corporation; *U.S. Public*, pg. 1825
THALES-RAYTHEON SYSTEMS COMPANY SAS—See Thales S.A.; *Int'l*, pg. 7601
THALES RESEARCH & TECHNOLOGY—See Thales S.A.; *Int'l*, pg. 7605
THALES RESEARCH & TECHNOLOGY UK LTD—See Thales S.A.; *Int'l*, pg. 7605
THALES SAFARE—See Thales S.A.; *Int'l*, pg. 7605
THALES SAIC TRANSPORT—See Thales S.A.; *Int'l*, pg. 7605
THALES S.A.; *Int'l*, pg. 7598
THALES SECURITY ASIA PTE LTD—See Thales S.A.; *Int'l*, pg. 7605
THALES SECURITY SOLUTIONS AND SERVICES CO.—See Thales S.A.; *Int'l*, pg. 7605
THALES SECURITY SOLUTIONS AND SERVICES (PTY) LTD—See Thales S.A.; *Int'l*, pg. 7605
THALES SECURITY SOLUTIONS & SERVICES COMPANY—See Thales S.A.; *Int'l*, pg. 7605
THALES SECURITY SOLUTIONS & SERVICES S.A. DE C.V.—See Thales S.A.; *Int'l*, pg. 7605

THALES SECURITY SOLUTIONS & SERVICES SAS—See Thales S.A.; *Int'l*, pg. 7601
THALES - SECURITY SOLUTIONS & SERVICES SPA—See Thales S.A.; *Int'l*, pg. 7601
THALES SECURITY SYSTEMS SAS—See Thales S.A.; *Int'l*, pg. 7605
THALES SERVICES INDUSTRIE S.A—See Thales S.A.; *Int'l*, pg. 7605
THALES SERVICES INDUSTRIE—See Thales S.A.; *Int'l*, pg. 7605
THALES SERVICES LTD.—See Thales S.A.; *Int'l*, pg. 7605
THALES SERVICES SA—See Thales S.A.; *Int'l*, pg. 7606
THALES SERVICES S.A.S.—See Thales S.A.; *Int'l*, pg. 7605
THALES SERVICES—See Thales S.A.; *Int'l*, pg. 7605
THALES SINGAPORE PTE LTD—See Thales S.A.; *Int'l*, pg. 7606
THALES SIX GTS FRANCE SAS—See Thales S.A.; *Int'l*, pg. 7606
THALES—See VINCI S.A.; *Int'l*, pg. 8229
THALES SOUTH AFRICA PTY LTD—See Thales S.A.; *Int'l*, pg. 7606
THALES SUISSE SA—See Thales S.A.; *Int'l*, pg. 7603
THALES SVERIGE AB—See Thales S.A.; *Int'l*, pg. 7606
THALES SYSTEMS AEROPORTES S.A—See Thales S.A.; *Int'l*, pg. 7606
THALES SYSTEMS CANADA, INC.—See Thales S.A.; *Int'l*, pg. 7606
THALES SYSTEMS ROMANIA—See Thales S.A.; *Int'l*, pg. 7606
THALES TECHNOLOGIES & SERVICES—See Thales S.A.; *Int'l*, pg. 7606
THALES (TIANJIN) RADAR TECHNOLOGIES CO., LTD—See Thales S.A.; *Int'l*, pg. 7601
THALES TRAINING & SIMULATION LTD—See Thales S.A.; *Int'l*, pg. 7603
THALES TRAINING & SIMULATION SAS—See Thales S.A.; *Int'l*, pg. 7606
THALES TRANSPORTATION SYSTEMS GMBH—See Thales S.A.; *Int'l*, pg. 7606
THALES TRANSPORTATION SYSTEMS—See Thales S.A.; *Int'l*, pg. 7606
THALES TRANSPORT & SECURITY (HK) LTD—See Thales S.A.; *Int'l*, pg. 7606
THALES TRANSPORT & SECURITY, INC.—See Thales S.A.; *Int'l*, pg. 7606
THALES TRANSPORT & SECURITY LTD—See Thales S.A.; *Int'l*, pg. 7603
THALES TRANSPORT SIGNALLING & SECURITY SOLUTIONS, S.A.U.—See Thales S.A.; *Int'l*, pg. 7606
THALES UK LTD—See Thales S.A.; *Int'l*, pg. 7603
THALES UNDERWATER SYSTEMS LTD—See Thales S.A.; *Int'l*, pg. 7603
THALES UNDERWATER SYSTEMS SAS—See Thales S.A.; *Int'l*, pg. 7603
THALES UNDERWATER SYSTEMS SINGAPORE—See Thales S.A.; *Int'l*, pg. 7606
THALES UNIVERSITE LTD—See Thales S.A.; *Int'l*, pg. 7606
THALES UNIVERSITE S.A.—See Thales S.A.; *Int'l*, pg. 7606
THALES USA, INC.—See Thales S.A.; *Int'l*, pg. 7606
THALES VP—See Thales S.A.; *Int'l*, pg. 7601
THALETEC GMBH—See HLE Glascoat Limited; *Int'l*, pg. 3431
THALETEC INC.—See HLE Glascoat Limited; *Int'l*, pg. 3431
THALHEIMER BROTHERS, INC.—See Audax Group, Limited Partnership; *U.S. Private*, pg. 390
THALHEIMER'S JEWELERS, INC.; *U.S. Private*, pg. 3979
THALHIMER COMMERCIAL REAL ESTATE; *U.S. Private*, pg. 3979
THALIA BUCHER AG—See Thalia Bucher GmbH; *Int'l*, pg. 7607
THALIA BUCHER GMBH; *Int'l*, pg. 7606
THALIA BUCH & MEDIEN GMBH—See Thalia Bucher GmbH; *Int'l*, pg. 7607
THALIA MEDIENSERVICE GMBH—See Thalia Bucher GmbH; *Int'l*, pg. 7607
THALIA SA—See EFG International AG; *Int'l*, pg. 2320
THALIA UNIVERSITATSBUCHHANDLUNG GMBH—See Thalia Bucher GmbH; *Int'l*, pg. 7607
THE THAL INDUSTRIES CORPORATION LIMITED - LAYYAH SUGAR MILL—See The Thal Industries Corporation Limited; *Int'l*, pg. 7694
THE THAL INDUSTRIES CORPORATION LIMITED - SAFINA SUGAR MILL—See The Thal Industries Corporation Limited; *Int'l*, pg. 7694
THE THAL INDUSTRIES CORPORATION LIMITED; *Int'l*, pg. 7694
THALLE CONSTRUCTION CO., INC.; *U.S. Private*, pg. 3980
THAL LIMITED-LAMINATES DIVISION—See House of Habib; *Int'l*, pg. 3491
THAL LIMITED—See House of Habib; *Int'l*, pg. 3491
THAMES AND HUDSON (S) PRIVATE LTD—See Thames & Hudson Ltd; *Int'l*, pg. 7607

THANH THAI GROUP JOINT STOCK COMPANY

THAMES & HUDSON (AUSTRALIA) PTY LTD—See Thames & Hudson Ltd; *Int'l*, pg. 7607
THAMES & HUDSON CHINA LTD—See Thames & Hudson Ltd; *Int'l*, pg. 7607
THAMES & HUDSON LTD; *Int'l*, pg. 7607
THAMES & HUDSON (S) PRIVATE LTD—See Thames & Hudson Ltd; *Int'l*, pg. 7607
THAMESIDE INVESTMENT GROUP PLC; *Int'l*, pg. 7607
THAMES PROPERTIES LTD—See Bank of Cyprus Holdings Public Limited Company; *Int'l*, pg. 842
THAMES RIVER CAPITAL UK LIMITED—See Bank of Montreal; *Int'l*, pg. 847
THAMES RIVER MULTI-CAPITAL LLP—See Bank of Montreal; *Int'l*, pg. 847
THAMES TRAVEL (WALLINGFORD) LIMITED—See GLOBALVIA Inversiones, S.A.U.; *Int'l*, pg. 3005
THAMES TRAVEL (WALLINGFORD) LIMITED—See Kinetic Group Services Pty Ltd.; *Int'l*, pg. 4168
THAMES VALLEY APOTHECARY, LLC—See Acreage Holdings, Inc.; *U.S. Public*, pg. 36
THE THAMES VALLEY NUFFIELD HOSPITAL SLOUGH—See Nuffield Health; *Int'l*, pg. 5488
THAMES VENTURES VCT 2 PLC; *Int'l*, pg. 7607
THAMES WATER PLC—See Macquarie Group Limited; *Int'l*, pg. 4626
THAMMACHART SEAFOOD RETAIL CO., LTD.—See Thai Union Group Public Company Limited; *Int'l*, pg. 7597
THANACHART BANK PUBLIC CO. LTD.—See TMBThanachart Bank Public Company Limited; *Int'l*, pg. 7766
THANACHART BROKER CO., LTD.—See Thanachart Capital PCL; *Int'l*, pg. 7607
THANACHART CAPITAL PCL; *Int'l*, pg. 7607
THANACHART FUND MANAGEMENT COMPANY LIMITED—See Thanachart Capital PCL; *Int'l*, pg. 7607
THANACHART GROUP LEASING CO., LTD.—See Thanachart Capital PCL; *Int'l*, pg. 7607
THANACHART INSURANCE PUBLIC COMPANY LIMITED—See Thanachart Capital PCL; *Int'l*, pg. 7607
THANACHART MANAGEMENT & SERVICES CO., LTD.—See Thanachart Capital PCL; *Int'l*, pg. 7607
THANACHART PLUS CO., LTD.—See Thanachart Capital PCL; *Int'l*, pg. 7607
THANACHART SECURITIES PUBLIC COMPANY LIMITED—See Thanachart Capital PCL; *Int'l*, pg. 7608
THANACHART SPV 01 COMPANY LIMITED—See Thanachart Capital PCL; *Int'l*, pg. 7608
THANACHART SPV 2 CO., LTD.—See Thanachart Capital PCL; *Int'l*, pg. 7608
THANACHART TRAINING & DEVELOPMENT CO., LTD.—See Thanachart Capital PCL; *Int'l*, pg. 7608
THANA CITY GOLF & SPORTS CLUB CO., LTD.—See BTS Group Holdings Public Company Limited; *Int'l*, pg. 1206
THANAKOM INJECTION CO., LTD.—See Saha Pathanapibul Public Company Limited; *Int'l*, pg. 6479
THANAPAKDI CO., LTD.—See Thai Beverage Public Company Limited; *Int'l*, pg. 7592
THANAPIRIYA PUBLIC COMPANY LIMITED; *Int'l*, pg. 7608
THANASIRI GROUP PUBLIC COMPANY LIMITED; *Int'l*, pg. 7608
THANE DIRECT UK LTD.—See H.I.G. Capital, LLC; *U.S. Private*, pg. 1832
THANE GHODBUNDER TOLL ROAD PVT. LTD.—See IRB Infrastructure Developers Ltd.; *Int'l*, pg. 3805
THANE INTERNATIONAL, INC.—See H.I.G. Capital, LLC; *U.S. Private*, pg. 1832
THANGAMAYIL GOLD & DIAMOND PRIVATE LIMITED—See Thangamayil Jewellery Limited; *Int'l*, pg. 7608
THANGAMAYIL JEWELLERY LIMITED; *Int'l*, pg. 7608
THANG LONG INDUSTRIAL PARK II CORPORATION—See Sumitomo Corporation; *Int'l*, pg. 7276
THANG LONG INVEST LAND JSC—See ThangLong Investment Group Joint Stock Company; *Int'l*, pg. 7608
THANGLONG INVESTMENT GROUP JOINT STOCK COMPANY; *Int'l*, pg. 7608
THANG LONG JOINT OPERATING COMPANY—See Repsol, S.A.; *Int'l*, pg. 6293
THANG LONG PHUTHO INVESTMENT JOINT STOCK COMPANY—See ThangLong Investment Group Joint Stock Company; *Int'l*, pg. 7608
THANG LONG WINE JSC; *Int'l*, pg. 7608
THANH CHAU PHU YEN GRANITE COMPANY LIMITED—See Phu Tai Joint Stock Company; *Int'l*, pg. 5857
THANH CONG MEDICAL CENTER JOINT STOCK COMPANY—See Thanh Cong Textile Garment Investment Trading Joint Stock Company; *Int'l*, pg. 7608
THANH CONG TEXTILE GARMENT INVESTMENT TRADING JOINT STOCK COMPANY; *Int'l*, pg. 7608
THANH NAM FURNITURE & ARCHITECTURE JOINT STOCK COMPANY; *Int'l*, pg. 7608
THANH THAI GROUP JOINT STOCK COMPANY; *Int'l*, pg. 7608
THANH THAI VIET NAM INDUSTRY TECHNOLOGY COMPANY LIMITED—See Cherng Tay Technology Co., Ltd.; *Int'l*, pg. 1471

2735

THANH THANH CONG - BIEN HOA JOINT STOCK COMPANY

THANH THANH CONG - BIEN HOA JOINT STOCK COMPANY; *Int'l*, pg. 7608
THANH THANH JOINT STOCK COMPANY; *Int'l*, pg. 7608
THANH VAN HOTEL DEVELOPMENT INVESTMENT JOINT STOCK COMPANY—See Sotetsu Holdings, Inc.; *Int'l*, pg. 7113
THANKSGIVING COFFEE COMPANY, INC.; *U.S. Private*, pg. 3980
THANKSGIVING POINT; *U.S. Private*, pg. 3980
THANKS TEMP CO., LTD.—See Persol Holdings Co., Ltd.; *Int'l*, pg. 5819
THANTAWAN INDUSTRY PUBLIC COMPANY LIMITED; *Int'l*, pg. 7608
THANULUX PUBLIC COMPANY LIMITED; *Int'l*, pg. 7608
THANYATHAMRONGKIJ CO., LTD—See Kasikornbank Public Company Limited; *Int'l*, pg. 4088
THANYATHANATHAVEE CO., LTD.—See Kasikornbank Public Company Limited; *Int'l*, pg. 4088
THANYING RESTAURANT SINGAPORE PTE. LTD.—See Amara Holdings Ltd.; *Int'l*, pg. 411
THARALDSON DEVELOPMENT CO.; *U.S. Private*, pg. 3980
THARCO CONTAINERS, INC.—See Packaging Corporation of America; *U.S. Public*, pg. 1633
THARCO CONTAINERS TEXAS, INC.—See Packaging Corporation of America; *U.S. Public*, pg. 1633
THARCO PACKAGING, INC.—See Packaging Corporation of America; *U.S. Public*, pg. 1633
THARIMMUNE, INC.; *U.S. Public*, pg. 2030
THARISA PLC; *Int'l*, pg. 7608
THAR PHARMACEUTICALS, INC.—See Grunenthal GmbH; *Int'l*, pg. 3115
T. HASEGAWA CO LTD - FINE FOODS UNIT—See T. Hasegawa Co. Ltd.; *Int'l*, pg. 7396
T. HASEGAWA CO LTD - ITAKURA FACILITY—See T. Hasegawa Co. Ltd.; *Int'l*, pg. 7396
T. HASEGAWA CO. LTD.; *Int'l*, pg. 7396
T. HASEGAWA (SOUTH EAST ASIA) CO LTD.—See T. Hasegawa Co. Ltd.; *Int'l*, pg. 7396
T. HASEGAWA USA INC.—See T. Hasegawa Co. Ltd.; *Int'l*, pg. 7396
THAT'S GOOD HR; *U.S. Private*, pg. 3980
THATTA CEMENT COMPANY LIMITED; *Int'l*, pg. 7609
THATTA POWER (PRIVATE) LIMITED—See THATTA CEMENT COMPANY LIMITED; *Int'l*, pg. 7609
THAXTON BARCLAY GROUP; *U.S. Private*, pg. 3980
THAYERMAHAN, INC.; *U.S. Private*, pg. 3980
THAYER MEDIA, INC.; *U.S. Private*, pg. 3980
THAYER POWER & COMMUNICATION LINE CONTRUCTION CO., LLC—See The Anderson Group, LLC; *U.S. Private*, pg. 3986
THAYER PUBLISHING—See Taylor Corporation; *U.S. Private*, pg. 3938
TH BAKTI SDN. BHD.—See Lembaga Tabung Haji; *Int'l*, pg. 4449
THB GROUP LIMITED—See AmWINS Group, Inc.; *U.S. Private*, pg. 269
THB-IJM JOINT VENTURE SDN BHD—See IJM Corporation Berhad; *Int'l*, pg. 3609
THB INC.; *U.S. Private*, pg. 3980
THB INTERNATIONAL INC—See AmWINS Group, Inc.; *U.S. Private*, pg. 270
THB RISK SOLUTIONS LIMITED—See AmWINS Group, Inc.; *U.S. Private*, pg. 270
THB UK LIMITED—See AmWINS Group, Inc.; *U.S. Private*, pg. 270
THC BIOMED INTERNATIONAL LTD.; *Int'l*, pg. 7609
THC FARMACEUTICALS, INC.; *U.S. Public*, pg. 2030
THCG GROUP CO., LTD.—See Gunkul Engineering Co., Ltd.; *Int'l*, pg. 3184
T.H.C. INTERNATIONAL CO., LTD.—See Digilife Technologies Limited; *Int'l*, pg. 2120
THC THERAPEUTICS, INC.; *U.S. Public*, pg. 2030
THDC INDIA LTD.—See NTPC Limited; *Int'l*, pg. 5484
TH DENMARK APS—See PVH Corp.; *U.S. Public*, pg. 1739
THE7STARS; *Int'l*, pg. 7705
THE9 LIMITED; *Int'l*, pg. 7705
THEA & SCHOEN, INC.; *U.S. Private*, pg. 4140
THEATER COMPANY HIKOSEN INC.—See Bushiroad, Inc.; *Int'l*, pg. 1227
THEATERMANIA.COM, INC.—See AudienceView Ticketing Corporation; *Int'l*, pg. 701
THEATRE COMMUNICATIONS GROUP, INC.; *U.S. Private*, pg. 4140
THEATRE DEVELOPMENT FUND; *U.S. Private*, pg. 4141
THEATRE FOR A NEW AUDIENCE; *U.S. Private*, pg. 4141
THEATRE MANAGEMENT INC.; *U.S. Private*, pg. 4141
THEBE COMMUNITY FINANCIAL SERVICES (PTY) LTD.—See Thebe Investment Corporation; *Int'l*, pg. 7706
THEBE EMPLOYEE BENEFITS (PTY) LTD.—See Thebe Investment Corporation; *Int'l*, pg. 7706
THEBE INVESTMENT CORPORATION; *Int'l*, pg. 7706
THEBE REED EXHIBITIONS PTY LIMITED—See Futuregrowth Asset Management Pty. Ltd.; *Int'l*, pg. 2858
THEBE REED EXHIBITIONS PTY LIMITED—See RELX plc; *Int'l*, pg. 6267

THEBE STOCKBROKING (PTY) LTD.—See Thebe Investment Corporation; *Int'l*, pg. 7706
THEBE TOURISM GROUP PTY LIMITED—See Futuregrowth Asset Management Pty. Ltd.; *Int'l*, pg. 2858
THEBE YA BOPHELO HEALTHCARE ADMINISTRATORS (PTY) LTD—See Thebe Investment Corporation; *Int'l*, pg. 7706
THEBLAZE INC.; *U.S. Private*, pg. 4141
THEBRANDHOUSE LTD—See Cim Financial Services Limited; *Int'l*, pg. 1607
THECUS TECHNOLOGY CORP.—See Ennoconn Corporation; *Int'l*, pg. 2443
THECUS U.S.A., INC.—See Ennoconn Corporation; *Int'l*, pg. 2443
THEDACARE INC.—See Froedtert Memorial Lutheran Hospital, Inc.; *U.S. Private*, pg. 1613
THEDA OAKS GASTROENTEROLOGY & ENDOSCOPY CENTER, LLC—See Tenet Healthcare Corporation; *U.S. Public*, pg. 2005
THEDIRECTORY.COM, INC.; *U.S. Private*, pg. 4141
THEEGARTEN-PACTEC GMBH & CO. KG; *Int'l*, pg. 7706
THEGLOBE.COM, INC.; *U.S. Public*, pg. 2144
THEHUFFINGTONPOST.COM, INC.—See BuzzFeed, Inc.; *U.S. Public*, pg. 413
THEIPGUYS.NET LLC; *U.S. Private*, pg. 4141
THEISEN VENDING INC.; *U.S. Private*, pg. 4141
THEIS PRECISION STEEL INC.; *U.S. Private*, pg. 4141
THEJO AUSTRALIA PTY LTD.—See Thejo Engineering Limited; *Int'l*, pg. 7706
THEJO ENGINEERING LIMITED; *Int'l*, pg. 7706
THEJO HATCON INDUSTRIAL SERVICES COMPANY—See Thejo Engineering Limited; *Int'l*, pg. 7706
THELADDERS.COM, INC.; *U.S. Private*, pg. 4141
THELEN INC.; *U.S. Private*, pg. 4141
THELEN SAND & GRAVEL INC.; *U.S. Private*, pg. 4141
THELIOS S.P.A.—See LVMH Moet Hennessy Louis Vuitton SE; *Int'l*, pg. 4603
THELLE TEKNOLOGI AS—See INDEX-Werke GmbH & Co. KG; *Int'l*, pg. 3651
THELLO SAS—See Ferrovie dello Stato Italiane S.p.A.; *Int'l*, pg. 2645
THELLOY DEVELOPMENT GROUP; *Int'l*, pg. 7706
THELMA LAGER & ASSOCIATES; *U.S. Private*, pg. 4141
THELMA PTY LTD.—See ICSGlobal Limited; *Int'l*, pg. 3586
THELMA THERAPEUTICS CO., LTD.; *Int'l*, pg. 7706
THELONG AIRTECH JOINT STOCK COMPANY—See AIRTECH JAPAN, LTD.; *Int'l*, pg. 249
THELO ROLLING STOCK LEASING—See Industrial Development Corporation of South Africa, Ltd.; *Int'l*, pg. 3672
THEMAC RESOURCES GROUP LIMITED; *Int'l*, pg. 7706
THEM ADVERTISING (SA) PTY LTD; *Int'l*, pg. 7706
THEMART—See Vornado Realty Trust; *U.S. Public*, pg. 2310
THEMAVEN NETWORK, INC.—See The Arena Group Holdings, Inc; *U.S. Public*, pg. 2035
THEMED ATTRACTIONS RESORTS & HOTELS SDN. BHD.—See Khazanah Nasional Berhad; *Int'l*, pg. 4153
THEME INTERNATIONAL HOLDINGS LIMITED; *Int'l*, pg. 7706
THEMIS BIOSCIENCE NV—See Merck & Co., Inc.; *U.S. Public*, pg. 1421
THEMIS G.R.E.N. LTD; *Int'l*, pg. 7706
THEMIS MEDICARE LTD; *Int'l*, pg. 7706
THENERGY B.V.—See BayWa AG; *Int'l*, pg. 919
THENETHERLANDS622009 B. V.—See Deutsche Post AG; *Int'l*, pg. 2082
THEO. C. AUMAN, INC—See Service Corporation International; *U.S. Public*, pg. 1871
THEOCHEM LABORATORIES, INC.—See Theochem Laboratories, Inc.; *U.S. Private*, pg. 4141
THEOCHEM LABORATORIES, INC.; *U.S. Private*, pg. 4141
THEO DAVIS SONS, INCORPORATED—See Chatham Asset Management, LLC; *U.S. Public*, pg. 863
THEODOOR GILISSEN GLOBAL CUSTODY BV—See KBL European Private Bankers S.A.; *Int'l*, pg. 4107
THEODOR BUSCHMANN GMBH & CO KG—See Fairplay Schleppdampfschiffs-Reederei Richard Borchard GmbH; *Int'l*, pg. 2609
THEODORE PRESSER CO.; *U.S. Private*, pg. 4141
THEO FENNELL LTD.; *Int'l*, pg. 7706
THEO KALOMIRAKIS THEATERS; *U.S. Private*, pg. 4141
THEOLIA NATURENERGIEN GMBH—See Electricite de France S.A.; *Int'l*, pg. 2350
THEOREM CREATIONS—See Theorem Inc.; *U.S. Private*, pg. 4141
THEOREM ESPANOL—See Theorem Inc.; *U.S. Private*, pg. 4142
THEOREM INC.; *U.S. Private*, pg. 4141
THEOREM INDIA PVT. LTD.—See Theorem Inc.; *U.S. Private*, pg. 4142
THEORIA COMMUNICATIONS INC.—See AOI TYO Holdings Inc.; *Int'l*, pg. 488
THEORIS INC.—See Asseco Poland S.A.; *Int'l*, pg. 642
THEORY, LLC—See Fast Retailing Co., Ltd.; *Int'l*, pg. 2621
THEORY ONE; *U.S. Private*, pg. 4142

THEPENIER PHARMA INDUSTRIE S.A.S.—See Nippon Shikizai Inc.; *Int'l*, pg. 5332
THEPRINTERS.COM; *U.S. Private*, pg. 4142
THERACLION SA; *Int'l*, pg. 7706
THERACOM LLC—See Cencora, Inc.; *U.S. Public*, pg. 467
THERA COSMETIC GMBH—See Henkel AG & Co. KGaA; *Int'l*, pg. 3354
THERADIAG SA; *Int'l*, pg. 7706
THERADOC, INC.—See Premier, Inc.; *U.S. Public*, pg. 1715
THERAGEN BIO CO., LTD.—See Theragen Etex Co., Ltd.; *Int'l*, pg. 7706
THERAGEN ETEX CO., LTD.; *Int'l*, pg. 7706
THERAGENICS CORPORATION—See Juniper Investment Company, LLC; *U.S. Private*, pg. 2244
THERAKOS (UK), LTD—See Mallinckrodt Public Limited Company; *Int'l*, pg. 4663
THERALASE TECHNOLOGIES INC.; *Int'l*, pg. 7707
THERALINK TECHNOLOGIES, INC.; *U.S. Public*, pg. 2144
THERAMETRICS GMBH—See Linical Co., Ltd.; *Int'l*, pg. 4513
THERAMEX HQ UK LIMITED; *Int'l*, pg. 7707
THERANEXUS S.A.; *Int'l*, pg. 7707
THERANOSTIC MEDIZINTECHNIK GMBH—See Elekta AB; *Int'l*, pg. 2356
THERANOSTICS HEALTH—See Theralink Technologies, Inc.; *U.S. Public*, pg. 2144
THERAPAK LLC—See Avantor, Inc.; *U.S. Public*, pg. 241
THERAPEDIC ASSOCIATES, INC.; *U.S. Private*, pg. 4142
THERAPEDIC ASSOCIATES, INC. - THE BED FACTORY—See Therapedic Associates, Inc.; *U.S. Private*, pg. 4142
THER-A-PEDIC MIDWEST INC.; *U.S. Private*, pg. 4142
THERAPEIA GMBH & CO.KG—See Telix Pharmaceuticals Limited; *Int'l*, pg. 7545
THERAPEUTIC FAMILY LIFE; *U.S. Private*, pg. 4142
THERAPEUTIC RESEARCH CENTER LLC—See Levine Leichtman Capital Partners, LLC; *U.S. Private*, pg. 2436
THERAPEUTICSMD, INC.; *U.S. Public*, pg. 2144
THERAPEUTIC SOLUTIONS INTERNATIONAL, INC.; *U.S. Public*, pg. 2144
THERAPURE BIOPHARMA INC.—See The Catalyst Capital Group Inc.; *Int'l*, pg. 7631
THE THERAPY GROUP, INC.—See Apollo Global Management, Inc.; *U.S. Public*, pg. 158
THERAPYSITES.COM LLC; *U.S. Private*, pg. 4142
THERAPY SOURCE, INC.; *U.S. Private*, pg. 4142
THERAPY STAFF, LLC - DETROIT REGIONAL DIVISION—See L2 Capital Partners; *U.S. Private*, pg. 2367
THERAPY STAFF, LLC - DETROIT REGIONAL DIVISION—See Lakewood Capital, LLC; *U.S. Private*, pg. 2379
THERAPY STAFF, LLC - NATIONAL TRAVEL DIVISION—See L2 Capital Partners; *U.S. Private*, pg. 2367
THERAPY STAFF, LLC - NATIONAL TRAVEL DIVISION—See Lakewood Capital, LLC; *U.S. Private*, pg. 2379
THERAPY STAFF, LLC—See L2 Capital Partners; *U.S. Private*, pg. 2367
THERAPY STAFF, LLC—See Lakewood Capital, LLC; *U.S. Private*, pg. 2379
THERAPY SUPPORT, INC.—See New Mountain Capital, LLC; *U.S. Private*, pg. 2903
THERAPYWORKS PHYSICAL THERAPY, LLC—See U.S. Physical Therapy, Inc.; *U.S. Public*, pg. 2216
THERATECHNOLOGIES, INC.; *Int'l*, pg. 7707
THERAVALUES CORPORATION—See Handok Inc.; *Int'l*, pg. 3243
THERAVANCE BIOPHARMA, INC.; *U.S. Public*, pg. 2145
THERAVANCE BIOPHARMA IRELAND LIMITED—See Theravance Biopharma, Inc.; *U.S. Public*, pg. 2145
THERAVANCE BIOPHARMA US, INC.—See Theravance Biopharma, Inc.; *U.S. Public*, pg. 2145
THERAVET SA; *Int'l*, pg. 7707
THERICS, INC.—See Tredegar Corporation; *U.S. Public*, pg. 2187
THERIUM CAPITAL MANAGEMENT LIMITED—See Stone Point Capital LLC; *U.S. Private*, pg. 3821
THERIUM INC.—See Stone Point Capital LLC; *U.S. Private*, pg. 3821
THERIVA BIOLOGICS, INC.; *U.S. Public*, pg. 2145
THERMA BRIGHT, INC.; *Int'l*, pg. 7707
THERMACORE EUROPE LTD.—See The Goldman Sachs Group, Inc.; *U.S. Public*, pg. 2080
THERMACORE, INC.—See The Goldman Sachs Group, Inc.; *U.S. Public*, pg. 2080
THERMA CORPORATION—See Blackstone Inc.; *U.S. Public*, pg. 361
THERMADOR GROUPE; *Int'l*, pg. 7707
THERMADOR INTERNATIONAL SARL—See Thermador Groupe; *Int'l*, pg. 7707
THERMADOR SA—See Thermador Groupe; *Int'l*, pg. 7707
THERMADYNE BRAZIL HOLDINGS LTD—See Enovis Corporation; *U.S. Public*, pg. 773

THERMADYNE DE MEXICO S.A. DE C.V.—See Enovis Corporation; *U.S. Public*, pg. 773
THERMADYNE JAPAN LTD.—See Enovis Corporation; *U.S. Public*, pg. 771
THERMADYNE (SHANGHAI) CO. LTD.—See Enovis Corporation; *U.S. Public*, pg. 771
THERMADYNE VICTOR LTDA.—See Enovis Corporation; *U.S. Public*, pg. 773
THERMAFIBER, INC.—See Owens Corning; *U.S. Public*, pg. 1628
THERMAFREEZE PRODUCTS CORP.; *U.S. Public*, pg. 2145
THERM AIR AUSTRALIA PTY. LTD.—See Elders Limited; *Int'l*, pg. 2346
THERMAL CARE INC.—See Perma-Pipe International Holdings, Inc.; *U.S. Public*, pg. 1676
THERMALCAST, LLC; *U.S. Private*, pg. 4142
THERMAL CERAMICS ASIA PTE. LTD.—See Morgan Advanced Materials plc; *Int'l*, pg. 5044
THERMAL CERAMICS BENELUX B.V.—See Morgan Advanced Materials plc; *Int'l*, pg. 5043
THERMAL CERAMICS CARIBBEAN INC.—See Morgan Advanced Materials plc; *Int'l*, pg. 5043
THERMAL CERAMICS DE FRANCE S.A.—See Morgan Advanced Materials plc; *Int'l*, pg. 5043
THERMAL CERAMICS DE VENEUELA C.A.—See Morgan Advanced Materials plc; *Int'l*, pg. 5044
THERMAL CERAMICS ESPANA, S.L.—See Morgan Advanced Materials plc; *Int'l*, pg. 5043
THERMAL CERAMICS INC. - CANON CITY PLANT—See Morgan Advanced Materials plc; *Int'l*, pg. 5042
THERMAL CERAMICS INC. - ELKHART PLANT—See Morgan Advanced Materials plc; *Int'l*, pg. 5043
THERMAL CERAMICS INC. - EMPORIA PLANT—See Morgan Advanced Materials plc; *Int'l*, pg. 5043
THERMAL CERAMICS INC. - GIRARD PLANT—See Morgan Advanced Materials plc; *Int'l*, pg. 5043
THERMAL CERAMICS INC—See Morgan Advanced Materials plc; *Int'l*, pg. 5042
THERMAL CERAMICS ITALIANA S.R.L.—See Morgan Advanced Materials plc; *Int'l*, pg. 5043
THERMAL CERAMICS NZ LIMITED—See Morgan Advanced Materials plc; *Int'l*, pg. 5043
THERMAL CERAMICS POLSKA SP.ZOO—See Morgan Advanced Materials plc; *Int'l*, pg. 5044
THERMAL CERAMICS—See Morgan Advanced Materials plc; *Int'l*, pg. 5043
THERMAL CERAMICS SOUTH AFRICA PTY. LIMITED—See Morgan Advanced Materials plc; *Int'l*, pg. 5044
THERMAL CERAMICS UK LIMITED—See Morgan Advanced Materials plc; *Int'l*, pg. 5043
THERMAL CONCEPTS, LLC—See Halmos Capital Partners; *U.S. Private*, pg. 1845
THERMAL CONCEPTS, LLC—See Trivest Partners, LP; *U.S. Private*, pg. 4241
THERMAL CONTROL INSULATION, LLC—See Installed Building Products, Inc.; *U.S. Public*, pg. 1133
THERMAL CORPORATION—See Nailor Industries; *U.S. Private*, pg. 2831
THERMAL DEVICES, INC.—See Gryphon Investors, LLC; *U.S. Private*, pg. 1799
THERMAL DYNAMICS INTERNATIONAL, INC.—See Page Management Co., Inc.; *U.S. Private*, pg. 3074
THERMAL DYNAMICS, LLC.—See Zhejiang Yinlun Machinery Co., Ltd.; *Int'l*, pg. 8667
THERMAL EDGE, INC.; *U.S. Private*, pg. 4142
THERMAL ENERGY INTERNATIONAL (GUANGZHOU) LTD—See Thermal Energy International Inc.; *Int'l*, pg. 7707
THERMAL ENERGY INTERNATIONAL INC. - BRISTOL—See Thermal Energy International Inc.; *Int'l*, pg. 7707
THERMAL ENERGY INTERNATIONAL INC.; *Int'l*, pg. 7707
THERMAL ENERGY PRODUCTS, INC.—See HEICO Corporation; *U.S. Public*, pg. 1021
THERMAL ENGINEERING INTERNATIONAL LIMITED—See Babcock Power, Inc.; *U.S. Private*, pg. 422
THERMAL ENGINEERING INTERNATIONAL (USA) INC. - MSR DIVISION—See Babcock Power, Inc.; *U.S. Private*, pg. 422
THERMAL ENGINEERING INTERNATIONAL (USA), INC.—See Babcock Power, Inc.; *U.S. Private*, pg. 422
THERMAL ENGINEERING INTERNATIONAL (USA) INC. - STRUTHERS WELLS DIVISION—See Babcock Power, Inc.; *U.S. Private*, pg. 422
THERMAL EQUIPMENT SERVICE, INC.—See Comfort Systems USA, Inc.; *U.S. Public*, pg. 544
THERMALEX, INC.—See Investment Corporation of Dubai; *Int'l*, pg. 3785
THERMAL HAZARD TECHNOLOGY—See Judges Scientific plc; *Int'l*, pg. 4021
THERMAL INDUSTRIES, INC.—See Kenner & Company, Inc.; *U.S. Private*, pg. 2285
THERMAL INDUSTRIES, INC.—See North Cove Partners; *U.S. Private*, pg. 2944

THERMAL & MECHANICAL EQUIPMENT, LLC; *U.S. Private*, pg. 4142
THERMAL MECHANICS INC.; *U.S. Private*, pg. 4142
THERMAL PAPER DIRECT INC.; *U.S. Private*, pg. 4142
THERMAL SOLUTIONS LLC—See RTX Corporation; *U.S. Public*, pg. 1822
THERMAL SOLUTIONS MANUFACTURING, INC.—See Altus Capital Partners, Inc.; *U.S. Private*, pg. 211
THERMAL SPRAY INDUSTRIES LTD.—See Corrosion & Abrasion Solutions Ltd.; *Int'l*, pg. 1806
THERMAL SPRAY SOLUTIONS, INC.—See Palladium Equity Partners, LLC; *U.S. Private*, pg. 3078
THERMAL STRUCTURES, INC.—See HEICO Corporation; *U.S. Public*, pg. 1021
THERMAL SUPPLY INC.; *U.S. Private*, pg. 4142
THERMAL SYSTEMS KWC LTD.; *Int'l*, pg. 7707
THERMAL TECH, INC.—See ABC Supply Co. Inc.; *U.S. Private*, pg. 36
THERMAL TECHNOLOGY DISTRIBUTION SOLUTIONS—See Gryphon Investors, LLC; *U.S. Private*, pg. 1799
THERMAL TECHNOLOGY INC.—See GT Advanced Technologies Inc.; *U.S. Private*, pg. 1801
THERMALTEK, INC.—See Sandvik AB; *Int'l*, pg. 6535
THERMAL TREATMENT CENTER INC.—See HI TecMetal Group, Inc.; *U.S. Private*, pg. 1931
THERMAL WINDOWS INC.; *U.S. Private*, pg. 4142
THERMA MOBILE, INC.—See Aboitiz Equity Ventures, Inc.; *Int'l*, pg. 67
THERMA PRIME DRILLING CORPORATION—See Lopez, Inc.; *Int'l*, pg. 4557
THERMA-SEAL ROOFS INC.; *U.S. Private*, pg. 4142
THERMASERVE, INC.—See Huron Capital Partners LLC; *U.S. Private*, pg. 2012
THERMA SOUTH, INC.—See Aboitiz Equity Ventures, Inc.; *Int'l*, pg. 67
THERMASYS, CORP.—See Wellspring Capital Management LLC; *U.S. Private*, pg. 4478
THERMATECH NORTHWEST, INC.—See Alliance Environmental Group, LLC; *U.S. Private*, pg. 182
THERMA-TRON-X INC—See TTX Holdings Inc.; *U.S. Private*, pg. 4255
THERMA-TRU CORP.—See Fortune Brands Innovations, Inc.; *U.S. Public*, pg. 873
THERMA-TRU CORP.—See Fortune Brands Innovations, Inc.; *U.S. Public*, pg. 873
THERMAX BABCOCK & WILCOX ENERGY SOLUTIONS PRIVATE LIMITED—See Babcock & Wilcox Enterprises, Inc.; *U.S. Public*, pg. 263
THERMAX DENMARK APS—See Thermax Limited; *Int'l*, pg. 7708
THERMAX DO BRASIL - ENERGIA E EQUIPAMENTOS LTDA.—See Thermax Limited; *Int'l*, pg. 7708
THERMAX ENERGY & ENVIRONMENT LANKA (PRIVATE) LIMITED—See Thermax Limited; *Int'l*, pg. 7708
THERMAX ENERGY & ENVIRONMENT PHILIPPINES CORPORATION—See Thermax Limited; *Int'l*, pg. 7708
THERMAX ENGINEERING SINGAPORE PTE. LTD.—See Thermax Limited; *Int'l*, pg. 7708
THERMAX EUROPE LIMITED—See Thermax Limited; *Int'l*, pg. 7708
THERMAX INC.—See Thermax Limited; *Int'l*, pg. 7708
THERMAX LIMITED; *Int'l*, pg. 7707
THERMAX NIGERIA LIMITED—See Thermax Limited; *Int'l*, pg. 7708
THERMAX SDN. BHD.—See Thermax Limited; *Int'l*, pg. 7708
THERMAX (THAILAND) LIMITED—See Thermax Limited; *Int'l*, pg. 7707
THERM-CON, LLC—See Installed Building Products, Inc.; *U.S. Public*, pg. 1133
THERMEDICS DETECTION DE ARGENTINA S.A.—See Thermo Fisher Scientific Inc.; *U.S. Public*, pg. 2152
THERMEDX LLC—See Stryker Corporation; *U.S. Public*, pg. 1957
THERMENHOTEL VIKTORIA BAD GRIESBACH—See Schoeller Holdings Ltd.; *Int'l*, pg. 6637
THERME SEEWINKEL BETRIEBSGESELLSCHAFT M.B.H.—See Fresenius SE & Co. KGaA; *Int'l*, pg. 2781
THERMEX-THERMATRON SYSTEMS, LLC—See Druid Capital Partners, LLC; *U.S. Private*, pg. 1279
THERMIA AB—See STIEBEL ELTRON GmbH & Co. KG; *Int'l*, pg. 7215
THERMICO INC.; *U.S. Private*, pg. 4142
THERM, INC.; *U.S. Private*, pg. 4142
THERMIQUE INDUSTRIE VIDE—See AMG Critical Materials N.V.; *Int'l*, pg. 425
THERMISCHE RUCKSTANDSVERWERTUNG GMBH & CO. KG—See BASF SE; *Int'l*, pg. 885
THERMISOL FINLAND OY—See Jackon AS; *Int'l*, pg. 3864
THERMISSION AG; *Int'l*, pg. 7708
THERMIVAL JSC—See Hiolle Industries S.A.; *Int'l*, pg. 3401
THERMO ASSET MANAGEMENT SERVICES INC.—See Thermo Fisher Scientific Inc.; *U.S. Public*, pg. 2152
THERMO CIDTEC INC.—See Thermo Fisher Scientific Inc.; *U.S. Public*, pg. 2152

THERMOCOMPACT SA—See Groupe BPCE; *Int'l*, pg. 3097
THERMOCOPY OF TENNESSEE INC.; *U.S. Private*, pg. 4143
THERMO CRS LTD.—See Thermo Fisher Scientific Inc.; *U.S. Public*, pg. 2152
THERM-O-DISC EUROPE B.V.—See Emerson Electric Co.; *U.S. Public*, pg. 745
THERM-O-DISC, INC. - NORTHVILLE—See One Rock Capital Partners, LLC; *U.S. Private*, pg. 3023
THERM-O-DISC, INCORPORATED—See One Rock Capital Partners, LLC; *U.S. Private*, pg. 3023
THERMODOLE SAS—See Sintex Industries, Ltd.; *Int'l*, pg. 6957
THERMO EBERLINE LLC—See Thermo Fisher Scientific Inc.; *U.S. Public*, pg. 2152
THERMO EGS GAUGING, INC.—See Thermo Fisher Scientific Inc.; *U.S. Public*, pg. 2152
THERMO ELECTRIC COMPANY, INC.; *U.S. Private*, pg. 4142
THERMO ELECTRIC INSTRUMENTATION B.V.—See Indutrade AB; *Int'l*, pg. 3681
THERMO ELECTRON A/S—See Thermo Fisher Scientific Inc.; *U.S. Public*, pg. 2152
THERMO ELECTRON CORPORATION PROCESS INSTRUMENTS—See Thermo Fisher Scientific Inc.; *U.S. Public*, pg. 2152
THERMO ELECTRON INDUSTRIES—See Thermo Fisher Scientific Inc.; *U.S. Public*, pg. 2152
THERMO ELECTRON LABORATORY EQUIPMENT LLC—See Thermo Fisher Scientific Inc.; *U.S. Public*, pg. 2152
THERMO ELECTRON LED S.A.S.—See Thermo Fisher Scientific Inc.; *U.S. Public*, pg. 2152
THERMO ELECTRON LIMITED—See Thermo Fisher Scientific Inc.; *U.S. Public*, pg. 2152
THERMO ELECTRON S.A.—See Thermo Fisher Scientific Inc.; *U.S. Public*, pg. 2152
THERMO ELECTRON WEIGHING & INSPECTION LIMITED—See Thermo Fisher Scientific Inc.; *U.S. Public*, pg. 2152
THERMO ENERGY SOLUTIONS, INC.—See Gibraltar Industries, Inc.; *U.S. Public*, pg. 936
THERMO ENVIRONMENTAL INSTRUMENTS INC.—See Thermo Fisher Scientific Inc.; *U.S. Public*, pg. 2152
THERMO FAST U.K. LIMITED—See Thermo Fisher Scientific Inc.; *U.S. Public*, pg. 2152
THERMO FIBERGEN INC.—See Kadant Inc.; *U.S. Public*, pg. 1212
THERMO FISHER DIAGNOSTICS AB—See Thermo Fisher Scientific Inc.; *U.S. Public*, pg. 2152
THERMO FISHER DIAGNOSTICS AG—See Thermo Fisher Scientific Inc.; *U.S. Public*, pg. 2152
THERMO FISHER DIAGNOSTICS AUSTRIA GMBH—See Thermo Fisher Scientific Inc.; *U.S. Public*, pg. 2153
THERMO FISHER DIAGNOSTICS B.V.—See Thermo Fisher Scientific Inc.; *U.S. Public*, pg. 2152
THERMO FISHER DIAGNOSTICS NV—See Thermo Fisher Scientific Inc.; *U.S. Public*, pg. 2153
THERMO FISHER DIAGNOSTICS OY—See Thermo Fisher Scientific Inc.; *U.S. Public*, pg. 2152
THERMO FISHER DIAGNOSTICS SAS—See Thermo Fisher Scientific Inc.; *U.S. Public*, pg. 2152
THERMO FISHER DIAGNOSTICS, S.L.U.—See Thermo Fisher Scientific Inc.; *U.S. Public*, pg. 2153
THERMO FISHER DIAGNOSTICS, SOCIEDADE UNIPESSOAL LDA—See Thermo Fisher Scientific Inc.; *U.S. Public*, pg. 2153
THERMO FISHER DIAGNOSTICS SPA—See Thermo Fisher Scientific Inc.; *U.S. Public*, pg. 2148
THERMO FISHER FINANCIAL SERVICES INC.—See Thermo Fisher Scientific Inc.; *U.S. Public*, pg. 2152
THERMO FISHER IRELAND LTD.—See Thermo Fisher Scientific Inc.; *U.S. Public*, pg. 2152
THERMO FISHER ISRAEL LTD.—See Thermo Fisher Scientific Inc.; *U.S. Public*, pg. 2149
THERMO FISHER (KANDEL) GMBH—See Thermo Fisher Scientific Inc.; *U.S. Public*, pg. 2152
THERMO FISHER SCIENTIFIC AUSTRALIA PTY LTD—See Thermo Fisher Scientific Inc.; *U.S. Public*, pg. 2153
THERMO FISHER SCIENTIFIC BALTICS UAB—See Thermo Fisher Scientific Inc.; *U.S. Public*, pg. 2153
THERMO FISHER SCIENTIFIC BETEILIGUNGSVERWALTUNGS GMBH—See Thermo Fisher Scientific Inc.; *U.S. Public*, pg. 2153
THERMO FISHER SCIENTIFIC BIOPRODUCTION PTE. LTD.—See Thermo Fisher Scientific Inc.; *U.S. Public*, pg. 2153
THERMO FISHER SCIENTIFIC BRASIL SERVICOS DE LOGISTICA LTDA—See Thermo Fisher Scientific Inc.; *U.S. Public*, pg. 2147
THERMO FISHER SCIENTIFIC (BREDA) HOLDING BV—See Thermo Fisher Scientific Inc.; *U.S. Public*, pg. 2154
THERMO FISHER SCIENTIFIC (BREMEN) GMBH—See Thermo Fisher Scientific Inc.; *U.S. Public*, pg. 2153
THERMO FISHER SCIENTIFIC BRNO S.R.O.—See Thermo Fisher Scientific Inc.; *U.S. Public*, pg. 2153

THERMO FISHER SCIENTIFIC B.V.B.A.—See Thermo Fisher Scientific Inc.; *U.S. Public*, pg. 2153
THERMO FISHER SCIENTIFIC B.V.—See Thermo Fisher Scientific Inc.; *U.S. Public*, pg. 2154
THERMO FISHER SCIENTIFIC CHEMICALS INC.—See Thermo Fisher Scientific Inc.; *U.S. Public*, pg. 2153
THERMO FISHER SCIENTIFIC (CHINA) CO., LTD.—See Thermo Fisher Scientific Inc.; *U.S. Public*, pg. 2153
THERMO FISHER SCIENTIFIC - CONSOLIDATED TECHNOLOGIES—See Thermo Fisher Scientific Inc.; *U.S. Public*, pg. 2153
THERMO FISHER SCIENTIFIC (ECUBLENS) SARL—See Thermo Fisher Scientific Inc.; *U.S. Public*, pg. 2153
THERMO FISHER SCIENTIFIC FINANCE COMPANY BV—See Thermo Fisher Scientific Inc.; *U.S. Public*, pg. 2154
THERMO FISHER SCIENTIFIC - FRANKLIN BRANCH—See Thermo Fisher Scientific Inc.; *U.S. Public*, pg. 2153
THERMO FISHER SCIENTIFIC GENEART GMBH—See Thermo Fisher Scientific Inc.; *U.S. Public*, pg. 2149
THERMO FISHER SCIENTIFIC GERMANY BV & CO. KG—See Thermo Fisher Scientific Inc.; *U.S. Public*, pg. 2153
THERMO FISHER SCIENTIFIC GMBH—See Thermo Fisher Scientific Inc.; *U.S. Public*, pg. 2153
THERMO FISHER SCIENTIFIC INC. - CELLOMICS—See Thermo Fisher Scientific Inc.; *U.S. Public*, pg. 2154
THERMO FISHER SCIENTIFIC INC.—See Thermo Fisher Scientific Inc.; *U.S. Public*, pg. 2154
THERMO FISHER SCIENTIFIC INC.; *U.S. Public*, pg. 2145
THERMO FISHER SCIENTIFIC INDIA PVT LTD—See Thermo Fisher Scientific Inc.; *U.S. Public*, pg. 2154
THERMO FISHER SCIENTIFIC INDIA PVT LTD—See Thermo Fisher Scientific Inc.; *U.S. Public*, pg. 2154
THERMO FISHER SCIENTIFIC INFORMATICS—See Thermo Fisher Scientific Inc.; *U.S. Public*, pg. 2154
THERMO FISHER SCIENTIFIC IT SERVICES GMBH—See Thermo Fisher Scientific Inc.; *U.S. Public*, pg. 2154
THERMO FISHER SCIENTIFIC KOREA LTD.—See Thermo Fisher Scientific Inc.; *U.S. Public*, pg. 2146
THERMO FISHER SCIENTIFIC - LAB VISION IHC SYSTEM SOLUTIONS—See Thermo Fisher Scientific Inc.; *U.S. Public*, pg. 2153
THERMO FISHER SCIENTIFIC LIFE INVESTMENTS III S.A.R.L.—See Thermo Fisher Scientific Inc.; *U.S. Public*, pg. 2154
THERMO FISHER SCIENTIFIC LIFE SENIOR HOLDINGS II C.V.—See Thermo Fisher Scientific Inc.; *U.S. Public*, pg. 2154
THERMO FISHER SCIENTIFIC - MATRIX LIQUID HANDLING PRODUCTS—See Thermo Fisher Scientific Inc.; *U.S. Public*, pg. 2153
THERMO FISHER SCIENTIFIC MESSTECHNIK GMBH—See Thermo Fisher Scientific Inc.; *U.S. Public*, pg. 2154
THERMO FISHER SCIENTIFIC - METAVAC—See Thermo Fisher Scientific Inc.; *U.S. Public*, pg. 2153
THERMO FISHER SCIENTIFIC MEXICO CITY, S. DE R.L. DE C.V.—See Thermo Fisher Scientific Inc.; *U.S. Public*, pg. 2154
THERMO FISHER SCIENTIFIC MILANO SRL—See Thermo Fisher Scientific Inc.; *U.S. Public*, pg. 2152
THERMO FISHER SCIENTIFIC (MILWAUKEE) LLC—See Thermo Fisher Scientific Inc.; *U.S. Public*, pg. 2153
THERMO FISHER SCIENTIFIC (MISSISSAUGA) INC.—See Thermo Fisher Scientific Inc.; *U.S. Public*, pg. 2153
THERMO FISHER SCIENTIFIC - MOLECULAR BIOPRODUCTS—See Thermo Fisher Scientific Inc.; *U.S. Public*, pg. 2153
THERMO FISHER SCIENTIFIC - NALGENE & NUNC—See Thermo Fisher Scientific Inc.; *U.S. Public*, pg. 2153
THERMO FISHER SCIENTIFIC - NERL CLINICAL DIAGNOSTICS—See Thermo Fisher Scientific Inc.; *U.S. Public*, pg. 2153
THERMO FISHER SCIENTIFIC - NEWINGTON BRANCH—See Thermo Fisher Scientific Inc.; *U.S. Public*, pg. 2153
THERMO FISHER SCIENTIFIC NEW ZEALAND LTD—See Thermo Fisher Scientific Inc.; *U.S. Public*, pg. 2154
THERMO FISHER SCIENTIFIC - PITTSBURGH BRANCH—See Thermo Fisher Scientific Inc.; *U.S. Public*, pg. 2153
THERMO FISHER SCIENTIFIC (PRAHA) S.R.O.—See Thermo Fisher Scientific Inc.; *U.S. Public*, pg. 2153
THERMO FISHER SCIENTIFIC - SAN DIEGO BRANCH—See Thermo Fisher Scientific Inc.; *U.S. Public*, pg. 2153
THERMO FISHER SCIENTIFIC (SCHWEIZ) AG—See Thermo Fisher Scientific Inc.; *U.S. Public*, pg. 2153
THERMO FISHER SCIENTIFIC SL—See Thermo Fisher Scientific Inc.; *U.S. Public*, pg. 2154
THERMO FISHER SCIENTIFIC—See Thermo Fisher Scientific Inc.; *U.S. Public*, pg. 2153

THERMO FISHER SCIENTIFIC—See Thermo Fisher Scientific Inc.; *U.S. Public*, pg. 2153
THERMO FISHER SCIENTIFIC—See Thermo Fisher Scientific Inc.; *U.S. Public*, pg. 2153
THERMO FISHER SCIENTIFIC—See Thermo Fisher Scientific Inc.; *U.S. Public*, pg. 2152
THERMO FISHER SCIENTIFIC—See Thermo Fisher Scientific Inc.; *U.S. Public*, pg. 2153
THERMO FISHER SCIENTIFIC—See Thermo Fisher Scientific Inc.; *U.S. Public*, pg. 2153
THERMO FISHER SCIENTIFIC (THAILAND) CO., LTD.—See Thermo Fisher Scientific Inc.; *U.S. Public*, pg. 2149
THERMO FISHER SCIENTIFIC VERMOGENSVERWALTUNGS GMBH—See Thermo Fisher Scientific Inc.; *U.S. Public*, pg. 2154
THERMO FISHER SCIENTIFIC - WILMINGTON BRANCH—See Thermo Fisher Scientific Inc.; *U.S. Public*, pg. 2153
THERMO FISHER SCIENTIFIC WISSENSCHAFTLICHE GERATE GMBH—See Thermo Fisher Scientific Inc.; *U.S. Public*, pg. 2153
THERMO FISHER SCIENTIFIC (ZURICH) AG—See Thermo Fisher Scientific Inc.; *U.S. Public*, pg. 2153
THERMOFLEX AG—See Groupe Guillin SA; *Int'l*, pg. 3104
THERMO FLUIDS INC.; *U.S. Public*, pg. 4142
THERMOFORM ENGINEERED QUALITY LLC—See Sonoco Products Company; *U.S. Public*, pg. 1909
THERMOFORMING SYSTEMS, LLC—See ONEX Corporation; *Int'l*, pg. 5578
THERMO FUELS COMPANY, INC.—See The AES Corporation; *U.S. Public*, pg. 2032
THERMO GAMMA-METRICS LLC—See Thermo Fisher Scientific Inc.; *U.S. Public*, pg. 2154
THERMO GAMMA-METRICS PTY LTD—See Thermo Fisher Scientific Inc.; *U.S. Public*, pg. 2154
THERMOGAS GAS- UND GERATEVERTRIEBS-GMBH—See EnBW Energie Baden-Wurttemberg AG; *Int'l*, pg. 2400
THERMOGAS S.A.—See NIBE Industrier AB; *Int'l*, pg. 5263
THERMOGENESIS HOLDINGS, INC.—See Boyalife Group; *Int'l*, pg. 1124
THERMOGENICS INC.—See Audax Group, Limited Partnership; *U.S. Private*, pg. 390
THERMO GLASS DOOR S.P.A.—See LU-VE SpA; *Int'l*, pg. 4572
THERMOGRAPHICS, INC.—See Liquid Crystal Resources; *U.S. Private*, pg. 2465
THERMO HYPERSIL-KEYSTONE LLC—See Thermo Fisher Scientific Inc.; *U.S. Public*, pg. 2154
THERMO KEVEX X-RAY INC.—See Thermo Fisher Scientific Inc.; *U.S. Public*, pg. 2154
THERMO KEYTEK LLC—See Thermo Fisher Scientific Inc.; *U.S. Public*, pg. 2154
THERMO KING CENTRAL CAROLINAS, LLC; *U.S. Private*, pg. 4142
THERMO KING CHRISTENSEN INC.; *U.S. Private*, pg. 4142
THERMO KING CONTAINER ANTWERP—See Trane Technologies Plc; *Int'l*, pg. 7892
THERMO KING CONTAINER - DENMARK A/S—See Trane Technologies Plc; *Int'l*, pg. 7892
THERMO KING CONTAINER TEMPERATURE CONTROL (SUZHOU) CORPORATION LTD.—See Trane Technologies Plc; *Int'l*, pg. 7892
THERMO KING CORPORATION—See Trane Technologies Plc; *Int'l*, pg. 7891
THERMO KING CORPORATION—See Trane Technologies Plc; *Int'l*, pg. 7892
THERMO KING CORP.—See Trane Technologies Plc; *Int'l*, pg. 7892
THERMO KING DE PUERTO RICO—See Trane Technologies Plc; *Int'l*, pg. 7892
THERMO KING DO BRASIL, LTDA.—See Trane Technologies Plc; *Int'l*, pg. 7892
THERMO KING ENTERPRISES COMPANY—See Trane Technologies Plc; *Int'l*, pg. 7892
THERMO KING EUROPEAN MANUFACTURING LIMITED—See Trane Technologies Plc; *Int'l*, pg. 7892
THERMO KING INDIA PRIVATE LIMITED—See Trane Technologies Plc; *Int'l*, pg. 7892
THERMO KING INGERSOLL RAND SVENSKA AB—See Trane Technologies Plc; *Int'l*, pg. 7892
THERMO KING IRELAND LIMITED—See Trane Technologies Plc; *Int'l*, pg. 7892
THERMO KING MARITIMES INC.—See Trane Technologies Plc; *Int'l*, pg. 7892
THERMO KING MONTREAL INC.—See Trane Technologies Plc; *Int'l*, pg. 7892
THERMO KING OF HOUSTON, LP—See Kirby Corporation; *U.S. Public*, pg. 1235
THERMO KING OF INDIANA INC.; *U.S. Private*, pg. 4142
THERMO KING ONTARIO INC.—See Trane Technologies Plc; *Int'l*, pg. 7892
THERMO KING QUAD CITIES INC.; *U.S. Private*, pg. 4142
THERMO KING SALES & SERVICE, INC.; *U.S. Private*, pg. 4143

THERMO KING SERVICES LIMITED—See Trane Technologies Plc; *Int'l*, pg. 7892
THERMO KING SVC, INC.—See Trane Technologies Plc; *Int'l*, pg. 7892
THERMO KING TRANSPORTKOELING B.V.—See Trane Technologies Plc; *Int'l*, pg. 7892
THERMO KING WESTERN INC.; *Int'l*, pg. 7708
THERMOKON SENSORTECHNIK GMBH; *Int'l*, pg. 7708
THERMO LIFE SCIENCES AB—See Thermo Fisher Scientific Inc.; *U.S. Public*, pg. 2152
THERM-O-LINK INC.; *U.S. Private*, pg. 4142
THERMOLITH S.A.—See Viohalco SA/NV; *Int'l*, pg. 8244
THERMO LUXEMBOURG HOLDING S.A.R.L.—See Thermo Fisher Scientific Inc.; *U.S. Public*, pg. 2154
THERMOMED VERWALTUNGS GMBH—See Osterreichische Post AG; *Int'l*, pg. 5654
THERMONAMIC ELECTRONICS(JIANGXI) CORP., LTD.—See Jiangxi Copper Company Limited; *Int'l*, pg. 3959
THERMON AUSTRALIA PTY. LTD.—See Thermon Group Holdings, Inc.; *U.S. Public*, pg. 2155
THERMON BENELUX B.V.—See Thermon Group Holdings, Inc.; *U.S. Public*, pg. 2155
THERMON DEUTSCHLAND GMBH—See Thermon Group Holdings, Inc.; *U.S. Public*, pg. 2155
THERMO NESLAB LLC—See Thermo Fisher Scientific Inc.; *U.S. Public*, pg. 2154
THERMON EUROPE B.V.—See Thermon Group Holdings, Inc.; *U.S. Public*, pg. 2155
THERMON FAR EAST, LTD.—See Thermon Group Holdings, Inc.; *U.S. Public*, pg. 2155
THERMON FRANCE SAS—See Thermon Group Holdings, Inc.; *U.S. Public*, pg. 2155
THERMON GROUP HOLDINGS, INC.; *U.S. Public*, pg. 2155
THERMON HEATING SYSTEMS, INC.—See Thermon Group Holdings, Inc.; *U.S. Public*, pg. 2155
THERMON HEAT TRACERS PVT. LTD.—See Thermon Group Holdings, Inc.; *U.S. Public*, pg. 2155
THERMON HEAT TRACING SERVICES-I, INC.—See Thermon Group Holdings, Inc.; *U.S. Public*, pg. 2155
THERMONICS, INC.—See inTEST Corporation; *U.S. Public*, pg. 1159
THERMON INDUSTRIES, INC.—See Thermon Group Holdings, Inc.; *U.S. Public*, pg. 2155
THERMO NITON ANALYZERS LLC—See Thermo Fisher Scientific Inc.; *U.S. Public*, pg. 2154
THERMON KOREA, LTD.—See Thermon Group Holdings, Inc.; *U.S. Public*, pg. 2155
THERMON LATINOAMERICANA, S. DE R.L. DE C.V.—See Thermon Group Holdings, Inc.; *U.S. Public*, pg. 2155
THERMON MANUFACTURING COMPANY—See Thermon Group Holdings, Inc.; *U.S. Public*, pg. 2155
THERMON MIDDLE EAST, WLL—See Thermon Group Holdings, Inc.; *U.S. Public*, pg. 2155
THERMON SOLUCOES DE AQUECIMENTO LTDA.—See Thermon Group Holdings, Inc.; *U.S. Public*, pg. 2155
THERMON SOUTH AFRICA PTY. LTD.—See Thermon Group Holdings, Inc.; *U.S. Public*, pg. 2155
THERMON U.K. LTD.—See Thermon Group Holdings, Inc.; *U.S. Public*, pg. 2155
THERMO OPTEK S.A.—See Thermo Fisher Scientific Inc.; *U.S. Public*, pg. 2154
THERMOPAC (PTY) LTD—See Berry Global Group, Inc; *U.S. Public*, pg. 324
THERMOPAL-FIDERISSPAN AG—See Pfleiderer GmbH; *Int'l*, pg. 5836
THERMOPATCH B.V.—See Avery Dennison Corporation; *U.S. Public*, pg. 245
THERMOPATCH (CANADA) INC.—See Avery Dennison Corporation; *U.S. Public*, pg. 245
THERMOPATCH CORPORATION; *U.S. Private*, pg. 4143
THERMOPATCH DEUTSCHLAND GMBH—See Avery Dennison Corporation; *U.S. Public*, pg. 245
THERMOPATCH UK LTD.—See Avery Dennison Corporation; *U.S. Public*, pg. 245
THERMOPLASTICS ENGINEERING CORPORATION—See Broomfield Laboratories Inc.; *U.S. Private*, pg. 665
THERMOPLASTIC SERVICES INC.—See Netrix LLC; *U.S. Private*, pg. 2888
THERMOPLAST NEXTRUSIONS LIMITED; *Int'l*, pg. 7708
THERMOPLAST BRASIL SISTEMAS DE INJECAO LTDA—See Barnes Group Inc.; *U.S. Public*, pg. 278
THERMOPLAY DEUTSCHLAND GMBH—See Barnes Group Inc.; *U.S. Public*, pg. 278
THERMOPLAY HOT RUNNER SYSTEMS (BEIJING) CO. LTD—See Barnes Group Inc.; *U.S. Public*, pg. 278
THERMOPLAY INDIA PRIVATE LIMITED—See Barnes Group Inc.; *U.S. Public*, pg. 278
THERMOPLAY PORTUGAL UNIPESSOAL LDA—See Barnes Group Inc.; *U.S. Public*, pg. 278
THERMOPLAY S.P.A.—See Barnes Group Inc.; *U.S. Public*, pg. 278
THERMOPLAY U.K. LTD.—See Barnes Group Inc.; *U.S. Public*, pg. 278
THERMOPOL KUNSTSTOFTECHNIEK B.V.—See Nimbus B.V.; *Int'l*, pg. 5296

COMPANY NAME INDEX — THINK INK, INC.

THERMOPOL KUNSTSTOFTECHNIEK NV—See Nimbus B.V.; *Int'l*, pg. 5296
THERMO PRODUCTS, LLC—See Burnham Holdings, Inc.; *U.S. Public*, pg. 412
THERMO PROJECTS LIMITED—See Thermo Fisher Scientific Inc.; *U.S. Public*, pg. 2154
THERMOPYLAE SCIENCES + TECHNOLOGY—See Hexagon AB; *Int'l*, pg. 3369
THERMO RADIOMETRIE LIMITED—See Thermo Fisher Scientific Inc.; *U.S. Public*, pg. 2154
THERMO RAMSEY ITALIA S.R.L.—See Thermo Fisher Scientific Inc.; *U.S. Public*, pg. 2154
THERMO RAMSEY S.A.—See Thermo Fisher Scientific Inc.; *U.S. Public*, pg. 2154
THERMO REFRIGERATION SAS—See VINCI S.A.; *Int'l*, pg. 8229
THERMORETEC CORP.; *U.S. Private*, pg. 4143
THERMOR—See Atlantic Societe Francaise Develop Thermique S.A.; *Int'l*, pg. 675
THERMOSAFE BRANDS EUROPE LTD.—See Sonoco Products Company; *U.S. Public*, pg. 1909
THERMOSAFE BRANDS—See Sonoco Products Company; *U.S. Public*, pg. 1905
THERMOS (CHINA) HOUSEWARES CO. LTD.—See Thermos L.L.C.; *U.S. Private*, pg. 4143
THERMO SCIENTIFIC MICROBIOLOGY PTE LTD.—See Thermo Fisher Scientific Inc.; *U.S. Public*, pg. 2154
THERMO SCIENTIFIC PORTABLE ANALYTICAL INSTRUMENTS INC—See Thermo Fisher Scientific Inc.; *U.S. Public*, pg. 2154
THERMO SCIENTIFIC SERVICES, INC.—See Thermo Fisher Scientific Inc.; *U.S. Public*, pg. 2154
THERMOSEAL INDUSTRIES, LLC—See Audax Group, Limited Partnership; *U.S. Private*, pg. 386
THERMOSET INC.; *U.S. Private*, pg. 4143
THERMOSET TECHNOLOGIES (MIDDLE EAST) LLC—See Dubai Investments PJSC; *Int'l*, pg. 2219
THERMO SHANDON INC.—See Thermo Fisher Scientific Inc.; *U.S. Public*, pg. 2154
THERMOS HONG KONG LTD.—See Thermos L.L.C.; *U.S. Private*, pg. 4143
THERMOS K.K.—See Thermos L.L.C.; *U.S. Private*, pg. 4143
THERMOS L.L.C.; *U.S. Private*, pg. 4143
THERMOS PTY, LTD.—See Thermos L.L.C.; *U.S. Private*, pg. 4143
THERMOS RIVE NORD INC.; *Int'l*, pg. 7708
THERMOS (SINGAPORE) PTE LTD—See Thermos L.L.C.; *U.S. Private*, pg. 4143
THERMO-TECH PREMIUM WINDOWS & DOORS, INC.; *U.S. Private*, pg. 4143
THERMOTEC WEILBURG GMBH & CO. KG—See ESPEC Corp.; *Int'l*, pg. 2505
THERMOTEK, INC.—See Havencrest Capital Management, LLC; *U.S. Private*, pg. 1880
THERMO TELECOM PARTNERS, LLC; *U.S. Private*, pg. 4143
THERMOTEX NAGEL GMBH; *Int'l*, pg. 7708
THERMOTRAFFIC GMBH—See Nichirei Corporation; *Int'l*, pg. 5270
THERMOTRAFFIC HOLLAND B.V.—See Nichirei Corporation; *Int'l*, pg. 5270
THERMOTRON INDUSTRIES—See Venturedyne, Ltd.; *U.S. Private*, pg. 4358
THERMO-TWIN INDUSTRIES INC.; *U.S. Private*, pg. 4143
THERMOWATT PROFESSIONAL S.R.L.—See Ariston Holding N.V.; *Int'l*, pg. 567
THERMOX PERFORMANCE MATERIALS LTD.—See Amalgamated Metal Corporation PLC; *Int'l*, pg. 409
THERMOX ZINNOXIDE GMBH—See Amalgamated Metal Corporation PLC; *Int'l*, pg. 408
THERMOZELL ENTWICKLUNGS- UND VERTRIEBS GMBH—See Hirsch Servo AG; *Int'l*, pg. 3406
THERMTEC LTD—See NIBE Industrier AB; *Int'l*, pg. 5263
THERMWELL PRODUCTS CO., INC.; *U.S. Private*, pg. 4143
THERMWOOD CORPORATION; *U.S. Private*, pg. 4143
THERON RESOURCE GROUP; *Int'l*, pg. 7708
THEROX, INC.—See Asahi Kasei Corporation; *Int'l*, pg. 597
THESEUS PHARMACEUTICALS, INC.—See Concentra Biosciences, LLC; *U.S. Private*, pg. 1008
THESIA S.P.A.—See Cassa Depositi e Prestiti S.p.A.; *Int'l*, pg. 1354
THESIS, INC.; *U.S. Private*, pg. 4143
THESMIA S.A.—See Premia Real Estate Investment Company; *Int'l*, pg. 5959
THESPAC S.P.A.; *Int'l*, pg. 7708
THESSALONIKI CONTROLLED PARKING SYSTEM S.A.—See Intracom Holdings S.A.; *Int'l*, pg. 3768
THESSALONIKI PORT AUTHORITY S.A.; *Int'l*, pg. 7708
THESSALONIKI WATER SUPPLY & SEWERAGE CO. S.A.; *Int'l*, pg. 7708
THESSALY COTTON GINNING S.A—See Hellenic Fabrics S.A.; *Int'l*, pg. 3333
THESTREET.COM RATINGS, INC.—See The Arena Group Holdings, Inc; *U.S. Public*, pg. 2035
THESTREET, INC.—See The Arena Group Holdings, Inc; *U.S. Public*, pg. 2035

THETA EDGE BERHAD—See Lembaga Tabung Haji; *Int'l*, pg. 4449
THETA GOLD MINES LIMITED; *Int'l*, pg. 7708
THETA INDUSTRIES LTD.; *Int'l*, pg. 7708
THETFORD B.V.—See The Dyson-Kissner-Moran Corporation; *U.S. Private*, pg. 4024
THETFORD CORP. MANUFACTURING FACILITY—See The Dyson-Kissner-Moran Corporation; *U.S. Private*, pg. 4024
THETFORD CORPORATION—See The Dyson-Kissner-Moran Corporation; *U.S. Private*, pg. 4024
THETFORD CORP. - WAREHOUSING DIV—See The Dyson-Kissner-Moran Corporation; *U.S. Private*, pg. 4024
THEUT PRODUCTS INC.; *U.S. Private*, pg. 4143
THEVENIN SA; *Int'l*, pg. 7708
THEWEBDIGEST CORP.; *U.S. Private*, pg. 4143
THEWORKS.CO.UK PLC; *Int'l*, pg. 7708
THEXTON MANUFACTURING COMPANY, INC.; *U.S. Private*, pg. 4144
THEY INTEGRATED INC.; *Int'l*, pg. 7708
TH FOODS, INC.—See Kameda Seika Co., Ltd.; *Int'l*, pg. 4061
TH FOODS, INC.—See Mitsubishi Corporation; *Int'l*, pg. 4941
THG - BAUGESELLSCHAFT MBH—See VINCI S.A.; *Int'l*, pg. 8229
THG HOLDINGS PLC; *Int'l*, pg. 7708
THG HOLIDAYS LIMITED—See TUI AG; *Int'l*, pg. 7966
T&H GLOBAL HOLDINGS, LLC—See The Carlyle Group Inc.; *U.S. Public*, pg. 2054
THHEAVY ENGINEERING BERHAD; *Int'l*, pg. 7708
TH HEAVY ENGINEERING BHD; *Int'l*, pg. 7588
THHE FABRICATORS SDN. BHD.—See THHeavy Engineering Berhad; *Int'l*, pg. 7708
T.H. HIN HOME TECH SDN. BHD.—See Milux Corporation Berhad; *Int'l*, pg. 4897
THIBAULT BERGERON S A; *Int'l*, pg. 7709
THIBAUT, INC.—See The Riverside Company; *U.S. Private*, pg. 4110
THIBIANT INTERNATIONAL INC.—See Novacap Management Inc.; *Int'l*, pg. 5454
THIBODEAU PHYSICAL THERAPY, LIMITED PARTNERSHIP—See U.S. Physical Therapy, Inc.; *U.S. Public*, pg. 2216
THIELE KAOLIN COMPANY; *U.S. Private*, pg. 4144
THIELEN IDEACORP.; *U.S. Private*, pg. 4144
THIELE TECHNOLOGIES, INC.—See Barry-Wehmiller Companies, Inc.; *U.S. Private*, pg. 482
THIELE TECHNOLOGIES - REEDLEY—See Barry-Wehmiller Companies, Inc.; *U.S. Private*, pg. 482
THIELMANN ENERGIETECHNIK GMBH—See Itron, Inc.; *U.S. Public*, pg. 1176
THIELSCH ENGINEERING, INC.; *U.S. Private*, pg. 4144
THIEME INTERNATIONAL; *Int'l*, pg. 7709
THIEME MEDICAL AND SCIENTIFIC PUBLISHERS PRIVATE LIMITED—See Thieme International; *Int'l*, pg. 7709
THIEME MEDICAL PUBLISHERS, INC.—See Thieme International; *Int'l*, pg. 7709
THIENDORFER FRASDIENST GMBH & CO. KG—See L. Possehl & Co. mbH; *Int'l*, pg. 4385
THIENEMANN VERLAG GMBH—See Bonnier AB; *Int'l*, pg. 1108
THIEN HA KAMEDA JSC—See Kameda Seika Co., Ltd.; *Int'l*, pg. 4061
THIEN LONG GROUP CORPORATION; *Int'l*, pg. 7709
THIEN NAM CONFECTIONERY CO., LTD.—See Thien Nam Trading Import Export Corporation; *Int'l*, pg. 7709
THIEN NAM EDUCATION INVESTMENT CORPORATION—See Thien Nam Trading Import Export Corporation; *Int'l*, pg. 7709
THIEN NAM TRADING IMPORT EXPORT CORPORATION; *Int'l*, pg. 7709
THIEN QUANG GROUP JOINT STOCK COMPANY; *Int'l*, pg. 7709
THIENSURAT PUBLIC COMPANY LIMITED; *Int'l*, pg. 7709
THIERICA EQUIPMENT CORPORATION—See THI Inc.; *U.S. Private*, pg. 4144
THIERRY MUGLER PARFUMS—See L'Oreal S.A.; *Int'l*, pg. 4381
THIERRY PREVENT DEVELOPMENT PARIZ S.A.—See Prevent DEV GmbH; *Int'l*, pg. 5968
THIESS PTY. LIMITED—See ACS, Actividades de Construccion y Servicios, S.A.; *Int'l*, pg. 113
THIESS PTY. LIMITED—See Elliott Management Corporation; *U.S. Private*, pg. 1365
THIES & TALLE MANAGEMENT CO.; *U.S. Private*, pg. 4144
T.H.I. GROUP (CAMBODIA) CO., LTD.—See T3EX Global Holdings Corp.; *Int'l*, pg. 7398
T.H.I. GROUP LIMITED—See T3EX Global Holdings Corp.; *Int'l*, pg. 7398
T.H.I. GROUP (SHANGHAI) LTD.—See T3EX Global Holdings Corp.; *Int'l*, pg. 7398
T.H.I. GROUP SINGAPORE PTE. LTD.—See T3EX Global Holdings Corp.; *Int'l*, pg. 7398

T.H.I. GROUP VIETNAM CO., LTD.—See T3EX Global Holdings Corp.; *Int'l*, pg. 7398
THIIM A/S—See Addtech AB; *Int'l*, pg. 135
THI INC.; *U.S. Private*, pg. 4144
THI INVESTMENTS GMBH; *Int'l*, pg. 7708
T.H.I. JAPAN CO., LTD.—See T3EX Global Holdings Corp.; *Int'l*, pg. 7398
THILAWA GLOBAL LOGISTICS CO., LTD.—See Kamigumi Co., Ltd.; *Int'l*, pg. 4063
T.H.I. LOGISTICS (HONG KONG) CO., LIMITED—See T3EX Global Holdings Corp.; *Int'l*, pg. 7398
T.H.I. LOGISTICS (MALAYSIA) SDN. BHD.—See T3EX Global Holdings Corp.; *Int'l*, pg. 7398
T.H.I. LOGISTICS PHILIPPINES CORP.—See T3EX Global Holdings Corp.; *Int'l*, pg. 7398
T.H.I. & MARUZEN CO., LTD.—See T3EX Global Holdings Corp.; *Int'l*, pg. 7398
THE THINC GROUP—See Hakuhodo DY Holdings Incorporated; *Int'l*, pg. 3222
THINE ELECTRONICS, INC.; *Int'l*, pg. 7709
THINE ELECTRONICS SHENZHEN CO., LTD.—See THine Electronics, Inc.; *Int'l*, pg. 7709
THINE ELECTRONICS TAIWAN, INC.—See THine Electronics, Inc.; *Int'l*, pg. 7709
THIN FILM EQUIPMENT S.R.L.—See Plasma-Therm, LLC; *U.S. Private*, pg. 3198
THINFLEX CORP.—See Arisawa Manufacturing Co., Ltd.; *Int'l*, pg. 566
THING 5, LLC—See TZP Group LLC; *U.S. Private*, pg. 4269
THINGAP HOLDINGS, LLC—See Sensata Technologies Holding plc; *U.S. Public*, pg. 1866
THINGAP, INC.—See Allient Inc.; *U.S. Public*, pg. 81
THINGMAGIC INC.—See Novanta Inc.; *U.S. Public*, pg. 1548
THING ON ENTERPRISE LIMITED; *Int'l*, pg. 7709
THINGS REMEMBERED, INC.—See Gordon Brothers Group, LLC; *U.S. Private*, pg. 1742
THINGWORX, INC.—See PTC Inc.; *U.S. Public*, pg. 1735
THINK2ACT PARTNERS BVBA; *Int'l*, pg. 7709
THINK360 AI, INC.—See Computer Age Management Services Limited; *Int'l*, pg. 1759
THINKAES, INC.—See The AES Corporation; *U.S. Public*, pg. 2032
THINKAGENT CORPORATION—See World Co., Ltd.; *Int'l*, pg. 8457
THINK ANALYTICS INDIA PRIVATE LIMITED—See Computer Age Management Services Limited; *Int'l*, pg. 1759
THINKBDW LTD—See The Mission Group Public Limited Company; *Int'l*, pg. 7667
THINK BEYOND MEDIA LIMITED—See The Rank Group Plc; *Int'l*, pg. 7678
THINK BIG ANALYTICS, INC.—See Teradata Corporation; *U.S. Public*, pg. 2017
THINK BROWNSTONE INC.; *U.S. Private*, pg. 4144
THINK CHILDCARE LIMITED—See Ontario Teachers' Pension Plan; *Int'l*, pg. 5587
THINK COFFEE KOREA—See Seoul Food Industrial. Co., Ltd.; *Int'l*, pg. 6716
THINK: COLLEGES PTY LTD—See Strategic Education, Inc.; *U.S. Public*, pg. 1954
THINKDIRECT MARKETING GROUP, INC.—See Blackstreet Capital Management, LLC; *U.S. Private*, pg. 577
THINK: EDUCATION GROUP PTY LIMITED—See KKR & Co. Inc.; *U.S. Public*, pg. 1259
THINK: EDUCATION SERVICES PTY LIMITED—See KKR & Co. Inc.; *U.S. Public*, pg. 1259
THINK ELEVATION CAPITAL GROWTH OPPORTUNITIES; *U.S. Public*, pg. 2155
THINKER AGRICULTURAL MACHINERY CO., LTD.; *Int'l*, pg. 7709
THINKETHBANK CO., LTD.—See Bain Capital, LP; *U.S. Private*, pg. 435
THINKFARM PTE LTD—See Kingsmen Creatives Ltd; *Int'l*, pg. 4176
THINK FINANCE, INC.; *U.S. Private*, pg. 4144
THINK FITNESS CO., LTD.; *Int'l*, pg. 7709
THINKFUL, INC.—See Chegg Inc.; *U.S. Public*, pg. 483
THINKFUN, INC.—See Ravensburger AG; *Int'l*, pg. 6222
THINKGEEK, INC.—See GameStop Corp.; *U.S. Public*, pg. 896
THINKIFIC LABS INC.; *Int'l*, pg. 7709
THINK! INC.; *U.S. Private*, pg. 4144
THINKINGBOX MEDIA & DESIGN, INC.; *Int'l*, pg. 7709
THINKINGDOM MEDIA GROUP LTD.; *Int'l*, pg. 7710
THINKING (CHANGZHOU) ELECTRONIC CO., LTD.—See Thinking Electronic Industrial Co., Ltd.; *Int'l*, pg. 7709
THINKING ELECTRONIC INDUSTRIAL CO., LTD. - CHANGZHOU FACTORY—See Thinking Electronic Industrial Co., Ltd.; *Int'l*, pg. 7709
THINKING ELECTRONIC INDUSTRIAL CO., LTD. - KAOHSIUNG FACTORY—See Thinking Electronic Industrial Co., Ltd.; *Int'l*, pg. 7709
THINKING ELECTRONIC INDUSTRIAL CO., LTD.; *Int'l*, pg. 7709
THINKING GREEN; *U.S. Private*, pg. 4144
THINKING JUICE LTD.—See Sideshow Ltd.; *Int'l*, pg. 6883
THINKINGMAN.COM NEW MEDIA; *U.S. Private*, pg. 4144
THINK INK, INC.; *U.S. Private*, pg. 4144

THINK INK MARKETING & DIRECT MAIL SERVICES, INC.　　　　　CORPORATE AFFILIATIONS

THINK INK MARKETING & DIRECT MAIL SERVICES, INC.; *U.S. Private*, pg. 4144
THINKINK PICTUREZ LIMITED; *Int'l*, pg. 7710
THINK LIMITED—See EPAM Systems, Inc.; *U.S. Public*, pg. 783
THINKLOGICAL, LLC—See Belden, Inc.; *U.S. Public*, pg. 294
THINKME FINANCE PTY. LTD.—See Collection House Limited; *Int'l*, pg. 1699
THINKON SEMICONDUCTOR JINZHOU CORP.; *Int'l*, pg. 7710
THINKORSWIM—See The Charles Schwab Corporation; *U.S. Public*, pg. 2058
THINKPATH INC.; *U.S. Private*, pg. 4144
THINK RESEARCH CORPORATION—See Beedie Capital Partners; *Int'l*, pg. 939
THINK SILICON RESEARCH & TECHNOLOGY SINGLE MEMBER S.A.—See Applied Materials, Inc.; *U.S. Public*, pg. 172
THINK SILICON SINGLE MEMBER P.C.—See Applied Materials, Inc.; *U.S. Public*, pg. 172
THINKSMART LIMITED; *Int'l*, pg. 7710
THINKSMART LLC—See Ontario Teachers' Pension Plan; *Int'l*, pg. 5586
THE THINK TANK; *U.S. Private*, pg. 4126
THE THINK TANK—See The Think Tank; *U.S. Private*, pg. 4126
THE THINK TANK—See The Think Tank; *U.S. Private*, pg. 4126
THINKTECH, INC.—See The Charles Schwab Corporation; *U.S. Public*, pg. 2058
THINKTEL COMMUNICATIONS LTD.—See Distributel Communications Limited; *Int'l*, pg. 2136
THINKTRON LIMITED—See Japan Display Inc.; *Int'l*, pg. 3888
THINKWARE JAPAN CO., LTD.—See UbiVelox Co., Ltd.; *Int'l*, pg. 8004
THINKWARE SYSTEMS CORPORATION; *Int'l*, pg. 7710
THINKWAY TOYS—See Thinkway Trading Corporation; *Int'l*, pg. 7710
THINKWAY TRADING CORPORATION; *Int'l*, pg. 7710
THINKWELL GROUP, INC.—See Tait Towers Inc.; *U.S. Private*, pg. 3925
THINMANAGER—See Rockwell Automation, Inc.; *U.S. Public*, pg. 1807
THINSOLUTIONS; *U.S. Private*, pg. 4144
THINSPACE TECHNOLOGY, INC.; *U.S. Public*, pg. 2155
THINTECH MATERIALS TECHNOLOGY CO., LTD.; *Int'l*, pg. 7710
TH INTERNATIONAL LIMITED; *Int'l*, pg. 7588
TH INVERSIONES MEXICO, S.A. DE C.V.—See Temasek Holdings (Private) Limited; *Int'l*, pg. 7554
THIN-WALL, LLC—See Owens Corning; *U.S. Public*, pg. 1628
THINXXS MICROTECHNOLOGY AG—See IDEX Corp.; *U.S. Public*, pg. 1092
THIOGENESIS THERAPEUTICS, CORP.; *Int'l*, pg. 7710
THIOLAT PACKAGING SA—See Groupe Guillin SA; *Int'l*, pg. 3104
THIOLAT SAS—See Groupe Guillin SA; *Int'l*, pg. 3104
THIONVILLE LABORATORIES INC.; *U.S. Private*, pg. 4144
THIPCHALOTHORN CO., LTD.—See Thai Beverage Public Company Limited; *Int'l*, pg. 7592
THIRANI PROJECTS LIMITED; *Int'l*, pg. 7710
THIRA UTECH CO., LTD.; *Int'l*, pg. 7710
THIRD AVENUE MANAGEMENT LLC—See Quaestus Holdings, LLC; *U.S. Private*, pg. 3316
THIRD CANADIAN GENERAL INVESTMENT TRUST LIMITED—See Morgan Meighen & Associates Limited; *Int'l*, pg. 5044
THIRD CENTURY BANCORP; *U.S. Public*, pg. 2155
THIRD COAST BANCSHARES, INC.; *U.S. Public*, pg. 2155
THIRD COAST BANK, SSB—See Third Coast Bancshares, Inc.; *U.S. Public*, pg. 2155
THIRD COAST COMMERCIAL CAPITAL, INC.—See Third Coast Bancshares, Inc.; *U.S. Public*, pg. 2155
THIRD COAST MIDSTREAM, LLC—See ArcLight Capital Holdings, LLC; *U.S. Private*, pg. 312
THIRD COST TERMINALS; *U.S. Private*, pg. 4145
THIRD DOOR MEDIA INC.; *U.S. Private*, pg. 4145
THIRD ELEMENT AVIATION GMBH—See Hamburger Hafen und Logistik AG; *Int'l*, pg. 3237
THIRDEYE SYSTEMS LTD.; *Int'l*, pg. 7710
THIRD FEDERAL SAVINGS & LOAN ASSOCIATION OF CLEVELAND—See TFS Financial Corporation; *U.S. Public*, pg. 2029
THIRD FINANCIAL SOFTWARE LIMITED—See Grafton Capital Limited; *Int'l*, pg. 3050
THIRD HARMONIC BIO, INC.; *U.S. Public*, pg. 2155
THIRD LAW SOURCING; *U.S. Private*, pg. 4145
THIRD LEAF PARTNERS; *U.S. Private*, pg. 4145
THE THIRD NATIONAL BANK OF SEDALIA—See Central Bancompany, Inc.; *U.S. Public*, pg. 473
THIRD PARTY PLATFORM PTY LTD—See Bell Financial Group Limited; *Int'l*, pg. 966
THIRD PLANET WINDPOWER, LLC—See Morgan Stanley; *U.S. Public*, pg. 1475

THIRD POINT INVESTORS LTD.; *Int'l*, pg. 7710
THIRD POINT LLC; *U.S. Private*, pg. 4145
THIRD SECTOR NEW ENGLAND, INC.; *U.S. Private*, pg. 4145
THIRD SECURITY, LLC; *U.S. Private*, pg. 4145
THIRD SUN SOLAR & WIND POWER, LTD.; *U.S. Private*, pg. 4145
THIRD WAVE AGBIO, INC.—See Hologic, Inc.; *U.S. Public*, pg. 1045
THIRDWAVE FINANCIAL INTERMEDIARIES LIMITED; *Int'l*, pg. 7710
THIRD WAVE RESEARCH GROUP, LLC—See Vestar Capital Partners, LLC; *U.S. Private*, pg. 4372
THIRD WAVE SYSTEMS, INC.; *U.S. Private*, pg. 4145
THIRD WAVE TECHNOLOGIES, INC.—See Hologic, Inc.; *U.S. Public*, pg. 1045
THIRIX; *Int'l*, pg. 7710
THIRLBY AUTOMOTIVE INC.; *U.S. Private*, pg. 4145
THIRODE GRANDES CUISINES POLIGNY SAS—See Illinois Tool Works Inc.; *U.S. Public*, pg. 1111
THIRO LTEE.—See Brookfield Corporation; *Int'l*, pg. 1181
THIRSTY BEAR BREWING CO. LLC; *U.S. Private*, pg. 4145
THE THIRTY-EIGHT HUNDRED FUND, LLC—See Wells Fargo & Company; *U.S. Public*, pg. 2345
THIRTYTHREE APAC LIMITED—See Capita plc; *Int'l*, pg. 1308
THIRTY THREE (SHANGHAI) LTD.—See PCCS Group Berhad; *Int'l*, pg. 5767
THIRTYTHREE—See Capita plc; *Int'l*, pg. 1308
THIRTYTHREE USA INC.—See Capita plc; *Int'l*, pg. 1308
THIRU AROORAN SUGARS LIMITED; *Int'l*, pg. 7710
THIRUMALAI CHEMICALS LTD; *Int'l*, pg. 7710
THIS FILM STUDIO PTY. LTD.—See M&C Saatchi plc; *Int'l*, pg. 4611
THIS LIFE, INC.; *U.S. Private*, pg. 4145
THISMOMENT, INC.; *U.S. Private*, pg. 4145
THIS OLD HOUSE MAGAZINE—See Roku, Inc.; *U.S. Public*, pg. 1808
THIS OLD HOUSE VENTURES, LLC—See Roku, Inc.; *U.S. Public*, pg. 1808
THISTLEDOWN RACETRACK, LLC—See Caesars Entertainment, Inc.; *U.S. Public*, pg. 420
THISTLE HOTELS LIMITED—See Hong Leong Investment Holdings Pte. Ltd.; *Int'l*, pg. 3468
THISTLE INSURANCE SERVICES LIMITED—See Apax Partners LLP; *Int'l*, pg. 505
THISWEEK COMMUNITY NEWS—See Gannett Co., Inc.; *U.S. Public*, pg. 903
THITIKORN PUBLIC COMPANY LIMITED; *Int'l*, pg. 7710
THI VAI INTERNATIONAL PORT COMPANY LIMITED—See Kyoei Steel Ltd.; *Int'l*, pg. 4362
THIXOFORMING LLC—See ARC Group Worldwide, Inc.; *U.S. Public*, pg. 179
THIZ TECHNOLOGY GROUP LIMITED; *Int'l*, pg. 7711
TH. JANSEN-ARMATUREN GMBH—See IMI plc; *Int'l*, pg. 3627
THK AMERICA INC.—See THK CO., LTD.; *Int'l*, pg. 7712
THK BRASIL INDUSTRIA E COMERCIO LTDA.—See THK CO., LTD.; *Int'l*, pg. 7712
THK BRASIL LTDA.—See THK CO., LTD.; *Int'l*, pg. 7712
THK (CHINA) CO., LTD.—See THK CO., LTD.; *Int'l*, pg. 7712
THK CO., LTD. - GIFU PLANT—See THK CO., LTD.; *Int'l*, pg. 7712
THK CO., LTD. - KOFU PLANT—See THK CO., LTD.; *Int'l*, pg. 7712
THK CO., LTD. - MIE PLANT—See THK CO., LTD.; *Int'l*, pg. 7712
THK CO., LTD.; *Int'l*, pg. 7711
THK CO., LTD. - YAMAGATA PLANT—See THK CO., LTD.; *Int'l*, pg. 7712
THK EUROPE B.V.—See THK CO., LTD.; *Int'l*, pg. 7712
THK FRANCE S. A. S.—See THK CO., LTD.; *Int'l*, pg. 7712
THK GMBH—See THK CO., LTD.; *Int'l*, pg. 7712
THK GMBH—See THK CO., LTD.; *Int'l*, pg. 7712
THK INDIA PVT. LTD.—See THK CO., LTD.; *Int'l*, pg. 7712
THK INTECHS CO., LTD.—See THK CO., LTD.; *Int'l*, pg. 7712
THK LM SYSTEM PTE. LTD.—See THK CO., LTD.; *Int'l*, pg. 7712
THK MANUFACTURING OF AMERICA INC.—See THK CO., LTD.; *Int'l*, pg. 7712
THK MANUFACTURING OF CHINA (CHANGZHOU) CO., LTD.—See THK CO., LTD.; *Int'l*, pg. 7713
THK MANUFACTURING OF CHINA (LIAONING) CO., LTD.—See THK CO., LTD.; *Int'l*, pg. 7713
THK MANUFACTURING OF CHINA (WUXI) CO., LTD.—See THK CO., LTD.; *Int'l*, pg. 7713
THK MANUFACTURING OF EUROPE S.A.S.—See THK CO., LTD.; *Int'l*, pg. 7713
THK MANUFACTURING OF IRELAND LTD.—See THK CO., LTD.; *Int'l*, pg. 7713
THK MANUFACTURING OF VIETNAM CO., LTD.—See THK CO., LTD.; *Int'l*, pg. 7713
THK NIIGATA CO., LTD.—See THK CO., LTD.; *Int'l*, pg. 7713

THK RHYTHM AUTOMOTIVE CANADA LIMITED—See THK CO., LTD.; *Int'l*, pg. 7713
THK RHYTHM AUTOMOTIVE CZECH A.S.—See THK CO., LTD.; *Int'l*, pg. 7713
THK RHYTHM AUTOMOTIVE GMBH—See THK CO., LTD.; *Int'l*, pg. 7713
THK RHYTHM AUTOMOTIVE MICHIGAN CORPORATION—See THK CO., LTD.; *Int'l*, pg. 7713
THK RHYTHM CHANGZHOU CO., LTD.—See THK CO., LTD.; *Int'l*, pg. 7713
THK RHYTHM CO., LTD.—See THK CO., LTD.; *Int'l*, pg. 7713
THK RHYTHM GUANGZHOU CO., LTD.—See THK CO., LTD.; *Int'l*, pg. 7713
THK RHYTHM KHUSHU CO., LTD.—See THK CO., LTD.; *Int'l*, pg. 7713
THK RHYTHM MALAYSIA SDN. BHD.—See THK CO., LTD.; *Int'l*, pg. 7713
THK RHYTHM MEXICANA, S.A. DE C.V.—See THK CO., LTD.; *Int'l*, pg. 7713
THK RHYTHM (THAILAND) CO., LTD.—See THK CO., LTD.; *Int'l*, pg. 7713
THK (SHANGHAI) CO., LTD.—See THK CO., LTD.; *Int'l*, pg. 7712
THK TAIWAN CO., LTD.—See THK CO., LTD.; *Int'l*, pg. 7713
THL CREDIT ADVISORS LLC—See Blackstone Inc.; *U.S. Public*, pg. 353
THL CREDIT ADVISORS LLC—See Corsair Capital, LLC; *U.S. Private*, pg. 1059
THL CREDIT SENIOR LOAN FUND; *U.S. Public*, pg. 2156
TH LEE PUTNAM VENTURES; *U.S. Private*, pg. 3979
THL FOUNDATION EQUIPMENT (MYANMAR) COMPANY LIMITED—See CSC Holdings Limited; *Int'l*, pg. 1862
THL FOUNDATION EQUIPMENT (PHILIPPINES) INC.—See CSC Holdings Limited; *Int'l*, pg. 1863
THL FOUNDATION EQUIPMENT PTE. LTD.—See CSC Holdings Limited; *Int'l*, pg. 1863
THL INC.—See Tungtex (Holdings) Co. Ltd.; *Int'l*, pg. 7972
THL VIETNAM COMPANY LIMITED—See CSC Holdings Limited; *Int'l*, pg. 1863
T H MARCH & CO. LIMITED; *Int'l*, pg. 7394
T-H MARINE SUPPLIES INC.; *U.S. Private*, pg. 3910
T.H. MARSH CONSTRUCTION COMPANY; *U.S. Private*, pg. 3912
TH MIDWEST, INC.—See The Kroger Co.; *U.S. Public*, pg. 2109
THN CORPORATION; *Int'l*, pg. 7713
THN PARAGUAY. SA—See THN Corporation; *Int'l*, pg. 7713
THO-CELLO LOGITECH CORPORATION—See Sankyu, Inc.; *Int'l*, pg. 6545
THOELE INC.—See Warrenton Oil Co.; *U.S. Private*, pg. 4444
THOESEN TRACTOR & EQUIPMENT INC.—See Okada Aiyon Corporation; *Int'l*, pg. 5544
THOGUS PRODUCTS COMPANY; *U.S. Private*, pg. 4145
T-HOLDING CO LTD.—See Thai Union Group Public Company Limited; *Int'l*, pg. 7596
THOMA BRAVO ADVANTAGE; *U.S. Public*, pg. 2156
THOMA BRAVO, L.P.; *U.S. Private*, pg. 4145
THOMA INC.; *U.S. Private*, pg. 4154
THOMAS AMM GMBH—See Service Corporation International; *U.S. Public*, pg. 1871
THOMASARTS HOLDING, INC.—See Integrity Marketing Group LLC; *U.S. Private*, pg. 2104
THOMAS BENNETT & HUNTER INC.; *U.S. Private*, pg. 4154
THOMAS BETEILIGUNGEN GMBH; *Int'l*, pg. 7713
THOMAS & BETTS CARIBE, INC.—See ABB Ltd.; *Int'l*, pg. 52
THOMAS & BETTS CORPORATION—See ABB Ltd.; *Int'l*, pg. 52
THOMAS & BETTS POWER SOLUTIONS, LLC—See ABB Ltd.; *Int'l*, pg. 52
THOMAS BORTHWICK & SONS (AUSTRALIA) PTY. LTD.—See NH Foods Ltd.; *Int'l*, pg. 5257
THOMAS BOW LIMITED—See Breedon Group plc; *Int'l*, pg. 1144
THOMAS BROTHERS FOODS, LLC; *U.S. Private*, pg. 4154
THOMAS BROTHERS HAM CO. INC.; *U.S. Private*, pg. 4155
THOMAS BUILT BUSES, INC.—See Mercedes-Benz Group AG; *U.S. Public*, pg. 4823
THOMAS, CARROLL (BROKERS) LIMITED—See Thomas Carroll Group PLC; *Int'l*, pg. 7713
THOMAS CARROLL GROUP PLC; *Int'l*, pg. 7713
THOMAS, CARROLL INDEPENDENT FINANCIAL ADVISERS LIMITED—See Thomas Carroll Group PLC; *Int'l*, pg. 7713
THOMAS CAVANAGH CONSTRUCTION LIMITED; *Int'l*, pg. 7713
THE THOMAS COLACE COMPANY, LLC—See Lipman & Lipman, Inc.; *U.S. Private*, pg. 2465
THOMAS CONSTRUCTION INC.—See True Home Value, Inc.; *U.S. Private*, pg. 4247
THOMAS CONVEYOR COMPANY; *U.S. Private*, pg. 4155

COMPANY NAME INDEX

THOMAS COOK AUSTRIA AG—See Raiffeisen Touristik Group GmbH; *Int'l*, pg. 6185
THOMAS COOK GMBH—See Raiffeisen Touristik Group GmbH; *Int'l*, pg. 6185
THOMAS COOK (INDIA) LIMITED—See Fairfax Financial Holdings Limited; *Int'l*, pg. 2608
THOMAS COOK NORTHERN EUROPE AB; *Int'l*, pg. 7713
THOMAS COOK TOURISTIK GMBH—See Raiffeisen Touristik Group GmbH; *Int'l*, pg. 6185
THOMAS DAILY GMBH—See CoStar Group, Inc.; *U.S. Public*, pg. 586
THOMAS DESIGN BUILDERS LTD.; *Int'l*, pg. 7713
THOMAS DE SUDAMERICA S.A.—See Thyssen'sche Handelsgesellschaft m.b.H.; *Int'l*, pg. 7723
THOMAS D. MANGELSEN, INC.; *U.S. Private*, pg. 4155
THOMAS DURYEA LOGICALIS ASIA PACIFIC MSC SDN. BHD.—See Datatec Limited; *Int'l*, pg. 1981
THOMAS D. WOOD AND COMPANY - SARASOTA—See Thomas D. Wood and Company; *U.S. Private*, pg. 4155
THOMAS D. WOOD AND COMPANY; *U.S. Private*, pg. 4155
THOMAS D. WOOD AND COMPANY—See Thomas D. Wood and Company; *U.S. Private*, pg. 4155
THOMAS D. WOOD AND COMPANY—See Thomas D. Wood and Company; *U.S. Private*, pg. 4155
THOMAS DYNAMIC MATERIAL (JIANGSU) CO., LTD.—See Taiwan Paiho Limited; *Int'l*, pg. 7423
THOMAS ELECTRONICS INC.; *U.S. Private*, pg. 4155
THOMAS ENDUSTRIYEL MEDYA YAYINCILIK VE PAZ. LTD.—See Thomas Publishing Company LLC; *U.S. Private*, pg. 4157
THOMAS ENGINEERING COMPANY; *U.S. Private*, pg. 4155
THOMAS ENGINEERING INC.; *U.S. Private*, pg. 4155
THOMAS ERIE, INC.—See Thyssen'sche Handelsgesellschaft m.b.H.; *Int'l*, pg. 7723
THOMAS E. STRAUSS INC.; *U.S. Private*, pg. 4155
THOMAS FLEURS SA; *Int'l*, pg. 7713
THOMAS FOODS INTERNATIONAL; *Int'l*, pg. 7714
THOMAS FORD SALES INC.; *U.S. Private*, pg. 4155
THOMAS GAS COMPANY—See UGI Corporation; *U.S. Public*, pg. 2222
THOMAS G. GALLAGHER, INC.; *U.S. Private*, pg. 4155
THOMAS GLOVER ASSOCIATES, INC.; *U.S. Private*, pg. 4155
THOMAS GMBH—See Thyssen'sche Handelsgesellschaft m.b.H.; *Int'l*, pg. 7723
THOMAS HAND & REHABILITATION SPECIALISTS, LIMITED PARTNERSHIP—See U.S. Physical Therapy, Inc.; *U.S. Public*, pg. 2216
THOMAS H. BOYD MEMORIAL HOSPITAL; *U.S. Private*, pg. 4155
THOMAS HINE & CIE—See LVMH Moet Hennessy Louis Vuitton SE; *Int'l*, pg. 4600
THOMAS H. LEE PARTNERS, L.P.; *U.S. Private*, pg. 4155
THOMAS HOME HEALTH, LLC—See UnitedHealth Group Incorporated; *U.S. Public*, pg. 2247
THOMAS INDUSTRIAL MEDIA GMBH—See Thomas Publishing Company LLC; *U.S. Private*, pg. 4157
THOMAS INDUSTRIAL MEDIA SARL—See Thomas Publishing Company LLC; *U.S. Private*, pg. 4157
THOMAS INDUSTRIAL MEDIA SRL—See Thomas Publishing Company LLC; *U.S. Private*, pg. 4157
THOMAS INDUSTRIAL NETWORK ADVERTISING—See Thomas Publishing Company LLC; *U.S. Private*, pg. 4157
THOMAS INDUSTRIAL ROLLS, INC.—See Talon Group LLC; *U.S. Private*, pg. 3927
THOMAS INDUSTRIES INC.—See Ingersoll Rand Inc.; *U.S. Public*, pg. 1120
THOMAS INTERIOR SYSTEMS INC.; *U.S. Private*, pg. 4156
THOMAS INTERNATIONAL ADVERTISING CO. (BEIJING), LTD.—See Thomas Publishing Company LLC; *U.S. Private*, pg. 4157
THOMAS INTERNATIONAL PUBLISHING CO. INDIA PRIVATE LIMITED—See Thomas Publishing Company LLC; *U.S. Private*, pg. 4157
THOMAS INTERNATIONAL PUBLISHING COMPANY, INC.—See Thomas Publishing Company LLC; *U.S. Private*, pg. 4157
THOMAS INVESTMENT HOLDINGS, LLC—See Immobiliare Global Investments, Inc.; *U.S. Private*, pg. 2047
THOMAS INVESTMENTS INC.; *U.S. Private*, pg. 4156
THOMAS JAMES HOMES, INC.; *U.S. Private*, pg. 4156
THOMAS JEFFERSON FOUNDATION INC.; *U.S. Private*, pg. 4157
THOMAS J. FINNEGAN COMPANY; *U.S. Private*, pg. 4156
THOMAS J. O'BEIRNE & CO. INC.; *U.S. Private*, pg. 4156
THOMAS JOHNSON SURGERY CENTER, LLC—See UnitedHealth Group Incorporated; *U.S. Public*, pg. 2251
THOMAS J. PAYNE MARKET DEVELOPMENT; *U.S. Private*, pg. 4156

THOMAS J. PAYNE MARKET DEVELOPMENT—See Thomas J. Payne Market Development; *U.S. Private*, pg. 4156
THOMAS J. STEPHENS & ASSOCIATES, INC.—See SGS SA; *Int'l*, pg. 6745
THOMAS KAUBISCH GMBH—See Avnet, Inc.; *U.S. Public*, pg. 254
THOMAS & KING INC.; *U.S. Private*, pg. 4154
THE THOMAS KINKADE COMPANY; *U.S. Private*, pg. 4126
THOMAS L. CARDELLA & ASSOCIATES INC; *U.S. Private*, pg. 4157
THOMAS L. GREEN & COMPANY, INC.—See Markel Group Inc.; *U.S. Public*, pg. 1369
THOMAS/LUND PUBLICACOES INDUSTRIAIS LTDA.—See Thomas Publishing Company LLC; *U.S. Private*, pg. 4157
THOMAS & MARKER CONSTRUCTION COMPANY; *U.S. Private*, pg. 4154
THOMAS, MCNERNEY & PARTNERS II, LLC; *U.S. Private*, pg. 4157
THOMAS MEDIA GROUP, LLC; *U.S. Private*, pg. 4157
THOMAS MEDICAL PRODUCTS, INC.—See Merit Medical Systems, Inc.; *U.S. Public*, pg. 1425
THOMAS MEIKLE CENTRE (PRIVATE) LIMITED—See Meikles Limited; *Int'l*, pg. 4802
THOMAS MENZIES (BUILDERS) LIMITED—See J. Smart & Co. (Contractors) PLC; *Int'l*, pg. 3857
THE THOMAS MONAHAN COMPANY INC.; *U.S. Private*, pg. 4126
THOMAS MOTORS, INC.—See Morse Operations Inc.; *U.S. Private*, pg. 2790
THOMAS M. QUINN & SONS, LLC—See Service Corporation International; *U.S. Public*, pg. 1871
THOMAS NELSON, INC.—See Charlesbank Capital Partners, LLC; *U.S. Private*, pg. 854
THOMAS P. CARNEY INC.; *U.S. Private*, pg. 4157
THOMAS PETROLEUM, INC.; *U.S. Private*, pg. 4157
THOMAS PINK BELGIUM SA—See LVMH Moet Hennessy Louis Vuitton SE; *Int'l*, pg. 4597
THOMAS PINK BV—See LVMH Moet Hennessy Louis Vuitton SE; *Int'l*, pg. 4603
THOMAS PINK FRANCE—See LVMH Moet Hennessy Louis Vuitton SE; *Int'l*, pg. 4597
THOMAS PINK HOLDINGS LTD.—See LVMH Moet Hennessy Louis Vuitton SE; *Int'l*, pg. 4597
THOMAS PINK INC.—See LVMH Moet Hennessy Louis Vuitton SE; *Int'l*, pg. 4597
THOMAS PINK IRELAND LTD.—See LVMH Moet Hennessy Louis Vuitton SE; *Int'l*, pg. 4597
THOMAS PINK LTD.—See LVMH Moet Hennessy Louis Vuitton SE; *Int'l*, pg. 4597
THOMAS PIPE & SUPPLY CO.—See Winsupply, Inc.; *U.S. Private*, pg. 4545
THOMAS PLANT (BIRMINGHAM) LIMITED—See Lifetime Brands, Inc.; *U.S. Public*, pg. 1313
THOMAS P. PAPPAS & ASSOCIATES—See Kelley Cawthorne, LLC; *U.S. Private*, pg. 2275
THOMAS PUBLISHING COMPANY LLC - MADE2SPEC—See Thomas Publishing Company LLC; *U.S. Private*, pg. 4157
THOMAS PUBLISHING COMPANY LLC; *U.S. Private*, pg. 4157
THOMAS RAWLINGS ASSOCIATES—See Thomas Rawlings Group Inc.; *U.S. Private*, pg. 4157
THOMAS RAWLINGS GROUP INC.; *U.S. Private*, pg. 4157
THOMAS REGISTER OF AMERICAN MANUFACTURERS—See Thomas Publishing Company LLC; *U.S. Private*, pg. 4157
THOMAS REGOUT INTERNATIONAL B.V.—See Brd. Klee A/S; *Int'l*, pg. 1143
THOMAS REPROGRAPHICS, INC.; *U.S. Private*, pg. 4157
THOMAS ROAD SENIOR HOUSING, INC.—See The Ensign Group, Inc.; *U.S. Public*, pg. 2072
THOMAS RUTHERFOORD INC.—See Marsh & McLennan Companies, Inc.; *U.S. Public*, pg. 1388
THOMAS SAGAR INSURANCES LIMITED—See Brown & Brown, Inc.; *U.S. Public*, pg. 402
THOMAS SANDERSON; *Int'l*, pg. 7714
THOMAS SCIENTIFIC, LLC; *U.S. Private*, pg. 4157
THOMAS SCOTT (INDIA) LIMITED—See Bang Overseas Ltd.; *Int'l*, pg. 832
THOMASSEN AMCON INTERNATIONAL, LLC; *U.S. Private*, pg. 4158
THOMASSEN ENERGY B.V.—See Cassa Depositi e Prestiti S.p.A.; *Int'l*, pg. 1354
THOMAS SIGN & AWNING CO., INC.; *U.S. Private*, pg. 4158
THOMAS SILVEY LTD.—See Marquard & Bahls AG; *Int'l*, pg. 4701
THOMAS & SKINNER, INC.; *U.S. Private*, pg. 4154
THOMAS SOMERVILLE CO. INC.; *U.S. Private*, pg. 4158
THOMASSON COMPANY; *U.S. Private*, pg. 4158
THOMAS & SONS DISTRIBUTORS; *U.S. Private*, pg. 4154
THOMASSONS.NU GRUPP AB—See LKQ Corporation; *U.S. Public*, pg. 1336

THOMAS STEEL STRIP CORP.—See Tata Sons Limited; *Int'l*, pg. 7473
THOMAS SUPPLY COMPANY INC.; *U.S. Private*, pg. 4158
THOMAS (SUZHOU) METALS CO. LTD.—See Thyssen'sche Handelsgesellschaft m.b.H.; *Int'l*, pg. 7723
THOMASTECH, LLC; *U.S. Private*, pg. 4158
THOMAS TECHNOLOGY SOLUTIONS INC.—See Thomas Publishing Company LLC; *U.S. Private*, pg. 4157
THOMAS TECHNOLOGY SOLUTIONS (UK) LTD.—See Thomas Publishing Company LLC; *U.S. Private*, pg. 4157
THOMAS TITLE & ESCROW, LLC—See Stewart Information Services Corporation; *U.S. Public*, pg. 1948
THOMASTON SAVINGS BANK; *U.S. Private*, pg. 4158
THOMAS TURF SERVICES, INC.—See Labosport SAS; *Int'l*, pg. 4390
THOMASVILLE BANCSHARES, INC.; *U.S. Public*, pg. 2156
THOMASVILLE FORD LINCOLN MERCURY—See Thomasville Toyota Used Cars; *U.S. Private*, pg. 4158
THOMASVILLE FURNITURE INDUSTRIES, INC.—See Heritage Home Group, LLC; *U.S. Private*, pg. 1924
THOMASVILLE HOME FURNISHINGS OF ARIZONA—See Heritage Home Group, LLC; *U.S. Private*, pg. 1924
THOMASVILLE TOYOTA USED CARS; *U.S. Private*, pg. 4158
THOMAS WARBURTON PTY. LTD.—See Wurth Verwaltungsgesellschaft mbH; *Int'l*, pg. 8509
THOMAS WEISEL CAPITAL MANAGEMENT LLC—See Stifel Financial Corp.; *U.S. Public*, pg. 1950
THOMAS WEISEL PARTNERS GROUP, INC.—See Stifel Financial Corp.; *U.S. Public*, pg. 1950
THOMAS WEISEL PARTNERS LLC—See Stifel Financial Corp.; *U.S. Public*, pg. 1950
THOMAS WEST INC.; *U.S. Private*, pg. 4158
THOMAS WOOD PRESERVING INC.; *U.S. Private*, pg. 4158
THOMAS WYATT NIGERIA PLC.; *Int'l*, pg. 7714
THOM BROWNE, INC.—See Investindustrial Acquisition Corp.; *Int'l*, pg. 3779
THOMEE GRUPPEN AB—See Volati AB; *Int'l*, pg. 8301
THOMEKO EESTI OU—See Danish Crown AmbA; *Int'l*, pg. 1964
THOMEKO OY—See Danish Crown AmbA; *Int'l*, pg. 1964
THOMMEN-FURLER AG; *Int'l*, pg. 7714
THOMMEN MEDICAL AG; *Int'l*, pg. 7714
THOMMEN MEDICAL AUSTRIA GMBH—See Thommen Medical AG; *Int'l*, pg. 7714
THOMMEN MEDICAL BENELUX B.V.—See Thommen Medical AG; *Int'l*, pg. 7714
THOMMEN MEDICAL DEUTSCHLAND GMBH—See Thommen Medical AG; *Int'l*, pg. 7714
THOMMEN MEDICAL FRANCE SARL—See Thommen Medical AG; *Int'l*, pg. 7714
THOMMEN MEDICAL USA L.L.C.—See Thommen Medical AG; *Int'l*, pg. 7714
THOMPSON, AHERN & CO. LTD.; *Int'l*, pg. 7714
THOMPSON-ARTHUR PAVING & CONSTRUCTION—See CRH plc; *Int'l*, pg. 1847
THOMPSON AUTOMOTIVE GROUP INC.; *U.S. Private*, pg. 4158
THOMPSON & BENDER LLC; *U.S. Private*, pg. 4158
THOMPSON & BERRY—See Thompson & Company Marketing Communications; *U.S. Private*, pg. 4158
THOMPSON BRANDS LLC; *U.S. Private*, pg. 4158
THOMPSON BROOKS, INCORPORATED; *U.S. Private*, pg. 4158
THOMPSON BROS. (CONSTR.) LP.—See The Hillcore Group; *Int'l*, pg. 7652
THOMPSON BROTHERS INSURANCE CONSULTANTS LIMITED—See Brown & Brown, Inc.; *U.S. Public*, pg. 402
THOMPSON BUILDERS CORPORATION; *U.S. Private*, pg. 4159
THOMPSON & CAPPER LIMITED—See DCC plc; *Int'l*, pg. 1991
THOMPSON CHILD & FAMILY FOCUS; *U.S. Private*, pg. 4159
THOMPSON CIGAR—See Skandinavisk Holding A/S; *Int'l*, pg. 6977
THOMPSON COBB BAZILIO ASSOCIATES PC; *U.S. Private*, pg. 4159
THOMPSON COBURN LLP; *U.S. Private*, pg. 4159
THE THOMPSON COMPANIES; *U.S. Private*, pg. 4126
THOMPSON & COMPANY MARKETING COMMUNICATIONS; *U.S. Private*, pg. 4158
THOMPSON & COMPANY OF TAMPA, INC.—See Skandinavisk Holding A/S; *Int'l*, pg. 6977
THE THOMPSON COMPANY; *U.S. Private*, pg. 4126
THOMPSON & CO. NEW YORK—See Thompson & Co. Public Relations; *U.S. Private*, pg. 4158
THOMPSON CONSTRUCTION GROUP—See Thompson Industrial Services, LLC; *U.S. Private*, pg. 4159
THOMPSON CONSTRUCTION GROUP—See Thompson Industrial Services, LLC; *U.S. Private*, pg. 4159

THOMPSON & CO. PUBLIC RELATIONS — CORPORATE AFFILIATIONS

THOMPSON & CO. PUBLIC RELATIONS; *U.S. Private,* pg. 4158
THOMPSON CREEK METALS COMPANY INC.—See Centerra Gold Inc.; *Int'l,* pg. 1403
THOMPSON CREEK METALS COMPANY USA—See Centerra Gold Inc.; *Int'l,* pg. 1403
THOMPSON CREEK MINING CO.—See Centerra Gold Inc.; *Int'l,* pg. 1403
THOMPSON CREEK WINDOW COMPANY; *U.S. Private,* pg. 4159
THOMPSON DAYTON STEEL SERVICE - PAULDING—See The Thompson Companies; *U.S. Private,* pg. 4126
THOMPSON DAYTON STEEL SERVICE - ROSEVILLE—See The Thompson Companies; *U.S. Private,* pg. 4126
THOMPSON DAYTON STEEL SERVICE—See The Thompson Companies; *U.S. Private,* pg. 4126
THOMPSON DISTRIBUTION COMPANY, INC.; *U.S. Private,* pg. 4159
THOMPSON DISTRIBUTION, LLC; *U.S. Private,* pg. 4159
THOMPSON-DURKEE COMPANY INC.; *U.S. Private,* pg. 4162
THOMPSON ELECTRIC, INC.; *U.S. Private,* pg. 4159
THOMPSON ENERGY; *U.S. Private,* pg. 4159
THOMPSON FABRICATING LLC—See Ligon Industries LLC; *U.S. Private,* pg. 2455
THOMPSON FORD SALES; *Int'l,* pg. 7714
THOMPSON FUNERAL HOME, INC.—See Service Corporation International; *U.S. Public,* pg. 1871
THOMPSON HEATH & BOND LIMITED - EUROPEAN DIVISION—See AmWINS Group, Inc.; *U.S. Private,* pg. 270
THOMPSON HEATH & BOND LIMITED—See AmWINS Group, Inc.; *U.S. Private,* pg. 270
THOMPSON HINE LLP; *U.S. Private,* pg. 4159
THOMPSON HOSPITALITY INC.; *U.S. Private,* pg. 4159
THOMPSON HOTELS LLC—See Commune Hotels & Resorts, LLC; *U.S. Private,* pg. 987
THOMPSON HVAC—See Thompson Industrial Services, LLC; *U.S. Private,* pg. 4159
THOMPSON INDUSTRIAL SERVICES, LLC; *U.S. Private,* pg. 4159
THOMPSON INDUSTRIAL SUPPLY INC.; *U.S. Private,* pg. 4160
THOMPSON INDUSTRIAL SUPPLY—See Thompson Industrial Services, LLC; *U.S. Private,* pg. 4159
THOMPSON INSURANCE ENTERPRISES, LLC—See Markel Group Inc.; *U.S. Public,* pg. 1368
THOMPSON INSURANCE GROUP; *U.S. Private,* pg. 4160
THOMPSON INTERNATIONAL INC.; *U.S. Private,* pg. 4160
THOMPSON & JOHNSON EQUIPMENT CO.; *U.S. Private,* pg. 4158
THOMPSON KENYA LTD.—See WPP plc; *Int'l,* pg. 8482
THOMPSON & KNIGHT LLP—See Holland & Knight LLP; *U.S. Private,* pg. 1964
THOMPSON MACHINERY COMMERCE CORPORATION; *U.S. Private,* pg. 4160
THOMPSON MACHINES—See Burlington Basket Co.; *U.S. Private,* pg. 689
THOMPSON MARKETING; *U.S. Private,* pg. 4160
THOMPSON MEDIA GROUP LLC; *U.S. Private,* pg. 4160
THOMPSON MEDICAL & CHIROPRACTIC LLC—See Atlantic Health System Inc.; *U.S. Private,* pg. 373
THOMPSON & MORGAN (UK) LIMITED—See Primary Capital Limited; *Int'l,* pg. 5975
THOMPSON NEPAL PRIVATE LIMITED—See WPP plc; *Int'l,* pg. 8480
THOMPSON PEAK HEALTHCARE LLC—See The Ensign Group, Inc.; *U.S. Public,* pg. 2072
THOMPSON & PECK INC.; *U.S. Private,* pg. 4158
THOMPSON PETROLEUM CORP.; *U.S. Private,* pg. 4160
THOMPSON PRODUCTS, INC.; *U.S. Private,* pg. 4160
THOMPSON PUBLISHING GROUP—See Thompson Media Group LLC; *U.S. Private,* pg. 4160
THOMPSON PUMP AND MANUFACTURING CO., INC.; *U.S. Private,* pg. 4160
THOMPSON REALTY CORPORATION—See The Thompson Company; *U.S. Private,* pg. 4126
THOMPSON SALES CO.; *U.S. Private,* pg. 4160
THOMPSON SCHOOL BOOK DEPOSITORY; *U.S. Private,* pg. 4160
THOMPSONS GATEWAY (PTE) LTD—See Cullinan Holdings Limited; *Int'l,* pg. 1877
THOMPSON'S HONDA; *U.S. Private,* pg. 4162
THOMPSON, SIEGEL & WALMSLEY, LLC—See Perpetual Limited; *Int'l,* pg. 5812
THOMPSONS, KELLY & LEWIS PTY LTD—See Flowserve Corporation; *U.S. Public,* pg. 857
THOMPSONS LIMITED—See The Andersons Incorporated; *U.S. Public,* pg. 2034
THOMPSON'S MOVING & STORAGE; *Int'l,* pg. 7714
THOMPSON STREET CAPITAL MANAGER LLC; *U.S. Private,* pg. 4162
THOMPSONS USA LIMITED—See The Andersons Incorporated; *U.S. Public,* pg. 2035
THOMPSON TECHNOLOGIES, INC.; *U.S. Private,* pg. 4162

THOMPSON THRIFT DEVELOPMENT, INC.; *U.S. Private,* pg. 4162
THOMPSON TOYOTA INC.—See Thompson Automotive Group Inc.; *U.S. Private,* pg. 4158
THOMPSON TRACTOR COMPANY; *U.S. Private,* pg. 4162
THOMPSON TRACTOR COMPANY - THOMPSON TRUCK SOURCE DIVISION—See Thompson Tractor Company; *U.S. Private,* pg. 4162
THOMPSON TRUCK GROUP, LLC—See Thompson Distribution, LLC; *U.S. Private,* pg. 4159
THOMPSON TURNER CONSTRUCTION—See Thompson Industrial Services, LLC; *U.S. Private,* pg. 4160
THOMPSON TURNER CONSTRUCTION—See Thompson Industrial Services, LLC; *U.S. Private,* pg. 4160
THOMPSON TURNER CONSTRUCTION—See Thompson Industrial Services, LLC; *U.S. Private,* pg. 4159
THOMPSON VALVES LTD—See IMI plc; *Int'l,* pg. 3626
THOMSEN GROUP LLC; *U.S. Private,* pg. 4162
THOMSEN & NYBECK, P.A.—See DeWitt Ross & Stevens S.C.; *U.S. Private,* pg. 1219
THOMSON AIRWAYS LIMITED—See TUI AG; *Int'l,* pg. 7968
THOMSON AIRWAYS (SERVICES) LIMITED—See TUI AG; *Int'l,* pg. 7968
THOMSON ANGERS SAS—See Vantiva SA; *Int'l,* pg. 8131
THOMSON BROADCAST SAS—See Arelis SAS; *Int'l,* pg. 558
THOMSON BROTHERS LIMITED—See Ferguson plc; *Int'l,* pg. 2638
THOMSON CORPORATION FINANCIAL—See Thomson Reuters Corporation; *Int'l,* pg. 7716
THOMSON DIRECTORIES LTD.—See Foster Denovo Limited; *Int'l,* pg. 2749
THOMSON ELITE—See Thomson Reuters Corporation; *Int'l,* pg. 7715
THOMSON ELITE—See Thomson Reuters Corporation; *Int'l,* pg. 7715
THOMSON FINANCIAL LTD.—See Thomson Reuters Corporation; *Int'l,* pg. 7716
THOMSON FINANCIAL SA—See Thomson Reuters Corporation; *Int'l,* pg. 7716
THOMSON FINANCIAL S.A.—See Thomson Reuters Corporation; *Int'l,* pg. 7716
THOMSON FINANCIAL—See Thomson Reuters Corporation; *Int'l,* pg. 7716
THOMSON FINANCIAL—See Thomson Reuters Corporation; *Int'l,* pg. 7716
THOMSON FINANCIAL S.R.L.—See Thomson Reuters Corporation; *Int'l,* pg. 7716
THOMSON FINANCIAL VESTEK—See Thomson Reuters Corporation; *Int'l,* pg. 7716
THOMSON FLY—See TUI AG; *Int'l,* pg. 7968
THOMSON GLOBAL MARKETS INC.—See Thomson Reuters Corporation; *Int'l,* pg. 7716
THOMSON HOMES INC—See Thomson Properties Inc.; *U.S. Private,* pg. 4162
THOMSON, HORSTMANN & BRYANT, INC.—See Victory Capital Holdings, Inc.; *U.S. Public,* pg. 2296
THOMSON HOSPITALS SDN. BHD.—See Thomson Medical Group Limited; *Int'l,* pg. 7714
THOMSON INC.—See Vantiva SA; *Int'l,* pg. 8131
THOMSON LICENSING SAS—See Vantiva SA; *Int'l,* pg. 8131
THOMSON LINEAR LLC—See Regal Rexnord Corporation; *U.S. Public,* pg. 1772
THOMSON MACCONNELL CADILLAC, INC.; *U.S. Private,* pg. 4162
THOMSON MEDICAL GROUP LIMITED; *Int'l,* pg. 7714
THOMSON MEDICAL PTE. LTD.—See Thomson Medical Group Limited; *Int'l,* pg. 7714
THOMSON MOTOR CENTRE INC.; *U.S. Private,* pg. 4162
THOMSON NEFF GMBH—See Regal Rexnord Corporation; *U.S. Public,* pg. 1772
THOMSON PAEDIATRIC CENTRE PTE LTD—See Thomson Medical Group Limited; *Int'l,* pg. 7714
THOMSON PAEDIATRIC CLINIC PTE LTD—See OUE Limited; *Int'l,* pg. 5666
THOMSON PLASTICS, INC.; *U.S. Private,* pg. 4162
THOMSON PROPERTIES INC.; *U.S. Private,* pg. 4162
THOMSON RESOURCES LTD; *Int'l,* pg. 7714
THOMSON REUTERS AUSTRALIA—See Thomson Reuters Corporation; *Int'l,* pg. 7716
THOMSON REUTERS - CORPORATE HEADQUARTERS—See Thomson Reuters Corporation; *Int'l,* pg. 7715
THOMSON REUTERS CORPORATION; *Int'l,* pg. 7714
THOMSON REUTERS HONG KONG LIMITED—See Thomson Reuters Corporation; *Int'l,* pg. 7716
THOMSON REUTERS JAPAN—See Thomson Reuters Corporation; *Int'l,* pg. 7716
THOMSON REUTERS LEGAL—See Thomson Reuters Corporation; *Int'l,* pg. 7715
THOMSON REUTERS (MARKETS) DEUSCHLAND GMBH—See Thomson Reuters Corporation; *Int'l,* pg. 7716
THOMSON REUTERS MARKETS—See Thomson Reuters Corporation; *Int'l,* pg. 7715

THOMSON REUTERS/ONESOURCE—See Thomson Reuters Corporation; *Int'l,* pg. 7716
THOMSON REUTERS—See Thomson Reuters Corporation; *Int'l,* pg. 7716
THOMSON REUTERS TAX & ACCOUNTING—See Thomson Reuters Corporation; *Int'l,* pg. 7716
THOMSON-SHORE, INC.—See CJK Group, Inc.; *U.S. Private,* pg. 909
THOMSONS ONLINE BENEFITS LTD.—See Marsh & McLennan Companies, Inc.; *U.S. Public,* pg. 1386
THOMSON SPORT (UK) LIMITED—See TUI AG; *Int'l,* pg. 7968
THOMSON TELECOM SAS—See Vantiva SA; *Int'l,* pg. 8131
THOMSON WEST—See Thomson Reuters Corporation; *Int'l,* pg. 7715
THOMSON WOMEN CANCER CENTRE PTE. LTD.—See Thomson Medical Group Limited; *Int'l,* pg. 7714
THOMVEST ASSET MANAGEMENT LTD.—See Thomvest Ventures LLC; *U.S. Private,* pg. 4162
THOMVEST VENTURES LLC; *U.S. Private,* pg. 4162
THONAUER GESELLSCHAFT M.B.H.—See Komax Holding AG; *Int'l,* pg. 4241
THONAUER SPOL. S.R.O.—See Komax Holding AG; *Int'l,* pg. 4241
THONAUER S.R.O.—See Komax Holding AG; *Int'l,* pg. 4241
THONBURI BAMRUNGMUANG HOSPITAL CO., LTD.—See Thonburi Healthcare Group PCL; *Int'l,* pg. 7716
THONBURI HEALTHCARE GROUP PCL; *Int'l,* pg. 7716
THONBURI MEDICAL CENTRE PUBLIC COMPANY LIMITED; *Int'l,* pg. 7716
THONBURI REALTY DEVELOPMENT CO., LTD.—See Thonburi Healthcare Group PCL; *Int'l,* pg. 7716
THON DES MASCAREIGNES LTEE—See Ireland Blyth Limited; *Int'l,* pg. 3807
THONG GUAN INDUSTRIES BERHAD - FLEXIBLE PACKAGING DIVISION—See Thong Guan Industries Berhad; *Int'l,* pg. 7717
THONG GUAN INDUSTRIES BERHAD; *Int'l,* pg. 7717
THONG GUAN PLASTIC INDUSTRIES (SUZHOU) CO., LTD.—See Thong Guan Industries Berhad; *Int'l,* pg. 7717
THONG GUAN PLASTIC & PAPER INDUSTRIES SDN. BHD.—See Thong Guan Industries Berhad; *Int'l,* pg. 7717
THONG NHAT JOINT STOCK COMPANY; *Int'l,* pg. 7717
THONG NHAT THANH HOA DAIRY COW LIMITED COMPANY—See Vietnam Dairy Products Joint Stock Company; *Int'l,* pg. 8199
THONG SIA CO (S) PTE LTD—See Stelux Holdings International Limited; *Int'l,* pg. 7205
THONG SIA SDN BHD—See Stelux Holdings International Limited; *Int'l,* pg. 7205
THONG SIA WATCH CO. LTD—See Stelux Holdings International Limited; *Int'l,* pg. 7205
THORBAHN AND ASSOCIATES INSURANCE AGENCY, INC.—See Aon plc; *Int'l,* pg. 497
THOR BRASIL LTDA—See THOR GROUP LIMITED; *Int'l,* pg. 7717
THORBURN ASSOCIATES INC; *U.S. Private,* pg. 4162
THOR CAPTAIN SHIPPING CO., LTD.—See Thoresen Thai Agencies Public Company Limited; *Int'l,* pg. 7718
THOR CHAMPION SHIPPING CO., LTD.—See Thoresen Thai Agencies Public Company Limited; *Int'l,* pg. 7718
THOR COMMANDER SHIPPING CO., LTD.—See Thoresen Thai Agencies Public Company Limited; *Int'l,* pg. 7718
THORCO SHIPPING A/S—See Thornico A/S; *Int'l,* pg. 7720
THORENDAHL AS—See AF Gruppen ASA; *Int'l,* pg. 184
THOR ENERGY PLC; *Int'l,* pg. 7717
THORESEN & CO., (BANGKOK) LIMITED—See Thoresen Thai Agencies Public Company Limited; *Int'l,* pg. 7719
THORESEN & COMPANY (BANGKOK) LIMITED—See Thoresen Thai Agencies Public Company Limited; *Int'l,* pg. 7719
THORESEN SHIPPING FZE—See Thoresen Thai Agencies Public Company Limited; *Int'l,* pg. 7719
THORESEN SHIPPING GERMANY GMBH—See Thoresen Thai Agencies Public Company Limited; *Int'l,* pg. 7719
THORESEN SHIPPING SINGAPORE PTE. LTD.—See Thoresen Thai Agencies Public Company Limited; *Int'l,* pg. 7719
THORESEN THAI AGENCIES PUBLIC COMPANY LIMITED; *Int'l,* pg. 7718
THOR ESPECIALIDADES, S.A.—See THOR GROUP LIMITED; *Int'l,* pg. 7717
THOR EXPLORATIONS LIMITED; *Int'l,* pg. 7717
THOR GMBH—See THOR GROUP LIMITED; *Int'l,* pg. 7717
THOR GROUP LIMITED; *Int'l,* pg. 7717
THOR HARMONY SHIPPING CO., LTD—See Thoresen Thai Agencies Public Company Limited; *Int'l,* pg. 7718
THOR INDUSTRIES, INC.; *U.S. Public,* pg. 2156
THOR JAPAN LIMITED—See THOR GROUP LIMITED; *Int'l,* pg. 7717

COMPANY NAME INDEX — THREE NOTCH ELECTRIC MEMBERSHIP CORP.

THOR JASMINE SHIPPING CO., LTD.—See Thoresen Thai Agencies Public Company Limited; *Int'l*, pg. 7718

THORKILD LARSEN A/S—See A.A.G. STUCCHI s.r.l.; *Int'l*, pg. 23

THORLABS INC.; *U.S. Private*, pg. 4162

THORLEY INDUSTRIES LLC—See The Seidler Company, LLC; *U.S. Private*, pg. 4116

THOR-LO, INC.; *U.S. Private*, pg. 4162

THORLUX LIGHTING LIMITED—See F.W. Thorpe plc; *Int'l*, pg. 2597

THORLUX LIGHTING—See F.W. Thorpe plc; *Int'l*, pg. 2597

THORMAC ENGINEERING LTD.—See Madison Dearborn Partners, LLC; *U.S. Private*, pg. 2541

THOR MARINER SHIPPING CO., LTD.—See Thoresen Thai Agencies Public Company Limited; *Int'l*, pg. 7718

THOR MASTER SHIPPING CO., LTD.—See Thoresen Thai Agencies Public Company Limited; *Int'l*, pg. 7718

THOR MEDICAL ASA; *Int'l*, pg. 7717

THOR MERCHANT SHIPPING CO., LTD.—See Thoresen Thai Agencies Public Company Limited; *Int'l*, pg. 7718

THOR MOTOR COACH, INC.—See Thor Industries, Inc.; *U.S. Public*, pg. 2157

THOR MOTORS; *Int'l*, pg. 7717

THORN ABWASSERTECHNIK GMBH—See PORR AG; *Int'l*, pg. 5924

THORN AUSTRALIA PTY LTD—See Credit Corp Group Limited; *Int'l*, pg. 1835

THOR NAVIGATOR SHIPPING CO., LTD.—See Thoresen Thai Agencies Public Company Limited; *Int'l*, pg. 7718

THORNDON RUBBER CO LIMITED—See Skellerup Holdings Limited; *Int'l*, pg. 6980

THOR NECTAR SHIPPING CO., LTD.—See Thoresen Thai Agencies Public Company Limited; *Int'l*, pg. 7718

THORNE ELECTRIC COMPANY; *U.S. Private*, pg. 4162

THORNE HEALTHTECH, INC.—See Catterton Management Company, LLC; *U.S. Private*, pg. 794

THORNE MANAGEMENT INC.; *U.S. Private*, pg. 4162

THORN EQUIPMENT FINANCE PTY LTD—See ICM Limited; *Int'l*, pg. 3582

THORNE RESEARCH, INC.; *U.S. Private*, pg. 4162

THOR NEREUS SHIPPING CO., LTD.—See Thoresen Thai Agencies Public Company Limited; *Int'l*, pg. 7718

THORNES—See Source Atlantic Industrial Distribution & Services Group; *Int'l*, pg. 7115

THORNEY OPPORTUNITIES LIMITED; *Int'l*, pg. 7719

THORNEY TECHNOLOGIES LTD; *Int'l*, pg. 7719

THORN GROUP LIMITED—See ICM Limited; *Int'l*, pg. 3582

THORNHILL GM SUPERSTORE INC.; *U.S. Private*, pg. 4162

THORNHILL SECURITIES, INC.; *U.S. Private*, pg. 4163

THORNICO A/S; *Int'l*, pg. 7719

THORN LIGHTING GROUP PLC—See Zumtobel Group AG; *Int'l*, pg. 8695

THORN LIGHTING LTD.—See Zumtobel Group AG; *Int'l*, pg. 8695

THOR NORDIC—See THOR GROUP LIMITED; *Int'l*, pg. 7717

THORN SECURITY (HONG KONG) LIMITED—See Johnson Controls International plc; *Int'l*, pg. 3987

THORNTON FLATS JV, LLC—See Bluerock Residential Growth REIT, Inc.; *U.S. Public*, pg. 366

THORNTON KIDNEY CENTER, LLC—See Nautic Partners, LLC; *U.S. Private*, pg. 2871

THORNTON & ROSS LIMITED—See Bain Capital, LP; *U.S. Private*, pg. 444

THORNTON & ROSS LIMITED—See Cinven Limited; *Int'l*, pg. 1614

THORNTONS INC—See ArcLight Capital Holdings, LLC; *U.S. Private*, pg. 312

THORNTONS INC—See BP plc; *Int'l*, pg. 1131

THORNTONS LTD.—See Ferrero International S.A.; *Int'l*, pg. 2641

THORNTON & STEFANOVICH INC.; *U.S. Private*, pg. 4163

THORNTON-TOMASETTI, INC.; *U.S. Private*, pg. 4163

THORN VALLEY ENTERPRISES—See Norman-Spencer Agency, Inc.; *U.S. Private*, pg. 2938

THOROLD COGEN L.P.—See Northland Power Inc.; *Int'l*, pg. 5446

THO-RO PRODUCTS, INC.—See Eagle Button Co., Inc.; *U.S. Private*, pg. 1308

THOROUGHBRED DIRECT INTERMODAL SERVICES, INC.—See Norfolk Southern Corporation; *U.S. Public*, pg. 1536

THOROUGHBRED MORTGAGE, LLC—See Wells Fargo & Company; *U.S. Public*, pg. 2345

THOROUGHBRED RACING PRODUCTIONS (VICTORIA) PTY LTD—See Australian Turf Club (ATC); *Int'l*, pg. 722

THOROUGHBRED RESEARCH GROUP, INC.; *U.S. Private*, pg. 4163

THOROUGHBRED SOFTWARE INTERNATIONAL; *U.S. Private*, pg. 4163

THOROUGHBRED TECHNOLOGY AND TELECOMMUNICATIONS—See Norfolk Southern Corporation; *U.S. Public*, pg. 1536

THOROUGHBRED TIMES COMPANY INC.—See Fancy Publications Inc.; *U.S. Private*, pg. 1472

THORP & COMPANY; *U.S. Private*, pg. 4163

THORPE-BOWKER—See Cambridge Information Group, Inc.; *U.S. Private*, pg. 727

THORPE CANADA CORPORATION—See Terra Millenium Corporation; *U.S. Private*, pg. 3970

THORPE ELECTRIC SUPPLY INC.; *U.S. Private*, pg. 4163

THORPE PARK—See Merlin Entertainments plc; *Int'l*, pg. 4838

THOR PERSONAL CARE SAS—See THOR GROUP LIMITED; *Int'l*, pg. 7717

THORPE SPECIALTY SERVICES CORPORATION—See The CapStreet Group LLC; *U.S. Private*, pg. 4005

THORPE-SUNBELT, INC.—See The CapStreet Group LLC; *U.S. Private*, pg. 4005

THOR PILOT SHIPPING CO., LTD.—See Thoresen Thai Agencies Public Company Limited; *Int'l*, pg. 7718

THOR QUIMICOS DE MEXICO, SA DE CV—See THOR GROUP LIMITED; *Int'l*, pg. 7717

THOR SAILOR SHIPPING CO., LTD.—See Thoresen Thai Agencies Public Company Limited; *Int'l*, pg. 7718

THOR SARL—See THOR GROUP LIMITED; *Int'l*, pg. 7717

THOR SEA SHIPPING CO., LTD.—See Thoresen Thai Agencies Public Company Limited; *Int'l*, pg. 7718

THOR SKIPPER SHIPPING CO., LTD.—See Thoresen Thai Agencies Public Company Limited; *Int'l*, pg. 7718

THOR SKY SHIPPING CO., LTD.—See Thoresen Thai Agencies Public Company Limited; *Int'l*, pg. 7718

THORSON GMC TRUCK BUICK MOTOR COMPANY, INC.; *U.S. Private*, pg. 4163

THOR SPECIALITIES (UK) LIMITED—See THOR GROUP LIMITED; *Int'l*, pg. 7717

THOR SPECIALTIES, INC—See THOR GROUP LIMITED; *Int'l*, pg. 7717

THOR SPECIALTIES PTY LIMITED—See THOR GROUP LIMITED; *Int'l*, pg. 7717

THOR SPECIALTIES PTY LIMITED—See THOR GROUP LIMITED; *Int'l*, pg. 7717

THOR SPECIALTIES SDN BHD—See THOR GROUP LIMITED; *Int'l*, pg. 7717

THOR SPECIALTIES SRL—See THOR GROUP LIMITED; *Int'l*, pg. 7717

THOR SPECIALTIES SRL—See THOR GROUP LIMITED; *Int'l*, pg. 7717

THOR SPECIALTY CHEMICAL (SHANGHAI) CO LTD—See THOR GROUP LIMITED; *Int'l*, pg. 7717

THOR SPIRIT SHIPPING CO., LTD.—See Thoresen Thai Agencies Public Company Limited; *Int'l*, pg. 7718

THORSTAD CHEVROLET INC.; *U.S. Private*, pg. 4163

THOR STAR SHIPPING CO., LTD.—See Thoresen Thai Agencies Public Company Limited; *Int'l*, pg. 7718

THORS TRADING AB—See Sdiptech AB; *Int'l*, pg. 6659

THOR SUN SHIPPING CO., LTD.—See Thoresen Thai Agencies Public Company Limited; *Int'l*, pg. 7719

THORTEX—See Arlington Capital Partners LLC; *U.S. Private*, pg. 327

THOR TRANSPORTER SHIPPING CO., LTD.—See Thoresen Thai Agencies Public Company Limited; *Int'l*, pg. 7719

THOS. S. BYRNE, INC.; *U.S. Private*, pg. 4163

THOUGHTFUL BRANDS, INC.; *Int'l*, pg. 7720

THOUGHTWORKS HOLDING, INC.—See Apax Partners LLP; *Int'l*, pg. 507

THOUGHTWORKS, INC.—See Apax Partners LLP; *Int'l*, pg. 507

THOUSANDEYES GERMANY GMBH—See Cisco Systems, Inc.; *U.S. Public*, pg. 500

THOUSANDEYES, INC.—See Cisco Systems, Inc.; *U.S. Public*, pg. 500

THOUSAND OAKS PRINTING & SPECIALTIES, INC.—See Chatham Asset Management, LLC; *U.S. Private*, pg. 863

THOUSAND OAKS-S, INC.—See Lithia Motors, Inc.; *U.S. Public*, pg. 1326

THOUSANDPLAN, INC.—See Willtec Co., Ltd.; *Int'l*, pg. 8420

THOUSAND TRAILS LP—See Equity LifeStyle Properties, Inc.; *U.S. Public*, pg. 790

THPA SOFIA EAD—See Thessaloniki Port Authority S.A.; *Int'l*, pg. 7708

TH PELITA GEDONG SDN. BHD.—See Lembaga Tabung Haji; *Int'l*, pg. 4449

TH PELITA SADONG SDN. BHD.—See Lembaga Tabung Haji; *Int'l*, pg. 4449

THP KOTA BAHAGIA SDN. BHD.—See Lembaga Tabung Haji; *Int'l*, pg. 4449

TH PLANTATIONS BERHAD—See Lembaga Tabung Haji; *Int'l*, pg. 4449

TH PLASTICS INC.; *U.S. Private*, pg. 3979

TH PROPERTIES; *U.S. Private*, pg. 3979

THP SARIBAS SDN. BHD.—See Lembaga Tabung Haji; *Int'l*, pg. 4449

THQ ENTERTAINMENT GMBH—See THQ Inc.; *U.S. Private*, pg. 4163

THQ FRANCE S.A.R.L.—See THQ Inc.; *U.S. Private*, pg. 4163

THQ INC.; *U.S. Private*, pg. 4163

THQ NORDIC AB; *Int'l*, pg. 7720

THQ (UK) LIMITED—See THQ Inc.; *U.S. Private*, pg. 4163

TH QVILLER AS—See NIBE Industrier AB; *Int'l*, pg. 5262

THRACEAN GOLD MINING SA—See Eldorado Gold Corporation; *Int'l*, pg. 2347

THRACE INVESTMENTS BV—See Cyclone Metals Limited; *Int'l*, pg. 1894

THRACE IPOMA A.D.—See Thrace Plastics Holding and Commercial S.A.; *Int'l*, pg. 7720

THRACE LINQ INC.—See Thrace Plastics Holding and Commercial S.A.; *Int'l*, pg. 7720

THRACE MINERALS SA—See Eldorado Gold Corporation; *Int'l*, pg. 2347

THRACE NONWOVENS & GEOSYNTHETICS SA—See Thrace Plastics Holding and Commercial S.A.; *Int'l*, pg. 7720

THRACE PLASTICS HOLDING AND COMMERCIAL S.A.; *Int'l*, pg. 7720

THRACE PLASTICS PACKAGING DOO—See Thrace Plastics Holding and Commercial S.A.; *Int'l*, pg. 7720

THRACE PLASTICS PACK S.A.—See Thrace Plastics Holding and Commercial S.A.; *Int'l*, pg. 7720

THRACE POLYBULK A.S.—See Thrace Plastics Holding and Commercial S.A.; *Int'l*, pg. 7720

THRACE XPS S.A.—See Thrace Plastics Holding and Commercial S.A.; *Int'l*, pg. 7720

THRALL ENTERPRISES, INC.; *U.S. Private*, pg. 4163

THRALOW, INC.; *U.S. Private*, pg. 4163

THRANE & THRANE A/S—See Advent International Corporation; *U.S. Private*, pg. 100

THREADING & PRECISION MANUFACTURING LLC—See OFS International LLC; *U.S. Private*, pg. 3003

THREAD INNOVATION LIMITED—See M&C Saatchi plc; *Int'l*, pg. 4611

THREADNEEDLE ASSET MANAGEMENT HOLDINGS LIMITED—See Ameriprise Financial, Inc.; *U.S. Public*, pg. 114

THREADNEEDLE ASSET MANAGEMENT LTD.—See Ameriprise Financial, Inc.; *U.S. Public*, pg. 114

THREADNEEDLE CAPITAL MANAGEMENT LTD.—See Ameriprise Financial, Inc.; *U.S. Public*, pg. 114

THREADNEEDLE INTERNATIONAL LTD.—See Ameriprise Financial, Inc.; *U.S. Public*, pg. 114

THREADNEEDLE INVESTMENT SERVICES GMBH—See Ameriprise Financial, Inc.; *U.S. Public*, pg. 114

THREADNEEDLE INVESTMENT SERVICES LTD.—See Ameriprise Financial, Inc.; *U.S. Public*, pg. 114

THREADNEEDLE MANAGEMENT SERVICES LTD.—See Ameriprise Financial, Inc.; *U.S. Public*, pg. 114

THREADNEEDLE PENSIONS LTD.—See Ameriprise Financial, Inc.; *U.S. Public*, pg. 114

THREADNEEDLE PORTFOLIO SERVICES HONG KONG LTD.—See Ameriprise Financial, Inc.; *U.S. Public*, pg. 114

THREADNEEDLE PROPERTY INVESTMENTS LTD.—See Ameriprise Financial, Inc.; *U.S. Public*, pg. 114

THREATMETRIX, INC.—See RELX plc; *Int'l*, pg. 6267

THREAT STACK, INC.—See F5, Inc.; *U.S. Public*, pg. 819

THREATTRACK SECURITY, INC.; *U.S. Private*, pg. 4163

THREDUP, INC.; *U.S. Public*, pg. 2157

THREE ACE CO., LTD.—See Optex Group Co., Ltd.; *Int'l*, pg. 5602

THREE ACRE FARMS PLC—See Ceylon Grain Elevators PLC; *Int'l*, pg. 1426

THREE ALBERT EMBANKMENT LIMITED—See CLS Holdings plc; *Int'l*, pg. 1664

THREE-A RESOURCES BERHAD; *Int'l*, pg. 7720

THREE CHIMNEYS FARM; *U.S. Private*, pg. 4163

THREE COUNTIES FEEDS LTD—See Mole Valley Farmers Ltd; *Int'l*, pg. 5021

THREE COUNTY VOLKSWAGEN CORP; *U.S. Private*, pg. 4163

THREED CAPITAL INC.; *Int'l*, pg. 7721

THREE DEEP, INC.—See Bold Orange Company, LLC; *U.S. Private*, pg. 610

THREE D METALS CANADA, INC.—See Three D Metals Inc.; *U.S. Private*, pg. 4164

THREE D METALS INC.; *U.S. Private*, pg. 4163

THREE DOG LOGISTICS; *U.S. Private*, pg. 4164

THREE D TEC INC.—See Meitec Corporation; *Int'l*, pg. 4804

THREE F CO., LTD.; *Int'l*, pg. 7720

THREE FOREST (THAILAND) CO., LTD.—See OOTOYA Holdings Co., Ltd.; *Int'l*, pg. 5595

THREE HILLS CAPITAL PARTNERS LLP; *Int'l*, pg. 7720

THREE IRELAND (HUTCHISON) LIMITED—See CK Hutchison Holdings Limited; *Int'l*, pg. 1638

THREE J'S DISTRIBUTING, INC.; *U.S. Private*, pg. 4164

THREE L INC.; *U.S. Private*, pg. 4164

THREE LOWER COUNTIES COMMUNITY SERVICES, INC.; *U.S. Private*, pg. 4164

THREE MINDS LTD.—See Sansei Co., Ltd.; *Int'l*, pg. 6555

THREE M TOOL & MACHINE, INC.; *U.S. Private*, pg. 4164

THREE NOTCH ELECTRIC MEMBERSHIP CORP.; *U.S. Private*, pg. 4164

THREE PHASE LINE CONSTRUCTION, INC.—See MasTec, Inc.; *U.S. Public*, pg. 1393

2743

THREEPIPE REPLY LTD.—See Reply S.p.A.; *Int'l*, pg. 6291
THREE POINT MOTORS—See German Auto Import Network - Vancouver Island; *Int'l*, pg. 2943
THREE RINGS DESIGN, INC.—See Sega Sammy Holdings, Inc.; *Int'l*, pg. 6681
THREE RIVERS COMMUNITY FOUNDATION; *U.S. Private*, pg. 4164
THREE RIVERS ELECTRIC COOP; *U.S. Private*, pg. 4164
THREE RIVERS FS COMPANY; *U.S. Private*, pg. 4164
THREE RIVERS HOMECARE, LLC—See UnitedHealth Group Incorporated; *U.S. Public*, pg. 2247
THREE RIVERS LAND TRUST, INC.; *U.S. Private*, pg. 4164
THREE RIVERS MALL, L.L.C.—See Brookfield Corporation; *Int'l*, pg. 1185
THREE RIVERS MEDICAL CLINICS, INC.—See Quorum Health Corporation; *U.S. Private*, pg. 3330
THREE RIVERS OPERATING COMPANY LLC—See ConocoPhillips; *U.S. Public*, pg. 568
THREE RIVERS ORTHOPEDIC & SPINE PRODUCTS, INC.; *U.S. Private*, pg. 4164
THREE RIVERS PACKAGING, INC.—See The Cary Company; *U.S. Private*, pg. 4005
THREE RIVERS SYSTEMS, INC.—See Advent International Corporation; *U.S. Private*, pg. 107
THREE RIVERS TRUCKING, INC.; *U.S. Private*, pg. 4164
THREE'S COMPANY MEDIA GROUP CO., LTD.; *Int'l*, pg. 7720
THREE S FOODS CO., LTD—See Yamazaki Baking Co., Ltd.; *Int'l*, pg. 8556
THREE SHIRES HOSPITAL LP—See Centene Corporation; *U.S. Public*, pg. 470
THREE SHORES BANCORPORATION, INC.—See United Community Banks, Inc.; *U.S. Public*, pg. 2230
THREE SIXTY COMMUNICATIONS LIMITED—See Massy Holdings Ltd.; *Int'l*, pg. 4724
THREE SIXTY FIVE PCL; *Int'l*, pg. 7720
THREESIXTYFIVE PUBLIC COMPANY LIMITED; *Int'l*, pg. 7721
THREESIXTY GROUP LIMITED—See AEA Investors LP; *U.S. Private*, pg. 116
THREE SIXTY INSURE LIMITED—See Brown & Brown, Inc.; *U.S. Public*, pg. 402
THREESIXTY INVESTMENTS LIMITED; *Int'l*, pg. 7721
THREESIXTY SERVICES LLP—See Fintel plc; *Int'l*, pg. 2677
THREE SIXTY SOLAR LTD.; *Int'l*, pg. 7720
THREESIXTY TRADING NETWORKS (INDIA) PVT LTD—See Deutsche Borse AG; *Int'l*, pg. 2063
THREE SIX ZERO GROUP, INC.—See Live Nation Entertainment, Inc.; *U.S. Public*, pg. 1331
THREE SIX ZERO GRP LIMITED—See Live Nation Entertainment, Inc.; *U.S. Public*, pg. 1331
THREE SQUARE MARKET, INC.—See Cantaloupe, Inc.; *U.S. Public*, pg. 430
THREE SQUARE MARKET LIMITED—See Cantaloupe, Inc.; *U.S. Public*, pg. 430
THREE SQUIRRELS, INC.; *Int'l*, pg. 7720
THREE STATES SUPPLY COMPANY LLC—See Watsco, Inc.; *U.S. Public*, pg. 2337
THREE & THREE HARDWARE SDN BHD—See K. Seng Seng Corporation Bhd; *Int'l*, pg. 4043
THREE VALLEY COPPER CORP.—See Sprott Inc.; *Int'l*, pg. 7145
THREE WAY; *U.S. Private*, pg. 4164
THREEWIRE, INC.—See Leonard Green & Partners, L.P.; *U.S. Private*, pg. 2430
THREE WIRE SYSTEMS, LLC; *U.S. Private*, pg. 4164
THREE X COMMUNICATION LIMITED—See Compagnie Generale des Etablissements Michelin SCA; *Int'l*, pg. 1743
THRESHER INDUSTRIES, INC.; *U.S. Public*, pg. 2157
THRESHOLD ENTERPRISES, LTD.; *U.S. Private*, pg. 4164
THRESHOLD FOUNDATION; *U.S. Private*, pg. 4164
THE THRESHOLD GROUP, LLC—See AlTi Global, Inc.; *U.S. Public*, pg. 87
THRESHOLD INTERACTIVE—See Zealot Networks, Inc.; *U.S. Private*, pg. 4599
THRESHOLD REHABILITATION SERVICES, INC.; *U.S. Private*, pg. 4164
THRESHOLD VENTURES III, L.P.; *U.S. Private*, pg. 4164
THR HOTEL (JOHOR) SDN. BHD.—See Tradewinds Corporation Berhad; *Int'l*, pg. 7888
THR HOTEL (KUALA TAHAN) SDN. BHD.—See Tradewinds Corporation Berhad; *Int'l*, pg. 7888
THR HOTEL (PENANG) SDN. BHD.—See Tradewinds Corporation Berhad; *Int'l*, pg. 7888
THR HOTEL (SELANGOR) BERHAD—See Tradewinds Corporation Berhad; *Int'l*, pg. 7888
THRIACIO LOGISTICS CENTER S.A.—See Piraeus Financial Holdings S.A.; *Int'l*, pg. 5874
THRIFT TRUCKING INCORPORATED—See Assured Transportation Services; *U.S. Private*, pg. 359
THRIFTWAY INC.; *U.S. Private*, pg. 4164
THRIFTY AIR CONDITIONING & REFRIGERATION, INC.—See Freeman Spogli & Co. Incorporated; *U.S. Private*, pg. 1606

THRIFTY CAR SALES INC.—See Hertz Global Holdings, Inc.; *U.S. Public*, pg. 1029
THRIFTY DRUG STORES, INC.; *U.S. Private*, pg. 4164
THRIFTY FOODS INC.—See Empire Company Limited; *Int'l*, pg. 2387
THRIFTY, LLC—See Hertz Global Holdings, Inc.; *U.S. Public*, pg. 1029
THRIFTY OIL CO.; *U.S. Private*, pg. 4165
THRIFTY PAYLESS, INC.—See New Rite Aid, LLC; *U.S. Private*, pg. 2906
THRIFTY SUPPLY CO.; *U.S. Private*, pg. 4165
THRIGE ELECTRIC S.A.—See T-T Electric; *Int'l*, pg. 7396
THRILLIST MEDIA GROUP, INC.; *U.S. Private*, pg. 4165
THRIVE 365 LLC—See Mondelez International, Inc.; *U.S. Public*, pg. 1464
THRIVE ACQUISITION CORPORATION; *U.S. Public*, pg. 2157
THRIVEHIVE, INC.—See Gannett Co., Inc.; *U.S. Public*, pg. 906
THRIVE HOMES LLC—See Toll Brothers, Inc.; *U.S. Public*, pg. 2162
THRIVE, INC.—See Apax Partners LLP; *Int'l*, pg. 506
THRIVE LIFE, LLC; *U.S. Private*, pg. 4165
THRIVE MORTGAGE LLC; *U.S. Private*, pg. 4165
THRIVENT FINANCIAL FOR LUTHERANS FOUNDATION; *U.S. Private*, pg. 4165
THRIVENT FINANCIAL INVESTOR SERVICES INC.—See Thrivent Financial for Lutherans Foundation; *U.S. Private*, pg. 4165
THRIVENT INVESTMENT MANAGEMENT INC.—See Thrivent Financial for Lutherans Foundation; *U.S. Private*, pg. 4165
THRIVENT LIFE INSURANCE COMPANY—See Thrivent Financial for Lutherans Foundation; *U.S. Private*, pg. 4165
THRIVENT TRUST COMPANY—See Thrivent Financial for Lutherans Foundation; *U.S. Private*, pg. 4165
THRIVE OPERATIONS, LLC—See Court Square Capital Partners, L.P.; *U.S. Private*, pg. 1070
THRIVE PRECISION HEALTH INC.; *Int'l*, pg. 7721
THRIVE TRIBE TECHNOLOGIES LIMITED; *Int'l*, pg. 7721
THRIVE WORLD WIDE, INC.; *U.S. Private*, pg. 4165
THRIVUR HEALTH, LLC—See Corecivic, Inc.; *U.S. Public*, pg. 577
T.H. ROGERS LUMBER CO.; *U.S. Private*, pg. 3912
THROGMORTON FINANCIAL SERVICES LTD.; *Int'l*, pg. 7721
THROGMORTON PRIVATE CAPITAL LIMITED—See Throgmorton Financial Services Ltd.; *Int'l*, pg. 7721
THROGMORTON STREET CAPITAL LTD.—See ADVFN PLC; *Int'l*, pg. 168
THROGMORTON UK LTD.—See Apex Fund Services Holdings Ltd.; *Int'l*, pg. 510
THRO, LTD.—See Kohlberg & Company, LLC; *U.S. Private*, pg. 2338
THROMBODX BV—See Illumina, Inc.; *U.S. Public*, pg. 1112
THROMBOGENICS INC.—See Oxurion NV; *Int'l*, pg. 5676
THROMBOGENICS LTD.—See Oxurion NV; *Int'l*, pg. 5676
THROUGHTEK CO., LTD.; *Int'l*, pg. 7721
THRUSH AIRCRAFT, INC.; *U.S. Private*, pg. 4165
THRUSTMASTER OF TEXAS, INC.; *U.S. Private*, pg. 4165
THRU THE BIBLE RADIO NETWORK; *U.S. Private*, pg. 4165
THRU TUBING SOLUTIONS—See RPC, Inc.; *U.S. Public*, pg. 1816
THRUVISION GROUP PLC; *Int'l*, pg. 7721
THRUVISION INC.—See Thruvision Group plc; *Int'l*, pg. 7721
THRUWAY FASTENERS INC.; *U.S. Private*, pg. 4165
THRYV HOLDINGS, INC.; *U.S. Public*, pg. 2157
T&H SERVICES, LLC—See Tlingit Haida Tribal Business Corporation; *U.S. Private*, pg. 4179
TH STRALFORS (DATA PRODUCTS) LTD.—See PostNord AB; *Int'l*, pg. 5941
THT HEAT TRANSFER TECHNOLOGY, INC.; *Int'l*, pg. 7721
TH TRS CORP.—See Two Harbors Investment Corp.; *U.S. Public*, pg. 2207
THUAN AN WOOD PROCESSING JOINT STOCK COMPANY; *Int'l*, pg. 7721
THUAN HUNG CONSTRUCTION CORPORATION; *Int'l*, pg. 7721
THUASNE SA; *Int'l*, pg. 7721
THUDUC AGRICULTURE WHOLESALE MARKET CO., LTD—See Thuduc Housing Development Corporation; *Int'l*, pg. 7721
THUDUC HOUSING DEVELOPMENT CORPORATION; *Int'l*, pg. 7721
THU DUC HOUSING DEVELOPMENT CORP.; *Int'l*, pg. 7721
THU DUC TRADING IMPORT & EXPORT JOINT STOCK COMPANY; *Int'l*, pg. 7721
THUGA AKTIENGESELLSCHAFT; *Int'l*, pg. 7722
THUKELA REFRACTORIES ISITHEBE (PTY) LIMITED—See The Murugappa Group, Ltd.; *Int'l*, pg. 7668

THULE CANADA INC.—See Thule Group AB; *Int'l*, pg. 7722
THULE GMBH—See Thule Group AB; *Int'l*, pg. 7722
THULE GROUP AB; *Int'l*, pg. 7722
THULE, INC.—See Thule Group AB; *Int'l*, pg. 7722
THULE NV—See Thule Group AB; *Int'l*, pg. 7722
THULE TOWING SYSTEMS AB—See Thule Group AB; *Int'l*, pg. 7722
THUMANN & HEITKAMP HONG KONG LTD.—See Heitkamp & Thumann KG; *Int'l*, pg. 3326
THUMANN, INC.; *U.S. Private*, pg. 4165
THUMBAGE CO., LTD.; *Int'l*, pg. 7722
THUMB BANCORP, INC.; *U.S. Private*, pg. 4165
THUMB BANK & TRUST—See Thumb Bancorp, Inc.; *U.S. Private*, pg. 4165
THUMB CELLULAR LTD. PARTNERSHIP; *U.S. Private*, pg. 4165
THUMB ELECTRIC COOP OF MICHIGAN; *U.S. Private*, pg. 4165
THUMB PLASTICS INC.—See Gemini Group, Inc.; *U.S. Private*, pg. 1658
THUMBTACK, INC.; *U.S. Private*, pg. 4165
THUMB TOOL & ENGINEERING CO.—See Gemini Group, Inc.; *U.S. Private*, pg. 1658
THUMZUP MEDIA CORPORATION; *U.S. Public*, pg. 2157
THUNDER AIRLINES LIMITED; *Int'l*, pg. 7722
THUNDER BAY TERMINALS LTD.—See Russel Metals Inc.; *Int'l*, pg. 6430
THUNDER BAY TRUCK CENTRE INC.; *Int'l*, pg. 7722
THUNDER BAY HARLEY-DAVIDSON—See Scott Fischer Enterprises LLC; *U.S. Private*, pg. 3577
THUNDERBIRD HOTELES LAS AMERICAS, S.A.—See Thunderbird Resorts Inc.; *Int'l*, pg. 7722
THUNDERBIRD INVESTMENTS PLC—See BNP Paribas SA; *Int'l*, pg. 1093
THUNDERBIRD LLC; *U.S. Private*, pg. 4166
THUNDERBIRD METALS PTY. LTD.—See ATHA Energy Corp.; *Int'l*, pg. 669
THUNDERBIRD RESORTS INC.; *Int'l*, pg. 7722
THUNDERBIRD SCHOOL OF GLOBAL MANAGEMENT—See Arizona State University; *U.S. Private*, pg. 325
THUNDERBIRD TRUCKING INC.—See Omni Holding Company; *U.S. Private*, pg. 3016
THUNDERBUILD BV—See Topcon Corporation; *Int'l*, pg. 7814
THUNDERCAT TECHNOLOGY, LLC; *U.S. Private*, pg. 4166
THUNDER CREEK GAS SERVICES, LLC—See Western Midstream Partners, LP; *U.S. Public*, pg. 2356
THUNDER ENERGIES CORPORATION; *U.S. Public*, pg. 2157
THUNDERFUL GROUP AB; *Int'l*, pg. 7722
THUNDER GOLD CORP.; *Int'l*, pg. 7722
THUNDERHEAD LTD.; *Int'l*, pg. 7722
THUNDERHEAD PTY LTD—See Thunderhead Ltd.; *Int'l*, pg. 7722
THUNDER HEALTHCARE, INC.—See The Ensign Group, Inc.; *U.S. Public*, pg. 2072
THUNDERHILL ESTATES, L.L.C.—See Sun Communities, Inc.; *U.S. Public*, pg. 1963
THUNDER JET BOATS, INC.—See Brunswick Corporation; *U.S. Public*, pg. 408
THUNDERLINE Z, INC.—See Emerson Electric Co.; *U.S. Public*, pg. 1112
THUNDERMIST HEALTH CENTER; *U.S. Private*, pg. 4166
THUNDER MOUNTAIN GOLD, INC.; *U.S. Public*, pg. 2157
THUNDER MOUNTAIN WATER COMPANY—See EPCOR Utilities, Inc.; *Int'l*, pg. 2459
THUNDER PHYSICAL THERAPY, LIMITED PARTNERSHIP—See U.S. Physical Therapy, Inc.; *U.S. Public*, pg. 2216
THUNDER RIDGE TRANSPORT, INC.—See EVO Transportation & Energy Services, Inc.; *U.S. Public*, pg. 804
THUNDERSHIRT, LLC—See Ceva Sante Animale SA; *Int'l*, pg. 1425
THUNDER SOFTWARE TECHNOLOGY CO., LTD.; *Int'l*, pg. 7722
THUNDERSTRUCK RESOURCES LTD.; *Int'l*, pg. 7722
THUNDER TECH INC.; *U.S. Private*, pg. 4166
THUNDER TIGER CORP.; *Int'l*, pg. 7722
THUNDER TIGER EUROPE GMBH—See Thunder Tiger Corp.; *Int'l*, pg. 7722
THUNG SONG 888 CO., LTD.—See Thonburi Healthcare Group PCL; *Int'l*, pg. 7716
THUN TANKERS B.V.—See Erik Thun AB; *Int'l*, pg. 2493
THUN TANKERS B.V.—See Erik Thun AB; *Int'l*, pg. 2493
THUON SA—See Compagnie de Saint-Gobain SA; *Int'l*, pg. 1737
THURBO AG—See Schweizerische Bundesbahnen SBB AG; *Int'l*, pg. 6646
THURGAUER KANTONALBANK; *Int'l*, pg. 7722
THURGAUER ZEITUNG—See NZZ-Mediengruppe; *Int'l*, pg. 5502
THURINGER BEHALTERGLAS GMBH—See Wiegand-Glas GmbH; *Int'l*, pg. 8402
THURINGER ENERGIE AG; *Int'l*, pg. 7722
THURINGER ENERGIE NETZSERVICE GMBH—See E.ON SE; *Int'l*, pg. 2259

COMPANY NAME INDEX

THYSSENKRUPP AG

THURINGER NETKOM GMBH—See Thuringer Energie AG; *Int'l*, pg. 7723
THURINGIA GENERALI 1. IMMOBILIEN AG & CO. KG—See Cinven Limited; *Int'l*, pg. 1616
THURINGIA GENERALI 1. IMMOBILIEN AG & CO. KG—See Talanx AG; *Int'l*, pg. 7445
THURINGIA GENERALI 2. IMMOBILIEN AG & CO. KG—See Cinven Limited; *Int'l*, pg. 1616
THURINGIA GENERALI 2. IMMOBILIEN AG & CO. KG—See Talanx AG; *Int'l*, pg. 7445
THURLAND REAY FAMILY INVESTMENT CO.; *U.S. Private*, pg. 4166
THURMAN HOTEL CONSULTANTS; *U.S. Private*, pg. 4166
THUR MILCH RING AG—See HOCHDORF Holding AG; *Int'l*, pg. 3437
THURNE-MIDDLEBY LTD—See The Middleby Corporation; *U.S. Public*, pg. 2115
THURNE TEKNIK AB—See Addtech AB; *Int'l*, pg. 135
THURNE TEKNIK AB—See Addtech AB; *Int'l*, pg. 135
THURSBY SOFTWARE SYSTEMS, INC.—See Identiv, Inc.; *U.S. Public*, pg. 1089
THURSTON AUTO PLAZA; *U.S. Private*, pg. 4166
THURSTON GROUP, LLC; *U.S. Private*, pg. 4166
THUS GROUP PLC—See Vodafone Group Plc; *Int'l*, pg. 8284
THV COMPOZIT WINDOWS & DOORS—See True Home Value, Inc.; *U.S. Private*, pg. 4247
THWING-ALBERT INSTRUMENT COMPANY; *U.S. Private*, pg. 4166
THWING-ALBERT NETHERLANDS—See Thwing-Albert Instrument Company; *U.S. Private*, pg. 4166
TH. WITT KALTEMASCHINENFABRIK GMBH; *Int'l*, pg. 7588
THX LTD.—See Razer Inc.; *U.S. Private*, pg. 3359
THYBONY WALLCOVERINGS INC.; *U.S. Private*, pg. 4166
THYCOTIC SOFTWARE LIMITED—See TPG Capital, L.P.; *U.S. Public*, pg. 2169
THYE MING INDUSTRIAL CO., LTD.; *Int'l*, pg. 7723
THYE MING (VIETNAM) INDUSTRIAL CO., LTD.—See Thye Ming Industrial Co., Ltd.; *Int'l*, pg. 7723
THYME MATERNITY—See Reitmans (Canada) Limited; *Int'l*, pg. 6259
THE THYMES, LLC; *U.S. Private*, pg. 4127
THYMOORGAN PHARMAZIE GMBH—See Hikma Pharmaceuticals PLC; *Int'l*, pg. 3390
THYREGOD BYGNINGSINDUSTRI A/S—See VKR Holding A/S; *Int'l*, pg. 8281
THYROCARE BANGLADESH LIMITED—See Docon Technologies Private Limited; *Int'l*, pg. 2153
THYROCARE TECHNOLOGIES LIMITED—See Docon Technologies Private Limited; *Int'l*, pg. 2153
THYSSEN DOVER ELEVATOR (CANADA) LTD.—See Advent International Corporation; *U.S. Private*, pg. 107
THYSSEN DOVER ELEVATOR (CANADA) LTD.—See Cinven Limited; *Int'l*, pg. 1615
THYSSEN DOVER ELEVATOR (CANADA) LTD.—See RAG-Stiftung; *Int'l*, pg. 6181
THYSSEN ELEVATORS CO., LTD.—See ThyssenKrupp AG; *Int'l*, pg. 7726
THYSSENGAS GMBH—See DIF Management Holding B.V.; *Int'l*, pg. 2118
THYSSENGAS GMBH—See Electricite de France S.A.; *Int'l*, pg. 2352
THYSSENKRUPP ACADEMY GMBH—See ThyssenKrupp AG; *Int'l*, pg. 7734
THYSSENKRUPP ACCESS CHINA LTD.—See ThyssenKrupp AG; *Int'l*, pg. 7726
THYSSENKRUPP ACCESSIBILITY B.V.—See Advent International Corporation; *U.S. Private*, pg. 106
THYSSENKRUPP ACCESSIBILITY B.V.—See Cinven Limited; *Int'l*, pg. 1614
THYSSENKRUPP ACCESSIBILITY B.V.—See RAG-Stiftung; *Int'l*, pg. 6179
THYSSENKRUPP ACCESSIBILITY HOLDING GMBH—See Advent International Corporation; *U.S. Private*, pg. 106
THYSSENKRUPP ACCESSIBILITY HOLDING GMBH—See Cinven Limited; *Int'l*, pg. 1614
THYSSENKRUPP ACCESSIBILITY HOLDING GMBH—See RAG-Stiftung; *Int'l*, pg. 6179
THYSSENKRUPP ACCESS JAPAN CO., LTD.—See ThyssenKrupp AG; *Int'l*, pg. 7734
THYSSENKRUPP ACCESS LTD.—See ThyssenKrupp AG; *Int'l*, pg. 7726
THYSSENKRUPP ACEROS Y SERVICIOS S.A.—See ThyssenKrupp AG; *Int'l*, pg. 7726
THYSSENKRUPP AEROSPACE AUSTRALIA PTY. LTD.—See ThyssenKrupp AG; *Int'l*, pg. 7726
THYSSENKRUPP AEROSPACE FINLAND OY—See ThyssenKrupp AG; *Int'l*, pg. 7727
THYSSENKRUPP AEROSPACE GERMANY GMBH—See ThyssenKrupp AG; *Int'l*, pg. 7726
THYSSENKRUPP AEROSPACE MOROCCO SARL—See ThyssenKrupp AG; *Int'l*, pg. 7735
THYSSENKRUPP AEROSPACE NEDERLAND B.V.—See ThyssenKrupp AG; *Int'l*, pg. 7726

THYSSENKRUPP AEROSPACE (SHANGHAI) CO. LTD.—See ThyssenKrupp AG; *Int'l*, pg. 7726
THYSSENKRUPP AEROSPACE (SUZHOU) CO., LTD.—See ThyssenKrupp AG; *Int'l*, pg. 7735
THYSSENKRUPP AEROSPACE TUNISIA S.A.R.L.—See ThyssenKrupp AG; *Int'l*, pg. 7735
THYSSENKRUPP AEROSPACE UK LTD.—See ThyssenKrupp AG; *Int'l*, pg. 7726
THYSSENKRUPP AEROSPACE (XI'AN) CO., LTD.—See ThyssenKrupp AG; *Int'l*, pg. 7726
THYSSENKRUPP AG-SINGAPORE—See ThyssenKrupp AG; *Int'l*, pg. 7726
THYSSENKRUPP AG; *Int'l*, pg. 7723
THYSSENKRUPP AIRPORT SERVICES S.L.—See ThyssenKrupp AG; *Int'l*, pg. 7735
THYSSENKRUPP AIRPORT SOLUTIONS, S.A.—See ThyssenKrupp AG; *Int'l*, pg. 7735
THYSSENKRUPP AIRPORT SYSTEMS INC.—See ThyssenKrupp AG; *Int'l*, pg. 7729
THYSSENKRUPP ASANSOR SANAYI VE TIC. A.S.—See ThyssenKrupp AG; *Int'l*, pg. 7726
THYSSENKRUPP ASCENSEURS LUXEMBOURG S.A.R.L.—See ThyssenKrupp AG; *Int'l*, pg. 7726
THYSSENKRUPP ASCENSEURS S.A.S.—See ThyssenKrupp AG; *Int'l*, pg. 7726
THYSSENKRUPP AST USA INC.—See ThyssenKrupp AG; *Int'l*, pg. 7730
THYSSENKRUPP AT.PRO TEC GMBH—See ThyssenKrupp AG; *Int'l*, pg. 7734
THYSSENKRUPP AUFZUGE AG—See ThyssenKrupp AG; *Int'l*, pg. 7726
THYSSENKRUPP AUFZUGE GESELLSCHAFT M.B.H.—See ThyssenKrupp AG; *Int'l*, pg. 7726
THYSSENKRUPP AUFZUGE GMBH, NEUHAUSEN A. D.—See ThyssenKrupp AG; *Int'l*, pg. 7735
THYSSENKRUPP AUFZUGE GMBH—See Advent International Corporation; *U.S. Private*, pg. 106
THYSSENKRUPP AUFZUGE GMBH—See Cinven Limited; *Int'l*, pg. 1614
THYSSENKRUPP AUFZUGE GMBH—See RAG-Stiftung; *Int'l*, pg. 6179
THYSSENKRUPP AUFZUGE LTD.—See ThyssenKrupp AG; *Int'l*, pg. 7726
THYSSENKRUPP AUFZUGE NORGE A/S—See ThyssenKrupp AG; *Int'l*, pg. 7726
THYSSENKRUPP AUFZUGSWERKE GMBH—See ThyssenKrupp AG; *Int'l*, pg. 7726
THYSSENKRUPP AUFZUGSWERKE KONSTRUKTIONS GMBH—See ThyssenKrupp AG; *Int'l*, pg. 7726
THYSSENKRUPP AUSTRIA GMBH—See ThyssenKrupp AG; *Int'l*, pg. 7726
THYSSENKRUPP AUTOMATA INDUSTRIA DE PECAS LTDA.—See ThyssenKrupp AG; *Int'l*, pg. 7735
THYSSENKRUPP AUTOMATION ENGINEERING GMBH—See ThyssenKrupp AG; *Int'l*, pg. 7733
THYSSENKRUPP AUTOMOTIVE AG—See ThyssenKrupp AG; *Int'l*, pg. 7731
THYSSENKRUPP AUTOMOTIVE FRANCE S A R L—See ThyssenKrupp AG; *Int'l*, pg. 7732
THYSSENKRUPP AUTOMOTIVE SALES & TECHNICAL CENTER, INC.—See ThyssenKrupp AG; *Int'l*, pg. 7726
THYSSENKRUPP AUTOMOTIVE SYSTEMS DE MEXICO S.A. DE C.V.—See ThyssenKrupp AG; *Int'l*, pg. 7726
THYSSENKRUPP AUTOMOTIVE SYSTEMS GMBH—See ThyssenKrupp AG; *Int'l*, pg. 7732
THYSSENKRUPP AUTOMOTIVE SYSTEMS INDUSTRIAL DO BRASIL LTDA.—See ThyssenKrupp AG; *Int'l*, pg. 7726
THYSSENKRUPP BAUSERVICE GMBH—See ThyssenKrupp AG; *Int'l*, pg. 7726
THYSSENKRUPP BAUSYSTEME GMBH—See ThyssenKrupp AG; *Int'l*, pg. 7730
THYSSENKRUPP BILSTEIN BRASIL MOLAS E COMPONENTES DE SUSPENSAO LTDA.—See ThyssenKrupp AG; *Int'l*, pg. 7732
THYSSENKRUPP BILSTEIN COMPA S.A.—See ThyssenKrupp AG; *Int'l*, pg. 7732
THYSSENKRUPP BILSTEIN GMBH—See ThyssenKrupp AG; *Int'l*, pg. 7732
THYSSENKRUPP BILSTEIN OF AMERICA INC.—See ThyssenKrupp AG; *Int'l*, pg. 7732
THYSSEN KRUPP BILSTEIN OF AMERICA INC.—See ThyssenKrupp AG; *Int'l*, pg. 7732
THYSSENKRUPP BOUWSYSTEMEN B. V.—See ThyssenKrupp AG; *Int'l*, pg. 7727
THYSSENKRUPP BUDD CO.—See ThyssenKrupp AG; *Int'l*, pg. 7732
THYSSENKRUPP BULKTEC (CHINA) LTD.—See ThyssenKrupp AG; *Int'l*, pg. 7732
THYSSENKRUPP BYGGESYSTEM A/S—See ThyssenKrupp AG; *Int'l*, pg. 7727
THYSSENKRUPP CADILLAC PLASTIC S.A.S.—See ThyssenKrupp AG; *Int'l*, pg. 7727
THYSSENKRUPP CANADA, INC.—See ThyssenKrupp AG; *Int'l*, pg. 7727
THYSSENKRUPP CARBON COMPONENTS GMBH—See ThyssenKrupp AG; *Int'l*, pg. 7735
THYSSENKRUPP (CHINA) LTD.—See ThyssenKrupp AG; *Int'l*, pg. 7726

THYSSENKRUPP CHRISTON N.V.—See ThyssenKrupp AG; *Int'l*, pg. 7727
THYSSENKRUPP COMERCIAL COLOMBIA S.A.—See ThyssenKrupp AG; *Int'l*, pg. 7727
THYSSENKRUPP COMPONENTS TECHNOLOGY HUNGARY KFT.—See ThyssenKrupp AG; *Int'l*, pg. 7735
THYSSENKRUPP CRANKSHAFT COMPANY—See ThyssenKrupp AG; *Int'l*, pg. 7732
THYSSENKRUPP DELICATE GMBH—See ThyssenKrupp AG; *Int'l*, pg. 7727
THYSSENKRUPP DIZALA D.O.O.—See ThyssenKrupp AG; *Int'l*, pg. 7735
THYSSENKRUPP DVIGALA D.O.O.—See ThyssenKrupp AG; *Int'l*, pg. 7733
THYSSENKRUPP DYNAMIC COMPONENTS CHANGZHOU LTD.—See ThyssenKrupp AG; *Int'l*, pg. 7733
THYSSENKRUPP DYNAMIC COMPONENTS CHEMNITZ GMBH—See ThyssenKrupp AG; *Int'l*, pg. 7733
THYSSENKRUPP DYNAMIC COMPONENTS DANVILLE, LLC—See ThyssenKrupp AG; *Int'l*, pg. 7733
THYSSENKRUPP DYNAMIC COMPONENTS DANVILLE LLC—See ThyssenKrupp AG; *Int'l*, pg. 7733
THYSSENKRUPP DYNAMIC COMPONENTS TECCENTER AG—See ThyssenKrupp AG; *Int'l*, pg. 7733
THYSSENKRUPP EDELSTAHL-SERVICE-CENTER GMBH—See ThyssenKrupp AG; *Int'l*, pg. 7735
THYSSENKRUPP ELECTRICAL STEEL GMBH—See ThyssenKrupp AG; *Int'l*, pg. 7730
THYSSENKRUPP ELECTRICAL STEEL INDIA PRIVATE LTD.—See ThyssenKrupp AG; *Int'l*, pg. 7735
THYSSENKRUPP ELECTRICAL STEEL VERWALTUNGSGESELLSCHAFT MBH—See ThyssenKrupp AG; *Int'l*, pg. 7735
THYSSENKRUPP ELEVADORES S.A.C.—See Advent International Corporation; *U.S. Private*, pg. 106
THYSSENKRUPP ELEVADORES S.A.C.—See Cinven Limited; *Int'l*, pg. 1614
THYSSENKRUPP ELEVADORES S.A.C.—See RAG-Stiftung; *Int'l*, pg. 6180
THYSSENKRUPP ELEVADORES, S.A. DE C.V.—See Advent International Corporation; *U.S. Private*, pg. 106
THYSSENKRUPP ELEVADORES, S.A. DE C.V.—See Cinven Limited; *Int'l*, pg. 1614
THYSSENKRUPP ELEVADORES, S.A. DE C.V.—See RAG-Stiftung; *Int'l*, pg. 6180
THYSSENKRUPP ELEVADORES, S.A.—See Advent International Corporation; *U.S. Private*, pg. 106
THYSSENKRUPP ELEVADORES, S.A.—See Cinven Limited; *Int'l*, pg. 1614
THYSSENKRUPP ELEVADORES, S.A.—See RAG-Stiftung; *Int'l*, pg. 6180
THYSSENKRUPP ELEVADORES, S.A.—See Advent International Corporation; *U.S. Private*, pg. 106
THYSSENKRUPP ELEVADORES, S.A.—See Advent International Corporation; *U.S. Private*, pg. 106
THYSSENKRUPP ELEVADORES, S.A.—See Advent International Corporation; *U.S. Private*, pg. 106
THYSSENKRUPP ELEVADORES, S.A.—See Advent International Corporation; *U.S. Private*, pg. 106
THYSSENKRUPP ELEVADORES, S.A.—See Advent International Corporation; *U.S. Private*, pg. 106
THYSSENKRUPP ELEVADORES S.A.—See Cinven Limited; *Int'l*, pg. 1614
THYSSENKRUPP ELEVADORES, S.A.—See Cinven Limited; *Int'l*, pg. 1614
THYSSENKRUPP ELEVADORES, S.A.—See Cinven Limited; *Int'l*, pg. 1614
THYSSENKRUPP ELEVADORES, S.A.—See Cinven Limited; *Int'l*, pg. 1614
THYSSENKRUPP ELEVADORES, S.A.—See Cinven Limited; *Int'l*, pg. 1614
THYSSENKRUPP ELEVADORES, S.A.—See Cinven Limited; *Int'l*, pg. 1614
THYSSENKRUPP ELEVADORES S.A.—See RAG-Stiftung; *Int'l*, pg. 6180
THYSSENKRUPP ELEVADORES S.A.—See RAG-Stiftung; *Int'l*, pg. 6180
THYSSENKRUPP ELEVADORES, S.A.—See RAG-Stiftung; *Int'l*, pg. 6180
THYSSENKRUPP ELEVADORES, S.A.—See RAG-Stiftung; *Int'l*, pg. 6180
THYSSENKRUPP ELEVADORES, S.A.—See RAG-Stiftung; *Int'l*, pg. 6180
THYSSENKRUPP ELEVADORES, S.A.—See RAG-Stiftung; *Int'l*, pg. 6180
THYSSENKRUPP ELEVADORES, S.L.—See Advent International Corporation; *U.S. Private*, pg. 106
THYSSENKRUPP ELEVADORES, S.L.—See Cinven Limited; *Int'l*, pg. 1614
THYSSENKRUPP ELEVADORES, S.L.—See RAG-Stiftung; *Int'l*, pg. 6180
THYSSENKRUPP ELEVADORES, S.R.L.—See Advent International Corporation; *U.S. Private*, pg. 106
THYSSENKRUPP ELEVADORES, S.R.L.—See Cinven Limited; *Int'l*, pg. 1614

THYSSENKRUPP AG — CORPORATE AFFILIATIONS

THYSSENKRUPP ELEVADORES, S.R.L.—See RAG-Stiftung; *Int'l*, pg. 6180
THYSSENKRUPP ELEVADORES, S.R.L.—See ThyssenKrupp AG; *Int'l*, pg. 7735
THYSSENKRUPP ELEVATOR ALMOAYYED W.L.L.—See Advent International Corporation; *U.S. Private*, pg. 106
THYSSENKRUPP ELEVATOR ALMOAYYED W.L.L.—See Cinven Limited; *Int'l*, pg. 1615
THYSSENKRUPP ELEVATOR ALMOAYYED W.L.L.—See RAG-Stiftung; *Int'l*, pg. 6180
THYSSENKRUPP ELEVATOR AMERICAS CORP.—See Advent International Corporation; *U.S. Private*, pg. 106
THYSSENKRUPP ELEVATOR AMERICAS CORP.—See Cinven Limited; *Int'l*, pg. 1615
THYSSENKRUPP ELEVATOR AMERICAS CORP.—See RAG-Stiftung; *Int'l*, pg. 6180
THYSSENKRUPP ELEVATOR ASIA PACIFIC LTD.—See Advent International Corporation; *U.S. Private*, pg. 107
THYSSENKRUPP ELEVATOR ASIA PACIFIC LTD.—See Cinven Limited; *Int'l*, pg. 1615
THYSSENKRUPP ELEVATOR ASIA PACIFIC LTD.—See RAG-Stiftung; *Int'l*, pg. 6180
THYSSENKRUPP ELEVATOR A/S—See Advent International Corporation; *U.S. Private*, pg. 106
THYSSENKRUPP ELEVATOR A/S—See Advent International Corporation; *U.S. Private*, pg. 106
THYSSENKRUPP ELEVATOR A/S—See Cinven Limited; *Int'l*, pg. 1614
THYSSENKRUPP ELEVATOR A/S—See Cinven Limited; *Int'l*, pg. 1614
THYSSENKRUPP ELEVATOR A/S—See RAG-Stiftung; *Int'l*, pg. 6180
THYSSENKRUPP ELEVATOR A/S—See RAG-Stiftung; *Int'l*, pg. 6180
THYSSENKRUPP ELEVATOR AUSTRALIA PTY. LTD.—See ThyssenKrupp AG; *Int'l*, pg. 7735
THYSSENKRUPP ELEVATOR (BD) PVT. LTD.—See Advent International Corporation; *U.S. Private*, pg. 106
THYSSENKRUPP ELEVATOR (BD) PVT. LTD.—See Cinven Limited; *Int'l*, pg. 1614
THYSSENKRUPP ELEVATOR (BD) PVT. LTD.—See RAG-Stiftung; *Int'l*, pg. 6180
THYSSENKRUPP ELEVATOR BERGEN—See ThyssenKrupp AG; *Int'l*, pg. 7727
THYSSENKRUPP ELEVATOR B.V.—See Advent International Corporation; *U.S. Private*, pg. 106
THYSSENKRUPP ELEVATOR B.V.—See Cinven Limited; *Int'l*, pg. 1615
THYSSENKRUPP ELEVATOR B.V.—See RAG-Stiftung; *Int'l*, pg. 6180
THYSSENKRUPP ELEVATOR CANADA LTD.—See Advent International Corporation; *U.S. Private*, pg. 107
THYSSENKRUPP ELEVATOR CANADA LTD.—See Cinven Limited; *Int'l*, pg. 1615
THYSSENKRUPP ELEVATOR CANADA LTD.—See RAG-Stiftung; *Int'l*, pg. 6180
THYSSENKRUPP ELEVATOR CAPITAL CORP.—See Advent International Corporation; *U.S. Private*, pg. 106
THYSSENKRUPP ELEVATOR CAPITAL CORP.—See Cinven Limited; *Int'l*, pg. 1615
THYSSENKRUPP ELEVATOR CAPITAL CORP.—See RAG-Stiftung; *Int'l*, pg. 6180
THYSSENKRUPP ELEVATOR (CENE) INFRASTRUKTUR GMBH—See ThyssenKrupp AG; *Int'l*, pg. 7727
THYSSENKRUPP ELEVATOR CORP.—See Advent International Corporation; *U.S. Private*, pg. 106
THYSSENKRUPP ELEVATOR CORP.—See Cinven Limited; *Int'l*, pg. 1615
THYSSENKRUPP ELEVATOR CORP.—See RAG-Stiftung; *Int'l*, pg. 6180
THYSSENKRUPP ELEVATOR - EGYPT S.A.E.—See ThyssenKrupp AG; *Int'l*, pg. 7735
THYSSENKRUPP ELEVATOR & ESCALATOR (SHANGHAI) CO.LTD.—See Advent International Corporation; *U.S. Private*, pg. 106
THYSSENKRUPP ELEVATOR & ESCALATOR (SHANGHAI) CO.LTD.—See Cinven Limited; *Int'l*, pg. 1614
THYSSENKRUPP ELEVATOR & ESCALATOR (SHANGHAI) CO.LTD.—See RAG-Stiftung; *Int'l*, pg. 6180
THYSSENKRUPP ELEVATOR (HK) LTD.—See Advent International Corporation; *U.S. Private*, pg. 106
THYSSENKRUPP ELEVATOR (HK) LTD.—See Cinven Limited; *Int'l*, pg. 1614
THYSSENKRUPP ELEVATOR (HK) LTD.—See RAG-Stiftung; *Int'l*, pg. 6180
THYSSENKRUPP ELEVATOR HOLDING FRANCE S.A.S.—See Advent International Corporation; *U.S. Private*, pg. 107
THYSSENKRUPP ELEVATOR HOLDING FRANCE S.A.S.—See Cinven Limited; *Int'l*, pg. 1615
THYSSENKRUPP ELEVATOR HOLDING FRANCE S.A.S.—See RAG-Stiftung; *Int'l*, pg. 6180
THYSSENKRUPP ELEVATORI D.O.O.—See Advent International Corporation; *U.S. Private*, pg. 107
THYSSENKRUPP ELEVATORI D.O.O.—See Cinven Limited; *Int'l*, pg. 1615
THYSSENKRUPP ELEVATORI D.O.O.—See RAG-Stiftung; *Int'l*, pg. 6181
THYSSENKRUPP ELEVATOR INC.—See Advent International Corporation; *U.S. Private*, pg. 106
THYSSENKRUPP ELEVATOR INC.—See Cinven Limited; *Int'l*, pg. 1615
THYSSENKRUPP ELEVATOR INC.—See RAG-Stiftung; *Int'l*, pg. 6180
THYSSENKRUPP ELEVATOR (INDIA) PRIVATE LIMITED—See Advent International Corporation; *U.S. Private*, pg. 106
THYSSENKRUPP ELEVATOR (INDIA) PRIVATE LIMITED—See Cinven Limited; *Int'l*, pg. 1614
THYSSENKRUPP ELEVATOR (INDIA) PRIVATE LIMITED—See RAG-Stiftung; *Int'l*, pg. 6180
THYSSENKRUPP ELEVATOR INNOVATION CENTER, S.A.—See Advent International Corporation; *U.S. Private*, pg. 107
THYSSENKRUPP ELEVATOR INNOVATION CENTER, S.A.—See Cinven Limited; *Int'l*, pg. 1615
THYSSENKRUPP ELEVATOR INNOVATION CENTER, S.A.—See RAG-Stiftung; *Int'l*, pg. 6180
THYSSENKRUPP ELEVATOR IRELAND, LTD.—See Advent International Corporation; *U.S. Private*, pg. 107
THYSSENKRUPP ELEVATOR IRELAND, LTD.—See Cinven Limited; *Int'l*, pg. 1615
THYSSENKRUPP ELEVATOR IRELAND, LTD.—See RAG-Stiftung; *Int'l*, pg. 6180
THYSSENKRUPP ELEVATOR ISRAEL LP—See ThyssenKrupp AG; *Int'l*, pg. 7735
THYSSENKRUPP ELEVATOR ITALIA S.P.A.—See Advent International Corporation; *U.S. Private*, pg. 107
THYSSENKRUPP ELEVATOR ITALIA S.P.A.—See Cinven Limited; *Int'l*, pg. 1615
THYSSENKRUPP ELEVATOR ITALIA S.P.A.—See RAG-Stiftung; *Int'l*, pg. 6180
THYSSENKRUPP ELEVATOR/JORDAN LTD. CO.—See ThyssenKrupp AG; *Int'l*, pg. 7735
THYSSENKRUPP ELEVATOR (KOREA) LTD. - CHEONAN PLANT—See Advent International Corporation; *U.S. Private*, pg. 106
THYSSENKRUPP ELEVATOR (KOREA) LTD. - CHEONAN PLANT—See Cinven Limited; *Int'l*, pg. 1614
THYSSENKRUPP ELEVATOR (KOREA) LTD. - CHEONAN PLANT—See RAG-Stiftung; *Int'l*, pg. 6180
THYSSENKRUPP ELEVATOR (KOREA) LTD.—See Advent International Corporation; *U.S. Private*, pg. 106
THYSSENKRUPP ELEVATOR (KOREA) LTD.—See Cinven Limited; *Int'l*, pg. 1614
THYSSENKRUPP ELEVATOR (KOREA) LTD.—See RAG-Stiftung; *Int'l*, pg. 6180
THYSSENKRUPP ELEVATOR KUWAIT TRADING CO. WLL.—See ThyssenKrupp AG; *Int'l*, pg. 7735
THYSSENKRUPP ELEVATOR MALAYSIA SDN. BHD.—See Advent International Corporation; *U.S. Private*, pg. 107
THYSSENKRUPP ELEVATOR MALAYSIA SDN. BHD.—See Cinven Limited; *Int'l*, pg. 1615
THYSSENKRUPP ELEVATOR MALAYSIA SDN. BHD.—See RAG-Stiftung; *Int'l*, pg. 6180
THYSSENKRUPP ELEVATOR MANUFACTURING FRANCE S.A.S.—See Advent International Corporation; *U.S. Private*, pg. 107
THYSSENKRUPP ELEVATOR MANUFACTURING FRANCE S.A.S.—See Cinven Limited; *Int'l*, pg. 1615
THYSSENKRUPP ELEVATOR MANUFACTURING FRANCE S.A.S.—See RAG-Stiftung; *Int'l*, pg. 6180
THYSSENKRUPP ELEVATOR MANUFACTURING INC.—See Advent International Corporation; *U.S. Private*, pg. 107
THYSSENKRUPP ELEVATOR MANUFACTURING INC.—See Cinven Limited; *Int'l*, pg. 1615
THYSSENKRUPP ELEVATOR MANUFACTURING INC.—See RAG-Stiftung; *Int'l*, pg. 6180
THYSSENKRUPP ELEVATOR MANUFACTURING SPAIN S.L.—See Advent International Corporation; *U.S. Private*, pg. 107
THYSSENKRUPP ELEVATOR MANUFACTURING SPAIN S.L.—See Cinven Limited; *Int'l*, pg. 1615
THYSSENKRUPP ELEVATOR MANUFACTURING SPAIN S.L.—See RAG-Stiftung; *Int'l*, pg. 6181
THYSSENKRUPP ELEVATOR MYANMAR LIMITED—See ThyssenKrupp AG; *Int'l*, pg. 7735
THYSSENKRUPP ELEVATOR NEW ZEALAND LTD.—See ThyssenKrupp AG; *Int'l*, pg. 7735
THYSSENKRUPP ELEVATOR QUEENSLAND PTY. LTD.—See Advent International Corporation; *U.S. Private*, pg. 107
THYSSENKRUPP ELEVATOR QUEENSLAND PTY. LTD.—See Cinven Limited; *Int'l*, pg. 1615
THYSSENKRUPP ELEVATOR QUEENSLAND PTY. LTD.—See RAG-Stiftung; *Int'l*, pg. 6181
THYSSENKRUPP ELEVATOR SAUDI CO. LTD.—See Advent International Corporation; *U.S. Private*, pg. 107
THYSSENKRUPP ELEVATOR SAUDI CO. LTD.—See Cinven Limited; *Int'l*, pg. 1615
THYSSENKRUPP ELEVATOR SAUDI CO. LTD.—See RAG-Stiftung; *Int'l*, pg. 6181
THYSSENKRUPP ELEVATORS HELLAS S.A.—See Advent International Corporation; *U.S. Private*, pg. 107
THYSSENKRUPP ELEVATORS HELLAS S.A.—See Cinven Limited; *Int'l*, pg. 1615
THYSSENKRUPP ELEVATORS HELLAS S.A.—See RAG-Stiftung; *Int'l*, pg. 6181
THYSSENKRUPP ELEVATOR (SINGAPORE) PTE.LTD.—See Advent International Corporation; *U.S. Private*, pg. 106
THYSSENKRUPP ELEVATOR (SINGAPORE) PTE.LTD.—See Cinven Limited; *Int'l*, pg. 1614
THYSSENKRUPP ELEVATOR (SINGAPORE) PTE.LTD.—See RAG-Stiftung; *Int'l*, pg. 6180
THYSSENKRUPP ELEVATOR—See Advent International Corporation; *U.S. Private*, pg. 106
THYSSENKRUPP ELEVATOR—See Cinven Limited; *Int'l*, pg. 1615
THYSSENKRUPP ELEVATOR—See RAG-Stiftung; *Int'l*, pg. 6180
THYSSENKRUPP ELEVATOR—See Advent International Corporation; *U.S. Private*, pg. 106
THYSSENKRUPP ELEVATOR—See Cinven Limited; *Int'l*, pg. 1615
THYSSENKRUPP ELEVATOR—See RAG-Stiftung; *Int'l*, pg. 6180
THYSSENKRUPP ELEVATOR SOUTHERN EUROPE, AFRICA & MIDDLE EAST, S.L.U.—See Advent International Corporation; *U.S. Private*, pg. 107
THYSSENKRUPP ELEVATOR SOUTHERN EUROPE, AFRICA & MIDDLE EAST, S.L.U.—See Cinven Limited; *Int'l*, pg. 1615
THYSSENKRUPP ELEVATOR SOUTHERN EUROPE, AFRICA & MIDDLE EAST, S.L.U.—See RAG-Stiftung; *Int'l*, pg. 6181
THYSSENKRUPP ELEVATOR SP. Z O.O.—See Advent International Corporation; *U.S. Private*, pg. 107
THYSSENKRUPP ELEVATOR SP. Z O.O.—See Cinven Limited; *Int'l*, pg. 1615
THYSSENKRUPP ELEVATOR SP. Z O.O.—See RAG-Stiftung; *Int'l*, pg. 6181
THYSSENKRUPP ELEVATOR SRL—See Advent International Corporation; *U.S. Private*, pg. 107
THYSSENKRUPP ELEVATOR SRL—See Cinven Limited; *Int'l*, pg. 1615
THYSSENKRUPP ELEVATOR SRL—See RAG-Stiftung; *Int'l*, pg. 6181
THYSSENKRUPP ELEVATORS (SHANGHAI) CO., LTD.—See Advent International Corporation; *U.S. Private*, pg. 107
THYSSENKRUPP ELEVATORS (SHANGHAI) CO., LTD.—See Cinven Limited; *Int'l*, pg. 1615
THYSSENKRUPP ELEVATORS (SHANGHAI) CO., LTD.—See RAG-Stiftung; *Int'l*, pg. 6181
THYSSENKRUPP ELEVATOR SVERIGE AB—See Advent International Corporation; *U.S. Private*, pg. 107
THYSSENKRUPP ELEVATOR SVERIGE AB—See Cinven Limited; *Int'l*, pg. 1615
THYSSENKRUPP ELEVATOR SVERIGE AB—See RAG-Stiftung; *Int'l*, pg. 6181
THYSSENKRUPP ELEVATOR (TAIWAN) CO., LTD.—See ThyssenKrupp AG; *Int'l*, pg. 7735
THYSSENKRUPP ELEVATOR (THAILAND) CO., LTD.—See ThyssenKrupp AG; *Int'l*, pg. 7735
THYSSENKRUPP ELEVATOR UAE LLC—See ThyssenKrupp AG; *Int'l*, pg. 7735
THYSSENKRUPP ELEVATOR UK LTD.—See Advent International Corporation; *U.S. Private*, pg. 107
THYSSENKRUPP ELEVATOR UK LTD.—See Cinven Limited; *Int'l*, pg. 1615
THYSSENKRUPP ELEVATOR UK LTD.—See RAG-Stiftung; *Int'l*, pg. 6181
THYSSENKRUPP ELEVATOR VIETNAM CO., LTD.—See Advent International Corporation; *U.S. Private*, pg. 107
THYSSENKRUPP ELEVATOR VIETNAM CO., LTD.—See Cinven Limited; *Int'l*, pg. 1615
THYSSENKRUPP ELEVATOR VIETNAM CO., LTD.—See RAG-Stiftung; *Int'l*, pg. 6181
THYSSENKRUPP ENCASA AS—See ThyssenKrupp AG; *Int'l*, pg. 7727
THYSSENKRUPP ENCASA N.V.—See ThyssenKrupp AG; *Int'l*, pg. 7727
THYSSENKRUPP ENCASA S.L.—See ThyssenKrupp AG; *Int'l*, pg. 7727
THYSSENKRUPP ENGINE COMPONENTS (CHINA) CO., LTD.—See ThyssenKrupp AG; *Int'l*, pg. 7727
THYSSENKRUPP ENGINEERING (PROPRIETARY) LTD.—See ThyssenKrupp AG; *Int'l*, pg. 7727
THYSSENKRUPP EPITOELEMEK KFT—See ThyssenKrupp AG; *Int'l*, pg. 7730
THYSSENKRUPP ESCALATOR CO. (CHINA) LTD.—See ThyssenKrupp AG; *Int'l*, pg. 7735
THYSSENKRUPP FAHRTREPPEN GMBH—See ThyssenKrupp AG; *Int'l*, pg. 7727
THYSSENKRUPP FAWER LIAOYANG SPRING CO., LTD.—See ThyssenKrupp AG; *Int'l*, pg. 7727
THYSSENKRUPP FEDERN GMBH—See ThyssenKrupp AG; *Int'l*, pg. 7727
THYSSENKRUPP FEDERN UND STABILISATOREN GMBH—See ThyssenKrupp AG; *Int'l*, pg. 7735
THYSSENKRUPP FEROSTAV, SPOL. S R.O.—See ThyssenKrupp AG; *Int'l*, pg. 7727

COMPANY NAME INDEX

THYSSENKRUPP AG

THYSSENKRUPP FERROGLOBUS KERESKEDELMI ZRT—See ThyssenKrupp AG; *Int'l*, pg. 7734
THYSSENKRUPP FERTILIZER TECHNOLOGY GMBH—See ThyssenKrupp AG; *Int'l*, pg. 7735
THYSSENKRUPP FINANCE NEDERLAND B.V.—See ThyssenKrupp AG; *Int'l*, pg. 7727
THYSSENKRUPP FINANCE USA, INC.—See ThyssenKrupp AG; *Int'l*, pg. 7727
THYSSENKRUPP FOERDERTECHNIK GMBH—See ThyssenKrupp AG; *Int'l*, pg. 7732
THYSSENKRUPP GALMED, S.A.—See ThyssenKrupp AG; *Int'l*, pg. 7727
THYSSEN KRUPP GERLACH GMBH—See ThyssenKrupp AG; *Int'l*, pg. 7731
THYSSENKRUPP GERLACH GMBH—See ThyssenKrupp AG; *Int'l*, pg. 7727
THYSSENKRUPP GFT GLEISTECHNIK GMBH—See ThyssenKrupp AG; *Int'l*, pg. 7727
THYSSENKRUPP GFT POLSKA SP. Z O.O.—See ThyssenKrupp AG; *Int'l*, pg. 7727
THYSSENKRUPP GFT TIEFBAUTECHNIK GMBH—See ThyssenKrupp AG; *Int'l*, pg. 7727
THYSSENKRUPP GRUNDBESITZ-VERMIETUNGS GMBH & CO. KG—See ThyssenKrupp AG; *Int'l*, pg. 7727
THYSSENKRUPP HISERV S.R.O.—See ThyssenKrupp AG; *Int'l*, pg. 7727
THYSSENKRUPP HOHENLIMBURG KOMPETENZWERKSTATT GMBH—See ThyssenKrupp AG; *Int'l*, pg. 7735
THYSSENKRUPP HOME SOLUTIONS S.R.L.—See ThyssenKrupp AG; *Int'l*, pg. 7735
THYSSENKRUPP INDIA PRIVATE LIMITED—See ThyssenKrupp AG; *Int'l*, pg. 7735
THYSSENKRUPP INDUSTRIAL SERVICES CANADA, INC.—See ThyssenKrupp AG; *Int'l*, pg. 7729
THYSSENKRUPP INDUSTRIAL SERVICES NA, INC.—See ThyssenKrupp AG; *Int'l*, pg. 7727
THYSSENKRUPP INDUSTRIAL SOLUTIONS ARGENTINA S.A.—See ThyssenKrupp AG; *Int'l*, pg. 7734
THYSSENKRUPP INDUSTRIAL SOLUTIONS (ASIA PACIFIC) PTE. LTD.—See ThyssenKrupp AG; *Int'l*, pg. 7735
THYSSENKRUPP INDUSTRIAL SOLUTIONS (AUSTRALIA) PTY LTD—See ThyssenKrupp AG; *Int'l*, pg. 7732
THYSSENKRUPP INDUSTRIAL SOLUTIONS BRN SDN. BHD.—See ThyssenKrupp AG; *Int'l*, pg. 7735
THYSSENKRUPP INDUSTRIAL SOLUTIONS (CANADA) INC.—See ThyssenKrupp AG; *Int'l*, pg. 7735
THYSSENKRUPP INDUSTRIAL SOLUTIONS (CHILE) LIMITADA—See ThyssenKrupp AG; *Int'l*, pg. 7733
THYSSENKRUPP INDUSTRIAL SOLUTIONS (CHINA) CO., LTD.—See ThyssenKrupp AG; *Int'l*, pg. 7735
THYSSENKRUPP INDUSTRIAL SOLUTIONS (CZ) S.R.O.—See ThyssenKrupp AG; *Int'l*, pg. 7733
THYSSENKRUPP INDUSTRIAL SOLUTIONS EGYPT COMPANY S.A.E.—See ThyssenKrupp AG; *Int'l*, pg. 7734
THYSSENKRUPP INDUSTRIAL SOLUTIONS (FRANCE) S.A.S.—See ThyssenKrupp AG; *Int'l*, pg. 7733
THYSSENKRUPP INDUSTRIAL SOLUTIONS (INDIA) PVT. LTD.—See ThyssenKrupp AG; *Int'l*, pg. 7733
THYSSENKRUPP INDUSTRIAL SOLUTIONS (MALAYSIA) SDN. BHD.—See ThyssenKrupp AG; *Int'l*, pg. 7735
THYSSENKRUPP INDUSTRIAL SOLUTIONS (MEXICO) S.A. DE C.V.—See ThyssenKrupp AG; *Int'l*, pg. 7735
THYSSENKRUPP INDUSTRIAL SOLUTIONS—See ThyssenKrupp AG; *Int'l*, pg. 7732
THYSSENKRUPP INDUSTRIAL SOLUTIONS (SOUTH AFRICA) PTY LTD.—See ThyssenKrupp AG; *Int'l*, pg. 7727
THYSSENKRUPP INDUSTRIAL SOLUTIONS (THAILAND) LTD.—See ThyssenKrupp AG; *Int'l*, pg. 7734
THYSSENKRUPP INDUSTRIAL SOLUTIONS (USA), INC.—See ThyssenKrupp AG; *Int'l*, pg. 7735
THYSSENKRUPP INDUSTRIAL SOLUTIONS (USA), INC.—See ThyssenKrupp AG; *Int'l*, pg. 7727
THYSSENKRUPP INDUSTRIAL SOLUTIONS (VIETNAM) LTD.—See ThyssenKrupp AG; *Int'l*, pg. 7735
THYSSENKRUPP INDUSTRIES INDIA PVT. LTD.—See ThyssenKrupp AG; *Int'l*, pg. 7727
THYSSENKRUPP INFRASTRUCTURE BRASIL LTDA.—See ThyssenKrupp AG; *Int'l*, pg. 7735
THYSSENKRUPP INFRASTRUCTURE GMBH—See ThyssenKrupp AG; *Int'l*, pg. 7735
THYSSENKRUPP INGENIERIA CHILE LTDA.—See ThyssenKrupp AG; *Int'l*, pg. 7727
THYSSENKRUPP ITALIA HOLDING S.R.L.—See ThyssenKrupp AG; *Int'l*, pg. 7727
THYSSENKRUPP JAPAN K.K.—See ThyssenKrupp AG; *Int'l*, pg. 7735
THYSSENKRUPP KH MINERAL S.A.S.—See ThyssenKrupp AG; *Int'l*, pg. 7727
THYSSENKRUPP LIFTEN ASCENSEURS N.V.-S.A.—See ThyssenKrupp AG; *Int'l*, pg. 7727
THYSSENKRUPP LIFTEN B.V.—See ThyssenKrupp AG; *Int'l*, pg. 7727
THYSSENKRUPP LIFT KFT—See ThyssenKrupp AG; *Int'l*, pg. 7727
THYSSENKRUPP LOGISTICS, INC.—See ThyssenKrupp AG; *Int'l*, pg. 7727
THYSSENKRUPP MANAGEMENT CONSULTING GMBH—See ThyssenKrupp AG; *Int'l*, pg. 7727
THYSSENKRUPP MANNEX GMBH—See ThyssenKrupp AG; *Int'l*, pg. 7729
THYSSENKRUPP MANNEX PTY. LTD.—See ThyssenKrupp AG; *Int'l*, pg. 7727
THYSSENKRUPP MANNEX SVERIGE AB—See ThyssenKrupp AG; *Int'l*, pg. 7727
THYSSENKRUPP MANNEX UK LTD.—See ThyssenKrupp AG; *Int'l*, pg. 7728
THYSSENKRUPP MARINE SYSTEMS AG—See ThyssenKrupp AG; *Int'l*, pg. 7732
THYSSENKRUPP MARINE SYSTEMS AUSTRALIA PTY LTD—See ThyssenKrupp AG; *Int'l*, pg. 7733
THYSSENKRUPP MARINE SYSTEMS CANADA LTD.—See ThyssenKrupp AG; *Int'l*, pg. 7733
THYSSENKRUPP MARINE SYSTEMS GMBH—See OEP Capital Advisors, L.P.; *U.S. Private*, pg. 3000
THYSSENKRUPP MARINE SYSTEMS GMBH—See ThyssenKrupp AG; *Int'l*, pg. 7733
THYSSENKRUPP MARIN SISTEM GEMI SANAYI VE TICARET A.S.—See ThyssenKrupp AG; *Int'l*, pg. 7733
THYSSENKRUPP MATERIAL PROCESSING EUROPE GMBH—See ThyssenKrupp AG; *Int'l*, pg. 7734
THYSSENKRUPP MATERIALS AUSTRALIA PTY. LTD.—See ThyssenKrupp AG; *Int'l*, pg. 7735
THYSSENKRUPP MATERIALS AUSTRIA GMBH—See ThyssenKrupp AG; *Int'l*, pg. 7728
THYSSENKRUPP MATERIALS BELGIUM N.V.—See ThyssenKrupp AG; *Int'l*, pg. 7736
THYSSENKRUPP MATERIALS BULGARIA—See ThyssenKrupp AG; *Int'l*, pg. 7736
THYSSENKRUPP MATERIALS CA LTD.—See ThyssenKrupp AG; *Int'l*, pg. 7729
THYSSENKRUPP MATERIALS D.O.O.—See ThyssenKrupp AG; *Int'l*, pg. 7728
THYSSENKRUPP MATERIALS FRANCE S.A.S.—See ThyssenKrupp AG; *Int'l*, pg. 7728
THYSSENKRUPP MATERIALS HOLDING (THAILAND) LTD.—See ThyssenKrupp AG; *Int'l*, pg. 7728
THYSSENKRUPP MATERIALS HUNGARY ZRT.—See ThyssenKrupp AG; *Int'l*, pg. 7736
THYSSENKRUPP MATERIALS IBERICA S.A.—See ThyssenKrupp AG; *Int'l*, pg. 7729
THYSSENKRUPP MATERIALS IBERICA S.A.U.—See ThyssenKrupp AG; *Int'l*, pg. 7728
THYSSENKRUPP MATERIALS IOT GMBH—See ThyssenKrupp AG; *Int'l*, pg. 7736
THYSSENKRUPP MATERIALS KOREA COMPANY LTD.—See ThyssenKrupp AG; *Int'l*, pg. 7728
THYSSENKRUPP MATERIALS, LLC—See ThyssenKrupp AG; *Int'l*, pg. 7728
THYSSENKRUPP MATERIALS NA—See ThyssenKrupp AG; *Int'l*, pg. 7729
THYSSENKRUPP MATERIALS NEDERLAND B.V.—See ThyssenKrupp AG; *Int'l*, pg. 7728
THYSSENKRUPP MATERIALS POLAND SA—See ThyssenKrupp AG; *Int'l*, pg. 7728
THYSSENKRUPP MATERIALS PROCESSING EUROPE GMBH—See ThyssenKrupp AG; *Int'l*, pg. 7734
THYSSENKRUPP MATERIALS PROCESSING EUROPE, S.L.—See ThyssenKrupp AG; *Int'l*, pg. 7736
THYSSENKRUPP MATERIALS PROCESSING EUROPE SP. Z O.O.—See ThyssenKrupp AG; *Int'l*, pg. 7736
THYSSENKRUPP MATERIALS PROCESSING HUNGARY KFT.—See ThyssenKrupp AG; *Int'l*, pg. 7734
THYSSENKRUPP MATERIALS ROMANIA S.R.L.—See ThyssenKrupp AG; *Int'l*, pg. 7728
THYSSENKRUPP MATERIALS SCHWEIZ AG—See ThyssenKrupp AG; *Int'l*, pg. 7728
THYSSENKRUPP MATERIALS SERVICES GMBH—See ThyssenKrupp AG; *Int'l*, pg. 7734
THYSSENKRUPP MATERIALS (SHANGHAI) CO., LTD.—See ThyssenKrupp AG; *Int'l*, pg. 7729
THYSSENKRUPP MATERIALS SLOVAKIA SPOL. S R.O.—See ThyssenKrupp AG; *Int'l*, pg. 7736
THYSSENKRUPP MATERIALS SVERIGE AB—See ThyssenKrupp AG; *Int'l*, pg. 7728
THYSSENKRUPP MATERIALS SWEDEN—See ThyssenKrupp AG; *Int'l*, pg. 7730
THYSSENKRUPP MATERIALS SWITZERLAND AG—See ThyssenKrupp AG; *Int'l*, pg. 7728
THYSSENKRUPP MATERIALS (THAILAND) CO., LTD.—See ThyssenKrupp AG; *Int'l*, pg. 7728
THYSSENKRUPP MATERIALS TRADING ASIA PTE. LTD.—See ThyssenKrupp AG; *Int'l*, pg. 7736
THYSSENKRUPP MATERIALS TRADING CA, LTD.—See ThyssenKrupp AG; *Int'l*, pg. 7734
THYSSENKRUPP MATERIALS TRADING GMBH—See ThyssenKrupp AG; *Int'l*, pg. 7736
THYSSENKRUPP MATERIALS TURKEY METAL SANAYI VE TICARET A.S.—See ThyssenKrupp AG; *Int'l*, pg. 7736
THYSSENKRUPP MATERIALS (UK) LTD.—See ThyssenKrupp AG; *Int'l*, pg. 7729
THYSSENKRUPP MATERIALS VIETNAM LLC—See ThyssenKrupp AG; *Int'l*, pg. 7728
THYSSENKRUPP MAVILOR S.A.—See ThyssenKrupp AG; *Int'l*, pg. 7730
THYSSENKRUPP METALLURGICAL PRODUCTS CO., LTD. TIANJIN—See ThyssenKrupp AG; *Int'l*, pg. 7728
THYSSENKRUPP METALSERV GMBH—See ThyssenKrupp AG; *Int'l*, pg. 7728
THYSSENKRUPP METALURGICA CAMPO LIMPO LTDA.—See ThyssenKrupp AG; *Int'l*, pg. 7732
THYSSENKRUPP METALURGICA DE MEXICO S.A. DE C.V.—See ThyssenKrupp AG; *Int'l*, pg. 7732
THYSSENKRUPP METALURGICA SANTA LUZIA LTDA.—See ThyssenKrupp AG; *Int'l*, pg. 7728
THYSSENKRUPP METALURGICA SERVICIOS S.A. DE C.V.—See ThyssenKrupp AG; *Int'l*, pg. 7728
THYSSENKRUPP MEXINOX CREATEIT, S.A. DE C.V.—See ThyssenKrupp AG; *Int'l*, pg. 7728
THYSSENKRUPP MEXINOX S.A. DE C.V.—See ThyssenKrupp AG; *Int'l*, pg. 7730
THYSSENKRUPP MILLSERVICES & SYSTEMS GMBH—See ThyssenKrupp AG; *Int'l*, pg. 7728
THYSSENKRUPP NEDERLAND B.V.—See ThyssenKrupp AG; *Int'l*, pg. 7728
THYSSENKRUPP NEDERLAND HOLDING B.V.—See ThyssenKrupp AG; *Int'l*, pg. 7728
THYSSENKRUPP NEDERLAND INTERMEDIATE B.V.—See ThyssenKrupp AG; *Int'l*, pg. 7728
THYSSENKRUPP NIROSTA GMBH—See ThyssenKrupp AG; *Int'l*, pg. 7730
THYSSENKRUPP NORTE S.A.—See ThyssenKrupp AG; *Int'l*, pg. 7728
THYSSENKRUPP NORTHERN ELEVATOR LTD.—See Advent International Corporation; *U.S. Private*, pg. 107
THYSSENKRUPP NORTHERN ELEVATOR LTD.—See Cinven Limited; *Int'l*, pg. 1615
THYSSENKRUPP NORTHERN ELEVATOR LTD.—See RAG-Stiftung; *Int'l*, pg. 6181
THYSSENKRUPP NUCERA AG & CO. KGAA—See ThyssenKrupp AG; *Int'l*, pg. 7734
THYSSENKRUPP ONLINEMETALS, LLC—See ThyssenKrupp AG; *Int'l*, pg. 7728
THYSSENKRUPP OTTO WOLFF N.V./S.A—See ThyssenKrupp AG; *Int'l*, pg. 7728
THYSSENKRUPP PALMERS LTD.—See ThyssenKrupp AG; *Int'l*, pg. 7729
THYSSENKRUPP PARTICIPATIONS B.V.—See ThyssenKrupp AG; *Int'l*, pg. 7728
THYSSENKRUPP PLASTIC IBERICA SL—See ThyssenKrupp AG; *Int'l*, pg. 7728
THYSSENKRUPP PLASTICS AUSTRIA GMBH—See ThyssenKrupp AG; *Int'l*, pg. 7728
THYSSENKRUPP PLASTICS BELGIUM N.V./S.A.—See ThyssenKrupp AG; *Int'l*, pg. 7736
THYSSENKRUPP PLASTICS FRANCE S.A.S.—See ThyssenKrupp AG; *Int'l*, pg. 7734
THYSSENKRUPP PLASTICS GMBH—See ThyssenKrupp AG; *Int'l*, pg. 7736
THYSSENKRUPP POLYSIUS AG—See ThyssenKrupp AG; *Int'l*, pg. 7728
THYSSENKRUPP POLYSIUS GMBH—See ThyssenKrupp AG; *Int'l*, pg. 7734
THYSSENKRUPP POLYSIUS PERU S.A.C.—See ThyssenKrupp AG; *Int'l*, pg. 7734
THYSSENKRUPP PORTUGAL - ACOS E SERVICOS, LDA. - NON-FERROUS-METALS DIVISION—See ThyssenKrupp AG; *Int'l*, pg. 7728
THYSSENKRUPP PRECISION FORGE INC.—See ThyssenKrupp AG; *Int'l*, pg. 7729
THYSSENKRUPP PRESTA AG—See ThyssenKrupp AG; *Int'l*, pg. 7730
THYSSENKRUPP PRESTA CHEMNITZ GMBH—See ThyssenKrupp AG; *Int'l*, pg. 7728
THYSSENKRUPP PRESTA DALIAN CO. LTD.—See ThyssenKrupp AG; *Int'l*, pg. 7728
THYSSENKRUPP PRESTA ESSLINGEN GMBH—See ThyssenKrupp AG; *Int'l*, pg. 7728
THYSSENKRUPP PRESTA FRANCE S.A.S.—See ThyssenKrupp AG; *Int'l*, pg. 7729
THYSSENKRUPP PRESTA ILSENBURG GMBH—See ThyssenKrupp AG; *Int'l*, pg. 7729
THYSSENKRUPP PRESTA NORTH AMERICA, LLC—See ThyssenKrupp AG; *Int'l*, pg. 7734
THYSSENKRUPP PRESTA SHANGHAI CO. LTD.—See ThyssenKrupp AG; *Int'l*, pg. 7729
THYSSENKRUPP PRESTA TECCENTER AG—See ThyssenKrupp AG; *Int'l*, pg. 7729
THYSSENKRUPP PRESTA TERRE HAUTE, LLC—See ThyssenKrupp AG; *Int'l*, pg. 7729
THYSSENKRUPP RASSELSTEIN GMBH—See ThyssenKrupp AG; *Int'l*, pg. 7729
THYSSENKRUPP REAL ESTATE GMBH—See ThyssenKrupp AG; *Int'l*, pg. 7733
THYSSENKRUPP ROBINS INC.—See ThyssenKrupp AG; *Int'l*, pg. 7729
THYSSENKRUPP ROTHE ERDE GERMANY GMBH—See ThyssenKrupp AG; *Int'l*, pg. 7734
THYSSENKRUPP ROTHE ERDE ITALY S.P.A.—See ThyssenKrupp AG; *Int'l*, pg. 7736
THYSSENKRUPP ROTHE ERDE JAPAN LTD.—See ThyssenKrupp AG; *Int'l*, pg. 7736
THYSSENKRUPP ROTHE ERDE SLOVAKIA A.S.—See ThyssenKrupp AG; *Int'l*, pg. 7734

THYSSENKRUPP AG

THYSSENKRUPP ROTHE ERDE SPAIN S.A.—See ThyssenKrupp AG; *Int'l*, pg. 7734
THYSSENKRUPP ROTHE ERDE UK LTD.—See ThyssenKrupp AG; *Int'l*, pg. 7736
THYSSENKRUPP ROTHE ERDE USA INC.—See ThyssenKrupp AG; *Int'l*, pg. 7736
THYSSENKRUPP ROTHE ERDE (XUZHOU) RING MILL CO., LTD.—See ThyssenKrupp AG; *Int'l*, pg. 7734
THYSSENKRUPP RULLETRAPPER A/S—See ThyssenKrupp AG; *Int'l*, pg. 7729
THYSSENKRUPP SAGENSTAHLCENTER GMBH—See ThyssenKrupp AG; *Int'l*, pg. 7729
THYSSEN KRUPP SASA S.A. DE C.V.—See ThyssenKrupp AG; *Int'l*, pg. 7732
THYSSENKRUPP SASA SERVICIOS, S.A.DE C.V.—See ThyssenKrupp AG; *Int'l*, pg. 7732
THYSSENKRUPP SAUDI ARABIA CONTRACTING COMPANY LIMITED—See ThyssenKrupp AG; *Int'l*, pg. 7736
THYSSENKRUPP SAUDI ARABIA LIMITED—See ThyssenKrupp AG; *Int'l*, pg. 7736
THYSSENKRUPP SCHULTE GMBH—See ThyssenKrupp AG; *Int'l*, pg. 7729
THYSSENKRUPP SECURITIZATION CORP.—See ThyssenKrupp AG; *Int'l*, pg. 7729
THYSSENKRUPP SERVICES AG—See ThyssenKrupp AG; *Int'l*, pg. 7729
THYSSENKRUPP SERVICIOS S.A. DE C.V.—See ThyssenKrupp AG; *Int'l*, pg. 7729
THYSSENKRUPP SILCO-INOX SZERVIZKOZPONT KFT—See ThyssenKrupp AG; *Int'l*, pg. 7729
THYSSENKRUPP SISTEME PENTRU CONSTRUCTII S.R.L.—See ThyssenKrupp AG; *Int'l*, pg. 7730
THYSSENKRUPP SOFEDIT S.A.S.—See ThyssenKrupp AG; *Int'l*, pg. 7730
THYSSENKRUPP STAHL IMMOBILIEN GMBH—See ThyssenKrupp AG; *Int'l*, pg. 7729
THYSSENKRUPP STAHLKONTOR GMBH—See ThyssenKrupp AG; *Int'l*, pg. 7729
THYSSENKRUPP STAHLUNION POLSKA SP. Z O.O.—See ThyssenKrupp AG; *Int'l*, pg. 7729
THYSSENKRUPP STAINLESS AG—See ThyssenKrupp AG; *Int'l*, pg. 7729
THYSSEN KRUPP STAINLESS DVP S.A.—See ThyssenKrupp AG; *Int'l*, pg. 7729
THYSSENKRUPP STAL DANMARK A/S—See ThyssenKrupp AG; *Int'l*, pg. 7730
THYSSENKRUPP STAL SERWIS POLSKA SP. Z O.O.—See ThyssenKrupp AG; *Int'l*, pg. 7730
THYSSENKRUPP STAVEBNI SYSTEMY S.R.O.—See ThyssenKrupp AG; *Int'l*, pg. 7730
THYSSENKRUPP STEEL AND STAINLESS USA, LLC—See ThyssenKrupp AG; *Int'l*, pg. 7730
THYSSENKRUPP STEEL (ASIA PACIFIC) PTE LTD—See ThyssenKrupp AG; *Int'l*, pg. 7730
THYSSENKRUPP STEEL CHILE SPA—See ThyssenKrupp AG; *Int'l*, pg. 7736
THYSSENKRUPP STEEL COLOMBIA S.A.S.—See ThyssenKrupp AG; *Int'l*, pg. 7736
THYSSENKRUPP STEELCOM PTY. LTD.—See ThyssenKrupp AG; *Int'l*, pg. 7730
THYSSENKRUPP STEEL DISTRIBUTION, LLC—See ThyssenKrupp AG; *Int'l*, pg. 7730
THYSSENKRUPP STEEL EUROPE AG—See ThyssenKrupp AG; *Int'l*, pg. 7730
THYSSENKRUPP STEEL JAPAN GK—See ThyssenKrupp AG; *Int'l*, pg. 7736
THYSSENKRUPP STEEL NORTH AMERICA, INC.—See ThyssenKrupp AG; *Int'l*, pg. 7730
THYSSENKRUPP STEEL SWITZERLAND AG—See ThyssenKrupp AG; *Int'l*, pg. 7736
THYSSENKRUPP STEEL ZWEITE BETEILIGUNGSGESELLSCHAFT MBH—See ThyssenKrupp AG; *Int'l*, pg. 7730
THYSSENKRUPP STOKVIS PLASTICS B.V.—See ThyssenKrupp AG; *Int'l*, pg. 7731
THYSSENKRUPP SYSTEMBAU AUSTRIA GESELLSCHAFT M.B.H.—See ThyssenKrupp AG; *Int'l*, pg. 7731
THYSSENKRUPP SYSTEM ENGINEERING GMBH—See ThyssenKrupp AG; *Int'l*, pg. 7732
THYSSENKRUPP SYSTEM ENGINEERING GMBH—See ThyssenKrupp AG; *Int'l*, pg. 7732
THYSSENKRUPP SYSTEM ENGINEERING INC.—See ThyssenKrupp AG; *Int'l*, pg. 7732
THYSSENKRUPP SYSTEM ENGINEERING INDIA PRIVATE LIMITED—See ThyssenKrupp AG; *Int'l*, pg. 7736
THYSSENKRUPP SYSTEM ENGINEERING LTD.—See ThyssenKrupp AG; *Int'l*, pg. 7731
THYSSENKRUPP SYSTEM ENGINEERING, S.A. DE C.V.—See ThyssenKrupp AG; *Int'l*, pg. 7731
THYSSENKRUPP SYSTEM ENGINEERING S.A.—See ThyssenKrupp AG; *Int'l*, pg. 7731
THYSSENKRUPP SYSTEM ENGINEERING S.A.S.—See ThyssenKrupp AG; *Int'l*, pg. 7731
THYSSENKRUPP SYSTEM ENGINEERING (SHANGHAI) CO., LTD.—See ThyssenKrupp AG; *Int'l*, pg. 7731
THYSSENKRUPP SYSTEM ENGINEERING S.R.L.—See ThyssenKrupp AG; *Int'l*, pg. 7731
THYSSENKRUPP TAILORED BLANKS CELIK SANAYI VE TICARET LTD.—See ThyssenKrupp AG; *Int'l*, pg. 7731
THYSSENKRUPP TAILORED BLANKS S.A. DE C.V.—See ThyssenKrupp AG; *Int'l*, pg. 7731
THYSSENKRUPP TAILORED BLANKS (WUHAN) LTD.—See Advent International Corporation; *U.S. Private*, pg. 107
THYSSENKRUPP TAILORED BLANKS (WUHAN) LTD.—See Cinven Limited; *Int'l*, pg. 1615
THYSSENKRUPP TAILORED BLANKS (WUHAN) LTD.—See RAG-Stiftung; *Int'l*, pg. 6181
THYSSENKRUPP TECHNOLOGIES AG—See ThyssenKrupp AG; *Int'l*, pg. 7731
THYSSENKRUPP TECHNOLOGIES (CAMBODIA) CO., LTD.—See ThyssenKrupp AG; *Int'l*, pg. 7736
THYSSENKRUPP TIEFBAUTECHNIK GMBH—See ThyssenKrupp AG; *Int'l*, pg. 7733
THYSSENKRUPP TITANIUM S.P.A.—See ThyssenKrupp AG; *Int'l*, pg. 7730
THYSSENKRUPP TRANSRAPID GMBH—See ThyssenKrupp AG; *Int'l*, pg. 7733
THYSSENKRUPP TRATAMENTOS TERMICOS—See ThyssenKrupp AG; *Int'l*, pg. 7728
THYSSENKRUPP UHDE CHLORINE ELECTROLYSIS (USA) INC.—See ThyssenKrupp AG; *Int'l*, pg. 7736
THYSSENKRUPP UHDE CHLORINE ENGINEERS GMBH—See ThyssenKrupp AG; *Int'l*, pg. 7736
THYSSENKRUPP UHDE CHLORINE ENGINEERS (ITALIA) S.R.L.—See ThyssenKrupp AG; *Int'l*, pg. 7736
THYSSENKRUPP UHDE CHLORINE ENGINEERS (JAPAN) LTD.—See ThyssenKrupp AG; *Int'l*, pg. 7736
THYSSENKRUPP UHDE CHLORINE ENGINEERS (SHANGHAI) CO., LTD.—See ThyssenKrupp AG; *Int'l*, pg. 7736
THYSSENKRUPP UHDE ENGINEERING SERVICES GMBH—See ThyssenKrupp AG; *Int'l*, pg. 7733
THYSSENKRUPP UHDE GMBH—See ThyssenKrupp AG; *Int'l*, pg. 7733
THYSSENKRUPP UHDE USA, LLC—See ThyssenKrupp AG; *Int'l*, pg. 7734
THYSSENKRUPP UK PLC—See ThyssenKrupp AG; *Int'l*, pg. 7732
THYSSENKRUPP UMFORMTECHNIK GMBH—See ThyssenKrupp AG; *Int'l*, pg. 7733
THYSSENKRUPP USA, INC.—See ThyssenKrupp AG; *Int'l*, pg. 7733
THYSSENKRUPP VALVETRAIN GMBH—See ThyssenKrupp AG; *Int'l*, pg. 7736
THYSSENKRUPP VEERHAVEN B.V.—See ThyssenKrupp AG; *Int'l*, pg. 7733
THYSSENKRUPP VYTAHY S.R.O.—See ThyssenKrupp AG; *Int'l*, pg. 7733
THYSSENKRUPP VYTAHY S.R.O.—See ThyssenKrupp AG; *Int'l*, pg. 7733
THYSSENKRUPP WERK DAHLERBRUCK—See ThyssenKrupp AG; *Int'l*, pg. 7730
THYSSENKRUPP WERK KREFELD—See ThyssenKrupp AG; *Int'l*, pg. 7730
THYSSENKRUPP XERVON CO. LTD.—See ThyssenKrupp AG; *Int'l*, pg. 7733
THYSSENKRUPP XERVON CORP. SDN. BHD.—See ThyssenKrupp AG; *Int'l*, pg. 7733
THYSSENKRUPP XERVON MALAYSIA SDN. BHD.—See ThyssenKrupp AG; *Int'l*, pg. 7733
THYSSENKRUPP XERVON NORWAY AS—See ThyssenKrupp AG; *Int'l*, pg. 7733
THYSSENKRUPP XERVON SAUDI ARABIA L.L.C.—See ThyssenKrupp AG; *Int'l*, pg. 7733
THYSSENKRUPP XERVON SWEDEN AB—See ThyssenKrupp AG; *Int'l*, pg. 7733
THYSSENKRUPP XERVON U.A.E. - L.L.C.—See ThyssenKrupp AG; *Int'l*, pg. 7733
THYSSENKRUP STEEL B.V.—See ThyssenKrupp AG; *Int'l*, pg. 7730
THYSSEN POLYMER GMBH—See ThyssenKrupp AG; *Int'l*, pg. 7731
THYSSEN'SCHE HANDELSGESELLSCHAFT M.B.H.; *Int'l*, pg. 7723
THYSSEN STAHL GMBH—See ThyssenKrupp AG; *Int'l*, pg. 7726
THYSSEN TRADING S.A.—See ThyssenKrupp AG; *Int'l*, pg. 7726
THY TEKNIK A.S.—See Turk Hava Yollari Anonim Ortakligi; *Int'l*, pg. 7975
TIAA-CREF LIFE INSURANCE COMPANY—See Teachers Insurance Association - College Retirement Fund; *U.S. Private*, pg. 3948
TIAA FSB HOLDINGS, INC.—See Teachers Insurance Association - College Retirement Fund; *U.S. Private*, pg. 3948
TIAA, FSB—See Teachers Insurance Association - College Retirement Fund; *U.S. Private*, pg. 3948
TIAA HENDERSON REAL ESTATE LTD.—See Teachers Insurance Association - College Retirement Fund; *U.S. Private*, pg. 3945
TIAAN CONSUMER LIMITED; *Int'l*, pg. 7736
TIAA REAL ESTATE ACCOUNT—See Teachers Insurance Association - College Retirement Fund; *U.S. Private*, pg. 3948

CORPORATE AFFILIATIONS

TIAB SA—See VINCI S.A.; *Int'l*, pg. 8238
TIACLASSE INC.—See Onward Holdings Co., Ltd.; *Int'l*, pg. 5593
TIALIS ESSENTIAL IT PLC; *Int'l*, pg. 7736
TIA MARUCA ARGENTINA SA; *Int'l*, pg. 7736
TIAMA S.A.—See LBO France S.a.r.l.; *Int'l*, pg. 4430
TIAMONT PTY LTD—See Linde plc; *Int'l*, pg. 4508
TIAN AN AUSTRALIA LIMITED; *Int'l*, pg. 7737
TIAN AN CHINA INVESTMENTS COMPANY LIMITED; *Int'l*, pg. 7737
TIANAN INSURANCE CO., LTD.; *Int'l*, pg. 7737
TIAN'AN PHARMACEUTICAL CO., LTD.; *U.S. Public*, pg. 2157
TIAN AN (SHANGHAI) INVESTMENTS CO., LTD.—See Tian An China Investments Company Limited; *Int'l*, pg. 7737
TIANBAO HOLDINGS LIMITED; *Int'l*, pg. 7737
TIAN CHANG GROUP HOLDINGS LTD.; *Int'l*, pg. 7737
TIANDA GROUP LIMITED; *Int'l*, pg. 7737
TIANDA PHARMACEUTICALS (AUSTRALIA) PTY LTD.—See Tianda Group Limited; *Int'l*, pg. 7738
TIANDA PHARMACEUTICALS (CHINA) LTD.—See Tianda Group Limited; *Int'l*, pg. 7738
TIANDA PHARMACEUTICALS LIMITED—See Tianda Group Limited; *Int'l*, pg. 7737
TIANDE CHEMICAL HOLDINGS LIMITED; *Int'l*, pg. 7738
TIANDI SCIENCE & TECHNOLOGY CO., LTD.; *Int'l*, pg. 7738
TIANFENG SECURITIES CO., LTD.; *Int'l*, pg. 7738
TIAN GE INTERACTIVE HOLDINGS LTD.; *Int'l*, pg. 7737
TIANGONG INTERNATIONAL COMPANY LIMITED; *Int'l*, pg. 7738
TIANGUANG FIRE-FIGHTING INCORPORATED COMPANY; *Int'l*, pg. 7738
TIANHE CHEMICALS GROUP LTD.; *Int'l*, pg. 7738
TIANJIN 712 COMMUNICATION & BROADCASTING CO., LTD.; *Int'l*, pg. 7738
TIANJIN ACE PILLAR CO., LTD.—See ACE PILLAR Co., Ltd; *Int'l*, pg. 94
TIANJIN ACE PILLAR ENTERPRISE CO., LTD.—See ACE PILLAR Co., Ltd; *Int'l*, pg. 94
TIANJIN AIRLINES CO., LTD.—See Hainan Traffic Administration Holding Co., Ltd.; *Int'l*, pg. 3216
TIANJIN AISIN AUTOMOBILE PARTS CO., LTD.—See AISIN Corporation; *Int'l*, pg. 254
TIANJIN AKZO NOBEL PEROXIDES CO. LTD—See Akzo Nobel N.V.; *Int'l*, pg. 275
TIANJIN ALPS ELECTRONICS CO., LTD.—See Alps Alpine Co., Ltd.; *Int'l*, pg. 376
TIANJIN ALPS TEDA LOGISTICS CO., LTD.—See Tianjin Binhai Teda Logistics (Group) Corporation Limited; *Int'l*, pg. 7738
TIANJIN AMPHENOL KAE CO., LTD.—See Amphenol Corporation; *U.S. Public*, pg. 132
TIANJIN APPLE NORTHERN TECH CO., LTD.—See Apple Flavor & Fragrance Group Co., Ltd.; *Int'l*, pg. 520
TIANJIN ASMO AUTOMOTIVE SMALL MOTOR CO., LTD.—See Denso Corporation; *Int'l*, pg. 2033
TIANJIN ATLANTIC WELDING CONSUMABLES SALES CO., LTD.—See Atlantic China Welding Consumables, Inc.; *Int'l*, pg. 674
TIANJIN BEIT AUTO PARTS CO., LTD.—See Shanghai Beite Technology Co., Ltd.; *Int'l*, pg. 6762
TIANJIN BENEFO TEJING ELECTRIC CO., LTD.; *Int'l*, pg. 7738
TIANJIN BENNY TRADING CO., LTD.—See Marubeni Corporation; *Int'l*, pg. 4710
TIANJIN BERONI BIOTECHNOLOGY CO., LIMITED—See Beroni Group Limited; *Int'l*, pg. 989
TIANJIN BINHAI ENERGY & DEVELOPMENT CO., LTD.; *Int'l*, pg. 7738
TIANJIN BINHAI GLOBAL PRINTING CO., LTD.—See Xi'An Global Printing Co.,LTD.; *Int'l*, pg. 8522
TIANJIN BINHAI NEW DISTRICT ISETAN CO., LTD.—See Isetan Mitsukoshi Holdings Ltd.; *Int'l*, pg. 3815
TIANJIN BINHAI TEDA LOGISTICS (GROUP) CORPORATION LIMITED; *Int'l*, pg. 7738
TIANJIN BOAI NKY INTERNATIONAL LTD—See Boai NKY Medical Holdings Ltd.; *Int'l*, pg. 1094
TIAN JIN BOHAI CHEMICAL CO., LTD.; *Int'l*, pg. 7737
TIANJIN BOHAI INTERNATIONAL PAPER PACKAGING CO., LTD.—See International Paper Company; *U.S. Public*, pg. 1158
TIANJIN BRANCH OF WUHAN GEM URBAN MINERAL EQUIPMENT CO., LTD.—See GEM Co., Ltd.; *Int'l*, pg. 2914
TIANJIN CANON CO., LTD.—See Canon Inc.; *Int'l*, pg. 1292
TIANJIN CAPITAL ENVIRONMENTAL PROTECTION GROUP CO. LTD.; *Int'l*, pg. 7738
TIANJIN CEMENT INDUSTRY DESIGN & RESEARCH INSTITUTE CO., LTD.—See Sinoma International Engineering Co., Ltd.; *Int'l*, pg. 6952
TIANJIN CENTRAL ELECTRONIC CORPORATION—See Commax Co., Ltd.; *Int'l*, pg. 1714
TIANJIN CHAIN CHON STAINLESS STEEL CO., LTD.—See Chain Chon Industrial Co., Ltd.; *Int'l*, pg. 1437

COMPANY NAME INDEX

TIANJIN CHALTON TOMATO PRODUCT CO., LTD.—See Chalkis Health Industry Co., Ltd.; *Int'l*, pg. 1438
TIANJIN CHASE SUN PHARMACEUTICAL CO., LTD.; *Int'l*, pg. 7738
TIANJIN CHUHATSU HUAGUAN MACHINERY CO., LTD.—See Chuo Spring Co., Ltd.; *Int'l*, pg. 1599
TIANJIN CHUNG LOONG PAPER CO., LTD.—See Cheng Loong Corp.; *Int'l*, pg. 1466
TIANJIN CIMC LOGISTICS EQUIPMENTS CO., LTD.—See China International Marine Containers (Group) Co., Ltd.; *Int'l*, pg. 1512
TIANJIN CIMC NORTH OCEAN CONTAINER CO., LTD.—See China International Marine Containers (Group) Co., Ltd.; *Int'l*, pg. 1512
TIANJIN CMT INDUSTRY CO., LTD.—See China Metal Products Co., Ltd.; *Int'l*, pg. 1523
TIANJIN COSCO KANSAI PAINT & CHEMICALS CO., LTD.—See China COSCO Shipping Corporation Limited; *Int'l*, pg. 1492
TIANJIN COSCO KANSAI PAINT & CHEMICALS CO., LTD.—See Kansai Paint Co., Ltd.; *Int'l*, pg. 4073
TIANJIN COSLIGHT ELECTRICAL BICYCLE CO., LTD.—See Coslight Technology International Group Limited; *Int'l*, pg. 1810
TIANJIN COSMO POLYURETHANE CO., LTD.—See Mitsui Chemicals, Inc.; *Int'l*, pg. 4984
TIANJIN CPT M&E EQUIPMENT CO., LTD.—See Sichuan Dawn Precision Technology Co., Ltd.; *Int'l*, pg. 6878
TIANJIN CUSTOM WOOD PROCESSING, CO. LTD—See California Cedar Products Company; *U.S. Private*, pg. 718
TIANJIN DAGANG NEWSPRING CO., LTD.—See Hyflux Ltd; *Int'l*, pg. 3548
TIANJIN DAIYA VALVE CO., LTD.—See Seika Corporation; *Int'l*, pg. 6685
TIANJIN DANSUN PACKAGING CO., LTD.—See PSC Corporation Ltd.; *Int'l*, pg. 6015
TIANJIN DAXIN ELECTRONICS CO., LTD—See SangsinEDP; *Int'l*, pg. 6539
TIANJIN DEFENG FOODS CO., LTD.—See Daesang Corporation; *Int'l*, pg. 1909
TIANJIN DENSO AIR-CONDITIONER CO., LTD.—See Denso Corporation; *Int'l*, pg. 2033
TIANJIN DENSO ENGINE ELECTRICAL PRODUCTS CO., LTD—See Denso Corporation; *Int'l*, pg. 2033
TIANJIN DEVELOPMENT HOLDINGS LIMITED; *Int'l*, pg. 7739
TIANJIN DONGCHUN-TAIKI METAL FINISHING & CONVEYOR SYSTEM MANUFACTURING CO., LTD.—See Taikisha Ltd.; *Int'l*, pg. 7414
TIANJIN DONG HENG IMPORT & EXPORT CO., LTD.—See Korea Electric Terminal Co., Ltd.; *Int'l*, pg. 4284
TIANJIN ECO-CITY SUNWAY PROPERTY DEVELOPMENT CO., LTD.—See Sunway Berhad; *Int'l*, pg. 7331
TIANJIN ELECTRIC POWER COMPANY—See State Grid Corporation of China; *Int'l*, pg. 7183
TIANJIN EO TECHNICS CO., LTD—See EO Technics Co., Ltd.; *Int'l*, pg. 2457
TIANJIN EPSON CO., LTD.—See Seiko Epson Corporation; *Int'l*, pg. 6688
TIANJIN FAWER DENSO AIR-CONDITIONER CO., LTD.—See Denso Corporation; *Int'l*, pg. 2033
TIANJIN FAW TOYOTA MOTOR CO., LTD.—See China FAW Group Corporation; *Int'l*, pg. 1502
TIANJIN FAW TOYOTA MOTOR CO., LTD.—See Toyota Motor Corporation; *Int'l*, pg. 7872
TIANJIN FENGTIAN LOGISTICS CO., LTD.—See Toyota Tsusho Corporation; *Int'l*, pg. 7878
TIANJIN FIGARO ELECTRONIC CO., LTD.—See New Cosmos Electric Co., Ltd.; *Int'l*, pg. 5222
TIANJIN FRD SCIENCE & TECHNOLOGY CO., LTD.—See Shenzhen FRD Science & Technology Co., Ltd.; *Int'l*, pg. 6810
TIANJIN FUJI PROTEIN CO., LTD.—See Fuji Oil Holdings Inc.; *Int'l*, pg. 2816
TIANJIN FURUKAWA POWER COMPONENT CO., LTD.—See The Furukawa Electric Co., Ltd.; *Int'l*, pg. 7647
TIANJIN FUTABA SHYE CHAN MECHANICAL CO., LTD.—See Futaba Industrial Co., Ltd.; *Int'l*, pg. 2851
TIANJIN FUTONG XINMAO SCIENCE & TECHNOLOGY CO., LTD.; *Int'l*, pg. 7739
TIANJING FAR EASTERN DEPARTMENT STORE CO., LTD.—See The Far Eastern Group; *Int'l*, pg. 7642
TIANJIN GLOVIS AUTOMOTIVE PARTS CO., LTD.—See Hyundai Glovis Co., Ltd.; *Int'l*, pg. 3557
TIANJIN GOLDSUN WIRE ROPE LTD.—See Golik Holdings Limited; *Int'l*, pg. 3036
TIANJIN GOOD HAND RAILWAY HOLDING CO., LTD.; *Int'l*, pg. 7739
TIANJIN GUIFAXIANG 18TH STREET MAHUA FOOD CO., LTD.; *Int'l*, pg. 7739
TIANJIN HANA INTERNATIONAL TRADING CO., LTD.—See ABCO Electronics Co., Ltd.; *Int'l*, pg. 57
TIANJIN HEJIA XINGTAI CATERING MANAGEMENT COMPANY LIMITED—See Hop Hing Group Holdings Limited; *Int'l*, pg. 3473

TIANJIN HENKEL DETERGENTS & CLEANING PRODUCTS CO. LTD.—See Henkel AG & Co. KGaA; *Int'l*, pg. 3349
TIANJIN HERONG TITANIUM INDUSTRY CO., LTD.—See Atlantic China Welding Consumables, Inc.; *Int'l*, pg. 674
TIANJIN HEXING MECHATRONICS TECHNOLOGY CO., LTD.—See Hoden Seimitsu Kako Kenkyusho Co., Ltd.; *Int'l*, pg. 3438
TIANJIN HI-TECH DEVELOPMENT CO., LTD.; *Int'l*, pg. 7739
TIANJIN HOKURIKU ELECTRIC INDUSTRY CO., LTD.—See Hokuriku Electric Industry Co., Ltd.; *Int'l*, pg. 3445
TIANJIN HONGBANG DIE CASTING CO., LTD.—See Wencan Group Co., Ltd.; *Int'l*, pg. 8376
TIANJIN HOPERAY MINERAL LIMITED COMPANY—See Tewoo Group Co., Ltd.; *Int'l*, pg. 7581
TIANJIN HOPETONE CO. LTD.—See Tewoo Group Co., Ltd.; *Int'l*, pg. 7581
TIANJIN HOUSE CONSTRUCTION DEVELOPMENT GROUP CO., LTD.—See Shanghai Construction Group Co., Ltd.; *Int'l*, pg. 6764
TIANJIN HUADE MINERAL PRODUCT CO., LTD.—See L. Possehl & Co. mbH; *Int'l*, pg. 4385
TIANJIN HUANOU INTERNATIONAL SILICON MATERIALS CO., LTD.—See TCL Zhonghuan Renewable Energy Technology Co., Ltd.; *Int'l*, pg. 7484
TIANJIN HUAYI ZHICHENG TECHNOLOGY DEVELOPMENT CO., LTD.—See Beijing E-Hualu Information Technology Co., Ltd.; *Int'l*, pg. 949
TIANJIN HUMAN RESOURCE & EDUCATION CONSULTING CO., LTD.; *Int'l*, pg. 7739
TIANJIN INABATA TRADING CO., LTD.—See Inabata & Co. Ltd.; *Int'l*, pg. 3644
TIANJIN INOAC HUAXIANG AUTOMOTIVE PRODUCTS CO., LTD.—See INOAC Corporation; *Int'l*, pg. 3715
TIANJIN INOAC POLYMER CO., LTD.—See INOAC Corporation; *Int'l*, pg. 3715
TIANJIN INTEX AUTO PARTS CO., LTD.—See Toyota Boshoku Corporation; *Int'l*, pg. 7864
TIANJIN INVE AQUACULTURE CO., LTD.—See Benchmark Holdings Plc; *Int'l*, pg. 970
TIANJIN ISETAN CO., LTD.—See Isetan Mitsukoshi Holdings Ltd.; *Int'l*, pg. 3815
TIANJIN JIAHENG PLASTICS CO., LTD.—See Jahen Household Products Co., Ltd.; *Int'l*, pg. 3871
TIANJIN JIANFENG NATURAL PRODUCT R&D CO., LTD.—See Zhejiang Jianfeng Group Co., Ltd.; *Int'l*, pg. 8656
TIANJIN JIEQIANG EQUIPMENT CO., LTD.; *Int'l*, pg. 7739
TIANJIN JINBIN DEVELOPMENT CO., LTD.; *Int'l*, pg. 7739
TIANJIN JINGMING NEW TECHNOLOGICAL DEVELOPMENT CO., LTD—See Grand Pharmaceutical Group Limited; *Int'l*, pg. 3056
TIANJIN JINGWEI HUIKAI OPTOELECTRONIC CO., LTD.; *Int'l*, pg. 7739
TIANJIN JINHE ELECTRIC ENGINEERING CO., LTD.—See The Furukawa Electric Co., Ltd.; *Int'l*, pg. 7647
TIANJIN JINRAN PUBLIC UTILITIES COMPANY LIMITED; *Int'l*, pg. 7739
TIANJIN JINRONGTIAN NEW TECHNOLOGY CO., LTD.—See Tianjin Jinrong Tianyu Precision Machinery, Inc.; *Int'l*, pg. 7739
TIANJIN JINRONG TIANSHENG METAL SURFACE TREATMENT CO., LTD.—See Tianjin Jinrong Tianyu Precision Machinery, Inc.; *Int'l*, pg. 7739
TIANJIN JINRONG TIANYU PRECISION MACHINERY, INC.; *Int'l*, pg. 7739
TIANJIN JINXIN PRECISION PLASTIC COMPONENTS CO.—See Xin Point Holdings Limited; *Int'l*, pg. 8529
TIANJIN JINZHU WIRING SYSTEMS CO., LTD.—See Sumitomo Electric Industries, Ltd.; *Int'l*, pg. 7284
TIANJIN JIN-ZHU WIRING SYSTEMS COMPONENTS CO., LTD.—See Sumitomo Electric Industries, Ltd.; *Int'l*, pg. 7284
TIANJIN JIUHE INTERNATIONAL VILLA CO., LTD.—See Daiwa House Industry Co., Ltd.; *Int'l*, pg. 1947
TIANJIN JIURI NEW MATERIALS CO., LTD.; *Int'l*, pg. 7739
TIANJIN JL RAILWAY TRANSPORT EQUIPMENT LTD.—See CRRC Corporation Limited; *Int'l*, pg. 1859
TIANJIN KAMEDA FOOD CO., LTD.—See Kameda Seika Co., Ltd.; *Int'l*, pg. 4061
TIANJIN KAMEDA FOOD CO., LTD.—See Tingyi (Cayman Islands) Holding Corp.; *Int'l*, pg. 7754
TIANJIN KDS CORP.—See Daishinku Corp.; *Int'l*, pg. 1942
TIANJIN KEYVIA ELECTRIC CO., LTD.; *Int'l*, pg. 7739
TIANJIN KIBING ENERGY SAVING GLASS CO., LTD.—See Zhuzhou Kibing Group Co., Ltd.; *Int'l*, pg. 8680
TIANJIN KINGFA ADVANCED MATERIALS CO., LTD.—See Kingfa Sci &Tech Co., Ltd.; *Int'l*, pg. 4172
TIANJIN KUANGDA AUTOMOBILE FABRIC CO., LTD.—See Kuangda Technology Group Co., Ltd.; *Int'l*, pg. 4319

TIANJIN REALTY DEVELOPMENT(GROUP) CO., LTD.

TIANJIN KUO CHENG RUBBER INDUSTRY CO., LTD.—See JSR Corp.; *Int'l*, pg. 4014
TIANJIN LAIRD TECHNOLOGIES LIMITED—See DuPont de Nemours, Inc.; *U.S. Public*, pg. 694
TIANJIN LG BOHAI CHEMICAL CO., LTD.—See LG Chem Ltd.; *Int'l*, pg. 4474
TIANJIN LG BOTIAN CHEMICAL CO., LTD.—See LG Chem Ltd.; *Int'l*, pg. 4474
TIANJIN LG NEW BUILDING MATERIALS CO., LTD.—See LG Corp.; *Int'l*, pg. 4477
TIANJIN LION WINDOW & DOOR CO., LTD.—See Xinda Investment Holdings Limited; *Int'l*, pg. 8529
TIANJIN LISHENG PHARMACEUTICAL CO., LTD.; *Int'l*, pg. 7739
TIANJIN LONGXING CO., LTD.—See Chuo Spring Co., Ltd.; *Int'l*, pg. 1599
TIANJIN LVYIN LANDSCAPE CONSTRUCTION CO., LTD.; *Int'l*, pg. 7739
TIANJIN MASTERWORK GREEN PACKING TECHNOLOGY CO., LTD.—See ZRP Printing Group Co., Ltd.; *Int'l*, pg. 8691
TIANJIN MATERIALS & EQUIPMENT MERCHANT CO., LTD—See Tewoo Group Co., Ltd.; *Int'l*, pg. 7581
TIANJIN MATERIALS INDUSTRY & INTERNATIONAL ENERGY DEVELOPMENT CO., LTD—See Tewoo Group Co., Ltd.; *Int'l*, pg. 7581
TIANJIN MATTEL VACUUM TECHNOLOGY CO., LTD.—See Wuhu Token Sciences Co., Ltd.; *Int'l*, pg. 8502
TIANJIN MITSUMI ELECTRIC CO., LTD.—See Minebea Mitsumi Inc.; *Int'l*, pg. 4904
TIANJIN MOBIS AUTOMOTIVE PARTS CO., LTD.—See Hyundai MOBIS Co., Ltd.; *Int'l*, pg. 3558
TIANJIN MONOCON ALUMINOUS REFRACTORIES COMPANY LIMITED—See S K Bajoria Group; *Int'l*, pg. 6443
TIANJIN MORESCO TECHNOLOGY CO., LTD.—See MORESCO Corporation; *Int'l*, pg. 5040
TIANJIN MOTIMO MEMBRANE TECHNOLOGY CO., LTD.; *Int'l*, pg. 7740
TIANJIN MOTOR DIES CO., LTD.; *Int'l*, pg. 7740
TIANJIN NAGASE INTERNATIONAL TRADING CO., LTD.—See Nagase & Co., Ltd.; *Int'l*, pg. 5128
TIANJIN NEW UNIVERSAL SCIENCE & TECHNOLOGY CO., LTD.—See Beijing New Universal Science and Technology Co., Ltd.; *Int'l*, pg. 954
TIANJIN NISSIN INTERNATIONAL TRANSPORT CO., LTD.—See Nissin Corporation; *Int'l*, pg. 5376
TIANJIN O.R.G PACKAGING CO., LTD.—See ORG Technology Co., Ltd.; *Int'l*, pg. 5617
TIANJIN OTSUKA BEVERAGE CO., LTD.—See Otsuka Holdings Co., Ltd.; *Int'l*, pg. 5661
TIANJIN PACIFIC AUTO PARTS CO., LTD.—See PACIFIC INDUSTRIAL CO. LTD.; *Int'l*, pg. 5690
TIANJIN PACIFIC MILLENNIUM PACKAGING & PAPER INDUSTRIES CO., LTD.—See Pacific Millennium Packaging Group Corporation; *Int'l*, pg. 5691
TIANJIN PEARL BEACH INTERNATIONAL COUNTRY CLUB CO LTD—See Keppel Corporation Limited; *Int'l*, pg. 4132
TIANJIN PEGASUS-SHIMAMOTO AUTO PARTS CO., LTD.—See Pegasus Sewing Machine Manufacturing Co., Ltd.; *Int'l*, pg. 5780
TIANJIN PEGASUS SYSTEM ENGINEERING CO., LTD.—See Pegasus Sewing Machine Manufacturing Co., Ltd.; *Int'l*, pg. 5780
TIANJIN PENGLING GROUP CO., LTD.; *Int'l*, pg. 7740
TIANJIN PHARMACEUTICAL DA REN TANG GROUP CORPORATION LIMITED; *Int'l*, pg. 7740
TIANJIN PIGMENT ENGINEERING PLASTICS CO., LTD.—See NPK Co., Ltd.; *Int'l*, pg. 5473
TIANJIN POLY SAGAWA TRADING CO., LTD.—See China Poly Group Corporation; *Int'l*, pg. 1541
TIANJIN PORT ALLIANCE INTERNATIONAL CONTAINER TERMINAL CO., LTD.—See Tianjin Port Development Holdings Limited; *Int'l*, pg. 7740
TIANJIN PORT DEVELOPMENT HOLDINGS LIMITED; *Int'l*, pg. 7740
TIANJIN PORT HOLDINGS CO., LTD.; *Int'l*, pg. 7740
TIANJIN PORT MASTER LOGISTICS CO., LTD.—See China Master Logistics Co., Ltd.; *Int'l*, pg. 1518
TIANJIN PRINTRONICS CIRCUIT CORPORATION; *Int'l*, pg. 7740
TIANJIN PRODUCTS & ENERGY RESOURCES DEVELOPMENT CO., LTD—See Tewoo Group Co., Ltd.; *Int'l*, pg. 7581
TIANJIN PUMPS & MACHINERY GROUP CO., LTD.—See Tianjin Benefo Tejing Electric Co., Ltd.; *Int'l*, pg. 7738
TIANJIN REALTY DEVELOPMENT(GROUP) CO., LTD.; *Int'l*, pg. 7740
TIANJIN RENGO PACKAGING CO., LTD.—See Rengo Co., Ltd.; *Int'l*, pg. 6282
TIANJIN RICHPEACE AI CO., LIMITED—See Shang Gong Group Co., Ltd.; *Int'l*, pg. 6760
TIANJIN RIETER NITTOKU AUTOMOTIVE SOUNDPROOF CO. LTD—See Autoneum Holding Ltd.; *Int'l*, pg. 731

Company Index
TIANJIN REALTY DEVELOPMENT(GROUP) CO., LTD. CORPORATE AFFILIATIONS

TIANJIN RIETER NITTOKU AUTOMOTIVE SOUND-PROOF CO. LTD—See Nihon Tokushu Toryo Co., Ltd; *Int'l*, pg. 5287
TIANJIN RIKEVITA FOOD CO., LTD.—See Riken Vitamin Co., Ltd.; *Int'l*, pg. 6341
TIANJIN RINGPU BIO-TECHNOLOGY CO., LTD.; *Int'l*, pg. 7740
TIANJIN ROHTO HERBAL MEDICINE CO., LTD.—See Rohto Pharmaceutical Co. Ltd.; *Int'l*, pg. 6387
TIANJIN RUIXIN TECHNOLOGY CO., LTD.; *Int'l*, pg. 7740
TIANJIN SAINTEAGLE WELDING CO., LTD.—See Advanced Technology & Materials Co., Ltd.; *Int'l*, pg. 162
TIANJIN SAIXIANG TECHNOLOGY CO., LTD.; *Int'l*, pg. 7740
TIANJIN SAMSUNG LED CO., LTD.—See Samsung Group; *Int'l*, pg. 6514
TIANJIN SAMSUNG OPTO-ELECTRONICS CO., LTD.—See Samsung Group; *Int'l*, pg. 6514
TIANJIN SAMSUNG SDI CO., LTD.—See Samsung Group; *Int'l*, pg. 6514
TIANJIN SAMWHA ELECTRIC CO., LTD.—See Samwha Capacitor Group; *Int'l*, pg. 6518
TIANJIN SAMWHA ELECTRIC CO., LTD. - TIANJIN PLANT 1—See Samwha Capacitor Group; *Int'l*, pg. 6518
TIANJIN SAMWHA ELECTRIC CO., LTD. - TIANJIN PLANT 2—See Samwha Capacitor Group; *Int'l*, pg. 6518
TIANJIN SAN'AN OPTOELECTRONICS CO., LTD.—See San'an Optoelectronics Co., Ltd.; *Int'l*, pg. 6522
TIANJIN SANDEN AUTOMOTIVE AIR-CONDITIONING CO., LTD.—See Sanden Corporation; *Int'l*, pg. 6525
TIANJIN SANGO AUTOMOTIVE PARTS CO., LTD.—See Sango Co., Ltd.; *Int'l*, pg. 6538
TIANJIN SANHE FRUITS & VEGETABLES CO., LTD.—See Xinjiang Guannong Fruit and Velvet Co., Ltd.; *Int'l*, pg. 8531
TIANJIN SANHUAN LUCKY NEW MATERIAL INC.—See Beijing Zhong Ke San Huan High-tech Co., Ltd.; *Int'l*, pg. 961
TIANJIN SANKO GOSEI CO., LTD.—See Sanko Gosei Ltd.; *Int'l*, pg. 6542
TIANJIN SCAS AUTOMOBILE SALES SERVICES CO., LTD.—See China ZhengTong Auto Services Holdings Limited; *Int'l*, pg. 1567
TIANJIN SCHWAN COSMETICS CO. LTD.—See Schwan-STABILO Cosmetics GmbH & Co. KG; *Int'l*, pg. 6645
TIANJIN SECOM SECURITY CO., LTD.—See SECOM Co., Ltd.; *Int'l*, pg. 6672
TIANJIN-SHIMADZU HYDRAULIC EQUIPMENT CO., LTD.—See Shimadzu Corporation; *Int'l*, pg. 6833
TIANJIN SHUANG SHYE MECHANICAL INDUSTRIAL CO., LTD.—See Futaba Industrial Co., Ltd.; *Int'l*, pg. 2851
TIANJIN SINGAMAS CONTAINER CO., LTD.—See Singamas Container Holdings Limited; *Int'l*, pg. 6939
TIANJIN SMART SENSOR TECHNOLOGY CO., LTD.—See OYO Corporation; *Int'l*, pg. 5678
TIANJIN SOUTH CHINA LEESHENG SPORTING GOODS CO. LTD.—See South China Holdings Company Limited; *Int'l*, pg. 7116
TIAN JIN STANLEY ELECTRIC CO., LTD.—See Stanley Electric Co., Ltd.; *Int'l*, pg. 7171
TIANJIN STANLEY ELECTRIC TECHNOLOGY CO., LTD.—See Stanley Electric Co., Ltd.; *Int'l*, pg. 7171
TIANJIN STAR LIGHT RUBBER AND PLASTIC CO., LTD.—See Toyoda Gosei Co., Ltd.; *Int'l*, pg. 7862
TIANJIN SUNDIRO ELECTRIC VEHICLE CO., LTD.—See Sundiro Holding Co., Ltd.; *Int'l*, pg. 7313
TIANJIN SUNG MOON ELECTRONICS CO., LTD.—See Sungmoon Electronics Co., Ltd.; *Int'l*, pg. 7315
TIANJIN SUNSHINE PLASTICS CO., LTD.—See P.T. Trias Sentosa, Tbk; *Int'l*, pg. 5683
TIANJIN SYNOPEX CO., LTD.—See Synopex Inc.; *Int'l*, pg. 7386
TIANJIN SYP ENGINEERING GLASS CO., LTD.—See Shanghai Yaohua Pilkington Glass Group Co., Ltd.; *Int'l*, pg. 6782
TIANJIN SYP GLASS CO.,LTD.—See Shanghai Yaohua Pilkington Glass Group Co., Ltd.; *Int'l*, pg. 6782
TIANJIN TAIKISHA PAINT FINISHING SYSTEM LTD.—See Taikisha Ltd.; *Int'l*, pg. 7414
TIANJIN TAI RONG CHEMICAL TRADING CO., LTD.—See BRENNTAG SE; *Int'l*, pg. 1150
TIANJIN TAKEDA PHARMACEUTICALS CO., LTD.—See Takeda Pharmaceutical Company Limited; *Int'l*, pg. 7440
TIANJIN TANABE SEIYAKU CO., LTD.—See Grand Pharmaceutical Group Limited; *Int'l*, pg. 3056
TIANJIN TANGGU WATTS VALVE CO., LTD.—See Watts Water Technologies, Inc.; *U.S. Public*, pg. 2337
TIANJIN TEDA BIOMEDICAL ENGINEERING COMPANY LIMITED; *Int'l*, pg. 7740
TIANJIN TEDA CO., LTD.; *Int'l*, pg. 7740
TIANJIN TENAX INDUSTRIAL PLASTICS CO., LTD—See Tenax International BV; *Int'l*, pg. 7558
TIANJIN TENGLONG UNITED AUTO PARTS CO., LTD.—See Changzhou Tenglong Auto Parts Co., Ltd.; *Int'l*, pg. 1445
TIANJIN TIANBAO ENERGY CO., LTD.; *Int'l*, pg. 7740
TIANJIN TIANBAO INFRASTRUCTURE CO.,LTD.; *Int'l*, pg. 7740
TIANJIN TIANFA PHARMACEUTICALS IMP & EXP CORP.—See Tianjin Tianyao Pharmaceutical Co., Ltd.; *Int'l*, pg. 7741
TIANJIN TIANLING CARBIDE TOOLS CO., LTD.—See Mitsubishi Materials Corporation; *Int'l*, pg. 4965
TIANJIN TIANSHI BIOLOGICAL DEVELOPMENT CO., LTD.—See Tiens Biotech Group (USA), Inc.; *Int'l*, pg. 7744
TIANJIN TIAN XING PROPERTY MANAGEMENT CO., LTD—See KSH Holdings Limited; *Int'l*, pg. 4313
TIANJIN TIANYAO PHARMACEUTICAL CO., LTD.; *Int'l*, pg. 7740
TIANJIN TINCI MATERIALS TECHNOLOGY CO., LTD.—See Guangzhou Tinci Materials Technology Company Limited; *Int'l*, pg. 3168
TIANJIN TINGYI INTERNATIONAL FOOD CO., LTD.—See Tingyi (Cayman Islands) Holding Corp.; *Int'l*, pg. 7754
TIANJIN TINGYU CONSULTING CO., LTD.—See Tingyi (Cayman Islands) Holding Corp.; *Int'l*, pg. 7754
TIANJIN TOKAIRIKA AUTOMOTIVE PARTS CO., LTD—See Tokai Rika Co., Ltd.; *Int'l*, pg. 7780
TIAN JIN TONG DE TECHNOLOGY & TRADING CO., LTD.—See Kendrion N.V.; *Int'l*, pg. 4127
TIAN JIN TON YI INDUSTRIAL CO., LTD.—See Uni-President Enterprises Corporation; *Int'l*, pg. 8029
TIANJIN TOYODENKI INTERNATIONAL TRADE CO., LTD.—See TOYO DENKI SEIZO K.K.; *Int'l*, pg. 7852
TIANJIN TOYO INK CO., LTD.—See Toyo Ink SC Holdings Co., Ltd.; *Int'l*, pg. 7854
TIANJIN TOYOTA TSUSHO STEEL CO., LTD.—See Toyota Tsusho Corporation; *Int'l*, pg. 7878
TIANJIN TOYOTETSU AUTOMOBILE PARTS CO., LTD.—See Toyoda Iron Works Co., Ltd.; *Int'l*, pg. 7863
TIANJIN TOYOTSU ALUMINIUM SMELTING TECHNOLOGY CO., LTD.—See Toyota Tsusho Corporation; *Int'l*, pg. 7878
TIANJIN TOYOTSU AUTOMOTIVE EQUIPMENT MANUFACTURING CO., LTD.—See Toyota Tsusho Corporation; *Int'l*, pg. 7878
TIANJIN TRANSWELL INTERNATIONAL LOGISTICS CO., LTD.—See Beijing Properties (Holdings) Limited; *Int'l*, pg. 955
TIANJIN TSC AUTO ID TECHNOLOGY CO., LTD.—See TSC Auto ID Technology Co., Ltd.; *Int'l*, pg. 7949
TIANJIN TSUBAKIMOTO CONVEYOR SYSTEMS CO., LTD.—See Sinoma International Engineering Co., Ltd.; *Int'l*, pg. 6952
TIANJIN TUBE-COTE PETROLEUM PIPE COATING CO., LTD.—See Hilong Holding Limited; *Int'l*, pg. 3393
TIANJIN UNIVERSITY OF COMMERCE-BOUSTEAD INFORMATICS, LTD.—See Boustead Singapore Limited; *Int'l*, pg. 1121
TIANJIN UNIVTECH CO., LTD.—See China National Chemical Corporation; *Int'l*, pg. 1530
TIANJIN VANKE REAL ESTATE COMPANY LIMITED—See China Vanke Co., Ltd.; *Int'l*, pg. 1562
TIANJIN-VEGA CO. LTD.—See Grieshaber Holding GmbH; *Int'l*, pg. 3083
TIANJIN VIAM AUTOMOTIVE PRODUCTS CO., LTD.—See Freudenberg SE; *Int'l*, pg. 2790
TIANJIN VOKE MOLD & PLASTIC TECHNOLOGY CO., LTD.—See Xiamen Voke Mold & Plastic Engineering Co., Ltd.; *Int'l*, pg. 8526
TIANJIN WALKMAN BIOMATERIAL CO., LTD.—See PW Medtech Group Limited; *Int'l*, pg. 6126
TIANJIN WEIKAI BIOENG LTD.—See China Regenerative Medicine International Co., Ltd.; *Int'l*, pg. 1547
TIANJIN WINFIELD KANSAI PAINT & CHEMICALS CO., LTD.—See Kansai Paint Co., Ltd.; *Int'l*, pg. 4073
TIANJIN WOORY ELECTRONICS CO LTD—See Woory Industrial Holdings Co., Ltd.; *Int'l*, pg. 8454
TIANJIN WUHUA MINING INDUSTRY CO., LTD—See Tewoo Group Co., Ltd.; *Int'l*, pg. 7582
TIANJIN XINDAFENG IMPORT AND EXPORT TRADE CO. LTD.—See GCH Technology Co., Ltd.; *Int'l*, pg. 2895
TIANJIN XINGANG SHIPBUILDING HEAVY INDUSTRY CO., LTD.—See China Shipbuilding Industry Company Limited; *Int'l*, pg. 1551
TIANJIN YAKULT CO,. LTD.—See Yakult Honsha Co., Ltd.; *Int'l*, pg. 8546
TIANJIN YAMAHA ELECTRONIC MUSICAL INSTRUMENTS, INC.—See Yamaha Corporation; *Int'l*, pg. 8549
TIANJIN YAZAKI AUTOMOTIVE PARTS CO., LTD.—See Yazaki Corporation; *Int'l*, pg. 8572
TIANJIN YIYAO PRINTING CO., LTD.—See Tianjin Development Holdings Limited; *Int'l*, pg. 7739
TIANJIN YIYI HYGIENE PRODUCTS CO., LTD.; *Int'l*, pg. 7741
TIANJIN YOU FA STEEL PIPE GROUP STOCK CO., LTD.; *Int'l*, pg. 7741
TIANJIN YOUNG CHANG MUSICAL INSTRUMENT CO LTD—See Young Chang Akki Co. Ltd.; *Int'l*, pg. 8602
TIANJIN YUANHUA SHIPPING CO., LTD—See COSCO Shipping Holdings Co., Ltd.; *Int'l*, pg. 1810
TIANJIN YUASA BATTERIES CO., LTD.—See GS Yuasa Corporation; *Int'l*, pg. 3143
TIANJIN ZHONGFU IN-LINE CONTAINER CO., LTD—See Zhuhai Zhongfu Enterprise Co., Ltd.; *Int'l*, pg. 8679
TIANJIN ZHONG RONG CHEMICAL STORAGE CO., LTD.—See BRENNTAG SE; *Int'l*, pg. 1150
TIANJIN ZHONGWANG ALUMINIUM COMPANY LIMITED—See China Zhongwang Holdings Limited; *Int'l*, pg. 1567
TIANJIN ZHONGXING AUTOMOTIVE COMPONENTS CO., LTD.—See Chuo Spring Co., Ltd.; *Int'l*, pg. 1599
TIANJIN ZHUODA TECHNOLOGY DEVELOPMENT CO., LTD.—See Shenzhen Zowee Technology Co., Ltd.; *Int'l*, pg. 6825
TIANJIN ZHUOLANG INFORMATION TECHNOLOGY CO., LTD.; *Int'l*, pg. 7741
TIANJIN ZRP PRINTING TECHNOLOGY CO., LTD.—See ZRP Printing Group Co., Ltd.; *Int'l*, pg. 8691
TIANLI HOLDINGS GROUP LTD.; *Int'l*, pg. 7741
TIANLI INTERNATIONAL HOLDINGS LIMITED; *Int'l*, pg. 7741
TIAN-LI PHARMACEUTICAL CO.,LTD.—See Sinphar Pharmaceutical Co., Ltd.; *Int'l*, pg. 6956
TIAN LUN GAS HOLDINGS LIMITED; *Int'l*, pg. 7737
TIANMA BEARING GROUP CO., LTD.; *Int'l*, pg. 7741
TIANMA EUROPE GMBH—See AVIC International Holdings Limited; *Int'l*, pg. 742
TIANMA MICRO-ELECTRONICS CO., LTD.—See AVIC International Holdings Limited; *Int'l*, pg. 742
TIANMA MICROELECTRONICS KOREA CO., LTD—See AVIC International Holdings Limited; *Int'l*, pg. 742
TIANMA MICROELECTRONICS (USA) INC.—See AVIC International Holdings Limited; *Int'l*, pg. 742
TIANMEI BEVERAGE GROUP CORPORATION LIMITED; *Int'l*, pg. 7741
TIANMEN KAIDI WATER SERVICES CO., LTD.—See SIIC Environment Holdings Ltd.; *Int'l*, pg. 6913
TIANNENG BATTERY GROUP COMPANY LIMITED; *Int'l*, pg. 7741
TIANNENG POWER INTERNATIONAL LIMITED; *Int'l*, pg. 7741
TIAN POH RESOURCES LIMITED; *Int'l*, pg. 7737
TIANQI LITHIUM CORPORATION—See Chengdu Tianqi Industry (Group) Co., Ltd.; *Int'l*, pg. 1469
TIANRONG INTERNET PRODUCTS & SERVICES, INC.; *U.S. Public*, pg. 2157
TIANRUI GROUP CEMENT CO., LTD.—See Tianrui Group Co., Ltd.; *Int'l*, pg. 7741
TIANRUI GROUP CO., LTD.; *Int'l*, pg. 7741
TIANRUI GROUP FOUNDRY CO., LTD.—See Tianrui Group Co., Ltd.; *Int'l*, pg. 7741
TIANRUI GROUP NANZHAO CEMENT COMPANY LIMITED—See China Tianrui Group Cement Company Limited; *Int'l*, pg. 1559
TIANRUI GROUP ZHOUKOU CEMENT COMPANY LIMITED—See China Tianrui Group Cement Company Limited; *Int'l*, pg. 1559
TIAN RUIXIANG HOLDINGS LTD.; *Int'l*, pg. 7737
TIANRUI XINDENG ZHENGZHOU CEMENT COMPANY LIMITED—See China Tianrui Group Cement Company Limited; *Int'l*, pg. 1559
TIANRUN INDUSTRY TECHNOLOGY CO., LTD.; *Int'l*, pg. 7741
TIANSHAN ALUMINUM GROUP CO., LTD.; *Int'l*, pg. 7741
TIAN SHAN DEVELOPMENT (HOLDING) LIMITED; *Int'l*, pg. 7737
TIANSHAN MATERIAL CO.,LTD.; *Int'l*, pg. 7741
TIAN SHAN REAL ESTATE DEVELOPMENT COMPANY LIMITED—See Tian Shan Development (Holding) Limited; *Int'l*, pg. 7737
TIANSHENG PHARMACEUTICAL GROUP CO., LTD.; *Int'l*, pg. 7741
TIANSHUI CHANGCHENG SWITCHGEAR CO., LTD.—See Lanzhou Greatwall Electrical Co., Ltd.; *Int'l*, pg. 4416
TIANSHUI ELECTRIC DRIVE RESEARCH INSTITUTE CO., LTD.—See Lanzhou Greatwall Electrical Co., Ltd.; *Int'l*, pg. 4416
TIANSHUI GREAT WALL CONTROL ELECTRICAL CO., LTD.—See Lanzhou Greatwall Electrical Co., Ltd.; *Int'l*, pg. 4416
TIANSHUI GREATWALL FRUIT JUICE & BEVERAGE GROUP CO., LTD.—See Lanzhou Greatwall Electrical Co., Ltd.; *Int'l*, pg. 4416
TIANSHUI HUATIAN TECHNOLOGY CO., LTD.; *Int'l*, pg. 7741
TIANSHUI ZHONGXING BIO-TECHNOLOGY CO., LTD.; *Int'l*, pg. 7742
TIAN TECK LAND LTD.; *Int'l*, pg. 7737
TIANTIAN CJ HOME SHOPPING CO., LTD.—See CJ Corporation; *Int'l*, pg. 1634
TIAN WANG ELECTRONICS (SHENZHEN) COMPANY LIMITED—See Time Watch Investments Ltd; *Int'l*, pg. 7751
TIANWEN DIGITAL MEDIA TECHNOLOGY (BEIJING) CO., LTD.—See China South Publishing & Media Group Co., Ltd.; *Int'l*, pg. 1553
TIANYANG NEW MATERIALS (SHANGHAI) TECHNOLOGY CO., LTD.; *Int'l*, pg. 7742

COMPANY NAME INDEX

TIANYIN PHARMACEUTICAL CO.; *Int'l*, pg. 7742
TIAN YUAN GROUP HOLDINGS LIMITED; *Int'l*, pg. 7737
TIANYU BIO-TECHNOLOGY CO., LTD.; *Int'l*, pg. 7742
TIANYUN INTERNATIONAL HOLDINGS LIMITED; *Int'l*, pg. 7742
TIAN ZHENG INTERNATIONAL PRECISION MACHINERY CO., LTD.; *Int'l*, pg. 7737
TIARA BAY RESORTS BHD.—See Oilcorp Berhad; *Int'l*, pg. 5535
TIASANG BATTERY JOINT STOCK COMPANY—See Masan Consumer Corp.; *Int'l*, pg. 4719
TI AUTOMOTIVE EURO HOLDINGS LIMITED—See Bain Capital, LP; *U.S. Private*, pg. 447
TI AUTOMOTIVE LIMITED—See Bain Capital, LP; *U.S. Private*, pg. 447
TI AUTOMOTIVE, LLC—See Bain Capital, LP; *U.S. Private*, pg. 447
TIAX LLC; *U.S. Private*, pg. 4166
TIBA AG—See Tulikivi Corporation; *Int'l*, pg. 7969
TIBAH CHEMICALS—See Obegi Chemicals Group; *Int'l*, pg. 5510
TIBA PARKING LLC; *U.S. Private*, pg. 4166
TIBBETTS LUMBER CO., LLC; *U.S. Private*, pg. 4166
TIB CHAMICALS AG; *Int'l*, pg. 7742
TIBCO EXTENDED RESULTS, INC.—See Vista Equity Partners, LLC; *U.S. Private*, pg. 4402
TIBCO LOGLOGIC LLC—See Vista Equity Partners, LLC; *U.S. Private*, pg. 4402
TIBCO SOFTWARE AB—See Vista Equity Partners, LLC; *U.S. Private*, pg. 4402
TIBCO SOFTWARE (BEIJING) CO., LTD.—See Vista Equity Partners, LLC; *U.S. Private*, pg. 4402
TIBCO SOFTWARE HONG KONG LIMITED—See Vista Equity Partners, LLC; *U.S. Private*, pg. 4402
TIBCO SOFTWARE INC. - BOSTON—See Vista Equity Partners, LLC; *U.S. Private*, pg. 4402
TIBCO SOFTWARE INC. - PRINCETON—See Vista Equity Partners, LLC; *U.S. Private*, pg. 4402
TIBCO SOFTWARE INC.—See Vista Equity Partners, LLC; *U.S. Private*, pg. 4401
TIBCO SOFTWARE KOREA LTD.—See Vista Equity Partners, LLC; *U.S. Private*, pg. 4402
TIBCO SOFTWARE LIMITED—See Vista Equity Partners, LLC; *U.S. Private*, pg. 4402
TIBCO SOFTWARE N.V.—See Vista Equity Partners, LLC; *U.S. Private*, pg. 4402
TIBCO SOFTWARE PORTUGAL—See Vista Equity Partners, LLC; *U.S. Private*, pg. 4402
TIBCO SOFTWARE SA DE CV—See Vista Equity Partners, LLC; *U.S. Private*, pg. 4402
TIBCO SOFTWARE SINGAPORE PTE LTD.—See Vista Equity Partners, LLC; *U.S. Private*, pg. 4402
TIBCO YAZILIM SANAYI VE TICARET LIMITED SIRKETI—See Vista Equity Partners, LLC; *U.S. Private*, pg. 4402
TI BELGIUM S.P.R.L.-B.V.B.A—See TIM S.p.A.; *Int'l*, pg. 7750
TIBERIUS ACQUISITION CORPORATION; *U.S. Public*, pg. 2158
TIBERIUS HOLDING AG; *Int'l*, pg. 7742
TIBERSOFT CORPORATION; *U.S. Private*, pg. 4167
THE TIBERTI FENCE COMPANY—See Tiberti Organization; *U.S. Private*, pg. 4167
TIBERTI ORGANIZATION; *U.S. Private*, pg. 4167
TIBET AIM PHARM INC; *Int'l*, pg. 7742
TIBET CHEEZHENG TIBETAN MEDICINE CO. LTD.; *Int'l*, pg. 7742
TIBET DEVELOPMENT CO LTD.; *Int'l*, pg. 7742
TIBET DUO RUI PHARMACEUTICAL CO., LTD.; *Int'l*, pg. 7742
TIBET GAOZHENG EXPLOSIVE CO., LTD.; *Int'l*, pg. 7742
TIBET HUAYU MINING CO., LTD.; *Int'l*, pg. 7742
TIBET MINERAL DEVELOPMENT CO., LTD.; *Int'l*, pg. 7742
TIBET RHODIOLA PHARMACEUTICAL HOLDING COMPANY; *Int'l*, pg. 7742
TIBET SUMMIT RESOURCES CO., LTD.; *Int'l*, pg. 7743
TIBET TIANLU CO., LTD.; *Int'l*, pg. 7743
TIBET TOURISM CO., LTD.; *Int'l*, pg. 7743
TIBET URBAN DEVELOPMENT & INVESTMENT CO., LTD.; *Int'l*, pg. 7743
TIBET WATER RESOURCES LTD.; *Int'l*, pg. 7743
TIBET WEIXINKANG MEDICINE CO., LTD.; *Int'l*, pg. 7743
TIBNOR AB—See SSAB AB; *Int'l*, pg. 7155
TIBNOR A/S—See SSAB AB; *Int'l*, pg. 7155
TIBNOR A/S—See SSAB AB; *Int'l*, pg. 7155
TIBNOR OY—See Ovako Holdings AB; *Int'l*, pg. 5670
TIBNOR SIA—See SSAB AB; *Int'l*, pg. 7155
TIBOR MACHINE PRODUCTS INC.; *U.S. Private*, pg. 4167
TIBOTEC BVBA—See Johnson & Johnson; *U.S. Public*, pg. 1200
TIBOTEC PHARMACEUTICALS LTD.—See Johnson & Johnson; *U.S. Public*, pg. 1200
TIBOTEC-VIRCO VIROLOGY BVBA—See Johnson & Johnson; *U.S. Public*, pg. 1200
TIB THE INDEPENDENT BANKERSBANK, NATIONAL ASSOCIATION—See Independent Bankers Financial Corporation; *U.S. Private*, pg. 2058

TIBURON GOLF VENTURES LIMITED PARTNERSHIP—See Host Hotels & Resorts, Inc.; *U.S. Public*, pg. 1055
TIBUS—See Anderson Spratt Group; *Int'l*, pg. 450
T.I.C.-CITIZEN CO., LTD.—See Citizen Watch Co., Ltd.; *Int'l*, pg. 1625
TIC ENERGY & CHEMICAL—See Peter Kiewit Sons', Inc.; *U.S. Private*, pg. 3158
TIC GROUP (EUROPE) LTD.—See Pact Group Holdings Ltd.; *Int'l*, pg. 5693
TIC GUMS CHINA.—See Ingredion Incorporated; *U.S. Public*, pg. 1124
TIC GUMS, INC.—See Ingredion Incorporated; *U.S. Public*, pg. 1124
TIC HOLDINGS INC.—See Peter Kiewit Sons', Inc.; *U.S. Private*, pg. 3158
TIC INDUSTRIAL CO., LTD—See Joincare Pharmaceutical Industry Group Co., Ltd; *Int'l*, pg. 3995
TIC INTERNATIONAL CORPORATION; *U.S. Private*, pg. 4167
TICK DATA, INC.; *U.S. Private*, pg. 4167
TICKER COMMUNICATIONS, INC; *Int'l*, pg. 7743
TICKERPLANT LIMITED—See 63 moons technologies limited; *Int'l*, pg. 14
TICKET ALTERNATIVE, LLC; *U.S. Private*, pg. 4167
TICKETBISCUIT, LLC—See Intelli-Mark Technologies, Inc.; *U.S. Private*, pg. 2105
TICKETCITY INC.; *U.S. Private*, pg. 4167
TICKETCORNER AG—See CTS Eventim AG & Co. KGAA; *Int'l*, pg. 1874
TICKETCORNER AG—See Ringier Holding AG; *Int'l*, pg. 6344
TICKETECH, INC.—See FlashParking, Inc.; *U.S. Private*, pg. 1540
TICKETEK ARGENTINA S.A.—See T4F Entretenimento S.A.; *Int'l*, pg. 7398
TICKETEK PTY. LTD.—See Nine Entertainment Co. Holdings Limited; *Int'l*, pg. 5300
THE TICKET EXPERIENCE, LLC; *U.S. Private*, pg. 4127
TICKET EXPRESS HUNGARY KFT.—See CTS Eventim AG & Co. KGAA; *Int'l*, pg. 1874
TICKETFLY, LLC—See Eventbrite, Inc.; *U.S. Public*, pg. 799
TICKETFORCE, LLC—See Intelli-Mark Technologies, Inc.; *U.S. Private*, pg. 2105
TICKETLEAP INC.; *U.S. Private*, pg. 4167
TICKETMASTER B.V.—See Live Nation Entertainment, Inc.; *U.S. Public*, pg. 1331
TICKETMASTER CANADA LTD.—See Live Nation Entertainment, Inc.; *U.S. Public*, pg. 1331
TICKETMASTER CHILE S.A.—See T4F Entretenimento S.A.; *Int'l*, pg. 7398
TICKETMASTER ENTERTAINMENT LLC—See Live Nation Entertainment, Inc.; *U.S. Public*, pg. 1331
TICKETMASTER GMBH—See Live Nation Entertainment, Inc.; *U.S. Public*, pg. 1331
TICKETMASTER ISRAEL LTD—See Live Nation Entertainment, Inc.; *U.S. Public*, pg. 1331
TICKETMASTER LLC—See Live Nation Entertainment, Inc.; *U.S. Public*, pg. 1331
TICKETMASTER NZ LIMITED—See Live Nation Entertainment, Inc.; *U.S. Public*, pg. 1331
TICKETMASTER POLAND SP. Z.O.O.—See Live Nation Entertainment, Inc.; *U.S. Public*, pg. 1331
TICKETMASTER SCHWEIZ AG—See Live Nation Entertainment, Inc.; *U.S. Public*, pg. 1331
TICKETMASTER-SINGAPORE PTE. LTD.—See Live Nation Entertainment, Inc.; *U.S. Public*, pg. 1331
TICKETMASTER SUOMI OY—See Live Nation Entertainment, Inc.; *U.S. Public*, pg. 1330
TICKETMASTER SYSTEMS LIMITED—See Live Nation Entertainment, Inc.; *U.S. Public*, pg. 1331
TICKETMASTER UK LIMITED—See Live Nation Entertainment, Inc.; *U.S. Public*, pg. 1331
TICKETNETWORK, INC.; *U.S. Private*, pg. 4167
TICKETONE S.P.A.—See CTS Eventim AG & Co. KGAA; *Int'l*, pg. 1874
TICKETPRO POLSKA SP ZOO—See Live Nation Entertainment, Inc.; *U.S. Public*, pg. 1331
TICKETS.COM, INC.—See Major League Baseball; *U.S. Private*, pg. 2555
TICKET SERVICE, S.R.O.—See Edenred S.A.; *Int'l*, pg. 2308
TICKET SERVICOS S.A.—See Edenred S.A.; *Int'l*, pg. 2308
TICKETS FOR KIDS CHARITIES; *U.S. Private*, pg. 4167
TICKETSNOW.COM, INC.—See Live Nation Entertainment, Inc.; *U.S. Public*, pg. 1331
TICKETSOFT LLC—See Vista Group International Limited; *Int'l*, pg. 8254
TICKETS PLUS, INC.—See Intelli-Mark Technologies, Inc.; *U.S. Private*, pg. 2105
TICKETS & TOURS—See Entertainment Benefits Group, LLC; *U.S. Private*, pg. 1404
TICKETSWEST.COM, INC.—See The RMR Group Inc.; *U.S. Public*, pg. 2126
TICKETWEB LLC—See Live Nation Entertainment, Inc.; *U.S. Public*, pg. 1331
TICKETZOOM.COM; *U.S. Private*, pg. 4167

TICKFAW PIT STOP INC.—See Amar Oil Co. Inc.; *U.S. Private*, pg. 216
TICK TRADING SOFTWARE AKTIENGESELLSCHAFT; *Int'l*, pg. 7743
TI CLOUD INC.; *Int'l*, pg. 7736
TIC-MS, LLC—See Transcat, Inc.; *U.S. Public*, pg. 2179
TICOM GEOMATICS, INC.—See CACI International Inc.; *U.S. Public*, pg. 418
TICOMIX, INC.; *U.S. Private*, pg. 4167
TICOMO VALLEY CORP; *U.S. Private*, pg. 4167
TICONA GMBH—See Celanese Corporation; *U.S. Public*, pg. 465
TICON, INC.; *U.S. Private*, pg. 4167
TICONTRACT GMBH—See The Riverside Company; *U.S. Private*, pg. 4110
TICOR TITLE INSURANCE COMPANY—See Fidelity National Financial, Inc.; *U.S. Public*, pg. 831
TICO TITANIUM INC.; *U.S. Private*, pg. 4167
TIC PROPERTIES, LLC; *U.S. Private*, pg. 4167
TIC-THE INDUSTRIAL COMPANY—See Peter Kiewit Sons', Inc.; *U.S. Private*, pg. 3158
TIC-THE INDUSTRIAL COMPANY WYOMING, INC.—See Peter Kiewit Sons', Inc.; *U.S. Private*, pg. 3158
TIC TOC; *U.S. Private*, pg. 4167
TIC WESTERN—See Peter Kiewit Sons', Inc.; *U.S. Private*, pg. 3158
TI CYCLES OF INDIA LTD - NOIDA PLANT—See The Murugappa Group, Ltd.; *Int'l*, pg. 7669
TI CYCLES OF INDIA LTD—See The Murugappa Group, Ltd.; *Int'l*, pg. 7669
TIDAL BASIN GOVERNMENT CONSULTING, LLC—See D.C. Capital Partners, LLC; *U.S. Private*, pg. 1141
TIDAL ENERGY MARKETING INC.—See Enbridge Inc.; *Int'l*, pg. 2397
TIDAL LOGISTICS, INC.—See Select Water Solutions, Inc.; *U.S. Public*, pg. 1862
TIDAL POWER SERVICES, LLC.; *U.S. Private*, pg. 4167
TIDC INDIA LIMITED - HARIDWAR PLANT—See The Murugappa Group, Ltd.; *Int'l*, pg. 7669
TIDC INDIA LIMITED - MEDAK PLANT—See The Murugappa Group, Ltd.; *Int'l*, pg. 7669
TIDC INDIA LIMITED—See The Murugappa Group, Ltd.; *Int'l*, pg. 7669
TIDE CO., LTD.; *Int'l*, pg. 7743
TIDEHOLD DEVELOPMENT CO., LTD.; *Int'l*, pg. 7743
TIDELAND ELECTRIC MEMBERSHIP CORPORATION; *U.S. Private*, pg. 4168
TIDELANDS FORD - LINCOLN; *U.S. Private*, pg. 4168
TIDELANDS GEOPHYSICAL CO., INC.—See Wilks Brothers LLC; *U.S. Private*, pg. 4521
TIDELAND SIGNAL CORPORATION—See Xylem Inc.; *U.S. Public*, pg. 2395
TIDELAND SIGNAL LIMITED—See Xylem Inc.; *U.S. Public*, pg. 2395
TIDELANDS ROYALTY TRUST B; *U.S. Public*, pg. 2158
TIDEL ENGINEERING, L.P.—See Littlejohn & Co., LLC; *U.S. Private*, pg. 2472
TIDE PETROLEUM CORP.; *U.S. Private*, pg. 4167
TIDEPOOL PROJECT; *U.S. Private*, pg. 4168
TIDE ROCK HOLDINGS, LLC; *U.S. Private*, pg. 4167
TIDES AT CALABASH NORTH CAROLINA, LLC—See Independence Realty Trust, Inc.; *U.S. Public*, pg. 1116
TIDES; *U.S. Private*, pg. 4168
TIDESTONE SOFTWARE (SHANGHAI) CORPORATION LIMITED—See Vodatel Networks Holdings Limited; *Int'l*, pg. 8286
TIDEWATCH SELECT, LLC—See B. Riley Financial, Inc.; *U.S. Public*, pg. 261
TIDEWATER BARGE LINES INC.—See Tidewater Holdings, Inc.; *U.S. Private*, pg. 4168
TIDEWATER COMMUNICATIONS, LLC—See Saga Communications, Inc.; *U.S. Public*, pg. 1835
TIDEWATER DE MEXICO, S.A. DE C.V.—See Tidewater Inc.; *U.S. Public*, pg. 2158
TIDEWATER DIRECT LLC; *U.S. Private*, pg. 4168
TIDEWATER ENVIRONMENTAL SERVICES, INC.—See Artesian Resources Corporation; *U.S. Public*, pg. 202
TIDEWATER EQUIPMENT COMPANY; *U.S. Private*, pg. 4168
TIDEWATER FLEET SUPPLY—See Falcon Affiliates, LLC; *U.S. Private*, pg. 1466
TIDEWATER HOLDINGS, INC.; *U.S. Private*, pg. 4168
TIDEWATER INC.; *U.S. Public*, pg. 2158
TIDEWATER (INDIA) PRIVATE LIMITED—See Tidewater Inc.; *U.S. Public*, pg. 2158
TIDEWATER INSULATORS, LLC—See Installed Building Products, Inc.; *U.S. Public*, pg. 1134
TIDEWATER MANAGEMENT GROUP—See Integrity Marketing Group LLC; *U.S. Private*, pg. 2104
TIDEWATER MARINE AS—See Tidewater Inc.; *U.S. Public*, pg. 2158
TIDEWATER MARINE INTERNATIONAL PTE. LTD.—See Tidewater Inc.; *U.S. Public*, pg. 2158
TIDEWATER MARINE, L.L.C.—See Tidewater Inc.; *U.S. Public*, pg. 2158
TIDEWATER MARINE WESTERN, INC.—See Tidewater Inc.; *U.S. Public*, pg. 2158
TIDEWATER MIDDLE EAST CO. PLC; *Int'l*, pg. 7743

TIDEWATER MIDSTREAM AND INFRASTRUCTURE LTD.; *Int'l*, pg. 7743
TIDE WATER OIL CO. (INDIA) LTD. - FARIDABAD PLANT—See Tide Water Oil Co. (India) Ltd.; *Int'l*, pg. 7743
TIDE WATER OIL CO. (INDIA) LTD.; *Int'l*, pg. 7743
TIDE WATER OIL CO. (INDIA) LTD. - TURBHE PLANT—See Tide Water Oil Co. (India) Ltd.; *Int'l*, pg. 7743
TIDEWATER PIZZA TIME INC.; *U.S. Private*, pg. 4168
TIDEWATER RENEWABLES LTD.; *Int'l*, pg. 7743
TIDEWATER SUPPORT SERVICES LIMITED—See Tidewater Inc.; *U.S. Public*, pg. 2158
TIDEWATER TERMINAL COMPANY INC.—See Tidewater Holdings, Inc.; *U.S. Private*, pg. 4168
TIDEWATER TRANSIT CO., INC.; *U.S. Private*, pg. 4168
TIDEWATER UTILITIES, INC.—See Middlesex Water Company; *U.S. Public*, pg. 1445
TIDEWELL HOSPICE INC.; *U.S. Private*, pg. 4168
TIDI PRODUCTS LLC—See The Jordan Company, L.P.; *U.S. Private*, pg. 4062
TIDLAND CORPORATION—See Berwind Corporation; *U.S. Private*, pg. 541
TIDNINGSTJANST AB—See PostNord AB; *Int'l*, pg. 5941
TIDONENERGIE SRL—See A2A S.p.A.; *Int'l*, pg. 29
TID TECHNISCHE INFORMATIONEN & DIENSTLEISTUNGEN P. TSCHANNEN GMBH—See BKW AG; *Int'l*, pg. 1056
TIDWELL GROUP, LLC; *U.S. Private*, pg. 4168
TIDY CAR INTERNATIONAL, INC.—See Ziebart International Corporation; *U.S. Private*, pg. 4603
TIDY FILES (SA) (PTY) LTD—See Metrofile Holdings Limited; *Int'l*, pg. 4862
TIE COMMERCE INC.—See TIE Kinetix NV; *Int'l*, pg. 7743
TIEDEMANN-BEVS INDUSTRIES, INC.—See Strength Capital Partners, LLC; *U.S. Private*, pg. 3839
TIEDEMANN WEALTH MANAGEMENT, LLC—See AiTi Global, Inc.; *U.S. Public*, pg. 87
TIE DOWN ENGINEERING, INC.; *U.S. Private*, pg. 4168
TIE INTERNATIONAL BV—See TIE Kinetix NV; *Int'l*, pg. 7743
TIE KINETIX DACH GMBH—See SPS Commerce, Inc.; *U.S. Public*, pg. 1920
TIE KINETIX NV; *Int'l*, pg. 7743
TIE KINETIX S.A.S.—See TIE Kinetix NV; *Int'l*, pg. 7743
TIELING SUNJIN CO., LTD.—See SUNJIN CO., LTD.; *Int'l*, pg. 7316
TIELI ZHONGYU GAS CO., LTD.—See Zhongyu Energy Holdings Limited; *Int'l*, pg. 8676
TIEMCO LTD.; *Int'l*, pg. 7743
TIEMPO BBDO—See Omnicom Group Inc.; *U.S. Public*, pg. 1577
TIEMPO BBDO—See Omnicom Group Inc.; *U.S. Public*, pg. 1577
TIEMPO DEVELOPMENT CENTER—See 3Pillar Global, Inc.; *U.S. Private*, pg. 14
TIEMPO DEVELOPMENT CENTER—See 3Pillar Global, Inc.; *U.S. Private*, pg. 14
TIEMPO DEVELOPMENT LLC—See 3Pillar Global, Inc.; *U.S. Private*, pg. 14
TIENDAS CHEDRAUI S.A. DE C.V.—See Grupo Comercial Chedraui S.A.B. de C.V.; *Int'l*, pg. 3125
TIENDAS LA GLORIA INC.; *U.S. Private*, pg. 4168
TIENDAS LA GRAN VIA INC.; *U.S. Private*, pg. 4168
TIENDAS SORIANA, S.A. DE C. V.—See Organizacion Soriana, S.A.B. de C.V.; *Int'l*, pg. 5618
TIE NEDERLAND BV—See TIE Kinetix NV; *Int'l*, pg. 7743
TIEN GIANG INVESTMENT & CONSTRUCTION COMPANY; *Int'l*, pg. 7743
TIEN LEE HONG CO., LTD.—See DIC Corporation; *Int'l*, pg. 2111
TIEN LEN STEEL CORPORATION JOINT-STOCK COMPANY; *Int'l*, pg. 7744
TIEN LIANG BIOTECH CO., LTD.; *Int'l*, pg. 7744
TIEN PHONG PLASTIC JOINT-STOCK COMPANY; *Int'l*, pg. 7744
TIEN PHONG PLASTIC SOUTH JOINT STOCK COMPANY—See Tien Phong Plastic Joint-Stock company; *Int'l*, pg. 7744
TIEN PHONG SECURITIES CORPORATION; *Int'l*, pg. 7744
TIENS BIOTECH GROUP (USA), INC.; *Int'l*, pg. 7744
TIEN SON CEMENT JOINT STOCK COMPANY; *Int'l*, pg. 7744
TIEN THANH SERVICE & TRADING JOINT STOCK COMPANY; *Int'l*, pg. 7744
TIEN TRUNG JOINT STOCK COMPANY; *Int'l*, pg. 7744
TIEN WAH PRESS HOLDINGS BERHAD; *Int'l*, pg. 7744
TIEN WAH PRESS (MALAYA) SDN. BHD.—See Tien Wah Press Holdings Berhad; *Int'l*, pg. 7744
TIEN WAH PRESS (PTE.) LTD.—See Dai Nippon Printing Co., Ltd.; *Int'l*, pg. 1916
TIEPOLO S.R.L.—See Hera S.p.A.; *Int'l*, pg. 3356
TIER10; *U.S. Private*, pg. 4169
TIER1 FINANCIALS SOLUTIONS, INC.; *Int'l*, pg. 7744
TIER 1 PERFORMANCE SOLUTIONS, LLC; *U.S. Private*, pg. 4168
TIE RACK FRANCE SAS—See Fingen S.p.A.; *Int'l*, pg. 2675

TIE RACK LIMITED—See Fingen S.p.A.; *Int'l*, pg. 2675
TIE RACK RETAIL GROUP LIMITED—See Fingen S.p.A.; *Int'l*, pg. 2675
TIERCEL TECHNOLOGY CORP.; *Int'l*, pg. 7744
TIERCON—See J2 Management Corporation; *Int'l*, pg. 3859
TIERNAHRUNG DEUERER GMBH; *Int'l*, pg. 7744
TIERNEY COMMUNICATIONS—See The Interpublic Group of Companies, Inc.; *U.S. Public*, pg. 2104
TIER ONE CAPITAL LIMITED PARTNERSHIP; *Int'l*, pg. 7744
TIER ONE, LLC—See The Jordan Company, L.P.; *U.S. Private*, pg. 4060
TIER ONE PARTNERS; *U.S. Private*, pg. 4169
TIER ONE SILVER INC.; *Int'l*, pg. 7744
TIERPOINT, LLC—See Cequel III, LLC; *U.S. Private*, pg. 835
TIERPOINT, LLC—See Charterhouse Group, Inc.; *U.S. Private*, pg. 859
TIERPOINT, LLC—See Thompson Street Capital Manager LLC; *U.S. Private*, pg. 4160
TIERRA AGROTECH PRIVATE LIMITED—See Grandeur Products Limited; *Int'l*, pg. 3058
TIERRA ARMADA C.A.—See VINCI S.A.; *Int'l*, pg. 8229
TIERRA ARMADA S.A.—See VINCI S.A.; *Int'l*, pg. 8233
TIER-RACK CORPORATION; *U.S. Private*, pg. 4169
TIERRA, INC; *U.S. Private*, pg. 4169
TIERRA PRODUCTS AB—See Fenix Outdoor International AG; *Int'l*, pg. 2634
TIERRA SEED SCIENCE PRIVATE LIMITED—See Grandeur Products Limited; *Int'l*, pg. 3058
TIERRA SOLUTIONS INC.—See Repsol, S.A.; *Int'l*, pg. 6294
TIERRA S.P.A.—See Topcon Corporation; *Int'l*, pg. 7814
TIER REIT, INC.—See Cousins Properties Incorporated; *U.S. Public*, pg. 587
TIERRE VERDE MARINA—See HCI Group, Inc.; *U.S. Public*, pg. 1014
TIES.COM; *U.S. Private*, pg. 4169
TIESSE ROBOT S.P.A.—See Kawasaki Heavy Industries, Ltd.; *Int'l*, pg. 4098
TIES; *U.S. Private*, pg. 4169
TIE TECHNOLOGIES, INC.; *U.S. Public*, pg. 2158
TIETEK, INC.—See North American Technologies Group, Inc. (NAMC); *Int'l*, pg. 2941
TIETGENS ENTERPRISES INC.; *U.S. Private*, pg. 4169
TIE TIE INTELLIGENCE LOGISTICS CO., LTD.—See HBIS Group Co., Ltd.; *Int'l*, pg. 3296
TIE TIE IOT TECHNOLOGY CO., LTD.—See HBIS Group Co., Ltd.; *Int'l*, pg. 3296
TIETO AUSTRIA GMBH—See TietoEVRY Oyj; *Int'l*, pg. 7745
TIETO (BEIJING) TECHNOLOGY CO., LTD.—See TietoEVRY Oyj; *Int'l*, pg. 7745
TIETO BELGIUM N.V.—See TietoEVRY Oyj; *Int'l*, pg. 7745
TIETO CHINA CO., LTD—See TietoEVRY Oyj; *Int'l*, pg. 7745
TIETO CZECH S.R.O.—See TietoEVRY Oyj; *Int'l*, pg. 7745
TIETO CZECH SUPPORT SERVICES S.R.O.—See TietoEVRY Oyj; *Int'l*, pg. 7745
TIETO DENMARK A/S—See TietoEVRY Oyj; *Int'l*, pg. 7745
TIETOENATOR AB—See TietoEVRY Oyj; *Int'l*, pg. 7745
TIETOENATOR CONSULTING B.V.—See TietoEVRY Oyj; *Int'l*, pg. 7746
TIETOENATOR SIA—See TietoEVRY Oyj; *Int'l*, pg. 7745
TIETO ESTONIA AS—See TietoEVRY Oyj; *Int'l*, pg. 7745
TIETO ESTONIA SERVICES OU—See TietoEVRY Oyj; *Int'l*, pg. 7745
TIETO ESY OY—See TietoEVRY Oyj; *Int'l*, pg. 7745
TIETOEVRY OYJ; *Int'l*, pg. 7744
TIETO FINLAND OY—See TietoEVRY Oyj; *Int'l*, pg. 7745
TIETO FINLAND SUPPORT SERVICES OY—See TietoEVRY Oyj; *Int'l*, pg. 7745
TIETO GERMANY GMBH—See TietoEVRY Oyj; *Int'l*, pg. 7745
TIETO HEALTHCARE & WELFARE OY—See TietoEVRY Oyj; *Int'l*, pg. 7745
TIETO INDIA PVT. LTD.—See TietoEVRY Oyj; *Int'l*, pg. 7745
TIETO ITALY S.P.A.—See TietoEVRY Oyj; *Int'l*, pg. 7745
TIETOKARHU OY—See TietoEVRY Oyj; *Int'l*, pg. 7746
TIETO LATVIA SIA—See TietoEVRY Oyj; *Int'l*, pg. 7745
TIETO LIETUVA, UAB—See TietoEVRY Oyj; *Int'l*, pg. 7745
TIETO NORWAY AS—See TietoEVRY Oyj; *Int'l*, pg. 7745
TIETO RUS OOO—See TietoEVRY Oyj; *Int'l*, pg. 7745
TIETO SDN BHD—See TietoEVRY Oyj; *Int'l*, pg. 7745
TIETO SOFTWARE TECHNOLOGIES PVT. LTD—See TietoEVRY Oyj; *Int'l*, pg. 7745
TIETO SUPPORT SERVICES SP. Z O.O.—See TietoEVRY Oyj; *Int'l*, pg. 7745
TIETO SWEDEN AB—See TietoEVRY Oyj; *Int'l*, pg. 7745
TIETO SWEDEN AB—See TietoEVRY Oyj; *Int'l*, pg. 7745
TIETO SWEDEN SUPPORT SERVICES AB—See TietoEVRY Oyj; *Int'l*, pg. 7745
TIETO TELECOM R&D SERVICES INDIA PVT. LTD—See TietoEVRY Oyj; *Int'l*, pg. 7746
TIETO UKRAINE SUPPORT SERVICES LLC—See TietoEVRY Oyj; *Int'l*, pg. 7746
TIETTO MINERALS LTD.; *Int'l*, pg. 7746

TIFANY INDUSTRIES SAS; *Int'l*, pg. 7746
TIFCO (DONGGUAN) CO., LTD.—See Nifco Inc.; *Int'l*, pg. 5282
TIFCO INDUSTRIES INC.; *U.S. Private*, pg. 4169
TIFFANY & CO. (AUSTRALIA) PTY. LTD.—See LVMH Moet Hennessy Louis Vuitton SE; *Int'l*, pg. 4603
TIFFANY & CO. BELGIUM SPRL—See LVMH Moet Hennessy Louis Vuitton SE; *Int'l*, pg. 4603
TIFFANY & CO. (CANADA) LP—See LVMH Moet Hennessy Louis Vuitton SE; *Int'l*, pg. 4603
TIFFANY & CO. INTERNATIONAL—See LVMH Moet Hennessy Louis Vuitton SE; *Int'l*, pg. 4603
TIFFANY & CO. ITALIA S.P.A.—See LVMH Moet Hennessy Louis Vuitton SE; *Int'l*, pg. 4603
TIFFANY & CO. JAPAN INC.—See LVMH Moet Hennessy Louis Vuitton SE; *Int'l*, pg. 4603
TIFFANY & CO. LIMITED—See LVMH Moet Hennessy Louis Vuitton SE; *Int'l*, pg. 4603
TIFFANY & CO. MEXICO, S.A. DE C.V.—See LVMH Moet Hennessy Louis Vuitton SE; *Int'l*, pg. 4603
TIFFANY & CO. NETHERLANDS B.V.—See LVMH Moet Hennessy Louis Vuitton SE; *Int'l*, pg. 4603
TIFFANY CONSTRUCTION COMPANY; *U.S. Private*, pg. 4169
TIFFANY & CO. OF NEW YORK LIMITED—See LVMH Moet Hennessy Louis Vuitton SE; *Int'l*, pg. 4603
TIFFANY & CO. PTE. LTD.—See LVMH Moet Hennessy Louis Vuitton SE; *Int'l*, pg. 4603
TIFFANY & CO. (SHANGHAI) COMMERCIAL COMPANY LIMITED—See LVMH Moet Hennessy Louis Vuitton SE; *Int'l*, pg. 4603
TIFFANY & CO.—See LVMH Moet Hennessy Louis Vuitton SE; *Int'l*, pg. 4603
TIFFANY & CO.—See LVMH Moet Hennessy Louis Vuitton SE; *Int'l*, pg. 4603
TIFFANY & CO. (SWITZERLAND) JEWELERS S.A.R.L.—See LVMH Moet Hennessy Louis Vuitton SE; *Int'l*, pg. 4603
TIFFANY & CO. TAIWAN LIMITED—See LVMH Moet Hennessy Louis Vuitton SE; *Int'l*, pg. 4603
TIFFANY & CO. (UK) HOLDINGS LIMITED—See LVMH Moet Hennessy Louis Vuitton SE; *Int'l*, pg. 4603
TIFFANY KOREA LTD.—See LVMH Moet Hennessy Louis Vuitton SE; *Int'l*, pg. 4603
TIFFANY MOTOR COMPANY INC.; *U.S. Private*, pg. 4169
TIFFANY (NJ) LLC—See LVMH Moet Hennessy Louis Vuitton SE; *Int'l*, pg. 4603
TIFFANY OF NEW YORK (SPAIN) S.L.—See LVMH Moet Hennessy Louis Vuitton SE; *Int'l*, pg. 4603
TIFFANY SWITZERLAND WATCH COMPANY SAGL—See LVMH Moet Hennessy Louis Vuitton SE; *Int'l*, pg. 4603
TIFFANY WATCH CO. LTD—See The Swatch Group Ltd.; *Int'l*, pg. 7693
THE TIFFEN COMPANY LLC—See Topspin Partners, L.P.; *U.S. Private*, pg. 4188
TIFFEN INTERNATIONAL LTD.—See Topspin Partners, L.P.; *U.S. Private*, pg. 4188
TIFFEN MANUFACTURING CORP.—See Topspin Partners, L.P.; *U.S. Private*, pg. 4188
TIFFIN FORD-LINCOLN-MERCURY INC.—See Reineke Family Dealerships; *U.S. Private*, pg. 3392
TIFFIN LOADER CRANE COMPANY—See Palfinger AG; *Int'l*, pg. 5708
TIFFIN METAL PRODUCTS CO.—See Wellspring Capital Management LLC; *U.S. Private*, pg. 4477
TIFFIN MOTOR HOMES, INC.—See Thor Industries, Inc.; *U.S. Public*, pg. 2157
TIFFIN PAPER COMPANY; *U.S. Private*, pg. 4169
TIFFIN PARTS LLC—See The Heico Companies, L.L.C.; *U.S. Private*, pg. 4051
TIFICO FIBER INDONESIA TBK; *Int'l*, pg. 7746
TIFLEX LIMITED—See The James Walker Group Ltd; *Int'l*, pg. 7658
TI FLUID SYSTEMS PLC; *Int'l*, pg. 7736
TIFON D.O.O.—See MOL Magyar Olaj- es Gazipari Nyrt.; *Int'l*, pg. 5021
TIFORP, INC.; *U.S. Private*, pg. 4169
TIGA GAMING, INC.—See Firich Enterprises Co., Ltd.; *Int'l*, pg. 2679
TIGAR A.D. PIROT; *Int'l*, pg. 7746
TIGAR INCON DOO—See Tigar a.d. Pirot; *Int'l*, pg. 7746
TIGAR TYRES D.O.O.—See Compagnie Generale des Etablissements Michelin SCA; *Int'l*, pg. 1745
TIGAZ TISZANTULI GAZSZOLGALTATO RESZVENYTARSASAG; *Int'l*, pg. 7746
TIGBUR-TEMPORARY PROFESSIONAL PERSONNEL LTD.; *Int'l*, pg. 7746
TIGER AIRWAYS AUSTRALIA PTY. LTD.—See Virgin Australia Holdings Limited; *Int'l*, pg. 8247
TIGER ANALYTICS LLC; *U.S. Private*, pg. 4169
TIGER BALM (MALAYSIA) SDN BHD—See Haw Par Corporation Limited; *Int'l*, pg. 3287
TIGER BRANDS LTD.; *Int'l*, pg. 7746
TIGER CALCIUM SERVICES INC. - SLAVE LAKE PLANT—See Tricor Pacific Capital, Inc.; *Int'l*, pg. 7920
TIGER CALCIUM SERVICES INC.—See Tricor Pacific Capital, Inc.; *Int'l*, pg. 7920
TIGER COMMISSARY SERVICES, INC.; *U.S. Private*, pg. 4169

TIGERCONNECT, INC.; *U.S. Private*, pg. 4170
TIGER CORP. DIRECT, INC.—See Insight Enterprises, Inc.; *U.S. Public*, pg. 1130
TIGER CORRECTIONAL SERVICES; *U.S. Private*, pg. 4169
TIGERDIRECT, INC.—See Insight Enterprises, Inc.; *U.S. Public*, pg. 1130
TIGER DISTRIBUTION & LOGISTICS CO., LTD.—See Saha Pathanapibul Public Company Limited; *Int'l*, pg. 6479
TIGER DISTRIBUTORS INC.; *U.S. Private*, pg. 4169
TIGER DRYLAC USA INC.; *U.S. Private*, pg. 4169
TIGERELEC CO.,LTD.; *Int'l*, pg. 7746
TIGER ENERGY TRADING PTE. LTD.—See PTT Public Company Limited; *Int'l*, pg. 6092
TIGER ENTERPRISES INC.; *U.S. Private*, pg. 4169
TIGER ENTERPRISES LTD—See Giordano International Limited; *Int'l*, pg. 2978
TIGER FILTRATION LIMITED—See Xebec Adsorption Inc.; *Int'l*, pg. 8520
TIGER FITNESS INC.; *U.S. Private*, pg. 4169
TIGERFLEX CORPORATION—See Tigers Polymer Corporation; *Int'l*, pg. 7747
TIGER GLOBAL MANAGEMENT LLC; *U.S. Private*, pg. 4169
TIGERGPS.COM, LTD.; *U.S. Private*, pg. 4170
TIGER HOME SERVICES, INC.—See Universal Insurance Holdings, Inc.; *U.S. Public*, pg. 2261
TIGER INFORMATION SYSTEMS INC.; *U.S. Private*, pg. 4169
TIGER INFRASTRUCTURE PARTNERS LP; *U.S. Private*, pg. 4170
TIGER INTERNATIONAL RESOURCES INC.; *U.S. Public*, pg. 2158
TIGERJET NETWORK, INC.—See B. Riley Financial, Inc.; *U.S. Public*, pg. 262
TIGERLOGIC CORPORATION; *U.S. Private*, pg. 4170
TIGERLOGIC FRANCE—See TigerLogic Corporation; *U.S. Private*, pg. 4170
TIGERLOGIC GERMANY GMBH—See TigerLogic Corporation; *U.S. Private*, pg. 4170
TIGERLOGIC UK, LTD.—See TigerLogic Corporation; *U.S. Private*, pg. 4170
TIGER LOGISTICS (INDIA) LIMITED; *Int'l*, pg. 7746
TIGER NATURAL GAS, INC.; *U.C. Private*, pg. 4170
TIGER OF SWEDEN AB—See Friheden Invest A/S; *Int'l*, pg. 2792
TIGER OIL AND ENERGY, INC.; *U.S. Public*, pg. 2158
TIGER OPTICS LLC; *U.S. Private*, pg. 4170
TIGERPAW SOFTWARE, INC.—See Rev.io, LLC; *U.S. Private*, pg. 3413
TIGERPOLY INDUSTRIA DE MEXICO S.A. DE C.V.—See Tigers Polymer Corporation; *Int'l*, pg. 7747
TIGERPOLY MANUFACTURING, INC.—See Tigers Polymer Corporation; *Int'l*, pg. 7747
TIGERPOLY (THAILAND) LTD.—See Tigers Polymer Corporation; *Int'l*, pg. 7747
TIGER REEF, INC.; *Int'l*, pg. 7746
TIGER RESOURCES LIMITED; *Int'l*, pg. 7746
TIGER ROYALTIES AND INVESTMENTS PLC; *Int'l*, pg. 7746
TIGERS GLOBAL LOGISTICS PTY LTD—See JAS Worldwide, Inc.; *U.S. Private*, pg. 2189
TIGERS GLOBAL LOGISTICS—See JAS Worldwide, Inc.; *U.S. Private*, pg. 2189
TIGERS (HK) CO., LTD.—See JAS Worldwide, Inc.; *U.S. Private*, pg. 2189
TIGERS LIMITED—See JAS Worldwide, Inc.; *U.S. Private*, pg. 2189
TIGER SOFT (1998) COMPANY LIMITED—See Humanica Public Company Limited; *Int'l*, pg. 3530
TIGERSPIKE FZ-LLC—See TD Synnex Corp; *U.S. Public*, pg. 1987
TIGERSPIKE, INC.—See TD Synnex Corp; *U.S. Public*, pg. 1987
TIGERSPIKE KK—See TD Synnex Corp; *U.S. Public*, pg. 1987
TIGERSPIKE LTD—See TD Synnex Corp; *U.S. Public*, pg. 1987
TIGERSPIKE PTE. LTD.—See TD Synnex Corp; *U.S. Public*, pg. 1987
TIGERSPIKE PTY LTD—See TD Synnex Corp; *U.S. Public*, pg. 1987
TIGERS POLYMER CORPORATION; *Int'l*, pg. 7746
TIGERS POLYMER (M) SDN BHD—See Tigers Polymer Corporation; *Int'l*, pg. 7747
TIGERS REALM COAL LIMITED; *Int'l*, pg. 7747
TIGER-SUL PRODUCTS (CANADA) CO.—See Platte River Ventures, LLC; *U.S. Private*, pg. 3211
TIGER-SUL PRODUCTS LLC—See Platte River Ventures, LLC; *U.S. Private*, pg. 3211
TIGER-SUL PRODUCTS LLC—See Platte River Ventures, LLC; *U.S. Private*, pg. 3211
TIGER-SUL PRODUCTS LLC - STOCKTON PLANT—See Platte River Ventures, LLC; *U.S. Private*, pg. 3211
TIGERS (USA) GLOBAL LOGISTICS, INC.—See JAS Worldwide, Inc.; *U.S. Private*, pg. 2189
TIGER TASMAN MINERALS LIMITED; *Int'l*, pg. 7746
TIGERTEL COMMUNICATIONS INC.; *Int'l*, pg. 7747

TIGERTMS LIMITED—See Searchlight Capital Partners, L.P.; *U.S. Private*, pg. 3589
TIGERTURF AUSTRALIA PTY LTD—See ABN AMRO Group N.V.; *Int'l*, pg. 65
TIGERTURF AUSTRALIA PTY LTD—See Gilde Buy Out Partners B.V.; *Int'l*, pg. 2975
TIGERTURF AUSTRALIA PTY LTD—See Parcom Capital Management B.V.; *Int'l*, pg. 5740
TIGERTURF NZ LIMITED—See ABN AMRO Group N.V.; *Int'l*, pg. 65
TIGERTURF NZ LIMITED—See Gilde Buy Out Partners B.V.; *Int'l*, pg. 2975
TIGERTURF NZ LIMITED—See Parcom Capital Management B.V.; *Int'l*, pg. 5740
TIGERTURF (UK) LIMITED—See ABN AMRO Group N.V.; *Int'l*, pg. 65
TIGERTURF (UK) LIMITED—See Gilde Buy Out Partners B.V.; *Int'l*, pg. 2975
TIGERTURF (UK) LIMITED—See Parcom Capital Management B.V.; *Int'l*, pg. 5740
TIGER WHEELS LIMITED; *Int'l*, pg. 7746
TIGHE & BOND, INC.; *U.S. Private*, pg. 4170
TIGHE PUBLISHING SERVICES, INC.—See PLDT Inc.; *Int'l*, pg. 5896
TIGHE WAREHOUSING & DISTRIBUTION; *U.S. Private*, pg. 4170
TIG HOLDINGS, INC.—See Fairfax Financial Holdings Limited; *Int'l*, pg. 2608
TIGI HAIRCARE GMBH—See Unilever PLC; *Int'l*, pg. 8045
TIGI LTD.; *Int'l*, pg. 7747
TIG INSURANCE CO.—See Fairfax Financial Holdings Limited; *Int'l*, pg. 2608
T & I GLOBAL LTD.; *Int'l*, pg. 7394
TIGNE MALL P.L.C.; *Int'l*, pg. 7747
TIGO ENERGY, INC; *U.S. Public*, pg. 2158
TIGO ENERGY MERGECO, INC—See Tigo Energy, Inc; *U.S. Public*, pg. 2158
TIGOLD CORPORATION - CHIBA PLANT—See ULVAC, Inc.; *Int'l*, pg. 8020
TIGOLD CORPORATION—See ULVAC, Inc.; *Int'l*, pg. 8020
TIGO PVT LTD.—See Empresas Publicas de Medellin ESP; *Int'l*, pg. 2392
TIGRE-ADS COLOMBIA LIMITADA—See Advanced Drainage Systems, Inc.; *U.S. Public*, pg. 46
TIGRE-ADS PERU S.A.C.—See Advanced Drainage Systems, Inc.; *U.S. Public*, pg. 46
TIGRE S.A; *Int'l*, pg. 7747
TIGRE USA, INC.—See Tigre S.A; *Int'l*, pg. 7747
TIGROUP—See Thompson Industrial Services, LLC; *U.S. Private*, pg. 4160
TIHAMA ADVERTISING & PUBLIC RELATIONS COMPANY; *Int'l*, pg. 7747
TIHATI PRODUCTIONS LTD., INC.; *U.S. Private*, pg. 4170
TIHERT - EAD—See Herti AD; *Int'l*, pg. 3365
TIH LIMITED; *Int'l*, pg. 7747
TII FIBER OPTICS, INC.—See Kelta, Inc.; *U.S. Private*, pg. 2281
TI INC. AFFLUENT MEDIA GROUP—See Meredith Corporation; *U.S. Public*, pg. 1423
TII NETWORK TECHNOLOGIES, INC.—See Kelta, Inc.; *U.S. Private*, pg. 2281
T&I INNOVATION CENTER, CO. LTD.—See The Chiba Bank, Ltd.; *Int'l*, pg. 7632
TIIVITUOTE OY—See Ratos AB; *Int'l*, pg. 6220
TIJARA & REAL ESTATE INVESTMENT COMPANY K.S.C.C.; *Int'l*, pg. 7747
TIJARIA POLYPIPES LTD; *Int'l*, pg. 7747
TIJUANA PARTNERS, S. DE R.L. DE C.V.—See Hyatt Hotels Corporation; *U.S. Public*, pg. 1078
TIKCRO TECHNOLOGIES LTD.; *Int'l*, pg. 7747
TIKEHAU ACE CAPITAL—See Tikehau Capital Advisors SAS; *Int'l*, pg. 7747
TIKEHAU CAPITAL ADVISORS SAS; *Int'l*, pg. 7747
TIKEHAU CAPITAL NORTH AMERICA LLC—See Tikehau Capital Advisors SAS; *Int'l*, pg. 7747
TIKEHAU CAPITAL SCA—See Tikehau Capital Advisors SAS; *Int'l*, pg. 7747
TIKEHAU INVESTMENT MANAGEMENT ASIA PTE. LTD.—See Tikehau Capital Advisors SAS; *Int'l*, pg. 7747
TIKEHAU INVESTMENT MANAGEMENT JAPAN K.K.—See Tikehau Capital Advisors SAS; *Int'l*, pg. 7747
TIKFORCE LIMITED; *Int'l*, pg. 7747
TIK, INC.—See Ship Healthcare Holdings, Inc.; *Int'l*, pg. 6852
TIKI RESTAURANT, LOUNGE & MARINA, INC.; *U.S. Private*, pg. 4170
TIKIT GROUP PLC—See Vista Equity Partners, LLC; *U.S. Private*, pg. 4395
TIKKURILA AB—See PPG Industries, Inc.; *U.S. Public*, pg. 1710
TIKKURILA (CHINA) PAINTS CO., LTD.—See PPG Industries, Inc.; *U.S. Public*, pg. 1710
TIKKURILA COATINGS SP. Z.O.O.—See PPG Industries, Inc.; *U.S. Public*, pg. 1710
TIKKURILA DANMARK A/S—See PPG Industries, Inc.; *U.S. Public*, pg. 1710

TIKKURILA D.O.O.E.L.—See PPG Industries, Inc.; *U.S. Public*, pg. 1711
TIKKURILA NORGE A/S—See PPG Industries, Inc.; *U.S. Public*, pg. 1710
TIKKURILA OYJ—See PPG Industries, Inc.; *U.S. Public*, pg. 1710
TIKKURILA POLSKA S.A.—See PPG Industries, Inc.; *U.S. Public*, pg. 1710
TIKKURILA SVERIGE AB—See PPG Industries, Inc.; *U.S. Public*, pg. 1711
TIKKURILA ZORKA D.O.O.—See PPG Industries, Inc.; *U.S. Public*, pg. 1710
TIKO VERTRIEBSGESELLSCHAFT MBH—See FRoSTA AG; *Int'l*, pg. 2797
TIKTAK/SEGAFREDO ZANETTI NEDERLAND B.V.—See Segafredo Zanetti S.p.A.; *Int'l*, pg. 6682
TIKUN OLAM CANNBIT PHARMACEUTICALS LTD.; *Int'l*, pg. 7748
TILA COMMERCIAL LIMITED—See Places for People Group Limited; *Int'l*, pg. 5888
TILAKNAGAR INDUSTRIES LTD; *Int'l*, pg. 7748
TILAK VENTURES LIMITED; *Int'l*, pg. 7748
TILBURY GREEN POWER LIMITED—See KKR & Co. Inc.; *U.S. Public*, pg. 1252
TILCON CONNECTICUT INC.—See CRH plc; *Int'l*, pg. 1848
TILCON NEW YORK INC. - NEW JERSEY—See CRH plc; *Int'l*, pg. 1848
TILCON NEW YORK INC.—See CRH plc; *Int'l*, pg. 1848
TILDA INDIA PRIVATE LIMITED—See Ebro Foods S.A.; *Int'l*, pg. 2287
TILDA LIMITED—See Ebro Foods S.A.; *Int'l*, pg. 2287
TILDA MARKETING INC.—See The Hain Celestial Group, Inc.; *U.S. Public*, pg. 2087
TILDA RICE LIMITED—See The Hain Celestial Group, Inc.; *U.S. Public*, pg. 2087
TILDEN FARM NURSERY, LLC—See SiteOne Landscape Supply, Inc.; *U.S. Public*, pg. 1889
TILDEN MINING COMPANY LC—See Cleveland-Cliffs, Inc.; *U.S. Public*, pg. 514
TILE AFRICA GROUP (PTY) LTD.—See Norcros plc; *Int'l*, pg. 5415
TILE & CARPET TOWN EAST INCORPORATED; *U.S. Private*, pg. 4170
TILE CONTRACTORS SUPPLY COMPANY; *U.S. Private*, pg. 4170
TILE GIANT LIMITED—See Travis Perkins plc; *Int'l*, pg. 7908
TILE IMPORTS LLC; *U.S. Private*, pg. 4170
TIL ENVIRO LTD.; *Int'l*, pg. 7748
TILES4LESS LIMITED—See Topps Tiles Plc; *Int'l*, pg. 7820
TILE SHOP HOLDINGS, INC.; *U.S. Public*, pg. 2158
THE TILE SHOP, LLC—See Tile Shop Holdings, Inc.; *U.S. Public*, pg. 2159
TILE TOP INDUSTRY CO., LTD.—See Dynasty Ceramic Public Company Limited; *Int'l*, pg. 2242
TILETORIA CAPE (PTY) LTD.—See Invicta Holdings Limited; *Int'l*, pg. 3788
TILE WEST INC.; *U.S. Private*, pg. 4170
TILIA HOLDINGS LLC; *U.S. Private*, pg. 4170
TILIBRA PRODUTOS DE PAPELARIA LTDA—See ACCO Brands Corporation; *U.S. Public*, pg. 33
TILIN TALAN SPAIN, S.L.—See Scientia School, S.A.; *Int'l*, pg. 6648
TILLAGE CONSTRUCTION L.L.C.; *U.S. Private*, pg. 4170
TILLAMOOK CHEESE INC.—See Tillamook County Creamery Association; *U.S. Private*, pg. 4171
TILLAMOOK COUNTRY SMOKER INC.—See Insignia Capital Group, L.P.; *U.S. Private*, pg. 2091
TILLAMOOK COUNTY CREAMERY ASSOCIATION; *U.S. Private*, pg. 4170
TILLAMOOK LUMBER COMPANY—See Hampton Affiliates; *U.S. Private*, pg. 1851
TILL CAPITAL CORPORATION; *Int'l*, pg. 7748
TILLEMAN MOTOR COMPANY; *U.S. Private*, pg. 4171
TILLER CORP.—See Martin Marietta Materials, Inc.; *U.S. Public*, pg. 1389
TILLERY CAPITAL LLC; *U.S. Private*, pg. 4171
TILLERY CHEVROLET GMC INC.; *U.S. Private*, pg. 4171
TILLEY CHEMICAL CO., INC.—See SK Capital Partners, LP; *U.S. Private*, pg. 3680
TILLEY FIRE EQUIPMENT COMPANY INC—See Tustin Mechanical Services (Lehigh Valley), LLC; *U.S. Private*, pg. 4262
TIL LIMITED; *Int'l*, pg. 7748
TILLING TIMBER PTY. LIMITED; *Int'l*, pg. 7748
TILLLATE SCHWEIZ AG—See TX Group AG; *Int'l*, pg. 7992
TILLMAN, ALLEN, GREER; *U.S. Private*, pg. 4171
TILLOTSON COMMERCIAL MOTORS LIMITED—See Heidelberg Materials AG; *Int'l*, pg. 3320
TILLOTTS PHARMA AB—See Zeria Pharmaceutical Co., Ltd.; *Int'l*, pg. 8638
TILLOTTS PHARMA AG—See Zeria Pharmaceutical Co., Ltd.; *Int'l*, pg. 8638
TILLOTTS PHARMA CZECH S.R.O.—See Zeria Pharmaceutical Co., Ltd.; *Int'l*, pg. 8638

TILLOTTS PHARMA GMBH—See Zeria Pharmaceutical Co., Ltd.; *Int'l*, pg. 8638
TILLOTTS PHARMA LTD—See Zeria Pharmaceutical Co., Ltd.; *Int'l*, pg. 8638
TILLOTTS PHARMA SPAIN S.L.U.—See Zeria Pharmaceutical Co., Ltd.; *Int'l*, pg. 8638
TILLOTTS PHARMA UK LTD—See Zeria Pharmaceutical Co., Ltd.; *Int'l*, pg. 8638
TILLY'S, INC.; *U.S. Public*, pg. 2159
TILNEY INVESTMENT MANAGEMENT SERVICES LIMITED—See Permira Advisers LLP; *Int'l*, pg. 5809
TILNEY INVESTMENT MANAGEMENT—See Permira Advisers LLP; *Int'l*, pg. 5808
TILNEY SMITH & WILLIAMSON LTD.—See Permira Advisers LLP; *Int'l*, pg. 5808
TILON INC.; *Int'l*, pg. 7748
TIL OVERSEAS PTE. LIMITED.—See TIL Limited; *Int'l*, pg. 7748
TILRAY BRANDS, INC.; *Int'l*, pg. 7748
TILSON HR, INC.; *U.S. Private*, pg. 4171
TILSON TECHNOLOGY MANAGEMENT; *U.S. Private*, pg. 4171
TILT CREATIVE + PRODUCTION, LLC; *U.S. Private*, pg. 4171
TILTED KILT PUB & EATERY!; *U.S. Private*, pg. 4171
TILT HOLDINGS INC.; *U.S. Public*, pg. 2159
TILTING CAPITAL CORP.; *Int'l*, pg. 7748
TILTON EQUIPMENT COMPANY; *U.S. Private*, pg. 4171
TILT RENEWABLES LIMITED—See Mercury NZ Limited; *Int'l*, pg. 4834
TIMAB MAGNESIUM SAS—See Compagnie Financiere et de Participations Roullier SA; *Int'l*, pg. 1740
TIMAC AGRO ALGERIE, SARL—See Compagnie Financiere et de Participations Roullier SA; *Int'l*, pg. 1740
TIMAC AGRO ARGENTINA S.A.—See Compagnie Financiere et de Participations Roullier SA; *Int'l*, pg. 1740
TIMAC AVRASYA ZIRAAT SAN.VE TIC. A.S.—See Compagnie Financiere et de Participations Roullier SA; *Int'l*, pg. 1740
TIMAC AGRO INTERNATIONAL SAS—See Compagnie Financiere et de Participations Roullier SA; *Int'l*, pg. 1740
TIMAC AGRO LATVIA SIA—See Compagnie Financiere et de Participations Roullier SA; *Int'l*, pg. 1740
TIMAC AGRO LT, UAB—See Compagnie Financiere et de Participations Roullier SA; *Int'l*, pg. 1740
TIMAC AGRO MAROC SA—See Compagnie Financiere et de Participations Roullier SA; *Int'l*, pg. 1740
TIMAC AGRO NEDERLAND B.V.—See Compagnie Financiere et de Participations Roullier SA; *Int'l*, pg. 1740
TIMAC AGRO PARAGUAY S.A.—See Compagnie Financiere et de Participations Roullier SA; *Int'l*, pg. 1740
TIMAC AGRO POLSKA SP.Z.O.O.—See Compagnie Financiere et de Participations Roullier SA; *Int'l*, pg. 1740
TIMAC AGRO ROMANIA SRL—See Compagnie Financiere et de Participations Roullier SA; *Int'l*, pg. 1740
TIMAC AGRO SLOVAKIA, S.R.O.—See Compagnie Financiere et de Participations Roullier SA; *Int'l*, pg. 1740
TIMAC AGRO SVERIGE AB—See Compagnie Financiere et de Participations Roullier SA; *Int'l*, pg. 1740
TIMAC AGRO UK LTD.—See Compagnie Financiere et de Participations Roullier SA; *Int'l*, pg. 1740
TIMAC AGRO UKRAINE LLC—See Compagnie Financiere et de Participations Roullier SA; *Int'l*, pg. 1740
TIMAC AGRO URUGUAY S.A.—See Compagnie Financiere et de Participations Roullier SA; *Int'l*, pg. 1740
TIMAC AGRO USA INC.—See Compagnie Financiere et de Participations Roullier SA; *Int'l*, pg. 1740
TIMAH INTERNATIONAL INVESTMENT PTE. LTD.—See PT Timah Tbk.; *Int'l*, pg. 6078
TIMARPUR-OKHLA WASTE MANAGEMENT COMPANY PRIVATE LIMITED - OLD NDMC COMPOST PLANT—See JITF Infralogistics Limited; *Int'l*, pg. 3971
TIMAR SA—See Clasquin S.A.; *Int'l*, pg. 1652
TIMARU MOTORS LTD—See The Colonial Motor Company Limited; *Int'l*, pg. 7635
TIMAS A.D.; *Int'l*, pg. 7750
TIMBER AND HARDWARE EXCHANGE PTY. LTD.—See Metcash Limited; *Int'l*, pg. 4852
TIMBER & BUILDING SUPPLIES HOLLAND N.V.—See HAL Trust N.V.; *Int'l*, pg. 3227
TIMBERCON, INC.—See Radiall S.A.; *Int'l*, pg. 6174
TIMBERCREEK ASSET MANAGEMENT INC.; *Int'l*, pg. 7750
TIMBERCREEK FINANCIAL CORP.—See Timbercreek Asset Management Inc.; *Int'l*, pg. 7750
TIMBER CREEK RESOURCE, LLC.—See Delos Capital, LLC; *U.S. Private*, pg. 1198
TIMBERFENCE CAPITAL PARTNERS, LLC; *U.S. Private*, pg. 4171
TIMBER HILL EUROPE AG—See Interactive Brokers Group, Inc.; *U.S. Public*, pg. 1140
TIMBERHORN, LLC.—See ManpowerGroup Inc.; *U.S. Public*, pg. 1362
TIMBER INDUSTRIES INC.; *U.S. Private*, pg. 4171
TIMBERLAND ASIA LLC—See V. F. Corporation; *U.S. Public*, pg. 2268
TIMBERLAND BANCORP, INC.; *U.S. Public*, pg. 2159

TIMBERLAND BANK—See Timberland Bancorp, Inc.; *U.S. Public*, pg. 2159
TIMBERLAND CANADA CO.—See V. F. Corporation; *U.S. Public*, pg. 2268
THE TIMBERLAND COMPANY—See V. F. Corporation; *U.S. Public*, pg. 2268
TIMBERLAND ESPANA, S.A.—See V. F. Corporation; *U.S. Public*, pg. 2268
TIMBERLAND EUROPE B.V.—See V. F. Corporation; *U.S. Public*, pg. 2268
TIMBERLAND EUROPE SERVICES LTD.—See V. F. Corporation; *U.S. Public*, pg. 2268
TIMBERLAND (GIBRALTAR) HOLDING LIMITED—See V. F. Corporation; *U.S. Public*, pg. 2268
TIMBERLAND HARVESTERS INC.; *U.S. Private*, pg. 4171
TIMBERLAND HONG KONG LTD.—See V. F. Corporation; *U.S. Public*, pg. 2268
TIMBERLAND INTERNATIONAL, LLC—See V. F. Corporation; *U.S. Public*, pg. 2269
TIMBERLAND ITALY SRL.—See V. F. Corporation; *U.S. Public*, pg. 2269
TIMBERLAND LLC—See V. F. Corporation; *U.S. Public*, pg. 2269
TIMBERLAND RETAIL, INC.—See V. F. Corporation; *U.S. Public*, pg. 2269
TIMBERLAND SERVICE CORPORATION—See Timberland Bancorp, Inc.; *U.S. Public*, pg. 2159
TIMBERLAND SERVICES—See Landvest Inc.; *U.S. Private*, pg. 2387
TIMBERLAND SWITZERLAND HOLDING GMBH—See V. F. Corporation; *U.S. Public*, pg. 2269
TIMBERLINE FASTENERS, INC.; *U.S. Private*, pg. 4172
TIMBERLINE FOREST PRODUCTS LLC; *U.S. Private*, pg. 4172
TIMBERLINE LAND CO. INC.; *U.S. Private*, pg. 4172
TIMBERLINE, LLC; *U.S. Private*, pg. 4172
TIMBERLINE PLASTICS, INC.; *U.S. Private*, pg. 4172
TIMBERLINE RESOURCES CORPORATION—See McEwen Mining Inc.; *U.S. Public*, pg. 4758
TIMBERLINE SOFTWARE CORPORATION—See The Sage Group plc; *Int'l*, pg. 7680
TIMBERLINK AUSTRALIA PTY. LTD.—See New Forests Pty. Limited; *Int'l*, pg. 5223
TIMBERMAN DENMARK A/S—See Volati AB; *Int'l*, pg. 8301
THE TIMBERMEN, INC.; *U.S. Private*, pg. 4127
TIMBER PRODUCTS COMPANY, LP; *U.S. Private*, pg. 4171
TIMBER PRODUCTS COMPANY—See Timber Products Company, LP; *U.S. Private*, pg. 4171
TIMBER PRODUCTS CO.—See Timber Products Company, LP; *U.S. Private*, pg. 4171
TIMBERPRO, INC.—See Komatsu Ltd.; *Int'l*, pg. 4239
TIMBER PRO LOGGING LTD.; *Int'l*, pg. 7750
TIMBER SPECIALTIES CO.—See Koppers Holdings Inc.; *U.S. Public*, pg. 1272
TIMBERTECH, INC.; *U.S. Private*, pg. 4172
TIMBERWELL BERHAD; *Int'l*, pg. 7750
TIMBERWEST FOREST CORP.—See British Columbia Investment Management Corp.; *Int'l*, pg. 1170
TIMBERWEST FOREST CORP.—See Public Sector Pension Investment Board; *Int'l*, pg. 6097
TIMBERWOLF PLANTING PTY LTD—See PeopleIn Limited; *Int'l*, pg. 5794
TIMBES & YEAGER, LLC; *U.S. Private*, pg. 4172
TIMBIL MECHANICAL CORP; *U.S. Private*, pg. 4172
TIM BRASIL SERVICIOS E PARTICIPACOES S.A.—See TIM S.p.A.; *Int'l*, pg. 7750
TIM-BR MARTS LTD.; *Int'l*, pg. 7750
TIMBUK2 DESIGNS, INC.—See Exemplis LLC; *U.S. Private*, pg. 1448
TIMBUS—See Regie Autonome des Transports Parisiens; *Int'l*, pg. 6253
TIM CASTELLAW AUTOMOTIVE; *U.S. Private*, pg. 4171
TIM CELULAR S.A.—See TIM S.p.A.; *Int'l*, pg. 7750
TIMCO AEROSYSTEMS—See John Swire & Sons Limited; *Int'l*, pg. 3980
TIMCO AVIATION SERVICES, INC.—See John Swire & Sons Limited; *Int'l*, pg. 3980
TIMCO ENGINE CENTER—See John Swire & Sons Limited; *Int'l*, pg. 3981
TIME CARE AB—See Rothschild & Co SCA; *Int'l*, pg. 6403
TIME CARE AB—See TA Associates, Inc.; *U.S. Private*, pg. 3917
TIMEC COMPANY, INC.; *U.S. Private*, pg. 4172
TIME CITY (HONG KONG) LIMITED—See Asia Commercial Holdings Limited; *Int'l*, pg. 611
TIME CO., LTD.—See Valor Holdings Co., Ltd.; *Int'l*, pg. 8122
TIME COMMERCE CO., LTD.—See Prestige International Inc.; *Int'l*, pg. 5967
TIME DECO CORPORATION LIMITED—See MC Group Public Company Limited; *Int'l*, pg. 4755
TIME DEFINITE SERVICES INC.; *U.S. Private*, pg. 4172
TIME DESIGN CO., LTD.—See Kakaku.Com Inc.; *Int'l*, pg. 4056
TI MEDIA LIMITED—See Epiris Managers LLP; *Int'l*, pg. 2461

TIME DOMAIN CORP.—See Bonaventure Capital LLC; *U.S. Private*, pg. 613
TIME DOMAIN CORP.—See Fidelis Capital LLC; *U.S. Private*, pg. 1502
TIME DOTCOM BERHAD; *Int'l*, pg. 7750
TIME DOTNET BHD.—See TIME dotCom Berhad; *Int'l*, pg. 7750
TIME EQUITIES, INC.; *U.S. Private*, pg. 4172
TIME ERA SDN. BHD.—See Eden Inc. Berhad; *Int'l*, pg. 2306
TIME FINANCE PLC; *Int'l*, pg. 7750
TIME FLAGSHIP AG—See The Swatch Group Ltd.; *Int'l*, pg. 7693
THE TIME GROUP INC.; *U.S. Private*, pg. 4127
TIME INC. (UK) PROPERTY INVESTMENTS LTD—See Epiris Managers LLP; *Int'l*, pg. 2461
TIME INTERCONNECT TECHNOLOGY (HUIZHOU) LIMITED—See Time Interconnect Technology Limited; *Int'l*, pg. 7751
TIME INTERCONNECT TECHNOLOGY LIMITED; *Int'l*, pg. 7751
TIME INTERNATIONAL; *Int'l*, pg. 7751
TIMELESS CAPITAL CORP.; *Int'l*, pg. 7751
TIMELESS INC.—See Polaris Capital Group Co., Ltd.; *Int'l*, pg. 5907
TIMELESS INVESTMENTS BV; *Int'l*, pg. 7751
TIMELESS RESOURCES HOLDINGS LIMITED; *Int'l*, pg. 7751
TIMELINE RECRUITING, LLC—See Maxim Healthcare Services, Inc.; *U.S. Private*, pg. 2618
TIME LINK INTERNATIONAL CORP.—See Hellman & Friedman LLC; *U.S. Private*, pg. 1911
TIMELOX AB—See ASSA ABLOY AB; *Int'l*, pg. 640
TIMELY ADVERTISING, INC.; *U.S. Private*, pg. 4172
TIME MAGAZINE EUROPE LIMITED—See Warner Bros. Discovery, Inc.; *U.S. Public*, pg. 2328
TIME MANUFACTURING COMPANY—See The Sterling Group, L.P.; *U.S. Private*, pg. 4123
TIME MATTERS GMBH—See Deutsche Lufthansa AG; *Int'l*, pg. 2071
TIME MOVING & STORAGE INC.; *U.S. Private*, pg. 4172
TIMEOUT AGENCY & CONCERTS AS—See Live Nation Entertainment, Inc.; *U.S. Public*, pg. 1331
TIME OUT CHICAGO LLC—See Time Out Group plc; *Int'l*, pg. 7751
TIME OUT GROUP PLC; *Int'l*, pg. 7751
TIME OUT MARKET PORTO, LDA—See Time Out Group plc; *Int'l*, pg. 7751
TIME OUT NEW YORK—See Oakley Capital Limited; *Int'l*, pg. 5504
TIMEPAYMENT CORPORATION—See SoftBank Group Corp.; *Int'l*, pg. 7053
TIME PRODUCTS LTD.; *Int'l*, pg. 7751
TIME PUBLISHING AND MEDIA CO., LTD.; *Int'l*, pg. 7751
TIMERACK INC.; *U.S. Private*, pg. 4172
TIMES24 CO., LTD.—See PARK24 Co. Ltd.; *Int'l*, pg. 5743
TIMESAVERS INC.—See Holden Industries, Inc.; *U.S. Private*, pg. 1962
TIMESAVERS INTERNATIONAL BV—See Holden Industries, Inc.; *U.S. Private*, pg. 1962
TIMESCAN LOGISTICS (INDIA) LIMITED; *Int'l*, pg. 7752
TIMES CHINA HOLDINGS LIMITED; *Int'l*, pg. 7752
TIMES COLONIST—See Glacier Media Inc.; *Int'l*, pg. 2987
TIMES COMMUNICATION CO., LTD.—See PARK24 Co. Ltd.; *Int'l*, pg. 5743
TIMES COMMUNITY NEWS—See Los Angeles Times Communications, LLC; *U.S. Private*, pg. 2497
TIMES COMMUNITY NEWS - SOUTH—See Los Angeles Times Communications, LLC; *U.S. Private*, pg. 2497
TIMESDAILY—See Tennessee Valley Printing Co.; *U.S. Private*, pg. 3968
TIMES DEVELOPMENT PTE LTD—See Singapore Press Holdings Ltd.; *Int'l*, pg. 6943
TIMES EDUCATIONAL SERVICES PTE LTD—See Thai Beverage Public Company Limited; *Int'l*, pg. 7590
TIMES FIBER CANADA LTD.—See Amphenol Corporation; *U.S. Public*, pg. 132
TIMES FIBER COMMUNICATIONS, INC.—See Amphenol Corporation; *U.S. Public*, pg. 132
TIMES GREEN ENERGY INDIA LIMITED; *Int'l*, pg. 7752
TIMES GUARANTY LTD.—See Team India Managers Ltd.; *Int'l*, pg. 7500
TIMESHARE RELIEF, INC.; *U.S. Private*, pg. 4173
TIMESHARES BY OWNER; *U.S. Private*, pg. 4173
THE TIMES HERALD COMPANY—See Gannett Co., Inc.; *U.S. Public*, pg. 901
TIMES HERALD-RECORD—See Gannett Co., Inc.; *U.S. Public*, pg. 904
TIMES-HERALD—See Alden Global Capital LLC; *U.S. Private*, pg. 155
THE TIMES HERALD—See Alden Global Capital LLC; *U.S. Private*, pg. 159
TIMES HOLDING CO.; *U.S. Private*, pg. 4172
THE TIMES INC.—See Paxton Media Group LLC; *U.S. Private*, pg. 3116
THE TIMES INC.—See Small Newspaper Group Inc.; *U.S. Private*, pg. 3690
TIMES INNOVATION CAPITAL LLC—See PARK24 Co. Ltd.; *Int'l*, pg. 5743

COMPANY NAME INDEX

TIMES JOURNAL INC.; *U.S. Private*, pg. 4172
THE TIMES LEADER—See The Nutting Company, Inc.; *U.S. Private*, pg. 4087
TIMES MEDIA GROUP LIMITED—See Tiso Blackstar Group SE; *Int'l*, pg. 7759
TIMES MEDIA (PTY) LIMITED - BOOKS DIVISION—See Tiso Blackstar Group SE; *Int'l*, pg. 7759
TIMES MEDIA (PTY) LIMITED - MEDIA DIVISION—See Tiso Blackstar Group SE; *Int'l*, pg. 7759
TIMES MEDIA (PTY) LIMITED—See Tiso Blackstar Group SE; *Int'l*, pg. 7759
TIMES MOBILITY CO., LTD.—See PARK24 Co. Ltd.; *Int'l*, pg. 5743
TIMES NEIGHBORHOOD HOLDINGS LIMITED; *Int'l*, pg. 7752
TIMES NEWSPAPERS LTD.—See News Corporation; *U.S. Public*, pg. 1521
THE TIMES-NEWS—See Gannett Co., Inc.; *U.S. Public*, pg. 906
TIMES OFFSET (MALAYSIA) SDN BHD—See Thai Beverage Public Company Limited; *Int'l*, pg. 7590
THE TIMES OF INDIA—See Bennett, Coleman & Co. Ltd.; *Int'l*, pg. 975
THE TIMES OF TRENTON—See Advance Publications, Inc.; *U.S. Private*, pg. 87
TIMES OIL CORPORATION; *U.S. Private*, pg. 4172
TIME & SPACE—See Williams Whittle Associates, Inc.; *U.S. Private*, pg. 4527
THE TIMES-PICAYUNE PUBLISHING CORP.—See Advance Publications, Inc.; *U.S. Private*, pg. 87
TIMES-POST—See Home News Enterprises, LLC; *U.S. Private*, pg. 1971
TIMES PRINTERS PTE LTD—See Thai Beverage Public Company Limited; *Int'l*, pg. 7590
TIMES PRINTING COMPANY, INC.—See PDQ Print Center, Inc.; *U.S. Private*, pg. 3122
TIMES PROPERTIES PRIVATE LIMITED—See Singapore Press Holdings Ltd.; *Int'l*, pg. 6943
TIMES PUBLISHING COMPANY—See Times Holding Co.; *U.S. Private*, pg. 4172
TIMES PUBLISHING CO.—See Gannett Co., Inc.; *U.S. Public*, pg. 906
TIMES PUBLISHING (HONG KONG) LIMITED—See Thai Beverage Public Company Limited; *Int'l*, pg. 7590
TIMES PUBLISHING LIMITED—See Thai Beverage Public Company Limited; *Int'l*, pg. 7590
TIMES PUBLISHING NEWSPAPERS INC.—See O'Rourke Media Group, LLC; *U.S. Private*, pg. 2980
TIMES RECORDER—See Gannett Co., Inc.; *U.S. Public*, pg. 901
THE TIMES REPORTER—See Gannett Co., Inc.; *U.S. Public*, pg. 905
TIMES SERVICE CO., LTD.—See PARK24 Co. Ltd.; *Int'l*, pg. 5743
TIMES-SHAMROCK, INC.; *U.S. Private*, pg. 4173
THE TIMES—See Gannett Co., Inc.; *U.S. Public*, pg. 901
TIMESSQUARE CAPITAL MANAGEMENT, LLC—See Affiliated Managers Group, Inc.; *U.S. Public*, pg. 56
TIMES SQUARE PROPERTIES; *U.S. Private*, pg. 4172
TIMES-STANDARD—See Alden Global Capital LLC; *U.S. Private*, pg. 156
TIMES SUPPORT CO., LTD.—See PARK24 Co. Ltd.; *Int'l*, pg. 5743
TIME-STEPS AG—See PSI Software SE; *Int'l*, pg. 6017
TIMES THE BOOKSHOP PTE LTD—See Thai Beverage Public Company Limited; *Int'l*, pg. 7590
TIMES UNIVERSAL GROUP HOLDINGS LIMITED; *Int'l*, pg. 7752
TI METAL FORMING LTD - AHMEDABAD PLANT—See The Murugappa Group, Ltd.; *Int'l*, pg. 7669
TI METAL FORMING LTD - BARODA PLANT—See The Murugappa Group, Ltd.; *Int'l*, pg. 7669
TI METAL FORMING LTD - BHAWAL PLANT—See The Murugappa Group, Ltd.; *Int'l*, pg. 7669
TI METAL FORMING LTD - KAKKALUR PLANT—See The Murugappa Group, Ltd.; *Int'l*, pg. 7669
TI METAL FORMING LTD - PUNE PLANT—See The Murugappa Group, Ltd.; *Int'l*, pg. 7669
TI METAL FORMING LTD—See The Murugappa Group, Ltd.; *Int'l*, pg. 7669
TIMETARGET PTY LTD—See Accel Partners L.P.; *U.S. Private*, pg. 49
TIMETARGET PTY LTD—See KKR & Co. Inc.; *U.S. Public*, pg. 1239
TIME TECH (HONG KONG) LTD.—See Seiko Epson Corporation; *Int'l*, pg. 6688
TIME TECHNOLOGY CO., LTD.; *Int'l*, pg. 7751
TIME TECHNOPLAST LIMITED; *Int'l*, pg. 7751
TIMET GERMANY, GMBH—See Berkshire Hathaway Inc.; *U.S. Public*, pg. 315
TIME TIMER LLC; *U.S. Private*, pg. 4172
TIMETRADE SYSTEMS, INC.—See Clearhaven Partners LP; *U.S. Private*, pg. 933
TIMET SAVOIE, SA—See Berkshire Hathaway Inc.; *U.S. Public*, pg. 315
TIMET UK LIMITED—See Berkshire Hathaway Inc.; *U.S. Public*, pg. 315
TIME USA, LLC—See Meredith Corporation; *U.S. Public*, pg. 1423

TIME WARNER BUSINESS SERVICES LLC—See Warner Bros. Discovery, Inc.; *U.S. Public*, pg. 2328
TIME WARNER CABLE ENTERPRISES LLC—See Charter Communications, Inc.; *U.S. Public*, pg. 483
TIME WARNER GLOBAL MEDIA GROUP—See Warner Bros. Discovery, Inc.; *U.S. Public*, pg. 2328
TIME WATCH INVESTMENTS LTD; *Int'l*, pg. 7751
TIMEWEAVE LIMITED—See Swiss Life Holding; *Int'l*, pg. 7368
TIMEWORTH LTD.—See PPF Group N.V.; *Int'l*, pg. 5951
TIMEX GROUP B.V.; *Int'l*, pg. 7752
TIMEX GROUP INDIA LTD.—See Timex Group B.V.; *Int'l*, pg. 7752
TIMEX GROUP LUXURY WATCHES BV—See Timex Group B.V.; *Int'l*, pg. 7752
TIMEX GROUP USA, INC.—See Timex Group B.V.; *Int'l*, pg. 7752
TIME ZONE MULTIMEDIA; *U.S. Private*, pg. 4172
TIM FOOD CO., LTD.—See House Foods Group Inc.; *Int'l*, pg. 3491
TIM HAPERT BV—See VDL Groep B.V.; *Int'l*, pg. 8141
TIMICO LIMITED—See Horizon Capital LLP; *Int'l*, pg. 3479
TIMICO PARTNER SERVICES LIMITED—See Horizon Capital LLP; *Int'l*, pg. 3479
TIMICO TECHNOLOGY GROUP LIMITED—See Horizon Capital LLP; *Int'l*, pg. 3479
TIMIOS APPRAISAL MANAGEMENT, INC.—See Ideanomics, Inc.; *U.S. Public*, pg. 1088
TIMIOS DEFAULT SERVICES, INC.—See Ideanomics, Inc.; *U.S. Public*, pg. 1088
TIMIOS HOLDINGS CORP.—See Ideanomics, Inc.; *U.S. Public*, pg. 1088
TIMIOS, INC.—See Ideanomics, Inc.; *U.S. Public*, pg. 1088
TIMIOS TITLE, A CALIFORNIA CORPORATION—See Ideanomics, Inc.; *U.S. Public*, pg. 1088
TIMJAMWAY PTY. LTD.—See Steadfast Group Limited; *Int'l*, pg. 7188
TIMKEN AEROSPACE TRANSMISSIONS, LLC—See The Timken Company; *U.S. Public*, pg. 2133
TIMKEN ARGENTINA S.R.L.—See The Timken Company; *U.S. Public*, pg. 2133
TIMKEN BORING SPECIALTIES, LLC—See The Timken Company; *U.S. Public*, pg. 2133
TIMKEN CANADA LP—See The Timken Company; *U.S. Public*, pg. 2133
THE TIMKEN COMPANY; *U.S. Public*, pg. 2132
TIMKEN DE MEXICO, S.A. DE C.V.—See The Timken Company; *U.S. Public*, pg. 2134
TIMKEN DEUTSCHLAND GMBH—See The Timken Company; *U.S. Public*, pg. 2133
TIMKEN DO BRASIL S.A. COMERCIO E INDUSTRIA LTDA.—See The Timken Company; *U.S. Public*, pg. 2134
TIMKEN DRIVES LLC—See The Timken Company; *U.S. Public*, pg. 2133
TIMKEN ENGINEERING AND RESEARCH-INDIA PRIVATE LIMITED—See The Timken Company; *U.S. Public*, pg. 2133
TIMKEN ESPANA, S.L.—See The Timken Company; *U.S. Public*, pg. 2133
TIMKEN EUROPE—See The Timken Company; *U.S. Public*, pg. 2133
TIMKEN GEARS & SERVICES INC.—See The Timken Company; *U.S. Public*, pg. 2133
TIMKEN GMBH—See The Timken Company; *U.S. Public*, pg. 2133
TIMKEN ILS CHELTENHAM LIMITED—See The Timken Company; *U.S. Public*, pg. 2133
TIMKEN ILS DAYTON, INC.—See The Timken Company; *U.S. Public*, pg. 2133
TIMKEN INDIA LTD.—See The Timken Company; *U.S. Public*, pg. 2133
TIMKEN INDIA MANUFACTURING PRIVATE LIMITED—See The Timken Company; *U.S. Public*, pg. 2133
TIMKEN ITALIA S.R.L.—See The Timken Company; *U.S. Public*, pg. 2133
TIMKEN MOTOR & CRANE SERVICES LLC—See The Timken Company; *U.S. Public*, pg. 2133
TIMKEN ROMANIA SA—See The Timken Company; *U.S. Public*, pg. 2133
TIMKEN (SHANGHAI) DISTRIBUTION AND SALES CO., LTD.—See The Timken Company; *U.S. Public*, pg. 2133
TIMKEN SINGAPORE PTE LTD—See The Timken Company; *U.S. Public*, pg. 2133
TIMKEN SOUTH AFRICA PROPRIETARY LTD.—See The Timken Company; *U.S. Public*, pg. 2133
TIMKENSTEEL (SHANGHAI) CORPORATION LIMITED—See Metallus Inc.; *U.S. Public*, pg. 1427
TIMKENSTEEL UK LIMITED—See Metallus Inc.; *U.S. Public*, pg. 1427
TIMKEN SUPER PRECISION—See The Timken Company; *U.S. Public*, pg. 2133
TIMKEN UK LTD.—See The Timken Company; *U.S. Public*, pg. 2134
TIMLOC BUILDING PRODUCTS LTD.—See The Alumasc Group plc; *Int'l*, pg. 7613

TIML RADIO LTD.—See Bennett, Coleman & Co. Ltd.; *Int'l*, pg. 975
TIMMERIJE B.V.—See Hydratec Industries NV; *Int'l*, pg. 3546
TIMMERMAN GEOTECHNICAL GROUP INC—See GPD Group; *U.S. Private*, pg. 1748
TIMM HEALTH CARE BV—See Fagron NV; *Int'l*, pg. 2603
TIMMINS DAILY PRESS—See Chatham Asset Management, LLC; *U.S. Private*, pg. 861
TIMMINS GARAGE INC.; *Int'l*, pg. 7752
TIMMINS GOLD CORP MEXICO S.A DE C.V—See Argonaut Gold Inc.; *U.S. Public*, pg. 191
TIMMONS & COMPANY, INC.; *U.S. Private*, pg. 4173
TIMMONS GROUP, INC.; *U.S. Private*, pg. 4173
TIMMONS INTERNATIONAL INC.; *U.S. Private*, pg. 4173
TIM O'BRIEN HOMES, INC.; *U.S. Private*, pg. 4171
TIMOK A.D.; *Int'l*, pg. 7752
TIMOLOR LEROUX ET LOTZ SAS—See Altawest Group; *Int'l*, pg. 388
TIMONEER STRATEGIC PARTNERS, LLC; *U.S. Private*, pg. 4173
TIMONIUM SURGERY CENTER, LLC—See Tenet Healthcare Corporation; *U.S. Public*, pg. 2009
TIMONIUM TOYOTA INCORPORATED; *U.S. Private*, pg. 4173
TIMOR PORT SA—See Financiere de L'Odet; *Int'l*, pg. 2668
TIMOTHY F. PASCH INC.; *U.S. Private*, pg. 4173
TIMOTHY OFF HEATING & AIR CONDITIONING; *U.S. Private*, pg. 4173
TIMOTHY P. DE MARTINI AUTO SALES; *U.S. Private*, pg. 4173
TIMPANI CAPITAL MANAGEMENT, LLC—See Calamos Asset Management, Inc.; *U.S. Private*, pg. 716
TIMPANOGOS REGIONAL HOSPITAL—See HCA Healthcare, Inc.; *U.S. Public*, pg. 1012
TIM PARTICIPACOES S.A.—See TIM S.p.A.; *Int'l*, pg. 7750
TIMPSON GROUP PLC; *Int'l*, pg. 7752
TIMPSON LOCKSMITHS LTD.—See Timpson Group PLC; *Int'l*, pg. 7752
TIMPSON LTD.—See Timpson Group PLC; *Int'l*, pg. 7752
TIMPTE INDUSTRIES INC.; *U.S. Private*, pg. 4173
TIMPURI NOI S.A.; *Int'l*, pg. 7752
TIM RHODES ELECTRIC CO., INC.—See Shoals MPE, LLC; *U.S. Private*, pg. 3639
TIMSAMLEE ASSOCIATES INC.; *U.S. Private*, pg. 4173
TIM S.A.—See Wurth Verwaltungsgesellschaft mbH; *Int'l*, pg. 8504
TIM'S BUICK PONTIAC GMC TOYOTA; *U.S. Private*, pg. 4171
TIM S.P.A. - ROME CORPORATE OFFICE—See TIM S.p.A.; *Int'l*, pg. 7749
TIM S.P.A.; *Int'l*, pg. 7748
TIM W.E. SGPS, S.A.; *Int'l*, pg. 7750
TIM WHITEHEAD CHRYSLER DODGE JEEP RAM; *U.S. Private*, pg. 4171
TINAU MISSION DEVELOPMENT BANK LIMITED—See Citizens Bank International Limited; *Int'l*, pg. 1626
THE TIN BOX COMPANY; *U.S. Private*, pg. 4127
TINBY AB—See SP Group A/S; *Int'l*, pg. 7122
TINBY SKUMPLAST A/S—See SP Group A/S; *Int'l*, pg. 7122
TINBY SP. Z O.O.—See SP Group A/S; *Int'l*, pg. 7122
TINC COMM. VA; *Int'l*, pg. 7752
TINCHER-WILLIAMS CHEVROLET, INC.; *U.S. Private*, pg. 4173
TINCI HOLDINGS LIMITED; *Int'l*, pg. 7753
TINCO TOYS COMPANY LIMITED—See Kader Holdings Company Limited; *Int'l*, pg. 4046
TINDALL CORPORATION; *U.S. Private*, pg. 4173
TINDALL RECORD STORAGE LTD.—See Berkshire Partners LLC; *U.S. Private*, pg. 534
TINDELL'S INC.; *U.S. Private*, pg. 4173
TINDER, INC.—See IAC Inc.; *U.S. Public*, pg. 1082
TINE AGRO LTD.; *Int'l*, pg. 7753
TINEL SA—See Eiffage S.A.; *Int'l*, pg. 2331
TINE MEIERIET VEST BA—See TINE SA; *Int'l*, pg. 7753
TINE SA; *Int'l*, pg. 7753
TINEXTA CYBER S.P.A.—See Tinexta S.p.A.; *Int'l*, pg. 7753
TINEXTA S.P.A.; *Int'l*, pg. 7753
TING INC.—See EchoStar Corporation; *U.S. Public*, pg. 711
TINGLEV ELEMENTFABRIK GMBH—See Heidelberg Materials AG; *Int'l*, pg. 3320
TINGLEY RUBBER CORPORATION—See Bunzl plc; *Int'l*, pg. 1219
TINGO GROUP, INC.; *U.S. Public*, pg. 2159
TING SIN CO., LTD.; *Int'l*, pg. 7753
TINGUE, BROWN & CO.; *U.S. Private*, pg. 4173
TINGUE, BROWN & CO.—See Tingue, Brown & Co.; *U.S. Private*, pg. 4173
TING VIRGINIA, LLC—See EchoStar Corporation; *U.S. Public*, pg. 711
TINGYI (CAYMAN ISLANDS) HOLDING CORP.; *Int'l*, pg. 7754
TINHORN CREEK VINEYARDS LTD.—See Andrew Peller Limited; *Int'l*, pg. 452

TINGYI (CAYMAN ISLANDS) HOLDING CORP.   CORPORATE AFFILIATIONS

TINHVAN TECHNOLOGIES JSC.—See TIS Inc.; *Int'l*, pg. 7758
TINICUM ENTERPRISES, INC.; *U.S. Private*, pg. 4173
TINICUM INCORPORATED—See Tinicum Enterprises, Inc.; *U.S. Private*, pg. 4173
TIN INC.—See International Paper Company; *U.S. Public*, pg. 1158
TINITRON, INC.; *U.S. Private*, pg. 4175
TINIUS OLSEN, INC.; *U.S. Private*, pg. 4175
TINIUS OLSEN, LTD.—See Tinius Olsen, Inc.; *U.S. Private*, pg. 4175
TINKA RESOURCES LIMITED; *Int'l*, pg. 7754
TINKA RESOURCES S.A.C.—See Tinka Resources Limited; *Int'l*, pg. 7754
TINKER FEDERAL CREDIT UNION; *U.S. Private*, pg. 4175
TINKERINE STUDIOS LTD.; *Int'l*, pg. 7754
TINKER OMEGA SINTO LLC—See Sintokogio Ltd.; *Int'l*, pg. 6959
TINKOFF BANK JSC; *Int'l*, pg. 7754
THE TINLEY BEVERAGE COMPANY INC.; *Int'l*, pg. 7694
TIN MAN BREWING CO.—See Neace Ventures; *U.S. Private*, pg. 2877
TINNA RUBBER & INFRASTRUCTURE LIMITED; *Int'l*, pg. 7754
TIN NGHIA - A CHAU JOINT-STOCK COMPANY—See Tin Nghia Corp.; *Int'l*, pg. 7752
TIN NGHIA CORP.; *Int'l*, pg. 7752
TIN NGHIA CORP. - TIN NGHIA GRANITE FACTORY—See Tin Nghia Corp.; *Int'l*, pg. 7752
TIN NGHIA LAOS JOINT STOCK COMPANY—See Tin Nghia Corp.; *Int'l*, pg. 7752
TIN NGHIA LOGISTICS JOINT-STOCK COMPANY—See Tin Nghia Corp.; *Int'l*, pg. 7752
TIN NGHIA PETROL JOINT STOCK COMPANY—See Tin Nghia Corp.; *Int'l*, pg. 7752
TIN NGHIA PROJECT MANAGEMENT COMPANY LIMITED—See Tin Nghia Corp.; *Int'l*, pg. 7752
TIN ONE MINING JSC; *Int'l*, pg. 7752
TINONE RESOURCES INC.; *Int'l*, pg. 7754
TINOPOLIS PLC—See Vitruvian Partners LLP; *Int'l*, pg. 8263
TIN PAN ALLEY CO., LTD.—See World Co., Ltd.; *Int'l*, pg. 8457
TINPLATE COMPANY OF INDIA LTD—See Tata Sons Limited; *Int'l*, pg. 7473
TIN ROOF SOFTWARE LLC; *U.S. Private*, pg. 4173
TINSA—See Advent International Corporation; *U.S. Private*, pg. 107
TINSELTOWN INVESTMENTS B.V.; *Int'l*, pg. 7754
TIN SING CHEMICAL ENGINEERS LIMITED—See Yau Lee Holdings Limited; *Int'l*, pg. 8572
TINSLEY ADVERTISING; *U.S. Private*, pg. 4175
TINSLEY GROUP - PS&W, INC.—See Olympic Steel Inc.; *U.S. Public*, pg. 1571
TINTA FRESCA EDICIONES S.A.—See Grupo Clarin S.A.; *Int'l*, pg. 3125
TINTARONA PUBLICATIONS SDN BHD—See Utusan Melayu (Malaysia) Berhad; *Int'l*, pg. 8102
TINTAS CORAL LTDA—See Akzo Nobel N.V.; *Int'l*, pg. 271
TINTAS DYRUP, S.A.—See PPG Industries, Inc.; *U.S. Public*, pg. 1707
TINTAS ROBBIALAC S.A.; *Int'l*, pg. 7754
TIN TEA IMPORT NETWORK B.A.—See Miko NV; *Int'l*, pg. 4892
TINTELINGEN B.V.—See Sligro Food Group N.V.; *Int'l*, pg. 6997
TIN THANH PACKING JOINT STOCK COMPANY—See Rengo Co., Ltd.; *Int'l*, pg. 6282
TINTINA MINES LIMITED; *Int'l*, pg. 7754
TINTOMETER AG—See Tintometer GmbH; *Int'l*, pg. 7754
TINTOMETER CHINA—See Tintometer GmbH; *Int'l*, pg. 7754
TINTOMETER GMBH; *Int'l*, pg. 7754
TINTOMETER INC.—See Tintometer GmbH; *Int'l*, pg. 7754
THE TINTOMETER LIMITED—See Tintometer GmbH; *Int'l*, pg. 7754
TINTOMETER SOUTH EAST ASIA—See Tintometer GmbH; *Int'l*, pg. 7754
TINTRA PLC; *Int'l*, pg. 7754
TINTRI INC.—See DataDirect Networks Inc.; *U.S. Private*, pg. 1165
TINT WORLD; *U.S. Private*, pg. 4175
TINUITI INC.—See New Mountain Capital, LLC; *U.S. Private*, pg. 2903
TINV LTD.—See Wise Plc; *Int'l*, pg. 8436
TINYBEANS; *Int'l*, pg. 7754
TINYBEANS USA LTD—See Tinybeans; *Int'l*, pg. 7755
TINYCO, INC.—See Netmarble Corp.; *Int'l*, pg. 5215
TINY TOTS THERAPY INC.; *U.S. Private*, pg. 4175
TIOGA GARDENS LP—See Edison International; *U.S. Public*, pg. 719
TIOGA PIPE SUPPLY CO. INC.; *U.S. Private*, pg. 4175
TIOGA STATE BANK—See TSB Services Inc.; *U.S. Private*, pg. 4252
TIOMAN DRILLING COMPANY SDN BHD—See Sapura Energy Berhad; *Int'l*, pg. 6574
TIOMAN ISLAND RESORT BERHAD—See Berjaya Corporation Berhad; *Int'l*, pg. 983

TIONA TRUCK LINE INC.; *U.S. Private*, pg. 4175
TIONG AIK CONSTRUCTION PTE LTD.—See TA Corporation Ltd.; *Int'l*, pg. 7399
TIONG AIK RESOURCES (S) PTE LTD—See TA Corporation Ltd.; *Int'l*, pg. 7399
TIONG NAM HEAVY TRANSPORT & LIFTING SDN. BHD.—See Tiong Nam Logistics Holdings Berhad; *Int'l*, pg. 7755
TIONG NAM LOGISTICS HOLDINGS BERHAD; *Int'l*, pg. 7755
TIONG NAM LOGISTICS SOLUTIONS (LAO) CO., LTD.—See Tiong Nam Logistics Holdings Berhad; *Int'l*, pg. 7755
TIONG NAM LOGISTICS SOLUTIONS SDN. BHD.—See Tiong Nam Logistics Holdings Berhad; *Int'l*, pg. 7755
TIONG NAM PROPERTIES SDN. BHD.—See Tiong Nam Logistics Holdings Berhad; *Int'l*, pg. 7755
TIONG SENG HOLDINGS LIMITED; *Int'l*, pg. 7755
TIONG WOON CHINA CONSORTIUM PTE. LTD.—See Tiong Woon Corporation Holding Ltd.; *Int'l*, pg. 7755
TIONG WOON CORPORATION HOLDING LTD.; *Int'l*, pg. 7755
TIONG WOON CRANE AND TRANSPORT (PTE) LTD—See Tiong Woon Corporation Holding Ltd.; *Int'l*, pg. 7755
TIONG WOON CRANE PTE LTD—See Tiong Woon Corporation Holding Ltd.; *Int'l*, pg. 7755
TIONG WOON CRANE & TRANSPORT LANKA (PVT) LTD.—See Tiong Woon Corporation Holding Ltd.; *Int'l*, pg. 7755
TIONG WOON CRANE & TRANSPORT (M) SDN BHD—See Tiong Woon Corporation Holding Ltd.; *Int'l*, pg. 7755
TIONG WOON ENTERPRISE PTE LTD—See Tiong Woon Corporation Holding Ltd.; *Int'l*, pg. 7755
TIONG WOON (HUIZHOU) INDUSTRIAL SERVICES CO., LTD—See Tiong Woon Corporation Holding Ltd.; *Int'l*, pg. 7755
TIONG WOON INTERNATIONAL PTE LTD—See Tiong Woon Corporation Holding Ltd.; *Int'l*, pg. 7755
TIONG WOON MARINE PTE LTD—See Tiong Woon Corporation Holding Ltd.; *Int'l*, pg. 7755
TIONG WOON MYANMAR COMPANY LIMITED—See Tiong Woon Corporation Holding Ltd.; *Int'l*, pg. 7755
TIONG WOON OFFSHORE PTE LTD—See Tiong Woon Corporation Holding Ltd.; *Int'l*, pg. 7755
TIONG WOON PHILIPPINES, INC.—See Tiong Woon Corporation Holding Ltd.; *Int'l*, pg. 7755
TIONG WOON PROJECT & CONTRACTING INDIA PRIVATE LIMITED—See Tiong Woon Corporation Holding Ltd.; *Int'l*, pg. 7755
TIONG WOON PROJECT & CONTRACTING PTE LTD—See Tiong Woon Corporation Holding Ltd.; *Int'l*, pg. 7755
TIONG WOON THAI CO., LTD.—See Tiong Woon Corporation Holding Ltd.; *Int'l*, pg. 7755
TIONG WOON TOWER CRANE PTE. LTD.—See Tiong Woon Corporation Holding Ltd.; *Int'l*, pg. 7755
TIONG WOON VIETNAM COMPANY LIMITED—See Tiong Woon Corporation Holding Ltd.; *Int'l*, pg. 7755
TION RENEWABLES AG—See EQT AB; *Int'l*, pg. 2481
TIORCO LLC—See Ecolab Inc.; *U.S. Public*, pg. 716
TIO TECH A; *Int'l*, pg. 7755
TIOXIDE AMERICAS LLC—See Huntsman Corporation; *U.S. Public*, pg. 1075
TIOXIDE EUROPE SAS—See Huntsman Corporation; *U.S. Public*, pg. 1075
TIOXIDE EUROPE S.R.L.—See Huntsman Corporation; *U.S. Public*, pg. 1075
TIOXIDE (MALAYSIA) SDN. BHD.—See Huntsman Corporation; *U.S. Public*, pg. 1075
TIOXIDE SOUTHERN AFRICA (PTY) LTD.—See Huntsman Corporation; *U.S. Public*, pg. 1075
TIPCO ASPHALT PUBLIC COMPANY LIMITED—See Tipco Foods Public Company Limited; *Int'l*, pg. 7756
TIPCO BIOTECH CO., LTD.—See Tipco Foods Public Company Limited; *Int'l*, pg. 7756
TIPCO F&B CO., LTD.—See Tipco Foods Public Company Limited; *Int'l*, pg. 7756
TIPCO FOOD CO., LTD.—See Tipco Foods Public Company Limited; *Int'l*, pg. 7756
TIPCO FOODS PUBLIC COMPANY LIMITED; *Int'l*, pg. 7756
TIPDATA MEDICAL SOFTWARE—See CompuGroup Medical SE & Co. KGaA; *Int'l*, pg. 1757
T.I.P. ENGINEERING D.O.O.—See Inles d.d.; *Int'l*, pg. 3705
TIPEX PTE LTD.—See Hanoi Beer Trading JSC; *Int'l*, pg. 3258
TIPEX TRADING PTE LTD—See PSC Corporation Ltd.; *Int'l*, pg. 6015
TIP GROUP (UK) PTY. LTD.—See Teaminvest Private Group Limited; *Int'l*, pg. 7501
TI (PHILIPPINES), INC.—See Texas Instruments Incorporated; *U.S. Public*, pg. 2026
TIPIAK INC—See Tipiak S.A.; *Int'l*, pg. 7756
TIPIAK INTERNATIONAL—See Tipiak S.A.; *Int'l*, pg. 7756
TIPIAK S.A.; *Int'l*, pg. 7756

TIPIK COMMUNICATION AGENCY S.A.—See Sword Group SE; *Int'l*, pg. 7376
TIPIK S.A.; *Int'l*, pg. 7756
TIPMEFAST, INC.; *Int'l*, pg. 7756
TIPMONT RURAL ELECTRIC MEMBERSHIP CORPORATION; *U.S. Private*, pg. 4175
TIPNESS, LTD.—See Nippon Television Holdings Inc.; *Int'l*, pg. 5356
TIPO DIRECT SERV SRL—See ANY Security Printing Company PLC; *Int'l*, pg. 486
TIPOGRAFIA MANSON, LIMITADA—See TOPPAN Holdings Inc.; *Int'l*, pg. 7817
TI POLAND SP Z O.O.—See Bain Capital, LP; *U.S. Private*, pg. 447
TIPOPLASTIKA A.D.; *Int'l*, pg. 7756
TIPOTEX CHEVROLET, INC.; *U.S. Private*, pg. 4175
TIPPAGRAL S.A.—See Tipperary Co-operative Creamery Ltd.; *Int'l*, pg. 7756
TIPPERARY CO-OPERATIVE CREAMERY LTD.; *Int'l*, pg. 7756
TIPPER TIE, INC.—See John Bean Technologies Corporation; *U.S. Public*, pg. 1192
TIPPETT STUDIO, INC; *U.S. Private*, pg. 4175
TIPPING POINT COMMUNITY; *U.S. Private*, pg. 4176
TIPPING POINT SOLUTIONS, INC.; *U.S. Private*, pg. 4176
TIPPS PTE. LTD.—See Toyo Ink SC Holdings Co., Ltd.; *Int'l*, pg. 7854
TIPS INDUSTRIES LIMITED; *Int'l*, pg. 7756
TIPS INDUSTRY (M) SDN. BHD—See PSC Corporation Ltd.; *Int'l*, pg. 6015
TIPSY ELVES LLC; *U.S. Private*, pg. 4176
TIP TECHNOLOGIES, INC.—See Roper Technologies, Inc.; *U.S. Public*, pg. 1811
TIPTEH D.O.O.; *Int'l*, pg. 7756
TIPTEL AG; *Int'l*, pg. 7756
TIPTON AND COSELEY BUILDING SOCIETY; *Int'l*, pg. 7756
TIPTON FARMERS COOPERATIVE—See Tennessee Farmers Cooperative; *U.S. Private*, pg. 3967
TIPTON FARMERS COOPERATIVE—See WinField United, LLC; *U.S. Private*, pg. 4541
TIPTON HONDA; *U.S. Private*, pg. 4176
TIPTON & MAGLIONE INC.; *U.S. Private*, pg. 4176
TIP TOP CANNING COMPANY; *U.S. Private*, pg. 4175
TIP TOP CONSTRUCTION CORP; *U.S. Private*, pg. 4175
TIP TOP MEAT SDN. BHD.—See MKH Berhad; *Int'l*, pg. 5002
TIP TOP POULTRY, INC. - ROCKMART FACILITY—See Tip Top Poultry, Inc.; *U.S. Private*, pg. 4175
TIP TOP POULTRY, INC.; *U.S. Private*, pg. 4175
TIPTREE INC.; *U.S. Public*, pg. 2159
TIPTREE OPERATING COMPANY, LLC—See Tiptree Inc.; *U.S. Public*, pg. 2159
TIP ZILINA, S.R.O.—See Hamburger Hafen und Logistik AG; *Int'l*, pg. 3237
TIRAD S.R.O.—See Hillenbrand, Inc.; *U.S. Public*, pg. 1037
TIRAM JAYA SDN BHD—See Berjaya Corporation Berhad; *Int'l*, pg. 983
TIRANA BANK S.A.—See Piraeus Financial Holdings S.A.; *Int'l*, pg. 5874
TIRANA INTERNATIONAL AIRPORT SHPK—See China Everbright Group Limited; *Int'l*, pg. 1501
TIRATHAI PUBLIC COMPANY LIMITED; *Int'l*, pg. 7756
TIRE AND OIL INC.; *U.S. Private*, pg. 4176
TIRE CENTERS WEST, LLC—See Compagnie Generale des Etablissements Michelin SCA; *Int'l*, pg. 1745
TIRE COMPANY DEBICA S.A.—See The Goodyear Tire & Rubber Company; *U.S. Public*, pg. 2084
TIRECORP GMBH—See Compagnie Generale des Etablissements Michelin SCA; *Int'l*, pg. 1745
TIRE CURING BLADDERS LLC—See LANXESS AG; *Int'l*, pg. 4416
TIRE DEN INC.; *U.S. Private*, pg. 4176
TIRE DISCOUNTERS, INC.—See Four Corners Property Trust, Inc.; *U.S. Public*, pg. 875
TIRE GROUP INTERNATIONAL, LLC; *U.S. Private*, pg. 4176
TIRE GUYS INC.; *U.S. Private*, pg. 4176
TIRE KINGDOM, INC.—See Golden Gate Capital Management II, LLC; *U.S. Private*, pg. 1731
TIRE MACHINERY DIVISION—See Mitsubishi Heavy Industries, Ltd.; *Int'l*, pg. 4957
TIREMAN AUTO SERVICE CENTERS LTD.—See Belle Tire Distributors, Inc.; *U.S. Private*, pg. 520
TIREMASTER LIMITED; *Int'l*, pg. 7756
TIREMAXX INC.; *U.S. Private*, pg. 4176
TIRENDO DEUTSCHLAND GMBH—See Delticom AG; *Int'l*, pg. 2021
TIRENDO GMBH—See Delticom AG; *Int'l*, pg. 2021
THE TIRE RACK INC.; *U.S. Private*, pg. 4127
TIRESOLES OF BROWARD INC.; *U.S. Private*, pg. 4176
TIRES PLUS TOTAL CAR CARE—See Bridgestone Corporation; *Int'l*, pg. 1160
TIRES PLUS TOTAL CAR CARE—See Bridgestone Corporation; *Int'l*, pg. 1157
TIRE'S WAREHOUSE, INC.; *U.S. Private*, pg. 4176

COMPANY NAME INDEX

TIRE WAREHOUSE CENTRAL INC.—See Monro, Inc.; *U.S. Public*, pg. 1465
TIRE WHOLESALERS COMPANY, LLC—See Kingswood Capital Management LLC; *U.S. Private*, pg. 2312
TIRE WORLD KAN BEST CO., LTD.—See PROTO CORPORATION; *Int'l*, pg. 6006
TIRMADRID, S.A.—See ACS, Actividades de Construccion y Servicios, S.A.; *Int'l*, pg. 116
TIROLER SPARKASSE BANK AG—See Erste Group Bank AG; *Int'l*, pg. 2498
TIROLINVEST KAPITALANLAGEGESELLSCHAFT MBH.—See Erste Group Bank AG; *Int'l*, pg. 2499
TIRRENO POWER SPA—See ENGIE SA; *Int'l*, pg. 2434
TIRRENO SOLAR S.R.L.—See ENGIE SA; *Int'l*, pg. 2434
TIRSCHWELL & LOEWY, INC.—See Provident Financial Services, Inc.; *U.S. Public*, pg. 1730
TIRTHA CO., LTD—See Tsukada Global Holdings Inc.; *Int'l*, pg. 7956
TIRTHA HARAPAN BALI.PT—See Prasidha Aneka Niaga Tbk; *Int'l*, pg. 5955
TIRTH PLASTICS LIMITED; *Int'l*, pg. 7756
TIRUNA AMERICA INC.—See Guangdong Dongfang Science & Technology Co., Ltd.; *Int'l*, pg. 3153
TIRUPATI DEVELOPMENT (U) LTD—See Tirupati Sarjan Ltd.; *Int'l*, pg. 7757
TIRUPATI FINCORP LTD.; *Int'l*, pg. 7756
TIRUPATI FINLEASE LTD.; *Int'l*, pg. 7756
TIRUPATI FOAM LTD.; *Int'l*, pg. 7756
TIRUPATI FORGE LTD.; *Int'l*, pg. 7757
TIRUPATI GRAPHITE PLC; *Int'l*, pg. 7757
TIRUPATI INDUSTRIES (INDIA) LIMITED; *Int'l*, pg. 7757
TIRUPATI INKS LIMITED; *Int'l*, pg. 7757
TIRUPATI SARJAN LTD.; *Int'l*, pg. 7757
TIRUPATI STARCH & CHEMICALS LIMITED; *Int'l*, pg. 7757
TIRUPATI TYRES LTD.; *Int'l*, pg. 7757
TIRUS INTERNATIONAL SA—See VSMPO - AVISMA Corporation; *Int'l*, pg. 8314
TIRU TEA COMPANY LIMITED—See Camellia Plc; *Int'l*, pg. 1271
TISA A.D.; *Int'l*, pg. 7758
TISCALI INTERNATIONAL NETWORK B.V.—See Tiscali S.p.A.; *Int'l*, pg. 7758
TISCALI S.P.A.; *Int'l*, pg. 7758
TIS CHIYODA SYSTEMS INC.—See Chiyoda Corporation; *Int'l*, pg. 1575
TISCHLER FINER FOODS INC.; *U.S. Private*, pg. 4176
TISCHLER UND SOHN USA LIMITED; *U.S. Private*, pg. 4176
TISCO ASSET MANAGEMENT COMPANY LIMITED—See TISCO Financial Group Public Company Limited; *Int'l*, pg. 7758
TISCO BANK PUBLIC COMPANY LIMITED—See TISCO Financial Group Public Company Limited; *Int'l*, pg. 7758
TISCO FINANCIAL GROUP PUBLIC COMPANY LIMITED; *Int'l*, pg. 7758
TISCO INFORMATION TECHNOLOGY COMPANY LIMITED—See TISCO Financial Group Public Company Limited; *Int'l*, pg. 7758
TISCO INSURANCE SOLUTION COMPANY LIMITED—See TISCO Financial Group Public Company Limited; *Int'l*, pg. 7758
TISCO LEARNING CENTER COMPANY LIMITED—See TISCO Financial Group Public Company Limited; *Int'l*, pg. 7758
TISCO SECURITIES COMPANY LIMITED—See TISCO Financial Group Public Company Limited; *Int'l*, pg. 7758
TISDALE CLEAN ENERGY CORP.; *Int'l*, pg. 7758
TIS FRANCE S.A.S.—See TIM S.p.A.; *Int'l*, pg. 7750
TISHCON CORP.; *U.S. Private*, pg. 4176
TISHMAN CONSTRUCTION CORPORATION—See AECOM; *U.S. Public*, pg. 51
TISHMAN HOTEL CORPORATION—See AECOM; *U.S. Public*, pg. 52
TISHMAN REALTY CORPORATION—See AECOM; *U.S. Public*, pg. 52
TISHMAN SPEYER PROPERTIES LP; *U.S. Private*, pg. 4176
TIS HOKKAIDO INC.—See TIS Inc.; *Int'l*, pg. 7758
TIS HOLDINGS INC.—See Munchener Ruckversicherungs AG; *Int'l*, pg. 5092
TISHOMINGO ACQUISITION, LLC—See Federal Signal Corporation; *U.S. Public*, pg. 826
TIS INC.; *U.S. Private*, pg. 4176
TIS INC.; *Int'l*, pg. 7757
TIS INC—See TIS Inc.; *Int'l*, pg. 7758
TIS INSURANCE SERVICES INC.—See Edwards Capital, LLC; *U.S. Private*, pg. 1342
TIS LOGISTICS, INC.—See Toll Brothers, Inc.; *U.S. Public*, pg. 2162
TISO BLACKSTAR GROUP PROPRIETARY LIMITED—See Tiso Blackstar Group SE; *Int'l*, pg. 7759
TISO BLACKSTAR GROUP SE; *Int'l*, pg. 7758
TI SPARKLE ARGENTINA S.A.—See TIM S.p.A.; *Int'l*, pg. 7748

TI SPARKLE AUSTRIA GMBH—See TIM S.p.A.; *Int'l*, pg. 7748
TI SPARKLE BRASIL PARTICIPACOES LTDA.—See TIM S.p.A.; *Int'l*, pg. 7749
TI SPARKLE FRANCE S.A.S.—See TIM S.p.A.; *Int'l*, pg. 7749
TI SPARKLE GERMANY GMBH—See TIM S.p.A.; *Int'l*, pg. 7749
TI SPARKLE GREECE S.A.—See TIM S.p.A.; *Int'l*, pg. 7749
TI SPARKLE ROMANIA S.R.L.—See TIM S.p.A.; *Int'l*, pg. 7749
TI SPARKLE RUSSIA LLC—See TIM S.p.A.; *Int'l*, pg. 7749
TI SPARKLE SINGAPORE PTE. LTD.—See TIM S.p.A.; *Int'l*, pg. 7749
TI SPARKLE TURKEY TELEKOMUNIKASYON ANONIM SIRKETI—See TIM S.p.A.; *Int'l*, pg. 7749
TI SPARKLE UK LTD.—See TIM S.p.A.; *Int'l*, pg. 7749
TIS SOLUTION LINK INC.—See TIS Inc.; *Int'l*, pg. 7758
TISSOT SA—See The Swatch Group Ltd.; *Int'l*, pg. 7693
TISSUE BANKS INTERNATIONAL; *U.S. Private*, pg. 4176
TISSUE GENESIS, INC.—See Orgenesis Inc.; *U.S. Public*, pg. 1617
TISSUE MACHINERY COMPANY S.P.A.—See I.M.A. Industria Macchine Automatiche S.p.A.; *Int'l*, pg. 3566
TISSUE REGENIX GROUP PLC; *Int'l*, pg. 7759
TISSUE REPAIR COMPANY—See Gene Biotherapeutics Inc.; *U.S. Public*, pg. 911
TISSUE REPAIR LTD.; *Int'l*, pg. 7759
TIS SYSTEM SERVICE INC.—See TIS Inc.; *Int'l*, pg. 7758
TISTA SCIENCE AND TECHNOLOGY CORP; *U.S. Private*, pg. 4176
TIS TOHOKU INC.—See TIS Inc.; *Int'l*, pg. 7758
TIS TOTAL SERVICE CO,. LTD.—See TIS Inc.; *Int'l*, pg. 7758
TIS WEST JAPAN INC.—See TIS Inc.; *Int'l*, pg. 7758
TISZA AUTOMOTIVE KFT—See AD Plastik d.d.; *Int'l*, pg. 122
TITAANIUM TEN ENTERPRISE LIMITED; *Int'l*, pg. 7759
TITAGARH FIREMA S.P.A.—See Titagarh Rail Systems Limited.; *Int'l*, pg. 7759
TITAGARH RAIL SYSTEMS LIMITED.; *Int'l*, pg. 7759
TITAGARH STEEL LTD.—See TSL Industries Limited; *Int'l*, pg. 7952
TITAN AG PTY LTD—See Elders Limited; *Int'l*, pg. 2346
TITAN AMERICA LLC—See Titan Cement Company S.A.; *Int'l*, pg. 7760
TITAN ASIA JANT SANAYI VE TICARET A.S.—See Titan International, Inc.; *U.S. Public*, pg. 2160
TITAN AUSTRALIA PTY. LTD.—See TKPH Pty Ltd.; *Int'l*, pg. 7766
TITAN BIOTECH LIMITED; *Int'l*, pg. 7759
TITAN BROADCASTING, LLC—See Pritchard Broadcasting Corp.; *U.S. Private*, pg. 3268
TITAN BROADCAST MANAGEMENT LLC—See Ellis, McQuary, Stanley & Associates LLC; *U.S. Private*, pg. 1374
TITAN CEMENT COMPANY S.A.; *Int'l*, pg. 7759
TITAN CEMENT INTERNATIONAL SA; *Int'l*, pg. 7760
TITAN CEMENT UK LTD.—See Titan Cement Company S.A.; *Int'l*, pg. 7760
TITAN CLOUD SOFTWARE, LLC; *U.S. Private*, pg. 4177
TITAN COMPANY LIMITED; *Int'l*, pg. 7760
TITAN CONSTRUCTION SUPPLY, INC.—See The Sterling Group, L.P.; *U.S. Private*, pg. 4122
TITAN CONSULTING LLC; *U.S. Private*, pg. 4177
TITAN CONTRACTING & LEASING CO. INC.—See Charlesbank Capital Partners, LLC; *U.S. Private*, pg. 856
TITAN CORRUGATED, INC.—See UFP Industries, Inc.; *U.S. Public*, pg. 2220
TITAN D.D.—See Groupe SFPI SA; *Int'l*, pg. 3111
TITAN DISTRIBUTION (UK) LIMITED—See Titan International, Inc.; *U.S. Public*, pg. 2160
TITAN ECHIPAMENTE NUCLEARE S.A.; *Int'l*, pg. 7760
TITAN ENERGY, LLC—See Atlas Energy Group, LLC; *U.S. Public*, pg. 223
TITAN ENERGY PARTNERS, L.P.—See UGI Corporation; *U.S. Public*, pg. 2222
TITAN ENERGY SYSTEMS INC.—See PIONEER POWER SOLUTIONS, INC.; *U.S. Public*, pg. 1693
TITAN ENVIRONMENTAL LIMITED—See Kingspan Group PLC; *Int'l*, pg. 4179
TITAN ENVIRONMENTAL LIMITED—See Kingspan Group PLC; *Int'l*, pg. 4179
TITAN ENVIRONMENTAL SURVEYS LTD—See HAL Trust N.V.; *Int'l*, pg. 3226
TITAN EUROPE PLC—See Titan International, Inc.; *U.S. Public*, pg. 2160
TITAN FABRICATORS, INC.—See INNOVATE Corp.; *U.S. Public*, pg. 1126
TITAN FACILITIES MANAGEMENT PTE. LTD.—See Hygieia Group Limited; *Int'l*, pg. 3549
TITAN FASTENER PRODUCTS, INC.—See Nautic Partners, LLC; *U.S. Private*, pg. 2871
TITAN FOUNDATION LIMITED—See Build King Holdings Limited; *Int'l*, pg. 1212
TITAN FRANCE SAS—See Titan International, Inc.; *U.S. Public*, pg. 2160

TITAN

TITAN GLOBAL DISTRIBUTION, INC.—See Atlas World Group, Inc.; *U.S. Private*, pg. 381
TITAN HEALTH MANAGEMENT SOLUTIONS, INC.—See Certive Solutions Inc.; *U.S. Public*, pg. 476
TITAN HOA MANAGEMENT, LLC; *U.S. Private*, pg. 4177
TITAN HOME IMPROVEMENT INC.—See York Capital Management Global Advisors, LLC; *U.S. Private*, pg. 4590
TITAN, INC.—See The Burke Porter Group; *U.S. Private*, pg. 4003
TITAN INDUSTRIES INCORPORATED; *U.S. Private*, pg. 4177
TITAN INTECH LIMITED; *Int'l*, pg. 7760
TITAN INTERNATIONAL, INC.; *U.S. Public*, pg. 2159
TITAN INTERNATIONAL LTD.; *Int'l*, pg. 7760
TITAN INTERTRACTOR GMBH—See Titan International, Inc.; *U.S. Public*, pg. 2160
TITAN INTERTRACTOR GMBH—See Titan International, Inc.; *U.S. Public*, pg. 2160
TITAN INVO TECHNOLOGY LIMITED; *Int'l*, pg. 7760
TITAN ITALIA SPA—See Titan International, Inc.; *U.S. Public*, pg. 2160
TITAN ITM HOLDING SPA—See Titan International, Inc.; *U.S. Public*, pg. 2160
TITAN ITM (TIANJIN) CO. LTD.—See Titan International, Inc.; *U.S. Public*, pg. 2160
TITANIUM AMERICAN TRUCKING, INC.—See Titanium Transportation Group Inc.; *Int'l*, pg. 7761
TITANIUM DENTAL BV—See PAO Severstal; *Int'l*, pg. 5732
TITANIUM FABRICATION CORPORATION - PHOENIX GROUP DIVISION—See Titanium Fabrication Corporation; *U.S. Private*, pg. 4177
TITANIUM FABRICATION CORPORATION; *U.S. Private*, pg. 4177
TITANIUM GROUP LIMITED; *Int'l*, pg. 7761
TITANIUM HEALTHCARE, INC.; *U.S. Private*, pg. 4177
TITANIUM HOLDINGS GROUP, INC.; *U.S. Public*, pg. 2160
TITANIUM INDUSTRIES, INC.; *U.S. Private*, pg. 4177
TITANIUM, LTD.—See Titanium Fabrication Corporation; *U.S. Private*, pg. 4177
TITANIUM METALS CORPORATION—See Berkshire Hathaway Inc.; *U.S. Public*, pg. 315
TITANIUM & STEEL MANUFACTURING COMPANY LIMITED—See Saudi Steel Pipe Company; *Int'l*, pg. 6594
TITANIUM TRANSPORTATION GROUP INC.; *Int'l*, pg. 7761
TITAN KOGYO, LTD.; *Int'l*, pg. 7760
TITAN KOGYO, LTD. - UBE NISHI PLANT—See Titan Kogyo, Ltd.; *Int'l*, pg. 7760
TITAN LANSING, LLC—See The Andersons Incorporated; *U.S. Public*, pg. 2035
TITANLINER, INC.—See Capital Southwest Corporation; *U.S. Public*, pg. 432
TITAN LOGIX CORP. - OVERLAND PARK BRANCH—See Titan Logix Corp.; *Int'l*, pg. 7760
TITAN LOGIX CORP.; *Int'l*, pg. 7760
TITAN MACHINERY BULGARIA AD—See Titan Machinery Inc.; *U.S. Public*, pg. 2160
TITAN MACHINERY D.O.O.—See Titan Machinery Inc.; *U.S. Public*, pg. 2160
TITAN MACHINERY INC. - AGRICULTURAL DIVISION—See Titan Machinery Inc.; *U.S. Public*, pg. 2160
TITAN MACHINERY INC. - CONSTRUCTION DIVISION—See Titan Machinery Inc.; *U.S. Public*, pg. 2160
TITAN MACHINERY INC. - INTERNATIONAL MARKETS—See Titan Machinery Inc.; *U.S. Public*, pg. 2160
TITAN MACHINERY INC.; *U.S. Public*, pg. 2160
TITAN MARITIME, LLC—See Crowley Maritime Corporation; *U.S. Private*, pg. 1110
TITAN MARKETING SERVICES, INC.—See Titan International, Inc.; *U.S. Public*, pg. 2160
TITAN MEDICAL INC.; *Int'l*, pg. 7760
TITAN MINERALS LIMITED; *Int'l*, pg. 7760
TITAN MINING CORP.; *Int'l*, pg. 7760
TITAN MINING (US) CORPORATION—See Titan Mining Corp.; *Int'l*, pg. 7760
TITAN MOBILE HOMES, INC.—See Champion Homes, Inc.; *U.S. Public*, pg. 477
TITAN OIL & GAS, INC.; *U.S. Private*, pg. 4177
TITAN OUTDOOR—See Titan; *U.S. Private*, pg. 4176
TITAN PETROCHEMICALS GROUP LIMITED; *Int'l*, pg. 7760
TITAN PHARMACEUTICALS, INC.; *U.S. Public*, pg. 2160
TITAN PROPANE LLC—See UGI Corporation; *U.S. Public*, pg. 2222
TITAN PROPERTY & CASUALTY INSURANCE COMPANY—See Western National Mutual Insurance Co.; *U.S. Private*, pg. 4494
TITAN ROOFING INC.; *U.S. Public*, pg. 4177
TITAN SECURITIES LIMITED; *Int'l*, pg. 7761
TITAN SEO INC.; *U.S. Private*, pg. 4177
TITAN; *U.S. Private*, pg. 4176
TITAN SPINE, LLC—See Medtronic plc; *Int'l*, pg. 4790

TITAN
CORPORATE AFFILIATIONS

TITANS POWER HOLDING PTE LTD—See NITTO KOGYO CORPORATION; *Int'l,* pg. 5387
TITANS POWER SYSTEM PTE LTD—See NITTO KOGYO CORPORATION; *Int'l,* pg. 5387
TITAN STAIRS INC.—See McDonough Corporation; *U.S. Private,* pg. 2633
TITAN STEEL CORP.; *U.S. Private,* pg. 4177
TITAN STEEL WHEELS LIMITED—See Titan International, Inc.; *U.S. Public,* pg. 2160
TITAN TECHNOLOGY PARTNERS, LTD.—See Accenture plc; *Int'l,* pg. 87
TITAN TELEVISION—See Modern Times Group MTG AB; *Int'l,* pg. 5015
TITAN TIRE CORPORATION OF BRYAN—See Titan International, Inc.; *U.S. Public,* pg. 2160
TITAN TIRE CORPORATION OF FREEPORT—See Titan International, Inc.; *U.S. Public,* pg. 2160
TITAN TIRE CORPORATION OF UNION CITY—See Titan International, Inc.; *U.S. Public,* pg. 2160
TITAN TIRE CORPORATION—See Titan International, Inc.; *U.S. Public,* pg. 2160
TITAN TOOL & DIE LIMITED; *Int'l,* pg. 7761
TITAN TOOL, INC.—See J. Wagner AG; *Int'l,* pg. 3857
TITANTV.COM—See Benedek Investment Group, LLC; *U.S. Private,* pg. 525
TITAN WHEEL CORPORATION OF ILLINOIS—See Titan International, Inc.; *U.S. Public,* pg. 2160
TITAN WHEEL CORPORATION OF VIRGINIA—See Titan International, Inc.; *U.S. Public,* pg. 2160
TITAN WHEELS AUSTRALIA PTY. LTD. - MUSWELLBROOK WHEEL AND UNDERCARRIAGE REFURBISH FACILITY—See TKPH Pty Ltd.; *Int'l,* pg. 7766
TITAN WIND ENERGY (EUROPE) A/S—See Titan Wind Energy (Suzhou) Co., Ltd.; *Int'l,* pg. 7761
TITAN WIND ENERGY (SUZHOU) CO., LTD.; *Int'l,* pg. 7761
TITAN WIRELESS LLC—See ISP Supplies LLC; *U.S. Private,* pg. 2146
TITAN WOOD INC.—See AccSys Technologies PLC; *Int'l,* pg. 93
TITAN WOOD LIMITED—See AccSys Technologies PLC; *Int'l,* pg. 93
TITAN WOOD TECHNOLOGY B.V.—See AccSys Technologies PLC; *Int'l,* pg. 93
TITAN WORLDWIDE—See Titan; *U.S. Private,* pg. 4177
TITAN WORLDWIDE—See Titan; *U.S. Private,* pg. 4177
TITAN WORLDWIDE—See Titan; *U.S. Private,* pg. 4177
TITAS GAS TRANSMISSION & DISTRIBUTION COMPANY LIMITED; *Int'l,* pg. 7761
TITAS TOPRAK INSAAT VE TAAHHUT ANONIM SIRKETI—See Enka Insaat ve Sanayi A.S.; *Int'l,* pg. 2440
TITEFLEX EUROPE S.A.S.—See Smiths Group plc; *Int'l,* pg. 7012
TITIJAYA LAND BERHAD; *Int'l,* pg. 7761
TIT INTERNATIONAL CO., LTD.—See TYC Brother Industrial Co., Ltd.; *Int'l,* pg. 7994
TITLE365 COMPANY—See Mr. Cooper Group Inc.; *U.S. Public,* pg. 1480
THE TITLE COMPANY OF NORTH CAROLINA—See Old Republic International Corporation; *U.S. Public,* pg. 1569
TITLE FIRST AGENCY, INC.; *U.S. Private,* pg. 4177
TITLEONE CORP.—See Anywhere Real Estate Inc.; *U.S. Public,* pg. 142
TITLEONE EXCHANGE COMPANY—See Anywhere Real Estate Inc.; *U.S. Public,* pg. 143
TITLE RESOURCE GROUP LLC—See Anywhere Real Estate Inc.; *U.S. Public,* pg. 142
TITLE RESOURCE GROUP SETTLEMENT SERVICES, LLC—See Anywhere Real Estate Inc.; *U.S. Public,* pg. 142
TITLE RESOURCES GUARANTY COMPANY—See Centerbridge Partners, L.P.; *U.S. Private,* pg. 816
TITLE SECURITY AGENCY OF PINAL COUNTY, LLC—See First American Financial Corporation; *U.S. Public,* pg. 838
THE TITLE SECURITY GROUP, INC.—See First American Financial Corporation; *U.S. Public,* pg. 838
TITLE SOURCE, INC.—See RockBridge Growth Equity, LLC; *U.S. Private,* pg. 3465
TITLEVEST AGENCY, INC.—See First American Financial Corporation; *U.S. Public,* pg. 838
TITLEZOOM COMPANY—See Lennar Corporation; *U.S. Public,* pg. 1307
TITMAN TIP TOOLS GMBH—See Checkit plc; *Int'l,* pg. 1459
TITMAN TIP TOOLS LIMITED—See Checkit plc; *Int'l,* pg. 1459
TITMAN TIP TOOLS LTD—See Checkit plc; *Int'l,* pg. 1459
TITOMIC LIMITED; *Int'l,* pg. 7761
TITON HARDWARE LIMITED—See Titon Holdings Plc; *Int'l,* pg. 7761
TITON HOLDINGS PLC; *Int'l,* pg. 7761
TITON INC—See Titon Holdings Plc; *Int'l,* pg. 7761
TITRON INDUSTRIES LIMITED—See AMCO United Holding Limited; *Int'l,* pg. 416
TITSCH & ASSOCIATES ARCHITECTS, INC.; *U.S. Private,* pg. 4177

TITTOT COMPANY LIMITED; *Int'l,* pg. 7761
TITUSFIELD LIMITED—See Kerry Group plc; *Int'l,* pg. 4139
TITUS—See Canada Pension Plan Investment Board; *Int'l,* pg. 1278
TITUSVILLE CENTER FOR SURGICAL EXCELLENCE, LLC—See Tenet Healthcare Corporation; *U.S. Public,* pg. 2013
TITUS WEALTH MANAGEMENT, INC.—See TA Associates, Inc.; *U.S. Private,* pg. 3919
TIUMBIO CO., LTD.; *Int'l,* pg. 7761
TIVA HEALTHCARE, INC.—See KKR & Co. Inc.; *U.S. Public,* pg. 1249
TIVERSA, INC.; *U.S. Private,* pg. 4177
TIVIC HEALTH SYSTEMS, INC.; *U.S. Public,* pg. 2161
TIVIT TERCEIRIZACAO DE PROCESSOS, SERVICOS E TECNOLOGIA S.A.—See Apax Partners LLP; *Int'l,* pg. 507
TIVITY HEALTH, INC.—See Stone Point Capital LLC; *U.S. Private,* pg. 3825
TIVIX, INC.—See Kellton Tech Solutions Ltd.; *Int'l,* pg. 4121
TIVO CORPORATION—See Adeia Inc.; *U.S. Public,* pg. 41
TIVO.KK—See Adeia Inc.; *U.S. Public,* pg. 41
TIVO KOREA CO. LTD.—See Adeia Inc.; *U.S. Public,* pg. 41
TIVOLI A/S; *Int'l,* pg. 7761
TIVOLI BEIRA, LDA.—See Teixeira Duarte SA; *Int'l,* pg. 7525
TIVOLICASINO.COM LIMITED—See Tivoli A/S; *Int'l,* pg. 7761
TIVOLI CONSTRUCTION LIMITED; *Int'l,* pg. 7761
TIVOLI ENTERPRISES INC.; *U.S. Private,* pg. 4177
TIVOLI GRUNDSTUCKS-AKTIENGESELLSCHAFT—See UniCredit S.p.A.; *Int'l,* pg. 8035
TIVOLI HOMES OF SARASOTA; *U.S. Private,* pg. 4177
TIVOLI, LLC—See 3F Filippi SpA; *Int'l,* pg. 7
TIVOLI PARTNERS; *U.S. Private,* pg. 4177
TIVOLY DF S.A. DE C.V.—See Tivoly S.A.; *Int'l,* pg. 7762
TIVOLY INC.—See Tivoly S.A.; *Int'l,* pg. 7762
TIVOLY S.A.; *Int'l,* pg. 7762
TIVO POLAND SP. Z O. O.—See Adeia Inc.; *U.S. Public,* pg. 41
TIVO SINGAPORE PTE. LTD.—See Adeia Inc.; *U.S. Public,* pg. 41
TIVO TECH PRIVATE LIMITED—See Adeia Inc.; *U.S. Public,* pg. 41
TIV TAAM HOLDINGS 1 LTD.; *Int'l,* pg. 7761
TIV TEXTILE GROUP 1969 LTD.; *Int'l,* pg. 7761
TIW CORPORATION—See Dril-Quip, Inc.; *U.S. Public,* pg. 687
TIW HUNGARY LLC—See Dril-Quip, Inc.; *U.S. Public,* pg. 687
TIW INTERNATIONAL, LLC—See Dril-Quip, Inc.; *U.S. Public,* pg. 688
TIW STEEL PLATEWORK INC.—See Canerector Inc.; *Int'l,* pg. 1290
TIW WESTERN, INC.—See Canerector Inc.; *Int'l,* pg. 1290
TIX CORPORATION; *U.S. Public,* pg. 2161
TIXIT—See Blackstone Inc.; *U.S. Public,* pg. 348
TIYO A.S.; *Int'l,* pg. 7762
TIZ A.D.; *Int'l,* pg. 7762
TIZER LIMITED—See A.G. Barr plc; *Int'l,* pg. 24
TIZIANA LIFE SCIENCES PLC; *Int'l,* pg. 7762
TIZIANI & WHITMYRE; *U.S. Private,* pg. 4177
TIZIR LTD.—See Eramet SA; *Int'l,* pg. 2489
TIZIR TITANIUM & IRON A/S—See Eramet SA; *Int'l,* pg. 2489
TJADER & HIGHSTROM UTILITY SERVICES, LLC—See Dycom Industries, Inc.; *U.S. Public,* pg. 699
TJADER & HIGHSTROM UTILITY SERVICES, LLC—See Dycom Industries, Inc.; *U.S. Public,* pg. 699
T.J. CAMPBELL CONSTRUCTION CO.; *U.S. Private,* pg. 3912
T.J.C. CHEMICAL CO., LTD.—See Kumiai Chemical Industry Co., Ltd.; *Int'l,* pg. 4331
TJ COPE INC.—See Clayton, Dubilier & Rice, LLC; *U.S. Private,* pg. 919
T. JERULLE CONSTRUCTION, LLC; *U.S. Private,* pg. 3911
T.J. HAGGERTY, INC.; *U.S. Private,* pg. 3912
T.J. HALE COMPANY INC.; *U.S. Private,* pg. 3912
T.J. HARKINS BASIC COMMODITY BROKERS, INC—See Bay State Milling Company; *U.S. Private,* pg. 494
TJ HUGHES LIMITED—See Silverfleet Capital Limited; *Int'l,* pg. 6926
TJIKO GMBH—See BayWa AG; *Int'l,* pg. 919
TJK MACHINERY (TIANJIN) CO., LTD.; *Int'l,* pg. 7762
T.J. LAMBRECHT CONSTRUCTION; *U.S. Private,* pg. 3912
T.J. MAXX OF CA, LLC—See The TJX Companies, Inc.; *U.S. Public,* pg. 2134
T.J. MAXX—See The TJX Companies, Inc.; *U.S. Public,* pg. 2134
T.J. MCGEEHAN'S SALES & SERVICE LTD.; *U.S. Private,* pg. 3912
TJ MEDIA CO., LTD.; *Int'l,* pg. 7762
TJ MEDIA PHIL. CO., LTD.—See TJ media Co., Ltd.; *Int'l,* pg. 7762

TJ MEDIA THAILAND CO., LTD.—See TJ media Co., Ltd.; *Int'l,* pg. 7762
TJM ELECTRONICS WEST, INC.—See DarkPulse, Inc.; *U.S. Public,* pg. 633
T J MORRIS LTD.; *Int'l,* pg. 7394
TJM PRODUCTS PTY. LTD.—See Eastern Polymer Group Public Company Limited; *Int'l,* pg. 2273
TJM PROPERTIES, INC.; *U.S. Private,* pg. 4177
TJOD COMPANY INC.; *U.S. Private,* pg. 4177
TJ PALM BEACH ASSOCIATES LIMITED PARTNERSHIP—See Simon Property Group, Inc.; *U.S. Public,* pg. 1881
T&J RESTAURANTS LLC; *U.S. Private,* pg. 3909
TJR PROCUREMENT, LLC; *U.S. Private,* pg. 4178
TJS & COMPANY, LLC—See TJS Deemer Dana LLP; *U.S. Private,* pg. 4178
TJS DEEMER DANA - DULUTH—See TJS Deemer Dana LLP; *U.S. Private,* pg. 4178
TJS DEEMER DANA LLP; *U.S. Private,* pg. 4178
T. J. SMITH & NEPHEW, LIMITED—See Smith & Nephew plc; *Int'l,* pg. 7009
T.J.'S SPORTS GARDEN RESTAURANT—See Boury Enterprises; *U.S. Private,* pg. 624
T.J.T., INC.; *U.S. Private,* pg. 1978
TJX AUSTRALIA PTY. LTD.—See The TJX Companies, Inc.; *U.S. Public,* pg. 2134
TJX AUSTRIA HOLDING GMBH—See The TJX Companies, Inc.; *U.S. Public,* pg. 2134
THE TJX COMPANIES, INC.; *U.S. Public,* pg. 2134
TJX DEUTSCHLAND LTD. & CO. KG—See The TJX Companies, Inc.; *U.S. Public,* pg. 2134
TJX DISTRIBUTION LTD. & CO. KG—See The TJX Companies, Inc.; *U.S. Public,* pg. 2134
TJX EUROPEAN DISTRIBUTION SP. Z O.O.—See The TJX Companies, Inc.; *U.S. Public,* pg. 2134
TJX EUROPE BUYING (DEUTSCHLAND) LTD—See The TJX Companies, Inc.; *U.S. Public,* pg. 2134
TJX EUROPE BUYING LTD—See The TJX Companies, Inc.; *U.S. Public,* pg. 2134
TJX EUROPE BUYING (POLSKA) LTD—See The TJX Companies, Inc.; *U.S. Public,* pg. 2134
TJX EUROPE LIMITED—See The TJX Companies, Inc.; *U.S. Public,* pg. 2134
TJX INCENTIVE SALES, INC.—See The TJX Companies, Inc.; *U.S. Public,* pg. 2134
TJX NEDERLAND B.V.—See The TJX Companies, Inc.; *U.S. Public,* pg. 2134
TJX OESTERREICH LTD. & CO. KG—See The TJX Companies, Inc.; *U.S. Public,* pg. 2134
TJX UK—See The TJX Companies, Inc.; *U.S. Public,* pg. 2134
TK6, INC.; *U.S. Private,* pg. 4178
TKA CO., LTD.—See Taikisha Ltd.; *Int'l,* pg. 7413
T.KAWABE & CO., LTD.—See Ichihiro Co., Ltd.; *Int'l,* pg. 3580
TKB BNP PARIBAS INVESTMENT PARTNERS JSC—See BNP Paribas SA; *Int'l,* pg. 1082
TKB BNP PARIBAS INVESTMENT PARTNERS JSC—See PJSC VTB Bank; *Int'l,* pg. 5886
TK BEHAVIORAL, LLC—See Acadia Healthcare Company, Inc.; *U.S. Public,* pg. 30
TK CARBURETTOR CO., LTD.—See Aisan Industry Co., Ltd.; *Int'l,* pg. 251
TKC CO LTD; *Int'l,* pg. 7762
TKC CORPORATION; *Int'l,* pg. 7762
TKC FINANCIAL GURANTEE CO., LTD.—See TKC Corporation; *Int'l,* pg. 7762
TKC FINE CHEMICAL (KUN-SHAN) CO., LTD.—See Tah Kong Chemical Industrial Corp.; *Int'l,* pg. 7407
TK CHEMICAL CORPORATION; *Int'l,* pg. 7762
TK CHEMICAL CORPORATION - SYNTHETIC RESIN PLANT—See TK Chemical Corporation; *Int'l,* pg. 7762
TKC METALS CORPORATION; *Int'l,* pg. 7762
T.K. CONSTRUCTORS INC.; *U.S. Private,* pg. 3912
TK CORPORATION - HWAJEON PLANT—See TK Corporation; *Int'l,* pg. 7762
TK CORPORATION; *Int'l,* pg. 7762
TKC PROSJEKT AS—See AF Gruppen ASA; *Int'l,* pg. 184
TKC SHUPPAN CORPORATION—See TKC Corporation; *Int'l,* pg. 7762
TKD CABLE (SUZHOU) CO., LTD—See TKH Group N.V.; *Int'l,* pg. 7764
TKD ITALIA S.R.L.—See TKH Group N.V.; *Int'l,* pg. 7764
TKD KABEL GMBH—See TKH Group N.V.; *Int'l,* pg. 7764
TKD KABEL MEXICO S. DE R.L. DE C.V.—See TKH Group N.V.; *Int'l,* pg. 7764
TKD POLSKA SP. Z O.O.—See TKH Group N.V.; *Int'l,* pg. 7764
TKD SCIENCE AND TECHNOLOGY CO., LTD.; *Int'l,* pg. 7762
TKDZ GMBH—See PORR AG; *Int'l,* pg. 5925
TK ELEVATOR GMBH—See Advent International Corporation; *U.S. Private,* pg. 106
TK ELEVATOR GMBH—See Cinven Limited; *Int'l,* pg. 1614
TK ELEVATOR GMBH—See RAG-Stiftung; *Int'l,* pg. 6179
TK ELEVATOR—See Advent International Corporation; *U.S. Private,* pg. 106
TK ELEVATOR—See Cinven Limited; *Int'l,* pg. 1614

COMPANY NAME INDEX

TK ELEVATOR—See RAG-Stiftung; *Int'l*, pg. 6179
TKF GMBH—See TKH Group N.V.; *Int'l*, pg. 7764
TKF NORDICS—See TKH Group N.V.; *Int'l*, pg. 7764
T&K FOODS INC.; *U.S. Private*, pg. 3909
TKG HUCHEMS CO.,LTD; *Int'l*, pg. 7762
TK GROUP (HOLDINGS) LIMITED; *Int'l*, pg. 7762
TKG-STORAGEMART PARTNERS PORTFOLIO, LLC; *U.S. Private*, pg. 4178
TKH AIRPORT SOLUTIONS A/S—See TKH Group N.V.; *Int'l*, pg. 7764
TKH AIRPORT SOLUTIONS B.V.—See TKH Group N.V.; *Int'l*, pg. 7764
TKH BUILDING SOLUTIONS SHANGHAI CO. LTD.—See TKH Group N.V.; *Int'l*, pg. 7765
TKH GROUP N.V.; *Int'l*, pg. 7763
TK-HOLD PLC; *Int'l*, pg. 7762
TKH SECURITY & AIRPORT SOLUTIONS PTE. LTD.—See TKH Group N.V.; *Int'l*, pg. 7765
TKH SECURITY B.V.—See TKH Group N.V.; *Int'l*, pg. 7765
TKH SECURITY SOLUTIONS USA—See Vector Capital Management, L.P.; *U.S. Private*, pg. 4352
TKH SECURITY UK LTD.—See TKH Group N.V.; *Int'l*, pg. 7765
TKH TECHNOLOGIE DEUTSCHLAND AG—See TKH Group N.V.; *Int'l*, pg. 7765
T.K INDIA PRIVATE LIMITED—See Teleflex Incorporated; *U.S. Public*, pg. 1995
TK KONTOR FREITAG GMBH—See Hexatronic Group AB; *Int'l*, pg. 3371
TKK PLANT ENGINEERING K.K.—See TOYO KANETSU K.K.; *Int'l*, pg. 7855
TK LAS VEGAS, LLC—See Las Vegas Sands Corp.; *U.S. Public*, pg. 1293
TKL CO., LTD.—See TOYO KANETSU K.K.; *Int'l*, pg. 7855
TKL & FAMILY PTE. LTD.; *Int'l*, pg. 7765
TK LOGISTICA DE MEXICO S. DE R.L. DE C.V.—See Kimura-Unity Co., Ltd.; *Int'l*, pg. 4164
T.K. MAXX HOLDING GMBH—See The TJX Companies, Inc.; *U.S. Public*, pg. 2134
T.K. MAXX MANAGEMENT GMBH—See The TJX Companies, Inc.; *U.S. Public*, pg. 2134
TK MAXX—See The TJX Companies, Inc.; *U.S. Public*, pg. 2134
TK MAXX—See The TJX Companies, Inc.; *U.S. Public*, pg. 2134
T&K MECHANICAL INC.; *U.S. Private*, pg. 3909
TK MODULAR PTE. LTD.—See TA Corporation Ltd.; *Int'l*, pg. 7399
TK MOLD (SHENZHEN) LIMITED—See TK Group (Holdings) Limited; *Int'l*, pg. 7762
TKO APPAREL, INC.; *U.S. Private*, pg. 4178
TKO DOORS—See ASSA ABLOY AB; *Int'l*, pg. 633
TKO GROUP HOLDINGS, INC.—See Silver Lake Group, LLC; *U.S. Private*, pg. 3654
TKO MILLER, LLC; *U.S. Private*, pg. 4178
TKO POWER INC.—See Enel S.p.A.; *Int'l*, pg. 2411
TKP CORPORATION; *Int'l*, pg. 7766
TKPH PTY LTD.; *Int'l*, pg. 7766
TKP INTERNATIONAL LIMITED—See TKP Corporation; *Int'l*, pg. 7766
TKP KRACHAN GMBH—See VINCI S.A.; *Int'l*, pg. 8229
TK PLASTIC PRODUCTS (SUZHOU) LIMITED—See TK Group (Holdings) Limited; *Int'l*, pg. 7762
TKP MEDICALINK CO., LTD.—See TKP Corporation; *Int'l*, pg. 7766
TKP NEW YORK, INC.—See TKP Corporation; *Int'l*, pg. 7766
TKP PENSIOEN B.V.—See Aegon N.V.; *Int'l*, pg. 175
TKP TELEMARKETING CORPORATION—See TKP Corporation; *Int'l*, pg. 7766
TKR DE MEXICO S.A DE C.V.—See nms Holdings Corporation; *Int'l*, pg. 5393
TK RENTALS SDN. BHD.—See Hextar Industries Berhad; *Int'l*, pg. 3373
TKR HONG KONG LIMITED—See nms Holdings Corporation; *Int'l*, pg. 5393
TKR HUANAN ELECTRONICS CO., LTD.—See nms Holdings Corporation; *Int'l*, pg. 5393
TKR MANUFACTURING (MALAYSIA) SDN. BHD.—See nms Holdings Corporation; *Int'l*, pg. 5393
TKR MANUFACTURING VIETNAM CO., LTD.—See nms Holdings Corporation; *Int'l*, pg. 5393
TKR PRECISION (MALAYSIA) SDN. BHD.—See nms Holdings Corporation; *Int'l*, pg. 5393
T. KRUNGTHAI INDUSTRIES PUBLIC COMPANY LIMITED; *Int'l*, pg. 7396
TKR USA, INC.—See nms Holdings Corporation; *Int'l*, pg. 5393
TK SERVICES, INC.—See Sonsray, Inc.; *U.S. Private*, pg. 3714
TKS FARMACEUTICA LTDA—See Sun Pharmaceutical Industries Ltd.; *Int'l*, pg. 7308
TKS HEIS AS—See Investment AB Latour; *Int'l*, pg. 3784
TK SIMPLEX—See Enerpac Tool Group Corp.; *U.S. Public*, pg. 766
TKS INDUSTRIAL COMPANY—See Taikisha Ltd.; *Int'l*, pg. 7413
TKSOFT SINGAPORE PTE. LTD.—See TIS Inc.; *Int'l*, pg. 7758

TK SPECIALTY RISKS PTY.—See Ensurance Ltd.; *Int'l*, pg. 2449
T&K SPOLKA Z.O.O.—See Darling Ingredients Inc.; *U.S. Public*, pg. 634
T.K. STANLEY, INC.; *U.S. Private*, pg. 3912
T.K.S. TECHNOLOGIES PHET BURY FACTORY—See T.K.S. Technologies Public Company Limited; *Int'l*, pg. 7397
T.K.S. TECHNOLOGIES PUBLIC COMPANY LIMITED; *Int'l*, pg. 7397
TKS TELEPOST KABEL-SERVICE KAISERSLAUTERN GMBH—See Vodafone Group Plc; *Int'l*, pg. 8284
TKS (U.S.A.), INC.—See TOKYO KIKAI SEISAKUSHO LTD.; *Int'l*, pg. 7793
T&K TOKA CORPORATION; *Int'l*, pg. 7395
TKW CONSULTING ENGINEERS INC.—See Keystone Capital, Inc.; *U.S. Private*, pg. 2295
T. KYLBERG NORDEN AB—See SGL Carbon SE; *Int'l*, pg. 6742
TLA ENTERTAINMENT GROUP, INC.; *U.S. Private*, pg. 4178
TLA INC.; *U.S. Private*, pg. 4178
TLA WORLDWIDE PLC; *Int'l*, pg. 7766
TLB CO., LTD.; *Int'l*, pg. 7766
TL CANNON CORPORATION; *U.S. Private*, pg. 4178
TLC BEATRICE INTERNATIONAL HOLDINGS INC.; *U.S. Private*, pg. 4178
TLC BIOPHARMACEUTICALS, B.V.—See Taiwan Liposome Company, Ltd.; *Int'l*, pg. 7422
TLC CO LTD—See TBS Holdings, Inc.; *Int'l*, pg. 7481
TLC CORPORATE SERVICES LLC—See The Kroger Co.; *U.S. Public*, pg. 2109
TLC DIVERSIFIED INC.; *U.S. Private*, pg. 4178
TLC ELECTRONICS, INC.; *U.S. Private*, pg. 4178
TLC ENGINEERING FOR ARCHITECTURE, INC.; *U.S. Private*, pg. 4178
THE T.L.C. GROUP, LTD.; *U.S. Private*, pg. 4126
TLC HEALTH NETWORK; *U.S. Private*, pg. 4178
TLC INGREDIENTS, INC.—See Gemspring Capital Management, LLC; *U.S. Private*, pg. 1659
TLC MEDIPARK PROPRIETARY LIMITED—See Dis-Chem Pharmacies Ltd.; *Int'l*, pg. 2131
TLC MODULAR CONSTRUCTION JOINT STOCK—See SHS Holdings Ltd.; *Int'l*, pg. 6867
T&L CO., LTD.; *Int'l*, pg. 7395
TLC PLUS OF TEXAS, INC.—See Humana, Inc.; *U.S. Public*, pg. 1070
TLC REIT MANAGEMENT INC.—See Tokyu Fudosan Holdings Corporation; *Int'l*, pg. 7798
TLC TECHNOLOGIES, INC.; *U.S. Private*, pg. 4178
TLC VISION CORPORATION—See Charlesbank Capital Partners, LLC; *U.S. Private*, pg. 856
TLC VISION CORPORATION—See Charlesbank Capital Partners, LLC; *U.S. Private*, pg. 856
TLC (WALES) INDEPENDENT FOSTERING LIMITED—See Sheikh Holdings Group (Investments) Limited; *Int'l*, pg. 6794
TLC WILDLIFE RANCHES INC.—See Moore Holdings Inc.; *U.S. Private*, pg. 2780
TLD3 ENTERTAINMENT GROUP, INC.; *U.S. Public*, pg. 2161
TLD ACQUISITION CO. LLC; *U.S. Private*, pg. 4178
TLD AMERICA CORPORATION—See Power Corporation of Canada; *Int'l*, pg. 5945
TLD ASIA LIMITED—See Power Corporation of Canada; *Int'l*, pg. 5945
TLD CHINA—See Power Corporation of Canada; *Int'l*, pg. 5945
TLD EUROPE SAS—See Power Corporation of Canada; *Int'l*, pg. 5945
TLD GROUP SAS—See Power Corporation of Canada; *Int'l*, pg. 5945
T&L DISTRIBUTING COMPANY INC.; *U.S. Private*, pg. 3909
TLD MIDDLE EAST—See Power Corporation of Canada; *Int'l*, pg. 5945
TLDS, LLC—See Siris Capital Group, LLC; *U.S. Private*, pg. 3675
T.L. EDWARDS INC.; *U.S. Private*, pg. 3912
TL FORWARDING SERVICE (PHILIPPINES) CORPORATION—See SBS Holdings Inc.; *Int'l*, pg. 6608
TLG IMMOBILIEN AG—See Aroundtown SA; *Int'l*, pg. 578
TLG INSURANCE CO., LTD.—See CTBC Financial Holding Co., Ltd.; *Int'l*, pg. 1869
TLG MULTICULTURAL COMMUNICATIONS; *U.S. Private*, pg. 4178
TLG SERVICES, INC—See Entergy Corporation; *U.S. Public*, pg. 777
TLGY ACQUISITION CORPORATION; *U.S. Public*, pg. 2161
TLH ENTERPRISES INC.; *U.S. Private*, pg. 4178
TLH LLC—See Icahn Enterprises L.P.; *U.S. Public*, pg. 1085
TLHM CO. LTD.—See dormakaba Holding AG; *U.S. Public*, pg. 2178
TLI CHO LANDTRAN TRANSPORT LTD.—See Landtran Systems Inc.; *U.S. Private*, pg. 4408
TLI CO., LTD.—See Wonik Corporation; *Int'l*, pg. 8448

TLI ENTERPRISES INC.; *U.S. Private*, pg. 4178
T LIFE ASSURANCE PLC—See Thanachart Capital PCL; *Int'l*, pg. 7607
TLINGIT-HAIDA REGIONAL HOUSING AUTHORITY; *U.S. Private*, pg. 4179
TLINGIT HAIDA TRIBAL BUSINESS CORPORATION; *U.S. Private*, pg. 4179
T-L IRRIGATION CO.; *U.S. Private*, pg. 3910
T.L. JONES LIMITED—See Halma plc; *Int'l*, pg. 3233
TL LOGISTICS SERVICE CO., LTD.—See SBS Holdings Inc.; *Int'l*, pg. 6608
TLL PRINTING & PACKAGING LTD—See Aga Khan Development Network; *Int'l*, pg. 199
TL MACHINE.; *U.S. Private*, pg. 4178
TLM FINANCE CORP.—See Repsol, S.A.; *Int'l*, pg. 6293
T. L. MONTGOMERY & ASSOCIATES; *U.S. Private*, pg. 3911
TL NATURAL GAS HOLDINGS LTD.; *Int'l*, pg. 7766
TLOGOS S.R.L.—See TXT e-Solutions S.p.A.; *Int'l*, pg. 7993
TLOU ENERGY LIMITED; *Int'l*, pg. 7766
TLS ASSOCIAZIONE PROFESSIONALE DI AVVOCATI E COMMERCIALISTI—See PricewaterhouseCoopers S.p.A.; *Int'l*, pg. 5972
TLS ENERGIMATNING AB—See Addtech AB; *Int'l*, pg. 135
TLS PRODUCTIONS, INC.—See Hibino Corporation; *Int'l*, pg. 3383
TLT BABCOCK EUROPE KFT.—See Enovis Corporation; *U.S. Public*, pg. 773
TLT-BABCOCK, INC.—See The New York Blower Company, Inc.; *U.S. Public*, pg. 4083
TLT BABCOCK INDIA PRIVATE LIMITED—See Enovis Corporation; *U.S. Public*, pg. 773
TLT-TURBO GMBH—See Power Construction Corporation of China; *Int'l*, pg. 5943
TLT URLAUBSREISEN GMBH—See TUI AG; *Int'l*, pg. 7966
TL VENTURES INC.; *U.S. Private*, pg. 4178
TLX TECHNOLOGIES, LLC; *U.S. Private*, pg. 4179
TM4 INC.—See Hydro-Quebec; *Int'l*, pg. 3547
TM5 PROPERTIES, LP; *U.S. Private*, pg. 4179
TMA CORPORATION PTY. LTD.—See Nippon Filcon Co., Ltd.; *Int'l*, pg. 5318
TMAC RESOURCES, INC.—See Agnico Eagle Mines Limited; *Int'l*, pg. 212
TM ADVERTISING, LLC; *U.S. Private*, pg. 4179
TMA GROUP OF COMPANIES LIMITED; *Int'l*, pg. 7766
T. MARZETTI COMPANY—See Lancaster Colony Corporation; *U.S. Public*, pg. 1291
T. MARZETTI COMPANY - WEST—See Lancaster Colony Corporation; *U.S. Public*, pg. 1292
T & M ASPHALT PAVING; *U.S. Private*, pg. 3908
T&M ASSOCIATES - COLUMBUS—See T&M Associates; *U.S. Private*, pg. 3910
T&M ASSOCIATES - MOORESTOWN—See T&M Associates; *U.S. Private*, pg. 3910
T&M ASSOCIATES; *U.S. Private*, pg. 3909
T&M ASSOCIATES—See T&M Associates; *U.S. Private*, pg. 3909
T&M ASSOCIATES—See T&M Associates; *U.S. Private*, pg. 3909
T&M ASSOCIATES—See T&M Associates; *U.S. Private*, pg. 3909
T&M ASSOCIATES—See T&M Associates; *U.S. Private*, pg. 3909
T&M ASSOCIATES—See T&M Associates; *U.S. Private*, pg. 3909
T&M ASSOCIATES—See T&M Associates; *U.S. Private*, pg. 3909
T&M ASSOCIATES—See T&M Associates; *U.S. Private*, pg. 3909
T&M ASSOCIATES—See T&M Associates; *U.S. Private*, pg. 3910
T&M ASSOCIATES—See T&M Associates; *U.S. Private*, pg. 3910
T&M ASSOCIATES—See T&M Associates; *U.S. Private*, pg. 3910
TMA SYSTEMS, LLC—See Silversmith Management, L.P.; *U.S. Private*, pg. 3664
TM AVIATION INC.; *U.S. Private*, pg. 4179
TMB ASSET MANAGEMENT CO., LTD.—See Prudential plc; *Int'l*, pg. 6009
TMB INDUSTRIES INC.; *U.S. Private*, pg. 4179
TM BROKER CO., LTD.—See Thanachart Capital PCL; *Int'l*, pg. 7607
TMBTHANACHART BANK PUBLIC COMPANY LIMITED; *Int'l*, pg. 7766
TM CASUALTY INSURANCE COMPANY—See Tokio Marine Holdings, Inc.; *U.S. Public*, pg. 7783
TMC BIOTECH SDN. BHD.—See Thomson Medical Group Limited; *Int'l*, pg. 7714
TMC BONDS, LLC—See Intercontinental Exchange, Inc.; *U.S. Public*, pg. 1143
TMC CONTENT GROUP AG; *Int'l*, pg. 7766
TMC DESIGN CORPORATION—See KBR, Inc.; *U.S. Public*, pg. 1216
TMC FOODS LLC; *U.S. Private*, pg. 4179
TMC GROUP INC.; *U.S. Private*, pg. 4179
TMC HEALTHCARE; *U.S. Private*, pg. 4179

T.M.C. INDUSTRIAL PUBLIC COMPANY LIMITED

T.M.C. INDUSTRIAL PUBLIC COMPANY LIMITED; *Int'l,* pg. 7397
TM CLAIMS SERVICE ASIA PTE. LTD.—See Tokio Marine Holdings, Inc.; *Int'l,* pg. 7784
TM CLAIMS SERVICE, INC.—See Tokio Marine Holdings, Inc.; *Int'l,* pg. 7783
TM CLAIMS SERVICE, INC.—See Tokio Marine Holdings, Inc.; *Int'l,* pg. 7783
TMC LIFE SCIENCES BERHAD—See Thomson Medical Group Limited; *Int'l,* pg. 7714
TMC MATERIALS INC.—See Ravago Holding S.A.; *Int'l,* pg. 6222
TMC NORTH AMERICA INC.—See I.M.A. Industria Macchine Automatiche S.p.A.; *Int'l,* pg. 3566
T. M. COBB COMPANY; *U.S. Private,* pg. 3911
TMC PEST MANAGEMENT, INC.—See Sprague Pest Solutions, Inc.; *U.S. Private,* pg. 3762
TMC PIONEER AGGREGATES LIMITED—See Heidelberg Materials AG; *Int'l,* pg. 3320
TMC SERVICES, INC.; *U.S. Private,* pg. 4179
TMC THE METALS COMPANY INC.; *Int'l,* pg. 7766
TMD FRICTION ESPANA S.L.—See Nisshinbo Holdings Inc.; *Int'l,* pg. 5374
TMD FRICTION FRANCE S.A.S.—See Nisshinbo Holdings Inc.; *Int'l,* pg. 5374
TMD FRICTION GMBH—See Nisshinbo Holdings Inc.; *Int'l,* pg. 5374
TMD FRICTION HOLDINGS GMBH & CO. KG—See Nisshinbo Holdings Inc.; *Int'l,* pg. 5374
TMD FRICTION, INC.—See Nisshinbo Holdings Inc.; *Int'l,* pg. 5374
TMD FRICTION ITALIA S.R.L.—See Nisshinbo Holdings Inc.; *Int'l,* pg. 5374
TMD FRICTION MALAYSIA—See Nisshinbo Holdings Inc.; *Int'l,* pg. 5374
TMD FRICTION MEXICO, S.A. DE C.V.—See Nisshinbo Holdings Inc.; *Int'l,* pg. 5374
TMD FRICTION UK LTD.—See Nisshinbo Holdings Inc.; *Int'l,* pg. 5374
TMDG, LLC—See PBMares, LLP; *U.S. Private,* pg. 3119
TMDWEK NORTH, LLC—See Grammer AG; *Int'l,* pg. 3053
T & MEDIA—See WPP plc; *Int'l,* pg. 8477
T MEDICAL SERVICE INC.—See Takashima & Co., Ltd.; *Int'l,* pg. 7435
TMEDIX CORPORATION—See Olympus Corporation; *Int'l,* pg. 5558
TME GMBH—See GlassBridge Enterprises, Inc.; *U.S. Public,* pg. 939
T-MELMAX SDN. BHD.—See Censof Holdings Berhad; *Int'l,* pg. 1402
TMES CORPORATION—See Takasago Thermal Engineering Co., Ltd.; *Int'l,* pg. 7434
TMF ADMINISTRATIVE SERVICES MALAYSIA SDN. BHD.—See icapital.biz Berhad; *Int'l,* pg. 3578
TMF AUTOLEASE SDN BHD—See Telekom Malaysia Berhad; *Int'l,* pg. 7537
TMF GROUP—See CVC Capital Partners SICAV-FIS S.A.; *Int'l,* pg. 1886
TMF HEALTH QUALITY INSTITUTE; *U.S. Private,* pg. 4179
TMF OPERATING SAS; *Int'l,* pg. 7766
TMG CONSULTING LLC—See Avance Investment Management, LLC; *U.S. Private,* pg. 403
TMG ENERGY CORP.; *U.S. Private,* pg. 4179
T.M.G. GMBH—See SOL S.p.A.; *Int'l,* pg. 7068
TMG HEALTH, INC.—See Cognizant Technology Solutions Corporation; *U.S. Public,* pg. 525
TM GLOBAL INCORPORATED—See Telekom Malaysia Berhad; *Int'l,* pg. 7537
T.M.G. PREPRESS TOPPAN CO., LTD.—See TOPPAN Holdings Inc.; *Int'l,* pg. 7817
TMG STRATEGIES—See Publicis Groupe S.A.; *Int'l,* pg. 6103
TMI HOLDINGS, INC.—See Tuesday Morning Corporation; *U.S. Public,* pg. 2204
TMI INTERNATIONAL, LLC—See ShoreView Industries, LLC; *U.S. Private,* pg. 3642
TM IMMO D.O.O—See Starwood Capital Group Global I, LLC; *U.S. Private,* pg. 3789
T. M. INC.; *U.S. Private,* pg. 3911
TM INFO-MEDIA SDN BHD—See Telekom Malaysia Berhad; *Int'l,* pg. 7537
TM INSURANCE HF.; *Int'l,* pg. 7766
TMI SOLUTIONS, LLC—See Stone Point Capital LLC; *U.S. Private,* pg. 3821
TMI TRADING CORP.—See CJ Corporation; *Int'l,* pg. 1631
TMI TRANSPORTGESELLSCHAFT DER MOBELINDUSTRIE MBH—See G. Peter Reber Mobel-Logistik GmbH; *Int'l,* pg. 2864
TMJ, INC.—See SECOM Co., Ltd.; *Int'l,* pg. 6672
TMJ SOLUTIONS, LLC—See Stryker Corporation; *U.S. Public,* pg. 1957
TMK A/S—See Axcel Management A/S; *Int'l,* pg. 762
TMK CORPORATE SCIENTIFIC AND TECHNICAL CENTRE—See PAO TMK; *Int'l,* pg. 5732
TMK ENERGY LTD.; *Int'l,* pg. 7767
TMK FARM CO., LTD.—See Thai Union Group Public Company Limited; *Int'l,* pg. 7596
TMK GLOBAL AG—See PAO TMK; *Int'l,* pg. 5732

TMK INDUSTRIAL SOLUTIONS LLC—See PAO TMK; *Int'l,* pg. 5732
TMK ITALIA S.R.L.—See PAO TMK; *Int'l,* pg. 5732
TMK KAZAKHSTAN LLC—See PAO TMK; *Int'l,* pg. 5732
TMK LOGISTICS—See PAO TMK; *Int'l,* pg. 5733
TMK MANUFACTURING, INC.—See Aterian Investment Management, L.P.; *U.S. Private,* pg. 367
TMK MIDDLE EAST—See PAO TMK; *Int'l,* pg. 5733
TMK NGS-NIZHNEVARTOVSK AO—See PAO TMK; *Int'l,* pg. 5733
TMK-RESITA SA—See PAO TMK; *Int'l,* pg. 5733
TMLC SAFES, S.A. DE C.V.—See Fortune Brands Innovations, Inc.; *U.S. Public,* pg. 873
TML INTERGOVERNMENTAL RISK POOL; *U.S. Private,* pg. 4179
TMLUC ARGENTINA S.A.—See Grupo Nutresa S.A.; *Int'l,* pg. 3133
TMM AGENCIAS ACAPULCO—See Grupo TMM, S.A.B.; *Int'l,* pg. 3137
TMM AGENCIAS COATZACOALCOS—See Grupo TMM, S.A.B.; *Int'l,* pg. 3137
TMM AGENCIAS DOS BOCAS—See Grupo TMM, S.A.B.; *Int'l,* pg. 3138
TM MANILA SHIPMANAGEMENT INC.—See Mitsui O.S.K. Lines, Ltd.; *Int'l,* pg. 4991
TMM CAR CARRIER CIUDAD DE MEXICO—See Grupo TMM, S.A.B.; *Int'l,* pg. 3138
TMM GROUP PTY. LTD.—See Macmahon Holdings Limited; *Int'l,* pg. 4623
TMM LOGISTICS CIUDAD DE MEXICO—See Grupo TMM, S.A.B.; *Int'l,* pg. 3138
TMM LOGISTICS MONTERREY—See Grupo TMM, S.A.B.; *Int'l,* pg. 3138
TMM REAL ESTATE DEVELOPMENT PUBLIC LTD.; *Int'l,* pg. 7767
TMNG LTD.—See Kardan N.V.; *Int'l,* pg. 4079
T-MOBILE AUSTRIA GMBH—See Deutsche Telekom AG; *Int'l,* pg. 2084
T-MOBILE CZECH REPUBLIC A.S.—See Deutsche Telekom AG; *Int'l,* pg. 2084
T-MOBILE INTERNATIONAL AG & CO. KG—See Deutsche Telekom AG; *Int'l,* pg. 2084
T-MOBILE NETHERLANDS BV—See Deutsche Telekom AG; *Int'l,* pg. 2084
T-MOBILE POLSKA S.A.—See Vivendi SE; *Int'l,* pg. 8278
T-MOBILE USA, INC.—See Deutsche Telekom AG; *Int'l,* pg. 2084
T-MOBILE US, INC.—See Deutsche Telekom AG; *Int'l,* pg. 2084
TMOP LEGACY COMPANY—See Bee Street Holdings LLC; *U.S. Private,* pg. 513
TM PACK CO., LTD.—See Toyo Seikan Group Holdings, Ltd.; *Int'l,* pg. 7857
TMP GROUP S.P.A.; *Int'l,* pg. 7767
T&M PHAEDRA PUBLIC COMPANY LTD.; *Int'l,* pg. 7395
TMP INTERNATIONAL, INC.; *U.S. Private,* pg. 4179
TMP (UK) LIMITED—See TrueBlue, Inc.; *U.S. Public,* pg. 2198
TMP WORLDWIDE ADVERTISING & COMMUNICATIONS LLC—See Gemspring Capital Management, LLC; *U.S. Private,* pg. 1659
TMP WORLDWIDE/ADVERTISING & COMMUNICATIONS—See Gemspring Capital Management, LLC; *U.S. Private,* pg. 1659
TMP WORLDWIDE/ADVERTISING & COMMUNICATIONS—See Gemspring Capital Management, LLC; *U.S. Private,* pg. 1659
TMP WORLDWIDE/ADVERTISING & COMMUNICATIONS—See Gemspring Capital Management, LLC; *U.S. Private,* pg. 1659
TMP WORLDWIDE/ADVERTISING & COMMUNICATIONS—See Gemspring Capital Management, LLC; *U.S. Private,* pg. 1659
TMP WORLDWIDE/ADVERTISING & COMMUNICATIONS—See Gemspring Capital Management, LLC; *U.S. Private,* pg. 1659
TMP WORLDWIDE/ADVERTISING & COMMUNICATIONS—See Gemspring Capital Management, LLC; *U.S. Private,* pg. 1659
TMP WORLDWIDE/ADVERTISING & COMMUNICATIONS—See Gemspring Capital Management, LLC; *U.S. Private,* pg. 1659
TMP WORLDWIDE/ADVERTISING & COMMUNICATIONS—See Gemspring Capital Management, LLC; *U.S. Private,* pg. 1659
TMP WORLDWIDE/DIRECTIONAL MARKETING—See Gemspring Capital Management, LLC; *U.S. Private,* pg. 1659
TMRC CO., LTD.—See RaQualia Pharma Inc.; *Int'l,* pg. 6211
TMRG, INC.—See comScore, Inc.; *U.S. Public,* pg. 561
TMR INC.—See 1-800 We Answer, Inc.; *U.S. Private,* pg. 1

CORPORATE AFFILIATIONS

TMR TECHNOLOGIES CO., LTD.—See NEXCOM International Co., Ltd.; *Int'l,* pg. 5242
TMR URUSHARTA (M) SDN. BHD.—See Damansara Realty Berhad; *Int'l,* pg. 1955
TMS CONTACT SARL—See CVC Capital Partners SICAV-FIS S.A.; *Int'l,* pg. 1882
TM,S CORPORATION—See LIXIL Group Corporation; *Int'l,* pg. 4534
TMS ENTERTAINMENT, LTD.—See Sega Sammy Holdings, Inc.; *Int'l,* pg. 6681
TMS EUROPE B.V.—See V-One Tech Co., Ltd.; *Int'l,* pg. 8105
TMS FASHION (H.K.) LIMITED—See Shangtex Holding Co., Ltd.; *Int'l,* pg. 6784
TMS FIJI LIMITED—See Jumbo Interactive Limited; *Int'l,* pg. 4026
TMS GLOBAL SERVICES PTY. LTD.—See Jumbo Interactive Limited; *Int'l,* pg. 4026
TM SHIPMANAGEMENT CO., LTD.—See Mitsui O.S.K. Lines, Ltd.; *Int'l,* pg. 4992
TMS INTERNATIONAL CORPORATION—See The Pritzker Organization, LLC; *U.S. Private,* pg. 4100
TMS INTERNATIONAL, LLC—See The Pritzker Organization, LLC; *U.S. Private,* pg. 4100
TMS INTERNATIONAL SERVICES UK LIMITED—See The Pritzker Organization, LLC; *U.S. Private,* pg. 4100
TMS MANAGEMENT GROUP, INC.; *U.S. Private,* pg. 4179
TMS MUSIC, CO., LTD—See Sega Sammy Holdings, Inc.; *Int'l,* pg. 6681
TM SOFTWARE ORIGO EHF.—See Origo hf.; *Int'l,* pg. 5630
TM SPECIALTY INSURANCE COMPANY—See Tokio Marine Holdings, Inc.; *Int'l,* pg. 7783
TM S.R.L.—See Apollo Global Management, Inc.; *U.S. Public,* pg. 162
TMST TIBBI SISTEMLER PAZARLAMA TICARET VE SERVIS A.S.—See Japan Industrial Partners, Inc.; *Int'l,* pg. 3891
TM STUDIOS, INC.—See Brookfield Corporation; *Int'l,* pg. 1184
T.M. SUTTON LIMITED—See Lone Star Global Acquisitions, LLC; *U.S. Private,* pg. 2487
TMS VT, LLC—See AdaptHealth Corp.; *U.S. Public,* pg. 39
TM SYSTEMS, LLC; *U.S. Private,* pg. 4179
TMT ACQUISITION CORP; *U.S. Private,* pg. 4180
TM TECHNOLOGY, INC.; *Int'l,* pg. 7766
TM TELFORD DAIRY LTD.—See Unternehmensgruppe Theo Muller S.e.c.s.; *Int'l,* pg. 8085
TM TEXTILES & GARMENTS LIMITED—See Toray Industries, Inc.; *Int'l,* pg. 7823
TMT FINANCE SA; *Int'l,* pg. 7767
TMT (INDIA) LTD.; *Int'l,* pg. 7767
TMT INVESTMENTS PLC; *Int'l,* pg. 7767
TMT LOGISTICS INC.; *U.S. Private,* pg. 4180
TMT MOTORS CORPORATION; *Int'l,* pg. 7767
TMT SERVICE & ENGINEERING CO LTD—See Japan Industrial Partners, Inc.; *Int'l,* pg. 3891
TMT SERVICES AND SUPPLIES (PTY) LTD.—See Kapsch-Group Beteiligungs GmbH; *Int'l,* pg. 4078
TMT STEEL PUBLIC COMPANY LIMITED; *Int'l,* pg. 7767
TM UNIMECH CO. LTD.—See UNIMECH Group Berhad; *Int'l,* pg. 8049
TMW ENTERPRISES INC.; *U.S. Private,* pg. 4180
TMW LIMITED; *Int'l,* pg. 7767
TMW MARKETING COMPANY, INC.—See Tailored Brands, Inc.; *U.S. Public,* pg. 1979
TMW MERCHANTS LLC—See Tailored Brands, Inc.; *U.S. Public,* pg. 1979
TMW PURCHASING LLC—See Tailored Brands, Inc.; *U.S. Public,* pg. 1979
TMW SYSTEMS, INC. - NASHVILLE—See Trimble, Inc.; *U.S. Public,* pg. 2191
TMW SYSTEMS, INC.—See Trimble, Inc.; *U.S. Public,* pg. 2191
TMX CANADA CORP.—See LISI S.A.; *Int'l,* pg. 4524
TMX GROUP INC.—See TMX Group Limited; *Int'l,* pg. 7767
TMX GROUP LIMITED; *Int'l,* pg. 7767
TMX, S.A. DE C.V.—See LISI S.A.; *Int'l,* pg. 4524
T&N ASPHALT SERVICES, INC.; *U.S. Private,* pg. 3910
TNB BILGISAYAR SISTEMLERI A.S.—See Japan Industrial Partners, Inc.; *Int'l,* pg. 3891
TNB CAPITAL (L) LTD.—See Tenaga Nasional Berhad; *Int'l,* pg. 7557
TNB ENGINEERING & COOPERATION SDN BHD (TNEC)—See Tenaga Nasional Berhad; *Int'l,* pg. 7558
TNB ENGINEERING CORPORATION SDN. BHD.—See Tenaga Nasional Berhad; *Int'l,* pg. 7558
TNB ENGINEERS SDN BHD—See Tenaga Nasional Berhad; *Int'l,* pg. 7558
TNB FUEL SERVICES SDN. BHD.—See Tenaga Nasional Berhad; *Int'l,* pg. 7558
TNB GENERATION SDN BHD—See Tenaga Nasional Berhad; *Int'l,* pg. 7558
TNB INTEGRATED LEARNING SOLUTION SDN BHD—See Tenaga Nasional Berhad; *Int'l,* pg. 7558
TNB JANAMANJUNG SDN. BHD.—See Tenaga Nasional Berhad; *Int'l,* pg. 7558

TNB LABS SDN. BHD.—See Tenaga Nasional Berhad; *Int'l*, pg. 7558
TNB POWER DAHARKI LTD.—See Tenaga Nasional Berhad; *Int'l*, pg. 7558
TNB REMACO PAKISTAN (PRIVATE) LIMITED—See Tenaga Nasional Berhad; *Int'l*, pg. 7558
TNB REPAIR & MAINTENANCE SDN BHD.—See Tenaga Nasional Berhad; *Int'l*, pg. 7558
TNB RESEARCH SDN. BHD.—See Tenaga Nasional Berhad; *Int'l*, pg. 7558
TNB VENTURES SDN. BHD.—See Tenaga Nasional Berhad; *Int'l*, pg. 7558
TNB WORKSHOP SERVICES SDN. BHD.—See Tenaga Nasional Berhad; *Int'l*, pg. 7558
TN CDJR MOTORS, LLC—See AutoNation, Inc.; *U.S. Public*, pg. 238
TN CHEMIE SDN. BHD.—See Samchem Holdings Berhad; *Int'l*, pg. 6503
TNC INDUSTRIAL CO., LTD. - COATING RAW MATERIALS DIVISION—See TNC Industrial Co., Ltd.; *Int'l*, pg. 7767
TNC INDUSTRIAL CO., LTD.; *Int'l*, pg. 7767
TNCI OPERATING COMPANY, LLC—See Blue Casa Communications, Inc.; *U.S. Private*, pg. 586
TNCI OPERATING COMPANY, LLC—See Garrison Investment Group LP; *U.S. Private*, pg. 1646
TNCI—See Blue Casa Communications, Inc.; *U.S. Private*, pg. 586
TNCI—See Garrison Investment Group LP; *U.S. Private*, pg. 1646
TND BEVERAGE, LLC—See Energy Transfer LP; *U.S. Public*, pg. 764
T&N DE MEXICO SA DE CV—See Apollo Global Management, Inc.; *U.S. Public*, pg. 162
TN(DK) EXPRESSWAYS LIMITED—See Madhucon Projects Limited; *Int'l*, pg. 4633
TNEMEC COMPANY INC.; *U.S. Private*, pg. 4180
TN FINE CHEMICALS CO., LTD.—See Nissui Corporation; *Int'l*, pg. 5379
TNF PHARMACEUTICALS, INC; *U.S. Public*, pg. 2161
TNG - ALBUQUERQUE—See The Jim Pattison Group; *Int'l*, pg. 7660
TNG - COLUMBIA—See The Jim Pattison Group; *Int'l*, pg. 7660
TNG INVESTMENT & TRADING JSC; *Int'l*, pg. 7767
TNG LIMITED; *Int'l*, pg. 7767
TNG - NORTH FORT MYERS—See The Jim Pattison Group; *Int'l*, pg. 7660
TNG—See The Jim Pattison Group; *Int'l*, pg. 7660
TNG WORLDWIDE, INC.; *U.S. Private*, pg. 4180
TNH SPECIALTY PHARMACY II; *U.S. Private*, pg. 4180
TNI INDUSTRY CORPORATION—See Nikon Corporation; *Int'l*, pg. 5294
TNI MEDICAL AG—See Masimo Corporation; *U.S. Public*, pg. 1392
T & N, INC.; *U.S. Private*, pg. 3908
TN INTERNATIONAL SA—See Orano SA; *Int'l*, pg. 5611
TNI PARTNERS—See Gannett Co., Inc.; *U.S. Public*, pg. 899
TNI PARTNERS—See Lee Enterprises, Incorporated; *U.S. Public*, pg. 1300
TN-K ENERGY GROUP INC.; *U.S. Private*, pg. 4180
TN MARKETING, LLC—See Apple Leisure Group; *U.S. Private*, pg. 297
TNN TELECOM—See Inter-Gamma Investment Company Ltd.; *Int'l*, pg. 3735
TNP CO., LTD.—See Nomad Foods Limited; *Int'l*, pg. 5409
TNP ENTERPRISES, INC.—See TXNM Energy, Inc.; *U.S. Public*, pg. 2208
TNR GOLD CORP.; *Int'l*, pg. 7767
TNR INDUSTRIAL DOORS INC.—See Hörmann KG Verkaufsgesellschaf; *Int'l*, pg. 3481
TNR TECHNICAL, INC.; *U.S. Public*, pg. 2161
TNS CANADIAN FACTS—See Bain Capital, LP; *U.S. Private*, pg. 447
TNS EMNID—See Bain Capital, LP; *U.S. Private*, pg. 447
TNS ENERGO KARELIA JSC—See GK TNS Energo PAO; *Int'l*, pg. 2983
TNS ENERGO KUBAN PJSC; *Int'l*, pg. 7768
TNS ENERGO MARI EL PJSC; *Int'l*, pg. 7768
TNS ENERGO NIZHNIY NOVG; *Int'l*, pg. 7768
TNS ENERGO NN PJSC—See GK TNS Energo PAO; *Int'l*, pg. 2983
TNS ENERGO PENZA LLC—See GK TNS Energo PAO; *Int'l*, pg. 2983
TNS ENERGO ROSTOV-ON-DON PJSC; *Int'l*, pg. 7768
TNS ENERGO TULA JSC—See GK TNS Energo PAO; *Int'l*, pg. 2983
TNS ENERGO VELIKIY NOVGOROD LLC—See GK TNS Energo PAO; *Int'l*, pg. 2983
TNS ENERGO VORONEZH PJSC; *Int'l*, pg. 7768
TNS ENERGO YAROSLAVL AO; *Int'l*, pg. 7768
TNS GALLUP AS—See Bain Capital, LP; *U.S. Private*, pg. 447
TNS GALLUP SA—See Bain Capital, LP; *U.S. Private*, pg. 447
TNS GROUP HOLDINGS PLC—See Bain Capital, LP; *U.S. Private*, pg. 447

TNSI EUROPE GMBH—See NEC Corporation; *Int'l*, pg. 5185
TNS, INC.—See High Wire Networks Inc.; *U.S. Public*, pg. 1035
TNS, INC.—See Koch Industries, Inc.; *U.S. Private*, pg. 2333
TNS INDIA PVT. LTD.—See Bain Capital, LP; *U.S. Private*, pg. 447
TNS INTERSEARCH—See Bain Capital, LP; *U.S. Private*, pg. 448
TNS LANDIS STRATEGY & INNOVATION—See Bain Capital, LP; *U.S. Private*, pg. 448
TNS MALAYSIA SDN. BHD.—See Bain Capital, LP; *U.S. Private*, pg. 447
TNS MEDIA INTELLIGENCE/CMR—See Bain Capital, LP; *U.S. Private*, pg. 448
TNS NEW ZEALAND—See Bain Capital, LP; *U.S. Private*, pg. 448
TNS OCEAN LINES (S) PTE. LTD.—See GKE Corporation Limited; *Int'l*, pg. 2983
TNS PHARMA PRIVATE LIMITED—See Trident Lifeline Limited; *Int'l*, pg. 7920
TNS PHILIPPINES—See Bain Capital, LP; *U.S. Private*, pg. 448
TNS PROGNOSTICS LTD—See Bain Capital, LP; *U.S. Private*, pg. 448
TNS PROGNOSTICS—See Bain Capital, LP; *U.S. Private*, pg. 448
TNS SECODIP—See Bain Capital, LP; *U.S. Private*, pg. 448
TNS SINGAPORE—See Bain Capital, LP; *U.S. Private*, pg. 448
TNS UK LIMITED—See Bain Capital, LP; *U.S. Private*, pg. 448
TNS US, LLC—See Bain Capital, LP; *U.S. Private*, pg. 448
TNS US, LLC - TOLEDO OFFICE—See Bain Capital, LP; *U.S. Private*, pg. 448
TNT AUSTRALIA PTY. LIMITED—See FedEx Corporation; *U.S. Public*, pg. 828
TNT CRANE & RIGGING, INC. - OKLAHOMA CITY—See First Reserve Management, L.P.; *U.S. Private*, pg. 1526
TNT CRANE & RIGGING, INC.—See First Reserve Management, L.P.; *U.S. Private*, pg. 1526
TNT CRANE & RIGGING, INC.—See First Reserve Management, L.P.; *U.S. Private*, pg. 1526
T.N.T. EQUIPMENT INC.; *U.S. Private*, pg. 3912
TNT EQUIPMENT SALES & RENTALS, LLC—See Utility One Source L.P.; *U.S. Private*, pg. 4326
TNT EXPRESS GMBH—See FedEx Corporation; *U.S. Public*, pg. 828
TNT EXPRESS NEDERLAND B.V.—See FedEx Corporation; *U.S. Public*, pg. 828
TNT EXPRESS N.V.—See FedEx Corporation; *U.S. Public*, pg. 828
TNT EXPRESS ROAD NETWORK B.V.—See FedEx Corporation; *U.S. Public*, pg. 828
TNT GROUP JOINT STOCK COMPANY; *Int'l*, pg. 7768
TNT INC.; *U.S. Private*, pg. 4180
TNT, JSC—See OAO AK Transneft; *Int'l*, pg. 5505
TNT NEDERLAND B.V.—See FedEx Corporation; *U.S. Public*, pg. 828
TNT PAPERCRAFT, INC.—See The Millcraft Paper Company, Inc.; *U.S. Private*, pg. 4079
TNT PARTS INC.—See Falcon Affiliates, LLC; *U.S. Private*, pg. 1466
TNT PETROLEUM INC.; *U.S. Private*, pg. 4180
TNT POWER WASH, INC.; *U.S. Private*, pg. 4180
T&N TRADING & INVESTMENT COMPANY LIMITED; *Int'l*, pg. 7395
TNTT PACKAGES EXPRESS SDN. BHD.—See Tiong Nam Logistics Holdings Berhad; *Int'l*, pg. 7755
TNT UK LIMITED—See FedEx Corporation; *U.S. Public*, pg. 828
TNUVA FOOD INDUSTRIES LTD.—See Bright Food (Group) Co., Ltd.; *Int'l*, pg. 1161
T.N. WARD COMPANY; *U.S. Private*, pg. 3912
TOA ACTIVE NOISE CONTROL DIVISION—See TOA Corporation; *Int'l*, pg. 7768
TOABO CORPORATION; *Int'l*, pg. 7769
TOA BUSINESS ASSOCIE CO., LTD.—See Toagosei Co. Ltd.; *Int'l*, pg. 7770
TOA CANADA CORPORATION—See TOA Corporation; *Int'l*, pg. 7768
TOACHI MINING INC.—See Atico Mining Corporation; *Int'l*, pg. 670
TOA (CHINA) LIMITED—See TOA Corporation; *Int'l*, pg. 7768
TOA COMMUNICATION SYSTEMS, INC.—See TOA Corporation; *Int'l*, pg. 7768
TOA CORPORATION; *Int'l*, pg. 7768
TOA CORPORATION—See TOA Corporation; *Int'l*, pg. 7768
TOA CORPORATION (UK) LIMITED—See TOA Corporation; *Int'l*, pg. 7768
TOA CREATE CO., LTD.—See TVE Co., Ltd.; *Int'l*, pg. 7988
TOAD HOLLOW VINEYARDS, INC.; *U.S. Private*, pg. 4180

TOA-DIC ZHANGJIAGANG CHEMICAL CO., LTD.—See DIC Corporation; *Int'l*, pg. 2111
TOADMAN INTERACTIVE AB; *Int'l*, pg. 7769
TOA EIYO LTD.—See Katakura Industries Co., Ltd.; *Int'l*, pg. 4089
TOA ELECTRONICS EUROPE G.M.B.H—See TOA Corporation; *Int'l*, pg. 7768
TOA ELECTRONICS EUROPE GMBH—See TOA Corporation; *Int'l*, pg. 7769
TOA ELECTRONICS EUROPE G.M.B.H. SP. Z.O.O.—See TOA Corporation; *Int'l*, pg. 7769
TOA ELECTRONICS, INC.—See TOA Corporation; *Int'l*, pg. 7769
TOA ELECTRONICS (M) SDN. BHD.—See TOA Corporation; *Int'l*, pg. 7768
TOA ELECTRONICS PTE LTD—See TOA Corporation; *Int'l*, pg. 7768
TOA ELECTRONICS SOUTHERN AFRICA (PROPRIETARY) LIMITED—See TOA Corporation; *Int'l*, pg. 7768
TOA ELECTRONICS TAIWAN CORPORATION—See TOA Corporation; *Int'l*, pg. 7769
TOA ELECTRONICS (THAILAND) CO., LTD.—See TOA Corporation; *Int'l*, pg. 7768
TOA ENGINEERING CORPORATION—See TOA Corporation; *Int'l*, pg. 7769
TOAGOSEI AMERICA, INC.—See Toagosei Co. Ltd.; *Int'l*, pg. 7770
TOAGOSEI CO. LTD. - HIRONO PLANT—See Toagosei Co. Ltd.; *Int'l*, pg. 7770
TOAGOSEI CO. LTD. - KAWASAKI PLANT—See Toagosei Co. Ltd.; *Int'l*, pg. 7770
TOAGOSEI CO. LTD. - NAGOYA PLANT—See Toagosei Co. Ltd.; *Int'l*, pg. 7770
TOAGOSEI CO. LTD. - SAKAIDE PLANT—See Toagosei Co. Ltd.; *Int'l*, pg. 7770
TOAGOSEI CO. LTD.; *Int'l*, pg. 7769
TOAGOSEI CO. LTD. - TAKAOKA PLANT—See Toagosei Co. Ltd.; *Int'l*, pg. 7770
TOAGOSEI CO. LTD. - TOKUSHIMA PLANT—See Toagosei Co. Ltd.; *Int'l*, pg. 7770
TOAGOSEI CO. LTD. - YOKOHAMA PLANT—See Toagosei Co. Ltd.; *Int'l*, pg. 7770
TOAGOSEI HONG KONG LIMITED—See Toagosei Co. Ltd.; *Int'l*, pg. 7770
TOAGOSEI KOREA CO., LTD.—See Toagosei Co. Ltd.; *Int'l*, pg. 7770
TOAGOSEI (SHANGHAI) MANAGEMENT CO., LTD.—See Toagosei Co. Ltd.; *Int'l*, pg. 7770
TOAGOSEI SINGAPORE PTE LTD.—See Toagosei Co. Ltd.; *Int'l*, pg. 7770
TOAGOSEI (THAILAND) CO., LTD.—See Toagosei Co. Ltd.; *Int'l*, pg. 7770
TOAGOSEI (ZHANGJIAGANG) NEW TECHNOLOGY CO., LTD.—See Toagosei Co. Ltd.; *Int'l*, pg. 7770
TOAGOSEI (ZHUHAI) LIMITED—See Toagosei Co. Ltd.; *Int'l*, pg. 7770
TOA GROUP HOLDING CO., LTD.; *Int'l*, pg. 7769
TOA HOLDINGS, INC.; *Int'l*, pg. 7769
TOA (HONG KONG) LTD.—See TOA Corporation; *Int'l*, pg. 7768
TOA INTERNATIONAL DIVISION—See TOA Corporation; *Int'l*, pg. 7769
TOA-JET CHEMICAL CO., LTD.—See Toagosei Co. Ltd.; *Int'l*, pg. 7770
TOA KENSO CO., LTD.—See Toagosei Co. Ltd.; *Int'l*, pg. 7770
TOA KOGYO CO., LTD.—See Toagosei Co. Ltd.; *Int'l*, pg. 7770
TOA LOGISTICS CO., LTD.—See Toagosei Co. Ltd.; *Int'l*, pg. 7770
TOAMI CORPORATION; *Int'l*, pg. 7770
TOAN GIA HIEP PHUOC TRADING & FOOD PROCESSING JOIN STOCK COMPANY—See Kato Sangyo Co., Ltd.; *Int'l*, pg. 4090
TOAN MY CORPORATION-JSC; *Int'l*, pg. 7770
TOA OIL CO., LTD.—See Idemitsu Kosan Co., Ltd.; *Int'l*, pg. 3592
TOA PAINT (LAOS) LTD.—See TOA Group Holding Co., Ltd.; *Int'l*, pg. 7769
TOA PAINT (THAILAND) PUBLIC COMPANY LIMITED—See TOA Group Holding Co., Ltd.; *Int'l*, pg. 7769
TOA PAINT (VIETNAM) CO., LTD.—See TOA Group Holding Co., Ltd.; *Int'l*, pg. 7769
TOA PERFORMANCE COATING CORPORATION CO., LTD.—See TOA Group Holding Co., Ltd.; *Int'l*, pg. 7769
THE TOA REINSURANCE COMPANY, LTD.; *Int'l*, pg. 7694
THE TOA REINSURANCE COMPANY OF AMERICA—See The Toa Reinsurance Company, Ltd.; *Int'l*, pg. 7694
TOA ROAD CORPORATION; *Int'l*, pg. 7769
TOA SERVICE CO., LTD.—See TVE Co., Ltd.; *Int'l*, pg. 7988
TOAST, INC.; *U.S. Public*, pg. 2161
TOAST (MAIL ORDER) LIMITED—See Bestseller A/S; *Int'l*, pg. 1000
TOASTMASTER DE MEXICO S.A.—See Spectrum Brands Holdings, Inc.; *U.S. Public*, pg. 1917

TOAST, INC.   CORPORATE AFFILIATIONS

TOA TECHNO-GAS CO., LTD.—See Toagosei Co. Ltd.; *Int'l*, pg. 7770
TOA TOKYO OFFICE—See TOA Corporation; *Int'l*, pg. 7769
TOA-TONE BORING CO., LTD.—See Toa Road Corporation; *Int'l*, pg. 7769
TOA TOTAL QUALITY ASSEMBLY LLC—See init innovation in traffic systems SE; *Int'l*, pg. 3704
TOA VENTURE HOLDING COMPANY LIMITED—See TOA Group Holding Co., Ltd.; *Int'l*, pg. 7769
TOA VIETNAM CO., LTD.—See TOA Corporation; *Int'l*, pg. 7769
THE TOBACCO HUT INC.; *U.S. Private*, pg. 4127
TOBACCOLAND AUTOMATEN GMBH & CO KG—See Japan Tobacco Inc.; *Int'l*, pg. 3906
TOBACCO MARKETING CONSULTANT BURKINA FASO SARL—See British American Tobacco plc; *Int'l*, pg. 1168
TOBACCO MERCHANTS ASSOCIATION OF THE UNITED STATES, INC.; *U.S. Private*, pg. 4180
TOBACCOR S.A.—See Imperial Brands PLC; *Int'l*, pg. 3633
TOBACCO SUPERSTORES INC.; *U.S. Private*, pg. 4180
TOBACNA 3DVA, TRGOVSKO PODJETJE, D.O.O.—See Imperial Brands PLC; *Int'l*, pg. 3634
TOBACNA GROSIST D.O.O.—See Imperial Brands PLC; *Int'l*, pg. 3634
TOBACNA LJUBLJANA D.O.O.—See Imperial Brands PLC; *Int'l*, pg. 3634
TOBAGO MARKETING COMPANY LIMITED—See ANSA McAL Limited; *Int'l*, pg. 477
TOBAGO SERVICES LIMITED—See Massy Holdings Ltd.; *Int'l*, pg. 4724
TOBAHMAOZ, INC., *U.S. Private*, pg. 4180
TOBA, INC.; *Int'l*, pg. 7770
TOBAN KOGYO CO., LTD.—See Marubeni Construction Material Lease Co., Ltd.; *Int'l*, pg. 4705
TOBA PNC CO. LTD.—See Piovan SpA; *Int'l*, pg. 5873
TOBA PULP LESTARI TBK; *Int'l*, pg. 7770
TOBAR LTD.; *Int'l*, pg. 7770
TOBA SEASIDE HOTEL CO., LTD.—See Mie Kotsu Group Holdings, Inc.; *Int'l*, pg. 4888
TOBA (SHANGHAI) TRADING CO., LTD.—See TOBA, INC.; *Int'l*, pg. 7770
TOBATA DAIICHI TRAFFIC INDUSTRIAL CO., LTD.—See Daiichi Koutsu Sangyo Co., Ltd.; *Int'l*, pg. 1929
TOBA (THAILAND) CO., LTD.—See TOBA, INC.; *Int'l*, pg. 7770
TOB BRENNTAG UKRAINE LLC—See BRENNTAG SE; *Int'l*, pg. 1150
TOB DYCKERHOFF UKRAINA—See Buzzi SpA; *Int'l*, pg. 1230
TOBE DIRECT; *U.S. Private*, pg. 4180
TOBESOFT CO., LTD.; *Int'l*, pg. 7771
TOBI-GNG PP—See PJSC Concern Galnaftogaz; *Int'l*, pg. 5878
TOBII AB; *Int'l*, pg. 7771
TOBII DYNAVOX LLC—See Tobii AB; *Int'l*, pg. 7771
TOBII TECHNOLOGY INC.—See Tobii AB; *Int'l*, pg. 7771
TOBII TECHNOLOGY JAPAN LTD.—See Tobii AB; *Int'l*, pg. 7771
TOBILA SYSTEMS, INC.; *Int'l*, pg. 7771
TOBIN & COLLINS CPA, PA.—See Aprio, LLP; *U.S. Private*, pg. 301
TOBIN PROPERTIES AB—See Klovern AB; *Int'l*, pg. 4203
TOBINSNET OIL & GAS LTD.; *Int'l*, pg. 7771
TOBIRA THERAPEUTICS, INC.—See AbbVie Inc.; *U.S. Public*, pg. 23
TOBISHIMA (BRUNEI) SDN BHD—See Tobishima Corporation; *Int'l*, pg. 7771
TOBISHIMA CORPORATION; *Int'l*, pg. 7771
TOBLER S.A.S.; *Int'l*, pg. 7771
TO BOOT NEW YORK INC.; *U.S. Private*, pg. 4180
TOB OVB ALLFINANZ—See OVB Holding AG; *Int'l*, pg. 5671
TOB THYSSENKRUPP ELEVATOR UKRAINE—See ThyssenKrupp AG; *Int'l*, pg. 7726
TOBU BUS CO., LTD.—See Tobu Railway Co., Ltd.; *Int'l*, pg. 7771
TOBU CHEMICAL CO., LTD.—See Kaneka Corporation; *Int'l*, pg. 4067
TOBU CO., LTD.—See Daiki Axis Co., Ltd.; *Int'l*, pg. 1932
TOBU CONSTRUCTION CO., LTD.—See Tobu Railway Co., Ltd.; *Int'l*, pg. 7771
TOBU DELIVERY CO., LTD.—See Tobu Railway Co., Ltd.; *Int'l*, pg. 7771
TOBU DEPARTMENT STORE CO., LTD.—See Tobu Railway Co., Ltd.; *Int'l*, pg. 7771
TOBU HOTEL MANAGEMENT CO., LTD.—See Tobu Railway Co., Ltd.; *Int'l*, pg. 7771
TOBU KAIHATSU CO., LTD.—See Tobu Railway Co., Ltd.; *Int'l*, pg. 7771
TOBU KEIBI SUPPORT CO., LTD.—See Tobu Railway Co., Ltd.; *Int'l*, pg. 7771
TOBU KOGYO CO., LTD.—See Tobu Railway Co., Ltd.; *Int'l*, pg. 7771
TOBUL ACCUMULATOR INCORPORATED—See Freudenberg SE; *Int'l*, pg. 2790
TOBU RAILWAY CO., LTD.; *Int'l*, pg. 7771

TOBU RYOKUCHI CO., LTD.—See Tobu Railway Co., Ltd.; *Int'l*, pg. 7772
TOBU STORE CO., LTD.—See Tobu Railway Co., Ltd.; *Int'l*, pg. 7771
TOBU TOP TOURS CO., LTD.—See Tobu Railway Co., Ltd.; *Int'l*, pg. 7771
TOBU TRANSPORTATION CO., LTD.—See Tobu Railway Co., Ltd.; *Int'l*, pg. 7771
TOBUTSU TECHNO CO., LTD.—See Sumitomo Electric Industries, Ltd.; *Int'l*, pg. 7285
TOBU UTSUNOMIYA DEPARTMENT STORE CO., LTD.—See Tobu Railway Co., Ltd.; *Int'l*, pg. 7771
TOBU WORLD SQUARE—See Tobu Railway Co., Ltd.; *Int'l*, pg. 7771
TOBU YACHIDA CONSTRUCTION CO., LTD.—See Tobu Railway Co., Ltd.; *Int'l*, pg. 7771
TOBU ZOOLOGICAL GARDEN—See Tobu Railway Co., Ltd.; *Int'l*, pg. 7772
TOBY/O, INC.; *U.S. Private*, pg. 4180
TOCA BOCA AB—See Spin Master Corp.; *Int'l*, pg. 7136
TOCALO CO., LTD. - AKASHI NO.2 PLANT—See Tocalo Co., Ltd.; *Int'l*, pg. 7772
TOCALO CO., LTD. - AKASHI NO.4 PLANT—See Tocalo Co., Ltd.; *Int'l*, pg. 7772
TOCALO CO., LTD. - AKASHI PLANT—See Tocalo Co., Ltd.; *Int'l*, pg. 7772
TOCALO CO., LTD. - KITA-KYUSYU PLANT—See Tocalo Co., Ltd.; *Int'l*, pg. 7772
TOCALO CO., LTD. - MIZUSHIMA PLANT—See Tocalo Co., Ltd.; *Int'l*, pg. 7772
TOCALO CO., LTD. - NAGOYA PLANT—See Tocalo Co., Ltd.; *Int'l*, pg. 7772
TOCALO CO., LTD.; *Int'l*, pg. 7772
TOCALO CO., LTD. - TOKYO PLANT—See Tocalo Co., Ltd.; *Int'l*, pg. 7772
TOCALO & HAN TAI CO., LTD.—See Tocalo Co., Ltd.; *Int'l*, pg. 7772
TOCALO & HAN TAI (KUNSHAN) CO., LTD.—See Tocalo Co., Ltd.; *Int'l*, pg. 7772
TOCCA LIFE HOLDINGS, INC.; *U.S. Public*, pg. 2161
TOC CO., LTD.; *Int'l*, pg. 7772
TOC GLYCOL COMPANY LIMITED—See PTT Global Chemical Public Company Limited; *Int'l*, pg. 6091
THE TOCHIGI BANK, LTD.; *Int'l*, pg. 7694
TOCHIGI ELECTRONICS INDUSTRY CO., LTD.—See Di-Nikko Engineering Co., Ltd.; *Int'l*, pg. 2101
TOCHIGI HIGH TRUST CO., LTD.—See Takuma Co., Ltd.; *Int'l*, pg. 7443
TOCHIGI KANEKA CORPORATION—See Kaneka Corporation; *Int'l*, pg. 4067
TOCHIGI NIKON CORPORATION—See Nikon Corporation; *Int'l*, pg. 5294
TOCHIGI NIKON PRECISION CO., LTD.—See Nikon Corporation; *Int'l*, pg. 5294
TOCHIGI NIPPON SHEET GLASS CO., LTD.—See Nippon Sheet Glass Co. Ltd.; *Int'l*, pg. 5332
TOCHIGI NISSHIN CO., LTD.—See Nippon Signal Co., Ltd.; *Int'l*, pg. 5334
TOCHIGI NITTO KOHKI CO., LTD.—See NITTO KOHKI Co., Ltd.; *Int'l*, pg. 5388
TOCHIGI SHEARING CORPORATION—See JFE Holdings, Inc.; *Int'l*, pg. 3937
TOCHIKU CORPORATION—See Toyo Corporation; *Int'l*, pg. 7852
TOC HOLDINGS CO.; *U.S. Private*, pg. 4180
TOC INTERNATIONAL—See Doppelmayr Group; *Int'l*, pg. 2175
TOC JIT INTERNATIONAL SERV S.R.L.—See Doppelmayr Group; *Int'l*, pg. 2175
TOCLAS CORPORATION—See Sumitomo Forestry Co., Ltd.; *Int'l*, pg. 7286
TOCO CHANNEL SHIZUOKA CORPORATION—See TOKAI Holdings Corporation; *Int'l*, pg. 7779
TOCOS AMERICA, INC.—See Tokyo Cosmos Electric Co., Ltd.; *Int'l*, pg. 7790
TOCQUIGNY DESIGN, INC.; *U.S. Private*, pg. 4180
TOCRIS COOKSON LIMITED—See Bio-Techne Corporation; *U.S. Public*, pg. 334
T.O.C. (SCHWEIZ) AG—See Mercedes-Benz Group AG; *Int'l*, pg. 4829
TOCSIS INC—See Sega Sammy Holdings, Inc.; *Int'l*, pg. 6681
TOCVAN VENTURES CORP.; *Int'l*, pg. 7772
TODA AMERICA, INC.—See Toda Corporation; *Int'l*, pg. 7773
TODA BLDG. PARTNERS CO., LTD.—See Toda Corporation; *Int'l*, pg. 7773
TODA CONSTRUCTION (SHANGHAI) CO., LTD.—See Toda Corporation; *Int'l*, pg. 7773
TODA CORPORATION; *Int'l*, pg. 7772
TODA FINANCE CO., LTD.—See Toda Corporation; *Int'l*, pg. 7773
TODA FOODS CO., LTD.—See Marudai Food Co., Ltd.; *Int'l*, pg. 4711
TODAI FRANCHISING LLC; *U.S. Private*, pg. 4180
TODA INTERNATIONAL HOLDINGS INC.; *Int'l*, pg. 7773
TODAKA CORPORATION—See NANYO Corporation; *Int'l*, pg. 5146

TODA KOGYO CORP.—See Moririn Co., Ltd.; *Int'l*, pg. 5047
TODAK PJSC; *Int'l*, pg. 7773
TODA REFORM CO., LTD.—See Toda Corporation; *Int'l*, pg. 7773
TODA ROAD CO., LTD.—See Toda Corporation; *Int'l*, pg. 7773
TODA STAFF SERVICE CO., LTD.—See Toda Corporation; *Int'l*, pg. 7773
TODA VIETNAM CO., LTD.—See Toda Corporation; *Int'l*, pg. 7773
TODAY CARD, LLC—See Continental Finance; *U.S. Private*, pg. 1029
TODAY'S BANK—See Mathias Bancshares, Inc.; *U.S. Private*, pg. 2611
TODAY'S BUSINESS PRODUCTS; *U.S. Private*, pg. 4180
TODAY'S CAR WASH, L.L.C.—See Red Dog Equity LLC; *U.S. Private*, pg. 3374
TODAY'S GROWTH CONSULTANT, INC.; *U.S. Private*, pg. 4180
THE TODAY SHOW CHARITABLE FOUNDATION INC.; *U.S. Private*, pg. 4127
TODAY'S OFFICE INC.; *U.S. Private*, pg. 4180
TODAYSURE MATTHEWS LIMITED—See Matthews International Corporation; *U.S. Public*, pg. 1401
TODAYTEC CANADA INC.—See Hangzhou Todaytec Digital Co., Ltd.; *Int'l*, pg. 3251
TODAYTEC INDIA PRIVATE LIMITED—See Hangzhou Todaytec Digital Co., Ltd.; *Int'l*, pg. 3251
TODAYTEC INDUSTRIA DE CODIGOS DE BARRAS LTDA.—See Hangzhou Todaytec Digital Co., Ltd.; *Int'l*, pg. 3251
TODAYTIX INC.—See Great Hill Partners, L.P.; *U.S. Private*, pg. 1763
TODCO, INC.—See Sanwa Holdings Corporation; *Int'l*, pg. 6561
THE TODD AGENCY, INC.—See Reverence Capital Partners LLC; *U.S. Private*, pg. 3415
TODD AND CASSANELLI INC.; *U.S. Private*, pg. 4181
THE TODD-AO CORPORATION—See Empire Investment Holdings, LLC; *U.S. Private*, pg. 1385
THE TODD CORPORATION LIMITED; *Int'l*, pg. 7694
TODD & DUNCAN LTD.—See Ningxia Zhongyin Cashmere Co., Ltd.; *Int'l*, pg. 5308
TODD ENERGY INTERNATIONAL LIMITED—See The Todd Corporation Limited; *Int'l*, pg. 7694
TODD ENERGY LIMITED—See The Todd Corporation Limited; *Int'l*, pg. 7694
TODD ENTERPRISES INC.; *U.S. Private*, pg. 4181
TODD ENTERPRISES—See Chem-Tainer Industries, Inc.; *U.S. Private*, pg. 871
TODD-FORD INC.—See Todd-Ford Management Inc.; *U.S. Private*, pg. 4181
TODD-FORD MANAGEMENT INC.; *U.S. Private*, pg. 4181
TODD-FORD SHEETMETAL INC.—See Todd-Ford Management Inc.; *U.S. Private*, pg. 4181
THE TODD GROUP, INC.; *U.S. Private*, pg. 4127
TODD HARRIS CO. INC.; *U.S. Private*, pg. 4181
TODD HSU CONSULTANTS, INC.—See Elliott Management Corporation; *U.S. Private*, pg. 1367
TODD HSU CONSULTANTS, INC.—See Vista Equity Partners, LLC; *U.S. Private*, pg. 4396
TODD MCFARLANE ENTERTAINMENT—See TMP International, Inc.; *U.S. Private*, pg. 4179
TODD MCFARLANE PRODUCTIONS—See TMP International, Inc.; *U.S. Private*, pg. 4179
TODD PROPERTY GROUP LIMITED—See The Todd Corporation Limited; *Int'l*, pg. 7694
TODD RESEARCH LIMITED—See Image Scan Holdings plc; *Int'l*, pg. 3618
TODD RIVER RESOURCES LIMITED; *Int'l*, pg. 7773
TODD & SARGENT, INC.; *U.S. Private*, pg. 4180
TODDS FOODS—See 3G Capital Inc.; *U.S. Private*, pg. 10
TODDS FOODS—See Berkshire Hathaway Inc.; *U.S. Public*, pg. 318
TODD SOUNDELUX—See Empire Investment Holdings, LLC; *U.S. Private*, pg. 1385
TODDS—See 3G Capital Inc.; *U.S. Private*, pg. 10
TODDS—See Berkshire Hathaway Inc.; *U.S. Public*, pg. 318
TODD WADENA ELECTRIC COOPERATIVE; *U.S. Private*, pg. 4181
TODD WENZEL BUICK GMC OF DAVISON, INC.—See General Motors Company; *U.S. Public*, pg. 929
TODD WENZEL BUICK GMC OF WESTLAND—See General Motors Company; *U.S. Public*, pg. 929
TODD WENZEL CHEVROLET; *U.S. Private*, pg. 4181
TODEN KOGYO CO., LTD.—See Tokyo Electric Power Company Holdings, Incorporated; *Int'l*, pg. 7790
TODEN KOKOKU CO., LTD.—See Tokyo Electric Power Company Holdings, Incorporated; *Int'l*, pg. 7790
TODEN REAL ESTATE CO., INC.—See Tokyo Electric Power Company Holdings, Incorporated; *Int'l*, pg. 7790
TODENTSU ACCESS CORPORATION—See MIRAIT ONE Corporation; *Int'l*, pg. 4918
TODEY MOTOR CO. INC.; *U.S. Private*, pg. 4181
TODINI & CO. S.P.A.—See Umicore S.A./N.V.; *Int'l*, pg. 8024

COMPANY NAME INDEX

TODINI COSTRUZIONI GENERALI S.P.A.—See Prime System Kz Ltd.; *Int'l*, pg. 5978
TODINI DEUTSCHLAND GMBH—See Umicore S.A./N.V.; *Int'l*, pg. 8024
TODINI METALS AND CHEMICALS INDIA PRIVATE LIMITED—See Umicore S.A./N.V.; *Int'l*, pg. 8024
TODINI QUIMICA IBERICA, S.L.—See Umicore S.A./N.V.; *Int'l*, pg. 8024
TODINO ENGINEERING SALES INC.; *U.S. Private*, pg. 4181
TODOROFF AD-SOFIA; *Int'l*, pg. 7773
TODO SEISAKUSHO LTD.; *Int'l*, pg. 7773
TODOS MEDICAL LTD.; *Int'l*, pg. 7773
TODOS QINGDAO CO. LTD—See Thales S.A.; *Int'l*, pg. 7600
TOD'S AUSTRIA GMBH—See Tod's S.p.A.; *Int'l*, pg. 7772
TOD'S BELGIQUE S.P.R.L.—See Tod's S.p.A.; *Int'l*, pg. 7772
TOD'S DEUTSCHLAND GMBH—See Tod's S.p.A.; *Int'l*, pg. 7772
TOD'S ESPANA SL—See Tod's S.p.A.; *Int'l*, pg. 7772
TODS FRANCE SAS—See Tod's S.p.A.; *Int'l*, pg. 7772
TOD'S HONG KONG LIMITED—See Tod's S.p.A.; *Int'l*, pg. 7772
TOD'S INTERNATIONAL BV—See Tod's S.p.A.; *Int'l*, pg. 7772
TOD'S JAPAN KK—See Tod's S.p.A.; *Int'l*, pg. 7772
TOD'S MASSACHUSSETS INC.—See Tod's S.p.A.; *Int'l*, pg. 7772
TOD'S S.P.A.; *Int'l*, pg. 7772
TOEBOX KOREA, LTD.; *Int'l*, pg. 7773
TOEI ADVERTISING, LTD.—See Toei Co., Ltd.; *Int'l*, pg. 7774
TOEI ANIMATION CO., LTD.; *Int'l*, pg. 7773
TOEI ANIMATION EUROPE S.A.S—See TOEI ANIMATION CO., LTD.; *Int'l*, pg. 7773
TOEI ANIMATION INCORPORATED—See TOEI ANIMATION CO., LTD.; *Int'l*, pg. 7773
TOEI ANIMATION MUSIC PUBLISHING CO., LTD.—See TOEI ANIMATION CO., LTD.; *Int'l*, pg. 7773
TOEI ANIMATION PHILS., INC.—See TOEI ANIMATION CO., LTD.; *Int'l*, pg. 7773
TOEI CO., LTD.; *Int'l*, pg. 7773
TOEI COMMERCIAL FILM CO., LTD.—See Toei Co., Ltd.; *Int'l*, pg. 7774
TOEI DIGITAL LABO TECH CO., LTD.—See Toei Co., Ltd.; *Int'l*, pg. 7774
TOEI FOODS CO., LTD.—See Toei Co., Ltd.; *Int'l*, pg. 7774
TOEI HOTEL CHAIN CO., LTD.—See Toei Co., Ltd.; *Int'l*, pg. 7774
TOEI INOAC LIMITED—See Inoue Rubber (Thailand) Public Company Limited; *Int'l*, pg. 3715
TOEI KASEI CO., LTD.—See Mitsubishi Chemical Group Corporation; *Int'l*, pg. 4934
TOEI KENKO CO., LTD.—See Toei Co., Ltd.; *Int'l*, pg. 7774
TOEI KYOTO STUDIO CO., LTD.—See Toei Co., Ltd.; *Int'l*, pg. 7774
TOEI LABO TECH CO., LTD.—See Toei Co., Ltd.; *Int'l*, pg. 7774
TOEI MUSIC PUBLISHING CO., LTD.—See Toei Co., Ltd.; *Int'l*, pg. 7774
TOEI REEFER LINE LTD.; *Int'l*, pg. 7774
TOEI VIDEO COMPANY, LTD.—See Toei Co., Ltd.; *Int'l*, pg. 7774
TOEKI ECO LIFE CORPORATION—See Toho Gas Co., Ltd.; *Int'l*, pg. 7775
TOELL CO., LTD.; *Int'l*, pg. 7774
TOENEC CONSTRUCTION (SHANGHAI) CO., LTD.—See Toenec Corporation; *Int'l*, pg. 7774
TOENEC CORPORATION—See Toenec Corporation; *Int'l*, pg. 7774
TOENEC CORPORATION—See Toenec Corporation; *Int'l*, pg. 7774
TOENEC CORPORATION—See Toenec Corporation; *Int'l*, pg. 7774
TOENEC CORPORATION; *Int'l*, pg. 7774
TOENEC PHILIPPINES INC.—See Toenec Corporation; *Int'l*, pg. 7774
TOENEC SERVICE CORPORATION—See Toenec Corporation; *Int'l*, pg. 7774
TOENEC (THAILAND) CO., LTD.—See Toenec Corporation; *Int'l*, pg. 7774
T-O ENGINEERS, INC.—See Littlejohn & Co., LLC; *U.S. Private*, pg. 2470
TOENSMEIER ADJUSTMENT SERVICE; *U.S. Private*, pg. 4181
TOEPFER SECURITY CORP.—See Alpine Investors; *U.S. Private*, pg. 201
TOFANE GLOBAL SAS; *Int'l*, pg. 7774
TOFAS TURK OTOMOBIL FABRIKASI A.S.—See Koc Holding A.S.; *Int'l*, pg. 4224
TOFAS TURK OTOMOBIL FABRIKASI A.S.—See Stellantis N.V.; *Int'l*, pg. 7200
TOFER EUROPE SOLUTIONS SRL—See Figeac-Aero SA; *Int'l*, pg. 2661
TOFIC CO. LTD—See AT&S Austria Technologie & Systemtechnik Aktiengesellschaft; *Int'l*, pg. 665

TOFTA PLAT & VENTILATION AB—See Instalco AB; *Int'l*, pg. 3722
TOFT DAIRY, INC.; *U.S. Private*, pg. 4181
TOFUKU FLOUR MILLS CO., LTD.—See NIPPN Corporation; *Int'l*, pg. 5310
TOFUTTI BRANDS INC.; *U.S. Public*, pg. 2161
TOGA MANUFACTURING, INC.—See Kinplex Corp.; *U.S. Private*, pg. 2313
TOGAMA S.A.—See Fluidra SA; *Int'l*, pg. 2714
TOGAMI CONTROL CO., LTD.—See Togami Electric Mfg. Co., Ltd.; *Int'l*, pg. 7774
TOGAMI DENSO CO., LTD.—See Togami Electric Mfg. Co., Ltd.; *Int'l*, pg. 7774
TOGAMI ELECTRICAL SOFT CO., LTD.—See Togami Electric Mfg. Co., Ltd.; *Int'l*, pg. 7774
TOGAMI ELECTRIC MFG. CO., LTD.; *Int'l*, pg. 7774
TOGAMI KASEI CO., LTD.—See Togami Electric Mfg. Co., Ltd.; *Int'l*, pg. 7774
TOGAMI METALIX CO., LTD.—See Togami Electric Mfg. Co., Ltd.; *Int'l*, pg. 7774
TOGC @GLENEAGLES PTE. LTD.—See Singapore Medical Group Limited; *Int'l*, pg. 6941
TOGE DIIBEL GMBH & CO. KG—See Wurth Verwaltungsgesellschaft mbH; *Int'l*, pg. 8508
TOGETHER LTD.—See Otto GmbH & Co. KG; *Int'l*, pg. 5663
TOGETHER PHARMA LTD.; *Int'l*, pg. 7774
TOGETHERWORK HOLDINGS, LLC—See GI Manager L.P.; *U.S. Private*, pg. 1694
TOGGLE3D.AI INC.; *Int'l*, pg. 7775
TOG MANUFACTURING CO., INC.; *U.S. Private*, pg. 4181
TOGO CABLE CO., LTD.—See Chuo Spring Co., Ltd.; *Int'l*, pg. 1599
TOGO ELECTRICITE—See ENGIE SA; *Int'l*, pg. 2431
TOG ORTHOTICS INTERNATIONAL LONDON LTD.—See The Orthotic Group Inc.; *Int'l*, pg. 7672
TOG ORTHOTICS INTERNATIONAL LTD—See The Orthotic Group Inc.; *Int'l*, pg. 7672
TOGORUN; *U.S. Private*, pg. 4181
TOGO TELECOM; *Int'l*, pg. 7775
THE TOG SHOP—See Bluestem Brands, Inc.; *U.S. Private*, pg. 598
TOHAN CORPORATION; *Int'l*, pg. 7775
TOHAN STEEL CO., LTD.—See Hanwa Co., Ltd.; *Int'l*, pg. 3263
TOHATO INC.—See Yamazaki Baking Co., Ltd.; *Int'l*, pg. 8557
TOHATSU AMERICA CORPORATION; *U.S. Private*, pg. 4181
TOHBU NETWORK CO., LTD.; *Int'l*, pg. 7775
TOHCELLO LOGISTICS CO., LTD.—See Mitsui Chemicals, Inc.; *Int'l*, pg. 4984
TOHCELLO SLITTER CO., LTD.—See Mitsui Chemicals, Inc.; *Int'l*, pg. 4984
TOHCHO CO., LIMITED—See Chori Co., Ltd.; *Int'l*, pg. 1583
TOHEI CO., LTD.—See NICHIMO CO., LTD.; *Int'l*, pg. 5269
TOHKI ELECTRONICS CO., LTD.—See TOKYO KIKAI SEISAKUSHO LTD.; *Int'l*, pg. 7793
TOHKOHJUSHI CO., LTD.—See Fujikura Kasei Co., Ltd.; *Int'l*, pg. 2827
TOHMA GREEN LIFE INC.—See Watami Co., Ltd.; *Int'l*, pg. 8355
TOHMEI SHIPPING CO., LTD.—See Meiji Shipping Co., Ltd.; *Int'l*, pg. 4802
TOHO ACETYLENE CO., LTD.—See Tosoh Corporation; *Int'l*, pg. 7833
TOHO AIR SERVICE CO., LTD.—See Kawada Technologies Inc.; *Int'l*, pg. 4093
THE TOHO BANK, LTD.; *Int'l*, pg. 7694
TOHO BUSSAN KAISHA, LTD.—See Mitsui & Co., Ltd.; *Int'l*, pg. 4980
TOHO CAR CORPORATION—See ShinMaywa Industries, Ltd.; *Int'l*, pg. 6847
THE TOHO CARD CO., LTD.—See The Toho Bank, Ltd.; *Int'l*, pg. 7694
TOHO CAREER CO., LTD.—See Toho Zinc Co., Ltd.; *Int'l*, pg. 7776
TOHO CHEMICAL INDUSTRY CO., LTD.; *Int'l*, pg. 7775
TOHO CHEMICAL (THAILAND) CO., LTD.—See Toho Chemical Industry Co., Ltd.; *Int'l*, pg. 7775
TOHO CO., LTD.; *Int'l*, pg. 7775
TOHO CO., LTD.; *Int'l*, pg. 7775
THE TOHO COMPUTER SERVICE CO., LTD.—See The Toho Bank, Ltd.; *Int'l*, pg. 7694
THE TOHO CREDIT SERVICE CO., LTD.—See The Toho Bank, Ltd.; *Int'l*, pg. 7694
TOHO DEVELOPMENT ENGINEERING CO., LTD.—See Toho Zinc Co., Ltd.; *Int'l*, pg. 7776
TOHO EARTHTECH, INC.—See Nippon Light Metal Holdings Company, Inc.; *Int'l*, pg. 5324
TOHO ELECTRONICS, INC.—See Oki Electric Industry Co., Ltd.; *Int'l*, pg. 5549
TOHO GAS CO., LTD.; *Int'l*, pg. 7775
TOHO GAS CUSTOMER SERVICE CO., LTD.—See Toho Gas Co., Ltd.; *Int'l*, pg. 7775
TOHO GAS ENGINEERING CO., LTD.—See Toho Gas Co., Ltd.; *Int'l*, pg. 7775

TOHO GAS INFORMATION SYSTEM CO., LTD.—See Toho Gas Co., Ltd.; *Int'l*, pg. 7775
TOHO GAS LIVING CO., LTD.—See Toho Gas Co., Ltd.; *Int'l*, pg. 7775
TOHO GAS SAFETY LIFE CO., LTD.—See Toho Gas Co., Ltd.; *Int'l*, pg. 7775
TOHO GAS TECHNO CO., LTD.—See Toho Gas Co., Ltd.; *Int'l*, pg. 7775
TOHO HOLDINGS CO., LTD.; *Int'l*, pg. 7776
TOHO HUAIJI CHEMICAL CO., LTD.—See Toho Chemical Industry Co., Ltd.; *Int'l*, pg. 7775
TOHO INDUSTRIAL CO., LTD.—See Yamazen Corporation; *Int'l*, pg. 8558
TOHO KAKEN MANUFACTURING INC.—See Origin Co., Ltd.; *Int'l*, pg. 5629
TOHO KASEI CO., LTD.—See Daikin Industries, Ltd.; *Int'l*, pg. 1936
TOHO KINZOKU CO., LTD.—See TAIYO KOKO Co Ltd; *Int'l*, pg. 7426
TOHO KOJI CO., LTD.—See COMSYS Holdings Corporation; *Int'l*, pg. 1762
TOHO KOKI CO., LTD.; *Int'l*, pg. 7776
TOHOKU ALFRESA CORPORATION—See Alfresa Holdings Corporation; *Int'l*, pg. 317
TOHOKU ALPS, CO., LTD.—See Alps Alpine Co., Ltd.; *Int'l*, pg. 376
TOHOKU ANRITSU CO., LTD.—See Anritsu Corporation; *Int'l*, pg. 476
TOHOKU AOHATA CO., LTD.—See Aohata Corporation; *Int'l*, pg. 487
TOHOKU ASAHI DANBORU CO., LTD.—See Rengo Co., Ltd.; *Int'l*, pg. 6280
THE TOHOKU BANK LTD.; *Int'l*, pg. 7694
TOHOKU BORING CO.,LTD.—See OYO Corporation; *Int'l*, pg. 5678
TOHOKU CHEMICAL CO., LTD.; *Int'l*, pg. 7776
TOHOKU CHEMICAL INDUSTRIES, LTD.—See F.C.C. Co., Ltd.; *Int'l*, pg. 2596
TOHOKU CHEMICAL INDUSTRIES (VIETNAM), LTD.—See F.C.C. Co., Ltd.; *Int'l*, pg. 2596
TOHOKU DAIICHI TRAFFIC CO., LTD.—See Daiichi Koutsu Sangyo Co., Ltd.; *Int'l*, pg. 1929
TOHOKU DENKI TEKKO CO., LTD.—See Tosoh Corporation; *Int'l*, pg. 7833
TOHOKU ELECTRIC POWER CO., INC.; *Int'l*, pg. 7777
TOHOKU ELECTRIC POWER ENGINEERING & CONSTRUCTION CO., INC.—See Tohoku Electric Power Co., Inc.; *Int'l*, pg. 7777
TOHOKU FUJIKURA LTD.—See Fujikura Ltd.; *Int'l*, pg. 2829
TOHOKU GAS CORPORATION—See Kamei Corporation; *Int'l*, pg. 4062
TOHOKU GRAIN TERMINAL CO., LTD.—See Toyota Tsusho Corporation; *Int'l*, pg. 7878
TOHOKU GUNZE CO., LTD.—See Gunze Limited; *Int'l*, pg. 3186
TOHOKU HAKUHODO INC.—See Hakuhodo DY Holdings Incorporated; *Int'l*, pg. 3222
TOHOKU HIROSE ELECTRIC CO., LTD.—See Hirose Electric Co., Ltd.; *Int'l*, pg. 3405
TOHOKU HITACHI CO., LTD.—See Hitachi, Ltd.; *Int'l*, pg. 3424
TOHOKU INFORMATION CENTER CO., LTD.—See Core Corporation; *Int'l*, pg. 1797
TOHOKU INFORMATION SYSTEMS CO., INC.—See Tohoku Electric Power Co., Inc.; *Int'l*, pg. 7777
TOHOKU INOAC CO., LTD. - KITAKAMI PLANT—See INOAC Corporation; *Int'l*, pg. 3715
TOHOKU INOAC CO., LTD. - KOGOTA PLANT—See INOAC Corporation; *Int'l*, pg. 3715
TOHOKU INOAC CO., LTD. - WAKAYANAGI PLANT—See INOAC Corporation; *Int'l*, pg. 3715
TOHOKU INTELLIGENT TELECOMMUNICATION CO., INC.—See Tohoku Electric Power Co., Inc.; *Int'l*, pg. 7777
TOHOKU KANADEN TELECOM ENGINEERING CORPORATION—See Kanaden Corporation; *Int'l*, pg. 4063
TOHOKU KEISYA CO., LTD.—See Toyo Seikan Group Holdings, Ltd.; *Int'l*, pg. 7857
TOHOKU KOGYO CO., LTD.—See Marubeni Construction Material Lease Co., Ltd.; *Int'l*, pg. 4705
TOHOKU MANUFACTURING (THAILAND)CO., LTD.—See Tohoku Steel Co., Ltd.; *Int'l*, pg. 7777
TOHOKU MARUWA LOGISTICS CO., LTD.—See AZ-COM MARUWA Holdings Inc.; *Int'l*, pg. 776
TOHOKU MAZDA CO., LTD.—See Mazda Motor Corporation; *Int'l*, pg. 4749
TOHOKU MEIHAN CO., LTD.—See Meiji Holdings Co., Ltd.; *Int'l*, pg. 4801
TOHOKU METAL CHEMICAL CO., LTD.—See Resonac Holdings Corporation; *Int'l*, pg. 6301
TOHOKU MISAWA HOMES CO., LTD.—See Toyota Motor Corporation; *Int'l*, pg. 7873
TOHOKU MORI SHIGYO CO., LTD.—See Oji Holdings Corporation; *Int'l*, pg. 5537
TOHOKU MURATA MANUFACTURING COMPANY, LTD. - KANUMA PLANT—See Murata Manufacturing Co., Ltd.; *Int'l*, pg. 5098

TOHOKU ELECTRIC POWER CO., INC.   CORPORATE AFFILIATIONS

TOHOKU MURATA MANUFACTURING COMPANY, LTD. - MOTOMIYA PLANT—See Murata Manufacturing Co., Ltd.; *Int'l*, pg. 5098
TOHOKU MURATA MANUFACTURING COMPANY, LTD.—See Murata Manufacturing Co., Ltd.; *Int'l*, pg. 5098
TOHOKU NATURAL GAS CO., INC.—See Japan Petroleum Exploration Co. Ltd.; *Int'l*, pg. 3900
TOHOKU NICHIREI SERVICE INC.—See Nichirei Corporation; *Int'l*, pg. 5270
TOHOKU NIPPATSU CO., LTD.—See NHK Spring Co., Ltd.; *Int'l*, pg. 5258
TOHOKU NITTO KOGYO CORPORATION—See NITTO KOGYO CORPORATION; *Int'l*, pg. 5387
TOHOKU NS SOLUTIONS CORPORATION—See Nippon Steel Corporation; *Int'l*, pg. 5335
TOHOKU OKAYA CO., LTD.—See Okaya & Co., Ltd.; *Int'l*, pg. 5547
TOHOKU PIONEER CORPORATION—See EQT AB; *Int'l*, pg. 2471
TOHOKU PIONEER CORPORATION - YONEZAWA PLANT—See EQT AB; *Int'l*, pg. 2471
TOHOKU PIONEER EG CORPORATION—See Denso Corporation; *Int'l*, pg. 2033
TOHOKU PIONEER (THAILAND) CO., LTD.—See EQT AB; *Int'l*, pg. 2471
TOHOKU PIONEER (VIETNAM) CO., LTD.—See EQT AB; *Int'l*, pg. 2471
TOHOKU ROYAL PARK HOTEL CO., LTD.—See Mitsubishi Estate Co., Ltd.; *Int'l*, pg. 4947
TOHOKU RUBBER CO., LTD.—See Hitachi, Ltd.; *Int'l*, pg. 3424
TOHOKU RYOKKA KANKYOHOZEN CO., LTD.—See Tohoku Electric Power Co., Inc.; *Int'l*, pg. 7777
TOHOKU SEKISUI SHOJI CO., LTD.—See Sekisui Chemical Co., Ltd.; *Int'l*, pg. 6696
TOHOKU SENKO TRANSPORT CO., LTD.—See Senko Group Holdings Co., Ltd.; *Int'l*, pg. 6712
TOHOKU SHANON CO., LTD.—See Tokuyama Corporation; *Int'l*, pg. 7787
TOHOKU SHIKI CO., LTD.—See Rengo Co., Ltd.; *Int'l*, pg. 6282
TOHOKUSHINSHA CREATES INC.—See Tohokushinsha Film Corporation; *Int'l*, pg. 7777
TOHOKUSHINSHA FILM CORPORATION; *Int'l*, pg. 7777
TOHOKU SOLUTIONS COMPANY LIMITED—See SVI Public Co., Ltd.; *Int'l*, pg. 7359
TOHOKU STEEL CO., LTD.; *Int'l*, pg. 7777
TOHOKU STEEL CO., LTD. - TSUCHIURA PLANT—See Tohoku Steel Co., Ltd.; *Int'l*, pg. 7777
TOHOKU SUMIDEN PRECISION CO., LTD.—See Sumitomo Electric Industries, Ltd.; *Int'l*, pg. 7285
TOHOKU SYSTEMS CO., LTD.—See TOHOKU CHEMICAL CO., LTD.; *Int'l*, pg. 7777
TOHOKU TATSUMI KK; *Int'l*, pg. 7777
TOHOKU TOKUSUI, LTD. - SHIOGAMA FACTORY—See Tokusui Corporation; *Int'l*, pg. 7786
TOHOKU TOKUSUI, LTD.—See Tokusui Corporation; *Int'l*, pg. 7786
TOHOKU TOSOH CHEMICAL CO., LTD.—See Tosoh Corporation; *Int'l*, pg. 7833
TOHOKU U-LOID INDUSTRY CO., LTD.—See Gun Ei Chemical Industry Co., Ltd.; *Int'l*, pg. 3183
TOHO LAMAC CO., LTD.; *Int'l*, pg. 7776
T.O. HOLDINGS CO., LTD.; *Int'l*, pg. 7397
THE TOHO LEASE CO., LTD.—See The Toho Bank, Ltd.; *Int'l*, pg. 7694
TOHO LIQUEFIED GAS CO., LTD.—See Toho Gas Co., Ltd.; *Int'l*, pg. 7775
TOHO LNG SHIPPING CO., LTD.—See Toho Gas Co., Ltd.; *Int'l*, pg. 7775
TOHOPEKALIGA WATER AUTHORITY; *U.S. Private*, pg. 4181
TOHO PHARMACEUTICAL CO., LTD.—See Toho Holdings Co., Ltd.; *Int'l*, pg. 7776
TOHO POWERLARKS CO., LTD.—See TOHO Co., Ltd.; *Int'l*, pg. 7775
TOHO REAL ESTATE CO., LTD.—See Toho Gas Co., Ltd.; *Int'l*, pg. 7775
TOHO REAL ESTATE CO., LTD.—See Toho Co., Ltd.; *Int'l*, pg. 7775
TOHO SECURITIES CO., LTD.—See The Toho Bank, Ltd.; *Int'l*, pg. 7694
TOHO SERVICE CO., LTD.—See Toho Gas Co., Ltd.; *Int'l*, pg. 7775
TOHO SHINYO HOSHO COMPANY—See Prudential Financial, Inc.; *U.S. Public*, pg. 1733
TOHO SYSTEM SCIENCE CO., LTD.; *Int'l*, pg. 7776
TOHO SYSTEM SERVICE CO., LTD.—See Toho Holdings Co., Ltd.; *Int'l*, pg. 7776
TOHO TANSO KOGYO CO., LTD.—See Nippon Carbon Co., Ltd.; *Int'l*, pg. 5312
TOHO TENAX AMERICA, INC.—See Teijin Limited; *Int'l*, pg. 7523
TOHO TENAX CO., LTD.—See Teijin Limited; *Int'l*, pg. 7523
TOHO TENAX EUROPE GMBH—See Teijin Limited; *Int'l*, pg. 7524

TOHO TITANIUM CO., LTD. - HITACHI PLANT—See Toho Titanium Co., Ltd.; *Int'l*, pg. 7776
TOHO TITANIUM CO., LTD. - KUROBE PLANT—See Toho Titanium Co., Ltd.; *Int'l*, pg. 7776
TOHO TITANIUM CO., LTD.; *Int'l*, pg. 7776
TOHO TITANIUM CO., LTD. - WAKAMATSU PLANT—See Toho Titanium Co., Ltd.; *Int'l*, pg. 7776
TOHO TITANIUM CO., LTD. - YAHATA PLANT—See Toho Titanium Co., Ltd.; *Int'l*, pg. 7776
TOHO TITANIUM EUROPE CO., LTD.—See Toho Titanium Co., Ltd.; *Int'l*, pg. 7776
TOHO TOKUSHU PULP CO., LTD.—See Mitsubishi Paper Mills Limited; *Int'l*, pg. 4967
TOHO TRADE CO LTD—See Toho Zinc Co., Ltd.; *Int'l*, pg. 7776
TOHO TRANSPORTATION CO., LTD.—See Topre Corporation; *Int'l*, pg. 7820
TOHO UNYU CO., LTD.—See Tosoh Corporation; *Int'l*, pg. 7833
TOHO ZINC CO., LTD.; *Int'l*, pg. 7776
TOHPE CORPORATION—See Zeon Corporation; *Int'l*, pg. 8635
TOHSEN CORPORATION—See JFE Holdings, Inc.; *Int'l*, pg. 3937
TOHSUI FOODS K.K.—See TOHTO SUISAN Co., Ltd.; *Int'l*, pg. 7778
TOHTO CO., LTD.—See Relo Group, Inc.; *Int'l*, pg. 6265
TOHTO SUISAN CO., LTD.; *Int'l*, pg. 7777
TOHUN CO., LTD.—See Tomoku Co., Ltd.; *Int'l*, pg. 7802
TOHUN LOGITEM CO., LTD.—See Tomoku Co., Ltd.; *Int'l*, pg. 7802
TOHUN RYUTSU SERVICE CO., LTD.—See Tomoku Co., Ltd.; *Int'l*, pg. 7802
TOHUN SERVICE CO., LTD.—See Tomoku Co., Ltd.; *Int'l*, pg. 7802
TOHUN TRAFFIC CO., LTD.—See Tomoku Co., Ltd.; *Int'l*, pg. 7802
TOICHI LOGISTICS CO., LTD.—See Tsukiji Uoichiba Co., Ltd.; *Int'l*, pg. 7956
TOICHI TSUKIJI FISH (SHANGHAI) CO., LTD.—See Tsukiji Uoichiba Co., Ltd.; *Int'l*, pg. 7956
TOIMEX OY—See Panostaja Oyj; *Int'l*, pg. 5730
TOIN CORPORATION - KASHIWA FACTORY—See TOIN CORPORATION; *Int'l*, pg. 7778
TOIN CORPORATION - NODA FACTORY—See TOIN CORPORATION; *Int'l*, pg. 7778
TOIN CORPORATION; *Int'l*, pg. 7778
TOITURES COUTURE ET ASSOCIES INC.; *Int'l*, pg. 7778
TOJITSU, LTD.—See Topy Industries, Ltd.; *Int'l*, pg. 7822
TOJU KOSAN, LTD.—See Sintokogio Ltd.; *Int'l*, pg. 6959
TOKACHI GRAIN TERMINAL CO., LTD.—See Marubeni Corporation; *Int'l*, pg. 4710
TOKACHI PACKAGE CO., LTD.—See Tomoku Co., Ltd.; *Int'l*, pg. 7802
TOK ADVANCED MATERIALS CO., LTD.—See Tokyo Ohka Kogyo Co., Ltd.; *Int'l*, pg. 7794
TOKAI BAY NETWORK CO., LTD.—See TOKAI Holdings Corporation; *Int'l*, pg. 7779
TOKAI CABLE NETWORK CORPORATION—See TOKAI Holdings Corporation; *Int'l*, pg. 7779
TOKAI CAPSULE CO., LTD.—See Ono Pharmaceutical Co., Ltd.; *Int'l*, pg. 5582
TOKAI CARBON CB LTD.—See Tokai Carbon Co., Ltd.; *Int'l*, pg. 7778
TOKAI CARBON CO., LTD. - CHITA PLANT—See Tokai Carbon Co., Ltd.; *Int'l*, pg. 7778
TOKAI CARBON CO., LTD. - HOFU PLANT—See Tokai Carbon Co., Ltd.; *Int'l*, pg. 7778
TOKAI CARBON CO., LTD. - KYUSHU-WAKAMATSU PLANT—See Tokai Carbon Co., Ltd.; *Int'l*, pg. 7778
TOKAI CARBON CO., LTD. - SHONAN PLANT—See Tokai Carbon Co., Ltd.; *Int'l*, pg. 7778
TOKAI CARBON CO., LTD.; *Int'l*, pg. 7778
TOKAI CARBON CO., LTD. - TANOURA PLANT—See Tokai Carbon Co., Ltd.; *Int'l*, pg. 7778
TOKAI CARBON (DALIAN) CO., LTD.—See Tokai Carbon Co., Ltd.; *Int'l*, pg. 7778
TOKAI CARBON DEUTSCHLAND GMBH—See Tokai Carbon Co., Ltd.; *Int'l*, pg. 7778
TOKAI CARBON EUROPE GMBH—See Tokai Carbon Co., Ltd.; *Int'l*, pg. 7778
TOKAI CARBON EUROPE LTD.—See Tokai Carbon Co., Ltd.; *Int'l*, pg. 7778
TOKAI CARBON GE LLC—See Tokai Carbon Co., Ltd.; *Int'l*, pg. 7778
TOKAI CARBON ITALIA S.R.L.—See Tokai Carbon Co., Ltd.; *Int'l*, pg. 7778
TOKAI CARBON KOREA CO., LTD.—See Tokai Carbon Co., Ltd.; *Int'l*, pg. 7778
TOKAI CARBON (SHANGHAI) CO., LTD.—See Tokai Carbon Co., Ltd.; *Int'l*, pg. 7778
TOKAI CARBON (SUZHOU) CO., LTD.—See Tokai Carbon Co., Ltd.; *Int'l*, pg. 7778
TOKAI CARBON (TIANJIN) CO., LTD.—See Cabot Corporation; *U.S. Public*, pg. 417
TOKAI CARBON U.S.A., INC.—See Tokai Carbon Co., Ltd.; *Int'l*, pg. 7778
TOKAI CARBON US HOLDINGS INC—See Tokai Carbon Co., Ltd.; *Int'l*, pg. 7778

TOKAI CARBON US HOLDINGS INC—See Tokai Carbon Co., Ltd.; *Int'l*, pg. 7778
TOKAI CHEMICAL INDUSTRIES, LTD.—See Sumitomo Riko Company Limited; *Int'l*, pg. 7298
TOKAI CHEMICAL KYUSHU, LTD.—See Sumitomo Riko Company Limited; *Int'l*, pg. 7298
TOKAI CHEMICAL (TIANJIN) AUTO PARTS CO., LTD.—See Sumitomo Riko Company Limited; *Int'l*, pg. 7298
TOKAI CITY SERVICE CORPORATION—See TOKAI Holdings Corporation; *Int'l*, pg. 7779
TOKAI COBEX POLSKA SP. Z O.O.—See Tokai Carbon Co., Ltd.; *Int'l*, pg. 7778
TOKAI COBEX SAVOIE S.A.S.—See Tokai Carbon Co., Ltd.; *Int'l*, pg. 7778
TOKAI COMMUNICATIONS CORPORATION—See TOKAI Holdings Corporation; *Int'l*, pg. 7779
TOKAI CONCRETE INDUSTRIES CO., LTD.—See Chubu Electric Power Co., Inc.; *Int'l*, pg. 1593
TOKAI CORPORATION—See TOKAI Holdings Corporation; *Int'l*, pg. 7779
TOKAI CORP.; *Int'l*, pg. 7779
TOKAI DALIAN HOSE CO., LTD.—See Sumitomo Riko Company Limited; *Int'l*, pg. 7298
TOKAIDO REIT, INC.; *Int'l*, pg. 7781
TOKAI DYEING CO., (THAILAND) LTD.—See Tokai Senko K.K.; *Int'l*, pg. 7781
TOKAI EASTERN RUBBER (THAILAND) CO., LTD.—See Sumitomo Riko Company Limited; *Int'l*, pg. 7298
TOKAI ENGINEERING & CONSTRUCTION CO., LTD.—See RAIZNEXT Corporation; *Int'l*, pg. 6192
TOKAI ERFTCARBON GMBH—See Tokai Carbon Co., Ltd.; *Int'l*, pg. 7778
TOKAI FINE CARBON CO., LTD.—See Tokai Carbon Co., Ltd.; *Int'l*, pg. 7778
TOKAI FOREST CO., LTD.—See Tokushu Tokai Paper Co., Ltd.; *Int'l*, pg. 7786
TOKAI GAS CORPORATION—See TOKAI Holdings Corporation; *Int'l*, pg. 7779
TOKAI HOLDINGS CORPORATION; *Int'l*, pg. 7779
TOKAI HOME GAS CORPORATION—See TOKAI Holdings Corporation; *Int'l*, pg. 7779
TOKAI HUMAN RESOURCES EVOL CORPORATION—See TOKAI Holdings Corporation; *Int'l*, pg. 7779
TOKAI IMPERIAL RUBBER INDIA PRIVATE LIMITED—See Imperial Auto Industries Ltd.; *Int'l*, pg. 3632
TOKAI IMPERIAL RUBBER INDIA PRIVATE LIMITED—See Sumitomo Riko Company Limited; *Int'l*, pg. 7298
TOKAI INDUSTRIAL SEWING MACHINE CO., LTD.—See Tajima Industries Ltd.; *Int'l*, pg. 7428
TOKAI JIDOSHA CO., LTD.—See Odakyu Electric Railway Co., Ltd.; *Int'l*, pg. 5524
TOKAI KIDS TOUCH CORPORATION—See TOKAI Holdings Corporation; *Int'l*, pg. 7779
TOKAI KIOSK COMPANY—See Central Japan Railway Company; *Int'l*, pg. 1408
TOKAI KISEN CO., LTD.; *Int'l*, pg. 7780
TOKAIKOEI INC.—See MIRAIT ONE Corporation; *Int'l*, pg. 4918
TOKAI KOGYO CO., LTD.—See AGC Inc.; *Int'l*, pg. 204
TOKAI KONETSU ENGINEERING CO., LTD.—See Tokai Carbon Co., Ltd.; *Int'l*, pg. 7778
TOKAI KONETSU ENGINEERING CO., LTD.—See Tokai Carbon Co., Ltd.; *Int'l*, pg. 7778
TOKAI KONETSU KOGYO CO., LTD.—See Tokai Carbon Co., Ltd.; *Int'l*, pg. 7779
TOKAI KONETSU (SUZHOU) CO., LTD.—See Tokai Carbon Co., Ltd.; *Int'l*, pg. 7778
TOKAI LEASE CO., LTD.; *Int'l*, pg. 7780
TOKAI LIFE PLUS CORPORATION—See TOKAI Holdings Corporation; *Int'l*, pg. 7779
TOKAI MANAGEMENT SERVICE CORPORATION—See TOKAI Holdings Corporation; *Int'l*, pg. 7779
TOKAI MATERIAL CO., LTD.—See MK Kashiyama Corp.; *Int'l*, pg. 5000
TOKAI MAZDA SALES CO., LTD.—See Mazda Motor Corporation; *Int'l*, pg. 4749
TOKAI MEIJI CO., LTD.—See Meiji Holdings Co., Ltd.; *Int'l*, pg. 4801
TOKAI MELTEX INC.—See Astena Holdings Co., Ltd.; *Int'l*, pg. 653
TOKAI MORI SHIGYO CO., LTD.—See Oji Holdings Corporation; *Int'l*, pg. 5538
TOKAI MYANMAR COMPANY LIMITED—See TOKAI Holdings Corporation; *Int'l*, pg. 7779
TOKA INK (BANGLADESH) LTD—See T&K TOKA Corporation; *Int'l*, pg. 7395
TOKAI NONDESTRUCTIVE INSPECTION CO., LTD.—See TOKAI Holdings Corporation; *Int'l*, pg. 7779
TOKAI NOSHIRO SEIKO CO., LTD.—See Tokai Carbon Co., Ltd.; *Int'l*, pg. 7779
TOKAI NUTS CO., LTD.—See Meiji Holdings Co., Ltd.; *Int'l*, pg. 4801
TOKAI OKAYA KIZAI CO., LTD.—See Okaya & Co., Ltd.; *Int'l*, pg. 5547

TOKAI PAPER CONVERTING CO., LTD.—See Tokushu Tokai Paper Co., Ltd.; *Int'l*, pg. 7786
TOKAI PRESSING CO., LTD.—See Okaya & Co., Ltd.; *Int'l*, pg. 5547
TOKAI RIKA ASIA CO., LTD.—See Tokai Rika Co., Ltd.; *Int'l*, pg. 7780
TOKAI RIKA BELGIUM NV—See Tokai Rika Co., Ltd.; *Int'l*, pg. 7780
TOKAI RIKA CO., LTD. - HAGI PLANT—See Tokai Rika Co., Ltd.; *Int'l*, pg. 7780
TOKAI RIKA CO., LTD. - OTOWA PLANT—See Tokai Rika Co., Ltd.; *Int'l*, pg. 7780
TOKAI RIKA CO., LTD.; *Int'l*, pg. 7780
TOKAI RIKA CO., LTD. - TOYOTA PLANT—See Tokai Rika Co., Ltd.; *Int'l*, pg. 7780
TOKAI RIKA CREATE CORPORATION—See Tokai Rika Co., Ltd.; *Int'l*, pg. 7780
TOKAI RIKA ELETEC CO., LTD.—See Tokai Rika Co., Ltd.; *Int'l*, pg. 7780
TOKAI RIKA ELETECH CO., LTD.—See Tokai Rika Co., Ltd.; *Int'l*, pg. 7780
TOKAI RIKA MEXICO, S.A. DE C.V.—See Tokai Rika Co., Ltd.; *Int'l*, pg. 7780
TOKAI RIKA MINDA INDIA PRIVATE LIMITED—See Tokai Rika Co., Ltd.; *Int'l*, pg. 7780
TOKAI RIKA NEXT CO., LTD.—See Tokai Rika Co., Ltd.; *Int'l*, pg. 7780
TOKAI RIKA SERVICE CO., LTD.—See Tokai Rika Co., Ltd.; *Int'l*, pg. 7780
TOKAI RIKA THAILAND CO LTD—See Tokai Rika Co., Ltd.; *Int'l*, pg. 7780
TOKAI ROLLING STOCK & MACHINERY CO., LTD.—See Central Japan Railway Company; *Int'l*, pg. 1408
TOKAI RUBBER AUTO-PARTS INDIA PRIVATE LTD.—See Sumitomo Riko Company Limited; *Int'l*, pg. 7298
TOKAI RUBBER (DONGGUAN) CO., LTD.—See Sumitomo Riko Company Limited; *Int'l*, pg. 7298
TOKAI RUBBER (GUANGZHOU) CO., LTD.—See Sumitomo Riko Company Limited; *Int'l*, pg. 7298
TOKAI RUBBER INDUSTRIES (H.K.) LTD.—See Sumitomo Riko Company Limited; *Int'l*, pg. 7298
TOKAI RUBBER (JIAXING) CO., LTD.—See Sumitomo Riko Company Limited; *Int'l*, pg. 7298
TOKAI RUBBER MOLDINGS (TIANJIN) CO., LTD.—See Sumitomo Riko Company Limited; *Int'l*, pg. 7298
TOKAI RUBBER TECHNICAL CENTER (CHINA) CO., LTD.—See Sumitomo Riko Company Limited; *Int'l*, pg. 7298
TOKAI RUBBER (TIANJIN) CO., LTD.—See Sumitomo Riko Company Limited; *Int'l*, pg. 7298
TOKAISEIKI CO., LTD.—See Toyota Industries Corporation; *Int'l*, pg. 7866
TOKAI SEINO TRANSPORTATION CO., LTD.—See Seino Holdings Co., Ltd.; *Int'l*, pg. 6691
TOKAI SENKO K.K.; *Int'l*, pg. 7781
TOKAI SENKO TRANSPORT CO., LTD.—See Senko Group Holdings Co., Ltd.; *Int'l*, pg. 6712
TOKAI (SHANGHAI) TRADE & COMMERCE CO., LTD.—See TOKAI Holdings Corporation; *Int'l*, pg. 7779
TOKAI SHIKI CO., LTD.—See Rengo Co., Ltd.; *Int'l*, pg. 6282
TOKAI SOFTWARE CO., LTD.; *Int'l*, pg. 7781
TOKAI SPECIALTY STEEL CO. LTD.—See Aichi Steel Corporation; *Int'l*, pg. 230
TOKAI SPRING MFG. (FOSHAN) CO., LTD.—See Nagase & Co., Ltd.; *Int'l*, pg. 5128
TOKAI STEEL CORPORATION—See Godo Steel, Ltd.; *Int'l*, pg. 3020
TOKAI SUMICE SALES CO., LTD.—See Sumitomo Osaka Cement Co Ltd; *Int'l*, pg. 7297
TOKAI SUMIDEN PRECISION CO., LTD.—See Sumitomo Electric Industries, Ltd.; *Int'l*, pg. 7285
TOKAI SUMISE SALES CO., LTD.—See Sumitomo Osaka Cement Co Ltd; *Int'l*, pg. 7297
TOKAI TECHNO CO., LTD.—See Takeei Corporation; *Int'l*, pg. 7440
TOKAI TELEVISION BROADCASTING CO., LTD.—See Fuji Media Holdings, Inc.; *Int'l*, pg. 2814
TOKAITEX PHILS. INC.—See Tokai Senko K.K.; *Int'l*, pg. 7781
TOKAI TOKYO ACADEMY CO., LTD.—See Tokai Tokyo Financial Holdings, Inc.; *Int'l*, pg. 7781
TOKAI TOKYO BUSINESS SERVICE CO., LTD.—See Tokai Tokyo Financial Holdings, Inc.; *Int'l*, pg. 7781
TOKAI TOKYO FINANCIAL HOLDINGS, INC.; *Int'l*, pg. 7781
TOKAI TOKYO GLOBAL INVESTMENTS PTE. LTD.—See Tokai Tokyo Financial Holdings, Inc.; *Int'l*, pg. 7781
TOKAI TOKYO INVESTMENT CO., LTD.—See Tokai Tokyo Financial Holdings, Inc.; *Int'l*, pg. 7781
TOKAI TOKYO INVESTMENT MANAGEMENT PTE. LTD.—See Tokai Tokyo Financial Holdings, Inc.; *Int'l*, pg. 7781
TOKAI TOKYO INVESTMENT MANAGEMENT SINGAPORE PTE. LTD.—See Tokai Tokyo Financial Holdings, Inc.; *Int'l*, pg. 7781
TOKAI TOKYO RESEARCH CENTER CO., LTD.—See Tokai Tokyo Financial Holdings, Inc.; *Int'l*, pg. 7781
TOKAI TOKYO RESEARCH INSTITUTE CO., LTD.—See Tokai Tokyo Financial Holdings, Inc.; *Int'l*, pg. 7781
TOKAI TOKYO SECURITIES (ASIA) LTD.—See Tokai Tokyo Financial Holdings, Inc.; *Int'l*, pg. 7781
TOKAI TOKYO SECURITIES CO., LTD—See Tokai Tokyo Financial Holdings, Inc.; *Int'l*, pg. 7781
TOKAI TOKYO SECURITIES EUROPE LIMITED—See Tokai Tokyo Financial Holdings, Inc.; *Int'l*, pg. 7781
TOKAI TOKYO SECURITIES (USA), INC.—See Tokai Tokyo Financial Holdings, Inc.; *Int'l*, pg. 7781
TOKAI TOKYO SERVICES CO., LTD.—See Tokai Tokyo Financial Holdings, Inc.; *Int'l*, pg. 7781
TOKAI TOKYO WEALTH CONSULTING CO., LTD.—See Tokai Tokyo Financial Holdings, Inc.; *Int'l*, pg. 7781
TOKAI TRADING CO., LTD.—See Tokai Senko K.K.; *Int'l*, pg. 7781
TOKAI TRANSPORT SERVICE COMPANY—See Central Japan Railway Company; *Int'l*, pg. 1408
TOKAI UNYU CO., LTD.—See Tokai Carbon Co., Ltd.; *Int'l*, pg. 7779
TOKAI YOGYO CO., LTD.—See Alconix Corporation; *Int'l*, pg. 303
TOKAIZOSEN-UNYU CORPORATION—See TOKAI Holdings Corporation; *Int'l*, pg. 7779
TOKAL CORPORATION—See TOKAI Holdings Corporation; *Int'l*, pg. 7779
TOKAN (CHANGSHU) HIGH TECHNOLOGY CONTAINERS CO., LTD.—See Toyo Seikan Group Holdings, Ltd.; *Int'l*, pg. 7857
TOKAN KOGYO CO., LTD.—See Toyo Seikan Group Holdings, Ltd.; *Int'l*, pg. 7857
TOKAN KOSAN CO., LTD.—See Toyo Seikan Group Holdings, Ltd.; *Int'l*, pg. 7857
TOKAN KYOEI KAISHA, LTD.—See Toyo Seikan Group Holdings, Ltd.; *Int'l*, pg. 7857
TOKAN LOGITECH CO., LTD.—See Toyo Seikan Group Holdings, Ltd.; *Int'l*, pg. 7857
TOKAN TAKAYAMA CO., LTD.—See Toyo Seikan Group Holdings, Ltd.; *Int'l*, pg. 7857
TOKAN TRADING CORPORATION—See Toyo Seikan Group Holdings, Ltd.; *Int'l*, pg. 7857
THE TOKARZ GROUP ADVISERS, LLC; *U.S. Private*, pg. 4127
TOKATSU FOODS CO., LTD.—See Nisshin Seifun Group, Inc.; *Int'l*, pg. 5372
TOKATSU HOLDINGS CO., LTD.; *Int'l*, pg. 7781
TOK CHINA CO., LTD.—See Tokyo Ohka Kogyo Co., Ltd.; *Int'l*, pg. 7794
TOKEN BUILDING MANAGEMENT CO., LTD.—See Token Corporation; *Int'l*, pg. 7781
TOKEN CO., LTD.—See KOMATSU MATERE Co.,Ltd.; *Int'l*, pg. 4239
TOKEN COMMUNITIES LTD.—See ASC Global Inc.; *U.S. Private*, pg. 345
TOKEN CORPORATION; *Int'l*, pg. 7781
TOKENEX, LLC; *U.S. Private*, pg. 4181
TOK ENGINEERING CO., LTD.—See Tokyo Ohka Kogyo Co., Ltd.; *Int'l*, pg. 7794
TOKEN INDUSTRY CO., LTD.—See Tokyu Construction Co., Ltd.; *Int'l*, pg. 7797
TOKEN INTERIOR & DESIGN CO., LTD.—See Taikisha Ltd.; *Int'l*, pg. 7414
TOKEN LEASE FUND CO., LTD.—See Token Corporation; *Int'l*, pg. 7781
TOKEN MYANMAR CO., LTD.—See Taikisha Ltd.; *Int'l*, pg. 7414
TOKEN RESORT JAPAN CO., LTD.—See Token Corporation; *Int'l*, pg. 7781
TOKEN SCIENCES JAPAN CO. LTD.—See Wuhu Token Sciences Co., Ltd.; *Int'l*, pg. 8502
TOKENS.COM CORP.; *Int'l*, pg. 7782
TOKENS.COM CORP.; *Int'l*, pg. 7782
TOKEN SHOJI CO., LTD.—See Toyo Construction Co., Ltd.; *Int'l*, pg. 7852
TOKEN TADO COUNTRY CO., LTD.—See Token Corporation; *Int'l*, pg. 7781
TOKEN TADO COUNTRY K.K.—See Token Corporation; *Int'l*, pg. 7782
TOKEN TECHNO CO., LTD.—See Toyo Construction Co., Ltd.; *Int'l*, pg. 7852
TOKENTUS INVESTMENT AG; *Int'l*, pg. 7782
TOKHEIM BELGIUM—See Dover Corporation; *U.S. Public*, pg. 683
TOKHEIM GMBH—See Motion Equity Partners S.A.S.; *Int'l*, pg. 5053
TOKHEIM GROUP S.A.S.—See Motion Equity Partners S.A.S.; *Int'l*, pg. 5053
TOKHEIM GUARDIAN VENTURE SDN. BHD—See Dover Corporation; *U.S. Public*, pg. 683
TOKHEIM HENGSHAN TECHNOLOGIES (GUANGZHOU) CO. LTD.—See Dover Corporation; *U.S. Public*, pg. 683
TOKHEIM INDIA PRIVATE LIMITED—See Dover Corporation; *U.S. Public*, pg. 683
TOKHEIM NETHERLANDS B.V.—See Dover Corporation; *U.S. Public*, pg. 683
TOKHEIM SOFITAM APPLICATIONS—See Dover Corporation; *U.S. Public*, pg. 683
TOKHEIM SOUTH AFRICA (PTY) LTD.—See Motion Equity Partners S.A.S.; *Int'l*, pg. 5053
TOKI-BUYUKSEHIR BELEDIYESI INSAAT EMLAK VE PROJE A.S.—See T.C. Toplu Konut Idaresi Baskanligi; *Int'l*, pg. 7396
TOKICO (THAILAND) LTD.—See Hitachi Astemo, Ltd.; *Int'l*, pg. 3410
TOKI DYNAPAC CO., LTD. - NAKATSUGAWA PLANT—See Dynapac Co., Ltd.; *Int'l*, pg. 2241
TOKI DYNAPAC CO., LTD.—See Dynapac Co., Ltd.; *Int'l*, pg. 2241
TOKI FUDOSAN CO., LTD—See TOKYO KIKAI SEISAKUSHO LTD.; *Int'l*, pg. 7793
TOKIMEC AVIATION INC.—See TOKYO KEIKI INC.; *Int'l*, pg. 7792
TOKIMEC CONSTRUCTION SYSTEMS INC—See TOKYO KEIKI INC.; *Int'l*, pg. 7792
TOKIMEC INFORMATION SYSTEMS INC.—See TOKYO KEIKI INC.; *Int'l*, pg. 7792
TOKIMEC KOREA POWER CONTROL CO. LTD.—See TOKYO KEIKI INC.; *Int'l*, pg. 7792
TOKIMEC RAIL TECHNO INC.—See TOKYO KEIKI INC.; *Int'l*, pg. 7792
TOKIMO CO., LTD.—See Medipal Holdings Corporation; *Int'l*, pg. 4779
TOKIN ELECTRONICS (VIETNAM) CO. LTD.—See Yageo Corporation; *Int'l*, pg. 8545
TOKIN HONG KONG LTD.—See Yageo Corporation; *Int'l*, pg. 8545
TOKIO MARINE ASIA PTE. LTD.—See Tokio Marine Holdings, Inc.; *Int'l*, pg. 7784
TOKIO MARINE ASSET MANAGEMENT CO., LTD.—See Tokio Marine Holdings, Inc.; *Int'l*, pg. 7785
TOKIO MARINE ASSET MANAGEMENT INTERNATIONAL PTE. LTD.—See Tokio Marine Holdings, Inc.; *Int'l*, pg. 7785
TOKIO MARINE ASSET MANAGEMENT (LONDON) LIMITED—See Tokio Marine Holdings, Inc.; *Int'l*, pg. 7785
TOKIO MARINE ASSET MANAGEMENT (USA) LTD.—See Tokio Marine Holdings, Inc.; *Int'l*, pg. 7785
TOKIO MARINE BRASIL SEGURADORA S.A.—See Tokio Marine Holdings, Inc.; *Int'l*, pg. 7785
TOKIO MARINE BRASIL—See Tokio Marine Holdings, Inc.; *Int'l*, pg. 7786
TOKIO MARINE BRASIL—See Tokio Marine Holdings, Inc.; *Int'l*, pg. 7786
TOKIO MARINE BUSINESS SUPPORT CO., LTD.—See Tokio Marine Holdings, Inc.; *Int'l*, pg. 7785
THE TOKIO MARINE CLAIMS SERVICE CO., LTD.—See Tokio Marine Holdings, Inc.; *Int'l*, pg. 7784
TOKIO MARINE COMPANIA DE SEGUROS, S.A. DE C.V.—See Tokio Marine Holdings, Inc.; *Int'l*, pg. 7785
TOKIO MARINE COMPANIA DE SEGUROS, S.A. DE C.V.—See Tokio Marine Holdings, Inc.; *Int'l*, pg. 7785
TOKIO MARINE COMPANIA DE SEGUROS, S.A. DE C.V.—See Tokio Marine Holdings, Inc.; *Int'l*, pg. 7785
THE TOKIO MARINE EUROPE INSURANCE LIMITED—See Tokio Marine Holdings, Inc.; *Int'l*, pg. 7783
THE TOKIO MARINE EUROPE INSURANCE LIMITED—See Tokio Marine Holdings, Inc.; *Int'l*, pg. 7783
THE TOKIO MARINE EUROPE INSURANCE LIMITED—See Tokio Marine Holdings, Inc.; *Int'l*, pg. 7783
THE TOKIO MARINE EUROPE INSURANCE LIMITED—See Tokio Marine Holdings, Inc.; *Int'l*, pg. 7783
THE TOKIO MARINE EUROPE INSURANCE LIMITED, SPAIN BRANCH—See Tokio Marine Holdings, Inc.; *Int'l*, pg. 7783
THE TOKIO MARINE EUROPE INSURANCE LTD.—See Tokio Marine Holdings, Inc.; *Int'l*, pg. 7783
THE TOKIO MARINE EUROPE INSURANCE LTD.—See Tokio Marine Holdings, Inc.; *Int'l*, pg. 7783
TOKIO MARINE EUROPE INSURANCE LTD.—See Tokio Marine Holdings, Inc.; *Int'l*, pg. 7785
TOKIO MARINE EUROPE LIMITED—See Tokio Marine Holdings, Inc.; *Int'l*, pg. 7785
TOKIO MARINE EUROPE—See Tokio Marine Holdings, Inc.; *Int'l*, pg. 7785
TOKIO MARINE FINANCIAL SOLUTIONS LTD.—See Tokio Marine Holdings, Inc.; *Int'l*, pg. 7785
THE TOKIO MARINE & FIRE INSURANCE COMPANY (HONG KONG) LIMITED—See Tokio Marine Holdings, Inc.; *Int'l*, pg. 7782
THE TOKIO MARINE & FIRE INSURANCE COMPANY, LTD.—See Tokio Marine Holdings, Inc.; *Int'l*, pg. 7783
THE TOKIO MARINE & FIRE INSURANCE COMPANY, LTD.—See Tokio Marine Holdings, Inc.; *Int'l*, pg. 7783
THE TOKIO MARINE & FIRE INSURANCE COMPANY, LTD.—See Tokio Marine Holdings, Inc.; *Int'l*, pg. 7783
THE TOKIO MARINE & FIRE INSURANCE COMPANY, LTD.—See Tokio Marine Holdings, Inc.; *Int'l*, pg. 7783
THE TOKIO MARINE & FIRE INSURANCE COMPANY (SINGAPORE) PTE. LIMITED—See Tokio Marine Holdings, Inc.; *Int'l*, pg. 7783

TOKENTUS INVESTMENT AG — CORPORATE AFFILIATIONS

THE TOKIO MARINE & FIRE INSURANCE COMPANY (UK) LIMITED—See Tokio Marine Holdings, Inc.; *Int'l*, pg. 7783
TOKIO MARINE HOLDINGS, INC.; *Int'l*, pg. 7782
TOKIO MARINE INSURANCE (MALAYSIA) BHD.—See Tokio Marine Holdings, Inc.; *Int'l*, pg. 7782
TOKIO MARINE INSURANCE (MALAYSIA) BHD.—See Tokio Marine Holdings, Inc.; *Int'l*, pg. 7785
TOKIO MARINE INSURANCE (MALAYSIA) BHD.—See Tokio Marine Holdings, Inc.; *Int'l*, pg. 7785
TOKIO MARINE INSURANCE SINGAPORE LTD.—See Tokio Marine Holdings, Inc.; *Int'l*, pg. 7784
TOKIO MARINE INVESTMENT SERVICES, LIMITED—See Tokio Marine Holdings, Inc.; *Int'l*, pg. 7785
TOKIO MARINE KILN GROUP LIMITED—See Tokio Marine Holdings, Inc.; *Int'l*, pg. 7785
TOKIO MARINE KILN INSURANCE SERVICES LIMITED—See Tokio Marine Holdings, Inc.; *Int'l*, pg. 7784
TOKIO MARINE LIFE INSURANCE MALAYSIA BHD—See Tokio Marine Holdings, Inc.; *Int'l*, pg. 7785
TOKIO MARINE LIFE INSURANCE SINGAPORE LTD.—See Tokio Marine Holdings, Inc.; *Int'l*, pg. 7785
TOKIO MARINE LIFE INSURANCE (THAILAND) PUBLIC COMPANY LIMITED—See Tokio Marine Holdings, Inc.; *Int'l*, pg. 7784
TOKIO MARINE MALAYAN INSURANCE CO., INC.—See Tokio Marine Holdings, Inc.; *Int'l*, pg. 7782
TOKIO MARINE MANAGEMENT (AUSTRALASIA) PTY. LTD.—See Tokio Marine Holdings, Inc.; *Int'l*, pg. 7785
TOKIO MARINE MANAGEMENT (AUSTRALASIA) PTY. LTD.—See Tokio Marine Holdings, Inc.; *Int'l*, pg. 7785
TOKIO MARINE MANAGEMENT, INC.—See Tokio Marine Holdings, Inc.; *Int'l*, pg. 7785
TOKIO MARINE MIDDLE EAST LIMITED—See Tokio Marine Holdings, Inc.; *Int'l*, pg. 7785
TOKIO MARINE MILLEA SAST INSURANCE CO., LTD.—See Tokio Marine Holdings, Inc.; *Int'l*, pg. 7785
TOKIO MARINE NEWA INSURANCE CO. LTD.; *Int'l*, pg. 7786
TOKIO MARINE & NICHIDO ADJUSTING SERVICES CO., LTD.—See Tokio Marine Holdings, Inc.; *Int'l*, pg. 7784
TOKIO MARINE & NICHIDO AGENT SUPPORT CO., LTD.—See Tokio Marine Holdings, Inc.; *Int'l*, pg. 7784
TOKIO MARINE & NICHIDO ANSHIN 110 CO., LTD.—See Tokio Marine Holdings, Inc.; *Int'l*, pg. 7784
TOKIO MARINE & NICHIDO ANSHIN CONSULTING CO., LTD.—See Tokio Marine Holdings, Inc.; *Int'l*, pg. 7783
TOKIO MARINE NICHIDO BETTER LIFE SERVICE CO., LTD.—See Tokio Marine Holdings, Inc.; *Int'l*, pg. 7785
TOKIO MARINE & NICHIDO CAREER SERVICE CO., LTD.—See Tokio Marine Holdings, Inc.; *Int'l*, pg. 7783
TOKIO MARINE & NICHIDO COMMUNICATIONS CO., LTD.—See Tokio Marine Holdings, Inc.; *Int'l*, pg. 7784
TOKIO MARINE & NICHIDO FACILITIES, INC.—See Tokio Marine Holdings, Inc.; *Int'l*, pg. 7783
TOKIO MARINE & NICHIDO FINANCE CO., LTD.—See Tokio Marine Holdings, Inc.; *Int'l*, pg. 7784
TOKIO MARINE & NICHIDO FIRE INSURANCE CO., LTD. FRANCE—See Tokio Marine Holdings, Inc.; *Int'l*, pg. 7785
TOKIO MARINE & NICHIDO FIRE INSURANCE CO., LTD.—See Tokio Marine Holdings, Inc.; *Int'l*, pg. 7783
THE TOKIO MARINE & NICHIDO FIRE INSURANCE COMPANY (CHINA) LIMITED—See Tokio Marine Holdings, Inc.; *Int'l*, pg. 7784
TOKIO MARINE & NICHIDO FIRE INSURANCE COMPANY, LTD.—See Tokio Marine Holdings, Inc.; *Int'l*, pg. 7785
TOKIO MARINE & NICHIDO FIRE INSURANCE CO.—See Tokio Marine Holdings, Inc.; *Int'l*, pg. 7785
TOKIO MARINE & NICHIDO HUMAN RESOURCES ACADEMY CO., LTD.—See Tokio Marine Holdings, Inc.; *Int'l*, pg. 7784
TOKIO MARINE & NICHIDO LIFE INSURANCE CO., LTD.—See Tokio Marine Holdings, Inc.; *Int'l*, pg. 7785
TOKIO MARINE & NICHIDO MEDICAL SERVICE CO., LTD.—See Tokio Marine Holdings, Inc.; *Int'l*, pg. 7785
TOKIO MARINE & NICHIDO RISK CONSULTING CO., LTD.—See Tokio Marine Holdings, Inc.; *Int'l*, pg. 7785
TOKIO MARINE NICHIDO SAMUEL CO., LTD—See Tokio Marine Holdings, Inc.; *Int'l*, pg. 7785
TOKIO MARINE PACIFIC INSURANCE LIMITED—See Calvo Enterprises, Inc.; *U.S. Private*, pg. 725
TOKIO MARINE PROPERTY INVESTMENT MANAGEMENT, INC.—See Tokio Marine Holdings, Inc.; *Int'l*, pg. 7785
TOKIO MARINE PROPERTY LIMITED—See Tokio Marine Holdings, Inc.; *Int'l*, pg. 7785
TOKIO MARINE RETAKAFUL PTE. LTD.—See Tokio Marine Holdings, Inc.; *Int'l*, pg. 7785
TOKIO MARINE SAFETY INSURANCE (THAILAND) PUBLIC COMPANY LIMITED—See Tokio Marine Holdings, Inc.; *Int'l*, pg. 7786
TOKIO MARINE SEGURADORA S.A.—See PBG S/A; *Int'l*, pg. 5765

TOKIO MARINE SOUTH-EAST SERVICING COMPANY LIMITED—See Tokio Marine Holdings, Inc.; *Int'l*, pg. 7786
TOKIO MILLENNIUM RE LTD.—See Tokio Marine Holdings, Inc.; *Int'l*, pg. 7785
TOKIO MILLENNIUM RE (UK) LTD—See RenaissanceRe Holdings Ltd.; *Int'l*, pg. 6273
TOKIO PROPERTY SERVICES PTE. LTD.—See Nomura Real Estate Holdings, Inc.; *Int'l*, pg. 5412
TOKI SERVICE CO., LTD.—See TOKYO KIKAI SEISAKUSHO LTD.; *Int'l*, pg. 7793
TOKIWA DORO CO., LTD.—See Sala Corporation; *Int'l*, pg. 6490
TOKIWA INDUSTRY CO., LTD.—See NOK Corporation; *Int'l*, pg. 5403
TOKIWA KAIUN COMPANY LIMITED—See KKR & Co. Inc.; *U.S. Public*, pg. 1259
TOKIWAKEN FOODS CO., LTD.—See TKP Corporation; *Int'l*, pg. 7766
TOKIWA MACHINERY WORKS LTD.—See Mitsubishi Heavy Industries, Ltd.; *Int'l*, pg. 4962
TOKIWA MEDICAL SERVICE CO., LTD.—See Noevir Holdings Co., Ltd.; *Int'l*, pg. 5399
TOKIWA PHARMACEUTICAL CO., LTD.—See Noevir Holdings Co., Ltd.; *Int'l*, pg. 5399
TOK KOREA CO., LTD.—See Tokyo Ohka Kogyo Co., Ltd.; *Int'l*, pg. 7794
TOKMANNI GROUP CORPORATION; *Int'l*, pg. 7786
TOKMANNI OY—See Tokmanni Group Corporation; *Int'l*, pg. 7786
TOKO CO., LTD.—See Tokyo Aircraft Instrument Co., Ltd.; *Int'l*, pg. 7788
TOKO ELECTRIC CORPORATION—See Takaoka Toko Co., Ltd.; *Int'l*, pg. 7431
TOKO ELECTRIC (SUZHOU) CO., LTD.—See Takaoka Toko Co., Ltd.; *Int'l*, pg. 7431
TOKO ELECTRONICS (THAILAND) CO., LTD—See Murata Manufacturing Co., Ltd.; *Int'l*, pg. 5099
TOKO ENGINEERING CO., LTD.—See Tokyo Aircraft Instrument Co., Ltd.; *Int'l*, pg. 7788
TOKO GEOTECH CO., LTD.—See Takamatsu Construction Group Co., Ltd.; *Int'l*, pg. 7430
TOKOH EDARAN SDN BHD—See Tambun Indah Land Berhad; *Int'l*, pg. 7450
TOKO, INC.—See Murata Manufacturing Co., Ltd.; *Int'l*, pg. 5098
TOKO KIZAI CORPORATION—See Takaoka Toko Co., Ltd.; *Int'l*, pg. 7431
TOKO MARURAKU TRANSPORTATION CO., LTD.—See Mitsui-Soko Holdings Co., Ltd.; *Int'l*, pg. 4993
TOKOROZAWA FACTORY OF KANTOH DIETCOOK CO., LTD.—See Kenko Mayonnaise Co., Ltd.; *Int'l*, pg. 4127
TOKO (SHANGHAI WAIGAOQIAO F.T.Z.) INC. - BEIJING OFFICE—See Murata Manufacturing Co., Ltd.; *Int'l*, pg. 5098
TOKO (SHANGHAI WAIGAOQIAO F.T.Z.) INC.—See Murata Manufacturing Co., Ltd.; *Int'l*, pg. 5098
TOKO STEEL CORD CO., LTD.—See Tokyo Rope Manufacturing Co., Ltd.; *Int'l*, pg. 7794
TOKO TAKAOKA KOREA CO., LTD.—See Takaoka Toko Co., Ltd.; *Int'l*, pg. 7431
TOKSOZ SPOR MALZEMELERI TIC. A.S.—See Turkiye Is Bankasi A.S.; *Int'l*, pg. 7976
TOK & STOK LTDA.—See The Carlyle Group Inc.; *U.S. Public*, pg. 2056
TOK TAIWAN CO., LTD.—See ChangChun Group; *Int'l*, pg. 1442
TOK TAIWAN CO., LTD.—See Tokyo Ohka Kogyo Co., Ltd.; *Int'l*, pg. 7794
TOK TECHNO SERVICE CO., LTD.—See Tokyo Ohka Kogyo Co., Ltd.; *Int'l*, pg. 7794
TOKUDEN CO., LTD.; *Int'l*, pg. 7786
TOKUDEN TOPAL CO., LTD.—See TOKUDEN CO., LTD.; *Int'l*, pg. 7786
TOKUGIN CAPITAL CO., LTD.—See TOMONY Holdings, Inc.; *Int'l*, pg. 7802
TOKUHATSU CO., LTD—See NHK Spring Co., Ltd.; *Int'l*, pg. 5258
TOKUHON CORPORATION—See Taisho Pharmaceutical Holdings Co., Ltd.; *Int'l*, pg. 7417
TOKUPI CO., LTD.—See Fukuda Corporation; *Int'l*, pg. 2839
TOKURA CONSTRUCTION CO., LTD.; *Int'l*, pg. 7786
TOKUSEN KOGYO CO., LTD.—See Kanai Juyo Kogyo Co., Ltd; *Int'l*, pg. 4063
TOKUSEN U.S.A., INC.—See Kanai Juyo Kogyo Co., Ltd; *Int'l*, pg. 4064
THE TOKUSHIMA BANK, LTD.—See TOMONY Holdings, Inc.; *Int'l*, pg. 7802
TOKUSHIMA DAIICHI TRAFFIC CO., LTD.—See Daiichi Koutsu Sangyo Co., Ltd.; *Int'l*, pg. 1929
TOKUSHIMA JAMCO CORPORATION—See JAMCO Corporation; *Int'l*, pg. 3875
TOKUSHIMA TSUSHINKENSETSU CO., LTD.—See COMSYS Holdings Corporation; *Int'l*, pg. 1762
TOKUSHIN CO., LTD.—See Tokuyama Corporation; *Int'l*, pg. 7787
TOKUSHOU CO., LTD.—See Tokuyama Corporation; *Int'l*, pg. 7787

TOKUSHU MATEL CO., LTD.—See Tokushu Tokai Paper Co., Ltd.; *Int'l*, pg. 7786
TOKUSHU PAPER TRADING CO., LTD.—See Tokushu Tokai Paper Co., Ltd.; *Int'l*, pg. 7786
TOKUSHU TOKAI MATERIALZ CO., LTD.—See Tokushu Tokai Paper Co., Ltd.; *Int'l*, pg. 7786
TOKUSHU TOKAI PAPER CO., LTD. - GIFU PLANT—See Tokushu Tokai Paper Co., Ltd.; *Int'l*, pg. 7786
TOKUSHU TOKAI PAPER CO., LTD. - MISHIMA MILL—See Tokushu Tokai Paper Co., Ltd.; *Int'l*, pg. 7786
TOKUSHU TOKAI PAPER CO., LTD.; *Int'l*, pg. 7786
TOKUSUI CORPORATION; *Int'l*, pg. 7786
TOKUSUI FOODS CO., LTD.—See Iwata Sangyo Co., Ltd.; *Int'l*, pg. 3849
TOKUTEK, INC.—See Percona LLC.; *U.S. Private*, pg. 3147
TOKUYAMA AMERICA INC.—See Tokuyama Corporation; *Int'l*, pg. 7787
TOKUYAMA ASIA PACIFIC PTE. LTD.—See Tokuyama Corporation; *Int'l*, pg. 7787
TOKUYAMA CHEMICALS (ZHEJIANG) CO., LTD.—See Tokuyama Corporation; *Int'l*, pg. 7787
TOKUYAMA CHIYODA GYPSUM CO., LTD.—See Tokuyama Corporation; *Int'l*, pg. 7787
TOKUYAMA CORPORATION; *Int'l*, pg. 7786
TOKUYAMA DAIICHI TRAFFIC LTD—See Daiichi Koutsu Sangyo Co., Ltd.; *Int'l*, pg. 1929
TOKUYAMA DENTAL CORPORATION—See Tokuyama Corporation; *Int'l*, pg. 7787
TOKUYAMA-DOWA POWER MATERIALS CO., LTD.—See Tokuyama Corporation; *Int'l*, pg. 7788
TOKUYAMA ELECTRONIC CHEMICALS PTE. LTD.—See Tokuyama Corporation; *Int'l*, pg. 7787
TOKUYAMA EUROPE GMBH—See Tokuyama Corporation; *Int'l*, pg. 7787
TOKUYAMA INFORMATION SERVICE CORPORATION—See Tokuyama Corporation; *Int'l*, pg. 7787
TOKUYAMA KAIRIKU UNSO K.K.—See Tokuyama Corporation; *Int'l*, pg. 7787
TOKUYAMA KOREA CO., LTD.—See Tokuyama Corporation; *Int'l*, pg. 7787
TOKUYAMA KOUUN CO., LTD.—See Sankyu, Inc.; *Int'l*, pg. 6545
TOKUYAMA METEL CORPORATION—See Tokuyama Corporation; *Int'l*, pg. 7787
TOKUYAMA MTECH CORPORATION—See Tokuyama Corporation; *Int'l*, pg. 7787
TOKUYAMA NOUVELLE CALEDONIE S.A.—See Tokuyama Corporation; *Int'l*, pg. 7787
TOKUYAMA POLYPROPYLENE CO., LTD.—See Tokuyama Corporation; *Int'l*, pg. 7787
TOKUYAMA SEKISUI CO., LTD.—See Tosoh Corporation; *Int'l*, pg. 7833
TOKUYAMA (SHANGHAI) CO., LTD.—See Tokuyama Corporation; *Int'l*, pg. 7787
TOKUYAMA SIAM SILICA CO., LTD.—See Tokuyama Corporation; *Int'l*, pg. 7787
TOKUYAMA SINGAPORE PTE. LTD.—See Tokuyama Corporation; *Int'l*, pg. 7788
TOKUYAMA SODA TRADING CO., LTD.—See Tokuyama Corporation; *Int'l*, pg. 7788
TOKUYAMA TRADING (SHANGHAI) CO., LTD.—See Tokuyama Corporation; *Int'l*, pg. 7788
TOKUYAMA TSUSHO TRADING CO., LTD.—See Tokuyama Corporation; *Int'l*, pg. 7788
TOKYO AIRCRAFT INSTRUMENT CO., LTD.; *Int'l*, pg. 7788
TOKYO ALLIED COFFEE ROASTERS CO., LTD.—See S. ISHIMITSU & Co., LTD.; *Int'l*, pg. 6446
TOKYO ALUMINUM WIRE CORPORATION—See Resonac Holdings Corporation; *Int'l*, pg. 6301
TOKYO AUTOMATIC MACHINERY WORKS, LTD. - KASHIWA FACTORY—See Tokyo Automatic Machinery Works, Ltd.; *Int'l*, pg. 7788
TOKYO AUTOMATIC MACHINERY WORKS, LTD.; *Int'l*, pg. 7788
TOKYO BASE CO., LTD.; *Int'l*, pg. 7788
TOKYO BAY HILTON CO. LTD.—See Hilton Worldwide Holdings Inc.; *U.S. Public*, pg. 1041
TOKYO BAY NETWORK CO., LTD.—See TOKAI Holdings Corporation; *Int'l*, pg. 7780
TOKYO BED CO., LTD.—See FRANCE BED HOLDINGS CO. LTD.; *Int'l*, pg. 2759
TOKYO BIJUTSU CO., LTD.—See Citizen Watch Co., Ltd.; *Int'l*, pg. 1625
TOKYO BOARD INDUSTRIES CO., LTD.; *Int'l*, pg. 7788
TOKYO BROADCASTING SYSTEM INTERNATIONAL, INC.—See TBS Holdings, Inc.; *Int'l*, pg. 7481
TOKYO BROADCASTING SYSTEM TELEVISION, INC.—See TBS Holdings, Inc.; *Int'l*, pg. 7481
TOKYO BUILDING SERVICE CO., LTD.—See Tokyo Tatemono Co., Ltd.; *Int'l*, pg. 7796
TOKYO CAPITAL MANAGEMENT CO., LTD.—See NIPPON KANZAI Holdings Co.,Ltd.; *Int'l*, pg. 5320
TOKYO CEMENT COMPANY (LANKA) PLC; *Int'l*, pg. 7788

COMPANY NAME INDEX

TOKYO CENTURY CAPITAL (MALAYSIA) SDN. BHD.—See Tokyo Century Corporation; *Int'l*, pg. 7789
TOKYO CENTURY CORPORATION; *Int'l*, pg. 7788
TOKYO CENTURY LEASING CHINA CORPORATION—See Tokyo Century Corporation; *Int'l*, pg. 7789
TOKYO CENTURY LEASING (SINGAPORE) PTE. LTD.—See Tokyo Century Corporation; *Int'l*, pg. 7789
TOKYO CENTURY (USA) INC.—See Tokyo Century Corporation; *Int'l*, pg. 7789
TOKYO CHUO AUCTION CO., LTD.—See Tokyo Chuo Auction Holdings Ltd.; *Int'l*, pg. 7789
TOKYO CHUO AUCTION HOLDINGS LTD.; *Int'l*, pg. 7789
TOKYO CHUO SATO PRODUCT SALES CO., LTD.—See Pixel Companyz Inc.; *Int'l*, pg. 5877
TOKYO CHUO TAIWAN AUCTION COMPANY LIMITED—See Tokyo Chuo Auction Holdings Ltd.; *Int'l*, pg. 7789
TOKYO CITIZEN CORPORATION—See Citizen Watch Co., Ltd.; *Int'l*, pg. 1625
TOKYO CLINICAL CRO CO., LTD.—See Toho Holdings Co., Ltd.; *Int'l*, pg. 7776
TOKYO COMMERCIAL CO., LTD.—See Toyo Suisan Kaisha, Ltd.; *Int'l*, pg. 7858
TOKYO COMMODITY EXCHANGE, INC.; *Int'l*, pg. 7789
TOKYO CONCRETE CO., LTD.—See Shimizu Corporation; *Int'l*, pg. 6836
TOKYO CONE PAPER MFG. CO., LTD.; *Int'l*, pg. 7789
TOKYO COSMOS ELECTRIC CO., LTD.; *Int'l*, pg. 7789
TOKYO CREDIT SERVICES, LTD.—See Mitsubishi UFJ Financial Group, Inc.; *Int'l*, pg. 4972
TOKYO DAIICHI HIRE(CHAUFFEUR DRIVEN HIRED CAR) LTD—See Daiichi Koutsu Sangyo Co., Ltd.; *Int'l*, pg. 1929
(TOKYO) DAIICHI TRAFFIC CO., LTD.—See Daiichi Koutsu Sangyo Co., Ltd.; *Int'l*, pg. 1928
TOKYO DENPA CO., LTD.—See Murata Manufacturing Co., Ltd.; *Int'l*, pg. 5099
TOKYO DIA SERVICE CO., LTD.—See Mitsubishi Logistics Corporation; *Int'l*, pg. 4963
TOKYO DOME CORPORATION—See Mitsui Fudosan Co., Ltd.; *Int'l*, pg. 4988
TOKYO DOME HOTEL CORPORATION—See Mitsui Fudosan Co., Ltd.; *Int'l*, pg. 4988
TOKYO DORYOKU CO., LTD.—See Taihei Dengyo Kaisha Ltd.; *Int'l*, pg. 7411
TOKYO ECO RECYCLE CO., LTD.—See Hitachi, Ltd.; *Int'l*, pg. 3424
TOKYO EDUCATIONAL INSTITUTE CO., LTD.—See EQT AB; *Int'l*, pg. 2467
TOKYO ELECTRICA DE MEXICO S.A. DE C.V.—See MITSUBA Corporation; *Int'l*, pg. 4928
THE TOKYO ELECTRIC GENERATION COMPANY, INCORPORATED—See Tokyo Electric Power Company Holdings, Incorporated; *Int'l*, pg. 7790
TOKYO ELECTRIC POWER COMPANY HOLDINGS, INCORPORATED; *Int'l*, pg. 7790
TOKYO ELECTRIC POWER COMPANY INTERNATIONAL B.V.—See Tokyo Electric Power Company Holdings, Incorporated; *Int'l*, pg. 7790
TOKYO ELECTRIC POWER SERVICES COMPANY, LIMITED—See Tokyo Electric Power Company Holdings, Incorporated; *Int'l*, pg. 7790
TOKYO ELECTRON AGENCY LIMITED—See Tokyo Electron Limited; *Int'l*, pg. 7791
TOKYO ELECTRON AMERICA, INC.—See Tokyo Electron Limited; *Int'l*, pg. 7791
TOKYO ELECTRON AMERICA—See Tokyo Electron Limited; *Int'l*, pg. 7791
TOKYO ELECTRON BP LIMITED—See Tokyo Electron Limited; *Int'l*, pg. 7791
TOKYO ELECTRON DEVICE ASIA PACIFIC LIMITED—See Tokyo Electron Limited; *Int'l*, pg. 7791
TOKYO ELECTRON DEVICE LIMITED—See Tokyo Electron Limited; *Int'l*, pg. 7791
TOKYO ELECTRON DEVICE SINGAPORE PTE. LTD.—See Tokyo Electron Limited; *Int'l*, pg. 7791
TOKYO ELECTRON EE LIMITED—See Tokyo Electron Limited; *Int'l*, pg. 7791
TOKYO ELECTRON EUROPE LIMITED-FRANCE—See Tokyo Electron Limited; *Int'l*, pg. 7791
TOKYO ELECTRON EUROPE LIMITED-GERMANY—See Tokyo Electron Limited; *Int'l*, pg. 7791
TOKYO ELECTRON EUROPE LIMITED-IRELAND—See Tokyo Electron Limited; *Int'l*, pg. 7791
TOKYO ELECTRON EUROPE LIMITED-ITALY—See Tokyo Electron Limited; *Int'l*, pg. 7791
TOKYO ELECTRON EUROPE LIMITED-NETHERLANDS—See Tokyo Electron Limited; *Int'l*, pg. 7791
TOKYO ELECTRON EUROPE LIMITED—See Tokyo Electron Limited; *Int'l*, pg. 7791
TOKYO ELECTRON FE LIMITED—See Tokyo Electron Limited; *Int'l*, pg. 7791
TOKYO ELECTRON ISRAEL LIMITED—See Tokyo Electron Limited; *Int'l*, pg. 7791
TOKYO ELECTRON KOREA LIMITED—See Tokyo Electron Limited; *Int'l*, pg. 7791
TOKYO ELECTRON KOREA SOLUTION LIMITED—See Tokyo Electron Limited; *Int'l*, pg. 7791
TOKYO ELECTRON (KUNSHAN) LIMITED—See Tokyo Electron Limited; *Int'l*, pg. 7791
TOKYO ELECTRON LIMITED; *Int'l*, pg. 7790
TOKYO ELECTRON (MALAYSIA) SDN. BHD.—See Tokyo Electron Limited; *Int'l*, pg. 7790
TOKYO ELECTRON MIYAGI LIMITED—See Tokyo Electron Limited; *Int'l*, pg. 7791
TOKYO ELECTRON (SHANGHAI) LIMITED—See Tokyo Electron Limited; *Int'l*, pg. 7791
TOKYO ELECTRON (SHANGHAI) LOGISTIC CENTER LIMITED—See Tokyo Electron Limited; *Int'l*, pg. 7791
TOKYO ELECTRON SINGAPORE PTE. LTD.—See Tokyo Electron Limited; *Int'l*, pg. 7791
TOKYO ELECTRON TAIWAN LIMITED—See Tokyo Electron Limited; *Int'l*, pg. 7791
TOKYO ELECTRON TECHNOLOGY DEVELOPMENT INSTITUTE, INC.—See Tokyo Electron Limited; *Int'l*, pg. 7791
TOKYO ELECTRON TECHNOLOGY SOLUTIONS LTD.—See Tokyo Electron Limited; *Int'l*, pg. 7791
TOKYO ENERGY ALLIANCE CO., LTD.—See Nippon Gas Co., Ltd.; *Int'l*, pg. 5318
TOKYO ENERGY SERVICE CO., LTD.—See Sapporo Holdings Limited; *Int'l*, pg. 6574
TOKYO ENERGY & SYSTEMS INC.; *Int'l*, pg. 7791
TOKYO ENVIRONMENTAL MEASUREMENT CENTER CO., LTD.—See Adeka Corporation; *Int'l*, pg. 142
TOKYO ENVIRONMENT OPERATION LTD.—See Mitsubishi Heavy Industries, Ltd.; *Int'l*, pg. 4962
TOKYO FINANCE LIMITED; *Int'l*, pg. 7791
TOKYO FINANCIAL EXCHANGE INC.; *Int'l*, pg. 7791
TOKYO FINE CHEMICAL CO., LTD.—See Nippon Shokubai Co., Ltd.; *Int'l*, pg. 5333
TOKYO FOOTBALL CLUB CO., LTD.—See mixi, Inc.; *Int'l*, pg. 4996
TOKYO FUDOSAN KANRI CO., LTD.—See Tokyo Tatemono Co. Ltd.; *Int'l*, pg. 7796
TOKYO FUJI CO., LTD.—See Sakai Heavy Industries Ltd; *Int'l*, pg. 6487
TOKYO GARAGE CO., LTD.—See Mitsubishi Estate Co., Ltd.; *Int'l*, pg. 4947
TOKYO GAS AMERICA LTD.—See Tokyo Gas Co., Ltd.; *Int'l*, pg. 7792
TOKYO GAS AUSTRALIA PTY LTD—See Tokyo Gas Co., Ltd.; *Int'l*, pg. 7792
TOKYO GAS CHEMICALS CO., LTD.—See Tokyo Gas Co., Ltd.; *Int'l*, pg. 7792
TOKYO GAS CO., LTD.; *Int'l*, pg. 7791
TOKYO GAS CO., LTD. - US OFFICE—See Tokyo Gas Co., Ltd.; *Int'l*, pg. 7792
TOKYO GLASRON CO., LTD.—See Meiwa Corporation; *Int'l*, pg. 4805
TOKYO GLOBAL GATEWAY CO., LTD.—See Gakken Holdings Co., Ltd.; *Int'l*, pg. 2869
TOKYO GREEN SYSTEMS CORPORATION—See Sumitomo Corporation; *Int'l*, pg. 7270
TOKYO HINO MOTOR LTD.—See Toyota Motor Corporation; *Int'l*, pg. 7872
TOKYO HOSO KOGYO CO., LTD.—See Mitsubishi Materials Corporation; *Int'l*, pg. 4965
TOKYO HUMANIA ENTERPRISE, INC.—See Japan Airlines Co., Ltd.; *Int'l*, pg. 3882
TOKYO ICHIBAN FOODS CO., LTD.; *Int'l*, pg. 7792
TOKYO INDIVIDUALIZED EDUCATIONAL INSTITUTE, INC.—See EQT AB; *Int'l*, pg. 2467
TOKYO INFRASTRUCTURE ENERGY INVESTMENT CORP.; *Int'l*, pg. 7792
TOKYO INK (THAILAND) CO., LTD.—See Tokyo Printing Ink Manufacturing Co., Ltd.; *Int'l*, pg. 7792
TOKYO INTERNATIONAL AIR CARGO TERMINAL LTD.—See Mitsui & Co., Ltd.; *Int'l*, pg. 4980
TOKYO INTERNATIONAL AIR TERMINAL CORPORATION—See Japan Airport Terminal Co., Ltd.; *Int'l*, pg. 3885
TOKYO IPO—See FinanTec Co., Ltd.; *Int'l*, pg. 2669
TOKYO JUKI INTERNATIONAL TRADING (SHANGHAI) CO. LTD.—See Juki Corporation; *Int'l*, pg. 4024
TOKYO KAIKAN CO., LTD.; *Int'l*, pg. 7792
TOKYO KAKOKI CO., LTD.—See Astena Holdings Co., Ltd.; *Int'l*, pg. 653
TOKYO KAKOKI (SHANGHAI) CO., LTD.—See Astena Holdings Co., Ltd.; *Int'l*, pg. 653
TOKYO KANEKA FOODS MANUFACTURING CORPORATION—See Kaneka Corporation; *Int'l*, pg. 4067
TOKYO KEIKI AVIATION INC.—See TOKYO KEIKI INC.; *Int'l*, pg. 7792
TOKYO KEIKI CUSTOMER SERVICE INC.—See TOKYO KEIKI INC.; *Int'l*, pg. 7792
TOKYO KEIKI INC. - HANNO PLANT—See TOKYO KEIKI INC.; *Int'l*, pg. 7792
TOKYO KEIKI INC. - NASU PLANT—See TOKYO KEIKI INC.; *Int'l*, pg. 7792
TOKYO KEIKI INC. - SANO PLANT—See TOKYO KEIKI INC.; *Int'l*, pg. 7792
TOKYO KEIKI INC.; *Int'l*, pg. 7792
TOKYO KEIKI INC. - TANUMA PLANT—See TOKYO KEIKI INC.; *Int'l*, pg. 7792
TOKYO KEIKI INC. - YAITA PLANT—See TOKYO KEIKI INC.; *Int'l*, pg. 7792
TOKYO KEIKI INFORMATION SYSTEMS INC.—See TOKYO KEIKI INC.; *Int'l*, pg. 7792
TOKYO KEIKI POWER SYSTEMS INC.—See TOKYO KEIKI INC.; *Int'l*, pg. 7792
TOKYO KEIKI POWER SYSTEMS INC.—See TOKYO KEIKI INC.; *Int'l*, pg. 7792
TOKYO KEIKI PRECISION TECHNOLOGY CO., LTD.—See TOKYO KEIKI INC.; *Int'l*, pg. 7792
TOKYO KEIKI RAIL TECHNO INC.—See TOKYO KEIKI INC.; *Int'l*, pg. 7792
TOKYO KEIKI TECHNOPORT INC.—See TOKYO KEIKI INC.; *Int'l*, pg. 7792
TOKYO KEIKI U.S.A., INC.—See TOKYO KEIKI INC.; *Int'l*, pg. 7792
TOKYO KEISO (BEIJING) CO., LTD.—See Tokyo Keiso Co., Ltd.; *Int'l*, pg. 7792
TOKYO KEISO CO., LTD.; *Int'l*, pg. 7792
TOKYO KEISO CORPORATION OF AMERICA—See Tokyo Keiso Co., Ltd.; *Int'l*, pg. 7792
TOKYO KEISO EUROPE B.V.—See Tokyo Keiso Co., Ltd.; *Int'l*, pg. 7792
TOKYO KEISO KOREA CO., LTD.—See Tokyo Keiso Co., Ltd.; *Int'l*, pg. 7793
TOKYO KEISO (MALAYSIA) SDN.BHD.—See Tokyo Keiso Co., Ltd.; *Int'l*, pg. 7792
TOKYO KEISO SALES (THAILAND) CO., LTD.—See Tokyo Keiso Co., Ltd.; *Int'l*, pg. 7793
TOKYO KEISO (SHANGHAI) CO., LTD.—See Tokyo Keiso Co., Ltd.; *Int'l*, pg. 7792
TOKYO KEISO TAIWAN CO., LTD.—See Tokyo Keiso Co., Ltd.; *Int'l*, pg. 7792
TOKYO KEISO (XIA MEN) CO., LTD.—See Tokyo Keiso Co., Ltd.; *Int'l*, pg. 7792
TOKYO KIHO CO., LTD.; *Int'l*, pg. 7793
TOKYO KIKAI SEISAKUSHO LTD.; *Int'l*, pg. 7793
TOKYO KIKAI SEISAKUSHO LTD. - TAMAGAWA FACTORY—See TOKYO KIKAI SEISAKUSHO LTD.; *Int'l*, pg. 7793
TOKYO KINZOKU CO. LTD.—See Topre Corporation; *Int'l*, pg. 7820
TOKYO KIRABOSHI FINANCIAL GROUP, INC.; *Int'l*, pg. 7793
TOKYO KIRIN BEVERAGE SERVICE CO., LTD.—See Kirin Holdings Company, Limited; *Int'l*, pg. 4189
TOKYO KISEN CO., LTD.; *Int'l*, pg. 7793
TOKYO KITAUO CO., LTD.—See Chuo Gyorui Co., Ltd.; *Int'l*, pg. 1598
TOKYO KOHTETSU CO., LTD.—See Nippon Steel Corporation; *Int'l*, pg. 5339
TOKYO KOKI CO., LTD.; *Int'l*, pg. 7793
TOKYO KOKUSAI KOUN KAISHA, LTD.—See Kawasaki Kisen Kaisha, Ltd.; *Int'l*, pg. 4101
TOKYO KOSHUEISEI LABORATORIES, INC.—See BML, Inc.; *Int'l*, pg. 1076
TOKYO KOTSU KAIKAN CO., LTD.—See Mitsubishi Estate Co., Ltd.; *Int'l*, pg. 4947
TOKYO KOUJI KEIBI CO., LTD—See Kandenko Co., Ltd.; *Int'l*, pg. 4065
TOKYO KUTSUSHITA CO., LTD.—See Chori Co., Ltd.; *Int'l*, pg. 1583
TOKYO LEASING (HONG KONG) LTD.—See Tokyo Century Corporation; *Int'l*, pg. 7789
TOKYO LEASING (UK) PLC—See Tokyo Century Corporation; *Int'l*, pg. 7789
TOKYO LIGHT ALLOY CO., LTD.—See Ryobi Limited; *Int'l*, pg. 6440
TOKYO LIQUEFIED OXYGEN CO., LTD.—See Resonac Holdings Corporation; *Int'l*, pg. 6301
TOKYO LIVING SERVICE CO., LTD.; *Int'l*, pg. 7793
TOKYO MARINE ASIA PTE. LTD.—See Mitsui O.S.K. Lines, Ltd.; *Int'l*, pg. 4992
TOKYO MARINE BRASIL SEGURADORA SA—See Tokio Marine Holdings, Inc.; *Int'l*, pg. 7786
TOKYO MARINE CO., LTD.—See Mitsui O.S.K. Lines, Ltd.; *Int'l*, pg. 4991
TOKYO MEIJI FOODS CO., LTD.—See Meiji Holdings Co., Ltd.; *Int'l*, pg. 4801
TOKYO METAL PACK CO., LTD.—See Topre Corporation; *Int'l*, pg. 7820
TOKYO METRO CO., LTD.; *Int'l*, pg. 7793
TOKYO MIDTOWN MANAGEMENT CO., LTD.—See Mitsui Fudosan Co., Ltd.; *Int'l*, pg. 4988
TOKYO MIDTOWN MEDICINE CO., LTD.—See RESORT TRUST INC.; *Int'l*, pg. 6301
TOKYO MULTIFASTENER CO. LTD.—See Topre Corporation; *Int'l*, pg. 7820
TOKYO MUTUAL TRADING CO., LTD.—See Takara Holdings, Inc.; *Int'l*, pg. 7433
TOKYO NICHIREI SERVICE INC.—See Nichirei Corporation; *Int'l*, pg. 5270
TOKYO NISSAN COMPUTER SYSTEM CO., LTD.—See Canon Inc.; *Int'l*, pg. 1296
TOKYO NOHIN DAIKO CO., LTD.—See Senko Group Holdings Co., Ltd.; *Int'l*, pg. 6712

TOKYO METRO CO., LTD.   CORPORATE AFFILIATIONS

TOKYO NOHIN DAIKO WEST JAPAN CO., LTD.—See Senko Group Holdings Co., Ltd.; *Int'l*, pg. 6712
TOKYO OHKA KOGYO AMERICA, INC.—See Tokyo Ohka Kogyo Co., Ltd.; *Int'l*, pg. 7794
TOKYO OHKA KOGYO CO., LTD. - ASO PLANT—See Tokyo Ohka Kogyo Co., Ltd.; *Int'l*, pg. 7794
TOKYO OHKA KOGYO CO., LTD. - ELECTRONIC MATERIAL MARKETING DIVISION—See Tokyo Ohka Kogyo Co., Ltd.; *Int'l*, pg. 7794
TOKYO OHKA KOGYO CO., LTD. - GOTEMBA PLANT—See Tokyo Ohka Kogyo Co., Ltd.; *Int'l*, pg. 7794
TOKYO OHKA KOGYO CO., LTD. - KORIYAMA PLANT—See Tokyo Ohka Kogyo Co., Ltd.; *Int'l*, pg. 7794
TOKYO OHKA KOGYO CO., LTD. - KUMAGAYA PLANT—See Tokyo Ohka Kogyo Co., Ltd.; *Int'l*, pg. 7794
TOKYO OHKA KOGYO CO., LTD.; *Int'l*, pg. 7793
TOKYO OHKA KOGYO CO., LTD. - UTSUNOMIYA PLANT—See Tokyo Ohka Kogyo Co., Ltd.; *Int'l*, pg. 7794
TOKYO OPERA CITY BUILDING CO., LTD.—See Nippon Life Insurance Company; *Int'l*, pg. 5323
TOKYO OPTO-ELECTRONICS CO., LTD.—See Optex Group Co., Ltd.; *Int'l*, pg. 5602
TOKYO OTSUKA FURNITURE SALES CO., LTD.—See Otsuka Holdings Co., Ltd.; *Int'l*, pg. 5661
TOKYO PLANT-KAWASAKI—See Mitsubishi Motors Corporation; *Int'l*, pg. 4967
TOKYO PLAST INTERNATIONAL LIMITED; *Int'l*, pg. 7794
TOKYO POWER TECHNOLOGY LTD.—See Tokyo Electric Power Company Holdings, Incorporated; *Int'l*, pg. 7790
TOKYO PRINTING INK CORPORATION U.S.A.—See Tokyo Printing Ink Manufacturing Co., Ltd.; *Int'l*, pg. 7794
TOKYO PRINTING INK MANUFACTURING CO., LTD.; *Int'l*, pg. 7794
TOKYO PROCESS SERVICE CO., LTD.—See Takeda iP Holdings Co.,Ltd.; *Int'l*, pg. 7437
TOKYO PROPERTY SERVICE CO., LTD.—See Tokyotokeiba Co., Ltd.; *Int'l*, pg. 7797
TOKYO RADIATOR MFG. CO.,LTD.—See Nissan Motor Co., Ltd; *Int'l*, pg. 5369
TOKYO RAKUTENCHI CO., LTD.; *Int'l*, pg. 7794
TOKYO REALTY INVESTMENT MANAGEMENT, INC.—See Tokyo Tatemono Co. Ltd.; *Int'l*, pg. 7796
TOKYO RECORDS MANAGEMENT CO., INC.—See Tokyo Electric Power Company Holdings, Incorporated; *Int'l*, pg. 7790
TOKYO REINE, LTD.—See Hoyu Co., Ltd.; *Int'l*, pg. 3499
TOKYO RESEARCH CENTER OF CLINICAL PHARMACOLOGY CO., LTD.—See Toho Holdings Co., Ltd.; *Int'l*, pg. 7776
TOKYO ROCK STUDIO CO. LTD.—See KeyHolder, Inc.; *Int'l*, pg. 4146
TOKYO ROPE (CHANGZHOU) CO., LTD.—See Tokyo Rope Manufacturing Co., Ltd.; *Int'l*, pg. 7794
TOKYO ROPE DO BRASIL LTDA.—See Tokyo Rope Manufacturing Co., Ltd.; *Int'l*, pg. 7794
TOKYO ROPE ENGINEERING LLC—See Tokyo Rope Manufacturing Co., Ltd.; *Int'l*, pg. 7794
TOKYO ROPE (HONG KONG) CO., LTD.—See Tokyo Rope Manufacturing Co., Ltd.; *Int'l*, pg. 7794
TOKYO ROPE MANUFACTURING CO., LTD. - SAKAI PLANT—See Tokyo Rope Manufacturing Co., Ltd.; *Int'l*, pg. 7794
TOKYO ROPE MANUFACTURING CO., LTD.; *Int'l*, pg. 7794
TOKYO ROPE MANUFACTURING CO., LTD. - TSUCHIURA PLANT—See Tokyo Rope Manufacturing Co., Ltd.; *Int'l*, pg. 7794
TOKYO ROPE (SHANGHAI) TRADING CO., LTD.—See Tokyo Rope Manufacturing Co., Ltd.; *Int'l*, pg. 7794
TOKYO ROPE USA, INC.—See Tokyo Rope Manufacturing Co., Ltd.; *Int'l*, pg. 7794
TOKYO ROPE VIETNAM CO., LTD.—See Tokyo Rope Manufacturing Co., Ltd.; *Int'l*, pg. 7794
TOKYO RUBBER MFG. CO.. LTD.—See Fukoku Co., Ltd.; *Int'l*, pg. 2839
TOKYO RYOKO CONCRETE CO., LTD.—See Mitsubishi Materials Corporation; *Int'l*, pg. 4965
TOKYO SANGYO ASIA TRADING CO., LTD.—See Tokyo Sangyo Co., Ltd.; *Int'l*, pg. 7795
TOKYO SANGYO CO., LTD.; *Int'l*, pg. 7794
TOKYO SANGYO EUROPE GMBH—See Tokyo Sangyo Co., Ltd.; *Int'l*, pg. 7795
TOKYO SANGYO FUDOSAN CO., LTD.—See Tokyo Sangyo Co., Ltd.; *Int'l*, pg. 7795
TOKYO SANGYO JAPAN CO., LTD.—See Tokyo Sangyo Co., Ltd.; *Int'l*, pg. 7795
TOKYO SANGYO MACHINERY, S. A. DE C. V.—See Tokyo Sangyo Co., Ltd.; *Int'l*, pg. 7795
TOKYO SANGYO MALAYSIA SDN. BHD.—See Tokyo Sangyo Co., Ltd.; *Int'l*, pg. 7795
TOKYO SANGYO SINGAPORE (PTE.) LTD.—See Tokyo Sangyo Co., Ltd.; *Int'l*, pg. 7795
TOKYO SANGYO (THAILAND) CO., LTD.—See Tokyo Sangyo Co., Ltd.; *Int'l*, pg. 7795

TOKYO SANGYO VIETNAM CO., LTD.—See Tokyo Sangyo Co., Ltd.; *Int'l*, pg. 7795
TOKYO SANGYO YOSHI CO., LTD.—See Japan Pulp and Paper Company Limited; *Int'l*, pg. 3905
TOKYO SANSHO K.K.—See Koike Sanso Kogyo Co., Ltd.; *Int'l*, pg. 4230
TOKYO SECURITIES TRANSFER AGENT CO., LTD.; *Int'l*, pg. 7795
TOKYO SEIKO CO., LTD.—See TBK Co. Ltd.; *Int'l*, pg. 7480
TOKYO SEIKO ROPE MFG. CO.—See Tokyo Rope Manufacturing Co., Ltd.; *Int'l*, pg. 7794
TOKYO SEIMITSU CO., LTD. - HACHIOJI PLANT—See Tokyo Seimitsu Co., Ltd.; *Int'l*, pg. 7795
TOKYO SEIMITSU CO., LTD.; *Int'l*, pg. 7795
TOKYO SEIMITSU CO., LTD. - TSUCHIURA PLANT—See Tokyo Seimitsu Co., Ltd.; *Int'l*, pg. 7795
TOKYO SEISEN CO., LTD.—See Nippon Steel Corporation; *Int'l*, pg. 5339
TOKYO SHELL PACK K.K.—See Idemitsu Kosan Co., Ltd.; *Int'l*, pg. 3592
TOKYO SHIRTS CO., LTD.—See Nisshinbo Holdings Inc.; *Int'l*, pg. 5375
TOKYO SHOKAI, LTD.—See Mitsubishi Gas Chemical Company, Inc.; *Int'l*, pg. 4950
TOKYO SHOSEKI CO., LTD—See TOPPAN Holdings Inc.; *Int'l*, pg. 7817
TOKYO SOC CO., LTD.—See Sumitomo Osaka Cement Co Ltd; *Int'l*, pg. 7297
TOKYO SOIR CO., LTD.; *Int'l*, pg. 7796
TOKYO SOKUTEIKIZAI CO., LTD.—See Minebea Mitsumi Inc.; *Int'l*, pg. 4905
TOKYO SOUND PRODUCTION INC.—See TV Asahi Holdings Corporation; *Int'l*, pg. 7987
TOKYO SPECIAL COACH MANUFACTURE CO., LTD.—See Keio Corporation; *Int'l*, pg. 4118
THE TOKYO STAR BANK, LIMITED—See CTBC Financial Holding Co., Ltd.; *Int'l*, pg. 1869
TOKYO STAR BUSINESS FINANCE, LTD.—See CTBC Financial Holding Co., Ltd.; *Int'l*, pg. 1869
TOKYO STATION DEVELOPMENT CO., LTD.—See Central Japan Railway Company; *Int'l*, pg. 1408
TOKYO STEEL MANUFACTURING CO., LTD.; *Int'l*, pg. 7796
TOKYO STOCK EXCHANGE, INC.—See Japan Exchange Group, Inc.; *Int'l*, pg. 3888
TOKYO STYLE CO., LTD.—See TSI Holdings Co., Ltd.; *Int'l*, pg. 7951
TOKYO SUBARU INC.—See Subaru Corporation; *Int'l*, pg. 7248
TOKYOSUISANUNYU CORPORAITION—See Nissui Corporation; *Int'l*, pg. 5379
TOKYO SUMMERLAND CO., LTD.—See Tokyotokeiba Co., Ltd.; *Int'l*, pg. 7797
TOKYO SUPERMIX (PRIVATE) LIMITED—See Tokyo Cement Company (Lanka) PLC; *Int'l*, pg. 7788
TOKYO TAIKISHA SERVICE LTD.—See Taikisha Ltd.; *Int'l*, pg. 7414
TOKYO TATEMONO AMENITY SUPPORT CO., LTD.—See Tokyo Tatemono Co. Ltd.; *Int'l*, pg. 7796
TOKYO TATEMONO ASIA PTE. LTD.—See Tokyo Tatemono Co. Ltd.; *Int'l*, pg. 7796
TOKYO TATEMONO CO. LTD.; *Int'l*, pg. 7796
TOKYO TATEMONO FUND MANAGEMENT CO., LTD.—See Tokyo Tatemono Co. Ltd.; *Int'l*, pg. 7796
TOKYO TATEMONO INVESTMENT ADVISORS CO., LTD.—See Tokyo Tatemono Co. Ltd.; *Int'l*, pg. 7796
TOKYO TATEMONO KIDS CO., LTD.—See Tokyo Tatemono Co. Ltd.; *Int'l*, pg. 7796
TOKYO TATEMONO REAL ESTATE SALES CO., LTD.—See Tokyo Tatemono Co. Ltd.; *Int'l*, pg. 7796
TOKYO TATEMONO RESORT CO., LTD.—See Tokyo Tatemono Co. Ltd.; *Int'l*, pg. 7796
TOKYO TATEMONO SENIOR LIFE SUPPORT CO., LTD.—See Tokyo Tatemono Co. Ltd.; *Int'l*, pg. 7796
TOKYO TATEMONO (SHANGHAI) REAL ESTATE CONSULTING CO., LTD.—See Tokyo Tatemono Co. Ltd.; *Int'l*, pg. 7796
TOKYO TATEMONO STAFFING CO., LTD.—See Tokyo Tatemono Co. Ltd.; *Int'l*, pg. 7796
TOKYO TATEMONO (U.S.A.) INC.—See Tokyo Tatemono Co. Ltd.; *Int'l*, pg. 7796
TOKYO TEKKO CO., LTD.; *Int'l*, pg. 7796
TOKYO THEATRES COMPANY INCORPORATED; *Int'l*, pg. 7796
TOKYOTO BUSINESS SERVICE CO., LTD.—See Systena Corporation; *Int'l*, pg. 7393
TOKYO TOGAMI ELECTRIC SALES CO., LTD.—See Togami Electric Mfg. Co., Ltd.; *Int'l*, pg. 7774
TOKYOTOKEIBA CO., LTD.; *Int'l*, pg. 7797
TOKYO TOKUYAMA CONCRETE CO., LTD.—See Tokuyama Corporation; *Int'l*, pg. 7788
THE TOKYO TOMIN BANK, LIMITED—See Tokyo Kiraboshi Financial Group , Inc.; *Int'l*, pg. 7793
TOKYO TSUSHIN GROUP CO., LTD.; *Int'l*, pg. 7796
TOKYO YOSHIOKA CO., LTD—See Yoshikawa Inc.; *Int'l*, pg. 8600
TOKYO YUSO CO., LTD.—See Sojitz Corporation; *Int'l*, pg. 7066

TOKYO ZAIRYO CZECH, S.R.O.—See Zeon Corporation; *Int'l*, pg. 8636
TOKYO ZAIRYO (GUANGZHOU) CO., LTD.—See Zeon Corporation; *Int'l*, pg. 8635
TOKYO ZAIRYO (INDIA) PVT. LTD.—See Zeon Corporation; *Int'l*, pg. 8635
TOKYO ZAIRYO MEXICO, SA DE C.V.—See Zeon Corporation; *Int'l*, pg. 8636
TOKYO ZAIRYO (SHANGHAI) CO., LTD.—See Zeon Corporation; *Int'l*, pg. 8635
TOKYO ZAIRYO (SINGAPORE) PTE. LTD.—See Zeon Corporation; *Int'l*, pg. 8635
TOKYO ZAIRYO (THAILAND) CO., LTD.—See Zeon Corporation; *Int'l*, pg. 8635
TOKYO ZAIRYO (TIANJIN) CO., LTD.—See Zeon Corporation; *Int'l*, pg. 8635
TOKYO ZAIRYO (U.S.A.) INC.—See Zeon Corporation; *Int'l*, pg. 8635
TOKYO ZAIRYO (VIETNAM) LLC—See Zeon Corporation; *Int'l*, pg. 8636
TOKYU AGENCY INC.; *Int'l*, pg. 7797
TOKYU BUILDING MAINTENANCE CO., LTD.—See Tokyu Fudosan Holdings Corporation; *Int'l*, pg. 7798
TOKYU BUS CORPORATION—See Tokyu Corporation; *Int'l*, pg. 7797
TOKYU CARD, INC.—See Tokyu Corporation; *Int'l*, pg. 7797
TOKYU CO., LTD.—See Toyota Industries Corporation; *Int'l*, pg. 7866
TOKYU CONSTRUCTION CO., LTD.; *Int'l*, pg. 7797
TOKYU CORPORATE HOUSING MANAGEMENT INC.—See Tokyu Fudosan Holdings Corporation; *Int'l*, pg. 7798
TOKYU CORPORATION - BUILDING MANAGEMENT DIVISION—See Tokyu Corporation; *Int'l*, pg. 7797
TOKYU CORPORATION - RESORT DEVELOPMENT DIVISION—See Tokyu Corporation; *Int'l*, pg. 7797
TOKYU CORPORATION; *Int'l*, pg. 7797
TOKYU CORPORATION - TRANSPORT DIVISION—See Tokyu Corporation; *Int'l*, pg. 7797
TOKYU DEPARTMENT STORE CO., LTD.—See Tokyu Corporation; *Int'l*, pg. 7797
TOKYU E-LIFE DESIGN INC.—See Tokyu Fudosan Holdings Corporation; *Int'l*, pg. 7798
TOKYU FUDOSAN HOLDINGS CORPORATION; *Int'l*, pg. 7797
TOKYU GEOX CO., LTD.—See Tokyu Corporation; *Int'l*, pg. 7797
TOKYU HANDS SINGAPORE PTE. LTD.—See Tokyu Fudosan Holdings Corporation; *Int'l*, pg. 7798
TOKYU HOSPITAL—See Tokyu Corporation; *Int'l*, pg. 7797
TOKYU HOTELS CO., LTD.—See Tokyu Corporation; *Int'l*, pg. 7797
TOKYU KIDSBASECAMP CO., LTD.—See Tokyu Corporation; *Int'l*, pg. 7797
TOKYU LAND CAPITAL MANAGEMENT INC.—See Tokyu Fudosan Holdings Corporation; *Int'l*, pg. 7798
TOKYU LAND CORPORATION—See Tokyu Fudosan Holdings Corporation; *Int'l*, pg. 7798
TOKYU LAND US CORPORATION—See Tokyu Fudosan Holdings Corporation; *Int'l*, pg. 7798
TOKYU LIVABLE, INC.—See Tokyu Fudosan Holdings Corporation; *Int'l*, pg. 7798
TOKYU LIVABLE STAFF CORPORATION—See Tokyu Fudosan Holdings Corporation; *Int'l*, pg. 7798
TOKYU LIVABLE TEXAS INVESTMENT ADVISORS, LLC—See Tokyu Fudosan Holdings Corporation; *Int'l*, pg. 7798
TOKYU MALLS DEVELOPMENT CORPORATION—See Tokyu Corporation; *Int'l*, pg. 7797
TOKYU PM VIETNAM CO., LTD.—See Tokyu Fudosan Holdings Corporation; *Int'l*, pg. 7798
TOKYU RECREATION CO., LTD.—See Tokyu Corporation; *Int'l*, pg. 7797
TOKYU REIT, INC.; *Int'l*, pg. 7798
TOKYU RENEWAL CO., LTD.—See Tokyu Construction Co., Ltd.; *Int'l*, pg. 7797
TOKYU RESORT CORPORATION—See Tokyu Fudosan Holdings Corporation; *Int'l*, pg. 7798
TOKYU SECURITY CO., LTD.—See Tokyu Corporation; *Int'l*, pg. 7797
TOKYU SPORTS OASIS INC.—See Tokyu Fudosan Holdings Corporation; *Int'l*, pg. 7798
TOKYU STATION RETAIL SERVICE CO., LTD.—See Lawson, Inc.; *Int'l*, pg. 4426
TOKYU STAY CO., LTD.—See Tokyu Corporation; *Int'l*, pg. 7797
TOKYU STORE CHAIN CO., LTD.—See Tokyu Corporation; *Int'l*, pg. 7797
TOKYU TECHNOSYSTEM CO., LTD.—See Tokyu Corporation; *Int'l*, pg. 7797
TOKYU WORLD TRANSPORT (U.S.A.) INC.—See Tokyu Corporation; *Int'l*, pg. 7797
TOLAND INTERNATIONAL LIMITED—See Kiu Hung International Holdings Limited; *Int'l*, pg. 4197
TOLBERT ENTERPRISES INC.; *U.S. Private*, pg. 4181
TOLCON-LEHUMO (PROPRIETARY) LIMITED—See Murray & Roberts Holdings Ltd.; *Int'l*, pg. 5100

COMPANY NAME INDEX

TOLEDO BEND PROJECT JOINT OPERATIONS—See Sabine River Authority of Texas; *U.S. Private,* pg. 3521
TOLEDO BEND PROJECT JOINT OPERATIONS—See Sabine River Authority, State of Louisiana; *U.S. Private,* pg. 3521
TOLEDO COMMUTATOR CO.—See Kirkwood Holding, Inc.; *U.S. Private,* pg. 2315
THE TOLEDO EDISON COMPANY—See FirstEnergy Corp.; *U.S. Public,* pg. 849
TOLEDO ELEVATOR & MACHINE, CO.—See Carroll Capital LLC; *U.S. Private,* pg. 773
THE TOLEDO ENDOSCOPY ASC, LLC—See KKR & Co. Inc.; *U.S. Public,* pg. 1248
TOLEDO ENGENERING COMPANY INC.; *U.S. Private,* pg. 4181
TOLEDO FINANCE CORP.; *U.S. Private,* pg. 4181
TO-LE-DO FOODSERVICE; *Int'l,* pg. 7768
TOLEDO GAMING VENTURES, LLC—See PENN Entertainment, Inc.; *U.S. Public,* pg. 1663
TOLEDO MINING CORPORATION PLC—See DMCI Holdings, Inc.; *Int'l,* pg. 2143
TOLEDO MOLDING CZ S.R.O.—See Grammer AG; *Int'l,* pg. 3053
TOLEDO MOLDING & DIE INC.—See Grammer AG; *Int'l,* pg. 3053
TOLEDO MOLDING & DIE, LLC—See Grammer AG; *Int'l,* pg. 3053
TOLEDO MUSEUM OF ART; *U.S. Private,* pg. 4181
TOLEDO, PEORIA & WESTERN RAILWAY CORP.—See Brookfield Infrastructure Partners L.P.; *Int'l,* pg. 1193
TOLEDO, PEORIA & WESTERN RAILWAY CORP.—See GIC Pte. Ltd.; *Int'l,* pg. 2967
TOLEDO REFINING COMPANY LLC—See PBF Energy Inc.; *U.S. Public,* pg. 1657
TOLEDO SYMPHONY; *U.S. Private,* pg. 4181
TOLEDO TERMINALING COMPANY LLC—See PBF Energy Inc.; *U.S. Public,* pg. 1657
TOLEDO WEB SHOP; *U.S. Private,* pg. 4181
THE TOLEDO ZOOLOGICAL SOCIETY; *U.S. Private,* pg. 4127
TOLEETO FASTENERS INTERNATIONAL, INC.—See SpeedTech International, Inc.; *U.S. Private,* pg. 3754
TOLERANZIA AB; *Int'l,* pg. 7798
TOLERIE FOREZIENNE S.A.S.—See Poujoulat SA; *Int'l,* pg. 5942
TOLERO PHARMACEUTICALS, INC.—See Sumitomo Chemical Company, Limited; *Int'l,* pg. 7267
TOLEXO ONLINE PRIVATE LIMITED—See Indiamart Intermesh Limited; *Int'l,* pg. 3653
TOLI CORPORATION; *Int'l,* pg. 7798
TOLID DAROU PHARMACEUTICAL COMPANY—See Alborz Investment Company; *Int'l,* pg. 299
TOLIMA GOLD S.A.S.—See Amilot Capital Inc.; *Int'l,* pg. 427
TOLIN MECHANICAL SYSTEMS CO.—See The Jordan Company, Inc.; *U.S. Private,* pg. 4062
TOLKO INDUSTRIES LTD. - ARMSTRONG LUMBER-PLYWOOD/VENEER MILL—See Tolko Industries Ltd.; *Int'l,* pg. 7798
TOLKO INDUSTRIES LTD. - ATHABASCA MILL—See Tolko Industries Ltd.; *Int'l,* pg. 7798
TOLKO INDUSTRIES LTD. - EAGLE ROCK REFORESTATION CENTRE DIVISION—See Tolko Industries Ltd.; *Int'l,* pg. 7798
TOLKO INDUSTRIES LTD. - HEFFLEY CREEK MILL—See Tolko Industries Ltd.; *Int'l,* pg. 7798
TOLKO INDUSTRIES LTD. - HIGH LEVEL LUMBER MILL—See Tolko Industries Ltd.; *Int'l,* pg. 7798
TOLKO INDUSTRIES LTD. - KRAFT PAPER MILL—See Tolko Industries Ltd.; *Int'l,* pg. 7798
TOLKO INDUSTRIES LTD. - LAKE COUNTRY DIVISION—See Tolko Industries Ltd.; *Int'l,* pg. 7799
TOLKO INDUSTRIES LTD. - LAKEVIEW LUMBER DIVISION—See Tolko Industries Ltd.; *Int'l,* pg. 7799
TOLKO INDUSTRIES LTD. - LAVINGTON PLANER MILL—See Tolko Industries Ltd.; *Int'l,* pg. 7799
TOLKO INDUSTRIES LTD.; *Int'l,* pg. 7798
TOLKO INDUSTRIES LTD. - WHITE VALLEY DIVISION—See Tolko Industries Ltd.; *Int'l,* pg. 7799
TOLL ARCHITECTURE, INC.—See Toll Brothers, Inc.; *U.S. Public,* pg. 2162
TOLL (ASIA) PTE. LTD.—See Japan Post Holdings Co., Ltd.; *Int'l,* pg. 3901
TOLL AVIATION PTY LTD—See Japan Post Holdings Co., Ltd.; *Int'l,* pg. 3901
TOLL BROOKLYN L.P.—See Toll Brothers, Inc.; *U.S. Public,* pg. 2162
TOLL BROTHERS CANADA USA, INC.—See Toll Brothers, Inc.; *U.S. Public,* pg. 2162
TOLL BROTHERS, INC.; *U.S. Public,* pg. 2161
TOLL BROTHERS MORTGAGE COMPANY—See Toll Brothers, Inc.; *U.S. Public,* pg. 2162
TOLL BROTHERS REAL ESTATE, INC.—See Toll Brothers, Inc.; *U.S. Public,* pg. 2162
TOLL BROTHERS SMART HOME TECHNOLOGIES, INC.—See Toll Brothers, Inc.; *U.S. Public,* pg. 2162
TOLL COLLECT GMBH—See VINCI S.A.; *Int'l,* pg. 8229
TOLL COMPANY; *U.S. Private,* pg. 4182

TOLLEFSON'S RETAIL GROUP INC.; *U.S. Private,* pg. 4182
TOLL ENERGY & MARINE LOGISTICS PTY LTD—See Japan Post Holdings Co., Ltd.; *Int'l,* pg. 3902
TOLL EXPRESS (ASIA) PTE LTD—See Japan Post Holdings Co., Ltd.; *Int'l,* pg. 3901
TOLL EXPRESS JAPAN CO., LTD.—See Japan Post Holdings Co., Ltd.; *Int'l,* pg. 3901
TOLL FAST—See Japan Post Holdings Co., Ltd.; *Int'l,* pg. 3902
TOLL FL XIII LIMITED PARTNERSHIP—See Toll Brothers, Inc.; *U.S. Public,* pg. 2162
TOLL GLOBAL FORWARDING AB—See Japan Post Holdings Co., Ltd.; *Int'l,* pg. 3902
TOLL GLOBAL FORWARDING (BEIJING) LTD—See Japan Post Holdings Co., Ltd.; *Int'l,* pg. 3901
TOLL GLOBAL FORWARDING (CANADA) LTD—See Japan Post Holdings Co., Ltd.; *Int'l,* pg. 3902
TOLL GLOBAL FORWARDING COOPERATIEF U.A.—See Japan Post Holdings Co., Ltd.; *Int'l,* pg. 3902
TOLL GLOBAL FORWARDING (FRANCE) SAS—See Japan Post Holdings Co., Ltd.; *Int'l,* pg. 3901
TOLL GLOBAL FORWARDING (GERMANY) GMBH—See Japan Post Holdings Co., Ltd.; *Int'l,* pg. 3901
TOLL GLOBAL FORWARDING GROUP (UK) LIMITED—See Japan Post Holdings Co., Ltd.; *Int'l,* pg. 3902
TOLL GLOBAL FORWARDING (HONG KONG) LIMITED—See Japan Post Holdings Co., Ltd.; *Int'l,* pg. 3901
TOLL GLOBAL FORWARDING (INDIA) PRIVATE LTD—See Japan Post Holdings Co., Ltd.; *Int'l,* pg. 3901
TOLL GLOBAL FORWARDING (IRELAND) LTD—See Japan Post Holdings Co., Ltd.; *Int'l,* pg. 3902
TOLL GLOBAL FORWARDING LIMITED—See Japan Post Holdings Co., Ltd.; *Int'l,* pg. 3901
TOLL GLOBAL FORWARDING (MALAYSIA) SDN BHD—See Japan Post Holdings Co., Ltd.; *Int'l,* pg. 3902
TOLL GLOBAL FORWARDING (NETHERLANDS) B.V.—See Japan Post Holdings Co., Ltd.; *Int'l,* pg. 3902
TOLL GLOBAL FORWARDING (SHENZHEN) LTD—See Japan Post Holdings Co., Ltd.; *Int'l,* pg. 3902
TOLL GLOBAL FORWARDING (SINGAPORE) PTE LTD—See Japan Post Holdings Co., Ltd.; *Int'l,* pg. 3902
TOLL GLOBAL FORWARDING (TAIWAN) LTD—See Japan Post Holdings Co., Ltd.; *Int'l,* pg. 3902
TOLL GLOBAL FORWARDING (UAE) LLC—See Japan Post Holdings Co., Ltd.; *Int'l,* pg. 3902
TOLL GLOBAL FORWARDING (UK) LTD—See Japan Post Holdings Co., Ltd.; *Int'l,* pg. 3902
TOLL GLOBAL FORWARDING (USA) INC—See Japan Post Holdings Co., Ltd.; *Int'l,* pg. 3902
TOLL GLOBAL LOGISTICS LANKA (PVT) LTD—See Japan Post Holdings Co., Ltd.; *Int'l,* pg. 3901
TOLL GLOBAL LOGISTICS VIETNAM LIMITED—See Japan Post Holdings Co., Ltd.; *Int'l,* pg. 3901
TOLLGRADE COMMUNICATIONS, INC.—See Enghouse Systems Limited; *Int'l,* pg. 2428
TOLLGRADE GERMANY GMBH—See Enghouse Systems Limited; *Int'l,* pg. 2428
TOLLGRADE UK LIMITED—See Enghouse Systems Limited; *Int'l,* pg. 2428
TOLL HOLDINGS LIMITED—See Japan Post Holdings Co., Ltd.; *Int'l,* pg. 3900
TOLL (INDIA) LOGISTICS PVT LTD—See Japan Post Holdings Co., Ltd.; *Int'l,* pg. 3901
TOLLINK (PTY) LTD—See STRABAG SE; *Int'l,* pg. 7230
TOLL INTEGRATED FEEDER PTE LTD—See Japan Post Holdings Co., Ltd.; *Int'l,* pg. 3901
TOLL INTEGRATED LOGISTICS (M) SDN BHD—See Japan Post Holdings Co., Ltd.; *Int'l,* pg. 3901
TOLL INTERMODAL—See Japan Post Holdings Co., Ltd.; *Int'l,* pg. 3902
TOLL IPEC PTY LTD—See Japan Post Holdings Co., Ltd.; *Int'l,* pg. 3902
TOLL LOGISTICS (ASIA) LIMITED—See Japan Post Holdings Co., Ltd.; *Int'l,* pg. 3901
TOLL LOGISTICS (THAILAND) CO., LTD.—See Japan Post Holdings Co., Ltd.; *Int'l,* pg. 3901
TOLLMAN SPRING COMPANY INC.; *U.S. Private,* pg. 4182
TOLL MICROELECTRONICS CO., LTD.—See Fortune Oriental Company Limited; *Int'l,* pg. 2744
TOLL NETWORKS (NZ) LIMITED—See Japan Post Holdings Co., Ltd.; *Int'l,* pg. 3901
TOLL (NEW ZEALAND) LTD—See Japan Post Holdings Co., Ltd.; *Int'l,* pg. 3901
TOLL NORTH PTY. LTD.—See Japan Post Holdings Co., Ltd.; *Int'l,* pg. 3902
TOLL NQX—See Japan Post Holdings Co., Ltd.; *Int'l,* pg. 3902
TOLL OAK CREEK GOLF LLC—See Toll Brothers, Inc.; *U.S. Public,* pg. 2162

TOMAR INDUSTRIES, INC.

TOLL OFFSHORE PETROLEUM SERVICES PTE LTD—See Japan Post Holdings Co., Ltd.; *Int'l,* pg. 3901
TOLLO LINEAR AB—See Regal Rexnord Corporation; *U.S. Public,* pg. 1772
TOLLO SHIPPING CO. S.A.—See Compania Sudamericana de Vapores, S.A.; *Int'l,* pg. 1749
TOLL PERISHABLES (UK) LIMITED—See Japan Post Holdings Co., Ltd.; *Int'l,* pg. 3902
TOLL PERSONNEL PTY LTD—See Japan Post Holdings Co., Ltd.; *Int'l,* pg. 3902
TOLL PROPERTIES PTY LTD—See Japan Post Holdings Co., Ltd.; *Int'l,* pg. 3902
TOLL PTY LIMITED—See Japan Post Holdings Co., Ltd.; *Int'l,* pg. 3901
TOLL REMOTE LOGISTICS PTY LTD—See Japan Post Holdings Co., Ltd.; *Int'l,* pg. 3902
TOLL RESOURCES & GOVERNMENT LOGISTICS—See Japan Post Holdings Co., Ltd.; *Int'l,* pg. 3902
TOLL ROAD CONCESSIONAIRES (PROPRIETARY) LIMITED—See Murray & Roberts Holdings Ltd.; *Int'l,* pg. 5100
TOLL (SCL) LTD—See Japan Post Holdings Co., Ltd.; *Int'l,* pg. 3901
TOLL SHIPPING—See Japan Post Holdings Co., Ltd.; *Int'l,* pg. 3902
TOLL STRATFORD LLC—See Toll Brothers, Inc.; *U.S. Public,* pg. 2162
TOLL (TAIWAN) LTD—See Japan Post Holdings Co., Ltd.; *Int'l,* pg. 3901
TOLLTICKETS GMBH—See Kapsch-Group Beteiligungs GmbH; *Int'l,* pg. 4078
TOLL TRANSPORT PTY. LIMITED—See Japan Post Holdings Co., Ltd.; *Int'l,* pg. 3902
TOLL WAREHOUSE (THAILAND) LIMITED—See Japan Post Holdings Co., Ltd.; *Int'l,* pg. 3901
TOLMAR, INC.; *U.S. Private,* pg. 4182
TOLMAR PHARMACEUTICALS, INC.—See TOLMAR, Inc.; *U.S. Private,* pg. 4182
TOLMAR PHARMACEUTICALS, INC.—See TOLMAR, Inc.; *U.S. Private,* pg. 4182
TOLONA JAPAN CO., LTD.—See Zensho Holdings Co., Ltd.; *Int'l,* pg. 8635
TOLO TOYS LEARNING LTD.—See Tolo Toys Ltd.; *Int'l,* pg. 7799
TOLO TOYS LTD.; *Int'l,* pg. 7799
TOLTEQ GROUP, LLC—See NOV, Inc.; *U.S. Public,* pg. 1546
TOLUNA AUSTRALIA PTY LTD.—See Verlinvest S.A.; *Int'l,* pg. 8172
TOLUNA GERMANY GMBH—See Verlinvest S.A.; *Int'l,* pg. 8172
TOLUNA GROUP LIMITED.—See Brookfield Corporation; *Int'l,* pg. 1180
TOLUNA GROUP LIMITED.—See Elliott Management Corporation; *U.S. Private,* pg. 1373
TOLUNA (ISRAEL) LTD—See Verlinvest S.A.; *Int'l,* pg. 8172
TOLUNA NEDERLAND BV—See Verlinvest S.A.; *Int'l,* pg. 8172
TOLUNA PLC—See Verlinvest S.A.; *Int'l,* pg. 8172
TOLUNA SAS—See Verlinvest S.A.; *Int'l,* pg. 8172
TOLUNA USA INC—See Verlinvest S.A.; *Int'l,* pg. 8172
TOLUNAY-WONG ENGINEERS, INC.; *U.S. Private,* pg. 4182
TOLY BREAD CO., LTD.; *Int'l,* pg. 7799
TOLYPERS COMPANY; *Int'l,* pg. 7799
TOMA A.S.; *Int'l,* pg. 7799
TOMAGOLD CORPORATION; *Int'l,* pg. 7799
TOMAHAWK LOG & COUNTRY HOMES, INC.; *U.S. Private,* pg. 4183
TOMAHAWK RAILWAY LIMITED PARTNERSHIP—See Brookfield Infrastructure Partners L.P.; *Int'l,* pg. 1193
TOMAHAWK RAILWAY LIMITED PARTNERSHIP—See GIC Pte. Ltd.; *Int'l,* pg. 2967
TOMAHAWK STRATEGIC SOLUTIONS LLC; *U.S. Private,* pg. 4183
TOM AHL BUICK GMC; *U.S. Private,* pg. 4182
TOMAKOMAI HEAT SUPPLY CO., LTD.—See Takasago Thermal Engineering Co., Ltd.; *Int'l,* pg. 7435
TOMAKOMAI STEEL CENTER CO., LTD.—See Nippon Steel Corporation; *Int'l,* pg. 5339
TOMAL AB; *Int'l,* pg. 7799
TOMALES BAY FOODS INC.—See Emmi AG; *Int'l,* pg. 2385
TOMA METAL, INC.—See Reliance Steel & Aluminum Co.; *U.S. Public,* pg. 1781
TOMA METALS, INC.—See Reliance Steel & Aluminum Co.; *U.S. Public,* pg. 1782
TOMARCO CONTRACTOR SPECIALTIES; *U.S. Private,* pg. 4183
TOMAR COMPUTER INTEGRATION, INC.—See Trinity Hunt Management, L.P.; *U.S. Private,* pg. 4234
TOMAR INDUSTRIES, INC.; *U.S. Private,* pg. 4183
TOMARTA SDN. BHD.—See Far East Consortium International Limited; *Int'l,* pg. 2615
TOMASSEN DUCK-TO B.V.—See Bangkok Ranch Public Company Limited; *Int'l,* pg. 835

TOMAR INDUSTRIES, INC. — CORPORATE AFFILIATIONS

Company Index

TOMASSEN TRANSPORT B.V.—See Bangkok Ranch Public Company Limited; *Int'l*, pg. 835
TOMASSO BROTHERS INC.; *U.S. Private*, pg. 4183
TOMASZ GENERAL CONTRACTING LTD.; *Int'l*, pg. 7799
TOMATEC AMERICA, INC.—See Toyo Seikan Group Holdings, Ltd.; *Int'l*, pg. 7857
TOMATEC CO., LTD.—See Toyo Seikan Group Holdings, Ltd.; *Int'l*, pg. 7857
TOMATEC (SHANGHAI) FINE MATERIALS CO., LTD.—See Toyo Seikan Group Holdings, Ltd.; *Int'l*, pg. 7857
TOMATEC (XIAMEN) FINE MATERIAL CO., LTD.—See Toyo Seikan Group Holdings, Ltd.; *Int'l*, pg. 7857
TOMATES DEL SUR S.L.—See Sugalidal Industrias de Alimentacao SA; *Int'l*, pg. 7254
TOMATIN DISTILLERY CO LTD—See Takara Holdings, Inc.; *Int'l*, pg. 7433
TOMATO BANK LTD.; *Int'l*, pg. 7799
TOMATO CARD, LTD—See Tomato Bank Ltd.; *Int'l*, pg. 7799
TOMATO COAL CENTER—See Hokkaido Electric Power Co., Inc.; *Int'l*, pg. 3443
TOMATO SYSTEM CO., LTD.; *Int'l*, pg. 7799
TOMBADOR IRON LIMITED; *Int'l*, pg. 7799
TOMBALL TEXAS HOME CARE SERVICES, LLC—See Community Health Systems, Inc.; *U.S. Public*, pg. 557
TOMBAO ANTIQUES & ART GROUP; *Int'l*, pg. 7799
TOMBARI STRUCTURAL PRODUCTS, INC.—See Slate Capital Group LLC; *U.S. Private*, pg. 3687
TOM BARROW COMPANY—See Ardian SAS; *Int'l*, pg. 554
TOMBELL CHEVROLET INC.; *U.S. Private*, pg. 4183
TOMBIGBEE ELECTRIC POWER ASSOCIATION; *U.S. Private*, pg. 4183
TOMBO INDUSTRY CO., LTD.—See Nikko Co., Ltd.; *Int'l*, pg. 5291
TOMBOLA GOLD LTD.; *Int'l*, pg. 7799
TOMBOLA INTERNATIONAL MALTA PLC—See Flutter Entertainment plc; *Int'l*, pg. 2715
TOMBSTONE EXPLORATION CORPORATION; *U.S. Public*, pg. 2162
TOM BUSH MOTORS INC.—See Tom Bush Regency Motors Inc.; *U.S. Private*, pg. 4182
TOM BUSH REGENCY MOTORS INC.; *U.S. Private*, pg. 4182
TOM BUSH VOLKSWAGEN INC.—See Tom Bush Regency Motors Inc.; *U.S. Private*, pg. 4182
TOM CAT BAKERY, INC.—See Yamazaki Baking Co., Ltd.; *Int'l*, pg. 8557
TOM + CHEE; *U.S. Private*, pg. 4182
TOM CLARK CHEVROLET INC.; *U.S. Private*, pg. 4182
TOMCO2 EQUIPMENT COMPANY; *U.S. Private*, pg. 4183
TOMCO ENERGY PLC; *Int'l*, pg. 7799
TOM, DICK & HARRY ADVERTISING; *U.S. Private*, pg. 4183
TOMEC CORPORATION—See Aktio Holdings Corporation; *Int'l*, pg. 267
TOMEI CONSOLIDATED BERHAD; *Int'l*, pg. 7799
TOMEI KASEI CO., LTD.—See Kurabo Industries Ltd.; *Int'l*, pg. 4336
TOMEI SHOJI CO., LTD.—See Lightron, Inc.; *Int'l*, pg. 4497
TOMEI TSUSHIN KOGYO CO., LTD.—See COMSYS Holdings Corporation; *Int'l*, pg. 1762
TOME MURATA MANUFACTURING CO., LTD.—See Murata Manufacturing Co., Ltd.; *Int'l*, pg. 5099
TOMEN DEVICES CORPORATION; *Int'l*, pg. 7799
TOMEN ELECTRONICS CORPORATION—See Toyota Tsusho Corporation; *Int'l*, pg. 7878
TOMEN ELECTRONICS INDIA PRIVATE LIMITED—See Toyota Tsusho Corporation; *Int'l*, pg. 7878
TOMEN ELECTRONICS MALAYSIA SDN. BHD.—See Toyota Tsusho Corporation; *Int'l*, pg. 7878
TOMEN ELECTRONICS (SHENZHEN) CO., LTD—See Toyota Tsusho Corporation; *Int'l*, pg. 7877
TOMEN GRAIN CO.—See Toyota Tsusho Corporation; *Int'l*, pg. 7879
TOMEN IRAN LTD.—See Toyota Tsusho Corporation; *Int'l*, pg. 7878
TOMEN POWER (SINGAPORE) PTE. LTD.—See Toyota Tsusho Corporation; *Int'l*, pg. 7878
TOMEN TOYOTA TSUSHO PETROLEUM (S) PTE. LTD.—See Toyota Tsusho Corporation; *Int'l*, pg. 7878
TOMER ENERGY ROYALTIES 2012 LTD.; *Int'l*, pg. 7800
TOM FITTS TOBACCO CO INC.; *U.S. Private*, pg. 4182
TOM FORD INTERNATIONAL, LLC—See The Estee Lauder Companies Inc.; *U.S. Public*, pg. 2073
TOM GEORGE YACHT GROUP; *U.S. Private*, pg. 4182
TOM GRADDY ENTERPRISES INC.; *U.S. Private*, pg. 4182
TOM GREENAUER DEVELOPMENT, INC.—See Greenauer Holding Inc.; *U.S. Private*, pg. 1774
TOM GROUP LIMITED—See CK Hutchison Holdings Limited; *Int'l*, pg. 1638
TOM HESSER AUTO GROUP; *U.S. Private*, pg. 4182
TOM HESSER CHEVROLET/BMW INC.—See Tom Hesser Auto Group; *U.S. Private*, pg. 4182
TOMI ENVIRONMENTAL SOLUTIONS, INC.; *U.S. Public*, pg. 2162

TOMIE RAINES, INC.—See Berkshire Hathaway Inc.; *U.S. Public*, pg. 307
TOMINAGA SANGYO CO., LTD.—See Nippon Steel Corporation; *Int'l*, pg. 5339
TOMIN CARD CO., LTD.—See Tokyo Kiraboshi Financial Group , Inc.; *Int'l*, pg. 7793
TOMIN COMPUTER SYSTEM CO., LTD.—See Tokyo Kiraboshi Financial Group , Inc.; *Int'l*, pg. 7793
TOMIN CREDIT GUARANTEE CO., LTD.—See Tokyo Kiraboshi Financial Group , Inc.; *Int'l*, pg. 7793
TOMIN MANAGEMENT RESEARCH INSTITUTE CO., LTD.—See Tokyo Kiraboshi Financial Group , Inc.; *Int'l*, pg. 7793
TOMI-REMONT A.S.—See Grupo Villar Mir, S.A.U.; *Int'l*, pg. 3139
TOMI S.A.I.E.D.W.; *Int'l*, pg. 7800
TOMI SA—See ELLAKTOR S.A.; *Int'l*, pg. 2365
TOMISATO SHOJI KABUSHIKI KAISHA—See Delta Air Lines, Inc.; *U.S. Public*, pg. 652
TOMISO CO.,LTD—See Nissui Corporation; *Int'l*, pg. 5379
TOMITA ASIA CO., LTD.—See TOMITA CO., LTD.; *Int'l*, pg. 7800
TOMITA CANADA INC.—See TOMITA CO., LTD.; *Int'l*, pg. 7800
TOMITA CHINA CO., LTD.—See TOMITA CO., LTD.; *Int'l*, pg. 7800
TOMITA CO., LTD.; *Int'l*, pg. 7800
TOMITA ELECTRIC CO., LTD.; *Int'l*, pg. 7800
TOMITA FERRITE LTD.—See Tomita Electric Co., Ltd.; *Int'l*, pg. 7800
TOMITA INDIA PVT. LTD.—See TOMITA CO., LTD.; *Int'l*, pg. 7800
TOMITA MEXICO, S.DE R.L.DE C.V.—See TOMITA CO., LTD.; *Int'l*, pg. 7800
TOMITA UK LTD.—See TOMITA CO., LTD.; *Int'l*, pg. 7800
TOMITEC CO., LTD.—See Tokuyama Corporation; *Int'l*, pg. 7788
TOMIZONE LIMITED; *Int'l*, pg. 7800
TOM JAMES COMPANY—See Individualized Apparel Group; *U.S. Private*, pg. 2064
TOM JAMES OF ATLANTA, INC.—See Individualized Apparel Group; *U.S. Private*, pg. 2064
TOM JOHNSON CAMPING CENTER CHARLOTTE, INC.—See Camping World Holdings, Inc.; *U.S. Public*, pg. 428
TOM JOHNSON INVESTMENT MANAGEMENT, LLC (TJIM); *U.S. Private*, pg. 4182
TOM JONES FORD; *U.S. Private*, pg. 4182
TOM JONES INC.; *U.S. Private*, pg. 4182
TOM JONES INC.; *U.S. Private*, pg. 4182
TOMKINS BUILDERS, INC.—See ACS, Actividades de Construccion y Servicios, S.A.; *Int'l*, pg. 113
TOM LANGE COMPANY, INC.; *U.S. Private*, pg. 4182
TOM LIGHT CHEVROLET; *U.S. Private*, pg. 4182
TOMLIN INDUSTRIES INC; *Int'l*, pg. 7800
TOMLINSON BOILERS PTY LTD—See RCR Tomlinson Ltd.; *Int'l*, pg. 6229
TOMLINSON/ERWIN-LAMBETH, INC.; *U.S. Private*, pg. 4183
TOM LOFTUS INC.; *U.S. Private*, pg. 4182
TOM LOPES DISTRIBUTING INC.; *U.S. Private*, pg. 4183
TOM MASANO INC.; *U.S. Private*, pg. 4183
TOM-MEDIC INC.—See Ship Healthcare Holdings, Inc.; *Int'l*, pg. 6852
TOMMIE VAUGHN MOTORS INC.; *U.S. Private*, pg. 4184
TOMM MURSTAD FRILUFTSBARNEHAGE AS—See AcadeMedia AB; *Int'l*, pg. 77
TOMMY BAHAMA AUSTRALIA PTY LTD—See Oxford Industries, Inc.; *U.S. Public*, pg. 1629
TOMMY BAHAMA CANADA ULC—See Oxford Industries, Inc.; *U.S. Public*, pg. 1629
TOMMY BAHAMA GLOBAL SOURCING LIMITED—See Oxford Industries, Inc.; *U.S. Public*, pg. 1629
TOMMY BAHAMA GROUP, INC.—See Oxford Industries, Inc.; *U.S. Public*, pg. 1629
TOMMY BAHAMA LIMITED—See Oxford Industries, Inc.; *U.S. Public*, pg. 1629
TOMMY BAHAMA SARASOTA LLC—See Oxford Industries, Inc.; *U.S. Public*, pg. 1629
TOMMY BAHAMA TEXAS BEVERAGES LLC—See Oxford Industries, Inc.; *U.S. Public*, pg. 1629
TOMMY BARTLETT, INC.; *U.S. Private*, pg. 4184
TOMMY BROOKS OIL COMPANY; *U.S. Private*, pg. 4184
TOMMY HILFIGER ASIA-PACIFIC LIMITED—See Dickson Concepts (International) Limited; *Int'l*, pg. 2112
TOMMY HILFIGER CORPORATION—See PVH Corp.; *U.S. Public*, pg. 1739
TOMMY HILFIGER EUROPE B.V.—See PVH Corp.; *U.S. Public*, pg. 1739
TOMMY HILFIGER (HK) LTD.—See PVH Corp.; *U.S. Public*, pg. 1739
TOMMY HILFIGER MARKETING LIMITED—See Dickson Concepts (International) Limited; *Int'l*, pg. 2112
TOMMY HILFIGER (SHANGHAI) APPAREL CO., LTD.—See PVH Corp.; *U.S. Public*, pg. 1739
TOMMY HOUSE TIRE COMPANY; *U.S. Private*, pg. 4184
TOMMY'S QUALITY USED CARS; *U.S. Private*, pg. 4184
TOM NEHL TRUCK CO.; *U.S. Private*, pg. 4183

TOM O'BRIEN CHRYSLER JEEP GREENWOOD; *U.S. Private*, pg. 4183
TOMO-CSE AUTOTRIM PTE. LTD.—See TOMO Holdings Limited; *Int'l*, pg. 7800
TOMO-DIGI CORPORATION—See TBS Holdings, Inc.; *Int'l*, pg. 7481
TOMOE ADVANCED MATERIALS S.R.O.—See TOMOE Engineering Co., Ltd.; *Int'l*, pg. 7800
TOMOE CORPORATION—See Natoco Co.,Ltd.; *Int'l*, pg. 5165
TOMOE ENGINEERING CO., LTD. - SAGAMI FACTORY—See TOMOE Engineering Co., Ltd.; *Int'l*, pg. 7800
TOMOE ENGINEERING CO., LTD. - SHONAN FACTORY—See TOMOE Engineering Co., Ltd.; *Int'l*, pg. 7800
TOMOE ENGINEERING CO., LTD.; *Int'l*, pg. 7800
TOMOE ENGINEERING (HONG KONG) CO., LTD.—See TOMOE Engineering Co., Ltd.; *Int'l*, pg. 7800
TOMOEGAWA CO., LTD.; *Int'l*, pg. 7801
TOMOEGAWA EUROPE B.V.—See Tomoegawa Co., Ltd.; *Int'l*, pg. 7801
TOMOEGAWA HONG KONG CO., LTD.—See Tomoegawa Co., Ltd.; *Int'l*, pg. 7801
TOMOEGAWA IMAGING TECHNOLOGY HUIZHOU CO., LTD.—See Tomoegawa Co., Ltd.; *Int'l*, pg. 7801
TOMOEGAWA KOREA CO., LTD.—See Tomoegawa Co., Ltd.; *Int'l*, pg. 7801
TOMOEGAWA LOGISTICS SERVICE CO., LTD.—See Tomoegawa Co., Ltd.; *Int'l*, pg. 7801
TOMOEGAWA PAPER CO., LTD.—See Tomoegawa Co., Ltd.; *Int'l*, pg. 7801
TOMOEGAWA (U.S.A.) INC.—See Tomoegawa Co., Ltd.; *Int'l*, pg. 7801
TOMOE MACHINERY CO., LTD.—See TOMOE Engineering Co., Ltd.; *Int'l*, pg. 7800
TOMOE MACHINERY SERVICE CO., LTD.—See TOMOE Engineering Co., Ltd.; *Int'l*, pg. 7800
TOMOE SHOKAI CO., LTD.; *Int'l*, pg. 7801
TOMOE WINES & SPIRITS CO., LTD.—See NAC Co., Ltd.; *Int'l*, pg. 5121
TOMO HOLDINGS LIMITED; *Int'l*, pg. 7800
TOMOIKE ELECTRONICS (SHANGHAI) CO., LIMITED; *Int'l*, pg. 7801
TOMOIKE INDUSTRIAL CO., LTD.—See CDW Holding Ltd.; *Int'l*, pg. 1372
TOMOIKE INDUSTRIAL (H.K.) LIMITED—See CDW Holding Ltd.; *Int'l*, pg. 1372
TOMOIKE PRECISION MACHINERY (SHANGHAI) CO., LIMITED—See CDW Holding Ltd.; *Int'l*, pg. 1372
TOMO IZAKAYA PTE LTD—See Katrina Group Ltd.; *Int'l*, pg. 4092
TOMOKU CO., LTD. - AOMORI WORKS—See Tomoku Co., Ltd.; *Int'l*, pg. 7802
TOMOKU CO., LTD. - ATSUGI WORKS—See Tomoku Co., Ltd.; *Int'l*, pg. 7802
TOMOKU CO., LTD. - CHIBA FOLDING CARTON WORKS—See Tomoku Co., Ltd.; *Int'l*, pg. 7802
TOMOKU CO., LTD. - HAMAMATSU WORKS—See Tomoku Co., Ltd.; *Int'l*, pg. 7802
TOMOKU CO., LTD. - IWATSUKI WORKS—See Tomoku Co., Ltd.; *Int'l*, pg. 7802
TOMOKU CO., LTD. - KYUSHU WORKS—See Tomoku Co., Ltd.; *Int'l*, pg. 7802
TOMOKU CO., LTD. - NIIGATA WORKS—See Tomoku Co., Ltd.; *Int'l*, pg. 7802
TOMOKU CO., LTD. - OSAKA WORKS—See Tomoku Co., Ltd.; *Int'l*, pg. 7802
TOMOKU CO., LTD. - SAPPORO WORKS—See Tomoku Co., Ltd.; *Int'l*, pg. 7802
TOMOKU CO., LTD. - SENDAI WORKS—See Tomoku Co., Ltd.; *Int'l*, pg. 7802
TOMOKU CO., LTD.; *Int'l*, pg. 7801
TOMOKU CO., LTD. - TATEBAYASHI WORKS—See Tomoku Co., Ltd.; *Int'l*, pg. 7802
TOMOKU CO., LTD. - TOMOPREST WORKS—See Tomoku Co., Ltd.; *Int'l*, pg. 7802
TOMOKU CO., LTD. - YAMAGATA WORKS—See Tomoku Co., Ltd.; *Int'l*, pg. 7802
TOMOKU HUS AB—See Tomoku Co., Ltd.; *Int'l*, pg. 7802
TOMOKU VIETNAM CO., LTD.—See Tomoku Co., Ltd.; *Int'l*, pg. 7802
TOM ONLINE INC.—See CK Hutchison Holdings Limited; *Int'l*, pg. 1638
TOMONY CARD, INC.—See TOMONY Holdings, Inc.; *Int'l*, pg. 7802
TOMONY HOLDINGS, INC.; *Int'l*, pg. 7802
TOMORROW LTD—See Saturday Group Ltd; *Int'l*, pg. 6588
TOMORROW NETWORKS, LLC—See KKR & Co. Inc.; *U.S. Public*, pg. 1253
TOMORROWNOW, INC.—See SAP SE; *Int'l*, pg. 6568
TOMOS D.O.O.—See Hidria d.o.o.; *Int'l*, pg. 3384
TOMOTHERAPY BELGIUM BVBA—See Accuray Incorporated; *U.S. Public*, pg. 33
TOMOTHERAPY INCORPORATED—See Accuray Incorporated; *U.S. Public*, pg. 33
TOMOWEL PAYMENT SERVICE CO., LTD.—See Kyodo Printing Co. Ltd.; *Int'l*, pg. 4361

COMPANY NAME INDEX

TOM PECK FORD OF HUNTLEY, INC.; *U.S. Private*, pg. 4183
TOMPKINS FINANCIAL CORPORATION; *U.S. Public*, pg. 2162
TOMPKINS INDUSTRIES, INC.; *U.S. Private*, pg. 4184
TOMPKINS INSURANCE AGENCIES, INC.—See Tompkins Financial Corporation; *U.S. Public*, pg. 2162
TOMPKINS TRUST COMPANY—See Tompkins Financial Corporation; *U.S. Public*, pg. 2162
TOMPKINS VIST BANK—See Tompkins Financial Corporation; *U.S. Public*, pg. 2162
TOMRA AG—See Tomra Systems ASA; *Int'l*, pg. 7803
TOMRA BRASIL SOLUCOES EM SEGREGACAO LTDA.—See Tomra Systems ASA; *Int'l*, pg. 7802
TOMRA BUTIKKSYSTEMER AS—See Tomra Systems ASA; *Int'l*, pg. 7802
TOMRA CANADA INC—See Tomra Systems ASA; *Int'l*, pg. 7802
TOMRA/CBSI, LLC—See Tomra Systems ASA; *Int'l*, pg. 7803
TOMRA COLLECTION PORTUGAL, UNIPESSOAL LTDA.—See Tomra Systems ASA; *Int'l*, pg. 7802
TOMRA COLLECTION ROMANIA S.R.L.—See Tomra Systems ASA; *Int'l*, pg. 7802
TOMRA COLLECTION SLOVAKIA S.R.O.—See Tomra Systems ASA; *Int'l*, pg. 7803
TOMRA COLLECTION SOLUTIONS TAIWAN CO., LTD.—See Tomra Systems ASA; *Int'l*, pg. 7802
TOMRA COLLECTION TURKEY MAKINE TEKNOLOJI SANAYI VE TICARET ANONIM SIRKETI—See Tomra Systems ASA; *Int'l*, pg. 7803
TOMRA ENVIRONMENTAL PROTECTION TECHNOLOGY (XIAMEN) CO.LTD.—See Tomra Systems ASA; *Int'l*, pg. 7803
TOMRA EUROPE AS—See Tomra Systems ASA; *Int'l*, pg. 7803
TOMRA FOOD (VALENCIA) S.L.—See Tomra Systems ASA; *Int'l*, pg. 7803
TOMRA LEERGUTSYSTEME GMBH—See Tomra Systems ASA; *Int'l*, pg. 7803
TOMRA MASS LLC—See Tomra Systems ASA; *Int'l*, pg. 7803
TOMRA METRO, LLC—See Tomra Systems ASA; *Int'l*, pg. 7803
TOM RANDALL DISTRIBUTING CO.; *U.S. Private*, pg. 4183
TOMRA NY RECYCLING LLC—See Tomra Systems ASA; *Int'l*, pg. 7803
TOMRA OF NORTH AMERICA, INC.—See Tomra Systems ASA; *Int'l*, pg. 7803
TOMRA PRODUCTION AS—See Tomra Systems ASA; *Int'l*, pg. 7803
TOMRA RECYCLING TECHNOLOGY (XIAMEN) CO. LTD.—See Tomra Systems ASA; *Int'l*, pg. 7803
TOMRA SORTING AS—See Tomra Systems ASA; *Int'l*, pg. 7803
TOMRA SORTING CO., LTD.—See Tomra Systems ASA; *Int'l*, pg. 7803
TOMRA SORTING GMBH—See Tomra Systems ASA; *Int'l*, pg. 7803
TOMRA SORTING GMBH—See Tomra Systems ASA; *Int'l*, pg. 7803
TOMRA SORTING INC.—See Tomra Systems ASA; *Int'l*, pg. 7803
TOMRA SORTING INDIA PRIVATE LIMITED—See Tomra Systems ASA; *Int'l*, pg. 7803
TOMRA SORTING JLT—See Tomra Systems ASA; *Int'l*, pg. 7803
TOMRA SORTING K.K.—See Tomra Systems ASA; *Int'l*, pg. 7803
TOMRA SORTING LTD. IRELAND—See Tomra Systems ASA; *Int'l*, pg. 7802
TOMRA SORTING LTD.—See Tomra Systems ASA; *Int'l*, pg. 7803
TOMRA SORTING N.V.—See Tomra Systems ASA; *Int'l*, pg. 7803
TOMRA SORTING (PTY) LTD.—See Tomra Systems ASA; *Int'l*, pg. 7803
TOMRA SORTING , S.L.—See Tomra Systems ASA; *Int'l*, pg. 7803
TOMRA SORTING SOLUTIONS AS—See Tomra Systems ASA; *Int'l*, pg. 7803
TOMRA SORTING SOLUTIONS SRL—See Tomra Systems ASA; *Int'l*, pg. 7803
TOMRA SORTING SP. Z O.O.—See Tomra Systems ASA; *Int'l*, pg. 7803
TOMRA SORTING S.R.L.—See Tomra Systems ASA; *Int'l*, pg. 7803
TOMRA S.R.O.—See Tomra Systems ASA; *Int'l*, pg. 7803
TOMRA SYSTEM AS—See Tomra Systems ASA; *Int'l*, pg. 7803
TOMRA SYSTEMS AB—See Tomra Systems ASA; *Int'l*, pg. 7803
TOMRA SYSTEMS ASA; *Int'l*, pg. 7802
TOMRA SYSTEMS B.V.—See Tomra Systems ASA; *Int'l*, pg. 7803
TOMRA SYSTEMS GMBH—See Tomra Systems ASA; *Int'l*, pg. 7803

TOMRA SYSTEMS LTD—See Tomra Systems ASA; *Int'l*, pg. 7803
TOMRA SYSTEMS N.V.—See Tomra Systems ASA; *Int'l*, pg. 7803
TOMRA SYSTEMS SAS—See Tomra Systems ASA; *Int'l*, pg. 7803
TOM ROUSH INC.; *U.S. Private*, pg. 4183
TOM'S AMUSEMENT COMPANY, INC.—See Accel Entertainment, Inc.; *U.S. Public*, pg. 32
TOM'S CAMPERLAND, INC.—See Redwood Capital Investments, LLC; *U.S. Private*, pg. 3380
TOM'S CO., LTD.; *Int'l*, pg. 7799
TOMS CO., LTD—See Yamashita Health Care Holdings, Inc.; *Int'l*, pg. 8553
TOMS CREATIVE CO., LTD.—See SANKO SANGYO CO., LTD.; *Int'l*, pg. 6542
TOM'S FOOD MARKETS INC.; *U.S. Private*, pg. 4183
TOM'S FORD INC.; *U.S. Private*, pg. 4183
TOMSHEEHAN WORLDWIDE; *U.S. Private*, pg. 4184
TOMSHEEHAN WORLDWIDE—See tomsheehan worldwide; *U.S. Private*, pg. 4184
TOMSKGAZSTROY PJSC—See HMS Hydraulic Machines & Systems Group plc; *Int'l*, pg. 3432
TOMS KITCHEN LTD—See Dogus Holding AS; *Int'l*, pg. 2155
TOMSKPROMSTROYBANK PJSC; *Int'l*, pg. 7804
TOMSK RASPREDELIT KOMP AP; *Int'l*, pg. 7804
TOMSKTRANSGAZ—See PJSC Gazprom; *Int'l*, pg. 5880
TOM'S OF MAINE, INC.—See Colgate-Palmolive Company; *U.S. Public*, pg. 533
TOMSON (CHINA) LIMITED—See Tomson Group Limited; *Int'l*, pg. 7804
TOMSON GOLF (SHANGHAI) LIMITED—See Tomson Group Limited; *Int'l*, pg. 7804
TOMSON GROUP LIMITED; *Int'l*, pg. 7804
TOMS PHOTO CO., LTD.—See Sega Sammy Holdings, Inc.; *Int'l*, pg. 6681
TOMS-PRICE CO.; *U.S. Private*, pg. 4184
TOMS RIVER LINCOLN MERCURY MAZDA, INC.; *U.S. Private*, pg. 4184
TOMS RIVER SURGERY CENTER, L.L.C.—See Tenet Healthcare Corporation; *U.S. Public*, pg. 2013
TOMS SHOES, LLC—See Bain Capital, LP; *U.S. Private*, pg. 447
TOM STINNETT HOLIDAY RV CENTER INC.; *U.S. Private*, pg. 4183
TOM'S TRUCK CENTER INC.; *U.S. Private*, pg. 4183
TOM TAILOR FRANCE S.A.R.L.—See Tom Tailor Holding SE; *Int'l*, pg. 7799
TOM TAILOR GESELLSCHAFT M.B.H.—See Tom Tailor Holding SE; *Int'l*, pg. 7799
TOM TAILOR GMBH—See Tom Tailor Holding SE; *Int'l*, pg. 7799
TOM TAILOR HOLDING SE; *Int'l*, pg. 7799
TOM TAILOR INTERNATIONAL HOLDING B.V.—See Tom Tailor Holding SE; *Int'l*, pg. 7799
TOM TAILOR RETAIL GMBH—See Tom Tailor Holding SE; *Int'l*, pg. 7799
TOM TAILOR (SCHWEIZ) AG—See Tom Tailor Holding SE; *Int'l*, pg. 7799
TOM THUMB FOOD & PHARMACY—See Cerberus Capital Management, L.P.; *U.S. Public*, pg. 836
TOMTOM ASIA LTD.—See TomTom N.V.; *Int'l*, pg. 7804
TOMTOM DEVELOPMENT GERMANY GMBH—See TomTom N.V.; *Int'l*, pg. 7804
TOMTOM INC—See TomTom N.V.; *Int'l*, pg. 7804
TOMTOM INC.—See TomTom N.V.; *Int'l*, pg. 7804
TOMTOM INTERNATIONAL BV—See TomTom N.V.; *Int'l*, pg. 7804
TOMTOM N.V.; *Int'l*, pg. 7804
TOMTOM PLACES B.V—See TomTom N.V.; *Int'l*, pg. 7804
TOMTOM PLACES DEVELOPMENT B.V—See TomTom N.V.; *Int'l*, pg. 7804
TOMTOM POLSKA SP. Z.O.O—See TomTom N.V.; *Int'l*, pg. 7804
TOMTOM SALES BV—See TomTom N.V.; *Int'l*, pg. 7804
TOMTOM SOFTWARE LTD.—See TomTom N.V.; *Int'l*, pg. 7804
TOMTOM TREASURY I B.V—See TomTom N.V.; *Int'l*, pg. 7804
TOMTOM WORK GMBH—See TomTom N.V.; *Int'l*, pg. 7804
TOMUKI CORPORATION—See Toyota Tsusho Corporation; *Int'l*, pg. 7878
TOMUSINSKY OPEN PIT MINE OAO—See Mechel PAO; *Int'l*, pg. 4766
TOM VIETNAM CO., LTD.—See Rengo Co., Ltd.; *Int'l*, pg. 6281
TOM WESSEL CONSTRUCTION CORP.; *U.S. Private*, pg. 4183
TOM WHEAT LANDSCAPING; *U.S. Private*, pg. 4183
TOM YATES PETROLEUM CO. INC.; *U.S. Private*, pg. 4183
TOMY COMPANY, LTD.; *Int'l*, pg. 7804
TOMY FRANCE SARL—See Tomy Company, Ltd.; *Int'l*, pg. 7805
TOMY (HONG KONG) LTD.—See Tomy Company, Ltd.; *Int'l*, pg. 7805

TONGA COMMUNICATIONS CORPORATION

TOMY INTERNATIONAL-AUSTRALIA—See Tomy Company, Ltd.; *Int'l*, pg. 7805
TOMY INTERNATIONAL-CHINA—See Tomy Company, Ltd.; *Int'l*, pg. 7805
TOMY INTERNATIONAL-GERMANY—See Tomy Company, Ltd.; *Int'l*, pg. 7805
TOMY INTERNATIONAL-HONG KONG—See Tomy Company, Ltd.; *Int'l*, pg. 7805
TOMY INTERNATIONAL, INC.—See Tomy Company, Ltd.; *Int'l*, pg. 7805
TOMY INTERNATIONAL-UNITED KINGDOM—See Tomy Company, Ltd.; *Int'l*, pg. 7805
TOMYPAK FLEXIBLE PACKAGING SDN BHD—See Tomypak Holdings Berhad; *Int'l*, pg. 7805
TOMYPAK FLEXIBLE PACKAGING (S) PTE. LTD.—See Tomypak Holdings Berhad; *Int'l*, pg. 7805
TOMYPAK HOLDINGS BERHAD; *Int'l*, pg. 7805
TOMY (SHENZHEN) LTD.—See Tomy Company, Ltd.; *Int'l*, pg. 7805
TOMY (THAILAND) LTD.—See Tomy Company, Ltd.; *Int'l*, pg. 7805
TOMY UK LTD.—See Tomy Company, Ltd.; *Int'l*, pg. 7805
TOMZEL, JSC—See OAO AK Transneft; *Int'l*, pg. 5505
TONAMI HOLDINGS CO., LTD.; *Int'l*, pg. 7805
TONAMINO KOGYO CO., LTD.—See AISIN Corporation; *Int'l*, pg. 254
TONAMI SYSTEM SOLUTIONS CO., LTD.—See TONAMI HOLDINGS CO., LTD.; *Int'l*, pg. 7805
TONAQUINT DATA CENTERS, INC.; *U.S. Private*, pg. 4184
TONAR INDUSTRIES INC.; *U.S. Private*, pg. 4184
TONAWANDA COKE CORP; *U.S. Private*, pg. 4184
TONDACH BETEILIGUNGS GMBH—See Wienerberger AG; *Int'l*, pg. 8406
TONDACH BOSNA I HERCEGOVINA D.O.O.—See Wienerberger AG; *Int'l*, pg. 8406
TONDACH BULGARIA EOOD—See Wienerberger AG; *Int'l*, pg. 8406
TONDACH CESKA REPUBLIKA S.R.O.—See Wienerberger AG; *Int'l*, pg. 8406
TONDACH GLEINSTATTEN AG—See Wienerberger AG; *Int'l*, pg. 8406
TONDACH HRVATSKA D.D.—See Wienerberger AG; *Int'l*, pg. 8406
TONDACH MAGYARORSZAG RT.—See Wienerberger AG; *Int'l*, pg. 8406
TONDACH MAKEDONIJA D.O.O.—See Wienerberger AG; *Int'l*, pg. 8406
TONDACH ROMANIA SRL—See Wienerberger AG; *Int'l*, pg. 8406
TONDACH SLOVENIJA D.O.O.—See Wienerberger AG; *Int'l*, pg. 8406
TONDACH SLOVENSKO, S.R.O.—See Wienerberger AG; *Int'l*, pg. 8406
TONDA CONSTRUCTION LIMITED; *Int'l*, pg. 7805
TONDO SMART LTD.; *Int'l*, pg. 7805
TONE COMPANY LTD - KAWACHINAGANO FACTORY—See Tone Company Ltd; *Int'l*, pg. 7805
TONE COMPANY LTD; *Int'l*, pg. 7805
TONELI NUTRITION TITU SA; *Int'l*, pg. 7805
TONEN CHEMICAL CORPORATION—See ENEOS Holdings, Inc.; *Int'l*, pg. 2417
TONE PRODUCTS INC.; *U.S. Private*, pg. 4184
TONER CABLE EQUIPMENT INC.; *U.S. Private*, pg. 4184
TONER CABLE EQUIPMENT UK LTD—See Toner Cable Equipment Inc.; *U.S. Private*, pg. 4184
TONE RESOURCES LIMITED—See McEwen Mining Inc.; *Int'l*, pg. 4758
TONEREX TECHNOLOGIES SDN. BHD.—See LYC Healthcare Berhad; *Int'l*, pg. 4605
TONER GRAHAM LIMITED—See Kelly Services, Inc.; *U.S. Public*, pg. 1219
TONERS PLUS OFFICE PRODUCTS; *U.S. Private*, pg. 4184
TONETSU KOSAN CO., LTD.—See Dowa Holdings Co., Ltd.; *Int'l*, pg. 2184
TONE ZOOM INDUSTRY CO., LTD.—See Chung-Hsin Electric & Machinery Manufacturing Corp.; *Int'l*, pg. 1597
TONGAAT HULETT ACUCAREIRA DE MOCAMBIQUE, SARL—See Tongaat Hulett Limited; *Int'l*, pg. 7807
TONGAAT HULETT ACUCAR LIMITADA—See Tongaat Hulett Limited; *Int'l*, pg. 7807
TONGAAT HULETT DEVELOPMENTS (PTY) LTD—See Tongaat Hulett Limited; *Int'l*, pg. 7807
TONGAAT HULETT ESTATES (PTY) LIMITED—See Tongaat Hulett Limited; *Int'l*, pg. 7807
TONGAAT HULETT LIMITED; *Int'l*, pg. 7807
TONGAAT HULETT STARCH (PTY) LIMITED—See Tongaat Hulett Limited; *Int'l*, pg. 7807
TONGAAT HULETT SUGAR LIMITED—See Tongaat Hulett Limited; *Int'l*, pg. 7807
TONGAAT HULETT SUGAR SOUTH AFRICA LIMITED—See Tongaat Hulett Limited; *Int'l*, pg. 7807
TONGA COMMUNICATIONS CORPORATION; *Int'l*, pg. 7807
TONGALA & DISTRICT FINANCIAL SERVICES LIMITED—See Bendigo & Adelaide Bank Ltd.; *Int'l*, pg. 971

2771

TONGCHENG TRAVEL HOLDINGS LIMITED

CORPORATE AFFILIATIONS

TONGCHENG TRAVEL HOLDINGS LIMITED; *Int'l*, pg. 7807
TONGDA ELECTRICS COMPANY LIMITED—See Tongda Group Holdings Limited; *Int'l*, pg. 7807
TONG DA GENERAL HOLDINGS (H.K.) LIMITED—See Tongda Group Holdings Limited; *Int'l*, pg. 7807
TONGDA GROUP HOLDINGS LIMITED; *Int'l*, pg. 7807
TONGDA HONG TAI HOLDINGS LIMITED; *Int'l*, pg. 7807
TONGDAO LIEPIN GROUP; *Int'l*, pg. 7807
TONGDING INTERCONNECTION INFORMATION CO., LTD.; *Int'l*, pg. 7807
TONGFANG TECHNOVATOR INT (BEIJING) CO., LTD.—See Technovator International Limited; *Int'l*, pg. 7512
TONGFU MICROELECTRONICS CO., LTD.; *Int'l*, pg. 7807
TONGGUAN GOLD GROUP LTD.; *Int'l*, pg. 7807
TONG HEER ALUMINIUM INDUSTRIES SDN. BHD.—See Tong Herr Resources Berhad; *Int'l*, pg. 7805
TONG HEER FASTENERS CO. SDN. BHD.—See Tong Herr Resources Berhad; *Int'l*, pg. 7805
TONG HEER FASTENERS THAILAND CO., LTD.—See Tong Herr Resources Berhad; *Int'l*, pg. 7805
TONGHE NEW ENERGY (JINTANG) CO., LTD.—See Tongwei Co., Ltd.; *Int'l*, pg. 7808
TONG HERR RESOURCES BERHAD; *Int'l*, pg. 7805
TONG HSING ELECTRONIC INDUSTRIES, LTD. - CHUNG-LI PLANT—See Tong Hsing Electronic Industries, Ltd.; *Int'l*, pg. 7805
TONG HSING ELECTRONIC INDUSTRIES, LTD. - LONGTAN PLANT—See Tong Hsing Electronic Industries, Ltd.; *Int'l*, pg. 7805
TONG HSING ELECTRONIC INDUSTRIES, LTD.; *Int'l*, pg. 7805
TONG HSING ELECTRONICS PHILS INC.—See Tong Hsing Electronic Industries, Ltd.; *Int'l*, pg. 7805
TONGHUA DONGBAO PHARMACEUTICAL CO., LTD.; *Int'l*, pg. 7807
TONGHUA GOLDEN-HORSE PHARMACEUTICAL INDUSTRY CO.; *Int'l*, pg. 7807
TONGHUA GRAPE WINE CO., LTD.; *Int'l*, pg. 7808
TONG HUA HOLDING PUBLIC COMPANY LIMITED; *Int'l*, pg. 7806
TONG HWA SYNTHETIC FIBER COMPANY LIMITED; *Int'l*, pg. 7806
TONGJITANG CHINESE MEDICINES COMPANY; *Int'l*, pg. 7808
TONG JOO SHIPPING PTE LTD—See PDZ Holdings Berhad; *Int'l*, pg. 5771
TONGKAH HARBOUR PUBLIC COMPANY LIMITED; *Int'l*, pg. 7808
TONG KEE (HOLDING) LTD.; *Int'l*, pg. 7806
TONGKUN GROUP CO., LTD.; *Int'l*, pg. 7808
TONGKUN GROUP ZHEJIANG HENGTONG CHEMICAL FIBRE CO., LTD.—See Tongkun Group Co., Ltd.; *Int'l*, pg. 7808
TONG LE PRIVATE DINING PTE. LTD.—See Tung Lok Restaurants (2000) Ltd; *Int'l*, pg. 7971
TONGLING JIEYA BIOLOGIC TECHNOLOGY CO., LTD.; *Int'l*, pg. 7808
TONGLING JINGDA SPECIAL MAGNET WIRE CO., LTD.; *Int'l*, pg. 7808
TONGLING JINGXUN SPECIAL ENAMELLED WIRE CO., LTD.—See Tongling Jingda Special Magnet Wire Co., Ltd.; *Int'l*, pg. 7808
TONGLING NONFERROUS METALS GROUP CO., LTD.—See Tongling Nonferrous Metals Group Holdings Co., Ltd; *Int'l*, pg. 7808
TONGLING NONFERROUS METALS GROUP HOLDINGS CO., LTD; *Int'l*, pg. 7808
TONGLI PHARMACEUTICALS (USA), INC.; *U.S. Private*, pg. 4184
TONG LUNG METAL INDUSTRY CO., LTD.—See Stanley Black & Decker, Inc.; *U.S. Public*, pg. 1936
TONG LUNG PHILIPPINES METAL INDUSTRY CO., INC.—See Spectrum Brands Holdings, Inc.; *U.S. Public*, pg. 1917
TONG MING ENTERPRISE CO., LTD.; *Int'l*, pg. 7806
TONG PETROTECH CORP.; *Int'l*, pg. 7806
TONGQINGLOU DINING CO., LTD.; *Int'l*, pg. 7808
TONG REN TANG TECHNOLOGIES CO., LTD.; *Int'l*, pg. 7806
TONG SENG CO. LTD.—See Bridgestone Corporation; *Int'l*, pg. 1160
TONG-SHENG FINANCE LEASING CO., LTD.—See Uni-President Enterprises Corporation; *Int'l*, pg. 8029
TONG SHING, INC.—See Toray Industries, Inc.; *Int'l*, pg. 7824
TONGSUH PETROCHEMICAL CORP., LTD.—See Asahi Kasei Corporation; *Int'l*, pg. 595
TONG SUH PETROCHEMICAL CORP.—See Asahi Kasei Corporation; *Int'l*, pg. 597
TONGTAI EUROPE B.V.—See Tong-Tai Machine Tool Co., Ltd.; *Int'l*, pg. 7806
TONG-TAI MACHINE TOOL CO., LTD.; *Int'l*, pg. 7806
TONGTAI MACHINE & TOOL JAPAN CO., LTD.—See Tong-Tai Machine Tool Co., Ltd.; *Int'l*, pg. 7806
TONG-TAI SEIKI USA INC.—See Tong-Tai Machine Tool Co., Ltd.; *Int'l*, pg. 7806

TONGTAI SEIKI VIETNAM CO., LTD.—See Tong-Tai Machine Tool Co., Ltd.; *Int'l*, pg. 7806
TONG TEIK (NANTONG) TRADING LTD—See Tong Teik Pte Ltd; *Int'l*, pg. 7806
TONG TEIK PTE LTD; *Int'l*, pg. 7806
TONG TEIK (THAILAND) LIMITED—See Tong Teik Pte Ltd; *Int'l*, pg. 7806
TONGWEI CO., LTD.; *Int'l*, pg. 7808
TONGWEI NEW ENERGY CO., LTD.—See Tongwei Co., Ltd.; *Int'l*, pg. 7808
TONGXIANG ZHONGCEN CHEMICAL FIBRE CO., LTD.—See Xinfengming Group Co., Ltd.; *Int'l*, pg. 8529
TONGXIANG ZHONGCHI CHEMICAL FIBER CO., LTD.—See Xinfengming Group Co., Ltd.; *Int'l*, pg. 8529
TONGXIANG ZHONGWEI CHEMICAL FIBRE CO., LTD.—See Xinfengming Group Co., Ltd.; *Int'l*, pg. 8529
TONGXIANG ZHONGXIN CHEMICAL FIBRE CO., LTD.—See Xinfengming Group Co., Ltd.; *Int'l*, pg. 8529
TONGXINGDA (HONG KONG) TRADING CO., LTD.—See Shenzhen TXD Technology Co Ltd; *Int'l*, pg. 6823
TONGXING ENVIRONMENTAL PROTECTION TECHNOLOGY CO., LTD.; *Int'l*, pg. 7809
TONGXIN INTERNATIONAL LTD.; *Int'l*, pg. 7809
TONGYANG A&D CO., LTD.—See TONGYANG Group; *Int'l*, pg. 7809
TONGYANG CEMENT E&C—See TONGYANG Group; *Int'l*, pg. 7809
TONGYANG ENGINEERING & CONSTRUCTION GROUP—See TONGYANG Group; *Int'l*, pg. 7809
TONGYANG GROUP; *Int'l*, pg. 7809
TONGYANG INC.—See TONGYANG Group; *Int'l*, pg. 7809
TONG YANG INDUSTRY CO., LTD.; *Int'l*, pg. 7806
TONGYANG INVESTMENT CO.—See TONGYANG Group; *Int'l*, pg. 7809
TONGYANG LEISURE CO., LTD.—See TONGYANG Group; *Int'l*, pg. 7809
TONGYANG LIFE INSURANCE CO., LTD.—See Anbang Insurance Group Co., Ltd.; *Int'l*, pg. 447
TONGYANG LIFE SCIENCE CORP.—See TONGYANG Group; *Int'l*, pg. 7809
TONGYANG NETWORKS INC.—See TONGYANG Group; *Int'l*, pg. 7809
TONGYANG ONLINE CO., LTD.—See TONGYANG Group; *Int'l*, pg. 7809
TONGYANG PILE INC.; *Int'l*, pg. 7809
TONGYU COMMUNICATION INC.; *Int'l*, pg. 7809
TONGYU HEAVY INDUSTRY CO., LTD; *Int'l*, pg. 7809
TONGYU TECHNOLOGY INDIA PRIVATE LIMITED—See Tongyu Communication Inc.; *Int'l*, pg. 7809
TONGYU TECHNOLOGY OY—See Tongyu Communication Inc.; *Int'l*, pg. 7809
TONGZHOU CDB VILLAGE BANK CO., LTD.—See China Development Bank Corporation; *Int'l*, pg. 1497
TONIC DESIGN CO.—See Printfly Corp.; *U.S. Private*, pg. 3266
TONICHI FERRITE CO., LTD.—See CEC International Holdings Limited; *Int'l*, pg. 1372
TONICHI KYOUSAN CABLE, LTD.—See Hitachi, Ltd.; *Int'l*, pg. 3424
TONIC LIFE COMMUNICATIONS LTD.—See Clayton, Dubilier & Rice, LLC; *U.S. Private*, pg. 925
TONIC PHARMA SDN. BHD.—See 7-Eleven Malaysia Holdings Berhad; *Int'l*, pg. 14
TONIES FRANCE S.A.S.—See Tonies SE; *Int'l*, pg. 7809
TONIES SE; *Int'l*, pg. 7809
TONI & GUY USA, INC.; *U.S. Private*, pg. 4184
TONIPHARM S.A.S—See Recordati S.p.A.; *Int'l*, pg. 6240
TONI TRADING SRL—See Bog'Art S.R.L.; *Int'l*, pg. 1100
TONIX PHARMACEUTICALS HOLDING CORP.; *U.S. Public*, pg. 2162
TONKA BAY DIALYSIS, LLC—See DaVita Inc.; *U.S. Public*, pg. 643
TONKA BAY EQUITY PARTNERS LLC; *U.S. Private*, pg. 4184
TONKENS AGRAR AG; *Int'l*, pg. 7809
TONKING NEW ENERGY GROUP HOLDINGS LIMITED; *Int'l*, pg. 7809
TONKIN SPRINGS LLC—See McEwen Mining Inc.; *Int'l*, pg. 4758
TONLIN DEPARTMENT STORE CO., LTD.; *Int'l*, pg. 7809
TONLY ELECTRONICS HOLDINGS LIMITED—See TCL Technology Group Corp.; *Int'l*, pg. 7484
TONLY ELECTRONICS LTD.—See TCL Technology Group Corp.; *Int'l*, pg. 7484
TONNA ELECTRONIQUE S.A.; *Int'l*, pg. 7810
TONNELERIE RADOUX; *Int'l*, pg. 7810
TONNELLERIE DEMPTOS SA—See Tonnellerie Francois Freres; *Int'l*, pg. 7810
TONNELLERIE FRANCOIS FRERES; *Int'l*, pg. 7810
TONNELLERIE PROVENCALE—See Tonnellerie Francois Freres; *Int'l*, pg. 7810
TONNER DOLL COMPANY, INC.; *U.S. Private*, pg. 4185
TONOGA INC.; *U.S. Private*, pg. 4185
TONOGOLD RESOURCES, INC.; *U.S. Public*, pg. 2162
TONO GRINDING CO., LTD.—See Noritake Co., Limited; *Int'l*, pg. 5429
TONO KENMA CO., LTD.—See Noritake Co., Limited; *Int'l*, pg. 5429
TONOLLI CANADA LTD.; *Int'l*, pg. 7810

TONOPAH DIVIDE MINING CO.; *U.S. Public*, pg. 2162
TONO SEIKI CO., LTD.—See Seiko Group Corporation; *Int'l*, pg. 6688
TONOWO INC.—See Hoftex Group AG; *Int'l*, pg. 3441
TONROL BIO-PHARMACEUTICAL CO., LTD.—See Shanghai RAAS Blood Products Co., Ltd.; *Int'l*, pg. 6777
TONSA AUTOMOTIVE INC.; *U.S. Private*, pg. 4185
TONSAN ADHESIVE, INC.—See H.B. Fuller Company; *U.S. Public*, pg. 978
TONSAN ADHESIVE U.S., INC.—See H.B. Fuller Company; *U.S. Public*, pg. 978
TONS LIGHTOLOGY, INC.; *Int'l*, pg. 7810
TONTEK DESIGN TECHNOLOGY CO., LTD.; *Int'l*, pg. 7810
TONTEK TECHNOLOGY (SHENZHEN) CO., LTD.—See Tontek Design Technology Co., Ltd.; *Int'l*, pg. 7810
TONY DOMIANO AUTO DEALERSHIPS; *U.S. Private*, pg. 4185
TONY DOWNS FOODS—See Downs Food Group; *U.S. Private*, pg. 1269
TONY FUN, INC.; *Int'l*, pg. 7810
TONY GULLO MOTORS OF TEXAS, INC.; *U.S. Private*, pg. 4185
TON YI INDUSTRIAL CORP.—See Uni-President Enterprises Corporation; *Int'l*, pg. 8029
TONY MARTERIE & ASSOCIATES; *U.S. Private*, pg. 4185
TONYMOLY CO., LTD.; *Int'l*, pg. 7810
TONY'S EXPRESS INC.; *U.S. Private*, pg. 4185
TONY'S FINE FOODS INC.—See United Natural Foods, Inc.; *U.S. Public*, pg. 2233
TONY'S SEAFOOD LTD; *U.S. Private*, pg. 4185
TONY VOLKSWAGEN; *U.S. Private*, pg. 4185
TONZE NEW ENERGY TECHNOLOGY CO., LTD.; *Int'l*, pg. 7810
TOO ALFAR—See Ading AD; *Int'l*, pg. 149
TOO APS ENERGIA KAZAKHSTAN—See APS Energia SA; *Int'l*, pg. 523
TOO AVENA ASTANA—See Apetit Plc; *Int'l*, pg. 509
TOOELE CLINIC CORP.—See Quorum Health Corporation; *U.S. Private*, pg. 3330
TOO FACED COSMETICS, LLC—See The Estee Lauder Companies Inc.; *U.S. Public*, pg. 2073
TOOF COMMERCIAL PRINTING; *U.S. Private*, pg. 4185
TOOHEYS PTY. LIMITED—See Kirin Holdings Company, Limited; *Int'l*, pg. 4189
TOOJAY'S MANAGEMENT CORP.; *U.S. Private*, pg. 4185
TOO KARL STORZ ENDOSCOPY KAZAKHSTAN—See Karl Storz GmbH & Co.; *Int'l*, pg. 4083
TOO KNAUF GIPS KAPTSCHAGAJ—See Gebr. Knauf KG; *Int'l*, pg. 2908
TOO KSB KAZAKHSTAN—See KSB SE & Co. KGaA; *Int'l*, pg. 4313
TOOL & ABRASIVE SUPPLY, INC.—See DoALL Company; *U.S. Private*, pg. 1250
TOOLBARN.COM, INC.; *U.S. Private*, pg. 4186
TOOLBOX.CO.UK—See Grafton Group plc; *Int'l*, pg. 3051
TOOLBOX NO. 9 INC.—See Band of Coders, LP; *U.S. Private*, pg. 464
TOOL CENTER, INC.—See Mattsco Supply Co.; *U.S. Private*, pg. 2614
TOO LEIPURIN—See Aspo Oyj; *Int'l*, pg. 631
TOO LEMKEN KAZ—See Lemken GmbH & Co. KG; *Int'l*, pg. 4449
TOOL FABRICATION CORPORATION—See TruArc Partners, L.P.; *U.S. Private*, pg. 4245
TOOL FRANCE S.A.R.L.—See Tenex Capital Management, L.P.; *U.S. Private*, pg. 3966
TOOLGEN, INC.; *Int'l*, pg. 7810
TOOLING & EQUIPMENT INTERNATIONAL CORP.—See General Motors Company; *U.S. Public*, pg. 929
TOOLING INTERNATIONAL LTD.—See Wurth Verwaltungsgesellschaft mbH; *Int'l*, pg. 8508
TOOLING SPECIALISTS INC.; *U.S. Private*, pg. 4186
TOOLING TECHNOLOGY, LLC—See GenNx360 Capital Partners, L.P.; *U.S. Private*, pg. 1672
TOOL KING; *U.S. Private*, pg. 4185
TOOL MART INC.; *U.S. Private*, pg. 4185
TOOLMEX CORPORATION—See Mex Holdings Co. Ltd.; *Int'l*, pg. 4869
TOOLPUSHER SUPPLY CO.—See True Companies; *U.S. Private*, pg. 4247
TOOLROOM TECHNOLOGY LTD.—See Starrag Group Holding AG; *Int'l*, pg. 7179
TOOLS ACT COMPANY LIMITED—See Einhell Germany AG; *Int'l*, pg. 2334
TOOL SERVICE CORPORATION—See TruArc Partners, L.P.; *U.S. Private*, pg. 4245
TOOLS FOR SCHOOLS, INC.—See Alvarez & Marsal, Inc.; *U.S. Private*, pg. 213
TOOLS FOR SCHOOLS, INC.—See Highview Capital, LLC; *U.S. Private*, pg. 1942
TOOLS INDUSTRIBEHOV GJOVIK AS; *Int'l*, pg. 7810
TOOL-SMITH COMPANY, INC.; *U.S. Private*, pg. 4185
TOOL SOURCE WAREHOUSE, INC.—See GMS Inc.; *U.S. Public*, pg. 948

COMPANY NAME INDEX

TOOLSPEC MANUFACTURING COMPANY LTD.—See Cooper Coated Coil Management Limited; *Int'l*, pg. 1791
TOOLSRENT24 VERMIETUNGS- UND HANDELSGESELLSCHAFT MBH—See United Rentals, Inc.; *U.S. Public*, pg. 2235
TOOL STEEL SERVICE, INC.; *U.S. Private*, pg. 4185
TOOL SUPPLY, INC.—See DXP Enterprises, Inc.; *U.S. Public*, pg. 698
TOOL TECH, INC.; *U.S. Private*, pg. 4185
TOOLTEC (QINGDAO) TOOL CO LTD—See Atlas Copco AB; *Int'l*, pg. 684
TOOLUX SANDING S.A.; *Int'l*, pg. 7810
TOOLWATCH CORP.; *U.S. Private*, pg. 4186
TOOLWIRE, INC.; *U.S. Private*, pg. 4186
TOOLWORX INFORMATION PRODUCTS, INC.—See Raco Industries, Inc.; *U.S. Private*, pg. 3342
TOO NOKIAN TYRES—See Nokian Renkaat Oyj; *Int'l*, pg. 5407
TOONTEC SOLUTIONS CO., LTD.—See Amiya Corporation; *Int'l*, pg. 428
TOO PETRO WELT KAZAKHSTAN—See Petro Welt Technologies AG; *Int'l*, pg. 5825
TOOPLE PLC; *Int'l*, pg. 7810
TOO PLUS MICRO KAZAKHSTAN LP—See EPAM Systems, Inc.; *U.S. Public*, pg. 783
TOO RENOLIT—See RENOLIT SE; *Int'l*, pg. 6285
TOO RHENUS LOGISTICS—See RETHMANN AG & Co. KG; *Int'l*, pg. 6309
TOO ROBERT BOSCH—See Robert Bosch GmbH; *Int'l*, pg. 6368
TOOSLA SA; *Int'l*, pg. 7810
TOO TGLL KAZ LOGISTICS—See Taewoong Logistics Co., Ltd.; *Int'l*, pg. 7406
TOOTH & NAIL, LLC—See Universal Music Group N.V.; *Int'l*, pg. 8079
TOOTIE PIE COMPANY, INC.; *U.S. Private*, pg. 4186
TOO TIKKURILA—See PPG Industries, Inc.; *U.S. Public*, pg. 1710
TOOT'N TOTUM FOOD STORES LLC; *U.S. Private*, pg. 4186
THE TOOTSIE ROLL COMPANY—See Tootsie Roll Industries, Inc.; *U.S. Public*, pg. 2163
TOOTSIE ROLL INDUSTRIES, INC.; *U.S. Public*, pg. 2163
TOOTSIE ROLL MANAGEMENT INC—See Tootsie Roll Industries, Inc.; *U.S. Public*, pg. 2163
TOOTSIE ROLLS-LATIN AMERICA, INC.—See Tootsie Roll Industries, Inc.; *U.S. Public*, pg. 2163
TOO VBH—See VBH Holding AG; *Int'l*, pg. 8139
TOOWOOMBA DIAGNOSTIC IMAGING PTY. LTD.—See Healius Limited; *Int'l*, pg. 3303
TOP 10 CANADIAN FINANCIAL TRUST; *Int'l*, pg. 7811
TOP 10 SPLIT TRUST; *Int'l*, pg. 7811
TOP 20 EUROPE DIVIDEND TRUST—See The Bank of Nova Scotia; *Int'l*, pg. 7617
TOP 20 U.S. DIVIDEND TRUST—See The Bank of Nova Scotia; *Int'l*, pg. 7617
TOPAC GMBH—See Bertelsmann SE & Co. KGaA; *Int'l*, pg. 997
TOPA EQUITIES LTD, INC.; *U.S. Private*, pg. 4186
TOP AG COOPERATIVE—See Top Egg; *U.S. Private*, pg. 4186
TOPA INSURANCE COMPANY—See Topa Equities Ltd, Inc.; *U.S. Private*, pg. 4186
TOPA INSURANCE SERVICES—See Topa Equities Ltd, Inc.; *U.S. Private*, pg. 4187
TOPAK MARKETING INC.—See The Peter Group, Inc.; *U.S. Private*, pg. 4094
TOPALLIANCE BIOSCIENCES INC.—See Shanghai Junshi Biosciences Co., Ltd.; *Int'l*, pg. 6773
TOPA MANAGEMENT COMPANY—See Topa Equities Ltd, Inc.; *U.S. Private*, pg. 4187
TOPA PROPERTIES, LTD.—See Topa Equities Ltd, Inc.; *U.S. Private*, pg. 4187
TOPAQ PTY LIMITED—See Pentair plc; *Int'l*, pg. 5791
TOPAS ADVANCED POLYMERS GMBH—See Daicel Corporation; *Int'l*, pg. 1920
TOPAS GMBH—See DZ BANK AG Deutsche Zentral-Genossenschaftsbank; *Int'l*, pg. 2245
TOPASIA COMPUTER LIMITED; *Int'l*, pg. 7813
TOPAS VATTENAB—See Sdiptech AB; *Int'l*, pg. 6659
TOPAS VATTEN SERVICE AB—See Sdiptech AB; *Int'l*, pg. 6659
TOPAZ CO., LTD.—See Lumens Co., Ltd.; *Int'l*, pg. 4578
TOPAZ ENERGY GROUP LIMITED—See Alimentation Couche-Tard Inc.; *Int'l*, pg. 328
THE TOPAZ GROUP, INC.; *Int'l*, pg. 7694
TOPAZ HOTEL—See Pebblebrook Hotel Trust; *U.S. Public*, pg. 1660
TOPAZ LIGHTING CORP; *U.S. Private*, pg. 4187
TOPAZ RESOURCES, INC.; *U.S. Public*, pg. 2163
TOPAZ SYSTEMS, INC.; *U.S. Private*, pg. 4187
TOPBAND INDIA PRIVATE LIMITED—See Shenzhen Topband Co., Ltd.; *Int'l*, pg. 6823
TOPBI INTERNATIONAL HOLDINGS LIMITED; *Int'l*, pg. 7813
TOPBRANDS EUROPE B.V.—See B&S Group S.A.; *Int'l*, pg. 784
TOP BRANDS, INC.; *U.S. Private*, pg. 4186

TOP BRIGHT HOLDING CO., LTD.; *Int'l*, pg. 7811
TOPBUILD CORP.; *U.S. Public*, pg. 2163
TOP BUILDERS CAPITAL BERHAD; *Int'l*, pg. 7811
TOPCARD SERVICE AG—See UBS Group AG; *Int'l*, pg. 8007
TOPCELL SOLAR INTERNATIONAL CO. LTD.—See United Microelectronics Corporation; *Int'l*, pg. 8070
TOP CHANCE PROPERTIES PTE LTD—See Second Chance Properties Ltd.; *Int'l*, pg. 6672
TOPCHEM MATERIALS CORP—See TOPCO Scientific Co., Ltd.; *Int'l*, pg. 7814
TOPCHOICE MEDICAL CORPORATION; *Int'l*, pg. 7813
TOP CLASS ACTIONS LLC; *U.S. Private*, pg. 4186
TOPCLIMA - CLIMAVENETA SPAIN—See Mitsubishi Electric Corporation; *Int'l*, pg. 4944
TOPCO ASSOCIATES LLC—See Topco Holdings Inc.; *U.S. Private*, pg. 4187
TOPCODER, INC.—See Wipro Limited; *Int'l*, pg. 8432
TOPCODI S.L.—See Vivendi SE; *Int'l*, pg. 8276
TOPCO HOLDINGS INC.; *U.S. Private*, pg. 4187
TOP-COMMENT RESOURCES COMPANY LIMITED—See Cleanaway Company Limited; *Int'l*, pg. 1654
TOPCON AGRICULTURE CANADA, INC.—See Topcon Corporation; *Int'l*, pg. 7814
TOPCON AGRICULTURE S.P.A.—See Topcon Corporation; *Int'l*, pg. 7814
TOPCON AMERICA CORPORATION—See Topcon Corporation; *Int'l*, pg. 7814
TOPCON AUSTRALIA PTY. LTD.—See Topcon Corporation; *Int'l*, pg. 7814
TOPCON (BEIJING) MEDICAL TECHNOLOGY CO., LTD.—See Topcon Corporation; *Int'l*, pg. 7814
TOPCON (BEIJING) OPTO-ELECTRONICS CORPORATION—See Topcon Corporation; *Int'l*, pg. 7814
TOPCON CANADA, INC.—See Topcon Corporation; *Int'l*, pg. 7814
TOPCON CORPORATION; *Int'l*, pg. 7814
TOPCON DEUTSCHLAND GMBH—See Topcon Corporation; *Int'l*, pg. 7815
TOPCON DEUTSCHLAND MEDICAL GMBH—See Topcon Corporation; *Int'l*, pg. 7814
TOPCON DEUTSCHLAND POSITIONING G.M.B.H.—See Topcon Corporation; *Int'l*, pg. 7814
TOPCON ELECTRONICS GMBH & CO. KG—See Topcon Corporation; *Int'l*, pg. 7815
TOPCON ESPANA S.A.—See Topcon Corporation; *Int'l*, pg. 7815
TOPCON ESSILOR JAPAN, CO., LTD.—See Topcon Corporation; *Int'l*, pg. 7815
TOPCON EUROPE B.V.—See Topcon Corporation; *Int'l*, pg. 7815
TOPCON EUROPE MEDICAL B.V.—See Topcon Corporation; *Int'l*, pg. 7815
TOPCON EUROPE POSITIONING B.V.—See Japan Industrial Partners, Inc.; *Int'l*, pg. 3891
TOPCON FRANCE MEDICAL S.A.S.—See Topcon Corporation; *Int'l*, pg. 7815
TOPCON (GREAT BRITAIN) LTD.—See Topcon Corporation; *Int'l*, pg. 7815
TOPCON (GREAT BRITAIN) MEDICAL LTD.—See Topcon Corporation; *Int'l*, pg. 7814
TOPCON G.S. CORPORATION—See Topcon Corporation; *Int'l*, pg. 7815
TOPCON HEALTHCARE SOLUTIONS ASIA PACIFIC PTE. LTD.—See Topcon Corporation; *Int'l*, pg. 7815
TOPCON HEALTHCARE SOLUTIONS AUSTRALIA PTY LTD.—See Topcon Corporation; *Int'l*, pg. 7815
TOPCON HEALTHCARE SOLUTIONS EMEA OY—See Topcon Corporation; *Int'l*, pg. 7815
TOPCON HEALTHCARE SOLUTIONS, INC.—See Topcon Corporation; *Int'l*, pg. 7815
TOPCON HK (BD) LTD.—See Topcon Corporation; *Int'l*, pg. 7815
TOPCON INFOMOBILITY S.R.L.—See Topcon Corporation; *Int'l*, pg. 7815
TOPCON INSTRUMENTS (MALAYSIA) SDN. BHD.—See Topcon Corporation; *Int'l*, pg. 7815
TOPCON INSTRUMENTS (THAILAND) CO., LTD.—See Topcon Corporation; *Int'l*, pg. 7815
TOPCON KOREA CORPORATION—See Topcon Corporation; *Int'l*, pg. 7815
TOPCON MEDICAL JAPAN CO., LTD.—See Topcon Corporation; *Int'l*, pg. 7815
TOPCON MEDICAL LASER SYSTEMS, INC.—See Topcon Corporation; *Int'l*, pg. 7814
TOPCON MEDICAL SYSTEMS, INC.—See Topcon Corporation; *Int'l*, pg. 7814
TOPCON MIRAGE TECHNOLOGIES. S.L.—See Topcon Corporation; *Int'l*, pg. 7815
TOPCON OPTICAL (DONGGUAN) TECHNOLOGY LTD.—See Topcon Corporation; *Int'l*, pg. 7815
TOPCON OPTICAL (H.K.) LTD.—See Topcon Corporation; *Int'l*, pg. 7815
TOPCON OPTONEXUS CO., LTD.—See Topcon Corporation; *Int'l*, pg. 7815
TOPCON POLSKA SP. ZO. O.—See Topcon Corporation; *Int'l*, pg. 7815

TOP ENGINEERING CO., LTD.

TOPCON POSITIONING ASIA CO., LTD.—See Topcon Corporation; *Int'l*, pg. 7815
TOPCON POSITIONING ASIA (MALAYSIA) SDN. BHD.—See Topcon Corporation; *Int'l*, pg. 7815
TOPCON POSITIONING BELGIUM BV BA—See Topcon Corporation; *Int'l*, pg. 7815
TOPCON POSITIONING CANARIAS, S.L.—See Topcon Corporation; *Int'l*, pg. 7815
TOPCON POSITIONING FRANCE S.A.S.—See Topcon Corporation; *Int'l*, pg. 7815
TOPCON POSITIONING (GREAT BRITAIN) LTD.—See Topcon Corporation; *Int'l*, pg. 7815
TOPCON POSITIONING ITALY S.R.L.—See Topcon Corporation; *Int'l*, pg. 7815
TOPCON POSITIONING MIDDLE EAST AND AFRICA FZE—See Topcon Corporation; *Int'l*, pg. 7815
TOPCON POSITIONING PORTUGAL, LDA.—See Topcon Corporation; *Int'l*, pg. 7815
TOPCON POSITIONING SPAIN, S.L.U.—See Topcon Corporation; *Int'l*, pg. 7815
TOPCON POSITIONING SYSTEMS (AUSTRALIA) PTY LTD.—See Topcon Corporation; *Int'l*, pg. 7815
TOPCON POSITIONING SYSTEMS, INC—See Topcon Corporation; *Int'l*, pg. 7815
TOPCON PRECISION AG EUROPE S.L.—See Topcon Corporation; *Int'l*, pg. 7815
TOPCON PRECISION AGRICULTURE PTY LTD.—See Topcon Corporation; *Int'l*, pg. 7815
TOPCON S.A.R.L.—See Topcon Corporation; *Int'l*, pg. 7815
TOPCON SCANDINAVIA AB—See Topcon Corporation; *Int'l*, pg. 7815
TOPCON SINGAPORE HOLDINGS PTE. LTD.—See Topcon Corporation; *Int'l*, pg. 7815
TOPCON SINGAPORE MEDICAL PTE LTD—See Topcon Corporation; *Int'l*, pg. 7815
TOPCON SINGAPORE POSITIONING PTE. LTD.—See Topcon Corporation; *Int'l*, pg. 7815
TOPCON SINGAPORE POSITIONING SALES PTE LTD—See Topcon Corporation; *Int'l*, pg. 7815
TOPCON SOKKIA INDIA PVT. LTD.—See Topcon Corporation; *Int'l*, pg. 7815
TOPCON SOKKIA POSITIONING JAPAN CO., LTD.—See Topcon Corporation; *Int'l*, pg. 7815
TOPCON TECHNOHOUSE CORPORATION—See Topcon Corporation; *Int'l*, pg. 7816
TOPCON TECHNOLOGY FINLAND OY—See Topcon Corporation; *Int'l*, pg. 7816
TOPCON TECHNOLOGY LTD.—See Topcon Corporation; *Int'l*, pg. 7816
TOPCONTRACTS GMBH—See HTC Global Services Inc.; *U.S. Private*, pg. 1999
TOPCON YAMAGATA CO., LTD.—See Topcon Corporation; *Int'l*, pg. 7816
TOPCO OILSITE PRODUCTS LTD.; *Int'l*, pg. 7813
TOPCO OILSITE PRODUCTS (USA) INC.—See Topco Oilsite Products Ltd.; *Int'l*, pg. 7814
TOPCO QUARTZ PRODUCT CO., LTD.—See Shin-Etsu Chemical Co. Ltd.; *Int'l*, pg. 6841
TOPCO QUARTZ PRODUCTS CO., LTD.—See TOPCO Scientific Co., Ltd.; *Int'l*, pg. 7814
TOPCO SCIENTIFIC CO., LTD.; *Int'l*, pg. 7814
TOPCO SCIENTIFIC (SHANGHAI) CO., LTD.—See Federmann Enterprises, Ltd.; *Int'l*, pg. 2631
TOPCO SCIENTIFIC USA CORP.—See TOPCO Scientific Co., Ltd.; *Int'l*, pg. 7814
TOPCO (SHANGHAI) CO., LTD.—See Evermore Chemical Industry Co., Ltd.; *Int'l*, pg. 2568
TOPCRAFT PRECISION MOLDERS, INC.; *U.S. Private*, pg. 4187
TOP CREATION INVESTMENTS LTD; *Int'l*, pg. 7811
TOP CREATION LIMITED—See Dickson Concepts (International) Limited; *Int'l*, pg. 2112
TOP CULTURE CO., LTD.; *Int'l*, pg. 7811
TOPDANMARK A/S; *Int'l*, pg. 7816
TOPDANMARK EJENDOM A/S—See Topdanmark A/S; *Int'l*, pg. 7816
TOP DEGREE (M) SDN. BHD.—See RGT Berhad; *Int'l*, pg. 6319
TOPDEK, INC.; *U.S. Private*, pg. 4187
THE TOP DIE CASTING CO. INC.; *U.S. Private*, pg. 4127
TOP DYNAMIC ENTERPRISES LIMITED - DONGGUAN FACTORY—See Brainhole Technology Limited; *Int'l*, pg. 1137
TOP EDUCATION GROUP LTD.; *Int'l*, pg. 7811
TOP EGG; *U.S. Private*, pg. 4186
THE TOPEKA CAPITAL-JOURNAL—See Gannett Co., Inc.; *U.S. Public*, pg. 905
TOPEKA METAL SPECIALTIES—See L B Industries, Inc.; *U.S. Private*, pg. 2361
TOPEKA PRODUCTION CENTER—See Hallmark Cards, Inc.; *U.S. Private*, pg. 1845
TOP ELECTRODES SDN. BHD.—See Atlantic China Welding Consumables, Inc.; *Int'l*, pg. 674
TOP END ENERGY LIMITED; *Int'l*, pg. 7811
TOP ENERGY COMPANY LTD.; *Int'l*, pg. 7811
TOP ENGINEERING CO., LTD.; *Int'l*, pg. 7811
TOP ENGINEERING INC.—See Hirayama Holdings Co., Ltd.; *Int'l*, pg. 3404

TOP ENGINEERING CO., LTD. CORPORATE AFFILIATIONS

TOPERA, INC.—See Abbott Laboratories; *U.S. Public*, pg. 21
TOPETE/STONEFIELD, INCORPORATED; *U.S. Private*, pg. 4187
TOP FINANCIAL GROUP LIMITED; *Int'l*, pg. 7811
TOPFLIGHT AB—See Indutrade AB; *Int'l*, pg. 3681
TOPFLIGHT CORPORATION; *U.S. Private*, pg. 4187
TOPFLIGHT GRAIN COOPERATIVE INC.; *U.S. Private*, pg. 4187
TOP FLIGHT, INC.; *U.S. Private*, pg. 4186
TOP FLITE CONSTRUCTION INC.; *U.S. Private*, pg. 4186
TOP FLITE FINANCIAL, INC.; *U.S. Private*, pg. 4186
TOPFLOOR SYSTEMS LIMITED—See Software Circle plc.; *Int'l*, pg. 7057
TOPFOND PHARMACEUTICAL CO., LTD.—See China Meheco Group Co., Ltd.; *Int'l*, pg. 1519
TOP FORM INTERNATIONAL LTD - CHINA NANHOI FACTORY—See Top Form International Ltd; *Int'l*, pg. 7811
TOP FORM INTERNATIONAL LTD - CHINA SHENZHEN FACTORY—See Top Form International Ltd; *Int'l*, pg. 7811
TOP FORM INTERNATIONAL LTD; *Int'l*, pg. 7811
TOP FRONTIER INVESTMENT HOLDINGS, INC.; *Int'l*, pg. 7811
TOP GAARKEUKEN B.V.—See Sweco AB; *Int'l*, pg. 7364
TOP GLASS S.P.A.—See Kemrock Industries & Exports Ltd.; *Int'l*, pg. 4125
TOP GLOBAL LIMITED; *Int'l*, pg. 7812
TOP GLOBAL REAL ESTATE INVESTMENT PTE. LTD.—See Top Global Limited; *Int'l*, pg. 7812
TOP GLORY ELECTRONICS CO., LTD.—See Behavior Tech Computer Corporation; *Int'l*, pg. 941
TOP GLOVE CORPORATION BHD.; *Int'l*, pg. 7812
TOP GLOVE EUROPE GMBH—See Top Glove Corporation Bhd.; *Int'l*, pg. 7812
TOP GLOVE MEDICAL (THAILAND) CO. LTD.—See Top Glove Corporation Bhd.; *Int'l*, pg. 7812
TOP GLOVE SDN. BHD. - FACTORY 11—See Top Glove Corporation Bhd.; *Int'l*, pg. 7812
TOP GLOVE SDN. BHD. - FACTORY 13—See Top Glove Corporation Bhd.; *Int'l*, pg. 7812
TOP GLOVE SDN. BHD. - FACTORY 19—See Top Glove Corporation Bhd.; *Int'l*, pg. 7812
TOP GLOVE SDN. BHD. - FACTORY 4—See Top Glove Corporation Bhd.; *Int'l*, pg. 7812
TOP GLOVE SDN. BHD. - FACTORY 5—See Top Glove Corporation Bhd.; *Int'l*, pg. 7812
TOP GLOVE SDN. BHD.—See Top Glove Corporation Bhd.; *Int'l*, pg. 7812
TOP GLOVE TECHNOLOGY (THAILAND) CO. LTD.—See Top Glove Corporation Bhd.; *Int'l*, pg. 7812
TOPGOLF CALLAWAY BRANDS CORP.; *U.S. Public*, pg. 2164
TOPGOLF INTERNATIONAL, INC.—See Topgolf Callaway Brands Corp.; *U.S. Public*, pg. 2164
TOP GRADE CONSTRUCTION, INC.—See Goodfellow Bros., Inc.; *U.S. Private*, pg. 1739
TOPGREEN TECHNOLOGY CO., LTD; *Int'l*, pg. 7812
TOP GUN PRESSURE WASHING, INC.—See Osceola Capital Management, LLC; *U.S. Private*, pg. 3047
TOP GUN SALES PERFORMANCE; *U.S. Private*, pg. 4186
TOP GUN SECURITY SERVICES—See BC Partners LLP; *Int'l*, pg. 924
TOPHAT LOGISTICAL SOLUTIONS, LLC—See Atlas World Group, Inc.; *U.S. Private*, pg. 380
TOPHATMONOCLE CORP.; *Int'l*, pg. 7816
TOPHEDGE AKTIENGESELLSCHAFT; *Int'l*, pg. 7816
TOP HIGH IMAGE CORP.; *Int'l*, pg. 7812
TOP HITS INC.; *U.S. Private*, pg. 4186
TOPICA, INC.; *U.S. Private*, pg. 4187
TOPIC CO., LTD.—See DIC Corporation; *Int'l*, pg. 2111
TOPICS ENTERTAINMENT INC.; *U.S. Private*, pg. 4187
TOPICUS.COM INC.—See Constellation Software Inc.; *Int'l*, pg. 1774
TOP INFORMATION TECHNOLOGIES CO., LTD.—See Brookfield Corporation; *Int'l*, pg. 1181
TOPJECTS GMBH—See Allgeier SE; *Int'l*, pg. 337
TOPKAPI DANISMANLIK ELEKTRONIK HIZMETLER PAZARLAMA VE TICARET A.S.—See Turkiye Is Bankasi A.S.; *Int'l*, pg. 7976
TOPKEY CORPORATION; *Int'l*, pg. 7816
TOP KINGWIN LTD.; *Int'l*, pg. 7812
TOP KINISIS HELLAS—See Top Kinisis Travel Public Ltd; *Int'l*, pg. 7813
TOP KINISIS TRAVEL PUBLIC LTD; *Int'l*, pg. 7813
TOP KNOBS USA, INC.—See The Jordan Company, L.P.; *U.S. Private*, pg. 4062
TOP LABEL INTERNATIONAL LIMITED—See Continental Holdings Limited; *Int'l*, pg. 1784
TOPLAK GMBH—See EVN AG; *Int'l*, pg. 2571
T.O. PLASTICS, INC.—See Otter Tail Corporation; *U.S. Public*, pg. 1624
TOP LAYER REINSURANCE LTD.—See RenaissanceRe Holdings Ltd.; *Int'l*, pg. 6273
TOP LAYER REINSURANCE LTD.—See State Farm Mutual Automobile Insurance Company; *U.S. Private*, pg. 3792

TOPLEVEL COMPUTING LIMITED—See Siris Capital Group, LLC; *U.S. Private*, pg. 3673
TOPLINE FINANCIAL CREDIT UNION; *U.S. Private*, pg. 4187
TOPLINE FOOTWEAR CHINA, LTD.—See Topline Imports, Inc.; *U.S. Private*, pg. 4187
TOPLINE IMPORTS, INC.; *U.S. Private*, pg. 4187
TOPLINE KERAMIEK B.V.—See New Wave Group AB; *Int'l*, pg. 5231
TOP LINE PROCESS EQUIPMENT COMPANY—See Edgewater Services, LLC; *U.S. Private*, pg. 1335
TOPLINGO DEVELOPMENT, INC.; *U.S. Private*, pg. 4187
TOPLIVO AD—See Synergon Holding PLC; *Int'l*, pg. 7384
TOPLIVO GAS LTD.—See Synergon Holding PLC; *Int'l*, pg. 7384
TOPLOFIKATSIA ROUSSE EAD; *Int'l*, pg. 7816
TOPLUS GLOBAL CO., LTD.; *Int'l*, pg. 7816
T.O.P. MARKETING GROUP INC.; *U.S. Private*, pg. 3912
TOP MASTER, INC.—See O2 Investment Partners, LLC; *U.S. Private*, pg. 2982
TOP MASTER, INC.—See Oakland Standard Co., LLC; *U.S. Private*, pg. 2985
TOP MATERIAL CO., LTD.; *Int'l*, pg. 7813
TOP MEDIA NICARAGUA, S.A.—See JCDecaux S.A.; *Int'l*, pg. 3923
TOP MEERHOUT NV—See Group de Cloedt SA; *Int'l*, pg. 3088
TOP METAL BUYERS INC.; *U.S. Private*, pg. 4186
TOP METAL WORKS CO., LTD. - INCHEON FACILITY—See Seoyon Topmetal Co., Ltd.; *Int'l*, pg. 6717
TOP MIX CONCRETE PTE LTD—See EnGro Corporation Limited; *Int'l*, pg. 2436
TOPMOST GAMING CORP.—See Leisure & Resorts World Corporation; *Int'l*, pg. 4447
TOP NATION ELECTRONIC (SUZHOU) CO., LTD.—See Yao Sheng Electronics Co., Ltd.; *Int'l*, pg. 8566
TOP NORDIC FINLAND OY—See Atea ASA; *Int'l*, pg. 667
TOP NOTCH ENERGY SERVICES, INC.—See Intervale Capital, LLC; *U.S. Private*, pg. 2127
TOPNOTCH FOODS, INC.—See ReConserve, Inc.; *U.S. Private*, pg. 3371
TOPNOTCH RESORT & SPA—See Winston Harton Holdings, LLC; *U.S. Private*, pg. 4544
THE TOPOCEAN GROUP; *U.S. Private*, pg. 4127
TOP OF MIND NETWORKS, LLC—See Intercontinental Exchange, Inc.; *U.S. Public*, pg. 1142
TOP OF THE WORLD HOTEL—See Arctic Slope Regional Corporation; *U.S. Public*, pg. 316
TOPOINT TECHNOLOGY CO., LTD.; *Int'l*, pg. 7816
TOPOLA A.D. BACKA TOPOLA; *Int'l*, pg. 7816
TOPOLA LIVAR A.D.; *Int'l*, pg. 7816
TOPOLA UNIVERZAL A.D.; *Int'l*, pg. 7816
TOPO PLANIFICATION INC.—See Tetra Tech, Inc.; *U.S. Public*, pg. 2024
TOP OPTO TEC CO., LTD.—See Ability Opto-Electronics Technology Co., Ltd.; *Int'l*, pg. 61
TOPO TECHNOLOGY (SUZHOU) CO., LTD.—See Catcher Technology Co., Ltd.; *Int'l*, pg. 1359
TOPO TECHNOLOGY (TAIZHOU) CO., LTD.—See Catcher Technology Co., Ltd.; *Int'l*, pg. 1359
TOPPAN BEST-SET PREMEDIA (GUANGZHOU) LTD.—See TOPPAN Holdings Inc.; *Int'l*, pg. 7817
TOPPAN BEST-SET PREMEDIA LTD.—See TOPPAN Holdings Inc.; *Int'l*, pg. 7817
TOPPAN CHARACTER PRODUCTION CO., LTD.—See TOPPAN Holdings Inc.; *Int'l*, pg. 7817
TOPPAN CHUNGHWA ELECTRONICS CORPORATION—See TOPPAN Holdings Inc.; *Int'l*, pg. 7817
TOPPAN CO., LTD.—See TOPPAN Holdings Inc.; *Int'l*, pg. 7817
TOPPAN COMMUNICATION PRODUCTS CO., LTD.—See TOPPAN Holdings Inc.; *Int'l*, pg. 7817
TOPPAN COSMO EUROPE GMBH—See TOPPAN Holdings Inc.; *Int'l*, pg. 7818
TOPPAN COSMO, INC.—See TOPPAN Holdings Inc.; *Int'l*, pg. 7818
TOPPAN EDGE INC.—See TOPPAN Holdings Inc.; *Int'l*, pg. 7817
TOPPAN EDITORIAL COMMUNICATIONS CO., LTD.—See TOPPAN Holdings Inc.; *Int'l*, pg. 7818
TOPPAN ELECTRONICS CO., LTD.—See TOPPAN Holdings Inc.; *Int'l*, pg. 7818
TOPPAN ELECTRONICS FUJI CO., LTD.—See TOPPAN Holdings Inc.; *Int'l*, pg. 7818
TOPPAN ELECTRONICS, INC.—See TOPPAN Holdings Inc.; *Int'l*, pg. 7818
TOPPAN ELECTRONICS (TAIWAN) CO., LTD.—See TOPPAN Holdings Inc.; *Int'l*, pg. 7818
TOPPAN EUROPE GMBH—See TOPPAN Holdings Inc.; *Int'l*, pg. 7818
TOPPAN EUROPE GMBH—See TOPPAN Holdings Inc.; *Int'l*, pg. 7818
TOPPAN EXCEL PRINTING (GUANGZHOU) CO., LTD.—See TOPPAN Holdings Inc.; *Int'l*, pg. 7818
TOPPAN EXCEL (THAILAND) CO., LTD—See TOPPAN Holdings Inc.; *Int'l*, pg. 7818

TOPPAN FORMS CARD TECHNOLOGIES LTD.—See TOPPAN Holdings Inc.; *Int'l*, pg. 7818
TOPPAN FORMS CO., LTD.—See TOPPAN Holdings Inc.; *Int'l*, pg. 7818
TOPPAN FORMS COMPUTER SYSTEMS LTD.—See TOPPAN Holdings Inc.; *Int'l*, pg. 7818
TOPPAN FORMS (HONG KONG) LTD.—See TOPPAN Holdings Inc.; *Int'l*, pg. 7818
TOPPAN FORMS KANSAI CO., LTD.—See TOPPAN Holdings Inc.; *Int'l*, pg. 7818
TOPPAN FORMS NISHINIHON CO., LTD.—See TOPPAN Holdings Inc.; *Int'l*, pg. 7818
TOPPAN FORMS OPERATION CO., LTD.—See TOPPAN Holdings Inc.; *Int'l*, pg. 7818
TOPPAN FORMS (SANYO) CO., LTD.—See TOPPAN Holdings Inc.; *Int'l*, pg. 7818
TOPPAN FORMS (S) PTE. LTD.—See TOPPAN Holdings Inc.; *Int'l*, pg. 7818
TOPPAN FORMS TOKAI CO., LTD—See TOPPAN Holdings Inc.; *Int'l*, pg. 7818
TOPPAN GRAPHIC COMMUNICATIONS CO., LTD.—See TOPPAN Holdings Inc.; *Int'l*, pg. 7818
TOPPAN GRAVITY LIMITED—See TOPPAN Holdings Inc.; *Int'l*, pg. 7818
TOPPAN HALL CO., LTD.—See TOPPAN Holdings Inc.; *Int'l*, pg. 7818
TOPPAN HARIMA PRODUCTS CO., LTD.—See TOPPAN Holdings Inc.; *Int'l*, pg. 7818
TOPPAN HOKKAIDO INSATSUKAKO CO., LTD.—See TOPPAN Holdings Inc.; *Int'l*, pg. 7818
TOPPAN HOLDINGS INC.; *Int'l*, pg. 7816
TOPPAN HUMAN INFORMATION SERVICES CO., LTD.—See TOPPAN Holdings Inc.; *Int'l*, pg. 7818
TOPPAN INFOMEDIA CO., LTD.—See TOPPAN Holdings Inc.; *Int'l*, pg. 7818
TOPPAN INSURANCE SERVICE CO., LTD.—See TOPPAN Holdings Inc.; *Int'l*, pg. 7818
TOPPAN INTERAMERICA, INC.—See TOPPAN Holdings Inc.; *Int'l*, pg. 7818
TOPPAN LEEFUNG ADVERTISING (SHANGHAI) CO., LTD.—See TOPPAN Holdings Inc.; *Int'l*, pg. 7818
TOPPAN LEEFUNG (HONG KONG) LTD.—See TOPPAN Holdings Inc.; *Int'l*, pg. 7818
TOPPAN LEEFUNG PACKAGING & PRINTING (BEIJING) CO., LTD.—See TOPPAN Holdings Inc.; *Int'l*, pg. 7818
TOPPAN LEEFUNG PRINTING LTD.—See TOPPAN Holdings Inc.; *Int'l*, pg. 7818
TOPPAN LEEFUNG PTE. LTD.—See TOPPAN Holdings Inc.; *Int'l*, pg. 7818
TOPPAN LOGISTICS CO., LTD.—See TOPPAN Holdings Inc.; *Int'l*, pg. 7819
TOPPAN MANAGEMENT SYSTEMS (S) PTE. LTD.—See TOPPAN Holdings Inc.; *Int'l*, pg. 7819
TOPPAN MEDIA PRINTEC KANSAI CO., LTD.—See TOPPAN Holdings Inc.; *Int'l*, pg. 7819
TOPPAN MEDIA PRINTEC TOKYO CO., LTD—See TOPPAN Holdings Inc.; *Int'l*, pg. 7819
TOPPAN MEDIA PRINTING HOKKAIDO CO., LTD.—See TOPPAN Holdings Inc.; *Int'l*, pg. 7819
TOPPAN M&I LTD.—See TOPPAN Holdings Inc.; *Int'l*, pg. 7819
TOPPAN MIND WELLNESS CO., LTD.—See TOPPAN Holdings Inc.; *Int'l*, pg. 7819
TOPPAN PACKS CO., LTD.—See TOPPAN Holdings Inc.; *Int'l*, pg. 7819
TOPPAN PHOTOMASKS FRANCE S.A.S.—See TOPPAN Holdings Inc.; *Int'l*, pg. 7819
TOPPAN PHOTOMASKS GERMANY GMBH—See TOPPAN Holdings Inc.; *Int'l*, pg. 7819
TOPPAN PHOTOMASKS GMBH—See TOPPAN Holdings Inc.; *Int'l*, pg. 7819
TOPPAN PHOTOMASKS, INC. - COLORADO SPRINGS—See TOPPAN Holdings Inc.; *Int'l*, pg. 7819
TOPPAN PHOTOMASKS, INC. - SANTA CLARA—See TOPPAN Holdings Inc.; *Int'l*, pg. 7819
TOPPAN PHOTOMASKS, INC.—See TOPPAN Holdings Inc.; *Int'l*, pg. 7819
TOPPAN PLASTIC CO., LTD.—See TOPPAN Holdings Inc.; *Int'l*, pg. 7819
TOPPAN PRINTING CO. (AMERICA), INC.—See TOPPAN Holdings Inc.; *Int'l*, pg. 7819
TOPPAN PRINTING CO., (HK) LTD.—See TOPPAN Holdings Inc.; *Int'l*, pg. 7819
TOPPAN PRINTING CO., LTD. - CHUBU DIVISION—See TOPPAN Holdings Inc.; *Int'l*, pg. 7819
TOPPAN PRINTING CO., LTD. - ELECTRONICS DIVISION—See TOPPAN Holdings Inc.; *Int'l*, pg. 7819
TOPPAN PRINTING CO., LTD. - HIGASHINIHON DIVISION—See TOPPAN Holdings Inc.; *Int'l*, pg. 7819
TOPPAN PRINTING CO., LTD. - HOKKAIDO DIVISION—See TOPPAN Holdings Inc.; *Int'l*, pg. 7819
TOPPAN PRINTING CO., LTD. - INFORMATION AND COMMUNICATION DIVISION—See TOPPAN Holdings Inc.; *Int'l*, pg. 7819
TOPPAN PRINTING CO., LTD. INTERNATIONAL BUSINESS LAW CENTER—See TOPPAN Holdings Inc.; *Int'l*, pg. 7819
TOPPAN PRINTING CO., LTD. - INTERNATIONAL DIVISION—See TOPPAN Holdings Inc.; *Int'l*, pg. 7819

COMPANY NAME INDEX — TOP WEALTH GROUP HOLDING LIMITED

TOPPAN PRINTING CO., LTD. - KANSAI DIVISION—See TOPPAN Holdings Inc.; *Int'l*, pg. 7819
TOPPAN PRINTING CO., LTD. - LIVING ENVIRONMENT DIVISION—See TOPPAN Holdings Inc.; *Int'l*, pg. 7819
TOPPAN PRINTING CO., LTD. - NISHINIHON DIVISION—See TOPPAN Holdings Inc.; *Int'l*, pg. 7819
TOPPAN PRINTING CO., LTD.—See TOPPAN Holdings Inc.; *Int'l*, pg. 7819
TOPPAN PRINTING CO., LTD.—See TOPPAN Holdings Inc.; *Int'l*, pg. 7819
TOPPAN PRINTING CO., LTD.—See TOPPAN Holdings Inc.; *Int'l*, pg. 7819
TOPPAN PRINTING CO., (SHANGHAI) LTD.—See TOPPAN Holdings Inc.; *Int'l*, pg. 7819
TOPPAN PRINTING CO., (SHENZHEN) LTD.—See TOPPAN Holdings Inc.; *Int'l*, pg. 7819
TOPPAN PRINTING CO. (UK) LTD.—See TOPPAN Holdings Inc.; *Int'l*, pg. 7819
TOPPAN PRINTING GREECE S.A.—See TOPPAN Holdings Inc.; *Int'l*, pg. 7819
TOPPAN PROSPRINT CO., LTD.—See TOPPAN Holdings Inc.; *Int'l*, pg. 7819
TOPPAN SECURITY PRINTING PTE. LTD.—See TOPPAN Holdings Inc.; *Int'l*, pg. 7818
TOPPAN SECURITY SERVICE CO., LTD.—See TOPPAN Holdings Inc.; *Int'l*, pg. 7819
TOPPAN SEIHON CO., LTD.—See TOPPAN Holdings Inc.; *Int'l*, pg. 7819
TOPPAN SEMICONDUCTOR SINGAPORE PTE. LTD.—See TOPPAN Holdings Inc.; *Int'l*, pg. 7819
TOPPAN (SHANGHAI) MANAGEMENT CO., LTD.—See TOPPAN Holdings Inc.; *Int'l*, pg. 7817
TOPPAN SMIC ELECTRONICS (SHANGHAI) CO., LTD.—See TOPPAN Holdings Inc.; *Int'l*, pg. 7819
TOPPAN SYSTEM SOLUTIONS CO., LTD.—See TOPPAN Holdings Inc.; *Int'l*, pg. 7819
TOPPAN TDK LABEL CO., LTD. - FUKUSHIMA PLANT—See TOPPAN Holdings Inc.; *Int'l*, pg. 7819
TOPPAN TDK LABEL CO., LTD. - SAGAMIHARA PLANT—See TOPPAN Holdings Inc.; *Int'l*, pg. 7819
TOPPAN TDK LABEL CO., LTD.—See TOPPAN Holdings Inc.; *Int'l*, pg. 7819
TOPPAN TDK LABEL CO., LTD. - TAKINO PLANT—See TOPPAN Holdings Inc.; *Int'l*, pg. 7820
TOPPAN TECHNICAL DESIGN CENTER CO., LTD.—See TOPPAN Holdings Inc.; *Int'l*, pg. 7820
TOPPAN TECHNO CO., LTD.—See TOPPAN Holdings Inc.; *Int'l*, pg. 7820
TOPPAN TOMOEGAWA OPTICAL FILMS CO., LTD.—See TOPPAN Holdings Inc.; *Int'l*, pg. 7820
TOPPAN TRAVEL SERVICE CORP.—See TOPPAN Holdings Inc.; *Int'l*, pg. 7820
TOPPAN USA, INC.—See TOPPAN Holdings Inc.; *Int'l*, pg. 7820
TOPPAN VITE LTD.—See TOPPAN Holdings Inc.; *Int'l*, pg. 7818
TOPPAN VITE PTE. LTD.—See TOPPAN Holdings Inc.; *Int'l*, pg. 7818
TOPPAN YAU YUE PAPER PRODUCTS LTD.—See TOPPAN Holdings Inc.; *Int'l*, pg. 7818
TOPPER EUROPE B.V.—See Tong-Tai Machine Tool Co., Ltd.; *Int'l*, pg. 7807
TOPPER INDUSTRIAL INC.; *U.S. Private*, pg. 4187
TOPPERS LLC—See Camsing Global, LLC; *U.S. Private*, pg. 732
TOP PERSONNEL S. DE R.L. DE CV—See Randstad N.V.; *Int'l*, pg. 6206
TOPPESFIELD LTD; *Int'l*, pg. 7820
TOPPFRYS AB—See Nomad Foods Limited; *Int'l*, pg. 5409
TOPPINO'S INC.; *U.S. Private*, pg. 4187
TOP PLANNING JAPAN CO., LTD.—See Takeei Corporation; *Int'l*, pg. 7440
TOPPOINT BV—See New Wave Group AB; *Int'l*, pg. 5231
TOPPOINT NEDERLAND B.V.—See New Wave Group AB; *Int'l*, pg. 5231
TOP PRODUCER SYSTEMS COMPANY ULC—See Constellation Real Estate Group, Inc.; *U.S. Private*, pg. 1023
TOP PROPERTY COMPANY LIMITED—See King Wai Group (Thailand) Public Company Limited; *Int'l*, pg. 4170
TOPPS ARGENTINA SRL—See Madison Dearborn Partners, LLC; *U.S. Private*, pg. 2542
TOPPS CANADA, INC.—See Madison Dearborn Partners, LLC; *U.S. Private*, pg. 2542
THE TOPPS COMPANY, INC.—See Madison Dearborn Partners, LLC; *U.S. Private*, pg. 2542
TOPPS EUROPE LIMITED—See Madison Dearborn Partners, LLC; *U.S. Private*, pg. 2542
TOPPS IRELAND LTD—See Madison Dearborn Partners, LLC; *U.S. Private*, pg. 2542
TOPPS ITALIA SRL—See Madison Dearborn Partners, LLC; *U.S. Private*, pg. 2542
TOPPS SAFETY APPAREL, INC.—See Pinnacle Textile Industries, LLC; *U.S. Private*, pg. 3186
TOPPS TILES PLC; *Int'l*, pg. 7820
TOPPS TILES (UK) LTD—See Topps Tiles Plc; *Int'l*, pg. 7820

TOP RACING GROUP LTD.—See HKS CO., LTD.; *Int'l*, pg. 3429
TOP RAMDOR SYSTEMS & COMPUTERS 1990 CO LTD.; *Int'l*, pg. 7813
TOPRANK ONLINE MARKETING; *U.S. Private*, pg. 4187
TOPRAY SOLAR CO., LTD.; *Int'l*, pg. 7820
TOPRAY SOLAR GMBH—See Topray Solar Co., Ltd.; *Int'l*, pg. 7820
TOPRAY SOLAR (UNITED STATES) CO., LTD.—See Topray Solar Co., Ltd.; *Int'l*, pg. 7820
TOPREALITY.SK S.R.O.—See Axel Springer SE; *Int'l*, pg. 767
TOPRE AMERICA CORPORATION—See Topre Corporation; *Int'l*, pg. 7820
TOPRE AUTOPARTS MEXICO, S.A. DE C.V.—See Topre Corporation; *Int'l*, pg. 7820
TOPREC CORPORATION—See Topre Corporation; *Int'l*, pg. 7820
TOPRE CORPORATION; *Int'l*, pg. 7820
TOPRE (FOSHAN) AUTOPARTS CORPORATION—See Topre Corporation; *Int'l*, pg. 7820
TOPRE GIFU CORPORATION—See Topre Corporation; *Int'l*, pg. 7820
TOPRE INDIA PVT. LTD.—See Topre Corporation; *Int'l*, pg. 7820
TOPRE KYUSHU CORPORATION—See Topre Corporation; *Int'l*, pg. 7820
TOP REL S.R.L.—See TUV NORD AG; *Int'l*, pg. 7980
TOPRE SAITAMA CORPORATION—See Topre Corporation; *Int'l*, pg. 7820
TOP RESOURCE ENERGY CO., LTD.; *Int'l*, pg. 7813
TOPRE (THAILAND) CO., LTD.—See Topre Corporation; *Int'l*, pg. 7820
TOPRE TOKAI CORPORATION—See Topre Corporation; *Int'l*, pg. 7820
TOPRE (WUHAN) AUTOPARTS CORPORATION—See Topre Corporation; *Int'l*, pg. 7820
TOPRE (XIANGYANG) AUTOPARTS CORPORATION—See Topre Corporation; *Int'l*, pg. 7820
TOP RIGHT GROUP LIMITED—See Apax Partners LLP; *Int'l*, pg. 507
TOP RIGHT GROUP LIMITED—See The Scott Trust Limited; *Int'l*, pg. 7681
TO PROSPERITY TECHNOLOGY INC.; *Int'l*, pg. 7768
TOP RX INC.; *U.S. Private*, pg. 4186
THE TOPSAIL ADVERTISER—See Gannett Co., Inc.; *U.S. Public*, pg. 906
TOPSCIENCE (S) PTE. LTD.—See TOPCO Scientific Co., Ltd.; *Int'l*, pg. 7814
TOP SCORE FASHION CO., LTD.; *Int'l*, pg. 7813
TOPSEARCH PRINTED CIRCUITS (HK) LIMITED—See Renco Holdings Group Limited; *Int'l*, pg. 6274
TOPSEARCH PRINTED CIRCUITS MACAO COMMERCIAL OFFSHORE COMPANY LIMITED—See Renco Holdings Group Limited; *Int'l*, pg. 6274
TOPSEED TECHNOLOGY CORP.—See Jess-Link Products Co., Ltd.; *Int'l*, pg. 3932
TOP-SERVICE FUR LINGUALTECHNIK GMBH—See Solventum Corporation; *U.S. Public*, pg. 1902
TOPS FOOD & BEVERAGES—See Murree Brewery Company Limited; *Int'l*, pg. 5101
TOPS FOODS NV—See Charoen Pokphand Foods Public Company Limited; *Int'l*, pg. 1453
TOPSHEEN SHIPPING SINGAPORE PTE. LTD.—See Caravelle International Group; *Int'l*, pg. 1320
TOP SHELF DRILLING—See Haines & Kibblehouse Inc.; *U.S. Private*, pg. 1841
TOP SHELF ENTERTAINMENT, LLC—See RCI Hospitality Holdings, Inc.; *U.S. Public*, pg. 1767
TOP SHELF INTERNATIONAL HOLDINGS LTD.; *Int'l*, pg. 7813
TOP SHELF SPIRITS & WINE; *U.S. Private*, pg. 4186
TOP SHIPS, INC.; *Int'l*, pg. 7813
TOPS HOLDING II CORPORATION; *U.S. Private*, pg. 4188
TOPS HOLDING LLC—See Tops Holding II Corporation; *U.S. Private*, pg. 4188
TOPSIM GMBH—See MPS Limited; *Int'l*, pg. 5063
TOPS MARKETS, LLC—See Golub Corporation; *U.S. Private*, pg. 1737
TOPSOE A/S; *Int'l*, pg. 7821
TOPSOE FUEL CELL A/S—See Topsoe A/S; *Int'l*, pg. 7821
TOP SOLVENT COMPANY LIMITED—See Thai Oil Public Company Limited; *Int'l*, pg. 7594
TOPSON DOWNS OF CALIFORNIA, INC.; *U.S. Private*, pg. 4188
TOPSOURCE INC.; *U.S. Private*, pg. 4188
TOPSPIN PARTNERS, L.P.; *U.S. Private*, pg. 4188
TOPSPORTS INTERNATIONAL HOLDINGS LIMITED; *Int'l*, pg. 7821
TOPSPOT INTERNET MARKETING; *U.S. Private*, pg. 4188
TOP SPRING INTERNATIONAL HOLDINGS LIMITED; *Int'l*, pg. 7813
TOPS PRODUCTS; *U.S. Private*, pg. 4188
TOPS SOFTWARE, LLC; *U.S. Private*, pg. 4188
TOPS SPECIALTY HOSPITAL, LTD.—See Tenet Healthcare Corporation; *U.S. Public*, pg. 2013

TOPS STAFFING, LLC; *U.S. Private*, pg. 4188
TOP STANDARD CORPORATION; *Int'l*, pg. 7813
TOP STAR LIMITED—See Victory City International Holdings Limited; *Int'l*, pg. 8189
TOPSTEPTRADER, LLC; *U.S. Private*, pg. 4188
TOPSUN CO., LTD.; *Int'l*, pg. 7821
TOP SUPER SPORTSWEAR (SHENZHEN) CO., LTD.—See Mainland Headwear Holdings Ltd.; *Int'l*, pg. 4651
TOP TASTE HOLDING BV; *Int'l*, pg. 7813
TOPTEC CO., LTD.; *Int'l*, pg. 7821
TOPTECH CO. LIMITED—See Great Eagle Holdings Limited; *Int'l*, pg. 3064
TOPTECH DIAMOND TOOL COMPANY LIMITED—See SNC Holding Company Limited; *Int'l*, pg. 7025
TOP TECH INC.—See Nidec Corporation; *Int'l*, pg. 5275
TOP TECHNOLOGY VENTURES LIMITED—See IP Group plc; *Int'l*, pg. 3795
TOPTECH (SHANGHAI) BUILDING MATERIAL LTD.—See Great Eagle Holdings Limited; *Int'l*, pg. 3064
TOPTECH SYSTEMS, INC.—See IDEX Corp; *U.S. Public*, pg. 1092
TOPTECH SYSTEMS N.V.—See IDEX Corp; *U.S. Public*, pg. 1092
TOP THERMO MFG. (MALAYSIA) SDN. BHD—See Thermos L.L.C.; *U.S. Private*, pg. 4143
TOPTICA PHOTONICS AG; *Int'l*, pg. 7821
TOPTICA PHOTONICS INC—See TOPTICA Photonics AG; *Int'l*, pg. 7821
TOPTIP (R. MULLER AG)—See Coop-Gruppe Genossenschaft; *Int'l*, pg. 1790
TOPTONE ACOUSTICS (MALAYSIA) SDN. BHD.—See Tokyo Cone Paper Mfg. Co., Ltd.; *Int'l*, pg. 7789
TOP TREND DEVELOPMENTS LIMITED—See Far East Consortium International Limited; *Int'l*, pg. 2615
TOP TREND MANUFACTURING CO., LTD.—See Saha Pathanapibul Public Company Limited; *Int'l*, pg. 6479
TOP TURF BOTSWANA (PTY) LIMITED—See The Bidvest Group Limited; *Int'l*, pg. 7626
TOP TURF MAURITIUS (PTY) LIMITED—See The Bidvest Group Limited; *Int'l*, pg. 7626
TOP UNION ELECTRONICS CORP.; *Int'l*, pg. 7813
TOPURA CO., LTD.—See NHK Spring Co., Ltd.; *Int'l*, pg. 5258
TOPVALU COLLECTION CO., LTD.—See AEON Co., Ltd.; *Int'l*, pg. 178
TOP VALUE FABRICS INC.; *U.S. Private*, pg. 4186
TOP VENTURES HONG KONG LIMITED—See Thai Oil Public Company Limited; *Int'l*, pg. 7594
TOP VERSICHERUNGSSERVICE GMBH—See Allianz SE; *Int'l*, pg. 356
TOP VERSICHERUNGS-VERMITTLER SERVICE GMBH—See Allianz SE; *Int'l*, pg. 356
TOP VICTORY ELECTRONICS (FUJIAN) COMPANY LIMITED—See TPV Technology Co., Ltd.; *Int'l*, pg. 7885
TOP VICTORY ELECTRONICS (TAIWAN) COMPANY LIMITED—See TPV Technology Co., Ltd.; *Int'l*, pg. 7885
TOP VICTORY INVESTMENTS LIMITED—See TPV Technology Co., Ltd.; *Int'l*, pg. 7885
TOPVIEW OPTRONICS CORP.; *Int'l*, pg. 7821
TOP VISION EYE SPECIALIST CENTRE; *Int'l*, pg. 7813
TOP VORSORGE-MANAGEMENT GMBH—See Allianz SE; *Int'l*, pg. 356
TOP WEALTH GROUP HOLDING LIMITED; *Int'l*, pg. 7813
TOPWELL GROUP DEVELOPMENT LTD—See Carry Wealth Holdings Limited; *Int'l*, pg. 1346
TOP WIN INTERNATIONAL TRADING LIMITED—See Citychamp Watch & Jewellery Group Limited; *Int'l*, pg. 1629
TOPY AGENCY—See Topy Industries, Ltd.; *Int'l*, pg. 7822
TOPY AMERICA, INC.—See Topy Industries, Ltd.; *Int'l*, pg. 7822
TOPY ENTERPRISES (DALIAN FREE TRADE ZONE) CO., LTD.—See Topy Industries, Ltd.; *Int'l*, pg. 7822
TOPY ENTERPRISES, LTD.—See Topy Industries, Ltd.; *Int'l*, pg. 7822
TOPY FASTENERS, LTD. - KANRA FACTORY—See Topy Industries, Ltd.; *Int'l*, pg. 7822
TOPY FASTENERS, LTD.—See Topy Industries, Ltd.; *Int'l*, pg. 7822
TOPY FASTENERS MEXICO S.A. DE C.V.—See Topy Industries, Ltd.; *Int'l*, pg. 7822
TOPY FASTENERS (THAILAND) LTD.—See Topy Industries, Ltd.; *Int'l*, pg. 7822
TOPY FASTENERS VIETNAM CO., LTD.—See Topy Industries, Ltd.; *Int'l*, pg. 7822
TOPY FASTENER (THAILAND) LTD.—See Topy Industries, Ltd.; *Int'l*, pg. 7822
TOPY INDUSTRIES LTD. - AKEMI PLANT—See Topy Industries, Ltd.; *Int'l*, pg. 7822
TOPY INDUSTRIES LTD. - AYASE FACTORY—See Topy Industries, Ltd.; *Int'l*, pg. 7822
TOPY INDUSTRIES LTD. - HAMURA PLANT—See Topy Industries, Ltd.; *Int'l*, pg. 7822
TOPY INDUSTRIES LTD. - KANAGAWA FACTORY—See Topy Industries, Ltd.; *Int'l*, pg. 7822

TOP WEALTH GROUP HOLDING LIMITED — CORPORATE AFFILIATIONS

TOPY INDUSTRIES LTD. - KURATE PLANT—See Topy Industries, Ltd.; *Int'l*, pg. 7822
TOPY INDUSTRIES LTD. - SAGAMI PLANT—See Topy Industries, Ltd.; *Int'l*, pg. 7822
TOPY INDUSTRIES, LTD.; *Int'l*, pg. 7821
TOPY INDUSTRIES LTD. - TOYOHASHI FACTORY—See Topy Industries, Ltd.; *Int'l*, pg. 7822
TOPY INDUSTRIES LTD. - TOYOKAWA FACTORY—See Topy Industries, Ltd.; *Int'l*, pg. 7822
TOPY MARINE TRANSPORT, LTD.—See Topy Industries, Ltd.; *Int'l*, pg. 7822
TOPY MW MANUFACTURING MEXICO S.A. DE C.V.—See Topy Industries, Ltd.; *Int'l*, pg. 7822
TOPY PRECISION MFG., INC.—See Topy Industries, Ltd.; *Int'l*, pg. 7822
TOPY-REC, LTD.—See Topy Industries, Ltd.; *Int'l*, pg. 7822
TOPY UNDERCARRIAGE (CHINA) CO., LTD.—See Topy Industries, Ltd.; *Int'l*, pg. 7822
TORADEX AG—See Verium AG; *Int'l*, pg. 8169
TORADEX, INC.—See Verium AG; *Int'l*, pg. 8169
TORAKU FOODS CO., LTD.—See Marudai Food Co., Ltd.; *Int'l*, pg. 4711
TORA SP. Z O.O.—See LPP S.A.; *Int'l*, pg. 4568
TORAU SPORT AG—See Goldwin, Inc.; *Int'l*, pg. 3035
TORA WALLET SINGLE MEMBER S.A.—See Greek Organisation of Football Prognostics S.A.; *Int'l*, pg. 3069
TORAX MEDICAL, INC.—See Johnson & Johnson; *U.S. Public*, pg. 1196
TORAY ACE CO., LTD.—See Toray Industries, Inc.; *Int'l*, pg. 7824
TORAY ADVANCED COMPOSITES ADS LLC—See Toray Industries, Inc.; *Int'l*, pg. 7824
TORAY ADVANCED COMPOSITES B.V.—See Toray Industries, Inc.; *Int'l*, pg. 7824
TORAY ADVANCED COMPOSITES NETHERLANDS B.V.—See Toray Industries, Inc.; *Int'l*, pg. 7824
TORAY ADVANCED COMPOSITES—See Toray Industries, Inc.; *Int'l*, pg. 7824
TORAY ADVANCED COMPOSITES UK LTD.—See Toray Industries, Inc.; *Int'l*, pg. 7824
TORAY ADVANCED COMPOSITES USA INC.—See Toray Industries, Inc.; *Int'l*, pg. 7824
TORAY ADVANCED COMPOSITES USA INC.—See Toray Industries, Inc.; *Int'l*, pg. 7824
TORAY ADVANCED COMPUTER SOLUTION, INC.—See Toray Industries, Inc.; *Int'l*, pg. 7824
TORAY ADVANCED FILM CO., LTD.—See Toray Industries, Inc.; *Int'l*, pg. 7824
TORAY ADVANCED FILM KAOHSIUNG CO., LTD.—See Toray Industries, Inc.; *Int'l*, pg. 7824
TORAY ADVANCED MATERIALS KOREA INC.—See Toray Industries, Inc.; *Int'l*, pg. 7824
TORAY ADVANCED MATERIALS RESEARCH LABORATORIES (CHINA) CO., LTD.—See Toray Industries, Inc.; *Int'l*, pg. 7824
TORAY ADVANCED TEXTILE MEXICO, S.A. DE C.V.—See Toray Industries, Inc.; *Int'l*, pg. 7824
TORAY ASIA PTE. LTD.—See Toray Industries, Inc.; *Int'l*, pg. 7824
TORAY BASF PBT RESIN SDN. BERHAD—See Toray Industries, Inc.; *Int'l*, pg. 7824
TORAY BATTERY SEPARATOR FILM KOREA LIMITED—See Toray Industries, Inc.; *Int'l*, pg. 7824
TORAY BLUESTAR MEMBRANE CO., LTD.—See Toray Industries, Inc.; *Int'l*, pg. 7824
TORAY BSF COATING KOREA LIMITED—See Toray Industries, Inc.; *Int'l*, pg. 7824
TORAY CAPITAL (AMERICA), INC.—See Toray Industries, Inc.; *Int'l*, pg. 7825
TORAY CARBON FIBERS AMERICA, INC.—See Toray Industries, Inc.; *Int'l*, pg. 7825
TORAY CARBON FIBERS EUROPE S.A.—See Toray Industries, Inc.; *Int'l*, pg. 7824
TORAY CHEMICAL KOREA - GUMI I PLANT—See Toray Industries, Inc.; *Int'l*, pg. 7824
TORAY CHEMICAL KOREA INC.—See Toray Industries, Inc.; *Int'l*, pg. 7824
TORAY CHEMICAL KOREA - YUGU PLANT—See Toray Industries, Inc.; *Int'l*, pg. 7824
TORAY COATEX CO., LTD.—See Toray Industries, Inc.; *Int'l*, pg. 7824
TORAY COMPOSITE MATERIALS AMERICA, INC.—See Toray Industries, Inc.; *Int'l*, pg. 7824
TORAY COMPOSITES (AMERICA), INC.—See Toray Industries, Inc.; *Int'l*, pg. 7825
TORAY COMS CHIBA CO., LTD.—See Toray Industries, Inc.; *Int'l*, pg. 7824
TORAY CONSTRUCTION CO., LTD.; *Int'l*, pg. 7822
TORAY CORPORATE BUSINESS RESEARCH, INC.—See Toray Industries, Inc.; *Int'l*, pg. 7824
TORAY DIPLOMODE, INC.—See Toray Industries, Inc.; *Int'l*, pg. 7824
TORAY DO BRASIL LTDA.—See Toray Industries, Inc.; *Int'l*, pg. 7824
TORAY ECSAINE PLAZA, INC.—See Toray Industries, Inc.; *Int'l*, pg. 7824
TORAY ENGINEERING CO., LTD.—See Toray Industries, Inc.; *Int'l*, pg. 7824

TORAY ENGINEERING (KOREA) CO., LTD.—See Toray Industries, Inc.; *Int'l*, pg. 7824
TORAY ENGINEERING WEST CO., LTD.—See Toray Industries, Inc.; *Int'l*, pg. 7824
TORAY ENTERPRISE CORP.—See Toray Industries, Inc.; *Int'l*, pg. 7824
TORAY EUROPE LTD.—See Toray Industries, Inc.; *Int'l*, pg. 7824
TORAY FIBERS (NANTONG) CO., LTD.—See Toray Industries, Inc.; *Int'l*, pg. 7825
TORAY FIBERS (NANTONG) CO., LTD. (TFNL)—See Toray Industries, Inc.; *Int'l*, pg. 7825
TORAY FIBERS & TEXTILES RESEARCH LABORATORIES (CHINA) CO., LTD.—See Toray Industries, Inc.; *Int'l*, pg. 7825
TORAY FILM PRODUCTS (HONG KONG) LTD.—See Toray Industries, Inc.; *Int'l*, pg. 7825
TORAY FILM PRODUCTS (ZHONGSHAN) LTD.—See Toray Industries, Inc.; *Int'l*, pg. 7825
TORAY FILM PRODUCTS (ZHOUGSHAN) LTD.—See Toray Industries, Inc.; *Int'l*, pg. 7825
TORAY FILMS EUROPE S.A.S.—See Toray Industries, Inc.; *Int'l*, pg. 7825
TORAY FINE CHEMICALS CO., LTD. - CHIBA PLANT—See Toray Industries, Inc.; *Int'l*, pg. 7825
TORAY FINE CHEMICALS CO., LTD. - MATSUYAMA PLANT—See Toray Industries, Inc.; *Int'l*, pg. 7825
TORAY FINE CHEMICALS CO., LTD. - MORIYAMA PLANT—See Toray Industries, Inc.; *Int'l*, pg. 7825
TORAY FINE CHEMICALS CO., LTD.—See Toray Industries, Inc.; *Int'l*, pg. 7825
TORAY FINE CHEMICALS CO., LTD. - TOKAI PLANT—See Toray Industries, Inc.; *Int'l*, pg. 7825
TORAY FLUOROFIBERS (AMERICA), INC.—See Toray Industries, Inc.; *Int'l*, pg. 7825
TORAY HYBRID CORD, INC.—See Toray Industries, Inc.; *Int'l*, pg. 7825
TORAY INDUSTRIES (AMERICA), INC.—See Toray Industries, Inc.; *Int'l*, pg. 7825
TORAY INDUSTRIES (CHINA) CO., LTD.—See Toray Industries, Inc.; *Int'l*, pg. 7825
TORAY INDUSTRIES EUROPE GMBH—See Toray Industries, Inc.; *Int'l*, pg. 7825
TORAY INDUSTRIES (H.K.) LTD.—See Toray Industries, Inc.; *Int'l*, pg. 7825
TORAY INDUSTRIES HUNGARY KFT.—See Toray Industries, Inc.; *Int'l*, pg. 7825
TORAY INDUSTRIES, INC. - AICHI PLANT—See Toray Industries, Inc.; *Int'l*, pg. 7825
TORAY INDUSTRIES, INC. - CHIBA PLANT—See Toray Industries, Inc.; *Int'l*, pg. 7825
TORAY INDUSTRIES, INC. - EHIME PLANT—See Toray Industries, Inc.; *Int'l*, pg. 7825
TORAY INDUSTRIES, INC. - GIFU PLANT—See Toray Industries, Inc.; *Int'l*, pg. 7825
TORAY INDUSTRIES, INC. - ISHIKAWA PLANT—See Toray Industries, Inc.; *Int'l*, pg. 7825
TORAY INDUSTRIES, INC. - NAGOYA PLANT—See Toray Industries, Inc.; *Int'l*, pg. 7825
TORAY INDUSTRIES, INC. - OKAZAKI PLANT—See Toray Industries, Inc.; *Int'l*, pg. 7825
TORAY INDUSTRIES, INC. - SETA PLANT—See Toray Industries, Inc.; *Int'l*, pg. 7825
TORAY INDUSTRIES, INC. - SHIGA PLANT—See Toray Industries, Inc.; *Int'l*, pg. 7826
TORAY INDUSTRIES, INC.; *Int'l*, pg. 7822
TORAY INDUSTRIES, INC. - TOKAI PLANT—See Toray Industries, Inc.; *Int'l*, pg. 7826
TORAY INDUSTRIES (INDIA) PRIVATE LIMITED—See Toray Industries, Inc.; *Int'l*, pg. 7825
TORAY INDUSTRIES KOREA INC.—See Toray Industries, Inc.; *Int'l*, pg. 7825
TORAY INDUSTRIES (SINGAPORE) PTE. LTD.—See Toray Industries, Inc.; *Int'l*, pg. 7825
TORAY INDUSTRIES (SOUTH CHINA) CO., LTD.—See Toray Industries, Inc.; *Int'l*, pg. 7825
TORAY INDUSTRIES (THAILAND) CO., LTD.—See Toray Industries, Inc.; *Int'l*, pg. 7825
TORAY INDUSTRIES (THAILAND) CO., LTD. (TTH)—See Toray Industries, Inc.; *Int'l*, pg. 7825
TORAY INTERNATIONAL AMERICA INC.—See Toray Industries, Inc.; *Int'l*, pg. 7825
TORAY INTERNATIONAL (CHINA) CO., LTD.—See Toray Industries, Inc.; *Int'l*, pg. 7826
TORAY INTERNATIONAL DE MEXICO, S.A. DE C.V.—See Toray Industries, Inc.; *Int'l*, pg. 7826
TORAY INTERNATIONAL EUROPE GMBH—See Toray Industries, Inc.; *Int'l*, pg. 7826
TORAY INTERNATIONAL GUANGZHOU TRADING CO., LTD.—See Toray Industries, Inc.; *Int'l*, pg. 7826
TORAY INTERNATIONAL, INC.—See Toray Industries, Inc.; *Int'l*, pg. 7826
TORAY INTERNATIONAL INDIA PRIVATE LIMITED—See Toray Industries, Inc.; *Int'l*, pg. 7826
TORAY INTERNATIONAL ITALY S.R.L.—See Toray Industries, Inc.; *Int'l*, pg. 7826
TORAY INTERNATIONAL (KOREA), INC.—See Toray Industries, Inc.; *Int'l*, pg. 7826

TORAY INTERNATIONAL SINGAPORE PTE. LTD.—See Toray Industries, Inc.; *Int'l*, pg. 7826
TORAY INTERNATIONAL TAIPEI INC.—See Toray Industries, Inc.; *Int'l*, pg. 7826
TORAY INTERNATIONAL TRADING (THAILAND) CO., LTD.—See Toray Industries, Inc.; *Int'l*, pg. 7826
TORAY INTERNATIONAL U.K. LTD.—See Toray Industries, Inc.; *Int'l*, pg. 7826
TORAY INTERNATIONAL VIETNAM CO., LTD.—See Toray Industries, Inc.; *Int'l*, pg. 7826
TORAY ITALIA S.R.L.—See Toray Industries, Inc.; *Int'l*, pg. 7826
TORAY KP FILMS INC.—See Toray Industries, Inc.; *Int'l*, pg. 7826
TORAY KUSUMGAR ADVANCED TEXTILE PRIVATE LIMITED—See Toray Industries, Inc.; *Int'l*, pg. 7826
TORAY MALAYSIA SYSTEMS SOLUTION SDN. BHD.—See Toray Industries, Inc.; *Int'l*, pg. 7826
TORAY MARKETING AND SALES (AMERICA), INC.—See Toray Industries, Inc.; *Int'l*, pg. 7825
TORAY MARKETING E VENDAS (BRASIL) LTDA.—See Toray Industries, Inc.; *Int'l*, pg. 7826
TORAY MEDICAL CO., LTD.—See Toray Industries, Inc.; *Int'l*, pg. 7826
TORAY MEDICAL (QINGDAO) CO., LTD.—See Toray Industries, Inc.; *Int'l*, pg. 7826
TORAY MEMBRANE (BEIJING) CO.,LTD.—See Toray Industries, Inc.; *Int'l*, pg. 7826
TORAY MEMBRANE EUROPE AG—See Toray Industries, Inc.; *Int'l*, pg. 7826
TORAY MEMBRANE (FOSHAN) CO.—See Toray Industries, Inc.; *Int'l*, pg. 7826
TORAY MEMBRANE MIDDLE EAST LLC—See Toray Industries, Inc.; *Int'l*, pg. 7826
TORAY MEMBRANE SPAIN S.L.—See Toray Industries, Inc.; *Int'l*, pg. 7826
TORAY MEMBRANE USA, INC.—See Toray Industries, Inc.; *Int'l*, pg. 7825
TORAY MONOFILAMENT CO., LTD.—See Toray Industries, Inc.; *Int'l*, pg. 7826
TORAY OPELONTEX CO., LTD.—See Toray Industries, Inc.; *Int'l*, pg. 7826
TORAY PEF PRODUCTS INC.—See Toray Industries, Inc.; *Int'l*, pg. 7826
TORAY PERFORMANCE MATERIALS CORPORATION—See Toray Industries, Inc.; *Int'l*, pg. 7824
TORAY PLASTICS (AMERICA), INC.—See Toray Industries, Inc.; *Int'l*, pg. 7825
TORAY PLASTICS (CHENGDU) CO., LTD.—See Toray Industries, Inc.; *Int'l*, pg. 7826
TORAY PLASTICS (CHINA) CO., LTD.—See Toray Industries, Inc.; *Int'l*, pg. 7826
TORAY PLASTICS EUROPE S.A.—See Toray Industries, Inc.; *Int'l*, pg. 7826
TORAY PLASTICS (MALAYSIA) SDN. BHD.—See Toray Industries, Inc.; *Int'l*, pg. 7826
TORAY PLASTICS PRECISION CO., LTD.—See Toray Industries, Inc.; *Int'l*, pg. 7826
TORAY PLASTICS PRECISION (HONG KONG) LTD.—See Toray Industries, Inc.; *Int'l*, pg. 7826
TORAY PLASTICS PRECISION (ZHONGSHAN) LTD.—See Toray Industries, Inc.; *Int'l*, pg. 7826
TORAY PLASTICS (SHENZHEN) LTD.—See Toray Industries, Inc.; *Int'l*, pg. 7826
TORAY PLASTICS (SUZHOU) CO., LTD.—See Toray Industries, Inc.; *Int'l*, pg. 7826
TORAY POLYTECH (FOSHAN) CO., LTD.—See Toray Industries, Inc.; *Int'l*, pg. 7826
TORAY POLYTECH (NANTONG) CO., LTD.—See Toray Industries, Inc.; *Int'l*, pg. 7826
TORAY PRECISION CO., LTD.—See Toray Industries, Inc.; *Int'l*, pg. 7826
TORAY RESEARCH CENTER, INC.—See Toray Industries, Inc.; *Int'l*, pg. 7827
TORAY RESIN CO. - INDIANA FACTORY—See Toray Industries, Inc.; *Int'l*, pg. 7825
TORAY RESIN COMPANY—See Toray Industries, Inc.; *Int'l*, pg. 7825
TORAY RESIN MEXICO, S.A. DE C.V.—See Toray Industries, Inc.; *Int'l*, pg. 7827
TORAY RESINS EUROPE GMBH—See Toray Industries, Inc.; *Int'l*, pg. 7827
TORAY SAKAI WEAVING & DYEING (NANTONG) CO., LTD.—See Toray Industries, Inc.; *Int'l*, pg. 7827
TORAY SAKAI WEAVING & DYEING (NANTONG) CO., LTD. (TSD)—See Toray Industries, Inc.; *Int'l*, pg. 7827
TORAY SANKO PRECISION (HONG KONG) LTD.—See Toray Industries, Inc.; *Int'l*, pg. 7827
TORAY SANKO PRECISION (ZHONGSHAN) LTD.—See Toray Industries, Inc.; *Int'l*, pg. 7827
TORAY SYSTEMS CENTER, INC.—See Toray Industries, Inc.; *Int'l*, pg. 7827
TORAY TEXTILES CENTRAL EUROPE S.R.O.—See Toray Industries, Inc.; *Int'l*, pg. 7827
TORAY TEXTILES EUROPE LTD.—See Toray Industries, Inc.; *Int'l*, pg. 7827
TORAY TEXTILES INC.—See Toray Industries, Inc.; *Int'l*, pg. 7827

COMPANY NAME INDEX

TORAY TEXTILES (THAILAND) PUBLIC COMPANY LIMITED—See Toray Industries, Inc.; *Int'l*, pg. 7827
TORAY TRADING (SHANGHAI) CO., LTD.—See Toray Industries, Inc.; *Int'l*, pg. 7827
TORAY TRAVEL CO., LTD.—See Toray Industries, Inc.; *Int'l*, pg. 7827
TORAY WBD MEMBRANE TECHNOLOGY (JS) CO., LTD.—See Toray Industries, Inc.; *Int'l*, pg. 7827
TORBA INSAAT VE TURISTIK A.S—See Global Yatirim Holding A.S.; *Int'l*, pg. 3003
TORBJORN SUNDH ENTREPRENAD AB—See Nordisk Bergteknik AB; *Int'l*, pg. 5424
TORBRAM ELECTRIC SUPPLY CORPORATION; *Int'l*, pg. 7827
TORCH ENERGY ADVISORS INCORPORATED; *U.S. Private*, pg. 4188
TORCHLIGHT INC.—See Metaps Inc.; *Int'l*, pg. 4851
TORCHMATE, INC.—See Lincoln Electric Holdings, Inc.; *U.S. Public*, pg. 1318
TORCHMEDIA PTY LTD—See TVG Capital Partners Limited; *Int'l*, pg. 7988
TORCH TECHNOLOGIES; *U.S. Private*, pg. 4188
TOR COATINGS LIMITED—See RPM International Inc.; *U.S. Public*, pg. 1820
TORC OIL & GAS LTD.—See Whitecap Resources Inc.; *Int'l*, pg. 8399
TORCON, INC.; *U.S. Private*, pg. 4188
TORCO TERMITE & PEST CONTROL COMPANY, LLC; *U.S. Private*, pg. 4188
TORC ROBOTICS, INC.—See Mercedes-Benz Group AG; *Int'l*, pg. 4824
TOREAD HOLDINGS GROUP CO., LTD.; *Int'l*, pg. 7827
TOREDAL VERKSTAD AB—See Nederman Holding AB; *Int'l*, pg. 5188
T&O REFRIGERATION, INC.—See Ares Management Corporation; *U.S. Public*, pg. 189
TORESCO ENTERPRISES; *U.S. Private*, pg. 4188
TOREX GOLD RESOURCES INC.; *Int'l*, pg. 7827
TOREX (HONG KONG) LIMITED—See Torex Semiconductor Ltd.; *Int'l*, pg. 7827
TOREX SEMICONDUCTOR DEVICE (SHANGHAI) CO., LTD.—See Torex Semiconductor Ltd.; *Int'l*, pg. 7828
TOREX SEMICONDUCTOR LTD. - SALES DIVISION—See Torex Semiconductor Ltd.; *Int'l*, pg. 7828
TOREX SEMICONDUCTOR LTD.; *Int'l*, pg. 7827
TOREX SEMICONDUCTOR (S) PTE LTD—See Torex Semiconductor Ltd.; *Int'l*, pg. 7827
TOREX SEMICONDUCTOR TAIWAN LTD.—See Torex Semiconductor Ltd.; *Int'l*, pg. 7828
TOREX S.P.A.—See WAMGROUP S.p.A.; *Int'l*, pg. 8338
TOREX VIETNAM SEMICONDUCTOR CO., LTD.—See Torex Semiconductor Ltd.; *Int'l*, pg. 7828
TORGAN MANAGEMENT INC; *Int'l*, pg. 7828
TORGERSON PROPERTIES INC.; *U.S. Private*, pg. 4188
TORGO, LTD.; *U.S. Private*, pg. 4189
TORGOTERM PLC; *Int'l*, pg. 7828
TORGOVYI DOM KOPEYKA OAO—See X5 Retail Group N.V.; *Int'l*, pg. 8518
TORIASE PUBLIC COMPANY LTD.; *Int'l*, pg. 7828
TORICA INC.—See Wacoal Holdings Corp.; *Int'l*, pg. 8326
TORIDEN-SHOJI CO.—See METAWATER Co., Ltd.; *Int'l*, pg. 4851
TORIDOLL HOLDINGS CORPORATION; *Int'l*, pg. 7828
THE TORIGOE CO., LTD.; *Int'l*, pg. 7694
TORII PHARMACEUTICAL CO., LTD. - SAKURA PLANT—See Astena Holdings Co., Ltd.; *Int'l*, pg. 653
TORII PHARMACEUTICAL CO., LTD.; *Int'l*, pg. 7828
TORIKA HOSO SHIZAI CO., LTD.—See Oji Holdings Corporation; *Int'l*, pg. 5537
TORIKIZOKU CO., LTD.; *Int'l*, pg. 7828
TORINDO CO., LTD.—See CDS Co., Ltd.; *Int'l*, pg. 1371
TORIN INDUSTRIES (MALAYSIA) SDN. BHD.—See Regal Rexnord Corporation; *U.S. Public*, pg. 1773
TORIN-SIFAN LIMITED—See Volution Group plc; *Int'l*, pg. 8304
TORISHIMA ELECTRIC WORKS LTD.—See NICHICON CORPORATION; *Int'l*, pg. 5268
TORISHIMA EUROPE LTD—See Torishima Pump Mfg. Co., Ltd.; *Int'l*, pg. 7828
TORISHIMA (HONG KONG) LIMITED—See Torishima Pump Mfg. Co., Ltd.; *Int'l*, pg. 7828
TORISHIMA MALAYSIA SDN.BHD—See Torishima Pump Mfg. Co., Ltd.; *Int'l*, pg. 7828
TORISHIMA PUMP MFG. CO., LTD.; *Int'l*, pg. 7828
TORISHIMA SERVICE SOLUTIONS EUROPE LTD.—See Torishima Pump Mfg. Co., Ltd.; *Int'l*, pg. 7828
TORISHIMA SERVICE SOLUTIONS FZCO—See Torishima Pump Mfg. Co., Ltd.; *Int'l*, pg. 7828
TORIT DCE GMBH—See Donaldson Company, Inc.; *U.S. Public*, pg. 675
TORITON, INC—See GMO GlobalSign Holdings K.K.; *Int'l*, pg. 3013
TORKE COFFEE ROASTING COMPANY; *U.S. Private*, pg. 4189
TORKIAN-ZARGARI TRADING CORP.—See B.H.T. Electronics Purchasing Inc.; *U.S. Private*, pg. 420
TORKKELIN PAPERI OY—See Wulff-Group Plc; *Int'l*, pg. 8502

TORK PRODUCTS, INC.; *U.S. Private*, pg. 4189
TORKRET GMBH—See STRABAG SE; *Int'l*, pg. 7233
TORKZADEH LAW FIRM, PLC; *U.S. Private*, pg. 4189
TORLYS INC.; *Int'l*, pg. 7828
TORM A/S; *Int'l*, pg. 7828
TORMEE CONSTRUCTION INC.; *U.S. Private*, pg. 4189
TORME LAURICELLA; *U.S. Private*, pg. 4189
TOR MINERALS INTERNATIONAL INC.; *U.S. Public*, pg. 2164
TOR MINERALS MALAYSIA, SDN. BHD.—See TOR Minerals International Inc.; *U.S. Public*, pg. 2164
TORM PLC; *Int'l*, pg. 7828
TORM SHIPPING INDIA PTE LTD—See TORM A/S; *Int'l*, pg. 7828
TORM SINGAPORE PTE. LTD.—See TORM A/S; *Int'l*, pg. 7828
TORM USA LLC—See TORM A/S; *Int'l*, pg. 7828
TORNADO AIR PLC; *Int'l*, pg. 7828
TORNADO GLOBAL HYDROVACS LTD.; *Int'l*, pg. 7828
TORNADO GROUP LTD.—See Storskogen Group AB; *Int'l*, pg. 7228
TORNADO INDUSTRIES, INC.—See Tacony Corporation; *U.S. Private*, pg. 3921
TORNADO LIMITED—See Ireland Blyth Limited; *Int'l*, pg. 3807
TORNEOS Y COMPETENCIAS S.A.—See AT&T Inc.; *U.S. Public*, pg. 220
TORN & GLASSER INC.; *U.S. Private*, pg. 4189
TORNIER AG—See Wright Medical Group N.V.; *Int'l*, pg. 8494
TORNIER BELGIUM N.V.—See Wright Medical Group N.V.; *Int'l*, pg. 8494
TORNIER ESPANA SA—See Wright Medical Group N.V.; *Int'l*, pg. 8494
TORNIER GMBH—See Wright Medical Group N.V.; *Int'l*, pg. 8494
TORNIER, INC.—See Wright Medical Group N.V.; *Int'l*, pg. 8495
TORNIER ORTHOPEDICS, INC.—See Wright Medical Group N.V.; *Int'l*, pg. 8494
TORNIER ORTHOPEDICS IRELAND, LTD.—See Wright Medical Group N.V.; *Int'l*, pg. 8494
TORNIER PTY LTD—See Wright Medical Group N.V.; *Int'l*, pg. 8494
TORNIER SAS—See Wright Medical Group N.V.; *Int'l*, pg. 8494
TORNIER SCANDINAVIA A/S—See Wright Medical Group N.V.; *Int'l*, pg. 8494
TORNIER SRL—See Wright Medical Group N.V.; *Int'l*, pg. 8494
TORNIER UK, LTD.—See Wright Medical Group N.V.; *Int'l*, pg. 8494
TORNIK INC.—See WESCO International, Inc.; *U.S. Public*, pg. 2350
TORNOS AUTOMATICOS IND. E COM. LTDA.—See INDEX-Werke GmbH & Co. KG; *Int'l*, pg. 3651
TORNOS HOLDINGS S.A; *Int'l*, pg. 7828
TORNOS (TAICHUNG) MACHINE WORKS LTD.—See Tornos Holdings S.A; *Int'l*, pg. 7829
TORNOS TECHNOLOGIES ASIA LIMITED—See Tornos Holdings S.A; *Int'l*, pg. 7829
TORNOS TECHNOLOGIES DEUTSCHLAND GMBH—See Tornos Holdings S.A; *Int'l*, pg. 7829
TORNOS TECHNOLOGIES FRANCE SAS—See Tornos Holdings S.A; *Int'l*, pg. 7829
TORNOS TECHNOLOGIES ITALIA SRL—See Tornos Holdings S.A; *Int'l*, pg. 7829
TORNOS TECHNOLOGIES (THAILAND) CO. LTD.—See Tornos Holdings S.A; *Int'l*, pg. 7829
TORNOS (XI'AN) MACHINE WORKS CO., LTD.—See Tornos Holdings S.A; *Int'l*, pg. 7829
TORNUM AB—See Volati AB; *Int'l*, pg. 8301
TORNUM ASIA CO., LTD.—See Volati AB; *Int'l*, pg. 8301
TORNUM KFT.—See Volati AB; *Int'l*, pg. 8301
TORNUM LLC—See Volati AB; *Int'l*, pg. 8301
TORNUM POLSKA SP. Z.O.O.—See Volati AB; *Int'l*, pg. 8301
TORNUM S.R.L.—See Volati AB; *Int'l*, pg. 8301
TORO-AIRE INC.; *U.S. Private*, pg. 4189
TORO AUSTRALIA GROUP SALES PTY. LTD—See The Toro Company; *U.S. Public*, pg. 2135
TORO AUSTRALIA PTY. LTD.—See The Toro Company; *U.S. Public*, pg. 2135
THE TORO COMPANY IRRIGATION PRODUCTS—See The Toro Company; *U.S. Public*, pg. 2135
THE TORO COMPANY; *U.S. Public*, pg. 2134
TORO CORP.; *Int'l*, pg. 7829
THE TORO CO.—See The Toro Company; *U.S. Public*, pg. 2135
THE TORO CO.—See The Toro Company; *U.S. Public*, pg. 2135
THE TORO CO.—See The Toro Company; *U.S. Public*, pg. 2135
TORO CREDIT COMPANY—See The Toro Company; *U.S. Public*, pg. 2135
TORO DATA LABS, INC.; *U.S. Private*, pg. 4189
TORO ENERGY LTD; *Int'l*, pg. 7829
TORO EUROPE N.V.—See The Toro Company; *U.S. Public*, pg. 2135

TORQX CAPITAL PARTNERS B.V.

TOROFLEX GMBH—See Comet Umetni brusi in nekovine, d.d.; *Int'l*, pg. 1711
TORO MANUFACTURING LLC—See The Toro Company; *U.S. Public*, pg. 2135
TOROMONT CAT - QUEBEC—See Toromont Industries Ltd.; *Int'l*, pg. 7829
TOROMONT CAT—See Toromont Industries Ltd.; *Int'l*, pg. 7829
TOROMONT ENERGY—See Toromont Industries Ltd.; *Int'l*, pg. 7829
TOROMONT INDUSTRIES LTD.; *Int'l*, pg. 7829
TOROMONT MATERIAL HANDLING—See Toromont Industries Ltd.; *Int'l*, pg. 7829
TORONTO AIRWAYS LTD.; *Int'l*, pg. 7829
TORONTO BLUE JAYS BASEBALL CLUB—See Rogers Communications Inc.; *Int'l*, pg. 6383
TORONTO DODGE CHRYSLER LTD.—See AutoCanada Inc.; *Int'l*, pg. 726
THE TORONTO-DOMINION BANK; *Int'l*, pg. 7694
TORONTO DOMINION HOLDINGS (U.K.) LIMITED—See The Toronto-Dominion Bank; *Int'l*, pg. 7696
TORONTO DOMINION INTERNATIONAL INC.—See The Toronto-Dominion Bank; *Int'l*, pg. 7696
TORONTO DOMINION (NEW YORK) LLC—See The Toronto-Dominion Bank; *Int'l*, pg. 7696
TORONTO DOMINION (SOUTH EAST ASIA) LIMITED—See The Toronto-Dominion Bank; *Int'l*, pg. 7696
TORONTO HONDA; *Int'l*, pg. 7829
TORONTO HYDRO CORPORATION; *Int'l*, pg. 7829
TORONTO HYDRO-ELECTRIC SYSTEM LIMITED—See Toronto Hydro Corporation; *Int'l*, pg. 7829
TORONTO HYDRO ENERGY SERVICES INC.—See Toronto Hydro Corporation; *Int'l*, pg. 7829
TORONTO HYDRO STREET LIGHTING INC.—See Toronto Hydro Corporation; *Int'l*, pg. 7829
TORONTO LIFE—See St. Joseph Communications Inc.; *Int'l*, pg. 7159
TORONTO MAPLE LEAFS HOCKEY CLUB INC.—See BCE Inc.; *Int'l*, pg. 927
TORONTO MAPLE LEAFS HOCKEY CLUB INC.—See Rogers Communications Inc.; *Int'l*, pg. 6383
TORONTO MARRIOTT DOWNTOWN CENTRE HOTEL—See Marriott International, Inc.; *U.S. Public*, pg. 1373
TORONTO RAPTORS BASKETBALL CLUB INC.—See BCE Inc.; *Int'l*, pg. 927
TORONTO RAPTORS BASKETBALL CLUB INC.—See Rogers Communications Inc.; *Int'l*, pg. 6383
TORONTO STAR NEWSPAPERS LTD.—See Torstar Corporation; *Int'l*, pg. 7831
THE TORONTO SUN PUBLISHING CORPORATION—See Chatham Asset Management, LLC; *U.S. Private*, pg. 861
TORONTO SYMPHONY ORCHESTRA; *Int'l*, pg. 7829
TORO PETROLEUM CORP.; *U.S. Private*, pg. 4189
TORO R&D COMPANY—See The Toro Company; *U.S. Public*, pg. 2135
TOROS TARIM SANAYI VE TICARET A.S.—See Tekfen Holding A.S.; *Int'l*, pg. 7527
TOROS TARIM—See Tekfen Holding A.S.; *Int'l*, pg. 7527
TOROTEL, INC.—See TT Electronics plc; *Int'l*, pg. 7959
TOROTEL PRODUCTS, INC.—See TT Electronics plc; *Int'l*, pg. 7959
TORO WASTE EQUIPMENT (AUST) PTY. LTD.—See Macquarie Group Limited; *Int'l*, pg. 4626
TORO-WHEEL HORSE—See The Toro Company; *U.S. Public*, pg. 2135
TORO WORLDWIDE PARTS DISTRIBUTION CENTER—See The Toro Company; *U.S. Public*, pg. 2135
TORPEDO FACTORY GROUP LIMITED—See Aukett Swanke Group Plc; *Int'l*, pg. 704
TORPEDO SPECIALTY WIRE INC.; *U.S. Private*, pg. 4189
TORPOL S.A.; *Int'l*, pg. 7829
TOR PROCESSING & TRADE BV—See TOR Minerals International Inc.; *U.S. Public*, pg. 2164
TORPROJEKT SP. Z O.O.—See Trakcja PRKiI S.A.; *Int'l*, pg. 7891
TORQ CORPORATION; *U.S. Private*, pg. 4189
TORQEEDO GMBH—See Yamaha Corporation; *Int'l*, pg. 8550
TORQEEDO INC.—See Yamaha Corporation; *Int'l*, pg. 8550
TORQ INC.; *Int'l*, pg. 7829
TORQ RESOURCES INC.; *Int'l*, pg. 7829
TORQTEK DESIGN & MANUFACTURING, LLC; *U.S. Private*, pg. 4189
TORQUE CAPITAL GROUP, LLC; *U.S. Private*, pg. 4189
TORQUE CONTROL SPECIALISTS PTY LTD—See Snap-on Incorporated; *U.S. Public*, pg. 1899
TORQUEST PARTNERS INC.; *Int'l*, pg. 7829
TORQX CAPITAL PARTNERS B.V.; *Int'l*, pg. 7830
THE TORRANCE CA MULTI-SPECIALTY ASC, LLC—See KKR & Co. Inc.; *U.S. Public*, pg. 1248
TORRANCE NISSAN, LLC—See AutoNation, Inc.; *U.S. Public*, pg. 238
TORRANCE REFINING COMPANY—See PBF Energy Inc.; *U.S. Public*, pg. 1657

TORQX CAPITAL PARTNERS B.V. — CORPORATE AFFILIATIONS

TORRANCE SURGERY CENTER, L.P.—See KKR & Co. Inc.; *U.S. Public*, pg. 1249
TORRASPAPEL PORTUGAL LDA—See CVC Capital Partners SICAV-FIS S.A.; *Int'l*, pg. 1888
TORRASPAPEL, S.A.—See CVC Capital Partners SICAV-FIS S.A.; *Int'l*, pg. 1888
TORREAL, S.A.; *Int'l*, pg. 7830
TORRE AUTOMOTIVE (PTY) LIMITED—See Apex Partners Proprietary Limited; *Int'l*, pg. 512
TORRE AUTOMOTIVE (PTY) LIMITED—See TRG Management LP; *U.S. Private*, pg. 4220
TORRE & BRUGLIO INC.; *U.S. Private*, pg. 4189
TORRE DE COLLSEROLA, S.A.—See Telefonica, S.A.; *Int'l*, pg. 7536
TORREFAZIONE ITALIA LLC—See Starbucks Corporation; *U.S. Public*, pg. 1939
TORRE HOLDINGS (PTY) LTD.—See Apex Partners Proprietary Limited; *Int'l*, pg. 512
TORRE HOLDINGS (PTY) LTD.—See TRG Management LP; *U.S. Private*, pg. 4220
TORRE IBERDROLA, A.I.E.—See Iberdrola, S.A.; *Int'l*, pg. 3574
TORRE INDUSTRIES LIMITED—See Apex Partners Proprietary Limited; *Int'l*, pg. 512
TORRE INDUSTRIES LIMITED—See TRG Management LP; *U.S. Private*, pg. 4219
TORRE LAZUR HEALTHCARE GROUP, LLC—See The Interpublic Group of Companies, Inc.; *U.S. Public*, pg. 2102
TORRE MARENOSTRUM, S.L.—See Inmobiliaria Colonial SOCIMI SA; *Int'l*, pg. 3706
TORRENS MINING LTD.—See Coda Minerals Ltd.; *Int'l*, pg. 1687
TORRENT CAPITAL LTD.; *Int'l*, pg. 7830
TORRENT DO BRASIL LTDA.—See Torrent Pharmaceuticals Limited; *Int'l*, pg. 7831
TORRENT GOLD INC.; *Int'l*, pg. 7830
TORRENT GOVERNMENT CONTRACTING SERVICES, LLC—See Marsh & McLennan Companies, Inc.; *U.S. Public*, pg. 1388
TORRENT PHARMACEUTICALS LIMITED; *Int'l*, pg. 7830
TORRENT PHARMA INC.—See Torrent Pharmaceuticals Limited; *Int'l*, pg. 7831
TORRENT PHARMA PHILIPPINES INC.—See Torrent Pharmaceuticals Limited; *Int'l*, pg. 7831
TORRENT PHARMA (UK) LTD.—See Torrent Pharmaceuticals Limited; *Int'l*, pg. 7831
TORRENT POWER LIMITED; *Int'l*, pg. 7831
TORRENT RESOURSES INC; *U.S. Private*, pg. 4189
TORRENT TECHNOLOGIES, INC.—See Marsh & McLennan Companies, Inc.; *U.S. Public*, pg. 1388
TORRENT TRACKSIDE LTD.—See Vp PLC; *Int'l*, pg. 8312
TORRE PARTS AND COMPONENTS—See Apex Partners Proprietary Limited; *Int'l*, pg. 512
TORRE PARTS AND COMPONENTS—See TRG Management LP; *U.S. Private*, pg. 4220
TORRES INSURANCE AGENCY, INC.; *U.S. Private*, pg. 4190
TORREVIEJA SALUD S.L.U.—See Centene Corporation; *U.S. Public*, pg. 470
TORREX CHIESI PHARMA GMBH—See Chiesi Farmaceutici SpA; *Int'l*, pg. 1478
TORREYA PARTNERS LLC—See Stifel Financial Corp.; *U.S. Public*, pg. 1950
TORREY HILLS TECHNOLOGIES, LLC; *U.S. Private*, pg. 4190
TORREY PINES BANK—See Western Alliance Bancorporation; *U.S. Public*, pg. 2354
TORREY PINES CARE CENTER—See Apollo Global Management, Inc.; *U.S. Public*, pg. 158
TORREY PINES TRANSPORTATION—See Marcou Transportation Group LLC; *U.S. Private*, pg. 2572
TORRID HOLDINGS INC.; *U.S. Public*, pg. 2164
TORRID INC.; *U.S. Public*, pg. 2164
THE TORRINGTON SAVINGS BANK INC.; *U.S. Private*, pg. 4127
TORRINGTON SUPPLY COMPANY, INCORPORATED; *U.S. Private*, pg. 4190
TORRINGTON WATER COMPANY—See Eversource Energy; *U.S. Public*, pg. 802
TORRMETAL CORPORATION; *U.S. Private*, pg. 4190
TORR METALS INC.; *Int'l*, pg. 7830
TORRY HARRYS INC.; *U.S. Private*, pg. 4190
TORSION CONTROL PRODUCTS, INC.—See The Timken Company; *U.S. Public*, pg. 2134
TORSIT BV—See Henkel + Gerlach GmbH & Co. KG; *Int'l*, pg. 3348
TORSLANDA PROPERTY INVESTMENT AB; *Int'l*, pg. 7831
TORSTAR CORPORATION; *Int'l*, pg. 7831
TOR SYSTEM TECHNIK GMBH—See Sanwa Holdings Corporation; *Int'l*, pg. 6561
TORTEC BRANDSCHUTZTOR GMBH—See Hormann KG Verkaufsgesellschaf; *Int'l*, pg. 3481
TORTEC GROUP CORP.; *U.S. Public*, pg. 2164
TORTEL COMMUNICATIONS INC.; *Int'l*, pg. 7831
TORTEL USA LLC—See Tortel Communications Inc.; *Int'l*, pg. 7831
TORTILLA KING INC.; *U.S. Private*, pg. 4190

TORTILLA MEXICAN GRILL PLC; *Int'l*, pg. 7831
TORTILLERIA ATOTONILCO INC.; *U.S. Private*, pg. 4190
TORTIMASA, S.A.—See Gruma, S.A.B. de C.V.; *Int'l*, pg. 3114
TORTOISE CAPITAL ADVISORS, LLC—See Lovell Minnick Partners LLC; *U.S. Private*, pg. 2503
TORTOISE CO., LTD.—See Sumitomo Corporation; *Int'l*, pg. 7276
TORTOISE CREDIT STRATEGIES, LLC—See Lovell Minnick Partners LLC; *U.S. Private*, pg. 2503
TORTOISE ENERGY INDEPENDENCE FUND, INC.—See Lovell Minnick Partners LLC; *U.S. Private*, pg. 2503
TORTOISE ENERGY INFRASTRUCTURE CORPORATION—See Lovell Minnick Partners LLC; *U.S. Private*, pg. 2503
TORTOISE INVESTMENTS, LLC—See Lovell Minnick Partners LLC; *U.S. Private*, pg. 2503
TORTOISE MIDSTREAM ENERGY FUND, INC.—See Lovell Minnick Partners LLC; *U.S. Private*, pg. 2503
TORTOISE PIPELINE & ENERGY FUND, INC.—See Lovell Minnick Partners LLC; *U.S. Private*, pg. 2503
TORTOISE POWER & ENERGY INFRASTRUCTURE FUND, INC.—See Lovell Minnick Partners LLC; *U.S. Private*, pg. 2503
TORTOLITA HEALTHCARE, INC.—See The Ensign Group, Inc.; *U.S. Public*, pg. 2072
TORTUGAS DIALYSIS, LLC—See DaVita Inc.; *U.S. Public*, pg. 643
TORTUGA TRADING INC.; *U.S. Private*, pg. 4190
TORTUM ELEKTRIK URETIM A.S.—See Verusaturk Girisim Sermayesi Yatirim Ortakligi A.S.; *Int'l*, pg. 8176
TORUNLAR GAYRIMENKUL YATIRIM ORTAKLIGI AS; *Int'l*, pg. 7831
TORUS CORPORATE CAPITAL LTD.—See Enstar Group Limited; *Int'l*, pg. 2449
TORUS NATIONAL INSURANCE COMPANY—See Enstar Group Limited; *Int'l*, pg. 2449
TORUS UNDERWRITING MANAGEMENT LTD.—See Enstar Group Limited; *Int'l*, pg. 2449
TORUS US INTERMEDIARIES INC—See Enstar Group Limited; *Int'l*, pg. 2449
TORVBYEN SENTER AS—See BNP Paribas SA; *Int'l*, pg. 1093
TORVBYEN UTVIKLING AS—See BNP Paribas SA; *Int'l*, pg. 1093
TORVHJORNET LILLESTROM ANS—See BNP Paribas SA; *Int'l*, pg. 1093
TORY BURCH LLC; *U.S. Private*, pg. 4190
TOSAI GAS, INC.—See Nippon Gas Co., Ltd.; *Int'l*, pg. 5318
TOSAS (PTY.) LTD.—See Raubex Group Limited; *Int'l*, pg. 6221
TOSAY MEDICAL.CO., LTD.—See WIN-Partners Co., Ltd.; *Int'l*, pg. 8424
TOSCA ASCENSORI S.R.L.—See KONE Oyj; *Int'l*, pg. 4250
TOSCAFUND ASSET MANAGEMENT LLP—See Old Oak Holdings Limited; *Int'l*, pg. 5552
TOSCA LIMITED—See Apax Partners LLP; *Int'l*, pg. 507
TOSCANA AEROPORTI S.P.A.—See Corporacion America Airports S.A.; *Int'l*, pg. 1803
TOSCANA CAPITAL CORPORATION—See Sprott Inc.; *Int'l*, pg. 7145
TOSCANA ENERGIA GREEN S.P.A.—See Italgas S.p.A.; *Int'l*, pg. 3828
TOSCANA ENERGIA S.P.A.—See Italgas S.p.A.; *Int'l*, pg. 3828
TOSCANA ENERGY INCOME CORPORATION—See i3 Energy Plc; *Int'l*, pg. 3566
TOSCANA ONDULATI SPA—See DS Smith Plc; *Int'l*, pg. 2209
TOSCANA (WA) PTY LTD.; *Int'l*, pg. 7831
TOSCOTEC S.P.A.—See Voith GmbH & Co. KGaA; *Int'l*, pg. 8297
T.O.S.C. - TICKETONE SISTEMI CULTURALI S.R.L.—See CTS Eventim AG & Co. KGAA; *Int'l*, pg. 1874
TOSE CO., LTD.; *Int'l*, pg. 7831
TOSE-E MELLI GROUP INVESTMENT COMPANY; *Int'l*, pg. 7832
TOSEE MELLI INVESTMENT COMPANY; *Int'l*, pg. 7832
TOSEI AMERICA, INC.—See Tokyo Seimitsu Co., Ltd.; *Int'l*, pg. 7795
TOSEI BOX CORP.—See Tokyo Seimitsu Co., Ltd.; *Int'l*, pg. 7795
TOSEI CANADA MEASURING INC.—See Tokyo Seimitsu Co., Ltd.; *Int'l*, pg. 7796
TOSEI CORPORATION—See Electrolux Professional AB; *Int'l*, pg. 2353
TOSEI ENGINEERING CORP.—See Tokyo Seimitsu Co., Ltd.; *Int'l*, pg. 7796
TOSEI ENGINEERING PVT. LTD.—See Tokyo Seimitsu Co., Ltd.; *Int'l*, pg. 7796
TOSEI KOREA CO., LTD.—See Tokyo Seimitsu Co., Ltd.; *Int'l*, pg. 7796
TOSEI MEXICO, S.A. DE C.V.—See Tokyo Seimitsu Co., Ltd.; *Int'l*, pg. 7796
TOSEI PHILIPPINES CORP.—See Tokyo Seimitsu Co., Ltd.; *Int'l*, pg. 7796

TOSEI REIT INVESTMENT CORPORATION; *Int'l*, pg. 7832
TOSEI SYSTEMS CO., LTD.—See Tokyo Seimitsu Co., Ltd.; *Int'l*, pg. 7796
TOSEI TAIWAN CO., LTD.—See Tokyo Seimitsu Co., Ltd.; *Int'l*, pg. 7796
TOSEI (THAILAND) CO., LTD.—See Tokyo Seimitsu Co., Ltd.; *Int'l*, pg. 7795
TOSE PHILIPPINES, INC.—See Tose Co., Ltd.; *Int'l*, pg. 7832
TOSE SOFTWARE (HANGZHOU) CO., LTD.—See Tose Co., Ltd.; *Int'l*, pg. 7832
TOSHBRO SHIMADZU PRIVATE LTD.—See Shimadzu Corporation; *Int'l*, pg. 6833
TOSHIBA AKITA DENKI CO., LTD.—See Japan Industrial Partners, Inc.; *Int'l*, pg. 3891
TOSHIBA AMERICA BUSINESS SOLUTIONS - ARLINGTON HEIGHTS—See Japan Industrial Partners, Inc.; *Int'l*, pg. 3891
TOSHIBA AMERICA BUSINESS SOLUTIONS - ATLANTA—See Japan Industrial Partners, Inc.; *Int'l*, pg. 3892
TOSHIBA AMERICA BUSINESS SOLUTIONS - CHICAGO—See Japan Industrial Partners, Inc.; *Int'l*, pg. 3892
TOSHIBA AMERICA BUSINESS SOLUTIONS - DENVER—See Japan Industrial Partners, Inc.; *Int'l*, pg. 3892
TOSHIBA AMERICA BUSINESS SOLUTIONS - ELECTRONIC IMAGING DIVISION—See Japan Industrial Partners, Inc.; *Int'l*, pg. 3892
TOSHIBA AMERICA BUSINESS SOLUTIONS, INC.—See Japan Industrial Partners, Inc.; *Int'l*, pg. 3891
TOSHIBA AMERICA BUSINESS SOLUTIONS - IRVING—See Japan Industrial Partners, Inc.; *Int'l*, pg. 3892
TOSHIBA AMERICA BUSINESS SOLUTIONS - LAS VEGAS—See Japan Industrial Partners, Inc.; *Int'l*, pg. 3892
TOSHIBA AMERICA BUSINESS SOLUTIONS - LEES SUMMIT—See Japan Industrial Partners, Inc.; *Int'l*, pg. 3892
TOSHIBA AMERICA BUSINESS SOLUTIONS - MITCHELL—See Japan Industrial Partners, Inc.; *Int'l*, pg. 3892
TOSHIBA AMERICA BUSINESS SOLUTIONS - MOUNT GILEAD—See Japan Industrial Partners, Inc.; *Int'l*, pg. 3892
TOSHIBA AMERICA BUSINESS SOLUTIONS - PARSIPPANY—See Japan Industrial Partners, Inc.; *Int'l*, pg. 3892
TOSHIBA AMERICA BUSINESS SOLUTIONS - RICHLAND HILLS—See Japan Industrial Partners, Inc.; *Int'l*, pg. 3892
TOSHIBA AMERICA BUSINESS SOLUTIONS - SAINT PAUL—See Japan Industrial Partners, Inc.; *Int'l*, pg. 3892
TOSHIBA AMERICA BUSINESS SOLUTIONS - SAN ANTONIO—See Japan Industrial Partners, Inc.; *Int'l*, pg. 3892
TOSHIBA AMERICA BUSINESS SOLUTIONS - TAMARAC—See Japan Industrial Partners, Inc.; *Int'l*, pg. 3892
TOSHIBA AMERICA CAPITAL CORPORATION—See Japan Industrial Partners, Inc.; *Int'l*, pg. 3892
TOSHIBA AMERICA CONSUMER PRODUCTS-LATIN AMERICA—See Japan Industrial Partners, Inc.; *Int'l*, pg. 3892
TOSHIBA AMERICA CONSUMER PRODUCTS, LLC—See Japan Industrial Partners, Inc.; *Int'l*, pg. 3892
TOSHIBA AMERICA ELECTRONIC COMPONENTS, INC. - ADVANCED MATERIALS DIVISION—See Japan Industrial Partners, Inc.; *Int'l*, pg. 3892
TOSHIBA AMERICA ELECTRONIC COMPONENTS, INC.—See Japan Industrial Partners, Inc.; *Int'l*, pg. 3892
TOSHIBA AMERICA ELECTRONIC COMPONENTS, INC. - STORAGE PRODUCTS BUSINESS UNIT—See Japan Industrial Partners, Inc.; *Int'l*, pg. 3892
TOSHIBA AMERICA ELECTRONICS—See Japan Industrial Partners, Inc.; *Int'l*, pg. 3892
TOSHIBA AMERICA, INC.—See Japan Industrial Partners, Inc.; *Int'l*, pg. 3891
TOSHIBA AMERICA MEDICAL SYSTEMS, INC.—See Japan Industrial Partners, Inc.; *Int'l*, pg. 3892
TOSHIBA AMERICA RESEARCH, INC.—See Japan Industrial Partners, Inc.; *Int'l*, pg. 3892
TOSHIBA ASIA PACIFIC PTE., LTD.—See Japan Industrial Partners, Inc.; *Int'l*, pg. 3892
TOSHIBA ASIA PACIFIC PTE., LTD. (TAPL)—See Japan Industrial Partners, Inc.; *Int'l*, pg. 3893
TOSHIBA (AUSTRALIA) PTY., LTD.—See Japan Industrial Partners, Inc.; *Int'l*, pg. 3891
TOSHIBA BAIYUN VACUUM INTERRUPTERS (JINZHOU) CO., LTD.—See Japan Industrial Partners, Inc.; *Int'l*, pg. 3893
TOSHIBA BATTERY CO., LTD.—See Japan Industrial Partners, Inc.; *Int'l*, pg. 3893

COMPANY NAME INDEX

TOSHIBA BUILDING & LEASE CO., LTD.—See Nomura Real Estate Holdings, Inc.; *Int'l*, pg. 5412
TOSHIBA BUSINESS AND LIFE SERVICE CORPORATION—See Japan Industrial Partners, Inc.; *Int'l*, pg. 3893
TOSHIBA BUSINESS SOLUTIONS OF NY & NJ—See Japan Industrial Partners, Inc.; *Int'l*, pg. 3892
TOSHIBA CAPITAL (ASIA) LTD.—See Japan Industrial Partners, Inc.; *Int'l*, pg. 3893
TOSHIBA CAPITAL CORPORATION—See Japan Industrial Partners, Inc.; *Int'l*, pg. 3893
TOSHIBA CARRIER AIR CONDITIONING (CHINA) CO., LTD.—See Carrier Global Corporation; *U.S. Public*, pg. 444
TOSHIBA CARRIER AIRCONDITIONING SALES (SHANGHAI) CO., LTD.—See Carrier Global Corporation; *U.S. Public*, pg. 444
TOSHIBA CARRIER CORPORATION—See Carrier Global Corporation; *U.S. Public*, pg. 444
TOSHIBA CARRIER EUROPE S.A.S.—See Carrier Global Corporation; *U.S. Public*, pg. 444
TOSHIBA CARRIER NORTH AMERICA, INC.—See Carrier Global Corporation; *U.S. Public*, pg. 444
TOSHIBA CARRIER (THAILAND) CO., LTD.—See Carrier Global Corporation; *U.S. Public*, pg. 444
TOSHIBA CARRIER UK LIMITED—See Carrier Global Corporation; *U.S. Public*, pg. 444
TOSHIBA (CHINA) CO., LTD.—See Japan Industrial Partners, Inc.; *Int'l*, pg. 3891
TOSHIBA COMPONENTS CO., LTD.—See Japan Industrial Partners, Inc.; *Int'l*, pg. 3893
TOSHIBA COMPRESSOR (TAIWAN) CORP.—See Japan Industrial Partners, Inc.; *Int'l*, pg. 3893
TOSHIBA COMPUTER TECHNOLOGY CORP.—See Japan Industrial Partners, Inc.; *Int'l*, pg. 3893
TOSHIBA CONSUMER & LIGHTING PRODUCTS TRADING (SHANGHAI) CO., LTD.—See Japan Industrial Partners, Inc.; *Int'l*, pg. 3893
TOSHIBA CONSUMER MARKETING CORPORATION—See Japan Industrial Partners, Inc.; *Int'l*, pg. 3893
TOSHIBA CONSUMER MARKETING CORPORATION—See Japan Industrial Partners, Inc.; *Int'l*, pg. 0000
TOSHIBA CONSUMER MARKETING CORPORATION—See Japan Industrial Partners, Inc.; *Int'l*, pg. 3893
TOSHIBA CONSUMER MARKETING CORPORATION—See Japan Industrial Partners, Inc.; *Int'l*, pg. 3893
TOSHIBA CONSUMER MARKETING CORPORATION—See Japan Industrial Partners, Inc.; *Int'l*, pg. 3893
TOSHIBA CONSUMER MARKETING CORPORATION—See Japan Industrial Partners, Inc.; *Int'l*, pg. 3893
TOSHIBA CONSUMER PRODUCTS (THAILAND) CO., LTD.—See Japan Industrial Partners, Inc.; *Int'l*, pg. 3893
TOSHIBA CORPORATION - FUCHU COMPLEX FACTORY—See Japan Industrial Partners, Inc.; *Int'l*, pg. 3893
TOSHIBA CORPORATION - FUKAYA COMPLEX FACTORY—See Japan Industrial Partners, Inc.; *Int'l*, pg. 3893
TOSHIBA CORPORATION - KASHIWAZAKI OPERATIONS FACTORY—See Japan Industrial Partners, Inc.; *Int'l*, pg. 3893
TOSHIBA CORPORATION - KEIHIN PRODUCT OPERATIONS FACTORY—See Japan Industrial Partners, Inc.; *Int'l*, pg. 3893
TOSHIBA CORPORATION - KOMUKAI COMPLEX FACTORY—See Japan Industrial Partners, Inc.; *Int'l*, pg. 3893
TOSHIBA CORPORATION - MIE OPERATIONS FACTORY—See Japan Industrial Partners, Inc.; *Int'l*, pg. 3893
TOSHIBA CORPORATION - OITA OPERATIONS FACTORY—See Japan Industrial Partners, Inc.; *Int'l*, pg. 3894
TOSHIBA CORPORATION - OME COMPLEX FACTORY—See Japan Industrial Partners, Inc.; *Int'l*, pg. 3894
TOSHIBA CORPORATION—See Japan Industrial Partners, Inc.; *Int'l*, pg. 3889
TOSHIBA CORPORATION - WEST TURBINE WORKS—See Japan Industrial Partners, Inc.; *Int'l*, pg. 3894
TOSHIBA CORPORATION - YOKKAICHI OPERATIONS FACTORY—See Japan Industrial Partners, Inc.; *Int'l*, pg. 3894
TOSHIBA CORPORATION - YOKOHAMA COMPLEX FACTORY—See Japan Industrial Partners, Inc.; *Int'l*, pg. 3894
TOSHIBA DALIAN CO. LTD.—See Japan Industrial Partners, Inc.; *Int'l*, pg. 3894
TOSHIBA DATA DYNAMICS PTE. LTD.—See Japan Industrial Partners, Inc.; *Int'l*, pg. 3894
TOSHIBA DE COLUMBIA C.A.—See Japan Industrial Partners, Inc.; *Int'l*, pg. 3898
TOSHIBA DE MEXICO, S.A. DE C.V.—See Japan Industrial Partners, Inc.; *Int'l*, pg. 3898
TOSHIBA DE VENEZUELA C.A.—See Japan Industrial Partners, Inc.; *Int'l*, pg. 3898
TOSHIBA DIGITAL MEDIA ENGINEERING CORP.—See Japan Industrial Partners, Inc.; *Int'l*, pg. 3894
TOSHIBA DIGITAL MEDIA NETWORK KOREA CORP.—See Japan Industrial Partners, Inc.; *Int'l*, pg. 3893
TOSHIBA DIGITAL MEDIA NETWORK TAIWAN CORPORATION—See Japan Industrial Partners, Inc.; *Int'l*, pg. 3894
TOSHIBA DISK PRODUCTS DIVISION—See Japan Industrial Partners, Inc.; *Int'l*, pg. 3892
TOSHIBA DISPLAY DEVICES (THAILAND) CO., LTD.—See Japan Industrial Partners, Inc.; *Int'l*, pg. 3894
TOSHIBA DO BRASIL S.A.—See Japan Industrial Partners, Inc.; *Int'l*, pg. 3898
TOSHIBA ELECTRIC SERVICE CORP.—See Japan Industrial Partners, Inc.; *Int'l*, pg. 3894
TOSHIBA ELECTRONIC DEVICES & STORAGE CORPORATION—See Japan Industrial Partners, Inc.; *Int'l*, pg. 3893
TOSHIBA ELECTRONIC ENGINEERING CORPORATION—See Japan Industrial Partners, Inc.; *Int'l*, pg. 3894
TOSHIBA ELECTRONIC IMAGING DIVISION—See Japan Industrial Partners, Inc.; *Int'l*, pg. 3892
TOSHIBA ELECTRONICS ASIA (HONG KONG), LTD.—See Japan Industrial Partners, Inc.; *Int'l*, pg. 3896
TOSHIBA ELECTRONICS ASIA, LTD.—See Japan Industrial Partners, Inc.; *Int'l*, pg. 3894
TOSHIBA ELECTRONICS ASIA (SINGAPORE) PTE. LTD.—See Japan Industrial Partners, Inc.; *Int'l*, pg. 3894
TOSHIBA ELECTRONICS ASIA—See Japan Industrial Partners, Inc.; *Int'l*, pg. 3894
TOSHIBA ELECTRONICS ASIA—See Japan Industrial Partners, Inc.; *Int'l*, pg. 3894
TOSHIBA ELECTRONICS (DALIAN) CO., LTD.—See Japan Industrial Partners, Inc.; *Int'l*, pg. 3893
TOSHIBA ELECTRONICS ESPANA S.A.—See Japan Industrial Partners, Inc.; *Int'l*, pg. 3895
TOSHIBA ELECTRONICS EUROPE GMBH—See Japan Industrial Partners, Inc.; *Int'l*, pg. 3895
TOSHIBA ELECTRONICS EUROPE GMBH—See Japan Industrial Partners, Inc.; *Int'l*, pg. 3895
TOSHIBA ELECTRONICS FRANCE S.A.R.L.—See Japan Industrial Partners, Inc.; *Int'l*, pg. 3895
TOSHIBA ELECTRONICS ITALIANA S.R.L.—See Japan Industrial Partners, Inc.; *Int'l*, pg. 3895
TOSHIBA ELECTRONICS KOREA CORPORATION—See Japan Industrial Partners, Inc.; *Int'l*, pg. 3894
TOSHIBA ELECTRONICS KOREA CORPORATION—See Japan Industrial Partners, Inc.; *Int'l*, pg. 3894
TOSHIBA ELECTRONICS SCANDINAVIA AB—See Japan Industrial Partners, Inc.; *Int'l*, pg. 3895
TOSHIBA ELECTRONICS SERVICE (THAILAND) CO., LTD.—See Japan Industrial Partners, Inc.; *Int'l*, pg. 3893
TOSHIBA ELECTRONICS (SHANGHAI) CO., LTD.—See Japan Industrial Partners, Inc.; *Int'l*, pg. 3893
TOSHIBA ELECTRONICS (SHENZHEN) CO., LTD.—See Japan Industrial Partners, Inc.; *Int'l*, pg. 3893
TOSHIBA ELECTRONICS TAIWAN CORP.—See Japan Industrial Partners, Inc.; *Int'l*, pg. 3894
TOSHIBA ELECTRONICS TRADING (MALAYSIA) SDN. BHD.—See Japan Industrial Partners, Inc.; *Int'l*, pg. 3894
TOSHIBA ELECTRONICS TRADING (MALAYSIA) SDN. BHD.—See Japan Industrial Partners, Inc.; *Int'l*, pg. 3894
TOSHIBA ELEVATOR & BUILDING SYSTEMS CORPORATION—See Japan Industrial Partners, Inc.; *Int'l*, pg. 3894
TOSHIBA ELEVATOR (CHINA) CO.,LTD.—See Japan Industrial Partners, Inc.; *Int'l*, pg. 3894
TOSHIBA ELEVATOR (INDIA) PVT., LTD—See Japan Industrial Partners, Inc.; *Int'l*, pg. 3894
TOSHIBA ELEVATOR KOREA INC.—See Japan Industrial Partners, Inc.; *Int'l*, pg. 3894
TOSHIBA ELEVATOR SHENYANG CO., LTD.—See Japan Industrial Partners, Inc.; *Int'l*, pg. 3894
TOSHIBA ENERGY SYSTEMS & SOLUTIONS CORPORATION—See Japan Industrial Partners, Inc.; *Int'l*, pg. 3894
TOSHIBA EUROPE RESEARCH LTD.—See Japan Industrial Partners, Inc.; *Int'l*, pg. 3896
TOSHIBA EUROPE (SWITZERLAND) GMBH—See Japan Industrial Partners, Inc.; *Int'l*, pg. 3895
TOSHIBA GULF FZE—See Japan Industrial Partners, Inc.; *Int'l*, pg. 3895
TOSHIBA HANGZHOU CO., LTD.—See Japan Industrial Partners, Inc.; *Int'l*, pg. 3893
TOSHIBA HOKUTO ELECTRONICS CORPORATION—See Japan Industrial Partners, Inc.; *Int'l*, pg. 3895
TOSHIBA HOKUTO ELECTRONICS CORPORATION—See Japan Industrial Partners, Inc.; *Int'l*, pg. 3895
TOSHIBA HOME APPLIANCES CORPORATION—See Japan Industrial Partners, Inc.; *Int'l*, pg. 3895
TOSHIBA HOME APPLIANCES SALES (NANHAI) CO., LTD.—See Japan Industrial Partners, Inc.; *Int'l*, pg. 3893
TOSHIBA HOME TECHNOLOGY CORPORATION—See Japan Industrial Partners, Inc.; *Int'l*, pg. 3895
TOSHIBA HONG KONG LIMITED.—See Japan Industrial Partners, Inc.; *Int'l*, pg. 3895
TOSHIBA HYDRO POWER (HANGZHOU) CO., LTD.—See Japan Industrial Partners, Inc.; *Int'l*, pg. 3893
TOSHIBA INDUSTRIAL PRODUCTS MANUFACTURING CORPORATION—See Japan Industrial Partners, Inc.; *Int'l*, pg. 3895
TOSHIBA INDUSTRIAL PRODUCTS SALES CORPORATION—See Japan Industrial Partners, Inc.; *Int'l*, pg. 3895
TOSHIBA INFORMATION EQUIPMENT (PHILIPPINES), INC.—See Japan Industrial Partners, Inc.; *Int'l*, pg. 3895
TOSHIBA INFORMATION, INDUSTRIAL AND POWER SYSTEMS TAIWAN CORPORATION—See Japan Industrial Partners, Inc.; *Int'l*, pg. 3895
TOSHIBA INFORMATION SYSTEMS (UK) LTD.—See Japan Industrial Partners, Inc.; *Int'l*, pg. 3895
TOSHIBA INFRASTRUCTURE SYSTEMS SOUTH AMERICA LTD.—See Japan Industrial Partners, Inc.; *Int'l*, pg. 3895
TOSHIBA INSURANCE SERVICE CORPORATION—See Japan Industrial Partners, Inc.; *Int'l*, pg. 3895
TOSHIBA INTERNATIONAL CORP., INDUSTRIAL PRODUCTS DIV.—See Japan Industrial Partners, Inc.; *Int'l*, pg. 3892
TOSHIBA INTERNATIONAL CORPORATION - INDUSTRIAL SYSTEMS DIVISION—See Japan Industrial Partners, Inc.; *Int'l*, pg. 3892
TOSHIBA INTERNATIONAL CORPORATION - LED DISPLAY SYSTEMS DIVISION—See Japan Industrial Partners, Inc.; *Int'l*, pg. 3892
TOSHIBA INTERNATIONAL CORPORATION PTY., LTD.—See Japan Industrial Partners, Inc.; *Int'l*, pg. 3896
TOSHIBA INTERNATIONAL CORPORATION—See Japan Industrial Partners, Inc.; *Int'l*, pg. 3892
TOSHIBA INTERNATIONAL (EUROPE) LTD—See Japan Industrial Partners, Inc.; *Int'l*, pg. 3895
TOSHIBA INTERNATIONAL (EUROPE) LTD.—See Japan Industrial Partners, Inc.; *Int'l*, pg. 3895
TOSHIBA INTERNATIONAL FINANCE (NETHERLANDS) B.V.—See Japan Industrial Partners, Inc.; *Int'l*, pg. 3895
TOSHIBA INTERNATIONAL FINANCE (UK) PLC—See Japan Industrial Partners, Inc.; *Int'l*, pg. 3895
TOSHIBA IT & CONTROL SYSTEMS CORPORATION—See Japan Industrial Partners, Inc.; *Int'l*, pg. 3895
TOSHIBA KN SYSTEM CO., LTD.—See Japan Industrial Partners, Inc.; *Int'l*, pg. 3896
TOSHIBA KYUSHU MARKETING CO., LTD.—See Japan Industrial Partners, Inc.; *Int'l*, pg. 3896
TOSHIBA LIGHTING (BEIJING) CO., LTD.—See Japan Industrial Partners, Inc.; *Int'l*, pg. 3893
TOSHIBA LIGHTING & DISPLAY SYSTEMS (SHANGHAI) CO., LTD.—See Japan Industrial Partners, Inc.; *Int'l*, pg. 3893
TOSHIBA LIGHTING (FUZHOU) CO.,LTD.—See Japan Industrial Partners, Inc.; *Int'l*, pg. 3893
TOSHIBA LIGHTING & TECHNOLOGY CORPORATION—See Japan Industrial Partners, Inc.; *Int'l*, pg. 3896
TOSHIBA LOCATION INFORMATION CO., LTD.—See Japan Industrial Partners, Inc.; *Int'l*, pg. 3896
TOSHIBA LOGISTICS AMERICA, INC.—See Japan Industrial Partners, Inc.; *Int'l*, pg. 3892
TOSHIBA LOGISTICS CORPORATION—See Japan Industrial Partners, Inc.; *Int'l*, pg. 3896
TOSHIBA LOGISTICS (DALIAN) CO., LTD.—See SBS Holdings Inc.; *Int'l*, pg. 6608
TOSHIBA LOGISTICS (HANGZHOU) CO., LTD.—See SBS Holdings Inc.; *Int'l*, pg. 6608
TOSHIBA LOGISTICS (HONG KONG) CO., LTD.—See SBS Holdings Inc.; *Int'l*, pg. 6608
TOSHIBA LOGISTICS MALAYSIA SDN. BHD.—See SBS Holdings Inc.; *Int'l*, pg. 6608
TOSHIBA LOGISTICS (PHILIPPINES) CORPORATION—See SBS Holdings Inc.; *Int'l*, pg. 6608
TOSHIBA LOGISTICS (SINGAPORE) PTE. LTD.—See SBS Holdings Inc.; *Int'l*, pg. 6608
TOSHIBA LOGISTICS VIETNAM CO., LTD.—See SBS Holdings Inc.; *Int'l*, pg. 6608

TOSHIBA MACHINE (CHENNAI) PVT. LTD.—See Japan Industrial Partners, Inc.; *Int'l*, pg. 3891
TOSHIBA MACHINE CO., LTD - GOTEMBA PLANT—See Japan Industrial Partners, Inc.; *Int'l*, pg. 3891
TOSHIBA MACHINE CO., LTD - SAGAMI PLANT—See Japan Industrial Partners, Inc.; *Int'l*, pg. 3891
TOSHIBA MACHINE CO., LTD. - SHANGHAI PLANT—See Japan Industrial Partners, Inc.; *Int'l*, pg. 3891
TOSHIBA MACHINE COMPANY AMERICA LTD.—See Japan Industrial Partners, Inc.; *Int'l*, pg. 3892
TOSHIBA MACHINE COMPANY CANADA LTD.—See Japan Industrial Partners, Inc.; *Int'l*, pg. 3891
TOSHIBA MACHINE (EUROPE) GMBH—See Japan Industrial Partners, Inc.; *Int'l*, pg. 3891
TOSHIBA MACHINE HONG KONG LTD—See Japan Industrial Partners, Inc.; *Int'l*, pg. 3891
TOSHIBA MACHINE S.E ASIA PTE. LTD.—See Japan Industrial Partners, Inc.; *Int'l*, pg. 3891
TOSHIBA MACHINE (SHANGHAI) CO., LTD.—See Japan Industrial Partners, Inc.; *Int'l*, pg. 3890
TOSHIBA MACHINE (SHENZHEN) CO., LTD.—See Japan Industrial Partners, Inc.; *Int'l*, pg. 3891
TOSHIBA MACHINE TAIWAN CO., LTD.—See Japan Industrial Partners, Inc.; *Int'l*, pg. 3891
TOSHIBA MACHINE (THAILAND) CO., LTD.—See Japan Industrial Partners, Inc.; *Int'l*, pg. 3891
TOSHIBA MACHINE (VIETNAM) CO., LTD.—See Japan Industrial Partners, Inc.; *Int'l*, pg. 3891
TOSHIBA MATERIAL SALES CO., LTD.—See Japan Industrial Partners, Inc.; *Int'l*, pg. 3896
TOSHIBA MATERIALS CO., LTD.—See Japan Industrial Partners, Inc.; *Int'l*, pg. 3896
TOSHIBA-MEDICAL DIVISION—See Japan Industrial Partners, Inc.; *Int'l*, pg. 3891
TOSHIBA MEDICAL DO BRASIL LTDA.—See Japan Industrial Partners, Inc.; *Int'l*, pg. 3896
TOSHIBA MEDICAL FRANCE S.A.—See Japan Industrial Partners, Inc.; *Int'l*, pg. 3895
TOSHIBA MEDICAL SYSTEMS AG—See Japan Industrial Partners, Inc.; *Int'l*, pg. 3895
TOSHIBA MEDICAL SYSTEMS ASIA PTE., LTD.—See Japan Industrial Partners, Inc.; *Int'l*, pg. 3896
TOSHIBA MEDICAL SYSTEMS CORPORATION—See Canon, Inc.; *Int'l*, pg. 1298
TOSHIBA MEDICAL SYSTEMS EUROPE B.V.—See Japan Industrial Partners, Inc.; *Int'l*, pg. 3895
TOSHIBA MEDICAL SYSTEMS GMBH—See Japan Industrial Partners, Inc.; *Int'l*, pg. 3895
TOSHIBA MEDICAL SYSTEMS GMBH—See Japan Industrial Partners, Inc.; *Int'l*, pg. 3895
TOSHIBA MEDICAL SYSTEMS LTD.—See Japan Industrial Partners, Inc.; *Int'l*, pg. 3895
TOSHIBA MEDICAL SYSTEMS NV/SA—See Japan Industrial Partners, Inc.; *Int'l*, pg. 3895
TOSHIBA MEDICAL SYSTEMS S.A.—See Japan Industrial Partners, Inc.; *Int'l*, pg. 3896
TOSHIBA MEDICAL SYSTEMS S.R.L.—See Japan Industrial Partners, Inc.; *Int'l*, pg. 3896
TOSHIBA MEDICAL SYSTEMS SWEDEN—See Japan Industrial Partners, Inc.; *Int'l*, pg. 3896
TOSHIBA MEMORY ADVANCED PACKAGE CORPORATION—See Japan Industrial Partners, Inc.; *Int'l*, pg. 3896
TOSHIBA MEMORY SEMICONDUCTOR TAIWAN CORPORATION—See Japan Industrial Partners, Inc.; *Int'l*, pg. 3896
TOSHIBA METAL PARTS CO., LTD.—See Japan Industrial Partners, Inc.; *Int'l*, pg. 3896
TOSHIBA MITSUBISHI-ELECTRIC INDUSTRIAL SYSTEMS CORPORATION—See Japan Industrial Partners, Inc.; *Int'l*, pg. 3896
TOSHIBA MITSUBISHI-ELECTRIC INDUSTRIAL SYSTEMS—See Mitsubishi Electric Corporation; *Int'l*, pg. 4946
TOSHIBA MULTIMEDIA DEVICES CO., LTD.—See Japan Industrial Partners, Inc.; *Int'l*, pg. 3896
TOSHIBA MULTI MEDIA DEVICES CO., LTD.—See Japan Industrial Partners, Inc.; *Int'l*, pg. 3896
TOSHIBA NANOANALYSIS CORPORATION—See L'Air Liquide S.A.; *Int'l*, pg. 4373
TOSHIBA NANO ANALYSIS K.K.—See L'Air Liquide S.A.; *Int'l*, pg. 4373
TOSHIBA NISHI NIHON SERVICE & ENGINEERING CO., LTD.—See Japan Industrial Partners, Inc.; *Int'l*, pg. 3896
TOSHIBA OF CANADA, LTD.—See Japan Industrial Partners, Inc.; *Int'l*, pg. 3898
TOSHIBA OF EUROPE LTD. - NEW LIGHTING SYSTEMS—See Japan Industrial Partners, Inc.; *Int'l*, pg. 3898
TOSHIBA OSAKA BUILDING CO., LTD.—See Japan Industrial Partners, Inc.; *Int'l*, pg. 3896
TOSHIBA OU DENKI CO., LTD.—See Japan Industrial Partners, Inc.; *Int'l*, pg. 3896
TOSHIBA PERSONAL COMPUTER & NETWORK (SHANGHAI) CO., LTD.—See Japan Industrial Partners, Inc.; *Int'l*, pg. 3896

TOSHIBA PERSONAL COMPUTER SYSTEM CORP.—See Japan Industrial Partners, Inc.; *Int'l*, pg. 3896
TOSHIBA PLANT SYSTEMS & SERVICES CORPORATION—See Japan Industrial Partners, Inc.; *Int'l*, pg. 3896
TOSHIBA PORTUGAL—See Japan Industrial Partners, Inc.; *Int'l*, pg. 3896
TOSHIBA PRODUCTS & SERVICES (SHANGHAI) CO., LTD.—See Japan Industrial Partners, Inc.; *Int'l*, pg. 3893
TOSHIBA RESEARCH EUROPE, LTD.—See Japan Industrial Partners, Inc.; *Int'l*, pg. 3896
TOSHIBA RUS LLC.—See Japan Industrial Partners, Inc.; *Int'l*, pg. 3896
TOSHIBA SALES & SERVICES SDN. BHD.—See Japan Industrial Partners, Inc.; *Int'l*, pg. 3896
TOSHIBA SANGYO KIKI SYSTEM CORPORATION—See Japan Industrial Partners, Inc.; *Int'l*, pg. 3896
TOSHIBA SCHNEIDER INVERTER CORP.—See Schneider Electric SE; *Int'l*, pg. 6635
TOSHIBA SEMICONDUCTOR GMBH—See Japan Industrial Partners, Inc.; *Int'l*, pg. 3896
TOSHIBA SEMICONDUCTOR (THAILAND) CO., LTD.—See Japan Industrial Partners, Inc.; *Int'l*, pg. 3896
TOSHIBA SERVICE & ENGINEERING CO., LTD.—See Japan Industrial Partners, Inc.; *Int'l*, pg. 3897
TOSHIBA SHIKOKU SERVICE & ENGINEERING CO. LTD.—See Japan Industrial Partners, Inc.; *Int'l*, pg. 3897
TOSHIBA SHOMEI PRECISION CORPORATION—See Japan Industrial Partners, Inc.; *Int'l*, pg. 3897
TOSHIBA SOCIO-ENGINEERING CO., LTD.—See Japan Industrial Partners, Inc.; *Int'l*, pg. 3897
TOSHIBA STORAGE DEVICE CORPORATION—See Japan Industrial Partners, Inc.; *Int'l*, pg. 3897
TOSHIBA STORAGE DEVICE (PHILLIPINES), INC.—See Japan Industrial Partners, Inc.; *Int'l*, pg. 3897
TOSHIBA SYSTEM TECHNOLOGY CORP.—See Japan Industrial Partners, Inc.; *Int'l*, pg. 3897
TOSHIBA TEC AMERICA RETAIL INFORMATION SYSTEMS, INC.—See Japan Industrial Partners, Inc.; *Int'l*, pg. 3897
TOSHIBA TEC AUSTRALIA PTY. LTD.—See Japan Industrial Partners, Inc.; *Int'l*, pg. 3897
TOSHIBA TEC CANADA INC—See Japan Industrial Partners, Inc.; *Int'l*, pg. 3897
TOSHIBA TEC CORPORATION—See Japan Industrial Partners, Inc.; *Int'l*, pg. 3897
TOSHIBA TEC FRANCE IMAGING SYSTEMS S.A.—See Japan Industrial Partners, Inc.; *Int'l*, pg. 3891
TOSHIBA TEC GERMANY IMAGING SYSTEMS GMBH—See Japan Industrial Partners, Inc.; *Int'l*, pg. 3897
TOSHIBA TECHNICAL SERVICES INTERNATIONAL CORPORATION—See Japan Industrial Partners, Inc.; *Int'l*, pg. 3897
TOSHIBA TECHNOLOGY DEVELOPMENT (SHANGHAI) CO., LTD.—See Japan Industrial Partners, Inc.; *Int'l*, pg. 3897
TOSHIBA TEC KOREA CO., LTD.—See Japan Industrial Partners, Inc.; *Int'l*, pg. 3897
TOSHIBA TEC MALAYSIA SDN BHD—See Japan Industrial Partners, Inc.; *Int'l*, pg. 3897
TOSHIBA TEC NETHERLANDS RETAIL INFORMATION SYSTEMS B.V.—See Japan Industrial Partners, Inc.; *Int'l*, pg. 3897
TOSHIBA TEC NORDIC AB—See Japan Industrial Partners, Inc.; *Int'l*, pg. 3897
TOSHIBA TEC SINGAPORE PTE LTD—See Japan Industrial Partners, Inc.; *Int'l*, pg. 3897
TOSHIBA TEC SPAIN IMAGING SYSTEMS—See Japan Industrial Partners, Inc.; *Int'l*, pg. 3897
TOSHIBA TEC SUISSE AG—See Japan Industrial Partners, Inc.; *Int'l*, pg. 3897
TOSHIBA-TELECOMMUNICATIONS RESEARCH LABORATORY—See Japan Industrial Partners, Inc.; *Int'l*, pg. 3896
TOSHIBA TELI CORP.—See Japan Industrial Partners, Inc.; *Int'l*, pg. 3897
TOSHIBA THAILAND CO., LTD.—See Japan Industrial Partners, Inc.; *Int'l*, pg. 3897
TOSHIBA TLC, INC.—See Japan Industrial Partners, Inc.; *Int'l*, pg. 3897
TOSHIBA TOKO METER SYSTEMS CO., LTD.—See Takaoka Toko Co., Ltd.; *Int'l*, pg. 7431
TOSHIBA TOURIST CORPORATION—See Japan Industrial Partners, Inc.; *Int'l*, pg. 3897
TOSHIBA TRADING INC.—See Japan Industrial Partners, Inc.; *Int'l*, pg. 3897
TOSHIBA TRANSMISSION AND DISTRIBUTION BRAZIL LTD.—See Japan Industrial Partners, Inc.; *Int'l*, pg. 3897
TOSHIBA TRANSMISSION AND DISTRIBUTION SYSTEMS BRAZIL LTD.—See Japan Industrial Partners, Inc.; *Int'l*, pg. 3897

TOSHIBA VIDEO PRODUCTS JAPAN CO., LTD.—See Japan Industrial Partners, Inc.; *Int'l*, pg. 3897
TOSHIBA VIETNAM CONSUMER PRODUCTS CO., LTD.—See Japan Industrial Partners, Inc.; *Int'l*, pg. 3897
TOSHIBA (VIETNAM) HOME APPLIANCES CO., LTD. - BEN CAT FACTORY—See Japan Industrial Partners, Inc.; *Int'l*, pg. 3893
TOSHIBA VISUAL-EQUIPMENT CORPORATION—See Japan Industrial Partners, Inc.; *Int'l*, pg. 3897
TOSHIBA VISUAL IMAGING SYSTEMS (SHENZHEN) LTD.—See Japan Industrial Partners, Inc.; *Int'l*, pg. 3893
TOSHICHI INC.—See Medipal Holdings Corporation; *Int'l*, pg. 4779
TOSHI KANKYO ENGINEERING CO., LTD.—See Kajima Corporation; *Int'l*, pg. 4056
TOSHIN DEVELOPMENT CO. LTD.—See Takashimaya Company, Limited; *Int'l*, pg. 7435
TOSHIN GROUP CO., LTD.; *Int'l*, pg. 7832
TOSHIN HOLDINGS CO., LTD.; *Int'l*, pg. 7832
TOSHIN PACKAGE CO., LTD.—See Tomoku Co., Ltd.; *Int'l*, pg. 7802
TOSHIN SEISAKUSYO CO., LTD.—See RAIZNEXT Corporation; *Int'l*, pg. 6192
TOSHINSHOKAI CO., LTD.—See Cominix Co., Ltd.; *Int'l*, pg. 1714
TOSHKENT REPUBLIC STOCK EXCHANGE; *Int'l*, pg. 7832
TOSHO ASSET MANAGEMENT CO., LTD.—See TOSHO Co., Ltd.; *Int'l*, pg. 7832
TOSHO CENTRAL CO., LTD.—See Central Glass Co. Ltd.; *Int'l*, pg. 1407
TOSHO CO., LTD.; *Int'l*, pg. 7832
TOSHO COMPUTER SYSTEMS CO., LTD.—See FUJISOFT INCORPORATED; *Int'l*, pg. 2830
TOSHO ESTATE CO., LTD.—See TOPPAN Holdings Inc.; *Int'l*, pg. 7820
TOSHO GLASS CO., LTD.—See Toyo Seikan Group Holdings, Ltd.; *Int'l*, pg. 7857
TOSHOKAN RYUTSU CENTER CO., LTD.—See Dai Nippon Printing Co., Ltd.; *Int'l*, pg. 1916
TOSHOKU AMERICA, INC.—See Cargill, Inc.; *U.S. Private*, pg. 760
TOSHOKU LTD.—See Cargill, Inc.; *U.S. Private*, pg. 760
TOSHO PRINTING COMPANY LIMITED—See TOPPAN Holdings Inc.; *Int'l*, pg. 7817
TOSNET CORPORATION; *Int'l*, pg. 7832
TOSO CO., LTD.; *Int'l*, pg. 7832
TOSOH AMERICA, INC.—See Tosoh Corporation; *Int'l*, pg. 7833
TOSOH ANALYSIS AND RESEARCH CENTER CO., LTD.—See Tosoh Corporation; *Int'l*, pg. 7833
TOSOH ASIA PTE. LTD.—See Tosoh Corporation; *Int'l*, pg. 7833
TOSOH BIOSCIENCE, A.G.—See Tosoh Corporation; *Int'l*, pg. 7833
TOSOH BIOSCIENCE GMBH—See Tosoh Corporation; *Int'l*, pg. 7833
TOSOH BIOSCIENCE, INC.—See Tosoh Corporation; *Int'l*, pg. 7833
TOSOH BIOSCIENCE LLC—See Tosoh Corporation; *Int'l*, pg. 7833
TOSOH BIOSCIENCE LTD.—See Tosoh Corporation; *Int'l*, pg. 7833
TOSOH BIOSCIENCE N.V.—See Tosoh Corporation; *Int'l*, pg. 7833
TOSOH BIOSCIENCE S.A.—See Tosoh Corporation; *Int'l*, pg. 7833
TOSOH BIOSCIENCE SHANGHAI CO., LTD.—See Tosoh Corporation; *Int'l*, pg. 7833
TOSOH BIOSCIENCE SRL—See Tosoh Corporation; *Int'l*, pg. 7833
TOSOH BIOSCIENCE WISCONSIN, INC.—See Tosoh Corporation; *Int'l*, pg. 7833
TOSOH BIOSEP GMBH—See Tosoh Corporation; *Int'l*, pg. 7833
TOSOH CERAMICS CO., LTD.—See Tosoh Corporation; *Int'l*, pg. 7833
TOSOH CORPORATION - FUKUOKA REGIONAL OFFICE—See Tosoh Corporation; *Int'l*, pg. 7834
TOSOH CORPORATION - OSAKA REGIONAL OFFICE—See Tosoh Corporation; *Int'l*, pg. 7834
TOSOH CORPORATION; *Int'l*, pg. 7832
TOSOH CORPORATION—See Tosoh Corporation; *Int'l*, pg. 7833
TOSOH CORPORATION—See Tosoh Corporation; *Int'l*, pg. 7833
TOSOH CORPORATION—See Tosoh Corporation; *Int'l*, pg. 7833
TOSOH EUROPE B.V.—See Tosoh Corporation; *Int'l*, pg. 7834
TOSOH EUROPE N.V.—See Tosoh Corporation; *Int'l*, pg. 7834
TOSOH FINECHEM CORPORATION—See Tosoh Corporation; *Int'l*, pg. 7834
TOSOH F-TECH, INC. - NANYO PLANT—See Tosoh Corporation; *Int'l*, pg. 7834

COMPANY NAME INDEX

TOTALENERGIES SE

TOSOH F-TECH, INC.—See Tosoh Corporation; *Int'l,* pg. 7834
TOSOH (GUANGZHOU) CHEMICAL INDUSTRIES, INC.—See Tosoh Corporation; *Int'l,* pg. 7833
TOSOH HELLAS A.I.C.—See Tosoh Corporation; *Int'l,* pg. 7834
TOSOH HYUGA CORPORATION—See Tosoh Corporation; *Int'l,* pg. 7834
TOSOH INDIA PVT. LTD.—See Tosoh Corporation; *Int'l,* pg. 7834
TOSOH INFORMATION SYSTEMS CORPORATION—See Tosoh Corporation; *Int'l,* pg. 7834
TOSOH KASUMI ENGI INC.—See Tosoh Corporation; *Int'l,* pg. 7834
TOSOH LOGISTICS CORPORATION—See Tosoh Corporation; *Int'l,* pg. 7834
TOSOH LOGISTICS WAREHOUSE CO., LTD.—See Tosoh Corporation; *Int'l,* pg. 7834
TOSOH ORGANIC CHEMICAL CO., LTD.—See Tosoh Corporation; *Int'l,* pg. 7834
TOSOH POLYVIN CORPORATION—See Tosoh Corporation; *Int'l,* pg. 7834
TOSOH QUARTZ CO., LTD.—See Tosoh Corporation; *Int'l,* pg. 7834
TOSOH QUARTZ CO., LTD.—See Tosoh Corporation; *Int'l,* pg. 7834
TOSOH QUARTZ, INC.—See Tosoh Corporation; *Int'l,* pg. 7833
TOSOH QUARTZ, LTD.—See Tosoh Corporation; *Int'l,* pg. 7834
TOSOH SET, INC.—See Tosoh Corporation; *Int'l,* pg. 7833
TOSOH SGM CORPORATION—See Tosoh Corporation; *Int'l,* pg. 7834
TOSOH (SHANGHAI) CO., LTD.—See Tosoh Corporation; *Int'l,* pg. 7833
TOSOH SILICA CORPORATION—See Tosoh Corporation; *Int'l,* pg. 7834
TOSOH SMD, INC.—See Tosoh Corporation; *Int'l,* pg. 7833
TOSOH SMD KOREA, LTD.—See Tosoh Corporation; *Int'l,* pg. 7834
TOSOH SMD TAIWAN, LTD.—See Tosoh Corporation; *Int'l,* pg. 7834
TOSOH SPECIALITY MATERIALS CORPORATION—See Tosoh Corporation; *Int'l,* pg. 7834
TOSOH SPECIALTY CHEMICALS USA, INC.—See Tosoh Corporation; *Int'l,* pg. 7834
TOSOH TECHNO-SYSTEM, INC.—See Tosoh Corporation; *Int'l,* pg. 7834
TOSOH USA, INC.—See Tosoh Corporation; *Int'l,* pg. 7833
TOSO RYUTSU SERVICE CO., LTD.—See TOSO Co., Ltd.; *Int'l,* pg. 7832
TOSO WINDOW TREATMENT (SHANGHAI) CO., LTD.—See TOSO Co., Ltd.; *Int'l,* pg. 7832
TOSRIFA INDUSTRIES LTD.; *Int'l,* pg. 7834
T&O S.R.L.—See Sesa S.p.A.; *Int'l,* pg. 6729
TOSTEM HONG KONG LTD.—See LIXIL Group Corporation; *Int'l,* pg. 4535
TOSTEM HOUSING PRODUCTS (DALIAN) CO., LTD.—See LIXIL Group Corporation; *Int'l,* pg. 4534
TOSTEM MANAGEMENT SYSTEMS CO., LTD.—See LIXIL Group Corporation; *Int'l,* pg. 4534
TOSTEM THAI CO., LTD.—See LIXIL Group Corporation; *Int'l,* pg. 4534
TOSTEM THAI MARKETING CO., LTD.—See LIXIL Group Corporation; *Int'l,* pg. 4534
TOSTEM VIVA CORPORATION—See LIXIL Group Corporation; *Int'l,* pg. 4535
TOSU DELICA CO., LTD.—See Kewpie Corporation; *Int'l,* pg. 4144
TOSYALI TOYO CELIK ANONIM SIRKETI—See Toyo Seikan Group Holdings, Ltd.; *Int'l,* pg. 7857
TOSYS NIIGATA CO., LTD.—See COMSYS Holdings Corporation; *Int'l,* pg. 1762
TOTAKU INDUSTRIES, INC.—See Nagase & Co., Ltd.; *Int'l,* pg. 5128
TOTAKU INDUSTRIES SUZHOU CO., LTD—See Nagase & Co., Ltd.; *Int'l,* pg. 5128
TOTAL ABU AL BU KHOOSH S.A.—See TotalEnergies SE; *Int'l,* pg. 7840
TOTAL ACCESS COMMUNICATION PUBLIC CO., LTD.—See Charoen Pokphand Group Co., Ltd.; *Int'l,* pg. 1453
TOTAL ACCIDENT MANAGEMENT LIMITED—See ZIGUP plc; *Int'l,* pg. 8683
TOTAL ACRYLIC POLYMER INDUSTRY CORPORATION—See Seiko PMC Corporation; *Int'l,* pg. 6689
TOTAL ACTION AGAINST POVERTY; *U.S. Private,* pg. 4190
TOTAL ADDITIFS ET CARBURANTS SPECIAUX SA—See TotalEnergies SE; *Int'l,* pg. 7839
TOTAL ADMINISTRATIVE SERVICES CORPORATION; *U.S. Private,* pg. 4190
TOTAL AIR POLLUTION CONTROL PTY LIMITED—See The Environmental Group Limited; *Int'l,* pg. 7640
TOTAL AMERICAN SERVICES, INC.—See TotalEnergies SE; *Int'l,* pg. 7838

TOTAL APPLIANCE & AIR CONDITIONING REPAIRS, INC.; *U.S. Private,* pg. 4190
TOTAL AUSTRAL S.A.—See TotalEnergies SE; *Int'l,* pg. 7839
TOTAL AUSTRIA GMBH—See TotalEnergies SE; *Int'l,* pg. 7839
TOTAL AUTOS (1990) PTY LTD—See Eagers Automotive Limited; *Int'l,* pg. 2263
TOTAL AVIATION LTD.—See TotalEnergies SE; *Int'l,* pg. 7839
TOTALBANKEN A/S; *Int'l,* pg. 7835
TOTAL BEAUTY MEDIA, INC.—See Evolve Media, LLC; *U.S. Private,* pg. 1444
TOTAL BELGIUM SA/NV—See TotalEnergies SE; *Int'l,* pg. 7839
TOTAL BEVERAGE SOLUTION; *U.S. Private,* pg. 4190
TOTAL BITUMEN DEUTSCHLAND GMBH—See TotalEnergies SE; *Int'l,* pg. 7839
TOTAL - BITUMEN—See TotalEnergies SE; *Int'l,* pg. 7839
TOTAL BITUMEN UK LTD—See TotalEnergies SE; *Int'l,* pg. 7839
TOTAL BOTSWANA—See TotalEnergies SE; *Int'l,* pg. 7843
TOTAL BRAIN LIMITED; *U.S. Public,* pg. 2164
TOTAL BUILDING ENVIRONMENTS SOUTH, INC.—See Energy Control Consultants, Inc.; *U.S. Private,* pg. 1394
TOTAL BURKINA S.A.—See TotalEnergies SE; *Int'l,* pg. 7839
TOTAL BUSINESS SOLUTIONS LIMITED—See Belize Telecommunications Limited; *Int'l,* pg. 965
TOTAL CAMBODGE—See TotalEnergies SE; *Int'l,* pg. 7838
TOTAL CAPITAL S.A.—See TotalEnergies SE; *Int'l,* pg. 7839
TOTAL CARBIDE LIMITED—See Versarien plc; *Int'l,* pg. 8173
TOTAL CARBON NEUTRALITY VENTURES EUROPE SA—See TotalEnergies SE; *Int'l,* pg. 7839
TOTAL CARE; *U.S. Private,* pg. 4190
TOTAL CAR FRANCHISING CORP.; *U.S. Private,* pg. 4190
TOTAL CAROLINA CARE, INC.—See Centene Corporation; *U.S. Public,* pg. 471
TOTAL CESKA REPUBLIKA S.R.O.—See TotalEnergies SE; *Int'l,* pg. 7838
TOTAL CHEMICAL DIVISION—See TotalEnergies SE; *Int'l,* pg. 7839
TOTAL CHILE SA—See TotalEnergies SE; *Int'l,* pg. 7838
TOTAL CHINA INVESTMENT COMPANY LIMITED—See TotalEnergies SE; *Int'l,* pg. 7839
TOTAL COMFORT SOLUTIONS LLC; *U.S. Private,* pg. 4190
TOTAL COMMUNICATIONS GROUP; *U.S. Private,* pg. 4190
TOTAL COMMUNICATIONS INC.; *U.S. Private,* pg. 4190
TOTAL COMMUNITY ACTION, INC.; *U.S. Private,* pg. 4190
TOTAL CONCEPTS OF DESIGN, INC.; *U.S. Private,* pg. 4190
TOTAL CONGO SA—See TotalEnergies SE; *Int'l,* pg. 7840
TOTAL CORROSION CONTROL PTY. LTD.—See Altrad Investment Authority SAS; *Int'l,* pg. 398
TOTAL COSTA RICA—See TotalEnergies SE; *Int'l,* pg. 7840
TOTAL COTE D'IVOIRE SA—See TotalEnergies SE; *Int'l,* pg. 7840
TOTAL CREDIT SERVICES LIMITED—See Jamaica National Building Society; *Int'l,* pg. 3874
TOTAL - CSTJF—See TotalEnergies SE; *Int'l,* pg. 7839
TOTAL DEFENSE, INC.—See Open Text Corporation; *Int'l,* pg. 5598
TOTAL DENMARK A/S—See TotalEnergies SE; *Int'l,* pg. 7838
TOTAL DEUTSCHLAND GMBH—See TotalEnergies SE; *Int'l,* pg. 7840
TOTAL DIRECT ENERGIE S.A.—See TotalEnergies SE; *Int'l,* pg. 7840
TOTAL DIRECTION GENERALE GAZ & ELECTRICITE—See TotalEnergies SE; *Int'l,* pg. 7840
TOTAL DISTRIBUTION INC.—See Peoples Services Inc.; *U.S. Private,* pg. 3142
TOTAL DISTRIBUTION SERVICES, INC. (TDSI)—See CSX Corporation; *U.S. Public,* pg. 602
TOTAL DISTRIBUTION—See Peoples Services Inc.; *U.S. Private,* pg. 3142
TOTAL DOLLAR MANAGEMENT EFFORT LTD; *U.S. Private,* pg. 4190
TOTAL EDEN MCCRACKENS GROUP PTY LIMITED—See Nutrien Ltd.; *Int'l,* pg. 5493
TOTAL EDEN PTY LIMITED—See Nutrien Ltd.; *Int'l,* pg. 5493
TOTAL ELECTRICAL SERVICE & SUPPLY CO.—See Primoris Services Corporation; *U.S. Public,* pg. 1719
TOTAL ELECTRONICS, LLC—See Cal-Comp Electronics (Thailand) pcl; *Int'l,* pg. 1261
TOTAL ENERGI AS—See Hafslund ASA; *Int'l,* pg. 3206
TOTAL ENERGIE DEVELOPPEMENT SAS—See TotalEnergies SE; *Int'l,* pg. 7840

TOTAL ENERGIE GAS GMBH—See TotalEnergies SE; *Int'l,* pg. 7840
TOTAL ENERGIE GAZ SA—See TotalEnergies SE; *Int'l,* pg. 7838
TOTALENERGIES ADDITIVES AND FUELS SOLUTIONS—See TotalEnergies SE; *Int'l,* pg. 7843
TOTALENERGIES (BEIJING) CORPORATE MANAGEMENT CO., LTD.—See TotalEnergies SE; *Int'l,* pg. 7843
TOTALENERGIES DISTRIBUIDORA BRASIL LTDA.—See TotalEnergies SE; *Int'l,* pg. 7843
TOTALENERGIES EP CANADA LTD.—See Suncor Energy Inc.; *Int'l,* pg. 7311
TOTALENERGIES EP DANMARK A/S—See TotalEnergies SE; *Int'l,* pg. 7843
TOTALENERGIES EP NEDERLAND B.V.—See TotalEnergies SE; *Int'l,* pg. 7843
TOTALENERGIES EP NIGERIA LTD.—See TotalEnergies SE; *Int'l,* pg. 7843
TOTALENERGIES EP NORGE AS—See TotalEnergies SE; *Int'l,* pg. 7843
TOTALENERGIES EP PNG LTD.—See TotalEnergies SE; *Int'l,* pg. 7843
TOTALENERGIES GLASS LUBRICANTS EUROPE GMBH—See TotalEnergies SE; *Int'l,* pg. 7843
TOTAL ENERGIES LUBRIFIANTS ALGERIE SPA—See TotalEnergies SE; *Int'l,* pg. 7840
TOTALENERGIES MARINE FUELS PTE. LTD.—See TotalEnergies SE; *Int'l,* pg. 7843
TOTAL ENERGIES MARKETING (CAMBODIA) CO. LTD.—See TotalEnergies SE; *Int'l,* pg. 7840
TOTALENERGIES MARKETING CESKA REPUBLIKA S.R.O.—See TotalEnergies SE; *Int'l,* pg. 7844
TOTALENERGIES MARKETING EGYPTE—See TotalEnergies SE; *Int'l,* pg. 7844
TOTAL ENERGIES MARKETING ESPANA, S.A.U.—See TotalEnergies SE; *Int'l,* pg. 7840
TOTALENERGIES MARKETING ETHIOPIA SHARE COMPANY—See TotalEnergies SE; *Int'l,* pg. 7844
TOTALENERGIES MARKETING (FIJI) PTE. LTD.—See TotalEnergies SE; *Int'l,* pg. 7844
TOTALENERGIES MARKETING GHANA PLC—See TotalEnergies SE; *Int'l,* pg. 7844
TOTAL ENERGIES MARKETING ITALIA S.P.A.—See TotalEnergies SE; *Int'l,* pg. 7844
TOTALENERGIES MARKETING JAMAICA LTD.—See TotalEnergies SE; *Int'l,* pg. 7844
TOTALENERGIES MARKETING KENYA PLC—See TotalEnergies SE; *Int'l,* pg. 7844
TOTALENERGIES MARKETING LUXEMBOURG S.A.—See TotalEnergies SE; *Int'l,* pg. 7844
TOTALENERGIES MARKETING MADAGASIKARA S.A.—See TotalEnergies SE; *Int'l,* pg. 7844
TOTALENERGIES MARKETING MALAWI LTD.—See TotalEnergies SE; *Int'l,* pg. 7844
TOTALENERGIES MARKETING MAROC S.A.; *Int'l,* pg. 7835
TOTALENERGIES MARKETING MAURITIUS LTD.—See TotalEnergies SE; *Int'l,* pg. 7844
TOTALENERGIES MARKETING MEXICO S.A. DE C.V.—See TotalEnergies SE; *Int'l,* pg. 7844
TOTALENERGIES MARKETING MOCAMBIQUE S.A.—See TotalEnergies SE; *Int'l,* pg. 7844
TOTALENERGIES MARKETING NAMIBIA (PTY.) LTD.—See TotalEnergies SE; *Int'l,* pg. 7844
TOTALENERGIES MARKETING NIGERIA PLC—See TotalEnergies SE; *Int'l,* pg. 7844
TOTALENERGIES MARKETING ROMANIA S.A.—See TotalEnergies SE; *Int'l,* pg. 7844
TOTALENERGIES MARKETING SOUTH AFRICA (PTY.) LTD.—See TotalEnergies SE; *Int'l,* pg. 7844
TOTALENERGIES MARKETING TAIWAN LTD.—See TotalEnergies SE; *Int'l,* pg. 7844
TOTALENERGIES MARKETING TANZANIA LTD.—See TotalEnergies SE; *Int'l,* pg. 7844
TOTAL ENERGIES MARKETING UGANDA LTD.—See TotalEnergies SE; *Int'l,* pg. 7840
TOTAL ENERGIES MARKETING UK LIMITED—See TotalEnergies SE; *Int'l,* pg. 7840
TOTALENERGIES MARKETING USA INC.—See TotalEnergies SE; *Int'l,* pg. 7844
TOTALENERGIES MARKETING VIETNAM COMPANY LTD.—See TotalEnergies SE; *Int'l,* pg. 7844
TOTAL ENERGIES MARKETING ZAMBIA LTD.—See TotalEnergies SE; *Int'l,* pg. 7840
TOTALENERGIES MARKETING ZIMBABWE (PRIVATE) LTD.—See TotalEnergies SE; *Int'l,* pg. 7844
TOTALENERGIES RAFFINERIE MITTELDEUTSCHLAND GMBH—See TotalEnergies SE; *Int'l,* pg. 7844
TOTALENERGIES SE—See TotalEnergies SE; *Int'l,* pg. 7844
TOTALENERGIES SE; *Int'l,* pg. 7835
TOTALENERGIES TRADING CANADA L.P.—See TotalEnergies SE; *Int'l,* pg. 7844
TOTALENERGIES TURKEY PAZARLAMA A.S.—See TotalEnergies SE; *Int'l,* pg. 7844
TOTALENERGIES UPSTREAM DANMARK A/S—See TotalEnergies SE; *Int'l,* pg. 7844

TOTALENERGIES SE

CORPORATE AFFILIATIONS

TOTALENERGIES WARME&KRAFTSTOFF DEUTSCHLAND GMBH—See TotalEnergies SE; *Int'l*, pg. 7844
TOTAL ENERGY CONCEPTS INC.—See SmartCool Systems Inc.; *Int'l*, pg. 7001
TOTAL ENERGY SERVICES INC.; *Int'l*, pg. 7834
TOTAL ENGINEERING INC.; *U.S. Private*, pg. 4191
TOTAL E&P ALGERIE—See TotalEnergies SE; *Int'l*, pg. 7840
TOTAL E&P ANGOLA SA—See TotalEnergies SE; *Int'l*, pg. 7840
TOTAL E&P AUSTRALIA—See TotalEnergies SE; *Int'l*, pg. 7840
TOTAL E&P AZERBAIDJAN B.V.—See TotalEnergies SE; *Int'l*, pg. 7840
TOTAL E&P BOLIVIE S.A.—See TotalEnergies SE; *Int'l*, pg. 7840
TOTAL E&P BORNEO B.V.—See TotalEnergies SE; *Int'l*, pg. 7840
TOTAL E&P BULGARIA B.V.—See TotalEnergies SE; *Int'l*, pg. 7840
TOTAL E&P CAMEROON—See TotalEnergies SE; *Int'l*, pg. 7840
TOTAL E&P CANADA LTD.—See TotalEnergies SE; *Int'l*, pg. 7840
TOTAL E&P DANMARK A/S—See TotalEnergies SE; *Int'l*, pg. 7840
TOTAL E&P DO BRASIL—See TotalEnergies SE; *Int'l*, pg. 7841
TOTAL E&P FRANCE—See TotalEnergies SE; *Int'l*, pg. 7840
TOTAL E&P IRAN—See TotalEnergies SE; *Int'l*, pg. 7840
TOTAL E&P IRAQ—See TotalEnergies SE; *Int'l*, pg. 7840
TOTAL E&P ITALIA SPA—See TotalEnergies SE; *Int'l*, pg. 7840
TOTAL E&P KUWAIT—See TotalEnergies SE; *Int'l*, pg. 7840
TOTAL E&P LIBYE—See TotalEnergies SE; *Int'l*, pg. 7840
TOTAL E & P MALAYSIA—See TotalEnergies SE; *Int'l*, pg. 7838
TOTAL E&P MAURITANIE—See TotalEnergies SE; *Int'l*, pg. 7840
TOTAL E&P MOZAMBIQUE AREA 1, LIMITADA—See TotalEnergies SE; *Int'l*, pg. 7840
TOTAL E&P NEDERLAND B.V.—See TotalEnergies SE; *Int'l*, pg. 7841
TOTAL E&P NEDERLAND B.V.—See TotalEnergies SE; *Int'l*, pg. 7838
TOTAL E&P NIGERIA LIMITED—See TotalEnergies SE; *Int'l*, pg. 7840
TOTAL E&P NORGE AS - HARSTAD—See TotalEnergies SE; *Int'l*, pg. 7841
TOTAL E&P NORGE AS - OSLO—See TotalEnergies SE; *Int'l*, pg. 7841
TOTAL E&P NORGE AS—See TotalEnergies SE; *Int'l*, pg. 7841
TOTAL E&P NORTH SEA UK LIMITED—See TotalEnergies SE; *Int'l*, pg. 7840
TOTAL E&P OMAN—See TotalEnergies SE; *Int'l*, pg. 7841
TOTAL E&P PNG LIMITED—See TotalEnergies SE; *Int'l*, pg. 7840
TOTAL E&P QATAR—See TotalEnergies SE; *Int'l*, pg. 7841
TOTAL E&P RUSSIA—See TotalEnergies SE; *Int'l*, pg. 7841
TOTAL E&P SYRIE—See TotalEnergies SE; *Int'l*, pg. 7841
TOTAL E&P THAILAND—See TotalEnergies SE; *Int'l*, pg. 7841
TOTAL E&P UGANDA B.V.—See TotalEnergies SE; *Int'l*, pg. 7840
TOTAL E&P UK LIMITED—See TotalEnergies SE; *Int'l*, pg. 7841
TOTAL E&P UK LTD. - LONDON EXECUTIVE OFFICE—See TotalEnergies SE; *Int'l*, pg. 7841
TOTAL E&P USA INC.—See TotalEnergies SE; *Int'l*, pg. 7841
TOTAL E&P YEMEN—See TotalEnergies SE; *Int'l*, pg. 7841
TOTAL EQUIPMENT COMPANY; *U.S. Private*, pg. 4191
TOTAL ESPANA SA—See TotalEnergies SE; *Int'l*, pg. 7840
TOTAL ESPECIALIDADES ARGENTINA S.A.—See TotalEnergies SE; *Int'l*, pg. 7840
TOTAL ESPECIALIDADES VENEZUELA, C.A.—See TotalEnergies SE; *Int'l*, pg. 7840
TOTAL ETHIOPIA S.C.—See TotalEnergies SE; *Int'l*, pg. 7840
TOTAL EXPERT INC; *U.S. Private*, pg. 4191
TOTAL EXPLORATION & PRODUCTION—See TotalEnergies SE; *Int'l*, pg. 7840
TOTALFACILITY, INC.—See Lincolnshire Management, Inc.; *U.S. Private*, pg. 2459
TOTAL FACILITY SOLUTIONS, INC.—See M+W Group GmbH; *Int'l*, pg. 4614
TOTAL FEUERSCHUTZ GMBH—See Johnson Controls International plc; *Int'l*, pg. 3987
TOTAL FIJI LIMITED—See TotalEnergies SE; *Int'l*, pg. 7838
TOTAL FILTRATION SERVICES, INC.—See Parker Hannifin Corporation; *U.S. Public*, pg. 1650

TOTAL FINANCE EXPLOITATION—See TotalEnergies SE; *Int'l*, pg. 7838
TOTAL FINANCE USA, INC.—See TotalEnergies SE; *Int'l*, pg. 7838
TOTAL FINANCIAL & INSURANCE SERVICES, LLC—See Simplicity Financial Marketing Holdings Inc.; *U.S. Private*, pg. 3667
TOTAL FIRESTOP GMBH—See London Security PLC; *Int'l*, pg. 4547
TOTAL FLUIDES S.A.—See TotalEnergies SE; *Int'l*, pg. 7841
TOTAL FOODS CORPORATION; *U.S. Private*, pg. 4191
TOTAL FUELS (WUHAN) CO., LTD.—See TotalEnergies SE; *Int'l*, pg. 7841
TOTAL GABON—See TotalEnergies SE; *Int'l*, pg. 7841
TOTAL GASANDES S.A.—See TotalEnergies SE; *Int'l*, pg. 7838
TOTAL GAS AND POWER LIMITED—See TotalEnergies SE; *Int'l*, pg. 7841
TOTAL GAS & POWER NEW ENERGIES USA, INC.—See TotalEnergies SE; *Int'l*, pg. 7841
TOTAL GAS & POWER NORTH AMERICA, INC—See TotalEnergies SE; *Int'l*, pg. 7841
TOTAL GAS & POWER NORTH EUROPE S.A.—See TotalEnergies SE; *Int'l*, pg. 7839
TOTAL GAS & POWER—See TotalEnergies SE; *Int'l*, pg. 7841
TOTAL GAS & POWER VENTURES USA, INC—See TotalEnergies SE; *Int'l*, pg. 7841
TOTAL GAZ & ELECTRICITE HOLDINGS FRANCE—See TotalEnergies SE; *Int'l*, pg. 7838
TOTAL GUADELOUPE—See TotalEnergies SE; *Int'l*, pg. 7838
TOTAL GUINEA ECUATORIAL SA—See TotalEnergies SE; *Int'l*, pg. 7841
TOTAL GUINEE SA—See TotalEnergies SE; *Int'l*, pg. 7841
TOTAL HEALTH CONCEPT SDN BHD—See Holista ColITech Limited; *Int'l*, pg. 3450
TOTAL HELIUM LTD.; *Int'l*, pg. 7835
TOTAL HELLAS S.A.—See TotalEnergies SE; *Int'l*, pg. 7841
TOTAL HOCKEY, INC.; *U.S. Private*, pg. 4191
TOTAL HOLDINGS EUROPE S.A.S.—See TotalEnergies SE; *Int'l*, pg. 7841
TOTAL HOLDINGS UK LIMITED—See TotalEnergies SE; *Int'l*, pg. 7841
TOTAL HOME HEALTH CARE, INC.—See Capitol Partners LLC; *U.S. Private*, pg. 744
TOTAL HONDURAS, S.A. DE C.V.—See TotalEnergies SE; *Int'l*, pg. 7841
TOTAL HOSPITALITY LTD.; *Int'l*, pg. 7835
TOTAL HUNGARIA KFT—See TotalEnergies SE; *Int'l*, pg. 7838
TOTALIGENT, INC.; *U.S. Public*, pg. 2165
TOTAL IMAGING - PARSONS, LLC—See HCA Healthcare, Inc.; *U.S. Public*, pg. 1012
TOTAL INDUSTRIAL SERVICES COMPANY LIMITED—See JCK International Public Limited Company; *Int'l*, pg. 3923
TOTAL INFRASTRUCTURES GAZ FRANCE SA—See Electricite de France S.A.; *Int'l*, pg. 2352
TOTAL INFRASTRUCTURES GAZ FRANCE SA—See Eni S.p.A.; *Int'l*, pg. 2438
TOTAL INFRASTRUCTURES GAZ FRANCE SA—See GIC Pte. Ltd.; *Int'l*, pg. 2965
TOTAL INNOVATIVE PACKAGING, INC.—See AptarGroup, Inc.; *U.S. Public*, pg. 175
TOTAL INSIGHT, LLC; *U.S. Private*, pg. 4191
TOTAL INSURANCE BROKERS, LLC—See Madison Dearborn Partners, LLC; *U.S. Private*, pg. 2540
TOTAL ITALIA S.P.A—See TotalEnergies SE; *Int'l*, pg. 7841
TOTALIZATOR ENGINEERING LIMITED—See Fujitsu Limited; *Int'l*, pg. 2834
TOTAL JAMAICA LIMITED—See TotalEnergies SE; *Int'l*, pg. 7841
TOTALJOBS GROUP LIMITED—See Axel Springer SE; *Int'l*, pg. 767
TOTAL JOINT CENTER OF THE NORTHLAND, LLC—See Tenet Healthcare Corporation; *U.S. Public*, pg. 2009
TOTAL JORDAN PSC—See TotalEnergies SE; *Int'l*, pg. 7841
TOTAL KENYA PLC—See TotalEnergies SE; *Int'l*, pg. 7841
TOTALKREDIT A/S—See Nykredit A/S; *Int'l*, pg. 5500
TOTAL LENDER SOLUTIONS, INC.; *U.S. Private*, pg. 4191
TOTALLE PROCUREMENT LOGISTICS (MACAO COMMERCIAL OFFSHORE) LIMITED—See Yips Chemical Holdings Limited; *Int'l*, pg. 8585
TOTAL LESOTHO (PTY) LTD—See TotalEnergies SE; *Int'l*, pg. 7843
TOTAL LIBAN SAL—See TotalEnergies SE; *Int'l*, pg. 7841
TOTAL LIVING NETWORK; *U.S. Private*, pg. 4191
TOTAL LUBRICANTES DO BRASIL LTDA—See TotalEnergies SE; *Int'l*, pg. 7841
TOTAL LUBRICANTS ALGERIE—See TotalEnergies SE; *Int'l*, pg. 7841
TOTAL LUBRICANTS BLENDING UAE CO LTD—See TotalEnergies SE; *Int'l*, pg. 7841

TOTAL LUBRICANTS CHINA CO., LTD.—See TotalEnergies SE; *Int'l*, pg. 7842
TOTAL LUBRICANTS HONG KONG LTD.—See TotalEnergies SE; *Int'l*, pg. 7842
TOTAL LUBRICANTS JAPAN CO, LTD.—See TotalEnergies SE; *Int'l*, pg. 7838
TOTAL LUBRICANTS USA—See TotalEnergies SE; *Int'l*, pg. 7842
TOTAL LUBRIFIANTS ALGERIE SPA—See TotalEnergies SE; *Int'l*, pg. 7842
TOTAL LUBRIFIANTS SA—See TotalEnergies SE; *Int'l*, pg. 7842
TOTAL LUXEMBOURG S.A.—See TotalEnergies SE; *Int'l*, pg. 7838
TOTALLY CHOCOLATE, INC.—See Tricor Pacific Founders Capital, Inc.; *Int'l*, pg. 7920
TOTALLY HEALTHCARE LIMITED—See Totally Plc; *Int'l*, pg. 7844
TOTALLY HEALTH LIMITED—See Totally Plc; *Int'l*, pg. 7844
TOTALLY HIP TECHNOLOGIES INC.; *Int'l*, pg. 7844
TOTALLY PLC; *Int'l*, pg. 7844
TOTALLY TICKETS INC.; *U.S. Private*, pg. 4192
TOTAL MACHINE SOLUTIONS, INC.—See Applied Industrial Technologies, Inc.; *U.S. Public*, pg. 171
TOTAL MALAWI LIMITED—See TotalEnergies SE; *Int'l*, pg. 7842
TOTAL MANAGEMENT BUSINESS CO., LTD.—See Takara Holdings, Inc.; *Int'l*, pg. 7433
TOTAL - MARINE FUELS—See TotalEnergies SE; *Int'l*, pg. 7839
TOTAL MARINE TECHNOLOGY (MALAYSIA) SDN. BHD.—See Sapura Energy Berhad; *Int'l*, pg. 6574
TOTAL MARINE TECHNOLOGY PTY, LTD.—See Sapura Energy Berhad; *Int'l*, pg. 6574
TOTAL MARKETING MIDDLE EAST LLC—See TotalEnergies SE; *Int'l*, pg. 7842
TOTAL MAURITIUS LTD—See TotalEnergies SE; *Int'l*, pg. 7842
TOTAL MAYOTTE SAS—See TotalEnergies SE; *Int'l*, pg. 7842
TOTAL MEAL SOLUTION SDN BHD—See KPJ Healthcare Berhad; *Int'l*, pg. 4297
TOTAL MECHANICAL, INC.; *U.S. Private*, pg. 4191
TOTAL MEDIA DEVELOPMENT INSTITUTE CO., LTD.—See TOPPAN Holdings Inc.; *Int'l*, pg. 7820
TOTAL MEDIA DIRECT—See Total Media Group Ltd.; *Int'l*, pg. 7835
TOTAL MEDIA GGI—See The Interpublic Group of Companies, Inc.; *U.S. Public*, pg. 2105
TOTAL MEDIA GROUP LTD.; *Int'l*, pg. 7835
TOTAL MEDIA NORTH—See Total Media Group Ltd.; *Int'l*, pg. 7835
TOTAL MEDIA; *U.S. Private*, pg. 4191
TOTAL MEDICAL SERVICE CO., LTD.—See Medical System Network Co., Ltd.; *Int'l*, pg. 4775
TOTAL MEXICO S.A DE C.V—See TotalEnergies SE; *Int'l*, pg. 7842
TOTAL MINERALOEL UND CHEMIE GMBH—See TotalEnergies SE; *Int'l*, pg. 7838
TOTAL MOMENTUM PTY. LTD.—See Engenco Limited; *Int'l*, pg. 2427
TOTAL MORTGAGE SERVICES, LLC; *U.S. Private*, pg. 4191
TOTAL MOZAMBIQUE SA—See TotalEnergies SE; *Int'l*, pg. 7842
TOTAL MULTIMEDIA INCORPORATED; *U.S. Public*, pg. 2165
TOTAL NAMIBIA (PTY) LTD—See TotalEnergies SE; *Int'l*, pg. 7843
TOTAL NEDERLAND N V—See TotalEnergies SE; *Int'l*, pg. 7842
TOTAL NIGERIA PLC—See TotalEnergies SE; *Int'l*, pg. 7842
TOTAL OFFICE PLANNING SERVICES; *U.S. Private*, pg. 4191
TOTAL OIL ASIA-PACIFIC PTE LTD. - LUBRICANTS PLANT—See TotalEnergies SE; *Int'l*, pg. 7838
TOTAL OIL ASIA-PACIFIC PTE LTD.—See TotalEnergies SE; *Int'l*, pg. 7838
TOTAL OILFIELD RENTALS INC.—See Total Energy Services Inc.; *Int'l*, pg. 7835
TOTAL OILFIELD RENTALS—See Total Energy Services Inc.; *Int'l*, pg. 7835
TOTAL OIL INDIA PVT LTD—See TotalEnergies SE; *Int'l*, pg. 7842
TOTAL OIL INDIA PVT. LTD.—See TotalEnergies SE; *Int'l*, pg. 7842
TOTAL OIL MALAYSIA SDN BHD—See TotalEnergies SE; *Int'l*, pg. 7842
TOTAL OIL (THAILAND) CO. LTD—See TotalEnergies SE; *Int'l*, pg. 7842
TOTAL OIL TURKEY A.S.—See TotalEnergies SE; *Int'l*, pg. 7842
TOTAL OPSLAG EN PIJPLEIDING NEDERLAND NV—See TotalEnergies SE; *Int'l*, pg. 7842
TOTAL ORTHODONTICS LIMITED—See The British United Provident Association Limited; *Int'l*, pg. 7630

COMPANY NAME INDEX

TOTAL OUTRE-MER S.A.—See TotalEnergies SE; *Int'l*, pg. 7842
TOTAL OUTSOURCE, INC.—See UCA Group Component Specialty Inc.; *U.S. Private*, pg. 4273
TOTALPAAS, INC.; *U.S. Private*, pg. 4192
TOTAL PACIFIQUE SA—See TotalEnergies SE; *Int'l*, pg. 7842
TOTAL PARCO PAKISTAN LIMITED—See TotalEnergies SE; *Int'l*, pg. 7842
TOTAL PARCO PAKISTAN LTD.—See TotalEnergies SE; *Int'l*, pg. 7842
TOTAL PETROCHEMICALS ANTWERPEN—See TotalEnergies SE; *Int'l*, pg. 7842
TOTAL PETROCHEMICALS FELUY—See TotalEnergies SE; *Int'l*, pg. 7842
TOTAL PETROCHEMICALS (FOSHAN) CO., LTD.—See TotalEnergies SE; *Int'l*, pg. 7842
TOTAL PETROCHEMICALS (HONG KONG) LTD—See TotalEnergies SE; *Int'l*, pg. 7842
TOTAL PETROCHEMICALS, INC.—See TotalEnergies SE; *Int'l*, pg. 7842
TOTAL PETROCHEMICALS & REFINING USA, INC. - BAYPORT—See TotalEnergies SE; *Int'l*, pg. 7842
TOTAL PETROCHEMICALS & REFINING USA, INC.—See TotalEnergies SE; *Int'l*, pg. 7842
TOTAL PETROCHEMICALS—See TotalEnergies SE; *Int'l*, pg. 7842
TOTAL PETROCHEMICALS—See TotalEnergies SE; *Int'l*, pg. 7842
TOTAL PETROCHEMICALS TAIPEI—See TotalEnergies SE; *Int'l*, pg. 7842
TOTAL PETROCHEMICALS UK LIMITED—See TotalEnergies SE; *Int'l*, pg. 7842
TOTAL PETROCHEMICALS USA, INC. - LA PORTE—See TotalEnergies SE; *Int'l*, pg. 7842
TOTAL PETROCHEMICALS USA, INC. - PORT ARTHUR—See TotalEnergies SE; *Int'l*, pg. 7842
TOTAL PETROLEO COSTA RICA S.A.—See TotalEnergies SE; *Int'l*, pg. 7839
TOTAL PETROLEUM GHANA PLC—See TotalEnergies SE; *Int'l*, pg. 7841
TOTAL PETROLEUM HONG KONG LTD.—See TotalEnergies SE; *Int'l*, pg. 7843
TOTAL PETROLEUM PUERTO RICO CORP.—See TotalEnergies SE; *Int'l*, pg. 7843
TOTAL (PHILIPPINES) CORP.—See TotalEnergies SE; *Int'l*, pg. 7838
TOTALPLAN INC.; *Int'l*, pg. 7845
TOTAL PLASTICS, INC. - GRAND RAPIDS—See Prophet Equity L.P.; *U.S. Private*, pg. 3286
TOTAL PLASTICS, INC. - LIFE SCIENCES—See Prophet Equity L.P.; *U.S. Private*, pg. 3286
TOTAL PLASTICS, INC.—See Prophet Equity L.P.; *U.S. Private*, pg. 3286
TOTAL POLSKA S.P. ZO.O.—See TotalEnergies SE; *Int'l*, pg. 7839
TOTAL POLYNESIE S.A.—See TotalEnergies SE; *Int'l*, pg. 7843
TOTAL PORT ARTHUR REFINERY—See TotalEnergies SE; *Int'l*, pg. 7841
TOTAL POWERGEN SOLUTIONS—See Audax Group, Limited Partnership; *U.S. Private*, pg. 390
TOTAL POWER LTD.—See Audax Group, Limited Partnership; *U.S. Private*, pg. 390
TOTAL PRODUCE HOLDINGS B.V.—See Dole plc; *Int'l*, pg. 2158
TOTAL PRODUCE IRELAND LIMITED—See Dole plc; *Int'l*, pg. 2158
TOTAL PRODUCE NORDIC A/S—See Dole plc; *Int'l*, pg. 2158
TOTAL PRODUCE PLC—See Dole plc; *Int'l*, pg. 2158
TOTAL PRODUCTION LINE (TPL)—See Total Media Group Ltd.; *Int'l*, pg. 7835
TOTAL PROFILS PETROLIERS—See TotalEnergies SE; *Int'l*, pg. 7839
TOTAL PROGRAM MANAGEMENT, LLC—See Stone Point Capital LLC; *U.S. Private*, pg. 3821
TOTAL PROJECTS INDIA LTD—See TotalEnergies SE; *Int'l*, pg. 7843
TOTAL PROMOTIONS; *U.S. Private*, pg. 4191
TOTAL QUADRAN SAS—See TotalEnergies SE; *Int'l*, pg. 7844
TOTAL QUALITY, INC. - MECOSTA TERMINAL—See Forward Air Corporation; *U.S. Private*, pg. 874
TOTAL QUALITY, INC.—See Forward Air Corporation; *U.S. Public*, pg. 874
TOTAL QUALITY LOGISTICS INC.; *U.S. Private*, pg. 4191
TOTAL RAFFINADERIJ ANTWERPEN—See TotalEnergies SE; *Int'l*, pg. 7843
TOTAL RAFFINAGE FRANCE SA—See TotalEnergies SE; *Int'l*, pg. 7843
TOTAL RAFFINERIE MITTELDEUTSCHLAND GMBH—See TotalEnergies SE; *Int'l*, pg. 7840
TOTAL RDC SA—See TotalEnergies SE; *Int'l*, pg. 7843
TOTAL RECALL CORPORATION—See Ares Management Corporation; *U.S. Public*, pg. 189
TOTAL RECOVERY GROUP, LLC; *U.S. Private*, pg. 4191
TOTAL RENAL CARE/CRYSTAL RIVER DIALYSIS, L.C.—See DaVita Inc.; *U.S. Public*, pg. 643

TOTAL RENAL CARE/EATON CANYON DIALYSIS CENTER PARTNERSHIP—See DaVita Inc.; *U.S. Public*, pg. 643
TOTAL RENAL CARE NORTH CAROLINA, LLC—See DaVita Inc.; *U.S. Public*, pg. 643
TOTAL RENAL CARE TEXAS LIMITED PARTNERSHIP—See DaVita Inc.; *U.S. Public*, pg. 643
TOTAL RENAL LABORATORIES, INC.—See DaVita Inc.; *U.S. Public*, pg. 644
TOTAL RESEARCH & TECHNOLOGY FELUY—See TotalEnergies SE; *Int'l*, pg. 7843
TOTAL RESOURCE MANAGEMENT, INC.; *U.S. Private*, pg. 4191
TOTAL REUNION S.A.—See TotalEnergies SE; *Int'l*, pg. 7843
TOTAL R&M TRINIDAD & TOBAGO LTD.—See TotalEnergies SE; *Int'l*, pg. 7843
TOTAL ROMANIA S.A.—See TotalEnergies SE; *Int'l*, pg. 7843
TOTALRUBBER LIMITED—See Sunway Berhad; *Int'l*, pg. 7331
TOTAL SAFETY SUPPLY BELGIUM BVBA—See Bunzl plc; *Int'l*, pg. 1219
TOTAL SAFETY U.S., INC.—See Littlejohn & Co., LLC; *U.S. Private*, pg. 2472
TOTALSEAL GROUP AUSTRALIA PTY LIMITED—See Diploma PLC; *Int'l*, pg. 2129
TOTAL SENEGAL SA—See TotalEnergies SE; *Int'l*, pg. 7839
TOTAL SERVICE SUPPLY INC.; *U.S. Private*, pg. 4191
TOTAL SITE SOLUTIONS—See TSS, Inc.; *U.S. Public*, pg. 2202
TOTAL SLOVENSKO S.R.O.—See TotalEnergies SE; *Int'l*, pg. 7839
TOTAL SOFT BANK LTD.; *Int'l*, pg. 7835
TOTAL SOFT S.A.—See Logo Yazilim Sanayi ve Ticaret A.S.; *Int'l*, pg. 4543
TOTAL SOLAR INTERNATIONAL SAS—See TotalEnergies SE; *Int'l*, pg. 7843
TOTAL SOLAR INTL SAS—See TotalEnergies SE; *Int'l*, pg. 7843
TOTAL SOUTH AFRICA (PTY.) LTD.—See TotalEnergies SE; *Int'l*, pg. 7843
TOTAL SOUTH PARS—See TotalEnergies SE; *Int'l*, pg. 7839
TOTAL SPECIAL FLUIDS—See TotalEnergies SE; *Int'l*, pg. 7843
TOTAL SPECIAL FLUIDS - THE OUDALLE PLANT—See TotalEnergies SE; *Int'l*, pg. 7843
TOTAL SPECIALTIES USA INC—See TotalEnergies SE; *Int'l*, pg. 7843
TOTAL SPECIFIC SOLUTIONS (TSS) B.V.—See Constellation Software Inc.; *Int'l*, pg. 1774
TOTAL SPECTRUM, LLC—See Gryphon Investors, LLC; *U.S. Public*, pg. 1799
TOTAL SPORTS MEDIA, INC.; *U.S. Private*, pg. 4191
TOTAL STAFFING SOLUTIONS INC.; *U.S. Private*, pg. 4191
TOTALSTAY LIMITED—See Vitruvian Partners LLP; *Int'l*, pg. 8263
TOTAL STRENGTH AND SPEED—See Performance Strength Designs, Inc.; *U.S. Private*, pg. 3150
TOTAL (SUISSE) S.A.—See TotalEnergies SE; *Int'l*, pg. 7839
TOTAL SWAZILAND (PTY) LTD—See TotalEnergies SE; *Int'l*, pg. 7843
TOTAL SWEDEN AB—See TotalEnergies SE; *Int'l*, pg. 7839
TOTAL SYSTEM SERVICES HOLDING EUROPE LP—See Global Payments Inc.; *U.S. Public*, pg. 944
TOTAL SYSTEM SERVICES, INC.—See Global Payments Inc.; *U.S. Public*, pg. 944
TOTAL SYSTEM SERVICES PROCESSING EUROPE LIMITED—See Global Payments Inc.; *U.S. Public*, pg. 945
TOTAL SYSTEM SERVICES SALES EUROPE LIMITED—See Global Payments Inc.; *U.S. Public*, pg. 945
TOTAL SYSTEMS PLC; *Int'l*, pg. 7835
TOTAL SYSTEMS TECHNOLOGY INC.; *U.S. Private*, pg. 4191
TOTAL TANZANIE LTD—See TotalEnergies SE; *Int'l*, pg. 7843
TOTAL TELCOM INC.; *Int'l*, pg. 7835
TOTAL TELCO SPECIALIST INC.; *U.S. Private*, pg. 4191
TOTAL TEMPERATURE INSTRUMENTATION, INC.; *U.S. Private*, pg. 4192
TOTAL TERMINALS INTERNATIONAL LLC—See Mediterranean Shipping Company, S.A.; *Int'l*, pg. 4784
TOTAL TITLE SOLUTIONS, LLC—See Florida Agency Network, LLC; *U.S. Private*, pg. 1547
TOTAL TOGO SA—See TotalEnergies SE; *Int'l*, pg. 7843
TOTAL TOOLS MOORABBIN STORE PTY. LTD.—See Metcash Limited; *Int'l*, pg. 4852
TOTAL TOOLS PRESTON PTY. LTD.—See Metcash Limited; *Int'l*, pg. 4852
TOTAL TOOL SUPPLY INC., CRANE & HOIST DIVISION—See Total Tool Supply Inc.; *U.S. Private*, pg. 4192

TOTAL TOOL SUPPLY INC.; *U.S. Private*, pg. 4192
TOTAL TOSHISEIBI CO., LTD.—See Takamiya Co., Ltd.; *Int'l*, pg. 7430
TOTAL TRADING ASIA PTE LTD—See TotalEnergies SE; *Int'l*, pg. 7839
TOTAL TRADING CANADA LIMITED—See TotalEnergies SE; *Int'l*, pg. 7843
TOTAL TRADING INTERNATIONAL S.A—See TotalEnergies SE; *Int'l*, pg. 7839
TOTAL TRADING & SHIPPING—See TotalEnergies SE; *Int'l*, pg. 7839
TOTAL TRANSPORTATION CONCEPT; *U.S. Private*, pg. 4192
TOTAL TRANSPORTATION OF MISSISSIPPI LLC—See Knight-Swift Transportation Holdings Inc.; *U.S. Public*, pg. 1269
TOTAL TRANSPORTATION SERVICES, INC.—See UniGroup, Inc.; *U.S. Private*, pg. 4283
TOTAL TRANSPORTATION TRUCKING, INC.—See RJW, Inc.; *U.S. Private*, pg. 3450
TOTAL TRANSPORT MARITIME—See TotalEnergies SE; *Int'l*, pg. 7843
TOTAL TRANSPORT SOLUTIONS MALDIVES (PVT) LTD.—See Hayleys PLC; *Int'l*, pg. 3292
TOTAL TRANSPORT SYSTEMS LIMITED; *Int'l*, pg. 7835
TOTALTRAX, INC.—See Pharos Capital Group, LLC; *U.S. Private*, pg. 3166
TOTAL TREASURY—See TotalEnergies SE; *Int'l*, pg. 7839
TOTAL TRIAL MANAGEMENT CONSULTING CO., LTD.—See EPS Holdings, Inc.; *Int'l*, pg. 2466
TOTAL TRUCK PARTS INC.; *U.S. Private*, pg. 4192
TOTAL TUNISIA—See TotalEnergies SE; *Int'l*, pg. 7839
TOTAL UGANDA LIMITED—See TotalEnergies SE; *Int'l*, pg. 7843
TOTAL UK LTD—See TotalEnergies SE; *Int'l*, pg. 7841
TOTAL UPSTREAM DANMARK A/S—See TotalEnergies SE; *Int'l*, pg. 7843
TOTAL UPSTREAM NIGERIA LTD.—See TotalEnergies SE; *Int'l*, pg. 7843
TOTAL VALUE RV; *U.S. Private*, pg. 4192
TOTAL VENEZUELA SA—See TotalEnergies SE; *Int'l*, pg. 7839
TOTAL VIDEO PRODUCTS, INC.—See Fernandez Holdings, Inc.; *U.S. Private*, pg. 1497
TOTAL VIETNAM LIMITED—See TotalEnergies SE; *Int'l*, pg. 7843
TOTAL VISION, INC.—See Centene Corporation; *U.S. Public*, pg. 471
TOTAL VOSTOK OOO—See TotalEnergies SE; *Int'l*, pg. 7843
TOTAL VVS AS—See Instalco AB; *Int'l*, pg. 3722
TOTAL-WESTERN, INC.; *U.S. Private*, pg. 4192
TOTAL WORKOUT PREMIUM MANAGEMENT INC.—See Tsuburaya Fields Holdings Inc.; *Int'l*, pg. 7955
TOTAL YEMEN LNG COMPANY LTD.—See TotalEnergies SE; *Int'l*, pg. 7839
TOTAL ZIMBABWE PVT. LTD.—See TotalEnergies SE; *Int'l*, pg. 7843
TOTAN KAKO CO., LTD.—See Toyo Tanso Co., Ltd.; *Int'l*, pg. 7858
TOT BIOPHARM INTERNATIONAL COMPANY LIMITED; *Int'l*, pg. 7834
TOTECH CORPORATION; *Int'l*, pg. 7845
TOTEMCO B.V.—See New Wave Group AB; *Int'l*, pg. 5231
TOTEM ELECTRIC OF TACOMA INC.; *U.S. Private*, pg. 4192
TOTEM ELECTRO SRL—See SEMIKRON International GmbH; *Int'l*, pg. 6705
TOTEM OCEAN TRAILER EXPRESS—See Saltchuk Resources Inc.; *U.S. Private*, pg. 3534
TOTEM—See Yellow Pages Limited; *Int'l*, pg. 8576
TOTENKO CO., LTD.; *Int'l*, pg. 7845
TOTENS SPAREBANK—See Sparebank 1 Oestlandet; *Int'l*, pg. 7125
TOTER, LLC—See H.I.G. Capital, LLC; *U.S. Private*, pg. 1832
TOTES ISOTONER CANADA LTD.—See Freeman Spogli & Co. Incorporated; *U.S. Private*, pg. 1606
TOTES ISOTONER CANADA LTD.—See Investcorp Holdings B.S.C.; *Int'l*, pg. 3776
TOTES ISOTONER CORPORATION—See Freeman Spogli & Co. Incorporated; *U.S. Private*, pg. 1606
TOTES ISOTONER CORPORATION—See Investcorp Holdings B.S.C.; *Int'l*, pg. 3776
TOTES ISOTONER (UK) LIMITED—See Freeman Spogli & Co. Incorporated; *U.S. Private*, pg. 1606
TOTES ISOTONER (UK) LIMITED—See Investcorp Holdings B.S.C.; *Int'l*, pg. 3776
TOTETSU KOGYO CO., LTD.; *Int'l*, pg. 7845
TOTETSU MAINTENANCE KOJI CO., LTD.—See Totetsu Kogyo Co., Ltd.; *Int'l*, pg. 7845
TOTETSU SOKEN CO., LTD.—See Totetsu Kogyo Co., Ltd.; *Int'l*, pg. 7845
TOT GROUP CYPRUS—See Mullen Automotive, Inc.; *U.S. Public*, pg. 1486
TOT GROUP, INC.—See Mullen Automotive, Inc.; *U.S. Public*, pg. 1486
TOT GROUP KAZAKHSTAN LLC—See Mullen Automotive, Inc.; *U.S. Public*, pg. 1486

TOTH BUICK-GMC

TOTH BUICK-GMC; *U.S. Private*, pg. 4192
TO THE GAME, LLC—See Delta Apparel, Inc.; *U.S. Public*, pg. 652
TOTH, INC.; *U.S. Private*, pg. 4192
TOTH INDUSTRIES, INC.; *U.S. Private*, pg. 4192
TOTIPOTENTRX CELL THERAPY PVT LTD.—See Boyalife Group; *Int'l*, pg. 1124
TOTM TECHNOLOGIES LIMITED—See Shanghai Yinda Technology Industrial Co. Ltd.; *Int'l*, pg. 6782
TOT NEW EDGE, LLC—See Mullen Automotive, Inc.; *U.S. Public*, pg. 1486
TOTO AMERICAS HOLDINGS, INC.—See Toto Ltd.; *Int'l*, pg. 7845
TOTO AQUAIR LTD.—See Toto Ltd.; *Int'l*, pg. 7845
TOTO ASIA OCEANIA PTE. LTD.—See Toto Ltd.; *Int'l*, pg. 7845
TOTO BATH CREATE LTD.—See Toto Ltd.; *Int'l*, pg. 7845
TOTO (BEIJING) CO., LTD.—See Toto Ltd.; *Int'l*, pg. 7846
TOTO BUSINETZ LTD.—See Toto Ltd.; *Int'l*, pg. 7845
TOTO (CHINA) CO., LTD., - BEIJING—See Toto Ltd.; *Int'l*, pg. 7846
TOTO (CHINA) CO. LTD.—See Toto Ltd.; *Int'l*, pg. 7846
TOTO (CHINA) LTD.—See Toto Ltd.; *Int'l*, pg. 7846
TOTO CHUBU SALES LTD.—See Toto Ltd.; *Int'l*, pg. 7845
TOTO DALIAN CO., LTD.—See Toto Ltd.; *Int'l*, pg. 7846
TOTO DO BRASIL DISTRIBUICAO E COMERCIO, LTDA.—See Toto Ltd.; *Int'l*, pg. 7845
TOTO EAST CHINA CO., LTD.—See Toto Ltd.; *Int'l*, pg. 7845
TOTO ENGINEERING LTD.—See Toto Ltd.; *Int'l*, pg. 7845
TOTO ENPLA LTD.—See Toto Ltd.; *Int'l*, pg. 7845
TOTO EUROPE GMBH—See Toto Ltd.; *Int'l*, pg. 7845
TOTO EXCERA LTD.—See Toto Ltd.; *Int'l*, pg. 7845
TOTO EXPERT LTD.—See Toto Ltd.; *Int'l*, pg. 7845
TOTO FINANCE LTD.—See Toto Ltd.; *Int'l*, pg. 7845
TOTO FINE CERAMICS LTD.—See Toto Ltd.; *Int'l*, pg. 7845
TOTO (FUJIAN) CO., LTD.—See Toto Ltd.; *Int'l*, pg. 7846
TOTO GERMANY GMBH—See Toto Ltd.; *Int'l*, pg. 7845
TOTO (GUANGZHOU) CO., LTD.—See Toto Ltd.; *Int'l*, pg. 7846
TOTO HIGH LIVING LTD.—See Toto Ltd.; *Int'l*, pg. 7845
TOTO (H.K.) LTD.—See Toto Ltd.; *Int'l*, pg. 7846
TOTO INDIA INDUSTRIES PVT. LTD.—See Toto Ltd.; *Int'l*, pg. 7845
TOTO INFOM LTD.—See Toto Ltd.; *Int'l*, pg. 7845
TOTO KIKI (H.K.) LTD.—See Toto Ltd.; *Int'l*, pg. 7846
TOTO KOREA LTD.—See Toto Ltd.; *Int'l*, pg. 7846
TOTOKU ELECTRIC CO., LTD.—See The Carlyle Group Inc.; *U.S. Public*, pg. 2055
TOTO LOGICOM LTD.—See Toto Ltd.; *Int'l*, pg. 7846
TOTOLOTEK S.A.—See Gauselmann AG; *Int'l*, pg. 2890
TOTO LTD.; *Int'l*, pg. 7845
TOTO MAINTENANCE LTD.—See Toto Ltd.; *Int'l*, pg. 7846
TOTO MALAYSIA SDN. BHD.—See Toto Ltd.; *Int'l*, pg. 7846
TOTO MATERIA LTD.—See Toto Ltd.; *Int'l*, pg. 7846
TOTO MEXICO, S.A. DE C.V.—See Toto Ltd.; *Int'l*, pg. 7846
TOTO MTEC LTD.—See Toto Ltd.; *Int'l*, pg. 7846
TOTO SEKISUI CO., LTD.—See Sekisui Chemical Co., Ltd.; *Int'l*, pg. 6696
TOTO (SHANGHAI) CO., LTD.—See Toto Ltd.; *Int'l*, pg. 7845
TOTO (THAILAND) CO., LTD.—See Toto Ltd.; *Int'l*, pg. 7846
TOTO USA, INC.—See Toto Ltd.; *Int'l*, pg. 7846
TOTO VIETNAM CO., LTD.—See Toto Ltd.; *Int'l*, pg. 7846
TOTO WASHLET TECHNO LTD.—See Toto Ltd.; *Int'l*, pg. 7846
TOT PUBLIC COMPANY LIMITED; *Int'l*, pg. 7834
TOTRAMA SUPERMARKET INC.; *U.S. Private*, pg. 4192
TOTSA TOTAL OIL TRADING S.A—See TotalEnergies SE; *Int'l*, pg. 7839
TOTSU AGENCY CO., LTD.—See Token Corporation; *Int'l*, pg. 7782
TOTSU INC—See TBS Holdings, Inc.; *Int'l*, pg. 7481
TOTSU TRAVEL CO., LTD.—See Token Corporation; *Int'l*, pg. 7782
TOTSY MANUFACTURING COMPANY, INC.; *U.S. Private*, pg. 4192
TOTTA & ACORES INC.—See Banco Santander, S.A.; *Int'l*, pg. 828
TOTTA (IRELAND), PLC—See Banco Santander, S.A.; *Int'l*, pg. 828
TOTTENHAM ACQUISITION I LTD.; *Int'l*, pg. 7846
TOTTENHAM HOTSPUR FOOTBALL AND ATHLETIC CO. LIMITED—See Tottenham Hotspur plc; *Int'l*, pg. 7846
TOTTENHAM HOTSPUR PLC; *Int'l*, pg. 7846
TOTTEN INSURANCE GROUP INC—See Hellman & Friedman LLC; *U.S. Private*, pg. 1909
TOTTEN TUBES, INC.; *U.S. Private*, pg. 4192
THE TOTTORI BANK LTD.; *Int'l*, pg. 7696
TOTTORI BUILCON CORPORATION—See Totech Corporation; *Int'l*, pg. 7845
TOTTORI DAIMARU CO., LTD.—See J. Front Retailing Co., Ltd.; *Int'l*, pg. 3855
TOTTORI SANYO ELECTRIC CO., LTD.—See Panasonic Holdings Corporation; *Int'l*, pg. 5725

TOTTORI SEIRYO ELECTRIC CORPORATION—See Seiryo Electric Corporation; *Int'l*, pg. 6692
TOTT'S CHAMPAGNE CELLARS—See E. & J. Gallo Winery; *U.S. Private*, pg. 1303
TOTUS ENERGY TRADING LLC—See Dron & Dickson Ltd.; *Int'l*, pg. 2205
TOTUS PRO DEO; *U.S. Private*, pg. 4192
TOTVS S.A.; *Int'l*, pg. 7846
TOUBANI RESOURCES LIMITED; *Int'l*, pg. 7846
TOUBANI RESOURCES LIMITED; *Int'l*, pg. 7846
TOUBUJYUHAN CO., LTD.; *Int'l*, pg. 7847
TOUCAN INC.; *U.S. Private*, pg. 4192
TOUCAN INTERACTIVE CORP.; *U.S. Public*, pg. 2165
TOUCH CLOUD INC.—See Chroma ATE Inc.; *Int'l*, pg. 1588
TOUCHCORP LIMITED—See Block, Inc.; *U.S. Public*, pg. 361
TOUCHE PHD—See Omnicom Group Inc.; *U.S. Public*, pg. 1590
TOUCHETTE REGIONAL HOSPITAL; *U.S. Private*, pg. 4192
TOUCH HOLDINGS PTY. LIMITED—See Block, Inc.; *U.S. Public*, pg. 361
TOUCH LOCAL LIMITED—See Siris Capital Group, LLC; *U.S. Private*, pg. 3675
TOUCHMARK BANCSHARES, INC.; *U.S. Public*, pg. 2165
TOUCH-N-BUY, LLC—See IDT Corporation; *U.S. Public*, pg. 1094
TOUCHNET INFORMATION SYSTEMS, INC.—See Global Payments Inc.; *U.S. Public*, pg. 944
TOUCH NETWORKS PTY. LTD.—See Block, Inc.; *U.S. Public*, pg. 362
TOUCH 'N GO SDN. BHD.—See CIMB Group Holdings Berhad; *Int'l*, pg. 1608
TOUCH PANEL SYSTEMS K.K.—See TE Connectivity Ltd.; *Int'l*, pg. 7496
TOUCHPAPER TELEVISION—See De Agostini S.p.A.; *Int'l*, pg. 1994
TOUCHPOINT GROUP HOLDINGS, INC.; *U.S. Public*, pg. 2165
TOUCHPOINT SUPPORT SERVICES, LLC—See Compass Group PLC; *Int'l*, pg. 1752
TOUCH PROPERTY CO., LTD.—See Sansiri pcl; *Int'l*, pg. 6557
TOUCHSENSOR TECHNOLOGIES, L.L.C.—See Methode Electronics, Inc.; *U.S. Public*, pg. 1429
TOUCHSTAR PLC; *Int'l*, pg. 7847
TOUCHSTAR TECHNOLOGIES LTD.—See TouchStar plc; *Int'l*, pg. 7847
TOUCHSTONE BANK; *U.S. Public*, pg. 2165
TOUCHSTONE BEHAVIORAL HEALTH; *U.S. Private*, pg. 4192
TOUCHSTONE CAPITAL MANAGEMENT CO., LTD.—See Danto Holdings Corporation; *Int'l*, pg. 1969
TOUCHSTONE (CI) LIMITED—See Touchstone Group plc; *Int'l*, pg. 7847
TOUCHSTONE CORPORATE PROPERTY SERVICES LIMITED—See Places for People Group Limited; *Int'l*, pg. 5888
TOUCHSTONE CORPORATION—See Urban Renaissance Group LLC; *U.S. Private*, pg. 4315
TOUCHSTONE CRM LIMITED—See Touchstone Group plc; *Int'l*, pg. 7847
TOUCHSTONE ENERGY COOPERATIVE, INC.; *U.S. Private*, pg. 4192
TOUCHSTONE EXPLORATION INC.; *Int'l*, pg. 7847
TOUCHSTONE EXPLORATION (TRINIDAD) LTD.—See Touchstone Exploration Inc.; *Int'l*, pg. 7847
TOUCHSTONE GROUP PLC; *Int'l*, pg. 7847
TOUCHSTONE INTERNATIONAL MEDICAL SCIENCE CO., LTD.; *Int'l*, pg. 7847
TOUCHSTONE LTD.—See Touchstone Group plc; *Int'l*, pg. 7847
TOUCHSTONE MERCHANDISE GROUP, LLC; *U.S. Private*, pg. 4193
TOUCHSTONE PRECISION, INC.—See I-PEX Inc.; *Int'l*, pg. 3564
TOUCHSTONE SECURITIES, INC.—See Western & Southern Financial Group, Inc.; *U.S. Private*, pg. 4490
TOUCHSUITE; *U.S. Private*, pg. 4193
TOUCHTEK CORPORATION—See Hong Tai Electric Industrial Co., Ltd.; *Int'l*, pg. 3469
TOUCHTOWN INC.—See Atlantic Street Capital Management LLC; *U.S. Private*, pg. 374
TOUCHTUNES MUSIC CORPORATION—See Searchlight Capital Partners, L.P.; *U.S. Private*, pg. 3590
TOUCHTURNS LLC—See CN Innovations Holdings Limited; *Int'l*, pg. 1673
TOUCHUPDIRECT, LLC; *U.S. Private*, pg. 4193
TOUCH VENTURES LIMITED; *Int'l*, pg. 7847
TOUCHWOOD ENTERTAINMENT LTD.; *Int'l*, pg. 7847
TOUEI FUJIYOSHI CONSTRUCTION CORPORATION—See Iida Group Holdings Co., Ltd.; *Int'l*, pg. 3607
TOUEI HOME SERVICE CORPORATION—See Iida Group Holdings Co., Ltd.; *Int'l*, pg. 3607
TOUEI HOUSING CORPORATION—See Iida Group Holdings Co., Ltd.; *Int'l*, pg. 3607

CORPORATE AFFILIATIONS

TOUEN JAPAN CO., LTD.—See Abundance International Ltd.; *Int'l*, pg. 74
TOUGHBUILT INDUSTRIES, INC.; *U.S. Public*, pg. 2165
TOUGHER INDUSTRIES ENTERPRISES, LLC—See JWD Group Inc.; *U.S. Private*, pg. 2247
TOUGH MUDDER LLC; *U.S. Private*, pg. 4193
TOUHOKU BORING CO., LTD.—See OYO Corporation; *Int'l*, pg. 5678
TOUHOKU CARTON CO., LTD.—See Rengo Co., Ltd.; *Int'l*, pg. 6282
TOUHOKU DIAMOND COMPUTER SERVICE CO., LTD.—See Mitsubishi Research Institute, Inc.; *Int'l*, pg. 4968
TOUHOKU MARUHACHI UNYU COMPANY LTD.—See Maruhachi Warehouse Company Limited; *Int'l*, pg. 4712
TOUJYUKOUSAN CO., LTD.—See Sintokogio Ltd.; *Int'l*, pg. 6959
TOUKEI COMPUTER CO., LTD.; *Int'l*, pg. 7847
TOUKEI (THAILAND) CO., LTD.—See Toukei Computer Co., Ltd.; *Int'l*, pg. 7847
TOU KEWPIE CO., LTD.—See Kewpie Corporation; *Int'l*, pg. 4144
TOULON DIFFUSION AUTO; *Int'l*, pg. 7847
TOULOUSE LOCATION S.A.R.L.—See AerCap Holdings N.V.; *Int'l*, pg. 179
TOUMAZ HEALTHCARE LIMITED—See Science Group plc; *Int'l*, pg. 6647
TOUMAZ MICROSYSTEMS LIMITED—See Science Group plc; *Int'l*, pg. 6647
TOUMEI CO., LTD.; *Int'l*, pg. 7847
TOUNG LOONG TEXTILE MFG CO., LTD.; *Int'l*, pg. 7847
TOUPARGEL GROUPE SA; *Int'l*, pg. 7847
TOUPARGEL SAS—See Toupargel Groupe SA; *Int'l*, pg. 7847
TOUQUET SAVOUR S.A.S.; *Int'l*, pg. 7847
TOURAH PORTLAND CEMENT COMPANY—See Heidelberg Materials AG; *Int'l*, pg. 3320
TOURAMA (PVT) LTD.—See The Autodrome PLC; *Int'l*, pg. 7614
TOURAM LIMITED PARTNERSHIP—See Air Canada; *Int'l*, pg. 236
TOUR & ANDERSSON A/S—See IMI plc; *Int'l*, pg. 3626
TOUR & ANDERSSON NV/SA—See IMI plc; *Int'l*, pg. 3626
TOUR & ANDERSSON OY—See IMI plc; *Int'l*, pg. 3626
TOUR & ANDERSSON SA—See IMI plc; *Int'l*, pg. 3626
TOUR & ANDERSSON SA—See IMI plc; *Int'l*, pg. 3626
TOURAVENTURE S.A.—See TUI AG; *Int'l*, pg. 7968
TOUR CREATE, INC.—See Japan Airlines Co., Ltd.; *Int'l*, pg. 3884
TOUR EAST (2009) SDN BHD—See JTB Corp.; *Int'l*, pg. 4016
TOUR EAST AUSTRALIA PTY LIMITED—See JTB Corp.; *Int'l*, pg. 4016
TOUR EAST (HONG KONG) LIMITED—See JTB Corp.; *Int'l*, pg. 4016
TOUR EAST SINGAPORE (1996) PTE LTD—See JTB Corp.; *Int'l*, pg. 4016
TOUR EIFFEL ASSET MANAGEMENT—See Societe Mutuelle d'Assurance du Batiment et des Travaux Publics; *Int'l*, pg. 7043
TOUR EL GHAZAL-BNPI—See BNP Paribas SA; *Int'l*, pg. 1093
TOUR HOCKEY, INC.—See Roller Derby Skate Corp.; *U.S. Private*, pg. 3474
TOUR-HOUSE VERANSTALTUNGS-, KONZERT-, TV- UND MEDIA-CONSULTING GMBH—See CTS Eventim AG & Co. KGAA; *Int'l*, pg. 1874
TOURICO HOLIDAYS, INC.—See Canada Pension Plan Investment Board; *Int'l*, pg. 1279
TOURICO HOLIDAYS, INC.—See Cinven Limited; *Int'l*, pg. 1612
TOURIN PROPERTIES REIT; *Int'l*, pg. 7847
TOURISM ENTERPRISES COMPANY; *Int'l*, pg. 7847
TOURISM FINANCE CORPORATION OF INDIA LTD.; *Int'l*, pg. 7848
TOURISM HOLDINGS AUSTRALIA PTY LIMITED—See Tourism Holdings Limited; *Int'l*, pg. 7848
TOURISM HOLDINGS LIMITED; *Int'l*, pg. 7848
TOURISM & LEISURE ADVISORY SERVICE S.L.—See Indra Sistemas, S.A.; *Int'l*, pg. 3660
TOURISM NEW ZEALAND—See Tourism New Zealand; *Int'l*, pg. 7848
TOURISM NEW ZEALAND; *Int'l*, pg. 7848
TOURISM & SHIPPING SERVICES SARL—See Albert Ballin KG; *Int'l*, pg. 296
TOURIST BUREAU MARKETING, INC.—See Travel & Leisure Co.; *U.S. Public*, pg. 2185
TOURIST COMPANY OF NIGERIA PLC—See Ikeja Hotel Plc; *Int'l*, pg. 3610
TOURISTIC ENTERPRISES COMPANY; *Int'l*, pg. 7848
TOURIST TRANSPORT (FIJI) LIMITED; *Int'l*, pg. 7848
TOURIST VILLAGE OF MOSUL DAM; *Int'l*, pg. 7848
TOURMALINE BIO, INC.; *U.S. Public*, pg. 2165
TOURMALINE OIL CORP.; *Int'l*, pg. 7848
TOURNAMENT GOLF FOUNDATION; *U.S. Private*, pg. 4193
TOURNAMENT SOLUTIONS LLC—See New Wave Group AB; *Int'l*, pg. 5231

COMPANY NAME INDEX

TOURNAMENT SPORTS MARKETING INC.; *Int'l*, pg. 7848
TOURNEAU, LLC—See Bucherer AG; *Int'l*, pg. 1209
TOURNIER BOTTU SAS—See Innothera SA; *Int'l*, pg. 3711
TOUR SCOTIA—See The Bank of Nova Scotia; *Int'l*, pg. 7619
TOURS ON LOCATION INC; *U.S. Private*, pg. 4193
TOURTECH SUPPORT, INC.—See CES Power LLC; *U.S. Private*, pg. 842
TOUR WAVE CO., LTD.—See H.I.S. Co., Ltd.; *Int'l*, pg. 3196
TOURYO KIGYO CO.,LTD.—See Mitsubishi Logistics Corporation; *Int'l*, pg. 4963
TOUSA, INC.—See Technical Olympic SA; *Int'l*, pg. 7506
TOUS LES JOURS INTERNATIONAL CORP.—See CJ Corporation; *Int'l*, pg. 1632
TOUSLEY FORD, INC.—See AutoNation, Inc.; *U.S. Public*, pg. 238
TOUS WOOLLEN COMPANY; *Int'l*, pg. 7848
TOUTATIS CLIENT SERVICES DO BRASIL S.A.; *Int'l*, pg. 7848
TOUT L'TEMPS PRESSE SAS—See VINCI S.A.; *Int'l*, pg. 8229
TOUTON HOLDINGS LTD; *U.S. Private*, pg. 4193
TOUTO SYSTEMS, LTD.—See Tsuzuki Denki Co., Ltd.; *Int'l*, pg. 7958
TOUYUN BIOTECH GROUP LTD—See CC Land Holdings Limited; *Int'l*, pg. 1366
TOV ALGOL CHEMICALS—See Algol Oy; *Int'l*, pg. 318
TOV ALPINA UA—See Alpina, d.d.; *Int'l*, pg. 371
TOVANO B.V.—See ACOMO N.V.; *Int'l*, pg. 108
TOVARNA OLJA GEA D.D.; *Int'l*, pg. 7848
TOVAR SNOW PROFESSIONALS, INC.—See Guggenheim Partners, LLC; *U.S. Private*, pg. 1811
TOV DELFI—See AS Ekspress Grupp; *Int'l*, pg. 590
TOV EGGER HOLZWERKSTOFFE—See Fritz Egger GmbH & Co.; *Int'l*, pg. 2794
TOV EUROSOFTWARE-UA—See Fujitsu Limited; *Int'l*, pg. 2837
TOV GEA-UKRAYINA—See Triton Advisers Limited; *Int'l*, pg. 7931
TOV GREINER PACKAGING—See Greiner Holding AG; *Int'l*, pg. 3080
TOVIS CO., LTD; *Int'l*, pg. 7849
TOVIS CO., LTD - WONJU FACTORY—See Tovis CO., Ltd; *Int'l*, pg. 7849
TOV KARL STORZ UKRAINE—See Karl Storz GmbH & Co.; *Int'l*, pg. 4083
TOV KRKA UKRAINA—See Krka, d.d., Novo Mesto; *Int'l*, pg. 4303
TOV KSB UKRAINE—See KSB Limited; *Int'l*, pg. 4310
TOV MARY KAY (UKRAINE) LTD—See Mary Kay Holding Corporation; *U.S. Private*, pg. 2599
TOV POLYSIUS UKRAINE—See ThyssenKrupp AG; *Int'l*, pg. 7726
TOV RAISIO UKRAINA—See Raisio PLC; *Int'l*, pg. 6191
TOV REMONDIS ARTEMIWSK—See RETHMANN AG & Co. KG; *Int'l*, pg. 6309
TOV RHENUS REVIVAL—See RETHMANN AG & Co. KG; *Int'l*, pg. 6309
TOV STOCKMANN—See Stockmann plc; *Int'l*, pg. 7220
TOV VAMED UKRAINE—See Fresenius SE & Co. KGaA; *Int'l*, pg. 2781
TOV VBH—See VBH Holding AG; *Int'l*, pg. 8139
TOV WIKA PRYLAD—See WIKA Alexander-Wiegand GmbH & Co. KG; *Int'l*, pg. 8408
TOWA ASIA-PACIFIC PTE. LTD.—See TOWA Corporation; *Int'l*, pg. 7849
THE TOWA BANK, LTD.; *Int'l*, pg. 7696
THE TOWA CARD CO., LTD.—See The Towa Bank, Ltd.; *Int'l*, pg. 7696
TOWA CONCRETE PUMPING INC.—See Fujii Sangyo Corporation; *Int'l*, pg. 2826
TOWA CORPORATION - KYOTO EAST PLANT—See TOWA Corporation; *Int'l*, pg. 7849
TOWA CORPORATION; *Int'l*, pg. 7849
TOWA EUROPE B.V.—See TOWA Corporation; *Int'l*, pg. 7849
TOWA EUROPE GMBH—See TOWA Corporation; *Int'l*, pg. 7849
TOWA FOOD SERVICE CO., LTD.; *Int'l*, pg. 7849
TOWA GIKEN CO., LTD.—See Tokuyama Corporation; *Int'l*, pg. 7788
THE TOWAGIN LEASE CO., LTD.—See The Towa Bank, Ltd.; *Int'l*, pg. 7696
TOWA HI SYSTEM CO., LTD.; *Int'l*, pg. 7849
TOWA KANKO KAIHATSU CO., LTD—See Toda Corporation; *Int'l*, pg. 7773
TOWA KENSETSU CO., LTD.—See Tekken Corporation; *Int'l*, pg. 7527
TOWA KOREA CO., LTD.—See TOWA Corporation; *Int'l*, pg. 7849
TOWA LASERFRONT CORPORATION—See TOWA Corporation; *Int'l*, pg. 7849
TOWAM SDN. BHD.—See TOWA Corporation; *Int'l*, pg. 7849
TOWA (NANTONG) CO., LTD.—See TOWA Corporation; *Int'l*, pg. 7849

TOWANDA PRINTING CO.—See Times-Shamrock, Inc.; *U.S. Private*, pg. 4173
TOWA ORIMONO CO., LTD.—See Toray Industries, Inc.; *Int'l*, pg. 7827
TOWA PHARMACEUTICAL CO. LTD.; *Int'l*, pg. 7849
TOWARDS GREEN SDN. BHD.—See Chasen Holdings Limited; *Int'l*, pg. 1457
TOWA REAL ESTATE BROKERAGE CO., LTD.—See Mitsubishi Estate Co., Ltd.; *Int'l*, pg. 4947
TOWA REAL ESTATE CO., LTD.—See Toyota Motor Corporation; *Int'l*, pg. 7872
TOWA REAL ESTATE DEVELOPMENT CO., LTD.—See Mitsubishi Estate Co., Ltd.; *Int'l*, pg. 4947
TOWAROWA GIELDA ENERGII SA—See Gielda Papierow Wartosciowych w Warszawie S.A.; *Int'l*, pg. 2969
TOWARZYSTWO FUNDUSZY INWESTYCYJNYCH CAPITAL PARTNERS SA—See Capital Partners S.A.; *Int'l*, pg. 1312
TOWARZYSTWO UBEZPIECZEN EULER HERMES S.A.—See Allianz SE; *Int'l*, pg. 356
TOWARZYSTWO UBEZPIECZEN EUROPA S.A.—See Talanx AG; *Int'l*, pg. 7445
TOWARZYSTWO UBEZPIECZEN I REASEKURACJI ALLIANZ POLSKA S.A.—See Allianz SE; *Int'l*, pg. 356
TOWARZYSTWO UBEZPIECZEN I REASEKURACJI WARTA S.A.—See Talanx AG; *Int'l*, pg. 7445
TOWARZYSTWO UBEZPIECZEN NA ZYCIE EUROPA S.A.—See Talanx AG; *Int'l*, pg. 7445
TOWARZYSTWO UBEZPIECZEN WZAJEMNYCH CUPRUM SP. Z O.O.—See KGHM Polska Miedz S.A.; *Int'l*, pg. 4149
TOWA SEMICONDUCTOR EQUIPMENT PHILIPPINES CORPORATION—See TOWA Corporation; *Int'l*, pg. 7849
TOWA (SHANGHAI) CO., LTD.—See TOWA Corporation; *Int'l*, pg. 7849
TOWA SHOKO CO., LTD.—See Japan Material Co., Ltd.; *Int'l*, pg. 3899
TOWA (SUZHOU) CO., LTD.—See TOWA Corporation; *Int'l*, pg. 7849
TOWA TAIWAN CO., LTD.—See TOWA Corporation; *Int'l*, pg. 7849
TOWATEC CO., LTD.—See TOWA Corporation; *Int'l*, pg. 7849
TOWA THAI COMPANY LIMITED—See TOWA Corporation; *Int'l*, pg. 7849
TOWBIN AUTOMOTIVE ENTERPRISES; *U.S. Private*, pg. 4193
TOW CO., LTD.; *Int'l*, pg. 7849
TOWEL AUTO CENTRE LLC—See W.J. Towell & Co. LLC; *Int'l*, pg. 8322
TOWELL CONSTRUCTION & MAINTENANCE CO. LLC—See W.J. Towell & Co. LLC; *Int'l*, pg. 8322
TOWELLERS LIMITED; *Int'l*, pg. 7849
TOWELL FURNITURE CO LLC—See W.J. Towell & Co. LLC; *Int'l*, pg. 8322
TOWELL MATTRESS & FURNITURE INDUSTRY—See W.J. Towell & Co. LLC; *Int'l*, pg. 8322
TOWELL TAKE SOLUTIONS LLC—See TAKE Solutions Limited; *Int'l*, pg. 7436
TOWELL TOOLS & ENGINEERING CO. LLC—See W.J. Towell & Co. LLC; *Int'l*, pg. 8322
TOWEL TRACKER, LLC; *U.S. Private*, pg. 4193
TOWER 16, INC.—See Sun Capital Partners, Inc.; *U.S. Private*, pg. 3860
TOWER ARCH CAPITAL LLC; *U.S. Private*, pg. 4193
TOWER ASPHALT INC.—See Hardrives, Inc.; *U.S. Private*, pg. 1863
TOWER AUTOMOTIVE AUSLANDSBETEILIGUNGEN GMBH—See Financiere SNOP Dunois SA; *Int'l*, pg. 2669
TOWER AUTOMOTIVE BELGIUM B.V.B.A.—See Financiere SNOP Dunois SA; *Int'l*, pg. 2669
TOWER AUTOMOTIVE DO BRASIL, LTDA.—See KPS Capital Partners, LP; *U.S. Private*, pg. 2347
TOWER AUTOMOTIVE HOLDING GMBH—See Financiere SNOP Dunois SA; *Int'l*, pg. 2669
TOWER AUTOMOTIVE HOLDINGS EUROPE B.V.—See Financiere SNOP Dunois SA; *Int'l*, pg. 2669
TOWER AUTOMOTIVE INDIA PVT. LTD.—See KPS Capital Partners, LP; *U.S. Private*, pg. 2347
TOWER AUTOMOTIVE JAPAN CO., LTD.—See KPS Capital Partners, LP; *U.S. Private*, pg. 2347
TOWER AUTOMOTIVE MELFI, S.R.L.—See Financiere SNOP Dunois SA; *Int'l*, pg. 2669
TOWER AUTOMOTIVE MEXICO, S.DE R.L. DE C.V.—See KPS Capital Partners, LP; *U.S. Private*, pg. 2347
TOWER AUTOMOTIVE POLSKA SP. ZO.O.—See Financiere SNOP Dunois SA; *Int'l*, pg. 2669
TOWER AUTOMOTIVE PRESSWERK ZWICKAU GMBH—See Financiere SNOP Dunois SA; *Int'l*, pg. 2669
TOWER AUTOMOTIVE S.A.—See Financiere SNOP Dunois SA; *Int'l*, pg. 2669
TOWER AUTOMOTIVE SPAIN SL—See Financiere SNOP Dunois SA; *Int'l*, pg. 2669
TOWER AUTOMOTIVE S.R.L.—See Financiere SNOP Dunois SA; *Int'l*, pg. 2669

TOWER SEMICONDUCTOR LTD.

TOWER AUTOMOTIVE SUD S.R.L.—See Financiere SNOP Dunois SA; *Int'l*, pg. 2669
TOWER AUTOMOTIVE UMFORMTECHNICK GMBH—See Financiere SNOP Dunois SA; *Int'l*, pg. 2669
TOWER AUTOMOTIVE (WUHU) CO. LTD—See KPS Capital Partners, LP; *U.S. Private*, pg. 2347
TOWERBANK INTERNATIONAL, INC.; *Int'l*, pg. 7850
TOWERBROOK CAPITAL PARTNERS, L.P.; *U.S. Private*, pg. 4196
TOWERBROOK CAPITAL PARTNERS (U.K.) L.L.P.—See TowerBrook Capital Partners, L.P.; *U.S. Private*, pg. 4196
TOWER CANCER RESEARCH FOUNDATION; *U.S. Private*, pg. 4193
TOWER CAPITAL ASIA PTE. LTD.; *Int'l*, pg. 7849
TOWER CLEANING SYSTEMS INC.; *U.S. Private*, pg. 4193
TOWER CLUB PENANG BERHAD—See Only World Group Holdings Berhad; *Int'l*, pg. 5582
TOWERCO; *U.S. Private*, pg. 4196
TOWER CRANES SERVICES PTE. LTD.—See Tiong Woon Corporation Holding Ltd.; *Int'l*, pg. 7756
TOWERDATA, INC.; *U.S. Private*, pg. 4196
TOWER DEFENSE & AEROSPACE, LLC—See KPS Capital Partners, LP; *U.S. Private*, pg. 2347
TOWER ENGINEERING PROFESSIONALS, INC.—See H.I.G. Capital, LLC; *U.S. Private*, pg. 1834
TOWER FASTENERS CO. INC.—See MSC Industrial Direct Co., Inc.; *U.S. Public*, pg. 1483
TOWER FORD; *U.S. Private*, pg. 4193
TOWERGATE FINANCIAL (WEST) LTD.—See Towergate Partnership Limited; *Int'l*, pg. 7850
TOWERGATE PARTNERSHIP LIMITED; *Int'l*, pg. 7850
TOWER GENERAL PARTNER LIMITED—See BlackRock, Inc.; *U.S. Public*, pg. 347
TOWER GOLDEN RING - CHANGCHUN—See KPS Capital Partners, LP; *U.S. Private*, pg. 2347
TOWER HEALTH & LIFE LIMITED—See Tower Limited; *Int'l*, pg. 7850
TOWER HEALTH; *U.S. Private*, pg. 4193
TOWER HILL INSURANCE GROUP; *U.S. Private*, pg. 4194
TOWER HOLDING BV—See LVMH Moet Hennessy Louis Vuitton SE; *Int'l*, pg. 4603
TOWER HOLDINGS, INC.—See Amneal Pharmaceuticals, Inc.; *U.S. Public*, pg. 125
TOWER INDUSTRIES INC.; *U.S. Private*, pg. 4194
TOWER INSURANCE COMPANY LIMITED—See Intact Financial Corporation; *Int'l*, pg. 3727
TOWER INSURANCE COMPANY LIMITED—See Tryg A/S; *Int'l*, pg. 7947
TOWER INSURANCE (FIJI) LIMITED—See Noble Group Holdings Limited; *Int'l*, pg. 5397
TOWER INSURANCE (PNG) LIMITED—See Alpha Insurance Limited; *Int'l*, pg. 368
TOWER INTERNATIONAL, INC.—See KPS Capital Partners, LP; *U.S. Private*, pg. 2346
TOWER INVESTMENTS S.A.; *Int'l*, pg. 7850
TOWER INWESTYCJE SP. Z O.O.—See Powszechny Zaklad Ubezpieczen S.A.; *Int'l*, pg. 5949
TOWER ITALIA S.R.L.—See Financiere SNOP Dunois SA; *Int'l*, pg. 2669
TOWER LEGAL STAFFING, INC.—See Surge Private Equity LLC; *U.S. Private*, pg. 3884
TOWER LIMITED; *Int'l*, pg. 7850
TOWER LOAN OF MISSISSIPPI, INC.—See Prospect Capital Corporation; *U.S. Public*, pg. 1728
TOWER MANUFACTURING CORPORATION; *U.S. Private*, pg. 4194
TOWER MOTOR CO. INC.; *U.S. Private*, pg. 4194
TOWER ONE WIRELESS CORP.; *Int'l*, pg. 7850
TOWER PERFORMANCE, INC.—See Hastings Equity Partners, LLC; *U.S. Private*, pg. 1879
TOWER PERFORMANCE, INC.—See ORIX Corporation; *Int'l*, pg. 5636
TOWER PROPERTIES COMPANY; *U.S. Public*, pg. 2165
TOWER REAL ESTATE INVESTMENT TRUST; *Int'l*, pg. 7850
TOWER REALTY PARTNERS, INC.; *U.S. Private*, pg. 4194
TOWER RECORDS JAPAN INC.; *Int'l*, pg. 7850
TOWER RESOURCES LTD.; *Int'l*, pg. 7850
TOWER RESOURCES PLC; *Int'l*, pg. 7850
TOWER ROCK STONE COMPANY INC.; *U.S. Private*, pg. 4194
TOWERS DEVELOPMENT CORPORATION—See Crown Castle Inc.; *U.S. Public*, pg. 596
TOWER SEMICONDUCTOR LTD.; *Int'l*, pg. 7850
TOWER SEMICONDUCTOR NEWPORT BEACH, INC.—See Tower Semiconductor Ltd.; *Int'l*, pg. 7850
TOWER SEMICONDUCTOR SAN ANTONIO, INC.—See Tower Semiconductor Ltd.; *Int'l*, pg. 7850
TOWER SEMICONDUCTOR USA INC.—See Tower Semiconductor Ltd.; *Int'l*, pg. 7850
TOWERSENTRY LLC—See Hughey & Phillips, LLC; *U.S. Private*, pg. 2004
TOWER-SERVICE SP. Z O.O.—See CPI Property Group, S.A.; *Int'l*, pg. 1825

TOWER SEMICONDUCTOR LTD.

TOWER (SHANGHAI) AUTOMOTIVE TECH SERVICE CO. LTD.—See KPS Capital Partners, LP; *U.S. Private*, pg. 2347
TOWERSTONE, INC.—See IMA Financial Group, Inc.; *U.S. Private*, pg. 2043
TOWERSTREAM CORP.; *U.S. Public*, pg. 2165
TOWER STRUCTURAL LAMINATING—See WABASH NATIONAL CORPORATION; *U.S. Public*, pg. 2320
TOWERS WATSON AB—See Willis Towers Watson Public Limited Company; *Int'l*, pg. 8415
TOWERS WATSON AG—See Willis Towers Watson Public Limited Company; *Int'l*, pg. 8415
TOWERS WATSON AUSTRALIA PTY. LTD.—See Willis Towers Watson Public Limited Company; *Int'l*, pg. 8415
TOWERS WATSON AUSTRIA GMBH—See Willis Towers Watson Public Limited Company; *Int'l*, pg. 8415
TOWERS WATSON (BERMUDA) LTD.—See Willis Towers Watson Public Limited Company; *Int'l*, pg. 8415
TOWERS WATSON CANADA INC.—See Willis Towers Watson Public Limited Company; *Int'l*, pg. 8415
TOWERS WATSON CONSULTING (SHANGHAI) LIMITED—See Willis Towers Watson Public Limited Company; *Int'l*, pg. 8415
TOWERS WATSON CONSULTORES COLOMBIA S.A.—See Willis Towers Watson Public Limited Company; *Int'l*, pg. 8415
TOWERS WATSON CONSULTORIA LTDA.—See Willis Towers Watson Public Limited Company; *Int'l*, pg. 8415
TOWERS WATSON DATA SERVICES, INC.—See Willis Towers Watson Public Limited Company; *Int'l*, pg. 8415
TOWERS WATSON DE ESPANA, S.A.—See Willis Towers Watson Public Limited Company; *Int'l*, pg. 8415
TOWERS WATSON HONG KONG LIMITED—See Willis Towers Watson Public Limited Company; *Int'l*, pg. 8415
TOWERS WATSON INDIA PRIVATE LIMITED—See Willis Towers Watson Public Limited Company; *Int'l*, pg. 8415
TOWERS WATSON INVESTMENT MANAGEMENT (IRELAND) LIMITED—See Willis Towers Watson Public Limited Company; *Int'l*, pg. 8415
TOWERS WATSON ITALIA S.R.L.—See Willis Towers Watson Public Limited Company; *Int'l*, pg. 8415
TOWERS WATSON K.K.—See Willis Towers Watson Public Limited Company; *Int'l*, pg. 8415
TOWERS WATSON LIMITED—See Willis Towers Watson Public Limited Company; *Int'l*, pg. 8415
TOWERS WATSON LLC—See Willis Towers Watson Public Limited Company; *Int'l*, pg. 8415
TOWERS WATSON (MALAYSIA) SDN. BHD.—See Willis Towers Watson Public Limited Company; *Int'l*, pg. 8415
TOWERS WATSON MANAGEMENT CONSULTING (SHENZHEN) CO., LTD.—See Willis Towers Watson Public Limited Company; *Int'l*, pg. 8415
TOWERS WATSON MEXICO, AGENTE DE SEGUROS, S.A. DE C.V.—See Willis Towers Watson Public Limited Company; *Int'l*, pg. 8415
TOWERS WATSON MIDDLE EAST FZ-LLC—See Willis Towers Watson Public Limited Company; *Int'l*, pg. 8415
TOWERS WATSON NETHERLANDS B.V.—See Willis Towers Watson Public Limited Company; *Int'l*, pg. 8415
TOWERS WATSON NV—See Willis Towers Watson Public Limited Company; *Int'l*, pg. 8415
TOWERS WATSON PENSION SERVICES BV—See Willis Towers Watson Public Limited Company; *Int'l*, pg. 8415
TOWERS WATSON (PTY) LIMITED—See Willis Towers Watson Public Limited Company; *Int'l*, pg. 8415
TOWERS WATSON SA (PROPRIETARY) LIMITED—See Willis Towers Watson Public Limited Company; *Int'l*, pg. 8415
TOWERS WATSON SUPERANNUATION PTY LTD—See Willis Towers Watson Public Limited Company; *Int'l*, pg. 8415
TOWERS WATSON (THAILAND) LIMITED—See Willis Towers Watson Public Limited Company; *Int'l*, pg. 8415
TOWERS WATSON VIETNAM COMPANY LIMITED—See Willis Towers Watson Public Limited Company; *Int'l*, pg. 8415
TOWER TAG & LABEL, LLC—See Do-It Corporation; *U.S. Private*, pg. 1250
TOWERTEL S.P.A.—See EI Towers S.p.A.; *Int'l*, pg. 2328
TOWER THREE PARTNERS, LLC; *U.S. Private*, pg. 4194
TOWER VENTURES HOLDINGS LLC—See Blackstone Inc.; *U.S. Public*, pg. 356
TOWERVIEW, LLC—See COPT Defense Properties; *U.S. Public*, pg. 575
TOWLIFT INC.; *U.S. Private*, pg. 4196
TOWN AND COUNTRY PROPERTIES SDN. BHD—See Oilcorp Berhad; *Int'l*, pg. 5535
TOWN AND COUNTRY SUPERMARKETS, INC.; *U.S. Private*, pg. 4197
TOWN ART CO., LTD.—See Kotobuki Corporation; *Int'l*, pg. 4292
TOWN BANK—See Wintrust Financial Corporation; *U.S. Public*, pg. 2375
TOWN BUILDING SYSTEMS, LLC—See Installed Building Products, Inc.; *U.S. Public*, pg. 1134
TOWN CENTER AT AURORA, LLC—See Washington Prime Group Inc.; *U.S. Private*, pg. 4449
TOWN CENTER BANK; *U.S. Public*, pg. 2165

TOWN CENTER SELF STORAGE, LLC—See National Storage Affiliates Trust; *U.S. Public*, pg. 1498
TOWN CENTRE SECURITIES PLC; *Int'l*, pg. 7850
TOWN & COUNTRY AGENCY LLC—See Community Bank System, Inc.; *U.S. Public*, pg. 550
TOWN & COUNTRY AGRIMERCHANTS PTY LIMITED—See Nutrien Ltd.; *Int'l*, pg. 5493
TOWN & COUNTRY BANCORP INC.; *U.S. Private*, pg. 4196
TOWN & COUNTRY BANCORP, INC.; *U.S. Private*, pg. 4196
TOWN & COUNTRY BANK SPRINGFIELD—See Town & Country Bancorp Inc.; *U.S. Private*, pg. 4196
TOWN & COUNTRY BANK & TRUST COMPANY; *U.S. Private*, pg. 4196
TOWN & COUNTRY CEDAR HOMES; *U.S. Private*, pg. 4196
TOWN & COUNTRY CHRYSLER JEEP, INC.—See AutoNation, Inc.; *U.S. Public*, pg. 238
TOWN & COUNTRY CO-OP INC.; *U.S. Private*, pg. 4196
TOWN & COUNTRY CO-OP; *U.S. Private*, pg. 4196
TOWN & COUNTRY CREDIT CORP.—See Ameriquest Capital Corporation; *U.S. Private*, pg. 260
TOWN & COUNTRY CREDIT UNION; *U.S. Private*, pg. 4196
TOWN & COUNTRY DISTRIBUTORS; *U.S. Private*, pg. 4196
TOWN & COUNTRY FOODS, INC.—See Pine State Trading Co.; *U.S. Private*, pg. 3183
TOWN & COUNTRY FORD INC.; *U.S. Private*, pg. 4196
TOWN & COUNTRY HARDWARE STORES, LLC—See Tyndale Advisors, LLC; *U.S. Private*, pg. 4268
TOWN & COUNTRY HONDA; *U.S. Private*, pg. 4196
TOWN & COUNTRY HOTEL, LLC—See Atlas Hotels, Inc.; *U.S. Private*, pg. 378
TOWN & COUNTRY INDUSTRIES—See Hendricks Holding Company, Inc.; *U.S. Private*, pg. 1915
TOWN & COUNTRY LANDSCAPE SUPPLY CO.; *U.S. Private*, pg. 4196
TOWN & COUNTRY LINEN CORP.—See H.I.G. Capital, LLC; *U.S. Private*, pg. 1832
TOWN & COUNTRY MARKET INC.; *U.S. Private*, pg. 4196
TOWN-COUNTRY NATIONAL BANK—See United Bancorporation of Alabama, Inc.; *U.S. Public*, pg. 2229
TOWN & COUNTRY PHYSICAL THERAPY, LTD.—See U.S. Physical Therapy, Inc.; *U.S. Public*, pg. 2216
TOWN & COUNTRY SERVICES; *U.S. Private*, pg. 4196
TOWN & COUNTRY—See The Hearst Corporation; *U.S. Private*, pg. 4047
TOWN & COUNTRY SURF SHOP INC.—See T&C Holding Ltd; *U.S. Private*, pg. 3909
TOWNE AIR FREIGHT INC.—See Towne Holdings Inc.; *U.S. Private*, pg. 4198
TOWN EAST HEALTHCARE, INC.—See The Ensign Group, Inc.; *U.S. Public*, pg. 2072
TOWNE BANCORP, INC.; *U.S. Private*, pg. 4198
TOWNEBANK COMMERCIAL MORTGAGE, LLC—See Towne Bank; *U.S. Public*, pg. 2166
TOWNEBANK MORTGAGE—See Towne Bank; *U.S. Public*, pg. 2166
TOWNE BANK; *U.S. Public*, pg. 2165
TOWNECRAFT HOMEWARES, LLC; *U.S. Private*, pg. 4198
TOWNECRAFT, INC.; *U.S. Private*, pg. 4198
TOWNE DEVELOPMENT OF HAWAII, INC.—See Zilber Ltd.; *U.S. Private*, pg. 4604
TOWNE HOLDINGS INC.; *U.S. Private*, pg. 4198
TOWNE HYUNDAI; *U.S. Private*, pg. 4198
TOWNE INSURANCE AGENCY, LLC—See Towne Bank; *U.S. Public*, pg. 2166
TOWNE INVESTMENTS, LLC—See Towne Bank; *U.S. Public*, pg. 2166
TOWNE PARK LTD—See Greenbriar Equity Group, L.P.; *U.S. Private*, pg. 1776
TOWNE PROPERTIES; *U.S. Private*, pg. 4198
TOWNER COUNTY MEDICAL CENTER; *U.S. Private*, pg. 4198
TOWNE REALTY, INC.—See Zilber Ltd.; *U.S. Private*, pg. 4604
TOWNE REALTY, LLC—See Towne Bank; *U.S. Public*, pg. 2166
TOWNES TELE-COMMUNICATIONS; *U.S. Private*, pg. 4198
TOWNE WEST SQUARE, LLC—See Washington Prime Group Inc.; *U.S. Private*, pg. 4449
TOWN FAIR TIRE CENTERS INC.; *U.S. Private*, pg. 4197
TOWNGAS ENTERPRISE LIMITED—See Henderson Land Development Co. Ltd.; *Int'l*, pg. 3344
TOWNGAS INTERNATIONAL COMPANY LIMITED—See Henderson Land Development Co. Ltd.; *Int'l*, pg. 3344
TOWNGAS SMART ENERGY COMPANY LIMITED; *Int'l*, pg. 7851
TOWNGAS TELECOMMUNICATIONS FIXED NETWORK LIMITED—See Henderson Land Development Co. Ltd.; *Int'l*, pg. 3344
TOWN HEALTH INTERNATIONAL MEDICAL GROUP LIMITED; *Int'l*, pg. 7851

CORPORATE AFFILIATIONS

TOWN HEALTH MEDICAL & DENTAL SERVICES LIMITED—See Town Health International Medical Group Limited; *Int'l*, pg. 7851
TOWNHOMES AT RIVERFRONT PARK, LLC—See Goff Capital, Inc.; *U.S. Private*, pg. 1726
TOWNHOMES MANAGEMENT, INC.; *U.S. Private*, pg. 4198
THE TOWNHOMES OF BEVERLY—See Lone Star Global Acquisitions, LLC; *U.S. Private*, pg. 2488
TOWNLEY INC.; *U.S. Private*, pg. 4198
TOWNLEY MANUFACTURING COMPANY; *U.S. Private*, pg. 4198
TOWN MANAGEMENT CORP; *U.S. Private*, pg. 4197
TOWN MOTOR CAR CORPORATION; *U.S. Private*, pg. 4197
TOWNNEWS-SHA CO., LTD.; *Int'l*, pg. 7851
TOWN NORTH MAZDA; *U.S. Private*, pg. 4197
TOWN OF PARADISE VALLEY INDEPENDENT—See Independent Newspapers, Inc.; *U.S. Private*, pg. 2060
TOWN PLAZA FAMILY PRACTICE, LLC—See HCA Healthcare, Inc.; *U.S. Public*, pg. 1012
TOWN PLAZA FAMILY PRACTICE, LLC—See HCA Healthcare, Inc.; *U.S. Public*, pg. 1012
TOWN PUMP, INC.; *U.S. Private*, pg. 4197
TOWN RAY HOLDINGS LIMITED; *Int'l*, pg. 7851
TOWNSEND CAPITAL, LLC; *U.S. Private*, pg. 4198
TOWNSEND COATES LTD.—See discoverIE Group plc; *Int'l*, pg. 2134
THE TOWNSEND CORPORATION; *U.S. Private*, pg. 4127
TOWNSEND DIALYSIS, LLC—See DaVita Inc.; *U.S. Public*, pg. 644
TOWNSEND DOOR & HARDWARE—See MSCO Inc.; *U.S. Private*, pg. 2806
TOWNSEND FORD INC.; *U.S. Private*, pg. 4198
TOWNSEND GROUP ASIA LIMITED—See Aon plc; *Int'l*, pg. 495
THE TOWNSEND GROUP, INC.—See SmithBucklin Corporation; *U.S. Private*, pg. 3697
TOWNSEND OIL CO. INC.; *U.S. Private*, pg. 4198
TOWNSEND RECOVERY CENTER NEW ORLEANS, LLC—See AAC Holdings, Inc.; *U.S. Private*, pg. 31
TOWNSEND; *U.S. Private*, pg. 4198
TOWNSEND SYSTEMS—See MSCO Inc.; *U.S. Private*, pg. 2806
TOWNSEND TIMES—See Alden Global Capital LLC; *U.S. Private*, pg. 157
TOWNSEND TREE SERVICE—See The Townsend Corporation; *U.S. Private*, pg. 4127
TOWN SPORTS INTERNATIONAL HOLDINGS, INC.; *U.S. Private*, pg. 4197
TOWN SPORTS INTERNATIONAL, LLC—See Town Sports International Holdings, Inc.; *U.S. Private*, pg. 4197
TOWN SQUARE COMMONS, LLC—See UDR, Inc.; *U.S. Public*, pg. 2218
TOWNSQUARE MEDIA ABILENE, LLC—See Brookfield Corporation; *Int'l*, pg. 1183
TOWNSQUARE MEDIA AMARILLO, LLC—See Brookfield Corporation; *Int'l*, pg. 1183
TOWNSQUARE MEDIA BILLINGS, LLC—See Brookfield Corporation; *Int'l*, pg. 1184
TOWNSQUARE MEDIA BINGHAMTON, LLC—See Brookfield Corporation; *Int'l*, pg. 1184
TOWNSQUARE MEDIA BROADCASTING, LLC—See Brookfield Corporation; *Int'l*, pg. 1183
TOWNSQUARE MEDIA CASPER, LLC—See Brookfield Corporation; *Int'l*, pg. 1184
TOWNSQUARE MEDIA FARIBAULT, LLC—See Brookfield Corporation; *Int'l*, pg. 1184
TOWNSQUARE MEDIA, INC.—See Brookfield Corporation; *Int'l*, pg. 1183
TOWNSQUARE MEDIA LANSING, LLC—See Brookfield Corporation; *Int'l*, pg. 1184
TOWNSQUARE MEDIA LAWTON, LLC—See Brookfield Corporation; *Int'l*, pg. 1183
TOWNSQUARE MEDIA LUBBOCK, LLC—See Brookfield Corporation; *Int'l*, pg. 1184
TOWNSQUARE MEDIA LUFKIN, LLC—See Brookfield Corporation; *Int'l*, pg. 1184
TOWNSQUARE MEDIA NEW BEDFORD, LLC—See Brookfield Corporation; *Int'l*, pg. 1184
TOWNSQUARE MEDIA ODESSA-MIDLAND II, LLC—See Brookfield Corporation; *Int'l*, pg. 1184
TOWNSQUARE MEDIA OF ALBANY, INC.—See Brookfield Corporation; *Int'l*, pg. 1184
TOWNSQUARE MEDIA OF BLOOMINGTON, INC.—See Brookfield Corporation; *Int'l*, pg. 1184
TOWNSQUARE MEDIA OF BUFFALO, INC.—See Brookfield Corporation; *Int'l*, pg. 1184
TOWNSQUARE MEDIA OF EL PASO, INC.—See Brookfield Corporation; *Int'l*, pg. 1184
TOWNSQUARE MEDIA OF EVANSVILLE/OWENSBORO, INC.—See Brookfield Corporation; *Int'l*, pg. 1184
TOWNSQUARE MEDIA OF FLINT, INC.—See Brookfield Corporation; *Int'l*, pg. 1184
TOWNSQUARE MEDIA OF FT. COLLINS, INC.—See Brookfield Corporation; *Int'l*, pg. 1184
TOWNSQUARE MEDIA OF GRAND RAPIDS, INC.—See Brookfield Corporation; *Int'l*, pg. 1184

COMPANY NAME INDEX

TOWNSQUARE MEDIA OF KILLEEN-TEMPLE, INC.—See Brookfield Corporation; *Int'l*, pg. 1184
TOWNSQUARE MEDIA OF LAFAYETTE, INC.—See Brookfield Corporation; *Int'l*, pg. 1184
TOWNSQUARE MEDIA OF OWENSBORO—See Brookfield Corporation; *Int'l*, pg. 1184
TOWNSQUARE MEDIA OF ST. CLOUD, INC.—See Brookfield Corporation; *Int'l*, pg. 1184
TOWNSQUARE MEDIA OF UTICA/ROME, INC.—See Brookfield Corporation; *Int'l*, pg. 1184
TOWNSQUARE MEDIA PORTSMOUTH, LLC—See Brookfield Corporation; *Int'l*, pg. 1184
TOWNSQUARE MEDIA - SQUARE DIVISION—See Brookfield Corporation; *Int'l*, pg. 1183
TOWNSQUARE MEDIA TEXARKANA, LLC—See Brookfield Corporation; *Int'l*, pg. 1184
TOWNSQUARE MEDIA - TOWN DIVISION—See Brookfield Corporation; *Int'l*, pg. 1184
TOWNSQUARE MEDIA TWIN FALLS, LLC—See Brookfield Corporation; *Int'l*, pg. 1184
TOWNSQUARE MEDIA TYLER, LLC—See Brookfield Corporation; *Int'l*, pg. 1184
TOWNSQUARE MEDIA VICTORIA, LLC—See Brookfield Corporation; *Int'l*, pg. 1184
TOWNSQUARE MEDIA WICHITA FALLS, LLC—See Brookfield Corporation; *Int'l*, pg. 1184
THE TOWN TALK—See Gannett Co., Inc.; *U.S. Public*, pg. 896
TOWN VILLAGE STERLING HEIGHTS, LLC—See Chicago Pacific Founders; *U.S. Private*, pg. 878
TOWN VILLAGE VESTAVIA HILLS, LLC—See Chicago Pacific Founders; *U.S. Private*, pg. 878
TOW SMT SCHARF UKRAINIA—See Yankuang Group Co., Limited; *Int'l*, pg. 8562
TOWSON PROMENADE, LLC—See UDR, Inc.; *U.S. Public*, pg. 2218
TOWSON SURGICAL CENTER, LLC—See KKR & Co. Inc.; *U.S. Public*, pg. 1249
TOXCO INC.—See *U.S. Private*, pg. 4198
TOXEMENT, S.A.—See RPM International Inc.; *U.S. Public*, pg. 1820
TOX FREE (AUSTRALIA) PTY LTD—See Cleanaway Waste Management Limited; *Int'l*, pg. 1655
TOX FREE (HENDERSON) PTY LTD—See Cleanaway Waste Management Limited; *Int'l*, pg. 1655
TOX FREE (KWINANA) PTY LTD—See Cleanaway Waste Management Limited; *Int'l*, pg. 1655
TOX FREE (NEW SOUTH WALES) PTY LTD—See Cleanaway Waste Management Limited; *Int'l*, pg. 1655
TOX FREE (QUEENSLAND) PTY LTD—See Cleanaway Waste Management Limited; *Int'l*, pg. 1655
TOXIDO PEST CONTROL LLC—See Al Jaber Group; *Int'l*, pg. 280
TOXIKON CORPORATION—See Laboratory Corporation of America Holdings; *U.S. Public*, pg. 1287
TOXIKOS PTY LTD—See EnviroSuite Limited; *Int'l*, pg. 2455
TOXLAB SAS—See Eurofins Scientific S.E.; *Int'l*, pg. 2543
TOX PATH SPECIALISTS, LLC—See Ampersand Management LLC; *U.S. Private*, pg. 265
TOX PRESSOTECHNIK DO BRASIL LTDA.—See TOX Pressotechnik GmbH & Co. KG; *Int'l*, pg. 7851
TOX PRESSOTECHNIK GMBH & CO. KG; *Int'l*, pg. 7851
TOX PRESSOTECHNIK INDIA PVT LTD—See TOX Pressotechnik GmbH & Co. KG; *Int'l*, pg. 7851
TOX PRESSOTECHNIK LLC—See TOX Pressotechnik GmbH & Co. KG; *Int'l*, pg. 7851
TOX PRESSOTECHNIK LTD.—See TOX Pressotechnik GmbH & Co. KG; *Int'l*, pg. 7851
TOX PRESSOTECHNIK (PTY) LTD—See TOX Pressotechnik GmbH & Co. KG; *Int'l*, pg. 7851
TOX PRESSOTECHNIK SDN BHD—See TOX Pressotechnik GmbH & Co. KG; *Int'l*, pg. 7851
TOX-RIX PRESSOTECHNIK CO.—See TOX Pressotechnik GmbH & Co. KG; *Int'l*, pg. 7851
TOXSTRATEGIES INC.—See Renovus Capital Partners; *U.S. Private*, pg. 3399
TOYAL AMERICA INC.—See Nippon Light Metal Holdings Company, Ltd.; *Int'l*, pg. 5324
TOYAL EUROPE S.A.S.U.—See Nippon Light Metal Holdings Company, Ltd.; *Int'l*, pg. 5324
TOYAL ZHAOQING CO., LTD.—See Nippon Light Metal Holdings Company, Ltd.; *Int'l*, pg. 5324
TOYAMA ATSUEN CO., LTD.—See Nachi-Fujikoshi Corp.; *Int'l*, pg. 5123
TOYAMA CHEMICAL CO., LTD.—See FUJIFILM Holdings Corporation; *Int'l*, pg. 2826
TOYAMA DAIKEN CORPORATION—See Daiken Corporation; *Int'l*, pg. 1931
TOYAMA ELECTRIC LTD.; *Int'l*, pg. 7851
TOYAMA JUKI CO., LTD.—See Daiken Corporation; *Int'l*, pg. 1931
TOYAMA KOBAYASHI PHARMACEUTICAL CO., LTD.—See Kobayashi Pharmaceutical Co., Ltd.; *Int'l*, pg. 4216
TOYAMA MURATA MANUFACTURING CO., LTD.—See Murata Manufacturing Co., Ltd.; *Int'l*, pg. 5099
TOYAMA SHOWA CO., LTD.—See SMK Corporation; *Int'l*, pg. 7013

TOYAMA TELEPHONE CONSTRUCTION CORPORATION—See COMSYS Holdings Corporation; *Int'l*, pg. 1761
TOYAMA TERMINAL BUILDING COMPANY—See West Japan Railway Company; *Int'l*, pg. 8385
TOYAM SPORTS LIMITED; *Int'l*, pg. 7851
TOYA ROMANIA S.A.—See Toya S.A.; *Int'l*, pg. 7851
TOYA S.A.; *Int'l*, pg. 7851
TOYE & CO. PLC; *Int'l*, pg. 7851
TOYE, KENNING & SPENCER LIMITED—See Toye & Co. plc; *Int'l*, pg. 7852
TOY ISLAND MANUFACTURING COMPANY LIMITED—See Li & Fung Limited; *Int'l*, pg. 4481
TOY MARINE S.P.A; *Int'l*, pg. 7851
TOYO ADL CO., LTD.—See Toyo Ink SC Holdings Co., Ltd.; *Int'l*, pg. 7854
TOYO ADL CORP. - CHIBA PLANT—See Toyo Ink SC Holdings Co., Ltd.; *Int'l*, pg. 7854
TOYO ADTEC CO., LTD.—See Denki Company Limited; *Int'l*, pg. 2027
TOYO ADVANCED SCIENCE TAIWAN CO., LTD.—See Toyo Ink SC Holdings Co., Ltd.; *Int'l*, pg. 7854
TOYO ADVANCED TECHNOLOGIES CO., LTD. - AUTOMOBILE COMPONENTS SALES DIVISION—See ITOCHU Corporation; *Int'l*, pg. 3841
TOYO ADVANCED TECHNOLOGIES CO., LTD. - HARD COATING SALES DIVISION (HARD COATING)—See ITOCHU Corporation; *Int'l*, pg. 3841
TOYO ADVANCED TECHNOLOGIES CO., LTD. - HIROSHIMA PLANT—See ITOCHU Corporation; *Int'l*, pg. 3841
TOYO ADVANCED TECHNOLOGIES CO., LTD. - NAGOYA PLANT (HARD COATING)—See ITOCHU Corporation; *Int'l*, pg. 3841
TOYO ADVANCED TECHNOLOGIES CO., LTD.—See ITOCHU Corporation; *Int'l*, pg. 3841
TOYO ADVANCED TECHNOLOGIES CO., LTD. - TOKYO PLANT (HARD COATING)—See ITOCHU Corporation; *Int'l*, pg. 3841
TOYO AEROSOL INDUSTRY CO., LTD.—See Toyo Seikan Group Holdings, Ltd.; *Int'l*, pg. 7857
TOYO ALUMINIUM EKCO PRODUCTS CO., LTD.—See Nippon Light Metal Holdings Company, Ltd.; *Int'l*, pg. 5324
TOYO ALUMINIUM K.K.—See Nippon Light Metal Holdings Company, Ltd.; *Int'l*, pg. 5324
TOYO ALUMINIUM (SHANGHAI) MANAGEMENT CO., LTD.—See Nippon Light Metal Holdings Company, Ltd.; *Int'l*, pg. 5324
TOYO ASANO FOUNDATION CO., LTD.; *Int'l*, pg. 7852
TOYO AUTOMOTIVE PARTS DE MEXICO, S.A. DE C.V.—See Toyo Tire Corporation; *Int'l*, pg. 7859
TOYO AUTOMOTIVE PARTS (GUANGZHOU) CO., LTD.—See Toyo Tire Corporation; *Int'l*, pg. 7859
TOYO AUTOMOTIVE PARTS (USA) INC—See Toyo Tire Corporation; *Int'l*, pg. 7859
TOYO BEAUTY SUPPLY CORPORATION—See Mitsui Chemicals, Inc.; *Int'l*, pg. 4984
TOYO B NET CO., LTD.—See Toyo Ink SC Holdings Co., Ltd.; *Int'l*, pg. 7854
TOYOBO AMERICA INC.—See Toyobo Co., Ltd.; *Int'l*, pg. 7861
TOYOBO AUTOMOTIVE TEXTILES (CHANGSHU) CO., LTD.—See Toyobo Co., Ltd.; *Int'l*, pg. 7861
TOYOBO BINH DUONG CO., LTD.—See Toyobo Co., Ltd.; *Int'l*, pg. 7861
TOYOBO CHEMICALS EUROPE GMBH—See Toyobo Co., Ltd.; *Int'l*, pg. 7861
TOYOBO CHEMICALS (THAILAND) CO., LTD.—See Toyobo Co., Ltd.; *Int'l*, pg. 7861
TOYOBO CO., LTD.; *Int'l*, pg. 7860
TOYOBO DO BRASIL PARTICIPACOES LTDA.—See Toyobo Co., Ltd.; *Int'l*, pg. 7861
TOYOBO ENGINEERING CO., LTD.—See Toyobo Co., Ltd.; *Int'l*, pg. 7861
TOYOBO INDIA PRIVATE LIMITED—See Toyobo Co., Ltd.; *Int'l*, pg. 7861
TOYOBO INDUSTRIAL MATERIALS AMERICA, INC.—See Toyobo Co., Ltd.; *Int'l*, pg. 7861
TOYOBO INDUSTRIAL MATERIAL (THAILAND) LTD.—See Toyobo Co., Ltd.; *Int'l*, pg. 7861
TOYOBO INFORMATION SYSTEM CREATE CO., LTD.—See Toyobo Co., Ltd.; *Int'l*, pg. 7861
TOYOBO KANKYO TECHNO CO., LTD.—See The Japan Wool Textile Co., Ltd.; *Int'l*, pg. 7659
TOYOBO KOREA CO., LTD.—See Toyobo Co., Ltd.; *Int'l*, pg. 7861
TOYOBO KUREHA AMERICA CO., LTD.—See Toyobo Co., Ltd.; *Int'l*, pg. 7860
TOYOBO LOGISTICS CO., LTD.—See Toyobo Co., Ltd.; *Int'l*, pg. 7861
TOYOBO MC MEXICO S.A. DE C.V.—See Toyobo Co., Ltd.; *Int'l*, pg. 7861
TOYOBO MC U.S.A. INC.—See Toyobo Co., Ltd.; *Int'l*, pg. 7861
TOYOBO MEXICO, S.A. DE C.V.—See Toyobo Co., Ltd.; *Int'l*, pg. 7861
TOYOBO PHOTO CHEMICALS CO., LTD.—See Toyobo Co., Ltd.; *Int'l*, pg. 7861

TOYO CORPORATION

TOYOBO REAL ESTATE CO., LTD.—See Toyobo Co., Ltd.; *Int'l*, pg. 7861
TOYOBO SAHA SAFETY WEAVE CO., LTD.—See Toyobo Co., Ltd.; *Int'l*, pg. 7861
TOYOBO (SHANGHAI) BIOTECH CO., LTD.—See Toyobo Co., Ltd.; *Int'l*, pg. 7861
TOYOBO (SHANGHAI) CO., LTD.—See Toyobo Co., Ltd.; *Int'l*, pg. 7861
TOYOBOSHI KOGYO CO., LTD.—See Shima Seiki Mfg., Ltd.; *Int'l*, pg. 6831
TOYOBO STC CO., LTD.—See Toyobo Co., Ltd.; *Int'l*, pg. 7861
TOYOBO (TAIWAN) CO., LTD.—See Toyobo Co., Ltd.; *Int'l*, pg. 7861
TOYOBO TEXTILE (MALAYSIA) SDN. BHD.—See Toyobo Co., Ltd.; *Int'l*, pg. 7861
TOYOBO (THAILAND) CO., LTD.—See Toyobo Co., Ltd.; *Int'l*, pg. 7861
TOYO BUSINESS SUPPORT INC.—See Toray Industries, Inc.; *Int'l*, pg. 7827
TOYO CAPITAL CO., LTD.—See Toyo Securities Co., Ltd.; *Int'l*, pg. 7856
TOYOCHEM CO., LTD. - KAWAGOE FACTORY—See Toyo Ink SC Holdings Co., Ltd.; *Int'l*, pg. 7855
TOYOCHEM CO., LTD. - SEISHIN PLANT—See Toyo Ink SC Holdings Co., Ltd.; *Int'l*, pg. 7855
TOYOCHEM CO., LTD.—See Toyo Ink SC Holdings Co., Ltd.; *Int'l*, pg. 7855
TOYOCHEM CORPORATION SDN. BHD.—See Toyo Ink SC Holdings Co., Ltd.; *Int'l*, pg. 7855
TOYO CHEMICAL INDUSTRIAL PRODUCTS CO., LTD.—See Toyo Tire Corporation; *Int'l*, pg. 7859
TOYO CHEMICAL / INDUSTRIAL PRODUCTS SALES CORPORATION—See Toyo Tire Corporation; *Int'l*, pg. 7859
TOYOCHEM PRINTING CHEMICAL SDN. BHD.—See Toyo Ink SC Holdings Co., Ltd.; *Int'l*, pg. 7855
TOYOCHEM SPECIALTY CHEMICAL SDN. BHD. - SEREMBAN PLANT—See Toyo Ink SC Holdings Co., Ltd.; *Int'l*, pg. 7855
TOYOCHEM SPECIALTY CHEMICAL SDN. BHD.—See Toyo Ink SC Holdings Co., Ltd.; *Int'l*, pg. 7855
TOYO CLOTH CO., LTD.—See Toyobo Co., Ltd.; *Int'l*, pg. 7861
TOYO CLUTCH CO., LTD.—See OGURA CLUTCH CO., LTD.; *Int'l*, pg. 5531
TOYOCOLOR CO., LTD.- FUJI FACTORY—See Toyo Ink SC Holdings Co., Ltd.; *Int'l*, pg. 7855
TOYOCOLOR CO., LTD. - MORIYAMA FACTORY—See Toyo Ink SC Holdings Co., Ltd.; *Int'l*, pg. 7855
TOYOCOLOR CO., LTD. - OKAYAMA PLANT—See Toyo Ink SC Holdings Co., Ltd.; *Int'l*, pg. 7855
TOYOCOLOR CO., LTD.—See Toyo Ink SC Holdings Co., Ltd.; *Int'l*, pg. 7855
TOYOCOLOR CO., LTD.—See Toyo Ink SC Holdings Co., Ltd.; *Int'l*, pg. 7855
TOYO CO., LTD.—See Seino Holdings Co., Ltd.; *Int'l*, pg. 6691
TOYOCOM ASIA PTE. LTD.—See Seiko Epson Corporation; *Int'l*, pg. 6687
TOYOCOM ENGINEERING CO., LTD.—See Seiko Epson Corporation; *Int'l*, pg. 6687
TOYOCOM EUROPE GMBH—See Seiko Epson Corporation; *Int'l*, pg. 6687
TOYOCOM TRADING CO., LTD.—See Seiko Epson Corporation; *Int'l*, pg. 6687
TOYO CONSTRUCTION CO., LTD.; *Int'l*, pg. 7852
TOYO CONSTRUCTION CHINA—See Toyo Corporation; *Int'l*, pg. 7852
TOYO CORPORATION; *Int'l*, pg. 7852
TOYO COTTON COMPANY—See Toyota Tsusho Corporation; *Int'l*, pg. 7878
TOYO COTTON (JAPAN) CO.—See Toyota Tsusho Corporation; *Int'l*, pg. 7878
TOYO CR SDN. BHD.—See Mitsubishi Heavy Industries, Ltd.; *Int'l*, pg. 4962
TOYO CUSHION LANKA (PVT) LTD.—See Hayleys PLC; *Int'l*, pg. 3292
TOYODA BOSHOKU CORPORATION—See Toyota Motor Corporation; *Int'l*, pg. 7872
TOYODA GOSEI ASIA CO., LTD.—See Toyoda Gosei Co., Ltd.; *Int'l*, pg. 7862
TOYODA GOSEI AUSTRALIA PTY. LTD.—See Toyoda Gosei Co., Ltd.; *Int'l*, pg. 7862
TOYODA GOSEI AUTOMOTIVE SEALING MEXICO S.A. DE C.V.—See Toyoda Gosei Co., Ltd.; *Int'l*, pg. 7862
TOYODA GOSEI CO., LTD. - BISAI PLANT—See Toyoda Gosei Co., Ltd.; *Int'l*, pg. 7862
TOYODA GOSEI CO., LTD. - FUKUOKA PLANT—See Toyoda Gosei Co., Ltd.; *Int'l*, pg. 7862
TOYODA GOSEI CO., LTD. - HARUHI PLANT—See Toyoda Gosei Co., Ltd.; *Int'l*, pg. 7862
TOYODA GOSEI CO., LTD. - HEIWACHO PLANT—See Toyoda Gosei Co., Ltd.; *Int'l*, pg. 7862
TOYODA GOSEI CO., LTD. - INAZAWA PLANT—See Toyoda Gosei Co., Ltd.; *Int'l*, pg. 7862
TOYODA GOSEI CO., LTD. - IWATE PLANT—See Toyoda Gosei Co., Ltd.; *Int'l*, pg. 7862

TOYO CORPORATION — CORPORATE AFFILIATIONS

TOYODA GOSEI CO., LTD. - KITAKYUSHU PLANT—See Toyoda Gosei Co., Ltd.; *Int'l*, pg. 7862
TOYODA GOSEI CO., LTD. - MORIMACHI PLANT—See Toyoda Gosei Co., Ltd.; *Int'l*, pg. 7862
TOYODA GOSEI CO., LTD. - NISHIMIZOGUCHI PLANT—See Toyoda Gosei Co., Ltd.; *Int'l*, pg. 7862
TOYODA GOSEI CO., LTD. - SAGA PLANT—See Toyoda Gosei Co., Ltd.; *Int'l*, pg. 7862
TOYODA GOSEI CO., LTD. - SETO PLANT—See Toyoda Gosei Co., Ltd.; *Int'l*, pg. 7862
TOYODA GOSEI CO., LTD.; *Int'l*, pg. 7861
TOYODA GOSEI CZECH, S.R.O.—See Toyoda Gosei Co., Ltd.; *Int'l*, pg. 7862
TOYODA GOSEI EAST JAPAN CO., LTD.—See Toyoda Gosei Co., Ltd.; *Int'l*, pg. 7862
TOYODA GOSEI EUROPE N.V.—See Toyoda Gosei Co., Ltd.; *Int'l*, pg. 7862
TOYODA GOSEI FOSHAN RUBBER PARTS CO., LTD.—See Toyoda Gosei Co., Ltd.; *Int'l*, pg. 7862
TOYODA GOSEI HAIPHONG CO., LTD.—See Toyoda Gosei Co., Ltd.; *Int'l*, pg. 7862
TOYODA GOSEI HINODE CO., LTD.—See Toyoda Gosei Co., Ltd.; *Int'l*, pg. 7862
TOYODA GOSEI INDIA PVT. LTD.—See Toyoda Gosei Co., Ltd.; *Int'l*, pg. 7862
TOYODA GOSEI INTERIOR MANUFACTURING CO., LTD.—See Toyoda Gosei Co., Ltd.; *Int'l*, pg. 7862
TOYODA GOSEI KYUSHU CO., LTD.—See Toyoda Gosei Co., Ltd.; *Int'l*, pg. 7862
TOYODA GOSEI NORTH AMERICA CORPORATION—See Toyoda Gosei Co., Ltd.; *Int'l*, pg. 7862
TOYODA GOSEI OPTO-ELECTRONICS SHANGHAI CO., LTD.—See Toyoda Gosei Co., Ltd.; *Int'l*, pg. 7863
TOYODA GOSEI SHANGHAI CO., LTD.—See Toyoda Gosei Co., Ltd.; *Int'l*, pg. 7863
TOYODA GOSEI SOUTH AFRICA PTY. LTD.—See Toyoda Gosei Co., Ltd.; *Int'l*, pg. 7863
TOYODA GOSEI SOUTH INDIA PVT. LTD.—See Toyoda Gosei Co., Ltd.; *Int'l*, pg. 7862
TOYODA GOSEI TEXAS, LLC—See Toyoda Gosei Co., Ltd.; *Int'l*, pg. 7862
TOYODA GOSEI (THAILAND) CO., LTD.—See Toyoda Gosei Co., Ltd.; *Int'l*, pg. 7862
TOYODA GOSEI TIANJIN PRECISE PLASTIC CO., LTD.—See Toyoda Gosei Co., Ltd.; *Int'l*, pg. 7863
TOYODA GOSEI UK LTD.—See Toyoda Gosei Co., Ltd.; *Int'l*, pg. 7863
TOYODA GOSEI ZHANGJIAGANG CO., LTD.—See Toyoda Gosei Co., Ltd.; *Int'l*, pg. 7863
TOYODA GOSEI ZHANGJIAGANG PLASTIC PARTS CO., LTD.—See Toyoda Gosei Co., Ltd.; *Int'l*, pg. 7863
TOYODA HIGH SYSTEM, INCORPORATED—See Toyota Industries Corporation; *Int'l*, pg. 7866
TOYODA IRON WORKS CO., LTD. - HIROKUTE PLANT—See Toyoda Iron Works Co., Ltd.; *Int'l*, pg. 7863
TOYODA IRON WORKS CO., LTD. - NUKATA PLANT—See Toyoda Iron Works Co., Ltd.; *Int'l*, pg. 7863
TOYODA IRON WORKS CO., LTD. - SASAHARA PLANT—See Toyoda Iron Works Co., Ltd.; *Int'l*, pg. 7863
TOYODA IRON WORKS CO., LTD.; *Int'l*, pg. 7863
TOYODA KOKI DO BRASIL INDUSTRIA E COMERCIO DE MAQUINAS, LTDA.—See JTEKT Corporation; *Int'l*, pg. 4019
TOYODA MACHINERY (DALIAN) CO., LTD—See Toyota Tsusho Corporation; *Int'l*, pg. 7878
TOYODA MACHINERY & ENGINEERING EUROPE SAS—See JTEKT Corporation; *Int'l*, pg. 4019
TOYODA MACHINERY S.E. ASIA CO., LTD—See JTEKT Corporation; *Int'l*, pg. 4019
TOYODA MACHINERY USA CORP.—See JTEKT Corporation; *Int'l*, pg. 4019
TOYODA MICROMATIC MACHINERY INDIA PVT.LTD.—See JTEKT Corporation; *Int'l*, pg. 4019
TOYODA TEXTILE MACHINERY, INC.—See Toyota Industries Corporation; *Int'l*, pg. 7869
TOYODA VAN MOPPES LTD.—See JTEKT Corporation; *Int'l*, pg. 4019
TOYO DENKI (BEIJING) CO., LTD.—See TOYO DENKI SEIZO K.K.; *Int'l*, pg. 7852
TOYO DENKI KOUJI CO., LTD.—See Sumitomo Densetsu Co., Ltd.; *Int'l*, pg. 7277
TOYO DENKI SEIZO K.K.; *Int'l*, pg. 7852
TOYO DENKI USA, INC.—See TOYO DENKI SEIZO K.K.; *Int'l*, pg. 7852
TOYO DO BRASIL - CONSULTORIA E CONSTRUCOES INDUSTRIAIS LTDA.—See Toyo Engineering Corporation; *Int'l*, pg. 7853
TOYO DRILUBE CO., LTD.; *Int'l*, pg. 7852
TOYO ELECTRIC CORPORATION—See Mitsubishi Electric Corporation; *Int'l*, pg. 4946
TOYO ELECTRIC MANUFACTURING CO., LTD.—See MITSUBA Corporation; *Int'l*, pg. 4930
TOYO ELECTRONICS CORP.—See Mitsui E&S Holdings Co., Ltd.; *Int'l*, pg. 4986

TOYO EMC ENGINEERING CO., LTD.—See Toyo Corporation; *Int'l*, pg. 7852
TOYO ENERGY CO., LTD.—See Hanwa Co., Ltd.; *Int'l*, pg. 3263
TOYO ENGINEERING CANADA LTD.—See Toyo Engineering Corporation; *Int'l*, pg. 7853
TOYO ENGINEERING & CONSTRUCTION SDN. BHD.—See Toyo Engineering Corporation; *Int'l*, pg. 7853
TOYO ENGINEERING CORPORATION (CHINA)—See Toyo Engineering Corporation; *Int'l*, pg. 7853
TOYO ENGINEERING CORPORATION; *Int'l*, pg. 7852
TOYO ENGINEERING EUROPE S.A.—See Toyo Engineering Corporation; *Int'l*, pg. 7853
TOYO ENGINEERING EUROPE, S.R.L—See Toyo Engineering Corporation; *Int'l*, pg. 7853
TOYO ENGINEERING INDIA LIMITED—See Toyo Engineering Corporation; *Int'l*, pg. 7853
TOYO ENGINEERING INDIA PRIVATE LIMITED—See Toyo Engineering Corporation; *Int'l*, pg. 7853
TOYO ENGINEERING KOREA LIMITED—See Toyo Engineering Corporation; *Int'l*, pg. 7853
TOYO ENGINEERING WORKS, LTD.; *Int'l*, pg. 7853
TOYO FILLING INTERNATIONAL CO., LTD.—See Toyo Seikan Group Holdings, Ltd.; *Int'l*, pg. 7857
TOYOFLEX CEBU CORPORATION—See Asahi Intecc Co., Ltd.; pg. 594
TOYOFLEX CORPORATION—See Asahi Intecc Co., Ltd.; *Int'l*, pg. 594
TOYO FPP CO., LTD. - 1ST PLANT—See Toyo Ink SC Holdings Co., Ltd.; *Int'l*, pg. 7854
TOYO FPP CO., LTD.—See Toyo Ink SC Holdings Co., Ltd.; *Int'l*, pg. 7854
TOYO GAS ENGINEERING CO., LTD.—See INPEX CORPORATION; *Int'l*, pg. 3717
TOYO GLASS CO., LTD.—See Toyo Seikan Group Holdings, Ltd.; *Int'l*, pg. 7857
TOYO GLASS LOGISTICS CO., LTD.—See Toyo Seikan Group Holdings, Ltd.; *Int'l*, pg. 7857
TOYO GLASS MACHINERY CO., LTD.—See Toyo Seikan Group Holdings, Ltd.; *Int'l*, pg. 7857
TOYO GOSEI CO., LTD.; *Int'l*, pg. 7853
TOYO GRAIN TERMINAL CO., LTD.—See Toyota Tsusho Corporation; *Int'l*, pg. 7878
TOYOHASHI SENKO TRANSPORT CO., LTD.—See Senko Group Holdings, Co., Ltd.; *Int'l*, pg. 6712
TOYOHASHI STATION BUILDING CO., LTD.—See Central Japan Railway Company; *Int'l*, pg. 1408
TOYO HEISEI POLYMER CO., LTD.—See Hagihara Industries Inc.; *Int'l*, pg. 3207
TOYO HUMAN ASSET CO., LTD.—See Toyo Ink SC Holdings Co., Ltd.; *Int'l*, pg. 7854
TOYO HYDRO ELEVATOR CO., LTD.—See Yuken Kogyo Co., Ltd.; *Int'l*, pg. 8612
TOYO INGENIERIA DE VENEZUELA, C.A.—See Toyo Engineering Corporation; *Int'l*, pg. 7853
TOYO INK AMERICA, LLC—See Toyo Ink SC Holdings Co., Ltd.; *Int'l*, pg. 7855
TOYO INK ARETS INDIA PVT. LTD.—See Toyo Ink SC Holdings Co., Ltd.; *Int'l*, pg. 7854
TOYO INK ARETS MIDDLE EAST FZE.—See Toyo Ink SC Holdings Co., Ltd.; *Int'l*, pg. 7854
TOYO INK ASIA LTD.—See Toyo Ink SC Holdings Co., Ltd.; *Int'l*, pg. 7854
TOYO INK AUSTRALIA PTY. LTD.—See Toyo Ink SC Holdings Co., Ltd.; *Int'l*, pg. 7854
TOYO INK BRASIL LTDA—See Toyo Ink SC Holdings Co., Ltd.; *Int'l*, pg. 7854
TOYO INK CHEMICALS TAIWAN CO., LTD.—See Toyo Ink SC Holdings Co., Ltd.; *Int'l*, pg. 7854
TOYO INK CHUSHIKOKU CO., LTD.—See Toyo Ink SC Holdings Co., Ltd.; *Int'l*, pg. 7854
TOYO INK CO., LTD.—See Toyo Ink SC Holdings Co., Ltd.; *Int'l*, pg. 7854
TOYO INK COMPOUNDS CORPORATION—See Toyo Ink SC Holdings Co., Ltd.; *Int'l*, pg. 7854
TOYO INK COMPOUNDS VIETNAM CO., LTD.—See Toyo Ink SC Holdings Co., Ltd.; *Int'l*, pg. 7854
TOYO INK ENGINEERING CO., LTD.—See Toyo Ink SC Holdings Co., Ltd.; *Int'l*, pg. 7854
TOYO INK EUROPE DEUTSCHLAND GMBH—See Toyo Ink SC Holdings Co., Ltd.; *Int'l*, pg. 7854
TOYO INK EUROPE FRANCE S.A.S.—See Toyo Ink SC Holdings Co., Ltd.; *Int'l*, pg. 7854
TOYO INK EUROPE (PARIS) S.A.S.—See Toyo Ink SC Holdings Co., Ltd.; *Int'l*, pg. 7854
TOYO INK EUROPE PLASTIC COLORANT S.A.S.—See Toyo Ink SC Holdings Co., Ltd.; *Int'l*, pg. 7854
TOYO INK EUROPE SA—See Toyo Ink SC Holdings Co., Ltd.; *Int'l*, pg. 7854
TOYO INK EUROPE SPECIALTY CHEMICALS S.A.—See Toyo Ink SC Holdings Co., Ltd.; *Int'l*, pg. 7854
TOYO INK EUROPE UK LTD.—See Toyo Ink SC Holdings Co., Ltd.; *Int'l*, pg. 7854
TOYO INK GRAPHICS CO., LTD.—See Toyo Ink SC Holdings Co., Ltd.; *Int'l*, pg. 7854
TOYO INK GRAPHICS NISHINIHON CO., LTD.—See Toyo Ink SC Holdings Co., Ltd.; *Int'l*, pg. 7854

TOYO INK GROUP BERHAD—See Toyo Ventures Holdings Berhad; *Int'l*, pg. 7860
TOYO INK HOKKAIDO CO., LTD.—See Toyo Ink SC Holdings Co., Ltd.; *Int'l*, pg. 7854
TOYO INK INDIA PVT. LTD.—See Toyo Ink SC Holdings Co., Ltd.; *Int'l*, pg. 7854
TOYO INK INTERNATIONAL CORP.—See Toyo Ink SC Holdings Co., Ltd.; *Int'l*, pg. 7854
TOYO INK KOREA CO., LTD.—See Toyo Ink SC Holdings Co., Ltd.; *Int'l*, pg. 7854
TOYO INK KYUSHU CO., LTD.—See Toyo Ink SC Holdings Co., Ltd.; *Int'l*, pg. 7854
TOYO INK MEXICO, S.A. DE C.V.—See Toyo Ink SC Holdings Co., Ltd.; *Int'l*, pg. 7855
TOYO INK MFG. AMERICA, LLC—See Toyo Ink SC Holdings Co., Ltd.; *Int'l*, pg. 7855
TOYO INK MFG. AMERICA, LLC - TEXAS FACTORY—See Toyo Ink SC Holdings Co., Ltd.; *Int'l*, pg. 7855
TOYO INK MFG. CO., LTD. - SAITAMA FACTORY—See Toyo Ink SC Holdings Co., Ltd.; *Int'l*, pg. 7855
TOYO INK (MIDDLE EAST) FZE—See Toyo Ink SC Holdings Co., Ltd.; *Int'l*, pg. 7854
TOYO INK MYANMAR CO., LTD.—See Toyo Ink SC Holdings Co., Ltd.; *Int'l*, pg. 7855
TOYO INK NEW ZEALAND LTD.—See Toyo Ink SC Holdings Co., Ltd.; *Int'l*, pg. 7854
TOYO INK NORTH AFRICA S.A.R.L.—See Toyo Ink SC Holdings Co., Ltd.; *Int'l*, pg. 7855
TOYO INK PAN PACIFIC PTE. LTD.—See Toyo Ink SC Holdings Co., Ltd.; *Int'l*, pg. 7854
TOYO INK (PHILIPPINES) CO., INC.—See Toyo Ink SC Holdings Co., Ltd.; *Int'l*, pg. 7854
TOYO INK SC HOLDINGS CO., LTD.; *Int'l*, pg. 7853
TOYO INK SDN. BHD.—See Toyo Ventures Holdings Berhad; *Int'l*, pg. 7860
TOYO INK (SHANGHAI) RHQ CO., LTD.—See Toyo Ink SC Holdings Co., Ltd.; *Int'l*, pg. 7854
TOYO INK TAIWAN CO., LTD.—See Toyo Ink SC Holdings Co., Ltd.; *Int'l*, pg. 7855
TOYO INK (THAILAND) CO., LTD. - PLASTIC COLORANT FACTORY—See Toyo Ink SC Holdings Co., Ltd.; *Int'l*, pg. 7854
TOYO INK (THAILAND) CO., LTD.—See Toyo Ink SC Holdings Co., Ltd.; *Int'l*, pg. 7854
TOYO INK TOHOKU CO., LTD.—See Toyo Ink SC Holdings Co., Ltd.; *Int'l*, pg. 7854
TOYO INK VIETNAM CO., LTD.—See Toyo Ink SC Holdings Co., Ltd.; *Int'l*, pg. 7854
TOYO INSURANCE AGENCY CO., LTD—See T&D Holdings, Inc.; *Int'l*, pg. 7395
TOYO JIDOKI AMERICA CORPORATION - CA BRANCH—See Nabtesco Corporation; *Int'l*, pg. 5121
TOYO JIDOKI CO., LTD. - IWAKUNI PLANT—See Nabtesco Corporation; *Int'l*, pg. 5121
TOYO JIDOKI CO., LTD.—See Nabtesco Corporation; *Int'l*, pg. 5121
TOYO JIDOKI EUROPE GMBH—See Nabtesco Corporation; *Int'l*, pg. 5121
TOYO JITSUGYO CO., LTD.—See Toray Industries, Inc.; *Int'l*, pg. 7827
TOYO KAGAKU CO., LTD—See Mitsubishi Gas Chemical Company, Inc.; *Int'l*, pg. 4950
TOYO KANETSU K.K. - CHIBA PLANT—See TOYO KANETSU K.K.; *Int'l*, pg. 7855
TOYO KANETSU K.K.; *Int'l*, pg. 7855
TOYO KANETSU SINGAPORE PTE. LTD.—See TOYO KANETSU K.K.; *Int'l*, pg. 7855
TOYO KANETSU SOLUTIONS K.K.—See TOYO KANETSU K.K.; *Int'l*, pg. 7855
TOYO KANKOU CO., LTD.—See Keikyu Corporation; *Int'l*, pg. 4117
TOYO KINZOKU CORPORATION—See JFE Holdings, Inc.; *Int'l*, pg. 3937
TOYO KNIFE COMPANY, LTD—See Ferrotec Holdings Corporation; *Int'l*, pg. 2643
TOYO KNIFE (SHANGHAI) CO., LTD.; *Int'l*, pg. 7856
TOYO KNIT CO., LTD.—See Toyobo Co., Ltd.; *Int'l*, pg. 7861
TOYO KNITEX (CEPZ) LIMITED; *Int'l*, pg. 7856
TOYO KOHAN CO., LTD.—See Toyo Seikan Group Holdings, Ltd.; *Int'l*, pg. 7857
TOYO KOHAN SHANGHAI CO., LTD.—See Toyo Seikan Group Holdings, Ltd.; *Int'l*, pg. 7857
TOYO KOKEN K.K.—See TOYO KANETSU K.K.; *Int'l*, pg. 7856
TOYO KOKU DENSHI CO., LTD.—See Imasen Electric Industrial Co., Ltd.; *Int'l*, pg. 3620
TOYOKOUKI CO., LTD.—See TOYO DENKI SEIZO K.K.; *Int'l*, pg. 7852
TOYOKUMO, INC.; *Int'l*, pg. 7863
TOYO KUNI ELECTRONICS CO. LTD.—See Audix Corporation; *Int'l*, pg. 702
TOYO LOGISTICS AMERICA, INC.—See Toyo Logistics Co., Ltd.; *Int'l*, pg. 7856
TOYO LOGISTICS CO., LTD.; *Int'l*, pg. 7856
TOYO LOGISTICS CO., LTD.—See Toyo Logistics Co., Ltd.; *Int'l*, pg. 7856

COMPANY NAME INDEX

TOYO LOGISTICS (S) PTE LTD—See Toyo Logistics Co., Ltd.; *Int'l*, pg. 7856
TOYO MACHINERY (CHANGSHU) CO., LTD.—See Toyo Machinery & Metal Co., Ltd.; *Int'l*, pg. 7856
TOYO MACHINERY & METAL CO., LTD.; *Int'l*, pg. 7856
TOYO MACHINERY & METAL (GUANGZHOU) CO., LTD.—See Toyo Machinery & Metal Co., Ltd.; *Int'l*, pg. 7856
TOYO MACHINERY & METAL (SHANGHAI) CO., LTD.—See Toyo Machinery & Metal Co., Ltd.; *Int'l*, pg. 7856
TOYO MACHINERY & METAL (TAIWAN) CO., LTD.—See Toyo Machinery & Metal Co., Ltd.; *Int'l*, pg. 7856
TOYO MACHINERY (M) SDN. BHD.—See Toyo Machinery & Metal Co., Ltd.; *Int'l*, pg. 7856
TOYO MACHINERY VIETNAM CO., LTD.—See Toyo Machinery & Metal Co., Ltd.; *Int'l*, pg. 7856
TOYO MANAGEMENT SERVICE CO., LTD.—See Toyo Ink SC Holdings Co., Ltd.; *Int'l*, pg. 7855
TOYO MATBAA MUREKKEPLERI SANAYI VE TICARET A.S.—See Toyo Ink SC Holdings Co., Ltd.; *Int'l*, pg. 7855
TOYO MEBIUS CO., LTD.—See Toyo Seikan Group Holdings, Ltd.; *Int'l*, pg. 7857
TOYO MEBIUS LOGISTICS (THAILAND) CO., LTD.—See Toyo Seikan Group Holdings, Ltd.; *Int'l*, pg. 7857
TOYO-MEMORY TECHNOLOGY SDN. BHD.—See Toyo Seikan Group Holdings, Ltd.; *Int'l*, pg. 7858
TOYOMI CO., LTD.—See Tokuyama Corporation; *Int'l*, pg. 7788
TOYOMI ENGINEERING SDN. BHD.—See MSM International Limited; *Int'l*, pg. 5069
TOYOMI TOHTO SUISAN REIZO K.K.—See TOHTO SUISAN Co., Ltd.; *Int'l*, pg. 7778
TOYOMI TOICHI REIZO CO., LTD.—See Tsukiji Uoichiba Co., Ltd.; *Int'l*, pg. 7956
TOYO-MORTON, LTD. - SAITAMA PLANT—See K+S Aktiengesellschaft; *Int'l*, pg. 4041
TOYO-MORTON, LTD. - SAITAMA PLANT—See Toyo Ink SC Holdings Co., Ltd.; *Int'l*, pg. 7855
TOYO-MORTON, LTD.—See K+S Aktiengesellschaft; *Int'l*, pg. 4041
TOYO-MORTON, LTD.—See Toyo Ink SC Holdings Co., Ltd.; *Int'l*, pg. 7855
TOYONAKA & ITAMI RECYCLE FOREST CO., LTD.—See Hitachi Zosen Corporation; *Int'l*, pg. 3412
TOYO NETWORKS & SYSTEM INTEGRATION CO., LTD.—See NEC Corporation; *Int'l*, pg. 5185
TOYOOKA ENERGY CO., LTD.—See Osaka Gas Co., Ltd.; *Int'l*, pg. 5646
TOYOOKI KOGYO CO., LTD.—See JTEKT Corporation; *Int'l*, pg. 4019
TOYO PACK (CHANGSHU) CO., LTD.—See Toyo Seikan Group Holdings, Ltd.; *Int'l*, pg. 7857
TOYO PACKS CO., LTD.—See Toyo Seikan Group Holdings, Ltd.; *Int'l*, pg. 7857
TOYO PARTNER CO., LTD.—See Toyo Seikan Group Holdings, Ltd.; *Int'l*, pg. 7857
TOYO PHOSPHORIC ACID, INC.—See Mitsui Chemicals, Inc.; *Int'l*, pg. 4984
TOYO PLASTICS INDUSTRIES CORP.—See Sekisui Chemical Co., Ltd.; *Int'l*, pg. 6696
TOYO POLYMER CO., LTD.—See Tosoh Corporation; *Int'l*, pg. 7834
TOYO PRECISION APPLIANCE (KUNSHAN) CO., LTD.—See Nippon Light Metal Holdings Company, Ltd.; *Int'l*, pg. 5324
TOY OPTIONS (FAR EAST) LIMITED—See The Character Group plc; *Int'l*, pg. 7631
TOYO QUALITY ONE (GUANGZHOU) CO., LTD.—See Nagase & Co., Ltd.; *Int'l*, pg. 5128
TOYO QUALITY ONE NINGBO CO., LTD.—See Nagase & Co., Ltd.; *Int'l*, pg. 5128
TOYO REIFEN GMBH—See Toyo Tire Corporation; *Int'l*, pg. 7859
TOYO REITO KAISHA, LTD.—See Toyo Suisan Kaisha, Ltd.; *Int'l*, pg. 7858
TOYO REIZO CO., LTD.—See Mitsubishi Corporation; *Int'l*, pg. 4943
TOYO RIKAGAKU KENKYUSHO CO., LTD.—See Nippon Light Metal Holdings Company, Ltd.; *Int'l*, pg. 5324
TOYO RIKUUN CO., LTD.—See Sumitomo Forestry Co., Ltd.; *Int'l*, pg. 7286
TOYO RUBBER CHEMICAL & INDUSTRIAL PRODUCTS (HK) LTD—See Toyo Tire Corporation; *Int'l*, pg. 7859
TOYO RUBBER CHEMICAL PRODUCTS (THAILAND) LIMITED—See Toyo Tire Corporation; *Int'l*, pg. 7859
TOYO RUBBER CHIP CO., LTD.—See Envipro Holdings Inc.; *Int'l*, pg. 2454
TOYO SANGYO CO., LTD.—See Daido Steel Co., Ltd.; *Int'l*, pg. 1923
TOYOSANGYO K.K.—See TOYO DENKI SEIZO K.K.; *Int'l*, pg. 7852
TOYO - SASAKI GLASS CO., LTD.—See Toyo Seikan Group Holdings, Ltd.; *Int'l*, pg. 7857
TOYOS CLINIC; *U.S. Private*, pg. 4198
TOYO SC TRADING CO., LTD.—See Toyo Ink SC Holdings Co., Ltd.; *Int'l*, pg. 7855

TOYO SECURITIES ASIA LTD.—See Toyo Securities Co., Ltd.; *Int'l*, pg. 7856
TOYO SECURITIES CO., LTD.; *Int'l*, pg. 7856
TOYO SEIHAN CO., LTD.—See Toyo Seikan Group Holdings, Ltd.; *Int'l*, pg. 7858
TOYO SEIKAN CO., LTD.—See Toyo Seikan Group Holdings, Ltd.; *Int'l*, pg. 7858
TOYO SEIKAN GROUP ENGINEERING CO., LTD.—See Toyo Seikan Group Holdings, Ltd.; *Int'l*, pg. 7858
TOYO SEIKAN GROUP HOLDINGS, LTD.; *Int'l*, pg. 7856
TOYO SEIKAN (THAILAND) CO., LTD.—See Toyo Seikan Group Holdings, Ltd.; *Int'l*, pg. 7858
TOYO SEIKI CO.,LTD—See Toyo Tire Corporation; *Int'l*, pg. 7859
TOYO SERVICE CO., LTD.—See Nishio Holdings Co., Ltd.; *Int'l*, pg. 5366
TOYO SERVICE SYSTEM K.K.—See TOYO KANETSU K.K.; *Int'l*, pg. 7856
TOYO SETAL EMPREENDIMENTOS LTDA.—See Toyo Engineering Corporation; *Int'l*, pg. 7853
TOYOSHIMA (ASIA) CO., LTD.—See Toyoshima & Co., Ltd.; *Int'l*, pg. 7863
TOYOSHIMA & CO., LTD.; *Int'l*, pg. 7863
TOYOSHIMA DO BRASIL COMERCIAL IMPORTADORA E EXPORTADORA LTDA.—See Toyoshima & Co., Ltd.; *Int'l*, pg. 7863
TOYOSHIMA INTERNATIONAL AMERICA, INC.—See Toyoshima & Co., Ltd.; *Int'l*, pg. 7863
TOYOSHIMA INTERNATIONAL (SHANGHAI) CO., LTD.—See Toyoshima & Co., Ltd.; *Int'l*, pg. 7863
TOYOSHIMA LONG AN GARMENT CO., LTD.—See Toyoshima & Co., Ltd.; *Int'l*, pg. 7863
TOYOSHIMA (U.S.A.), INC.—See Toyoshima & Co., Ltd.; *Int'l*, pg. 7863
TOYOSHIMA VIETNAM CO., LTD.—See Toyoshima & Co., Ltd.; *Int'l*, pg. 7863
TOYOSHINA FILM CO., LTD.—See Daicel Corporation; *Int'l*, pg. 1920
TOYO SHINKO CO., LTD - NAGAOKA FACTORY—See Toray Industries, Inc.; *Int'l*, pg. 7824
TOYO SHINKO CO., LTD—See Toray Industries, Inc.; *Int'l*, pg. 7824
TOYO SHOJI K.K.—See TOYO DENKI SEIZO K.K.; *Int'l*, pg. 7852
TOYO SHOKUSAN INC.—See Toray Industries, Inc.; *Int'l*, pg. 7827
TOYO SHUTTER CO., LTD.; *Int'l*, pg. 7858
TOYO SOFLAN CO.,LTD—See Osaka Gas Co., Ltd.; *Int'l*, pg. 5646
TOYO SOFLAN TEC CO., LTD—See Toyo Tire Corporation; *Int'l*, pg. 7859
TOYO SPRING INDUSTRIAL CO., LTD.—See Carlit Co., Ltd.; *Int'l*, pg. 1338
TOYO STYRENE CO., LTD.—See Daicel Corporation; *Int'l*, pg. 1920
TOYOSU CO., LTD.—See Kameda Seika Co., Ltd.; *Int'l*, pg. 4061
TOYO SUGAR REFINING CO., LTD.—See Marubeni Corporation; *Int'l*, pg. 4710
TOYO SUISAN KAISHA, LTD.; *Int'l*, pg. 7858
TOYOTA ADRIA, PODJETJE ZA IZVOZ IN PROMET Z VOZILI, D.O.O.—See Toyota Tsusho Corporation; *Int'l*, pg. 7878
TOYOTA ADVANCE LOGISTICS NORTH AMERICA—See Toyota Industries Corporation; *Int'l*, pg. 7866
TOYOTA ALGERIE SPA—See Toyota Motor Corporation; *Int'l*, pg. 7872
TOYOTA ANYAGMOZGATAS MAGYARORSZAG KFT.—See Toyota Industries Corporation; *Int'l*, pg. 7867
TOYOTA ARGENTINA S.A.—See Toyota Motor Corporation; *Int'l*, pg. 7872
TOYOTA AUTO BODY CO., LTD. - INABE PLANT—See Toyota Motor Corporation; *Int'l*, pg. 7872
TOYOTA AUTO BODY CO., LTD. - KARIYA PLANT—See Toyota Motor Corporation; *Int'l*, pg. 7872
TOYOTA AUTO BODY CO., LTD.—See Toyota Motor Corporation; *Int'l*, pg. 7872
TOYOTA AUTO BODY CO., LTD. - YOSHIWARA PLANT—See Toyota Motor Corporation; *Int'l*, pg. 7872
TOYOTA AUTO BODY THAILAND CO., LTD.—See Toyota Motor Corporation; *Int'l*, pg. 7875
TOYOTA BALKANS EOOD—See Inchcape plc; *Int'l*, pg. 3647
TOYOTA BELGIUM NV/SA—See Inchcape plc; *Int'l*, pg. 3647
TOYOTA BILIA AS—See Bilia AB; *Int'l*, pg. 1029
TOYOTA BOSHOKU AMERICA, INC.—See Toyota Boshoku Corporation; *Int'l*, pg. 7864
TOYOTA BOSHOKU ARGENTINA S.R.L.—See Toyota Boshoku Corporation; *Int'l*, pg. 7864
TOYOTA BOSHOKU ASIA CO., LTD.—See Toyota Boshoku Corporation; *Int'l*, pg. 7864
TOYOTA BOSHOKU AUSTRALIA PTY. LTD.—See Toyota Boshoku Corporation; *Int'l*, pg. 7864
TOYOTA BOSHOKU AUTOMOTIVE INDIA PRIVATE LIMITED—See Toyota Boshoku Corporation; *Int'l*, pg. 7864

TOYOTA BOSHOKU CANADA, INC.—See Toyota Boshoku Corporation; *Int'l*, pg. 7864
TOYOTA BOSHOKU (CHINA) CO. LTD.—See Toyota Boshoku Corporation; *Int'l*, pg. 7864
TOYOTA BOSHOKU CORPORATION - FUJIOKA PLANT—See Toyota Boshoku Corporation; *Int'l*, pg. 7864
TOYOTA BOSHOKU CORPORATION - FUJISUSONO PLANT—See Toyota Boshoku Corporation; *Int'l*, pg. 7864
TOYOTA BOSHOKU CORPORATION - GIFU PLANT—See Toyota Boshoku Corporation; *Int'l*, pg. 7864
TOYOTA BOSHOKU CORPORATION - INABE PLANT—See Toyota Boshoku Corporation; *Int'l*, pg. 7865
TOYOTA BOSHOKU CORPORATION - KARIYA PLANT—See Toyota Boshoku Corporation; *Int'l*, pg. 7865
TOYOTA BOSHOKU CORPORATION - KISOGAWA PLANT—See Toyota Boshoku Corporation; *Int'l*, pg. 7865
TOYOTA BOSHOKU CORPORATION - OGUCHI PLANT—See Toyota Boshoku Corporation; *Int'l*, pg. 7865
TOYOTA BOSHOKU CORPORATION - SANAGE PLANT—See Toyota Boshoku Corporation; *Int'l*, pg. 7865
TOYOTA BOSHOKU CORPORATION; *Int'l*, pg. 7863
TOYOTA BOSHOKU CORPORATION - TAHARA PLANT—See Toyota Boshoku Corporation; *Int'l*, pg. 7865
TOYOTA BOSHOKU CORPORATION - TAKAOKA PLANT—See Toyota Boshoku Corporation; *Int'l*, pg. 7865
TOYOTA BOSHOKU CORPORATION - TOKYO PLANT—See Toyota Boshoku Corporation; *Int'l*, pg. 7865
TOYOTA BOSHOKU CORPORATION - TOYOHASHI-HIGASHI PLANT—See Toyota Boshoku Corporation; *Int'l*, pg. 7865
TOYOTA BOSHOKU CORPORATION - TOYOHASHI-KITA PLANT—See Toyota Boshoku Corporation; *Int'l*, pg. 7865
TOYOTA BOSHOKU CORPORATION - TOYOHASHI-MINAMI PLANT—See Toyota Boshoku Corporation; *Int'l*, pg. 7865
TOYOTA BOSHOKU CORPORATION - TSUCHIHASHI PLANT—See Toyota Boshoku Corporation; *Int'l*, pg. 7865
TOYOTA BOSHOKU CORPORATION - TSUTSUMI PLANT—See Toyota Boshoku Corporation; *Int'l*, pg. 7865
TOYOTA BOSHOKU DO BRASIL LTDA.—See Toyota Boshoku Corporation; *Int'l*, pg. 7865
TOYOTA BOSHOKU EUROPE N.V.—See Toyota Boshoku Corporation; *Int'l*, pg. 7864
TOYOTA BOSHOKU FILTRATION SYSTEM (THAILAND) CO., LTD.—See Denso Corporation; *Int'l*, pg. 2033
TOYOTA BOSHOKU FOSHAN CO., LTD.—See Toyota Boshoku Corporation; *Int'l*, pg. 7864
TOYOTA BOSHOKU FRANCE S.A.S.—See Toyota Boshoku Corporation; *Int'l*, pg. 7865
TOYOTA BOSHOKU GATEWAY (THAILAND) CO., LTD.—See Tamura Corporation; *Int'l*, pg. 7452
TOYOTA BOSHOKU (GUANGZHOU) AUTOMOTIVE PARTS CO., LTD.—See Toyota Boshoku Corporation; *Int'l*, pg. 7864
TOYOTA BOSHOKU HAIPHONG CO., LTD.—See Toyota Boshoku Corporation; *Int'l*, pg. 7865
TOYOTA BOSHOKU HANOI CO., LTD.—See Toyota Boshoku Corporation; *Int'l*, pg. 7865
TOYOTA BOSHOKU HIROSE CORPORATION—See Toyota Boshoku Corporation; *Int'l*, pg. 7865
TOYOTA BOSHOKU ILLINOIS, LLC—See Toyota Boshoku Corporation; *Int'l*, pg. 7865
TOYOTA BOSHOKU INDIANA, LLC—See Toyota Boshoku Corporation; *Int'l*, pg. 7864
TOYOTA BOSHOKU KENTUCKY, LLC—See Toyota Boshoku Corporation; *Int'l*, pg. 7865
TOYOTA BOSHOKU KYUSHU CORPORATION—See Toyota Boshoku Corporation; *Int'l*, pg. 7865
TOYOTA BOSHOKU LEGNICA SP. Z O.O.—See Toyota Boshoku Corporation; *Int'l*, pg. 7865
TOYOTA BOSHOKU MANUFACTURING KENTUCKY LLC—See Toyota Boshoku Corporation; *Int'l*, pg. 7865
TOYOTA BOSHOKU MISSISSIPPI LLC—See Toyota Boshoku Corporation; *Int'l*, pg. 7865
TOYOTA BOSHOKU PHILIPPINES CORPORATION—See Toyota Boshoku Corporation; *Int'l*, pg. 7865
TOYOTA BOSHOKU POLAND SP. Z O.O.—See Toyota Boshoku Corporation; *Int'l*, pg. 7865
TOYOTA BOSHOKU SEIKO CORPORATION—See Toyota Boshoku Corporation; *Int'l*, pg. 7865
TOYOTA BOSHOKU SHIGA CORPORATION—See Toyota Boshoku Corporation; *Int'l*, pg. 7865
TOYOTA BOSHOKU SIAM METAL COM., LTD.—See Toyota Boshoku Corporation; *Int'l*, pg. 7865

TOYOTA BOSHOKU CORPORATION

CORPORATE AFFILIATIONS

TOYOTA BOSHOKU SOMAIN S.A.S.—See Toyota Boshoku Corporation; *Int'l*, pg. 7865
TOYOTA BOSHOKU SOUTH AFRICA (PTY) LTD.—See Toyota Boshoku Corporation; *Int'l*, pg. 7865
TOYOTA BOSHOKU TENNESSEE, LLC—See Toyota Boshoku Corporation; *Int'l*, pg. 7865
TOYOTA BOSHOKU (TIANJIN) AUTOMOTIVE PARTS CO., LTD.—See Toyota Boshoku Corporation; *Int'l*, pg. 7864
TOYOTA BOSHOKU TOHOKU CORPORATION—See Toyota Boshoku Corporation; *Int'l*, pg. 7865
TOYOTA BOSHOKU TURKIYE OTOMOTIV SANAYI VE TICARET A.S.—See Toyota Boshoku Corporation; *Int'l*, pg. 7865
TOYOTA CAETANO PORTUGAL S.A.; *Int'l*, pg. 7865
TOYOTA (CAMBODIA) CO., LTD.—See Toyota Tsusho Corporation; *Int'l*, pg. 7878
TOYOTA CANADA, INC.—See Mitsui & Co., Ltd.; *Int'l*, pg. 4980
TOYOTA CANADA, INC.—See Toyota Motor Corporation; *Int'l*, pg. 7872
TOYOTA CANARIAS, S.A.—See Sumitomo Corporation; *Int'l*, pg. 7276
TOYOTA CARRELLI ELEVATORI ITALIA S.R.L.—See Toyota Industries Corporation; *Int'l*, pg. 7867
TOYOTA CENTER; *U.S. Private*, pg. 4198
TOYOTA CENTRAL ASIA FZE—See Sumitomo Corporation; *Int'l*, pg. 7276
TOYOTA CENTRAL R&D LABS., INC.—See Toyota Motor Corporation; *Int'l*, pg. 7872
TOYOTA CHEMICAL ENGINEERING CO., LTD.—See Toyota Tsusho Corporation; *Int'l*, pg. 7878
TOYOTA CHILE S.A.—See Toyota Motor Corporation; *Int'l*, pg. 7872
TOYOTA COROLLA GIFU CO., LTD.—See Seino Holdings Co., Ltd.; *Int'l*, pg. 6691
TOYOTA CREDIT CANADA, INC.—See Toyota Motor Corporation; *Int'l*, pg. 7872
TOYOTA DEL PERU S.A.—See Toyota Motor Corporation; *Int'l*, pg. 7875
TOYOTA DE PUERTO RICO CORP.—See Toyota Motor Corporation; *Int'l*, pg. 7875
TOYOTA DEUTSCHLAND GMBH—See Toyota Motor Corporation; *Int'l*, pg. 7872
TOYOTA DE VENEZUELA C.A.—See Toyota Motor Corporation; *Int'l*, pg. 7875
TOYOTA DIGITAL CRUISE, INC.—See Toyota Tsusho Corporation; *Int'l*, pg. 7878
TOYOTA DO BRASIL LTDA.—See Toyota Motor Corporation; *Int'l*, pg. 7875
TOYOTA EUROPE ENGINEERING & MAINTENANCE, NV/SA—See Toyota Tsusho Corporation; *Int'l*, pg. 7878
TOYOTA FINANCE FINLAND OY—See Toyota Motor Corporation; *Int'l*, pg. 7872
TOYOTA FINANCIAL SERVICES CORPORATION—See Toyota Motor Corporation; *Int'l*, pg. 7873
TOYOTA FINANCIAL SERVICES—See Toyota Motor Corporation; *Int'l*, pg. 7872
TOYOTA FINANCIAL SERVICES (UK) PLC—See Toyota Motor Corporation; *Int'l*, pg. 7872
TOYOTA FRANCE S.A.—See Toyota Motor Corporation; *Int'l*, pg. 7873
TOYOTA FUDOSAN CO., LTD.—See Toyota Motor Corporation; *Int'l*, pg. 7873
TOYOTA GABON S.A.—See Toyota Motor Corporation; *Int'l*, pg. 7870
TOYOTA (GB) PLC—See Toyota Motor Corporation; *Int'l*, pg. 7872
TOYOTA GHANA COMPANY LTD.—See Marubeni Corporation; *Int'l*, pg. 4710
TOYOTA HELLAS SA—See Inchcape plc; *Int'l*, pg. 3647
TOYOTA HOME GIFU CO., LTD.—See Seino Holdings Co., Ltd.; *Int'l*, pg. 6691
TOYOTA HOUSING CORPORATION—See Toyota Motor Corporation; *Int'l*, pg. 7873
TOYOTA INDUSTRIAL EQUIPMENT EUROPE, S.A.R.L.—See Toyota Industries Corporation; *Int'l*, pg. 7867
TOYOTA INDUSTRIAL EQUIPMENT MFG., INC.—See Toyota Industries Corporation; *Int'l*, pg. 7869
TOYOTA INDUSTRIAL EQUIPMENT, S.A.—See Toyota Industries Corporation; *Int'l*, pg. 7867
TOYOTA INDUSTRIAL EQUIPMENT VIETNAM CO., LTD.—See Toyota Industries Corporation; *Int'l*, pg. 7866
TOYOTA INDUSTRIES CORPORATION - ANJO PLANT—See Toyota Industries Corporation; *Int'l*, pg. 7866
TOYOTA INDUSTRIES CORPORATION - HEKINAN PLANT—See Toyota Industries Corporation; *Int'l*, pg. 7866
TOYOTA INDUSTRIES CORPORATION - HIGASHICHITA PLANT—See Toyota Industries Corporation; *Int'l*, pg. 7867
TOYOTA INDUSTRIES CORPORATION - HIGASHIURA PLANT—See Toyota Industries Corporation; *Int'l*, pg. 7867

TOYOTA INDUSTRIES CORPORATION - KYOWA PLANT—See Toyota Industries Corporation; *Int'l*, pg. 7867
TOYOTA INDUSTRIES CORPORATION - MORIOKA WORKS—See Toyota Industries Corporation; *Int'l*, pg. 7867
TOYOTA INDUSTRIES CORPORATION - NAGAKUSA PLANT—See Toyota Industries Corporation; *Int'l*, pg. 7867
TOYOTA INDUSTRIES CORPORATION - OBU PLANT—See Toyota Industries Corporation; *Int'l*, pg. 7867
TOYOTA INDUSTRIES CORPORATION; *Int'l*, pg. 7865
TOYOTA INDUSTRIES CORPORATION - TAKAHAMA PLANT—See Toyota Industries Corporation; *Int'l*, pg. 7867
TOYOTA INDUSTRIES ENGINE INDIA PVT LTD.—See Toyota Industries Corporation; *Int'l*, pg. 7867
TOYOTA INDUSTRIES EUROPE AB—See Toyota Industries Corporation; *Int'l*, pg. 7867
TOYOTA INDUSTRIES FINANCE INTERNATIONAL AB—See Toyota Industries Corporation; *Int'l*, pg. 7867
TOYOTA INDUSTRIES IT SOLUTIONS INC.—See Toyota Industries Corporation; *Int'l*, pg. 7868
TOYOTA INDUSTRIES NORTH AMERICA, INC.—See Toyota Industries Corporation; *Int'l*, pg. 7868
TOYOTA INDUSTRIES PERSONNEL SERVICE OF AMERICA, INC.—See Toyota Industries Corporation; *Int'l*, pg. 7869
TOYOTA INDUSTRIES SWEDEN AB—See Toyota Industries Corporation; *Int'l*, pg. 7867
TOYOTA INDUSTRIES WELL SUPPORT CORPORATION—See Toyota Industries Corporation; *Int'l*, pg. 7869
TOYOTA INDUSTRY AUTOMOBILE (KUNSHAN) PARTS CO.,LTD.—See Universal Cement Corporation; *Int'l*, pg. 8078
TOYOTA INDUSTRY (KUNSHAN) CO.,LTD.—See Universal Cement Corporation; *Int'l*, pg. 8078
TOYOTA IRELAND—See Toyota Motor Corporation; *Int'l*, pg. 7873
TOYOTA ISTIF MAKINELERI A.S.—See Toyota Tsusho Corporation; *Int'l*, pg. 7878
TOYOTA JAMAICA LTD.—See Toyota Tsusho Corporation; *Int'l*, pg. 7878
TOYOTA KENYA LTD.—See Toyota Tsusho Corporation; *Int'l*, pg. 7878
TOYOTA KIRLOSKAR MOTOR PRIVATE LTD.—See Toyota Motor Corporation; *Int'l*, pg. 7873
TOYOTA KREDITBANK GMBH—See Toyota Motor Corporation; *Int'l*, pg. 7872
TOYOTA LAKOZY AUTO PRIVATE LTD.—See Toyota Tsusho Corporation; *Int'l*, pg. 7878
TOYOTA LANKA (PRIVATE) LIMITED—See Toyota Tsusho Corporation; *Int'l*, pg. 7878
TOYOTA LEASING GMBH—See Toyota Motor Corporation; *Int'l*, pg. 7872
TOYOTA LEASING (THAILAND) CO., LTD.—See Toyota Motor Corporation; *Int'l*, pg. 7873
TOYOTA L&F AKITA CO., LTD.—See Toyota Industries Corporation; *Int'l*, pg. 7866
TOYOTA L&F FUKUI CO., LTD.—See Toyota Industries Corporation; *Int'l*, pg. 7869
TOYOTA L&F HYOGO CO., LTD.—See Toyota Industries Corporation; *Int'l*, pg. 7866
TOYOTA L&F KINKI CO., LTD.—See Toyota Industries Corporation; *Int'l*, pg. 7869
TOYOTA L&F SHIZUOKA CO., LTD.—See Toyota Industries Corporation; *Int'l*, pg. 7866
TOYOTA L&F TOKYO CO., LTD.—See Toyota Industries Corporation; *Int'l*, pg. 7866
TOYOTA LIFT OF SOUTH TEXAS—See Doggett Equipment Services, Ltd.; *U.S. Private*, pg. 1253
TOYOTA LY THUONG KIET—See Sumitomo Corporation; *Int'l*, pg. 7276
TOYOTA MAKATI, INC.—See GT Capital Holdings, Inc.; *Int'l*, pg. 3151
TOYOTA MALAWI LTD.—See Toyota Tsusho Corporation; *Int'l*, pg. 7878
TOYOTA MAQUINAS TEXTEIS BRASIL LTDA—See Toyota Industries Corporation; *Int'l*, pg. 7869
TOYOTA MATERIAL HANDLING AUSTRALIA PTY LIMITED—See Toyota Industries Corporation; *Int'l*, pg. 7869
TOYOTA MATERIAL HANDLING AUSTRIA GMBH—See Toyota Industries Corporation; *Int'l*, pg. 7867
TOYOTA MATERIAL HANDLING BELGIUM NV/SA—See Toyota Industries Corporation; *Int'l*, pg. 7867
TOYOTA MATERIAL HANDLING CZ S.R.O.—See Toyota Industries Corporation; *Int'l*, pg. 7867
TOYOTA MATERIAL HANDLING DANMARK A/S—See Toyota Industries Corporation; *Int'l*, pg. 7867
TOYOTA MATERIAL HANDLING DEUTSCHLAND GMBH—See Toyota Industries Corporation; *Int'l*, pg. 7867
TOYOTA MATERIAL HANDLING EESTI AS—See Toyota Industries Corporation; *Int'l*, pg. 7867
TOYOTA MATERIAL HANDLING ESPANA, S.A.—See Toyota Industries Corporation; *Int'l*, pg. 7867

TOYOTA MATERIAL HANDLING EUROPE AB—See Toyota Industries Corporation; *Int'l*, pg. 7867
TOYOTA MATERIAL HANDLING EUROPE BRUSSELS NV/SA—See Toyota Industries Corporation; *Int'l*, pg. 7867
TOYOTA MATERIAL HANDLING EUROPE, NV/SA—See Toyota Industries Corporation; *Int'l*, pg. 7867
TOYOTA MATERIAL HANDLING FINLAND OY—See Toyota Industries Corporation; *Int'l*, pg. 7867
TOYOTA MATERIAL HANDLING GREECE SA—See Toyota Industries Corporation; *Int'l*, pg. 7867
TOYOTA MATERIAL HANDLING, INC.—See Toyota Industries Corporation; *Int'l*, pg. 7869
TOYOTA MATERIAL HANDLING INDIA PVT. LTD.—See Toyota Industries Corporation; *Int'l*, pg. 7869
TOYOTA MATERIAL HANDLING IRELAND—See Toyota Industries Corporation; *Int'l*, pg. 7867
TOYOTA MATERIAL HANDLING ITALIA S.R.L.—See Toyota Industries Corporation; *Int'l*, pg. 7867
TOYOTA MATERIAL HANDLING LATVIJA LTD.—See Toyota Industries Corporation; *Int'l*, pg. 7867
TOYOTA MATERIAL HANDLING LIETUVA UAB—See Toyota Industries Corporation; *Int'l*, pg. 7867
TOYOTA MATERIAL HANDLING MERCOSUR COMERCIO DE EQUIPAMENTOS LTDA—See Toyota Industries Corporation; *Int'l*, pg. 7869
TOYOTA MATERIAL HANDLING NEDERLAND B.V.—See Toyota Industries Corporation; *Int'l*, pg. 7867
TOYOTA MATERIAL HANDLING NORWAY AS—See Toyota Industries Corporation; *Int'l*, pg. 7868
TOYOTA MATERIAL HANDLING POLSKA SP. Z O.O.—See Toyota Industries Corporation; *Int'l*, pg. 7868
TOYOTA MATERIAL HANDLING ROMANIA S.R.L.—See Toyota Industries Corporation; *Int'l*, pg. 7868
TOYOTA MATERIAL HANDLING SCHWEIZ AG—See Toyota Industries Corporation; *Int'l*, pg. 7868
TOYOTA MATERIAL HANDLING (SHANGHAI) CO., LTD.—See Toyota Industries Corporation; *Int'l*, pg. 7869
TOYOTA MATERIAL HANDLING SLOVENSKO S.R.O.—See Toyota Industries Corporation; *Int'l*, pg. 7868
TOYOTA MATERIAL HANDLING SWEDEN AB—See Toyota Industries Corporation; *Int'l*, pg. 7868
TOYOTA MATERIAL HANDLING TAIWAN LTD.—See Toyota Industries Corporation; *Int'l*, pg. 7866
TOYOTA MATERIAL HANDLING UK LIMITED—See Toyota Industries Corporation; *Int'l*, pg. 7868
TOYOTA MATERIAL HANDLING, U.S.A., INC.—See Toyota Industries Corporation; *Int'l*, pg. 7869
TOYOTA MAURITANIE S.A.—See Toyota Motor Corporation; *Int'l*, pg. 7870
TOYOTA MOTOR ASIA PACIFIC ENGINEERING AND MANUFACTURING CO., LTD.—See Toyota Motor Corporation; *Int'l*, pg. 7873
TOYOTA MOTOR ASIA PACIFIC PTE LTD.—See Toyota Motor Corporation; *Int'l*, pg. 7873
TOYOTA MOTOR ASIA PTE. LTD.—See Toyota Motor Corporation; *Int'l*, pg. 7873
TOYOTA MOTOR (CHINA) INVESTMENT CO., LTD.—See Toyota Motor Corporation; *Int'l*, pg. 7873
TOYOTA MOTOR (CHINA) LTD.—See Toyota Motor Corporation; *Int'l*, pg. 7873
TOYOTA MOTOR CORPORATION AUSTRALIA LTD. - CARINGBAH—See Toyota Motor Corporation; *Int'l*, pg. 7873
TOYOTA MOTOR CORPORATION AUSTRALIA LTD.—See Toyota Motor Corporation; *Int'l*, pg. 7873
TOYOTA MOTOR CORPORATION - HIROSE PLANT—See Toyota Motor Corporation; *Int'l*, pg. 7873
TOYOTA MOTOR CORPORATION - HONSHA PLANT—See Toyota Motor Corporation; *Int'l*, pg. 7873
TOYOTA MOTOR CORPORATION; *Int'l*, pg. 7869
TOYOTA MOTOR CORPORATION - TAHARA PLANT—See Toyota Motor Corporation; *Int'l*, pg. 7873
TOYOTA MOTOR CREDIT CORPORATION—See Toyota Motor Corporation; *Int'l*, pg. 7873
TOYOTA MOTOR EAST JAPAN, INC. - HIGASHI FUJI PLANT—See Toyota Motor Corporation; *Int'l*, pg. 7873
TOYOTA MOTOR EAST JAPAN, INC. - IWATE PLANT—See Toyota Motor Corporation; *Int'l*, pg. 7874
TOYOTA MOTOR EAST JAPAN, INC. - MIYGAGI-TAIWA PLANT—See Toyota Motor Corporation; *Int'l*, pg. 7874
TOYOTA MOTOR EAST JAPAN, INC.—See Toyota Motor Corporation; *Int'l*, pg. 7873
TOYOTA MOTOR EAST JAPAN, INC. - SUYAMA PLANT—See Toyota Motor Corporation; *Int'l*, pg. 7874
TOYOTA MOTOR ENGINEERING & MANUFACTURING NORTH AMERICA, INC.—See Toyota Motor Corporation; *Int'l*, pg. 7874
TOYOTA MOTOR FINANCE (NETHERLANDS) B.V.—See Toyota Motor Corporation; *Int'l*, pg. 7874
TOYOTA MOTOR FINLAND OY—See Toyota Motor Corporation; *Int'l*, pg. 7874
TOYOTA MOTOR HOKKAIDO INC.—See Toyota Motor Corporation; *Int'l*, pg. 7874
TOYOTA MOTOR HUNGARY KFT.—See Toyota Motor Corporation; *Int'l*, pg. 7874

COMPANY NAME INDEX

TOYOTA MOTOR INDUSTRIES POLAND SP. Z.O.O.—See Toyota Motor Corporation; *Int'l*, pg. 7874
TOYOTA MOTOR INSURANCE SERVICES—See Toyota Motor Corporation; *Int'l*, pg. 7874
TOYOTA MOTOR ITALIA S.P.A.—See Toyota Motor Corporation; *Int'l*, pg. 7874
TOYOTA MOTOR KYUSHU, INC. - KANDA PLANT—See Toyota Motor Corporation; *Int'l*, pg. 7874
TOYOTA MOTOR KYUSHU, INC.—See Toyota Motor Corporation; *Int'l*, pg. 7874
TOYOTA MOTOR MANUFACTURING, ALABAMA, INC.—See Toyota Motor Corporation; *Int'l*, pg. 7874
TOYOTA MOTOR MANUFACTURING CANADA, INC.—See Toyota Motor Corporation; *Int'l*, pg. 7874
TOYOTA MOTOR MANUFACTURING DE BAJA CALIFORNIA S .DE R.L.DE C.V.—See Toyota Motor Corporation; *Int'l*, pg. 7874
TOYOTA MOTOR MANUFACTURING FRANCE S.A.S.—See Toyota Motor Corporation; *Int'l*, pg. 7874
TOYOTA MOTOR MANUFACTURING, INDIANA, INC.—See Toyota Motor Corporation; *Int'l*, pg. 7874
TOYOTA MOTOR MANUFACTURING, KENTUCKY, INC.—See Toyota Motor Corporation; *Int'l*, pg. 7874
TOYOTA MOTOR MANUFACTURING, MISSISSIPPI, INC.—See Toyota Motor Corporation; *Int'l*, pg. 7874
TOYOTA MOTOR MANUFACTURING POLAND SP. Z.O.O.—See Toyota Motor Corporation; *Int'l*, pg. 7874
TOYOTA MOTOR MANUFACTURING, TEXAS, INC.—See Toyota Motor Corporation; *Int'l*, pg. 7874
TOYOTA MOTOR MANUFACTURING TURKEY INC.—See Toyota Motor Corporation; *Int'l*, pg. 7874
TOYOTA MOTOR MANUFACTURING (UK) LTD—See Toyota Motor Corporation; *Int'l*, pg. 7874
TOYOTA MOTOR MANUFACTURING (UK) LTD—See Toyota Motor Corporation; *Int'l*, pg. 7874
TOYOTA MOTOR MANUFACTURING, WEST VIRGINIA, INC.—See Toyota Motor Corporation; *Int'l*, pg. 7874
TOYOTA MOTOR NORTH AMERICA, INC.—See Toyota Motor Corporation; *Int'l*, pg. 7874
TOYOTA MOTOR PHILIPPINES CORPORATION—See GT Capital Holdings, Inc.; *Int'l*, pg. 3150
TOYOTA MOTOR POLAND COMPANY, LTD. SP ZOO—See Toyota Motor Corporation; *Int'l*, pg. 7875
TOYOTA MOTOR SALES, U.S.A., INC.—See Toyota Motor Corporation; *Int'l*, pg. 7874
TOYOTA MOTORSPORT GMBH—See Toyota Motor Corporation; *Int'l*, pg. 7875
TOYOTA MOTOR THAILAND CO., LTD.—See Toyota Motor Corporation; *Int'l*, pg. 7875
TOYOTA MOTOR VIETNAM CO., LTD.—See Toyota Motor Corporation; *Int'l*, pg. 7875
TOYOTA NEW ZEALAND LTD.—See Toyota Motor Corporation; *Int'l*, pg. 7875
TOYOTA NIGERIA LIMITED—See Elizade Nigeria Limited; *Int'l*, pg. 2363
TOYOTA NORGE A/S—See Toyota Motor Corporation; *Int'l*, pg. 7875
TOYO TANSO CO., LTD.; *Int'l*, pg. 7858
TOYO TANSO EUROPE S.P.A.—See Toyo Tanso Co., Ltd.; *Int'l*, pg. 7858
TOYO TANSO FRANCE S.A.—See Toyo Tanso Co., Ltd.; *Int'l*, pg. 7859
TOYO TANSO KOREA CO., LTD.—See Toyo Tanso Co., Ltd.; *Int'l*, pg. 7859
TOYO TANSO MEXICO, S.A. DE C.V.—See Toyo Tanso Co., Ltd.; *Int'l*, pg. 7859
TOYO TANSO SINGAPORE PTE. LTD.—See Toyo Tanso Co., Ltd.; *Int'l*, pg. 7859
TOYO TANSO TAIWAN CO., LTD.—See Toyo Tanso Co., Ltd.; *Int'l*, pg. 7859
TOYO TANSO (THAILAND) CO., LTD.—See Toyo Tanso Co., Ltd.; *Int'l*, pg. 7858
TOYO TANSO USA INC.—See Toyo Tanso Co., Ltd.; *Int'l*, pg. 7859
TOYO TANSO (ZHEJIANG) CO., LTD.—See Toyo Tanso Co., Ltd.; *Int'l*, pg. 7858
TOYOTA NYUGYOU CO., LTD.—See Kobe Bussan Co., Ltd.; *Int'l*, pg. 4217
TOYOTA OF BOWLING GREEN; *U.S. Private*, pg. 4198
TOYOTA OF CLOVIS—See Penske Automotive Group, Inc.; *U.S. Public*, pg. 1666
TOYOTA OF DES MOINES; *U.S. Private*, pg. 4198
TOYOTA OF EASLEY; *U.S. Private*, pg. 4198
TOYOTA OF GLENDALE; *U.S. Private*, pg. 4199
TOYOTA OF GREENVILLE; *U.S. Private*, pg. 4199
TOYOTA OF HATTIESBURG, INC.; *U.S. Private*, pg. 4199
TOYOTA OF IRVING INC.; *U.S. Private*, pg. 4199
TOYOTA OF KIRKLAND—See Michael O'Brien Enterprises, Inc.; *U.S. Private*, pg. 2698
TOYOTA OF LOUISVILLE, INC.; *U.S. Private*, pg. 4199
TOYOTA OF MELBOURNE; *U.S. Private*, pg. 4199
TOYOTA OF MORRISTOWN; *U.S. Private*, pg. 4199
TOYOTA OF PASADENA; *U.S. Private*, pg. 4199
TOYOTA OF REDLANDS; *U.S. Private*, pg. 4199
TOYOTA OF RENTON—See Michael O'Brien Enterprises, Inc.; *U.S. Private*, pg. 2698
TOYOTA OF RIVERSIDE INC.; *U.S. Private*, pg. 4199
TOYOTA OF RUNNEMEDE; *U.S. Private*, pg. 4199
TOYOTA OF TRI-CITIES; *U.S. Private*, pg. 4199

TOYOTA ON NICHOLASVILLE; *U.S. Private*, pg. 4199
TOYOTA RENT-A-CAR; *U.S. Private*, pg. 4199
TOYOTA RENT-A-LEASE GIFU CO., LTD.—See Seino Holdings Co., Ltd.; *Int'l*, pg. 6691
TOYOTA SAN FERNANDO PAMPANGA, INC.—See GT Capital Holdings, Inc.; *Int'l*, pg. 3151
TOYOTA SCION OF GOLDSBORO; *U.S. Private*, pg. 4199
TOYOTA SCION OF SAN BERNARDINO; *U.S. Private*, pg. 4199
TOYOTA SENDAI RENTAL & LEASING CO., LTD.—See Kamei Corporation; *Int'l*, pg. 4062
TOYOTA SOUTH AFRICA LIMITED—See Toyota Motor Corporation; *Int'l*, pg. 7875
TOYOTA SOUTH AFRICA MOTORS (PTY.) LTD.—See Toyota Motor Corporation; *Int'l*, pg. 7875
TOYOTA SOUTH, INC.; *U.S. Private*, pg. 4199
TOYOTA STEEL CENTER CO., LTD.—See Toyota Tsusho Corporation; *Int'l*, pg. 7878
TOYOTA SUBIC, INC.—See GT Capital Holdings, Inc.; *Int'l*, pg. 3151
TOYOTA SWEDEN AB—See Toyota Motor Corporation; *Int'l*, pg. 7875
TOYOTA TANZANIA LIMITED—See Toyota Motor Corporation; *Int'l*, pg. 7872
TOYOTA TECHNICAL CENTER, U.S.A., INC.—See Toyota Motor Corporation; *Int'l*, pg. 7874
TOYOTA TECHNO PARK INDIA PVT. LTD.—See Toyota Tsusho Corporation; *Int'l*, pg. 7878
TOYOTA TEXTILE MACHINERY CORP. IN U.S.A.—See Toyota Motor Corporation; *Int'l*, pg. 7874
TOYOTA TEXTILE MACHINERY EUROPE, AG—See Toyota Industries Corporation; *Int'l*, pg. 7868
TOYOTA TEXTILE MACHINERY (SHANGHAI) CO., LTD.—See Toyota Industries Corporation; *Int'l*, pg. 7869
TOYOTA TOWN OF STOCKTON; *U.S. Private*, pg. 4199
TOYOTA TSUSHO AFRICA (PTY) LTD. - GREEN METALS DIVISION—See Toyota Tsusho Corporation; *Int'l*, pg. 7879
TOYOTA TSUSHO AFRICA (PTY) LTD.—See Toyota Tsusho Corporation; *Int'l*, pg. 7879
TOYOTA TSUSHO AMERICA, INC.—See Toyota Tsusho Corporation; *Int'l*, pg. 7879
TOYOTA TSUSHO ARGENTINA S.A.—See Toyota Tsusho Corporation; *Int'l*, pg. 7879
TOYOTA TSUSHO (AUSTRALASIA) PTY. LTD.—See Toyota Tsusho Corporation; *Int'l*, pg. 7878
TOYOTA TSUSHO AUTOMOBILE LONDON HOLDINGS LIMITED—See Toyota Tsusho Corporation; *Int'l*, pg. 7879
TOYOTA TSUSHO AUTOMOBILES PARIS EST S.A.S.—See Toyota Tsusho Corporation; *Int'l*, pg. 7879
TOYOTA TSUSHO AUTO VALENCIENNES S.A.R.L.—See Toyota Tsusho Corporation; *Int'l*, pg. 7879
TOYOTA TSUSHO CANADA, INC.—See Toyota Tsusho Corporation; *Int'l*, pg. 7879
TOYOTA TSUSHO (CHINA) CO., LTD.—See Toyota Tsusho Corporation; *Int'l*, pg. 7879
TOYOTA TSUSHO CORPORATION; *Int'l*, pg. 7875
TOYOTA TSUSHO (DALIAN) CO., LTD.—See Toyota Tsusho Corporation; *Int'l*, pg. 7879
TOYOTA TSUSHO DE VENEZUELA, C.A.—See Toyota Tsusho Corporation; *Int'l*, pg. 7880
TOYOTA TSUSHO ELECTRONICS CORPORATION—See Toyota Tsusho Corporation; *Int'l*, pg. 7879
TOYOTA TSUSHO EUROLEASING HUNGARY KFT—See Toyota Tsusho Corporation; *Int'l*, pg. 7879
TOYOTA TSUSHO EUROPE SA—See Toyota Tsusho Corporation; *Int'l*, pg. 7879
TOYOTA TSUSHO EUROPE SA—See Toyota Tsusho Corporation; *Int'l*, pg. 7879
TOYOTA TSUSHO FOODS CORPORATION—See Toyota Tsusho Corporation; *Int'l*, pg. 7879
TOYOTA TSUSHO FORKLIFT (THAILAND) CO., LTD.—See Toyota Tsusho Corporation; *Int'l*, pg. 7879
TOYOTA TSUSHO (GUANGZHOU) CO., LTD.—See Toyota Tsusho Corporation; *Int'l*, pg. 7879
TOYOTA TSUSHO (H.K.) CORPORATION LIMITED—See Toyota Tsusho Corporation; *Int'l*, pg. 7879
TOYOTA TSUSHO (HONG KONG) CO., LTD.—See Toyota Tsusho Corporation; *Int'l*, pg. 7879
TOYOTA TSUSHO ID SYSTEMS GMBH—See Toyota Tsusho Corporation; *Int'l*, pg. 7879
TOYOTA TSUSHO INSURANCE PARTNERS CORPORATION.—See Toyota Tsusho Corporation; *Int'l*, pg. 7879
TOYOTA TSUSHO KOREA CORPORATION—See Toyota Tsusho Corporation; *Int'l*, pg. 7879
TOYOTA TSUSHO MACHINERY, LLC—See Toyota Tsusho Corporation; *Int'l*, pg. 7879
TOYOTA TSUSHO (MALAYSIA) SDN. BHD.—See Toyota Tsusho Corporation; *Int'l*, pg. 7879
TOYOTA TSUSHO MATERIAL HANDLING AMERICA, INC.—See Toyota Tsusho Corporation; *Int'l*, pg. 7879
TOYOTA TSUSHO MEXICO, S.A. DE C.V.—See Toyota Tsusho Corporation; *Int'l*, pg. 7880
TOYOTA TSUSHO NEXTY ELECTRONICS (DALIAN) CO., LTD.—See STMicroelectronics N.V.; *Int'l*, pg. 7218

TOYOTA TSUSHO NEXTY ELECTRONICS HONG KONG CO., LTD.—See STMicroelectronics N.V.; *Int'l*, pg. 7218
TOYOTA TSUSHO NEXTY ELECTRONICS SHANGHAI CO., LTD.—See STMicroelectronics N.V.; *Int'l*, pg. 7218
TOYOTA TSUSHO NEXTY ELECTRONICS SHENZHEN CO., BEIJING BRANCH LTD.—See STMicroelectronics N.V.; *Int'l*, pg. 7218
TOYOTA TSUSHO NEXTY ELECTRONICS SHENZHEN CO., CHENGDU BRANCH LTD.—See STMicroelectronics N.V.; *Int'l*, pg. 7218
TOYOTA TSUSHO NEXTY ELECTRONICS SHENZHEN CO., WUHAN BRANCH LTD.—See STMicroelectronics N.V.; *Int'l*, pg. 7218
TOYOTA TSUSHO NEXTY ELECTRONICS (THAILAND) CO., LTD.—See STMicroelectronics N.V.; *Int'l*, pg. 7218
TOYOTA TSUSHO RE SINGAPORE PTE. LTD.—See Toyota Tsusho Corporation; *Int'l*, pg. 7880
TOYOTA TSUSHO (SHANGHAI) CO., LTD.—See Toyota Tsusho Corporation; *Int'l*, pg. 7879
TOYOTA TSUSHO (SINGAPORE) PTE., LTD.—See Toyota Tsusho Corporation; *Int'l*, pg. 7879
TOYOTA TSUSHO SOUTH SEA LIMITED; *Int'l*, pg. 7880
TOYOTA TSUSHO (TAIWAN) CO., LTD.—See Toyota Tsusho Corporation; *Int'l*, pg. 7879
TOYOTA TSUSHO TECHNICS CENTRAL ASIA LLP—See Toyota Tsusho Corporation; *Int'l*, pg. 7878
TOYOTA TSUSHO TEKHNIKA LLC—See Toyota Tsusho Corporation; *Int'l*, pg. 7880
TOYOTA TSUSHO U.K. LTD.—See Toyota Tsusho Corporation; *Int'l*, pg. 7880
TOYOTA TSUSHO VIETNAM CO., LTD.—See Toyota Tsusho Corporation; *Int'l*, pg. 7880
TOYOTA TURKIYE MOTORLU ARACLAR A.S.—See Abdul Latif Jameel Group of Companies; *Int'l*, pg. 58
TOYOTA TURKIYE MOTORLU ARACLAR A.S.—See Mitsui & Co., Ltd.; *Int'l*, pg. 4980
TOYOTA TURKIYE MOTORLU ARACLAR A.S.—See Toyota Motor Corporation; *Int'l*, pg. 7875
TOYOTA UGANDA LIMITED—See Toyota Tsusho Corporation; *Int'l*, pg. 7880
TOYOTA UKRAINE—See Sumitomo Corporation; *Int'l*, pg. 7276
TOYOTA WALNUT CREEK, INC.; *U.S. Private*, pg. 4199
TOYOTA ZIMBABWE (PRIVATE) LTD.—See Toyota Tsusho Corporation; *Int'l*, pg. 7880
TOYO TEC CO., LTD.; *Int'l*, pg. 7859
TOYOTETSU AMERICA, INC.—See Toyoda Iron Works Co., Ltd.; *Int'l*, pg. 7863
TOYOTETSU FUKUOKA CO., LTD.—See Toyoda Iron Works Co., Ltd.; *Int'l*, pg. 7863
TOYOTETSU INDIA, AUTO PARTS PVT. LTD.—See Toyoda Iron Works Co., Ltd.; *Int'l*, pg. 7863
TOYOTETSU OTOMOTIV PARCALARI SANAYI VE TICARET A.S.—See Toyoda Iron Works Co., Ltd.; *Int'l*, pg. 7863
TOYOTETSU (THAILAND) CO., LTD.—See Toyoda Iron Works Co., Ltd.; *Int'l*, pg. 7863
TOYOTETSU TOHOKU CO., LTD.—See Toyoda Iron Works Co., Ltd.; *Int'l*, pg. 7863
TOYO TIRE BENELUX B.V.—See Toyo Tire Corporation; *Int'l*, pg. 7860
TOYO TIRE & BENELUX—See Toyo Tire Corporation; *Int'l*, pg. 7859
TOYO TIRE CANADA, INC.—See Toyo Tire Corporation; *Int'l*, pg. 7860
TOYO TIRE CORPORATION; *Int'l*, pg. 7859
TOYO TIRE DEUTSCHLAND GMBH—See Toyo Tire Corporation; *Int'l*, pg. 7860
TOYO TIRE EUROPE GMBH—See Toyo Tire Corporation; *Int'l*, pg. 7860
TOYO TIRE HOLDINGS OF AMERICAS INC.—See Toyo Tire Corporation; *Int'l*, pg. 7859
TOYO TIRE HOLDINGS OF EUROPE GMBH—See Toyo Tire Corporation; *Int'l*, pg. 7860
TOYO TIRE ITALIA S.P.A—See Toyo Tire Corporation; *Int'l*, pg. 7860
TOYO TIRE JAPAN CO.,LTD—See Toyo Tire Corporation; *Int'l*, pg. 7860
TOYO TIRE MEXICO LLC—See Toyo Tire Corporation; *Int'l*, pg. 7860
TOYO TIRE NORTH AMERICA MANUFACTURING INC—See Toyo Tire Corporation; *Int'l*, pg. 7859
TOYO TIRE NORTH AMERICA OE SALES LLC—See Toyo Tire Corporation; *Int'l*, pg. 7859
TOYO TIRE REFINE CORPORATION—See Toyo Tire Corporation; *Int'l*, pg. 7860
TOYO TIRE RUS LLC—See Toyo Tire Corporation; *Int'l*, pg. 7859
TOYO TIRES CANADA INC.—See Toyo Tire Corporation; *Int'l*, pg. 7860
TOYO TIRE (SHANGAI) CO LTD—See Toyo Tire Corporation; *Int'l*, pg. 7859
TOYO TIRES LOGISTICS CO.,LTD—See Toyo Tire Corporation; *Int'l*, pg. 7860
TOYO TIRE (U.S.A.) CORPORATION—See Toyo Tire Corporation; *Int'l*, pg. 7860
TOYO TIRE ZHANGJIAGANG CO., LTD.—See Toyo Tire Corporation; *Int'l*, pg. 7860

TOYO TIRE CORPORATION / CORPORATE AFFILIATIONS

TOYO TOKAI ALUMINUM HANBAI K.K.—See Nippon Light Metal Holdings Company, Ltd.; *Int'l*, pg. 5324
TOYO TOKAI ALUMINUM HANBAI (SHANGHAI) CO., LTD.—See Nippon Light Metal Holdings Company, Ltd.; *Int'l*, pg. 5324
TOYO TRANSPORT ENGINEERING CO., LTD.—See Toyo Engineering Corporation; *Int'l*, pg. 7853
TOYOTSU AUTO SERVICE CO., LTD.—See Toyota Tsusho Corporation; *Int'l*, pg. 7880
TOYOTSU BUSINESS SERVICE CORPORATION—See Toyota Tsusho Corporation; *Int'l*, pg. 7880
TOYOTSU CHEMIPLAS CORPORATION—See Toyota Tsusho Corporation; *Int'l*, pg. 7880
TOYOTSU ENERGY CORPORATION—See Toyota Tsusho Corporation; *Int'l*, pg. 7880
TOYOTSU FAMILY LIFE CORPORATION—See Toyota Tsusho Corporation; *Int'l*, pg. 7880
TOYOTSU FASHION EXPRESS CO., LTD.—See Toyota Tsusho Corporation; *Int'l*, pg. 7880
TOYOTSU HITETSU CENTER CORPORATION—See Toyota Tsusho Corporation; *Int'l*, pg. 7880
TOYOTSU HOKEN CUSTOMER CENTER CORPORATION—See Toyota Tsusho Corporation; *Int'l*, pg. 7880
TOYOTSU HUMAN RESOURCES CORPORATION—See Toyota Tsusho Corporation; *Int'l*, pg. 7880
TOYOTSU KAMIGUMI LOGISTICS (CHANGSHU) CO., LTD.—See Kamigumi Co., Ltd.; *Int'l*, pg. 4063
TOYOTSU LIFECARE CORPORATION—See Toyota Tsusho Corporation; *Int'l*, pg. 7880
TOYOTSU-LIVING CO., LTD.—See Toyota Tsusho Corporation; *Int'l*, pg. 7880
TOYOTSU MACHINERY CORPORATION—See Toyota Tsusho Corporation; *Int'l*, pg. 7880
TOYOTSU MATERIAL INC.—See Toyota Tsusho Corporation; *Int'l*, pg. 7880
TOYOTSU NEW PACK CO., LTD.—See Toyota Tsusho Corporation; *Int'l*, pg. 7880
TOYOTSU NONFERROUS CENTER CORPORATION—See Kobe Steel, Ltd.; *Int'l*, pg. 4221
TOYOTSU OFFICE SERVICE CORPORATION—See Toyota Tsusho Corporation; *Int'l*, pg. 7880
TOYOTSU PETROTEX CORPORATION—See Toyota Tsusho Corporation; *Int'l*, pg. 7880
TOYOTSU RARE EARTHS CORPORATION—See Toyota Tsusho Corporation; *Int'l*, pg. 7880
TOYOTSU RECYCLE CORPORATION—See Toyota Tsusho Corporation; *Int'l*, pg. 7880
TOYOTSU SYSCOM CORPORATION—See Toyota Tsusho Corporation; *Int'l*, pg. 7880
TOYOTSU TEKKOU HAMBAI CO., LTD.—See Toyota Tsusho Corporation; *Int'l*, pg. 7880
TOYOTSU TEKKOU HANBAI CO., LTD.—See Toyota Tsusho Corporation; *Int'l*, pg. 7880
TOYO TYRE AND RUBBER AUSTRALIA LIMITED—See Toyo Tire Corporation; *Int'l*, pg. 7860
TOYO TYRE AUSTRALIA PTY. LTD.—See Toyo Tire Corporation; *Int'l*, pg. 7860
TOYO TYRE MALAYSIA SDN. BHD.—See Toyo Tire Corporation; *Int'l*, pg. 7860
TOYO TYRE SALES & MARKETING MALAYSIA SDN. BHD.—See Toyo Tire Corporation; *Int'l*, pg. 7860
TOYO TYRE (UK) LTD—See Toyo Tire Corporation; *Int'l*, pg. 7860
TOYOU FEIJI ELECTRONICS CO., LTD.; *Int'l*, pg. 7880
TOYO U.S.A., INC.—See Toyo Engineering Corporation; *Int'l*, pg. 7853
TOYO VALVE CO., LTD.—See KITZ CORPORATION; *Int'l*, pg. 4197
TOYO VENTURES HOLDINGS BERHAD; *Int'l*, pg. 7880
TOYO VISUAL SOLUTIONS CO., LTD.—See Toyo Ink SC Holdings Co., Ltd.; *Int'l*, pg. 7855
TOYO WHARF & WAREHOUSE CO., LTD.; *Int'l*, pg. 7860
TOYOX SOFTWARE CO., LTD.—See Uchida Yoko Co., Ltd.; *Int'l*, pg. 8012
TOYS "R" US AG—See Smyths Toys Holding Unlimited Company; *Int'l*, pg. 7024
TOYS "R" US (CANADA) LTD.—See Fairfax Financial Holdings Limited; *Int'l*, pg. 2608
TOYS "R" US GMBH—See Smyths Toys Holding Unlimited Company; *Int'l*, pg. 7024
TOYS "R" US HANDELSGESELLSCHAFT M.B.H.—See Smyths Toys Holding Unlimited Company; *Int'l*, pg. 7024
TOYS "R" US IBERIA, S.A.U.; *Int'l*, pg. 7880
TOYS "R" US, INC.—See WHP Global; *U.S. Private*, pg. 4515
TOYS "R" US INTERNATIONAL, LLC—See WHP Global; *U.S. Private*, pg. 4515
TOYS "R" US JAPAN, LTD.—See WHP Global; *U.S. Private*, pg. 4515
TOYS "R" US PORTUGAL, LIMITADA—See WHP Global; *U.S. Private*, pg. 4515
TOYS "R" US S.A.R.L.—See Cyrus Capital Partners, L.P.; *U.S. Private*, pg. 1135
TOYS R US ANZ LIMITED; *Int'l*, pg. 7880
TOYSRUS.COM (JAPAN), LTD.—See WHP Global; *U.S. Private*, pg. 4515

TOYU DISTRIBUTION CO., LTD.—See The Sumitomo Warehouse Co. Ltd.; *Int'l*, pg. 7689
TOZAI CAPITAL CO. LTD.; *Int'l*, pg. 7881
TOZAI JITSUGYO CO., LTD.—See Seika Corporation; *Int'l*, pg. 6685
TOZAI OIL TERMINAL CO., LTD.—See Cosmo Energy Holdings Co., Ltd.; *Int'l*, pg. 1812
TOZAI OIL TERMINAL CO., LTD.—See ENEOS Holdings, Inc.; *Int'l*, pg. 2417
TOZA MARKOVIC D.O.O.; *Int'l*, pg. 7881
TOZOUR ENERGY SYSTEMS, INC.; *U.S. Private*, pg. 4199
TPA CR S.R.O.—See STRABAG SE; *Int'l*, pg. 7233
TPA GESELLSCHAFT FUR QUALITATSSICHERUNG UND INNOVATII GMBH—See STRABAG SE; *Int'l*, pg. 7233
TPA HU KFT.—See STRABAG SE; *Int'l*, pg. 7233
TPA INST YTUT BA DAN TECHNICZNYCH SP.Z O.O.—See STRABAG SE; *Int'l*, pg. 7233
TPAM SAS—See Eiffage S.A.; *Int'l*, pg. 2331
TPA PORTABLE ROADWAYS—See Vp PLC; *Int'l*, pg. 8312
TP ARN INTERNATIONAL TRADING (SHANGHAI) CO.,LTD.—See TPR Co., Ltd.; *Int'l*, pg. 7884
TPA SOCIETATE PENTRU ASIGURAREA CALITATII SI INOVATII SRL—See STRABAG SE; *Int'l*, pg. 7233
TPA SP. Z O.O.—See STRABAG SE; *Int'l*, pg. 7233
TP ASSOCIATES INC.—See Timber Products Company, LP; *U.S. Private*, pg. 4171
TPA TRAFFIC & PARKING AUTOMATION SYSTEMS—See Ascom Holding AG; *Int'l*, pg. 603
TPBI PUBLIC COMPANY LIMITED; *Int'l*, pg. 7882
TPC ASSET COMPANY LIMITED—See Thai Polycons Public Company Limited; *Int'l*, pg. 7594
TPC BANGKOK SUPPLY COMPANY LIMITED—See Thai Polycons Public Company Limited; *Int'l*, pg. 7594
TPC CO., LTD.; *Int'l*, pg. 7882
TPC CONSOLIDATED LIMITED; *Int'l*, pg. 7882
TPC FZE - PROCESS PACKAGE DIVISION—See Bhatia Brothers Group; *Int'l*, pg. 1014
TPC FZE—See Bhatia Brothers Group; *Int'l*, pg. 1014
TPC GROUP INC.—See First Reserve Management, L.P.; *U.S. Private*, pg. 1526
TPC GROUP INC.—See SK Capital Partners, LP; *U.S. Private*, pg. 3680
TP CHILI (CHILE)—See Teleperformance SE; *Int'l*, pg. 7540
TPC HOLDINGS, INC.; *U.S. Private*, pg. 4199
TPC HOLDINGS, LLC—See Audax Group, Limited Partnership; *U.S. Private*, pg. 390
TPC (MALAYSIA) SDN. BHD.—See KYOCERA Corporation; *Int'l*, pg. 4359
TPC MECHATRONICS CORPORATION; *Int'l*, pg. 7882
TPCNIC CO., LTD. - CHONBURI FACTORY—See Dynic Corporation; *Int'l*, pg. 2243
TPCNIC CO., LTD.—See Dynic Corporation; *Int'l*, pg. 2243
TP COMPOSITES, INC.—See SK Capital Partners, LP; *U.S. Private*, pg. 3680
TP CONCEPT SDN. BHD.—See Pentamaster Corporation Berhad; *Int'l*, pg. 5791
TPC PASTE RESIN CO.,LTD.—See The Siam Cement Public Company Limited; *Int'l*, pg. 7685
TPC PLUS BERHAD; *Int'l*, pg. 7882
TPC PNEUMATICS INC.—See TPC Mechatronics Corporation; *Int'l*, pg. 7882
TPC POWER HOLDING PUBLIC COMPANY LIMITED; *Int'l*, pg. 7882
TPC SAS—See KYOCERA Corporation; *Int'l*, pg. 4360
TPCS PUBLIC COMPANY LIMITED; *Int'l*, pg. 7882
TPC THE PENSION CONSULTANCY GMBH—See MLP SE; *Int'l*, pg. 5004
TPC TRAINING SYSTEMS, INC.—See Frontenac Company LLC; *U.S. Private*, pg. 1614
TPC VINA PLASTIC & CHEMICAL CORPORATION LIMITED—See The Siam Cement Public Company Limited; *Int'l*, pg. 7685
TPC WIRE & CABLE CORP.—See Audax Group, Limited Partnership; *U.S. Private*, pg. 390
TPCW MEXICO, S. DE R.L. DE C.V.—See Amphenol Corporation; *U.S. Public*, pg. 132
TP DC SARAJEVO D.D. SARAJEVO; *Int'l*, pg. 7881
TP DENTAL SURGEONS PTE. LTD.—See Q&M Dental Group (Singapore) Limited; *Int'l*, pg. 6131
TP DUNAV A.D.; *Int'l*, pg. 7881
TPE DE MEXICO, S. DE R.L. DE C.V.—See RBC Bearings Incorporated; *U.S. Public*, pg. 1766
TPFM THE PHOENIX FUND MANAGEMENT LTD.—See Inverite Insights Inc.; *Int'l*, pg. 3774
TPFUSION CORP.—See Sigurd Microelectronics Corp.; *Int'l*, pg. 6913
TPFUSION, INC.—See Sigurd Microelectronics Corp.; *Int'l*, pg. 6913
TPG AERONAUTIK SDN. BHD.—See CB Industrial Product Holding Berhad; *Int'l*, pg. 1364
TPG CAPITAL LLP—See TPG Capital, L.P.; *U.S. Public*, pg. 2175
TPG CAPITAL, L.P.; *U.S. Public*, pg. 2166
TPG CORPORATION LIMITED—See CK Hutchison Holdings Limited; *Int'l*, pg. 1638

TPG CORPORATION LIMITED—See Vodafone Group Plc; *Int'l*, pg. 8284
TPG DEVELOPMENT MANAGEMENT CONSULTANTS—See The Plasencia Group, Inc.; *U.S. Private*, pg. 4096
TPG DIRECT—See Omnicom Group Inc.; *U.S. Public*, pg. 1599
TPG GROWTH - SAN FRANCISCO OFFICE—See TPG Capital, L.P.; *U.S. Public*, pg. 2177
TPG GROWTH—See TPG Capital, L.P.; *U.S. Public*, pg. 2175
TPG HOLDINGS LIMITED—See CK Hutchison Holdings Limited; *Int'l*, pg. 1638
TPG HOLDINGS LIMITED—See Vodafone Group Plc; *Int'l*, pg. 8284
TPG INTERNET PTY. LTD.—See CK Hutchison Holdings Limited; *Int'l*, pg. 1638
TPG INTERNET PTY. LTD.—See Vodafone Group Plc; *Int'l*, pg. 8285
TPG NETWORK PTY LTD—See CK Hutchison Holdings Limited; *Int'l*, pg. 1638
TPG NETWORK PTY LTD—See Vodafone Group Plc; *Int'l*, pg. 8285
TPG OIL & GAS SDN. BHD.—See CB Industrial Product Holding Berhad; *Int'l*, pg. 1364
TPG PACE BENEFICIAL FINANCE CORP.; *U.S. Public*, pg. 2177
TPG PACE SOLUTIONS CORP.—See Vacasa, Inc.; *U.S. Public*, pg. 2270
TPG RE FINANCE TRUST, INC.; *U.S. Public*, pg. 2178
TPG RESEARCH PTY LTD—See CK Hutchison Holdings Limited; *Int'l*, pg. 1638
TPG RESEARCH PTY LTD—See Vodafone Group Plc; *Int'l*, pg. 8285
TP GROUP PLC—See Science Group plc; *Int'l*, pg. 6647
TPG SOFTWARE, INC.—See The Carlyle Group Inc.; *U.S. Public*, pg. 2045
TPG TELECOM LIMITED—See CK Hutchison Holdings Limited; *Int'l*, pg. 1638
TPG TELECOM LIMITED—See Vodafone Group Plc; *Int'l*, pg. 8284
TPG TELEMANAGEMENT INC.; *U.S. Private*, pg. 4200
TPH ACQUISITION, LLLP; *U.S. Private*, pg. 4200
TPHCOM GMBH—See mobilezone holding ag; *Int'l*, pg. 5011
TPH (UK) LIMITED—See Dole plc; *Int'l*, pg. 2158
TPI ADVISORY SERVICES INDIA PVT. LTD.—See Information Services Group, Inc.; *U.S. Public*, pg. 1118
TPI-ARCADE, INC.—See Ligon Industries LLC; *U.S. Private*, pg. 2455
TPI BILLING SOLUTIONS; *U.S. Private*, pg. 4200
TP ICAP (DUBAI) LIMITED—See TP ICAP Finance PLC; *Int'l*, pg. 7881
TP ICAP EMEA INVESTMENTS LIMITED—See TP ICAP Finance PLC; *Int'l*, pg. 7881
TP ICAP FINANCE PLC; *Int'l*, pg. 7881
TP ICAP MANAGEMENT SERVICES (SINGAPORE) PTE. LTD.—See TP ICAP Finance PLC; *Int'l*, pg. 7881
TPI CESKA REPUBLIKA S.R.O.—See VINCI S.A.; *Int'l*, pg. 8238
TPI COMPOSITES INC.—See Landmark Growth Capital Partners, LP; *U.S. Private*, pg. 2385
TPI CONCRETE CO., LTD.—See TPI Polene Public Company Limited; *Int'l*, pg. 7883
TPI CORP.; *U.S. Private*, pg. 4200
TPI EUROPE LTD.—See Information Services Group, Inc.; *U.S. Public*, pg. 1118
TPI INDIA LIMITED; *Int'l*, pg. 7883
TPI INTERNATIONAL, INC.; *U.S. Public*, pg. 2178
T.P. INDUSTRIAL HOLDING S.P.A.—See China National Chemical Corporation; *Int'l*, pg. 1529
TPI OCHRONA PRZECIWPOZAROWA SP. Z O. O.—See VINCI S.A.; *Int'l*, pg. 8238
TPI POLENE POWER PCL; *Int'l*, pg. 7883
TPI POLENE PUBLIC COMPANY LIMITED; *Int'l*, pg. 7883
TPI POLYTECHNIEK B.V.—See SP Group A/S; *Int'l*, pg. 7122
TPI S.R.O.—See VINCI S.A.; *Int'l*, pg. 8229
TPI TECNIMONT PLANUNG UND INDUSTRIEANLAGEN-BAU GMBH—See Maire Tecnimont S.p.A.; *Int'l*, pg. 4652
TPI TRAVEL (CANADA), LTD.—See JTB Corp.; *Int'l*, pg. 4015
TPI - TRIUNFO PARTICIPACOES E INVESTIMENTOS S.A.; *Int'l*, pg. 7883
T.P.J. D.O.O.—See SOL S.p.A.; *Int'l*, pg. 7068
TPK HOLDING CO., LTD.; *Int'l*, pg. 7883
TPK TOUCH SOLUTIONS INC.—See TPK Holding Co., Ltd.; *Int'l*, pg. 7883
TPK TOUCH SOLUTIONS (XIAMEN) INC.—See TPK Holding Co., Ltd.; *Int'l*, pg. 7883
TPL ARKOMA MIDSTREAM LLC—See Targa Resources Corp.; *U.S. Public*, pg. 1981
TPL CORP LIMITED; *Int'l*, pg. 7883
TPLEX CO.; *Int'l*, pg. 7883
T-PLEX INDUSTRIES, INC.—See Federated Healthcare Supply Holdings, Inc.; *U.S. Private*, pg. 1491
TP-LINK CORPORATION LIMITED—See Ban Leong Technologies Limited; *Int'l*, pg. 814

COMPANY NAME INDEX

TPL INSURANCE LIMITED—See TPL Corp Limited; *Int'l*, pg. 7883
TPL LIFE INSURANCE LIMITED—See TPL Corp Limited; *Int'l*, pg. 7883
TPL PLASTECH LIMITED—See Time Technoplast Limited; *Int'l*, pg. 7751
T-PLUS GMBH—See EnBW Energie Baden-Wurttemberg AG; *Int'l*, pg. 2400
T PLUS IMPLANT TECH CO. LTD.—See Straumann Holding AG; *Int'l*, pg. 7238
T PLUS PJSC; *Int'l*, pg. 7394
TPM (1998) LTD—See Mohammed Enterprises Tanzania Limited; *Int'l*, pg. 5018
TP MANAGEMENT SA—See TalkPool AG; *Int'l*, pg. 7447
TP MANUFACTURING LTD.—See The Alumasc Group plc; *Int'l*, pg. 7613
TP MLAVA A.D.; *Int'l*, pg. 7882
TPM TECHNOPARK SDN BHD—See Johor Corporation; *Int'l*, pg. 3994
TPN INC.—See Omnicom Group Inc.; *U.S. Public*, pg. 1599
TP OF MACON, INC.—See HI-Boy Group Inc.; *U.S. Private*, pg. 1931
TPO HOLZ-SYSTEME GMBH—See Arbonia AG; *Int'l*, pg. 538
TP ORTHODONTICS INC.; *U.S. Private*, pg. 4199
TP PLUMBING & HEATING—See Travis Perkins plc; *Int'l*, pg. 7908
TP RACING L.L.L.P.; *U.S. Private*, pg. 4199
TPR ALTEC CO., LTD.—See TPR Co., Ltd.; *Int'l*, pg. 7884
TPR AMERICA, INC.—See TPR Co., Ltd.; *Int'l*, pg. 7884
TPR ASIAN SALES (THAILAND) LTD.—See TPR Co., Ltd.; *Int'l*, pg. 7884
TPR AUTOPARTS MFG. INDIA PVT LTD.—See TPR Co., Ltd.; *Int'l*, pg. 7884
TPR BUSINESS CO., LTD.—See TPR Co., Ltd.; *Int'l*, pg. 7884
TPR CO., LTD.; *Int'l*, pg. 7883
TPR EK METALS CO., LTD.—See TPR Co., Ltd.; *Int'l*, pg. 7884
TPR ENGINEERING CO., LTD.—See TPR Co., Ltd.; *Int'l*, pg. 7884
TPR ENPLA CO., LTD.—See TPR Co., Ltd.; *Int'l*, pg. 7884
TPR EUROPE GMBH—See TPR Co., Ltd.; *Int'l*, pg. 7884
TPR FIBERDUR GMBH & CO. KG; *Int'l*, pg. 7884
TPR INDUSTRIA DE PECAS AUTOMOTIVAS DO BRASIL LTDA.—See TPR Co., Ltd.; *Int'l*, pg. 7884
TPR INDUSTRY CO., LTD.—See TPR Co., Ltd.; *Int'l*, pg. 7884
TPR NOBUKAWA CO., LTD.—See TPR Co., Ltd.; *Int'l*, pg. 7884
TPR NOBUKAWA TRADING CO., LTD.—See TPR Co., Ltd.; *Int'l*, pg. 7884
T-PRODUCTION TESTING LLC—See TETRA Technologies, Inc.; *U.S. Public*, pg. 2024
T PROJECT CO., LTD.—See DMG MORI Co., Ltd.; *Int'l*, pg. 2145
TP ROMANIA SERVICES 800 CSP—See Teleperformance SE; *Int'l*, pg. 7540
TPR PREMEC CO., LTD.—See TPR Co., Ltd.; *Int'l*, pg. 7884
TPR SUNLIGHT CO., LTD.—See TPR Co., Ltd.; *Int'l*, pg. 7884
TPR THERMAL ENGINEERING CO., LTD.—See TPR Co., Ltd.; *Int'l*, pg. 7884
TPR (TIANJIN) CO., LTD.—See TPR Co., Ltd.; *Int'l*, pg. 7884
TPR TOTAL SERVICE CO., LTD.—See TPR Co., Ltd.; *Int'l*, pg. 7884
TPR TRADING CO., LTD.—See TPR Co., Ltd.; *Int'l*, pg. 7884
TPR VIETNAM CO., LTD.—See TPR Co., Ltd.; *Int'l*, pg. 7884
T.P.S. AVIATION INC.; *U.S. Private*, pg. 3912
TPS CONSULT LIMITED—See Carillion plc; *Int'l*, pg. 1330
TPS EASTERN AFRICA LIMITED; *Int'l*, pg. 7884
TPSEF INC.—See TP ICAP Finance PLC; *Int'l*, pg. 7882
THE TPS HEALTHCARE GROUP LIMITED—See DCC plc; *Int'l*, pg. 1991
TPSH S.A.; *Int'l*, pg. 7885
TPS, LLC—See Resilience Capital Partners, LLC; *U.S. Private*, pg. 3405
TP SOLAR LTD.—See Tata Power Company Limited; *Int'l*, pg. 7468
TPS PARKING MANAGEMENT, LLC—See Green Courte Partners, LLC; *U.S. Private*, pg. 1772
TPS S.P.A.; *Int'l*, pg. 7885
TPT GLOBAL TECH, INC.; *U.S. Public*, pg. 2178
TPT MAQUINAS-FERRAMENTAS E LASER, UNIPES-SOAL, LDA.—See TRUMPF SE + Co. KG; *Int'l*, pg. 7942
TP TRUCKING LLC—See Timber Products Company, LP; *U.S. Private*, pg. 4171
TP&T (TOR PROCESSING & TRADE) B.V.—See TOR Minerals International Inc.; *U.S. Public*, pg. 2164
TPT WEALTH LIMITED—See MyState Limited; *Int'l*, pg. 5114
T & P VASTGOED STUTTGART B.V.—See UniCredit S.p.A.; *Int'l*, pg. 8035

TPV CIS LTD.—See TPV Technology Co., Ltd.; *Int'l*, pg. 7885
TPV ELECTRONICS (FUJIAN) COMPANY LIMITED—See TPV Technology Co., Ltd.; *Int'l*, pg. 7885
TPV TECHNOLOGY CO., LTD.; *Int'l*, pg. 7885
TPV TECHNOLOGY LIMITED—See TPV Technology Co., Ltd.; *Int'l*, pg. 7885
TPV TECHNOLOGY (WUHAN) COMPANY LIMITED—See TPV Technology Co., Ltd.; *Int'l*, pg. 7885
TPXIMPACT HOLDINGS PLC; *Int'l*, pg. 7885
TP ZVEZDA A.D.; *Int'l*, pg. 7882
TQ-1 DE MEXICO S.A. DE C.V.—See Nagase & Co., Ltd.; *Int'l*, pg. 5128
TQ CATALIS LIMITED—See Pearson plc; *Int'l*, pg. 5778
TQ CLAPHAM LTD—See Pearson plc; *Int'l*, pg. 5778
TQC QUANTIUM QUALITY, S.A. DE C.V.—See Dover Corporation; *U.S. Public*, pg. 682
TQ EDUCATION & TRAINING LTD—See Pearson plc; *Int'l*, pg. 5778
TQ GROUP LTD—See Pearson plc; *Int'l*, pg. 5778
TQ HOLDINGS LTD.—See Pearson plc; *Int'l*, pg. 5778
TQI EXCHANGE, LLC—See Deutsche Bank Aktiengesellschaft; *Int'l*, pg. 2062
TQL TECHNOLOGY LIMITED—See K & P International Holdings Limited; *Int'l*, pg. 4037
TQM CORP PCL; *Int'l*, pg. 7885
TQM EUROPE GMBH—See Tianjin Motor Dies Co., Ltd.; *Int'l*, pg. 7740
TQMP GLASS MANUFACTURING CORP.; *Int'l*, pg. 7885
TQR PUBLIC COMPANY LIMITED; *Int'l*, pg. 7885
TQS INTEGRATION AG—See Cognizant Technology Solutions Corporation; *U.S. Public*, pg. 525
TQT S.R.L.—See FLY Srl; *Int'l*, pg. 2716
TQTVD SOFTWARE LTDA.—See TOTVS S.A.; *Int'l*, pg. 7846
TQUILA AUTOMATION, INC.—See Delta-v Capital, LLC; *U.S. Private*, pg. 1202
TR3 SOLUTIONS, INC.—See Rock Solid UK Ltd.; *U.S. Private*, pg. 3465
TRAAS ON PRODUCT INC.; *Int'l*, pg. 7885
TRABAJOS INDUSTRIALES Y MECANICOS, C.A.; *Int'l*, pg. 7885
TRABAJOS MARITIMOS S.A.—See Grupo Romero; *Int'l*, pg. 3135
TRABIT S.A.U.—See VINCI S.A.; *Int'l*, pg. 8229
TRABOCCA B.V.—See SunOpta Inc.; *Int'l*, pg. 7320
TRABON PRINTING COMPANY INC.; *U.S. Private*, pg. 4200
TRABZON LIMAN ISLETMECILI AS; *Int'l*, pg. 7885
TRABZONSPOR SPORTIF YATIRIM VE FUTBOL A.S.; *Int'l*, pg. 7885
TRABZONSPOR SPORTIF YATIRIM VE FUTBOL ISLET-MECILIGI TAS; *Int'l*, pg. 7885
TRACE3, INC.—See American Securities LLC; *U.S. Private*, pg. 250
TRACE-A-MATIC CORPORATION; *U.S. Private*, pg. 4200
TRACE AVIATION, INC.—See GenNx360 Capital Partners, L.P.; *U.S. Private*, pg. 1672
TRACE BG EOOD LTD.—See Trace Group Hold PLC; *Int'l*, pg. 7886
TRACE BG JSC—See Trace Group Hold PLC; *Int'l*, pg. 7886
TRACE - BOURGAS JSC—See Trace Group Hold PLC; *Int'l*, pg. 7886
TRACE FINANCIAL—See Trace Group; *Int'l*, pg. 7886
TRACEGAINS, INC.—See Veralto Corporation; *U.S. Public*, pg. 2280
TRACE GROUP HOLD PLC; *Int'l*, pg. 7886
TRACE GROUP; *Int'l*, pg. 7886
TRACEGUARD TECHNOLOGIES, INC.; *U.S. Private*, pg. 4200
TRACE ISYS LIMITED—See Trace Group; *Int'l*, pg. 7886
TRACE KARJALI JSC—See Trace Group Hold PLC; *Int'l*, pg. 7886
TRACE LABORATORIES CHICAGO—See Methode Electronics, Inc.; *U.S. Public*, pg. 1429
TRACE LABORATORIES EAST—See Methode Electronics, Inc.; *U.S. Public*, pg. 1429
TRACELOGISTICS, S.A.—See Fluidra SA; *Int'l*, pg. 2714
TRAC EMC & SAFETY LTD—See Ecolab Inc.; *U.S. Public*, pg. 712
TRAC ENERGY SERVICES LTD.—See Zedcor Inc.; *Int'l*, pg. 8629
TRACEN TECHNOLOGIES, INC.; *U.S. Private*, pg. 4200
TRAC ENVIRONMENTAL & ANALYSIS LTD.—See Ecolab Inc.; *U.S. Public*, pg. 712
TRACE ONE SAS—See Symphony Technology Group, LLC; *U.S. Private*, pg. 3902
TRACE ONE UK—See M. Abuhab Participacoes S.A.; *Int'l*, pg. 4615
TRACEPARTS GMBH—See Trace Software International; *Int'l*, pg. 7886
TRACEPARTS INC.—See Trace Software International; *Int'l*, pg. 7886
TRACEPARTS S.A.—See Trace Software International; *Int'l*, pg. 7886
TRACEPARTS SRL—See Trace Software International; *Int'l*, pg. 7886

TRACEPARTS UK LTD.—See Trace Software International; *Int'l*, pg. 7886
TRACE PAYROLL SERVICES LIMITED—See Trace Group; *Int'l*, pg. 7886
TRACE PLOVDIV LTD.—See Trace Group Hold PLC; *Int'l*, pg. 7886
TRACE PROPERTIES LTD.—See Trace Group Hold PLC; *Int'l*, pg. 7886
TRACERCO DO BRASIL - DIAGNOSTICOS DE PROCESSOS INDUSTRIAIS LTDA.—See Johnson Matthey PLC; *Int'l*, pg. 3993
TRACERCO EUROPE BVBA—See Johnson Matthey PLC; *Int'l*, pg. 3993
TRACERCO LIMITED—See Souter Capital LLP; *Int'l*, pg. 7115
TRACERCO LIMITED—See Sullivan Street Partners Limited; *Int'l*, pg. 7256
TRACERCO NORGE AS—See Johnson Matthey PLC; *Int'l*, pg. 3993
TRACER CONSTRUCTION LLC—See Pentair plc; *Int'l*, pg. 5790
TRACERCO RADIOACTIVE DIAGNOSTIC SERVICES CANADA INC.—See Johnson Matthey PLC; *Int'l*, pg. 3993
TRACERCO—See Johnson Matthey PLC; *Int'l*, pg. 3992
TRACER INDUSTRIES CANADA LIMITED—See Pentair plc; *Int'l*, pg. 5790
TRACER INDUSTRIES, INC.—See Pentair plc; *Int'l*, pg. 5790
TRACE ROADS JSC—See Trace Group Hold PLC; *Int'l*, pg. 7886
TRACER PRODUCTS—See Spectronics Corporation; *U.S. Private*, pg. 3752
TRACER TECHNOLOGY PTE LTD—See Trek 2000 International Ltd; *Int'l*, pg. 7910
TRACESECURITY INC.; *U.S. Private*, pg. 4200
TRACE SERBIA JSC—See Trace Group Hold PLC; *Int'l*, pg. 7886
TRACE SERVICES INC.; *U.S. Private*, pg. 4200
TRACESMART LTD.—See RELX plc; *Int'l*, pg. 6268
TRACE SOFTWARE CHINA—See Trace Software International; *Int'l*, pg. 7886
TRACE SOFTWARE IBERIA—See Trace Software International; *Int'l*, pg. 7886
TRACE SOFTWARE INTERNATIONAL; *Int'l*, pg. 7886
TRACE SOFTWARE MOROCCO—See Trace Software International; *Int'l*, pg. 7886
TRACE SOFTWARE PRIVATE LIMITED; *Int'l*, pg. 7886
TRACE SOLUTIONS—See Trace Group; *Int'l*, pg. 7886
TRACE VFX LLC—See Vantiva SA; *Int'l*, pg. 8131
TRACEVIA DO BRAZIL -SISTEMAS DE TELEMTICA RODOVIARIA LTDA.—See Mota-Engil SGPS, S.A.; *Int'l*, pg. 5052
TRACE WORLDWIDE CORP.; *U.S. Private*, pg. 4200
TRACE YAMBOL JSC—See Trace Group Hold PLC; *Int'l*, pg. 7886
TRACEY ROAD EQUIPMENT INC.; *U.S. Private*, pg. 4200
TRACFONE WIRELESS, INC.—See Verizon Communications Inc.; *U.S. Public*, pg. 2285
TRACHTE BUILDING SYSTEMS INC.; *U.S. Private*, pg. 4200
TRACHTE LLC—See nVent Electric plc; *Int'l*, pg. 5498
TRACINDA CORPORATION; *U.S. Private*, pg. 4200
TRAC INTERMODAL LLC—See Stonepeak Partners L.P.; *U.S. Private*, pg. 3829
TRAC INTERSTAR LLC—See Stonepeak Partners L.P.; *U.S. Private*, pg. 3829
TRACKCOM SYSTEMS INTERNATIONAL (TSI)—See Kavveri Telecom Products Ltd; *Int'l*, pg. 4093
TRACK DATA CORPORATION; *U.S. Private*, pg. 4201
TRACK ENTERTAINMENT; *U.S. Private*, pg. 4201
TRACKER BOAT CENTERS CORBIN—See The Great American Outdoors Group LLC; *U.S. Private*, pg. 4038
TRACKER BOATING CENTER - SNOWDEN—See The Great American Outdoors Group LLC; *U.S. Private*, pg. 4038
TRACKER LOGISTICS INC.—See Deutsche Post AG; *Int'l*, pg. 2082
TRACKER LTD.—See General Atlantic Service Company, L.P.; *U.S. Private*, pg. 1661
TRACKER MARINE - ARLINGTON—See The Great American Outdoors Group LLC; *U.S. Private*, pg. 4038
TRACKER MARINE - BEAUMONT—See The Great American Outdoors Group LLC; *U.S. Private*, pg. 4038
TRACKER MARINE GROUP LLC—See The Great American Outdoors Group LLC; *U.S. Private*, pg. 4038
TRACKER NETWORK (UK) LTD—See Tantalum Corporation Limited; *Int'l*, pg. 7460
TRACK EXPERTS D.O.O.—See PORR AG; *Int'l*, pg. 5925
TRACK GROUP, INC.; *U.S. Public*, pg. 2178
TRACKMOBILE, INC.—See Berkshire Hathaway Inc.; *U.S. Public*, pg. 311
TRACKNET HOLDING; *Int'l*, pg. 7886
TRACK ONLINE B.V.—See Unith Ltd; *Int'l*, pg. 8074
TRACKPOINT SYSTEMS LLC—See Genstar Capital, LLC; *U.S. Private*, pg. 1676
TRACK—See Omnicom Group Inc.; *U.S. Public*, pg. 1592
TRACKSPARES (AUSTRALIA) PTY. LTD.—See Hoe Leong Corporation Ltd.; *Int'l*, pg. 3439

TRACKWISE DESIGNS PLC

TRACKWISE DESIGNS PLC; *Int'l*, pg. 7886
TRACKWORK & SUPPLIES SDN. BHD.—See AWC Berhad; *Int'l*, pg. 752
TRACKX HOLDINGS INC.; *Int'l*, pg. 7886
TRACMEC SRL—See BAUER Aktiengesellschaft; *Int'l*, pg. 894
TRACO ADVERTISING, INC.; *U.S. Private*, pg. 4201
TRACOE MEDICAL GMBH; *Int'l*, pg. 7887
TRACO INC.—See Howmet Aerospace Inc.; *U.S. Public*, pg. 1062
TRACOMA HOLDINGS BERHAD; *Int'l*, pg. 7887
TRACOMEX B.V.—See BayWa AG; *Int'l*, pg. 919
TRACONF S.R.L.—See Nippon Express Holdings, Inc.; *Int'l*, pg. 5317
TRACON PHARMACEUTICALS, INC.; *U.S. Public*, pg. 2178
TRAC-RITE DOOR INC.—See Trachte Building Systems Inc.; *U.S. Private*, pg. 4200
TRACSIS PASSENGER COUNTS LIMITED—See Tracsis Plc; *Int'l*, pg. 7887
TRACSIS PLC; *Int'l*, pg. 7887
TRACSIS RAIL CONSULTANCY LIMITED—See Tracsis Plc; *Int'l*, pg. 7887
TRACSTAR SYSTEMS, INC.—See Advent International Corporation; *U.S. Private*, pg. 100
TRACTAMENT METROPOLITA DE FANGS, S.L.—See GS Holdings Corp.; *Int'l*, pg. 3142
TRACTEBEL DEVELOPMENT ENGINEERING S.A.—See ENGIE SA; *Int'l*, pg. 2432
TRACTEBEL ENERGIA COMERCIALIZADORA LIMITADA—See ENGIE SA; *Int'l*, pg. 2433
TRACTEBEL ENERGIA S.A. - HPP CANA BRAVA - UHCB PLANT—See ENGIE SA; *Int'l*, pg. 2432
TRACTEBEL ENERGIA S.A. - HPP MACHADINHO - UHMA PLANT—See ENGIE SA; *Int'l*, pg. 2432
TRACTEBEL ENERGIA S.A. - HPP PONTE DE PEDRA - UHPP PLANT—See ENGIE SA; *Int'l*, pg. 2432
TRACTEBEL ENERGIA S.A. - HPP SALTO OSORIO - UHSO PLANT—See ENGIE SA; *Int'l*, pg. 2432
TRACTEBEL ENERGIA S.A. - HPP SALTO SANTIAGO - UHSS PLANT—See ENGIE SA; *Int'l*, pg. 2432
TRACTEBEL ENERGIA S.A. - HPP SAO SALVADOR - UHSA PLANT—See ENGIE SA; *Int'l*, pg. 2432
TRACTEBEL ENERGIA S.A. - JORGE LACERDA THERMOELECTRIC COMPLEX - CJL PLANT—See ENGIE SA; *Int'l*, pg. 2432
TRACTEBEL ENERGIA S.A. - LAGES COGENERATION UNIT - UCLA PLANT—See ENGIE SA; *Int'l*, pg. 2432
TRACTEBEL ENERGIA S.A. - TPP ALEGRETE - UTAL PLANT—See ENGIE SA; *Int'l*, pg. 2432
TRACTEBEL ENERGIA S.A. - TPP CHARQUEADAS - UTCH PLANT—See ENGIE SA; *Int'l*, pg. 2432
TRACTEBEL ENERGIA S.A. - TPP WILLIAM ARJONA - UTWA PLANT—See ENGIE SA; *Int'l*, pg. 2432
TRACTEBEL ENGINEERING—See ENGIE SA; *Int'l*, pg. 2432
TRACTEBEL S.A.—See ENGIE SA; *Int'l*, pg. 2432
TRAC TELECOMS & RADIO LTD.—See Ecolab Inc.; *U.S. Public*, pg. 712
TRACTION CORPORATION; *U.S. Private*, pg. 4201
TRACTION—See Genuine Parts Company; *U.S. Public*, pg. 932
TRACTION URANIUM INC.; *Int'l*, pg. 7887
TRACTION WHOLESALE CENTER; *U.S. Private*, pg. 4201
TRACTMANAGER, INC.—See Clearlake Capital Group, L.P.; *U.S. Private*, pg. 937
TRACTMANAGER, INC.—See SkyKnight Capital LLC; *U.S. Private*, pg. 3685
TRACTOR AND GRADER SUPPLIES (PTY) LTD—See Apex Partners Proprietary Limited; *Int'l*, pg. 512
TRACTOR AND GRADER SUPPLIES (PTY) LTD—See TRG Management LP; *U.S. Private*, pg. 4220
TRACTORBEAM; *U.S. Private*, pg. 4201
TRACTOR CENTRAL LLC; *U.S. Private*, pg. 4201
TRACTOR CENTRAL - MONDOVI—See Tractor Central LLC; *U.S. Private*, pg. 4201
TRACTOR CENTRAL—See Tractor Central LLC; *U.S. Private*, pg. 4201
TRACTOR ENGINEERS LIMITED—See Larsen & Toubro Limited; *Int'l*, pg. 4420
TRACTOR & EQUIPMENT COMPANY; *U.S. Private*, pg. 4201
TRACTOR & EQUIPMENT COMPANY—See Tractor & Equipment Company; *U.S. Private*, pg. 4201
THE TRACTORS & ENGINEERING CO.—See Chemical Industries Holding Company; *Int'l*, pg. 1462
TRACTORS INDIA PVT. LTD.—See TIL Limited; *Int'l*, pg. 7748
TRACTORS MALAYSIA 1982 SDN. BHD.—See Sime Darby Berhad; *Int'l*, pg. 6930
TRACTORS PETROLEUM SERVICES SDN BHD—See Sime Darby Berhad; *Int'l*, pg. 6930
TRACTORS SINGAPORE LIMITED—See Sime Darby Berhad; *Int'l*, pg. 6930
TRACTORS SINGAPORE (MALDIVES) PRIVATE LIMITED—See Sime Darby Berhad; *Int'l*, pg. 6930
TRACTOR SUPPLY COMPANY; *U.S. Public*, pg. 2178

TRACTOR SUPPLY CO. OF TEXAS, LP—See Tractor Supply Company; *U.S. Public*, pg. 2178
TRACTOR TRAILER SUPPLY CO.; *U.S. Private*, pg. 4201
TRAC-WORK INC.; *U.S. Private*, pg. 4200
TRACXN TECHNOLOGIES LIMITED; *Int'l*, pg. 7887
TRACY-DRISCOLL & CO., INC.—See ABRY Partners, LLC; *U.S. Private*, pg. 42
TRACY EVANS LTD. INC.; *U.S. Private*, pg. 4201
TRACY INDUSTRIES INC.; *U.S. Private*, pg. 4201
TRACY INTERNATIONAL—See Chem-Tainer Industries, Inc.; *U.S. Private*, pg. 871
TRACYLOCKE—See Omnicom Group Inc.; *U.S. Public*, pg. 1599
TRACYLOCKE—See Omnicom Group Inc.; *U.S. Public*, pg. 1599
TRACYLOCKE - WILTON OFFICE—See Omnicom Group Inc.; *U.S. Public*, pg. 1599
TRACY & RYDER LANDSCAPE INC.—See Tracy Industries Inc.; *U.S. Private*, pg. 4201
TRACY TOYOTA SCION; *U.S. Private*, pg. 4201
TRACY VOLKSWAGEN, INC.; *U.S. Private*, pg. 4201
TRACY VOLKSWAGEN; *U.S. Private*, pg. 4201
TRADA; *U.S. Private*, pg. 4201
TRADAVO INC; *U.S. Private*, pg. 4201
T.RAD (CHANGSHU) CO., LTD.—See T.RAD Co., Ltd.; *Int'l*, pg. 7397
T.RAD (CHANGSHU) R&D CENTER CO., LTD.—See T.RAD Co., Ltd.; *Int'l*, pg. 7397
T.RAD CO., LTD. - HATANO WORKS—See T.RAD Co., Ltd.; *Int'l*, pg. 7397
T.RAD CO., LTD. - NAGOYA WORKS—See T.RAD Co., Ltd.; *Int'l*, pg. 7397
T.RAD CO., LTD. - SHIGA WORKS—See T.RAD Co., Ltd.; *Int'l*, pg. 7397
T.RAD CO., LTD.; *Int'l*, pg. 7397
T.RAD CONNECT CO., LTD.—See T.RAD Co., Ltd.; *Int'l*, pg. 7397
TRADCORP S.A.—See BERICAP GmbH & Co. KG; *Int'l*, pg. 981
T.RAD CZECH S.R.O.—See T.RAD Co., Ltd.; *Int'l*, pg. 7397
TRADE ALERT, LLC—See Cboe Global Markets, Inc.; *U.S. Public*, pg. 459
TRADE AM INTERNATIONAL INC.; *U.S. Private*, pg. 4201
TRADE AREA SYSTEMS INC.—See Hanover Investors Management LLP; *Int'l*, pg. 3258
TRADEBE BRASIL—See Grupo Tradebe Medioambiente S.L.; *Int'l*, pg. 3138
TRADEBE ENVIRONMENTAL SERVICES, LLC—See Grupo Tradebe Medioambiente S.L.; *Int'l*, pg. 3138
TRADEBE S.A.R.L.—See Grupo Tradebe Medioambiente S.L.; *Int'l*, pg. 3138
TRADEBE SOLVENT RECYCLING LTD.—See Grupo Tradebe Medioambiente S.L.; *Int'l*, pg. 3138
TRADEBE UK LIMITED—See Grupo Tradebe Medioambiente S.L.; *Int'l*, pg. 3138
TRADEBE USA HOLDINGS, INC—See Grupo Tradebe Medioambiente S.L.; *Int'l*, pg. 3138
TRADE CITY BARTER PRIVATE LIMITED—See Lohia Securities Ltd; *Int'l*, pg. 4543
TRADE CITY REAL ESTATE PRIVATE LIMITED—See Lohia Securities Ltd; *Int'l*, pg. 4543
TRADE CITY SECURITIES PRIVATE LIMITED—See Lohia Securities Ltd; *Int'l*, pg. 4543
TRADECORP DO BRASIL LTDA—See Sapec S.A.; *Int'l*, pg. 6571
TRADECORP FRANCE—See Sapec S.A.; *Int'l*, pg. 6571
TRADE CORPORATION INTERNATIONAL S.A.—See Sapec S.A.; *Int'l*, pg. 6571
TRADE CREDIT BROKERS LIMITED—See Willis Towers Watson Public Limited Company; *Int'l*, pg. 8415
THE TRADE DESK AUSTRALIA PTY LTD—See The Trade Desk, Inc.; *U.S. Public*, pg. 2135
THE TRADE DESK GMBH—See The Trade Desk, Inc.; *U.S. Public*, pg. 2135
THE TRADE DESK, INC.; *U.S. Public*, pg. 2135
THE TRADE DESK JAPAN K.K.—See The Trade Desk, Inc.; *U.S. Public*, pg. 2135
THE TRADE DESK KOREA YUHAN HOESA—See The Trade Desk, Inc.; *U.S. Public*, pg. 2135
THE TRADE DESK (SINGAPORE) PTE. LTD.—See The Trade Desk, Inc.; *U.S. Public*, pg. 2135
THE TRADE DESK SPAIN SRL—See The Trade Desk, Inc.; *U.S. Public*, pg. 2135
TRADE & DEVELOPMENT BANK OF MONGOLIA LLC; *Int'l*, pg. 7887
TRADE DIMENSIONS INTERNATIONAL, INC.—See Brookfield Corporation; *Int'l*, pg. 1180
TRADE DIMENSIONS INTERNATIONAL, INC.—See Elliott Management Corporation; *U.S. Private*, pg. 1373
TRADEDOUBLER AB; *Int'l*, pg. 7887
TRADEDOUBLER BV—See TradeDoubler AB; *Int'l*, pg. 7888
TRADEDOUBLER ESPANA SL—See TradeDoubler AB; *Int'l*, pg. 7888
TRADEDOUBLER GMBH—See TradeDoubler AB; *Int'l*, pg. 7888
TRADEDOUBLER INTERNATIONAL AB—See TradeDoubler AB; *Int'l*, pg. 7888

CORPORATE AFFILIATIONS

TRADEDOUBLER LTD.—See TradeDoubler AB; *Int'l*, pg. 7888
TRADEDOUBLER SP ZOO—See TradeDoubler AB; *Int'l*, pg. 7888
TRADEEASY HOLDINGS LIMITED—See CCT Fortis Holdings Limited; *Int'l*, pg. 1370
TRADE FAIR CORP.; *U.S. Private*, pg. 4201
TRADE & FAIRS CONSULTING—See Messe Munchen GmbH; *Int'l*, pg. 4842
TRADEFLOW CAPITAL MANAGEMENT PTE. LTD.—See Supply@Me Capital plc; *Int'l*, pg. 7340
TRADEGATE AG WERTPAPIERHANDELSBANK; *Int'l*, pg. 7888
TRADEGATE EXCHANGE GMBH—See Deutsche Borse AG; *Int'l*, pg. 2064
TRADEGECKO PTE LTD—See Intuit Inc.; *U.S. Public*, pg. 1160
TRADEGO FINTECH LTD.; *Int'l*, pg. 7888
TRADEGO S.A./N.V.—See Euroclear S.A./N.V.; *Int'l*, pg. 2534
TRADEHOLD LIMITED; *Int'l*, pg. 7888
TRADEHOME SHOE STORES, INC.; *U.S. Private*, pg. 4202
TRADE HOUSE BRP, LTD.—See JSC Borovichi Refractories Plant; *Int'l*, pg. 4008
TRADE HOUSE HILONG-RUS CO. LTD.—See Hilong Holding Limited; *Int'l*, pg. 3393
TRADE HOUSE TMK—See PAO TMK; *Int'l*, pg. 5733
TRADE INSURANCE SERVICES INC—See Munchener Ruckversicherungs AG; *Int'l*, pg. 5092
TRADE LAKE MUTUAL INSURANCE CO, INC.—See River Falls Mutual Insurance Company; *U.S. Private*, pg. 3444
TRADELINK ELECTRONIC COMMERCE LIMITED; *Int'l*, pg. 7888
TRADELINK PLUMBING CENTRES—See Fletcher Building Limited; *Int'l*, pg. 2699
TRADELINK PTY LTD—See Fletcher Building Limited; *Int'l*, pg. 2701
THE TRADEMARK COMPANY; *U.S. Private*, pg. 4127
TRADE MARK CONSTRUCTION, INC.—See Chastain Construction Inc.; *U.S. Private*, pg. 860
TRADEMARK CONSTRUCTION, INC.—See HITT Contracting, Inc.; *U.S. Private*, pg. 1953
TRADEMARK GLOBAL, LLC—See Bertram Capital Management, LLC; *U.S. Private*, pg. 540
TRADEMARK HARDWARE INC.; *U.S. Private*, pg. 4202
TRADE-MARK INDUSTRIAL INC.; *U.S. Private*, pg. 7887
TRADEMARK METALS RECYCLING LLC—See Nucor Corporation; *U.S. Public*, pg. 1554
TRADEMARK RECRUITING INC.; *U.S. Private*, pg. 4202
TRADEMARK ROOFING COMPANY, INC.—See Installed Building Products, Inc.; *U.S. Public*, pg. 1134
TRADE ME GROUP LIMITED—See Apax Partners LLP; *Int'l*, pg. 507
TRADEMOTION, LLC—See The Reynolds & Reynolds Company; *U.S. Private*, pg. 4106
TRADEON AG—See Lloyd Capital AG; *Int'l*, pg. 4536
TRADEONE; *U.S. Private*, pg. 4202
TRADE ONLY DESIGN LIBRARY; *U.S. Private*, pg. 4201
TRADE ONLY INC.—See Altitude Group plc; *Int'l*, pg. 393
TRADE ONLY LIMITED—See Altitude Group plc; *Int'l*, pg. 393
TRADE PARTNERS LIMITED; *Int'l*, pg. 7887
TRADEPORT AB—See Investment AB Latour; *Int'l*, pg. 3784
TRADEPORT FRANKFURT GMBH—See Fraport AG; *Int'l*, pg. 2764
TRADEPORT HONG KONG LTD.—See Fraport AG; *Int'l*, pg. 2764
TRADE PRESS PUBLISHING CORP.; *U.S. Private*, pg. 4202
TRADEPRINT DISTRIBUTION LIMITED—See Cimpress plc; *Int'l*, pg. 1609
TRADE PRODUCTS CORP; *U.S. Private*, pg. 4202
TRADE PROMOTERS LTD.—See Schindler Holding AG; *Int'l*, pg. 6571
TRADE PROMOTION SERVICES LTD.—See Messe Munchen GmbH; *Int'l*, pg. 4842
TRADER.COM (POLSKA) SP. Z O.O—See Agora S.A.; *Int'l*, pg. 213
TRADER CORPORATION—See Thoma Bravo, L.P.; *U.S. Private*, pg. 4154
TRADER DEALER ONLINE PTY. LTD.—See Sequoia Financial Group Limited; *Int'l*, pg. 6720
TRADEREV USA LLC—See OPENLANE, Inc.; *U.S. Public*, pg. 1607
TRADERFOX GMBH—See Axel Springer SE; *Int'l*, pg. 767
TRADER JOE'S CO.—See Aldi Einkauf SE & Co. oHG; *Int'l*, pg. 304
TRADEROS TECHNOLOGIES INC.—See ParcelPal Logistics Inc.; *Int'l*, pg. 5739
TRADERPLANET.COM, LLC; *U.S. Private*, pg. 4202
TRADER'S COVE—See Miller Yacht Sales, Inc.; *U.S. Private*, pg. 2736
TRADERS & FARMERS BANK; *U.S. Private*, pg. 4202
TRADERS HOLDINGS CO., LTD.; *Int'l*, pg. 7888
TRADE SCIENCE CORP.—See Monex Group, Inc.; *Int'l*, pg. 5032

2794

COMPANY NAME INDEX

TRADE SERVICE CO. LLC—See Trimble, Inc.; *U.S. Public*, pg. 2191
TRADE SERVICE HOLDINGS INC.—See Trimble, Inc.; *U.S. Public*, pg. 2191
TRADE SETTLEMENT, INC.—See Virtus Partners LLC; *U.S. Private*, pg. 4389
TRADESHIFT INC.; *U.S. Private*, pg. 4202
TRADESIGNAL GMBH—See TMX Group Limited; *Int'l*, pg. 7767
TRADESMEN INTERNATIONAL, LLC—See Blackstone Inc.; *U.S. Public*, pg. 361
TRADESOURCE INC.; *U.S. Private*, pg. 4202
TRADE SOURCE INTERNATIONAL, INC.—See Craftmade International, Inc.; *U.S. Private*, pg. 1082
TRADESTAR CORPORATION—See Incitec Pivot Limited; *Int'l*, pg. 3648
TRADESTAR INVESTMENTS, INC.—See Fiserv, Inc.; *U.S. Public*, pg. 851
TRADESTATION EUROPE LIMITED—See Monex Group, Inc.; *Int'l*, pg. 5032
TRADESTATION GROUP, INC.—See Monex Group, Inc.; *Int'l*, pg. 5032
TRADESTATION SECURITIES, INC.—See Monex Group, Inc.; *Int'l*, pg. 5032
TRADES UNLIMITED; *U.S. Private*, pg. 4202
TRADE SUPPLIES, LLC—See Sole Source Capital LLC; *U.S. Private*, pg. 3708
TRADETEAM LIMITED—See Deutsche Post AG; *Int'l*, pg. 2078
TRADETECH CONSULTING SCANDINAVIA AB—See EQT AB; *Int'l*, pg. 2472
TRADETEC SKYLINE; *U.S. Private*, pg. 4202
TRADETHEMARKETS.COM; *U.S. Private*, pg. 4202
TRADE THE MARKETS; *U.S. Private*, pg. 4202
TRADETICITY D.O.O.—See Antares Vision SpA; *Int'l*, pg. 482
TRADETICITY SERVICE D.O.O.—See Antares Vision SpA; *Int'l*, pg. 482
TRADETOOL AUTO CO., LTD.; *Int'l*, pg. 7888
TRADE UNION COOPERATIVE INSURANCE & REINSURANCE COMPANY; *Int'l*, pg. 7887
TRADEUP 88 CORP.; *U.S. Private*, pg. 2178
TRADEUP SECURITIES INC.—See UP Fintech Holding Limited; *Int'l*, pg. 8086
TRADE-VAN INFORMATION SERVICES CO.; *Int'l*, pg. 7887
TRADE VISION, LTD.—See BIPROGY Inc.; *Int'l*, pg. 1045
TRADEWAY (SHIPPING) LIMITED—See Santova Ltd.; *Int'l*, pg. 6559
TRADEWEB COMMERCIAL INFORMATION CONSULTING (SHANGHAI) CO., LTD.—See Tradeweb Markets Inc.; *U.S. Public*, pg. 2178
TRADEWEB EU B.V.—See Tradeweb Markets Inc.; *U.S. Public*, pg. 2178
TRADEWEB EUROPE LIMITED—See Tradeweb Markets Inc.; *U.S. Public*, pg. 2178
TRADEWEB JAPAN K.K.—See Tradeweb Markets Inc.; *U.S. Public*, pg. 2178
TRADEWEB LLC—See Tradeweb Markets Inc.; *U.S. Public*, pg. 2178
TRADEWEB MARKETS INC.; *U.S. Public*, pg. 2178
TRADEWEB MARKETS LLC—See Tradeweb Markets Inc.; *U.S. Public*, pg. 2178
TRADEWIND INSURANCE COMPANY, LTD.—See Island Holdings, Inc.; *U.S. Private*, pg. 2145
TRADEWINDS A/S—See Fred. Olsen & Co.; *Int'l*, pg. 2768
TRADEWINDS-ATHENS—See Fred. Olsen & Co.; *Int'l*, pg. 2768
TRADEWINDS CHEMICALS CORPORATION—See BASF SE; *Int'l*, pg. 876
TRADEWINDS CORPORATION BERHAD; *Int'l*, pg. 7888
TRADEWINDS DISTRIBUTING COMPANY, LLC—See Watsco, Inc.; *U.S. Public*, pg. 2337
TRADEWINDS GLOBAL INVESTORS, LLC—See Teachers Insurance Association - College Retirement Fund; *U.S. Private*, pg. 3948
TRADEWINDS HOTELS & RESORTS SDN. BHD.—See Tradewinds Corporation Berhad; *Int'l*, pg. 7888
TRADEWINDS INSURANCE, INC.—See Linde plc; *Int'l*, pg. 4510
TRADEWINDS INTERNATIONAL INSURANCE BROKERS SDN. BHD.—See Tradewinds Corporation Berhad; *Int'l*, pg. 7888
TRADEWINDS ISLANDS RESORTS ON SAINT PETE BEACH—See Resort Inns of America Inc.; *U.S. Private*, pg. 3406
TRADEWINDS-ITALY—See Fred. Olsen & Co.; *Int'l*, pg. 2768
TRADEWINDS JOHOR SDN. BHD.—See Tradewinds Corporation Berhad; *Int'l*, pg. 7889
TRADEWINDS-LONDON—See Fred. Olsen & Co.; *Int'l*, pg. 2768
TRADEWINDS MECHANICAL SERVICES, LLC.; *U.S. Private*, pg. 4202
TRADEWINDS-NEW DELHI—See Fred. Olsen & Co.; *Int'l*, pg. 2768
TRADEWINDS PLANTATION BERHAD; *Int'l*, pg. 7889
TRADEWINDS POWER CORP.—See Southeast Diesel Corp.; *U.S. Private*, pg. 3725

TRADEWINDS PROPERTIES SDN. BHD.—See Tradewinds Corporation Berhad; *Int'l*, pg. 7889
TRADEWINDS TOURS & TRAVEL PTE LTD.—See Temasek Holdings (Private) Limited; *Int'l*, pg. 7551
TRADEWINDS TRAVEL & TOURS SDN. BHD.—See Tradewinds Corporation Berhad; *Int'l*, pg. 7889
TRADE WINGS, INC.; *U.S. Private*, pg. 4202
TRADE WINGS LIMITED; *Int'l*, pg. 7887
TRADEWISE ADVISORS, INC.—See The Charles Schwab Corporation; *U.S. Public*, pg. 2058
TRADE WORKS ASIA LIMITED—See Transaction Co., Ltd.; *Int'l*, pg. 7895
TRADE WORKS CO., LTD.—See Transaction Co., Ltd.; *Int'l*, pg. 7895
TRADE WORKS CO., LTD.; *Int'l*, pg. 7887
TRADEWORKS GROUP INC.—See One Rock Capital Partners, LLC; *U.S. Private*, pg. 3022
TRADEX FOODS INC.; *Int'l*, pg. 7889
TRADEX INTERNATIONAL, INC.; *U.S. Private*, pg. 4202
TRADE X PARTNERS LLC—See Stagwell, Inc.; *U.S. Public*, pg. 1928
TRAD HIRE & SALES LTD.—See Altrad Investment Authority SAS; *Int'l*, pg. 398
TRADIA CORPORATION; *Int'l*, pg. 7889
TRADINCO INSTRUMENTEN-APPARATEN B.V.—See Indutrade AB; *Int'l*, pg. 3681
TRADING AND DISTRIBUTION LIMITED—See Massy Holdings Ltd.; *Int'l*, pg. 4724
TRADING CO. STORES, FOOD & DRUG—See Bonner Foods Inc.; *U.S. Private*, pg. 614
TRADING COVE ASSOCIATES—See Kerzner International Limited; *Int'l*, pg. 4141
TRADING COVE ASSOCIATES—See Waterford Group, LLC; *U.S. Private*, pg. 4453
TRADING EMISSIONS PLC; *Int'l*, pg. 7889
TRADING HOUSE KAMA LLC—See PJSC Tatneft; *Int'l*, pg. 5885
TRADING PLACES INTERNATIONAL, LLC—See Marriott Vacations Worldwide Corporation; *U.S. Public*, pg. 1374
TRADING POST MANAGEMENT COMPANY, LLC; *U.S. Private*, pg. 4202
TRADING TECHNOLOGIES INTERNATIONAL, INC.; *U.S. Private*, pg. 4202
TRADIN ORGANICS USA, INC.—See SunOpta Inc.; *Int'l*, pg. 7320
TRADINSA INDUSTRIAL, S.L.—See Construcciones y Auxiliar de Ferrocarriles S.A.; *Int'l*, pg. 1777
TRADI S.A.; *Int'l*, pg. 7889
TRADITAL S.P.A.—See Domus Fin S.A.; *Int'l*, pg. 2162
TRADITIE N. V.—See HEINRICH DE FRIES GmbH; *Int'l*, pg. 3324
TRADITIONAL BAKERY INC.; *U.S. Private*, pg. 4202
TRADITIONAL BAKERY INC.—See Traditional Bakery Inc.; *U.S. Private*, pg. 4202
TRADITIONAL BANCORPORATION; *U.S. Private*, pg. 4203
TRADITIONAL BANK, INC.—See Traditional Bancorporation; *U.S. Private*, pg. 4203
TRADITIONAL HOME—See Meredith Corporation; *U.S. Public*, pg. 1423
TRADITIONAL JEWELERS, INC.; *U.S. Private*, pg. 4203
TRADITIONAL SERVICE COMPANY, LLC—See Traditional Service Corporation; *U.S. Private*, pg. 4203
TRADITIONAL SERVICE CORPORATION; *U.S. Private*, pg. 4203
TRADITIONAL TRADE MANAGEMENT CO., LTD.—See Thai Beverage Public Company Limited; *Int'l*, pg. 7592
TRADITION ARGENTINA SA—See Viel & Compagnie SA; *Int'l*, pg. 8193
TRADITION (ASIA) LTD.—See Viel & Compagnie SA; *Int'l*, pg. 8193
TRADITION ASIEL SECURITIES INC.—See Viel & Compagnie SA; *Int'l*, pg. 8193
TRADITION (BEAUFORT HOUSE) LTD—See Viel & Compagnie SA; *Int'l*, pg. 8193
TRADITION BOND BROKERS LTD—See Viel & Compagnie SA; *Int'l*, pg. 8193
TRADITION CHEVROLET BUICK, INC.—See General Motors Company; *U.S. Public*, pg. 929
TRADITION CHILE AGENTES DE VALORES LIMITADA—See Viel & Compagnie SA; *Int'l*, pg. 8193
TRADITION FINANCIAL SERVICES GMBH—See Viel & Compagnie SA; *Int'l*, pg. 8193
TRADITION FINANCIAL SERVICES INC.—See Viel & Compagnie SA; *Int'l*, pg. 8193
TRADITION FINANCIAL SERVICES JAPAN LTD—See Viel & Compagnie SA; *Int'l*, pg. 8193
TRADITION FINANCIAL SERVICES LTD—See Viel & Compagnie SA; *Int'l*, pg. 8193
TRADITION FINE FOODS LTD.; *Int'l*, pg. 7889
TRADITION (GLOBAL CLEARING) INC.—See Viel & Compagnie SA; *Int'l*, pg. 8193
TRADITION (GOVERNMENT SECURITIES) INC.—See Viel & Compagnie SA; *Int'l*, pg. 8193
TRADITION HILTON HEAD, LLC—See Hilton Grand Vacations Inc.; *U.S. Public*, pg. 1040
TRADITION ITALIA SIM S.P.A—See Viel & Compagnie SA; *Int'l*, pg. 8193

TRAFIGURA BEHEER B.V.

TRADITION (LONDON CLEARING) LTD—See Viel & Compagnie SA; *Int'l*, pg. 8193
TRADITION LUXEMBOURG S.A.—See Viel & Compagnie SA; *Int'l*, pg. 8193
TRADITION (NORTH AMERICA) INC.—See Viel & Compagnie SA; *Int'l*, pg. 8193
TRADITION REALTY, LLC—See Hilton Grand Vacations Inc.; *U.S. Public*, pg. 1040
TRADITION SECURITIES AND FUTURES S.A.—See Viel & Compagnie SA; *Int'l*, pg. 8193
TRADITION SERVICES S.A. DE C.V.—See Viel & Compagnie SA; *Int'l*, pg. 8193
TRADITIONS HEALTH, LLC—See Dorilton Capital Advisors LLC; *U.S. Private*, pg. 1263
TRADITION SINGAPORE (PTE) LTD—See Viel & Compagnie SA; *Int'l*, pg. 8193
TRADITION TITLE COMPANY, LLC—See Hilton Grand Vacations Inc.; *U.S. Public*, pg. 1040
TRADITION (UK) LTD—See Viel & Compagnie SA; *Int'l*, pg. 8193
T.RAD NORTH AMERICA, INC.—See T.RAD Co., Ltd.; *Int'l*, pg. 7397
T.RAD NORTH AMERICA, INC. - TRA C/B DIVISION—See T.RAD Co., Ltd.; *Int'l*, pg. 7397
TRADOS GMBH—See RWS Holdings plc; *Int'l*, pg. 6438
T.RAD SALES EUROPE GMBH—See T.RAD Co., Ltd.; *Int'l*, pg. 7397
TRAD SCAFFOLDING COMPANY LTD—See Altrad Investment Authority SAS; *Int'l*, pg. 398
T.RAD (THAILAND) CO., LTD.—See T.RAD Co., Ltd.; *Int'l*, pg. 7397
T.RAD (ZHONGSHAN) CO., LTD.—See T.RAD Co., Ltd.; *Int'l*, pg. 7397
TRAEGER, INC.; *U.S. Public*, pg. 2179
TRAEGER PELLET GRILLS LLC; *U.S. Private*, pg. 4203
TRAFAIR CAPITAL AG; *Int'l*, pg. 7889
THE TRAFALGAR COMPANY—See Randa Corp.; *U.S. Private*, pg. 3353
TRAFALGAR CORPORATE PTY. LIMITED—See Centuria Capital Limited; *Int'l*, pg. 1416
THE TRAFALGAR GROUP; *Int'l*, pg. 7696
TRAFALGAR INSURANCE COMPANY OF CANADA—See Intact Financial Corporation; *Int'l*, pg. 3726
TRAFALGAR INSURANCE PUBLIC LIMITED COMPANY—See Allianz SE; *Int'l*, pg. 356
TRAFALGAR MANAGED INVESTMENTS LIMITED—See Centuria Capital Limited; *Int'l*, pg. 1416
TRAFALGAR PROPERTY GROUP PLC; *Int'l*, pg. 7889
TRAFALGAR RETIREMENT + LIMITED—See Trafalgar Property Group Plc; *Int'l*, pg. 7889
TRAFALGAR SECURITIES LIMITED—See The Trafalgar Group; *Int'l*, pg. 7696
TRAFCO GROUP B.S.C.; *Int'l*, pg. 7889
TRAFCON INC.—See Constructors Inc.; *U.S. Private*, pg. 1025
TRAFERA, LLC—See Rotunda Capital Partners LLC; *U.S. Private*, pg. 3488
TRAFFICCAST INTERNATIONAL, INC—See Almaviva S.p.A.; *Int'l*, pg. 363
TRAFFIC.CLUB IT GMBH—See Team Internet Group plc; *Int'l*, pg. 7500
TRAFFIC CONTROL DEVICES INC.; *U.S. Private*, pg. 4203
TRAFFIC CONTROL TECHNOLOGY CO., LTD.; *Int'l*, pg. 7889
TRAFFIC MANAGEMENT PRODUCTS LTD.—See Dewhurst Group plc; *Int'l*, pg. 2091
THE TRAFFIC MARSHAL PTY LTD.—See AVADA Group Limited; *Int'l*, pg. 734
TRAFFICMASTER LTD—See Vector Capital Management, L.P.; *U.S. Private*, pg. 4353
TRAFFIC & PARKING CONTROL CO., INC.; *U.S. Private*, pg. 4203
TRAFFIC PLANNING & DESIGN, INC.; *U.S. Private*, pg. 4203
TRAFFIC PLANNING & DESIGN INC.—See Traffic Planning & Design, Inc.; *U.S. Private*, pg. 4203
TRAFFIC RESEARCH & ANALYSIS, INC.—See Rekor Systems, Inc.; *U.S. Public*, pg. 1778
TRAFFIC SERVICES, INC.—See Jacobs Engineering Group, Inc.; *U.S. Public*, pg. 1186
TRAFFIC TECHNOLOGIES LTD.; *Int'l*, pg. 7889
TRAFFIPAX, LLC—See Jenoptik AG; *Int'l*, pg. 3929
TRAFFIX, INC.—See Protagenic Therapeutics, Inc.; *U.S. Public*, pg. 1729
TRAFFORD HOLDINGS LTD.; *Int'l*, pg. 7889
TRAFFORD PUBLISHING, INC.—See Trafford Holdings Ltd.; *Int'l*, pg. 7889
TRAFFORD VAN CENTRE LTD—See Ballyvesey Holdings Limited; *Int'l*, pg. 809
TRAFICO DE MERCANCIAS S.A—See Israel Corporation Ltd.; *Int'l*, pg. 3823
TRAFICTOURS DE MEXICO S.A. DE C.V.—See Transat A.T., Inc.; *Int'l*, pg. 7896
TRAFIGURA AG—See Trafigura Beheer B.V.; *Int'l*, pg. 7890
TRAFIGURA BEHEER B.V.; *Int'l*, pg. 7889
TRAFIGURA CALGARY LTD.—See Trafigura Beheer B.V.; *Int'l*, pg. 7890

TRAFIGURA BEHEER B.V.   CORPORATE AFFILIATIONS

TRAFIGURA CHILE LIMITADA—See Trafigura Beheer B.V.; *Int'l*, pg. 7890
TRAFIGURA EURASIA LLC—See Trafigura Beheer B.V.; *Int'l*, pg. 7890
TRAFIGURA INDIA PRIVATE LIMITED—See Trafigura Beheer B.V.; *Int'l*, pg. 7890
TRAFIGURA INVESTMENT (CHINA) CO., LTD.—See Trafigura Beheer B.V.; *Int'l*, pg. 7890
TRAFIGURA MEXICO, S.A. DE C.V.—See Trafigura Beheer B.V.; *Int'l*, pg. 7890
TRAFIGURA PERU S.A.C.—See Trafigura Beheer B.V.; *Int'l*, pg. 7890
TRAFIGURA PTE. LTD.—See Trafigura Beheer B.V.; *Int'l*, pg. 7890
TRAFIGURA SERVICES SOUTH AFRICA (PTY) LTD—See Trafigura Beheer B.V.; *Int'l*, pg. 7890
TRAFIURBE, S.A.—See ACS, Actividades de Construccion y Servicios, S.A.; *Int'l*, pg. 116
TRAFO CZ, A.S.—See CEZ, a.s.; *Int'l*, pg. 1429
TRAFON GROUP; *U.S. Private*, pg. 4203
TRAIANA, INC.—See CME Group, Inc.; *U.S. Public*, pg. 517
TRAIANA TECHNOLOGIES LIMITED—See CME Group, Inc.; *U.S. Public*, pg. 518
TRAIL APPLIANCES; *Int'l*, pg. 7890
TRAILAR LIMITED—See Deutsche Post AG; *Int'l*, pg. 2082
TRAILBLAZER RESOURCES, INC.; *U.S. Public*, pg. 2179
THE TRAILERBARROW CO.—See Elsan Ltd.; *Int'l*, pg. 2370
TRAILER BOSS; *U.S. Private*, pg. 4203
TRAILER BRIDGE, INC.; *U.S. Private*, pg. 4203
THE TRAILERFARM LIMITED—See Canada Pension Plan Investment Board; *Int'l*, pg. 1281
THE TRAILERFARM LIMITED—See EQT AB; *Int'l*, pg. 2483
THE TRAILERFARM LIMITED—See Temasek Holdings (Private) Limited; *Int'l*, pg. 7548
TRAILER PARK; *U.S. Private*, pg. 4203
TRAILERS DIRECT—See Bain Capital, LP; *U.S. Private*, pg. 436
TRAILER SOURCE INC.; *U.S. Private*, pg. 4203
TRAILER WHEEL & FRAME COMPANY; *U.S. Private*, pg. 4204
TRAIL-EZE TRAILERS—See Dakota Manufacturing Co. Inc.; *U.S. Private*, pg. 1147
TRAILINER CORP.; *U.S. Private*, pg. 4204
TRAIL KING INDUSTRIES, INC.—See Henry Crown & Company; *U.S. Private*, pg. 1918
TRAIL MOUNTAIN INC.—See EOG Resources, Inc.; *U.S. Public*, pg. 782
TRAIL RIDGE LANDFILL, INC.—See Waste Management, Inc.; *U.S. Public*, pg. 2332
TRAILS AT NORTHPOINT MISSISSIPPI MEMBER, LLC—See RAIT Financial Trust; *U.S. Private*, pg. 3349
TRAILS EDGE SURGERY CENTER, LLC—See UnitedHealth Group Incorporated; *U.S. Public*, pg. 2251
TRAILSIDE CAMPERS RV SALES, INC.; *U.S. Private*, pg. 4204
TRAILSTONE AUSTRALIA PTY LTD—See TrailStone LLP; *Int'l*, pg. 7890
TRAILSTONE DIALYSIS, LLC—See DaVita Inc.; *U.S. Public*, pg. 644
TRAILSTONE GMBH—See TrailStone LLP; *Int'l*, pg. 7890
TRAILSTONE LLP; *Int'l*, pg. 7890
TRAILSTONE MANAGEMENT CORP—See TrailStone LLP; *Int'l*, pg. 7890
TRAILSTONE NETHERLANDS I COOPERATIEF U.A.—See TrailStone LLP; *Int'l*, pg. 7890
TRAILWOOD TRANSPORTATION INC.; *U.S. Private*, pg. 4204
TRAINELEC, S.L.—See Construcciones y Auxiliar de Ferrocarriles S.A.; *Int'l*, pg. 1777
TRAINER COMMUNICATIONS; *U.S. Private*, pg. 4204
TRAINERS' HOUSE PLC; *Int'l*, pg. 7890
TRAINICO TRAINING UND AUSBILDUNG COOPERATION IN BERLIN BRANDENBURG GMBH—See Deutsche Lufthansa AG; *Int'l*, pg. 2070
TRAINING AND RESEARCH FOUNDATION; *U.S. Private*, pg. 4204
THE TRAINING ASSOCIATES (TTA); *U.S. Private*, pg. 4127
TRAININGFOLKS; *U.S. Private*, pg. 4204
TRAINING FORCE (PROPRIETARY) LIMITED—See Workforce Holdings Ltd.; *Int'l*, pg. 8456
TRAINING TOWARD SELF-RELIANCE, INC.; *U.S. Private*, pg. 4204
TRAINLINE PLC—See Exponent Private Equity LLP; *Int'l*, pg. 2590
TRAIN OILFIELD SERVICES LTD.—See APi Group Corporation; *Int'l*, pg. 514
TRAINOR GRAIN & SUPPLY CO.; *U.S. Private*, pg. 4204
TRAINOSE SA—See Ferrovie dello Stato Italiane S.p.A.; *Int'l*, pg. 2645
TRAIN SIGNAL INC.; *U.S. Private*, pg. 4204
TRAIN TRAILER RENTALS LIMITED—See Bravia Capital Hong Kong Limited; *Int'l*, pg. 1141
TRAIN TRAVEL, INC.—See United Rail, Inc.; *U.S. Public*, pg. 2234
TRAIS CO., LTD.; *Int'l*, pg. 7890

TRAITAFINA AG; *Int'l*, pg. 7890
TRAITAL S.R.L.—See BKW AG; *Int'l*, pg. 1056
TRAITOMIC A/S—See Carlsberg A/S; *Int'l*, pg. 1341
TRAJAN GROUP HOLDINGS LIMITED; *Int'l*, pg. 7891
TRAJANO IBERIA SOCIMI SA; *Int'l*, pg. 7891
TRAJAN SCIENTIFIC & MEDICAL PTY LTD.—See Trajan Group Holdings Limited; *Int'l*, pg. 7891
TRAJECTOR, INC.; *U.S. Private*, pg. 4204
TRAJEN FLIGHT SUPPORT, LP—See Macquarie Group Limited; *Int'l*, pg. 4628
TRAJEN INC.; *U.S. Private*, pg. 4204
TRAJEN LIMITED, LLC—See Macquarie Group Limited; *Int'l*, pg. 4628
TRAKA PLC—See ASSA ABLOY AB; *Int'l*, pg. 640
TRAKA RESOURCES LIMITED; *Int'l*, pg. 7891
TRAKCJA PRKII S.A.; *Int'l*, pg. 7891
TRAKIISKO PIVO AD; *Int'l*, pg. 7891
TRAKKER MIDDLE EAST LLC—See Al Jaber Group; *Int'l*, pg. 280
TRAKM8 HOLDINGS PLC; *Int'l*, pg. 7891
TRAKM8 LIMITED—See Trakm8 Holdings PLC; *Int'l*, pg. 7891
TRAKM8 S.R.O.—See Trakm8 Holdings PLC; *Int'l*, pg. 7891
TRAK MICROWAVE CORPORATION—See Smiths Group plc; *Int'l*, pg. 7012
TRAK MICROWAVE LTD.—See Smiths Group plc; *Int'l*, pg. 7012
TRAKNIAGA SDN. BHD; *Int'l*, pg. 7891
TRAKOPOLIS IOT CORP.; *Int'l*, pg. 7891
TRAKYA CAM SANAYII A.S.—See Turkiye Is Bankasi A.S.; *Int'l*, pg. 7976
TRAKYA ET VE SUT URUNLERI SAN. TIC. A.S.—See Siniora Food Industries P.L.C.; *Int'l*, pg. 6945
TRAKYA GLASS BULGARIA EAD—See Turkiye Sise ve Cam Fabrikalari A.S.; *Int'l*, pg. 7977
TRAKYA GLASS RUS AO—See Turkiye Sise ve Cam Fabrikalari A.S.; *Int'l*, pg. 7977
TRAKYA POLATLI CAM SANAYII A.S.—See Turkiye Sise ve Cam Fabrikalari A.S.; *Int'l*, pg. 7977
TRAKYA YENISEHIR CAM SANAYII A.S.—See Turkiye Sise ve Cam Fabrikalari A.S.; *Int'l*, pg. 7977
TRALLIANCE CORPORATION—See theglobe.com, inc.; *U.S. Public*, pg. 2144
TRAMAC CORPORATION; *U.S. Private*, pg. 4204
TRAMADA SYSTEMS PTY. LTD.—See Corporate Travel Management Limited; *Int'l*, pg. 1806
TRAMCO EUROPE LIMITED—See Ag Growth International Inc.; *Int'l*, pg. 198
TRAMCO INC.—See Ag Growth International Inc.; *Int'l*, pg. 198
TRAM DATA, LLC; *U.S. Private*, pg. 4204
TRAMEC CONTINENTAL-AERO, LLC—See MacLean-Fogg Company; *U.S. Private*, pg. 2537
TRAMEC HILL FASTENER, LLC—See MacLean-Fogg Company; *U.S. Private*, pg. 2537
TRAMEC LLC—See MacLean-Fogg Company; *U.S. Private*, pg. 2537
TRAMEC SLOAN, LLC—See MacLean-Fogg Company; *U.S. Private*, pg. 2537
TRAM, INC.—See Tokai Rika Co., Ltd.; *Int'l*, pg. 7780
TRAMMELL CROW COMPANY, LLC—See CBRE Group, Inc.; *U.S. Public*, pg. 460
TRAMMELL CROW SERVICES, INC.—See CBRE Group, Inc.; *U.S. Public*, pg. 460
TRAMMO AG—See Trammo, Inc.; *U.S. Private*, pg. 4204
TRAMMO AG—See Trammo, Inc.; *U.S. Private*, pg. 4204
TRAMMOCHEM A.G.—See Trammo, Inc.; *U.S. Private*, pg. 4204
TRAMMOCHEM—See Trammo, Inc.; *U.S. Private*, pg. 4204
TRAMMO GAS DOMESTIC—See Trammo, Inc.; *U.S. Private*, pg. 4204
TRAMMO GAS INTERNATIONAL, INC.—See Trammo, Inc.; *U.S. Private*, pg. 4204
TRAMMO, INC.; *U.S. Private*, pg. 4204
TRAMMO INDIA PVT. LIMITED—See Trammo, Inc.; *U.S. Private*, pg. 4204
TRAMMO LTD.—See Trammo, Inc.; *U.S. Private*, pg. 4204
TRAMMO MAGHREB S.A.R.L.—See Trammo, Inc.; *U.S. Private*, pg. 4204
TRAMMO PETROLEUM, INC.—See Trammo, Inc.; *U.S. Private*, pg. 4204
TRAMMO PTE LTD.—See Trammo, Inc.; *U.S. Private*, pg. 4204
TRAM OPERATIONS LIMITED—See FirstGroup plc; *Int'l*, pg. 2689
TRAMP OIL (BRASIL) LIMITADA—See World Kinect Corporation; *U.S. Public*, pg. 2381
TRAMP OIL DISTRIBUIDORA LTDA.—See World Kinect Corporation; *U.S. Public*, pg. 2381
TRAMP OIL GERMANY GMBH & CO KG—See World Kinect Corporation; *U.S. Public*, pg. 2381
TRAMP OIL SCHIFFAHRTS-UND HANDELSGESELLSCHAFT GMBH—See World Kinect Corporation; *U.S. Public*, pg. 2381
TRAMZ HOTELS INC.; *U.S. Private*, pg. 4205
TRANAB MARKBYGGNAD AB—See Peab AB; *Int'l*, pg. 5773

TRAN ANH DIGITAL WORLD JOINT STOCK COMPANY—See Mobile World Investment Corporation; *Int'l*, pg. 5011
TRANAUTO; *Int'l*, pg. 7891
TRANAX TECHNOLOGIES INC.; *U.S. Private*, pg. 4205
TRANBERG AS—See R. STAHL AG; *Int'l*, pg. 6170
TRANCE PACIFIC INSURANCE COMPANY—See Tokio Marine Holdings, Inc.; *Int'l*, pg. 7785
TRANCOM BANGKOK CO., LTD.—See Japan Logistic Systems Corp.; *Int'l*, pg. 3899
TRANCOM CO., LTD.; *Int'l*, pg. 7891
TRANCOM DS CO., LTD.—See Trancom Co., Ltd.; *Int'l*, pg. 7891
TRANCOM ITS CO., LTD.—See Trancom Co., Ltd.; *Int'l*, pg. 7891
TRANCOS, INC.; *U.S. Private*, pg. 4205
TRANCY LOGISTICS AMERICA—See Japan Transcity Corporation; *Int'l*, pg. 3907
TRANCY LOGISTICS (EUROPE) GMBH—See Japan Transcity Corporation; *Int'l*, pg. 3907
TRANCY LOGISTICS (H.K.) LTD—See Japan Transcity Corporation; *Int'l*, pg. 3907
TRANCY LOGISTICS (MALAYSIA) SDN. BHD—See Japan Transcity Corporation; *Int'l*, pg. 3907
TRANCY LOGISTICS MEXICO S.A. DE C.V.—See Japan Transcity Corporation; *Int'l*, pg. 3907
TRANCY LOGISTICS (PHILIPPINES), INC—See Japan Transcity Corporation; *Int'l*, pg. 3907
TRANCY LOGISTICS(SHANGHAI)CO.,LTD.—See Japan Transcity Corporation; *Int'l*, pg. 3907
TRANCY LOGISTICS (SINGAPORE) PTE LTD—See Japan Transcity Corporation; *Int'l*, pg. 3907
TRANCY LOGISTICS (THAILAND) CO., LTD.—See Japan Transcity Corporation; *Int'l*, pg. 3907
TRANCY LOGISTICS(VIETNAM)CO.,LTD.—See Japan Transcity Corporation; *Int'l*, pg. 3907
TRANDES CORPORATION; *U.S. Private*, pg. 4205
TRANDS AD VIETNAM JOINT STOCK COMPANY—See BTS Group Holdings Public Company Limited; *Int'l*, pg. 1206
TRANE AIRCONDITIONING BV—See Trane Technologies Plc; *Int'l*, pg. 7892
TRANE AIR CONDITIONING SYSTEMS (CHINA) CO. LTD.—See Trane Technologies Plc; *Int'l*, pg. 7892
TRANE AIRE ACONDICIANDO S.L.—See Trane Technologies Plc; *Int'l*, pg. 7892
TRANE BELO HORIZONTE—See Trane Technologies Plc; *Int'l*, pg. 7893
TRANE CANADA LP—See Trane Technologies Plc; *Int'l*, pg. 7892
TRANE CANADA ULC—See Trane Technologies Plc; *Int'l*, pg. 7892
TRANE CENTRAL AMERICA, INC.—See Trane Technologies Plc; *Int'l*, pg. 7893
TRANE CENTRAL ONTARIO—See Trane Technologies Plc; *Int'l*, pg. 7893
TRANE COMFORT SOLUTIONS INC.—See Trane Technologies Plc; *Int'l*, pg. 7893
THE TRANE COMPANY—See Trane Technologies Plc; *Int'l*, pg. 7892
TRANE CR SPOL. S.R.O.—See Trane Technologies Plc; *Int'l*, pg. 7893
TRANE DE ARGENTINA S.A.—See Trane Technologies Plc; *Int'l*, pg. 7893
TRANE DE CHILE SA—See Trane Technologies Plc; *Int'l*, pg. 7893
TRANE DE COLOMBIA, SA—See Trane Technologies Plc; *Int'l*, pg. 7893
TRANE DE MEXICO, S.A. DE C.V.—See Trane Technologies Plc; *Int'l*, pg. 7892
TRANE DESIGN CENTRE PRIVATE LTD.—See Trane Technologies Plc; *Int'l*, pg. 7892
TRANE DEUTSCHLAND GMBH—See Ingersoll Rand Inc.; *U.S. Public*, pg. 1122
TRANE DISTRIBUTION PTE LTD—See Trane Technologies Plc; *Int'l*, pg. 7892
TRANE DO BRASIL INDUSTRIA E COMERCIO DE PRODUCTOS PARA CONDICIONAMENTO DE AR LTDA.—See Trane Technologies Plc; *Int'l*, pg. 7892
TRANE DOMINCANA, C. POR A.—See Trane Technologies Plc; *Int'l*, pg. 7892
TRANE EQUIPMENT/CONTROLS/PARTS—See Trane Technologies Plc; *Int'l*, pg. 7893
TRANE EUROPE HOLDINGS B.V.—See Trane Technologies Plc; *Int'l*, pg. 7892
TRANE GMBH—See Trane Technologies Plc; *Int'l*, pg. 7893
TRANE HELLAS SA—See Trane Technologies Plc; *Int'l*, pg. 7893
TRANE HUNGARY KFT.—See Trane Technologies Plc; *Int'l*, pg. 7893
TRANE INC. OF DELAWARE—See Trane Technologies Plc; *Int'l*, pg. 7893
TRANE INC.—See Trane Technologies Plc; *Int'l*, pg. 7892
TRANE (IRELAND) LTD.—See Trane Technologies Plc; *Int'l*, pg. 7893
TRANE ITALIA S.R.L—See Trane Technologies Plc; *Int'l*, pg. 7892

COMPANY NAME INDEX

TRANE JAPAN, LTD.—See Trane Technologies Plc; *Int'l*, pg. 7893
TRANE KLIMA TICARET A.S.—See Trane Technologies Plc; *Int'l*, pg. 7893
TRANE KOREA, INC.—See Trane Technologies Plc; *Int'l*, pg. 7893
TRANE LEASING SERVICES—See Trane Technologies Plc; *Int'l*, pg. 7893
TRANE MALAYSIA SALES & SERVICES SDN. BHD.—See Trane Technologies Plc; *Int'l*, pg. 7893
TRANE - NASHVILLE—See Trane Technologies Plc; *Int'l*, pg. 7893
TRANE PHILLIPINES—See Trane Technologies Plc; *Int'l*, pg. 7893
TRANE POLSKA SP. Z.O.O.—See Trane Technologies Plc; *Int'l*, pg. 7893
TRANE PUERTO RICO INC.—See Trane Technologies Plc; *Int'l*, pg. 7893
TRANE REINETSU SERVICE, LTD.—See Trane Technologies Plc; *Int'l*, pg. 7893
TRANE ROMANIA S.R.L—See Trane Technologies Plc; *Int'l*, pg. 7892
TRANE, S.A. DE C.V.—See Trane Technologies Plc; *Int'l*, pg. 7892
TRANE (SCHWEIZ) AG—See Trane Technologies Plc; *Int'l*, pg. 7893
TRANE SERVICE HONG KONG—See Trane Technologies Plc; *Int'l*, pg. 7893
TRANE SERVICFIRST C.A.—See Trane Technologies Plc; *Int'l*, pg. 7893
TRANE SINGAPORE—See Trane Technologies Plc; *Int'l*, pg. 7893
TRANE SWEDEN AB—See Trane Technologies Plc; *Int'l*, pg. 7893
TRANE TECHNOLOGIES LLC—See Trane Technologies Plc; *Int'l*, pg. 7893
TRANE TECHNOLOGIES PLC; *Int'l*, pg. 7891
TRANE THAILAND LTD.—See Trane Technologies Plc; *Int'l*, pg. 7893
TRANE (UNITED KINGDOM) LTD.—See Trane Technologies Plc; *Int'l*, pg. 7893
TRANE U.S. INC.—See Trane Technologies Plc; *Int'l*, pg. 7893
TRANE VIDALIA LLC—See Trane Technologies Plc; *Int'l*, pg. 7000
TRANE VIETNAM SERVICES COMPANY LTD.—See Trane Technologies Plc; *Int'l*, pg. 7892
TRANG AN SECURITIES JOINT STOCK COMPANY; *Int'l*, pg. 7893
TRANG CORPORATION; *Int'l*, pg. 7893
TRANGLO SDN. BHD.—See Currenc Group Inc.; *U.S. Public*, pg. 611
TRANGS CHINA CORPORATION—See Trang Corporation; *Int'l*, pg. 7893
THE TRANG SEAFOOD PRODUCTS PUBLIC COMPANY LIMITED; *Int'l*, pg. 7696
TRANGS FOOD PTY LTD—See Trang Corporation; *Int'l*, pg. 7893
TRANGS GROUP USA INCORPORATED—See Trang Corporation; *Int'l*, pg. 7893
TRANGS UK LIMITED—See Trang Corporation; *Int'l*, pg. 7894
TRANQUILITY (PTE) LTD—See John Keells Holdings PLC; *Int'l*, pg. 3979
TRANQUIL PC LTD.—See 2Crsi SA; *Int'l*, pg. 4
TRANSACT24 LIMITED—See Lesaka Technologies, Inc.; *Int'l*, pg. 4469
TRANSACT ELEKTRONISCHE ZAHLUNGSSYSTEME GMBH—See Euronet Worldwide, Inc.; *U.S. Public*, pg. 798
TRANSACT ENERGY CORP.; *U.S. Public*, pg. 2179
TRANSACTION ASSOCIATES, INC.; *U.S. Private*, pg. 4206
TRANSACTION CAPITAL LIMITED; *Int'l*, pg. 7894
TRANSACTION CAPITAL TRANSACTIONAL SERVICES PROPRIETARY LIMITED—See Transaction Capital Limited; *Int'l*, pg. 7895
TRANSACTION CO., LTD.; *Int'l*, pg. 7895
TRANSACTION DATA SYSTEMS INC.—See BlackRock, Inc.; *U.S. Public*, pg. 347
TRANSACTION JUNCTION (PROPRIETARY) LIMITED—See Blue Label Telecoms Limited; *Int'l*, pg. 1068
TRANSACTION MEDIA NETWORKS INC.; *Int'l*, pg. 7895
TRANSACTION NETWORK SERVICES, INC.—See Koch Industries, Inc.; *U.S. Private*, pg. 2333
TRANSACTION NETWORK SERVICES (INDIA) PRIVATE LTD—See Koch Industries, Inc.; *U.S. Private*, pg. 2333
TRANSACTION NETWORK SERVICES PTY LIMITED—See Koch Industries, Inc.; *U.S. Private*, pg. 2333
TRANSACTION NETWORK SERVICES SG PTE LIMITED—See Koch Industries, Inc.; *U.S. Private*, pg. 2333
TRANSACTION NETWORK SERVICES (UK) LIMITED—See Koch Industries, Inc.; *U.S. Private*, pg. 2333
TRANSACTION PROCESSING SPECIALISTS, INC.—See Xerox Holdings Corporation; *U.S. Public*, pg. 2388

TRANSACTION PUBLISHERS, INC.; *U.S. Private*, pg. 4206
TRANSACTION SOLUTIONS INTERNATIONAL (INDIA) PRIVATE LIMITED—See CX Advisors LLP; *Int'l*, pg. 1891
TRANSACTION SOLUTIONS INTERNATIONAL PTY LTD—See Vortiv Limited; *Int'l*, pg. 8307
TRANSACTION WIRELESS, INC.—See Fiserv, Inc.; *U.S. Public*, pg. 851
TRANSACTIS, INC.—See Mastercard Incorporated; *U.S. Public*, pg. 1394
TRANSACT TECHNOLOGIES INCORPORATED; *U.S. Public*, pg. 2179
TRANSACT TECHNOLOGIES LTD.—See TransAct Technologies Incorporated; *U.S. Public*, pg. 2179
TRANSACT TECHNOLOGIES (MACAU) LIMITED—See TransAct Technologies Incorporated; *U.S. Public*, pg. 2179
TRANSACTTOOLS, INC.; *U.S. Private*, pg. 4206
TRANSADRIA MEDUNARODNA SPEDICIJA D.D.; *Int'l*, pg. 7895
TRANS.AD SOLUTIONS COMPANY LIMITED—See BTS Group Holdings Public Company Limited; *Int'l*, pg. 1206
TRANSAERO INC.; *U.S. Private*, pg. 4206
TRANSAFRICA MOTORS LTD.—See Honda Motor Co., Ltd.; *Int'l*, pg. 3464
TRANSAKT LTD.; *Int'l*, pg. 7895
TRANS-ALARM, INC.—See iVerify US, Inc.; *U.S. Private*, pg. 2151
TRANSALL AG—See Bystronic AG; *Int'l*, pg. 1236
TRANSALLIANCE; *Int'l*, pg. 7895
TRANSALPINA GMBH—See SKion GmbH; *Int'l*, pg. 6987
TRANSALTA CENTRALIA GENERATION LLC—See TransAlta Corporation; *Int'l*, pg. 7895
TRANSALTA CORPORATION; *Int'l*, pg. 7895
TRANSALTA ENERGY (AUSTRALIA) PTY. LTD.—See TransAlta Corporation; *Int'l*, pg. 7895
TRANSALTA ENERGY MARKETING CORP.—See TransAlta Corporation; *Int'l*, pg. 7895
TRANSALTA ENERGY MARKETING (U.S.) INC.—See TransAlta Corporation; *Int'l*, pg. 7895
TRANSALTA GENERATION PARTNERSHIP—See TransAlta Corporation; *Int'l*, pg. 7895
TRANSALTA POWER, L.P.—See CK Hutchison Holdings Limited; *Int'l*, pg. 1637
TRANSALTA RENEWABLES INC.—See TransAlta Corporation; *Int'l*, pg. 7895
TRANSAMERICA ADVISORS LIFE INSURANCE COMPANY—See Aegon N.V.; *Int'l*, pg. 174
TRANSAMERICA BROKERAGE GROUP—See Aegon N.V.; *Int'l*, pg. 174
TRANSAMERICA CAPITAL, INC.—See Aegon N.V.; *Int'l*, pg. 174
TRANSAMERICA CORPORATION—See Aegon N.V.; *Int'l*, pg. 174
TRANSAMERICA EXPRESS LOGISTICS, LLC; *U.S. Private*, pg. 4207
TRANSAMERICA FINANCIAL ADVISORS, INC.—See Aegon N.V.; *Int'l*, pg. 174
TRANSAMERICA FINANCIAL ADVISORS, INC.—See Aegon N.V.; *Int'l*, pg. 174
TRANSAMERICA INVESTMENT MANAGEMENT—See Aegon N.V.; *Int'l*, pg. 174
TRANSAMERICA LIFE (BERMUDA) LTD.—See Aegon N.V.; *Int'l*, pg. 175
TRANSAMERICA LIFE CANADA—See Vestar Capital Partners, LLC; *U.S. Private*, pg. 4373
TRANSAMERICA LIFE INSURANCE COMPANY—See Aegon N.V.; *Int'l*, pg. 174
TRANSAMERICA LIFE INSURANCE OF NEW YORK—See Aegon N.V.; *Int'l*, pg. 174
TRANSAMERICAN AUTO PARTS CO.—See Polaris, Inc.; *U.S. Public*, pg. 1701
TRANS AMERICAN CUSTOMHOUSE BROKERS, INC.—See Expolanka Holdings PLC; *Int'l*, pg. 2589
TRANS AMERICAN TRUCKING SERVICE; *U.S. Private*, pg. 4205
TRANSAMERICA RETIREMENT SOLUTIONS, LLC—See Aegon N.V.; *Int'l*, pg. 174
TRANSAMMONIA AG—See Trammo, Inc.; *U.S. Private*, pg. 4205
TRANSAMMONIA AG—See Trammo, Inc.; *U.S. Private*, pg. 4205
TRANSAMMONIA B.V.—See Trammo, Inc.; *U.S. Private*, pg. 4205
TRANSAMMONIA DIS TICARET LIMITED COMPANY—See Trammo, Inc.; *U.S. Private*, pg. 4205
TRANSAMMONIA INTERNACIONAL REPRESENTACOES LTDA.—See Trammo, Inc.; *U.S. Private*, pg. 4205
TRANSAMMONIA LTD.—See Trammo, Inc.; *U.S. Private*, pg. 4205
TRANSAMMONIA S.A.R.L.—See Trammo, Inc.; *U.S. Private*, pg. 4205
TRANSAMMONIA (SHANGHAI) TRADING CO., LTD.—See Trammo, Inc.; *U.S. Private*, pg. 4205
TRANSAM TRUCKING INC.; *U.S. Private*, pg. 4207
TRANSANDINA DE COMERCIO S.A.—See Owens Corning; *U.S. Public*, pg. 1628

TRANSART EUROPE B.V.—See Transart Graphics Co., Ltd.; *Int'l*, pg. 7895
TRANSART GRAPHICS CO., LTD.; *Int'l*, pg. 7895
TRANSART GRAPHICS (SHENZHEN) CO., LTD.—See Transart Graphics Co., Ltd.; *Int'l*, pg. 7895
TRANSART GRAPHICS (TAICANG) CO,. LTD.—See Transart Graphics Co., Ltd.; *Int'l*, pg. 7895
TRANSART GRAPHICS (TIANJIN) CO,. LTD.—See Transart Graphics Co., Ltd.; *Int'l*, pg. 7895
TRANSART GRAPHICS (VIETNAM) CO., LTD.—See Transart Graphics Co., Ltd.; *Int'l*, pg. 7895
TRANSASIA BIO-MEDICALS LTD.; *Int'l*, pg. 7895
TRANS ASIA CORPORATION LIMITED; *Int'l*, pg. 7894
TRANS ASIA HOTELS PLC; *Int'l*, pg. 7894
TRANS ASIAN SHIPPING SERVICES PVT. LTD.; *Int'l*, pg. 7894
TRANS-ASIA PETROLEUM CORPORATION—See Ayala Corporation; *Int'l*, pg. 773
TRANS-ASIA SHIPPING LINES, INCORPORATED—See Chelsea Logistics and Infrastructure Holdings Corp.; *Int'l*, pg. 1460
TRANSAS MARINE GMBH—See Wartsila Corporation; *Int'l*, pg. 8347
TRANSAS NAVIGATOR LTD.—See Wartsila Corporation; *Int'l*, pg. 8347
TRANSA SPEDITION GMBH—See Deutsche Bahn AG; *Int'l*, pg. 2054
TRANSAT A.T., INC.; *Int'l*, pg. 7896
TRANSATEL SA—See Nippon Telegraph & Telephone Corporation; *Int'l*, pg. 5355
TRANSAT HOLIDAYS USA INC.—See Transat A.T., Inc.; *Int'l*, pg. 7896
TRANSATLANTIC AB—See Kistefos AS; *Int'l*, pg. 4193
TRANSATLANTIC CAPITAL INC.; *U.S. Public*, pg. 2179
TRANSATLANTIC HOLDINGS, INC.—See Berkshire Hathaway Inc.; *U.S. Public*, pg. 299
TRANS-ATLANTIC MOTORS INC.; *U.S. Private*, pg. 4205
TRANSATLANTIC PETROLEUM LTD.; *U.S. Public*, pg. 2179
TRANSATLANTIC PETROLEUM (USA) CORP.—See TransAtlantic Petroleum Ltd.; *U.S. Public*, pg. 2179
TRANSATLANTIC RE (ARGENTINA) S.A.—See Berkshire Hathaway Inc.; *U.S. Public*, pg. 299
TRANSATLANTIC REINSURANCE COMPANY—See Berkshire Hathaway Inc.; *U.S. Public*, pg. 299
TRANSATLANTIC SERVICES AB—See Kistefos AS; *Int'l*, pg. 4193
TRANSATLANTIC UK LTD.—See Kistefos AS; *Int'l*, pg. 4193
TRANS AUSTRIA GASLEITUNG GMBH—See Eni S.p.A.; *Int'l*, pg. 2438
TRANS-AUTO AB—See ZF Friedrichshafen AG; *Int'l*, pg. 8641
TRANSAVIA AIRLINES B.V.—See Air France-KLM S.A.; *Int'l*, pg. 238
TRANSAVIA AIRLINES C.V.—See Air France-KLM S.A.; *Int'l*, pg. 238
TRANSAVIA FRANCE S.A.S.—See Air France-KLM S.A.; *Int'l*, pg. 238
TRANSAXLE LLC—See Crossplane Capital Management LP; *U.S. Private*, pg. 1107
TRANSBAY CONTAINER TERMINAL, INC.—See Kawasaki Kisen Kaisha, Ltd.; *Int'l*, pg. 4099
TRANSBEAM, INC.—See GTT Communications, Inc.; *U.S. Private*, pg. 1808
TRANSBOTHNIA AB—See PostNord AB; *Int'l*, pg. 5941
TRANSBOTICS CORP.—See JBS S.A.; *Int'l*, pg. 3918
TRANS-BRIDGE LINES, INC.; *U.S. Private*, pg. 4205
TRANSCANADA ENERGY LTD. - HALTON HILLS PLANT—See Ontario Power Generation, Inc.; *Int'l*, pg. 5585
TRANSCANADA ENERGY LTD.—See TC Energy Corporation; *Int'l*, pg. 7482
TRANS CANADA GOLD CORP.; *Int'l*, pg. 7894
TRANSCANADA GTN SYSTEM—See TC Energy Corporation; *Int'l*, pg. 7482
TRANSCANADA INTERNATIONAL LTD.—See TC Energy Corporation; *Int'l*, pg. 7482
TRANSCANADA KEYSTONE PIPELINE, LP—See TC Energy Corporation; *Int'l*, pg. 7482
TRANSCANADA PIPELINES LIMITED—See TC Energy Corporation; *Int'l*, pg. 7482
TRANSCANADA PIPELINE USA LTD.—See TC Energy Corporation; *Int'l*, pg. 7482
TRANSCANADA POWER L.P.—See TC Energy Corporation; *Int'l*, pg. 7482
TRANSCANNA HOLDINGS, INC.; *Int'l*, pg. 7896
TRANSCARD FINANCIAL SERVICES EAD; *Int'l*, pg. 7896
TRANSCARE NEW YORK INC.; *U.S. Private*, pg. 4207
TRANSCARE OF MARYLAND INC—See Transcare New York Inc.; *U.S. Private*, pg. 4207
TRANSCARE SERVICE GMBH—See B. Braun Melsungen AG; *Int'l*, pg. 788
TRANSCARE SUPPLY CHAIN MANAGEMENT INC.—See Deutsche Post AG; *Int'l*, pg. 2082
TRANSCARGO; *Int'l*, pg. 7896
TRANS CARRIER LIMITED—See Petrowest Corp.; *Int'l*, pg. 5833

TRANSCARGO

TRANS-CARRIERS INC.—See Daco Corporation; *U.S. Private*, pg. 1144
TRANS C.A.S. S.R.L.—See Compa S.A.; *Int'l*, pg. 1721
TRANSCAT, INC.; *U.S. Public*, pg. 2179
TRANSCENDENT INVESTMENT MANAGEMENT; *U.S. Private*, pg. 4207
TRANSCENDENT ONE, INC.—See AppTech Inc.; *U.S. Private*, pg. 300
TRANSCEND INFORMATION, INC.; *Int'l*, pg. 7896
TRANSCEND INFORMATION INC—See Transcend Information, Inc.; *Int'l*, pg. 7896
TRANSCEND INFORMATION (SHANGHAI), LTD.—See Transcend Information, Inc.; *Int'l*, pg. 7896
TRANSCEND INFORMATION TRADING GMBH—See Transcend Information, Inc.; *Int'l*, pg. 7896
TRANSCEND INFORMATION UK LIMITED—See Transcend Information, Inc.; *Int'l*, pg. 7896
TRANSCEND INFRASTRUCTURE LIMITED—See American Tower Corporation; *U.S. Public*, pg. 111
TRANSCEND INFRASTRUCTURE PRIVATE LIMITED—See American Tower Corporation; *U.S. Public*, pg. 111
TRANSCEND INSIGHTS, INC.—See Humana, Inc.; *U.S. Public*, pg. 1070
TRANSCEND KOREA INC.—See Transcend Information, Inc.; *Int'l*, pg. 7896
TRANSCEND LOGISTICS, INC.—See P.A.M. Transportation Services, Inc.; *U.S. Public*, pg. 1630
TRANSCEND MEDIA LLC; *U.S. Private*, pg. 4207
TRANSCEND RESIDENTIAL PROPERTY FUND LTD.; *Int'l*, pg. 7896
TRANSCEND SERVICES, INC.—See Microsoft Corporation; *U.S. Public*, pg. 1443
TRANSCEND UNITED TECHNOLOGIES LLC—See Black Box Limited; *Int'l*, pg. 1058
TRANSCENTA HOLDING LIMITED; *Int'l*, pg. 7896
TRANSCENTRA FTS PRIVATE LTD.—See Exela Technologies, Inc.; *U.S. Public*, pg. 806
TRANSCENTRA, INC.—See Gainline Capital Partners LP; *U.S. Private*, pg. 1635
TRANSCENTURY LIMITED; *Int'l*, pg. 7896
TRANSCEPTA LLC; *U.S. Private*, pg. 4207
TRANSCHEM, INC.; *U.S. Private*, pg. 4207
TRANSCHEM LTD.; *Int'l*, pg. 7896
TRANSCOASTAL CORPORATION OF TEXAS—See TransCoastal Corporation; *U.S. Private*, pg. 4207
TRANSCOASTAL CORPORATION; *U.S. Private*, pg. 4207
TRANSCODE THERAPEUTICS, INC.; *U.S. Public*, pg. 2180
TRANSCO GAS PIPE LINE CORPORATION—See The Williams Companies, Inc.; *U.S. Public*, pg. 2143
TRANSCO GAS PIPE LINE CORPORATION—See The Williams Companies, Inc.; *U.S. Public*, pg. 2143
TRANSCO GAS PIPE LINE CORP.—See The Williams Companies, Inc.; *U.S. Public*, pg. 2143
TRANSCO GAS PIPE LINE CORP.—See The Williams Companies, Inc.; *U.S. Public*, pg. 2143
TRANSCO GAS PIPE LINE CORP.—See The Williams Companies, Inc.; *U.S. Public*, pg. 2143
TRANSCO GAS PIPE LINE CORP.—See The Williams Companies, Inc.; *U.S. Public*, pg. 2143
TRANSCO GAS PIPE LINE CORP.—See The Williams Companies, Inc.; *U.S. Public*, pg. 2143
TRANSCO GAS PIPE LINE CORP.—See The Williams Companies, Inc.; *U.S. Public*, pg. 2143
TRANSCO GAS PIPELINES—See The Williams Companies, Inc.; *U.S. Public*, pg. 2143
TRANSCO INC.; *U.S. Private*, pg. 4207
TRANSCO LEASING INC.; *U.S. Private*, pg. 4207
TRANSCO LEASING INC.—See P&S Investment Company Inc.; *U.S. Private*, pg. 3059
TRANS CO., LTD.—See Transaction Co., Ltd.; *Int'l*, pg. 7895
TRANSCOM AB—See Altor Equity Partners AB; *Int'l*, pg. 396
TRANSCOM A/S—See Altor Equity Partners AB; *Int'l*, pg. 396
TRANSCOM ELECTRONICS LIMITED—See Daikin Industries, Ltd.; *Int'l*, pg. 1936
TRANSCOM LLP—See Eurasian Natural Resources Corporation Limited; *Int'l*, pg. 2527
TRANSCOMMUNICATIONS INC.; *U.S. Private*, pg. 4207
TRANSCOM NORGE AS—See Altor Equity Partners AB; *Int'l*, pg. 396
TRANSCOM S.A.; *Int'l*, pg. 7896
TRANSCOM TECHNIK, SPOL. S R.O.—See Endress+Hauser (International) Holding AG; *Int'l*, pg. 2409
TRANSCOM WORLDWIDE AB—See Altor Equity Partners AB; *Int'l*, pg. 396
TRANSCOM WORLDWIDE BELGIUM SA—See Altor Equity Partners AB; *Int'l*, pg. 396
TRANSCOM WORLDWIDE CZECH REPUBLIC S.R.O.—See Altor Equity Partners AB; *Int'l*, pg. 396
TRANSCOM WORLDWIDE D.O.O.—See Altor Equity Partners AB; *Int'l*, pg. 396
TRANSCOM WORLDWIDE FRANCE SAS—See Altor Equity Partners AB; *Int'l*, pg. 396
TRANSCOM WORLDWIDE ROSTOCK GMBH—See Altor Equity Partners AB; *Int'l*, pg. 396
TRANSCOM WORLDWIDE SPAIN SL—See Altor Equity Partners AB; *Int'l*, pg. 396
TRANSCOM WORLDWIDE S.P.A.—See Altor Equity Partners AB; *Int'l*, pg. 396
TRANSCOM WORLDWIDE VILNIUS UAB—See Altor Equity Partners AB; *Int'l*, pg. 396
TRANSCON BUILDERS INC.; *U.S. Private*, pg. 4207
TRANS CONSULT INTERNATIONAL SA; *Int'l*, pg. 7894
TRANSCONTAINER LIMITED—See Nippon Yusen Kabushiki Kaisha; *Int'l*, pg. 5360
TRANSCONTAINER LOGISTICS (THAILAND) CO., LTD.—See Nippon Yusen Kabushiki Kaisha; *Int'l*, pg. 5360
TRANSCONTAINER (TCL) PHILIPPINES, INC.—See Nippon Yusen Kabushiki Kaisha; *Int'l*, pg. 5359
TRANSCONTINENTAL ACME DIRECT—See Transcontinental Inc.; *Int'l*, pg. 7897
TRANSCONTINENTAL CORPORATION; *U.S. Private*, pg. 4207
TRANSCONTINENTAL DEPOSITORY SERVICES, LLC—See A-Mark Precious Metals, Inc.; *U.S. Public*, pg. 10
TRANSCONTINENTAL DIGITAL SERVICES INC.—See Transcontinental Inc.; *Int'l*, pg. 7897
TRANSCONTINENTAL DIRECT, INC.—See Transcontinental Inc.; *Int'l*, pg. 7897
TRANSCONTINENTAL GAS PIPE LINE COMPANY, LLC—See The Williams Companies, Inc.; *U.S. Public*, pg. 2143
TRANSCONTINENTAL GAS PIPE LINE CORP.—See The Williams Companies, Inc.; *U.S. Public*, pg. 2143
TRANSCONTINENTAL GAS PIPE LINE CORP.—See The Williams Companies, Inc.; *U.S. Public*, pg. 2143
TRANSCONTINENTAL GOLD CORP.; *Int'l*, pg. 7896
TRANSCONTINENTAL INC.; *Int'l*, pg. 7897
TRANSCONTINENTAL INTERWEB INC—See Transcontinental Inc.; *Int'l*, pg. 7897
TRANSCONTINENTAL LGM GRAPHICS—See Transcontinental Inc.; *Int'l*, pg. 7897
TRANSCONTINENTAL PLM—See Transcontinental Inc.; *Int'l*, pg. 7897
TRANSCONTINENTAL PRINTING INC. - AURORA—See Transcontinental Inc.; *Int'l*, pg. 7897
TRANSCONTINENTAL PRINTING INC. - BRAMPTON—See Transcontinental Inc.; *Int'l*, pg. 7897
TRANSCONTINENTAL PRINTING INC. - CALGARY PLANT—See Transcontinental Inc.; *Int'l*, pg. 7897
TRANSCONTINENTAL PRINTING INC. - CONCORD PLANT—See Transcontinental Inc.; *Int'l*, pg. 7897
TRANSCONTINENTAL PRINTING INC. - HALIFAX PLANT—See Transcontinental Inc.; *Int'l*, pg. 7897
TRANSCONTINENTAL PRINTING INC. - LASALLE PLANT—See Transcontinental Inc.; *Int'l*, pg. 7897
TRANSCONTINENTAL PRINTING INC. - METROPOLITAN PLANT—See Transcontinental Inc.; *Int'l*, pg. 7897
TRANSCONTINENTAL PRINTING INC. - NORTHERN CALIFORNIA PLANT—See Transcontinental Inc.; *Int'l*, pg. 7897
TRANSCONTINENTAL PRINTING INC. - PRINCE EDWARD ISLAND PLANT—See Transcontinental Inc.; *Int'l*, pg. 7897
TRANSCONTINENTAL PRINTING INC. - QUALIMAX PLANT—See Transcontinental Inc.; *Int'l*, pg. 7897
TRANSCONTINENTAL PRINTING INC. - SAINT-HYACINTHE—See Transcontinental Inc.; *Int'l*, pg. 7897
TRANSCONTINENTAL PRINTING INC.—See Transcontinental Inc.; *Int'l*, pg. 7897
TRANSCONTINENTAL PRINTING INC. - TRANSMAG—See Transcontinental Inc.; *Int'l*, pg. 7897
TRANSCONTINENTAL PRINTING INC. - VAUGHAN PLANT—See Transcontinental Inc.; *Int'l*, pg. 7897
TRANS-CONTINENTAL PRINTING USA INC—See Transcontinental Inc.; *Int'l*, pg. 7897
TRANSCONTINENTAL RBW GRAPHICS—See Transcontinental Inc.; *Int'l*, pg. 7897
TRANSCONTINENTAL REALTY INVESTORS, INC.—See American Realty Investors, Inc.; *U.S. Public*, pg. 108
TRANSCONTINENTAL ROSS-ELLIS—See Transcontinental Inc.; *Int'l*, pg. 7897
TRANSCO PRODUCTS INC.—See Transco Inc; *U.S. Private*, pg. 4207
TRANSCO PRODUCTS INC. - TPI FABRICATION FACILITY—See Transco Inc.; *U.S. Private*, pg. 4207
TRANSCO RAILWAY PRODUCTS INC—See Berkshire Hathaway Inc.; *U.S. Public*, pg. 312
TRANSCO RAILWAY PRODUCTS, INC—See Transco Inc.; *U.S. Private*, pg. 4207
TRANSCOR AMERICA, LLC—See Corecivic, Inc.; *U.S. Public*, pg. 577
TRANSCOR ASTRA GROUP S.A.; *Int'l*, pg. 7897
TRANSCOR ASTRA LUXEMBOURG S.A.—See Transcor Astra Group S.A.; *Int'l*, pg. 7897
TRANSCOR CORPORATION (ENERGY)—See Transcor Astra Group S.A.; *Int'l*, pg. 7898
TRANSCORE COMMERCIAL SERVICES, LLC—See Roper Technologies, Inc.; *U.S. Public*, pg. 1814
TRANSCORE HOLDINGS INC.—See Roper Technologies, Inc.; *U.S. Public*, pg. 1813
TRANSCORE LINK LOGISTICS CORPORATION—See Roper Technologies, Inc.; *U.S. Public*, pg. 1814
TRANSCORE, LP—See Roper Technologies, Inc.; *U.S. Public*, pg. 1813
TRANSCORE MARKETING COMMUNICATIONS—See Roper Technologies, Inc.; *U.S. Public*, pg. 1814
TRANSCORP HOLDINGS LIMITED; *Int'l*, pg. 7898
TRANSCORP HOTELS PLC.—See Transnational Corporation of Nigeria Plc.; *Int'l*, pg. 7902
TRANSCORP INTERNATIONAL LIMITED; *Int'l*, pg. 7898
TRANSCORR LLC; *U.S. Private*, pg. 4207
TRANSCOSMOS AMERICA INC.—See Transcosmos Inc.; *Int'l*, pg. 7898
TRANSCOSMOS ANALYTICS INC.—See Transcosmos Inc.; *Int'l*, pg. 7898
TRANSCOSMOS ASIA PHILIPPINES, INC.—See Transcosmos Inc.; *Int'l*, pg. 7899
TRANSCOSMOS BUSINESS SERVICE OUTSOURCING (DALIAN) CO.,LTD.—See Transcosmos Inc.; *Int'l*, pg. 7898
TRANSCOSMOS BUSINESS SERVICE OUTSOURCING SUZHOU CO., LTD.—See Transcosmos Inc.; *Int'l*, pg. 7898
TRANSCOSMOS CRM MIYAZAKI INC.—See Transcosmos Inc.; *Int'l*, pg. 7898
TRANSCOSMOS FIELD MARKETING INC.—See Transcosmos Inc.; *Int'l*, pg. 7898
TRANSCOSMOS INC.; *Int'l*, pg. 7898
TRANSCOSMOS INFORMATION CREATIVE (CHINA) CO., LTD.—See Transcosmos Inc.; *Int'l*, pg. 7899
TRANSCOSMOS INFORMATION CREATIVE JAPAN INC.—See Transcosmos Inc.; *Int'l*, pg. 7899
TRANSCOSMOS INFORMATION SYSTEMS LIMITED—See Transcosmos Inc.; *Int'l*, pg. 7899
TRANSCOSMOS KOREA INC.—See Transcosmos Inc.; *Int'l*, pg. 7899
TRANSCOSMOS LOGICALL INC.—See Transcosmos Inc.; *Int'l*, pg. 7899
TRANSCOSMOS (MALAYSIA) SDN. BHD.—See Transcosmos Inc.; *Int'l*, pg. 7898
TRANSCOSMOS OMNICONNECT, LLC—See Transcosmos Inc.; *Int'l*, pg. 7899
TRANSCOSMOS TAIWAN INC.—See Transcosmos Inc.; *Int'l*, pg. 7899
TRANSCOSMOS TECHNOLOGIC ARTS CO., LTD.—See Transcosmos Inc.; *Int'l*, pg. 7899
TRANSCOSMOS TECHNOLOGIES INC.—See Transcosmos Inc.; *Int'l*, pg. 7899
TRANSCOSMOS (THAILAND) CO., LTD.—See Transcosmos Inc.; *Int'l*, pg. 7898
TRANSCOSMOS VIETNAM CO., LTD.—See Transcosmos Inc.; *Int'l*, pg. 7899
TRANSCO UNION OFFICE; *U.S. Private*, pg. 4207
TRANSCOUNTY TITLE AGENCY LLC—See Heartland BancCorp; *U.S. Public*, pg. 1017
TRANSCRAFT CORPORATION—See WABASH NATIONAL CORPORATION; *U.S. Public*, pg. 2320
THE TRANSCRIPTION AGENCY (VIQ) COMPANY—See VIQ Solutions Inc.; *Int'l*, pg. 8245
TRANSCRIPTION EXPRESS, INC.—See VIQ Solutions Inc.; *Int'l*, pg. 8245
TRANSCRIPT PHARMACY, INC.; *U.S. Private*, pg. 4207
TRANSCU LTD.; *Int'l*, pg. 7899
TRANSCULTURAL HEALTH DEVELOPMENT, INC.—See Acadia Healthcare Company, Inc.; *U.S. Public*, pg. 31
TRANSDEV AUCKLAND LTD—See Veolia Environnement S.A.; *Int'l*, pg. 8156
TRANSDEV GROUP S.A.—See Caisse des Depots et Consignations; *Int'l*, pg. 1258
TRANSDEV NORTH AMERICA, INC.—See Caisse des Depots et Consignations; *Int'l*, pg. 1258
TRANSDEV PLC—See Caisse des Depots et Consignations; *Int'l*, pg. 1259
TRANSDEV S.A.—See Caisse des Depots et Consignations; *Int'l*, pg. 1258
TRANSDEV SVERIGE AB—See Caisse des Depots et Consignations; *Int'l*, pg. 1258
TRANSDEV SYDNEY PTY LTD—See Caisse des Depots et Consignations; *Int'l*, pg. 1259
TRANSDIGM GROUP INCORPORATED; *U.S. Public*, pg. 2180
TRANSDIGM INC.—See TransDigm Group Incorporated; *U.S. Public*, pg. 2181
TRANSDIGM TECHNOLOGIES INDIA PRIVATE LIMITED—See TransDigm Group Incorporated; *U.S. Public*, pg. 2183
TRANSDUCERS DIRECT, LLC; *U.S. Private*, pg. 4207
TRANSEASTERN POWER TRUST; *Int'l*, pg. 7899
TRANS EAST TRADING (KOREA) LTD.—See Trammo, Inc.; *U.S. Private*, pg. 4205
TRANSEAWAYS SHIPPING. SDN. BHD.—See Asdion Berhad.; *Int'l*, pg. 604
TRANSEC POWER SERVICES CO., LTD.—See Samart Corporation Public Company Limited; *Int'l*, pg. 6502
TRANSEJES TRANSMISSIONES HOMOCINETICAS DE COLUMBIA S.A.—See Dana Incorporated; *U.S. Public*, pg. 623

COMPANY NAME INDEX

TRANSEL ELEVATOR & ELECTRIC INC.—See Analogue Holdings Limited; *Int'l*, pg. 446
TRANSEND CORPORATION—See ACI Worldwide, Inc.; *U.S. Public*, pg. 35
TRANSENGEN, INC.—See General Atlantic Service Company, L.P.; *U.S. Private*, pg. 1662
TRANSENSE TECHNOLOGIES PLC; *Int'l*, pg. 7899
TRANSENTERIX ASIA PTE LTD.—See Karl Storz GmbH & Co.; *Int'l*, pg. 4083
TRANSENTERIX EUROPE SARL—See Karl Storz GmbH & Co.; *Int'l*, pg. 4083
TRANS EQUATORIAL ENGINEERING PTE LTD—See TEE International Limited; *Int'l*, pg. 7520
TRANSERVICE LEASE CORP.—See ZS Fund L.P.; *U.S. Private*, pg. 4609
TRANSERVICE LOGISTICS INC.—See ZS Fund L.P.; *U.S. Private*, pg. 4609
TRANSERVI S.A.—See Deutsche Bahn AG; *Int'l*, pg. 2051
TRANS EURO HOTEL S.A.—See SIF Banat-Crisana S.A.; *Int'l*, pg. 6905
TRANS EXPEDITE, INC.; *U.S. Private*, pg. 4205
TRANSFAR - AGENCIA DE VIAGENS E TURISMO LDA.—See TUI AG; *Int'l*, pg. 7968
TRANSFAR GROUP CO., LTD.; *Int'l*, pg. 7899
TRANSFAR ZHILIAN CO., LTD.—See Transfar Group Co., Ltd.; *Int'l*, pg. 7899
TRANS FAST REMITTANCE, INC.—See Mastercard Incorporated; *U.S. Public*, pg. 1394
TRANSFENNICA BELGIUM B.V.B.A.—See Spliethoff's Bevrachtingskantoor B.V.; *Int'l*, pg. 7141
TRANSFENNICA DEUTSCHLAND GMBH—See Spliethoff's Bevrachtingskantoor B.V.; *Int'l*, pg. 7141
TRANSFENNICA LTD—See Spliethoff's Bevrachtingskantoor B.V.; *Int'l*, pg. 7141
TRANSFENNICA OU—See Spliethoff's Bevrachtingskantoor B.V.; *Int'l*, pg. 7141
TRANSFENNICA POLSKA SP. Z O.O.—See Spliethoff's Bevrachtingskantoor B.V.; *Int'l*, pg. 7141
TRANSFENNICA (UK) LTD—See Spliethoff's Bevrachtingskantoor B.V.; *Int'l*, pg. 7141
TRANSFERASE CONSULTING & MEDIA RELATIONS MILAN—See WPP plc; *Int'l*, pg. 8492
TRANSFER ENTERPRISES, INC.; *U.S. Private*, pg. 4207
TRANSFER MARKETING INC.; *U.S. Private*, pg. 4207
TRANSFERMARKT GMBH & CO. KG—See Axel Springer SE; *Int'l*, pg. 767
TRANSFER NV—See The Walt Disney Company; *U.S. Public*, pg. 2140
TRANSFESA LOGISTICS, S.A.—See Deutsche Bahn AG; *Int'l*, pg. 2054
TRANSFESA PORTUGAL LDA.—See Deutsche Bahn AG; *Int'l*, pg. 2051
TRANSFESA RAIL S.A.—See Deutsche Bahn AG; *Int'l*, pg. 2051
TRANSFESA UK LTD—See Deutsche Bahn AG; *Int'l*, pg. 2051
TRANSFINDER CORPORATION; *U.S. Private*, pg. 4207
TRANSFIN-M OJSC; *Int'l*, pg. 7899
TRANSFIRST, LLC—See Global Payments Inc.; *U.S. Public*, pg. 944
TRANSFLO CORPORATION—See CSX Corporation; *U.S. Public*, pg. 602
TRANSFOAM S.L.—See Recticel S.A.; *Int'l*, pg. 6242
TRANSFORCE, INC.—See Palladium Equity Partners, LLC; *U.S. Private*, pg. 3078
TRANSFORMACIONES METALURGICAS NORMA, S.A.—See Cie Automotive S.A.; *Int'l*, pg. 1605
TRANSFORMACIONES METALURGICAS S.A.—See Zeleziarne Podbrezova a.s.; *Int'l*, pg. 8631
TRANSFORMADORES TUSAN S.A.—See State Grid Corporation of China; *Int'l*, pg. 7183
TRANSFORMA RESOURCES CORP.; *Int'l*, pg. 7899
TRANSFORMATEUR FEDERAL LTEE.; *Int'l*, pg. 7899
TRANSFORMATION ADVISORS GROUP, LLC; *U.S. Private*, pg. 4208
TRANSFORMATIONAL CPG ACQUISITION CORP.; *U.S. Private*, pg. 4208
TRANSFORMATIONAL SECURITY, LLC—See HEICO Corporation; *U.S. Public*, pg. 1021
TRANSFORMATION SYSTEMS, INC.; *U.S. Private*, pg. 4208
TRANSFORMERS & RECTIFIERS INDIA LTD; *Int'l*, pg. 7899
TRANSFORM EXPLORATION PTY LTD.; *Int'l*, pg. 7899
TRANSFORM HOLDCO LLC; *U.S. Private*, pg. 4208
TRANSFORM HOSPITAL GROUP LTD.—See Aurelius Equity Opportunities SE & Co. KGaA; *Int'l*, pg. 710
TRANSFORMING RETAIL PRIVATE LIMITED—See PC Jeweller Limited; *Int'l*, pg. 5766
TRANSFORM MASTER SDN. BHD.—See Luxchem Corporation Berhad; *Int'l*, pg. 4588
TRANSFORM SR BRANDS LLC—See Transform Holdco LLC; *U.S. Private*, pg. 4208
TRANSFORM-X, INC.; *U.S. Private*, pg. 4208
TRANSFO SERVICES SAS—See Schneider Electric SE; *Int'l*, pg. 6635
TRANS FREIGHT CONTAINERS LTD.; *Int'l*, pg. 7894
TRANSFREIGHT, LLC—See Penske Corporation; *U.S. Private*, pg. 3138

TRANSFRESH CORPORATION—See Banco Safra S.A.; *Int'l*, pg. 824
TRANSFRESH CORPORATION—See Sucocitrico Cutrale Ltda.; *Int'l*, pg. 7251
TRANSGAS ARMAZENAGEM - SOC. PORTUGUESA DE ARMAZENAGEM DE GAS NATURAL, S.A.—See Galp Energia SGPS, S.A.; *Int'l*, pg. 2876
TRANSGAS DE OCCIDENTE S.A.—See TC Energy Corporation; *Int'l*, pg. 7482
TRANSGAS INC.—See National Grid plc; *Int'l*, pg. 5158
TRANSGAZ S.A.; *Int'l*, pg. 7900
TRANSGENE BIOTEK LTD.; *Int'l*, pg. 7900
TRANSGENE S.A.—See Institut Merieux; *Int'l*, pg. 3723
TRANS GENIC INC.; *Int'l*, pg. 7894
TRANSGENOMIC LTD.—See Precipio, Inc.; *U.S. Public*, pg. 1713
TRANSGLOBAL ASSETS, INC.; *U.S. Public*, pg. 2183
TRANSGLOBAL COMMUNICATIONS INC.; *U.S. Private*, pg. 4208
TRANSGLOBAL GAS & OIL COMPANY; *U.S. Private*, pg. 4208
TRANS GLOBAL GROUP, INC.; *U.S. Public*, pg. 2179
TRANS-GLOBAL PRODUCTS INC.; *U.S. Private*, pg. 4206
TRANS-GLOBAL SOLUTIONS INC.; *U.S. Private*, pg. 4206
TRANS-GLOBAL SOLUTIONS, INC.—See Trans-Global Solutions Inc.; *U.S. Private*, pg. 4206
TRANS GLOBAL S.R.L.—See Albert Ballin KG; *Int'l*, pg. 296
TRANSGLOBE ENERGY CORPORATION—See VAALCO Energy, Inc.; *U.S. Public*, pg. 2270
TRANSGLOBE FOODS LIMITED; *Int'l*, pg. 7900
TRANSGLOBE LIFE INSURANCE INC.; *Int'l*, pg. 7900
TRANSGLOBE PETROLEUM EGYPT INC.—See VAALCO Energy, Inc.; *U.S. Public*, pg. 2270
TRANSGLOBE PETROLEUM INTERNATIONAL INC.—See VAALCO Energy, Inc.; *U.S. Public*, pg. 2270
TRANSGLOB MEDNARODNA SPEDICIJA D.O.O. LJUBLJANA—See Transadria Medunarodna Spedicija d.d.; *Int'l*, pg. 7895
TRANSGOODS AMERICA INC.—See China Railway Materials Co., Ltd.; *Int'l*, pg. 1544
TRANSGOURMET IMMOBILIEN GMBH & CO. KG—See Coop-Gruppe Genossenschaft; *Int'l*, pg. 1790
TRANSGOURMET SCHWEIZ AG—See Coop-Gruppe Genossenschaft; *Int'l*, pg. 1790
TRANSGOURMET SEAFOOD—See Coop-Gruppe Genossenschaft; *Int'l*, pg. 1790
TRANSGROUP AS, LTD.; *Int'l*, pg. 7900
TRANS HEX GROUP LIMITED; *Int'l*, pg. 7894
TRANSHIELD, INC.—See Patrick Industries, Inc.; *U.S. Public*, pg. 1653
TRANSHUMANCE HOLDING COMPANY INC.; *U.S. Private*, pg. 4208
TRANSICOIL LLC—See TransDigm Group Incorporated; *U.S. Public*, pg. 2183
TRANSICOIL (MALAYSIA) SENDIRIAN BERHAD—See TransDigm Group Incorporated; *U.S. Public*, pg. 2183
TRANSICO INCORPORATED; *U.S. Private*, pg. 4208
TRANSICS BELUX BVBA—See ZF Friedrichshafen AG; *Int'l*, pg. 8641
TRANSICS BELUX NV—See ZF Friedrichshafen AG; *Int'l*, pg. 8641
TRANSICS DEUTSCHLAND GMBH—See ZF Friedrichshafen AG; *Int'l*, pg. 8641
TRANSICS FRANCE SARL—See ZF Friedrichshafen AG; *Int'l*, pg. 8641
TRANSICS INTERNATIONAL NV—See ZF Friedrichshafen AG; *Int'l*, pg. 8641
TRANSICS IRELAND LIMITED—See ZF Friedrichshafen AG; *Int'l*, pg. 8641
TRANSICS ITALIA S.R.L—See ZF Friedrichshafen AG; *Int'l*, pg. 8641
TRANSICS NEDERLAND BV—See ZF Friedrichshafen AG; *Int'l*, pg. 8641
TRANSICS NV—See ZF Friedrichshafen AG; *Int'l*, pg. 8641
TRANSICS TELEMATICA ESPANA S.L.U—See ZF Friedrichshafen AG; *Int'l*, pg. 8641
TRANSIGO LTD.—See Evolution AB; *Int'l*, pg. 2572
TRANSILVANIA BROKER DE ASIGURARE S.A.; *Int'l*, pg. 7900
TRANSILVANIA INVESTMENTS ALLIANCE S.A.; *Int'l*, pg. 7900
TRANSILVANIA LEASING & CREDIT IFN S.A.; *Int'l*, pg. 7900
TRANSILWRAP COMPANY, INC. - HEBRON PLANT—See Nicolet Capital Partners, LLC; *U.S. Private*, pg. 2926
TRANSILWRAP COMPANY, INC. - LAMINATION/ID SECURITIES DIVISION—See Nicolet Capital Partners, LLC; *U.S. Private*, pg. 2926
TRANSILWRAP COMPANY, INC. - NORTHEAST DIVISION—See Nicolet Capital Partners, LLC; *U.S. Private*, pg. 2926
TRANSILWRAP COMPANY, INC. - PRINTABLE PLASTICS DIVISION—See Nicolet Capital Partners, LLC; *U.S. Private*, pg. 2926

TRANSILWRAP COMPANY, INC.—See Nicolet Capital Partners, LLC; *U.S. Private*, pg. 2926.
TRANSILWRAP COMPANY, INC.—See Nicolet Capital Partners, LLC; *U.S. Private*, pg. 2926.
TRANSILWRAP COMPANY, INC. - SPECIALTY & INDUSTRIAL FILMS DIVISION—See Nicolet Capital Partners, LLC; *U.S. Private*, pg. 2926.
TRANSIMEX CORPORATION; *Int'l*, pg. 7900
TRANSIMEX HI TECH PARK LOGISTICS CO., LTD.—See Transimex Corporation; *Int'l*, pg. 7900
TRANSIMEX PROPERTY COMPANY LTD.—See Transimex Corporation; *Int'l*, pg. 7900
TRANSIM TECHNOLOGY CORPORATION—See Arrow Electronics, Inc.; *U.S. Public*, pg. 200
TRANS INDIA HOUSE IMPEX LIMITED; *Int'l*, pg. 7894
TRANS-INDIA PRODUCTS, INC.; *U.S. Private*, pg. 4206
TRANS INNS MANAGEMENT INC.; *U.S. Private*, pg. 4205
TRANS INTER EUROPE, S.A.S—See ACS, Actividades de Construccion y Servicios, S.A.; *Int'l*, pg. 116
TRANSINTRA GMBH; *Int'l*, pg. 7900
TRANSINTRA SHIPPING AND FORWARDING SP. Z O.O.—See Transintra GmbH; *Int'l*, pg. 7900
TRANSINVESTMENT SPV; *Int'l*, pg. 7900
TRANSIP GROUP BV—See Combell NV; *Int'l*, pg. 1708
TRANS-ISLAND LIMOUSINE SERVICE LIMITED—See KWOON CHUNG BUS HOLDINGS LIMITED; *Int'l*, pg. 4351
TRANSISTOR DEVICES EUROPE LTD.—See TDI Power Systems; *U.S. Private*, pg. 3944
TRANSITCENTER, INC.; *U.S. Private*, pg. 4208
TRANSIT ENGINEERING SERVICES, INC.—See Mattei Compressors Inc.; *U.S. Private*, pg. 2613
TRANSIT FREIGHT FORWARDING PROPRIETARY LIMITED—See Frontier Services Group Limited; *Int'l*, pg. 2796
TRANSITIONAL FAMILY SERVICES, INC.—See ATAR Capital, LLC; *U.S. Private*, pg. 365
TRANSITIONAL SERVICES FOR NEW YORK, INC.; *U.S. Private*, pg. 4208
TRANSITIONAL SERVICES, LLC—See Centerbridge Partners, L.P.; *U.S. Private*, pg. 814
TRANSITION CAPITAL PARTNERS LTD.; *U.S. Private*, pg. 4208
THE TRANSITION COMPANIES LLC; *U.S. Private*, pg. 4128
TRANSITION EVERGREEN; *Int'l*, pg. 7900
TRANSITION HOUSE; *U.S. Private*, pg. 4208
TRANSITION METALS CORP.; *Int'l*, pg. 7901
TRANSITION NETWORKS—See Pineapple Energy Inc.; *U.S. Public*, pg. 1691
TRANSITION SA; *Int'l*, pg. 7901
TRANSITIONS GROUP INC.; *U.S. Private*, pg. 4208
TRANSITIONS OPTICAL, INC.—See EssilorLuxottica SA; *Int'l*, pg. 2514
TRANSITIONS OPTICAL LIMITED—See EssilorLuxottica SA; *Int'l*, pg. 2514
TRANSITIONS OPTICAL PHILIPPINES, INC.—See EssilorLuxottica SA; *Int'l*, pg. 2514
TRANSITIONS OPTICAL (S) PTE. LTD—See EssilorLuxottica SA; *Int'l*, pg. 2514
TRANSITIONS OPTICAL (THAILAND) LTD.—See EssilorLuxottica SA; *Int'l*, pg. 2514
TRANSITIONS WEALTH MANAGEMENT LLC—See Genstar Capital, LLC; *U.S. Private*, pg. 1677
TRANSITIONS WEALTH MANAGEMENT LLC—See Keystone Group, L.P.; *U.S. Private*, pg. 2298
TRANSITION THERAPEUTICS INC.—See OPKO Health, Inc.; *U.S. Public*, pg. 1608
TRANSIT LINK PTE. LTD.—See Land Transport Authority of Singapore; *Int'l*, pg. 4404
TRANSIT MANAGEMENT OF VOLUSIA, INC.—See FirstGroup plc; *Int'l*, pg. 2689
TRANSIT MEDIA GROUP; *U.S. Private*, pg. 4208
TRANSIT MIX CONCRETE CO.—See Holcim Ltd.; *Int'l*, pg. 3446
TRANSITOWNE HYUNDAI LLC—See West Herr Automotive Group, Inc.; *U.S. Private*, pg. 4485
TRANSIT SA—See Burelle S.A.; *Int'l*, pg. 1223
TRANSIT SOLUTIONS PROPRIETARY LIMITED—See Fortive Corporation; *U.S. Public*, pg. 872
TRANSIT SUPPORT SERVICES LTD.; *Int'l*, pg. 7900
TRANSIT SYSTEMS INC.; *U.S. Private*, pg. 4208
TRANSIT UNDERWRITING MANAGERS (PTY.) LTD.—See Talanx AG; *Int'l*, pg. 7445
TRANSIT WASTE, LLC—See BC Partners LLP; *Int'l*, pg. 924
TRANSITYRE B.V.—See Compagnie Generale des Etablissements Michelin SCA; *Int'l*, pg. 1745
TRANSLAB NV—See ABO-Group NV/SA; *Int'l*, pg. 66
TRANSLATE BIO, INC.—See Sanofi; *Int'l*, pg. 6552
TRANSLATEMEDIA ASIA LTD—See TranslateMedia Ltd.; *Int'l*, pg. 7901
TRANSLATEMEDIA GMBH—See TranslateMedia Ltd.; *Int'l*, pg. 7901
TRANSLATEMEDIA LTD.; *Int'l*, pg. 7901
TRANSLATEMEDIA TRANSLATION SERVICES LLC—See TranslateMedia Ltd.; *Int'l*, pg. 7901

TRANSLATEMEDIA LTD.

TRANSLATE PLUS UK LIMITED—See Publicis Groupe S.A.; *Int'l*, pg. 6112
TRANSLATION LLC—See The Interpublic Group of Companies, Inc.; *U.S. Public*, pg. 2104
TRANSLATIONS.COM—See Translations.com; *U.S. Private*, pg. 4208
TRANSLATIONS.COM; *U.S. Private*, pg. 4208
TRANS-LEASE GROUP; *U.S. Private*, pg. 4206
TRANSLEC LIMITED—See Methode Electronics, Inc.; *U.S. Public*, pg. 1429
TRANSLIMP CO—See Interserve Plc; *Int'l*, pg. 3760
TRANSLINK SHIPPING INC.; *U.S. Private*, pg. 4208
TRANSLOAD SERVICES, LLC—See Kinder Morgan, Inc.; *U.S. Public*, pg. 1233
TRANSLOC INC.—See Constellation Software Inc.; *Int'l*, pg. 1775
TRANS-LOGO-TECH (TLT) GMBH—See Super Group Limited; *Int'l*, pg. 7335
TRANS LOUISIANA GAS PIPELINE, INC.—See Atmos Energy Corporation; *U.S. Public*, pg. 224
TRANSLUCENT INC.—See Silex Systems Ltd.; *Int'l*, pg. 6919
TRANS-LUX COCTEAU CORPORATION—See Trans-Lux Corporation; *U.S. Public*, pg. 2179
TRANS-LUX CORPORATION; *U.S. Public*, pg. 2179
TRANS-LUX PTY. LTD.—See Trans-Lux Corporation; *U.S. Public*, pg. 2179
TRANS MACHINE TECHNOLOGIES; *U.S. Private*, pg. 4205
TRANSMARKET GROUP INC.; *U.S. Private*, pg. 4209
TRANS-MARKET LLC—See Krones AG; *Int'l*, pg. 4306
TRANS-MARKET SALES & EQUIPMENT, INC.—See Krones AG; *Int'l*, pg. 4305
TRANSMART TECHNOLOGIES, INC.—See GI Manager L.P.; *U.S. Private*, pg. 1691
TRANSMASHHOLDING JSC; *Int'l*, pg. 7901
TRANS-MATE, INC.—See Highlander Partners, LP.; *U.S. Private*, pg. 1940
TRANS-MATIC MFG.; *U.S. Private*, pg. 4206
TRANSMATION (CANADA) LTD.—See Transcat, Inc.; *U.S. Public*, pg. 2179
TRANSMEC ENGINEERING PTE LTD—See Invicta Holdings Limited; *Int'l*, pg. 3788
TRANSMEDIA GROUP; *U.S. Private*, pg. 4209
TRANSMEDIA—See Transcontinental Inc.; *Int'l*, pg. 7897
TRANSMEDIC CHINA LTD.—See EBOS Group Limited; *Int'l*, pg. 2286
TRANSMEDIC COMPANY LTD.—See EBOS Group Limited; *Int'l*, pg. 2286
TRANSMEDIC PHILIPPINES, INC.—See EBOS Group Limited; *Int'l*, pg. 2286
TRANSMEDIC PTE. LTD.—See EBOS Group Limited; *Int'l*, pg. 2286
TRANSMEDICS GROUP, INC.; *U.S. Public*, pg. 2183
TRANSMEDICS, INC.; *U.S. Private*, pg. 4209
TRANSMEDIC (THAILAND) CO. LTD.—See EBOS Group Limited; *Int'l*, pg. 2286
TRANS MEDITERRANEAN AIRLINES S.A.L.; *Int'l*, pg. 7894
TRANSMED TRANSPORT GMBH—See PHOENIX Pharmahandel GmbH & Co. KG; *Int'l*, pg. 5855
TRANS-MED USA INC.; *U.S. Private*, pg. 4206
TRANSMERES S.A. DE C.V.—See Albert Ballin KG; *Int'l*, pg. 296
TRANSMERIDIAN S.A.C.—See Nippon Yusen Kabushiki Kaisha; *Int'l*, pg. 5360
TRANSMETANO E.S.P. S.A.—See Grupo Aval Acciones y Valores S.A.; *Int'l*, pg. 3121
TRANSMETRO CORPORATION LIMITED; *Int'l*, pg. 7901
TRANSMILE AIR SERVICES SDN. BHD. - ENGINEERING DIVISION—See Transmile Air Services Sdn. Bhd.; *Int'l*, pg. 7901
TRANSMILE AIR SERVICES SDN. BHD.; *Int'l*, pg. 7901
TRANSMISIONES Y EQUIPOS MECANICOS, S.A. DE C.V.—See Grupo Kuo, S.A.B. de C.V.; *Int'l*, pg. 3131
TRANSMISSION AUSTRALIA PTY., LTD.—See Regal Rexnord Corporation; *U.S. Public*, pg. 1773
TRANSMISSION CO LIMITED—See Renold plc; *Int'l*, pg. 6284
TRANSMISSION ENGINEERING INDUSTRIES LIMITED; *Int'l*, pg. 7901
TRANSMISSION & FLUID EQUIPMENT COMPANY; *U.S. Private*, pg. 4209
TRANSMISSION LINE CONSTRUCTION CO., LTD.—See Kandenko Co.; *Int'l*, pg. 4405
TRANSMISSORA ALIANCA DE ENERGIA ELETRICA S.A.; *Int'l*, pg. 7901
TRANSMIT ENTERTAINMENT LIMITED; *Int'l*, pg. 7901
TRANSMODE LTD.—See Infinera Corporation; *U.S. Public*, pg. 1117
TRANSMODE SYSTEMS, INC.—See Infinera Corporation; *U.S. Public*, pg. 1117
TRANSMONTAIGNE GP L.L.C.—See ArcLight Capital Holdings, LLC; *U.S. Private*, pg. 312
TRANSMONTAIGNE, INC.—See NGL Energy Partners LP; *U.S. Public*, pg. 1527
TRANSMONTAIGNE MARKETING CANADA INC.—See Morgan Stanley; *U.S. Public*, pg. 1475
TRANSMONTAIGNE PARTNERS LLC—See ArcLight Capital Holdings, LLC; *U.S. Private*, pg. 312
TRANSMONTAIGNE PRODUCT SERVICES, LLC—See Berkshire Hathaway Inc.; *U.S. Public*, pg. 313
TRANSMONTAIGNE TRANSPORT INC.—See NGL Energy Partners LP; *U.S. Public*, pg. 1527
TRANSMOUNTAIN DIALYSIS, L.P.—See DaVita Inc.; *U.S. Public*, pg. 644
TRANSNATIONAL AERO CORPORATION—See Transnational Diversified Group of Companies; *Int'l*, pg. 7902
TRANSNATIONAL CANNABIS LTD; *Int'l*, pg. 7902
TRANSNATIONAL COMPANY KAZCHROME JSC; *Int'l*, pg. 7902
TRANSNATIONAL CORPORATION OF NIGERIA PLC.; *Int'l*, pg. 7902
TRANSNATIONAL DIVERSIFIED GROUP, INC.—See Transnational Diversified Group of Companies; *Int'l*, pg. 7902
TRANSNATIONAL DIVERSIFIED GROUP OF COMPANIES; *Int'l*, pg. 7902
TRANSNATIONAL FINANCIAL SERVICES, INC.—See Transnational Diversified Group of Companies; *Int'l*, pg. 7902
TRANSNATIONAL FOODS; *U.S. Private*, pg. 4209
TRANSNATIONAL GROUP, INC.; *U.S. Public*, pg. 2183
TRANS NATIONAL GROUP SERVICES, LLC—See Apple Leisure Group; *U.S. Private*, pg. 297
TRANS NATIONAL GROUP SERVICES; *U.S. Private*, pg. 4205
TRANSNATIONAL LOGISTICS SOLUTIONS CORP.—See Transnational Diversified Group of Companies; *Int'l*, pg. 7902
TRANSNATIONAL MEDICAL & DIAGNOSTIC CENTER, INC.—See Transnational Diversified Group of Companies; *Int'l*, pg. 7902
TRANSNATIONAL SHIP MANAGEMENT, INC.—See Transnational Diversified Group of Companies; *Int'l*, pg. 7902
TRANS-NATIONWIDE EXPRESS PLC.; *Int'l*, pg. 7894
TRANSNEFT BALTIC, LLC—See OAO AK Transneft; *Int'l*, pg. 5505
TRANSNEFT DIASCAN, JSC—See OAO AK Transneft; *Int'l*, pg. 5506
TRANSNEFT DRUZHBA, JSC—See OAO AK Transneft; *Int'l*, pg. 5506
TRANSNEFT EAST, LLC—See OAO AK Transneft; *Int'l*, pg. 5506
TRANSNEFT ENERGY, LLC—See OAO AK Transneft; *Int'l*, pg. 5506
TRANSNEFTEPRODUCT, JSC—See OAO AK Transneft; *Int'l*, pg. 5506
TRANSNEFT FAR EAST, LLC—See OAO AK Transneft; *Int'l*, pg. 5506
TRANSNEFT INVEST MANAGEMENT COMPANY, LLC—See OAO AK Transneft; *Int'l*, pg. 5506
TRANSNEFT KAMA REGION, JSC—See OAO AK Transneft; *Int'l*, pg. 5506
TRANSNEFT KOZMINO PORT, LLC—See OAO AK Transneft; *Int'l*, pg. 5506
TRANSNEFT-LOGISTICS, LLC—See OAO AK Transneft; *Int'l*, pg. 5506
TRANSNEFT MEDIA, LLC—See OAO AK Transneft; *Int'l*, pg. 5506
TRANSNEFT METROLOGY, JSC—See OAO AK Transneft; *Int'l*, pg. 5506
TRANSNEFT NORTH, JSC—See OAO AK Transneft; *Int'l*, pg. 5506
TRANSNEFT OIL PUMPS, JSC—See OAO AK Transneft; *Int'l*, pg. 5506
TRANSNEFT PCD, LLC—See OAO AK Transneft; *Int'l*, pg. 5506
TRANSNEFT PRIMORSK PORT, LLC—See OAO AK Transneft; *Int'l*, pg. 5506
TRANSNEFT SECURITY SERVICES, LLC—See OAO AK Transneft; *Int'l*, pg. 5506
TRANSNEFT SERVICE, JSC—See OAO AK Transneft; *Int'l*, pg. 5506
TRANSNEFT-SERVICE, LLC—See OAO AK Transneft; *Int'l*, pg. 5506
TRANSNEFT SUPERVISION, LLC—See OAO AK Transneft; *Int'l*, pg. 5506
TRANSNEFT TECHNOLOGY, LLC—See OAO AK Transneft; *Int'l*, pg. 5506
TRANSNEFT TELECOM, LLC—See OAO AK Transneft; *Int'l*, pg. 5506
TRANSNEFT UPPER VOLGA, JSC—See OAO AK Transneft; *Int'l*, pg. 5506
TRANSNEFT URALS, JSC—See OAO AK Transneft; *Int'l*, pg. 5506
TRANSNEFT UST-LUGA PORT, LLC—See OAO AK Transneft; *Int'l*, pg. 5506
TRANSNEFT UW SERVICE, JSC—See OAO AK Transneft; *Int'l*, pg. 5506
TRANSNEFT VOLGA REGION, JSC—See OAO AK Transneft; *Int'l*, pg. 5506
TRANSNEFT WESTERN SIBERIA, JSC—See OAO AK Transneft; *Int'l*, pg. 5506
TRANS-NEMWIL INSURANCE (GRENADA) LTD—See Guardian Holdings Limited; *Int'l*, pg. 3171

CORPORATE AFFILIATIONS

TRANSNETBW GMBH—See EnBW Energie Baden-Wurttemberg AG; *Int'l*, pg. 2400
TRANSNETBW GMBH—See EnBW Energie Baden-Wurttemberg AG; *Int'l*, pg. 2400
TRANSNET FREIGHT RAIL—See Transnet Ltd.; *Int'l*, pg. 7902
TRANSNET LTD.; *Int'l*, pg. 7902
TRANSNET PIPELINES—See Transnet Ltd.; *Int'l*, pg. 7902
TRANSNET S.A.—See State Grid Corporation of China; *Int'l*, pg. 7183
TRANSNETYX, INC.—See Thompson Street Capital Manager LLC; *U.S. Private*, pg. 4161
TRANSNORM SYSTEM GMBH—See Honeywell International Inc.; *U.S. Public*, pg. 1052
TRANSNUCLEAR, LTD.—See Kobe Steel, Ltd.; *Int'l*, pg. 4221
TRANSOCEANA CIA. LTDA.—See Albert Ballin KG; *Int'l*, pg. 296
TRANSOCEAN BRASIL LTDA.—See Transocean Ltd.; *Int'l*, pg. 7903
TRANSOCEAN DISTRIBUTION HUB SDN. BHD.—See Transocean Holdings Bhd.; *Int'l*, pg. 7902
TRANSOCEAN DRILLING LIMITED—See Transocean Ltd.; *Int'l*, pg. 7903
TRANSOCEAN DRILLING (NIGERIA) LTD.—See Transocean Ltd.; *Int'l*, pg. 7903
TRANSOCEAN DRILLING OFFSHORE S.A.R.L.—See Transocean Ltd.; *Int'l*, pg. 7903
TRANSOCEAN EASTERN PTE LTD.—See Transocean Ltd.; *Int'l*, pg. 7903
TRANSOCEAN ENTERPRISE INC.—See Transocean Ltd.; *Int'l*, pg. 7903
TRANSOCEAN HOLDING CORPORATION—See Assicurazioni Generali S.p.A.; *Int'l*, pg. 648
TRANSOCEAN HOLDINGS BHD.; *Int'l*, pg. 7902
TRANSOCEAN I AS—See Transocean Ltd.; *Int'l*, pg. 7903
TRANSOCEAN INC.—See Transocean Ltd.; *Int'l*, pg. 7903
TRANSOCEAN (KL) SDN. BHD.—See Transocean Holdings Bhd.; *Int'l*, pg. 7902
TRANSOCEAN LOGISTICS SDN. BHD.—See Transocean Holdings Bhd.; *Int'l*, pg. 7902
TRANSOCEAN LTD.; *Int'l*, pg. 7903
TRANSOCEAN MANAGEMENT LTD.—See Transocean Ltd.; *Int'l*, pg. 7903
TRANSOCEAN NORWAY DRILLING AS—See Transocean Ltd.; *Int'l*, pg. 7903
TRANSOCEAN OFFSHORE CANADA SERVICES LTD.—See Transocean Ltd.; *Int'l*, pg. 7903
TRANSOCEAN OFFSHORE DEEPWATER DRILLING INC.—See Transocean Ltd.; *Int'l*, pg. 7903
TRANSOCEAN OFFSHORE INTERNATIONAL VENTURES LIMITED—See Transocean Ltd.; *Int'l*, pg. 7903
TRANSOCEAN OFFSHORE (NORTH SEA) LTD.—See Transocean Ltd.; *Int'l*, pg. 7903
TRANSOCEAN OFFSHORE USA, INC.—See Transocean Ltd.; *Int'l*, pg. 7903
TRANSOCEAN ONSHORE SUPPORT SERVICES LIMITED—See Transocean Ltd.; *Int'l*, pg. 7903
TRANS OCEAN PRODUCTS INC.—See Maruha Nichiro Corporation; *Int'l*, pg. 4712
TRANSOCEAN PTY LTD.—See Transocean Ltd.; *Int'l*, pg. 7903
TRANSOCEAN SUPPORT SERVICES PVT. LTD.—See Transocean Ltd.; *Int'l*, pg. 7903
TRANSODA SP. Z.O.O.—See Kulczyk Investments S.A.; *Int'l*, pg. 4328
TRANS-O-FLEX ACCOUNTING SERVICE GMBH—See Osterreichische Post AG; *Int'l*, pg. 5654
TRANS-O-FLEX GERMANY GMBH—See Osterreichische Post AG; *Int'l*, pg. 5654
TRANS-O-FLEX IT-SERVICE GMBH—See Osterreichische Post AG; *Int'l*, pg. 5654
TRANS-O-FLEX LINIENVERKEHR GMBH—See Osterreichische Post AG; *Int'l*, pg. 5654
TRANS-O-FLEX SCHNELL-LIEFERDIENST GMBH—See Schoeller Holdings Ltd.; *Int'l*, pg. 6637
TRANS-O-FLEX THERMOMED AUSTRIA GMBH—See Osterreichische Post AG; *Int'l*, pg. 5654
TRANS-O-FLEX THERMOMED GMBH & CO KG—See Osterreichische Post AG; *Int'l*, pg. 5654
TRANS-O-FLEX VERWALTUNG GMBH—See Osterreichische Post AG; *Int'l*, pg. 5654
TRANSOFT GROUP LTD.—See HgCapital Trust plc; *Int'l*, pg. 3377
TRANSOHIO RESIDENTIAL TITLE AGENCY, LTD.—See M/I Homes, Inc.; *U.S. Public*, pg. 1351
TRANSOLID, INC.—See TRM Inc.; *U.S. Private*, pg. 4241
TRANSOM CAPITAL GROUP, LLC; *U.S. Private*, pg. 4209
TRANSONIC ASIA INC.—See Measurement Innovations Corp.; *U.S. Private*, pg. 2648
TRANSONIC COMBUSTION, INC.; *U.S. Private*, pg. 4210
TRANSONIC EUROPE B.V.—See Measurement Innovations Corp.; *U.S. Private*, pg. 2648
TRANSONIC JAPAN INC.—See Measurement Innovations Corp.; *U.S. Private*, pg. 2648
TRANSONIC SCISENSE INC—See Measurement Innovations Corp.; *U.S. Private*, pg. 2648
TRANSONIC SYSTEMS INC.—See Measurement Innovations Corp.; *U.S. Private*, pg. 2648

COMPANY NAME INDEX

TRANSON MEDIA LLC; *U.S. Private,* pg. 4210
TRANSOURCE INC.; *U.S. Private,* pg. 4210
TRANSOURCE SERVICES CORP; *U.S. Private,* pg. 4210
TRANS-OVERSEAS B.V.—See AG der Dillinger Huttenwerke; *Int'l,* pg. 197
TRANS-OVERSEAS CORPORATION; *U.S. Private,* pg. 4206
TRANS-PACIFIC AEROSPACE COMPANY, INC.; *U.S. Public,* pg. 2179
TRANS PACIFIC BANCORP; *U.S. Private,* pg. 4205
TRANSPACIFIC BITUMINOUS PRODUCTS PTY LTD—See Cleanaway Waste Management Limited; *Int'l,* pg. 1655
TRANSPACIFIC BROADBAND GROUP INTERNATIONAL, INC.; *Int'l,* pg. 7903
TRANSPACIFIC CLEANAWAY PTY. LTD.—See Cleanaway Waste Management Limited; *Int'l,* pg. 1655
TRANS-PACIFIC CREDIT PRIVATE LIMITED—See UOB-Kay Hian Holdings Limited; *Int'l,* pg. 8085
TRANSPACIFIC INDUSTRIES PTY LTD—See Cleanaway Waste Management Limited; *Int'l,* pg. 1655
TRANS PACIFIC INSURANCE COMPANY—See Tokio Marine Holdings, Inc.; *Int'l,* pg. 7786
TRANSPACIFIC MANUFACTURING SYSTEMS PTY LTD—See Cleanaway Waste Management Limited; *Int'l,* pg. 1655
TRANS PACIFIC NATIONAL BANK—See Trans Pacific Bancorp; *U.S. Private,* pg. 4205
TRANSPACIFIC PARAMOUNT SERVICES PTY LTD—See Cleanaway Waste Management Limited; *Int'l,* pg. 1655
TRANSPACIFIC RECYCLING PTY LTD—See Cleanaway Waste Management Limited; *Int'l,* pg. 1655
TRANSPACIFIC RESOURCES PTY LTD—See Cleanaway Waste Management Limited; *Int'l,* pg. 1655
TRANS PACIFIC SHIPPING LIMITED—See Singularity Future Technology Ltd.; *U.S. Public,* pg. 1888
TRANSPACIFIC SUPERIOR PAK PTY LTD—See Cleanaway Waste Management Limited; *Int'l,* pg. 1655
TRANS PACIFIC TEXTILE (M) SDN. BHD.—See Techbase Industries Berhad; *Int'l,* pg. 7503
TRANSPACIFIC WASTE MANAGEMENT PTY LTD—See Cleanaway Waste Management Limited; *Int'l,* pg. 1655
TRANSPAC IMPORTS INC.; *U.S. Private,* pg. 4210
TRANSPACO ADMINISTRATIVE AND FINANCIAL SERVICES (PTY) LTD—See Transpaco Ltd.; *Int'l,* pg. 7904
TRANSPACO CORES & TUBES (PTY) LTD.—See Transpaco Ltd.; *Int'l,* pg. 7904
TRANSPACO FLEXIBLES MPUMALANGA (PTY) LTD—See Transpaco Ltd.; *Int'l,* pg. 7904
TRANSPACO FLEXIBLES PTY LIMITED—See Transpaco Ltd.; *Int'l,* pg. 7904
TRANSPACO LTD.; *Int'l,* pg. 7903
TRANSPACO PACKAGING (PTY) LTD—See Transpaco Ltd.; *Int'l,* pg. 7904
TRANSPACO POLYMER RECYCLERS (PTY) LTD—See Transpaco Ltd.; *Int'l,* pg. 7904
TRANSPACO RECYCLING (PTY) LTD—See Transpaco Ltd.; *Int'l,* pg. 7904
TRANSPACO SPECIALISED FILMS (PTY) LTD—See Transpaco Ltd.; *Int'l,* pg. 7904
TRANSPACT ENTERPRISES LIMITED; *Int'l,* pg. 7904
TRANSPAK CORPORATION—See Delos Capital, LLC; *U.S. Private,* pg. 1198
TRANS PAPA LOGISTICS, INC.—See Papa John's International, Inc.; *U.S. Public,* pg. 1636
TRANSPARENT CONTAINER CO., INC. - MEXICO FACILITY—See Wellspring Capital Management LLC; *U.S. Private,* pg. 4477
TRANSPARENT CONTAINER CO., INC. - PAPERBOARD FACILITY—See Wellspring Capital Management LLC; *U.S. Private,* pg. 4477
TRANSPARENT CONTAINER CO., INC.—See Wellspring Capital Management LLC; *U.S. Private,* pg. 4477
TRANSPARES LIMITED—See Transformers & Rectifiers India Ltd; *Int'l,* pg. 7900
TRANSPASS B.V.—See Caisse des Depots et Consignations; *Int'l,* pg. 1258
TRANSPAVE, INC.—See CRH plc; *Int'l,* pg. 1849
TRANSPEC LEASING INC.—See TSL Companies; *U.S. Private,* pg. 4254
TRANSPED A.D.; *Int'l,* pg. 7904
TRANSPEED HONG KONG LIMITED—See Janco Holdings Limited; *Int'l,* pg. 3879
TRANSPEK CREATIVE CHEMISTRY PRIVATE LIMITED—See Transpek Industry Limited; *Int'l,* pg. 7904
TRANSPEK INDUSTRY (EUROPE) LTD.—See Transpek Industry Limited; *Int'l,* pg. 7904
TRANSPEK INDUSTRY LIMITED; *Int'l,* pg. 7904
TRANSPERFECT DOCUMENT MANAGEMENT, INC.—See TransPerfect Global, Inc.; *U.S. Private,* pg. 4210
TRANSPERFECT GLOBAL, INC.; *U.S. Private,* pg. 4210
TRANSPERFECT LEGAL SOLUTIONS—See TransPerfect Global, Inc.; *U.S. Private,* pg. 4210
TRANSPERFECT TRANSLATIONS INTERNATIONAL INC.—See TransPerfect Global, Inc.; *U.S. Private,* pg. 4210

TRANSPHORM, INC.—See Renesas Electronics Corporation; *Int'l,* pg. 6277
TRANSPHORM JAPAN EPI, INC.—See Renesas Electronics Corporation; *Int'l,* pg. 6277
TRANSPHORM JAPAN, INC.—See Renesas Electronics Corporation; *Int'l,* pg. 6277
TRANSPHORM TECHNOLOGY, INC.—See Renesas Electronics Corporation; *Int'l,* pg. 6277
TRANSPIRE BIO INC.—See Smoore International Holdings Limited; *Int'l,* pg. 7014
TRANSPLACE CANADA - LAKESIDE DIVISION—See TPG Capital, L.P.; *U.S. Public,* pg. 2177
TRANSPLACE, LLC—See TPG Capital, L.P.; *U.S. Public,* pg. 2177
TRANSPLANT GENOMICS, INC.—See Eurofins Scientific S.E.; *Int'l,* pg. 2552
TRANSPLATINUM SERVICE, LLC—See WEX, Inc.; *U.S. Public,* pg. 2364
TRANSPLY INC.; *U.S. Private,* pg. 4210
TRANS POLONIA S.A.; *Int'l,* pg. 7894
TRANSPORCIAN MARITIMA MEXICANA, S.A. DE C.V.—See Grupo TMM, S.A.B.; *Int'l,* pg. 3137
TRANSPOREON GMBH—See Trimble, Inc.; *U.S. Public,* pg. 2193
TRANSPOREON SP. Z O. O.—See Trimble, Inc.; *U.S. Public,* pg. 2193
TRANSPORT 4, L.L.C.—See Enterprise Products Partners L.P.; *U.S. Public,* pg. 779
TRANSPORTADORA DE ELECTRICIDAD S.A.—See Redeia Corporation, *Int'l,* pg. 6246
TRANSPORTADORA DE ENERGIA DE CENTROAMERICA S.A.—See Grupo Energia Bogota S.A. E.S.P.; *Int'l,* pg. 3128
TRANSPORTADORA DE GAS DEL PERU S.A.; *Int'l,* pg. 7905
TRANSPORTADORA DE GAS DEL SUR S.A.—See Grupo EMES S.A.; *Int'l,* pg. 3126
TRANSPORTATION ALLIANCE BANK—See FJ Management, Inc.; *U.S. Private,* pg. 1538
TRANSPORTATION AND LOGISTICS SYSTEMS, INC.; *U.S. Public,* pg. 2184
TRANSPORTATION AUCKLAND CORPORATION LIMITED—See Infratil Limited; *Int'l,* pg. 3698
TRANSPORTATION CLAIMS LIMITED—See FirstGroup plc; *Int'l,* pg. 2689
TRANSPORTATION COMMUNICATIONS UNIONIAM; *U.S. Private,* pg. 4211
TRANSPORTATION CONSULTANTS OF AMERICA, INC.; *U.S. Private,* pg. 4211
TRANSPORTATION DESIGN & MANUFACTURING CO.; *U.S. Private,* pg. 4211
TRANSPORTATION EQUIPMENT SALES CORP. (TESCO); *U.S. Private,* pg. 4211
TRANSPORTATION GENERAL INC.; *U.S. Private,* pg. 4211
TRANSPORTATION GROUP—See Van Eerden Trucking Company; *U.S. Private,* pg. 4340
TRANSPORTATION IMPACT LLC—See The Jordan Company, L.P.; *U.S. Private,* pg. 4062
TRANSPORTATION INSIGHT, LLC—See Gryphon Investors, LLC; *U.S. Private,* pg. 1799
TRANSPORTATION INSURANCE COMPANY—See Loews Corporation; *U.S. Public,* pg. 1340
TRANSPORTATION LEASING CO.; *U.S. Private,* pg. 4211
TRANSPORTATION POWER, INC.—See Cummins Inc.; *U.S. Public,* pg. 609
TRANSPORTATION RESOURCE PARTNERS, LP; *U.S. Private,* pg. 4211
TRANSPORTATION SERVICES, INC.; *U.S. Private,* pg. 4211
TRANSPORTATION SOLUTIONS GROUP, LLC.; *U.S. Private,* pg. 4211
TRANSPORTATION SPECIALISTS LTD.—See TSL Companies; *U.S. Private,* pg. 4254
TRANSPORTATION TECHNOLOGY SERVICES, INC.—See Berkshire Hathaway Inc.; *U.S. Public,* pg. 303
TRANSPORTATION & TRADING SERVICES JOINT STOCK COMPANY; *Int'l,* pg. 7905
TRANSPORTATION & TRANSIT ASSOCIATES, LLC; *U.S. Private,* pg. 4211
TRANSPORTATION WORLDWIDE INC.; *U.S. Private,* pg. 4211
TRANSPORTBEDRIJF VAN VLIET B.V.—See Renewi plc; *Int'l,* pg. 6279
TRANSPORTBETON BAD WALDSEE GESCHAFTSFUHRUNGS GMBH—See Heidelberg Materials AG; *Int'l,* pg. 3320
TRANSPORTBETON UND ASPHALTGESELLSCHAFT M.B.H.—See Swietelsky Baugesellschaft m.b.H.; *Int'l,* pg. 7367
TRANSPORT BROKERS (PTY) LIMITED—See Super Group Limited; *Int'l,* pg. 7335
TRANSPORT CO OF INDIA (MAURITIUS) LTD.—See Transport Corporation of India Ltd.; *Int'l,* pg. 7905
TRANSPORT CORPORATION OF AMERICA, INC.—See TFI International Inc.; *Int'l,* pg. 7586
TRANSPORT CORPORATION OF INDIA LTD.; *Int'l,* pg. 7904

TRANSPORT COUTURE & FILS LTEE—See TFI International Inc.; *Int'l,* pg. 7586
TRANSPORT DISTRIBUTION COMPANY; *U.S. Private,* pg. 4210
TRANSPORT & DISTRIBUTION INC.—See Siemens Aktiengesellschaft; *Int'l,* pg. 6891
TRANSPORT & DISTRIBUTION SERVICE, INC.—See Taiyo Kogyo Corporation; *Int'l,* pg. 7426
TRANSPORT DRIVERS INC.; *U.S. Private,* pg. 4210
TRANSPORTE AEREO S.A.—See LATAM Airlines Group S.A.; *Int'l,* pg. 4422
TRANSPORT & ENGINEERING CO—See Chemical Industries Holding Company; *Int'l,* pg. 1462
TRANSPORT ENGINEERING SOLUTIONS PTY LIMITED—See Sime Darby Berhad; *Int'l,* pg. 6930
TRANSPORT ENTERPRISE LEASING, LLC—See Covenant Logistics Group, Inc.; *U.S. Public,* pg. 588
THE TRANSPORTER, INC.—See Ridgemont Partners Management LLC; *U.S. Private,* pg. 3433
TRANSPORTES AEREOS PORTUGUESES, S.A.—See TAP-Transportes Aereos Portugueses, SGPS, S.A.; *Int'l,* pg. 7461
TRANSPORTES MARITIMOS INSULARES, S.A.; *Int'l,* pg. 7905
TRANSPORTES POR CABLE S.A.—See Doppelmayr Group; *Int'l,* pg. 2175
TRANSPORTES SUL DO TEJO S.A.—See Deutsche Bahn AG; *Int'l,* pg. 2055
TRANSPORTES TPG S.A.—See Quinenco S.A.; *Int'l,* pg. 6164
TRANSPORTES UNIDOS DE ASTURIAS, S.L.—See Mobico Group PLC; *Int'l,* pg. 5009
TRANSPORTES URBANOS DE GUADALAJARA, S.L.—See Mobico Group PLC; *Int'l,* pg. 5009
TRANSPORTES VICONTO LTDA.—See Vina Concha y Toro S.A.; *Int'l,* pg. 8209
TRANSPORT EXPRESS LLC; *U.S. Private,* pg. 4210
TRANSPORT FINANCIAL SERVICES—See AB Volvo; *Int'l,* pg. 42
TRANSPORT HERVE LEMIEUX; *Int'l,* pg. 7905
TRANSPORT INDIANA, LLC—See Patrick Industries, Inc.; *U.S. Public,* pg. 1653
TRANSPORT INTERNATIONAL HOLDINGS LIMITED; *Int'l,* pg. 7905
TRANSPORT & INVESTMENT BARTER COMPANY; *Int'l,* pg. 7904
TRANSPORT INVESTMENTS, INC.; *U.S. Private,* pg. 4210
TRANSPORTIQ, INC.—See TraQiQ, Inc.; *U.S. Public,* pg. 2185
TRANSPORT JACQUES AUGER INC.; *Int'l,* pg. 7905
TRANSPORT KOBELT INC.—See TFI International Inc.; *Int'l,* pg. 7587
TRANSPORT LABOR CONTRACT/LEASING—See Berggruen Holdings, Inc.; *U.S. Private,* pg. 531
TRANSPORT LABOR CONTRACT/LEASING—See High Street Capital Management, Inc.; *U.S. Private,* pg. 1937
TRANSPORT LABOR CONTRACT/LEASING—See SE Capital, LLC; *U.S. Private,* pg. 3582
TRANSPORT LEASING COMPANY LLP; *U.S. Private,* pg. 4210
TRANSPORT LEASING/CONTRACT; *U.S. Private,* pg. 4210
TRANSPORT LEASING SYSTEMS, LLC.—See US 1 Industries, Inc.; *U.S. Private,* pg. 4317
TRANSPORT NANUK INC.—See Blue Wolf Capital Partners LLC; *U.S. Private,* pg. 595
TRANSPORT REFRIGERATION INC.; *U.S. Private,* pg. 4210
TRANSPORT REFRIGERATION OF SOUTH DAKOTA INC.; *U.S. Private,* pg. 4210
TRANSPORT RISK MANAGEMENT INC.—See Kelso & Company, L.P.; *U.S. Private,* pg. 2280
TRANSPORTS BAUDOUIN; *Int'l,* pg. 7905
TRANSPORTS BERNIS—See SNCF; *Int'l,* pg. 7026
TRANSPORTS DESERT SA; *Int'l,* pg. 7905
TRANSPORTS DUSOLIER—See SNCF; *Int'l,* pg. 7026
TRANSPORT SERVICE CO.—See Caisse de Depot et Placement du Quebec; *Int'l,* pg. 1255
TRANSPORT SERVICE CO.—See The Goldman Sachs Group, Inc.; *U.S. Public,* pg. 2081
TRANSPORT SERVICES, INC.—See Bennett International Group, Inc.; *U.S. Private,* pg. 527
TRANSPORT SERVICES INC.; *U.S. Private,* pg. 4210
TRANSPORTS GAZEAU SAS—See Groupement FLO; *Int'l,* pg. 3112
TRANSPORTS GODFROY S.A.S—See Nichirei Corporation; *Int'l,* pg. 5270
TRANSPORTS GOUBET; *Int'l,* pg. 7905
TRANSPORTS GUIDEZ; *Int'l,* pg. 7905
TRANSPORTS JOLLIVET CHRISTIAN; *Int'l,* pg. 7905
TRANSPORTS KLINZING FRERES ET CIE; *Int'l,* pg. 7905
TRANSPORTS LACASSAGNE—See SNCF; *Int'l,* pg. 7026
TRANSPORTS MOULINOIS—See SNCF; *Int'l,* pg. 7026
TRANSPORT SPECIALISTS INCORPORATED; *U.S. Private,* pg. 4211

TRANSPORTS RAPIDES LOZERIENS—See SNCF; *Int'l*, pg. 7026
TRANSPORT TECHNOLOGIE-CONSULT KARLSRUHE GMBH—See Porsche Automobil Holding SE; *Int'l*, pg. 5926
TRANSPORT TELEMATIC SYSTEMS LLC—See Kapsch-Group Beteiligungs GmbH; *Int'l*, pg. 4078
TRANSPORT TERTIAIRE INDUSTRIE SAS—See FAYAT SAS; *Int'l*, pg. 2626
TRANSPORT THIBODEAU INC.—See TFI International Inc.; *Int'l*, pg. 7587
TRANSPORT TOPICS PUBLISHING GROUP; *U.S. Private*, pg. 4211
TRANSPORTURI AUTO GIULESTI SA; *Int'l*, pg. 7905
TRANSPORT VOZDOVAC A.D.; *Int'l*, pg. 7905
TRANSPORT WATSON MONTREAL LTEE—See TFI International Inc.; *Int'l*, pg. 7587
TRANSPOSAFE SYSTEMS HOLLAND B.V.—See Brady Corporation; *U.S. Public*, pg. 379
TRANSPOSAFE SYSTEMS POLSKA SP. Z.O.O.—See Brady Corporation; *U.S. Public*, pg. 379
TRANSPO SERVICE LTD. INC.—See Centre Limited Inc.; *U.S. Private*, pg. 828
TRANS POWER UTILITY CONTRACTORS INC.; *Int'l*, pg. 7894
TRANSPRINT USA, INC.—See Colorep, Inc.; *U.S. Private*, pg. 975
TRANSPRO FREIGHT SYSTEMS LTD.; *Int'l*, pg. 7905
TRANSPROM A.D.; *Int'l*, pg. 7905
TRANSPROTECTION SERVICE COMPANY—See American Financial Group, Inc.; *U.S. Public*, pg. 103
TRANS QUEBEC & MARITIMES PIPELINE INC.—See Caisse de Depot et Placement du Quebec; *Int'l*, pg. 1256
TRANS QUEBEC & MARITIMES PIPELINE INC.—See TC Energy Corporation; *Int'l*, pg. 7482
TRANSQUERCY—See SNCF; *Int'l*, pg. 7026
TRANSQUEST TAG & TRACING SOLUTIONS B.V.—See dormakaba Holding AG; *Int'l*, pg. 2178
TRANSRAIL LIGHTING LIMITED; *Int'l*, pg. 7905
TRANSRE EUROPE S.A.—See Berkshire Hathaway Inc.; *U.S. Public*, pg. 299
TRANSRE LONDON LIMITED—See Berkshire Hathaway Inc.; *U.S. Public*, pg. 299
TRANSRE S.A.—See Berkshire Hathaway Inc.; *U.S. Public*, pg. 299
TRANS RESOURCES CORPORATION SDN. BHD.—See TRC Synergy Berhad; *Int'l*, pg. 7909
TRANS-RESOURCES, INC.; *U.S. Private*, pg. 4206
TRANSRE ZURICH LTD.—See Berkshire Hathaway Inc.; *U.S. Public*, pg. 299
TRANS RE ZURICH REINSURANCE COMPANY LTD—See Berkshire Hathaway Inc.; *U.S. Public*, pg. 299
TRANSROL S.A.S.—See SKF AB; *Int'l*, pg. 6983
TRANSROUTE SA—See Eiffage S.A.; *Int'l*, pg. 2331
TRANS-SERVIS, SPOL. S R.O.—See Heidelberg Materials AG; *Int'l*, pg. 3320
TRANS-SIBERIAN GOLD MANAGEMENT, LLC—See Horvik Limited; *Int'l*, pg. 3482
TRANS-SIBERIAN GOLD PLC—See Horvik Limited; *Int'l*, pg. 3482
TRANS SP. Z O.O—See Decora S.A.; *Int'l*, pg. 2001
TRANS STATES AIRLINES INC.; *U.S. Private*, pg. 4205
TRANSSTROY-AM AD; *Int'l*, pg. 7905
TRANSSTROY-BURGAS AD; *Int'l*, pg. 7905
TRANS-SYSTEM INC.; *U.S. Private*, pg. 4206
TRANSTAR AUTOBODY TECHNOLOGIES, INC.—See Blue Point Capital Partners, LLC; *U.S. Private*, pg. 591
TRANSTAR HOLDING COMPANY—See Blue Point Capital Partners, LLC; *U.S. Private*, pg. 590
TRANSTAR INDUSTRIES, INC.—See Blue Point Capital Partners, LLC; *U.S. Private*, pg. 590
TRANSTAR, LLC—See SoftBank Group Corp.; *Int'l*, pg. 7053
TRANSTAR METALS LIMITED—See A. M. Castle & Co.; *U.S. Public*, pg. 11
TRANSTEC AG—See Adiuva Capital GmbH; *Int'l*, pg. 149
TRANSTEC COMPUTER AG—See Adiuva Capital GmbH; *Int'l*, pg. 149
TRANSTEC COMPUTERS LTD.—See Adiuva Capital GmbH; *Int'l*, pg. 149
TRANSTECH CONSULTING, INC.—See Blue Horseshoe Solutions, Inc.; *U.S. Private*, pg. 589
TRANS-TECH, INC.—See Skyworks Solutions, Inc.; *U.S. Public*, pg. 1893
TRANSTECH INDUSTRIES, INC.; *U.S. Public*, pg. 2184
TRANSTECH INTERACTIVE TRAINING INC.—See John Wood Group PLC; *Int'l*, pg. 3982
TRANSTECHNIK GMBH & CO. KG—See Knorr-Bremse AG; *Int'l*, pg. 4212
TRANSTECH OF SC, INC.—See Westinghouse Air Brake Technologies Corporation; *U.S. Public*, pg. 2358
TRANSTECH OPTELECOM SCIENCE HOLDINGS LTD.; *Int'l*, pg. 7905
TRANSTECH OPTICAL COMMUNICATION CO., LTD.—See Futong Group Co., Ltd.; *Int'l*, pg. 2852
TRANSTECH OY—See Skoda Transportation a.s.; *Int'l*, pg. 6991

TRANSTECH SOLUTIONS, INC.; *U.S. Private*, pg. 4211
TRANSTECH SP. Z O.O.—See Zaklady Chemiczne POLICE S.A.; *Int'l*, pg. 8621
TRANSTECNO AANDRIJFTECHNIEK BV—See Interpump Group S.p.A.; *Int'l*, pg. 3757
TRANSTECNO BV—See Interpump Group S.p.A.; *Int'l*, pg. 3757
TRANSTECNO IBERICA THE MODULAR GEARMOTOR S.A.—See Interpump Group S.p.A.; *Int'l*, pg. 3757
TRANSTECNO S.R.L.—See Interpump Group S.p.A.; *Int'l*, pg. 3757
TRANSTEC S.A.R.L.—See Adiuva Capital GmbH; *Int'l*, pg. 149
TRANSTECTOR SYSTEMS, INC.—See Smiths Group plc; *Int'l*, pg. 7012
TRANSTELCO HOLDING, INC.; *U.S. Private*, pg. 4211
TRANSTELE - CANAL FRANCE INTERNATIONAL; *Int'l*, pg. 7905
TRANSTEL ENGINEERING ARABIA LIMITED CO—See CSE Global Ltd.; *Int'l*, pg. 1864
TRANSTEL ENGINEERING ARABIAN LIMITED CO.—See CSE Global Ltd.; *Int'l*, pg. 1864
TRANSTEL ENGINEERING (NIGERIA) LTD.—See CSE Global Ltd.; *Int'l*, pg. 1864
TRANSTEL ENGINEERING PNG LTD—See CSE Global Ltd.; *Int'l*, pg. 1864
TRANSTEL ENGINEERING PTE LTD.—See CSE Global Ltd.; *Int'l*, pg. 1864
TRANSTEL ENGINEERING (THAILAND) CO LIMITED—See CSE Global Ltd.; *Int'l*, pg. 1864
TRANSTEL LIMITED—See Fiji National Provident Fund; *Int'l*, pg. 2661
TRANSTEMA AB—See Transtema Group AB; *Int'l*, pg. 7906
TRANSTEMA GROUP AB; *Int'l*, pg. 7905
TRANSTEX BELTING—See Forbo Holding Ltd.; *Int'l*, pg. 2729
TRANS-TEX FABRICATING CO., INC.; *U.S. Private*, pg. 4206
TRANSTEX HUNTER, LLC—See Expand Energy Corporation; *U.S. Public*, pg. 808
TRANSTEX LLC; *U.S. Private*, pg. 4211
TRANSTOUCH TECHNOLOGY, INC.; *Int'l*, pg. 7906
TRANSTRACK INTERNATIONAL B.V.—See Giesecke & Devrient GmbH; *Int'l*, pg. 2970
TRANS-TRADE, INC.; *U.S. Private*, pg. 4206
TRANS-TRADE, INC.—See Trans-Trade, Inc.; *U.S. Private*, pg. 4206
TRANSTREND B.V.—See ORIX Corporation; *Int'l*, pg. 5636
TRANSTRON AMERICA, INC.—See Fujitsu Limited; *Int'l*, pg. 2838
TRANSTRUCTURE CO., LTD.—See Miroku Jyoho Service Co., Ltd.; *Int'l*, pg. 4920
TRANS TUNISIAN PIPELINE CO LTD—See Eni S.p.A.; *Int'l*, pg. 2438
TRANSTURIST D.D.; *Int'l*, pg. 7906
TRANSTURK HOLDING A.S.; *Int'l*, pg. 7906
TRANSUNION BRASIL SISTEMAS EM INFORMATICA LTDA.—See TransUnion; *U.S. Public*, pg. 2184
TRANSUNION CIBIL LIMITED—See TransUnion; *U.S. Public*, pg. 2184
TRANSUNION CORP.—See TransUnion; *U.S. Public*, pg. 2184
TRANS UNION COSTA RICA, S.A.—See TransUnion; *U.S. Public*, pg. 2184
TRANSUNION CREDIT BUREAU NAMIBIA (PTY) LTD.—See TransUnion; *U.S. Public*, pg. 2184
TRANSUNION CREDIT BUREAU (PTY) LTD.—See TranSunion; *U.S. Public*, pg. 2184
TRANS UNION GUATEMALA, S.A.—See TransUnion; *U.S. Public*, pg. 2184
TRANSUNION INFORMATION GROUP LIMITED—See TransUnion; *U.S. Public*, pg. 2184
TRANSUNION INFORMATION SOLUTIONS, INC.—See TransUnion; *U.S. Public*, pg. 2184
TRANSUNION LIMITED—See American Express Company; *U.S. Public*, pg. 101
TRANSUNION LLC—See TransUnion; *U.S. Public*, pg. 2184
TRANS UNION OF CANADA, INC.—See TransUnion; *U.S. Public*, pg. 2184
TRANSUNION RWANDA LIMITED—See TransUnion; *U.S. Public*, pg. 2184
TRANSUNION; *U.S. Public*, pg. 2184
TRANSUNIVERS VOYAGE; *Int'l*, pg. 7906
TRANSUP JAPAN CO., LTD.—See Screen Holdings Co., Ltd.; *Int'l*, pg. 6656
TRANSURBAN INFRASTRUCTURE MANAGEMENT LIMITED—See Transurban Limited; *Int'l*, pg. 7906
TRANSURBAN LIMITED; *Int'l*, pg. 7906
TRANSURE SERVICES, INC.—See Aquiline Capital Partners LLC; *U.S. Private*, pg. 305
TRANSVAL TEOLLISUUSPALVELUT VINDEA OY—See Posti Group Oyj; *Int'l*, pg. 5940
TRANSVER AG—See Rotzinger AG; *Int'l*, pg. 6407
TRANSVERSE INSURANCE GROUP LLC—See MS&AD Insurance Group Holdings, Inc.; *Int'l*, pg. 5066

TRANSVIARIA - GESTAO DE TRANSPORTES S.A.—See Camargo Correa S.A.; *Int'l*, pg. 1268
TRANSVICTORY WINCH SYSTEM PTE. LTD.—See Union Steel Holdings Limited; *Int'l*, pg. 8054
TRANSVIEW LIFESTYLE PTE. LTD.—See XEBIO Holdings Co., Ltd.; *Int'l*, pg. 8520
TRANSVOICE AB—See Altor Equity Partners AB; *Int'l*, pg. 396
TRANSVOY LOGISTICS INDIA LIMITED; *Int'l*, pg. 7906
TRANSWARRANTY FINANCE LIMITED; *Int'l*, pg. 7906
TRANSWASTE TECHNOLOGIES PTY LTD—See Cleanaway Waste Management Limited; *Int'l*, pg. 1655
TRANSWEIGH INDIA LTD.—See FLSmidth & Co. A/S; *Int'l*, pg. 2711
TRANSWERK—See Transnet Ltd.; *Int'l*, pg. 7902
TRANSWESTERN COMMERCIAL SERVICES—See Pearlmark Real Estate Partners LLC; *U.S. Private*, pg. 3125
TRANSWESTERN PIPELINE COMPANY, LLC—See Energy Transfer LP; *U.S. Public*, pg. 764
TRANS-WEST INC.; *U.S. Private*, pg. 4206
TRANSWEST MONGOLIA LLC—See Sumitomo Corporation; *Int'l*, pg. 7276
TRANSWEST PARTNERS; *U.S. Private*, pg. 4211
TRANSWHEEL CORPORATION; *U.S. Private*, pg. 4211
TRANSWIND INFRASTRUCTURES LIMITED; *Int'l*, pg. 7906
TRANSWIRE (PTY.) LTD.—See ACTOM (Pty) Ltd.; *Int'l*, pg. 121
TRANSWOOD CARRIERS INC.; *U.S. Private*, pg. 4211
TRANSWOOD INC.—See Transwood Carriers Inc.; *U.S. Private*, pg. 4211
TRANSWOOD LOGISTICS INC—See Transwood Carriers Inc.; *U.S. Private*, pg. 4212
TRANSWORKS COMPANY—See Norfolk Southern Corporation; *U.S. Public*, pg. 1536
TRANSWORLD ADVERTISING, INC.; *U.S. Private*, pg. 4212
TRANS WORLD ASSURANCE INC.; *U.S. Private*, pg. 4205
TRANSWORLD BUSINESS ADVISORS OF COLORADO LLC; *U.S. Private*, pg. 4212
TRANSWORLD CARGO CARRIERS, S.A.—See TBS INTERNATIONAL PLC; *Int'l*, pg. 7481
TRANS WORLD CONNECTION—See Unlimited Services of Wisconsin, Inc.; *U.S. Private*, pg. 4310
TRANS WORLD CORPORATION—See Far East Consortium International Limited; *Int'l*, pg. 2616
TRANS WORLD FEEDERS FZCO—See Shreyas Shipping & Logistics Limited; *Int'l*, pg. 6865
TRANS WORLD HOTELS AUSTRIA GMBH—See Far East Consortium International Limited; *Int'l*, pg. 2616
TRANS WORLD HOTELS & ENTERTAINMENT A.S.—See Far East Consortium International Limited; *Int'l*, pg. 2616
TRANS WORLD HOTELS GERMANY GMBH—See Far East Consortium International Limited; *Int'l*, pg. 2616
TRANSWORLD INFORMATION SYSTEMS—See Agnite Education Limited; *Int'l*, pg. 212
TRANS WORLD MARKETING CORP.; *U.S. Private*, pg. 4205
TRANSWORLD PRODUCTS, INC.—See Peterson Manufacturing Company Inc.; *U.S. Private*, pg. 3160
TRANSWORLD PUBLISHERS—See Bertelsmann SE & Co. KGaA; *Int'l*, pg. 991
TRANS WORLD RADIO INC.; *U.S. Private*, pg. 4205
TRANSWORLD SHIPPING & LOGISTICS LLC—See Shreyas Shipping & Logistics Limited; *Int'l*, pg. 6865
TRANSWORLD SYSTEMS, INC.—See Platinum Equity, LLC; *U.S. Private*, pg. 3209
TRANSYLVANIA COMMUNITY HOSPITAL, INC.; *U.S. Private*, pg. 4212
TRANSYOKI - TRANSPORTES YOKI LTDA—See General Mills, Inc.; *U.S. Public*, pg. 922
TRANSYSTEMS CORP.—See OceanSound Partners, LP; *U.S. Private*, pg. 2991
TRANSYSTEMS INC.—See Little Brownie Properties Inc.; *U.S. Private*, pg. 2468
TRANSYSTEMS LLC - IDAHO DIVISION—See Transystems LLC; *U.S. Private*, pg. 4212
TRANSYSTEMS LLC - MINNESOTA DIVISION—See Transystems LLC; *U.S. Private*, pg. 4212
TRANSYSTEMS LLC - RED RIVER VALLEY DIVISION—See Transystems LLC; *U.S. Private*, pg. 4212
TRANSYSTEMS LLC—See Transystems LLC; *U.S. Private*, pg. 4212
TRANSYSTEMS LLC; *U.S. Private*, pg. 4212
TRANSYSTEMS—See Transystems LLC; *U.S. Private*, pg. 4212
TRANSZAP, INC.—See Hellman & Friedman LLC; *U.S. Private*, pg. 1908
TRANTECH RADIATOR PRODUCTS, INC.—See Industrial Opportunity Partners, LLC; *U.S. Private*, pg. 2067
TRANTECHS, LTD.—See Toyota Motor Corporation; *Int'l*, pg. 7872
TRANTER ENERGY & MINING SERVICES—See Tranter Holdings (Pty) Limited; *Int'l*, pg. 7906
TRANTER HEAT EXCHANGERS (BEIJING) CO LTD—See Alfa Laval AB; *Int'l*, pg. 308

COMPANY NAME INDEX

TRANTER HEAT EXCHANGERS CANADA INC.—See Alfa Laval AB; *Int'l*, pg. 310
TRANTER HES GMBH—See Alfa Laval AB; *Int'l*, pg. 310
TRANTER HOLDINGS (PTY) LIMITED; *Int'l*, pg. 7906
TRANTER INC.—See Alfa Laval AB; *Int'l*, pg. 309
TRANTER INDIA PVT LTD—See Alfa Laval AB; *Int'l*, pg. 310
TRANTER INTERNATIONAL AB—See Alfa Laval AB; *Int'l*, pg. 310
TRANTER PHE, INC.—See Alfa Laval AB; *Int'l*, pg. 310
TRANTER ROCK DRILLS—See Tranter Holdings (Pty) Limited; *Int'l*, pg. 7906
TRANTER SAS—See Alfa Laval AB; *Int'l*, pg. 310
TRANTER SOLARICE GMBH—See Alfa Laval AB; *Int'l*, pg. 310
TRANTER SRL—See Alfa Laval AB; *Int'l*, pg. 311
TRANTER WARMETAUSCHER GMBH—See Alfa Laval AB; *Int'l*, pg. 309
TRANUM AUTO GROUP; *U.S. Private*, pg. 4212
TRANWAY TECHNOLOGIES LIMITED; *Int'l*, pg. 7906
TRANZACT CORPORATION—See Metalico Inc.; *U.S. Private*, pg. 2681
TRANZACT TECHNOLOGIES INC.; *U.S. Private*, pg. 4212
TRANZAS ASIA PACIFIC PTE. LTD.—See TRaaS On Product Inc.; *Int'l*, pg. 7885
TRANZCOM NV—See VINCI S.A.; *Int'l*, pg. 8229
TRANZION, LLC—See National HealthCare Corporation; *U.S. Public*, pg. 1497
THE TRANZONIC COMPANIES—See The PNC Financial Services Group, Inc.; *U.S. Public*, pg. 2120
TRAPAC, LLC—See Kawasaki Kisen Kaisha, Ltd.; *Int'l*, pg. 4101
TRAPAC, LLC—See Mitsui O.S.K. Lines, Ltd.; *Int'l*, pg. 4991
TRAPAC, LLC—See Nippon Yusen Kabushiki Kaisha; *Int'l*, pg. 5359
TRAPANANDA SEAFARMS LLC—See Joyvio Food Co., Ltd.; *Int'l*, pg. 4005
TRAPEZE GROUP DEUTSCHLAND GMBH—See Constellation Software Inc.; *Int'l*, pg. 1775
TRAPEZE GROUP EUROPE A/S—See Constellation Software Inc.; *Int'l*, pg. 1775
TRAPEZE GROUP (UK) LIMITED—See Constellation Software Inc.; *Int'l*, pg. 1775
TRAPEZE ITS GERMANY GMBH—See Constellation Software Inc.; *Int'l*, pg. 1775
TRAPEZE ITS SWITZERLAND GMBH—See Constellation Software Inc.; *Int'l*, pg. 1775
TRAPEZE POLAND SP. Z O.O.—See Constellation Software Inc.; *Int'l*, pg. 1775
TRAPEZE SOFTWARE GROUP, INC.—See Constellation Software Inc.; *Int'l*, pg. 1775
TRAPEZE SOFTWARE INC.—See Constellation Software Inc.; *Int'l*, pg. 1775
TRAPHACO JOINT STOCK COMPANY; *Int'l*, pg. 7906
TRAPOFIT GMBH—See Mercedes-Benz Group AG; *Int'l*, pg. 4829
TRAP OIL LTD.; *Int'l*, pg. 7906
TRAPO KUNG AG—See ThyssenKrupp AG; *Int'l*, pg. 7734
TRAPOLLO, LLC—See Validic, Inc.; *U.S. Private*, pg. 4332
TRAPP FAMILY LODGE, INC.; *U.S. Private*, pg. 4212
TRAPP TECHNOLOGY, INC.; *U.S. Private*, pg. 4212
TRAP ROCK INDUSTRIES, INC.; *U.S. Private*, pg. 4212
TRAPROCK MINING LIMITED; *Int'l*, pg. 7906
TRAPY PRO; *Int'l*, pg. 7906
TRAQER CORP.; *Int'l*, pg. 7906
TRAQIQ, INC.; *U.S. Public*, pg. 2185
TRAQIQ SOLUTIONS, PVT. LTD.—See TraQiQ, Inc.; *U.S. Public*, pg. 2185
TRAQUEUR S.A.—See Coyote System SAS; *Int'l*, pg. 1823
TRARYDS METALL AB—See Metso Oyj; *Int'l*, pg. 4866
TRASFOR SA—See ABB Ltd.; *Int'l*, pg. 56
TRASFOTEX S.R.L.—See Freudenberg SE; *Int'l*, pg. 2790
TRASH BUTLER, LLC—See Republic Services, Inc.; *U.S. Public*, pg. 1787
TRASHCO INC.—See Waste Management, Inc.; *U.S. Public*, pg. 2332
TRASHCO INC.—See Waste Management, Inc.; *U.S. Public*, pg. 2332
TR ASIA INVESTMENT HOLDINGS PTE LTD—See Trifast plc; *Int'l*, pg. 7921
TRASTOR REAL ESTATE INVESTMENT COMPANY S.A.—See Piraeus Financial Holdings S.A.; *Int'l*, pg. 5874
TRASYS CHARLEROI—See Ackermans & van Haaren NV; *Int'l*, pg. 106
TRASYS CHARLEROI—See BNP Paribas SA; *Int'l*, pg. 1090
TRASYS CHARLEROI—See Frere-Bourgeois; *Int'l*, pg. 2774
TRASYS GREECE—See Ackermans & van Haaren NV; *Int'l*, pg. 106
TRASYS GREECE—See BNP Paribas SA; *Int'l*, pg. 1090
TRASYS GREECE—See Frere-Bourgeois; *Int'l*, pg. 2774
TRASYS LUXEMBOURG—See Ackermans & van Haaren NV; *Int'l*, pg. 106

TRASYS LUXEMBOURG—See BNP Paribas SA; *Int'l*, pg. 1090
TRASYS LUXEMBOURG—See Frere-Bourgeois; *Int'l*, pg. 2774
TRASYS S.A—See Ackermans & van Haaren NV; *Int'l*, pg. 106
TRASYS S.A—See BNP Paribas SA; *Int'l*, pg. 1090
TRASYS S.A—See Frere-Bourgeois; *Int'l*, pg. 2774
TRATAMAQ CA—See Ingersoll Rand Inc.; *U.S. Public*, pg. 1122
TRATAMENT BALNEAR BUZIAS S.A.—See Transilvania Investments Alliance S.A.; *Int'l*, pg. 7900
TRATAMIENTO INTEGRAL DE RESIDUOS DE CANTABRIA S.L.U.—See ACS, Actividades de Construccion y Servicios, S.A.; *Int'l*, pg. 116
TRATEL AIRVAULT—See E B Trans SA; *Int'l*, pg. 2246
TRATEL AIRVAULT—See Groupe GARNIER; *Int'l*, pg. 3103
TRATEL AIRVAULT—See Transports Desert SA; *Int'l*, pg. 7905
TRATEL MOULT—See E B Trans SA; *Int'l*, pg. 2246
TRATEL MOULT—See Groupe GARNIER; *Int'l*, pg. 3103
TRATEL MOULT—See Transports Desert SA; *Int'l*, pg. 7905
TRATEL PESSAC—See E B Trans SA; *Int'l*, pg. 2246
TRATEL PESSAC—See Groupe GARNIER; *Int'l*, pg. 3103
TRATEL PESSAC—See Transports Desert SA; *Int'l*, pg. 7905
TRATEL S.A.S—See E B Trans SA; *Int'l*, pg. 2246
TRATEL S.A.S—See Groupe GARNIER; *Int'l*, pg. 3103
TRATEL S.A.S—See Transports Desert SA; *Int'l*, pg. 7905
TRATON CORP.; *U.S. Private*, pg. 4212
TRATON SE—See Porsche Automobil Holding SE; *Int'l*, pg. 5929
TRAUB CAPITAL—See Marvin Traub Associates, Inc.; *U.S. Private*, pg. 2598
TRAUB DREHMASCHINEN GMBH—See INDEX-Werke GmbH & Co. KG; *Int'l*, pg. 3651
TRAUBE TENT COMPANY, INC.; *U.S. Private*, pg. 4212
TRAU & LOEVNER INCORPORATED; *U.S. Private*, pg. 4212
TRAULSEN—See Illinois Tool Works Inc.; *U.S. Public*, pg. 1104
TRAUMAFX SOLUTIONS, INC.—See CNL Strategic Capital Management LLC; *U.S. Private*, pg. 952
TRAUMA HEALING CENTERS INC.—See MediPharm Labs Corp.; *Int'l*, pg. 4779
TRAUMA MEDICINE SERVICES OF TN, LLC—See HCA Healthcare, Inc.; *U.S. Public*, pg. 1012
TRAUMHAUS AG; *Int'l*, pg. 7906
TRAUSON (CHINA) MEDICAL INSTRUMENT COMPANY LIMITED—See Stryker Corporation; *U.S. Public*, pg. 1957
TRAUSON HOLDINGS COMPANY LIMITED—See Stryker Corporation; *U.S. Public*, pg. 1957
TRAUTMANN, MAHER & ASSOCIATES, INC.—See Northwest Plan Services, Inc.; *U.S. Private*, pg. 2961
TRAUTMAN & SHREVE, INC.—See EMCOR Group, Inc.; *U.S. Public*, pg. 739
TRAVAGLINI ENTERPRISES, INC.; *U.S. Private*, pg. 4212
TRAVAUX DU MIDI VAR SAS—See VINCI S.A.; *Int'l*, pg. 8235
TRAVAUX PUBLICS ET ASSAINISSEMENT—See Eiffage S.A.; *Int'l*, pg. 2331
TRAVAUX PUBLICS GOULARD SAS—See VINCI S.A.; *Int'l*, pg. 8229
TRAVCOA CORPORATION—See TUI AG; *Int'l*, pg. 7966
TRAVCO HOTELS LIMITED—See Co-operative Group Limited; *Int'l*, pg. 1679
TRAVCO INC.; *U.S. Private*, pg. 4212
TRAVCO SERVICES INC.; *U.S. Private*, pg. 4212
TRAVEL & ALLIED SERVICES LLC—See Oman Holdings International Company SAOG; *Int'l*, pg. 5560
TRAVEL ALL RUSSIA LLC; *U.S. Private*, pg. 4212
TRAVEL AUDIENCE, GMBH—See Amadeus IT Group, S.A.; *Int'l*, pg. 407
TRAVEL-BA.SYS GMBH & CO KG—See TUI AG; *Int'l*, pg. 7969
TRAVELBOARD GMBH—See Bayer Aktiengesellschaft; *Int'l*, pg. 407
TRAVELBOUND EUROPEAN TOURS LIMITED—See TUI AG; *Int'l*, pg. 7968
TRAVEL-BY-NET, INC.—See Cappy Devlin International; *U.S. Private*, pg. 745
TRAVELCARD, B.V.—See Corpay, Inc.; *U.S. Public*, pg. 580
TRAVEL CARE INC.—See Allianz SE; *Int'l*, pg. 356
TRAVELCENTERS OF AMERICA INC.—See BP plc; *Int'l*, pg. 1127
TRAVEL CLASS LIMITED—See TUI AG; *Int'l*, pg. 7968
TRAVELCLICK, INC.—See Amadeus IT Group, S.A.; *Int'l*, pg. 407
TRAVEL CLUB (PTE) LTD—See John Keells Holdings PLC; *Int'l*, pg. 3979
TRAVEL CONNECTIONS (PTY) LIMITED—See The Bidvest Group Limited; *Int'l*, pg. 7626
TRAVELCORP HOLDINGS PTY LTD.—See Corporate Travel Management Limited; *Int'l*, pg. 1806

TRAVELEX HOLDINGS LIMITED

TRAVEL COUNSELLORS LTD.—See Vitruvian Partners LLP; *Int'l*, pg. 8263
TRAVEL COVENTRY—See Mobico Group PLC.; *Int'l*, pg. 5009
TRAVEL DESTINATIONS MANAGEMENT GROUP, INC.—See ABRY Partners, LLC; *U.S. Private*, pg. 41
TRAVELDOO SAS—See Expedia Group, Inc.; *U.S. Public*, pg. 810
TRAVEL DUNDEE LTD—See Mobico Group PLC.; *Int'l*, pg. 5009
TRAVELERS CASUALTY AND SURETY COMPANY—See The Travelers Companies, Inc.; *U.S. Public*, pg. 2136
THE TRAVELERS COMPANIES, INC.; *U.S. Public*, pg. 2135
TRAVELERS CONSTITUTION STATE INSURANCE COMPANY—See The Travelers Companies, Inc.; *U.S. Public*, pg. 2136
TRAVELERS FINANCIAL (ALBERTA) CORPORATION—See Travelers Financial Group Limited; *Int'l*, pg. 7907
TRAVELERS FINANCIAL CORPORATION—See Travelers Financial Group Limited; *Int'l*, pg. 7907
TRAVELERS FINANCIAL GROUP LIMITED; *Int'l*, pg. 7907
TRAVELERS HAVEN, LLC—See Blueground US Inc; *U.S. Private*, pg. 597
THE TRAVELERS INDEMNITY COMPANY OF AMERICA—See The Travelers Companies, Inc.; *U.S. Public*, pg. 2136
TRAVELERS INSURANCE COMPANY LIMITED—See The Travelers Companies, Inc.; *U.S. Public*, pg. 2136
TRAVELERS INSURANCE COMPANY OF CANADA—See The Travelers Companies, Inc.; *U.S. Public*, pg. 2136
TRAVELERS INSURANCE DESIGNATED ACTIVITY COMPANY—See The Travelers Companies, Inc.; *U.S. Public*, pg. 2136
TRAVELERS LIABILITY INSURANCE—See The Travelers Companies, Inc.; *U.S. Public*, pg. 2136
TRAVELERS LLOYDS OF TEXAS INSURANCE COMPANY—See The Travelers Companies, Inc.; *U.S. Public*, pg. 2136
TRAVELERS LONDON LIMITED—See The Travelers Companies, Inc.; *U.S. Public*, pg. 2136
TRAVELERS MANAGEMENT LIMITED—See The Travelers Companies, Inc.; *U.S. Public*, pg. 2136
THE TRAVELERS MARINE CORPORATION—See The Travelers Companies, Inc.; *U.S. Public*, pg. 2136
TRAVELERS MARINE, LLC—See The Travelers Companies, Inc.; *U.S. Public*, pg. 2136
TRAVELERS MARKETING LLC; *U.S. Private*, pg. 4214
TRAVELERS PROPERTY CASUALTY COMPANY OF AMERICA—See The Travelers Companies, Inc.; *U.S. Public*, pg. 2136
TRAVELERS PROPERTY CASUALTY CORP.—See The Travelers Companies, Inc.; *U.S. Public*, pg. 2136
TRAVELERS RENTAL CO. INC.; *U.S. Public*, pg. 4214
TRAVELER'S RV SALES; *U.S. Private*, pg. 4214
TRAVELERS SEGUROS BRASIL S.A.—See The Travelers Companies, Inc.; *U.S. Public*, pg. 2136
TRAVELERS—See The Travelers Companies, Inc.; *U.S. Public*, pg. 2136
TRAVELERS SYNDICATE MANAGEMENT LIMITED—See The Travelers Companies, Inc.; *U.S. Public*, pg. 2136
TRAVELERS SYNDICATE MANAGEMENT LIMITED—See The Travelers Companies, Inc.; *U.S. Public*, pg. 2136
TRAVELERS TRANSPORTATION SERVICES; *Int'l*, pg. 7907
TRAVELERS UNDERWRITING AGENCY LIMITED—See The Travelers Companies, Inc.; *U.S. Public*, pg. 2136
TRAVEL & EVENT SERVICES, LLC—See Viad Corp.; *U.S. Public*, pg. 2291
TRAVELEX BAHRAIN WLL—See Travelex Holdings Limited; *Int'l*, pg. 7907
TRAVEL EXCHANGE; *U.S. Private*, pg. 4213
TRAVELEX CURRENCY EXCHANGE (CHINA) CO., LTD.—See Travelex Holdings Limited; *Int'l*, pg. 7907
TRAVELEX CURRENCY SERVICES INC.—See Travelex Holdings Limited; *Int'l*, pg. 7907
TRAVELEX DEUTSCHLAND GMBH—See Travelex Holdings Limited; *Int'l*, pg. 7907
TRAVELEX EMIRATES LLC—See Travelex Holdings Limited; *Int'l*, pg. 7907
TRAVELEX GLOBAL BUSINESS PAYMENTS, INC.—See The Western Union Company; *U.S. Public*, pg. 2141
TRAVELEX HOLDINGS LIMITED; *Int'l*, pg. 7907
TRAVELEX INDIA PVT LIMITED—See Travelex Holdings Limited; *Int'l*, pg. 7907
TRAVELEX INSURANCE SERVICES, INC.—See Zurich Insurance Group Limited; *Int'l*, pg. 8697
TRAVELEX ITALIA LTD—See Travelex Holdings Limited; *Int'l*, pg. 7907
TRAVELEX JAPAN KK—See Travelex Holdings Limited; *Int'l*, pg. 7907
TRAVELEX LIMITED—See Travelex Holdings Limited; *Int'l*, pg. 7907
TRAVELEX MALAYSIA SDN BHD—See Travelex Holdings Limited; *Int'l*, pg. 7907
TRAVELEX MONEY EXCHANGE LIMITED—See Travelex Holdings Limited; *Int'l*, pg. 7907

TRAVEL EXPERT (ASIA) ENTERPRISES LIMITED

TRAVEL EXPERT (ASIA) ENTERPRISES LIMITED; *Int'l*, pg. 7906
TRAVEL EXPERT BUSINESS SERVICES LIMITED—See Travel Expert (Asia) Enterprises Limited; *Int'l*, pg. 7906
TRAVEL EXPERT ONLINE LIMITED—See Travel Expert (Asia) Enterprises Limited; *Int'l*, pg. 7906
TRAVELEX QATAR Q.S.C.—See Travelex Holdings Limited; *Int'l*, pg. 7907
TRAVELEX SA/NV—See Travelex Holdings Limited; *Int'l*, pg. 7907
TRAVEL GUARD AMERICAS LLC—See American International Group, Inc.; *U.S. Public*, pg. 106
TRAVEL GUARD EMEA LIMITED—See American International Group, Inc.; *U.S. Public*, pg. 106
TRAVEL GUARD GROUP, INC.—See American International Group, Inc.; *U.S. Public*, pg. 106
TRAVEL GUARD WORLDWIDE, INC.—See American International Group, Inc.; *U.S. Public*, pg. 106
THE TRAVEL HAMMOCK INC.; *U.S. Private*, pg. 4128
TRAVEL HOLDINGS, INC.; *U.S. Private*, pg. 4213
TRAVELHOST, INC.; *U.S. Private*, pg. 4214
TRAVEL IMPRESSIONS, LTD.—See Apple Leisure Group; *U.S. Private*, pg. 297
TRAVEL INCORPORATED; *U.S. Private*, pg. 4213
TRAVELING COACHES, INC; *U.S. Private*, pg. 4214
TRAVEL INVESTMENT & SEAFOOD DEVELOPMENT CORP.; *Int'l*, pg. 7906
TRAVELITE HOLDINGS LTD.; *Int'l*, pg. 7907
TRAVEL-IT GMBH & CO. KG—See Elliott Management Corporation; *U.S. Private*, pg. 1373
TRAVEL-IT GMBH & CO. KG—See Siris Capital Group, LLC; *U.S. Private*, pg. 3674
TRAVELJIGSAW HOLDINGS LIMITED—See Booking Holdings, Inc.; *U.S. Public*, pg. 368
TRAVELJIGSAW LTD.—See Booking Holdings, Inc.; *U.S. Public*, pg. 368
TRAVEL LEADERS FRANCHISE GROUP, LLC—See Travel Leaders Group, LLC; *U.S. Private*, pg. 4213
TRAVEL LEADERS GROUP, LLC; *U.S. Private*, pg. 4213
TRAVEL LEADERS OF CHARLESTON—See Travel Leaders Group, LLC; *U.S. Private*, pg. 4213
TRAVEL & LEISURE CO.; *U.S. Public*, pg. 2185
TRAVEL + LEISURE—See Travel & Leisure Co.; *U.S. Public*, pg. 2185
TRAVELLERS INTERNATIONAL HOTEL GROUP, INC.—See Alliance Global Group, Inc.; *Int'l*, pg. 339
TRAVELLERS INTERNATIONAL HOTEL GROUP, INC.—See Genting Hong Kong Limited; *Int'l*, pg. 2929
TRAVEL MANAGEMENT PARTNERS INC.; *U.S. Private*, pg. 4213
TRAVELMATE.COM.AU PTY. LTD.—See Helloworld Travel Limited; *Int'l*, pg. 3337
TRAVELNET SOLUTIONS, INC.; *U.S. Private*, pg. 4214
THE TRAVEL NETWORK CORP.; *Int'l*, pg. 7697
THE TRAVEL NETWORK—See Travel Network Vacation Central; *U.S. Private*, pg. 4213
TRAVEL NETWORK VACATION CENTRAL; *U.S. Private*, pg. 4213
TRAVEL NURSE ACROSS AMERICA, LLC; *U.S. Private*, pg. 4213
TRAVELODGE BARRIE ON BAYFIELD—See Clarke Inc.; *Int'l*, pg. 1650
TRAVELODGE HOTEL BELLEVILLE—See Clarke Inc.; *Int'l*, pg. 1650
TRAVELODGE HOTELS, INC.—See Travel & Leisure Co.; *U.S. Public*, pg. 2185
TRAVELODGE LAKESHORE; *Int'l*, pg. 7907
TRAVELODGE OTTAWA WEST—See Clarke Inc.; *Int'l*, pg. 1650
TRAVELODGE TIMMINS—See Clarke Inc.; *Int'l*, pg. 1650
TRAVEL-ON LTD., INC.; *U.S. Private*, pg. 4213
TRAVEL PARTNER BULGARIA EOOD—See TUI AG; *Int'l*, pg. 7968
TRAVELPERK SL; *Int'l*, pg. 7907
TRAVELPLANET.PL S.A.—See MCI Capital Alternatywna Spolka Inwestycyjna S.A.; *Int'l*, pg. 4758
TRAVEL PLAZA (EUROPE) B.V.—See JTB Corp.; *Int'l*, pg. 4016
TRAVELPLUS GROUP GMBH—See Cox & Kings Limited; *Int'l*, pg. 1823
TRAVEL PLUS N.V.—See Exmar N.V.; *Int'l*, pg. 2585
TRAVELPORT DIGITAL LIMITED—See Elliott Management Corporation; *U.S. Private*, pg. 1373
TRAVELPORT DIGITAL LIMITED—See Siris Capital Group, LLC; *U.S. Private*, pg. 3674
TRAVELPORT GDS—See Elliott Management Corporation; *U.S. Private*, pg. 1373
TRAVELPORT GDS—See Siris Capital Group, LLC; *U.S. Private*, pg. 3674
TRAVELPORT INC.—See Elliott Management Corporation; *U.S. Private*, pg. 1373
TRAVELPORT INC.—See Siris Capital Group, LLC; *U.S. Private*, pg. 3674
TRAVELPORT, LP—See Elliott Management Corporation; *U.S. Private*, pg. 1373
TRAVELPORT, LP—See Siris Capital Group, LLC; *U.S. Private*, pg. 3674
TRAVELPORT WORLDWIDE LIMITED—See Elliott Management Corporation; *U.S. Private*, pg. 1373

TRAVELPORT WORLDWIDE LIMITED—See Siris Capital Group, LLC; *U.S. Private*, pg. 3674
TRAVELPRO PRODUCTS, INC.—See MidOcean Partners, LLP; *U.S. Private*, pg. 2717
TRAVEL & RECREATION GROUP—See Viad Corp.; *U.S. Public*, pg. 2291
TRAVEL REPUBLIC HOLDINGS LIMITED—See The Emirates Group; *Int'l*, pg. 7639
TRAVEL RESOURCES LIMITED—See Corporate Travel Management Limited; *Int'l*, pg. 1806
TRAVELSCAPE, LLC—See Expedia Group, Inc.; *U.S. Public*, pg. 810
TRAVEL SECURITY S.A.—See Grupo Security S.A.; *Int'l*, pg. 3135
TRAVEL SENSE A/S—See TUI AG; *Int'l*, pg. 7968
TRAVEL SERVICES EUROPE SPAIN SL—See TUI AG; *Int'l*, pg. 7968
TRAVELSKY TECHNOLOGY (JAPAN) LIMITED—See TravelSky Technology Limited; *Int'l*, pg. 7907
TRAVELSKY TECHNOLOGY LIMITED; *Int'l*, pg. 7907
TRAVEL SMART VIP CLUB—See Sunwing Travel Group, Inc.; *Int'l*, pg. 7332
TRAVELSMITH OUTFITTERS, INC.—See DAI Holding, LLC; *U.S. Private*, pg. 1145
TRAVEL SPIKE, LLC; *U.S. Private*, pg. 4213
TRAVELSTART ONLINE TRAVEL OPERATIONS PTY. LTD; *Int'l*, pg. 7907
TRAVEL STATION; *U.S. Private*, pg. 4213
TRAVEL TAGS, INC.—See Taylor Corporation; *U.S. Private*, pg. 3939
TRAVELTAINMENT AG—See Amadeus IT Group, S.A.; *Int'l*, pg. 407
TRAVELTAINMENT POLSKA SP. Z O.O.—See Amadeus IT Group, S.A.; *Int'l*, pg. 407
TRAVELTAINMENT UK LTD.—See Amadeus IT Group, S.A.; *Int'l*, pg. 407
THE TRAVEL TEAM, INC.—See Rich Holdings, Inc.; *U.S. Private*, pg. 3426
TRAVEL TECHNOLOGY INTERACTIVE SA; *Int'l*, pg. 7907
TRAVEL TOPIA INC.—See Yamazen Corporation; *Int'l*, pg. 8558
TRAVEL & TRANSPORT INC.; *U.S. Private*, pg. 4212
TRAVEL TRIPPER, LLC; *U.S. Private*, pg. 4213
TRAVEL TURF, INC.—See TUI AG; *Int'l*, pg. 7968
TRAVEL VIVA GMBH—See Unister Holding GmbH; *Int'l*, pg. 8062
TRAVELZOO (EUROPE) LIMITED—See Travelzoo; *U.S. Public*, pg. 2186
TRAVELZOO LOCAL (AUSTRALIA) PTY LIMITED—See Travelzoo; *U.S. Public*, pg. 2186
TRAVELZOO; *U.S. Public*, pg. 2186
TRAVERE THERAPEUTICS, INC.; *U.S. Public*, pg. 2186
TRAVERS & COMPANY INC.; *U.S. Private*, pg. 4214
TRAVERSE CITY AUTO PLAZA INC.; *U.S. Private*, pg. 4214
TRAVERSE CITY FILM FESTIVAL; *U.S. Private*, pg. 4214
TRAVERSE CITY RECORD-EAGLE—See The Retirement Systems of Alabama; *U.S. Private*, pg. 4106
TRAVERSE ENERGY LTD.; *Int'l*, pg. 7908
TRAVERSE POINTE PARTNERS LLC; *U.S. Private*, pg. 4214
TRAVERS FOOD SERVICE LTD.—See Aramark; *U.S. Public*, pg. 176
TRAVERS MECHANICAL SERVICES—See Ontario Municipal Employees Retirement System; *Int'l*, pg. 5584
TRAVERS REALTY CORP.; *U.S. Private*, pg. 4214
TRAVERS REALTY CORP.—See Travers Realty Corp.; *U.S. Private*, pg. 4214
TRAVERS REALTY CORP.—See Travers Realty Corp.; *U.S. Private*, pg. 4214
TRAVERS REALTY CORP.—See Travers Realty Corp.; *U.S. Private*, pg. 4214
TRAVERS REALTY CORP.—See Travers Realty Corp.; *U.S. Private*, pg. 4214
TRAVERS TOOL COMPANY INC.; *U.S. Private*, pg. 4214
TRAVERTINE COMPANY PLC; *Int'l*, pg. 7908
TRAVERTINE, INC.; *U.S. Private*, pg. 4214
TRAVESSET SAS—See VINCI S.A.; *Int'l*, pg. 8229
TRAVIAUSTRIA DATENSERVICE FUR REISE UND TOURISTIK GESELLSCHAFT M.B.H. & CO NFG. KG—See Deutsche Lufthansa AG; *Int'l*, pg. 2070
TRAVIAUSTRIA GMBH—See Deutsche Lufthansa AG; *Int'l*, pg. 2071
TRAVIS BOATS & MOTORS BATON ROUGE INC.—See The Great American Outdoors Group LLC; *U.S. Private*, pg. 4038
TRAVIS BODY AND TRAILER, INC.—See Federal Signal Corporation; *U.S. Public*, pg. 826
TRAVIS BUSINESS SYSTEMS INC.; *U.S. Private*, pg. 4214
TRAVIS COMMERCIAL REAL ESTATE SERVICES, LTD.—See Jones Lang LaSalle Incorporated; *U.S. Public*, pg. 1206
TRAVIS CREDIT UNION; *U.S. Private*, pg. 4214
TRAVIS INDUSTRIES INC.; *U.S. Private*, pg. 4214
TRAVISMATHEW, LLC—See Topgolf Callaway Brands Corp.; *U.S. Public*, pg. 2164

CORPORATE AFFILIATIONS

TRAVIS MATHEW RETAIL, LLC—See Topgolf Callaway Brands Corp.; *U.S. Public*, pg. 2164
TRAVIS MEATS INC.; *U.S. Private*, pg. 4214
TRAVIS PERKINS PLC; *Int'l*, pg. 7908
TRAVIS PERKINS (PROPERTIES) LIMITED—See Travis Perkins plc; *Int'l*, pg. 7908
TRAVIS PERKINS TRADING COMPANY—See Travis Perkins plc; *Int'l*, pg. 7908
TRAVIS TILE SALES INC.; *U.S. Private*, pg. 4214
TRAVIX INTERNATIONAL B.V.—See Trip.com Group Ltd.; *Int'l*, pg. 7926
TRAVTECH INC.—See Omega World Travel, Inc.; *U.S. Private*, pg. 3015
TRAVUNIJA A.D.; *Int'l*, pg. 7908
TRAWICK CONSTRUCTION COMPANY, LLC—See Dycom Industries, Inc.; *U.S. Public*, pg. 699
TRAWS PHARMA, INC; *U.S. Public*, pg. 2186
TRAXALL INTERNATIONAL LTD.; *Int'l*, pg. 7908
TRAXCOMM LIMITED—See MTR Corporation Limited; *Int'l*, pg. 5072
TRAX INTERNATIONAL CORPORATION; *U.S. Private*, pg. 4215
TRAXION SOLUTIONS, S.A. DE C.V.—See Grupo Traxion, S. A. B. de C. V.; *Int'l*, pg. 3138
TRAXLE MFG. LTD.—See Linamar Corporation; *Int'l*, pg. 4502
TRAXON TECHNOLOGIES EUROPE GMBH—See ams AG; *Int'l*, pg. 440
TRAXON TECHNOLOGIES LLC—See ams AG; *Int'l*, pg. 440
TRAXON TECHNOLOGIES LTD.—See ams AG; *Int'l*, pg. 440
TRAX TECHNOLOGIES, INC.; *U.S. Private*, pg. 4215
TRAX TECHNOLOGY SOLUTIONS PTE LTD.; *Int'l*, pg. 7908
TRAX USA, CORP.—See AAR Corp.; *U.S. Public*, pg. 13
TRAXYS AFRICA PTY. LTD.—See The Carlyle Group Inc.; *U.S. Public*, pg. 2056
TRAXYS COMETALS USA LLC—See The Carlyle Group Inc.; *U.S. Public*, pg. 2056
TRAXYS NORTH AMERICA LLC—See The Carlyle Group Inc.; *U.S. Public*, pg. 2056
TRAXYS S.A.—See The Carlyle Group Inc.; *U.S. Public*, pg. 2056
TRAYAL KORPORACIJA A.D.; *Int'l*, pg. 7908
TRAYER PRODUCTS, INC.; *U.S. Private*, pg. 4215
TRAY, INC.; *U.S. Private*, pg. 4215
TRAYLOR BROTHERS, INC.; *U.S. Private*, pg. 4215
TRAYLOR CHEMICAL & SUPPLY CO.; *U.S. Private*, pg. 4215
TRAYLOR MINING, LLC—See Traylor Brothers, Inc.; *U.S. Private*, pg. 4215
TRAY-PAK CORP.—See Archbrook Capital Management LLC; *U.S. Private*, pg. 310
TRAYPORT LIMITED—See TMX Group Limited; *Int'l*, pg. 7767
TRAYPORT PTE LTD—See TMX Group Limited; *Int'l*, pg. 7767
TRB APOKPA LLC—See BRT Apartments Corp.; *U.S. Public*, pg. 403
TRB ARLINGTON LLC—See BRT Apartments Corp.; *U.S. Public*, pg. 403
TRB CHEMEDICA S.A.—See MyunMoon Pharm Co., Ltd.; *Int'l*, pg. 5115
TR BIG SUR MANAGEMENT LLC—See Hyatt Hotels Corporation; *U.S. Public*, pg. 1078
T&R BIOFAB; *Int'l*, pg. 7395
TRB LIMITED—See Tokai Rika Co., Ltd.; *Int'l*, pg. 7780
TRB (LONDON) LTD.—See PT Pertamina (Persero); *Int'l*, pg. 6064
TRB NO. 1 CORP.—See BRT Apartments Corp.; *U.S. Public*, pg. 403
TR BRICKS SDN. BHD.—See Naim Holdings Berhad; *Int'l*, pg. 5131
TRBR INDUSTRIA E COMERCIO LTDA.—See Tokai Rika Co., Ltd.; *Int'l*, pg. 7780
TRB SYSTEMS INTERNATIONAL, INC.; *U.S. Public*, pg. 2186
TRC ACQUISITION, LLC—See Argan, Inc.; *U.S. Public*, pg. 191
TRC ALBUQUERQUE—See TRC Companies, Inc.; *U.S. Private*, pg. 4215
TR CAMINO MANAGEMENT LLC—See Hyatt Hotels Corporation; *U.S. Public*, pg. 1078
TR CANADA INC.—See Tecnicas Reunidas, S.A.; *Int'l*, pg. 7515
TRC COMPANIES, INC. - CINCINNATI—See TRC Companies, Inc.; *U.S. Private*, pg. 4215
TRC COMPANIES, INC. - MOUNT LAUREL—See TRC Companies, Inc.; *U.S. Private*, pg. 4215
TRC COMPANIES, INC.; *U.S. Private*, pg. 4215
TRC COMPANIES, LTD.—See TRC Companies, Inc.; *U.S. Private*, pg. 4215
TRC CONSTRUCTION PUBLIC COMPANY LIMITED; *Int'l*, pg. 7908
TRC DEVELOPMENT SDN. BHD.—See TRC Synergy Berhad; *Int'l*, pg. 7909
TRC ENGINEERING LLC—See TRC Construction Public Company Limited; *Int'l*, pg. 7908

COMPANY NAME INDEX

TRC ENGINEERS INC.—See TRC Companies, Inc.; *U.S. Private*, pg. 4215
TRC ENGINEERS LLC—See TRC Companies, Inc.; *U.S. Private*, pg. 4215
TRC ENVIRONMENTAL CORPORATION—See TRC Companies, Inc.; *U.S. Private*, pg. 4215
TRC ENVIRONMENTAL - LARAMIE—See TRC Companies, Inc.; *U.S. Private*, pg. 4215
TRC-FOUR CORNERS DIALYSIS CLINICS, LLC—See DaVita Inc.; *U.S. Public*, pg. 643
TRC GLOBAL SOLUTIONS, INC.; *U.S. Private*, pg. 4215
TRC HONDURAS S.A. DE C.V.—See Southwire Company, LLC; *U.S. Private*, pg. 3742
TRC, INC.—See Dai Nippon Printing Co., Ltd.; *Int'l*, pg. 1916
TRC - INDIANA, LLC—See DaVita Inc.; *U.S. Public*, pg. 643
TRC LAND SDN. BHD.—See TRC Synergy Berhad; *Int'l*, pg. 7908
TRC LIBRARY SERVICE INC.—See Dai Nippon Printing Co., Ltd.; *Int'l*, pg. 1916
TRC MIDDLE EAST LLC—See TRC Construction Public Company Limited; *Int'l*, pg. 7908
TRC OF NEW YORK, INC.—See DaVita Inc.; *U.S. Public*, pg. 643
TR CONSULTING KFT.—See 4iG Nyrt.; *Int'l*, pg. 12
TRC-PETERSBURG, LLC—See DaVita Inc.; *U.S. Public*, pg. 643
TRC PINNACLE TOWERS, L.L.C.—See COPT Defense Properties; *U.S. Public*, pg. 575
TRC SOFTWARE—See TRC Companies, Inc.; *U.S. Private*, pg. 4215
TRC STAFFING SERVICES, INC.; *U.S. Private*, pg. 4215
TRC SYNERGY BERHAD; *Int'l*, pg. 7908
TR CUTLER, INC.; *U.S. Private*, pg. 4200
TRC WEST, INC.—See DaVita Inc.; *U.S. Public*, pg. 643
TRC WORLDWIDE ENGINEERING, INC.; *U.S. Private*, pg. 4215
TRCZ S.R.O.—See Tokai Rika Co., Ltd.; *Int'l*, pg. 7780
T.R. DILLON LOGGING INC.; *U.S. Private*, pg. 3912
TRD MANUFACTURING, INC.—See IMI plc; *Int'l*, pg. 3624
TRDT BRASIL TECNOLOGIA LTDA.—See Teradata Corporation; *U.S. Public*, pg. 2016
TRD USA INC.—See Toyota Motor Corporation; *Int'l*, pg. 7074
TREA ASSET MANAGEMENT S.G.I.I.C., S.A.—See TREA Capital Partners, Sociedad de Valores S.A.; *Int'l*, pg. 7909
TREA CAPITAL PARTNERS, SOCIEDAD DE VALORES S.A.; *Int'l*, pg. 7909
TREACE MEDICAL CONCEPTS, INC.; *U.S. Public*, pg. 2186
TREACY & COMPANY, INC.—See Cherry Bekaert LLP; *U.S. Private*, pg. 874
TREADMILLDOCTOR.COM, INC.; *U.S. Private*, pg. 4216
TREADWELL CORPORATION; *U.S. Private*, pg. 4216
TREALITY SVS LLC—See TransDigm Group Incorporated; *U.S. Public*, pg. 2181
TREAN CORPORATION—See Altaris Capital Partners, LLC; *U.S. Private*, pg. 206
TREAN INSURANCE GROUP, INC.—See Altaris Capital Partners, LLC; *U.S. Private*, pg. 206
TREASURE ASA—See Wilh. Wilhelmsen Holding ASA; *Int'l*, pg. 8410
TREASURE CHEST CASINO, L.L.C.—See Boyd Gaming Corporation; *U.S. Public*, pg. 378
TREASURE CHEST, LLC—See Boyd Gaming Corporation; *U.S. Public*, pg. 378
TREASURE COAST BEHAVIORAL HEALTH, LLC—See Universal Health Services, Inc.; *U.S. Public*, pg. 2260
TREASURE COAST BOATING CENTER, INC.; *U.S. Private*, pg. 4216
TREASURE COAST NEWSPAPERS, LLC—See Gannett Co., Inc.; *U.S. Public*, pg. 898
TREASURE FACTORY CO., LTD.; *Int'l*, pg. 7909
TREASURE GLOBAL, INC.; *U.S. Public*, pg. 2186
TREASURE ISLAND COMMUNITY DEVELOPMENT, LLC—See Lennar Corporation; *U.S. Public*, pg. 1307
TREASURE ISLAND CORP.; *U.S. Private*, pg. 4216
TREASURE ISLAND FOOD MARTS INC.; *U.S. Private*, pg. 4216
TREASURE ISLAND RESORT FLORIDA, LLC—See RAIT Financial Trust; *U.S. Private*, pg. 3349
TREASURE ISLAND ROYALTY TRUST; *U.S. Public*, pg. 2186
TREASURE VALLEY FIRE PROTECTION, INC.—See Pye-Barker Fire & Safety, LLC; *U.S. Private*, pg. 3309
TREASURY CHATEAU & ESTATES—See Treasury Wine Estates Limited; *Int'l*, pg. 7909
TREASURY CORPORATION OF VICTORIA; *Int'l*, pg. 7909
TREASURY WINE ESTATES CANADA, INC.—See Treasury Wine Estates Limited; *Int'l*, pg. 7909
TREASURY WINE ESTATES (CHINA) HOLDING CO. PTY. LTD.—See Treasury Wine Estates Limited; *Int'l*, pg. 7909
TREASURY WINE ESTATES EMEA LTD.—See Treasury Wine Estates Limited; *Int'l*, pg. 7909
TREASURY WINE ESTATES LIMITED; *Int'l*, pg. 7909

TREASURY WINE ESTATES (NZ) LIMITED—See Treasury Wine Estates Limited; *Int'l*, pg. 7909
TREASURY WINE ESTATES PTE. LTD.—See Treasury Wine Estates Limited; *Int'l*, pg. 7909
TREASURY WINE ESTATES—See Treasury Wine Estates Limited; *Int'l*, pg. 7909
TREAT AMERICA FOOD SERVICES, INC. - INDIANAPOLIS—See Treat America Food Services, Inc.; *U.S. Private*, pg. 4216
TREAT AMERICA FOOD SERVICES, INC.; *U.S. Private*, pg. 4216
TREAT AMERICA OMAHA—See Treat America Food Services, Inc.; *U.S. Private*, pg. 4216
TREATCO, INC.; *U.S. Private*, pg. 4216
TREAT ENTERTAINMENT INC.; *U.S. Private*, pg. 4216
THE TREATMENT AND LEARNING CENTERS, INC.; *U.S. Private*, pg. 4128
TREATMENT AND RECYCLING OF WISCONSIN, LLC—See Grupo Tradebe Medioambiente S.L.; *Int'l*, pg. 3138
TREATMENT ASSOCIATES, INC.—See Acadia Healthcare Company, Inc.; *U.S. Public*, pg. 31
TREATMENT.COM INTERNATIONAL INC.; *U.S. Public*, pg. 2186
TREATMENT EQUIPMENT COMPANY; *U.S. Private*, pg. 4216
TREATMENT RESEARCH INSTITUTE—See Public Health Management Corporation; *U.S. Private*, pg. 3299
TREATT PLC; *Int'l*, pg. 7909
TREATT USA INC.—See Treatt Plc; *Int'l*, pg. 7909
TREATY RADIO LIMITED—See News Corporation; *U.S. Public*, pg. 1520
TREBBIANNO LLC; *U.S. Private*, pg. 4216
TREBI GENERALCONSULT S.R.L.—See Gruppo Mutui-Online S.p.A; *Int'l*, pg. 3141
TREBOLIT AB—See Axcel Management A/S; *Int'l*, pg. 762
TREBOL MAQUINARIA Y SUMINISTROS S.A.—See Emak S.p.A.; *Int'l*, pg. 2373
TREBOL MOTORS CORPORATION; *U.S. Private*, pg. 4216
TREBOR BASSETT SHARPS GMBH—See Mondelez International, Inc.; *U.S. Public*, pg. 1461
TREBOR INC.; *U.S. Private*, pg. 4216
TREBOR INTERNATIONAL, INC.—See IDEX Corp; *U.S. Public*, pg. 1092
TRECEK CHEVROLET OLDSMOBILE GEO; *U.S. Private*, pg. 4216
TRECORA CHEMICAL, INC—See Balmoral Funds LLC; *U.S. Private*, pg. 462
TRECORA, LLC—See Balmoral Funds LLC; *U.S. Private*, pg. 461
TRECO S.R.L.—See Akoya Capital LLC; *U.S. Private*, pg. 146
TRECO S.R.L.—See Century Park Capital Partners, LLC; *U.S. Private*, pg. 834
TREDCOR KENYA LIMITED—See The Goodyear Tire & Rubber Company; *U.S. Public*, pg. 2085
TREDEC Z IMMOBILIEN LEASING GESELLSCHAFT M.B.H.—See UniCredit S.p.A.; *Int'l*, pg. 8037
TREDEGAR BRASIL INDUSTRIA DE PLASTICOS LTDA.—See Tredegar Corporation; *U.S. Public*, pg. 2187
TREDEGAR CORPORATION; *U.S. Public*, pg. 2186
TREDEGAR FILM PRODUCTS B.V.—See Tredegar Corporation; *U.S. Public*, pg. 2187
TREDEGAR FILM PRODUCTS COMPANY SHANGHAI, LIMITED—See Tredegar Corporation; *U.S. Public*, pg. 2187
TREDEGAR FILM PRODUCTS CORPORATION - TERRE HAUTE PLANT—See Tredegar Corporation; *U.S. Public*, pg. 2187
TREDEGAR FILM PRODUCTS KFT—See Tredegar Corporation; *U.S. Public*, pg. 2187
TREDEGAR FILM PRODUCTS - LAKE ZURICH, LLC—See Tredegar Corporation; *U.S. Public*, pg. 2187
TREDEX GMBH—See Foot Locker, Inc.; *U.S. Public*, pg. 864
TREDIA CHINA CO., LTD.—See Mitsubishi Corporation; *Int'l*, pg. 4943
TREDIA FASHION CO., LTD.—See Mitsubishi Corporation; *Int'l*, pg. 4943
TREDI ARGENTINA—See Groupe Seche SAS; *Int'l*, pg. 3110
TREDIA VIETNAM CO., LTD.—See Mitsubishi Corporation; *Int'l*, pg. 4943
TREDI SA—See Groupe Seche SAS; *Int'l*, pg. 3110
TREDIT TIRE & WHEEL COMPANY, INC.; *U.S. Private*, pg. 4216
TREDJE AP-FONDEN; *Int'l*, pg. 7909
TREDO AB—See Orkla ASA; *Int'l*, pg. 5639
TREDROC TIRE SERVICES; *U.S. Private*, pg. 4216
TREDROC TIRE SERVICES—See Tredroc Tire Services; *U.S. Private*, pg. 4216
TREDROC TIRE SERVICES—See Tredroc Tire Services; *U.S. Private*, pg. 4216
TREDROC TIRE SERVICES—See Tredroc Tire Services; *U.S. Private*, pg. 4216
TREDZ LIMITED—See Halfords Group plc; *Int'l*, pg. 3229
TREE BRAND PACKAGING, INC.; *U.S. Private*, pg. 4216

TREE CITY DIALYSIS, LLC—See DaVita Inc.; *U.S. Public*, pg. 644
TREECON RESOURCES, INC.; *U.S. Public*, pg. 2187
TREE DIGITAL COMPANY—See The Company for Cooperative Insurance; *Int'l*, pg. 7635
TREEFIN GMBH—See Wuestenrot & Wuerttembergische AG; *Int'l*, pg. 8499
TREEFROG DATA SOLUTIONS; *U.S. Private*, pg. 4217
TREE HOUSE EDUCATION & ACCESSORIES LIMITED; *Int'l*, pg. 7909
TREEHOUSE FOODS, INC.; *U.S. Public*, pg. 2187
TREEHOUSE INTERACTIVE HOLDING, INC.—See Kennet Partners Ltd; *Int'l*, pg. 4127
TREEHOUSE ISLAND INC.; *U.S. Private*, pg. 4217
TREE ISLAND STEEL LTD. - RANCHO CUCAMONGA PLANT—See Tree Island Steel Ltd.; *Int'l*, pg. 7910
TREE ISLAND STEEL LTD.; *Int'l*, pg. 7910
TREELINE DIESEL CENTER LLC—See Legend Oil and Gas, Ltd.; *U.S. Public*, pg. 1301
TREELINE, INCORPORATED; *U.S. Private*, pg. 4217
TREELINE WELL SERVICES INC.; *Int'l*, pg. 7910
TREE MEDIC, LLC; *U.S. Private*, pg. 4216
TREE MEDICS, INC.—See The F.A. Bartlett Tree Expert Company; *U.S. Private*, pg. 4027
TREE MEN INC.—See A Plus Tree, LLC; *U.S. Private*, pg. 19
TREEN BOX & PALLET CORP.; *U.S. Private*, pg. 4217
TREEN BOX & PALLET, INC.—See Treen Box & Pallet Corp.; *U.S. Private*, pg. 4217
TREENO SOFTWARE, INC.—See LoneTree Capital LLC; *U.S. Private*, pg. 2490
TREE OF LIFE FOUNDATION NPO—See Bank of Georgia Group PLC; *Int'l*, pg. 843
TREE OF LIFE UK LTD.—See Petty Wood & Co. Ltd.; *Int'l*, pg. 5834
TREESAP FARMS, LLC; *U.S. Private*, pg. 4217
TREES CORPORATION; *U.S. Public*, pg. 2188
TREES N TRENDS INC.; *U.S. Private*, pg. 4217
TREESOURCE INDUSTRIES, INC.; *U.S. Private*, pg. 4217
TREET BATTERY LIMITED—See Treet Corporation Limited; *Int'l*, pg. 7910
TREET CORPORATION LIMITED; *Int'l*, pg. 7910
TREE-TECH, INC.—See Apax Partners LLP; *Int'l*, pg. 506
TREE TOP, INC. - MEDFORD OREGON PLANT—See Tree Top, Inc.; *U.S. Private*, pg. 4216
TREE TOP, INC. - OXNARD CALIFORNIA PLANT—See Tree Top, Inc.; *U.S. Private*, pg. 4216
TREE TOP, INC. - PROSSER PLANT—See Tree Top, Inc.; *U.S. Private*, pg. 4216
TREE TOP, INC. - ROSS PLANT—See Tree Top, Inc.; *U.S. Private*, pg. 4216
TREE TOP, INC. - SELAH PLANT—See Tree Top, Inc.; *U.S. Private*, pg. 4217
TREE TOP, INC.; *U.S. Private*, pg. 4216
TREE TOP, INC. - WENATCHEE PLANT—See Tree Top, Inc.; *U.S. Private*, pg. 4217
TREE TOP, INC. - WOODBURN OREGON PLANT—See Tree Top, Inc.; *U.S. Private*, pg. 4217
TREETOP TECHNOLOGIES, INC.—See MobileDataforce, Inc.; *U.S. Private*, pg. 2758
TREET SERVICES (PRIVATE) LIMITED—See Treet Corporation Limited; *Int'l*, pg. 7910
TREFILERIAS QUIJANO, S.A.—See Celsa Group; *Int'l*, pg. 1395
TREFILKIN SPRL—See Aga Khan Development Network; *Int'l*, pg. 199
TREFINOS, S.L—See CORTICEIRA AMORIM, S.G.P.S., S.A.; *Int'l*, pg. 1808
TREFZ CORPORATION; *U.S. Private*, pg. 4217
TREFZ & TREFZ INC.; *U.S. Private*, pg. 4217
TREGARON MANAGEMENT, LLC; *U.S. Private*, pg. 4217
TREHEL CORPORATION; *U.S. Private*, pg. 4217
TRE HOLDINGS CORPORATION; *Int'l*, pg. 7909
TREIBACHER INDUSTRIE AG; *Int'l*, pg. 7910
TREIBACHER INDUSTRIE INC.—See Treibacher Industrie AG; *Int'l*, pg. 7910
TREIBACHER SCHLEIFMITTEL AG—See Groupe Bruxelles Lambert SA; *Int'l*, pg. 3100
TREIBACHER SCHLEIFMITTEL NORTH AMERICA, INC.—See Groupe Bruxelles Lambert SA; *Int'l*, pg. 3100
TREI REAL ESTATE AUSTRIA GMBH—See Tengelmann Warenhandelsgesellschaft KG; *Int'l*, pg. 7560
TREI REAL ESTATE CZECH REPUBLIC S.R.O.—See Tengelmann Warenhandelsgesellschaft KG; *Int'l*, pg. 7560
TREI REAL ESTATE HUNGARY KFT.—See Tengelmann Warenhandelsgesellschaft KG; *Int'l*, pg. 7560
TREI REAL ESTATE POLAND SP. Z O.O.—See Tengelmann Warenhandelsgesellschaft KG; *Int'l*, pg. 7560
TREI REAL ESTATE PORTUGAL, LDA.—See Tengelmann Warenhandelsgesellschaft KG; *Int'l*, pg. 7560
TREJHARA PTE. LIMITED—See Trejhara Solutions Ltd.; *Int'l*, pg. 7910
TREJHARA SOLUTIONS LTD.; *Int'l*, pg. 7910
TREJO OIL CO. INC.; *U.S. Private*, pg. 4217
TREK 2000 INTERNATIONAL LTD; *Int'l*, pg. 7910
TREK AMERICA TRAVEL LIMITED—See TUI AG; *Int'l*, pg. 7968

TREK BICYCLE CORPORATION — CORPORATE AFFILIATIONS

TREK BICYCLE CORPORATION; *U.S. Private*, pg. 4217
TREK DIAGNOSTIC SYSTEMS LTD.—See Thermo Fisher Scientific Inc.; *U.S. Public*, pg. 2155
TREK, INC.—See Advanced Energy Industries, Inc.; *U.S. Public*, pg. 48
TREK INTERNATIONAL TRAVEL CORP—See TUI AG; *Int'l*, pg. 7969
TREK JAPAN K.K.—See Advanced Energy Industries, Inc.; *U.S. Public*, pg. 48
TREKKER TRACTOR, LLC; *U.S. Private*, pg. 4217
TREK METALS LTD.; *Int'l*, pg. 7910
TREK RESOURCES, INC.; *U.S. Public*, pg. 2188
TREKSTOR GMBH—See Link-Asia International MedTech Group Limited; *Int'l*, pg. 4514
TREK SYSTEMS (M) SDN BHD—See Trek 2000 International Ltd; *Int'l*, pg. 7910
TREK TECHNOLOGY (HK) CO. LTD.—See Trek 2000 International Ltd; *Int'l*, pg. 7910
TREK TECHNOLOGY (SINGAPORE) PTE LTD—See Trek 2000 International Ltd; *Int'l*, pg. 7910
TREL AB—See Instalco AB; *Int'l*, pg. 3722
TRELAWNY PLACE (FELIXSTOWE) RESIDENTS MANAGEMENT COMPANY LIMITED—See Persimmon plc; *Int'l*, pg. 5818
TRELAWNY SPT LIMITED—See Indutrade AB; *Int'l*, pg. 3681
TRELEC, S. A.—See Empresas Publicas de Medellin ESP; *Int'l*, pg. 2392
T&R ELECTRIC SUPPLY COMPANY, INC.; *U.S. Private*, pg. 3910
TRELLANCE, INC.; *U.S. Private*, pg. 4217
TRELLEBOG CEILING SOLUTIONS—See Trelleborg AB; *Int'l*, pg. 7911
TRELLEBORG AB; *Int'l*, pg. 7910
TRELLEBORG ANTIVIBRATION SOLUTIONS GERMANY GMBH—See Trelleborg AB; *Int'l*, pg. 7911
TRELLEBORG APPLIED TECHNOLOGY—See Trelleborg AB; *Int'l*, pg. 7911
TRELLEBORG AUTOMOTIVE AVS EUROPE—See Trelleborg AB; *Int'l*, pg. 7911
TRELLEBORG AUTOMOTIVE CHINA HOLDING AB—See Trelleborg AB; *Int'l*, pg. 7911
TRELLEBORG AUTOMOTIVE CZECH REPUBLIC S.R.O—See Trelleborg AB; *Int'l*, pg. 7911
TRELLEBORG AUTOMOTIVE DO BRASIL INDUSTRIA E COMERCIO DE AUTOPECAS LTD—See Trelleborg AB; *Int'l*, pg. 7911
TRELLEBORG AUTOMOTIVE FORSHEDA AB—See Trelleborg AB; *Int'l*, pg. 7911
TRELLEBORG AUTOMOTIVE GROUP AB—See Trelleborg AB; *Int'l*, pg. 7911
TRELLEBORG AUTOMOTIVE MEXICO SA DE CV—See Trelleborg AB; *Int'l*, pg. 7911
TRELLEBORG AUTOMOTIVE—See Trelleborg AB; *Int'l*, pg. 7911
TRELLEBORG AUTOMOTIVE SPAIN SA—See Trelleborg AB; *Int'l*, pg. 7911
TRELLEBORG AUTOMOTIVE TOLUCA SA DE CV—See Freudenberg SE; *Int'l*, pg. 2790
TRELLEBORG BOHEMIA A.S—See Trelleborg AB; *Int'l*, pg. 7911
TRELLEBORG BOOTS FRANCE SAS—See Trelleborg AB; *Int'l*, pg. 7911
TRELLEBORG BUILDING SYSTEMS UK LTD.—See Trelleborg AB; *Int'l*, pg. 7912
TRELLEBORG BV—See The Yokohama Rubber Co., Ltd.; *Int'l*, pg. 7702
TRELLEBORG CHINA HOLDING AB—See Trelleborg AB; *Int'l*, pg. 7911
TRELLEBORG COATED SYSTEM FRANCE SAS—See Trelleborg AB; *Int'l*, pg. 7911
TRELLEBORG COATED SYSTEMS (SHANGHAI) CO., LTD.—See Trelleborg AB; *Int'l*, pg. 7912
TRELLEBORG COATED SYSTEMS US INC.—See Trelleborg AB; *Int'l*, pg. 7912
TRELLEBORG CORPORATION—See Trelleborg AB; *Int'l*, pg. 7912
TRELLEBORG CROATIA D.O.O.—See Trelleborg AB; *Int'l*, pg. 7912
TRELLEBORG DO BRASIL LTDA.—See The Yokohama Rubber Co., Ltd.; *Int'l*, pg. 7703
TRELLEBORG DO BRASIL SOLUCOES EM VEDACAO LTDA—See Trelleborg AB; *Int'l*, pg. 7914
TRELLEBORG EDE BV—See Trelleborg AB; *Int'l*, pg. 7912
TRELLEBORG ENGINEERED SYSTEMS AUSTRALIA PTY LTD—See Trelleborg AB; *Int'l*, pg. 7912
TRELLEBORG ENGINEERED SYSTEMS CHINA HOLDING AB—See Trelleborg AB; *Int'l*, pg. 7912
TRELLEBORG ENGINEERED SYSTEMS GROUP AB—See Trelleborg AB; *Int'l*, pg. 7912
TRELLEBORG ENGINEERED SYSTEMS ITALY S.P.A.—See Trelleborg AB; *Int'l*, pg. 7912
TRELLEBORG ENGINEERED SYSTEMS LTD—See Trelleborg AB; *Int'l*, pg. 7912
TRELLEBORG ERSMARK AB—See Trelleborg AB; *Int'l*, pg. 7912
TRELLEBORG ETM GMBH—See Trelleborg AB; *Int'l*, pg. 7912
TRELLEBORG FILLITE INC.—See Trelleborg AB; *Int'l*, pg. 7911
TRELLEBORG FILLITE LTD.—See Trelleborg AB; *Int'l*, pg. 7911
TRELLEBORG FITTINGS SAS—See Trelleborg AB; *Int'l*, pg. 7912
TRELLEBORG FORSHEDA AB—See Trelleborg AB; *Int'l*, pg. 7912
TRELLEBORG HOLDING DANMARK A/S—See Trelleborg AB; *Int'l*, pg. 7912
TRELLEBORG HOLDINGS ITALY S.R.L—See Trelleborg AB; *Int'l*, pg. 7912
TRELLEBORG HORDA AB- MATERIALS DIVISION—See Trelleborg AB; *Int'l*, pg. 7912
TRELLEBORG IBERCAUCHO ALAVA S.A.—See Trelleborg AB; *Int'l*, pg. 7912
TRELLEBORG INDIA PVT LTD.—See Trelleborg AB; *Int'l*, pg. 7912
TRELLEBORG INDUSTRI AB—See Trelleborg AB; *Int'l*, pg. 7912
TRELLEBORG INDUSTRIAL AB—See Trelleborg AB; *Int'l*, pg. 7912
TRELLEBORG INDUSTRIAL AVS AB—See Trelleborg AB; *Int'l*, pg. 7912
TRELLEBORG INDUSTRIAL AVS—See Trelleborg AB; *Int'l*, pg. 7912
TRELLEBORG INDUSTRIAL AVS USA, INC.—See Trelleborg AB; *Int'l*, pg. 7912
TRELLEBORG INDUSTRIAL PRODUCTS ESTONIA OU—See Trelleborg AB; *Int'l*, pg. 7912
TRELLEBORG INDUSTRIAL PRODUCTS FINLAND OY—See Trelleborg AB; *Int'l*, pg. 7913
TRELLEBORG INDUSTRIAL PRODUCTS GERMANY GMBH—See Trelleborg AB; *Int'l*, pg. 7913
TRELLEBORG INDUSTRIAL PRODUCTS INDIA PVT LTD—See Trelleborg AB; *Int'l*, pg. 7913
TRELLEBORG INDUSTRIAL PRODUCTS NORWAY AS—See Trelleborg AB; *Int'l*, pg. 7913
TRELLEBORG INDUSTRIAL PRODUCTS SANCHEVILLE SAS—See Trelleborg AB; *Int'l*, pg. 7913
TRELLEBORG INDUSTRIAL PRODUCTS SWEDEN AB—See Trelleborg AB; *Int'l*, pg. 7913
TRELLEBORG INDUSTRIAL PRODUCTS UK LTD—See Trelleborg AB; *Int'l*, pg. 7913
TRELLEBORG INDUSTRIAL TYRES UK LTD—See Trelleborg AB; *Int'l*, pg. 7913
TRELLEBORG INDUSTRI BENELUX—See Trelleborg AB; *Int'l*, pg. 7912
TRELLEBORG INDUSTRIE S.A.—See Trelleborg AB; *Int'l*, pg. 7912
TRELLEBORG INDUSTRIES POLSKA SP. Z O.O.—See Trelleborg AB; *Int'l*, pg. 7913
TRELLEBORG INDUSTRI IBERICA S.A.—See Trelleborg AB; *Int'l*, pg. 7912
TRELLEBORG INDUSTRI O.O.O—See Trelleborg AB; *Int'l*, pg. 7912
TRELLEBORG ITM—See Trelleborg AB; *Int'l*, pg. 7912
TRELLEBORG IZARRA, S.A.U.—See Trelleborg AB; *Int'l*, pg. 7912
TRELLEBORG IZARRA S.A.U.—See Trelleborg AB; *Int'l*, pg. 7913
TRELLEBORG JAPAN K.K.—See Trelleborg AB; *Int'l*, pg. 7913
TRELLEBORG KUNHWA CO LTD—See Trelleborg AB; *Int'l*, pg. 7913
TRELLEBORG LANKA (PVT) LTD.—See The Yokohama Rubber Co., Ltd.; *Int'l*, pg. 7702
TRELLEBORG MALAYSIA SDN. BHD.—See The Yokohama Rubber Co., Ltd.; *Int'l*, pg. 7702
TRELLEBORG MARINE SYSTEMS ASIA PTE LTD—See Trelleborg AB; *Int'l*, pg. 7913
TRELLEBORG MARINE SYSTEMS AUSTRALIA PTY LTD—See Trelleborg AB; *Int'l*, pg. 7913
TRELLEBORG MARINE SYSTEMS FZE—See Trelleborg AB; *Int'l*, pg. 7913
TRELLEBORG MARINE SYSTEMS INDIA PVT LTD—See Trelleborg AB; *Int'l*, pg. 7913
TRELLEBORG MARINE SYSTEMS MELBOURNE PTY LTD—See Trelleborg AB; *Int'l*, pg. 7913
TRELLEBORG MARINE SYSTEMS USA—See Trelleborg AB; *Int'l*, pg. 7912
TRELLEBORG MATERIALS & MIXING FORSHEDA AB—See Trelleborg AB; *Int'l*, pg. 7913
TRELLEBORG MODYN SAS—See Trelleborg AB; *Int'l*, pg. 7913
TRELLEBORG OFFSHORE BOSTON, INC.—See Trelleborg AB; *Int'l*, pg. 7912
TRELLEBORG OFFSHORE & CONSTRUCTION AB—See Trelleborg AB; *Int'l*, pg. 7913
TRELLEBORG OFFSHORE NORWAY AS—See Trelleborg AB; *Int'l*, pg. 7913
TRELLEBORG OFFSHORE UK LTD; *Int'l*, pg. 7914
TRELLEBORG OFFSHORE US INC—See Trelleborg AB; *Int'l*, pg. 7912
TRELLEBORG PIPE SEALS DUISBURG GMBH—See Trelleborg AB; *Int'l*, pg. 7913
TRELLEBORG PIPE SEALS LELYSTAD BV—See Trelleborg AB; *Int'l*, pg. 7911
TRELLEBORG PIPE SEALS MILFORD, INC.—See Trelleborg AB; *Int'l*, pg. 7912
TRELLEBORG PIPE SEALS ROCHEFORT SAS—See Trelleborg AB; *Int'l*, pg. 7913
TRELLEBORG PIPE SEALS SANTANDER S.A.—See Trelleborg AB; *Int'l*, pg. 7913
TRELLEBORG PIPE SEALS SPYDEBERG AS—See Trelleborg AB; *Int'l*, pg. 7913
TRELLEBORG PPL—See Trelleborg AB; *Int'l*, pg. 7913
TRELLEBORG PRAHA S.R.O.—See Trelleborg AB; *Int'l*, pg. 7913
TRELLEBORG REIMS SAS—See Trelleborg AB; *Int'l*, pg. 7913
TRELLEBORG RIDDERKERK BV—See Trelleborg AB; *Int'l*, pg. 7913
TRELLEBORG RUBORE AB—See Trelleborg AB; *Int'l*, pg. 7911
TRELLEBORG RUBORE-AUSTRALIA—See Trelleborg AB; *Int'l*, pg. 7911
TRELLEBORG RUBORE INC.—See Trelleborg AB; *Int'l*, pg. 7911
TRELLEBORG SEALING PROFILES GERMANY GMBH—See Trelleborg AB; *Int'l*, pg. 7913
TRELLEBORG SEALING PROFILES HUNGARY LTD—See Trelleborg AB; *Int'l*, pg. 7913
TRELLEBORG SEALING PROFILES NORTH AMERICA INC.—See Trelleborg AB; *Int'l*, pg. 7913
TRELLEBORG SEALING PROFILES SWEDEN AB—See Trelleborg AB; *Int'l*, pg. 7912
TRELLEBORG SEALING PROFILES U.S., INC—See Trelleborg AB; *Int'l*, pg. 7913
TRELLEBORG SEALING SOLUTIONS A/S—See Trelleborg AB; *Int'l*, pg. 7913
TRELLEBORG SEALING SOLUTIONS AUSTRIA GMBH—See Trelleborg AB; *Int'l*, pg. 7913
TRELLEBORG SEALING SOLUTIONS BELGIUM SA—See Trelleborg AB; *Int'l*, pg. 7913
TRELLEBORG SEALING SOLUTIONS BULGARIA EOOD—See Trelleborg AB; *Int'l*, pg. 7913
TRELLEBORG SEALING SOLUTIONS CANADA INC.—See Trelleborg AB; *Int'l*, pg. 7913
TRELLEBORG SEALING SOLUTIONS (CHINA) CO., LTD.—See Trelleborg AB; *Int'l*, pg. 7913
TRELLEBORG SEALING SOLUTIONS CZECH S.R.O.—See Trelleborg AB; *Int'l*, pg. 7914
TRELLEBORG SEALING SOLUTIONS DELANO, LLC—See Trelleborg AB; *Int'l*, pg. 7914
TRELLEBORG SEALING SOLUTIONS DENMARK A/S—See Trelleborg AB; *Int'l*, pg. 7914
TRELLEBORG SEALING SOLUTIONS DETROIT, INC—See Trelleborg AB; *Int'l*, pg. 7913
TRELLEBORG SEALING SOLUTIONS EL SEGUNDO, INC.—See Trelleborg AB; *Int'l*, pg. 7913
TRELLEBORG SEALING SOLUTIONS ESPANA SAU—See Trelleborg AB; *Int'l*, pg. 7914
TRELLEBORG SEALING SOLUTIONS FINLAND OY—See Trelleborg AB; *Int'l*, pg. 7914
TRELLEBORG SEALING SOLUTIONS FRANCE SAS—See Trelleborg AB; *Int'l*, pg. 7914
TRELLEBORG SEALING SOLUTIONS GERMANY GMBH—See Trelleborg AB; *Int'l*, pg. 7914
TRELLEBORG SEALING SOLUTIONS HONG KONG LTD.—See Trelleborg AB; *Int'l*, pg. 7914
TRELLEBORG SEALING SOLUTIONS HUNGARY KFT—See Trelleborg AB; *Int'l*, pg. 7914
TRELLEBORG SEALING SOLUTIONS ITALIA S.P.A.—See Trelleborg AB; *Int'l*, pg. 7914
TRELLEBORG SEALING SOLUTIONS ITALY SPA—See Trelleborg AB; *Int'l*, pg. 7914
TRELLEBORG SEALING SOLUTIONS JAPAN KK—See Trelleborg AB; *Int'l*, pg. 7914
TRELLEBORG SEALING SOLUTIONS KALMAR AB—See Trelleborg AB; *Int'l*, pg. 7914
TRELLEBORG SEALING SOLUTIONS KOREA LTD—See Trelleborg AB; *Int'l*, pg. 7914
TRELLEBORG SEALING SOLUTIONS MEXICO S.A DE C.V—See Trelleborg AB; *Int'l*, pg. 7914
TRELLEBORG SEALING SOLUTIONS NETHERLANDS BV—See Trelleborg AB; *Int'l*, pg. 7914
TRELLEBORG SEALING SOLUTIONS NORWAY AS—See Trelleborg AB; *Int'l*, pg. 7914
TRELLEBORG SEALING SOLUTIONS O.O.O—See Trelleborg AB; *Int'l*, pg. 7914
TRELLEBORG SEALING SOLUTIONS POLSKA SP.ZO.O—See Trelleborg AB; *Int'l*, pg. 7914
TRELLEBORG SEALING SOLUTIONS SILCOTECH SWITZERLAND AG—See Trelleborg AB; *Int'l*, pg. 7914
TRELLEBORG SEALING SOLUTIONS SINGAPORE PTE LTD—See Trelleborg AB; *Int'l*, pg. 7914
TRELLEBORG SEALING SOLUTIONS SWEDEN AB—See Trelleborg AB; *Int'l*, pg. 7914
TRELLEBORG SEALING SOLUTIONS SWITZERLAND SA—See Trelleborg AB; *Int'l*, pg. 7914
TRELLEBORG SEALING SOLUTIONS TAIWAN LTD—See Trelleborg AB; *Int'l*, pg. 7914
TRELLEBORG SEALING SOLUTIONS UK LTD.—See Trelleborg AB; *Int'l*, pg. 7914
TRELLEBORG SIGMA AB—See Trelleborg AB; *Int'l*, pg. 7911

TRELLEBORG SINGAPORE PTE LTD—See Trelleborg AB; *Int'l*, pg. 7914
TRELLEBORG SLOVENIJA D.O.O—See Trelleborg AB; *Int'l*, pg. 7914
TRELLEBORG SOUTH AFRICA (PTY) LTD.—See The Yokohama Rubber Co., Ltd.; *Int'l*, pg. 7702
TRELLEBORG TRADING WUXI CO., LTD.—See Trelleborg AB; *Int'l*, pg. 7914
TRELLEBORG TREASURY—See Trelleborg AB; *Int'l*, pg. 7914
TRELLEBORG TYRES LANKA (PRIVATE) LTD—See Trelleborg AB; *Int'l*, pg. 7914
TRELLEBORGVIBRACOUSTIC—See Freudenberg SE; *Int'l*, pg. 2790
TRELLEBORG WHEELS AB—See The Yokohama Rubber Co., Ltd.; *Int'l*, pg. 7703
TRELLEBORG WHEEL SYSTEMS AB—See The Yokohama Rubber Co., Ltd.; *Int'l*, pg. 7703
TRELLEBORG WHEEL SYSTEMS AMERICAS, INC.—See The Yokohama Rubber Co., Ltd.; *Int'l*, pg. 7703
TRELLEBORG WHEEL SYSTEMS ARGENTINA S.A—See The Yokohama Rubber Co., Ltd.; *Int'l*, pg. 7703
TRELLEBORG WHEEL SYSTEMS AUSTRALIA PTY LTD—See The Yokohama Rubber Co., Ltd.; *Int'l*, pg. 7703
TRELLEBORG WHEEL SYSTEMS BELGIUM N.V.—See The Yokohama Rubber Co., Ltd.; *Int'l*, pg. 7703
TRELLEBORG WHEEL SYSTEMS FRANCE SAS—See The Yokohama Rubber Co., Ltd.; *Int'l*, pg. 7703
TRELLEBORG WHEEL SYSTEMS GMBH - INDUSTRIAL TIRES AND WHEELS—See The Yokohama Rubber Co., Ltd.; *Int'l*, pg. 7703
TRELLEBORG WHEEL SYSTEMS LANKA LTD.—See The Yokohama Rubber Co., Ltd.; *Int'l*, pg. 7703
TRELLEBORG WHEEL SYSTEMS LIEPAJA SIA—See The Yokohama Rubber Co., Ltd.; *Int'l*, pg. 7703
TRELLEBORG WHEEL SYSTEMS MIDDLE EAST LTD—See The Yokohama Rubber Co., Ltd.; *Int'l*, pg. 7703
TRELLEBORG WHEEL SYSTEMS MOTO D.O.O.—See Trelleborg AB; *Int'l*, pg. 7914
TRELLEBORG WHEEL SYSTEMS NETHERLANDS B.V.—See Trelleborg AB; *Int'l*, pg. 7914
TRELLEBORG WHEEL SYSTEMS NORDIC AB—See Trolleborg AB; *Int'l*, pg. 7914
TRELLEBORG WHEEL SYSTEMS SAVSJO AB—See The Yokohama Rubber Co., Ltd.; *Int'l*, pg. 7703
TRELLEBORG WHEEL SYSTEMS SEA PTE LTD—See The Yokohama Rubber Co., Ltd.; *Int'l*, pg. 7703
TRELLEBORG WHEEL SYSTEMS—See The Yokohama Rubber Co., Ltd.; *Int'l*, pg. 7702
TRELLEBORG WHEEL SYSTEMS—See The Yokohama Rubber Co., Ltd.; *Int'l*, pg. 7702
TRELLEBORG WHEEL SYSTEMS S.P.A.—See The Yokohama Rubber Co., Ltd.; *Int'l*, pg. 7703
TRELLEBORG WHEEL SYSTEMS UK LIMITED—See The Yokohama Rubber Co., Ltd.; *Int'l*, pg. 7703
TRELLEBORG YSH S.A. DE C.V.—See Trelleborg AB; *Int'l*, pg. 7911
TRELLEBORG YSH—See Trelleborg AB; *Int'l*, pg. 7911
TRELLEBORG YSH—See Trelleborg AB; *Int'l*, pg. 7911
TRELLEBORG YSH—See Trelleborg AB; *Int'l*, pg. 7911
TRELLEGRAV AB—See Storskogen Group AB; *Int'l*, pg. 7228
TRELLIDOR GHANA LIMITED—See Trellidor Holdings Limited; *Int'l*, pg. 7915
TRELLIDOR HOLDINGS LIMITED; *Int'l*, pg. 7914
TRELLIDOR INNOVATIONS PROPRIETARY LIMITED—See Trellidor Holdings Limited; *Int'l*, pg. 7915
TRELLIDOR PROPRIETARY LIMITED—See Trellidor Holdings Limited; *Int'l*, pg. 7915
TRELLIDOR UK LIMITED—See Trellidor Holdings Limited; *Int'l*, pg. 7915
TRELLIS BIOPLASTICS—See Trellis Earth Products, Inc.; *U.S. Private*, pg. 4217
TRELLIS EARTH PRODUCTS, INC.; *U.S. Private*, pg. 4217
TRELLIS S.R.O.—See VINCI S.A.; *Int'l*, pg. 8229
TRELLISWARE TECHNOLOGIES, INC.—See ViaSat, Inc.; *U.S. Public*, pg. 2292
TRELLO, INC—See Atlassian Corporation; *Int'l*, pg. 686
TRELLUS HEALTH INC.—See Trellus Health Plc; *Int'l*, pg. 7915
TRELLUS HEALTH PLC; *Int'l*, pg. 7915
TRELOCK ASIA PACIFIC LIMITED—See Allegion Public Limited Company; *Int'l*, pg. 335
TRELOCK GMBH—See Allegion Public Limited Company; *Int'l*, pg. 335
TREMA ENGINEERING 2 SH P.K—See STRABAG SE; *Int'l*, pg. 7233
TREMATON CAPITAL INVESTMENTS LTD.; *Int'l*, pg. 7915
TREMBLY ASSOCIATES INC.; *U.S. Private*, pg. 4217
TREMCAR INC.; *Int'l*, pg. 7915
TREMCAR INDUSTRIES INC.—See Tremcar Inc.; *Int'l*, pg. 7915
TREMCAR LONDON INC.—See Tremcar Inc.; *Int'l*, pg. 7915

TREMCAR ST-CESAIRE INC.—See Tremcar Inc.; *Int'l*, pg. 7915
TREMCAR USA INC.—See Tremcar Inc.; *Int'l*, pg. 7915
TREMCAR WEST INC.—See Tremcar Inc.; *Int'l*, pg. 7915
TREMCO ASIA PTE. LTD.—See RPM International Inc.; *U.S. Public*, pg. 1818
TREMCO AUSTRALIA—See RPM International Inc.; *U.S. Public*, pg. 1818
TREMCO BARRIER SOLUTIONS, INC.—See RPM International Inc.; *U.S. Public*, pg. 1818
TREMCO CPG GERMANY GMBH—See RPM International Inc.; *U.S. Public*, pg. 1820
TREMCO CPG (INDIA) PRIVATE LIMITED—See RPM International Inc.; *U.S. Public*, pg. 1820
TREMCO CPG SWEDEN AB—See RPM International Inc.; *U.S. Public*, pg. 1820
TREMCO ILLBRUCK CO., LTD.—See RPM International Inc.; *U.S. Public*, pg. 1820
TREMCO ILLBRUCK DIS TICARET A.S.—See RPM International Inc.; *U.S. Public*, pg. 1820
TREMCO ILLBRUCK GMBH—See RPM International Inc.; *U.S. Public*, pg. 1820
TREMCO ILLBRUCK GROUP GMBH—See RPM International Inc.; *U.S. Public*, pg. 1820
TREMCO ILLBRUCK KFT—See RPM International Inc.; *U.S. Public*, pg. 1820
TREMCO ILLBRUCK LIMITED—See RPM International Inc.; *U.S. Public*, pg. 1820
TREMCO ILLBRUCK OOO—See RPM International Inc.; *U.S. Public*, pg. 1820
TREMCO ILLBRUCK PRODUCTION SAS—See RPM International Inc.; *U.S. Public*, pg. 1820
TREMCO ILLBRUCK PRODUKTION GMBH—See RPM International Inc.; *U.S. Public*, pg. 1820
TREMCO ILLBRUCK SAS—See RPM International Inc.; *U.S. Public*, pg. 1820
TREMCO ILLBRUCK, S.L.U.—See RPM International Inc.; *U.S. Public*, pg. 1820
TREMCO ILLBRUCK S.R.O.—See RPM International Inc.; *U.S. Public*, pg. 1820
TREMCO ILLBRUCK SWISS AG—See RPM International Inc.; *U.S. Public*, pg. 1820
TREMCO INCORPORATED—See RPM International Inc.; *U.S. Public*, pg. 1817
TREMCO PTY. LTD.—See RPM International Inc.; *U.S. Public*, pg. 1818
TREMISIS ENERGY ACQUISITION CORPORATION II; *Int'l*, pg. 7915
TREMONT COOPERATIVE GRAIN CO; *U.S. Private*, pg. 4217
TREMONT GROUP, INC.; *U.S. Private*, pg. 4218
TREMONT HOMES INC.; *U.S. Private*, pg. 4218
TREMONT MORTGAGE TRUST—See The RMR Group Inc.; *U.S. Public*, pg. 2126
TREMONT REALTY ADVISORS LLC—See The RMR Group Inc.; *U.S. Public*, pg. 2126
TREMULA NAV SA; *Int'l*, pg. 7915
TRENARY WOOD PRODUCTS—See Holmquist Feedmill Inc.; *U.S. Private*, pg. 1968
TRENCAP L.P.—See Caisse de Depot et Placement du Quebec; *Int'l*, pg. 1255
TRENCHANT CAPITAL CORP.; *Int'l*, pg. 7915
TRENCH AUSTRIA GMBH—See Siemens Energy AG; *Int'l*, pg. 6903
TRENCH FRANCE S.A.—See Siemens Energy AG; *Int'l*, pg. 6903
TRENCH GERMANY GMBH—See Siemens Energy AG; *Int'l*, pg. 6903
TRENCH HIGH VOLTAGE PRODUCTS LTD.—See Siemens Energy AG; *Int'l*, pg. 6903
TRENCH ITALIA S.R.L.—See Siemens Energy AG; *Int'l*, pg. 6903
TRENCH LIMITED—See Siemens Energy AG; *Int'l*, pg. 6904
TRENCH METALS CORP.; *Int'l*, pg. 7915
TRENCH PLATE RENTAL COMPANY—See Brookfield Corporation; *Int'l*, pg. 1184
TRENCH SHORING COMPANY; *U.S. Private*, pg. 4218
TRENCOR, INC.—See The Toro Company; *U.S. Public*, pg. 2134
TRENCOR LIMITED; *Int'l*, pg. 7915
TRENDCHIP TECHNOLOGIES CORP.—See MediaTek Inc.; *U.S. Public*, pg. 4774
TRENDCO HAIR SUPPLIES CO., LTD—See Aderans Co., Ltd.; *Int'l*, pg. 144
TREND CONTROL SYSTEMS LIMITED—See Honeywell International Inc.; *U.S. Public*, pg. 1048
TREND ELECTRONICS LTD.; *Int'l*, pg. 7915
TRENDERS INC.—See CyberAgent, Inc.; *Int'l*, pg. 1892
TREND EXPLORATION, LTD.; *Int'l*, pg. 7915
TREND GAYRIMENKUL YATIRIM ORTAKLIGI A.S.; *Int'l*, pg. 7915
TREND HEALTH PARTNERS LLC; *U.S. Private*, pg. 4218
TRENDHR SERVICES; *U.S. Private*, pg. 4218
TRENDLINE OFFICE INTERIORS LTD.—See Dauphin HumanDesign Group GmbH & Co. KG; *Int'l*, pg. 1983
THE TRENDLINES GROUP LTD.; *Int'l*, pg. 7697

TREND MAGAZINES, INC.—See Times Holding Co.; *U.S. Private*, pg. 4172
TRENDMAKER HOMES, INC.—See Tri Pointe Homes, Inc.; *U.S. Public*, pg. 2188
TRENDMAKER, INC. LIMITED; *Int'l*, pg. 7916
TRENDMALL GALLERY LIMITED—See e Lighting Group Holdings Limited; *Int'l*, pg. 2246
TREND MARINE PRODUCTS LIMITED—See LCI Industries; *U.S. Public*, pg. 1295
TREND MICRO AUSTRALIA PTY. LTD.—See Trend Micro Inc.; *Int'l*, pg. 7915
TREND MICRO DEUTSCHLAND GMBH—See Trend Micro Inc.; *Int'l*, pg. 7915
TREND MICRO DO BRASIL, LTDA.—See Trend Micro Inc.; *Int'l*, pg. 7915
TREND MICRO (EMEA) LIMITED—See Trend Micro Inc.; *Int'l*, pg. 7915
TREND MICRO FRANCE S.A.—See Trend Micro Inc.; *Int'l*, pg. 7915
TREND MICRO INCORPORATED—See Trend Micro Inc.; *Int'l*, pg. 7915
TREND MICRO INC.; *Int'l*, pg. 7915
TREND MICRO, INC.—See Trend Micro Inc.; *Int'l*, pg. 7916
TREND MICRO LATIN AMERICA—See Trend Micro Inc.; *Int'l*, pg. 7915
TREND MICRO LATINOAMERICA BU—See Trend Micro Inc.; *Int'l*, pg. 7916
TREND MICRO MIDDLE EAST—See Trend Micro Inc.; *Int'l*, pg. 7916
TREND MICRO (UK) LTD.—See Trend Micro Inc.; *Int'l*, pg. 7915
TRENDMINER NV—See Silver Lake Group, LLC; *U.S. Private*, pg. 3660
TREND NETWORKS LIMITED; *Int'l*, pg. 7916
TREND OFFSET PRINTING SERVICES, INC.—See Mittera Group, Inc.; *U.S. Private*, pg. 2752
TREND OFFSET PRINTING SERVICES - SOUTHEAST DIVISION—See Mittera Group, Inc.; *U.S. Private*, pg. 2752
TREND OFFSET PRINTING SERVICES - SOUTHWEST DIVISION—See Mittera Group, Inc.; *U.S. Private*, pg. 2752
TREND SERVICE, S.A. DE C.V.—See RCS MediaGroup S.p.A.; *Int'l*, pg. 6229
TRENDSET CONCRETE PRODUCTS INC.—See SiteOne Landscape Supply, Inc.; *U.S. Public*, pg. 1889
TRENDSET GMBH—See Messe Munchen GmbH; *Int'l*, pg. 4842
TRENDSETTERS INC.—See May Trucking Company Inc.; *U.S. Private*, pg. 2620
TRENDS INTERNATIONAL LLC; *U.S. Private*, pg. 4218
TRENDS LEATHER (YANGZHOU) CO., LTD.—See Yihua Lifestyle Technology Co., Ltd.; *Int'l*, pg. 8582
TREND TECHNOLOGIES, LLC; *U.S. Private*, pg. 4218
TRENDTEST GMBH—See Ipsos S.A.; *Int'l*, pg. 3802
TREND TONE IMAGING, INC.—See Everlight Chemical Industrial Co.; *Int'l*, pg. 2567
TRENDWAY CORPORATION—See Fellowes, Inc.; *U.S. Private*, pg. 1494
TRENDWOOD INC.; *U.S. Private*, pg. 4218
THE TRENDY CONDOMINIUM—See Grande Asset Hotels & Property Public Company Limited; *Int'l*, pg. 3057
TRENDY IMPORTS S.A. DE C.V.—See Steven Madden, Ltd.; *U.S. Public*, pg. 1947
TRENDYLITE CORPORATION—See Ennostar Inc.; *Int'l*, pg. 2444
TRENDZON HOLDINGS GROUP LIMITED; *Int'l*, pg. 7916
TR ENERGY CO., LTD.—See Tokyo Sangyo Co., Ltd.; *Int'l*, pg. 7795
TRENES DE NAVARRA, S.A.U.—See Construcciones y Auxiliar de Ferrocarriles S.A.; *Int'l*, pg. 1777
TRENITALIA C2C LIMITED—See Ferrovie dello Stato Italiane S.p.A.; *Int'l*, pg. 2645
TRENITALIA S.P.A.—See Ferrovie dello Stato Italiane S.p.A.; *Int'l*, pg. 2645
TRENITALIA TPER SCARL—See Ferrovie dello Stato Italiane S.p.A.; *Int'l*, pg. 2645
TRENMEDIA, S.A.—See ACS, Actividades de Construccion y Servicios, S.A.; *Int'l*, pg. 116
TRENT BOX MFG. CO., INC.; *U.S. Private*, pg. 4218
TRENT CAPITAL PARTNERS, LLC; *U.S. Private*, pg. 4218
TRENT FOUNDRIES LTD.—See Westley Group Limited; *Int'l*, pg. 8391
TRENTHAM LEISURE LIMITED—See Blackstone Inc.; *U.S. Public*, pg. 358
TRENT, INC.; *U.S. Private*, pg. 4218
TRENTION AB; *Int'l*, pg. 7916
TRENT LIMITED; *Int'l*, pg. 7916
TRENTON COLD STORAGE, INC. - EDMONTON FACILITY—See Trenton Cold Storage, Inc.; *Int'l*, pg. 7916
TRENTON COLD STORAGE, INC.; *Int'l*, pg. 7916
TRENTON COLD STORAGE, INC. - TORONTO FACILITY—See Trenton Cold Storage, Inc.; *Int'l*, pg. 7916
TRENTON MARINE CENTER PERFORMANCE GROUP, INC.; *U.S. Private*, pg. 4218

TRENTON MARINE CENTER PERFORMANCE GROUP, INC. CORPORATE AFFILIATIONS

TRENTON PIPE NIPPLE COMPANY LLC—See Tailwind Capital Group, LLC; *U.S. Private*, pg. 3923
TRENTON S.P.A.—See FLY Srl; *Int'l*, pg. 2716
TRENTON SYSTEMS INC; *U.S. Private*, pg. 4218
TRENTON TECHNOLOGY INC.—See Trenton Systems Inc; *U.S. Private*, pg. 4218
TRENTON WATER WORKS; *U.S. Private*, pg. 4218
TRENTYRE (LESOTHO) (PTY) LTD—See The Goodyear Tire & Rubber Company; *U.S. Public*, pg. 2085
TRENWA, INC.; *U.S. Private*, pg. 4218
TREO DRILLING SERVICES L.P.—See Mullen Group Ltd.; *Int'l*, pg. 5080
TREOFAN GERMANY GMBH & CO. KG—See M&C S.p.A.; *Int'l*, pg. 4610
TREOFAN HOLDINGS GMBH—See M&C S.p.A.; *Int'l*, pg. 4610
TREOFAN ITALY S.P.A. - BATTIPAGLIA PLANT—See M&C S.p.A.; *Int'l*, pg. 4610
TREOFAN ITALY S.P.A. - TERNI PLANT—See M&C S.p.A.; *Int'l*, pg. 4610
TREPCO IMPORTS & DISTRIBUTION LTD.; *U.S. Private*, pg. 4218
TREPOINT BARC; *U.S. Private*, pg. 4218
TREPOINTBARC—See Trepoint Barc; *U.S. Private*, pg. 4218
TREPP, LLC—See Daily Mail & General Trust plc; *Int'l*, pg. 1938
TREPP UK LTD.—See Daily Mail & General Trust plc; *Int'l*, pg. 1938
TRESA AT ARROWHEAD ARIZONA, LLC—See RAIT Financial Trust; *U.S. Public*, pg. 3349
TRES AMIGAS, LLC—See American Superconductor Corporation; *U.S. Public*, pg. 110
THE TRESANTI SURGICAL CENTER, LLC—See Tenet Healthcare Corporation; *U.S. Public*, pg. 2005
TRES ARROYOS TELEVISORA COLOR S.A.—See Grupo Clarin S.A.; *Int'l*, pg. 3125
TRESCAL A/S—See Ontario Municipal Employees Retirement System; *Int'l*, pg. 5585
TRESCAL B.V.—See Ontario Municipal Employees Retirement System; *Int'l*, pg. 5585
TRESCAL ESPANA DE METROLOGIA SLU—See Ontario Municipal Employees Retirement System; *Int'l*, pg. 5585
TRESCAL GMBH—See Ontario Municipal Employees Retirement System; *Int'l*, pg. 5585
TRESCAL INC.—See Ontario Municipal Employees Retirement System; *Int'l*, pg. 5585
TRESCAL LIMITED—See Ontario Municipal Employees Retirement System; *Int'l*, pg. 5585
TRESCAL S.A.—See Ontario Municipal Employees Retirement System; *Int'l*, pg. 5585
TRESCAL S.R.L.—See Ontario Municipal Employees Retirement System; *Int'l*, pg. 5585
TRESCH ELECTRICAL COMPANY; *U.S. Private*, pg. 4218
TRESCON LIMTED; *Int'l*, pg. 7916
TRESENSA INC.—See Blackstone Inc.; *U.S. Public*, pg. 361
TRES HERMANOS, INC.; *U.S. Private*, pg. 4218
TRESMAN STEEL INDUSTRIES LTD.; *Int'l*, pg. 7916
TRES-OR RESOURCES LTD.; *Int'l*, pg. 7916
TRESPA INTERNATIONAL B.V.—See HAL Trust N.V.; *Int'l*, pg. 3224
T.R.E. S.R.L.—See Collecte Localisation Satellites; *Int'l*, pg. 1699
TRESSA, INC.; *U.S. Private*, pg. 4218
TRESSALLURE/GENERAL WIG—See Aderans Co., Ltd.; *Int'l*, pg. 144
TRESTLETREE, INC.—See Harvard Pilgrim Health Care, Inc.; *U.S. Private*, pg. 1875
TRESTON HOLDING, INC.—See Treston Oy; *Int'l*, pg. 7916
TRESTON IAC LLC—See Treston Oy; *Int'l*, pg. 7916
TRESTON OY; *Int'l*, pg. 7916
TRESYS TECHNOLOGY LLC—See Behrman Brothers Management Corp.; *U.S. Private*, pg. 515
TRETORN SWEDEN AB—See Leonard Green & Partners, L.P.; *U.S. Private*, pg. 2425
TRETT LTD.—See Dialles; *Int'l*, pg. 2104
TREUCONSULT BETEILIGUNGSGESELLSCHAFT M.B.H.—See UniCredit S.p.A.; *Int'l*, pg. 8040
TREUCONSULT PROPERTY BETA GMBH—See UniCredit S.p.A.; *Int'l*, pg. 8040
TREUCONSULT PROPERTY EPSILON GMBH—See UniCredit S.p.A.; *Int'l*, pg. 8040
TREUINVEST SERVICE GMBH—See Deutsche Bank Aktiengesellschaft; *Int'l*, pg. 2062
TREV-2 GRUPP AS—See VINCI S.A.; *Int'l*, pg. 8229
TREVALI MINING CORPORATION; *Int'l*, pg. 7916
TREVARROW INC.; *U.S. Private*, pg. 4219
TREVDAN INC.; *U.S. Private*, pg. 4219
TREVENA, INC.; *U.S. Public*, pg. 2188
TREVI ALGERIE E.U.R.L.—See Trevi Finanziaria Industriale SpA; *Int'l*, pg. 7917
TREVI AUSTRALIA PTY. LTD.—See Trevi Finanziaria Industriale SpA.; *Int'l*, pg. 7917
TREVI CHILE S.P.A.—See Trevi Finanziaria Industriale SpA.; *Int'l*, pg. 7917

TREVI CIMENTACIONES C.A.—See Trevi Finanziaria Industriale SpA.; *Int'l*, pg. 7917
TREVI CIMENTACONES Y CONSOLIDACIONES S.A.—See Trevi Finanziaria Industriale SpA.; *Int'l*, pg. 7917
TREVI CONSTRUCTION CO., LTD.—See Trevi Finanziaria Industriale SpA.; *Int'l*, pg. 7917
TREVI FINANZIARIA INDUSTRIALE SPA.; *Int'l*, pg. 7916
TREVI FONDATIONS SPECIALES S.A.S.—See Trevi Finanziaria Industriale SpA.; *Int'l*, pg. 7917
TREVI FOUNDATIONS KUWAIT CO. WLL—See Trevi Finanziaria Industriale SpA.; *Int'l*, pg. 7917
TREVI FOUNDATIONS NIGERIA LTD.—See Trevi Finanziaria Industriale SpA.; *Int'l*, pg. 7917
TREVI FOUNDATIONS PHILIPPINES INC.—See Trevi Finanziaria Industriale SpA.; *Int'l*, pg. 7917
TREVI GALANTE S.A.—See Trevi Finanziaria Industriale SpA.; *Int'l*, pg. 7917
TREVIGEN, INC.—See Bio-Techne Corporation; *U.S. Public*, pg. 334
TREVI GEOTECHNIK GMBH—See Trevi Finanziaria Industriale SpA.; *Int'l*, pg. 7917
TREVI ICOS CORPORATION—See Trevi Finanziaria Industriale SpA.; *Int'l*, pg. 7917
TREVIICOS SOLETANCHE JV—See Trevi Finanziaria Industriale SpA.; *Int'l*, pg. 7917
TREVI INSAAT VE MUHENDISLIK AS—See Trevi Finanziaria Industriale SpA.; *Int'l*, pg. 7917
TREVISA INVESTIMENTOS SA; *Int'l*, pg. 7917
TREVISAN COMETAL NORTH AMERICA INC—See Trevisan Cometal SpA; *Int'l*, pg. 7917
TREVISAN COMETAL SPA; *Int'l*, pg. 7917
TREVISAN NANHAI CO. LTD—See Trevisan Cometal SpA; *Int'l*, pg. 7917
TREVI S.P.A.—See Trevi Finanziaria Industriale SpA.; *Int'l*, pg. 7917
TREVI SPEZIALTIEFBAU GMBH—See Trevi Finanziaria Industriale SpA.; *Int'l*, pg. 7917
TREVI THERAPEUTICS, INC.; *U.S. Public*, pg. 2188
TREVOR BAYLIS BRANDS PLC; *Int'l*, pg. 7917
TREW AUTO BODY, INC.—See Susquehanna International Group, LLP; *U.S. Private*, pg. 3886
TREW MARKETING; *U.S. Private*, pg. 4219
T-REX ACQUISITION CORP.; *U.S. Public*, pg. 1977
TR EXCELSIOR MANAEMENT LLC—See Hyatt Hotels Corporation; *U.S. Public*, pg. 1078
TREX COMMERCIAL PRODUCTS, INC.—See Sightline Commercial Solutions LLC; *U.S. Private*, pg. 3648
TREX COMPANY, INC.; *U.S. Public*, pg. 2188
TREX ENTERPRISES CORPORATION; *U.S. Private*, pg. 4219
TREXIN CONSULTING LLC; *U.S. Private*, pg. 4219
T-REX SOLUTIONS, LLC; *U.S. Private*, pg. 3910
TREXTEL, LLC; *U.S. Private*, pg. 4219
TREX THAIRUNG CO., LTD.—See Kyokuto Kaihatsu Kogyo Co. Ltd.; *Int'l*, pg. 4363
TREYARCH CORPORATION—See Microsoft Corporation; *U.S. Public*, pg. 1439
TREYNOR BANCSHARES, INC.; *U.S. Private*, pg. 4219
TREYNOR STATE BANK—See Treynor Bancshares, Inc.; *U.S. Private*, pg. 4219
TREYO LEISURE AND ENTERTAINMENT LTD; *Int'l*, pg. 7917
TREZ COMMERCIAL FINANCES LP—See Groupe BPCE; *Int'l*, pg. 3099
TREZOS & ASSOCIATES S.A.—See Bischof + Klein GmbH & Co. KG; *Int'l*, pg. 1049
TR FASTENINGS AB—See Trifast plc; *Int'l*, pg. 7921
TR FASTENINGS ESPANA - INGENIERIA INDUSTRIAL, S.L.—See Trifast plc; *Int'l*, pg. 7921
TR FASTENINGS LTD—See Trifast plc; *Int'l*, pg. 7921
TRF LTD; *Int'l*, pg. 7917
T R FOODS, INC.; *U.S. Private*, pg. 3909
TR FORMAC CO. LTD.—See Trifast plc; *Int'l*, pg. 7921
TR FORMAC FASTENINGS PRIVATE LTD.—See Trifast plc; *Int'l*, pg. 7921
TR FORMAC PTE LTD—See Trifast plc; *Int'l*, pg. 7921
TR FORMAC (SHANGHAI) PTE LTD—See Trifast plc; *Int'l*, pg. 7921
TR FORMAC (SUZHOU) PTE LTD—See Trifast plc; *Int'l*, pg. 7921
TRG BERRYVILLE LLC—See Alter Trading Corporation; *U.S. Private*, pg. 207
TRG CHARLOTTE LLC—See Simon Property Group, Inc.; *U.S. Public*, pg. 1882
TRG HARRISON, LLC—See Alter Trading Corporation; *U.S. Private*, pg. 207
TRG HOLDINGS, LLC; *U.S. Private*, pg. 4219
TRG HOT SPRINGS, LLC—See Alter Trading Corporation; *U.S. Private*, pg. 207
TRG JONESBORO, LLC—See Alter Trading Corporation; *U.S. Private*, pg. 207
TRG MANAGEMENT LP; *U.S. Private*, pg. 4219
TRGOAUTO A.D.; *Int'l*, pg. 7918
TRGOCENTAR A.D.; *Int'l*, pg. 7918
TRGOPROMET A.D.; *Int'l*, pg. 7918
TRGOVINA 22 A.D.; *Int'l*, pg. 7918
TRGOVINA BORAC D.D. TRAVNIK; *Int'l*, pg. 7918
TRG PAKISTAN LIMITED; *Int'l*, pg. 7918

TRG ROGERS, LLC—See Alter Trading Corporation; *U.S. Private*, pg. 207
TRGRP, INC.—See Vista Equity Partners, LLC; *U.S. Private*, pg. 4402
TRG TRADING (PTY) LIMITED—See Basil Read Holdings Limited; *Int'l*, pg. 887
T.R. HINAN CONTRACTORS INC.; *Int'l*, pg. 7397
TR HOTEL JARDIN DEL MAR SA; *Int'l*, pg. 7885
TRH SERVICES LIMITED—See NZ WINDFARMS LIMITED; *Int'l*, pg. 5502
TR HUNGARY KFT—See Trifast plc; *Int'l*, pg. 7921
TRIA BEAUTY, INC.; *U.S. Private*, pg. 4225
TRIA CAPITAL PARTNERS, LLC; *U.S. Private*, pg. 4225
TRIACOS CONSULTING & ENGINEERING GMBH—See Krones AG; *Int'l*, pg. 4306
TRIACTA BV; *Int'l*, pg. 7918
TRIACT CANADA MARKETPLACE LP—See Cboe Global Markets, Inc.; *U.S. Public*, pg. 459
TRIAD ADVISORS, INC.—See Reverence Capital Partners LLC; *U.S. Private*, pg. 3415
TRIAD COMPONENTS GROUP; *U.S. Private*, pg. 4225
TRIAD CONTROL SYSTEMS INC.—See The Newtron Group Inc.; *U.S. Private*, pg. 4084
TRIADE INFORMATIONSYSTEMS GMBH—See SER Solutions Deutschland GmbH; *Int'l*, pg. 6720
TRIAD ELECTRIC & CONTROLS INC.—See The Newtron Group Inc.; *U.S. Private*, pg. 4084
TRIAD ENVIRONMENTAL CONSULTANT—See Montrose Environmental Group, LLC; *U.S. Public*, pg. 1466
TRIAD-FABCO INC.; *U.S. Private*, pg. 4225
TRIAD FINANCIAL ADVISORS INC.—See New Mountain Capital, LLC; *U.S. Private*, pg. 2901
TRIAD FINANCIAL SERVICE, INC—See ECN Capital Corp.; *Int'l*, pg. 2292
TRIAD FINANCIAL SERVICES, INC.—See ECN Capital Corp.; *Int'l*, pg. 2292
TRIAD FOODS GROUP; *U.S. Private*, pg. 4225
TRIAD FREIGHTLINER OF GREENSBORO INC.; *U.S. Private*, pg. 4225
TRIAD GROUP PLC; *Int'l*, pg. 7918
TRIAD HYBRID SOLUTIONS, LLC—See Reverence Capital Partners LLC; *U.S. Private*, pg. 3415
TRIAD, INC.; *U.S. Private*, pg. 4225
TRIAD INTERACTIVE, INC.—See Platinum Equity, LLC; *U.S. Private*, pg. 3206
TRIADIS ETAMPES—See Groupe Seche SAS; *Int'l*, pg. 3111
TRIAD ISOTOPES, INC.—See Jubilant Bhartia Group; *Int'l*, pg. 4020
TRIADIS SERVICES S.A.S.—See Groupe Seche SAS; *Int'l*, pg. 3111
TRIAD MACHINERY INC.; *U.S. Private*, pg. 4225
TRIAD MANUFACTURING, INC.; *U.S. Private*, pg. 4225
TRIAD MARKETING INC.; *U.S. Private*, pg. 4225
TRIAD MECHANICAL INC.; *U.S. Private*, pg. 4225
TRIAD METAL PRODUCTS COMPANY INC.; *U.S. Private*, pg. 4225
TRIAD MINING INC.—See James River Coal Company; *U.S. Private*, pg. 2185
TRIAD OF ALABAMA, LLC—See Community Health Systems, Inc.; *U.S. Public*, pg. 557
TRIAD OIL MANITOBA LTD.—See Repsol, S.A.; *Int'l*, pg. 6293
TRIAD PACKAGING DESIGN & DISPLAY INC.; *U.S. Private*, pg. 4225
TRIAD PACKAGING, INC. ATHENS, ALABAMA—See Triad Packaging Design & Display Inc.; *U.S. Private*, pg. 4225
TRIAD PERSONNEL SERVICES, INC.—See GEE Group Inc.; *U.S. Public*, pg. 910
TRIAD PLASTICS INC.; *U.S. Private*, pg. 4225
TRIAD PRO INNOVATORS, INC.; *U.S. Public*, pg. 2189
TRIAD RF SYSTEMS INC.—See Comrod Inc.; *U.S. Private*, pg. 1006
TRIAD SEMICONDUCTOR; *U.S. Private*, pg. 4225
TRIAD SERVICE SOLUTIONS, INC—See Tide Rock Holdings, LLC; *U.S. Private*, pg. 4168
TRIAD SPEAKERS, INC.—See Resideo Technologies, Inc.; *U.S. Public*, pg. 1790
TRIAD TECHNOLOGIES; *U.S. Private*, pg. 4225
TRIAD TRANSPORT INC.; *U.S. Private*, pg. 4225
TRIAD UNDERGROUND MINING, LLC—See James River Coal Company; *U.S. Private*, pg. 2185
TRIAD WEB DESIGN; *U.S. Private*, pg. 4225
TRIAGE FIRST INC.—See Emergency Nurses Association; *U.S. Public*, pg. 1380
TRIAGE PARTNERS, LLC—See Broadtree Partners, LLC; *U.S. Private*, pg. 659
TRIAGE STAFFING INC.; *U.S. Private*, pg. 4225
TRIALCARD INCORPORATED—See Odyssey Investment Partners, LLC; *U.S. Private*, pg. 2996
TRIALCO INC.; *U.S. Private*, pg. 4225
TRIAL EXHIBITS, INC.—See U.S. Legal Support, Inc.; *U.S. Private*, pg. 4271
TRIALGRAPHIX INC.—See Odyssey Investment Partners, LLC; *U.S. Private*, pg. 2995
TRIALON CORPORATION—See Resilience Capital Partners, LLC; *U.S. Private*, pg. 3405

COMPANY NAME INDEX

TRIAL PARTNERS, INC.—See U.S. Legal Support, Inc.; *U.S. Private*, pg. 4271
TRIALPAY, INC.—See Visa, Inc.; *U.S. Public*, pg. 2301
TRIAL SOLUTIONS OF TEXAS LLC; *U.S. Private*, pg. 4225
TRIALTO WINE GROUP LTD.; *Int'l*, pg. 7918
TRI-AM RV CENTER; *U.S. Private*, pg. 4221
TRIAMUN AG—See CSL Limited; *Int'l*, pg. 1866
TRIANA ENERGY, LLC—See Morgan Stanley; *U.S. Public*, pg. 1474
TRIAN FUND MANAGEMENT, L.P.; *U.S. Private*, pg. 4226
TRIANGEL FRANKFURT IMMOBILIEN GMBH & CO. KG—See Aroundtown SA; *Int'l*, pg. 578
TRIANGLE AGGREGATES LLC.; *U.S. Private*, pg. 4226
TRIANGLE AUTO CENTER, INC.; *U.S. Private*, pg. 4226
TRIANGLE BIOSYSTEMS INC.—See Harvard Bioscience, Inc.; *U.S. Public*, pg. 987
TRIANGLE BRASS MANUFACTURING COMPANY, INC.; *U.S. Private*, pg. 4226
TRIANGLE BUSINESS JOURNALS OF NORTH CAROLINA, LLC—See Advance Publications, Inc.; *U.S. Private*, pg. 85
TRIANGLE CAR WASH INC.; *U.S. Private*, pg. 4226
TRIANGLE CHEMICAL CO. INC.; *U.S. Private*, pg. 4226
TRIANGLE CONTRACTORS INC.; *U.S. Private*, pg. 4226
TRIANGLE DISTRIBUTING COMPANY; *U.S. Private*, pg. 4226
TRIANGLE ELECTRIC COMPANY; *U.S. Private*, pg. 4226
TRIANGLE ENDOSCOPY CENTER, LLC—See KKR & Co. Inc.; *U.S. Public*, pg. 1249
TRIANGLE ENERGY (GLOBAL) LIMITED; *Int'l*, pg. 7919
TRIANGLE ENTERPRISES INC.; *U.S. Private*, pg. 4226
TRIANGLE FASTENER CORPORATION—See SFS Group AG; *Int'l*, pg. 6739
TRIANGLE GRADING & PAVING INC.; *U.S. Private*, pg. 4226
TRIANGLE (GUANGZHOU) DIGITAL MATERIALS CO., LTD.—See Sakata INX Corporation; *Int'l*, pg. 6488
TRIANGLE LANDSCAPE SUPPLIES, INC.—See SiteOne Landscape Supply, Inc.; *U.S. Public*, pg. 1889
TRIANGLE LIFE INSURANCE—See First Citizens BancShares, Inc.; *U.S. Public*, pg. 842
TRIANGLE MACHINE PRODUCT CO.—See Freeway Corporation; *U.S. Private*, pg. 1607
TRIANGLE MANUFACTURING CO. INC.; *U.S. Private*, pg. 4226
TRIANGLE METALS INC.—See Thomas Engineering Inc.; *U.S. Private*, pg. 4155
TRIANGLE NORTH HEALTHCARE FOUNDATION, INC.; *U.S. Private*, pg. 4226
TRIANGLE PACKAGE MACHINERY CO.; *U.S. Private*, pg. 4226
TRIANGLE PETROLEUM CORPORATION; *U.S. Public*, pg. 2189
TRIANGLE REFRIGERATION CO.—See Ares Management Corporation; *U.S. Public*, pg. 189
TRIANGLE SALES INC.; *U.S. Private*, pg. 4226
TRIANGLE SERVICES, INC.; *U.S. Private*, pg. 4226
TRIANGLE SUGAR CORPORATION LIMITED—See Tongaat Hulett Limited; *Int'l*, pg. 7807
TRIANGLE SUSPENSION SYSTEMS, INC.—See Berkshire Hathaway Inc.; *U.S. Public*, pg. 310
TRIANGLE SYSTEMS INC.; *U.S. Private*, pg. 4226
TRIANGLE TELEPHONE COOP ASSOCIATION; *U.S. Private*, pg. 4226
TRIANGLE TIRE CO. LTD; *Int'l*, pg. 7919
TRIANGLE TOOL CORPORATION; *U.S. Private*, pg. 4226
TRIANGLE TOOL CO.—See The Plastek Group; *U.S. Private*, pg. 4096
TRIANGLE TOWN CENTER, LLC—See CBL & Associates Properties, Inc.; *U.S. Public*, pg. 459
TRIANGLE TRAINING LTD.—See Interserve Plc; *Int'l*, pg. 3760
TRIANGLE TRUSS INC.; *U.S. Private*, pg. 4226
TRIANGLE USA PETROLEUM CORPORATION—See Triangle Petroleum Corporation; *U.S. Public*, pg. 2189
TRIANGULAR FORCE CONSTRUCTION ENGINEERING LIMITED—See Beaver Group (HOLDING) Company Limited; *Int'l*, pg. 935
TRI-ANIM HEALTH SERVICES, INC.—See Investor AB; *Int'l*, pg. 3787
TRIAN INVESTORS 1 LIMITED; *Int'l*, pg. 7918
TRIANON HOTEL CO.; *U.S. Private*, pg. 4227
TRIARC LTD; *U.S. Private*, pg. 4227
TRIARCO INDUSTRIES, LLC—See One Rock Capital Partners, LLC; *U.S. Private*, pg. 3022
TRI-ARROWS ALUMINUM INC.—See UACJ Corporation; *Int'l*, pg. 7999
TRIARTISAN CAPITAL ADVISORS LLC—See The Toronto-Dominion Bank; *Int'l*, pg. 7695
TRI-ARTISAN PARTNERS ADVISORS EUROPE LLP—See Morgan Joseph TriArtisan Group Inc.; *U.S. Private*, pg. 2784
TRIATHLON HOLDING GMBH—See Sunlight Group Energy Storage Systems Industrial and Commercial Singlemember Societe Anonyme; *Int'l*, pg. 7317
TRI-AUTO ENTERPRISES, LLC; *U.S. Private*, pg. 4221

TRIAZA - TRATAMENTO DE RESIDUOS INDUSTRIAIS DA AZAMBUJA, S.A.—See Mota-Engil SGPS, S.A.; *Int'l*, pg. 5052
TRIBAL CONSULTING LIMITED—See Tribal Group plc; *Int'l*, pg. 7919
TRIBAL DDB ATHENS—See Omnicom Group Inc.; *U.S. Public*, pg. 1582
TRIBAL DDB BARCELONA—See Omnicom Group Inc.; *U.S. Public*, pg. 1582
TRIBAL DDB BUDAPEST—See Omnicom Group Inc.; *U.S. Public*, pg. 1582
TRIBAL DDB CHICAGO—See Omnicom Group Inc.; *U.S. Public*, pg. 1582
TRIBAL DDB COLOMBIA—See Omnicom Group Inc.; *U.S. Public*, pg. 1582
TRIBAL DDB COPENHAGEN—See Omnicom Group Inc.; *U.S. Public*, pg. 1582
TRIBAL DDB HONG KONG—See Omnicom Group Inc.; *U.S. Public*, pg. 1582
TRIBAL DDB INDIA—See Omnicom Group Inc.; *U.S. Public*, pg. 1582
TRIBAL DDB MADRID—See Omnicom Group Inc.; *U.S. Public*, pg. 1582
TRIBAL DDB MALAYSIA—See Omnicom Group Inc.; *U.S. Public*, pg. 1582
TRIBAL DDB MELBOURNE—See Omnicom Group Inc.; *U.S. Public*, pg. 1582
TRIBAL DDB MILAN—See Omnicom Group Inc.; *U.S. Public*, pg. 1582
TRIBAL DDB NORTH AMERICA/NEW YORK—See Omnicom Group Inc.; *U.S. Public*, pg. 1582
TRIBAL DDB OSLO—See Omnicom Group Inc.; *U.S. Public*, pg. 1582
TRIBAL DDB PARIS—See Omnicom Group Inc.; *U.S. Public*, pg. 1582
TRIBAL DDB SAN FRANCISCO—See Omnicom Group Inc.; *U.S. Public*, pg. 1582
TRIBAL DDB SAO PAULO—See Omnicom Group Inc.; *U.S. Public*, pg. 1582
TRIBAL DDB SINGAPORE—See Omnicom Group Inc.; *U.S. Public*, pg. 1582
TRIBAL DDB—See Omnicom Group Inc.; *U.S. Public*, pg. 1582
TRIBAL DDB SYDNEY—See Omnicom Group Inc.; *U.S. Public*, pg. 1582
TRIBAL DDB TEL AVIV—See Omnicom Group Inc.; *U.S. Public*, pg. 1582
TRIBAL DDB TOKYO—See Omnicom Group Inc.; *U.S. Public*, pg. 1582
TRIBAL DDB TORONTO—See Omnicom Group Inc.; *U.S. Public*, pg. 1582
TRIBAL DDB VANCOUVER—See Omnicom Group Inc.; *U.S. Public*, pg. 1582
TRIBAL DDB WORLDWIDE—See Omnicom Group Inc.; *U.S. Public*, pg. 1582
TRIBAL EDUCATION LIMITED—See Tribal Group plc; *Int'l*, pg. 7919
TRIBAL FUSION, INC.; *U.S. Private*, pg. 4227
TRIBAL GROUP PLC; *Int'l*, pg. 7919
TRIBAL GROUP PTY LIMITED—See Tribal Group plc; *Int'l*, pg. 7919
TRIBAL HOLDINGS INC.—See Rizal Resources Corporation; *Int'l*, pg. 6354
TRIBAL LAW AND POLICY INSTITUTE; *U.S. Private*, pg. 4227
TRIBAL NOVA, INC.—See Veritas Capital Fund Management, LLC; *U.S. Private*, pg. 4363
TRIBAL RESOURCING LIMITED—See Tribal Group plc; *Int'l*, pg. 7919
TRIBAL RIDES INTERNATIONAL CORP.; *U.S. Public*, pg. 2189
TRIBAL SYSTEMS CANADA LIMITED—See Tribal Group plc; *Int'l*, pg. 7919
TRIBAL WORLDWIDE LONDON—See Omnicom Group Inc.; *U.S. Public*, pg. 1582
TRIBBLE & STEPHENS CONSTRUCTORS LIMITED; *U.S. Private*, pg. 4227
TRIBE 9 FOODS LLC; *U.S. Private*, pg. 4227
TRIBECA FILM INSTITUTE LLC; *U.S. Private*, pg. 4227
TRIBECA FLASHPOINT MEDIA ARTS ACADEMY; *U.S. Private*, pg. 4227
TRIBECA GLOBAL NATURAL RESOURCES LIMITED; *Int'l*, pg. 7919
TRIBECA GRILL—See Myriad Restaurant Group; *U.S. Private*, pg. 2825
TRIBECA LEARNING PTY LIMITED—See Graham Holdings Company; *U.S. Public*, pg. 956
TRIBECA OVEN, INC.—See The Pritzker Group - Chicago, LLC; *U.S. Private*, pg. 4098
TRIBECA RESOURCES CORPORATION; *Int'l*, pg. 7919
TRIBECA TECHNOLOGY SOLUTIONS INC.; *U.S. Private*, pg. 4227
TRIBECK INC.—See Miroku Jyoho Service Co., Ltd.; *Int'l*, pg. 4920
TRIBECO BINH DUONG CO., LTD.—See Uni-President Enterprises Corporation; *Int'l*, pg. 8029
TRIBELT B.V.—See Beijer Alma AB; *Int'l*, pg. 943
TRIBE MEDIA CORP.; *U.S. Private*, pg. 4227

TRI-CHEM, INC.

TRIBE MEDITERRANEAN FOODS INC.—See Lakeview Farms LLC; *U.S. Private*, pg. 2378
TRIBE; *U.S. Private*, pg. 4227
TRIBHOVANDAS BHIMJI ZAVERI LIMITED; *Int'l*, pg. 7919
TRIBIA AB—See Addnode Group AB; *Int'l*, pg. 131
TRIBIA AS—See Addnode Group AB; *Int'l*, pg. 131
TRIBLES INC.; *U.S. Private*, pg. 4227
TRIBON SOLUTIONS (UK) LTD.—See Schneider Electric SE; *Int'l*, pg. 6623
TRIBOO SPA; *Int'l*, pg. 7919
TRI-BORO CONSTRUCTION SUPPLIES INC.—See Clayton, Dubilier & Rice, LLC; *U.S. Private*, pg. 930
TRIBORON INTERNATIONAL AB; *Int'l*, pg. 7919
TRIBORO QUILT MANUFACTURING CORP.—See Gerber Childrenswear LLC; *U.S. Private*, pg. 1686
TRIBOTEC AB—See Indutrade AB; *Int'l*, pg. 3681
TRIBRIDGE RESIDENTIAL, LLC; *U.S. Private*, pg. 4227
TRIBRIDGE RESIDENTIAL PROPERTY MANAGEMENT ADVISORS, LLC—See Tribridge Residential, LLC; *U.S. Private*, pg. 4227
TRIBUILD CONTRACTING (CALGARY) LTD.; *Int'l*, pg. 7919
TRIBU/NAZCA SAATCHI & SAATCHI—See Publicis Groupe S.A.; *Int'l*, pg. 6110
TRIBUNE 365, LLC—See Tribune Publishing Company; *U.S. Private*, pg. 4228
TRIBUNE BROADCASTING COMPANY—See Nexstar Media Group, Inc.; *U.S. Public*, pg. 1524
TRIBUNE BROADCASTING DENVER, LLC—See Nexstar Media Group, Inc.; *U.S. Public*, pg. 1525
TRIBUNE BROADCASTING HARTFORD, LLC—See Nexstar Media Group, Inc.; *U.S. Public*, pg. 1525
TRIBUNE BROADCASTING INDIANAPOLIS, LLC—See Nexstar Media Group, Inc.; *U.S. Public*, pg. 1525
TRIBUNE BROADCASTING OKLAHOMA CITY LICENSE, LLC—See Nexstar Media Group, Inc.; *U.S. Public*, pg. 1525
TRIBUNE CNLBC, LLC—See Nexstar Media Group, Inc.; *U.S. Public*, pg. 1525
TRIBUNE CONTENT AGENCY, LLC—See Tribune Publishing Company; *U.S. Private*, pg. 4228
THE TRIBUNE-DEMOCRAT—See The Retirement Systems of Alabama; *U.S. Public*, pg. 4106
TRIBUNE DIRECT MARKETING, INC.—See Tribune Publishing Company; *U.S. Private*, pg. 4228
TRIBUNE DIRECT MARKETING—See Tribune Publishing Company; *U.S. Private*, pg. 4228
TRIBUNE ENTERTAINMENT COMPANY—See Nexstar Media Group, Inc.; *U.S. Public*, pg. 1524
TRIBUNE INTERACTIVE, INC.—See Nexstar Media Group, Inc.; *U.S. Public*, pg. 1525
TRIBUNE MEDIA COMPANY—See Nexstar Media Group, Inc.; *U.S. Public*, pg. 1524
TRIBUNE PROPERTIES, INC.—See Nexstar Media Group, Inc.; *U.S. Public*, pg. 1525
TRIBUNE PUBLISHING COMPANY, LLC—See Tribune Publishing Company; *U.S. Private*, pg. 4228
TRIBUNE PUBLISHING COMPANY—See TPC Holdings, Inc.; *U.S. Private*, pg. 4200
TRIBUNE PUBLISHING COMPANY; *U.S. Private*, pg. 4227
TRIBUNE RESOURCES LTD.; *Int'l*, pg. 7919
TRIBUNE-REVIEW PUBLISHING COMPANY; *U.S. Private*, pg. 4228
THE TRIBUNE—See Chatham Asset Management, LLC; *U.S. Public*, pg. 867
THE TRIBUNE—See Home News Enterprises, LLC; *U.S. Private*, pg. 1971
TRIBUNE TELEVISION NEW ORLEANS, INC.—See Nexstar Media Group, Inc.; *U.S. Public*, pg. 1524
TRIBUNE TELEVISION NORTHWEST, INC.—See Nexstar Media Group, Inc.; *U.S. Public*, pg. 1524
TRIBUNE WASHINGTON BUREAU, LLC—See Tribune Publishing Company; *U.S. Private*, pg. 4228
TRIBURY CONSTRUCTION (1995) INC.; *Int'l*, pg. 7919
TRIBUS AEROSPACE LLC—See Shorehill Capital LLC; *U.S. Private*, pg. 3641
TRIBUS ENTERPRISES, INC.; *U.S. Private*, pg. 4228
TRIBUTE INC.—See Constellation Software Inc.; *Int'l*, pg. 1776
TRIBUTE RESOURCES INC.; *Int'l*, pg. 7919
TRICAL INC.; *U.S. Private*, pg. 4228
TRICAN WELL SERVICE, L.P.—See Trican Well Service, Ltd.; *Int'l*, pg. 7919
TRICAN WELL SERVICE, LTD.; *Int'l*, pg. 7919
TRICAP CHICAGO, LLC; *U.S. Private*, pg. 4228
TRI-C BUSINESS FORMS, INC.—See Ennis, Inc.; *U.S. Public*, pg. 769
TRICE MEDICAL, INC; *U.S. Private*, pg. 4228
TRICENTIS USA CORP.; *U.S. Private*, pg. 4229
TRI CENTRAL CO-OP; *U.S. Private*, pg. 4220
TRICENTURION INC.—See GuideWell Mutual Holding Corporation; *U.S. Public*, pg. 1814
TRI CHEMICAL LABORATORIES INC.; *Int'l*, pg. 7918
TRI-CHEM, INC.; *U.S. Private*, pg. 4221
TRICHOME FINANCIAL CORP.—See IM Cannabis Corp.; *Int'l*, pg. 3617

TRI-CHEM, INC.

TRICHROMATIC MEXICO S.DE.R.L.—See SK Capital Partners, LP; *U.S. Private*, pg. 3680
TRICHROMATIC MISR—See SK Capital Partners, LP; *U.S. Private*, pg. 3680
TRICHROMATIC WEST INC.—See SK Capital Partners, LP; *U.S. Private*, pg. 3680
TRICIDA, INC.; *U.S. Public*, pg. 2189
TRI-CITIES HOME HEALTH, LLC.—See Amedisys, Inc.; *U.S. Public*, pg. 94
TRI-CITIES LABORATORY, LLC—See Laboratory Corporation of America Holdings; *U.S. Public*, pg. 1287
TRI-CITY AUTO SALVAGE INC.—See Stellex Capital Management LP; *U.S. Private*, pg. 3800
TRI CITY BANKSHARES CORPORATION; *U.S. Public*, pg. 2188
TRI-CITY CHARTER OF BOSSIER, INC.—See Lone Star Coaches, Inc.; *U.S. Private*, pg. 2484
TRI-CITY COMMUNITY ACTION PROGRAM INC.; *U.S. Private*, pg. 4221
TRI CITY DISTRIBUTORS LP; *U.S. Private*, pg. 4220
TRI-CITY ELECTRICAL CONTRACTORS, INC.; *U.S. Private*, pg. 4221
TRI-CITY ELECTRICAL CONTRACTORS, INC. - TAMPA DIVISION—See Tri-City Electrical Contractors, Inc.; *U.S. Private*, pg. 4221
TRI-CITY ELECTRIC CO.; *U.S. Private*, pg. 4221
TRI-CITY EXTRUSION, INC.—See The Dyson-Kissner-Moran Corporation; *U.S. Private*, pg. 4024
TRI CITY FOODS INC.; *U.S. Private*, pg. 4220
TRI CITY FORD INC.; *U.S. Private*, pg. 4221
TRI-CITY HERALD—See Chatham Asset Management, LLC; *U.S. Private*, pg. 867
TRI-CITY MEATS INCORPORATED; *U.S. Private*, pg. 4221
TRICITY NATIONAL BANK INC—See Tri City Bankshares Corporation; *U.S. Public*, pg. 2188
TRICITY PAIN ASSOCIATES PA—See Spindletop Capital Management LLC; *U.S. Private*, pg. 3757
TRI CITY PAVING INC.; *U.S. Private*, pg. 4220
TRI CITY PETCT LLC—See Akumin, Inc.; *U.S. Public*, pg. 70
TRI CITY RENTAL; *U.S. Private*, pg. 4220
TRI CITY SUPPLY, INC.—See Freeman Spogli & Co. Incorporated; *U.S. Private*, pg. 1606
TRI-CITY WEEKLY—See Alden Global Capital LLC; *U.S. Private*, pg. 156
TRICKETT HONDA; *U.S. Private*, pg. 4229
TRICKEY JENNUS INC.; *U.S. Private*, pg. 4229
TRICKLESTAR LIMITED; *Int'l*, pg. 7919
TRICKS WROUGHT IRON SERVICES PROPRIETARY LIMITED—See ARGENT INDUSTRIAL LIMITED; *Int'l*, pg. 561
TRICKY JIGSAW PTY. LTD.—See M&C Saatchi plc; *Int'l*, pg. 4611
TRI COASTAL DESIGN GROUP INC; *U.S. Private*, pg. 4220
TRICO AUTOMOTIVE SYSTEMS CO., LTD—See Crowne Group LLC; *U.S. Private*, pg. 1112
TRICO BANCSHARES; *U.S. Public*, pg. 2189
TRICOCI UNIVERSITY OF BEAUTY CULTURE—See NCK Capital LLC; *U.S. Private*, pg. 2876
TRICO COMPONENTES S.A. DE C.V.—See Crowne Group LLC; *U.S. Private*, pg. 1112
TRICO ELECTRIC CO-OP.; *U.S. Private*, pg. 4229
TRICO ENTERPRISES LLC.; *U.S. Private*, pg. 4229
TRICO EQUIPMENT SERVICES LLC; *U.S. Private*, pg. 4229
TRICOFLEX SA—See Exel Industries SA; *Int'l*, pg. 2583
TRICO LATINOAMERICANA DO BRASIL LTDA—See Crowne Group LLC; *U.S. Private*, pg. 1112
TRICO LATINOAMERICANA SA—See Crowne Group LLC; *U.S. Private*, pg. 1112
TRICOL BIOMEDICAL, INC.—See Weifang Tricol Trading Co. Ltd.; *Int'l*, pg. 8369
TRICO LIMITED—See Crowne Group LLC; *U.S. Private*, pg. 1112
TRICOLOR AUTO GROUP; *U.S. Private*, pg. 4229
TRICOLORE CO., LTD.—See Key Coffee Inc.; *Int'l*, pg. 4145
TRICO MARINE ASSETS, INC.—See Trico Marine Services, Inc.; *U.S. Private*, pg. 4229
TRICO MARINE INTERNATIONAL, INC.—See Trico Marine Services, Inc.; *U.S. Private*, pg. 4229
TRICO MARINE OPERATORS, INC.—See Trico Marine Services, Inc.; *U.S. Private*, pg. 4229
TRICO MARINE SERVICES, INC.; *U.S. Private*, pg. 4229
TRICOM FRUIT PRODUCTS LIMITED; *Int'l*, pg. 7919
TRICOM, INC.—See Wintrust Financial Corporation; *U.S. Public*, pg. 2375
TRICOM S.A.—See Altice Europe N.V.; *Int'l*, pg. 393
TRICON AMERICAN HOMES LLC—See Blackstone Inc.; *U.S. Public*, pg. 352
TRICON DRILLING SOLUTIONS PTY. LTD.—See Sandvik AB; *Int'l*, pg. 6535
TRI-CON INC.; *U.S. Private*, pg. 4221
TRI-CON INDUSTRIES LTD.—See TS Tech Co Ltd; *Int'l*, pg. 7948
TRICONNEX LIMITED—See Nexus Infrastructure plc; *Int'l*, pg. 5251

TRICON RESIDENTIAL INC.—See Blackstone Inc.; *U.S. Public*, pg. 351
TRICON RESTAURANT INTERNATIONAL (PR), INC.—See Encanto Restaurants, Inc; *U.S. Private*, pg. 1389
TRI-CONSTRUCTION COMPANY, INC.; *U.S. Private*, pg. 4221
TRI-CONTINENTAL CORPORATION; *U.S. Public*, pg. 2188
TRICONTINENT SCIENTIFIC, INC.—See Ingersoll Rand Inc.; *U.S. Public*, pg. 1120
TRI-CONTROL AUTOMATION COMPANY LIMITED—See China Automation Group Limited; *Int'l*, pg. 1483
TRICOOL REEFER SDN BHD—See Eng Kong Holdings Pte Ltd.; *Int'l*, pg. 2426
TRICO PTY. LIMITED—See Crowne Group LLC; *U.S. Private*, pg. 1112
TRICOR AMERICA, INC.; *U.S. Private*, pg. 4229
TRICOR AXCELASIA SDN BHD—See Axington Inc.; *Int'l*, pg. 768
TRICOR AXCELASIA (SG) PTE LTD—See Axington Inc.; *Int'l*, pg. 768
TRICORBRAUN DESIGN & ENGINEERING—See Ares Management Corporation; *U.S. Public*, pg. 191
TRICORBRAUN DESIGN & ENGINEERING—See Ontario Teachers' Pension Plan; *Int'l*, pg. 5591
TRICORBRAUN INC.—See Ares Management Corporation; *U.S. Public*, pg. 191
TRICORBRAUN INC.—See Ontario Teachers' Pension Plan; *Int'l*, pg. 5590
TRICOR (B) SDN BHD—See The Bank of East Asia, Limited; *Int'l*, pg. 7615
TRICOR CARIBBEAN LIMITED—See The Bank of East Asia, Limited; *Int'l*, pg. 7615
TRICOR CONSULTANCY (BEIJING) LIMITED—See The Bank of East Asia, Limited; *Int'l*, pg. 7615
TRICOR DIRECT INC.—See Brady Corporation; *U.S. Public*, pg. 379
TRICOR INC.; *U.S. Private*, pg. 4229
TRICORE REFERENCE LABORATORIES; *U.S. Private*, pg. 4229
TRICORE SOLUTIONS LLC—See Apollo Global Management, Inc.; *U.S. Public*, pg. 154
TRICOR GROUPE S.A.—See Brady Corporation; *U.S. Public*, pg. 379
TRICOR HOLDINGS PTE. LTD.—See The Bank of East Asia, Limited; *Int'l*, pg. 7615
TRICOR, INC.; *U.S. Private*, pg. 4229
TRICOR JAPAN LIMITED—See The Bank of East Asia, Limited; *Int'l*, pg. 7615
TRICOR K.K.—See The Bank of East Asia, Limited; *Int'l*, pg. 7615
TRICORN CORPORATION—See Septeni Holdings Co., Ltd.; *Int'l*, pg. 6718
TRICORN GROUP PLC; *Int'l*, pg. 7920
TRICORONA AB; *Int'l*, pg. 7920
TRICORONA CARBON ASSET MANAGEMENT PTE. LTD.—See Tricorona AB; *Int'l*, pg. 7920
TRICORONA CLIMATE PARTNER AB—See Tricorona AB; *Int'l*, pg. 7920
TRICOR PACIFIC CAPITAL, INC.; *Int'l*, pg. 7919
TRICOR PACIFIC FOUNDERS CAPITAL, INC.; *Int'l*, pg. 7920
TRICOR PLC; *Int'l*, pg. 7920
TRICOR PRAESIDIUM LIMITED—See The Bank of East Asia, Limited; *Int'l*, pg. 7615
TRICOR REFINING, LLC—See Ergon, Inc.; *U.S. Private*, pg. 1418
TRICOR REFINING, LLC—See San Joaquin Refining Co., Inc.; *U.S. Private*, pg. 3541
TRICOR ROOTS SDN BHD—See Axington Inc.; *Int'l*, pg. 768
TRICOR SERVICES EUROPE LLP—See The Bank of East Asia, Limited; *Int'l*, pg. 7615
TRICOR SERVICES LIMITED—See The Bank of East Asia, Limited; *Int'l*, pg. 7615
TRICOR SERVICES (MACAU) LIMITED—See The Bank of East Asia, Limited; *Int'l*, pg. 7615
TRICOR SERVICES (MALAYSIA) SDN. BHD—See The Bank of East Asia, Limited; *Int'l*, pg. 7615
TRICOR SINGAPORE PTE LTD—See The Bank of East Asia, Limited; *Int'l*, pg. 7615
TRICOR TRUSTCO (LABUAN) LTD—See The Bank of East Asia, Limited; *Int'l*, pg. 7615
TRICOSAL GMBH & CO. KG—See Sika AG; *Int'l*, pg. 6916
TRICO SERVICOS MARITIMOS LTDA—See Trico Marine Services, Inc.; *U.S. Private*, pg. 4229
TRICOT, INC.—See Pola Orbis Holdings Inc.; *Int'l*, pg. 5905
TRI-COUNTIES ASSOCIATION FOR THE DEVELOPMENTALLY DISABLED; *U.S. Private*, pg. 4222
TRI COUNTIES BANK—See TriCo Bancshares; *U.S. Public*, pg. 2189
TRI COUNTY AIR CONDITIONING & HEATING, INC.; *U.S. Private*, pg. 4220
TRI - COUNTY BEVERAGE; *U.S. Private*, pg. 4220
TRI-COUNTY BUILDING SUPPLIES; *U.S. Private*, pg. 4222

CORPORATE AFFILIATIONS

TRI-COUNTY COMMUNICATIONS COOPERATIVE, INC.; *U.S. Private*, pg. 4222
TRI-COUNTY COMMUNICATIONS CORP.—See Telephone & Data Systems, Inc.; *U.S. Public*, pg. 1998
TRI COUNTY COMMUNITY ACTION AGENCY, INC.; *U.S. Private*, pg. 4220
TRI-COUNTY ELECTRIC COMPANY, INC.—See Penn Line Corp.; *U.S. Private*, pg. 3134
TRI-COUNTY ELECTRIC COOPERATIVE, INC.; *U.S. Private*, pg. 4222
TRI-COUNTY ELECTRIC COOPERATIVE INC.; *U.S. Private*, pg. 4222
TRI-COUNTY ELECTRIC COOP; *U.S. Private*, pg. 4222
TRI-COUNTY ELECTRIC COOP; *U.S. Private*, pg. 4222
TRI-COUNTY ELECTRIC COOP; *U.S. Private*, pg. 4222
TRI-COUNTY ELECTRIC COOP; *U.S. Private*, pg. 4222
TRI-COUNTY ELECTRIC MEMBERSHIP CORP.; *U.S. Private*, pg. 4222
TRI-COUNTY ELECTRIC MEMBERSHIP CORP; *U.S. Private*, pg. 4222
TRI COUNTY FARMERS EQUIPMENT; *U.S. Private*, pg. 4220
TRI-COUNTY FINANCIAL GROUP, INC.; *U.S. Public*, pg. 2188
TRI-COUNTY INTERNATIONAL TRUCKS INC.—See C&S Motors, Inc.; *U.S. Private*, pg. 704
TRI-COUNTY LOGGING, INC.—See Hardwoods Distribution Inc.; *Int'l*, pg. 3273
TRI-COUNTY MEDICAL & OSTOMY SUPPLIES, INC.—See Becton, Dickinson & Company; *U.S. Public*, pg. 291
TRI-COUNTY MENTAL HEALTH SERVICES—See Spurwink Services Incorporated; *U.S. Private*, pg. 3765
TRI COUNTY OFFICE FURNITURE; *U.S. Private*, pg. 4220
TRI-COUNTY-PETROLEUM; *U.S. Private*, pg. 4222
TRI-COUNTY RURAL ELECTRIC CO; *U.S. Private*, pg. 4222
TRI-COUNTY SURGICAL SPECIALISTS, LLC—See HCA Healthcare, Inc.; *U.S. Public*, pg. 1012
TRI-COUNTY TRUCK COMPANY; *U.S. Private*, pg. 4222
TRI COUNTY TRUSS—See The Truss Company, Inc.; *U.S. Private*, pg. 4128
TRI COUNTY WHOLESALE DISTRIBUTORS INC.; *U.S. Private*, pg. 4220
TRICO USA, LLC.; *U.S. Private*, pg. 4229
TRICO WELDING SUPPLIES, INC.—See BBHC, Inc.; *U.S. Public*, pg. 284
TRICOYA TECHNOLOGIES LIMITED—See AccSys Technologies PLC; *Int'l*, pg. 93
TRICYCLE, INC.—See Berkshire Hathaway Inc.; *U.S. Public*, pg. 316
TRI DAL LTD.; *U.S. Private*, pg. 4220
TRI-DAM PROJECT; *U.S. Private*, pg. 4222
TRIDATA INC.—See System Planning Corporation; *U.S. Private*, pg. 3907
TRIDEA PARTNERS, LLC.—See Columbus A/S; *Int'l*, pg. 1706
TRIDELTA MEIDENSHA GMBH—See Meidensha Corporation; *Int'l*, pg. 4799
TRIDEM SPORTS AG—See Sport1 Medien AG; *Int'l*, pg. 7142
TRIDENT ABSTRACT TITLE AGENCY, LLC—See OceanFirst Financial Corp.; *U.S. Public*, pg. 1563
TRIDENT BEHAVIORAL HEALTH SERVICES, LLC—See HCA Healthcare, Inc.; *U.S. Public*, pg. 1012
TRIDENT BRANDS INCORPORATED; *U.S. Public*, pg. 2189
TRIDENT BUILDING SYSTEMS, INC.—See Behlen Mfg. Co.; *U.S. Private*, pg. 515
TRIDENT B.V—See Wartsila Corporation; *Int'l*, pg. 8347
TRIDENT CAPITAL, INC.; *U.S. Private*, pg. 4229
TRIDENT CAPITAL—See Trident Capital, Inc.; *U.S. Private*, pg. 4229
TRIDENT COMPUTER RESOURCES, INC.—See Harvest Partners L.P.; *U.S. Private*, pg. 1877
TRIDENT CONTRACT MANAGEMENT; *U.S. Private*, pg. 4229
TRIDENT DEVELOPMENTS LIMITED—See Simonds Farsons Cisk plc; *Int'l*, pg. 6933
TRIDENT ENERGY MANAGEMENT LIMITED—See Warburg Pincus LLC; *U.S. Private*, pg. 4440
TRIDENT EXPLORATION CORP.—See Trident Limited Partnership; *Int'l*, pg. 7920
TRIDENT EXPLORATION (WX) CORP.—See Trident Limited Partnership; *Int'l*, pg. 7920
TRIDENT FOODS, LTD.—See Cedar Enterprises Inc.; *U.S. Private*, pg. 804
TRIDENT GRAPHICS CANADA CORPORATION—See Sonoco Products Company; *U.S. Public*, pg. 1909
TRIDENT GRAPHICS NA LLC—See Sonoco Products Company; *U.S. Public*, pg. 1909
TRIDENT HEALTH SYSTEM—See HCA Healthcare, Inc.; *U.S. Public*, pg. 1012
TRIDENT INDUSTRI AB—See AdderaCare AB; *Int'l*, pg. 128
TRIDENT INFOSOL PVT. LTD.—See HUB Cyber Security Ltd.; *Int'l*, pg. 3516

TRIDENT INSURANCE COMPANY LIMITED—See ANSA McAL Limited; *Int'l*, pg. 476
TRIDENT INSURANCE GROUP PTY LTD—See Steadfast Group Limited; *Int'l*, pg. 7188
TRIDENT INSURANCE SERVICES, LLC—See Paragon Insurance Holdings, LLC; *U.S. Private*, pg. 3091
TRIDENT ITALIA SRL—See Wartsila Corporation; *Int'l*, pg. 8347
TRIDENT LAS PALMAS S.L.—See Wartsila Corporation; *Int'l*, pg. 8347
TRIDENT LIFELINE LIMITED; *Int'l*, pg. 7920
TRIDENT LIMITED PARTNERSHIP; *Int'l*, pg. 7920
TRIDENT LIMITED; *Int'l*, pg. 7920
TRIDENT MACHINE TOOLS, LLC—See Morris Group, Inc.; *U.S. Private*, pg. 2787
TRIDENT MANUFACTURING, INC.—See Clean Energy Technologies, Inc.; *U.S. Public*, pg. 508
TRIDENT MARITIME SYSTEMS, LLC—See J.F. Lehman & Company, Inc.; *U.S. Private*, pg. 2164
TRIDENT MARKETING; *U.S. Private*, pg. 4229
TRIDENT MEDICAL CENTER, LLC—See HCA Healthcare, Inc.; *U.S. Public*, pg. 1013
TRIDENT MICROELECTRONICS, LTD.—See Trident Microsystems, Inc.; *U.S. Private*, pg. 4230
TRIDENT MICROSYSTEMS (EUROPE) B.V.—See Trident Microsystems, Inc.; *U.S. Private*, pg. 4230
TRIDENT MICROSYSTEMS (EUROPE) GMBH—See Trident Microsystems, Inc.; *U.S. Private*, pg. 4230
TRIDENT MICROSYSTEMS (FAR EAST) LTD.—See Trident Microsystems, Inc.; *U.S. Private*, pg. 4230
TRIDENT MICROSYSTEMS, INC.; *U.S. Private*, pg. 4230
TRIDENT MICROSYSTEMS (JAPAN) GK—See Trident Microsystems, Inc.; *U.S. Private*, pg. 4230
TRIDENT MICROSYSTEMS (KOREA) LTD.—See Trident Microsystems, Inc.; *U.S. Private*, pg. 4230
TRIDENT NEONATOLOGY SERVICES, LLC—See HCA Healthcare, Inc.; *U.S. Public*, pg. 1013
TRIDENT PRECISION MANUFACTURING INC.; *U.S. Private*, pg. 4230
TRIDENT ROYALTIES PLC—See Deterra Royalties Limited; *Int'l*, pg. 2048
TRIDENT SEAFOODS CORPORATION; *U.S. Private*, pg. 4230
TRIDENT STEEL CORP.; *U.S. Private*, pg. 4230
TRIDENT STEEL INTELLECTUAL PROPERTY (PTY) LIMITED—See Aveng Limited; *Int'l*, pg. 738
TRIDENT STEEL (PTY) LIMITED—See Aveng Limited; *Int'l*, pg. 738
TRIDENT SYSTEMS INCORPORATED—See ATL Partners, LLC; *U.S. Private*, pg. 369
TRIDENT TECHLABS LIMITED; *Int'l*, pg. 7920
TRIDENT TEXOFAB LIMITED; *Int'l*, pg. 7920
TRIDENT TOOLS LIMITED; *Int'l*, pg. 7921
TRIDENT TRANSPORT, LLC; *U.S. Private*, pg. 4230
TRIDE RUS OOO—See BRENNTAG SE; *Int'l*, pg. 1150
TRIDEUM CORP.; *U.S. Private*, pg. 4230
TRI-DIM FILTER CORPORATION—See Team Solutions Project Group, Inc.; *U.S. Private*, pg. 3950
TRIDIUM, INC.—See Honeywell International Inc.; *U.S. Public*, pg. 1052
TRIDONIC AG—See Zumtobel Group AG; *Int'l*, pg. 8695
TRIDONIC AUSTRALIA PTY. LTD.—See Zumtobel Group AG; *Int'l*, pg. 8695
TRIDONIC AYDINLATMA TICARET LIMITED SIRKETI—See Zumtobel Group AG; *Int'l*, pg. 8695
TRIDONIC DEUTSCHLAND GMBH—See Zumtobel Group AG; *Int'l*, pg. 8696
TRIDONIC FRANCE SARL—See Zumtobel Group AG; *Int'l*, pg. 8696
TRIDONIC GMBH & CO KG—See Zumtobel Group AG; *Int'l*, pg. 8696
TRIDONIC IBERIA SL—See Zumtobel Group AG; *Int'l*, pg. 8696
TRIDONIC ITALIA SRL—See Zumtobel Group AG; *Int'l*, pg. 8696
TRIDONIC KOREA LLC—See Zumtobel Group AG; *Int'l*, pg. 8696
TRIDONIC (MALAYSIA) SDN. BHD.—See Zumtobel Group AG; *Int'l*, pg. 8695
TRIDONIC (ME) FZE—See Zumtobel Group AG; *Int'l*, pg. 8695
TRIDONIC PORTUGAL UNIPESSOA LDA—See Zumtobel Group AG; *Int'l*, pg. 8696
TRIDONIC SA (PROPRIETARY) LIMITED—See Zumtobel Group AG; *Int'l*, pg. 8696
TRIDONIC (S.E.A.) PTE. LTD.—See Zumtobel Group AG; *Int'l*, pg. 8695
TRIDONIC (SHANGHAI) CO. LTD.—See Zumtobel Group AG; *Int'l*, pg. 8695
TRIDONIC UK LTD.—See Zumtobel Group AG; *Int'l*, pg. 8696
TRIDON INC.—See TruArc Partners, L.P.; *U.S. Private*, pg. 4245
TRIDYNE PROCESS SYSTEMS, INC.; *U.S. Private*, pg. 4230
TRIEAGLE ENERGY LP—See Vistra Corp.; *U.S. Public*, pg. 2306
TRI-ED DISTRIBUTION INC.—See WESCO International, Inc.; *U.S. Public*, pg. 2351

TRI-ED PUERTO RICO LTD. INC.—See WESCO International, Inc.; *U.S. Public*, pg. 2351
TRI-ELECTRONICS INC.; *U.S. Private*, pg. 4222
TRIENA INVESTMENTS PUBLIC COMPANY LTD—See SFS Group Public Company Limited; *Int'l*, pg. 6740
TRIENDA HOLDINGS, LLC—See Kruger Brown Holdings, LLC; *U.S. Private*, pg. 2353
TRI ENGINEERING, LTD.—See Sumitomo Riko Company Limited; *Int'l*, pg. 7298
TRIENT, LLC—See Audax Group, Limited Partnership; *U.S. Private*, pg. 387
TRIER & COMPANY; *U.S. Private*, pg. 4230
TRIERER WALZWERK GMBH—See Tata Sons Limited; *Int'l*, pg. 7473
TRIERWEILER CONSTRUCTION & SUPPLY CO. INC.; *U.S. Private*, pg. 4230
TRIESSE LIMITED; *Int'l*, pg. 7921
TRIESTA SCIENCES, INC.—See Healthcare Global Enterprises Limited; *Int'l*, pg. 3304
TRI-EXCELLENCE, INC.—See Gulfside Supply Inc.; *U.S. Private*, pg. 1817
TRIFACTA GMBH—See Clearlake Capital Group, L.P.; *U.S. Private*, pg. 933
TRIFACTA GMBH—See Insight Venture Management, LLC; *U.S. Private*, pg. 2087
TRIFACTA, INC.—See Clearlake Capital Group, L.P.; *U.S. Private*, pg. 933
TRIFACTA, INC.—See Insight Venture Management, LLC; *U.S. Private*, pg. 2087
TRIFACTOR LLC—See Air Transport Services Group, Inc.; *U.S. Public*, pg. 67
TRIFA LAMPS, GERMANY GMBH—See Suprajit Engineering Limited; *Int'l*, pg. 7340
TRIFAST PLC; *Int'l*, pg. 7921
TRIFAST SYSTEMS LTD—See Trifast plc; *Int'l*, pg. 7921
TRIFECTA GOLD LTD.; *Int'l*, pg. 7921
TRIFECTA MULTIMEDIA, LLC—See Leonard Green & Partners, L.P.; *U.S. Private*, pg. 2430
TRIFECTA TECHNOLOGIES, INC.; *U.S. Private*, pg. 4230
TRIFFID INVESTMENTS PTY LTD—See Brickworks Limited; *Int'l*, pg. 1152
THE TRIFFID PTY. LTD.—See Live Nation Entertainment, Inc.; *U.S. Public*, pg. 1331
TRIFLO INTERNATIONAL, INC.; *U.S. Private*, pg. 4230
TRIFOIL IMAGING—See Psilos Group Managers, LLC; *U.S. Private*, pg. 3297
TRI-FORCE CONSULTING SERVICES, INC.; *U.S. Private*, pg. 4222
TRIFORCE CORPORATION—See Mitsuuroko Group Holdings Co., Ltd.; *Int'l*, pg. 4994
TRI-FORD INC.; *U.S. Private*, pg. 4222
TRI-FROST CORPORATION—See Cullen/Frost Bankers, Inc.; *U.S. Public*, pg. 604
TRIFUSION, LP; *U.S. Private*, pg. 4230
TRIGA COLOR, A.S.—See PPG Industries, Inc.; *U.S. Public*, pg. 1710
TRI-GAS & OIL CO. INC.; *U.S. Private*, pg. 4222
TRIGATE CAPITAL, LLC; *U.S. Private*, pg. 4230
TRIGEM COMPUTER, INC.; *Int'l*, pg. 7921
TRIG ENGINEERING LIMITED—See Ensinger GmbH; *Int'l*, pg. 2448
TRIGEN LABORATORIES, LLC—See RVL Pharmaceuticals plc; *U.S. Public*, pg. 1827
TRI-GEN PHARMA INT'L (PVT) LTD.—See Tasly Pharmaceutical Group Co., Ltd.; *Int'l*, pg. 7465
TRIGGER APPARELS LIMITED—See KG DENIM LIMITED; *Int'l*, pg. 4148
TRIGGER COMMUNICATION & DESIGN LTD.; *Int'l*, pg. 7921
TRIGGER POINT TECHNOLOGIES; *U.S. Private*, pg. 4230
TRIGG LABORATORIES, INC.; *U.S. Private*, pg. 4230
TRIGG MINERALS LIMITED; *Int'l*, pg. 7921
TRIGIANT GROUP LIMITED; *Int'l*, pg. 7921
TRIGINTA CAPITAL; *Int'l*, pg. 7921
TRIGLA LTD.—See Endress+Hauser (International) Holding AG; *Int'l*, pg. 2409
TRIGLAV AVTOSERVIS D.O.O.—See Zavarovalnica Triglav, d.d.; *Int'l*, pg. 8626
TRIGLAV AVTOSERVIS D.O.O.—See Zavarovalnica Triglav, d.d.; *Int'l*, pg. 8626
TRIGLAV DRUZBA ZA UPRAVLJANJE, D.O.O.—See Zavarovalnica Triglav, d.d.; *Int'l*, pg. 8626
TRIGLAV INT, D.O.O.—See Zavarovalnica Triglav, d.d.; *Int'l*, pg. 8626
TRIGLAV KRAJINA KOPAONIK A.D.—See Zavarovalnica Triglav, d.d.; *Int'l*, pg. 8626
TRIGLAV NALOZBE, FINANCNA DRUZBA D.D.—See Zavarovalnica Triglav, d.d.; *Int'l*, pg. 8626
TRIGLAV NETHERLANDS B.V.—See Zavarovalnica Triglav, d.d.; *Int'l*, pg. 8626
TRIGLAV OSIGURANJE, A.D.O., BEOGRAD—See Zavarovalnica Triglav, d.d.; *Int'l*, pg. 8626
TRIGLAV OSIGURANJE, D.D., SARAJEVO—See Zavarovalnica Triglav, d.d.; *Int'l*, pg. 8626
TRIGLAV OSIGURANJE, D.D.; *Int'l*, pg. 7921
TRIGLAV OSIGURANJE D.D.—See Zavarovalnica Triglav, d.d.; *Int'l*, pg. 8626
TRIGLAV OSIGURUVANE AD; *Int'l*, pg. 7921

TRIGLAV OSIGURUVANJE AD—See Zavarovalnica Triglav, d.d.; *Int'l*, pg. 8626
TRIGLAV OSIGURUVANJE A.D.—See Zavarovalnica Triglav, d.d.; *Int'l*, pg. 8626
TRIGLAV OSIGURUVANJE ZIVOT A.D.—See Zavarovalnica Triglav, d.d.; *Int'l*, pg. 8626
TRIGLAV PENZIJSKI FONDOVI A.D.—See Zavarovalnica Triglav, d.d.; *Int'l*, pg. 8626
TRIGLAV PENZISKO DRUSTVO A.D.—See Zavarovalnica Triglav, d.d.; *Int'l*, pg. 8627
TRIGLAV, POKOJNINSKA DRUZBA D.D.—See Zavarovalnica Triglav, d.d.; *Int'l*, pg. 8627
TRIGLAV POKOKNINSKA DRUZBA DD.—See Zavarovalnica Triglav, d.d.; *Int'l*, pg. 8627
TRIGLAV SAVJETOVANJE D.O.O.—See Zavarovalnica Triglav, d.d.; *Int'l*, pg. 8626
TRIGLAV SKLADI D.O.O.—See Zavarovalnica Triglav, d.d.; *Int'l*, pg. 8626
TRIGLAV SVETOVANJE, D.O.O.—See Zavarovalnica Triglav, d.d.; *Int'l*, pg. 8626
TRIGLAV, UPRAVLJANJE NEPREMICNIN D.O.O.—See Zavarovalnica Triglav, d.d.; *Int'l*, pg. 8627
TRIGLAV, ZDRAVSTVENA DEJAVNOST D.O.O.—See Zavarovalnica Triglav, d.d.; *Int'l*, pg. 8627
TRIGLAV, ZDRAVSTVENA ZAVAROVALNICA D.D.—See Zavarovalnica Triglav, d.d.; *Int'l*, pg. 8627
TRI GLOBAL ENERGY LLC—See Enbridge Inc.; *Int'l*, pg. 2397
TRIGLORY (H.K.) LIMITED—See Heng Tai Consumables Group Limited; *Int'l*, pg. 3345
TRIGOLD HOLDINGS LTD.; *Int'l*, pg. 7922
TRIGON INTERNATIONAL LLC—See NN, Inc.; *U.S. Public*, pg. 1531
TRIGON METALS, INC.; *Int'l*, pg. 7922
TRIGON PROPERTY DEVELOPMENT AS; *Int'l*, pg. 7922
TRIGO SAS—See Ardian SAS; *Int'l*, pg. 556
TRIGREEN EQUIPMENT LLC; *U.S. Private*, pg. 4231
TRI GREEN TRACTOR, LLC—See TTG Equipment, LLC; *U.S. Private*, pg. 4254
TRI-G TECHNOLOGIES SDN. BHD.—See Nexgram Holdings Berhad; *Int'l*, pg. 5244
TRIGYN TECHNOLOGIES, INC.—See Trigyn Technologies Limited; *Int'l*, pg. 7922
TRIGYN TECHNOLOGIES, INC.—See Trigyn Technologies Limited; *Int'l*, pg. 7922
TRIGYN TECHNOLOGIES LIMITED; *Int'l*, pg. 7922
TRIHEALTH INC.—See Catholic Health Initiatives; *U.S. Private*, pg. 790
TRIHEDRAL UK LIMITED—See Delta Electronics, Inc.; *Int'l*, pg. 2018
TRI HOSE SALES, LTD.—See Sumitomo Riko Company Limited; *Int'l*, pg. 7298
TRIHYDRO CORPORATION; *U.S. Private*, pg. 4231
TRI INTERNATIONAL COMPANY—See Tootsie Roll Industries, Inc.; *U.S. Public*, pg. 2163
TRI INTERNATIONAL, INC.—See Tootsie Roll Industries, Inc.; *U.S. Public*, pg. 2163
TRIIS, INC.; *Int'l*, pg. 7922
TRIIS INTERNATIONAL CO., LTD.—See TRiiS, Inc.; *Int'l*, pg. 7922
TRI-JAY TIRE DISTRIBUTORS INC.; *U.S. Private*, pg. 4222
TRIKEENAN TILEWORK, INC.—See Elgin-Butler Brick Company; *U.S. Private*, pg. 1359
TRI-K INDUSTRIES, INC.—See Galaxy Surfactants Limited; *Int'l*, pg. 2872
TRI-K INDUSTRIES - PROTEINS DIV—See Galaxy Surfactants Limited; *Int'l*, pg. 2872
TRIKOTAZA PELISTER AD; *Int'l*, pg. 7922
TRILAB ADVANCED SOLUTIONS B.V.—See IEX Group N.V.; *Int'l*, pg. 3598
TRILAND METALS AMERICAS INC.—See Mitsubishi Corporation; *Int'l*, pg. 4943
TRILAND METALS LTD.—See Mitsubishi Corporation; *Int'l*, pg. 4943
TRILAND METALS SINGAPORE PTE. LTD.—See Mitsubishi Corporation; *Int'l*, pg. 4943
TRILAND METALS TOKYO LTD.—See Mitsubishi Corporation; *Int'l*, pg. 4943
TRILAND USA INC.—See Mitsubishi Corporation; *Int'l*, pg. 4943
TRILANTIC CAPITAL MANAGEMENT L.P.; *U.S. Private*, pg. 4231
TRILANTIC CAPITAL PARTNERS LLP—See Trilantic Capital Management L.P.; *U.S. Private*, pg. 4231
TRILBY MISSO LAWYERS LIMITED—See Allegro Funds Pty. Ltd.; *Int'l*, pg. 336
TRILBY TRADING LIMITED—See Endless LLP; *Int'l*, pg. 2403
TRILEGIANT CORPORATION—See JPMorgan Chase & Co.; *U.S. Public*, pg. 1210
TRILIANCE POLYMERS LTD; *Int'l*, pg. 7922
TRI-LIFT INC.; *U.S. Private*, pg. 4222
TRILINC GLOBAL IMPACT FUND, LLC; *U.S. Public*, pg. 2189
TRI-LINE CARRIERS LP—See TFI International Inc.; *Int'l*, pg. 7586
TRI-LINE DISPOSAL INC.—See BC Partners LLP; *Int'l*, pg. 924

TRILINC GLOBAL IMPACT FUND, LLC

TRILINK BIOTECHNOLOGIES, INC.—See Maravai Life-Sciences Holdings, Inc.; *U.S. Public*, pg. 1364
TRILINK ENERGY, INC.; *U.S. Private*, pg. 4231
TRILITERAL LLC—See Atlas Holdings, LLC; *U.S. Private*, pg. 377
TRILIX S.R.L.—See Tata Motors Limited; *Int'l*, pg. 7468
TRILLACORPE CONSTRUCTION; *U.S. Private*, pg. 4231
TRILLIANT INCORPORATED; *U.S. Private*, pg. 4231
TRILLIANT SURGICAL, LTD.—See Envois Corporation; *U.S. Public*, pg. 772
TRILLION DEVELOPMENT CO LTD—See AP (Thailand) Public Company Limited; *Int'l*, pg. 499
TRILLION ENERGY INTERNATIONAL INC.; *Int'l*, pg. 7922
TRILLIUM ACQUISITION CORP.; *Int'l*, pg. 7922
TRILLIUM ASSET MANAGEMENT, LLC—See Perpetual Limited; *Int'l*, pg. 5812
TRILLIUM ASSET MANAGEMENT UK LIMITED—See Perpetual Limited; *Int'l*, pg. 5812
TRILLIUM COMMUNITY HEALTH PLAN, INC.—See Centene Corporation; *U.S. Public*, pg. 471
TRILLIUM CORPORATION; *U.S. Private*, pg. 4231
TRILLIUM FAMILY SERVICES; *U.S. Private*, pg. 4231
TRILLIUM HOLDINGS LIMITED—See The William Pears Group of Companies Limited; *Int'l*, pg. 7701
TRILLIUM SOFTWARE, INC.—See Harte Hanks, Inc.; *U.S. Public*, pg. 986
TRILLIUM SOLUTIONS GROUP, INC.—See Element 78 LLC; *U.S. Private*, pg. 1357
TRILLIUM THERAPEUTICS INC.—See Pfizer Inc.; *U.S. Public*, pg. 1683
TRILLIUM TRANSPORTATION FUELS, LLC—See Love's Travel Stops & Country Stores, Inc.; *U.S. Private*, pg. 2501
TRILOGIC OUTDOOR; *U.S. Private*, pg. 4231
TRILOGIQ AUSTRALIA PTY LTD—See Trilogiq SA; *Int'l*, pg. 7922
TRILOGIQ BENELUX BVBA—See Trilogiq SA; *Int'l*, pg. 7922
TRILOGIQ CZ S.R.O—See Trilogiq SA; *Int'l*, pg. 7922
TRILOGIQ DEUTSCHLAND GMBH—See Trilogiq SA; *Int'l*, pg. 7922
TRILOGIQ DO BRASIL LTDA—See Trilogiq SA; *Int'l*, pg. 7922
TRILOGIQ HUNGARIA KFT.—See Trilogiq SA; *Int'l*, pg. 7922
TRILOGIQ IBERIA SL—See Trilogiq SA; *Int'l*, pg. 7922
TRILOGIQ INDIA MODULAR SYSTEM PRIVATE LIMITED—See Trilogiq SA; *Int'l*, pg. 7922
TRILOGIQ ITALIA SRL—See Trilogiq SA; *Int'l*, pg. 7922
TRILOGIQ MAROC—See Trilogiq SA; *Int'l*, pg. 7922
TRILOGIQ MEXICO, S.A DE C.V—See Trilogiq SA; *Int'l*, pg. 7922
TRILOGIQ POLAND SP. Z O.O.—See Trilogiq SA; *Int'l*, pg. 7922
TRILOGIQ ROMANIA SRL—See Trilogiq SA; *Int'l*, pg. 7922
TRILOGIQ RUSSIA—See Trilogiq SA; *Int'l*, pg. 7922
TRILOGIQ SA LTD—See Trilogiq SA; *Int'l*, pg. 7922
TRILOGIQ SA; *Int'l*, pg. 7922
TRILOGIQ SLOVAKIA S.R.O—See Trilogiq SA; *Int'l*, pg. 7922
TRILOGIQ SWEDEN AB—See Trilogiq SA; *Int'l*, pg. 7922
TRILOGIQ USA CORP.—See Trilogiq SA; *Int'l*, pg. 7922
TRI LOGITECH, LTD.—See Sumitomo Riko Company Limited; *Int'l*, pg. 7298
TRILOGY AI CORP.; *Int'l*, pg. 7923
TRILOGY CAPITAL GROUP, LLC; *U.S. Private*, pg. 4232
TRILOGY COMMUNICATIONS, INC; *U.S. Private*, pg. 4232
TRILOGY ENTERPRISES, INC.—See ESW Capital, LLC; *U.S. Private*, pg. 1430
TRILOGY EYE MEDICAL GROUP INC.; *U.S. Private*, pg. 4232
TRILOGY FUNDS MANAGEMENT LIMITED—See Balmain Corp.; *Int'l*, pg. 810
TRILOGY GLOBAL ADVISORS INTERNATIONAL LLP—See Affiliated Managers Group, Inc.; *U.S. Public*, pg. 56
TRILOGY GLOBAL ADVISORS, LP—See Affiliated Managers Group, Inc.; *U.S. Public*, pg. 56
TRILOGY HEALTH SERVICES LLC—See American Healthcare Investors LLC; *U.S. Private*, pg. 236
TRILOGY HEALTH SERVICES LLC—See DigitalBridge Group, Inc.; *U.S. Public*, pg. 665
TRILOGY HEALTH SERVICES LLC—See Griffin Capital Corporation; *U.S. Private*, pg. 1787
TRILOGY INTERNATIONAL LIMITED—See CITIC Group Corporation; *Int'l*, pg. 1620
TRILOGY INTERNATIONAL PARTNERS INC.—See SG Enterprises II, LLC; *U.S. Private*, pg. 3622
TRILOGY INTERNATIONAL PARTNERS LLC—See SG Enterprises II, LLC; *U.S. Private*, pg. 3622
TRILOGY METALS INC.; *Int'l*, pg. 7923
TRILOGY RETAIL ENTERPRISES L.P.; *Int'l*, pg. 7923
TRILOGY RISK SPECIALISTS, INC.—See Regions Financial Corporation; *U.S. Public*, pg. 1776
TRILOGY TECHNOLOGIES LIMITED—See BC Partners LLP; *Int'l*, pg. 925

TRILOQ TURQUIE METAL VE KINYA—See Trilogiq SA; *Int'l*, pg. 7922
TRILUX FRANCE SAS; *Int'l*, pg. 7922
TRIMACO LLC—See Trimaco LLC; *U.S. Private*, pg. 4232
TRIMACO LLC; *U.S. Private*, pg. 4232
TRIMACO LLC—See Trimaco LLC; *U.S. Private*, pg. 4232
TRIMAC TRANSPORTATION CENTRAL INC.—See Trimac Transportation Ltd.; *Int'l*, pg. 7923
TRIMAC TRANSPORTATION EAST INC.—See Trimac Transportation Ltd.; *Int'l*, pg. 7923
TRIMAC TRANSPORTATION INC.—See Trimac Transportation Ltd.; *Int'l*, pg. 7923
TRIMAC TRANSPORTATION LTD.; *Int'l*, pg. 7923
TRIMAC TRANSPORTATION SERVICES INC.—See Trimac Transportation Ltd.; *Int'l*, pg. 7923
TRIMAC TRANSPORTATION SERVICES—See Trimac Transportation Ltd.; *Int'l*, pg. 7923
TRIMAC TRANSPORTATION SERVICES (WESTERN), INC.—See Trimac Transportation Ltd.; *Int'l*, pg. 7923
TRIMAC TRANSPORTATION SOUTH INC.—See Trimac Transportation Ltd.; *Int'l*, pg. 7923
TRIMAG DIE CASTINGS—See Spectra Premium Industries Inc.; *Int'l*, pg. 7130
TRIMAN INDUSTRIES, INC.—See AE Industrial Partners, LP; *U.S. Private*, pg. 112
TRIMARAN CAPITAL PARTNERS, LLC; *U.S. Private*, pg. 4232
TRIMAR CONSTRUCTION, INC.; *U.S. Private*, pg. 4232
TRI-MARINE FISH COMPANY—See Tri-Star Marine International, Inc.; *U.S. Private*, pg. 4223
TRIMARK DIGITAL, LLC; *U.S. Private*, pg. 4232
TRIMARK MARLIN INC.—See Warburg Pincus LLC; *U.S. Private*, pg. 4440
TRIMARK RAYGAL INC—See Warburg Pincus LLC; *U.S. Private*, pg. 4440
TRIMARK ROBERTCLARK—See Warburg Pincus LLC; *U.S. Private*, pg. 4440
TRIMARK SPORTSWEAR GROUP INC.—See Charlesbank Capital Partners, LLC; *U.S. Private*, pg. 856
TRIMARK SS KEMP—See Warburg Pincus LLC; *U.S. Private*, pg. 4440
TRIMARK USA LLC—See Warburg Pincus LLC; *U.S. Private*, pg. 4440
TRIMAS CORPORATION; *U.S. Public*, pg. 2189
TRIMASTER MANUFACTURING, INC.—See GenNx360 Capital Partners, L.P.; *U.S. Private*, pg. 1672
TRIMAX BUILDING PRODUCTS; *U.S. Private*, pg. 4232
TRIMAX STEEL INC.; *Int'l*, pg. 7923
TRIMBLE AB—See Trimble, Inc.; *U.S. Public*, pg. 2191
TRIMBLE BRASIL SOLUCOES LTDA—See Trimble, Inc.; *U.S. Public*, pg. 2192
TRIMBLE CORVALLIS—See Trimble, Inc.; *U.S. Public*, pg. 2192
TRIMBLE DAYTON—See Trimble, Inc.; *U.S. Public*, pg. 2192
TRIMBLE DBO INFORMATION TECHNOLOGY (SHANGHAI) CO, LTD.—See Trimble, Inc.; *U.S. Public*, pg. 2192
TRIMBLE ELECTRONIC PRODUCTS (SHANGHAI) CO., LTD.—See Trimble, Inc.; *U.S. Public*, pg. 2192
TRIMBLE EUROPE B.V.—See Trimble, Inc.; *U.S. Public*, pg. 2192
TRIMBLE FORESTRY CORPORATION—See Trimble, Inc.; *U.S. Public*, pg. 2192
TRIMBLE FORESTRY GMBH—See Trimble, Inc.; *U.S. Public*, pg. 2192
TRIMBLE FORESTRY LTDA—See Trimble, Inc.; *U.S. Public*, pg. 2192
TRIMBLE FRANCE S.A.S.—See Trimble, Inc.; *U.S. Public*, pg. 2192
TRIMBLE GERMANY GMBH—See Trimble, Inc.; *U.S. Public*, pg. 2192
TRIMBLE GMBH—See Trimble, Inc.; *U.S. Public*, pg. 2192
TRIMBLE HOLDINGS GMBH—See Trimble, Inc.; *U.S. Public*, pg. 2192
TRIMBLE HUNGARY KFT—See Trimble, Inc.; *U.S. Public*, pg. 2192
TRIMBLE, INC.; *U.S. Public*, pg. 2189
TRIMBLE INTERNATIONAL (SCHWEIZ) SEESTRASSE SA—See Trimble, Inc.; *U.S. Public*, pg. 2192
TRIMBLE ITALIA SRL—See Trimble, Inc.; *U.S. Public*, pg. 2192
TRIMBLE JEAN GMBH—See Trimble, Inc.; *U.S. Public*, pg. 2192
TRIMBLE KAISERSLAUTERN GMBH—See Trimble, Inc.; *U.S. Public*, pg. 2192
TRIMBLE LOADRITE AUCKLAND LIMITED—See Trimble, Inc.; *U.S. Public*, pg. 2192
TRIMBLE LOADRITE CHILE SPA—See Trimble, Inc.; *U.S. Public*, pg. 2192
TRIMBLE MEP—See Trimble, Inc.; *U.S. Public*, pg. 2192
TRIMBLE MEXICO S DE RL—See Trimble, Inc.; *U.S. Public*, pg. 2192
TRIMBLE MOBILE SOLUTIONS, INC.—See Trimble, Inc.; *U.S. Public*, pg. 2192
TRIMBLE MOBILITY SOLUTIONS INDIA LIMITED—See Trimble, Inc.; *U.S. Public*, pg. 2192
TRIMBLE MRM—See Trimble, Inc.; *U.S. Public*, pg. 2192

CORPORATE AFFILIATIONS

TRIMBLE NANTES S.A.S—See Trimble, Inc.; *U.S. Public*, pg. 2192
TRIMBLE NAVIGATION AUSTRALIA PTY. LIMITED—See Trimble, Inc.; *U.S. Public*, pg. 2192
TRIMBLE NAVIGATION CHILE LIMITADA—See Trimble, Inc.; *U.S. Public*, pg. 2192
TRIMBLE NAVIGATION IBERICA S.L.—See Trimble, Inc.; *U.S. Public*, pg. 2192
TRIMBLE NAVIGATION INDIA PVT LIMITED—See Trimble, Inc.; *U.S. Public*, pg. 2192
TRIMBLE NAVIGATION LTD.—See Trimble, Inc.; *U.S. Public*, pg. 2192
TRIMBLE NAVIGATION NEW ZEALAND LIMITED—See Trimble, Inc.; *U.S. Public*, pg. 2192
TRIMBLE NAVIGATION SINGAPORE PTE LIMITED—See Trimble, Inc.; *U.S. Public*, pg. 2192
TRIMBLE NV—See Trimble, Inc.; *U.S. Public*, pg. 2192
TRIMBLE POLAND SP. Z.O.O.—See Trimble, Inc.; *U.S. Public*, pg. 2192
TRIMBLE RAILWAY LIMITED—See Trimble, Inc.; *U.S. Public*, pg. 2192
TRIMBLE RAILWAYS GMBH—See Trimble, Inc.; *U.S. Public*, pg. 2192
TRIMBLE RUS LLC—See Trimble, Inc.; *U.S. Public*, pg. 2192
TRIMBLE SOLUTIONS AARHUS A/S—See Trimble, Inc.; *U.S. Public*, pg. 2192
TRIMBLE SOLUTIONS FRANCE SARL—See Trimble, Inc.; *U.S. Public*, pg. 2192
TRIMBLE SOLUTIONS GOTHENBURG AB—See Trimble, Inc.; *U.S. Public*, pg. 2193
TRIMBLE SOLUTIONS INDIA PVT. LTD.—See Trimble, Inc.; *U.S. Public*, pg. 2193
TRIMBLE SOLUTIONS KOREA CO., LTD.—See Trimble, Inc.; *U.S. Public*, pg. 2193
TRIMBLE SOLUTIONS MALAYSIA SDN BHD—See Trimble, Inc.; *U.S. Public*, pg. 2193
TRIMBLE SOLUTIONS OY—See Trimble, Inc.; *U.S. Public*, pg. 2193
TRIMBLE SOLUTIONS SANDVIKA AS—See Trimble, Inc.; *U.S. Public*, pg. 2193
TRIMBLE SOLUTIONS SEA PTE. LTD.—See Trimble, Inc.; *U.S. Public*, pg. 2193
TRIMBLE SOLUTIONS SWEDEN AB—See Trimble, Inc.; *U.S. Public*, pg. 2193
TRIMBLE SOLUTIONS UK LTD—See Trimble, Inc.; *U.S. Public*, pg. 2193
TRIMBLE SOLUTIONS USA INC.—See Trimble, Inc.; *U.S. Public*, pg. 2193
TRIMBLE SOUTH AFRICA DISTRIBUTION HOLDINGS PTY LTD.—See Trimble, Inc.; *U.S. Public*, pg. 2193
TRIMBLE SWEDEN A.B.—See Trimble, Inc.; *U.S. Public*, pg. 2193
TRIMBLE TERRASAT GMBH—See Trimble, Inc.; *U.S. Public*, pg. 2192
TRIMBLE TRAILBLAZER GMBH—See Trimble, Inc.; *U.S. Public*, pg. 2193
TRIMBLE TRANSPORTATION ENTERPRISE SOLUTIONS INC.—See Trimble, Inc.; *U.S. Public*, pg. 2193
TRIMBLE UK LIMITED—See Trimble, Inc.; *U.S. Public*, pg. 2193
TRIM CO., LTD.—See Medipal Holdings Corporation; *Int'l*, pg. 4779
TRIMCO MILLWORK—See Hoff Companies, Inc; *U.S. Private*, pg. 1959
TRI-MEATS INC.; *U.S. Private*, pg. 4222
TRIMECH SOLUTIONS, LLC—See Sentinel Capital Partners, L.L.C.; *U.S. Private*, pg. 3609
TRIMED HELLAS S.A—See Wright Medical Group N.V.; *Int'l*, pg. 8495
TRIMEDIA K.K.—See ad-comm Co., Ltd.; *Int'l*, pg. 123
TRIMEDX INDIA PVT. LTD.—See Ascension Health Alliance; *U.S. Private*, pg. 346
TRIMEDX INTERNATIONAL, LLC—See Ascension Health Alliance; *U.S. Private*, pg. 346
TRIMEDX, LLC—See Ascension Health Alliance; *U.S. Private*, pg. 346
TRIMEDYNE, INC.; *U.S. Private*, pg. 4232
TRIM ELECTRIC MACHINERY CO., LTD.—See Nihon Trim Co., Ltd.; *Int'l*, pg. 5288
TRIMETALS MINING INC. - CHILE OFFICE—See Gold Springs Resource Corp.; *Int'l*, pg. 3026
TRIMET ALUMINIUM SE; *Int'l*, pg. 7923
TRIMET AUTOMOTIVE SOMMERDA GMBH & CO. KG—See TRIMET Aluminium SE; *Int'l*, pg. 7923
TRI METEX, LTD.—See Sumitomo Riko Company Limited; *Int'l*, pg. 7298
TRIMET FRANCE SAS—See TRIMET Aluminium SE; *Int'l*, pg. 7923
TRIMET ITALIA S.R.L.—See TRIMET Aluminium SE; *Int'l*, pg. 7923
TRI-MET; *U.S. Private*, pg. 4222
TRIMEVAC PTY. LTD.—See WSP Global, Inc.; *Int'l*, pg. 8497
TRIMEX GMBH—See Innova Capital Sp. z o.o.; *Int'l*, pg. 3711
TRIMEX TRANSIT IMPORT EXPORT CARL NIELSEN GMBH & CO. KG—See REWE-Zentral-Aktiengesellschaft; *Int'l*, pg. 6315

COMPANY NAME INDEX

TRIMFIT COMPANY LIMITED—See Trimfit, Inc.; *U.S. Private*, pg. 4232
TRIMFIT, INC.; *U.S. Private*, pg. 4232
TRIMFOOT CO., LLC; *U.S. Private*, pg. 4232
TRIMGEN CORPORATION; *U.S. Private*, pg. 4232
TRIM (GUANGZHOU) WATER & HEALTH CO., LTD.—See Nihon Trim Co., Ltd.; *Int'l*, pg. 5288
TRIMIL SA—See Giorgio Armani S.p.A.; *Int'l*, pg. 2978
TRIMIN CAPITAL CORP.; *Int'l*, pg. 7923
TRI-M, INC.—See DAIICHIKOUSHO CO., LTD.; *Int'l*, pg. 1930
TRIMIN SYSTEMS INC.; *U.S. Private*, pg. 4232
TRIM JOIST CORPORATION—See Sanford Resources Corporation; *U.S. Private*, pg. 3546
TRIMLITE LLC—See Wynnchurch Capital, L.P.; *U.S. Private*, pg. 4578
TRIM NUTRITION INC.; *U.S. Private*, pg. 4232
TRIMO BULGARIA OOD—See Innova Capital Sp. z o.o.; *Int'l*, pg. 3711
TRI-MODAL DISTRIBUTION SERVICES; *U.S. Private*, pg. 4222
TRI-MODE SYSTEM (M) BHD; *Int'l*, pg. 7918
TRIMO, D.O.O.—See Innova Capital Sp. z o.o.; *Int'l*, pg. 3711
TRIMO-INZENJERING D.O.O.—See Innova Capital Sp. z o.o.; *Int'l*, pg. 3711
TRIMOLD LLC—See TS Tech Co Ltd; *Int'l*, pg. 7948
TRIMO MAGYARORSZAG KER. KEP.—See Innova Capital Sp. z o.o.; *Int'l*, pg. 3711
TRIMON INC.; *U.S. Private*, pg. 4232
TRIMONT, D.O.O.—See Innova Capital Sp. z o.o.; *Int'l*, pg. 3711
TRIMONT MFG. INC.—See TS Tech Co Ltd; *Int'l*, pg. 7948
TRIMONT REAL ESTATE ADVISORS LLC—See Varde Partners, Inc.; *U.S. Private*, pg. 4346
TRIMO POLSKA SP.Z.O.O.—See Innova Capital Sp. z o.o.; *Int'l*, pg. 3711
TRIM OPTIMAL HEALTH CO., LTD—See Nihon Trim Co., Ltd.; *Int'l*, pg. 5288
TRIMO UK LTD.—See Innova Capital Sp. z o.o.; *Int'l*, pg. 3711
TRIM PARTS, INC.—See Dubin Clark & Company, Inc.; *U.S. Private*, pg. 1283
TRIMPROOF LIMITED; *Int'l*, pg. 7923
TRIMSEAL PLASTICS LTD.; *Int'l*, pg. 7923
TRIMSEAL USA INC.—See Trimseal Plastics Ltd.; *Int'l*, pg. 7923
TRIMSOL BRAZIL, LTDA.—See DUAL Co Ltd; *Int'l*, pg. 2217
TRIMSOL CZECH REPUBLIC S.R.O.—See DUAL Co Ltd; *Int'l*, pg. 2217
TRIMSOL CZECH S.R.O.—See DUAL Co Ltd; *Int'l*, pg. 2217
TRIMSOL ROMANIA SRL—See DUAL Co Ltd; *Int'l*, pg. 2217
TRIMSOL SP. Z O.O.—See DUAL Co Ltd; *Int'l*, pg. 2217
TRIMS UNLIMITED; *U.S. Private*, pg. 4232
TRIM SYSTEMS OPERATING CORP.—See Commercial Vehicle Group, Inc.; *U.S. Public*, pg. 547
TRIMTABS INVESTMENT RESEARCH, INC.—See Informa plc; *Int'l*, pg. 3693
TRIMTEX CO. INC.; *U.S. Private*, pg. 4232
TRIMUDA NUANSA CITRA PT; *Int'l*, pg. 7923
TRIMURTHI LIMITED; *Int'l*, pg. 7923
TRINAMIC, INC.—See Analog Devices, Inc.; *U.S. Public*, pg. 136
TRINAMIC MOTION CONTROL GMBH & CO. KG—See Analog Devices, Inc.; *U.S. Public*, pg. 136
TRINAMIX GMBH—See BASF SE; *Int'l*, pg. 885
TRINA SOLAR (AUSTRALIA) PTY LTD.—See Trina Solar Limited; *Int'l*, pg. 7924
TRINA SOLAR (CHANGZHOU) SCIENCE AND TECHNOLOGY CO., LTD.—See Trina Solar Limited; *Int'l*, pg. 7924
TRINA SOLAR ENERGY (SHANGHAI) CO., LTD.—See Trina Solar Limited; *Int'l*, pg. 7924
TRINA SOLAR (GERMANY) GMBH—See Trina Solar Limited; *Int'l*, pg. 7924
TRINA SOLAR (ITALY) S.R.L—See Trina Solar Limited; *Int'l*, pg. 7924
TRINA SOLAR (JAPAN) LIMITED—See Trina Solar Limited; *Int'l*, pg. 7924
TRINA SOLAR LIMITED; *Int'l*, pg. 7924
TRINA SOLAR (SCHWEIZ) AG—See Trina Solar Limited; *Int'l*, pg. 7924
TRINA SOLAR (SPAIN) S.L.U—See Trina Solar Limited; *Int'l*, pg. 7924
TRINA SOLAR (SWITZERLAND) LTD—See Trina Solar Limited; *Int'l*, pg. 7924
TRINA SOLAR (U.S.) INC.—See Trina Solar Limited; *Int'l*, pg. 7924
TRINCHERO FAMILY ESTATES; *U.S. Private*, pg. 4232
TRINEL C.A.—See Trabajos Industriales y Mecanicos, C.A.; *Int'l*, pg. 7885
TRINERGI AB—See Addtech AB; *Int'l*, pg. 135
TRINET - BRADENTON—See General Atlantic Service Company, L.P.; *U.S. Private*, pg. 1663
TRINET GROUP, INC.—See General Atlantic Service Company, L.P.; *U.S. Private*, pg. 1663

TRINETHRA INFRA VENTURES LIMITED; *Int'l*, pg. 7924
TRINET INDUSTRIES INC.—See SinSin Pharm.Co.,Ltd.,; *Int'l*, pg. 6956
TRINET INTERNET SOLUTIONS, INC.; *U.S. Private*, pg. 4232
TRINET INTERNET SOLUTIONS, INC.—See Trinet Internet Solutions, Inc.; *U.S. Private*, pg. 4232
TRI-NET LOGISTICS (ASIA) PTE. LTD.—See Mitsui & Co., Ltd.; *Int'l*, pg. 4980
TRINET LOGISTICS CO., LTD.—See Mitsui & Co., Ltd.; *Int'l*, pg. 4980
TRINET SYSTEMS, INC.—See American Securities LLC; *U.S. Private*, pg. 250
TRINFICO INVESTMENT GROUP; *Int'l*, pg. 7924
TRINIDAD AREA HEALTH ASSOCIATION; *U.S. Private*, pg. 4233
TRINIDAD/BENHAM CORP.—See Trinidad/Benham Holding Co; *U.S. Private*, pg. 4233
TRINIDAD/BENHAM HOLDING CO; *U.S. Private*, pg. 4233
TRINIDAD CEMENT LIMITED—See CEMEX, S.A.B. de C.V.; *Int'l*, pg. 1400
TRINIDAD COLOMBIA SAS—See Ensign Energy Services Inc.; *Int'l*, pg. 2447
TRINIDAD DISTILLERS LIMITED—See Angostura Holdings Limited; *Int'l*, pg. 463
TRINIDAD DRILLING LIMITED PARTNERSHIP—See Ensign Energy Services Inc.; *Int'l*, pg. 2447
TRINIDAD DRILLING LTD.—See Ensign Energy Services Inc.; *Int'l*, pg. 2447
TRINIDAD MATCH LIMITED—See ANSA McAL Limited; *Int'l*, pg. 477
TRINIDAD PUBLISHING COMPANY LIMITED—See ANSA McAL Limited; *Int'l*, pg. 477
TRINIDAD RESORT & CLUB, LLC—See Apex Oil Company, Inc.; *U.S. Private*, pg. 293
TRINIDAD & TOBAGO INSURANCE LIMITED—See ANSA McAL Limited; *Int'l*, pg. 477
TRINIDAD & TOBAGO STOCK EXCHANGE LIMITED; *Int'l*, pg. 7924
TRIN, INC.—See Tokai Rika Co., Ltd.; *Int'l*, pg. 7781
TRINISYS, LLC—See Novacap Management Inc.; *Int'l*, pg. 5453
TRINITAS PRIVATE EQUITY (PROPRIETARY) LIMITED; *Int'l*, pg. 7924
TRINITAS REGIONAL MEDICAL CENTER; *U.S. Private*, pg. 4233
TRINITE INC.; *U.S. Private*, pg. 4233
TRINITY ACQUISITION CORPORATION; *Int'l*, pg. 7924
TRINITY AIR MEDICAL, INC.—See Blade Air Mobility, Inc.; *U.S. Public*, pg. 361
TRINITY ARGENTINA S.R.L.—See Trinity Industries, Inc.; *U.S. Public*, pg. 2193
TRINITY BANK N.A; *U.S. Public*, pg. 2193
TRINITY BENEFIT ADVISORS, INC.—See The Baldwin Insurance Group, Inc.; *U.S. Public*, pg. 2036
TRINITY BIOTECH PLC; *Int'l*, pg. 7924
TRINITY BRANDS UK LIMITED—See Trinity Limited; *Int'l*, pg. 7925
TRINITY BUILDING & CONSTRUCTION MANAGEMENT CORP.; *U.S. Private*, pg. 4233
TRINITY CAPITAL CORPORATION—See Enterprise Financial Services Corp; *U.S. Public*, pg. 778
TRINITY CAPITAL CORP.; *U.S. Private*, pg. 4233
TRINITY CAPITAL, LLC—See Citizens Financial Group, Inc.; *U.S. Public*, pg. 506
TRINITYCARE L.L.C.—See Catholic Health Initiatives; *U.S. Private*, pg. 789
TRINITY CARPET BROKERS INC.; *U.S. Private*, pg. 4233
TRINITY CARPET INC.—See Trinity Carpet Brokers Inc.; *U.S. Private*, pg. 4233
TRINITY CO2 INVESTMENTS LLC—See Morgan Stanley; *U.S. Public*, pg. 1474
TRINITY COATING SYSTEMS (SHANGHAI) CO., LTD.—See Trinity Industrial Corporation; *Int'l*, pg. 7924
TRINITY COMMERCIAL SERVICES, INC.; *U.S. Private*, pg. 4233
TRINITY CONSTRUCTION MATERIALS, INC.—See Trinity Industries, Inc.; *U.S. Public*, pg. 2193
TRINITY CONSULTANTS, INC.—See Keystone Group, L.P.; *U.S. Private*, pg. 2299
TRINITY CONSULTING, INC.; *U.S. Private*, pg. 4233
TRINITY CONTAINERS, LLC—See Trinity Industries, Inc.; *U.S. Public*, pg. 2194
TRINITY CONTINUING CARE SERVICES—See Trinity Health Corporation; *U.S. Private*, pg. 4233
TRINITY CRYOGENICS, LLC—See Trinity Industries, Inc.; *U.S. Public*, pg. 2194
TRINITY DEFENSE LLC—See Unibail-Rodamco-Westfield SE; *Int'l*, pg. 8030
TRINITY ENVIRONMENTAL SERVICES, L.L.C; *U.S. Private*, pg. 4233
TRINITY EXPLORATION & PRODUCTION PLC—See Lease Operators Limited; *Int'l*, pg. 4435
TRINITY FOREST INDUSTRIES INC.; *U.S. Private*, pg. 4233
TRINITY FUNDS MANAGEMENT LIMITED—See Unity Pacific Group; *Int'l*, pg. 8076

TRINITY MANOR INC.

TRINITY GLASS INTERNATIONAL INC.; *U.S. Private*, pg. 4233
TRINITY GRAPHIC USA, INC.; *U.S. Private*, pg. 4233
TRINITY HARDWOOD DISTRIBUTORS, INC.—See Transom Capital Group, LLC; *U.S. Private*, pg. 4209
TRINITY HEADS, INC.—See Trinity Industries, Inc.; *U.S. Public*, pg. 2194
TRINITY HEALTH CORPORATION; *U.S. Private*, pg. 4233
TRINITY HEALTH GROUP, LTD.—See NAC, Inc.; *U.S. Private*, pg. 2829
TRINITY HEALTH OF NEW ENGLAND/USP SURGERY CENTERS, L.L.C.—See Tenet Healthcare Corporation; *U.S. Public*, pg. 2009
TRINITY HEALTH PLANS—See Trinity Health Corporation; *U.S. Public*, pg. 4234
TRINITY HEALTH SYSTEM INC.; *U.S. Private*, pg. 4234
TRINITY HEALTH SYSTEMS, INC.—See UnityPoint Health; *U.S. Private*, pg. 4303
TRINITY HIGHWAY LEASING, INC.—See Trinity Industries, Inc.; *U.S. Public*, pg. 2194
TRINITY HIGHWAY PRODUCTS, LLC—See Trinity Industries, Inc.; *U.S. Public*, pg. 2194
TRINITY HIGHWAY PRODUCTS—See Trinity Industries, Inc.; *U.S. Public*, pg. 2194
TRINITY HIGHWAY RENTALS, INC.—See Trinity Industries, Inc.; *U.S. Public*, pg. 2194
TRINITY HOMECARE LLC—See Walgreens Boots Alliance, Inc.; *U.S. Public*, pg. 2323
TRINITY HOSPICE OF TEXAS, LLC—See Apollo Global Management, Inc.; *U.S. Public*, pg. 158
TRINITY HUNT MANAGEMENT, L.P.; *U.S. Private*, pg. 4234
TRINITY INC.—See Hirata Corporation; *Int'l*, pg. 3404
TRINITY INDUSTRIAL CORPORATION - MIYOSHI PLANT—See Trinity Industrial Corporation; *Int'l*, pg. 7924
TRINITY INDUSTRIAL CORPORATION; *Int'l*, pg. 7924
TRINITY INDUSTRIAL CORPORATION - TOYOTA PLANT—See Trinity Industrial Corporation; *Int'l*, pg. 7924
TRINITY INDUSTRIES DE MEXICO, S. DE R.L. DE C.V.—See Trinity Industries, Inc.; *U.S. Public*, pg. 2194
TRINITY INDUSTRIES DE MEXICO—See Trinity Industries, Inc.; *U.S. Public*, pg. 2194
TRINITY INDUSTRIES, INC. - FORT WORTH—See Trinity Industries, Inc.; *U.S. Public*, pg. 2194
TRINITY INDUSTRIES, INC.; *U.S. Public*, pg. 2193
TRINITY INDUSTRIES LEASING COMPANY—See Trinity Industries, Inc.; *U.S. Public*, pg. 2194
TRINITY INDUSTRIES—See Trinity Industries, Inc.; *U.S. Public*, pg. 2194
TRINITY INDUSTRIES—See Trinity Industries, Inc.; *U.S. Public*, pg. 2194
TRINITY INDUSTRIES—See Trinity Industries, Inc.; *U.S. Public*, pg. 2194
TRINITY INDUSTRIES—See Trinity Industries, Inc.; *U.S. Public*, pg. 2194
TRINITY INDUSTRIES—See Trinity Industries, Inc.; *U.S. Public*, pg. 2194
TRINITY INDUSTRIES—See Trinity Industries, Inc.; *U.S. Public*, pg. 2194
TRINITY INDUSTRIES—See Trinity Industries, Inc.; *U.S. Public*, pg. 2194
TRINITY INDUSTRIES—See Trinity Industries, Inc.; *U.S. Public*, pg. 2194
TRINITY INSIGHT, LLC—See WILsquare Capital LLC; *U.S. Private*, pg. 4532
TRINITY LEAGUE INDIA LIMITED; *Int'l*, pg. 7924
TRINITY LIMITED; *Int'l*, pg. 7924
TRINITY LOGISTICS GROUP, INC.—See Trinity Industries, Inc.; *U.S. Public*, pg. 2194
TRINITY LOGISTICS INC.; *U.S. Private*, pg. 4235
TRINITY LOGISTICS—See Trinity Industries, Inc.; *U.S. Public*, pg. 2194
TRINITY LOGISTICS—See Trinity Industries, Inc.; *U.S. Public*, pg. 2194
TRINITY LOGISTICS—See Trinity Industries, Inc.; *U.S. Public*, pg. 2194
TRINITY MANOR INC.; *U.S. Private*, pg. 4235
TRINITY MERGER CORP.—See Waterfall Asset Management LLC; *U.S. Private*, pg. 4453
TRINITY MEYER UTILITY STRUCTURES, LLC—See Trinity Industries, Inc.; *U.S. Public*, pg. 2194
TRINITY MINING AND CONSTRUCTION EQUIPMENT, INC.—See Trinity Industries, Inc.; *U.S. Public*, pg. 2194
TRINITY MIRROR CHESHIRE LIMITED—See Reach PLC; *Int'l*, pg. 6231
TRINITY MIRROR DIGITAL RECRUITMENT LTD.—See Reach PLC; *Int'l*, pg. 6231
TRINITY MIRROR HUDDERSFIELD LTD.—See Reach PLC; *Int'l*, pg. 6231
TRINITY MIRROR MERSEYSIDE LIMITED—See Reach PLC; *Int'l*, pg. 6231
TRINITY MIRROR PRINTING (BLANTYRE) LIMITED—See Reach PLC; *Int'l*, pg. 6231
TRINITY MIRROR PRINTING (CARDIFF) LIMITED—See Reach PLC; *Int'l*, pg. 6231
TRINITY MIRROR PRINTING LIMITED—See Reach PLC; *Int'l*, pg. 6231

TRINITY MANOR INC.

TRINITY MIRROR PRINTING (MIDLANDS) LIMITED—See Reach PLC; *Int'l*, pg. 6231
TRINITY MIRROR PRINTING (OLDHAM) LIMITED—See Reach PLC; *Int'l*, pg. 6231
TRINITY MIRROR PRINTING (WATFORD) LIMITED—See Reach PLC; *Int'l*, pg. 6231
TRINITY MIRROR REGIONALS PLC—See Reach PLC; *Int'l*, pg. 6231
TRINITY MIRROR SOUTHERN LTD—See Reach PLC; *Int'l*, pg. 6231
TRINITY MRI LIMITED—See Integral Diagnostics Limited; *Int'l*, pg. 3730
TRINITY PACKAGING CORPORATION—See The Pritzker Group - Chicago, LLC; *U.S. Private*, pg. 4099
TRINITY PARK SURGERY CENTER—See HCA Healthcare, Inc.; *U.S. Public*, pg. 1013
TRINITY PARTNERS, LLC—See Kohlberg & Company, LLC; *U.S. Private*, pg. 2339
TRINITY PARTS & COMPONENTS, LLC—See Trinity Industries, Inc.; *U.S. Public*, pg. 2194
TRINITY PASTURES (CALVERT LANE HULL) RESIDENTS MANAGEMENT COMPANY LIMITED—See Persimmon plc; *Int'l*, pg. 5818
TRINITY PETROLEUM TRUST; *U.S. Public*, pg. 2194
TRINITY PHARMA PROPRIETARY LIMITED—See Strides Pharma Science Limited; *Int'l*, pg. 7241
TRINITY (PHILIPPINES) CORPORATION—See Trinity Industrial Corporation; *Int'l*, pg. 7924
TRINITY PIPELINE, L.P.—See Morgan Stanley; *U.S. Public*, pg. 1474
TRINITY PLACE HOLDINGS, INC.; *U.S. Public*, pg. 2194
TRINITY PRECISION TECHNOLOGY CO., LTD.; *Int'l*, pg. 7925
TRINITY PRIVATE EQUITY GROUP, LLC; *U.S. Private*, pg. 4235
TRINITY PRODUCTS INC.; *U.S. Private*, pg. 4235
TRINITY PUBLICATIONS LTD—See Reach PLC; *Int'l*, pg. 6231
TRINITY RAIL GROUP, LLC—See Trinity Industries, Inc.; *U.S. Public*, pg. 2194
TRINITYRAIL MAINTENANCE SERVICES, INC.—See Trinity Industries, Inc.; *U.S. Public*, pg. 2194
TRINITY REAL ESTATE SOLUTIONS, INC.; *U.S. Private*, pg. 4235
TRINITY RECYCLERS LLC—See Green Tree Electronic Recycling, LLC; *U.S. Private*, pg. 1774
TRINITY SCIENTIFIC LTD—See DDD Ltd.; *Int'l*, pg. 1993
TRINITY SERVICES GROUP, INC.—See H.I.G. Capital, LLC; *U.S. Private*, pg. 1832
TRINITY SHORING PRODUCTS, INC.—See Trinity Industries, Inc.; *U.S. Public*, pg. 2194
TRINITY SOLAR, INC.; *U.S. Private*, pg. 4235
TRINITY SPECIALTY PRODUCTS, INC.—See Trinity Industries, Inc.; *U.S. Public*, pg. 2194
TRINITY SQUARE INSURANCE LIMITED—See Willis Towers Watson Public Limited Company; *Int'l*, pg. 8416
TRINITY STEEL FABRICATORS, INC.—See The CapStreet Group LLC; *U.S. Private*, pg. 4005
TRINITY STERILE; *U.S. Private*, pg. 4235
TRINITY TECHNOLOGIES, INC.; *U.S. Private*, pg. 4235
TRINITY TECHNOLOGY GROUP, INC.; *U.S. Private*, pg. 4235
TRINITY TOWERS LIMITED PARTNERSHIP—See Brookdale Senior Living Inc.; *U.S. Public*, pg. 395
TRINITY TRADELINK LIMITED; *Int'l*, pg. 7925
TRINITY TRAILER SALES & SERVICE, INC.—See Great Western Leasing & Sales, LLC; *U.S. Private*, pg. 1768
TRINITY TRANSPORTATION—See Trinity Industries, Inc.; *U.S. Public*, pg. 2194
TRINITY TRANSPORT, INC.; *U.S. Private*, pg. 4236
TRINITY UNDERWRITING MANAGERS, INC.—See AmWINS Group, Inc.; *U.S. Private*, pg. 270
TRINITY UNIVERSAL INSURANCE CO.—See Kemper Corporation; *U.S. Public*, pg. 1221
TRINITY UTILITY STRUCTURES, LLC—See Trinity Industries, Inc.; *U.S. Public*, pg. 2194
TRINITY VALLEY ELECTRIC COOP (ATHENS OFFICE)—See Trinity Valley Electric Coop; *U.S. Private*, pg. 4236
TRINITY VALLEY ELECTRIC COOP (CEDAR CREEK SUB-OFFICE)—See Trinity Valley Electric Coop; *U.S. Private*, pg. 4236
TRINITY VALLEY ELECTRIC COOP; *U.S. Private*, pg. 4236
TRINITY VENTURE CAPITAL NOMINEES LIMITED—See TVC Holdings plc; *Int'l*, pg. 7988
TRINITY VENTURES; *U.S. Private*, pg. 4236
TRINITY WATTHANA PUBLIC COMPANY LIMITED; *Int'l*, pg. 7925
TRINITY WHOLESALE DISTRIBUTORS, INC.; *U.S. Private*, pg. 4236
TRINITY YACHTS, LLC; *U.S. Private*, pg. 4236
TRINKKONTOR BITBURGER BIER GMBH—See Bitburger Braugruppe GmbH; *Int'l*, pg. 1049
TRINKS GMBH—See Krombacher Brauerei Bernhard Schadeberg GmbH & Co. KG; *Int'l*, pg. 4304
TRINNO TECHNOLOGY CO., LTD.—See iA Inc.; *Int'l*, pg. 3568

TRINOM BUSINESS APARTMENTS GMBH—See TAG Immobilien AG; *Int'l*, pg. 7407
TRI-NORTH BUILDERS INC.; *U.S. Private*, pg. 4223
TRINOS VAKUUM-SYSTEME GMBH—See Dr. Ing. K. Busch GmbH; *Int'l*, pg. 2194
TRINOVA INC.—See Gold Eagle Company; *U.S. Private*, pg. 1728
TRINOX SA—See Jacquet Metal Service SA; *Int'l*, pg. 3868
TRINSEO EUROPE GMBH—See Bain Capital, LP; *U.S. Private*, pg. 450
TRINSEO JAPAN Y.K.—See Bain Capital, LP; *U.S. Private*, pg. 450
TRINSEO NETHERLANDS B.V.—See Bain Capital, LP; *U.S. Private*, pg. 450
TRINSEO S.A.—See Bain Capital, LP; *U.S. Private*, pg. 449
TRINTECH GROUP LIMITED—See Summit Partners, L.P.; *U.S. Private*, pg. 3856
TRINTECH INC.—See Summit Partners, L.P.; *U.S. Private*, pg. 3856
TRINTECH TECHNOLOGIES LIMITED—See Summit Partners, L.P.; *U.S. Private*, pg. 3856
TRINTECH UK LTD.—See Summit Partners, L.P.; *U.S. Private*, pg. 3856
TRIO ADVERTISING. DESIGN. SOLUTIONS; *U.S. Private*, pg. 4236
TRIOAK FOODS, INC.; *U.S. Private*, pg. 4236
TRIOCEAN INDUSTRIAL CORPORATION CO., LTD.; *Int'l*, pg. 7925
TRIOCHEM PRODUCTS LIMITED; *Int'l*, pg. 7925
TRIO DANMARK A/S—See Enghouse Systems Limited; *Int'l*, pg. 2428
TRIO DATACOM INC.—See Schneider Electric SE; *Int'l*, pg. 6635
TRIO DATACOM PTY. LTD.—See Schneider Electric SE; *Int'l*, pg. 6635
TRIODETIC INC—See Plaintree Systems Inc.; *Int'l*, pg. 5888
TRIODOS BANK N.V.; *Int'l*, pg. 7925
TRIO ENGINEERING COMPANY LIMITED—See Trio Industrial Electronics Group Limited; *Int'l*, pg. 7925
TRIO ENGINEERING GMBH—See Trio Industrial Electronics Group Limited; *Int'l*, pg. 7925
TRIO ENTERPRISE AB—See Enghouse Systems Limited; *Int'l*, pg. 2428
TRIOGEN LTD—See Veolia Environnement S.A.; *Int'l*, pg. 8154
TRIO, INC.; *U.S. Private*, pg. 4236
TRIO INDUSTRIAL ELECTRONICS GROUP LIMITED; *Int'l*, pg. 7925
TRI OITA ADVANCED ELASTOMER, LTD.—See Sumitomo Riko Company Limited; *Int'l*, pg. 7298
TRIOLAB AB—See AddLife AB; *Int'l*, pg. 130
TRIOLAB A/S—See Addtech AB; *Int'l*, pg. 135
TRIOLAB OY—See HORIBA Ltd; *Int'l*, pg. 3478
TRIO MERCANTILE & TRADING LIMITED; *Int'l*, pg. 7925
TRIO MOTION TECHNOLOGY LLC—See Nanjing Estun Automation Co., Ltd.; *Int'l*, pg. 5140
TRION CHEMICALS PVT. LTD.—See Bodal Chemicals Ltd.; *Int'l*, pg. 1097
TRION, INC.—See Johnson Controls International plc; *Int'l*, pg. 3985
TRIONIS SCRL—See Fiserv, Inc.; *U.S. Public*, pg. 851
TRIO NORGE AS—See Enghouse Systems Limited; *Int'l*, pg. 2428
TRIO PACKAGING CORP; *U.S. Private*, pg. 4236
TRIO PAPER MILLS SDN. BHD.—See HPI Resources Berhad; *Int'l*, pg. 3501
TRIO PETROLEUM CORP.; *U.S. Public*, pg. 2194
TRIOPLANEX FRANCE SAS—See Altor Equity Partners AB; *Int'l*, pg. 396
TRIOPLAST LANDSKRONA AB—See Altor Equity Partners AB; *Int'l*, pg. 396
TRIOPLAST NYBORG A/S—See Altor Equity Partners AB; *Int'l*, pg. 396
TRIOPLAST SIFAB AB—See Altor Equity Partners AB; *Int'l*, pg. 396
TRIOPTICS BERLIN GMBH—See Jenoptik AG; *Int'l*, pg. 3929
TRIOPTICS GMBH—See Jenoptik AG; *Int'l*, pg. 3929
TRIOPTICS JAPAN CO., LTD.—See Jenoptik AG; *Int'l*, pg. 3929
TRIOPTICS KOREA CO., LTD.—See Jenoptik AG; *Int'l*, pg. 3929
TRIOPTICS SINGAPORE PTE. LTD.—See Jenoptik AG; *Int'l*, pg. 3929
TRIOPTICS TAIWAN LTD.—See Jenoptik AG; *Int'l*, pg. 3929
TRIOPTIMA AB—See CME Group, Inc.; *U.S. Public*, pg. 518
TRIOPTIMA ASIA PACIFIC PTE LIMITED—See CME Group, Inc.; *U.S. Public*, pg. 518
TRIOPTIMA JAPAN K.K.—See CME Group, Inc.; *U.S. Public*, pg. 518
TRIOPTIMA NORTH AMERICA LLC—See CME Group, Inc.; *U.S. Public*, pg. 517
TRIOPTIMA UK LIMITED—See CME Group, Inc.; *U.S. Public*, pg. 518

CORPORATE AFFILIATIONS

TRIO RESOURCES, INC.; *Int'l*, pg. 7925
TRIOSE, INC.; *U.S. Private*, pg. 4236
TRIOSIM CORPORATION; *U.S. Private*, pg. 4236
TRIO SUPPLY COMPANY—See The ODP Corporation; *U.S. Public*, pg. 2118
TRIO-TECH BANGKOK CO., LTD.—See Trio-Tech International; *Int'l*, pg. 7925
TRIO-TECH (CHONGQING) CO., LTD.—See Trio-Tech International; *Int'l*, pg. 7925
TRIO-TECH INTERNATIONAL PTE., LTD.—See Trio-Tech International; *Int'l*, pg. 7925
TRIO-TECH INTERNATIONAL - SINGAPORE FACILITY—See Trio-Tech International; *Int'l*, pg. 7925
TRIO-TECH INTERNATIONAL; *Int'l*, pg. 7925
TRIO-TECH (MALAYSIA) SDN. BHD.—See Trio-Tech International; *Int'l*, pg. 7925
TRIO-TECH (SIP) CO., LTD.—See Trio-Tech International; *Int'l*, pg. 7925
TRIO-TECH (TIANJIN) CO., LTD.—See Trio-Tech International; *Int'l*, pg. 7925
TRIO-TRONICS MANUFACTURING GLOBAL LIMITED—See Trio Industrial Electronics Group Limited; *Int'l*, pg. 7925
TRIO-TRONICS (THAILAND) LIMITED—See Trio Industrial Electronics Group Limited; *Int'l*, pg. 7925
TRIO TRUCKING INC.; *U.S. Private*, pg. 4236
TRIOVING A.S.—See ASSA ABLOY AB; *Int'l*, pg. 641
TRIOWORLD BOTTNARYD AB—See Altor Equity Partners AB; *Int'l*, pg. 396
TRIOWORLD GMBH—See Altor Equity Partners AB; *Int'l*, pg. 396
TRIOWORLD INDUSTRIER AB—See Altor Equity Partners AB; *Int'l*, pg. 396
TRIOWORLD LUNDIN AS—See Altor Equity Partners AB; *Int'l*, pg. 396
TRIOWORLD OMBREE D'ANJOU SAS—See Altor Equity Partners AB; *Int'l*, pg. 397
TRIOWORLD OY—See Altor Equity Partners AB; *Int'l*, pg. 397
TRIOWORLD VARBERG AB—See Altor Equity Partners AB; *Int'l*, pg. 397
TRI-PACK ENTERPRISES INC.—See Clearlake Capital Group, L.P.; *U.S. Private*, pg. 937
TRIPACK PACKAGING (M) SDN. BHD.—See Ornapaper Berhad; *Int'l*, pg. 5641
TRIPADVISOR, INC.; *U.S. Public*, pg. 2195
TRIPADVISOR LLC—See TripAdvisor, Inc.; *U.S. Public*, pg. 2195
TRI PAK, INC.—See Saybrook Corporate Opportunity Fund LP; *U.S. Private*, pg. 3558
TRI-PARISH COMMUNITY HOMECARE, LLC—See UnitedHealth Group Incorporated; *U.S. Public*, pg. 2247
TRIPAR TRANSPORTATION LP—See TFI International Inc.; *Int'l*, pg. 7586
TRIPATH IMAGING, INC.—See Becton, Dickinson & Company; *U.S. Public*, pg. 288
TRIPATH ONCOLOGY, INC.—See Becton, Dickinson & Company; *U.S. Public*, pg. 288
TRIPBORN, INC.; *U.S. Public*, pg. 2195
TRIP.COM GROUP LTD.; *Int'l*, pg. 7926
TRIPCON CO., LTD.—See Shobunsha Holdings Inc.; *Int'l*, pg. 6857
TRIP DRINK LTD.—See 029 Group SE; *Int'l*, pg. 1
TRI PETCH ISUZU LEASING CO., LTD.—See Mitsubishi Corporation; *Int'l*, pg. 4943
TRI PETCH ISUZU SALES CO., LTD.—See Isuzu Motors Limited; *Int'l*, pg. 3826
TRI PETCH ISUZU SALES CO., LTD.—See Mitsubishi Motors Corporation; *Int'l*, pg. 4967
TRIP HOLDINGS, INC.; *Int'l*, pg. 7925
TRIPICTURES, S.A.—See Vocento, S.A.; *Int'l*, pg. 8284
TRIPIFOODS INC.; *U.S. Private*, pg. 4236
TRIPIT LLC—See SAP SE; *Int'l*, pg. 6567
TRIPLA GRUNDSTUCKS-VERMIETUNGSGESELLSCHAFT MBH—See Deutsche Bank Aktiengesellschaft; *Int'l*, pg. 2062
TRIPLAN GEBAUDETECHNIK AG—See TTP GmbH; *Int'l*, pg. 7961
TRIPLAN GMBH—See TTP GmbH; *Int'l*, pg. 7961
TRIPLAN INDIA PVT. LTD.—See TTP GmbH; *Int'l*, pg. 7961
TRIPLAN INGENIEUR AG—See TTP GmbH; *Int'l*, pg. 7961
TRIPLAY, INC.; *U.S. Private*, pg. 4236
TRIPLC BERHAD—See Puncak Niaga Holdings Berhad; *Int'l*, pg. 6118
TRIPLE A SERVICES INC.; *U.S. Private*, pg. 4236
TRIPLE B CORP; *U.S. Private*, pg. 4236
TRIPLE B FORWARDERS, INC.; *U.S. Private*, pg. 4236
TRIPLE CANOPY, INC.—See Apollo Global Management, Inc.; *U.S. Public*, pg. 150
TRIPLE C, INC.—See HCC, Inc.; *U.S. Private*, pg. 1888
TRIPLE-C, INC.—See Triple-S Management Corp.; *U.S. Public*, pg. 2195
TRIPLE CITIES ACQUISITION LLC; *U.S. Private*, pg. 4236
TRIPLE CREEK ASSOCIATES, INC.—See MentorcliQ, Inc.; *U.S. Private*, pg. 2667

TRIPLE CROWN SERVICES, CO.—See Norfolk Southern Corporation; *U.S. Public*, pg. 1536
TRIPLE-D COMMUNICATIONS, LLC—See Dycom Industries, Inc.; *U.S. Public*, pg. 699
TRIPLE D OF BREVARD INC—See Outdoor Resorts of America; *U.S. Private*, pg. 3051
TRIPLE ENERGY LIMITED; *Int'l*, pg. 7926
TRIPLE F HOLDINGS, LLC—See Bain Capital, LP; *U.S. Private*, pg. 441
TRIPLEFIN LLC—See JLL Partners, LLC; *U.S. Private*, pg. 2212
TRIPLEFIN LLC—See Water Street Healthcare Partners, LLC; *U.S. Private*, pg. 4452
TRIPLE FLAG PRECIOUS METALS CORP.; *Int'l*, pg. 7926
TRIPLE G CONSTRUCTION INC.; *Int'l*, pg. 7926
TRIPLE H FOOD PROCESSORS INCORPORATED; *U.S. Private*, pg. 4237
TRIPLE H SPECIALTY CO. INC.; *U.S. Private*, pg. 4237
TRIPLE I ASIA CARGO CO., LTD.—See Triple i Logistics Public Company Limited; *Int'l*, pg. 7926
TRIPLE-I CORP—See Triple-I Investments Inc.; *U.S. Private*, pg. 4237
TRIPLE-I INVESTMENTS INC.; *U.S. Private*, pg. 4237
TRIPLE I LOGISTICS PUBLIC COMPANY LIMITED; *Int'l*, pg. 7926
TRIPLE I MARITIME AGENCIES CO., LTD.—See Triple i Logistics Public Company Limited; *Int'l*, pg. 7927
TRIPLE INDUSTRIES TAIWAN CORP.—See Star Micronics Co Ltd; *Int'l*, pg. 7175
TRIPLEINK—See Omnicom Group Inc.; *U.S. Public*, pg. 1588
TRIPLE-I OF COLORADO INC.—See Triple-I Investments Inc.; *U.S. Private*, pg. 4237
TRIPLE I SUPPLYCHAIN CO., LTD.—See Triple i Logistics Public Company Limited; *Int'l*, pg. 7927
TRIPLE J ENTERPRISES, INC.; *U.S. Private*, pg. 4237
TRIPLE LEAF TEA, INC.; *U.S. Private*, pg. 4237
TRIPLE 'M' FIRE—See BSA Limited; *Int'l*, pg. 1201
TRIPLE M MECHANICAL SERVICES PTY LTD—See BSA Limited; *Int'l*, pg. 1201
TRIPLE M MECHANICAL SERVICES PTY LTD—See BSA Limited; *Int'l*, pg. 1202
TRIPLE M ROOFING CORP.; *U.S. Private*, pg. 4237
TRIPLE PEAKS, LLC—See Vail Resorts, Inc.; *U.S. Public*, pg. 2271
TRIPLE P N.V.; *Int'l*, pg. 7927
TRIPLE POINT ENERGY TRANSITION PLC; *Int'l*, pg. 7927
TRIPLEPOINT ENVIRONMENTAL, LLC—See KKR & Co. Inc.; *U.S. Public*, pg. 1239
TRIPLEPOINT ENVIRONMENTAL, LLC—See XPV Water Partners; *Int'l*, pg. 8538
TRIPLE POINT INCOME VCT PLC; *Int'l*, pg. 7927
TRIPLEPOINT PRIVATE VENTURE CREDIT INC.; *U.S. Private*, pg. 4237
TRIPLE POINT SOCIAL HOUSING REIT PLC; *Int'l*, pg. 7927
TRIPLE POINT TECHNOLOGY, INC.—See TA Associates, Inc.; *U.S. Private*, pg. 3918
TRIPLE POINT TECHNOLOGY PTY LTD.—See TA Associates, Inc.; *U.S. Private*, pg. 3919
TRIPLE POINT VCT 2011 PLC; *Int'l*, pg. 7927
TRIPLEPOINT VENTURE GROWTH BDC CORP.; *U.S. Public*, pg. 2195
TRIPLE P PACKAGING & PAPER PRODUCTS, INC.; *U.S. Private*, pg. 4237
TRIPLE-S ADVANTAGE, INC.—See Triple-S Management Corp.; *U.S. Public*, pg. 2195
TRIPLE S AIR SYSTEMS, INC.; *U.S. Private*, pg. 4237
TRIPLE-S AS—See Addtech AB; *Int'l*, pg. 131
TRIPLE/S DYNAMICS, INC.; *U.S. Private*, pg. 4237
TRIPLESEAT SOFTWARE, LLC—See Vista Equity Partners, LLC; *U.S. Private*, pg. 4402
TRIPLESENSE REPLY GMBH—See Reply S.p.A.; *Int'l*, pg. 6291
TRIPLE SEVEN CHRYSLER; *Int'l*, pg. 7927
TRIPLE-S, INC.—See Triple-S Management Corp.; *U.S. Public*, pg. 2195
TRIPLE-S INSURANCE AGENCY, INC.—See Triple-S Management Corp.; *U.S. Public*, pg. 2195
TRIPLE-S MANAGEMENT CORP.; *U.S. Public*, pg. 2195
TRIPLE S PETROLEUM COMPANY INC.; *U.S. Private*, pg. 4237
TRIPLE S&P, INC.; *U.S. Private*, pg. 4237
TRIPLE-S PROPIEDAD, INC.—See Triple-S Management Corp.; *U.S. Public*, pg. 2195
TRIPLE-S STEEL HOLDINGS INC.; *U.S. Private*, pg. 4237
TRIPLE-S STEEL SUPPLY CO. INC.—See Triple-S Steel Holdings Inc.; *U.S. Private*, pg. 4237
TRIPLE S TIRE CO. INC.; *U.S. Private*, pg. 4237
TRIPLE S TOWERS, INC.—See Microwave Transmission Systems, Inc.; *U.S. Private*, pg. 2705
TRIPLE-S VIDA, INC.—See Triple-S Management Corp.; *U.S. Public*, pg. 2195
TRIPLE T BROADBAND PUBLIC COMPANY LIMITED—See Advanced Info Service Plc; *Int'l*, pg. 160
TRIPLE-T FOODS INC.—See Darling Ingredients Inc.; *U.S. Public*, pg. 634
TRIPLE T INTERNET CO., LTD.—See Advanced Info Service Plc; *Int'l*, pg. 160
TRIPLE T PARTS & EQUIPMENT CO—See Matt Management Inc.; *U.S. Private*, pg. 2613
TRIPLETT INC.; *U.S. Private*, pg. 4237
TRIPLETT OFFICE ESSENTIALS; *U.S. Private*, pg. 4238
TRIPLE T TRANSPORT, INC.; *U.S. Private*, pg. 4237
TRIPLE V INC.; *U.S. Private*, pg. 4237
TRIPLE W. EQUIPMENT INC.—See Missoula Cartage Co. Inc.; *U.S. Private*, pg. 2748
TRIPLE WEST MEDICAL LIMITED—See Servoca Plc; *Int'l*, pg. 6726
TRIPLEX CHILE LTDA.—See Cargotec Corporation; *Int'l*, pg. 1329
TRIPLEX INC.; *U.S. Private*, pg. 4238
TRIPLINGO, LLC—See Travel & Transport Inc.; *U.S. Private*, pg. 4212
TRI PLUS GRUPA D.O.O—See SmartRent, Inc.; *U.S. Public*, pg. 1896
TRIP NETWORK, INC.—See Expedia Group, Inc.; *U.S. Public*, pg. 809
TRIPOD TECHNOLOGY CORPORATION; *Int'l*, pg. 7927
TRIPOD TECHNOLOGY CORPORATION - TAIWAN PLANT—See Tripod Technology Corporation; *Int'l*, pg. 7927
TRI POINTE ADVANTAGE INSURANCE SERVICES, INC.—See Tri Pointe Homes, Inc.; *U.S. Public*, pg. 2188
TRI POINTE COMMUNITIES, INC.—See Tri Pointe Homes, Inc.; *U.S. Public*, pg. 2188
TRI POINTE CONNECT, L.L.C.—See Tri Pointe Homes, Inc.; *U.S. Public*, pg. 2188
TRI POINTE HOLDINGS, INC.—See Tri Pointe Homes, Inc.; *U.S. Public*, pg. 2188
TRI POINTE HOMES ARIZONA, LLC—See Tri Pointe Homes, Inc.; *U.S. Public*, pg. 2188
TRI POINTE HOMES DC METRO, INC.—See Tri Pointe Homes, Inc.; *U.S. Public*, pg. 2188
TRI POINTE HOMES, INC.; *U.S. Public*, pg. 2188
TRI POINTE HOMES, INC.—See Tri Pointe Homes, Inc.; *U.S. Public*, pg. 2188
TRI POINTE HOMES WASHINGTON, INC.—See Tri Pointe Homes, Inc.; *U.S. Public*, pg. 2188
TRI-POINT OIL & GAS PRODUCTION SYSTEMS, LLC—See First Reserve Management, L.P.; *U.S. Private*, pg. 1526
TRI (POLAND) SP.ZO.O.—See Sumitomo Riko Company Limited; *Int'l*, pg. 7298
TRIPOL AS—See Marsh & McLennan Companies, Inc.; *U.S. Public*, pg. 1376
TRIPOLI COUNTRY CLUB, INC.—See University Club of Milwaukee; *U.S. Private*, pg. 4307
TRIPOS TRAVEL PROPRIETARY LIMITED—See AYO Technology Solutions Ltd.; *Int'l*, pg. 775
TRI-POWER MPT, INC.—See Genstar Capital, LLC; *U.S. Private*, pg. 1678
TRIPPE MANUFACTURING COMPANY; *U.S. Private*, pg. 4238
TRIPP ENTERPRISES INC.; *U.S. Private*, pg. 4238
TRIPPIES INC.; *U.S. Private*, pg. 4238
TRIPPLE GEE & COMPANY PLC; *Int'l*, pg. 7927
TRIPPLEX APS—See ROCKWOOL A/S; *Int'l*, pg. 6381
TRIPRESERVATIONS.COM—See Prestige Travel, Inc.; *U.S. Private*, pg. 3256
TRI -PRO BH D.O.O.—See Zavarovalnica Triglav, d.d.; *Int'l*, pg. 8626
TRI-PRO D.O.O.—See Zavarovalnica Triglav, d.d.; *Int'l*, pg. 8626
TRIPSITTER CLINIC LIMITED; *Int'l*, pg. 7927
TRIPSPARK TECHNOLOGIES—See Constellation Software Inc.; *Int'l*, pg. 1775
TRIP TECHNOLOGIES, INC.; *U.S. Public*, pg. 2194
TRIPUL - SOC. DE GESTAO DE NAVIOS, LDA.—See Galp Energia SGPS, S.A.; *Int'l*, pg. 2875
TRIPWIRE ASIA-PACIFIC—See HGGC, LLC; *U.S. Private*, pg. 1929
TRIPWIRE EMEA—See HGGC, LLC; *U.S. Private*, pg. 1929
TRIPWIRE, INC.—See HGGC, LLC; *U.S. Private*, pg. 1929
TRIPWIRE JAPAN KK—See HGGC, LLC; *U.S. Private*, pg. 1929
TRIREME MEDICAL, LLC—See Quantum Healthcare Limited; *Int'l*, pg. 6155
TRIRIGA INC.—See International Business Machines Corporation; *U.S. Public*, pg. 1150
TRI RINSE, INC.; *U.S. Private*, pg. 4220
TRI-RIVER VENTURES INC.; *Int'l*, pg. 7918
TRI SAGE CONSULTING—See Qualus Corporation; *U.S. Private*, pg. 3322
TRISALUS LIFE SCIENCES, INC.; *U.S. Public*, pg. 2195
TRISCO TAILORED AND WOVEN INTERNATIONAL LTD.—See PT Trisula International Tbk; *Int'l*, pg. 6080
TRI-SEAL, INC.—See Genstar Capital, LLC; *U.S. Private*, pg. 1679
TRI-SEAL, INC.—See Genstar Capital, LLC; *U.S. Private*, pg. 1679
TRISEN ASIA CONTROL PTE. LIMITED—See China Automation Group Limited; *Int'l*, pg. 1484
TRI-SEN SYSTEMS CORPORATION—See China Automation Group Limited; *Int'l*, pg. 1483
TRI-S ENVIRONMENTAL SERVICES INC.; *U.S. Private*, pg. 4223
TRISEP CORP.—See Mann+Hummel GmbH; *Int'l*, pg. 4673
TRISHAKTI INDUSTRIES LTD.; *Int'l*, pg. 7927
TRISH MCEVOY LTD.; *U.S. Private*, pg. 4238
TRISHYIRAYA RECYCLING INDIA PRIVATE LTD.—See Sims Limited; *U.S. Public*, pg. 1884
TRI-SIGNAL INTEGRATION, INC.; *U.S. Private*, pg. 4223
TRISKO S.A.—See Industria de Diseno Textil, S.A.; *Int'l*, pg. 3667
TRISLOT N.V.; *Int'l*, pg. 7927
TRISOME FOODS, INC.; *U.S. Private*, pg. 4238
TRISON CONSTRUCTION, INC.—See LSB Industries, Inc.; *U.S. Public*, pg. 1344
TRISONICS, INC.—See Avista Capital Partners, L.P.; *U.S. Private*, pg. 409
TRISON TECHNOLOGY CORPORATION—See Tripod Technology Corporation; *Int'l*, pg. 7927
TRISOURCE SOLUTIONS, LLC—See Repay Holdings Corporation; *U.S. Public*, pg. 1784
TRISPAN LLP; *Int'l*, pg. 7927
TRIS PHARMA, INC.; *U.S. Private*, pg. 4238
TRISSEL, GRAHAM & TOOLE INC.; *U.S. Private*, pg. 4238
TRISSENTIAL, LLC—See Assystem S.A.; *Int'l*, pg. 650
TRI-STAGE, INC.—See Bain Capital, LP; *U.S. Private*, pg. 449
TRISTAR ACQUISITION GROUP; *Int'l*, pg. 7927
TRISTAR ASHLAND CITY MEDICAL CENTER—See HCA Healthcare, Inc.; *U.S. Public*, pg. 997
TRISTAR BONE MARROW TRANSPLANT, LLC—See HCA Healthcare, Inc.; *U.S. Public*, pg. 1012
TRI-STAR CABINET & TOP CO.; *U.S. Private*, pg. 4223
TRISTAR CARDIOVASCULAR SURGERY, LLC—See HCA Healthcare, Inc.; *U.S. Public*, pg. 1012
TRISTAR CENTENNIAL MEDICAL CENTER—See HCA Healthcare, Inc.; *U.S. Public*, pg. 997
TRISTAR ELECTRIC INC.—See Aecon Group Inc.; *Int'l*, pg. 172
TRI-STAR ELECTRONICS INTERNATIONAL, INC.—See Carlisle Companies Incorporated; *U.S. Public*, pg. 437
TRISTAR ELECTRONICS SA—See Carlisle Companies Incorporated; *U.S. Public*, pg. 437
TRI STAR ENERGY, LLC; *U.S. Private*, pg. 4220
TRI-STAR ENGINEERING, INC.; *U.S. Private*, pg. 4223
TRISTAR ENTERPRISES, LLC; *U.S. Private*, pg. 4238
TRISTAR FAMILY CARE, LLC—See HCA Healthcare, Inc.; *U.S. Public*, pg. 1012
TRI-STAR FORD-MERCURY, INC.; *U.S. Private*, pg. 4223
TRI STAR FREIGHT SYSTEM INC.; *U.S. Private*, pg. 4221
TRISTAR GOLD INC.; *U.S. Public*, pg. 2196
TRISTAR GREENVIEW REGIONAL HOSPITAL—See HCA Healthcare, Inc.; *U.S. Public*, pg. 1012
TRISTAR GYNECOLOGY ONCOLOGY, LLC—See HCA Healthcare, Inc.; *U.S. Public*, pg. 1012
TRISTAR HEALTH SYSTEM—See HCA Healthcare, Inc.; *U.S. Public*, pg. 1012
TRISTAR HENDERSONVILLE MEDICAL CENTER—See HCA Healthcare, Inc.; *U.S. Public*, pg. 1012
TRISTAR HOLDINGS INC.; *U.S. Private*, pg. 4238
TRISTAR HORIZON MEDICAL CENTER—See HCA Healthcare, Inc.; *U.S. Public*, pg. 1012
TRI-STAR INDUSTRIES, INC.—See American Securities LLC; *U.S. Private*, pg. 250
TRISTAR INSURANCE GROUP, INC.; *U.S. Private*, pg. 4238
TRISTAR JOINT REPLACEMENT INSTITUTE, LLC—See HCA Healthcare, Inc.; *U.S. Public*, pg. 1012
TRISTAR MANAGING GENERAL AGENCY; *U.S. Private*, pg. 4238
TRI-STAR MARINE INTERNATIONAL, INC.; *U.S. Private*, pg. 4223
TRISTAR MEDICAL GROUP - LEGACY HEALTH, LLC—See HCA Healthcare, Inc.; *U.S. Public*, pg. 1012
TRI STAR METALS INC.; *U.S. Private*, pg. 4221
TRI-STAR MUTUAL FUND LIMITED; *Int'l*, pg. 7918
TRI-STAR PACKAGING SUPPLIES LIMITED—See Bunzl plc; *Int'l*, pg. 1219
TRI-STAR PLASTICS CORPORATION; *U.S. Private*, pg. 4223
TRI-STAR PLASTICS INC.; *U.S. Private*, pg. 4223
TRI-STAR POWER LIMITED; *Int'l*, pg. 7918
TRISTAR PRODUCTS INC.; *U.S. Private*, pg. 4238
TRISTAR RADIATION ONCOLOGY, LLC—See HCA Healthcare, Inc.; *U.S. Public*, pg. 1012
TRI-STAR RESOURCES PLC; *Int'l*, pg. 7918
TRISTAR RISK MANAGEMENT INC.; *U.S. Private*, pg. 4238
TRI-STAR SEMI TRUCK & TRAILER SERVICES, LLC; *U.S. Private*, pg. 4223
TRISTAR SKYLINE MADISON CAMPUS—See HCA Healthcare, Inc.; *U.S. Public*, pg. 1012
TRISTAR SKYLINE MEDICAL CENTER—See HCA Healthcare, Inc.; *U.S. Public*, pg. 1012

TRI-STAR SEMI TRUCK & TRAILER SERVICES, LLC
CORPORATE AFFILIATIONS
Company Index

TRISTAR SOUTHERN HILLS MEDICAL CENTER—See HCA Healthcare, Inc.; *U.S. Public*, pg. 997
TRISTAR STONECREST MEDICAL CENTER—See HCA Healthcare, Inc.; *U.S. Public*, pg. 997
TRISTAR SUMMIT MEDICAL CENTER—See HCA Healthcare, Inc.; *U.S. Public*, pg. 997
TRISTAR TENNESSEE HEART AND VASCULAR, LLC—See HCA Healthcare, Inc.; *U.S. Public*, pg. 1012
TRISTAR TERMINALS GUAM INC.—See Agility; *Int'l*, pg. 210
TRISTAR TRANSPORT LLC—See Agility; *Int'l*, pg. 210
TRI-STAR WASTE SYSTEMS, INC.—See Watts Trucking Service, Inc.; *U.S. Private*, pg. 4456
TRISTAR WEB GRAPHICS INC—See Tristar Holdings Inc.; *U.S. Private*, pg. 4238
TRISTAR WEB SOLUTIONS, INC.—See Tristar Holdings Inc.; *U.S. Private*, pg. 4238
TRISTAR WELLNESS SOLUTIONS, INC.; *U.S. Public*, pg. 2196
TRI-STATE ADVERTISING CO., INC.; *U.S. Private*, pg. 4223
TRI-STATE ARMATURE & ELECTRIC WORKS, INC.; *U.S. Private*, pg. 4223
TRI-STATE AUCTION CO., INC.—See OPENLANE, Inc.; *U.S. Public*, pg. 1607
TRI-STATE AUTO AUCTION LLC; *U.S. Private*, pg. 4223
TRI-STATE BAKING CO.—See Affiliated Foods, Inc.; *U.S. Private*, pg. 122
TRI-STATE BANK OF MEMPHIS; *U.S. Private*, pg. 4223
TRI-STATE BUILDING MATERIALS; *U.S. Private*, pg. 4223
TRISTATE CAPITAL BANK—See Raymond James Financial, Inc.; *U.S. Public*, pg. 1765
TRISTATE CAPITAL HOLDINGS, INC.—See Raymond James Financial, Inc.; *U.S. Public*, pg. 1765
TRI STATE CHRISTIAN TELEVISION—See TCT Ministries, Inc.; *U.S. Private*, pg. 3943
TRI-STATE CONSTRUCTION, INC.; *U.S. Private*, pg. 4223
TRISTATE CONTAINER CORP.—See Connecticut Container Corporation; *U.S. Private*, pg. 1016
TRI-STATE DIESEL INC.; *U.S. Private*, pg. 4223
TRI-STATE DISPLAYS INC.—See Capital Properties, Inc.; *U.S. Public*, pg. 432
TRI-STATE DISTRIBUTORS INCORPORATED; *U.S. Private*, pg. 4223
TRI STATE DISTRIBUTORS INC.; *U.S. Private*, pg. 4221
TRI-STATE DISTRIBUTORS INC.; *U.S. Private*, pg. 4223
TRI-STATE ELECTRIC OF CORINTH—See Tri-State Armature & Electric Works, Inc.; *U.S. Private*, pg. 4223
TRI-STATE ELECTRIC OF JONESBORO—See Tri-State Armature & Electric Works, Inc.; *U.S. Private*, pg. 4223
TRI-STATE ENGINEERING, INC.—See Olsson Associates, Inc.; *U.S. Private*, pg. 3012
TRI-STATE ENTERPRISES INC.; *U.S. Private*, pg. 4223
TRI-STATE ENVELOPE CORPORATION; *U.S. Private*, pg. 4224
TRI-STATE FOREST PRODUCTS; *U.S. Private*, pg. 4224
TRI-STATE GARDEN SUPPLY INC.; *U.S. Private*, pg. 4224
TRI-STATE GENERATION AND TRANSMISSION ASSOCIATION, INC.; *U.S. Private*, pg. 4224
TRI-STATE GRINDING—See Colter & Peterson Inc.; *U.S. Private*, pg. 976
TRISTATE HOLDINGS LIMITED; *Int'l*, pg. 7927
TRI-STATE HOME SERVICES LLC—See Morgan Stanley; *U.S. Public*, pg. 1474
TRI-STATE HOSE & FITTING, INC.—See Frontenac Company LLC; *U.S. Private*, pg. 1614
TRISTATE HVAC EQUIPMENT LLP; *U.S. Private*, pg. 4238
TRI-STATE INDUSTRIAL GROUP; *U.S. Private*, pg. 4224
TRI-STATE JOINT FUND; *U.S. Private*, pg. 4224
TRI-STATE LEASING—See Tri-State Truck Center, Inc.; *U.S. Private*, pg. 4224
TRI-STATE MACHINE, INC.; *U.S. Private*, pg. 4224
TRISTATE MACHINERY, INC.; *U.S. Private*, pg. 4238
TRI-STATE MEMORIAL HOSPITAL & MEDICAL CAMPUS; *U.S. Private*, pg. 4224
TRI-STATE MOTOR TRANSIT CO.; *U.S. Private*, pg. 4224
TRI-STATE OIL COMPANY, INC.; *U.S. Private*, pg. 4224
TRI-STATE PAVING & SEALCOATING, INC.—See Energy Services of America Corporation; *U.S. Public*, pg. 762
TRI-STATE PETROLEUM CORPORATION; *U.S. Private*, pg. 4224
TRI-STATE PETROLEUM INC.; *U.S. Private*, pg. 4224
TRISTATE PETROLEUM—See Exxon Mobil Corporation; *U.S. Public*, pg. 817
TRI-STATES AUTOMOTIVE WAREHOUSE, INC.—See Replacement Parts Inc.; *U.S. Private*, pg. 3401
TRI STATE SUPPLY COMPANY, INC.; *U.S. Private*, pg. 4221
TRI-STATE SURGICAL SUPPLY & EQUIPMENT LTD.; *U.S. Private*, pg. 4224
TRI-STATE TECHNICAL SERVICES, INC.—See EVI Industries, Inc.; *U.S. Public*, pg. 803
TRI-STATE TRUCK CENTER, INC.; *U.S. Private*, pg. 4224
TRI-STATE TRUCK & EQUIPMENT, INC.; *U.S. Private*, pg. 4224
TRISTATE US INC.—See Tristate Holdings Limited; *Int'l*, pg. 7927
TRI-STATE UTILITIES, CO.—See ORIX Corporation; *Int'l*, pg. 5636
TRI-STATE UTILITY PRODUCTS INC.—See American Water Works Company, Inc.; *U.S. Public*, pg. 112
TRI-STATE WHOLESALE FLOORING, INC.—See ShoreView Industries, LLC; *U.S. Private*, pg. 3642
TRI-STATE WINDOW & DOOR FACTORY, INC.; *U.S. Private*, pg. 4224
TRI-STATE WINDOW FACTORY, CORP.; *U.S. Private*, pg. 4224
TRISTEL GMBH—See TRISTEL PLC; *Int'l*, pg. 7928
TRISTEL ITALIA SRL.—See TRISTEL PLC; *Int'l*, pg. 7928
TRISTEL NEW ZEALAND LTD.—See TRISTEL PLC; *Int'l*, pg. 7928
TRISTEL PLC; *Int'l*, pg. 7927
TRISTEL PTY. LTD.—See TRISTEL PLC; *Int'l*, pg. 7928
TRISTEL SAS—See TRISTEL PLC; *Int'l*, pg. 7928
TRISTEL SOLUTIONS LIMITED—See TRISTEL PLC; *Int'l*, pg. 7928
TRISTONE FLOWTECH GERMANY GMBH—See BAVARIA Industries Group AG; *Int'l*, pg. 899
TRISTRATA INC.; *U.S. Private*, pg. 4238
TRISTRATA TECHNOLOGY INC—See Tristrata Inc.; *U.S. Private*, pg. 4238
TRISTYLE MODE GMBH—See Equistone Partners Europe Limited; *Int'l*, pg. 2487
TRISUL S.A.; *Int'l*, pg. 7928
TRI-SUPPLY AND EQUIPMENT INC.—See Clayton, Dubilier & Rice, LLC; *U.S. Private*, pg. 930
TRI SUPPLY COMPANY; *U.S. Private*, pg. 4221
TRI SUPREME OPTICAL LLC—See EssilorLuxottica SA; *Int'l*, pg. 2514
TRISURA GROUP LTD.; *Int'l*, pg. 7928
TRISURA GUARANTEE INSURANCE COMPANY—See Trisura Group Ltd.; *Int'l*, pg. 7928
TRI-SURE CLOSURES NETHERLANDS—See Greif, Inc.; *U.S. Public*, pg. 968
TRISURE CORPORATION—See Hellman & Friedman LLC; *U.S. Private*, pg. 1910
TRITAX BIG BOX REIT PLC; *Int'l*, pg. 7928
TRITAX EUROBOX PLC; *Int'l*, pg. 7928
TRITEC AG—See EnBW Energie Baden-Wurttemberg AG; *Int'l*, pg. 2400
TRITEC BUILDING COMPANY INC.; *U.S. Private*, pg. 4238
TRI TECH CONSTRUCTION CORP.; *U.S. Private*, pg. 4221
TRITECH CONSULTANTS PTE LTD—See Tritech Group Limited; *Int'l*, pg. 7928
TRITECH DISTRIBUTION LIMITED—See MTT Group Holdings Limited; *Int'l*, pg. 5072
TRITECH ENGINEERING & TESTING (SINGAPORE) PTE LTD—See Tritech Group Limited; *Int'l*, pg. 7928
TRITECH-GEOKON SINGAPORE PTE LTD—See Tritech Group Limited; *Int'l*, pg. 7928
TRITECH GEOTECHNIC PTE LTD—See Tritech Group Limited; *Int'l*, pg. 7928
TRITECH GROUP LIMITED; *Int'l*, pg. 7928
TRI-TECH HOLDING INC.; *Int'l*, pg. 7918
TRI-TECH INFRASTRUCTURES, LLC. - J&Y WATER DIVISION—See Tri-Tech Holding Inc.; *Int'l*, pg. 7918
TRITECH INTERNATIONAL LIMITED—See Moog Inc.; *U.S. Public*, pg. 1471
TRITECH INTERNATIONAL, LLC—See C&G SYSTEMS INC.; *Int'l*, pg. 1238
TRI TECH LABORATORIES, INC.; *U.S. Private*, pg. 4221
TRI TECHNICAL CENTER USA, INC.—See Sumitomo Riko Company Limited; *Int'l*, pg. 7298
TRI TECHNO, LTD.—See Sumitomo Riko Company Limited; *Int'l*, pg. 7298
TRITECH SOFTWARE SYSTEMS INC.—See Vista Equity Partners, LLC; *U.S. Private*, pg. 4395
TRI-TECH SOLUTIONS, INC.—See 5th Gear Technologies Concepts, Inc.; *U.S. Private*, pg. 16
TRITECH VAVIE (SINGAPORE) PTE. LTD.—See Tritech Group Limited; *Int'l*, pg. 7928
TRITECH WATER TECHNOLOGIES PTE LTD—See Tritech Group Limited; *Int'l*, pg. 7928
TRI-TEC SEAL LLC—See Trelleborg AB; *Int'l*, pg. 7914
TRITEL AUSTRALIA PTY LIMITED—See Reverse Corp Limited; *Int'l*, pg. 6313
TRITEN CORPORATION; *U.S. Private*, pg. 4238
TRITENT INTERNATIONAL, CORP.; *Int'l*, pg. 7928
TRITENT INT'L AGRICULTURE, INC.; *U.S. Public*, pg. 2196
TRITERRAS, INC.; *Int'l*, pg. 7928
TRI TEST RESEARCH EUROPE GMBH—See Test Research Inc.; *Int'l*, pg. 7575
TRI-TEX CO INC—See SK Capital Partners, LP; *U.S. Private*, pg. 3680
TRITEX CORPORATION—See AMETEK, Inc.; *U.S. Public*, pg. 122
TRITEX SP. Z O.O.—See Marie Brizard Wine & Spirits S.A.; *Int'l*, pg. 4694
TRITIUM DCFC LIMITED—See Exicom Tele-Systems Limited; *Int'l*, pg. 2584
TRITIUM PARTNERS, LLC; *U.S. Private*, pg. 4238
TRITON ADVISERS LIMITED; *Int'l*, pg. 7928
TRITON ADVISERS S.A.R.L.—See Triton Advisers Limited; *Int'l*, pg. 7934
TRITON ADVISERS (SHANGHAI) CO. LTD—See Triton Advisers Limited; *Int'l*, pg. 7934
TRITON ADVISERS (SWEDEN) AB—See Triton Advisers Limited; *Int'l*, pg. 7934
TRITON ADVISERS (UK) LTD.—See Triton Advisers Limited; *Int'l*, pg. 7934
TRITON ASSET LEASING GMBH—See Transocean Ltd.; *Int'l*, pg. 7903
TRITON BETEILIGUNGSBERATUNG GMBH—See Triton Advisers Limited; *Int'l*, pg. 7934
TRITON CAPITAL PARTNERS LIMITED; *U.S. Private*, pg. 4238
TRITON COMMERCE, LLC; *U.S. Private*, pg. 4239
TRITON CONSOLIDATED, INC.; *U.S. Private*, pg. 4239
TRITON CONSTRUCTION LIMITED; *Int'l*, pg. 7935
TRITON CONTAINER INTERNATIONAL B.V.—See Brookfield Infrastructure Partners L.P.; *Int'l*, pg. 1190
TRITON CONTAINER INTERNATIONAL, GMBH—See Brookfield Infrastructure Partners L.P.; *Int'l*, pg. 1190
TRITON CONTAINER INTERNATIONAL LIMITED—See Brookfield Infrastructure Partners L.P.; *Int'l*, pg. 1190
TRITON CONTAINER INTERNATIONAL LIMITED—See Brookfield Infrastructure Partners L.P.; *Int'l*, pg. 1190
TRITON CONTAINER SOUTH AFRICA (PTY) LTD—See Brookfield Infrastructure Partners L.P.; *Int'l*, pg. 1190
TRITON CONTAINER (S) PTE LTD—See Brookfield Infrastructure Partners L.P.; *Int'l*, pg. 1190
TRITON CONTAINER SUL AMERICANA-TRANSPORTE E COMERCIO LTDA.—See Brookfield Infrastructure Partners L.P.; *Int'l*, pg. 1190
TRITON CONTAINER UK LIMITED—See Brookfield Infrastructure Partners L.P.; *Int'l*, pg. 1190
TRITON CORP. LTD.; *Int'l*, pg. 7935
TRITON CORP.; *U.S. Private*, pg. 4239
TRITON DEVELOPMENT S.A.; *Int'l*, pg. 7935
TRITON DIGITAL CANADA, INC.—See The E.W. Scripps Company; *U.S. Public*, pg. 2069
TRITON DIGITAL INC.—See iHeartMedia, Inc.; *U.S. Public*, pg. 1097
TRITON DIVING SERVICES, LLC; *U.S. Private*, pg. 4239
TRITON EMISSION SOLUTIONS INC.; *Int'l*, pg. 7935
TRITON GLOBAL SERVICES INC.—See NeoMedia Technologies, Inc.; *U.S. Public*, pg. 1506
TRITON HOLDING PUBLIC COMPANY LIMITED; *Int'l*, pg. 7935
TRITON INDUSTRIES, INC.; *U.S. Private*, pg. 4239
TRITON INTERNATIONAL AUSTRALIA PTY LTD—See Brookfield Infrastructure Partners L.P.; *Int'l*, pg. 1190
TRITON INTERNATIONAL DE MEXICO S.A. DE C.V.—See Noble Corporation plc; *Int'l*, pg. 5397
TRITON INTERNATIONAL, INC—See Noble Corporation plc; *Int'l*, pg. 5397
TRITON INTERNATIONAL LIMITED—See Brookfield Infrastructure Partners L.P.; *Int'l*, pg. 1189
TRITON INVESTMENT MANAGEMENT LIMITED—See Triton Advisers Limited; *Int'l*, pg. 7934
TRITON ITALY S.R.L.—See Brookfield Infrastructure Partners L.P.; *Int'l*, pg. 1190
TRITON LIMITED—See Brookfield Infrastructure Partners L.P.; *Int'l*, pg. 1190
TRITON MARINE CONSTRUCTION; *U.S. Private*, pg. 4239
TRITON MARKETING COMPANY; *U.S. Private*, pg. 4239
TRITON MEDIA, LLC—See Brookfield Corporation; *Int'l*, pg. 1184
TRITON PACIFIC CAPITAL PARTNERS LLC; *U.S. Private*, pg. 4239
TRITON PLC—See Norcros plc; *Int'l*, pg. 5415
TRITON PROJECTS—See Jacobs Engineering Group, Inc.; *U.S. Public*, pg. 1185
TRITON SERVICES INC.; *U.S. Private*, pg. 4239
TRITON SUBMARINES, LLC; *U.S. Private*, pg. 4239
TRITON SYSTEMS INC.; *U.S. Private*, pg. 4239
TRITON TECHNOLOGIES, INC.; *U.S. Private*, pg. 4239
TRITON TIMBER S.A.S.—See Voltalia S.A.; *Int'l*, pg. 8303
TRITON VALVES LTD.; *Int'l*, pg. 7936
TRITON WATER AG; *Int'l*, pg. 7936
TRI TOOL INC.; *U.S. Private*, pg. 4221
TRI TOOL INTERNATIONAL—See Tri Tool Inc.; *U.S. Private*, pg. 4221
TRI TOOL POWER SERVICES, INC.—See Tri Tool Inc.; *U.S. Private*, pg. 4221
TRITRONICS, INC.—See Bain Capital, LP; *U.S. Private*, pg. 444
TRITTON RESOURCES LIMITED—See Aeris Resources Limited; *Int'l*, pg. 180
TRIULZI AG—See Burkhalter Holding AG; *Int'l*, pg. 1226
TRIUMFUS ONION PRODUCTS ONIONS B.V.—See Top Taste Holding BV; *Int'l*, pg. 7813
TRIUM N.V.—See London Security PLC; *Int'l*, pg. 4547
TRIUMPH ACCESSORY SERVICES-GRAND PRAIRIE, INC.—See Triumph Group, Inc.; *U.S. Public*, pg. 2196
TRIUMPH ACTUATION SYSTEMS-CONNECTICUT, LLC—See Triumph Group, Inc.; *U.S. Public*, pg. 2196
TRIUMPH ACTUATION SYSTEMS - ISLE OF MAN, LTD.—See Triumph Group, Inc.; *U.S. Public*, pg. 2196

COMPANY NAME INDEX

TRIUMPH ACTUATION SYSTEMS, LLC—See Triumph Group, Inc.; *U.S. Public*, pg. 2196
TRIUMPH ACTUATION SYSTEMS-UK, LTD. - CHELTENHAM—See Triumph Group, Inc.; *U.S. Public*, pg. 2196
TRIUMPH ACTUATION SYSTEMS-VALENCIA, LLC—See Triumph Group, Inc.; *U.S. Public*, pg. 2196
TRIUMPH ACTUATION SYSTEMS-YAKIMA, LLC—See Triumph Group, Inc.; *U.S. Public*, pg. 2196
TRIUMPH-ADLER EXPERTS AT OUTPUT GMBH—See KYOCERA Corporation; *Int'l*, pg. 4358
TRIUMPH AEROSPACE SYSTEMS GROUP, LLC—See Triumph Group, Inc.; *U.S. Public*, pg. 2196
TRIUMPH AEROSTRUCTURES GROUP—See Triumph Group, Inc.; *U.S. Public*, pg. 2196
TRIUMPH AEROSTRUCTURES - TULSA, LLC—See Triumph Group, Inc.; *U.S. Public*, pg. 2196
TRIUMPH AFTERMARKET SERVICES GROUP, LLC—See Triumph Group, Inc.; *U.S. Public*, pg. 2197
TRIUMPH AIRBORNE STRUCTURES, LLC—See Triumph Group, Inc.; *U.S. Public*, pg. 2197
TRIUMPHAL ASSOCIATES BHD.; *Int'l*, pg. 7936
TRIUMPHAL EQUIPMENT SPARE PARTS SDN. BHD.—See Triumphal Associates Bhd.; *Int'l*, pg. 7936
TRIUMPHAL MACHINERY SUPPLY SDN. BHD.—See Triumphal Associates Bhd.; *Int'l*, pg. 7936
TRIUMPH AVIATION SERVICES - NAAS DIVISION—See STS Aviation Group; *U.S. Private*, pg. 3842
TRIUMPH BUDAPEST—See Triumph Motorcycles Limited; *Int'l*, pg. 7936
TRIUMPH BUENOS AIRES—See Triumph Motorcycles Limited; *Int'l*, pg. 7936
TRIUMPH CAPITAL, L.P.; *U.S. Private*, pg. 4239
TRIUMPH COLOMBIA S.A.S.—See Triumph Motorcycles Limited; *Int'l*, pg. 7936
TRIUMPH COMPOSITE SYSTEMS, INC.—See Triumph Group, Inc.; *U.S. Public*, pg. 2196
TRIUMPH CONTROLS FRANCE SAS—See Triumph Group, Inc.; *U.S. Public*, pg. 2197
TRIUMPH CONTROLS, LLC—See Triumph Group, Inc.; *U.S. Public*, pg. 2196
TRIUMPH CONTROLS-UK, LTD.—See Triumph Group, Inc.; *U.S. Public*, pg. 2196
TRIUMPH CORPORATION, LTD.; *Int'l*, pg. 7936
TRIUMPH COSTA RICA—See Triumph Motorcycles Limited; *Int'l*, pg. 7936
TRIUMPH ENGINE CONTROL SYSTEMS, LLC—See Triumph Group, Inc.; *U.S. Public*, pg. 2197
TRIUMPH ENGINEERED SOLUTIONS, INC.—See Triumph Group, Inc.; *U.S. Public*, pg. 2197
TRIUMPH ENGINEERING SERVICES, INC.—See Triumph Group, Inc.; *U.S. Public*, pg. 2197
TRIUMPH ENTERPRISES INC; *U.S. Private*, pg. 4239
TRIUMPH FABRICATIONS-FORT WORTH, INC.—See Arlington Capital Partners LLC; *U.S. Private*, pg. 328
TRIUMPH FABRICATIONS - ORANGEBURG, INC.—See Triumph Group, Inc.; *U.S. Public*, pg. 2197
TRIUMPH FABRICATIONS-SAN DIEGO, INC.—See Arlington Capital Partners LLC; *U.S. Private*, pg. 328
TRIUMPH FABRICATIONS-ST. LOUIS, INC.—See Triumph Group, Inc.; *U.S. Public*, pg. 2196
TRIUMPH FINANCIAL, INC.; *U.S. Public*, pg. 2196
TRIUMPH FRANCE SA—See Triumph Motorcycles Limited; *Int'l*, pg. 7936
TRIUMPH GEAR SYSTEMS, INC.—See Triumph Group, Inc.; *U.S. Public*, pg. 2196
TRIUMPH GEAR SYSTEMS-MACOMB, INC.—See Triumph Group, Inc.; *U.S. Public*, pg. 2196
TRIUMPH GEAR SYSTEMS-TORONTO, ULC—See Triumph Group, Inc.; *U.S. Public*, pg. 2197
TRIUMPH GEO-SYNTHETICS, INC.—See Clayton, Dubilier & Rice, LLC; *U.S. Private*, pg. 930
TRIUMPH GOLD CORP.; *Int'l*, pg. 7936
TRIUMPH GROUP, INC.; *U.S. Public*, pg. 2196
TRIUMPH GROUP -MEXICO S. DE R.L. DE C.V.—See Triumph Group, Inc.; *U.S. Public*, pg. 2197
TRIUMPH GUATEMALA—See Triumph Motorcycles Limited; *Int'l*, pg. 7936
TRIUMPH HIGHER EDUCATION GROUP, LLC; *U.S. Private*, pg. 4239
TRIUMPH HOSPITAL NORTHWEST INDIANA, LLC—See Apollo Global Management, Inc.; *U.S. Public*, pg. 157
TRIUMPH INSTRUMENTS-BURBANK, INC.—See Triumph Group, Inc.; *U.S. Public*, pg. 2197
TRIUMPH INSULATION SYSTEMS, LLC—See Triumph Group, Inc.; *U.S. Public*, pg. 2196
TRIUMPH INSULATION SYSTEMS—See Triumph Group, Inc.; *U.S. Public*, pg. 2197
TRIUMPH INTERIORS, LLC—See Triumph Group, Inc.; *U.S. Public*, pg. 2196
TRIUMPH INTERNATIONAL AG; *Int'l*, pg. 7936
TRIUMPH INTERNATIONAL FINANCE INDIA LTD.; *Int'l*, pg. 7936
TRIUMPH INTERNATIONAL INDIA (PVT) LTD—See Triumph International AG; *Int'l*, pg. 7936
TRIUMPH INTERNATIONAL—See Triumph International AG; *Int'l*, pg. 7936
TRIUMPH LEARNING, LLC—See School Specialty, Inc.; *U.S. Public*, pg. 1848

TRIUMPH LUCK LIMITED—See Fountain Set (Holdings) Limited; *Int'l*, pg. 2754
TRIUMPH MODULAR, INC.—See Tecno Fast SA; *Int'l*, pg. 7516
TRIUMPH MOTOCICLETAS ESPANA S. L.—See Triumph Motorcycles Limited; *Int'l*, pg. 7936
TRIUMPH MOTORCYCLES AB—See Triumph Motorcycles Limited; *Int'l*, pg. 7936
TRIUMPH MOTORCYCLES BENELUX B.V.—See Triumph Motorcycles Limited; *Int'l*, pg. 7936
TRIUMPH MOTORCYCLES (INDIA) PRIVATE LIMITED—See Triumph Motorcycles Limited; *Int'l*, pg. 7936
TRIUMPH MOTORCYCLES LIMITED; *Int'l*, pg. 7936
TRIUMPH MOTORCYCLES SLOVAKIA S.R.O.—See Triumph Motorcycles Limited; *Int'l*, pg. 7936
TRIUMPH MOTORCYCLES SOUTH AFRICA—See Triumph Motorcycles Limited; *Int'l*, pg. 7936
TRIUMPH MOTORCYCLES SRL—See Triumph Motorcycles Limited; *Int'l*, pg. 7936
TRIUMPH MOTORRAD DEUTSCHLAND GMBH—See Triumph Motorcycles Limited; *Int'l*, pg. 7936
TRIUMPH ON-DEMAND, INC.—See Genpact Limited; *Int'l*, pg. 2927
TRIUMPH PET INDUSTRIES, INC.—See Sunshine Mills Inc.; *U.S. Private*, pg. 3872
TRIUMPH POLSKA—See Triumph Motorcycles Limited; *Int'l*, pg. 7936
TRIUMPH PROCESSING, INC.—See ATL Partners, LLC; *U.S. Private*, pg. 369
TRIUMPH PROCESSING, INC.—See British Columbia Investment Management Corp.; *Int'l*, pg. 1170
TRIUMPH REHABILITATION HOSPITAL OF NORTHEAST HOUSTON, LLC—See Apollo Global Management, Inc.; *U.S. Public*, pg. 157
TRIUMPH RESOURCES INC—See Chaparral Energy, Inc.; *U.S. Private*, pg. 849
TRIUMPH RUSSIA—See Triumph Motorcycles Limited; *Int'l*, pg. 7936
TRIUMPH S.A.S.—See Triumph Motorcycles Limited; *Int'l*, pg. 7936
TRIUMPH SCIENCE & TECHNOLOGY CO., LTD.; *Int'l*, pg. 7936
TRIUMPH STRUCTURES-EAST TEXAS, INC.—See Triumph Group, Inc.; *U.S. Public*, pg. 2196
TRIUMPH STRUCTURES - FARNBOROUGH, LTD.—See Triumph Group, Inc.; *U.S. Public*, pg. 2197
TRIUMPH STRUCTURES-KANSAS CITY, INC.—See Triumph Group, Inc.; *U.S. Public*, pg. 2197
TRIUMPH STRUCTURES-LONG ISLAND, LLC—See Triumph Group, Inc.; *U.S. Public*, pg. 2197
TRIUMPH STRUCTURES-LOS ANGELES, INC.—See ATL Partners, LLC; *U.S. Private*, pg. 369
TRIUMPH STRUCTURES-LOS ANGELES, INC.—See British Columbia Investment Management Corp.; *Int'l*, pg. 1170
TRIUMPH STRUCTURES-WICHITA, INC.—See Triumph Group, Inc.; *U.S. Public*, pg. 2197
TRIUMPH THERMAL SYSTEMS, LLC—See Triumph Group, Inc.; *U.S. Public*, pg. 2196
TRIUMPH TUBULAR & SUPPLY LTD—See Russel Metals Inc.; *Int'l*, pg. 6430
TRIUNE IP, LLC—See Semtech Corporation; *U.S. Public*, pg. 1864
TRIUNE SYSTEMS, LLC—See Semtech Corporation; *U.S. Public*, pg. 1864
TRIUNFO IMPORT & EXPORT FOOD—See Seabra Group; *U.S. Private*, pg. 3583
TRI-UNION FROZEN PRODUCTS, INC.—See Thai Union Group Public Company Limited; *Int'l*, pg. 7597
TRI-UNION FROZEN PRODUCTS NORTH AMERICA, LLC—See Thai Union Group Public Company Limited; *Int'l*, pg. 7597
TRI-UNION SEAFOODS LLC—See Thai Union Group Public Company Limited; *Int'l*, pg. 7597
TRIUNITY ENGINEERING & MANAGEMENT, INC.—See H.W. Lochner, Inc.; *U.S. Private*, pg. 1836
TRI USA, INC.—See Sumitomo Riko Company Limited; *Int'l*, pg. 7298
TRIUS TRAPS, LLC—See Lyman Products Corporation; *U.S. Private*, pg. 2520
TRIVAGO N.V.; *Int'l*, pg. 7937
TRIVAGO SPAIN, S.L.—See Expedia Group, Inc.; *U.S. Public*, pg. 810
TRI-VALLEY HERALD—See Alden Global Capital LLC; *U.S. Public*, pg. 155
TRI-VALLEY MINOR HOCKEY ASSOCIATION; *U.S. Private*, pg. 4224
TRI-VALLEY OPPORTUNITY COUNCIL, INC.; *U.S. Private*, pg. 4224
TRI-VALLEY RESELLER, LLC—See Workday, Inc.; *U.S. Public*, pg. 2378
TRI-VALLEY TRANSPORT & STORAGE; *U.S. Private*, pg. 4224
TRIVANTAGE, LLC—See Glen Raven, Inc.; *U.S. Private*, pg. 1709
TRIVANTAGE PTY LTD.—See Southern Cross Electrical Engineering Limited; *Int'l*, pg. 7119

TRIYARDS HOLDINGS LIMITED

TRIVANTIS CORPORATION—See Fundos Group LLC; *U.S. Private*, pg. 1623
TRIVANTIS CORPORATION—See Trinity Private Equity Group, LLC; *U.S. Private*, pg. 4235
TRIVASCULAR GERMANY GMBH—See Endologix, Inc.; *U.S. Private*, pg. 1392
TRIVASCULAR, INC.—See Endologix, Inc.; *U.S. Private*, pg. 1392
TRIVASCULAR TECHNOLOGIES, INC.—See Endologix, Inc.; *U.S. Private*, pg. 1392
TRI-VAX ENTERPRISES LTD.—See Clean Harbors, Inc.; *U.S. Public*, pg. 510
TRIVE CAPITAL INC.; *U.S. Private*, pg. 4239
TRIVE CAPITAL MANAGEMENT LLC—See Trive Capital Inc.; *U.S. Private*, pg. 4240
TRIVEC-AVANT CORPORATION—See Advent International Corporation; *U.S. Private*, pg. 100
TRIVENI ENGINEERING & INDUSTRIES LTD; *Int'l*, pg. 7937
TRIVENI ENTERPRISES LIMITED; *Int'l*, pg. 7937
TRIVENI GLASS LIMITED; *Int'l*, pg. 7937
TRIVENI TURBINE LIMITED—See Triveni Engineering & Industries Ltd; *Int'l*, pg. 7937
TRIVENTO BODEGAS Y VINEDOS S.A.—See Vina Concha y Toro S.A.; *Int'l*, pg. 8209
TRI-VENTURE MARKETING LLC—See Leonard Green & Partners, L.P.; *U.S. Private*, pg. 2423
TRIVE PROPERTY GROUP BERHAD; *Int'l*, pg. 7937
TRIVERIO SAS—See VINCI S.A.; *Int'l*, pg. 8235
TRIVEST PARTNERS, LP; *U.S. Private*, pg. 4240
TRIVIDIA HEALTH, INC.—See Sinocare Inc.; *Int'l*, pg. 6949
TRIVIDIA MANUFACTURING SOLUTIONS, INC.—See Sinocare Inc.; *Int'l*, pg. 6949
TRI VIET ASSET MANAGEMENT CORPORATION JOINT STOCK COMPANY; *Int'l*, pg. 7918
TRI VIET SECURITIES JSC; *Int'l*, pg. 7918
TRIVIT MLIN A.D.; *Int'l*, pg. 7937
TRIVIT PEK A.D.; *Int'l*, pg. 7937
TRIVIUM SYSTEMS, INC.—See Provana LLC; *U.S. Private*, pg. 3291
TRIVNET LTD—See Thales S.A.; *Int'l*, pg. 7600
TRI-WALL (ASIA) PTE. LTD.—See Rengo Co., Ltd.; *Int'l*, pg. 6282
TRI-WALL AUSTRIA PACKAGING SYSTEMS GMBH—See Rengo Co., Ltd.; *Int'l*, pg. 6282
TRI-WALL INTERNATIONAL TRADING CO., LTD.—See Rengo Co., Ltd.; *Int'l*, pg. 6282
TRI-WALL JAPAN CO., LTD.—See Rengo Co., Ltd.; *Int'l*, pg. 6282
TRI-WALL K.K.; *Int'l*, pg. 7918
TRI-WALL KOREA CO., LTD.—See Rengo Co., Ltd.; *Int'l*, pg. 6282
TRI-WALL LIMITED—See Rengo Co., Ltd.; *Int'l*, pg. 6282
TRI-WALL LTD—See Veridis Environment Ltd; *Int'l*, pg. 8168
TRI-WALL (MALAYSIA) SDN. BHD.—See Rengo Co., Ltd.; *Int'l*, pg. 6282
TRI-WALL PACKAGING (FUZHOU) CO., LTD.—See Rengo Co., Ltd.; *Int'l*, pg. 6282
TRI-WALL PACKAGING (JIANGSU) CO., LTD.—See Rengo Co., Ltd.; *Int'l*, pg. 6282
TRI-WALL PACKAGING (THAI) LTD.—See Rengo Co., Ltd.; *Int'l*, pg. 6282
TRI-WALL PAK PRIVATE LIMITED—See Rengo Co., Ltd.; *Int'l*, pg. 6282
TRI-WALL POLSKA SP. Z O.O.—See Rengo Co., Ltd.; *Int'l*, pg. 6282
TRI-WALL SLOVAKIA, S.R.O.—See Rengo Co., Ltd.; *Int'l*, pg. 6282
TRI-WALL SWANSEA LIMITED—See Rengo Co., Ltd.; *Int'l*, pg. 6282
TRI-WALL (THAILAND) LTD.—See Rengo Co., Ltd.; *Int'l*, pg. 6282
TRI-WALL UK LIMITED—See Rengo Co., Ltd.; *Int'l*, pg. 6282
TRI-WALL VINA PACK COMPANY LIMITED—See Rengo Co., Ltd.; *Int'l*, pg. 6282
TRIWAYS LOGISTICS USA INC.; *U.S. Private*, pg. 4241
TRIWEST CAPITAL MANAGEMENT CORP.; *Int'l*, pg. 7937
TRI-WEST LTD.; *U.S. Private*, pg. 4224
TRI-WEST OF HAWAII INC.—See Tri-West Ltd.; *U.S. Private*, pg. 4225
TRI-W GROUP, INC.—See OEP Capital Advisors, L.P.; *U.S. Private*, pg. 3000
TRI-WIN; *U.S. Private*, pg. 4225
TRI-WIRE ENGINEERING SOLUTIONS, INC.; *U.S. Private*, pg. 4225
TRI-WORTH SOLUTIONS, LLC—See The Advanced Group of Companies; *U.S. Private*, pg. 3982
TRIXELL—See Thales S.A.; *Int'l*, pg. 7603
TRIX S.R.L.—See Tinexta S.p.A.; *Int'l*, pg. 7753
TRIYARDS HOLDINGS LIMITED; *Int'l*, pg. 7937
TRI YEOVIL UK LIMITED—See Frasers Group plc; *Int'l*, pg. 2765
TRIZETTO CORPORATION—See Cognizant Technology Solutions Corporation; *U.S. Public*, pg. 525

TRIZETTO CORP. - UNION REGIONAL OFFICE—See Cognizant Technology Solutions Corporation; *U.S. Public*, pg. 525
TRIZETTO INDIA PRIVATE LIMITED—See Cognizant Technology Solutions Corporation; *U.S. Public*, pg. 525
TRIZETTO PROVIDER SOLUTIONS, LLC - NHXS—See Cognizant Technology Solutions Corporation; *U.S. Public*, pg. 525
TRIZETTO PROVIDER SOLUTIONS, LLC—See Cognizant Technology Solutions Corporation; *U.S. Public*, pg. 525
TRIZETTO SERVICES INDIA PRIVATE LIMITED—See Cognizant Technology Solutions Corporation; *U.S. Public*, pg. 525
TR KEBA LTD—See Trifast plc; *Int'l*, pg. 7921
TR KENZAI CO., LTD.—See Bunka Shutter Co., Ltd.; *Int'l*, pg. 1216
TR KUHLMANN GMBH—See Trifast plc; *Int'l*, pg. 7921
TR LAKESHORE MANAGEMENT LLC—See Hyatt Hotels Corporation; *U.S. Public*, pg. 1078
TRL CHINA LIMITED—See Tata Sons Limited; *Int'l*, pg. 7468
TRL COMPLIANCE SERVICES LIMITED—See Ecolab Inc.; *U.S. Public*, pg. 712
TRL KROSAKI CHINA LIMITED—See Krosaki Harima Corporation; *Int'l*, pg. 4307
TRL KROSAKI REFRACTORIES LIMITED—See Tata Sons Limited; *Int'l*, pg. 7468
TRL TECHNOLOGY LIMITED—See L3Harris Technologies, Inc.; *U.S. Public*, pg. 1284
TR MANUFACTURING, LLC—See Corning Incorporated; *U.S. Public*, pg. 579
T&R MARKET INC.; *U.S. Private*, pg. 3910
TRM COPY CENTERS, LLC—See Marlin Equity Partners, LLC; *U.S. Private*, pg. 2584
TRMC SAS—See VINCI S.A.; *Int'l*, pg. 8229
T.R. MCTAGGART—See Forward Corporation; *U.S. Private*, pg. 1578
TRM EQUITY LLC; *U.S. Private*, pg. 4241
TRMI, INC.—See Tokai Rika Co., Ltd.; *Int'l*, pg. 7780
T.R. MILLER CO., INC.—See Stran & Company, Inc.; *U.S. Public*, pg. 1953
TR MILLER HOLDING B.V.—See Trifast plc; *Int'l*, pg. 7921
TRM INC.; *U.S. Private*, pg. 4241
TRM LLC—See T.RAD Co., Ltd.; *Int'l*, pg. 7397
TRM S.P.A.—See Iren S.p.A.; *Int'l*, pg. 3808
TRM S.R.L.—See Marangoni S.p.A.; *Int'l*, pg. 4688
TRN CAPITAL MANAGEMENT, INC.—See Huxley Corporation; *Int'l*, pg. 3538
TRND SARL—See Bertelsmann SE & Co. KGaA; *Int'l*, pg. 997
TR NEW YORK MANAGEMENT LLC—See Hyatt Hotels Corporation; *U.S. Public*, pg. 1078
TRN INVESTMENT MANAGEMENT, INC.—See Huxley Corporation; *Int'l*, pg. 3538
TRNLWB, LLC—See Trinity Industries, Inc.; *U.S. Public*, pg. 2193
TRNLWS, LLC—See Trinity Industries, Inc.; *U.S. Public*, pg. 2193
TR NORGE AS—See Trifast plc; *Int'l*, pg. 7921
TROAX AB—See Troax Group AB; *Int'l*, pg. 7938
TROAX BV—See Troax Group AB; *Int'l*, pg. 7938
TROAX DENMARK A/S—See Troax Group AB; *Int'l*, pg. 7938
TROAX GMBH—See Troax Group AB; *Int'l*, pg. 7938
TROAX GROUP AB; *Int'l*, pg. 7937
TROAX GUVENLIK SISTEMLERI HIZ, VE TIC. LTD.STI.—See Troax Group AB; *Int'l*, pg. 7938
TROAX, INC.—See Troax Group AB; *Int'l*, pg. 7938
TROAX LEE MANUFACTURING LTD.—See Troax Group AB; *Int'l*, pg. 7938
TROAX NORDIC AB—See Troax Group AB; *Int'l*, pg. 7938
TROAX NORDIC AS—See Troax Group AB; *Int'l*, pg. 7938
TROAX SAFETY SYSTEMS CO., LTD.—See Troax Group AB; *Int'l*, pg. 7938
TROAX SAFETY SYSTEMS INDIA PRIVATE LIMITED—See Troax Group AB; *Int'l*, pg. 7938
TROAX SAFETY SYSTEMS POLAND SP.Z.O.O—See Troax Group AB; *Int'l*, pg. 7938
TROAX SAFETY SYSTEMS PTY LTD—See Troax Group AB; *Int'l*, pg. 7938
TROAX SA—See Troax Group AB; *Int'l*, pg. 7938
TROAX SCHWEIZ AG—See Troax Group AB; *Int'l*, pg. 7938
TROAX SHANGHAI SAFETY SYSTEM CO., LTD.—See Troax Group AB; *Int'l*, pg. 7938
TROAX SYSTEM SL—See Troax Group AB; *Int'l*, pg. 7938
TROAX UK LTD.—See Troax Group AB; *Int'l*, pg. 7938
T-ROBOTICS CO., LTD.; *Int'l*, pg. 7396
TROC DE L ILE SA; *Int'l*, pg. 7938
TROCELLEN GMBH—See The Furukawa Electric Co., Ltd.; *Int'l*, pg. 7647
TROCELLEN IBERICA S.A.—See The Furukawa Electric Co., Ltd.; *Int'l*, pg. 7647
TROCELLEN ITALIA HOLDING S.R.L.—See The Furukawa Electric Co., Ltd.; *Int'l*, pg. 7647
TROCELLEN ITALY S.P.A.—See The Furukawa Electric Co., Ltd.; *Int'l*, pg. 7647
TROCELLEN S.E.A. SDN. BHD.—See The Furukawa Electric Co., Ltd.; *Int'l*, pg. 7647

TRODAT GMBH; *Int'l*, pg. 7938
TROFHOLZ TECHNOLOGIES, INC.; *U.S. Private*, pg. 4241
TROIA EMPREENDIMENTOS IMOBILIARIOS LTDA.—See Mercedes-Benz Group AG; *Int'l*, pg. 4829
TROIKA, INC.—See Troika Media Group, Inc.; *U.S. Public*, pg. 2197
TROIKA MEDIA GROUP, INC.; *U.S. Public*, pg. 2197
TROILUS GOLD CORP.; *Int'l*, pg. 7938
TROILUS GOLD CORP.; *Int'l*, pg. 7938
TROIS ELECTRONICS (WUXI) CO., LTD.—See Di-Nikko Engineering Co., Ltd.; *Int'l*, pg. 2101
TROIS ENGINEERING PRETEC HONG KONG LTD—See Di-Nikko Engineering Co., Ltd.; *Int'l*, pg. 2101
TROIS TAKAYA ELECTRONICS (THAILAND) CO., LTD.—See Di-Nikko Engineering Co., Ltd.; *Int'l*, pg. 2101
TROIS (THAILAND) CO., LTD.—See Di-Nikko Engineering Co., Ltd.; *Int'l*, pg. 2101
TROIS VIETNAM CO., LTD.—See Di-Nikko Engineering Co., Ltd.; *Int'l*, pg. 2101
TROITEC AUTOMOTIVE ELECTRONICS CO., LTD.—See Titan Invo Technology Limited; *Int'l*, pg. 7760
TROJAN BATTERY COMPANY—See KPS Capital Partners, LP; *U.S. Private*, pg. 2347
TROJAN CONSTRUCTION GROUP - SOLE PROPRIETORSHIP LLC—See Alpha Dhabi Holding PJSC; *Int'l*, pg. 368
TROJAN ELECTRONIC SUPPLY CO., INC.; *U.S. Private*, pg. 4241
TROJAN GENERAL CONTRACTING LLC—See Alpha Dhabi Holding PJSC; *Int'l*, pg. 368
TROJAN GOLD INC.; *Int'l*, pg. 7938
TROJAN HOLDINGS LTD.; *Int'l*, pg. 7938
TROJANLABEL APS—See AstroNova, Inc.; *U.S. Public*, pg. 218
TROJAN LITHOGRAPH CORPORATION—See Great Mill Rock LLC; *U.S. Private*, pg. 1766
TROJAN RECYCLING INC—See Waste Connections, Inc.; *Int'l*, pg. 8352
TROJAN TECHNOLOGIES GROUP ULC—See Danaher Corporation; *U.S. Public*, pg. 631
TROJAN TECHNOLOGIES, INC.—See Danaher Corporation; *U.S. Public*, pg. 631
TROJANUV TECHNOLOGIES LIMITED—See Danaher Corporation; *U.S. Public*, pg. 631
TROKOST GMBH; *Int'l*, pg. 7938
TROLEX CORP.; *U.S. Private*, pg. 4241
TROLLANDTOAD.COM; *U.S. Private*, pg. 4241
TROLLHATTANS TERMINAL AB—See Katoen Natie N.V.; *Int'l*, pg. 4091
TROMA ENTERTAINMENT INC.; *U.S. Private*, pg. 4241
TR OMAN LLC—See W.J. Towell & Co. LLC; *Int'l*, pg. 8322
TROMBETTA MOTION TECHNOLOGIES, INC.—See Fulham & Co., Inc.; *U.S. Private*, pg. 1620
TROMBO EXTRACTIONS LIMITED; *Int'l*, pg. 7938
TROMMSDORFF GMBH & CO. KG—See Dermapharm Holding SE; *Int'l*, pg. 2043
TROMP GROUP AMERICAS, LLC—See Markel Group Inc.; *U.S. Public*, pg. 1369
TROMP GROUP B.V.—See Markel Group Inc.; *U.S. Public*, pg. 1369
TROMS BILDELSENTER AS—See LKQ Corporation; *U.S. Public*, pg. 2193
TROMS OFFSHORE FLEET 2 AS—See Tidewater Inc.; *U.S. Public*, pg. 2158
TRONAIR, INC.—See Golden Gate Capital Management II, LLC; *U.S. Private*, pg. 1732
TRONA RAILWAY COMPANY LLC—See NIRMA LIMITED; *Int'l*, pg. 5363
TRONDHEIM ENERGI AS—See Statkraft AS; *Int'l*, pg. 7185
TRONDHEIM KRAFT AS—See Statkraft AS; *Int'l*, pg. 7185
TRONE BRAND ENERGY, INC.; *U.S. Private*, pg. 4241
TRONEX INTERNATIONAL INC.; *U.S. Private*, pg. 4241
TRON GROUP INC.; *Int'l*, pg. 7938
TRONICOM CORP.; *U.S. Private*, pg. 4241
TRONICS MICROSYSTEMS S.A.—See TDK Corporation; *Int'l*, pg. 7489
TRONOX B.V.—See Tronox Holdings plc; *U.S. Public*, pg. 2197
TRONOX FINANCE B.V.—See Tronox Holdings plc; *U.S. Public*, pg. 2197
TRONOX GLOBAL HOLDINGS PTY LIMITED—See Tronox Holdings plc; *U.S. Public*, pg. 2197
TRONOX HOLDINGS PLC; *U.S. Public*, pg. 2197
TRONOX INCORPORATED—See Tronox Holdings plc; *U.S. Public*, pg. 2197
TRONOX KZN SANDS PROPRIETARY LIMITED—See Tronox Holdings plc; *U.S. Public*, pg. 2197
TRONOX LLC - GREEN RIVER SODA ASH PLANT—See Tronox Holdings plc; *U.S. Public*, pg. 2197
TRONOX LLC—See Tronox Holdings plc; *U.S. Public*, pg. 2197
TRONOX PIGMENTOS DO BRASIL S.A.—See LyondellBasell Industries N.V.; *Int'l*, pg. 4608
TRONOX PIGMENTS (HOLLAND) B.V.—See Tronox Holdings plc; *U.S. Public*, pg. 2197

TRONOX PIGMENTS (NETHERLANDS) B.V.—See Tronox Holdings plc; *U.S. Public*, pg. 2197
TRONOX PIGMENTS PTY. LIMITED—See Tronox Holdings plc; *U.S. Public*, pg. 2197
TRONOX PIGMENTS (SINGAPORE) PTE. LTD.—See Tronox Holdings plc; *U.S. Public*, pg. 2197
TRONOX US HOLDINGS INC.—See Tronox Holdings plc; *U.S. Public*, pg. 2197
TRONOX WESTERN AUSTRALIA PTY. LTD.—See Tronox Holdings plc; *U.S. Public*, pg. 2197
TRONSER, INC.—See Alfred Tronser GmbH; *Int'l*, pg. 317
TRONY EAST AFRICA LIMITED—See Trony Solar Holdings Company Limited; *Int'l*, pg. 7938
TRONY SOLAR HOLDINGS COMPANY LIMITED; *Int'l*, pg. 7938
TRONY SOLAR HOLDINGS (HONG KONG) LIMITED—See Trony Solar Holdings Company Limited; *Int'l*, pg. 7939
TROON ENTERPRISES INC.; *U.S. Private*, pg. 4242
TROON GOLF L.L.C.; *U.S. Private*, pg. 4242
TROON MANAGEMENT CORPORATION—See Old Republic International Corporation; *U.S. Public*, pg. 1569
TROOPSDIRECT; *U.S. Private*, pg. 4242
TROOPS, INC.; *Int'l*, pg. 7939
TROPAR MFG. CO., INC.—See Tropar Mfg. Co., Inc.; *U.S. Private*, pg. 4242
TROPAR MFG. CO., INC.; *U.S. Private*, pg. 4242
TROPAR MFG. CO., INC.—See Tropar Mfg. Co., Inc.; *U.S. Private*, pg. 4242
TROPEX PLANT SALES LEASING & MAINTENANCE, INC.; *U.S. Private*, pg. 4242
TROPHIC CANADA LTD.—See Nestle S.A.; *Int'l*, pg. 5206
TROPHY CLUB MEDICAL CENTER, L.P.—See Tenet Healthcare Corporation; *U.S. Public*, pg. 2013
TROPHY HOLDINGS INC.; *U.S. Private*, pg. 4242
TROPHY NISSAN, INC.; *U.S. Private*, pg. 4242
TROPHY NUT CO.; *U.S. Private*, pg. 4242
TROPHY RESOURCES, INC.; *U.S. Public*, pg. 2198
TROPHY SIGNATURE HOMES, LLC—See Green Brick Partners, Inc.; *U.S. Public*, pg. 963
TROPIC AIR; *Int'l*, pg. 7939
TROPICAL AQUACULTURE PRODUCTS, INC.—See GeneSeas Aquacultura Ltda.; *Int'l*, pg. 2921
TROPICAL BATTERY COMPANY LIMITED; *U.S. Public*, pg. 2198
TROPICAL BATTERY USA, LLC—See Tropical Battery Company Limited; *U.S. Public*, pg. 2198
TROPICAL BLOSSOM HONEY CO, INC.; *U.S. Private*, pg. 4242
TROPICAL BOTANICS SDN BHD—See Holista ColiTech Limited; *Int'l*, pg. 3451
TROPICAL CANNING (THAILAND) PUBLIC COMPANY LIMITED; *Int'l*, pg. 7939
TROPICAL CHEESE INDUSTRIES, INC.; *U.S. Private*, pg. 4242
TROPICAL COFFEE COMPANY S.A.S.—See Grupo Nutresa S.A.; *Int'l*, pg. 3133
TROPICAL COMMUNICATIONS, INC.—See High Wire Networks Inc.; *U.S. Public*, pg. 1035
TROPICAL CORPORATION—See Tropical Canning (Thailand) Public Company Limited; *Int'l*, pg. 7939
TROPICALE FOODS, LLC—See Wind Point Advisors LLC; *U.S. Private*, pg. 4536
TROPICAL EXTERMINATORS LIMITED—See Rentokil Initial plc; *Int'l*, pg. 6289
TROPICAL FOOD MANUFACTURING (NINGBO) CO LTD—See Tropical Canning (Thailand) Public Company Limited; *Int'l*, pg. 7939
TROPICAL ISLAND MANAGEMENT GMBH—See Newgate Private Equity LLP; *Int'l*, pg. 5235
TROPICAL LAUNDRIES—See Goddard Enterprises Limited; *Int'l*, pg. 3019
TROPICAL MARINE CENTRE LTD.—See Westland Horticulture Ltd.; *Int'l*, pg. 8390
TROPICAL NUT & FRUIT CO; *U.S. Private*, pg. 4242
TROPICAL SHELL & GIFTS INC—See Historic Tours of America Inc.; *U.S. Private*, pg. 1952
TROPICAL SHIPPING & CONSTRUCTION COMPANY LIMITED—See Saltchuk Resources Inc.; *U.S. Private*, pg. 3534
TROPICAL SKY LTD.; *Int'l*, pg. 7939
TROPICAL SMOOTHIE CAFE, LLC—See Levine Leichtman Capital Partners, LLC; *U.S. Private*, pg. 2436
TROPICAL SMOOTHIE FRANCHISE DEVELOPMENT CORP.—See BIP Opportunities Fund, LP; *U.S. Private*, pg. 563
TROPICAL TRANSPORTES IPIRANGA LTDA.—See Ultrapar Participacoes S.A.; *Int'l*, pg. 8019
TROPICANA ALVALLE S.L.—See PepsiCo, Inc.; *U.S. Public*, pg. 1672
TROPICANA BRANDS GROUP, INC.—See PAI Partners S.A.S.; *Int'l*, pg. 5702
TROPICANA CHERAS SDN. BHD.—See Tropicana Corporation Berhad; *Int'l*, pg. 7939
TROPICANA CITY MANAGEMENT SDN. BHD.—See Tropicana Corporation Berhad; *Int'l*, pg. 7939
TROPICANA CORPORATION BERHAD; *Int'l*, pg. 7939
TROPICANA DANGA BAY SDN. BHD.—See Tropicana Corporation Berhad; *Int'l*, pg. 7939

COMPANY NAME INDEX

TROPICANA ENTERTAINMENT INC.—See Caesars Entertainment, Inc.; *U.S. Public*, pg. 420
TROPICANA EUROPE N.V.—See PepsiCo, Inc.; *U.S. Public*, pg. 1672
TROPICANA GOLF & COUNTRY RESORT BERHAD—See Tropicana Corporation Berhad; *Int'l*, pg. 7939
TROPICANA GP VIEWS SDN BHD—See Tropicana Corporation Berhad; *Int'l*, pg. 7939
TROPICANA HOTEL - GOLDEN MILE—See Gooderson Leisure Corporation; *Int'l*, pg. 3040
TROPICANA INDAH SDN. BHD.—See Tropicana Corporation Berhad; *Int'l*, pg. 7939
TROPICANA LANDMARK SDN. BHD.—See Tropicana Corporation Berhad; *Int'l*, pg. 7939
TROPICANA LAS VEGAS HOTEL & CASINO, INC.—See PENN Entertainment, Inc.; *U.S. Public*, pg. 1663
TROPICANA LAS VEGAS, INC.—See PENN Entertainment, Inc.; *U.S. Public*, pg. 1663
TROPICANA LAUGHLIN, LLC—See Caesars Entertainment, Inc.; *U.S. Public*, pg. 421
TROPICANA LOOZA BENELUX BVBA—See PepsiCo, Inc.; *U.S. Public*, pg. 1672
TROPICANA MANUFACTURING COMPANY, INC.—See PepsiCo, Inc.; *U.S. Public*, pg. 1672
TROPICANA MEDICAL CENTRE (M) SDN. BHD.—See Thomson Medical Group Limited; *Int'l*, pg. 7714
TROPICANA MEDICAL CENTRE (PENANG) SDN. BHD.—See Thomson Medical Group Limited; *Int'l*, pg. 7714
TROPICANA PRODUCTS, INC.—See PAI Partners S.A.S.; *Int'l*, pg. 5702
TROPICANA TRANSPORTATION CORP.—See PAI Partners S.A.S.; *Int'l*, pg. 5702
TROPIC FISHERY (PVT) LTD—See Tess Agro PLC; *Int'l*, pg. 7573
TROPIC FISH & VEGETABLE CENTER INC.; *U.S. Private*, pg. 4242
TROPIC FROZEN FOODS LTD.—See Tess Agro PLC; *Int'l*, pg. 7573
TROPICS SOFTWARE TECHNOLOGIES, INC.—See GI Manager L.P.; *U.S. Private*, pg. 1692
TROPIC SUPPLY INC.; *U.S. Private*, pg. 4242
TROPIKAL BAHCE VE EVCIL HAYVAN URUNLERI A.S.—See The Riverside Company; *U.S. Private*, pg. 4110
TROPITONE FURNITURE COMPANY, INC.—See Littlejohn & Co., LLC; *U.S. Private*, pg. 2470
TROPRIA HOLDING B.V.—See Edgewell Personal Care Company; *U.S. Public*, pg. 718
TROSS DIALYSIS, LLC—See DaVita Inc.; *U.S. Public*, pg. 644
TROSTEL LTD.—See HEXPOL AB; *Int'l*, pg. 3372
TROTTER & MORTON BUILDING TECHNOLOGIES INC—See Trotter & Morton Ltd.; *Int'l*, pg. 7939
TROTTER & MORTON LTD.; *Int'l*, pg. 7939
TROTTHOLMEN AB; *Int'l*, pg. 7939
TROUBADOUR RESOURCES, INC.; *Int'l*, pg. 7939
TROUILLET CARROSSIER CONSTRUCTEUR; *Int'l*, pg. 7939
TROUSDALE LIMITED—See The Pritzker Group - Chicago, LLC; *U.S. Private*, pg. 4098
TROUSDALE MEDICAL CENTER, LLC—See Apollo Global Management, Inc.; *U.S. Public*, pg. 159
TROUT-BLUE CHELAN, INC.; *U.S. Private*, pg. 4243
TROUTDALE MINI STORAGE, LLC—See National Storage Affiliates Trust; *U.S. Public*, pg. 1498
TROUTLODGE, INC.; *U.S. Private*, pg. 4243
TROUTMAN PEPPER HAMILTON SANDERS LLP; *U.S. Private*, pg. 4243
TROUTMAN SANDERS LLP; *U.S. Private*, pg. 4243
TROUT UNLIMITED INC.; *U.S. Private*, pg. 4243
TROUTWINE AUTO SALES, INC.; *U.S. Private*, pg. 4243
TROUW NUTRITION BELGIUM—See SHV Holdings N.V.; *Int'l*, pg. 6872
TROUW NUTRITION CHINA—See SHV Holdings N.V.; *Int'l*, pg. 6872
TROUW NUTRITION DENMARK—See SHV Holdings N.V.; *Int'l*, pg. 6872
TROUW NUTRITION DEUTSCHLAND GMBH—See SHV Holdings N.V.; *Int'l*, pg. 6872
TROUW NUTRITION FRANCE—See SHV Holdings N.V.; *Int'l*, pg. 6872
TROUW NUTRITION HUNGARY—See SHV Holdings N.V.; *Int'l*, pg. 6872
TROUW NUTRITION INTERNATIONAL B.V.—See SHV Holdings N.V.; *Int'l*, pg. 6872
TROUW NUTRITION IRELAND—See SHV Holdings N.V.; *Int'l*, pg. 6872
TROUW NUTRITION ITALIA S.P.A.—See SHV Holdings N.V.; *Int'l*, pg. 6872
TROUW NUTRITION MEXICO—See SHV Holdings N.V.; *Int'l*, pg. 6872
TROUW NUTRITION NEDERLAND B.V.—See SHV Holdings N.V.; *Int'l*, pg. 6872
TROUW NUTRITION SOUTH AFRICA—See SHV Holdings N.V.; *Int'l*, pg. 6872
TROUW NUTRITION USA, LLC—See SHV Holdings N.V.; *Int'l*, pg. 6872

TROVATAR A.S.—See Manutan International SA; *Int'l*, pg. 4680
TROVICOR GMBH—See Perusa GmbH; *Int'l*, pg. 5821
TROV INC.—See The Travelers Companies, Inc.; *U.S. Public*, pg. 2136
TROVIX INC.—See Ontario Teachers' Pension Plan; *Int'l*, pg. 5588
TROWBRIDGE ENTERPRISES; *U.S. Private*, pg. 4243
TROWEL TRADES SUPPLY, INC.—See GMS Inc.; *U.S. Public*, pg. 949
T. ROWE PRICE ADVISORY SERVICES, INC.—See T. Rowe Price Group Inc.; *U.S. Public*, pg. 1978
T. ROWE PRICE ASSOCIATES, INC.—See T. Rowe Price Group Inc.; *U.S. Public*, pg. 1978
T. ROWE PRICE AUSTRALIA, LTD.—See T. Rowe Price Group Inc.; *U.S. Public*, pg. 1978
T. ROWE PRICE FUNDS SICAV—See T. Rowe Price Group Inc.; *U.S. Public*, pg. 1978
T. ROWE PRICE GROUP INC.; *U.S. Public*, pg. 1978
T. ROWE PRICE INTERNATIONAL, INC.—See T. Rowe Price Group Inc.; *U.S. Public*, pg. 1978
T. ROWE PRICE INTERNATIONAL LTD—See T. Rowe Price Group Inc.; *U.S. Public*, pg. 1978
T. ROWE PRICE INVESTMENT SERVICES INC.—See T. Rowe Price Group Inc.; *U.S. Public*, pg. 1978
T. ROWE PRICE JAPAN, INC.—See T. Rowe Price Group Inc.; *U.S. Public*, pg. 1978
T. ROWE PRICE RETIREMENT PLAN SERVICES, INC.—See T. Rowe Price Group Inc.; *U.S. Public*, pg. 1978
T. ROWE PRICE (SWITZERLAND) GMBH—See T. Rowe Price Group Inc.; *U.S. Public*, pg. 1978
THE TROXEL COMPANY; *U.S. Private*, pg. 4128
TROXEL EQUIPMENT CO.—See TTG Equipment, LLC; *U.S. Private*, pg. 4254
TROXELL COMMUNICATIONS, INC.—See AEA Investors LP; *U.S. Private*, pg. 116
TROY-ALAN CHEVROLET; *U.S. Private*, pg. 4243
TROY BANK & TRUST COMPANY—See Henderson Bancshares, Inc.; *U.S. Private*, pg. 1913
TROY-BILT LLC—See Stanley Black & Decker, Inc.; *U.S. Public*, pg. 1936
TROY BIOSCIENCES, INC.—See Troy Corporation; *U.S. Private*, pg. 4243
TROY CHEMICAL COMPANY B.V.—See Troy Corporation; *U.S. Private*, pg. 4243
TROY CHEMICAL COMPANY LIMITED—See Troy Corporation; *U.S. Private*, pg. 4243
TROY CHEMICAL COMPANY SP. Z O.O.—See Troy Corporation; *U.S. Private*, pg. 4243
TROY CHEMICAL CORPORATION—See Troy Corporation; *U.S. Private*, pg. 4243
TROY CHEMIE GMBH—See Troy Corporation; *U.S. Private*, pg. 4243
TROY-CJD, LLC—See Lithia Motors, Inc.; *U.S. Public*, pg. 1326
TROY COLLISION, LLC—See Lithia Motors, Inc.; *U.S. Public*, pg. 1326
TROY CORPORATION; *U.S. Private*, pg. 4243
TROY DAILY NEWS—See Independence Capital Partners, LLC; *U.S. Private*, pg. 2057
TROY ELEVATOR, INC.—See The Mennel Milling Company; *U.S. Private*, pg. 4078
TROYER CHEESE, INC.—See Littlejohn & Co., LLC; *U.S. Private*, pg. 2472
TROYER FOODS, INC.; *U.S. Private*, pg. 4243
TROYER POTATO PRODUCTS, INC.—See Hanover Foods Corporation; *U.S. Public*, pg. 984
TROY FAIN INSURANCE INC.—See Loews Corporation; *U.S. Public*, pg. 1340
TROY FOODS LTD—See Fylde Fresh & Fabulous Ltd.; *Int'l*, pg. 2860
TROY FRANCE S.A.R.L.—See Troy Corporation; *U.S. Private*, pg. 4243
TROY GOLD & MINERAL CORP.; *U.S. Public*, pg. 2198
TROY GROUP INC.; *U.S. Private*, pg. 4243
TROY GROUP, INC.—See Troy Group Inc.; *U.S. Private*, pg. 4243
TROY HEALTHCARE SOLUTIONS—See Troy Group Inc.; *U.S. Private*, pg. 4243
TROY-I, LLC—See Lithia Motors, Inc.; *U.S. Public*, pg. 1326
TROY INCOME & GROWTH TRUST PLC—See STS Global Income & Growth Trust plc; *Int'l*, pg. 7244
TROY INDUSTRIAL SOLUTIONS LLC; *U.S. Private*, pg. 4243
TROY INFORMATION TECHNOLOGY CO., LTD.; *Int'l*, pg. 7939
TROY LAMINATING & COATING, INC.—See Chargeurs SA; *Int'l*, pg. 1449
TROY MINERALS INC.; *Int'l*, pg. 7940
TROY MOTORS, INC.—See Elder Automotive Group; *U.S. Private*, pg. 1350
TROY NISSAN INC.; *U.S. Private*, pg. 4243
TROYRESEARCH; *U.S. Private*, pg. 4243
TROY RESOURCES ARGENTINA LTD.—See Troy Resources Limited; *Int'l*, pg. 7940
TROY RESOURCES LIMITED; *Int'l*, pg. 7940

TRUCK EQUIPMENT INC.

TROY TUBE & MANUFACTURING, CO.; *U.S. Private*, pg. 4243
TROY VINES, INC.—See Summit Materials, Inc.; *U.S. Public*, pg. 1960
TROZZOLO COMMUNICATIONS GROUP; *U.S. Private*, pg. 4244
TR PARK SOUTH MANAGEMENT LLC—See Hyatt Hotels Corporation; *U.S. Public*, pg. 1078
TRP BAU GMBH; *Int'l*, pg. 7940
TRP CONNECTOR B.V.—See Bel Fuse Inc.; *U.S. Public*, pg. 293
TRP CONNECTOR LIMITED—See Bel Fuse Inc.; *U.S. Public*, pg. 293
TRP, INC.—See Tokai Rika Co., Ltd.; *Int'l*, pg. 7780
TR POST MANAGEMENT LLC—See Hyatt Hotels Corporation; *U.S. Public*, pg. 1078
TR PRESIDIO MANAGEMENT LLC—See Hyatt Hotels Corporation; *U.S. Public*, pg. 1078
TRP RESTAURANT ENTERPRISES, INC.; *U.S. Private*, pg. 4244
TR PROPERTY INVESTMENT TRUST PLC; *Int'l*, pg. 7885
TRQSS, INC—See Tokai Rika Co., Ltd.; *Int'l*, pg. 7780
T. R. RIZZUTO PIZZA CRUST, INC.—See Rich Holdings, Inc.; *U.S. Private*, pg. 3427
TR SAGEMIS INTERNATIONAL SRL—See Tecnicas Reunidas, S.A.; *Int'l*, pg. 7515
TR SANTA CLARA MANAGEMENT LLC—See Hyatt Hotels Corporation; *U.S. Public*, pg. 1078
TRS BEHAVIORAL CARE, INC.—See Elements Behavioral Health, Inc.; *U.S. Private*, pg. 1357
TRSB GROUPE SA; *Int'l*, pg. 7940
TRS CONSULTANTS JLT—See Fluor Corporation; *U.S. Public*, pg. 858
TR SEATTLE MANAGEMENT LLC—See Hyatt Hotels Corporation; *U.S. Public*, pg. 1078
TR SEDONA MANAGEMENT LLC—See Hyatt Hotels Corporation; *U.S. Public*, pg. 1078
TRS GLOBAL SERVICES, LLC—See Knox Capital Holdings, LLC; *U.S. Private*, pg. 2324
TR SOUTHERN FASTENERS LTD—See Trifast plc; *Int'l*, pg. 7921
TRS-RENTELCO INC.—See McGrath RentCorp.; *U.S. Public*, pg. 1407
TRS STAFFING SOLUTIONS (AUSTRALIA) PTY LTD—See Fluor Corporation; *U.S. Public*, pg. 860
TRS STAFFING SOLUTIONS BELGIUM B.V.—See Fluor Corporation; *U.S. Public*, pg. 860
TRS STAFFING SOLUTIONS BV—See Fluor Corporation; *U.S. Public*, pg. 858
TRS STAFFING SOLUTIONS (CANADA), INC.—See Fluor Corporation; *U.S. Public*, pg. 859
TRS STAFFING SOLUTIONS GMBH—See Fluor Corporation; *U.S. Public*, pg. 860
TRS STAFFING SOLUTIONS, INC.—See Fluor Corporation; *U.S. Public*, pg. 860
TRS STAFFING SOLUTIONS INDIA PRIVATE LIMITED—See Fluor Corporation; *U.S. Public*, pg. 860
TRS STAFFING SOLUTIONS LIMITED—See Fluor Corporation; *U.S. Public*, pg. 860
TRS STAFFING SOLUTIONS (PTY) LTD—See Fluor Corporation; *U.S. Public*, pg. 860
TRS STAFFING SOLUTIONS, S. DE R.L. DE C.V.—See Fluor Corporation; *U.S. Public*, pg. 860
TRS TECHNOLOGIES, INC.—See Tayca Corporation; *Int'l*, pg. 7478
TRS TRADING GROUP PTY. LTD.—See The Reject Shop Limited; *Int'l*, pg. 7678
TRS TYRE & WHEEL LIMITED—See The Yokohama Rubber Co., Ltd.; *Int'l*, pg. 7703
TR SUNNYVALE MANAGEMENT LLC—See Hyatt Hotels Corporation; *U.S. Public*, pg. 1078
TR TECH CO., LTD.—See Tung-Jetek Co., Ltd.; *Int'l*, pg. 7971
TRT HOLDINGS, INC.; *U.S. Private*, pg. 4244
TRT LIGHTING LIMITED—See F.W. Thorpe plc; *Int'l*, pg. 2597
TRUARC PARTNERS, L.P.; *U.S. Private*, pg. 4244
TRUAX CORPORATION; *U.S. Private*, pg. 4246
TRUBRIDGE, INC.; *U.S. Public*, pg. 2198
TRUCCHIS MARKETS; *U.S. Private*, pg. 4246
TRUCEPT INC.; *U.S. Public*, pg. 2198
TRUCK BODIES & EQUIPMENT INTERNATIONAL, INC.—See Federal Signal Corporation; *U.S. Public*, pg. 826
TRUCKCENTER.COM, LLC—See Liquidity Services, Inc.; *U.S. Public*, pg. 1321
TRUCK CENTER INCORPORATED; *U.S. Private*, pg. 4246
TRUCK CENTERS INC.; *U.S. Private*, pg. 4246
TRUCK CITY OF GARY INC.; *U.S. Private*, pg. 4246
TRUCK COUNTRY INC.; *U.S. Private*, pg. 4246
TRUCKEE GAMING LLC; *U.S. Private*, pg. 4246
TRUCKEE-TAHOE LUMBER CO; *U.S. Private*, pg. 4246
TRUCK ENTERPRISES INCORPORATED; *U.S. Private*, pg. 4246
TRUCK ENTERPRISES, INC.—See Doggett Equipment Services, Ltd.; *U.S. Public*, pg. 1253
TRUCK EQUIPMENT INC.; *U.S. Private*, pg. 4246

TRUCK EQUIPMENT INC. — CORPORATE AFFILIATIONS

TRUCKER PUBLICATIONS INC.—See Digital Air Strike Inc.; *U.S. Private*, pg. 1230
TRUCKERSB2B, INC.—See Celadon Group, Inc.; *U.S. Public*, pg. 464
TRUCKERS B2B, LLC—See WEX, Inc.; *U.S. Public*, pg. 2364
TRUCK ETAPE BEZIER SAS—See VINCI S.A.; *Int'l*, pg. 8229
TRUCK FREIGHT INTERNATIONAL—See Paterson GlobalFoods Inc.; *Int'l*, pg. 5756
TRUCK HERO, INC.—See CCMP Capital Advisors, LP; *U.S. Private*, pg. 801
TRUCK HERO, INC.—See TA Associates, Inc.; *U.S. Private*, pg. 3919
TRUCK INSURANCE MART INC.—See Aquiline Capital Partners LLC; *U.S. Private*, pg. 305
TRUCK LEASE SERVICES, INC.; *U.S. Private*, pg. 4246
TRUCK LIGHTHOUSE; *U.S. Private*, pg. 4246
TRUCK-LITE CO., LLC—See Genstar Capital, LLC; *U.S. Private*, pg. 1676
TRUCK-LITE EUROPE LTD.—See Genstar Capital, LLC; *U.S. Private*, pg. 1677
TRUCKNET ENTERPRISE LTD.; *Int'l*, pg. 7940
TRUCKOMAN LLC—See Al Yousef Group; *Int'l*, pg. 283
TRUCKOMAT CORPORATION—See Iowa 80 Group, Inc.; *U.S. Private*, pg. 2134
TRUCK ONE, INC.; *U.S. Private*, pg. 4246
TRUCK PARTS AND EQUIPMENT CO.; *U.S. Private*, pg. 4246
TRUCK PARTS & EQUIPMENT INC.—See American Securities LLC; *U.S. Private*, pg. 248
TRUCKPRO, LLC—See Platinum Equity, LLC; *U.S. Private*, pg. 3209
TRUCKQUIP SDN. BHD.—See Tan Chong Motor Holdings Berhad; *Int'l*, pg. 7454
TRUCK SALES & SERVICE INC. - MANSFIELD—See Midvale Truck Sales & Service Inc.; *U.S. Private*, pg. 2718
TRUCK SALES & SERVICE INC.; *U.S. Private*, pg. 4246
TRUCKS-E-QUIP INC.; *U.S. Private*, pg. 4246
TRUCKS FOR YOU, INC.; *U.S. Private*, pg. 4246
TRUCKS & PARTS OF TAMPA INC.; *U.S. Private*, pg. 4246
TRUCK TRACK LOGISTICS LTD.—See TSL Companies; *U.S. Private*, pg. 4254
TRUCK TRAILER & EQUIPMENT INC.; *U.S. Private*, pg. 4246
TRUCK & TRAILER INDUSTRY AS—See VDL Groep B.V.; *Int'l*, pg. 8141
TRUCK UTILITIES, INC.—See Custom Truck One Source, Inc.; *U.S. Public*, pg. 612
TRUCKWAY LEASING INC.; *U.S. Private*, pg. 4246
TRUCK WORLD INC.; *U.S. Private*, pg. 4246
TRUCO ENTERPRISES INC.; *U.S. Private*, pg. 4247
TRUCO ENTERPRISES, LP—See Utz Brands, Inc.; *U.S. Public*, pg. 2268
TRUCO INC.; *U.S. Private*, pg. 4247
TRUCOM CORPORATION—See Windstream Holdings, Inc.; *U.S. Public*, pg. 2373
TRU COMMUNITY CARE; *U.S. Private*, pg. 4244
TRUDEAU DISTRIBUTING COMPANY; *U.S. Private*, pg. 4247
TRUDEAU FOODS, LLC—See United Natural Foods, Inc.; *U.S. Public*, pg. 2233
TRUDECO—See Trulite Glass & Aluminum Solutions, LLC; *U.S. Private*, pg. 4249
TRUDELA PARTNERS LLC—See Coltala Holdings, LLC; *U.S. Private*, pg. 976
TRUDELL CONSULTING ENGINEERS, INC.—See Bowman Consulting Group Ltd.; *U.S. Public*, pg. 377
TRUDELL TRAILERS OF GRAND RAPIDS, INC.; *U.S. Private*, pg. 4247
TRUDY'S TEXAS STAR INC.; *U.S. Private*, pg. 4247
TRUE2FORM COLLISION REPAIR CENTERS, INC.—See Boyd Group Services Inc.; *Int'l*, pg. 1125
TRUE2FORM COLLISION REPAIR CENTERS, LLC—See Boyd Group Services Inc.; *Int'l*, pg. 1125
TRUEABILITY INC.—See ALUMINUM.IO, INC.; *U.S. Private*, pg. 211
TRUEBLOOD OIL CO. INC.; *U.S. Private*, pg. 4248
TRUE BLUE HOLDINGS, INC.; *U.S. Public*, pg. 2198
TRUEBLUE, INC.; *U.S. Public*, pg. 2198
TRUEBLUE OUTSOURCING SOLUTIONS—See TrueBlue, Inc.; *U.S. Public*, pg. 2198
TRUE CAPITAL MANAGEMENT, LLC—See Cresset Asset Management, LLC; *U.S. Private*, pg. 1095
TRUECAR, INC.; *U.S. Public*, pg. 2199
TRUECLAIM EXPLORATION INC.; *Int'l*, pg. 7941
TRUE COLORS STUDIO; *U.S. Private*, pg. 4247
TRUECOMMERCE, INC.—See Welsh, Carson, Anderson & Stowe; *U.S. Private*, pg. 4480
TRUE COMPANIES; *U.S. Private*, pg. 4247
TRUE.COM; *U.S. Private*, pg. 4248
TRUECONTEXT CORPORATION—See Battery Ventures, L.P.; *U.S. Private*, pg. 489
TRUECONTEXT INC.—See Battery Ventures, L.P.; *U.S. Private*, pg. 489
TRUECORE BEHAVIORAL SOLUTIONS, LLC; *U.S. Private*, pg. 4248

TRUECORE, LLC—See Nucor Corporation; *U.S. Public*, pg. 1554
TRUE CORPORATION PUBLIC COMPANY LIMITED—See Charoen Pokphand Group Co., Ltd.; *Int'l*, pg. 1453
TRUE & CO.—See PVH Corp.; *U.S. Public*, pg. 1739
TRUE DATA INC.; *Int'l*, pg. 7940
TRU-EDGE GRINDING INC.—See MSC Industrial Direct Co., Inc.; *U.S. Public*, pg. 1483
TRUE DIGITAL SECURITY, INC.; *U.S. Private*, pg. 4247
TRUE DRILLING CO.—See True Companies; *U.S. Private*, pg. 4247
TRUEDYNE SENSORS AG—See Endress+Hauser (International) Holding AG; *Int'l*, pg. 2409
TRUE ENERGY; *Int'l*, pg. 7940
TRUE FABRICATIONS; *U.S. Private*, pg. 4247
TRUEFFECT, INC.; *U.S. Private*, pg. 4248
TRUE FITNESS TECHNOLOGY INC.; *U.S. Private*, pg. 4247
TRUEFORM ENGINEERING LIMITED—See GIL Investments Ltd.; *Int'l*, pg. 2973
TRUE GREEN CAPITAL MANAGEMENT LLC; *U.S. Private*, pg. 4247
TRUE GREEN ENERGY GROUP CORP; *Int'l*, pg. 7940
TRUE HEALTHCARE INDIA PVT. LTD.—See Berjaya Corporation Berhad; *Int'l*, pg. 985
TRUE HEALTHCARE (THAILAND) CO., LTD.—See Berjaya Corporation Berhad; *Int'l*, pg. 984
TRUE HEALTH NEW MEXICO, INC.—See NeueHealth, Inc.; *U.S. Public*, pg. 1510
TRUE HEALTH STUDIO, INC.—See CARBON GREEN INC.; *Int'l*, pg. 1320
TRUE HOME VALUE, INC.; *U.S. Private*, pg. 4247
TRUE INFLUENCE, LLC; *U.S. Private*, pg. 4247
TRUELEARN, LLC; *U.S. Private*, pg. 4248
TRUE LENS SERVICES LTD—See Procam Television Ltd.; *Int'l*, pg. 5986
TRUELIGHT CORPORATION; *Int'l*, pg. 7941
TRUELOVE & MACLEAN INC.; *U.S. Private*, pg. 4248
TRUE MEDIA; *U.S. Private*, pg. 4247
TRUEN CO., LTD.; *Int'l*, pg. 7941
TRU ENERGY SERVICES, LLC—See NACCO Industries, Inc.; *U.S. Public*, pg. 1490
TRUENET COMMUNICATIONS, CORP.—See Fujitsu Limited; *Int'l*, pg. 2833
TRUE NORTH COMMERCIAL REAL ESTATE INVESTMENT TRUST—See Starlight Investments Ltd.; *Int'l*, pg. 7177
TRUENORTH COMPANIES L.C.; *U.S. Private*, pg. 4248
TRUE NORTH CONSULTING LLC—See GSE Systems, Inc.; *U.S. Public*, pg. 973
TRUE NORTH ENERGY CORPORATION; *U.S. Public*, pg. 2198
TRUE NORTH ENERGY, LLC; *U.S. Private*, pg. 4247
TRUE NORTH ENTERTAINMENT COMPLEX LP—See True North Sports & Entertainment Limited; *Int'l*, pg. 7941
TRUE NORTH EQUIPMENT CO.; *U.S. Private*, pg. 4248
TRUE NORTH FORD; *Int'l*, pg. 7940
TRUE NORTH GEMS INC.; *Int'l*, pg. 7940
TRUE NORTH HOTEL GROUP, INC.; *U.S. Private*, pg. 4248
TRUENORTH, INC.—See IMA Financial Group, Inc.; *U.S. Private*, pg. 2044
TRUE NORTH INC.; *U.S. Private*, pg. 4248
TRUE NORTH INTERACTIVE—See True North Inc.; *U.S. Private*, pg. 4248
TRUENORTHLOGIC; *U.S. Private*, pg. 4249
TRUE NORTH MANAGERS LLP; *Int'l*, pg. 7940
TRUE NORTH NUTRITION LTD.; *Int'l*, pg. 7940
TRUE NORTH PRODUCTIONS LIMITED—See Comcast Corporation; *U.S. Public*, pg. 542
TRUE NORTH REAL ESTATE LLC—See DallasNews Corporation; *U.S. Public*, pg. 621
TRUE NORTH RECRUITING, LLC; *U.S. Private*, pg. 4248
TRUE NORTH SALMON CO. LTD.—See Cooke, Inc.; *Int'l*, pg. 1788
TRUE NORTH SPORTS & ENTERTAINMENT LIMITED; *Int'l*, pg. 7940
TRUENORTH STEEL - BILLINGS—See TrueNorth Steel Inc.; *U.S. Private*, pg. 4249
TRUENORTH STEEL - BLAINE—See TrueNorth Steel Inc.; *U.S. Private*, pg. 4249
TRUENORTH STEEL - HURON—See TrueNorth Steel Inc.; *U.S. Private*, pg. 4249
TRUENORTH STEEL INC.; *U.S. Private*, pg. 4249
TRUENORTH STEEL - MANDAN—See TrueNorth Steel Inc.; *U.S. Private*, pg. 4249
TRUE OIL CO.—See True Companies; *U.S. Private*, pg. 4247
TRUE PARTNER ADVISOR HONG KONG LIMITED—See True Partner Capital Holding Limited; *Int'l*, pg. 7941
TRUE PARTNER CAPITAL HOLDING LIMITED; *Int'l*, pg. 7941
TRUE PARTNER CAPITAL USA HOLDING INC.—See True Partner Capital Holding Limited; *Int'l*, pg. 7941
TRUE PARTNER CHINA HOLDING LIMITED—See True Partner Capital Holding Limited; *Int'l*, pg. 7941

TRUE PARTNERS CONSULTING LLC—See Baker Tilly US, LLP; *U.S. Private*, pg. 457
TRUEPATH.COM—See Etica Entertainment Inc.; *U.S. Private*, pg. 1432
TRUEPATH TECHNOLOGIES, INC.—See Antin Infrastructure Partners SAS; *Int'l*, pg. 483
TRUEPOINT COMMUNICATIONS, LLC; *U.S. Private*, pg. 4249
TRUEPOINT INC.; *U.S. Private*, pg. 4249
TRUEPOINT TECHNOLOGY CO., LTD.—See Beijing BDStar Navigation Co., Ltd.; *Int'l*, pg. 946
TRUEPOSITION, INC.—See Liberty Broadband Corporation; *U.S. Public*, pg. 1311
TRUE PROCESS, INC.—See Baxter International Inc.; *U.S. Public*, pg. 284
TRUE RANCHES—See True Companies; *U.S. Private*, pg. 4247
TRUE RELIGION APPAREL, INC.—See TowerBrook Capital Partners, L.P.; *U.S. Private*, pg. 4196
TRUE RELIGION BRAND JEANS GERMANY GMBH—See TowerBrook Capital Partners, L.P.; *U.S. Private*, pg. 4196
TRUE RELIGION BRAND JEANS ITALY, S.R.L.—See TowerBrook Capital Partners, L.P.; *U.S. Private*, pg. 4196
TRUE RELIGION BRAND JEANS U.K. LIMITED—See TowerBrook Capital Partners, L.P.; *U.S. Private*, pg. 4196
TRUE RELIGION JAPAN K.K.—See TowerBrook Capital Partners, L.P.; *U.S. Private*, pg. 4196
TRUE SECURITIZADORA S.A.; *Int'l*, pg. 7941
TRUESHORE S.R.I.—See Humana, Inc.; *U.S. Public*, pg. 1070
TRUESTONE, LLC—See Nana Regional Corporation, Inc.; *U.S. Private*, pg. 2832
TRUETECH CO., LTD.—See Techwing Inc.; *Int'l*, pg. 7514
TRUE TEMPER SPORTS, INC.; *U.S. Private*, pg. 4248
TRUE TEXTILES, INC.—See Duvaltex Inc.; *Int'l*, pg. 2236
TRUETT-HURST, INC.; *U.S. Public*, pg. 2199
TRUETZSCHLER CARD CLOTHING GMBH—See Trutzschler GmbH & Co. KG; *Int'l*, pg. 7945
TRUETZSCHLER DE MEXICO, S.A. DE C.V.—See Trutzschler GmbH & Co. KG; *Int'l*, pg. 7946
TRUETZSCHLER INDIA PRIVATE LIMITED—See Trutzschler GmbH & Co. KG; *Int'l*, pg. 7946
TRUETZSCHLER TEKSTIL MAKINALARI TICARET LTD.—See Trutzschler GmbH & Co. KG; *Int'l*, pg. 7946
TRUETZSCHLER TEXTILE MACHINERY (SHANGHAI) CO., LTD.—See Trutzschler GmbH & Co. KG; *Int'l*, pg. 7946
TRUE VALUE COMPANY, L.L.C.—See ACON Investments, LLC; *U.S. Private*, pg. 63
TRUE VALUE SOLAR PTY. LTD.—See M+W Group GmbH; *Int'l*, pg. 4614
TRUE VENTURES; *U.S. Private*, pg. 4248
TRUE VIEW REALTY PARTNERS ONE LP; *U.S. Private*, pg. 4248
TRUE WIND CAPITAL MANAGEMENT, L.P.; *U.S. Private*, pg. 4248
TRUE WIRELESS, INC; *U.S. Private*, pg. 4248
TRUEWOOD—See RD Merrill Company; *U.S. Private*, pg. 3362
TRUE WORLD FOODS-ALASKA—See Family Federation for World Peace & Unification; *U.S. Private*, pg. 1469
TRUE WORLD FOODS CHICAGO LLC—See Family Federation for World Peace & Unification; *U.S. Private*, pg. 1469
TRUE WORLD FOODS, INC. OF HAWAII—See Family Federation for World Peace & Unification; *U.S. Private*, pg. 1469
TRUE WORLD FOODS INTERNATIONAL, INC.—See Family Federation for World Peace & Unification; *U.S. Private*, pg. 1469
TRUE WORLD FOODS MIAMI LLC—See Family Federation for World Peace & Unification; *U.S. Private*, pg. 1469
TRUE WORLD FOODS NEW YORK LLC—See Family Federation for World Peace & Unification; *U.S. Private*, pg. 1469
TRUE WORLD FOODS SAN FRANCISCO LLC—See Family Federation for World Peace & Unification; *U.S. Private*, pg. 1469
TRUE WORLD FOODS SEATTLE LLC—See Family Federation for World Peace & Unification; *U.S. Private*, pg. 1469
TRUE WORLD GROUP, INC.—See Family Federation for World Peace & Unification; *U.S. Private*, pg. 1469
TRUE YOGA PTE. LTD.—See Kontafarma China Holdings Limited; *Int'l*, pg. 4276
TRUFFLE ASSET MANAGEMENT (PTY) LTD.; *Int'l*, pg. 7941
TRUFFLE CAPITAL SAS; *Int'l*, pg. 7941
TRUFIN PLC; *Int'l*, pg. 7941
TRU-FIRE CORP.—See TruArc Partners, L.P.; *U.S. Private*, pg. 4245
TRU FLEET PTY. LTD.—See SSH Group Limited; *Int'l*, pg. 7156
TRU-FLEX, LLC—See Wind Point Advisors LLC; *U.S. Private*, pg. 4534

COMPANY NAME INDEX

TRUFLO INTERNATIONAL PLC—See IMI plc; *Int'l*, pg. 3627
TRUFLO MARINE LTD—See IMI plc; *Int'l*, pg. 3627
TRUFLO RONA S.R.L.—See IMI plc; *Int'l*, pg. 3627
TRU-FLOW LLC—See Wynnchurch Capital, L.P.; *U.S. Private*, pg. 4577
TRUFOODS LLC; *U.S. Private*, pg. 4249
TRU-FORM INC.—See General Electric Company; *U.S. Public*, pg. 919
TRUFORM METALSERVICE INC—See McCarty Corporation; *U.S. Private*, pg. 2628
TRUFORM ORTHOTICS & PROSTHETICS—See Surgical Appliance Industries, Inc.; *U.S. Private*, pg. 3884
TRUFUSION, LLC; *U.S. Private*, pg. 4249
TRUGLO, INC.—See Good Sportsman Marketing, LLC; *U.S. Private*, pg. 1738
TRUGREEN COMPANIES LLC—See TruGreen Limited Partnership; *U.S. Private*, pg. 4249
TRUGREEN LIMITED PARTNERSHIP; *U.S. Private*, pg. 4249
TRUHEARING, INC.—See EQT AB; *Int'l*, pg. 2480
TRUIMPH ACCESSORY SERVICES—See Triumph Group, Inc.; *U.S. Public*, pg. 2197
TRU INDEPENDCE LLC; *U.S. Private*, pg. 4244
TRUIST BANK—See Truist Financial Corporation; *U.S. Public*, pg. 2200
TRUIST FINANCIAL CORPORATION; *U.S. Public*, pg. 2199
TRUIST INSURANCE HOLDINGS, INC.—See Clayton, Dubilier & Rice, LLC; *U.S. Private*, pg. 927
TRUIST INSURANCE HOLDINGS, INC.—See Mubadala Investment Company PJSC; *Int'l*, pg. 5076
TRUIST INSURANCE HOLDINGS, INC.—See Stone Point Capital LLC; *U.S. Private*, pg. 3825
TRUIST INVESTMENT SERVICES, INC.—See Truist Financial Corporation; *U.S. Public*, pg. 2201
TRUIST LEADERSHIP INSTITUTE, INC.—See Truist Financial Corporation; *U.S. Public*, pg. 2201
TRUIST SECURITIES, INC.—See Truist Financial Corporation; *U.S. Public*, pg. 2200
TRUITT BROS., INC.—See Seneca Foods Corporation; *U.S. Public*, pg. 1865
TRUITT & WHITE; *U.S. Private*, pg. 4249
TRUKAI INDUSTRIES LIMITED—See Ricegrowers Limited; *Int'l*, pg. 6329
TRUKING FEIYUN PHARMACEUTICAL EQUIPMENT (CHANGSHA) LIMITED—See Truking Technology Limited; *Int'l*, pg. 7941
TRUKING TECHNOLOGY LIMITED; *Int'l*, pg. 7941
TRULAND HOMES, LLC—See D.R. Horton, Inc.; *U.S. Public*, pg. 620
TRULEUM, INC.; *U.S. Public*, pg. 2201
TRULIA, LLC—See Zillow Group, Inc.; *U.S. Public*, pg. 2405
TRULIEVE CANNABIS CORP.; *U.S. Public*, pg. 2201
TRULIEVE, INC.—See Trulieve Cannabis Corp.; *U.S. Public*, pg. 2201
TRULIFE, INC.—See Trulife Limited; *Int'l*, pg. 7942
TRULIFE LIMITED-BIRMINGHAM—See Trulife Limited; *Int'l*, pg. 7941
TRULIFE LIMITED-CORK—See Trulife Limited; *Int'l*, pg. 7941
TRULIFE LIMITED; *Int'l*, pg. 7941
TRULIFE LIMITED—See Trulife Limited; *Int'l*, pg. 7941
TRULITE GLASS & ALUMINUM SOLUTIONS, LLC - ATLANTA—See Trulite Glass & Aluminum Solutions, LLC; *U.S. Private*, pg. 4249
TRULITE GLASS & ALUMINUM SOLUTIONS, LLC - CHESWICK—See Trulite Glass & Aluminum Solutions, LLC; *U.S. Private*, pg. 4249
TRULITE GLASS & ALUMINUM SOLUTIONS, LLC - GRENADA—See Trulite Glass & Aluminum Solutions, LLC; *U.S. Private*, pg. 4249
TRULITE GLASS & ALUMINUM SOLUTIONS, LLC - NEW BERLIN—See Trulite Glass & Aluminum Solutions, LLC; *U.S. Private*, pg. 4250
TRULITE GLASS & ALUMINUM SOLUTIONS, LLC; *U.S. Private*, pg. 4249
TRULITE, INC.; *U.S. Public*, pg. 2201
TRULLER KNABBER-GEBACK GMBH—See Intersnack Group GmbH & Co. KG; *Int'l*, pg. 3761
TRULY ELECTRICAL PRODUCTS COMPANY LIMITED—See Truly International Holdings Limited; *Int'l*, pg. 7942
TRULY ELECTRONICS MANUFACTURING LIMITED—See Truly International Holdings Limited; *Int'l*, pg. 7942
TRULY INDUSTRIAL LIMITED—See Truly International Holdings Limited; *Int'l*, pg. 7942
TRULY INSTRUMENT LIMITED—See Truly International Holdings Limited; *Int'l*, pg. 7942
TRULY INTERNATIONAL HOLDINGS LIMITED - SHANWEI FACTORY—See Truly International Holdings Limited; *Int'l*, pg. 7942
TRULY INTERNATIONAL HOLDINGS LIMITED; *Int'l*, pg. 7942
TRULY NOLEN OF AMERICA INC.; *U.S. Private*, pg. 4250
TRULY OPTO-ELECTRONICS LIMITED—See Truly International Holdings Limited; *Int'l*, pg. 7942

TRULY SEMICONDUCTORS LIMITED—See Truly International Holdings Limited; *Int'l*, pg. 7942
TRULY SEMICONDUCTORS LIMITED—See Truly International Holdings Limited; *Int'l*, pg. 7942
TRULY SEMICONDUCTORS (SINGAPORE) PTE. LTD.—See Truly International Holdings Limited; *Int'l*, pg. 7942
TRULY (USA) INC.—See Truly International Holdings Limited; *Int'l*, pg. 7942
TRUMAN ARNOLD COMPANIES; *U.S. Private*, pg. 4250
TRUMANSBURG TELEPHONE COMPANY, INC.—See Keystone Group, L.P.; *U.S. Private*, pg. 2300
TRUMARK FINANCIAL CREDIT UNION; *U.S. Private*, pg. 4250
TRUMBALL CORPORATION/P.J. DICK, INC.—See P.J. Dick Incorporated; *U.S. Private*, pg. 3060
TRUMBO ELECTRIC, INCORPORATED—See Comfort Systems USA, Inc.; *U.S. Public*, pg. 544
TRUMBULL INDUSTRIES INC.; *U.S. Private*, pg. 4250
TRUMBULL PRINTING INC.—See Hersam Acorn Newspapers LLC; *U.S. Private*, pg. 1926
TRUMETHODS, LLC—See Insight Venture Management, LLC; *U.S. Private*, pg. 2091
TRUMP CARD, LLC—See Littlejohn & Co., LLC; *U.S. Private*, pg. 2470
TRUMP CENTRAL PARK WEST CORP.—See The Trump Organization, Inc.; *U.S. Private*, pg. 4128
TRUMPET INTERNATIONAL SDN. BHD.—See XOX Networks Berhad; *Int'l*, pg. 8536
TRUMPET LLC; *U.S. Private*, pg. 4250
TRUMPF AMSA SAS—See TRUMPF SE + Co. KG; *Int'l*, pg. 7942
TRUMPF BULGARIA LTD.—See TRUMPF SE + Co. KG; *Int'l*, pg. 7942
TRUMPF CANADA, INC.—See TRUMPF SE + Co. KG; *Int'l*, pg. 7942
TRUMPF (CHINA) CO., LTD.—See TRUMPF SE + Co. KG; *Int'l*, pg. 7942
TRUMPF CHINA (HONG KONG) LTD.—See TRUMPF SE + Co. KG; *Int'l*, pg. 7942
TRUMPF CORPORATION—See TRUMPF SE + Co. KG; *Int'l*, pg. 7942
TRUMPF ENGINEERING SERVICES ITALY S.R.L—See TRUMPF SE + Co. KG; *Int'l*, pg. 7942
TRUMPF FINANCE (SCHWEIZ) AG—See TRUMPF SE + Co. KG; *Int'l*, pg. 7942
TRUMPF FINANCIAL SERVICES GMBH—See TRUMPF SE + Co. KG; *Int'l*, pg. 7942
TRUMPF GRUSCH AG—See TRUMPF SE + Co. KG; *Int'l*, pg. 7943
TRUMPF HOMBERGER S.R.L.—See TRUMPF SE + Co. KG; *Int'l*, pg. 7943
TRUMPF HUETTINGER ELECTRONIC K.K.—See TRUMPF SE + Co. KG; *Int'l*, pg. 7943
TRUMPF HUETTINGER, INC.—See TRUMPF SE + Co. KG; *Int'l*, pg. 7943
TRUMPF HUETTINGER K.K.—See TRUMPF SE + Co. KG; *Int'l*, pg. 7943
TRUMPF HUETTINGER SP. Z O. O.—See TRUMPF SE + Co. KG; *Int'l*, pg. 7943
TRUMPF HUNGARY KFT.—See TRUMPF SE + Co. KG; *Int'l*, pg. 7943
TRUMPF HUTTINGER GMBH + CO. KG—See TRUMPF SE + Co. KG; *Int'l*, pg. 7943
TRUMPF HUTTINGER (SHANGHAI) CO., LTD.—See TRUMPF SE + Co. KG; *Int'l*, pg. 7943
TRUMPF INC.—See TRUMPF SE + Co. KG; *Int'l*, pg. 7943
TRUMPF (INDIA) PVT. LTD.—See TRUMPF SE + Co. KG; *Int'l*, pg. 7942
TRUMPF KOREA CO., LTD.—See TRUMPF SE + Co. KG; *Int'l*, pg. 7943
TRUMPF LASER GMBH—See TRUMPF SE + Co. KG; *Int'l*, pg. 7943
TRUMPF LIBEREC, SPOL. S.R.O.—See TRUMPF SE + Co. KG; *Int'l*, pg. 7943
TRUMPF LTD.—See TRUMPF SE + Co. KG; *Int'l*, pg. 7943
TRUMPF LTD.—See TRUMPF SE + Co. KG; *Int'l*, pg. 7943
TRUMPF MACCHINE ITALIA S.R.L.—See TRUMPF SE + Co. KG; *Int'l*, pg. 7943
TRUMPF MACHINES SARL—See TRUMPF SE + Co. KG; *Int'l*, pg. 7943
TRUMPF MAKINA SANAYII A.S.—See TRUMPF SE + Co. KG; *Int'l*, pg. 7943
TRUMPF MALAYSIA SDN. BHD.—See TRUMPF SE + Co. KG; *Int'l*, pg. 7943
TRUMPF MAQUINARIA S.A.—See TRUMPF SE + Co. KG; *Int'l*, pg. 7943
TRUMPF MAQUINAS IND. E. COM. LTDA.—See TRUMPF SE + Co. KG; *Int'l*, pg. 7943
TRUMPF MASCHINEN AUSTRIA GMBH + CO. KG—See TRUMPF SE + Co. KG; *Int'l*, pg. 7943
TRUMPF MASKIN AB—See TRUMPF SE + Co. KG; *Int'l*, pg. 7943
TRUMPF MED (AUST) PTY. LIMITED—See Baxter International Inc.; *U.S. Public*, pg. 283

TRUMPF MEDICAL SYSTEMS, INC.—See Baxter International Inc.; *U.S. Public*, pg. 283
TRUMPF MEDICAL SYSTEMS LTD.—See Baxter International Inc.; *U.S. Public*, pg. 283
TRUMPF MEDICAL SYSTEMS (TAICANG) CO., LTD.—See Baxter International Inc.; *U.S. Public*, pg. 283
TRUMPF MED ITALIA S.R.L.—See Baxter International Inc.; *U.S. Public*, pg. 283
TRUMPF MEDIZIN SYSTEME BETEILIGUNGS GMBH—See Baxter International Inc.; *U.S. Public*, pg. 283
TRUMPF MEDIZIN SYSTEME GMBH & CO. KG—See Baxter International Inc.; *U.S. Public*, pg. 283
TRUMPF MEDIZINSYSTEMS OSTERREICH GMBH—See Baxter International Inc.; *U.S. Public*, pg. 282
TRUMPF MEDIZINSYSTEMS OSTERREICH GMBH—See Baxter International Inc.; *U.S. Public*, pg. 282
TRUMPF MEXICO S. DE R.L. DE C.V.—See TRUMPF SE + Co. KG; *Int'l*, pg. 7943
TRUMPF MIDDLE EAST—See TRUMPF SE + Co. KG; *Int'l*, pg. 7943
TRUMPF NEDERLAND B.V.—See TRUMPF SE + Co. KG; *Int'l*, pg. 7943
TRUMPF OOO—See TRUMPF SE + Co. KG; *Int'l*, pg. 7943
TRUMPF PHILIPPINES INC.—See TRUMPF SE + Co. KG; *Int'l*, pg. 7943
TRUMPF PHOTONICS, INC.—See TRUMPF SE + Co. KG; *Int'l*, pg. 7943
TRUMPF POLSKA SP. Z O.O.—See TRUMPF SE + Co. KG; *Int'l*, pg. 7943
TRUMPF PRAHA, SPOL. S.R.O.—See TRUMPF SE + Co. KG; *Int'l*, pg. 7943
TRUMPF (PTE.) LTD.—See TRUMPF SE + Co. KG; *Int'l*, pg. 7942
TRUMPF SACHSEN GMBH—See TRUMPF SE + Co. KG; *Int'l*, pg. 7943
TRUMPF SAS—See TRUMPF SE + Co. KG; *Int'l*, pg. 7943
TRUMPF SCIENTIFIC LASERS GMBH + CO. KG—See TRUMPF SE + Co. KG; *Int'l*, pg. 7943
TRUMPF SE + CO. KG; *Int'l*, pg. 7942
TRUMPF SHEET METAL PRODUCTS (DONGGUAN) CO., LTD.—See TRUMPF SE + Co. KG; *Int'l*, pg. 7943
TRUMPF SLOVAKIA, S.R.O.—See TRUMPF SE + Co. KG; *Int'l*, pg. 7943
TRUMPF TAIWAN INDUSTRIES CO., LTD.—See TRUMPF SE + Co. KG; *Int'l*, pg. 7943
TRUMPF VIETNAM PTE LTD—See TRUMPF SE + Co. KG; *Int'l*, pg. 7943
TRUMPF WERKZEUGMASCHINEN GMBH + CO. KG—See TRUMPF SE + Co. KG; *Int'l*, pg. 7943
TRUMPF WERKZEUGMASCHINEN TENINGEN GMBH—See TRUMPF SE + Co. KG; *Int'l*, pg. 7943
TRUMP INTERNATIONAL GOLF CLUB, INC.—See The Trump Organization, Inc.; *U.S. Private*, pg. 4128
TRUMP INTERNATIONAL HOTELS MANAGEMENT LLC—See The Trump Organization, Inc.; *U.S. Private*, pg. 4128
TRUMP INTERNATIONAL REALTY—See The Trump Organization, Inc.; *U.S. Private*, pg. 4128
TRUMP MEDIA & TECHNOLOGY GROUP CORP.; *U.S. Public*, pg. 2201
TRUMP NATIONAL GOLF CLUB, LLC—See The Trump Organization, Inc.; *U.S. Private*, pg. 4128
THE TRUMP ORGANIZATION, INC.; *U.S. Private*, pg. 4128
TRUMP ORGANIZATION LLC—See The Trump Organization, Inc.; *U.S. Private*, pg. 4128
TRUMP PALACE—See The Trump Organization, Inc.; *U.S. Private*, pg. 4128
TRUMP PAVILION FOR NURSING AND REHABILITATION; *U.S. Private*, pg. 4250
TRUNG AN HI-TECH FARMING JOINT STOCK COMPANY; *Int'l*, pg. 7943
TRUNKBOW ASIA PACIFIC (SHANDONG) CO., LTD.—See Trunkbow International Holdings Limited; *Int'l*, pg. 7943
TRUNKBOW ASIA PACIFIC (SHENZHEN) CO., LTD.—See Trunkbow International Holdings Limited; *Int'l*, pg. 7943
TRUNKBOW INTERNATIONAL HOLDINGS LIMITED; *Int'l*, pg. 7943
TRUNK CLUB, INC.—See Nordstrom, Inc.; *U.S. Public*, pg. 1535
TRUNKI INC.—See Heroes Technology Ltd.; *Int'l*, pg. 3364
TRUNKLINE GAS COMPANY—See Energy Transfer LP; *U.S. Public*, pg. 763
TRUONG HAI AUTO CORPORATION; *Int'l*, pg. 7944
TRUONG LONG ENGINEERING & AUTO JOINT STOCK COMPANY; *Int'l*, pg. 7944
TRUONG THANH FURNITURE CORPORATION; *Int'l*, pg. 7944
TRUONG TIEN GROUP JSC; *Int'l*, pg. 7944
TRUPAL MEDIA, INC.; *U.S. Private*, pg. 4250
TRUPANION, INC.; *U.S. Public*, pg. 2201
TRUPAY; *U.S. Private*, pg. 4250
TRUPET LLC—See Better Choice Company, Inc.; *U.S. Public*, pg. 326

TRUPHATEK (BEIJING) TRADING CO., LTD.—See Teleflex Incorporated; *U.S. Public*, pg. 1996
TRUPHATEK INTERNATIONAL LIMITED—See Teleflex Incorporated; *U.S. Public*, pg. 1996
TRUPHATEK PRODUCT RESOURCES INDIA PRIVATE LIMITED—See Teleflex Incorporated; *U.S. Public*, pg. 1996
TRUPHONE AUSTRALIA PTY LTD—See Truphone Limited; *Int'l*, pg. 7944
TRUPHONE BV—See Truphone Limited; *Int'l*, pg. 7944
TRUPHONE GMBH—See Truphone Limited; *Int'l*, pg. 7944
TRUPHONE HONG KONG LIMITED—See Truphone Limited; *Int'l*, pg. 7944
TRUPHONE, INC.—See Truphone Limited; *Int'l*, pg. 7944
TRUPHONE LIMITED; *Int'l*, pg. 7944
TRUPHONE POLAND SP Z.O.O.—See Truphone Limited; *Int'l*, pg. 7944
TRUPOINT INC.; *U.S. Private*, pg. 4250
TRU-POWER INC.; *U.S. Private*, pg. 4244
TRU PRECIOUS METALS CORP.; *Int'l*, pg. 7940
TRURX, LLC—See Bansk Group LLC; *U.S. Private*, pg. 469
TRUSANT TECHNOLOGIES, LLC.; *U.S. Private*, pg. 4250
TRUSCANIAN FOUNDRIES LIMITED—See W. Lucy & Co. Ltd.; *Int'l*, pg. 8321
TRUSCO NAKAYAMA CORPORATION; *Int'l*, pg. 7944
TRUSCO NAKAYAMA CORPORATION (THAILAND) LIMITED—See Trusco Nakayama Corporation; *Int'l*, pg. 7944
TRUSCOTT MINING CORPORATION LIMITED; *Int'l*, pg. 7944
TRUSCREEN GROUP LIMITED; *Int'l*, pg. 7944
THE TRU SHRIMP COMPANIES, INC.; *U.S. Public*, pg. 2136
TRU SIMULATION + TRAINING INC.—See Textron Inc.; *U.S. Public*, pg. 2028
TRU SIMULATION + TRAINING LLC—See Textron Inc.; *U.S. Public*, pg. 2029
TRUSSBILT, LLC.; *U.S. Private*, pg. 4250
TRUSSCO, INC.—See Gibson Energy Inc.; *Int'l*, pg. 2963
THE TRUSS COMPANY, INC.; *U.S. Private*, pg. 4128
TRUSSES UNLIMITED INC.; *U.S. Private*, pg. 4250
TRUSS FAB, LLC—See Bain Capital, LP; *U.S. Private*, pg. 451
TRUSS-PRO'S, INC.; *U.S. Private*, pg. 4250
TRUSS SYSTEMS, INC.; *U.S. Private*, pg. 4250
TRUSS TECH INDUSTRIES INC.; *U.S. Private*, pg. 4250
TRUSS-T STRUCTURES, INC.—See Roots Equity Group LLC; *U.S. Private*, pg. 3480
TRUSSVILLE GAS & WATER DEPARTMENTS; *U.S. Private*, pg. 4250
TRUSSWAY LTD.; *U.S. Private*, pg. 4250
TRUST ABSOLUT AUTO (PTY.) LTD.—See VT Holdings Co., Ltd.; *Int'l*, pg. 8315
TRUST ADVISERS CORPORATION—See Striders Corporation; *Int'l*, pg. 7240
TRUSTAFF, INC.; *U.S. Private*, pg. 4251
TRUST ALGERIA ASSURANCES REASSURANCE—See Trust International Insurance Company E.C.; *Int'l*, pg. 7945
TRUST ALLIANCE INFORMATION DEVELOPMENT INC. LTD.; *Int'l*, pg. 7944
TRUSTAR ENERGY LLC—See Fortistar LLC; *U.S. Private*, pg. 1576
TRUST AXIATA DIGITAL LIMITED—See Trust Bank Limited; *Int'l*, pg. 7944
THE TRUST BANK LIMITED; *Int'l*, pg. 7697
TRUST BANK LIMITED; *Int'l*, pg. 7944
THE TRUST BANK LTD.—See Social Security & National Insurance Trust; *Int'l*, pg. 7031
TRUSTBIX, INC.; *Int'l*, pg. 7945
TRUSTBRIDGE PARTNERS; *Int'l*, pg. 7945
TRUSTCO BANK CORP NY; *U.S. Public*, pg. 2201
TRUSTCO BANK—See TrustCo Bank Corp NY; *U.S. Public*, pg. 2201
TRUSTCO BANK TRUST DEPT—See TrustCo Bank Corp NY; *U.S. Public*, pg. 2202
TRUSTCO FINANCIAL SERVICES (PTY) LTD—See Trustco Group Holdings Limited; *Int'l*, pg. 7945
TRUSTCO GROUP HOLDINGS LIMITED; *Int'l*, pg. 7945
TRUSTCO INSURANCE LTD—See Trustco Group Holdings Limited; *Int'l*, pg. 7945
TRUST CO., LTD.—See VT Holdings Co., Ltd.; *Int'l*, pg. 8315
TRUST COMPANIES OF AMERICA, INC.; *U.S. Private*, pg. 4250
TRUST COMPANY OF THE WEST—See The Carlyle Group Inc.; *U.S. Public*, pg. 2056
THE TRUST COMPANY—See Argent Financial Group, Inc.; *U.S. Private*, pg. 320
TRUST COMPASS INSURANCE CO. S.A.L.—See Trust International Insurance Company E.C.; *Int'l*, pg. 7945
TRUST & CUSTODY SERVICES BANK, LTD.—See Japan Trustee Services Bank, Ltd.; *Int'l*, pg. 3908
TRUSTED BRAND 2016, INC.; *Int'l*, pg. 7945
TRUSTED CHOICE, INC.—See Independent Insurance Agents & Brokers of America, Inc.; *U.S. Private*, pg. 2059
TRUSTED HEALTH PLAN, INC.; *U.S. Private*, pg. 4251

TRUSTED HEALTH PLAN MICHIGAN, INC.—See Henry Ford Health System; *Int'l*, pg. 1918
TRUSTEDID, INC.—See Equifax Inc.; *U.S. Public*, pg. 787
TRUSTED LABS, INC.—See IAC Inc.; *U.S. Public*, pg. 1082
TRUSTED LABS S.A.S.U.—See Thales S.A.; *Int'l*, pg. 7600
TRUSTED LOGIC AFRICA (PTY) LTD—See Thales S.A.; *Int'l*, pg. 7600
TRUSTED LOGIC ASIA (PTE) LTD—See Thales S.A.; *Int'l*, pg. 7600
TRUSTED LOGIC S.A.—See Thales S.A.; *Int'l*, pg. 7600
TRUSTED NOVUS BANK LIMITED; *Int'l*, pg. 7945
TRUSTED POSITIONING, INC—See TDK Corporation; *Int'l*, pg. 7489
TRUSTED PROPERTIES (KPO) PRIVATE LIMITED—See Marg Ltd; *Int'l*, pg. 4692
TRUSTED SENIOR SPECIALISTS—See Integrity Marketing Group LLC; *U.S. Private*, pg. 2104
TRUSTED SUPPLY CHAIN PARTNERS; *U.S. Private*, pg. 4251
TRUSTEE PRINCIPLES LIMITED—See Willis Towers Watson Public Limited Company; *Int'l*, pg. 8415
THE TRUSTEES OF RESERVATIONS; *U.S. Private*, pg. 4128
TRUSTE; *U.S. Private*, pg. 4251
TRUST FINANCE INDONESIA TBK; *Int'l*, pg. 7944
TRUSTFORD - POTTERS BAR—See Ford Motor Company; *U.S. Public*, pg. 866
TRUSTGARD INSURANCE COMPANY—See Grange Mutual Casualty Company; *U.S. Private*, pg. 1754
THE TRUST FOR PUBLIC LAND; *U.S. Private*, pg. 4128
TRUST HOLDINGS INC.; *Int'l*, pg. 7944
TRUST HOSPITALITY LLC; *U.S. Private*, pg. 4250
TRUSTHOUSE SERVICES GROUP, INC.—See Charterhouse Capital Partners LLP; *Int'l*, pg. 1455
TRUSTILE DOORS LLC—See Marvin Windows & Doors Inc.; *U.S. Private*, pg. 2598
TRUST INSURANCE SERVICES LIMITED—See PSC Insurance Group Limited; *Int'l*, pg. 6016
TRUST INTERNATIONAL INSURANCE COMPANY (CYPRUS) LTD—See Trust International Insurance Company E.C.; *Int'l*, pg. 7945
TRUST INTERNATIONAL INSURANCE COMPANY E.C.; *Int'l*, pg. 7944
TRUST INTERNATIONAL INSURANCE COMPANY P.L.C—See Trust International Insurance Company E.C.; *Int'l*, pg. 7945
TRUST INVESTMENT BANK LIMITED; *Int'l*, pg. 7945
TRUST IT SP. Z O.O.—See Atende S.A.; *Int'l*, pg. 668
TRUST K PORTER CO., LTD.—See Warabeya Nichiyo Holdings Co., Ltd.; *Int'l*, pg. 8344
TRUSTMARK CORPORATION; *U.S. Public*, pg. 2202
TRUSTMARK MUTUAL HOLDING COMPANY; *U.S. Private*, pg. 4251
TRUSTMARK NATIONAL BANK—See Trustmark Corporation; *U.S. Public*, pg. 2202
TRUSTMARQUE SOLUTIONS LIMITED—See Capita plc; *Int'l*, pg. 1309
TRUST MODARABA; *Int'l*, pg. 7945
TRUST MOTORS LIMITED—See Pinewood Technologies Group PLC; *Int'l*, pg. 5869
TRUST NETWORKS INC.—See Internet Initiative Japan Inc.; *Int'l*, pg. 3753
TRUST NEXT SOLUTIONS, INC.—See Open Up Group Inc; *Int'l*, pg. 5599
TRU-STONE TECHNOLOGIES, INC.—See MiddleGround Management, LP; *U.S. Private*, pg. 2713
TRUST PHARMATECH CO., LTD.—See Sawai Group Holdings Co., Ltd.; *Int'l*, pg. 6602
TRUSTPILOT A/S—See Trustpilot Group Plc; *Int'l*, pg. 7945
TRUSTPILOT GROUP PLC; *Int'l*, pg. 7945
TRUSTPILOT LTD.—See Trustpilot Group Plc; *Int'l*, pg. 7945
TRUSTPILOT S.R.L.—See Trustpilot Group Plc; *Int'l*, pg. 7945
TRUSTPILOT UAB—See Trustpilot Group Plc; *Int'l*, pg. 7945
TRUSTPOINT HOSPITAL, LLC—See Acadia Healthcare Company, Inc.; *U.S. Public*, pg. 31
TRUSTPOINT INTERNATIONAL, LLC; *U.S. Private*, pg. 4251
TRUST RE—See Trust International Insurance Company E.C.; *Int'l*, pg. 7945
TRUST-SEARCH CORP., LTD.; *Int'l*, pg. 7945
TRUST SECURITIES & BROKERAGE LIMITED; *Int'l*, pg. 7945
TRUST TECH WITH INC.—See Open Up Group Inc; *Int'l*, pg. 5599
TRUSTTEXAS BANK; *U.S. Private*, pg. 4251
TRUST UNDERWRITING LIMITED—See Trust International Insurance Company E.C.; *Int'l*, pg. 7945
TRUSTWAVE CANADA, INC.—See Temasek Holdings (Private) Limited; *Int'l*, pg. 7554
TRUSTWAVE HOLDINGS, INC.—See The Chertoff Group, LLC; *U.S. Private*, pg. 4008
TRUSTWAVE LIMITED—See Temasek Holdings (Private) Limited; *Int'l*, pg. 7554

TRUST YEMEN INSURANCE & REINSURANCE COMPANY—See Trust International Insurance Company E.C.; *Int'l*, pg. 7945
TRUSVAL TECHNOLOGY CO., LTD.; *Int'l*, pg. 7945
TRUS-WAY, INC.; *U.S. Private*, pg. 4250
TRUSWOOD INC.; *U.S. Private*, pg. 4251
TRUS Y 7 REIT CO., LTD.; *Int'l*, pg. 7944
TRUTAC LIMITED—See Microlise Group Plc; *Int'l*, pg. 4879
TRUTANKLESS INC.; *U.S. Public*, pg. 2202
TRUTEAM, LLC—See TopBuild Corp.; *U.S. Public*, pg. 2163
TRUTEAM OF CALIFORNIA, INC.—See TopBuild Corp.; *U.S. Public*, pg. 2163
TRU TECH SYSTEMS INC.—See Star Cutter Company; *U.S. Public*, pg. 3784
TRU-TEST BRASIL S.A.—See Tru-Test Group; *Int'l*, pg. 7940
TRU-TEST GROUP; *Int'l*, pg. 7940
TRU-TEST, INC.—See Tru-Test Group; *Int'l*, pg. 7940
TRU-TEST LIMITED—See Tru-Test Group; *Int'l*, pg. 7940
TRU-TEST PTY LIMITED—See Tru-Test Group; *Int'l*, pg. 7940
TRUTH HARDWARE INC.—See Quanex Building Products Corp.; *U.S. Public*, pg. 1750
TRUTH HONOUR ELECTRONIC LIMITED—See China Technology Industry Group Limited; *Int'l*, pg. 1557
TRUTH PUBLISHING COMPANY INC.—See Federated Media Inc.; *U.S. Private*, pg. 1492
TRUTRACE TECHNOLOGIES INC.; *Int'l*, pg. 7945
TRUTZSCHLER GMBH & CO. KG; *Int'l*, pg. 7945
TRUTZSCHLER INDUSTRIA E COMERCIO DE MAQUINAS LTDA—See Trutzschler GmbH & Co. KG; *Int'l*, pg. 7946
TRUTZSCHLER NONWOVENS GMBH—See Trutzschler GmbH & Co. KG; *Int'l*, pg. 7946
TRUTZSCHLER NONWOVENS & MAN-MADE FIBERS GMBH—See Trutzschler GmbH & Co. KG; *Int'l*, pg. 7946
TRUTZSCHLER SWITZERLAND AG—See Trutzschler GmbH & Co. KG; *Int'l*, pg. 7946
TRUVALUE MANUFACTURING CO.—See ACON Investments, LLC; *U.S. Private*, pg. 63
TRUVEN HEALTH ANALYTICS INC.—See International Business Machines Corporation; *U.S. Public*, pg. 1151
TRUVERIS, INC.; *U.S. Private*, pg. 4251
TRUVISO LLC—See Cisco Systems, Inc.; *U.S. Public*, pg. 500
TRUVO NV/SA—See Apax Partners LLP; *Int'l*, pg. 507
TRUVO NV/SA—See Cinven Limited; *Int'l*, pg. 1615
TRUVOX INTERNATIONAL LIMITED—See Tacony Corporation; *U.S. Private*, pg. 3921
TRU VUE, INC.—See Apogee Enterprises, Inc.; *U.S. Public*, pg. 145
TRU VUE, INC.—See Apogee Enterprises, Inc.; *U.S. Public*, pg. 145
TRUWATER COOLING TOWERS SDN. BHD.—See Jiangsu Seagull Cooling Tower Co., Ltd.; *Int'l*, pg. 3953
TRUWEST CREDIT UNION; *U.S. Private*, pg. 4251
TRUWIN CO., LTD.; *Int'l*, pg. 7946
TRUWORTHS INTERNATIONAL LIMITED; *Int'l*, pg. 7946
TRUWORTHS LIMITED; *Int'l*, pg. 7946
TRUXMART, INC.—See Worksport, Ltd.; *Int'l*, pg. 8456
TRUXOR WETLAND EQUIPMENT AB—See Lagercrantz Group AB; *Int'l*, pg. 4395
TRUXTON CORP.; *U.S. Public*, pg. 2202
TRV HOLDINGS LLC—See Citigroup Inc.; *U.S. Public*, pg. 504
TRV INVESTMENTS LLC—See Citigroup Inc.; *U.S. Public*, pg. 504
TRV THERMISCHE RUCKSTANDSVERWERTUNG GMBH & CO. KG—See LyondellBasell Industries N.V.; *Int'l*, pg. 4608
TRV THERMISCHE RUCKSTANDSVERWERTUNG VERWALTUNGS-GMBH—See LyondellBasell Industries N.V.; *Int'l*, pg. 4608
TRW AFTERMARKET ASIA PACIFIC PTE LTD—See ZF Friedrichshafen AG; *Int'l*, pg. 8645
TRW AFTERMARKET JAPAN CO., LTD.—See ZF Friedrichshafen AG; *Int'l*, pg. 8645
TRW AIRBAG SYSTEMS GMBH-LAAGE—See ZF Friedrichshafen AG; *Int'l*, pg. 8646
TRW AIRBAG SYSTEMS GMBH—See ZF Friedrichshafen AG; *Int'l*, pg. 8646
TRW ASIA PACIFIC CO.,LTD—See ZF Friedrichshafen AG; *Int'l*, pg. 8645
TRW ASIATIC CO., LTD.—See ZF Friedrichshafen AG; *Int'l*, pg. 8645
TRW ASIATIC (M) SDN BHD—See ZF Friedrichshafen AG; *Int'l*, pg. 8645
TRW AUTOELEKTRONIKA S.R.O.—See ZF Friedrichshafen AG; *Int'l*, pg. 8645
TRW AUTOMOTIVE BONNEVAL S.A.S.—See ZF Friedrichshafen AG; *Int'l*, pg. 8645
TRW AUTOMOTIVE COMPONENTS (LANGFANG) CO., LTD.—See ZF Friedrichshafen AG; *Int'l*, pg. 8645
TRW AUTOMOTIVE COMPONENTS (SHANGHAI) CO., LTD.—See ZF Friedrichshafen AG; *Int'l*, pg. 8645

COMPANY NAME INDEX

TRW AUTOMOTIVE COMPONENTS TECHNICAL SERVICE SHANGHAI CO. LTD.—See ZF Friedrichshafen AG; *Int'l*, pg. 8645
TRW AUTOMOTIVE CZECH S.R.O—See ZF Friedrichshafen AG; *Int'l*, pg. 8646
TRW AUTOMOTIVE ELECTRONICS & COMPONENTS GMBH—See ZF Friedrichshafen AG; *Int'l*, pg. 8646
TRW AUTOMOTIVE ESPANA SL—See ZF Friedrichshafen AG; *Int'l*, pg. 8646
TRW AUTOMOTIVE HOLDING GMBH & CO. KG—See ZF Friedrichshafen AG; *Int'l*, pg. 8646
TRW AUTOMOTIVE INC.—See ZF Friedrichshafen AG; *Int'l*, pg. 8646
TRW AUTOMOTIVE ITALIA S.R.L.—See ZF Friedrichshafen AG; *Int'l*, pg. 8646
TRW AUTOMOTIVE JAPAN CO. LTD.—See ZF Friedrichshafen AG; *Int'l*, pg. 8646
TRW AUTOMOTIVE LTDA. - ENGENHEIRO COELHO—See ZF Friedrichshafen AG; *Int'l*, pg. 8646
TRW AUTOMOTIVE LTDA.—See ZF Friedrichshafen AG; *Int'l*, pg. 8646
TRW AUTOMOTIVE PORTUGAL LDA—See ZF Friedrichshafen AG; *Int'l*, pg. 8646
TRW AUTOMOTIVE SAFETY SYSTEMS GMBH—See ZF Friedrichshafen AG; *Int'l*, pg. 8646
TRW AUTOMOTIVE (SLOVAKIA) S.R.O.—See ZF Friedrichshafen AG; *Int'l*, pg. 8645
TRW AUTOMOTIVE TECHNOLOGIES (SHANGHAI) CO., LTD.—See ZF Friedrichshafen AG; *Int'l*, pg. 8645
TRW AUTOMOTIVE U.S. LLC - COMMERCIAL STEERING SYSTEMS, LAFAYETTE PLANT—See ZF Friedrichshafen AG; *Int'l*, pg. 8646
TRW AUTOMOTIVE U.S. LLC - COMMERCIAL STEERING SYSTEMS, LEBANON PLANT—See ZF Friedrichshafen AG; *Int'l*, pg. 8646
TRW AUTOMOTIVE U.S. LLC - STEERING SYSTEMS, WASHINGTON PLANT—See ZF Friedrichshafen AG; *Int'l*, pg. 8646
TRW B.V.—See ZF Friedrichshafen AG; *Int'l*, pg. 8641
TRW CANADA LIMITED/TRW CANADA LIMITEE—See ZF Friedrichshafen AG; *Int'l*, pg. 8646
TRW-CARR S.R.O.—See ZF Friedrichshafen AG; *Int'l*, pg. 8646
TRW CONTROLS & FASTENERS INC.—See ZF Friedrichshafen AG; *Int'l*, pg. 8646
TRW DEUTSCHLAND HOLDING GMBH—See ZF Friedrichshafen AG; *Int'l*, pg. 8646
TRW DONGFANG (XIAN) AIRBAG INFLATOR CO., LTD.—See ZF Friedrichshafen AG; *Int'l*, pg. 8645
TRW FAWER AUTOMOBILE SAFETY SYSTEMS (CHANGCHUN) CO., LTD.—See ZF Friedrichshafen AG; *Int'l*, pg. 8645
TRW FAWER COMMERCIAL VEHICLE STEERING (CHANGCHUN) CO., LTD.—See ZF Friedrichshafen AG; *Int'l*, pg. 8645
T.R. WINSTON & COMPANY, LLC; *U.S. Private*, pg. 3912
TRW KFZ AUSRUSTUNG GMBH—See ZF Friedrichshafen AG; *Int'l*, pg. 8646
TRW LIMITED—See ZF Friedrichshafen AG; *Int'l*, pg. 8646
TRW LOGISTIC SERVICES GMBH—See ZF Friedrichshafen AG; *Int'l*, pg. 8646
TRW OCCUPANT RESTRAINTS SOUTH AFRICA INC.—See ZF Friedrichshafen AG; *Int'l*, pg. 8646
TRW OVERSEAS SEOUL INC.—See ZF Friedrichshafen AG; *Int'l*, pg. 8646
TRW POLSKA SP. Z O.O.—See ZF Friedrichshafen AG; *Int'l*, pg. 8646
TRW RECEIVABLES FINANCE GMBH—See ZF Friedrichshafen AG; *Int'l*, pg. 8646
TRW SISTEMAS DE DIRECCIONES, S. DE R.L. DE C.V.—See ZF Friedrichshafen AG; *Int'l*, pg. 8646
TRW STEERING CO. LTD.—See ZF Friedrichshafen AG; *Int'l*, pg. 8646
TRW STEERING & SUSPENSION CO., LTD.—See ZF Friedrichshafen AG; *Int'l*, pg. 8646
TRW SUN STEERING WHEELS PVT. LTD.—See Rane Holdings Limited; *Int'l*, pg. 6206
TRW SUN STEERING WHEELS PVT. LTD.—See ZF Friedrichshafen AG; *Int'l*, pg. 8646
TRW (SUZHOU) AUTOMOTIVE ELECTRONICS CO., LTD.—See ZF Friedrichshafen AG; *Int'l*, pg. 8641
TRW SYSTEMES DE FREINAGE SAS—See ZF Friedrichshafen AG; *Int'l*, pg. 8646
TRW VEHICLE SAFETY SYSTEMS DE MEXICO, S. DE R.L. DE C.V.—See ZF Friedrichshafen AG; *Int'l*, pg. 8646
TRW VEHICLE SAFETY SYSTEMS, INC. - MESA PLANT—See ZF Friedrichshafen AG; *Int'l*, pg. 8646
TRW VEHICLE SAFETY SYSTEMS, INC.—See ZF Friedrichshafen AG; *Int'l*, pg. 8646
TRX GOLD CORPORATION; *Int'l*, pg. 7946
TRYAD SERVICE CORPORATION—See J.D. Rush Company Inc.; *U.S. Private*, pg. 2161
TRYANGLE CO., LTD.—See Bain Capital, LP; *U.S. Private*, pg. 435
TRYBA ENERGIES SAS—See Atrya SAS; *Int'l*, pg. 694
TRYCERA FINANCIAL, INC.; *U.S. Private*, pg. 4251
TRYCHEM FZCO—See BRENNTAG SE; *Int'l*, pg. 1150
TRYFFELSVINET AB—See Viva Wine Group AB; *Int'l*, pg. 8265
TRYG A/S; *Int'l*, pg. 7946
TRYG FORSIKRING A/S—See Tryg A/S; *Int'l*, pg. 7947
TRYGG-HANSA FORSAKRING AB—See Intact Financial Corporation; *Int'l*, pg. 3727
TRYGG-HANSA FORSAKRING AB—See Tryg A/S; *Int'l*, pg. 7946
TRYGHEDSGRUPPEN SMBA; *Int'l*, pg. 7947
TRY, INC.—See Tokyo Century Corporation; *Int'l*, pg. 7789
TRY-IT DISTRIBUTING CO. INC.; *U.S. Private*, pg. 4251
TRYKO PARTNERS, LLC; *U.S. Private*, pg. 4251
TRYKSAGSOMDELINGEN FYN A/S—See North Media A/S; *Int'l*, pg. 5440
TRYLON SMR; *U.S. Private*, pg. 4252
TRYM ANLEGG AS—See Per Aarsleff Holding A/S; *Int'l*, pg. 5796
TRYNET HOLDINNGS CO.,LTD.—See Nakano Corporation; *Int'l*, pg. 5133
TRYNEX, INC.—See Douglas Dynamics, Inc.; *U.S. Public*, pg. 677
TRYON DISTRIBUTING CO. LLC; *U.S. Private*, pg. 4252
THE TRYON GROUP INC.—See O2 Investment Partners, LLC; *U.S. Private*, pg. 2982
THE TRYON GROUP INC.—See Oakland Standard Co., LLC; *U.S. Private*, pg. 2984
TRYON MANAGEMENT, INC.—See Wells Fargo & Company; *U.S. Public*, pg. 2347
TRYP FRANCOIS SAS—See Melia Hotels International, S.A.; *Int'l*, pg. 4809
TRYSILFJELLET ALPIN AS—See SkiStar AB; *Int'l*, pg. 6990
TRYSILFJELLET GOLF AS—See SkiStar AB; *Int'l*, pg. 6990
TRYSPORTS, LLC; *U.S. Private*, pg. 4252
TRYSTAR, LLC; *U.S. Private*, pg. 4252
TRYTEC CORPORATION—See Seiko Electric Co., Ltd.; *Int'l*, pg. 6686
TRYTECH CO., LTD.—See WIN-Partners Co., Ltd.; *Int'l*, pg. 8424
TRYT INC.; *Int'l*, pg. 7947
TRYTO CORPORATION—See AIFUL Corporation; *Int'l*, pg. 232
TRYTON TOOL SERVICES LTD.—See Element Technical Services Inc.; *Int'l*, pg. 2358
TRZNICA A.D.; *Int'l*, pg. 7947
TS3; *Int'l*, pg. 7949
TSA CONSULTING GROUP, INC.; *U.S. Private*, pg. 4252
TSA GRIDDLE SYSTEMS INC.—See Gilbert Global Equity Partners; *U.S. Private*, pg. 1699
TSA, INC.—See Cross Financial Corporation; *U.S. Private*, pg. 1105
TSA INDUSTRIES (IPOH) SDN. BHD.—See TSA Industries Sdn. Bhd.; *Int'l*, pg. 7949
TSA INDUSTRIES (JOHOR) SDN. BHD.—See TSA Industries Sdn. Bhd.; *Int'l*, pg. 7949
TSA INDUSTRIES (PENANG) SDN. BHD.—See TSA Industries Sdn. Bhd.; *Int'l*, pg. 7949
TSA INDUSTRIES SDN. BHD. - SABAH—See TSA Industries Sdn. Bhd.; *Int'l*, pg. 7949
TSA INDUSTRIES SDN. BHD.; *Int'l*, pg. 7949
TSA INDUSTRIES (SEA) PTE LTD—See TSA Industries Sdn. Bhd.; *Int'l*, pg. 7949
TSAKER NEW ENERGY TECH CO., LIMITED; *Int'l*, pg. 7949
TSAKIRIS S.A.—See Coca-Cola HBC AG; *Int'l*, pg. 1686
TSAKOS ENERGY NAVIGATION LIMITED; *Int'l*, pg. 7949
TS ALFRESA CORPORATION—See Alfresa Holdings Corporation; *Int'l*, pg. 317
T S ALLOYS LIMITED—See Tata Sons Limited; *Int'l*, pg. 7471
TSAMOUTALES STRATEGIES; *U.S. Private*, pg. 4252
TSANG YOW INDUSTRIAL CO., LTD.; *Int'l*, pg. 7949
TSANN KUEN (CHINA) ENTERPRISE CO., LTD.; *Int'l*, pg. 7949
TSANN KUEN ENTERPRISE CO., LTD.; *Int'l*, pg. 7949
TSA PIPES MANUFACTURING SDN. BHD.—See TSA Industries Sdn. Bhd.; *Int'l*, pg. 7949
TSA PROCESSING DALLAS, LLC—See Ryerson Holding Corporation; *U.S. Public*, pg. 1829
TS ASSET MANAGEMENT CO., LTD.—See Thanachart Capital PCL; *Int'l*, pg. 7607
TSAVO POWER COMPANY LTD—See Aga Khan Development Network; *Int'l*, pg. 199
TSAWORLD INC.; *U.S. Private*, pg. 4252
TSAY CONSTRUCTION & SERVICES, LLC—See Tsay Corporation; *U.S. Private*, pg. 4252
TSAY CORPORATION; *U.S. Private*, pg. 4252
TSAYTA RESOURCES CORP.—See NorthWest Copper Corp.; *Int'l*, pg. 5446
TSB BANKING GROUP PLC—See Banco de Sabadell, S.A.; *Int'l*, pg. 821
TSB BANK PLC—See Banco de Sabadell, S.A.; *Int'l*, pg. 821
TSB BANKSHARES, INC.; *U.S. Private*, pg. 4252
TSB BANK; *U.S. Private*, pg. 4252
TSB BORRENTREPRENAD AB—See Nordisk Bergteknik AB; *Int'l*, pg. 5424
TS BELMONT (TAIWAN) CO.,LTD.—See Takara Belmont Corporation; *Int'l*, pg. 7432
TS BIG CREEK, LLC—See Independence Realty Trust, Inc.; *U.S. Public*, pg. 1116
TSB LOSS CONTROL CONSULTANTS, INC.—See Factory Mutual Insurance Company; *U.S. Public*, pg. 1461
T&S BRASS & BRONZE WORKS, INC.; *U.S. Private*, pg. 3910
TS BRIER CREEK, LLC—See Independence Realty Trust, Inc.; *U.S. Public*, pg. 1116
TSB SERVICES INC.; *U.S. Private*, pg. 4252
TSB SUGAR HOLDINGS (PTY) LIMITED—See Remgro Limited; *Int'l*, pg. 6271
TSB TRIMEDIA INC—See TBS Holdings, Inc.; *Int'l*, pg. 7481
TSC ACQUISITION CORP.; *U.S. Private*, pg. 4252
TSCAN THERAPEUTICS, INC.; *U.S. Public*, pg. 2202
TSC APPAREL, LLC—See Clayton, Dubilier & Rice, LLC; *U.S. Private*, pg. 926
TSC AUTO ID TECHNOLOGY AMERICA INC.—See TSC Auto ID Technology Co., Ltd.; *Int'l*, pg. 7949
TSC AUTO ID TECHNOLOGY CO., LTD.; *Int'l*, pg. 7949
TSC AUTO ID TECHNOLOGY EMEA GMBH—See TSC Auto ID Technology Co., Ltd.; *Int'l*, pg. 7949
TSC AUTO ID TECHNOLOGY EMEA GMBH—See TSC Auto ID Technology Co., Ltd.; *Int'l*, pg. 7949
TSC AUTO ID TECHNOLOGY ME LTD.—See TSC Auto ID Technology Co., Ltd.; *Int'l*, pg. 7949
TSC ENGINEERING LIMITED—See CM Energy Tech Co., Ltd.; *Int'l*, pg. 1666
T SCIENTIFIC CO., LTD; *Int'l*, pg. 7394
TSC MANUFACTURING & SUPPLY, LLC—See CM Energy Tech Co., Ltd.; *Int'l*, pg. 1666
TSC OFFSHORE CHINA LTD.—See CM Energy Tech Co., Ltd.; *Int'l*, pg. 1666
TSC OFFSHORE CORPORATION—See CM Energy Tech Co., Ltd.; *Int'l*, pg. 1666
TSC OFFSHORE LIMITEDA—See CM Energy Tech Co., Ltd.; *Int'l*, pg. 1666
TSC OFFSHORE PTE. LIMITED—See CM Energy Tech Co., Ltd.; *Int'l*, pg. 1666
TSC OFFSHORE (UK) LIMITED—See CM Energy Tech Co., Ltd.; *Int'l*, pg. 1666
T&S COMMUNICATIONS CO., LTD. - SHENZHEN FACTORY—See T&S Communications Co.,Ltd.; *Int'l*, pg. 7395
T&S COMMUNICATIONS CO.,LTD.; *Int'l*, pg. 7395
TS CONSULTING INTERNATIONAL, INC.—See Persol Holdings Co., Ltd.; *Int'l*, pg. 5820
TS CORPORATION CO., LTD.—See TS Tech Co Ltd; *Int'l*, pg. 7948
TS CORPORATION - FEED DIVISION—See TS Corporation; *Int'l*, pg. 7947
TS CORPORATION - OXAN PLANT—See TS Corporation; *Int'l*, pg. 7947
TS CORPORATION; *Int'l*, pg. 7947
TS CORPORATION - SUGAR & FOODSTUFF DIVISION—See TS Corporation; *Int'l*, pg. 7947
TS CRAIG RANCH, LLC—See Independence Realty Trust, Inc.; *U.S. Public*, pg. 1116
TS CREDIT & INVESTMENT CORP.—See TS Corporation; *Int'l*, pg. 7947
TS CREEKSTONE, LLC—See Independence Realty Trust, Inc.; *U.S. Public*, pg. 1116
TSC (SHANGHAI) CO., LTD.—See Tokyo Sangyo Co., Ltd.; *Int'l*, pg. 7795
TSC STORES L.P.—See Peavey Industries LP; *Int'l*, pg. 5778
TSC TECH ASIA CO., LTD.—See Sumitomo Densetsu Co., Ltd.; *Int'l*, pg. 7277
TSC TELEFON-SERVICECENTER GMBH—See Raiffeisenlandesbank Oberosterreich Aktiengesellschaft; *Int'l*, pg. 6187
TS DE SAN PEDRO INDUSTRIES, S. DE R.L. DE C.V.—See TS Tech Co Ltd; *Int'l*, pg. 7948
TSD GLOBAL INC.—See Career Horizons, Inc.; *U.S. Private*, pg. 752
TS DOCK & LIFT SERVICES—See TS Recreational, Inc.; *U.S. Private*, pg. 4252
TSEBO SOLUTIONS GROUP PTY LTD.—See Wendel S.A.; *Int'l*, pg. 8376
TSEC AMERICA INC.—See TSEC Corporation; *Int'l*, pg. 7950
TSEC CORPORATION - HSINCHU PLANT—See TSEC Corporation; *Int'l*, pg. 7950
TSEC CORPORATION - PINGTUNG PLANT—See TSEC Corporation; *Int'l*, pg. 7950
TSEC CORPORATION; *Int'l*, pg. 7950
TSE CO., LTD.; *Int'l*, pg. 7949
TSE CONSULTING SA—See WPP plc; *Int'l*, pg. 8468
TSE CONSULTING TURKIYE—See WPP plc; *Int'l*, pg. 8468
TSE INDUSTRIES INC.; *U.S. Private*, pg. 4252
TSE ENGINEERING CO., LTD.—See Takebishi Corporation; *Int'l*, pg. 7436
TSE NORTH AMERICA—See WPP plc; *Int'l*, pg. 8468
T&S ENTERPRISES (LONDON) LIMITED—See JFLA Holdings Inc.; *Int'l*, pg. 3939
TSE SCANDINAVIA—See WPP plc; *Int'l*, pg. 8468

TSE

CORPORATE AFFILIATIONS

Company Index

TSE; *U.S. Private*, pg. 4252
TSE STEEL LTD.; *Int'l*, pg. 7949
TSE SUI LUEN JEWELLERY COMPANY LIMITED—See Tse Sui Luen Jewellery (International) Limited; *Int'l*, pg. 7950
TSE SUI LUEN JEWELLERY (INTERNATIONAL) LIMITED; *Int'l*, pg. 7950
TSE WALL ARLIDGE LIMITED—See Downer EDI Limited; *Int'l*, pg. 2186
TSEYU INTERNATIONAL TRADING COMPANY LIMITED—See Harbour Equine Holdings Limited; *Int'l*, pg. 3272
TSF-A GMBH—See voestalpine AG; *Int'l*, pg. 8289
TSF ENGINEERING PTY LTD—See EVZ Limited; *Int'l*, pg. 2574
T S FLOUR MILL PUBLIC COMPANY LIMITED; *Int'l*, pg. 7394
TSF MANAGEMENT COMPANY LIMITED—See ThreeSixtyFive Public Company Limited; *Int'l*, pg. 7721
TSF POWER PTY LTD—See EVZ Limited; *Int'l*, pg. 2574
TSG CONSUMER PARTNERS LLC - NEW YORK OFFICE—See TSG Consumer Partners LLC; *U.S. Private*, pg. 4253
TSG CONSUMER PARTNERS LLC; *U.S. Private*, pg. 4252
TSG EDV-TERMINAL SERVICE GMBH—See Atos SE; *Int'l*, pg. 692
TSG INC.; *U.S. Private*, pg. 4253
TSG INTERNATIONAL AG; *Int'l*, pg. 7950
TS GLOBAL NETWORK SDN. BHD.—See Perusahaan Perseroan Indonesia Tbk; *Int'l*, pg. 5822
TSG NORWAY AS—See Austriacard Holdings AG; *Int'l*, pg. 724
TS GOOSECREEK, LLC—See Independence Realty Trust, Inc.; *U.S. Public*, pg. 1116
TSG PREMIUM FINANCE, LLC—See Brown & Brown, Inc.; *U.S. Public*, pg. 402
TS GROUP GMBH; *Int'l*, pg. 7947
T&S GROUP INC.; *Int'l*, pg. 7395
TSG SOLUTIONS, INC.—See Bluestone Investment Partners, LLC; *U.S. Private*, pg. 598
TSH AGRI PTE. LTD.—See TSH Resources Berhad; *Int'l*, pg. 7950
TSH BIOPHARM CORP LTD.; *Int'l*, pg. 7950
TSH CORPORATION LIMITED; *Int'l*, pg. 7950
TS HEATRONICS CO., LTD.—See Nabtesco Corporation; *Int'l*, pg. 5121
TSHIRTBORDELLO.COM; *U.S. Private*, pg. 4253
T-SHIRT INTERNATIONAL INC.; *U.S. Private*, pg. 3911
T SHIRT PRINTERS PTY LIMITED—See Live Nation Entertainment, Inc.; *U.S. Public*, pg. 1331
TSH PLANTATION SDN. BHD—See TSH Resources Berhad; *Int'l*, pg. 7950
TSH PRODUCTS SDN. BHD.—See TSH Resources Berhad; *Int'l*, pg. 7950
TSH RESOURCES BERHAD; *Int'l*, pg. 7950
TSI 1231 3RD AVENUE, LLC—See Town Sports International Holdings, Inc.; *U.S. Private*, pg. 4197
TSI 30 BROAD STREET, LLC—See Town Sports International Holdings, Inc.; *U.S. Private*, pg. 4197
TSI 555 6TH AVENUE, LLC—See Town Sports International Holdings, Inc.; *U.S. Private*, pg. 4197
TSI AB—See TSI Incorporated; *U.S. Private*, pg. 4253
TSI ALEXANDRIA, LLC—See Town Sports International Holdings, Inc.; *U.S. Private*, pg. 4198
TSI ARDMORE, LLC—See Town Sports International Holdings, Inc.; *U.S. Private*, pg. 4198
TSI ASSET HOLDINGS, LLC—See Lezzer Lumber, Inc.; *U.S. Private*, pg. 2441
TSI ASTOR PLACE, LLC—See Town Sports International Holdings, Inc.; *U.S. Private*, pg. 4197
TSI BRADFORD, LLC—See Town Sports International Holdings, Inc.; *U.S. Private*, pg. 4197
TSI CLARENDON, LLC—See Town Sports International Holdings, Inc.; *U.S. Private*, pg. 4198
TSI CO., LTD.; *Int'l*, pg. 7950
TSI EAST 86, LLC—See Town Sports International Holdings, Inc.; *U.S. Private*, pg. 4198
TSI EC STRATEGY CO., LTD.—See TSI Holdings Co., Ltd.; *Int'l*, pg. 7950
TSI EQUIPMENT INC.—See Transportation Services, Inc.; *U.S. Private*, pg. 4211
TSI FRANCE, INC.—See TSI Incorporated; *U.S. Private*, pg. 4253
TSI GLOBAL COMPANIES; *U.S. Private*, pg. 4253
TSI GMBH—See TSI Incorporated; *U.S. Private*, pg. 4253
TSI GRAPHICS INC.; *U.S. Private*, pg. 4253
TSI HEALTHCARE, INC; *U.S. Private*, pg. 4253
TSI HELL'S KITCHEN, LLC—See Town Sports International Holdings, Inc.; *U.S. Private*, pg. 4197
TSI HOLDING COMPANY; *U.S. Private*, pg. 4253
TSI HOLDINGS CO., LTD.; *Int'l*, pg. 7950
TSI HOLDINGS, LLC; *U.S. Private*, pg. 4253
TSI INCORPORATED; *U.S. Private*, pg. 4253
TSI INSTRUMENT (BEIJING) CO.,LTD.—See TSI Incorporated; *U.S. Private*, pg. 4253
TSI INSTRUMENTS INDIA PRIVATE LIMITED—See TSI Incorporated; *U.S. Private*, pg. 4253
TSI INSTRUMENTS LTD.—See TSI Incorporated; *U.S. Private*, pg. 4253
TSI INSTRUMENTS SINGAPORE PTE LTD.—See TSI Incorporated; *U.S. Private*, pg. 4253
TSI-LIV CONDADO, LLC—See Town Sports International Holdings, Inc.; *U.S. Private*, pg. 4197
TSI-LIV GUAYNABO, LLC—See Town Sports International Holdings, Inc.; *U.S. Private*, pg. 4197
TSI - LUCILLE 38TH AVENUE, LLC—See Town Sports International Holdings, Inc.; *U.S. Private*, pg. 4197
TSI - LUCILLE 42ND STREET, LLC—See Town Sports International Holdings, Inc.; *U.S. Private*, pg. 4197
TSI - LUCILLE 89TH STREET, LLC—See Town Sports International Holdings, Inc.; *U.S. Private*, pg. 4197
TSI - LUCILLE ASTORIA, LLC—See Town Sports International Holdings, Inc.; *U.S. Private*, pg. 4197
TSI - LUCILLE AUSTIN STREET, LLC—See Town Sports International Holdings, Inc.; *U.S. Private*, pg. 4197
TSI - LUCILLE BAYSHORE, LLC—See Town Sports International Holdings, Inc.; *U.S. Private*, pg. 4197
TSI - LUCILLE BRONX, LLC—See Town Sports International Holdings, Inc.; *U.S. Private*, pg. 4197
TSI - LUCILLE CLIFTON, LLC—See Town Sports International Holdings, Inc.; *U.S. Private*, pg. 4197
TSI - LUCILLE COMMACK, LLC—See Town Sports International Holdings, Inc.; *U.S. Private*, pg. 4197
TSI - LUCILLE HOLBROOK, LLC—See Town Sports International Holdings, Inc.; *U.S. Private*, pg. 4197
TSI - LUCILLE JERSEY CITY, LLC—See Town Sports International Holdings, Inc.; *U.S. Private*, pg. 4197
TSI - LUCILLE KINGS HIGHWAY, LLC—See Town Sports International Holdings, Inc.; *U.S. Private*, pg. 4197
TSI - LUCILLE RALPH AVENUE, LLC—See Town Sports International Holdings, Inc.; *U.S. Private*, pg. 4197
TSI - LUCILLE ROCKVILLE CENTRE, LLC—See Town Sports International Holdings, Inc.; *U.S. Private*, pg. 4197
TSI - LUCILLE ST. NICHOLAS AVENUE, LLC—See Town Sports International Holdings, Inc.; *U.S. Private*, pg. 4197
TSI - LUCILLE VALLEY STREAM, LLC—See Town Sports International Holdings, Inc.; *U.S. Private*, pg. 4197
TSI MAHWAH, LLC—See Town Sports International Holdings, Inc.; *U.S. Private*, pg. 4198
TSI METHUEN, LLC—See Town Sports International Holdings, Inc.; *U.S. Private*, pg. 4197
TSIMIS S.A.—See Mondelez International, Inc.; *U.S. Public*, pg. 1464
TSIM SHA TSUI PROPERTIES LIMITED; *Int'l*, pg. 7951
TSI (NA) LIMITED—See Tata Sons Limited; *Int'l*, pg. 7470
TS INDUSTRIES INC.—See Graycliff Partners LP; *U.S. Private*, pg. 1761
TSINGHUA HOLDINGS CO., LTD.; *Int'l*, pg. 7951
TSINGHUA TONGFANG CO., LTD.; *Int'l*, pg. 7951
TSINGHUA UNIGROUP LTD.—See Tsinghua Holdings Co., Ltd.; *Int'l*, pg. 7951
TSINGSHAN HOLDING GROUP CO., LTD.; *Int'l*, pg. 7952
TSINGTAO BREWERY COMPANY LIMITED—See Tsingtao Brewery Group Company Ltd.; *Int'l*, pg. 7952
TSINGTAO BREWERY GROUP COMPANY LTD.; *Int'l*, pg. 7952
TSI - NORTHRIDGE, LLC—See Town Sports International Holdings, Inc.; *U.S. Private*, pg. 4197
TSINPO, D.O.O.—See Telekom Slovenije, d.d.; *Int'l*, pg. 7538
TS INSURANCE SERVICE CO., LTD.—See TS Tech Co Ltd; *Int'l*, pg. 7948
TS INVESTMENT CORP; *Int'l*, pg. 7947
TSI PEABODY, LLC—See Town Sports International Holdings, Inc.; *U.S. Private*, pg. 4197
TSI - PEACOCK, PORT ST. LUCIE, LLC—See Town Sports International Holdings, Inc.; *U.S. Private*, pg. 4197
TSI - PLACENTIA, LLC—See Town Sports International Holdings, Inc.; *U.S. Private*, pg. 4197
TSI PRINCETON, LLC—See Town Sports International Holdings, Inc.; *U.S. Private*, pg. 4198
TSI PRISM—See Black Creek Integrated Systems Corporation; *U.S. Private*, pg. 570
TSI PRODUCTION NETWORK CO., LTD.—See TSI Holdings Co., Ltd.; *Int'l*, pg. 7951
TSI SALISBURY, LLC—See Town Sports International Holdings, Inc.; *U.S. Private*, pg. 4197
TSI - SAN JOSE, LLC—See Town Sports International Holdings, Inc.; *U.S. Private*, pg. 4197
TSI; *U.S. Private*, pg. 4253
TSI SPRINGFIELD, LLC—See Town Sports International Holdings, Inc.; *U.S. Private*, pg. 4198
TSI - STUDIO CITY, LLC—See Town Sports International Holdings, Inc.; *U.S. Private*, pg. 4197
TSI - TOPANGA, LLC—See Town Sports International Holdings, Inc.; *U.S. Private*, pg. 4197
TSI - TORRANCE, LLC—See Town Sports International Holdings, Inc.; *U.S. Private*, pg. 4197
TSIT WING INTERNATIONAL HOLDINGS LIMITED; *Int'l*, pg. 7952
TSI - US HIGHWAY, JUPITER, LLC—See Town Sports International Holdings, Inc.; *U.S. Private*, pg. 4197
TSI - VALENCIA, LLC—See Town Sports International Holdings, Inc.; *U.S. Private*, pg. 4197
TSI WEST CALDWELL, LLC—See Town Sports International Holdings, Inc.; *U.S. Private*, pg. 4198
TSI - WESTLAKE, LLC—See Town Sports International Holdings, Inc.; *U.S. Private*, pg. 4197
TSKB GAYRIMENKUL DEGERLEME A.S.—See Turkiye Is Bankasi A.S.; *Int'l*, pg. 7976
TSKB GAYRIMENKUL YATIRIM ORTAKLIGI A.S.—See Turkiye Sinai Kalkinma Bankasi A.S.; *Int'l*, pg. 7977
TSKB SURDURULEBILIRLIK DANISMANLIGI A.S.—See Turkiye Is Bankasi A.S.; *Int'l*, pg. 7976
TSKB SURDURULEBIRLIK DANISMANLIGI A.S.—See Turkiye Sinai Kalkinma Bankasi A.S.; *Int'l*, pg. 7977
TSK DO BRASIL LTDA.—See Komax Holding AG; *Int'l*, pg. 4241
TSK ELECTRONICA Y ELECTRICIDAD, S.A.; *Int'l*, pg. 7952
TSK ENGINEERING TAIWAN CO., LTD.—See Tsukishima Holdings Co., Ltd.; *Int'l*, pg. 7956
TSK ENGINEERING THAILAND CO., LTD.—See Tsukishima Holdings Co., Ltd.; *Int'l*, pg. 7956
TSK FLAGSOL ENGINEERING GMBH—See TSK Electronica y Electricidad, S.A.; *Int'l*, pg. 7952
TSK INNOVATIONS CO.—See Komax Holding AG; *Int'l*, pg. 4241
TSK (KOREA) CO., LTD—See Hi-Lex Corporation; *Int'l*, pg. 3381
TSK PARTNERS, INC.; *U.S. Private*, pg. 4253
TSK PRUFSYSTEME GMBH—See Komax Holding AG; *Int'l*, pg. 4241
TSK SERVICES LTD.—See Komax Holding AG; *Int'l*, pg. 4241
TSK SISTEMAS DE TESTES DO BRASIL LTDA.—See Komax Holding AG; *Int'l*, pg. 4241
TSK TEST SISTEMLERI SAN. LTD. STI.—See Komax Holding AG; *Int'l*, pg. 4241
TSK TEST SYSTEMS SRL—See Komax Holding AG; *Int'l*, pg. 4241
TSK TUNISIA S.A.R.L.—See Komax Holding AG; *Int'l*, pg. 4241
TS LAW HOLDING SDN. BHD.; *Int'l*, pg. 7947
TSL COMPANIES; *U.S. Private*, pg. 4254
TS-LEAR AUTOMOTIVE (MALAYSIA) SDN. BHD.—See Lear Corporation; *U.S. Public*, pg. 1298
TSLELAY GITIT LTD.—See Aiphone Co., Ltd.; *Int'l*, pg. 235
TSL ENGINEERED PRODUCTS, LLC—See Tinicum Enterprises, Inc.; *U.S. Private*, pg. 4174
TSL INDUSTRIES LIMITED; *Int'l*, pg. 7952
TSL JEWELLERY (EXPORT) COMPANY LIMITED—See Tse Sui Luen Jewellery (International) Limited; *Int'l*, pg. 7950
TSL JEWELLERY (H.K.) CO. LIMITED—See Tse Sui Luen Jewellery (International) Limited; *Int'l*, pg. 7950
TSL JEWELLERY (MACAU) LIMITED—See Tse Sui Luen Jewellery (International) Limited; *Int'l*, pg. 7950
TSL LIMITED; *Int'l*, pg. 7952
TSL LOGISTICS CO., LTD.—See Triple i Logistics Public Company Limited; *Int'l*, pg. 7926
TSL LTD.; *U.S. Private*, pg. 4254
TS LOGISTICS CO., LTD.—See TS Tech Co Ltd; *Int'l*, pg. 7948
TS-MAV GEPESZET SERVICES KFT.—See OBB-Holding AG; *Int'l*, pg. 5510
TSMC CHINA COMPANY LIMITED—See Taiwan Semiconductor Manufacturing Company Ltd.; *Int'l*, pg. 7423
TSMC DESIGN TECHNOLOGY CANADA INC.—See Taiwan Semiconductor Manufacturing Company Ltd.; *Int'l*, pg. 7423
TSMC DESIGN TECHNOLOGY JAPAN, INC.—See Taiwan Semiconductor Manufacturing Company Ltd.; *Int'l*, pg. 7423
TSMC EUROPE B.V.—See Taiwan Semiconductor Manufacturing Company Ltd.; *Int'l*, pg. 7423
TSM CHAMP, LLC—See Altus Capital Partners, Inc.; *U.S. Private*, pg. 211
TSMC JAPAN 3DIC R&D CENTER, INC.—See Taiwan Semiconductor Manufacturing Company Ltd.; *Int'l*, pg. 7423
TSMC JAPAN KK—See Taiwan Semiconductor Manufacturing Company Ltd.; *Int'l*, pg. 7423
TSMC KOREA LIMITED—See Taiwan Semiconductor Manufacturing Company Ltd.; *Int'l*, pg. 7424
TSMC NANJING COMPANY LIMITED—See Taiwan Semiconductor Manufacturing Company Ltd.; *Int'l*, pg. 7424
TSMC NORTH AMERICA INC.—See Taiwan Semiconductor Manufacturing Company Ltd.; *Int'l*, pg. 7424
TSM CORP.—See Parsons Corporation; *U.S. Public*, pg. 1651
TSMC SOLAR EUROPE GMBH—See Taiwan Semiconductor Manufacturing Company Ltd.; *Int'l*, pg. 7424
TSMC SOLAR LTD.—See Taiwan Semiconductor Manufacturing Company Ltd.; *Int'l*, pg. 7424
TSMC TECHNOLOGY, INC.—See Taiwan Semiconductor Manufacturing Company Ltd.; *Int'l*, pg. 7424
T.S.MECHATECH CO., LTD.—See Nabtesco Corporation; *Int'l*, pg. 5121
TS METALS LTD—See Quartzelec Ltd.; *Int'l*, pg. 6156
TSM GLOBAL BERHAD; *Int'l*, pg. 7952

COMPANY NAME INDEX

TS MILLER CREEK, LLC—See Independence Realty Trust, Inc.; *U.S. Public*, pg. 1116
TSML INNOVATIONS, LLC—See TS Tech Co Ltd; *Int'l*, pg. 7948
TSM SERVICES INC.—See National Amusements, Inc.; *U.S. Public*, pg. 2844
TS&M SUPPLY—See NOV, Inc.; *U.S. Public*, pg. 1546
TSMT TECHNOLOGY (INDIA) PVT. LTD.—See Taiwan Surface Mounting Technology Corp.; *Int'l*, pg. 7424
TSM WELLNESS SDN. BHD.—See TSM Global Berhad; *Int'l*, pg. 7952
TSN EAST, LLC—See Bunzl plc; *Int'l*, pg. 1219
TS NETWORK CO., LTD—See Japan Tobacco Inc.; *Int'l*, pg. 3907
TS NEXGEN CO., LTD.; *Int'l*, pg. 7947
TSN TURMBAU STEFFENS & NOLLE GMBH—See INDUS Holding AG; *Int'l*, pg. 3664
TSN WEST, LLC—See Bunzl plc; *Int'l*, pg. 1219
TSN WIRES CO. LTD—See Tata Sons Limited; *Int'l*, pg. 7468
TSO3 CORPORATION—See Stryker Corporation; *U.S. Public*, pg. 1957
TSO3 INC.—See Stryker Corporation; *U.S. Public*, pg. 1957
TSODILO RESOURCES LIMITED; *Int'l*, pg. 7952
TSOGO INVESTMENT HOLDING COMPANY (PTY) LIMITED—See Hosken Consolidated Investments Limited; *Int'l*, pg. 3485
TSOGO SUN EMONTI (PTY) LTD.—See Hosken Consolidated Investments Limited; *Int'l*, pg. 3485
TSOGO SUN GAMING (PTY) LIMTED—See Hosken Consolidated Investments Limited; *Int'l*, pg. 3485
TSOGO SUN KWAZULU-NATAL (PTY) LTD.—See Hosken Consolidated Investments Limited; *Int'l*, pg. 3485
TSOGO SUN LIMITED—See Hosken Consolidated Investments Limited; *Int'l*, pg. 3485
TSO HOLDINGS A LIMITED—See Deutsche Post AG; *Int'l*, pg. 2082
TSO HOLDINGS B LIMITED—See Deutsche Post AG; *Int'l*, pg. 2082
TSO INDUSTRIEANLAGEN PLANUNG UND VERTRIEB GMBH—See ATON GmbH; *Int'l*, pg. 689
T-SOLAR GLOBAL S.A.; *Int'l*, pg. 7396
TSON CO., LTD.; *Int'l*, pg. 7952
TS OPERATIONS LIMITED—See Gordon Brothers Group, LLC; *U.S. Private*, pg. 1742
TS OPTO CO., LTD.—See Toyoda Gosei Co., Ltd.; *Int'l*, pg. 7862
TSOU SEEN CHEMICAL INDUSTRIES CORPORATION—See China Petrochemical Development Corp.; *Int'l*, pg. 1540
T&S PERFECTION CHAIN PRODUCTS, INC.; *U.S. Private*, pg. 3910
T. SPIRITUAL WORLD LIMITED; *Int'l*, pg. 7396
TS PLANET SPORTS PTE. LTD.—See Tuan Sing Holdings Limited; *Int'l*, pg. 7962
TS PLASTICS SDN. BHD.—See Nippon Paper Industries Co., Ltd.; *Int'l*, pg. 5328
TSP PROJECTS LIMITED—See SYSTRA Ltd.; *Int'l*, pg. 7393
TS PRECISION CO., LTD.—See Nabtesco Corporation; *Int'l*, pg. 5121
TS PRESS ENGINEERING CO., LTD.—See TS Tech Co Ltd; *Int'l*, pg. 7948
T&S PRODUCTS INC.; *U.S. Private*, pg. 3910
TSPS CORP—See KEC Holdings Co., Ltd.; *Int'l*, pg. 4113
T-SQUARE SOLUTIONS CO., LTD—See TOWA PHARMACEUTICAL CO. LTD.; *Int'l*, pg. 7849
TSR BINA SDN. BHD.—See TSR Capital Berhad; *Int'l*, pg. 7952
TSR CAPITAL BERHAD; *Int'l*, pg. 7952
TSRC CORPORATION - GANGSHAN FACTORY—See TSRC Corporation; *Int'l*, pg. 7953
TSRC CORPORATION - KAOHSIUNG FACTORY—See TSRC Corporation; *Int'l*, pg. 7953
TSRC CORPORATION; *Int'l*, pg. 7952
TSRC (JINAN) INDUSTRIES LTD.—See TSRC Corporation; *Int'l*, pg. 7952
TSRC (LUX.) CORPORATION S.A R.L.—See TSRC Corporation; *Int'l*, pg. 7953
TSRC (NANTONG) INDUSTRIES LTD.—See TSRC Corporation; *Int'l*, pg. 7953
TSR CONCRETE PRODUCTS SDN. BHD. - SEPANG FACTORY—See TSR Capital Berhad; *Int'l*, pg. 7952
TSR CONCRETE PRODUCTS SDN. BHD.—See TSR Capital Berhad; *Int'l*, pg. 7952
TSR CONCRETE PRODUCTS SDN. BHD. - TERENGGANU FACTORY—See TSR Capital Berhad; *Int'l*, pg. 7952
TSR CONSULTANTS PRIVATE LIMITED—See Mitsubishi UFJ Financial Group, Inc.; *Int'l*, pg. 4971
TSR CONSULTING SERVICES, INC.—See TSR, Inc.; *U.S. Public*, pg. 2202
TSR CONSULTING SERVICES, INC.—See TSR, Inc.; *U.S. Public*, pg. 2202
TSR CONSULTING SERVICES, INC.—See TSR, Inc.; *U.S. Public*, pg. 2202
TSRC (SHANGHAI) INDUSTRIES LTD.—See TSRC Corporation; *Int'l*, pg. 7953

TSRC-UBE (NANTONG) CHEMICAL INDUSTRIES LIMITED CORPORATION—See TSRC Corporation; *Int'l*, pg. 7953
TSRC (VIETNAM) CO., LTD.—See TSRC Corporation; *Int'l*, pg. 7953
TS RECREATIONAL, INC.; *U.S. Private*, pg. 4252
TSR, INC.; *U.S. Public*, pg. 2202
TSR RECYCLING GMBH & CO. KG—See Alfa Acciai SpA; *Int'l*, pg. 307
TSR RECYCLING GMBH & CO. KG—See CRONIMET Holding GmbH; *Int'l*, pg. 1855
TSR RECYCLING GMBH & CO. KG—See RETHMANN AG & Co. KG; *Int'l*, pg. 6307
TSS GLOBAL PTE. LTD.—See TS Wonders Holding Limited; *Int'l*, pg. 7949
TS SHIPPING OU—See Tallinna Sadam AS; *Int'l*, pg. 7448
T.S. SIMMS & CO., LIMITED; *Int'l*, pg. 7397
TSS, INC.; *U.S. Public*, pg. 2202
TSSI SYSTEMS LTD; *Int'l*, pg. 7953
TSSK LOGISTIC CO., LTD.—See AMA Marine Public Company Limited; *Int'l*, pg. 403
TSSLINK, INC.—See Avnet, Inc.; *U.S. Public*, pg. 254
TS SOLARTECH SDN. BHD.—See Tek Seng Holdings Berhad; *Int'l*, pg. 7526
T+S SP. Z O.O.—See Norsk Hydro ASA; *Int'l*, pg. 5433
TSS-RADIO; *U.S. Private*, pg. 8
TSS REDMOND LLC—See 360training.com, Inc.; *U.S. Private*, pg. 8
TSS TECHNOLOGIES INCORPORATED; *U.S. Private*, pg. 4254
T-STAFF, INC.; *U.S. Private*, pg. 3911
TS TALISON ROW, LLC—See Independence Realty Trust, Inc.; *U.S. Public*, pg. 1116
T STAMP, INC.; *U.S. Public*, pg. 1977
T STATS SUPPLY INC.; *U.S. Private*, pg. 3909
TST CO., LTD.—See Sigurd Microelectronics Corp.; *Int'l*, pg. 6913
T-ST CORPORATION—See Toyota Tsusho Corporation; *Int'l*, pg. 7877
TS TECH ALABAMA LLC—See TS Tech Co Ltd; *Int'l*, pg. 7948
TS TECH BUSINESS SERVICES PHILIPPINES, INC.—See TS Tech Co Ltd; *Int'l*, pg. 7948
TS TECH CANADA INC.—See TS Tech Co Ltd; *Int'l*, pg. 7948
TS TECH CO., LTD. - HAMAMATSU PLANT—See TS Tech Co Ltd; *Int'l*, pg. 7948
TS TECH CO., LTD. - SAITAMA PLANT (GYODA)—See TS Tech Co Ltd; *Int'l*, pg. 7948
TS TECH CO., LTD. - SAITAMA PLANT (KAWAGOE)—See TS Tech Co Ltd; *Int'l*, pg. 7948
TS TECH CO., LTD. - SAITAMA PLANT (KONOSU)—See TS Tech Co Ltd; *Int'l*, pg. 7948
TS TECH CO., LTD. - SAITAMA PLANT (SAYAMA)—See TS Tech Co Ltd; *Int'l*, pg. 7948
TS TECH CO LTD; *Int'l*, pg. 7947
TS TECH CO., LTD. - SUZUKA PLANT—See TS Tech Co Ltd; *Int'l*, pg. 7948
TS TECH DEUTSCHLAND GMBH—See TS Tech Co Ltd; *Int'l*, pg. 7948
TS TECH DO BRASIL LTDA—See TS Tech Co Ltd; *Int'l*, pg. 7948
TS TECH (HONG KONG) CO., LTD.—See TS Tech Co Ltd; *Int'l*, pg. 7948
TS TECH HUNGARY KFT.—See TS Tech Co Ltd; *Int'l*, pg. 7948
TS TECH INDIANA, LLC—See TS Tech Co Ltd; *Int'l*, pg. 7948
TS TECH (MANDAL) PRIVATE LIMITED—See TS Tech Co Ltd; *Int'l*, pg. 7948
TS TECH NORTH AMERICA INC.—See TS Tech Co Ltd; *Int'l*, pg. 7948
TS TECH POLAND SP. Z O.O.—See TS Tech Co Ltd; *Int'l*, pg. 7948
TS TECH SUN (INDIA) LIMITED—See TS Tech Co Ltd; *Int'l*, pg. 7948
TS TECH SUN RAJASTHAN PRIVATE LIMITED—See TS Tech Co Ltd; *Int'l*, pg. 7948
TS TECH (THAILAND) CO., LTD.—See TS Tech Co Ltd; *Int'l*, pg. 7948
TS TECH TRIM PHILIPPINES, INC.—See TS Tech Co Ltd; *Int'l*, pg. 7948
TS TECH UK LTD.—See TS Tech Co Ltd; *Int'l*, pg. 7948
TS TECH USA CORPORATION—See TS Tech Co Ltd; *Int'l*, pg. 7948
TST EXPEDITED SERVICES INC.—See TFI International Inc.; *Int'l*, pg. 7586
TST/IMPRESO, INC.—See Impreso, Inc.; *U.S. Public*, pg. 1114
TST/IMPRESO, INC.—See Impreso, Inc.; *U.S. Public*, pg. 1114
TST INC.; *U.S. Private*, pg. 4254
TST INC. - STANDARD METALS DIVISION—See TST Inc.; *U.S. Private*, pg. 4254
TST MANUFACTURING DE MEXICO, S. DE R.L. DE C.V.—See TS Tech Co Ltd; *Int'l*, pg. 7948
TSTM CO., LTD.—See Nabtesco Corporation; *Int'l*, pg. 5121

TSUBAKIMOTO KOGYO CO., LTD.

TS TRAFFIC SYSTEMS GMBH—See VINCI S.A.; *Int'l*, pg. 8229
TS TRANSPORT & SERVICES SPEDITIONS GMBH—See G. Peter Reber Mobel-Logistik GmbH; *Int'l*, pg. 2864
TS TRILLION CO., LTD.; *Int'l*, pg. 7948
TS TRIM BRASIL S.A.—See TS Tech Co Ltd; *Int'l*, pg. 7948
TS TRIM INDUSTRIES INC.—See TS Tech Co Ltd; *Int'l*, pg. 7948
T&S TRUCKING COMPANY; *U.S. Private*, pg. 3910
TST SUNRISE SERVICE, LTD.—See KKR & Co. Inc.; *U.S. Public*, pg. 1259
TSUBACO (HONG KONG) CO., LTD.—See Tsubakimoto Kogyo Co., Ltd.; *Int'l*, pg. 7955
TSUBACO KOREA CO., LTD.—See Tsubakimoto Kogyo Co., Ltd.; *Int'l*, pg. 7955
TSUBACO KTE CO., LTD.—See Tsubakimoto Kogyo Co., Ltd.; *Int'l*, pg. 7955
TSUBACO SINGAPORE PTE LTD—See Tsubakimoto Kogyo Co., Ltd.; *Int'l*, pg. 7955
TSUBAKI AUSTRALIA PTE. LIMITED—See Tsubakimoto Chain Co.; *Int'l*, pg. 7953
TSUBAKI AUTOMOTIVE CZECH REPUBLIC S.R.O.—See Tsubakimoto Chain Co.; *Int'l*, pg. 7953
TSUBAKI BRASIL EQUIPAMENTOS INDUSTRIAIS LTDA—See Tsubakimoto Chain Co.; *Int'l*, pg. 7953
TSUBAKI CAPT POWER TRANSMISSION (SHIJIAZHUANG) CO., LTD.—See Tsubakimoto Chain Co.; *Int'l*, pg. 7953
TSUBAKI DEUTSCHLAND GMBH—See Tsubakimoto Chain Co.; *Int'l*, pg. 7953
TSUBAKI EVERBEST GEAR (TIANJIN) CO., LTD.—See Tsubakimoto Chain Co.; *Int'l*, pg. 7953
TSUBAKI IBERICA POWER TRANSMISSION S.L.—See Tsubakimoto Chain Co.; *Int'l*, pg. 7953
TSUBAKI INDIA POWER TRANSMISSION PRIVATE LIMITED—See Tsubakimoto Chain Co.; *Int'l*, pg. 7954
TSUBAKI KABELSCHLEPP GMBH—See Tsubakimoto Chain Co.; *Int'l*, pg. 7954
TSUBAKI KABELSCHLEPP SHANGHAI CO., LTD.—See Tsubakimoto Chain Co.; *Int'l*, pg. 7954
TSUBAKI MOTION CONTROL (SHANGHAI) CO., LTD.—See Tsubakimoto Chain Co.; *Int'l*, pg. 7954
TSUBAKI MOTION CONTROL (THAILAND) CO., LTD.—See Tsubakimoto Chain Co.; *Int'l*, pg. 7954
TSUBAKIMOTO AUTOMOTIVE KOREA CO., LTD.—See Tsubakimoto Chain Co.; *Int'l*, pg. 7953
TSUBAKIMOTO AUTOMOTIVE MEXICO S.A. DE C.V.—See Tsubakimoto Chain Co.; *Int'l*, pg. 7954
TSUBAKIMOTO AUTOMOTIVE (SHANGHAI) CO., LTD.—See Tsubakimoto Chain Co.; *Int'l*, pg. 7953
TSUBAKIMOTO AUTOMOTIVE (THAILAND) CO., LTD.—See Tsubakimoto Chain Co.; *Int'l*, pg. 7953
TSUBAKIMOTO BULK SYSTEMS CORP—See Tsubakimoto Chain Co.; *Int'l*, pg. 7953
TSUBAKIMOTO BULK SYSTEMS (SHANGHAI) CORP.—See Tsubakimoto Chain Co.; *Int'l*, pg. 7954
TSUBAKIMOTO CHAIN CO. - HYOGO PLANT—See Tsubakimoto Chain Co.; *Int'l*, pg. 7954
TSUBAKIMOTO CHAIN CO. - SAITAMA PLANT—See Tsubakimoto Chain Co.; *Int'l*, pg. 7954
TSUBAKIMOTO CHAIN CO.; *Int'l*, pg. 7953
TSUBAKIMOTO CHAIN CO.—See Tsubakimoto Chain Co.; *Int'l*, pg. 7954
TSUBAKIMOTO CHAIN CO.—See Tsubakimoto Chain Co.; *Int'l*, pg. 7954
TSUBAKIMOTO CHAIN CO.—See Tsubakimoto Chain Co.; *Int'l*, pg. 7954
TSUBAKIMOTO CHAIN ENGINEERING (SHANGHAI) CO., LTD.—See Tsubakimoto Chain Co.; *Int'l*, pg. 7954
TSUBAKIMOTO CHAIN (SHANGHAI) CO., LTD.—See Tsubakimoto Chain Co.; *Int'l*, pg. 7954
TSUBAKIMOTO CHAIN (TIANJIN) CO., LTD.—See Tsubakimoto Chain Co.; *Int'l*, pg. 7954
TSUBAKIMOTO CHAIN TRADING (SHANGHAI) CO., LTD.—See Tsubakimoto Chain Co.; *Int'l*, pg. 7953
TSUBAKIMOTO CUSTOM CHAIN CO.—See Tsubakimoto Chain Co.; *Int'l*, pg. 7954
TSUBAKIMOTO EUROPE B.V.—See Tsubakimoto Chain Co.; *Int'l*, pg. 7954
TSUBAKIMOTO IRON CASTING CO., LTD—See Tsubakimoto Chain Co.; *Int'l*, pg. 7953
TSUBAKIMOTO KOGYO CO., LTD.; *Int'l*, pg. 7955
TSUBAKIMOTO KOREA CO., LTD.—See Tsubakimoto Chain Co.; *Int'l*, pg. 7954
TSUBAKIMOTO MACHINERY CO—See Tsubakimoto Chain Co.; *Int'l*, pg. 7954
TSUBAKIMOTO MAYFRAN CONVEYOR (SHANGHAI) CO., LTD—See Tsubakimoto Chain Co.; *Int'l*, pg. 7953
TSUBAKIMOTO MAYFRAN INC.—See Tsubakimoto Chain Co.; *Int'l*, pg. 7954
TSUBAKIMOTO PHILIPPINES CORPORATION—See Tsubakimoto Chain Co.; *Int'l*, pg. 7954
TSUBAKIMOTO SINGAPORE PTE., LTD.—See Tsubakimoto Chain Co.; *Int'l*, pg. 7954
TSUBAKIMOTO SPROCKET CO—See Tsubakimoto Chain Co.; *Int'l*, pg. 7953
TSUBAKIMOTO (THAILAND) CO., LTD.—See Tsubakimoto Chain Co.; *Int'l*, pg. 7953

TSUBAKIMOTO KOGYO CO., LTD. — CORPORATE AFFILIATIONS

TSUBAKIMOTO UK LTD.—See Tsubakimoto Chain Co.; *Int'l*, pg. 7954
TSUBAKIMOTO VIETNAM CO., LTD.—See Tsubakimoto Chain Co.; *Int'l*, pg. 7954
TSUBAKI NAKASHIMA CO., LTD.—See The Carlyle Group Inc.; *U.S. Public*, pg. 2055
TSUBAKI OF CANADA LIMITED—See Tsubakimoto Chain Co.; *Int'l*, pg. 7954
TSUBAKI POWER TRANSMISSION (MALAYSIA) SDN. BHD.—See Tsubakimoto Chain Co.; *Int'l*, pg. 7954
TSUBAKI SUPPORT CENTER CO.—See Tsubakimoto Chain Co.; *Int'l*, pg. 7954
TSUBAKI YAMAKYU CHAIN CO—See Tsubakimoto Chain Co.; *Int'l*, pg. 7953
TSUBAMEX CO., LTD.—See Sunstar Suisse S.A.; *Int'l*, pg. 7324
TSUBOI INDUSTRIAL CO., LTD.; *Int'l*, pg. 7955
TSUBURAYA FIELDS HOLDINGS INC.; *Int'l*, pg. 7955
TSUBURAYA PRODUCTIONS CO., LTD.—See BANDAI NAMCO Holdings Inc.; *Int'l*, pg. 828
TSUBURAYA PRODUCTIONS CO., LTD.—See Tsuburaya Fields Holdings Inc.; *Int'l*, pg. 7955
TSUCHIURA SHOKUSAN INC.—See Toray Industries, Inc.; *Int'l*, pg. 7827
TSUCHIYA HOLDINGS CO., LTD.; *Int'l*, pg. 7955
TSUDAKOMA CORPORATION; *Int'l*, pg. 7955
TSUDAKOMA SHANGHAI CO LTD—See Tsudakoma Corporation; *Int'l*, pg. 7955
TSUDOIE CORPORATION—See Kowa Co., Ltd.; *Int'l*, pg. 4294
TSUGAMI CORPORATION - NAGAOKA FACTORY—See TSUGAMI CORPORATION; *Int'l*, pg. 7955
TSUGAMI CORPORATION; *Int'l*, pg. 7955
TSUGAMI GENERAL SERVICE CO., LTD.—See TSUGAMI CORPORATION; *Int'l*, pg. 7955
TSUGAMI GMBH—See TSUGAMI CORPORATION; *Int'l*, pg. 7955
TSUGAMI (THAI) CO., LTD.—See TSUGAMI CORPORATION; *Int'l*, pg. 7955
TSUI WAH HOLDINGS LIMITED; *Int'l*, pg. 7955
TSUKADA ELECTRICAL CONSTRUCTION CO., LTD.—See MIRAIT ONE Corporation; *Int'l*, pg. 4918
TSUKADA GLOBAL HOLDINGS INC.; *Int'l*, pg. 7955
TSUKAMOTO CORPORATION CO., LTD.; *Int'l*, pg. 7956
TSUKAMOTO ICHIDA CO., LTD.—See Tsukamoto Corporation Co., Ltd.; *Int'l*, pg. 7956
TSUKASA CHEMICAL INDUSTRY CO. LTD. - FUKUOKA BRANCH—See Tsukasa Chemical Industry Co. Ltd.; *Int'l*, pg. 7956
TSUKASA CHEMICAL INDUSTRY CO. LTD. - KOKUBU PLANT—See Tsukasa Chemical Industry Co. Ltd.; *Int'l*, pg. 7956
TSUKASA CHEMICAL INDUSTRY CO. LTD. - OSAKA BRANCH—See Tsukasa Chemical Industry Co. Ltd.; *Int'l*, pg. 7956
TSUKASA CHEMICAL INDUSTRY CO. LTD. - SAPPORO BRANCH—See Tsukasa Chemical Industry Co. Ltd.; *Int'l*, pg. 7956
TSUKASA CHEMICAL INDUSTRY CO. LTD.; *Int'l*, pg. 7956
TSUKASA CHEMICAL INDUSTRY CO. LTD. - TSUKUBA PLANT—See Tsukasa Chemical Industry Co. Ltd.; *Int'l*, pg. 7956
TSUKEN CORPORATION—See COMSYS Holdings Corporation; *Int'l*, pg. 1762
TSUKEN ELECTRIC IND CO., LTD.—See Tohoku Electric Power Co., Inc.; *Int'l*, pg. 7777
TSUKIBOSHI ART CO., LTD.—See Nippon Steel Corporation; *Int'l*, pg. 5336
TSUKIBOSHI LOGISTICS CO., LTD.—See Nippon Steel Corporation; *Int'l*, pg. 5336
TSUKIBOSHI MANUFACTURING CO., LTD.—See Daido Kogyo Co., Ltd.; *Int'l*, pg. 1921
TSUKIBOSHI SHOJI CO., LTD.—See Nippon Steel Corporation; *Int'l*, pg. 5336
TSUKIJI ICHIKAWA SUISAN CO., LTD.—See Tsukiji Uoichiba Co., Ltd.; *Int'l*, pg. 7956
TSUKIJI KIGYO CO., LTD.—See Tsukiji Uoichiba Co., Ltd.; *Int'l*, pg. 7956
TSUKIJI UOICHIBA CO., LTD.; *Int'l*, pg. 7956
TSUKISHIMA BUSINESS SUPPORT CO., LTD.—See Tsukishima Holdings Co., Ltd.; *Int'l*, pg. 7956
TSUKISHIMA ENGINEERING MALAYSIA SDN. BHD.—See Tsukishima Holdings Co., Ltd.; *Int'l*, pg. 7956
TSUKISHIMA HOLDINGS CO., LTD.; *Int'l*, pg. 7956
TSUKISHIMA KANKYO ENGINEERING, LTD.—See Tsukishima Holdings Co., Ltd.; *Int'l*, pg. 7956
TSUKISHIMA KIKAI CO., LTD. - ICHIKAWA FACTORY—See Tsukishima Holdings Co., Ltd.; *Int'l*, pg. 7956
TSUKISHIMA MACHINE SALES CO., LTD.—See Tsukishima Holdings Co., Ltd.; *Int'l*, pg. 7957
TSUKISHIMA TECHNOLOGY MAINTENANCE SERVICE CO., LTD—See Tsukishima Holdings Co., Ltd.; *Int'l*, pg. 7957
TSUKIYONO DENSHI CO., LTD.—See Taiyo Yuden Company Ltd.; *Int'l*, pg. 7427

TSU-KONG CO., LTD.—See ChangChun Group; *Int'l*, pg. 1442
TSUKUBA BANK, LTD.; *Int'l*, pg. 7957
TSUKUBA FOOD EVALUATION CENTER CO., LTD.—See Prima Meat Packers Ltd.; *Int'l*, pg. 5975
TSUKUBA KOKI CO., LTD.—See SNT Corporation; *Int'l*, pg. 7029
TSUKUBA SEIKO CO., LTD.; *Int'l*, pg. 7957
TSUKUI CORPORATION; *Int'l*, pg. 7957
TSUKUMI COOPERATIVE MINING CO., LTD.—See Nittetsu Mining Co., Ltd.; *Int'l*, pg. 5383
TSUKUMI LIMESTONE CO., LTD.—See Nittetsu Mining Co., Ltd.; *Int'l*, pg. 5384
TSUKUMI VEHICLE REPAIR CO., LTD.—See Nittetsu Mining Co., Ltd.; *Int'l*, pg. 5384
TSUKURUBA, INC.; *Int'l*, pg. 7957
TSUKUSHI FACTORY CO., LTD.—See Itoham Yonekyu Holdings Inc.; *Int'l*, pg. 3843
TSUMIKI SECURITIES CO., LTD.—See Marui Group Co., Ltd.; *Int'l*, pg. 4713
TSUMURA & CO.; *Int'l*, pg. 7957
TSUMURA USA, INC.—See Tsumura & Co.; *Int'l*, pg. 7957
TSUNAGU GROUP HOLDINGS INC.; *Int'l*, pg. 7957
TSUNAGU NETWORK COMMUNICATIONS, INC.—See Arteria Networks Corp.; *Int'l*, pg. 583
TSUNAMI MARKETING; *U.S. Private*, pg. 4254
TSUNE AMERICA LLC—See Tsune Seiki Co., Ltd.; *Int'l*, pg. 7957
TSUNE EUROPA GMBH—See Tsune Seiki Co., Ltd.; *Int'l*, pg. 7957
TSUNEISHI GROUP (ZHOUSHAN) SHIPBUILDING INC.—See Tsuneishi Holdings Corporation; *Int'l*, pg. 7957
TSUNEISHI HEAVY INDUSTRIES (CEBU) INC.—See Tsuneishi Holdings Corporation; *Int'l*, pg. 7957
TSUNEISHI HOLDINGS CORPORATION; *Int'l*, pg. 7957
TSUNE SEIKI CO., LTD. - NYUZEN FACTORY—See Tsune Seiki Co., Ltd.; *Int'l*, pg. 7957
TSUNE SEIKI CO., LTD. - OSAWANO FACTORY—See Tsune Seiki Co., Ltd.; *Int'l*, pg. 7957
TSUNE SEIKI CO., LTD.; *Int'l*, pg. 7957
TSUNE SEIKI CO., LTD. - YATSUO FACTORY—See Tsune Seiki Co., Ltd.; *Int'l*, pg. 7957
TSUNE SEIKI (THAILAND) CO., LTD.—See Tsune Seiki Co., Ltd.; *Int'l*, pg. 7957
TSUNE WAGNER CARBIDE CO., LTD.—See Tsune Seiki Co., Ltd.; *Int'l*, pg. 7957
TSUN FAT (HUI ZHOU) BISCUIT FACTORY LIMITED—See Four Seas Mercantile Holdings Limited; *Int'l*, pg. 2755
TS UNIVERSAL TRADING SDN. BHD.—See The Store Corporation Berhad; *Int'l*, pg. 7689
TSUNO FOOD INDUSTRIAL CO., LTD. - OSAKA TSUNO FACTORY—See Tsuno Food Industrial Co., Ltd.; *Int'l*, pg. 7957
TSUNO FOOD INDUSTRIAL CO., LTD.; *Int'l*, pg. 7957
TSUNO FOOD INDUSTRIAL CO., LTD. - TAKARAZUKA TSUNO FACTORY—See Tsuno Food Industrial Co., Ltd.; *Int'l*, pg. 7957
TSUNO FOOD INDUSTRIAL CO., LTD. - YASHIRO FACTORY—See Tsuno Food Industrial Co., Ltd.; *Int'l*, pg. 7957
TSUNO RICE FINE CHEMICALS CO., LTD.—See Tsuno Food Industrial Co., Ltd.; *Int'l*, pg. 7957
TSUNO TRANSPORTATION, LTD.—See Tsuno Food Industrial Co., Ltd.; *Int'l*, pg. 7957
TSURIYOSHI CO., LTD.—See Shimano, Inc.; *Int'l*, pg. 6834
TSURONG XIAMEN XIANGYU TRADING CO., LTD.—See Japan Industrial Partners, Inc.; *Int'l*, pg. 3898
TSURUHA HOLDINGS INC.; *Int'l*, pg. 7957
TSURUMI (AMERICA), INC.—See Tsurumi Manufacturing Co., Ltd.; *Int'l*, pg. 7958
TSURUMI (EUROPE) GMBH—See Tsurumi Manufacturing Co., Ltd.; *Int'l*, pg. 7958
TSURUMI FRANCE S.A.S.—See Seika Corporation; *Int'l*, pg. 6686
TSURUMI-INTEC PUMP AB—See Seika Corporation; *Int'l*, pg. 6686
TSURUMI KOZAI CENTER CO., LTD.—See Okaya & Co., Ltd.; *Int'l*, pg. 5547
TSURUMI MANUFACTURING CO., LTD. - KYOTO PLANT—See Tsurumi Manufacturing Co., Ltd.; *Int'l*, pg. 7958
TSURUMI MANUFACTURING CO., LTD.; *Int'l*, pg. 7958
TSURUMI MANUFACTURING CO., LTD. - YONAGO PLANT—See Tsurumi Manufacturing Co., Ltd.; *Int'l*, pg. 7958
TSURUMI PUMP KOREA CO., LTD. - CHUNGJU PLANT—See Tsurumi Manufacturing Co., Ltd.; *Int'l*, pg. 7958
TSURUMI PUMP KOREA CO., LTD.—See Tsurumi Manufacturing Co., Ltd.; *Int'l*, pg. 7958
TSURUMI PUMP TAIWAN CO., LTD.—See Tsurumi Manufacturing Co., Ltd.; *Int'l*, pg. 7958
TSURUMI PUMP (THAILAND) CO., LTD.—See Tsurumi Manufacturing Co., Ltd.; *Int'l*, pg. 7958
TSURUMISEKIYU CO., LTD.—See Mitani Corporation; *Int'l*, pg. 4924

TSURUMI (SINGAPORE) PTE LTD—See Tsurumi Manufacturing Co., Ltd.; *Int'l*, pg. 7958
TSURUMI SODA CO., LTD.—See Toagosei Co. Ltd.; *Int'l*, pg. 7770
TSURUMI VACUUM ENGINEERING (SHANGHAI) CO., LTD.—See Tsurumi Manufacturing Co., Ltd.; *Int'l*, pg. 7958
TSURUYA CO., LTD.; *Int'l*, pg. 7958
TSUSHIMA DIE-ENGINEERING CORP.—See Honda Motor Co.; *Int'l*, pg. 3464
TSUSHIN DENSETSU CO., LTD.—See COMSYS Holdings Corporation; *Int'l*, pg. 1762
TSUTAYA ONLINE CO., LTD.—See Culture Convenience Club Co., Ltd.; *Int'l*, pg. 1877
TSUTAYA STORES HOLDINGS CO., LTD.—See Culture Convenience Club Co., Ltd.; *Int'l*, pg. 1877
TSUTSUMI JEWELRY CO., LTD.; *Int'l*, pg. 7958
TSUTSUNAKA KOSAN CO., LTD.—See Sumitomo Bakelite Co., Ltd.; *Int'l*, pg. 7263
TSUYAMA GUNZE CO., LTD.—See Gunze Limited; *Int'l*, pg. 3186
TSUYAMA KEN-IKI ENVIRONMENT TECHNOLOGY CO., LTD.—See Hitachi Zosen Corporation; *Int'l*, pg. 3412
TSUZUKI DENKI CO., LTD.; *Int'l*, pg. 7958
TSUZUKI DENSAN HONG KONG CO., LTD.—See Tsuzuki Denki Co., Ltd.; *Int'l*, pg. 7958
TSUZUKI DENSAN SINGAPORE PTE. LTD.—See Tsuzuki Denki Co., Ltd.; *Int'l*, pg. 7958
TSUZUKI DENSAN TRADING (SHANGHAI) CO., LTD.—See Tsuzuki Denki Co., Ltd.; *Int'l*, pg. 7958
TSUZUKI EMBEDDED SOLUTIONS CO., LTD.—See Tsuzuki Denki Co., Ltd.; *Int'l*, pg. 7958
TSUZUKI INFO-TECHNO EAST JAPAN CO., LTD.—See Tsuzuki Denki Co., Ltd.; *Int'l*, pg. 7958
TSUZUKI INFO-TECHNO WEST JAPAN CO., LTD.—See Tsuzuki Denki Co., Ltd.; *Int'l*, pg. 7958
TSUZUKI MANUFACTURING CO., LTD.—See Honda Motor Co., Ltd.; *Int'l*, pg. 3464
TSUZUKI SOFTWARE CO., LTD.—See Tsuzuki Denki Co., Ltd.; *Int'l*, pg. 7958
TSUZUKI TECHNO SERVICE CO., LTD.—See Tsuzuki Denki Co., Ltd.; *Int'l*, pg. 7958
TSUZUKI XROSS SUPPORT CO., LTD.—See Tsuzuki Denki Co., Ltd.; *Int'l*, pg. 7958
TS WESTMONT, LLC—See Independence Realty Trust, Inc.; *U.S. Public*, pg. 1116
TS WONDERS HOLDING LIMITED; *Int'l*, pg. 7948
TS WOOIN CO., LTD—See TS Corporation; *Int'l*, pg. 7947
TSX INC.—See TMX Group Limited; *Int'l*, pg. 7767
TSYMMETRY, INC.; *U.S. Private*, pg. 4254
TSYS ACQUIRING SOLUTIONS, LLC—See Global Payments Inc.; *U.S. Public*, pg. 944
TSYS CARD TECH LIMITED—See Global Payments Inc.; *U.S. Public*, pg. 944
TSYS CARD TECH SERVICES LIMITED—See Global Payments Inc.; *U.S. Public*, pg. 944
TSYS INTERNATIONAL MANAGEMENT LIMITED—See Global Payments Inc.; *U.S. Public*, pg. 944
TSYS MANAGED SERVICES CANADA, INC.—See Global Payments Inc.; *U.S. Public*, pg. 944
TSYS MANAGED SERVICES EMEA LIMITED—See Global Payments Inc.; *U.S. Public*, pg. 944
TSYS MANAGED SERVICES EMEA (NETHERLANDS) B.V.—See Global Payments Inc.; *U.S. Public*, pg. 944
TSYS MERCHANT SOLUTIONS - ATLANTA—See Global Payments Inc.; *U.S. Public*, pg. 944
TSYS MERCHANT SOLUTIONS, LLC—See Global Payments Inc.; *U.S. Public*, pg. 944
T-SYSTEM, INC.—See Fidelity National Financial, Inc.; *U.S. Public*, pg. 831
T-SYSTEMS AUSTRIA GES.M.B.H—See Deutsche Telekom AG; *Int'l*, pg. 2084
T-SYSTEMS BELGIUM S.A.—See Deutsche Telekom AG; *Int'l*, pg. 2084
T-SYSTEMS BUSINESS SERVICES—See Deutsche Telekom AG; *Int'l*, pg. 2084
T-SYSTEMS CHINA LTD.—See Deutsche Telekom AG; *Int'l*, pg. 2084
T-SYSTEMS DANMARK AS—See Deutsche Telekom AG; *Int'l*, pg. 2084
T-SYSTEMS DEBIS SYSTEMHAUS—See Deutsche Telekom AG; *Int'l*, pg. 2085
T-SYSTEMS DO BRASIL LTDA.—See Deutsche Telekom AG; *Int'l*, pg. 2085
T-SYSTEMS HUNGARY KFT.—See Deutsche Telekom AG; *Int'l*, pg. 2084
T-SYSTEMS INTERNATIONAL GMBH—See Deutsche Telekom AG; *Int'l*, pg. 2084
T-SYSTEMS ITALIA S.P.A.—See Deutsche Telekom AG; *Int'l*, pg. 2084
T-SYSTEMS JAPAN K.K.—See Deutsche Telekom AG; *Int'l*, pg. 2084
T-SYSTEMS LTD.—See Deutsche Telekom AG; *Int'l*, pg. 2084
T-SYSTEMS LUXEMBURG S.A.—See Deutsche Telekom AG; *Int'l*, pg. 2084
T-SYSTEMS NEDERLAND B.V.—See Deutsche Telekom AG; *Int'l*, pg. 2085

COMPANY NAME INDEX

T-SYSTEMS NORTH AMERICA INC.—See Deutsche Telekom AG; *Int'l*, pg. 2085
T-SYSTEMS POLSKA SP. Z O.O.—See Deutsche Telekom AG; *Int'l*, pg. 2085
T-SYSTEMS SINGAPORE PTE. LTD.—See Deutsche Telekom AG; *Int'l*, pg. 2085
T-SYSTEMS—See Deutsche Telekom AG; *Int'l*, pg. 2084
T-SYSTEMS SOUTH AFRICA (PTY) LTD.—See Deutsche Telekom AG; *Int'l*, pg. 2085
T-SYSTEMS SWITZERLAND LTD.—See Deutsche Telekom AG; *Int'l*, pg. 2085
T&T2 INC—See Hellman & Friedman LLC; *U.S. Private*, pg. 1909
TTA HOLDINGS LIMITED—See TT International Limited; *Int'l*, pg. 7960
TTA, INC.—See Altour International, Inc.; *U.S. Private*, pg. 210
T.T.A.S. CO., LTD.—See Toyota Tsusho Corporation; *Int'l*, pg. 7877
TT AUTOMOTIVE ELECTRONICS (SUZHOU) CO LTD—See TT Electronics plc; *Int'l*, pg. 7959
T T BARGE SERVICES MILE 237, LLC.; *U.S. Private*, pg. 3909
TTBIO CORP.; *Int'l*, pg. 7960
TTC AIR BRAKE CENTRE LTD—See Unipart Group of Companies Limited; *Int'l*, pg. 8055
TTC ANALYTICAL SERVICE CORP.—See Abbott Laboratories; *U.S. Public*, pg. 20
TTC GROUP, INC.; *U.S. Private*, pg. 4254
TTC INNOVATIONS; *U.S. Private*, pg. 4254
TTCL PUBLIC COMPANY LIMITED—See Italian-Thai Development pcl; *Int'l*, pg. 3829
TTCL PUBLIC COMPANY LIMITED—See Toyo Engineering Corporation; *Int'l*, pg. 7853
TTC MARKETING SOLUTIONS; *U.S. Private*, pg. 4254
TTC NORGE AS—See Beijer Ref AB; *Int'l*, pg. 945
TT-COIL A/S—See Beijer Ref AB; *Int'l*, pg. 945
TT COIL LTD.—See Beijer Ref AB; *Int'l*, pg. 945
TT-COIL NORGE AS—See Beijer Ref AB; *Int'l*, pg. 945
T&T CO., LTD.—See TANSEISHA CO. LTD.; *Int'l*, pg. 7459
T&T COMPUTERS, INC.; *U.S. Private*, pg. 3910
TTCP MANAGEMENT SERVICES, LLC.; *U.S. Private*, pg. 4254
TTC SALES AND MARKETING (SA) (PROPRIETARY) LIMITED—See TT International Limited; *Int'l*, pg. 7960
TTC TRAINING CENTER UNTERNEHMENSBERATUNG GMBH—See Assicurazioni Generali S.p.A.; *Int'l*, pg. 645
TTCU THE CREDIT UNION; *U.S. Private*, pg. 4254
TT DOTCOM SDN. BHD—See TIME dotCom Berhad; *Int'l*, pg. 7750
TTD—See Tereos; *Int'l*, pg. 7564
TTEC COMPUTER B.V.—See Adiuva Capital GmbH; *Int'l*, pg. 149
TTEC DIGITAL LLC—See TTEC Holdings, Inc.; *U.S. Public*, pg. 2203
TTEC EASTERN EUROPE EAD—See TTEC Holdings, Inc.; *U.S. Public*, pg. 2203
TTEC HOLDINGS, INC.; *U.S. Public*, pg. 2202
T.T.E. ENGINEERING (MALAYSIA) SDN. BHD.—See Takasago Thermal Engineering Co., Ltd.; *Int'l*, pg. 7434
TTE FILTERS, LLC—See The Jordan Company, L.P.; *U.S. Private*, pg. 4063
TTE LABORATORIES INC.—See Transcat, Inc.; *U.S. Public*, pg. 2179
T-T ELECTRIC GMBH—See T-T Electric; *Int'l*, pg. 7396
T-T ELECTRIC; *Int'l*, pg. 7396
TT ELECTRONICS GMBH—See TT Electronics plc; *Int'l*, pg. 7959
TT ELECTRONICS INTEGRATED MANUFACTURING SERVICES LIMITED—See TT Electronics plc; *Int'l*, pg. 7959
TT ELECTRONICS INTEGRATED MANUFACTURING SERVICES (SUZHOU) CO LTD—See TT Electronics plc; *Int'l*, pg. 7959
TT ELECTRONICS IOT SOLUTIONS LIMITED—See Cicor Technologies Ltd.; *Int'l*, pg. 1603
TT ELECTRONICS PLC; *Int'l*, pg. 7958
TT ELECTRONICS SRL—See TT Electronics plc; *Int'l*, pg. 7959
T&T ENERGY CO., LTD.—See TOKAI Holdings Corporation; *Int'l*, pg. 7779
T&T ENERTECHNO CO., LTD.—See TOPPAN Holdings Inc.; *Int'l*, pg. 7817
T. TERMICOS METASA, S.A.—See Aalberts N.V.; *Int'l*, pg. 35
T. TERMICOS SARASKETA, S.L.U—See Aalberts N.V.; *Int'l*, pg. 35
T. TERMICOS SOHETRASA, S.A.—See Aalberts N.V.; *Int'l*, pg. 36
T. TERMICOS TEY, S.L.—See Aalberts N.V.; *Int'l*, pg. 36
T. TERMICOS TRATERH, S.A.U—See Aalberts N.V.; *Int'l*, pg. 36
TTET UNION CORP.; *Int'l*, pg. 7960
TTF AEROSPACE, INC.—See Commercial Aircraft Interiors, LLC; *U.S. Private*, pg. 983
TTFB CO., LTD.; *Int'l*, pg. 7960
T&T FOODS INC.; *U.S. Private*, pg. 3910

TTG ASIA MEDIA PTE. LTD—See Sino Splendid Holdings Limited; *Int'l*, pg. 6947
TTG EQUIPMENT, LLC; *U.S. Private*, pg. 4254
TTG GLOBAL GROUP LIMITED; *Int'l*, pg. 7960
TTGROUP FRANCE SA—See Tong-Tai Machine Tool Co., Ltd.; *Int'l*, pg. 7806
TT GROUP, INC.—See TT Group Ltd.; *Int'l*, pg. 7959
TT GROUP LTD.; *Int'l*, pg. 7959
TTH DEVELOPMENT PTE LTD—See Amara Holdings Ltd.; *Int'l*, pg. 411
T-THERMAL COMPANY—See Linde plc; *Int'l*, pg. 4505
T. T. H. K. CO., LTD.—See Toyota Tsusho Corporation; *Int'l*, pg. 7877
T&T HONDA LTD—See Aga Khan Development Network; *Int'l*, pg. 199
TT HOTELS CROATIA D.O.O.—See TUI AG; *Int'l*, pg. 7966
TT HOTELS TURKEY OTEL HIZMETLERI TURIZM VE TICARET AS—See TUI AG; *Int'l*, pg. 7966
TT HUMAN ASSET SERVICE CORPORATION—See Transcosmos Inc.; *Int'l*, pg. 7898
TTI ELLEBEAU, INC.—See Transcu Ltd.; *Int'l*, pg. 7899
TTI ENTERPRISE LIMITED; *Int'l*, pg. 7960
TTI GLOBAL—See Learning Technologies Group plc; *Int'l*, pg. 4435
TTI GROUP LIMITED—See Aalberts N.V.; *Int'l*, pg. 36
TTI HOLDINGS INC.; *U.S. Private*, pg. 4254
TTI, INC.—See P-Duke Technology Co., Ltd.; *Int'l*, pg. 5682
TTI, INC.—See Berkshire Hathaway Inc.; *U.S. Public*, pg. 316
TTI, INC.; *U.S. Private*, pg. 4255
TTIK INC.; *U.S. Private*, pg. 4255
TTI LAGUNA PHILIPPINES INC.—See The Carlyle Group Inc.; *U.S. Public*, pg. 2055
T&T INSPECTIONS & ENGINEERING LTD.—See Hyduke Energy Services Inc.; *Int'l*, pg. 3548
TT INTERNATIONAL ADVISORS INC.—See Sumitomo Mitsui Financial Group, Inc.; *Int'l*, pg. 7295
TT INTERNATIONAL (HONG KONG) LIMITED—See Sumitomo Mitsui Financial Group, Inc.; *Int'l*, pg. 7295
TT INTERNATIONAL LIMITED; *Int'l*, pg. 7960
TT INTERNATIONAL—See Sumitomo Mitsui Financial Group, Inc.; *Int'l*, pg. 7295
T. T. INTERNATIONAL TRADEPARK PTE. LTD.—See TT International Limited; *Int'l*, pg. 7960
TTI PERU S.A.C.—See Learning Technologies Group plc; *Int'l*, pg. 4435
TTI TACTICAL TECHNOLOGIES INC.—See Leonardo S.p.A.; *Int'l*, pg. 4461
TTI TEAM TELECOM INTERNATIONAL LTD.—See TEOCO Corporation; *U.S. Private*, pg. 3969
TTI TELECOM—See TEOCO Corporation; *U.S. Private*, pg. 3969
TTI- TUBACEX TUBOS INOXIDABLES S.A.U.—See Tubacex S.A.; *Int'l*, pg. 7962
TTJ DESIGN AND ENGINEERING PTE LTD—See TTJ Holdings Limited; *Int'l*, pg. 7960
T T J DESIGN & ENGINEERING (INDIA) PRIVATE LIMITED—See TTJ Holdings Limited; *Int'l*, pg. 7960
TTJ HOLDINGS LIMITED; *Int'l*, pg. 7960
TTK BANK AD SKOPJE; *Int'l*, pg. 7960
TTK CO., LTD.—See MIRAIT ONE Corporation; *Int'l*, pg. 4918
TTK CORPORATION—See Shimizu Corporation; *Int'l*, pg. 6836
TTK ENG AKITA CO., LTD.—See MIRAIT ONE Corporation; *Int'l*, pg. 4918
TTK ENG AOMORI CO., LTD.—See MIRAIT ONE Corporation; *Int'l*, pg. 4918
TTK ENG FUKUSHIMA CO., LTD.—See MIRAIT ONE Corporation; *Int'l*, pg. 4918
TTK ENG IWATE CO., LTD.—See MIRAIT ONE Corporation; *Int'l*, pg. 4918
TTK ENG MIYAGI CO., LTD.—See MIRAIT ONE Corporation; *Int'l*, pg. 4918
TTK ENG YAMAGATA CO., LTD.—See MIRAIT ONE Corporation; *Int'l*, pg. 4918
TTK HEALTHCARE LTD; *Int'l*, pg. 7960
TTK KOREA CO., LTD.—See Tokyo Tekko Co., Ltd.; *Int'l*, pg. 7796
TTK PRESTIGE LIMITED; *Int'l*, pg. 7961
TTK PROTECTIVE DEVICES LIMITED—See TTK Prestige Limited; *Int'l*, pg. 7961
TTL BETEILIGUNGS UND GRUNDBESITZ AG; *Int'l*, pg. 7961
TTL ENTERPRISES LIMITED; *Int'l*, pg. 7961
TTL GMBH—See Systemair AB; *Int'l*, pg. 7392
T.T.LIMITED - TIRUPATHI SPINNING MILL—See TT Ltd; *Int'l*, pg. 7960
T.T.LIMITED - TIRUPUR UNIT—See TT Ltd; *Int'l*, pg. 7960
TTL INDUSTRIES PUBLIC COMPANY LIMITED; *Int'l*, pg. 7961
TTL MANUFACTURING (SHANGHAI) CO., LTD.—See Scintronix Corporation Ltd.; *Int'l*, pg. 6649
TTL LOGISTICS (AUSTRALASIA) PTY LTD—See Toyota Tsusho Corporation; *Int'l*, pg. 7878
TTL PROMEX MANUFACTURING (SHANGHAI) CO., LTD.—See Scintronix Corporation Ltd.; *Int'l*, pg. 6649

TUANCHE LIMITED

TTL PROMEX PRECISION ENGINEERING (SHANGHAI) CO., LTD.—See Scintronix Corporation Ltd.; *Int'l*, pg. 6649
TT LTD; *Int'l*, pg. 7960
T & T MANUFACTURING, LLC—See C. G. Bretting Manufacturing Co., Inc.; *U.S. Private*, pg. 705
TT MIDDLE EAST FZE—See TT International Limited; *Int'l*, pg. 7960
TTM INC.—See Open Up Group Inc; *Int'l*, pg. 5599
T&T MOTORS INC.; *U.S. Private*, pg. 3910
TTM RESOURCES INC.; *Int'l*, pg. 7961
TTM TECHNOLOGIES ADVANCED CIRCUITS DIV.—See TTM Technologies, Inc.; *U.S. Public*, pg. 2203
TTM TECHNOLOGIES, INC.; *U.S. Public*, pg. 2203
TTM TECHNOLOGIES TORONTO, INC.—See TTM Technologies, Inc.; *U.S. Public*, pg. 2203
TT NETWORK INTEGRATION INDIA PRIVATE LIMITED—See Toyota Tsusho Corporation; *Int'l*, pg. 7878
TT NETWORK INTEGRATION (THAILAND) CO., LTD.—See Toyota Tsusho Corporation; *Int'l*, pg. 7878
TT OF COLUMBIA, INC.; *U.S. Private*, pg. 4254
TTP GMBH; *Int'l*, pg. 7961
TT PROCESS MANAGEMENT INC.—See Transcosmos Inc.; *Int'l*, pg. 7898
T T R AUTOMOBILES; *Int'l*, pg. 7394
TTR THAIRUNG CO., LTD.—See Kyokuto Kaihatsu Kogyo Co. Ltd.; *Int'l*, pg. 4363
TTS BOHAI MACHINERY CO., LTD.—See Cargotec Corporation; *Int'l*, pg. 1329
TTS CRANES NORWAY AS—See Nekkar ASA; *Int'l*, pg. 5193
TTS GREECE LTD.—See Cargotec Corporation; *Int'l*, pg. 1329
TTS GROUP LTD—See RM plc; *Int'l*, pg. 6356
TTS GROUP - PORT & LOGISTICS—See Nekkar ASA; *Int'l*, pg. 5193
TTS HANDLING SYSTEMS AS—See Nekkar ASA; *Int'l*, pg. 5193
TTS HUA HAI AB—See Cargotec Corporation; *Int'l*, pg. 1329
TTS HUA HAI SHIPS EQUIPMENT CO., LTD.—See Cargotec Corporation; *Int'l*, pg. 1329
TTS KOREA INC—See Cargotec Corporation; *Int'l*, pg. 1329
TTS, LLC; *U.S. Private*, pg. 4255
TTS MARINE AB—See Cargotec Corporation; *Int'l*, pg. 1329
TTS MARINE AS—See Cargotec Corporation; *Int'l*, pg. 1329
TTS MARINE EQUIPMENT (DALIAN) CO., LTD.—See Cargotec Corporation; *Int'l*, pg. 1329
TTS MARINE GMBH—See Cargotec Corporation; *Int'l*, pg. 1329
TTS MARINE INC.—See Cargotec Corporation; *Int'l*, pg. 1329
TTS MARINE KOREA CO., LTD.—See Cargotec Corporation; *Int'l*, pg. 1329
TTS MARINE OSTRAVA S.R.O—See Cargotec Corporation; *Int'l*, pg. 1329
TTS MARINE SHANGHAI CO., LTD.—See Cargotec Corporation; *Int'l*, pg. 1329
TTS MARINE S.R.L—See Cargotec Corporation; *Int'l*, pg. 1329
TTS OFFSHORE HANDLING EQUIPMENT AS—See Cargotec Corporation; *Int'l*, pg. 1329
T&T SOLUTIONS, INC.; *U.S. Private*, pg. 3910
TTS PORT EQUIPMENT AB—See Nekkar ASA; *Int'l*, pg. 5193
TTS SHIPS EQUIPMENT AS—See Nekkar ASA; *Int'l*, pg. 5193
TTS SINGAPORE PTE. LTD.—See Cargotec Corporation; *Int'l*, pg. 1329
TTSS LIMITED—See TUI AG; *Int'l*, pg. 7968
TT STEEL CENTRE (AUSTRALASIA) PTY LTD—See Toyota Tsusho Corporation; *Int'l*, pg. 7878
T & T SUPERMARKET, INC.—See George Weston Limited; *Int'l*, pg. 2939
TTS VIETNAM—See Cargotec Corporation; *Int'l*, pg. 1329
TTT-CUBED, INC.—See HEICO Corporation; *U.S. Public*, pg. 1021
TTT MONEYCORP LIMITED; *Int'l*, pg. 7961
T&T PUBLIC COMPANY LIMITED; *Int'l*, pg. 7960
T&T TRUCKING INCORPORATED; *U.S. Private*, pg. 3910
TTT WEST COAST INC.; *U.S. Private*, pg. 4255
TTU ENERGETIK D.O.O.—See JP Elektroprivreda BiH d.d.; *Int'l*, pg. 4005
TT VISION HOLDINGS BERHAD; *Int'l*, pg. 7960
TTV, S.A.; *Int'l*, pg. 7961
TTW PUBLIC COMPANY LIMITED; *Int'l*, pg. 7961
TTX CO.; *U.S. Private*, pg. 4255
TTX HOLDINGS INC.; *U.S. Private*, pg. 4255
TTY BIOPHARM CO., LTD.; *Int'l*, pg. 7961
TUALATIN SLEEP PRODUCTS INC.; *U.S. Private*, pg. 4255
TUALITY HEALTHCARE; *U.S. Private*, pg. 4255
TU ALLIANZ ZYCIE POLSKA S.A.—See Allianz SE; *Int'l*, pg. 356
TUANCHE LIMITED; *Int'l*, pg. 7962

TUANCHE LIMITED

TUAN DAT MINERALS CO., LTD.—See Phu Tai Joint Stock Company; *Int'l*, pg. 5857
TUAN SING HOLDINGS LIMITED; *Int'l*, pg. 7961
TUAPSE BULK TERMINAL, LLC—See Kovdorskiy GOK JSC; *Int'l*, pg. 4293
TUAPSE COMMERCIAL SEAPORT—See Novolipetski Metallurgicheski Komb OAO; *Int'l*, pg. 5466
TUAS LTD.; *Int'l*, pg. 7962
TUBACEX; *Int'l*, pg. 7962
TUBACEX AMERICA INC,—See Tubacex S.A.; *Int'l*, pg. 7962
TUBACEX AWAJI (THAILAND) LTD.—See Tubacex S.A.; *Int'l*, pg. 7962
TUBACEX & COTUBES CANADA, INC.—See Tubacex S.A.; *Int'l*, pg. 7962
TUBACEX DISTRIBUCAO DE ACOS, LTDA.—See Tubacex S.A.; *Int'l*, pg. 7962
TUBACEX INDIA PVT LTD.—See Tubacex S.A.; *Int'l*, pg. 7962
TUBACEX S.A.; *Int'l*, pg. 7962
TUBACEX TAYLOR ACCESORIOS, S.A.—See Tubacex S.A.; *Int'l*, pg. 7962
TUBA CITY GOLD CORP.; *Int'l*, pg. 7962
TUBA CITY REGIONAL HEALTH CARE CORPORATION; *U.S. Private*, pg. 4255
TUBACOAT S.L.—See Tubacex S.A.; *Int'l*, pg. 7962
TUBAG TRASS-ZEMENT-STEINWERKE GMBH—See Buzzi SpA; *Int'l*, pg. 1231
TUBAUTO S.A.S.—See Hormann KG Verkaufsgesellschaf; *Int'l*, pg. 3481
TUBBS CORDAGE INC.—See Frank W. Winne & Son, Inc.; *U.S. Private*, pg. 1596
TUBBS SNOWSHOE COMPANY—See Kohlberg & Company, LLC; *U.S. Private*, pg. 2338
TUBBY'S SUB SHOPS, INC.; *U.S. Private*, pg. 4255
THE TUBE AND BRACKET COMPANY—See Trilogiq SA; *Int'l*, pg. 7922
TUBE ART DISPLAYS INC.; *U.S. Private*, pg. 4255
TUBE BEND FORM INTERNATIONAL LIMITED—See Cooper Coated Coil Management Limited; *Int'l*, pg. 1791
TUBE CITY IMS BELGIUM BVBA—See The Pritzker Organization, LLC; *U.S. Private*, pg. 4100
TUBE CITY IMS CANADA LIMITED—See The Pritzker Organization, LLC; *U.S. Private*, pg. 4100
TUBE CITY IMS DE MEXICO S. DE R.L. DE C.V.—See The Pritzker Organization, LLC; *U.S. Private*, pg. 4100
TUBE CITY IMS FRANCE CENTRE S.A.S.—See The Pritzker Organization, LLC; *U.S. Private*, pg. 4100
TUBE CITY IMS HOLDING B.V.—See The Pritzker Organization, LLC; *U.S. Private*, pg. 4100
TUBE CITY IMS KOSICE S.R.O.—See The Pritzker Organization, LLC; *U.S. Private*, pg. 4100
TUBE CITY IMS SERVICIOS DE MEXICO S. DE R.L. DE C.V.—See The Pritzker Organization, LLC; *U.S. Private*, pg. 4100
TUBE CITY IMS SOUTH AFRICA (PTY) LTD.—See The Pritzker Organization, LLC; *U.S. Private*, pg. 4100
TUBE CITY IMS TAIWAN LIMITED—See The Pritzker Organization, LLC; *U.S. Private*, pg. 4100
TUBE CITY IMS TRINIDAD LIMITED—See The Pritzker Organization, LLC; *U.S. Private*, pg. 4100
TUBE CLEAN GMBH—See Fouad Alghanim & Sons Group of Companies; *Int'l*, pg. 2753
TUBE CONTROL AB—See Addtech AB; *Int'l*, pg. 135
TUBED COAL MINES LIMITED—See The Aditya Birla Group; *Int'l*, pg. 7612
TUBE DUDE, LLC; *U.S. Private*, pg. 4255
TUBE FABRICATION INDUSTRIES, INC.; *U.S. Private*, pg. 4255
TUBE FABRICATION MACHINERY LIMITED—See Addison Saws Limited; *Int'l*, pg. 129
TUBE FORGINGS OF AMERICA INC.; *U.S. Private*, pg. 4255
TUBE INVESTMENTS OF INDIA LIMITED—See The Murugappa Group, Ltd.; *Int'l*, pg. 7669
TUBELITE COMPANY INC.; *U.S. Private*, pg. 4255
TUBELITE COMPANY INC.—See Tubelite Company Inc.; *U.S. Private*, pg. 4255
TUBELITE COMPANY INC.—See Tubelite Company Inc.; *U.S. Private*, pg. 4255
TUBELITE COMPANY INC.—See Tubelite Company Inc.; *U.S. Private*, pg. 4255
TUBELITE COMPANY INC.—See Tubelite Company Inc.; *U.S. Private*, pg. 4255
TUBELITE COMPANY INC.—See Tubelite Company Inc.; *U.S. Private*, pg. 4255
TUBELITE COMPANY INC.—See Tubelite Company Inc.; *U.S. Private*, pg. 4256
TUBELITE INC.—See Apogee Enterprises, Inc.; *U.S. Public*, pg. 145
TUBE-MAC INDUSTRIES LTD.; *Int'l*, pg. 7962
TUBEMOGUL, INC.—See Adobe Inc.; *U.S. Public*, pg. 43
TUBE PROCESSING CORP.; *U.S. Private*, pg. 4255
TUBE PRODUCTS OF INDIA LTD. - MOHALI PLANT—See The Murugappa Group, Ltd.; *Int'l*, pg. 7669
TUBE PRODUCTS OF INDIA LTD. - SHIRWAL PLANT—See The Murugappa Group, Ltd.; *Int'l*, pg. 7669

TUBE PRODUCTS OF INDIA LTD.—See The Murugappa Group, Ltd.; *Int'l*, pg. 7669
TUBERIAS PROCARSA S.A. DE C.V.—See Industrias CH, S.A.B. de C.V.; *Int'l*, pg. 3674
TUBES INC.; *U.S. Private*, pg. 4256
TUBESOLAR AG; *Int'l*, pg. 7962
TUBE SPECIALTIES CO. INC.; *U.S. Private*, pg. 4255
TUBE SUPPLY, LLC—See Triple-S Steel Holdings Inc.; *U.S. Private*, pg. 4237
TUBETECH INC.; *U.S. Private*, pg. 4256
TUBETEX NV—See Sonoco Products Company; *U.S. Public*, pg. 1909
TUBEWORKX B.V.—See Indutrade AB; *Int'l*, pg. 3682
TUBEX HOLDING GMBH—See CAG Holding GmbH; *Int'l*, pg. 1251
TUBEX LIMITED—See Berry Global Group, Inc; *U.S. Public*, pg. 326
TUBEX PACKAGING MATERIALS CO. LTD.—See CAG Holding GmbH; *Int'l*, pg. 1251
TUBEX SDN. BHD.—See Terengganu Incorporated Sdn. Bhd.; *Int'l*, pg. 7564
TUBEX TUBENFABRIK WOLFSBERG GMBH—See CAG Holding GmbH; *Int'l*, pg. 1251
TUBEX WASUNGEN GMBH—See CAG Holding GmbH; *Int'l*, pg. 1251
TUBEX ZAO—See CAG Holding GmbH; *Int'l*, pg. 1251
TUBIFICIO DI TERNI S.R.L.—See ThyssenKrupp AG; *Int'l*, pg. 7730
TUBIFLEX S.P.A.—See Interpump Group S.p.A.; *Int'l*, pg. 3757
TUBING SEAL CAP—See Pacific Precision Metals, Inc.; *U.S. Private*, pg. 3070
TUBIZE PARTS SERVICE S.R.L.—See LKQ Corporation; *U.S. Public*, pg. 1336
TUBO-FGS, L.L.C.—See NOV, Inc.; *U.S. Public*, pg. 1547
TUBORG PAZARLAMA A.S.—See Turk Tuborg Bira Ve Malt Sanayii A.S.; *Int'l*, pg. 7975
TUBOS ARGENTINOS S.A.—See CAP S.A.; *Int'l*, pg. 1301
TUBOSCOPE BRANDT DE VENEZUELA S.A.—See NOV, Inc.; *U.S. Public*, pg. 1547
TUBOSCOPE NORGE AS—See NOV, Inc.; *U.S. Public*, pg. 1547
TUBOSCOPE PIPELINE SERVICES INC.—See NOV, Inc.; *U.S. Public*, pg. 1546
TUBOSCOPE VETCO CANADA ULC—See NOV, Inc.; *U.S. Public*, pg. 1547
TUBOSCOPE VETCO DE ARGENTINA S.A.—See NOV, Inc.; *U.S. Public*, pg. 1547
TUBOSCOPE VETCO MEXICO, S.A. DE C.V.—See NOV, Inc.; *U.S. Public*, pg. 1547
TUBOSCOPE VETCO MOSCOW CJSC—See NOV, Inc.; *U.S. Public*, pg. 1547
TUBOSCOPE VETCO (OSTERREICH) GMBH—See NOV, Inc.; *U.S. Public*, pg. 1547
TUBOS DE ACERO DE MEXICO, S.A.—See Techint S.p.A.; *Int'l*, pg. 7504
TUBOS MECANICOS NORTE, S.A.—See Tubacex S.A.; *Int'l*, pg. 7962
TUBOS MECANICOS S.A.—See Tubacex S.A.; *Int'l*, pg. 7962
TUBOS REUNIDOS AMERICA, INC.—See Tubos Reunidos, S.A.; *Int'l*, pg. 7963
TUBOS REUNIDOS INDUSTRIAL, S.L.—See Tubos Reunidos, S.A.; *Int'l*, pg. 7963
TUBOS REUNIDOS, S.A.; *Int'l*, pg. 7963
TUBOS SAMUEL DE MEXICO, S.A. DE C.V.—See Samuel, Son & Co., Limited; *Int'l*, pg. 6516
TUBOS SOLDADOS ATLANTICO LTDA.—See Vallourec SA; *Int'l*, pg. 8117
TUBOS TIGRE-ADS DO BRASIL LIMITADA—See Advanced Drainage Systems, Inc.; *U.S. Public*, pg. 46
TUBOS Y ACTIVOS, S. DE R.L. DE C.V.—See NOV, Inc.; *U.S. Public*, pg. 1546
TUBOS Y PLASTICOS ADS CHILE LIMITADA—See Advanced Drainage Systems, Inc.; *U.S. Public*, pg. 46
TUBO-TEC NORDESTE INDUSTRIA—See Sonoco Products Company; *U.S. Public*, pg. 1909
TUBULAR & EQUIPMENT SERVICES, LLC; *U.S. Private*, pg. 4256
TUBULAR INSTRUMENTATION & CONTROLS LP; *U.S. Private*, pg. 4256
TUBULAR LEASING ASTRALIA PTY LTD—See Magnus Energy Group Ltd.; *Int'l*, pg. 4642
TUBULAR METAL SYSTEMS—See Patriarch Partners, LLC; *U.S. Private*, pg. 3109
TUBULAR PRODUCTS COMPANY—See Samuel, Son & Co., Limited; *Int'l*, pg. 6516
TUBULAR SERVICES LP - JACINTOPORT PLANT—See Tubular Services LP; *U.S. Private*, pg. 4256
TUBULAR SERVICES LP - MCCARTY TUBING PLANT—See Tubular Services LP; *U.S. Private*, pg. 4256
TUBULAR SERVICES LP; *U.S. Private*, pg. 4256
TUBULAR STEEL, INC.—See Reliance Steel & Aluminum Co.; *U.S. Public*, pg. 1782
TUBULAR TEXTILE MACHINERY, INC.; *U.S. Private*, pg. 4256
TUC AMU CENTER TUC MIDTJYLLAND APS—See DEKRA e.V.; *Int'l*, pg. 2009

CORPORATE AFFILIATIONS

TUC AMU CENTER TUC SYD A/S—See DEKRA e.V.; *Int'l*, pg. 2010
TUC BRANDS LTD.; *Int'l*, pg. 7963
TUC DANSK VOGNMANDSSKOLE A/S—See DEKRA e.V.; *Int'l*, pg. 2010
TUC DUCAS APS—See DEKRA e.V.; *Int'l*, pg. 2010
TUC FYN APS—See DEKRA e.V.; *Int'l*, pg. 2010
TUCHMAN CLEANERS INC.—See U.S. Dry Cleaning Services Corporation; *U.S. Private*, pg. 4270
TUCKAHOE SAND & GRAVEL CO., INC.—See Johnston Enterprises Inc.; *U.S. Private*, pg. 2230
TUCKER ACOUSTICAL PRODUCTS, INC.—See GMS Inc.; *U.S. Public*, pg. 948
TUCKER ALBIN & ASSOCIATES, INC.; *U.S. Private*, pg. 4256
TUCKER CHRYSLER JEEP, INC.; *U.S. Private*, pg. 4256
TUCKER CONSTRUCTION CO.—See First Reserve Management, L.P.; *U.S. Private*, pg. 1526
TUCKER COUNTY COMMISSION; *U.S. Private*, pg. 4256
TUCKER COUNTY SOLID WASTE AUTHORITY, INC.—See Tucker County Commission; *U.S. Private*, pg. 4256
TUCKER-DAVIS TECHNOLOGIES, INC.; *U.S. Private*, pg. 4256
TUCKER ENERGY SERVICES HOLDINGS, INC.—See STEP Energy Services Ltd.; *Int'l*, pg. 7208
TUCKER GMBH—See Stanley Black & Decker, Inc.; *U.S. Public*, pg. 1935
TUCKER/HALL, INC.; *U.S. Private*, pg. 4256
TUCKER MATERIALS, INC.—See GMS Inc.; *U.S. Public*, pg. 948
TUCKER MECHANICAL—See EMCOR Group, Inc.; *U.S. Public*, pg. 739
TUCKER MIDSTREAM, INC.—See First Reserve Management, L.P.; *U.S. Private*, pg. 1526
TUCKER NURSING CENTER, LLC—See Apollo Global Management, Inc.; *U.S. Public*, pg. 158
TUCKER OIL COMPANY INC.; *U.S. Private*, pg. 4256
TUCKER PAVING, INC.; *U.S. Private*, pg. 4256
TUCKER PRINTERS, INC.—See Chatham Asset Management, LLC; *U.S. Private*, pg. 863
TUCKER-ROCKY DISTRIBUTING—See LDI Ltd., LLC; *U.S. Private*, pg. 2404
TUCKERTON LUMBER CO. INC.; *U.S. Private*, pg. 4256
TUCO INDUSTRIAL PRODUCTS, INC.—See I Squared Capital Advisors (US) LLC; *U.S. Private*, pg. 2021
TUCO INDUSTRIAL PRODUCTS, INC.—See TDR Capital LLP; *Int'l*, pg. 7490
TUCOWS.COM CO.—See Tucows, Inc.; *Int'l*, pg. 7963
TUCOWS, INC.; *Int'l*, pg. 7963
TUCSON AIRPORT AUTHORITY INC.; *U.S. Private*, pg. 4256
TUCSON ARIZONA SURGICAL CENTER, LLC—See UnitedHealth Group Incorporated; *U.S. Public*, pg. 2251
TUCSON COMMUNICATIONS LLC—See Cascade Broadcasting Group LLC; *U.S. Public*, pg. 778
TUCSON DODGE, INC.; *U.S. Private*, pg. 4256
TUCSON ELECTRIC POWER COMPANY—See Fortis Inc.; *Int'l*, pg. 2740
TUCSON EMBEDDED SYSTEMS, INC.; *U.S. Private*, pg. 4256
TUCSON EXPLORER—See 10/13 Communications LLC; *U.S. Private*, pg. 2
TUCSON HEART HOSPITAL—See Ascension Health Alliance; *U.S. Public*, pg. 347
TUCSON HOSPITALITY PROPERTIES, LTD—See InnSuites Hospitality Trust; *U.S. Public*, pg. 1128
TUCSON ST. MARY'S SUITE HOSPITALITY LLC—See InnSuites Hospitality Trust; *U.S. Public*, pg. 1128
TUCSON SYMPHONY ORCHESTRA; *U.S. Private*, pg. 4256
TUC STRANDENS UDDANNELSES-CENTER APS—See DEKRA e.V.; *Int'l*, pg. 2010
TUDELEY HOLDINGS LIMITED; *Int'l*, pg. 7963
TUDO EVENTOS E PROMOCOES LTDA—See Omnicom Group Inc.; *U.S. Public*, pg. 1585
TUDOR CAPITAL AUSTRALIA PTY. LTD.—See Tudor Investment Corporation; *U.S. Private*, pg. 4257
TUDOR CAPITAL EUROPE LLP—See Tudor Investment Corporation; *U.S. Private*, pg. 4257
TUDOR GOLD CORP.; *Int'l*, pg. 7963
TUDOR GOLD SERVICE CORPORATION—See Tudor Gold Corp.; *Int'l*, pg. 7963
TUDOR INSURANCE COMPANY—See American International Group, Inc.; *U.S. Public*, pg. 107
TUDOR INVESTMENT CORPORATION; *U.S. Private*, pg. 4257
TUDOR, PICKERING, HOLT & CO., LLC—See Perella Weinberg Partners LP; *U.S. Public*, pg. 1674
TUDOR, PICKERING, HOLT & CO. SECURITIES-CANADA ULC—See Perella Weinberg Partners LP; *U.S. Public*, pg. 1674
TUDOR RANCH, INC.; *U.S. Private*, pg. 4257
TUDOR REALTY SERVICES CORP.—See FirstService Corporation; *Int'l*, pg. 2691
T&U ELECTRONICS, CO., LTD.—See UBE Corporation; *Int'l*, pg. 8002
TUENTI TECHNOLOGIES, S.L.—See Telefonica, S.A.; *Int'l*, pg. 7536

COMPANY NAME INDEX

TUERFF-DAVIS ENVIROMEDIA; *U.S. Private*, pg. 4257
TUESDAY MORNING CORPORATION; *U.S. Public*, pg. 2203
TUFCO TECHNOLOGIES, INC.—See Griffin Holdings, LLC; *U.S. Private*, pg. 1788
TUFENKIAN IMPORT/EXPORT VENTURES, INC.; *U.S. Private*, pg. 4257
TUFFCARE INC.; *U.S. Private*, pg. 4257
TUFF GROUP AG; *Int'l*, pg. 7963
TUFFIEH FUNDS SICAV PLC; *Int'l*, pg. 7963
TUFF SHED, INC.; *U.S. Private*, pg. 4257
TUFF TORQ CORPORATION—See Yanmar Co., Ltd.; *Int'l*, pg. 8563
TUFFY ADVERTISING; *U.S. Private*, pg. 4257
TUFFY ASSOCIATES CORPORATION; *U.S. Private*, pg. 4257
TUFFY MANUFACTURING INDUSTRIES, INC.—See Myers Industries, Inc.; *U.S. Public*, pg. 1488
TUFFYS PET FOODS INC—See KLN Enterprises Inc.; *U.S. Private*, pg. 2320
TU FILAR S.A.—See UNIQA Insurance Group AG; *Int'l*, pg. 8059
TUFIN SOFTWARE TECHNOLOGIES LTD.—See Turn/River Management LLC; *U.S. Private*, pg. 4259
TUFPAK, INC.—See The Jordan Company, L.P.; *U.S. Private*, pg. 4062
TUFTCO CORPORATION; *U.S. Private*, pg. 4257
TUFTON OCEANIC ASSETS LIMITED; *Int'l*, pg. 7963
TUF-TRANSPORTES URBANOS DE FAMALICAO, LDA—See Deutsche Bahn AG; *Int'l*, pg. 2054
TUFVASSONS TRANSFORMATOR AB—See Addtech AB; *Int'l*, pg. 135
TUFVASSON TESCH AB—See Addtech AB; *Int'l*, pg. 135
TUGA INNOVATIONS, INC.; *Int'l*, pg. 7963
TUGCELIK ALUMINYUM VE METAL MAMULLERI SANAYI VE TIC. A.S.; *Int'l*, pg. 7963
TUG TECHNOLOGIES CORPORATION—See Textron Inc.; *U.S. Public*, pg. 2029
TUGU INSURANCE COMPANY LIMITED—See PT Pertamina (Persero); *Int'l*, pg. 6064
TUGWELL OIL CO. INC.; *U.S. Private*, pg. 4257
TUHAMA FOR FINANCIAL INVESTMENT P.L.C; *Int'l*, pg. 7963
TUHC ANESTHESIOLOGY GROUP, LLC—See HCA Healthcare, Inc.; *U.S. Public*, pg. 1011
TUHC PHYSICIAN GROUP, LLC—See HCA Healthcare, Inc.; *U.S. Public*, pg. 1011
TUI 4 U GMBH—See TUI AG; *Int'l*, pg. 7967
TUI AG; *Int'l*, pg. 7963
TUI AIRLINES BELGIUM N.V.—See TUI AG; *Int'l*, pg. 7967
TUI AIRLINES NEDERLAND B.V.—See TUI AG; *Int'l*, pg. 7967
TUI AMBASSADOR TOURS UNIPESSOAL LDA—See TUI AG; *Int'l*, pg. 7967
TUI AUSTRIA HOLDING GMBH—See TUI AG; *Int'l*, pg. 7967
TUI BELGIUM RETAIL N.V.—See TUI AG; *Int'l*, pg. 7967
TUI BETEILIGUNGS GMBH—See TUI AG; *Int'l*, pg. 7967
TUI BLUE DE GMBH—See TUI AG; *Int'l*, pg. 7967
TUI BULGARIA EOOD—See TUI AG; *Int'l*, pg. 7967
TUI BUSINESS SERVICES GMBH—See TUI AG; *Int'l*, pg. 7967
TUI CHINA TRAVEL CO. LTD.—See TUI AG; *Int'l*, pg. 7967
TUI CONSULTING & SERVICES GMBH—See TUI AG; *Int'l*, pg. 7967
TUI CRUISES GMBH—See Royal Caribbean Cruises Ltd.; *U.S. Public*, pg. 1815
TUI CRUISES GMBH—See TUI AG; *Int'l*, pg. 7967
TUI DANMARK A/S—See TUI AG; *Int'l*, pg. 7967
TUI DEUTSCHLAND GMBH—See TUI AG; *Int'l*, pg. 7967
TUI ESPANA TURISMO S.A—See TUI AG; *Int'l*, pg. 7967
TUI FINLAND OY AB—See TUI AG; *Int'l*, pg. 7967
TUI FINLAND OY AB—See TUI AG; *Int'l*, pg. 7967
TUI FINLAND OY AB—See TUI AG; *Int'l*, pg. 7967
TUI FINLAND OY AB—See TUI AG; *Int'l*, pg. 7967
TUIFLY.COM—See TUI AG; *Int'l*, pg. 7967
TUIFLY GMBH—See TUI AG; *Int'l*, pg. 7968
TUIFLY NORDIC AB—See TUI AG; *Int'l*, pg. 7968
TUIFLY VERMARKTUNGS GMBH—See TUI AG; *Int'l*, pg. 7968
TUI FRANCE SA—See TUI AG; *Int'l*, pg. 7967
TUI HELLAS S.A.—See TUI AG; *Int'l*, pg. 7967
TUI HOLIDAYS IRELAND LIMITED—See TUI AG; *Int'l*, pg. 7967
TUI HOTEL BETRIEBSGESELLSCHAFT MBH—See TUI AG; *Int'l*, pg. 7967
TUI INDIA PRIVATE LIMITED—See TUI AG; *Int'l*, pg. 7967
TUI INFOTEC GMBH—See Sonata Software Limited; *Int'l*, pg. 7089
TUI INFOTEC GMBH—See TUI AG; *Int'l*, pg. 7967
TUI INTERNATIONAL HOLIDAY (MALAYSIA) SDN. BHD.—See TUI AG; *Int'l*, pg. 7967
TUI IRELAND LIMITED—See TUI AG; *Int'l*, pg. 7967
TUI LEISURE TRAVEL SERVICE GMBH—See TUI AG; *Int'l*, pg. 7967
TUI LEISURE TRAVEL SPECIAL TOURS GMBH—See TUI AG; *Int'l*, pg. 7967
TUI LIFESTYLE, LLC; *U.S. Private*, pg. 4257
TUI MAGIC LIFE GMBH—See TUI AG; *Int'l*, pg. 7967
TUI MAGYARORSZAG UTAZASI IRODA KFT.—See TUI AG; *Int'l*, pg. 7967
TUI NEDERLAND HOLDING N.V.—See TUI AG; *Int'l*, pg. 7967
TUI NEDERLAND N.V.—See TUI AG; *Int'l*, pg. 7967
TUI NORDIC HOLDING AB—See TUI AG; *Int'l*, pg. 7967
TUI NORGE AS—See TUI AG; *Int'l*, pg. 7967
TUI NORTHERN EUROPE LTD.—See TUI AG; *Int'l*, pg. 7967
TU INTERRISK S.A.—See Vienna Insurance Group AG Wiener Versicherung Gruppe; *Int'l*, pg. 8194
TUI POLAND SP. Z O.O.—See TUI AG; *Int'l*, pg. 7968
TUI PORTUGAL - AGENCIA DE VIAGENS E TURISMO S.A.—See TUI AG; *Int'l*, pg. 7968
TUI REISECENTER SLOVENSKO S.R.O.—See TUI AG; *Int'l*, pg. 7968
TUI SERVICE AG—See TUI AG; *Int'l*, pg. 7968
TUI SPAIN, SLU—See TUI AG; *Int'l*, pg. 7968
TUI (SUISSE) AG—See TUI AG; *Int'l*, pg. 7967
TUI SUISSE RETAIL AG—See TUI AG; *Int'l*, pg. 7968
TUI SVERIGE AG—See TUI AG; *Int'l*, pg. 7968
TUITION MANAGEMENT SYSTEMS, LLC—See Nelnet, Inc.; *U.S. Public*, pg. 1504
TUI TRAVEL AVIATION FINANCE LIMITED—See TUI AG; *Int'l*, pg. 7967
TUI TRAVEL HEALTHCARE LIMITED—See TUI AG; *Int'l*, pg. 7967
TUI UK LTD.—See TUI AG; *Int'l*, pg. 7967
TUI UK TRANSPORT LTD.—See TUI AG; *Int'l*, pg. 7968
TUJA ZEITARBEIT GMBH—See Adecco Group AG; *Int'l*, pg. 141
TUJUAN EHSAN SDN. BHD.—See Global Oriental Berhad; *Int'l*, pg. 3000
TU-KA CELLULAR TOKYO, INC.—See KDDI Corporation; *Int'l*, pg. 4112
TUKAIZ LLC; *U.S. Private*, pg. 4257
TUKAS GIDA SANAYI VE TICARET A.S.; *Int'l*, pg. 7969
TUKATECH INC.; *U.S. Private*, pg. 4257
TUKA TRANSPORTATION CO.; *Int'l*, pg. 7969
TUKIRAHOITUS OY—See Nordea Bank Abp; *Int'l*, pg. 5417
TUKSU ENGINEERING & CONSTRUCTION LTD. - ASAN FACTORY—See Taikisha Ltd.; *Int'l*, pg. 7414
THE TUKWILA REPORTER—See Black Press Group Ltd.; *Int'l*, pg. 1059
TULACEMENT LIMITED LIABILITY COMPANY—See Heidelberg Materials AG; *Int'l*, pg. 3320
TULA LIFE, INC.—See The Procter & Gamble Company; *U.S. Public*, pg. 2124
TULALIP CASINO—See Tulalip Tribes; *U.S. Private*, pg. 4257
TULALIP TRIBES; *U.S. Private*, pg. 4257
TULANE MEDICAL CENTER—See HCA Healthcare, Inc.; *U.S. Public*, pg. 1013
TULARE ADVANCE-REGISTER—See Gannett Co., Inc.; *U.S. Public*, pg. 901
TULARE COUNTY ASSOCIATION OF REALTORS, INC.; *U.S. Private*, pg. 4257
TULASEE BIO-ETHANOL LIMITED; *Int'l*, pg. 7969
TULE WIND LLC—See Iberdrola, S.A.; *Int'l*, pg. 3571
TU LIEM URBAN DEVELOPMENT JOINT STOCK COMPANY; *Int'l*, pg. 7961
TULIKIVI CORPORATION; *Int'l*, pg. 7969
TULIKIVI UK LIMITED—See Tulikivi Corporation; *Int'l*, pg. 7969
TULIKIVI US INC.—See Tulikivi Corporation; *Int'l*, pg. 7969
TULINTECH S.A.R.L.—See Komax Holding AG; *Int'l*, pg. 4241
TULIPA ROKYTKA S.R.O.—See Africa Israel Investments Ltd.; *Int'l*, pg. 190
TULIPA VOKOVICE S.R.O.—See Africa Israel Investments Ltd.; *Int'l*, pg. 190
TULIP CORP., MILWAUKEE DIV.—See Tulip Corporation; *U.S. Private*, pg. 4257
TULIP CORPORATION; *U.S. Private*, pg. 4257
TULIP DEVELOPMENT LABORATORY, INC.—See Orbit International Corp.; *U.S. Public*, pg. 1615
TULIP DIAGNOSTICS PVT LTD.—See Revvity, Inc.; *U.S. Public*, pg. 1795
TULIP DRUG DISPENSARY CO., LTD.—See FALCO Holdings Co., Ltd.; *Int'l*, pg. 2610
TULIP FLEISCHWAREN OLDENBURG GMBH—See Danish Crown AmbA; *Int'l*, pg. 1965
TULIP FOOD COMPANY AB—See Danish Crown AmbA; *Int'l*, pg. 1965
TULIP FOOD COMPANY FRANCE S.A.—See Danish Crown AmbA; *Int'l*, pg. 1965
TULIP FOOD COMPANY GMBH—See Danish Crown AmbA; *Int'l*, pg. 1965
TULIP FOOD COMPANY ITALIANA S.R.L.—See Danish Crown AmbA; *Int'l*, pg. 1965
TULIP FOOD COMPANY JAPAN CO. LTD—See Danish Crown AmbA; *Int'l*, pg. 1965
TULIP FOOD COMPANY—See Danish Crown AmbA; *Int'l*, pg. 1965
TULIP LTD.—See JBS S.A.; *Int'l*, pg. 3919
TULIP MANAGEMENT SRL—See Africa Israel Investments Ltd.; *Int'l*, pg. 190

TULIP MOLDED PLASTICS CORP - NIAGARA FALLS DIV.—See Tulip Corporation; *U.S. Private*, pg. 4257
TULIP NORGE AS—See Danish Crown AmbA; *Int'l*, pg. 1965
TULIP STAR HOTELS LTD.; *Int'l*, pg. 7969
TULIVE DEVELOPERS LIMITED; *Int'l*, pg. 7969
TULKOFF FOOD PRODUCTS, INC.—See The Graham Group, Inc.; *U.S. Private*, pg. 4037
TULLAHOMA HMA, INC.—See Community Health Systems, Inc.; *U.S. Public*, pg. 557
TULLAMORE HARDWARE LIMITED—See Grafton Group plc; *Int'l*, pg. 3051
TULLETT LIBERTY (BAHRAIN) CO. W.L.L.—See TP ICAP Finance PLC; *Int'l*, pg. 7881
TULLETT PREBON AMERICAS CORP.—See TP ICAP Finance PLC; *Int'l*, pg. 7882
TULLETT PREBON AMERICAS CORP.—See TP ICAP Finance PLC; *Int'l*, pg. 7882
TULLETT PREBON (AUSTRALIA) PTY. LIMITED—See TP ICAP Finance PLC; *Int'l*, pg. 7881
TULLETT PREBON BRASIL CORRETORA DE VALORES E CAMBIO LTDA.—See TP ICAP Finance PLC; *Int'l*, pg. 7882
TULLETT PREBON (CANADA) LIMITED—See TP ICAP Finance PLC; *Int'l*, pg. 7881
TULLETT PREBON ENERGY (JAPAN) LIMITED—See TP ICAP Finance PLC; *Int'l*, pg. 7882
TULLETT PREBON ENERGY (SINGAPORE) PTE. LTD.—See TP ICAP Finance PLC; *Int'l*, pg. 7882
TULLETT PREBON (EQUITIES) LIMITED—See TP ICAP Finance PLC; *Int'l*, pg. 7881
TULLETT PREBON ETP (JAPAN) LTD.—See TP ICAP Finance PLC; *Int'l*, pg. 7882
TULLETT PREBON (EUROPE) LIMITED—See TP ICAP Finance PLC; *Int'l*, pg. 7881
TULLETT PREBON (HONG KONG) LIMITED—See TP ICAP Finance PLC; *Int'l*, pg. 7881
TULLETT PREBON (JAPAN) LIMITED—See TP ICAP Finance PLC; *Int'l*, pg. 7881
TULLETT PREBON (LUXEMBOURG) S.A.—See TP ICAP Finance PLC; *Int'l*, pg. 7881
TULLETT PREBON MEXICO S.A. DE C.V.—See TP ICAP Finance PLC; *Int'l*, pg. 7882
TULLETT PREBON MONEY BROKERAGE (KOREA) LIMITED—See TP ICAP Finance PLC; *Int'l*, pg. 7882
TULLETT PREBON (PHILIPPINES) INC.—See TP ICAP Finance PLC; *Int'l*, pg. 7882
TULLETT PREBON (POLSKA) SA—See TP ICAP Finance PLC; *Int'l*, pg. 7882
TULLETT PREBON (SINGAPORE) LIMITED—See TP ICAP Finance PLC; *Int'l*, pg. 7882
TULLETT PREBON SITICO (CHINA) LIMITED—See TP ICAP Finance PLC; *Int'l*, pg. 7882
TULLETT PREBON SOUTH AFRICA (PTY) LIMITED—See TP ICAP Finance PLC; *Int'l*, pg. 7882
TULLETT PREBON (UK) LIMITED—See TP ICAP Finance PLC; *Int'l*, pg. 7882
TULLOCH PETROLEUM SERVICES PTY LTD—See Ampol Limited; *Int'l*, pg. 437
TULLO MARSHALL WARREN LTD.—See Accenture plc; *Int'l*, pg. 87
TULLOW COTE D'IVOIRE LIMITED—See Tullow Oil plc; *Int'l*, pg. 7970
TULLOW GHANA LIMITED—See Tullow Oil plc; *Int'l*, pg. 7970
TULLOW HARDMAN HOLDINGS B.V.—See Tullow Oil plc; *Int'l*, pg. 7970
TULLOW KENYA B.V.—See Tullow Oil plc; *Int'l*, pg. 7970
TULLOW MADAGASCAR LIMITED—See Tullow Oil plc; *Int'l*, pg. 7970
TULLOW OIL GABON SA—See Tullow Oil plc; *Int'l*, pg. 7970
TULLOW OIL LIMITED—See Tullow Oil plc; *Int'l*, pg. 7970
TULLOW OIL PLC; *Int'l*, pg. 7969
TULLOW OIL SK LIMITED—See Tullow Oil plc; *Int'l*, pg. 7970
TULLOW OIL SPE LIMITED—See Tullow Oil plc; *Int'l*, pg. 7970
TULLOW OIL UK LIMITED—See Tullow Oil plc; *Int'l*, pg. 7970
TULLOW OVERSEAS HOLDINGS B.V.—See Tullow Oil plc; *Int'l*, pg. 7970
TULLOW PAKISTAN (DEVELOPMENTS) LIMITED—See Pakistan Petroleum Ltd.; *Int'l*, pg. 5704
TULLOW SOUTH AFRICA (PTY) LTD—See Tullow Oil plc; *Int'l*, pg. 7970
TULLOW TANZANIA B.V.—See Tullow Oil plc; *Int'l*, pg. 7970
TULLOW UGANDA OPERATIONS PTY LTD—See Tullow Oil plc; *Int'l*, pg. 7970
TULLP B.V.—See GEA Group Aktiengesellschaft; *Int'l*, pg. 2903
TULLY CONSTRUCTION CO., INC.; *U.S. Private*, pg. 4257
TULLY RINCKEY PLLC; *U.S. Private*, pg. 4258
TULLYS COFFEE JAPAN CO., LTD.—See ITO EN Ltd.; *Int'l*, pg. 3834
TULLY-WIHR COMPANY; *U.S. Private*, pg. 4258
TULPAR JOINT STOCK COMPANY; *Int'l*, pg. 7970

TULSA AIRPORT AUTHORITY

TULSA AIRPORT AUTHORITY; *U.S. Private*, pg. 4258
TULSA CEMEMT LLC—See Eagle Materials Inc.; *U.S. Public*, pg. 702
TULSACK, INC.—See The Pritzker Group - Chicago, LLC; *U.S. Private*, pg. 4099
TULSA DIALYSIS, LLC—See DaVita Inc.; *U.S. Public*, pg. 644
TULSA INSPECTION RESOURCES - CANADA, ULC—See Cypress Environmental Partners, L.P.; *U.S. Public*, pg. 618
TULSA INSPECTION RESOURCES, LLC—See Cypress Environmental Partners, L.P.; *U.S. Public*, pg. 618
TULSA MANUFACTURING PLANT—See T.D. Williamson, Inc.; *U.S. Private*, pg. 3911
THE TULSA OK OPHTHALMOLOGY ASC, LLC—See KKR & Co. Inc.; *U.S. Public*, pg. 1248
TULSA POWER, INC; *U.S. Private*, pg. 4258
TULSA RIG IRON INC.; *U.S. Private*, pg. 4258
TULSA ROUTE 66 MARATHON INC.; *U.S. Private*, pg. 4258
TULSARR INDUSTRIAL RESEARCH B.V.—See Barco N.V.; *Int'l*, pg. 864
TULSA SPECIALTY HOSPITAL, LLC—See Select Rehabilitation, LLC; *U.S. Private*, pg. 3601
TULSAT-ATLANTA LLC—See Leveling 8, Inc.; *U.S. Private*, pg. 2434
TULSAT CORP.—See ADDvantage Technologies Group, Inc.; *U.S. Public*, pg. 40
TULSAT-NEBRASKA—See ADDvantage Technologies Group, Inc.; *U.S. Public*, pg. 40
TULSA TRENCHLESS INC—See Tulsa Rig Iron Inc.; *U.S. Private*, pg. 4258
TULSA WINCH, INC.—See Dover Corporation; *U.S. Public*, pg. 679
TULSI EXTRUSIONS LIMITED; *Int'l*, pg. 7970
TULSI EXTRUSIONS LIMITED, UNIT -III—See Tulsi Extrusions Limited; *Int'l*, pg. 7970
TULSI EXTRUSIONS LIMITED, UNIT -II—See Tulsi Extrusions Limited; *Int'l*, pg. 7970
TULSI EXTRUSIONS LIMITED, UNIT -I—See Tulsi Extrusions Limited; *Int'l*, pg. 7970
TULSYAN NEC LIMITED; *Int'l*, pg. 7970
TUMAC LUMBER CO. INC.; *U.S. Private*, pg. 4258
TUMAD MADENCILIK SANAYI VE TICARET A.S.—See Nurol Holding A.S.; *Int'l*, pg. 5491
TUMAD MINING INDUSTRY & TRADE INC.—See Nurol Holding A.S.; *Int'l*, pg. 5491
TUM-A-LUM LUMBER, INC.—See TAL Holdings LLC; *U.S. Private*, pg. 3925
TUMBLE FORMS INC.—See Patterson Companies, Inc.; *U.S. Public*, pg. 1654
TUMBLEWEED, INC.; *U.S. Private*, pg. 4258
TUMBLR, INC.—See Apollo Global Management, Inc.; *U.S. Public*, pg. 167
TUMEDEI S.P.A.—See Skellerup Holdings Limited; *Int'l*, pg. 6980
TUM FINANCE PLC; *Int'l*, pg. 7970
TUMI CANADA ULC—See Samsonite International S.A.; *Int'l*, pg. 6510
TUMI CHARLOTTE AIRPORT LLC—See Samsonite International S.A.; *Int'l*, pg. 6510
TUMI D2C GMBH—See Samsonite International S.A.; *Int'l*, pg. 6510
TUMIDEI SPA—See Skellerup Holdings Limited; *Int'l*, pg. 6980
TUMI HOLDINGS, INC.—See Samsonite International S.A.; *Int'l*, pg. 6510
TUMI HOUSTON AIRPORT LLC—See Samsonite International S.A.; *Int'l*, pg. 6510
TUMI, INC.—See Samsonite International S.A.; *Int'l*, pg. 6510
TUMI (UK) LIMITED—See Samsonite International S.A.; *Int'l*, pg. 6510
TUMON AQUARIUM LLC—See LVMH Moet Hennessy Louis Vuitton SE; *Int'l*, pg. 4603
TUMOR DIAGNOSIS SUPPORT CO., LTD.—See Nippon Kayaku Co., Ltd.; *Int'l*, pg. 5321
TUMORGENESIS INC.—See Predictive Oncology Inc.; *U.S. Public*, pg. 1713
TUMOSAN DOKUM A.S.—See Tumosan Motor ve Traktor Sanayi A.S.; *Int'l*, pg. 7970
TUMOSAN MOTOR VE TRAKTOR SANAYI A.S.; *Int'l*, pg. 7970
TUMPEER CHEMICAL CO. INC.; *U.S. Private*, pg. 4258
TUMRIIN ZAVOD JOINT STOCK COMPANY; *Int'l*, pg. 7970
TUNA ADVERTISING CO., LTD.—See Plan B Media Public Company Limited; *Int'l*, pg. 5888
TUNABYGDENS VVS INSTALLATOR AB—See Instalco AB; *Int'l*, pg. 3722
TUNA ENVIROTECH PRIVATE LIMITED—See Zhejiang Tuna Environmental Science & Technology Co., Ltd.; *Int'l*, pg. 8664
TUNAP AG—See Wurth Verwaltungsgesellschaft mbH; *Int'l*, pg. 8508
TUNAP BENELUX NV—See Wurth Verwaltungsgesellschaft mbH; *Int'l*, pg. 8508

TUNAP CHEMISCH-TECHNISCHE PRODUKTE PRODUKTIONS-UND HANDELSGESELLSCHAFT M.B.H.—See Wurth Verwaltungsgesellschaft mbH; *Int'l*, pg. 8508
TUNAP COSMETICS GMBH—See Wurth Verwaltungsgesellschaft mbH; *Int'l*, pg. 8508
TUNAP DO BRASIL COMERCIO DE PRODUTOS QUIMICOS LTDA.—See Wurth Verwaltungsgesellschaft mbH; *Int'l*, pg. 8508
TUNAP FRANCE SAS—See Wurth Verwaltungsgesellschaft mbH; *Int'l*, pg. 8508
TUNAP GMBH & CO. KG—See Wurth Verwaltungsgesellschaft mbH; *Int'l*, pg. 8508
TUNAP ITALIA S.R.L.—See Wurth Verwaltungsgesellschaft mbH; *Int'l*, pg. 8508
TUNAP KIMYASAL URUNLER PAZARLAMA LTD. STI.—See Wurth Verwaltungsgesellschaft mbH; *Int'l*, pg. 8508
TUNAP NORGE AS—See Wurth Verwaltungsgesellschaft mbH; *Int'l*, pg. 8508
TUNAP POLSKA SP. Z O.O.—See Wurth Verwaltungsgesellschaft mbH; *Int'l*, pg. 8508
TUNAP PRODUCTOS QUIMICOS SA.—See Wurth Verwaltungsgesellschaft mbH; *Int'l*, pg. 8508
TUNAP RUSSIA OOO—See Wurth Verwaltungsgesellschaft mbH; *Int'l*, pg. 8508
TUNAP (SHANGHAI) INTERNATIONAL TRADING CO., LTD.—See Wurth Verwaltungsgesellschaft mbH; *Int'l*, pg. 8508
TUNAP SPORTS GMBH—See Wurth Verwaltungsgesellschaft mbH; *Int'l*, pg. 8508
TUNAP SVERIGE AB—See Wurth Verwaltungsgesellschaft mbH; *Int'l*, pg. 8508
TUNAR (UK) LIMITED—See Wurth Verwaltungsgesellschaft mbH; *Int'l*, pg. 8508
TUNAS PELANGI SDN. BHD.—See Pelangi Publishing Group Bhd; *Int'l*, pg. 5782
TU NA ZYCIE COMPENSA S.A.—See Vienna Insurance Group AG Wiener Versicherung Gruppe; *Int'l*, pg. 8194
TUNBOW GROUP LIMITED—See Town Ray Holdings Limited; *Int'l*, pg. 7851
TUNBRIDGE WELLS FIRE PROTECTION LIMITED—See London Security PLC; *Int'l*, pg. 4547
THE TUNBRIDGE WELLS NUFFIELD HOSPITAL—See Nuffield Health; *Int'l*, pg. 5488
TUNDRA BOOKS INC.—See Bertelsmann SE & Co. KGaA; *Int'l*, pg. 991
TUNDRA GOLD CORP.; *U.S. Public*, pg. 2204
TUNDRA HOLDINGS, INC.—See Cadence Design Systems, Inc.; *U.S. Public*, pg. 419
TUNDRA RESTAURANT SUPPLY, INC.—See New Mountain Capital, LLC; *U.S. Public*, pg. 2902
TUNDRA TOURS, INC.—See Arctic Slope Regional Corporation; *U.S. Private*, pg. 316
TUNECORE, INC.—See Believe SAS; *Int'l*, pg. 964
TUNEHOUSE PTY. LTD.—See HKS CO., LTD.; *Int'l*, pg. 3429
TUNE INSURANCE MALAYSIA BERHAD—See Tune Protect Group Berhad; *Int'l*, pg. 7970
TUNELES CONCESIONADOS DE ACAPULCO, S.A. DE C.V.—See Empresas ICA S.A.B. de C.V.; *Int'l*, pg. 2391
TUNE PROTECT GROUP BERHAD; *Int'l*, pg. 7970
TUNGALOY CORP.—See Berkshire Hathaway Inc.; *U.S. Public*, pg. 308
TUNGALOY FRICTION MATERIAL VIETNAM LTD.—See Honda Motor Co., Ltd.; *Int'l*, pg. 3463
TUNGA LYFT I SVERIGE AB—See Storskogen Group AB; *Int'l*, pg. 7228
TUNG FENG INC.—See Chailease Holding Company Limited; *Int'l*, pg. 1437
TUNG HO STEEL ENTERPRISE CORPORATION - KAOHSIUNG WORKS—See Tung Ho Steel Enterprise Corporation; *Int'l*, pg. 7970
TUNG HO STEEL ENTERPRISE CORPORATION - MIAOLI WORKS—See Tung Ho Steel Enterprise Corporation; *Int'l*, pg. 7970
TUNG HO STEEL ENTERPRISE CORPORATION; *Int'l*, pg. 7970
TUNG HO STEEL ENTERPRISE CORPORATION - TAOYUAN WORKS—See Tung Ho Steel Enterprise Corporation; *Int'l*, pg. 7971
TUNG HO STEEL VIETNAM CORPORATION LIMITED—See Tung Ho Steel Enterprise Corporation; *Int'l*, pg. 7971
TUNG HO TEXTILE CO., LTD.; *Int'l*, pg. 7971
TUNGHSU AZURE RENEWABLE ENERGY CO., LTD.; *Int'l*, pg. 7971
TUNG-JETEK CO., LTD.; *Int'l*, pg. 7971
TUNG KANG ENGINEERING & CONSTRUCTION CORP.—See Tung Ho Steel Enterprise Corporation; *Int'l*, pg. 7971
TUNG KANG STEEL STRUCTURE CORP.—See Tung Ho Steel Enterprise Corporation; *Int'l*, pg. 7971
TUNG KANG WIND POWER CORP.—See Tung Ho Steel Enterprise Corporation; *Int'l*, pg. 7971
TUNGKONG CO., LTD.; *Int'l*, pg. 7971
TUNG KONG SECURITY PRINTING CO., LTD. - BEIJING FACTORY—See Tungkong Co., Ltd.; *Int'l*, pg. 7971

CORPORATE AFFILIATIONS

TUNG KONG SECURITY PRINTING CO., LTD. - CHENGDU FACTORY—See Tungkong Co., Ltd.; *Int'l*, pg. 7971
TUNG KONG SECURITY PRINTING CO., LTD. - GUANGZHOU FACTORY—See Tungkong Co., Ltd.; *Int'l*, pg. 7971
TUNG KONG SECURITY PRINTING CO., LTD. - QINGHAI FACTORY—See Tungkong Co., Ltd.; *Int'l*, pg. 7971
TUNG KONG SECURITY PRINTING CO., LTD. - SHANGHAI FACTORY—See Tungkong Co., Ltd.; *Int'l*, pg. 7971
TUNG KONG SECURITY PRINTING CO., LTD. - XINJIANG FACTORY—See Tungkong Co., Ltd.; *Int'l*, pg. 7971
TUNG KONG SECURITY PRINTING CO., LTD. - ZHENGZHOU FACTORY—See Tungkong Co., Ltd.; *Int'l*, pg. 7971
TUNGKUANG INDUSTRIAL JOINT STOCK COMPANY - HAI DUONG FACTORY—See TungKuang Industrial Joint Stock Company; *Int'l*, pg. 7971
TUNGKUANG INDUSTRIAL JOINT STOCK COMPANY - NHON TRACH FACTORY—See TungKuang Industrial Joint Stock Company; *Int'l*, pg. 7971
TUNGKUANG INDUSTRIAL JOINT STOCK COMPANY; *Int'l*, pg. 7971
TUNG LOK ARENA PTE LTD—See Tung Lok Restaurants (2000) Ltd; *Int'l*, pg. 7971
TUNG LOK CENTRAL RESTAURANT PTE LTD—See Tung Lok Restaurants (2000) Ltd; *Int'l*, pg. 7971
TUNG LOK MILLENNIUM PTE LTD—See Tung Lok Restaurants (2000) Ltd; *Int'l*, pg. 7971
TUNG LOK RESTAURANTS (2000) LTD; *Int'l*, pg. 7971
TUNG LOK SIGNATURES PTE LTD—See Tung Lok Restaurants (2000) Ltd; *Int'l*, pg. 7971
TUNG PEI INDUSTRIAL CO., LTD.—See NTN Corporation; *Int'l*, pg. 5482
TUNGRAY TECHNOLOGIES INC.; *Int'l*, pg. 7972
TUNGSTEN CORPORATION PLC—See Clearlake Capital Group, L.P.; *U.S. Private*, pg. 936
TUNGSTEN CORPORATION PLC—See TA Associates, Inc.; *U.S. Private*, pg. 3916
TUNGSTEN MINING NL; *Int'l*, pg. 7972
TUNGSTEN NETWORK INC—See Clearlake Capital Group, L.P.; *U.S. Private*, pg. 936
TUNGSTEN NETWORK INC—See TA Associates, Inc.; *U.S. Private*, pg. 3916
TUNGSTEN WEST PLC; *Int'l*, pg. 7972
TUNGTEX FASHIONS (VIETNAM) LIMITED—See Tungtex (Holdings) Co. Ltd.; *Int'l*, pg. 7972
TUNGTEX (HOLDINGS) CO. LTD.; *Int'l*, pg. 7972
TUNGTEX INTERNATIONAL LIMITED—See Tungtex (Holdings) Co. Ltd.; *Int'l*, pg. 7972
TUNGTEX TRADING COMPANY LIMITED—See Tungtex (Holdings) Co. Ltd.; *Int'l*, pg. 7972
TUNGTEX (UK) LIMITED—See Tungtex (Holdings) Co. Ltd.; *Int'l*, pg. 7972
TUNG THAI FASHIONS LIMITED—See Tungtex (Holdings) Co. Ltd.; *Int'l*, pg. 7972
TUNG THIH ELECTRONIC CO., LTD.; *Int'l*, pg. 7971
TUNHEIM PARTNERS; *U.S. Private*, pg. 4258
TUNICA GOLF COURSE, LLC—See Boyd Gaming Corporation; *U.S. Public*, pg. 378
TUNISIE TELECOM; *Int'l*, pg. 7972
TUNISIE VOYAGES S.A.—See TUI AG; *Int'l*, pg. 7969
TUNIS INTERNATIONAL BANK—See Kuwait Projects Company (Holding) K.S.C.P.; *Int'l*, pg. 4347
TUNI TEXTILE MILLS LIMITED; *Int'l*, pg. 7972
TUNIU CORPORATION; *Int'l*, pg. 7972
TUNKHANNOCK CLINIC COMPANY, LLC—See Community Health Systems, Inc.; *U.S. Public*, pg. 557
TUNNEL DETROIT MOD DRO-2—See VINCI S.A.; *Int'l*, pg. 8235
TUNNEL DIALYSIS, LLC—See DaVita Inc.; *U.S. Public*, pg. 644
TUNNEL HILL PARTNERS LP—See Macquarie Group Limited; *Int'l*, pg. 4628
TUNNELL CONSULTING; *U.S. Private*, pg. 4258
TUNNELL CONSULTING—See Tunnell Consulting; *U.S. Private*, pg. 4258
TUNNEL NETWORK SERVICES PTY LTD.—See Groupe Egis S.A.; *Int'l*, pg. 3102
TUNNEL SAFETY TESTING, S.A.—See I Squared Capital Advisors (US) LLC; *U.S. Private*, pg. 2023
TUNNEL SAFETY TESTING, S.A.—See TDR Capital LLP; *Int'l*, pg. 7492
TUNROCK S.R.L.—See MAHLE GmbH; *Int'l*, pg. 4648
TUNSTALL AB—See Tunstall Group Limited; *Int'l*, pg. 7972
TUNSTALL AG—See Tunstall Group Limited; *Int'l*, pg. 7972
TUNSTALL AMERICAS—See ConnectAmerica.com, LLC; *U.S. Private*, pg. 1015
TUNSTALL A/S—See Tunstall Group Limited; *Int'l*, pg. 7972
TUNSTALL AUSTRALASIA PTY LTD—See Tunstall Group Limited; *Int'l*, pg. 7972
TUNSTALL B.V.—See Tunstall Group Limited; *Int'l*, pg. 7972
TUNSTALL CANADA INC—See Tunstall Group Limited; *Int'l*, pg. 7972
TUNSTALL CONSULTING, INC.; *U.S. Private*, pg. 4258

COMPANY NAME INDEX

TUNSTALL EMERGENCY RESPONSE LTD.—See Tunstall Group Limited; *Int'l*, pg. 7972
TUNSTALL GMBH—See Tunstall Group Limited; *Int'l*, pg. 7973
TUNSTALL GROUP LIMITED; *Int'l*, pg. 7972
TUNSTALL HEALTHCARE A/S—See Tunstall Group Limited; *Int'l*, pg. 7973
TUNSTALL HEALTHCARE GROUP LIMITED—See Tunstall Group Limited; *Int'l*, pg. 7973
TUNSTALL HEALTHCARE (UK) LIMITED—See Tunstall Group Limited; *Int'l*, pg. 7973
TUNSTALL IBERICA, S.A.—See Tunstall Group Limited; *Int'l*, pg. 7973
TUNSTALL NEW ZEALAND LIMITED—See Tunstall Group Limited; *Int'l*, pg. 7973
TUNSTALL OY—See Tunstall Group Limited; *Int'l*, pg. 7973
TUNSTALL S.A./N.V.—See Tunstall Group Limited; *Int'l*, pg. 7973
TUNSTALL TECHNOLOGIES S.A.—See Tunstall Group Limited; *Int'l*, pg. 7973
TUNTEX DISTINCT CORP.; *Int'l*, pg. 7973
TUNTEX EXECUTIVE PARK INC.—See Universal Paragon Corporation; *U.S. Private*, pg. 4306
TUNTEX INCORPORATION—See Tuntex Distinct Corp.; *Int'l*, pg. 7973
TUNTEX (THAILAND) PUBLIC COMPANY LIMITED—See Tuntex Distinct Corp.; *Int'l*, pg. 7973
TUNTURI-HELLBERG OY LTD.—See Accell Group N.V.; *Int'l*, pg. 81
TUNTURI NEW FITNESS B.V.—See Accell Group N.V.; *Int'l*, pg. 81
TUNZINI ANTILLES SAS—See VINCI S.A.; *Int'l*, pg. 8229
TUNZINI BORDEAUX SAS—See VINCI S.A.; *Int'l*, pg. 8230
TUNZINI GUADELOUPE SAS—See VINCI S.A.; *Int'l*, pg. 8230
TUNZINI LIMOGES SAS—See VINCI S.A.; *Int'l*, pg. 8230
TUNZINI MAINTENANCE NUCLEAIRE SAS—See VINCI S.A.; *Int'l*, pg. 8230
TUNZINI NUCLEAIRE SAS—See VINCI S.A.; *Int'l*, pg. 8230
TUNZINI PROTECTION INC.ENDIE SAS—See VINCI S.A.; *Int'l*, pg. 8230
TUNZINI—See VINCI S.A.; *Int'l*, pg. 8238
TUNZINI TOULOUSE S.A.S.—See VINCI S.A.; *Int'l*, pg. 8238
TUOHY FURNITURE CORPORATION; *U.S. Private*, pg. 4258
TUONG AIK SHIPYARD SDN. BHD.—See TAS Offshore Berhad; *Int'l*, pg. 7464
TUONG AN VEGETABLE OIL JOINT STOCK COMPANY—See KIDO Group Corp.; *Int'l*, pg. 4158
TUOXIN PHARMACEUTICAL GROUP CO., LTD.; *Int'l*, pg. 7973
TUPELO-HONEY RAYCOM, LLC—See Gray Television, Inc.; *U.S. Public*, pg. 959
TU-PLAST TUBE PRODUCING LTD.—See Hoffmann Neopac; *Int'l*, pg. 3440
TU POLSKI ZWIAZEK MOROROWY S.A.—See Vienna Insurance Group AG Wiener Versicherung Gruppe; *Int'l*, pg. 8194
TUPPER, INC.; *Int'l*, pg. 7973
TUPPERWARE AUSTRALIA PTY. LTD.—See Tupperware Brands Corporation; *U.S. Public*, pg. 2204
TUPPERWARE BELGIUM N.V.—See Tupperware Brands Corporation; *U.S. Public*, pg. 2204
TUPPERWARE BRANDS CORPORATION; *U.S. Public*, pg. 2204
TUPPERWARE BRANDS FOUNDATION—See Tupperware Brands Corporation; *U.S. Public*, pg. 2204
TUPPERWARE BRANDS KOREA LTD.—See Tupperware Brands Corporation; *U.S. Public*, pg. 2204
TUPPERWARE DEUTSCHLAND GMBH—See Tupperware Brands Corporation; *U.S. Public*, pg. 2204
TUPPERWARE D.O.O.—See Tupperware Brands Corporation; *U.S. Public*, pg. 2205
TUPPERWARE ESPANA, S.A.—See Tupperware Brands Corporation; *U.S. Public*, pg. 2204
TUPPERWARE FRANCE S.A.—See Tupperware Brands Corporation; *U.S. Public*, pg. 2204
TUPPERWARE GENERAL SERVICES N.V.—See Tupperware Brands Corporation; *U.S. Public*, pg. 2204
TUPPERWARE GLOBAL CENTER SARL—See Tupperware Brands Corporation; *U.S. Public*, pg. 2204
TUPPERWARE NORDIC A/S—See Tupperware Brands Corporation; *U.S. Public*, pg. 2204
TUPPERWARE OSTERREICH G.M.B.H.—See Tupperware Brands Corporation; *U.S. Public*, pg. 2204
TUPPERWARE POLSKA SP.Z O.O.—See Tupperware Brands Corporation; *U.S. Public*, pg. 2204
TUPPERWARE PRODUCTS, INC. WILMINGTON—See Tupperware Brands Corporation; *U.S. Public*, pg. 2204
TUPPERWARE ROMANIA S.R.L.—See Tupperware Brands Corporation; *U.S. Public*, pg. 2204
TUPPERWARE SERVICES GMBH—See Tupperware Brands Corporation; *U.S. Public*, pg. 2204

TUPPERWARE SOUTHERN AFRICA (PROPRIETARY) LIMITED—See Tupperware Brands Corporation; *U.S. Public*, pg. 2204
TUPPERWARE (SUISSE) SA—See Tupperware Brands Corporation; *U.S. Public*, pg. 2204
TUPPERWARE TRADING LTD.—See Tupperware Brands Corporation; *U.S. Public*, pg. 2204
TUPPERWARE TURKEY, INC.—See Tupperware Brands Corporation; *U.S. Public*, pg. 2204
TUPPERWARE UNITED KINGDOM & IRELAND LIMITED—See Tupperware Brands Corporation; *U.S. Public*, pg. 2205
TUPPERWARE U.S., INC.—See Tupperware Brands Corporation; *U.S. Public*, pg. 2205
TUPPERWARE VIETNAM LLC—See Tupperware Brands Corporation; *U.S. Public*, pg. 2205
TUPRAG METAL MADENCILIK SANAYI VE TICARET LIMITED SIRKETI—See Eldorado Gold Corporation; *Int'l*, pg. 2347
TUPRAS TRADING LTD.—See Koc Holding A.S.; *Int'l*, pg. 4224
TUPY AMERICAN FOUNDRY CORP—See TUPY S.A.; *Int'l*, pg. 7973
TUPY EUROPE GMBH—See TUPY S.A.; *Int'l*, pg. 7973
TUPY MEXICO SALTILLO, S.A. DE C.V.—See TUPY S.A.; *Int'l*, pg. 7973
TUPY S.A.; *Int'l*, pg. 7973
TURACO GOLD LIMITED; *Int'l*, pg. 7973
TURA INC.—See Equistone Partners Europe Limited; *Int'l*, pg. 2486
TURANBANK OJSC; *Int'l*, pg. 7973
TURAN-FOLEY MOTORS INC.; *U.S. Private*, pg. 4258
TURANLI ELEKTRONIK LTD.—See Billionton Systems Inc.; *Int'l*, pg. 1031
TURANO BAKING COMPANY; *U.S. Private*, pg. 4258
TURBIGAS SOLAR S.A.—See Fugro N.V.; *Int'l*, pg. 2808
TURBINAS SOLAR DE VENEVUELA C.A.—See Caterpillar, Inc.; *U.S. Public*, pg. 454
TURBINAS SOLAR, S.A. DE C.V.—See Caterpillar, Inc.; *U.S. Public*, pg. 454
TURBINATE INTERNATIONAL, B.V.—See Team, Inc.; *U.S. Public*, pg. 1988
TURBINE AVIATION, INC.; *U.S. Public*, pg. 2205
TURBINE CONTROLS, LLC—See VSE Corporation; *U.S. Public*, pg. 2313
TURBINE DIAGNOSTIC SERVICES, INC.; *U.S. Private*, pg. 4258
TURBINE ENGINE COMPONENTS TECHNOLOGIES CORP.—See Stony Point Group, Inc.; *U.S. Private*, pg. 3830
TURBINE ENGINE COMPONENTS TEXTRON, INC.—See UCA Holdings Inc.; *U.S. Private*, pg. 4273
TURBINE GENERATOR MAINTENANCE, INC.; *U.S. Private*, pg. 4259
TURBINE INCUBATOR LIMITED—See ENL Limited; *Int'l*, pg. 2442
TURBINE KINETICS, INC.—See HEICO Corporation; *U.S. Public*, pg. 1020
TURBINE REPAIR SERVICES GLOBAL IRELAND LTD—See The Carlyle Group Inc.; *U.S. Public*, pg. 2054
TURBINE; *U.S. Private*, pg. 4258
TURBINE SURFACE TECHNOLOGIES LIMITED—See Rolls-Royce Holdings plc; *Int'l*, pg. 6394
TURBOATOM JSC; *Int'l*, pg. 7973
TURBOCAM INTERNATIONAL; *U.S. Private*, pg. 4259
TURBOCARE B.V.—See Siemens Aktiengesellschaft; *Int'l*, pg. 6901
TURBOCARE C.A.—See Siemens Aktiengesellschaft; *Int'l*, pg. 6901
TURBOCARE, INC.—See Siemens Aktiengesellschaft; *Int'l*, pg. 6891
TURBOCARE S.P.A.—See Siemens Aktiengesellschaft; *Int'l*, pg. 6901
TURBOCARE SP. Z.O.O.—See Siemens Aktiengesellschaft; *Int'l*, pg. 6901
TURBOCHEF INTERNATIONAL—See The Middleby Corporation; *U.S. Public*, pg. 2115
TURBOCHEF TECHNOLOGIES EUROPE, LTD—See The Middleby Corporation; *U.S. Public*, pg. 2115
TURBOCHEF TECHNOLOGIES, INC.—See The Middleby Corporation; *U.S. Public*, pg. 2115
TURBOCHROME LTD.—See First Israel Mezzanine Investors Ltd.; *Int'l*, pg. 2685
TURBOCOMBUSTOR KFT.—See AeroEquity Partners, LLC; *U.S. Private*, pg. 119
TURBOCOMBUSTOR KFT.—See The Carlyle Group Inc.; *U.S. Public*, pg. 2046
TURBOCOMBUSTOR TECHNOLOGY, INC.—See AeroEquity Partners, LLC; *U.S. Private*, pg. 119
TURBOCOMBUSTOR TECHNOLOGY, INC.—See The Carlyle Group Inc.; *U.S. Public*, pg. 2046
TURBODEN S.P.A.—See Mitsubishi Heavy Industries, Ltd.; *Int'l*, pg. 4962
TURBODEN TURKEY ORC TURBO JENERATOR SANAYI ANONIM SIRKETI—See Mitsubishi Heavy Industries, Ltd.; *Int'l*, pg. 4962
TURBO DRIVE LTD.—See Cummins Inc.; *U.S. Public*, pg. 609

TURBODYNE TECHNOLOGIES, INC.; *U.S. Private*, pg. 4259
TURBO ENERGY PRIVATE LTD.—See BorgWarner Inc.; *U.S. Public*, pg. 371
TURBO FILTRATION, LLC—See AIP, LLC; *U.S. Private*, pg. 136
TURBOFLAME AB—See NIBE Industrier AB; *Int'l*, pg. 5263
TURBOGAS - PRODUTORA ENERGIA S.A.—See ENGIE SA; *Int'l*, pg. 2433
TURBOGENERADORES DEL PERU, S.A.C.—See Duro Felguera, S.A.; *Int'l*, pg. 2229
TURBOGEN LTD.; *Int'l*, pg. 7973
TURBO HOLDINGS INC.; *U.S. Private*, pg. 4259
TURBOLIN PR—See Omnicom Group Inc.; *U.S. Public*, pg. 1578
TURBOLINUX, INC.—See SRA Holdings Inc; *Int'l*, pg. 7148
TURBOLINUX, JAPAN K.K.—See SRA Holdings Inc; *Int'l*, pg. 7148
TURBOMACH FRANCE S.A.R.L.—See Caterpillar, Inc.; *U.S. Public*, pg. 454
TURBOMACH GMBH—See Caterpillar, Inc.; *U.S. Public*, pg. 454
TURBO MACHINERY REPAIR, INC.—See DXP Enterprises, Inc.; *U.S. Public*, pg. 698
TURBOMACH NETHERLANDS B.V.—See Caterpillar, Inc.; *U.S. Public*, pg. 454
TURBOMACH PAKISTAN (PRIVATE) LIMITED—See Caterpillar, Inc.; *U.S. Public*, pg. 454
TURBOMACH S.A.—See Caterpillar, Inc.; *U.S. Public*, pg. 454
TURBOMAX CO., LTD.—See ShinMaywa Industries, Ltd.; *Int'l*, pg. 6847
TURBOMAX INDIA PRIVATE LIMITED—See ShinMaywa Industries, Ltd.; *Int'l*, pg. 6847
TURBOMECA AMERICA LATINA S.A.—See Safran SA; *Int'l*, pg. 6476
TURBOMECA AUSTRALASIA PTY. LTD.—See Safran SA; *Int'l*, pg. 6476
TURBOMECA BEIJING HELICOPTER ENGINES TRADING CIE LTD.—See Safran SA; *Int'l*, pg. 6476
TURBOMECA CANADA INC.—See Safran SA; *Int'l*, pg. 6476
TURBOMECA GMBH—See Safran SA; *Int'l*, pg. 6476
TURBOMECA HELICOPTER ENGINES TRADING LTD—See Safran SA; *Int'l*, pg. 6476
TURBOMECA INDIA ENGINES PVT LTD—See Safran SA; *Int'l*, pg. 6476
TURBOMECA JAPAN K.K—See Safran SA; *Int'l*, pg. 6476
TURBOMECA MEXICO S.A DE C.V—See Safran SA; *Int'l*, pg. 6476
TURBOMECANICA S.A.; *Int'l*, pg. 7973
TURBOMECA SA—See Safran SA; *Int'l*, pg. 6476
TURBOMECA—See Safran SA; *Int'l*, pg. 6476
TURBOMECA SUD AMERICANA—See Safran SA; *Int'l*, pg. 6476
TURBOMECA TIANJING HELICOPTER ENGINES TRADING CIE LTD.—See Safran SA; *Int'l*, pg. 6476
TURBO-MECH ASIA PTE. LTD.—See Turbo-Mech Berhad; *Int'l*, pg. 7973
TURBO-MECH BERHAD; *Int'l*, pg. 7973
TURBO-MECH (THAILAND) CO. LTD.—See Turbo-Mech Berhad; *Int'l*, pg. 7973
TURBO-MECH (THAIL) CO. LTD.—See Turbo-Mech Berhad; *Int'l*, pg. 7973
TURBOMED EDV GMBH—See CompuGroup Medical SE & Co. KGaA; *Int'l*, pg. 1757
TURBOMED VERTRIEBS- UND SERVICE GMBH—See CompuGroup Medical SE & Co. KGaA; *Int'l*, pg. 1756
TURBON AG; *Int'l*, pg. 7973
TURBONETICS HOLDINGS, INC.—See Westinghouse Air Brake Technologies Corporation; *U.S. Public*, pg. 2359
TURBONOMIC, INC.; *U.S. Private*, pg. 4259
TURBON (THAILAND) CO. LTD.—See Turbon AG; *Int'l*, pg. 7974
TURBON USA, INC.—See Turbon AG; *Int'l*, pg. 7974
TURBO POWER SYSTEMS INC.; *Int'l*, pg. 7973
TURBO PRECLEANER INC—See Dreison International, Inc.; *U.S. Private*, pg. 1276
TURBOSERVICES SDN. BHD.—See Deleum Berhad; *Int'l*, pg. 2012
TURBOSQUID, INC.—See Shutterstock, Inc.; *U.S. Public*, pg. 1876
TURBOTEC PRODUCTS, INC.; *U.S. Private*, pg. 4259
TURBOTVILLE NATIONAL BANK; *U.S. Public*, pg. 2205
TURBO-UNION LTD.—See Airbus SE; *Int'l*, pg. 243
TURBO WHOLESALE TIRES, INC.—See Kingswood Capital Management LLC; *U.S. Private*, pg. 2312
TURCAS PETROL A.S.; *Int'l*, pg. 7974
TURCHETTE ADVERTISING AGENCY LLC; *U.S. Private*, pg. 4259
TURCK AUSTRALIA PTY. LTD.—See Turck Holding GmbH; *Int'l*, pg. 7974
TURCK AUTOMATION ROMANIA SRL—See Turck Holding GmbH; *Int'l*, pg. 7974
TURCK BANNER S.A.S.—See Turck Holding GmbH; *Int'l*, pg. 7974

TURCHETTE ADVERTISING AGENCY LLC

Company Index

TURCK BANNER S.R.L.—See Turck Holding GmbH; *Int'l*, pg. 7974
TURCK B.V.—See Turck Holding GmbH; *Int'l*, pg. 7974
TURCK CHARTWELL CANADA INC.—See Turck Holding GmbH; *Int'l*, pg. 7974
TURCK DO BRASIL AUTOMACAO LTDA.—See Turck Holding GmbH; *Int'l*, pg. 7974
TURCK ELECTRONICS GMBH—See Turck Holding GmbH; *Int'l*, pg. 7974
TURCK GMBH—See Turck Holding GmbH; *Int'l*, pg. 7974
TURCK HOLDING GMBH; *Int'l*, pg. 7974
TURCK HUNGARY KFT.—See Turck Holding GmbH; *Int'l*, pg. 7974
TURCK INC.; *U.S. Private*, pg. 4259
TURCK INDIA AUTOMATION PVT. LTD.—See Turck Holding GmbH; *Int'l*, pg. 7974
TURCK JAPAN CORPORATION—See Turck Holding GmbH; *Int'l*, pg. 7974
TURCK KOREA CO, LTD.—See Turck Holding GmbH; *Int'l*, pg. 7974
TURCK MIDDLE EAST S.P.C.—See Turck Holding GmbH; *Int'l*, pg. 7974
TURCK OTOMASYON TICARET LIMITED SIRKETI—See Turck Holding GmbH; *Int'l*, pg. 7974
TURCK RUS OOO—See Turck Holding GmbH; *Int'l*, pg. 7974
TURCK SINGAPORE PTE. LTD.—See Turck Holding GmbH; *Int'l*, pg. 7974
TURCK SP.Z.O.O.—See Turck Holding GmbH; *Int'l*, pg. 7974
TURCK S.R.O.—See Turck Holding GmbH; *Int'l*, pg. 7974
TURCK (TIANJIN) SENSOR CO. LTD.—See Turck Holding GmbH; *Int'l*, pg. 7974
TURCO NEDERLAND B.V.—See Henkel AG & Co. KGaA; *Int'l*, pg. 3351
TURCO PRODUKTEN B.V.—See Henkel AG & Co. KGaA; *Int'l*, pg. 3351
TURCOTEL TURIZM A.S.—See TUI AG; *Int'l*, pg. 7969
TURCOTTE O'KEEFFE, INC.; *U.S. Private*, pg. 4259
TURDAPAN SA; *Int'l*, pg. 7974
TUREC ADVERTISING ASSOCIATES, INC.; *U.S. Private*, pg. 4259
TURELK INC.; *U.S. Private*, pg. 4259
TURENFABRIK SAFENWIL AG—See Indutrade AB; *Int'l*, pg. 3682
TURENNE CAPITAL PARTENAIRES SAS; *Int'l*, pg. 7974
TUREX A.S.—See Kiler Holding A.S.; *Int'l*, pg. 4161
TURF CARE SUPPLY CORP—See Platinum Equity, LLC; *U.S. Private*, pg. 3209
TURF FACTORY DIRECT LLC—See Sentinel Capital Partners, L.L.C.; *U.S. Private*, pg. 3609
TURF & GARDEN, INC.—See Pool Corporation; *U.S. Public*, pg. 1701
TURFGRASS, LLC; *U.S. Private*, pg. 4259
TURF MASTERS BRANDS, INC.—See CenterOak Partners LLC; *U.S. Private*, pg. 816
TURF MASTERS LAWN CARE, INC.—See CenterOak Partners LLC; *U.S. Private*, pg. 816
TURF MERCHANTS, INC.; *U.S. Private*, pg. 4259
TURF PRODUCTS CORPORATION; *U.S. Private*, pg. 4259
TURF STAR INC.; *U.S. Private*, pg. 4259
TURFTENDERS LANDSCAPE SERVICES INC—See Greenscape, Inc.; *U.S. Private*, pg. 1780
TURFWAY PARK, LLC—See Churchill Downs, Inc.; *U.S. Public*, pg. 494
TURGIS TECHNOLOGY PTY LTD.—See Koninklijke HaskoningDHV Groep B.V.; *U.S. Private*, pg. 4266
TURIS BEST D.D. KONJIC; *Int'l*, pg. 7974
TURISCAR RENT A CAR, S.A.—See Avis Budget Group, Inc.; *U.S. Public*, pg. 249
TURISM, HOTELURI, RESTAURANTE MAREA NEAGRA S.A.—See Transilvania Investments Alliance S.A.; *Int'l*, pg. 7900
TURISMO ASIA COMPANY LTD.—See TUI AG; *Int'l*, pg. 7969
TURIYA BERHAD; *Int'l*, pg. 7974
TURK BAKIM EVI PFLEGEEINRICHTUNG BERLIN KREUZBERG GMBH—See MK-Kliniken AG; *Int'l*, pg. 5002
TURK BANKASI LTD.—See Turkish Bank A.S.; *Int'l*, pg. 7975
TURKCELL FINANSMAN A.S.; *Int'l*, pg. 7975
TURKCELL HOLDING AS—See Cukurova Holding A.S.; *Int'l*, pg. 1876
TURKCELL ILETISIM HIZMETLERI A.S.; *Int'l*, pg. 7975
TURK EKONOMI BANKASI A.S.—See BNP Paribas SA; *Int'l*, pg. 1093
TURKEL; *U.S. Private*, pg. 4259
TURKENT GIDA VE TURIZM SANAYI VE TICARET A.S.—See Yum! Brands, Inc.; *U.S. Public*, pg. 2400
TURKER PROJE GAYRIMENKUL VE YATIRIM GELISTIRME AS; *Int'l*, pg. 7975
TURKEY CORPORATION—See Hyundai Glovis Co., Ltd.; *Int'l*, pg. 3557
TURKEY CREEK PORK SKINS, LLC—See Wind Point Advisors LLC; *U.S. Private*, pg. 4534
TURKEY HILL DAIRY, INC.—See Peak Rock Capital LLC; *U.S. Private*, pg. 3124

TURKEY HILL, L.P.—See Peak Rock Capital LLC; *U.S. Private*, pg. 3124
TURK HAVA YOLLARI ANONIM ORTAKLIGI; *Int'l*, pg. 7974
TURK HENKEL KIMYA SANAYI VE TICARET A.S.—See Henkel AG & Co. KGaA; *Int'l*, pg. 3354
TURK ILAC VE SERUM SANAYI A.S.; *Int'l*, pg. 7975
TURKISH BANK A.S.; *Int'l*, pg. 7975
TURKISH BILGI ISLEM HIZMETLERI A.S.—See Turkish Bank A.S.; *Int'l*, pg. 7975
TURKISH INVESTMENT SECURITIES INC.—See Turkish Bank A.S.; *Int'l*, pg. 7975
TURKISH YATIRIM A.S.—See Turkish Bank A.S.; *Int'l*, pg. 7975
TURKISH ZIRAAT BANK BOSNIA DD—See Turkiye Cumhuriyeti Ziraat Bankasi A.S.; *Int'l*, pg. 7975
TURKIYE CUMHURIYETI ZIRAAT BANKASI A.S.; *Int'l*, pg. 7975
TURKIYE CUMHURIYET MERKEZ BANKASI; *Int'l*, pg. 7975
TURKIYE GARANTI BANKASI A.S.; *Int'l*, pg. 7975
TURKIYE HALK BANKASI A.S.; *Int'l*, pg. 7975
TURKIYE IHRACAT KREDI BANKASI A.S.; *Int'l*, pg. 7976
TURKIYE IS BANKASI A.S.; *Int'l*, pg. 7976
TURKIYE KALKINMA VE YATIRIM BANKASI AS; *Int'l*, pg. 7976
TURKIYE PETROL RAFINERILERI A.S.—See Koc Holding A.S.; *Int'l*, pg. 4224
TURKIYE SINAI KALKINMA BANKASI A.S.; *Int'l*, pg. 7977
TURKIYE SISE VE CAM FABRIKALAN A.S.—See Turkiye Is Bankasi A.S.; *Int'l*, pg. 7976
TURKIYE SISE VE CAM FABRIKALARI A.S.; *Int'l*, pg. 7977
TURKIYE VAKIFLAR BANKASI T.A.O.; *Int'l*, pg. 7977
TURKIYE VARLIK FONU YONETIMI AS; *Int'l*, pg. 7978
TURK MAADIN SIRKETI A.S.—See Afarak Group SE; *Int'l*, pg. 185
TURKMENISTAN COCA-COLA BOTTLERS—See Coca-Cola Icecek A.S.; *Int'l*, pg. 1686
TURK NIPPON SIGORTA A.S.—See Harel Insurance Investments & Financial Services Ltd.; *Int'l*, pg. 3274
TURK PHILIPS TICARET A.S.—See Koninklijke Philips N.V.; *Int'l*, pg. 4271
TURK PRYSMIAN KABLO VE SISTEMLERI A.S.—See Prysmian S.p.A.; *Int'l*, pg. 6013
TURKTRAKTOR VE ZIRAAT MAKINELERI AS—See CNH Industrial N.V.; *Int'l*, pg. 1676
TURKTRAKTOR VE ZIRAAT MAKINELERI AS—See Koc Holding A.S.; *Int'l*, pg. 4224
TURK TUBORG BIRA VE MALT SANAYII A.S.; *Int'l*, pg. 7975
TURKU REPAIR YARD LTD—See BLRT Grupp AS; *Int'l*, pg. 1066
TURKVEN PRIVATE EQUITY; *Int'l*, pg. 7978
TURLEY PUBLICATIONS INC.; *U.S. Private*, pg. 4259
TURLEY RESIDENTIAL CENTER, LLC—See Corecivic, Inc.; *U.S. Public*, pg. 644
TURLOCK DIALYSIS CENTER, LLC—See DaVita Inc.; *U.S. Public*, pg. 644
TURLOCK IMAGING SERVICES, LLC—See Tenet Healthcare Corporation; *U.S. Public*, pg. 2003
TURLOCK IRRIGATION DISTRICT; *U.S. Private*, pg. 4259
TURMALINA METALS CORP.; *Int'l*, pg. 7978
TURMERIC ACQUISITION CORP.; *U.S. Public*, pg. 2205
TURM-SAHNE GMBH—See DMK Deutsches Milchkontor GmbH; *Int'l*, pg. 2146
TURN5, INC.; *U.S. Private*, pg. 4260
TURNALL HOLDINGS LIMITED; *Int'l*, pg. 7978
TURNBERRY ASSOCIATES—See Turnberry, Ltd.; *U.S. Private*, pg. 4260
TURNBERRY HOMES; *U.S. Private*, pg. 4260
TURNBERRY ISLE RESORT & SPA—See Turnberry, Ltd.; *U.S. Private*, pg. 4260
TURNBERRY, LTD.; *U.S. Private*, pg. 4260
TURNBERRY SOLUTIONS; *U.S. Private*, pg. 4260
TURNBRIDGE CAPITAL, LLC; *U.S. Private*, pg. 4260
TURNBULL LLC; *U.S. Private*, pg. 4260
TURNBULL-WAHLERT CONSTRUCTION, INC.; *U.S. Private*, pg. 4260
TURNER AVIATION LTD—See Turner & Co. (Glasgow) Limited; *Int'l*, pg. 7978
TURNER BROADCASTING SALES, INC.—See Warner Bros. Discovery, Inc.; *U.S. Public*, pg. 2328
TURNER BROADCASTING SALES TAIWAN INC.—See Warner Bros. Discovery, Inc.; *U.S. Public*, pg. 2328
TURNER BROADCASTING SYSTEM ASIA PACIFIC INC.—See Warner Bros. Discovery, Inc.; *U.S. Public*, pg. 2328
TURNER BROADCASTING SYSTEM EUROPE LIMITED—See Warner Bros. Discovery, Inc.; *U.S. Public*, pg. 2328
TURNER BROADCASTING SYSTEM, INC.—See Warner Bros. Discovery, Inc.; *U.S. Public*, pg. 2328
TURNER BROS TRUCKING LLC; *U.S. Private*, pg. 4260
TURNER & CO. (GLASGOW) LIMITED; *Int'l*, pg. 7978
TURNER CONSTRUCTION COMPANY—See ACS, Actividades de Construccion y Servicios, S.A.; *Int'l*, pg. 113

CORPORATE AFFILIATIONS

TURNER CONSTRUCTION INTERNATIONAL LLC—See ACS, Actividades de Construccion y Servicios, S.A.; *Int'l*, pg. 113
TURNER CONSULTING GROUP, INC.; *U.S. Private*, pg. 4260
TURNER DAIRY FARMS, INC.; *U.S. Private*, pg. 4260
TURNER DUCKWORTH LIMITED—See Publicis Groupe S.A.; *Int'l*, pg. 6112
TURNER DUCKWORTH, LLC—See Publicis Groupe S.A.; *Int'l*, pg. 6112
TURNER ENGINE CONTROL SOLUTIONS BV—See Turner & Co. (Glasgow) Limited; *Int'l*, pg. 7978
TURNER ENGINE POWERED SERVICES LIMITED—See Turner & Co. (Glasgow) Limited; *Int'l*, pg. 7978
TURNER ENGINE POWERED SOLUTIONS LTD.—See Turner & Co. (Glasgow) Limited; *Int'l*, pg. 7978
TURNER ENTERTAINMENT NETWORKS INCORPORATED—See Warner Bros. Discovery, Inc.; *U.S. Public*, pg. 2328
TURNER ENTERTAINMENT NETWORKS INTERNATIONAL LIMITED—See Warner Bros. Discovery, Inc.; *U.S. Public*, pg. 2328
TURNER EQUIPMENT DIVISION—See Turner Industries Group, L.L.C.; *U.S. Private*, pg. 4260
TURNER FABRICATION LTD—See Turner & Co. (Glasgow) Limited; *Int'l*, pg. 7978
TURNER GAS COMPANY INC.; *U.S. Private*, pg. 4260
TURNER GROUNDSCARE—See Turner & Co. (Glasgow) Limited; *Int'l*, pg. 7978
TURNER HOCHTIEF CONSTRUCTION MANAGEMENT GMBH—See ACS, Actividades de Construccion y Servicios, S.A.; *Int'l*, pg. 114
TURNER IMAGING SYSTEMS, INC.—See RadNet, Inc.; *U.S. Public*, pg. 1761
TURNER INDUSTRIAL SUPPLY CO.; *U.S. Private*, pg. 4260
TURNER INDUSTRIES GROUP, L.L.C. - CORPUS CHRISTI FACILITY—See Turner Industries Group, L.L.C.; *U.S. Private*, pg. 4261
TURNER INDUSTRIES GROUP, L.L.C. - DECATUR FACILITY—See Turner Industries Group, L.L.C.; *U.S. Private*, pg. 4261
TURNER INDUSTRIES GROUP, L.L.C. - HOUSTON FACILITY—See Turner Industries Group, L.L.C.; *U.S. Private*, pg. 4261
TURNER INDUSTRIES GROUP LLC PIPE FABRICATION DIV—See Turner Industries Group, L.L.C.; *U.S. Private*, pg. 4261
TURNER INDUSTRIES GROUP, L.L.C. - PORT ALLEN FACILITY—See Turner Industries Group, L.L.C.; *U.S. Private*, pg. 4261
TURNER INDUSTRIES GROUP L.L.C.—See Turner Industries Group, L.L.C.; *U.S. Private*, pg. 4261
TURNER INDUSTRIES GROUP, L.L.C.; *U.S. Private*, pg. 4260
TURNER INDUSTRIES GROUP L.L.C.—See Turner Industries Group, L.L.C.; *U.S. Private*, pg. 4261
TURNER INDUSTRIES LTD.; *Int'l*, pg. 7978
TURNER INDUSTRIES—See Turner Industries Group, L.L.C.; *U.S. Private*, pg. 4261
TURNER INDUSTRIES—See Turner Industries Group, L.L.C.; *U.S. Private*, pg. 4260
TURNER INTERNATIONAL, INC.—See Warner Bros. Discovery, Inc.; *U.S. Public*, pg. 2328
TURNER INVESTMENTS, INC.—See Veracen Funds LP; *U.S. Private*, pg. 4359
TURNER KIA; *U.S. Private*, pg. 4261
TURNER LABORATORIES, INC.; *U.S. Private*, pg. 4261
TURNER MACHINE COMPANY, INC.; *U.S. Private*, pg. 4261
TURNER MAINTENANCE CORPORATION—See Turner Industries Group, L.L.C.; *U.S. Private*, pg. 4261
TURNER MCS S.R.L.—See Turner & Co. (Glasgow) Limited; *Int'l*, pg. 7978
TURNER NETWORK SALES, INC.—See Warner Bros. Discovery, Inc.; *U.S. Public*, pg. 2328
TURNER NETWORK TELEVISION, INC.—See Warner Bros. Discovery, Inc.; *U.S. Public*, pg. 2328
TURNER POWERTRAIN SYSTEMS LIMITED—See Caterpillar, Inc.; *U.S. Public*, pg. 454
TURNER PUBLIC RELATIONS, INC. - NEW YORK—See Peopletomysite.com, LLC; *U.S. Private*, pg. 3143
TURNER PUBLIC RELATIONS, INC.—See Peopletomysite.com, LLC; *U.S. Private*, pg. 3143
TURNERS AUCTIONS LIMITED - DAMAGED VEHICLES TRUCKS AND MOBILE PLANT—See Turners Auctions Limited; *Int'l*, pg. 7979
TURNERS AUCTIONS LIMITED; *Int'l*, pg. 7979
TURNERS AUTOMOTIVE GROUP LIMITED; *Int'l*, pg. 7979
TURNER SCAFFOLDING SERVICES—See Turner Industries Group, L.L.C.; *U.S. Private*, pg. 4261
TURNERS FLEET LTD.—See Turners Auctions Limited; *Int'l*, pg. 7979
TURNERS GROUP NZ LIMITED—See Turners Automotive Group Limited; *Int'l*, pg. 7979
TURNERS GROUP NZ LIMITED—See Turners Automotive Group Limited; *Int'l*, pg. 7979

COMPANY NAME INDEX

TURNERS GROUP NZ LIMITED—See Turners Automotive Group Limited; *Int'l*, pg. 7979
TURNERS GROUP NZ LIMITED—See Turners Automotive Group Limited; *Int'l*, pg. 7979
TURNERS MARINE TRADING LTD—See James Fisher & Sons Public Limited Company; *Int'l*, pg. 3875
TURNER'S OUTDOORS, INC.; *U.S. Private*, pg. 4261
TURNER SPORTS, INC.—See Warner Bros. Discovery, Inc.; *U.S. Public*, pg. 2328
TURNERS (SOHAM) LTD; *Int'l*, pg. 7979
TURNER SUPPLY COMPANY; *U.S. Private*, pg. 4261
TURNERSVILLE AUTO MALL—See Penske Automotive Group, Inc.; *U.S. Public*, pg. 1666
TURNERSVILLE AUTO OUTLET, LLC—See Penske Automotive Group, Inc.; *U.S. Public*, pg. 1666
TURNER & TOWNSEND LTD.—See CBRE Group, Inc.; *U.S. Public*, pg. 460
TURNER VALLEY OIL & GAS, INC.; *U.S. Public*, pg. 2205
TURNER & WRIGHTS LIMITED—See Kitwave Group Plc; *Int'l*, pg. 4196
TURN, INC.—See Nexxen International Ltd.; *Int'l*, pg. 5251
TURNING POINT BRANDS, INC.; *U.S. Public*, pg. 2205
TURNINGPOINT GLOBAL SOLUTIONS; *U.S. Private*, pg. 4261
TURNING POINT HOSPITAL—See Universal Health Services, Inc.; *U.S. Public*, pg. 2260
TURNING POINT THERAPEUTICS, INC.—See Bristol-Myers Squibb Company; *U.S. Public*, pg. 387
TURNING TECHNOLOGIES, LLC—See Centre Lane Partners, LLC; *U.S. Private*, pg. 828
TURNITIN, LLC—See Advance Publications, Inc.; *U.S. Private*, pg. 87
TURNKEY BENEFITS INC.—See Key Family of Companies; *U.S. Private*, pg. 2293
TURNKEY CAPITAL, INC.; *U.S. Public*, pg. 2205
TURNKEY COMPUTER SYSTEMS, LLC—See Patterson Companies, Inc.; *U.S. Public*, pg. 1654
TURN KEY DESIGN B.V.—See Goodbaby International Holdings Limited; *Int'l*, pg. 3039
TURNKEY INDUSTRIES, LLC—See K-Solv Group, LLC; *U.S. Private*, pg. 2251
TURN KEY PIPELINE SERVICES B.V.—See Wah Seong Corporation Berhad; *Int'l*, pg. 6629
TURN KEY STAFFING SOLUTIONS INC—See Keith Bagg Staffing Resources Inc.; *Int'l*, pg. 4118
TURNKEY TECHNOLOGIES, INC.; *U.S. Private*, pg. 4261
TURNKEY VACATION RENTALS LLC—See Vacasa, Inc.; *U.S. Public*, pg. 2270
TURNKEY VENTURES LLC—See Schneider National, Inc.; *U.S. Public*, pg. 1847
TURNONGREEN, INC.—See Ault Alliance, Inc.; *U.S. Public*, pg. 227
TURN-ON PRODUCTS INC—See Steven Madden, Ltd.; *U.S. Public*, pg. 1947
TURNPIKE FORD INC.; *U.S. Private*, pg. 4261
TURNPOINT SERVICES, LLC—See Ontario Municipal Employees Retirement System; *Int'l*, pg. 5585
TURN/RIVER MANAGEMENT LLC; *U.S. Private*, pg. 4259
TURNSPIRE CAPITAL PARTNERS LLC; *U.S. Private*, pg. 4261
TURNSTILE PUBLISHING COMPANY; *U.S. Private*, pg. 4261
TURNSTONE BIOLOGICS CORP.; *U.S. Public*, pg. 2205
TURNSTONE CAPITAL MANAGEMENT LLC; *U.S. Private*, pg. 4261
TURNSTONE—See Steelcase Inc.; *U.S. Public*, pg. 1944
TURNTIDE TECHNOLOGIES INC.; *U.S. Private*, pg. 4261
TURNTO NETWORKS, INC.—See Pixlee, Inc.; *U.S. Private*, pg. 3193
TURNUPSEED ELECTRIC SERVICE, INC.; *U.S. Private*, pg. 4261
TURO INC.—See General Motors Company; *U.S. Public*, pg. 929
TUROTEST MEDIDORES LTDA—See Enerpac Tool Group Corp.; *U.S. Public*, pg. 766
TURPAK ELEKTROMANYETIK YAKIT IKMAL SISTEMLERI TICARET A.S.—See Vontier Corporation; *U.S. Public*, pg. 2309
TURPAZ INDUSTRIES LTD; *Int'l*, pg. 7979
TURPIN DODGE OF DUBUQUE; *U.S. Private*, pg. 4261
TURQUINO EQUITY LLC; *U.S. Private*, pg. 4261
TURQUOISE COUNCIL OF AMERICANS & EURASIANS; *U.S. Private*, pg. 4261
TURQUOISE HEALTH & WELLNESS, INC.; *U.S. Private*, pg. 4262
TURQUOISE HILL RESOURCES LTD.—See Rio Tinto plc; *Int'l*, pg. 6348
TURQUOISE SERVICES LTD—See London Stock Exchange Group plc; *Int'l*, pg. 4548
TURRET STEEL INDUSTRIES, INC.—See Ryerson Holding Corporation; *U.S. Public*, pg. 1829
TURRI'S ITALIAN FOODS, INC.; *U.S. Private*, pg. 4262
TURRI S.R.L.—See Dexelance S.p.A.; *Int'l*, pg. 2092
TURRI UK LTD.—See Dexelance S.p.A.; *Int'l*, pg. 2092
TURRI USA CORP.—See Dexelance S.p.A.; *Int'l*, pg. 2092
TURSACK INCORPORATED—See Chatham Asset Management, LLC; *U.S. Private*, pg. 863
TURSER TOURISM PUBLISHING AND TRADE INC.—See Nurol Holding A.S.; *Int'l*, pg. 5491
TURSER TURIZM SERVIS VE TICARET A.S.—See Nurol Holding A.S.; *Int'l*, pg. 5491
TURSSO COMPANIES INCORPORATED; *U.S. Private*, pg. 4262
TURTLE BEACH CORPORATION; *U.S. Public*, pg. 2205
TURTLE BEACH EUROPE LIMITED—See Turtle Beach Corporation; *U.S. Public*, pg. 2205
TURTLE BEACH PRESERVE—See Equity LifeStyle Properties, Inc.; *U.S. Public*, pg. 790
TURTLEDOVE CLEMENS, INC.; *U.S. Private*, pg. 4262
TURTLE & HUGHES, INC.; *U.S. Private*, pg. 4262
TURTLE ISLAND FOODS INC.—See Morinaga Milk Industry Co., Ltd.; *Int'l*, pg. 5046
TURTLE MAGAZINE FOR PRESCHOOL KIDS—See Saturday Evening Post Society; *U.S. Private*, pg. 3553
TURTLE MOUNTAIN BAND OF CHIPPEWA INDIANS INC.; *U.S. Private*, pg. 4262
TURTLE SURVIVAL ALLIANCE FOUNDATION; *U.S. Private*, pg. 4262
TURTLE WAX, INC.; *U.S. Private*, pg. 4262
TURUN KONEKESKUS OY—See AB Sagax; *Int'l*, pg. 41
TURUN TORIPARKKI OY—See Taaleri Oyj; *Int'l*, pg. 7401
TURUN VV-AUTO OY—See Kesko Corporation; *Int'l*, pg. 4143
TURVAC D.O.O.—See Recticel S.A.; *Int'l*, pg. 6242
TURVO INTERNATIONAL CO., LTD.; *Int'l*, pg. 7979
TUSCALOOSA HYUNDAI, INC.; *U.S. Private*, pg. 4262
THE TUSCALOOSA NEWS—See Gannett Co., Inc.; *U.S. Public*, pg. 906
TUSCAN IMPORTS INC.—See Salt Creek Capital Management, LLC; *U.S. Private*, pg. 3533
TUSCANO-MAHER ROOFING, INC.—See Altas Partners LP; *Int'l*, pg. 387
TUSCAN SURGERY CENTER AT LAS COLINAS, LLC—See Tenet Healthcare Corporation; *U.S. Public*, pg. 2013
TUSCAN VENTURES PVT. LTD.; *Int'l*, pg. 7979
TUSCANY BAY APARTMENTS FLORIDA, LLC—See RAIT Financial Trust; *U.S. Private*, pg. 3349
TUSCANY HOLDINGS - BOGOTA—See Tuscany Holdings GP, LLC; *Int'l*, pg. 7979
TUSCANY HOLDINGS GP, LLC; *Int'l*, pg. 7979
TUSCANY HOLDINGS - QUITO—See Tuscany Holdings GP, LLC; *Int'l*, pg. 7979
TUSCANY PAVERS; *U.S. Private*, pg. 4262
TUSCANY—See Set Point Group Limited; *Int'l*, pg. 6730
TUSCARORA GAS TRANSMISSION COMPANY—See TC Energy Corporation; *Int'l*, pg. 7482
TUSCARORA WAYNE INSURANCE CO.—See Mutual Capital Group, Inc.; *U.S. Private*, pg. 2819
TUSCARORA YARNS INC.; *U.S. Private*, pg. 4262
TUSCOLA COUNTY ROAD COMMISSION; *U.S. Private*, pg. 4262
TUSCO LIMITED—See NTPC Limited; *Int'l*, pg. 5484
TUS-DESIGN GROUP CO., LTD.; *Int'l*, pg. 7979
TUS ENVIRONMENTAL SCIENCE AND TECHNOLOGY DEVELOPMENT CO., LTD.; *Int'l*, pg. 7979
TU-SERVICE ANLAGENTECHNIK GMBH & CO. KG—See TUV NORD AG; *Int'l*, pg. 7980
TU SERVICE INGENIEURGESELLSCHAFT MBH & CO. KG—See TUV NORD AG; *Int'l*, pg. 7980
TUSHACO PUMPS PRIVATE LIMITED—See Envois Corporation; *U.S. Public*, pg. 773
TUS-HOLDINGS CO., LTD.—See Tsinghua Holdings Co., Ltd.; *Int'l*, pg. 7951
TUSIMPLE HOLDINGS INC.; *U.S. Public*, pg. 2205
TUSKERDIRECT LTD.—See Lloyds Banking Group plc; *Int'l*, pg. 4538
TUSNAD SA—See Transilvania Investments Alliance S.A.; *Int'l*, pg. 7900
TUSONIX INC.—See CTS Corporation; *U.S. Public*, pg. 603
TUS PHARMACEUTICAL GROUP CO., LTD.—See Tsinghua Holdings Co., Ltd.; *Int'l*, pg. 7951
TUSTIN BUICK GMC; *U.S. Private*, pg. 4262
TUSTIN DIALYSIS CENTER, LLC—See DaVita Inc.; *U.S. Public*, pg. 644
TUSTIN MECHANICAL SERVICES (LEHIGH VALLEY), LLC; *U.S. Private*, pg. 4262
TUSTIN MOTORS INC.—See Lithia Motors, Inc.; *U.S. Public*, pg. 1326
TUSTIN TOYOTA; *U.S. Private*, pg. 4262
TUTA HEALTH CARE PTY LTD—See Otsuka Holdings Co., Ltd.; *Int'l*, pg. 5661
TUTCH MOBILE MEDIA B.V.—See Nippon Telegraph & Telephone Corporation; *Int'l*, pg. 5349
TUTCO INC—See Smiths Group plc; *Int'l*, pg. 7012
TUTELAR OIL SERVICES CO. (PVT) LTD.—See Desh Garments Limited; *Int'l*, pg. 2045
TUTERA GROUP INC.; *U.S. Private*, pg. 4262
TUTHILL CORPORATION PUMP GROUP—See Tuthill Corporation; *U.S. Private*, pg. 4263
TUTHILL CORPORATION; *U.S. Private*, pg. 4262
TUTHILL CORP; *U.S. Private*, pg. 4262
TUTHILL FILL-RITE DIVISION—See Tuthill Corporation; *U.S. Private*, pg. 4263
TUTHILL FINANCE; *U.S. Private*, pg. 4263
TUTHILL MEXICO, S RL CV—See Tuthill Corporation; *U.S. Private*, pg. 4262
TUTHILL PLASTICS GROUP—See Tuthill Corporation; *U.S. Private*, pg. 4263
TUTHILLTOWN SPIRITS, LLC—See William Grant & Sons Ltd.; *Int'l*, pg. 8413
TUTHILL TRANSFER SYSTEMS—See Tuthill Corporation; *U.S. Private*, pg. 4263
TUTHILL UK LTD—See Tuthill Corporation; *U.S. Private*, pg. 4263
TUTHILL VACUUM & BLOWER SYSTEMS, INC.—See Ingersoll Rand Inc.; *U.S. Public*, pg. 1122
TUTICORIN ALKALI CHEMICALS & FERTILISERS LTD.; *Int'l*, pg. 7979
TUTOGEN MEDICAL GMBH—See Montagu Private Equity LLP; *Int'l*, pg. 5036
TUTON TEXTILE (NINGBO) CO., LTD.—See Shenzhou International Group Holdings Limited; *Int'l*, pg. 6825
TUTOR.COM, INC.—See IAC Inc.; *U.S. Public*, pg. 1083
TUTORFLY HOLDINGS INC.—See Kip McGrath Education Centres Ltd; *Int'l*, pg. 4184
TUTORIA.AT GMBH—See Verlagsgruppe Georg von Holtzbrinck GmbH; *Int'l*, pg. 8172
TUTORIA GMBH—See Verlagsgruppe Georg von Holtzbrinck GmbH; *Int'l*, pg. 8172
TUTOR MICRONESIA CONSTRUCTION, LLC—See Tutor Perini Corporation; *U.S. Public*, pg. 2206
TUTOR PERINI BUILDING CORP.—See Tutor Perini Corporation; *U.S. Public*, pg. 2206
TUTOR PERINI CORPORATION; *U.S. Public*, pg. 2205
TUTOR-SALIBA CORPORATION—See Tutor Perini Corporation; *U.S. Public*, pg. 2206
TUTS INTERNATIONAL EXPORT & IMPORT COMPANY—See Littlejohn & Co., LLC; *U.S. Private*, pg. 2472
TUTSI S.A. DE C.V.—See Tootsie Roll Industries, Inc.; *U.S. Public*, pg. 2163
TUTT BRYANT GROUP LIMITED - CARADEL HIRE—See Affirma Capital Limited; *Int'l*, pg. 188
TUTT BRYANT GROUP LIMITED - CRANE HIRE DIVISION—See Affirma Capital Limited; *Int'l*, pg. 188
TUTT BRYANT GROUP LIMITED—See Affirma Capital Limited; *Int'l*, pg. 187
TUTT BRYANT HEAVY LIFT & SHIFT—See Affirma Capital Limited; *Int'l*, pg. 188
TUTT BRYANT HEAVY LIFT & SHIFT—See Affirma Capital Limited; *Int'l*, pg. 188
TUTT BRYANT HIRE PORTSMITH—See Affirma Capital Limited; *Int'l*, pg. 188
TUTT BRYANT HIRE—See Affirma Capital Limited; *Int'l*, pg. 188
TUTTLE-CLICK AUTOMOTIVE GROUP; *U.S. Private*, pg. 4263
TUTTLE-CLICK COLLISION CENTER; *U.S. Private*, pg. 4263
TUTTLE GROUP INC.; *U.S. Private*, pg. 4263
TUTTLE, INC.—See LFM Capital LLC; *U.S. Public*, pg. 2441
TUTTNAUER LTD.—See Fortissimo Capital Management Ltd.; *Int'l*, pg. 2740
TUTTNAUER U.S.A. CO., LTD.—See Fortissimo Capital Management Ltd.; *Int'l*, pg. 2740
TUTTON INSURANCE SERVICES, INC.—See GTCR LLC; *U.S. Private*, pg. 1804
TUTUBAN PROPERTIES, INC.—See Ayalaland Logistics Holdings Corp.; *Int'l*, pg. 774
TUTUNSKI KOMBINAT AD PRILEP—See Imperial Brands PLC; *Int'l*, pg. 3634
TUV AKADEMIA POLSKA SP. Z O.O—See TUV Rheinland Berlin-Brandenburg Pfalz e.V.; *Int'l*, pg. 7982
TUVALU MEDIA BV—See Television Francaise 1 S.A.; *Int'l*, pg. 7543
TUVAN-STANGSEL AB—See CRH plc; *Int'l*, pg. 1848
TUV ASIA PACIFIC LTD—See TUV NORD AG; *Int'l*, pg. 7980
TUV BERLIN BRANDENBURG VERWALTUNGS-GMBH—See TUV Rheinland Berlin-Brandenburg Pfalz e.V.; *Int'l*, pg. 7982
TUV CROATIA D.O.O.—See TUV NORD AG; *Int'l*, pg. 7980
TUV CYPRUS LTD.—See TUV NORD AG; *Int'l*, pg. 7980
TUV DCTA SAS—See TUV Rheinland Berlin-Brandenburg Pfalz e.V.; *Int'l*, pg. 7982
TUV EESTI OU—See TUV NORD AG; *Int'l*, pg. 7980
TUV FRANCE SAS-GROUPE TUV RHEINLAND—See TUV Rheinland Berlin-Brandenburg Pfalz e.V.; *Int'l*, pg. 7982
TUV HANSE GMBH—See TUV SUD AG; *Int'l*, pg. 7985
TUV HELLAS S.A.—See TUV NORD AG; *Int'l*, pg. 7980
TUV HESSEN MOBILITAT UND BERATUNG GMBH—See TUV SUD AG; *Int'l*, pg. 7984
TUV INDIA PVT LIMITED—See TUV NORD AG; *Int'l*, pg. 7980
TUV INFORMATIONSTECHNIK GMBH—See TUV NORD AG; *Int'l*, pg. 7980
TUV INTERNATIONAL RUS OOO—See TUV Rheinland Berlin-Brandenburg Pfalz e.V.; *Int'l*, pg. 7982
TUV INTERNATIONAL S.R.O.—See TUV Rheinland Berlin-Brandenburg Pfalz e.V.; *Int'l*, pg. 7982

TUTTLE GROUP INC.

TUV ITALIA S.R.L.—See TUV SUD AG; *Int'l*, pg. 7985
TUV-MIDDLE EAST LTD—See National Industrialization Company; *Int'l*, pg. 5159
TUV NEDERLAND QA B.V.—See TUV NORD AG; *Int'l*, pg. 7981
TUV NORD AG; *Int'l*, pg. 7979
TUV NORD AKADEMIE GMBH & CO. KG—See TUV NORD AG; *Int'l*, pg. 7980
TUV NORD ARGENTINA S.A.—See TUV NORD AG; *Int'l*, pg. 7980
TUV NORD AUSTRIA GMBH—See TUV NORD AG; *Int'l*, pg. 7980
TUV NORD AUTO GMBH—See TUV NORD AG; *Int'l*, pg. 7980
TUV NORD BALTIK SIA—See TUV NORD AG; *Int'l*, pg. 7981
TUV NORD BILDUNG GMBH & CO. KG—See TUV NORD AG; *Int'l*, pg. 7980
TUV NORD BILDUNG SAAR GMBH—See TUV NORD AG; *Int'l*, pg. 7980
TUV NORD BULGARIEN GMBH—See TUV NORD AG; *Int'l*, pg. 7980
TUV NORD CERTIFICATION (TIANJIN) CO., LTD.—See TUV NORD AG; *Int'l*, pg. 7981
TUV NORD CZECH S.R.O.—See TUV NORD AG; *Int'l*, pg. 7981
TUV NORD DANMARK APS—See TUV NORD AG; *Int'l*, pg. 7981
TUV NORD EGYPT S.A.E.—See TUV NORD AG; *Int'l*, pg. 7981
TUV NORD FINLAND OY—See TUV NORD AG; *Int'l*, pg. 7981
TUV NORD FRANCE S.A.S.—See TUV NORD AG; *Int'l*, pg. 7981
TUV NORD INTEGRA BVBA—See TUV NORD AG; *Int'l*, pg. 7981
TUV NORD IRAN PJS—See TUV NORD AG; *Int'l*, pg. 7981
TUV NORD ITALIA S.R.L.—See TUV NORD AG; *Int'l*, pg. 7981
TUV NORD KFT.—See TUV NORD AG; *Int'l*, pg. 7981
TUV NORD LUXEMBOURG S.A.R.L.—See TUV NORD AG; *Int'l*, pg. 7981
TUV NORD (MALAYSIA) SDN. BHD.—See TUV NORD AG; *Int'l*, pg. 7980
TUV NORD MATERIAL TESTING GMBH—See TUV NORD AG; *Int'l*, pg. 7981
TUV NORD MEXICO S.A. DE C.V.—See TUV NORD AG; *Int'l*, pg. 7981
TUV NORD MOBILITAT IMMOBILIEN GMBH—See TUV NORD AG; *Int'l*, pg. 7981
TUV NORD MPA GESELLSCHAFT FUR MATERIALPRUFUNG UND ANLAGENSICHERHEIT MBH & CO. KG—See TUV NORD AG; *Int'l*, pg. 7981
TUV NORD PHILIPPINES. INC.—See TUV NORD AG; *Int'l*, pg. 7981
TUV NORD POLSKA SP. Z O.O.—See TUV NORD AG; *Int'l*, pg. 7981
TUV NORD ROMANIA S.R.L.—See TUV NORD AG; *Int'l*, pg. 7981
TUV NORD SLOVAKIA. S.R.O.—See TUV NORD AG; *Int'l*, pg. 7981
TUV NORD SOUTHERN AFRICA (PTY) LTD.—See TUV NORD AG; *Int'l*, pg. 7981
TUV NORD SWEDEN AB—See TUV NORD AG; *Int'l*, pg. 7981
TUV NORD SYSTEC GMBH & CO. KG—See TUV NORD AG; *Int'l*, pg. 7981
TUV NORD SYSTEMS GMBH & CO. KG—See TUV NORD AG; *Int'l*, pg. 7981
TUV NORD TECHNISCHES SCHULUNGSZENTRUM GMBH & CO. KG—See TUV NORD AG; *Int'l*, pg. 7981
TUV NORD (THAILAND) LTD.—See TUV NORD AG; *Int'l*, pg. 7980
TUV NORD TRANSFER GMBH—See TUV NORD AG; *Int'l*, pg. 7981
TUV NORD UKRAINA GMBH—See TUV NORD AG; *Int'l*, pg. 7981
TUV NORD VIETNAM LTD.—See TUV NORD AG; *Int'l*, pg. 7981
TUV PFALZ ANLAGEN UND BETRIEBSTECHNIK GMBH—See TUV Rheinland Berlin-Brandenburg Pfalz e.V.; *Int'l*, pg. 7982
TUV QUALITY CONTROL LTD.—See TUV Rheinland Berlin-Brandenburg Pfalz e.V.; *Int'l*, pg. 7982
TUV RHEINLAND AG—See TUV Rheinland Berlin-Brandenburg Pfalz e.V.; *Int'l*, pg. 7981
TUV RHEINLAND AIA SERVICES, LLC—See TUV Rheinland Berlin-Brandenburg Pfalz e.V.; *Int'l*, pg. 7982
TUV RHEINLAND AIMEX LTD.—See TUV Rheinland Berlin-Brandenburg Pfalz e.V.; *Int'l*, pg. 7983
TUV RHEINLAND AKADEMIE CHILE LTDA.—See TUV Rheinland Berlin-Brandenburg Pfalz e.V.; *Int'l*, pg. 7983
TUV RHEINLAND ARABIA LLC—See TUV Rheinland Berlin-Brandenburg Pfalz e.V.; *Int'l*, pg. 7983
TUV RHEINLAND ARGENTINA S.A.—See TUV Rheinland Berlin-Brandenburg Pfalz e.V.; *Int'l*, pg. 7982
TUV RHEINLAND AUSTRALIA PTY. LTD.—See TUV Rheinland Berlin-Brandenburg Pfalz e.V.; *Int'l*, pg. 7983

TUV RHEINLAND BANGLADESH PVT. LTD.—See TUV Rheinland Berlin-Brandenburg Pfalz e.V.; *Int'l*, pg. 7983
TUV RHEINLAND BELGIUM A.S.B.L.—See TUV Rheinland Berlin-Brandenburg Pfalz e.V.; *Int'l*, pg. 7982
TUV RHEINLAND BELGIUM NV—See TUV Rheinland Berlin-Brandenburg Pfalz e.V.; *Int'l*, pg. 7982
TUV RHEINLAND BERLIN-BRANDENBURG PFALZ E.V.; *Int'l*, pg. 7981
TUV RHEINLAND CAMBODIA CO., LTD.—See TUV Rheinland Berlin-Brandenburg Pfalz e.V.; *Int'l*, pg. 7983
TUV RHEINLAND CANADA INC.—See TUV Rheinland Berlin-Brandenburg Pfalz e.V.; *Int'l*, pg. 7983
TUV RHEINLAND / CCIC (QINGDAO) CO., LTD.—See TUV Rheinland Berlin-Brandenburg Pfalz e.V.; *Int'l*, pg. 7983
TUV RHEINLAND CHINA LTD.—See TUV Rheinland Berlin-Brandenburg Pfalz e.V.; *Int'l*, pg. 7982
TUV RHEINLAND COLOMBIA S.A.S.—See TUV Rheinland Berlin-Brandenburg Pfalz e.V.; *Int'l*, pg. 7982
TUV RHEINLAND DE MEXICO S.A. DE C.V.—See TUV Rheinland Berlin-Brandenburg Pfalz e.V.; *Int'l*, pg. 7982
TUV RHEINLAND DO BRASIL LTDA.—See TUV Rheinland Berlin-Brandenburg Pfalz e.V.; *Int'l*, pg. 7982
TUV RHEINLAND GREBNER RUCHAY CONSULTING GMBH—See TUV Rheinland Berlin-Brandenburg Pfalz e.V.; *Int'l*, pg. 7983
TUV RHEINLAND GRUNDSTUCKSGESELLSCHAFT MBH & CO. KG—See TUV Rheinland Berlin-Brandenburg Pfalz e.V.; *Int'l*, pg. 7983
TUV RHEINLAND (GUANGDONG) LTD.—See TUV Rheinland Berlin-Brandenburg Pfalz e.V.; *Int'l*, pg. 7983
TUV RHEINLAND (HAINAN) CO., LTD.—See TUV Rheinland Berlin-Brandenburg Pfalz e.V.; *Int'l*, pg. 7983
TUV RHEINLAND HONG KONG LIMITED.—See TUV Rheinland Berlin-Brandenburg Pfalz e.V.; *Int'l*, pg. 7982
TUV RHEINLAND IBERICA INSPECTION CERTIFICATION & TESTING S.A.—See TUV Rheinland Berlin-Brandenburg Pfalz e.V.; *Int'l*, pg. 7983
TUV RHEINLAND IBERICA, S.A.—See TUV Rheinland Berlin-Brandenburg Pfalz e.V.; *Int'l*, pg. 7982
TUV RHEINLAND (INDIA) PRIVATE LTD.—See TUV Rheinland Berlin-Brandenburg Pfalz e.V.; *Int'l*, pg. 7983
TUV RHEINLAND INTERCERT D.O.O.—See TUV Rheinland Berlin-Brandenburg Pfalz e.V.; *Int'l*, pg. 7983
TUV RHEINLAND ITALIA S.R.L.—See TUV Rheinland Berlin-Brandenburg Pfalz e.V.; *Int'l*, pg. 7983
TUV RHEINLAND JAPAN LTD.—See TUV Rheinland Berlin-Brandenburg Pfalz e.V.; *Int'l*, pg. 7982
TUV RHEINLAND KOREA LTD.—See TUV Rheinland Berlin-Brandenburg Pfalz e.V.; *Int'l*, pg. 7982
TUV RHEINLAND - KTI KFT.—See TUV Rheinland Berlin-Brandenburg Pfalz e.V.; *Int'l*, pg. 7983
TUV RHEINLAND LICHTTECHNIK GMBH—See TUV Rheinland Berlin-Brandenburg Pfalz e.V.; *Int'l*, pg. 7983
TUV RHEINLAND LUXEMBURG GMBH—See TUV Rheinland Berlin-Brandenburg Pfalz e.V.; *Int'l*, pg. 7983
TUV RHEINLAND MALAYSIA SDN BHD—See TUV Rheinland Berlin-Brandenburg Pfalz e.V.; *Int'l*, pg. 7983
TUV RHEINLAND MANDY LTD.—See TUV Rheinland Berlin-Brandenburg Pfalz e.V.; *Int'l*, pg. 7983
TUV RHEINLAND MIDDLE EAST FZE—See TUV Rheinland Berlin-Brandenburg Pfalz e.V.; *Int'l*, pg. 7983
TUV RHEINLAND MIDDLE EAST LLC—See TUV Rheinland Berlin-Brandenburg Pfalz e.V.; *Int'l*, pg. 7982
TUV RHEINLAND MOBILITY, INC.—See TUV Rheinland Berlin-Brandenburg Pfalz e.V.; *Int'l*, pg. 7983
TUV RHEINLAND NAVARRA SA—See TUV Rheinland Berlin-Brandenburg Pfalz e.V.; *Int'l*, pg. 7983
TUV RHEINLAND NEDERLAND B.V.—See TUV Rheinland Berlin-Brandenburg Pfalz e.V.; *Int'l*, pg. 7983
TUV RHEINLAND NIFE ACADEMY PRIVATE LTD.—See TUV Rheinland Berlin-Brandenburg Pfalz e.V.; *Int'l*, pg. 7983
TUV RHEINLAND NORTH AMERICA HOLDING, INC.—See TUV Rheinland Berlin-Brandenburg Pfalz e.V.; *Int'l*, pg. 7983
TUV RHEINLAND PERU S.A.C.—See TUV Rheinland Berlin-Brandenburg Pfalz e.V.; *Int'l*, pg. 7983
TUV RHEINLAND PHILIPPINES, INC.—See TUV Rheinland Berlin-Brandenburg Pfalz e.V.; *Int'l*, pg. 7983
TUV RHEINLAND POLSKA SP. Z O.O.—See TUV Rheinland Berlin-Brandenburg Pfalz e.V.; *Int'l*, pg. 7983
TUV RHEINLAND PORTUGAL INSPECCOES TECNICAS, LDA.—See TUV Rheinland Berlin-Brandenburg Pfalz e.V.; *Int'l*, pg. 7983
TUV RHEINLAND PTL LLC—See TUV Rheinland Berlin-Brandenburg Pfalz e.V.; *Int'l*, pg. 7983
TUV RHEINLAND ROMANIA S.R.L.—See TUV Rheinland Berlin-Brandenburg Pfalz e.V.; *Int'l*, pg. 7983
TUV RHEINLAND SCHNIERING GMBH—See TUV Rheinland Berlin-Brandenburg Pfalz e.V.; *Int'l*, pg. 7983
TUV RHEINLAND (SHANGHAI) CO., LTD.—See TUV Rheinland Berlin-Brandenburg Pfalz e.V.; *Int'l*, pg. 7983
TUV RHEINLAND (SHENZHEN) CO., LTD.—See TUV Rheinland Berlin-Brandenburg Pfalz e.V.; *Int'l*, pg. 7983
TUV RHEINLAND SINGAPORE PTE. LTD.—See TUV Rheinland Berlin-Brandenburg Pfalz e.V.; *Int'l*, pg. 7983
TUV RHEINLAND SLOVENSKO S.R.O.—See TUV Rheinland Berlin-Brandenburg Pfalz e.V.; *Int'l*, pg. 7983

CORPORATE AFFILIATIONS

TUV RHEINLAND STEP INTERNATIONAL GMBH—See TUV Rheinland Berlin-Brandenburg Pfalz e.V.; *Int'l*, pg. 7983
TUV RHEINLAND TAIWAN LTD.—See TUV Rheinland Berlin-Brandenburg Pfalz e.V.; *Int'l*, pg. 7983
TUV RHEINLAND THAILAND LTD.—See TUV Rheinland Berlin-Brandenburg Pfalz e.V.; *Int'l*, pg. 7984
TUV RHEINLAND TURKIYE A. S.—See TUV Rheinland Berlin-Brandenburg Pfalz e.V.; *Int'l*, pg. 7983
TUV RHEINLAND UK LTD.—See TUV Rheinland Berlin-Brandenburg Pfalz e.V.; *Int'l*, pg. 7984
TUV RHEINLAND UKRAINE GMBH—See TUV Rheinland Berlin-Brandenburg Pfalz e.V.; *Int'l*, pg. 7984
TUV RHEINLAND VIETNAM CO. LTD.—See TUV Rheinland Berlin-Brandenburg Pfalz e.V.; *Int'l*, pg. 7984
TUV RHEINLAND VISTORIAS LTDA.—See TUV Rheinland Berlin-Brandenburg Pfalz e.V.; *Int'l*, pg. 7983
TUV RHEINLAND (WUXI) AUTOMOTIVE TESTING CO., LTD.—See TUV Rheinland Berlin-Brandenburg Pfalz e.V.; *Int'l*, pg. 7983
TUV SUD ADVIMO GMBH—See TUV SUD AG; *Int'l*, pg. 7985
TUV SUD AG; *Int'l*, pg. 7984
TUV SUD AKADEMIE GMBH—See TUV SUD AG; *Int'l*, pg. 7985
TUV SUD AMERICA DE MEXICO S.A. DE C.V.—See TUV SUD AG; *Int'l*, pg. 7985
TUV SUD AMERICA INC.—See TUV SUD AG; *Int'l*, pg. 7985
TUV SUD ASIA PACIFIC PTE. LTD.—See TUV SUD AG; *Int'l*, pg. 7985
TUV SUD AUTOMOTIVE GMBH—See TUV SUD AG; *Int'l*, pg. 7985
TUV SUD AUTO PARTNER GMBH—See TUV SUD AG; *Int'l*, pg. 7985
TUV SUD AUTO PLUS GMBH—See TUV SUD AG; *Int'l*, pg. 7985
TUV SUD AUTO SERVICE GMBH—See TUV SUD AG; *Int'l*, pg. 7985
TUV SUD BANGLADESH (PVT.) LTD.—See TUV SUD AG; *Int'l*, pg. 7985
TUV SUD BATTERY TESTING GMBH—See TUV SUD AG; *Int'l*, pg. 7985
TUV SUD BENELUX B.V.B.A.—See TUV SUD AG; *Int'l*, pg. 7985
TUV SUD BRASIL ENGENHARIA E CONSULTORIA LTDA.—See TUV SUD AG; *Int'l*, pg. 7985
TUV SUD BURSA TASIT MUAYENE ISTASYONLARI ISLETIM A.S.—See TUV SUD AG; *Int'l*, pg. 7985
TUV SUD CANADA INC.—See TUV SUD AG; *Int'l*, pg. 7985
TUV SUD CENTRAL EASTERN EUROPE S.R.O.—See TUV SUD AG; *Int'l*, pg. 7985
TUV SUD CERTIFICATION AND TESTING (CHINA) CO., LTD.—See TUV SUD AG; *Int'l*, pg. 7985
TUV SUD CHEMIE SERVICE GMBH—See TUV SUD AG; *Int'l*, pg. 7985
TUV SUD DANMARK APS—See TUV SUD AG; *Int'l*, pg. 7985
TUV SUD DO BRASIL LTDA.—See TUV SUD AG; *Int'l*, pg. 7986
TUV SUD ELAB GMBH—See TUV SUD AG; *Int'l*, pg. 7985
TUV SUD ENERGIETECHNIK GMBH BADEN-WURTTEMBERG—See TUV SUD AG; *Int'l*, pg. 7985
TUV SUD FOOD SAFETY INSTITUTE GMBH—See TUV SUD AG; *Int'l*, pg. 7985
TUV SUD FRANCE S.A.S.—See TUV SUD AG; *Int'l*, pg. 7985
TUV SUD GLOBAL INSPECTION LIMITED—See TUV SUD AG; *Int'l*, pg. 7985
TUV SUD IMMOWERT GMBH—See TUV SUD AG; *Int'l*, pg. 7985
TUV SUD INDUSTRIE SERVICE GMBH—See TUV SUD AG; *Int'l*, pg. 7985
TUV SUD INDUSTRY SERVICE, INC.—See TUV SUD AG; *Int'l*, pg. 7985
TUV SUD JAPAN LTD.—See TUV SUD AG; *Int'l*, pg. 7985
TUV SUD KOCEN LTD.—See TUV SUD AG; *Int'l*, pg. 7985
TUV SUD KOREA LTD.—See TUV SUD AG; *Int'l*, pg. 7985
TUV SUD LANDESGESELLSCHAFT OSTERREICH GMBH—See TUV SUD AG; *Int'l*, pg. 7985
TUV SUD LBERIA, S.L.U.—See TUV SUD AG; *Int'l*, pg. 7986
TUV SUD LIFE SERVICE GMBH—See TUV SUD AG; *Int'l*, pg. 7985
TUV SUD MANAGEMENT SERVICE GMBH—See TUV SUD AG; *Int'l*, pg. 7985
TUV SUD MIDDLE EAST LLC—See TUV SUD AG; *Int'l*, pg. 7985
TUV SUD MIDDLE EAST LLC—See TUV SUD AG; *Int'l*, pg. 7985
TUV SUD MIDDLE EAST LLC—See TUV SUD AG; *Int'l*, pg. 7985
TUV SUD NEL LIMITED—See TUV SUD AG; *Int'l*, pg. 7986
TUV SUD NUCLEAR TECHNOLOGIES PLC—See TUV SUD AG; *Int'l*, pg. 7986

TUV SUD PLUSPUNKT GMBH—See TUV SUD AG; Int'l, pg. 7986
TUV SUD PMSS LTD.—See TUV SUD AG; Int'l, pg. 7986
TUV SUD PMSS—See TUV SUD AG; Int'l, pg. 7986
TUV SUD POLSKA SP. Z.O.O.—See TUV SUD AG; Int'l, pg. 7986
TUV SUD PROCESS SAFETY—See TUV SUD AG; Int'l, pg. 7986
TUV SUD PRODUCT SERVICE GMBH—See TUV SUD AG; Int'l, pg. 7986
TUV SUD PSB INDONESIA, PT.—See TUV SUD AG; Int'l, pg. 7986
TUV SUD PSB (MALAYSIA) SDN. BHD.—See TUV SUD AG; Int'l, pg. 7986
TUV SUD PSB PHILIPPINES INC.—See TUV SUD AG; Int'l, pg. 7986
TUV SUD PSB PRODUCTS TESTING (SHANGHAI) CO., LTD—See TUV SUD AG; Int'l, pg. 7986
TUV SUD PSB PTE. LTD.—See TUV SUD AG; Int'l, pg. 7986
TUV SUD PSB (THAILAND) LTD.—See TUV SUD AG; Int'l, pg. 7986
TUV SUD PSB VIETNAM CO. LTD.—See TUV SUD AG; Int'l, pg. 7986
TUV SUD RAIL GMBH—See TUV SUD AG; Int'l, pg. 7986
TUV SUD ROMANIA S.R.L.—See TUV SUD AG; Int'l, pg. 7986
TUV SUD SAVA D.O.O.—See TUV SUD AG; Int'l, pg. 7986
TUV SUD SEC-IT GMBH—See TUV SUD AG; Int'l, pg. 7985
TUV SUD SENTON GMBH—See TUV SUD AG; Int'l, pg. 7986
TUV SUD SERVICES (UK) LIMITED—See TUV SUD AG; Int'l, pg. 7986
TUV SUD SLOVAKIA S.R.O.—See TUV SUD AG; Int'l, pg. 7986
TUV SUD SOUTH AFRICA PRO-TEC (PTY) LTD.—See TUV SUD AG; Int'l, pg. 7986
TUV SUD SOUTH AFRICA (PTY) LTD—See TUV SUD AG; Int'l, pg. 7986
TUV SUD SOUTH AFRICA REAL ESTATE SERVICES (PTY) LTD.—See TUV SUD AG; Int'l, pg. 7986
TUV SUD TGK LTD. STI.—See TUV SUD AG; Int'l, pg. 7986
TUV SUD WALLACE WHITTLE LTD. See TUV SUD AG; Int'l, pg. 7986
TUV TEKNIK KONTROL VE BELGELENDIRME A.S.—See TUV NORD AG; Int'l, pg. 7981
TUV THURINGEN ANLAGENTECHNIK GMBH & CO. KG—See TUV NORD AG; Int'l, pg. 7981
TUVTURK A.S.—See TUV SUD AG; Int'l, pg. 7986
TUV UK LTD.—See TUV NORD AG; Int'l, pg. 7981
TUV USA. INC.—See TUV NORD AG; Int'l, pg. 7981
TUV US JOINT STOCK COMPANY; Int'l, pg. 7986
TUXEDO JUNCTION INC.; U.S. Private, pg. 4263
TUXIS CORP.; U.S. Public, pg. 2206
TUYA INC.; U.S. Public, pg. 7986
TUYAR MIKROELEKTRONIK SANAYI VE TICARET ANONIM SIRKETI—See Aselsan Elektronik Sanayi Ve Ticaret AS; Int'l, pg. 606
TUYAUX ET AGGLOMERES VENDEENS—See Compagnie de Saint-Gobain SA; Int'l, pg. 1737
TU YI HOLDING COMPANY LIMITED; Int'l, pg. 7961
TUZLA-REMONT D.D. TUZLA; Int'l, pg. 7986
TUZODENT S.A. DE C.V.—See DENTSPLY SIRONA Inc.; U.S. Public, pg. 655
TV18 BROADCAST LIMITED—See Reliance - ADA Group Limited; Int'l, pg. 6262
TV 2 AS—See Egmont Fonden; Int'l, pg. 2326
TV 2 TORGET AS—See Egmont Fonden; Int'l, pg. 2326
TV2U INTERNATIONAL LIMITED; Int'l, pg. 7988
TV2U PTY. LTD.—See TV2U International Limited; Int'l, pg. 7988
TV3 A/S DANMARK—See Modern Times Group MTG AB; Int'l, pg. 5014
TV3 AS NORGE—See Modern Times Group MTG AB; Int'l, pg. 5014
TV3 NORWAY—See Modern Times Group MTG AB; Int'l, pg. 5014
TV3—See Modern Times Group MTG AB; Int'l, pg. 5015
TV3 SWEDEN—See Modern Times Group MTG AB; Int'l, pg. 5015
TV3 TELEVISION NETWORK LIMITED—See Liberty Global plc; Int'l, pg. 4486
TV3 TELEVISION NETWORK LIMITED—See Telefonica, S.A.; Int'l, pg. 7536
TV3 TELEVISION NETWORK—See Brookfield Corporation; Int'l, pg. 1181
TV4 AB—See Telia Company AB; Int'l, pg. 7544
TV4 AS NORGE—See Modern Times Group MTG AB; Int'l, pg. 5014
TV4 STOCKHOLM AB—See Telia Company AB; Int'l, pg. 7544
TV6 SWEDEN—See Modern Times Group MTG AB; Int'l, pg. 5015
TV8 MEDIA CENTER—See Vail Resorts, Inc.; U.S. Public, pg. 2271
TV8 REDAKTION—See Modern Times Group MTG AB; Int'l, pg. 5015

TV8 SWEDEN—See Modern Times Group MTG AB; Int'l, pg. 5015
TVA COMMUNITY CREDIT UNION; U.S. Private, pg. 4263
TVA FILMS—See Quebecor Inc.; Int'l, pg. 6159
TVA GROUP, INC.—See Quebecor Inc.; Int'l, pg. 6159
TVA MEDICAL, INC.—See Becton, Dickinson & Company; U.S. Public, pg. 292
TVA PUBLICATIONS INC.—See Quebecor Inc.; Int'l, pg. 6159
TVA PUBLICATIONS, INC.—See Quebecor Inc.; Int'l, pg. 6159
TV ASAHI ASK CO., LTD.—See TV Asahi Holdings Corporation; Int'l, pg. 7987
TV ASAHI BEST CO., LTD.—See TV Asahi Holdings Corporation; Int'l, pg. 7987
TV ASAHI CREATE CORPORATION—See TV Asahi Holdings Corporation; Int'l, pg. 7987
TV ASAHI HOLDINGS CORPORATION; Int'l, pg. 7986
TV ASAHI MEDIAPLEX CORPORATION—See TV Asahi Holdings Corporation; Int'l, pg. 7987
TV ASAHI MUSIC CO., LTD.—See TV Asahi Holdings Corporation; Int'l, pg. 7987
TV ASAHI PRODUCTIONS CO., LTD.—See TV Asahi Holdings Corporation; Int'l, pg. 7987
TVAX BIOMEDICAL, INC.; U.S. Private, pg. 4263
TV AZTECA S.A.B DE C.V.—See Grupo Salinas, S.A. de C.V.; Int'l, pg. 3135
TVB 3 NETWORK CO., LTD.—See BEC World Public Company Limited; Int'l, pg. 936
TVB (AUSTRALIA) PTY. LTD.—See Television Broadcasts Limited; Int'l, pg. 7542
TV BREIZH SA—See Television Francaise 1 S.A.; Int'l, pg. 7543
TVB (USA) INC.—See Television Broadcasts Limited; Int'l, pg. 7542
TVC CAPITAL LLC; U.S. Private, pg. 4263
TVC CO., LTD.—See NOK Corporation; Int'l, pg. 5403
TVC COMMUNICATIONS, LLC—See WESCO International, Inc.; U.S. Public, pg. 2352
TVC GROUP LIMITED—See The Economist Group Limited; Int'l, pg. 7637
TVC HOLDINGS PLC; Int'l, pg. 7988
TV DIRECT PUBLIC COMPANY LIMITED; Int'l, pg. 7987
TV FARS; U.S. Private, pg. 4263
TVE CO., LTD.; Int'l, pg. 7988
TVE GLOBAL ASIA PACIFIC PTE. LTD.—See TVE Co., Ltd.; Int'l, pg. 7988
TVELEM LTD.—See LEM Holding SA; Int'l, pg. 4448
T-VENTURE HOLDING GMBH—See Deutsche Telekom AG; Int'l, pg. 2085
T-VENTURE INDUSTRIES (M) SDN. BHD.—See RGT Berhad; Int'l, pg. 6319
T-VENTURE OF AMERICA, INC.—See Deutsche Telekom AG; Int'l, pg. 2085
TVE REFINING METAL CO., LTD.—See TVE Co., Ltd.; Int'l, pg. 7988
TVER INC—See Dentsu Group Inc.; Int'l, pg. 2039
TVF ALTWERT GMBH—See Alba SE; Int'l, pg. 293
TVF (UK) LIMITED—See London Security PLC; Int'l, pg. 4547
TVG CAPITAL PARTNERS LIMITED; Int'l, pg. 7988
TV GUIDE MAGAZINE GROUP, INC.—See OpenGate Capital Management, LLC; U.S. Private, pg. 3031
TV GUIDE ONLINE HOLDINGS LLC—See National Amusements, Inc.; U.S. Private, pg. 2844
TV GUIDE—See NTVB Media, Inc.; U.S. Private, pg. 2971
TV.GUSTO GMBH—See Hubert Burda Media Holding Kommanditgesellschaft; Int'l, pg. 3520
TVG-ZIMSEN EHF.—See Eimskipafelag Islands Hf.; Int'l, pg. 2332
TVH AUSTRALASIA PTY LTD.—See Group Thermote & Vanhalst; Int'l, pg. 3090
TVH AUSTRALIA PTY LTD—See Group Thermote & Vanhalst; Int'l, pg. 3090
TVH BRASIL PECAS LTDA.—See Group Thermote & Vanhalst; Int'l, pg. 3090
TVH CANADA LTD—See Group Thermote & Vanhalst; Int'l, pg. 3090
TVH DEUTSCHLAND GMBH—See Group Thermote & Vanhalst; Int'l, pg. 3090
TVH FRANCE SASU—See Group Thermote & Vanhalst; Int'l, pg. 3090
TVH INDIA PRIVATE LTD.—See Group Thermote & Vanhalst; Int'l, pg. 3090
TVH ITALIA SRL—See Group Thermote & Vanhalst; Int'l, pg. 3090
TVH MALAYSIA SDN. BHD.—See Group Thermote & Vanhalst; Int'l, pg. 3090
TVH MEXICO, S DE RL DE CV—See Group Thermote & Vanhalst; Int'l, pg. 3090
TVH MIDDLE EAST FZE—See Group Thermote & Vanhalst; Int'l, pg. 3090
TVH NEW ZEALAND LTD.—See Group Thermote & Vanhalst; Int'l, pg. 3090
TVH NORDIC AB—See Group Thermote & Vanhalst; Int'l, pg. 3090
TVH PARTS CO.—See Group Thermote & Vanhalst; Int'l, pg. 3090

TVH PARTS MEXICO S. DE R.L. DE C.V.—See Group Thermote & Vanhalst; Int'l, pg. 3090
TVH PARTS SOUTH AFRICA (PTY) LTD—See Group Thermote & Vanhalst; Int'l, pg. 3090
TVH POLSKA SP.Z O.O.—See Group Thermote & Vanhalst; Int'l, pg. 3090
TVH RUS, LLC—See Group Thermote & Vanhalst; Int'l, pg. 3090
TVH SINGAPORE PTE LTD—See Group Thermote & Vanhalst; Int'l, pg. 3090
TVH TRADING CO., LTD.—See Group Thermote & Vanhalst; Int'l, pg. 3090
TVH TRADING (XIAMEN) CO. LTD.—See Group Thermote & Vanhalst; Int'l, pg. 3090
TVH UK LTD.—See Group Thermote & Vanhalst; Int'l, pg. 3090
TVH YEDEK PARCA TICARET A.S.—See Group Thermote & Vanhalst; Int'l, pg. 3090
TVILUM—See Masco Corporation; U.S. Public, pg. 1391
TV, INC.; U.S. Private, pg. 4263
TV, INC.—See TV, Inc.; U.S. Private, pg. 4263
TVI PACIFIC INC.; Int'l, pg. 7988
TVI RESOURCE DEVELOPMENT PHILS. INC—See Prime Asset Ventures, Inc.; Int'l, pg. 5976
TVI SA—See Bertelsmann SE & Co. KGaA; Int'l, pg. 995
TVL AUSTRALIA PTY LTD—See Sabre Corporation; U.S. Public, pg. 1834
TVLINE MEDIA, LLC—See Penske Media Corporation; U.S. Private, pg. 3139
TVL-MARUZEN GLOBAL LOGISTICS CO., LTD.—See Maruzen Showa Unyu Co., Ltd.; Int'l, pg. 4716
TVNET, SIA—See UP Invest OU; Int'l, pg. 8087
TV NORGE AS—See Warner Bros. Discovery, Inc.; U.S. Public, pg. 2326
TVNORTE, S. DE R.L. DE C.V.—See Entravision Communications Corporation; U.S. Public, pg. 779
TVN S.A.; Int'l, pg. 7988
TVNU SWEDEN AB—See Schibsted ASA; Int'l, pg. 6617
TVNZ SATELLITE SERVICES LIMITED—See TVNZ; Int'l, pg. 7988
TVNZ; Int'l, pg. 7988
TVO GROUPE; U.S. Private, pg. 4263
TV ONE, LLC—See Urban One, Inc.; U.S. Public, pg. 2265
TVO NORTH AMERICA—See TVO Groupe; U.S. Private, pg. 4263
TVO REALTY PARTNERS; U.S. Private, pg. 4263
TVORNICA CARAPA KLJUC D.D.; Int'l, pg. 7988
TVORNICA CEMENTA KAKANJ D.D.; Int'l, pg. 7988
TVORNICA ELEKTRO OPREME D.D. SARAJEVO; Int'l, pg. 7988
TVORNICA OPEKE SARAJEVO D.O.O.—See Nexe Grupa d.d.; Int'l, pg. 5243
TVORNICA STOCNE HRANE D.D.; Int'l, pg. 7988
TVORNICA ZA OBRADU METALA EKSPLOZIJOM A.D.; Int'l, pg. 7988
TV PROFILE, LLC—See Finbond Group Limited; Int'l, pg. 2670
TV SANTA FE, S.A. DE C.V.—See Grupo Televisa, S.A.B.; Int'l, pg. 3136
TVS AUTOMOBILE SOLUTIONS PVT. LTD.; Int'l, pg. 7988
TVS CAPITAL FUNDS PRIVATE LIMITED—See TVS Electronics Limited; Int'l, pg. 7989
TVS CHERRY LIMITED—See ZF Friedrichshafen AG; Int'l, pg. 8643
TVS CREDIT SERVICES LIMITED—See TVS Electronics Limited; Int'l, pg. 7989
TVS DIGITAL PTE. LIMITED—See TVS Motor Company Ltd.; Int'l, pg. 7989
TVS DYNAMIC GLOBAL FREIGHT SERVICES LIMITED—See TVS Logistics Services Ltd.; Int'l, pg. 7989
TVS ELECTRONICS LIMITED; Int'l, pg. 7988
TVS FILTERS—See Align Capital Partners, LLC; U.S. Private, pg. 167
TVS LOGISTICS SERVICES LTD.; Int'l, pg. 7989
TVS MOTOR COMPANY LTD.; Int'l, pg. 7989
TV SPECIALISTS INC.; U.S. Private, pg. 4263
TVS SCS LIMITED—See TVS Logistics Services Ltd.; Int'l, pg. 7989
TVS SENSING SOLUTIONS PRIVATE LIMITED—See TVS Srichakra Ltd; Int'l, pg. 7989
TVS SRICHAKRA LTD; Int'l, pg. 7989
TVS SUPPLY CHAIN SOLUTIONS LTD.—See TVS Logistics Services Ltd.; Int'l, pg. 7989
TV SUNDRAM IYENGAR & SONS LIMITED; Int'l, pg. 7987
TVS UPASNA LIMITED—See TVS Electronics Limited; Int'l, pg. 7989
TV+SYNCHRON BERLIN GMBH—See Canada Pension Plan Investment Board; Int'l, pg. 1280
TV+SYNCHRON BERLIN GMBH—See EQT AB; Int'l, pg. 2483
TV+SYNCHRON BERLIN GMBH—See Temasek Holdings (Private) Limited; Int'l, pg. 7548
TVTAGLICH AG—See TX Group AG; Int'l, pg. 7992
TVTEL TELECOMUNICACOES S.A.—See NOS SGPS, S.A.; Int'l, pg. 5448

TV THUNDER PUBLIC COMPANY LIMITED

CORPORATE AFFILIATIONS

TV THUNDER PUBLIC COMPANY LIMITED; *Int'l*, pg. 7987
TVT MEDIA; *Int'l*, pg. 7989
TV TODAY NETWORK LIMITED; *Int'l*, pg. 7987
TV TOKYO AMERICA, INC.—See TV TOKYO Holdings Corporation; *Int'l*, pg. 7988
TV TOKYO ART, INC.—See TV TOKYO Holdings Corporation; *Int'l*, pg. 7987
TV TOKYO BUILDING, INC.—See TV TOKYO Holdings Corporation; *Int'l*, pg. 7987
TV TOKYO BUSINESS SERVICE, INC.—See TV TOKYO Holdings Corporation; *Int'l*, pg. 7988
TV TOKYO COMMERCIAL, INC.—See TV TOKYO Holdings Corporation; *Int'l*, pg. 7987
TV TOKYO COMMUNICATIONS CORPORATION—See TV TOKYO Holdings Corporation; *Int'l*, pg. 7987
TV TOKYO CORPORATION—See TV TOKYO Holdings Corporation; *Int'l*, pg. 7987
TV TOKYO DIRECT, INC.—See TV TOKYO Holdings Corporation; *Int'l*, pg. 7987
TV TOKYO HOLDINGS CORPORATION; *Int'l*, pg. 7987
TV TOKYO HUMAN, INC.—See TV TOKYO Holdings Corporation; *Int'l*, pg. 7987
TV TOKYO MEDIANET INC.—See TV TOKYO Holdings Corporation; *Int'l*, pg. 7987
TV TOKYO MEDIAWORKS, INC.—See TV TOKYO Holdings Corporation; *Int'l*, pg. 7987
TV TOKYO MUSIC, INC.—See TV TOKYO Holdings Corporation; *Int'l*, pg. 7987
TV TOKYO PRODUCTION, INC.—See TV TOKYO Holdings Corporation; *Int'l*, pg. 7987
TV TOKYO SYSTEMS, INC.—See TV TOKYO Holdings Corporation; *Int'l*, pg. 7987
TV TOKYO TECHNOMAX, INC.—See TV TOKYO Holdings Corporation; *Int'l*, pg. 7987
TV TOOLS OY—See Transition Evergreen; *Int'l*, pg. 7901
TVT VIDEO TECHNOLOGIES, INC.—See Vista Equity Partners, LLC; *U.S. Private*, pg. 4401
TV VISION LIMITED; *Int'l*, pg. 7988
TVWORKS, LLC—See Comcast Corporation; *U.S. Public*, pg. 541
TVZONE MEDIA CO., LTD.; *Int'l*, pg. 7989
TW AGRICULTURAL DEVELOPMENT CO., LTD.—See Tongwei Co., Ltd.; *Int'l*, pg. 7988
T&WA, INC.—See The Goodyear Tire & Rubber Company; *U.S. Public*, pg. 2084
TW-ASIA CONSULTANTS PTE. LTD.—See WMCH Global Investment Limited; *Int'l*, pg. 8441
TWASOL BUSINESS MEN SERVICE LLC—See Alpha Dhabi Holding PJSC; *Int'l*, pg. 368
T'WAY AIR CO., LTD.; *Int'l*, pg. 7395
TWAY HOLDINGS CO LTD; *Int'l*, pg. 7989
TWB COMPANY, LLC—See ThyssenKrupp AG; *Int'l*, pg. 7730
TWB COMPANY, LLC—See Worthington Industries, Inc.; *U.S. Public*, pg. 2382
TWB INDUSTRIES, S.A. DE C.V.—See ThyssenKrupp AG; *Int'l*, pg. 7726
TWC ARABIA LTD.—See Tiong Woon Corporation Holding Ltd.; *Int'l*, pg. 7755
TWC AVIATION, INC.; *U.S. Private*, pg. 4263
TWC CHANDLER LLC—See The Macerich Company; *U.S. Public*, pg. 2111
TWC ENTERPRISE LIMITED; *Int'l*, pg. 7989
TWC II-PRESCOTT MALL, LLC—See The Macerich Company; *U.S. Public*, pg. 2111
T.W. COOPER INSURANCE, LLC—See Russ Smale, Inc.; *U.S. Private*, pg. 3506
TWC PRODUCT AND TECHNOLOGY, LLC—See International Business Machines Corporation; *U.S. Public*, pg. 1151
TWC TECH HOLDINGS II CORP.—See Sun Corporation; *Int'l*, pg. 7303
TWD & ASSOCIATES INC.; *U.S. Private*, pg. 4263
TWDC ENTERPRISES 18 CORP.—See The Walt Disney Company; *U.S. Public*, pg. 2137
TWEAKERS.NET B.V.—See DPG Media Group NV; *Int'l*, pg. 2188
TWEDDLE LITHO COMPANY; *U.S. Private*, pg. 4264
TWEEDDALE PRESS LTD—See JPIMedia Holdings Limited; *Int'l*, pg. 4007
TWEED HEADS COOLANGATTA TAXI SERVICE PTY. LTD.—See ComfortDelGro Corporation Limited; *Int'l*, pg. 1712
TWEED HEADS MAZDA PTY. LIMITED—See Peter Warren Automotive Holdings Ltd.; *Int'l*, pg. 5824
TWEEDS LIMITED—See Tetra Tech, Inc.; *U.S. Public*, pg. 2024
TWEEDY, BROWNE COMPANY LLC—See Affiliated Managers Group, Inc.; *U.S. Public*, pg. 56
T/WEE LIMITED—See ANSA McAL Limited; *Int'l*, pg. 477
TWEEN BRANDS, INC.—See Mahwah Bergen Retail Group, Inc.; *U.S. Private*, pg. 2550
TWEET-GAROT MECHANICAL INC.; *U.S. Private*, pg. 4264
TWEEZERMAN INTERNATIONAL—See Henkel AG & Co. KGaA; *Int'l*, pg. 3354
TWELVE CONSULTING GROUP, INC.; *U.S. Private*, pg. 4264

TWELVE NYC; *U.S. Private*, pg. 4264
TWELVE OAKS MALL LLC—See Simon Property Group, Inc.; *U.S. Public*, pg. 1882
TWELVE POINTS WEALTH MANAGEMENT, LLC; *U.S. Private*, pg. 4264
TWENTIETH CENTURY FOX FILM COMPANY LIMITED—See The Walt Disney Company; *U.S. Public*, pg. 2140
TWENTIETH CENTURY FOX FILM CORPORATION—See The Walt Disney Company; *U.S. Public*, pg. 2140
TWENTIETH CENTURY FOX FILM DISTRIBUTORS PTY LIMITED—See The Walt Disney Company; *U.S. Public*, pg. 2141
TWENTIETH CENTURY FOX HOME ENTERTAINMENT FRANCE S.A.—See The Walt Disney Company; *U.S. Public*, pg. 2140
TWENTIETH CENTURY FOX HOME ENTERTAINMENT GERMANY GMBH—See The Walt Disney Company; *U.S. Public*, pg. 2140
TWENTIETH CENTURY FOX HOME ENTERTAINMENT JAPAN K.K.—See The Walt Disney Company; *U.S. Public*, pg. 2140
TWENTIETH CENTURY FOX HOME ENTERTAINMENT LIMITED—See The Walt Disney Company; *U.S. Public*, pg. 2140
TWENTIETH CENTURY FOX HOME ENTERTAINMENT LLC—See The Walt Disney Company; *U.S. Public*, pg. 2140
TWENTIETH CENTURY FOX HOME ENTERTAINMENT SOUTH PACIFIC PTY. LIMITED—See The Walt Disney Company; *U.S. Public*, pg. 2140
TWENTIETH CENTURY FOX OF GERMANY GMBH—See The Walt Disney Company; *U.S. Public*, pg. 2140
TWENTIETH CENTURY MARKETS, INC.—See The Fiore Companies; *U.S. Private*, pg. 4028
TWENTIETH TELEVISION, INC.—See The Walt Disney Company; *U.S. Public*, pg. 2140
TWENTSCHE COURANT TUBANTIA BV—See DPG Media Group NV; *Int'l*, pg. 2189
TWENTSCHE (NANJING) FIBRE OPTICS CO. LTD.—See TKH Group N.V.; *Int'l*, pg. 7765
TWENTY20 MEDIA GROUP LIMITED—See SEC Newgate S.p.A.; *Int'l*, pg. 6670
TWENTYCI HOLDINGS LIMITED; *Int'l*, pg. 7990
TWENTYEIGHTY, INC.—See Providence Equity Partners L.L.C.; *U.S. Private*, pg. 3294
TWENTYEIGHTY STRATEGY EXECUTION (GERMANY) GMBH—See Korn Ferry; *U.S. Public*, pg. 1273
TWENTYEIGHTY STRATEGY EXECUTION, INC.—See Korn Ferry; *U.S. Public*, pg. 1273
TWENTYEIGHTY STRATEGY EXECUTION (UK) LTD.—See Korn Ferry; *U.S. Public*, pg. 1274
TWENTY FIRST CENTURY ENGINEERING CORP.—See Kelso & Company, L.P.; *U.S. Private*, pg. 2278
TWENTY-FIRST CENTURY FOX, INC.—See The Walt Disney Company; *U.S. Public*, pg. 2140
TWENTY-FIRST CENTURY GRAIN PROCESSING COOPERATIVE; *U.S. Private*, pg. 4264
TWENTY FIRST CENTURY LP; *U.S. Private*, pg. 4264
TWENTYFIRST CENTURY MANAGEMENT SERVICES LTD.; *Int'l*, pg. 7990
TWENTYFOUR ASSET MANAGEMENT LLP—See Vontobel Holding AG; *Int'l*, pg. 8306
TWENTY-FOUR CON & SUPPLY PUBLIC COMPANY LIMITED; *Int'l*, pg. 7990
TWENTYFOUR INCOME FUND LTD.; *Int'l*, pg. 7990
TWENTYFOUR SELECT MONTHLY INCOME FUND LTD.; *Int'l*, pg. 7990
TWENTY FOUR SEVEN, INC.; *U.S. Private*, pg. 4264
TWENTY FOUR SEVEN—See Twenty Four Seven, Inc.; *U.S. Private*, pg. 4264
TWENTY SEVEN CO. LIMITED; *Int'l*, pg. 7990
TWENTY TWENTY PRODUCTIONS LIMITED—See Warner Bros. Discovery, Inc.; *U.S. Public*, pg. 2329
TWENTY/TWENTY WORLDWIDE HOSPITALITY, LLC; *U.S. Private*, pg. 4264
TWENTY WEB LIMITED—See TwentyCi Holdings Limited; *Int'l*, pg. 7990
TWEPPY S.P.A.; *Int'l*, pg. 7990
T-WEST SALES & SERVICE, INC.—See AutoNation, Inc.; *U.S. Public*, pg. 238
T.W.E. WHOLESALE, INC. OF SAN DIEGO; *U.S. Private*, pg. 3912
T&W FORGE, LLC—See SIFCO Industries, Inc.; *U.S. Public*, pg. 1877
TWG BENEFITS, INC.; *U.S. Private*, pg. 4264
TWG EUROPE LIMITED—See Assurant, Inc.; *U.S. Public*, pg. 215
TWG MAURITIUS LTD.—See Workforce Holdings Ltd.; *Int'l*, pg. 8456
TWG REPAIR SERVICES (SHANGHAI) CO., LTD.—See Assurant, Inc.; *U.S. Public*, pg. 215
TW GROUP, INC.—See World Insurance Associates LLC; *U.S. Private*, pg. 4566
TWG SERVICES LIMITED—See Assurant, Inc.; *U.S. Public*, pg. 215
TWIDDY AND COMPANY REALTORS; *U.S. Private*, pg. 4264

TWIFLEX LTD.—See Regal Rexnord Corporation; *U.S. Public*, pg. 1772
TWIG COM LTD.; *Int'l*, pg. 7990
TWIGG EXPLORATION & MINING, LIMITADA—See Syrah Resources Limited; *Int'l*, pg. 7387
TWIGG GOLD LIMITED—See African Eagle Resources PLC; *Int'l*, pg. 191
TWIGG RESOURCES LIMITED—See African Eagle Resources PLC; *Int'l*, pg. 191
TWI GROUP, INC.; *U.S. Private*, pg. 4264
TWI GROUP INC.—See TWI Group, Inc.; *U.S. Private*, pg. 4264
TWIG TECHNOLOGIES, LLC—See The Will Group, Inc.; *U.S. Private*, pg. 4136
TWI INTERNATIONAL, INC.—See Waxman Industries, Inc.; *U.S. Private*, pg. 4459
TWI INTERNATIONAL TAIWAN, INC.—See Waxman Industries, Inc.; *U.S. Private*, pg. 4459
TWILIGHT NOW, LLC—See Now Electronics, Inc.; *U.S. Private*, pg. 2968
TWILIGHT NOW, LLC—See Twilight Technology, Inc.; *U.S. Private*, pg. 4264
TWILIGHT TECHNOLOGY, INC.; *U.S. Private*, pg. 4264
TWILIO BERLIN GMBH—See Twilio Inc.; *U.S. Public*, pg. 2206
TWILIO INC.; *U.S. Public*, pg. 2206
TWILIO SWEDEN AB—See Twilio Inc.; *U.S. Public*, pg. 2206
TWILL, INC.—See Ace Lithographers of Morris County, Inc.; *U.S. Private*, pg. 57
TWIM CORP.; *Int'l*, pg. 7990
TWINAPLATE LIMITED—See Illinois Tool Works Inc.; *U.S. Public*, pg. 1111
TWINBIRD CORPORATION; *Int'l*, pg. 7990
TWINBIRD ELECTRICAL APPLIANCE (SHENZHEN) CO., LTD.—See Twinbird Corporation; *Int'l*, pg. 7990
TWIN BRIDGE CAPITAL CORPORATION—See ConnectOne Bancorp, Inc.; *U.S. Public*, pg. 568
TWIN BRIDGES GOLF CLUB, L.P.—See Waste Management, Inc.; *U.S. Public*, pg. 2332
TWIN BRIDGES TRUCK CITY INC.; *U.S. Private*, pg. 4264
TWIN BUTTES WIND, LLC—See Iberdrola, S.A.; *Int'l*, pg. 3571
TWINCARE GROUP—See TRG Management LP; *U.S. Private*, pg. 4220
TWIN CITIES AD; *U.S. Private*, pg. 4264
TWIN CITIES AMBULATORY SURGERY CENTER, L.P.—See Tenet Healthcare Corporation; *U.S. Public*, pg. 2013
TWIN CITIES COMMUNITY HOSPITAL, INC.—See Adventist Health System; *U.S. Private*, pg. 108
TWIN CITIES FINANCIAL SERVICES; *U.S. Private*, pg. 4264
TWIN CITIES HOSPITAL—See HCA Healthcare, Inc.; *U.S. Public*, pg. 1013
TWIN CITIES PUBLIC TELEVISION, INC.; *U.S. Private*, pg. 4264
TWIN CITY BAGEL, INC—See Grupo Bimbo, S.A.B. de C.V.; *Int'l*, pg. 3123
TWIN CITY CHRISTIAN HOMES, INC.; *U.S. Private*, pg. 4264
TWIN CITY CONCRETE PRODUCTS CO.; *U.S. Private*, pg. 4264
TWIN CITY CRANE & HOIST INC.—See Balance Point Capital Advisors, LLC; *U.S. Private*, pg. 457
TWIN CITY DIE CASTINGS CO.; *U.S. Private*, pg. 4264
TWIN CITY DIE CASTINGS CO.—See Twin City Die Castings Co.; *U.S. Private*, pg. 4265
TWIN CITY DIE CASTINGS CO. - WATERTOWN FACILITY—See Twin City Die Castings Co.; *U.S. Private*, pg. 4265
TWIN CITY FAN & BLOWER—See Twin City Fan Companies, Ltd.; *U.S. Private*, pg. 4265
TWIN CITY FAN COMPANIES, LTD.; *U.S. Private*, pg. 4265
TWIN CITY FOODS, INC.; *U.S. Private*, pg. 4265
TWIN CITY GARAGE DOOR COMPANY—See APi Group Corporation; *Int'l*, pg. 514
TWIN CITY HARDWARE COMPANY; *U.S. Private*, pg. 4265
TWIN CITY HOLLAND INDUSTRIES—See Twin City Fan Companies, Ltd.; *U.S. Private*, pg. 4265
TWIN CITY KNITTING CO, INC.—See Huron Capital Partners LLC; *U.S. Private*, pg. 2012
TWIN CITY MAZDA; *U.S. Private*, pg. 4265
TWIN CITY MOTORS INC.—See Southeast Texas Classic Automotive; *U.S. Private*, pg. 3726
TWIN CITY SECURITY, INC.; *U.S. Private*, pg. 4265
TWIN CITY TRACTOR & EQUIPMENT INC.; *U.S. Private*, pg. 4265
TWIN CITY TRAILER SALES & SERVICE, INC.; *U.S. Private*, pg. 4265
TWIN CITY VENTCO—See Twin City Fan Companies, Ltd.; *U.S. Private*, pg. 4265
TWIN CITY WIRE, INC.; *U.S. Private*, pg. 4265
TWINCO AUTOMOTIVE WAREHOUSE, INC.; *U.S. Private*, pg. 4266
TWINCO INC.; *U.S. Private*, pg. 4266

COMPANY NAME INDEX

TWIN COMMANDER AIRCRAFT LLC—See Hicks Holdings, LLC; *U.S. Private*, pg. 1934
TWIN COMMANDER AIRCRAFT LLC—See The Riverside Company; *U.S. Private*, pg. 4108
TWIN COMMANDER AIRCRAFT LLC—See Weinberg Capital Group, Inc.; *U.S. Private*, pg. 4471
TWIN COUNTY ELECTRIC POWER ASSOCIATION; *U.S. Private*, pg. 4265
TWINCRAFT, INC.—See PC GROUP, INC.; *U.S. Private*, pg. 3119
TWIN DISC (FAR EAST) LTD.—See Twin Disc, Incorporated; *U.S. Public*, pg. 2206
TWIN DISC, INCORPORATED; *U.S. Public*, pg. 2206
TWIN DISC INTERNATIONAL, S.A.—See Twin Disc, Incorporated; *U.S. Public*, pg. 2207
TWIN DISC ITALIA SRL—See Twin Disc, Incorporated; *U.S. Public*, pg. 2207
TWIN DISC (PACIFIC) PTY. LTD.—See Twin Disc, Incorporated; *U.S. Public*, pg. 2207
TWIN DISC POWER TRANSMISSION (SHANGHAI) CO. LTD.—See Twin Disc, Incorporated; *U.S. Public*, pg. 2207
TWIN DISC SRL—See Twin Disc, Incorporated; *U.S. Public*, pg. 2207
TWIN DOLPHIN MARINA—See Miller Enterprises of Manatee, Inc.; *U.S. Private*, pg. 2734
TWIN DRAGON MARKETING, INC.—See Texhong Textile Group Limited; *Int'l*, pg. 7584
TWIN EAGLE RESOURCE MANAGEMENT, LLC—See Blackstone Inc.; *U.S. Public*, pg. 349
TWIN EAGLE RESOURCE MANAGEMENT, LLC—See Five Point Energy LLC; *U.S. Private*, pg. 1537
TWINEAGLES BROKERAGE INC—See Ronto Group, Inc.; *U.S. Private*, pg. 3478
TWINE & CORDAGE MANUFACTURING CO. (PVT) LIMITED—See TT Electronics plc; *Int'l*, pg. 7959
TWINFAKTOR GMBH—See Vienna Insurance Group AG Wiener Versicherung Gruppe; *Int'l*, pg. 8196
TWIN FILTER N.A., INC.—See Parker Hannifin Corporation; *U.S. Public*, pg. 1650
TWIN FILTER SOUTH AMERICA LTDA—See Parker Hannifin Corporation; *U.S. Public*, pg. 1650
TWINFORMATICS GMBH—See Vienna Insurance Group AG Wiener Versicherung Gruppe; *Int'l*, pg. 8195
TWINHEAD INTERNATIONAL CORP.; *Int'l*, pg. 7990
TWIN HILLS FORD LINCOLN; *Int'l*, pg. 7990
TWIN INDUSTRIAL (H.K.) COMPANY LIMITED—See Ta Win Holdings Berhad; *Int'l*, pg. 7400
TWINING & CO. LTD.—See The Garfield Weston Foundation; *Int'l*, pg. 7649
TWINING INC.; *U.S. Private*, pg. 4266
TWININGS NORTH AMERICA, INC.—See The Garfield Weston Foundation; *Int'l*, pg. 7649
TWINLAB CONSOLIDATED HOLDINGS, INC.; *U.S. Public*, pg. 2207
TWINLAB CONSOLIDATION CORPORATION—See Twinlab Consolidated Holdings, Inc.; *U.S. Public*, pg. 2207
TWINLAB CORPORATION—See Twinlab Consolidated Holdings, Inc.; *U.S. Public*, pg. 2207
TWINLAB CORP. - UTAH FACILITY—See Twinlab Consolidated Holdings, Inc.; *U.S. Public*, pg. 2207
TWINLAB HOLDINGS, INC.—See Twinlab Consolidated Holdings, Inc.; *U.S. Public*, pg. 2207
TWIN LAKES COMMUNITY BANK—See First National Bancorp, Inc.; *U.S. Private*, pg. 1521
TWIN LAKES HOME HEALTH AGENCY, LLC—See UnitedHealth Group Incorporated; *U.S. Public*, pg. 2247
TWIN LAKES TELEPHONE COOP. CORP.; *U.S. Private*, pg. 4265
TWIN LIQUORS; *U.S. Private*, pg. 4265
TWIN MEDICAL TRANSACTION SERVICES, INC—See Firstsource Solutions Limited; *Int'l*, pg. 2691
TWIN MED LLC—See TA Associates, Inc.; *U.S. Private*, pg. 3919
TWIN METALS MINNESOTA LLC—See Antofagasta plc; *Int'l*, pg. 484
TWIN OAKS COMMUNITY SERVICES INC.; *U.S. Private*, pg. 4265
TWIN PALMS DEVELOPMENT SDN. BHD.—See Lum Chang Holdings Limited; *Int'l*, pg. 4577
TWIN POINT CAPITAL, LLC; *U.S. Private*, pg. 4265
TWIN PONDS EAST ARENA—See Blackstreet Capital Holdings LLC; *U.S. Private*, pg. 576
TWINPUTKI OY—See Instalco AB; *Int'l*, pg. 3722
TWIN RIDGE AUTO AND LIGHT TRUCK SERVICE, INC.—See Bueso & Forman, Inc.; *U.S. Private*, pg. 680
TWIN RIDGE CAPITAL ACQUISITION CORP.; *U.S. Public*, pg. 2207
TWIN RIVER NATIONAL BANK; *U.S. Private*, pg. 4265
TWIN RIVERS CENTER—See Formation Capital, LLC; *U.S. Private*, pg. 1571
TWIN RIVERS FOODS INC.—See Twin Rivers Group Inc.; *U.S. Private*, pg. 4266
TWIN RIVERS GROUP INC.; *U.S. Private*, pg. 4265
TWIN RIVERS PACKAGING INC.—See Twin Rivers Group Inc.; *U.S. Private*, pg. 4266
TWIN RIVERS PAPER COMPANY; *U.S. Private*, pg. 4266
TWIN RIVERS PLUMBING INC.; *U.S. Private*, pg. 4266

TWIN RIVERS RESPIRATORY CARE, INC.—See AdaptHealth Corp.; *U.S. Public*, pg. 39
TWIN RIVERS TECHNOLOGIES HOLDINGS, INC.—See FGV Holdings Bhd; *Int'l*, pg. 2649
TWIN RIVER - TIVERTON, LLC—See Bally's Corporation; *U.S. Public*, pg. 268
TWIN ROSES TRADES & AGENCIES LTD.; *Int'l*, pg. 7990
TWINSAVER GROUP—See TRG Management LP; *U.S. Private*, pg. 4220
TWINSPIRES—See Churchill Downs, Inc.; *U.S. Public*, pg. 494
TWINS SPORTS, INC.—See Pohlad Companies; *U.S. Private*, pg. 3220
TWINSTAR CREDIT UNION; *U.S. Private*, pg. 4266
TWINSTAR INDUSTRIES LIMITED; *Int'l*, pg. 7990
TWIN-STAR INTERNATIONAL, INC.—See Z Capital Group, LLC; *U.S. Private*, pg. 4595
TWIN STATE INC.; *U.S. Private*, pg. 4266
TWIN STATES PUBLISHING CO. INC.—See Community Media Group; *U.S. Private*, pg. 995
TWIN STATE TRUCKS INC.; *U.S. Private*, pg. 4266
TWINTEC TECHNOLOGIE GMBH—See Baumot Group AG; *Int'l*, pg. 895
TWINTEK INVESTMENT HOLDINGS LIMITED; *Int'l*, pg. 7990
TWIN TIER HOSPITALITY, LLC; *U.S. Private*, pg. 4266
TWIN TOWERS; *U.S. Private*, pg. 4266
TWIN TOWERS TRADING, INC.; *U.S. Private*, pg. 4266
TWIN TOWNS MARKETING MANAGEMENT L.L.C.—See National Bank of Umm Al Qaiwain; *Int'l*, pg. 5154
TWIN TOWNS SERVICES CLUB LIMITED; *Int'l*, pg. 7990
TWIN TRAFFIC MARKING CORP.—See Tricor Pacific Capital, Inc.; *Int'l*, pg. 7920
TWIN VEE POWERCATS CO.; *U.S. Public*, pg. 2207
TWINVISION—See Audax Group, Limited Partnership; *U.S. Private*, pg. 389
TWI PHARMACEUTICALS USA, INC.—See Bora Pharmaceuticals Co., Ltd.; *Int'l*, pg. 1112
TWISS COLD STORAGE, INC.—See Bulova Technologies Group, Inc.; *U.S. Private*, pg. 685
TWISS LOGISTICS INC.—See Bulova Technologies Group, Inc.; *U.S. Private*, pg. 685
TWISS TRANSPORT, INC.—See Bulova Technologies Group, Inc.; *U.S. Private*, pg. 685
TWIST BIOSCIENCE CORPORATION; *U.S. Public*, pg. 2207
TWISTBOX ENTERTAINMENT, INC.—See Digital Turbine, Inc.; *U.S. Public*, pg. 664
TWISTBOX GAMES LTD. & CO KG—See Digital Turbine, Inc.; *U.S. Public*, pg. 664
TWISTDX LIMITED—See Abbott Laboratories; *U.S. Public*, pg. 19
TWISTED PAIR SOLUTIONS, INC.—See Motorola Solutions, Inc.; *U.S. Public*, pg. 1479
TWISTED SCHOLAR, INC.; *U.S. Private*, pg. 4266
TWISTED TECHNOLOGIES, INC.—See TheIPGuys.Net LLC; *U.S. Private*, pg. 4141
THE TWISTER GROUP, INC.; *U.S. Private*, pg. 4128
TWIST INC.; *U.S. Private*, pg. 4266
TWIST INVESTMENT CORPORATION; *U.S. Private*, pg. 4266
TWISTO PAYMENTS A.S.—See Zip Co Limited; *Int'l*, pg. 8685
TWISTO POLSKA SP. Z O.O.—See Zip Co Limited; *Int'l*, pg. 8685
TWIST SOLUTIONS, LP—See The Aldridge Company; *U.S. Private*, pg. 3983
TWITCHELL CORPORATION—See Highlander Partners, LP.; *U.S. Private*, pg. 1940
TWITCH INTERACTIVE, INC.—See Amazon.com, Inc.; *U.S. Public*, pg. 91
T.W.L CORP; *U.S. Private*, pg. 3912
T.W. LEWIS COMPANY INC.; *U.S. Private*, pg. 3912
TWL HOLDINGS BHD; *Int'l*, pg. 7991
TWL PRECISION INC.—See VTL (Holdings) Ltd; *Int'l*, pg. 8317
TW MANUFACTURING CO.—See Park-Ohio Holdings Corp.; *U.S. Public*, pg. 1640
TWMB ASSOCIATES, LLC—See Tanger Inc.; *U.S. Public*, pg. 1980
TW METALS—See O'Neal Industries, Inc.; *U.S. Private*, pg. 2979
TW MEXICO PACKAGING SOLUTIONS, S. DE R.L DE C.V.—See Rengo Co., Ltd.; *Int'l*, pg. 6281
TW MEXICO PLANTA PUEBLA, S. DE R.L DE C.V.—See Rengo Co., Ltd.; *Int'l*, pg. 6281
TW MICHIGAN INC.—See Rengo Co., Ltd.; *Int'l*, pg. 6281
TWM INDUSTRIES; *U.S. Private*, pg. 4266
TWNKLS B.V.—See PTC Inc.; *U.S. Public*, pg. 1735
TWOADAY OIL, INC.; *U.S. Private*, pg. 4267
TWO BALLSTON PLAZA CO. LLC—See Brookfield Corporation; *Int'l*, pg. 1186
TWO DEGREES MOBILE LIMITED—See SG Enterprises II, LLC; *U.S. Private*, pg. 3622
TWO DOT WIND FARM, LLC—See New Jersey Resources Corporation; *U.S. Public*, pg. 1512
TWO FARMS, INC.; *U.S. Private*, pg. 4266
T&W OF KNOXVILLE INC.; *U.S. Private*, pg. 3910
TWOFOUR AMERICA, LLC—See ITV plc; *Int'l*, pg. 3845

TWYFORD VENTURES INC.

TWOFOUR GROUP LTD.—See ITV plc; *Int'l*, pg. 3845
TWO FREEDOM SQUARE, L.L.C.—See Boston Properties, Inc.; *U.S. Public*, pg. 373
TWO HANDS CORPORATION; *Int'l*, pg. 7991
TWO HARBORS INVESTMENT CORP.; *U.S. Public*, pg. 2207
TWO MEN & A TRUCK/INTERNATIONAL INC.—See Roark Capital Group Inc.; *U.S. Private*, pg. 3456
TWO OCEANS ABALONE PTY. LTD.—See Rare Foods Australia Ltd.; *Int'l*, pg. 6211
TWO RIVER BANCORP—See OceanFirst Financial Corp.; *U.S. Public*, pg. 1563
TWO RIVER COMMUNITY BANK—See OceanFirst Financial Corp.; *U.S. Public*, pg. 1563
TWO RIVER GROUP HOLDINGS, LLC; *U.S. Private*, pg. 4266
TWO RIVER GROUP MANAGEMENT, LLC—See Two River Group Holdings, LLC; *U.S. Private*, pg. 4266
TWO RIVERS BANK & TRUST—See Two Rivers Financial Group, Inc.; *U.S. Public*, pg. 2207
TWO RIVERS CONSUMERS COOP ASSOCIATION; *U.S. Private*, pg. 4266
TWO RIVERS COOPERATIVE; *U.S. Private*, pg. 4266
TWO RIVERS DEVELOPMENT LIMITED—See Centum Investment Company Limited; *Int'l*, pg. 1416
TWO RIVERS FINANCIAL GROUP, INC.; *U.S. Public*, pg. 2207
TWO RIVERS PHYSICIAN PRACTICES, LLC—See Apollo Global Management, Inc.; *U.S. Public*, pg. 159
TWO RIVERS PLATINUM (PROPRIETARY) LIMITED—See African Rainbow Minerals Limited; *Int'l*, pg. 192
TWO RIVERS PSYCHIATRIC HOSPITAL—See Universal Health Services, Inc.; *U.S. Public*, pg. 2260
TWO RIVERS WATER & FARMING COMPANY; *U.S. Private*, pg. 4266
TWO ROADS LAS VEGAS, LLC—See Las Vegas Sands Corp.; *U.S. Public*, pg. 1293
TWO'S COMPANY INC.; *U.S. Private*, pg. 4267
TWOSE OF TIVERTON LTD.—See Aramark; *U.S. Public*, pg. 178
TWO SHEA CONSULTING, INC.—See ChrysCapital Investment Advisors (India) Private Limited; *Int'l*, pg. 1588
TWO SHIELDS INVESTMENTS PLC; *Int'l*, pg. 7991
TWO SIGMA INVESTMENTS, LP; *U.S. Private*, pg. 4267
TWO SIX TECHNOLOGIES, INC.—See The Carlyle Group Inc.; *U.S. Public*, pg. 2056
TWO; *U.S. Public*, pg. 2207
TWO-STATE CONSTRUCTION COMPANY, INC.; *U.S. Private*, pg. 4267
TWO TECHNOLOGIES, INC.; *U.S. Private*, pg. 4267
TWOTON INC.; *U.S. Private*, pg. 4267
TWO TREES INN—See Mashantucket Pequot Gaming Enterprise Inc.; *U.S. Private*, pg. 2601
TWO-TWO-FREE LIMITED—See Huasheng International Holding Limited; *Int'l*, pg. 3514
TWO-WAY COMMUNICATIONS INC.; *U.S. Private*, pg. 4267
TWO WEST, INC.; *U.S. Private*, pg. 4267
TW PACKAGING LTD.—See Rengo Co., Ltd.; *Int'l*, pg. 6281
TW PERRY ENTERPRISES, INC.; *U.S. Private*, pg. 4263
TWP LIMPOPO ENGINEERING (PTY) LIMITED—See Worley Limited; *Int'l*, pg. 8459
TWP SENDIRIAN BERHAD—See Dai Nippon Printing Co., Ltd.; *Int'l*, pg. 1916
TW (SABAH) PTE LTD—See Tiong Woon Corporation Holding Ltd.; *Int'l*, pg. 7755
T&W SALES INC.; *U.S. Private*, pg. 3910
TWSCO; *U.S. Private*, pg. 4267
TW SOLAR (CHENGDU) CO., LTD.—See Tongwei Co., Ltd.; *Int'l*, pg. 7808
TW SOLAR (HEFEI) CO., LTD.—See Tongwei Co., Ltd.; *Int'l*, pg. 7808
TW SOLAR (JINTANG) CO., LTD.—See Tongwei Co., Ltd.; *Int'l*, pg. 7808
TW SOLAR (MEISHAN) CO., LTD.—See Tongwei Co., Ltd.; *Int'l*, pg. 7808
TWS PARTNERSHIP LLC; *U.S. Private*, pg. 4267
TWSP PTY. LTD.—See Worley Limited; *Int'l*, pg. 8459
TWSP PTY. LTD.—See WSP Global, Inc.; *Int'l*, pg. 8497
TWS TECHNISCHE WERKE DER GEMEINDE SAAR-WELLINGEN GMBH—See RWE AG; *Int'l*, pg. 6436
TWT GROUP LIMITED; *Int'l*, pg. 7991
T&W TIRE COMPANY; *U.S. Private*, pg. 3910
TWT MANUFACTURING CO., LTD.—See WW Holding Inc; *Int'l*, pg. 8517
T-W TRANSPORT, INC.—See Trans-System Inc.; *U.S. Private*, pg. 4206
TWT REFRIGERATED SERVICE—See Trans-System Inc.; *U.S. Private*, pg. 4206
T W WARD CNC MACHINERY LTD.—See Nidec Corporation; *Int'l*, pg. 5280
T & W WATER SERVICE COMPANY—See Northwest Natural Holding Company; *U.S. Public*, pg. 1542
TWX GROUP HOLDING LIMITED; *Int'l*, pg. 7991
TWX GROUP HOLDING LIMITED; *Int'l*, pg. 7991
TWYFORD VENTURES INC.; *Int'l*, pg. 7991

TWYVER SWITCHGEAR LIMITED—See VINCI S.A.; *Int'l*, pg. 8239
TWZ CORPORATION PUBLIC COMPANY LIMITED; *Int'l*, pg. 7991
TX3 SERVICES, LLC—See Tricentis USA Corp.; *U.S. Private*, pg. 4229
TX ALLIANCE MOTORS, INC.—See AutoNation, Inc.; *U.S. Public*, pg. 238
TX-CC DALLAS, INC.—See AutoNation, Inc.; *U.S. Public*, pg. 238
TX-CC GALLERIA, INC.—See AutoNation, Inc.; *U.S. Public*, pg. 238
TXC (CHONGQING) CORPORATION—See TXC Corporation; *Int'l*, pg. 7992
TXC CORPORATION - NINGBO FACTORY—See TXC Corporation; *Int'l*, pg. 7993
TXC CORPORATION; *Int'l*, pg. 7992
TX-CC SPRING, INC.—See AutoNation, Inc.; *U.S. Public*, pg. 238
TXC EUROPE GMBH—See TXC Corporation; *Int'l*, pg. 7993
TXC JAPAN CORPORATION—See TXC Corporation; *Int'l*, pg. 7993
TXC (NINGBO) CORPORATION—See TXC Corporation; *Int'l*, pg. 7992
TXCOM S.A.; *Int'l*, pg. 7993
TXC TECHNOLOGY INC.—See TXC Corporation; *Int'l*, pg. 7993
TXDC, LP—See Signet Jewelers Limited; *Int'l*, pg. 6911
TX ENERGY SERVICES, LLC—See Forbes Energy Services Ltd.; *U.S. Public*, pg. 864
TXEX ENERGY INVESTMENTS, LLC; *U.S. Private*, pg. 4267
TX GROUP AG; *Int'l*, pg. 7991
TXI RIVERSIDE INC.—See Martin Marietta Materials, Inc.; *U.S. Public*, pg. 1389
TX LOGISTIK AB—See Ferrovie dello Stato Italiane S.p.A.; *Int'l*, pg. 2645
TX LOGISTIK A/S—See Ferrovie dello Stato Italiane S.p.A.; *Int'l*, pg. 2645
TX LOGISTIK GMBH—See Ferrovie dello Stato Italiane S.p.A.; *Int'l*, pg. 2645
TX LOGISTIK TRANSALPINE GMBH—See Ferrovie dello Stato Italiane S.p.A.; *Int'l*, pg. 2645
TX MOTORS OF NORTH RICHLAND HILLS, INC.—See AutoNation, Inc.; *U.S. Public*, pg. 238
TX MOTORS ON KATY FREEWAY, INC.—See AutoNation, Inc.; *U.S. Public*, pg. 238
TX NEWCO, L.L.C.—See Waste Management, Inc.; *U.S. Public*, pg. 2332
TXNM ENERGY, INC.; *U.S. Public*, pg. 2208
TXOL INTERNET, INC.—See Rural Telecommunications of America, Inc.; *U.S. Private*, pg. 3504
TXO PARTNERS, L.P.; *U.S. Public*, pg. 2208
TXO PLC; *Int'l*, pg. 7993
TX RAIL PRODUCTS, INC.; *U.S. Public*, pg. 2208
TXRB HOLDINGS, INC.; *U.S. Private*, pg. 4267
TX RX SYSTEMS INC.—See Indutrade AB; *Int'l*, pg. 3681
TX SOLAR I LLC—See Duke Energy Corporation; *U.S. Public*, pg. 691
TXTB.COM LLC—See Barnes & Noble Education, Inc.; *U.S. Public*, pg. 276
TX TECHNOLOGY CORP.—See EXX Inc.; *U.S. Private*, pg. 1453
TXT E-SOLUTIONS GMBH—See TXT e-Solutions S.p.A.; *Int'l*, pg. 7993
TXT E-SOLUTIONS LTD.—See TXT e-Solutions S.p.A.; *Int'l*, pg. 7993
TXT E-SOLUTIONS S.A.G.L.—See TXT e-Solutions S.p.A.; *Int'l*, pg. 7993
TXT E-SOLUTIONS SARL—See TXT e-Solutions S.p.A.; *Int'l*, pg. 7993
TXT E-SOLUTIONS S.L.—See TXT e-Solutions S.p.A.; *Int'l*, pg. 7993
TXT E-SOLUTIONS S.P.A.; *Int'l*, pg. 7993
TXT E-TECH S.R.L.—See TXT e-Solutions S.p.A.; *Int'l*, pg. 7993
TXTLOCAL LTD.—See Cisco Systems, Inc.; *U.S. Public*, pg. 499
TXT NOVIGO S.R.L.—See TXT e-Solutions S.p.A.; *Int'l*, pg. 7993
TXT QUENCE S.R.L.—See TXT e-Solutions S.p.A.; *Int'l*, pg. 7993
TXU ENERGY RETAIL COMPANY LLC—See Vistra Corp.; *U.S. Public*, pg. 2306
TXU WARM FRONT LIMITED—See E.ON SE; *Int'l*, pg. 2256
TX WEST HOUSTON MOTORS, INC.—See AutoNation, Inc.; *U.S. Public*, pg. 238
TYAN COMPUTER CORPORATION—See MiTAC International Corp.; *Int'l*, pg. 4923
TYAN COMPUTER GMBH—See MiTAC International Corp.; *Int'l*, pg. 4923
TYAN COMPUTER (USA) CORPORATION—See MiTAC International Corp.; *Int'l*, pg. 4923
TYAZHMASH JOINT STOCK COMPANY—See United Wagon Company Research & Production Corporation PJSC; *Int'l*, pg. 8073

TYBRIN CORPORATION—See Jacobs Engineering Group, Inc.; *U.S. Public*, pg. 1185
TYC AMERICAS INC.—See TYC Brother Industrial Co., Ltd.; *Int'l*, pg. 7994
TYC BALTIC UAB—See TYC Brother Industrial Co., Ltd.; *Int'l*, pg. 7994
TYC BROTHER INDUSTRIAL CO., LTD.; *Int'l*, pg. 7993
TYC EUROPE B.V.—See TYC Brother Industrial Co., Ltd.; *Int'l*, pg. 7994
TYCHE INDUSTRIES LTD; *Int'l*, pg. 7994
TYCHE SPA—See Matthews International Corporation; *U.S. Public*, pg. 1400
TYCO BUILDING SERVICES PRODUCTS (GERMANY) GMBH—See Johnson Controls International plc; *Int'l*, pg. 3987
TYCO BUILDING SERVICES PRODUCTS (HUNGARY) KFT—See Johnson Controls International plc; *Int'l*, pg. 3987
TYCO BUILDING SERVICES PRODUCTS (ITALY) S.R.L.—See Johnson Controls International plc; *Int'l*, pg. 3987
TYCO BUILDING SERVICES PRODUCTS (NORWAY) AS—See Johnson Controls International plc; *Int'l*, pg. 3987
TYCO BUILDING SERVICES PRODUCTS S.A.S.—See Johnson Controls International plc; *Int'l*, pg. 3987
TYCO BUILDING SERVICES PRODUCTS (SWEDEN) AB—See Johnson Controls International plc; *Int'l*, pg. 3987
TYCO BUILDING SERVICES PRODUCTS (UK) LIMITED—See Johnson Controls International plc; *Int'l*, pg. 3987
TYCO (CHINA) INVESTMENT CO., LTD.—See Johnson Controls International plc; *Int'l*, pg. 3987
TYCO CONNECTIVITY—See TE Connectivity Ltd.; *Int'l*, pg. 7497
TYCO ELECTRONICS AMP ESPANA, S.A.—See TE Connectivity Ltd.; *Int'l*, pg. 7497
TYCO ELECTRONICS AMP GMBH—See TE Connectivity Ltd.; *Int'l*, pg. 7498
TYCO ELECTRONICS AMP K.K.—See TE Connectivity Ltd.; *Int'l*, pg. 7497
TYCO ELECTRONICS AMP KOREA LIMITED—See TE Connectivity Ltd.; *Int'l*, pg. 7497
TYCO ELECTRONICS AMP QINGDAO LTD.—See TE Connectivity Ltd.; *Int'l*, pg. 7497
TYCO ELECTRONICS AMP SHANGHAI LTD.—See TE Connectivity Ltd.; *Int'l*, pg. 7497
TYCO ELECTRONICS ARGENTINA S.A.—See TE Connectivity Ltd.; *Int'l*, pg. 7497
TYCO ELECTRONICS AUSTRIA GMBH—See TE Connectivity Ltd.; *Int'l*, pg. 7497
TYCO ELECTRONICS BELGIUM EC BVBA—See TE Connectivity Ltd.; *Int'l*, pg. 7497
TYCO ELECTRONICS BRASIL S.A.—See TE Connectivity Ltd.; *Int'l*, pg. 7497
TYCO ELECTRONICS CANADA ULC—See TE Connectivity Ltd.; *Int'l*, pg. 7497
TYCO ELECTRONICS COLOMBIA LTDA.—See TE Connectivity Ltd.; *Int'l*, pg. 7497
TYCO ELECTRONICS COMPONENTES ELECTROMECANICOS LDA.—See TE Connectivity Ltd.; *Int'l*, pg. 7497
TYCO ELECTRONICS - CORCOM—See TE Connectivity Ltd.; *Int'l*, pg. 7497
TYCO ELECTRONICS CORPORATION INDIA PVT LIMITED—See TE Connectivity Ltd.; *Int'l*, pg. 7498
TYCO ELECTRONICS CORPORATION—See TE Connectivity Ltd.; *Int'l*, pg. 7497
TYCO ELECTRONICS - CROMPTON INSTRUMENTS—See TE Connectivity Ltd.; *Int'l*, pg. 7498
TYCO ELECTRONICS CZECH S.R.O.—See TE Connectivity Ltd.; *Int'l*, pg. 7498
TYCO ELECTRONICS DENMARK A/S—See TE Connectivity Ltd.; *Int'l*, pg. 7498
TYCO ELECTRONICS EC TRUTNOV S.R.O.—See TE Connectivity Ltd.; *Int'l*, pg. 7498
TYCO ELECTRONICS ENERGY PTY LTD—See TE Connectivity Ltd.; *Int'l*, pg. 7498
TYCO ELECTRONICS FINLAND OY—See TE Connectivity Ltd.; *Int'l*, pg. 7498
TYCO ELECTRONICS FRANCE—See TE Connectivity Ltd.; *Int'l*, pg. 7498
TYCO ELECTRONICS FRANCE—See TE Connectivity Ltd.; *Int'l*, pg. 7498
TYCO ELECTRONICS GERMANY HOLDINGS GMBH—See TE Connectivity Ltd.; *Int'l*, pg. 7498
TYCO ELECTRONICS (GIBRALTAR) HOLDING LIMITED—See TE Connectivity Ltd.; *Int'l*, pg. 7497
TYCO ELECTRONICS GROUP S.A.—See TE Connectivity Ltd.; *Int'l*, pg. 7497
TYCO ELECTRONICS HELLAS MEPE—See TE Connectivity Ltd.; *Int'l*, pg. 7498
TYCO ELECTRONICS H.K. LIMITED—See TE Connectivity Ltd.; *Int'l*, pg. 7498
TYCO ELECTRONICS HUNGARY TERMELO KFT—See TE Connectivity Ltd.; *Int'l*, pg. 7498

TYCO ELECTRONICS IDENTO SAS—See TE Connectivity Ltd.; *Int'l*, pg. 7498
TYCO ELECTRONICS INDUSTRIAL Y COMERCIAL CHILE LIMITADA—See TE Connectivity Ltd.; *Int'l*, pg. 7498
TYCO ELECTRONICS INTEGRATED CABLE SYSTEMS LLC—See TE Connectivity Ltd.; *Int'l*, pg. 7498
TYCO ELECTRONICS IRELAND LTD.—See TE Connectivity Ltd.; *Int'l*, pg. 7498
TYCO ELECTRONICS ISRAEL LTD.—See TE Connectivity Ltd.; *Int'l*, pg. 7498
TYCO ELECTRONICS ITALIA HOLDING S.R.L.—See TE Connectivity Ltd.; *Int'l*, pg. 7498
TYCO ELECTRONICS JAPAN G.K.—See TE Connectivity Ltd.; *Int'l*, pg. 7498
TYCO ELECTRONICS - KILOVAC—See TE Connectivity Ltd.; *Int'l*, pg. 7498
TYCO ELECTRONICS LOGISTICS AG—See TE Connectivity Ltd.; *Int'l*, pg. 7498
TYCO ELECTRONICS MEXICO, S. DE R.L. DE C.V.—See TE Connectivity Ltd.; *Int'l*, pg. 7498
TYCO ELECTRONICS MIDDLE EAST FZE—See TE Connectivity Ltd.; *Int'l*, pg. 7498
TYCO ELECTRONICS (M) SDN. BHD.—See TE Connectivity Ltd.; *Int'l*, pg. 7497
TYCO ELECTRONICS NEDERLAND B.V.—See TE Connectivity Ltd.; *Int'l*, pg. 7498
TYCO ELECTRONICS NETHERLANDS (INDIA) COOPERATIEF U.A.—See TE Connectivity Ltd.; *Int'l*, pg. 7498
TYCO ELECTRONICS NORGE AS—See TE Connectivity Ltd.; *Int'l*, pg. 7498
TYCO ELECTRONICS NZ LIMITED—See TE Connectivity Ltd.; *Int'l*, pg. 7498
TYCO ELECTRONICS PHILIPPINES, INC.—See TE Connectivity Ltd.; *Int'l*, pg. 7498
TYCO ELECTRONICS POLSKA SP Z O.O.—See TE Connectivity Ltd.; *Int'l*, pg. 7498
TYCO ELECTRONICS PRECISION ENGINEERING LTD.—See TE Connectivity Ltd.; *Int'l*, pg. 7496
TYCO ELECTRONICS PTY LIMITED—See TE Connectivity Ltd.; *Int'l*, pg. 7498
TYCO ELECTRONICS (QINGDAO) LTD.—See TE Connectivity Ltd.; *Int'l*, pg. 7497
TYCO ELECTRONICS RAYCHEM GMBH—See TE Connectivity Ltd.; *Int'l*, pg. 7498
TYCO ELECTRONICS RAYCHEM KOREA LIMITED—See TE Connectivity Ltd.; *Int'l*, pg. 7498
TYCO ELECTRONICS RAYCHEM N.V.—See TE Connectivity Ltd.; *Int'l*, pg. 7498
TYCO ELECTRONICS RUS OOO—See TE Connectivity Ltd.; *Int'l*, pg. 7498
TYCO ELECTRONICS SAUDI ARABIA LIMITED—See TE Connectivity Ltd.; *Int'l*, pg. 7499
TYCO ELECTRONICS (SCHWEIZ) AG—See TE Connectivity Ltd.; *Int'l*, pg. 7497
TYCO ELECTRONICS SERVICES GMBH—See TE Connectivity Ltd.; *Int'l*, pg. 7499
TYCO ELECTRONICS SERVICIOS DE MEXICO, S. DE R. L. DE C.V.—See TE Connectivity Ltd.; *Int'l*, pg. 7499
TYCO ELECTRONICS (SHANGHAI) CO., LTD—See TE Connectivity Ltd.; *Int'l*, pg. 7497
TYCO ELECTRONICS SIMEL SAS—See TE Connectivity Ltd.; *Int'l*, pg. 7498
TYCO ELECTRONICS SINGAPORE PTE LTD—See TE Connectivity Ltd.; *Int'l*, pg. 7499
TYCO ELECTRONICS—See TE Connectivity Ltd.; *Int'l*, pg. 7497
TYCO ELECTRONICS—See TE Connectivity Ltd.; *Int'l*, pg. 7497
TYCO ELECTRONICS—See TE Connectivity Ltd.; *Int'l*, pg. 7497
TYCO ELECTRONICS—See TE Connectivity Ltd.; *Int'l*, pg. 7497
TYCO ELECTRONICS SOUTH AFRICA (PROPRIETARY) LIMITED—See TE Connectivity Ltd.; *Int'l*, pg. 7499
TYCO ELECTRONICS SUBSEA COMMUNICATIONS LLC—See TE Connectivity Ltd.; *Int'l*, pg. 7498
TYCO ELECTRONICS (SUZHOU) LTD.—See TE Connectivity Ltd.; *Int'l*, pg. 7497
TYCO ELECTRONICS SVENSKA AB—See TE Connectivity Ltd.; *Int'l*, pg. 7499
TYCO ELECTRONICS SVENSKA HOLDINGS AB—See TE Connectivity Ltd.; *Int'l*, pg. 7499
TYCO ELECTRONICS SYSTEMS INDIA PVT LTD—See TE Connectivity Ltd.; *Int'l*, pg. 7499
TYCO ELECTRONICS TAIWAN CO., LTD.—See TE Connectivity Ltd.; *Int'l*, pg. 7499
TYCO ELECTRONICS TECHNOLOGY (KUNSHAN) CO., LTD.—See TE Connectivity Ltd.; *Int'l*, pg. 7499
TYCO ELECTRONICS TECNOLOGIAS S. DE R.L. DE C.V.—See TE Connectivity Ltd.; *Int'l*, pg. 7499
TYCO ELECTRONICS TELECOM OSP—See TE Connectivity Ltd.; *Int'l*, pg. 7498
TYCO ELECTRONICS (THAILAND) LIMITED—See TE Connectivity Ltd.; *Int'l*, pg. 7497

COMPANY NAME INDEX

TYCO ELECTRONICS UK INFRASTRUCTURE LIMITED—See TE Connectivity Ltd.; *Int'l*, pg. 7496
TYCO ELECTRONICS UK LTD.—See TE Connectivity Ltd.; *Int'l*, pg. 7496
TYCO ELECTRONICS UKRAINE LIMITED—See TE Connectivity Ltd.; *Int'l*, pg. 7499
TYCO ELECTRONICS (US), INC.—See Johnson Controls International plc; *Int'l*, pg. 3987
TYCO ELECTRONICS VERMOGENSVERWALTUNGS GMBH & CO KG—See TE Connectivity Ltd.; *Int'l*, pg. 7499
TYCO ELECTRONICS (WUXI) LTD—See TE Connectivity Ltd.; *Int'l*, pg. 7497
TYCO ELECTRONICS (ZHUHAI) LTD—See TE Connectivity Ltd.; *Int'l*, pg. 7497
TYCO ELECTRONICS (ZIBO) CO., LTD.—See TE Connectivity Ltd.; *Int'l*, pg. 7497
TYCO ELEKTRONIK AMP TICARET LIMITED—See TE Connectivity Ltd.; *Int'l*, pg. 7499
TYCO EUROPE S.A.S.—See Johnson Controls International plc; *Int'l*, pg. 3987
TYCO FIRE & BUILDING PRODUCTS ASIA PTE. LTD.—See Johnson Controls International plc; *Int'l*, pg. 3987
TYCO FIRE & INTEGRATED SOLUTIONS FRANCE S.A.S.—See Johnson Controls International plc; *Int'l*, pg. 3988
TYCO FIRE & INTEGRATED SOLUTIONS (NORWAY) AS—See Johnson Controls International plc; *Int'l*, pg. 3988
TYCO FIRE & INTEGRATED SOLUTIONS (SCHWEIZ) AG—See Johnson Controls International plc; *Int'l*, pg. 3988
TYCO FIRE & INTEGRATED SOLUTIONS (SLOVAKIA) S.R.O.—See Johnson Controls International plc; *Int'l*, pg. 3987
TYCO FIRE & INTEGRATED SOLUTIONS S.R.O.—See Johnson Controls International plc; *Int'l*, pg. 3987
TYCO FIRE & INTEGRATED SOLUTIONS (UK) LIMITED—See Johnson Controls International plc; *Int'l*, pg. 3988
TYCO FIRE & INTEGRATED SYSTEMS (GUANGZHOU) CO., LTD.—See Johnson Controls International plc; *Int'l*, pg. 3988
TYCO FIRE PRODUCTS, LP—See Johnson Controls International plc; *Int'l*, pg. 3988
TYCO FIRE PRODUCTS MANUFACTURING LIMITED—See Johnson Controls International plc; *Int'l*, pg. 3988
TYCO FIRE PROTECTION PRODUCTS—See Johnson Controls International plc; *Int'l*, pg. 3989
TYCO FIRE PROTECTION PRODUCTS—See Johnson Controls International plc; *Int'l*, pg. 3989
TYCO FIRE & SECURITY CZECH REPUBLIC S.R.O.—See Johnson Controls International plc; *Int'l*, pg. 3988
TYCO FIRE & SECURITY FINANCE S.C.A.—See Johnson Controls International plc; *Int'l*, pg. 3988
TYCO FIRE & SECURITY GMBH—See Johnson Controls International plc; *Int'l*, pg. 3987
TYCO FIRE & SECURITY HOLDING GERMANY GMBH—See Johnson Controls International plc; *Int'l*, pg. 3988
TYCO FIRE & SECURITY LLC—See Johnson Controls International plc; *Int'l*, pg. 3988
TYCO FIRE & SECURITY NEDERLAND BV—See Johnson Controls International plc; *Int'l*, pg. 3988
TYCO FIRE & SECURITY PTY. LIMITED—See Johnson Controls International plc; *Int'l*, pg. 3988
TYCO FIRE & SECURITY SERVICES INTERNATIONAL TRADING (SHANGHAI) CO. LTD.—See Johnson Controls International plc; *Int'l*, pg. 3988
TYCO FIRE, SECURITY & SERVICES MALAYSIA SDN BHD—See Johnson Controls International plc; *Int'l*, pg. 3989
TYCO FIRE, SECURITY & SERVICES PTE. LTD.—See Johnson Controls International plc; *Int'l*, pg. 3989
TYCO FIRE & SECURITY S.P.A.—See Johnson Controls International plc; *Int'l*, pg. 3989
TYCO HOLDING VIII (DENMARK) APS—See Johnson Controls International plc; *Int'l*, pg. 3989
TYCO INTEGRATED FIRE & SECURITY AUSTRIA GMBH—See Johnson Controls International plc; *Int'l*, pg. 3989
TYCO INTEGRATED FIRE & SECURITY CANADA, INC.—See Johnson Controls International plc; *Int'l*, pg. 3989
TYCO INTEGRATED FIRE & SECURITY (SCHWEIZ) AG—See Johnson Controls International plc; *Int'l*, pg. 3989
TYCO INTEGRATED FIRE & SECURITY—See Johnson Controls International plc; *Int'l*, pg. 3989
TYCO INTEGRATED FIRE & SECURITY—See Johnson Controls International plc; *Int'l*, pg. 3989
TYCO INTEGRATED SECURITY LLC—See Johnson Controls International plc; *Int'l*, pg. 3989
TYCO INTERNATIONAL MANAGEMENT COMPANY, LLC—See Johnson Controls International plc; *Int'l*, pg. 3986

TYCO INTERNATIONAL OF CANADA LTD.—See Johnson Controls International plc; *Int'l*, pg. 3989
TYCO INTERNATIONAL PTY LIMITED—See Johnson Controls International plc; *Int'l*, pg. 3989
TYCO MARINE, S.A.—See TE Connectivity Ltd.; *Int'l*, pg. 7499
TYCO NETWORKS IBERICA, S.L.—See TE Connectivity Ltd.; *Int'l*, pg. 7499
TYCO NETWORKS (NETHERLANDS) B.V.—See TE Connectivity Ltd.; *Int'l*, pg. 7499
TYCO NEW ZEALAND LIMITED—See Johnson Controls International plc; *Int'l*, pg. 3989
TYCOON GROUP HOLDINGS LIMITED; *Int'l*, pg. 7994
TYCOONS GROUP ENTERPRISE CO., LTD.; *Int'l*, pg. 7994
TYCOONS WORLDWIDE GROUP (THAILAND) PUBLIC CO., LTD.—See Tycoons Group Enterprise Co., Ltd.; *Int'l*, pg. 7994
TYCORE BUILT LLC.; *U.S. Private*, pg. 4267
TYCO SAFETY PRODUCTS CANADA LTD.—See Johnson Controls International plc; *Int'l*, pg. 3989
TYCO SAFETY PRODUCTS FRANCE SARL—See Johnson Controls International plc; *Int'l*, pg. 3989
TYCO SAFETY PRODUCTS (SHANGHAI) CO., LTD.—See Johnson Controls International plc; *Int'l*, pg. 3989
TYCO SAFETY PRODUCTS (SHENYANG) CO., LTD.—See Johnson Controls International plc; *Int'l*, pg. 3989
TYCO SANMAR LTD.—See Sanmar Holdings Ltd.; *Int'l*, pg. 6546
TYCO SERVICE & MONTAGE GMBH - MERSEBURG—See Johnson Controls International plc; *Int'l*, pg. 3989
TYCO SERVICE & MONTAGE GMBH—See Johnson Controls International plc; *Int'l*, pg. 3989
TYCO SERVICES S.A.—See Johnson Controls International plc; *Int'l*, pg. 3989
TYCO SERVICES S.A.—See Johnson Controls International plc; *Int'l*, pg. 3989
TYCO SIMPLEXGRINNELL—See Johnson Controls International plc; *Int'l*, pg. 3988
TYCO SIMPLEXGRINNELL—See Johnson Controls International plc; *Int'l*, pg. 3988
TYCO TELECOMMUNICATIONS (US) INC.—See TE Connectivity Ltd.; *Int'l*, pg. 7498
TYCO THERMAL CONTROLS FINLAND OY—See Pentair plc; *Int'l*, pg. 5790
TYCO THERMAL CONTROLS (SHANGHAI) ENGINEERING CO., LTD.—See Pentair plc; *Int'l*, pg. 5790
TYCO THERMAL CONTROLS (SHANGHAI) TRADING CO. LTD—See Pentair plc; *Int'l*, pg. 5790
TYCO VALVES & CONTROLS DE MEXICO, S.A. DE C.V.—See Emerson Electric Co.; *U.S. Public*, pg. 751
TYCO VALVES & CONTROLS (SICHUAN) CO., LTD.—See Emerson Electric Co.; *U.S. Public*, pg. 751
TYCROP MANUFACTURING LTD.; *Int'l*, pg. 7994
TYC SPORTS—See Grupo Clarin S.A.; *Int'l*, pg. 3125
TYCZKA INDUSTRIE-GASE GMBH—See Air Products & Chemicals, Inc.; *U.S. Public*, pg. 67
TYDENBROOKS SECURITY PRODUCTS GROUP—See Bertram Capital Management, LLC; *U.S. Private*, pg. 540
TYDENBROOKS SECURITY PRODUCTS GROUP—See Bertram Capital Management, LLC; *U.S. Private*, pg. 540
TYDENBROOKS SECURITY PRODUCTS GROUP—See Crimson Investment; *U.S. Private*, pg. 1100
TYDENBROOKS SECURITY PRODUCTS GROUP—See Crimson Investment; *U.S. Private*, pg. 1100
TYDENBROOKS STOFFEL SEALS CORPORATION—See Bertram Capital Management, LLC; *U.S. Private*, pg. 540
TYDENBROOKS STOFFEL SEALS CORPORATION—See Crimson Investment; *U.S. Private*, pg. 1100
TYDEN GROUP INC.—See Bertram Capital Management, LLC; *U.S. Private*, pg. 540
TYDEN GROUP INC.—See Crimson Investment; *U.S. Private*, pg. 1100
TYDEN (SUZHOU) SECURITY SEAL CO., LTD.—See Bertram Capital Management, LLC; *U.S. Private*, pg. 540
TYDEN (SUZHOU) SECURITY SEAL CO., LTD.—See Crimson Investment; *U.S. Private*, pg. 1100
TYDIPACKS NIGERIA LIMITED—See May & Baker Nigeria Plc.; *Int'l*, pg. 4743
TYEE PRODUCTS INC.—See Ta-I Technology Co., Ltd.; *Int'l*, pg. 7400
TYE SOON LIMITED; *Int'l*, pg. 7994
TYGA-BOX SYSTEMS, INC.; *U.S. Private*, pg. 4267
TYGAFLOR LTD.—See Compagnie de Saint-Gobain SA; *Int'l*, pg. 1732
TYGAR MANUFACTURING, INC.; *U.S. Private*, pg. 4267
TYGAVAC ADVANCED MATERIALS LTD.—See Airtech International Inc.; *U.S. Private*, pg. 142
TYGON PEAK CAPITAL; *U.S. Private*, pg. 4267
TYGRIS ASSET FINANCE, INC—See Teachers Insurance Association - College Retirement Fund; *U.S. Private*, pg. 3948
TYHEE GOLD CORP.; *Int'l*, pg. 7994

TY HOLDINGS CO. LTD.; *Int'l*, pg. 7993
TY INC.; *U.S. Private*, pg. 4267
TYK AMERICA, INC.—See TYK Corporation; *Int'l*, pg. 7994
TYK CORPORATION; *Int'l*, pg. 7994
T.Y.K INDUSTRY CO., LTD.—See The Steel Public Company Limited; *Int'l*, pg. 7688
TYKMA, INC.—See The 600 Group PLC; *Int'l*, pg. 7609
TYLDIN CORP.; *U.S. Private*, pg. 4267
THE TYLENOL COMPANY—See Johnson & Johnson; *U.S. Public*, pg. 1200
TYLER 2 CONSTRUCTION, INC.; *U.S. Private*, pg. 4267
TYLER AUTOMOTIVE INC.; *U.S. Private*, pg. 4267
TYLER BUILDING SYSTEMS, L.P.; *U.S. Private*, pg. 4267
TYLER & CO.—See Jackson Healthcare, LLC; *U.S. Private*, pg. 2177
TYLER DIALYSIS, LLC—See DaVita Inc.; *U.S. Public*, pg. 644
TYLER DISTRIBUTION CENTERS—See Port Jersey Logistics; *U.S. Private*, pg. 3230
TYLER EQUIPMENT CORPORATION; *U.S. Private*, pg. 4267
TYLER FORD; *U.S. Private*, pg. 4268
TYLER GRIFFIN CO., INC.—See G&G Technical Inc.; *U.S. Private*, pg. 1629
TYLER INSURANCE AGENCY, LLC—See Arthur J. Gallagher & Co.; *U.S. Public*, pg. 207
TYLER IRON & METAL COMPANY—See M. Lipsitz & Co., Ltd.; *U.S. Private*, pg. 2527
TYLER MOUNTAIN WATER COMPANY; *U.S. Private*, pg. 4268
TYLER REFRIGERATION CORP.—See Haier Smart Home Co., Ltd.; *Int'l*, pg. 3210
TYLER REHABILITATION HOSPITAL, INC.—See Encompass Health Corporation; *U.S. Public*, pg. 759
TYLERS AUTOMOTIVE INC.; *U.S. Private*, pg. 4268
TYLER'S JEFFERSON MOTORS; *U.S. Private*, pg. 4268
TYLER STAFFING SERVICES INC.; *U.S. Private*, pg. 4268
TYLER TECHNOLOGIES - EAGLE DIVISION—See Tyler Technologies, Inc.; *U.S. Public*, pg. 2209
TYLER TECHNOLOGIES: FUNDBALANCE SOLUTIONS—See Tyler Technologies, Inc.; *U.S. Public*, pg. 2209
TYLER TECHNOLOGIES, INC. - CLT—See Tyler Technologies, Inc.; *U.S. Public*, pg. 2209
TYLER TECHNOLOGIES INCODE SOLUTIONS—See Tyler Technologies, Inc.; *U.S. Public*, pg. 2209
TYLER TECHNOLOGIES, INC.; *U.S. Public*, pg. 2208
TYLER TECHNOLOGIES, INC.—See Tyler Technologies, Inc.; *U.S. Public*, pg. 2209
TYLER (XIANXIAN) FOUNDRY CO., LTD.—See McWane, Inc.; *U.S. Private*, pg. 2645
T.Y. LIMITED, INC.; *Int'l*, pg. 7398
T.Y. LIN INTERNATIONAL GROUP LTD.; *U.S. Private*, pg. 3912
T.Y. LIN INTERNATIONAL - MEDINA—See T.Y. Lin International Group Ltd.; *U.S. Private*, pg. 3913
TYLITE HOLDINGS, INC.—See Northwest Fiber LLC; *U.S. Private*, pg. 2960
TYLKO PRACOWNICY S.A.—See IQ Partners S.A.; *Int'l*, pg. 3803
TYLOON, INC.—See 2GM Corporation; *U.S. Private*, pg. 6
TYMAN PLC—See Quanex Building Products Corp.; *U.S. Public*, pg. 1749
TYMBAL RESOURCES LTD.; *Int'l*, pg. 7995
TYM CENTRAL EUROPE S.R.O.—See Tym Corporation; *Int'l*, pg. 7995
TYMCO INTERNATIONAL LTD.; *U.S. Private*, pg. 4268
TYM CORPORATION; *Int'l*, pg. 7994
THE TYMETAL CORP.—See The Fort Miller Group Inc.; *U.S. Private*, pg. 4030
TYME TECHNOLOGIES, INC.—See Syros Pharmaceuticals, Inc.; *U.S. Public*, pg. 1972
TYMLEZ GROUP LTD.; *Int'l*, pg. 7995
TYM MEDICAL—See HORIBA Ltd; *Int'l*, pg. 3478
TYMPHANY ACOUSTIC TECHNOLOGY EUROPE, S.R.O.—See Primax Electronics Ltd.; *Int'l*, pg. 5976
TYMPHANY-CHINA—See Tymphany Corp.; *U.S. Private*, pg. 4268
TYMPHANY CORP.; *U.S. Private*, pg. 4268
TYMPHANY-HONG KONG—See Tymphany Corp.; *U.S. Private*, pg. 4268
TYM-USA INC.—See Tym Corporation; *Int'l*, pg. 7995
TYNAGH ENERGY LTD.—See Energeticky a Prumyslovy Holding, a.s.; *Int'l*, pg. 2420
TYNAN'S VOLKSWAGEN, INC.; *U.S. Private*, pg. 4268
TYNDALE ADVISORS, LLC; *U.S. Private*, pg. 4268
TYNDALE HOUSE PUBLISHERS, INC.; *U.S. Private*, pg. 4268
TYNDALL FEDERAL CREDIT UNION INC.; *U.S. Private*, pg. 4268
TYNDALL INVESTMENT MANAGEMENT LIMITED—See Sumitomo Mitsui Trust Holdings, Inc.; *Int'l*, pg. 7296
TYNER RESOURCES LTD.; *Int'l*, pg. 7995
TYNET CORPORATION—See Tyson Foods, Inc.; *U.S. Public*, pg. 2210
TYNRICH TECHNOLOGY CORPORATION—See Tyntek Corporation; *Int'l*, pg. 7995

TYNER RESOURCES LTD.
CORPORATE AFFILIATIONS

TYNSOLAR CORPORATION—See Tyntek Corporation; *Int'l*, pg. 7995
TYNTEK CORPORATION; *Int'l*, pg. 7995
TYO INC.—See AOI TYO Holdings Inc.; *Int'l*, pg. 488
TYONEK CONSTRUCTION GROUP, INC.—See The Tyonek Native Corporation; *U.S. Private*, pg. 4128
TYONEK MANUFACTURING GROUP, INC.—See The Tyonek Native Corporation; *U.S. Private*, pg. 4128
THE TYONEK NATIVE CORPORATION; *U.S. Private*, pg. 4128
TYONEK SERVICES GROUP, INC.—See The Tyonek Native Corporation; *U.S. Private*, pg. 4128
TYONEK SERVICES OVERHAUL FACILITY-STENNIS, LLC—See The Tyonek Native Corporation; *U.S. Private*, pg. 4128
TYO TECHNICAL RANCH INC.—See AOI TYO Holdings Inc.; *Int'l*, pg. 488
TYPHOON FINANCIAL SERVICES LTD.; *Int'l*, pg. 7995
TYPHOON INTERNATIONAL LIMITED—See Safety & Survival Systems International Ltd.; *U.S. Private*, pg. 3524
TYPHOON TOUCH TECHNOLOGIES, INC.; *U.S. Private*, pg. 4269
TYPHOO TEA LTD.—See Zetland Capital Partners LLP; *Int'l*, pg. 8639
TYPICAL INTERNATIONAL CORPORATION—See Xi'an Typical Industries Co., Ltd.; *Int'l*, pg. 8522
TYPOCAR LTD—See Vertu Motors plc; *Int'l*, pg. 8175
TYP RESTAURANT GROUP INC.; *U.S. Private*, pg. 4268
TYPTAP INSURANCE COMPANY—See HCI Group, Inc.; *U.S. Public*, pg. 1014
TYRA BIOSCIENCES, INC.; *U.S. Public*, pg. 2209
TYRANNA RESOURCES LIMITED; *Int'l*, pg. 7995
TYRATECH, INC.—See American Vanguard Corporation; *U.S. Public*, pg. 112
TYREE MAINTENANCE CO. INC.—See Tyree Organization, Ltd; *U.S. Private*, pg. 4269
TYREE OIL INC.; *U.S. Private*, pg. 4269
TYREE ORGANIZATION, LTD; *U.S. Private*, pg. 4269
TYREFIX UK LTD.—See Literacy Capital Plc; *Int'l*, pg. 4526
TYR ENERGY, INC.—See ITOCHU Corporation; *Int'l*, pg. 3839
TYRENS AB; *Int'l*, pg. 7995
TYRENS UK LIMITED—See Tyrens AB; *Int'l*, pg. 7995
TYRE PACIFIC (HK) LTD—See Stamford Tyres Corporation Limited; *Int'l*, pg. 7165
TYR EQUITY, INC.; *U.S. Private*, pg. 4269
TYRES INTERNATIONAL INC.; *U.S. Private*, pg. 4269
TYRESNET INC—See Delticom AG; *Int'l*, pg. 2021
TYREX ENGINEERING GROUP—See TyRex Group, Ltd.; *U.S. Private*, pg. 4269
TYREX GROUP, LTD.; *U.S. Private*, pg. 4269
TYRHOLM BIG R STORES; *U.S. Private*, pg. 4269
TYROC CONSTRUCTION, LLC—See Blunt Enterprises LLC; *U.S. Private*, pg. 600
TYROLEAN AIRWAYS TIROLER LUFTFAHRT GMBH—See Deutsche Lufthansa AG; *Int'l*, pg. 2066
TYROL EQUITY AG; *Int'l*, pg. 7996
TYROLIA TECHNOLOGY GMBH—See Head B.V.; *Int'l*, pg. 3300
TYROLIT SCHLEIFMITTELWERKE SWAROVSKI KG—See Swarovski & Co.; *Int'l*, pg. 7362
TYROLIT WICKMAN INC.—See Swarovski & Co.; *Int'l*, pg. 7362
TYROLMED GMBH—See Nissha Co., Ltd.; *Int'l*, pg. 5372
TYROO MEDIA PVT. LTD.—See Dentsu Group Inc.; *Int'l*, pg. 2038
TYROON TEA COMPANY LIMITED; *Int'l*, pg. 7996
TYRO PAYMENTS LIMITED; *Int'l*, pg. 7995
TYRRELL-DOYLE CHEVROLET CO.; *U.S. Private*, pg. 4269
TYRRELL-MARXEN CHEVROLET OLDSMOBILE CADILLAC INC.; *U.S. Private*, pg. 4269
TYRRELLS POTATO CRISPS LTD.—See The Hershey Co.; *U.S. Public*, pg. 2088
TYRRELLTECH, INC.; *U.S. Private*, pg. 4269
TYRX, INC.—See Medtronic plc; *Int'l*, pg. 4790
TYSAN FOUNDATION LIMITED—See Blackstone Inc.; *U.S. Public*, pg. 351
TYSAN HOLDINGS LIMITED—See Blackstone Inc.; *U.S. Public*, pg. 351
TYSAN MACHINERY HIRE LIMITED—See Blackstone Inc.; *U.S. Public*, pg. 351
TYSENS COUNTRY GROCERY INC.; *U.S. Private*, pg. 4269
TYSK-SVENSKA HANDELSKAMMAREN—See Messe Munchen GmbH; *Int'l*, pg. 4842
TYSNES SPAREBANK; *Int'l*, pg. 7996
TYSON BREEDERS, INC.—See Tyson Foods, Inc.; *U.S. Public*, pg. 2210
TYSON CHICKEN, INC.—See Tyson Foods, Inc.; *U.S. Public*, pg. 2210
TYSON DELI, INC.—See Tyson Foods, Inc.; *U.S. Public*, pg. 2210
TYSON DE MEXICO, S. DE R.L. DE C.V.—See JBS S.A.; *Int'l*, pg. 3919
TYSON EXPORT SALES, INC.—See Tyson Foods, Inc.; *U.S. Public*, pg. 2210

TYSON FOODS CANADA, INC.—See Tyson Foods, Inc.; *U.S. Public*, pg. 2210
TYSON FOODS, INC. - ALBERTVILLE—See Tyson Foods, Inc.; *U.S. Public*, pg. 2210
TYSON FOODS, INC. - CARTHAGE—See Tyson Foods, Inc.; *U.S. Public*, pg. 2210
TYSON FOODS, INC. - CHICAGO—See Tyson Foods, Inc.; *U.S. Public*, pg. 2210
TYSON FOODS, INC.; *U.S. Public*, pg. 2209
TYSON FOODS ITALIA S.P.A.—See Tyson Foods, Inc.; *U.S. Public*, pg. 2210
TYSON FOODS UK HOLDING LTD.—See Tyson Foods, Inc.; *U.S. Public*, pg. 2210
TYSON FRESH MEATS, INC.—See Tyson Foods, Inc.; *U.S. Public*, pg. 2210
TYSON FRESH MEATS, INC.—See Tyson Foods, Inc.; *U.S. Public*, pg. 2210
TYSON FRESH MEATS, INC.—See Tyson Foods, Inc.; *U.S. Public*, pg. 2210
TYSON FRESH MEATS, INC.—See Tyson Foods, Inc.; *U.S. Public*, pg. 2210
TYSON FRESH MEATS, INC.—See Tyson Foods, Inc.; *U.S. Public*, pg. 2210
TYSON FRESH MEATS, INC.—See Tyson Foods, Inc.; *U.S. Public*, pg. 2210
TYSON FRESH MEATS, INC.—See Tyson Foods, Inc.; *U.S. Public*, pg. 2210
TYSON FRESH MEATS, INC.—See Tyson Foods, Inc.; *U.S. Public*, pg. 2210
TYSON FRESH MEATS, INC.—See Tyson Foods, Inc.; *U.S. Public*, pg. 2210
TYSON FRESH MEATS, INC.—See Tyson Foods, Inc.; *U.S. Public*, pg. 2210
TYSON MEXICAN ORIGINAL, INC.—See Tyson Foods, Inc.; *U.S. Public*, pg. 2210
TYSON PREPARED FOODS, INC.—See Tyson Foods, Inc.; *U.S. Public*, pg. 2210
TYSON REFRIGERATED PROCESSED MEATS, INC.—See Tyson Foods, Inc.; *U.S. Public*, pg. 2210
TYTAN HOLDINGS, INC.; *U.S. Public*, pg. 2211
TYTO ATHENE, LLC—See Arlington Capital Partners LLC; *U.S. Private*, pg. 328
TYUMENNIIGIPROGAZ—See PJSC Gazprom; *Int'l*, pg. 5880
TYVAENERGOSBYT OPEN JOINT-STOCK COMPANY—See JSC ROSSETI; *Int'l*, pg. 4011
TZAH-SERAFON LTD.—See The Kusto Group Inc.; *Int'l*, pg. 7663
TZELL TRAVEL GROUP—See Travel Leaders Group, LLC; *U.S. Private*, pg. 4213
TZERO ATS, LLC—See Beyond, Inc.; *U.S. Public*, pg. 327
TZE SHIN INTERNATIONAL CO., LTD.; *Int'l*, pg. 7996
TZ FINANCIAL COMPANY; *U.S. Private*, pg. 4269
TZI AUSTRALIA PTY LIMITED—See TZ LIMITED; *Int'l*, pg. 7996
TZI SINGAPORE PTE LTD.—See TZ LIMITED; *Int'l*, pg. 7996
TZI UK LIMITED—See TZ LIMITED; *Int'l*, pg. 7996
TZ LIMITED; *Int'l*, pg. 7996
TZOW PETRO CARBO CHEM—See PCC SE; *Int'l*, pg. 5767
TZP GROUP LLC; *U.S. Private*, pg. 4269
TZP STRATEGIES ACQUISITION CORP.; *U.S. Public*, pg. 2211
TZ STROMAG—See Burkhalter Holding AG; *Int'l*, pg. 1226

U

U105 LIMITED—See News Corporation; *U.S. Public*, pg. 1520
U10 CORP SA; *Int'l*, pg. 7998
U2BIO CO., LTD.; *Int'l*, pg. 7998
U3O8 HOLDINGS PLC; *Int'l*, pg. 7998
U3 PHARMA GMBH—See Daiichi Sankyo Co., Ltd.; *Int'l*, pg. 1930
UAA DENMARK—See Albert Ballin KG; *Int'l*, pg. 296
UAA FINLAND—See Albert Ballin KG; *Int'l*, pg. 296
UAASC NORWAY—See Albert Ballin KG; *Int'l*, pg. 296
UAB AARSLEFF—See Per Aarsleff Holding A/S; *Int'l*, pg. 5796
UAB ABBOTT MEDICAL LITHUANIA—See Abbott Laboratories; *U.S. Public*, pg. 21
UAB ABC DATA LIETUVA—See Droege Group AG; *Int'l*, pg. 2205
UAB ACHEMOS MOKYMO CENTRAS—See Koncernas Achemos Grupe; *Int'l*, pg. 4246
UAB ACNIELSEN BALTICS—See Brookfield Corporation; *Int'l*, pg. 1177
UAB ACNIELSEN BALTICS—See Elliott Management Corporation; *U.S. Private*, pg. 1369
UAB ACTA JUVENTUS—See City Service SE; *Int'l*, pg. 1628
UAB AEROC—See Aeroc International AS; *Int'l*, pg. 180
UAB AGRO MANAGEMENT TEAM—See AUGA group, AB; *Int'l*, pg. 703

UAB AGROSS—See AUGA group, AB; *Int'l*, pg. 703
UAB AGROTECHNIKOS CENTRAS—See AUGA group, AB; *Int'l*, pg. 703
UAB AIRO CATERING SERVICES LIETUVA—See Deutsche Lufthansa AG; *Int'l*, pg. 2068
UAB ALD AUTOMOTIVE—See ALD Automotive; *Int'l*, pg. 304
UAB ALGOL CHEMICALS—See Algol Oy; *Int'l*, pg. 318
UAB ALL MEDIA LITHUANIA—See Providence Equity Partners L.L.C.; *U.S. Private*, pg. 3291
UAB ALSO LIETUVA—See Droege Group AG; *Int'l*, pg. 2205
UAB AMADEUS LIETUVA—See Amadeus IT Group, S.A.; *Int'l*, pg. 407
UAB AVENA NORDIC GRAIN—See Apetit Plc; *Int'l*, pg. 509
UAB AVON COSMETICS—See Natura & Co Holding S.A.; *Int'l*, pg. 5167
UAB AZARTO TECHNIKA—See Novomatic AG; *Int'l*, pg. 5467
UAB BALTIC ENGINEERS; *Int'l*, pg. 7998
UAB BAYER—See Bayer Aktiengesellschaft; *Int'l*, pg. 910
UAB BEIJER REF—See Beijer Ref AB; *Int'l*, pg. 945
UAB BENTELER DISTRIBUTION LITHUANIA—See Benteler International AG; *Int'l*, pg. 977
UAB BITE LIETUVA—See Mid Europa Partners LLP; *Int'l*, pg. 4882
UAB BOSKALIS BALTIC—See HAL Trust N.V.; *Int'l*, pg. 3227
UAB BRENNTAG LIETUVA—See BRENNTAG SE; *Int'l*, pg. 1150
UAB BRITISH AMERICAN TOBACCO LIETUVA—See British American Tobacco plc; *Int'l*, pg. 1168
UAB BULL BALTIJA—See Atos SE; *Int'l*, pg. 692
UAB CAMARGO—See Floridienne SA; *Int'l*, pg. 2708
UAB CAVERION LIETUVA—See Triton Advisers Limited; *Int'l*, pg. 7935
UAB CGI LITHUANIA—See CGI Inc.; *Int'l*, pg. 1433
UAB CITY24—See Alma Media Corporation; *Int'l*, pg. 362
UAB CITY SERVICE ENGINEERING—See City Service SE; *Int'l*, pg. 1628
UAB CLEAR CHANNEL LITHUANIA—See iHeartMedia, Inc.; *U.S. Public*, pg. 1096
UAB COCA-COLA HBC LIETUVA—See Coca-Cola HBC AG; *Int'l*, pg. 1686
UAB COLUMBUS LIETUVA—See Columbus A/S; *Int'l*, pg. 1706
UAB DEKRA INDUSTRIAL—See DEKRA e.V.; *Int'l*, pg. 2010
UAB DHL LIETUVA—See Deutsche Post AG; *Int'l*, pg. 2078
UAB DOUGLAS LT—See CVC Capital Partners SICAV-FIS S.A.; *Int'l*, pg. 1883
UAB DS SMITH PACKAGING LITHUANIA—See DS Smith Plc; *Int'l*, pg. 2209
UAB ECKES-GRANINI LIETUVA—See Eckes AG; *Int'l*, pg. 2291
UAB ECONOMUS—See City Service SE; *Int'l*, pg. 1628
UAB EDEN SPRINGS LIETUVA—See Eden International SA; *Int'l*, pg. 2307
UAB EGMONT LIETUVA—See Egmont Fonden; *Int'l*, pg. 2326
UAB ELEKTROBALT—See Wurth Verwaltungsgesellschaft mbH; *Int'l*, pg. 8508
UAB ELEKTROSKANDIA LT—See Rexel, S.A.; *Int'l*, pg. 6316
UAB ELEKTROS TINKLO PASLAUGOS—See UAB Ignitis grupe; *Int'l*, pg. 7998
UAB ELME MESSER LIT—See BLRT Grupp AS; *Int'l*, pg. 1066
UAB ELTEL NETWORKS—See Eltel AB; *Int'l*, pg. 2371
UAB EMAS—See Orlen S.A.; *Int'l*, pg. 5641
UAB ENERGETIKOS PAJEGOS—See UAB Ignitis grupe; *Int'l*, pg. 7998
UAB ERICSSON LIETUVA—See Telefonaktiebolaget LM Ericsson; *Int'l*, pg. 7534
UAB ETERNIT BALTIC—See Etex SA/NV; *Int'l*, pg. 2523
UAB FAZER LIETUVA—See Oy Karl Fazer Ab; *Int'l*, pg. 5677
UAB FERRATUM FINANCE—See Multitude SE; *Int'l*, pg. 5084
UAB FINOMARK—See NEO Finance AB; *Int'l*, pg. 5195
UAB FORTUM EKOSILUMA—See Fortum Oyj; *Int'l*, pg. 2742
UAB FORTUM HEAT LIETUVA—See Fortum Oyj; *Int'l*, pg. 2742
UAB FORTUM KLAIPEDA—See Fortum Oyj; *Int'l*, pg. 2742
UAB FORUM CINEMAS—See Sanoma Oyj; *Int'l*, pg. 6553
UAB FUGRO BALTIC—See Fugro N.V.; *Int'l*, pg. 2808
UAB FURNMASTER—See Gabriel Holding A/S; *Int'l*, pg. 2867
UAB FUTURE ELECTRONICS—See Future Electronics Inc.; *Int'l*, pg. 2856
UAB GARSU PASAULIS; *Int'l*, pg. 7998
UAB GERDUKAS—See Heidelberg Materials AG; *Int'l*, pg. 3320
UAB GILBARCO VEEDER-ROOT—See Vontier Corporation; *U.S. Public*, pg. 2309

2840

COMPANY NAME INDEX

UAB GREEN TERMINAL—See Caiano AS; *Int'l*, pg. 1252
UAB HC BETONAS—See Heidelberg Materials AG; *Int'l*, pg. 3320
UAB HEIDELBERG CEMENT KLAIPEDA—See Heidelberg Materials AG; *Int'l*, pg. 3320
UAB HELLA LITHUANIA—See Hella GmbH & Co. KGaA; *Int'l*, pg. 3333
UAB HEWLETT-PACKARD—See HP Inc.; *U.S. Public*, pg. 1065
UAB HKSCAN LIETUVA—See HKFoods Plc; *Int'l*, pg. 3429
UAB IGNITIS GRUPE; *Int'l*, pg. 7998
UAB INDEEL LT—See Yokogawa Electric Corporation; *Int'l*, pg. 8592
UAB INDUSTEK—See Indutrade AB; *Int'l*, pg. 3682
UAB INTRUM JUSTITIA—See Intrum AB; *Int'l*, pg. 3771
UAB INWIDO SUPPORT—See Ratos AB; *Int'l*, pg. 6220
UAB IVECO CAPITAL BALTIC—See CNH Industrial N.V.; *Int'l*, pg. 1676
UAB JOHNSON & JOHNSON—See Johnson & Johnson; *U.S. Public*, pg. 1200
UAB JONISKIO ENERGIJA—See Fortum Oyj; *Int'l*, pg. 2742
UAB JZP OPTIKA LITUANIA—See EssilorLuxottica SA; *Int'l*, pg. 2516
UAB KALNAPILIO-TAURO GRUPE—See Royal Unibrew A/S; *Int'l*, pg. 6414
UAB KAROLINISKIU TURGUS—See City Service SE; *Int'l*, pg. 1628
UAB KAUNO ENERGETIKOS REMONTAS—See UAB Ignitis grupe; *Int'l*, pg. 7998
UAB KENTEK LIETUVA—See Diploma PLC; *Int'l*, pg. 2129
UAB KIA AUTO—See Tallinna Kaubamaja AS; *Int'l*, pg. 7448
UAB KINGSPAN—See Kingspan Group PLC; *Int'l*, pg. 4179
UAB KINNARPS—See Kinnarps AB; *Int'l*, pg. 4181
UAB KITRON REAL ESTATE—See Kitron ASA; *Int'l*, pg. 4195
UAB KITRON—See Kitron ASA; *Int'l*, pg. 4195
UAB KONCERNAS SBA; *Int'l*, pg. 7998
UAB KONECRANES—See Konecranes Plc; *Int'l*, pg. 4253
UAB KONE—See KONE Oyj; *Int'l*, pg. 4250
UAB KRANTAS TRAVEL—See DFDS A/S; *Int'l*, pg. 2095
UAB KRKA LIETUVA—See Krka, d.d., Novo Mesto; *Int'l*, pg. 4303
UAB KROVINIU TERMINALAS—See Koncernas Achemos Grupe; *Int'l*, pg. 4246
UAB KRUZAS NORDIC COSMETICS DISTRIBUTION—See Berner Oy; *Int'l*, pg. 988
UAB LAISVAS IR NEPRIKLAUSOMAS KANALAS—See MG Baltic UAB; *Int'l*, pg. 4871
UAB LEIPURIN—See Aspo Oyj; *Int'l*, pg. 631
UAB LEMMINKAINEN LIETUVA—See YIT Corporation; *Int'l*, pg. 8587
UAB LIETLINEN—See Marzotto S.p.A.; *Int'l*, pg. 4718
UAB LIETUVOS SPAUDOS VILNIAUS AGENTURA—See Sanoma Oyj; *Int'l*, pg. 6553
UAB LINDAB—See Lindab International AB; *Int'l*, pg. 4504
UAB LITHUANIAN SNACKS—See PepsiCo, Inc.; *U.S. Public*, pg. 1672
UAB LITSPIN—See Egetaepper A/S; *Int'l*, pg. 2324
UAB LOTOS BALTIJA—See Grupa LOTOS S.A.; *Int'l*, pg. 3117
UABL PARAGUAY S.A—See Southern Cross Capital Management SA; *Int'l*, pg. 7118
UABL S.A.—See Southern Cross Capital Management SA; *Int'l*, pg. 7118
UAB LUMEN INTELLECTUS—See Kitron ASA; *Int'l*, pg. 4195
UAB LUNDBECK LITHUANIA—See Lundbeckfonden; *Int'l*, pg. 4582
UAB MANO APLINKA—See City Service SE; *Int'l*, pg. 1628
UAB MANO BUSTAS ALYTUS—See City Service SE; *Int'l*, pg. 1628
UAB MANO BUSTAS KAUNAS—See City Service SE; *Int'l*, pg. 1628
UAB MANO BUSTAS KLAIPEDA—See City Service SE; *Int'l*, pg. 1628
UAB MANO BUSTAS SIAULIAI—See City Service SE; *Int'l*, pg. 1628
UAB MANO BUSTAS—See City Service SE; *Int'l*, pg. 1628
UAB MANO BUSTAS VILNIUS—See City Service SE; *Int'l*, pg. 1628
UAB MANO SAUGA LT—See City Service SE; *Int'l*, pg. 1628
UAB MAZEIKIU NAFTOS SVEIKATOS PRIEZIUROS CENTRAS—See Orlen S.A.; *Int'l*, pg. 5641
UAB MEGRAME; *Int'l*, pg. 7999
UAB MERCK SHARP & DOHME—See Merck & Co., Inc.; *U.S. Public*, pg. 1421
UAB MERKO STATYBA—See AS Merko Ehitus; *Int'l*, pg. 590
UAB MG BALTIC TRADE—See MG Baltic UAB; *Int'l*, pg. 4871
UAB MG VALDA—See MG Baltic UAB; *Int'l*, pg. 4871
UAB MIKRON—See Mikron Holding AG; *Int'l*, pg. 4893
UAB MINERALINIAI VANDENYS—See MG Baltic UAB; *Int'l*, pg. 4871
UAB MINORDIJA—See Orkla ASA; *Int'l*, pg. 5639
UAB MITNIJA—See MG Baltic UAB; *Int'l*, pg. 4871
UAB NESTE LIETUVA—See Fortum Oyj; *Int'l*, pg. 2742
UAB NESTE LIETUVA—See Neste Oyj; *Int'l*, pg. 5202
UAB NIF LIETUVA—See AS Reverta; *Int'l*, pg. 591
UAB NURMINEN MARITIME—See Nurminen Logistics Plc; *Int'l*, pg. 5490
UAB ONEMED—See Interogo Holding AG; *Int'l*, pg. 3754
UAB ORIOLA VILNIUS—See Oriola Corporation; *Int'l*, pg. 5631
UAB ORION GLOBAL PET—See Indorama Ventures Public Company Limited; *Int'l*, pg. 3658
UAB ORION PHARMA—See Orion Corporation; *Int'l*, pg. 5632
UAB ORKLA FOODS LIETUVA—See Orkla ASA; *Int'l*, pg. 5639
UAB PALANGOS VETRA—See Koncernas Achemos Grupe; *Int'l*, pg. 4246
UAB PAPYRUS LIETUVA—See Altor Equity Partners AB; *Int'l*, pg. 395
UAB PAREX INVESTICIJU VALDYMAS—See AS Reverta; *Int'l*, pg. 591
UAB PAROC—See Owens Corning; *U.S. Public*, pg. 1628
UAB PASTATU PRIEZIURA—See City Service SE; *Int'l*, pg. 1628
UAB PASTATU VALDYMAS—See City Service SE; *Int'l*, pg. 1628
UAB PERNOD RICARD LIETUVA—See Pernod Ricard S.A.; *Int'l*, pg. 5811
UAB PHARMASWISS—See Bausch Health Companies Inc.; *Int'l*, pg. 898
UAB PHILIP MORRIS BALTIC—See Philip Morris International Inc.; *U.S. Public*, pg. 1687
UAB PHILIP MORRIS LIETUVA—See Philip Morris International Inc.; *U.S. Public*, pg. 1687
UAB PLASTIMA—See REHAU Verwaltungszentrale AG; *Int'l*, pg. 6256
UAB PORTALPRO—See City Service SE; *Int'l*, pg. 1628
UAB PREKYBOS CENTRAS MANDARINAS—See Citycon Oyj; *Int'l*, pg. 1629
UAB PRICEWATERHOUSECOOPERS; *Int'l*, pg. 7999
UAB PUUMERKKI—See Stora Enso Oyj; *Int'l*, pg. 7224
UAB "ECE PROJEKTMANAGEMENT VILNIUS"—See ECE Projektmanagement GmbH & Co KG; *Int'l*, pg. 2288
UAB "SANOFI-AVENTIS LIETUVA"—See Sanofi; *Int'l*, pg. 6551
UAB RAISIO LIETUVA—See Raisio PLC; *Int'l*, pg. 6191
UAB RAMIRENT—See Loxam SAS; *Int'l*, pg. 4566
UAB RENERGA—See Koncernas Achemos Grupe; *Int'l*, pg. 4246
UAB RHENUS SVORIS—See RETHMANN AG & Co. KG; *Int'l*, pg. 6309
UAB ROBERT BOSCH—See Robert Bosch GmbH; *Int'l*, pg. 6368
UAB ROCKWOOL—See ROCKWOOL A/S; *Int'l*, pg. 6381
UAB RUUKKI LIETUVA—See SSAB AB; *Int'l*, pg. 7154
UAB SARIA—See RETHMANN AG & Co. KG; *Int'l*, pg. 6310
UAB SCHENKER—See Deutsche Bahn AG; *Int'l*, pg. 2054
UAB SCHINDLER LIFTAS—See Schindler Holding AG; *Int'l*, pg. 6621
UAB SCHNEIDER ELECTRIC LIETUVA—See Schneider Electric SE; *Int'l*, pg. 6635
UAB SELECTA—See Allianz SE; *Int'l*, pg. 356
UAB SERGEL—See Telia Company AB; *Int'l*, pg. 7545
UAB S-GROUP LIETUVA—See Addnode Group AB; *Int'l*, pg. 131
UAB SHERWIN-WILLIAMS BALTIC—See The Sherwin-Williams Company; *U.S. Public*, pg. 2130
UAB SHERWIN-WILLIAMS LIETUVA—See The Sherwin-Williams Company; *U.S. Public*, pg. 2130
UAB SIEMENS—See Siemens Aktiengesellschaft; *Int'l*, pg. 6901
UAB SLO LITHUANIA—See Sonepar S.A.; *Int'l*, pg. 7094
UAB SMC PNEUMATICS—See SMC Corporation; *Int'l*, pg. 7006
UAB SPORTLAND LT—See Frasers Group plc; *Int'l*, pg. 2765
UAB STAPPERT LIETUVA—See Jacquet Metal Service SA; *Int'l*, pg. 3868
UAB STORA ENSO LIETUVA—See Stora Enso Oyj; *Int'l*, pg. 7224
UAB STORMGEO—See Alfa Laval AB; *Int'l*, pg. 312
UAB STUMBRAS—See MG Baltic UAB; *Int'l*, pg. 4871
UAB SWECO HIDROPROJEKTAS—See Sweco AB; *Int'l*, pg. 7363
UAB SWECO LIETUVA—See Sweco AB; *Int'l*, pg. 7364
UAB TAMRO—See PHOENIX Pharmahandel GmbH & Co. KG; *Int'l*, pg. 5855
UAB TECH-COAT—See Sto SE & Co. KGaA; *Int'l*, pg. 7219
UAB TELE-FONIKA BALTIC—See TELE-FONIKA Kable Sp. z o.o. S.K.A.; *Int'l*, pg. 7529
UAB THYSSENKRUPP BALTIJA—See ThyssenKrupp AG; *Int'l*, pg. 7734
UAB TIBNOR—See SSAB AB; *Int'l*, pg. 7155

UAB TIKKURILA—See PPG Industries, Inc.; *U.S. Public*, pg. 1711
UAB TOYO INK EUROPE BALTICA—See Toyo Ink SC Holdings Co., Ltd.; *Int'l*, pg. 7855
UAB TROMINA—See MG Baltic UAB; *Int'l*, pg. 4871
UAB UNIS STEEL BALTIJA—See UNIS Fabrika Cijevi a.d.; *Int'l*, pg. 8060
UAB VALBRA; *Int'l*, pg. 7999
UAB VALIO INTERNATIONAL—See Valio Ltd.; *Int'l*, pg. 8116
UAB VILKMERGES ALUS—See Royal Unibrew A/S; *Int'l*, pg. 6414
UAB VILNIAUS DUONA—See Lantmannen ek for; *Int'l*, pg. 4414
UAB VILNIUS ENERGIJA—See Veolia Environnement S.A.; *Int'l*, pg. 8156
UAB VMG FOOD—See Orkla ASA; *Int'l*, pg. 5637
UAB VYDMANTAI WIND PARK—See JSC INTER RAO UES; *Int'l*, pg. 4009
UAB WAVIN BALTIC—See Bharti Enterprises Limited; *Int'l*, pg. 1012
UAB WESTERN BALTIJA SHIPBUILDING—See BLRT Grupp AS; *Int'l*, pg. 1066
UAB WTE BALTIC—See EVN AG; *Int'l*, pg. 2571
UAB XIRGO GLOBAL—See Sensata Technologies Holding plc; *U.S. Public*, pg. 1866
UAB YAZAKI WIRING TECHNOLOGIES LIETUVA—See Yazaki Corporation; *Int'l*, pg. 8572
UAB ZEMAITIJOS GRUDAI—See Koncernas Achemos Grupe; *Int'l*, pg. 4246
UAC ADVANCE POLYMER & CHEMICALS CO., LTD.—See UAC Global Public Company Limited; *Int'l*, pg. 7999
UAC BERHAD—See Lembaga Tabung Angkatan Tentera; *Int'l*, pg. 4449
UAC ENERGY HOLDINGS PTY. LTD.; *Int'l*, pg. 7999
UAC GLOBAL PUBLIC COMPANY LIMITED; *Int'l*, pg. 7999
UACJ AUTOMOTIVE WHITEHALL INDUSTRIES, INC.—See UACJ Corporation; *Int'l*, pg. 7999
UACJBUTSURYU.CO., LTD.—See Senko Group Holdings Co., Ltd.; *Int'l*, pg. 6712
UACJ CORPORATION; *Int'l*, pg. 7999
UACJ EXTRUSION CZECH S.R.O.—See UACJ Corporation; *Int'l*, pg. 7999
UACJ FOIL CORPORATION—See UACJ Corporation; *Int'l*, pg. 7999
UACJ FOIL MALAYSIA SDN. BHD.—See UACJ Corporation; *Int'l*, pg. 7999
UACJ FOIL SANGYO CORPORATION—See UACJ Corporation; *Int'l*, pg. 7999
UACJ FOIL SERVICE CORPORATION—See UACJ Corporation; *Int'l*, pg. 7999
UACJ FOUNDRY & FORGING CORPORATION—See UACJ Corporation; *Int'l*, pg. 7999
UACJ FOUNDRY & FORGING (VIETNAM) CO., LTD.—See UACJ Corporation; *Int'l*, pg. 7999
UACJ MARKETING & PROCESSING AMERICA, INC.—See UACJ Corporation; *Int'l*, pg. 7999
UACJ MARKETING & PROCESSING CORPORATION—See UACJ Corporation; *Int'l*, pg. 8000
UACJ METAL COMPONENTS CENTRAL MEXICO, S.A. DE C.V.—See UACJ Corporation; *Int'l*, pg. 8000
UACJ METAL COMPONENTS MEXICO, S.A. DE C.V.—See UACJ Corporation; *Int'l*, pg. 8000
UACJ METAL COMPONENTS NORTH AMERICA, INC.—See UACJ Corporation; *Int'l*, pg. 8000
UACJ MH (THAILAND) CO., LTD.—See UACJ Corporation; *Int'l*, pg. 7999
UACJ (THAILAND) CO., LTD.—See UACJ Corporation; *Int'l*, pg. 7999
UACJ TRADING CORPORATION—See UACJ Corporation; *Int'l*, pg. 8000
UACJ TRADING (KUNSHAN) METAL PRODUCTS CO., LTD.—See UACJ Corporation; *Int'l*, pg. 8000
UACJ TRADING (SHANGHAI) CO., LTD.—See UACJ Corporation; *Int'l*, pg. 8000
UACJ TRADING (THAILAND) CO., LTD.—See UACJ Corporation; *Int'l*, pg. 8000
UAC OF NIGERIA PLC; *Int'l*, pg. 7999
UADBB AON BALTIC—See Aon plc; *Int'l*, pg. 495
UAD BB MARSH LIETUVA—See Marsh & McLennan Companies, Inc.; *U.S. Public*, pg. 1388
UAE EXCHANGE AUSTRALIA PTY LTD—See NMC Health PLC; *Int'l*, pg. 5392
UAE EXCHANGE CENTRE LLC—See NMC Health PLC; *Int'l*, pg. 5392
UAE OIL SERVICES PLC; *Int'l*, pg. 8000
UAE SPONSORSHIP CENTRE—See NMC Health PLC; *Int'l*, pg. 5392
UAG ATLANTA H1, LLC—See Penske Automotive Group, Inc.; *U.S. Public*, pg. 1666
UAG FAIRFIELD CA, LLC—See Penske Automotive Group, Inc.; *U.S. Public*, pg. 1666
UAG FAIRFIELD CM, LLC—See Penske Automotive Group, Inc.; *U.S. Public*, pg. 1666
UAG FAYETTEVILLE III, LLC—See Penske Automotive Group, Inc.; *U.S. Public*, pg. 1666

UAE OIL SERVICES PLC

UAG LANDERS SPRINGDALE, LLC—See Penske Automotive Group, Inc.; *U.S. Public*, pg. 1666
UAG WEST BAY IA, LLC—See Penske Automotive Group, Inc.; *U.S. Public*, pg. 1666
UAH LIMITED—See Capricorn Energy PLC; *Int'l*, pg. 1316
UALA SRL; *Int'l*, pg. 8000
UA LOCAL UNION 669 ROAD SPRINKLER FITTERS; *U.S. Private*, pg. 4272
UAM PHILIPPINES, INC.—See Okaya & Co., Ltd.; *Int'l*, pg. 5547
UA MULTIMEDIA, INC.; *U.S. Public*, pg. 2217
U AND I GROUP PLC; *Int'l*, pg. 7996
UANGEL BRAZIL—See UANGEL Corporation; *Int'l*, pg. 8000
UANGEL CORPORATION; *Int'l*, pg. 8000
UANGEL ITALY—See UANGEL Corporation; *Int'l*, pg. 8000
UANGEL KOREA—See UANGEL Corporation; *Int'l*, pg. 8000
UANGEL THAILAND CO., LTD.—See UANGEL Corporation; *Int'l*, pg. 8000
UANGEL U.S.A.—See UANGEL Corporation; *Int'l*, pg. 8000
UAN POWER CORP.; *U.S. Public*, pg. 2217
UAP AUSTRALIA PTY LTD; *Int'l*, pg. 8000
THE UAP GROUP LIMITED; *Int'l*, pg. 7697
UAP, INC. (CADEL DIV.)—See Genuine Parts Company; *U.S. Public*, pg. 932
UAP INC.—See Genuine Parts Company; *U.S. Public*, pg. 932
UAPRO INC—See Genuine Parts Company; *U.S. Public*, pg. 933
UASAC CEE (AUSTRIA) GMBH—See Albert Ballin KG; *Int'l*, pg. 296
UASAC CEE (HUNGARY) KFT.—See Albert Ballin KG; *Int'l*, pg. 296
UASAC CEE (SLOVAKIA) S.R.O.—See Albert Ballin KG; *Int'l*, pg. 296
UASAC DENIZCILIK NAKLIYAT A.S.—See Albert Ballin KG; *Int'l*, pg. 296
UASAC FRANCE SAS—See Albert Ballin KG; *Int'l*, pg. 296
UASAC IBERIA S.L.—See Albert Ballin KG; *Int'l*, pg. 296
UASAC (ITALY) SRL—See Albert Ballin KG; *Int'l*, pg. 296
UASAC POLSKA—See Albert Ballin KG; *Int'l*, pg. 296
UASAC (UK) LTD.—See Albert Ballin KG; *Int'l*, pg. 296
UASC AGENCIES GHANA—See Albert Ballin KG; *Int'l*, pg. 296
UASC AGENCIES NIGERIA—See Albert Ballin KG; *Int'l*, pg. 296
UAS DRONE CORP.; *U.S. Public*, pg. 2217
UAS LABORATORIES, INC.—See Novonesis A/S; *Int'l*, pg. 5468
UAT—See AXA S.A.; *Int'l*, pg. 759
UAV AND DRONE SOLUTIONS PTY. LTD.—See The Bidvest Group Limited; *Int'l*, pg. 7626
UAV ENGINES LTD.—See Elbit Systems Limited; *Int'l*, pg. 2345
UAV FACTORY LTD.—See AE Industrial Partners, LP; *U.S. Private*, pg. 112
UAV FACTORY USA LLC—See AE Industrial Partners, LP; *U.S. Private*, pg. 112
U A VIE—See AXA S.A.; *Int'l*, pg. 759
UBA CHAD S.A.—See United Bank for Africa Plc; *Int'l*, pg. 8064
UBA CONGO BRAZZAVILLE SA—See United Bank for Africa Plc; *Int'l*, pg. 8064
UBA CONGO DRC SA—See United Bank for Africa Plc; *Int'l*, pg. 8065
UBA GHANA LIMITED—See United Bank for Africa Plc; *Int'l*, pg. 8065
UBA GUINEA SA—See United Bank for Africa Plc; *Int'l*, pg. 8065
UBA INVESTMENTS LIMITED; *Int'l*, pg. 8000
UBAJAY DAS S.A.—See Corteva, Inc.; *U.S. Public*, pg. 582
UBA LIBERIA LIMITED—See United Bank for Africa Plc; *Int'l*, pg. 8065
UBA MOZAMBIQUE SA—See United Bank for Africa Plc; *Int'l*, pg. 8065
UBANK LTD.—See FIBI Holdings Ltd.; *Int'l*, pg. 2652
UBANK—See Huntington Bancshares Inc.; *U.S. Private*, pg. 2010
UBANK TRUST COMPANY LTD.—See FIBI Holdings Ltd.; *Int'l*, pg. 2652
UBA SENEGAL SA—See United Bank for Africa Plc; *Int'l*, pg. 8065
UBA TANZANIA LIMITED—See United Bank for Africa Plc; *Int'l*, pg. 8065
UBA UGANDA LIMITED—See United Bank for Africa Plc; *Int'l*, pg. 8065
UBA UK LIMITED—See United Bank for Africa Plc; *Int'l*, pg. 8065
UBB ASSET MANAGEMENT AD—See KBC Group NV; *Int'l*, pg. 4107
UBB FACTORING E.O.O.D.—See KBC Group NV; *Int'l*, pg. 4107
UBBINK B.V.—See CENTROTEC SE; *Int'l*, pg. 1414
UBBINK FRANCE S.A.S.—See CENTROTEC SE; *Int'l*, pg. 1415

UBBINK GARTEN GMBH—See Outside Living Industries France SARL; *Int'l*, pg. 5669
UBBINK NV—See CENTROTEC SE; *Int'l*, pg. 1415
UBBINK (UK) LTD.—See CENTROTEC SE; *Int'l*, pg. 1415
UBB INSURANCE BROKER A.D.—See KBC Group NV; *Int'l*, pg. 4107
UBB USEDOMER BADERBAHN GMBH—See Deutsche Bahn AG; *Int'l*, pg. 2055
UBCARE CO., LTD.—See GC Biopharma Corp.; *Int'l*, pg. 2894
UBC CABLE NETWORK PUBLIC COMPANY LIMITED—See Charoen Pokphand Group Co., Ltd.; *Int'l*, pg. 1453
U.B. CHEMICAL INDUSTRIES CO., LTD.—See Saha Pathanapibul Public Company Limited; *Int'l*, pg. 6479
UBC INVESTMENTS, INC.—See United Bancshares, Inc.; *U.S. Public*, pg. 2229
UBC LATE STAGE, INC.—See The Cigna Group; *U.S. Public*, pg. 2062
UBC PRECISION BEARING MANUFACTURING CO., LTD.—See Nippon Thompson Co., Ltd.; *Int'l*, pg. 5357
UBCR LLC—See Tomra Systems ASA; *Int'l*, pg. 7803
UBC SCIENTIFIC SOLUTIONS, LIMITED—See The Cigna Group; *U.S. Public*, pg. 2062
UBE ALUMINUM WHEELS LTD.—See UBE Corporation; *Int'l*, pg. 8001
UBE AMERICA INC.—See UBE Corporation; *Int'l*, pg. 8001
UBE AMMONIA INDUSTRY, LTD.—See UBE Corporation; *Int'l*, pg. 8001
UBE ASSET & INSURANCE, LTD.—See UBE Corporation; *Int'l*, pg. 8001
UBE AUTOMOTIVE—See UBE Corporation; *Int'l*, pg. 8001
UBE BOARD CO., LTD.—See UBE Corporation; *Int'l*, pg. 8001
UBE-C&A CO., LTD.—See UBE Corporation; *Int'l*, pg. 8002
UBE CHEMICAL EUROPE, S.A.—See UBE Corporation; *Int'l*, pg. 8002
UBE CHEMICALS (ASIA) PUBLIC CO., LTD.—See UBE Corporation; *Int'l*, pg. 8001
UBE CONCRETE INDUSTRY CO., LTD.—See UBE Corporation; *Int'l*, pg. 8001
UBE CONSTRUCTION MATERIALS CO., LTD.—See UBE Corporation; *Int'l*, pg. 8001
UBE CONSTRUCTION MATERIALS SALES CO., LTD.—See UBE Corporation; *Int'l*, pg. 8001
UBE CORPORATION EUROPE, S.A.—See UBE Corporation; *Int'l*, pg. 8001
UBE CORPORATION; *Int'l*, pg. 8000
UBE INTERACTIVE, INC.; *U.S. Private*, pg. 4273
UBE ELASTOMER CO., LTD.—See UBE Corporation; *Int'l*, pg. 8001
UBE ELECTRONICS, LTD.—See UBE Corporation; *Int'l*, pg. 8002
UBE ELECTRONICS (WUXI) CO., LTD.—See UBE Corporation; *Int'l*, pg. 8002
UBE ENGINEERING PLASTICS, S.A.—See UBE Corporation; *Int'l*, pg. 8002
UBE EUROPE GMBH—See UBE Corporation; *Int'l*, pg. 8002
UBE EXSYMO CO., LTD.—See UBE Corporation; *Int'l*, pg. 8002
UBE FINE CHEMICALS (ASIA) CO., LTD.—See UBE Corporation; *Int'l*, pg. 8002
UBE (HONG KONG) LTD.—See UBE Corporation; *Int'l*, pg. 8001
UBE INDUSTRIES, LTD. - CHIBA PETROCHEMICAL FACTORY—See UBE Corporation; *Int'l*, pg. 8002
UBE INDUSTRIES, LTD. - ISA CEMENT FACTORY—See UBE Corporation; *Int'l*, pg. 8002
UBE INDUSTRIES, LTD. - KANDA CEMENT FACTORY—See UBE Corporation; *Int'l*, pg. 8002
UBE INDUSTRIES, LTD. - SAKAI FACTORY—See UBE Corporation; *Int'l*, pg. 8002
UBE INDUSTRIES, LTD. - UBE CEMENT FACTORY—See UBE Corporation; *Int'l*, pg. 8002
UBE INDUSTRIES, LTD. - UBE CHEMICAL FACTORY—See UBE Corporation; *Int'l*, pg. 8002
UBE INDUSTRIES TOTAL SERVICE CO., LTD.—See UBE Corporation; *Int'l*, pg. 8002
UBE INFORMATION SYSTEMS INC.—See UBE Corporation; *Int'l*, pg. 8002
UBE KOREA CO., LTD.—See UBE Corporation; *Int'l*, pg. 8002
UBE LATIN AMERICA SERVICOS LTDA.—See UBE Corporation; *Int'l*, pg. 8002
UBEL BV—See Sonepar S.A.; *Int'l*, pg. 7094
UBE MACHINERY CORPORATION, LTD.—See UBE Corporation; *Int'l*, pg. 8002
UBE MACHINERY INC.—See UBE Corporation; *Int'l*, pg. 8002
UBE MACHINERY (SHANGHAI) LTD.—See UBE Corporation; *Int'l*, pg. 8002
UBE MATERIAL INDUSTRIES, LTD.—See UBE Corporation; *Int'l*, pg. 8001
UBE-MC HYDROGEN PEROXIDE LTD.—See UBE Corporation; *Int'l*, pg. 8001
UBE MEXICO S. DE R.L. DE C.V.—See UBE Corporation; *Int'l*, pg. 8001

CORPORATE AFFILIATIONS

UBE-MITSUBISHI CEMENT CORPORATION—See Mitsubishi Materials Corporation; *Int'l*, pg. 4965
UBE-MITSUBISHI CEMENT CORPORATION—See UBE Corporation; *Int'l*, pg. 8001
UBENCH INTERNATIONAL NV—See BASF SE; *Int'l*, pg. 885
UBE NISSHIN LIME CO., LTD.—See UBE Corporation; *Int'l*, pg. 8002
UBE NYLON (THAILAND) LIMITED—See UBE Corporation; *Int'l*, pg. 8002
UBEO, LLC—See Sentinel Capital Partners, L.L.C.; *U.S. Private*, pg. 3609
UBE PORT SERVICE CO., LTD.—See Mitsui O.S.K. Lines, Ltd.; *Int'l*, pg. 4992
UBERALL; *Int'l*, pg. 8002
UBER AUSTRIA GMBH—See Uber Technologies, Inc.; *U.S. Public*, pg. 2217
UBER B.V.—See Uber Technologies, Inc.; *U.S. Public*, pg. 2217
UBE REALTY & DEVELOPMENT CO., LTD.—See UBE Corporation; *Int'l*, pg. 8002
UBER FRANCE SAS—See Uber Technologies, Inc.; *U.S. Public*, pg. 2217
UBER GERMANY GMBH—See Uber Technologies, Inc.; *U.S. Public*, pg. 2217
UBER INDIA SYSTEMS PRIVATE LIMITED—See Uber Technologies, Inc.; *U.S. Public*, pg. 2217
UBER JAPAN CO. LTD.—See Uber Technologies, Inc.; *U.S. Public*, pg. 2217
UBERLANDWERK KRUMBACH GMBH—See RWE AG; *Int'l*, pg. 6436
UBER LONDON LIMITED—See Uber Technologies, Inc.; *U.S. Public*, pg. 2217
UBER POLAND SP. Z O.O.—See Uber Technologies, Inc.; *U.S. Public*, pg. 2217
UBERSMITH, INC.—See Internap Holding LLC; *U.S. Private*, pg. 2114
UBER SOUTH AFRICA TECHNOLOGY (PTY) LTD.—See Uber Technologies, Inc.; *U.S. Public*, pg. 2217
UBER TECHNOLOGIES, INC.; *U.S. Public*, pg. 2217
UBE SAND CO., LTD.—See UBE Corporation; *Int'l*, pg. 8002
UBE SCIENTIFIC ANALYSIS LABORATORY, INC.—See UBE Corporation; *Int'l*, pg. 8002
UBE (SHANGHAI) LTD.—See UBE Corporation; *Int'l*, pg. 8001
UBE SHIPPING & LOGISTICS, LTD.—See UBE Corporation; *Int'l*, pg. 8002
UBE SINGAPORE PTE. LTD.—See UBE Corporation; *Int'l*, pg. 8002
UBE STEEL CO., LTD.—See UBE Corporation; *Int'l*, pg. 8002
UBE TECHNICAL CENTER (ASIA) LIMITED—See UBE Corporation; *Int'l*, pg. 8002
UBE TECHNO ENG CO., LTD.—See UBE Corporation; *Int'l*, pg. 8002
UBE YOSHINO GYPSUM CO., LTD.—See Central Glass Co., Ltd.; *Int'l*, pg. 1407
UB FINANCE COMPANY LIMITED—See Union Bank of Colombo Limited; *Int'l*, pg. 8051
UB GREENSFELDER LLP; *U.S. Private*, pg. 4273
UB GROUP LIMITED—See Barclays PLC; *Int'l*, pg. 863
UBH OF OREGON, LLC—See Universal Health Services, Inc.; *U.S. Public*, pg. 2260
UBH OF PHOENIX, LLC—See Universal Health Services, Inc.; *U.S. Public*, pg. 2260
UBI BANCA DI VALLE CAMONICA S.P.A.—See Intesa Sanpaolo S.p.A.; *Int'l*, pg. 3766
UBI BANCA INTERNATIONAL S.A.—See EFG International AG; *Int'l*, pg. 2321
UBI BANCO DI BRESCIA SPA—See Intesa Sanpaolo S.p.A.; *Int'l*, pg. 3766
UBI BLOCKCHAIN INTERNET, LTD.; *Int'l*, pg. 8003
UBICARE; *U.S. Private*, pg. 4273
UBIC NORTH AMERICA, INC. HONG KONG—See Fronteo, Inc.; *Int'l*, pg. 2794
UBIC NORTH AMERICA, INC. SOUTH KOREA—See Fronteo, Inc.; *Int'l*, pg. 2794
UBICOM HOLDINGS, INC.; *Int'l*, pg. 8003
UBICS, INC.—See United Breweries (Holdings) Ltd.; *Int'l*, pg. 8065
UBID.COM, INC.—See Enable Holdings, Inc.; *U.S. Public*, pg. 754
UBI FACTOR S.P.A.—See Intesa Sanpaolo S.p.A.; *Int'l*, pg. 3766
UBI GAMES SA—See Ubisoft Entertainment S.A.; *Int'l*, pg. 8003
UBI GESTIONI FIDUCIARIE SIM S.P.A.—See Intesa Sanpaolo S.p.A.; *Int'l*, pg. 3766
UBI INSURANCE BROKER SRL—See Intesa Sanpaolo S.p.A.; *Int'l*, pg. 3766
UBI LEASE FINANCE 5 SRL—See Intesa Sanpaolo S.p.A.; *Int'l*, pg. 3766
UBI LEASING S.P.A.—See Intesa Sanpaolo S.p.A.; *Int'l*, pg. 3766
UBI LOGISTICS (CHINA) LIMITED—See A-Sonic Aerospace Limited; *Int'l*, pg. 21
UBI LOGISTICS (HK) LIMITED—See A-Sonic Aerospace Limited; *Int'l*, pg. 21

COMPANY NAME INDEX

UBI MANAGEMENT COMPANY SA—See EFG International AG; *Int'l*, pg. 2321
UBINETICS (VPT) LIMITED—See QUALCOMM Incorporated; *U.S. Public*, pg. 1748
UBION CO., LTD.; *Int'l*, pg. 8003
UBI PRAMERICA SGR S.P.A.—See Intesa Sanpaolo S.p.A.; *Int'l*, pg. 3766
UBIQCONN TECHNOLOGY INC.—See FIC Global, INC; *Int'l*, pg. 2653
UBIQLINK LTD.—See Nomura Research Institute, Ltd.; *Int'l*, pg. 5413
UBIQUE MINERALS LTD.; *Int'l*, pg. 8003
UBIQUITI INC.; *U.S. Public*, pg. 2217
UBIQUITOUS AI CORPORATION; *Int'l*, pg. 8003
UBIQUITY MANAGEMENT, L.P.; *U.S. Private*, pg. 4273
UBIQUOSS HOLDINGS INC.; *Int'l*, pg. 8003
UBIQUOSS JAPAN, INC.—See Ubiquoss Holdings Inc.; *Int'l*, pg. 8003
UBIQUS REPORTING, INC.—See Euromezzanine Conseil SAS; *Int'l*, pg. 2554
UBIQUS REPORTING, INC.—See Indigo Capital LLP; *Int'l*, pg. 3655
UBIQUS SAS—See Euromezzanine Conseil SAS; *Int'l*, pg. 2554
UBIQUS SAS—See Indigo Capital LLP; *Int'l*, pg. 3655
UBIQUS UK LIMITED—See Euromezzanine Conseil SAS; *Int'l*, pg. 2554
UBIQUS UK LIMITED—See Indigo Capital LLP; *Int'l*, pg. 3655
UBIS (ASIA) PUBLIC CO., LTD.; *Int'l*, pg. 8003
UBISENSE AMERICA LLC—See KKR & Co. Inc.; *U.S. Public*, pg. 1253
UBISENSE GMBH—See KKR & Co. Inc.; *U.S. Public*, pg. 1253
UBISENSE JAPAN K.K.—See KKR & Co. Inc.; *U.S. Public*, pg. 1253
UBISENSE LIMITED; *Int'l*, pg. 8003
UBISENSE SAS—See KKR & Co. Inc.; *U.S. Public*, pg. 1253
UBI SERVICES LTD.—See Union Bank of India; *Int'l*, pg. 8051
UBI SISTEMI E SERVIZI SCPA—See Intesa Sanpaolo S.p.A.; *Int'l*, pg. 3766
UBISOFT ANNECY SAS—See Ubisoft Entertainment S.A.; *Int'l*, pg. 8003
UBISOFT BARCELONA MOBILE SL—See Ubisoft Entertainment S.A.; *Int'l*, pg. 8003
UBISOFT BLUE BYTE GMBH—See Ubisoft Entertainment S.A.; *Int'l*, pg. 8003
UBISOFT BV—See Ubisoft Entertainment S.A.; *Int'l*, pg. 8003
UBISOFT CANADA INC.—See Ubisoft Entertainment S.A.; *Int'l*, pg. 8003
UBISOFT EMEA SARL—See Ubisoft Entertainment S.A.; *Int'l*, pg. 8003
UBISOFT ENTERTAINMENT INDIA PRIVATE LTD—See Ubisoft Entertainment S.A.; *Int'l*, pg. 8004
UBISOFT ENTERTAINMENT LTD.—See Ubisoft Entertainment S.A.; *Int'l*, pg. 8004
UBISOFT ENTERTAINMENT S.A.; *Int'l*, pg. 8003
UBISOFT ENTERTAINMENT—See Ubisoft Entertainment S.A.; *Int'l*, pg. 8004
UBISOFT ENTERTAINMENT SWEDEN AB—See Ubisoft Entertainment S.A.; *Int'l*, pg. 8004
UBISOFT EOOD—See Ubisoft Entertainment S.A.; *Int'l*, pg. 8004
UBISOFT FINLAND OY—See Ubisoft Entertainment S.A.; *Int'l*, pg. 8004
UBISOFT FRANCE SAS—See Ubisoft Entertainment S.A.; *Int'l*, pg. 8004
UBISOFT GMBH—See Ubisoft Entertainment S.A.; *Int'l*, pg. 8004
UBISOFT GMBH—See Ubisoft Entertainment S.A.; *Int'l*, pg. 8004
UBISOFT INC.—See Ubisoft Entertainment S.A.; *Int'l*, pg. 8004
UBISOFT KK—See Ubisoft Entertainment S.A.; *Int'l*, pg. 8004
UBISOFT LIMITED—See Ubisoft Entertainment S.A.; *Int'l*, pg. 8004
UBISOFT LTD—See Ubisoft Entertainment S.A.; *Int'l*, pg. 8004
UBISOFT MANUFACTURING & ADMINISTRATION SARL—See Ubisoft Entertainment S.A.; *Int'l*, pg. 8004
UBISOFT MARKETING FRANCE SARL—See Ubisoft Entertainment S.A.; *Int'l*, pg. 8004
UBISOFT MOBILE GAMES SARL—See Ubisoft Entertainment S.A.; *Int'l*, pg. 8004
UBISOFT MONTPELLIER SAS—See Ubisoft Entertainment S.A.; *Int'l*, pg. 8004
UBISOFT MONTREAL—See Ubisoft Entertainment S.A.; *Int'l*, pg. 8004
UBISOFT NORDIC AS—See Ubisoft Entertainment S.A.; *Int'l*, pg. 8004
UBISOFT OSAKA KK—See Ubisoft Entertainment S.A.; *Int'l*, pg. 8004
UBISOFT PRODUCTION FRANCE SAS—See Ubisoft Entertainment S.A.; *Int'l*, pg. 8004

UBISOFT PTY LTD—See Ubisoft Entertainment S.A.; *Int'l*, pg. 8004
UBISOFT SA—See Ubisoft Entertainment S.A.; *Int'l*, pg. 8004
UBISOFT SIMULATIONS SAS—See Ubisoft Entertainment S.A.; *Int'l*, pg. 8004
UBISOFT SINGAPORE PTE LTD—See Ubisoft Entertainment S.A.; *Int'l*, pg. 8004
UBISOFT SPA—See Ubisoft Entertainment S.A.; *Int'l*, pg. 8004
UBISOFT SRL—See Ubisoft Entertainment S.A.; *Int'l*, pg. 8004
UBISOFT STUDIOS SRL—See Ubisoft Entertainment S.A.; *Int'l*, pg. 8004
UBISOFT TORONTO INC.—See Ubisoft Entertainment S.A.; *Int'l*, pg. 8004
UBISOFT WINNIPEG INC.—See Ubisoft Entertainment S.A.; *Int'l*, pg. 8004
UBIS PRIMATECH COMPANY LIMITED—See UBIS (Asia) Public Co., Ltd.; *Int'l*, pg. 8003
UBIS SOLUTIONS INFORMATION TECHNOLOGY GMBH—See UniCredit S.p.A.; *Int'l*, pg. 8035
UBI STUDIOS SL—See Ubisoft Entertainment S.A.; *Int'l*, pg. 8003
UBITEQ, INC.—See ORIX Corporation; *Int'l*, pg. 5636
UBI TRUSTEE SA—See EFG International AG; *Int'l*, pg. 2321
UBIVELOX CO., LTD.; *Int'l*, pg. 8004
UBIVELOX MOBILE CORP.—See UbiVelox Co., Ltd.; *Int'l*, pg. 8004
UBIWAY NV-SA—See bpost NV/SA; *Int'l*, pg. 1133
U-BIX CORPORATION; *Int'l*, pg. 7997
UBL BANK (TANZANIA) LIMITED—See Bestway (Holdings) Limited; *Int'l*, pg. 1001
UBL FUND MANAGERS LIMITED—See Bestway (Holdings) Limited; *Int'l*, pg. 1001
U-BLOX AG—See u-blox Holding AG; *Int'l*, pg. 7997
U-BLOX AMERICA INC.—See u-blox Holding AG; *Int'l*, pg. 7997
U-BLOX BERLIN GMBH—See u-blox Holding AG; *Int'l*, pg. 7997
U-BLOX CORK LTD.—See u-blox Holding AG; *Int'l*, pg. 7997
U-BLOX ESPOO OY—See u-blox Holding AG; *Int'l*, pg. 7997
U-BLOX HOLDING AG; *Int'l*, pg. 7997
U-BLOX ITALIA S.P.A.—See u-blox Holding AG; *Int'l*, pg. 7997
U-BLOX JAPAN K.K.—See u-blox Holding AG; *Int'l*, pg. 7997
U-BLOX LAHORE (PRIVATE) LTD.—See u-blox Holding AG; *Int'l*, pg. 7997
U-BLOX MALMO AB—See u-blox Holding AG; *Int'l*, pg. 7997
U-BLOX SINGAPORE PTE. LTD.—See u-blox Holding AG; *Int'l*, pg. 7997
U-BLOX UK LTD.—See u-blox Holding AG; *Int'l*, pg. 7997
UBM AGRI TRADE SRL—See UBM Holding Public Company Limited; *Int'l*, pg. 8005
UBM AGRO SLOVAKIA S.R.O.—See UBM Holding Public Company Limited; *Int'l*, pg. 8005
UBM ASIA LTD.—See Informa plc; *Int'l*, pg. 3694
UBM ASIA (THAILAND) CO., LTD.—See Informa plc; *Int'l*, pg. 3694
UBM CANON—See Informa plc; *Int'l*, pg. 3694
UBM CHINA (GUANGZHOU) CO. LTD.—See Informa plc; *Int'l*, pg. 3694
UBM CHINA (HANGZHOU) COMPANY LIMITED—See Informa plc; *Int'l*, pg. 3693
UBM CHINA (SHANGHAI) CO., LIMITED—See Informa plc; *Int'l*, pg. 3693
UBM DEVELOPMENT AG—See PORR AG; *Int'l*, pg. 5925
UBM D.O.O. ZA POSLOVANJE NEKRETNINAMA—See PORR AG; *Int'l*, pg. 5925
UBM EXHIBITIONS PHILIPPINES, INC.—See Informa plc; *Int'l*, pg. 3693
UBM FEED ROMANIA SRL—See UBM Holding Public Company Limited; *Int'l*, pg. 8005
UBM HOLDING PUBLIC COMPANY LIMITED; *Int'l*, pg. 8004
UBMI B.V.—See Informa plc; *Int'l*, pg. 3694
UBM INDIA PVT. LTD—See Informa plc; *Int'l*, pg. 3694
UBM JAPAN CO., LTD.—See Informa plc; *Int'l*, pg. 3694
UBM KOREA CORPORATION—See Informa plc; *Int'l*, pg. 3694
UBM LIFE SCIENCES VETERINARY GROUP—See Informa plc; *Int'l*, pg. 3694
UBM LLC—See Informa plc; *Int'l*, pg. 3694
UBM MEDICA ASIA PTE LIMITED—See Informa plc; *Int'l*, pg. 3694
UBM PLC—See Informa plc; *Int'l*, pg. 3693
UBM ROTAFORTE ULLARARASI FUARCOLIK—See Informa plc; *Int'l*, pg. 3693
UBM SEEVILLEN ERRICHTUNGS-GMBH—See PORR AG; *Int'l*, pg. 5925
UBM TECH—See Informa plc; *Int'l*, pg. 3694
UBM TRUST COMPANY LIMITED—See Informa plc; *Int'l*, pg. 3693
UBM (UK) LIMITED—See Informa plc; *Int'l*, pg. 3694

UBN TOWER SDN BHD—See Shangri-La Asia Limited; *Int'l*, pg. 6784
UBOMBO SUGAR LIMITED—See The Garfield Weston Foundation; *Int'l*, pg. 7648
UB ORANGEBURG, LLC—See Regency Centers Corporation; *U.S. Public*, pg. 1774
UBOUR LOGISTICS SERVICES P.L.C.; *Int'l*, pg. 8005
UBP ASSET MANAGEMENT ASIA LIMITED—See Union Bancaire Privee, UBP SA; *Int'l*, pg. 8051
UBP ASSET MANAGEMENT ASIA LTD.—See Union Bancaire Privee, UBP SA; *Int'l*, pg. 8051
UBP ASSET MANAGEMENT (EUROPE) S.A.—See Union Bancaire Privee, UBP SA; *Int'l*, pg. 8051
UBP ASSET MANAGEMENT (EUROPE) S,A.—See Union Bancaire Privee, UBP SA; *Int'l*, pg. 8051
UBP ASSET MANAGEMENT LLC—See Union Bancaire Privee, UBP SA; *Int'l*, pg. 8051
UBP ASSET MANAGEMENT TAIWAN LTD.—See Union Bancaire Privee, UBP SA; *Int'l*, pg. 8051
UBP CAPITAL CORPORATION—See UnionBank of the Philippines; *Int'l*, pg. 8054
UBP GESTION INSTITUCIONAL S.A.U.—See Union Bancaire Privee, UBP SA; *Int'l*, pg. 8051
UBP INVESTMENT MANAGEMENT (SHANGHAI) LTD.—See Union Bancaire Privee, UBP SA; *Int'l*, pg. 8051
UBP INVESTMENT MANAGEMENT (ZHEJIANG) LTD.—See Union Bancaire Privee, UBP SA; *Int'l*, pg. 8051
UBP INVESTMENTS CO., LTD.—See Union Bancaire Privee, UBP SA; *Int'l*, pg. 8051
UBP INVESTMENT SERVICES LTD.—See Union Bancaire Privee, UBP SA; *Int'l*, pg. 8051
UBREAKIFIX—See Asurion LLC; *U.S. Private*, pg. 363
UBS AG - HONG KONG—See UBS Group AG; *Int'l*, pg. 8007
UBS AG JERSEY—See UBS Group AG; *Int'l*, pg. 8010
UBS AG MIAMI AGENCY—See UBS Group AG; *Int'l*, pg. 8008
UBS AG - SINGAPORE—See UBS Group AG; *Int'l*, pg. 8007
UBS AG—See UBS Group AG; *Int'l*, pg. 8007
UBS ASESORES S.A.—See UBS Group AG; *Int'l*, pg. 8008
UBS ASIA EQUITIES LIMITED—See UBS Group AG; *Int'l*, pg. 8008
UBS ASSET MANAGEMENT NEW YORK—See UBS Group AG; *Int'l*, pg. 8009
UBS ASSET MANAGEMENT (SINGAPORE) LTD.—See UBS Group AG; *Int'l*, pg. 8008
UBS ASSET MANAGEMENT SWITZERLAND AG—See UBS Group AG; *Int'l*, pg. 8010
UBS ASSET MANAGEMENT (UK) LTD.—See UBS Group AG; *Int'l*, pg. 8010
UBS AUSTRALIA LTD.—See UBS Group AG; *Int'l*, pg. 8008
UBS (BAHAMAS) LTD.—See UBS Group AG; *Int'l*, pg. 8007
UBS BANK (CANADA)—See UBS Group AG; *Int'l*, pg. 8008
UBS BANK (NETHERLANDS) B.V.—See UBS Group AG; *Int'l*, pg. 8008
UBS BANK—See UBS Group AG; *Int'l*, pg. 8008
UBS BANK USA—See UBS Group AG; *Int'l*, pg. 8008
UBS CAPITAL ASIA PACIFIC (HK) LTD.—See UBS Group AG; *Int'l*, pg. 8008
UBS CAPITAL GMBH—See UBS Group AG; *Int'l*, pg. 8008
UBS CAPITAL LLC—See UBS Group AG; *Int'l*, pg. 8008
UBS CAPITAL MARKETS—See UBS Group AG; *Int'l*, pg. 8008
UBS CAPITAL SECURITIES (JERSEY) LIMITED—See UBS Group AG; *Int'l*, pg. 8008
UBS CAPITAL S.P.A.—See UBS Group AG; *Int'l*, pg. 8008
UBS CARD CENTER AG—See UBS Group AG; *Int'l*, pg. 8008
UBS DERIVATIVES HONG KONG LIMITED—See UBS Group AG; *Int'l*, pg. 8008
UBSECURE, INC.—See Nomura Research Institute, Ltd.; *Int'l*, pg. 5413
UBS ESPANA, S.A.—See UBS Group AG; *Int'l*, pg. 8008
UBS EUROPE SE—See UBS Group AG; *Int'l*, pg. 8010
UBS FIDUCIARIA S.P.A.—See UBS Group AG; *Int'l*, pg. 8008
UBS FINANCIAL SERVICES INC.—See UBS Group AG; *Int'l*, pg. 8008
UBS FINANCIAL SERVICES INC.—See UBS Group AG; *Int'l*, pg. 8008
UBS FINANCIAL SERVICES INC.—See UBS Group AG; *Int'l*, pg. 8008
UBS FINANCIAL SERVICES INC—See UBS Group AG; *Int'l*, pg. 8009
UBS (FRANCE) SA—See UBS Group AG; *Int'l*, pg. 8007
UBS FUND ADVISOR, L.L.C.—See UBS Group AG; *Int'l*, pg. 8008
UBS FUND MANAGEMENT (SWITZERLAND) AG—See Northern Trust Corporation; *U.S. Public*, pg. 1539
UBS FUND SERVICES (CAYMAN) LTD.—See UBS Group AG; *Int'l*, pg. 8008

UBOUR LOGISTICS SERVICES P.L.C. — CORPORATE AFFILIATIONS

UBS FUND SERVICES (IRELAND) LIMITED—See UBS Group AG; *Int'l*, pg. 8008
UBS FUND SERVICES (LUXEMBOURG) S.A.—See Northern Trust Corporation; *U.S. Public*, pg. 1539
UBS GLOBAL ALLOCATION TRUST; *Int'l*, pg. 8005
UBS GLOBAL ASSET MANAGEMENT (AMERICAS) INC.—See UBS Group AG; *Int'l*, pg. 8008
UBS GLOBAL ASSET MANAGEMENT (AUSTRALIA) LTD.—See UBS Group AG; *Int'l*, pg. 8008
UBS GLOBAL ASSET MANAGEMENT (CANADA) CO.—See UBS Group AG; *Int'l*, pg. 8008
UBS GLOBAL ASSET MANAGEMENT (DEUTSCHLAND) GMBH—See UBS Group AG; *Int'l*, pg. 8008
UBS GLOBAL ASSET MANAGEMENT (FRANCE) SA—See UBS Group AG; *Int'l*, pg. 8008
UBS GLOBAL ASSET MANAGEMENT FUNDS LTD—See UBS Group AG; *Int'l*, pg. 8009
UBS GLOBAL ASSET MANAGEMENT HOLDING LTD—See UBS Group AG; *Int'l*, pg. 8009
UBS GLOBAL ASSET MANAGEMENT (HONG KONG) LIMITED—See UBS Group AG; *Int'l*, pg. 8008
UBS GLOBAL ASSET MANAGEMENT (JAPAN) LIMITED—See UBS Group AG; *Int'l*, pg. 8008
UBS GLOBAL ASSET MANAGEMENT (SINGAPORE) LTD—See UBS Group AG; *Int'l*, pg. 8009
UBS GLOBAL ASSET MANAGEMENT (TAIWAN) LTD—See UBS Group AG; *Int'l*, pg. 8009
UBS GLOBAL ASSET MANAGEMENT (UK) LTD.—See UBS Group AG; *Int'l*, pg. 8009
UBS GLOBAL ASSET MANAGEMENT (US) INC.—See UBS Group AG; *Int'l*, pg. 8008
UBS GLOBAL TRUST CORPORATION—See UBS Group AG; *Int'l*, pg. 8009
UBS GROUP AG; *Int'l*, pg. 8005
UBS HONG KONG NOMINEES LTD.—See UBS Group AG; *Int'l*, pg. 8009
UBS (INDIA) PRIVATE LTD—See UBS Group AG; *Int'l*, pg. 8007
UBS INFRASTRUCTURE ASSET MANAGEMENT—See UBS Group AG; *Int'l*, pg. 8008
UBS INTERNATIONAL HOLDINGS B.V.—See UBS Group AG; *Int'l*, pg. 8009
UBS INVEST KAPITALANLAGEGESELLSCHAFT MBH—See UBS Group AG; *Int'l*, pg. 8007
UBS INVESTMENT BANK AG—See UBS Group AG; *Int'l*, pg. 8009
UBS INVESTMENT BANK NEDERLAND B.V.—See UBS Group AG; *Int'l*, pg. 8009
UBS INVESTMENT BANK—See UBS Group AG; *Int'l*, pg. 8009
UBS INVESTMENT BANK—See UBS Group AG; *Int'l*, pg. 8009
UBS INVESTMENT BANK UK—See UBS Group AG; *Int'l*, pg. 8009
UBS INVESTMENT MANAGEMENT CANADA INC.—See UBS Group AG; *Int'l*, pg. 8009
UBS INVESTMENTS LTD.—See UBS Group AG; *Int'l*, pg. 8009
UBS INVESTMENTS PHILIPPINES, INC.—See UBS Group AG; *Int'l*, pg. 8009
UBS ITALIA SIM S.P.A.—See UBS Group AG; *Int'l*, pg. 8007
UBS (ITALIA) S.P.A.—See UBS Group AG; *Int'l*, pg. 8007
UBS LA MAISON DE GESTION SAS—See UBS Group AG; *Int'l*, pg. 8007
UBS LEASING AG—See UBS Group AG; *Int'l*, pg. 8009
UBS (LUXEMBOURG) S.A.—See UBS Group AG; *Int'l*, pg. 8007
UBS (MONACO) SA—See UBS Group AG; *Int'l*, pg. 8007
UBS NEW ZEALAND HOLDINGS LTD.—See UBS Group AG; *Int'l*, pg. 8009
UBS NEW ZEALAND LTD.—See UBS Group AG; *Int'l*, pg. 8009
UBS O'CONNOR LIMITED—See UBS Group AG; *Int'l*, pg. 8010
UBS O'CONNOR LLC—See UBS Group AG; *Int'l*, pg. 8010
UBS PREFERRED FUNDING COMPANY LLC IV—See UBS Group AG; *Int'l*, pg. 8010
UBS PRINCIPAL CAPITAL ASIA LTD.—See UBS Group AG; *Int'l*, pg. 8010
UBS PRIVATE BANKING (DUETSCHLAND) AG—See UBS Group AG; *Int'l*, pg. 8010
UBS PRIVATE BANKING—See UBS Group AG; *Int'l*, pg. 8010
UBS REAL ESTATE GMBH—See UBS Group AG; *Int'l*, pg. 8010
UBS REAL ESTATE SECURITIES INC—See UBS Group AG; *Int'l*, pg. 8010
UBS REALTY INVESTORS LLC—See UBS Group AG; *Int'l*, pg. 8010
UBS SAUDI ARABIA COMPANY—See UBS Group AG; *Int'l*, pg. 8010
UBS SECURITES INDIA PRIVATE LTD—See UBS Group AG; *Int'l*, pg. 8010
UBS SECURITIES ASIA LIMITED—See UBS Group AG; *Int'l*, pg. 8010
UBS SECURITIES AUSTRALIA LTD.—MELBOURNE—See UBS Group AG; *Int'l*, pg. 8009

UBS SECURITIES AUSTRALIA LTD.—See UBS Group AG; *Int'l*, pg. 8009
UBS SECURITIES CANADA, INC.—See UBS Group AG; *Int'l*, pg. 8009
UBS SECURITIES (CANADA), INC.—See UBS Group AG; *Int'l*, pg. 8008
UBS SECURITIES CANADA, INC.—See UBS Group AG; *Int'l*, pg. 8009
UBS SECURITIES CJSC—See UBS Group AG; *Int'l*, pg. 8009
UBS SECURITIES (ESPANA) S.V., S.A.—See UBS Group AG; *Int'l*, pg. 8009
UBS SECURITIES FRANCE S.A.—See UBS Group AG; *Int'l*, pg. 8009
UBS SECURITIES HONG KONG LIMITED—See UBS Group AG; *Int'l*, pg. 8010
UBS SECURITIES INDIA PRIVATE LIMITED—See UBS Group AG; *Int'l*, pg. 8009
UBS SECURITIES ISRAEL LTD.—See UBS Group AG; *Int'l*, pg. 8009
UBS SECURITIES JAPAN PREPARATION CO., LTD.—See UBS Group AG; *Int'l*, pg. 8009
UBS SECURITIES, LLC—See UBS Group AG; *Int'l*, pg. 8008
UBS SECURITIES, LLC—See UBS Group AG; *Int'l*, pg. 8009
UBS SECURITIES LTD—See UBS Group AG; *Int'l*, pg. 8009
UBS SECURITIES MALAYSIA SDN. BHD.—See UBS Group AG; *Int'l*, pg. 8009
UBS SECURITIES PHILIPPINES, INC.—See UBS Group AG; *Int'l*, pg. 8009
UBS SECURITIES PTE. LTD.—See UBS Group AG; *Int'l*, pg. 8010
UBS SECURITIES THAILAND CO., LTD.—See UBS Group AG; *Int'l*, pg. 8010
UBS (SOUTH AFRICA) (PTY) LTD.—See UBS Group AG; *Int'l*, pg. 8009
UBS SUMI TRUST WEALTH MANAGEMENT CO., LTD.—See UBS Group AG; *Int'l*, pg. 8010
UBS SWISS FINANCIAL ADVISERS AG—See Vontobel Holding AG; *Int'l*, pg. 8306
UBS (TRUST & BANKING) LIMITED—See UBS Group AG; *Int'l*, pg. 8007
UBS TRUSTEE COMPANY LIMITED—See UBS Group AG; *Int'l*, pg. 8010
UBS TRUSTEES (BAHAMAS) LTD.—See UBS Group AG; *Int'l*, pg. 8010
UBS TRUSTEES (CAYMAN) LTD.—See UBS Group AG; *Int'l*, pg. 8010
UBS TRUSTEES (CHANNEL ISLANDS) LTD.—See UBS Group AG; *Int'l*, pg. 8010
UBS TRUSTEES (JERSEY) LTD.—See UBS Group AG; *Int'l*, pg. 8010
UBS TRUSTEES (SINGAPORE) LTD.—See UBS Group AG; *Int'l*, pg. 8010
UBS (URUGUAY) LTDA.—See UBS Group AG; *Int'l*, pg. 8007
UBS WEALTH MANAGEMENT ISRAEL LTD—See UBS Group AG; *Int'l*, pg. 8010
U-BTECH SOLUTIONS LTD.; *Int'l*, pg. 7997
UBUBELE HOLDINGS LIMITED; *Int'l*, pg. 8010
UBU HOLDINGS INC.; *U.S. Public*, pg. 2217
UBUYHOLDINGS, INC.; *U.S. Public*, pg. 2217
UB VERKTYG AB—See AGES Industri AB; *Int'l*, pg. 206
U-BX TECHNOLOGY LTD.; *Int'l*, pg. 7997
UB YRITYSRAHOITUS OY—See United Bankers Plc; *Int'l*, pg. 8065
U.C.A. AG; *Int'l*, pg. 7998
UCA GROUP COMPONENT SPECIALTY INC.; *U.S. Private*, pg. 4273
UCA HOLDINGS INC.; *U.S. Private*, pg. 4273
UCAL LTD.; *Int'l*, pg. 8010
UCAL POLYMER INDUSTRIES LIMITED—See Ucal Ltd.; *Int'l*, pg. 8010
UCAL SYSTEMS INC.—See Ucal Ltd.; *Int'l*, pg. 8010
UCAMCO N.V.—See ESO Partners L.P.; *Int'l*, pg. 2504
UCANDO GMBH—See Hella GmbH & Co. KGaA; *Int'l*, pg. 3333
UCANDO SP. Z O.O.—See Hella GmbH & Co. KGaA; *Int'l*, pg. 3333
UCAP CLOUD INFORMATION TECHNOLOGY CO., LTD.; *Int'l*, pg. 8010
UCAPITAL24 S.P.A.; *Int'l*, pg. 8010
UCAPITAL GLOBAL PLC; *Int'l*, pg. 8010
UCAR EMULSION SYSTEMS INTERNATIONAL, INC.—See Dow Inc.; *U.S. Public*, pg. 686
UCAR SA; *Int'l*, pg. 8010
UCA SYSTEMS INC.; *U.S. Private*, pg. 4273
UCB A.E.—See UCB S.A.; *Int'l*, pg. 8011
UCB ASSET MANAGEMENT, INC.—See UCBH Holdings, Inc.; *U.S. Private*, pg. 4273
UCB AUSTRALIA PTY. LTD.—See UCB S.A.; *Int'l*, pg. 8011
UCB AUSTRIA—See National Industries Group Holding S.A.K.; *Int'l*, pg. 5159
UCB BELGIUM S.A.—See UCB S.A.; *Int'l*, pg. 8011
UCB BIOPHARMA LTDA.—See UCB S.A.; *Int'l*, pg. 8011
UCB-BIOPRODUCTS S.A.—See UCB S.A.; *Int'l*, pg. 8012

UCB BIOSCIENCES GMBH—See UCB S.A.; *Int'l*, pg. 8011
UCB BIOSCIENCES, INC.—See UCB S.A.; *Int'l*, pg. 8012
UCB BULGARIA EOOD—See UCB S.A.; *Int'l*, pg. 8011
UCB CANADA INC.—See UCB S.A.; *Int'l*, pg. 8011
UCB COMERCIAL CAST-PROFIL S.A.—See National Industries Group Holding S.A.K.; *Int'l*, pg. 5159
UCB DE MEXICO S.A. DE C.V.—See UCB S.A.; *Int'l*, pg. 8012
UCB FARCHIM S.A.—See UCB S.A.; *Int'l*, pg. 8011
UCB FERROCAST LIMITED—See National Industries Group Holding S.A.K.; *Int'l*, pg. 5159
UCB FINANCE N.V.—See UCB S.A.; *Int'l*, pg. 8011
UCB FINTECH COMPANY LIMITED—See United Commercial Bank Limited; *Int'l*, pg. 8066
UCB GERMANY GMBH—See National Industries Group Holding S.A.K.; *Int'l*, pg. 5159
UCB GMBH—See UCB S.A.; *Int'l*, pg. 8011
UCBH HOLDINGS, INC.; *U.S. Private*, pg. 4273
UCB HOME LOANS CORPORATION LIMITED—See Nationwide Building Society; *Int'l*, pg. 5165
UCB HUNGARY LTD—See UCB S.A.; *Int'l*, pg. 8011
UCB, INC.—See UCB S.A.; *Int'l*, pg. 8012
UCB INDIA PRIVATE LTD—See UCB S.A.; *Int'l*, pg. 8011
UCB INGATLANHITEL RT—See BNP Paribas SA; *Int'l*, pg. 1093
UCB INVESTISSEMENTS S.A.—See UCB S.A.; *Int'l*, pg. 8011
UCB (INVESTMENTS) LTD—See UCB S.A.; *Int'l*, pg. 8011
UCB JAPAN CO. LTD.—See UCB S.A.; *Int'l*, pg. 8011
UCB KOREA CO., LTD.—See UCB S.A.; *Int'l*, pg. 8011
UCB LOCABAIL IMMOBILIER 2—See BNP Paribas SA; *Int'l*, pg. 1093
UCB LUX S.A.—See UCB S.A.; *Int'l*, pg. 8011
UCB MANUFACTURING IRELAND LTD—See UCB S.A.; *Int'l*, pg. 8011
UCB MEDICAL DEVICES SA—See UCB S.A.; *Int'l*, pg. 8011
UCB NORDIC AS—See UCB S.A.; *Int'l*, pg. 8011
UCB NOVOBANK PJSC; *Int'l*, pg. 8010
UCB PHARMA AB—See UCB S.A.; *Int'l*, pg. 8011
UCB-PHARMA AG—See UCB S.A.; *Int'l*, pg. 8012
UCB PHARMA A.S.—See UCB S.A.; *Int'l*, pg. 8011
UCB PHARMA A.S.—See UCB S.A.; *Int'l*, pg. 8011
UCB PHARMA B.V.—See UCB S.A.; *Int'l*, pg. 8011
UCB PHARMACEUTICALS (TAIWAN) LTD.—See UCB S.A.; *Int'l*, pg. 8012
UCB PHARMA GESELLSCHAFT M.B.H.—See UCB S.A.; *Int'l*, pg. 8011
UCB PHARMA GMBH—See UCB S.A.; *Int'l*, pg. 8011
UCB PHARMA (HONG KONG) LTD—See UCB S.A.; *Int'l*, pg. 8011
UCB (PHARMA) IRELAND LTD—See UCB S.A.; *Int'l*, pg. 8011
UCB PHARMA IRELAND LTD.—See UCB S.A.; *Int'l*, pg. 8011
UCB PHARMA LLC—See UCB S.A.; *Int'l*, pg. 8011
UCB PHARMA OY—See UCB S.A.; *Int'l*, pg. 8011
UCB PHARMA (PRODUTOS FARMACEUTICOS) LDA.—See UCB S.A.; *Int'l*, pg. 8011
UCB PHARMA (PRODUTOS FARMACEUTICOS) LDA.—See UCB S.A.; *Int'l*, pg. 8011
UCB PHARMA ROMANIA S.R.L.—See UCB S.A.; *Int'l*, pg. 8011
UCB PHARMA S.A.—See UCB S.A.; *Int'l*, pg. 8011
UCB PHARMA S.A.—See UCB S.A.; *Int'l*, pg. 8011
UCB PHARMA S.A.—See UCB S.A.; *Int'l*, pg. 8012
UCB PHARMA SP. Z.O.O.—See UCB S.A.; *Int'l*, pg. 8012
UCB PHARMA (ZHUHAI) COMPANY LTD.—See UCB S.A.; *Int'l*, pg. 8011
UCB S.A.; *Int'l*, pg. 8010
UCB S.R.O.—See UCB S.A.; *Int'l*, pg. 8012
UCB STOCK BROKERAGE LIMITED—See United Commercial Bank Limited; *Int'l*, pg. 8066
UCB TRADING (SHANGHAI) CO LTD—See UCB S.A.; *Int'l*, pg. 8012
UCB WATFORD LTD—See UCB S.A.; *Int'l*, pg. 8012
UCC DIRECT—See Wolters Kluwer n.v.; *Int'l*, pg. 8444
UCDP FINANCE, INC.—See Comcast Corporation; *U.S. Public*, pg. 541
UCEM SISTEMAS DE SEGURIDAD S.A.—See Groupe SFPI SA; *Int'l*, pg. 3111
UCESS PARTNERS CO., LTD.—See LG Corp.; *Int'l*, pg. 4475
UCG INFORMATION SERVICES LLC—See United Communications Group; *U.S. Private*, pg. 4289
UCHEALTH BROOMFIELD HOSPITAL LLC—See Adeptus Health Inc.; *U.S. Private*, pg. 78
UCHICAGO MEDICINE INGALLS MEMORIAL—See University of Chicago; *U.S. Private*, pg. 4308
UCHIDA BUSINESS SOLUTIONS CO., LTD.—See Uchida Yoko Co., Ltd.; *Int'l*, pg. 8012
UCHIDA ESCO CO., LTD.—See Uchida Yoko Co., Ltd.; *Int'l*, pg. 8012
UCHIDA HUMAN DEVELOPMENT CO., LTD.—See Uchida Yoko Co., Ltd.; *Int'l*, pg. 8013
UCHIDA MK SDN. BHD.—See Uchida Yoko Co., Ltd.; *Int'l*, pg. 8013

COMPANY NAME INDEX

UCHIDA OF AMERICA, CORP.—See Uchida Yoko Co., Ltd.; *Int'l*, pg. 8013
UCHIDA SPECTRUM INC.—See Uchida Yoko Co., Ltd.; *Int'l*, pg. 8013
UCHIDA SYSTEMS CO., LTD.—See Uchida Yoko Co., Ltd.; *Int'l*, pg. 8013
UCHIDA TECHNO CO., LTD.—See Uchida Yoko Co., Ltd.; *Int'l*, pg. 8013
UCHIDA YOKO BUSINESS EXPERT CO., LTD.—See Uchida Yoko Co., Ltd.; *Int'l*, pg. 8013
UCHIDA YOKO CO., LTD.; *Int'l*, pg. 8012
UCHIDA YOKO GLOBAL LIMITED—See Uchida Yoko Co., Ltd.; *Int'l*, pg. 8013
UCHIDA YOKO IT SOLUTIONS CO., LTD.—See Uchida Yoko Co., Ltd.; *Int'l*, pg. 8013
UCHIDA YOKO OFFICE FACILITIES (SHANGHAI) CO., LTD.—See Uchida Yoko Co., Ltd.; *Int'l*, pg. 8013
UCHIHASHI ESTEC CO., LTD.; *Int'l*, pg. 8013
UCHI OPTOELECTRONIC (M) SDN. BHD.—See Uchi Technologies Berhad; *Int'l*, pg. 8012
UCHI TECHNOLOGIES BERHAD; *Int'l*, pg. 8012
UCHIYAMA HOLDINGS CO., LTD.; *Int'l*, pg. 8013
UCH POWER LIMITED—See ENGIE SA; *Int'l*, pg. 2435
UCHUMI SUPERMARKETS LIMITED; *Int'l*, pg. 8013
UCI AIRFREIGHT JAPAN, INC.—See Naigai Trans Line Ltd.; *Int'l*, pg. 5130
UCI CO., LTD.; *Int'l*, pg. 8013
UCI COMMUNICATIONS LLC—See Black Box Limited; *Int'l*, pg. 1058
UCI CONSTRUCTION INC.; *U.S. Private*, pg. 4273
UCI HEALTH; *U.S. Private*, pg. 4273
UCI HOLDINGS LIMITED—See Rank Group Ltd.; *Int'l*, pg. 6208
UCI INTERNATIONAL, INC.—See Rank Group Ltd.; *Int'l*, pg. 6208
UCI—See BNP Paribas SA; *Int'l*, pg. 1093
U CITY PUBLIC COMPANY LIMITED; *Int'l*, pg. 7996
UCI UNION DE CREDITOS IMOBILIARIOS—See BNP Paribas SA; *Int'l*, pg. 1093
UCKELE HEALTH NUTRITION; *U.S. Private*, pg. 4274
UCL CO., LTD. - INCHEON FACTORY—See Daebong LS Co., Ltd.; *Int'l*, pg. 1906
UCL CO., LTD. - JEJU FACTORY—See Daebong LS Co., Ltd.; *Int'l*, pg. 1906
UCL CO., LTD.—See Daebong LS Co., Ltd.; *Int'l*, pg. 1906
UCLOUDLINK GROUP, INC.; *Int'l*, pg. 8013
UCLOUD TECHNOLOGY CO., LTD.; *Int'l*, pg. 8013
UCL PRESS—See Informa plc; *Int'l*, pg. 3693
UCM AG—See Durr AG; *Int'l*, pg. 2233
UC MALAMPAYA PHILIPPINES PTE. LTD.—See Udenna Corporation; *Int'l*, pg. 8014
U.C.M. RESITA S.A.; *Int'l*, pg. 7998
UCO BANK LIMITED; *Int'l*, pg. 8013
UCO EQUIPMENT, LLC—See Utility One Source L.P.; *U.S. Private*, pg. 4326
UCOMMUNE GROUP HOLDINGS LIMITED—See Ucommune International Ltd.; *U.S. Private*, pg. 2217
UCOMMUNE INTERNATIONAL LTD.; *U.S. Public*, pg. 2217
UCORE RARE METALS INC.; *Int'l*, pg. 8013
UCP AUSTRALIA PTY LIMITED—See WPIL Limited; *Int'l*, pg. 8462
UCPLUS A/S—See Deutsche Bahn AG; *Int'l*, pg. 2055
UCREST BERHAD; *Int'l*, pg. 8013
UCR SA; *Int'l*, pg. 8013
UC SAN DIEGO HEALTH; *U.S. Private*, pg. 4273
UCS CO., LTD.—See Pan Pacific International Holdings Corporation; *Int'l*, pg. 5715
U.C.S. CO., LTD.—See Unitika Ltd.; *Int'l*, pg. 8074
U.C.S.-CUIDADOS INTEGRADOS DE SAUDE, S.A—See TAP-Transportes Aereos Portugueses, SGPS, S.A.; *Int'l*, pg. 7461
UCSF MEDICAL CENTER; *U.S. Private*, pg. 4274
UCS SOFTWARE MANUFACTURING (PROPRIETARY) LIMITED—See Capital Eye Investments Limited; *Int'l*, pg. 1311
UCS SOLUTIONS (PROPRIETARY) LIMITED—See Business Connexion Group Limited; *Int'l*, pg. 1228
UCS SOLUTIONS—See Business Connexion Group Limited; *Int'l*, pg. 1228
UCS; *U.S. Private*, pg. 4274
UCT FLUID DELIVERY SOLUTIONS S.R.O—See Ultra Clean Holdings, Inc.; *U.S. Public*, pg. 2223
UCW LIMITED; *Int'l*, pg. 8013
UCYCLYD PHARMA, INC.—See Bausch Health Companies Inc.; *Int'l*, pg. 898
UDACITY, INC.—See Asas Capital Ltd; *Int'l*, pg. 599
UDAIPUR CEMENT WORKS LIMITED; *Int'l*, pg. 8013
UDARNIK D.D. BREZA; *Int'l*, pg. 8013
UDAY JEWELLERY INDUSTRIES LTD.; *Int'l*, pg. 8014
UDAYSHIVAKUMAR INFRA LTD.; *Int'l*, pg. 8014
UDC FINANCE LTD.—See SBI Shinsei Bank, Limited; *Int'l*, pg. 6606
UDC JCDECAUX—See JCDecaux S.A.; *Int'l*, pg. 3923
U&D COAL LIMITED; *Int'l*, pg. 7997
UDDEHOLM A/S—See voestalpine AG; *Int'l*, pg. 8292
UDDEHOLM AB—See voestalpine AG; *Int'l*, pg. 8292
UDDEHOLM EIENDOM AS—See voestalpine AG; *Int'l*, pg. 8289

UDDEHOLM HOLDING AB—See voestalpine AG; *Int'l*, pg. 8289
UDDEHOLM KK—See voestalpine AG; *Int'l*, pg. 8292
UDDEHOLM N.V.—See voestalpine AG; *Int'l*, pg. 8292
UDDEHOLMS AB—See voestalpine AG; *Int'l*, pg. 8289
UDDEHOLM SVENSKA AKTIEBOLAG—See voestalpine AG; *Int'l*, pg. 8289
UDDEHOLM TOOLING AB—See voestalpine AG; *Int'l*, pg. 8292
UDEA B.V.; *Int'l*, pg. 8014
UDELHOVEN OILFIELD SYSTEMS SERVICES INC.—See Harding Holdings Inc.; *U.S. Private*, pg. 1863
UDELL ASSOCIATES, INC.—See Aon plc; *Int'l*, pg. 497
UDEMY, INC.; *U.S. Public*, pg. 2217
UDENNA CORPORATION; *Int'l*, pg. 8014
UDER ELEKTROMECHANIK GMBH—See KSB SE & Co. KGaA; *Int'l*, pg. 4313
UDG HEALTHCARE PLC—See Clayton, Dubilier & Rice, LLC; *U.S. Private*, pg. 927
UDG, INC. - ATLANTA STUDIO—See UDG, Inc.; *U.S. Private*, pg. 4274
UDG, INC.; *U.S. Private*, pg. 4274
UD HOSPITALITY MANAGEMENT CORPORATION—See Nippon Telegraph & Telephone Corporation; *Int'l*, pg. 5355
UDICARE S.R.L.—See Demant A/S; *Int'l*, pg. 2025
U.D. INDUSTRIES SDN. BHD.—See SWS Capital Berhad; *Int'l*, pg. 7376
UD INFO CORP.—See Apacer Technology Inc.; *Int'l*, pg. 500
U&D MINING INDUSTRY (AUSTRALIA) PTY. LTD.—See U&D Coal Limited; *Int'l*, pg. 7997
U. DORI CONSTRUCTION LTD.—See Amos Luzon Development and Energy Group Ltd.; *Int'l*, pg. 430
U.D. PANELFORM LAMINATION AND SDN. BHD.—See SWS Capital Berhad; *Int'l*, pg. 7376
UDP TECHNOLOGY LTD.; *Int'l*, pg. 8014
UDRA MEXICO S.A. DE C.V.—See Grupo Empresarial San Jose, S.A.; *Int'l*, pg. 3128
UDR BRIO LLC—See UDR, Inc.; *U.S. Public*, pg. 2218
UDR CANAL I LLC—See UDR, Inc.; *U.S. Public*, pg. 2218
UDR CANTERBURY LLC—See UDR, Inc.; *U.S. Public*, pg. 2218
UDR COOL SPRINGS I LLC—See UDR, Inc.; *U.S. Public*, pg. 2218
UDR CURRENTS ON THE CHARLES LLC—See UDR, Inc.; *U.S. Public*, pg. 2218
UD-RD HOLDING COMPANY LIMITED—See Lone Star Funds; *U.S. Private*, pg. 2487
UDR, INC.; *U.S. Public*, pg. 2217
UDR INWOOD LLC—See UDR, Inc.; *U.S. Public*, pg. 2218
UDR LEONARD POINTE LLC—See UDR, Inc.; *U.S. Public*, pg. 2218
UDR PERIDOT PALMS LLC—See UDR, Inc.; *U.S. Public*, pg. 2218
UDR PRESERVE AT GATEWAY LLC—See UDR, Inc.; *U.S. Public*, pg. 2218
UDR PRESIDENTIAL GREENS, L.L.C.—See UDR, Inc.; *U.S. Public*, pg. 2218
UDR RED STONE RANCH LLC—See UDR, Inc.; *U.S. Public*, pg. 2218
UDR SMITH LLC—See UDR, Inc.; *U.S. Public*, pg. 2218
UDR UNION PLACE LLC—See UDR, Inc.; *U.S. Public*, pg. 2218
UDS (NO 3) LIMITED—See Heidelberg Materials AG; *Int'l*, pg. 3320
UD TRUCKS CORPORATION—See AB Volvo; *Int'l*, pg. 45
UD TRUCKS JAPAN CO., LTD. - HANYU PLANT—See AB Volvo; *Int'l*, pg. 45
UD TRUCKS JAPAN CO., LTD. - KONOSU PLANT—See AB Volvo; *Int'l*, pg. 46
UD TRUCKS JAPAN CO., LTD.—See AB Volvo; *Int'l*, pg. 45
UD TRUCKS NORTH AMERICA, INC.—See AB Volvo; *Int'l*, pg. 46
UD TRUCKS SOUTH AFRICA (PTY) LTD.—See AB Volvo; *Int'l*, pg. 46
UD-UNION DISTRIBUTION S.A.S.—See Madrigall SA; *Int'l*, pg. 4635
UDUPI POWER CORPORATION LIMITED—See Adani Enterprises Limited; *Int'l*, pg. 125
UEBELHOR DEVELOPMENT INC.; *U.S. Private*, pg. 4274
UEBELHOR & SONS; *U.S. Private*, pg. 4274
UEBERLANDWERK LEINETAL GMBH—See E.ON SE; *Int'l*, pg. 2254
UEB (SWITZERLAND)—See BNP Paribas SA; *Int'l*, pg. 1093
UEC ELECTRONICS, LLC—See Greenbriar Equity Group, L.P.; *U.S. Private*, pg. 1775
UEC - GAS TURBINES, JSC—See Russian Technologies State Corporation; *Int'l*, pg. 6431
UEC GROUP LTD.; *Int'l*, pg. 8014
UE CHINA (SHANGHAI) CO LTD—See Yanlord Land Group Limited; *Int'l*, pg. 8562
UECOMM LTD—See Temasek Holdings (Private) Limited; *Int'l*, pg. 7553
UE COMPRESSION, LLC—See Lion Equity Partners, LLC; *U.S. Private*, pg. 2463

UEC RESOURCES LTD.—See Uranium Energy Corp.; *Int'l*, pg. 8094
UEC SAIL INFORMATION TECHNOLOGY LIMITED—See Steel Authority of India Limited; *Int'l*, pg. 7189
UEDA JAPAN RADIO CO., LTD.—See Nisshinbo Holdings Inc.; *Int'l*, pg. 5373
UE ENVIROTECH PTE LTD—See Yanlord Land Group Limited; *Int'l*, pg. 8563
UE FURNITURE CO., LTD.; *Int'l*, pg. 8014
UEG ARAUCARIA S.A.—See Companhia Paranaense de Energia; *Int'l*, pg. 1748
UEGA - USINA ELETRICA A GAS DE ARAUCARIA LTDA.—See Companhia Paranaense de Energia; *Int'l*, pg. 1748
UEG-GREEN ENERGY SOLUTIONS/ALBERTA, INC.; *Int'l*, pg. 8014
UEHARA FOODS INDUSTRY CO., LTD—See Adeka Corporation; *Int'l*, pg. 142
UEHARA SEI SHOJI CO., LTD.; *Int'l*, pg. 8014
UE HUDSON MALL HOLDING LLC—See URBAN EDGE PROPERTIES; *U.S. Public*, pg. 2265
UEI DO BRASIL CONTROLES REMOTOS LTDA.—See Universal Electronics, Inc.; *U.S. Public*, pg. 2255
UEKI CORPORATION; *Int'l*, pg. 8014
UEKI REAL ESTATE CO., LTD.—See UEKI Corporation; *Int'l*, pg. 8014
UEL CORPORATION—See BIPROGY Inc.; *Int'l*, pg. 1045
UELS HOLDING, LLC—See Wells Fargo & Company; *U.S. Public*, pg. 2345
UELS, LLC—See Wells Fargo & Company; *U.S. Public*, pg. 2345
UE MANAGED SOLUTIONS TAIWAN LTD—See Yanlord Land Group Limited; *Int'l*, pg. 8563
UE MANUFACTURING LLC—See Kirby Corporation; *U.S. Public*, pg. 1235
UEMATSU SHOKAI CO., LTD.; *Int'l*, pg. 8014
UEM EDGENTA BERHAD—See Khazanah Nasional Berhad; *Int'l*, pg. 4153
UEMET GMBH—See uesa GmbH; *Int'l*, pg. 8015
UEM GROUP BERHAD—See Khazanah Nasional Berhad; *Int'l*, pg. 4153
UEMS SOLUTIONS PTE. LTD.—See Khazanah Nasional Berhad; *Int'l*, pg. 4154
UEM SUNRISE BERHAD—See Khazanah Nasional Berhad; *Int'l*, pg. 4154
UEMURA TEC CO., LTD.—See Honda Motor Co., Ltd.; *Int'l*, pg. 3464
UENO CANON MATERIALS INC.—See Canon Inc.; *Int'l*, pg. 1298
UENO FINE CHEMICALS INDUSTRIES USA—See Ueno Fine Chemicals Industry, Ltd.; *Int'l*, pg. 8014
UENO FINE CHEMICALS INDUSTRY, LTD.; *Int'l*, pg. 8014
UENO, LLC; *U.S. Private*, pg. 4274
UENO SHOKAI CO., LTD.—See TSI Holdings Co., Ltd.; *Int'l*, pg. 7951
UE NOVO (MALAYSIA) SDN. BHD.—See CITIC Group Corporation; *Int'l*, pg. 1620
UE PARK AVENUE INTERNATIONAL PTE. LTD.—See Yanlord Land Group Limited; *Int'l*, pg. 8562
UESA GMBH; *Int'l*, pg. 8014
UESATRANS GMBH—See uesa GmbH; *Int'l*, pg. 8015
UE SERVICECORP (TAIWAN) LIMITED—See Yanlord Land Group Limited; *Int'l*, pg. 8563
UESHIMA CO., LTD.—See Kato Sangyo Co., Ltd.; *Int'l*, pg. 4090
UES HOLDINGS PTE. LTD.; *Int'l*, pg. 8014
UES, INC.; *U.S. Private*, pg. 4274
UES INTERNATIONAL SDN. BHD.—See MB Holding Company LLC; *Int'l*, pg. 4750
UESTRA HANNOVERSCHE VERKEHRSBETRIEBE AG; *Int'l*, pg. 8015
UE SUPPORT SERVICES PTE LTD—See Yanlord Land Group Limited; *Int'l*, pg. 8563
UE TRADE CORPORATION PTE LTD—See Yanlord Land Group Limited; *Int'l*, pg. 8563
UET UNITED ELECTRONIC TECHNOLOGY AG; *Int'l*, pg. 8015
UEX CORPORATION—See Uranium Energy Corp.; *Int'l*, pg. 8094
UEX, LTD.; *Int'l*, pg. 8015
UFA CINEMA GMBH—See Bertelsmann SE & Co. KGaA; *Int'l*, pg. 995
UFA FILM UND FERNSEH GMBH—See Bertelsmann SE & Co. KGaA; *Int'l*, pg. 996
UFA RADIO-PROGRAMMGESELLSCHAFT IN BAYERN MBH—See Bertelsmann SE & Co. KGaA; *Int'l*, pg. 995
UFA SHOW GMBH—See Bertelsmann SE & Co. KGaA; *Int'l*, pg. 995
UFA SPORTS ASIA PTE LTD—See Bertelsmann SE & Co. KGaA; *Int'l*, pg. 995
UFA SPORTS GMBH—See Bertelsmann SE & Co. KGaA; *Int'l*, pg. 995
UFA SPORTS SLOVAKIA S.R.O—See Bertelsmann SE & Co. KGaA; *Int'l*, pg. 995
UFD DISTRIBUCION ELECTRICIDAD, S.A.—See Naturgy Energy Group, S.A.; *Int'l*, pg. 5169
UFFICIUM IMMOBILIEN LEASING GESELLSCHAFT M.B.H.—See UniCredit S.p.A.; *Int'l*, pg. 8037
UFG GROUP, INC.; *U.S. Private*, pg. 4274

UFI CHARITABLE TRUST

UFI CHARITABLE TRUST; *Int'l,* pg. 8015
UFINET ARGENTINA SA—See Enel S.p.A.; *Int'l,* pg. 2415
UFINET BRASIL SA—See Enel S.p.A.; *Int'l,* pg. 2415
UFINET CHILE SA—See Enel S.p.A.; *Int'l,* pg. 2415
UFINET COLOMBIA SA—See Enel S.p.A.; *Int'l,* pg. 2415
UFINET COSTA RICA SA—See Enel S.p.A.; *Int'l,* pg. 2415
UFINET ECUADOR UFIEC SA—See Enel S.p.A.; *Int'l,* pg. 2415
UFINET EL SALVADOR SA DE CV—See Enel S.p.A.; *Int'l,* pg. 2415
UFINET FTTH GUATEMALA LTDA.—See Enel S.p.A.; *Int'l,* pg. 2415
UFINET GUATEMALA SA—See Enel S.p.A.; *Int'l,* pg. 2415
UFINET HONDURAS SA—See Enel S.p.A.; *Int'l,* pg. 2415
UFINET LATAM SLU—See Enel S.p.A.; *Int'l,* pg. 2415
UFINET MEXICO S DE RL DE CV—See Enel S.p.A.; *Int'l,* pg. 2415
UFINET NICARAGUA SA—See Enel S.p.A.; *Int'l,* pg. 2415
UFINET PANAMA SA—See Enel S.p.A.; *Int'l,* pg. 2415
UFINET PARAGUAY SA—See Enel S.p.A.; *Int'l,* pg. 2415
UFINET PERU SAC—See Enel S.p.A.; *Int'l,* pg. 2415
UFIT CO., LTD.—See TIS Inc.; *Int'l,* pg. 7758
UFLEX EUROPE LIMITED—See Uflex Ltd; *Int'l,* pg. 8015
UFLEX LTD; *Int'l,* pg. 8015
UFLEX PACKAGING INC.—See Uflex Ltd; *Int'l,* pg. 8015
UFO LANKA PRIVATE LIMITED—See UFO Moviez India Ltd; *Int'l,* pg. 8015
UFO MOVIEZ INDIA LTD; *Int'l,* pg. 8015
UFOOD RESTAURANT GROUP, INC.; *U.S. Private,* pg. 4274
UFP ASHBURN, LLC—See UFP Industries, Inc.; *U.S. Public,* pg. 2219
UFP AUBURNDALE, LLC—See UFP Industries, Inc.; *U.S. Public,* pg. 2219
UFP BELCHERTOWN, LLC—See UFP Industries, Inc.; *U.S. Public,* pg. 2219
UFP BERLIN, LLC—See UFP Industries, Inc.; *U.S. Public,* pg. 2219
UFP BLANCHESTER, LLC—See UFP Industries, Inc.; *U.S. Public,* pg. 2219
UFP CALDWELL, LLC—See UFP Industries, Inc.; *U.S. Public,* pg. 2219
UFP CHANDLER, LLC—See UFP Industries, Inc.; *U.S. Public,* pg. 2219
UFP CONSTRUCTION, LLC—See UFP Industries, Inc.; *U.S. Public,* pg. 2219
UFP DISTRIBUTION, LLC—See UFP Industries, Inc.; *U.S. Public,* pg. 2219
UFP EATONTON, LLC—See UFP Industries, Inc.; *U.S. Public,* pg. 2219
UFP ELIZABETH CITY, LLC—See UFP Industries, Inc.; *U.S. Public,* pg. 2219
UFP ELKWOOD, LLC—See UFP Industries, Inc.; *U.S. Public,* pg. 2219
UFP FOLKSTON, LLC—See UFP Industries, Inc.; *U.S. Public,* pg. 2219
UFP FRANKLINTON, LLC—See UFP Industries, Inc.; *U.S. Public,* pg. 2219
UFP GORDON, LLC—See UFP Industries, Inc.; *U.S. Public,* pg. 2220
UFP GRANDVIEW, LLC—See UFP Industries, Inc.; *U.S. Public,* pg. 2220
UFP GRANGER, LLC—See UFP Industries, Inc.; *U.S. Public,* pg. 2220
UFP HALEYVILLE, LLC—See UFP Industries, Inc.; *U.S. Public,* pg. 2220
UFP HAMILTON, LLC—See UFP Industries, Inc.; *U.S. Public,* pg. 2220
UFP HARRISONVILLE, LLC—See UFP Industries, Inc.; *U.S. Public,* pg. 2220
UFP HILLSBORO, LLC—See UFP Industries, Inc.; *U.S. Public,* pg. 2220
UFP INDUSTRIES, INC.; *U.S. Public,* pg. 2218
UFP JANESVILLE, LLC—See UFP Industries, Inc.; *U.S. Public,* pg. 2220
UFP LAFAYETTE, LLC—See UFP Industries, Inc.; *U.S. Public,* pg. 2220
UFP LODI, LLC—See UFP Industries, Inc.; *U.S. Public,* pg. 2220
UFP MAGNA, LLC—See UFP Industries, Inc.; *U.S. Public,* pg. 2220
UFP MCMINNVILLE, LLC—See UFP Industries, Inc.; *U.S. Public,* pg. 2220
UFP MID-ATLANTIC, LLC - JEFFERSON—See UFP Industries, Inc.; *U.S. Public,* pg. 2220
UFP MID-ATLANTIC, LLC - LIBERTY—See UFP Industries, Inc.; *U.S. Public,* pg. 2220
UFP MID-ATLANTIC, LLC—See UFP Industries, Inc.; *U.S. Public,* pg. 2220
UFP MILLRY, LLC—See UFP Industries, Inc.; *U.S. Public,* pg. 2220
UFP MINNEOTA, LLC—See UFP Industries, Inc.; *U.S. Public,* pg. 2220
UFP MORRISTOWN, LLC—See UFP Industries, Inc.; *U.S. Public,* pg. 2220
UFP MOULTRIE, LLC—See UFP Industries, Inc.; *U.S. Public,* pg. 2220
UFP NAPPANEE, LLC—See UFP Industries, Inc.; *U.S. Public,* pg. 2220
UFP NEW LONDON, LLC—See UFP Industries, Inc.; *U.S. Public,* pg. 2220
UFP NEW WAVERLY, LLC—See UFP Industries, Inc.; *U.S. Public,* pg. 2220
UFP NEW WINDSOR, LLC—See UFP Industries, Inc.; *U.S. Public,* pg. 2220
UFP NEW YORK, LLC - CHAFFEE—See UFP Industries, Inc.; *U.S. Public,* pg. 2220
UFP NEW YORK, LLC - HUDSON—See UFP Industries, Inc.; *U.S. Public,* pg. 2220
UFP NEW YORK, LLC - SIDNEY—See UFP Industries, Inc.; *U.S. Public,* pg. 2220
UFP PACKAGING, LLC—See UFP Industries, Inc.; *U.S. Public,* pg. 2220
UFP PARKER, LLC—See UFP Industries, Inc.; *U.S. Public,* pg. 2220
UFP PURCHASING, INC.—See UFP Industries, Inc.; *U.S. Public,* pg. 2220
UFP RANSON, LLC—See UFP Industries, Inc.; *U.S. Public,* pg. 2220
UFP RIVERSIDE, LLC—See UFP Industries, Inc.; *U.S. Public,* pg. 2220
UFP SAGINAW, LLC—See UFP Industries, Inc.; *U.S. Public,* pg. 2220
UFP SALISBURY, LLC—See UFP Industries, Inc.; *U.S. Public,* pg. 2220
UFP SAN ANTONIO, LLC—See UFP Industries, Inc.; *U.S. Public,* pg. 2220
UFP SAUK RAPIDS, LLC—See UFP Industries, Inc.; *U.S. Public,* pg. 2220
UFP SCHERTZ, LLC—See UFP Industries, Inc.; *U.S. Public,* pg. 2220
UFP SHAWNEE, LLC—See UFP Industries, Inc.; *U.S. Public,* pg. 2220
UFP STOCKERTOWN, LLC—See UFP Industries, Inc.; *U.S. Public,* pg. 2220
UFP TAMPA, LLC—See UFP Industries, Inc.; *U.S. Public,* pg. 2220
UFP TECHNOLOGIES, INC. - GRAND RAPIDS—See UFP Technologies, Inc.; *U.S. Public,* pg. 2221
UFP TECHNOLOGIES, INC.; *U.S. Public,* pg. 2221
UFP THORNTON, LLC—See UFP Industries, Inc.; *U.S. Public,* pg. 2220
UFP TRANSPORTATION, INC.—See UFP Industries, Inc.; *U.S. Public,* pg. 2220
UFP UNION CITY, LLC—See UFP Industries, Inc.; *U.S. Public,* pg. 2220
UFP VENTURES II, INC.—See UFP Industries, Inc.; *U.S. Public,* pg. 2220
UFP WARRENS, LLC—See UFP Industries, Inc.; *U.S. Public,* pg. 2220
UFP WHITE BEAR LAKE, LLC—See UFP Industries, Inc.; *U.S. Public,* pg. 2221
UFP WINDSOR, LLC—See UFP Industries, Inc.; *U.S. Public,* pg. 2221
UFP WOODBURN, LLC—See UFP Industries, Inc.; *U.S. Public,* pg. 2221
U-FREIGHT AMERICA INC.; *U.S. Private,* pg. 4269
UFS BANCORP; *U.S. Private,* pg. 4274
UFS BETEILIGUNGS-GMBH—See Allianz SE; *Int'l,* pg. 356
UF TECH, LTD.—See ULVAC, Inc.; *Int'l,* pg. 8020
UFUK YATIRIM YONETIM VE GAYRIMENKUL AS; *Int'l,* pg. 8015
UGANDA BREWERIES LTD—See Diageo plc; *Int'l,* pg. 2102
UGANDA CLAYS LTD.; *Int'l,* pg. 8015
UGANDA SECURITIES EXCHANGE LTD.; *Int'l,* pg. 8015
UGANDA TOWERS LIMITED—See Bharti Enterprises Limited; *Int'l,* pg. 1013
UGAR QUALITY PACKAGING PVT. LTD.—See The Ugar Sugar Works Limited; *Int'l,* pg. 7697
UGAR—See AXA S.A.; *Int'l,* pg. 759
THE UGAR SUGAR WORKS LIMITED; *Int'l,* pg. 7697
UGE INTERNATIONAL LTD.—See Nova Infrastructure Management, LLC; *U.S. Private,* pg. 2965
UGENIUS TECHNOLOGY, LLC.; *U.S. Private,* pg. 4274
UG HEALTHCARE CORPORATION LIMITED; *Int'l,* pg. 8015
UGI CENTRAL PENN GAS, INC.—See UGI Corporation; *U.S. Public,* pg. 2223
UGI CORPORATION; *U.S. Public,* pg. 2221
UGI DEVELOPMENT COMPANY—See UGI Corporation; *U.S. Public,* pg. 2223
UGI ENERGY SERVICES, INC.—See UGI Corporation; *U.S. Public,* pg. 2223
UGI ENERGY SERVICES, LLC—See UGI Corporation; *U.S. Public,* pg. 2222
UGI ENTERPRISES, LLC—See UGI Corporation; *U.S. Public,* pg. 2222
UGI HVAC ENTERPRISES, INC.—See UGI Corporation; *U.S. Public,* pg. 2223
UGI PENN NATURAL GAS, INC.—See UGI Corporation; *U.S. Public,* pg. 2223
UGI STORAGE COMPANY—See UGI Corporation; *U.S. Public,* pg. 2223
UGITECH S.A.—See Swiss Steel Holding AG; *Int'l,* pg. 7373

CORPORATE AFFILIATIONS

UGI UTILITIES, INC.—See UGI Corporation; *U.S. Public,* pg. 2223
UGIVIS S.A.S.—See Acciaierie Valbruna; *Int'l,* pg. 89
UGL CANADA INC.—See ACS, Actividades de Construccion y Servicios, S.A.; *Int'l,* pg. 113
UGL ENGINEERING PTY LTD—See ACS, Actividades de Construccion y Servicios, S.A.; *Int'l,* pg. 113
UGL (NZ) LIMITED—See ACS, Actividades de Construccion y Servicios, S.A.; *Int'l,* pg. 113
UGL OPERATIONS AND MAINTENANCE PTY LTD—See ACS, Actividades de Construccion y Servicios, S.A.; *Int'l,* pg. 113
UGL PTY LIMITED—See ACS, Actividades de Construccion y Servicios, S.A.; *Int'l,* pg. 113
UGL RAIL PTY LTD—See ACS, Actividades de Construccion y Servicios, S.A.; *Int'l,* pg. 113
UGL RAIL SERVICES PTY LIMITED—See ACS, Actividades de Construccion y Servicios, S.A.; *Int'l,* pg. 113
UGL (SINGAPORE) PTE LTD—See ACS, Actividades de Construccion y Servicios, S.A.; *Int'l,* pg. 113
UG M&E PTE LTD—See Southern Capital Group Pte. Ltd.; *Int'l,* pg. 7118
UGM HOLDINGS PTY LTD; *Int'l,* pg. 8015
UGN DE MEXICO, S. DE R.L. DE C.V.—See Autoneum Holding Ltd.; *Int'l,* pg. 731
UGN, INC.—See Autoneum Holding Ltd.; *Int'l,* pg. 731
UGN, INC.—See Nihon Tokushu Toryo Co., Ltd; *Int'l,* pg. 5287
UGOPROM A.D.; *Int'l,* pg. 8015
U-GO STATIONS INC.—See Blink Charging Co.; *U.S. Public,* pg. 361
UGOTURS A.D.; *Int'l,* pg. 8016
UGRO CAPITAL LIMITED; *Int'l,* pg. 8016
U-GRO LEARNING CENTRES, INC.—See American Securities LLC; *U.S. Private,* pg. 249
UGS AMERICA SALES INC.—See UTAC Holdings Ltd.; *Int'l,* pg. 8100
UGS CHINA SALES LTD—See UTAC Holdings Ltd.; *Int'l,* pg. 8100
UGS EUROPE LLC—See UTAC Holdings Ltd.; *Int'l,* pg. 8100
UGS EUROPE SALES SRL—See UTAC Holdings Ltd.; *Int'l,* pg. 8100
UGS GMBH—See VINCI S.A.; *Int'l,* pg. 8218
UGS ISRAELI HOLDINGS (ISRAEL) LTD.—See Siemens Aktiengesellschaft; *Int'l,* pg. 6901
U-HAUL CO. OF ALABAMA, INC.—See U-Haul Holding Company; *U.S. Public,* pg. 2211
U-HAUL CO. OF ALASKA, INC.—See U-Haul Holding Company; *U.S. Public,* pg. 2211
U-HAUL CO. OF ARIZONA, INC.—See U-Haul Holding Company; *U.S. Public,* pg. 2211
U-HAUL CO. OF ARKANSAS—See U-Haul Holding Company; *U.S. Public,* pg. 2211
U-HAUL CO. OF CHARLESTON—See U-Haul Holding Company; *U.S. Public,* pg. 2211
U-HAUL CO. OF COLORADO—See U-Haul Holding Company; *U.S. Public,* pg. 2211
U-HAUL CO. OF DISTRICT OF COLUMBIA, INC.—See U-Haul Holding Company; *U.S. Public,* pg. 2211
U-HAUL CO. OF FLORIDA—See U-Haul Holding Company; *U.S. Public,* pg. 2211
U-HAUL CO. OF GEORGIA—See U-Haul Holding Company; *U.S. Public,* pg. 2211
U-HAUL CO. OF IDAHO, INC.—See U-Haul Holding Company; *U.S. Public,* pg. 2211
U-HAUL CO. OF INDIANA, INC.—See U-Haul Holding Company; *U.S. Public,* pg. 2211
U-HAUL CO. OF KANSAS, INC.—See U-Haul Holding Company; *U.S. Public,* pg. 2211
U-HAUL CO. OF KENTUCKY—See U-Haul Holding Company; *U.S. Public,* pg. 2211
U-HAUL CO. OF LOUISIANA—See U-Haul Holding Company; *U.S. Public,* pg. 2211
U-HAUL CO. OF MAINE, INC.—See U-Haul Holding Company; *U.S. Public,* pg. 2211
U-HAUL CO. OF MARYLAND, INC.—See U-Haul Holding Company; *U.S. Public,* pg. 2211
U-HAUL CO. OF MICHIGAN—See U-Haul Holding Company; *U.S. Public,* pg. 2211
U-HAUL CO. OF MINNESOTA—See U-Haul Holding Company; *U.S. Public,* pg. 2211
U-HAUL CO. OF MISSISSIPPI—See U-Haul Holding Company; *U.S. Public,* pg. 2211
U-HAUL CO. OF NEBRASKA—See U-Haul Holding Company; *U.S. Public,* pg. 2211
U-HAUL CO. OF NEVADA, INC.—See U-Haul Holding Company; *U.S. Public,* pg. 2211
U-HAUL CO. OF NEW JERSEY, INC.—See U-Haul Holding Company; *U.S. Public,* pg. 2211
U-HAUL CO. OF NEW YORK AND VERMONT, INC.—See U-Haul Holding Company; *U.S. Public,* pg. 2211
U-HAUL CO. OF PENNSYLVANIA—See U-Haul Holding Company; *U.S. Public,* pg. 2211
U-HAUL CO. OF SOUTH CAROLINA, INC.—See U-Haul Holding Company; *U.S. Public,* pg. 2212
U-HAUL CO. OF SOUTH DAKOTA, INC.—See U-Haul Holding Company; *U.S. Public,* pg. 2212

U-HAUL CO. OF UTAH, INC.—See U-Haul Holding Company; *U.S. Public*, pg. 2212
U-HAUL CO. OF VIRGINIA—See U-Haul Holding Company; *U.S. Public*, pg. 2212
U-HAUL CO. OF WISCONSIN, INC.—See U-Haul Holding Company; *U.S. Public*, pg. 2212
U-HAUL HOLDING COMPANY; *U.S. Public*, pg. 2211
U-HAUL INTERNATIONAL, INC.—See U-Haul Holding Company; *U.S. Public*, pg. 2211
U-HAUL OF HAWAII, INC.—See U-Haul Holding Company; *U.S. Public*, pg. 2212
UHC OF CALIFORNIA—See UnitedHealth Group Incorporated; *U.S. Public*, pg. 2251
UHC OF CALIFORNIA—See UnitedHealth Group Incorporated; *U.S. Public*, pg. 2251
UHDE ARABIA LTD.—See ThyssenKrupp AG; *Int'l*, pg. 7734
UHDE ASIA PACIFIC PTY. LTD.—See ThyssenKrupp AG; *Int'l*, pg. 7734
UHDE DO BRASIL LTDA.—See ThyssenKrupp AG; *Int'l*, pg. 7734
UHDE EDELEANU S.E. ASIA PTE. LTD.—See ThyssenKrupp AG; *Int'l*, pg. 7734
UHDE EDELEANU S.R.O.—See ThyssenKrupp AG; *Int'l*, pg. 7734
UHDE ENGINEERING CONSULTING (SHANGHAI) CO., LTD.—See ThyssenKrupp AG; *Int'l*, pg. 7734
UHDE ENGINEERING DE MEXICO, S.A. DE C.V.—See ThyssenKrupp AG; *Int'l*, pg. 7734
UHDE ENGINEERING EGYPT COMPANY (S.A.E.)—See ThyssenKrupp AG; *Int'l*, pg. 7734
UHDE GMBH—See ThyssenKrupp AG; *Int'l*, pg. 7733
UHDE HIGH PRESSURE TECHNOLOGIES GMBH—See ThyssenKrupp AG; *Int'l*, pg. 7734
UHDE INVENTA-FISCHER AG—See ThyssenKrupp AG; *Int'l*, pg. 7733
UHDE INVENTA-FISCHER CHEMICAL FIBER EQUIPMENT (SHANGHAI) LTD.—See ThyssenKrupp AG; *Int'l*, pg. 7733
UHDE INVENTA-FISCHER GMBH—See ThyssenKrupp AG; *Int'l*, pg. 7733
UHDE MEXICO S.A. DE C.V.—See ThyssenKrupp AG; *Int'l*, pg. 7734
UHDE SERVICES SLOVAKIA S.R.O.—See ThyssenKrupp AG; *Int'l*, pg. 7734
UHDE SHEDDEN (AUSTRALIA) PTY. LTD.—See ThyssenKrupp AG; *Int'l*, pg. 7734
UH INDUSTRIES & DEVELOPMENT SDN. BHD.—See Bertam Alliance Berhad; *Int'l*, pg. 989
UHINENUD AJAKIRJAD OU; *Int'l*, pg. 8016
UHLENBRUCK ENERGIE GMBH—See Marquard & Bahls AG; *Int'l*, pg. 4701
UHLIG HOLDING GMBH—See NORD Holding Unternehmensbeteiligungsgesellschaft mbH; *Int'l*, pg. 5416
THE UHLMANN COMPANY; *U.S. Private*, pg. 4128
UHL TRUCK SALES INC.; *U.S. Private*, pg. 4274
UHP, LP—See Universal Health Services, Inc.; *U.S. Public*, pg. 2260
UHRHAN & SCHWILL SCHWEISSTECHNIK GMBH—See Lincoln Electric Holdings, Inc.; *U.S. Public*, pg. 1318
UHRHAN & SCHWILL SCHWEISSTECHNIK GMBH—See Lincoln Electric Holdings, Inc.; *U.S. Public*, pg. 1318
UHRIG CONSTRUCTION INC.; *U.S. Private*, pg. 4274
UHS ESSENTIAL HEALTH PHILIPPINES, INC.—See Gull Holdings, Ltd.; *U.S. Public*, pg. 1817
UHS IMAGING LLC—See Universal Health Services, Inc.; *U.S. Public*, pg. 2260
UHS MIDWEST CENTER FOR YOUTH AND FAMILIES, LLC—See Universal Health Services, Inc.; *U.S. Public*, pg. 2260
UHS OF CENTENNIAL PEAKS, LLC—See Universal Health Services, Inc.; *U.S. Public*, pg. 2260
UHS OF DELAWARE, INC.—See Universal Health Services, Inc.; *U.S. Public*, pg. 2260
UHS OF PARKWOOD, INC.—See Universal Health Services, Inc.; *U.S. Public*, pg. 2260
UHS OF PHOENIX, LLC—See Universal Health Services, Inc.; *U.S. Public*, pg. 2260
UHS OF ROCKFORD, LLC—See Universal Health Services, Inc.; *U.S. Public*, pg. 2260
UHS OF SPRINGWOODS, L.L.C.—See Universal Health Services, Inc.; *U.S. Public*, pg. 2260
UHS OF TUCSON, LLC—See Universal Health Services, Inc.; *U.S. Public*, pg. 2260
UHSOME, LLC; *U.S. Private*, pg. 4274
UHS PRODUCTS (MALAYSIA) SDN BHD—See Gull Holdings, Ltd.; *U.S. Public*, pg. 1817
UHS PTY LTD—See Carrier Global Corporation; *U.S. Public*, pg. 444
UHV DESIGN LIMITED—See Judges Scientific plc; *Int'l*, pg. 4021
UHY ADVISORS, INC.; *U.S. Private*, pg. 4275
UHY LLP; *U.S. Private*, pg. 4275
U.H. ZAVERI LIMITED; *Int'l*, pg. 7998
UI2 CORPORATION—See FUJISOFT INCORPORATED; *Int'l*, pg. 2830
UIC ASIAN COMPUTER SERVICES PTE LTD—See Singapore Land Group Limited; *Int'l*, pg. 6940
UIC COMMERCIAL SERVICES, LLC—See Ukpeagvik Inupiat Corporation; *U.S. Private*, pg. 4275
UIC DEVELOPMENT (PRIVATE) LIMITED—See Singapore Land Group Limited; *Int'l*, pg. 6940
UIC GMBH—See BDI - BioEnergy International AG; *Int'l*, pg. 929
U & I CONSTRUCTION BANGKOK CO., LTD.—See Property Perfect Public Company Limited; *Int'l*, pg. 5998
UI CORPORATION—See NIHON DENKEI CO., LTD.; *Int'l*, pg. 5284
UIC TECHNICAL SERVICES, LLC—See Ukpeagvik Inupiat Corporation; *U.S. Private*, pg. 4275
UIC TECHNOLOGIES PTE LTD—See Singapore Land Group Limited; *Int'l*, pg. 6940
U.I. DISPLAY CO., LTD.; *Int'l*, pg. 7998
UIE PLC; *Int'l*, pg. 8016
UIE SERVICES A/S—See UIE Plc; *Int'l*, pg. 8016
U & I FINANCIAL CORP.; *U.S. Public*, pg. 2211
UILA, INC.—See Toyo Corporation; *Int'l*, pg. 7852
UIL CO., LTD.; *Int'l*, pg. 8016
U&I LEARNING NV; *Int'l*, pg. 7997
UIL ENERGY LTD.; *Int'l*, pg. 8016
UIL FINANCE LIMITED; *Int'l*, pg. 8016
UIL HOLDINGS CORPORATION—See Iberdrola, S.A.; *Int'l*, pg. 3571
UIL LIMITED—See ICM Limited; *Int'l*, pg. 3581
UINTA BREWING CO.—See Riverside Partners, LLC; *U.S. Private*, pg. 3446
UINTAH BASIN MEDICAL CENTER; *U.S. Private*, pg. 4275
UINTA TITLE AND INSURANCE, INC.—See First American Financial Corporation; *U.S. Public*, pg. 837
UIPATH, INC.; *U.S. Public*, pg. 2223
UIRAPURU TRANSMISSORA DE ENERGIA, LTDA—See Companhia Paranaense de Energia; *Int'l*, pg. 1748
UIR VERWALTUNGSGESELLSCHAFT MBH—See DZ BANK AG Deutsche Zentral-Genossenschaftsbank; *Int'l*, pg. 2245
UI TECHNO SERVICE CO., LTD.—See Uchida Yoko Co., Ltd.; *Int'l*, pg. 8013
UITGEVERIJ BN/DE STEM B.V.—See DPG Media Group NV; *Int'l*, pg. 2189
UITGEVERIJ ESSENER B.V.—See Sanoma Oyj; *Int'l*, pg. 6553
UITGEVERIJ VAN IN N.V.—See DPG Media Group NV; *Int'l*, pg. 2188
UITGEVERSMAATSCHAPPIJ THE READER'S DIGEST N.V.—See RDA Holding Co.; *Int'l*, pg. 3364
UITZENDBUREAU OTTER-WESTELAKEN B.V.—See Randstad N.V.; *Int'l*, pg. 6206
UJAAS ENERGY LIMITED; *Int'l*, pg. 8016
UJA FEDERATION OF NEW YORK; *U.S. Private*, pg. 4275
UJENA SWIMWEAR AND FASHION; *U.S. Private*, pg. 4275
UJIA E-COMMERCE CO., LTD.—See NetEase, Inc.; *Int'l*, pg. 5214
UJI KAIHATSU DEVELOPMENT CO., LTD.—See Nissin Foods Holdings Co., Ltd.; *Int'l*, pg. 5377
U-JIN CABLE INDUSTRIAL CO., LTD.—See Amphenol Corporation; *U.S. Public*, pg. 132
UJJIVAN FINANCIAL SERVICES LTD.; *Int'l*, pg. 8016
UJJIVAN SMALL FINANCE BANK LIMITED—See Ujjivan Financial Services Ltd.; *Int'l*, pg. 8016
UJ-TRADING AB—See Moelven Industrier ASA; *Int'l*, pg. 5017
UJU ELECTRONICS CO., LTD.; *Int'l*, pg. 8016
UJU HOLDING LIMITED; *Int'l*, pg. 8016
UJV REZ, A. S.—See CEZ, a.s.; *Int'l*, pg. 1429
UK2 GROUP LTD.—See THG Holdings Plc; *Int'l*, pg. 7708
UKAI CO., LTD.; *Int'l*, pg. 8016
UK ARSAGERA OAO; *Int'l*, pg. 8016
UKAS BIG SAVER FOODS INC.; *U.S. Private*, pg. 4275
UKC ELECTRONICS (H.K.) CO.,LTD.—See Restar Holdings Corporation; *Int'l*, pg. 6303
UKC ELECTRONICS (S) PTE,LTD.—See Restar Holdings Corporation; *Int'l*, pg. 6303
UKC ELECTRONICS (THAILAND) CO.,LTD.—See Restar Holdings Corporation; *Int'l*, pg. 6303
UK CIRCUITS & ELECTRONICS SOLUTIONS LIMITED—See Light Science Technologies Holdings Plc; *Int'l*, pg. 4496
UK COAL MINING LIMITED—See Harworth Group plc; *Int'l*, pg. 3282
UK COMMERCIAL PROPERTY REIT LIMITED—See Tritax Big Box REIT plc; *Int'l*, pg. 7928
UK CRBS LIMITED—See MITIE Group Plc; *Int'l*, pg. 4927
UKC SYSTEMS LTD.; *Int'l*, pg. 8016
UKDN WATERFLOW LIMITED—See Horizon Capital LLP; *Int'l*, pg. 3479
UK ELITE SOCCER INC.—See Steel Partners Holdings L.P.; *U.S. Public*, pg. 1943
UK ENERGY SYSTEMS, LTD.—See Biogas Energy Solutions, LLC; *U.S. Private*, pg. 562
UK FACILITIES LIMITED—See PSC Insurance Group Limited; *Int'l*, pg. 6016
UKFAST.NET LTD.; *Int'l*, pg. 8016
UKFH LIMITED—See SEC Newgate S.p.A.; *Int'l*, pg. 6670
UK FLOORING DIRECT LTD.; *Int'l*, pg. 8016
UKFM GROUP LTD—See Cordant Group PLC; *Int'l*, pg. 1796
UKFOREX LIMITED—See OFX Group Limited; *Int'l*, pg. 5531
UKG INC.; *U.S. Private*, pg. 4275
UKG INC.—See Hellman & Friedman LLC; *U.S. Private*, pg. 1910
UK GREETINGS LIMITED—See Clayton, Dubilier & Rice, LLC; *U.S. Public*, pg. 919
UK GRID SOLUTIONS LIMITED—See General Electric Company; *U.S. Public*, pg. 918
UK HEALTHCARE GOOD SAMARITAN HOSPITAL; *U.S. Private*, pg. 4275
THE UKIAH DAILY JOURNAL—See Alden Global Capital LLC; *U.S. Private*, pg. 156
UKIAH DIALYSIS, LLC—See DaVita Inc.; *U.S. Public*, pg. 644
UKIAH FORD; *U.S. Private*, pg. 4275
UK INDEPENDENT MEDICAL SERVICES LIMITED—See GIC Pte. Ltd.; *Int'l*, pg. 2964
UK INDEPENDENT MEDICAL SERVICES LIMITED—See Leonard Green & Partners, L.P.; *U.S. Private*, pg. 2425
UK MAIL GROUP LIMITED—See Deutsche Post AG; *Int'l*, pg. 2083
UK MAIL LTD—See Deutsche Post AG; *Int'l*, pg. 2083
U.K. MEDICAL LIMITED—See Becton, Dickinson & Company; *U.S. Public*, pg. 292
U.K. MEDICAL, LTD.—See Becton, Dickinson & Company; *U.S. Public*, pg. 292
UKM FAHRZEUGTEILE GMBH—See CMP Capital Management-Partners GmbH; *Int'l*, pg. 1672
UK-NSI CO., LTD.—See Nippon Seiki Co., Ltd.; *Int'l*, pg. 5330
UK OIL & GAS PLC; *Int'l*, pg. 8016
UKO TECHNIK GMBH—See Nayax Ltd.; *Int'l*, pg. 5178
UK PACKAGING SUPPLIES LIMITED; *Int'l*, pg. 8016
UKPEAGVIK INUPIAT CORPORATION; *U.S. Private*, pg. 4275
UK POLYFILM LIMITED—See Berry Global Group, Inc; *U.S. Public*, pg. 326
UK POLYTHENE LIMITED—See Berry Global Group, Inc; *U.S. Public*, pg. 326
UKRAINIAN LEASING COMPANY—See BNP Paribas SA; *Int'l*, pg. 1093
UKRAINIAN MOBILE COMMUNICATIONS—See MOBILE TELESYSTEMS PUBLIC JOINT STOCK COMPANY; *Int'l*, pg. 5011
UKRAINIAN MUSIC PC—See Universal Music Group N.V.; *Int'l*, pg. 8079
UKRAINIAN NATIONAL ASSOCIATION, INC.; *U.S. Private*, pg. 4275
UKRAINIAN STOCK EXCHANGE; *Int'l*, pg. 8017
UKRAINISCH-DEUTSCHE GESCHLOSSENE AKTIENGESELLSCHAFT—See Mayr-Melnhof Karton AG; *Int'l*, pg. 4747
UKRAS A.D.; *Int'l*, pg. 8017
UKRAS A.D.; *Int'l*, pg. 8017
UKRAVTOMATIKA—See MARAC ELECTRONICS SA; *Int'l*, pg. 4687
UKRGASVYDOBUVANNIA AC—See National Joint-Stock Company Naftogaz of Ukraine; *Int'l*, pg. 5160
UKRGAZBANK, PJSC; *Int'l*, pg. 8017
UKRHIMFORMACIA LIMITED COMPANY—See GHW International; *Int'l*, pg. 2960
UKRNAFTA PJSC—See Societe Generale S.A.; *Int'l*, pg. 7042
UKRON—See ARCADIS N.V.; *Int'l*, pg. 542
UKROP'S HOMESTYLE FOODS, LLC.; *U.S. Private*, pg. 4275
UKRPRODUCT GROUP CJSC—See UKRPRODUCT GROUP LTD; *Int'l*, pg. 8017
UKRPRODUCT GROUP LTD; *Int'l*, pg. 8017
UKRSIBBANK—See BNP Paribas SA; *Int'l*, pg. 1093
UKRTELECOM JSC; *Int'l*, pg. 8017
UKRTRANSNAFTA JOINT STOCK COMPANY—See National Joint-Stock Company Naftogaz of Ukraine; *Int'l*, pg. 5160
UK SEAFOOD INVESTMENTS LIMITED—See Thai Union Group Public Company Limited; *Int'l*, pg. 7596
UK SINBON ELECTRONICS CO., LTD.—See SINBON Electronics Co., Ltd.; *Int'l*, pg. 6937
U.K. SPAC PLC; *Int'l*, pg. 7998
UK STONE DIRECT LIMITED—See Breedon Group plc; *Int'l*, pg. 1043
THE UK TRADE DESK LTD—See The Trade Desk, Inc.; *U.S. Public*, pg. 2135
UKTV INTERACTIVE LIMITED—See British Broadcasting Corporation; *Int'l*, pg. 1169
UKTV MEDIA LIMITED—See British Broadcasting Corporation; *Int'l*, pg. 1169
UKUS A.D.; *Int'l*, pg. 8017
UK WISDOM LTD.; *Int'l*, pg. 8016
ULAANBAATAR KHIVS JOINT STOCK COMPANY; *Int'l*, pg. 8017
ULAN BATOR ZHONGFU CO., LTD—See Zhuhai Zhongfu Enterprise Co., Ltd.; *Int'l*, pg. 8679
ULANQAB DARSEN GRAPHITE NEW MATERIALS CO., LTD.—See Anhui Tatfook Technology Co., Ltd; *Int'l*, pg. 469

ULASLAR TURIZM YATIRIMLARI VE DAYANIKLI A.S.; *Int'l*, pg. 8017
ULBA-CHINA CO. LTD.—See JSC National Atomic Company Kazatomprom; *Int'l*, pg. 4009
ULBA FA LLP—See JSC National Atomic Company Kazatomprom; *Int'l*, pg. 4009
ULBA METALLURGICAL PLANT JSC—See JSC National Atomic Company Kazatomprom; *Int'l*, pg. 4009
ULBRICH ASIA METALS MALAYSIA SDN BHD—See Ulbrich Stainless Steel & Special Metals, Inc.; *U.S. Private*, pg. 4275
ULBRICH OF CALIFORNIA, INC.—See Ulbrich Stainless Steel & Special Metals, Inc.; *U.S. Private*, pg. 4276
ULBRICH OF ILLINOIS, INC.—See Ulbrich Stainless Steel & Special Metals, Inc.; *U.S. Private*, pg. 4276
ULBRICH OF NEW ENGLAND—See Ulbrich Stainless Steel & Special Metals, Inc.; *U.S. Private*, pg. 4276
ULBRICH PRECISION FLAT WIRE, INC.—See Ulbrich Stainless Steel & Special Metals, Inc.; *U.S. Private*, pg. 4275
ULBRICH PRECISION SPECIAL METALS (SUZHOU) CO., LTD.—See Ulbrich Stainless Steel & Special Metals, Inc.; *U.S. Private*, pg. 4275
ULBRICH SHAPED WIRE, INC.—See Ulbrich Stainless Steel & Special Metals, Inc.; *U.S. Private*, pg. 4275
ULBRICH SOLAR TECHNOLOGIES, INC.—See Ulbrich Stainless Steel & Special Metals, Inc.; *U.S. Private*, pg. 4276
ULBRICH SOLAR TECHNOLOGIES OREGON LLC—See Ulbrich Stainless Steel & Special Metals, Inc.; *U.S. Private*, pg. 4275
ULBRICH SPECIALTY STRIP MILL—See Ulbrich Stainless Steel & Special Metals, Inc.; *U.S. Private*, pg. 4276
ULBRICH STAINLESS STEEL & SPECIAL METALS, INC.; *U.S. Private*, pg. 4275
ULBRINOX—See Ulbrich Stainless Steel & Special Metals, Inc.; *U.S. Private*, pg. 4276
ULCOAT TAIWAN, INC.—See ULVAC, Inc.; *Int'l*, pg. 8020
ULC ROBOTICS, INC.—See SPX Technologies, Inc.; *U.S. Public*, pg. 1922
ULDAL AS—See Byggma ASA; *Int'l*, pg. 1235
UL DE MEXICO, S.A. DE C.V.—See Underwriters Laboratories Inc.; *U.S. Private*, pg. 4280
ULEAD SYSTEMS GMBH—See KKR & Co. Inc.; *U.S. Public*, pg. 1243
ULEAD SYSTEMS, INC.—See KKR & Co. Inc.; *U.S. Public*, pg. 1243
ULEAD SYSTEMS K.K.—See KKR & Co. Inc.; *U.S. Public*, pg. 1243
ULFERTS INTERNATIONAL LIMITED; *Int'l*, pg. 8017
ULFERTS OF SWEDEN (FAR EAST) LIMITED—See Ulferts International Limited; *Int'l*, pg. 8017
ULICO STANDARD OF AMERICA CASUALTY COMPANY—See Ullico Inc.; *U.S. Private*, pg. 4276
ULI INTERNATIONAL CO., LTD.—See Unique Logistics International Inc.; *U.S. Public*, pg. 2227
UL INDIA PRIVATE LTD.—See Underwriters Laboratories Inc.; *U.S. Private*, pg. 4280
U-LINE CORPORATION—See The Middleby Corporation; *U.S. Public*, pg. 2115
ULINE, INC.; *U.S. Private*, pg. 4276
ULI (NORTH & EAST CHINA) CO. LTD.—See Unique Logistics International Inc.; *U.S. Public*, pg. 2227
UL INTERNATIONAL DEMKO A/S—See Underwriters Laboratories Inc.; *U.S. Private*, pg. 4280
UL INTERNATIONAL FRANCE S.A.—See Underwriters Laboratories Inc.; *U.S. Private*, pg. 4280
UL INTERNATIONAL GERMANY GMBH—See Underwriters Laboratories Inc.; *U.S. Private*, pg. 4280
UL INTERNATIONAL ITALIA S.R.L.—See Underwriters Laboratories Inc.; *U.S. Private*, pg. 4280
UL INTERNATIONAL ITALIA S.R.L.—See Underwriters Laboratories Inc.; *U.S. Private*, pg. 4280
UL INTERNATIONAL LTD.—See Underwriters Laboratories Inc.; *U.S. Private*, pg. 4280
UL INTERNATIONAL (NETHERLANDS) B.V.—See Underwriters Laboratories Inc.; *U.S. Private*, pg. 4280
UL INTERNATIONAL NEW ZEALAND LIMITED—See Underwriters Laboratories Inc.; *U.S. Private*, pg. 4280
UL INTERNATIONAL NEW ZEALAND LTD—See Underwriters Laboratories Inc.; *U.S. Private*, pg. 4280
UL INTERNATIONAL (SWEDEN) AB—See Underwriters Laboratories Inc.; *U.S. Private*, pg. 4280
UL INTERNATIONAL (UK) LTD.—See Underwriters Laboratories Inc.; *U.S. Private*, pg. 4280
ULISSE BIOMED S.P.A.; *Int'l*, pg. 8017
ULITEP, SPOL. S R O.—See CEZ, a.s.; *Int'l*, pg. 1429
UL JAPAN, INC.—See Underwriters Laboratories Inc.; *U.S. Private*, pg. 4280
ULKER BISKUVI SANAYI A.S.—See Yildiz Holding AS; *Int'l*, pg. 8583
ULKER CIKOLATA SANAYI A.S.—See Yildiz Holding AS; *Int'l*, pg. 8583
UL KOREA LTD.—See Underwriters Laboratories Inc.; *U.S. Private*, pg. 4280
ULLAND BROTHERS INC.; *U.S. Private*, pg. 4276
ULLA POPKEN LTD.; *U.S. Private*, pg. 4276
ULLENSAKER BOLIGBYGGELAG AS—See Storebrand ASA; *Int'l*, pg. 7226

ULLICO CASUALTY COMPANY—See Ullico Inc.; *U.S. Private*, pg. 4276
ULLICO CASUALTY GROUP, INC.—See Ullico Inc.; *U.S. Private*, pg. 4276
ULLICO INC.—See Ullico Inc.; *U.S. Private*, pg. 4276
ULLICO INC.; *U.S. Private*, pg. 4276
ULLICO INDEMNITY—See Ullico Inc.; *U.S. Private*, pg. 4276
ULLICO INVESTMENT ADVISORS, INC.—See Ullico Inc.; *U.S. Private*, pg. 4276
ULLICO INVESTMENT COMPANY, INC.—See Ullico Inc.; *U.S. Private*, pg. 4276
ULLICO MORTGAGE CORPORATION—See Ullico Inc.; *U.S. Private*, pg. 4276
ULLIMAN SCHUTTE CONSTRUCTION LLC; *U.S. Private*, pg. 4276
ULLINK GLOBAL SAS—See Broadridge Financial Solutions, Inc.; *U.S. Public*, pg. 392
ULLINK INC.—See Broadridge Financial Solutions, Inc.; *U.S. Public*, pg. 392
ULLINK LIMITED—See Broadridge Financial Solutions, Inc.; *U.S. Public*, pg. 392
ULLMAN DEVICES CORPORATION; *U.S. Private*, pg. 4276
ULLMAN OIL, INC.; *U.S. Private*, pg. 4277
ULLSTEIN BUCHVERLAGE GMBH—See Bonnier AB; *Int'l*, pg. 1108
ULMA AGRICOLA, S. COOP.—See Mondragon Corporation; *Int'l*, pg. 5029
ULMA ANDAMIOS Y ENCOFRADOS ARGENTINA, S.A.—See Mondragon Corporation; *Int'l*, pg. 5029
ULMA BETONSCHALUNGEN UND GERUSTE GMBH—See Mondragon Corporation; *Int'l*, pg. 5029
ULMA BRASIL - FORMAS E ESCORAMENTOS LTDA.—See Mondragon Corporation; *Int'l*, pg. 5029
ULMA CHILE - ANDAMIOS Y MOLDAJES, S.A.—See Mondragon Corporation; *Int'l*, pg. 5029
ULMA CIMBRAS Y ANDAMIOS DE MEXICO S.A. DE C.V.—See Mondragon Corporation; *Int'l*, pg. 5029
ULMA COFRAJE S.R.L.—See Mondragon Corporation; *Int'l*, pg. 5029
ULMA CONSTRUCCION CZ, S.R.O.—See Mondragon Corporation; *Int'l*, pg. 5030
ULMA CONSTRUCCION POLSKA S.A.; *Int'l*, pg. 8017
ULMA CONSTRUCCION SK, S.R.O.—See Mondragon Corporation; *Int'l*, pg. 5030
ULMA CONSTRUCTION SYSTEMS CANADA INC.—See Mondragon Corporation; *Int'l*, pg. 5030
ULMA CONVEYOR COMPONENTS S.COOP.—See Mondragon Corporation; *Int'l*, pg. 5030
ULMA C Y E, S. COOP.—See Mondragon Corporation; *Int'l*, pg. 5029
ULMA ENCOFRADOS PERU, S.A.—See Mondragon Corporation; *Int'l*, pg. 5030
ULMA FORMWORKS CHINA R.O.—See Mondragon Corporation; *Int'l*, pg. 5030
ULMA FORM WORKS, INC.—See Mondragon Corporation; *Int'l*, pg. 5030
ULMA FORMWORK SINGAPORE PTE. LTD.—See Mondragon Corporation; *Int'l*, pg. 5030
ULMA FORMWORKS UAE L.L.C.—See Mondragon Corporation; *Int'l*, pg. 5030
ULMA FORMWORK SYSTEMS INDIA PVT. LTD.—See Mondragon Corporation; *Int'l*, pg. 5030
ULMA FORMWORK UKRAINE LTD.—See Mondragon Corporation; *Int'l*, pg. 5030
ULMA HANDLING SYSTEMS DO BRASIL LTDA—See Mondragon Corporation; *Int'l*, pg. 5031
ULMA HANDLING SYSTEMS FRANCE S.A.R.L.—See Mondragon Corporation; *Int'l*, pg. 5031
ULMA HORMIGON POLIMERO, S. COOP.—See Mondragon Corporation; *Int'l*, pg. 5030
ULMA INOXTRUCK—See Mondragon Corporation; *Int'l*, pg. 5030
ULMA INTERNATIONAL GMBH—See Southern Capital Group Pte. Ltd.; *Int'l*, pg. 7118
ULMA KAZAKHSTAN—See Mondragon Corporation; *Int'l*, pg. 5030
ULMA LAZKAO FORGING, S.L.—See Mondragon Corporation; *Int'l*, pg. 5030
ULMA MANUTENCION, S. COOP.—See Mondragon Corporation; *Int'l*, pg. 5030
THE ULMAN CANCER FUND FOR YOUNG ADULTS; *U.S. Private*, pg. 4128
ULMA PACKAGING B.V.—See Mondragon Corporation; *Int'l*, pg. 5030
ULMA PACKAGING GMBH—See Mondragon Corporation; *Int'l*, pg. 5030
ULMA PACKAGING LDA—See Mondragon Corporation; *Int'l*, pg. 5030
ULMA PACKAGING LIMITED—See Mondragon Corporation; *Int'l*, pg. 5030
ULMA PACKAGING LLC—See Mondragon Corporation; *Int'l*, pg. 5030
ULMA PACKAGING LTDA—See Mondragon Corporation; *Int'l*, pg. 5030
ULMA PACKAGING POLSKA SP.Z.O.O.—See Mondragon Corporation; *Int'l*, pg. 5030

ULMA PACKAGING PTY LTD—See Mondragon Corporation; *Int'l*, pg. 5030
ULMA PACKAGING SARL—See Mondragon Corporation; *Int'l*, pg. 5030
ULMA PACKAGING SRL—See Mondragon Corporation; *Int'l*, pg. 5030
ULMA PACKAGING SYSTEMS (SA) (PTY) LTD—See Mondragon Corporation; *Int'l*, pg. 5030
ULMA PACKAGING UKRAINE—See Mondragon Corporation; *Int'l*, pg. 5030
ULMA PIPING—See Mondragon Corporation; *Int'l*, pg. 5030
ULMA PORTUGAL LDA.—See Mondragon Corporation; *Int'l*, pg. 5030
ULMA PRECINOX S.COOP.—See Mondragon Corporation; *Int'l*, pg. 5030
ULMA, S.A.R.L.—See Mondragon Corporation; *Int'l*, pg. 5030
ULMA SERVICIOS DE MANUTENCION, S. COOP.—See Mondragon Corporation; *Int'l*, pg. 5030
ULMER MASCHINENTEILE GMBH—See Rupf Industries GmbH; *Int'l*, pg. 6429
ULMER WERKZEUGSCHLEIFTECHNIK GMBH & CO. KG—See Rupf Industries GmbH; *Int'l*, pg. 6429
ULRIC DE VARENS S.A.; *Int'l*, pg. 8017
ULRICH ALBER GMBH; *Int'l*, pg. 8017
ULRICH HUBER AG—See Burkhalter Holding AG; *Int'l*, pg. 1226
ULRICH MOTOR COMPANY; *U.S. Private*, pg. 4277
ULRICH STEIN GESELLSCHAFT MIT BESCHRANKTER HAFTUNG—See Hamburger Hafen und Logistik AG; *Int'l*, pg. 3237
ULRIKSDAL UTVECKLING AB—See Peab AB; *Int'l*, pg. 5773
ULSAN ENGINEERING CO.,LTD.—See Honda Motor Co., Ltd.; *Int'l*, pg. 3464
ULSAN MARITIME AGENCY CO., LTD—See KSS LINE LTD.; *Int'l*, pg. 4314
ULSAN PORT OPERATING CO., LTD.—See CJ Corporation; *Int'l*, pg. 1634
UL SERVICES (MALAYSIA) SDN. BHD.—See Underwriters Laboratories Inc.; *U.S. Private*, pg. 4280
ULS EXPRESS—See Universal Warehouse Co.; *U.S. Private*, pg. 4307
ULS GROUP, INC.; *Int'l*, pg. 8017
ULSHOFER IT GMBH & CO. KG.—See Iron Mountain Incorporated; *U.S. Public*, pg. 1174
ULS TECHNOLOGY PLC; *Int'l*, pg. 8017
ULSTER BANK IRELAND LIMITED—See NatWest Group plc; *Int'l*, pg. 5172
ULSTER BANK LIMITED—See NatWest Group plc; *Int'l*, pg. 5172
ULSTERBUS—See Northern Ireland Transport Holding Company; *Int'l*, pg. 5444
ULSTER ELECTRIC SUPPLY CO. INC.; *U.S. Private*, pg. 4277
ULSTER INDUSTRIAL EXPLOSIVES LTD.—See Societe Anonyme d'Explosifs et de Produits Chimiques; *Int'l*, pg. 7035
ULSTER SAVINGS BANK; *U.S. Private*, pg. 4277
ULSTER WEAVERS HOME FASHION LTD—See John Hogg & Co. Ltd.; *Int'l*, pg. 3978
ULSTER WEAVERS—See John Hogg & Co. Ltd.; *Int'l*, pg. 3978
ULTA BEAUTY, INC.; *U.S. Public*, pg. 2223
ULTA-LIT TECHNOLOGIES INC.; *U.S. Private*, pg. 4277
ULTEAM SARL—See Derichebourg S.A.; *Int'l*, pg. 2042
ULTERRA DRILLING TECHNOLOGIES, L.P.—See Patterson-UTI Energy, Inc.; *U.S. Public*, pg. 1654
ULTHERA, INC.—See Merz Pharma GmbH & Co. KGaA; *Int'l*, pg. 4839
ULTIMA FOODS INC.—See Groupe Lactalis SA; *Int'l*, pg. 3106
ULTIMA HOSPITALITY, LLC—See Waterford Group, LLC; *U.S. Private*, pg. 4453
ULTIMA ITALIA S.R.L.—See Bhartiya International Ltd.; *Int'l*, pg. 1013
ULTIMA RX, LLC—See UnitedHealth Group Incorporated; *U.S. Public*, pg. 2251
ULTIMATE ACQUISITION PARTNERS, L.P.; *U.S. Private*, pg. 4277
ULTIMATE DIRECTION, INC.—See Exxel Outdoors, Inc.; *U.S. Private*, pg. 1453
ULTIMATE EVERCARE HOLDINGS, LLC; *U.S. Private*, pg. 4277
ULTIMATE FINANCE GROUP LIMITED—See Ultimate Finance Holdings Limited; *Int'l*, pg. 8017
ULTIMATE FINANCE HOLDINGS LIMITED; *Int'l*, pg. 8017
ULTIMATE GAMES SA; *Int'l*, pg. 8017
ULTIMATE HOLDINGS GROUP, INC.; *Int'l*, pg. 8018
ULTIMATE INVOICE FINANCE LIMITED—See Ultimate Finance Holdings Limited; *Int'l*, pg. 8017
ULTIMATE JETCHARTERS, INC.; *U.S. Private*, pg. 4277
ULTIMATE KITCHENS (PIMLICO) LTD.—See Nobia AB; *Int'l*, pg. 5396
ULTIMATE MACHINING SOLUTIONS (M) SDN. BHD.—See UMS Holdings Limited; *Int'l*, pg. 8027

COMPANY NAME INDEX

ULTIMATE NURSING SERVICES OF IOWA, INC.; *U.S. Private*, pg. 4277
ULTIMATE POWERLINE CONTRACTING LTD.—See Quanta Services, Inc.; *U.S. Public*, pg. 1753
ULTIMATE POWER TRUCK, LLC—See Cool Technologies, Inc.; *U.S. Public*, pg. 573
ULTIMATE PRECISION METAL PRODUCTS; *U.S. Private*, pg. 4277
ULTIMATE RACK, INC.; *U.S. Private*, pg. 4277
ULTIMATE RB, INC.—See Carlisle Companies Incorporated; *U.S. Public*, pg. 436
ULTIMATE SERVICES AGENCY, LLC—See BancInsurance Corporation; *U.S. Private*, pg. 464
THE ULTIMATE SOFTWARE GROUP, INC.—See Hellman & Friedman LLC; *U.S. Private*, pg. 1911
THE ULTIMATE SOFTWARE GROUP OF CANADA, INC.—See Hellman & Friedman LLC; *U.S. Private*, pg. 1911
THE ULTIMATE SOFTWARE GROUP OF CANADA, INC.—See Permira Advisers LLP; *Int'l*, pg. 5808
ULTIMATE SPORTS INC.; *U.S. Public*, pg. 2223
ULTIMATE SUPPORT SYSTEMS INC.; *U.S. Private*, pg. 4277
ULTIMATE TECHNOLOGIES GROUP, INC.; *U.S. Private*, pg. 4277
ULTIMATE TECHNOLOGY CORPORATION; *U.S. Private*, pg. 4277
ULTIMATE VEHICLE PTY LTD—See JACKSPEED CORPORATION LIMITED; *Int'l*, pg. 3865
ULTIMATTE CORPORATION—See Blackmagic Design Pty. Ltd.; *Int'l*, pg. 1061
ULTIMA UNITED LIMITED; *Int'l*, pg. 8017
ULTIMED, INC.—See CNL Strategic Capital Management LLC; *U.S. Private*, pg. 952
ULTIMO SOFTWARE SOLUTIONS, INC.; *U.S. Private*, pg. 4277
ULTIMO SP. Z O.O.—See B2Holding AS; *Int'l*, pg. 791
ULTIMOVACS ASA; *Int'l*, pg. 8018
ULTIMUS ASSET SERVICES, LLC—See GTCR LLC; *U.S. Private*, pg. 1806
ULTIMUS FUND SOLUTIONS, LLC—See GTCR LLC; *U.S. Private*, pg. 1806
ULTISALES RETAIL SOFTWARE (PROPRIETARY) LIMITED—See Capital Eye Investments Limited; *Int'l*, pg. 1311
ULTISAT, INC.—See SpeedCast International Limited; *Int'l*, pg. 7133
ULTJE GMBH—See Intersnack Group GmbH & Co. KG; *Int'l*, pg. 3761
ULTOCO, S.A.—See Universal Corporation; *U.S. Public*, pg. 2254
ULTOCO SERVICES, S.A.—See Universal Corporation; *U.S. Public*, pg. 2254
ULTRA ADDITIVES INC.; *U.S. Private*, pg. 4277
ULTRA AIR CARGO, INC.—See A-Sonic Aerospace Limited; *Int'l*, pg. 21
ULTRA ALUMINUM MANUFACTURING INC.—See UFP Industries, Inc.; *U.S. Public*, pg. 2219
ULTRA-BRAG AG; *Int'l*, pg. 8018
ULTRA BRANDS LTD.; *Int'l*, pg. 8018
ULTRABULK DO BRASIL LTDA.—See Ultramar Ltda.; *Int'l*, pg. 8018
ULTRABULK (GERMANY) GMBH—See Ultramar Ltda.; *Int'l*, pg. 8018
ULTRABULK (HONG KONG) LIMITED—See Ultramar Ltda.; *Int'l*, pg. 8018
ULTRABULK SHIPPING A/S—See Ultramar Ltda.; *Int'l*, pg. 8018
ULTRABULK (SINGAPORE) PTE LTD.—See Ultramar Ltda.; *Int'l*, pg. 8018
ULTRABULK (USA) INC—See Ultramar Ltda.; *Int'l*, pg. 8018
ULTRACAB (INDIA) LIMITED; *Int'l*, pg. 8018
ULTRACHARGE LTD; *Int'l*, pg. 8018
ULTRACHEM INC.—See FUCHS SE; *Int'l*, pg. 2804
ULTRA-CHEM INC.; *U.S. Private*, pg. 4277
ULTRACHIP INC.; *Int'l*, pg. 8018
ULTRA CLEAN ASIA PACIFIC, PTE LTD—See Ultra Clean Holdings, Inc.; *U.S. Public*, pg. 2223
ULTRA CLEAN HOLDINGS, INC.; *U.S. Public*, pg. 2223
ULTRA CLEAN PRECISION TECHNOLOGIES CORP.—See ULVAC, Inc.; *Int'l*, pg. 8020
ULTRA CLEAN SYSTEMS INC.—See Getinge AB; *Int'l*, pg. 2952
ULTRA CLEAN TECHNOLOGY SYSTEMS AND SERVICE, INC.—See Ultra Clean Holdings, Inc.; *U.S. Public*, pg. 2223
ULTRA ELECTRONICS ADVANCED TACTICAL SYSTEMS, INC.—See Advent International Corporation; *U.S. Private*, pg. 100
ULTRA ELECTRONICS AIRPORT SYSTEMS—See Advent International Corporation; *U.S. Private*, pg. 100
ULTRA ELECTRONICS AUSTRALIA PTY LIMITED—See Advent International Corporation; *U.S. Private*, pg. 100
ULTRA ELECTRONICS CANADA INC.—See Advent International Corporation; *U.S. Private*, pg. 100
ULTRA ELECTRONICS CARD SYSTEMS INC—See Advent International Corporation; *U.S. Private*, pg. 101
ULTRA ELECTRONICS CARD SYSTEMS LTD—See Advent International Corporation; *U.S. Private*, pg. 100
ULTRA ELECTRONICS COMMAND & CONTROL SYSTEMS—See Advent International Corporation; *U.S. Private*, pg. 101
ULTRA ELECTRONICS CONTROLS DIVISION—See Advent International Corporation; *U.S. Private*, pg. 101
ULTRA ELECTRONICS DNE TECHNOLOGIES, INC.—See Advent International Corporation; *U.S. Private*, pg. 101
ULTRA ELECTRONICS FLIGHTLINE SYSTEMS—See Advent International Corporation; *U.S. Private*, pg. 101
ULTRA ELECTRONICS FORENSIC TECHNOLOGY INC.—See Advent International Corporation; *U.S. Private*, pg. 101
ULTRA ELECTRONICS HERLEY—See Advent International Corporation; *U.S. Private*, pg. 101
ULTRA ELECTRONICS HOLDINGS LIMITED—See Advent International Corporation; *U.S. Private*, pg. 100
ULTRA ELECTRONICS ICE, INC.—See Advent International Corporation; *U.S. Private*, pg. 101
ULTRA ELECTRONICS LIMITED—See Advent International Corporation; *U.S. Private*, pg. 101
ULTRA ELECTRONICS MARITIME SYSTEMS—See Advent International Corporation; *U.S. Private*, pg. 100
ULTRA ELECTRONICS MEASUREMENT SYSTEMS, INC.—See Advent International Corporation; *U.S. Private*, pg. 101
ULTRA ELECTRONICS, NUCLEAR SENSORS & PROCESS INSTRUMENTATION—See Advent International Corporation; *U.S. Private*, pg. 100
ULTRA ELECTRONICS OCEAN SYSTEMS INC.—See Advent International Corporation; *U.S. Private*, pg. 101
ULTRA ELECTRONICS PMES—See Advent International Corporation; *U.S. Private*, pg. 101
ULTRA ELECTRONICS PRECISION AIR SYSTEMS INC—See Advent International Corporation; *U.S. Private*, pg. 101
ULTRA ELECTRONICS PRECISION AIR SYSTEMS LTD—See Advent International Corporation; *U.S. Private*, pg. 101
ULTRA ELECTRONICS SML TECHNOLOGIES LTD.—See Advent International Corporation; *U.S. Private*, pg. 101
ULTRA ELECTRONICS SONAR & COMMUNICATIONS SYSTEMS—See Advent International Corporation; *U.S. Private*, pg. 101
ULTRA EQUITY INVESTMENTS LTD.; *Int'l*, pg. 8018
ULTRAEUROPA SP. Z O.O.—See DBAY Advisors Limited; *Int'l*, pg. 1987
ULTRAEX, INC.; *U.S. Private*, pg. 4278
ULTRAFAB INC.; *U.S. Private*, pg. 4278
ULTRAFILTER AG—See Donaldson Company, Inc.; *U.S. Public*, pg. 676
ULTRAFILTER S.A.S.—See Donaldson Company, Inc.; *U.S. Public*, pg. 675
ULTRA FINISH TECHNOLOGY CO., LTD.—See Hitachi Zosen Corporation; *Int'l*, pg. 3412
ULTRAFLEX SYSTEMS INC.; *U.S. Private*, pg. 4278
ULTRAFRAME (UK) LTD.—See Epwin Group Plc; *Int'l*, pg. 2466
ULTRAFRESH MODULAR SOLUTIONS LIMITED—See TTK Prestige Limited; *Int'l*, pg. 7961
ULTRAFRYER SYSTEMS, INC.—See Standex International; *U.S. Public*, pg. 1931
ULTRAGENDA N.V—See DXC Technology Company; *U.S. Public*, pg. 906
ULTRAGENYX GERMANY GMBH—See Ultragenyx Pharmaceutical Inc.; *U.S. Public*, pg. 2224
ULTRAGENYX PHARMACEUTICAL INC.; *U.S. Public*, pg. 2223
ULTRA GREEN SDN. BHD.—See Oriental Holdings Berhad; *Int'l*, pg. 5625
ULTRAHAPTICS LTD.; *Int'l*, pg. 8018
ULTRAIMPRESSION INC.—See TV Asahi Holdings Corporation; *Int'l*, pg. 7987
ULTRA INC.; *U.S. Private*, pg. 4277
ULTRALAT CAPITAL MARKET INC.—See Credicorp Ltd.; *Int'l*, pg. 1834
ULTRALIFE BATTERIES INDIA PRIVATE LIMITED—See Ultralife Corporation; *U.S. Public*, pg. 2224
ULTRALIFE BATTERIES (UK) LTD.—See Ultralife Corporation; *U.S. Public*, pg. 2224
ULTRALIFE CORPORATION; *U.S. Public*, pg. 2224
ULTRA LITHIUM INC.; *Int'l*, pg. 8018
ULTRALON PRODUCTS (NZ) LIMITED—See Skellerup Holdings Limited; *Int'l*, pg. 6980
ULTRALOX TECHNOLOGY, LLC—See The AZEK Company Inc.; *U.S. Public*, pg. 2035
ULTRAMARA AGENCIA MARITIMA LTDA.—See Ultramar Ltda.; *Int'l*, pg. 8019
ULTRAMAR ENERGY INC.—See Valero Energy Corporation; *U.S. Public*, pg. 2272
ULTRAMAR EXPRESS TRANSPORT S.A.—See TUI AG; *Int'l*, pg. 7969
ULTRAMARINE & PIGMENTS LTD.—See Thirumalai Chemicals Ltd; *Int'l*, pg. 7710
ULTRAMAR LTDA.; *Int'l*, pg. 8018
ULTRAMAR LTD.—See Valero Energy Corporation; *U.S. Public*, pg. 2272
ULTRAMAR NETWORK BRAZIL—See Ultramar Ltda.; *Int'l*, pg. 8019
ULTRAMAR NETWORK COLOMBIA—See Ultramar Ltda.; *Int'l*, pg. 8019
ULTRAMAR NETWORK ECUADOR REMAR—See Ultramar Ltda.; *Int'l*, pg. 8019
ULTRAMAR NETWORK URUGUAY SCHANDY—See Ultramar Ltda.; *Int'l*, pg. 8019
ULTRAMATICS, INC.; *U.S. Private*, pg. 4278
ULTRA MONTES C.V.—See TUI AG; *Int'l*, pg. 7969
ULTRA-PAK INDUSTRIES CO. LTD. - KUN SHAN FACTORY—See Ocean Plastics Co., Ltd.; *Int'l*, pg. 5516
ULTRA-PAK INDUSTRIES CO. LTD. - PHILIPPINE FACTORY—See Ocean Plastics Co., Ltd.; *Int'l*, pg. 5516
ULTRA-PAK INDUSTRIES CO. LTD.—See Ocean Plastics Co., Ltd.; *Int'l*, pg. 5516
ULTRAPAK MANUFACTURING COMPANY LIMITED—See Takween Advanced Industries; *Int'l*, pg. 7443
ULTRAPAR PARTICIPACOES S.A.; *Int'l*, pg. 8019
ULTRA PET COMPANY, INC.—See Oil-Dri Corporation of America; *U.S. Public*, pg. 1566
ULTRAPETROL (BAHAMAS) LIMITED—See Southern Cross Capital Management SA; *Int'l*, pg. 7118
ULTRA PETROLEUM CORP.; *U.S. Public*, pg. 2223
ULTRAPETROL S.A.—See Southern Cross Capital Management SA; *Int'l*, pg. 7118
ULTRA PLAY SYSTEMS, INC.—See Court Square Capital Partners, L.P.; *U.S. Private*, pg. 1070
ULTRAPORT LTDA.—See Ultramar Ltda.; *Int'l*, pg. 8019
ULTRA POWER CORP.; *U.S. Private*, pg. 4277
ULTRAPURE & INDUSTRIAL SERVICES, LLC—See Driessen Water I Inc.; *U.S. Private*, pg. 1277
ULTRA PURE WATER TECHNOLOGIES, LLC; *U.S. Public*, pg. 2223
ULTRARAD HOLDINGS PTY LIMITED—See Sonic Healthcare Limited; *Int'l*, pg. 7099
ULTRA RESOURCES, INC.—See Ultra Petroleum Corp.; *U.S. Public*, pg. 2223
ULTRASEAL CHONGQING LIMITED—See Quaker Chemical Corporation; *U.S. Public*, pg. 1747
ULTRASEAL INTERNATIONAL GROUP LTD.—See Quaker Chemical Corporation; *U.S. Public*, pg. 1747
ULTRASEAL SHANGHAI LIMITED—See Quaker Chemical Corporation; *U.S. Public*, pg. 1747
ULTRASEAL USA INC.—See Quaker Chemical Corporation; *U.S. Public*, pg. 1747
ULTRA SEATING COMPANY—See VSE Corporation; *U.S. Public*, pg. 2313
ULTRA SOLUTIONS—See E&A Industries, Inc.; *U.S. Private*, pg. 1301
ULTRASONIC AG; *Int'l*, pg. 8019
ULTRA SONIC SEAL INC.—See Sonics & Materials, Inc.; *U.S. Private*, pg. 3714
ULTRASONIX MEDICAL CORPORATION—See Altaris Capital Partners, LLC; *U.S. Private*, pg. 205
ULTRASON (UK) LTD.—See Lalique Group S.A.; *Int'l*, pg. 4399
ULTRA SOURCE ELECTRONICS (SZ) CO, LTD—See Arrow Electronics, Inc.; *U.S. Public*, pg. 200
ULTRASOURCE LLC; *U.S. Private*, pg. 4278
ULTRA SOURCE TECHNOLOGY CORP.—See Arrow Electronics, Inc.; *U.S. Public*, pg. 200
ULTRASUN AG—See Lalique Group S.A.; *Int'l*, pg. 4399
ULTRASUN GERMANY GMBH—See Lalique Group S.A.; *Int'l*, pg. 4399
ULTRATAPE INDUSTRIES—See Delphon Industries, LLC; *U.S. Public*, pg. 1199
ULTRATECH CEMENT LTD.—See The Aditya Birla Group; *Int'l*, pg. 7611
ULTRATECH, INC.—See Veeco Instruments Inc.; *U.S. Public*, pg. 2276
ULTRATECH INTERNATIONAL, INC.—See Veeco Instruments Inc.; *U.S. Public*, pg. 2276
ULTRATECH KABUSHIKI KAISHA—See Veeco Instruments Inc.; *U.S. Public*, pg. 2276
ULTRA TECHNOLOGIES INC.; *U.S. Private*, pg. 4277
ULTRATEC, INC.; *U.S. Private*, pg. 4278
ULTRATEC JEWELRY SUPPLIES (GUANGZHOU) LTD.—See Goodwin PLC; *Int'l*, pg. 3042
ULTRATEC LIMITED—See Restore plc; *Int'l*, pg. 6305
ULTRATEST SOLUTIONS LIMITED—See Restore plc; *Int'l*, pg. 6305
ULTRA-VIOLET PRODUCTS LTD.—See Endress+Hauser (International) Holding AG; *Int'l*, pg. 2405
ULTRAVOLT, INC.—See Advanced Energy Industries, Inc.; *U.S. Public*, pg. 48
ULTRA WHEEL COMPANY INC.; *U.S. Private*, pg. 4277
ULTRA WIRING CONNECTIVITY SYSTEM LTD.; *Int'l*, pg. 8018
ULTROID TECHNOLOGIES, INC.; *U.S. Private*, pg. 4278
ULTRO RESOURCES PTE LTD—See Ley Choon Group Holdings Limited; *Int'l*, pg. 4472
ULUKOM BILGISAYAR YAZILIM DONANIM DANISMANLIK VE TICARET A.S.—See WiseTech Global Limited; *Int'l*, pg. 8437
ULULA ASH (PTY) LTD.—See PPC Ltd.; *Int'l*, pg. 5950
THE ULUM GROUP; *U.S. Private*, pg. 4129

ULURU CO., LTD.; *Int'l*, pg. 8019
ULUSAL FAKTORING A.S.; *Int'l*, pg. 8019
ULUSOY ELEKTRIK IMALAT TAAHHUT VE TICARET A.S.—See Eaton Corporation plc; *Int'l*, pg. 2282
ULUSOY UN SANAYI VE TICARET A.S.; *Int'l*, pg. 8019
ULVAC AUTOMATION TAIWAN INC.—See ULVAC, Inc.; *Int'l*, pg. 8020
ULVAC AUTOMATION TECHNOLOGY (SHANGHAI) CORPORATION—See ULVAC, Inc.; *Int'l*, pg. 8020
ULVAC (CHINA) HOLDING CO., LTD.—See ULVAC, Inc.; *Int'l*, pg. 8020
ULVAC COATING CORPORATION—See ULVAC, Inc.; *Int'l*, pg. 8020
ULVAC COATING TECHNOLOGY (HEFEI) CO., LTD.—See ULVAC, Inc.; *Int'l*, pg. 8020
ULVAC CORPORATION—See ULVAC, Inc.; *Int'l*, pg. 8020
ULVAC CRYOGENICS, INC.—See ULVAC, Inc.; *Int'l*, pg. 8020
ULVAC CRYOGENICS KOREA INC.—See Azenta, Inc.; *U.S. Public*, pg. 258
ULVAC CRYOGENICS NINGBO INC.—See Azenta, Inc.; *U.S. Public*, pg. 258
ULVAC EQUIPMENT SALES, INC.—See ULVAC, Inc.; *Int'l*, pg. 8020
ULVAC GMBH—See ULVAC, Inc.; *Int'l*, pg. 8020
ULVAC, INC. - CHIBA TOMISATO PLANT—See ULVAC, Inc.; *Int'l*, pg. 8021
ULVAC, INC. - FUJI SUSONO PLANT—See ULVAC, Inc.; *Int'l*, pg. 8021
ULVAC, INC. - KAGOSHIMA PLANT—See ULVAC, Inc.; *Int'l*, pg. 8021
ULVAC, INC.; *Int'l*, pg. 8020
ULVAC KIKO, INC. - OVERSEAS DIVISION—See ULVAC, Inc.; *Int'l*, pg. 8020
ULVAC KIKO, INC.—See ULVAC, Inc.; *Int'l*, pg. 8020
ULVAC KOREA, LTD.—See ULVAC, Inc.; *Int'l*, pg. 8020
ULVAC KOREA PRECISION CO., LTD.—See ULVAC, Inc.; *Int'l*, pg. 8020
ULVAC KYUSHU CORPORATION—See ULVAC, Inc.; *Int'l*, pg. 8020
ULVAC MALAYSIA SDN. BHD.—See ULVAC, Inc.; *Int'l*, pg. 8020
ULVAC MATERIALS KOREA, LTD.—See ULVAC, Inc.; *Int'l*, pg. 8020
ULVAC MATERIALS (SUZHOU) CO., LTD.—See ULVAC, Inc.; *Int'l*, pg. 8020
ULVAC MATERIALS TAIWAN, INC.—See ULVAC, Inc.; *Int'l*, pg. 8020
ULVAC (NINGBO) CO., LTD.—See ULVAC, Inc.; *Int'l*, pg. 8021
ULVAC ORIENT TEST AND MEASUREMENT TECHNOLOGY (CHENGDU) CO., LTD.—See ULVAC, Inc.; *Int'l*, pg. 8021
ULVAC-PHI, INC.—See ULVAC, Inc.; *Int'l*, pg. 8021
ULVAC (SHANGHAI) TRADING CO., LTD.—See ULVAC, Inc.; *Int'l*, pg. 8020
ULVAC (SHENYANG) CO., LTD.—See ULVAC, Inc.; *Int'l*, pg. 8020
ULVAC SINGAPORE PTE LTD—See ULVAC, Inc.; *Int'l*, pg. 8020
ULVAC SOFTWARE CREATIVE TECHNOLOGY, CO., LTD.—See ULVAC, Inc.; *Int'l*, pg. 8020
ULVAC (SUZHOU) CO., LTD.—See ULVAC, Inc.; *Int'l*, pg. 8020
ULVAC TAIWAN INC—See ULVAC, Inc.; *Int'l*, pg. 8020
ULVAC TECHNOLOGIES, INC.—See ULVAC, Inc.; *Int'l*, pg. 8021
ULVAC TECHNO, LTD.—See ULVAC, Inc.; *Int'l*, pg. 8021
ULVAC (THAILAND) LTD.—See ULVAC, Inc.; *Int'l*, pg. 8021
ULVAC TIANMA ELECTRIC (JINGJIANG) CO., LTD.—See ULVAC, Inc.; *Int'l*, pg. 8021
ULVAC TOHOKU, INC.—See ULVAC, Inc.; *Int'l*, pg. 8021
ULVAC VACUUM EQUIPMENT (SHANGHAI) CO., LTD.—See ULVAC, Inc.; *Int'l*, pg. 8021
ULVAC VACUUM FURNACE (SHENYANG) CO., LTD.—See ULVAC, Inc.; *Int'l*, pg. 8021
ULYANOVSK AUTOMOBILE PLANT PJSC—See OJSC Sollers; *Int'l*, pg. 5542
ULYSSE NARDIN (ASIA PACIFIC) LTD.—See Kering S.A.; *Int'l*, pg. 4136
ULYSSE NARDIN LE LOCLE SA—See Kering S.A.; *Int'l*, pg. 4136
ULYSSE NARDIN RUSSIA LLC—See Kering S.A.; *Int'l*, pg. 4136
ULYSSES MANAGEMENT, LLC; *U.S. Private*, pg. 4278
U-MACHINE (CHINA) CO., LTD.—See Mitsubishi HC Capital Inc.; *Int'l*, pg. 4952
U-MACHINE INC—See Mitsubishi HC Capital Inc.; *Int'l*, pg. 4952
U-MACHINE (THAILAND) CO., LTD.—See Mitsubishi HC Capital Inc.; *Int'l*, pg. 4952
UMAC MANUFACTURING (HUIZHOU) CO., LTD.—See Onamba Co., Ltd.; *Int'l*, pg. 5573
UMA EXPORTS LIMITED; *Int'l*, pg. 8021
UMALIS GROUP SA; *Int'l*, pg. 8021
UMA MANUFACTURING CO., LTD.—See Onamba Co., Ltd.; *Int'l*, pg. 5573

UMA MANUFACTURING (HUIZHOU) CO., LTD.—See Onamba Co., Ltd.; *Int'l*, pg. 5573
UMANA MEDICAL TECHNOLOGIES LTD.—See GPI S.p.A.; *Int'l*, pg. 3046
UMANDIAGNOSTICS AB—See Quanterix Corporation; *U.S. Public*, pg. 1753
UMANG DAIRIES LTD.—See Bengal & Assam Company Ltd.; *Int'l*, pg. 973
UMANIS S.A.—See CGI Inc.; *Int'l*, pg. 1434
U-MARKET PLACE ENTERPRISE PTE. LTD.—See Neo Group Limited; *Int'l*, pg. 5196
UMARO S.A.; *Int'l*, pg. 8021
UMASS MEMORIAL HEALTH CARE, INC.; *U.S. Private*, pg. 4278
UMATAC INDUSTRIAL PROCESSES INC.—See ThyssenKrupp AG; *Int'l*, pg. 7732
UMATILLA ELECTRIC COOPERATIVE INC.; *U.S. Private*, pg. 4278
UMATRIN HOLDING LIMITED; *Int'l*, pg. 8021
UMAX SYSTEMS GMBH—See Hiyes International Co., Ltd.; *Int'l*, pg. 3427
UMAX TECHNOLOGIES INC.—See Hiyes International Co., Ltd.; *Int'l*, pg. 3427
UMB BANC LEASING CORP.—See UMB Financial Corporation; *U.S. Public*, pg. 2224
UMB BANK, N.A.—See UMB Financial Corporation; *U.S. Public*, pg. 2224
UMB CAPITAL CORPORATION—See UMB Financial Corporation; *U.S. Public*, pg. 2224
UMB COMMUNICATION AG—See BKW AG; *Int'l*, pg. 1056
UMBC TRAINING CENTERS; *U.S. Private*, pg. 4278
UMB DISTRIBUTION SERVICES, LLC—See UMB Financial Corporation; *U.S. Public*, pg. 2224
UMBELINO MONTEIRO S.A.—See Groupe Bruxelles Lambert SA; *Int'l*, pg. 3100
UMB FINANCIAL CORPORATION; *U.S. Public*, pg. 2224
UMB FINANCIAL SERVICES, INC.—See UMB Financial Corporation; *U.S. Public*, pg. 2224
UMB FUND SERVICES, INC.—See UMB Financial Corporation; *U.S. Public*, pg. 2224
UMBRA ACQUE S.P.A.—See ACEA S.p.A.; *Int'l*, pg. 95
UMBRA APPLIED TECHNOLOGIES GROUP, INC.; *U.S. Public*, pg. 2224
UMBRACO A/S—See Monterro Investment AB; *Int'l*, pg. 5037
UMBRAGROUP S.P.A.; *Int'l*, pg. 8021
UMBRA INC.; *U.S. Private*, pg. 4278
UMBRELLA GRAPHICS LTD.—See Publicis Groupe S.A.; *Int'l*, pg. 6110
UMBRELLA SOLAR INVESTMENT SA; *Int'l*, pg. 8021
UMBRO INC.—See Iconix Acquisition LLC; *U.S. Private*, pg. 2033
UMB (SWITZERLAND) LTD.—See Mizrahi Tefahot Bank Ltd.; *Int'l*, pg. 4997
UMB UNTERNEHMENS-MANAGEMENTBERATUNGS GMBH—See DZ BANK AG Deutsche Zentral-Genossenschaftsbank; *Int'l*, pg. 2245
U M CABLES LIMITED—See Usha Martin Limited; *Int'l*, pg. 8097
UMC ACQUISITION CORP.; *U.S. Private*, pg. 4278
UMC CAPITAL (U.S.A)—See United Microelectronics Corporation; *Int'l*, pg. 8070
UMC ELECTRONICS CO., LTD.; *Int'l*, pg. 8021
UMC ELECTRONICS (DONGGUAN) CO., LTD.—See UMC Electronics Co., Ltd.; *Int'l*, pg. 8021
UMC ELECTRONICS EUROPE GMBH—See UMC Electronics Co., Ltd.; *Int'l*, pg. 8021
UMC ELECTRONICS HONG KONG LTD.—See UMC Electronics Co., Ltd.; *Int'l*, pg. 8021
UMC ELECTRONICS MANUFACTURING (DONGGUAN) CO., LTD.—See UMC Electronics Co., Ltd.; *Int'l*, pg. 8021
UMC ELECTRONICS MEXICO, S.A. DE C.V.—See UMC Electronics Co., Ltd.; *Int'l*, pg. 8021
UMC ELECTRONICS PRODUCTS (DONGGUAN) CO., LTD.—See UMC Electronics Co., Ltd.; *Int'l*, pg. 8021
UMC ELECTRONICS (THAILAND) LIMITED—See UMC Electronics Co., Ltd.; *Int'l*, pg. 8021
UMC ELECTRONICS VIETNAM LIMITED—See UMC Electronics Co., Ltd.; *Int'l*, pg. 8021
UMC GROUP (USA)—See United Microelectronics Corporation; *Int'l*, pg. 8070
UMC H. ELECTORONICS CO., LTD.—See UMC Electronics Co., Ltd.; *Int'l*, pg. 8021
U.M.C. INTERNATIONAL PLC—See Ackermans & van Haaren NV; *Int'l*, pg. 106
U.M.C. INTERNATIONAL PLC—See STAR Capital Partners Limited; *Int'l*, pg. 7173
UMC JUST IN STAFF CO., LTD.—See UMC Electronics Co., Ltd.; *Int'l*, pg. 8021
UMCOR AG; *Int'l*, pg. 8021
UM CORPORATION, SAS—See Unipres Corporation; *Int'l*, pg. 8056
UMC SERVICEMASTER PTE LTD—See Yanlord Land Group Limited; *Int'l*, pg. 8563
UMC SERVICEMASTER TAIWAN LIMITED—See Yanlord Land Group Limited; *Int'l*, pg. 8563

UMC-SG—See United Microelectronics Corporation; *Int'l*, pg. 8070
UMC USA—See United Microelectronics Corporation; *Int'l*, pg. 8070
UMDASCH GROUP AG; *Int'l*, pg. 8022
UMDASCH SHOP-CONCEPT AG—See Umdasch Group AG; *Int'l*, pg. 8023
UMDASCH SHOP-CONCEPT SPOL. S.R.O.—See Umdasch Group AG; *Int'l*, pg. 8023
UMDASCH SHOPFITTING AG—See Umdasch Group AG; *Int'l*, pg. 8023
UMDASCH SHOPFITTING GMBH—See Umdasch Group AG; *Int'l*, pg. 8023
UMDASCH SHOPFITTING GMBH—See Umdasch Group AG; *Int'l*, pg. 8023
UMDASCH SHOPFITTING GMBH—See Umdasch Group AG; *Int'l*, pg. 8023
UMDASCH SHOPFITTING GROUP GMBH—See Umdasch Group AG; *Int'l*, pg. 8023
UMDASCH SHOPFITTING LIMITED—See Umdasch Group AG; *Int'l*, pg. 8023
UMDASCH SHOPFITTING LLC—See Umdasch Group AG; *Int'l*, pg. 8023
UMDASCH SHOPFITTING LTD.—See Umdasch Group AG; *Int'l*, pg. 8023
UMDASCH SHOPFITTING SAS—See Umdasch Group AG; *Int'l*, pg. 8023
UMDASCH SHOPFITTING S.R.L.—See Umdasch Group AG; *Int'l*, pg. 8023
UM DEVELOPMENT SDN. BHD.—See Seleksi Juang Sdn Bhd; *Int'l*, pg. 6700
UMEC CO.,LTD.—See Universal Microelectronics Co., Ltd.; *Int'l*, pg. 8079
UMECO, INC.—See Cesar Castillo, Inc.; *U.S. Private*, pg. 842
UMEC USA INC.—See Universal Microelectronics Co., Ltd.; *Int'l*, pg. 8079
UMEDA ARTS THEATER CO., LTD.—See Hankyu Hanshin Holdings Inc.; *Int'l*, pg. 3256
UMEDIA SPORTS ADVERTISING S.L.—See WPP plc; *Int'l*, pg. 8477
UMEDIC GROUP BERHAD; *Int'l*, pg. 8023
UMEDISC LIMITED—See Anwell Technologies Ltd.; *Int'l*, pg. 486
UMENOHANA CO., LTD.; *Int'l*, pg. 8023
UMENOHANA S&P CO., LTD.—See S&P Syndicate Public Company Limited; *Int'l*, pg. 6445
UME SERVICE & TRADING SDN. BHD.—See UNIMECH Group Berhad; *Int'l*, pg. 8049
UMETCO MINERALS CORPORATION—See Dow Inc.; *U.S. Public*, pg. 686
UMETNOST A.D.; *Int'l*, pg. 8023
UMETRICS, INC.—See MKS Instruments, Inc.; *U.S. Public*, pg. 1453
UMETSUGUMI CORPORATION—See Toa Road Corporation; *Int'l*, pg. 7769
UMEWORLD, LIMITED; *U.S. Public*, pg. 2224
UMEYA CO., LTD.—See Marudai Food Co., Ltd.; *Int'l*, pg. 4711
UMEZAWA MUSEN DENKI CO.,LTD.—See Takebishi Corporation; *Int'l*, pg. 7437
UMFORMTECHNIK BAEUERLE GMBH—See Georgsmarienhutte Holding GmbH; *Int'l*, pg. 2941
UMFORMTECHNIK STENDAL GMBH—See Klockner & Co. SE; *Int'l*, pg. 4201
UMG ABS, LTD.—See Mitsubishi Chemical Group Corporation; *Int'l*, pg. 4934
UMG ABS, LTD.—See UBE Corporation; *Int'l*, pg. 8001
UMG / DEL MEDICAL—See United Marketing Group, Inc.; *U.S. Private*, pg. 4294
UMG RECORDINGS, INC.—See Universal Music Group N.V.; *Int'l*, pg. 8079
UMH IN HIGHLAND, LLC—See UMH Properties, Inc.; *U.S. Public*, pg. 2225
UMH IN HOLIDAY VILLAGE, LLC—See UMH Properties, Inc.; *U.S. Public*, pg. 2225
UMH IN MEADOWS, LLC—See UMH Properties, Inc.; *U.S. Public*, pg. 2225
UMH IN SUMMIT VILLAGE, LLC—See UMH Properties, Inc.; *U.S. Public*, pg. 2225
UMH IN WOODS EDGE, LLC—See UMH Properties, Inc.; *U.S. Public*, pg. 2225
U-MHI PLATECH CO., LTD.—See UBE Corporation; *Int'l*, pg. 8002
UMH MI CANDLEWICK COURT, LLC—See UMH Properties, Inc.; *U.S. Public*, pg. 2225
UMH MI NORTHTOWNE MEADOWS, LLC—See UMH Properties, Inc.; *U.S. Public*, pg. 2225
UMH NY BROOKVIEW MHP, LLC—See UMH Properties, Inc.; *U.S. Public*, pg. 2225
UMH NY D&R VILLAGE, LLC—See UMH Properties, Inc.; *U.S. Public*, pg. 2225
UMH OH CATALINA, LLC—See UMH Properties, Inc.; *U.S. Public*, pg. 2225
UMH OH HAYDEN HEIGHTS, LLC—See UMH Properties, Inc.; *U.S. Public*, pg. 2225
UMH OH LAKE SHERMAN VILLAGE, LLC—See UMH Properties, Inc.; *U.S. Public*, pg. 2225

UMH OH OLMSTED FALLS, LLC—See UMH Properties, Inc.; *U.S. Public*, pg. 2225
UMH OH WORTHINGTON ARMS, LLC—See UMH Properties, Inc.; *U.S. Public*, pg. 2225
UM HOLDINGS LIMITED; *U.S. Private*, pg. 4278
UMH PA CAMELOT WOODS, LLC—See UMH Properties, Inc.; *U.S. Public*, pg. 2225
UMH PA CRANBERRY VILLAGE, LLC—See UMH Properties, Inc.; *U.S. Public*, pg. 2225
UMH PA FOREST PARK, LLC—See UMH Properties, Inc.; *U.S. Public*, pg. 2225
UMH PA HIGHLAND ESTATES. LLC—See UMH Properties, Inc.; *U.S. Public*, pg. 2225
UMH PA HOLLY ACRES, LLC—See UMH Properties, Inc.; *U.S. Public*, pg. 2225
UMH PA HUNTINGTON POINTE, LLC—See UMH Properties, Inc.; *U.S. Public*, pg. 2225
UMH PA SUBURBAN ESTATES, LLC—See UMH Properties, Inc.; *U.S. Public*, pg. 2225
UMH PA SUNNY ACRES, LLC—See UMH Properties, Inc.; *U.S. Public*, pg. 2225
UMH PA VALLEY STREAM, LLC—See UMH Properties, Inc.; *U.S. Public*, pg. 2225
UMH PA VOYAGER ESTATES, LLC—See UMH Properties, Inc.; *U.S. Public*, pg. 2225
UMH PROPERTIES, INC.; *U.S. Public*, pg. 2224
UMH TN ALLENTOWN, LLC—See UMH Properties, Inc.; *U.S. Public*, pg. 2225
UMH TN WEATHERLY ESTATES, LLC—See UMH Properties, Inc.; *U.S. Public*, pg. 2225
UMIAQ, LLC—See Ukpeagvik Inupiat Corporation; *U.S. Private*, pg. 4275
UMI COMPANY, INC. - MINNEAPOLIS PLANT—See UMI Company, Inc.; *U.S. Private*, pg. 4278
UMI COMPANY, INC.; *U.S. Private*, pg. 4278
UMI COMPANY, INC. - SPANTEK DIVISION—See UMI Company, Inc.; *U.S. Private*, pg. 4278
UMICORE ABRASIVES S.A—See Umicore S.A./N.V.; *Int'l*, pg. 8024
UMICORE AG & CO. KG—See Umicore S.A./N.V.; *Int'l*, pg. 8024
UMICORE ARGENTINA S.A—See Umicore S.A./N.V.; *Int'l*, pg. 8024
UMICORE AUSTRALIA LTD.—See Umicore S.A./N.V.; *Int'l*, pg. 8024
UMICORE AUTOCATALYST RECYCLING BELGIUM N.V.—See Umicore S.A./N.V.; *Int'l*, pg. 8024
UMICORE AUTOCAT CANADA CORP—See Umicore S.A./N.V.; *Int'l*, pg. 8024
UMICORE AUTOCAT (CHINA) CO. LTD.—See Umicore S.A./N.V.; *Int'l*, pg. 8024
UMICORE AUTOCAT FRANCE S.A.S.—See Umicore S.A./N.V.; *Int'l*, pg. 8024
UMICORE AUTOCAT INDIA PVT. LTD.—See Umicore S.A./N.V.; *Int'l*, pg. 8024
UMICORE AUTOCAT LUXEMBOURG SA—See Umicore S.A./N.V.; *Int'l*, pg. 8024
UMICORE AUTOCAT POLAND SP. Z O.O.—See Umicore S.A./N.V.; *Int'l*, pg. 8024
UMICORE AUTOCAT SOUTH AFRICA (PTY) LTD.—See Umicore S.A./N.V.; *Int'l*, pg. 8024
UMICORE AUTOCAT SWEDEN AB—See Umicore S.A./N.V.; *Int'l*, pg. 8024
UMICORE AUTOCAT (THAILAND) CO., LTD.—See Umicore S.A./N.V.; *Int'l*, pg. 8024
UMICORE AUTOCAT USA INC.—See Umicore S.A./N.V.; *Int'l*, pg. 8025
UMICORE BAUSYSTEME GMBH—See Umicore S.A./N.V.; *Int'l*, pg. 8024
UMICORE BRAZIL LTDA.—See Umicore S.A./N.V.; *Int'l*, pg. 8024
UMICORE BUILDING PRODUCTS FRANCE S.A.S.—See Fedrus International NV; *Int'l*, pg. 2631
UMICORE BUILDING PRODUCTS HUNGARY KFT.—See Fedrus International NV; *Int'l*, pg. 2631
UMICORE BUILDING PRODUCTS IBERICA S.L.—See Fedrus International NV; *Int'l*, pg. 2631
UMICORE BUILDING PRODUCTS ITALIA S.R.L.—See Fedrus International NV; *Int'l*, pg. 2631
UMICORE BUILDING PRODUCTS USA INC.—See Fedrus International NV; *Int'l*, pg. 2631
UMICORE CATALISADORES LTDA.—See Umicore S.A./N.V.; *Int'l*, pg. 8024
UMICORE CATALYSIS KOREA CO.,LTD.—See Umicore S.A./N.V.; *Int'l*, pg. 8024
UMICORE CATALYST (CHINA) CO., LTD.—See Umicore S.A./N.V.; *Int'l*, pg. 8024
UMICORE CATALYST SOUTH AFRICA (PTY) LTD.—See Umicore S.A./N.V.; *Int'l*, pg. 8024
UMICORE CATALYST USA, LLC—See Umicore S.A./N.V.; *Int'l*, pg. 8024
UMICORE CLIMETA S.A.S.—See Umicore S.A./N.V.; *Int'l*, pg. 8024
UMICORE COATING SERVICES LTD.—See Umicore S.A./N.V.; *Int'l*, pg. 8024
UMICORE ELECTRICAL MATERIALS USA INC.—See Trent Capital Partners, LLC; *U.S. Private*, pg. 4218
UMICORE FINANCIAL SERVICES NV/SA—See Umicore S.A./N.V.; *Int'l*, pg. 8024

UMICORE GALVANOTECHNIK GMBH—See Umicore S.A./N.V.; *Int'l*, pg. 8024
UMICORE HUNAN FUHONG ZINC CHEMICALS CO., LTD.—See Umicore S.A./N.V.; *Int'l*, pg. 8024
UMICORE INDIUM PRODUCTS—See Umicore S.A./N.V.; *Int'l*, pg. 8024
UMICORE IR GLASS S.A.S.—See Umicore S.A./N.V.; *Int'l*, pg. 8024
UMICORE JAPAN KK—See Umicore S.A./N.V.; *Int'l*, pg. 8024
UMICORE JAPAN KK - TSUKUBA TECH. CENTER/PLANT—See Umicore S.A./N.V.; *Int'l*, pg. 8024
UMICORE JUBO THIN FILM PRODUCTS (BEIJING) CO., LTD.—See Umicore S.A./N.V.; *Int'l*, pg. 8024
UMICORE KOREA LTD—See Umicore S.A./N.V.; *Int'l*, pg. 8024
UMICORE MALAYSIA SDN BHD—See Umicore S.A./N.V.; *Int'l*, pg. 8024
UMICORE MARKETING SERVICES AFRICA (PTY) LTD.—See Umicore S.A./N.V.; *Int'l*, pg. 8025
UMICORE MARKETING SERVICES AUSTRALIA PTY. LTD.—See Umicore S.A./N.V.; *Int'l*, pg. 8025
UMICORE MARKETING SERVICES BELGIUM S.A./NV—See Umicore S.A./N.V.; *Int'l*, pg. 8025
UMICORE MARKETING SERVICES FRANCE S.A.S.—See Umicore S.A./N.V.; *Int'l*, pg. 8025
UMICORE MARKETING SERVICES (HONG KONG) LTD.—See Umicore S.A./N.V.; *Int'l*, pg. 8025
UMICORE MARKETING SERVICES KOREA CO., LTD.—See Umicore S.A./N.V.; *Int'l*, pg. 8025
UMICORE MARKETING SERVICES LUSITANA METAIS, LDA.—See Umicore S.A./N.V.; *Int'l*, pg. 8025
UMICORE MARKETING SERVICES (SHANGHAI) CO., LTD.—See Umicore S.A./N.V.; *Int'l*, pg. 8025
UMICORE MARKETING SERVICES UK LTD.—See Umicore S.A./N.V.; *Int'l*, pg. 8025
UMICORE MARKETING SERVICES USA INC.—See Umicore S.A./N.V.; *Int'l*, pg. 8025
UMICORE MATERIALS AG—See Umicore S.A./N.V.; *Int'l*, pg. 8025
UMICORE NORWAY AS—See Umicore S.A./N.V.; *Int'l*, pg. 8025
UMICORE OPTICAL MATERIALS INC.—See Umicore S.A./N.V.; *Int'l*, pg. 8025
UMICORE OXYDE BELGIUM NV—See Umicore S.A./N.V.; *Int'l*, pg. 8025
UMICORE PORTUGAL S.A.—See Umicore S.A./N.V.; *Int'l*, pg. 8025
UMICORE PRECIOUS METALS CANADA INC.—See Umicore S.A./N.V.; *Int'l*, pg. 8025
UMICORE PRECIOUS METALS NJ LLC—See Umicore S.A./N.V.; *Int'l*, pg. 8025
UMICORE PRECIOUS METALS USA INC.—See Umicore S.A./N.V.; *Int'l*, pg. 8025
UMICORE S.A./N.V.; *Int'l*, pg. 8024
UMICORE SHANGHAI CO., LTD.—See Umicore S.A./N.V.; *Int'l*, pg. 8025
UMICORE SHOKUBAI BRASIL INDUSTRIAL LTDA—See Umicore S.A./N.V.; *Int'l*, pg. 8025
UMICORE SHOKUBAI (CHINA) CO., LTD.—See Umicore S.A./N.V.; *Int'l*, pg. 8025
UMICORE SHOKUBAI GERMANY GMBH—See Umicore S.A./N.V.; *Int'l*, pg. 8025
UMICORE SHOKUBAI JAPAN CO., LTD.—See Umicore S.A./N.V.; *Int'l*, pg. 8025
UMICORE SHOKUBAI (THAILAND) CO., LTD.—See Umicore S.A./N.V.; *Int'l*, pg. 8025
UMICORE SHOKUBAI USA INC.—See Umicore S.A./N.V.; *Int'l*, pg. 8025
UMICORE SOUTH AFRICA (PTY) LTD—See Umicore S.A./N.V.; *Int'l*, pg. 8025
UMICORE SPECIALTY CHEMICALS SUBIC INC.—See Umicore S.A./N.V.; *Int'l*, pg. 8025
UMICORE SPECIALTY MATERIALS BRUGGE NV—See Umicore S.A./N.V.; *Int'l*, pg. 8025
UMICORE SPECIALTY MATERIALS RECYCLING, LLC—See Umicore S.A./N.V.; *Int'l*, pg. 8025
UMICORE SPECIALTY POWDERS FRANCE S.A.S.—See Umicore S.A./N.V.; *Int'l*, pg. 8025
UMICORE STRUB AG—See Umicore S.A./N.V.; *Int'l*, pg. 8025
UMICORE TECHNICAL MATERIALS (SUZHOU) CO., LTD.—See Umicore S.A./N.V.; *Int'l*, pg. 8025
UMICORE THIN FILM PRODUCTS AG—See Umicore S.A./N.V.; *Int'l*, pg. 8025
UMICORE THIN FILM PRODUCTS TAIWAN CO., LTD.—See Umicore S.A./N.V.; *Int'l*, pg. 8025
UMICORE USA INC.—See Umicore S.A./N.V.; *Int'l*, pg. 8025
UMIDA GROUP AB; *Int'l*, pg. 8025
UMINA BROS INC.; *U.S. Private*, pg. 4278
U-MIND CLUB, INC.—See PHMC, Inc.; *U.S. Private*, pg. 3172
U-MING MARINE TRANSPORT CORP.; *Int'l*, pg. 7997
U-MING MARINE TRANSPORT (SINGAPORE) PTE. LTD.—See U-Ming Marine Transport Corp.; *Int'l*, pg. 7997

UMISO (LAEM CHABANG) CO., LTD.—See The Sumitomo Warehouse Co. Ltd.; *Int'l*, pg. 7691
UMI SPECIAL STEEL LTD.—See Jindal Holdings Limited; *Int'l*, pg. 3966
UM ITALIA SRL—See W&R Barnett Ltd.; *Int'l*, pg. 8320
UMIYA TUBES LIMITED; *Int'l*, pg. 8025
UM KOREA LTD—See W&R Barnett Ltd.; *Int'l*, pg. 8320
UMLAUT; *U.S. Private*, pg. 4278
UMM AL HOUL POWER COMPANY—See Mitsubishi Corporation; *Int'l*, pg. 4943
UMM AL QAIWAIN GENERAL INVESTMENTS P.S.C.; *Int'l*, pg. 8026
UMM AL-QURA CEMENT COMPANY; *Int'l*, pg. 8026
UMM SAID BAKERY—See Zad Holding Company S.A.Q.; *Int'l*, pg. 8619
UMNIAH MOBILE COMPANY PSC—See Bahrain Telecommunications Company BSC; *Int'l*, pg. 801
UMN PHARMA INC.; *Int'l*, pg. 8026
UMOE ADVANCED COMPOSITES AS—See Umoe Gruppen AS; *Int'l*, pg. 8026
UMOE BIOENERGY S.A—See Umoe Gruppen AS; *Int'l*, pg. 8026
UMOE CONSULTING AS—See Umoe Gruppen AS; *Int'l*, pg. 8026
UMOE GRUPPEN AS; *Int'l*, pg. 8026
UMOE MANDAL INC.—See Umoe Gruppen AS; *Int'l*, pg. 8026
UMOE RESTAURANT GROUP AS—See Umoe Gruppen AS; *Int'l*, pg. 8026
UMOE SCHAT-HARDING EQUIPMENT AS—See Umoe Gruppen AS; *Int'l*, pg. 8026
UMOE SCHAT-HARDING GROUP AS—See Umoe Gruppen AS; *Int'l*, pg. 8026
UMOE SCHAT-HARDING, INC.—See Umoe Gruppen AS; *Int'l*, pg. 8026
UMOE SCHAT-HARDING SERVICES AS—See Umoe Gruppen AS; *Int'l*, pg. 8026
UMOYA COMMUNICATIONS (PTY) LTD—See African Media Entertainment Limited; *Int'l*, pg. 192
UMPAS HOLDING A.S.; *Int'l*, pg. 8026
UMP HEALTHCARE HOLDINGS LTD.; *Int'l*, pg. 8026
UMP JSC—See JSC National Atomic Company Kazatomprom; *Int'l*, pg. 4009
UMPO JSC; *Int'l*, pg. 8026
UMPQUA BANK—See Columbia Banking System, Inc.; *U.S. Public*, pg. 534
UMPQUA BANK—See Columbia Banking System, Inc.; *U.S. Public*, pg. 534
UMPQUA BANK—See Columbia Banking System, Inc.; *U.S. Public*, pg. 534
UMPQUA BANK—See Columbia Banking System, Inc.; *U.S. Public*, pg. 534
UMPQUA DAIRY PRODUCTS CO. INC.; *U.S. Private*, pg. 4279
UMPQUA INSURANCE AGENCY INC.; *U.S. Private*, pg. 4279
UMRAH HOLIDAYS INTERNATIONAL FZ LLC—See Webjet Limited; *Int'l*, pg. 8366
UM RESIDENCES SDN. BHD.—See Seleksi Juang Sdn Bhd; *Int'l*, pg. 6700
UMR, INC.—See UnitedHealth Group Incorporated; *U.S. Public*, pg. 2251
UMS APS—See Thoma Bravo, L.P.; *U.S. Private*, pg. 4148
UMS CORPORATION SDN. BHD.—See UMS Holdings Berhad; *Int'l*, pg. 8026
UMS ENGINEERING (S) PTE. LTD.—See UMS Holdings Berhad; *Int'l*, pg. 8026
UMS-GENERALI MARINE S.P.A.—See Assicurazioni Generali S.p.A.; *Int'l*, pg. 648
UMS GROUP, INC.—See Align Capital Partners, LLC; *U.S. Private*, pg. 167
UMS HOLDINGS BERHAD; *Int'l*, pg. 8026
UMS HOLDINGS LIMITED; *Int'l*, pg. 8026
UMSI INCORPORATED; *U.S. Private*, pg. 4279
UMS (JB) SDN. BHD.—See UMS Holdings Berhad; *Int'l*, pg. 8026
UMS (KUANTAN) SDN. BHD.—See UMS Holdings Berhad; *Int'l*, pg. 8026
UMS-NEIKEN GROUP BERHAD; *Int'l*, pg. 8027
UMS OY—See Thoma Bravo, L.P.; *U.S. Private*, pg. 4148
UMS (PENANG) SDN. BHD.—See UMS Holdings Berhad; *Int'l*, pg. 8026
UMS PTE LTD—See UMS Holdings Limited; *Int'l*, pg. 8027
UMS (SARAWAK) SDN. BHD.—See UMS Holdings Berhad; *Int'l*, pg. 8026
UMS TECHNOLOGIES LIMITED; *Int'l*, pg. 8027
UMT INTERNATIONAL CO., LTD.—See Onamba Co., Ltd.; *Int'l*, pg. 5573
UMT (THAILAND)—See Onamba Co., Ltd.; *Int'l*, pg. 5573
UMT UNITED MOBILITY TECHNOLOGY AG; *Int'l*, pg. 8027
UMW ADVANTECH SDN BHD—See Sime Darby Berhad; *Int'l*, pg. 6930
UMW AERO ASSETS SDN BHD—See Sime Darby Berhad; *Int'l*, pg. 6930
UMW CORPORATION SDN BHD—See Sime Darby Berhad; *Int'l*, pg. 6930
UMW DEVELOPMENT SDN BHD—See Sime Darby Berhad; *Int'l*, pg. 6930

UMT UNITED MOBILITY TECHNOLOGY AG

UMW (EAST MALAYSIA) SDN BHD—See Komatsu Ltd.; *Int'l*, pg. 4239
UMWELTBANK AG; *Int'l*, pg. 8027
UMWELT-SERVICE NORDSCHWARZWALD GMBH—See Alba SE; *Int'l*, pg. 293
UMWELT- UND INGENIEURTECHNIK GMBH DRESDEN—See General Atomics; *U.S. Private*, pg. 1664
UMW ENGINEERING SERVICES LIMITED—See Komatsu Ltd.; *Int'l*, pg. 4239
UMW EQUIPMENT & ENGINEERING PTE. LTD.—See Sime Darby Berhad; *Int'l*, pg. 6930
UMW EQUIPMENT SDN BHD—See Komatsu Ltd.; *Int'l*, pg. 4239
UMW EQUIPMENT SYSTEMS (VIETNAM) COMPANY LIMITED—See Sime Darby Berhad; *Int'l*, pg. 6931
UMW GRANTT INTERNATIONAL SDN BHD—See Sime Darby Berhad; *Int'l*, pg. 6930
UMW HOLDINGS BERHAD—See Sime Darby Berhad; *Int'l*, pg. 6930
UMW INDUSTRIAL EQUIPMENT (SHANGHAI) CO. LTD.—See Sime Darby Berhad; *Int'l*, pg. 6930
UMW INDUSTRIAL POWER SERVICES SDN. BHD.—See Sime Darby Berhad; *Int'l*, pg. 6931
UMW INDUSTRIAL TRADING (SHANGHAI) CO. LTD.—See Sime Darby Berhad; *Int'l*, pg. 6930
UMW INDUSTRIES (1985) SDN BHD—See Sime Darby Berhad; *Int'l*, pg. 6930
UMW KOMATSU HEAVY EQUIPMENT SDN BHD—See Komatsu Ltd.; *Int'l*, pg. 4239
UMW LUBRICANT INTERNATIONAL SDN BHD—See Sime Darby Berhad; *Int'l*, pg. 6930
UMW M&E SDN BHD—See Sime Darby Berhad; *Int'l*, pg. 6930
UMW NIUGINI LIMITED—See Komatsu Ltd.; *Int'l*, pg. 4239
UMW PENNZOIL DISTRIBUTORS SDN BHD—See Sime Darby Berhad; *Int'l*, pg. 6931
UMW TOYOTA MOTOR SDN. BHD.—See Sime Darby Berhad; *Int'l*, pg. 6931
UMW TOYOTSU MOTORS SDN. BHD.—See Toyota Tsusho Corporation; *Int'l*, pg. 7880
UMW TRAINING CENTRE SDN BHD—See Sime Darby Berhad; *Int'l*, pg. 6931
UMZUGSAUKTION GMBH & CO. KG—See Axel Springer SE; *Int'l*, pg. 767
UNACAST, INC.; *U.S. Private*, pg. 4279
UNADILLA LAMINATED PRODUCTS—See Unadilla Silo Company Inc.; *U.S. Private*, pg. 4279
UNADILLA SILO COMPANY INC.; *U.S. Private*, pg. 4279
UNAKA COMPANY INC.; *U.S. Private*, pg. 4279
UNALLOY-IWRC—See Samuel, Son & Co., Limited; *Int'l*, pg. 6516
UNAMGEN MINERACAO E METALURGIA S/A—See Eldorado Gold Corporation; *Int'l*, pg. 2347
UNAMIC/HCN B.V.—See Conduent Incorporated; *U.S. Public*, pg. 566
UNARCO INDUSTRIES LLC—See Berkshire Hathaway Inc.; *U.S. Public*, pg. 310
UNARCO MATERIAL HANDLING, INC.—See The Renco Group Inc.; *U.S. Private*, pg. 4104
UNARETI SERVIZI METRICI S.R.L.—See A2A S.p.A.; *Int'l*, pg. 29
UNARETI S.P.A.—See A2A S.p.A.; *Int'l*, pg. 29
UNA VEZ MAS, LP; *U.S. Private*, pg. 4279
UNBANKED INC.; *Int'l*, pg. 8027
UNBENCH B.V.—See BASF SE; *Int'l*, pg. 885
UNBOUNDED SOLUTIONS; *U.S. Private*, pg. 4279
UNBOUND GROUP PLC—See Epiris Managers LLP; *Int'l*, pg. 2461
UNBOUNDID CORP.—See Vista Equity Partners, LLC; *U.S. Private*, pg. 4399
UNCAS (HK) COMPANY LTD.—See Uncas Manufacturing Company; *U.S. Private*, pg. 4279
UNCAS MANUFACTURING COMPANY; *U.S. Private*, pg. 4279
UNCLAIMED FREIGHT COMPANY LLC; *U.S. Private*, pg. 4279
UNCLE CHARLEY'S SAUSAGE CO.; *U.S. Private*, pg. 4279
UNCLE DANS, LTD—See Gearhead Outfitters, Inc.; *U.S. Private*, pg. 1655
UNCLE GREY A/S—See WPP plc; *Int'l*, pg. 8472
UNCLE GREY OSLO—See WPP plc; *Int'l*, pg. 8472
UNCLE JULIO'S CORPORATION—See Catterton Management Company, LLC; *U.S. Private*, pg. 794
UNCLE LEE'S TEA INC.; *U.S. Private*, pg. 4279
UNCLE MATT'S ORGANIC INC.—See Dean Foods Company; *U.S. Private*, pg. 1184
UNCLE RAY'S, LLC—See The H.T. Hackney Company; *U.S. Private*, pg. 4041
UNCLE WALLY'S LLC; *U.S. Private*, pg. 4279
UNCLICK SRL—See Indra Sistemas, S.A.; *Int'l*, pg. 3661
UNCO DATA SYSTEMS, INC.—See Culligan Soft Water Service Co.; *U.S. Private*, pg. 1121
UNDACAR PARTS (QLD) PTY LTD.—See Wisr Finance Pty Ltd; *Int'l*, pg. 8437
UNDACAR PARTS (TAS) PTY LTD.—See Wisr Finance Pty Ltd; *Int'l*, pg. 8438

UNDACAR PARTS (WA) PTY LTD.—See Wisr Finance Pty Ltd; *Int'l*, pg. 8438
UNDA S.A—See Boiron Group; *Int'l*, pg. 1101
UNDER ARMOUR EUROPE B.V.—See Under Armour, Inc.; *U.S. Public*, pg. 2225
UNDER ARMOUR, INC.; *U.S. Public*, pg. 2225
UNDERCARRIAGE SPECIALISTS INC.—See Clarence L. Boyd Company; *U.S. Private*, pg. 911
UNDERCURRENT LLC—See Quirky Inc.; *U.S. Private*, pg. 3329
THE UNDERFLOOR HEATING COMPANY LIMITED—See Georg Fischer AG; *Int'l*, pg. 2937
THE UNDERFLOOR HEATING STORE LIMITED—See Travis Perkins plc; *Int'l*, pg. 7908
UNDERGROUND CONSTRUCTION CO., INC.—See Quanta Services, Inc.; *U.S. Public*, pg. 1753
UNDERGROUND ELEPHANT INC.; *U.S. Private*, pg. 4279
UNDERGROUND IMAGING TECHNOLOGIES LLC—See Caterpillar, Inc.; *U.S. Public*, pg. 454
UNDERGROUND INFRASTRUCTURE TECHNOLOGIES CORPORATION—See Hitachi Zosen Corporation; *Int'l*, pg. 3412
UNDERGROUND LOCATING & EXCAVATING—See Complete General Construction Co. Inc.; *U.S. Private*, pg. 1000
UNDERGROUND PIERCING, INC.—See Comlink Contractors Inc.; *U.S. Private*, pg. 982
UNDERGROUND PRINTING; *U.S. Private*, pg. 4279
UNDERGROUND SERVICE LOCATORS—See Downer EDI Limited; *Int'l*, pg. 2186
UNDERGROUND SERVICES AUSTRALIA PTY LTD—See CFC Group Pty. Ltd.; *Int'l*, pg. 1429
UNDERGROUND SOLUTIONS, INC.—See New Mountain Capital, LLC; *U.S. Private*, pg. 2900
UNDERGROUND SPECIALISTS INC.; *U.S. Private*, pg. 4279
UNDERGROUND SPECIALTIES INC.—See Crestone Services Group LLC; *U.S. Private*, pg. 1097
UNDERGROUND SPECIALTIES, LLC—See Dycom Industries, Inc.; *U.S. Public*, pg. 699
UNDERPINNING & FOUNDATION CONSTRUCTORS, INC.—See Skanska AB; *Int'l*, pg. 6979
UNDER PRESSURE WASHING, LLC—See ACON Investments, LLC; *U.S. Private*, pg. 62
UNDERRINER BUICK, INC.; *U.S. Private*, pg. 4279
UNDERSCORE MARKETING LLC; *U.S. Private*, pg. 4279
UNDERSCORE.VC MANAGEMENT CO. LLC; *U.S. Private*, pg. 4279
UNDERSEA SENSOR SYSTEMS INC.—See Advent International Corporation; *U.S. Private*, pg. 101
UNDERSEA SOLUTIONS CORPORATION—See Huntington Ingalls Industries, Inc.; *U.S. Public*, pg. 1072
UNDERWATER CONSTRUCTION CORP.; *U.S. Private*, pg. 4279
UNDERWATER ENGINEERING SERVICES LIMITED—See National Bank of Greece S.A.; *Int'l*, pg. 5153
UNDERWATER WORLD LANGKAWI SDN. BHD.—See Eden Inc. Berhad; *Int'l*, pg. 2306
UNDERWATER WORLD PATTAYA LTD.—See Haw Par Corporation Limited; *Int'l*, pg. 3287
UNDERWATER WORLD SINGAPORE PTE. LTD.—See Haw Par Corporation Limited; *Int'l*, pg. 3288
UNDERWATER WORLD SUNSHINE COAST PTY LTD.—See Merlin Entertainments plc; *Int'l*, pg. 4838
UNDERWATER WORLD XIAMEN CO., LTD.—See Straco Corporation, Ltd.; *Int'l*, pg. 7234
UNDERWOOD BROS INCORPORATED; *U.S. Private*, pg. 4280
UNDERWOOD CHEVROLET-BUICK, INC.; *U.S. Private*, pg. 4280
UNDERWOOD SURGERY CENTER, LLC—See Tenet Healthcare Corporation; *U.S. Public*, pg. 2014
UNDERWRITER FOR THE PROFESSIONS INSURANCE COMPANY—See The Doctors Company; *U.S. Private*, pg. 4022
UNDERWRITERS LABORATORIES AG—See Underwriters Laboratories Inc.; *U.S. Private*, pg. 4280
UNDERWRITERS LABORATORIES INC.; *U.S. Private*, pg. 4280
UNDERWRITERS LABORATORIES OF CANADA—See Underwriters Laboratories Inc.; *U.S. Private*, pg. 4280
UNDERWRITERS LABORATORIES OF CANADA - VANCOUVER BRANCH—See Underwriters Laboratories Inc.; *U.S. Private*, pg. 4280
UNDERWRITERS MARINE SERVICES, INC.—See Aon plc; *Int'l*, pg. 495
UNDERWRITERS SAFETY AND CLAIMS, INC.; *U.S. Private*, pg. 4280
UNDERWRITING AGENCIES OF AUSTRALIA PTY. LTD.—See Steadfast Group Limited; *Int'l*, pg. 7188
UNDERWRITING AGENCIES OF NEW ZEALAND LIMITED—See Steadfast Group Limited; *Int'l*, pg. 7188
UNDERWRITING AGENCIES OF SINGAPORE PTE LTD—See Steadfast Group Limited; *Int'l*, pg. 7188
UNDERWRITING RISK SERVICES S.A.—See American International Group, Inc.; *U.S. Public*, pg. 107
UND SPORTS FACILITIES INC.; *U.S. Private*, pg. 4279
UNECO CO., LTD.; *Int'l*, pg. 8027

CORPORATE AFFILIATIONS

UNEDISA COMUNICACIONES S.L.U.—See RCS MediaGroup S.p.A.; *Int'l*, pg. 6229
UNEDISA TELECOMUNICACIONES S.L.U.—See RCS MediaGroup S.p.A.; *Int'l*, pg. 6230
UNEDITE SAS—See Lonsdale Group; *Int'l*, pg. 4552
UNEEDA DOLL COMPANY, LTD.; *U.S. Private*, pg. 4281
UNEEDKOREA; *Int'l*, pg. 8027
UNEEK 4X4 AUSTRALIA PTY LTD—See Arnotiv Limited; *Int'l*, pg. 431
UNEEK CLOTHING COMPANY LTD.; *Int'l*, pg. 8027
UNE EPM TELECOMUNICACIONES SA—See Empresas Publicas de Medellin ESP; *Int'l*, pg. 2392
UNEKEL, S. COOP.—See Mondragon Corporation; *Int'l*, pg. 5031
UNENANA COOL CORP.—See Wacoal Holdings Corp.; *Int'l*, pg. 8326
UNEO INCORPORATED—See Universal Cement Corporation; *Int'l*, pg. 8078
UNE PIECE EN PLUS SAS—See Safestore Holdings plc; *Int'l*, pg. 6470
UNET CREDIT FINANCE SERVICES LTD.; *Int'l*, pg. 8027
UNETIXS VASCULAR INC—See Opto Circuits (India) Limited; *Int'l*, pg. 5605
U-NETRANS CO., LTD.—See Kimura-Unity Co., Ltd.; *Int'l*, pg. 4164
UNETTE CORPORATION; *U.S. Private*, pg. 4281
UNEVIT D.D.; *Int'l*, pg. 8027
UNEX GROUP; *Int'l*, pg. 8027
UNEX (GUATEMALA), S.A.—See ITOCHU Corporation; *Int'l*, pg. 3841
UNEX MANUFACTURING, INC.; *U.S. Private*, pg. 4281
UNEXO SAS; *Int'l*, pg. 8027
U-NEXT HOLDINGS CO.,LTD; *Int'l*, pg. 7997
UNFI CANADA, INC.—See United Natural Foods, Inc.; *U.S. Public*, pg. 2233
UNFOLD.VC ASI S.A.; *Int'l*, pg. 8027
UNFORS RAYSAFE AB—See Fortive Corporation; *U.S. Public*, pg. 872
UNGA FARMCARE (EAST AFRICA) LIMITED—See Seaboard Corporation; *U.S. Public*, pg. 1851
UNGA GROUP PLC; *Int'l*, pg. 8027
THE UNGAR GROUP; *U.S. Private*, pg. 4129
UNGER COMPANY; *U.S. Private*, pg. 4281
UNGERER AUSTRALIA—See Givaudan S.A.; *Int'l*, pg. 2982
UNGERER & COMPANY—See Givaudan S.A.; *Int'l*, pg. 2982
UNGERER DE COLOMBIA LTDA—See Givaudan S.A.; *Int'l*, pg. 2982
UNGERER DE MEXICO S.A. DE C.V.—See Givaudan S.A.; *Int'l*, pg. 2982
UNGERER FRAGRANCE & FLAVOUR (SHANGHAI) CO. LTD.—See Givaudan S.A.; *Int'l*, pg. 2982
UNGERER INDUSTRIES, INC.—See Givaudan S.A.; *Int'l*, pg. 2982
UNGERER LIMITED—See Givaudan S.A.; *Int'l*, pg. 2982
UNGER FABRIK LLC; *U.S. Private*, pg. 4281
UNGO SECURITY CORPORATION—See FORVIA SE; *Int'l*, pg. 2745
UNGRICHT GMBH + CO KG—See Matthews International Corporation; *U.S. Public*, pg. 1400
UNI 3 PTE LTD—See Polaris Ltd.; *Int'l*, pg. 5907
UNI ABEX ALLOY PRODUCTS LTD.; *Int'l*, pg. 8027
UNIADEX, LTD.—See BIPROGY Inc.; *Int'l*, pg. 1045
UNIAID CO., LTD.—See BIPROGY Inc.; *Int'l*, pg. 1045
UNI'ANG PLASTIC INDUSTRIES (SABAH) SDN. BHD.—See Thong Guan Industries Berhad; *Int'l*, pg. 7717
UNIAO PARTICIPACOES LTDA—See Banco Bradesco S.A.; *Int'l*, pg. 819
UNIAO VOPAK - ARMAZENS GERAIS LTDA.—See Ultrapar Participacoes S.A.; *Int'l*, pg. 8019
UNIAQUE SPA; *Int'l*, pg. 8029
UNIASFALT S. R. O.—See VINCI S.A.; *Int'l*, pg. 8230
UNI-ASIA CAPITAL (JAPAN) LTD.—See Uni-Asia Group Limited; *Int'l*, pg. 8028
UNI-ASIA GROUP LIMITED; *Int'l*, pg. 8028
UNI-ASIA SHIPPING LIMITED—See Uni-Asia Group Limited; *Int'l*, pg. 8028
UNIA SP. Z O.O.; *Int'l*, pg. 8029
UNIASSELVI - SOCIEDADE EDUCACIONAL LEONARDO DA VINCI S/S LTDA.—See Vitru Limited; *Int'l*, pg. 8263
UNIASSURANCES S.A.—See Unibank S.A.; *Int'l*, pg. 8030
UNI AUTO PARTS MANUFACTURE CO., LTD.—See NHK Spring Co., Ltd.; *Int'l*, pg. 5258
UNIAXIS SRL—See MARAC ELECTRONICS SA; *Int'l*, pg. 4687
UNIBAIL-RODAMCO BETEILIGUNGSVERWALTUNG GMBH—See Unibail-Rodamco-Westfield SE; *Int'l*, pg. 8030
UNIBAIL-RODAMCO DEVELOPMENT NEDERLAND BV—See Unibail-Rodamco-Westfield SE; *Int'l*, pg. 8030
UNIBAIL-RODAMCO INVEST GMBH—See Unibail-Rodamco-Westfield SE; *Int'l*, pg. 8030
UNIBAIL-RODAMCO LIEGENSCHAFTSERWERBS GMBH—See Unibail-Rodamco-Westfield SE; *Int'l*, pg. 8030
UNIBAIL-RODAMCO NEDERLAND WINKELS BV—See Unibail-Rodamco-Westfield SE; *Int'l*, pg. 8030

COMPANY NAME INDEX

UNIBAIL-RODAMCO POLSKA SP ZOO—See Unibail-Rodamco-Westfield SE; *Int'l*, pg. 8030
UNIBAIL-RODAMCO SPAIN SA—See Unibail-Rodamco-Westfield SE; *Int'l*, pg. 8030
UNIBAIL-RODAMCO-WESTFIELD GERMANY GMBH—See Unibail-Rodamco-Westfield SE; *Int'l*, pg. 8030
UNIBAIL-RODAMCO-WESTFIELD SE; *Int'l*, pg. 8029
UNIBAN CANADA, INC.; *Int'l*, pg. 8030
UNIBANCO LEASING S.A.—See Itau Unibanco Holding S.A.; *Int'l*, pg. 3830
UNIBANCO-UNIAO DE BANCOS BRASILEIROS S.A.—See Itau Unibanco Holding S.A.; *Int'l*, pg. 3830
UNIBAND ENTERPRISES—See Turtle Mountain Band of Chippewa Indians Inc.; *U.S. Private*, pg. 4262
UNIBANKA AD; *Int'l*, pg. 8031
UNIBANK CJSC; *Int'l*, pg. 8030
UNIBANK COMMERCIAL BANK OJSC; *Int'l*, pg. 8030
UNIBANK FOR SAVINGS—See UFS Bancorp; *U.S. Private*, pg. 4274
UNIBANK S.A.; *Int'l*, pg. 8030
UNIBANK, S.A.; *Int'l*, pg. 8031
UNIBANK—See U & I Financial Corp.; *U.S. Public*, pg. 2211
UNIBAP AB; *Int'l*, pg. 8031
UNIBAR, INC.—See Nextworld, LLC; *U.S. Private*, pg. 2921
UNIBAR MAINTENANCE SERVICES; *U.S. Private*, pg. 4281
UNIBEL SA; *Int'l*, pg. 8031
UNIBEP S.A.; *Int'l*, pg. 8031
UNIBETAO - INDUSTRIAS DE BETAO PREPARADO, S.A.—See SODIM, SGPS, SA; *Int'l*, pg. 7049
UNIBET (HOLDING) LIMITED—See Kindred Group plc; *Int'l*, pg. 4166
UNIBETON EST—See Heidelberg Materials AG; *Int'l*, pg. 3316
UNIBETON ILE DE FRANCE—See Heidelberg Materials AG; *Int'l*, pg. 3316
UNIBETON MEDITERRANEE—See Heidelberg Materials AG; *Int'l*, pg. 3316
UNIBETON OUEST PAYS DE LOIRE—See Heidelberg Materials AG; *Int'l*, pg. 3316
UNIBETON S.A.S.—See Heidelberg Materials AG; *Int'l*, pg. 3316
UNIBETON SUD OUEST—See Heidelberg Materials AG; *Int'l*, pg. 3316
UNIBEV LIMITED—See Globus Spirits Ltd; *Int'l*, pg. 3008
UNI-BIO SCIENCE GROUP LTD; *Int'l*, pg. 8028
UNI-BIO SCIENCE HEALTHCARE (BEIJING) CO. LIMITED—See Uni-Bio Science Group Ltd; *Int'l*, pg. 8028
UNIBIOS HOLDINGS S.A.; *Int'l*, pg. 8031
UNIBLOC-PUMP, INC.—See May River Capital, LLC; *U.S. Private*, pg. 2620
UNIBOARD CANADA, INC.-LDI DIVISION—See Compagnie de Saint-Gobain SA; *Int'l*, pg. 1724
UNIBOARD CANADA INC.—See Compagnie de Saint-Gobain SA; *Int'l*, pg. 1723
UNIBOARD FOSTORIA INC.—See Compagnie de Saint-Gobain SA; *Int'l*, pg. 1724
UNIBOARD MONT LAURIER INC.—See Compagnie de Saint-Gobain SA; *Int'l*, pg. 1724
UNIBOARD NEW LISKEARD, INC.—See Compagnie de Saint-Gobain SA; *Int'l*, pg. 1724
UNIBOARD SAYABEC, INC.—See Compagnie de Saint-Gobain SA; *Int'l*, pg. 1724
UNIBOARD SURFACE INC.—See Compagnie de Saint-Gobain SA; *Int'l*, pg. 1724
UNIBOARD UNIRES, INC.—See Compagnie de Saint-Gobain SA; *Int'l*, pg. 1724
UNIBOARD VAL D'OR, INC.—See Compagnie de Saint-Gobain SA; *Int'l*, pg. 1724
UNIBUS, INC.—See Powell Industries, Inc.; *U.S. Public*, pg. 1705
UNICABLE INCORPORATED; *U.S. Private*, pg. 4281
UNICA CO., LTD.—See Toyota Industries Corporation; *Int'l*, pg. 7869
UNICA ENERGY SOLUTIONS B.V.—See Triton Advisers Limited; *Int'l*, pg. 7935
UNICAFE INC. - KANAGAWA GENERAL FACTORY—See Unicafe Inc.; *Int'l*, pg. 8031
UNICAFE INC.; *Int'l*, pg. 8031
UNICA GROEP B.V.—See Triton Advisers Limited; *Int'l*, pg. 7935
UNICA IMMOBILIENGESELLSCHAFT MBH—See Commerzbank AG; *Int'l*, pg. 1719
UNICA INDUSTRY SOLUTIONS B.V.—See Triton Advisers Limited; *Int'l*, pg. 7935
UNICA INSTALLATIETECHNIEK B.V.—See Triton Advisers Limited; *Int'l*, pg. 7935
UNICA INSURANCE INC.—See La Capitale Civil Service Mutual; *Int'l*, pg. 4387
UNICAJA BANCO, S.A.; *Int'l*, pg. 8031
UNICAP INVESTMENT & FINANCE COMPANY K.S.C.P.; *Int'l*, pg. 8031
UNICAPITAL, INC.; *Int'l*, pg. 8031
UNICAP MODARABA; *Int'l*, pg. 8031

UNICAP SECURITIES LIMITED—See Union Capital Limited; *Int'l*, pg. 8052
UNICARE HEALTH PLAN OF KANSAS, INC.—See Elevance Health, Inc.; *U.S. Public*, pg. 730
UNICARE HEALTH PLAN OF WEST VIRGINIA, INC.—See Elevance Health, Inc.; *U.S. Public*, pg. 730
UNI-CARE, INC.—See Arthur J. Gallagher & Co.; *U.S. Public*, pg. 207
UNICARRIERS AMERICAS CORPORATION—See Mitsubishi Heavy Industries, Ltd.; *Int'l*, pg. 4959
UNICARRIERS CORPORATION—See Mitsubishi Heavy Industries, Ltd.; *Int'l*, pg. 4959
UNICARRIERS DENMARK A/S—See Mitsubishi Heavy Industries, Ltd.; *Int'l*, pg. 4959
UNICARRIERS EUROPE AB—See Mitsubishi Heavy Industries, Ltd.; *Int'l*, pg. 4959
UNICARRIERS FORKLIFT (ANHUI) CO., LTD.—See Mitsubishi Heavy Industries, Ltd.; *Int'l*, pg. 4962
UNICARRIERS FRANCE SAS—See Mitsubishi Heavy Industries, Ltd.; *Int'l*, pg. 4959
UNICARRIERS GERMANY GMBH—See Mitsubishi Heavy Industries, Ltd.; *Int'l*, pg. 4959
UNICARRIERS MANUFACTURING SPAIN, S.A.—See Mitsubishi Heavy Industries, Ltd.; *Int'l*, pg. 4959
UNICARRIERS NETHERLANDS B.V.—See Mitsubishi Heavy Industries, Ltd.; *Int'l*, pg. 4959
UNICARRIERS UK LIMITED—See Mitsubishi Heavy Industries, Ltd.; *Int'l*, pg. 4959
UNICARS HONDA; *U.S. Private*, pg. 4281
UNICARS LIMITED—See P.M. Tseriotis Ltd.; *Int'l*, pg. 5682
UNICASA INDUSTRIA DE MOVEIS S.A.; *Int'l*, pg. 8031
UNICASA PTY LTD—See Casa Holdings Ltd.; *Int'l*, pg. 1349
UNI-CAST, INC.; *U.S. Private*, pg. 4281
UNICAST INC.—See Decisive Dividend Corporation; *Int'l*, pg. 2001
UNICAT CATALYST TECHNOLOGIES, INC.—See White Deer Management LLC; *U.S. Private*, pg. 4509
UNICCOMP GMBH—See BAUER COMP Holding AG; *Int'l*, pg. 894
UNICELL HOLDINGS INC.; *U.S. Private*, pg. 4281
UNICELL NORDIC A/S—See Flugger Group A/S; *Int'l*, pg. 2712
UNICENTER S.A.—See Cencosud S.A.; *Int'l*, pg. 1400
UNICEP COMMERCE A.D.; *Int'l*, pg. 8031
UNICEP COMPANY A.D.; *Int'l*, pg. 8031
UNICER - AGUAS S.A.—See Unicer - Bebidas de Portugal, SGPS, SA; *Int'l*, pg. 8032
UNICER - BEBIDAS DE PORTUGAL, SGPS, SA; *Int'l*, pg. 8031
UNICER - BEBIDAS, SA—See Unicer - Bebidas de Portugal, SGPS, SA; *Int'l*, pg. 8032
UNICER - CERVEJAS SA—See Unicer - Bebidas de Portugal, SGPS, SA; *Int'l*, pg. 8032
UNICER.COM - TECNOLOGIAS DE INFORMACAO S.A.—See Unicer - Bebidas de Portugal, SGPS, SA; *Int'l*, pg. 8032
UNICER - DISTRIBUICAO DE BEBIDAS S.A.—See Unicer - Bebidas de Portugal, SGPS, SA; *Int'l*, pg. 8032
UNICERGESTE - GESTAO DE SERVICOS DE DISTRIBUICAO S.A.—See Unicer - Bebidas de Portugal, SGPS, SA; *Int'l*, pg. 8032
UNICER INTERNACIONAL - EXPORTACAO E IMPORTACAO DE BEBIDAS S.A.—See Unicer - Bebidas de Portugal, SGPS, SA; *Int'l*, pg. 8032
UNICER - SERVICOS DE GESTAO EMPRESARIAL S.A.—See Unicer - Bebidas de Portugal, SGPS, SA; *Int'l*, pg. 8032
UNICER - SUMOS E REFRIGERANTES S.A.—See Unicer - Bebidas de Portugal, SGPS, SA; *Int'l*, pg. 8032
UNICER - VINHOS S.A.—See Unicer - Bebidas de Portugal, SGPS, SA; *Int'l*, pg. 8032
UNICHARM AUSTRALASIA PTY. LTD.—See Unicharm Corporation; *Int'l*, pg. 8032
UNICHARM CONSUMER PRODUCTS (CHINA) CO., LTD.—See Unicharm Corporation; *Int'l*, pg. 8032
UNI-CHARM CORPORATION SDN. BHD.—See Unicharm Corporation; *Int'l*, pg. 8032
UNICHARM CORPORATION; *Int'l*, pg. 8032
UNICHARM HUMANCARE CORPORATION—See Unicharm Corporation; *Int'l*, pg. 8032
UNICHARM INDIA PRIVATE LTD.—See Unicharm Corporation; *Int'l*, pg. 8032
UNICHARM KOKKO NONWOVEN CO., LTD.—See Unicharm Corporation; *Int'l*, pg. 8032
UNICHARM MIDDLE EAST & NORTH AFRICA HYGIENIC INDUSTRIES COMPANY S.A.E.—See Unicharm Corporation; *Int'l*, pg. 8032
UNICHARM MIDDLE EAST & NORTH AFRICA INDUSTRIES COMPANY S.A.E.—See Unicharm Corporation; *Int'l*, pg. 8032
UNI.CHARM MOLNLYCKE BABY B.V.—See Unicharm Corporation; *Int'l*, pg. 8032
UNI-CHARM MOLNLYCKE B.V.—See Unicharm Corporation; *Int'l*, pg. 8032
UNI.CHARM MOLNLYCKE INCONTINENCE B.V.—See Unicharm Corporation; *Int'l*, pg. 8032
UNICHARM MOLNLYCKE K.K.—See Unicharm Corporation; *Int'l*, pg. 8032

UNICORN MINERAL RESOURCES PLC

UNI-CHARM (THAILAND) CO., LTD.—See Unicharm Corporation; *Int'l*, pg. 8032
UNICHEM (CHINA) PRIVATE LIMITED—See Ipca Laboratories Ltd.; *Int'l*, pg. 3796
UNI CHEM CO., LTD.; *Int'l*, pg. 8027
UNICHEM FARMACEUTICA DO BRASIL LTDA.—See Ipca Laboratories Ltd.; *Int'l*, pg. 3796
UNICHEMICALS INDUSTRIA E COMERCIO LTDA.—See Illinois Tool Works Inc.; *U.S. Public*, pg. 1111
UNICHEM LABORATORIES LIMITED—See Ipca Laboratories Ltd.; *Int'l*, pg. 3796
UNICHEM PHARMACEUTICALS (USA) INC.—See Ipca Laboratories Ltd.; *Int'l*, pg. 3796
UNICIRCUIT, INC.—See TTM Technologies, Inc.; *U.S. Public*, pg. 2203
UNICK CORPORATION - ASAN PLANT—See Unick Corporation; *Int'l*, pg. 8032
UNICK CORPORATION - GIMHAE 1ST PLANT—See Unick Corporation; *Int'l*, pg. 8032
UNICK CORPORATION; *Int'l*, pg. 8032
UNICK FIX-A-FORM & PRINTERS LTD.; *Int'l*, pg. 8033
UNICLIP VERPACKUNGSTECHNIK GMBH—See Dover Corporation; *U.S. Public*, pg. 683
UNICLIQ SDN BHD—See Telekom Malaysia Berhad; *Int'l*, pg. 7537
UNICO AMERICAN CORPORATION; *U.S. Public*, pg. 2225
UNICO BANK - PARAGOULD, KINGSHIGHWAY—See Washco Bancshares, Inc.; *U.S. Private*, pg. 4445
UNICO BANK—See Washco Bancshares, Inc.; *U.S. Private*, pg. 4445
UNICOBE CORP.; *Int'l*, pg. 8033
UNICO CHINA AUTOMATION CO. LTD.—See Regal Rexnord Corporation; *U.S. Public*, pg. 1774
UNICO CORPORATION—See ITOCHU Corporation; *Int'l*, pg. 3841
UNICO DEUTSCHLAND GMBH—See Regal Rexnord Corporation; *U.S. Public*, pg. 1774
UNICO HABERKORN AG—See Haberkorn Holding AG; *Int'l*, pg. 3202
UNICOI DIALYSIS, LLC—See DaVita Inc.; *U.S. Public*, pg. 644
UNICO, INC.—See Regal Rexnord Corporation; *U.S. Public*, pg. 1774
UNICO INC.—See Sun-Brite Foods Inc.; *Int'l*, pg. 7309
UNICOIN INC.; *U.S. Private*, pg. 4281
UNICO JAPAN CO. LTD.—See Regal Rexnord Corporation; *U.S. Public*, pg. 1774
UNICOL LTD.—See Cherat Cement Company Limited; *Int'l*, pg. 1471
UNICOM ENGINEERING, INC.—See UNICOM Global, Inc.; *U.S. Private*, pg. 4281
UNICOM GLOBAL IBERIA, INC.—See UNICOM Global, Inc.; *U.S. Private*, pg. 4281
UNICOM GLOBAL, INC.; *U.S. Private*, pg. 4281
UNICOM GOVERNMENT, INC.—See UNICOM Global, Inc.; *U.S. Private*, pg. 4282
UNICOM IMMOBILIEN LEASING GESELLSCHAFT M.B.H.—See UniCredit S.p.A.; *Int'l*, pg. 8037
UNI COMMUNICATIONS INC—See Ildong Pharmaceutical Co., Ltd.; *Int'l*, pg. 3613
UNICOM NEW CENTURY TELECOMMUNICATIONS CORPORATION LIMITED—See China United Network Communications Group Company Limited; *Int'l*, pg. 1561
UNICOMP, INC.; *U.S. Private*, pg. 4282
UNICOMP INC.; *U.S. Private*, pg. 4282
UNICOM SOLUTIONS GROUP INC.—See Hill, Barth & King LLC; *U.S. Private*, pg. 1945
UNICOM SYSTEMS INC.—See UNICOM Global, Inc.; *U.S. Private*, pg. 4282
UNICON A/S—See Cementir Holding N.V.; *Int'l*, pg. 1397
UNICON INTERNATIONAL INC.; *U.S. Private*, pg. 4282
UNICON OPTICAL CO., LTD.; *Int'l*, pg. 8033
UNICONS INVESTMENT CONSTRUCTION CO., LTD.—See Coteccons Construction Joint Stock Company; *Int'l*, pg. 1815
UNICOOP COOPERATIVE AGRICOLE; *Int'l*, pg. 8033
UNICO PROPERTIES INC.; *U.S. Private*, pg. 4281
UNICORD CORPORATION; *U.S. Private*, pg. 4282
UNICORD INTERNATIONAL LLC—See Unicord Corporation; *U.S. Private*, pg. 4282
UNICORD PUBLIC CO. LTD. - PLANT 1—See Unicord Public Co. Ltd.; *Int'l*, pg. 8033
UNICORD PUBLIC CO. LTD. - PLANT 2—See Unicord Public Co. Ltd.; *Int'l*, pg. 8033
UNICORD PUBLIC CO. LTD.; *Int'l*, pg. 8033
UNI CORE HOLDINGS CORPORATION; *Int'l*, pg. 8027
UNICORN AIM VCT PLC; *Int'l*, pg. 8033
UNICORN CAPITAL PARTNERS LIMITED; *Int'l*, pg. 8033
THE UNICORN GROUP; *U.S. Private*, pg. 4129
UNICORN HRO—See The Unicorn Group; *U.S. Private*, pg. 4129
UNICORN HRO—See The Unicorn Group; *U.S. Private*, pg. 4129
UNICORN MINERAL RESOURCES PLC; *Int'l*, pg. 8033
UNICORN PRECIDIA SA—See Compagnie de Saint-Gobain SA; *Int'l*, pg. 1737

UNICORP NATIONAL DEVELOPMENTS, INC.

UNICORP NATIONAL DEVELOPMENTS, INC.; *U.S. Private,* pg. 4282
UNICORP TOWER PLAZA, S.A.; *Int'l,* pg. 8033
UNICORR PACKAGING GROUP—See Connecticut Container Corporation; *U.S. Private,* pg. 1016
UNICO SIGORTA A.S.—See EMF Capital Partners Limited; *Int'l,* pg. 2380
UNICO SILVER LIMITED; *Int'l,* pg. 8033
UNICO SYNDICATE PAKISTAN PVT. LTD.—See WAM-GROUP S.p.A.; *Int'l,* pg. 8338
UNICOTE CORPORATION—See Howard Finishing LLC; *U.S. Private,* pg. 1994
UNICO (UK) LTD.—See Regal Rexnord Corporation; *U.S. Public,* pg. 1774
UNICOVEN C. A.—See Regal Rexnord Corporation; *U.S. Public,* pg. 1774
UNICOVER CORPORATION; *U.S. Private,* pg. 4282
UNICREDIT AURORA LEASING GMBH—See UniCredit S.p.A.; *Int'l,* pg. 8037
UNICREDIT BANCA S.P.A.—See UniCredit S.p.A.; *Int'l,* pg. 8038
UNICREDIT BANK A.D.—See UniCredit S.p.A.; *Int'l,* pg. 8040
UNICREDIT BANK AG—See UniCredit S.p.A.; *Int'l,* pg. 8039
UNICREDIT BANK AKTIENGESELLSCHAFT—See UniCredit S.p.A.; *Int'l,* pg. 8038
UNICREDIT BANK AUSTRIA AG - GLOBAL SECURITIES SERVICES DIVISION—See UniCredit S.p.A.; *Int'l,* pg. 8040
UNICREDIT BANK AUSTRIA AG—See UniCredit S.p.A.; *Int'l,* pg. 8039
UNICREDIT BANK CZECH REPUBLIC A.S.—See UniCredit S.p.A.; *Int'l,* pg. 8040
UNICREDIT BANK CZECH REPUBLIC & SLOVAKIA AS—See UniCredit S.p.A.; *Int'l,* pg. 8033
UNICREDIT BANK D.D.—See UniCredit S.p.A.; *Int'l,* pg. 8040
UNICREDIT BANK HUNGARY ZRT.—See UniCredit S.p.A.; *Int'l,* pg. 8040
UNICREDIT BANK OJSC—See UniCredit S.p.A.; *Int'l,* pg. 8039
UNICREDIT BANK SA—See UniCredit S.p.A.; *Int'l,* pg. 8033
UNICREDIT BANK SA—See UniCredit S.p.A.; *Int'l,* pg. 8040
UNICREDIT BANK SERBIA JSC—See UniCredit S.p.A.; *Int'l,* pg. 8040
UNICREDIT BETEILIGUNGS GMBH—See UniCredit S.p.A.; *Int'l,* pg. 8039
UNICREDIT BPC MORTGAGE S.R.L.—See UniCredit S.p.A.; *Int'l,* pg. 8035
UNICREDIT BULBANK INC.—See UniCredit S.p.A.; *Int'l,* pg. 8041
UNICREDIT BUSINESS PARTNER SOCIETA CONSORTILE PER AZIONI—See UniCredit S.p.A.; *Int'l,* pg. 8035
UNICREDIT CAIB CZECH REPUBLIC A.S.—See UniCredit S.p.A.; *Int'l,* pg. 8040
UNICREDIT CAIB ROMENIA SRL—See UniCredit S.p.A.; *Int'l,* pg. 8040
UNICREDIT CAIB SLOVENIJA, D.O.O.—See UniCredit S.p.A.; *Int'l,* pg. 8040
UNICREDIT CENTER AM KAISERWASSER GMBH—See UniCredit S.p.A.; *Int'l,* pg. 8042
UNICREDIT CONSUMER FINANCING IFN S.A.—See UniCredit S.p.A.; *Int'l,* pg. 8035
UNICREDIT CORPORATE BANKING SERVICES S.P.A.—See UniCredit S.p.A.; *Int'l,* pg. 8041
UNICREDIT DIRECT SERVICES GMBH—See UniCredit S.p.A.; *Int'l,* pg. 8039
UNICREDIT FACTORING CZECH REPUBLIC ANDSLOVAKIA, A.S.—See UniCredit S.p.A.; *Int'l,* pg. 8042
UNICREDIT FACTORING S.P.A.—See UniCredit S.p.A.; *Int'l,* pg. 8041
UNICREDIT FAMILY FINANCING BANK S.P.A.—See UniCredit S.p.A.; *Int'l,* pg. 8041
UNICREDIT FLEET MANAGEMENT, S.R.O.—See UniCredit S.p.A.; *Int'l,* pg. 8038
UNICREDIT FUGGETLEN BIZTOSITASKOZVETITO KFT—See UniCredit S.p.A.; *Int'l,* pg. 8035
UNICREDIT GARAGEN ERRICHTUNG UND VERWERTUNG GMBH—See UniCredit S.p.A.; *Int'l,* pg. 8037
UNICREDIT GLOBAL BUSINESS SERVICES GMBH—See UniCredit S.p.A.; *Int'l,* pg. 8039
UNICREDIT GLOBAL INFORMATION SERVICES SOCIETA CONSORTILE PER AZIONI—See UniCredit S.p.A.; *Int'l,* pg. 8035
UNICREDIT GLOBAL LEASING EXPORT GMBH—See UniCredit S.p.A.; *Int'l,* pg. 8036
UNICREDIT GLOBAL LEASING PARTICIPATION MANAGEMENT GMBH—See UniCredit S.p.A.; *Int'l,* pg. 8036
UNICREDIT GLOBAL LEASING VERSICHERUNGSSERVICE GMBH—See UniCredit S.p.A.; *Int'l,* pg. 8036
UNICREDIT INSURANCE BROKER SRL—See UniCredit S.p.A.; *Int'l,* pg. 8042
UNICREDIT INTERNATIONAL BANK (LUXEMBOURG) SA—See UniCredit S.p.A.; *Int'l,* pg. 8035
UNICREDIT JELZALOGBANK ZRT.—See UniCredit S.p.A.; *Int'l,* pg. 8042
UNICREDIT LEASED ASSET MANAGEMENT SPA—See UniCredit S.p.A.; *Int'l,* pg. 8042
UNICREDIT LEASING AD—See UniCredit S.p.A.; *Int'l,* pg. 8036
UNICREDIT LEASING (AUSTRIA) GMBH—See UniCredit S.p.A.; *Int'l,* pg. 8036
UNICREDIT LEASING BAUTRAGER GMBH—See UniCredit S.p.A.; *Int'l,* pg. 8037
UNICREDIT LEASING CORPORATION IFN S.A.—See UniCredit S.p.A.; *Int'l,* pg. 8036
UNICREDIT LEASING CROATIA D.O.O.—See UniCredit S.p.A.; *Int'l,* pg. 8036
UNICREDIT LEASING CZ A.S.—See UniCredit S.p.A.; *Int'l,* pg. 8038
UNICREDIT LEASING, D.O.O.—See UniCredit S.p.A.; *Int'l,* pg. 8038
UNICREDIT LEASING D.O.O.—See UniCredit S.p.A.; *Int'l,* pg. 8036
UNICREDIT LEASING FINANCE GMBH—See UniCredit S.p.A.; *Int'l,* pg. 8035
UNICREDIT LEASING FUHRPARKMANAGEMENT GMBH—See UniCredit S.p.A.; *Int'l,* pg. 8035
UNICREDIT LEASING GMBH—See UniCredit S.p.A.; *Int'l,* pg. 8039
UNICREDIT LEASING HUNGARY ZRT—See UniCredit S.p.A.; *Int'l,* pg. 8036
UNICREDIT LEASING REAL ESTATE S.R.O.—See UniCredit S.p.A.; *Int'l,* pg. 8036
UNICREDIT LEASING S.P.A.—See UniCredit S.p.A.; *Int'l,* pg. 8036
UNICREDIT LEASING TECHNIKUM GMBH—See UniCredit S.p.A.; *Int'l,* pg. 8038
UNICREDIT LEASING TOB—See UniCredit S.p.A.; *Int'l,* pg. 8036
UNICREDIT LEASING VERSICHERUNGSSERVICE GMBH & CO KG—See UniCredit S.p.A.; *Int'l,* pg. 8037
UNICREDIT LUNA LEASING GMBH—See UniCredit S.p.A.; *Int'l,* pg. 8038
UNICREDIT LUXEMBOURG FINANCE SA—See UniCredit S.p.A.; *Int'l,* pg. 8035
UNICREDIT LUXEMBOURG S.A.—See UniCredit S.p.A.; *Int'l,* pg. 8041
UNICREDIT MOBILIEN LEASING GMBH—See UniCredit S.p.A.; *Int'l,* pg. 8038
UNICREDITO ITALIANO BANK (IRELAND) P.L.C.—See UniCredit S.p.A.; *Int'l,* pg. 8041
UNICREDITO ITALIANO S.P.A.—See UniCredit S.p.A.; *Int'l,* pg. 8033
UNICREDIT PARTNER D.O.O—See UniCredit S.p.A.; *Int'l,* pg. 8038
UNICREDIT PEGASUS LEASING GMBH—See UniCredit S.p.A.; *Int'l,* pg. 8037
UNICREDIT POJIST'OVACI MAKLERSKA SPOL. S.R.O.—See UniCredit S.p.A.; *Int'l,* pg. 8038
UNICREDIT POLARIS LEASING GMBH—See UniCredit S.p.A.; *Int'l,* pg. 8038
UNICREDIT PRIVATE BANKING S.P.A.—See UniCredit S.p.A.; *Int'l,* pg. 8041
UNICREDIT REAL ESTATE SOCIETA CONSORTILE PER AZIONI—See UniCredit S.p.A.; *Int'l,* pg. 8038
UNICREDIT RENT D.O.O. BEOGRAD—See UniCredit S.p.A.; *Int'l,* pg. 8038
UNICREDIT SERVICES GMBH—See UniCredit S.p.A.; *Int'l,* pg. 8033
UNICREDIT SERVICES GMBH—See UniCredit S.p.A.; *Int'l,* pg. 8033
UNICREDIT SERVICES S.C.P.A—See UniCredit S.p.A.; *Int'l,* pg. 8041
UNICREDIT S.P.A.; *Int'l,* pg. 8033
UNICREDIT TECHRENT LEASING GMBH—See UniCredit S.p.A.; *Int'l,* pg. 8037
UNICREDIT TURN-AROUND MANAGEMENT CEE GMBH—See UniCredit S.p.A.; *Int'l,* pg. 8038
UNICYCIVE THERAPEUTICS, INC.; *U.S. Public,* pg. 2226
UNIDAD EDITORIAL INFORMACION DEPORTIVA S.L.U.—See RCS MediaGroup S.p.A.; *Int'l,* pg. 6230
UNIDAD EDITORIAL INFORMACION GENERAL S.L.U.—See RCS MediaGroup S.p.A.; *Int'l,* pg. 6230
UNIDAD EDITORIAL REVISTAS S.L.U.—See RCS MediaGroup S.p.A.; *Int'l,* pg. 6230
UNIDAD EDITORIAL, S.A.—See RCS MediaGroup S.p.A.; *Int'l,* pg. 6229
UNIDAD MOVIL DE DIAGNOSTICO, S.A.—See MAPFRE S.A.; *Int'l,* pg. 4684
UNIDAL D.O.O.—See Unior Kovaska industrija d.d.; *Int'l,* pg. 8055
UNIDAL VENEZUELA S.A.—See Arcor Sociedad Anonima, Industrial y Comercial; *Int'l,* pg. 550
UNIDAS LOCADORA DE VEICULOS LTDA.; *Int'l,* pg. 8042
UNI-DATA SERVICES, LLC—See Unity Electric Co. Inc.; *U.S. Private,* pg. 4302
UNIDATA S.P.A.; *Int'l,* pg. 8042
UNID BTPLUS CO., LTD.; *Int'l,* pg. 8042
UNID CO., LTD.; *Int'l,* pg. 8042
UNIDEL, D.O.O.—See Impol d.d.; *Int'l,* pg. 3637
UNIDEL FOUNDATION, INC.; *U.S. Private,* pg. 4282
UNIDEN AMERICA CORPORATION—See Uniden Holdings Corporation; *Int'l,* pg. 8042
UNIDEN AUSTRALIA PROPRIETARY LIMITED—See Uniden Holdings Corporation; *Int'l,* pg. 8042
UNIDEN AUSTRALIA PTY. LIMITED—See Uniden Holdings Corporation; *Int'l,* pg. 8042
UNIDEN CORPORATION-MARINE COMMUNICATIONS DIV.—See Uniden Holdings Corporation; *Int'l,* pg. 8042
UNIDEN HOLDINGS CORPORATION; *Int'l,* pg. 8042
UNIDEN HONK KONG LTD.—See Uniden Holdings Corporation; *Int'l,* pg. 8042
UNIDEN NEW ZEALAND LTD.—See Uniden Holdings Corporation; *Int'l,* pg. 8042
UNIDENT S.A.—See L'Air Liquide S.A.; *Int'l,* pg. 4375
UNIDESK CORPORATION—See Elliott Management Corporation; *U.S. Private,* pg. 1367
UNIDESK CORPORATION—See Vista Equity Partners, LLC; *U.S. Public,* pg. 4396
UNIDEVELOPMENT SA—See UNIBEP S.A.; *Int'l,* pg. 8031
UNIDEVICE AG; *Int'l,* pg. 8042
UNI DEVICE CORPORATION CO., LTD—See Restar Holdings Corporation; *Int'l,* pg. 6303
UNI DEVICE (SHANGHAI) CO., LTD—See Restar Holdings Corporation; *Int'l,* pg. 6303
UNI DEVICE (S) PTE LTD—See Restar Holdings Corporation; *Int'l,* pg. 6303
UNIDEX GROUP INC.; *U.S. Private,* pg. 4282
UNI-DIL PACKAGING LTD.—See Lanka Walltile PLC; *Int'l,* pg. 4412
UNIDINE CORPORATION; *U.S. Private,* pg. 4282
UNID JIANGSU CHEMICAL CO., LTD.—See Unid Co., Ltd.; *Int'l,* pg. 8042
UNIDOC HEALTH CORP.; *Int'l,* pg. 8042
UNIDRIVE PTY. LTD.—See GKN plc; *Int'l,* pg. 2986
UNIDRIVE PTY. LTD.—See NTN Corporation; *Int'l,* pg. 5483
UNIDRO CONTARINI S.A.S.—See Interpump Group S.p.A.; *Int'l,* pg. 3757
UNIDRO S.A.R.L.—See Interpump Group S.p.A.; *Int'l,* pg. 3755
UNIDUX ELECTRONICS LIMITED—See Avnet, Inc.; *U.S. Public,* pg. 251
UNIDUX (MALAYSIA) SDN BHD—See Avnet, Inc.; *U.S. Public,* pg. 251
UNIDUX (SINGAPORE) PTE LTD—See Avnet, Inc.; *U.S. Public,* pg. 251
UNIDUX (THAILAND) CO., LTD.—See Avnet, Inc.; *U.S. Public,* pg. 251
UNIDYM, INC.—See Wisepower Co., Ltd.; *Int'l,* pg. 8436
UNIECHEMIE B.V.—See Beijer Ref AB; *Int'l,* pg. 945
UNI-ELECTRONICS (HONG KONG) LTD.—See O-Well Corporation; *Int'l,* pg. 5503
UNI-ELECTRONICS, INC.—See O-Well Corporation; *Int'l,* pg. 5503
UNI-ELECTRONICS PTE. LTD.—See O-Well Corporation; *Int'l,* pg. 5503
UNI ELEKTRO FACHGROSSHANDEL GMBH & CO. KG—See Wurth Verwaltungsgesellschaft mbH; *Int'l,* pg. 8508
UNIEQUIP LABORGERATEBAU- UND VERTRIEBS GMBH; *Int'l,* pg. 8042
UNIEURO S.P.A.—See Rhone Group, LLC; *U.S. Private,* pg. 3424
UNIFAB EXPORT CO., LTD.—See Saha Pathanapibul Public Company Limited; *Int'l,* pg. 6479
UNIFAITH MACHINE TOOLS COMPANY LIMITED—See Combine Will International Holdings Limited; *Int'l,* pg. 1709
UNIFARM AD; *Int'l,* pg. 8042
UNIFAST FINANCE & INVESTMENT PLC; *Int'l,* pg. 8042
UNIFAX INSURANCE SYSTEMS, INC.—See Unico American Corporation; *U.S. Public,* pg. 2225
UNIFENCE LLC—See PAO Severstal; *Int'l,* pg. 5732
UNIFERM GMBH & CO.—See The Garfield Weston Foundation; *Int'l,* pg. 7648
UNI-FIBRE CO., LTD.—See Saha-Union Public Company Limited; *Int'l,* pg. 6480
UNIFI CENTRAL AMERICA, LTDA. DE CV—See Unifi, Inc.; *U.S. Public,* pg. 2226
UNIFI DO BRASIL, LTDA—See Unifi, Inc.; *U.S. Public,* pg. 2226
UNIFIED AIRCRAFT SERVICES INC.; *U.S. Private,* pg. 4282
UNIFIED BANK—See United Bancorp, Inc.; *U.S. Public,* pg. 2229
UNIFIED BRANDS INC.—See Electrolux Professional AB; *Int'l,* pg. 2353
UNIFIED COMMERCE GROUP; *U.S. Private,* pg. 4282
UNIFIEDCOMMUNICATIONS.COM; *U.S. Private,* pg. 4283
UNIFIED COMMUNICATIONS (OHQ) SDN. BHD.—See Advance Synergy Berhad; *Int'l,* pg. 157
UNIFIED COMMUNICATIONS PTE LTD—See Captii Limited; *Int'l,* pg. 1317
UNIFIED DEVELOPMENT, INC.; *U.S. Private,* pg. 4282
UNIFIED DOOR & HARDWARE GROUP, LLC—See American Securities LLC; *U.S. Private,* pg. 249
UNIFIED FINANCIAL SECURITIES, LLC—See GTCR LLC; *U.S. Private,* pg. 1806

COMPANY NAME INDEX

UNIFIED FINANCIAL SERVICES, INC.; *U.S. Private*, pg. 4282
UNIFIED GROCERS INSURANCE SERVICES—See Stone Point Capital LLC; *U.S. Private*, pg. 3821
UNIFIED HOUSING FOUNDATION, INC.; *U.S. Private*, pg. 4282
UNIFIED INDUSTRIES, INC.—See Columbus McKinnon Corporation; *U.S. Public*, pg. 536
UNIFIED INDUSTRIES INC.; *U.S. Private*, pg. 4282
UNIFIED INVESTIGATIONS & SCIENCES, INC.—See The Carlyle Group Inc.; *U.S. Public*, pg. 2054
UNIFIED LIFE INSURANCE COMPANY—See Obra Capital, Inc.; *U.S. Private*, pg. 2987
UNIFIED LOGISTICS HOLDINGS LLC—See ACI Capital Co. LLC; *U.S. Private*, pg. 59
UNIFIED MARINE INC.; *U.S. Private*, pg. 4282
UNIFIED MARINE, INC.; *U.S. Private*, pg. 4283
UNIFIED MESSAGING SYSTEMS AS—See Thoma Bravo, L.P.; *U.S. Private*, pg. 4148
UNIFIEDONLINE, INC.; *U.S. Private*, pg. 4283
UNIFIED PACKAGING, INC.; *U.S. Private*, pg. 4283
UNIFIED PARTNERS, LTD—See Nomura Holdings, Inc.; *Int'l*, pg. 5412
UNIFIED PAYMENTS, LLC—See Mullen Automotive, Inc.; *U.S. Public*, pg. 1486
UNIFIED PORT OF SAN DIEGO; *U.S. Private*, pg. 4283
UNIFIEDPOST AG—See Unifiedpost Group SA; *Int'l*, pg. 8043
UNIFIEDPOST AS—See Unifiedpost Group SA; *Int'l*, pg. 8043
UNIFIEDPOST BV—See Nimbus B.V.; *Int'l*, pg. 5297
UNIFIEDPOST D.O.O.—See Unifiedpost Group SA; *Int'l*, pg. 8043
UNIFIEDPOST GROUP SA; *Int'l*, pg. 8042
UNIFIEDPOST LIMITED LIABILITY COMPANY—See Unifiedpost Group SA; *Int'l*, pg. 8043
UNIFIEDPOST LIMITED—See Unifiedpost Group SA; *Int'l*, pg. 8043
UNIFIEDPOST SARL—See Nimbus B.V.; *Int'l*, pg. 5297
UNIFIEDPOST SA—See Nimbus B.V.; *Int'l*, pg. 5296
UNIFIEDPOST SOLUTIONS D.O.O.—See Unifiedpost Group SA; *Int'l*, pg. 8043
UNIFIEDPOST SRL—See Nimbus B.V.; *Int'l*, pg. 5297
UNIFIEDPOST S.R.O.—See Unifiedpost Group SA; *Int'l*, pg. 8043
UNIFIEDPOST UAB—See Unifiedpost Group SA; *Int'l*, pg. 8043
UNIFIEDPOST, UNIPESSOAL LDA.—See Unifiedpost Group SA; *Int'l*, pg. 8043
UNIFIED POWER, LLC—See Incline MGMT Corp.; *U.S. Private*, pg. 2054
UNIFIED RESOURCES IN DISPLAY; *U.S. Private*, pg. 4283
UNIFIED SIGNAL, INC.; *U.S. Private*, pg. 4283
UNIFIED TRANSPORT & LOGISTICS CO; *Int'l*, pg. 8042
UNIFIED TRUST COMPANY, N.A.—See Unified Financial Services, Inc.; *U.S. Private*, pg. 4282
UNIFIED VALVE LTD; *Int'l*, pg. 8042
UNIFI FINANCIAL, INC.; *U.S. Private*, pg. 4282
UNIFI, INC.; *U.S. Public*, pg. 2226
UNIFI LATIN AMERICA, S.A.S.—See Unifi, Inc.; *U.S. Public*, pg. 2226
UNIFILLER SYSTEMS UK LTD.—See Hillenbrand, Inc.; *U.S. Public*, pg. 1037
UNIFILL S.P.A.—See Ferd AS; *Int'l*, pg. 2636
UNIFI MANUFACTURING, INC.—See Unifi, Inc.; *U.S. Public*, pg. 2226
UNIFIN FINANCIERA, S.A.B. DE C.V., SOFOM, E.N.R.; *Int'l*, pg. 8043
UNIFINZ CAPITAL INDIA LIMITED; *Int'l*, pg. 8043
UNIFIRST CANADA LTD.—See UniFirst Corporation; *U.S. Public*, pg. 2226
UNIFIRST CORPORATION; *U.S. Public*, pg. 2226
UNIFIRST CORPORATION—See UniFirst Corporation; *U.S. Public*, pg. 2226
UNIFIRST HOLDINGS INC—See UniFirst Corporation; *U.S. Public*, pg. 2226
UNIFI TEXTILES—See Unifi, Inc.; *U.S. Public*, pg. 2226
UNIFI TEXTURED POLYESTER, LLC—See Unifi, Inc.; *U.S. Public*, pg. 2226
UNIFI TEXTURED YARNS EUROPE, LTD.—See Unifi, Inc.; *U.S. Public*, pg. 2226
UNIFIX SWG S.R.L.—See Wurth Verwaltungsgesellschaft mbH; *Int'l*, pg. 8508
UNIFLAIR GMBH—See Schneider Electric SE; *Int'l*, pg. 6635
UNIFLAIR IBERICA SA—See Schneider Electric SE; *Int'l*, pg. 6635
UNIFLAIR SOUTH AFRICA (PTY) LTD—See Schneider Electric SE; *Int'l*, pg. 6635
UNIFLAIR SPA—See Schneider Electric SE; *Int'l*, pg. 6635
UNIFLAIR (ZHUHAI) ELECTR. APPLI. MANUF. CO. LTD—See Schneider Electric SE; *Int'l*, pg. 6635
UNI FLEX CO LTD.—See NHK Spring Co., Ltd.; *Int'l*, pg. 5258
UNIFLEX TECHNOLOGY INC.; *Int'l*, pg. 8043
UNIFLEX TECHNOLOGY INC. - TAICHUNG CHINGNIAN PLANT—See Uniflex Technology Inc.; *Int'l*, pg. 8043
UNIFLEX TECHNOLOGY INC. - YANGZHOU PLANT—See Uniflex Technology Inc.; *Int'l*, pg. 8043
UNIFLOTTE SRL—See Hera S.p.A.; *Int'l*, pg. 3357
UNIFOCUS, LP; *U.S. Private*, pg. 4283
UNIFOIL CORPORATION; *U.S. Private*, pg. 4283
UNIFORM COLOR COMPANY—See Audia International, Inc.; *U.S. Private*, pg. 390
UNI-FORM COMPONENTS CO.—See Berkshire Hathaway Inc.; *U.S. Public*, pg. 311
UNIFORMED SERVICES BENEFIT ASSOCIATION; *U.S. Private*, pg. 4283
UNIFORMES DE SAN LUIS S.A. DE C.V.—See UniFirst Corporation; *U.S. Public*, pg. 2226
UNIFORM INDUSTRIAL CORPORATION; *Int'l*, pg. 8043
UNIFORM INDUSTRIAL CORP.USA—See Uniform Industrial Corporation; *Int'l*, pg. 8043
UNIFORM NEXT CO., LTD.; *Int'l*, pg. 8043
UNIFORMS UNLIMITED, INC.—See Charlesbank Capital Partners, LLC; *U.S. Private*, pg. 855
UNIFORS RAYSAFE AB—See Fortive Corporation; *U.S. Public*, pg. 872
UNIFOSA CORP.; *Int'l*, pg. 8043
UNIFRAX I LLC—See Clearlake Capital Group, L.P.; *U.S. Private*, pg. 937
UNIFREE DUTY FREE ISLETMECILIGI A.S.—See Bank of Georgia Group PLC; *Int'l*, pg. 843
UNIFREIGHT AFRICA LIMITED; *Int'l*, pg. 8043
UNIFUJI SDN. BHD.—See Fuji Oil Holdings Inc.; *Int'l*, pg. 2816
UNIFUNDS LIMITED; *Int'l*, pg. 8043
UNIFUSION INC.—See UniTest Inc.; *Int'l*, pg. 8074
UNIFY GMBH & CO. KG—See Searchlight Capital Partners, L.P.; *U.S. Private*, pg. 3590
UNIFY SMART TECH JOINT STOCK COMPANY—See The Siam Cement Public Company Limited; *Int'l*, pg. 7685
UNIFY SOFTWARE & SOLUTIONS GMBH & CO. KG—See Searchlight Capital Partners, L.P.; *U.S. Private*, pg. 3589
UNIFY SQUARE, INC.—See Unisys Corporation; *U.S. Public*, pg. 2228
UNIGARD INSURANCE GROUP—See QBE Insurance Group Limited; *Int'l*, pg. 6137
UNIGAS TRANSPORT FUELS PTY LTD—See Linde plc; *Int'l*, pg. 4508
UNIGATE TELECOM INC.—See Chunghwa Telecom Co., Ltd.; *Int'l*, pg. 1598
UNIGEL GROUP PLC; *Int'l*, pg. 8043
UNIGEN CORPORATION; *U.S. Private*, pg. 4283
UNIGLASS LTD—See Nippon Sheet Glass Co. Ltd.; *Int'l*, pg. 5332
UNIGLOBE ADVANCE TRAVEL LTD; *Int'l*, pg. 8043
UNIGLOBE MOD TRAVELS PVT. LTD.—See Modi Rubber Limited; *Int'l*, pg. 5016
UNIGLOBE TRAVEL INTERNATIONAL LIMITED PARTNERSHIP—See Charlwood Pacific Group; *Int'l*, pg. 1450
UNIGOLD INC.; *Int'l*, pg. 8043
UNIGRADE TRADING PTE LTD—See Sim Lian Group Limited; *Int'l*, pg. 6927
UNIGRADNJA DD SARAJEVO; *Int'l*, pg. 8043
UNIGRAINS; *Int'l*, pg. 8044
UNIGRAPHIC, INC.—See Quad/Graphics, Inc.; *U.S. Public*, pg. 1745
UNIGROUP GUOXIN MICROELECTRONICS CO., LTD.; *Int'l*, pg. 8044
UNIGROUP, INC.; *U.S. Private*, pg. 4283
UNIGROUP RELOCATION—See UniGroup, Inc.; *U.S. Private*, pg. 4283
UNIGROUP WORLDWIDE, INC.—See UniGroup, Inc.; *U.S. Private*, pg. 4283
UNIGROUP WORLDWIDE LOGISTICS, LLC—See UniGroup, Inc.; *U.S. Private*, pg. 4283
UNIGROWTH INVESTMENTS PUBLIC LTD; *Int'l*, pg. 8044
UNIHAN CORPORATION—See Pegatron Corporation; *Int'l*, pg. 5781
UNIHEALTH CONSULTANCY LIMITED; *Int'l*, pg. 8044
UNIHOLDINGS INC.; *Int'l*, pg. 8044
UNIHORN, INC.—See Unison Pacific Corporation; *U.S. Private*, pg. 4286
UNI HOSIERY CO. INC.; *U.S. Private*, pg. 4281
UNIHOUSE SA—See UNIBEP S.A.; *Int'l*, pg. 8031
UNI INDUSTRY CO., LTD.—See Mitsubishi Pencil Co., Ltd.; *Int'l*, pg. 4967
UNIINFO TELECOM SERVICES LIMITED; *Int'l*, pg. 8044
UNI IT SRL—See GPI S.p.A.; *Int'l*, pg. 3046
UNIIUMIN GROUP CO., LTD.—See Unilumin Group Co., Ltd.; *Int'l*, pg. 8048
UNIJIN INSTRUMENTS INDUSTRIES SDN. BHD.—See UNIMECH Group Berhad; *Int'l*, pg. 8049
UNI JOINT B.V.—See Triton Advisers Limited; *Int'l*, pg. 7934
UNIKAI & COMPANY LLC—See Unikai Foods P.J.S.C.; *Int'l*, pg. 8044
UNIKAI FOODS P.J.S.C.; *Int'l*, pg. 8044
UNIKAI HAFENBETRIEB GMBH—See Hamburger Hafen und Logistik AG; *Int'l*, pg. 3237
UNIKAI LAGEREI- UND SPEDITIONSGESELLSCHAFT MBH—See Hamburger Hafen und Logistik AG; *Int'l*, pg. 3237
UNIKORN SEMICONDUCTOR CORPORATION—See Ennostar Inc.; *Int'l*, pg. 2444
UNILABS AB—See Apax Partners LLP; *Int'l*, pg. 507
UNILABS S.A.—See Apax Partners LLP; *Int'l*, pg. 507
UNILAC, INC.—See Nestle S.A.; *Int'l*, pg. 5211
UNILAD GROUP LIMITED—See LBG Media Plc; *Int'l*, pg. 4429
UNI-LAND PROPERTY CONSULTANTS LIMITED—See Zhongchang International Holdings Group Limited; *Int'l*, pg. 8672
UNI LAND S.P.A.; *Int'l*, pg. 8028
UNILAVA CORPORATION; *U.S. Private*, pg. 4283
UNILENS VISION INC.—See Bausch Health Companies Inc.; *Int'l*, pg. 897
UNILES, A.S.—See Agrofert Holding, a.s.; *Int'l*, pg. 219
UNILEVER ALGERIE SPA—See Unilever PLC; *Int'l*, pg. 8045
UNILEVER ANDINA BOLIVIA S.A.—See Unilever PLC; *Int'l*, pg. 8045
UNILEVER ANDINA COLOMBIA LTDA.—See Unilever PLC; *Int'l*, pg. 8045
UNILEVER ANDINA PERU S.A.—See Unilever PLC; *Int'l*, pg. 8045
UNILEVER ANDINA VENEZUELA S.A.—See Unilever PLC; *Int'l*, pg. 8045
UNILEVER AUSTRALIA LTD.—See Unilever PLC; *Int'l*, pg. 8045
UNILEVER AUSTRIA GMBH—See Unilever PLC; *Int'l*, pg. 8045
UNILEVER BANGLADESH LIMITED—See Unilever PLC; *Int'l*, pg. 8045
UNILEVER BELGIUM BVBA—See Unilever PLC; *Int'l*, pg. 8045
UNILEVER BESTFOODS BRASIL LTDA—See Unilever PLC; *Int'l*, pg. 8045
UNILEVER BESTFOODS HK LTD.—See Unilever PLC; *Int'l*, pg. 8045
UNILEVER BRASIL LTDA.—See Unilever PLC; *Int'l*, pg. 8045
UNILEVER CANADA INC.—See Unilever PLC; *Int'l*, pg. 8045
UNILEVER CAPITAL CORPORATION—See Unilever PLC; *Int'l*, pg. 8048
UNILEVER CARIBBEAN LIMITED—See Unilever PLC; *Int'l*, pg. 8045
UNILEVER CHILE SA—See Unilever PLC; *Int'l*, pg. 8045
UNILEVER COTE D'IVOIRE SA—See Unilever PLC; *Int'l*, pg. 8045
UNILEVER - COVINGTON—See Unilever PLC; *Int'l*, pg. 8048
UNILEVER CR SPOL. S R. O.—See Unilever PLC; *Int'l*, pg. 8045
UNILEVER DANMARK A/S—See Unilever PLC; *Int'l*, pg. 8045
UNILEVER DE ARGENTINA SA—See Unilever PLC; *Int'l*, pg. 8048
UNILEVER DE MEXICO S DE RL DE CV—See Unilever PLC; *Int'l*, pg. 8048
UNILEVER DEUTSCHLAND GMBH—See Unilever PLC; *Int'l*, pg. 8045
UNILEVER DEUTSCHLAND HOLDING GMBH—See Unilever PLC; *Int'l*, pg. 8045
UNILEVER DEUTSCHLAND IMMOBILIEN LEASING GMBH & CO. OHG—See Unilever PLC; *Int'l*, pg. 8045
UNILEVER DEUTSCHLAND PRODUKTIONS GMBH & CO. OHG—See Unilever PLC; *Int'l*, pg. 8045
UNILEVER DEUTSCHLAND PRODUKTIONS GMBH & CO. OHG - WERK AUERBACH—See Unilever PLC; *Int'l*, pg. 8045
UNILEVER DEUTSCHLAND PRODUKTIONS GMBH & CO. OHG - WERK BUXTEHUDE—See Unilever PLC; *Int'l*, pg. 8045
UNILEVER DEUTSCHLAND PRODUKTIONS GMBH & CO. OHG - WERK HEILBRONN—See Unilever PLC; *Int'l*, pg. 8045
UNILEVER DEUTSCHLAND PRODUKTIONS GMBH & CO. OHG - WERK HEPPENHEIM—See Unilever PLC; *Int'l*, pg. 8045
UNILEVER DEUTSCHLAND PRODUKTIONS GMBH & CO. OHG - WERK KLEVE—See Unilever PLC; *Int'l*, pg. 8045
UNILEVER DEUTSCHLAND PRODUKTIONS GMBH & CO. OHG - WERK MANNHEIM—See Unilever PLC; *Int'l*, pg. 8045
UNILEVER DEUTSCHLAND PRODUKTIONS GMBH & CO. OHG - WERK PRATAU—See Unilever PLC; *Int'l*, pg. 8045
UNILEVER DEUTSCHLAND SUPPLY CHAIN SERVICES GMBH—See Unilever PLC; *Int'l*, pg. 8045
UNILEVER ESPANA, S.A.—See Unilever PLC; *Int'l*, pg. 8045
UNILEVER FINLAND OY—See Unilever PLC; *Int'l*, pg. 8045
UNILEVER FOOD SOLUTIONS - LITTLE ROCK—See Unilever PLC; *Int'l*, pg. 8047

UNILAVA CORPORATION

UNILEVER FOOD SOLUTIONS - MILWAUKEE—See Unilever PLC; *Int'l*, pg. 8047
UNILEVER FOOD SOLUTIONS—See Unilever PLC; *Int'l*, pg. 8047
UNILEVER FRANCE SAS—See Unilever PLC; *Int'l*, pg. 8046
UNILEVER FRANCE—See Unilever PLC; *Int'l*, pg. 8046
UNILEVER GHANA PLC—See Unilever PLC; *Int'l*, pg. 8046
UNILEVER HOME & PERSONAL CARE USA—See Unilever PLC; *Int'l*, pg. 8047
UNILEVER HOME & PERSONAL CARE USA—See Unilever PLC; *Int'l*, pg. 8047
UNILEVER HONG KONG LTD.—See Unilever PLC; *Int'l*, pg. 8046
UNILEVER HPC USA, INC.—See Unilever PLC; *Int'l*, pg. 8048
UNILEVER HRVATSKA D.O.O.—See Unilever PLC; *Int'l*, pg. 8046
UNILEVER IRAN P.J.S.C—See Unilever PLC; *Int'l*, pg. 8046
UNILEVER IRELAND LTD.—See Unilever PLC; *Int'l*, pg. 8047
UNILEVER ISRAEL MARKETING LTD—See Unilever PLC; *Int'l*, pg. 8046
UNILEVER ITALIA SRL—See Unilever PLC; *Int'l*, pg. 8046
UNILEVER ITALY HOLDINGS S.R.L.—See Unilever PLC; *Int'l*, pg. 8046
UNILEVER JAPAN HOLDINGS K.K.—See Unilever PLC; *Int'l*, pg. 8046
UNILEVER JAPAN KK—See Unilever PLC; *Int'l*, pg. 8046
UNILEVER KENYA LTD.—See Unilever PLC; *Int'l*, pg. 8046
UNILEVER KOREA LTD.—See Unilever PLC; *Int'l*, pg. 8046
UNILEVER MAGHREB EXPORT SA—See Unilever PLC; *Int'l*, pg. 8046
UNILEVER MAGHREB S.A.—See Unilever PLC; *Int'l*, pg. 8046
UNILEVER MAGYARORSZAG KFT.—See Unilever PLC; *Int'l*, pg. 8046
UNILEVER (MALAYSIA) HOLDINGS SDN BHD—See Unilever PLC; *Int'l*, pg. 8045
UNILEVER MARKET DEVELOPMENT (PTY) LTD—See Unilever PLC; *Int'l*, pg. 8046
UNILEVER MOCAMBIQUE LIMITADA—See Unilever PLC; *Int'l*, pg. 8046
UNILEVER NEDERLAND B.V.—See Unilever PLC; *Int'l*, pg. 8046
UNILEVER NEDERLAND HOLDINGS B.V.—See Unilever PLC; *Int'l*, pg. 8046
UNILEVER NEW ZEALAND LTD.—See Unilever PLC; *Int'l*, pg. 8045
UNILEVER NIGERIA PLC—See Unilever PLC; *Int'l*, pg. 8046
UNILEVER NORGE AS—See Unilever PLC; *Int'l*, pg. 8046
UNILEVER PAKISTAN FOODS LIMITED—See Unilever PLC; *Int'l*, pg. 8047
UNILEVER PAKISTAN LTD.—See Unilever PLC; *Int'l*, pg. 8046
UNILEVER PERU S.A—See Unilever PLC; *Int'l*, pg. 8046
UNILEVER PHILIPPINES INC.—See Unilever PLC; *Int'l*, pg. 8046
UNILEVER PLC; *Int'l*, pg. 8044
UNILEVER POLSKA S.A.—See Unilever PLC; *Int'l*, pg. 8046
UNILEVER RESEARCH & DEVELOPMENT CO.—See Unilever PLC; *Int'l*, pg. 8047
UNILEVER ROMANIA S.A.—See Unilever PLC; *Int'l*, pg. 8046
UNILEVER RUSSIA—See Unilever PLC; *Int'l*, pg. 8046
UNILEVER SANAYI VE TURK A.S.—See Unilever PLC; *Int'l*, pg. 8046
UNILEVER SCHWEIZ GMBH—See Unilever PLC; *Int'l*, pg. 8046
UNILEVER SERVICES (HEI FEI) CO. LIMITED—See Unilever PLC; *Int'l*, pg. 8046
UNILEVER SINGAPORE PTE. LTD.—See Unilever PLC; *Int'l*, pg. 8045
UNILEVER SLOVENSKO, SPOL. S R.O.—See Unilever PLC; *Int'l*, pg. 8046
UNILEVER—See Unilever PLC; *Int'l*, pg. 8047
UNILEVER SOUTH AFRICA (PTY) LTD—See Unilever PLC; *Int'l*, pg. 8046
UNILEVER SOUTH CENTRAL EUROPE SA—See Unilever PLC; *Int'l*, pg. 8046
UNILEVER SOUTH EAST AFRICA LTD—See Unilever PLC; *Int'l*, pg. 8046
UNILEVER SRI LANKA LIMITED—See Unilever PLC; *Int'l*, pg. 8046
UNILEVER SUPPLY CHAIN COMPANY AG—See Unilever PLC; *Int'l*, pg. 8046
UNILEVER SVERIGE AB—See Unilever PLC; *Int'l*, pg. 8046
UNILEVER TANZANIA LIMITED—See Unilever PLC; *Int'l*, pg. 8046
UNILEVER TEA RWANDA LIMITED—See Unilever PLC; *Int'l*, pg. 8046

UNILEVER THAI TRADING LIMITED—See Unilever PLC; *Int'l*, pg. 8047
UNILEVER TUNISIA S.A.—See Unilever PLC; *Int'l*, pg. 8047
UNILEVER UGANDA LIMITED—See Unilever PLC; *Int'l*, pg. 8047
UNILEVER UK & CN HOLDINGS LIMITED—See Unilever PLC; *Int'l*, pg. 8047
UNILEVER UK HOLDINGS LTD.—See Unilever PLC; *Int'l*, pg. 8047
UNILEVER UK LTD.—See Unilever PLC; *Int'l*, pg. 8047
UNILEVER UKRAINE LLC—See Unilever PLC; *Int'l*, pg. 8047
UNILEVER UNITED STATES, INC.—See Unilever PLC; *Int'l*, pg. 8047
UNILEVER US GOVERNMENT & PUBLIC AFFAIRS—See Unilever PLC; *Int'l*, pg. 8048
UNILEVER VIETNAM INTERNATIONAL COMPANY LIMITED—See Unilever PLC; *Int'l*, pg. 8048
UNILEVER ZIMBABWE PVT LTD—See Unilever PLC; *Int'l*, pg. 8048
UNILFARMA-UNIAO INTERNACIONAL DE LABORATORIOS FARMACEUTICOS, LDA.—See C.H. Boehringer Sohn AG & Co. KG; *Int'l*, pg. 1242
UNILIFE CORPORATION; *U.S. Private*, pg. 4283
UNILIFE MEDICAL SOLUTIONS, INC.—See Unilife Corporation; *U.S. Private*, pg. 4283
UNILIFT S.R.L.—See KONE Oyj; *Int'l*, pg. 4250
UNILIN BVBA-DIVISION SYSTEMS—See Mohawk Industries, Inc.; *U.S. Public*, pg. 1458
UNILIN FLOORING NC, LLC—See Mohawk Industries, Inc.; *U.S. Public*, pg. 1458
UNILIN INDUSTRIES BVBA—See Mohawk Industries, Inc.; *U.S. Public*, pg. 1458
UNILIN ITALIA S.R.L.—See Mohawk Industries, Inc.; *U.S. Public*, pg. 1458
UNILINK DATA SYSTEMS PTY LTD—See Nelnet, Inc.; *U.S. Public*, pg. 1504
UNILIN NORTH AMERICA, LLC—See Mohawk Industries, Inc.; *U.S. Public*, pg. 1458
UNILIN NORWAY AS—See Mohawk Industries, Inc.; *U.S. Public*, pg. 1458
UNILIN POLAND SP.Z O.O.—See Mohawk Industries, Inc.; *U.S. Public*, pg. 1458
UNILIN SWISS GMBH—See Mohawk Industries, Inc.; *U.S. Public*, pg. 1458
UNILIVING CO., LTD.—See Mitsui Fudosan Co., Ltd.; *Int'l*, pg. 4988
UNILOCK CAPITAL CORP.; *Int'l*, pg. 8048
UNILOGIC B.V.—See Dustin Group AB; *Int'l*, pg. 2235
UNILUMIN AUSTRALIA PTY. LTD.—See Unilumin Group Co., Ltd.; *Int'l*, pg. 8048
UNILUMIN GERMANY GMBH—See Unilumin Group Co., Ltd.; *Int'l*, pg. 8048
UNILUMIN GROUP CO., LTD.; *Int'l*, pg. 8048
UNILUMIN LED EUROPE BV—See Unilumin Group Co., Ltd.; *Int'l*, pg. 8048
UNILUMIN MIDDLE EAST DMCC—See Unilumin Group Co., Ltd.; *Int'l*, pg. 8048
UNILUMIN SAUDI ARABIA LLC—See Unilumin Group Co., Ltd.; *Int'l*, pg. 8048
UNILUMIN SOUTH KOREA LTD.—See Unilumin Group Co., Ltd.; *Int'l*, pg. 8048
UNILUMIN TECHNOLOGIES PTE. LTD.—See Unilumin Group Co., Ltd.; *Int'l*, pg. 8048
UNILUMIN THAILAND LIMITED—See Unilumin Group Co., Ltd.; *Int'l*, pg. 8048
UNILUMIN UK CO., LTD.—See Unilumin Group Co., Ltd.; *Int'l*, pg. 8048
UNILUMIN USA LLC—See Unilumin Group Co., Ltd.; *Int'l*, pg. 8048
UNILUX, INC.; *U.S. Private*, pg. 4283
UNIMA 2000 SYSTEMY TELEINFORMATYCZNE S.A.; *Int'l*, pg. 8048
UNIMAC GRAPHICS; *U.S. Private*, pg. 4283
UNIMAC PACKAGING GROUP—See Unimac Graphics; *U.S. Private*, pg. 4284
UNIMAC RUBBER CO., LTD.—See Marubeni Corporation; *Int'l*, pg. 4710
UNIMARK TRUCK TRANSPORT LLC—See TFI International Inc.; *Int'l*, pg. 7586
UNIMAS SPORTSWEAR LTD.—See Mainland Headwear Holdings Ltd.; *Int'l*, pg. 4651
UNIMATEC CHEMICALS AMERICA, INC.—See NOK Corporation; *Int'l*, pg. 5403
UNIMATEC CHEMICALS (CHINA) CO., LTD.—See NOK Corporation; *Int'l*, pg. 5403
UNIMATEC CHEMICALS EUROPE GMBH & CO. KG.—See NOK Corporation; *Int'l*, pg. 5403
UNIMATEC CHEMICALS SINGAPORE PTE. LTD.—See NOK Corporation; *Int'l*, pg. 5403
UNIMATEC CO., LTD. - PLANT NO. 1—See NOK Corporation; *Int'l*, pg. 5403
UNIMATEC CO., LTD. - PLANT NO. 2—See NOK Corporation; *Int'l*, pg. 5403
UNIMATEX SDN. BHD.—See Matex International Limited; *Int'l*, pg. 4727
UNIMAT LIFE CORPORATION; *Int'l*, pg. 8048

CORPORATE AFFILIATIONS

UNIMAT RETIREMENT COMMUNITY CO., LTD.—See MBK Partners Ltd.; *Int'l*, pg. 4754
UNIMAX ELECTRONICS INCORPORATION—See ASUSTeK Computer Inc.; *Int'l*, pg. 664
UNIMAX PRECISION METAL FORMING CO., LTD.—See Right Way Industrial Co., Ltd.; *Int'l*, pg. 6340
UNIMAX SANITARIO (M) SDN. BHD.—See UNIMECH Group Berhad; *Int'l*, pg. 8049
UNIMECH (ASIA PACIFIC) PTY. LTD.—See UNIMECH Group Berhad; *Int'l*, pg. 8049
UNIMECH ENGINEERING (AUST) PTY. LTD.—See UNIMECH Group Berhad; *Int'l*, pg. 8049
UNIMECH ENGINEERING (JB) SDN. BHD.—See UNIMECH Group Berhad; *Int'l*, pg. 8049
UNIMECH ENGINEERING (KL) SDN. BHD.—See UNIMECH Group Berhad; *Int'l*, pg. 8049
UNIMECH ENGINEERING (KUANTAN) SDN. BHD.—See UNIMECH Group Berhad; *Int'l*, pg. 8049
UNIMECH ENGINEERING (M) SDN. BHD.—See UNIMECH Group Berhad; *Int'l*, pg. 8049
UNIMECH FLOW SYSTEM SDN. BHD.—See UNIMECH Group Berhad; *Int'l*, pg. 8049
UNIMECH GROUP BERHAD; *Int'l*, pg. 8048
UNIMECH INSTRUMENTS & CONTROL SDN. BHD.—See UNIMECH Group Berhad; *Int'l*, pg. 8049
UNIMECH INTERNATIONAL SDN. BHD.—See UNIMECH Group Berhad; *Int'l*, pg. 8049
UNIMECH MARINE EQUIPMENT SDN. BHD.—See UNIMECH Group Berhad; *Int'l*, pg. 8049
UNIMECH MARINE & SANITARY EQUIPMENT SDN. BHD.—See UNIMECH Group Berhad; *Int'l*, pg. 8049
UNIMECH VALVE TECHNOLOGY SDN. BHD.—See UNIMECH Group Berhad; *Int'l*, pg. 8049
UNIMECH VIETNAM CO., LTD.—See UNIMECH Group Berhad; *Int'l*, pg. 8049
UNIMECH WORLDWIDE (SHANGHAI) SDN. BHD.—See UNIMECH Group Berhad; *Int'l*, pg. 8049
UNIMED INNOVATION AS—See SINTEF; *Int'l*, pg. 6957
UNIMED LABORATORIES; *Int'l*, pg. 8049
UNIMED MEDICAL SUPPLIES INC.—See Yunda Holding Co., Ltd.; *Int'l*, pg. 8613
UNIMELT GMBH—See RETHMANN AG & Co. KG; *Int'l*, pg. 6310
UNIMER GROUP; *Int'l*, pg. 8050
UNIMET GMBH; *Int'l*, pg. 8050
UNIMICRONCARRIER TECHNOLOGY (HUANGSHI) INC.—See Unimicron Technology Corporation; *Int'l*, pg. 8050
UNIMICRON GERMANY GMBH—See Unimicron Technology Corporation; *Int'l*, pg. 8050
UNIMICRON JAPAN CO., LTD.—See Unimicron Technology Corporation; *Int'l*, pg. 8050
UNIMICRON MANAGEMENT (KUNSHAN) CO., LTD.—See Unimicron Technology Corporation; *Int'l*, pg. 8050
UNIMICRON TECHNOLOGY CORPORATION; *Int'l*, pg. 8050
UNIMICRON TECHNOLOGY (SHENZHEN) CORP.—See Unimicron Technology Corporation; *Int'l*, pg. 8050
UNIMICRON TECHNOLOGY (SUZHOU) CORP.—See Unimicron Technology Corporation; *Int'l*, pg. 8050
UNIMILLS A.S.—See Raiffeisen-Holding Niederosterreich-Wien reg. Gen.m.b.H.; *Int'l*, pg. 6185
UNIMIN CORPORATION—See Covia Holdings Corporation; *U.S. Private*, pg. 1072
UNIMIN INDIA LTD; *Int'l*, pg. 8050
UNIMIT ENGINEERING PUBLIC COMPANY LIMITED; *Int'l*, pg. 8050
UNI-MIX CONCRETE PRODUCTS SDN. BHD.—See B.I.G. Industries Berhad; *Int'l*, pg. 790
UNI-MIX SDN. BHD.—See B.I.G. Industries Berhad; *Int'l*, pg. 790
UNIMODE OVERSEAS LIMITED; *Int'l*, pg. 8050
UNIMO ENTERPRISES LIMITED—See United Motors Lanka PLC; *Int'l*, pg. 8071
UNIMORE LTD.—See Unitika Ltd.; *Int'l*, pg. 8074
UNIMOT ENERGIA I GAZ SP. Z O.O.—See Unimot SA; *Int'l*, pg. 8050
UNIMOT ENERGY LLC—See Unimot SA; *Int'l*, pg. 8050
UNIMOT SA; *Int'l*, pg. 8050
UNIOIL PETROLEUM PHILIPPINES, INC.—See AT Capital Pte Limited; *Int'l*, pg. 664
UNIOIL RESOURCES & HOLDINGS COMPANY INC.; *Int'l*, pg. 8050
UNION ACCEPTANCE COMPANY LLC—See PCP Enterprise, L.P.; *U.S. Private*, pg. 3121
UNION ADVANCED INDUSTRIES CO. PLC—See Union Group; *Int'l*, pg. 8052
THE UNION ADVERTISING AGENCY; *Int'l*, pg. 7697
THE UNION ADVERTISING AGENCY—See The Union Advertising Agency; *Int'l*, pg. 7697
UNION ADVERTISING CANADA LP—See Stagwell, Inc.; *U.S. Public*, pg. 1928
UNION AGENCY, INC.—See Farmers & Merchants Investment Inc.; *U.S. Private*, pg. 1476
UNION AGRICULTURE GROUP CORP.; *Int'l*, pg. 8050
UNION ANDINA DE CEMENTOS S.A.A.; *Int'l*, pg. 8050

COMPANY NAME INDEX

UNION PACIFIC RAILROAD EMPLOYEE HEALTH SYSTEMS INC.

UNION ARMAZENAGEM E OPERACOES PORTUARIA S.A.—See Santos Brasil Participacoes SA; *Int'l*, pg. 6559

UNION ASSET MANAGEMENT HOLDING AG; *Int'l*, pg. 8050

UNION ASSURANCE PLC—See John Keells Holdings PLC; *Int'l*, pg. 3979

UNION AUCTION PUBLIC COMPANY LIMITED; *Int'l*, pg. 8051

UNION AUTOPARTS MANUFACTURING CO., LTD. - FACTORY III—See Okaya & Co., Ltd.; *Int'l*, pg. 5547

UNION AUTOPARTS MANUFACTURING CO., LTD. - FACTORY II—See Okaya & Co., Ltd.; *Int'l*, pg. 5547

UNION AUTOPARTS MANUFACTURING CO., LTD.—See Okaya & Co., Ltd.; *Int'l*, pg. 5547

UNION BANCAIRE ASSET MANAGEMENT (JERSEY) LTD.—See Union Bancaire Privee, UBP SA; *Int'l*, pg. 8051

UNION BANCAIRE PRIVEE ASSET MANAGEMENT (BERMUDA) LTD.—See Union Bancaire Privee, UBP SA; *Int'l*, pg. 8051

UNION BANCAIRE PRIVEE ASSET MANAGEMENT LLC—See Union Bancaire Privee, UBP SA; *Int'l*, pg. 8051

UNION BANCAIRE PRIVEE (EUROPE) SA—See Union Bancaire Privee, UBP SA; *Int'l*, pg. 8051

UNION BANCAIRE PRIVEE, UBP SA; *Int'l*, pg. 8051

UNION BANKA D.D. SARAJEVO; *Int'l*, pg. 8051

THE UNION BANK COMPANY—See United Bancshares, Inc.; *U.S. Public*, pg. 2229

UNION BANK OF COLOMBO LIMITED; *Int'l*, pg. 8051

UNION BANK OF INDIA; *Int'l*, pg. 8051

UNION BANK OF INDIA UK LIMITED—See Union Bank of India; *Int'l*, pg. 8051

UNION BANK OF IRAQ; *Int'l*, pg. 8051

UNION BANK OF ISRAEL LTD.—See Mizrahi Tefahot Bank Ltd.; *Int'l*, pg. 4997

UNION BANK OF NIGERIA PLC; *Int'l*, pg. 8051

UNION BANK OF TAIWAN; *Int'l*, pg. 8051

UNIONBANK OF THE PHILIPPINES; *Int'l*, pg. 8051

UNION BANKSHARES, INC.; *U.S. Public*, pg. 2226

UNION BANK—See Union Bankshares, Inc.; *U.S. Public*, pg. 2226

UNION BANK; *U.S. Private*, pg. 4284

UNION BANK & TRUST COMPANY—See Farmers & Merchants Investment Inc.; *U.S. Private*, pg. 1475

UNION BANK & TRUST COMPANY—See First Union Financial Corp.; *U.S. Private*, pg. 1530

UNION BAUZENTRUM HORNBACH GMBH—See Hornbach Holding AG & Co. KGaA; *Int'l*, pg. 3482

UNION BAY RISK ADVISORS LLC; *U.S. Private*, pg. 4284

UNION BEARINGS (INDIA) LTD.; *Int'l*, pg. 8052

UNION BENEFITS TRUST; *U.S. Private*, pg. 4284

UNION BERKLEY, COMPANIA DE SEGUROS S.A.—See W.R. Berkley Corporation; *U.S. Public*, pg. 2318

UNION BRIDGE HOLDINGS LIMITED; *Int'l*, pg. 8052

UNION BUTTON CORP., LTD.—See Saha-Union Public Company Limited; *Int'l*, pg. 6480

UNION CAPITAL LIMITED; *Int'l*, pg. 8052

UNION CAPITAL MORTGAGE CORPORATION—See First Niles Financial, Inc.; *U.S. Public*, pg. 846

UNION CARBIDE CORPORATION—See Dow Inc.; *U.S. Public*, pg. 686

UNION CARBIDE CORPORATION—See Dow Inc.; *U.S. Public*, pg. 686

UNION CARBIDE CORPORATION—See Dow Inc.; *U.S. Public*, pg. 686

UNION CATALANA DE VALORES SA; *Int'l*, pg. 8052

UNION CEMENT COMPANY—See Shree Cement Limited; *Int'l*, pg. 6862

UNION CEMENT CORPORATION—See FLSmidth & Co. A/S; *Int'l*, pg. 2712

UNION CHEMICAL & PHARMACEUTICAL CO., LTD.—See Bora Pharmaceuticals Co., Ltd.; *Int'l*, pg. 1112

UNION CHEMICALS LANKA PLC; *Int'l*, pg. 8052

UNION CHEMICAL & VEGETABLE OIL INDUSTRIES CO. PLC—See Union Group; *Int'l*, pg. 8052

UNION CHLORINE L.L.C—See Oman Chlorine S.A.O.G.; *Int'l*, pg. 5559

UNION CITY NISSAN INC.; *U.S. Private*, pg. 4284

THE UNION CLUB OF THE CITY OF NEW YORK; *U.S. Private*, pg. 4129

UNION CO., LTD.—See Unitika Ltd.; *Int'l*, pg. 8074

UNION COMMERCIAL BANK PLC—See E. Sun Financial Holding Co., Ltd.; *Int'l*, pg. 2250

UNION COMMERCIAL BANK PUBLIC LIMITED CORPORATION—See E. Sun Financial Holding Co., Ltd.; *Int'l*, pg. 2250

UNION COMMERCIAL BANK S.A.—See The Mauritius Commercial Bank Ltd.; *Int'l*, pg. 7666

UNION COMMUNITY BANK FSB—See Northwest Bancshares, Inc.; *U.S. Public*, pg. 1541

UNION COMMUNITY BANK FSB—See Northwest Bancshares, Inc.; *U.S. Public*, pg. 1541

UNION COMMUNITY HEALTH CENTER; *U.S. Private*, pg. 4284

UNION CONSTRUCTION AND INVESTMENT; *Int'l*, pg. 8052

UNION CONSTRUCTION CORP., LTD.—See Saha-Union Public Company Limited; *Int'l*, pg. 6480

UNION CORPORATION; *Int'l*, pg. 8052

UNION CORRUGATING COMPANY—See Clayton, Dubilier & Rice, LLC; *U.S. Private*, pg. 921

UNION COUNTY SAVINGS BANK; *U.S. Private*, pg. 4284

UNION DE CERVECERIAS PERUANAS BACKUS Y JOHNSTON S.A.A.—See Anheuser-Busch InBev SA/NV; *Int'l*, pg. 464

UNION DE CONCRETERAS S.A.—See Union Andina de Cementos S.A.A.; *Int'l*, pg. 8050

UNION DE INDUSTRIAS C.A., S.A.—See HEXPOL AB; *Int'l*, pg. 3373

THE UNION DEMOCRAT—See Western Communications Inc.; *U.S. Private*, pg. 4492

UNION DE PHARMACOLOGIE SCIENTIFIQUE APPLIQUEE S.A.S.—See Taisho Pharmaceutical Holdings Co., Ltd; *Int'l*, pg. 7418

UNION DIAGNOSTIC & CLINICAL SERVICES PLC.; *Int'l*, pg. 8052

UNION DICON SALT PLC.; *Int'l*, pg. 8052

UNION DIGITAL—See The Union Advertising Agency; *Int'l*, pg. 7697

UNION DIRECT—See The Union Advertising Agency; *Int'l*, pg. 7697

UNIONE DI BANCHE ITALIANE SPA—See Intesa Sanpaolo S.p.A.; *Int'l*, pg. 3766

UNIONE FARMACEUTICA DISTRIBUZIONE SA—See CSL Limited; *Int'l*, pg. 1866

UNION ELECTRICA DE CANARIAS GENERACION SAU—See Enel S.p.A.; *Int'l*, pg. 2415

UNION ELECTRIC COMPANY—See Ameren Corporation; *U.S. Public*, pg. 94

UNION ELECTRIC STEEL BVBA—See Ampco-Pittsburgh Corporation; *U.S. Public*, pg. 126

UNION ELECTRIC STEEL CORP.—See Ampco-Pittsburgh Corporation; *U.S. Public*, pg. 126

UNION ELECTRIC STEEL CORP.—See Ampco-Pittsburgh Corporation; *U.S. Public*, pg. 126

UNION ELECTRIC STEEL UK LIMITED—See Ampco-Pittsburgh Corporation; *U.S. Public*, pg. 126

UNIONELEKTRO A.D.; *Int'l*, pg. 8054

UNION EL GOLF S.A.; *Int'l*, pg. 8052

UNION ENGINEERING A/S—See Pentair plc; *Int'l*, pg. 5791

UNION ENGINEERING CO., LTD.—See Union Tool Co.; *Int'l*, pg. 8054

UNION ENGINEERING NORTH AMERICA LLC—See Pentair plc; *Int'l*, pg. 5791

UNION EUROPEA DE INVERSIONES, S.A.; *Int'l*, pg. 8052

UNION FINANCIAL CORP.; *U.S. Public*, pg. 2226

UNION FINANCIERE DE FRANCE BANQUE SA—See Aema Groupe; *Int'l*, pg. 175

UNION FROST COMPANY LIMITED—See Lam Soon (Thailand) Public Company Limited; *Int'l*, pg. 4400

UNION GALVASTEEL CORPORATION—See PHINMA Corporation; *Int'l*, pg. 5848

UNION GARMENT CO., LTD.—See Saha-Union Public Company Limited; *Int'l*, pg. 6480

UNION GAS HOLDINGS LIMITED; *Int'l*, pg. 8052

UNION GOSPEL MISSION; *U.S. Private*, pg. 4284

THE UNION GROUP; *U.S. Private*, pg. 4129

UNION GROUP; *Int'l*, pg. 8052

UNION HARVEST (M) SDN.BHD—See Sumitomo Corporation; *Int'l*, pg. 7276

UNION HEALTH CENTER; *U.S. Private*, pg. 4284

UNION HEALTH SERVICE, INC.; *U.S. Private*, pg. 4284

UNION HILL APARTMENTS, L.P.—See Synovus Financial Corp.; *U.S. Public*, pg. 1971

UNION HILL APARTMENTS, L.P.—See Synovus Financial Corp.; *U.S. Public*, pg. 1972

UNION HILL HEALTHCARE, INC.—See The Ensign Group, Inc.; *U.S. Public*, pg. 2072

UNION HOME MORTGAGE CORP.; *U.S. Private*, pg. 4284

UNION HOMES SAVINGS & LOANS PLC.—See Union Bank of Nigeria Plc.; *Int'l*, pg. 8051

UNION HOSPITAL; *U.S. Private*, pg. 4284

UNION HOSPITAL—See Barnabas Health, Inc.; *U.S. Private*, pg. 477

UNION HOTELS D.D.—See Grand Hotel Union d.d.; *Int'l*, pg. 3055

UNION ICE LTD.; *U.S. Private*, pg. 4284

UNION INFORMATION TECHNOLOGY CORPORATION—See Union Bank of Taiwan; *Int'l*, pg. 8051

UNION INMOBILIARIA S.A.; *Int'l*, pg. 8052

UNION INSURANCE CO., LTD.—See Want Want China Holdings Ltd.; *Int'l*, pg. 8342

UNION INSURANCE COMPANY P.S.C.; *Int'l*, pg. 8052

UNION INSURANCE CO. P.S.C.—See Al-Sagr National Insurance Company; *Int'l*, pg. 288

UNION INSURANCE GROUP, LLC—See Atlantic Union Bankshares Corporation; *U.S. Public*, pg. 223

UNIONINVEST D.D.; *Int'l*, pg. 8054

UNIONINVEST INZENJERING I PROJEKTOVANJE A.D.; *Int'l*, pg. 8054

UNION INVESTMENT AUSTRIA GMBH—See DZ BANK AG Deutsche Zentral-Genossenschaftsbank; *Int'l*, pg. 2245

UNION INVESTMENT CORPORATION; *Int'l*, pg. 8052

UNION INVESTMENT FINANCIAL SERVICES S.A.—See DZ BANK AG Deutsche Zentral-Genossenschaftsbank; *Int'l*, pg. 2245

UNION INVESTMENT INSTITUTIONAL GMBH—See DZ BANK AG Deutsche Zentral-Genossenschaftsbank; *Int'l*, pg. 2245

UNION INVESTMENT INSTITUTIONAL PROPERTY GMBH—See DZ BANK AG Deutsche Zentral-Genossenschaftsbank; *Int'l*, pg. 2245

UNION INVESTMENT REAL ESTATE ASIA PACIFIC PTE. LTD.—See DZ BANK AG Deutsche Zentral-Genossenschaftsbank; *Int'l*, pg. 2245

UNION INVESTMENT REAL ESTATE AUSTRIA AG—See DZ BANK AG Deutsche Zentral-Genossenschaftsbank; *Int'l*, pg. 2245

UNION INVESTMENT REAL ESTATE FRANCE S.A.S.—See DZ BANK AG Deutsche Zentral-Genossenschaftsbank; *Int'l*, pg. 2245

UNION INVESTMENT SERVICE BANK AG—See DZ BANK AG Deutsche Zentral-Genossenschaftsbank; *Int'l*, pg. 2245

UNIONINVEST PLASTIKA D.D. SEMIZOVAC; *Int'l*, pg. 8054

UNION INVIVO - UNION DE COOPERATIVES AGRICOLES; *Int'l*, pg. 8053

UNION IRON INC.—See Ag Growth International Inc.; *Int'l*, pg. 198

UNION IT-SERVICES GMBH—See DZ BANK AG Deutsche Zentral-Genossenschaftsbank; *Int'l*, pg. 2245

UNIONIZGRADNJA SIP D.D. SARAJEVO; *Int'l*, pg. 8054

UNION JACK OIL PLC; *Int'l*, pg. 8053

UNION KOREA PHARM CO., LTD.; *Int'l*, pg. 8053

UNION KOSAN CO., LTD.—See Unitika Ltd.; *Int'l*, pg. 8074

THE UNION LABOR LIFE INSURANCE CO.—See Ullico Inc.; *U.S. Private*, pg. 4276

UNION LAND DEVELOPMENT; *Int'l*, pg. 8053

UNION LEADER CORPORATION; *U.S. Private*, pg. 4284

THE UNION LEAGUE CLUB; *U.S. Private*, pg. 4129

UNION LEASING, INC.—See Sasser Family Holdings, Inc.; *U.S. Private*, pg. 3552

UNION MACHINERY CO., LTD.—See Onamba Co., Ltd.; *Int'l*, pg. 5573

UNIONMAN TECHNOLOGY CO., LTD.; *Int'l*, pg. 8054

UNION MARKETING GROUP—See Union Group; *Int'l*, pg. 8052

UNION MATERIALS CORP.—See Union Corporation; *Int'l*, pg. 8052

UNION MATERIAL TECHNOLOGY CORP.—See MiTAC International Corp.; *Int'l*, pg. 4923

UNION MEADOWS ASSOCIATES LLC—See Edison International; *U.S. Public*, pg. 719

UNION MEDICA LA FUENCISLA, SA COMPANIA DE SEGUROS—See Munchener Ruckversicherungs AG; *Int'l*, pg. 5087

UNION METAL CORPORATION; *U.S. Private*, pg. 4284

UNION METALLURGIQUE DE LA HAUTE SEINE SA; *Int'l*, pg. 8053

UNION MICRONCLEAN CO.,LTD.—See Saha-Union Public Company Limited; *Int'l*, pg. 6480

UNION MINERA DEL SUR, S.A. DE C.V.—See Grupo Empresarial Kaluz S.A. de C.V.; *Int'l*, pg. 3128

UNION MORTGAGE GROUP, INC.—See Atlantic Union Bankshares Corporation; *U.S. Public*, pg. 223

THE UNION MOSAIC INDUSTRY PUBLIC COMPANY LIMITED; *Int'l*, pg. 7697

UNION MOTORS CAR SALES S.R.L.—See General Motors Company; *U.S. Public*, pg. 929

UNION MUSICAL EDICIONES SL—See Music Sales Corporation; *U.S. Public*, pg. 2818

UNION MUTUAL FIRE INSURANCE CO.; *U.S. Private*, pg. 4284

UNION NACIONAL DE EMPRESAS, S.A.; *Int'l*, pg. 8053

UNION NATIONAL BANK PJSC—See Abu Dhabi Commercial Bank PJSC; *Int'l*, pg. 71

UNION NIFCO CO., LTD.—See Nifco Inc.; *Int'l*, pg. 5282

UNION N.V.; *Int'l*, pg. 8053

UNION OFFSET CO. PTY LIMITED—See OPUS Group Limited; *Int'l*, pg. 5606

UNION & OJI INTERPACK CO., LTD.—See Oji Holdings Corporation; *Int'l*, pg. 5538

UNION OPTECH CO., LTD.; *Int'l*, pg. 8053

UNION ORTHOPEDIC CORP.; *Int'l*, pg. 8053

UNION PACIFIC CORPORATION; *U.S. Public*, pg. 2226

UNION PACIFIC DISTRIBUTION SERVICES—See Union Pacific Corporation; *U.S. Public*, pg. 2227

UNION PACIFIC RAILROAD COMPANY—See Union Pacific Corporation; *U.S. Public*, pg. 2227

UNION PACIFIC RAILROAD EMPLOYEE HEALTH SYSTEMS INC.; *U.S. Private*, pg. 4284

UNION PACIFIC RAILROAD—See Union Pacific Corporation; *U.S. Public*, pg. 2227

UNION PACIFIC RAILROAD EMPLOYEE HEALTH SYSTEMS INC.

CORPORATE AFFILIATIONS

UNION PAPELERA MERCHANTING SL—See KPP Group Holdings Co., Ltd.; *Int'l*, pg. 4298
UNION PARK AUTOMOTIVE GROUP, INC.; *U.S. Private*, pg. 4284
UNION PARK CAPITAL; *U.S. Private*, pg. 4284
UNION PEN COMPANY; *U.S. Private*, pg. 4285
UNION PETROCHEMICAL PUBLIC COMPANY LIMITED; *Int'l*, pg. 8053
UNION PIONEER PUBLIC COMPANY LIMITED; *Int'l*, pg. 8053
UNION PLASTIC PUBLIC CO., LTD.—See Saha-Union Public Company Limited; *Int'l*, pg. 6480
UNION PLASTIC SA—See Groupe OMERIN; *Int'l*, pg. 3109
UNION POIST'OVNA A.S.—See Achmea B.V.; *Int'l*, pg. 104
UNION POUR LE NEGOCE EN PRODUITS CHIMIQUES S.A.—See OMV Aktiengesellschaft; *Int'l*, pg. 5569
UNION POWER COOPERATIVE; *U.S. Private*, pg. 4285
UNION PRECISION DIE CO., LTD.—See Kawasaki Heavy Industries, Ltd.; *Int'l*, pg. 4098
UNION PRINTING—See The Union Group; *U.S. Private*, pg. 4129
UNION PROPERTIES, INC.—See UnionBank of the Philippines; *Int'l*, pg. 8054
UNION PROPERTIES PJSC—See Emirates NBD PJSC; *Int'l*, pg. 2382
UNION QUALITY PLASTICS LIMITED; *Int'l*, pg. 8053
UNION QUIMICO FARMACEUTICA SA—See Vivimed Labs Limited; *Int'l*, pg. 8279
UNION RAILROAD COMPANY—See United States Steel Corporation; *U.S. Public*, pg. 2237
UNION REAL ESTATE COMPANY K.S.C.C.; *Int'l*, pg. 8053
THE UNION-RECORDER—See The Retirement Systems of Alabama; *U.S. Private*, pg. 4106
UNION RUBBER PRODUCTS CORP. LTD.—See Saha-Union Public Company Limited; *Int'l*, pg. 6480
UNION SANITARY DISTRICT; *U.S. Private*, pg. 4285
UNION SAVINGS BANK; *U.S. Private*, pg. 4285
UNION SAVINGS BANK; *U.S. Private*, pg. 4285
UNION SAVINGS & LOAN ASSOCIATION; *U.S. Private*, pg. 4285
UNION SECURITY INSURANCE COMPANY—See Assurant, Inc.; *U.S. Public*, pg. 216
UNION SECURITY LIFE INSURANCE COMPANY OF NEW YORK—See Assurant, Inc.; *U.S. Public*, pg. 216
UNION SERVICE INDUSTRIES INC.; *U.S. Private*, pg. 4285
UNION SERVICES (SINGAPORE) PTE LTD - FORWARDING DIVISION—See The Sumitomo Warehouse Co. Ltd.; *Int'l*, pg. 7690
UNION SERVICES (SINGAPORE) PTE. LTD.—See The Sumitomo Warehouse Co. Ltd.; *Int'l*, pg. 7690
UNION SERVICES (SINGAPORE) PTE LTD - TRAFFIC DIVISION—See The Sumitomo Warehouse Co. Ltd.; *Int'l*, pg. 7690
UNION SERVICES (SINGAPORE) PTE LTD - TRANSPORT DIVISION—See The Sumitomo Warehouse Co. Ltd.; *Int'l*, pg. 7690
UNION SHOWA K.K.—See Resonac Holdings Corporation; *Int'l*, pg. 6301
UNION SPECIAL CORPORATION; *U.S. Private*, pg. 4285
UNION SPINNING MILLS CO., LTD.—See Saha-Union Public Company Limited; *Int'l*, pg. 6480
UNION SPORTSMEN'S ALLIANCE; *U.S. Private*, pg. 4285
UNION SPRING & MANUFACTURING CORP.; *U.S. Private*, pg. 4285
UNION SQUARE DEVELOPMENTS LIMITED—See Hammerson plc; *Int'l*, pg. 3238
UNION SQUARE MUSIC LTD.—See Bertelsmann SE & Co. KGaA; *Int'l*, pg. 990
UNION SQUARE VENTURES LLC; *U.S. Private*, pg. 4285
UNION STAINLESS STEEL PRODUCTS CO., LTD.—See Saha-Union Public Company Limited; *Int'l*, pg. 6480
UNION STANDARD INSURANCE COMPANY—See W.R. Berkley Corporation; *U.S. Public*, pg. 2318
UNION STANDARD OF AMERICA LIFE INSURANCE CO.—See Ullico Inc.; *U.S. Private*, pg. 4276
UNION STATE BANCSHARES, INC.; *U.S. Private*, pg. 4285
UNION STATE BANK; *U.S. Private*, pg. 4285
THE UNION STATE BANK—See Docking Bancshares, Inc.; *U.S. Private*, pg. 1251
UNION STATE BANK—See Greenfield Bancorporation Ltd.; *U.S. Private*, pg. 1777
UNION STATE BANK—See Union State Bancshares, Inc.; *U.S. Private*, pg. 4285
UNION STATION REDEVELOPMENT CORPORATION; *U.S. Private*, pg. 4285
UNION STEEL HOLDINGS LIMITED; *Int'l*, pg. 8053
UNION STEEL PTE. LTD.—See Union Steel Holdings Limited; *Int'l*, pg. 8053
UNION SUPPLY GROUP, INC.—See Aramark; *U.S. Public*, pg. 178
UNION TANK CAR COMPANY—See Berkshire Hathaway Inc.; *U.S. Public*, pg. 311

UNION TECH AUTOMATION SDN. BHD.—See Aimflex Berhad; *Int'l*, pg. 233
UNION TECHNIQUE DE L'AUTOMOBILE, DU MOTOCYCLE ET DU SASU; *Int'l*, pg. 8054
UNION TECHNOLOGIES INFORMATIQUE GROUP SA; *Int'l*, pg. 8054
UNION TECHNOLOGY CORP.—See Arcline Investment Management LP; *U.S. Private*, pg. 315
UNION TECNICO COMERCIAL S.R.L.—See Henkel AG & Co. KGaA; *Int'l*, pg. 3354
UNION TELECARD ALLIANCE, LLC—See IDT Corporation; *U.S. Public*, pg. 1094
UNION TELECARD ARIZONA, LLC—See IDT Corporation; *U.S. Public*, pg. 1094
UNION TELECOM TEXAS LLC—See IDT Corporation; *U.S. Public*, pg. 1094
UNION TELEPHONE COMPANY INC.; *U.S. Private*, pg. 4285
UNION TELEPHONE COMPANY—See Telephone & Data Systems, Inc.; *U.S. Public*, pg. 1998
UNION TEXTILE INDUSTRIES PLC—See Saha-Union Public Company Limited; *Int'l*, pg. 6480
UNION THAI-NICHIBAN CO.,LTD.—See Saha-Union Public Company Limited; *Int'l*, pg. 6480
UNION TITLE COMPANY, LLC—See Farmers & Merchants Investment Inc.; *U.S. Private*, pg. 1476
UNION TOBACCO & CIGARETTE INDUSTRIES CO. PLC—See Union Group; *Int'l*, pg. 8052
UNION TOOL CO. - MITSUKE PLANT—See Union Tool Co.; *Int'l*, pg. 8054
UNION TOOL CO. - NAGAOKA PLANT—See Union Tool Co.; *Int'l*, pg. 8054
UNION TOOL CO.; *Int'l*, pg. 8054
UNION TOOL EUROPE S.A.—See Union Tool Co.; *Int'l*, pg. 8054
UNION TOOL HONG KONG LTD.—See Union Tool Co.; *Int'l*, pg. 8054
UNION TOOL (SHANGHAI) CO., LTD.—See Union Tool Co.; *Int'l*, pg. 8054
UNION TOOL SINGAPORE PTE., LTD.—See Union Tool Co.; *Int'l*, pg. 8054
UNION TOOL (THAILAND) CO., LTD.—See Union Tool Co.; *Int'l*, pg. 8054
UNION TOOL (WAIGAOQIAO SHANGHAI) CO., LTD.—See Union Tool Co.; *Int'l*, pg. 8054
UNIONTOWN NEWSPAPERS INC.—See The Nutting Company, Inc.; *U.S. Private*, pg. 4087
UNION TOWNSHIP ADULT COMMUNITY DEVELOPMENT CORPORATION; *U.S. Private*, pg. 4285
UNION TRACTOR LTD.; *Int'l*, pg. 8054
UNION TRADING COMPANY—See Belhasa Group of Companies; *Int'l*, pg. 964
UNION UHRENFABRIK GMBH—See The Swatch Group Ltd.; *Int'l*, pg. 7693
UNION UNDERWEAR COMPANY, INC.—See Berkshire Hathaway Inc.; *U.S. Public*, pg. 305
UNIONVALE COAL CO. INC.; *U.S. Private*, pg. 4285
UNION VERSICHERUNGS-AKTIENGESELLSCHAFT; *Int'l*, pg. 8054
UNION VIENNA INSURANCE GROUP BIZTOSITO ZRT.—See Vienna Insurance Group AG Wiener Versicherung Gruppe; *Int'l*, pg. 8195
UNION ZOJIRUSHI CO., LTD.—See Saha-Union Public Company Limited; *Int'l*, pg. 6480
UNIOR BIONIC, D.O.O.—See Unior Kovaska industrija d.d.; *Int'l*, pg. 8055
UNIOR BULGARIA, LTD.—See Unior Kovaska industrija d.d.; *Int'l*, pg. 8055
UNIOR COFRAMA SP. Z O.O.—See Unior Kovaska industrija d.d.; *Int'l*, pg. 8055
UNIOR COMPONENTS A.D.; *Int'l*, pg. 8055
UNIOR DEUTSCHLAND GMBH—See Unior Kovaska industrija d.d.; *Int'l*, pg. 8055
UNIOR ESPANA, S.L.—See Unior Kovaska industrija d.d.; *Int'l*, pg. 8055
UNIOR HUNGARIA KFT.—See Unior Kovaska industrija d.d.; *Int'l*, pg. 8055
UNIOR IN D.O.O.—See Unior Kovaska industrija d.d.; *Int'l*, pg. 8055
UNIOR ITALIA S.R.L.—See Unior Kovaska industrija d.d.; *Int'l*, pg. 8055
UNIOR KOVASKA INDUSTRIJA D.D.; *Int'l*, pg. 8055
UNIOR - NORTH AMERICA INC.—See Unior Kovaska industrija d.d.; *Int'l*, pg. 8055
UNIOR PROFESSIONAL TOOLS, LTD.—See Unior Kovaska industrija d.d.; *Int'l*, pg. 8055
UNIOR SAVJETOVANJE I TRGOVINA D.O.O.—See Unior Kovaska industrija d.d.; *Int'l*, pg. 8055
UNIOR VINKOVCI D.O.O.—See Unior Kovaska industrija d.d.; *Int'l*, pg. 8055
UNIO SA SATU MARE; *Int'l*, pg. 8050
UNIPACK, INC.—See BelHealth Investment Partners LLC; *U.S. Private*, pg. 518
UNIPAL GENERAL TRADING COMPANY PSC—See Arab Palestinian Investment Company; *Int'l*, pg. 531
UNIPAR CARBOCLORO S.A.; *Int'l*, pg. 8055
UNIPAR INDUPA S.A.I.C.—See Unipar Carbocloro S.A.; *Int'l*, pg. 8055

UNIPART GROUP OF COMPANIES LIMITED; *Int'l*, pg. 8055
UNIPART POLYMER AND COMPOSITE SOLUTIONS—See Unipart Group of Companies Limited; *Int'l*, pg. 8055
UNIPART RAIL—See Unipart Group of Companies Limited; *Int'l*, pg. 8055
UNIPART SECURITY SOLUTIONS LTD—See Unipart Group of Companies Limited; *Int'l*, pg. 8055
UNIPART SERVICES AMERICA INC.—See Unipart Group of Companies Limited; *Int'l*, pg. 8055
UNIPART SERVICES INDIA PRIVATE LIMITED—See Unipart Group of Companies Limited; *Int'l*, pg. 8055
UNIPARTS INDIA GMBH—See Uniparts India Limited; *Int'l*, pg. 8055
UNIPARTS INDIA LIMITED; *Int'l*, pg. 8055
UNIPEC ASIA CO. LTD.—See China Petrochemical Corporation; *Int'l*, pg. 1540
UNIPEC UK CO. LTD.—See China Petrochemical Corporation; *Int'l*, pg. 1540
UNIPER ANLAGENSERVICE GMBH—See Fortum Oyj; *Int'l*, pg. 2742
UNIPER BELGIUM N.V.—See Fortum Oyj; *Int'l*, pg. 2742
UNIPER BENELUX N.V.—See Fortum Oyj; *Int'l*, pg. 2742
UNIPER ENERGY DMCC—See Montfort Group; *Int'l*, pg. 5037
UNIPER ENERGY DMCC—See Sheikh Ahmed bin Dalmook Al Maktoum Private Office LLC; *Int'l*, pg. 6793
UNIPER ENERGY SALES GMBH—See Fortum Oyj; *Int'l*, pg. 2742
UNIPER ENERGY SOUTHERN AFRICA (PTY) LTD.—See Fortum Oyj; *Int'l*, pg. 2742
UNIPER SE—See Fortum Oyj; *Int'l*, pg. 2742
UNIPER TECHNOLOGIES B.V.—See Fortum Oyj; *Int'l*, pg. 2742
UNIPER TECHNOLOGIES GMBH—See Fortum Oyj; *Int'l*, pg. 2742
UNIPER TECHNOLOGIES LIMITED—See Fortum Oyj; *Int'l*, pg. 2742
UNIPER WARME GMBH—See Fortum Oyj; *Int'l*, pg. 2742
UNIPETROL, A.S.—See Orlen S.A.; *Int'l*, pg. 5641
UNIPETROL DEUTSCHLAND GMBH—See Orlen S.A.; *Int'l*, pg. 5641
UNIPETROL RAFINERIE, A.S.—See Orlen S.A.; *Int'l*, pg. 5641
UNIPETROL SERVICES S.R.O.—See Orlen S.A.; *Int'l*, pg. 5641
UNIPETROL SLOVENSKO S.R.O.—See Orlen S.A.; *Int'l*, pg. 5641
UNIPEX BENELUX NV—See Groupe Unipex SAS; *Int'l*, pg. 3112
UNIPEX SOLUTIONS FRANCE S.A.S.—See Groupe Unipex SAS; *Int'l*, pg. 3112
UNIPHARM INC.; *U.S. Private*, pg. 4285
UNIPHARM JSC—See Sopharma AD; *Int'l*, pg. 7108
UNIPHAR PLC; *Int'l*, pg. 8055
UNIPHOENIX JAYA SDN. BHD.—See Fiamma Holdings Berhad; *Int'l*, pg. 2650
UNIPIPE LTD.—See NIBE Industrier AB; *Int'l*, pg. 5263
UNIPLAST KNAUER VERWALTUNGS GMBH—See Blue Cap AG; *Int'l*, pg. 1067
UNIPLEX SOFTWARE, INC.—See CP Software Group, Inc.; *U.S. Private*, pg. 1079
UNIPLUMO (IRELAND) LIMITED—See Dole plc; *Int'l*, pg. 2158
UNIPLY BLAZE PRIVATE LIMITED—See Uniply Industries Limited; *Int'l*, pg. 8056
UNIPLY DECOR LIMITED; *Int'l*, pg. 8056
UNIPLY INDUSTRIES LIMITED; *Int'l*, pg. 8056
UNIPOINT CORP.; *Int'l*, pg. 8056
UNIPOINT ELECTRIC MFG CO., LTD.—See Robert Bosch GmbH; *Int'l*, pg. 6368
UNI POINT MARKETING (M) SDN BHD—See Solid Automotive Berhad; *Int'l*, pg. 7071
UNIPOL BANCA S.P.A.—See BPER BANCA S.p.A; *Int'l*, pg. 1132
UNIPOL GRUPPO S.P.A.; *Int'l*, pg. 8056
UNIPOL HOLLAND B.V.—See CRH plc; *Int'l*, pg. 1849
UNIPOL LEASING S.P.A.—See BPER BANCA S.p.A; *Int'l*, pg. 1132
UNIPOL MERCHANT S.P.A.—See BPER BANCA S.p.A; *Int'l*, pg. 1132
UNIPOLSAI ASSICURAZIONI S.P.A.—See Unipol Gruppo S.p.A.; *Int'l*, pg. 8056
UNI POLYMER CO., LTD.—See Mitsubishi Pencil Co., Ltd.; *Int'l*, pg. 4967
UNIPOWER AB—See Sdiptech AB; *Int'l*, pg. 6659
UNIPOWER, LLC—See Sdiptech AB; *Int'l*, pg. 6658
UNIPRES ALABAMA, INC.—See Unipres Corporation; *Int'l*, pg. 8056
UNIPRES BUTSURYU CO., LTD.—See Unipres Corporation; *Int'l*, pg. 8056
UNIPRES (CHINA) CORPORATION—See Unipres Corporation; *Int'l*, pg. 8056
UNIPRES CORPORATION; *Int'l*, pg. 8056
UNIPRES CORPORATION - TOCHIGI PLANT—See Unipres Corporation; *Int'l*, pg. 8056
UNIPRES CORPORATION - TOOL & DIE PLANT—See Unipres Corporation; *Int'l*, pg. 8056

COMPANY NAME INDEX

UNIPRES EUROPE, SAS—See Unipres Corporation; *Int'l*, pg. 8056
UNIPRES GUANGZHOU CORPORATION—See Unipres Corporation; *Int'l*, pg. 8056
UNI-PRESIDENT CHINA HOLDINGS LTD; *Int'l*, pg. 8028
UNI-PRESIDENT COLD-CHAIN CORP.—See Uni-President Enterprises Corporation; *Int'l*, pg. 8029
UNI-PRESIDENT DEPARTMENT STORE CORP.—See Uni-President Enterprises Corporation; *Int'l*, pg. 8029
UNI-PRESIDENT ENTERPRISES CORPORATION; *Int'l*, pg. 8028
UNI-PRESIDENT GLASS INDUSTRIAL CO., LTD.—See Uni-President Enterprises Corporation; *Int'l*, pg. 8029
UNI-PRESIDENT MARKETING CO., LTD.—See Uni-President Enterprises Corporation; *Int'l*, pg. 8029
UNI-PRESIDENT (PHILIPPINES) CORP.—See Uni-President Enterprises Corporation; *Int'l*, pg. 8029
UNI-PRESIDENT (THAILAND) LTD.—See Uni-President Enterprises Corporation; *Int'l*, pg. 8029
UNI-PRESIDENT VIETNAM AQUATIC BREEDING CO., LTD.—See Uni-President Enterprises Corporation; *Int'l*, pg. 8029
UNI-PRESIDENT (VIETNAM) CO., LTD.—See Uni-President Enterprises Corporation; *Int'l*, pg. 8029
UNIPRES INDIA PRIVATE LIMITED—See Unipres Corporation; *Int'l*, pg. 8056
UNIPRES KYUSHU CORPORATION—See Unipres Corporation; *Int'l*, pg. 8056
UNIPRES MEXICANA, S.A. DE C.V.—See Unipres Corporation; *Int'l*, pg. 8056
UNIPRES MOLD CORPORATION—See Unipres Corporation; *Int'l*, pg. 8056
UNIPRES NORTH AMERICA, INC.—See Unipres Corporation; *Int'l*, pg. 8056
UNIPRES PRECISION CORPORATION—See Unipres Corporation; *Int'l*, pg. 8057
UNIPRES PRECISION GUANGZHOU CORPORATION—See Unipres Corporation; *Int'l*, pg. 8057
UNIPRES R & D CO., LTD.—See Unipres Corporation; *Int'l*, pg. 8057
UNIPRES SERVICE CORPORATION—See Unipres Corporation; *Int'l*, pg. 8057
UNIPRES SOUTHEAST U.S.A., INC.—See Unipres Corporation; *Int'l*, pg. 8057
UNIPRES SUNRISE CORPORATION—See Unipres Corporation; *Int'l*, pg. 8057
UNIPRES (THAILAND) CO., LTD.—See Unipres Corporation; *Int'l*, pg. 8056
UNIPRES (UK) LIMITED—See Unipres Corporation; *Int'l*, pg. 8056
UNIPRES U.S.A., INC.—See Unipres Corporation; *Int'l*, pg. 8057
UNIPRES WUHAN CORPORATION—See Unipres Corporation; *Int'l*, pg. 8057
UNIPRES ZHENGZHOU CORPORATION—See Unipres Corporation; *Int'l*, pg. 8057
UNIPRIX INC.—See McKesson Corporation; *U.S. Public*, pg. 1408
UNIPRO-BELGIE N.V.—See Uzin Utz AG; *Int'l*, pg. 8103
UNIPRO B.V.—See Uzin Utz AG; *Int'l*, pg. 8103
UNIPRO FOODSERVICE INC.; *U.S. Private*, pg. 4285
UNIPROF REAL ESTATE HOLDING AG; *Int'l*, pg. 8057
UNIPROJECT S.R.L.—See Iren S.p.A.; *Int'l*, pg. 3808
UN IPRO JEKT BAU- UND INNENBAU GMBH—See STRABAG SE; *Int'l*, pg. 7233
UNIPROM A.D.; *Int'l*, pg. 8057
UNIPROMET D.D.; *Int'l*, pg. 8057
UNIPROM HOMES INC.—See Uniprop, Inc.; *U.S. Private*, pg. 4286
UNIPROP, INC.; *U.S. Private*, pg. 4285
UNIPRO PJSC—See Fortum Oyj; *Int'l*, pg. 2742
UNIPRO TECHNOLOGIES LIMITED; *Int'l*, pg. 8057
UNIPUBLIC S.A.—See Atresmedia Corporacion de Medios de Comunicacion, S.A.; *Int'l*, pg. 693
UNIPULSE ASIA PACIFIC PTE. LTD.—See Unipulse Corporation; *Int'l*, pg. 8057
UNIPULSE CORPORATION; *Int'l*, pg. 8057
UNIPULSE INSTRUMENTS PVT. LTD.—See Unipulse Corporation; *Int'l*, pg. 8057
UNIPULSE INSTRUMENTS THAILAND CO., LTD.—See Unipulse Corporation; *Int'l*, pg. 8057
UNIPULSE TRADING (WUXI) CO., LTD.—See Unipulse Corporation; *Int'l*, pg. 8057
UNIQA A.D.O.—See UNIQA Insurance Group AG; *Int'l*, pg. 8059
UNIQA A.D. SKOPJE—See UNIQA Insurance Group AG; *Int'l*, pg. 8058
UNIQA ALTERNATIVE INVESTMENTS GMBH—See UNIQA Insurance Group AG; *Int'l*, pg. 8058
UNIQA ASIGURARI DE VIATA—See UNIQA Insurance Group AG; *Int'l*, pg. 8058
UNIQA ASIGURARI S.A.—See UNIQA Insurance Group AG; *Int'l*, pg. 8058
UNIQA ASSICURAZIONI S.P.A.—See Societa Reale Mutua di Assicurazioni; *Int'l*, pg. 7034
UNIQA ASSURANCES S.A.—See UNIQA Insurance Group AG; *Int'l*, pg. 8058

UNIQA BETEILIGUNGS-HOLDING GMBH—See UNIQA Insurance Group AG; *Int'l*, pg. 8058
UNIQA BIZTOSITO ZRT.—See UNIQA Insurance Group AG; *Int'l*, pg. 8058
UNIQA ERWERB VON BETEILIGUNGEN GESELLSCHAFT M.B.H.—See UNIQA Insurance Group AG; *Int'l*, pg. 8058
UNIQA FINANZ-SERVICE GMBH—See UNIQA Insurance Group AG; *Int'l*, pg. 8058
UNIQA GLOBALCARE SA—See UNIQA Insurance Group AG; *Int'l*, pg. 8058
UNIQA IMMOBILIEN-SERVICE GMBH—See UNIQA Insurance Group AG; *Int'l*, pg. 8058
UNIQA INSURANCE GROUP AG; *Int'l*, pg. 8057
UNIQA INSURANCE PLC—See UNIQA Insurance Group AG; *Int'l*, pg. 8058
UNIQA INTERNATIONAL VERSICHERUNGS-HOLDING GMBH—See UNIQA Insurance Group AG; *Int'l*, pg. 8058
UNIQA INVESTICNI SPOLECNOST, A.S.—See UNIQA Insurance Group AG; *Int'l*, pg. 8058
UNIQA LEBENSVERSICHERUNG AG—See UNIQA Insurance Group AG; *Int'l*, pg. 8058
UNIQA LIFE AD-SKOPJE—See UNIQA Insurance Group AG; *Int'l*, pg. 8058
UNIQA LIFE INSURANCE COMPANY—See UNIQA Insurance Group AG; *Int'l*, pg. 8058
UNIQA LIFE INSURANCE PLC—See UNIQA Insurance Group AG; *Int'l*, pg. 8058
UNIQA LIFE PRIVATE JOINT STOCK COMPANY—See UNIQA Insurance Group AG; *Int'l*, pg. 8058
UNIQA LIFE S.P.A.—See Societa Reale Mutua di Assicurazioni; *Int'l*, pg. 7034
UNIQA NEZIVOTNO OSIGURANJE A.D.O.—See UNIQA Insurance Group AG; *Int'l*, pg. 8059
UNIQA NEZIVOTNO OSIGURANJE A.D.—See UNIQA Insurance Group AG; *Int'l*, pg. 8059
UNIQA OSIGURANJE D.D.—See UNIQA Insurance Group AG; *Int'l*, pg. 8058
UNIQA OSIGURANJE D.D.—See UNIQA Insurance Group AG; *Int'l*, pg. 8059
UNIQA OSTERREICH VERSICHERUNGEN AG—See UNIQA Insurance Group AG; *Int'l*, pg. 8058
UNIQA PERSONENVERSICHERUNG AG—See UNIQA Insurance Group AG; *Int'l*, pg. 8058
UNIQA POISTOVNA A.S.—See UNIQA Insurance Group AG; *Int'l*, pg. 8059
UNIQA POJISTOVNA A.S.—See UNIQA Insurance Group AG; *Int'l*, pg. 8059
UNIQA POSLOVNI CENTAR KORZO D.O.O.—See UNIQA Insurance Group AG; *Int'l*, pg. 8059
UNIQA PREVIDENZA S.P.A.—See Societa Reale Mutua di Assicurazioni; *Int'l*, pg. 7034
UNIQA RAIFFEISEN SOFTWARE SERVICE KFT.—See UNIQA Insurance Group AG; *Int'l*, pg. 8058
UNIQA RAIFFEISEN SOFTWARE SERVICE S.R.L.—See UNIQA Insurance Group AG; *Int'l*, pg. 8058
UNIQA RE AG—See UNIQA Insurance Group AG; *Int'l*, pg. 8058
UNIQA REAL ESTATE AG—See UNIQA Insurance Group AG; *Int'l*, pg. 8059
UNIQA REAL ESTATE BH NEKRETNINE, D.O.O.—See UNIQA Insurance Group AG; *Int'l*, pg. 8059
UNIQA REAL ESTATE DRITTE BETEILIGUNGSVERWALTUNG GMBH—See UNIQA Insurance Group AG; *Int'l*, pg. 8059
UNIQA REAL ESTATE HOLDING GMBH—See UNIQA Insurance Group AG; *Int'l*, pg. 8059
UNIQA REAL ESTATE MANAGEMENT GMBH—See UNIQA Insurance Group AG; *Int'l*, pg. 8059
UNIQA REAL ESTATE VIERTE BETEILIGUNGSVERWALTUNG GMBH—See UNIQA Insurance Group AG; *Int'l*, pg. 8059
UNIQARTA, INC.—See Kulicke & Soffa Industries, Inc.; *Int'l*, pg. 4329
UNIQA SACHVERSICHERUNG AG—See UNIQA Insurance Group AG; *Int'l*, pg. 8059
UNIQA SOFTWARE SERVICE BULGARIA OOD—See UNIQA Insurance Group AG; *Int'l*, pg. 8059
UNIQA SOFTWARE SERVICE D.O.O.—See UNIQA Insurance Group AG; *Int'l*, pg. 8059
UNIQA SOFTWARE-SERVICE GMBH—See UNIQA Insurance Group AG; *Int'l*, pg. 8059
UNIQA SOFTWARE SERVICE KFT.—See UNIQA Insurance Group AG; *Int'l*, pg. 8059
UNIQA TA NA ZYCIE S.A.—See UNIQA Insurance Group AG; *Int'l*, pg. 8059
UNIQA TU S.A.—See UNIQA Insurance Group AG; *Int'l*, pg. 8059
UNIQA VENTURES GMBH—See UNIQA Insurance Group AG; *Int'l*, pg. 8059
UNIQA VERSICHERUNG AG—See UNIQA Insurance Group AG; *Int'l*, pg. 8059
UNIQA ZIVOTNO OSIGURANJE A.D.—See UNIQA Insurance Group AG; *Int'l*, pg. 8059
UNIQA ZIVOTNO OSIGURANJE A.D.—See UNIQA Insurance Group AG; *Int'l*, pg. 8059
UNIQLO AUSTRALIA PTY LTD—See Fast Retailing Co., Ltd.; *Int'l*, pg. 2621

UNIQLO HONG KONG, LTD.—See Fast Retailing Co., Ltd.; *Int'l*, pg. 2621
UNIQLO VIETNAM CO., LTD.—See Fast Retailing Co., Ltd.; *Int'l*, pg. 2621
UNIQ SECURITY SOLUTIONS PRIVATE LIMITED—See Security & Intelligence Services (INDIA) Limited; *Int'l*, pg. 6677
UNIQUE AIR SERVICES INC.; *U.S. Private*, pg. 4286
UNIQUE BALANCE, INC.; *U.S. Private*, pg. 4286
UNIQUE BETRIEBSSYSTEME AG—See Flughafen Zurich AG; *Int'l*, pg. 2713
UNIQUE BROADBAND SYSTEMS LTD.; *Int'l*, pg. 8059
UNIQUE DIGITAL TECHNOLOGY; *U.S. Private*, pg. 4286
UNIQUE ELEVATOR INTERIORS, INC.—See P4G Capital Management, LLC; *U.S. Private*, pg. 3062
UNIQUE ENGINEERING AND CONSTRUCTION PUBLIC COMPANY LIMITED; *Int'l*, pg. 8059
UNIQUE ENGINEERING AUSTRALIA PTY. LTD.—See Schunk GmbH; *Int'l*, pg. 6643
UNIQUE FABRICATING, INC.—See Taglich Private Equity LLC; *U.S. Private*, pg. 3922
UNIQUE FASHION CO., LTD.—See Saha Pathanapibul Public Company Limited; *Int'l*, pg. 6479
UNIQUE FINANCE LIMITED—See Civil Bank Limited; *Int'l*, pg. 1630
UNIQUE FINANCIAL PLANNING LIMITED—See Schroders plc; *Int'l*, pg. 6641
UNIQUE FIRE HOLDINGS BERHAD; *Int'l*, pg. 8059
UNIQUE FOODS CORP.; *U.S. Public*, pg. 2227
UNIQUE FURNITURE A/S; *Int'l*, pg. 8059
UNIQUE HOME HEALTH CARE LIMITED—See Apollo Hospitals Enterprise Limited; *Int'l*, pg. 518
UNIQUE HOTEL & RESORTS LIMITED; *Int'l*, pg. 8059
UNIQUE INGREDIENTS LIMITED—See International Flavors & Fragrances Inc.; *U.S. Public*, pg. 1154
UNIQUE-INTASCO USA, INC.—See Taglich Private Equity LLC; *U.S. Private*, pg. 3922
UNIQUE INTERNATIONAL LOGISTICS (M) SDN BHD—See Unique Logistics International Inc.; *U.S. Public*, pg. 2227
UNIQUE LIMOUSINE, INC.; *U.S. Private*, pg. 4286
UNIQUE LOGISTICS HOLDINGS LTD.—See Unique Logistics International Inc.; *U.S. Public*, pg. 2227
UNIQUE LOGISTICS INTERNATIONAL (ATL) LLC—See Unique Logistics International Inc.; *U.S. Public*, pg. 2227
UNIQUE LOGISTICS INTERNATIONAL (BOS), INC.—See Unique Logistics International Inc.; *U.S. Public*, pg. 2227
UNIQUE LOGISTICS INTERNATIONAL (CAMBODIA) CO., LTD.—See Unique Logistics International Inc.; *U.S. Public*, pg. 2227
UNIQUE LOGISTICS INTERNATIONAL (CHICAGO), LLC.—See Unique Logistics International Inc.; *U.S. Public*, pg. 2227
UNIQUE LOGISTICS INTERNATIONAL (FUZHOU) LTD.—See Unique Logistics International Inc.; *U.S. Public*, pg. 2227
UNIQUE LOGISTICS INTERNATIONAL (H.K.) LTD.—See Unique Logistics International Inc.; *U.S. Public*, pg. 2227
UNIQUE LOGISTICS INTERNATIONAL INC.; *U.S. Public*, pg. 2227
UNIQUE LOGISTICS INTERNATIONAL (INDIA) PRIVATE LIMITED—See Unique Logistics International Inc.; *U.S. Public*, pg. 2227
UNIQUE LOGISTICS INTERNATIONAL (LAX), INC.—See Unique Logistics International Inc.; *U.S. Public*, pg. 2227
UNIQUE LOGISTICS INTERNATIONAL (MACAU) LTD.—See Unique Logistics International Inc.; *U.S. Public*, pg. 2227
UNIQUE LOGISTICS INTERNATIONAL (NYC), LLC—See Unique Logistics International Inc.; *U.S. Public*, pg. 2227
UNIQUE LOGISTICS INTERNATIONAL PHILIPPINES INC.—See Unique Logistics International Inc.; *U.S. Public*, pg. 2227
UNIQUE LOGISTICS INTERNATIONAL (S) PTE LTD—See Unique Logistics International Inc.; *U.S. Public*, pg. 2227
UNIQUE LOGISTICS INTERNATIONAL (THAILAND) CO., LTD.—See Unique Logistics International Inc.; *U.S. Public*, pg. 2227
UNIQUE LOGISTICS INTERNATIONAL (VIETNAM) LTD.—See Unique Logistics International Inc.; *U.S. Public*, pg. 2227
UNIQUE LOGISTICS INTERNATIONAL XIAMEN LIMITED—See Unique Logistics International Inc.; *U.S. Public*, pg. 2227
UNIQUE LOGISTICS INTERNATIONAL (ZHONGSHAN) LTD.—See Unique Logistics International Inc.; *U.S. Public*, pg. 2227
UNIQUE LOGISTICS (KOREA) CO., LTD.—See Unique Logistics International Inc.; *U.S. Public*, pg. 2227
UNIQUE MACHINE, LLC—See Sumitomo Corporation; *Int'l*, pg. 7274

UNIQUE LOGISTICS INTERNATIONAL, INC.

CORPORATE AFFILIATIONS

UNIQUE MINING SERVICES PUBLIC COMPANY LIMITED—See Thoresen Thai Agencies Public Company Limited; *Int'l*, pg. 7719
UNIQUE MIX (PENANG) SDN. BHD.—See Oriental Holdings Berhad; *Int'l*, pg. 5625
UNIQUE MIX SDN. BHD.—See Oriental Holdings Berhad; *Int'l*, pg. 5625
UNIQUE NEDERLAND BV—See Recruit Holdings Co., Ltd.; *Int'l*, pg. 6241
UNIQUE ORGANICS LIMITED; *Int'l*, pg. 8059
UNIQUE PAVE SDN. BHD.—See Oriental Holdings Berhad; *Int'l*, pg. 5625
UNIQUE PERSONALSERVICE GMBH—See Recruit Holdings Co., Ltd.; *Int'l*, pg. 6241
UNIQUE PERSONALSERVICE GMBH—See Recruit Holdings Co., Ltd.; *Int'l*, pg. 6241
UNIQUE PERSONNEL SERVICE GMBH—See Recruit Holdings Co., Ltd.; *Int'l*, pg. 6241
UNIQUE PHARMACY (IPOH) SDN BHD—See Batu Kawan Berhad; *Int'l*, pg. 891
UNIQUE PLAYGROUNDS LTD.—See KOMPAN A/S; *Int'l*, pg. 4243
UNIQUE-PRESCOTECH, INC.—See Taglich Private Equity LLC; *U.S. Private*, pg. 3922
UNIQUE PUB PROPERTIES LIMITED—See Stonegate Pub Company Limited; *Int'l*, pg. 7222
UNIQUE REGULUS SUPPLY CHAIN SOLUTIONS INDIA PRIVATE LIMITED—See Unique Logistics International Inc.; *U.S. Public*, pg. 2227
UNIQUE SCM (H.K) LIMITED—See Unique Logistics International Inc.; *U.S. Public*, pg. 2227
UNIQUESOURCE; *U.S. Private*, pg. 4286
UNIQUEST AMERICA INC.—See Uniquest Corporation; *Int'l*, pg. 8060
UNIQUEST CORPORATION; *Int'l*, pg. 8060
UNIQUEST HONG KONG—See Uniquest Corporation; *Int'l*, pg. 8060
UNIQUEST KOREA INC.—See Uniquest Corporation; *Int'l*, pg. 8060
UNIQUE SUGARS LIMITED—See Universal Starch-Chem Allied Limited; *Int'l*, pg. 8082
UNIQUE TECHNOLOGY EUROPE B.V.—See Unitech Computer Co., Ltd.; *Int'l*, pg. 8064
UNIQUE VASTU NIRMAN PRIVATE LIMITED—See Setubandhan Infrastructure Limited; *Int'l*, pg. 6730
UNIQUE WHOLESALE DISTRIBUTORS, INC.; *U.S. Private*, pg. 4286
UNIQUE WINDOWS & DOORS; *U.S. Private*, pg. 4286
UNIQURE N.V.—See Ampersand Management LLC; *U.S. Private*, pg. 265
UNIRAC, INC.—See Tenex Capital Management, L.P.; *U.S. Private*, pg. 3966
UNIREA SA; *Int'l*, pg. 8060
UNIRISC, INC.—See Kelso & Company, L.P.; *U.S. Private*, pg. 2280
UNIRITA INC.; *Int'l*, pg. 8060
UNIROSS BATTERIES HK LTD.—See Eveready Industries India Ltd; *Int'l*, pg. 2563
UNIROSS BATTERIES SAS—See Eveready Industries India Ltd; *Int'l*, pg. 2563
UNIROSS SA—See Eveready Industries India Ltd; *Int'l*, pg. 2563
UNIROYAL ENGINEERED PRODUCTS, LLC—See Uniroyal Global Engineered Products, Inc.; *U.S. Public*, pg. 2228
UNIROYAL GLOBAL ENGINEERED PRODUCTS, INC.; *U.S. Public*, pg. 2227
UNIROYAL GLOBAL LIMITED—See Uniroyal Global Engineered Products, Inc.; *U.S. Public*, pg. 2228
UNIROYAL GOODRICH CANADA, INC.—See Compagnie Generale des Etablissements Michelin SCA; *Int'l*, pg. 1744
UNIROYAL GOODRICH INTELLECTUAL—See Compagnie Generale des Etablissements Michelin SCA; *Int'l*, pg. 1744
UNIROYAL INDUSTRIES LTD.; *Int'l*, pg. 8060
UNIROYAL MARINE EXPORTS LIMITED; *Int'l*, pg. 8060
UNIR S.A.—See Grupo Clarin S.A.; *Int'l*, pg. 3124
UNISA AMERICA INC.—See Unisa Holdings Incorporated; *U.S. Private*, pg. 4286
UNISA EUROPA HOLDINGS INC.—See Unisa Holdings Incorporated; *U.S. Private*, pg. 4286
UNISA EUROPA SA—See Unisa Holdings Incorporated; *U.S. Private*, pg. 4286
UNISA HOLDINGS INCORPORATED; *U.S. Private*, pg. 4286
UNISALUTE S.P.A.—See Unipol Gruppo S.p.A.; *Int'l*, pg. 8056
UNISA—See Unisa Holdings Incorporated; *U.S. Private*, pg. 4286
UNISEA, INC.—See Nissui Corporation; *Int'l*, pg. 5379
UNISEAL, INC.—See LG Chem Ltd.; *Int'l*, pg. 4474
UNI-SELECT INC.—See LKQ Corporation; *U.S. Public*, pg. 1336
UNISEM CHENGDU CO., LTD.—See Tianshui Huatian Technology Co., Ltd.; *Int'l*, pg. 7742
UNISEM CO., LTD.; *Int'l*, pg. 8060
UNISEM (M) BERHAD—See Tianshui Huatian Technology Co., Ltd.; *Int'l*, pg. 7741

UNISEM SA; *Int'l*, pg. 8060
UNISEM (SUNNYVALE) INC.—See Tianshui Huatian Technology Co., Ltd.; *Int'l*, pg. 7742
UNISENSE TECHNOLOGY CO., LTD.—See Unimicron Technology Corporation; *Int'l*, pg. 8050
UNISENSOR AG—See Investor AB; *Int'l*, pg. 3786
UNISERVE COMMUNICATIONS CORPORATION; *Int'l*, pg. 8061
UNI-SERVICE OPERATIONS CORPORATION—See Utica National Insurance Group; *U.S. Private*, pg. 4325
UNISERVICE SA—See Bouygues S.A.; *Int'l*, pg. 1123
UNISERVICE UNISAFE S.R.L—See OTI Greentech AG; *Int'l*, pg. 5657
UNIS FABRIKA CIJEVI A.D.; *Int'l*, pg. 8060
UNIS-FEROS A.D.; *Int'l*, pg. 8060
UNIS GINEX D.D. GORAZDE; *Int'l*, pg. 8060
UNISHIPPERS ASSOCIATION INC.; *U.S. Private*, pg. 4286
UNISHIPPERS GLOBAL LOGISTICS, LLC—See Ridgemont Partners Management LLC; *U.S. Private*, pg. 3433
UNISHIRE URBAN INFRA LTD; *Int'l*, pg. 8061
UNISISTEMAS PANAMA, SA—See Hewlett Packard Enterprise Company; *U.S. Public*, pg. 1032
UNISKA AG—See Indutrade AB; *Int'l*, pg. 3682
UNIS KOMERC D.D. SARAJEVO; *Int'l*, pg. 8060
UNISON CAPITAL, INC.; *Int'l*, pg. 8061
UNISON CO., LTD.; *Int'l*, pg. 8061
UNISON CONSULTING, INC.; *U.S. Private*, pg. 4286
UNISON E&C CO., LTD.—See Unison Co., Ltd.; *Int'l*, pg. 8061
UNISON ENGINE COMPONENTS—See General Electric Company; *U.S. Public*, pg. 919
UNISON ENGINE COMPONENTS—See General Electric Company; *U.S. Public*, pg. 919
UNISON ENVIRO PRIVATE LIMITED—See Mahanagar Gas Limited; *Int'l*, pg. 4644
UNISON HEALTH PLAN OF DELAWARE, INC.—See UnitedHealth Group Incorporated; *U.S. Public*, pg. 2251
UNISON INDUSTRIES, LLC—See General Electric Company; *U.S. Public*, pg. 919
UNISON INDUSTRIES LLC—See General Electric Company; *U.S. Public*, pg. 919
UNISON INDUSTRIES LLC—See General Electric Company; *U.S. Public*, pg. 919
UNISON INDUSTRIES, LLC—See General Electric Company; *U.S. Public*, pg. 919
UNISON INDUSTRIES, LLC—See General Electric Company; *U.S. Public*, pg. 919
UNISON INDUSTRIES—See General Electric Company; *U.S. Public*, pg. 919
UNISON INTERNATIONAL CORP.—See Unison Pacific Corporation; *U.S. Private*, pg. 4286
UNISON MARKETPLACE, INC.—See The Carlyle Group Inc.; *U.S. Public*, pg. 2056
UNISON METALS LTD.; *Int'l*, pg. 8062
UNISONO FIELDMARKETING—See Omnicom Group Inc.; *U.S. Public*, pg. 1599
UNISONO FIELDMARKETING—See Omnicom Group Inc.; *U.S. Public*, pg. 1599
UNISONO FIELDMARKETING—See Omnicom Group Inc.; *U.S. Public*, pg. 1599
UNISON PACIFIC CORPORATION; *U.S. Private*, pg. 4286
UNISON SOFTWARE, INC.—See The Carlyle Group Inc.; *U.S. Public*, pg. 2056
UNISON—See UnitedHealth Group Incorporated; *U.S. Public*, pg. 2238
UNISONSTEADFAST AG—See Steadfast Group Limited; *Int'l*, pg. 7188
UNISON SYSTEMS, INC.; *U.S. Private*, pg. 4286
UNISON TRANSFORMER SERVICES, INC.—See Dow Inc.; *U.S. Public*, pg. 686
UNISOR MULTISYSTEMS LTD.—See STG International Ltd; *Int'l*, pg. 7213
UNISOURCE BELGIUM BVBA—See Clayton, Dubilier & Rice, LLC; *U.S. Private*, pg. 928
UNISOURCE CANADA INC.—See Clayton, Dubilier & Rice, LLC; *U.S. Private*, pg. 929
UNISOURCE ENERGY SERVICES, INC.—See Fortis Inc.; *Int'l*, pg. 2740
UNISOURCE ENTERPRISES LIMITED—See Tongjitang Chinese Medicines Company; *Int'l*, pg. 7808
UNISOURCE MANUFACTURING, INC.—See AEA Investors LP; *U.S. Public*, pg. 115
UNISOURCE SAS—See Britvic plc; *Int'l*, pg. 1171
UNISOURCE SOLUTIONS INC.; *U.S. Private*, pg. 4286
UNISPACE GLOBAL PTY LTD.—See PAG Capital; *Int'l*, pg. 5697
UNISPAN AUSTRALIA PTY LTD—See Acrow Limited; *Int'l*, pg. 109
UNISPLENDOUR CORPORATION LIMITED; *Int'l*, pg. 8062
UNIS-PRETIS NIS D.D. VOGOSCA; *Int'l*, pg. 8060
UNISSANT, INC.; *U.S. Private*, pg. 4286
UNIS STEEL DISTRIBUTION ROMANIA SRL; *Int'l*, pg. 8060
UNISTAN INC.; *U.S. Private*, pg. 4286
UNISTAR FOODS, INC.; *U.S. Private*, pg. 4287
UNISTAR MULTIMEDIA LIMITED; *Int'l*, pg. 8062
UNISTAR PLASTICS LLC; *U.S. Private*, pg. 4287

UNISTARS CORP.—See United Microelectronics Corporation; *Int'l*, pg. 8070
UNISTAR-SPARCO COMPUTERS INC.; *U.S. Private*, pg. 4287
UNIS TAS A.D.; *Int'l*, pg. 8060
UNISTEEL FASTENING SYSTEMS (SHANGHAI) CO., LTD.—See SFS Group AG; *Int'l*, pg. 6739
UNISTEEL, LLC—See Ellwood Group, Inc.; *U.S. Private*, pg. 1375
UNISTEEL PRECISION (SUZHOU) CO., LTD.—See SFS Group AG; *Int'l*, pg. 6739
UNISTEEL TECHNOLOGY (CHINA) CO., LTD.—See SFS Group AG; *Int'l*, pg. 6740
UNISTEEL TECHNOLOGY LIMITED—See SFS Group AG; *Int'l*, pg. 6739
UNISTEEL TECHNOLOGY (M) SDN. BHD.—See SFS Group AG; *Int'l*, pg. 6740
UNIS TELEKOM D.D.; *Int'l*, pg. 8060
UNISTER HOLDING GMBH; *Int'l*, pg. 8062
UNISTER TRAVEL RETAIL GMBH & CO. KG—See Unister Holding GmbH; *Int'l*, pg. 8062
UNISTOCK JSC—See REISSWOLF International AG; *Int'l*, pg. 6258
UNISTREAM COMMERCIAL BANK OJSC; *Int'l*, pg. 8062
UNISTRESS CORPORATION—See Petricca Industries, Inc.; *U.S. Private*, pg. 3161
UNISTRING TECH SOLUTIONS PRIVATE LIMITED—See Zen Technologies Ltd; *Int'l*, pg. 8632
UNISTRONG TECHNOLOGY (S) PTE. LTD.—See Beijing UniStrong Science & Technology Co., Ltd.; *Int'l*, pg. 959
UNISTRUCTURAL SUPPORT SYSTEMS, LTD.—See Brixey & Meyer, Inc.; *U.S. Private*, pg. 658
UNISTRUT CORPORATION—See Clayton, Dubilier & Rice, LLC; *U.S. Private*, pg. 920
UNISTRUT CORPORATION—See Clayton, Dubilier & Rice, LLC; *U.S. Private*, pg. 920
UNIS - UDRUZENA METALNA INDUSTRIJA D.D.; *Int'l*, pg. 8060
UNIS USHA A.D. VISEGRAD; *Int'l*, pg. 8060
UNIS-USHA D.O.O.—See Unis USHA a.d. Visegrad; *Int'l*, pg. 8060
UNIS VALJCICI D.D.; *Int'l*, pg. 8060
UNISYNC CORP.; *Int'l*, pg. 8062
UNISYN VOTING SOLUTIONS, INC.—See Berjaya Corporation Berhad; *Int'l*, pg. 983
UNISYS AUSTRALIA PROPRIETY LTD—See Unisys Corporation; *U.S. Public*, pg. 2228
UNISYS BELGIUM—See Unisys Corporation; *U.S. Public*, pg. 2228
UNISYS CORPORATION; *U.S. Public*, pg. 2228
UNISYS DEUTSCHLAND GMBH—See Unisys Corporation; *U.S. Public*, pg. 2228
UNISYS ESPANA S.A.—See Unisys Corporation; *U.S. Public*, pg. 2228
UNISYS FRANCE—See Unisys Corporation; *U.S. Public*, pg. 2228
UNISYS ITALIA S.P.A.—See Unisys Corporation; *U.S. Public*, pg. 2228
UNISYS LIMITED—See Unisys Corporation; *U.S. Public*, pg. 2228
UNISYS NEDERLAND N.V.—See Unisys Corporation; *U.S. Public*, pg. 2228
UNISYS (SCHWEIZ) A.G.—See Unisys Corporation; *U.S. Public*, pg. 2228
UNISYS SOFTWARES & HOLDING INDUSTRIES LIMITED; *Int'l*, pg. 8062
UNISYSTEMS BELGIUM S.A.—See Quest Holdings S.A.; *Int'l*, pg. 6160
UNI SYSTEMS BULGARIA LTD—See Quest Holdings S.A.; *Int'l*, pg. 6160
UNISYSTEMS INFORMATION TECHNOLOGY SYSTEMS SRL—See Quest Holdings S.A.; *Int'l*, pg. 6160
UNI SYSTEMS ROMANIA SRL—See Quest Holdings S.A.; *Int'l*, pg. 6160
UNISYSTEMS S.A.—See Quest Holdings S.A.; *Int'l*, pg. 6160
UNISYST ENGINEERING PLC; *Int'l*, pg. 8062
UNIT4 ACCOUNTANCY B.V.—See UNIT4 N.V.; *Int'l*, pg. 8062
UNIT4 AGRESSO AB—See UNIT4 N.V.; *Int'l*, pg. 8063
UNIT4 AGRESSO AS—See UNIT4 N.V.; *Int'l*, pg. 8063
UNIT4 AGRESSO GMBH—See UNIT4 N.V.; *Int'l*, pg. 8062
UNIT4 ASIA PACIFIC PTE LTD.—See UNIT4 N.V.; *Int'l*, pg. 8062
UNIT4 BUSINESS SOFTWARE BENELUX B.V.—See UNIT4 N.V.; *Int'l*, pg. 8062
UNIT4 BUSINESS SOFTWARE B.V.—See UNIT4 N.V.; *Int'l*, pg. 8062
UNIT4 BUSINESS SOFTWARE HOLDING B.V.—See UNIT4 N.V.; *Int'l*, pg. 8063
UNIT4 BUSINESS SOFTWARE IBERICA S.A.—See Oakley Capital Limited; *Int'l*, pg. 5504
UNIT4 BUSINESS SOFTWARE INC.—See UNIT4 N.V.; *Int'l*, pg. 8063
UNIT4 BUSINESS SOFTWARE LTD.—See UNIT4 N.V.; *Int'l*, pg. 8063
UNIT4 BUSINESS SOFTWARE LTD.—See UNIT4 N.V.; *Int'l*, pg. 8063

COMPANY NAME INDEX

UNIT4 BUSINESS SOFTWARE LTD.—See UNIT4 N.V.; *Int'l*, pg. 8063
UNIT4 BUSINESS SOFTWARE LTD.—See UNIT4 N.V.; *Int'l*, pg. 8063
UNIT4 BUSINESS SOFTWARE N.V.—See UNIT4 N.V.; *Int'l*, pg. 8063
UNIT4 BUSINESS SOFTWARE SRL—See UNIT4 N.V.; *Int'l*, pg. 8063
UNIT4 C-LOGIC N.V.—See UNIT4 N.V.; *Int'l*, pg. 8063
UNIT4 CODA CZECH S.R.O—See UNIT4 N.V.; *Int'l*, pg. 8063
UNIT4 CODA INC—See UNIT4 N.V.; *Int'l*, pg. 8063
UNIT4 CONSIST B.V.—See UNIT4 N.V.; *Int'l*, pg. 8062
UNIT4 CURRENT SOFTWARE AS—See UNIT4 N.V.; *Int'l*, pg. 8063
UNIT4 EESTI OU—See UNIT4 N.V.; *Int'l*, pg. 8063
UNIT4 FINANCIELE INTERMEDIAIRS B.V.—See UNIT4 N.V.; *Int'l*, pg. 8062
UNIT4 IT SOLUTIONS B.V.—See UNIT4 N.V.; *Int'l*, pg. 8062
UNIT4 MAP AB—See UNIT4 N.V.; *Int'l*, pg. 8063
UNIT4 N.V.; *Int'l*, pg. 8062
UNIT4 NV—See Advent International Corporation; *U.S. Private*, pg. 107
UNIT4 OCRA AB—See UNIT4 N.V.; *Int'l*, pg. 8063
UNIT4 OOST NEDERLAND B.V.—See UNIT4 N.V.; *Int'l*, pg. 8062
UNIT4 PORTUGAL LDA—See UNIT4 N.V.; *Int'l*, pg. 8063
UNIT4 R&D AS—See UNIT4 N.V.; *Int'l*, pg. 8062
UNIT4 SOFTWARE B.V.—See UNIT4 N.V.; *Int'l*, pg. 8063
UNIT4 SOFTWARE ENGINEERING SP. Z O.O.—See UNIT4 N.V.; *Int'l*, pg. 8063
UNIT4 TETA S.A.—See UNIT4 N.V.; *Int'l*, pg. 8063
UNITAB MEDIC SDN. BHD.—See Khazanah Nasional Berhad; *Int'l*, pg. 4152
UNITAINER TRADING GMBH; *Int'l*, pg. 8063
UNITAINER TRADING (UAE) FZE—See UNITAINER Trading GmbH; *Int'l*, pg. 8063
UNITAS CAPITAL INVESTMENT CONSULTING (SHANGHAI) CO. LTD.—See Unitas Capital Pte. Ltd.; *Int'l*, pg. 8063
UNITAS CAPITAL PTE. LTD.; *Int'l*, pg. 8063
UNITAS CAPITAL YUHAN HOESA—See Unitas Capital Pte. Ltd.; *Int'l*, pg. 8063
UNITAS GLOBAL LLC; *U.S. Private*, pg. 4287
UNITAS HOLDINGS LIMITED; *Int'l*, pg. 8063
UNITATA BERHAD—See United Plantations Berhad; *Int'l*, pg. 8072
UNIT.COM INC.—See MCJ Co., Ltd.; *Int'l*, pg. 4759
UNIT CORPORATION; *U.S. Public*, pg. 2228
UNIT DRILLING COMPANY—See Unit Corporation; *U.S. Public*, pg. 2228
UNIT DROP FORGE CO., INC.; *U.S. Private*, pg. 4287
UNITEAM HOLDING AS—See IKM Gruppen AS; *Int'l*, pg. 3612
UNITECH COMPUTER CO., LTD.; *Int'l*, pg. 8064
UNITECH ELECTRICAL CONTRACTING INC.; *Int'l*, pg. 8064
UNITECH INTERNATIONAL LIMITED; *Int'l*, pg. 8064
UNITECH JAPAN CO., LTD.—See Unitech Computer Co., Ltd.; *Int'l*, pg. 8064
UNITECH LIMITED; *Int'l*, pg. 8064
UNITECH LIMITED—See Clayton, Dubilier & Rice, LLC; *U.S. Private*, pg. 928
UNITECH NEW ENERGY ENGINEERING CO., LTD.—See TOPCO Scientific Co., Ltd.; *Int'l*, pg. 7814
UNITECH POWER SYSTEMS AS—See Aker Solutions ASA; *Int'l*, pg. 263
UNITECH POWER TRANSMISSION LIMITED—See Unitech Limited; *Int'l*, pg. 8064
UNITECH PRINTED CIRCUIT BOARD CORP. - FACTORY NO. 2—See Unitech Printed Circuit Board Corp.; *Int'l*, pg. 8064
UNITECH PRINTED CIRCUIT BOARD CORP. - FACTORY NO. 3—See Unitech Printed Circuit Board Corp.; *Int'l*, pg. 8064
UNITECH PRINTED CIRCUIT BOARD CORP. - PLANT II—See Unitech Printed Circuit Board Corp.; *Int'l*, pg. 8064
UNITECH PRINTED CIRCUIT BOARD CORP.; *Int'l*, pg. 8064
UNITECH SERVICES B.V.—See UniFirst Corporation; *U.S. Public*, pg. 2226
UNITECH SERVICES GMBH—See UniFirst Corporation; *U.S. Public*, pg. 2226
UNITECH SERVICES GROUP, INC.—See UniFirst Corporation; *U.S. Public*, pg. 2226
UNITECH SERVICES GROUP LTD.—See UniFirst Corporation; *U.S. Public*, pg. 2226
UNITECH SERVICES GROUP—See UniFirst Corporation; *U.S. Public*, pg. 2226
UNITECH SERVICES SAS—See UniFirst Corporation; *U.S. Public*, pg. 2226
UNITEC LLC—See New Mountain Capital, LLC; *U.S. Private*, pg. 2900
UNITECNIC MEDIA SOLUTIONS—See WPP plc; *Int'l*, pg. 8477
UNITE CO., LTD.—See Kanamoto Co., Ltd.; *Int'l*, pg. 4064

UNITECTA ITALIANA S.P.A.—See Akzo Nobel N.V.; *Int'l*, pg. 271
UNITED ABRASIVES INC.; *U.S. Private*, pg. 4287
UNITED ACQUISITION CORP.—See Red Apple Group, Inc.; *U.S. Private*, pg. 3373
UNITED ADMINISTRATIVE SERVICES; *U.S. Private*, pg. 4287
UNITED ADVERTISING PUBLICATIONS, INC.—See Irish Times; *U.S. Private*, pg. 2138
UNITED ADVISORS, LLC—See Aon plc; *Int'l*, pg. 498
UNITED AEROSPACE CORP.—See YMC Aviation Inc.; *U.S. Private*, pg. 4589
UNITED AGRICULTURAL COOPERATIVE INC.; *U.S. Private*, pg. 4287
UNITED AGRI PRODUCTS CANADA INC.—See Nutrien Ltd.; *Int'l*, pg. 5492
UNITED AG SERVICE INC.; *U.S. Private*, pg. 4287
UNITED AIR CONDITIONING & HEATING COMPANY, INC.; *U.S. Private*, pg. 4287
UNITED AIR LINES CREDIT UNION—See United Airlines Holdings, Inc.; *U.S. Public*, pg. 2229
UNITED AIRLINES HOLDINGS, INC.; *U.S. Public*, pg. 2228
UNITED AIRLINES, INC.—See United Airlines Holdings, Inc.; *U.S. Public*, pg. 2228
UNITED AIRLINES, INC.—See United Airlines Holdings, Inc.; *U.S. Public*, pg. 2228
UNITED AIRLINES OPERATIONS CENTER—See United Airlines Holdings, Inc.; *U.S. Public*, pg. 2229
UNITED AIR-TEMP AC & HEATING; *U.S. Private*, pg. 4287
UNITED AIRWAYS BANGLADESH LTD.; *Int'l*, pg. 8064
UNITED AIRWAYS (BD) LTD.; *Int'l*, pg. 8064
UNITED AJOD INSURANCE LIMITED; *Int'l*, pg. 8064
UNITED ALLOY, INC.; *U.S. Private*, pg. 4287
UNITED ALLOYS & METALS. INC—See CRONIMET Holding GmbH; *Int'l*, pg. 1855
UNITED ALUMINUM CORPORATION; *U.S. Private*, pg. 4287
UNITED ALUMINUM & METAL COATING CO. W.L.L—See Fouad Alghanim & Sons Group of Companies; *Int'l*, pg. 2753
UNITED AMERICAN HEALTHCARE CORP.; *U.S. Public*, pg. 2229
UNITED AMERICAN INSURANCE COMPANY—See Globe Life Inc.; *U.S. Public*, pg. 946
UNITED AMERICAN PETROLEUM CORP.; *U.S. Private*, pg. 4287
UNITED AMERICAN SECURITY, LLC—See BC Partners LLP; *Int'l*, pg. 924
THE UNITED ANIMAL HEALTHCARE (INNER MONGOLIA) CO., LTD.—See The United Laboratories International Holdings Ltd.; *Int'l*, pg. 7697
UNITED ANIMAL HEALTH, INC.; *U.S. Private*, pg. 4287
UNITED ANODISERS UK LIMITED—See Coil S.A./N.V.; *Int'l*, pg. 1696
UNITED ARAB AGENCIES AB—See Albert Ballin KG; *Int'l*, pg. 296
UNITED ARAB AGENCIES AUSTRALIA PTY LTD—See Albert Ballin KG; *Int'l*, pg. 296
UNITED ARAB AGENCIES, INC.—See Albert Ballin KG; *Int'l*, pg. 296
UNITED ARAB BANK PJSC; *Int'l*, pg. 8064
UNITED ARAB EMIRATES LPT (FZC); *Int'l*, pg. 8064
UNITED ARAB JORDAN COMPANY FOR INVESTMENT & FINANCIAL BROKERAGE—See Arab Jordan Investment Bank; *Int'l*, pg. 530
UNITED ARAB SHIPPING AGENCIES COMPANY (EMIRATES)—See Albert Ballin KG; *Int'l*, pg. 296
UNITED ARAB SHIPPING AGENCIES COMPANY—See Albert Ballin KG; *Int'l*, pg. 296
UNITED ARAB SHIPPING AGENCIES COMPANY W.L.L.—See Albert Ballin KG; *Int'l*, pg. 296
UNITED ARAB SHIPPING AGENCIES CO. (SAUDIA) LTD.—See Albert Ballin KG; *Int'l*, pg. 296
UNITED ARAB SHIPPING AGENCIES CO. (SAUDIA) LTD.—See Albert Ballin KG; *Int'l*, pg. 296
UNITED ARAB SHIPPING AGENCIES CO. (SAUDIA) LTD.—See Albert Ballin KG; *Int'l*, pg. 296
UNITED ARAB SHIPPING AGENCIES (PAKISTAN) PVT. LTD.—See Albert Ballin KG; *Int'l*, pg. 296
UNITED ARAB SHIPPING AGENCY COMPANY (BENELUX) B.V.—See Albert Ballin KG; *Int'l*, pg. 297
UNITED ARAB SHIPPING AGENCY COMPANY (DEUTSCHLAND) GMBH—See Albert Ballin KG; *Int'l*, pg. 297
UNITED ARAB SHIPPING AGENCY COMPANY (HONG KONG) LIMITED—See Albert Ballin KG; *Int'l*, pg. 297
UNITED ARAB SHIPPING AGENCY COMPANY (NINGBO) LTD.—See Albert Ballin KG; *Int'l*, pg. 297
UNITED ARAB SHIPPING AGENCY COMPANY (QATAR) WLL—See Albert Ballin KG; *Int'l*, pg. 297
UNITED ARAB SHIPPING AGENCY COMPANY (SHANGHAI) LTD.—See Albert Ballin KG; *Int'l*, pg. 297
UNITED ARAB SHIPPING AGENCY COMPANY (SHENZHEN) LTD.—See Albert Ballin KG; *Int'l*, pg. 297
UNITED ARAB SHIPPING AGENCY COMPANY (SINGAPORE)—See Albert Ballin KG; *Int'l*, pg. 297

UNITED BIOMEDICAL INC.

UNITED ARAB SHIPPING AGENCY COMPANY (TAIWAN) LTD.—See Albert Ballin KG; *Int'l*, pg. 297
UNITED ARAB SHIPPING AGENCY COMPANY (THAILAND) LTD.—See Albert Ballin KG; *Int'l*, pg. 297
UNITED ARAB SHIPPING AGENCY COMPANY (VIETNAM) LIMITED—See Albert Ballin KG; *Int'l*, pg. 297
UNITED ARAB SHIPPING AGENCY CO. (M) SDN BHD—See Albert Ballin KG; *Int'l*, pg. 297
UNITED ARAB SHIPPING AGENCY (INDIA) PVT LTD—See Albert Ballin KG; *Int'l*, pg. 296
UNITED ARAB SHIPPING COMPANY (S.A.G.)—See Albert Ballin KG; *Int'l*, pg. 296
UNITED ARAB SHIPPING COMPANY—See Albert Ballin KG; *Int'l*, pg. 297
UNITED ARAB SHIPPING COMPANY—See Albert Ballin KG; *Int'l*, pg. 297
UNITED ARAB SHIPPING COMPANY—See Albert Ballin KG; *Int'l*, pg. 297
UNITED ARAB SHIPPING COMPANY—See Albert Ballin KG; *Int'l*, pg. 297
UNITED ARAB SHIPPING COMPANY—See Albert Ballin KG; *Int'l*, pg. 297
UNITED ARAB SHIPPING COMPANY—See Albert Ballin KG; *Int'l*, pg. 297
UNITED ARROWS LTD.; *Int'l*, pg. 8064
UNITED ARTISTS CORPORATION—See Amazon.com, Inc.; *U.S. Public*, pg. 91
UNITED ARTISTS THEATRE CIRCUIT, INC.—See Cineworld Group plc; *Int'l*, pg. 1611
UNITED ASATSU INTERNATIONAL LTD.—See Bain Capital, LP; *U.S. Private*, pg. 428
UNITED ASIA FINANCE LIMITED—See Allied Group Limited; *Int'l*, pg. 357
UNITED AUTO CREDIT CORPORATION—See Pine Brook Partners, LLC; *U.S. Private*, pg. 3182
UNITED AUTOMOBILE INSURANCE GROUP, INC.; *U.S. Private*, pg. 4287
UNITED AUTOMOTIVE DISTRIBUTORS LTD; *Int'l*, pg. 8064
UNITED AUTOMOTIVE ELECTRONIC SYSTEMS CO., LTD.—See Robert Bosch GmbH; *Int'l*, pg. 6368
UNITED AUTO SERVICE & MAINTENANCE CO LTD—See Sumitomo Corporation; *Int'l*, pg. 7274
UNITED AUTO SUPPLY INC.; *U.S. Private*, pg. 4287
UNITED AUTO SUPPLY; *U.S. Private*, pg. 4287
UNITED AVIATION (SINGAPORE) PTE. LTD.—See Samson Paper Holdings Limited; *Int'l*, pg. 6509
UNITED BAKING CO., INC.; *U.S. Private*, pg. 4288
UNITED BANCORP, INC.; *U.S. Public*, pg. 2229
UNITED BANCORPORATION OF ALABAMA, INC.; *U.S. Public*, pg. 2229
UNITED BANCSHARES, INC.; *U.S. Private*, pg. 4288
UNITED BANCSHARES, INC.; *U.S. Public*, pg. 2229
UNITED BANK AG—See Bestway (Holdings) Limited; *Int'l*, pg. 1001
UNITED BANK CORPORATION; *U.S. Private*, pg. 4288
UNITED BANKERS PLC; *Int'l*, pg. 8065
UNITED BANK FOR AFRICA PLC; *Int'l*, pg. 8064
UNITED BANK FOR COMMERCE & INVESTMENT S.A.C.—See Kuwait Finance House K.S.C.; *Int'l*, pg. 4344
UNITED BANK INSURANCE AGENCY—See United Community Financial; *U.S. Private*, pg. 4290
UNITED BANK LIMITED—See Bestway (Holdings) Limited; *Int'l*, pg. 1001
UNITED BANK OF INDIA—See Punjab National Bank; *Int'l*, pg. 6120
UNITED BANK OF IOWA—See Ida Grove Bancshares, Inc.; *U.S. Private*, pg. 2034
UNITED BANK OF MICHIGAN INC—See United Community Financial; *U.S. Private*, pg. 4290
UNITED BANK OF PHILADELPHIA—See United Bancshares, Inc.; *U.S. Private*, pg. 4288
UNITED BANKSHARES, INC.; *U.S. Public*, pg. 2229
UNITED BANK—See United Bancorporation of Alabama, Inc.; *U.S. Public*, pg. 2229
UNITED BANK—See United Bank Corporation; *U.S. Private*, pg. 4288
UNITED BANK—See United Bankshares, Inc.; *U.S. Public*, pg. 2229
UNITED BANK—See Park National Corporation; *U.S. Public*, pg. 1638
UNITED BANK & TRUST COMPANY; *U.S. Private*, pg. 4288
UNITED BANK & TRUST NA—See Ames National Corporation; *U.S. Public*, pg. 116
UNITED BASALT PRODUCTS LIMITED; *Int'l*, pg. 8065
UNITED BEARING INDUSTRIAL CORP.—See THK CO., LTD.; *Int'l*, pg. 7713
UNITED BEHAVIORAL HEALTH—See UnitedHealth Group Incorporated; *U.S. Public*, pg. 2252
UNITED BEVERAGES S.A.; *Int'l*, pg. 8065
UNITED BILT HOMES INCORPORATED; *U.S. Private*, pg. 4288
UNITED BINTANG MACHINERY SDN. BHD.—See Ideal United Bintang Berhad; *Int'l*, pg. 3589
UNITED BIOMEDICAL INC.; *U.S. Private*, pg. 4288
UNITED BIOSOURCE CORPORATION LLC—See Avista Capital Partners, L.P.; *U.S. Private*, pg. 409

UNITED BIOMEDICAL INC.

CORPORATE AFFILIATIONS

UNITED BIOSOURCE (GERMANY) GMBH—See Avista Capital Partners, L.P.; *U.S. Private*, pg. 409
UNITED BIOSOURCE HOLDING (UK) LIMITED—See Avista Capital Partners, L.P.; *U.S. Private*, pg. 409
UNITED BIOSOURCE PATIENT SOLUTIONS, INC.—See The Cigna Group; *U.S. Public*, pg. 2062
UNITED BIOSOURCE (SUISSE) SA—See Avista Capital Partners, L.P.; *U.S. Private*, pg. 409
UNITED BISCUITS (HOLDINGS) LIMITED—See Yildiz Holding AS; *Int'l*, pg. 8583
UNITED BMEC PTE. LTD.—See Boustead Singapore Limited; *Int'l*, pg. 1121
UNITED BRANDS LIMITED; *Int'l*, pg. 8065
UNITED BRANDS OF SCANDINAVIA IRE LTD.—See New Wave Group AB; *Int'l*, pg. 5231
UNITED BRANDS OF SCANDINAVIA LTD.—See New Wave Group AB; *Int'l*, pg. 5231
UNITED BRASS WORKS INC.; *U.S. Private*, pg. 4288
UNITED BREWERIES (HOLDINGS) LTD.; *Int'l*, pg. 8065
UNITED BREWERIES LTD.—See L'Arche Green N.V.; *Int'l*, pg. 4377
UNITED BRIGHTENING DEVELOPING CORP.—See Yieh Phui Enterprise Co., Ltd.; *Int'l*, pg. 8581
UNITED BRINE PIPELINE COMPANY LLC—See United Salt Corporation; *U.S. Private*, pg. 4297
UNITED BROKERAGE SERVICES, INC.—See United Bankshares, Inc.; *U.S. Public*, pg. 2229
UNITED BUILDING MAINTENANCE, INC.; *U.S. Private*, pg. 4288
UNITED BUILDING MATERIALS, INC.—See GMS Inc.; *U.S. Public*, pg. 948
UNITED BULGARIAN BANK A.D.—See KBC Group NV; *Int'l*, pg. 4106
UNITED BULK PROPRIETARY LIMITED—See OneLogix Group Limited; *Int'l*, pg. 5576
UNITED BULK SHIPPING PTE LTD—See Pan-United Corporation Ltd.; *Int'l*, pg. 5716
UNITED BULK TERMINALS DAVANT LLC—See Marquard & Bahls AG; *Int'l*, pg. 4700
UNITED BULLION EXCHANGE, INC.; *U.S. Public*, pg. 2229
UNITED BUSINESS BANK—See BayCom Corp; *U.S. Public*, pg. 284
UNITED BUS SERVICE LTD.; *Int'l*, pg. 8065
UNITED CABINET COMPANY, LLC; *U.S. Private*, pg. 4288
UNITED CABLE INDUSTRIES COMPANY; *Int'l*, pg. 8065
UNITED CANADIAN MALT LIMITED; *Int'l*, pg. 8065
UNITED CANNABIS CORPORATION; *U.S. Private*, pg. 4288
UNITED CAPITAL BANK; *Int'l*, pg. 8065
UNITED CAPITAL CONSULTANTS, INC.; *U.S. Private*, pg. 4288
UNITED CAPITAL CORP.; *U.S. Private*, pg. 4288
UNITED CAPITAL FINANCIAL ADVISERS, LLC - SILICON VALLEY—See The Goldman Sachs Group, Inc.; *U.S. Public*, pg. 2082
UNITED CAPITAL FINANCIAL ADVISERS, LLC—See The Goldman Sachs Group, Inc.; *U.S. Public*, pg. 2082
UNITED CAPITAL FUNDING CORP.; *U.S. Private*, pg. 4288
UNITED CAPITAL MARKETS HOLDINGS, INC.; *U.S. Private*, pg. 4288
UNITED CAPITAL PARTNERS ADVISORY LLC; *Int'l*, pg. 8065
UNITED CARPARKS SDN BHD—See United Overseas Australia Ltd; *Int'l*, pg. 8071
UNITED CARPET COMPANY, INC.—See Rainier Partners LP; *U.S. Private*, pg. 3348
UNITED CARPET MANUFACTURING CO., LTD.—See TCM Corporation Public Company Limited; *Int'l*, pg. 7484
UNITED CARPETS GROUP PLC; *Int'l*, pg. 8065
UNITED CARPETS (NORTHERN) LIMITED—See United Carpets Group PLC; *Int'l*, pg. 8065
UNITED CARTON INDUSTRIES COMPANY LTD.—See Hayel Saeed Anam Group of Companies; *Int'l*, pg. 3291
UNITED CAST BAR (UK) LIMITED—See National Industries Group Holding S.A.K.; *Int'l*, pg. 5159
UNITED CASTINGS LIMITED—See Sims Limited; *U.S. Public*, pg. 1884
UNITED CASUALTY INSURANCE COMPANY OF AMERICA—See Kemper Corporation; *U.S. Public*, pg. 1221
UNITED CASUALTY & SURETY INSURANCE COMPANY—See Boston Omaha Corporation; *U.S. Public*, pg. 372
UNITED CEMENT PTE LTD—See Pan-United Corporation Ltd.; *Int'l*, pg. 5716
UNITED CENTRAL BAKERIES LTD.—See Xaver Fassin GmbH; *Int'l*, pg. 8520
UNITED CENTRAL INDUSTRIAL SUPPLY COMPANY—See Clayton, Dubilier & Rice, LLC; *U.S. Private*, pg. 926
UNITED CHARITABLE PROGRAMS; *U.S. Private*, pg. 4288
UNITED CHARM CO., LTD.—See Unicharm Corporation; *Int'l*, pg. 8032

UNITED CHEMI-CON, INC.—See Nippon Chemi-Con Corporation; *Int'l*, pg. 5313
UNITED CHURCH HOMES AND SERVICES; *U.S. Private*, pg. 4288
UNITED CHURCH OF CHRIST HOMES, INC.; *U.S. Private*, pg. 4289
UNITED CINEMAS CO., LTD.—See Advantage Partners LLP; *Int'l*, pg. 164
UNITED CLAIM SOLUTIONS, LLC; *U.S. Private*, pg. 4289
UNITED CLASSIFIEDS S.R.O.—See Axel Springer SE; *Int'l*, pg. 767
UNITED C & N CO., LTD.—See NANYO Corporation; *Int'l*, pg. 5146
UNITED COAL HOLDINGS LTD.; *Int'l*, pg. 8065
UNITED COASTAL INSURANCE COMPANY—See ACMAT Corporation; *U.S. Public*, pg. 35
UNITED COGEN, INC.—See United Airlines Holdings, Inc.; *U.S. Public*, pg. 2229
UNITED & COLLECTIVE CO., LTD.; *Int'l*, pg. 8064
UNITED COLLIERIES PTY LIMITED—See Glencore plc; *Int'l*, pg. 2990
UNITED COLOR MANUFACTURING; *U.S. Private*, pg. 4289
UNITED COMMERCE CENTERS INC.; *U.S. Private*, pg. 4289
UNITED COMMERCIAL AGENCIES W.L.L.—See Shoei Co., Ltd.; *Int'l*, pg. 6858
UNITED COMMERCIAL BANK LIMITED; *Int'l*, pg. 8065
UNITED COMMERCIAL TRAVELERS OF AMERICA; *U.S. Private*, pg. 4289
UNITED COMMUNICATION GROUP—See Hakuhodo DY Holdings Incorporated; *Int'l*, pg. 3221
UNITED COMMUNICATION INDUSTRY PUBLIC COMPANY LIMITED—See Charoen Pokphand Group Co., Ltd.; *Int'l*, pg. 1453
UNITED COMMUNICATION PARTNERS INC.; *U.S. Public*, pg. 2229
UNITED COMMUNICATIONS CORPORATION; *U.S. Private*, pg. 4289
UNITED COMMUNICATIONS GROUP; *U.S. Private*, pg. 4289
UNITED COMMUNICATIONS, INC.—See Warburg Pincus LLC; *U.S. Private*, pg. 4438
UNITED COMMUNICATION SYSTEMS; *U.S. Private*, pg. 4289
UNITED COMMUNITY ACTION NETWORK; *U.S. Private*, pg. 4289
UNITED COMMUNITY BANCORP, INC.; *U.S. Private*, pg. 4289
UNITED COMMUNITY BANK OF NORTH DAKOTA—See American Bancor, Ltd.; *U.S. Private*, pg. 223
UNITED COMMUNITY BANK OF WEST KENTUCKY, INC.; *U.S. Private*, pg. 4290
UNITED COMMUNITY BANKS, INC.; *U.S. Public*, pg. 2229
UNITED COMMUNITY BANK—See Community Bancorp of Louisiana, Inc.; *U.S. Private*, pg. 989
UNITED COMMUNITY BANK—See United Community Banks, Inc.; *U.S. Public*, pg. 2230
UNITED COMMUNITY BANK—See United Community Bancorp, Inc.; *U.S. Private*, pg. 4289
UNITED COMMUNITY CENTER, INC.; *U.S. Private*, pg. 4290
UNITED COMMUNITY & FAMILY SERVICES INC.; *U.S. Private*, pg. 4289
UNITED COMMUNITY FINANCIAL; *U.S. Private*, pg. 4290
UNITED COMMUNITY MORTGAGE SERVICES, INC.—See United Community Banks, Inc.; *U.S. Public*, pg. 2230
UNITED COMPANIES OF MESA COUNTY—See CRH plc; *Int'l*, pg. 1848
UNITED COMPANY OF PHARMACISTS SAE—See Walgreens Boots Alliance, Inc.; *U.S. Public*, pg. 2323
UNITED COMPANY RUSAL PLC; *Int'l*, pg. 8066
THE UNITED COMPANY; *U.S. Private*, pg. 4129
UNITED COMPONENTS, INC.—See Rank Group Ltd.; *Int'l*, pg. 6208
UNITED COMPUTER SALES & SERVICES, INC.—See Konica Minolta, Inc.; *Int'l*, pg. 4258
UNITED COM-SERVE; *U.S. Private*, pg. 4289
UNITED CONCORDIA COMPANIES INC.—See Highmark Health; *U.S. Private*, pg. 1941
UNITED CONCRETE PRODUCTS, LLC—See Eagle Manufacturing Group; *U.S. Private*, pg. 1309
UNITED CONCRETE PRODUCTS, LLC—See Eagle Manufacturing Group; *U.S. Private*, pg. 1309
UNITED CONSTRUCTION CO. INC.; *U.S. Private*, pg. 4290
UNITED CONSTRUCTION & FORESTRY, LLC—See Fernandez Holdings, Inc.; *U.S. Private*, pg. 1497
UNITED CONSTRUCTION PRODUCTS, INC.—See GMS Inc.; *U.S. Public*, pg. 948
UNITED CONSTRUCTION & REALTY; *U.S. Private*, pg. 4290
UNITED CONSUMER FINANCIAL SERVICES COMPANY—See Berkshire Hathaway Inc.; *U.S. Public*, pg. 300
UNITED CONTRACTORS INC.; *U.S. Private*, pg. 4290
UNITED CONTRACTORS INC.; *U.S. Private*, pg. 4290

UNITED CONTRACTORS MIDWEST, INC.; *U.S. Private*, pg. 4290
UNITED CONTROLS GROUP, INC.—See Roper Technologies, Inc.; *U.S. Public*, pg. 1814
UNITED CONVEYOR CORPORATION; *U.S. Private*, pg. 4290
UNITED COOPERATIVE ASSURANCE COMPANY; *Int'l*, pg. 8066
UNITED COOPERATIVE SERVICES; *U.S. Private*, pg. 4290
UNITED COOPERATIVE; *U.S. Private*, pg. 4290
UNITED COOPERATIVE; *U.S. Private*, pg. 4290
UNITED COOPERATIVE—See United Cooperative; *U.S. Private*, pg. 4290
UNITED CORPORATIONS LTD.; *Int'l*, pg. 8066
UNITED CORP.; *U.S. Private*, pg. 4290
UNITED CORRSTACK LLC—See Interstate Resources, Inc.; *U.S. Private*, pg. 2125
UNITED COUNSELING SERVICE; *U.S. Private*, pg. 4290
UNITED COURIERS S.A.R.L.—See United Parcel Service, Inc.; *U.S. Public*, pg. 2234
UNITED CREDIT BUREAU CJSC—See OJSC Sberbank of Russia; *Int'l*, pg. 5542
UNITED CREDIT CORP.; *U.S. Private*, pg. 4290
UNITED CREDIT LTD; *Int'l*, pg. 8066
UNITED CREDIT SYSTEMS OAO; *Int'l*, pg. 8066
UNITED CUSTOMHOUSE BROKERS; *U.S. Private*, pg. 4290
UNITED DAIRY FARMERS, INC.; *U.S. Private*, pg. 4290
UNITED DAIRY, INC.; *U.S. Private*, pg. 4290
UNITED DAIRYMEN OF ARIZONA; *U.S. Private*, pg. 4291
UNITED DAIRY—See United Dairy, Inc.; *U.S. Private*, pg. 4291
UNITED DATA TECHNOLOGIES, INC.; *U.S. Private*, pg. 4291
UNITED DEALER SERVICES L.L.C.—See Arthur J. Gallagher & Co.; *U.S. Public*, pg. 207
UNITED DEVELOPMENT COMPANY PSC; *Int'l*, pg. 8066
UNITED DEVELOPMENT FUNDING INCOME FUND V; *U.S. Private*, pg. 4291
UNITED DEVELOPMENT FUNDING IV; *U.S. Private*, pg. 4291
UNITED DEVELOPMENT SYSTEMS, INC.—See Brown & Brown, Inc.; *U.S. Public*, pg. 399
UNITED DIAGNOSTICS, INC.—See Thermo Fisher Scientific Inc.; *U.S. Public*, pg. 2155
THE UNITED DISTRIBUTION GROUP, INC.—See Clayton, Dubilier & Rice, LLC; *U.S. Private*, pg. 926
UNITED DISTRIBUTORS, INC.—See Unistan Inc.; *U.S. Private*, pg. 4286
UNITED DISTRIBUTORS PAKISTAN LIMITED—See International Brands Private Limited; pg. 3744
UNITED DOCKS LTD; *Int'l*, pg. 8066
UNITED-DOMAINS AG—See United Internet AG; *Int'l*, pg. 8069
UNITED DOMAINS, INC.—See United Internet AG; *Int'l*, pg. 8069
UNITED-DOMAINS RESELLING GMBH—See United Internet AG; *Int'l*, pg. 8069
UNITED DOMINION REALTY L.P.—See UDR, Inc.; *U.S. Public*, pg. 2218
UNITED DRILLING INC.; *U.S. Private*, pg. 4291
UNITED DRILLING TOOLS LTD.; *Int'l*, pg. 8066
THE UNITED DRUG (1996) CO. LTD.—See Diethelm Keller Holding Limited; *Int'l*, pg. 2117
UNITED DRUG WHOLESALE LIMITED—See McKesson Corporation; *U.S. Public*, pg. 1409
UNITED DRYWALL LTD.; *Int'l*, pg. 8066
UNITED EDUCATORS INC.; *U.S. Private*, pg. 4291
UNITED EDUCATORS INSURANCE, A RECIPROCAL RISK RETENTION GROUP, INC.; *U.S. Private*, pg. 4291
UNITED EGG PRODUCERS; *U.S. Private*, pg. 4291
UNITED ELECTRICAL, RADIO & MACHINE WORKERS OF AMERICA; *U.S. Private*, pg. 4291
UNITED ELECTRIC CO. INC.; *U.S. Private*, pg. 4291
UNITED ELECTRIC COMPANY, L.P.—See Carrier Global Corporation; *U.S. Public*, pg. 442
UNITED ELECTRIC CONTROLS COMPANY INC.; *U.S. Private*, pg. 4291
UNITED ELECTRIC COOPERATIVE, INC.; *U.S. Private*, pg. 4291
UNITED ELECTRIC INDUSTRIES CO., LTD.—See Sumitomo Electric Industries, Ltd.; *Int'l*, pg. 7285
UNITED ELECTRIC INDUSTRY CO., LTD.—See Ta Ya Electric Wire & Cable Co., Ltd.; *Int'l*, pg. 7400
UNITED ELECTRIC SUPPLY COMPANY, INC.; *U.S. Private*, pg. 4291
UNITED ELECTRIC WIRE (KUNSHAN) CO., LTD.—See Copartner Technology Corporation; *Int'l*, pg. 1793
UNITED ELECTRONICS COMPANY-EXTRA L.L.C.—See United Electronics Company KSA; *Int'l*, pg. 8066
UNITED ELECTRONICS COMPANY KSA; *Int'l*, pg. 8066
UNITED EL SEGUNDO INC.; *U.S. Private*, pg. 4291
UNITED ENERGEX LP—See Michelson Energy Company; *U.S. Private*, pg. 2700
UNITED ENERGIES DEVELOPMENT CORPORATION; *U.S. Private*, pg. 4291

COMPANY NAME INDEX

UNITED ENERGY A.S.—See Energeticky a Prumyslovy Holding, a.s.; *Int'l*, pg. 2420
UNITED ENERGY CORPORATION; *U.S. Public*, pg. 2230
UNITED ENERGY DISTRIBUTION PTY LIMITED—See CK Hutchison Holdings Limited; *Int'l*, pg. 1637
UNITED ENERGY GROUP LIMITED; *Int'l*, pg. 8066
UNITED ENERGY PAKISTAN LIMITED—See United Energy Group Limited; *Int'l*, pg. 8067
UNITED ENERTECH CORP.—See S&P Sistemas de Ventilación, S.L.U.; *Int'l*, pg. 6445
UNITED ENGINEERING SERVICES LLC—See MB Holding Company LLC; *Int'l*, pg. 4750
UNITED ENGINEERS (B) SDN BHD—See Yanlord Land Group Limited; *Int'l*, pg. 8563
UNITED ENGINEERS DEVELOPMENTS PTE LTD—See Yanlord Land Group Limited; *Int'l*, pg. 8563
UNITED ENGINEERS LIMITED—See Yanlord Land Group Limited; *Int'l*, pg. 8562
UNITED ENGINEERS MANAGED SOLUTIONS MALAYSIA SDN. BHD.—See Yanlord Land Group Limited; *Int'l*, pg. 8563
UNITED ENGINE & MACHINE COMPANY; *U.S. Private*, pg. 4291
UNITED ENGINES, LLC—See Kirby Corporation; *U.S. Public*, pg. 1235
UNITED ENTERTAINMENT CORP.; *U.S. Private*, pg. 4291
UNITED ENVELOPE LLC—See Palm Beach Capital Partners LLC; *U.S. Private*, pg. 3079
UNITED E&P, INC.; *U.S. Public*, pg. 2230
UNITED EQUIPMENT PTY LTD—See Elphinstone Pty Ltd; *Int'l*, pg. 2369
UNITED ERIE—See Interstate Chemical Co., Inc.; *U.S. Private*, pg. 2124
UNITED ESOTERIC CORP.; *U.S. Private*, pg. 4291
UNITED EUROPEAN BANK & TRUST (NASSAU) LTD.—See BNP Paribas SA; *Int'l*, pg. 1093
UNITED EUROPEAN CAR CARRIERS AS—See Nippon Yusen Kabushiki Kaisha; *Int'l*, pg. 5360
UNITED EUROPHIL, S.A.—See Palladium Equity Partners, LLC; *U.S. Private*, pg. 3077
UNITED EXPRESS, INC.; *U.S. Public*, pg. 2230
UNITED EXPRESS SERVICE, INC.—See NFI Industries, Inc.; *U.S. Private*, pg. 2923
UNITED FABRICARE SUPPLY INC.; *U.S. Private*, pg. 4291
UNITED FACILITIES, INC.; *U.S. Private*, pg. 4292
UNITED FACILITIES MANAGEMENT COMPANY O.M.C—See United Development Company PSC; *Int'l*, pg. 8066
UNITED FACILITIES MANAGEMENT L.L.C.—See Kuwait Projects Company (Holding) K.S.C.P.; *Int'l*, pg. 4347
UNITED FAITH AUTO ENGINEERING CO., LTD.; *Int'l*, pg. 8067
UNITED FAMILY PRACTICE HEALTH CENTER; *U.S. Private*, pg. 4292
UNITED FARMERS COOPERATIVE; *U.S. Private*, pg. 4292
UNITED FARMERS COOPERATIVE; *U.S. Private*, pg. 4292
UNITED FARMERS OF ALBERTA CO-OPERATIVE LIMITED; *Int'l*, pg. 8067
UNITED FARM FAMILY INSURANCE COMPANY—See Brookfield Corporation; *Int'l*, pg. 1175
UNITED FARM INDUSTRIES INCORPORATED; *U.S. Private*, pg. 4292
UNITED FASHIONS OF TEXAS LTD.; *U.S. Private*, pg. 4292
UNITED FEATHER & DOWN INC.; *U.S. Private*, pg. 4292
UNITED FEDERAL CREDIT UNION; *U.S. Private*, pg. 4292
UNITED FEED COMPANY—See Hayel Saeed Anam Group of Companies; *Int'l*, pg. 3291
UNITED FEED COOP INC.; *U.S. Private*, pg. 4292
UNITED FIBERGLASS OF AMERICA, INC.—See Hill & Smith PLC; *Int'l*, pg. 3392
UNITED FIBER OPTIC COMMUNICATION, INC.; *Int'l*, pg. 8067
UNITED FIDELITY BANK, FSB—See Fidelity Federal Bancorp; *U.S. Public*, pg. 830
UNITED FIDELITY INSURANCE CO PSC; *Int'l*, pg. 8067
UNITED FIDELITY LIFE INSURANCE COMPANY—See Financial Holding Corp.; *U.S. Private*, pg. 1507
UNITED FINANCE COMPANY SAOG; *Int'l*, pg. 8067
UNITED FINANCE CO.; *U.S. Private*, pg. 4292
UNITED FINANCE LIMITED; *Int'l*, pg. 8067
UNITED FINANCE PLC; *Int'l*, pg. 8067
UNITED FINANCIAL CASUALTY COMPANY—See The Progressive Corporation; *U.S. Public*, pg. 2125
UNITED FINANCIAL INVESTMENTS CO.—See Jordan Kuwait Bank PLC; *Int'l*, pg. 3998
UNITED FINANCIAL OF ILLINOIS INC; *U.S. Private*, pg. 4292
UNITED FINANCIAL SERVICES, INC.—See Nicolet Bankshares, Inc.; *U.S. Public*, pg. 1528
UNITED FIRE ALARMS LIMITED—See London Security PLC; *Int'l*, pg. 4547
UNITED FIRE & CASUALTY COMPANY—See United Fire Group, Inc.; *U.S. Public*, pg. 2230
UNITED FIRE GROUP, INC.; *U.S. Public*, pg. 2230

UNITED FIRE GROUP, INC.—See United Fire Group, Inc.; *U.S. Public*, pg. 2231
UNITED FIRE & INDEMNITY COMPANY—See United Fire Group, Inc.; *U.S. Public*, pg. 2231
UNITED FIRE LLOYDS—See United Fire Group, Inc.; *U.S. Public*, pg. 2231
UNITED FISH INDUSTRIES (UK) LIMITED—See Austevoll Seafood ASA; *Int'l*, pg. 718
UNITED FISH INDUSTRIES (UK) LIMITED—See Kverva AS; *Int'l*, pg. 4349
UNITED FLEA MARKETS; *U.S. Private*, pg. 4292
UNITED FLOW TECHNOLOGIES—See H.I.G. Capital, LLC; *U.S. Private*, pg. 1834
UNITED FOAM—See UFP Technologies, Inc.; *U.S. Public*, pg. 2221
UNITED FOOD & COMMERCIAL WORKERS & EMPS ARIZONA HEALTH & WELFARE TRUST; *U.S. Private*, pg. 4292
UNITED FOOD HOLDINGS LIMITED; *Int'l*, pg. 8067
UNITED FOODS COMPANY (PSC) - JABEL ALI PLANT—See United Foods Company (PSC); *Int'l*, pg. 8067
UNITED FOODS COMPANY (PSC); *Int'l*, pg. 8067
UNITED FOOD STORE INC.; *U.S. Private*, pg. 4292
UNITED FOODSTUFF INDUSTRIES GROUP CO. K.S.C.C.; *Int'l*, pg. 8067
UNITED FOREST PRODUCTS INC.; *U.S. Private*, pg. 4292
UNITED FORKTRUCKS LTD—See CorpAcq Holdings Limited; *Int'l*, pg. 1802
UNITED FORMING INC.; *U.S. Private*, pg. 4292
UNITED FOR RESPECT EDUCATION FUND; *U.S. Private*, pg. 4292
UNITED FREIGHT & LOGISTICS, LTD.; *U.S. Private*, pg. 4292
UNITED FREIGHT SERVICE INC.; *U.S. Private*, pg. 4292
UNITED FURNITURE INDUSTRIES; *U.S. Private*, pg. 4292
UNITED GALVANIZING, INC.—See Valmont Industries, Inc.; *U.S. Public*, pg. 2274
UNITED GAMING, LLC; *U.S. Private*, pg. 4292
UNITED GAS TRANSMISSIONS COMPANY LIMITED—See Dana Gas PJSC; *Int'l*, pg. 1957
UNITED GEAR & ASSEMBLY—See United Stars Inc.; *U.S. Private*, pg. 4298
UNITED GENETICS HOLDING LLC—See Kagome Co., Ltd.; *Int'l*, pg. 4050
UNITED GENETICS TURKEY TOHUM FIDE A.S.—See Kagome Co., Ltd.; *Int'l*, pg. 4050
UNITED GHS INC.—See United Airlines Holdings, Inc.; *U.S. Public*, pg. 2229
UNITED GILSONITE LABORATORIES—See Sika AG; *Int'l*, pg. 6918
UNITED GLASS GROUP LTD.—See O-I Glass, Inc.; *U.S. Public*, pg. 1560
UNITEDGLOBALCOM, INC.—See Liberty Global plc; *Int'l*, pg. 4485
UNITED GLOBAL LIMITED; *Int'l*, pg. 8067
UNITED GLOBAL RESOURCES LIMITED—See Emivest Berhad; *Int'l*, pg. 2383
UNITED GLOBAL TECHNOLOGIES, INC.; *U.S. Private*, pg. 4293
UNITED GOVERNMENT SERVICES, LLC—See Elevance Health, Inc.; *U.S. Public*, pg. 730
UNITED GRAIN COMPANY JSC; *Int'l*, pg. 8067
UNITED GRAIN INDUSTRY CO., LTD.—See TPI Polene Public Company Limited; *Int'l*, pg. 7883
UNITED GRANITE LLC—See CARYSIL LIMITED; *Int'l*, pg. 1349
UNITED GREENERIES LTD.—See Hygrovest Limited; *Int'l*, pg. 3549
UNITED GRINDING GROUP AG; *Int'l*, pg. 8067
UNITED GRINDING NORTH AMERICA, INC.—See United Grinding Group AG; *Int'l*, pg. 8067
UNITED GROUP FOR PUBLISHING ADVERTISING & MARKETING; *Int'l*, pg. 8068
THE UNITED GROUP; *U.S. Private*, pg. 4129
UNITED GUARANTY COMMERCIAL INSURANCE COMPANY OF NORTH CAROLINA—See Arch Capital Group Ltd.; *Int'l*, pg. 546
UNITED GUARANTY CORPORATION—See Arch Capital Group Ltd.; *Int'l*, pg. 546
UNITED GUARANTY CREDIT INSURANCE COMPANY—See Arch Capital Group Ltd.; *Int'l*, pg. 546
UNITED GUARANTY SERVICES, INC.—See Arch Capital Group Ltd.; *Int'l*, pg. 547
UNITED-GUARDIAN, INC.; *U.S. Public*, pg. 2238
UNITED GULF BANK B.S.C.—See Kuwait Projects Company (Holding) K.S.C.P.; *Int'l*, pg. 4347
UNITED GULF BANK SECURITIES COMPANY B.S.C.—See Kuwait Projects Company (Holding) K.S.C.P.; *Int'l*, pg. 4347
UNITED GULF CONSTRUCTION CO. W.L.L—See Jeeran Holding Company K.S.C.C.; *Int'l*, pg. 3927
UNITED GULF FINANCIAL SERVICES COMPANY—See United Gulf Holding Company BSC; *Int'l*, pg. 8068
UNITED GULF FINANCIAL SERVICES-NORTH AFRICA SA—See United Gulf Holding Company BSC; *Int'l*, pg. 8068

UNITED HERITAGE CREDIT UNION

UNITED GULF HOLDING COMPANY BSC; *Int'l*, pg. 8068
UNITED GULF INVESTMENT CORPORATION B.S.C.; *Int'l*, pg. 8068
UNITED GULF MANAGEMENT LTD.—See Kuwait Projects Company (Holding) K.S.C.P.; *Int'l*, pg. 4347
UNITED GULF TRADING S.P.C.—See United Gulf Investment Corporation B.S.C.; *Int'l*, pg. 8068
UNITED HAMPSHIRE US REAL ESTATE INVESTMENT TRUST; *Int'l*, pg. 8068
UNITED HARDWARE DISTRIBUTING CO.; *U.S. Private*, pg. 4293
UNITED HARVEST LLC.; *U.S. Private*, pg. 4293
UNITED HEALTH ACTUARIAL SERVICES, INC.—See Kelso & Company, L.P.; *U.S. Private*, pg. 2280
UNITEDHEALTHCARE ARIZONA PHYSICIANS IPA—See UnitedHealth Group Incorporated; *U.S. Public*, pg. 2252
UNITEDHEALTHCARE BENEFITS OF TEXAS, INC.—See UnitedHealth Group Incorporated; *U.S. Public*, pg. 2251
UNITEDHEALTHCARE GLOBAL—See UnitedHealth Group Incorporated; *U.S. Public*, pg. 2241
UNITEDHEALTHCARE, INC.—See UnitedHealth Group Incorporated; *U.S. Public*, pg. 2251
UNITEDHEALTHCARE INDIA PRIVATE LIMITED—See UnitedHealth Group Incorporated; *U.S. Public*, pg. 2251
UNITEDHEALTHCARE INSURANCE COMPANY—See UnitedHealth Group Incorporated; *U.S. Public*, pg. 2252
UNITEDHEALTHCARE LIFE INSURANCE COMPANY—See UnitedHealth Group Incorporated; *U.S. Public*, pg. 2251
UNITEDHEALTHCARE NEVADA—See UnitedHealth Group Incorporated; *U.S. Public*, pg. 2252
UNITEDHEALTHCARE OF ALABAMA, INC.—See UnitedHealth Group Incorporated; *U.S. Public*, pg. 2252
UNITEDHEALTHCARE OF ARKANSAS, INC.—See UnitedHealth Group Incorporated; *U.S. Public*, pg. 2252
UNITEDHEALTHCARE OF COLORADO, INC.—See UnitedHealth Group Incorporated; *U.S. Public*, pg. 2252
UNITEDHEALTHCARE OF FLORIDA, INC.—See UnitedHealth Group Incorporated; *U.S. Public*, pg. 2252
UNITEDHEALTHCARE OF GEORGIA, INC.—See UnitedHealth Group Incorporated; *U.S. Public*, pg. 2252
UNITEDHEALTHCARE OF ILLINOIS, INC.—See UnitedHealth Group Incorporated; *U.S. Public*, pg. 2252
UNITEDHEALTHCARE OF MISSISSIPPI, INC.—See UnitedHealth Group Incorporated; *U.S. Public*, pg. 2252
UNITEDHEALTHCARE OF NEW ENGLAND, INC.—See UnitedHealth Group Incorporated; *U.S. Public*, pg. 2252
UNITEDHEALTHCARE OF NORTH CAROLINA, INC.—See UnitedHealth Group Incorporated; *U.S. Public*, pg. 2252
UNITEDHEALTHCARE OF OHIO, INC.—See UnitedHealth Group Incorporated; *U.S. Public*, pg. 2252
UNITEDHEALTHCARE OF OKLAHOMA, INC.—See UnitedHealth Group Incorporated; *U.S. Public*, pg. 2251
UNITEDHEALTHCARE OF OREGON, INC.—See UnitedHealth Group Incorporated; *U.S. Public*, pg. 2251
UNITEDHEALTHCARE OF TEXAS, INC.—See UnitedHealth Group Incorporated; *U.S. Public*, pg. 2251
UNITEDHEALTHCARE OF THE MIDLANDS, INC.—See UnitedHealth Group Incorporated; *U.S. Public*, pg. 2252
UNITEDHEALTHCARE OF THE MIDWEST, INC.—See UnitedHealth Group Incorporated; *U.S. Public*, pg. 2252
UNITEDHEALTHCARE OF WASHINGTON, INC.—See UnitedHealth Group Incorporated; *U.S. Public*, pg. 2252
UNITEDHEALTHCARE OF WISCONSIN, INC.—See UnitedHealth Group Incorporated; *U.S. Public*, pg. 2252
UNITEDHEALTHCARE PLAN OF THE RIVER VALLEY, INC.—See UnitedHealth Group Incorporated; *U.S. Public*, pg. 2251
UNITEDHEALTHCARE SERVICE LLC—See UnitedHealth Group Incorporated; *U.S. Public*, pg. 2251
UNITED HEALTHCARE SERVICES, INC.—See UnitedHealth Group Incorporated; *U.S. Public*, pg. 2251
UNITEDHEALTH GROUP GLOBAL HEALTHCARE SERVICES LIMITED—See UnitedHealth Group Incorporated; *U.S. Public*, pg. 2251
UNITEDHEALTH GROUP GLOBAL SERVICES, INC.—See UnitedHealth Group Incorporated; *U.S. Public*, pg. 2251
UNITEDHEALTH GROUP INCORPORATED; *U.S. Public*, pg. 2238
UNITED HEALTH PRODUCTS, INC.; *U.S. Public*, pg. 2231
UNITED HEAVY MACHINERY PLANTS OJSC—See Gazprombank JSC; *Int'l*, pg. 2892
UNITED HELICHARTERS PRIVATE LIMITED—See Exhicon Events Media Solutions Ltd.; *Int'l*, pg. 2584
UNITED HELIUM, INCORPORATED; *U.S. Private*, pg. 4293
UNITED HERITAGE CREDIT UNION; *U.S. Private*, pg. 4293

UNITED HERITAGE MUTUAL LIFE INSURANCE COMPANY INC.

UNITED HERITAGE MUTUAL LIFE INSURANCE COMPANY INC.; *U.S. Private*, pg. 4293
UNITED HOLDING COMPANY SAE—See Orascom Construction PLC; *Int'l*, pg. 5613
UNITED HOLDINGS LLC—See Kirby Corporation; *U.S. Public*, pg. 1235
UNITED HOME CARE SERVICES INC.; *U.S. Private*, pg. 4293
UNITED HOME INSURANCE COMPANY, A RISK RETENTION GROUP—See Beazer Homes USA, Inc.; *U.S. Public*, pg. 288
UNITED HOMES GROUP, INC; *U.S. Public*, pg. 2231
UNITED HUNTER OIL & GAS CORP.; *Int'l*, pg. 8068
UNITED HYDROGEN GROUP, INC.—See Plug Power Inc.; *U.S. Public*, pg. 1699
THE UNITED ILLUMINATING COMPANY—See Iberdrola, S.A.; *Int'l*, pg. 3571
UNITED, INC.—See Anthem Works Ltd.; *Int'l*, pg. 483
UNITED, INC.; *Int'l*, pg. 8074
UNITED INDUSTRIAL CORPORATION—See Textron Inc.; *U.S. Public*, pg. 2029
UNITED INDUSTRIAL GASES CO, LTD.—See MiTAC International Corp.; *Int'l*, pg. 4924
UNITED INDUSTRIES COMPANY K.S.C.C.—See Kuwait Projects Company (Holding) K.S.C.P.; *Int'l*, pg. 4347
UNITED INDUSTRIES CORP. - BRIDGETON—See Spectrum Brands Holdings, Inc.; *U.S. Public*, pg. 1917
UNITED INDUSTRIES CORPORATION—See Spectrum Brands Holdings, Inc.; *U.S. Public*, pg. 1917
UNITED INDUSTRIES CORPORATION—See Spectrum Brands Holdings, Inc.; *U.S. Public*, pg. 1917
UNITED INDUSTRIES CO—See Hayel Saeed Anam Group of Companies; *Int'l*, pg. 3291
UNITED INDUSTRIES, INC.—See United Stars Inc.; *U.S. Private*, pg. 4298
UNITED INDUSTRIES; *U.S. Private*, pg. 4293
UNITED INFORMATION HIGHWAY CO., LTD.—See Charoen Pokphand Group Co., Ltd.; *Int'l*, pg. 1453
UNITED INITIATORS GMBH & CO. KG—See Equistone Partners Europe Limited; *Int'l*, pg. 2487
UNITED INITIATORS, INC.—See Equistone Partners Europe Limited; *Int'l*, pg. 2487
UNITED INITIATORS PTY. LTD.—See Equistone Partners Europe Limited; *Int'l*, pg. 2487
UNITED INSTRUMENTS, INC.—See Tokyo Aircraft Instrument Co., Ltd.; *Int'l*, pg. 7788
UNITED INSURANCE COMPANY LTD.; *Int'l*, pg. 8068
UNITED INSURANCE COMPANY OF VIETNAM—See Sompo Holdings, Inc.; *Int'l*, pg. 7087
UNITED INSURANCE COMPANY—See Barbados Shipping & Trading Co. Ltd.; *Int'l*, pg. 858
UNITED INSURANCE CO.—See Hayel Saeed Anam Group of Companies; *Int'l*, pg. 3291
UNITED INSURANCE LIMITED; *Int'l*, pg. 8068
UNITED INSURANCE MANAGEMENT, L.C.—See American Coastal Insurance Corporation; *U.S. Public*, pg. 98
UNITED INTEGRATED SERVICES CO., LTD.; *Int'l*, pg. 8068
UNITED INTERNATIONAL BANK N.V.—See United International Holdings B.V.; *Int'l*, pg. 8068
UNITED INTERNATIONAL ENTERPRISES (M) SDN. BHD.—See United Plantations Berhad; *Int'l*, pg. 8072
UNITED INTERNATIONAL HOLDINGS B.V.; *Int'l*, pg. 8068
UNITED INTERNATIONAL INSURANCE CO.—See American European Group, Inc.; *U.S. Private*, pg. 232
UNITED INTERNATIONAL MANAGEMENT B.V.—See United International Holdings B.V.; *Int'l*, pg. 8068
UNITED INTERNATIONAL MANAGEMENT LTD—See United International Holdings B.V.; *Int'l*, pg. 8068
UNITED INTERNATIONAL MANAGEMENT S.A.—See United International Holdings B.V.; *Int'l*, pg. 8068
UNITED INTERNATIONAL PICTURES OF PANAMA, INC.—See Comcast Corporation; *U.S. Public*, pg. 542
UNITED INTERNATIONAL PICTURES—See Comcast Corporation; *U.S. Public*, pg. 541
UNITED INTERNATIONAL PICTURES—See National Amusements, Inc.; *U.S. Private*, pg. 2843
UNITED INTERNATIONAL TRANSPORTATION COMPANY; *Int'l*, pg. 8068
UNITED INTERNET AG; *Int'l*, pg. 8068
UNITED INTERNET BETEILIGUNGEN GMBH—See United Internet AG; *Int'l*, pg. 8069
UNITED INTERNET MEDIA AG—See United Internet AG; *Int'l*, pg. 8069
UNITED INTERNET MEDIA AUSTRIA GMBH—See United Internet AG; *Int'l*, pg. 8069
UNITED INVESTMENTS LTD.; *Int'l*, pg. 8069
UNITED INVESTMENTS PORTUGAL—See International Financial Advisors K.S.C.C.; *Int'l*, pg. 3748
UNITED IRON & STEEL MANUFACTURING CO. P.L.C.—See State Grid Corporation of China; *Int'l*, pg. 7182
UNITED ISRAEL APPEAL, INC.; *U.S. Private*, pg. 4293
UNITED JUICE COMPANIES OF AMERICA, INC.; *U.S. Private*, pg. 4293
UNITED KENNEL CLUB, INC.; *U.S. Private*, pg. 4293
UNITED KENNING RENTAL GROUP LTD.—See Sixt SE; *Int'l*, pg. 6968

UNITED KOTAK BERHAD—See Oji Holdings Corporation; *Int'l*, pg. 8070
UNITED-KUC, INC.—See Liberty Broadband Corporation; *U.S. Public*, pg. 1311
UNITED LABELS AG; *Int'l*, pg. 8070
UNITED LABEL S.A.—See CI GAMES S.A.; *Int'l*, pg. 1601
UNITEDLABELS BELGIUM N.V.—See United Labels AG; *Int'l*, pg. 8070
UNITEDLABELS FRANCE S.A.S.—See United Labels AG; *Int'l*, pg. 8070
UNITEDLABELS IBERICA S.A.—See United Labels AG; *Int'l*, pg. 8070
UNITEDLABELS ITALIA S.R.L.—See United Labels AG; *Int'l*, pg. 8070
UNITED LABORATORIES (CHENGDU) CO., LTD.—See The United Laboratories International Holdings Ltd.; *Int'l*, pg. 7697
THE UNITED LABORATORIES CO., LTD.—See The United Laboratories International Holdings Ltd.; *Int'l*, pg. 7697
UNITED LABORATORIES, INC.; *U.S. Private*, pg. 4293
UNITED LABORATORIES (INNER MONGOLIA) CO., LTD.—See The United Laboratories International Holdings Ltd.; *Int'l*, pg. 7697
THE UNITED LABORATORIES INTERNATIONAL HOLDINGS LTD.; *Int'l*, pg. 7697
UNITED LANDMARK ASSOCIATES, INC.; *U.S. Private*, pg. 4293
UNITED LAND SERVICES, INC.—See Centre Partners Management LLC; *U.S. Private*, pg. 2507
UNITED LAND SERVICES, INC.—See LP First Capital; *U.S. Private*, pg. 2507
UNITED LANGUAGE GROUP, INC.—See Leonard Green & Partners, L.P.; *U.S. Private*, pg. 2428
UNITED LANGUAGE GROUP, INC.—See TTCP Management Services, LLC.; *U.S. Private*, pg. 4254
UNITEDLAYER, INC.—See Accelon Capital LLC; *U.S. Private*, pg. 50
UNITED LEASING COMPANY LIMITED—See Camellia Plc; *Int'l*, pg. 1271
UNITED LEASING & INDUSTRIES LIMITED; *Int'l*, pg. 8070
UNITED LEBANESE REAL ESTATE COMPANY S.A.L—See Kuwait Projects Company (Holding) K.S.C.P.; *Int'l*, pg. 4347
UNITED LED CORPORATION (SHANDONG) LIMITED—See Ennostar Inc.; *Int'l*, pg. 2444
UNITED LEGAL SERVICES LTD.; *Int'l*, pg. 8070
UNITED LEGWEAR & APPAREL CO.; *U.S. Private*, pg. 4293
UNITEDLEX CORPORATION; *U.S. Private*, pg. 4302
UNITED LIFE INSURANCE COMPANY—See Kuvare US Holdings, Inc.; *U.S. Private*, pg. 2359
UNITED LIGHTING AND SUPPLY CO.; *U.S. Private*, pg. 4293
UNITED LIGHTING OPTO-ELECTRONIC INC.—See United Microelectronics Corporation; *Int'l*, pg. 8070
UNITED LINEN SERVICES INC.; *U.S. Private*, pg. 4293
UNITED LIQUID GAS COMPANY—See Superior Plus Corp.; *Int'l*, pg. 7338
UNITED LITHIUM CORP.; *Int'l*, pg. 8070
UNITED LITHO, INC.—See CJK Group, Inc.; *U.S. Private*, pg. 909
UNITED LIVING GROUP—See Elysian Capital LLP; *Int'l*, pg. 2372
UNITED LUMBER & REMAN, LLC—See UFP Industries, Inc.; *U.S. Public*, pg. 2221
UNITED LUTHERAN PROGRAM FOR THE AGING, INC.; *U.S. Private*, pg. 4293
UNITED MACHINING INC.—See Wescast Industries Inc.; *Int'l*, pg. 8380
UNITED MAILING SERVICES, INC.; *U.S. Private*, pg. 4293
UNITED MALACCA BERHAD; *Int'l*, pg. 8070
UNITED MALAYAN LAND BHD—See Seleksi Juang Sdn Bhd; *Int'l*, pg. 6700
UNITED MALT GROUP LIMITED—See Perpetual Equity Investment Company Limited; *Int'l*, pg. 5812
UNITED MANUFACTURERS SUPPLIES, INC.; *U.S. Private*, pg. 4294
UNITED MARINE AGENCIES (PVT) LTD.—See Regional Container Lines Public Company Limited; *Int'l*, pg. 6254
UNITED MARITIME CORPORATION; *Int'l*, pg. 8070
UNITED MARKETING GROUP, INC.; *U.S. Private*, pg. 4294
UNITED MARKETING GROUP LLC; *U.S. Private*, pg. 4294
UNITED MARKETING INC.; *U.S. Private*, pg. 4294
UNITED MATERIALS, INC.—See Guggenheim Partners, LLC; *U.S. Private*, pg. 1811
UNITED MATERIALS LLC—See Votorantim S.A.; *Int'l*, pg. 8310
UNITED MAYFLOWER CONTAINER SERVICES, LLC—See UniGroup, Inc.; *U.S. Private*, pg. 4283
UNITED MCGILL CORPORATION - BENNINGTON PLANT—See The McGill Corporation; *U.S. Private*, pg. 4076

CORPORATE AFFILIATIONS

UNITED MCGILL CORPORATION - FOUNTAIN INN PLANT—See The McGill Corporation; *U.S. Private*, pg. 4076
UNITED MCGILL CORPORATION - GRAND PRAIRIE PLANT—See The McGill Corporation; *U.S. Private*, pg. 4076
UNITED MCGILL CORPORATION - GRINNELL PLANT—See The McGill Corporation; *U.S. Private*, pg. 4076
UNITED MCGILL CORPORATION - HILLSBORO PLANT—See The McGill Corporation; *U.S. Private*, pg. 4076
UNITED MCGILL CORPORATION - SAN ANTONIO PLANT—See The McGill Corporation; *U.S. Private*, pg. 4076
UNITED MCGILL CORPORATION—See The McGill Corporation; *U.S. Private*, pg. 4076
UNITED MCGILL CORPORATION - STOCKTON PLANT—See The McGill Corporation; *U.S. Private*, pg. 4076
UNITED MECHANICAL, INC.; *U.S. Private*, pg. 4294
UNITED MECHANICAL INC.; *U.S. Private*, pg. 4294
UNITED MECHANICAL; *U.S. Private*, pg. 4294
UNITED MEDCO, LLC—See Medline Industries, LP; *U.S. Private*, pg. 2658
UNITED MEDIA HOLDING RUSSIA—See United Media Holding; *Int'l*, pg. 8070
UNITED MEDIA HOLDING; *Int'l*, pg. 8070
UNITED MEDIA, INC.—See The E.W. Scripps Company; *U.S. Public*, pg. 2069
UNITED MEDIA SERVICES LLC—See Muscat Overseas Co., L.L.C.; *Int'l*, pg. 5102
UNITED MEDICAL PARK ASC, LLC—See UnitedHealth Group Incorporated; *U.S. Public*, pg. 2251
UNITED MEDICAL SYSTEMS (DE), INC.; *U.S. Private*, pg. 4294
UNITED MEMORIES INC.—See ProMOS Technologies Inc.; *Int'l*, pg. 5994
UNITED MERCHANT SERVICES INC.; *U.S. Private*, pg. 4294
UNITED METAL FABRICATORS, INC.; *U.S. Private*, pg. 4294
UNITED METALS COMPANY—See El Sewedy Electric Company; *Int'l*, pg. 2341
UNITED METHODIST FAMILY SERVICES OF VIRGINIA, INC.; *U.S. Private*, pg. 4294
UNITED METHODIST PUBLISHING HOUSE; *U.S. Private*, pg. 4294
UNITED METHODIST RETIREMENT CENTER; *U.S. Private*, pg. 4294
UNITED METHODIST RETIREMENT COMMUNITIES; *U.S. Private*, pg. 4294
UNITED MICROELECTRONICS CORPORATION; *Int'l*, pg. 8070
UNITED MICROELECTRONICS (EUROPE) B.V.—See United Microelectronics Corporation; *Int'l*, pg. 8070
UNITED MIDWEST SAVINGS BANK, N.A.; *U.S. Private*, pg. 4294
UNITED MIGRANT OPPORTUNITY SERVICES, INC.; *U.S. Private*, pg. 4294
UNITED MINERAL AND CHEMICAL CORPORATION—See ICD Group International Inc.; *U.S. Private*, pg. 2030
UNITED MINERALS COMPANY, LLC—See Peabody Energy Corporation; *U.S. Public*, pg. 1659
UNITED MIZRAHI BANK (SWITZERLAND) LTD.—See Mizrahi Tefahot Bank Ltd.; *Int'l*, pg. 4997
UNITED MOBILE HOMES OF BUFFALO, INC.—See UMH Properties, Inc.; *U.S. Public*, pg. 2225
UNITED MOLASSES ESPANA SA—See W&R Barnett Ltd.; *Int'l*, pg. 8320
UNITED MOLASSES GB LIMITED—See W&R Barnett Ltd.; *Int'l*, pg. 8320
UNITED MOLASSES GROUP LIMITED—See W&R Barnett Ltd.; *Int'l*, pg. 8320
UNITED MOLASSES (IRELAND) LTD—See W&R Barnett Ltd.; *Int'l*, pg. 8320
UNITED MOLASSES MARKETING LIMITED—See W&R Barnett Ltd.; *Int'l*, pg. 8320
UNITED MOLASSES MARKETING PHILIPPINES INC.—See W&R Barnett Ltd.; *Int'l*, pg. 8320
UNITED MOLASSES STORAGE—See W&R Barnett Ltd.; *Int'l*, pg. 8320
UNITED MOLASSES TRADING LIMITED—See W&R Barnett Ltd.; *Int'l*, pg. 8321
UNITED MOTOR CLUB OF AMERICA, INC.—See Tiptree Inc.; *U.S. Public*, pg. 2159
UNITED MOTORS LANKA PLC; *Int'l*, pg. 8071
UNITED MS ELECTRICAL MFG (M) SDN. BHD.—See UMS-Neiken Group Berhad; *Int'l*, pg. 8027
UNITED MUSLIM RELIEF; *U.S. Private*, pg. 4294
UNITED NANOTECHNOLOGIES PRIVATE LIMITED—See United Credit Ltd; *Int'l*, pg. 8066
UNITED NATIONAL BANK LIMITED—See Bestway (Holdings) Limited; *Int'l*, pg. 1001
UNITED NATIONAL BANK LIMITED—See State Bank of Pakistan; *Int'l*, pg. 7182
UNITED NATIONAL BANK; *U.S. Public*, pg. 2231

UNITED NATIONAL BREWERIES (SA) PTY LTD.—See Delta Corporation Limited; *Int'l*, pg. 2016
UNITED NATIONAL CLOSEOUT STORES, INC.; *U.S. Private*, pg. 4294
UNITED NATIONAL CORPORATION; *U.S. Private*, pg. 4295
UNITED NATIONAL GROUP LTD.—See Paine Schwartz Partners, LLC; *U.S. Private*, pg. 3076
UNITED NATIONAL INSURANCE COMPANY—See Paine Schwartz Partners, LLC; *U.S. Private*, pg. 3076
UNITED NATIONS DEVELOPMENT CORPORATION; *U.S. Private*, pg. 4295
UNITED NATURAL FOODS, INC.—See United Natural Foods, Inc.; *U.S. Public*, pg. 2233
UNITED NATURAL FOODS, INC.; *U.S. Public*, pg. 2231
UNITED NATURAL FOODS, INC.—See United Natural Foods, Inc.; *U.S. Public*, pg. 2233
UNITED NATURAL FOODS, INC.—See United Natural Foods, Inc.; *U.S. Public*, pg. 2233
UNITED NATURAL FOODS, INC.—See United Natural Foods, Inc.; *U.S. Public*, pg. 2233
UNITED NATURAL FOODS WEST, INC.—See United Natural Foods, Inc.; *U.S. Public*, pg. 2233
UNITED NATURAL TRADING, LLC—See United Natural Foods, Inc.; *U.S. Public*, pg. 2233
UNITED NEGRO COLLEGE FUND, INC.; *U.S. Private*, pg. 4295
THE UNITED NETWORK—See WPP plc; *Int'l*, pg. 8467
THE UNITED NILGIRI TEA ESTATES CO. LTD.; *Int'l*, pg. 7698
UNITED NOTIONS INC.; *U.S. Private*, pg. 4295
UNITED OF OMAHA LIFE INSURANCE COMPANY—See Mutual of Omaha Insurance Company; *U.S. Private*, pg. 2820
UNITED OHANA, LLC; *U.S. Private*, pg. 4295
UNITED OIL CORPORATION—See Forestar Group Inc.; *U.S. Public*, pg. 867
UNITED OIL CORP; *U.S. Private*, pg. 4295
UNITED OIL CO.; *U.S. Private*, pg. 4295
UNITED OIL & GAS PLC; *Int'l*, pg. 8071
UNITED OIL PROJECTS COMPANY K.S.C.—See Kuwait Projects Company (Holding) K.S.C.P.; *Int'l*, pg. 4347
UNITED OIL RECOVERY, INC.—See Grupo Tradebe Medioambiente S.L.; *Int'l*, pg. 3138
UNITED ONLINE, INC.—See B. Riley Financial, Inc.; *U.S. Public*, pg. 262
UNITED OVERSEAS AUSTRALIA LTD.; *Int'l*, pg. 8071
UNITED OVERSEAS BANK (CHINA) LIMITED—See United Overseas Bank Limited; *Int'l*, pg. 8072
UNITED OVERSEAS BANK LIMITED; *Int'l*, pg. 8071
UNITED OVERSEAS BANK (MALAYSIA) BHD.—See United Overseas Bank Limited; *Int'l*, pg. 8072
UNITED OVERSEAS BANK (THAI) PUBLIC COMPANY LIMITED—See United Overseas Bank Limited; *Int'l*, pg. 8072
UNITED OVERSEAS BANK (VIETNAM) LIMITED—See United Overseas Bank Limited; *Int'l*, pg. 8072
UNITED PACIFIC MORTGAGE CO., INC.; *U.S. Private*, pg. 4295
UNITED PACIFIC PET, LLC—See Pet Food Experts Inc.; *U.S. Private*, pg. 3156
UNITED PACKAGING CO., LTD.—See Oji Holdings Corporation; *Int'l*, pg. 5538
UNITED PACKAGING INDUSTRIES PTE. LTD—See PSC Corporation Ltd.; *Int'l*, pg. 6015
UNITED PACKAGING SUPPLY CO.—See Kelso & Company, L.P.; *U.S. Private*, pg. 2279
UNITED PACKAGING SUPPLY CO.—See Warburg Pincus LLC; *U.S. Private*, pg. 4437
UNITED PAINT & CHEMICAL CORPORATION—See Piceu Group Limited, Inc.; *U.S. Private*, pg. 3176
UNITED PAINTS & CHEMICALS S.A.E—See Compagnie de Saint-Gobain SA; *Int'l*, pg. 1737
UNITED PALM OIL INDUSTRY PUBLIC COMPANY LIMITED; *Int'l*, pg. 8072
UNITED PANAM FINANCIAL CORP.—See Pine Brook Partners, LLC; *U.S. Private*, pg. 3182
UNITED PAPER INDUSTRIES BSC; *Int'l*, pg. 8072
UNITED PAPER PUBLIC COMPANY LIMITED - MUANG FACTORY—See United Paper Public Company Limited; *Int'l*, pg. 8072
UNITED PAPER PUBLIC COMPANY LIMITED; *Int'l*, pg. 8072
UNITED PARADYNE CORPORATION; *U.S. Private*, pg. 4295
UNITED PARAGON MINING CORPORATION; *Int'l*, pg. 8072
UNITED PARCEL SERVICE (BY)—See United Parcel Service, Inc.; *U.S. Public*, pg. 2234
UNITED PARCEL SERVICE CANADA LTD.—See United Parcel Service, Inc.; *U.S. Public*, pg. 2234
UNITED PARCEL SERVICE CO.—See United Parcel Service, Inc.; *U.S. Public*, pg. 2233
UNITED PARCEL SERVICE CZECH REPUBLIC, S.R.O.—See United Parcel Service, Inc.; *U.S. Public*, pg. 2234
UNITED PARCEL SERVICE DEUTSCHLAND S.A.R.L. & CO. OHG—See United Parcel Service, Inc.; *U.S. Public*, pg. 2233

UNITED PARCEL SERVICE GENERAL SERVICES CO.—See United Parcel Service, Inc.; *U.S. Public*, pg. 2234
UNITED PARCEL SERVICE, INC.; *U.S. Public*, pg. 2233
UNITED PARCEL SERVICE ITALIA SRL—See United Parcel Service, Inc.; *U.S. Public*, pg. 2234
UNITED PARCEL SERVICE NEDERLAND BV—See United Parcel Service, Inc.; *U.S. Public*, pg. 2234
UNITED PARCEL SERVICE NEDERLANDS B.V.—See United Parcel Service, Inc.; *U.S. Public*, pg. 2234
UNITED PARCEL SERVICE OF AMERICA, INC.—See United Parcel Service, Inc.; *U.S. Public*, pg. 2234
UNITED PARCEL SERVICE (RUS) LLC—See United Parcel Service, Inc.; *U.S. Public*, pg. 2234
UNITED PARKS & RESORTS INC.; *U.S. Public*, pg. 2234
UNITED PAYMENT SERVICES, INC.—See Direct Connect LLC; *U.S. Private*, pg. 1235
UNITED PEOPLE POWER, INC.; *U.S. Private*, pg. 4295
UNITED PERFORMANCE MATERIALS CORP.—See Formosan Union Chemical Corp.; *Int'l*, pg. 2736
UNITED PERFORMANCE METALS, INC.—See O'Neal Industries, Inc.; *U.S. Private*, pg. 2979
UNITED PETFOOD PRODUCERS NV—See Waterland Private Equity Investments B.V.; *Int'l*, pg. 8357
UNITED PET GROUP, INC.—See Spectrum Brands Holdings, Inc.; *U.S. Public*, pg. 1917
UNITED PET POLSKA SP. Z.O.O.—See Spectrum Brands Holdings, Inc.; *U.S. Public*, pg. 1917
UNITED PETROLEUM DEVELOPMENT CO., LTD.—See ENEOS Holdings, Inc.; *Int'l*, pg. 2418
UNITED PETROLEUM PTY. LTD.; *Int'l*, pg. 8072
UNITED PETROLEUM TRANSPORTS, INC.—See Gregmar, Inc.; *U.S. Private*, pg. 1782
UNITED PET SUPPLY INC.; *U.S. Private*, pg. 4295
UNITED PHARMACEUTICAL DISTRIBUTORS (PROPRIETARY) LIMITED—See Clicks Group Limited; *Int'l*, pg. 1658
UNITED PHOSPHORUS HOLDINGS B.V.—See UPL Limited; *Int'l*, pg. 8089
UNITED PHOSPHORUS HOLDINGS COOPERATIEF U.A.—See UPL Limited; *Int'l*, pg. 8089
UNITED PHOSPHORUS, INC.—See UPL Limited; *Int'l*, pg. 8090
UNITED PHOSPHORUS (KOREA) LTD.—See UPL Limited; *Int'l*, pg. 8089
UNITED PHOSPHORUS LIMITED, JAPAN—See UPL Limited; *Int'l*, pg. 8089
UNITED PHOSPHORUS LTD. AUSTRALIA—See UPL Limited; *Int'l*, pg. 8089
UNITED PHOSPHORUS LTD. HONG KONG—See UPL Limited; *Int'l*, pg. 8089
UNITED PHOSPHORUS LTD. UK—See UPL Limited; *Int'l*, pg. 8090
UNITED PHOSPHORUS POLSKA SP.Z.O.O—See UPL Limited; *Int'l*, pg. 8090
UNITED PHOSPHORUS (SHANGHAI) COMPANY LIMITED.—See UPL Limited; *Int'l*, pg. 8090
UNITED PHOSPHORUS (TAIWAN) LIMITED.—See UPL Limited; *Int'l*, pg. 8089
UNITED PIG PLACEMENT SERVICES—See United Animal Health, Inc.; *U.S. Private*, pg. 4287
UNITED PIPELINE SYSTEMS, INC.—See New Mountain Capital, LLC; *U.S. Private*, pg. 2900
UNITED PIPE & STEEL CORP.—See Reliance Steel & Aluminum Co.; *U.S. Public*, pg. 1780
UNITED PIPING, INC.—See APi Group Corporation; *Int'l*, pg. 514
UNITED PISTON RING, INC.—See TPR Co., Ltd.; *Int'l*, pg. 7884
UNITED PLAINS AG—See CHS INC.; *U.S. Public*, pg. 493
UNITED PLANNERS' FINANCIAL SERVICES OF AMERICA—See Pacific Mutual Holding Company; *U.S. Private*, pg. 3069
UNITED PLANNING ORGANIZATION; *U.S. Private*, pg. 4295
UNITED PLANTATIONS BERHAD; *Int'l*, pg. 8072
UNITED PLASTIC FABRICATING; *U.S. Private*, pg. 4295
UNITED PLUMBING & HEATING SUPPLY CO.; *U.S. Private*, pg. 4295
UNITED PLUMBING SUPPLY CO.; *U.S. Private*, pg. 4295
UNITED PLUMBING TECHNOLOGIES; *U.S. Private*, pg. 4295
UNITED PLYWOODS & LUMBER INC.; *U.S. Private*, pg. 4295
UNITED POLYFAB GUJARAT LTD.; *Int'l*, pg. 8072
UNITED POWER GENERATION & DISTRIBUTION CO., LTD.; *Int'l*, pg. 8072
UNITED POWER INC.; *U.S. Private*, pg. 4295
UNITED POWER OF ASIA PUBLIC COMPANY LIMITED; *Int'l*, pg. 8072
UNITED POWER & RESOURCES PTE. LTD.—See Nishio Holdings Co., Ltd.; *Int'l*, pg. 5366
UNITED POWER TECHNOLOGY AG; *Int'l*, pg. 8072
UNITED PRAIRIE, LLC; *U.S. Private*, pg. 4295
UNITED PRECAST, INC.; *U.S. Private*, pg. 4295
UNITED PRECISION DRILLING COMPANY W.L.L.—See Weatherford International plc; *U.S. Public*, pg. 2339

UNITED PRESS INTERNATIONAL, INC.—See Family Federation for World Peace & Unification; *U.S. Private*, pg. 1469
UNITED PRINTING AND PUBLISHING—See Abu Dhabi Media; *Int'l*, pg. 72
UNITED PRODUCERS, INC.; *U.S. Private*, pg. 4296
UNITED PRODUCTION & CONSTRUCTION SERVICES; *U.S. Private*, pg. 4296
UNITED PRODUCTIONS, INC.—See KeyHolder, Inc.; *Int'l*, pg. 4146
UNITED PRODUCTS CO., LTD.—See Thai Beverage Public Company Limited; *Int'l*, pg. 7592
UNITED PRODUCTS CORP.—See Beacon Roofing Supply, Inc.; *U.S. Public*, pg. 285
UNITED PRODUCTS DISTRIBUTORS INC.; *U.S. Private*, pg. 4296
UNITED PROJECT MANAGEMENT COMPANY LIMITED—See Origin Property Public Company Limited; *Int'l*, pg. 5630
UNITED PROJECTS COMPANY FOR AVIATION SERVICES K.S.C.P.—See Agility; *Int'l*, pg. 210
UNITED PROPANE GAS COMPANIES INC.; *U.S. Private*, pg. 4296
UNITED PROPANE—See Suburban Propane Partners, L.P.; *U.S. Public*, pg. 1959
UNITED PROPERTIES LLC—See Pohlad Companies; *U.S. Private*, pg. 3221
UNITED PROPERTIES REIT; *Int'l*, pg. 8072
UNITED PROPERTIES; *U.S. Private*, pg. 4296
UNITED PROPERTY & CASUALTY INSURANCE COMPANY—See HCI Group, Inc.; *U.S. Public*, pg. 1014
UNITED PROPERTY FINANCE LIMITED—See Global Token Limited; *Int'l*, pg. 3001
UNITED PUBLISHING HOUSE (M) SDN. BHD.—See Sasbadi Holdings Berhad; *Int'l*, pg. 6582
UNITED PULP & PAPER CO., INC.—See The Siam Cement Public Company Limited; *Int'l*, pg. 7685
UNITED PULSE TRADING INC.—See AGT Food and Ingredients Inc.; *Int'l*, pg. 221
UNITED RADIANT TECHNOLOGY CORPORATION; *Int'l*, pg. 8073
UNITED RADIO, INCORPORATED; *U.S. Private*, pg. 4296
UNITED RADIO INC.; *U.S. Private*, pg. 4296
UNITED RAIL, INC.; *U.S. Public*, pg. 2234
UNITED READERS SERVICE LTD.; *U.S. Private*, pg. 4296
UNITED READY MIXED CONCRETE COMPANY, INC—See Vicat S.A.; *Int'l*, pg. 8186
UNITED REAL ESTATE COMPANY K.S.C.P.—See Kuwait Projects Company (Holding) K.S.C.P.; *Int'l*, pg. 4347
UNITED REAL ESTATE COMPANY S.A.K.—See Kuwait Projects Company (Holding) K.S.C.P.; *Int'l*, pg. 4347
UNITED REAL ESTATE GROUP, LLC; *U.S. Private*, pg. 4296
UNITED REALTY CORPORATION—See Atwood Enterprises Inc.; *U.S. Private*, pg. 384
UNITED RECORD PRESSING LLC; *U.S. Private*, pg. 4296
UNITED RECOVERY SYSTEMS, LP—See Audax Group, Limited Partnership; *U.S. Private*, pg. 390
UNITED REFINERIES LTD.—See Masawara PLC; *Int'l*, pg. 4720
UNITED REFINING COMPANY—See Red Apple Group, Inc.; *U.S. Private*, pg. 3373
UNITED REFINING INC.—See Red Apple Group, Inc.; *U.S. Private*, pg. 3373
UNITED REFRIGERATION, INC.; *U.S. Private*, pg. 4296
UNITED REFRIGERATION OF CANADA LTD.—See United Refrigeration, Inc.; *U.S. Private*, pg. 4296
UNITED REFRIGERATOR SDN BHD—See Carrier Global Corporation; *U.S. Public*, pg. 442
UNITED RENEWABLE ENERGY CO., LTD.; *Int'l*, pg. 8073
UNITED RENTAL GROUP LTD.—See Sixt SE; *Int'l*, pg. 6968
UNITED RENTALS BELGIUM BV—See United Rentals, Inc.; *U.S. Public*, pg. 2235
UNITED RENTALS GMBH—See United Rentals, Inc.; *U.S. Public*, pg. 2235
UNITED RENTALS, INC.; *U.S. Public*, pg. 2234
UNITED RENTALS INTERNATIONAL B.V.—See United Rentals, Inc.; *U.S. Public*, pg. 2235
UNITED RENTALS (NORTH AMERICA), INC.—See United Rentals, Inc.; *U.S. Public*, pg. 2235
UNITED RENTALS NORTHWEST, INC.—See United Rentals, Inc.; *U.S. Public*, pg. 2235
UNITED RENTALS OF CANADA, INC.—See United Rentals, Inc.; *U.S. Public*, pg. 2235
UNITED RESOURCE HOLDINGS GROUP, INC.; *U.S. Public*, pg. 2235
UNITED RESTAURANT SUPPLY INC.; *U.S. Private*, pg. 4296
UNITED RETIREMENT PLAN CONSULTANTS, INC.—See Aquiline Capital Partners LLC; *U.S. Public*, pg. 304
UNITED RETIREMENT PLAN CONSULTANTS, INC.—See Genstar Capital, LLC; *U.S. Private*, pg. 1675
UNITED RIGGERS & ERECTORS INC.; *U.S. Private*, pg. 4296

UNITED RIGGERS & ERECTORS INC. CORPORATE AFFILIATIONS

UNITED ROAD SERVICES, INC.—See The Carlyle Group Inc.; *U.S. Public*, pg. 2056
UNITED ROAD TOWING, INC.—See Guggenheim Partners, LLC; *U.S. Private*, pg. 1812
UNITED ROLLS INC.—See Park Corp.; *U.S. Private*, pg. 3096
UNITED ROMANIAN BREWERIES BEREPROD SRL—See Carlsberg A/S; *Int'l*, pg. 1341
UNITED ROTARY BRUSH CORPORATION EASTERN DIVISION—See United Rotary Brush Corporation; *U.S. Private*, pg. 4296
UNITED ROTARY BRUSH CORPORATION OF CANADA—See United Rotary Brush Corporation; *U.S. Private*, pg. 4296
UNITED ROTARY BRUSH CORPORATION; *U.S. Private*, pg. 4296
UNITED ROTARY BRUSH—See United Rotary Brush Corporation; *U.S. Private*, pg. 4296
UNITED ROTARY BRUSH—See United Rotary Brush Corporation; *U.S. Private*, pg. 4296
UNITED ROTORCRAFT SOLUTIONS, LLC—See American Securities LLC; *U.S. Private*, pg. 247
UNITED ROYALE HOLDINGS CORP.—See Cybernorth Ventures Inc.; *Int'l*, pg. 1893
UNITED SALES PARTNERS LLC—See Dubai Investments PJSC; *Int'l*, pg. 2219
UNITED SALON TECHNOLOGIES GMBH—See Wilh. Werhahn KG; *Int'l*, pg. 8410
UNITED SALT CORPORATION; *U.S. Private*, pg. 4296
UNITED SANOH INDUSTRIES SDN. BHD.—See Sanoh Industrial Co., Ltd.; *Int'l*, pg. 6553
UNITED SAVINGS BANK; *U.S. Private*, pg. 4297
UNITED SCALE & ENGINEERING CORPORATION—See Transcat, Inc.; *U.S. Public*, pg. 2179
UNITED SCIENCES TESTING INC.—See TRC Companies, Inc.; *U.S. Private*, pg. 4215
UNITED SEAFOOD IMPORTS INC.; *U.S. Private*, pg. 4297
UNITED SEATING & MOBILITY LLC—See AEA Investors LP; *U.S. Private*, pg. 116
UNITED SECURITY BANCSHARES; *U.S. Public*, pg. 2235
UNITED SECURITY BANK—See United Security Bancshares; *U.S. Public*, pg. 2235
UNITED SECURITY LIFE AND HEALTH INSURANCE COMPANY; *U.S. Private*, pg. 4297
UNITED SECURITY LIFE INSURANCE CO.—See United Security Life and Health Insurance Company; *U.S. Private*, pg. 4297
UNITED SECURITY PROVIDER LTD.—See Swisscom AG; *Int'l*, pg. 7374
UNITED-SEINO TRANSPORTATION (MALAYSIA) SDN. BHD.—See Seino Holdings Co., Ltd.; *Int'l*, pg. 6691
UNITED SERVICE COMPANIES INC.; *U.S. Private*, pg. 4297
UNITED SERVICE EQUIPMENT COMPANY—See Standex International; *U.S. Public*, pg. 1931
THE UNITED SERVICE ORGANIZATIONS, INC.; *U.S. Private*, pg. 4129
UNITED SERVICE PROTECTION, INC.—See Assurant, Inc.; *U.S. Public*, pg. 216
UNITED SERVICES AUTOMOBILE ASSOCIATION; *U.S. Private*, pg. 4297
UNITED SERVICES INC.; *U.S. Private*, pg. 4297
UNITED SERVICE TECHNOLOGIES, INC.—See HCI Equity Management, L.P.; *U.S. Private*, pg. 1889
UNITED SHAREHOLDER SERVICES, INC.—See U.S. Global Investors, Inc.; *U.S. Public*, pg. 2213
UNITED SHIPPERS LTD.—See Oricon Enterprises Ltd.; *Int'l*, pg. 5621
UNITED SHIPPING AGENCIES LTD.—See Albert Ballin KG; *Int'l*, pg. 297
UNITED SHIPPING CO. LTD.—See Albert Ballin KG; *Int'l*, pg. 297
UNITED SHIPPING SOLUTIONS; *U.S. Private*, pg. 4297
UNITED SHOE MACHINERY CORP.; *U.S. Private*, pg. 4297
UNITED SILICONE—See Illinois Tool Works Inc.; *U.S. Public*, pg. 1111
UNITED SISTEMA DE TUBERIAS LTDA.—See New Mountain Capital, LLC; *U.S. Private*, pg. 2900
UNITED SITE SERVICES, INC.—See Platinum Equity, LLC; *U.S. Private*, pg. 3209
UNITED SOLUTIONS, INC.—See Aktion Associates, Inc.; *U.S. Private*, pg. 147
UNITED SOUTH AND EASTERN TRIBES, INC.; *U.S. Private*, pg. 4297
UNITED SOUTHERN BANK; *U.S. Private*, pg. 4298
UNITED-SOUTHERN WASTE MATERIAL CO; *U.S. Private*, pg. 4302
UNITED SPECIAL TECHNICAL SERVICES LLC—See New Mountain Capital, LLC; *U.S. Private*, pg. 2900
UNITED SPINAL ASSOCIATION; *U.S. Private*, pg. 4298
UNITED SPIRITS LTD.—See Diageo plc; *Int'l*, pg. 2103
UNITED STAFFING ASSOCIATES; *U.S. Private*, pg. 4298
UNITED STAFFING SOLUTIONS INC.; *U.S. Private*, pg. 4298
UNITED STAINLESS, INC.—See United Stars Inc.; *U.S. Private*, pg. 4298

UNITED STARS INC.; *U.S. Private*, pg. 4298
UNITED STARS INDUSTRIES, INC.—See United Stars Inc.; *U.S. Private*, pg. 4298
UNITED STATES 12 MONTH NATURAL GAS FUND, LP—See The Marygold Companies, Inc.; *U.S. Public*, pg. 2112
UNITED STATES 12 MONTH OIL FUND, LP—See The Marygold Companies, Inc.; *U.S. Public*, pg. 2112
UNITED STATES AIRCRAFT INSURANCE GROUP—See Berkshire Hathaway Inc.; *U.S. Public*, pg. 302
UNITED STATES ALLIANCE FIRE PROTECTION, INC.—See APi Group Corporation; *Int'l*, pg. 514
UNITED STATES ALLIANCE FIRE PROTECTION, INC.—See APi Group Corporation; *Int'l*, pg. 514
UNITED STATES ALUMOWELD CO. INC.—See Fujikura Ltd.; *Int'l*, pg. 2829
UNITED STATES ANTIMONY CORPORATION; *U.S. Public*, pg. 2235
UNITED STATES APPRAISALS LLC—See Stewart Information Services Corporation; *U.S. Public*, pg. 1948
UNITED STATES BAKERY - PORTLAND PLANT—See United States Bakery; *U.S. Private*, pg. 4298
UNITED STATES BAKERY - SEATTLE, 6TH AVE PLANT—See United States Bakery; *U.S. Private*, pg. 4298
UNITED STATES BAKERY - SEATTLE, WELLER STREET PLANT—See United States Bakery; *U.S. Private*, pg. 4298
UNITED STATES BAKERY; *U.S. Private*, pg. 4298
UNITED STATES BAKERY - SPRINGFIELD PLANT—See United States Bakery; *U.S. Private*, pg. 4298
UNITED STATES BARTENDER'S GUILD; *U.S. Private*, pg. 4298
UNITED STATES BEEF CORPORATION; *U.S. Private*, pg. 4298
UNITED STATES BEVERAGE LLC; *U.S. Private*, pg. 4298
UNITED STATES BITCOIN AND TREASURY INVESTMENT TRUST; *U.S. Private*, pg. 4298
UNITED STATES BOX CORP.; *U.S. Private*, pg. 4298
UNITED STATES BRASS & COPPER CO.; *U.S. Private*, pg. 4298
UNITED STATES BRENT OIL FUND, LP—See The Marygold Companies, Inc.; *U.S. Public*, pg. 2112
UNITED STATES BUILDING SUPPLY; *U.S. Private*, pg. 4298
UNITED STATES BULLET PROOFING, INC.—See River Associates Investments, LLC; *U.S. Private*, pg. 3443
UNITED STATES CARGO & COURIER SERVICE, INC.—See U.S. Cargo, Inc.; *U.S. Private*, pg. 4270
UNITED STATES CELLULAR CORPORATION—See Telephone & Data Systems, Inc.; *U.S. Public*, pg. 1998
UNITED STATES COACHWORKS INC.; *U.S. Private*, pg. 4298
UNITED STATES COAST GUARD; *U.S. Private*, pg. 4298
UNITED STATES COLD STORAGE, INC.—See John Swire & Sons Limited; *Int'l*, pg. 3981
UNITED STATES COMMODITY FUNDS, LLC—See The Marygold Companies, Inc.; *U.S. Public*, pg. 2112
UNITED STATES COMMODITY INDEX FUNDS TRUST—See The Marygold Companies, Inc.; *U.S. Public*, pg. 2112
UNITED STATES COUNCIL FOR AUTOMOTIVE RESEARCH LLC—See General Motors Company; *U.S. Public*, pg. 929
UNITED STATES DIESEL-HEATING OIL FUND, LP—See The Marygold Companies, Inc.; *U.S. Public*, pg. 2112
UNITED STATES DISTILLED PRODUCTS CO., INC.; *U.S. Private*, pg. 4298
UNITED STATES ENDOSCOPY GROUP, INC.—See STERIS plc; *Int'l*, pg. 7211
UNITED STATES ENRICHMENT CORPORATION—See Centrus Energy Corp.; *U.S. Public*, pg. 474
UNITED STATES ENVIRONMENTAL PROTECTION AGENCY; *U.S. Private*, pg. 4299
UNITED STATES ENVIRONMENTAL SERVICES, LLC—See The Halifax Group LLC; *U.S. Private*, pg. 4042
UNITED STATES FIRE INSURANCE COMPANY—See Fairfax Financial Holdings Limited; *Int'l*, pg. 2606
UNITED STATES FOUNDRY MANUFACTURING INC.—See Eagle Manufacturing Group; *U.S. Private*, pg. 1309
UNITED STATES GASOLINE FUND, LP—See The Marygold Companies, Inc.; *U.S. Public*, pg. 2112
UNITED STATES GEAR CORPORATION; *U.S. Private*, pg. 4299
UNITED STATES GOLD AND TREASURY INVESTMENT TRUST; *U.S. Private*, pg. 4299
UNITED STATES HANG GLIDING & PARAGLIDING ASSOCIATION, INC.; *U.S. Private*, pg. 4299
UNITED STATES HOMELAND INVESTIGATIONS INC; *U.S. Private*, pg. 4299
UNITED STATES INFO SYSTEMS INC.; *U.S. Private*, pg. 4299
UNITED STATES JUSTICE FOUNDATION; *U.S. Private*, pg. 4299

UNITED STATES LIABILITY INSURANCE COMPANY—See Berkshire Hathaway Inc.; *U.S. Public*, pg. 319
THE UNITED STATES LIFE INSURANCE COMPANY IN THE CITY OF NEW YORK—See American International Group, Inc.; *U.S. Public*, pg. 105
UNITED STATES LIME & MINERALS, INC.; *U.S. Public*, pg. 2236
UNITED STATES LUGGAGE COMPANY, LLC; *U.S. Private*, pg. 4299
UNITED STATES MARBLE, INC.—See O2 Investment Partners, LLC; *U.S. Private*, pg. 2982
UNITED STATES MARBLE, INC.—See Oakland Standard Co., LLC; *U.S. Private*, pg. 2985
UNITED STATES MARITIME ALLIANCE, LTD.; *U.S. Private*, pg. 4299
UNITED STATES MEAT EXPORT FEDERATION INC.; *U.S. Private*, pg. 4299
UNITED STATES MEDICAL SUPPLY, INC.—See Court Square Capital Partners, L.P.; *U.S. Private*, pg. 1069
UNITED STATES MINERAL PRODUCTS COMPANY—See SK Capital Partners, LP; *U.S. Private*, pg. 3680
UNITED STATES MINT; *U.S. Private*, pg. 4299
UNITED STATES NAME PLATE—See LaFrance Corporation; *U.S. Private*, pg. 2373
UNITED STATES NATURAL GAS FUND, LP—See The Marygold Companies, Inc.; *U.S. Public*, pg. 2113
UNITED STATES OIL FUND, LP; *U.S. Public*, pg. 2236
UNITED STATES OIL & GAS CORPORATION; *U.S. Private*, pg. 4299
UNITED STATES OLYMPIC COMMITTEE; *U.S. Private*, pg. 4299
THE UNITED STATES PLAYING CARD COMPANY—See Cartamundi N.V.; *Int'l*, pg. 1348
UNITED STATES POLO ASSOCIATION, INC.; *U.S. Private*, pg. 4299
THE UNITED STATES PONY CLUBS INC.; *U.S. Private*, pg. 4129
UNITED STATES POSTAL SERVICE; *U.S. Private*, pg. 4299
UNITED STATES REALTY & INVESTMENT COMPANY; *U.S. Private*, pg. 4299
UNITED STATES SEAFOODS, LLC; *U.S. Private*, pg. 4299
UNITED STATES SERVICE INDUSTRIES INC.; *U.S. Private*, pg. 4300
UNITED STATES SERVICES GROUP, LLC; *U.S. Private*, pg. 4300
UNITED STATES SHORT OIL FUND, LP—See The Marygold Companies, Inc.; *U.S. Public*, pg. 2113
UNITED STATES SOCIETY ON DAMS; *U.S. Private*, pg. 4300
UNITED STATES STEEL, AIRCRAFT DIVISION—See United States Steel Corporation; *U.S. Public*, pg. 2237
UNITED STATES STEEL CORP. - BRADDOCK—See United States Steel Corporation; *U.S. Public*, pg. 2237
UNITED STATES STEEL CORP. - GARY—See United States Steel Corporation; *U.S. Public*, pg. 2237
UNITED STATES STEEL CORPORATION RESEARCH AND TECHNOLOGY CENTER—See United States Steel Corporation; *U.S. Public*, pg. 2237
UNITED STATES STEEL CORPORATION; *U.S. Public*, pg. 2236
UNITED STATES STEEL CORP.—See United States Steel Corporation; *U.S. Public*, pg. 2237
UNITED STATES STEEL CORP.—See United States Steel Corporation; *U.S. Public*, pg. 2237
UNITED STATES STEEL CORP.—See United States Steel Corporation; *U.S. Public*, pg. 2237
UNITED STATES STEEL CORP.—See United States Steel Corporation; *U.S. Public*, pg. 2237
UNITED STATES STEEL CORP.—See United States Steel Corporation; *U.S. Public*, pg. 2237
UNITED STATES STEEL CORP.—See United States Steel Corporation; *U.S. Public*, pg. 2237
UNITED STATES STEEL CORP.—See United States Steel Corporation; *U.S. Public*, pg. 2237
UNITED STATES STEEL GREAT LAKES WORKS—See United States Steel Corporation; *U.S. Public*, pg. 2237
UNITED STATES STEEL INTERNATIONAL, INC.—See United States Steel Corporation; *U.S. Public*, pg. 2237
UNITED STATES STEEL MIDWEST—See United States Steel Corporation; *U.S. Public*, pg. 2237
UNITED STATES STEEL TUBULAR PRODUCTS—See United States Steel Corporation; *U.S. Public*, pg. 2237
UNITED STATES STOVE COMPANY; *U.S. Private*, pg. 4300
UNITED STATES SUGAR CORPORATION; *U.S. Private*, pg. 4300
UNITED STATES SURETY COMPANY—See Tokio Marine Holdings, Inc.; *Int'l*, pg. 7784
UNITED STATES TELECOM ASSOCIATION; *U.S. Private*, pg. 4300
UNITED STATES TRAFFIC NETWORK, LLC; *U.S. Private*, pg. 4300
UNITED STATES UNIVERSITY, INC.—See Aspen Group, Inc.; *U.S. Public*, pg. 213
UNITED STATES WELDING, INC.; *U.S. Private*, pg. 4300
UNITED STATIONERS HONG KONG LIMITED—See Sycamore Partners Management, LP; *U.S. Private*, pg. 3897

COMPANY NAME INDEX

UNITED STATIONERS SUPPLY CO.—See Sycamore Partners Management, LP; *U.S. Private*, pg. 3896
UNITED STATIONERS TECHNOLOGY SERVICES LLC—See Sycamore Partners Management, LP; *U.S. Private*, pg. 3897
UNITED STATIONS PROPRIETARY LIMITED—See African Media Entertainment Limited; *Int'l*, pg. 192
UNITED STATIONS RADIO NETWORKS INC.; *U.S. Private*, pg. 4300
UNITED STEEL ENGINEERING & CONSTRUCTION CORP.—See China Steel Corporation; *Int'l*, pg. 1556
UNITED STEEL INC.; *U.S. Private*, pg. 4300
UNITED STEEL SERVICE, INC.; *U.S. Private*, pg. 4300
UNITED STEEL SUPPLY, LLC—See Steel Dynamics, Inc.; *U.S. Public*, pg. 1942
UNITED STEELWORKERS OF AMERICA; *Int'l*, pg. 8073
UNITED STRENGTH POWER HOLDINGS LIMITED; *Int'l*, pg. 8073
UNITED STRUCTURES OF AMERICA INC.; *U.S. Private*, pg. 4300
UNITED STUDENT AID FUNDS INC.; *U.S. Private*, pg. 4300
UNITED SUBCONTRACTORS, INC.—See TopBuild Corp.; *U.S. Public*, pg. 2163
UNITED SUGAR COMPANY—See A.K. Al-Muhaidib & Sons Group of Companies; *Int'l*, pg. 24
UNITED SUGARS CORP.—See American Crystal Sugar Company; *U.S. Public*, pg. 98
UNITED SUGARS CORP.—See Minn-Dak Farmers Cooperative; *U.S. Private*, pg. 2742
UNITED SUGARS CORP.—See United States Sugar Corporation; *U.S. Private*, pg. 4300
UNITED SUPER MARKETS HOLDINGS, INC.—See AEON Co., Ltd.; *Int'l*, pg. 178
UNITED SUPERMARKETS, LLC—See Cerberus Capital Management, LP; *U.S. Private*, pg. 836
UNITED SUPERMARKETS; *U.S. Private*, pg. 4300
UNITED SUPPLIERS, INC.—See Land O'Lakes, Inc.; *U.S. Private*, pg. 2383
UNITED SUPPLY; *U.S. Private*, pg. 4300
UNITED SURGICAL ASSISTANTS, INC.; *U.S. Private*, pg. 4300
UNITED SURGICAL PARTNERS INTERNATIONAL, INC.—See Tenet Healthcare Corporation; *U.S. Public*, pg. 2013
UNITED SWEETHEARTS GARMENT SDN BHD—See MWE Holdings Berhad; *Int'l*, pg. 5110
UNITED SYSTEMS, INC.; *U.S. Private*, pg. 4300
UNITED SYSTEMS TECHNOLOGY, INC.—See StarDyne Technologies Inc.; *Int'l*, pg. 7176
UNITED TACONITE, LLC—See Cleveland-Cliffs, Inc.; *U.S. Public*, pg. 514
UNITED TACTICAL SYSTEMS, LLC; *U.S. Private*, pg. 4301
UNITED TAIWAN BANK—See Taiwan Cooperative Financial Holding Co., Ltd.; *Int'l*, pg. 7419
UNITED TALENT AGENCY, INC.; *U.S. Private*, pg. 4301
UNITED TANK TECHNOLOGY INC.—See Tailwind Capital Group, LLC; *U.S. Private*, pg. 3924
UNITED TEACHER ASSOCIATES INSURANCE COMPANY—See INNOVATE Corp.; *U.S. Public*, pg. 1126
UNITED TEACHERS LOS ANGELES; *U.S. Private*, pg. 4301
THE UNITED TEACHERS OF DADE; *U.S. Private*, pg. 4129
UNITED TECHNICAL & ALLIED SERVICES LIMITED—See Chellarams Plc; *Int'l*, pg. 1460
UNITED TECHNICAL SERVICES—See Mechanical Equipment Company Inc.; *U.S. Private*, pg. 2648
UNITED TECHNOLOGIES AUSTRALIA HOLDINGS LIMITED—See RTX Corporation; *U.S. Public*, pg. 1825
UNITED TECHNOLOGIES CANADA, LTD.—See RTX Corporation; *U.S. Public*, pg. 1825
UNITED TECHNOLOGIES ELECTRONIC CONTROLS, INC.—See Carrier Global Corporation; *U.S. Public*, pg. 441
UNITED TECHNOLOGIES INTERNATIONAL CORPORATION-ASIA PRIVATE LIMITED—See RTX Corporation; *U.S. Public*, pg. 1825
UNITED TECHNOLOGIES RESEARCH CENTER—See RTX Corporation; *U.S. Public*, pg. 1825
UNITED TECHNOLOGY GROUP, LLC—See Wells Fargo & Company; *U.S. Public*, pg. 2344
UNITED TECH PARK PTE LTD—See Yanlord Land Group Limited; *Int'l*, pg. 8563
UNITED TELEPHONE COMPANY OF PENNSYLVANIA LLC, THE—See Lumen Technologies, Inc.; *U.S. Public*, pg. 1348
UNITED TELEPHONE SOUTHEAST LLC—See Lumen Technologies, Inc.; *U.S. Public*, pg. 1348
UNITED TENNESSEE BANKSHARES, INC.; *U.S. Public*, pg. 2237
UNITED TEST & ASSEMBLY CENTER LTD.—See UTAC Holdings Ltd.; *Int'l*, pg. 8100
UNITED TEXTILES LIMITED; *Int'l*, pg. 8073
UNITED THAI LOGISTICS CO., LTD.—See Maruzen Showa Unyu Co., Ltd.; *Int'l*, pg. 4716

UNITED THAI SHIPPING CORP LIMITED—See IMC Pan Asia Alliance Pte. Ltd.; *Int'l*, pg. 3621
UNITED THAI WAREHOUSE CO., LTD.—See Maruzen Showa Unyu Co., Ltd.; *Int'l*, pg. 4716
UNITED THERAPEUTICS CORPORATION; *U.S. Public*, pg. 2238
UNITED THERAPEUTICS EUROPE LTD.—See United Therapeutics Corporation; *U.S. Public*, pg. 2238
UNITED THROUGH READING; *U.S. Private*, pg. 4301
UNITED TITLE GUARANTY AGENCY, LLC—See Stewart Information Services Corporation; *U.S. Public*, pg. 1948
UNITED TITLE OF LOUISIANA, INC.—See Knox Capital Holdings, LLC; *U.S. Private*, pg. 2324
UNITED TOOL & DIE COMPANY; *U.S. Private*, pg. 4301
UNITED TOOL & FASTENER COMPANY; *U.S. Private*, pg. 4301
UNITED TOTE CANADA, INC.—See Churchill Downs, Inc.; *U.S. Public*, pg. 494
UNITED TRADING SYSTEM—See senata GmbH; *Int'l*, pg. 6707
UNITED TRANSFORMERS ELECTRIC COMPANY—See Bawan Company; *Int'l*, pg. 900
UNITED TRANSMISSION EXCHANGE, INC.—See Blue Point Capital Partners, LLC; *U.S. Private*, pg. 591
UNITED TRANSPORTATION UNION INSURANCE ASSOCIATION; *U.S. Private*, pg. 4301
UNITED TRUST (ANGUILLA) LIMITED—See United International Holdings B.V.; *Int'l*, pg. 8068
THE UNITED TRUST COMPANY N.V.—See United International Holdings B.V.; *Int'l*, pg. 8068
UNITED TRUST MANAGEMENT (ARUBA) UTM N.V.—See United International Holdings B.V.; *Int'l*, pg. 8068
UNITED TUBE CORPORATION; *U.S. Private*, pg. 4301
UNITED U-LI CORPORATION BERHAD; *Int'l*, pg. 8073
UNITED U-LI GOODLITE SDN. BHD.—See United U-LI Corporation Berhad; *Int'l*, pg. 8073
UNITED UNDERWRITERS INSURANCE; *U.S. Private*, pg. 4301
UNITED UNIFORM CO., INC.—See Kanders & Company, Inc.; *U.S. Private*, pg. 2259
UNITED UNIVERSAL REAL ESTATE CONSULTING COMPANY—See Kuwait Projects Company (Holding) K.S.C.P.; *Int'l*, pg. 4347
UNITED UNIVERSAL REAL ESTATE W.L.L—See Kuwait Projects Company (Holding) K.S.C.P.; *Int'l*, pg. 4347
UNITED URBAN INVESTMENT CORPORATION; *Int'l*, pg. 8073
UNITED UTILITIES GROUP PLC; *Int'l*, pg. 8073
UNITED UTILITIES, INC.—See Liberty Broadband Corporation; *U.S. Public*, pg. 1310
UNITED UTILITIES INTERNATIONAL LTD.—See United Utilities Group plc; *Int'l*, pg. 8073
UNITED UTILITIES PACIFIC HOLDINGS BV—See Manila Water Company, Inc.; *Int'l*, pg. 4671
UNITED UTILITY SERVICES, LLC—See Bernhard Capital Partners Management, LP; *U.S. Private*, pg. 537
UNITED UTILITY SUPPLY COOPERATIVE INC.; *U.S. Private*, pg. 4301
UNITED VACATIONS, INC.—See United Airlines Holdings, Inc.; *U.S. Public*, pg. 2229
UNITED VALLEY BANK; *U.S. Private*, pg. 4301
UNITED VAN DER HORST LTD.; *Int'l*, pg. 8073
UNITED VAN LINES, LLC—See UniGroup, Inc.; *U.S. Private*, pg. 4283
UNITED VASCULAR OF HUNTSVILLE, LLC—See Community Health Systems, Inc.; *U.S. Public*, pg. 557
UNITED VEGGIES CO., LTD.—See Zensho Holdings Co., Ltd.; *Int'l*, pg. 8635
UNITED VERTICAL MEDIA GMBH; *Int'l*, pg. 8073
UNITED VISION GROUP INC.; *U.S. Private*, pg. 4301
UNITED VISION LOGISTICS HOLDING CORP.—See Welsh, Carson, Anderson & Stowe; *U.S. Private*, pg. 4480
UNITED VISION LOGISTICS MEXICO—See Welsh, Carson, Anderson & Stowe; *U.S. Private*, pg. 4480
UNITED VISIONS GMBH—See WPP plc; *Int'l*, pg. 8463
UNITED WAGON COMPANY RESEARCH & PRODUCTION CORPORATION PJSC; *Int'l*, pg. 8073
UNITED WAREHOUSE CO. INC.; *U.S. Private*, pg. 4301
UNITED WAREHOUSE COMPANY; *U.S. Private*, pg. 4301
UNITED WATER INTERNATIONAL—See KBR, Inc.; *U.S. Public*, pg. 1216
UNITED WATER INTERNATIONAL—See Veolia Environnement S.A.; *Int'l*, pg. 8156
UNITED WATER SERVICES; *U.S. Private*, pg. 4301
UNITED WAY OF GREATER MERCER COUNTY, INC.—See United Way of the Virginia Peninsula; *U.S. Private*, pg. 4301
UNITED WAY OF THE VIRGINIA PENINSULA; *U.S. Private*, pg. 4301
UNITED WAY WORLDWIDE; *U.S. Private*, pg. 4301
UNITED WEHCO INC.—See Wehco Media, Inc.; *U.S. Private*, pg. 4469
UNITED WESTERN COOP; *U.S. Private*, pg. 4301
UNITED WESTERN ENTERPRISES, INC.—See Ancor Holdings, L.P.; *U.S. Private*, pg. 275
UNITED WHOLESALE LUMBER CO.—See Fruit Growers Supply Co.; *U.S. Private*, pg. 1617

UNITI GROUP INC.

UNITED WHOLESALE MORTGAGE, LLC—See The Gores Group, LLC; *U.S. Private*, pg. 4035
UNITED WHOLESALE (SCOTLAND) LTD.; *Int'l*, pg. 8073
UNITED WINDOW & DOOR MANUFACTURING; *U.S. Private*, pg. 4302
UNITED WIRE FACTORIES COMPANY; *Int'l*, pg. 8073
UNITED WISCONSIN GRAIN PRODUCERS, LLC; *U.S. Private*, pg. 4302
UNITED WISCONSIN INSURANCE COMPANY—See Accident Fund Insurance Company of America; *U.S. Private*, pg. 53
UNITED WORLD HOLDING GROUP LTD.; *Int'l*, pg. 8074
UNITED WORLD LIFE INSURANCE COMPANY—See Mutual of Omaha Insurance Company; *U.S. Private*, pg. 2820
U-NITE FASTENERS TECHNOLOGY AB—See Lindab International AB; *Int'l*, pg. 4504
UNITE FINANCE LTD.—See The Unite Group plc; *Int'l*, pg. 7697
UNITE FINANCE ONE (PROPERTY) LTD.—See The Unite Group plc; *Int'l*, pg. 7697
THE UNITE GROUP PLC; *Int'l*, pg. 7697
UNITE & GROW, INC.; *Int'l*, pg. 8063
UNITE HERE HEALTH; *U.S. Private*, pg. 4287
UNITE HERE; *U.S. Private*, pg. 4287
UNITE HOLDINGS PLC—See The Unite Group plc; *Int'l*, pg. 7697
UNITEK ELEKTRIK MAKINE OTOMASYON SAN. VE TIC. A.S.—See Komax Holding AG; *Int'l*, pg. 4241
UNITEK GLOBAL SERVICES, INC.—See Littlejohn & Co., LLC; *U.S. Private*, pg. 2472
UNITEK GLOBAL SERVICES, INC.—See New Mountain Capital, LLC; *U.S. Private*, pg. 2903
UNITEK INFORMATION SYSTEMS; *U.S. Private*, pg. 4302
UNITEK INSULATION INC.—See Pacific Marine & Supply Co. Ltd. Inc.; *U.S. Private*, pg. 3068
UNITEKNO CO., LTD. - AAAN FACTORY—See UNITEKNO Co.,Ltd.; *Int'l*, pg. 8074
UNITEKNO CO.,LTD.; *Int'l*, pg. 8074
UNITEK SERVICIOS DE ASESOIRIA ESPECIALIZAD S.A.—See Quaker Chemical Corporation; *U.S. Public*, pg. 1747
UNITEK SOLVENT SERVICES INC.; *U.S. Private*, pg. 4302
UNITEK TECHNICAL LLC—See Pacific Marine & Supply Co. Ltd. Inc.; *U.S. Private*, pg. 3068
UNITEL HIGH TECHNOLOGY CORP.; *Int'l*, pg. 8074
UNITELLER FINANCIAL SERVICES; *U.S. Private*, pg. 4302
UNITE LONDON LTD.—See The Unite Group plc; *Int'l*, pg. 7697
UNITEL S.A.; *Int'l*, pg. 8074
UNITE MODULAR SOLUTIONS LTD.—See The Unite Group plc; *Int'l*, pg. 7697
UNITEMP LIMITED—See ESPEC Corp.; *Int'l*, pg. 2505
UNITE PRIVATE NETWORKS, LLC—See Cox Enterprises, Inc.; *U.S. Private*, pg. 1078
UNITEST INC.; *Int'l*, pg. 8074
UNITEX AUSTRALIA PTY LTD.—See Sto SE & Co. KGaA; *Int'l*, pg. 7219
UNITEX-HARTMANN S.A.—See PAUL HARTMANN AG; *Int'l*, pg. 5762
UNIT & GUEST CO., LTD.—See TSI Holdings Co., Ltd.; *Int'l*, pg. 7951
UNITHAI MARUZEN LOGISTICS (VIETNAM) CORP.—See Maruzen Showa Unyu Co., Ltd.; *Int'l*, pg. 4716
UNITHAI SHIPYARD AND ENGINEERING LIMITED—See IMC Pan Asia Alliance Pte. Ltd.; *Int'l*, pg. 3621
UNITHERM BARUTH GMBH—See Pfleiderer GmbH; *Int'l*, pg. 5836
UNITHER PHARMACEUTICALS SAS—See Equistone Partners Europe Limited; *Int'l*, pg. 2487
UNITHER TELMED, LTD.—See United Therapeutics Corporation; *U.S. Public*, pg. 2238
UNITH LTD; *Int'l*, pg. 8074
UNITI FIBER—See Uniti Group Inc.; *U.S. Public*, pg. 2253
UNITI GROUP INC.; *U.S. Public*, pg. 2253
UNITIKA AMERICA CORPORATION—See Unitika Ltd.; *Int'l*, pg. 8074
UNITIKA (BEIJING) TRADING CO., LTD.—See Unitika Ltd.; *Int'l*, pg. 8074
UNITIKA DO BRASIL INDUSTIA TEXTIL LIMITADE—See Unitika Ltd.; *Int'l*, pg. 8075
UNITIKA EMBLEM CHINA LTD.—See Unitika Ltd.; *Int'l*, pg. 8075
UNITIKA ESTATE CO., LTD.—See Unitika Ltd.; *Int'l*, pg. 8075
UNITIKA EUROPE GMBH—See Unitika Ltd.; *Int'l*, pg. 8075
UNITIKA GARMENTS TECHNOLOGY & RESEARCH LABORATORISE LTD.—See Unitika Ltd.; *Int'l*, pg. 8075
UNITIKA GLASS FIBER CO., LTD.—See Unitika Ltd.; *Int'l*, pg. 8075
UNITIKA GOLFING TARUI CO., LTD.—See Unitika Ltd.; *Int'l*, pg. 8075
UNITIKA (HONG KONG) LTD.—See Unitika Ltd.; *Int'l*, pg. 8075
UNITIKA LOGISTICS CO., LTD.—See Unitika Ltd.; *Int'l*, pg. 8075

UNITI GROUP INC.

CORPORATE AFFILIATIONS

UNITIKA LTD. - ADVANCED MATERIALS DIVISION—See Unitika Ltd.; *Int'l*, pg. 8075
UNITIKA LTD. - ENVIRONMENT & ENGINEERING DIVISION—See Unitika Ltd.; *Int'l*, pg. 8075
UNITIKA LTD. - FILM DIVISION—See Unitika Ltd.; *Int'l*, pg. 8075
UNITIKA LTD. - HEALTH & AMENITY DIVISION—See Unitika Ltd.; *Int'l*, pg. 8075
UNITIKA LTD. - NONWOVEN DIVISION—See Unitika Ltd.; *Int'l*, pg. 8075
UNITIKA LTD. - OKAZAKI PLANT—See Unitika Ltd.; *Int'l*, pg. 8075
UNITIKA LTD. - PLASTICS DIVISION—See Unitika Ltd.; *Int'l*, pg. 8075
UNITIKA LTD. - SAKOSHI PLANT—See Unitika Ltd.; *Int'l*, pg. 8075
UNITIKA LTD.; *Int'l*, pg. 8074
UNITIKA LTD. - TARUI PLANT—See Unitika Ltd.; *Int'l*, pg. 8075
UNITIKA LTD. - TOKIWA MILL—See Unitika Ltd.; *Int'l*, pg. 8075
UNITIKA LTD. - TOYOHASHI PLANT—See Unitika Ltd.; *Int'l*, pg. 8075
UNITIKA LTD. - U IMIDE DIVISION—See Unitika Ltd.; *Int'l*, pg. 8075
UNITIKA LTD. - UJI PLANT—See Unitika Ltd.; *Int'l*, pg. 8075
UNITIKA MATE CO., LTD.—See Unitika Ltd.; *Int'l*, pg. 8075
UNITIKA NARIWA CO., LTD.—See Unitika Ltd.; *Int'l*, pg. 8075
UNITIKA NP CLOTH CO., LTD.—See Unitika Ltd.; *Int'l*, pg. 8075
UNITIKA PLANT ENGINEERING CO., LTD.—See Unitika Ltd.; *Int'l*, pg. 8075
UNITIKA (SHANGHAI) LTD.—See Unitika Ltd.; *Int'l*, pg. 8075
UNITIKA SPARKLITE LTD.—See Unitika Ltd.; *Int'l*, pg. 8075
UNITIKA TECHNOS CO., LTD.—See Unitika Ltd.; *Int'l*, pg. 8075
UNITIKA TRADING CO., LTD.—See Unitika Ltd.; *Int'l*, pg. 8075
UNITIL CORPORATION; *U.S. Public*, pg. 2253
UNITIL ENERGY SYSTEMS, INC.—See Unitil Corporation; *U.S. Public*, pg. 2253
UNITIL POWER CORPORATION—See Unitil Corporation; *U.S. Public*, pg. 2253
UNITIL REALTY CORP.—See Unitil Corporation; *U.S. Public*, pg. 2253
UNITIL RESOURCES, INC.—See Unitil Corporation; *U.S. Public*, pg. 2253
UNITIL SERVICE CORP.—See Unitil Corporation; *U.S. Public*, pg. 2253
UNITIL—See Unitil Corporation; *U.S. Public*, pg. 2253
UNITI SA; *Int'l*, pg. 8074
UNITIVE ELECTRONICS INC.; *U.S. Private*, pg. 4302
UNITIV, INC.—See Ludvik Holdings, Inc.; *U.S. Private*, pg. 2512
UNITIZE COMPANY INC.; *U.S. Private*, pg. 4302
UNIT L TRIDENT PKHALTON LEA—See United Carpets Group PLC; *Int'l*, pg. 8065
UNITOL SAS—See Tata Sons Limited; *Int'l*, pg. 7473
UNITO VERSAND & DIENSTLEISTUNGEN GMBH—See Otto GmbH & Co. KG; *Int'l*, pg. 5663
UNIT PETROLEUM COMPANY—See Unit Corporation; *U.S. Public*, pg. 2228
UNITPOOL AG—See Brambles Limited; *Int'l*, pg. 1139
UNITRAC RAILROAD MATERIALS, INC.—See Westinghouse Air Brake Technologies Corporation; *U.S. Public*, pg. 2359
UNITRACT SYRINGE PTY LIMITED—See Unilife Corporation; *U.S. Private*, pg. 4283
UNITRADE 745 (PTY) LTD.—See Metair Investments Limited; *Int'l*, pg. 4845
UNITRADE HOLLAND B.V.—See Dole plc; *Int'l*, pg. 2158
UNITRADE INDUSTRIES BERHAD; *Int'l*, pg. 8075
UNITRA INTERNATIONAL LLC—See Mezzan Holding Co KSC; *Int'l*, pg. 4870
UNITRANS ASIA PACIFIC PTY. LTD.—See Steinhoff International Holdings N.V.; *Int'l*, pg. 7195
UNITRANS CORPORATION, INC.—See Q International Courier, LLC; *U.S. Private*, pg. 3312
UNITRANSFER INTERNATIONAL LTD.—See Unibank S.A.; *Int'l*, pg. 8030
UNITRANS FREIGHT & LOGISTICS DIVISION—See Steinhoff International Holdings N.V.; *Int'l*, pg. 7195
UNITRANS HOLDINGS (PTY) LTD.—See Steinhoff International Holdings N.V.; *Int'l*, pg. 7194
UNITRANS INTERNATIONAL CORP.—See AIT Worldwide Logistics, Inc.; *U.S. Private*, pg. 143
UNITRANS PASSENGER (PTY) LIMITED—See Steinhoff International Holdings N.V.; *Int'l*, pg. 7194
UNITRANS SA; *Int'l*, pg. 8075
UNITRANS SUPPLY CHAIN SOLUTIONS (PTY) LTD.—See Steinhoff International Holdings N.V.; *Int'l*, pg. 7194
UNITREND LTD.—See The Interpublic Group of Companies, Inc.; *U.S. Public*, pg. 2102

UNITRENDS, INC.—See Insight Venture Management, LLC; *U.S. Private*, pg. 2091
UNI TREND TECHNOLOGY CHINA CO., LTD.; *Int'l*, pg. 8028
UNITRIN ADVANTAGE INSURANCE COMPANY—See Kemper Corporation; *U.S. Public*, pg. 1221
UNITRIN COUNTY MUTUAL INSURANCE COMPANY—See Kemper Corporation; *U.S. Public*, pg. 1221
UNITRIN DIRECT PROPERTY & CASUALTY COMPANY—See Kemper Corporation; *U.S. Public*, pg. 1221
UNITRON CUSTOMIZED SYSTEMS—See Unitron Inc.; *U.S. Private*, pg. 4302
UNITRONEX CORPORATION; *U.S. Private*, pg. 4302
UNITRON HEARING AB—See Sonova Holding AG; *Int'l*, pg. 7101
UNITRON HEARING AS—See Sonova Holding AG; *Int'l*, pg. 7101
UNITRON HEARING B.V.—See Sonova Holding AG; *Int'l*, pg. 7101
UNITRON HEARING COLOMBIA LTD.—See Sonova Holding AG; *Int'l*, pg. 7101
UNITRON HEARING GMBH—See Sonova Holding AG; *Int'l*, pg. 7101
UNITRON HEARING, INC.—See Sonova Holding AG; *Int'l*, pg. 7101
UNITRON HEARING LTD.—See Sonova Holding AG; *Int'l*, pg. 7101
UNITRON HEARING (SUZHOU) CO., LTD.—See Sonova Holding AG; *Int'l*, pg. 7101
UNITRONIC AG—See Lagercrantz Group AB; *Int'l*, pg. 4395
UNITRONICS (1989) (R"G) LTD.; *Int'l*, pg. 8075
UNITRONICS INC.—See Unitronics (1989) (R"G) Ltd.; *Int'l*, pg. 8075
UNITRON INC.; *U.S. Private*, pg. 4302
UNITRONIX CORP.; *Int'l*, pg. 8075
UNITRON LEISURE PRODS.—See Unitron Inc.; *U.S. Private*, pg. 4302
UNITRON TECH CO., LIMITED—See Serial System Ltd.; *Int'l*, pg. 6723
UNITRUST INDUSTRIAL CORP.; *U.S. Private*, pg. 4302
THE UNIT SERVICED APARTMENTS LIMITED—See Emperor International Holdings Limited; *Int'l*, pg. 2386
UNITS SETS, INC.—See Rotary Forms Press, Inc.; *U.S. Private*, pg. 3486
UNIT-T BV—See Solutions 30 SE; *Int'l*, pg. 7077
UNITTEC CO., LTD.; *Int'l*, pg. 8075
UNITUS COMMUNITY CREDIT UNION; *U.S. Private*, pg. 4302
UNITY4 HOLDINGS PTY LTD; *Int'l*, pg. 8076
UNITY ALUMINUM, INC.; *U.S. Private*, pg. 4302
UNITY BANCORP, INC.; *U.S. Public*, pg. 2253
UNITY BANK PLC.; *Int'l*, pg. 8076
UNITY BANK—See Unity Bancorp, Inc.; *U.S. Public*, pg. 2253
UNITY BIOTECHNOLOGY, INC.; *U.S. Public*, pg. 2253
UNITY DATA & ELECTRICAL SERVICES—See Unity Electric Co. Inc.; *U.S. Private*, pg. 4302
UNITY DELAWARE INVESTMENT 2, INC.—See Unity Bancorp, Inc.; *U.S. Public*, pg. 2253
UNITY ELECTRIC CO. INC.; *U.S. Private*, pg. 4302
UNITY ELECTRIC LLC—See Unity Electric Co. Inc.; *U.S. Private*, pg. 4302
UNITY ENTERPRISE HOLDINGS LIMITED; *Int'l*, pg. 8076
UNITY FINANCIAL LIFE INSURANCE COMPANY; *U.S. Private*, pg. 4302
UNITY FINANCIAL SERVICES, INC.—See Unity Bancorp, Inc.; *U.S. Public*, pg. 2253
UNITY GROUP HOLDINGS INTERNATIONAL LIMITED; *Int'l*, pg. 8076
UNITY HEALTH CARE, INC.; *U.S. Private*, pg. 4303
UNITY HEALTH HOSPICE—See Enhabit, Inc.; *U.S. Public*, pg. 768
UNITY HEALTH - WHITE COUNTY MEDICAL CENTER; *U.S. Private*, pg. 4303
UNITY HOUSE OF CAYUGA COUNTY, INC.; *U.S. Private*, pg. 4303
UNITY HOUSE OF TROY, INC.; *U.S. Private*, pg. 4303
UNITY LINE—See Polska Zegluga Morska; *Int'l*, pg. 5911
UNITY MANUFACTURING COMPANY; *U.S. Private*, pg. 4303
UNITYMEDIA GMBH—See Permira Advisers LLP; *Int'l*, pg. 5808
UNITYMEDIA INTERNATIONAL GMBH—See Liberty Global plc; *Int'l*, pg. 4485
UNITYMEDIA MANAGEMENT GMBH—See Permira Advisers LLP; *Int'l*, pg. 5808
UNITYMEDIA NRW GMBH—See Permira Advisers LLP; *Int'l*, pg. 5808
UNITY MICROELECTRONICS, INC.—See Unity Opto Technology Co., Ltd.; *Int'l*, pg. 8076
UNITY MORTGAGE CORP.; *U.S. Private*, pg. 4303
UNITY NATIONAL BANK—See Park National Corporation; *U.S. Public*, pg. 1638
UNITY NJ REIT, INC.—See Unity Bancorp, Inc.; *U.S. Public*, pg. 2253
UNITY OPTO TECHNOLOGY CO., LTD.; *Int'l*, pg. 8076

UNITY PACIFIC GROUP; *Int'l*, pg. 8076
UNITY PARTNERS LP; *U.S. Public*, pg. 2253
UNITYPOINT HEALTH; *U.S. Private*, pg. 4303
UNITY PRINTING CO., INC.; *U.S. Private*, pg. 4303
UNITY SEMICONDUCTOR CORPORATION—See Rambus Inc.; *U.S. Public*, pg. 1762
UNITY SOFTWARE INC.; *U.S. Public*, pg. 2254
UNIVACCO TECHNOLOGY, INC,; *Int'l*, pg. 8076
UNIVAC DESIGN & ENGINEERING PTE LTD—See Venture Corporation Limited; *Int'l*, pg. 8151
UNIVA CORPORATION—See Altair Engineering, Inc.; *U.S. Public*, pg. 86
UNIVAC PRECISION ENGINEERING PTE LTD—See Venture Corporation Limited; *Int'l*, pg. 8151
UNIVAC PRECISION, INC—See Venture Corporation Limited; *Int'l*, pg. 8151
UNIVAC PRECISION PLASTICS (SHANGHAI) CO., LTD—See Venture Corporation Limited; *Int'l*, pg. 8151
UNIVAC PRECISION PLASTICS (SUZHOU) CO., LTD.—See Venture Corporation Limited; *Int'l*, pg. 8151
UNIVA FOODS LIMITED; *Int'l*, pg. 8076
UNIVAIL-RODAMCO AS—See Unibail-Rodamco-Westfield SE; *Int'l*, pg. 8030
UNIVANCE CORPORATION - HAMAMATSU PLANT—See Univance Corporation; *Int'l*, pg. 8076
UNIVANCE CORPORATION - KOSAI PLANT—See Univance Corporation; *Int'l*, pg. 8076
UNIVANCE CORPORATION; *Int'l*, pg. 8076
UNIVANCE INC.—See Univance Corporation; *Int'l*, pg. 8076
UNIVANCE (THAILAND) CO., LTD.—See Univance Corporation; *Int'l*, pg. 8076
UNIVANICH PALM OIL PUBLIC COMPANY LIMITED; *Int'l*, pg. 8076
UNIVA OAK HOLDINGS LIMITED; *Int'l*, pg. 8076
UNIVAR AB—See Apollo Global Management, Inc.; *U.S. Public*, pg. 165
UNIVAR AG—See Apollo Global Management, Inc.; *U.S. Public*, pg. 165
UNIVAR BELGIUM NV—See Apollo Global Management, Inc.; *U.S. Public*, pg. 165
UNIVAR BENELUX—See Apollo Global Management, Inc.; *U.S. Public*, pg. 165
UNIVAR BRASIL LTDA.—See Apollo Global Management, Inc.; *U.S. Public*, pg. 165
UNIVAR BV—See Apollo Global Management, Inc.; *U.S. Public*, pg. 165
UNIVAR CANADA LTD.—See Apollo Global Management, Inc.; *U.S. Public*, pg. 165
UNIVAR CZECH SRO—See Apollo Global Management, Inc.; *U.S. Public*, pg. 165
UNIVAR EGYPT LLC—See Apollo Global Management, Inc.; *U.S. Public*, pg. 165
UNIVAR EUROPE HOLDINGS B.V.—See Apollo Global Management, Inc.; *U.S. Public*, pg. 165
UNIVAR FRANCE SNC—See Apollo Global Management, Inc.; *U.S. Public*, pg. 166
UNIVAR FRANCE—See Apollo Global Management, Inc.; *U.S. Public*, pg. 165
UNIVAR GMBH—See Apollo Global Management, Inc.; *U.S. Public*, pg. 165
UNIVAR HUNGARY SALES LIMITED LIABILITY CO—See Apollo Global Management, Inc.; *U.S. Public*, pg. 166
UNIVAR IBERIA S.A.—See Apollo Global Management, Inc.; *U.S. Public*, pg. 165
UNIVAR IRELAND—See Apollo Global Management, Inc.; *U.S. Public*, pg. 166
UNIVAR LIMITED—See Apollo Global Management, Inc.; *U.S. Public*, pg. 166
UNIVAR MIDDLE EAST-AFRICA FZE—See Apollo Global Management, Inc.; *U.S. Public*, pg. 166
UNIVAR NORDIC—See Apollo Global Management, Inc.; *U.S. Public*, pg. 166
UNIVAR POLAND SP.ZO.O—See Apollo Global Management, Inc.; *U.S. Public*, pg. 166
UNIVAR SINGAPORE PTE LTD—See Apollo Global Management, Inc.; *U.S. Public*, pg. 166
UNIVAR SOLUTIONS AS—See Apollo Global Management, Inc.; *U.S. Public*, pg. 166
UNIVAR SOLUTIONS CHINA LTD.—See Apollo Global Management, Inc.; *U.S. Public*, pg. 166
UNIVAR SOLUTIONS DENMARK A/S—See Apollo Global Management, Inc.; *U.S. Public*, pg. 166
UNIVAR SOLUTIONS HELLAS EPE—See Apollo Global Management, Inc.; *U.S. Public*, pg. 166
UNIVAR SOLUTIONS INC.—See Apollo Global Management, Inc.; *U.S. Public*, pg. 165
UNIVAR SOLUTIONS KIMYA SANAYI VE DIS TICARET LIMITED—See Apollo Global Management, Inc.; *U.S. Public*, pg. 166
UNIVAR SOLUTIONS LLC—See Apollo Global Management, Inc.; *U.S. Public*, pg. 166
UNIVAR SOLUTIONS OY—See Apollo Global Management, Inc.; *U.S. Public*, pg. 166
UNIVAR SOLUTIONS PORTUGAL SA—See Apollo Global Management, Inc.; *U.S. Public*, pg. 166
UNIVAR SOLUTIONS SAS—See Apollo Global Management, Inc.; *U.S. Public*, pg. 166

COMPANY NAME INDEX

UNIVAR SOLUTIONS SINGAPORE PTE LTD—See Apollo Global Management, Inc.; *U.S. Public*, pg. 166
UNIVAR SOLUTIONS SPAIN SA—See Apollo Global Management, Inc.; *U.S. Public*, pg. 166
UNIVAR SOLUTIONS UK LTD.—See Apollo Global Management, Inc.; *U.S. Public*, pg. 166
UNIVAR SOLUTIONS USA INC.—See Apollo Global Management, Inc.; *U.S. Public*, pg. 166
UNIVAR SOUTH-EAST EUROPE S.R.L.—See Apollo Global Management, Inc.; *U.S. Public*, pg. 166
UNIVAR S.P.A.—See Apollo Global Management, Inc.; *U.S. Public*, pg. 166
UNIVAR SPECIALTY CONSUMABLES LIMITED—See Apollo Global Management, Inc.; *U.S. Public*, pg. 166
UNIVAR UK LIMITED—See Apollo Global Management, Inc.; *U.S. Public*, pg. 166
UNIVAR ZWIJNDRECHT N.V.—See Apollo Global Management, Inc.; *U.S. Public*, pg. 166
UNIVASTU HVAC INDIA PRIVATE LIMITED—See Univastu India Ltd.; *Int'l*, pg. 8077
UNIVASTU INDIA LTD.; *Int'l*, pg. 8076
UNIVATION TECHNOLOGIES, LLC—See Dow Inc.; *U.S. Public*, pg. 686
UNIVEG DEUTSCHLAND GMBH—See CVC Capital Partners SICAV-FIS S.A.; *Int'l*, pg. 1886
UNIVEG FRUIT & VEGETABLES B.V.—See CVC Capital Partners SICAV-FIS S.A.; *Int'l*, pg. 1886
UNIVEG GROUP—See CVC Capital Partners SICAV-FIS S.A.; *Int'l*, pg. 1886
UNIVENTURES CONSULTING CO., LTD.—See Univentures Public Company Limited; *Int'l*, pg. 8077
UNIVENTURES PUBLIC COMPANY LIMITED; *Int'l*, pg. 8077
UNIVER CAPITAL LLC; *Int'l*, pg. 8077
UNIVERGAS ITALIA S.R.L.—See UGI Corporation; *U.S. Public*, pg. 2223
UNIVERMA AG; *Int'l*, pg. 8077
UNIVERSAL 1 CREDIT UNION, INC.; *U.S. Private*, pg. 4303
UNIVERSAL ACCOUNTING CENTER; *U.S. Private*, pg. 4303
UNIVERSAL ACIERS SARL—See Salzgitter AG; *Int'l*, pg. 6499
UNIVERSAL ACOUSTIC & EMISSION TECHNOLOGIES PVT. LTD.—See Durr AG; *Int'l*, pg. 2231
UNIVERSAL ADVANCED SYSTEMS; *Int'l*, pg. 8077
UNIVERSAL AEROSPACE CO. INC.—See Strength Capital Partners, LLC; *U.S. Private*, pg. 3839
UNIVERSAL AIR TOOL COMPANY LIMITED—See ShoreView Industries, LLC; *U.S. Private*, pg. 3642
UNIVERSAL ALLOY CORPORATION—See Global Equity Partners Beteiligungs-Management AG; *Int'l*, pg. 2996
UNIVERSAL AMERICAN CORP.—See Centene Corporation; *U.S. Public*, pg. 471
UNIVERSAL AMERICAN MORTGAGE COMPANY-LENNAR—See Lennar Corporation; *U.S. Public*, pg. 1307
UNIVERSAL AMERICAN MORTGAGE COMPANY OF CALIFORNIA—See Lennar Corporation; *U.S. Public*, pg. 1307
UNIVERSAL AMERICAN MORTGAGE COMPANY—See Lennar Corporation; *U.S. Public*, pg. 1307
UNIVERSAL ANALYZERS INC.—See AMETEK, Inc.; *U.S. Public*, pg. 118
UNIVERSAL ARTS LIMITED; *Int'l*, pg. 8077
UNIVERSAL ASSET MANAGEMENT, INC.—See China Aircraft Leasing Group Holdings Limited; *Int'l*, pg. 1481
UNIVERSAL ATHLETIC SERVICE, INC.; *U.S. Private*, pg. 4303
UNIVERSAL AUTO BODY SUPPLY—See KSI Trading Company; *U.S. Private*, pg. 2354
UNIVERSAL AUTOFOUNDRY LIMITED; *Int'l*, pg. 8077
UNIVERSAL BACKGROUND SCREENING, INC.—See Sackett National Holdings, Inc.; *U.S. Private*, pg. 3522
UNIVERSAL BANK PJSC—See TAS Group LLC; *Int'l*, pg. 7464
UNIVERSAL BANK; *U.S. Private*, pg. 4303
UNIVERSAL BEARINGS, INC.—See Hanwha Group; *Int'l*, pg. 3265
UNIVERSAL BIOENERGY, INC.; *U.S. Private*, pg. 4303
UNIVERSAL BIOFUELS PRIVATE LIMITED—See Aemetis, Inc.; *U.S. Public*, pg. 52
UNIVERSAL BIOSENSORS, INC.; *Int'l*, pg. 8077
UNIVERSAL BIOSENSORS PTY. LTD.—See Universal Biosensors, Inc.; *Int'l*, pg. 8077
UNIVERSAL BLANCHERS, LLC—See Temasek Holdings (Private) Limited; *Int'l*, pg. 7549
UNIVERSAL BLUEPRINT PAPER COMPANY, LLC; *U.S. Private*, pg. 4304
UNIVERSAL BOOT SHOPS, A CALIFORNIA GENERAL PARTNERSHIP—See Apartment Investment and Management Company; *U.S. Public*, pg. 144
UNIVERSAL BUILDERS SUPPLY, INC.; *U.S. Private*, pg. 4304
UNIVERSAL BUILDERS SUPPLY LTD.—See Universal Builders Supply, Inc.; *U.S. Private*, pg. 4304
UNIVERSAL BUILDING NORTH, INC.—See Vornado Realty Trust; *U.S. Public*, pg. 2310

UNIVERSAL BUILDING SPECIALTIES INCORPORATED; *U.S. Private*, pg. 4304
UNIVERSAL BUSINESS SOLUTIONS, NA; *U.S. Private*, pg. 4304
UNIVERSAL CABLE (M) BERHAD - PLENTONG MANUFACTURING PLANT—See Sarawak Cable Berhad; *Int'l*, pg. 6576
UNIVERSAL CABLE (M) BERHAD—See Sarawak Cable Berhad; *Int'l*, pg. 6576
UNIVERSAL CABLE (SARAWAK) SDN. BHD.—See Sarawak Cable Berhad; *Int'l*, pg. 6576
UNIVERSAL CABLES LIMITED; *Int'l*, pg. 8077
UNIVERSAL CAN CORP. - FUJI-OYAMA PLANT—See Mitsubishi Materials Corporation; *Int'l*, pg. 4965
UNIVERSAL CAN CORP. - GUNMA PLANT—See Mitsubishi Materials Corporation; *Int'l*, pg. 4965
UNIVERSAL CAN CORP. - OKAYAMA PLANT—See Mitsubishi Materials Corporation; *Int'l*, pg. 4966
UNIVERSAL CAN CORP. - SHIGA PLANT—See Mitsubishi Materials Corporation; *Int'l*, pg. 4966
UNIVERSAL CAN CORP.—See Mitsubishi Materials Corporation; *Int'l*, pg. 4965
UNIVERSAL CAN CORP. - YUKI PLANT—See Mitsubishi Materials Corporation; *Int'l*, pg. 4966
UNIVERSAL CAPACITY SOLUTIONS, LLC—See Universal Logistics Holdings, Inc.; *U.S. Public*, pg. 2261
UNIVERSAL CAPITAL SECURITIES PVT LTD—See Mitsubishi UFJ Financial Group, Inc.; *Int'l*, pg. 4971
UNIVERSAL CARE, INC.—See Molina Healthcare, Inc.; *U.S. Public*, pg. 1459
UNIVERSAL CARGO LOGISTICS HOLDING B.V.; *Int'l*, pg. 8077
UNIVERSAL CEMENT CORPORATION; *Int'l*, pg. 8078
UNIVERSAL CHEMICAL AND SUPPLY; *U.S. Private*, pg. 4304
UNIVERSAL CHEVROLET CO. INC.; *U.S. Private*, pg. 4304
UNIVERSAL CITY DEVELOPMENT PARTNERS, LTD.—See Comcast Corporation; *U.S. Public*, pg. 540
UNIVERSAL CITY NISSAN, INC.—See Sage Holding Company; *U.S. Private*, pg. 3526
UNIVERSAL CITY STUDIOS LLC—See Comcast Corporation; *U.S. Public*, pg. 540
UNIVERSAL CITY TRAVEL PARTNERS—See Comcast Corporation; *U.S. Public*, pg. 540
UNIVERSAL CLASSICS, INC.—See Universal Music Group N.V.; *Int'l*, pg. 8079
UNIVERSAL COAL DEVELOPMENT VIII (PTY.) LTD.—See TerraCom Limited; *Int'l*, pg. 7567
UNIVERSAL COAL PLC—See TerraCom Limited; *Int'l*, pg. 7567
UNIVERSAL COIN & BULLION LTD.; *U.S. Private*, pg. 4304
UNIVERSAL COMFORT PRODUCTS LIMITED—See Tata Sons Limited; *Int'l*, pg. 7473
UNIVERSAL COMMUNICATION—See The Interpublic Group of Companies, Inc.; *U.S. Public*, pg. 2103
UNIVERSAL COMMUNICATION—See The Interpublic Group of Companies, Inc.; *U.S. Public*, pg. 2103
UNIVERSAL CONCRETE PRODUCTS CORPORATION—See Bodon Industries Inc.; *U.S. Private*, pg. 608
UNIVERSAL CONCRETE PRODUCTS OF NEW JERSEY INC.—See Bodon Industries Inc.; *U.S. Private*, pg. 608
UNIVERSAL CONSOLIDATED SERVICES; *U.S. Private*, pg. 4304
UNIVERSAL CONSTRUCTION COMPANY, INC.; *U.S. Private*, pg. 4304
UNIVERSAL CONSULTING SERVICES, INC.; *U.S. Private*, pg. 4304
UNIVERSAL CONSUMER PRODUCTS, INC.—See UFP Industries, Inc.; *U.S. Public*, pg. 2221
UNIVERSAL CONVERSION TECHNOLOGIES—See EquiSoft Inc.; *U.S. Private*, pg. 1416
UNIVERSAL COOPERATIVES, INC.; *U.S. Private*, pg. 4304
UNIVERSAL COOPERATIVES, INC - UCPA CHEMICAL PLANT—See Universal Cooperatives, Inc.; *U.S. Private*, pg. 4304
UNIVERSAL COPPER LTD.—See Vizsla Copper Corp.; *Int'l*, pg. 8280
UNIVERSAL CORPORATION; *U.S. Public*, pg. 2254
UNIVERSAL CORPORATION LTD—See E.T. Browne Drug Company, Inc.; *U.S. Private*, pg. 1307
UNIVERSAL CORRUGATED B.V.—See MINDA Industrieanlagen GmbH; *Int'l*, pg. 4900
UNIVERSAL CREDIT LIMITED—See Paragon Banking Group PLC; *Int'l*, pg. 5736
UNIVERSAL CREDIT & SECURITIES LIMITED; *Int'l*, pg. 8078
UNIVERSAL DENTALCARE PTE LTD—See OUE Limited; *Int'l*, pg. 5666
UNIVERSAL DENTAL GROUP (BRADDELL) PTE LTD—See OUE Limited; *Int'l*, pg. 5666
UNIVERSAL DENTAL GROUP (WOODLANDS) PTE LTD—See OUE Limited; *Int'l*, pg. 5666
UNIVERSAL / DEVLIEG LLC—See Mistequay Group Ltd.; *U.S. Private*, pg. 2750

UNIVERSAL HERBS INC.

UNIVERSAL DIALYSIS CENTER, LLC—See Nautic Partners, LLC; *U.S. Private*, pg. 2871
UNIVERSAL DISPLAY CORPORATION HONG KONG, LIMITED—See Universal Display Corporation; *U.S. Public*, pg. 2255
UNIVERSAL DISPLAY CORPORATION; *U.S. Public*, pg. 2254
UNIVERSAL DISPLAY & FIXTURES COMPANY INC.; *U.S. Private*, pg. 4304
UNIVERSAL DRUM RECONDITIONING COMPANY; *Int'l*, pg. 8078
UNIVERSAL DYEING & PRINTING, INC.; *U.S. Private*, pg. 4304
UNIVERSAL DYNAMICS, INC.—See Mann+Hummel GmbH; *Int'l*, pg. 4674
UNIVERSAL E-BUSINESS SOLUTIONS; *U.S. Private*, pg. 4304
UNIVERSALE INTERNATIONAL REALITAETEN GMBH—See UniCredit S.p.A.; *Int'l*, pg. 8040
UNIVERSAL EISEN UND STAHL GMBH—See Salzgitter AG; *Int'l*, pg. 6499
UNIVERSAL ELECTRONICS BV—See Universal Electronics, Inc.; *U.S. Public*, pg. 2255
UNIVERSAL ELECTRONICS, INC.; *U.S. Public*, pg. 2255
UNIVERSAL ELECTRONICS—See Universal Electronics, Inc.; *U.S. Public*, pg. 2255
UNIVERSAL ENERGY CORP.; *U.S. Public*, pg. 2255
UNIVERSAL ENGEISHA CO., LTD.; *Int'l*, pg. 8078
UNIVERSAL ENGINEERING SCIENCES, LLC; *U.S. Private*, pg. 4304
UNIVERSAL ENGINEERING SCIENCES—See Universal Engineering Sciences, LLC; *U.S. Private*, pg. 4305
UNIVERSAL ENGINEERING SCIENCES—See Universal Engineering Sciences, LLC; *U.S. Private*, pg. 4305
UNIVERSAL ENGINEERING SCIENCES—See Universal Engineering Sciences, LLC; *U.S. Private*, pg. 4305
UNIVERSAL ENGINEERING SERVICES LLC—See Suhail Bahwan Group (Holding) LLC; *Int'l*, pg. 7254
UNIVERSAL ENGRAVING INC.; *U.S. Private*, pg. 4305
UNIVERSAL ENSCO, INC.—See PMC Capital Partners, LLC; *U.S. Private*, pg. 3218
UNIVERSAL ENTERTAINMENT CORPORATION; *Int'l*, pg. 8078
UNIVERSAL ENTERTAINMENT GMBH—See Universal Music Group N.V.; *Int'l*, pg. 8079
UNIVERSAL ENVIRONMENTAL SERVICES, LLC—See Avista Oil AG; *Int'l*, pg. 745
UNIVERSAL (FAR EAST) PTE. LTD.—See Trio-Tech International; *U.S. Public*, pg. 7925
UNIVERSAL FIBERS SYSTEMS LLC; *U.S. Private*, pg. 4305
UNIVERSAL FIDELITY HOLDING CO., INC.; *U.S. Private*, pg. 4305
UNIVERSAL FIDELITY LIFE INSURANCE CO.—See Universal Fidelity Holding Co., Inc.; *U.S. Private*, pg. 4305
UNIVERSAL FINANCIAL SERVICES, L.P.—See Bunge Limited; *U.S. Public*, pg. 412
UNIVERSAL FLOW MONITORS, INC.—See Arcline Investment Management LP; *U.S. Private*, pg. 313
UNIVERSAL FOOD CO., LTD.—See ITOCHU Corporation; *Int'l*, pg. 3841
UNIVERSAL FOOD PUBLIC COMPANY LIMITED—See Lam Soon (Thailand) Public Company Limited; *Int'l*, pg. 4400
UNIVERSAL FOODS LIMITED—See Associated Brands Industries Limited; *Int'l*, pg. 648
UNIVERSAL FOREST PRODUCTS FOUNDATION—See UFP Industries, Inc.; *U.S. Public*, pg. 2221
UNIVERSAL FOREST PRODUCTS OF CANADA, INC.—See UFP Industries, Inc.; *U.S. Public*, pg. 2221
UNIVERSAL FORKLIFT SUPPLY LLC—See Ranger Lift Trucks; *U.S. Private*, pg. 3355
UNIVERSAL FORWARDER LLC—See Universal Cargo Logistics Holding B.V.; *Int'l*, pg. 8078
UNIVERSAL GAMING CORPORATION; *U.S. Public*, pg. 2255
UNIVERSAL GENEVE S.A.—See CVC Capital Partners SICAV-FIS S.A.; *Int'l*, pg. 1883
UNIVERSAL GLOBAL HUB INC.; *U.S. Public*, pg. 2255
UNIVERSAL GLOBAL SCIENTIFIC INDUSTRIAL CO., LTD.—See ASE Technology Holding Co., Ltd.; *Int'l*, pg. 604
UNIVERSAL GOLF ENTERPISES PLC; *Int'l*, pg. 8078
UNIVERSAL GUARANTEE LIFE INSURANCE—See UTG, Inc.; *U.S. Public*, pg. 2267
UNIVERSAL HARDWARE & PLASTIC FACTORY LIMITED—See Aliaxis S.A./N.V.; *Int'l*, pg. 325
UNIVERSAL HARVESTER CO., INC.—See Art's-Way Manufacturing Co., Inc.; *U.S. Public*, pg. 201
UNIVERSAL HEALTH CARE, INC.; *U.S. Private*, pg. 4305
UNIVERSAL HEALTH INTERNATIONAL GROUP HOLDING LIMITED; *Int'l*, pg. 8078
UNIVERSAL HEALTH REALTY INCOME TRUST; *U.S. Public*, pg. 2255
UNIVERSAL HEALTH SERVICES, INC.; *U.S. Public*, pg. 2255
UNIVERSAL HEMP, LLC—See Acreage Holdings, Inc.; *U.S. Public*, pg. 36
UNIVERSAL HERBS INC.; *U.S. Private*, pg. 4305

UNIVERSAL HERBS INC.   CORPORATE AFFILIATIONS

UNIVERSAL HOLIDAYS, INC.—See Transnational Diversified Group of Companies; *Int'l*, pg. 7902
UNIVERSAL HOME EXPERTS; *U.S. Private*, pg. 4305
UNIVERSAL HYDRAULIK GMBH; *Int'l*, pg. 8078
UNIVERSAL IBOGAINE INC.—See P Squared Renewables, Inc.; *Int'l*, pg. 5681
UNIVERSAL INCORPORATION; *Int'l*, pg. 8078
UNIVERSAL INDUSTRIAL GASES, LLC—See Nucor Corporation; *U.S. Public*, pg. 1555
UNIVERSAL INDUSTRIAL PRODUCTS CO.; *U.S. Private*, pg. 4305
UNIVERSAL INDUSTRIAL SALES, INC.; *U.S. Private*, pg. 4305
UNIVERSAL INDUSTRIES CORPORATION (PTY) LIMITED—See TRG Management LP; *U.S. Private*, pg. 4220
UNIVERSAL INDUSTRIES LLC; *U.S. Private*, pg. 4305
UNIVERSAL INSPECTION & CERTIFICATION TECHNOLOGY CO., LTD.—See Solar Applied Materials Technology Corporation; *Int'l*, pg. 7069
UNIVERSAL INSPECTION CORPORATION—See Universal Insurance Holdings, Inc.; *U.S. Public*, pg. 2261
UNIVERSAL INSTRUMENTS CORPORATION—See Francisco Partners Management, LP; *U.S. Private*, pg. 1592
THE UNIVERSAL INSURANCE COMPANY LIMITED—See Bibojee Services Private Limited; *Int'l*, pg. 1018
UNIVERSAL INSURANCE COMPANY—See Carolina Motor Club, Inc.; *U.S. Private*, pg. 768
UNIVERSAL INSURANCE HOLDING CO.—See Universal Insurance Holdings, Inc.; *U.S. Public*, pg. 2261
UNIVERSAL INSURANCE HOLDINGS, INC.; *U.S. Public*, pg. 2261
UNIVERSAL INSURANCE SERVICES OF FLORIDA, INC.—See Keystone Group, L.P.; *U.S. Private*, pg. 2298
UNIVERSAL INTERCHEMICALS CORP. PTE., LTD.—See PT Unggul Indah Cahaya Tbk; *Int'l*, pg. 6080
UNIVERSAL INTERLOCK CORP.; *U.S. Private*, pg. 4305
UNIVERSAL INTERMODAL SERVICES, INC.—See Universal Logistics Holdings, Inc.; *U.S. Public*, pg. 2261
UNIVERSAL INTERNATIONAL MUSIC B.V.—See Universal Music Group N.V.; *Int'l*, pg. 8080
UNIVERSAL INVESTMENT BANK AD SKOPJE; *Int'l*, pg. 8078
UNIVERSAL INVESTMENT UNIVERSAL-KBAM-FONDS GMBH—See Knorr-Bremse AG; *Int'l*, pg. 4212
UNIVERSAL KNOWLEDGE SOFTWARE (PROPRIETARY) LIMITED—See Capital Eye Investments Limited; *Int'l*, pg. 1311
UNIVERSAL LANGUAGE SERVICE, INC.; *U.S. Private*, pg. 4305
UNIVERSAL LEAF (ASIA) PTE LTD.—See Universal Corporation; *U.S. Public*, pg. 2254
UNIVERSAL LEAF GERMANY GMBH—See Universal Corporation; *U.S. Public*, pg. 2254
UNIVERSAL LEAF NICARAGUA, S.A.—See Universal Corporation; *U.S. Public*, pg. 2254
UNIVERSAL LEAF NORTH AMERICA U. S., INC.—See Universal Corporation; *U.S. Public*, pg. 2254
UNIVERSAL LEAF PHILIPPINES INC.—See Universal Corporation; *U.S. Public*, pg. 2254
UNIVERSAL LEAF TABACOS S. A.—See Universal Corporation; *U.S. Public*, pg. 2254
UNIVERSAL LEAF TOBACCO COMPANY, INC.—See Universal Corporation; *U.S. Public*, pg. 2254
UNIVERSAL LEAF TOBACCO HUNGARY PRIVATE LIMITED COMPANY—See Universal Corporation; *U.S. Public*, pg. 2254
UNIVERSAL LEASING CO., LTD.—See Mizuho Leasing Company, Limited; *Int'l*, pg. 4999
UNIVERSAL LENDING CORPORATION; *U.S. Private*, pg. 4305
UNIVERSAL LEVEN N.V.—See Allianz SE; *Int'l*, pg. 349
UNIVERSAL LIGHTING TECHNOLOGIES, INC.—See Panasonic Holdings Corporation; *Int'l*, pg. 5722
UNIVERSAL LIMITED; *U.S. Private*, pg. 4305
UNIVERSAL LOGISTICS HOLDINGS, INC.; *U.S. Public*, pg. 2261
UNIVERSAL LOGISTICS INC.; *Int'l*, pg. 8079
UNIVERSAL LOGISTICS SOLUTIONS CANADA, LTD.—See Universal Logistics Holdings, Inc.; *U.S. Public*, pg. 2261
UNIVERSAL LOGISTICS SOLUTIONS INTERNATIONAL, INC.—See Universal Logistics Holdings, Inc.; *U.S. Public*, pg. 2262
UNIVERSAL MACHINE CO. OF POTTSTOWN; *U.S. Private*, pg. 4305
UNIVERSAL MACOMB AMBULANCE SERVICE, INC.; *U.S. Private*, pg. 4305
UNIVERSAL MANAGEMENT CORP.—See The Rados Companies; *U.S. Private*, pg. 4102
UNIVERSAL MANAGEMENT SERVICES, INC.—See Universal Logistics Holdings, Inc.; *U.S. Public*, pg. 2262
UNIVERSAL MANUFACTURING COMPANY—See WNC Corporation; *U.S. Private*, pg. 4552
UNIVERSAL MANUFACTURING COMPANY; *U.S. Private*, pg. 4305
UNIVERSAL MANUFACTURING CORP.; *U.S. Private*, pg. 4305

UNIVERSAL MARINE SYSTEMS CORPORATION—See JFE Holdings, Inc.; *Int'l*, pg. 3939
UNIVERSAL MCCANN GMBH—See The Interpublic Group of Companies, Inc.; *U.S. Public*, pg. 2101
UNIVERSAL MCCANN, S.A.—See The Interpublic Group of Companies, Inc.; *U.S. Public*, pg. 2103
UNIVERSAL MCCANN—See The Interpublic Group of Companies, Inc.; *U.S. Public*, pg. 2101
UNIVERSAL MCCANN—See The Interpublic Group of Companies, Inc.; *U.S. Public*, pg. 2101
UNIVERSAL MCCANN—See The Interpublic Group of Companies, Inc.; *U.S. Public*, pg. 2103
UNIVERSAL MCCANN—See The Interpublic Group of Companies, Inc.; *U.S. Public*, pg. 2103
UNIVERSAL MCCANN—See The Interpublic Group of Companies, Inc.; *U.S. Public*, pg. 2103
UNIVERSAL MCCANN—See The Interpublic Group of Companies, Inc.; *U.S. Public*, pg. 2103
UNIVERSAL MCCANN—See The Interpublic Group of Companies, Inc.; *U.S. Public*, pg. 2101
UNIVERSAL MCCANN—See The Interpublic Group of Companies, Inc.; *U.S. Public*, pg. 2103
UNIVERSAL MCCANN—See The Interpublic Group of Companies, Inc.; *U.S. Public*, pg. 2103
UNIVERSAL MCCANN—See The Interpublic Group of Companies, Inc.; *U.S. Public*, pg. 2103
UNIVERSAL MCCANN WORLDWIDE, INC.—See The Interpublic Group of Companies, Inc.; *U.S. Public*, pg. 2102
UNIVERSAL MEATS (UK) LIMITED—See Tyson Foods, Inc.; *U.S. Public*, pg. 2210
UNIVERSAL MEDIA GROUP INC.; *U.S. Public*, pg. 2262
UNIVERSAL MEDIA HELLAS SA—See The Interpublic Group of Companies, Inc.; *U.S. Public*, pg. 2103
UNIVERSAL MEDIA INC.; *U.S. Private*, pg. 4305
UNIVERSAL MEDIA JAPAN CO., LTD.—See Rentracks Co., Ltd.; *Int'l*, pg. 6289
UNIVERSAL MEDIA SEVEN FZ-LLC—See The Interpublic Group of Companies, Inc.; *U.S. Public*, pg. 2104
UNIVERSAL MEDIA—See The Interpublic Group of Companies, Inc.; *U.S. Public*, pg. 2103
UNIVERSAL MEDICAL, INC.—See Koninklijke Philips N.V.; *Int'l*, pg. 4267
UNIVERSAL MEDICAL, INC.—See Koninklijke Philips N.V.; *Int'l*, pg. 4267
UNIVERSAL MEDICAL SYSTEMS, INC.—See Merry X-Ray Corporation; *U.S. Private*, pg. 2676
UNIVERSAL METAL HOSE—See Hyspan Precision Products, Inc.; *U.S. Private*, pg. 2020
UNIVERSAL METAL PRODUCTS INC.; *U.S. Private*, pg. 4305
UNIVERSAL MICROELECTRONICS CO., LTD.; *Int'l*, pg. 8079
UNIVERSAL MIND; *U.S. Private*, pg. 4305
UNIVERSAL MODERN INDUSTRIES CO. PLC; *Int'l*, pg. 8079
UNIVERSAL MOLDING COMPANY INC.—See UMC Acquisition Corp.; *U.S. Private*, pg. 4278
UNIVERSAL MOLDING EXTRUSION CO.—See UMC Acquisition Corp.; *U.S. Private*, pg. 4278
UNIVERSAL MOTORS CORPORATION—See Nissan Motor Co., Ltd.; *Int'l*, pg. 5369
UNIVERSAL MOTORS ISRAEL LTD.—See General Motors Company; *U.S. Public*, pg. 929
UNIVERSAL MOTOWN RECORDS—See Universal Music Group N.V.; *Int'l*, pg. 8079
UNIVERSAL MOVERS CORPORATION; *Int'l*, pg. 8079
UNIVERSAL MUSIC AB—See Universal Music Group N.V.; *Int'l*, pg. 8080
UNIVERSAL MUSIC AUSTRALIA PTY. LTD.—See Universal Music Group N.V.; *Int'l*, pg. 8080
UNIVERSAL MUSIC (AUSTRIA) GMBH—See Universal Music Group N.V.; *Int'l*, pg. 8080
UNIVERSAL MUSIC CANADA INC.—See Universal Music Group N.V.; *Int'l*, pg. 8079
UNIVERSAL MUSIC COLOMBIA S.A.—See Universal Music Group N.V.; *Int'l*, pg. 8079
UNIVERSAL MUSIC DOMESTIC DIVISION—See Universal Music Group N.V.; *Int'l*, pg. 8080
UNIVERSAL MUSIC ENTERTAINMENT GMBH—See Universal Music Group N.V.; *Int'l*, pg. 8080
UNIVERSAL MUSIC FRANCE—See Universal Music Group N.V.; *Int'l*, pg. 8080
UNIVERSAL MUSIC GMBH—See Universal Music Group N.V.; *Int'l*, pg. 8081
UNIVERSAL MUSIC GROUP, INC.—See Universal Music Group N.V.; *Int'l*, pg. 8079
UNIVERSAL MUSIC GROUP INTERNATIONAL LTD.—See Universal Music Group N.V.; *Int'l*, pg. 8079
UNIVERSAL MUSIC GROUP NASHVILLE—See Universal Music Group N.V.; *Int'l*, pg. 8080
UNIVERSAL MUSIC GROUP N.V.; *Int'l*, pg. 8079
UNIVERSAL MUSIC GROUP—See Universal Music Group N.V.; *Int'l*, pg. 8079
UNIVERSAL MUSIC GROUP—See Universal Music Group N.V.; *Int'l*, pg. 8079
UNIVERSAL MUSIC HOLDINGS LIMITED—See Universal Music Group N.V.; *Int'l*, pg. 8080
UNIVERSAL MUSIC ITALIA SRL—See Universal Music Group N.V.; *Int'l*, pg. 8080

UNIVERSAL MUSIC (JAPAN) K.K.—See Universal Music Group N.V.; *Int'l*, pg. 8080
UNIVERSAL MUSIC LATIN AMERICA—See Universal Music Group N.V.; *Int'l*, pg. 8080
UNIVERSAL MUSIC LATIN ENTERTAINMENT—See Universal Music Group N.V.; *Int'l*, pg. 8080
UNIVERSAL MUSIC MEXICO, SA DE CV—See Universal Music Group N.V.; *Int'l*, pg. 8080
UNIVERSAL MUSIC NZ LTD.—See Universal Music Group N.V.; *Int'l*, pg. 8080
UNIVERSAL MUSIC OY—See Universal Music Group N.V.; *Int'l*, pg. 8080
UNIVERSAL MUSIC OY—See Universal Music Group N.V.; *Int'l*, pg. 8080
UNIVERSAL MUSIC PORTUGAL S.A.—See Universal Music Group N.V.; *Int'l*, pg. 8080
UNIVERSAL MUSIC PUBLISHING AB—See Universal Music Group N.V.; *Int'l*, pg. 8081
UNIVERSAL MUSIC PUBLISHING (AUSTRIA) GMBH—See Universal Music Group N.V.; *Int'l*, pg. 8081
UNIVERSAL MUSIC PUBLISHING, B.V.—See Universal Music Group N.V.; *Int'l*, pg. 8081
UNIVERSAL MUSIC PUBLISHING GMBH—See Universal Music Group N.V.; *Int'l*, pg. 8081
UNIVERSAL MUSIC PUBLISHING GROUP CANADA—See Universal Music Group N.V.; *Int'l*, pg. 8080
UNIVERSAL MUSIC PUBLISHING GROUP DENMARK—See Universal Music Group N.V.; *Int'l*, pg. 8080
UNIVERSAL MUSIC PUBLISHING GROUP LATIN AMERICA—See Universal Music Group N.V.; *Int'l*, pg. 8080
UNIVERSAL MUSIC PUBLISHING GROUP NASHVILLE—See Universal Music Group N.V.; *Int'l*, pg. 8080
UNIVERSAL MUSIC PUBLISHING GROUP—See Universal Music Group N.V.; *Int'l*, pg. 8080
UNIVERSAL MUSIC PUBLISHING GROUP THAILAND—See Universal Music Group N.V.; *Int'l*, pg. 8080
UNIVERSAL MUSIC PUBLISHING INTERNATIONAL LTD.—See Universal Music Group N.V.; *Int'l*, pg. 8081
UNIVERSAL MUSIC PUBLISHING KFT.—See Universal Music Group N.V.; *Int'l*, pg. 8081
UNIVERSAL MUSIC PUBLISHING LLC—See Universal Music Group N.V.; *Int'l*, pg. 8081
UNIVERSAL MUSIC PUBLISHING LTDA.—See Universal Music Group N.V.; *Int'l*, pg. 8081
UNIVERSAL MUSIC PUBLISHING LTDA—See Universal Music Group N.V.; *Int'l*, pg. 8081
UNIVERSAL MUSIC PUBLISHING LTD—See Universal Music Group N.V.; *Int'l*, pg. 8081
UNIVERSAL MUSIC PUBLISHING LTD.—See Universal Music Group N.V.; *Int'l*, pg. 8081
UNIVERSAL MUSIC PUBLISHING LTD.—See Universal Music Group N.V.; *Int'l*, pg. 8081
UNIVERSAL MUSIC PUBLISHING (PTY) LTD.—See Universal Music Group N.V.; *Int'l*, pg. 8080
UNIVERSAL MUSIC PUBLISHING PTY. LTD.—See Universal Music Group N.V.; *Int'l*, pg. 8081
UNIVERSAL MUSIC PUBLISHING S.A.—See Universal Music Group N.V.; *Int'l*, pg. 8080
UNIVERSAL MUSIC PUBLISHING S.A.—See Universal Music Group N.V.; *Int'l*, pg. 8081
UNIVERSAL MUSIC PUBLISHING S.A.—See Universal Music Group N.V.; *Int'l*, pg. 8081
UNIVERSAL MUSIC PUBLISHING SDN BHD—See Universal Music Group N.V.; *Int'l*, pg. 8081
UNIVERSAL MUSIC PUBLISHING SP. Z.O.O.—See Universal Music Group N.V.; *Int'l*, pg. 8081
UNIVERSAL MUSIC PUBLISHING SRL—See Universal Music Group N.V.; *Int'l*, pg. 8081
UNIVERSAL MUSIC PUBLISHING S.R.O.—See Universal Music Group N.V.; *Int'l*, pg. 8081
UNIVERSAL MUSIC ROMANIA SRL—See Universal Music Group N.V.; *Int'l*, pg. 8081
UNIVERSAL MUSIC SPAIN S.L.—See Universal Music Group N.V.; *Int'l*, pg. 8080
UNIVERSAL MUSIC SWITZERLAND GMBH—See Universal Music Group N.V.; *Int'l*, pg. 8080
UNIVERSAL MUSIC TAXIM EDITION—See Universal Music Group N.V.; *Int'l*, pg. 8081
UNIVERSAL MUSIC UK LTD.—See Universal Music Group N.V.; *Int'l*, pg. 8080
UNIVERSAL NETWORK TELEVISION LLC—See Comcast Corporation; *U.S. Public*, pg. 540
UNIVERSAL NUTRITION; *U.S. Private*, pg. 4306
UNIVERSAL OCEL SPOL. S.R.O.—See Salzgitter AG; *Int'l*, pg. 6499
UNIVERSAL OFFICE AUTOMATION LIMITED; *Int'l*, pg. 8082
UNIVERSAL OUTDOOR GROUP PLC; *Int'l*, pg. 8082
UNIVERSAL OVERALL COMPANY; *U.S. Private*, pg. 4306
UNIVERSAL PACKAGING SYSTEMS, INC.—See Universal Packaging Systems, Inc.; *U.S. Private*, pg. 4306

COMPANY NAME INDEX

UNIVERSAL PACKAGING SYSTEMS, INC.; *U.S. Private*, pg. 4306
UNIVERSAL PARAGON CORPORATION; *U.S. Private*, pg. 4306
UNIVERSAL PARKS & RESORTS MANAGEMENT SERVICES LLC—See Comcast Corporation; *U.S. Public*, pg. 540
UNIVERSAL PARTNERS LIMITED; *Int'l*, pg. 8082
UNIVERSALPAY, ENTIDAD DE PAGO, S.L.—See Global Payments Inc.; *U.S. Public*, pg. 943
UNIVERSALPEGASUS INTERNATIONAL CANADA, INC.—See Huntington Ingalls Industries, Inc.; *U.S. Public*, pg. 1072
UNIVERSALPEGASUS INTERNATIONAL, INC.—See PMC Capital Partners, LLC; *U.S. Private*, pg. 3218
UNIVERSALPEGASUS INTERNATIONAL TRINIDAD AND TOBAGO LIMITED—See Huntington Ingalls Industries, Inc.; *U.S. Public*, pg. 1072
UNIVERSAL PHARMACEUTICAL LABORATORIES LIMITED—See Li & Fung Limited; *Int'l*, pg. 4481
UNIVERSAL PHARMACEUTICAL MEDICAL SUPPLY CO, INC.—See Z Capital Group, LLC; *U.S. Private*, pg. 4595
UNIVERSAL PHOTONICS FAR EAST, INC—See Universal Photonics, Inc.; *U.S. Private*, pg. 4306
UNIVERSAL PHOTONICS HONG KONG LIMITED—See Universal Photonics, Inc.; *U.S. Private*, pg. 4306
UNIVERSAL PHOTONICS, INC.; *U.S. Private*, pg. 4306
UNIVERSAL PHOTONICS (SHENZHEN) CO., LTD.—See Universal Photonics, Inc.; *U.S. Private*, pg. 4306
UNIVERSAL PICTURES HOME ENTERTAINMENT LLC—See Comcast Corporation; *U.S. Public*, pg. 542
UNIVERSAL PICTURES INTERNATIONAL ENTERTAINMENT LIMITED—See Comcast Corporation; *U.S. Public*, pg. 541
UNIVERSAL PIPING INDUSTRIES, LLC—See Gallagher-Kaiser Corporation; *U.S. Private*, pg. 1639
UNIVERSAL PLASTICS CORP.—See Wembly Enterprises LLC; *U.S. Private*, pg. 4480
UNIVERSAL POLICY INVESTMENT VEHICLE LTD.; *Int'l*, pg. 8082
UNIVERSAL POLYMER & RUBBER LTD.; *U.S. Private*, pg. 4306
UNIVERSAL POOL CO. INC.; *U.S. Private*, pg. 4000
UNIVERSAL POSTAL UNION; *Int'l*, pg. 8082
UNIVERSAL POTASH CORPORATION; *U.S. Private*, pg. 4306
UNIVERSAL POWER GROUP, INC.; *U.S. Private*, pg. 4306
UNIVERSAL POWER INDUSTRY CORPORATION; *U.S. Public*, pg. 2262
UNIVERSAL POWER NORDIC AB—See Duc Long Gia Lai Group JSC; *Int'l*, pg. 2222
UNIVERSAL POWER SYSTEMS PRIVATE LIMITED—See Eros International Plc; *Int'l*, pg. 2497
UNIVERSAL PRESSURE PUMPING, INC.—See Patterson-UTI Energy, Inc.; *U.S. Public*, pg. 1654
UNIVERSAL PRIME ALUMINIUM LIMITED; *Int'l*, pg. 8082
UNIVERSAL PRINTING COMPANY; *U.S. Private*, pg. 4306
UNIVERSAL PRODUCTS INC.; *U.S. Private*, pg. 4306
UNIVERSAL PROPERTY & CASUALTY INSURANCE CO. (UPCIC)—See Universal Insurance Holdings, Inc.; *U.S. Public*, pg. 2261
UNIVERSAL PROPERTY MANAGEMENT—See Universal Insurance Holdings, Inc.; *U.S. Public*, pg. 2261
UNIVERSAL PROPTECH INC.; *Int'l*, pg. 8082
UNIVERSAL PROTECTION SECURITY SYSTEMS, LP—See Allied Universal Manager LLC; *U.S. Private*, pg. 191
UNIVERSAL PROTECTION SERVICE, LP—See Allied Universal Manager LLC; *U.S. Private*, pg. 191
UNIVERSAL PROVIDENT LIMITED—See Personal Group Holdings plc; *Int'l*, pg. 5820
UNIVERSAL PROVIDERS LIMITED—See Grafton Group plc; *Int'l*, pg. 3051
UNIVERSAL PULP & PAPER (SHANDONG) COMPANY LIMITED—See Samson Paper Holdings Limited; *Int'l*, pg. 6509
UNIVERSAL RAZOR INDUSTRIES, LLC—See KAI Corporation; *Int'l*, pg. 4050
UNIVERSAL RECYCLING TECHNOLOGIES, LLC—See Hendricks Holding Company, Inc.; *U.S. Private*, pg. 1915
UNIVERSAL REFRACTORIES INC.—See Vesuvius plc; *Int'l*, pg. 8179
UNIVERSAL RELAY—See Park Distributors, Inc.; *U.S. Private*, pg. 3096
UNIVERSAL RESOURCE & SERVICES LIMITED; *Int'l*, pg. 8082
UNIVERSAL RESTORATION, INC.—See Air Pros USA; *U.S. Private*, pg. 139
UNIVERSAL RISK SOLUTION COMPANY, LIMITED—See Tokio Marine Holdings, Inc.; *Int'l*, pg. 7782
UNIVERSAL ROBINA CORPORATION—See JG Summit Holdings, Inc.; *Int'l*, pg. 3939
UNIVERSAL ROBOTS A/S—See Teradyne, Inc.; *U.S. Public*, pg. 2018

UNIVERSAL ROBOTS GMBH—See Teradyne, Inc.; *U.S. Public*, pg. 2018
UNIVERSAL ROBOTS (INDIA) PTE. LTD.—See Teradyne, Inc.; *U.S. Public*, pg. 2018
UNIVERSAL ROBOTS (SHANGHAI) CO. LTD.—See Teradyne, Inc.; *U.S. Public*, pg. 2018
UNIVERSAL ROBOTS (SINGAPORE) PTE. LTD.—See Teradyne, Inc.; *U.S. Public*, pg. 2018
UNIVERSAL ROBOTS (SPAIN) S.L.—See Teradyne, Inc.; *U.S. Public*, pg. 2018
UNIVERSAL ROBOTS (USA), INC.—See Teradyne, Inc.; *U.S. Public*, pg. 2018
UNIVERSAL SCIENTIFIC INDUSTRIAL CO., LTD.—See ASE Technology Holding Co., Ltd.; *Int'l*, pg. 604
UNIVERSAL SCIENTIFIC INDUSTRIAL (SHANGHAI) CO., LTD.—See ASE Technology Holding Co., Ltd.; *Int'l*, pg. 604
UNIVERSAL SEALANTS (U.K.) LIMITED—See RPM International Inc.; *U.S. Public*, pg. 1820
UNIVERSAL SECURITY INSTRUMENTS, INC.; *U.S. Public*, pg. 2262
UNIVERSAL SELECT INC.; *U.S. Private*, pg. 4306
UNIVERSAL SELF STORAGE HESPERIA LLC—See National Storage Affiliates Trust; *U.S. Public*, pg. 1498
UNIVERSAL SELF STORAGE SAN BERNARDINO LLC—See National Storage Affiliates Trust; *U.S. Public*, pg. 1498
UNIVERSAL SELF STORAGE—See National Storage Affiliates Trust; *U.S. Public*, pg. 1498
UNIVERSAL SENSORS, INC.—See China Automotive Systems, Inc.; *Int'l*, pg. 1484
UNIVERSAL SERVICE CENTER COMPANY—See Universal Logistics Holdings, Inc.; *U.S. Public*, pg. 2262
UNIVERSAL SERVICE LLP—See Eurasian Natural Resources Corporation Limited; *Int'l*, pg. 2527
UNIVERSAL SERVICES OF AMERICA, LP—See Allied Universal Manager LLC; *U.S. Private*, pg. 190
UNIVERSAL SEWING SUPPLY INC.; *U.S. Private*, pg. 4306
UNIVERSAL SHIPBUILDING CORPORATION—See Hitachi Zosen Corporation; *Int'l*, pg. 3412
UNIVERSAL SMARTCOMP, LLC; *U.S. Private*, pg. 4306
UNIVERSAL SODEXHO CONGO—See Sodexo S.A.; *Int'l*, pg. 7047
UNIVERSAL SODEXHO GABON—See Sodexo S.A.; *Int'l*, pg. 7047
UNIVERSAL SODEXHO NIGERIA LTD—See Sodexo S.A.; *Int'l*, pg. 7047
UNIVERSAL SODEXHO PERU—See Sodexo S.A.; *Int'l*, pg. 7047
UNIVERSAL SOLAR TECHNOLOGY, INC.; *U.S. Public*, pg. 2262
UNIVERSAL SPACE NETWORK, INC.—See SSC Group; *Int'l*, pg. 7155
UNIVERSAL SPECTRUM CORPORATION—See Hamamatsu Photonics K.K.; *Int'l*, pg. 3235
UNIVERSAL STAINLESS & ALLOY PRODUCTS, INC.; *U.S. Public*, pg. 2262
UNIVERSAL STAL SP. Z.O.O.—See Salzgitter AG; *Int'l*, pg. 6499
UNIVERSAL STARCH-CHEM ALLIED LIMITED; *Int'l*, pg. 8082
UNIVERSAL STEEL AMERICA CHICAGO, INC.—See Salzgitter AG; *Int'l*, pg. 6499
UNIVERSAL STEEL AMERICA, INC.—See Salzgitter AG; *Int'l*, pg. 6499
THE UNIVERSAL STEEL CO.—See Columbia National Group Inc; *U.S. Private*, pg. 977
UNIVERSAL STEEL HOLLAND B.V.—See Salzgitter AG; *Int'l*, pg. 6499
UNIVERSAL STONE JSC—See Phu Tai Joint Stock Company; *Int'l*, pg. 5857
UNIVERSAL STORE HOLDINGS LIMITED; *Int'l*, pg. 8082
UNIVERSAL STUDIOS HOLLYWOOD—See Comcast Corporation; *U.S. Public*, pg. 541
UNIVERSAL STUDIOS HOME ENTERTAINMENT LLC—See Comcast Corporation; *U.S. Public*, pg. 541
UNIVERSAL STUDIOS INTERNATIONAL B.V.—See Comcast Corporation; *U.S. Public*, pg. 541
UNIVERSAL STUDIOS LLC—See Comcast Corporation; *U.S. Public*, pg. 540
UNIVERSAL SUPPLY COMPANY INC.—See Bain Capital, LP; *U.S. Private*, pg. 451
UNIVERSAL SYSTEM GROUP SA; *Int'l*, pg. 8082
UNIVERSAL SYSTEMS, INC.; *U.S. Public*, pg. 2262
UNIVERSAL TABLETOP, INC.—See EveryWare Global, Inc.; *U.S. Private*, pg. 1441
UNIVERSAL TECHNICAL INSTITUTE, INC.; *U.S. Public*, pg. 2262
UNIVERSAL TECHNICAL INSTITUTE OF ARIZONA, INC.—See Universal Technical Institute, Inc.; *U.S. Public*, pg. 2262
UNIVERSAL TECHNICAL INSTITUTE OF MASSACHUSETTS, INC.—See Universal Technical Institute, Inc.; *U.S. Public*, pg. 2262
UNIVERSAL TECHNICAL INSTITUTE OF PENNSYLVANIA, INC.—See Universal Technical Institute, Inc.; *U.S. Public*, pg. 2262

UNIVERSITY BANCORP, INC.

UNIVERSAL TECHNICAL RESOURCE SERVICES, INC.; *U.S. Private*, pg. 4306
UNIVERSAL TECHNIC SAS—See Danaher Corporation; *U.S. Public*, pg. 631
UNIVERSAL TECHNOLOGIES HOLDINGS LIMITED; *Int'l*, pg. 8082
UNIVERSAL TELESERVICES LLC; *U.S. Private*, pg. 4306
UNIVERSAL TEXTILE CO., LTD.; *Int'l*, pg. 8082
UNIVERSAL TEXTILE CO., LTD. - SPINNING FACTORY, CHANGBIN—See Universal Textile Co., Ltd.; *Int'l*, pg. 8082
UNIVERSAL TEXTILE CO., LTD. - WEAVING FACTORY, LUZHU—See Universal Textile Co., Ltd.; *Int'l*, pg. 8082
UNIVERSAL TEXTILE CO., LTD. - WEAVING FACTORY, TAOYUAN—See Universal Textile Co., Ltd.; *Int'l*, pg. 8082
UNIVERSAL THREAD GRINDING COMPANY; *U.S. Private*, pg. 4307
UNIVERSAL TRAFFIC SERVICE; *U.S. Private*, pg. 4307
UNIVERSAL TRAILER CORPORATION—See Corporate Partners LLC; *U.S. Private*, pg. 1055
UNIVERSAL TRANSPORT KANN GMBH; *Int'l*, pg. 8082
UNIVERSAL TRAVEL GROUP; *Int'l*, pg. 8082
UNIVERSAL TRUCK & TRAILER SALES II LLC; *U.S. Private*, pg. 4307
UNIVERSAL TURBINE PARTS, LLC; *U.S. Private*, pg. 4307
THE UNIVERSAL TYRE COMPANY (DEPTFORD) LIMITED—See Halfords Group plc; *Int'l*, pg. 3229
UNIVERSAL UNDERWRITERS INSURANCE COMPANY—See Zurich Insurance Group Limited; *Int'l*, pg. 8699
UNIVERSAL UNDERWRITERS LIFE INSURANCE—See Zurich Insurance Group Limited; *Int'l*, pg. 8699
UNIVERSAL UNDERWRITERS OF TEXAS INSURANCE COMPANY—See Zurich Insurance Group Limited; *Int'l*, pg. 8699
UNIVERSAL UNDERWRITING AGENCIES PTY LIMITED—See QBE Insurance Group Limited; *Int'l*, pg. 6138
UNIVERSAL UTILITIES LIMITED—See Vitruvian Partners LLP; *Int'l*, pg. 8263
UNIVERSAL UTILITIES PUBLIC COMPANY LIMITED—See Eastern Water Resources Development & Management Public Company Limited; *Int'l*, pg. 2274
UNIVERSAL VISION BIOTECHNOLOGY CO., LTD.; *Int'l*, pg. 8082
UNIVERSAL WAREHOUSE CO.; *U.S. Private*, pg. 4307
UNIVERSAL WARRANTY CORP.; *U.S. Private*, pg. 4307
UNIVERSAL WEATHER & AVIATION, INC.; *U.S. Private*, pg. 4307
UNIVERSAL WEAVERS CORPORATION—See Medtecs International Corporation Limited; *Int'l*, pg. 4786
UNIVERSAL WELL SERVICES, INC.—See Patterson-UTI Energy, Inc.; *U.S. Public*, pg. 1654
UNIVERSAL WILDE; *U.S. Private*, pg. 4307
UNIVERSAL WINDOW SOLUTIONS, LLC; *U.S. Private*, pg. 4307
UNIVERSAL YUMS LLC; *U.S. Private*, pg. 4307
UNIVERSE BEAUTY CO., LTD.—See Saha Pathanapibul Public Company Limited; *Int'l*, pg. 6479
UNIVERSE ENTERTAINMENT AND CULTURE GROUP COMPANY LIMITED; *Int'l*, pg. 8082
UNIVERSE GAS & OIL COMPANY, INC.—See Japan Petroleum Exploration Co. Ltd.; *Int'l*, pg. 3900
UNIVERSE GROUP PLC—See TA Associates, Inc.; *U.S. Private*, pg. 3917
UNIVERSELLE ENGINEERING U.N.L. GMBH—See Korber AG; *Int'l*, pg. 4280
UNIVERSE OPTICAL COMPANY LIMITED—See Universe Entertainment and Culture Group Company Limited; *Int'l*, pg. 8083
UNIVERSE PHARMACEUTICALS INC.; *Int'l*, pg. 8083
UNIVERSE PRINTSHOP HOLDINGS LTD.; *Int'l*, pg. 8083
UNIVERSIA BRASIL S.A.—See Banco Santander, S.A.; *Int'l*, pg. 828
UNIVERSIDAD CNCI, S.A. DE C.V.; *Int'l*, pg. 8083
UNIVERS INFORMATIQUE—See Micropole SA; *Int'l*, pg. 4880
UNIVERSITATSKLINIKUM GIEBEN UND MARBURG GMBH—See Asklepios Kliniken GmbH & Co. KGaA; *Int'l*, pg. 624
UNIVERSITATSKLINIKUM GIESSEN UND MARBURG GMBH—See Asklepios Kliniken GmbH & Co. KGaA; *Int'l*, pg. 624
UNIVERSITIES RESEARCH ASSOCIATION, INC.; *U.S. Private*, pg. 4307
UNIVERSITIES SUPERANNUATION SCHEME LIMITED; *Int'l*, pg. 8083
UNIVERSITI TENAGA NASIONAL SDN. BHD.—See Tenaga Nasional Berhad; *Int'l*, pg. 7558
UNIVERSITI TENAGA NASIONAL SDN BHD (UNITEN)—See Tenaga Nasional Berhad; *Int'l*, pg. 7558
UNIVERSITY AREA COMMUNITY DEVELOPMENT CORPORATION, INC.; *U.S. Private*, pg. 4307
UNIVERSITY AUTO RECYCLERS, INC.—See Stellex Capital Management LP; *U.S. Private*, pg. 3800
UNIVERSITY BANCORP, INC.; *U.S. Public*, pg. 2262

UNIVERSITY BANCORP, INC.

UNIVERSITY BANK—See University Bancorp, Inc.; *U.S. Public*, pg. 2262
UNIVERSITY BOOK STORE INC.; *U.S. Private*, pg. 4307
THE UNIVERSITY BOOK STORE; *U.S. Private*, pg. 4129
UNIVERSITY CHRYSLER DODGE JEEP RAM OF FLORENCE; *U.S. Private*, pg. 4307
UNIVERSITY CIRCLE INCORPORATED; *U.S. Private*, pg. 4307
UNIVERSITY CITY SCIENCE CENTER; *U.S. Private*, pg. 4307
UNIVERSITY CLUB OF MILWAUKEE; *U.S. Private*, pg. 4307
UNIVERSITY CORP.; *U.S. Private*, pg. 4307
UNIVERSITY DIALYSIS CENTER, LLC—See DaVita Inc.; *U.S. Public*, pg. 644
UNIVERSITY DIRECTORIES—See The AroundCampus Group; *U.S. Private*, pg. 3988
UNIVERSITY GAMES AUSTRALIA—See University Games Corporation; *U.S. Private*, pg. 4307
UNIVERSITY GAMES CORPORATION; *U.S. Private*, pg. 4307
UNIVERSITY GAMES EUROPE B.V.—See University Games Corporation; *U.S. Private*, pg. 4307
UNIVERSITY GAMES UK LTD.—See University Games Corporation; *U.S. Private*, pg. 4308
UNIVERSITY HEALTH CARE, INC.; *U.S. Private*, pg. 4308
UNIVERSITY HEALTH PLANS, INC—See Kelso & Company, L.P.; *U.S. Private*, pg. 2280
UNIVERSITY HEALTH SYSTEM; *U.S. Private*, pg. 4308
UNIVERSITY HOSPITAL, LTD.—See HCA Healthcare, Inc.; *U.S. Public*, pg. 1013
UNIVERSITY HOSPITAL & MEDICAL CENTER—See HCA Healthcare, Inc.; *U.S. Public*, pg. 1013
UNIVERSITY INSTRUCTORS, INC.—See Public Consulting Group, Inc.; *U.S. Private*, pg. 3299
UNIVERSITY KIDNEY CENTER BLUEGRASS, LLC—See Nautic Partners, LLC; *U.S. Private*, pg. 2871
UNIVERSITY MECHANICAL & ENGINEERING CONTRACTORS, INC.—See EMCOR Group, Inc.; *U.S. Public*, pg. 737
UNIVERSITY MECHANICAL & ENGINEERING CONTRACTORS, INC.—See EMCOR Group, Inc.; *U.S. Public*, pg. 737
UNIVERSITY MEDICAL GROUP; *U.S. Private*, pg. 4308
UNIVERSITY MOVING & STORAGE CO.; *U.S. Private*, pg. 4308
THE UNIVERSITY NATIONAL BANK OF LAWRENCE—See Lawrence Financial Corporation; *U.S. Private*, pg. 2401
UNIVERSITY OF AFRICA LTD.—See ADvTECH Limited; *Int'l*, pg. 169
UNIVERSITY OF ARIZONA; *U.S. Private*, pg. 4308
UNIVERSITY OF CALIFORNIA SAN FRANCISCO MEDICAL CENTER; *U.S. Private*, pg. 4308
UNIVERSITY OF CHICAGO MEDICINE—See University of Chicago; *U.S. Private*, pg. 4308
UNIVERSITY OF CHICAGO PRESS—See University of Chicago; *U.S. Private*, pg. 4308
UNIVERSITY OF CHICAGO; *U.S. Private*, pg. 4308
UNIVERSITY OF COLORADO HEALTH; *U.S. Private*, pg. 4308
UNIVERSITY OF CONNECTICUT COOPERATIVE CORPORATION; *U.S. Private*, pg. 4309
UNIVERSITY OF DREAMS, INC.; *U.S. Private*, pg. 4309
UNIVERSITY OF KANSAS MEM CORP.; *U.S. Private*, pg. 4309
UNIVERSITY OF LOUISVILLE; *U.S. Private*, pg. 4309
UNIVERSITY OF MIAMI TISSUE BANK—See Vivex Biomedical, Inc.; *U.S. Private*, pg. 4406
UNIVERSITY OF MICHIGAN; *U.S. Private*, pg. 4309
UNIVERSITY OF NEBRASKA FOUNDATION; *U.S. Private*, pg. 4309
UNIVERSITY OF NEW HAMPSHIRE FOUNDATION; *U.S. Private*, pg. 4309
THE UNIVERSITY OF NOTTINGHAM IN MALAYSIA SDN BHD—See Lembaga Tabung Angkatan Tentera; *Int'l*, pg. 4448
THE UNIVERSITY OF OKLAHOMA COLLEGE OF MEDICINE; *U.S. Private*, pg. 4129
UNIVERSITY OF OREGON BOOKSTORE; *U.S. Private*, pg. 4309
UNIVERSITY OF PANGASINAN, INC.—See PHINMA Corporation; *Int'l*, pg. 5848
UNIVERSITY OF PHOENIX, INC.—See Apollo Global Management, Inc.; *U.S. Public*, pg. 146
UNIVERSITY OF PHOENIX, INC.—See The Vistria Group, LP; *U.S. Private*, pg. 4131
UNIVERSITY OF PITTSBURGH MEDICAL CENTER; *U.S. Private*, pg. 4309
THE UNIVERSITY OF THE ROCKIES—See Zovio Inc.; *U.S. Public*, pg. 2411
UNIVERSITY OF TN MEDICAL CENTER HOME CARE SERVICES, LLC—See UnitedHealth Group Incorporated; *U.S. Public*, pg. 2247
UNIVERSITY OF VIRGINIA PHYSICIANS GROUP; *U.S. Private*, pg. 4310
UNIVERSITY OF WISCONSIN MEDICAL FOUNDATION; *U.S. Private*, pg. 4310

UNIVERSITY PARK MALL CC, LLC—See Washington Prime Group Inc.; *U.S. Private*, pg. 4449
UNIVERSITY PHYSICAL THERAPY, LIMITED PARTNERSHIP—See U.S. Physical Therapy, Inc.; *U.S. Public*, pg. 2216
UNIVERSITY PLUMBING & HEATING LTD; *Int'l*, pg. 8083
UNIVERSITY PRESS OF AMERICA, INC.—See The Rowman & Littlefield Publishing Group, Inc.; *U.S. Private*, pg. 4112
UNIVERSITY PRESS PLC; *Int'l*, pg. 8083
UNIVERSITY PRODUCTS INC.; *U.S. Private*, pg. 4310
UNIVERSITY SQUARE PARKING LLC—See Kite Realty Group Trust; *U.S. Public*, pg. 1237
UNIVERSITY SURGERY CENTER, LTD.—See Tenet Healthcare Corporation; *U.S. Public*, pg. 2014
UNIVERSITY SURGICENTER, LLC—See HCA Healthcare, Inc.; *U.S. Public*, pg. 1013
UNIVERSITY SWAGING CORPORATION—See Berkshire Hathaway Inc.; *U.S. Public*, pg. 315
UNIVERSITY TITLE COMPANY—See Investors Title Company; *U.S. Public*, pg. 1165
UNIVERSITY VENTURES FUNDS MANAGEMENT LLC; *U.S. Private*, pg. 4310
UNIVERSITY VILLAGE TOWERS, LLC—See Greystar Real Estate Partners, LLC; *U.S. Private*, pg. 1785
UNIVERSITY VOLKSWAGEN INC.; *U.S. Private*, pg. 4310
UNIVERSO ONLINE S.A; *Int'l*, pg. 8083
UNIVERSO SA—See The Swatch Group Ltd.; *Int'l*, pg. 7693
UNIVERS POCHE SA—See Vivendi SE; *Int'l*, pg. 8278
UNIVERSUM FILM GMBH—See KKR & Co. Inc.; *U.S. Public*, pg. 1266
UNIVERUS SOFTWARE, INC.; *Int'l*, pg. 8083
UNIVERZAL A.D.; *Int'l*, pg. 8083
UNIVERZAL BANKA A.D. BEOGRAD; *Int'l*, pg. 8083
UNIVERZALNI SPRAVA MAJETKU AS—See Assicurazioni Generali S.p.A.; *Int'l*, pg. 648
UNIVERZALPROMET D.D. TUZLA; *Int'l*, pg. 8083
UNIVESCO INC.; *U.S. Private*, pg. 4310
UNIVEST BANK & TRUST CO.—See Univest Financial Corporation; *U.S. Public*, pg. 2262
UNIVEST CAPITAL, INC.—See Univest Financial Corporation; *U.S. Public*, pg. 2263
UNIVEST FINANCIAL CORPORATION; *U.S. Public*, pg. 2262
UNIVEST GROUP—See International Financial Advisors K.S.C.C.; *Int'l*, pg. 3748
UNIVEST INSURANCE, INC.—See Univest Financial Corporation; *U.S. Public*, pg. 2263
UNIVEST INVESTMENTS, INC.—See Univest Financial Corporation; *U.S. Public*, pg. 2263
UNIVEX CORPORATION; *U.S. Private*, pg. 4310
UNIVID ASA; *Int'l*, pg. 8083
UNIVISION COMMUNICATIONS INC.—See ForgeLight, LLC; *U.S. Private*, pg. 1568
UNIVISION COMMUNICATIONS INC.—See Searchlight Capital Partners, L.P.; *U.S. Private*, pg. 3590
UNIVISION ENGINEERING LIMITED; *Int'l*, pg. 8083
UNIVISION HOLDINGS, INC.—See ForgeLight, LLC; *U.S. Private*, pg. 1568
UNIVISION HOLDINGS, INC.—See Searchlight Capital Partners, L.P.; *U.S. Private*, pg. 3590
UNIVISION RADIO NATIONAL SALES—See iHeartMedia, Inc.; *U.S. Public*, pg. 1096
UNIVISION RADIO—See ForgeLight, LLC; *U.S. Private*, pg. 1568
UNIVISION RADIO—See Searchlight Capital Partners, L.P.; *U.S. Private*, pg. 3590
UNIVISTA INSURANCE CORPORATION; *U.S. Private*, pg. 4310
UNIVOLT CANADA LTD.—See Dietzel GmbH; *Int'l*, pg. 2117
UNIVOLT (HK) LIMITED—See Dietzel GmbH; *Int'l*, pg. 2117
UNIVOLT HUNGARIA KFT.—See Dietzel GmbH; *Int'l*, pg. 2117
UNIVOLT REMAT S.R.O.—See Dietzel GmbH; *Int'l*, pg. 2117
UNIVOLT (UK) LTD.—See Dietzel GmbH; *Int'l*, pg. 2117
UNIVO PHARMACEUTICALS LTD.; *Int'l*, pg. 8083
UNIWAY—See Societe Pour L'Informatique Industrielle; *Int'l*, pg. 7044
UNIWEB INC.; *U.S. Private*, pg. 4310
UNIWELD PRODUCTS INC.; *U.S. Private*, pg. 4310
UNIWELL CORPORATION; *U.S. Private*, pg. 4310
UNIWHEELS AG—See SUPERIOR INDUSTRIES INTERNATIONAL INC; *U.S. Public*, pg. 1967
UNIWHEELS MANAGEMENT (SWITZERLAND) AG; *Int'l*, pg. 8083
UNIWIDE HOLDINGS INC.; *Int'l*, pg. 8083
UNIWILL INSURANCE BROKER CO., LTD.—See China United Insurance Service, Inc.; *Int'l*, pg. 1561
UNIWIZ TRADE SALES, INC.—See Razer Inc.; *U.S. Private*, pg. 3359
UNI-WORLD CAPITAL, L.P.; *U.S. Private*, pg. 4281
UNIWORLD GROUP-DETROIT—See Uniworld Group, Inc.; *U.S. Private*, pg. 4310
UNIWORLD GROUP, INC.; *U.S. Private*, pg. 4310
UNIWORTH INTERNATIONAL LTD.; *Int'l*, pg. 8083

CORPORATE AFFILIATIONS

UNIWORTH TEXTILES LTD.; *Int'l*, pg. 8084
UNI-X (BOLIVIA) LTDA—See Nippon Yusen Kabushiki Kaisha; *Int'l*, pg. 5360
UNI-X CORPORATION—See Nippon Yusen Kabushiki Kaisha; *Int'l*, pg. 5360
UNIXECURE CORP.—See SYSTEX Corporation; *Int'l*, pg. 7393
UNI-X NCT CORPORATION—See Nippon Yusen Kabushiki Kaisha; *Int'l*, pg. 5360
UNI YAZI GERECLERI KIRTASIYE VE SAN. TIC. A.S.—See Mitsubishi Pencil Co., Ltd.; *Int'l*, pg. 4967
UNIZAN CAPITAL, LLC—See Huntington Bancshares Incorporated; *U.S. Public*, pg. 1071
UNIZO HOLDINGS COMPANY LIMITED; *Int'l*, pg. 8084
UNIZYX HOLDING CORPORATION; *Int'l*, pg. 8084
UNJHA FORMULATIONS LIMITED; *Int'l*, pg. 8084
UNLEADED COMMUNICATIONS, INC.; *U.S. Private*, pg. 4310
UNLIMITED CONSTRUCTION SERVICES; *U.S. Private*, pg. 4310
UNLIMITED EXPRESS (GUANGZHOU) CORP.—See UEC Group Ltd.; *Int'l*, pg. 8014
UNLIMITED EXPRESS (JAKARTA) CORP.—See UEC Group Ltd.; *Int'l*, pg. 8014
UNLIMITED EXPRESS (MYANMAR) CORP.—See UEC Group Ltd.; *Int'l*, pg. 8014
UNLIMITED EXPRESS (SEMARANG) CORP.—See UEC Group Ltd.; *Int'l*, pg. 8014
UNLIMITED EXPRESS (SHENZHEN) CORP.—See UEC Group Ltd.; *Int'l*, pg. 8014
UNLIMITED EXPRESS (TAIWAN) CORP.—See UEC Group Ltd.; *Int'l*, pg. 8014
UNLIMITED EXPRESS (THAILAND) CORP.—See UEC Group Ltd.; *Int'l*, pg. 8014
UNLIMITED EXPRESS (USA) CORP.—See UEC Group Ltd.; *Int'l*, pg. 8014
UNLIMITED MERCHANT SERVICES—See I.T. Source; *U.S. Private*, pg. 2027
UNLIMITED QUEST, INC.—See Centerbridge Partners, L.P.; *U.S. Private*, pg. 814
UNLIMITED SERVICES OF WISCONSIN, INC.; *U.S. Private*, pg. 4310
UNLIMITED SKY HOLDINGS, INC.; *U.S. Private*, pg. 4310
UNLIMITED WORLDWIDE LOGISTICS CORP.—See UEC Group Ltd.; *Int'l*, pg. 8014
UNLIMIT HEALTH LIMITED—See Eisai Co., Ltd.; *Int'l*, pg. 2336
UNLOCK HEALTH, INC.—See Amulet Capital Partners, L.P.; *U.S. Private*, pg. 268
UNLU MENKUL DEGERLER A.S.; *Int'l*, pg. 8084
UN MONDE INTERNATIONAL LTD.; *U.S. Public*, pg. 2225
UNM PHARMA INC.; *Int'l*, pg. 8084
UNNA ENERGIA S.A.—See Aenza S.A.A.; *Int'l*, pg. 176
UNNO INDUSTRIES LTD.; *Int'l*, pg. 8084
UNO ALLA VOLTA, LLC.; *U.S. Private*, pg. 4310
UNOCHROME INDUSTRIES LIMITED—See Camellia Plc; *Int'l*, pg. 1271
UNO-EINKAUFSZENTRUM-VERWALTUNGSGESELLSCHAFT MBH—See Uni-Credit S.p.A.; *Int'l*, pg. 8038
UNOFI PATRIMOINE; *Int'l*, pg. 8084
UNOMEDICAL A/S—See Nordic Capital AB; *Int'l*, pg. 5421
UNO MINDA LIMITED; *Int'l*, pg. 8084
UNO RESTAURANT HOLDINGS CORPORATION—See Centre Partners Management LLC; *U.S. Private*, pg. 829
UNO S.A. DE C.V.—See Grupo Terra S.A. de C.V.; *Int'l*, pg. 3137
UNOSQUARE LLC—See Trivest Partners, LP; *U.S. Private*, pg. 4241
UNOS SDN. BHD.—See FSBM Holdings Berhad; *Int'l*, pg. 2798
UNO-X GRUPPEN AS—See Reitangruppen AS; *Int'l*, pg. 6259
UNOZAWA-GUMI IRON WORKS, LTD.; *Int'l*, pg. 8084
U.N.P.-HRSOLUTIONS GMBH—See Allgeier SE; *Int'l*, pg. 338
U.N.P. - SOFTWARE GMBH—See Allgeier SE; *Int'l*, pg. 338
UNQ HOLDINGS LIMITED; *Int'l*, pg. 8084
UNRAVEL S.A.—See Spyrosoft S.A.; *Int'l*, pg. 7146
THE UNREAL AGENCY; *U.S. Private*, pg. 4129
UNRIVALED BRANDS, INC.; *U.S. Public*, pg. 2263
U.N. RO-RO ISLETMELERI A.S.—See DFDS A/S; *Int'l*, pg. 2095
UNSA AMBALAJ SANAYI VE TICARET ANONIM SIRKETI—See Greif Inc.; *U.S. Public*, pg. 968
UNSDG ACQUISITION CORP.; *U.S. Public*, pg. 4311
UNS ELECTRIC, INC.—See Fortis Inc.; *Int'l*, pg. 2740
UNS ENERGY CORPORATION—See Fortis Inc.; *Int'l*, pg. 2740
UNSER LAGERHAUS WARENHANDELSGESELLSCHAFT M.B.H.—See BayWa AG; *Int'l*, pg. 919
UNS GAS, INC.—See Fortis Inc.; *Int'l*, pg. 2740
UNSW GLOBAL PTY. LTD.—See Janison Education Group Limited; *Int'l*, pg. 3879
UNTANGLE, INC.—See Providence Equity Partners L.L.C.; *U.S. Private*, pg. 3294

COMPANY NAME INDEX

UNTERNEHMENSGRUPPE THEO MULLER S.E.C.S.; *Int'l*, pg. 8085
UNTERNEHMENS INVEST AG; *Int'l*, pg. 8085
UNTERSTUETZUNGSKASSE DER SACHS FAHRZEUG- UND MOTORENTECHNIK GMBH—See ZF Friedrichshafen AG; *Int'l*, pg. 8644
UNTERSTUTZUNGSGESELLSCHAFT MBH DER DEUTZ AKTIENGESELLSCHAFT—See DEUTZ AG; *Int'l*, pg. 2086
UNTERTAGE-SPEICHER-GESELLSCHAFT MBH (USG)—See BASF SE; *Int'l*, pg. 885
UN TOIT POUR TOI SA; *Int'l*, pg. 8027
UNTRACHT EARLY, LLC; *U.S. Private*, pg. 4311
UNUM DENTAL—See Unum Group; *U.S. Public*, pg. 2263
UNUM EUROPEAN HOLDING COMPANY LIMITED—See Unum Group; *U.S. Public*, pg. 2263
UNUM GROUP; *U.S. Public*, pg. 2263
UNUM INSURANCE AGENCY, LLC—See Unum Group; *U.S. Public*, pg. 2263
UNUM LIFE INSURANCE COMPANY OF AMERICA—See Unum Group; *U.S. Public*, pg. 2263
UNUM LIMITED—See Unum Group; *U.S. Public*, pg. 2263
UNUM—See Unum Group; *U.S. Public*, pg. 2263
UNUM ZYCIE TOWARZYSTWO UBEZPIECZEN I REASEKURACJI SPOLKA AKCYJNA—See Unum Group; *U.S. Public*, pg. 2263
UNUS HOLDING B.V.—See Unilever PLC; *Int'l*, pg. 8045
UNUSUAL LIMITED—See mm2 Asia Ltd.; *Int'l*, pg. 5004
UNUSUAL MACHINES, INC.; *U.S. Public*, pg. 2263
UNUSUAL PRODUCTIONS (M) SDN. BHD.—See mm2 Asia Ltd.; *Int'l*, pg. 5004
UNVERFERTH MANUFACTURING COMPANY INC.; *U.S. Private*, pg. 4311
UNWIRED AUSTRALIA PTY. LIMITED—See Seven Group Holdings Limited; *Int'l*, pg. 6733
U.N.X. INCORPORATED; *U.S. Private*, pg. 4269
UNY CO., LTD.—See Pan Pacific International Holdings Corporation; *Int'l*, pg. 5715
UNYE CIMENTO SANAYI VE TICARET A.S.; *Int'l*, pg. 8085
UNZA CATHAY LIMITED—See Wipro Limited; *Int'l*, pg. 8432
UNZA CHINA LIMITED—See Wipro Limited; *Int'l*, pg. 8432
UNZA COMPANY PTE LTD—See Wipro Limited; *Int'l*, pg. 8432
UNZA HOLDINGS PTE LTD.—See Wipro Limited; *Int'l*, pg. 8432
UNZA HOLDINGS SDN BHD—See Wipro Limited; *Int'l*, pg. 8432
UNZ & COMPANY, INC.; *U.S. Private*, pg. 4311
UNZIPPED APPAREL LLC—See Iconix Acquisition LLC; *U.S. Private*, pg. 2033
UOA ASSET MANAGEMENT SDN BHD—See United Overseas Australia Ltd; *Int'l*, pg. 8071
UOA DEVELOPMENT BHD.—See United Overseas Australia Ltd; *Int'l*, pg. 8071
UOA HOLDINGS SDN BHD—See United Overseas Australia Ltd; *Int'l*, pg. 8071
UOA HOSPITALITY SDN BHD—See United Overseas Australia Ltd; *Int'l*, pg. 8071
UOA PROPERTY GALLERY - THE VILLAGE—See United Overseas Australia Ltd; *Int'l*, pg. 8071
UOA REAL ESTATE INVESTMENT TRUST; *Int'l*, pg. 8085
UOA (SINGAPORE) PTE LTD—See United Overseas Australia Ltd; *Int'l*, pg. 8071
UOB ALTERNATIVE INVESTMENT MANAGEMENT PTE. LTD.—See United Overseas Bank Limited; *Int'l*, pg. 8071
UOB APARTMENT PROPERTY FUND ONE—See U City Public Company Limited; *Int'l*, pg. 7996
UOB ASSET MANAGEMENT (B) SDN. BHD.—See United Overseas Bank Limited; *Int'l*, pg. 8071
UOB ASSET MANAGEMENT (JAPAN) LTD.—See United Overseas Bank Limited; *Int'l*, pg. 8071
UOB ASSET MANAGEMENT LTD.—See United Overseas Bank Limited; *Int'l*, pg. 8071
UOB ASSET MANAGEMENT (MALAYSIA) BERHAD—See United Overseas Bank Limited; *Int'l*, pg. 8071
UOB ASSET MANAGEMENT (TAIWAN) CO., LTD.—See United Overseas Bank Limited; *Int'l*, pg. 8071
UOB ASSET MANAGEMENT (THAI) CO., LTD.—See United Overseas Bank Limited; *Int'l*, pg. 8071
UOB ASSET MANAGEMENT (THAILAND) CO., LTD.—See United Overseas Bank Limited; *Int'l*, pg. 8071
UOB AUSTRALIA LIMITED—See United Overseas Bank Limited; *Int'l*, pg. 8071
UOB BULLION & FUTURES LIMITED—See United Overseas Bank Limited; *Int'l*, pg. 8071
UOB GLOBAL CAPITAL LLC—See United Overseas Bank Limited; *Int'l*, pg. 8071
UOB ISLAMIC ASSET MANAGEMENT SDN. BHD.—See United Overseas Bank Limited; *Int'l*, pg. 8071
UOB KAY HIAN CREDIT PTE LTD—See UOB-Kay Hian Holdings Limited; *Int'l*, pg. 8085
UOB-KAY HIAN HOLDINGS LIMITED; *Int'l*, pg. 8085
UOB KAY HIAN (HONG KONG) LIMITED—See UOB-Kay Hian Holdings Limited; *Int'l*, pg. 8085
UOB KAY HIAN INVESTMENT CONSULTING (SHANGHAI) COMPANY LIMITED—See UOB-Kay Hian Holdings Limited; *Int'l*, pg. 8085
UOB KAY HIAN (MALAYSIA) HOLDINGS SDN. BHD.—See UOB-Kay Hian Holdings Limited; *Int'l*, pg. 8085
UOB KAY HIAN PRIVATE LTD.—See UOB-Kay Hian Holdings Limited; *Int'l*, pg. 8085
UOB KAY HIAN SECURITIES (M) SDN. BHD.—See UOB-Kay Hian Holdings Limited; *Int'l*, pg. 8085
UOB KAY HIAN SECURITIES (PHILIPPINES), INC.—See UOB-Kay Hian Holdings Limited; *Int'l*, pg. 8085
UOB KAY HIAN SECURITIES (THAILAND) PUBLIC COMPANY LIMITED—See UOB-Kay Hian Holdings Limited; *Int'l*, pg. 8085
UOB KAY HIAN (U.K.) LIMITED—See UOB-Kay Hian Holdings Limited; *Int'l*, pg. 8085
UOB KAY HIAN (U.S.) INC.—See UOB-Kay Hian Holdings Limited; *Int'l*, pg. 8085
UOB TRAVEL PLANNERS PTE. LTD.—See United Overseas Bank Limited; *Int'l*, pg. 8072
UOB VENTURE MANAGEMENT PRIVATE LIMITED—See United Overseas Bank Limited; *Int'l*, pg. 8072
UOB VENTURE MANAGEMENT (SHANGHAI) CO., LTD.—See United Overseas Bank Limited; *Int'l*, pg. 8072
UOC SDN. BHD.—See Cyberjaya Education Group Berhad; *Int'l*, pg. 1893
UOEI SHOTEN CORPORATION—See Future Corporation; *Int'l*, pg. 2853
UOKI CO., LTD.; *Int'l*, pg. 8086
UOL GROUP LIMITED; *Int'l*, pg. 8086
UOMO MEDIA INC.; *Int'l*, pg. 8086
UOP CALLIDUS—See Honeywell International Inc.; *U.S. Public*, pg. 1052
UOP CH SARL—See Honeywell International Inc.; *U.S. Public*, pg. 1052
UOP LIMITED—See Honeywell International Inc.; *U.S. Public*, pg. 1052
UOP LLC - HOUSTON—See Honeywell International Inc.; *U.S. Public*, pg. 1052
UOP LLC—See Honeywell International Inc.; *U.S. Public*, pg. 1052
UOP RUSSELL LLC—See Honeywell International Inc.; *U.S. Public*, pg. 1052
UORIKI CO., LTD.; *Int'l*, pg. 8086
UPA CORPORATION BERHAD; *Int'l*, pg. 8087
UPAKARMA AYURVEDA PRIVATE LIMITED—See Mankind Pharma Ltd.; *Int'l*, pg. 4673
U-PAK FZC—See Kuwait Packing Materials Manufacturing Company K.S.C.C.; *Int'l*, pg. 4345
UPA MACHINERY SDN. BHD.—See UPA Corporation Berhad; *Int'l*, pg. 8087
UPA PRESS SDN. BHD.—See UPA Corporation Berhad; *Int'l*, pg. 8087
UPARC, INC.; *U.S. Private*, pg. 4311
UPARTMENTS REAL ESTATE GMBH—See CORESTATE Capital Holding SA; *Int'l*, pg. 1800
UPAY, INC.; *U.S. Public*, pg. 2263
U-PAYMENT LTD.—See DGB Financial Group Co., Ltd.; *Int'l*, pg. 2096
UPBEST ASSETS MANAGEMENT LIMITED—See Upbest Group Limited; *Int'l*, pg. 8087
UPBEST BULLION COMPANY LIMITED—See Upbest Group Limited; *Int'l*, pg. 8087
UPBEST COMMODITIES COMPANY LIMITED—See Upbest Group Limited; *Int'l*, pg. 8087
UPBEST CYBER TRADE COMPANY LIMITED—See Upbest Group Limited; *Int'l*, pg. 8087
UPBEST FINANCE COMPANY LIMITED—See Upbest Group Limited; *Int'l*, pg. 8087
UPBEST FINANCIAL SERVICES LIMITED—See Upbest Group Limited; *Int'l*, pg. 8087
UPBEST GROUP LIMITED; *Int'l*, pg. 8087
UPBEST INVESTMENT COMPANY LIMITED—See Upbest Group Limited; *Int'l*, pg. 8087
UPBEST SECURITIES COMPANY LIMITED—See Upbest Group Limited; *Int'l*, pg. 8087
UPBOUND GROUP, INC.; *U.S. Public*, pg. 2263
UPCAP SERVICES, INC.; *U.S. Private*, pg. 4311
UPC AUSTRIA GMBH—See Deutsche Telekom AG; *Int'l*, pg. 2084
UPC AUSTRIA SERVICES GMBH—See Deutsche Telekom AG; *Int'l*, pg. 2084
UPC BROADBAND N.V.—See Liberty Global plc; *Int'l*, pg. 4485
UPC BUSINESS AUSTRIA GMBH—See Liberty Global plc; *Int'l*, pg. 4485
UPC CABLECOM AUSTRIA GMBH—See Liberty Global plc; *Int'l*, pg. 4485
UPC CABLECOM GMBH—See Liberty Global plc; *Int'l*, pg. 4485
UPC CESKA REPUBLICA S.R.O—See Vodafone Group Plc; *Int'l*, pg. 8285
UPC DSL TELECOM GMBH—See Liberty Global plc; *Int'l*, pg. 4485
UP CHEMICAL CO. LTD. - PYEONGTAEK PLANT—See Jiangsu Yoke Technology Co., Ltd.; *Int'l*, pg. 3957

UPLAND HILLS HEALTH, INC.

UP CHEMICAL CO. LTD.—See Jiangsu Yoke Technology Co., Ltd.; *Int'l*, pg. 3957
UPCHURCH ELECTRIC SUPPLY CO.; *U.S. Private*, pg. 4311
UPCHURCH MANAGEMENT CO. INC.; *U.S. Private*, pg. 4311
UPC LTD.; *Int'l*, pg. 8087
UPC MAGYARORSZAG KFT—See Vodafone Group Plc; *Int'l*, pg. 8285
UPC NEDERLAND NETWERK 2 BV—See Liberty Global plc; *Int'l*, pg. 4485
UPCO SYSTEMS INC.—See Adamant Holding Inc.; *Int'l*, pg. 123
UPC ROMANIA SRL—See Vodafone Group Plc; *Int'l*, pg. 8285
UPC SCHWEIZ GMBH—See Liberty Global plc; *Int'l*, pg. 4485
UPC TELEKABEL-FERNSEHNETZ WIENER NEUSTADT/NEUNKIRCHEN BETRIEBSGESELLSCHAFT MBH—See Deutsche Telekom AG; *Int'l*, pg. 2084
UPC TELEKABEL KLAGENFURT GMBH—See Deutsche Telekom AG; *Int'l*, pg. 2084
UPC TELEKABEL WIEN GMBH—See Deutsche Telekom AG; *Int'l*, pg. 2084
UPCURVE CLOUD LLC—See Gannett Co., Inc.; *U.S. Public*, pg. 906
UPCURVE, INC.—See Gannett Co., Inc.; *U.S. Public*, pg. 906
UPDATA INFRASTRUCTURE UK LTD.—See Capita plc; *Int'l*, pg. 1309
UPDATA PARTNERS; *U.S. Private*, pg. 4311
UPDATE CRM INC.—See ESW Capital, LLC; *U.S. Private*, pg. 1429
UPDATE LEGAL, INC.—See Driven, Inc.; *U.S. Private*, pg. 1278
UPDATEPOWER CORPORATION; *U.S. Private*, pg. 4311
UPDATER INC.; *U.S. Private*, pg. 4311
UPDATER SERVICES LIMITED; *Int'l*, pg. 8087
UPDAY GMBH & CO. KG—See Axel Springer SE; *Int'l*, pg. 767
UPDC PLC.—See Custodian Investment PLC; *Int'l*, pg. 1880
UPDEGRAFF VISION; *U.S. Private*, pg. 4311
UPD HOLDING CORP.; *U.S. Public*, pg. 2263
UPDOWN INGENIEURTECHNIK FUR FORDERTECHNIK GMBH—See DEKRA e.V.; *Int'l*, pg. 2010
UPD STARI GRAD A.D.; *Int'l*, pg. 8087
UPECA AEROTECH SDN. BHD.—See Senior plc; *Int'l*, pg. 6709
UPECA FLOWTECH SDN. BHD.—See Senior plc; *Int'l*, pg. 6709
UPECA TECHNOLOGIES SDN. BHD.—See Senior plc; *Int'l*, pg. 6709
UP ENERGY DEVELOPMENT GROUP LIMITED; *Int'l*, pg. 8086
UPERGY; *Int'l*, pg. 8088
UPET S.A.; *Int'l*, pg. 8088
UPEX BRANDS—See Mapal Communications Ltd.; *Int'l*, pg. 4681
UPEXI, INC.; *U.S. Public*, pg. 2264
UP FINTECH HOLDING LIMITED; *Int'l*, pg. 8086
UPFRONT HEALTHCARE SERVICES, INC.; *U.S. Private*, pg. 4311
UPFRONT VENTURES; *U.S. Private*, pg. 4311
UPG BALTIC UAB—See MG Baltic UAB; *Int'l*, pg. 4871
UPG ENTERPRISES LLC; *U.S. Private*, pg. 4311
UP GLOBAL SOURCING HOLDINGS PLC; *Int'l*, pg. 8086
UP GLOBAL SOURCING HONG KONG LIMITED—See UP Global Sourcing Holdings plc; *Int'l*, pg. 8086
UPHAM OIL & GAS COMPANY; *U.S. Private*, pg. 4311
UPHEALTH, INC.; *U.S. Public*, pg. 2264
UPHOLSTERY INTERNATIONAL, INC.; *U.S. Private*, pg. 4311
U.P. HOTELS LIMITED; *Int'l*, pg. 7998
UP HUNTSMAN-NMG—See Huntsman Corporation; *U.S. Public*, pg. 1075
U-PICA RESIN (CHANGSHU) CO., LTD.—See Mitsubishi Gas Chemical Company, Inc.; *Int'l*, pg. 4949
UPI ENERGY LP—See Growmark, Inc.; *U.S. Private*, pg. 1795
UPI ENERGY LP—See Suncor Energy Inc.; *Int'l*, pg. 7311
UP IMAGING MANAGEMENT SERVICES, LLC—See Apollo Global Management, Inc.; *U.S. Public*, pg. 159
UP INVEST OU; *Int'l*, pg. 8086
UPI PHILIPPINES, INC.—See Okaya & Co., Ltd.; *Int'l*, pg. 5547
UPI POSLOVNI SISTEM D.D. SARAJEVO—See CID Adriatic Investments GmbH; *Int'l*, pg. 1603
UPJOHN MIDDLE EAST FZ-LLC—See Viatris Inc.; *U.S. Public*, pg. 2294
UPL AGRICULTURAL SOLUTIONS ROMANIA S.R.L.—See UPL Limited; *Int'l*, pg. 8089
UPL AGROSOLUTIONS CANADA INC.—See UPL Limited; *Int'l*, pg. 8089
UPLAND COMMUNITY CARE, INC.—See The Ensign Group, Inc.; *U.S. Public*, pg. 2072
UPLAND HILLS HEALTH, INC.; *U.S. Private*, pg. 4312

UPLAND HILLS HEALTH, INC.

UPLAND OUTPATIENT SURGICAL CENTER, L.P.—See UnitedHealth Group Incorporated; *U.S. Public*, pg. 2252
UPLAND RESOURCES LIMITED; *Int'l*, pg. 8090
UPLAND SOFTWARE II, INC.—See Upland Software, Inc.; *U.S. Public*, pg. 2264
UPLAND SOFTWARE I, INC.—See Upland Software, Inc.; *U.S. Public*, pg. 2264
UPLAND SOFTWARE, INC.; *U.S. Public*, pg. 2264
UPLAND SOFTWARE IV, INC.—See Upland Software, Inc.; *U.S. Public*, pg. 2264
UPLAND SOFTWARE VI, LLC—See Upland Software, Inc.; *U.S. Public*, pg. 2264
UPLAND UNIVERSAL SELF STORAGE—See National Storage Affiliates Trust; *U.S. Public*, pg. 1498
UPL ARGENTINA S.A.—See UPL Limited; *Int'l*, pg. 8089
UPL AUSTRALIA PTY. LIMITED—See UPL Limited; *Int'l*, pg. 8089
UPL BENELUX B.V.—See UPL Limited; *Int'l*, pg. 8089
UPL BULGARIA EOOD—See UPL Limited; *Int'l*, pg. 8089
UPL COLOMBIA SAS—See UPL Limited; *Int'l*, pg. 8089
UPL CZECH S.R.O.—See UPL Limited; *Int'l*, pg. 8089
UPL DEUTSCHLAND GMBH—See UPL Limited; *Int'l*, pg. 8089
UPL EUROPE LIMITED—See UPL Limited; *Int'l*, pg. 8089
UPL FRANCE SAS—See UPL Limited; *Int'l*, pg. 8089
UPL HELLAS S.A.—See UPL Limited; *Int'l*, pg. 8089
UPL HOLDINGS SA (PTY.) LTD.—See UPL Limited; *Int'l*, pg. 8089
UPL HUNGARY KERESKEDELMI ES SZOLGALTATO KORLATOLT FELELOSSEGU TARSASAG—See UPL Limited; *Int'l*, pg. 8089
UPL IBERIA S.A.—See UPL Limited; *Int'l*, pg. 8089
UPLIFT NUTRITION, INC.; *U.S. Private*, pg. 4312
UPLIGHT, INC.—See Schneider Electric SE; *Int'l*, pg. 6636
UPLIGHT, INC.—See The AES Corporation; *U.S. Public*, pg. 2032
UPLINK DIGITAL GMBH; *Int'l*, pg. 8090
UPLINK SECURITY, INC.—See Sierra Wireless, Inc.; *Int'l*, pg. 6904
UPL LIMITED; *Int'l*, pg. 8088
UPLOGIX, INC.—See Lantronix, Inc.; *U.S. Public*, pg. 1293
UPL PARAGUAY S.A.—See UPL Limited; *Int'l*, pg. 8089
UPL POLSKA SP. Z O.O.—See UPL Limited; *Int'l*, pg. 8089
UPL SLOVAKIA S.R.O.—See UPL Limited; *Int'l*, pg. 8089
UPL SOUTH AFRICA (PTY.) LTD.—See UPL Limited; *Int'l*, pg. 8089
UPL UKRAINE LLC—See UPL Limited; *Int'l*, pg. 8089
UPL ZIRAAT VE KIMYA SANAYI VE TICARET LIMITED SIRKETI—See UPL Limited; *Int'l*, pg. 8089
UP MADERA A.D.; *Int'l*, pg. 8087
UPMARITIME LONDON LTD.; *Int'l*, pg. 8092
UPM ASIA PACIFIC PTE. LTD—See UPM-Kymmene Corporation; *Int'l*, pg. 8090
UPM BIOCHEMICALS GMBH—See UPM-Kymmene Corporation; *Int'l*, pg. 8090
UPMC HEALTH PLAN, INC.—See University of Pittsburgh Medical Center; *U.S. Private*, pg. 4309
UPM (CHINA) CO., LTD. - CHANGSHU PAPER MILL #2—See UPM-Kymmene Corporation; *Int'l*, pg. 8090
UPM (CHINA) CO., LTD.—See UPM-Kymmene Corporation; *Int'l*, pg. 8090
UPMC JAMESON—See University of Pittsburgh Medical Center; *U.S. Private*, pg. 4309
UPMC PINNACLE CARLISLE—See University of Pittsburgh Medical Center; *U.S. Private*, pg. 4310
UPMC PINNACLE LANCASTER—See University of Pittsburgh Medical Center; *U.S. Private*, pg. 4310
UPMC PINNACLE LITITZ—See University of Pittsburgh Medical Center; *U.S. Private*, pg. 4310
UPMC PINNACLE MEMORIAL—See University of Pittsburgh Medical Center; *U.S. Private*, pg. 4310
UPMC PINNACLE—See University of Pittsburgh Medical Center; *U.S. Private*, pg. 4310
UPMC SOMERSET—See University of Pittsburgh Medical Center; *U.S. Private*, pg. 4310
UPMC WESTERN MARYLAND CORPORATION—See University of Pittsburgh Medical Center; *U.S. Private*, pg. 4310
UPMC WORKPARTNERS; *U.S. Private*, pg. 4312
UPM ENERGY—See UPM-Kymmene Corporation; *Int'l*, pg. 8090
UPM FOREST—See UPM-Kymmene Corporation; *Int'l*, pg. 8090
UPM FRANCE S.A.S. - AIGREFEUILLE FURTHER PROCESSING MILL—See UPM-Kymmene Corporation; *Int'l*, pg. 8090
UPM FRANCE S.A.S. - CHAPELLE DARBLAY PAPER MILL—See UPM-Kymmene Corporation; *Int'l*, pg. 8090
UPM FRANCE S.A.S. - DOCELLES PAPER MILL—See UPM-Kymmene Corporation; *Int'l*, pg. 8090
UPM FRANCE S.A.S.—See UPM-Kymmene Corporation; *Int'l*, pg. 8090
UPM FRANCE S.A.S. - STRACEL PAPER MILL—See UPM-Kymmene Corporation; *Int'l*, pg. 8090
UPM FRAY BENTOS S.A.—See UPM-Kymmene Corporation; *Int'l*, pg. 8090

UPM GMBH - ETTRINGEN PAPER MILL—See UPM-Kymmene Corporation; *Int'l*, pg. 8090
UPM GMBH - HURTH PAPER MILL—See UPM-Kymmene Corporation; *Int'l*, pg. 8090
UPM GMBH - PLATTLING PAPER MILL—See UPM-Kymmene Corporation; *Int'l*, pg. 8090
UPM GMBH - SCHONGAU PAPER MILL—See UPM-Kymmene Corporation; *Int'l*, pg. 8090
UPM GMBH - SCHWEDT PAPER MILL—See UPM-Kymmene Corporation; *Int'l*, pg. 8090
UPM GMBH—See UPM-Kymmene Corporation; *Int'l*, pg. 8090
UPM-KYMMENE AB—See UPM-Kymmene Corporation; *Int'l*, pg. 8091
UPM-KYMMENE AG—See UPM-Kymmene Corporation; *Int'l*, pg. 8091
UPM-KYMMENE AS—See UPM-Kymmene Corporation; *Int'l*, pg. 8092
UPM-KYMMENE A/S—See UPM-Kymmene Corporation; *Int'l*, pg. 8091
UPM-KYMMENE (AUSTRIA) GMBH—See Heinzel Holding GmbH; *Int'l*, pg. 3325
UPM-KYMMENE (AUSTRIA) GMBH - STEYRERMUHL PAPER MILL—See Heinzel Holding GmbH; *Int'l*, pg. 3325
UPM-KYMMENE (AUSTRIA) GMBH - STEYRERMUHL SAWMILL—See Heinzel Holding GmbH; *Int'l*, pg. 3325
UPM-KYMMENE (BELGIUM) S.A./N.V.—See UPM-Kymmene Corporation; *Int'l*, pg. 8091
UPM-KYMMENE B.V.—See UPM-Kymmene Corporation; *Int'l*, pg. 8092
UPM-KYMMENE CORP. - ALHOLMA SAWMILL—See UPM-Kymmene Corporation; *Int'l*, pg. 8092
UPM-KYMMENE CORP. - FRAY BENTOS PULP MILL—See UPM-Kymmene Corporation; *Int'l*, pg. 8092
UPM-KYMMENE CORP. - JAMSANKOSKI PAPER MILL—See UPM-Kymmene Corporation; *Int'l*, pg. 8092
UPM-KYMMENE CORP. - KAIPOLA PAPER MILL—See UPM-Kymmene Corporation; *Int'l*, pg. 8092
UPM-KYMMENE CORP. - KAUKAS PAPER/PULP MILL—See UPM-Kymmene Corporation; *Int'l*, pg. 8092
UPM-KYMMENE CORP. - KAUKAS SAWMILL—See UPM-Kymmene Corporation; *Int'l*, pg. 8092
UPM-KYMMENE CORP. - KORKEAKOSKI SAWMILL—See UPM-Kymmene Corporation; *Int'l*, pg. 8092
UPM-KYMMENE CORP. - KYMI PAPER/PULP MILL—See UPM-Kymmene Corporation; *Int'l*, pg. 8092
UPM-KYMMENE CORPORATION; *Int'l*, pg. 8090
UPM-KYMMENE CORP. - PIETARSAARI PULP MILL—See UPM-Kymmene Corporation; *Int'l*, pg. 8092
UPM-KYMMENE CORP. - RAUMA PAPER MILL—See UPM-Kymmene Corporation; *Int'l*, pg. 8092
UPM-KYMMENE CORP. - SEIKKU SAWMILL—See UPM-Kymmene Corporation; *Int'l*, pg. 8092
UPM-KYMMENE CORP. - TERVASAARI PAPER MILL—See UPM-Kymmene Corporation; *Int'l*, pg. 8092
UPM-KYMMENE HELLAS LTD—See UPM-Kymmene Corporation; *Int'l*, pg. 8092
UPM-KYMMENE INC.—See UPM-Kymmene Corporation; *Int'l*, pg. 8092
UPM-KYMMENE INDIA PVT LTD—See UPM-Kymmene Corporation; *Int'l*, pg. 8092
UPM-KYMMENE JAPAN K.K.—See UPM-Kymmene Corporation; *Int'l*, pg. 8092
UPM-KYMMENE KAGIT URUNLERI SANAYI VE TICARET LTD. STI.—See UPM-Kymmene Corporation; *Int'l*, pg. 8092
UPM-KYMMENE KAGIT URUNLERI SANOY VE TICARET LTD. STI—See UPM-Kymmene Corporation; *Int'l*, pg. 8092
UPM-KYMMENE KERESBEDELMI KFT.—See UPM-Kymmene Corporation; *Int'l*, pg. 8092
UPM-KYMMENE LDA—See UPM-Kymmene Corporation; *Int'l*, pg. 8091
UPM-KYMMENE OTEPAA AS—See UPM-Kymmene Corporation; *Int'l*, pg. 8092
UPM-KYMMENE PTY. LTD.—See UPM-Kymmene Corporation; *Int'l*, pg. 8092
UPM-KYMMENE S.A.—See UPM-Kymmene Corporation; *Int'l*, pg. 8092
UPM-KYMMENE SEVEN SEAS OY—See UPM-Kymmene Corporation; *Int'l*, pg. 8092
UPM-KYMMENE (S) PTE. LTD.—See UPM-Kymmene Corporation; *Int'l*, pg. 8090
UPM-KYMMENE S.R.L.—See UPM-Kymmene Corporation; *Int'l*, pg. 8092
UPM-KYMMENE S.R.O.—See UPM-Kymmene Corporation; *Int'l*, pg. 8092
UPM-KYMMENE (UK) HOLDINGS LIMITED—See UPM-Kymmene Corporation; *Int'l*, pg. 8091
UPM-KYMMENE (UK) LIMITED - SHOTTON PAPER MILL—See UPM-Kymmene Corporation; *Int'l*, pg. 8091
UPM-KYMMENE (UK) LIMITED—See UPM-Kymmene Corporation; *Int'l*, pg. 8091
UPM-KYMMENE WOOD OY - JOENSUU PLYWOOD MILL—See UPM-Kymmene Corporation; *Int'l*, pg. 8092
UPM-KYMMENE WOOD OY - JYVASKYLA PLYWOOD MILL—See UPM-Kymmene Corporation; *Int'l*, pg. 8092

CORPORATE AFFILIATIONS

UPM-KYMMENE WOOD OY - KALSO VENEER MILL—See UPM-Kymmene Corporation; *Int'l*, pg. 8092
UPM-KYMMENE WOOD OY - PELLOS PLYWOOD MILL—See UPM-Kymmene Corporation; *Int'l*, pg. 8092
UPM-KYMMENE WOOD OY - SAVONLINNA PLYWOOD MILL—See UPM-Kymmene Corporation; *Int'l*, pg. 8092
UPM-KYMMENE WOOD OY—See UPM-Kymmene Corporation; *Int'l*, pg. 8092
UPM PHARMACEUTICALS, INC.; *U.S. Private*, pg. 4312
UPM PROFI - BRUCHSAL—See UPM-Kymmene Corporation; *Int'l*, pg. 8091
UPM PROFI—See UPM-Kymmene Corporation; *Int'l*, pg. 8091
UPM PULP SALES OY—See UPM-Kymmene Corporation; *Int'l*, pg. 8091
UPM RAFLATAC (BEIJING) CO., LTD—See UPM-Kymmene Corporation; *Int'l*, pg. 8091
UPM RAFLATAC BRAZIL—See UPM-Kymmene Corporation; *Int'l*, pg. 8091
UPM RAFLATAC (CHANGSHU) CO., LTD.—See UPM-Kymmene Corporation; *Int'l*, pg. 8091
UPM RAFLATAC CHILE SPA—See UPM-Kymmene Corporation; *Int'l*, pg. 8091
UPM RAFLATAC CO., LTD—See UPM-Kymmene Corporation; *Int'l*, pg. 8091
UPM RAFLATAC IBERICA S.A.—See UPM-Kymmene Corporation; *Int'l*, pg. 8091
UPM RAFLATAC INC. - ILLINOIS LABELSTOCK FACTORY—See UPM-Kymmene Corporation; *Int'l*, pg. 8091
UPM RAFLATAC INC.—See UPM-Kymmene Corporation; *Int'l*, pg. 8091
UPM RAFLATAC LIMITED—See UPM-Kymmene Corporation; *Int'l*, pg. 8091
UPM RAFLATAC LTD.—See UPM-Kymmene Corporation; *Int'l*, pg. 8091
UPM RAFLATAC MEXICO S.A. DE C.V.—See UPM-Kymmene Corporation; *Int'l*, pg. 8091
UPM RAFLATAC NZ LIMITED—See UPM-Kymmene Corporation; *Int'l*, pg. 8091
UPM RAFLATAC OY—See UPM-Kymmene Corporation; *Int'l*, pg. 8091
UPM RAFLATAC PTY LTD—See UPM-Kymmene Corporation; *Int'l*, pg. 8091
UPM RAFLATAC PVT. LTD.—See UPM-Kymmene Corporation; *Int'l*, pg. 8091
UPM RAFLATAC RFID (GUANGZHOU) CO. LTD—See UPM-Kymmene Corporation; *Int'l*, pg. 8091
UPM RAFLATAC S.A.S.—See UPM-Kymmene Corporation; *Int'l*, pg. 8091
UPM RAFLATAC SDN. BHD.—See UPM-Kymmene Corporation; *Int'l*, pg. 8091
UPM RAFLATAC SDN. BHD.—See UPM-Kymmene Corporation; *Int'l*, pg. 8091
UPM RAFLATAC—See UPM-Kymmene Corporation; *Int'l*, pg. 8091
UPM RAFLATAC SP. Z O.O.—See UPM-Kymmene Corporation; *Int'l*, pg. 8091
UPM RAFLATAC S.R.L.—See UPM-Kymmene Corporation; *Int'l*, pg. 8091
UPM ROMANIA S.R.L.—See UPM-Kymmene Corporation; *Int'l*, pg. 8091
UPM SAHKONSIIRTO OY—See UPM-Kymmene Corporation; *Int'l*, pg. 8091
UPM SALES GMBH—See UPM-Kymmene Corporation; *Int'l*, pg. 8091
UPM SILVESTA OY—See UPM-Kymmene Corporation; *Int'l*, pg. 8091
UPM TILHILL FORESTRY LTD—See UPM-Kymmene Corporation; *Int'l*, pg. 8091
UPM TIMBER—See UPM-Kymmene Corporation; *Int'l*, pg. 8091
UPNEST, INC.—See News Corporation; *U.S. Public*, pg. 1519
UP-NXT—See Nimbus B.V.; *Int'l*, pg. 5296
UPOC NETWORKS INC.—See RCS MediaGroup S.p.A.; *Int'l*, pg. 6230
UP OFFSHORE APOIO MARITIMO LTDA—See Southern Cross Capital Management SA; *Int'l*, pg. 7118
UPONOR AB—See Georg Fischer AG; *Int'l*, pg. 2937
UPONOR A/S—See Georg Fischer AG; *Int'l*, pg. 2937
UPONOR AS—See Georg Fischer AG; *Int'l*, pg. 2937
UPONOR BETEILIGUNGS GMBH—See Georg Fischer AG; *Int'l*, pg. 2937
UPONOR BUSINESS SOLUTIONS OY—See Georg Fischer AG; *Int'l*, pg. 2937
UPONOR (DEUTSCHLAND) GMBH—See Georg Fischer AG; *Int'l*, pg. 2937
UPONOR EESTI OU—See Georg Fischer AG; *Int'l*, pg. 2937
UPONOR EPULETGEPESZETI KORLATOLT FELELOSSEGU TARSASAG—See Georg Fischer AG; *Int'l*, pg. 2937
UPONOR GMBH—See Georg Fischer AG; *Int'l*, pg. 2937
UPONOR HISPANIA, S.A.—See Georg Fischer AG; *Int'l*, pg. 2937
UPONOR INFRA OY—See Georg Fischer AG; *Int'l*, pg. 2937

COMPANY NAME INDEX

URALS ENERGY PUBLIC COMPANY LIMITED

UPONOR INNOVATION AB—See Georg Fischer AG; *Int'l*, pg. 2938
UPONOR KFT—See Georg Fischer AG; *Int'l*, pg. 2938
UPONOR LIMITED—See Georg Fischer AG; *Int'l*, pg. 2938
UPONOR NORTH AMERICA—See Georg Fischer AG; *Int'l*, pg. 2938
UPONOR OYJ—See Georg Fischer AG; *Int'l*, pg. 2937
UPONOR PORTUGAL - SISTEMAS PARA FLUIDOS LDA.—See Georg Fischer AG; *Int'l*, pg. 2938
UPONOR S.A.R.L.—See Georg Fischer AG; *Int'l*, pg. 2937
UPONOR SP. Z O.O.—See Georg Fischer AG; *Int'l*, pg. 2938
UPONOR S.R.O.—See Georg Fischer AG; *Int'l*, pg. 2938
UPONOR SUOMI OY—See Georg Fischer AG; *Int'l*, pg. 2938
UPONOR TEXNIKES LYSEIS GIA KTIRIA AE—See Georg Fischer AG; *Int'l*, pg. 2938
UPONOR USA—See Georg Fischer AG; *Int'l*, pg. 2938
UPONOR VERTRIEBS GMBH—See Georg Fischer AG; *Int'l*, pg. 2937
U POWER LIMITED; *Int'l*, pg. 7997
UPPER BAY SURGERY CENTER, LLC—See Tenet Healthcare Corporation; *U.S. Public*, pg. 2014
UPPER CANYON MINERALS CORP.; *Int'l*, pg. 8092
UPPERCASE LIVING, LLC—See JRjr33, Inc.; *U.S. Private*, pg. 2240
UPPER CONNECTICUT VALLEY HOSPITAL; *U.S. Private*, pg. 4312
UPPER CUMBERLAND ELECTRIC MEMBERSHIP CORPORATION; *U.S. Private*, pg. 4312
UPPER CUMBERLAND PHYSICIANS' SURGERY CENTER, LLC—See Tenet Healthcare Corporation; *U.S. Public*, pg. 2014
THE UPPER DECK COMPANY, LLC; *U.S. Private*, pg. 4129
UPPER DES MOINES OPPORTUNITY, INC.; *U.S. Private*, pg. 4312
UPPER EAST TENNESSEE HUMAN DEVELOPMENT AGENCY, INC.; *U.S. Private*, pg. 4312
UPPER EDGE TECHNOLOGIES, INC.; *U.S. Private*, pg. 4312
UPPER EGYPT CONTRACTING; *Int'l*, pg. 8092
UPPER EGYPT FLOUR MILLS; *Int'l*, pg. 8092
UPPER GANGES SUGAR INDUSTRIES LTD.—See K.K. Birla Group; *Int'l*, pg. 4044
UPPER LAKES COAL COMPANY INC.; *U.S. Private*, pg. 4312
UPPER LAKES FOODS INC.; *U.S. Private*, pg. 4312
UPPER LAKES GROUP INC.; *Int'l*, pg. 8093
UPPER MIDWEST ORGAN PROCUREMENT ORGANIZATION, INC.; *U.S. Private*, pg. 4312
UPPER PENINSULA POWER COMPANY—See Colliers International Group Inc.; *Int'l*, pg. 1700
UPPER RANCH COMPANY LLC; *U.S. Private*, pg. 4312
UPPER ROCK ISLAND COUNTY LANDFILL, INC.—See Republic Services, Inc.; *U.S. Public*, pg. 1788
THE UPPER ROOM; *U.S. Private*, pg. 4129
UPPER STREET MARKETING, INC.; *U.S. Public*, pg. 2264
UPPER TRINITY REGIONAL WATER DISTRICT; *U.S. Private*, pg. 4312
UPPER VALLEY DIALYSIS, L.P.—See DaVita Inc.; *U.S. Public*, pg. 644
UPPLEVELSEAKUTEN AB—See Verdane Capital Advisors AS; *Int'l*, pg. 8165
UPPSALA HISS MONTAGE OCH EL AB—See KONE Oyj; *Int'l*, pg. 4250
UPP TECHNOLOGY, INC.; *U.S. Private*, pg. 4312
UPPY'S CONVENIENCE STORES INC.—See Sunoco LP; *U.S. Public*, pg. 1965
UPRAW CAFE & JUICE BAR PTY LTD—See xReality Group Ltd; *Int'l*, pg. 8538
UPR CORPORATION; *Int'l*, pg. 8093
UP RHENUS LOGISTICS—See RETHMANN AG & Co. KG; *Int'l*, pg. 6309
UPRIGHT TECHNOLOGIES LLC—See DEVsource Technology Solutions, LLC; *U.S. Private*, pg. 1219
UPRINTING.COM; *U.S. Private*, pg. 4312
UPROMISE, INC.—See Great Hill Partners, L.P.; *U.S. Private*, pg. 1763
UPR SINGAPORE PTE. LTD.—See UPR Corporation; *Int'l*, pg. 8093
UPR SOLUTION (MALAYSIA) SDN. BHD.—See UPR Corporation; *Int'l*, pg. 8093
UPR (THAILAND) CO., LTD.—See UPR Corporation; *Int'l*, pg. 8093
UPR VIETNAM CO., LTD.—See UPR Corporation; *Int'l*, pg. 8093
UPSAMEDICA GMBH—See Taisho Pharmaceutical Holdings Co., Ltd; *Int'l*, pg. 7418
UPSA SAS—See Taisho Pharmaceutical Holdings Co., Ltd; *Int'l*, pg. 7417
UPS ASIA GROUP PTE. LTD.—See United Parcel Service, Inc.; *U.S. Public*, pg. 2233
UPSA SWITZERLAND A.G.—See Taisho Pharmaceutical Holdings Co., Ltd; *Int'l*, pg. 7418
UPS CAPITAL BUSINESS CREDIT—See United Parcel Service, Inc.; *U.S. Public*, pg. 2233

UPS CAPITAL CORPORATION—See United Parcel Service, Inc.; *U.S. Public*, pg. 2233
UPSCIENCE ITALIA S.R.L.—See Archer-Daniels-Midland Company; *U.S. Public*, pg. 185
UP SCIENTECH MATERIALS CORP.; *Int'l*, pg. 8087
UPS CUSTOMER SERVICE CENTER—See United Parcel Service, Inc.; *U.S. Public*, pg. 2233
UPSELLON BRANDS HOLDINGS LTD.; *Int'l*, pg. 8093
UPS EUROPE SA/NV—See United Parcel Service, Inc.; *U.S. Public*, pg. 2233
UPS GROUND FREIGHT, INC.—See TFI International Inc.; *Int'l*, pg. 7587
UPS GROUND FREIGHT, INC. - WESTERN REGIONAL OFFICE—See TFI International Inc.; *Int'l*, pg. 7587
UPSHE CO., LTD.—See TIS Inc.; *Int'l*, pg. 7758
UPSHER-SMITH LABORATORIES LLC—See Bora Pharmaceuticals Co., Ltd.; *Int'l*, pg. 1112
UPSHOT INC.—See Leonard Green & Partners, L.P.; *U.S. Private*, pg. 2423
UPS HUNGARY LTD.—See United Parcel Service, Inc.; *U.S. Public*, pg. 2233
UPSHUR FOREST PRODUCTS, LLC—See UFP Industries, Inc.; *U.S. Public*, pg. 2221
UPSHUR PROPERTY LLC—See Arch Resources, Inc.; *U.S. Public*, pg. 180
UPSHUR RURAL ELECTRIC COOPERATIVE CORPORATION; *U.S. Private*, pg. 4312
UPSIDE ENGINEERING LTD.; *Int'l*, pg. 8093
UPSIGHT, INC.; *U.S. Private*, pg. 4312
UPS INTERNATIONAL, INC.—See United Parcel Service, Inc.; *U.S. Public*, pg. 2233
UPS LIMITED—See United Parcel Service, Inc.; *U.S. Public*, pg. 2233
UPSNAP, INC.; *Int'l*, pg. 8093
UPSOLUT EVENT GMBH—See Vivendi SE; *Int'l*, pg. 8277
UP SOLUTIONS SRL—See Retelit S.p.A.; *Int'l*, pg. 6306
UPSOLUT MERCHANDISING GMBH & CO KG—See Vivendi SE; *Int'l*, pg. 8277
UPSOLUT SPORT AG—See Vivendi SE; *Int'l*, pg. 8277
UPSOLUT VERWALTUNGS GMBH—See Vivendi SE; *Int'l*, pg. 8277
UPSON ELECTRIC MEMBERSHIP CORPORATION; *U.S. Private*, pg. 4312
UPSON INTERNATIONAL CORPORATION; *Int'l*, pg. 8093
UPSON REGIONAL MEDICAL CENTER; *U.S. Private*, pg. 4312
UPS PARCEL DELIVERY (GUANGDONG) CO., LTD.—See United Parcel Service, Inc.; *U.S. Public*, pg. 2233
UPS PARCEL DELIVERY SERVICE LTD.—See United Parcel Service, Inc.; *U.S. Public*, pg. 2233
UPSPRING, LTD.—See Reckitt Benckiser Group plc; *Int'l*, pg. 6237
UPS SCS HOLDING LIMITED—See United Parcel Service, Inc.; *U.S. Public*, pg. 2233
UPS SCS, INC.—See United Parcel Service, Inc.; *U.S. Public*, pg. 2234
UPS SCS (NEDERLAND) B.V.—See United Parcel Service, Inc.; *U.S. Public*, pg. 2233
THE UPS STORE, INC.—See United Parcel Service, Inc.; *U.S. Public*, pg. 2233
UPS SUPPLY CHAIN SOLUTIONS GENERAL SERVICES, INC.—See United Parcel Service, Inc.; *U.S. Public*, pg. 2234
UPS SUPPLY CHAIN SOLUTIONS, INC. - COPPELL—See United Parcel Service, Inc.; *U.S. Public*, pg. 2234
UPS SUPPLY CHAIN SOLUTIONS, INC.—See United Parcel Service, Inc.; *U.S. Public*, pg. 2234
UPS SUPPLY CHAIN SOLUTIONS, INC. - SOUTH SAN FRANCISCO—See United Parcel Service, Inc.; *U.S. Public*, pg. 2234
UPSTACK, INC.; *U.S. Private*, pg. 4312
UPSTAIRS/Y & R POLAND SP. Z.O.O.—See WPP plc; *Int'l*, pg. 8493
UPSTART HOLDINGS, INC.; *U.S. Public*, pg. 2264
UPSTART NETWORK, INC.—See Upstart Holdings, Inc.; *U.S. Public*, pg. 2264
UPSTATE AGENCY, LLC—See Arrow Financial Corporation; *U.S. Public*, pg. 200
UPSTATE CEREBRAL PALSY; *U.S. Private*, pg. 4313
UPSTATE ELECTRONIC WHOLESALERS; *U.S. Private*, pg. 4313
UPSTATE MORTGAGE INC.; *U.S. Private*, pg. 4313
UPSTATE NIAGARA COOPERATIVE, INC.; *U.S. Private*, pg. 4313
UPSTATE PHARMACY, LTD.; *U.S. Private*, pg. 4313
UPSTATE PHARMA LLC—See UCB S.A.; *Int'l*, pg. 8012
UPSTATE ROOFING & PAINTING, INC.—See Roofed Right America, LLC; *U.S. Private*, pg. 3478
UPSTATE SHREDDING, LLC; *U.S. Private*, pg. 4313
UPSTONE MATERIALS INC.—See Barrett Industries, Inc.; *U.S. Private*, pg. 480
UPSTREAM ASIA (CHINA) CONSULTING LTD—See Next 15 Group plc; *Int'l*, pg. 5247
UPSTREAM AS—See Fred. Olsen & Co.; *Int'l*, pg. 2768
UPSTREAM HOUSTON—See Fred. Olsen & Co.; *Int'l*, pg. 2768

UPSTREAM LONDON—See Fred. Olsen & Co.; *Int'l*, pg. 2768
UPSTREAMNET COMMUNICATIONS GMBH—See DigitalBridge Group, Inc.; *U.S. Public*, pg. 665
UPSTREAMNET COMMUNICATIONS GMBH—See EQT AB; *Int'l*, pg. 2482
UPSTREAM PRINT SOLUTIONS AUSTRALIA PTY LTD—See FUJIFILM Holdings Corporation; *Int'l*, pg. 2826
UPSTREAM PRODUCTION SOLUTIONS PTY. LTD.—See GR Engineering Services Limited; *Int'l*, pg. 3047
UPSTREAM SINGAPORE—See Fred. Olsen & Co.; *Int'l*, pg. 2768
UPSTREAM TECHNICAL COMPUTING COMPANY—See Exxon Mobil Corporation; *U.S. Public*, pg. 817
UPSURGE INVESTMENT & FINANCE LTD.; *Int'l*, pg. 8093
UPS WORLDWIDE FORWARDING, INC.—See United Parcel Service, Inc.; *U.S. Public*, pg. 2234
U P SYSTEMS, INCORPORATED—See Vertiv Holdings Co; *U.S. Public*, pg. 2288
UPTAKE CANADA, INC.—See Uptake Technologies, LLC; *U.S. Private*, pg. 4313
UPTAKE MEDICAL CORP.—See Broncus Medical, Inc; *U.S. Private*, pg. 662
UPTAKE TECHNOLOGIES, LLC; *U.S. Private*, pg. 4313
UPT COMPONENT (S) PTE. LTD.—See Europtronic Group Ltd.; *Int'l*, pg. 2557
UPT CRYPSON COMPONENT (SHANGHAI) CO., LTD.—See Europtronic Group Ltd.; *Int'l*, pg. 2557
UPTIME INSTITUTE, LLC—See 451 Group, LLC; *U.S. Private*, pg. 15
UPTIME SYSTEMS OU—See Levikom Eesti OU; *Int'l*, pg. 4471
UPT ODEME HIZMETLERI A.S.—See Aktif Yatirim Bankasi A.S.; *Int'l*, pg. 267
UP TO ELEVEN DIGITAL SOLUTIONS GMBH; *Int'l*, pg. 8087
UPTON FULTON MCCANN PVT. LTD.—See The Interpublic Group of Companies, Inc.; *U.S. Public*, pg. 2103
UPTOWN CHEVROLET-CADILLAC, INC.—See General Motors Company; *U.S. Public*, pg. 929
UPTOWN NETWORK, LLC; *U.S. Private*, pg. 4313
UPT UNITED PRODUCT TANKERS GMBH & CO. KG—See Schoeller Holdings Ltd.; *Int'l*, pg. 6637
THE UPTURN, INC.; *U.S. Private*, pg. 4129
U-PULL U-SAVE AUTO PARTS—See Stellex Capital Management LP; *U.S. Private*, pg. 3800
UPWARD TITLE & CLOSING TEXAS LLC—See Anywhere Real Estate Inc.; *U.S. Public*, pg. 143
UPWARD TITLE CO., LTD.—See Anywhere Real Estate Inc.; *U.S. Public*, pg. 143
UPWARD TITLE & ESCROW CO., LTD.—See Anywhere Real Estate Inc.; *U.S. Public*, pg. 143
UPWARD UNLIMITED; *U.S. Private*, pg. 4313
UPWORK GLOBAL INC.; *U.S. Private*, pg. 4313
UPWORK INC—See Upwork Global Inc.; *U.S. Private*, pg. 4313
UQ COMMUNICATIONS INC.—See KDDI Corporation; *Int'l*, pg. 4112
UQM TECHNOLOGIES, INC.—See Danfoss A/S; *Int'l*, pg. 1961
UQUEST, LTD.—See Takaoka Toko Co., Ltd.; *Int'l*, pg. 7431
UQUIFA MEXICO S.A. DE C.V.—See Vivimed Labs Limited; *Int'l*, pg. 8280
UR A.B.—See UR Holding S.p.A; *Int'l*, pg. 8093
URAC; *U.S. Private*, pg. 4313
URA HOLDINGS PLC; *Int'l*, pg. 8093
URAI CO., LTD.; *Int'l*, pg. 8093
URAL AIRLINES JSC; *Int'l*, pg. 8093
THE URAL BANK FOR RECONSTRUCTION & DEVELOPMENT JSC; *Int'l*, pg. 7698
URALCHEM OJSC; *Int'l*, pg. 8094
URALCHEM TRADING DO BRASIL LTDA.—See Uralchem OJSC; *Int'l*, pg. 8094
URALCHEM-TRANS LLC—See Uralchem OJSC; *Int'l*, pg. 8094
URALCHIMPLAST HUTTENES-ALBERTUS LTD.—See Huettenes-Albertus Chemische Werke GmbH; *Int'l*, pg. 3523
URALITA SISTEMAS DE TUBERIAS, S.A.—See Nefinsa S.A.; *Int'l*, pg. 5192
URALITA TEJADOS, S.A.—See Nefinsa S.A.; *Int'l*, pg. 5192
URALKALI PJSC—See Rinsoco Trading Co. Limited; *Int'l*, pg. 6346
URALKALI TRADING S.A.—See Rinsoco Trading Co. Limited; *Int'l*, pg. 6346
URALS ENERGY PUBLIC COMPANY LIMITED; *Int'l*, pg. 8094
URALSIB SECURITIES LTD.—See ITI Group Ltd.; *Int'l*, pg. 3833
URALSK PLANT ZENIT JSC—See National Company Kazakhstan Engineering JSC; *Int'l*, pg. 5155
URALS STAMPINGS PLANT OAO—See Mechel PAO; *Int'l*, pg. 4766
URALTRANSGAZ—See PJSC Gazprom; *Int'l*, pg. 5880

URAN BARILGA JOINT STOCK COMPANY

URAN BARILGA JOINT STOCK COMPANY; *Int'l*, pg. 8094
URANENERGO LLP—See JSC National Atomic Company Kazatomprom; *Int'l*, pg. 4009
URANGAN FISHERIES PTY. LTD.—See Temasek Holdings (Private) Limited; *Int'l*, pg. 7550
URANGESELLSCHAFT GMBH—See Orano SA; *Int'l*, pg. 5611
URANIUM ENERGY CORP. - CORPORATE OFFICE—See Uranium Energy Corp.; *Int'l*, pg. 8094
URANIUM ENERGY CORP.; *Int'l*, pg. 8094
URANIUM MINERAL VENTURES INC.—See Mega Uranium Ltd.; *Int'l*, pg. 4793
URANIUM ONE AFRICA LTD—See State Atomic Energy Corporation ROSATOM; *Int'l*, pg. 7181
URANIUM ONE AMERICAS, INC—See State Atomic Energy Corporation ROSATOM; *Int'l*, pg. 7181
URANIUM ONE INC.—See State Atomic Energy Corporation ROSATOM; *Int'l*, pg. 7180
URANIUM ONE NETHERLANDS B.V.—See State Atomic Energy Corporation ROSATOM; *Int'l*, pg. 7181
URANIUM ONE USA, INC.—See State Atomic Energy Corporation ROSATOM; *Int'l*, pg. 7181
URANIUM PARTICIPATION CORPORATION; *Int'l*, pg. 8094
URANIUM ROYALTY CORP.; *Int'l*, pg. 8094
URANIUM TRADING CORPORATION; *U.S. Private*, pg. 4313
URANUS CHEMICALS CO., LTD.—See Coremax Corp.; *Int'l*, pg. 1799
URANUS INTERNATIONAL CO., LTD.—See Catcher Technology Co., Ltd.; *Int'l*, pg. 1359
URASIA ENERGY (U.S.A.) HOLDINGS INC—See State Atomic Energy Corporation ROSATOM; *Int'l*, pg. 7181
URATA & SONS CEMENT COMPANY; *U.S. Private*, pg. 4313
URAVAN MINERALS INC.; *Int'l*, pg. 8094
URAVI T & WEDGE LAMPS LTD.; *Int'l*, pg. 8094
URAWA POLYMER CO., LTD.—See Shin-Etsu Chemical Co. Ltd.; *Int'l*, pg. 6840
URAWA RED DIAMONDS CO., LTD.—See Mitsubishi Heavy Industries, Ltd.; *Int'l*, pg. 4962
URAYASU CONCRETE CO., LTD.—See UBE Corporation; *Int'l*, pg. 8002
URBACET, S.L.—See ACS, Actividades de Construccion y Servicios, S.A.; *Int'l*, pg. 116
URBAENERGIA, S.L.—See ACS, Actividades de Construccion y Servicios, S.A.; *Int'l*, pg. 117
URBAINE DES PETROLES SAS—See TotalEnergies SE; *Int'l*, pg. 7844
URBAIN PRO VALENTON SAS—See VINCI S.A.; *Int'l*, pg. 8230
URBAMAR LEVANTE RESIDUOS INDUSTRIALES, S.L.—See ACS, Actividades de Construccion y Servicios, S.A.; *Int'l*, pg. 117
URBANA CORPORATION; *Int'l*, pg. 8094
URBANA COUNTRY CLUB; *U.S. Private*, pg. 4315
URBAN AFFAIRS COALITION; *U.S. Private*, pg. 4313
URBAN APPAREL GROUP INC.; *U.S. Private*, pg. 4313
URBANARA HOME & LIVING GMBH—See The Social Chain AG; *Int'l*, pg. 7687
URBANA TELEUNION ROSTOCK GMBH & CO. KG—See Vodafone Group Plc; *Int'l*, pg. 8285
URBAN BARNS FOODS INC.; *Int'l*, pg. 8094
URBAN CABLE TECHNOLOGY INC.—See QualTek Services Inc.; *U.S. Public*, pg. 1748
URBAN&CIVIC PLC—See The Wellcome Trust, Ltd; *Int'l*, pg. 7700
URBAN COBOTS PTE. LTD.—See LS 2 Holdings Limited; *Int'l*, pg. 4568
URBAN COMMUNICATIONS INC.—See DigitalBridge Group, Inc.; *U.S. Public*, pg. 664
URBAN COMMUNICATIONS; *U.S. Private*, pg. 4313
URBAN CONCRETE CONTRACTORS, LTD.; *U.S. Private*, pg. 4313
URBAN CONTROL LIMITED—See Luceco PLC; *Int'l*, pg. 4573
URBANDADDY, INC.; *U.S. Private*, pg. 4315
URBANDALE-S, LLC—See Lithia Motors, Inc.; *U.S. Public*, pg. 1326
URBAN DECAY COSMETICS LLC—See Castanea Partners, Inc.; *U.S. Private*, pg. 784
URBAN DEVELOPMENT & CONSTRUCTION CORPORATION; *Int'l*, pg. 8094
URBAN EDGE CAGUAS LP—See URBAN EDGE PROPERTIES; *U.S. Public*, pg. 2265
URBAN EDGE PROPERTIES; *U.S. Public*, pg. 2264
URBAN ELEVATOR SERVICE CA LLC—See Urban Elevator Service, LLC; *U.S. Private*, pg. 4314
URBAN ELEVATOR SERVICE, LLC; *U.S. Private*, pg. 4314
URBAN ENERGY CORPORATION—See JFE Holdings, Inc.; *Int'l*, pg. 3935
URBAN ENGINEERS INC.; *U.S. Private*, pg. 4314
URBAN ENGINEERS OF NEW YORK, P.C.—See Urban Engineers Inc.; *U.S. Private*, pg. 4314
URBANET CORPORATION CO., LTD.; *Int'l*, pg. 8094
URBANEX CO., LTD—See Osaka Gas Co., Ltd.; *Int'l*, pg. 5646

URBAN EXPOSITIONS; *U.S. Private*, pg. 4314
URBANEX SA; *Int'l*, pg. 8094
THE URBAN FARMER STORE, INC.—See Leonard Green & Partners, L.P.; *U.S. Private*, pg. 2429
URBAN & FISCHER VERLAG GMBH & CO. KG—See Verlagsgruppe Georg von Holtzbrinck GmbH; *Int'l*, pg. 8171
URBANFOX PTE. LTD.—See Keppel Corporation Limited; *Int'l*, pg. 4132
URBAN FT GROUP, INC.; *U.S. Private*, pg. 4314
URBANFUND CORP.; *Int'l*, pg. 8094
URBANGOLD MINERALS INC.—See Troilus Gold Corp.; *Int'l*, pg. 7938
URBAN GREEN AB—See Kingspan Group PLC; *Int'l*, pg. 4179
URBAN-GRO, INC.; *U.S. Public*, pg. 2265
URBAN HABITAT; *U.S. Private*, pg. 4314
URBAN HEALTH PLAN, INC.; *U.S. Private*, pg. 4314
URBANIMMERSIVE, INC.; *Int'l*, pg. 8095
URBAN & INDUSTRIAL DEVELOPMENT INVESTMENT IDICO - QUE VO JSC—See Vietnam Urban Development Investment Corporation; *Int'l*, pg. 8204
URBAN INFRASTRUCTURE VENTURE CAPITAL LIMITED—See Jai Corp Ltd; *Int'l*, pg. 3871
URBAN INSIGHTS ASSOCIATES, INC.—See Elliott Management Corporation; *U.S. Private*, pg. 1368
URBAN INSIGHTS ASSOCIATES, INC.—See Veritas Capital Fund Management, LLC; *U.S. Private*, pg. 4362
URBAN INVESTMENT RESEARCH CORP.; *U.S. Private*, pg. 4314
URBANISE.COM LIMITED; *Int'l*, pg. 8095
URBAN LAND INSTITUTE; *U.S. Private*, pg. 4314
URBAN LENDING SOLUTIONS LLC; *U.S. Private*, pg. 4314
URBAN LIFE CO., LTD.—See Mitsubishi Estate Co., Ltd.; *Int'l*, pg. 4947
URBAN LOGISTICS REIT PLC; *Int'l*, pg. 8094
URBAN MINISTRY CENTER; *U.S. Private*, pg. 4314
URBAN NIRVANA; *U.S. Private*, pg. 4314
URBAN OFFICE PRODUCTS, INC.; *U.S. Private*, pg. 4314
URBAN ONE, INC.; *U.S. Public*, pg. 2265
URBAN OUTFITTERS BELGIUM BVBA—See Urban Outfitters, Inc.; *U.S. Public*, pg. 2265
URBAN OUTFITTERS CANADA, INC.—See Urban Outfitters, Inc.; *U.S. Public*, pg. 2265
URBAN OUTFITTERS, INC.; *U.S. Public*, pg. 2265
URBAN OUTFITTERS IRELAND LIMITED—See Urban Outfitters, Inc.; *U.S. Public*, pg. 2265
URBAN OUTFITTERS I SVERIGE AB—See Urban Outfitters, Inc.; *U.S. Public*, pg. 2265
URBAN OUTFITTERS UK, LIMITED—See Urban Outfitters, Inc.; *U.S. Public*, pg. 2265
URBAN PARTNERS, LLC; *U.S. Private*, pg. 4314
URBAN PREP ACADEMIES; *U.S. Private*, pg. 4314
URBAN RENAISSANCE GROUP LLC; *U.S. Private*, pg. 4314
URBAN RESOURCE INSTITUTE; *U.S. Private*, pg. 4315
URBAN RETAIL PROPERTIES CO. OF FLORIDA—See RAIT Financial Trust; *U.S. Public*, pg. 3349
URBAN RETAIL PROPERTIES CO. OF MASSACHUSETTS—See RAIT Financial Trust; *U.S. Private*, pg. 3349
URBAN RETAIL PROPERTIES, LLC; *U.S. Private*, pg. 4315
URBAN SCIENCE, INC.; *U.S. Private*, pg. 4315
URBAN-STAFF CO., LTD.—See Polaris Capital Group Co., Ltd.; *Int'l*, pg. 5907
URBANSTEMS INC.; *U.S. Private*, pg. 4315
URBAN STRATEGIES INC.; *U.S. Private*, pg. 4315
URBAN STUDIO ARCHITECTS, INC.; *U.S. Private*, pg. 4315
URBAN TANTRA INTERNATIONAL, INC.; *U.S. Private*, pg. 4315
URBAN TECHNOLOGY GMBH—See Straumann Holding AG; *Int'l*, pg. 7238
URBAN TELEVISION NETWORK CORP.; *U.S. Public*, pg. 2265
URBANYS—See DBAY Advisors Limited; *Int'l*, pg. 1987
URBAOIL, S.A.—See ACS, Actividades de Construccion y Servicios, S.A.; *Int'l*, pg. 117
URBAR INGENIEROS, S.A.; *Int'l*, pg. 8095
URBASER ENVIRONNEMENT, S.A.S.—See Platinum Equity, LLC; *U.S. Private*, pg. 3209
URBASER, LTD.—See Platinum Equity, LLC; *U.S. Private*, pg. 3209
URBASER, S.A.—See Platinum Equity, LLC; *U.S. Private*, pg. 3209
URBASER VENEZOLANA S.A.—See Platinum Equity, LLC; *U.S. Private*, pg. 3209
URBAS GRUPO FINANCIERO S.A.; *Int'l*, pg. 8095
URBASYS, S.A.S.—See ACS, Actividades de Construccion y Servicios, S.A.; *Int'l*, pg. 117
URBI, DESARROLLOS URBANOS, S.A. B. DE C. V.; *Int'l*, pg. 8095
URBIETA OIL CO.; *U.S. Private*, pg. 4315
URB INVESTMENTS LIMITED—See Centuria Capital Limited; *Int'l*, pg. 1416
URBIS ARMATURI SANITARE SA; *Int'l*, pg. 8095

CORPORATE AFFILIATIONS

URBISINVEST A.D.; *Int'l*, pg. 8095
URBIS PARK SAS—See Covivio; *Int'l*, pg. 1821
URBISPROJEKT A.D.; *Int'l*, pg. 8095
URB-IT AB—See Fin Mile Logistics Limited; *Int'l*, pg. 2664
URBN 640 OSTERIA LLC—See Urban Outfitters, Inc.; *U.S. Public*, pg. 2265
URBN CALLOWHILL LLC—See Urban Outfitters, Inc.; *U.S. Public*, pg. 2265
URBN CHANCELLOR LLC—See Urban Outfitters, Inc.; *U.S. Public*, pg. 2265
URBN FNB HOLDINGS LLC—See Urban Outfitters, Inc.; *U.S. Public*, pg. 2265
URBN NVY LOSP LLC—See Urban Outfitters, Inc.; *U.S. Public*, pg. 2265
URBN UK LIMITED—See Urban Outfitters, Inc.; *U.S. Public*, pg. 2265
URBN WAVERLY AMIS LLC—See Urban Outfitters, Inc.; *U.S. Public*, pg. 2265
URC SA; *Int'l*, pg. 8095
UREACH TECHNOLOGIES, INC.—See Ribbon Communications Inc.; *U.S. Public*, pg. 1797
URENCO CHEMPLANTS LIMITED—See Urenco Limited; *Int'l*, pg. 8095
URENCO DEUTSCHLAND GMBH—See Urenco Limited; *Int'l*, pg. 8095
URENCO, INC.—See Urenco Limited; *Int'l*, pg. 8095
URENCO LIMITED; *Int'l*, pg. 8095
URENCO NEDERLAND B.V.—See Urenco Limited; *Int'l*, pg. 8095
UR-ENERGY INC.; *U.S. Public*, pg. 2264
UR-ENERGY USA INC.—See Ur-Energy Inc.; *U.S. Public*, pg. 2264
URESCO CONSTRUCTION MATERIALS INC.; *U.S. Private*, pg. 4315
URETEK USA INC.; *U.S. Private*, pg. 4315
URETHANE ENGINEERING INC.—See Bunker Corporation; *U.S. Private*, pg. 685
URETHANES TECHNOLOGY INTERNATIONAL—See Crain Communications, Inc.; *U.S. Private*, pg. 1083
URGENT ACTION FUND FOR WOMEN'S HUMAN RIGHTS; *U.S. Private*, pg. 4315
URGENT CARE CENTERS OF ARIZONA, LLC—See Tenet Healthcare Corporation; *U.S. Public*, pg. 2005
URGENT CARE MSO, LLC—See UnitedHealth Group Incorporated; *U.S. Public*, pg. 2252
URGENT CARE PARTNERS, INC.; *U.S. Private*, pg. 4315
URGENT.LY, INC.; *U.S. Public*, pg. 2266
URGENT PLASTIC SERVICES INC.; *U.S. Private*, pg. 4315
URGENT TECHNOLOGY LTD.—See Techniche Limited; *Int'l*, pg. 7506
UR GMBH—See UR Holding S.p.A; *Int'l*, pg. 8093
UR GMBH—See UR Holding S.p.A; *Int'l*, pg. 8093
URGO GROUP SAS; *Int'l*, pg. 8095
URGO HOTELS LP; *U.S. Private*, pg. 4315
URGO MEDICAL NORTH AMERICA—See URGO Group SAS; *Int'l*, pg. 8095
URG PTE. LTD.—See Serial System Ltd.; *Int'l*, pg. 6723
UR GROUP INC.—See UR Holding S.p.A; *Int'l*, pg. 8093
UR HOLDING S.P.A; *Int'l*, pg. 8093
URIEL GAS HOLDINGS CORP.; *Int'l*, pg. 8095
URIGEN PHARMACEUTICALS, INC.; *U.S. Private*, pg. 4315
U-RIGHT GARMENTS LIMITED—See Fullsun International Holdings Group Co., Limited; *Int'l*, pg. 2843
U-RIGHT (HK) LIMITED—See Fullsun International Holdings Group Co., Limited; *Int'l*, pg. 2843
URI, INC.—See Westwater Resources, Inc.; *U.S. Public*, pg. 2363
URI, INC.; *U.S. Private*, pg. 4315
URIMAN INC.—See Halla Group; *Int'l*, pg. 3230
UR-ISRAEL LTD.—See UR Holding S.p.A; *Int'l*, pg. 8093
URJA BATTERIES LIMITED—See Urja Global Ltd.; *Int'l*, pg. 8095
URJA GLOBAL LTD.; *Int'l*, pg. 8095
URL AGRAR GMBH—See BayWa AG; *Int'l*, pg. 919
UR LTD.—See UR Holding S.p.A; *Int'l*, pg. 8093
U&R MANAGEMENT BV—See Unibail-Rodamco-Westfield SE; *Int'l*, pg. 8030
URM DEVELOPMENT CORP.—See URM Stores, Inc.; *Int'l*, pg. 4316
URMET FRANCE CAPTIV; *Int'l*, pg. 8095
URMIA CEMENT COMPANY LLP; *Int'l*, pg. 8095
URM INSURANCE AGENCY—See URM Stores, Inc.; *U.S. Private*, pg. 4316
URM STORES, INC.; *U.S. Private*, pg. 4316
URNERS INC.; *U.S. Private*, pg. 4316
UROGEN PHARMA LTD.; *U.S. Public*, pg. 2266
UROICA PRECISION INFORMATION ENGINEERING CO., LTD.; *Int'l*, pg. 8095
U.R.O.K. PRODUCTIONS, INC.—See Lions Gate Entertainment Corp.; *U.S. Private*, pg. 4521
UROLA, S.C.—See Mondragon Corporation; *Int'l*, pg. 5031
UROLOGY AMERICA, LLC—See Gauge Capital LLC; *U.S. Private*, pg. 1652
UROLOGY ASSOCIATES OF NORTH TEXAS, PLLC—See UnitedHealth Group Incorporated; *U.S. Public*, pg. 2240

COMPANY NAME INDEX

UROLOGY SPECIALISTS OF KINGWOOD, PLLC—See HCA Healthcare, Inc.; *U.S. Public*, pg. 1013
UROLOGY SPECIALISTS OF RICHMOND, LLC—See HCA Healthcare, Inc.; *U.S. Public*, pg. 1013
UROLOGY SURGERY CENTER OF COLORADO, LLC—See HCA Healthcare, Inc.; *U.S. Public*, pg. 1013
UROOJ LLC; *U.S. Private*, pg. 4316
URO PROPERTY HOLDINGS SOCIMI SA—See Banco Santander, S.A.; *Int'l*, pg. 828
UROVANT SCIENCES, INC.—See Sumitomo Chemical Company, Limited; *Int'l*, pg. 7267
UROVANT SCIENCES LTD.—See Sumitomo Chemical Company, Limited; *Int'l*, pg. 7267
URSA BENELUX BVBA—See Nefinsa S.A.; *Int'l*, pg. 5192
URSA BEOGRAD D.O.O.—See Nefinsa S.A.; *Int'l*, pg. 5192
URSA FARMERS COOPERATIVE CO.; *U.S. Private*, pg. 4316
URSA FRANCE, S.A.S.—See Nefinsa S.A.; *Int'l*, pg. 5192
URSA IBERICA AISLANTES, S.A.—See Nefinsa S.A.; *Int'l*, pg. 5192
URSA INFORMATION SYSTEMS INC.; *U.S. Private*, pg. 4316
URSA INSULATION, S.A.—See Lone Star Global Acquisitions, LLC; *U.S. Private*, pg. 2489
URSA ITALIA S.R.L.—See Nefinsa S.A.; *Int'l*, pg. 5192
URSANAV; *U.S. Private*, pg. 4316
URSA POLSKA SP. Z.O.O.—See Nefinsa S.A.; *Int'l*, pg. 5192
UR S.A.R.L.—See UR Holding S.p.A; *Int'l*, pg. 8093
URSA SK S.R.O—See Nefinsa S.A.; *Int'l*, pg. 5192
UR S.A.—See UR Holding S.p.A; *Int'l*, pg. 8093
URSA U.K. LTD—See Nefinsa S.A.; *Int'l*, pg. 5192
URSA ZAGREB D.O.O.—See Nefinsa S.A.; *Int'l*, pg. 5192
URS CARIBE, LLP—See AECOM; *U.S. Public*, pg. 51
URSCHEL ASIA PACIFIC PTE. LTD.—See Urschel Laboratories Incorporated; *U.S. Private*, pg. 4316
URSCHEL CHINA LTD.—See Urschel Laboratories Incorporated; *U.S. Private*, pg. 4316
URSCHEL ESPANA SL—See Urschel Laboratories Incorporated; *U.S. Private*, pg. 4316
URSCHEL HELLAS—See Urschel Laboratories Incorporated; *U.S. Private*, pg. 4316
URSCHEL INDIA TRADING PRIVATE LIMITED—See Urschel Laboratories Incorporated; *U.S. Private*, pg. 4316
URSCHEL INTERNATIONAL LTD.—See Urschel Laboratories Incorporated; *U.S. Private*, pg. 4316
URSCHEL INTERNATIONAL LTD.—See Urschel Laboratories Incorporated; *U.S. Private*, pg. 4316
URSCHEL INTERNATIONAL LTD.—See Urschel Laboratories Incorporated; *U.S. Private*, pg. 4316
URSCHEL INTERNATIONAL LTD.—See Urschel Laboratories Incorporated; *U.S. Private*, pg. 4316
URSCHEL INTERNATIONAL LTD.—See Urschel Laboratories Incorporated; *U.S. Private*, pg. 4316
URSCHEL INTERNATIONAL LTD.—See Urschel Laboratories Incorporated; *U.S. Private*, pg. 4316
URSCHEL INTERNATIONAL POLSKA SP. Z O.O.—See Urschel Laboratories Incorporated; *U.S. Private*, pg. 4316
URSCHEL JAPAN CO,. LTD.—See ITOCHU Corporation; *Int'l*, pg. 3839
URSCHEL JAPAN—See Urschel Laboratories Incorporated; *U.S. Private*, pg. 4316
URSCHEL LABORATORIES INCORPORATED; *U.S. Private*, pg. 4316
URSCHEL LATINOAMERICA S.R.L.—See Urschel Laboratories Incorporated; *U.S. Private*, pg. 4316
URSCHEL (THAILAND) LTD.—See Urschel Laboratories Incorporated; *U.S. Private*, pg. 4316
URS CONSULTING (SHANGHAI) LTD.—See AECOM; *U.S. Public*, pg. 51
URS CORPORATION BOLIVIA SA—See AECOM; *U.S. Public*, pg. 51
URS CORPORATION DE MEXICO S DE RL DE CV—See AECOM; *U.S. Public*, pg. 51
URS CORPORATION S.A.—See AECOM; *U.S. Public*, pg. 51
URS CORPORATION—See AECOM; *U.S. Public*, pg. 51
URS CORPORATION—See AECOM; *U.S. Public*, pg. 51
URS CORP. - RIYADH—See AECOM; *U.S. Public*, pg. 51
URS HOLDINGS, INC. - PANAMANIAN BRANCH—See AECOM; *U.S. Public*, pg. 51
URS NEW ZEALAND LTD.—See AECOM; *U.S. Public*, pg. 51
URS SAFETY MANAGEMENT SOLUTIONS—See AECOM; *U.S. Public*, pg. 51
URSSA MAROC SARLAU—See Mondragon Corporation; *Int'l*, pg. 5031
URSSAMEX, SA DE CV—See Mondragon Corporation; *Int'l*, pg. 5031
URSSA SARL—See Mondragon Corporation; *Int'l*, pg. 5031
URSSA, S. COOP. - PLANT 2—See Mondragon Corporation; *Int'l*, pg. 5031
URSSA, S. COOP.—See Mondragon Corporation; *Int'l*, pg. 5031
UR SUGAR INDUSTRIES LTD.; *Int'l*, pg. 8093
URSUIT AB—See Sioen Industries NV; *Int'l*, pg. 6960

URSUIT BALTICS AS—See Sioen Industries NV; *Int'l*, pg. 6960
URSUIT OY—See Sioen Industries NV; *Int'l*, pg. 6960
URSUS BREWERIES SA—See Anheuser-Busch InBev SA/NV; *Int'l*, pg. 465
URSUS S.A.; *Int'l*, pg. 8095
URSUS TRANSPORT INC.; *Int'l*, pg. 8095
URS WORLDWIDE HOLDINGS UK LIMITED—See AECOM; *U.S. Public*, pg. 52
U.R.T EUROPE APS—See United Radiant Technology Corporation; *Int'l*, pg. 8073
URTHECAST CORP.; *Int'l*, pg. 8095
URTHECAST IMAGING.S.L.U.—See UrtheCast Corp.; *Int'l*, pg. 8095
URTHECAST USA, INC.—See UrtheCast Corp.; *Int'l*, pg. 8096
URUK FOR COMPUTER SERVICES & OFFICE EQUIPMENT CO. LTD.—See Eng. Shabah Al-Shammery & Partners Co.; *Int'l*, pg. 2426
URU METALS LIMITED; *Int'l*, pg. 8096
URUSHI CO., LTD.—See Original Engineering Consultants Co., Ltd.; *Int'l*, pg. 5630
URWILER OIL & FERTILIZER INC.; *U.S. Private*, pg. 4316
US1COM INC.—See AFE Industries, Inc.; *U.S. Private*, pg. 121
US 1 INDUSTRIES, INC.; *U.S. Private*, pg. 4316
US 1 LOGISTICS, LLC—See US 1 Industries, Inc.; *U.S. Private*, pg. 4317
USAA ACCEPTANCE, LLC—See United Services Automobile Association; *U.S. Private*, pg. 4297
USAA ALLIANCE SERVICES COMPANY—See United Services Automobile Association; *U.S. Private*, pg. 4297
USAA FEDERAL SAVINGS BANK—See United Services Automobile Association; *U.S. Private*, pg. 4297
USAA INSURANCE AGENCY INC.—See United Services Automobile Association; *U.S. Private*, pg. 4297
USAA INVESTMENT MANAGEMENT CO.—See The Charles Schwab Corporation; *U.S. Public*, pg. 2058
USAA LIFE GENERAL AGENCY INC.—See United Services Automobile Association; *U.S. Private*, pg. 4297
USAA LIFE INSURANCE CO.—See United Services Automobile Association; *U.S. Private*, pg. 4297
USAA REAL ESTATE COMPANY; *U.S. Private*, pg. 4321
USAA REAL ESTATE SERVICES—See United Services Automobile Association; *U.S. Private*, pg. 4297
USAA RELOCATION SERVICES, INC.—See United Services Automobile Association; *U.S. Private*, pg. 4297
USAA SAVINGS BANK—See United Services Automobile Association; *U.S. Private*, pg. 4297
USA BABY; *U.S. Private*, pg. 4321
USA BANK; *U.S. Private*, pg. 4321
USABLE CORPORATION; *U.S. Private*, pg. 4322
USABLE LIFE INSURANCE COMPANY—See USAble Corporation; *U.S. Private*, pg. 4322
USABLE MCO—See USAble Corporation; *U.S. Private*, pg. 4322
USABLE MUTUAL INSURANCE COMPANY—See USAble Corporation; *U.S. Private*, pg. 4322
USABLENET, INC.; *U.S. Private*, pg. 4322
USABLENET UK LTD.—See Usablenet, Inc.; *U.S. Private*, pg. 4322
USA CAPITAL MANAGEMENT, INC.; *U.S. Private*, pg. 4321
USA COMPRESSION GP, LLC—See Energy Transfer LP; *U.S. Public*, pg. 765
USA COMPRESSION PARTNERS, LLC—See Riverstone Holdings LLC; *U.S. Private*, pg. 3448
USA COMPRESSION PARTNERS, LP—See Riverstone Holdings LLC; *U.S. Private*, pg. 3447
US ACRYLIC INC.; *U.S. Private*, pg. 4317
USA DEBUSK LLC—See H.I.G. Capital, LLC; *U.S. Private*, pg. 1834
USA DEVELOPMENT CORP.; *U.S. Private*, pg. 4321
USA DIRECT COMPUTER SYSTEMS—See USA Direct Holdings; *U.S. Private*, pg. 4321
USA DIRECT HOLDINGS; *U.S. Private*, pg. 4321
USA DISCOUNTERS, LTD.—See Parallel Investment Partners LLC; *U.S. Private*, pg. 3092
USA ENVIRONMENTAL, INC.; *U.S. Private*, pg. 4321
USA ENVIRONMENT, L.P.—See J.F. Lehman & Company, Inc.; *U.S. Private*, pg. 2163
USAEPAY, INC.—See Francisco Partners Management, LP; *U.S. Private*, pg. 1590
U.S. AEROSPACE, INC.; *U.S. Public*, pg. 2212
USA FASTENER GROUP INC—See American Securities LLC; *U.S. Private*, pg. 250
USA FINANCIAL MARKETING CORPORATION; *U.S. Private*, pg. 4321
USAGENCIES CASUALTY INSURANCE—See J.C. Flowers & Co. LLC; *U.S. Private*, pg. 2159
USAGENCIES, LLC—See J.C. Flowers & Co. LLC; *U.S. Private*, pg. 2159
USAGENCIES MANAGEMENT SERVICES, INC.—See J.C. Flowers & Co. LLC; *U.S. Private*, pg. 2159
U.S. AGGREGATES INC. - FRANCESVILLE PLANT—See Heritage Group; *U.S. Private*, pg. 1923

U.S. AGGREGATES INC. - LAFAYETTE PLANT—See Heritage Group; *U.S. Private*, pg. 1923
U.S. AGGREGATES INC. - LOWELL PLANT—See Heritage Group; *U.S. Private*, pg. 1923
U.S. AGGREGATES INC. - MONON PLANT—See Heritage Group; *U.S. Private*, pg. 1923
U.S. AGGREGATES INC. - SAND & GRAVEL - CRAWFORDSVILLE PLANT—See Heritage Group; *U.S. Private*, pg. 1923
U.S. AGGREGATES INC. - SAND & GRAVEL - PERKINSVILLE PLANT—See Heritage Group; *U.S. Private*, pg. 1923
U.S. AGGREGATES INC. - SAND & GRAVEL - RICHMOND PLANT—See Heritage Group; *U.S. Private*, pg. 1923
U.S. AGGREGATES INC. - SAND & GRAVEL - THORNTOWN PLANT—See Heritage Group; *U.S. Private*, pg. 1923
U.S. AGGREGATES INC.—See Heritage Group; *U.S. Private*, pg. 1923
U.S. AGGREGATES INC. - STONE QUARRY - COLUMBUS PLANT—See Heritage Group; *U.S. Private*, pg. 1923
U.S. AGGREGATES INC. - STONE QUARRY - DELPHI PLANT—See Heritage Group; *U.S. Private*, pg. 1923
U.S. AGGREGATES INC. - STONE QUARRY - LINN GROVE PLANT—See Heritage Group; *U.S. Private*, pg. 1923
U.S. AGGREGATES INC. - STONE QUARRY - PLEASANT MILLS PLANT—See Heritage Group; *U.S. Private*, pg. 1923
U.S. AGGREGATES INC. - STONE QUARRY - PORTLAND PLANT—See Heritage Group; *U.S. Private*, pg. 1923
U.S. AGGREGATES INC. - STONE QUARRY - RIDGEVILLE PLANT—See Heritage Group; *U.S. Private*, pg. 1923
US AGRI-CHEMICALS CORPORATION—See Sinochem Corporation; *Int'l*, pg. 6951
USA GYMNASTICS; *U.S. Private*, pg. 4321
USA HOCKEY, INC.; *U.S. Private*, pg. 4321
USA HOIST CO., INC.—See Mid-American Elevator Equipment Co., Inc.; *U.S. Private*, pg. 2707
USA HONGFUHAN TECHNOLOGY CO.—See Shenzhen Hongfuhan Technology Co., Ltd.; *Int'l*, pg. 6812
USA INSULATION FRANCHISE, LLC—See Riverside Partners, LLC; *U.S. Private*, pg. 3446
US AIRCONDITIONING DISTRIBUTORS, INC.; *U.S. Private*, pg. 4317
US AIRLINE PILOTS ASSOCIATION; *U.S. Private*, pg. 4317
U.S. AIRMOTIVE GSE; *U.S. Private*, pg. 4269
U.S. AIRPORTS FLIGHT SUPPORT LLC; *U.S. Private*, pg. 4269
USA JET AIRLINES, INC.—See Roadrunner Transportation Systems, Inc.; *U.S. Public*, pg. 1802
USAK SERAMIK SANAYI A.S.; *Int'l*, pg. 8096
USA LABS INC.; *U.S. Private*, pg. 4321
USA LABS INC.—See USA Labs Inc.; *U.S. Private*, pg. 4321
USALCO ASHTABULA PLANT, LLC—See H.I.G. Capital, LLC; *U.S. Private*, pg. 1832
USALCO BALTIMORE PLANT, LLC—See H.I.G. Capital, LLC; *U.S. Private*, pg. 1832
USALCO FAIRFIELD PLANT, LLC—See H.I.G. Capital, LLC; *U.S. Private*, pg. 1832
USALCO GAHANNA PLANT, LLC—See H.I.G. Capital, LLC; *U.S. Private*, pg. 1832
USALCO, LLC—See H.I.G. Capital, LLC; *U.S. Private*, pg. 1832
USALCO MICHIGAN CITY PLANT, LLC—See H.I.G. Capital, LLC; *U.S. Private*, pg. 1832
USALCO PORT ALLEN PLANT, LLC—See H.I.G. Capital, LLC; *U.S. Private*, pg. 1832
US ALLIANCE CORPORATION; *U.S. Private*, pg. 4317
US ALLIANCE LIFE & SECURITY COMPANY—See US Alliance Corporation; *U.S. Private*, pg. 4317
US ALUMINUM SERVICES, CORP.; *U.S. Private*, pg. 4317
USA MANAGED CARE ORGANIZATION; *U.S. Private*, pg. 4321
USA MASTER VALVE CO., LTD.—See Jiangsu Hongtian Technology Co., Ltd.; *Int'l*, pg. 3948
USANA AUSTRALIA PTY, LTD.—See Gull Holdings, Ltd.; *U.S. Private*, pg. 1817
USANA CANADA CO.—See Gull Holdings, Ltd.; *U.S. Private*, pg. 1817
USANA HEALTH SCIENCES, INC.—See Gull Holdings, Ltd.; *U.S. Private*, pg. 1817
USANA HEALTH SCIENCES KOREA LTD.—See Gull Holdings, Ltd.; *U.S. Private*, pg. 1818
USANA HEALTH SCIENCES (NZ) CORP.—See Gull Holdings, Ltd.; *U.S. Private*, pg. 1818
USANA HEALTH SCIENCES SINGAPORE PTE, LTD.—See Gull Holdings, Ltd.; *U.S. Private*, pg. 1818
USANA HONG KONG LTD.—See Gull Holdings, Ltd.; *U.S. Private*, pg. 1818
USANA JAPAN, INC.—See Gull Holdings, Ltd.; *U.S. Private*, pg. 1818

US-ANALYTICS SOLUTIONS GROUP, LLC

US-ANALYTICS SOLUTIONS GROUP, LLC; *U.S. Private*, pg. 4320
USA.NET, INC.; *U.S. Private*, pg. 4321
USAN, INC.; *U.S. Private*, pg. 4322
USA PARKING SYSTEM, INC.—See Eldridge Industries LLC; *U.S. Private*, pg. 1351
USA PARKING SYSTEMS, INC.—See The Frangos Group, LLC; *U.S. Private*, pg. 4030
USA PAWN & JEWELRY CO IV, LLC—See EZCORP, Inc.; *U.S. Public*, pg. 818
USA PAYROLLS INC.—See Asure Software, Inc.; *U.S. Public*, pg. 218
USA POULTRY & EGG EXPORT COUNCIL; *U.S. Private*, pg. 4321
US APPRAISAL GROUP, INC.; *U.S. Private*, pg. 4317
USA PROPERTIES FUND, INC.; *U.S. Private*, pg. 4321
USA REAL ESTATE HOLDING COMPANY; *Int'l*, pg. 8096
USA RECYCLING INDUSTRIES, INC.; *U.S. Public*, pg. 2267
USA RESTAURANTS, INC.; *U.S. Private*, pg. 4321
USA SCIENTIFIC, INC.—See Eppendorf AG; *Int'l*, pg. 2465
USA SERVICES OF FLORIDA, INC.—See Warburg Pincus LLC; *U.S. Private*, pg. 4440
US ASPHALT CO—See Omni Holding Company; *U.S. Private*, pg. 3016
U.S. ASSETS GROUP; *U.S. Private*, pg. 4270
U.S.A STARK TECHNOLOGY INC.—See Stark Technology, Inc.; *Int'l*, pg. 7177
USA SUMMIT DISTRIBUTION, LLC.; *U.S. Private*, pg. 4321
USA SWIMMING; *U.S. Private*, pg. 4321
USA SWITCH INC.—See Superior Capital Partners LLC; *U.S. Private*, pg. 3876
USA TAKARA HOLDING COMPANY—See Takara Holdings, Inc.; *Int'l*, pg. 7433
USA TANK SALES & ERECTION CO., INC.—See Cameron Holdings Corporation; *U.S. Private*, pg. 729
USA TECHNOLOGY SERVICES, LLC; *U.S. Private*, pg. 4321
USA TODAY—See Gannett Co., Inc.; *U.S. Public*, pg. 901
USA TODAY—See Gannett Co., Inc.; *U.S. Public*, pg. 901
USA TODAY SPORTS MEDIA GROUP, LLC—See Gannett Co., Inc.; *U.S. Public*, pg. 901
USA TRIATHLON; *U.S. Private*, pg. 4321
USA TRUCK, INC.—See Deutsche Bahn AG; *Int'l*, pg. 2054
U.S. AUTOFORCE—See U.S. Venture, Inc.; *U.S. Private*, pg. 4272
US AUTO GROUP LIMITED; *U.S. Private*, pg. 4317
US AUTO GROUP OF MASSACHUSETTS—See US Auto Group Limited; *U.S. Private*, pg. 4317
U.S. AUTOMOTIVE MANUFACTURING, INC.; *U.S. Public*, pg. 2212
US AUTO SALES INC.; *U.S. Private*, pg. 4317
USA VALLEY FACILITY, INC.—See Waste Management, Inc.; *U.S. Public*, pg. 2332
U-SAVE AUTO RENTAL OF AMERICA, INC.—See Franchise Services of North America Inc.; *U.S. Private*, pg. 1587
U-SAVE-IT PHARMACY, INC.; *U.S. Private*, pg. 4269
U-SAVE PHARMACY OF DAWSON COUNTY, LLC; *U.S. Private*, pg. 4269
USA VISION SYSTEMS INC.—See GeoVision Inc.; *Int'l*, pg. 2942
USA WASTE OF CALIFORNIA, INC.—See Waste Management, Inc.; *U.S. Public*, pg. 2332
USA WASTE OF TEXAS LANDFILLS, INC.—See Waste Management, Inc.; *U.S. Public*, pg. 2332
USA WASTE OF VIRGINIA LANDFILLS, INC.—See Waste Management, Inc.; *U.S. Public*, pg. 2332
USA WOOD DOOR, INC.—See Owens Corning; *U.S. Public*, pg. 1627
U.S. AXLE, INC.; *U.S. Private*, pg. 4270
USA ZAMA INC.—See Andreas Stihl AG & Co.; *Int'l*, pg. 451
U.S. BANCORP ADVISORS, LLC—See U.S. Bancorp; *U.S. Public*, pg. 2212
U.S. BANCORP COMMUNITY DEVELOPMENT CORPORATION—See U.S. Bancorp; *U.S. Public*, pg. 2212
U.S. BANCORP EQUIPMENT FINANCE, INC.—See U.S. Bancorp; *U.S. Public*, pg. 2212
U.S. BANCORP FOUNDATION—See U.S. Bancorp; *U.S. Public*, pg. 2212
U.S. BANCORP FUND SERVICES, LLC—See U.S. Bancorp; *U.S. Public*, pg. 2212
U.S. BANCORP FUND SERVICES, LTD.—See U.S. Bancorp; *U.S. Public*, pg. 2213
U.S. BANCORP INVESTMENTS, INC.—See U.S. Bancorp; *U.S. Public*, pg. 2213
U.S. BANCORP; *U.S. Public*, pg. 2212
U.S. BAND & ORCHESTRA SUPPLIES, INC.; *U.S. Private*, pg. 4270
U.S. BANK ASSET MANAGEMENT—See U.S. Bancorp; *U.S. Public*, pg. 2213
U.S. BANK BUSINESS CREDIT—See U.S. Bancorp; *U.S. Public*, pg. 2213
U.S. BANK HOME MORTGAGE—See U.S. Bancorp; *U.S. Public*, pg. 2213

U.S. BANK NATIONAL ASSOCIATION ND—See U.S. Bancorp; *U.S. Public*, pg. 2213
U.S. BANK NATIONAL ASSOCIATION—See U.S. Bancorp; *U.S. Public*, pg. 2213
U.S. BANK TRUSTEES LIMITED—See U.S. Bancorp; *U.S. Public*, pg. 2213
U.S. BANK TRUST NATIONAL ASSOCIATION SD—See U.S. Bancorp; *U.S. Public*, pg. 2213
USB BANK PLC—See BLC Bank SAL; *Int'l*, pg. 1063
USB CAPITAL IX—See U.S. Bancorp; *U.S. Public*, pg. 2213
U.S. BELLOWS, INC.—See Piping Technology & Products Inc.; *U.S. Private*, pg. 3190
US BENEFITS ALLIANCE, LLC—See Reliance Global Group, Inc.; *U.S. Public*, pg. 1778
USB GMBH—See Sopra Steria Group S.A.; *Int'l*, pg. 7109
USBID, INC.; *U.S. Private*, pg. 4322
US BIOSERVICES CORPORATION—See Cencora, Inc.; *U.S. Public*, pg. 467
US BIOSERVICES; *U.S. Private*, pg. 4317
US BIOTEC, INC.; *U.S. Public*, pg. 2266
U.S. BLADES SUB LLC—See SCIES B.G.R. INC.; *Int'l*, pg. 6648
US BORAX HOLDINGS INC. - CHANGSHU OPERATIONS - SHIPPING FACILITY—See Rio Tinto plc; *Int'l*, pg. 6348
US BORAX HOLDINGS INC. - ROTTERDAM OPERATIONS - SHIPPING FACILITY—See Rio Tinto plc; *Int'l*, pg. 6348
US BORAX HOLDINGS INC.—See Rio Tinto plc; *Int'l*, pg. 6348
U.S. BOTTLERS MACHINERY COMPANY; *U.S. Private*, pg. 4270
U.S. BROACH & MACHINE COMPANY—See Avis Industrial Corporation; *U.S. Private*, pg. 407
U.S. BRONZE FOUNDRY & MACHINE, INC.; *U.S. Private*, pg. 4270
USB TRADE SERVICES LIMITED—See U.S. Bancorp; *U.S. Public*, pg. 2213
US BUILDINGS LLC; *U.S. Private*, pg. 4318
US BULK TRANSPORT INC.; *U.S. Private*, pg. 4318
US CABLE GROUP; *U.S. Private*, pg. 4318
US CABLE OF COASTAL TEXAS LP—See US Cable Group; *U.S. Private*, pg. 4318
U.S. CAD, INC.—See Schneider Electric SE; *Int'l*, pg. 6625
U.S., CANADA AND MONTERREY MANUFACTURING GROUP—See Cox Enterprises, Inc.; *U.S. Private*, pg. 1075
U.S. CARGO, INC.; *U.S. Private*, pg. 4270
U.S. CASTINGS, LLC—See Advanced Metals Group, LLC; *U.S. Private*, pg. 91
USC ATLANTIC, INC.—See Vulcan Materials Company; *U.S. Public*, pg. 2314
US CAVALRY STORE INC.; *U.S. Private*, pg. 4318
USCB FINANCIAL HOLDINGS, INC.; *U.S. Public*, pg. 2267
USC CONSULTING GROUP, LLC; *U.S. Private*, pg. 4322
USC CORPORATION—See Restar Holdings Corporation; *Int'l*, pg. 6303
USC CREDIT UNION; *U.S. Private*, pg. 4322
USCC SERVICES, LLC—See Telephone & Data Systems, Inc.; *U.S. Public*, pg. 1998
USC-DAVITA DIALYSIS CENTER, LLC—See DaVita Inc.; *U.S. Public*, pg. 644
USC DISTRIBUTION SERVICES LLC—See Deutsche Post AG; *Int'l*, pg. 2083
USCE BOSNE VP A.D.; *Int'l*, pg. 8096
USC ELECTRONICS (CHINA) CO., LTD.—See Restar Holdings Corporation; *Int'l*, pg. 6303
USC ELECTRONICS (KOREA) CO.,LTD.—See Restar Holdings Corporation; *Int'l*, pg. 6303
USC ELECTRONICS (SHANGHAI) CO.,LTD.—See Restar Holdings Corporation; *Int'l*, pg. 6303
U.S. CENTER FOR SPORTS MEDICINE, L.L.C.—See Tenet Healthcare Corporation; *U.S. Public*, pg. 2009
USCF INVESTMENTS, INC.—See The Marygold Companies, Inc.; *U.S. Public*, pg. 2112
US-CHINA BIOMEDICAL TECHNOLOGY, INC.; *U.S. Private*, pg. 4320
U.S. CHINA MINING GROUP, INC.; *U.S. Private*, pg. 4270
US CHROME CORPORATION; *U.S. Private*, pg. 4318
USC LLC; *U.S. Private*, pg. 4322
US COAL CORPORATION; *U.S. Private*, pg. 4318
US COATINGS, LLC—See SK Capital Partners, LP; *U.S. Private*, pg. 3679
U.S. COATINGS LLC—See Henkel AG & Co. KGaA; *Int'l*, pg. 3354
U.S. COLLECTIONS, INC.—See HCA Healthcare, Inc.; *U.S. Public*, pg. 1013
U.S. COLO, LLC—See American Tower Corporation; *U.S. Public*, pg. 111
USCOM KFT—See USCOM LIMITED; *Int'l*, pg. 8096
USCOM LIMITED; *Int'l*, pg. 8096
US COMMERCIAL CORP. S.A. DE C.V.—See Grupo Carso, S.A.B. de C.V.; *Int'l*, pg. 3124
U.S. COMPANIES, INC.; *U.S. Private*, pg. 4270
U.S. COMPOUNDING, INC.—See DMK Pharmaceuticals Corporation; *U.S. Private*, pg. 671

CORPORATE AFFILIATIONS

U.S. CONCRETE, INC.—See Vulcan Materials Company; *U.S. Public*, pg. 2313
U.S. CONCRETE ON-SITE, INC.—See Vulcan Materials Company; *U.S. Public*, pg. 2314
US CONEC LTD.—See Fujikura Ltd.; *Int'l*, pg. 2829
US COPPER CORP.; *Int'l*, pg. 8096
US CORPORATION OF SHINHEUNG GLOBAL CO., LTD.—See Shinsung Delta Tech Co., Ltd.; *Int'l*, pg. 6849
U.S. CORRUGATED, INC. - CLEVELAND SHEET PLANT—See Bio Pappel, S.A.B. de C.V.; *Int'l*, pg. 1035
U.S. CORRUGATED, INC. - COAL CENTER CORRUGATOR PLANT—See Bio Pappel, S.A.B. de C.V.; *Int'l*, pg. 1035
U.S. CORRUGATED, INC. - MILWAUKEE SHEET PLANT—See Bio Pappel, S.A.B. de C.V.; *Int'l*, pg. 1035
U.S. CORRUGATED, INC.—See Bio Pappel, S.A.B. de C.V.; *Int'l*, pg. 1035
U.S. COTTON, LLC; *U.S. Private*, pg. 4270
US CRITICAL METALS CORP.; *Int'l*, pg. 8096
U.S. CUSTOM MANUFACTURING—See U.S. Venture, Inc.; *U.S. Private*, pg. 4272
USCUTTER INC.; *U.S. Private*, pg. 4322
US DAIRY SYSTEMS INC.; *U.S. Private*, pg. 4318
U.S. DATA MINING GROUP, INC.—See Hut 8 Corp.; *U.S. Public*, pg. 1076
US DATAWORKS, INC.—See Checkalt, LLC; *U.S. Private*, pg. 869
US DESIGN & CONSTRUCTION CORP.; *U.S. Private*, pg. 4318
US DESIGN & MILL, CORP.; *U.S. Private*, pg. 4318
USDIAGNOSTICS, INC.; *U.S. Private*, pg. 4322
US DIAGNOSTICS, INC.—See Abbott Laboratories; *U.S. Public*, pg. 19
US DISMANTLEMENT LLC; *U.S. Private*, pg. 4318
U.S. DISPLAY GROUP, INC.—See Four M Holdings LLC; *U.S. Private*, pg. 1582
U.S. DISPLAY GROUP—See Four M Holdings LLC; *U.S. Private*, pg. 1582
US DIVERS JAPAN—See L'Air Liquide S.A.; *Int'l*, pg. 4375
US DIVERS—See L'Air Liquide S.A.; *Int'l*, pg. 4375
USD PARTNERS LP; *U.S. Public*, pg. 2267
U.S. DRY CLEANING SERVICES CORPORATION; *U.S. Private*, pg. 4270
U.S. EAGLE CORPORATION; *U.S. Private*, pg. 4270
US ECOLOGY HOUSTON, INC.—See Republic Services, Inc.; *U.S. Public*, pg. 1788
US ECOLOGY IDAHO, INC.—See Republic Services, Inc.; *U.S. Public*, pg. 1788
US ECOLOGY ILLINOIS, INC.—See Republic Services, Inc.; *U.S. Public*, pg. 1788
US ECOLOGY, INC.—See Republic Services, Inc.; *U.S. Public*, pg. 1787
US ECOLOGY KARNES COUNTY DISPOSAL, LLC—See Republic Services, Inc.; *U.S. Public*, pg. 1788
US ECOLOGY MICHIGAN, INC.—See Republic Services, Inc.; *U.S. Public*, pg. 1788
US ECOLOGY NEVADA, INC.—See Republic Services, Inc.; *U.S. Public*, pg. 1788
US ECOLOGY ROMULUS, INC.—See Republic Services, Inc.; *U.S. Public*, pg. 1788
US ECOLOGY SULLIGENT, INC.—See Republic Services, Inc.; *U.S. Public*, pg. 1788
US ECOLOGY TAMPA, INC.—See Republic Services, Inc.; *U.S. Public*, pg. 1788
US ECOLOGY TAYLOR, INC.—See Republic Services, Inc.; *U.S. Public*, pg. 1788
US ECOLOGY TEXAS, INC.—See Republic Services, Inc.; *U.S. Public*, pg. 1788
US ECOLOGY TULSA, INC.—See Republic Services, Inc.; *U.S. Public*, pg. 1788
US ECOLOGY VERNON, INC.—See Republic Services, Inc.; *U.S. Public*, pg. 1788
US ECOLOGY WASHINGTON, INC.—See Republic Services, Inc.; *U.S. Public*, pg. 1788
US ECOLOGY WINNIE, LLC—See Republic Services, Inc.; *U.S. Public*, pg. 1788
USE CREDIT UNION; *U.S. Private*, pg. 4322
US EDIRECT INC.—See Tyler Technologies, Inc.; *U.S. Public*, pg. 2209
U-SELECT-IT CORPORATION—See The Wittern Group; *U.S. Private*, pg. 4138
U.S. ELECTRICAL MOTORS—See Emerson Electric Co.; *U.S. Public*, pg. 752
U.S. ELECTRICAL SERVICES, INC.—See Blackfriars Corp.; *U.S. Private*, pg. 574
U.S.E.M. DE MEXICO S.A. DE C.V.—See Nidec Corporation; *Int'l*, pg. 5277
USEM INC.; *U.S. Private*, pg. 4322
USEN CORPORATION—See U-NEXT HOLDINGS Co.,Ltd; *Int'l*, pg. 7997
U.S. ENDOWMENT FOR FORESTRY & COMMUNITIES, INC.; *U.S. Private*, pg. 4270
U.S. ENERGY CORP.; *U.S. Public*, pg. 2213
U.S. ENERGY DEVELOPMENT CORPORATION; *U.S. Private*, pg. 4270

COMPANY NAME INDEX

U.S. ENERGY INITIATIVES CORPORATION; *U.S. Public,* pg. 2213
U.S. ENERGY TECHNOLOGIES, INC.; *U.S. Private,* pg. 4270
US ENGINEERING COMPANY; *U.S. Private,* pg. 4318
U.S. ENGINE VALVE CORPORATION—See Eaton Corporation plc; *Int'l,* pg. 2280
U.S. ENGINE VALVE CORPORATION—See NITTAN Corporation; *Int'l,* pg. 5383
US ENTERPRISES INC.; *U.S. Private,* pg. 4318
US E & O BROKERS—See Caisse de Depot et Placement du Quebec; *Int'l,* pg. 1257
US E & O BROKERS—See KKR & Co. Inc.; *U.S. Public,* pg. 1265
US EQUIPMENT CO. INC.; *U.S. Private,* pg. 4318
USERADGENTS SAS—See HighCo S.A.; *Int'l,* pg. 3387
USER CENTRIC COMMUNICATIONS; *U.S. Private,* pg. 4322
USER FRIENDLY HOME SERVICES, LLC; *U.S. Private,* pg. 4322
USERFUL CORPORATION; *U.S. Private,* pg. 4322
USER INSIGHT, INC.; *U.S. Private,* pg. 4322
USERJOY TECHNOLOGY CO., LTD.; *Int'l,* pg. 8096
USERLIKE UG—See Lime Technologies AB; *Int'l,* pg. 4498
USER LOCAL, INC.; *Int'l,* pg. 8096
USERS INCORPORATED—See Fiserv, Inc.; *U.S. Public,* pg. 851
USERTESTING, INC.—See Sunstone Partners Management LLC; *U.S. Private,* pg. 3873
USERTESTING, INC.—See Thoma Bravo, L.P.; *U.S. Private,* pg. 4154
USER TREND LTD.; *Int'l,* pg. 8096
USERVOICE, INC.; *U.S. Private,* pg. 4323
USE-SYSTEM ENGINEERING HOLDING B.V.—See TKH Group N.V.; *Int'l,* pg. 7765
USEWALTER INC.; *Int'l,* pg. 8096
U.S. EXCHANGE HOLDINGS, INC.—See Deutsche Borse AG; *Int'l,* pg. 2064
US EXP GROUP, INC.; *U.S. Private,* pg. 4318
U.S. EXPRESS, INC.—See U.S. Logistics, Inc.; *U.S. Private,* pg. 4271
U.S. FACILITIES, INC.—See PRWT Services, Inc.; *U.S. Private,* pg. 3296
USFALCON, INC.; *U.S. Private,* pg. 4323
U.S. FARATHANE HOLDINGS CORP.—See The Gores Group, LLC; *U.S. Private,* pg. 4035
U.S. FARATHANE, LLC—See The Gores Group, LLC; *U.S. Private,* pg. 4035
USF COLLECTIONS INC.; *U.S. Private,* pg. 4323
US FEDERAL CONTRACTOR REGISTRATION INC.; *U.S. Private,* pg. 4318
US FEDERAL PROPERTIES TRUST, INC.; *U.S. Private,* pg. 4318
US-FEIWO AGRICULTURAL INDUSTRY INTERNATIONAL, INC.; *U.S. Private,* pg. 4320
USF FABRICATION, INC.—See Eagle Manufacturing Group; *U.S. Private,* pg. 1309
USF FABRICATION, INC. - UTAH FACILITY—See Eagle Manufacturing Group; *U.S. Private,* pg. 1309
USF FEDERAL CREDIT UNION; *U.S. Private,* pg. 4323
USF HEALTHCARE SA—See Ecolab Inc.; *U.S. Public,* pg. 717
USF HOLLAND INC.—See Yellow Corporation; *U.S. Public,* pg. 2398
U.S. FIBER, LLC—See Casella Waste Systems, Inc.; *U.S. Public,* pg. 446
U.S. FIDUCIARY SERVICES, INC.; *U.S. Private,* pg. 4270
USFI, INC.; *U.S. Private,* pg. 4323
US FINANCIAL 15 SPLIT CORP.—See Quadravest Capital Management Inc.; *Int'l,* pg. 6150
U.S. FINANCIAL ADVISORS LLC—See Great Valley Advisor Group, Inc.; *U.S. Private,* pg. 1768
U.S. FINANCIAL SERVICES, LLC; *U.S. Private,* pg. 4270
US FLEET TRACKING CORP.; *U.S. Private,* pg. 4318
US FOODS CO., LTD.—See S. ISHIMITSU & Co., LTD.; *Int'l,* pg. 6446
US FOODS CULINARY EQUIPMENT & SUPPLIES, LLC—See US Foods Holding Corp.; *U.S. Public,* pg. 2266
US FOODS HOLDING CORP.; *U.S. Public,* pg. 2266
US FOODS, INC.—See US Foods Holding Corp.; *U.S. Public,* pg. 2266
US FOOT & ANKLE SPECIALISTS, LLC—See NMS Capital Services, LLC; *U.S. Private,* pg. 2932
U.S. FRANCHISE SYSTEMS, INC.—See Travel & Leisure Co.; *U.S. Public,* pg. 2185
USF REDDAWAY INC.—See Yellow Corporation; *U.S. Public,* pg. 2398
U.S. GAS & ELECTRIC, INC.—See Crius Energy, LLC; *U.S. Private,* pg. 1102
USG BORAL BUILDING PRODUCTS PTY LIMITED—See Gebr. Knauf KG; *Int'l,* pg. 2908
USG BORAL BUILDING PRODUCTS PTY LIMITED—See Seven Group Holdings Limited; *Int'l,* pg. 6733
USG CORP.—See Gebr. Knauf KG; *Int'l,* pg. 2908
USG FAR EAST INTERNATIONAL TRADING (SHANGHAI) LTD.—See Triumphal Associates Bhd.; *Int'l,* pg. 7936
USG INTERIORS, INC.—See Gebr. Knauf KG; *Int'l,* pg. 2908

USG INTERNATIONAL, LTD.—See Gebr. Knauf KG; *Int'l,* pg. 2908
US GLASS & ALUMINUM INC.; *U.S. Private,* pg. 4318
U.S. GLOBAL INVESTORS, INC.; *U.S. Public,* pg. 2213
USG NETHERLANDS GLOBAL HOLDINGS B.V.—See Gebr. Knauf KG; *Int'l,* pg. 2908
US GOLD CANADIAN ACQUISITION CORPORATION—See McEwen Mining Inc.; *Int'l,* pg. 4758
U.S. GOLD CORP.; *U.S. Public,* pg. 2213
U.S. GOLDMINING INC.—See GoldMining Inc.; *Int'l,* pg. 3034
US GOLF INC.; *U.S. Private,* pg. 4318
USGP ALBANY DEA, LLC—See Easterly Government Properties, Inc.; *U.S. Public,* pg. 703
USGP DALLAS DEA LP—See Easterly Government Properties, Inc.; *U.S. Public,* pg. 703
USG PEOPLE BELGIUM SA—See Recruit Holdings Co., Ltd.; *Int'l,* pg. 6241
USG PEOPLE HOLDINGS B.V.—See Recruit Holdings Co., Ltd.; *Int'l,* pg. 6241
USG PRODUCTS (F.E.) PTE. LTD.—See Triumphal Associates Bhd.; *Int'l,* pg. 7937
USG PRODUCTS SDN. BHD.—See Triumphal Associates Bhd.; *Int'l,* pg. 7937
USG PROFESSIONALS NV—See Recruit Holdings Co., Ltd.; *Int'l,* pg. 6241
U.S. GREEN BUILDING COUNCIL, INC.; *U.S. Private,* pg. 4270
US GREENFIBER LLC; *U.S. Private,* pg. 4318
US GROUP INC.; *U.S. Private,* pg. 4318
US GROWERS COLD STORAGE INC.; *U.S. Private,* pg. 4318
USG TECH SOLUTIONS LIMITED; *Int'l,* pg. 8096
USHA INTERNATIONAL LIMITED—See Siddharth Shriram Group; *Int'l,* pg. 6883
USHAKIRAN FINANCE LIMITED; *Int'l,* pg. 8097
USHA MARTIN AMERICAS INC.—See Usha Martin Limited; *Int'l,* pg. 8097
USHA MARTIN AUSTRALIA PTY LIMITED—See Usha Martin Limited; *Int'l,* pg. 8097
USHA MARTIN EDUCATION & SOLUTIONS LTD.; *Int'l,* pg. 8096
USHA MARTIN EUROPE B.V.—See Usha Martin Limited; *Int'l,* pg. 8097
USHA MARTIN INTERNATIONAL LIMITED—See Usha Martin Limited; *Int'l,* pg. 8097
USHA MARTIN ITALIA S.R.L.—See Usha Martin Limited; *Int'l,* pg. 8097
USHA MARTIN LIMITED; *Int'l,* pg. 8096
USHA MARTIN SINGAPORE PTE. LIMITED—See Usha Martin Limited; *Int'l,* pg. 8097
USHA MARTIN TECHNOLOGIES LIMITED—See Usha Martin Education & Solutions Ltd.; *Int'l,* pg. 8096
USHA MARTIN UK LTD.—See Usha Martin Limited; *Int'l,* pg. 8097
USHA MARTIN VIETNAM COMPANY LIMITED—See Usha Martin Limited; *Int'l,* pg. 8097
USHANTI COLOUR CHEM LIMITED; *Int'l,* pg. 8097
USHA RESOURCES LTD.; *Int'l,* pg. 8097
USHA SIAM STEEL INDUSTRIES PUBLIC COMPANY LIMITED—See Usha Martin Limited; *Int'l,* pg. 8097
USHDEV INTERNATIONAL LIMITED; *Int'l,* pg. 8097
US HEALTH ADVISORS INC—See National Health Corporation; *U.S. Private,* pg. 2856
US HEALTH AND LIFE INSURANCE CO—See US Health Holdings Ltd.; *U.S. Private,* pg. 4319
USHEALTH CAREER—See UBS Group AG; *Int'l,* pg. 8006
U.S HEALTHCARE HOLDINGS, LLC—See CVS Health Corporation; *U.S. Public,* pg. 615
USHEALTH GROUP, INC.—See UBS Group AG; *Int'l,* pg. 8006
US HEALTH HOLDINGS LTD.; *U.S. Private,* pg. 4318
US HEALTHVEST LLC; *U.S. Private,* pg. 4319
U.S. HEALTHWORKS, INC.—See Select Medical Holdings Corporation; *U.S. Public,* pg. 1862
U.S. HEALTHWORKS MEDICAL GROUP OF KANSAS CITY, P.A.—See Select Medical Holdings Corporation; *U.S. Public,* pg. 1861
U.S. HEALTHWORKS MEDICAL GROUP OF MAINE, INC.—See Select Medical Holdings Corporation; *U.S. Public,* pg. 1861
U.S. HEALTHWORKS MEDICAL GROUP OF MINNESOTA, P.C.—See Select Medical Holdings Corporation; *U.S. Public,* pg. 1862
U.S. HEALTHWORKS MEDICAL GROUP OF NORTH CAROLINA, P.C.—See Select Medical Holdings Corporation; *U.S. Public,* pg. 1862
U.S. HEALTHWORKS MEDICAL GROUP OF OHIO, INC.—See Select Medical Holdings Corporation; *U.S. Public,* pg. 1862
U.S. HEALTHWORKS MEDICAL GROUP OF TENNESSEE, P.C.—See Select Medical Holdings Corporation; *U.S. Public,* pg. 1862
U.S. HEALTHWORKS MEDICAL GROUP OF WASHINGTON, P.S.—See Select Medical Holdings Corporation; *U.S. Public,* pg. 1862

USHIO, INC.

U.S. HEALTHWORKS MEDICAL GROUP, PROF. CORP.—See Catholic Health Initiatives; *U.S. Private,* pg. 790
U.S. HEALTHWORKS MEDICAL GROUP, PROF. CORP.—See Select Medical Holdings Corporation; *U.S. Public,* pg. 1857
U.S. HEALTHWORKS MEDICAL GROUP, PROF. CORP.—See Welsh, Carson, Anderson & Stowe; *U.S. Private,* pg. 4479
U.S. HEALTHWORKS OF INDIANA, INC.—See Select Medical Holdings Corporation; *U.S. Public,* pg. 1862
U.S. HEALTHWORKS OF WASHINGTON, INC.—See Select Medical Holdings Corporation; *U.S. Public,* pg. 1862
U.S. HEALTHWORKS PROVIDER NETWORK OF COLORADO, INC.—See Select Medical Holdings Corporation; *U.S. Public,* pg. 1862
USHER AGRO LTD.; *Int'l,* pg. 8097
USHER ENTERPRISES, INC.—See The Pritzker Group - Chicago, LLC; *U.S. Private,* pg. 4100
USHER INCORPORATED—See MicroStrategy, Inc.; *U.S. Public,* pg. 1444
USHER TRANSPORT INC.; *U.S. Private,* pg. 4323
USHG ACQUISITION CORP.; *U.S. Public,* pg. 2267
U-SHIN ACCESS SYSTEMS (WUXI) CO., LTD.—See Minebea Mitsumi Inc.; *Int'l,* pg. 4905
U-SHIN AMERICA INC.—See Minebea Mitsumi Inc.; *Int'l,* pg. 4905
U-SHIN AUTOPARTS MEXICO,S.A. DE C.V.—See Minebea Mitsumi Inc.; *Int'l,* pg. 4905
U-SHIN DEUTSCHLAND GMBH—See Minebea Mitsumi Inc.; *Int'l,* pg. 4905
U-SHIN DEUTSCHLAND GRUNDVERMOGEN GMBH—See Minebea Mitsumi Inc.; *Int'l,* pg. 4905
U-SHIN DEUTSCHLAND ZUGANGSSYSTEME GMBH—See Minebea Mitsumi Inc.; *Int'l,* pg. 4905
U-SHIN DO BRASIL SISTEMAS AUTOMOTIVOS LTDA.—See Minebea Mitsumi Inc.; *Int'l,* pg. 4905
USHINE PHOTONICS CORP.; *Int'l,* pg. 8097
U-SHIN EUROPE LTD.—See Minebea Mitsumi Inc.; *Int'l,* pg. 4905
U-SHIN FRANCE S.A.S.—See Minebea Mitsumi Inc.; *Int'l,* pg. 4905
U-SHIN HOLDINGS EUROPE BV—See Minebea Mitsumi Inc.; *Int'l,* pg. 4905
U-SHIN (HONG KONG) LIMITED—See Minebea Mitsumi Inc.; *Int'l,* pg. 4905
U-SHIN INDIA PRIVATE LIMITED—See Minebea Mitsumi Inc.; *Int'l,* pg. 4905
U-SHIN INTERNATIONAL TRADING (SHANGHAI) LTD—See Minebea Mitsumi Inc.; *Int'l,* pg. 4905
U-SHIN ITALIA S.P.A.—See Minebea Mitsumi Inc.; *Int'l,* pg. 4905
U-SHIN LTD.—See Minebea Mitsumi Inc.; *Int'l,* pg. 4905
U-SHIN MANUFACTURING (SUZHOU) CO., LTD.—See Minebea Mitsumi Inc.; *Int'l,* pg. 4905
U-SHIN MANUFACTURING (WUXI) CO., LTD.—See Minebea Mitsumi Inc.; *Int'l,* pg. 4905
U-SHIN MANUFACTURING (ZHONGSHAN) CO., LTD.—See Minebea Mitsumi Inc.; *Int'l,* pg. 4905
U-SHIN SHOWA LTD. - KYOTO PLANT—See Minebea Mitsumi Inc.; *Int'l,* pg. 4905
U-SHIN SHOWA LTD.—See Minebea Mitsumi Inc.; *Int'l,* pg. 4905
U-SHIN SLOVAKIA S.R.O.—See Minebea Mitsumi Inc.; *Int'l,* pg. 4905
U-SHIN SPAIN S.L.—See Minebea Mitsumi Inc.; *Int'l,* pg. 4905
U-SHIN (THAILAND) CO., LTD.—See Minebea Mitsumi Inc.; *Int'l,* pg. 4905
U-SHIN TRANSPORT LTD.—See Minebea Mitsumi Inc.; *Int'l,* pg. 4905
USHIO AMERICA, CENTRAL REGIONAL OFFICE—See Ushio, Inc.; *Int'l,* pg. 8098
USHIO AMERICA, EASTERN DIVISION BRANCH OFFICE—See Ushio, Inc.; *Int'l,* pg. 8098
USHIO AMERICA, INC.—See Ushio, Inc.; *Int'l,* pg. 8098
USHIO ASIA PACIFIC PTE. LTD.—See Ushio, Inc.; *Int'l,* pg. 8098
USHIO ASIA PACIFIC (THAILAND) LTD.—See Ushio, Inc.; *Int'l,* pg. 8098
USHIO ASIA PACIFIC VIETNAM CO., LTD.—See Ushio, Inc.; *Int'l,* pg. 8098
USHIO ASIA TRADING LTD.—See Ushio, Inc.; *Int'l,* pg. 8098
USHIO DEUTSCHLAND GMBH—See Ushio, Inc.; *Int'l,* pg. 8098
USHIO EUROPE B.V.—See Ushio, Inc.; *Int'l,* pg. 8098
USHIO FRANCE S.A.R.L.—See Ushio, Inc.; *Int'l,* pg. 8098
USHIO HONG KONG LTD.—See Ushio, Inc.; *Int'l,* pg. 8098
USHIO, INC., GOTEMBA DIVISION—See Ushio, Inc.; *Int'l,* pg. 8098
USHIO, INC., HARIMA DIVISION—See Ushio, Inc.; *Int'l,* pg. 8098
USHIO INC., OSAKA BRANCH—See Ushio, Inc.; *Int'l,* pg. 8098
USHIO, INC.—See Ushio, Inc.; *Int'l,* pg. 8098
USHIO, INC.; *Int'l,* pg. 8097

USHIO, INC.

USHIO, INC. - SYSTEM SALES DIVISION—See Ushio, Inc.; *Int'l*, pg. 8098
USHIO, INC., TOKYO SALES HEADQUARTERS—See Ushio, Inc.; *Int'l*, pg. 8098
USHIO, INC., YOKOHAMA DIVISION—See Ushio, Inc.; *Int'l*, pg. 8098
USHIO KOREA, INC.—See Ushio, Inc.; *Int'l*, pg. 8098
USHIO LIGHTING, INC. - FUKUSAKI DIVISION—See Ushio, Inc.; *Int'l*, pg. 8098
USHIO LIGHTING, INC.—See Ushio, Inc.; *Int'l*, pg. 8098
USHIO LIGHTING, INC.—See Ushio, Inc.; *Int'l*, pg. 8098
USHIO LIGHTING, INC. - TSUKUBA DIVISION—See Ushio, Inc.; *Int'l*, pg. 8098
USHIO LIGHTING, INC. - YOKOHAMA DIVISION—See Ushio, Inc.; *Int'l*, pg. 8098
USHIO PHILIPPINES, INC.—See Ushio, Inc.; *Int'l*, pg. 8098
USHIO POLAND SP. Z O.O.—See Ushio, Inc.; *Int'l*, pg. 8098
USHIO SHANGHAI, INC—See Ushio, Inc.; *Int'l*, pg. 8097
USHIO (SHAOGUAN) CO., LTD.—See Ushio, Inc.; *Int'l*, pg. 8097
USHIO SHENZHEN, INC.—See Ushio, Inc.; *Int'l*, pg. 8097
USHIO SINGAPORE PTE. LTD.—See Ushio, Inc.; *Int'l*, pg. 8098
USHIO SPAX, INC. - HORIKIRI PLANT—See Ushio, Inc.; *Int'l*, pg. 8098
USHIO SPAX, INC.—See Ushio, Inc.; *Int'l*, pg. 8098
USHIO (SUZHOU) CO., LTD.—See Ushio, Inc.; *Int'l*, pg. 8097
USHIO TAIWAN, INC.—See Ushio, Inc.; *Int'l*, pg. 8098
USHIO U.K., LTD.—See Ushio, Inc.; *Int'l*, pg. 8098
USHIP, INC.; *U.S. Private*, pg. 4323
USHKUY JSC; *Int'l*, pg. 8098
US-HM STRAW CONSTRUCTION MATERIAL INT'L, INC.; *U.S. Private*, pg. 4320
US HOLDINGS CORPORATION; *U.S. Private*, pg. 4319
U.S. HOME OF ARIZONA CONSTRUCTION CO.—See Lennar Corporation; *U.S. Public*, pg. 1307
U.S. HOSE CORP. - HOUSTON—See Smiths Group plc; *Int'l*, pg. 7012
U.S. HOSE CORP.—See Smiths Group plc; *Int'l*, pg. 7012
U.S. HOSPITALITY PUBLISHERS, INC.—See Atlantic Street Capital Management LLC; *U.S. Private*, pg. 374
USHUAIA TV—See Television Francaise 1 S.A.; *Int'l*, pg. 7543
US HYBRID CORPORATION—See Ideanomics, Inc.; *U.S. Public*, pg. 1088
USI AFFINITY—See Caisse de Depot et Placement du Quebec; *Int'l*, pg. 1257
USI AFFINITY—See KKR & Co. Inc.; *U.S. Public*, pg. 1265
USI AMERICA INC.—See ASE Technology Holding Co., Ltd.; *Int'l*, pg. 605
USIBELLI COAL MINE, INC.; *U.S. Private*, pg. 4323
USIC, LLC; *U.S. Private*, pg. 4323
USI COLORADO LLC—See Caisse de Depot et Placement du Quebec; *Int'l*, pg. 1257
USI COLORADO LLC—See KKR & Co. Inc.; *U.S. Public*, pg. 1265
USI CONSULTING GROUP—See Caisse de Depot et Placement du Quebec; *Int'l*, pg. 1257
USI CONSULTING GROUP—See KKR & Co. Inc.; *U.S. Public*, pg. 1265
USI CORPORATION - KAOHSIUNG PLANT—See Chun Yu Works & Co., Ltd.; *Int'l*, pg. 1596
USI CORPORATION; *Int'l*, pg. 8098
USI ELECTRIC, INC.—See Universal Security Instruments, Inc.; *U.S. Public*, pg. 2262
USIG (SHANGHAI) CO., LTD.—See USI Corporation; *Int'l*, pg. 8099
USI HOLDINGS CORPORATION—See Caisse de Depot et Placement du Quebec; *Int'l*, pg. 1256
USI HOLDINGS CORPORATION—See KKR & Co. Inc.; *U.S. Public*, pg. 1264
USI, INC.; *U.S. Private*, pg. 4323
USI INSURANCE SERVICES LLC - AUSTIN—See Caisse de Depot et Placement du Quebec; *Int'l*, pg. 1257
USI INSURANCE SERVICES LLC - AUSTIN—See KKR & Co. Inc.; *U.S. Public*, pg. 1265
USI INSURANCE SERVICES LLC - DALLAS—See Caisse de Depot et Placement du Quebec; *Int'l*, pg. 1257
USI INSURANCE SERVICES LLC - DALLAS—See KKR & Co. Inc.; *U.S. Public*, pg. 1265
USI INSURANCE SERVICES LLC - FORT LAUDERDALE—See Caisse de Depot et Placement du Quebec; *Int'l*, pg. 1257
USI INSURANCE SERVICES LLC - FORT LAUDERDALE—See KKR & Co. Inc.; *U.S. Public*, pg. 1266
USI INSURANCE SERVICES LLC - HOUSTON—See Caisse de Depot et Placement du Quebec; *Int'l*, pg. 1257
USI INSURANCE SERVICES LLC - HOUSTON—See KKR & Co. Inc.; *U.S. Public*, pg. 1266
USI INSURANCE SERVICES LLC - PHOENIX—See Caisse de Depot et Placement du Quebec; *Int'l*, pg. 1257
USI INSURANCE SERVICES LLC - PHOENIX—See KKR & Co. Inc.; *U.S. Public*, pg. 1266

USI INSURANCE SERVICES LLC - SAN ANGELO—See Caisse de Depot et Placement du Quebec; *Int'l*, pg. 1257
USI INSURANCE SERVICES LLC - SAN ANGELO—See KKR & Co. Inc.; *U.S. Public*, pg. 1266
USI INSURANCE SERVICES LLC—See Caisse de Depot et Placement du Quebec; *Int'l*, pg. 1256
USI INSURANCE SERVICES LLC—See KKR & Co. Inc.; *U.S. Public*, pg. 1264
USI INSURANCE SERVICES LLC - SOUTH PORTLAND—See Caisse de Depot et Placement du Quebec; *Int'l*, pg. 1257
USI INSURANCE SERVICES LLC - SOUTH PORTLAND—See KKR & Co. Inc.; *U.S. Public*, pg. 1266
USI INSURANCE SERVICES OF CONNECTICUT, LLC—See Caisse de Depot et Placement du Quebec; *Int'l*, pg. 1257
USI INSURANCE SERVICES OF CONNECTICUT, LLC—See KKR & Co. Inc.; *U.S. Public*, pg. 1266
U.S.I. INSURANCE SERVICES OF MASSACHUSETTS, INC.—See Caisse de Depot et Placement du Quebec; *Int'l*, pg. 1257
U.S.I. INSURANCE SERVICES OF MASSACHUSETTS, INC.—See KKR & Co. Inc.; *U.S. Public*, pg. 1265
USI INVESTMENT CO., LTD.—See USI Corporation; *Int'l*, pg. 8099
USI JAPAN CO., LTD.—See ASE Technology Holding Co., Ltd.; *Int'l*, pg. 604
USI MANAGEMENT CONSULTING CORP.—See USI Corporation; *Int'l*, pg. 8099
USIMINAS MECANICA SA—See Techint S.p.A.; *Int'l*, pg. 7505
USINA ESTIVAS LTDA.—See Raizen S.A.; *Int'l*, pg. 6192
USINAGE ET NOUVELLES TECHNOLOGIES S.A.S.—See Kering S.A.; *Int'l*, pg. 4136
USINAS SIDERURGICAS DE MINAS GERAIS S.A.—See Techint S.p.A.; *Int'l*, pg. 7505
US INDUSTRIAL TECHNOLOGIES, INC.—See Veolia Environnement S.A.; *Int'l*, pg. 8158
USINES CLAAS FRANCE S.A.S.—See Claas KGaA mbH; *Int'l*, pg. 1641
USINES DE ROSIERES S.A.S.—See Haier Smart Home Co., Ltd.; *Int'l*, pg. 3210
US INFORMATION TECHNOLOGIES CORPORATION; *U.S. Private*, pg. 4319
US INK CORPORATION, EASTERN REGION—See DIC Corporation; *Int'l*, pg. 2111
US INK CORPORATION, MIDWEST REGION—See DIC Corporation; *Int'l*, pg. 2111
US INK CORPORATION—See DIC Corporation; *Int'l*, pg. 2111
US INK CORPORATION, SOUTHERN REGION—See DIC Corporation; *Int'l*, pg. 2111
US INK CORPORATION, SOUTHWEST REGION—See DIC Corporation; *Int'l*, pg. 2111
US INK CORPORATION, WESTERN REGION—See DIC Corporation; *Int'l*, pg. 2111
U.S. INSPECT, INC.; *U.S. Private*, pg. 4271
U.S. INSULATION CORP.—See Installed Building Products, Inc.; *U.S. Public*, pg. 1134
U.S. INSURANCE SERVICES, INC.—See Paine Schwartz Partners, LLC; *U.S. Private*, pg. 3076
US INTERACTIVE INC; *U.S. Private*, pg. 4319
U.S. INTERNATIONAL MEDIA; *U.S. Private*, pg. 4271
US INTERNET CORPORATION; *U.S. Private*, pg. 4319
US INVESTIGATIONS SERVICES, LLC—See Corporate Risk Holdings LLC; *U.S. Private*, pg. 1056
US INVESTIGATIONS SERVICES PROFESSIONAL SERVICES DIVISION, INC.—See Corporate Risk Holdings LLC; *U.S. Private*, pg. 1056
U.S. INVESTMENT CORPORATION—See Berkshire Hathaway Inc.; *U.S. Public*, pg. 319
USIO INC.; *U.S. Public*, pg. 2267
USI OPTRONICS CORPORATION—See USI Corporation; *Int'l*, pg. 8099
USI SCIENTIFIC INDUSTRIAL (SHANGHAI) CO., LTD.—See ASE Technology Holding Co., Ltd.; *Int'l*, pg. 604
USIS COMMERCIAL SERVICES—See Corporate Risk Holdings LLC; *U.S. Private*, pg. 1056
USI SERVICES GROUP; *U.S. Private*, pg. 4323
USIS, INC.—See Brown & Brown, Inc.; *U.S. Public*, pg. 402
USIS INTELLIGENCE AND INVESTIGATIONS SERVICES—See Corporate Risk Holdings LLC; *U.S. Private*, pg. 1056
USI TECHNOLOGIES, INC.; *U.S. Private*, pg. 4323
USIT IRELAND LTD.—See Ion Equity Limited; *Int'l*, pg. 3793
USI TRADING(SHANGHAI) CO., LTD.—See USI Corporation; *Int'l*, pg. 8099
USI WIRELESS; *U.S. Private*, pg. 4323
USI@WORK, INC.—See ASE Technology Holding Co., Ltd.; *Int'l*, pg. 605
USJE CEMENTARNICA AD—See Titan Cement Company S.A.; *Int'l*, pg. 7760
USJ LLC—See Comcast Corporation; *U.S. Public*, pg. 540

CORPORATE AFFILIATIONS

US JOINER LLC - GULF COAST—See J.F. Lehman & Company, Inc.; *U.S. Private*, pg. 2164
US JOINER, LLC—See J.F. Lehman & Company, Inc.; *U.S. Private*, pg. 2164
USK-HUMAN CO., LTD.—See NIPPON CARBIDE INDUSTRIES CO., INC.; *Int'l*, pg. 5311
US KINDEN CORPORATION—See Kinden Corporation; *Int'l*, pg. 4166
USKUDAR TANKERCILIK A.S.—See Koc Holding A.S.; *Int'l*, pg. 4223
U.S. LABORATORIES; *U.S. Private*, pg. 4271
USL ASIA PACIFIC (M) SDN. BHD.—See Koh Brothers Group Limited; *Int'l*, pg. 4228
USL ASIA PACIFIC PTE LTD—See Koh Brothers Group Limited; *Int'l*, pg. 4228
U.S. LAWNS INC.—See The Riverside Company; *U.S. Private*, pg. 4110
US LBM HOLDINGS, INC.—See Bain Capital, LP; *U.S. Private*, pg. 450
U.S. LBM HOLDINGS, LLC—See Bain Capital, LP; *U.S. Private*, pg. 450
US LED, LTD.; *U.S. Private*, pg. 4319
U.S. LEGAL FORMS, INC.—See USLegal, Inc.; *U.S. Private*, pg. 4323
USLEGAL, INC.; *U.S. Private*, pg. 4323
U.S. LEGAL SUPPORT, INC.; *U.S. Private*, pg. 4271
US LETTER CARRIERS MUTUAL BENEFIT ASSOCIATION; *U.S. Private*, pg. 4319
US LIGHTING GROUP, INC.; *U.S. Public*, pg. 2266
U.S. LIGHTING TECH—See U.S. Energy Technologies, Inc.; *U.S. Private*, pg. 4270
US LIGITEK INC.—See Ligitek Electronics Co., Ltd.; *Int'l*, pg. 4497
U.S. LIME COMPANY - SHREVEPORT—See United States Lime & Minerals, Inc.; *U.S. Public*, pg. 2236
U.S. LIME COMPANY—See United States Lime & Minerals, Inc.; *U.S. Public*, pg. 2236
U.S. LIME COMPANY - ST. CLAIR—See United States Lime & Minerals, Inc.; *U.S. Public*, pg. 2236
U.S. LIME COMPANY-TRANSPORTATION—See United States Lime & Minerals, Inc.; *U.S. Public*, pg. 2236
U.S. LINER COMPANY—See Transtex LLC; *U.S. Private*, pg. 4211
US LINES—See CMA CGM S.A.; *Int'l*, pg. 1666
US LIQUIDATORS, LLC—See MarineMax, Inc.; *U.S. Public*, pg. 1367
U.S. LOGISTICS, INC.; *U.S. Private*, pg. 4271
US LOGISTICS LLC; *U.S. Private*, pg. 4319
USLP UNDERWRITING SOLUTIONS LP—See Aon plc; *Int'l*, pg. 495
USL SHIPPING DMCEST—See Oricon Enterprises Ltd.; *Int'l*, pg. 5621
U.S. LUBRICANTS—See U.S. Venture, Inc.; *U.S. Private*, pg. 4272
US LUMBER GROUP INC.—See Specialty Building Products, LLC; *U.S. Private*, pg. 3749
USLUZNE DJELATNOSTI A.D.; *Int'l*, pg. 8099
USMANIA GLASS SHEET FACTORY LIMITED; *Int'l*, pg. 8099
U.S. MANUFACTURING CORPORATION—See Wynnchurch Capital, L.P.; *U.S. Private*, pg. 4578
U.S. MARINE MANAGEMENT, INCORPORATED—See A.P. Moller-Maersk A/S; *Int'l*, pg. 28
US MARKERBOARD; *U.S. Private*, pg. 4319
US MASTERS RESIDENTIAL PROPERTY FUND; *Int'l*, pg. 8096
US MATERIALS HANDLING CORP.; *U.S. Private*, pg. 4319
USM BUSINESS SYSTEMS, INC.; *U.S. Private*, pg. 4323
USM CAPITAL, INC.—See U.S. Micro Corporation; *U.S. Private*, pg. 4271
USMD CANCER TREATMENT CENTERS, LLC—See UnitedHealth Group Incorporated; *U.S. Public*, pg. 2240
USM DE MEXICO, S. DE R.L. DE C.V.—See Wynnchurch Capital, L.P.; *U.S. Private*, pg. 4578
USMD HOLDINGS, INC.—See UnitedHealth Group Incorporated; *U.S. Public*, pg. 2240
USMD HOSPITAL AT ARLINGTON, L.P.—See UnitedHealth Group Incorporated; *U.S. Public*, pg. 2240
USMD HOSPITAL AT FT. WORTH, L.P.—See UnitedHealth Group Incorporated; *U.S. Public*, pg. 2240
USMD, INC.—See UnitedHealth Group Incorporated; *U.S. Public*, pg. 2240
U.S. MED-EQUIP, INC.—See Freeman Spogli & Co. Incorporated; *U.S. Private*, pg. 1606
U.S. MEDGROUP OF ILLINOIS, P.C.—See Select Medical Holdings Corporation; *U.S. Public*, pg. 1862
U.S. MEDGROUP OF KANSAS, P.A.—See Select Medical Holdings Corporation; *U.S. Public*, pg. 1862
U.S. MEDGROUP OF MICHIGAN, P.C.—See Select Medical Holdings Corporation; *U.S. Public*, pg. 1862
U.S. MEDGROUP, P.A.—See Select Medical Holdings Corporation; *U.S. Public*, pg. 1862
U.S. MEDGROUP, P.A.—See Select Medical Holdings Corporation; *U.S. Public*, pg. 1862
US MEDIA CONSULTING; *U.S. Private*, pg. 4319
US MEDICAL MANAGEMENT LLC—See Centene Corporation; *U.S. Public*, pg. 471

COMPANY NAME INDEX

U.S. MERCHANTS FINANCIAL GROUP, INC.; *U.S. Private*, pg. 4271
USMETALS, INC.; *U.S. Private*, pg. 4323
U.S. METALS POWDERS INC.; *U.S. Private*, pg. 4271
USMETA MANUFACTURING SDN. BHD.—See Transocean Holdings Bhd.; *Int'l*, pg. 7903
U.S. MICRO CORPORATION - DALLAS FACILITY—See Mountville Mills Inc.; *U.S. Private*, pg. 2801
U.S. MICRO CORPORATION; *U.S. Private*, pg. 4271
U.S. MICRO CORPORATION - TORONTO FACILITY—See Mountville Mills Inc.; *U.S. Private*, pg. 2801
US MICRON LLC; *U.S. Private*, pg. 4319
U.S. MICRO OPERATING COMPANY, LLC—See Arrow Electronics, Inc.; *U.S. Public*, pg. 200
US MICRO PRODUCTS, INC.; *U.S. Private*, pg. 4319
U.S. MILLS, LLC—See Susquehanna International Group, LLP; *U.S. Private*, pg. 3886
USM JSC—See Trace Group Hold PLC; *Int'l*, pg. 7886
US MOTION, INC.—See Frencken Group Limited; *Int'l*, pg. 2773
USMP—See Omnicom Group Inc.; *U.S. Public*, pg. 1599
USM-RGC, INC.—See CRH plc; *Int'l*, pg. 1845
U.S. MUNICIPAL SUPPLY, INC.; *U.S. Private*, pg. 4271
U'S MUSIC CO., LTD.—See U-NEXT HOLDINGS Co.,Ltd; *Int'l*, pg. 7997
U.S. MUSIC CORPORATION—See DCC plc; *Int'l*, pg. 1990
U.S. NATIONAL WHITEWATER CENTER, INC.; *U.S. Private*, pg. 4271
U.S. NAVAL INSTITUTE; *U.S. Private*, pg. 4271
U.S. NETTING, INC.—See Mativ Holdings, Inc.; *U.S. Public*, pg. 1397
US NEWSPAPERS; *U.S. Private*, pg. 4319
U.S. NEWS & WORLD REPORT, L.P.; *U.S. Private*, pg. 4271
US NISSHIN SHOKAI INC.—See The Nisshin OilliO Group, Ltd.; *Int'l*, pg. 7671
US NITTO; *U.S. Private*, pg. 4319
US-NOBEL PRIMARY EDUCATION DEVELOPMENT INT'L, INC.; *U.S. Private*, pg. 4320
US NONWOVENS CORP.—See Wind Point Advisors LLC; *U.S. Private*, pg. 4536
USNR—See USNR; *U.S. Private*, pg. 4323
USNR; *U.S. Private*, pg. 4323
US NUCLEAR CORP.; *U.S. Public*, pg. 2268
US NURSING CORPORATION—See Clarion Capital Partners, LLC; *U.S. Private*, pg. 911
USNY BANK; *U.S. Private*, pg. 4323
U.S. OIL - CHEBOYGAN TERMINAL—See U.S. Venture, Inc.; *U.S. Private*, pg. 4272
U.S. OILCHEK—See U.S. Venture, Inc.; *U.S. Private*, pg. 4272
US OIL SANDS INC.; *Int'l*, pg. 8096
U.S. OIL—See U.S. Venture, Inc.; *U.S. Private*, pg. 4272
U.S. OIL TRADING LLC—See Par Pacific Holdings, Inc.; *U.S. Public*, pg. 1636
USOL VIETNAM CO., LTD.—See BIPROGY Inc.; *Int'l*, pg. 1045
US ONCOLOGY, INC.—See McKesson Corporation; *U.S. Public*, pg. 1408
USON LP—See Roper Technologies, Inc.; *U.S. Public*, pg. 1814
U.S. ORTHOPAEDIC PARTNERS—See FFL Partners, LLC; *U.S. Private*, pg. 1500
US ORTHOTICS AND PROSTHETICS, INC.—See Patient Square Capital, L.P.; *U.S. Private*, pg. 3107
USOURCE LLC—See Unitil Corporation; *U.S. Public*, pg. 2253
US PACK LOGISTICS LLC—See NewSpring Capital LLC; *U.S. Private*, pg. 2918
USPA CORPORATION PTY. LTD.—See BWX Limited; *Int'l*, pg. 1233
US PAINT CORPORATION—See Kansai Paint Co., Ltd.; *Int'l*, pg. 4073
US PAPER CORPORATION—See Sappi Limited; *Int'l*, pg. 6572
U.S. PAPER MILLS CORP.—See Sonoco Products Company; *U.S. Public*, pg. 1909
U.S. PAVEMENT SERVICES INC.; *U.S. Private*, pg. 4271
USPC HOLDING, INC.—See Newell Brands Inc.; *U.S. Public*, pg. 1515
US PERISHABLES; *U.S. Private*, pg. 4319
U.S. PEROXIDE, LLC—See Danaher Corporation; *U.S. Public*, pg. 631
US PET NUTRITION, LLC—See Thai Union Group Public Company Limited; *Int'l*, pg. 7597
U.S. PETROLEUM EQUIPMENT—See U.S. Venture, Inc.; *U.S. Private*, pg. 4272
USP GROUP LIMITED; *Int'l*, pg. 8099
U.S. PHYSICAL THERAPY, INC.; *U.S. Public*, pg. 2213
USPI HOLDING COMPANY, INC.—See Tenet Healthcare Corporation; *U.S. Public*, pg. 2009
USPI HOLDINGS, INC.—See Tenet Healthcare Corporation; *U.S. Public*, pg. 2013
U.S. PIPELINE, INC.—See Dearborn Resources, Inc.; *U.S. Private*, pg. 1185
U.S. PIPE VALVE & HYDRANT, LLC—See Mueller Water Products, Inc.; *U.S. Public*, pg. 1486

US PIZZA COMPANY; *U.S. Private*, pg. 4319
USP MARYLAND, INC.—See Tenet Healthcare Corporation; *U.S. Public*, pg. 2013
US POLE LIGHTING CO.; *U.S. Private*, pg. 4319
US POLYMERS INC.; *U.S. Private*, pg. 4319
US POWER GENERATING COMPANY—See Tenaska, Inc.; *U.S. Private*, pg. 3965
USPP-TRI LAKES, LLC; *U.S. Private*, pg. 4323
US PRECAST CORP.—See Eagle Manufacturing Group; *U.S. Private*, pg. 1309
U.S. PREMIUM BEEF, LLC; *U.S. Private*, pg. 4271
US PREMIUM FINANCE, INC.—See Ameris Bancorp; *U.S. Public*, pg. 115
U.S. PRESS, LLC; *U.S. Private*, pg. 4272
US-PS ENERGYSAVE CONSTRUCTION MATERIAL INT'L, INC.; *U.S. Private*, pg. 4320
U.S. PT ALLIANCE REHABILITATION SERVICES, INCITATION SERVICES—See U.S. Physical Therapy, Inc.; *U.S. Public*, pg. 2216
U.S. PT THERAPY SERVICES, INC.—See U.S. Physical Therapy, Inc.; *U.S. Public*, pg. 2216
US PT THERAPY SERVICES INC.—See U.S. Physical Therapy, Inc.; *U.S. Public*, pg. 2216
US PT THERAPY SERVICES INC.—See U.S. Physical Therapy, Inc.; *U.S. Public*, pg. 2216
US PT THERAPY SERVICES INC.—See U.S. Physical Therapy, Inc.; *U.S. Public*, pg. 2216
US PT THERAPY SERVICES INC.—See U.S. Physical Therapy, Inc.; *U.S. Public*, pg. 2216
US PT THERAPY SERVICES INC.—See U.S. Physical Therapy, Inc.; *U.S. Public*, pg. 2216
US PT THERAPY SERVICES INC.—See U.S. Physical Therapy, Inc.; *U.S. Public*, pg. 2216
USP WERBEGESELLSCHAFT.MBH—See JCDecaux S.A.; *Int'l*, pg. 3923
US RADIOLOGY SPECIALISTS, INC.; *U.S. Private*, pg. 4319
U.S. RARE EARTHS, INC.; *U.S. Private*, pg. 4272
U.S. REGIONAL OCCUPATIONAL HEALTH II OF NJ, P.C.—See Select Medical Holdings Corporation; *U.S. Public*, pg. 1862
U.S. REGIONAL OCCUPATIONAL HEALTH II, P.C.—See Select Medical Holdings Corporation; *U.S. Public*, pg. 1862
U.S. RENAL CARE, INC.; *U.S. Private*, pg. 4272
U.S. REPEATING ARMS COMPANY—See Herstal, S.A.; *Int'l*, pg. 3365
US-REPORTS, INC.—See HGGC, LLC; *U.S. Private*, pg. 1929
US RESTAURANTS INC.; *U.S. Private*, pg. 4319
US RETAILERS LLC—See NRG Energy, Inc.; *U.S. Public*, pg. 1551
U.S. RETIREMENT PARTNERS, INC.—See Kohlberg & Company, LLC; *U.S. Private*, pg. 2339
USRG MANAGEMENT COMPANY, LLC; *U.S. Private*, pg. 4323
USR HOLDINGS, LLC—See Akumin, Inc.; *U.S. Public*, pg. 70
U.S. RISK BROKERS, INC.—See Caisse de Depot et Placement du Quebec; *Int'l*, pg. 1256
U.S. RISK BROKERS, INC.—See KKR & Co. Inc.; *U.S. Public*, pg. 1265
U.S. RISK FINANCIAL SERVICES, INC.—See Caisse de Depot et Placement du Quebec; *Int'l*, pg. 1257
U.S. RISK FINANCIAL SERVICES, INC.—See KKR & Co. Inc.; *U.S. Public*, pg. 1265
U.S. RISK INSURANCE GROUP, INC.—See Caisse de Depot et Placement du Quebec; *Int'l*, pg. 1256
U.S. RISK INSURANCE GROUP, INC.—See KKR & Co. Inc.; *U.S. Public*, pg. 1265
U.S. RISK, LLC—See Caisse de Depot et Placement du Quebec; *Int'l*, pg. 1256
U.S. RISK, LLC—See KKR & Co. Inc.; *U.S. Public*, pg. 1265
U.S. RISK MANAGEMENT, INC.—See Caisse de Depot et Placement du Quebec; *Int'l*, pg. 1257
U.S. RISK MANAGEMENT, INC.—See KKR & Co. Inc.; *U.S. Public*, pg. 1265
U.S. ROASTERIE, INC.—See Huron Capital Partners LLC; *U.S. Private*, pg. 2012
USROBOTICS CORPORATION; *U.S. Private*, pg. 4324
US SALT, LLC—See Crestwood Equity Partners LP; *U.S. Public*, pg. 594
U.S. SASSUOLO CALCIO SRL—See Mapei SpA; *Int'l*, pg. 4683
U.S. SATELLITE CORPORATION—See United Natural Foods, Inc.; *U.S. Public*, pg. 2232
USS CO., LTD.; *Int'l*, pg. 8099
US SCRIPT, INC.—See Centene Corporation; *U.S. Public*, pg. 421
US SEARCH.COM INC.—See Intelius, Inc.; *U.S. Private*, pg. 2105
U.S. SECURITY ASSOCIATES, INC.—See Allied Universal Manager LLC; *U.S. Private*, pg. 191
U.S. SECURITY ASSOCIATES, INC.—See Allied Universal Manager LLC; *U.S. Private*, pg. 191
US SECURITY INC.; *U.S. Private*, pg. 4320
U.S. SECURITY INSURANCE CO.—See Kingsway Financial Services Inc.; *U.S. Public*, pg. 1235

US SUPPLY COMPANY INC.

US SEEDS LLC—See Bayer Aktiengesellschaft; *Int'l*, pg. 903
U.S. SENSOR CORP.—See Littelfuse, Inc.; *U.S. Public*, pg. 1327
US SENSOR SYSTEMS INC.—See Acorn Energy, Inc.; *U.S. Public*, pg. 36
US SERVICE GROUP, LLC; *U.S. Private*, pg. 4320
U & S SERVICES, INC.; *U.S. Private*, pg. 4269
USS GALVANIZING, INC.—See United States Steel Corporation; *U.S. Public*, pg. 2237
U.S. SHIPPING CORP.—See AIP, LLC; *U.S. Private*, pg. 137
USS HOLDINGS, INC.—See Apollo Global Management, Inc.; *U.S. Public*, pg. 165
U.S. SHORING & EQUIPMENT CO.—See Road Machinery & Supplies Company; *U.S. Private*, pg. 3453
US SIGNAL COMPANY, LLC—See Mitsubishi UFJ Financial Group, Inc.; *Int'l*, pg. 4971
US SIGNS, INC.—See FM Facility Maintenance, LLC; *U.S. Private*, pg. 1553
U.S. SILICA COMPANY—See Apollo Global Management, Inc.; *U.S. Public*, pg. 165
U.S. SILICA HOLDINGS, INC.—See Apollo Global Management, Inc.; *U.S. Public*, pg. 164
U.S. SILVER IDAHO, INC.—See Americas Gold and Silver Corporation; *Int'l*, pg. 423
US SIRNAOMICS INC.—See Sirnaomics Ltd.; *Int'l*, pg. 6962
USS LOGISTICS INTERNATIONAL SERVICE CO., LTD.—See USS Co., Ltd.; *Int'l*, pg. 8099
USS MIDWAY MUSEUM; *U.S. Private*, pg. 4324
U.S. SMOKELESS TOBACCO COMPANY, LLC—See Altria Group, Inc.; *U.S. Public*, pg. 89
U.S. SMOKELESS TOBACCO MANUFACTURING COMPANY LLC—See Altria Group, Inc.; *U.S. Public*, pg. 89
USS OILWELL TUBULAR, INC.—See United States Steel Corporation; *U.S. Public*, pg. 2237
U.S. SOYBEAN EXPORT COUNCI; *U.S. Private*, pg. 4272
U.S. SPACE & ROCKET CENTER; *U.S. Private*, pg. 4272
US SPECIAL DELIVERY INC.; *U.S. Private*, pg. 4320
U.S. SPECIALTY INSURANCE COMPANY—See Tokio Marine Holdings, Inc.; *Int'l*, pg. 7784
USS PORTFOLIO DELAWARE, INC.—See United States Steel Corporation; *U.S. Public*, pg. 2237
USS-POSCO INDUSTRIES—See POSCO Holdings Inc.; *Int'l*, pg. 5936
USS-POSCO INDUSTRIES—See United States Steel Corporation; *U.S. Public*, pg. 2237
USS REAL ESTATE—See United States Steel Corporation; *U.S. Public*, pg. 2237
U. S. STEEL EUROPE - BOHEMIA A.S.—See United States Steel Corporation; *U.S. Public*, pg. 2237
U. S. STEEL EUROPE - FRANCE S.A.—See United States Steel Corporation; *U.S. Public*, pg. 2236
U. S. STEEL EUROPE - GERMANY GMBH—See United States Steel Corporation; *U.S. Public*, pg. 2236
U. S. STEEL EUROPE - ITALY S.R.L.—See United States Steel Corporation; *U.S. Public*, pg. 2237
U. S. STEEL EUROPE (UK) LIMITED—See United States Steel Corporation; *U.S. Public*, pg. 2236
U. S. STEEL KOSICE - LABORTEST, S.R.O.—See United States Steel Corporation; *U.S. Public*, pg. 2236
U.S. STEEL KOSICE - SBS, S.R.O.—See United States Steel Corporation; *U.S. Public*, pg. 2237
U.S. STEEL KOSICE, S.R.O.—See United States Steel Corporation; *U.S. Public*, pg. 2237
US STEEL MINNTAC—See United States Steel Corporation; *U.S. Public*, pg. 2237
U. S. STEEL OILWELL SERVICES, LLC—See United States Steel Corporation; *U.S. Public*, pg. 2237
U. S. STEEL RECEIVABLES LLC—See United States Steel Corporation; *U.S. Public*, pg. 2237
U. S. STEEL SERVICES S.R.O.—See United States Steel Corporation; *U.S. Public*, pg. 2237
U. S. STEEL TUBULAR PRODUCTS, INC.—See United States Steel Corporation; *U.S. Public*, pg. 2237
US STEM CELL CLINIC, LLC—See U.S. Stem Cell, Inc.; *U.S. Public*, pg. 2217
U.S. STEM CELL CLINIC OF THE VILLAGES LLC—See U.S. Stem Cell, Inc.; *U.S. Public*, pg. 2217
U.S. STEM CELL, INC.; *U.S. Public*, pg. 2216
US STORAGE SEARCH, INC.—See B2 Interactive; *U.S. Private*, pg. 421
US STUDENT HOUSING REIT; *Int'l*, pg. 8096
US SUITES OF SAN DIEGO INC.—See The Armco Group Inc.; *U.S. Private*, pg. 3988
US SUITES OF SEATTLE INC.—See The Armco Group Inc.; *U.S. Private*, pg. 3988
US SUPPLY COMPANY INC.; *U.S. Private*, pg. 4320
US SYNTHETIC CORPORATION—See Dover Corporation; *U.S. Public*, pg. 679
US TAG & TICKET—See Champion Industries, Inc.; *U.S. Public*, pg. 478
UST-ALDETEC GROUP—See Greenbriar Equity Group, L.P.; *U.S. Private*, pg. 1775
USTAR TECHNOLOGIES LIMITED—See UTStarcom Holdings Corp.; *Int'l*, pg. 8101
USTAV APLIKOVANE MECHANIKY BRNO, S.R.O.—See CEZ, a.s.; *Int'l*, pg. 1429

USTAV JADERNEHO VYZKUMU REZ, A.S.—See CEZ, a.s.; *Int'l*, pg. 1429
UST CORPORATION—See Heartwood Partners, LLC; *U.S. Private*, pg. 1901
U.S. TECHNOLOGIES INC.—See Greenbriar Equity Group, L.P.; *U.S. Private*, pg. 1776
US TECH SERVICES INC.; *U.S. Private*, pg. 4320
US TECH SOLUTIONS INC.; *U.S. Private*, pg. 4320
U.S. TELEPACIFIC CORP.—See Siris Capital Group, LLC; *U.S. Private*, pg. 3674
USTER TECHNOLOGIES AG—See Toyota Industries Corporation; *Int'l*, pg. 7868
USTER TECHNOLOGIES, INC. - CHARLOTTE—See Toyota Industries Corporation; *Int'l*, pg. 7868
USTER TECHNOLOGIES, INC.—See Toyota Industries Corporation; *Int'l*, pg. 7868
USTER TECHNOLOGIES LTD.—See Toyota Industries Corporation; *Int'l*, pg. 7868
USTER TECHNOLOGIES LTD.—See Toyota Industries Corporation; *Int'l*, pg. 7868
USTER TECHNOLOGIES VISION SYSTEMS INC.—See Toyota Industries Corporation; *Int'l*, pg. 7868
US TEXTILE CORP.—See Sculptz, Inc.; *U.S. Private*, pg. 3581
U.S. TEXTILES LLC; *U.S. Private*, pg. 4272
UST GLOBAL INC.; *U.S. Private*, pg. 4324
U.S. THERAPY, INC.—See Advent International Corporation; *U.S. Private*, pg. 96
US TITLE AGENCY, INC.—See Erie Title Agency, Inc.; *U.S. Private*, pg. 1420
U.S. TITLE GUARANTY COMPANY—See Anywhere Real Estate Inc.; *U.S. Public*, pg. 142
UST-KAMENOGORSK POULTRY PLANT JSC; *Int'l*, pg. 8099
UST-KAMENOGORSK TITANIUM MAGNESIUM PLANT JSC; *Int'l*, pg. 8099
UST MAMIYA; *U.S. Private*, pg. 4324
US TOOL GRINDING INC.; *U.S. Private*, pg. 4324
U-STORE-IT MINI WAREHOUSE CO.—See CubeSmart; *U.S. Public*, pg. 604
U.S. TOY CO., INC.—See Windy City Novelties, Inc.; *U.S. Private*, pg. 4540
US-TQ BEVERAGE PRODUCTS INT'L, INC.; *U.S. Private*, pg. 4320
U.S. TRANSLATION COMPANY; *U.S. Private*, pg. 4272
US TRANSPORT; *U.S. Private*, pg. 4320
USTREAM, INC.—See International Business Machines Corporation; *U.S. Public*, pg. 1151
U.S. TRUST, BANK OF AMERICA PRIVATE WEALTH MANAGEMENT—See Bank of America Corporation; *U.S. Public*, pg. 271
U.S. TRUST COMPANY, N.A.—See Bank of America Corporation; *U.S. Public*, pg. 271
U.S. TRUST COMPANY—See Bank of America Corporation; *U.S. Public*, pg. 271
U.S. TRUST COMPANY—See Bank of America Corporation; *U.S. Public*, pg. 271
U.S. TRUST COMPANY—See Bank of America Corporation; *U.S. Public*, pg. 271
U.S. TRUST COMPANY—See Bank of America Corporation; *U.S. Public*, pg. 271
U.S. TRUST COMPANY—See Bank of America Corporation; *U.S. Public*, pg. 271
U.S. TRUST COMPANY—See Bank of America Corporation; *U.S. Public*, pg. 271
U.S. TRUST COMPANY—See Bank of America Corporation; *U.S. Public*, pg. 271
U.S. TRUST COMPANY—See Bank of America Corporation; *U.S. Public*, pg. 271
U.S. TRUST COMPANY—See Bank of America Corporation; *U.S. Public*, pg. 271
U.S. TRUST COMPANY—See Bank of America Corporation; *U.S. Public*, pg. 271
U.S. TRUST COMPANY—See Bank of America Corporation; *U.S. Public*, pg. 271
U.S. TRUST COMPANY—See Bank of America Corporation; *U.S. Public*, pg. 271
U.S. TRUST COMPANY—See Bank of America Corporation; *U.S. Public*, pg. 271
U.S. TRUST COMPANY—See Bank of America Corporation; *U.S. Public*, pg. 271
U.S. TRUST COMPANY—See Bank of America Corporation; *U.S. Public*, pg. 271
U.S. TRUST COMPANY—See Bank of America Corporation; *U.S. Public*, pg. 271
U.S. TRUST COMPANY—See Bank of America Corporation; *U.S. Public*, pg. 271
U.S. TRUST COMPANY—See Bank of America Corporation; *U.S. Public*, pg. 271
U.S. TRUST COMPANY—See Bank of America Corporation; *U.S. Public*, pg. 271
U.S. TSUBAKI AUTOMOTIVE, LLC—See Tsubakimoto Chain Co.; *Int'l*, pg. 7954
U.S. TSUBAKI - DETROIT ENGINEERING OFFICE—See Tsubakimoto Chain Co.; *Int'l*, pg. 7954

U.S. TSUBAKI - ENGINEERING CHAIN DIVISION SANDUSKY PLANT—See Tsubakimoto Chain Co.; *Int'l*, pg. 7955
U.S. TSUBAKI HOLDINGS, INC.—See Tsubakimoto Chain Co.; *Int'l*, pg. 7954
U.S. TSUBAKI POWER TRANSMISSION, LLC - KABELSCHLEPP DIVISION—See Tsubakimoto Chain Co.; *Int'l*, pg. 7955
U.S. TSUBAKI POWER TRANSMISSION, LLC—See Tsubakimoto Chain Co.; *Int'l*, pg. 7954
U.S. TSUBAKI - ROLLER CHAIN DIVISION HOLYOKE PLANT—See Tsubakimoto Chain Co.; *Int'l*, pg. 7955
UST TECHNOLOGY PTE. LTD.; *Int'l*, pg. 8099
USU GMBH—See USU Software AG; *Int'l*, pg. 8099
USUM INVESTMENT GROUP CO., LTD.; *Int'l*, pg. 8099
U.S. UNDERWATER SERVICES, LLC—See Benford Capital Partners, LLC; *U.S. Private*, pg. 526
U.S. UNDERWATER SERVICES, LLC—See Coppermine Capital, LLC; *U.S. Private*, pg. 1045
U.S. UNDERWRITERS INSURANCE COMPANY—See Berkshire Hathaway Inc.; *U.S. Public*, pg. 319
USUN (FOSHAN) TECHNOLOGY CO., LTD.—See Usun Technology Co., Ltd.; *Int'l*, pg. 8099
US UNION TOOL INC.—See Union Tool Co.; *Int'l*, pg. 8054
USUN TECHNOLOGY CO., LTD.; *Int'l*, pg. 8099
U-SURE INSURANCE SERVICES LIMITED—See Brown & Brown, Inc.; *U.S. Public*, pg. 402
USU SAS—See USU Software AG; *Int'l*, pg. 8099
USU SOFTWARE AG; *Int'l*, pg. 8099
USU SOFTWARE S.R.O.—See USU Software AG; *Int'l*, pg. 8099
USU TECHNOLOGIES INC.—See USU Software AG; *Int'l*, pg. 8099
US VANADIUM LLC; *Int'l*, pg. 4320
U.S. VENTURE, INC. - EXPRESS CONVENIENCE CENTERS DIVISION—See U.S. Venture, Inc.; *U.S. Private*, pg. 4272
U.S. VENTURE, INC.; *U.S. Private*, pg. 4272
US VINYL MANUFACTURING CORP.; *U.S. Private*, pg. 4320
U.S. VISION, INC.—See ACON Investments, LLC; *U.S. Private*, pg. 63
USV PVT LTD.; *Int'l*, pg. 8099
US VR GLOBAL.COM, INC.; *Int'l*, pg. 8096
US VR GLOBAL.COM INC.; *U.S. Private*, pg. 4320
US WEB INCORPORATED; *U.S. Private*, pg. 4320
US WEEKLY MAGAZINE—See Chatham Asset Management, LLC; *U.S. Private*, pg. 860
U.S. WELL SERVICES, INC.—See ProFrac Holding Corp.; *U.S. Public*, pg. 1724
U.S. WHOLESALE PIPE AND TUBE, INC.; *U.S. Private*, pg. 4272
U.S. WIND FARMING, INC.; *U.S. Public*, pg. 2217
USWIRED INCORPORATED—See Trivest Partners, LP; *U.S. Private*, pg. 4241
U-SWIRL, INC.—See Rocky Mountain Chocolate Factory, Inc.; *U.S. Public*, pg. 1807
U-SWIRL INTERNATIONAL, INC.—See Rocky Mountain Chocolate Factory, Inc.; *U.S. Public*, pg. 1807
US WORLDMEDS, LLC; *U.S. Private*, pg. 4320
U.S. WORLDWIDE LOGISTICS, INC.—See LDI Ltd., LLC; *U.S. Private*, pg. 2404
U.S. XPRESS ENTERPRISES, INC.—See Knight-Swift Transportation Holdings Inc.; *U.S. Public*, pg. 1269
U.S. XPRESS, INC.—See Knight-Swift Transportation Holdings Inc.; *U.S. Public*, pg. 1269
US YACHIYO, INC.—See Honda Motor Co., Ltd.; *Int'l*, pg. 3464
US YOUTH SOCCER; *U.S. Private*, pg. 4320
U-SYSTEMS, INC.—See GE HealthCare Technologies Inc.; *U.S. Public*, pg. 909
U.S. ZINC CORPORATION—See Aterian Investment Management, L.P.; *U.S. Private*, pg. 367
UTA ACQUISITION CORPORATION; *U.S. Public*, pg. 2267
UTA BULGARIA OOD—See Edenred S.A.; *Int'l*, pg. 2308
UTAC DONGGUAN LIMITED—See UTAC Holdings Ltd.; *Int'l*, pg. 8100
UTAC HOLDINGS LTD.; *Int'l*, pg. 8100
UTAC JAPAN CO., LTD.—See UTAC Holdings Ltd.; *Int'l*, pg. 8100
UTAC MANUFACTURING SERVICES MALAYSIA SDN BHD—See UTAC Holdings Ltd.; *Int'l*, pg. 8100
UTAC (SHANGHAI) COMPANY, LTD—See UTAC Holdings Ltd.; *Int'l*, pg. 8100
UTAC TAIWAN CORPORATION—See UTAC Holdings Ltd.; *Int'l*, pg. 8100
UTAC THAI LTD—See UTAC Holdings Ltd.; *Int'l*, pg. 8100
UTA CZECH S.R.O.—See Edenred S.A.; *Int'l*, pg. 2308
UTA FINANZ UND LEASING—See ING Groep N.V.; *Int'l*, pg. 3701
UTA FRANCE S.A.R.L.—See Edenred S.A.; *Int'l*, pg. 2308
UTAH ASSOCIATED MUNICIPLE POWER SYSTEMS; *U.S. Private*, pg. 4324
UTAH AUTO AUCTION—See Cox Enterprises, Inc.; *U.S. Private*, pg. 1077
UTAH BROADBAND, LLC—See Boston Omaha Corporation; *U.S. Public*, pg. 372

UTAH DISASTER KLEENUP; *U.S. Private*, pg. 4324
UTAH FARM BUREAU FINANCIAL SERVICES (INC.)—See Iowa Farm Bureau Federation; *U.S. Private*, pg. 2134
UTAH HOUSING CORPORATION; *U.S. Private*, pg. 4324
UTAH LOGOS, INC.—See Lamar Advertising Company; *U.S. Public*, pg. 1291
UTAH MEDIA, INC.—See Alden Global Capital LLC; *U.S. Private*, pg. 159
UTAH MEDICAL PRODUCTS, INC.; *U.S. Public*, pg. 2267
UTAH MEDICAL PRODUCTS LTD.—See Utah Medical Products, Inc.; *U.S. Public*, pg. 2267
UTAH MUNICIPAL POWER AGENCY INC.; *U.S. Private*, pg. 4324
UTAH OFFICE OF TOURISM; *U.S. Private*, pg. 4324
UTAH PAPER BOX COMPANY INC.; *U.S. Private*, pg. 4324
UTAH PROPERTY MANAGEMENT ASSOCIATES, LLC—See Deseret Management Corporation; *U.S. Private*, pg. 1212
UTAH SCIENTIFIC, INC.; *U.S. Private*, pg. 4324
UTAH STATE UNIVERSITY, SPACE DYNAMICS LABORATORY; *U.S. Private*, pg. 4324
UTAH SURGICAL CENTER—See HCA Healthcare, Inc.; *U.S. Public*, pg. 1013
UTAH SYMPHONY & OPERA; *U.S. Private*, pg. 4324
UTAH TRANSIT AUTHORITY; *U.S. Private*, pg. 4324
UTAH ZOOLOGICAL SOCIETY; *U.S. Private*, pg. 4324
UT AIM CO., LTD.—See UT Group Co., Ltd.; *Int'l*, pg. 8100
UTAMA ASSOCIATES SDN. BHD.—See Southern Capital Group Pte. Ltd.; *Int'l*, pg. 7118
UTA ROMANIA SERVICES SRL—See Edenred S.A.; *Int'l*, pg. 2308
UTAX GMBH—See KYOCERA Corporation; *Int'l*, pg. 4358
UT BANK LIMITED; *Int'l*, pg. 8100
UTC ACCORD LOGISTICS AUSTRALIA PTY. LTD.—See UTC Overseas, Inc.; *U.S. Private*, pg. 4325
UTC AEROSPACE SYSTEMS - ACTUATION SYSTEMS, BUC—See RTX Corporation; *U.S. Public*, pg. 1821
UTC AEROSPACE SYSTEMS - AEROSTRUCTURES, COLOMIERS—See RTX Corporation; *U.S. Public*, pg. 1821
UTC AEROSPACE SYSTEMS - AEROSTRUCTURES, HAMBURG—See RTX Corporation; *U.S. Public*, pg. 1821
UTC AEROSPACE SYSTEMS - AEROSTRUCTURES, TIANJIN—See RTX Corporation; *U.S. Public*, pg. 1821
UTC AEROSPACE SYSTEMS - ENGINE CONTROL SERVICES—See RTX Corporation; *U.S. Public*, pg. 1823
UTC AEROSPACE SYSTEMS - LANDING GEAR, BURLINGTON—See RTX Corporation; *U.S. Public*, pg. 1821
UTC AEROSPACE SYSTEMS - LANDING GEAR, OAKVILLE—See RTX Corporation; *U.S. Public*, pg. 1821
UTC BENELUX, N.V.—See Industria de Diseno Textil, S.A.; *Int'l*, pg. 3668
UTC CANADA CORPORATION—See RTX Corporation; *U.S. Public*, pg. 1825
UTC ENGINEERING SDN. BHD.—See Dancomech Holdings Berhad; *Int'l*, pg. 1959
UTC FIRE & SECURITY CANADA—See Carrier Global Corporation; *U.S. Public*, pg. 441
UTC FIRE & SECURITY CORPORATION—See Carrier Global Corporation; *U.S. Public*, pg. 440
UTC INTERNATIONAL LOGISTICS LIMITED—See UTC Overseas, Inc.; *U.S. Private*, pg. 4325
UTCL INVESTMENTS B.V.—See RTX Corporation; *U.S. Public*, pg. 1825
UT CONNECT CO., LTD.—See UT Group Co., Ltd.; *Int'l*, pg. 8100
UT CONSTRUCTION CO., LTD.—See UT Group Co., Ltd.; *Int'l*, pg. 8100
UTC OVERSEAS, AB—See UTC Overseas, Inc.; *U.S. Private*, pg. 4325
UTC OVERSEAS BOLIVIA SRL.—See UTC Overseas, Inc.; *U.S. Private*, pg. 4325
UTC OVERSEAS BRASIL LTDA.—See UTC Overseas, Inc.; *U.S. Private*, pg. 4325
UTC OVERSEAS COLOMBIA SAS—See UTC Overseas, Inc.; *U.S. Private*, pg. 4325
UTC OVERSEAS ECUADOR S.A.—See UTC Overseas, Inc.; *U.S. Private*, pg. 4325
UTC OVERSEAS GMBH—See UTC Overseas, Inc.; *U.S. Private*, pg. 4325
UTC OVERSEAS (HK) LIMITED—See UTC Overseas, Inc.; *U.S. Private*, pg. 4325
UTC OVERSEAS, INC.; *U.S. Private*, pg. 4325
UTC OVERSEAS INC.—See UTC Overseas, Inc.; *U.S. Private*, pg. 4325
UTC OVERSEAS (INDIA) PVT. LTD.—See UTC Overseas, Inc.; *U.S. Private*, pg. 4325
UTC OVERSEAS IRELAND LTD—See UTC Overseas, Inc.; *U.S. Private*, pg. 4325
UTC OVERSEAS LOGISTICS LTD—See UTC Overseas, Inc.; *U.S. Private*, pg. 4325
UTC OVERSEAS LTD.—See UTC Overseas, Inc.; *U.S. Private*, pg. 4325

UTC OVERSEAS OY—See UTC Overseas, Inc.; *U.S. Private*, pg. 4325
UTC OVERSEAS (PERU) S.A.C.—See UTC Overseas, Inc.; *U.S. Private*, pg. 4325
UTC OVERSEAS S.A.—See UTC Overseas, Inc.; *U.S. Private*, pg. 4325
UTC OVERSEAS S DE RL DE CV—See UTC Overseas, Inc.; *U.S. Private*, pg. 4325
UTC OVERSEAS (TAIWAN) CO., LTD.—See UTC Overseas, Inc.; *U.S. Private*, pg. 4325
UTC UK LTD—See UTC Overseas, Inc.; *U.S. Private*, pg. 4325
UTC (US) LLC—See RTX Corporation; *U.S. Public*, pg. 1825
UTEBUTIKEN I UMEA AB—See Fenix Outdoor International AG; *Int'l*, pg. 2634
UTEC CONSTRUCTORS CORP.; *U.S. Private*, pg. 4325
UTECH ELECTRONICS; *Int'l*, pg. 8100
U-TECH ENGINEERING COMPANY LIMITED—See Henderson Land Development Co. Ltd.; *Int'l*, pg. 3344
U-TECH MEDIA CORPORATION; *Int'l*, pg. 7997
U-TECH MEDIA KOREA CO., LTD.—See U-TECH Media Corporation; *Int'l*, pg. 7998
UTECHZONE CO., LTD.; *Int'l*, pg. 8100
UTEC INC.—See Carrier Global Corporation; *U.S. Public*, pg. 444
UTE ENERGY LLC—See Quantum Energy Partners, LLC; *U.S. Private*, pg. 3323
UTEGRATION, LLC—See Cognizant Technology Solutions Corporation; *U.S. Public*, pg. 525
UTEK EUROPE LTD—See INNOVARO, INC.; *U.S. Private*, pg. 2081
UTELITE CORP.—See Holcim Ltd.; *Int'l*, pg. 3449
THE UTE MOUNTAINEER, LTD.; *U.S. Private*, pg. 4129
UTE NORTE FLUMINENSE S.A.—See Electricite de France S.A.; *Int'l*, pg. 2352
UTENOS TRIKOTAZAS AB—See UAB koncernas SBA; *Int'l*, pg. 7999
UTERON PHARMA SPRL—See AbbVie Inc.; *U.S. Public*, pg. 23
UTERQUE CIS, LTD—See Industria de Diseno Textil, S.A.; *Int'l*, pg. 3668
UTERQUE DISENO, S.L.—See Industria de Diseno Textil, S.A.; *Int'l*, pg. 3668
UTERQUE ESPANA, S.A.—See Industria de Diseno Textil, S.A.; *Int'l*, pg. 3668
UTERQUE GIYIM LIMITED—See Industria de Diseno Textil, S.A.; *Int'l*, pg. 3668
UTERQUE LOGISTICA, S.A.—See Industria de Diseno Textil, S.A.; *Int'l*, pg. 3668
UTERQUE S.A.—See Industria de Diseno Textil, S.A.; *Int'l*, pg. 3668
UTEST INC.; *U.S. Private*, pg. 4325
UTEXAM LOGISTICS LTD.—See BNP Paribas SA; *Int'l*, pg. 1093
UTEXBEL N.V.; *Int'l*, pg. 8100
UTEX HOLDING PLC; *Int'l*, pg. 8100
UTEX INDUSTRIES INC.—See Riverstone Holdings LLC; *U.S. Private*, pg. 3448
UTG, INC.; *U.S. Public*, pg. 2267
UTGR, INC.—See Bally's Corporation; *U.S. Public*, pg. 268
UT GROUP CO., LTD.; *Int'l*, pg. 8100
UTHE JAPAN CO., LTD.—See Crest Group Inc.; *U.S. Private*, pg. 1096
UTHE SINGAPORE PTE LTD—See Crest Group Inc.; *U.S. Private*, pg. 1096
UTHE TECHNOLOGY, INC.—See Crest Group Inc.; *U.S. Private*, pg. 1096
UTI ASSET MANAGEMENT CO. LTD.; *Int'l*, pg. 8100
UTICA ASC PARTNERS, LLC—See Tenet Healthcare Corporation; *U.S. Public*, pg. 2014
UTICA BOILERS—See TerraVest Industries, Inc.; *Int'l*, pg. 7568
UTICA CORPORATION—See UCA Holdings Inc.; *U.S. Private*, pg. 4273
UTICA EAST OHIO MIDSTREAM LLC—See The Williams Companies, Inc.; *U.S. Public*, pg. 2143
UTICA ENERGY, LLC.; *U.S. Private*, pg. 4325
UTICA ENTERPRISES, INC.; *U.S. Private*, pg. 4325
UTICA GENERAL TRUCK CO. INC.; *U.S. Private*, pg. 4325
UTICA LLOYDS OF TEXAS—See Utica National Insurance Group; *U.S. Private*, pg. 4325
UTICA MUTUAL INSURANCE COMPANY—See Utica National Insurance Group; *U.S. Private*, pg. 4325
UTICA NATIONAL INSURANCE CO. OF TEXAS—See Utica National Insurance Group; *U.S. Private*, pg. 4325
UTICA NATIONAL INSURANCE GROUP; *U.S. Private*, pg. 4325
UTICA PRODUCTS, INC.—See Utica Enterprises, Inc.; *U.S. Private*, pg. 4325
UTICA SERVICES INC.—See St. John Health System Inc.; *U.S. Private*, pg. 3771
UTICA SQUARE SHOPPING CENTER, INC.—See Helmerich & Payne, Inc.; *U.S. Public*, pg. 1024
THE UTICA SYMPHONY ORCHESTRA; *U.S. Private*, pg. 4130
UTICA WASHERS—See MNP Corporation; *U.S. Private*, pg. 2756

UTI EGYPT/JORDAN LTD.—See DSV A/S; *Int'l*, pg. 2216
UTI GROUP LTD.; *Int'l*, pg. 8100
UTI INSTAL CONSTRUCT INC—See UTI Group Ltd.; *Int'l*, pg. 8100
UTI INVENTORY MANAGEMENT SOLUTIONS INC.—See DSV A/S; *Int'l*, pg. 2216
UTILAJ GREU S.A.—See Transilvania Investments Alliance S.A.; *Int'l*, pg. 7900
UTILANT LLC—See Thoma Bravo, L.P.; *U.S. Private*, pg. 4149
UTILICO EMERGING MARKETS LIMITED—See ICM Limited; *Int'l*, pg. 3582
UTILICO EMERGING MARKETS TRUST PLC—See ICM Limited; *Int'l*, pg. 3582
UTILI-COMM SOUTH, INC.; *U.S. Private*, pg. 4326
UTILICON SOLUTIONS, LTD.—See Asplundh Tree Expert Co.; *U.S. Private*, pg. 353
UTILICRAFT AEROSPACE INDUSTRIES, INC.; *U.S. Public*, pg. 2267
UTILIMASTER HOLDINGS, INC.—See The Shyft Group, Inc.; *U.S. Public*, pg. 2130
UTILIPATH, LLC—See NewSpring Capital LLC; *U.S. Private*, pg. 2918
UTILIQUEST, LLC—See Dycom Industries, Inc.; *U.S. Public*, pg. 699
UTILITIES BOARD OF THE CITY OF FOLEY ALABAMA; *U.S. Private*, pg. 4326
UTILITIES BOARD OF TRUSSVILLE; *U.S. Private*, pg. 4326
UTILITIES DISTRICT OF WESTERN INDIANA REMC; *U.S. Private*, pg. 4326
UTILITIES, INC.; *U.S. Private*, pg. 4326
UTILITIES & INDUSTRIES—See BSI Diversified LLC; *U.S. Private*, pg. 675
UTILITIES PLUS ENERGY SERVICES—See New Mountain Capital, LLC; *U.S. Private*, pg. 2903
UTILITIES SUPPLY COMPANY—See F.W. Webb Company; *U.S. Private*, pg. 1457
UTILITY BUSINESS ALLIANCE COMPANY LIMITED - DINDAENG WASTEWATER TREATMENT PLANT—See Nawarat Patanakarn Public Company Limited; *Int'l*, pg. 5177
UTILITY BUSINESS ALLIANCE COMPANY LIMITED - NONG KHAEM WASTEWATER TREATMENT PLANT—See Nawarat Patanakarn Public Company Limited; *Int'l*, pg. 5177
UTILITY BUSINESS ALLIANCE COMPANY LIMITED—See Nawarat Patanakarn Public Company Limited; *Int'l*, pg. 5177
UTILITY BUSINESS ALLIANCE COMPANY LIMITED - THUNGKHRU WASTEWATER TREATMENT PLANT—See Nawarat Patanakarn Public Company Limited; *Int'l*, pg. 5177
UTILITY COATINGS & FABRICATION, LLC—See Victaulic Company; *U.S. Private*, pg. 4377
UTILITY CONCIERGE, LLC; *U.S. Private*, pg. 4326
UTILITY CONTRACTORS INC.; *U.S. Private*, pg. 4326
UTILITY CORP.—See The Bank of Nova Scotia; *Int'l*, pg. 7617
UTILITY DYNAMICS CORPORATION; *U.S. Private*, pg. 4326
UTILITY EQUIPMENT COMPANY; *U.S. Private*, pg. 4326
UTILITY FINANCIAL CORP.—See Southwest Gas Holdings, Inc.; *U.S. Public*, pg. 1913
UTILITY FLEET SALES, LTD.—See Utility One Source L.P.; *U.S. Private*, pg. 4326
UTILITY GARMENTS INC.—See Unisync Corp.; *Int'l*, pg. 8062
UTILITY HOLDINGS INC.; *U.S. Private*, pg. 4326
UTILITY/KEYSTONE TRAILER SALES; *U.S. Private*, pg. 4327
UTILITY LINE MANAGEMENT SERVICES, INC.—See Quanta Services, Inc.; *U.S. Public*, pg. 1753
UTILITY LINES CONSTRUCTION SERVICES, INC.—See Asplundh Tree Expert Co.; *U.S. Private*, pg. 353
UTILITY LINE SERVICES INC.; *U.S. Private*, pg. 4326
UTILITY MANAGEMENT & CONSTRUCTION, LLC—See Renavotio, Inc.; *U.S. Public*, pg. 1783
UTILITY ONE SOURCE L.P.; *U.S. Private*, pg. 4326
UTILITY PARTNERSHIP LIMITED—See Smart Metering Systems plc; *Int'l*, pg. 7000
UTILITY PROPERTIES INC.—See Utility Holdings Inc.; *U.S. Private*, pg. 4326
UTILITY PROTECTION SERVICES-EAST—See Heath Consultants Incorporated; *U.S. Private*, pg. 1902
UTILITY SALES ASSOCIATES, INC.—See Osceola Capital Management, LLC; *U.S. Private*, pg. 3047
UTILITY SALES & SERVICE, INC.; *U.S. Private*, pg. 4326
UTILITY SERVICE AFFILIATES, INC.—See Middlesex Water Company; *U.S. Public*, pg. 1445
UTILITY SERVICE AFFILIATES (PERTH AMBOY) INC.—See Middlesex Water Company; *U.S. Public*, pg. 1445
UTILITY SERVICES GROUP LIMITED—See Downer EDI Limited; *Int'l*, pg. 2185
UTILITY SERVICE & SUPPLY INC.; *U.S. Private*, pg. 4326
UTILITY SOFTWARE SERVICES PTY. LTD.—See AD1 Holdings Limited; *Int'l*, pg. 123

UTILITY SUPPORT GROUP (USG) BV—See Koninklijke DSM N.V.; *Int'l*, pg. 4266
UTILITY SUPPORT SYSTEMS INC.—See TRC Companies, Inc.; *U.S. Private*, pg. 4215
UTILITY TRAILER MANUFACTURING COMPANY, LLC; *U.S. Private*, pg. 4326
UTILITY TRAILER SALES COMPANY ARIZONA; *U.S. Private*, pg. 4326
UTILITY TRAILER SALES OF BOISE; *U.S. Private*, pg. 4327
UTILITY TRAILER SALES OF CENTRAL CALIFORNIA; *U.S. Private*, pg. 4327
UTILITY TRAILER SALES OF COLORADO LLC; *U.S. Private*, pg. 4327
UTILITY TRAILER SALES OF NEW JERSEY, INC.—See Atlantic Utility Trailer Sales, Inc.; *U.S. Private*, pg. 375
UTILITY TRAILER SALES SOUTHEAST TEXAS INC.—See Utility Trailer Manufacturing Company, LLC; *U.S. Private*, pg. 4326
UTILITY TRI-STATE INC.; *U.S. Private*, pg. 4327
UTILITY VAULT CO., INC.—See CRH plc; *Int'l*, pg. 1846
UTILIWORKS CONSULTING, LLC—See Align Capital Partners, LLC; *U.S. Private*, pg. 167
UTILLIGENT LLC—See Align Capital Partners, LLC; *U.S. Private*, pg. 167
UTIMACO GMBH—See EQT AB; *Int'l*, pg. 2481
UTI & MAINTENANCE SERVICES S.A.—See UTI Group Ltd.; *Int'l*, pg. 8100
UTIME LIMITED; *Int'l*, pg. 8100
UTINGAS ARMAZENADORA S.A.—See Ultrapar Participacoes S.A.; *Int'l*, pg. 8019
U.T.I. OF ILLINOIS, INC.—See Universal Technical Institute, Inc.; *U.S. Public*, pg. 2262
UTI PERSHIP (PVT) LIMITED—See DSV A/S; *Int'l*, pg. 2216
UTIQUE ENTERPRISES LTD.; *Int'l*, pg. 8100
UTIS CO., LTD—See Rogers Corporation; *U.S. Public*, pg. 1808
UTI SECURITY & FIRE SOLUTIONS—See UTI Group Ltd.; *Int'l*, pg. 8100
UTI SYSTEMS S.A.—See UTI Group Ltd.; *Int'l*, pg. 8100
UTI WORLDWIDE INC.—See DSV A/S; *Int'l*, pg. 2216
UTKAL ALUMINA INTERNATIONAL LIMITED—See The Aditya Birla Group; *Int'l*, pg. 7612
UTKARSH SMALL FINANCE BANK LIMITED; *Int'l*, pg. 8101
UTL INDUSTRIES LIMITED; *Int'l*, pg. 8101
UTLX COMPANY—See Berkshire Hathaway Inc.; *U.S. Public*, pg. 319
UTMOST BUILDING MATERIALS LLC—See Suhail Bahwan Group (Holding) LLC; *Int'l*, pg. 7254
UTMOST INTERNATIONAL GROUP HOLDINGS LIMITED; *Int'l*, pg. 8101
UTMOST LIMITED—See Utmost International Group Holdings Limited; *Int'l*, pg. 8101
UTMOST PANEUROPE—See Utmost International Group Holdings Limited; *Int'l*, pg. 8101
UTN SOLUTIONS (NORTH) LIMITED—See Onzima Ventures PLC; *Int'l*, pg. 5593
UTOC AMERICA, INC.—See Mitsui O.S.K. Lines, Ltd.; *Int'l*, pg. 4992
UTOC CORPORATION—See Mitsui O.S.K. Lines, Ltd.; *Int'l*, pg. 4992
UTOC ENGINEERING PTE. LTD.—See Mitsui O.S.K. Lines, Ltd.; *Int'l*, pg. 4992
UTOC (THAILAND) CO., LTD.—See Mitsui O.S.K. Lines, Ltd.; *Int'l*, pg. 4992
UTON S.A.; *Int'l*, pg. 8101
UTOPIA, INC.; *U.S. Private*, pg. 4327
UTOPY, INC.—See Permira Advisers LLP; *Int'l*, pg. 5805
UTOUR GROUP CO., LTD.; *Int'l*, pg. 8100
UT PABEC CO., LTD.—See UT Group Co., Ltd.; *Int'l*, pg. 8100
UTP BELA CRKVA A.D.; *Int'l*, pg. 8101
U.T.P. D.O.O—See SOL S.p.A.; *Int'l*, pg. 7068
UT PHYSICIANS; *U.S. Private*, pg. 4324
UTP KASTEL AD; *Int'l*, pg. 8101
UTRADE—See UOB-Kay Hian Holdings Limited; *Int'l*, pg. 8086
U-TRAVELWIDE SDN BHD—See Sime Darby Berhad; *Int'l*, pg. 6930
UTRECHT MANUFACTURING CORP.—See Dick Blick Holdings Inc.; *U.S. Private*, pg. 1225
U-TRON SYSTEMS INC.—See Unitronics (1989) (R"G) Ltd.; *Int'l*, pg. 8075
UTSCH DO BRASIL—See Erich Utsch AG; *Int'l*, pg. 2493
UTSCH INTERNATIONAL LTD.—See Erich Utsch AG; *Int'l*, pg. 2493
UTSCH TONNJES INTERNATIONAL AG—See Erich Utsch AG; *Int'l*, pg. 2493
UTS MARKETING SOLUTIONS HOLDINGS LIMITED; *Int'l*, pg. 8101
UTS MARKETING SOLUTIONS SDN. BHD.—See UTS Marketing Solutions Holdings Limited; *Int'l*, pg. 8101
UT SOUTHWESTERN DVA HEALTHCARE, LLP—See DaVita Inc.; *U.S. Public*, pg. 644
UTSTARCOM (BEIJING) TECHNOLOGIES CO., LTD.—See UTStarcom Holdings Corp.; *Int'l*, pg. 8101

UTSTARCOM (CHINA) LTD.—See UTStarcom Holdings Corp.; *Int'l*, pg. 8101
UTSTARCOM HOLDINGS CORP.; *Int'l*, pg. 8101
UTSTARCOM INC.—See UTStarcom Holdings Corp.; *Int'l*, pg. 8101
UTSTARCOM INDIA TELECOM PVT. LTD.—See UTStarcom Holdings Corp.; *Int'l*, pg. 8101
UTSTARCOM JAPAN KK—See UTStarcom Holdings Corp.; *Int'l*, pg. 8101
UTSTARCOM KOREA LIMITED—See UTStarcom Holdings Corp.; *Int'l*, pg. 8101
UTSTARCOM SE UTStarcom Holdings Corp.; *Int'l*, pg. 8101
UTSTARCOM TAIWAN LTD—See UTStarcom Holdings Corp.; *Int'l*, pg. 8101
UTSTARCOM TELECOM CO., LTD.—See UTStarcom Holdings Corp.; *Int'l*, pg. 8101
UTSTARCOM (THAILAND) LIMITED—See UTStarcom Holdings Corp.; *Int'l*, pg. 8101
UTSUNOMIYA CHEMICAL INDUSTRY CO., LTD—See Mitsui Chemicals, Inc.; *Int'l*, pg. 4984
UTSUNOMIYA DYNAPAC CO., LTD.—See Dynapac Co., Ltd.; *Int'l*, pg. 2242
UTSUNOMIYA KIKI CO., LTD.—See JTEKT Corporation; *Int'l*, pg. 4019
UT SURI-EMU CO., LTD.—See UT Group Co., Ltd.; *Int'l*, pg. 8100
UTTAM GALVA INTERNATIONAL, FZE—See Uttam Galva Steels Limited; *Int'l*, pg. 8101
UTTAM GALVA NORTH AMERICA, INC—See Uttam Galva Steels Limited; *Int'l*, pg. 8101
UTTAM GALVA STEELS LIMITED; *Int'l*, pg. 8101
UTTAM SUGAR MILLS LIMITED; *Int'l*, pg. 8101
UTTARA BANK PLC; *Int'l*, pg. 8102
UTTARA FINANCE AND INVESTMENTS LIMITED; *Int'l*, pg. 8102
UTTARKASHI TONS HYDRO POWER PRIVATE LTD.—See SPML Infra Limited; *Int'l*, pg. 7141
UTT DE MEXICO TECHNICAL TEXTILES, S.A. DE C.V.—See Indorama Ventures Public Company Limited; *Int'l*, pg. 3659
UTTOXETER ESTATES LIMITED—See Blackstone Inc.; *U.S. Public*, pg. 358
UTUSAN AIRTIME SDN BHD—See Utusan Melayu (Malaysia) Berhad; *Int'l*, pg. 8102
UTUSAN KARYA SDN BHD—See Utusan Melayu (Malaysia) Berhad; *Int'l*, pg. 8102
UTUSAN MELAYU (MALAYSIA) BERHAD - BANDAR BARU BANGI PLANT—See Utusan Melayu (Malaysia) Berhad; *Int'l*, pg. 8102
UTUSAN MELAYU (MALAYSIA) BERHAD; *Int'l*, pg. 8102
UTUSAN PRINTCORP SDN BHD—See Utusan Melayu (Malaysia) Berhad; *Int'l*, pg. 8102
UTUSAN PUBLICATIONS & DISTRIBUTORS SDN BHD—See Utusan Melayu (Malaysia) Berhad; *Int'l*, pg. 8102
UTVA PROING A.D.; *Int'l*, pg. 8102
UTVA SILOSI A.D. KOVIN; *Int'l*, pg. 8102
UTV SOFTWARE COMMUNICATIONS LIMITED; *Int'l*, pg. 8102
UT WORLDWIDE (INDIA) PVT. LTD.—See DSV A/S; *Int'l*, pg. 2216
UTXL, INC.—See Knight-Swift Transportation Holdings Inc.; *U.S. Public*, pg. 1269
UTXO ACQUISITION INC.; *U.S. Private*, pg. 4327
UTX TECHNOLOGIES LIMITED—See Verint Systems Inc.; *U.S. Public*, pg. 2281
UTZ BRANDS, INC.; *U.S. Public*, pg. 2267
UTZ QUALITY FOODS, LLC—See Utz Brands, Inc.; *U.S. Public*, pg. 2268
UUDENMAAN LVI-TALO OY—See Instalco AB; *Int'l*, pg. 3722
U&U HOLDINGS PTY LTD—See Will Group, Inc.; *Int'l*, pg. 8412
U & U INC.—See GENDAI AGENCY INC.; *Int'l*, pg. 2917
UUUM CO., LTD.—See FreakOut Holdings, Inc.; *Int'l*, pg. 2767
UUV AQUABOTIX LTD; *Int'l*, pg. 8102
UVA ENCOMPASS HEALTH REHABILITATION HOSPITAL, LLC—See Encompass Health Corporation; *U.S. Public*, pg. 759
UVAT TECHNOLOGY CO., LTD.; *Int'l*, pg. 8102
UVAXX PTE. LTD.—See Barramundi Group Ltd.; *Int'l*, pg. 867
UVET AMERICAN EXPRESS CORPORATE TRAVEL S.P.A.—See American Express Company; *U.S. Public*, pg. 102
UVEX SAFETY GROUP GMBH & CO. KG—See UVEX Winter Holding GmbH & Co KG; *Int'l*, pg. 8102
UVEX WINTER HOLDING GMBH & CO KG; *Int'l*, pg. 8102
UV FLU TECHNOLOGIES, INC.; *U.S. Public*, pg. 2268
UV GERMI SA; *Int'l*, pg. 8102
UVP, LLC—See Endress+Hauser (International) Holding AG; *Int'l*, pg. 2405
UV PURE TECHNOLOGIES INC.—See Clearford Water Systems Inc.; *Int'l*, pg. 1657
UVRE LIMITED; *Int'l*, pg. 8102

UV-TECHNIK INTERNATIONAL LTD.—See Dr. Honle AG; *Int'l*, pg. 2192
UV-TECHNIK SPEZIALLAMPEN GMBH—See Dr. Honle AG; *Int'l*, pg. 2192
UWAJIMAYA, INC.; *U.S. Private*, pg. 4327
UWATEC AG—See Johnson Outdoors Inc.; *U.S. Public*, pg. 1201
UWC BERHAD; *Int'l*, pg. 8102
UWHARRIE BANK—See Uwharrie Capital Corp.; *U.S. Public*, pg. 2268
UWHARRIE CAPITAL CORP.; *U.S. Public*, pg. 2268
UWHARRIE ENVIRONMENTAL—See Republic Services, Inc.; *U.S. Public*, pg. 1788
UWHARRIE INVESTMENT ADVISORS INC.—See Uwharrie Capital Corp.; *U.S. Public*, pg. 2268
UWIZ TECHNOLOGY CO., LTD.—See American Securities LLC; *U.S. Private*, pg. 252
U.W. MARX CONSTRUCTION COMPANY, INC.; *U.S. Private*, pg. 4272
UWM HOLDINGS CORPORATION—See The Gores Group, LLC; *U.S. Private*, pg. 4035
UWORLD LLC; *U.S. Private*, pg. 4327
UW PROVISION COMPANY, INC.; *U.S. Private*, pg. 4327
UXA RESOURCES LIMITED; *Int'l*, pg. 8102
UXC BSG HOLDINGS PTY. LTD.—See DXC Technology Company; *U.S. Public*, pg. 695
UXC CONSULTING PTE LTD—See DXC Technology Company; *U.S. Public*, pg. 697
UXC ECLIPSE SOLUTIONS (CANADA) LTD—See DXC Technology Company; *U.S. Public*, pg. 697
UXC ECLIPSE (USA) INC.—See DXC Technology Company; *U.S. Public*, pg. 695
UXC PROFESSIONAL SOLUTIONS HOLDINGS PTY LTD—See DXC Technology Company; *U.S. Public*, pg. 695
UXELLO GRAND OUEST SAS—See VINCI S.A.; *Int'l*, pg. 8230
UXELLO SUD OUEST SAS—See VINCI S.A.; *Int'l*, pg. 8230
UXIN LIMITED; *Int'l*, pg. 8102
UXN CO., LTD.; *Int'l*, pg. 8102
UYEMURA INTERNATIONAL CORPORATION—See C.Uyemura & Co., Ltd.; *Int'l*, pg. 1244
UYEMURA INTERNATIONAL (HONG KONG) CO., LTD.—See C.Uyemura & Co., Ltd.; *Int'l*, pg. 1244
UYEMURA INTERNATIONAL (SINGAPORE) PTE. LTD.—See C.Uyemura & Co., Ltd.; *Int'l*, pg. 1244
UYEMURA KOREA CO., LTD.—See C.Uyemura & Co., Ltd.; *Int'l*, pg. 1244
UYEMURA (MALAYSIA) SDN. BHD.—See C.Uyemura & Co., Ltd.; *Int'l*, pg. 1244
UYEMURA (SHANGHAI) CO., LTD.—See C.Uyemura & Co., Ltd.; *Int'l*, pg. 1244
UYEMURA (SHENZHEN) CO., LTD.—See C.Uyemura & Co., Ltd.; *Int'l*, pg. 1244
UYENO KOSAN LTD.; *Int'l*, pg. 8103
U. Y. FINCORP LIMITED; *Int'l*, pg. 7998
UYT LTD.—See Shandong Yongtai Chemical Group Co. Ltd.; *Int'l*, pg. 6759
UZABASE ASIA PACIFIC PTE. LTD.—See Uzabase, Inc.; *Int'l*, pg. 8103
UZABASE CHINA LIMITED—See Uzabase, Inc.; *Int'l*, pg. 8103
UZABASE HONG KONG LIMITED—See Uzabase, Inc.; *Int'l*, pg. 8103
UZABASE, INC.; *Int'l*, pg. 8103
UZARIJA A.D.; *Int'l*, pg. 8103
UZDAROJI AKCINE BENDROVE OZANTIS—See NEPI Rockcastle N.V.; *Int'l*, pg. 5200
UZEL DEUTZ MOTOR SANAYI VE TICARET A.S.—See Uzel Makina Sanayi A.S.; *Int'l*, pg. 8103
UZEL EMLAK HIZMETLERI A.S.—See Uzel Makina Sanayi A.S.; *Int'l*, pg. 8103
UZEL LOJISTIK VE SATINALMA HIZMETLERI A.S.—See Uzel Makina Sanayi A.S.; *Int'l*, pg. 8103
UZEL MAKINA SANAYI A.S.; *Int'l*, pg. 8103
UZEL PARK DANISMANLIK VE TICARET A.S.—See Uzel Makina Sanayi A.S.; *Int'l*, pg. 8103
UZEL SIGORTA ARACILIK HIZMETLERI A.S.—See Uzel Makina Sanayi A.S.; *Int'l*, pg. 8103
UZEL SINAI YATIRIM A.S.—See Uzel Makina Sanayi A.S.; *Int'l*, pg. 8103
UZEL SISTEM A.S.—See Uzel Makina Sanayi A.S.; *Int'l*, pg. 8103
UZEL TARIM MAKINALARI VE PARCA SANAYI VE TICARET A.S.—See Uzel Makina Sanayi A.S.; *Int'l*, pg. 8103
UZEL TUKETICI FINANSMANI VE KART HIZMETLERI A.S.—See Uzel Makina Sanayi A.S.; *Int'l*, pg. 8103
UZERTAS BOYA SANAYI TICARET VE YATIRIM AS; *Int'l*, pg. 8103
UZINEXPORT S.A.; *Int'l*, pg. 8104
UZIN FRANCE SAS—See Uzin Utz AG; *Int'l*, pg. 8103
UZIN LIMITED—See Uzin Utz AG; *Int'l*, pg. 8103
UZINSIDER ENGINEERING S.A.; *Int'l*, pg. 8104
UZIN S.R.O.—See Uzin Utz AG; *Int'l*, pg. 8104
UZIN TYRO AG—See Uzin Utz AG; *Int'l*, pg. 8103
UZIN UTZ AG; *Int'l*, pg. 8103
UZIN UTZ BELGIE N.V—See Uzin Utz AG; *Int'l*, pg. 8103

UZIN UTZ CESKA REPUBLIKA S.R.O.—See Uzin Utz AG; *Int'l*, pg. 8103
UZIN UTZ DENMARK APS—See Uzin Utz AG; *Int'l*, pg. 8103
UZIN UTZ FRANCE SAS—See Uzin Utz AG; *Int'l*, pg. 8104
UZIN UTZ HRVATSKA D.O.O.—See Uzin Utz AG; *Int'l*, pg. 8104
UZIN UTZ MAGYARORSZAG KFT.—See Uzin Utz AG; *Int'l*, pg. 8104
UZIN UTZ NEDERLAND B.V.—See Uzin Utz AG; *Int'l*, pg. 8104
UZIN UTZ NORGE AS—See Uzin Utz AG; *Int'l*, pg. 8104
UZIN UTZ NORTH AMERICA INC.—See Uzin Utz AG; *Int'l*, pg. 8103
UZIN UTZ NORTH AMERICA, INC.—See Uzin Utz AG; *Int'l*, pg. 8103
UZIN UTZ POLSKA SP. Z O. O.—See Uzin Utz AG; *Int'l*, pg. 8104
UZIN UTZ SCHWEIZ AG—See Uzin Utz AG; *Int'l*, pg. 8104
UZIN UTZ SINGAPORE PTE. LTD.—See Uzin Utz AG; *Int'l*, pg. 8104
UZIN UTZ SLOVENIJA D.O.O.—See Uzin Utz AG; *Int'l*, pg. 8104
UZIN UTZ SOUTH PACIFIC LTD.—See Uzin Utz AG; *Int'l*, pg. 8104
UZIN UTZ SRBIJA D.O.O.—See Uzin Utz AG; *Int'l*, pg. 8104
UZIN UTZ SVERIGE AB—See Uzin Utz AG; *Int'l*, pg. 8104
UZIN UTZ TOOLS VERWALTUNGS GMBH—See Uzin Utz AG; *Int'l*, pg. 8104
UZIN UTZ UNITED KINGDOM LTD.—See Uzin Utz AG; *Int'l*, pg. 8103
UZINVESTPROJECT LLC—See National Bank for Foreign Economic Activity of the Republic of Uzbekistan; *Int'l*, pg. 5151
UZLOMAC A.D.; *Int'l*, pg. 8104
UZMA BERHAD; *Int'l*, pg. 8104
UZTEL SA; *Int'l*, pg. 8104
UZUMINE COUNTRY CLUB CO., LTD.—See Dai Nippon Printing Co., Ltd.; *Int'l*, pg. 1916
UZUSHIO ENTERPRISE CO., LTD.—See Daeyang Electric Co., Ltd.; *Int'l*, pg. 1911

V

V2COM PARTICIPACOES S.A.—See WEG S.A.; *Int'l*, pg. 8368
V2 RETAIL LIMITED; *Int'l*, pg. 8106
V2R, LLC—See Revcor, Inc.; *U.S. Private*, pg. 3413
V2SOFT, INC.; *U.S. Private*, pg. 4328
V2 SYSTEMS, INC.; *U.S. Private*, pg. 4328
V2 TOBACCO A/S—See Philip Morris International Inc.; *U.S. Public*, pg. 1687
V2X, INC.; *U.S. Public*, pg. 2270
V2Y CORPORATION LTD.; *Int'l*, pg. 8106
V3 BROADSUITE, LLC; *U.S. Private*, pg. 4328
V3 MARKETS, LLC—See Global Brokerage, Inc.; *U.S. Public*, pg. 940
V3 PRINTING CORPORATION; *U.S. Private*, pg. 4328
V8 SUPERCARS AUSTRALIA PTY LTD—See Archer Capital Pty. Ltd.; *Int'l*, pg. 547
VAAGEN BROTHERS LUMBER, INC.; *U.S. Private*, pg. 4328
VAAHTO PAPER TECHNOLOGY LTD.—See Lone Star Funds; *U.S. Private*, pg. 2487
VAAHTO PULP & PAPER MACHINERY DISTRIBUTION (SHANGHAI) CO. LTD.—See Lone Star Funds; *U.S. Private*, pg. 2487
VAALCO ANGOLA (KWANZA), INC.—See VAALCO Energy, Inc.; *U.S. Public*, pg. 2270
VAALCO ENERGY, INC.; *U.S. Public*, pg. 2270
VAALCO ENERGY (USA), INC.—See VAALCO Energy, Inc.; *U.S. Public*, pg. 2270
VAALCO GABON (ETAME), INC.—See VAALCO Energy, Inc.; *U.S. Public*, pg. 2270
VAALCO GABON S.A.—See VAALCO Energy, Inc.; *U.S. Public*, pg. 2270
VAALCO INTERNATIONAL, INC.—See VAALCO Energy, Inc.; *U.S. Public*, pg. 2270
VAALCO PRODUCTION (GABON) INC.—See VAALCO Energy, Inc.; *U.S. Public*, pg. 2270
VAALDIAM DO BRASIL MINERACAO LTDA.—See Tres-Or Resources Ltd.; *Int'l*, pg. 7916
VAAL SANITARYWARE (PROPRIETARY) LIMITED—See DISTRIBUTION AND WAREHOUSING NETWORK LIMITED; *Int'l*, pg. 2136
VAAL TRIANGLE SYSTEMS PRIVATE LIMITED—See Sandvik AB; *Int'l*, pg. 6535
V.A. ANDERSON ENTERPRISES, INC.—See Apax Partners LLP; *Int'l*, pg. 503
VAARAD VENTURES LIMITED; *Int'l*, pg. 8107
VAARI DIGITAL CO., LTD.—See AP (Thailand) Public Company Limited; *Int'l*, pg. 499
VAASAN NORGE AS—See Lantmannen ek for; *Int'l*, pg. 4414
VAASAN OY—See Lantmannen ek for; *Int'l*, pg. 4414
VAASAN SVERIGE AB—See Lantmannen ek for; *Int'l*, pg. 4414

COMPANY NAME INDEX

VAASA OY—See Ilkka Yhtymae Oyj; *Int'l*, pg. 3615
VAASSEN, INC.—See Egeria Capital Management B.V.; *Int'l*, pg. 2323
VA AUTOMOTIVE AB; *Int'l*, pg. 8106
VABA GMBH—See Axactor SE; *Int'l*, pg. 761
VAB LEASING—See 4finance Holding S.A.; *Int'l*, pg. 12
VAB RIJSCHOOL NV—See KBC Group NV; *Int'l*, pg. 4106
VAC-ALL SERVICE, INC.—See Republic Services, Inc.; *U.S. Public*, pg. 1788
VACANCES (PTY) LTD—See Fosun International Limited; *Int'l*, pg. 2750
VACASA, INC.; *U.S. Public*, pg. 2270
VACATION ASIA (HK) LIMITED—See Avillion Berhad; *Int'l*, pg. 743
VACATION CENTRAL—See Travel Network Vacation Central; *U.S. Private*, pg. 4213
VACATION CLUB SERVICES CO.—See Melia Hotels International, S.A.; *Int'l*, pg. 4809
VACATION.COM, INC.—See Travel Leaders Group, LLC; *U.S. Private*, pg. 4213
VACATION EXPESS USA CORP.—See Sunwing Travel Group, Inc.; *Int'l*, pg. 7333
VACATION HOME RENTALS, INC.—See TripAdvisor, Inc.; *U.S. Public*, pg. 2195
VACATION HOME SWAP, INC.; *U.S. Private*, pg. 4328
VACATION PALM SPRINGS REAL ESTATE, INC.—See Travel & Leisure Co.; *U.S. Public*, pg. 2185
VACATION RESORTS INTERNATIONAL, LLC—See Marriott Vacations Worldwide Corporation; *U.S. Public*, pg. 1374
VACATIONROOST GROUP INC.; *U.S. Private*, pg. 4329
VACATION VILLAGE, INC.—See Golden Entertainment, Inc.; *U.S. Public*, pg. 950
VACATION VILLAGES OF AMERICA, INC.; *U.S. Private*, pg. 4329
VACAVILLE HONDA; *U.S. Private*, pg. 4329
VACCEX, INC.; *U.S. Private*, pg. 4329
VACCINES LAB SDN. BHD.—See Nexgram Holdings Berhad; *Int'l*, pg. 5244
VACCINEX, LP; *U.S. Private*, pg. 4329
VACCINOGEN, INC.; *U.S. Private*, pg. 4329
VACCO INDUSTRIES INC.—See ESCO Technologies, Inc.; *U.S. Public*, pg. 794
VACCON CO., INC.—See IMI plc; *Int'l*, pg. 3624
VAC-CON, INC.—See Holden Industries, Inc.; *U.S. Private*, pg. 1962
VAC GHANA—See General Atlantic Service Company, L.P.; *U.S. Private*, pg. 1661
VACHERIE MACHINE DIVISION; *U.S. Private*, pg. 4329
VACHERON AND CONSTANTIN S.A.—See Compagnie Financiere Richemont S.A.; *Int'l*, pg. 1741
VACI UTCA CENTER KFT—See Assicurazioni Generali S.p.A.; *Int'l*, pg. 645
VACLAV CIZEK S.R.O.—See Pilot Corporation; *Int'l*, pg. 5867
VAC MAGNETIC JAPAN K.K.—See Ara Partners Group; *U.S. Private*, pg. 306
VAC MAGNETIC KOREA LTD.—See Ara Partners Group; *U.S. Private*, pg. 306
VAC MAGNETICS LLC—See Ara Partners Group; *U.S. Private*, pg. 306
VAC-MET, INC.—See Solar Atmospheres, Inc.; *U.S. Private*, pg. 3707
VAC NETHERLANDS B.V.—See Ara Partners Group; *U.S. Private*, pg. 306
VACO BV—See Orior AG; *Int'l*, pg. 5633
VACO, LLC—See Olympus Partners; *U.S. Private*, pg. 3013
VACOM TECHNOLOGIES LLC—See BITZER SE; *Int'l*, pg. 1052
VACON AB—See Danfoss A/S; *Int'l*, pg. 1961
VACON AT ANTRIEBSSYSTEME GMBH—See Danfoss A/S; *Int'l*, pg. 1961
VACON BENELUX B.V.—See Danfoss A/S; *Int'l*, pg. 1961
VACON BENELUX N.V./S.A.—See Danfoss A/S; *Int'l*, pg. 1961
VACON DRIVES A/S—See Danfoss A/S; *Int'l*, pg. 1961
VACON DRIVES & CONTROLS PVT. LTD.—See Danfoss A/S; *Int'l*, pg. 1961
VACON DRIVES UK LTD.—See Danfoss A/S; *Int'l*, pg. 1961
VACON FRANCE S.A.S.—See Danfoss A/S; *Int'l*, pg. 1962
VACON GMBH—See Danfoss A/S; *Int'l*, pg. 1962
VACON LTD—See Danfoss A/S; *Int'l*, pg. 1961
VACON PACIFIC PTY LTD—See Danfoss A/S; *Int'l*, pg. 1962
VACON S.P.A.—See Danfoss A/S; *Int'l*, pg. 1962
V & A CONSULTING ENGINEERS, INC.; *U.S. Private*, pg. 4327
VA CONSULTING, INC.; *U.S. Private*, pg. 4328
VACO SAN ANTONIO—See Olympus Partners; *U.S. Private*, pg. 3014
VACTEK A/S—See Addtech AB; *Int'l*, pg. 135
VAC-TOGO S.A.—See General Atlantic Service Company, L.P.; *U.S. Private*, pg. 1661
VACTOR MANUFACTURING, INC.—See Federal Signal Corporation; *U.S. Public*, pg. 826
VACUDYNE INC.—See Altair Corporation; *U.S. Public*, pg. 86

VACUFORM 2000 (PROPRIETARY) LIMITED—See Samvardhana Motherson International Limited; *Int'l*, pg. 6518
VACUHEAT GMBH—See AMG Critical Materials N.V.; *Int'l*, pg. 425
VACUHEAT VERWALTUNGS GMBH—See AMG Critical Materials N.V.; *Int'l*, pg. 426
VACULUX B.V.—See H2 Equity Partners B.V.; *Int'l*, pg. 3199
VACUTEC MESSTECHNIK GMBH—See Hormann Holding GmbH & Co. KG; *Int'l*, pg. 3480
VACUUM ENGINEERING SERVICES LTD.—See Indutrade AB; *Int'l*, pg. 3682
VACUUM INSTRUMENT CORP.—See Valero Capital Partners LLC; *U.S. Private*, pg. 4331
VACUUMSCHMELZE GMBH & CO., KG—See Ara Partners Group; *U.S. Private*, pg. 306
VACUUM SYSTEMS INTERNATIONAL, INC.—See Lakewood Capital, LLC; *U.S. Private*, pg. 2379
VACUUM TECHNOLOGY ASSOCIATES, INC.—See Schunk GmbH; *Int'l*, pg. 6643
VADA BVBA—See Darling Ingredients Inc.; *U.S. Public*, pg. 634
VADATECH, INC.; *U.S. Private*, pg. 4329
VADDI CONCERTS GMBH—See CTS Eventim AG & Co. KGAA; *Int'l*, pg. 1874
VADDIO—See Legrand S.A.; *Int'l*, pg. 4445
VADEN HOLDING INC.; *U.S. Private*, pg. 4329
VADEN'S ACOUSTICS & DRYWALL, INC.; *U.S. Private*, pg. 4329
VADILAL ENTERPRISES LTD - FOREX DIVISION—See Vadilal Enterprises Ltd; *Int'l*, pg. 8107
VADILAL ENTERPRISES LTD - ICE-CREAM DIVISION—See Vadilal Enterprises Ltd; *Int'l*, pg. 8107
VADILAL ENTERPRISES LTD - PROCESSED FOOD DIVISION—See Vadilal Enterprises Ltd; *Int'l*, pg. 8107
VADILAL ENTERPRISES LTD - REAL ESTATE DIVISION—See Vadilal Enterprises Ltd; *Int'l*, pg. 8107
VADILAL ENTERPRISES LTD; *Int'l*, pg. 8107
VADILAL INDUSTRIES LIMITED; *Int'l*, pg. 8107
VADIM COMPUTER MANAGEMENT GROUP LTD.—See StarDyne Technologies Inc.; *Int'l*, pg. 7176
VADIVARHE SPECIALITY CHEMICALS LIMITED; *Int'l*, pg. 8107
VADNAIS TRENCHLESS SERVICES, INC.—See Primoris Services Corporation; *U.S. Public*, pg. 1719
VADO CORP.; *Int'l*, pg. 8107
VADOTECH JAPAN KK—See AB Dynamics plc; *Int'l*, pg. 39
VADO UK LTD.—See Norcros plc; *Int'l*, pg. 5415
VADS BERHAD—See Telekom Malaysia Berhad; *Int'l*, pg. 7537
VADS BUSINESS PROCESS SDN BHD—See Telekom Malaysia Berhad; *Int'l*, pg. 7537
VADS LYFE SDN. BHD.—See Telekom Malaysia Berhad; *Int'l*, pg. 7537
VADS SOLUTIONS SDN BHD—See Telekom Malaysia Berhad; *Int'l*, pg. 7537
VADTEK LLC.; *U.S. Private*, pg. 4329
VA DYNAMICS SDN. BHD.—See Mesiniaga Berhad; *Int'l*, pg. 4840
VAE AKTIENGESELLSCHAFT—See voestalpine AG; *Int'l*, pg. 8295
VAEGTKONSULENTERNE A/S—See Egmont Fonden; *Int'l*, pg. 2326
VAE INC.; *U.S. Private*, pg. 4329
VAE NORTRAK NORTH AMERICA—See voestalpine AG; *Int'l*, pg. 8295
VAESSEN INDUSTRIES NV; *Int'l*, pg. 8107
VAF INSTRUMENTS B.V.—See Aalberts N.V.; *Int'l*, pg. 36
VAGABOND FRANCHISE SYSTEM, INC.; *U.S. Private*, pg. 4329
VAGABOND MEDIA AB—See Egmont Fonden; *Int'l*, pg. 2326
VAGAR A.D.; *Int'l*, pg. 8108
VAG ARMATURA POLSKA SP.Z.O.O.—See Zurn Elkay Water Solutions Corporation; *U.S. Public*, pg. 2414
VAG ARMATUREN AT GMBH—See Zurn Elkay Water Solutions Corporation; *U.S. Public*, pg. 2414
VAG ARMATUREN CHILE LIMITADA—See Zurn Elkay Water Solutions Corporation; *U.S. Public*, pg. 2414
VAG ARMATUREN GMBH—See Zurn Elkay Water Solutions Corporation; *U.S. Public*, pg. 2414
VAGA SRL—See Mapei SpA; *Int'l*, pg. 4683
VAGA TEHNIKA EESTI OU—See Brodrene A & O Johansen A/S; *Int'l*, pg. 1173
VAGGMATERIAL SVERIGE AB—See Volati AB; *Int'l*, pg. 8301
VAG GMBH—See Aurelius Equity Opportunities SE & Co. KGaA; *Int'l*, pg. 710
VAGHANI TECHNO-BUILD LIMITED; *Int'l*, pg. 8108
V.A.G. HOLDING FINANCIERE S.A.—See Porsche Automobil Holding SE; *Int'l*, pg. 5931
VAG MIDDLE EAST DMCC—See Aurelius Equity Opportunities SE & Co. KGaA; *Int'l*, pg. 710
VAGROEN B.V.—See Sweco AB; *Int'l*, pg. 7364
VAG USA, LLC—See Zurn Elkay Water Solutions Corporation; *U.S. Public*, pg. 2414

VAG VALVES CHILE S.A.—See Zurn Elkay Water Solutions Corporation; *U.S. Public*, pg. 2414
VAG VALVES FRANCE SARL—See Zurn Elkay Water Solutions Corporation; *U.S. Public*, pg. 2414
VAG-VALVES INDIA (PRIVATE) LIMITED—See Zurn Elkay Water Solutions Corporation; *U.S. Public*, pg. 2414
VAG VALVES INDIA (PRIVATE) LTD.—See Aurelius Equity Opportunities SE & Co. KGaA; *Int'l*, pg. 710
VAG VALVES UK LIMITED—See Zurn Elkay Water Solutions Corporation; *U.S. Public*, pg. 2414
VAG VALVES USA INC.—See Zurn Elkay Water Solutions Corporation; *U.S. Public*, pg. 2414
VAG VALVOLE ITALIA SRL—See Zurn Elkay Water Solutions Corporation; *U.S. Public*, pg. 2414
VAG WATER SYSTEMS (TAICANG) CO., LTD.—See Zurn Elkay Water Solutions Corporation; *U.S. Public*, pg. 2414
VAHLE JAPAN CO., LTD.—See Kyokuto Boeki Kaisha, Ltd.; *Int'l*, pg. 4362
VAIBHAV GLOBAL LIMITED; *Int'l*, pg. 8108
VAIDYA SANE AYURVED LABORATORIES LTD.; *Int'l*, pg. 8108
VAIL ASSOCIATES INVESTMENTS, INC.—See Vail Resorts, Inc.; *U.S. Public*, pg. 2271
VAIL BEAVER CREEK RESORT PROPERTIES INC.—See Vail Resorts, Inc.; *U.S. Public*, pg. 2271
VAIL FOOD SERVICES INC.—See Vail Resorts, Inc.; *U.S. Public*, pg. 2271
VAIL HOLDINGS, INC.—See Vail Resorts, Inc.; *U.S. Public*, pg. 2271
VAIL INDUSTRIES, INC.; *U.S. Private*, pg. 4329
VAILLANT A/S—See Vaillant GmbH; *Int'l*, pg. 8108
VAILLANT CORP—See Vaillant GmbH; *Int'l*, pg. 8108
VAILLANT D.O.O.—See Vaillant GmbH; *Int'l*, pg. 8109
VAILLANT GMBH; *Int'l*, pg. 8108
VAILLANT GROUP AUSTRIA GMBH—See Vaillant GmbH; *Int'l*, pg. 8108
VAILLANT GROUP CZECH S.R.O.—See Vaillant GmbH; *Int'l*, pg. 8108
VAILLANT GROUP FRANCE SA—See Vaillant GmbH; *Int'l*, pg. 8108
VAILLANT GROUP GASERES AB—See Vaillant GmbH; *Int'l*, pg. 8108
VAILLANT GROUP ITALIA SPA—See Vaillant GmbH; *Int'l*, pg. 8108
VAILLANT GROUP NORGE A/S—See Vaillant GmbH; *Int'l*, pg. 8108
VAILLANT GROUP SLOVAKIA, S.R.O.—See Vaillant GmbH; *Int'l*, pg. 8108
VAILLANT GROUP UK LTD—See Vaillant GmbH; *Int'l*, pg. 8108
VAILLANT LIMITED—See Vaillant GmbH; *Int'l*, pg. 8108
VAILLANT LIMITED—See Vaillant GmbH; *Int'l*, pg. 8108
VAILLANT S.A.—See Vaillant GmbH; *Int'l*, pg. 8109
VAILLANT SAUNIER DUVAL KFT.—See Vaillant GmbH; *Int'l*, pg. 8109
VAILLANT, S.L.U.—See Vaillant GmbH; *Int'l*, pg. 8108
VAIL MOUNTAIN LODGE & SPA—See KSL Capital Partners, LLC; *U.S. Private*, pg. 2355
VAILOG S.R.L.—See SEGRO plc; *Int'l*, pg. 6683
VAIL RESORTS DEVELOPMENT COMPANY—See Vail Resorts, Inc.; *U.S. Public*, pg. 2272
VAIL RESORTS, INC.; *U.S. Public*, pg. 2270
VAIL RUBBER WORKS, INC.; *U.S. Private*, pg. 4329
VAIL SUMMIT RESORTS, INC.—See Vail Resorts, Inc.; *U.S. Public*, pg. 2272
VAIL SYSTEMS INC.; *U.S. Private*, pg. 4329
VAIMO AB—See Transcosmos Inc.; *Int'l*, pg. 7899
VA-INGENJORERNA AB—See Veolia Environnement S.A.; *Int'l*, pg. 8162
VAINO KORPINEN OY—See AddLife AB; *Int'l*, pg. 130
VAISALA CANADA INC.—See Vaisala Oyj; *Int'l*, pg. 8109
VAISALA CHINA LTD.—See Vaisala Oyj; *Int'l*, pg. 8109
VAISALA EAST AFRICA LIMITED—See Vaisala Oyj; *Int'l*, pg. 8109
VAISALA FRANCE SAS—See Vaisala Oyj; *Int'l*, pg. 8109
VAISALA GMBH—See Vaisala Oyj; *Int'l*, pg. 8109
VAISALA INC.—See Vaisala Oyj; *Int'l*, pg. 8109
VAISALA INC.—See Vaisala Oyj; *Int'l*, pg. 8109
VAISALA INC.—See Vaisala Oyj; *Int'l*, pg. 8109
VAISALA LIMITED—See Vaisala Oyj; *Int'l*, pg. 8109
VAISALA MEXICO LIMITED, S. DE R. L. DE C.V.—See Vaisala Oyj; *Int'l*, pg. 8109
VAISALA OYJ; *Int'l*, pg. 8109
VAISALA PTY. LTD.—See Vaisala Oyj; *Int'l*, pg. 8109
VAISALA SDN. BHD.—See Vaisala Oyj; *Int'l*, pg. 8109
VAISALA SERVICOS DE MARKETING LTDA.—See Vaisala Oyj; *Int'l*, pg. 8109
VAISALA SHANGHAI SENSORS LTD.—See Vaisala Oyj; *Int'l*, pg. 8109
VAISHALI PHARMA LTD.; *Int'l*, pg. 8109
VAISHNAVI BUILDERS & DEVELOPERS PRIVATE LIMITED—See Hubtown Limited; *Int'l*, pg. 3521
VAISHNAVI CORPORATE COMMUNICATIONS PVT. LTD.; *Int'l*, pg. 8109
VAISHNAVI GOLD LIMITED; *Int'l*, pg. 8109
VAIV COMPANY INC.; *Int'l*, pg. 8109

VAKIFBANK INTERNATIONAL WIEN AG—See Turkiye Vakiflar Bankasi T.A.O.; *Int'l*, pg. 7978
VAKIF EMEKLILIK AS—See Turkiye Varlik Fonu Yonetimi AS; *Int'l*, pg. 7978
VAKIF ENERJI VE MADENCILIK AS—See Turkiye Vakiflar Bankasi T.A.O.; *Int'l*, pg. 7978
VAKIF FAKTORING A.S.; *Int'l*, pg. 8109
VAKIF FINANSAL KIRALAMA AS—See Turkiye Vakiflar Bankasi T.A.O.; *Int'l*, pg. 7978
VAKIF FINANS FACTORING HIZMETLERI AS—See Turkiye Vakiflar Bankasi T.A.O.; *Int'l*, pg. 7978
VAKIF GAYRIMENKUL DEGERLEME AS—See Turkiye Vakiflar Bankasi T.A.O.; *Int'l*, pg. 7978
VAKIF GAYRIMENKUL YATIRIM ORTAKLIGI AS; *Int'l*, pg. 8109
VAKIF G.Y.O. A.S.—See T.C. Toplu Konut Idaresi Baskanligi; *Int'l*, pg. 7397
VAKIF INS. RESTORASYON VE TIC. A.S.—See T.C. Toplu Konut Idaresi Baskanligi; *Int'l*, pg. 7397
VAKIF MENKUL KIYMET YATIRIM ORTAKLIGI A.S.—See Turkiye Vakiflar Bankasi T.A.O.; *Int'l*, pg. 7978
VAKIF PORTFOY YONETIMI AS—See Turkiye Vakiflar Bankasi T.A.O.; *Int'l*, pg. 7978
VAKIF VARLIK KIRALAMA A.S.; *Int'l*, pg. 8109
VAKIF YATIRIM MENKUL DEGERLER AS—See Turkiye Vakiflar Bankasi T.A.O.; *Int'l*, pg. 7978
VAKKO TEKSTIL VE HAZIR GIYIM SANAYI ISLETMELERI A.S.; *Int'l*, pg. 8109
VAKRANGEE LIMITED; *Int'l*, pg. 8109
VAKSINDO ANIMAL HEALTH PVT. LTD.—See PT Japfa Comfeed Indonesia Tbk; *Int'l*, pg. 6049
VAKUFSKA BANKA D.D. SARAJEVO—See CID Adriatic Investments GmbH; *Int'l*, pg. 1603
VAKUTEK—See Dr. Ing. K. Busch GmbH; *Int'l*, pg. 2194
VAL-A CHICAGO, INC.—See LHB Industries, Inc.; *U.S. Private*, pg. 2442
VALADOR, INC.; *U.S. Private*, pg. 4330
VALAD PROPERTY HOLDINGS (UK) LIMITED—See Blackstone Inc.; *U.S. Public*, pg. 360
VALAMAR RIVIERA D.D.; *Int'l*, pg. 8110
VALANTIC GMBH—See DPE Deutsche Private Equity GmbH; *Int'l*, pg. 2188
VALANT MEDICAL SOLUTIONS INC.—See Resurgens Technology Partners, LLC; *U.S. Private*, pg. 3411
VALARD BEARINGS LTD—See Hudaco Industries Limited; *Int'l*, pg. 3521
VALARD CONSTRUCTION AUSTRALIA PTY. LTD.—See Quanta Services, Inc.; *U.S. Public*, pg. 1753
VALARD CONSTRUCTION LP—See Quanta Services, Inc.; *U.S. Public*, pg. 1753
VALARD GEOMATICS BC, LTD.—See Quanta Services, Inc.; *U.S. Public*, pg. 1753
VALARD GEOMATICS LTD.—See Quanta Services, Inc.; *U.S. Public*, pg. 1753
VALARD POLSKA SP. Z O.O.—See Quanta Services, Inc.; *U.S. Public*, pg. 1753
VALARIS LIMITED; *Int'l*, pg. 8110
VALARIS PLC—See Valaris Limited; *Int'l*, pg. 8110
VALARTIS ADVISORY SERVICES SA—See Valartis Group AG; *Int'l*, pg. 8111
VALARTIS FINANCIAL ADVISORY PTE. LTD.—See Valartis Group AG; *Int'l*, pg. 8111
VALARTIS GROUP AG; *Int'l*, pg. 8111
VALARTIS INTERNATIONAL LTD.—See Valartis Group AG; *Int'l*, pg. 8111
VALASSIS CANADA INC.—See Direct Response Media Group Inc.; *Int'l*, pg. 2130
VALASSIS COMMUNICATIONS, INC.—See MacAndrews & Forbes Incorporated; *U.S. Private*, pg. 2532
VALASSIS DIRECT MAIL, INC.—See MacAndrews & Forbes Incorporated; *U.S. Private*, pg. 2532
VALAYA LUXURY HOLDINGS PTY. LTD.; *Int'l*, pg. 8111
VALBART S.R.L.—See Flowserve Corporation; *U.S. Public*, pg. 857
VALBIOTIS SA; *Int'l*, pg. 8111
VALBRIDGE PROPERTY ADVISORS, INC.; *U.S. Private*, pg. 4330
VALBRUNA AG—See Acciaierie Valbruna S.p.A.; *Int'l*, pg. 89
VALBRUNA ASIA LIMITED—See Acciaierie Valbruna S.p.A.; *Int'l*, pg. 89
VALBRUNA AUSTRALIA PTY LTD—See Acciaierie Valbruna S.p.A.; *Int'l*, pg. 89
VALBRUNA CANADA LTD.—See Acciaierie Valbruna S.p.A.; *Int'l*, pg. 89
VALBRUNA EDEL INOX GMBH—See Acciaierie Valbruna S.p.A.; *Int'l*, pg. 89
VALBRUNA GULF FZE—See Acciaierie Valbruna S.p.A.; *Int'l*, pg. 89
VALBRUNA MEXICO, S.A. DE C.V.—See Acciaierie Valbruna S.p.A.; *Int'l*, pg. 89
VALBRUNA NEDERLAND B.V.—See Acciaierie Valbruna S.p.A.; *Int'l*, pg. 89
VALBRUNA NORDIC AB—See Acciaierie Valbruna S.p.A.; *Int'l*, pg. 89
VALBRUNA NORDIC OY—See Acciaierie Valbruna S.p.A.; *Int'l*, pg. 89
VALBRUNA POLSKA SP. Z O.O—See Acciaierie Valbruna S.p.A.; *Int'l*, pg. 89
VALBRUNA SLATER STAINLESS, INC.—See Acciaierie Valbruna S.p.A.; *Int'l*, pg. 89
VALBRUNA STAINLESS, INC.—See Acciaierie Valbruna S.p.A.; *Int'l*, pg. 89
VALBRUNA STAINLESS SDN. BHD—See Acciaierie Valbruna S.p.A.; *Int'l*, pg. 89
VALBRUNA STAINLESS—See Acciaierie Valbruna S.p.A.; *Int'l*, pg. 90
VALBRUNA STAINLESS—See Acciaierie Valbruna S.p.A.; *Int'l*, pg. 90
VALBRUNA UK LTD—See Acciaierie Valbruna S.p.A.; *Int'l*, pg. 90
VALCAMBI S.A.—See Newmont Corporation; *U.S. Public*, pg. 1516
VALCO CINCINNATI INC.; *U.S. Private*, pg. 4330
VALCO GROUP AS; *Int'l*, pg. 8111
VALCO INSTRUMENTS CO., INC.; *U.S. Private*, pg. 4330
VALCOM CO., LTD.—See Eagle Industry Co., Ltd.; *Int'l*, pg. 2266
VALCOM ENTERPRISES INCORPORATED; *U.S. Private*, pg. 4330
VALCOM, INC.; *U.S. Private*, pg. 4330
VALCOR ENGINEERING CORPORATION; *U.S. Private*, pg. 4330
VALCORP FINE FOODS PTY. LTD.; *Int'l*, pg. 8111
VALCO SRL; *Int'l*, pg. 8111
VAL.CO SRL—See GHM Messtechnik GmbH; *Int'l*, pg. 2959
VALCOUR PRINTING, INC.—See Chatham Asset Management, LLC; *U.S. Private*, pg. 863
VALCOURT BUILDING SERVICES LLC; *U.S. Private*, pg. 4330
VALDAK CORPORATION; *U.S. Private*, pg. 4330
VALDARNO AMBIENTE S.R.L.—See Iren S.p.A.; *Int'l*, pg. 3808
VAL DE LOIRE GRANULATS SAS—See VINCI S.A.; *Int'l*, pg. 8240
VAL DE LOIRE MAINTENANCE SERVICE SAS—See VINCI S.A.; *Int'l*, pg. 8240
VAL DE LYON SAS—See Coop-Gruppe Genossenschaft; *Int'l*, pg. 1790
VALDEMINGOMEZ 2000, S.A.—See Sacyr, S.A.; *Int'l*, pg. 6466
VALDEOLMILLOS GESTORES SLU—See Tessi S.A.; *Int'l*, pg. 7575
VALDESE WEAVERS, LLC—See CV Industries Inc.; *U.S. Private*, pg. 1132
VALDEYRON MATERIAUX SAS—See Bisca Materiaux SARL; *Int'l*, pg. 1048
VALDEZ & TORRY ADVERTISING LIMITED—See WPP plc; *Int'l*, pg. 8472
VALDOIE MICA SAS—See SKion GmbH; *Int'l*, pg. 6987
VALDOR FIBER OPTICS, INC.—See Valdor Technology International Inc.; *Int'l*, pg. 8111
VAL-D'OR MINING CORPORATION; *Int'l*, pg. 8109
VALDOR TECHNOLOGY INTERNATIONAL INC.; *Int'l*, pg. 8111
VALEANT CANADA HOLDINGS LIMITED—See Bausch Health Companies Inc.; *Int'l*, pg. 898
VALEANT CANADA LTD.—See Bausch Health Companies Inc.; *Int'l*, pg. 898
VALEANT CANADA S.E.C./VALEANT CANADA LP—See Bausch Health Companies Inc.; *Int'l*, pg. 898
VALEANT CZECH PHARMA S.R.O.—See Bausch Health Companies Inc.; *Int'l*, pg. 898
VALEANT FARMACEUTICA DO BRASIL LTDA.—See Bausch Health Companies Inc.; *Int'l*, pg. 898
VALEANT FARMACEUTICA, S.A. DE C.V.—See Bausch Health Companies Inc.; *Int'l*, pg. 898
VALEANT FARMACUETICA PANAMA S.A.—See Bausch Health Companies Inc.; *Int'l*, pg. 898
VALEANT GROUPE COSMODERME INC.—See Bausch Health Companies Inc.; *Int'l*, pg. 898
VALEANT LLC—See Bausch Health Companies Inc.; *Int'l*, pg. 898
VALEANT MED SP. Z O.O.—See Bausch Health Companies Inc.; *Int'l*, pg. 897
VALEANT PHARMACEUTICALS INTERNATIONAL CORPORATION—See Bausch Health Companies Inc.; *Int'l*, pg. 898
VALEANT PHARMACEUTICALS INTERNATIONAL—See Bausch Health Companies Inc.; *Int'l*, pg. 898
VALEANT PHARMACEUTICALS NORTH AMERICA LLC—See Bausch Health Companies Inc.; *Int'l*, pg. 898
VALEANT PHARMA HUNGARY COMMERCIAL LLC—See Bausch Health Companies Inc.; *Int'l*, pg. 898
VALE BATES S.A. DE C.V.—See Vivendi SE; *Int'l*, pg. 8269
VALE BROTHERS HOLDINGS LIMITED; *Int'l*, pg. 8111
VALE BROTHERS LIMITED—See Vale Brothers Holdings Limited; *Int'l*, pg. 8111
VALEDO PARTNERS AB; *Int'l*, pg. 8112
VALE DO RIO DOCE ALUMINIO S.A.—See Vale S.A.; *Int'l*, pg. 8112
VALE ENERGIA LIMPA S.A.—See Vale S.A.; *Int'l*, pg. 8112
VALE EXPLORATION PERU SAC—See Vale S.A.; *Int'l*, pg. 8112
VALE EXPLORATION PHILIPPINES INC—See Vale S.A.; *Int'l*, pg. 8112
VALE GENERAL, S.A.—See Banco General, S.A.; *Int'l*, pg. 822
VALE HEALTH PARTNERS LTD—See Nuffield Health; *Int'l*, pg. 5488
VALE HOLDINGS AG—See Vale S.A.; *Int'l*, pg. 8112
VALE INTERNATIONAL S.A.—See Vale S.A.; *Int'l*, pg. 8112
VALE INTERNATIONAL SINGAPORE—See Vale S.A.; *Int'l*, pg. 8112
VALE JAPAN LIMITED—See Vale S.A.; *Int'l*, pg. 8112
VALE MALAYSIA MINERALS SDN. BHD.—See Vale S.A.; *Int'l*, pg. 8112
VALE MINERALS CHINA CO. LTD.—See Vale S.A.; *Int'l*, pg. 8112
VALE MOCAMBIQUE LTDA.—See Vale S.A.; *Int'l*, pg. 8112
VALE NATIONAL TRAINING CENTER INC.—See The Carlyle Group Inc.; *U.S. Public*, pg. 2054
THE VALENCE GROUP, LLC—See Piper Sandler Companies; *U.S. Public*, pg. 1694
VALENCE HEALTH, LLC—See Evolent Health, Inc.; *U.S. Public*, pg. 804
VALENCE MEDIA GROUP; *U.S. Private*, pg. 4330
VALENCE SURFACE TECHNOLOGIES LLC—See ATL Partners, LLC; *U.S. Private*, pg. 369
VALENCE SURFACE TECHNOLOGIES LLC—See British Columbia Investment Management Corp.; *Int'l*, pg. 1170
VALENCE TECHNOLOGY, INC.; *U.S. Private*, pg. 4331
VALENCIA-A, INC.—See Lithia Motors, Inc.; *U.S. Public*, pg. 1326
VALENCIA AT DORAL, LLC—See Lennar Corporation; *U.S. Public*, pg. 1307
VALENCIA B. IMPORTS, INC.—See AutoNation, Inc.; *U.S. Public*, pg. 238
VALENCIA CAPITAL, INC.; *Int'l*, pg. 8112
VALENCIA DEVELOPMENT SDN. BHD.—See Gamuda Berhad; *Int'l*, pg. 2879
VALENCIA H. IMPORTS, INC.—See AutoNation, Inc.; *U.S. Public*, pg. 238
VALENCIA HOMES SDN. BHD.—See Insas Berhad; *Int'l*, pg. 3718
VALENCIA MODULOS DE PUERTA, S.L.—See Stellantis N.V.; *Int'l*, pg. 7203
VALENCIA NUTRITION LIMITED; *Int'l*, pg. 8112
VALENCIA POWER CONVERTERS S.A.—See Siemens Energy AG; *Int'l*, pg. 6903
VALENER INC.—See Caisse de Depot et Placement du Quebec; *Int'l*, pg. 1256
VALE NOUVELLE CALEDONIE S.A.S.—See Vale S.A.; *Int'l*, pg. 8112
THE VALENS COMPANY INC.; *Int'l*, pg. 7698
VALENS SEMICONDUCTOR LTD.; *Int'l*, pg. 8112
VALENS TECHNOLOGIES PRIVATE LIMITED—See Paramount Communications Limited; *Int'l*, pg. 5737
VALENT AEROSTRUCTURES - LENEXA, LLC—See SONACA S.A; *Int'l*, pg. 7088
VALENT AEROSTRUCTURES - WASHINGTON, LLC—See SONACA S.A; *Int'l*, pg. 7088
VALENT AEROSTRUCTURES - WICHITA, LLC—See SONACA S.A; *Int'l*, pg. 7088
VALENT BIOSCIENCES CORPORATION—See Sumitomo Chemical Company, Limited; *Int'l*, pg. 7266
VALENT CAPITAL PARTNERS LLC; *U.S. Private*, pg. 4331
VALENTE EQUIPMENT LEASING CORP.—See Vulcan Materials Company; *U.S. Public*, pg. 2314
VALENTI AUTO SALES, INC.; *U.S. Private*, pg. 4331
VALENTI MOTORS, INC.; *U.S. Private*, pg. 4331
VALENTINE MARK CORPORATION; *U.S. Public*, pg. 2272
VALENTIN ENVIRONNEMENT & TRAVAUX PUBLICS S.A.S.—See VINCI S.A.; *Int'l*, pg. 8220
VALENTINO FASHION GROUP S.P.A.—See Mayhoola for Investments LLC; *Int'l*, pg. 4745
VALENTIN SAS—See VINCI S.A.; *Int'l*, pg. 8240
VALENTINS GMBH—See Hubert Burda Media Holding Kommanditgesellschaft; *Int'l*, pg. 3520
VALENTI TOYOTA; *U.S. Private*, pg. 4331
VALENT U.S.A. CORPORATION—See Sumitomo Chemical Company, Limited; *Int'l*, pg. 7266
VALEO AUTO-ELECTRIC GMBH—See Valeo S.A.; *Int'l*, pg. 8113
VALEO AUTO-ELECTRIC HUNGARY LLC—See Valeo S.A.; *Int'l*, pg. 8113
VALEO AUTOKLIMATIZACE K.S.—See Valeo S.A.; *Int'l*, pg. 8113
VALEO AUTOMOTIVE AIR CONDITIONING HUBEI CO. LTD—See Valeo S.A.; *Int'l*, pg. 8113
VALEO AUTOMOTIVE SECURITY SYSTEMS (WUXI) CO. LTD—See Valeo S.A.; *Int'l*, pg. 8113
VALEO AUTOMOTIVE (THAILAND) CO. LTD.—See Valeo S.A.; *Int'l*, pg. 8113
VALEO AUTOSYSTEMY SP. Z.O.O.—See Valeo S.A.; *Int'l*, pg. 8113
VALEO BEHAVIORAL HEALTH CARE; *U.S. Private*, pg. 4331
VALEO CLIMATE CONTROL LIMITED—See Valeo S.A.; *Int'l*, pg. 8113

COMPANY NAME INDEX

VALEO CLIMATIZACAO DO BRASIL - VEICULOS COMERCIAIS S/A—See Valeo S.A.; *Int'l*, pg. 8115
VALEO CLIMATIZACION, S.A.—See Valeo S.A.; *Int'l*, pg. 8113
VALEO COMPRESSOR (CHANGCHUN) CO. LTD.—See Valeo S.A.; *Int'l*, pg. 8113
VALEO COMPRESSOR CLUTCH (THAILAND) CO. LTD—See Valeo S.A.; *Int'l*, pg. 8113
VALEO COMPRESSOR EUROPE S.R.O.—See Valeo S.A.; *Int'l*, pg. 8113
VALEO COMPRESSOR (THAILAND) CO. LTD.—See Valeo S.A.; *Int'l*, pg. 8113
VALEO ELECTRICAL SYSTEMS, INC. - WIPER SYSTEMS—See Valeo S.A.; *Int'l*, pg. 8114
VALEO EMBRAGUES ARGENTINA, SA—See Valeo S.A.; *Int'l*, pg. 8113
VALEO ENGINE COOLING (FOSHAN) CO. LTD.—See Valeo S.A.; *Int'l*, pg. 8113
VALEO EQUIPEMENT ELECTRIQUES MOTEUR—See Valeo S.A.; *Int'l*, pg. 8113
VALEO FOODS LTD.—See CapVest Limited; *Int'l*, pg. 1318
VALEO FRANKLIN—See Sheikh Holdings Group (Investments) Limited; *Int'l*, pg. 6794
VALEO FRICTION MATERIALS INDIA LTD.—See Valeo S.A.; *Int'l*, pg. 8113
VALEO GMBH—See Valeo S.A.; *Int'l*, pg. 8113
VALEO HOLDING NETHERLANDS B.V.—See Valeo S.A.; *Int'l*, pg. 8113
VALEO ILUMINACION, S.A.—See Valeo S.A.; *Int'l*, pg. 8113
VALEO INDIA PRIVATE LTD—See Valeo S.A.; *Int'l*, pg. 8113
VALEO INTERBRANCH AUTOMOTIVE SOFTWARE EGYPT—See Valeo S.A.; *Int'l*, pg. 8113
VALEO INTERIOR CONTROLS (SHENZHEN) CO. LTD—See Valeo S.A.; *Int'l*, pg. 8114
VALEO INTERIOR CONTROLS—See Valeo S.A.; *Int'l*, pg. 8114
VALEO KLIMASYSTEME GMBH—See Valeo S.A.; *Int'l*, pg. 8113
VALEO LIGHTING HUBEI TECHNICAL CENTER CO. LTD.—See Valeo S.A.; *Int'l*, pg. 8114
VALEO MANAGEMENT (BEIJING) CO. LTD.—See Valeo S.A.; *Int'l*, pg. 8114
VALEO MANAGEMENT SERVICES—See Valeo S.A.; *Int'l*, pg. 8114
VALEO MANAGEMENT SERVICES UK LIMITED—See Valeo S.A.; *Int'l*, pg. 8114
VALE OMAN PELLETIZING COMPANY LLC—See Vale S.A.; *Int'l*, pg. 8112
VALEO MOTHERSON THERMAL COMMERCIAL VEHICLES INDIA LTD.—See Valeo S.A.; *Int'l*, pg. 8114
VALEO NORTH AMERICA, INC.—See Valeo S.A.; *Int'l*, pg. 8114
VALEO OTOMOTIV SISTEMLERI ENDUSTRISI A.S.—See Valeo S.A.; *Int'l*, pg. 8114
VALEO PHARMA, INC.; *Int'l*, pg. 8112
VALEO RAYTHEON SYSTEMS, INC.—See Valeo S.A.; *Int'l*, pg. 8114
VALEO S.A.; *Int'l*, pg. 8112
VALEO SCHALTER UND SENSOREN GMBH—See Valeo S.A.; *Int'l*, pg. 8113
VALEO SERVICE BELGIQUE SA—See Valeo S.A.; *Int'l*, pg. 8114
VALEO SERVICE BENELUX B.V.—See Valeo S.A.; *Int'l*, pg. 8114
VALEO SERVICE DEUTSCHLAND GMBH—See Valeo S.A.; *Int'l*, pg. 8113
VALEO SERVICE EASTERN EUROPE SP. Z.O.O—See Valeo S.A.; *Int'l*, pg. 8114
VALEO SERVICE ESPANA, S.A.—See Valeo S.A.; *Int'l*, pg. 8114
VALEO SERVICE ITALIA, S.P.A.—See Valeo S.A.; *Int'l*, pg. 8114
VALEO SERVICE LIMITED LIABILITY COMPANY—See Valeo S.A.; *Int'l*, pg. 8114
VALEO SERVICE SAS—See Valeo S.A.; *Int'l*, pg. 8114
VALEO SERVICE UK LIMITED—See Valeo S.A.; *Int'l*, pg. 8114
VALEO SHANGHAI AUTOMOTIVE ELECTRIC MOTORS & WIPER SYSTEMS CO., LTD—See Valeo S.A.; *Int'l*, pg. 8114
VALEO SIAM THERMAL SYSTEMS CO. LTD—See Valeo S.A.; *Int'l*, pg. 8114
VALEO SICHERHEITSSYSTEME GMBH—See Valeo S.A.; *Int'l*, pg. 8113
VALEO SISTEMAS AUTOMOTIVOS LTDA—See Valeo S.A.; *Int'l*, pg. 8114
VALEO SISTEMAS ELECTRICOS SERVICIOS S DE RL DE CV—See Valeo S.A.; *Int'l*, pg. 8114
VALEO SISTEMAS ELECTRONICOS, S DE RL DE CV—See Valeo S.A.; *Int'l*, pg. 8114
VALEO SISTEME TERMICE S.R.L.—See Valeo S.A.; *Int'l*, pg. 8114
VALEO S.P.A.—See Valeo S.A.; *Int'l*, pg. 8113
VALEO SWITCHES AND DETECTION SYSTEMS, INC.—See Valeo S.A.; *Int'l*, pg. 8114
VALEO-SYLVANIA, LLC—See Valeo S.A.; *Int'l*, pg. 8115

VALEO SYSTEMES DE CONTROLE MOTEUR SASU—See Valeo S.A.; *Int'l*, pg. 8114
VALEO SYSTEMES D'ESSUYAGE SAS—See Valeo S.A.; *Int'l*, pg. 8114
VALEO SYSTEMES THERMIQUES SAS—See Valeo S.A.; *Int'l*, pg. 8114
VALEO SYSTEMS SOUTH AFRICA (PROPRIETARY) LTD.—See Valeo S.A.; *Int'l*, pg. 8114
VALEO TECHNOLOGIES LLC—See Ansell Limited; *Int'l*, pg. 478
VALEO TERMICO, S.A.—See Valeo S.A.; *Int'l*, pg. 8114
VALEO THERMAL COMMERCIAL VEHICLES AUSTRALIA PTY. LTD.—See Valeo S.A.; *Int'l*, pg. 8114
VALEO THERMAL COMMERCIAL VEHICLES FINLAND OY LTD.—See Valeo S.A.; *Int'l*, pg. 8114
VALEO THERMAL COMMERCIAL VEHICLES GERMANY GMBH—See Valeo S.A.; *Int'l*, pg. 8114
VALEO THERMAL COMMERCIAL VEHICLES MEXICO, SA DE CV—See Valeo S.A.; *Int'l*, pg. 8114
VALEO THERMAL COMMERCIAL VEHICLES MIDDLE EAST FZE—See Valeo S.A.; *Int'l*, pg. 8114
VALEOTHERMAL COMMERCIAL VEHICLES NORTH AMERICA, INC.—See Valeo S.A.; *Int'l*, pg. 8115
VALEO THERMAL COMMERCIAL VEHICLES SA (PTY) LTD.—See Valeo S.A.; *Int'l*, pg. 8114
VALEO THERMAL COMMERCIAL VEHICLES SYSTEM (SUZHOU) CO. LTD.—See Valeo S.A.; *Int'l*, pg. 8114
VALEO THERMAL SYSTEMS JAPAN CORPORATION—See Valeo S.A.; *Int'l*, pg. 8114
VALEO THERMAL SYSTEMS KOREA CO. LTD—See Valeo S.A.; *Int'l*, pg. 8114
VALEO TICARI TASITLAR TERMO SISTEMLERI AS—See Valeo S.A.; *Int'l*, pg. 8114
VALEO TRANSMISIONES SERVICIOS DE MEXICO S. DE R.L. DE C.V.—See Valeo S.A.; *Int'l*, pg. 8114
VALEO VISION BELGIQUE SA—See Valeo S.A.; *Int'l*, pg. 8114
VALEO VISION S.A.S.—See Valeo S.A.; *Int'l*, pg. 8114
VALEO VYMENIKY TEPLA S.R.O.—See Valeo S.A.; *Int'l*, pg. 8115
VALERA GLOBAL; *U.S. Private*, pg. 4331
VALERIE WILSON TRAVEL, INC.—See Frosch International Travel Inc.; *U.S. Private*, pg. 1616
VALER, INC.; *U.S. Private*, pg. 4331
VALERO CAPITAL PARTNERS LLC; *U.S. Private*, pg. 4331
VALERO ENERGY CORPORATION; *U.S. Public*, pg. 2272
VALERO ENERGY INC.—See Valero Energy Corporation; *U.S. Public*, pg. 2272
VALERO ENERGY (IRELAND) LIMITED—See Valero Energy Corporation; *U.S. Public*, pg. 2272
VALERO ENERGY LTD—See Valero Energy Corporation; *U.S. Public*, pg. 2272
VALERO ENERGY PARTNERS LP—See Valero Energy Corporation; *U.S. Public*, pg. 2272
VALERO EQUITY SERVICES LTD—See Valero Energy Corporation; *U.S. Public*, pg. 2272
VALERO MARKETING AND SUPPLY DE MEXICO S.A. DE C.V.—See Valero Energy Corporation; *U.S. Public*, pg. 2272
VALERO MARKETING IRELAND LIMITED—See Valero Energy Corporation; *U.S. Public*, pg. 2272
VALERO MARKETING & SUPPLY COMPANY—See Valero Energy Corporation; *U.S. Public*, pg. 2272
VALERON STRENGTH FILMS B.V.B.A.—See Illinois Tool Works Inc.; *U.S. Public*, pg. 1111
VALERON STRENGTH FILMS—See Illinois Tool Works Inc.; *U.S. Public*, pg. 1111
VALERO PARTNERS SOUTH TEXAS, LLC—See Valero Energy Corporation; *U.S. Public*, pg. 2272
VALERO PERU S.A.C.—See Valero Energy Corporation; *U.S. Public*, pg. 2272
VALERO REFINING COMPANY-ARUBA N.V.—See Valero Energy Corporation; *U.S. Public*, pg. 2272
VALERO REFINING COMPANY-CALIFORNIA—See Valero Energy Corporation; *U.S. Public*, pg. 2272
VALERO REFINING-MERAUX LLC—See Valero Energy Corporation; *U.S. Public*, pg. 2272
VALERO REFINING-TEXAS, L.P.—See Valero Energy Corporation; *U.S. Public*, pg. 2272
VALERO RENEWABLE FUELS CO., LLC - ALBION—See Valero Energy Corporation; *U.S. Public*, pg. 2272
VALERO RENEWABLE FUELS CO., LLC - AURORA—See Valero Energy Corporation; *U.S. Public*, pg. 2272
VALERO RENEWABLE FUELS CO., LLC - BLOOMINGBURG—See Valero Energy Corporation; *U.S. Public*, pg. 2273
VALERO RENEWABLE FUELS CO., LLC - CHARLES CITY—See Valero Energy Corporation; *U.S. Public*, pg. 2273
VALERO RENEWABLE FUELS CO., LLC - FORT DODGE—See Valero Energy Corporation; *U.S. Public*, pg. 2273
VALERO RENEWABLE FUELS CO., LLC - HARTLEY—See Valero Energy Corporation; *U.S. Public*, pg. 2273
VALERO RENEWABLE FUELS CO., LLC - LINDEN—See Valero Energy Corporation; *U.S. Public*, pg. 2273

VALIANT STEEL AND EQUIPMENT

VALERO RENEWABLE FUELS CO., LLC - WELCOME—See Valero Energy Corporation; *U.S. Public*, pg. 2273
VALERO RENEWABLE FUELS COMPANY, LLC—See Valero Energy Corporation; *U.S. Public*, pg. 2272
VALERO TERMINALING AND DISTRIBUTION DE MEXICO, S.A. DE C.V.—See Valero Energy Corporation; *U.S. Public*, pg. 2272
VALERO TERMINALING & DISTRIBUTION COMPANY—See Valero Energy Corporation; *U.S. Public*, pg. 2273
VALERUS COMPRESSION SERVICES, LP—See TPG Capital, L.P.; *U.S. Public*, pg. 2177
VALE S.A.; *Int'l*, pg. 8111
VALESCO INDUSTRIES, INC; *U.S. Private*, pg. 4331
VALESERVE MALAYSIA SDN. BHD.—See Vale S.A.; *Int'l*, pg. 8112
VALESUL ALUMINIO S.A.—See Vale S.A.; *Int'l*, pg. 8112
VALE TECHNOLOGY DEVELOPMENT (CANADA) LIMITED—See Vale S.A.; *Int'l*, pg. 8112
VALET LIVING, LLC—See GI Manager L.P.; *U.S. Private*, pg. 1694
VALET PARKING SERVICE, LIMITED PARTNERSHIP; *U.S. Private*, pg. 4331
VALE TRADING (SHANGHAI) CO., LTD—See Vale S.A.; *Int'l*, pg. 8112
VALETRON S.A.; *Int'l*, pg. 8115
VALETTA LOCOSHED OFFICES LTD.—See ENL Limited; *Int'l*, pg. 2442
VALETTE FINANCE B.V—See Immofinanz AG; *Int'l*, pg. 3628
VALEU CONSULTING SA—See Intracom Holdings S.A.; *Int'l*, pg. 3768
VALEURA ENERGY ASIA PTE. LTD.—See Valeura Energy Inc.; *Int'l*, pg. 8115
VALEURA ENERGY INC.; *Int'l*, pg. 8115
V. ALEXANDER & CO. INC.; *U.S. Private*, pg. 4328
VALEXCONSULTING; *U.S. Private*, pg. 4331
VALEX CORP.—See Reliance Steel & Aluminum Co.; *U.S. Public*, pg. 1782
VALEX KOREA CO., LTD.—See Reliance Steel & Aluminum Co.; *U.S. Public*, pg. 1782
VALFF ENROBES SAS—See VINCI S.A.; *Int'l*, pg. 8240
VALFILM - MG INDUSTRIA DE EMBALAGENS LTDA—See ValGroup Packaging Solutions; *Int'l*, pg. 8115
VALFILM NORTH AMERICA, INC. - FINDLAY PLANT—See ValGroup Packaging Solutions; *Int'l*, pg. 8115
VALFILM NORTH AMERICA, INC.—See ValGroup Packaging Solutions; *Int'l*, pg. 8115
VALFIVRE ITALIA SRL—See El.En. S.p.A.; *Int'l*, pg. 2342
VAL GLASS US LLC—See Dover Corporation; *U.S. Public*, pg. 683
VALGRAIN—See Groupe Limagrain Holding SA; *Int'l*, pg. 3108
VALGROUP PACKAGING SOLUTIONS - CAMACARI UNIT—See ValGroup Packaging Solutions; *Int'l*, pg. 8115
VALGROUP PACKAGING SOLUTIONS - ITAMONTE UNIT—See ValGroup Packaging Solutions; *Int'l*, pg. 8115
VALGROUP PACKAGING SOLUTIONS - LORENA UNIT—See ValGroup Packaging Solutions; *Int'l*, pg. 8115
VALGROUP PACKAGING SOLUTIONS - MANAUS UNIT—See ValGroup Packaging Solutions; *Int'l*, pg. 8115
VALGROUP PACKAGING SOLUTIONS; *Int'l*, pg. 8115
VALHALLA BUILDERS & DEVELOPERS INC.; *U.S. Private*, pg. 4331
THE VALHALLA CEMETERY COMPANY LLC—See Axar Capital Management L.P.; *U.S. Private*, pg. 412
VALHALLA PARTNERS INC.; *U.S. Private*, pg. 4331
VALHI, INC.—See Contran Corporation; *U.S. Private*, pg. 1033
VALIANCE PARTNERS, LLC—See Novo Nordisk Fonden; *Int'l*, pg. 5463
VALIANT BANK AG—See Valiant Holding AG; *Int'l*, pg. 8115
VALIANT BANK AG—See Valiant Holding AG; *Int'l*, pg. 8115
VALIANT CO., LTD.; *Int'l*, pg. 8115
VALIANT COMMUNICATIONS LIMITED; *Int'l*, pg. 8115
VALIANT GLOBAL DEFENSE SERVICES INC.—See Valiant Integrated Services LLC; *U.S. Private*, pg. 4331
VALIANT HOLDING AG; *Int'l*, pg. 8115
VALIANT INTEGRATED SERVICES LLC; *U.S. Private*, pg. 4331
VALIANT LABORATORIES LIMITED; *Int'l*, pg. 8115
VALIANT MORTGAGES LTD.—See Valiant Holding AG; *Int'l*, pg. 8115
VALIANT ORGANICS LIMITED; *Int'l*, pg. 8115
VALIANT PRODUCTS CORP.; *U.S. Private*, pg. 4331
VALIANT STEEL AND EQUIPMENT; *U.S. Private*, pg. 4332
VALIANT STEELWELD DEUTSCHLAND GMBH—See VDL Groep B.V.; *Int'l*, pg. 8142

VALIANT STEEL AND EQUIPMENT

VALICARE GMBH—See Robert Bosch GmbH; *Int'l*, pg. 6368
VALICARE S.R.O.—See Robert Bosch GmbH; *Int'l*, pg. 6368
VALICA SPA; *Int'l*, pg. 8115
VALIC CO., LTD.—See AOKI Holdings Inc.; *Int'l*, pg. 488
VALICOR ENVIRONMENTAL SERVICES, LLC—See The Pritzker Group - Chicago, LLC; *U.S. Private*, pg. 4100
VALICOR ENVIRONMENTAL TECHNOLOGIES, LLC—See The Pritzker Group - Chicago, LLC; *U.S. Private*, pg. 4100
VALICOR, INC.; *U.S. Private*, pg. 4332
VALIDA HOLDING AG—See Raiffeisen Bank International AG; *Int'l*, pg. 6184
VALIDA PLUS AG—See Raiffeisen Bank International AG; *Int'l*, pg. 6184
VALIDAR INC.; *U.S. Private*, pg. 4332
VALID ASIA PTE. LTD.—See Valid Solucoes S.A.; *Int'l*, pg. 8116
VALIDATEK INC.; *U.S. Private*, pg. 4332
VALIDATION RESOURCES LLC—See Temasek Holdings (Private) Limited; *Int'l*, pg. 7547
VALIDIAN CORPORATION; *Int'l*, pg. 8116
VALIDIC, INC.; *U.S. Private*, pg. 4332
VALIDITY, INC.—See Silversmith Management, L.P.; *U.S. Private*, pg. 3664
VALIDOR CAPITAL LLC; *U.S. Private*, pg. 4332
VALIDSOFT UK LIMITED; *Int'l*, pg. 8116
VALID SOLUCIONES Y SERVICIOS DE SEGURIDAD EN MEDIOS DE PAGO E IDENTIFICACION S.A.—See Valid Solucoes S.A.; *Int'l*, pg. 8116
VALID SOLUCOES S.A.; *Int'l*, pg. 8115
VALID SOUTH AFRICA (PTY.) LTD.—See Valid Solucoes S.A.; *Int'l*, pg. 8116
VALID USA INC.—See Valid Solucoes S.A.; *Int'l*, pg. 8116
VALIDUS AS; *Int'l*, pg. 8116
VALIDUS BUTIKKDRIFT AS—See Validus AS; *Int'l*, pg. 8116
VALIDUS DC SYSTEMS INC.—See ABB Ltd.; *Int'l*, pg. 52
VALIDUS HOLDINGS, LTD.—See American International Group, Inc.; *U.S. Public*, pg. 107
VALIDUS REASEGUROS, INC.—See American International Group, Inc.; *U.S. Public*, pg. 107
VALIDUS REINSURANCE, LTD.—See American International Group, Inc.; *U.S. Public*, pg. 107
VALIDUS REINSURANCE (SWITZERLAND) LTD—See American International Group, Inc.; *U.S. Public*, pg. 107
VALIDUS RESEARCH INC.—See American International Group, Inc.; *U.S. Public*, pg. 107
VALIDUS RISK SERVICES (IRELAND) LIMITED—See American International Group, Inc.; *U.S. Public*, pg. 107
VALIDUS VERIFICATION SERVICES—See Where Food Comes From, Inc.; *U.S. Public*, pg. 2366
VALIFY, INC.—See HCA Healthcare, Inc.; *U.S. Public*, pg. 1013
VALIKA SAS—See Intek Group S.p.A.; *Int'l*, pg. 3733
VALIMET INC.; *U.S. Private*, pg. 4332
VALIMO WIRELESS OY—See Thales S.A.; *Int'l*, pg. 7600
VALIN CORPORATION—See Graybar Electric Company, Inc.; *U.S. Private*, pg. 1760
VALINGE INNOVATION AB—See Valinge Invest AB; *Int'l*, pg. 8116
VALINGE INVEST AB; *Int'l*, pg. 8116
VALINOX NUCLEAIRE S.A.S.—See Electricite de France S.A.; *Int'l*, pg. 2351
VALIN TUBE—See Hunan Valin Steel Co., Ltd.; *Int'l*, pg. 3534
VALIO EESTI AS—See Valio Ltd.; *Int'l*, pg. 8116
VALIO LTD.; *Int'l*, pg. 8116
VALIO SHANGHAI LTD.—See Valio Ltd.; *Int'l*, pg. 8116
VALIO SVERIGE AB—See Valio Ltd.; *Int'l*, pg. 8116
VALIO USA, INC.—See Valio Ltd.; *Int'l*, pg. 8116
VALIO - VACHE BLEUE S.A.—See Valio Ltd.; *Int'l*, pg. 8116
VALIPHARMA LTD.—See Valirx plc; *Int'l*, pg. 8116
VALIRA ASSET MANAGEMENT SL—See Credit Andorra, S.A.; *Int'l*, pg. 1835
VALIR HEALTH; *U.S. Private*, pg. 4332
VALIR REHABILITATION HOSPITAL OF OKC, LLC—See Valir Health; *U.S. Private*, pg. 4332
VALIRX PLC; *Int'l*, pg. 8116
VALITON GMBH—See Hubert Burda Media Holding Kommanditgesellschaft; *Int'l*, pg. 3520
VALITOR HOLDING HF.—See Arion Bank hf.; *Int'l*, pg. 565
VALJAONICA BAKRA SEVOJNO AD; *Int'l*, pg. 8116
VALKA EHF.—See Marel hf; *Int'l*, pg. 4691
VALK MANUFACTURING COMPANY; *U.S. Private*, pg. 4332
VALKRY CORPORATION & EXOTIC CARS SOUTH; *U.S. Private*, pg. 4332
VALKYRIE COMPANY INC.; *U.S. Private*, pg. 4332
VALKYRIE ENTERPRISES, LLC—See D.C. Capital Partners, LLC; *U.S. Private*, pg. 1141
VALLABH POLY PLAST INTERNATIONAL LIMITED; *Int'l*, pg. 8116
VALLABH STEELS LTD.; *Int'l*, pg. 8116
VALLACOM AB—See Instalco AB; *Int'l*, pg. 3723
VALLANCE CARRUTHERS COLEMAN PRIEST; *Int'l*, pg. 8117

VALLCAL S.L.—See Nicolas Correa S.A.; *Int'l*, pg. 5273
VALLECITOS WATER DISTRICT; *U.S. Private*, pg. 4332
VALLEHERMOSO DIVISION DE PROMOCION, S.A.U.—See Sacyr, S.A.; *Int'l*, pg. 6466
VALLEN DISTRIBUTION INC.—See Nautic Partners, LLC; *U.S. Private*, pg. 2872
VALLEN, INC.—See Sonepar S.A.; *Int'l*, pg. 7094
VALLEN—See Sonepar S.A.; *Int'l*, pg. 7093
VALLERGAS DRIVE-IN MARKETS; *U.S. Private*, pg. 4332
VALLET FOOD SERVICE INC.; *U.S. Private*, pg. 4332
VALLETTA CRUISE PORT PLC—See Global Yatirim Holding A.S.; *Int'l*, pg. 3003
VALLEY ACQUISITION CO. LLC; *U.S. Private*, pg. 4332
VALLEY ADVOCATE—See Tribune Publishing Company; *U.S. Private*, pg. 4228
VALLEY AMBULATORY SURGERY CENTER, L.P.—See Bain Capital, LP; *U.S. Private*, pg. 447
VALLEY AUTOMOTIVE GROUP; *U.S. Private*, pg. 4332
VALLEY AUTO WORLD INCORPORATED; *U.S. Private*, pg. 4332
VALLEY BAKERS COOP ASSOCIATION; *U.S. Private*, pg. 4332
VALLEY BANK OF HELENA—See Glacier Bancorp, Inc.; *U.S. Public*, pg. 939
VALLEY BANK & TRUST; *U.S. Private*, pg. 4332
VALLEY BAPTIST LAB SERVICES, LLC—See Tenet Healthcare Corporation; *U.S. Public*, pg. 2015
VALLEY BEHAVIORAL HEALTH SYSTEM, LLC—See Acadia Healthcare Company, Inc.; *U.S. Public*, pg. 31
VALLEY BUILDING MATERIALS—See West Coast Materials, Inc.; *U.S. Private*, pg. 4484
VALLEY BUILDING PRODUCTS COMPANY—See The Sowles Company; *U.S. Private*, pg. 4120
VALLEY BUILDING SUPPLY INC.—See Eagle Corporation; *U.S. Private*, pg. 1309
VALLEY BUILDING SUPPLY INC.—See Eagle Corporation; *U.S. Private*, pg. 1309
VALLEY CABINET INC.; *U.S. Private*, pg. 4332
THE VALLEY CADILLAC CORP.; *U.S. Private*, pg. 4130
VALLEY CADILLAC OLDSMOBILE; *U.S. Private*, pg. 4332
VALLEY CAPITAL CORPORATION; *U.S. Private*, pg. 4332
VALLEY CASTING, INC.; *U.S. Private*, pg. 4333
VALLEY CHEVROLET INC.; *U.S. Private*, pg. 4333
VALLEY CHRYSLER DODGE, INC.; *U.S. Private*, pg. 4333
VALLEY COCA-COLA BOTTLING COMPANY, INC.—See The Coca-Cola Company; *U.S. Public*, pg. 2065
VALLEY COMMERCIAL CONTRACTORS; *U.S. Private*, pg. 4333
VALLEY CONSTRUCTION COMPANY—See The Valley Group, Inc.; *U.S. Private*, pg. 4130
VALLEY CONSTRUCTION SUPPLY; *U.S. Private*, pg. 4333
VALLEY CONVERTING CO., INC.; *U.S. Private*, pg. 4333
VALLEY CO-OP INC.; *U.S. Private*, pg. 4333
VALLEY CO-OP OIL MILL INC.; *U.S. Private*, pg. 4333
VALLEY CO-OPS INC.; *U.S. Private*, pg. 4333
VALLEY COURIERS; *U.S. Private*, pg. 4333
VALLEY DETROIT DIESEL ALLISON; *U.S. Private*, pg. 4333
VALLEY ELECTRIC COMPANY OF MOUNT VERNON, INC.; *U.S. Private*, pg. 4333
VALLEY ELECTRIC SUPPLY CORP.; *U.S. Private*, pg. 4333
THE VALLEY ENDOSCOPY CENTER, L.P.; *U.S. Private*, pg. 4130
VALLEY ENERGY CORP.; *U.S. Private*, pg. 4333
VALLEY ENTERPRISES, INC.—See Gemini Group, Inc.; *U.S. Private*, pg. 1658
VALLEY EXPRESS INC.; *U.S. Private*, pg. 4333
VALLEYFAIR—See Six Flags Entertainment Corporation; *U.S. Public*, pg. 1890
VALLEY FARMERS COOPERATIVE; *U.S. Private*, pg. 4333
VALLEY FARMS LIMITED—See McCain Foods Limited; *Int'l*, pg. 4757
VALLEY FARMS SUPPLY, INC.—See Franklin Electric Co., Inc.; *U.S. Public*, pg. 879
VALLEY FASTENER GROUP LLC - NORTH COAST RIVET DIVISION—See Valley Fastener Group LLC; *U.S. Private*, pg. 4333
VALLEY FASTENER GROUP LLC; *U.S. Private*, pg. 4333
VALLEY FENCE COMPANY—See Apache Construction Company, Inc.; *U.S. Private*, pg. 290
VALLEY FIG GROWERS INC.; *U.S. Private*, pg. 4333
VALLEY FIRST CREDIT UNION; *U.S. Private*, pg. 4333
VALLEY FOOD SERVICES, LLC; *U.S. Private*, pg. 4333
VALLEY FORD SALES INC.; *U.S. Private*, pg. 4333
VALLEY FORD TRUCK SALES INCORPORATED; *U.S. Private*, pg. 4333
VALLEY FORGE CONVENTION CENTER PARTNERS, LLC—See Boyd Gaming Corporation; *U.S. Public*, pg. 378
VALLEY FORGE FLAG COMPANY; *U.S. Private*, pg. 4334

CORPORATE AFFILIATIONS

VALLEY FORGE INVESTMENT CORP.; *U.S. Private*, pg. 4334
VALLEY FREIGHTLINER INC.; *U.S. Private*, pg. 4334
VALLEY FRESH AUSTRALIA PTY LTD—See Maui Capital Ltd.; *Int'l*, pg. 4731
VALLEYFRESH EXPORTS—See Maui Capital Ltd.; *Int'l*, pg. 4731
VALLEYFRESH NEW ZEALAND LIMITED—See Maui Capital Ltd.; *Int'l*, pg. 4731
VALLEYFRESH NORTH AMERICA, LLC—See Maui Capital Ltd.; *Int'l*, pg. 4731
VALLEY FURNITURE SHOP, INC.; *U.S. Private*, pg. 4334
VALLEY GLASS INC.; *U.S. Private*, pg. 4334
THE VALLEY GROUP, INC.; *U.S. Private*, pg. 4130
VALLEY GUTTER SUPPLY INC.—See TopBuild Corp.; *U.S. Public*, pg. 2163
VALLEY HEALTH CARE NETWORK—See Tenet Healthcare Corporation; *U.S. Public*, pg. 2015
VALLEY HEALTHCARE SYSTEMS, INC.; *U.S. Private*, pg. 4334
VALLEY-HI AUTOMOTIVE GROUP—See Dick Browning, Inc.; *U.S. Private*, pg. 1225
VALLEY-HI HONDA—See Dick Browning, Inc.; *U.S. Private*, pg. 1225
VALLEY-HI NISSAN—See Dick Browning, Inc.; *U.S. Private*, pg. 1225
VALLEY-HI TOYOTA SCION; *U.S. Private*, pg. 4336
VALLEY-HI TOYOTA—See Dick Browning, Inc.; *U.S. Private*, pg. 1225
VALLEY HONDA; *U.S. Private*, pg. 4334
VALLEY HOPE ASSOCIATION; *U.S. Private*, pg. 4334
VALLEY HOSPICE, INC.; *U.S. Private*, pg. 4334
VALLEY HOSPITAL ASSOCIATION; *U.S. Private*, pg. 4334
VALLEY HOSPITAL MEDICAL CENTER—See Universal Health Services, Inc.; *U.S. Public*, pg. 2260
VALLEY ICE, LLC—See Holtzman Oil Corp.; *U.S. Private*, pg. 1969
VALLEY IMAGING PARTNERS INC.—See RadNet, Inc.; *U.S. Public*, pg. 1761
VALLEY IMPLEMENT & MOTOR CO.; *U.S. Private*, pg. 4334
VALLEY IMPORTS, INC.—See W.W. Wallwork, Inc.; *U.S. Private*, pg. 4423
VALLEY IMPROVEMENT ASSOCIATION, INC.; *U.S. Private*, pg. 4334
VALLEY INDUSTRIES, LLP—See Emak S.p.A.; *Int'l*, pg. 2373
VALLEY INSULATION, INC.—See TopBuild Corp.; *U.S. Public*, pg. 2163
VALLEY INTERIOR SYSTEMS INC.; *U.S. Private*, pg. 4334
VALLEY ISLE PRODUCE, INC.; *U.S. Private*, pg. 4334
VALLEY JOIST, LLC—See Black Diamond Capital Holdings, LLC; *U.S. Private*, pg. 571
VALLEYLIFE; *U.S. Private*, pg. 4336
VALLEY LIGHTING, LLC; *U.S. Private*, pg. 4334
VALLEY MAGNESITE COMPANY LIMITED; *Int'l*, pg. 8117
VALLEY MANAGEMENT GROUP, INC.; *U.S. Private*, pg. 4334
VALLEY MANAGEMENT, INC.; *U.S. Private*, pg. 4334
VALLEY MARKETS, INCORPORATED; *U.S. Private*, pg. 4334
VALLEY MEATS LLC—See North American Company; *U.S. Private*, pg. 2940
VALLEY METALS, LLC—See Leggett & Platt, Incorporated; *U.S. Public*, pg. 1304
VALLEY MINING, INC.; *U.S. Private*, pg. 4334
VALLEY MORNING STAR—See AIM Media Texas, LLC; *U.S. Private*, pg. 133
VALLEY MOUNTAIN REGIONAL CENTER INC.; *U.S. Private*, pg. 4334
VALLEY NAILS LLC—See Hudson Blvd. Group LLC; *U.S. Private*, pg. 2001
VALLEY NATIONAL BANCORP; *U.S. Public*, pg. 2273
VALLEY NATIONAL BANK—See Valley National Bancorp; *U.S. Public*, pg. 2273
VALLEY NETWORK PARTNERSHIP—See Lumen Technologies, Inc.; *U.S. Public*, pg. 1348
VALLEY NETWORK SOLUTIONS, INC.; *U.S. Private*, pg. 4334
VALLEY NEWSPAPERS—See Independent Newspapers, Inc.; *U.S. Private*, pg. 2060
VALLEY OIL CORPORATION; *U.S. Private*, pg. 4334
VALLEY PACIFIC PETROLEUM SERVICES, INC.; *U.S. Private*, pg. 4334
VALLEY PACKAGING INC.; *U.S. Private*, pg. 4334
VALLEY PACKAGING INDUSTRIES, INC.; *U.S. Private*, pg. 4334
VALLEY PACKING SERVICE INC.—See The VPS Companies Inc.; *U.S. Private*, pg. 4132
VALLEY PALLET RECYCLERS INC.; *U.S. Private*, pg. 4335
VALLEY PAVING INC.; *U.S. Private*, pg. 4335
VALLEY PET CREMATORIUM LIMITED—See CVS Group Plc; *Int'l*, pg. 1890
VALLEY PHYSICIANS NETWORK, INC.—See UnitedHealth Group Incorporated; *U.S. Public*, pg. 2252
VALLEY PLATING WORKS; *U.S. Private*, pg. 4335

COMPANY NAME INDEX

VALLEY PONTIAC BUICK GMC, INC.; *U.S. Private,* pg. 4335
VALLEY POWER LIMITED PARTNERSHIP—See Algonquin Power & Utilities Corp.; *Int'l,* pg. 319
VALLEY PRIDE PACK INC.; *U.S. Private,* pg. 4335
VALLEY PROCESSING, INC.—See Wyckoff Farms, Incorporated; *U.S. Private,* pg. 4575
VALLEY PRODUCTS CO.; *U.S. Private,* pg. 4335
VALLEY PROTEINS, INC.—See Darling Ingredients Inc.; *U.S. Public,* pg. 634
VALLEY PROTEINS, INC.—See Darling Ingredients Inc.; *U.S. Public,* pg. 634
VALLEY PROTEINS, INC.—See Darling Ingredients Inc.; *U.S. Public,* pg. 634
VALLEY PROTEINS, INC.—See Darling Ingredients Inc.; *U.S. Public,* pg. 634
VALLEY PROTEINS, INC.—See Darling Ingredients Inc.; *U.S. Public,* pg. 634
VALLEY QUALITY HOMES INC.; *U.S. Private,* pg. 4335
VALLEY QUARRIES INC. - CHAMBERSBURG PLANT—See New Enterprise Stone & Lime Co., Inc.; *U.S. Private,* pg. 2895
VALLEY QUARRIES INC. - GETTYSBURG PLANT—See New Enterprise Stone & Lime Co., Inc.; *U.S. Private,* pg. 2895
VALLEY QUARRIES INC. - MT. CYDONIA PLANT II—See New Enterprise Stone & Lime Co., Inc.; *U.S. Private,* pg. 2895
VALLEY QUARRIES INC. - MT. CYDONIA PLANT I—See New Enterprise Stone & Lime Co., Inc.; *U.S. Private,* pg. 2895
VALLEY QUARRIES INC. - SHIPPENSBURG PLANT—See New Enterprise Stone & Lime Co., Inc.; *U.S. Private,* pg. 2895
VALLEY QUARRIES INC.—See New Enterprise Stone & Lime Co., Inc.; *U.S. Private,* pg. 2895
VALLEY RECYCLING; *U.S. Private,* pg. 4335
VALLEY REGIONAL MEDICAL CENTER—See HCA Healthcare, Inc.; *U.S. Public,* pg. 1013
VALLEY RELOCATION & STORAGE; *U.S. Private,* pg. 4335
VALLEY REPUBLIC BANK; *U.S. Private,* pg. 4335
VALLEY RIDGE INVESTMENT PARTNERS; *U.S. Private,* pg. 4000
VALLEY RIVER NURSING, LLC—See Regional Health Properties, Inc.; *U.S. Public,* pg. 1776
VALLEY ROADWAYS LTD.—See Landtran Systems Inc.; *Int'l,* pg. 4408
VALLEY ROLLER COMPANY, INC.—See Berwind Corporation; *U.S. Private,* pg. 541
VALLEY ROZ ORCHARDS INC.; *U.S. Private,* pg. 4335
VALLEY RUBBER & GASKET CO. INC.—See LKCM Headwater Investments; *U.S. Private,* pg. 2475
VALLEY RUBBER, LLC; *U.S. Private,* pg. 4335
VALLEY RURAL ELECTRIC COOPERATIVE, INC.; *U.S. Private,* pg. 4335
VALLEY SERVICES, INC.—See Charterhouse Capital Partners LLP; *Int'l,* pg. 1455
VALLEY SHEET METAL COMPANY—See Frank M. Booth Inc.; *U.S. Private,* pg. 1595
VALLEY SOLVENT COMPANY, INC.—See Apollo Global Management, Inc.; *U.S. Public,* pg. 166
VALLEY SPRINGS DIALYSIS, LLC—See DaVita Inc.; *U.S. Public,* pg. 644
THE VALLEY STATE BANK—See Morley Bancshares Corporation; *U.S. Private,* pg. 2785
VALLEY STREAM GREEN ACRES LLC—See The Macerich Company; *U.S. Public,* pg. 2111
VALLEY STREAM LINCOLN MERCURY; *U.S. Private,* pg. 4335
VALLEY STRONG CEMENTS (ASSAM) LIMITED—See Barak Valley Cements Limited; *Int'l,* pg. 858
VALLEY STRONG CREDIT UNION; *U.S. Private,* pg. 4335
VALLEY SUPPLY & EQUIPMENT CO.; *U.S. Private,* pg. 4335
VALLEY SUPPLY, INC.—See Clayton, Dubilier & Rice, LLC; *U.S. Private,* pg. 930
VALLEY SURGICAL CENTER, LTD.—See Bain Capital, LP; *U.S. Private,* pg. 447
VALLEY TELEPHONE COOPERATIVE INC; *U.S. Private,* pg. 4335
VALLEY TIRE CO., INC.; *U.S. Private,* pg. 4335
VALLEY TOOL & MANUFACTURING, INC.—See Harlow Aerostructures, LLC; *U.S. Private,* pg. 1865
VALLEY TRANSFORMER CO—See Trilantic Capital Management L.P.; *U.S. Private,* pg. 4231
VALLEY TRUCKING CO., INC.; *U.S. Private,* pg. 4335
VALLEY TRUCK PARTS, INC.; *U.S. Private,* pg. 4335
VALLEY TRUCK & TRACTOR CO.; *U.S. Private,* pg. 4335
VALLEY TRUSS COMPANY—See Builders FirstSource, Inc.; *U.S. Public,* pg. 410
VALLEY VIEW BANCSHARES, INC.; *U.S. Private,* pg. 4336
VALLEY VIEW FINANCIAL GROUP TRUST COMPANY—See Valley View Bancshares, Inc.; *U.S. Private,* pg. 4336
VALLEY VIEW HAVEN, INC.; *U.S. Private,* pg. 4336
VALLEY VIEW HEALTH SERVICES, INC.—See The Ensign Group, Inc.; *U.S. Public,* pg. 2072
VALLEY VIEW HOSPITAL; *U.S. Private,* pg. 4336
VALLEY VIEW PACKING; *U.S. Private,* pg. 4336
VALLEY VIEW TUBE, INC.; *U.S. Private,* pg. 4336
VALLEY VISTA CARE CORPORATION; *U.S. Private,* pg. 4336
VALLEY WATER SYSTEMS, INC.—See New England Services Company; *U.S. Public,* pg. 1511
VALLEY WHOLESALE COMPANY INC.; *U.S. Private,* pg. 4336
VALLEY WIDE COOPERATIVE INC.; *U.S. Private,* pg. 4336
VALLEY YOUTH HOUSE; *U.S. Private,* pg. 4336
VALLIANZ HOLDINGS LIMITED; *Int'l,* pg. 8117
VALLIANZ OFFSHORE CAPITAL MEXICO, A. DE C.V. SOFOM, E.N.R.—See Vallianz Holdings Limited; *Int'l,* pg. 8117
VALLIANZ SAMSON PTE LTD—See Vallianz Holdings Limited; *Int'l,* pg. 8117
VALLIBEL POWER ERATHNA PLC; *Int'l,* pg. 8117
VALLI INFORMATION SYSTEMS, INCORPORATED; *U.S. Private,* pg. 4336
VAL LIMITED; *U.S. Private,* pg. 4329
VALLIN BALTIC AS—See Addtech AB; *Int'l,* pg. 135
VALLI PRODUCE; *U.S. Private,* pg. 4336
VALLONE S.R.L.—See Encavis AG; *Int'l,* pg. 2401
VALLORTIGARA SERVIZI AMBIENTALI S.P.A.—See Hera S.p.A.; *Int'l,* pg. 3357
VALLOUREC DEUTSCHLAND GMBH—See Vallourec SA; *Int'l,* pg. 8117
VALLOUREC DRILLING OIL EQUIPMENT MANUFACTURING LLC—See NOV, Inc.; *U.S. Public,* pg. 1547
VALLOUREC DRILLING PRODUCTS USA, INC.—See NOV, Inc.; *U.S. Public,* pg. 1547
VALLOUREC FITTINGS SAS—See Vallourec SA; *Int'l,* pg. 8117
VALLOUREC FLORESTAL LTDA.—See Vallourec SA; *Int'l,* pg. 8117
VALLOUREC ITALIANA S.R.L.—See Vallourec SA; *Int'l,* pg. 8117
VALLOUREC MIDDLE EAST FZE—See Vallourec SA; *Int'l,* pg. 8117
VALLOUREC MINERACAO LTDA.—See Vallourec SA; *Int'l,* pg. 8117
VALLOUREC OIL & GAS FRANCE - AULNOYE-AYMERIES—See Vallourec SA; *Int'l,* pg. 8117
VALLOUREC OIL & GAS FRANCE—See Vallourec SA; *Int'l,* pg. 8117
VALLOUREC OIL & GAS MEXICO S.A. DE C.V.—See Vallourec SA; *Int'l,* pg. 8117
VALLOUREC OIL & GAS NEDERLAND B.V.—See Vallourec SA; *Int'l,* pg. 8117
VALLOUREC OIL & GAS NIGERIA LTD.—See Vallourec SA; *Int'l,* pg. 8117
VALLOUREC OIL & GAS UK LTD.—See Vallourec SA; *Int'l,* pg. 8117
VALLOUREC SA; *Int'l,* pg. 8117
VALLOUREC STAR, LP—See Vallourec SA; *Int'l,* pg. 8118
VALLOUREC TUBE-ALLOY, LLC - HOUMA—See Vallourec SA; *Int'l,* pg. 8118
VALLOUREC TUBES FRANCE - AULNOYE-AYMERIES MILL—See Vallourec SA; *Int'l,* pg. 8118
VALLOUREC TUBES FRANCE - ROUEN MILL—See Vallourec SA; *Int'l,* pg. 8118
VALLOUREC TUBES FRANCE - SAINT-SAULVE TUBE MILL—See Vallourec SA; *Int'l,* pg. 8118
VALLOUREC TUBES SAS—See Vallourec SA; *Int'l,* pg. 8118
VALLOUREC TUBOS DO BRASIL S.A.—See Vallourec SA; *Int'l,* pg. 8118
VALLOUREC USA CORPORATION—See Vallourec SA; *Int'l,* pg. 8118
VALLS QUIMICA S.A.—See Groupe Seche SAS; *Int'l,* pg. 3111
VALLVIKS BRUK AB—See Arctic Paper S.A.; *Int'l,* pg. 552
VALMARK INC.; *U.S. Private,* pg. 4336
VALMARK INDUSTRIES, INC.—See Jordan Industries, Inc.; *U.S. Private,* pg. 2235
VAL-MATIC VALVE AND MANUFACTURING CORP.; *U.S. Private,* pg. 4330
VALMEC LIMITED—See Altrad Investment Authority SAS; *Int'l,* pg. 398
VALMET AB - GAVLE—See Valmet Oyj; *Int'l,* pg. 8120
VALMET AB - GOTHENBURG—See Valmet Oyj; *Int'l,* pg. 8120
VALMET AB - GOTHENBURG WORKS—See Valmet Oyj; *Int'l,* pg. 8120
VALMET AB - HAGFORS—See Valmet Oyj; *Int'l,* pg. 8120
VALMET AB - KARLSTAD—See Valmet Oyj; *Int'l,* pg. 8120
VALMET AB—See Valmet Oyj; *Int'l,* pg. 8120
VALMET AUTOMACAO LTDA.—See Valmet Oyj; *Int'l,* pg. 8119
VALMET AUTOMATION AB—See Valmet Oyj; *Int'l,* pg. 8119
VALMET AUTOMATION A/S—See Valmet Oyj; *Int'l,* pg. 8119
VALMET AUTOMATION B.V.—See Valmet Oyj; *Int'l,* pg. 8119

VALMET OYJ

VALMET AUTOMATION CO., LTD.—See Valmet Oyj; *Int'l,* pg. 8119
VALMET AUTOMATION GESMBH—See Valmet Oyj; *Int'l,* pg. 8119
VALMET AUTOMATION GMBH—See Valmet Oyj; *Int'l,* pg. 8119
VALMET AUTOMATION JSC—See Valmet Oyj; *Int'l,* pg. 8119
VALMET AUTOMATION KK—See Valmet Oyj; *Int'l,* pg. 8119
VALMET AUTOMATION LIMITED—See Valmet Oyj; *Int'l,* pg. 8119
VALMET AUTOMATION LTD—See Valmet Oyj; *Int'l,* pg. 8119
VALMET AUTOMATION OY - KAJAANI—See Valmet Oyj; *Int'l,* pg. 8119
VALMET AUTOMATION OY—See Valmet Oyj; *Int'l,* pg. 8119
VALMET AUTOMATION OY - TAMPERE—See Valmet Oyj; *Int'l,* pg. 8119
VALMET AUTOMATION POLSKA SP. Z.O.O.—See Valmet Oyj; *Int'l,* pg. 8119
VALMET AUTOMATION PRIVATE LIMITED—See Valmet Oyj; *Int'l,* pg. 8120
VALMET AUTOMATION PTE. LTD.—See Valmet Oyj; *Int'l,* pg. 8120
VALMET AUTOMATION (PTY) LTD.—See Valmet Oyj; *Int'l,* pg. 8119
VALMET AUTOMATION PTY. LTD.—See Valmet Oyj; *Int'l,* pg. 8120
VALMET AUTOMATION S.A.S.—See Valmet Oyj; *Int'l,* pg. 8120
VALMET AUTOMATION (SHANGHAI) CO., LTD.—See Valmet Oyj; *Int'l,* pg. 8119
VALMET AUTOMATION S.R.O.—See Valmet Oyj; *Int'l,* pg. 8120
VALMET AUTOMOTIVE ENGINEERING GMBH—See Valmet Automotive Oy; *Int'l,* pg. 8118
VALMET AUTOMOTIVE ENGINEERING GMBH—See Valmet Automotive Oy; *Int'l,* pg. 8118
VALMET AUTOMOTIVE GMBH—See Valmet Automotive Oy; *Int'l,* pg. 8118
VALMET AUTOMOTIVE OY; *Int'l,* pg. 8118
VALMET AUTOMOTIVE SP. Z O.O.—See Valmet Automotive Oy; *Int'l,* pg. 8118
VALMET B.V.—See Valmet Oyj; *Int'l,* pg. 8120
VALMET CELULOSE PAPEL E ENERGIA LTDA. - SOROCABA—See Valmet Oyj; *Int'l,* pg. 8120
VALMET CELULOSE, PAPEL E ENERGIA LTDA.—See Valmet Oyj; *Int'l,* pg. 8120
VALMET CHENNAI PVT. LTD.—See Valmet Oyj; *Int'l,* pg. 8120
VALMET (CHINA) CO., LTD.—See Valmet Oyj; *Int'l,* pg. 8120
VALMET CO., LTD.—See Valmet Oyj; *Int'l,* pg. 8120
VALMET DEUTSCHLAND GMBH—See Valmet Oyj; *Int'l,* pg. 8120
VALME TECHNOLOGIES SAS—See Derichebourg S.A.; *Int'l,* pg. 2042
VALMET FABRICS (CHINA) CO., LTD.—See Valmet Oyj; *Int'l,* pg. 8120
VALMET FABRICS TECIDOS TECNICOS LTDA.—See Valmet Oyj; *Int'l,* pg. 8120
VALMET GESMBH—See Valmet Oyj; *Int'l,* pg. 8120
VALMET GMBH—See Valmet Oyj; *Int'l,* pg. 8120
VALMET, INC. - APPLETON—See Valmet Oyj; *Int'l,* pg. 8121
VALMET, INC. - BELOIT—See Valmet Oyj; *Int'l,* pg. 8121
VALMET, INC. - BIDDEFORD—See Valmet Oyj; *Int'l,* pg. 8121
VALMET, INC. - CLARKS SUMMIT—See Valmet Oyj; *Int'l,* pg. 8121
VALMET, INC.—See Valmet Oyj; *Int'l,* pg. 8121
VALMET INC.—See Valmet Oyj; *Int'l,* pg. 8120
VALMET KAUTTUA OY—See Valmet Oyj; *Int'l,* pg. 8120
VALMET K.K.—See Valmet Oyj; *Int'l,* pg. 8120
VALMET K.K.—See Valmet Oyj; *Int'l,* pg. 8120
VALMET LDA—See Valmet Oyj; *Int'l,* pg. 8120
VALMET LIMITED—See Valmet Oyj; *Int'l,* pg. 8120
VALMET LTD.—See Valmet Oyj; *Int'l,* pg. 8120
VALMET LTD—See Valmet Oyj; *Int'l,* pg. 8120
VALMET OYJ; *Int'l,* pg. 8118
VALMET PAPER (SHANGHAI) CO., LTD.—See Valmet Oyj; *Int'l,* pg. 8120
VALMET PAPER TECHNOLOGY (CHINA) CO., LTD.—See Valmet Oyj; *Int'l,* pg. 8120
VALMET PAPER TECHNOLOGY (GUANGZHOU) CO., LTD.—See Valmet Oyj; *Int'l,* pg. 8120
VALMET PAPER TECHNOLOGY (XI'AN) CO., LTD.—See Valmet Oyj; *Int'l,* pg. 8120
VALMET PLATTLING GMBH—See Valmet Oyj; *Int'l,* pg. 8120
VALMET PTY. LTD.—See Valmet Oyj; *Int'l,* pg. 8120
VALMET SA—See Valmet Oyj; *Int'l,* pg. 8121
VALMET SA—See Valmet Oyj; *Int'l,* pg. 8121
VALMET SAS—See Valmet Oyj; *Int'l,* pg. 8121
VALMET SAS—See Valmet Oyj; *Int'l,* pg. 8121
VALMET SELULOZ KAGIT VE ENERJI TEKNOLOJILERI A.S.—See Valmet Oyj; *Int'l,* pg. 8120

VALMET OYJ

VALMET SOUTH AFRICA (PTY) LTD—See Valmet Oyj; *Int'l*, pg. 8121
VALMET S.P.A.—See Valmet Oyj; *Int'l*, pg. 8121
VALMET SPA—See Valmet Oyj; *Int'l*, pg. 8121
VALMET S.R.O.—See Valmet Oyj; *Int'l*, pg. 8121
VALMET TECHNOLOGIES CO. PVT LTD—See Valmet Oyj; *Int'l*, pg. 8121
VALMET TECHNOLOGIES OU—See Valmet Oyj; *Int'l*, pg. 8121
VALMET TECHNOLOGIES OY - JARVENPAA—See Valmet Oyj; *Int'l*, pg. 8121
VALMET TECHNOLOGIES OY - JYVASKYLA—See Valmet Oyj; *Int'l*, pg. 8121
VALMET TECHNOLOGIES OY - PORI—See Valmet Oyj; *Int'l*, pg. 8121
VALMET TECHNOLOGIES OY - RAISIO—See Valmet Oyj; *Int'l*, pg. 8121
VALMET TECHNOLOGIES OY—See Valmet Oyj; *Int'l*, pg. 8120
VALMET TECHNOLOGIES SAU—See Valmet Oyj; *Int'l*, pg. 8121
VALMET TECHNOLOGIES, SAU—See Valmet Oyj; *Int'l*, pg. 8121
VALMET TECHNOLOGIES S. DE R.L. DE C.V.—See Valmet Oyj; *Int'l*, pg. 8121
VALMET TECHNOLOGIES SP. Z O.O.—See Valmet Oyj; *Int'l*, pg. 8121
VALMET TECHNOLOGIES ZARAGOZA, S.L.—See Valmet Oyj; *Int'l*, pg. 8121
VALMET ZAO—See Valmet Oyj; *Int'l*, pg. 8121
VALMICRO IND. E COM. DE VALVULAS LIMITADA—See Lupatech S.A.; *Int'l*, pg. 4585
VALMIERAS STIKLA SKIEDRA AS—See Warwick Capital Partners LLP; *Int'l*, pg. 8350
VALMIE RESOURCES, INC.; *U.S. Public*, pg. 2273
VALMINVEST—See Societe Generale S.A.; *Int'l*, pg. 7042
VALMONT AUSTRALIA IRRIGATION PTY. LTD.—See Valmont Industries, Inc.; *U.S. Public*, pg. 2274
VALMONT COATINGS INC—See Valmont Industries, Inc.; *U.S. Public*, pg. 2274
VALMONT COATINGS WEST POINT GALVANIZING—See Valmont Industries, Inc.; *U.S. Public*, pg. 2274
VALMONT COMPOSITE STRUCTURES, INC.—See Valmont Industries, Inc.; *U.S. Public*, pg. 2274
VALMONT FRANCE S.A.—See Valmont Industries, Inc.; *U.S. Public*, pg. 2274
VALMONT INDUSTRIA E COMERCIO, LTDA.—See Valmont Industries, Inc.; *U.S. Public*, pg. 2274
VALMONT INDUSTRIES HOLLAND B.V.—See Valmont Industries, Inc.; *U.S. Public*, pg. 2274
VALMONT INDUSTRIES, INC.; *U.S. Public*, pg. 2273
VALMONT INTERNATIONAL CORP.—See Valmont Industries, Inc.; *U.S. Public*, pg. 2274
VALMONT IRRIGATION DIVISION—See Valmont Industries, Inc.; *U.S. Public*, pg. 2274
VALMONT NEDERLAND B.V.—See Valmont Industries, Inc.; *U.S. Public*, pg. 2274
VALMONT NEWMARK, INC.—See Valmont Industries, Inc.; *U.S. Public*, pg. 2274
VALMONT NORTHWEST—See Valmont Industries, Inc.; *U.S. Public*, pg. 2274
VALMONT POLSKA SP.Z O.O—See Valmont Industries, Inc.; *U.S. Public*, pg. 2274
VALMONT SM A/S—See Euro Steel Danmark A/S; *Int'l*, pg. 2531
VALMONT—See Valmont Industries, Inc.; *U.S. Public*, pg. 2274
VALMONT STAINTON LTD.—See Valmont Industries, Inc.; *U.S. Public*, pg. 2274
VALMONT STRUCTURES PRIVATE LIMITED—See Valmont Industries, Inc.; *U.S. Public*, pg. 2274
VALNEVA AUSTRIA GMBH—See Valneva SE; *Int'l*, pg. 8121
VALNEVA CANADA INC.—See Valneva SE; *Int'l*, pg. 8121
VALNEVA FRANCE SAS—See Valneva SE; *Int'l*, pg. 8121
VALNEVA SCOTLAND LIMITED—See Valneva SE; *Int'l*, pg. 8121
VALNEVA SE; *Int'l*, pg. 8121
VALNEVA SWEDEN AB—See Valneva SE; *Int'l*, pg. 8121
VALNEVA UK LTD.—See Valneva SE; *Int'l*, pg. 8121
VALNEVA USA, INC.—See Valneva SE; *Int'l*, pg. 8121
VALNOR AS—See Addtech AB; *Int'l*, pg. 135
VALODE ET PISTRE; *Int'l*, pg. 8121
VALOE OYJ; *Int'l*, pg. 8121
VALOIS ESPANA S.A.—See AptarGroup, Inc.; *U.S. Public*, pg. 175
VALOIS (IRELAND) LIMITED—See AptarGroup, Inc.; *U.S. Public*, pg. 175
VALOIS S.A.S.—See AptarGroup, Inc.; *U.S. Public*, pg. 175
VALON KONE AB—See Kadant Inc.; *U.S. Public*, pg. 1213
VALON KONE AB—See Kadant Inc.; *U.S. Public*, pg. 1213
VALON KONE OOO—See Kadant Inc.; *U.S. Public*, pg. 1213
VALON KONE OOO—See Kadant Inc.; *U.S. Public*, pg. 1213
VALON KONE OY—See Kadant Inc.; *U.S. Public*, pg. 1212
VALON KONE OY—See Kadant Inc.; *U.S. Public*, pg. 1212
VALON KONE OY—See Kadant Inc.; *U.S. Public*, pg. 1213

VALON KONE OY—See Kadant Inc.; *U.S. Public*, pg. 1213
VALORA EFFEKTEN HANDEL AG; *Int'l*, pg. 8122
VALORA HOLDING AG—See Fomento Economico Mexicano, S.A.B. de C.V.; *Int'l*, pg. 2724
VALORA HOLDING FINANCE LTD.—See Fomento Economico Mexicano, S.A.B. de C.V.; *Int'l*, pg. 2724
VALORA HOLDING GERMANY GMBH—See Fomento Economico Mexicano, S.A.B. de C.V.; *Int'l*, pg. 2724
VALORA LUXEMBOURG S.A.R.L.—See Fomento Economico Mexicano, S.A.B. de C.V.; *Int'l*, pg. 2724
VALORA MANAGEMENT AG—See Fomento Economico Mexicano, S.A.B. de C.V.; *Int'l*, pg. 2724
VALORA SCHWEIZ AG—See Fomento Economico Mexicano, S.A.B. de C.V.; *Int'l*, pg. 2724
VALORA TRADE DENMARK A/S—See Fomento Economico Mexicano, S.A.B. de C.V.; *Int'l*, pg. 2724
VALORA TRADE NORWAY AS—See Fomento Economico Mexicano, S.A.B. de C.V.; *Int'l*, pg. 2724
VALORA TRADE SWEDEN AB—See Fomento Economico Mexicano, S.A.B. de C.V.; *Int'l*, pg. 2724
VALOR BRANDS LLC—See Ontex Group N.V.; *Int'l*, pg. 5591
VALORE BF 3D S.R.L.—See Solid World S.p.A.; *Int'l*, pg. 7072
VALOREC SERVICES AG—See Veolia Environnement S.A.; *Int'l*, pg. 8158
VALOREF SA—See Compagnie de Saint-Gobain SA; *Int'l*, pg. 1732
VALORE INC.—See Follett Corporation; *U.S. Private*, pg. 1559
VALORE INC.—See Follett Corporation; *U.S. Private*, pg. 1559
VALORE METALS CORP.; *Int'l*, pg. 8122
VALOREM LLC—See Reply S.p.A.; *Int'l*, pg. 6291
VALOREM S.A.; *Int'l*, pg. 8122
VALOR EQUITY PARTNERS L.P.; *U.S. Private*, pg. 4336
VALORES BANCOLOMBIA S.A.—See Bancolombia S.A.; *Int'l*, pg. 828
VALORE (SHENZHEN) PRIVATE LIMITED—See Challenger Technologies Ltd.; *Int'l*, pg. 1438
VALORES SIMESA SA; *Int'l*, pg. 8122
VALOR EUROPE GMBH—See Shanghai Baolong Automotive Corporation; *Int'l*, pg. 6762
VALORE VENTURES, INC.; *U.S. Private*, pg. 4337
VALORGA INTERNATIONAL, S.A.S.—See ACS, Actividades de Construccion y Servicios, S.A.; *Int'l*, pg. 117
VALOR HEALTHCARE, INC.—See Humana, Inc.; *U.S. Public*, pg. 1070
VALOR HK CO.—See Shanghai Baolong Automotive Corporation; *Int'l*, pg. 6762
VALOR HOLDINGS CO., LTD.; *Int'l*, pg. 8122
VALOR IT; *U.S. Private*, pg. 4336
VALORIZA FACILITIES CHILE, SPA—See Sacyr, S.A.; *Int'l*, pg. 6466
VALORIZA GESTION, S.A.U.—See Sacyr, S.A.; *Int'l*, pg. 6466
VALORIZA SERVICIOS MEDIOAMBIENTALES SA—See Morgan Stanley; *U.S. Public*, pg. 1473
VALOR LATITUDE ACQUISITION CORP.; *U.S. Public*, pg. 2274
VALOR LLC; *U.S. Private*, pg. 4336
VALOR LTD.—See The Glen Dimplex Group; *Int'l*, pg. 7650
VALORO RESOURCES INC.; *Int'l*, pg. 8122
VALOR PROPERTIES REIT; *Int'l*, pg. 8122
VALOR RESOURCES LIMITED; *Int'l*, pg. 8122
VALOR WATER ANALYTICS, INC.—See Xylem Inc.; *U.S. Public*, pg. 2395
VALPAK DIRECT MARKETING SYSTEMS, INC.; *U.S. Private*, pg. 4337
VALPARAISO SPORTING CLUB S.A.; *Int'l*, pg. 8122
VALPO MEDIOS, INC.; *U.S. Private*, pg. 4337
VAL PORT DISTRIBUTORS INC.; *U.S. Private*, pg. 4329
VALQUA AMERICA INC.—See VALQUA, LTD.; *Int'l*, pg. 8122
VALQUA INDUSTRIES (THAILAND) LTD.—See VALQUA, LTD.; *Int'l*, pg. 8122
VALQUA KOREA CO., LTD.—See VALQUA, LTD.; *Int'l*, pg. 8122
VALQUA, LTD.; *Int'l*, pg. 8122
VALQUA NGC, INC.—See VALQUA, LTD.; *Int'l*, pg. 8122
VALQUA SEAL PRODUCTS (SHANGHAI) CO., LTD—See VALQUA, LTD.; *Int'l*, pg. 8122
VALQUA (SHANGHAI) TRADING CO., LTD.—See VALQUA, LTD.; *Int'l*, pg. 8122
VALQUA VIETNAM CO., LTD.—See VALQUA, LTD.; *Int'l*, pg. 8122
VALS DISTRIBUTING COMPANY; *U.S. Private*, pg. 4337
VALSEF GROUP; *Int'l*, pg. 8122
VALSER SERVICES AG—See Coca-Cola HBC AG; *Int'l*, pg. 1686
VALSOFT CORPORATION INC.—See Valsef Group; *Int'l*, pg. 8122
VALSOIA S.P.A.; *Int'l*, pg. 8123
VALSON INDUSTRIES LIMITED; *Int'l*, pg. 8123
VALSPAR ARIES COATINGS, S. DE R.L. DE C.V.—See The Sherwin-Williams Company; *U.S. Public*, pg. 2129
THE VALSPAR (ASIA) CORPORATION LIMITED—See The Sherwin-Williams Company; *U.S. Public*, pg. 2129

CORPORATE AFFILIATIONS

VALSPAR AUTOMOTIVE AUSTRALIA PTY LIMITED—See The Sherwin-Williams Company; *U.S. Public*, pg. 2129
VALSPAR B.V.—See The Sherwin-Williams Company; *U.S. Public*, pg. 2130
THE VALSPAR CORPORATION LIMITADA—See The Sherwin-Williams Company; *U.S. Public*, pg. 2129
THE VALSPAR CORPORATION—See The Sherwin-Williams Company; *U.S. Public*, pg. 2129
VALSPAR D.O.O BEOGRAD—See The Sherwin-Williams Company; *U.S. Public*, pg. 2130
VALSPAR D.O.O—See The Sherwin-Williams Company; *U.S. Public*, pg. 2129
THE VALSPAR (FINLAND) CORPORATION OY—See The Sherwin-Williams Company; *U.S. Public*, pg. 2129
THE VALSPAR (FRANCE) CORPORATION, S.A.S.—See The Sherwin-Williams Company; *U.S. Public*, pg. 2129
THE VALSPAR (H.K.) CORPORATION LIMITED—See The Sherwin-Williams Company; *U.S. Public*, pg. 2129
VALSPAR INC.—See The Sherwin-Williams Company; *U.S. Public*, pg. 2129
VALSPAR INDUSTRIES GMBH—See The Sherwin-Williams Company; *U.S. Public*, pg. 2129
VALSPAR INDUSTRIES (IRELAND) LTD.—See The Sherwin-Williams Company; *U.S. Public*, pg. 2129
VALSPAR MEXICANA, S.A. DE C.V.—See The Sherwin-Williams Company; *U.S. Public*, pg. 2130
THE VALSPAR (NANTES) CORPORATION, S.A.S.—See The Sherwin-Williams Company; *U.S. Public*, pg. 2129
VALSPAR PAINT (AUSTRALIA) PTY LTD—See The Sherwin-Williams Company; *U.S. Public*, pg. 2129
VALSPAR POWDER COATINGS LTD.—See The Sherwin-Williams Company; *U.S. Public*, pg. 2129
VALSPAR REFINISH, INC.—See The Sherwin-Williams Company; *U.S. Public*, pg. 2129
VALSPAR ROCK CO., LTD.—See The Sherwin-Williams Company; *U.S. Public*, pg. 2129
THE VALSPAR (SOUTH AFRICA) CORPORATION (PTY) LTD.—See The Sherwin-Williams Company; *U.S. Public*, pg. 2129
THE VALSPAR (SWITZERLAND) CORPORATION AG—See The Sherwin-Williams Company; *U.S. Public*, pg. 2129
THE VALSPAR (UK) CORPORATION LIMITED—See The Sherwin-Williams Company; *U.S. Public*, pg. 2129
VALSTONE ASSET MANAGEMENT—See ValStone Partners, LLC; *U.S. Private*, pg. 4337
VALSTONE PARTNERS, LLC; *U.S. Private*, pg. 4337
VAL SURF INC.; *U.S. Private*, pg. 4329
VALTECH AB—See Verlinvest S.A.; *Int'l*, pg. 8172
VALTECH A/S—See Verlinvest S.A.; *Int'l*, pg. 8172
VALTECH CARDIO, LTD.—See Edwards Lifesciences Corporation; *U.S. Public*, pg. 721
VALTECH GMBH—See Verlinvest S.A.; *Int'l*, pg. 8172
VALTECH INDIA SYSTEMS PRIVATE LTD.—See Verlinvest S.A.; *Int'l*, pg. 8172
VALTECH LIMITED—See Verlinvest S.A.; *Int'l*, pg. 8172
VALTECH PARIS—See Verlinvest S.A.; *Int'l*, pg. 8172
VALTECH SE; *Int'l*, pg. 8123
VALTECH SOLUTIONS, INC.—See Verlinvest S.A.; *Int'l*, pg. 8172
VALTECNE S.P.A.; *Int'l*, pg. 8123
VALTEK SPA UNIPERSONALE—See Westport Fuel Systems Inc.; *Int'l*, pg. 8393
VALTERRA PRODUCTS, INC.; *U.S. Private*, pg. 4337
VALTERRA RESOURCE CORPORATION; *Int'l*, pg. 8123
VALTES ADVANCED TECHNOLOGY, INC.—See Valtes Co., Ltd.; *Int'l*, pg. 8123
VALTES CO., LTD.; *Int'l*, pg. 8123
VALTES MOBILE TECHNOLOGY CO., LTD.—See Valtes Co., Ltd.; *Int'l*, pg. 8123
VAL-TEX, LLC—See Entegris, Inc.; *U.S. Public*, pg. 777
VALTIMET GMBH—See Vallourec SA; *Int'l*, pg. 8118
VALTIMET INC. - BRUNSWICK PLANT—See Vallourec SA; *Int'l*, pg. 8118
VALTIMET SAS - LES LAUMES PLANT—See Vallourec SA; *Int'l*, pg. 8118
VALTIMET SAS—See Vallourec SA; *Int'l*, pg. 8118
VALTI—See Mutares SE & Co. KGaA; *Int'l*, pg. 5106
VALTIX LLC—See Cisco Systems, Inc.; *U.S. Public*, pg. 500
VALTRACTOR COMERCIO DE TRACTORES E MAQUINAS AGRICOLAS SA—See AGCO Corporation; *U.S. Public*, pg. 59
VALTRACTOR SA—See AGCO Corporation; *U.S. Public*, pg. 59
VALTRA DO BRASIL S.A.—See AGCO Corporation; *U.S. Public*, pg. 59
VALTRA GMBH—See AGCO Corporation; *U.S. Public*, pg. 59
VALTRA, INC.—See AGCO Corporation; *U.S. Public*, pg. 59
VALTRA INTERNATIONAL B.V.—See AGCO Corporation; *U.S. Public*, pg. 59
VALTRA TRACTORES S.A.—See AGCO Corporation; *U.S. Public*, pg. 59
VALTRA TRACTORES S.A.—See AGCO Corporation; *U.S. Public*, pg. 59
VALTRA TRACTORS (UK) LTD.—See AGCO Corporation; *U.S. Public*, pg. 59

COMPANY NAME INDEX — VAMA SUNDARI INVESTMENTS (DELHI) PRIVATE LIMITED

VALTRA TRAKTOR AB—See AGCO Corporation; *U.S. Public*, pg. 59
VALTRA TRAKTOR AB—See Lantmannen ek for; *Int'l*, pg. 4414
VALTRA VERTRIEBS GMBH—See AGCO Corporation; *U.S. Public*, pg. 59
VALTRA VOUKRAUS OY—See AGCO Corporation; *U.S. Public*, pg. 59
VALTROX SANITARY EQUIPMENT SDN. BHD.—See UNIMECH Group Berhad; *Int'l*, pg. 8049
VALUABLE CO., LTD.—See System Location Co., Ltd.; *Int'l*, pg. 7390
VALUAMERICA, INC.—See Radian Group, Inc.; *U.S. Public*, pg. 1759
VALUATION RESEARCH CORP.; *U.S. Private*, pg. 4337
VALU DISCOUNT, INCORPORATED; *U.S. Private*, pg. 4337
VALUE8 N.V.; *Int'l*, pg. 8124
VALUEACT CAPITAL MANAGEMENT, L.P.; *U.S. Private*, pg. 4338
VALUE ADDED LOGISTICS SP. Z O.O.—See Muller Die Lila Logistik AG; *Int'l*, pg. 5081
VALUE ARK CONSULTING CO., LTD.—See Copro Holdings Co., Ltd.; *Int'l*, pg. 1794
VALUEBANK TEXAS; *U.S. Private*, pg. 4338
VALUE BASED SOLUTIONS, LLC; *U.S. Private*, pg. 4337
THE VALUE BRANDS COMPANY DE ARGENTINA S.C.A.—See Grupo Romero; *Int'l*, pg. 3134
VALUECENTRIC MARKETING GROUP, INC.—See Fidelity National Infor; *U.S. Public*, pg. 833
VALUECLICK AB—See Publicis Groupe S.A.; *Int'l*, pg. 6099
VALUECLICK BRANDS, INC.—See Publicis Groupe S.A.; *Int'l*, pg. 6099
VALUECLICK MEDIA—See Publicis Groupe S.A.; *Int'l*, pg. 6099
VALUECLICK SARL—See Publicis Groupe S.A.; *Int'l*, pg. 6099
VALUECOMMERCE CO., LTD.—See SoftBank Group Corp.; *Int'l*, pg. 7052
VALUE COMMUNICATION SERVICES (SHANGHAI), INC.—See SECOM Co., Ltd.; *Int'l*, pg. 6672
VALUE CONVERGENCE HOLDINGS LIMITED; *Int'l*, pg. 8123
VALUE CREATION INC.; *Int'l*, pg. 8123
VALUEDESIGN, INC.—See Arara, Inc.; *Int'l*, pg. 536
VALUEDESIGN SINGAPORE PTE. LTD.—See Arara, Inc.; *Int'l*, pg. 536
VALUED MERCHANT SERVICES; *U.S. Private*, pg. 4338
VALUE DRUG COMPANY; *U.S. Private*, pg. 4337
THE VALUE ENGINEERS LIMITED—See Arsenal Capital Management LP; *U.S. Private*, pg. 338
VALUE ENHANCEMENT PARTNERS B.V.; *Int'l*, pg. 8123
VALUE EXCHANGE CORPORATION; *U.S. Private*, pg. 4337
VALUE EXCHANGE INTERNATIONAL, INC.; *Int'l*, pg. 8124
VALUE EXCHANGE INTERNATIONAL LIMITED—See Value Exchange International, Inc.; *Int'l*, pg. 8124
VALUE FINANCIAL SERVICES, INC.—See EZCORP, Inc.; *U.S. Public*, pg. 818
VALUEFIRST DIGITAL MEDIA PVT. LTD—See Tanla Platforms Limited; *Int'l*, pg. 7459
VALUE GOLF, INC.; *Int'l*, pg. 8124
VALUE GROUP LIMITED; *Int'l*, pg. 8124
VALUEHD CORPORATION; *Int'l*, pg. 8124
VALUE HEALTH CARE SERVICES, LLC—See CVS Health Corporation; *U.S. Public*, pg. 616
VALUEHEALTH LLC—See Nueterra Capital Management, LLC; *U.S. Private*, pg. 2972
VALUE HOLDINGS VERMOGENSMANAGEMENT GMBH—See Raiffeisenverband Salzburg reg. Gen.m.b.H.; *Int'l*, pg. 6188
VALUE HR CO., LTD.; *Int'l*, pg. 8124
VALUE IMPLEMENT; *U.S. Private*, pg. 4337
VALUE INDUSTRIES LIMITED; *Int'l*, pg. 8124
VALUE LIGHTING, INC.—See Revolution Lighting Technologies, Inc.; *U.S. Public*, pg. 1793
VALUE LINE DISTRIBUTION CENTER, INC.—See Arnold Bernhard & Co.; *U.S. Private*, pg. 333
VALUE LINE, INC.—See Arnold Bernhard & Co.; *U.S. Private*, pg. 333
VALUE LINE PUBLISHING LLC—See Arnold Bernhard & Co.; *U.S. Private*, pg. 333
VALUE LOGIC, INC.—See MPAC Group PLC; *Int'l*, pg. 5060
VALUE MANAGEMENT GROUP LLC—See Northlane Capital Partners, LLC; *U.S. Private*, pg. 2956
VALUE MANAGEMENT INSTITUTE, INC.—See Development Bank of Japan, Inc.; *Int'l*, pg. 2088
VALUEMART INFO TECHNOLOGIES LIMITED; *Int'l*, pg. 8124
VALUEMAX GROUP LIMITED; *Int'l*, pg. 8124
VALUEMAX PAWNSHOP (CCK) PTE. LTD.—See ValueMax Group Limited; *Int'l*, pg. 8125
VALUE MUSIC CONCEPTS INC.; *U.S. Private*, pg. 4337
VALUENCE HOLDINGS, INC.; *Int'l*, pg. 8125
VALUENCE INTERNATIONAL LIMITED—See Valuence Holdings, Inc.; *Int'l*, pg. 8125
VALUENCE VENTURES INC.—See Valuence Holdings, Inc.; *Int'l*, pg. 8125
VALUENEX JAPAN, INC.; *Int'l*, pg. 8125
VALUEOPTIONS, INC.—See Beacon Health Holdings LLC; *U.S. Private*, pg. 504
VALUEOPTIONS, INC.—See Beacon Health Holdings LLC; *U.S. Private*, pg. 504
VALUEPARK TERNEUZEN BEHEER B.V.—See Dow Inc.; *U.S. Public*, pg. 685
VALUEPART INC.—See Deere & Company; *U.S. Public*, pg. 647
VALUE PARTNERS ASSET MANAGEMENT SINGAPORE PTE. LTD.—See Value Partners Group Limited; *Int'l*, pg. 8124
VALUE PARTNERS FUND MANAGEMENT (SHANGHAI) LIMITED—See Value Partners Group Limited; *Int'l*, pg. 8124
VALUE PARTNERS GROUP LIMITED; *Int'l*, pg. 8124
VALUE PARTNERS INDEX SERVICES LIMITED—See Value Partners Group Limited; *Int'l*, pg. 8124
VALUE PARTNERS INVESTMENT MANAGEMENT (SHANGHAI) LIMITED—See Value Partners Group Limited; *Int'l*, pg. 8124
VALUE PARTNERS, LTD.; *U.S. Private*, pg. 4337
VALUE PARTNERS (UK) LIMITED—See Value Partners Group Limited; *Int'l*, pg. 8124
VALUE PAYMENT SYSTEMS, LLC.; *U.S. Private*, pg. 4337
VALUEPETSUPPLIES.COM; *U.S. Private*, pg. 4338
VALUEPHONE GMBH—See Fujitsu Limited; *Int'l*, pg. 2837
VALUE PLASTICS, INC.—See Nordson Corporation; *U.S. Public*, pg. 1534
VALUE PLUS FLOORING, INC.—See The Sterling Group, L.P.; *U.S. Private*, pg. 4122
VALUE RECOVERY GROUP, INC.; *U.S. Private*, pg. 4337
VALUES CULTURAL INVESTMENT LIMITED; *Int'l*, pg. 8125
VALUESOURCE NV—See Cognizant Technology Solutions Corporation; *U.S. Public*, pg. 525
VALUESOURCE TECHNOLOGIES PRIVATE LIMITED—See Cognizant Technology Solutions Corporation; *U.S. Public*, pg. 525
THE VALUE SYSTEMS CO., LTD.—See VSTECS Holdings Limited; *Int'l*, pg. 8315
VALUETEC ENGINEERING SOLUTIONS LIMITED—See Endress+Hauser (International) Holding AG; *Int'l*, pg. 2409
VALUETRONICS HOLDINGS LIMITED - MANUFACTURING FACILITY—See Valuetronics Holdings Limited; *Int'l*, pg. 8125
VALUETRONICS HOLDINGS LIMITED; *Int'l*, pg. 8125
VALUE-TRONICS INTERNATIONAL, INC.; *U.S. Private*, pg. 4338
VALUE VALVES CO., LTD.; *Int'l*, pg. 8124
VALUE VALVES (SUZHOU) LTD.—See Value Valves Co., Ltd.; *Int'l*, pg. 8124
VALUE VINYLS INC.; *U.S. Private*, pg. 4337
VALUGUARD SOLUTIONS, LLC—See Stewart Information Services Corporation; *U.S. Public*, pg. 1948
VALU HOME CENTERS INC.; *U.S. Private*, pg. 4337
VALUIKISAKHAR SUGAR—See Gruppa Kompaniy Rusagro OOO; *Int'l*, pg. 3140
VALU MART CO.—See KV Mart Co.; *U.S. Private*, pg. 2359
VALU.NET CORPORATION; *U.S. Private*, pg. 4337
VALURATE CO., LTD.—See Grcs Inc.; *Int'l*, pg. 3063
VALUTEC AB—See Addtech AB; *Int'l*, pg. 135
VALUTEC GROUP AB—See Addtech AB; *Int'l*, pg. 135
VALUTEC OY—See Addtech AB; *Int'l*, pg. 135
VALUTEC WOOD DRYERS INC.—See Addtech AB; *Int'l*, pg. 135
VALVE CONCEPTS, INC.—See May River Capital, LLC; *U.S. Private*, pg. 2620
VALVE CORPORATION; *U.S. Private*, pg. 4338
VALVEKITS LTD—See Rotork Plc; *Int'l*, pg. 6406
VALVE & PRIMER CORPORATION—See Granite Equity Partners LLC; *U.S. Private*, pg. 1755
VALVERDE CONSTRUCTION INC.; *U.S. Private*, pg. 4338
VAL VERDE HOSPITAL CORPORATION; *U.S. Private*, pg. 4329
VAL VERDE WINERY; *U.S. Private*, pg. 4329
VALVESOURCE LTD—See Azzalin Srl; *Int'l*, pg. 782
VALVEX S.A.—See Meridian International Group, Inc.; *U.S. Private*, pg. 2673
VALVISION AS—See HitecVision AS; *Int'l*, pg. 3426
VALVISION AS—See HitecVision AS; *Int'l*, pg. 3426
VALVOLINE (AUSTRALIA) PTY. LTD.—See Saudi Arabian Oil Company; *Int'l*, pg. 6589
VALVOLINE CUMMINS ARGENTINA S.A.—See Saudi Arabian Oil Company; *Int'l*, pg. 6589
VALVOLINE DE COLOMBIA S.A.S.—See Saudi Arabian Oil Company; *Int'l*, pg. 6589
VALVOLINE DO BRASIL LUBRIFICANTES LTDA.—See Saudi Arabian Oil Company; *Int'l*, pg. 6589
VALVOLINE INC.; *U.S. Public*, pg. 2274
VALVOLINE INSTANT OIL CHANGE FRANCHISING, INC.—See Valvoline Inc.; *U.S. Public*, pg. 2274
VALVOLINE INTERNATIONAL, INC.—See Saudi Arabian Oil Company; *Int'l*, pg. 6589
VALVOLINE LLC—See Valvoline Inc.; *U.S. Public*, pg. 2274
VALVOLINE (THAILAND) LTD.—See Saudi Arabian Oil Company; *Int'l*, pg. 6589
VALVOSACCO S.P.A.; *Int'l*, pg. 8125
VALVTECHNOLOGIES INC.; *U.S. Private*, pg. 4338
VALVTRONIC S.A.—See Bray International, Inc.; *U.S. Private*, pg. 642
VALVULAS, ACCESORIOS Y MAQUINARIAS S.A.C.—See Emerson Electric Co.; *U.S. Public*, pg. 752
VALVULAS, ACCESORIOS Y MAQUINARIAS S.A.C.—See Emerson Electric Co.; *U.S. Public*, pg. 752
VALVULAS CROSBY INDUSTRIA E COMERCIO LTDA.—See Pentair plc; *Int'l*, pg. 5791
VALVULAS VAG DE MEXICO, S.A. DE C.V.—See Zurn Elkay Water Solutions Corporation; *U.S. Public*, pg. 2414
VALVULAS WORCESTER DE ARGENTINA S.A.—See Sophia Capital S.A.; *Int'l*, pg. 7109
VAL WARD CADILLAC, INC.; *U.S. Private*, pg. 4329
VAMAC INC.; *U.S. Private*, pg. 4338
VAMAFIL, SPOL. S R O.—See Roblon A/S; *Int'l*, pg. 6371
VAMA INDUSTRIES LIMITED; *Int'l*, pg. 8125
VAMA SUNDARI INVESTMENTS (DELHI) PRIVATE LIMITED; *Int'l*, pg. 8125
VAMA TECHNOLOGIES PTE. LTD.—See VAMA Industries Limited; *Int'l*, pg. 8125
VAM CANADA INC - NEWFOUNDLAND PLANT—See Vallourec SA; *Int'l*, pg. 8118
VAM CHANGZHOU OIL & GAS PREMIUM EQUIPMENTS CO., LTD.—See Vallourec SA; *Int'l*, pg. 8117
VAM DRILLING MIDDLE EAST FZE—See Vallourec SA; *Int'l*, pg. 8117
VAMED AG—See Fresenius SE & Co. KGaA; *Int'l*, pg. 2781
VAMED CZ S.R.O.—See Fresenius SE & Co. KGaA; *Int'l*, pg. 2781
VAMED ENGINEERING GMBH & CO KG—See Fresenius SE & Co. KGaA; *Int'l*, pg. 2781
VAMED ENGINEERING NICARAGUA, SOCIEDAD ANONIMA—See Fresenius SE & Co. KGaA; *Int'l*, pg. 2781
VAMED ESTATE DEVELOPMENT & ENGINEERING GMBH & CO KG—See Fresenius SE & Co. KGaA; *Int'l*, pg. 2781
VAMED GESUNDHEIT HOLDING DEUTSCHLAND GMBH—See Fresenius SE & Co. KGaA; *Int'l*, pg. 2781
VAMED HEALTHCARE CO. LTD.—See Fresenius SE & Co. KGaA; *Int'l*, pg. 2781
VAMED HEALTHCARE SERVICES SA (PTY) LTD.—See Fresenius SE & Co. KGaA; *Int'l*, pg. 2781
VAMED HEALTHCARE SERVICES SDN. BHD.—See Fresenius SE & Co. KGaA; *Int'l*, pg. 2781
VAMED HEALTH PROJECT GMBH—See Fresenius SE & Co. KGaA; *Int'l*, pg. 2781
VAMED HEALTH PROJECTS CZ S.R.O.—See Fresenius SE & Co. KGaA; *Int'l*, pg. 2781
VAMED HEALTH PROJECTS MALAYSIA SDN. BHD.—See Fresenius SE & Co. KGaA; *Int'l*, pg. 2781
VAMED HEALTH PROJECTS UK LIMITED—See Fresenius SE & Co. KGaA; *Int'l*, pg. 2781
VAMED-HUNGARIA HEALTH CARE LTD.—See Fresenius SE & Co. KGaA; *Int'l*, pg. 2781
VAMED INTERNATIONAL HOSPITAL MANAGEMENT & CONSULTING (BEIJING) CO., LTD.—See Fresenius SE & Co. KGaA; *Int'l*, pg. 2781
VAMED-KMB—See Fresenius SE & Co. KGaA; *Int'l*, pg. 2781
VAMED LEBEN AM ROSENBERG KRONACH GMBH—See Fresenius SE & Co. KGaA; *Int'l*, pg. 2779
VAMED MANAGEMENT UND SERVICE GMBH & CO KG—See Fresenius SE & Co. KGaA; *Int'l*, pg. 2781
VAMED MEDITERRA, A.S.—See Fresenius SE & Co. KGaA; *Int'l*, pg. 2781
VAMED MEDIZINTECHNIK GMBH—See Fresenius SE & Co. KGaA; *Int'l*, pg. 2781
VAMED NEDERLAND B.V.—See Fresenius SE & Co. KGaA; *Int'l*, pg. 2781
VAMED POLSKA SP. Z O.O.—See Fresenius SE & Co. KGaA; *Int'l*, pg. 2781
VAMED PROJETS HOSPITALIERS INTERNATIONAUX FRANCE S.A.S—See Fresenius SE & Co. KGaA; *Int'l*, pg. 2781
VAMED ROMANIA S.R.L.—See Fresenius SE & Co. KGaA; *Int'l*, pg. 2781
VAMED SERVICE- UND BETEILIGUNGSGES MBH—See Fresenius SE & Co. KGaA; *Int'l*, pg. 2781
VAMED STANDORTENTWICKLUNG UND ENGINEERING GMBH—See Fresenius SE & Co. KGaA; *Int'l*, pg. 2781
VAMED TURKEY MUHENDISLIK INSAAT TAAHHUT MEDIKAL SAGLIK HIZMETLERI LIMITED SIRKETI—See Fresenius SE & Co. KGaA; *Int'l*, pg. 2781
VAMED UKK PROJEKTGESELLSCHAFT M.B.H.—See Fresenius SE & Co. KGaA; *Int'l*, pg. 2781
VAM FAR EAST PTE LTD—See Vallourec SA; *Int'l*, pg. 8117
VAM FIELD SERVICES ANGOLA LDA.—See Vallourec SA; *Int'l*, pg. 8117

VAM INVESTMENTS SPAC B.V.; Int'l, pg. 8125
VAMIX CR—See Vandemoortele N.V.; Int'l, pg. 8129
VAMIX SLOVENSKA REPUBLIKA SRO—See Vandemoortele N.V.; Int'l, pg. 8129
VAMONA DEVELOPERS PRIVATE LIMITED—See The Phoenix Mills Limited; Int'l, pg. 7673
VA MORTGAGE CENTER.COM; U.S. Private, pg. 4328
VAMP OY—See Schneider Electric SE; Int'l, pg. 6635
VAMP SOLUTIONS (PTY) LTD—See Schneider Electric SE; Int'l, pg. 6635
VAMSHI RUBBER LIMITED; Int'l, pg. 8125
VAM USA, LLC—See Vallourec SA; Int'l, pg. 8118
VANACHAI CHEMICAL INDUSTRIES CO., LTD.—See Vanachai Group Public Company Limited; Int'l, pg. 8128
VANACHAI GROUP PUBLIC COMPANY LIMITED; Int'l, pg. 8128
VANACHAI PANEL INDUSTRIES CO., LTD.—See Vanachai Group Public Company Limited; Int'l, pg. 8128
VANADIAN ENERGY CORPORATION; Int'l, pg. 8128
VANADIA UTAMA, PT; Int'l, pg. 8128
VANADIUMCORP RESOURCE INC.; Int'l, pg. 8128
VANADIUM RESOURCES LIMITED; Int'l, pg. 8128
VAN AIR, INC.; U.S. Private, pg. 4338
VAN AIR SYSTEMS INC—See Van Air, Inc.; U.S. Private, pg. 4338
VAN ANDEL & FLIKKEMA MOTOR SALES, INC.; U.S. Private, pg. 4338
VAN ANDEL INSTITUTE; U.S. Private, pg. 4338
VAN ARKEL GERECHTSDEURWAARDERS B.V.—See Munchener Ruckversicherungs AG; Int'l, pg. 5088
VANASSE HANGEN BRUSTLIN, INC.; U.S. Private, pg. 4341
VANASVERKEN AB—See Patria Oyj; Int'l, pg. 5758
VAN AUKEN AKINS ARCHITECTS LLC; U.S. Private, pg. 4338
VAN AUSDALL & FARRAR INC.; U.S. Private, pg. 4338
VANAVARALES LLC—See RusForest AB; Int'l, pg. 6429
VAN BEBBER & ASSOCIATES, INC.; U.S. Private, pg. 4338
VAN BEURDEN INSURANCE SERVICES; U.S. Private, pg. 4338
VAN BEUREN MANAGEMENT, INC.; U.S. Private, pg. 4338
VAN BLARCOM CLOSURES INC.; U.S. Private, pg. 4338
VAN BORTEL AIRCRAFT INC.; U.S. Private, pg. 4339
VAN BORTEL FINANCE CORPORATION—See Van Bortel Aircraft Inc.; U.S. Private, pg. 4339
VAN BORTEL FORD; U.S. Private, pg. 4339
VAN BORTEL SUBARU; U.S. Private, pg. 4339
VAN BOXTEL HOORWINKELS B.V.—See Demant A/S; Int'l, pg. 2025
VAN BREDA CAR FINANCE NV—See Ackermans & van Haaren NV; Int'l, pg. 106
VAN BREDA IMMO CONSULT NV—See Ackermans & van Haaren NV; Int'l, pg. 106
VANBREDA INTERNATIONAL LLC—See The Cigna Group; U.S. Public, pg. 2061
VANBREDA INTERNATIONAL N.V.—See The Cigna Group; U.S. Public, pg. 2061
VANBRIDGE LLC—See Keystone Group, L.P.; U.S. Private, pg. 2298
VAN BUREN TRUCK SALES CORP.; U.S. Private, pg. 4339
VANCAMEL AG; Int'l, pg. 8128
VAN CAMPEN MOTORS, INC.; U.S. Private, pg. 4339
THE VAN CARGOES & FOREIGN TRADE LOGISTICS JOINT STOCK COMPANY; Int'l, pg. 7698
VANCE BALDWIN, INC.—See Bain Capital, LP; U.S. Private, pg. 444
VANCE BROTHERS INCORPORATED; U.S. Private, pg. 4342
VANCE HOLDINGS INC.; U.S. Private, pg. 4342
VANCE INDUSTRIES, INC.; U.S. Private, pg. 4342
VANCE INTERNATIONAL DE MEXICO, S.A. DE C.V.—See Audax Group, Limited Partnership; U.S. Private, pg. 386
VANCE PUBLISHING CORPORATION; U.S. Private, pg. 4342
VANCE STREET CAPITAL LLC; U.S. Private, pg. 4342
VANCE THOMPSON VISION CLINIC PROF LLC; U.S. Private, pg. 4342
VAN CHEVROLET; U.S. Private, pg. 4339
VAN CLEEF & ARPELS, INC.—See Reinet Investments S.C.A.; Int'l, pg. 6257
VAN CLEEF & ARPELS SA—See Compagnie Financiere Richemont S.A.; Int'l, pg. 1741
VAN CLEEF ENGINEERING ASSOCIATES, INC.; U.S. Private, pg. 4339
VAN CLEEF ENGINEERING ASSOCIATES LLC—See Van Cleef Engineering Associates, Inc.; U.S. Private, pg. 4339
VANCO (ASIA PACIFIC) PTE. LTD.—See Reliance - ADA Group Limited; Int'l, pg. 6262
VANCO GMBH—See Reliance - ADA Group Limited; Int'l, pg. 6262
VANCO INTERNATIONAL LTD—See Reliance - ADA Group Limited; Int'l, pg. 6262
VANCO JAPAN KK—See Reliance - ADA Group Limited; Int'l, pg. 6262

VANCO NV—See Reliance - ADA Group Limited; Int'l, pg. 6262
VANCOREJONES COMMUNICATIONS INC.; U.S. Private, pg. 4342
VANCO SOUTH AMERICA LTDA—See Reliance - ADA Group Limited; Int'l, pg. 6262
VANCO SWEDEN AB—See Reliance - ADA Group Limited; Int'l, pg. 6262
VANCOUVER CANUCKS—See Aquilini Investment Group; Int'l, pg. 528
VANCOUVER DRYDOCK COMPANY LTD.—See Washington Corporations; U.S. Private, pg. 4446
VANCOUVER FUNERAL CHAPEL, INC.—See Service Corporation International; U.S. Public, pg. 1871
VANCOUVER OIL COMPANY INC.—See Jubitz Corporation; U.S. Private, pg. 2242
VANCOUVER PORT AUTHORITY; Int'l, pg. 8128
VANCOUVER SHIPYARDS CO. LTD.—See Washington Corporations; U.S. Private, pg. 4447
THE VANCOUVER SUN—See Chatham Asset Management, LLC; U.S. Private, pg. 861
VAN DALE INDUSTRIES INC.; U.S. Private, pg. 4339
VAN DAM S.A.—See Arcor Sociedad Anonima, Industrial y Comercial; Int'l, pg. 550
VANDANA KNITWEAR LIMITED; Int'l, pg. 8128
VANDA PHARMACEUTICALS GERMANY GMBH—See Vanda Pharmaceuticals Inc.; U.S. Public, pg. 2275
VANDA PHARMACEUTICALS INC.; U.S. Public, pg. 2274
VANDA PHARMACEUTICALS LIMITED—See Vanda Pharmaceuticals Inc.; U.S. Public, pg. 2275
VANDEGRIFT FORWARDING CO, INC.—See A.P. Moller-Maersk A/S; Int'l, pg. 28
VANDE HEY BRANTMEIER CHEVROLET-BUICK-PONTIAC-OLDSMOBILE, INC.—See Vande Hey Brantmeier Enterprises, Inc.; U.S. Private, pg. 4342
VANDE HEY BRANTMEIER ENTERPRISES, INC.; U.S. Private, pg. 4342
VANDE HEY RALEIGH ROOF TILE MANUFACTURING, INC.—See Hendricks Holding Company, Inc.; U.S. Private, pg. 1915
VANDEMOORTELE BAKERY PRODUCTS GHISLENGHIEN SA—See Vandemoortele N.V.; Int'l, pg. 8129
VANDEMOORTELE DEUTSCHLAND GMBH—See Vandemoortele N.V.; Int'l, pg. 8128
VANDEMOORTELE DOMMITZSCH GMBH—See Vandemoortele N.V.; Int'l, pg. 8129
VANDEMOORTELE FRANCE—See Vandemoortele N.V.; Int'l, pg. 8129
VANDEMOORTELE HUNGARY LTD.—See Vandemoortele N.V.; Int'l, pg. 8129
VANDEMOORTELE IBERICA S.A.—See Vandemoortele N.V.; Int'l, pg. 8129
VANDEMOORTELE ITALIA S.P.A.—See Vandemoortele N.V.; Int'l, pg. 8129
VANDEMOORTELE N.V.; Int'l, pg. 8128
VANDEMOORTELE POLSKA SP.Z.O.O.—See Vandemoortele N.V.; Int'l, pg. 8129
VANDEMOORTELE PPI UK—See Vandemoortele N.V.; Int'l, pg. 8129
VANDEMOORTELE RUCKVERSICHERUNG AG—See Vandemoortele N.V.; Int'l, pg. 8129
VANDEMOORTELE SENEFFE SA—See Vandemoortele N.V.; Int'l, pg. 8129
VANDEMOORTELE (UK) LTD.—See Vandemoortele N.V.; Int'l, pg. 8129
VAN DEN BERG N.V.—See Orascom Construction PLC; Int'l, pg. 5612
VANDEN BORRE—See Kingfisher plc; Int'l, pg. 4173
VANDEN BUSSCHE IRRIGATION & EQUIPMENT LIMITED; Int'l, pg. 8129
VANDENDORPE NV—See Ackermans & van Haaren NV; Int'l, pg. 106
VAN DEN ENDE & DEITMERS B.V.; Int'l, pg. 8125
VAN DEN HEUVEL & FOUNTAIN INC.—See Aon plc; Int'l, pg. 498
VAN DE POL ENTERPRISES, INC.; U.S. Private, pg. 4339
VANDERBEEK MOTORS, INC.—See AutoNation, Inc.; U.S. Public, pg. 238
VANDERBEEK MOTORS, INC.—See AutoNation, Inc.; U.S. Public, pg. 238
VANDER-BEND MANUFACTURING, LLC—See Aterian Investment Management, L.P.; U.S. Private, pg. 367
THE VANDERBILT ADVERTISING AGENCY, INC.—See Arnold Bernhard & Co.; U.S. Private, pg. 333
VANDERBILT CHEMICAL, LLC—See R.T. Vanderbilt Holding Company, Inc.; U.S. Private, pg. 3340
VANDERBILT-INGRAM CANCER CENTER AT TENNOVA HEALTHCARE-CLARKSVILLE—See Community Health Systems, Inc.; U.S. Public, pg. 557
VANDERBILT INTERNATIONAL SARL—See R.T. Vanderbilt Holding Company, Inc.; U.S. Private, pg. 3340
VANDERBILT MINERALS, LLC—See R.T. Vanderbilt Holding Company, Inc.; U.S. Private, pg. 3340
VANDERBILT MORTGAGE & FINANCE, INC.—See Berkshire Hathaway Inc.; U.S. Public, pg. 304
VANDERBURGH & CO., INC.; U.S. Private, pg. 4342
VANDERFIELD PTY LTD; Int'l, pg. 8129
VANDERGRIFF CHEVROLET; U.S. Private, pg. 4342

VANDER HAAG'S INC.; U.S. Private, pg. 4342
VAN DER HAEGHE B.V.—See Iseki & Co., Ltd.; Int'l, pg. 3814
VANDER HAEGHEN & CO SA—See Enstar Group Limited; Int'l, pg. 2449
VANDERHEYDEN HALL, INC.; U.S. Private, pg. 4343
VANDERHOUWEN & ASSOCIATES, INC.; U.S. Private, pg. 4343
VANDERHOYDONCKS ELEKTROTECHNIEKEN NV—See Ackermans & van Haaren NV; Int'l, pg. 105
VANDERLANDE INDUSTRIES B.V.—See Toyota Industries Corporation; Int'l, pg. 7869
VANDERLANDE INDUSTRIES HOLDING B.V.—See Toyota Industries Corporation; Int'l, pg. 7869
VANDERLANDE INDUSTRIES INC.—See Toyota Industries Corporation; Int'l, pg. 7869
VANDERLINDEN—See VINCI S.A.; Int'l, pg. 8238
VAN DER LINDEN & VELDHUIS ISOLATIE B.V.—See VINCI S.A.; Int'l, pg. 8238
VANDERLOOP EQUIPMENT, INC.; U.S. Private, pg. 4343
VAN DER LOO YACHTINTERIORS BV—See LVMH Moet Hennessy Louis Vuitton SE; Int'l, pg. 4603
VAN DER MEER CONSULTING VIETNAM CO LTD.—See VDM Group Limited; Int'l, pg. 8143
VANDERMEER FOREST PRODUCTS INC.—See Cerberus Capital Management, L.P.; U.S. Private, pg. 837
VAN DER MOLEN GMBH—See RADIAL Capital Partners GmbH & Co. KG; Int'l, pg. 6173
VAN DER NEUT SUPERMARKTEN B.V.—See Jumbo Supermarkten B.V.; Int'l, pg. 4026
VANDERPOL'S EGGS LTD.; Int'l, pg. 8129
VANDERVERT CONSTRUCTION INC.; U.S. Private, pg. 4343
VANDERWELL CONTRACTORS (1971) LTD; Int'l, pg. 8129
VAN DE VELDE NORTH AMERICA INC.—See Van de Velde N.V.; Int'l, pg. 8125
VAN DE VELDE N.V.; Int'l, pg. 8125
VAN DE WATER RAYMOND LTD; Int'l, pg. 8125
VANDHAM SECURITIES CORP.—See Wall Street Access Corp.; U.S. Private, pg. 4430
VAN DIEN FUSED MAGNESIUM PHOSPHATE JOINT STOCK COMPANY—See Masan Consumer Corp.; Int'l, pg. 4719
VAN DIEST FAMILY, LLC; U.S. Private, pg. 4339
VAN DIEST INVESTMENT COMPANY—See Van Diest Family, LLC; U.S. Private, pg. 4339
VAN DIEST SUPPLY COMPANY—See Van Diest Family, LLC; U.S. Private, pg. 4339
VANDIPAINT NV—See VINCI S.A.; Int'l, pg. 8240
THE VANDIVER GROUP, INC.—See Lambert & Co.; U.S. Private, pg. 2380
VAN DOMBURG PARTNERS B.V.—See Midwich Group Plc; Int'l, pg. 4888
VAN DON TOURISM DEVELOPMENT & INVESTMENT JOINT STOCK COMPANY—See C.E.O Group Joint Stock Company; Int'l, pg. 1240
VANDOR, LLC—See BioWorld Merchandising, Inc.; U.S. Private, pg. 563
VAN DORN DEMAG—See Sumitomo Heavy Industries, Ltd.; Int'l, pg. 7289
VANDOR REAL ESTATE SOCIMI, S.A.U.; Int'l, pg. 8129
VANDRA SAETERITUS AS—See Investment AB Latour; Int'l, pg. 3783
VAN DRUNEN FORD; U.S. Private, pg. 4339
VAN DYK BUSINESS SYSTEMS INC.; U.S. Private, pg. 4339
VAN DYK & COMPANY, INC.; U.S. Private, pg. 4339
VAN DYKE DODGE; U.S. Private, pg. 4339
VAN DYKE RANKIN & COMPANY INC.; U.S. Private, pg. 4339
VAN DYKE SUPPLY CO., INC.—See Gridiron Capital, LLC; U.S. Private, pg. 1786
THE VAN DYKE TECHNOLOGY GROUP, INC.—See Jacobs Engineering Group, Inc.; U.S. Public, pg. 1186
VAN ECK ASSOCIATES CORP.; U.S. Private, pg. 4339
VANECK MERK GOLD TRUST; U.S. Public, pg. 2275
VAN ECK SWITZERLAND AG—See Van Eck Associates Corp.; U.S. Private, pg. 4340
VANEDGE CAPITAL PARTNERS LTD; Int'l, pg. 8129
VANEE FOODS COMPANY INC.; U.S. Private, pg. 4343
VAN EERDEN FOODSERVICE COMPANY; U.S. Private, pg. 4340
VAN EERDEN TRUCKING COMPANY; U.S. Private, pg. 4340
VAN EIGHT PRODUCTIONS, INC.—See Fuji Media Holdings, Inc.; U.S. Public, pg. 2814
VAN EKERIS EXPO SERVICE B.V.—See Messe Munchen GmbH; Int'l, pg. 4842
VAN ELLE HOLDINGS PLC; Int'l, pg. 8125
VANE MINERALS (UK) LIMITED—See Zephyr Energy Plc; Int'l, pg. 8636
VAN ENTERPRISES INC.; U.S. Private, pg. 4340
VAN ERT ELECTRIC COMPANY INC.; U.S. Private, pg. 4340
VANESCH VERF GROEP B.V.—See LKQ Corporation; U.S. Public, pg. 1337
VANET GIDA SANAYI IC VE DIS TICARET A.S.; Int'l, pg. 8129

VANET PROPERTY ASSET MANAGEMENT LIMITED—See The Skipton Building Society; *Int'l*, pg. 7687
VANETTI INC.; *U.S. Private*, pg. 4343
VANEX, INC.—See PPG Industries, Inc.; *U.S. Public*, pg. 1711
VANEXPORT SA; *Int'l*, pg. 8129
VAN EYCK CHEMIE NV—See Apollo Global Management, Inc.; *U.S. Public*, pg. 166
VANFUND URBAN INVESTMENT&DEVELOPMENT CO., LTD.; *Int'l*, pg. 8129
VAN GANSEWINKEL GROEP B.V.—See Renewi plc; *Int'l*, pg. 6279
VAN GEND & LOOS - EURO EXPRESS NV—See Deutsche Post AG; *Int'l*, pg. 2083
VAN GENECHTEN PACKAGING N.V.; *Int'l*, pg. 8126
VANGEO TECHNOLOGY GROUP, LLC; *U.S. Private*, pg. 4343
VANGO MINING LIMITED—See Catalyst Metals Limited; *Int'l*, pg. 1358
VAN GORP CORPORATION—See Precision Inc.; *U.S. Private*, pg. 3245
VANGUARD ATLANTIC LTD.; *U.S. Private*, pg. 4343
VANGUARD BROKERAGE SERVICES—See The Vanguard Group, Inc.; *U.S. Private*, pg. 4130
VANGUARD CAPITAL; *U.S. Private*, pg. 4343
VANGUARD CAR RENTAL USA, LLC—See Enterprise Holdings, Inc.; *U.S. Private*, pg. 1403
VANGUARD CLEANING SYSTEMS INC; *U.S. Private*, pg. 4343
VANGUARDCOMM - CORAL GABLES—See Vanguard-Comm; *U.S. Private*, pg. 4344
VANGUARDCOMM; *U.S. Private*, pg. 4344
VANGUARD COMMUNICATIONS; *U.S. Private*, pg. 4343
VANGUARD DIRECT INC.; *U.S. Private*, pg. 4343
VANGUARD EMS, INC.; *U.S. Private*, pg. 4343
VANGUARD ENERGY PARTNERS, LLC; *U.S. Private*, pg. 4343
VANGUARDE PTE. LTD.—See Destini Berhad; *Int'l*, pg. 2047
VANGUARD FIRE SYSTEMS, L.P.; *U.S. Private*, pg. 4343
VANGUARD FURNITURE CO. INC.; *U.S. Private*, pg. 4343
VANGUARD GREEN INVESTMENT LIMITED; *Int'l*, pg. 8129
THE VANGUARD GROUP, INC.; *U.S. Private*, pg. 4130
VANGUARD HEALTHCARE SERVICES LLC; *U.S. Private*, pg. 4343
VANGUARD HEALTHCARE SOLUTIONS LTD.—See MML Capital Partners LLP; *Int'l*, pg. 5005
VANGUARD HEALTH SYSTEMS, INC.—See Tenet Healthcare Corporation; *U.S. Public*, pg. 2014
VANGUARD HOLDINGS; *U.S. Private*, pg. 4343
VANGUARD HOME CARE, LLC—See Tenet Healthcare Corporation; *U.S. Public*, pg. 2015
VANGUARD INSTRUMENTS CO., INC.—See ESCO Technologies, Inc.; *U.S. Public*, pg. 793
VANGUARD INTEGRATION INTERNATIONAL PTY LTD—See Capgemini SE; *Int'l*, pg. 1303
VANGUARD INTERNATIONAL SEMICONDUCTOR CORPORATION; *Int'l*, pg. 8129
VANGUARD INVESTMENTS AUSTRALIA LTD.—See The Vanguard Group, Inc.; *U.S. Private*, pg. 4130
VANGUARD INVESTMENTS—See The Vanguard Group, Inc.; *U.S. Private*, pg. 4130
VANGUARD LABEL, INC.; *U.S. Private*, pg. 4343
VANGUARD LOGISTICS SERVICES—See NACA Logistics (USA), Inc.; *U.S. Private*, pg. 2829
VANGUARD MEDIA GROUP; *U.S. Private*, pg. 4343
VANGUARD MODULAR BUILDING SYSTEMS, LLC; *U.S. Private*, pg. 4343
VANGUARD NATIONAL TRAILER CORPORATION—See China International Marine Containers (Group) Co., Ltd.; *Int'l*, pg. 1512
VANGUARD OPERATING, LLC—See Grizzly Energy, LLC; *U.S. Public*, pg. 970
VANGUARD PACKAGING; *U.S. Private*, pg. 4344
VANGUARD PETROLEUM CORPORATION; *U.S. Private*, pg. 4344
VANGUARD PRINTING LLC; *U.S. Private*, pg. 4344
VANGUARD PRODUCTS GROUP, INC.; *U.S. Private*, pg. 4344
VANGUARD PROPERTIES CO.; *U.S. Private*, pg. 4344
VANGUARD RECORDS—See Massachusetts Mutual Life Insurance Company; *U.S. Private*, pg. 2605
VANGUARD SOFTWARE CORP.—See Wolters Kluwer n.v.; *Int'l*, pg. 8445
VANGUARD SOFTWARE GROUP LLC—See Jack Henry & Associates, Inc.; *U.S. Public*, pg. 1183
VANGUARD SYSTEMS, INC.—See Strattam Capital, LLC; *U.S. Private*, pg. 3837
VANGUARD TEMPORARIES INC.; *U.S. Private*, pg. 4344
VANGUARD TRUCK CENTER OF ST. LOUIS—See SF Holding Corp.; *U.S. Private*, pg. 3621
VANGUARD TRUCK CENTERS, LLC—See SF Holding Corp.; *U.S. Private*, pg. 3621
VANGUARD VIDEO LLC—See Beamr Ltd.; *Int'l*, pg. 932
VANHAN RUUKIN KIINTEISTOPALVELU OY—See Componenta Corporation; *Int'l*, pg. 1753

VAN HATTUM EN BLANKEVOORT BV—See Koninklijke VolkerWessels N.V.; *Int'l*, pg. 4272
VAN HECK INTERPIECES N.V.—See LKQ Corporation; *U.S. Public*, pg. 1336
VAN HEES AG—See VAN HEES GmbH; *Int'l*, pg. 8126
VAN HEES BENELUX BV—See VAN HEES GmbH; *Int'l*, pg. 8126
VAN HEES GMBH - HALAL PRODUKTION FACTORY—See VAN HEES GmbH; *Int'l*, pg. 8126
VAN HEES GMBH; *Int'l*, pg. 8126
VAN HEES INC.—See VAN HEES GmbH; *Int'l*, pg. 8126
VAN HEES SARL—See VAN HEES GmbH; *Int'l*, pg. 8126
VAN HOECKEL B.V.—See Sligro Food Group N.V.; *Int'l*, pg. 6997
THE VAN HOOF COMPANIES; *U.S. Private*, pg. 4130
VAN HOOSE CONSTRUCTION CO.; *U.S. Private*, pg. 4340
VAN HOPPLYNUS OPHTALM SA—See Fagron NV; *Int'l*, pg. 2603
VAN HORN AUTOMOTIVE GROUP, INC.; *U.S. Private*, pg. 4340
VAN HORN BROS INC.; *U.S. Private*, pg. 4340
VAN HORN HYUNDAI OF FOND DU LAC INC.; *U.S. Private*, pg. 4340
VAN HORN INC.—See Nutrien Ltd.; *Int'l*, pg. 5494
VAN HORN METZ & CO. INC.; *U.S. Private*, pg. 4340
VANI COMMERCIALS LIMITED; *Int'l*, pg. 8129
VANILIA S.R.L.—See Solvay S.A.; *Int'l*, pg. 7082
VANITY CAPITAL INC.; *Int'l*, pg. 8129
VANITY FAIR BRANDS, LP—See Berkshire Hathaway Inc.; *U.S. Public*, pg. 319
VANITY FAIR—See Advance Publications, Inc.; *U.S. Private*, pg. 86
VANITY SHOP OF GRAND FORKS INC.; *U.S. Private*, pg. 4344
VANITYSTYLE SP. Z O.O.—See Benefit Systems SA; *Int'l*, pg. 972
VANJEE TECHNOLOGY CO., LTD.; *Int'l*, pg. 8129
VANJIA CORPORATION; *U.S. Public*, pg. 2275
VAN KAMPEN GELD B.V.—See ASR Nederland N.V.; *Int'l*, pg. 632
VAN KAMPEN GROEP HOLDING B.V.—See ASR Nederland N.V.; *Int'l*, pg. 632
VANKE HOLDINGS USA LLC—See China Vanke Co., Ltd.; *Int'l*, pg. 1562
VAN KEMPEN & BEGEER HONG KONG LTD—See Koninklijke Delftsch Aardewerkfabriek N.V.; *Int'l*, pg. 4262
VANKE OVERSEAS INVESTMENT HOLDING COMPANY LIMITED—See China Vanke Co., Ltd.; *Int'l*, pg. 1562
VANKE REAL ESTATE (HONG KONG) CO., LTD.—See China Vanke Co., Ltd.; *Int'l*, pg. 1562
VAN KEULEN BV—See Compagnie de Saint-Gobain SA; *Int'l*, pg. 1737
VAN KEULEN INTERIEURBOUW BV; *Int'l*, pg. 8126
VAN KING & STORAGE INC.; *U.S. Private*, pg. 4340
VANKON MODULAR PRIVATE LIMITED—See Veto Switchgears & Cables Limited; *Int'l*, pg. 8180
VANKSEN GROUP—See Datawords Datasia SARL; *Int'l*, pg. 1981
VAN LAAN CONCRETE CONSTRUCTION, INC.; *U.S. Private*, pg. 4340
VAN LANG TECHNOLOGY DEVELOPMENT AND INVESTMENT JOINT STOCK COMPANY; *Int'l*, pg. 8126
VAN LANSCHOT ARS MUNDI BV—See Van Lanschot Kempen NV; *Int'l*, pg. 8126
VAN LANSCHOT ASSET MANAGEMENT BV—See Van Lanschot Kempen NV; *Int'l*, pg. 8126
VAN LANSCHOT ASSURANTIEN BV—See Van Lanschot Kempen NV; *Int'l*, pg. 8126
VAN LANSCHOT BANKIERS BELGIE NV—See Van Lanschot Kempen NV; *Int'l*, pg. 8126
VAN LANSCHOT BANKIERS (CURACAO) NV—See Van Lanschot Kempen NV; *Int'l*, pg. 8126
VAN LANSCHOT KEMPEN NV; *Int'l*, pg. 8126
VANLAW FOOD PRODUCTS, INC.—See Wind Point Advisors LLC; *U.S. Private*, pg. 4536
VAN LEER CONTAINERS (NIGERIA) PLC—See Greif Inc.; *U.S. Public*, pg. 968
VAN LEEUWEN BORU SANAYI VE TICARET LTD—See Van Leeuwen Pipe & Tube Group B.V.; *Int'l*, pg. 8127
VAN LEEUWEN BUIZEN BELGIUM N.V.—See Van Leeuwen Pipe & Tube Group B.V.; *Int'l*, pg. 8127
VAN LEEUWEN BUIZEN EUROPA B.V.—See Van Leeuwen Pipe & Tube Group B.V.; *Int'l*, pg. 8127
VAN LEEUWEN LTD—See Van Leeuwen Pipe & Tube Group B.V.; *Int'l*, pg. 8127
VAN LEEUWEN PIPE AND TUBE GULF FZE—See Van Leeuwen Pipe & Tube Group B.V.; *Int'l*, pg. 8127
VAN LEEUWEN PIPE AND TUBE LCC—See Van Leeuwen Pipe & Tube Group B.V.; *Int'l*, pg. 8127
VAN LEEUWEN PIPE AND TUBE N.V.—See Van Leeuwen Pipe & Tube Group B.V.; *Int'l*, pg. 8127
VAN LEEUWEN PIPE AND TUBE S.R.O.—See Van Leeuwen Pipe & Tube Group B.V.; *Int'l*, pg. 8127
VAN LEEUWEN PIPE & TUBE AUSTRALIA PTY. LTD.—See Van Leeuwen Pipe & Tube Group B.V.; *Int'l*, pg. 8127

VAN LEEUWEN PIPE & TUBE (CANADA) INC.—See Van Leeuwen Pipe & Tube Group B.V.; *Int'l*, pg. 8127
VAN LEEUWEN PIPE & TUBE (CANADA) INC.—See Van Leeuwen Pipe & Tube Group B.V.; *Int'l*, pg. 8127
VAN LEEUWEN PIPE & TUBE GROUP B.V.; *Int'l*, pg. 8126
VAN LEEUWEN PIPE & TUBE INDONESIA PTE. LTD.—See Van Leeuwen Pipe & Tube Group B.V.; *Int'l*, pg. 8127
VAN LEEUWEN PIPE & TUBE (MALAYSIA) SDN. BHD.—See Van Leeuwen Pipe & Tube Group B.V.; *Int'l*, pg. 8127
VAN LEEUWEN PIPE & TUBE (MIDDLE EAST) LTD.—See Van Leeuwen Pipe & Tube Group B.V.; *Int'l*, pg. 8127
VAN LEEUWEN PIPE & TUBE S.A. DE C.V.—See Van Leeuwen Pipe & Tube Group B.V.; *Int'l*, pg. 8127
VAN LEEUWEN PIPE & TUBE SINGAPORE PTE. LTD.—See Van Leeuwen Pipe & Tube Group B.V.; *Int'l*, pg. 8127
VAN LEEUWEN PIPE & TUBE (THAILAND) LTD.—See Van Leeuwen Pipe & Tube Group B.V.; *Int'l*, pg. 8127
VAN LEEUWEN PIPE & TUBE (THAILAND) LTD.—See Van Leeuwen Pipe & Tube Group B.V.; *Int'l*, pg. 8127
VAN LEEUWEN PIPE & TUBE WESTERN AUSTRALIA PTY. LTD.—See Van Leeuwen Pipe & Tube Group B.V.; *Int'l*, pg. 8127
VAN LEEUWEN PRECISION B.V.—See Van Leeuwen Pipe & Tube Group B.V.; *Int'l*, pg. 8127
VAN LEEUWEN RURY SPOLKA Z.O.O.—See Van Leeuwen Pipe & Tube Group B.V.; *Int'l*, pg. 8127
VAN LEEUWEN (SHANGHAI) PIPE AND TUBE CO., LTD.—See Van Leeuwen Pipe & Tube Group B.V.; *Int'l*, pg. 8127
VAN LEEUWEN S.R.O.—See Van Leeuwen Pipe & Tube Group B.V.; *Int'l*, pg. 8127
VAN LEEUWEN STAINLESS—See Van Leeuwen Pipe & Tube Group B.V.; *Int'l*, pg. 8127
VAN LEEUWEN TUBES S.A.—See Van Leeuwen Pipe & Tube Group B.V.; *Int'l*, pg. 8127
VAN LEEUWEN WHEELER - SHEFFIELD—See Van Leeuwen Pipe & Tube Group B.V.; *Int'l*, pg. 8127
VANLEIGH RV, INC.—See Thor Industries, Inc.; *U.S. Public*, pg. 2157
VANLINER INSURANCE COMPANY—See American Financial Group, Inc.; *U.S. Public*, pg. 103
VAN LOOY GROUP B.V.—See Electricite de France S.A.; *Int'l*, pg. 2351
VAN LOOY GROUP N.V.—See Electricite de France S.A.; *Int'l*, pg. 2351
VAN LUMBER INC.; *U.S. Private*, pg. 4340
VAN MANEN PETROLEUM GROUP; *U.S. Private*, pg. 4340
VAN MANNEKUS & CO. B.V.—See Compagnie Financiere et de Participations Roullier SA; *Int'l*, pg. 1740
VAN MANNEKUS & CO. B.V.—See Grecian Magnesite S.A; *Int'l*, pg. 3068
VAN MANNEKUS UNIVERSAL V.O.F.—See Compagnie Financiere et de Participations Roullier SA; *Int'l*, pg. 1740
VAN MANNEKUS UNIVERSAL V.O.F.—See Grecian Magnesite S.A; *Int'l*, pg. 3068
VAN MATRE REHABILITATION CENTER LLC—See Encompass Health Corporation; *U.S. Public*, pg. 759
VAN MELLE A.G.—See Perfetti Van Melle Holding B.V.; *Int'l*, pg. 5801
VAN MELLE FAR EAST LIMITED—See Perfetti Van Melle Holding B.V.; *Int'l*, pg. 5800
VAN MELLE NEDERLAND B.V.—See Perfetti Van Melle Holding B.V.; *Int'l*, pg. 5800
VAN METER INC.; *U.S. Private*, pg. 4340
VAN METER INSURANCE GROUP—See Houchens Industries, Inc.; *U.S. Private*, pg. 1990
THE VAN METRE COMPANIES; *U.S. Private*, pg. 4130
VAN MOER GROUP - ZELLIK—See Koninklijke Ahold Delhaize N.V.; *Int'l*, pg. 4261
VAN NATTA MECHANICAL INC.; *U.S. Private*, pg. 4340
VANN CORPORATION—See Bando Chemical Industries, Ltd.; *Int'l*, pg. 831
VAN NEERBOS BELGIE N.V.—See CRH plc; *Int'l*, pg. 1849
VAN NELFEN DEURTECHNIEK B.V.—See ASSA ABLOY AB; *Int'l*, pg. 638
VAN NELLE TABAK NEDERLAND B.V.—See Imperial Brands PLC; *Int'l*, pg. 3634
VAN NELLE TOBACCO INTERNATIONAL HOLDINGS B.V.—See Imperial Brands PLC; *Int'l*, pg. 3634
VANNER, INC.—See Havis, Inc.; *U.S. Private*, pg. 1881
VANNER INSURANCE AGENCY; *U.S. Private*, pg. 4344
VAN NETTEN GMBH—See Gigaset AG; *Int'l*, pg. 2972
VANNMEISLING AS—See AF Gruppen ASA; *Int'l*, pg. 184
VAN NOORDENNE VERF B.V.—See Akzo Nobel N.V.; *Int'l*, pg. 275
VANN'S INCORPORATED; *U.S. Private*, pg. 4344
VAN NUYS APARTMENTS—See Apartment Investment and Management Company; *U.S. Public*, pg. 144
VAN NUYS-H, INC.—See Lithia Motors, Inc.; *U.S. Public*, pg. 1326
VANN YORK PONTIAC INC.; *U.S. Private*, pg. 4344

VANN YORK PONTIAC INC.

VAN OERLE ALBERTON B.V.—See Autoliv, Inc.; *Int'l*, pg. 730
VANOIL ENERGY LTD.; *Int'l*, pg. 8129
VAN OORD DREDGING AND MARINE CONTRACTORS B.V.—See Van Oord nv; *Int'l*, pg. 8127
VAN OORD NV; *Int'l*, pg. 8127
VANOV HOLDINGS COMPANY LIMITED; *Int'l*, pg. 8129
VAN OWEN GROUP ACQUISITION COMPANY; *U.S. Private*, pg. 4340
VAN-PAK INC.; *U.S. Private*, pg. 4341
VAN PARTNERS—See Toyota Tsusho Corporation; *Int'l*, pg. 7879
VANPEE AB—See A.A.G. STUCCHI s.r.l.; *Int'l*, pg. 23
VANPEE A/S—See Lagercrantz Group AB; *Int'l*, pg. 4395
VANPEE NORGE AS—See A.A.G. STUCCHI s.r.l.; *Int'l*, pg. 23
VANPEE & WESTERBERG A/S—See Lagercrantz Group AB; *Int'l*, pg. 4394
VAN PELT CORPORATION; *U.S. Private*, pg. 4340
VAN PELT - SERVICE STEEL DIVISION—See Van Pelt Corporation; *U.S. Private*, pg. 4340
VAN PHAT HUNG CORPORATION; *Int'l*, pg. 8127
VAN PHU - INVEST INVESTMENT JOINT STOCK COMPANY; *Int'l*, pg. 8127
VANPIKE INC.; *U.S. Private*, pg. 4344
VAN PLYCON LINES INC.; *U.S. Private*, pg. 4340
VANPORT CANADA, CO.—See Vanport Manufacturing, Inc.; *U.S. Private*, pg. 4344
VANPORT MANUFACTURING, INC.; *U.S. Private*, pg. 4344
VANPRO, INC.; *U.S. Private*, pg. 4344
VANQUIS BANKING GROUP PLC; *Int'l*, pg. 8130
VANQUIS BANK LIMITED—See Vanquis Banking Group plc; *Int'l*, pg. 8130
VAN RAALTE DE VENEZUELA C.A.; *Int'l*, pg. 8127
VAN REES B.V.—See ACOMO N.V.; *Int'l*, pg. 108
VAN REES CEYLON LTD.—See ACOMO N.V.; *Int'l*, pg. 108
VAN REES GROUP—See Blackstone Inc.; *U.S. Public*, pg. 356
VAN REES LLC—See ACOMO N.V.; *Int'l*, pg. 108
VAN REES NORTH AMERICA INC—See ACOMO N.V.; *Int'l*, pg. 108
VAN REES UK LTD—See ACOMO N.V.; *Int'l*, pg. 108
VAN RIJN B.V.; *Int'l*, pg. 8127
VAN RIJN FRANCE S.A.R.L.—See KWS SAAT SE & Co. KGaA; *Int'l*, pg. 4353
VAN-ROB, INC.—See KIRCHHOFF Gruppe; *Int'l*, pg. 4185
VAN ROB WAVERLY INC.—See KIRCHHOFF Gruppe; *Int'l*, pg. 4185
VAN ROIJ FASTENERS EUROPE B.V.—See Wurth Verwaltungsgesellschaft mbH; *Int'l*, pg. 8508
VAN ROIJ FASTENERS HUNGARIA KFT.—See Wurth Verwaltungsgesellschaft mbH; *Int'l*, pg. 8508
VAN RU CREDIT CORPORATION; *U.S. Private*, pg. 4341
VANRX PHARMASYSTEMS INC.—See Danaher Corporation; *U.S. Public*, pg. 631
VAN SCHOUWEN ASSOCIATES, LLC; *U.S. Private*, pg. 4341
VANSHI SHIPPING PTE. LTD—See Adani Enterprises Limited; *Int'l*, pg. 125
VANSH NIMAY INFRAPROJECTS LIMITED—See Infrastructure Leasing & Financial Services Limited; *Int'l*, pg. 3698
VAN'S HONDA; *U.S. Private*, pg. 4341
VAN SHUNG CHONG HONG LIMITED—See Hong Kong Shanghai Alliance Holdings Limited; *Int'l*, pg. 3467
VAN SILLEVOLDT RIJST B.V.—See Marbour SAS; *Int'l*, pg. 4688
VANS, INC.—See V. F. Corporation; *U.S. Public*, pg. 2269
VAN'S INC.; *U.S. Private*, pg. 4341
VAN'S INC.—See C.S. Wo & Sons Ltd.; *U.S. Private*, pg. 709
VANS INTERNATIONAL FOODS—See Tyson Foods, Inc.; *U.S. Public*, pg. 2210
VAN'S INTERNATIONAL FOODS—See Tyson Foods, Inc.; *U.S. Public*, pg. 2210
VAN'S LUMBER & CUSTOM BUILDERS; *U.S. Private*, pg. 4341
VAN'S OF MICHIGAN, INC.—See Van's Inc.; *U.S. Private*, pg. 4341
VANSOLIX S.A—See HORIBA Ltd; *Int'l*, pg. 3478
VANSON DEVELOPMENTS LTD.—See Virgin Management Limited; *Int'l*, pg. 8247
VANSON ENTERPRISES, INC.; *U.S. Private*, pg. 4344
VAN SON HOLLAND INK CORPORATION OF AMERICA; *U.S. Private*, pg. 4341
VAN'S PRO SHOP—See Worldwide Golf Enterprises, Inc.; *U.S. Private*, pg. 4569
VAN'S REALTY & CONSTRUCTION; *U.S. Private*, pg. 4341
VANSTAR MINING RESOURCES INC.—See IAMGOLD Corporation; *Int'l*, pg. 3569
VAN SYCKLE KIA INC.; *U.S. Private*, pg. 4341
VANTA BIOSCIENCE LTD.; *Int'l*, pg. 8130
VANTACO OY—See The Sherwin-Williams Company; *U.S. Public*, pg. 2130
VANTACORE PARTNERS LP—See Sun Capital Partners, Inc.; *U.S. Private*, pg. 3861

VANTAGE AGING; *U.S. Private*, pg. 4344
VANTAGE AUTOMOTIVE LIMITED—See Sime Darby Berhad; *Int'l*, pg. 6931
VANTAGE BANK TEXAS—See VBT Financial Corporation; *U.S. Private*, pg. 4348
VANTAGE BAY JB SDN. BHD.—See Thomson Medical Group Limited; *Int'l*, pg. 7714
VANTAGE CLIMICAL SOLUTIONS, LLC—See Level Equity Management, LLC; *U.S. Private*, pg. 2434
VANTAGE CLIMICAL SOLUTIONS, LLC—See Silversmith Management, L.P.; *U.S. Private*, pg. 3664
VANTAGE CLIMICAL SOLUTIONS, LLC—See The Carlyle Group Inc.; *U.S. Public*, pg. 2050
VANTAGE COMPANIES; *U.S. Private*, pg. 4344
VANTAGE CONTRACTORS, LLC; *U.S. Private*, pg. 4344
VANTAGE CONTROLS, INC.—See Legrand S.A.; *Int'l*, pg. 4446
VANTAGE CUSTOM CLASSICS, INC.; *U.S. Private*, pg. 4345
VANTAGE DELAWARE HOLDINGS LLC—See Vantage Drilling Company; *U.S. Public*, pg. 2275
VANTAGE DELUXE WORLD TRAVEL; *U.S. Private*, pg. 4345
VANTAGE DEVELOPMENT S.A.—See TAG Immobilien AG; *Int'l*, pg. 7407
VANTAGE DRILLING COMPANY; *U.S. Public*, pg. 2275
VANTAGE DRILLING INTERNATIONAL; *U.S. Public*, pg. 2275
VANTAGE DRILLING INTERNATIONAL; *Int'l*, pg. 8130
VANTAGE ELEVATOR SOLUTIONS—See Golden Gate Capital Management II, LLC; *U.S. Private*, pg. 1732
VANTAGE ENERGY ACQUISITION CORP.; *U.S. Private*, pg. 4345
VANTAGE ENERGY INC.—See Lime Rock Partners, LLC; *U.S. Private*, pg. 2456
VANTAGE ENERGY INC.—See Quantum Energy Partners, LLC; *U.S. Private*, pg. 3323
VANTAGE ENERGY INC.—See Riverstone Holdings LLC; *U.S. Private*, pg. 3448
VANTAGE ENERGY SERVICES, INC.—See Vantage Drilling Company; *U.S. Public*, pg. 2275
VANTAGE EQUITIES, INC.; *Int'l*, pg. 8130
VANTAGE GODOWN COMPANY LIMITED—See Hong Kong Shanghai Alliance Holdings Limited; *Int'l*, pg. 3467
VANTAGE GOLDFIELDS LIMITED; *Int'l*, pg. 8130
VANTAGE HEALTH PLAN INC.; *U.S. Private*, pg. 4345
VANTAGE INSURANCE SERVICES LIMITED—See White Mountains Insurance Group, Ltd.; *U.S. Public*, pg. 2369
VANTAGE INTERNATIONAL (HOLDINGS) LIMITED; *Int'l*, pg. 8130
VANTAGE INTERNATIONAL MANAGEMENT COMPANY PTE LTD—See Vantage Drilling Company; *U.S. Public*, pg. 2275
VANTAGE INVESTMENT CORP.; *U.S. Private*, pg. 4345
VANTAGE KNOWLEDGE ACADEMY LTD.—See Anupam Finserv Ltd.; *Int'l*, pg. 486
VANTAGE MANAGEMENT CO., INC.—See Belmont Group Inc.; *U.S. Private*, pg. 520
VANTAGE MEDIA, LLC; *U.S. Private*, pg. 4345
VANTAGE MEDICAL SUPPLIES, INC.—See Dealmed Medical Supplies LLC; *U.S. Private*, pg. 1183
VANTAGE MOBILITY INTERNATIONAL, LLC—See Nautic Partners, LLC; *U.S. Private*, pg. 2872
VANTAGE OLEOCHEMICALS, INC.—See H.I.G. Capital, LLC; *U.S. Private*, pg. 1832
VANTAGEPOINT AI, LLC; *U.S. Private*, pg. 4345
VANTAGEPOINT CAPITAL PARTNERS; *U.S. Private*, pg. 4345
VANTAGEPOINT, INC.; *U.S. Private*, pg. 4345
VANTAGEPOINT K.K.—See JAC Recruitment Co., Ltd.; *Int'l*, pg. 3864
VANTAGE PRESS, INC.; *U.S. Private*, pg. 4345
VANTAGE PRODUCTION, LLC.—See United Communications Group; *U.S. Private*, pg. 4289
VANTAGESCORE SOLUTIONS, LLC—See Equifax Inc.; *U.S. Public*, pg. 787
VANTAGESCORE SOLUTIONS, LLC—See Experian plc; *Int'l*, pg. 2587
VANTAGESCORE SOLUTIONS, LLC—See TransUnion; *U.S. Public*, pg. 2184
VANTAGE SOFTWARE—See First Rate, Inc.; *U.S. Private*, pg. 1525
VANTAGE SPECIALTIES, INC.—See H.I.G. Capital, LLC; *U.S. Private*, pg. 1832
VANTAGE SPECIALTY CHEMICALS, INC.—See H.I.G. Capital, LLC; *U.S. Private*, pg. 1832
VANTAGE SPECIALTY INGREDIENTS, INC.—See H.I.G. Capital, LLC; *U.S. Private*, pg. 1832
VANTAGE TOWERS AG—See KKR & Co. Inc.; *U.S. Public*, pg. 1266
VANTAGE TOWERS SINGLE MEMBER SOCIETE ANONYME—See Vodafone Group Plc; *Int'l*, pg. 8285
VANTAGE TOWERS ZARTKORUEN MUKODO RESZVENYTARSASAG—See Vodafone Group Plc; *Int'l*, pg. 8285
VANTAGE TRAILERS INC.; *U.S. Private*, pg. 4345

CORPORATE AFFILIATIONS

VANTAGE VEHICLE INTERNATIONAL, INC.—See Salt Creek Capital Management, LLC; *U.S. Private*, pg. 3533
VANTAGE WEST CREDIT UNION; *U.S. Private*, pg. 4345
VANTEA SMART S.P.A.; *Int'l*, pg. 8130
VANTEC CENTRAL CORPORATION—See KKR & Co. Inc.; *U.S. Public*, pg. 1259
VANTEC CENTRAL LOGISTICS CORPORATION—See KKR & Co. Inc.; *U.S. Public*, pg. 1259
VANTEC CO., LTD.—See Sekisui Chemical Co., Ltd.; *Int'l*, pg. 6696
VANTEC CORPORATION—See KKR & Co. Inc.; *U.S. Public*, pg. 1259
VANTEC EAST LOGISTICS CORPORATION—See KKR & Co. Inc.; *U.S. Public*, pg. 1259
VANTEC EUROPE LIMITED—See KKR & Co. Inc.; *U.S. Public*, pg. 1259
VANTEC RF SOLUTIONS CORPORATION—See KKR & Co. Inc.; *U.S. Public*, pg. 1259
VANTEC SHOJI CO., LTD.—See Sekisui Chemical Co., Ltd.; *Int'l*, pg. 6696
VANTEC SUMISO LOGISTICS (WUHAN) CO., LTD.—See The Sumitomo Warehouse Co. Ltd.; *Int'l*, pg. 7690
VANTEC TOKAI LOGISTICS CORPORATION—See KKR & Co. Inc.; *U.S. Public*, pg. 1259
VANTEM GLOBAL, INC.; *U.S. Private*, pg. 4345
VANTEON CORPORATION; *U.S. Private*, pg. 4345
VANTEX COMMERCIAL PROPERTY GROUP—See Sowell & Co., Inc.; *U.S. Private*, pg. 3743
VANTI SA., ESP—See Brookfield Corporation; *Int'l*, pg. 1189
VANTIVA SA; *Int'l*, pg. 8130
VANTIV, LLC—See GTCR LLC; *U.S. Private*, pg. 1806
VANTONE NEO DEVELOPMENT GROUP CO., LTD.; *Int'l*, pg. 8131
VAN-TROW TOYOTA; *U.S. Private*, pg. 4341
VAN TUYL GROUP, LLC—See Berkshire Hathaway Inc.; *U.S. Public*, pg. 300
VAN UNEN / MIERSMA PROPANE, INC.—See EDPO, LLC; *U.S. Private*, pg. 1338
VAN VREEDE TV & APPLIANCE INCORPORATED; *U.S. Private*, pg. 4341
VAN VYNCK ENVIRONMENTAL SERVICES LTD.—See Rollins, Inc.; *U.S. Public*, pg. 1809
VAN WAGNER COMMUNICATIONS, LLC; *U.S. Private*, pg. 4341
VAN WAGNER SPORTS GROUP LLC—See Van Wagner Communications, LLC; *U.S. Private*, pg. 4341
VAN WALL EQUIPMENT INC.; *U.S. Private*, pg. 4341
VAN WERT COUNTY HOSPITAL; *U.S. Private*, pg. 4341
VAN WEZEL AUTOPARTS GMBH—See Unipart Group of Companies Limited; *Int'l*, pg. 8055
VAN WEZEL GMBH—See Unipart Group of Companies Limited; *Int'l*, pg. 8055
VAN WEZEL NV—See Unipart Group of Companies Limited; *Int'l*, pg. 8055
VAN-WHOLE PRODUCE LTD.; *Int'l*, pg. 8128
VAN WIJK & BOERMA VERDER—See Verder International B.V.; *Int'l*, pg. 8167
VAN WYK INC.; *U.S. Private*, pg. 4341
VANZANDT CONTROLS, LLC; *U.S. Private*, pg. 4345
VAN ZANDT COUNTY HAVEN OF MEMORIES, INC.—See Service Corporation International; *U.S. Public*, pg. 1870
VAN ZEELAND OIL CO., INC.; *U.S. Private*, pg. 4341
VAN ZYVERDEN INC.; *U.S. Private*, pg. 4341
VAO INTOURIST—See Sistema PJSFC; *Int'l*, pg. 6963
VAPAROID AG—See swisspor Management AG; *Int'l*, pg. 7375
VAPE BRANDS INTERNATIONAL INC.—See Gilla Inc.; *U.S. Public*, pg. 938
VAPEK ACLANICA LUTRA GROUP A.D.; *Int'l*, pg. 8131
VAPEN, LLC—See Vext Science, Inc.; *Int'l*, pg. 8182
THE VAPE STORE, INC.—See Healthier Choices Management Corp.; *U.S. Public*, pg. 1016
VAPIANO SE; *Int'l*, pg. 8131
VAPI ENTERPRISE LTD.; *Int'l*, pg. 8131
VAP INC.—See Nippon Television Holdings Inc.; *Int'l*, pg. 5356
VAPIR INC.—See Home Bistro, Inc.; *U.S. Public*, pg. 1046
VAPIS STAVEBNI HMOTY S.R.O.—See Heidelberg Materials AG; *Int'l*, pg. 3320
VAPO OY; *Int'l*, pg. 8131
VAPOR BEAST LLC—See Turning Point Brands, Inc.; *U.S. Public*, pg. 2205
VAPORBRANDS INTERNATIONAL, INC.; *U.S. Public*, pg. 2275
VAPOR BUS INTERNATIONAL—See Westinghouse Air Brake Technologies Corporation; *U.S. Public*, pg. 2359
VAPOR EUROPE S.R.L.—See Westinghouse Air Brake Technologies Corporation; *U.S. Public*, pg. 2359
VAPOR HUB INTERNATIONAL INC.; *U.S. Public*, pg. 2275
VAPORJET LTD.; *Int'l*, pg. 8132
THE VAPORMATIC CO., LTD.—See Deere & Company; *U.S. Public*, pg. 647
VAPOR POWER INTERNATIONAL, LLC—See Thermon Group Holdings, Inc.; *U.S. Public*, pg. 2155

COMPANY NAME INDEX

VAPOR RAIL KAPI SISTEMLERI TICARET VE HIZMETLERI LIMITED SIRKETI—See Westinghouse Air Brake Technologies Corporation; *U.S. Public*, pg. 2359
VAPOR RICON EUROPE LTD.—See Westinghouse Air Brake Technologies Corporation; *U.S. Public*, pg. 2359
VAPOR SHARK, LLC—See Turning Point Brands, Inc.; *U.S. Public*, pg. 2205
VAPOR TECHNOLOGIES, INC.—See Masco Corporation; *U.S. Public*, pg. 1392
VAPOTHERM, INC.—See Perceptive Advisors, LLC; *U.S. Private*, pg. 3146
V-APPAREL INTERNATIONAL LIMITED—See Victory City International Holdings Limited; *Int'l*, pg. 8189
VAPS GMBH—See voestalpine AG; *Int'l*, pg. 8289
VAPTSAROV JSC; *Int'l*, pg. 8132
VA-Q-TEC AG; *Int'l*, pg. 8107
VA-Q-TEC INDIA LTD.—See Va-Q-tec AG; *Int'l*, pg. 8107
VA-Q-TEC JAPAN G.K.—See Va-Q-tec AG; *Int'l*, pg. 8107
VA-Q-TEC KOREA LTD.—See Va-Q-tec AG; *Int'l*, pg. 8107
VA-Q-TEC LIMITED—See Va-Q-tec AG; *Int'l*, pg. 8107
VA-Q-TEC SG PTE. LTD.—See Va-Q-tec AG; *Int'l*, pg. 8107
VA-Q-TEC URUGUAY S.A.—See Va-Q-tec AG; *Int'l*, pg. 8107
VA-Q-TEC USA INC.—See Va-Q-tec AG; *Int'l*, pg. 8107
VAQUERIA TRES MONJITAS INC.; *U.S. Private*, pg. 4345
VAR 4 ADVISORY S.P.A.—See Sesa S.p.A.; *Int'l*, pg. 6729
VAR4TEAM SRL—See Sesa S.p.A.; *Int'l*, pg. 6729
VARAAN B.V.; *Int'l*, pg. 8132
VARAGE MOUNTAIN CO. INC.; *U.S. Private*, pg. 4345
VARAGON CAPITAL CORPORATION; *U.S. Private*, pg. 4345
VARAGON CAPITAL PARTNERS, L.P.—See Aflac Incorporated; *U.S. Public*, pg. 57
VARANGIS AVEPE S.A.; *Int'l*, pg. 8132
VARANGIS QATAR L.L.C—See VARANGIS AVEPE S.A.; *Int'l*, pg. 8132
VARANGIS TURNKEY INTERIOR PROJECTS L.L.C—See VARANGIS AVEPE S.A.; *Int'l*, pg. 8132
VAR BMS S.P.A.—See Sesa S.p.A.; *Int'l*, pg. 6729
VARBROS CORPORATION; *U.S. Private*, pg. 4345
VAR BUSINESS ENGINEERING SRL—See Sesa S.p.A.; *Int'l*, pg. 6729
VARCO BJ BV—See NOV, Inc.; *U.S. Public*, pg. 1547
VARCO CANADA ULC—See NOV, Inc.; *U.S. Public*, pg. 1547
VARCO, L.P.—See NOV, Inc.; *U.S. Public*, pg. 1547
VARCOMAC LLC—See Blackstone Inc.; *U.S. Public*, pg. 361
VARCO PRUDEN BUILDINGS, INC.—See BlueScope Steel Limited; *Int'l*, pg. 1073
VARCO SARA (INDIA) PRIVATE LIMITED—See NOV, Inc.; *U.S. Public*, pg. 1547
VARD ACCOMMODATION AS—See Fincantieri S.p.A.; *Int'l*, pg. 2671
VARD ACCOMMODATION TULCEA S.R.L.—See Cassa Depositi e Prestiti S.p.A.; *Int'l*, pg. 1355
VARD ACCOMMODTION TULCEA SRL—See Fincantieri S.p.A.; *Int'l*, pg. 2671
VARD AQUA CHILE SA—See Fincantieri S.p.A.; *Int'l*, pg. 2671
VARD AQUA SCOTLAND LTD.—See Fincantieri S.p.A.; *Int'l*, pg. 2671
VARD AQUA SUNNDAL AS—See Fincantieri S.p.A.; *Int'l*, pg. 2671
VARDATA LLC; *U.S. Private*, pg. 4346
VARDAX S.A.—See HELLENiQ ENERGY Holdings S.A.; *Int'l*, pg. 3334
VARD BRAILA SA—See Fincantieri S.p.A.; *Int'l*, pg. 2671
VARD BRATTVAAG AS—See Fincantieri S.p.A.; *Int'l*, pg. 2671
VARD BREVIK HOLDING AS—See Fincantieri S.p.A.; *Int'l*, pg. 2671
VARD DESIGN AS—See Fincantieri S.p.A.; *Int'l*, pg. 2671
VARD DESIGN LIBURNA LTD.—See Fincantieri S.p.A.; *Int'l*, pg. 2671
VARD ELECTRICAL INSTALLATION AND ENGINEERING (INDIA) PRIVATE LIMITED—See Fincantieri S.p.A.; *Int'l*, pg. 2672
VARD ELECTRO AS—See Fincantieri S.p.A.; *Int'l*, pg. 2671
VARD ELECTRO BRAILA SRL—See Fincantieri S.p.A.; *Int'l*, pg. 2672
VARD ELECTRO BRAZIL (INSTALACOES ELETRICAS) LTDA.—See Fincantieri S.p.A.; *Int'l*, pg. 2671
VARD ELECTRO BRAZIL LTDA.—See Fincantieri S.p.A.; *Int'l*, pg. 2672
VARD ELECTRO TULCEA SRL—See Fincantieri S.p.A.; *Int'l*, pg. 2672
VARD ELECTRO US INC.—See Cassa Depositi e Prestiti S.p.A.; *Int'l*, pg. 1355
VARD ENGINEERING BREVIK AS—See Fincantieri S.p.A.; *Int'l*, pg. 2672
VARDE OVNE A/S—See NIBE Industrier AB; *Int'l*, pg. 5263
VARDE PARTNERS, INC.; *U.S. Private*, pg. 4346
VARD GROUP AS—See Fincantieri S.p.A.; *Int'l*, pg. 2671
VARDHAMAN LABORATORIES LIMITED; *Int'l*, pg. 8132

VARDHAN CAPITAL & FINANCE LTD.; *Int'l*, pg. 8132
VARDHAN ACRYLICS LIMITED—See Vardhman Group of Companies; *Int'l*, pg. 8132
VARDHAN CONCRETE LIMITED—See Vardhman Group of Companies; *Int'l*, pg. 8132
VARDHMAN GROUP OF COMPANIES; *Int'l*, pg. 8132
VARDHMAN HOLDINGS LIMITED—See Vardhman Group of Companies; *Int'l*, pg. 8132
VARDHMAN INDUSTRIES LTD.; *Int'l*, pg. 8132
VARDHMAN POLYTEX LIMITED—See Vardhman Group of Companies; *Int'l*, pg. 8132
VARDHMAN SPECIAL STEELS LIMITED—See Vardhman Group of Companies; *Int'l*, pg. 8132
VARDHMAN TEXTILES LIMITED—See Vardhman Group of Companies; *Int'l*, pg. 8132
VARD HOLDINGS LIMITED—See Fincantieri S.p.A.; *Int'l*, pg. 2671
VARD MARINE GDANSK SP. Z O.O.—See Fincantieri S.p.A.; *Int'l*, pg. 2672
VARD MARINE INC.—See Fincantieri S.p.A.; *Int'l*, pg. 2672
VARD NITEROI SA—See Fincantieri S.p.A.; *Int'l*, pg. 2672
VARD OFFSHORE BREVIK AS—See Fincantieri S.p.A.; *Int'l*, pg. 2672
VARD PIPING AS—See Fincantieri S.p.A.; *Int'l*, pg. 2672
VARD PIPING TULCEA SRL—See Fincantieri S.p.A.; *Int'l*, pg. 2672
VARD PROMAR SA—See Fincantieri S.p.A.; *Int'l*, pg. 2672
VARD SINGAPORE PTE. LTD.—See Fincantieri S.p.A.; *Int'l*, pg. 2672
VARD TULCEA SA—See Fincantieri S.p.A.; *Int'l*, pg. 2672
VARDVASKAN AB—See Storskogen Group AB; *Int'l*, pg. 7228
VARD VUNG TAU LTD.—See Fincantieri S.p.A.; *Int'l*, pg. 2672
VARELA AUTO GROUP, LLC; *U.S. Private*, pg. 4346
VARELAS S.A.—See Marfin Investment Group Holdings S.A.; *Int'l*, pg. 4692
VAREL INTERNATIONAL ENERGY SERVICES, INC.—See Blue Water Energy LLP; *Int'l*, pg. 1070
VAR ENERGI AS—See Eni S.p.A.; *Int'l*, pg. 2438
VARENGOLD BANK AG; *Int'l*, pg. 8132
VAREN TECHNOLOGIES, INC.—See Godspeed Capital Management LP; *U.S. Private*, pg. 1725
VARESE RISORSE S.P.A.—See A2A S.p.A.; *Int'l*, pg. 29
VARESE SARABANDE RECORDS, INC.; *U.S. Private*, pg. 4346
VAREX IMAGING AMERICAS CORPORATION—See Varex Imaging Corporation; *U.S. Public*, pg. 2275
VAREX IMAGING CORPORATION; *U.S. Public*, pg. 2275
VAREX IMAGING EQUIPMENT (CHINA) CO., LTD.—See Varex Imaging Corporation; *U.S. Public*, pg. 2275
VAREX IMAGING HOLDINGS, INC.—See Varex Imaging Corporation; *U.S. Public*, pg. 2275
VAREX IMAGING ITALIA SRL—See Varex Imaging Corporation; *U.S. Public*, pg. 2275
VAREX IMAGING JAPAN, K.K.—See Varex Imaging Corporation; *U.S. Public*, pg. 2275
VAREX IMAGING NEDERLAND B.V.—See Varex Imaging Corporation; *U.S. Public*, pg. 2275
VAREX IMAGING PHILIPPINES, INC.—See Varex Imaging Corporation; *U.S. Public*, pg. 2275
VARGON D.O.O.—See Wienerberger AG; *Int'l*, pg. 8406
VAR GROUP SUISSE S.A.—See Sesa S.p.A.; *Int'l*, pg. 6729
VAR HUB SRL—See Sesa S.p.A.; *Int'l*, pg. 6729
THE VARIABLE ANNUITY LIFE INSURANCE COMPANY—See American International Group, Inc.; *U.S. Public*, pg. 105
VARIAN KOREA LTD.—See Applied Materials, Inc.; *U.S. Public*, pg. 173
VARIAN MEDICAL FRANCE S.A.S.—See Siemens Aktiengesellschaft; *Int'l*, pg. 6894
VARIAN MEDICAL SYSTEM LATIN AMERICA, LTD.—See Siemens Aktiengesellschaft; *Int'l*, pg. 6894
VARIAN MEDICAL SYSTEMS AUSTRALASIA HOLDINGS PTY. LTD.—See Siemens Aktiengesellschaft; *Int'l*, pg. 6894
VARIAN MEDICAL SYSTEMS AUSTRALASIA PTY LTD.—See Siemens Aktiengesellschaft; *Int'l*, pg. 6894
VARIAN MEDICAL SYSTEMS BELGIUM N.V.—See Siemens Aktiengesellschaft; *Int'l*, pg. 6894
VARIAN MEDICAL SYSTEMS BRASIL LTDA.—See Siemens Aktiengesellschaft; *Int'l*, pg. 6894
VARIAN MEDICAL SYSTEMS CANADA, INC.—See Siemens Aktiengesellschaft; *Int'l*, pg. 6894
VARIAN MEDICAL SYSTEMS (CHINA) CO. LTD.—See Siemens Aktiengesellschaft; *Int'l*, pg. 6894
VARIAN MEDICAL SYSTEMS DEUTSCHLAND GMBH—See Siemens Aktiengesellschaft; *Int'l*, pg. 6894
VARIAN MEDICAL SYSTEMS FINLAND OY—See Siemens Aktiengesellschaft; *Int'l*, pg. 6894
VARIAN MEDICAL SYSTEMS FRANCE—See Siemens Aktiengesellschaft; *Int'l*, pg. 6894
VARIAN MEDICAL SYSTEMS GESELLSCHAFT M.B.H.—See Siemens Aktiengesellschaft; *Int'l*, pg. 6894

VARISCAN MINES LIMITED

VARIAN MEDICAL SYSTEMS HAAN G.M.B.H.—See Siemens Aktiengesellschaft; *Int'l*, pg. 6894
VARIAN MEDICAL SYSTEMS HUNGARY KFT—See Siemens Aktiengesellschaft; *Int'l*, pg. 6894
VARIAN MEDICAL SYSTEMS IBERICA S.L.—See Siemens Aktiengesellschaft; *Int'l*, pg. 6894
VARIAN MEDICAL SYSTEMS IMAGING LABORATORY GMBH—See Siemens Aktiengesellschaft; *Int'l*, pg. 6894
VARIAN MEDICAL SYSTEMS, INC. - ONCOLOGY SYSTEMS—See Siemens Aktiengesellschaft; *Int'l*, pg. 6895
VARIAN MEDICAL SYSTEMS, INC.—See Siemens Aktiengesellschaft; *Int'l*, pg. 6894
VARIAN MEDICAL SYSTEMS INDIA PVT LTD.—See Siemens Aktiengesellschaft; *Int'l*, pg. 6894
VARIAN MEDICAL SYSTEMS INTERNATIONAL AG—See Siemens Aktiengesellschaft; *Int'l*, pg. 6894
VARIAN MEDICAL SYSTEMS INTERNATIONAL (INDIA) PVT. LTD.—See Siemens Aktiengesellschaft; *Int'l*, pg. 6894
VARIAN MEDICAL SYSTEMS ITALIA SPA—See Siemens Aktiengesellschaft; *Int'l*, pg. 6894
VARIAN MEDICAL SYSTEMS KK—See Siemens Aktiengesellschaft; *Int'l*, pg. 6894
VARIAN MEDICAL SYSTEMS NEDERLAND B.V.—See Siemens Aktiengesellschaft; *Int'l*, pg. 6894
VARIAN MEDICAL SYSTEMS PACIFIC, INC.—See Siemens Aktiengesellschaft; *Int'l*, pg. 6894
VARIAN MEDICAL SYSTEMS POLAND SP. Z O.O.—See Siemens Aktiengesellschaft; *Int'l*, pg. 6894
VARIAN MEDICAL SYSTEMS SCANDINAVIA AS—See Siemens Aktiengesellschaft; *Int'l*, pg. 6894
VARIAN MEDICAL SYSTEMS TRADING (BEIJING) CO., LTD.—See Siemens Aktiengesellschaft; *Int'l*, pg. 6894
VARIAN MEDICAL SYSTEMS UK HOLDINGS LIMITED—See Siemens Aktiengesellschaft; *Int'l*, pg. 6895
VARIAN MEDICAL SYSTEMS UK LTD.—See Siemens Aktiengesellschaft; *Int'l*, pg. 6895
VARIAN SEMICONDUCTOR EQUIPMENT ASSOCIATES, INC.—See Applied Materials, Inc.; *U.S. Public*, pg. 173
VARIAN SEMICONDUCTOR EQUIPMENT ASSOCIATES PACRIM PTE. LTD.—See Applied Materials, Inc.; *U.S. Public*, pg. 172
VARIANT CAPITAL ADVISORS LLC—See Conway MacKenzie, Inc.; *U.S. Private*, pg. 1036
VARIANT EQUITY ADVISORS, LLC; *U.S. Private*, pg. 4346
VARIANT S.A.; *Int'l*, pg. 8133
VARIA-PACK NV—See Bunzl plc; *Int'l*, pg. 1219
VARIATION BIOTECHNOLOGIES (US), INC.—See VBI Vaccines Inc.; *U.S. Public*, pg. 2276
VARIA US PROPERTIES AG; *Int'l*, pg. 8132
VARI CORPORATION; *U.S. Private*, pg. 4346
VARIETY CARE; *U.S. Private*, pg. 4346
VARIETY CHILD LEARNING CENTER; *U.S. Private*, pg. 4347
VARIETY DISTRIBUTORS INC.; *U.S. Private*, pg. 4347
VARIETY FOOD FACTORY COMPANY—See Savola Group; *Int'l*, pg. 6602
VARIETY MEDIA, LLC—See Penske Media Corporation; *U.S. Private*, pg. 3139
VARIETY WHOLESALERS, INCORPORATED; *U.S. Private*, pg. 4347
VARIFLEX INC.—See Transom Capital Group, LLC; *U.S. Private*, pg. 4209
VARI-FORM CORPORATION—See Crowne Group LLC; *U.S. Private*, pg. 1112
VARILEASE TECHNOLOGY FINANCE GROUP INC.; *U.S. Private*, pg. 4347
VARIMAN GLOBAL ENTERPRISES LTD.; *Int'l*, pg. 8133
VARIMERX S.E. ASIA PTE. LTD.—See Stamford Land Corporation Ltd.; *Int'l*, pg. 7165
VARIMIXER A/S—See The Middleby Corporation; *U.S. Public*, pg. 2115
VARINAK BULGARIA LTD.—See Siemens Aktiengesellschaft; *Int'l*, pg. 6895
VARINAK EUROPE LTD.—See Siemens Aktiengesellschaft; *Int'l*, pg. 6895
VARINAK ONKOLOJI SISTEMLERI SATIS VE SERVIS A.S.—See Bozlu Holding; *Int'l*, pg. 1125
VARINDERA CONSTRUCTIONS LTD.; *Int'l*, pg. 8133
VARIOHM-EUROSENSOR LIMITED—See discoverIE Group plc; *Int'l*, pg. 2134
VARIOHM HOLDINGS LIMITED—See discoverIE Group plc; *Int'l*, pg. 2134
VARIO SECURE, INC.; *Int'l*, pg. 8133
VARIOUS EATERIES PLC; *Int'l*, pg. 8133
VARIOUS, INC.—See FriendFinder Networks Inc.; *U.S. Private*, pg. 1611
VARIPERM (CANADA) LIMITED; *Int'l*, pg. 8133
VARIQ CORPORATION; *U.S. Private*, pg. 4347
VARISCAN MINES LIMITED; *Int'l*, pg. 8133
VARISCITE LTD.—See Telsys Ltd.; *Int'l*, pg. 7546
VARISCO S.R.L.—See Atlas Copco AB; *Int'l*, pg. 684
VARISCO WELLPOINT SRL—See Atlas Copco AB; *Int'l*, pg. 684

VARISCAN MINES LIMITED

VARISPEED (PTY) LTD—See Hudaco Industries Limited; *Int'l*, pg. 3521
VARISTAR CORPORATION—See Otter Tail Corporation; *U.S. Public*, pg. 1624
VARITE, INC.; *U.S. Private*, pg. 4347
VARITRON GROUP INC.—See Investissement Quebec; *Int'l*, pg. 3780
VARI TRONICS COMPANY, INC.; *U.S. Private*, pg. 4346
VARLEY AND GULLIVER LTD—See Hill & Smith PLC; *Int'l*, pg. 3392
VARMA & VELAVERK EHF.—See Endress+Hauser (International) Holding AG; *Int'l*, pg. 2409
VARMENT GUARD ENVIRONMENTAL SERVICES, INC.—See Plunkett's Pest Control, Inc.; *U.S. Private*, pg. 3215
VARNA PLOD AD; *Int'l*, pg. 8133
VARNAVAS HADJIPANAYIS LIMITED—See HORIBA Ltd; *Int'l*, pg. 3478
VARNELL-STRUCK & ASSOCIATES INC.; *U.S. Private*, pg. 4347
VARNER-GRUPPEN AS; *Int'l*, pg. 8133
VARNER POLSKA LTD. SP.Z.O.O.—See Varner-Gruppen AS; *Int'l*, pg. 8133
VARNEY AGENCY, INC.; *U.S. Private*, pg. 4347
VARNEY INC.; *U.S. Private*, pg. 4347
VARNI BROTHERS CORPORATION—See KKR & Co. Inc.; *U.S. Public*, pg. 1263
VARNOST FITEP A.D.; *Int'l*, pg. 8133
VARO ENERGY GERMANY GMBH—See Vitol Holding B.V.; *Int'l*, pg. 8260
VARO ENERGY HOLDING S.A.—See AtlasInvest; *Int'l*, pg. 686
VARO ENERGY HOLDING S.A.—See Vitol Holding B.V.; *Int'l*, pg. 8261
VARO ENERGY MARKETING AG—See AtlasInvest; *Int'l*, pg. 686
VARO ENERGY MARKETING AG—See Vitol Holding B.V.; *Int'l*, pg. 8261
VAROLII CORPORATION—See Microsoft Corporation; *U.S. Public*, pg. 1443
VAR ONE NORD EST S.R.L.—See Sesa S.p.A.; *Int'l*, pg. 6729
VARONIS SYSTEMS (AUSTRALIA) PTY LTD—See Varonis Systems Inc.; *U.S. Public*, pg. 2275
VARONIS SYSTEMS INC.; *U.S. Public*, pg. 2275
VARONIS SYSTEMS (IRELAND) LIMITED—See Varonis Systems Inc.; *U.S. Public*, pg. 2276
VARONIS SYSTEMS (NETHERLANDS) B.V.—See Varonis Systems Inc.; *U.S. Public*, pg. 2276
VAROPAKORN PUBLIC CO., LTD.; *Int'l*, pg. 8133
VARO REFINING CRESSIER S.A.—See AtlasInvest; *Int'l*, pg. 686
VARO REFINING CRESSIER S.A.—See Vitol Holding B.V.; *Int'l*, pg. 8261
VAROSSIEAU SURINAME NV—See PPG Industries, Inc.; *U.S. Public*, pg. 1711
VAROUH OIL, INC.; *U.S. Private*, pg. 4347
VAROVA BV; *Int'l*, pg. 8133
VAR PRIME SRL—See Sesa S.p.A.; *Int'l*, pg. 6729
VAR RESOURCES CORP.; *Int'l*, pg. 8132
VARROC ENGINEERING LTD.; *Int'l*, pg. 8133
VARROC LIGHTING SYSTEMS BULGARIA EOOD—See Varroc Engineering Ltd.; *Int'l*, pg. 8133
VARROC LIGHTING SYSTEMS GMBH—See Varroc Engineering Ltd.; *Int'l*, pg. 8133
VARROC LIGHTING SYSTEMS INC.—See Varroc Engineering Ltd.; *Int'l*, pg. 8133
VARROC LIGHTING SYSTEMS (INDIA) PRIVATE LIMITED—See Varroc Engineering Ltd.; *Int'l*, pg. 8133
VARROC LIGHTING SYSTEMS, ITALY S.P.A.—See Varroc Engineering Ltd.; *Int'l*, pg. 8133
VARROC LIGHTING SYSTEMS S DE R.L. DE C.V.—See Varroc Engineering Ltd.; *Int'l*, pg. 8133
VARROC LIGHTING SYSTEMS SRO—See Varroc Engineering Ltd.; *Int'l*, pg. 8133
VARROC POLYMERS PRIVATE LIMITED—See Varroc Engineering Ltd.; *Int'l*, pg. 8133
VARROC TYC AUTO LAMPS CO., LTD.—See TYC Brother Industrial Co., Ltd.; *Int'l*, pg. 7994
VARSAV GAME STUDIOS SA; *Int'l*, pg. 8133
VARS BRNO A.S.—See VINCI S.A.; *Int'l*, pg. 8240
VARSHNEY CAPITAL CORP.; *Int'l*, pg. 8133
VARSITY BRANDS HOLDING CO., INC.—See Bain Capital, LP; *U.S. Private*, pg. 451
VARSITY BRANDS, INC.—See Bain Capital, LP; *U.S. Private*, pg. 452
VARSITY CLUBS OF AMERICA - SOUTH BEND—See Apollo Global Management, Inc.; *U.S. Public*, pg. 150
VARSITY CLUBS OF AMERICA - SOUTH BEND—See Reverence Capital Partners LLC; *U.S. Private*, pg. 3415
VARSITY CLUBS OF AMERICA - TUCSON—See Apollo Global Management, Inc.; *U.S. Public*, pg. 150
VARSITY CLUBS OF AMERICA - TUCSON—See Reverence Capital Partners LLC; *U.S. Private*, pg. 3415
VARSITY CONTRACTORS, INC.; *U.S. Private*, pg. 4347
VARSITY FORD LINCOLN MERCURY; *U.S. Private*, pg. 4347

VARSITY LINCOLN-MERCURY INC.; *U.S. Private*, pg. 4347
VARSITY LOGISTICS, INC.—See Constellation Software Inc.; *Int'l*, pg. 1773
VARSITY MANAGEMENT COMPANY, LP; *U.S. Private*, pg. 4347
VARSITY PACKAGING LIMITED—See Mayr-Melnhof Karton AG; *Int'l*, pg. 4747
VARSITY—See Pavone; *U.S. Private*, pg. 3115
VARSITY SPIRIT LLC—See Bain Capital, LP; *U.S. Private*, pg. 452
VARSITY TENTS INC; *Int'l*, pg. 8134
VARSITY TUTORS LLC; *U.S. Private*, pg. 4347
VARSTEEL LTD.; *Int'l*, pg. 8134
VARTA AG—See Global Equity Partners Beteiligungs-Management AG; *Int'l*, pg. 2996
VARTA BATERIE SPOL. S.R.O.—See Global Equity Partners Beteiligungs-Management AG; *Int'l*, pg. 2996
VARTA BATTERIE GES. M.B.H.—See Global Equity Partners Beteiligungs-Management AG; *Int'l*, pg. 2996
VARTA B.V.—See Global Equity Partners Beteiligungs-Management AG; *Int'l*, pg. 2996
VARTA CONSUMER BATTERIES GMBH & CO. KGAA—See Global Equity Partners Beteiligungs-Management AG; *Int'l*, pg. 2996
VARTA CONSUMER BATTERIES ITALIA, S.R.L.—See Energizer Holdings, Inc.; *U.S. Public*, pg. 761
VARTA HUNGARIA KERESKEDELMI ES SZOLGALTATO KFT.—See Global Equity Partners Beteiligungs-Management AG; *Int'l*, pg. 2996
VARTA LTD.—See Global Equity Partners Beteiligungs-Management AG; *Int'l*, pg. 2996
VARTA MICROBATTERY GMBH—See Global Equity Partners Beteiligungs-Management AG; *Int'l*, pg. 2996
VARTA MICROBATTERY, INC.—See Global Equity Partners Beteiligungs-Management AG; *Int'l*, pg. 2996
VARTA MICROBATTERY PTE. LTD.—See Global Equity Partners Beteiligungs-Management AG; *Int'l*, pg. 2996
VARTA PILLERI TICARET LIMITED SIRKETI—See Global Equity Partners Beteiligungs-Management AG; *Int'l*, pg. 2996
VARTA S.A.—See Global Equity Partners Beteiligungs-Management AG; *Int'l*, pg. 2996
VARTA STORAGE GMBH—See Global Equity Partners Beteiligungs-Management AG; *Int'l*, pg. 2996
VARTECH SYSTEMS, INC.; *U.S. Public*, pg. 2276
VARTEKS D.D.; *Int'l*, pg. 8134
VARTEX AB—See Accell Group N.V.; *Int'l*, pg. 81
VARUN BEVERAGES LIMITED—See Affirma Capital Limited; *Int'l*, pg. 188
VARUN BEVERAGES MOROCCO S.A.—See Affirma Capital Limited; *Int'l*, pg. 188
VARUN BEVERAGES (NEPAL) PRIVATE LIMITED—See Affirma Capital Limited; *Int'l*, pg. 188
VARUN MERCANTILE LIMITED; *Int'l*, pg. 8134
VARUN SHIPPING COMPANY LIMITED; *Int'l*, pg. 8134
VARUN TRAVELS PRIVATE LIMITED—See Sayaji Industries Limited; *Int'l*, pg. 6603
VARVAN J.—See Dentium Co., Ltd; *Int'l*, pg. 2034
VARVARESSOS S.A.; *Int'l*, pg. 8134
VARVSTADEN AB—See Peab AB; *Int'l*, pg. 5773
VASA BETONGSTATION OY—See Peab AB; *Int'l*, pg. 5773
VAS AERO SERVICES, LLC—See H.I.G. Capital, LLC; *U.S. Private*, pg. 1832
VASAMED, INC.; *U.S. Public*, pg. 2276
VASARA INC.—See Septeni Holdings Co., Ltd.; *Int'l*, pg. 6718
VASA RETAIL & OVERSEAS LTD.; *Int'l*, pg. 8134
VASC CO., LTD.—See Fuji Media Holdings, Inc.; *Int'l*, pg. 2814
VASCO BVBA—See Vaessen Industries nv; *Int'l*, pg. 8108
VASCO DATA SECURITY ASIA-PACIFIC PTE LTD—See OneSpan Inc.; *U.S. Public*, pg. 1604
VASCO DATA SECURITY AUSTRALIA PTY LTD—See OneSpan Inc.; *U.S. Public*, pg. 1603
VASCO DATA SECURITY AUSTRIA GMBH—See OneSpan Inc.; *U.S. Public*, pg. 1603
VASCO DATA SECURITY B.V.—See OneSpan Inc.; *U.S. Public*, pg. 1604
VASCO DATA SECURITY EUROPE NV/SA—See OneSpan Inc.; *U.S. Public*, pg. 1604
VASCO DATA SECURITY, INC.—See OneSpan Inc.; *U.S. Public*, pg. 1604
VASCO DATA SECURITY INTERNATIONAL, GMBH—See OneSpan Inc.; *U.S. Public*, pg. 1603
VASCO DATA SECURITY MIDDLE EAST FZE—See OneSpan Inc.; *U.S. Public*, pg. 1603
VASCO DATA SECURITY NV/SA—See OneSpan Inc.; *U.S. Public*, pg. 1604
VASCO DATA SECURITY PTY LTD—See OneSpan Inc.; *U.S. Public*, pg. 1604
VASCO GMBH—See Vaessen Industries nv; *Int'l*, pg. 8107
VASCO GROUP NV—See Vaessen Industries nv; *Int'l*, pg. 8107
VASCO GROUP SARL—See Vaessen Industries nv; *Int'l*, pg. 8107
VASCO GROUP SRL—See Vaessen Industries nv; *Int'l*, pg. 8107

CORPORATE AFFILIATIONS

VASCO LTD—See Vaessen Industries nv; *Int'l*, pg. 8107
VASCON ENGINEERS LIMITED; *Int'l*, pg. 8134
VASCO PAY PTY LTD—See Novatti Group Limited; *Int'l*, pg. 5461
VASCOR, LTD.—See Fujitrans Corporation; *Int'l*, pg. 2832
VASCOR, LTD.—See Kintetsu Group Holdings Co., Ltd.; *Int'l*, pg. 4183
VASC SOFTWARE AND MEDIA COMPANY—See Vietnam Posts & Telecommunications Corporation; *Int'l*, pg. 8203
VASCULAR BIOGENICS LTD.; *Int'l*, pg. 8134
VASCULAR SOLUTIONS, INC.—See Teleflex Incorporated; *U.S. Public*, pg. 1996
VASCULAR SPECIALISTS OF CENTRAL FLORIDA, INC.; *U.S. Private*, pg. 4347
VASCUTEK DEUTSCHLAND G.M.B.H.—See Terumo Corporation; *Int'l*, pg. 7571
VASCUTEK LTD.—See Terumo Corporation; *Int'l*, pg. 7571
VASEK INSURANCE SERVICES LIMITED—See Arthur J. Gallagher & Co.; *U.S. Public*, pg. 207
VASEY COMMERCIAL HEATING & AC; *U.S. Private*, pg. 4347
VASHAW SCIENTIFIC INC.; *U.S. Private*, pg. 4347
VASHU BHAGNANI INDUSTRIES LIMITED; *Int'l*, pg. 8134
VAS INFRASTRUCTURE LIMITED; *Int'l*, pg. 8134
VASOACTIVE PHARMACEUTICALS, INC.; *U.S. Private*, pg. 4347
VASO CORPORATION; *U.S. Public*, pg. 2276
VASONA MANAGEMENT; *U.S. Private*, pg. 4347
VASONA NETWORKS, INC.—See ESW Capital, LLC; *U.S. Private*, pg. 1430
VASONOVA, INC.—See Teleflex Incorporated; *U.S. Public*, pg. 1996
VASSALLO BUILDERS GROUP LIMITED; *Int'l*, pg. 8134
VASSALLO BUILDERS INTERNATIONAL DOO—See Vassallo Builders Group Limited; *Int'l*, pg. 8134
VASSALLO BUILDERS LTD.—See Vassallo Builders Group Limited; *Int'l*, pg. 8134
VASSALLO INTERNATIONAL GROUP, INC.; *U.S. Private*, pg. 4347
VASSETI BERHAD—See Zavarco PLC; *Int'l*, pg. 8626
VASSETI DATATECH BERHAD—See Zavarco PLC; *Int'l*, pg. 8626
VASSILICO CEMENT WORKS PUBLIC COMPANY LTD; *Int'l*, pg. 8134
VASSILOPOULOS SHIPPING LTD.—See Albert Ballin KG; *Int'l*, pg. 297
VASS PIPE & STEEL CO. INC.; *U.S. Private*, pg. 4347
VASTA PLATFORM LIMITED; *Int'l*, pg. 8134
VASTECH PLASTIC (SHANGHAI) INDUSTRIAL CO., LTD.—See COXON Precise Industrial Co., Ltd.; *Int'l*, pg. 1823
VASTEC MEDICAL LIMITED—See IVD Medical Holding Limited; *Int'l*, pg. 3846
VASTERBERGSLAGENS ELNAT AB—See Vattenfall AB; *Int'l*, pg. 8136
VASTERBERGSLAGENS ENERGI AB—See Vattenfall AB; *Int'l*, pg. 8136
VAST FURNITURE MANUFACTURING (KUNSHAN) CO. LTD.—See MKH Berhad; *Int'l*, pg. 5002
VASTINT HOLDING B.V.—See Interogo Holding AG; *Int'l*, pg. 3754
VAST MEDICAL LIMITED—See LifeTech Scientific Corporation; *Int'l*, pg. 4495
VASTNED EMLAK YATIRIM VE INSAAT TICARET A.S.; *Int'l*, pg. 8134
VASTNED INDUSTRIAL B.V.—See NSI N.V.; *Int'l*, pg. 5477
VASTNED MANAGEMENT B.V.—See Vastned Retail N.V.; *Int'l*, pg. 8135
VASTNED OFFICES/INDUSTRIAL N.V.—See NSI N.V.; *Int'l*, pg. 5477
VASTNED RETAIL BELGIUM NV—See Vastned Retail N.V.; *Int'l*, pg. 8135
VASTNED RETAIL N.V.; *Int'l*, pg. 8134
VASTRA HAMNEN CORPORATE FINANCE AB; *Int'l*, pg. 8135
VASTRA TORP MARK AB—See BNP Paribas SA; *Int'l*, pg. 1093
VAST RESOURCES PLC; *Int'l*, pg. 8134
VASUDHAGAMA ENTERPRISES LIMITED; *Int'l*, pg. 8135
VASUNDHARA RASAYANS LIMITED; *Int'l*, pg. 8135
VASWANI INDUSTRIES LIMITED; *Int'l*, pg. 8135
VAT DEUTSCHLAND GMBH—See VAT Group AG; *Int'l*, pg. 8135
VATECH 2000 APS—See AVK Holding A/S; *Int'l*, pg. 748
VATECH AMERICA INC.—See Vatech Co., Ltd.; *Int'l*, pg. 8135
VATECH BRASIL LTDA.—See Vatech Co., Ltd.; *Int'l*, pg. 8135
VATECH CHINA CO., LTD.—See Vatech Co., Ltd.; *Int'l*, pg. 8135
VATECH CO., LTD.; *Int'l*, pg. 8135
VATECH DENTAL MANUFACTURING LTD.—See Vatech Co., Ltd.; *Int'l*, pg. 8135
VATECH FRANCE CO., LTD.—See Vatech Co., Ltd.; *Int'l*, pg. 8135
VATECH GLOBAL ASIA HQ SDN. BHD.—See Vatech Co., Ltd.; *Int'l*, pg. 8135

COMPANY NAME INDEX

VATECH GLOBAL (HK) LTD.—See Vatech Co., Ltd.; *Int'l*, pg. 8135
VATECH GLOBAL MEXICO S DE RL DE CV.—See Vatech Co., Ltd.; *Int'l*, pg. 8135
VATECH INDIA PVT. LTD.—See Vatech Co., Ltd.; *Int'l*, pg. 8135
VATECH MEDICAL PTY. LTD.—See Vatech Co., Ltd.; *Int'l*, pg. 8135
VATECH SPAIN S.L.—See Vatech Co., Ltd.; *Int'l*, pg. 8135
VA TECH (UK) LTD.—See Siemens Aktiengesellschaft; *Int'l*, pg. 6901
VATECH VIETNAM CO., LTD.—See Vatech Co., Ltd.; *Int'l*, pg. 8135
VA TECH WABAG ALGERIE S.A.R.L—See VA TECH WABAG Limited; *Int'l*, pg. 8107
VA TECH WABAG BRNO SPOL. S R.O.—See Varindera Constructions Ltd.; *Int'l*, pg. 8133
VA TECH WABAG DEUTSCHLAND GMBH—See VA TECH WABAG Limited; *Int'l*, pg. 8107
VA TECH WABAG EGYPT LLC—See VA TECH WABAG Limited; *Int'l*, pg. 8107
VA TECH WABAG GMBH—See VA TECH WABAG Limited; *Int'l*, pg. 8107
VA TECH WABAG (HONG KONG) LIMITED—See VA TECH WABAG Limited; *Int'l*, pg. 8107
VA TECH WABAG LIMITED; *Int'l*, pg. 8106
VA TECH WABAG MUSCAT LLC—See VA TECH WABAG Limited; *Int'l*, pg. 8107
VA TECH WABAG (PHILIPPINES) INC.—See VA TECH WABAG Limited; *Int'l*, pg. 8107
VA TECH WABAG (SPAIN) S.L.—See VA TECH WABAG Limited; *Int'l*, pg. 8107
VA TECH WABAG SU TEKNOLOJISI VE TYCARET LYMYTED SIRKET—See VA TECH WABAG Limited; *Int'l*, pg. 8107
VA TECH WABAG TUNISIE S.A.R.L—See VA TECH WABAG Limited; *Int'l*, pg. 8107
VATEL COMPANHIA DE PRODUTOS ALIMENTARES S.A.—See K+S Aktiengesellschaft; *Int'l*, pg. 4041
VATER'S OF OKLAHOMA CITY INC.; *U.S. Private*, pg. 4348
VATE TECHNOLOGY CO., LTD.—See VIA Technologies, Inc.; *Int'l*, pg. 8183
VAT GROUP AG; *Int'l*, pg. 8135
VATICS INC.—See Vivotek Inc.; *Int'l*, pg. 8280
VATIC VENTURES CORP.; *Int'l*, pg. 8135
VATIKA GROUP; *Int'l*, pg. 8135
VAT KOREA LTD.—See VAT Group AG; *Int'l*, pg. 8135
VAT LTD.—See VAT Group AG; *Int'l*, pg. 8135
V.A. TRANSPORT INC.; *Int'l*, pg. 8106
V.A. TRANSPORT INC. - WAREHOUSING DIVISION—See V.A. Transport Inc.; *Int'l*, pg. 8106
VAT ROMANIA S.R.L.—See VAT Group AG; *Int'l*, pg. 8135
VATROSERVIS A.D.; *Int'l*, pg. 8136
VATROSPREM AD; *Int'l*, pg. 8136
VAT SARL—See VAT Group AG; *Int'l*, pg. 8135
VAT SINGAPORE PTE. LTD.—See VAT Group AG; *Int'l*, pg. 8135
VATS LIQUOR CHAIN STORE MANAGEMENT JOINT STOCK CO., LTD.; *Int'l*, pg. 8136
VAT TAIWAN CO. LTD.—See VAT Group AG; *Int'l*, pg. 8135
VATTENFALL AB; *Int'l*, pg. 8136
VATTENFALL AB VATTENKRAFT—See Vattenfall AB; *Int'l*, pg. 8136
VATTENFALL BRANSLE AB—See Vattenfall AB; *Int'l*, pg. 8136
VATTENFALL BUSINESS SERVICES NORDIC AB—See Vattenfall AB; *Int'l*, pg. 8136
VATTENFALL DANMARK A/S—See Vattenfall AB; *Int'l*, pg. 8137
VATTENFALL ELDISTRIBUTION AB—See Vattenfall AB; *Int'l*, pg. 8136
VATTENFALL ELDISTRIBUTION AB—See Vattenfall AB; *Int'l*, pg. 8137
VATTENFALL ENERGY SOLUTIONS GMBH—See Vattenfall AB; *Int'l*, pg. 8137
VATTENFALL ENERGY TRADING A/S—See Vattenfall AB; *Int'l*, pg. 8137
VATTENFALL ENERGY TRADING GMBH—See Vattenfall AB; *Int'l*, pg. 8137
VATTENFALL EUROPEAN AFFAIRS—See Vattenfall AB; *Int'l*, pg. 8137
VATTENFALL EUROPE NUCLEAR ENERGY GMBH—See Vattenfall AB; *Int'l*, pg. 8137
VATTENFALL EUROPE SALES GMBH—See Vattenfall AB; *Int'l*, pg. 8137
VATTENFALL GMBH—See Vattenfall AB; *Int'l*, pg. 8137
VATTENFALL IT SERVICES POLAND SP. Z O.O—See Vattenfall AB; *Int'l*, pg. 8137
VATTENFALL KLANTENSERVICE N.V.—See Vattenfall AB; *Int'l*, pg. 8137
VATTENFALL LITHUANIA UAB—See Vattenfall AB; *Int'l*, pg. 8137
VATTENFALL MEGA NORGE—See Vattenfall AB; *Int'l*, pg. 8137
VATTENFALL POLAND SP. Z O.O.—See Vattenfall AB; *Int'l*, pg. 8137
VATTENFALL REAL ESTATE ENERGY SALES GMBH—See Vattenfall AB; *Int'l*, pg. 8137
VATTENFALL SERVICES NORDIC AB—See Vattenfall AB; *Int'l*, pg. 8137
VATTENFALL SERVICE SYD AB—See Vattenfall AB; *Int'l*, pg. 8137
VATTENFALL SMARTER LIVING GMBH—See Vattenfall AB; *Int'l*, pg. 8137
VATTENFALL (SWEDEN) AB—See Vattenfall AB; *Int'l*, pg. 8136
VATTENFALL UTVECKLING AB—See Vattenfall AB; *Int'l*, pg. 8137
VATTENFALL VINDKRAFT A/S—See Vattenfall AB; *Int'l*, pg. 8137
VATTENFALL WARME BERLIN AG—See Vattenfall AB; *Int'l*, pg. 8137
VATTENFALL WIND POWER LTD—See Vattenfall AB; *Int'l*, pg. 8137
VATTENKRAFTENS MILJOFOND SVERIGE AB—See Statkraft AS; *Int'l*, pg. 7185
VATTI CORPORATION LIMITED; *Int'l*, pg. 8137
VATUKOULA GOLD MINES; *Int'l*, pg. 8137
VAT VACUUM PRODUCTS LTD.—See VAT Group AG; *Int'l*, pg. 8135
VAT VACUUM VALVES SHANGHAI COMPANY LTD.—See VAT Group AG; *Int'l*, pg. 8135
VAT VAKUUMVENTILE AG—See VAT Group AG; *Int'l*, pg. 8135
VAUBAN INFRASTRUCTURE PARTNERS SCA—See Groupe BPCE; *Int'l*, pg. 3099
VAUDAUX-EPPENDORF AG—See Eppendorf AG; *Int'l*, pg. 2465
VAUDE SPORT GMBH & CO. KG; *Int'l*, pg. 8137
VAUDOISE ASSURANCES HOLDING SA; *Int'l*, pg. 8137
VAUEN VEREINIGTE PFEIFENFABRIKEN NURNBERG GMBH; *Int'l*, pg. 8137
VAUGHAN-BASSETT FURNITURE COMPANY INC.; *U.S. Private*, pg. 4348
VAUGHAN & BUSHNELL MANUFACTURING COMPANY, INC.; *U.S. Private*, pg. 4348
VAUGHAN FOODS, INC.—See Reser's Fine Foods Inc.; *U.S. Private*, pg. 3404
VAUGHAN FURNITURE COMPANY INC.; *U.S. Private*, pg. 4348
VAUGHAN INTERESTS INC.; *U.S. Private*, pg. 4348
VAUGHAN NELSON INVESTMENT MANAGEMENT, L.P.—See Groupe BPCE; *Int'l*, pg. 3096
VAUGHAN NELSON TRUST COMPANY—See Groupe BPCE; *Int'l*, pg. 3097
VAUGHAN-P, LP—See Lithia Motors, Inc.; *U.S. Public*, pg. 1326
VAUGHAN REGIONAL MEDICAL CENTER, LLC—See Apollo Global Management, Inc.; *U.S. Public*, pg. 159
VAUGHAN & SONS, INC. MULTI-FAMILY SALES—See Vaughan & Sons, Inc.; *U.S. Private*, pg. 4348
VAUGHAN & SONS, INC.; *U.S. Private*, pg. 4348
VAUGHN CHEVROLET; *U.S. Private*, pg. 4348
THE VAUGHN COLLABORATIVE INC—See Design Resources Group Architects, A.I.A., Inc.; *U.S. Private*, pg. 1214
VAUGHN HOUSE, INC.—See Easter Seals Central Texas; *U.S. Private*, pg. 1319
VAUGHN INDUSTRIES, LLC.; *U.S. Private*, pg. 4348
VAUGHN PRINTERS INCORPORATED—See Cenveo, Inc.; *U.S. Private*, pg. 835
VAUGHN WEDEEN KUHN; *U.S. Private*, pg. 4348
VAUGHT, INC.; *U.S. Private*, pg. 4348
VAUGHT WRIGHT & BOND, INC.—See Inszone Insurance Services, LLC; *U.S. Private*, pg. 2096
VAULT ACQUIRING SOLUTIONS LLC—See Mobi724 Global Solutions Inc.; *Int'l*, pg. 5008
VAULT.COM, INC.—See Veronis Suhler Stevenson Partners LLC; *U.S. Private*, pg. 4368
VAULT CREDIT CORPORATION—See Chesswood Group Limited; *Int'l*, pg. 1473
VAULTED GOLD BULLION TRUST; *U.S. Private*, pg. 4348
VAULT INTELLIGENCE LIMITED—See Damstra Holdings Ltd.; *Int'l*, pg. 1957
VAULT IQ NZ LTD.—See Damstra Holdings Ltd.; *Int'l*, pg. 1957
VAULTIVE, INC.—See CyberArk Software Ltd.; *Int'l*, pg. 1892
VAULT PAYMENT SYSTEMS LLC—See Chesswood Group Limited; *Int'l*, pg. 1473
VAULT SPORTSWEAR, INC.; *U.S. Private*, pg. 4348
VAUPELL CHINA (DONGGUAN) CO., LTD.—See Sumitomo Bakelite Co., Ltd.; *Int'l*, pg. 7263
VAUPELL HOLDINGS, INC—See Sumitomo Bakelite Co., Ltd.; *Int'l*, pg. 7263
VAUPELL INC.—See Sumitomo Bakelite Co., Ltd.; *Int'l*, pg. 7263
VAUPELL INC. - VAUPELL CHINA MOLDING & TOOLING DIVISION—See Sumitomo Bakelite Co., Ltd.; *Int'l*, pg. 7263
VAUPELL INC. - VAUPELL MIDWEST MOLDING & TOOLING DIVISION—See Sumitomo Bakelite Co., Ltd.; *Int'l*, pg. 7263
VAUPELL INC. - VAUPELL NORTHEAST MOLDING & TOOLING DIVISION—See Sumitomo Bakelite Co., Ltd.; *Int'l*, pg. 7263
VAUPELL INC. - VAUPELL NW MOLDING & TOOLING DIVISION—See Sumitomo Bakelite Co., Ltd.; *Int'l*, pg. 7263
VAUPELL INC. - VAUPELL RAPID SOLUTIONS DIVISION—See Sumitomo Bakelite Co., Ltd.; *Int'l*, pg. 7263
VAUPELL INDUSTRIAL PLASTICS, INC.—See Sumitomo Bakelite Co., Ltd.; *Int'l*, pg. 7264
VAUPELL MOLDING & TOOLING, INC.—See Sumitomo Bakelite Co., Ltd.; *Int'l*, pg. 7264
VAUTHIER SEPAC SARL—See Vivescia; *Int'l*, pg. 8279
VAUTID AUSTRIA GMBH—See DZ BANK AG Deutsche Zentral-Genossenschaftsbank; *Int'l*, pg. 2245
VAUTID-BELGIUM PGMBH—See DZ BANK AG Deutsche Zentral-Genossenschaftsbank; *Int'l*, pg. 2245
VAUTID GMBH—See UP Scientech Materials Corp.; *Int'l*, pg. 8087
VAUTID INDIA PRIVATE LIMITED—See DZ BANK AG Deutsche Zentral-Genossenschaftsbank; *Int'l*, pg. 2245
VAUTID LATAM S.A.—See DZ BANK AG Deutsche Zentral-Genossenschaftsbank; *Int'l*, pg. 2245
VAUTID MIDDLE EAST F.Z.E—See DZ BANK AG Deutsche Zentral-Genossenschaftsbank; *Int'l*, pg. 2245
VAUTID NORTH AMERICA, INC.—See DZ BANK AG Deutsche Zentral-Genossenschaftsbank; *Int'l*, pg. 2245
VAUTO, INC.—See Cox Enterprises, Inc.; *U.S. Private*, pg. 1076
VAUXHALL CROSS LIMITED—See CLS Holdings plc; *Int'l*, pg. 1664
VAUXHALL MOTORS LIMITED—See General Motors Company; *U.S. Public*, pg. 927
VAUXHALL MOTORS LIMITED—See Stellantis N.V.; *Int'l*, pg. 7203
VAVINEL SAS—See HPS Investment Partners, LLC; *U.S. Private*, pg. 1997
VAVRINEK, TRINE, DAY AND CO., LLP; *U.S. Private*, pg. 4348
VAXART BIOSCIENCES, INC.—See Vaxart, Inc.; *U.S. Public*, pg. 2276
VAXART, INC.; *U.S. Public*, pg. 2276
VAXCELL BIOTHERAPEUTICS CO., LTD.; *Int'l*, pg. 8138
VAXCYTE, INC.; *U.S. Public*, pg. 2276
VAXFAB ENTERPRISES LTD; *Int'l*, pg. 8138
VAX HOUSING FINANCE CORPORATION LIMITED; *Int'l*, pg. 8138
VAXIL BIO LTD.; *Int'l*, pg. 8138
VAXIL BIO LTD.—See Vaxil Bio Ltd.; *Int'l*, pg. 8138
VAXIL BIOTHERAPEUTICS LTD.—See Vaxil Bio Ltd.; *Int'l*, pg. 8138
VAXJO LACKCENTER AB—See LKQ Corporation; *U.S. Public*, pg. 1337
VAX LIMITED—See Techtronic Industries Co., Ltd.; *Int'l*, pg. 7513
VAXSERVE INC.—See Sanofi; *Int'l*, pg. 6549
VAXTEX COTFAB LIMITED; *Int'l*, pg. 8138
VAXXINITY, INC.; *U.S. Public*, pg. 2276
VAYAN MARKETING GROUP, LLC; *U.S. Private*, pg. 4348
VAYA PHARMA, INC.—See International Flavors & Fragrances Inc.; *U.S. Public*, pg. 1154
VAZIVA S.A.; *Int'l*, pg. 8138
VB2, INC.—See Copart, Inc.; *U.S. Public*, pg. 575
VBARE IBERIAN PROPERTIES SOCIMI SA; *Int'l*, pg. 8138
VBC-BRISTOL INC.—See Van Blarcom Closures Inc.; *U.S. Private*, pg. 4339
VBC ENERGIA S.A.—See Camargo Correa S.A.; *Int'l*, pg. 1268
VBC FERRO ALLOYS LTD.; *Int'l*, pg. 8138
VBCJ, INC.—See Van Blarcom Closures Inc.; *U.S. Private*, pg. 4339
V. B. DESAI FINANCIAL SERVICES LIMITED.; *Int'l*, pg. 8105
V BEVERAGES LIMITED—See Momentous Holdings Corp.; *Int'l*, pg. 5023
V&B FLIESEN GMBH—See Eczacibasi Holding A.S.; *Int'l*, pg. 2301
VBG CONSULTING (BEIJING) CO., LTD.—See Hatcher Group Ltd.; *Int'l*, pg. 3284
VBG GROUP AB; *Int'l*, pg. 8138
VBG GROUP ETES NV—See VBG Group AB; *Int'l*, pg. 8138
VBG GROUP SALES A/S—See VBG Group AB; *Int'l*, pg. 8138
VBG GROUP SALES AS—See VBG Group AB; *Int'l*, pg. 8139
VBG GROUP SALES LTD—See VBG Group AB; *Int'l*, pg. 8139
VBG GROUP TRUCK EQUIPMENT AB—See VBG Group AB; *Int'l*, pg. 8139
VBG GROUP TRUCK EQUIPMENT GMBH—See VBG Group AB; *Int'l*, pg. 8139
VBG GROUP TRUCK EQUIPMENT NV—See VBG Group AB; *Int'l*, pg. 8139
VBG PRODUKTER AB—See VBG Group AB; *Int'l*, pg. 8139

VBG GROUP AB

VBG - VALE BSGR GUINEA LIMITAD—See Vale S.A.; *Int'l*, pg. 8112
VBH BELGIUM NV—See VBH Holding AG; *Int'l*, pg. 8139
VBH BUDAPEST KFT—See VBH Holding AG; *Int'l*, pg. 8139
VBH BULGARIEN OOD—See VBH Holding AG; *Int'l*, pg. 8139
VBH DEMS D.O.O.—See VBH Holding AG; *Int'l*, pg. 8139
VBH DEUTSCHLAND GMBH—See VBH Holding AG; *Int'l*, pg. 8139
VBH ESTONIA AS—See VBH Holding AG; *Int'l*, pg. 8139
VBH (GB) LTD—See VBH Holding AG; *Int'l*, pg. 8139
VBH HELLAS S.A.—See VBH Holding AG; *Int'l*, pg. 8139
VBH HODY BELGIUM SA—See VBH Holding AG; *Int'l*, pg. 8139
VBH HOLDING AG; *Int'l*, pg. 8139
VBH HOLDING INDIA PRIVATE LIMITED—See VBH Holding AG; *Int'l*, pg. 8140
VBH ITALIA S.R.L.—See VBH Holding AG; *Int'l*, pg. 8139
VBH KAPI VE PENCERE SISTEMLERI SAN. VE TIC. A.S.—See VBH Holding AG; *Int'l*, pg. 8139
VBH KUWAIT FOR GENERAL TRADING CO. (W.L.L)—See VBH Holding AG; *Int'l*, pg. 8139
VBH - MALUM S.L.—See VBH Holding AG; *Int'l*, pg. 8139
VBH MEXICO S.A. DE C.V.—See VBH Holding AG; *Int'l*, pg. 8139
VBH MONTENEGRO D.O.O.—See VBH Holding AG; *Int'l*, pg. 8139
VBH NEDERLAND BV—See VBH Holding AG; *Int'l*, pg. 8139
VBH-OFIR S.R.L.—See VBH Holding AG; *Int'l*, pg. 8139
VBH OKOVI D.O.O.—See VBH Holding AG; *Int'l*, pg. 8139
VB HOLDINGS LIMITED; *Int'l*, pg. 8138
V.B. HOOK & CO., INC.; *U.S. Private*, pg. 4328
V. B. HOOK VACUUM COOLING COMPANY—See V.B. Hook & Co., Inc.; *U.S. Private*, pg. 4328
VBH O.O.O.—See VBH Holding AG; *Int'l*, pg. 8139
VBH OOO (ST. PETERSBURG)—See VBH Holding AG; *Int'l*, pg. 8139
VBH POLSKA SP.Z.O.O.—See VBH Holding AG; *Int'l*, pg. 8139
VBH - SIB—See VBH Holding AG; *Int'l*, pg. 8139
VBH SINGAPORE PTE. LTD.—See VBH Holding AG; *Int'l*, pg. 8140
VBH - TBM UAB—See VBH Holding AG; *Int'l*, pg. 8139
V.B.H. TRADING (L.L.C.)—See VBH Holding AG; *Int'l*, pg. 8139
VBH TRGOVINA D.O.O.—See VBH Holding AG; *Int'l*, pg. 8140
VBH VEREINIGTER BAUBESCHLAG- HANDEL SPOL. S R.O.—See VBH Holding AG; *Int'l*, pg. 8140
VBI LTD—See Parker Hannifin Corporation; *U.S. Public*, pg. 1643
VB INDUSTRIES LTD.; *Int'l*, pg. 8138
VBI VACCINES INC.; *U.S. Public*, pg. 2276
VBI VERENIGDE BOUWPRODUKTEN INDUSTRIE B.V.—See Bain Capital, LP; *U.S. Private*, pg. 438
VB LEASING BH D.O.O.—See Osterreichische Volksbanken AG; *Int'l*, pg. 5654
VB LEASING BH D.O.O.—See VR-LEASING AG; *Int'l*, pg. 8313
VB LEASING D.O.O. BEOGRAD—See Osterreichische Volksbanken AG; *Int'l*, pg. 5654
VB LEASING D.O.O. BEOGRAD—See VR-LEASING AG; *Int'l*, pg. 8313
VB LEASING D.O.O.—See Osterreichische Volksbanken AG; *Int'l*, pg. 5654
VB LEASING D.O.O.—See Osterreichische Volksbanken AG; *Int'l*, pg. 5654
VB LEASING D.O.O.—See VR-LEASING AG; *Int'l*, pg. 8313
VB LEASING D.O.O.—See VR-LEASING AG; *Int'l*, pg. 8313
VB LEASING INTERNATIONAL HOLDING GMBH—See Osterreichische Volksbanken AG; *Int'l*, pg. 5654
VB LEASING INTERNATIONAL HOLDING GMBH—See VR-LEASING AG; *Int'l*, pg. 8313
VB LEASING SK, SPOL. S.R.O.—See Osterreichische Volksbanken AG; *Int'l*, pg. 5654
VB LEASING SK, SPOL. S.R.O.—See VR-LEASING AG; *Int'l*, pg. 8313
V BLOCKCHAIN GROUP INC.; *U.S. Private*, pg. 4327
V & B MANUFACTURING CO.—See Vaughan & Bushnell Manufacturing Company, Inc.; *U.S. Private*, pg. 4348
VBN CHINA - BEIJING—See STV Group, Inc.; *U.S. Private*, pg. 3846
VBN CORP.—See STV Group, Inc.; *U.S. Private*, pg. 3846
VBOA ASC PARTNERS, L.P.—See Tenet Healthcare Corporation; *U.S. Public*, pg. 2015
VB PENZUGYI LIZING RT. & KFT.—See Osterreichische Volksbanken AG; *Int'l*, pg. 5654
VB PENZUGYI LIZING RT. & KFT.—See VR-LEASING AG; *Int'l*, pg. 8313
VBQ ACQUISITION B.V.—See G-III Apparel Group, Ltd.; *U.S. Public*, pg. 894
VBRICK SYSTEMS INC.; *U.S. Private*, pg. 4348
VB SERVICIOS, COMERCIO E ADMINISTRACAO LTDA—See Corpay, Inc.; *U.S. Public*, pg. 580

VBS INC., MATERIAL HANDLING EQUIPMENT; *U.S. Private*, pg. 4348
VBS MORTGAGE, LLC—See F&M Bank Corp.; *U.S. Public*, pg. 818
VBT FINANCIAL CORPORATION; *U.S. Public*, pg. 4348
VBV - BETRIEBLICHE ALTERSVORSORGE AG—See Vienna Insurance Group AG Wiener Versicherung Gruppe; *Int'l*, pg. 8195
VB VICTORIA ZASTUPANJE U OSIGURANJU D.O.O.—See Munchener Ruckversicherungs AG; *Int'l*, pg. 5092
VC3, INC.; *U.S. Private*, pg. 4348
VCA ANIMAL HOSPITALS, INC.—See Mars, Incorporated; *U.S. Private*, pg. 2590
VCA INC.—See Mars, Incorporated; *U.S. Private*, pg. 2590
V CARE INDUSTRIES (MALAYSIA) SDN. BHD.—See Parlo Berhad; *Int'l*, pg. 5745
VCARGO CLOUD PTE. LTD.—See EXEO Group Inc.; *Int'l*, pg. 2584
VC ASSET MANAGEMENT LTD—See Value Convergence Holdings Limited; *Int'l*, pg. 8123
VCAT; *U.S. Private*, pg. 4349
VCB FINANCIAL GROUP, INC.—See Blue Ridge Bankshares, Inc.; *U.S. Public*, pg. 365
VC BROKERAGE LIMITED—See Value Convergence Holdings Limited; *Int'l*, pg. 8123
VC CAPITAL LIMITED—See Value Convergence Holdings Limited; *Int'l*, pg. 8123
VCCP BLUE LIMITED—See Providence Equity Partners L.L.C.; *U.S. Private*, pg. 3292
VCCP HEALTH LIMITED—See Providence Equity Partners L.L.C.; *U.S. Private*, pg. 3292
VCCP LIMITED—See Providence Equity Partners L.L.C.; *U.S. Private*, pg. 3292
VCCP PTY. LTD.—See Providence Equity Partners L.L.C.; *U.S. Private*, pg. 3292
VCCP SEARCH LIMITED—See Providence Equity Partners L.L.C.; *U.S. Private*, pg. 3292
VCCP S.R.O.—See Providence Equity Partners L.L.C.; *U.S. Private*, pg. 3292
VCD BUSINESS INTELLIGENCE B.V.—See VINCI S.A.; *Int'l*, pg. 8240
VCD BUSINESS SOLUTIONS B.V.—See VINCI S.A.; *Int'l*, pg. 8240
VCE ELEKTRARNY, S.R.O.—See CEZ, a.s.; *Int'l*, pg. 1429
VCE EUROPE GMBH—See HPI AG; *Int'l*, pg. 3500
VCE MONTAZE, A.S.—See CEZ, a.s.; *Int'l*, pg. 1429
VCF FILMS, INC.—See PMC Capital Partners, LLC; *U.S. Private*, pg. 3218
VC FUTURES LIMITED—See Value Convergence Holdings Limited; *Int'l*, pg. 8123
VCG&A, INC.—See IQVIA Holdings Inc.; *U.S. Public*, pg. 1170
VCG COLOURLINK LTD.—See Visual Communications Group Ltd; *Int'l*, pg. 8255
VCG CONNECT LIMITED—See Visual Communications Group Ltd; *Int'l*, pg. 8255
VCG HOLDING CORP.; *U.S. Private*, pg. 4349
VCG (HOLDINGS) LIMITED—See Matthews International Corporation; *U.S. Public*, pg. 1401
VCG KESTREL LIMITED—See Visual Communications Group Ltd; *Int'l*, pg. 8255
V&C GMBH—See EVN AG; *Int'l*, pg. 2571
VCHECK GLOBAL LLC; *U.S. Private*, pg. 4349
VCI CONSTRUCTION, INC.—See Dycom Industries, Inc.; *U.S. Public*, pg. 699
VCI GLOBAL LIMITED; *Int'l*, pg. 8140
VCI, INC.—See J Fitzgibbons LLC; *U.S. Private*, pg. 2153
VCM PRODUCTS, LLC; *U.S. Private*, pg. 4349
VCOM INTERNATIONAL MULTI-MEDIA CORPORATION; *U.S. Private*, pg. 4349
VCOM SOLUTIONS INC.; *U.S. Private*, pg. 4349
VCOM; *U.S. Private*, pg. 4349
VCORE TECHNOLOGY PARTNERS LLC—See Berkshire Partners LLC; *U.S. Private*, pg. 534
VCPLUS LIMITED; *Int'l*, pg. 8140
VCREATIVE, INC.—See Banyan Software, Inc.; *U.S. Private*, pg. 470
VCREDIT FINANCE LIMITED—See VCREDIT Holdings Limited; *Int'l*, pg. 8140
VCREDIT HOLDINGS LIMITED; *Int'l*, pg. 8140
VCS GROUP INC.—See Benefits Network Inc.; *U.S. Private*, pg. 525
VCS QUALITY SERVICES PVT. LTD—See I Squared Capital Advisors (US) LLC; *U.S. Private*, pg. 2023
VCS QUALITY SERVICES PVT, LTD—See TDR Capital LLP; *Int'l*, pg. 7493
VCS SA—See VINCI S.A.; *Int'l*, pg. 8235
VCST AUTOMOTIVE COMPONENTS (CHANGZHOU) CO, LTD.—See Gimv NV; *Int'l*, pg. 2976
VCST AUTOMOTIVE PRODUCTION ALBA SRL—See Gimv NV; *Int'l*, pg. 2976
VCST DE MEXICO S. DE R.L. DE C.V.—See Gimv NV; *Int'l*, pg. 2976
VCST, INC.—See Gimv NV; *Int'l*, pg. 2976
VCST INDUSTRIAL PRODUCTS BVBA—See Gimv NV; *Int'l*, pg. 2976
VCST N.V.—See Gimv NV; *Int'l*, pg. 2976

CORPORATE AFFILIATIONS

VCST REICHENBACH GMBH—See Gimv NV; *Int'l*, pg. 2976
VCT INTERNACIONAL S.A.—See Vina Concha y Toro S.A.; *Int'l*, pg. 8209
VCT VIDEOCATION CREATIVE TOOLS GMBH—See Avemio AG; *Int'l*, pg. 738
VCT VOGEL GMBH—See Chart Industries, Inc.; *U.S. Public*, pg. 482
V-CUBE, INC.; *Int'l*, pg. 8104
V-CUBE (THAILAND) CO., LTD.—See V-cube, Inc.; *Int'l*, pg. 8104
V-CUBE USA, INC.—See V-cube, Inc.; *Int'l*, pg. 8104
VCU DATA MANAGEMENT LIMITED; *Int'l*, pg. 8140
VC UK LP—See Freudenberg SE; *Int'l*, pg. 2790
VCUSTOMER; *U.S. Private*, pg. 4349
VDA GROUP S.P.A.—See METI Holding Sarl; *Int'l*, pg. 4854
VDARA CONDO HOTEL, LLC—See MGM Resorts International; *U.S. Public*, pg. 1435
VDART INC.; *U.S. Private*, pg. 4349
V&D B.V.—See Sun Capital Partners, Inc.; *U.S. Private*, pg. 3862
VDC DISPLAY SYSTEMS—See Video Display Corporation; *U.S. Public*, pg. 2296
V-DESIGN SERVICES (M) SDN. BHD.—See Venture Corporation Limited; *Int'l*, pg. 8152
VDF SUN-ROYAL CO., LTD.—See Yamazaki Baking Co., Ltd.; *Int'l*, pg. 8557
VDG SECURITY B.V.—See TKH Group N.V.; *Int'l*, pg. 7765
VDH DIRKSLAND—See VDH Moerdijk; *Int'l*, pg. 8140
VDH ELECTRIC INC.—See VHC Inc.; *U.S. Private*, pg. 4375
VDH MOERDIJK; *Int'l*, pg. 8140
VDI, I.L.—See LINTEC Corporation; *Int'l*, pg. 4516
VDI VEREIN DEUTSCHER INGENIEURE E.V; *Int'l*, pg. 8140
VDI VERLAG GMBH—See VDI Verein Deutscher Ingenieure e.V.; *Int'l*, pg. 8140
VDK BANK; *Int'l*, pg. 8140
VDL AGROTECH B.V.—See VDL Groep B.V.; *Int'l*, pg. 8141
VDL APPARATENBOUW BV—See VDL Groep B.V.; *Int'l*, pg. 8141
VDL BELGIUM N.V.—See VDL Groep B.V.; *Int'l*, pg. 8142
VDL BUS CENTER BV—See VDL Groep B.V.; *Int'l*, pg. 8141
VDL BUS & COACH BV—See VDL Groep B.V.; *Int'l*, pg. 8141
VDL BUS & COACH CZECH REPUBLIC S.R.O.—See VDL Groep B.V.; *Int'l*, pg. 8141
VDL BUS & COACH DANMARK A/S—See VDL Groep B.V.; *Int'l*, pg. 8141
VDL BUS & COACH DEUTSCHLAND GMBH—See VDL Groep B.V.; *Int'l*, pg. 8141
VDL BUS & COACH FRANCE SARL—See VDL Groep B.V.; *Int'l*, pg. 8141
VDL BUS & COACH ITALIA S.R.L.—See VDL Groep B.V.; *Int'l*, pg. 8141
VDL BUS & COACH POLSKA SP. Z O.O.—See VDL Groep B.V.; *Int'l*, pg. 8141
VDL BUS & COACH SERBIA D.O.O.—See VDL Groep B.V.; *Int'l*, pg. 8141
VDL BUS & COACH SOUTH AFRICA LTD—See VDL Groep B.V.; *Int'l*, pg. 8141
VDL BUS & COACH (SUISSE) GMBH—See VDL Groep B.V.; *Int'l*, pg. 8141
VDL BUS HEERENVEEN B.V.—See VDL Groep B.V.; *Int'l*, pg. 8141
VDL BUS INTERNATIONAL B.V.—See VDL Groep B.V.; *Int'l*, pg. 8141
VDL BUSLAND BV—See VDL Groep B.V.; *Int'l*, pg. 8141
VDL BUS MODULES BV—See VDL Groep B.V.; *Int'l*, pg. 8141
VDL BUS ROESALARE NV—See VDL Groep B.V.; *Int'l*, pg. 8141
VDL BUS VALKENSWAARD BV—See VDL Groep B.V.; *Int'l*, pg. 8141
VDL BUS VENLO BV—See VDL Groep B.V.; *Int'l*, pg. 8141
VDL CONTAINERSYSTEME GMBH—See VDL Groep B.V.; *Int'l*, pg. 8141
VDL CONTAINERSYSTEMEN B.V.—See VDL Groep B.V.; *Int'l*, pg. 8141
VDL DELMAS GMBH—See VDL Groep B.V.; *Int'l*, pg. 8141
V.D. LEDERMANN & CO. GMBH—See Edding AG; *Int'l*, pg. 2304
VD LEEGTE METAAL B.V.—See VDL Groep B.V.; *Int'l*, pg. 8141
VDL ENABLING TECHNOLOGIES GROUP ALMELO BV—See VDL Groep B.V.; *Int'l*, pg. 8141
VDL ENABLING TECHNOLOGIES GROUP EINDHOVEN BV—See VDL Groep B.V.; *Int'l*, pg. 8141
VDL ENABLING TECHNOLOGIES GROUP OF SUZHOU LTD.—See VDL Groep B.V.; *Int'l*, pg. 8141
VDL ENABLING TECHNOLOGIES GROUP PROJECTS BV—See VDL Groep B.V.; *Int'l*, pg. 8141
VDL ENABLING TECHNOLOGIES GROUP RESEARCH BV—See VDL Groep B.V.; *Int'l*, pg. 8141

COMPANY NAME INDEX

VDL ENABLING TECHNOLOGIES GROUP SINGAPORE PTE. LTD.—See VDL Groep B.V.; *Int'l*, pg. 8141
VDL ENABLING TECHNOLOGIES GROUP USA - EAST COAST—See VDL Groep B.V.; *Int'l*, pg. 8141
VDL ENABLING TECHNOLOGIES GROUP USA - WEST COAST—See VDL Groep B.V.; *Int'l*, pg. 8141
VDL ETG PROJECTS BV—See VDL Groep B.V.; *Int'l*, pg. 8141
VDL ETG RESEARCH BV—See VDL Groep B.V.; *Int'l*, pg. 8141
VDL ETG TECHNOLOGY & DEVELOPMENT BV—See VDL Groep B.V.; *Int'l*, pg. 8141
VDL FIBERTECH INDUSTRIES BV—See VDL Groep B.V.; *Int'l*, pg. 8142
VDL GEREEDSCHAPMAKERIJ B.V.—See VDL Groep B.V.; *Int'l*, pg. 8142
VDL GROEP B.V.; *Int'l*, pg. 8140
VDL HOLDING BELGIUM N.V.—See VDL Groep B.V.; *Int'l*, pg. 8142
VDL INDUSTRIAL MODULES BV—See VDL Groep B.V.; *Int'l*, pg. 8142
VDL INDUSTRIAL PRODUCTS BV—See VDL Groep B.V.; *Int'l*, pg. 8142
VDL KLIMA B.V.—See VDL Groep B.V.; *Int'l*, pg. 8142
VDL KLIMA FRANCE S.A.R.L.—See VDL Groep B.V.; *Int'l*, pg. 8142
VDL KONINGS BV—See VDL Groep B.V.; *Int'l*, pg. 8142
VDL KTI NV—See VDL Groep B.V.; *Int'l*, pg. 8142
VDL KUNSTSTOFFEN B.V.—See VDL Groep B.V.; *Int'l*, pg. 8142
VDL LAKTECHNIEK B.V.—See VDL Groep B.V.; *Int'l*, pg. 8142
VDL LASINDUSTRIE B.V.—See VDL Groep B.V.; *Int'l*, pg. 8142
VDL MPC BV—See VDL Groep B.V.; *Int'l*, pg. 8142
VDL MPC BV—See VDL Groep B.V.; *Int'l*, pg. 8142
VDL NEDCAR BV—See VDL Groep B.V.; *Int'l*, pg. 8142
VDL NETWORK SUPPLIES BV—See VDL Groep B.V.; *Int'l*, pg. 8142
VDL PARREE BV—See VDL Groep B.V.; *Int'l*, pg. 8142
VDL PARTS BV—See VDL Groep B.V.; *Int'l*, pg. 8142
VDL POSTMA BV—See VDL Groep B.V.; *Int'l*, pg. 8142
VDL ROTECH SRL—See VDL Groep B.V.; *Int'l*, pg. 8142
VDL STAALSERVICE BV—See VDL Groep B.V.; *Int'l*, pg. 8142
VDL STEELWELD BV—See VDL Groep B.V.; *Int'l*, pg. 8142
VDL SYSTEMS B.V.—See VDL Groep B.V.; *Int'l*, pg. 8142
VDL TECHNICS BV—See VDL Groep B.V.; *Int'l*, pg. 8142
VDL TIM HAPERT BV—See VDL Groep B.V.; *Int'l*, pg. 8142
VDL-USA—See VDL Groep B.V.; *Int'l*, pg. 8142
VDL WEWELER BV—See VDL Groep B.V.; *Int'l*, pg. 8142
VDL WEWELER PARTS BV—See VDL Groep B.V.; *Int'l*, pg. 8142
VDL WIENTJES EMMEN BV—See VDL Groep B.V.; *Int'l*, pg. 8142
VDL WIENTJES RODEN BV—See VDL Groep B.V.; *Int'l*, pg. 8142
VDM CONSTRUCTION—See VDM Group Limited; *Int'l*, pg. 8143
VDM EARTHMOVING CONTRACTORS PTY LTD.—See VDM Group Limited; *Int'l*, pg. 8142
VDM GROUP LIMITED; *Int'l*, pg. 8142
VDM-HILFE GMBH—See GEA Group Aktiengesellschaft; *Int'l*, pg. 2903
VDM METALS AUSTRALIA PTY. LTD.—See Acerinox, S.A.; *Int'l*, pg. 101
VDM METALS AUSTRIA GMBH—See Acerinox, S.A.; *Int'l*, pg. 101
VDM METALS BENELUX B.V.—See Acerinox, S.A.; *Int'l*, pg. 101
VDM METALS CANADA LIMITED—See Acerinox, S.A.; *Int'l*, pg. 101
VDM METALS DE MEXICO S.A. DE C.V.—See Acerinox, S.A.; *Int'l*, pg. 101
VDM METALS FRANCE S.A.S.—See Acerinox, S.A.; *Int'l*, pg. 101
VDM METALS GMBH—See Acerinox, S.A.; *Int'l*, pg. 101
VDM METALS (GUANGZHOU) TRADING CO., LTD.—See Acerinox, S.A.; *Int'l*, pg. 101
VDM METALS HOLDING GMBH—See Acerinox, S.A.; *Int'l*, pg. 101
VDM METALS INTERNATIONAL GMBH—See Acerinox, S.A.; *Int'l*, pg. 101
VDM METALS ITALIA S.R.L.—See Acerinox, S.A.; *Int'l*, pg. 101
VDM METALS JAPAN K.K.—See Acerinox, S.A.; *Int'l*, pg. 101
VDM METALS KOREA CO., LTD.—See Acerinox, S.A.; *Int'l*, pg. 101
VDM METALS SCHWEIZ AG—See Acerinox, S.A.; *Int'l*, pg. 101
VDM METALS U.K. LTD.—See Acerinox, S.A.; *Int'l*, pg. 101
VDM METALS USA, LLC—See Acerinox, S.A.; *Int'l*, pg. 101
VDM (QLD) PTY LTD.—See VDM Group Limited; *Int'l*, pg. 8142
VDM (SHANGHAI) HIGH PERFORMANCE METALS TRADING CO., LTD.—See Acerinox, S.A.; *Int'l*, pg. 101
VDM-UNTERSTUTZUNGSKASSE GMBH—See ThyssenKrupp AG; *Int'l*, pg. 7734
VDO-PH INTERNATIONAL, INC.; *U.S. Private*, pg. 4349
VDOSOFT SDN. BHD.—See AWC Berhad; *Int'l*, pg. 752
VDS ALUMINIUM; *Int'l*, pg. 8143
VDS—See Sonepar S.A.; *Int'l*, pg. 7094
VDS TECHNISCHE INDUSTRIE BV—See VDL Groep B.V.; *Int'l*, pg. 8142
VDZ SRO—See VINCI S.A.; *Int'l*, pg. 8240
VEAB HEAT TECH AB—See Systemair AB; *Int'l*, pg. 7392
VEALEIDJA OU—See Sweco AB; *Int'l*, pg. 7363
VEALLS LIMITED; *Int'l*, pg. 8143
VEATIVE GROUP PLC; *Int'l*, pg. 8143
VEAU DES TERROIRS BRETONS—See Serval SAS; *Int'l*, pg. 6724
VEAU DES TERROIRS DE FRANCE—See Serval SAS; *Int'l*, pg. 6724
VEBACOM GMBH—See E.ON SE; *Int'l*, pg. 2260
VEBNET (HOLDINGS) LIMITED—See Phoenix Group Holdings PLC; *Int'l*, pg. 5851
VEBNET LIMITED—See Phoenix Group Holdings PLC; *Int'l*, pg. 5851
VEB.RF; *Int'l*, pg. 8143
V E C A ELECTRIC COMPANY INC.; *U.S. Private*, pg. 4327
VECAST, INC.; *U.S. Private*, pg. 4349
VEC CIVIL ENGINEERING PTY. LTD.—See Downer EDI Limited; *Int'l*, pg. 2186
VECELLIO & GROGAN, INC.—See Vecellio Group, Inc.; *U.S. Private*, pg. 4349
VECELLIO GROUP, INC.; *U.S. Private*, pg. 4349
VECIMA NETWORKS, INC.; *Int'l*, pg. 8143
VECIMA TELECOM (P) LTD.—See Vecima Networks, Inc.; *Int'l*, pg. 8143
VECKS INC.—See Vector Inc.; *Int'l*, pg. 8144
VECNA TECHNOLOGIES, INC.; *U.S. Private*, pg. 4349
VECO B.V.—See Gilde Buy Out Partners B.V.; *Int'l*, pg. 2975
VE COMMERCIAL VEHICLES LTD—See Eicher Motors Limited; *Int'l*, pg. 2328
VECOPLAN AG—See MAX Automation SE; *Int'l*, pg. 4734
VECOPLAN IBERICA S.L.—See MAX Automation SE; *Int'l*, pg. 4734
VECOPLAN LIMITED—See MAX Automation SE; *Int'l*, pg. 4734
VECOPLAN MIDWEST LLC—See MAX Automation SE; *Int'l*, pg. 4734
VECOW CO., LTD.—See Ennoconn Corporation; *Int'l*, pg. 2443
VECSCAN AB—See Vector Informatik GmbH; *Int'l*, pg. 8144
VECTA INC.; *U.S. Private*, pg. 4349
VECTA—See Steelcase Inc.; *U.S. Public*, pg. 1944
VECTA VENDING SOLUTIONS S.P.A.—See AB Electrolux; *Int'l*, pg. 41
VECTEUR PLUS—See Bridgepoint Group Plc; *Int'l*, pg. 1155
VECTION CONSULTING PTY LTD.—See Vection Technologies Ltd.; *Int'l*, pg. 8143
VECTION TECHNOLOGIES LTD.; *Int'l*, pg. 8143
VECTIVBIO HOLDING AG—See Ironwood Pharmaceuticals, Inc.; *U.S. Public*, pg. 1174
VECTOR 21 HOLDINGS, INC.; *U.S. Public*, pg. 2276
VECTOR AEROSPACE FRANCE—See The Carlyle Group Inc.; *U.S. Public*, pg. 2054
VECTORA TRANSPORTATION; *U.S. Private*, pg. 4353
VECTOR AUSTRIA GMBH—See Vector Informatik GmbH; *Int'l*, pg. 8144
VECTOR AUTOMOTIVE TECHNOLOGY (SHANGHAI) CO., LTD.—See Vector Informatik GmbH; *Int'l*, pg. 8144
VECTOR CAPITAL MANAGEMENT, L.P.; *U.S. Private*, pg. 4349
VECTOR CAPITAL PLC; *Int'l*, pg. 8143
VECTOR CHOICE TECHNOLOGY SOLUTIONS, CORP.; *U.S. Private*, pg. 4353
VECTOR CONSTRUCTION INC.—See Vector Construction Ltd.; *Int'l*, pg. 8144
VECTOR CONSTRUCTION LTD.; *Int'l*, pg. 8144
VECTOR CONSULTANTS LIMITED—See Freudenberg SE; *Int'l*, pg. 2790
VECTOR CORROSION TECHNOLOGIES INC.—See Vector Construction Ltd.; *Int'l*, pg. 8144
VECTOR CORROSION TECHNOLOGIES LTD—See Vector Construction Ltd.; *Int'l*, pg. 8144
VECTORCSP, LLC; *U.S. Private*, pg. 4353
VECTOR DATA SERVICES, INC.—See Freudenberg SE; *Int'l*, pg. 2791
VECTOR ENVIRONMENTAL SERVICES LIMITED—See Aramark; *U.S. Public*, pg. 178
VECTOR EUROPE NV—See Viscofan SA; *Int'l*, pg. 8250
VECTORFORM LLC—See Nippon Telegraph & Telephone Corporation; *Int'l*, pg. 5348
VECTOR FRANCE S.A.S.—See Vector Informatik GmbH; *Int'l*, pg. 8145
VECTOR GB LTD.—See Vector Informatik GmbH; *Int'l*, pg. 8145
VECTOR GROUP INC.—See Freudenberg SE; *Int'l*, pg. 2790
VECTOR GROUP LTD.—See Japan Tobacco Inc.; *Int'l*, pg. 3907
VECTOR INC.—See SoftBank Group Corp.; *Int'l*, pg. 7052
VECTOR INC.; *Int'l*, pg. 8144
VECTOR INFORMATICA BRASIL LTDA.—See Vector Informatik GmbH; *Int'l*, pg. 8145
VECTOR INFORMATIK GMBH; *Int'l*, pg. 8144
VECTOR INFORMATIK INDIA PVT. LTD.—See Vector Informatik GmbH; *Int'l*, pg. 8145
VECTOR ITALIA S.R.L.—See Vector Informatik GmbH; *Int'l*, pg. 8145
VECTOR KOREA IT INC.—See Vector Informatik GmbH; *Int'l*, pg. 8145
VECTOR LABORATORIES, INC.—See Thompson Street Capital Manager LLC; *U.S. Private*, pg. 4161
VECTORLEARNING.COM, INC.—See Providence Equity Partners L.L.C.; *U.S. Private*, pg. 3294
VECTOR LIMITED; *Int'l*, pg. 8145
VECTOR MARKETING CORPORATION—See CUTCO Corporation; *U.S. Private*, pg. 1131
VECTOR MEDIA GROUP INC.; *U.S. Private*, pg. 4353
VECTOR NORTH AMERICA INC.—See Vector Informatik GmbH; *Int'l*, pg. 8145
VECTOR PIPELINE, L.P.—See DTE Energy Company; *U.S. Public*, pg. 689
VECTOR PIPELINE, L.P.—See Enbridge Inc.; *Int'l*, pg. 2397
VECTOR PLANNING & SERVICES, INC.—See Chugach Alaska Corporation; *U.S. Private*, pg. 893
VECTORPLY CORPORATION—See MSouth Equity Partners, LLC; *U.S. Private*, pg. 2808
VECTOR PROCUREMENT SOLUTIONS INC.—See Multitude SE; *Int'l*, pg. 5084
VECTOR RESOURCES LIMITED; *Int'l*, pg. 8145
VECTOR SECURITY, INC.—See The Philadelphia Contributionship; *U.S. Private*, pg. 4094
VECTOR SHINWA CO., LTD.—See Nisso Corporation; *Int'l*, pg. 5377
VECTOR SOFTWARE INC.—See Vector Informatik GmbH; *Int'l*, pg. 8145
VECTOR SOFTWARE SP. Z O. O.; *Int'l*, pg. 8145
VECTOR SOLUTIONS, INC.—See Genstar Capital, LLC; *U.S. Private*, pg. 1679
VECTOR SPACE SYSTEMS; *U.S. Private*, pg. 4353
VECTOR TECHNOLOGIES LTD.—See Holden Industries, Inc.; *U.S. Private*, pg. 1962
VECTOR TOBACCO INC.—See Japan Tobacco Inc.; *Int'l*, pg. 3907
VECTORUSA; *U.S. Private*, pg. 4353
VECTORVISION OCULAR HEALTH, INC.—See Guardion Health Sciences, Inc.; *U.S. Public*, pg. 973
VECTOR WEALTH MANAGEMENT—See Warburg Pincus LLC; *U.S. Private*, pg. 4439
VECTOR WORKPLACE AND FACILITY MANAGEMENT LIMITED—See Aramark; *U.S. Public*, pg. 178
VECTORWORKS CANADA, INC.—See Nemetschek SE; *Int'l*, pg. 5195
VECTORWORKS UK, LTD.—See Nemetschek SE; *Int'l*, pg. 5195
VECTRA BANK COLORADO—See Zions Bancorporation, National Association; *U.S. Public*, pg. 2408
VECTRA CO.—See Apollo Global Management, Inc.; *U.S. Public*, pg. 166
VECTRA, INC.—See Taylor Corporation; *U.S. Private*, pg. 3939
VECTRA S.A.; *Int'l*, pg. 8145
VECTREN CORPORATION—See CenterPoint Energy, Inc.; *U.S. Public*, pg. 472
VECTREN ENTERPRISES, INC.—See CenterPoint Energy, Inc.; *U.S. Public*, pg. 472
VECTREN UTILITY HOLDINGS, INC.—See CenterPoint Energy, Inc.; *U.S. Public*, pg. 472
VECTRONIX AG—See Safran SA; *Int'l*, pg. 6475
VECTRONIX INC.—See Safran SA; *Int'l*, pg. 6475
VECTRON SYSTEMS AG—See Shift4 Payments, Inc.; *U.S. Public*, pg. 1875
VECTRUS FEDERAL SERVICES GMBH—See V2X, Inc.; *U.S. Public*, pg. 2270
VECTRUS MISSION SOLUTIONS CORPORATION—See V2X, Inc.; *U.S. Public*, pg. 2270
VECTRUS SYSTEMS CORPORATION—See V2X, Inc.; *U.S. Public*, pg. 2270
VECTURA AS—See Arcus ASA; *Int'l*, pg. 552
VECTURA DELIVERY DEVICES LTD.—See Philip Morris International Inc.; *U.S. Public*, pg. 1688
VECTURA FASTIGHETER AB—See Investor AB; *Int'l*, pg. 3787
VECTURA FERTIN PHARMA RESEARCH LABORATORIES PTE. LTD.—See Philip Morris International Inc.; *U.S. Public*, pg. 1688
VECTURA GMBH—See Philip Morris International Inc.; *U.S. Public*, pg. 1688
VECTURA GROUP PLC - NOTTINGHAM—See Philip Morris International Inc.; *U.S. Public*, pg. 1688
VECTURA GROUP PLC—See Philip Morris International Inc.; *U.S. Public*, pg. 1688

VECTRA S.A.   CORPORATE AFFILIATIONS

VECTURA INC—See Philip Morris International Inc.; *U.S. Public*, pg. 1688
VECTUS BIOSYSTEMS LIMITED; *Int'l*, pg. 8145
VECV SOUTH AFRICA (PTY) LTD.—See Eicher Motors Limited; *Int'l*, pg. 2328
VEDA CORPORATE SERVICES LIMITED—See NOIZ Group Limited; *Int'l*, pg. 5401
VEDAG GMBH—See RHI Magnesita N.V.; *Int'l*, pg. 6326
VEDALEON TECHNOLOGIES PTY. LTD.—See Amadeus IT Group, S.A.; *Int'l*, pg. 407
VEDANG CELLULAR SERVICES PRIVATE LIMITED—See Quess Corp Limited; *Int'l*, pg. 6160
VEDAN INTERNATIONAL (HOLDINGS) LTD.; *Int'l*, pg. 8145
VEDANTA BIOSCIENCES, INC.—See PureTech Health plc; *U.S. Public*, pg. 1738
VEDANTA CREATIONS LIMITED—See Bang Overseas Ltd.; *Int'l*, pg. 832
VEDANTA LIMITED—See Vedanta Resources Ltd; *Int'l*, pg. 8145
VEDANTA LISHEEN MINING LIMITED—See Vedanta Resources Ltd; *Int'l*, pg. 8146
VEDANTA RESOURCES LTD; *Int'l*, pg. 8145
VEDANT ASSET LIMITED; *Int'l*, pg. 8145
VEDANT FASHIONS LIMITED; *Int'l*, pg. 8145
VEDAN (VIETNAM) ENTERPRISE CORPORATION LIMITED—See Vedan International (Holdings) Ltd.; *Int'l*, pg. 8145
VEDAVAAG SYSTEMS LIMITED; *Int'l*, pg. 8146
VEDDER GMBH—See Depa PLC; *Int'l*, pg. 2041
VEDDER HOLSTERS LLC; *U.S. Private*, pg. 4353
VEDDER PRICE P.C.; *U.S. Private*, pg. 4353
VEDER DO BRASIL LTDA; *Int'l*, pg. 8146
VEDIM PHARMA SA—See UCB S.A.; *Int'l*, pg. 8012
VEDIM SA DE C.V.—See UCB S.A.; *Int'l*, pg. 8012
VEDIM SP. Z.O.O.—See UCB S.A.; *Int'l*, pg. 8012
VEEAM SOFTWARE GROUP GMBH—See Insight Venture Management, LLC; *U.S. Private*, pg. 2091
VEECO ASIA PTE. LTD.—See Veeco Instruments Inc.; *U.S. Public*, pg. 2276
VEECO COMPOUND SEMICONDUCTOR INC.—See Veeco Instruments Inc.; *U.S. Public*, pg. 2276
VEECO INSTRUMENTS GMBH—See Veeco Instruments Inc.; *U.S. Public*, pg. 2276
VEECO INSTRUMENTS INC.; *U.S. Public*, pg. 2276
VEECO INSTRUMENTS LTD.—See Veeco Instruments Inc.; *U.S. Public*, pg. 2277
VEECO INSTRUMENTS (SHANGHAI) CO. LTD.—See Veeco Instruments Inc.; *U.S. Public*, pg. 2277
VEECO JAPAN—See Veeco Instruments Inc.; *U.S. Public*, pg. 2277
VEECO KOREA INC.—See Veeco Instruments Inc.; *U.S. Public*, pg. 2277
VEECO KOREA LLC—See Veeco Instruments Inc.; *U.S. Public*, pg. 2277
VEECO MALAYSIA SDN. BHD.—See Veeco Instruments Inc.; *U.S. Public*, pg. 2277
VEECO PRECISION SURFACE PROCESSING LLC—See Veeco Instruments Inc.; *U.S. Public*, pg. 2277
VEECO PROCESS EQUIPMENT INC.—See Veeco Instruments Inc.; *U.S. Public*, pg. 2277
VEECOR CO., INC—See Coastal Group; *U.S. Private*, pg. 956
VEECO SIC CVD SYSTEMS AB—See Veeco Instruments Inc.; *U.S. Public*, pg. 2277
VEECO SINGAPORE—See Veeco Instruments Inc.; *U.S. Public*, pg. 2277
VEECO SOLAR EQUIPMENT INC.—See Veeco Instruments Inc.; *U.S. Public*, pg. 2277
VEECO TAIWAN INC.—See Veeco Instruments Inc.; *U.S. Public*, pg. 2277
VEEDER-ROOT COMPANY—See Vontier Corporation; *U.S. Public*, pg. 2309
VEEDER-ROOT FINANCE COMPANY—See Danaher Corporation; *U.S. Public*, pg. 631
VEEDER-ROOT FUELQUEST, LLC—See Vontier Corporation; *U.S. Public*, pg. 2309
VEEFIN SOLUTIONS LIMITED; *Int'l*, pg. 8146
VEEGO CORPORATION—See Wuhan Raycus Fiber Laser Technologies Co., Ltd.; *Int'l*, pg. 8501
VEEGO PHARMA LLC; *U.S. Private*, pg. 4353
VEE-JAY CEMENT CONTRACTING CO., INC.; *U.S. Private*, pg. 4353
VEEJAY LAKSHMI ENGINEERING WORKS LTD; *Int'l*, pg. 8146
VEEKO INTERNATIONAL HOLDINGS LTD.; *Int'l*, pg. 8146
VEEM LTD; *Int'l*, pg. 8146
VEENENDAALCAVE, INC.; *U.S. Private*, pg. 4353
VEENHUIS MACHINES B.V.; *Int'l*, pg. 8146
VEENMAN B.V.—See Xerox Holdings Corporation; *U.S. Public*, pg. 2388
VEEPS INC.—See Live Nation Entertainment, Inc.; *U.S. Public*, pg. 1331
VEERAL ORGANICS PVT. LTD.—See Vinati Organics Ltd; *Int'l*, pg. 8210
VEERAM SECURITIES LIMITED; *Int'l*, pg. 8147
VEERAS INFOTEK PVT LTD.—See Gemini Communication Ltd.; *Int'l*, pg. 2916

VEER ENERGY & INFRASTRUCTURE LTD.; *Int'l*, pg. 8146
VEER ENTERPRISE GMBH—See Veer Energy & Infrastructure Ltd.; *Int'l*, pg. 8146
VEER GLOBAL INFRACONSTRUCTION LIMITED; *Int'l*, pg. 8146
VEERHEALTH CARE LIMITED; *Int'l*, pg. 8147
VEERKRUPA JEWELLERS LIMITED; *Int'l*, pg. 8147
VEETEE RICE LIMITED—See A.K. Al-Muhaidib & Sons Group of Companies; *Int'l*, pg. 24
VEETHREE ELECTRONICS & MARINE LLC; *U.S. Private*, pg. 4353
VEE TIME CORP.; *Int'l*, pg. 8146
VEEUZE GMBH—See Eleco Plc; *Int'l*, pg. 2348
VEEVA SYSTEMS, INC.; *U.S. Public*, pg. 2277
VEEVA U.K. HOLDINGS LIMITED—See Veeva Systems, Inc.; *U.S. Public*, pg. 2277
VEEX, INC; *U.S. Private*, pg. 4353
VEEZEE, INC—See Leonard Green & Partners, L.P.; *U.S. Private*, pg. 2424
VEF AS; *Int'l*, pg. 8147
VEF LTD; *Int'l*, pg. 8147
VEF RADIOTEHNIKA RRR; *Int'l*, pg. 8147
VEGA AD; *Int'l*, pg. 8147
VEGA AMERICAS, INC.—See Grieshaber Holding GmbH; *Int'l*, pg. 3083
VEGA AUSTRALIA PTY LTD—See Grieshaber Holding GmbH; *Int'l*, pg. 3083
VEGA-CONTROLS LTD.—See Grieshaber Holding GmbH; *Int'l*, pg. 3083
VEGA CONVEYORS & AUTOMATION PRIVATE LIMITED—See Daifuku Co., Ltd.; *Int'l*, pg. 1926
VEGA CORPORATION CO., LTD.; *Int'l*, pg. 8147
VEGA DEUTSCHLAND GMBH—See Leonardo S.p.A.; *Int'l*, pg. 4460
VEGA ENGENHARIA AMBIENTAL S.A.—See Solvi S.A.; *Int'l*, pg. 7082
VEGAGEST SGR SPA—See Arrow Global Group PLC; *Int'l*, pg. 579
VEGA GRIESHABER KG—See Grieshaber Holding GmbH; *Int'l*, pg. 3083
VEGA INDIA LEVEL & PRESSURE MEASUREMENT PVT. LTD.—See Grieshaber Holding GmbH; *Int'l*, pg. 3083
VEGA INDUSTRIES (MIDDLE EAST) F.Z.C.—See AIA Engineering Ltd.; *Int'l*, pg. 227
VEGA INFORMATICA E FARMACIA SRL—See CompuGroup Medical SE & Co. KGaA; *Int'l*, pg. 1756
VEGA INSTRUMENTOS S.A.—See Grieshaber Holding GmbH; *Int'l*, pg. 3083
VEGA INSTRUMENTS CO., LTD.—See Grieshaber Holding GmbH; *Int'l*, pg. 3083
VEGA INSTRUMENTS LTD.—See Grieshaber Holding GmbH; *Int'l*, pg. 3083
VEGA INSTRUMENTS SA PTY LTD—See Grieshaber Holding GmbH; *Int'l*, pg. 3083
VEGA INSTRUMENTS (SEA) PTE LTD.—See Grieshaber Holding GmbH; *Int'l*, pg. 3083
VEGA INVESTMENT MANAGERS—See Groupe BPCE; *Int'l*, pg. 3096
VEGA ITALIA S.R.L.—See Grieshaber Holding GmbH; *Int'l*, pg. 3083
VEGALAB, INC.; *U.S. Private*, pg. 4353
VEGALAB LLC—See Vegalab, Inc.; *U.S. Private*, pg. 4353
VEGA MESSTECHNIK AG—See Grieshaber Holding GmbH; *Int'l*, pg. 3083
VEGA MIDDLE EAST LLC—See Grieshaber Holding GmbH; *Int'l*, pg. 3083
VEGANO FOODS INC.; *Int'l*, pg. 8147
VEGA N.V./S.A.—See Grieshaber Holding GmbH; *Int'l*, pg. 3083
VEGANZ GROUP AG; *Int'l*, pg. 8147
VEGAS BRAZIL LLC; *U.S. Private*, pg. 4354
VEGAS.COM, LLC—See Vivid Seats, Inc.; *U.S. Public*, pg. 2307
VEGAS ELECTRIC SUPPLY—See Blackfriars Corp.; *U.S. Private*, pg. 575
VEGA SEVIYE VE BASINC OLCUM CIHAZLARI TICARET LTD. STI.—See Grieshaber Holding GmbH; *Int'l*, pg. 3083
VEGAS INC—See The Greenspun Corporation; *U.S. Private*, pg. 4039
VEGA SPACE GMBH—See Leonardo S.p.A.; *Int'l*, pg. 4461
VEGA S.R.L.—See Investment AB Latour; *Int'l*, pg. 3784
VEGA STYLE ITALIA LTDA—See Investment AB Latour; *Int'l*, pg. 3784
VEGA TECHNIQUE S.A.S.—See Grieshaber Holding GmbH; *Int'l*, pg. 3083
VEGA TECHNOLOGIES SAS—See Leonardo S.p.A.; *Int'l*, pg. 4461
VEGE AUTOMOTIVE SPAIN, S.L.U.—See LKQ Corporation; *U.S. Public*, pg. 1337
VEGETABLE GROWERS SUPPLY CO. INC.; *U.S. Private*, pg. 4354
VEGETABLE JUICES INC.—See Givaudan S.A.; *Int'l*, pg. 2981
THE VEGETABLE OIL INDUSTRIES COMPANY; *Int'l*, pg. 7698

VEGETABLE OIL PACKING JOINT STOCK COMPANY; *Int'l*, pg. 8147
VEGETABLE PRODUCTS LTD.; *Int'l*, pg. 8147
VEGETARIAN TIMES—See Active Interest Media, Inc.; *U.S. Private*, pg. 69
THE VEGETEXCO PORT JOINT - STOCK COMPANY; *Int'l*, pg. 7698
VEGGIE GRILL, INC.—See Next Level Burger Company, Inc.; *U.S. Private*, pg. 4354
VEGITALIA S.P.A.—See Kagome Co., Ltd.; *Int'l*, pg. 4050
VEGIWORKS, INC.; *U.S. Private*, pg. 4354
VEG-LAND INC.—See Veg-Land Sales Inc.; *U.S. Private*, pg. 4353
VEG-LAND SALES INC.; *U.S. Private*, pg. 4353
VEG-PAK PRODUCE LIMITED; *Int'l*, pg. 8147
VEG-PAK PRODUCE LIMITED WAREHOUSE & PRODUCTION FACILITY—See Veg-Pak Produce Limited; *Int'l*, pg. 8147
VEGREVILLE FORD SALES & SERVICE INC; *Int'l*, pg. 8147
VEG TECH AB—See Kingspan Group PLC; *Int'l*, pg. 4179
VEG TECH A/S—See Kingspan Group PLC; *Int'l*, pg. 4179
VEGTRUG USA INC.—See Takasho Co., Ltd.; *Int'l*, pg. 7436
VEHCO AB; *Int'l*, pg. 8147
VEHCO BV—See VEHCO AB; *Int'l*, pg. 8147
VEHCO FRANCE SAS—See VEHCO AB; *Int'l*, pg. 8147
VEHCO ICT GMBH—See VEHCO AB; *Int'l*, pg. 8147
VEHCOM MANUFACTURING LTD.—See Linamar Corporation; *Int'l*, pg. 4502
VEHCO NV—See VEHCO AB; *Int'l*, pg. 8147
VEHICLE ADMINISTRATIVE SERVICES, LTD.—See Brown & Brown, Inc.; *U.S. Public*, pg. 402
VEHICLE AXLE MANUFACTURING CO.; *Int'l*, pg. 8147
THE VEHICLE CONVERTERS LLC—See Ilustrato Pictures International Inc.; *Int'l*, pg. 3617
VEHICLE DATA SERVICES LIMITED—See LKQ Corporation; *U.S. Public*, pg. 1337
VEHICLE MAINTENANCE PROGRAM, INC.; *U.S. Private*, pg. 4354
VEHICLE SERVICE GROUP, LLC—See Dover Corporation; *U.S. Public*, pg. 679
VEHICLES MIDDLE EAST FZCO U.A.E.—See ITOCHU Corporation; *Int'l*, pg. 3841
VEHICLE STORAGE & ENGINEERING PTY. LTD.—See Eagers Automotive Limited; *Int'l*, pg. 2264
VEHICLE TESTING NEW ZEALAND LTD.—See DEKRA e.V.; *Int'l*, pg. 2010
VEHICLE TRACKING SOLUTIONS, LLC; *U.S. Private*, pg. 4354
VEHIX, INC.—See Comcast Corporation; *U.S. Public*, pg. 542
VEHO GROUP OY AB; *Int'l*, pg. 8147
VEHO OY AB; *Int'l*, pg. 8147
VEI CAPITAL—See Palladio Holding SpA; *Int'l*, pg. 5708
VEICHI ELECTRIC (INDIA) PRIVATE LIMITED—See Suzhou Veichi Electric Co., Ltd.; *Int'l*, pg. 7352
VEICHI ELECTRIC (M) SDN. BHD.—See Suzhou Veichi Electric Co., Ltd.; *Int'l*, pg. 7352
VEIDEKKE ASA; *Int'l*, pg. 8147
VEIDEKKE EIENDOM AS—See Veidekke ASA; *Int'l*, pg. 8148
VEIDEKKE ENTREPRENOR AS—See Veidekke ASA; *Int'l*, pg. 8148
VEIDEKKE LOGISTIKKBYGG AS—See Veidekke ASA; *Int'l*, pg. 8148
VEIDEKKE PREFAB AB—See Veidekke ASA; *Int'l*, pg. 8148
VEIDEKKE SVERIGE AB—See Veidekke ASA; *Int'l*, pg. 8148
VEI INC.—See Jacobs Engineering Group, Inc.; *U.S. Public*, pg. 1186
VEIT & COMPANY, INC.; *U.S. Private*, pg. 4354
VEITECH AB—See Veidekke ASA; *Int'l*, pg. 8148
VEITSCH-RADEX DIDIER REFRACTAIRES S.A.—See RHI Magnesita N.V.; *Int'l*, pg. 6326
VEITSCH-RADEX GMBH & CO OG—See RHI Magnesita N.V.; *Int'l*, pg. 6326
THE VEJTHANI HOSPITAL—See Krung Thai Bank Public Company Limited; *Int'l*, pg. 4308
VEKADA UAB—See Panevezio statybos trestas AB; *Int'l*, pg. 5727
VEKA ENTREPRENAD AB—See Triton Advisers Limited; *Int'l*, pg. 7931
VEKEN TECHNOLOGY CO., LTD.; *Int'l*, pg. 8148
VEKOBS S.R.O.; *Int'l*, pg. 8148
VEKO LIGHTSYSTEMS GMBH—See Fagerhult Group AB; *Int'l*, pg. 2602
VEKO LIGHTSYSTEMS INTERNATIONAL B.V.—See Fagerhult Group AB; *Int'l*, pg. 2602
VEKO LIGHTSYSTEMS S.L.—See Fagerhult Group AB; *Int'l*, pg. 2602
VEKTOR AG—See Girmatic AG; *Int'l*, pg. 2979
VEKTOR MANAGEMENT GMBH & CO ERSTE KG; *Int'l*, pg. 8148
VELA ABS S.R.L—See BNP Paribas SA; *Int'l*, pg. 1093
VELA HOME SRL—See BNP Paribas SA; *Int'l*, pg. 1093
VELA INSURANCE SERVICES, INC.—See W.R. Berkley Corporation; *U.S. Public*, pg. 2318

2900

COMPANY NAME INDEX VELTEX CORPORATION
Company Index

VELA INTERNATIONAL MARINE LIMITED—See National Shipping Company of Saudi Arabia; *Int'l*, pg. 5163
VELANA DD; *Int'l*, pg. 8149
VELAN GMBH—See Velan Inc.; *Int'l*, pg. 8148
VELAN GULF MANUFACTURING CO. LTD.—See Velan Inc.; *Int'l*, pg. 8148
VELAN HOTELS LTD.; *Int'l*, pg. 8148
VELAN INC.; *Int'l*, pg. 8148
VELAN LTD.—See Velan Inc.; *Int'l*, pg. 8148
VELAN S.A.S.—See Velan Inc.; *Int'l*, pg. 8148
VELAN VALVAC MANUFACTURING CO. LTD.—See Velan Inc.; *Int'l*, pg. 8148
VELAN VALVE CORP.—See Velan Inc.; *Int'l*, pg. 8148
VELAN VALVES LTD.—See Velan Inc.; *Int'l*, pg. 8149
VELAN VALVE (SUZHOU) CO. LTD.—See Velan Inc.; *Int'l*, pg. 8148
VELAN VALVULAS INDUSTRIAIS, LDA.—See Velan Inc.; *Int'l*, pg. 8149
VELAPAN SYSTEMS PRIVATE LIMITED—See Megasoft Ltd.; *Int'l*, pg. 4794
VELA SOFTWARE INTERNATIONAL INC.—See Constellation Software Inc.; *Int'l*, pg. 1775
VELA TECHNOLOGIES PLC; *Int'l*, pg. 8148
VELATEL GLOBAL COMMUNICATIONS, INC.; *U.S. Private*, pg. 4354
VELA TRADING SYSTEMS LLC—See Marlin Equity Partners, LLC; *U.S. Private*, pg. 2584
VELBAZHD AD; *Int'l*, pg. 8149
VELCAN HOLDINGS SA; *Int'l*, pg. 8149
VELCOR LEASING CORPORATION; *U.S. Private*, pg. 4354
VELCRO AUSTRALIA PTY. LTD.—See Velcro Industries N.V.; *Int'l*, pg. 8149
VELCRO CANADA, INC.—See Velcro Industries N.V.; *Int'l*, pg. 8149
VELCRO DE MEXICO S.A. DE C.V.—See Velcro Industries N.V.; *Int'l*, pg. 8149
VELCRO EUROPE S.A.—See Velcro Industries N.V.; *Int'l*, pg. 8149
VELCRO GMBH—See Velcro Industries N.V.; *Int'l*, pg. 8149
VELCRO GROUP CORPORATION—See Velcro Industries N.V.; *Int'l*, pg. 8149
VELCRO HOLDINGS B.V.—See Velcro Industries N.V.; *Int'l*, pg. 8149
VELCRO HONG KONG LTD.—See Velcro Industries N.V.; *Int'l*, pg. 8149
VELCRO INDUSTRIES B.V.—See Velcro Industries N.V.; *Int'l*, pg. 8149
VELCRO INDUSTRIES FRANCE S.A.—See Velcro Industries N.V.; *Int'l*, pg. 8149
VELCRO INDUSTRIES N.V.; *Int'l*, pg. 8149
VELCRO ITALIA, S.R.L.—See Velcro Industries N.V.; *Int'l*, pg. 8149
VELCRO LTD.—See Velcro Industries N.V.; *Int'l*, pg. 8149
VELCRO USA INC.—See Velcro Industries N.V.; *Int'l*, pg. 8149
VELDKAMPS INC.; *U.S. Private*, pg. 4354
VELEPREHRANA A.D.; *Int'l*, pg. 8149
VELEPROMET-ZENICA D.D.; *Int'l*, pg. 8149
VELES CAPITAL INVESTMENT COMPANY LLC; *Int'l*, pg. 8149
VELESCO PHARMACEUTICAL SERVICES LLC—See Leonard Green & Partners, L.P.; *U.S. Private*, pg. 2426
VELESTO DRILLING ACADEMY SDN BHD—See Velesto Energy Berhad; *Int'l*, pg. 8149
VELESTO ENERGY BERHAD; *Int'l*, pg. 8149
VELESTO WORKOVER SDN. BHD.—See Velesto Energy Berhad; *Int'l*, pg. 8149
VELETRGOVINA A.D.; *Int'l*, pg. 8149
VELFAC AB—See VKR Holding A/S; *Int'l*, pg. 8281
VELFAC A/S—See VKR Holding A/S; *Int'l*, pg. 8281
VELFAC GMBH—See VKR Holding A/S; *Int'l*, pg. 8281
VELFAC IRELAND LTD.—See VKR Holding A/S; *Int'l*, pg. 8282
VELFAC LTD.—See VKR Holding A/S; *Int'l*, pg. 8282
VELGRAF ASSET MANAGEMENT AD; *Int'l*, pg. 8149
VELICO MEDICAL; *U.S. Private*, pg. 4354
VELINA AD-VELINGRAD; *Int'l*, pg. 8149
VELIQ BV; *Int'l*, pg. 8149
VELIR; *U.S. Private*, pg. 4354
VELJAN DENISON LIMITED - PATANCHERU FACTORY—See VELJAN DENISON LIMITED; *Int'l*, pg. 8149
VELJAN DENISON LIMITED; *Int'l*, pg. 8149
VELLANO BROS., INC.; *U.S. Private*, pg. 4354
VELLEMAN COMPONENTS S.A./NV; *Int'l*, pg. 8149
VELLEMAN, INC.—See Velleman Components S.A./NV; *Int'l*, pg. 8150
VELLIV, PENSION & LIVSFORSIKRING A/S; *Int'l*, pg. 8150
VELLNER LEISURE PRODUCTS; *Int'l*, pg. 8150
VELMAR S.P.A—See Aeffe SpA; *Int'l*, pg. 173
VELMASH-S OOO—See Palfinger AG; *Int'l*, pg. 5708
VELMOS D.D. MOSTAR; *Int'l*, pg. 8150
VELO3D, INC.; *U.S. Public*, pg. 2277
VELOCE LOGISTICA SA—See Mitsui & Co., Ltd.; *Int'l*, pg. 4980
VELOCENT SYSTEMS, INC.—See DRW Holdings, LLC; *U.S. Private*, pg. 1280
VELOCENT SYSTEMS, INC.—See Emergence Capital Partners; *U.S. Private*, pg. 1380
VELOCENT SYSTEMS, INC.—See North Bridge Venture Management Company, Inc.; *U.S. Private*, pg. 2942
VELOCENT SYSTEMS, INC.—See Voyager Capital, LLC; *U.S. Private*, pg. 4414
VELOCIFY, INC.—See Intercontinental Exchange, Inc.; *U.S. Public*, pg. 1142
VELOCITEL INC.—See Willis Stein & Partners, LLC; *U.S. Private*, pg. 4528
VELOCITEL MANAGEMENT SERVICES—See Willis Stein & Partners, LLC; *U.S. Private*, pg. 4528
VELOCITI (PROPRIETARY) LIMITED—See Blue Label Telecoms Limited; *Int'l*, pg. 1068
VELOCITY ACQUISITION CORP.; *U.S. Public*, pg. 2277
VELOCITY CLINICAL RESEARCH, INC—See GHO Capital Partners LLP; *Int'l*, pg. 2959
VELOCITY COMMERCIAL CAPITAL, LLC; *U.S. Private*, pg. 4354
VELOCITY COMPOSITES PLC; *Int'l*, pg. 8150
VELOCITY CREDIT UNION; *U.S. Private*, pg. 4354
VELOCITY DATA INC.; *Int'l*, pg. 8150
VELOCITY DYNAMICS, LLC—See Baird Financial Group, Inc.; *U.S. Private*, pg. 453
VELOCITYEHS HOLDINGS, INC.—See CVC Capital Partners SICAV-FIS S.A.; *Int'l*, pg. 1885
VELOCITY FINANCIAL, INC.; *U.S. Public*, pg. 2277
THE VELOCITY GROUP, INC.; *U.S. Private*, pg. 4130
VELOCITY LOCAL, INC.—See Live Ventures Incorporated; *U.S. Public*, pg. 1332
VELOCITY MARKETING CONCEPTS, INC—See Live Ventures Incorporated; *U.S. Public*, pg. 1332
VELOCITY MERCHANT SERVICES; *U.S. Private*, pg. 4354
VELOCITY MERGER CORP.; *U.S. Private*, pg. 4354
VELOCITY MINERALS LTD.; *Int'l*, pg. 8150
VELOCITY OUTDOOR INC.—See Compass Diversified Holdings; *U.S. Public*, pg. 560
VELOCITY PARTNERS LIMITED—See Next 15 Group plc; *Int'l*, pg. 5247
VELOCITY PARTNERS US INC.—See Next 15 Group plc; *Int'l*, pg. 5247
VELOCITY PORTFOLIO GROUP, INC.; *U.S. Private*, pg. 4354
VELOCITY PRINT SOLUTIONS; *U.S. Private*, pg. 4354
VELOCITY RISK UNDERWRITERS, LLC—See Brookfield Corporation; *Int'l*, pg. 1182
VELOCITY SNACK BRANDS—See VMG Partners, LLC; *U.S. Private*, pg. 4408
VELOCITY TECHNOLOGY SOLUTIONS III, INC.—See Accenture plc; *Int'l*, pg. 87
VELOCITY TECHNOLOGY SOLUTIONS, INC.—See Accenture plc; *Int'l*, pg. 87
VELOCITY UK LIMITED—See Reece Group Ltd; *Int'l*, pg. 6249
VELOCITY VEHICLE GROUP; *U.S. Private*, pg. 4354
VELOCIX LIMITED—See Nokia Corporation; *Int'l*, pg. 5404
VELODRIVE GMBH—See Masterflex SE; *Int'l*, pg. 4725
VELODYNE ACOUSTICS, INC.; *U.S. Private*, pg. 4355
VELODYNE LIDAR, INC.—See Ouster, Inc.; *U.S. Public*, pg. 1624
VELO & OXYGEN OY—See Grimaldi Industri AB; *Int'l*, pg. 3086
VELOSI AMERICA LLC—See I Squared Capital Advisors (US) LLC; *U.S. Private*, pg. 2023
VELOSI AMERICA LLC—See TDR Capital LLP; *Int'l*, pg. 7493
VELOSI ANGOLA LDA—See I Squared Capital Advisors (US) LLC; *U.S. Private*, pg. 2024
VELOSI ANGOLA LDA—See TDR Capital LLP; *Int'l*, pg. 7493
VELOSI BAHRAIN WLL.—See I Squared Capital Advisors (US) LLC; *U.S. Private*, pg. 2023
VELOSI BAHRAIN WLL.—See TDR Capital LLP; *Int'l*, pg. 7492
VELOSI CBL (M) SDN BHD—See I Squared Capital Advisors (US) LLC; *U.S. Private*, pg. 2024
VELOSI CBL (M) SDN BHD—See TDR Capital LLP; *Int'l*, pg. 7493
VELOSI CERTIFICATION BUREAU LIMITED—See I Squared Capital Advisors (US) LLC; *U.S. Private*, pg. 2024
VELOSI CERTIFICATION BUREAU LIMITED—See TDR Capital LLP; *Int'l*, pg. 7493
VELOSI CERTIFICATION SERVICES L.L.C—See I Squared Capital Advisors (US) LLC; *U.S. Private*, pg. 2024
VELOSI CERTIFICATION SERVICES L.L.C—See TDR Capital LLP; *Int'l*, pg. 7493
VELOSI CERTIFICATION W.L.L—See I Squared Capital Advisors (US) LLC; *U.S. Private*, pg. 2024
VELOSI CERTIFICATION W.L.L—See TDR Capital LLP; *Int'l*, pg. 7493
VELOSI ENGINEERING MANAGEMENT CONSULTANCY (SHANGAI) LTD CO.—See I Squared Capital Advisors (US) LLC; *U.S. Private*, pg. 2023
VELOSI ENGINEERING MANAGEMENT CONSULTANCY (SHANGAI) LTD CO.—See TDR Capital LLP; *Int'l*, pg. 7492
VELOSI EUROPE LIMITED—See I Squared Capital Advisors (US) LLC; *U.S. Private*, pg. 2024
VELOSI EUROPE LIMITED—See TDR Capital LLP; *Int'l*, pg. 7493
VELOSI (GHANA) LTD.—See I Squared Capital Advisors (US) LLC; *U.S. Private*, pg. 2023
VELOSI (GHANA) LTD.—See TDR Capital LLP; *Int'l*, pg. 7493
VELOSI INDUSTRIES SDN BHD—See I Squared Capital Advisors (US) LLC; *U.S. Private*, pg. 2024
VELOSI INDUSTRIES SDN BHD—See TDR Capital LLP; *Int'l*, pg. 7493
VELOSI INTERNATIONAL ITALY SRL—See I Squared Capital Advisors (US) LLC; *U.S. Private*, pg. 2024
VELOSI INTERNATIONAL ITALY SRL—See TDR Capital LLP; *Int'l*, pg. 7493
VELOSI LIMITED—See I Squared Capital Advisors (US) LLC; *U.S. Private*, pg. 2023
VELOSI LIMITED—See TDR Capital LLP; *Int'l*, pg. 7493
VELOSI LLC—See I Squared Capital Advisors (US) LLC; *U.S. Private*, pg. 2023
VELOSI LLC—See TDR Capital LLP; *Int'l*, pg. 7492
VELOSIO, LLC; *U.S. Private*, pg. 4355
VELOSI PROMSERVICE LLC—See I Squared Capital Advisors (US) LLC; *U.S. Private*, pg. 2024
VELOSI PROMSERVICE LLC—See TDR Capital LLP; *Int'l*, pg. 7493
VELOSI QUALITY MANAGEMENT INTERNATIONAL L.L.C.—See I Squared Capital Advisors (US) LLC; *U.S. Private*, pg. 2024
VELOSI QUALITY MANAGEMENT INTERNATIONAL L.L.C.—See TDR Capital LLP; *Int'l*, pg. 7493
VELOSI SAUDI ARABIA CO LTD.—See I Squared Capital Advisors (US) LLC; *U.S. Private*, pg. 2024
VELOSI SAUDI ARABIA CO LTD.—See TDR Capital LLP; *Int'l*, pg. 7493
VELOSI THAI CO., LTD.—See I Squared Capital Advisors (US) LLC; *U.S. Private*, pg. 2024
VELOSI THAI CO., LTD.—See TDR Capital LLP; *Int'l*, pg. 7493
VELOSI UGANDA LTD.—See I Squared Capital Advisors (US) LLC; *U.S. Private*, pg. 2024
VELOSI UGANDA LTD.—See TDR Capital LLP; *Int'l*, pg. 7493
VELOSI (VIETNAM) CO LTD.—See I Squared Capital Advisors (US) LLC; *U.S. Private*, pg. 2023
VELOSI (VIETNAM) CO LTD.—See TDR Capital LLP; *Int'l*, pg. 7493
VELOX CMS S.R.O—See IMCD N.V.; *Int'l*, pg. 3622
VELOX COMPOSITES GMBH I.G.—See IMCD N.V.; *Int'l*, pg. 3622
VELOX DIS TIC.LTD.STI.—See IMCD N.V.; *Int'l*, pg. 3622
VELOX FRANCE S.A.S.—See IMCD N.V.; *Int'l*, pg. 3622
VELOX GMBH—See IMCD N.V.; *Int'l*, pg. 3622
VELOXION INC.; *U.S. Private*, pg. 4355
VELOXIS PHARMACEUTICALS A/S—See Asahi Kasei Corporation; *Int'l*, pg. 597
VELOXIS PHARMACEUTICALS, INC.—See Asahi Kasei Corporation; *Int'l*, pg. 597
VELOX ITALIA S.R.L.—See IMCD N.V.; *Int'l*, pg. 3622
VELOX OY—See IMCD N.V.; *Int'l*, pg. 3622
VELOX POLAND SP. Z O.O.—See IMCD N.V.; *Int'l*, pg. 3622
VELOX SPECIALITIES AB—See IMCD N.V.; *Int'l*, pg. 3622
VELOX SPECIALITIES AB—See IMCD N.V.; *Int'l*, pg. 3622
VELOX SYSTEMS, INC.—See Advanced Document Solutions, Inc.; *U.S. Private*, pg. 89
VELOX TRADING S.L.U.—See IMCD N.V.; *Int'l*, pg. 3623
VELOX U.K. LTD—See IMCD N.V.; *Int'l*, pg. 3623
VELPA ENVELOPPEN BV—See KPP Group Holdings Co., Ltd.; *Int'l*, pg. 4298
VELPA SOLUCIONES INTEGRALES S.A.—See Emek Elektrik Endustrisi A.S.; *Int'l*, pg. 2377
VELROQ OY—See Sandvik AB; *Int'l*, pg. 6535
VELSA OY—See SSAB AB; *Int'l*, pg. 7154
VELSERV A/S—See VKR Holding A/S; *Int'l*, pg. 8282
VELSICOL CHEMICAL CORPORATION—See Arsenal Capital Management LP; *U.S. Private*, pg. 339
VELSOL FRANCE S.A.S.—See VKR Holding A/S; *Int'l*, pg. 8282
VELTEC AS—See ELKA Beteiligungs GmbH; *Int'l*, pg. 2364
VELTEC GMBH—See ELKA Beteiligungs GmbH; *Int'l*, pg. 2364
VELTEC INDUSTRIAL SERVICES A/S—See ELKA Beteiligungs GmbH; *Int'l*, pg. 2364
VELTEC N.V.—See ELKA Beteiligungs GmbH; *Int'l*, pg. 2364
VELTERM A/S—See VKR Holding A/S; *Int'l*, pg. 8282
VELTEX CORPORATION; *U.S. Public*, pg. 2277
VELTI FZ LLC—See Velti plc; *Int'l*, pg. 8150
VELTI ISTANBUL MOBIL TEKNOLOJILERI—See Velti plc; *Int'l*, pg. 8150
VELTI LIMITED—See Velti plc; *Int'l*, pg. 8150
VELTI MOBILE MARKETING TECHNOLOGY LLC—See Velti plc; *Int'l*, pg. 8150

VELTI PLATFORMS AND SERVICES LIMITED—See Velti plc; *Int'l*, pg. 8150
VELTI PLC; *Int'l*, pg. 8150
VELTI S.A.—See Velti plc; *Int'l*, pg. 8150
VELTI UKRAINE MOBILE MARKETING SERVICES LLC—See Velti plc; *Int'l*, pg. 8150
VELTRA CORP.; *Int'l*, pg. 8150
VELUR LAND INVESTMENTS, INC.; *U.S. Private*, pg. 4355
VELUX AMERICA INC.—See VKR Holding A/S; *Int'l*, pg. 8282
VELUX ARGENTINA S.A.—See VKR Holding A/S; *Int'l*, pg. 8282
VELUX A/S—See VKR Holding A/S; *Int'l*, pg. 8282
VELUX AUSTRALIA PTY. LTD.—See VKR Holding A/S; *Int'l*, pg. 8282
VELUX BELGIUM S.A.—See VKR Holding A/S; *Int'l*, pg. 8282
VELUX BOSNA I HERCEGOVINA D.O.O.—See VKR Holding A/S; *Int'l*, pg. 8282
VELUX BULGARIA EOOD—See VKR Holding A/S; *Int'l*, pg. 8282
VELUX CANADA INC.—See VKR Holding A/S; *Int'l*, pg. 8282
VELUX CHILE LIMITADA—See VKR Holding A/S; *Int'l*, pg. 8282
VELUX (CHINA) CO., LTD.—See VKR Holding A/S; *Int'l*, pg. 8282
VELUX COMMERCIAL BRAMO AS—See VKR Holding A/S; *Int'l*, pg. 8282
VELUX COMMERCIAL DOMEX A/S—See VKR Holding A/S; *Int'l*, pg. 8282
VELUX COMPANY LTD.—See VKR Holding A/S; *Int'l*, pg. 8282
VELUX DANMARK A/S—See VKR Holding A/S; *Int'l*, pg. 8282
VELUX DEUTSCHLAND GMBH—See VKR Holding A/S; *Int'l*, pg. 8282
VELUX EESTI OU—See VKR Holding A/S; *Int'l*, pg. 8282
VELUX FRANCE S.A.S.—See VKR Holding A/S; *Int'l*, pg. 8282
VELUX HRVATSKA D.O.O.—See VKR Holding A/S; *Int'l*, pg. 8282
VELUX ITALIA S.P.A.—See VKR Holding A/S; *Int'l*, pg. 8282
VELUX-JAPAN LTD.—See VKR Holding A/S; *Int'l*, pg. 8282
VELUX LATVIA SIA—See VKR Holding A/S; *Int'l*, pg. 8282
VELUX LIETUVA, UAB—See VKR Holding A/S; *Int'l*, pg. 8282
VELUX NEDERLAND B.V.—See VKR Holding A/S; *Int'l*, pg. 8282
VELUX NEW ZEALAND LTD.—See VKR Holding A/S; *Int'l*, pg. 8282
VELUX NORGE AS—See VKR Holding A/S; *Int'l*, pg. 8282
VELUX OSTERREICH GMBH—See VKR Holding A/S; *Int'l*, pg. 8282
VELUX POLSKA SP. Z O.O.—See VKR Holding A/S; *Int'l*, pg. 8282
VELUX PORTUGAL, LDA.—See VKR Holding A/S; *Int'l*, pg. 8282
VELUX SCHWEIZ AG—See VKR Holding A/S; *Int'l*, pg. 8282
VELUX SLOVENIJA D.O.O.—See VKR Holding A/S; *Int'l*, pg. 8282
VELUX SLOVENSKO SPOL. S.R.O.—See VKR Holding A/S; *Int'l*, pg. 8282
VELUX SPAIN, S.A.—See VKR Holding A/S; *Int'l*, pg. 8282
VELUX SRBIJA D.O.O.—See VKR Holding A/S; *Int'l*, pg. 8282
VELUX SUOMI OY—See VKR Holding A/S; *Int'l*, pg. 8282
VELUX SVENSKA AB—See VKR Holding A/S; *Int'l*, pg. 8282
VELVAC INCORPORATED—See The Eastern Company; *U.S. Public*, pg. 2069
VELVA LIQUIDS (NORTH SHIELDS) LTD.—See Simon Group plc; *Int'l*, pg. 6932
VELVET DRIVE—See Regal Rexnord Corporation; *U.S. Public*, pg. 1774
VELVET ICE CREAM COMPANY INC.; *U.S. Private*, pg. 4355
VELVET, LLC—See Adastria Co., Ltd.; *Int'l*, pg. 126
VEMA B.V.—See Newmark Security Plc; *Int'l*, pg. 5235
VE.MA.C. SRL—See The Middleby Corporation; *U.S. Public*, pg. 2115
VEMAC SRL—See Compagnie de Saint-Gobain SA; *Int'l*, pg. 1737
VEMANTI GROUP, INC.; *U.S. Public*, pg. 2277
VEMDALENS SPORTAFFARER & SKIDUTHYRNING AB—See SkiStar AB; *Int'l*, pg. 6990
VEME OY—See Purso Group Oy; *Int'l*, pg. 6123
V-EMPOWER, INC.; *U.S. Private*, pg. 4327
V-EMPOWER SOLUTIONS PVT., LTD.—See V-Empower, Inc.; *U.S. Private*, pg. 4328
VENABLE LLP; *U.S. Private*, pg. 4355
VENABLES, BELL & PARTNERS; *U.S. Private*, pg. 4355
VENAC A.D.; *Int'l*, pg. 8150
VENADO OIL & GAS, LLC; *U.S. Private*, pg. 4355

VENADO WIND FARM, LLC—See E.ON SE; *Int'l*, pg. 2260
VENAFI, INC.—See CyberArk Software Ltd.; *Int'l*, pg. 1892
VENAIR A/S—See Kemp & Lauritzen A/S; *Int'l*, pg. 4125
VENANCO AG—See Hansa Chemie International AG; *Int'l*, pg. 3259
VENATOR GROUP—See Huntsman Corporation; *U.S. Public*, pg. 1075
VENATOR MATERIALS PLC—See Huntsman Corporation; *U.S. Public*, pg. 1075
VENCANNA VENTURES INC.; *Int'l*, pg. 8150
VENCAP INDUSTRIER AB—See Grimaldi Industri AB; *Int'l*, pg. 3086
VENCAP TECHNOLOGIES, LLC; *U.S. Private*, pg. 4356
VENCHURS PACKAGING, INC.; *U.S. Private*, pg. 4356
VENCLOSE, INC.—See Becton, Dickinson & Company; *U.S. Public*, pg. 292
VENCO FARMACEUTICA S.A.—See Merck & Co., Inc.; *U.S. Public*, pg. 1421
VENCOR INTERNATIONAL, INC.; *U.S. Private*, pg. 4356
VENDA LIMITED—See Oracle Corporation; *U.S. Public*, pg. 1611
VENDAVO, INC.—See Francisco Partners Management, LP; *U.S. Private*, pg. 1592
VENDEMORE NORDIC AB—See Ratos AB; *Int'l*, pg. 6218
VENDETTA MINING CORP.; *Int'l*, pg. 8150
VENDETTI MOTORS INC.; *U.S. Private*, pg. 4356
VEND FOOD SERVICES INC.; *U.S. Private*, pg. 4356
VENDIG AB—See Lagercrantz Group AB; *Int'l*, pg. 4395
VENDIGITAL LIMITED—See Siemens Aktiengesellschaft; *Int'l*, pg. 6901
VENDING AUTOMATER APS—See Nayax Ltd.; *Int'l*, pg. 5178
VENDING MANAGEMENT SERVICES LTD—See COCA-COLA EUROPACIFIC PARTNERS PLC; *Int'l*, pg. 1684
VENDING TIMES INC.—See Networld Alliance, LLC; *U.S. Private*, pg. 2889
VENDINI, INC.—See AudienceView Ticketing Corporation; *Int'l*, pg. 701
VENDIO SERVICES, INC.—See Alibaba Group Holding Limited; *Int'l*, pg. 326
VEND MART INC.; *U.S. Private*, pg. 4356
VENDO IBERIA, S.A.—See Sanden Corporation; *Int'l*, pg. 6525
VENDOMATIC INC.; *U.S. Private*, pg. 4356
VENDOME GROUP, LLC—See Conversion Capital Partners Ltd.; *Int'l*, pg. 1787
VENDOR CREDENTIALING SERVICE LLC—See Clearlake Capital Group, L.P.; *U.S. Private*, pg. 937
VENDOR CREDENTIALING SERVICE LLC—See SkyKnight Capital LLC; *U.S. Private*, pg. 3685
VENDORIN, INC.—See Corcentric, Inc.; *U.S. Private*, pg. 1047
VENDORMATE, INC.—See Temasek Holdings (Private) Limited; *Int'l*, pg. 7547
VENDORNET, INC.—See eBay Inc.; *U.S. Public*, pg. 709
VENDOR PUBLICIDAD EXTERIOR S DE RL DE CV—See National Amusements, Inc.; *U.S. Private*, pg. 2844
VENDOR SERVICE CO., LTD.—See Mitsui & Co., Ltd.; *Int'l*, pg. 4980
VENDORS EXCHANGE INTERNATIONAL, INC.; *U.S. Private*, pg. 4356
VENDORS SUPPLY COMPANY INC.; *U.S. Private*, pg. 4356
VENDWEB.COM—See American Green, Inc.; *U.S. Public*, pg. 103
VENEASISTENCIA, C.A.—See MAPFRE S.A.; *Int'l*, pg. 4684
VENEER TECHNOLOGIES INC.; *U.S. Private*, pg. 4356
VENEGAS CONSTRUCTION CORP.; *U.S. Private*, pg. 4356
VENE INTERNATIONAL GMBH—See freenet AG; *Int'l*, pg. 2770
VENERABLE VENTURES LTD.; *Int'l*, pg. 8150
VENERA D.O.O.; *Int'l*, pg. 8150
V ENERGY S.A.—See TotalEnergies SE; *Int'l*, pg. 7844
VENETA BLINDS PTY LTD.—See Nien Made Enterprise Co., Ltd.; *Int'l*, pg. 5280
VENETA B.V.—See Nien Made Enterprise Co., Ltd.; *Int'l*, pg. 5280
VENETEL SERVICIOS PUBLICITARIOS, S.A.—See Grupo Televisa, S.A.B.; *Int'l*, pg. 3136
VENETIAN BLIND & FLOOR; *U.S. Private*, pg. 4356
VENETIAN CASINO RESORT, LLC—See Las Vegas Sands Corp.; *U.S. Public*, pg. 1293
VENETIAN MARKETING SERVICES LIMITED—See Las Vegas Sands Corp.; *U.S. Public*, pg. 1293
VENEZCO, INC—See Fluor Corporation; *U.S. Public*, pg. 859
VENEZIA DESIGN INC.; *U.S. Private*, pg. 4356
VENEZIA HAULING INC.; *U.S. Private*, pg. 4356
VENEZIANA GAS S.P.A.—See Eni S.p.A.; *Int'l*, pg. 2437
VENEZIA TERMINAL PASSEGGERI S.P.A.—See Carnival Corporation; *U.S. Public*, pg. 438
VENEZOLANA DE LIMPIEZAS INDUSTRIALES, C.A.—See ACS, Actividades de Construccion y Servicios, S.A.; *Int'l*, pg. 117
VENEZUELA HOLDINGS (BVI) LTD.—See Rusoro Mining Ltd.; *Int'l*, pg. 6429

VENGROFF WILLIAMS, INC.; *U.S. Private*, pg. 4356
THE VENICE AUCTION COMPANY, INC.; *U.S. Private*, pg. 4130
VENICE ENERGY SERVICES COMPANY, L.L.C.—See Targa Resources Corp.; *U.S. Public*, pg. 1982
VENICE FAMILY CLINIC; *U.S. Private*, pg. 4356
VENICE GOLF ASSOCIATION, INC.; *U.S. Private*, pg. 4356
VENICE GONDOLIER SUN—See Sun Coast Media Group, Inc.; *U.S. Private*, pg. 3862
VENICE HMA, INC.—See Community Health Systems, Inc.; *U.S. Public*, pg. 557
VENICE SIMPLON-ORIENT-EXPRESS DEUTSCHLAND GMBH—See LVMH Moet Hennessy Louis Vuitton SE; *Int'l*, pg. 4591
VENICE SIMPLON-ORIENT-EXPRESS INC.—See LVMH Moet Hennessy Louis Vuitton SE; *Int'l*, pg. 4591
VENICE SIMPLON-ORIENT-EXPRESS LTD.—See LVMH Moet Hennessy Louis Vuitton SE; *Int'l*, pg. 4591
VENICE SIMPLON-ORIENT-EXPRESS VOYAGES S.A.—See LVMH Moet Hennessy Louis Vuitton SE; *Int'l*, pg. 4591
VENIGROS LIMITED—See Hayleys PLC; *Int'l*, pg. 3291
VENIO LLC—See Lovell Minnick Partners LLC; *U.S. Private*, pg. 2503
VENIQUE, INC.—See Sally Beauty Holdings, Inc.; *U.S. Public*, pg. 1839
VENISON ROTORUA LIMITED—See Silver Fern Farms Limited; *Int'l*, pg. 6923
VENITI, INC.—See Boston Scientific Corporation; *U.S. Public*, pg. 375
VENIX CO., LTD.—See Sanwa Holdings Corporation; *Int'l*, pg. 6561
VENKEL LTD.; *U.S. Private*, pg. 4356
VENKY'S (INDIA) LTD.; *Int'l*, pg. 8150
VENLON ENTERPRISES LIMITED; *Int'l*, pg. 8150
VENLOP B.V.—See Bong AB; *Int'l*, pg. 1107
VENMAN S.A.—See Mevaco S.A.; *Int'l*, pg. 4868
VENMAR VENTILATION ULC—See Melrose Industries PLC; *Int'l*, pg. 4813
VENMO INC.—See eBay Inc.; *U.S. Public*, pg. 709
VENNEBERG INSURANCE, INC.—See Caisse de Depot et Placement du Quebec; *Int'l*, pg. 1257
VENNEBERG INSURANCE, INC.—See KKR & Co. Inc.; *U.S. Public*, pg. 1266
VENNERBECK, STERN, LEACH; *U.S. Private*, pg. 4356
VENNERS LTD.—See Christie Group plc; *Int'l*, pg. 1587
VENNERS SYSTEMS & SERVICES CORPORATION—See Christie Group plc; *Int'l*, pg. 1587
VENNERSYS LIMITED—See Christie Group plc; *Int'l*, pg. 1587
VENNERSYS LTD.—See Christie Group plc; *Int'l*, pg. 1587
VENN LIFE SCIENCES HOLDINGS PLC—See Open Orphan plc; *Int'l*, pg. 5596
VENN LIFE SCIENCES (IRELAND) LIMITED—See Open Orphan plc; *Int'l*, pg. 5596
VENN LIFE SCIENCES UK LIMITED—See Open Orphan plc; *Int'l*, pg. 5596
VENN PARTNERS LLP—See ESR Group Limited; *Int'l*, pg. 2508
VENN SYNERGIE S.A.S—See Open Orphan plc; *Int'l*, pg. 5596
VENOM PRODUCTS, LLC; *U.S. Private*, pg. 4356
VENOSAN NORTH AMERICA, INC.—See Ames Walker International Inc.; *U.S. Private*, pg. 262
VENQUEST CAPITAL PARTNERS LLC; *U.S. Private*, pg. 4356
VENROCK ASSOCIATES; *U.S. Private*, pg. 4356
VENROCK ASSOCIATES—See Venrock Associates; *U.S. Private*, pg. 4357
VENRO PETROLEUM CORPORATION; *U.S. Private*, pg. 4356
V-ENS CO. LTD.—See LG Corp.; *Int'l*, pg. 4475
VENSHORE MECHANICAL LTD.; *Int'l*, pg. 8150
VENSTAR, INC.—See Daikin Industries, Ltd.; *Int'l*, pg. 1936
VENSUN PHARMACEUTICALS INC.—See Strides Pharma Science Limited; *Int'l*, pg. 7241
VENSURE EMPLOYER SERVICES, INC.; *U.S. Private*, pg. 4357
VENSYS ENERGY AG—See Xinjiang Goldwind Science & Technology Co., Ltd.; *Int'l*, pg. 8531
VENTA GLOBAL, INC.; *U.S. Private*, pg. 4357
VENT-ALARM CORPORATION; *U.S. Private*, pg. 4357
VENTAMATIC LTD.; *U.S. Private*, pg. 4357
VENTANA BEKLEIDUNGSFABRIKATION GMBH—See Li & Fung Limited; *Int'l*, pg. 4481
VENTANA DESIGN S.L.—See Inles d.d.; *Int'l*, pg. 3705
VENTANA MEDICAL SYSTEMS, INC.—See Roche Holding AG; *Int'l*, pg. 6373
VENTANA MEDICAL SYSTEMS S.A.—See Roche Holding AG; *Int'l*, pg. 6373
VENTANA SURGICAL CENTER, LLC—See Tenet Healthcare Corporation; *U.S. Public*, pg. 2015
VENTANA USA; *U.S. Private*, pg. 4357
VENTAPP GMBH—See G. Siempelkamp GmbH & Co. KG; *Int'l*, pg. 2865

VENTAS AMBERLEIGH, LLC—See Ventas, Inc.; *U.S. Public*, pg. 2279
VENTAS HEALTHCARE PROPERTIES, INC.—See Ventas, Inc.; *U.S. Public*, pg. 2279
VENTAS, INC.; *U.S. Public*, pg. 2277
VENTAS REALTY, LIMITED PARTNERSHIP—See Ventas, Inc.; *U.S. Public*, pg. 2279
VENTAS SSL, INC.—See Ventas, Inc.; *U.S. Public*, pg. 2279
VENT-AXIA LTD.—See Volution Group plc; *Int'l*, pg. 8304
VENTCROFT LTD.—See NKT A/S; *Int'l*, pg. 5391
VENTEC AS—See Instalco AB; *Int'l*, pg. 3723
VENTECH ENGINEERS INC.—See Ventech Inc.; *U.S. Private*, pg. 4357
VENTECH INC.; *U.S. Private*, pg. 4357
VENTECH INVESTMENT CO., INC.—See Ventech Inc.; *U.S. Private*, pg. 4357
VENTECH SOLUTIONS INC.; *U.S. Private*, pg. 4357
VENTECH—See Groupe BPCE; *Int'l*, pg. 3096
VENTELO GMBH—See q.beyond AG; *Int'l*, pg. 6131
VEN-TEL PLASTICS CORPORATION; *U.S. Private*, pg. 4355
VENTEON HOLDINGS, LLC.; *U.S. Private*, pg. 4357
VENTERA CORPORATION—See CI Capital Partners LLC; *U.S. Private*, pg. 896
VENTE-UNIQUE.COM SA—See Cafom SA; *Int'l*, pg. 1250
VENTIA NZ LIMITED—See Ventia Services Group Limited; *Int'l*, pg. 8151
VENTIA PTY LTD—See Apollo Global Management, Inc.; *U.S. Public*, pg. 166
VENTIA SERVICES GROUP LIMITED; *Int'l*, pg. 8151
VENTICENTO S.R.L.—See Relatech S.p.A.; *Int'l*, pg. 6260
VENTIFILT ZRT.—See Videoton Holding Zrt.; *Int'l*, pg. 8191
VENTILATIONSFORBATTRINGAR I MALMO AB—See Instalco AB; *Int'l*, pg. 3723
VENTILEX B.V.—See Electricite de France S.A.; *Int'l*, pg. 2352
VENTIM AB—See Indutrade AB; *Int'l*, pg. 3682
VENTION MEDICAL, INC. - GRAND RAPIDS—See Viant Medical, LLC; *U.S. Private*, pg. 4375
VENTION MEDICAL, INC. - KERRVILLE—See Viant Medical, LLC; *U.S. Private*, pg. 4375
VENTION MEDICAL, INC. - WEST HAVEN—See Viant Medical, LLC; *U.S. Private*, pg. 4375
VENTIV TECHNOLOGY INC.—See TA Associates, Inc.; *U.S. Private*, pg. 3918
VENTIV TECHNOLOGY—See Symphony Technology Group, LLC; *U.S. Private*, pg. 3902
VENTOS S.A.; *Int'l*, pg. 8151
VENTOTECH AB—See Volati AB; *Int'l*, pg. 8301
VENTRA ANGOLA, LLC—See Flex-N-Gate Corporation; *U.S. Private*, pg. 1543
VENTRA EVART, LLC—See Flex-N-Gate Corporation; *U.S. Private*, pg. 1543
VENTRA IONIA MAIN, LLC—See Flex-N-Gate Corporation; *U.S. Private*, pg. 1543
VENTRA LLC GRAND RAPIDS PLANT 5—See Flex-N-Gate Corporation; *U.S. Private*, pg. 1543
VENTRA PLASTICS - PETERBOROUGH—See Flex-N-Gate Corporation; *U.S. Private*, pg. 1543
VENTRAQ CORPORATION—See StoneCalibre, LLC; *U.S. Private*, pg. 3828
VENTRA SALEM, LLC; *U.S. Private*, pg. 4357
VENTREX AUTOMOTIVE GMBH—See Aalberts N.V.; *Int'l*, pg. 36
VENTRIPOINT DIAGNOSTICS LTD.; *Int'l*, pg. 8151
VENT-RITE VALVE CORPORATION; *U.S. Private*, pg. 4357
VENTROLLA LIMITED—See Quanex Building Products Corp.; *U.S. Public*, pg. 1750
VENTSPILS GASES LTD—See StealthGas Inc.; *Int'l*, pg. 7188
VENTSPILS NAFTA TERMINALS—See Vitol Holding B.V.; *Int'l*, pg. 8260
VENTURA ASSOCIATES INTERNATIONAL LLC; *U.S. Private*, pg. 4357
VENTURA BEACH MARRIOTT—See Brighton Management LLC; *U.S. Private*, pg. 652
VENTURA BUS COMPANY PTY LTD—See Ventura Bus Lines Pty Ltd; *Int'l*, pg. 8151
VENTURA BUS LINES PTY LTD; *Int'l*, pg. 8151
VENTURA CANNABIS AND WELLNESS CORP.; *U.S. Public*, pg. 2279
VENTURA COASTAL LLC; *U.S. Private*, pg. 4357
VENTURA COUNTY CREDIT UNION; *U.S. Private*, pg. 4357
VENTURA COUNTY RAILROAD COMPANY—See Brookfield Infrastructure Partners L.P.; *Int'l*, pg. 1193
VENTURA COUNTY RAILROAD COMPANY—See GIC Pte. Ltd.; *Int'l*, pg. 2967
VENTURA COUNTY STAR, LLC—See Gannett Co., Inc.; *U.S. Public*, pg. 898
VENTURA ENDOSCOPY CENTER PARTNERS, LLC—See Tenet Healthcare Corporation; *U.S. Public*, pg. 2015
VENTURA GROUP LIMITED—See NEXT plc; *Int'l*, pg. 5248
VENTURA GUARANTY LIMITED; *Int'l*, pg. 8151

VENTURA HEALTH PTY LTD—See EBOS Group Limited; *Int'l*, pg. 2286
VENTURA PACIFIC INSURANCE SERVICES—See GTCR LLC; *U.S. Private*, pg. 1804
VENTURA PROPERTY MANAGEMENT, LLC—See Morgan Stanley; *U.S. Public*, pg. 1475
VENTURA PUBLISHING LTD—See Pearson plc; *Int'l*, pg. 5778
VENTURA TEXTILES LIMITED - NASHIK WORKS—See Ventura Textiles Limited; *Int'l*, pg. 8151
VENTURA TEXTILES LIMITED; *Int'l*, pg. 8151
VENTURA WATCH AG—See Herald Holdings Limited; *Int'l*, pg. 3358
VENTURCAP INVESTMENT GROUP V LLC; *U.S. Private*, pg. 4357
VENTURE AEROBEARINGS LLC—See SKF AB; *Int'l*, pg. 6985
VENTURE AUTOMATION & ENGINEERING PTE. LTD.—See Beng Kuang Marine Limited; *Int'l*, pg. 973
VENTUREAXESS GROUP LIMITED; *Int'l*, pg. 8152
VENTURE CAPITAL BANK BSC—See Esterad Investment Company BSC; *Int'l*, pg. 2518
VENTURE CAR WASH—See Car Wash Partners, Inc.; *U.S. Private*, pg. 748
VENTURE COMMUNICATIONS LTD.; *Int'l*, pg. 8151
VENTURE CONSTRUCTION COMPANY INC.; *U.S. Private*, pg. 4357
VENTURE CORPORATION LIMITED; *Int'l*, pg. 8151
VENTURE DEVELOPMENT CORP.; *U.S. Private*, pg. 4357
VENTUREDYNE, LTD.; *U.S. Private*, pg. 4358
VENTURE ELECTRONICS SERVICES (MALAYSIA) SDN BHD—See Venture Corporation Limited; *Int'l*, pg. 8152
VENTURE ELECTRONICS (SHANGHAI) CO., LTD—See Venture Corporation Limited; *Int'l*, pg. 8152
VENTURE ELECTRONICS (SHENZHEN) CO., LTD—See Venture Corporation Limited; *Int'l*, pg. 8152
VENTURE ELECTRONICS SOLUTIONS PTE LTD—See Venture Corporation Limited; *Int'l*, pg. 8152
VENTURE ELECTRONICS SPAIN S.L.—See Venture Corporation Limited; *Int'l*, pg. 8152
VENTURE ENGINEERING & CONSTRUCTION; *U.S. Private*, pg. 4357
VENTURE ENTERPRISE INNOVATION, INC.—See Venture Corporation Limited; *Int'l*, pg. 8152
VENTURE EXPRESS, INC.; *U.S. Private*, pg. 4357
VENTURE FOR AMERICA; *U.S. Private*, pg. 4358
VENTUREFORTH, INC.; *U.S. Private*, pg. 4358
VENTURE GES SINGAPORE PTE. LTD.—See Venture Corporation Limited; *Int'l*, pg. 8151
VENTURE INC OF BEAUFORT; *U.S. Private*, pg. 4358
VENTURE INCORPORATION PCL; *Int'l*, pg. 8152
VENTURE INFORMATION MANAGEMENT LTD.—See Sword Group SE; *Int'l*, pg. 7376
VENTURE LIFE GROUP PLC; *Int'l*, pg. 8152
VENTURE LIGHTING EUROPE LTD.—See Saratoga Partners L.P.; *U.S. Private*, pg. 3549
VENTURE LIGHTING INDIA LTD.; *Int'l*, pg. 8152
VENTURE LIGHTING INTERNATIONAL FZE—See Saratoga Partners L.P.; *U.S. Private*, pg. 3550
VENTURE LIGHTING INTERNATIONAL, INC.—See Saratoga Partners L.P.; *U.S. Private*, pg. 3549
VENTURE LIGHTING SOUTH AFRICA (PTY.) LTD.—See Saratoga Partners L.P.; *U.S. Private*, pg. 3550
VENTURE LOGISTICS S.A. DE C.V.—See Deutsche Post AG; *Int'l*, pg. 2083
VENTURE MEASUREMENT COMPANY LLC—See Fortive Corporation; *U.S. Public*, pg. 872
VENTURE MINERALS LIMITED; *Int'l*, pg. 8152
VENTURENET, INC.; *U.S. Private*, pg. 4358
VENTURE NORTH SEA GAS LIMITED—See Centrica plc; *Int'l*, pg. 1413
VENTURE PIPE & SUPPLY; *U.S. Private*, pg. 4358
VENTURE PRODUCTS, INC.—See The Toro Company; *U.S. Public*, pg. 2135
VENTURE REALTY GROUP; *U.S. Private*, pg. 4358
VENTURE REPUBLIC INC.; *Int'l*, pg. 8152
VENTURE REVITALIZE INVESTMENT, INC.; *Int'l*, pg. 8152
VENTURES ASSOCIATES, INC.—See Naka's, Inc.; *U.S. Private*, pg. 2831
VENTURES HUB SP. Z.O.O.—See IQ Partners S.A.; *Int'l*, pg. 3803
VENTURE SOLAR, LLC; *U.S. Private*, pg. 4358
VENTURE SOLUTIONS INC.—See Taylor Corporation; *U.S. Private*, pg. 3939
VENTURE SOUTH DISTRIBUTORS; *U.S. Private*, pg. 4358
@VENTURES—See Steel Connect, Inc.; *U.S. Public*, pg. 1941
VENTURE TAPE CORP.—See 3M Company; *U.S. Public*, pg. 6
VENTURETECH ALLIANCE HOLDINGS, LLC—See Taiwan Semiconductor Manufacturing Company Ltd.; *Int'l*, pg. 7424
VENTURE TECHNOLOGIES, INC.—See CVC Capital Partners SICAV-FIS S.A.; *Int'l*, pg. 1883
VENTURETEC ROTATING SYSTEMS GMBH—See Berndorf AG; *Int'l*, pg. 987

VENTURI AUTOMOBILES S.A.M.; *Int'l*, pg. 8152
VENTURI, INC.; *U.S. Private*, pg. 4358
VENTURI RESTORATION - IRVINE—See Franklin Resources, Inc.; *U.S. Public*, pg. 879
VENTURITY FINANCIAL PARTNERS; *U.S. Private*, pg. 4358
VENTURO TECHNOLOGIES S.A.R.L.—See Corpay, Inc.; *U.S. Public*, pg. 580
VENTUS VCT PLC; *Int'l*, pg. 8152
VENTYX ASIA INC.—See ABB Ltd.; *Int'l*, pg. 52
VENTYX BARRANQUILLA—See ABB Ltd.; *Int'l*, pg. 52
VENTYX BIOSCIENCES, INC.; *U.S. Public*, pg. 2279
VENTYX FRANCE—See ABB Ltd.; *Int'l*, pg. 52
VENTYX JOHANNESBURG—See ABB Ltd.; *Int'l*, pg. 52
VENTYX LIMA—See ABB Ltd.; *Int'l*, pg. 52
VENTYX MANAGED SERVICES, INC.—See ABB Ltd.; *Int'l*, pg. 52
VENTYX POLAND—See ABB Ltd.; *Int'l*, pg. 52
VENTYX USA, INC.—See ABB Ltd.; *Int'l*, pg. 52
VENUE DRIVER, LLC—See Sphere Entertainment Co.; *U.S. Public*, pg. 1918
VENUE OF SCOTTSDALE; *U.S. Private*, pg. 4358
VENUEPOINT AB—See Egmont Fonden; *Int'l*, pg. 2326
VENUEPOINT AS—See Egmont Fonden; *Int'l*, pg. 2326
VENUSA DE MEXICO, S.A. DE C.V.—See Integer Holdings Corporation; *U.S. Public*, pg. 1135
VENUSA, LTD.—See Integer Holdings Corporation; *U.S. Public*, pg. 1135
VENUS CAPITAL CORPORATION SDN. BHD.—See Lum Chang Holdings Limited; *Int'l*, pg. 4577
VENUS CONCEPT ARGENTINA SA—See Venus Concept Inc.; *Int'l*, pg. 8152
VENUS CONCEPT INC.; *Int'l*, pg. 8152
VENUS CONCEPT KOREA LTD.—See Venus Concept Inc.; *Int'l*, pg. 8152
VENUS CONCEPT UK LIMITED—See Venus Concept Inc.; *Int'l*, pg. 8152
VENUS CONSOLIDATED (PVT.) LTD.—See Raigam Marketing Services (Pvt) Ltd.; *Int'l*, pg. 6188
VENUS JSC; *Int'l*, pg. 8152
VENUS LABORATORIES INC. - EASTERN DIVISION—See Venus Laboratories Inc.; *U.S. Private*, pg. 4358
VENUS LABORATORIES INC.; *U.S. Private*, pg. 4358
VENUS LABORATORIES INC. - SOUTH EASTERN DIVISION—See Venus Laboratories Inc.; *U.S. Private*, pg. 4358
VENUS LABORATORIES INC. - WESTERN DIVISION—See Venus Laboratories Inc.; *U.S. Private*, pg. 4358
VENUS MEDTECH (HANGZHOU) INC.; *Int'l*, pg. 8152
VENUS METALS CORPORATION; *Int'l*, pg. 8152
VENUS PHARMA GMBH—See Venus Remedies Limited; *Int'l*, pg. 8153
VENUS PIPES & TUBES LIMITED; *Int'l*, pg. 8152
VENUS REMEDIES LIMITED; *Int'l*, pg. 8153
VENUS SWIMWEAR, INC.—See Golden Gate Capital Management II, LLC; *U.S. Private*, pg. 1731
VENUSTECH GROUP INC.; *Int'l*, pg. 8153
VENUS THREAD, INC.—See Saha-Union Public Company Limited; *Int'l*, pg. 6480
VENUTI & ASSOCIATES—See Northwest Plan Services, Inc.; *U.S. Private*, pg. 2961
VENUWORKS; *U.S. Private*, pg. 4358
VENYU SOLUTIONS INC.—See Astra Capital Management LLC; *U.S. Private*, pg. 361
VENZEE TECHNOLOGIES INC.; *Int'l*, pg. 8153
VEOLIA AGUA S.A.—See Veolia Environnement S.A.; *Int'l*, pg. 8161
VEOLIA APA SERVICII SRL—See Veolia Environnement S.A.; *Int'l*, pg. 8156
VEOLIA DEUTSCHLAND GMBH—See Veolia Environnement S.A.; *Int'l*, pg. 8161
VEOLIA EAU - COMPAGNIE GENERALE DES EAUX S.C.A.—See Veolia Environnement S.A.; *Int'l*, pg. 8156
VEOLIA ENERGIA POLSKA S.A.—See Veolia Environnement S.A.; *Int'l*, pg. 8156
VEOLIA ENERGIA SLOVENSKO A.S.—See Veolia Environnement S.A.; *Int'l*, pg. 8156
VEOLIA ENERGIA VYCHODNE SLOVENSKO, S.R.O.—See Veolia Environnement S.A.; *Int'l*, pg. 8158
VEOLIA ENERGIA WARSZAWA S.A.—See Veolia Environnement S.A.; *Int'l*, pg. 8156
VEOLIA ENERGIE CR A.S.—See Veolia Environnement S.A.; *Int'l*, pg. 8158
VEOLIA ENERGIE PRAHA, A.S.—See Veolia Environnement S.A.; *Int'l*, pg. 8158
VEOLIA ENERGIE—See Veolia Environnement S.A.; *Int'l*, pg. 8156
VEOLIA ENERGY BALTIMORE CORPORATION—See Veolia Environnement S.A.; *Int'l*, pg. 8158
VEOLIA ENERGY BOSTON, INC.—See Veolia Environnement S.A.; *Int'l*, pg. 8158
VEOLIA ENERGY KANSAS CITY, INC.—See Veolia Environnement S.A.; *Int'l*, pg. 8158
VEOLIA ENERGY MISSOURI, INC.—See Veolia Environnement S.A.; *Int'l*, pg. 8158
VEOLIA ENERGY NORTH AMERICA, LLC—See Veolia Environnement S.A.; *Int'l*, pg. 8158

VENZEE TECHNOLOGIES INC.

VEOLIA ENERGY PHILADELPHIA CORPORATION—See Veolia Environnement S.A.; *Int'l*, pg. 8158
VEOLIA ENERGY ROMANIA—See Veolia Environnement S.A.; *Int'l*, pg. 8158
VEOLIA ENERGY TRENTON, L.P.—See Veolia Environnement S.A.; *Int'l*, pg. 8158
VEOLIA ENVIRONMENTAL SERVICES ASIA PTE LTD—See Veolia Environnement S.A.; *Int'l*, pg. 8158
VEOLIA ENVIRONMENTAL SERVICES AUSTRALIA—See Veolia Environnement S.A.; *Int'l*, pg. 8159
VEOLIA ENVIRONMENTAL SERVICES BELGIUM N.V.—See Veolia Environnement S.A.; *Int'l*, pg. 8160
VEOLIA ENVIRONMENTAL SERVICES (CHINA) CO., LTD.—See Veolia Environnement S.A.; *Int'l*, pg. 8159
VEOLIA ENVIRONMENTAL SERVICES EMIRATES LLC—See Al Jaber Group; *Int'l*, pg. 280
VEOLIA ENVIRONMENTAL SERVICES FRANCE—See Veolia Environnement S.A.; *Int'l*, pg. 8160
VEOLIA ENVIRONMENTAL SERVICES (HK) HONG-KONG CO., LTD—See Veolia Environnement S.A.; *Int'l*, pg. 8159
VEOLIA ENVIRONMENTAL SERVICES (IRELAND) LIMITED—See Veolia Environnement S.A.; *Int'l*, pg. 8159
VEOLIA ENVIRONMENTAL SERVICES LIETUVA UAB—See Veolia Environnement S.A.; *Int'l*, pg. 8160
VEOLIA ENVIRONMENTAL SERVICES NORTH AMERICA CORP.—See Veolia Environnement S.A.; *Int'l*, pg. 8160
VEOLIA ENVIRONMENTAL SERVICES QATAR L.L.C.—See Veolia Environnement S.A.; *Int'l*, pg. 8160
VEOLIA ENVIRONMENTAL SERVICES SINGAPORE—See Veolia Environnement S.A.; *Int'l*, pg. 8160
VEOLIA ENVIRONMENTAL SERVICES—See Veolia Environnement S.A.; *Int'l*, pg. 8159
VEOLIA ENVIRONMENTAL SERVICES—See Veolia Environnement S.A.; *Int'l*, pg. 8159
VEOLIA ENVIRONMENTAL SERVICES—See Veolia Environnement S.A.; *Int'l*, pg. 8159
VEOLIA ENVIRONMENTAL SERVICES—See Veolia Environnement S.A.; *Int'l*, pg. 8160
VEOLIA ENVIRONMENTAL SERVICES—See Veolia Environnement S.A.; *Int'l*, pg. 8160
VEOLIA ENVIRONMENTAL SERVICES—See Veolia Environnement S.A.; *Int'l*, pg. 8160
VEOLIA ENVIRONMENTAL SERVICES (UK) PLC—See Veolia Environnement S.A.; *Int'l*, pg. 8159
VEOLIA ENVIRONMENTAL SERVICES UKRAINE—See Veolia Environnement S.A.; *Int'l*, pg. 8160
VEOLIA ENVIRONNEMENT S.A.; *Int'l*, pg. 8153
VEOLIA ENVIRONNEMENT SUISSE S.A.—See Veolia Environnement S.A.; *Int'l*, pg. 8158
VEOLIA ES CANADA INDUSTRIAL SERVICES INC.—See Veolia Environnement S.A.; *Int'l*, pg. 8160
VEOLIA ES INDUSTRIAL SERVICES, INC.—See Veolia Environnement S.A.; *Int'l*, pg. 8160
VEOLIA ESPANA S.L.U.—See Veolia Environnement S.A.; *Int'l*, pg. 8158
VEOLIA ES TECHNICAL SOLUTIONS LLC—See Veolia Environnement S.A.; *Int'l*, pg. 8160
VEOLIA GEBAUDESERVICE DEUTSCHLAND GMBH—See Veolia Environnement S.A.; *Int'l*, pg. 8158
VEOLIA INDUSTRIAL SERVICES, INC.—See Veolia Environnement S.A.; *Int'l*, pg. 8160
VEOLIA INDUSTRIAL SERVICES—See Veolia Environnement S.A.; *Int'l*, pg. 8160
VEOLIA INDUSTRIAL SERVICES WA—See Veolia Environnement S.A.; *Int'l*, pg. 8160
VEOLIA INDUSTRIE DEUTSCHLAND GMBH—See Veolia Environnement S.A.; *Int'l*, pg. 8158
VEOLIA INDUSTRIEDIENSTEN B.V.—See Veolia Environnement S.A.; *Int'l*, pg. 8158
VEOLIA INDUSTRIEPARK DEUTSCHLAND GMBH—See Veolia Environnement S.A.; *Int'l*, pg. 8158
VEOLIA KLARSCHLAMMVERWERTUNG DEUTSCHLAND GMBH—See Veolia Environnement S.A.; *Int'l*, pg. 8158
VEOLIA NEDERLAND BV—See Veolia Environnement S.A.; *Int'l*, pg. 8158
VEOLIA NORDIC AB—See Veolia Environnement S.A.; *Int'l*, pg. 8158
VEOLIA NORTH AMERICA, LLC—See Veolia Environnement S.A.; *Int'l*, pg. 8158
VEOLIA NORTH AMERICA REGENERATION SERVICES LLC—See Veolia Environnement S.A.; *Int'l*, pg. 8158
VEOLIA NUCLEAR SOLUTIONS, INC.—See Veolia Environnement S.A.; *Int'l*, pg. 8158
VEOLIA NV-SA—See Veolia Environnement S.A.; *Int'l*, pg. 8158
VEOLIA PET GERMANY GMBH—See Veolia Environnement S.A.; *Int'l*, pg. 8159
VEOLIA PET SVENSKA AB—See Veolia Environnement S.A.; *Int'l*, pg. 8159
VEOLIA PROPRETE SENEGAL—See Veolia Environnement S.A.; *Int'l*, pg. 8160
VEOLIA PROPRETE—See Veolia Environnement S.A.; *Int'l*, pg. 8159
VEOLIA PROPRETE—See Veolia Environnement S.A.; *Int'l*, pg. 8160

VEOLIA RECYCLING & RECOVERY HOLDINGS ANZ PTY. LTD.—See Veolia Environnement S.A.; *Int'l*, pg. 8160
VEOLIA TERM SA—See Veolia Environnement S.A.; *Int'l*, pg. 8160
VEOLIA TRANSPORTATION, INC.—See Caisse des Depots et Consignations; *Int'l*, pg. 1258
VEOLIA TRANSPORT AUSTRALASIA—See Caisse des Depots et Consignations; *Int'l*, pg. 1259
VEOLIA TRANSPORT AUSTRALIA PTY LTD—See Caisse des Depots et Consignations; *Int'l*, pg. 1259
VEOLIA TRANSPORT FINLAND OY—See Caisse des Depots et Consignations; *Int'l*, pg. 1259
VEOLIA TRANSPORT IRELAND—See Caisse des Depots et Consignations; *Int'l*, pg. 1259
VEOLIA TRANSPORT ISRAEL—See Veolia Environnement S.A.; *Int'l*, pg. 8160
VEOLIA TRANSPORT NEDERLAND BV—See Caisse des Depots et Consignations; *Int'l*, pg. 1259
VEOLIA TRANSPORT POLSKA SP. Z O.O. UL.—See Caisse des Depots et Consignations; *Int'l*, pg. 1259
VEOLIA TRANSPORT RATP INDIA PVT. LTD.—See Caisse des Depots et Consignations; *Int'l*, pg. 1259
VEOLIA UMWELTSERVICE & CONSULTING GMBH—See Veolia Environnement S.A.; *Int'l*, pg. 8160
VEOLIA UMWELTSERVICE DUAL GMBH—See Veolia Environnement S.A.; *Int'l*, pg. 8160
VEOLIA UMWELTSERVICE GMBH—See Veolia Environnement S.A.; *Int'l*, pg. 8160
VEOLIA UMWELTSERVICE GMBH—See Veolia Environnement S.A.; *Int'l*, pg. 8160
VEOLIA UMWELTSERVICE INDUSTRIE REINIGUNG GMBH & CO. KG—See Veolia Environnement S.A.; *Int'l*, pg. 8160
VEOLIA UMWELTSERVICE NORD GMBH—See Veolia Environnement S.A.; *Int'l*, pg. 8160
VEOLIA UMWELTSERVICE OST GMBH & CO. KG—See Veolia Environnement S.A.; *Int'l*, pg. 8160
VEOLIA UMWELTSERVICE PET RECYCLING GMBH—See Veolia Environnement S.A.; *Int'l*, pg. 8160
VEOLIA UMWELTSERVICE RESSOURCENMANAGEMENT GMBH—See Veolia Environnement S.A.; *Int'l*, pg. 8160
VEOLIA UMWELTSERVICE SUD GMBH & CO. KG.—See Veolia Environnement S.A.; *Int'l*, pg. 8160
VEOLIA UMWELTSERVICE WERTSTOFFMANAGEMENT GMBH—See Veolia Environnement S.A.; *Int'l*, pg. 8160
VEOLIA UMWELTSERVICE WEST GMBH—See Veolia Environnement S.A.; *Int'l*, pg. 8160
VEOLIA USLUGI DLA SRODOWISKA S.A.—See Veolia Environnement S.A.; *Int'l*, pg. 8160
VEOLIA VERKHER GMBH—See Caisse des Depots et Consignations; *Int'l*, pg. 1259
VEOLIA VIZ ZRT.—See Veolia Environnement S.A.; *Int'l*, pg. 8160
VEOLIA VODA SA—See Veolia Environnement S.A.; *Int'l*, pg. 8160
VEOLIA WASSER DEUTSCHLAND GMBH—See Veolia Environnement S.A.; *Int'l*, pg. 8160
VEOLIA WASSER GMBH—See Veolia Environnement S.A.; *Int'l*, pg. 8160
VEOLIA WASSER STORKOW GMBH—See Veolia Environnement S.A.; *Int'l*, pg. 8160
VEOLIA WASSER WAGENFELD GMBH—See Veolia Environnement S.A.; *Int'l*, pg. 8161
VEOLIA WATER AB—See Veolia Environnement S.A.; *Int'l*, pg. 8161
VEOLIA WATER ARMENIA—See Veolia Environnement S.A.; *Int'l*, pg. 8161
VEOLIA WATER ASIA PACIFIC LTD—See Veolia Environnement S.A.; *Int'l*, pg. 8161
VEOLIA WATER AUSTRALIA—See Veolia Environnement S.A.; *Int'l*, pg. 8161
VEOLIA WATER BRASIL—See Veolia Environnement S.A.; *Int'l*, pg. 8161
VEOLIA WATER CANADA INC.—See Veolia Environnement S.A.; *Int'l*, pg. 8163
VEOLIA WATER CZECH REPUBLIC—See Veolia Environnement S.A.; *Int'l*, pg. 8161
VEOLIA WATER FRANCE—See Veolia Environnement S.A.; *Int'l*, pg. 8161
VEOLIA WATER - GABON—See Veolia Environnement S.A.; *Int'l*, pg. 8161
VEOLIA WATER INDIANAPOLIS, LLC; *U.S. Private*, pg. 4358
VEOLIA WATER INDIA PVT LTD—See Veolia Environnement S.A.; *Int'l*, pg. 8161
VEOLIA WATER INDUSTRIAL OUTSOURCING LIMITED—See Veolia Environnement S.A.; *Int'l*, pg. 8163
VEOLIA WATER IRELAND—See Veolia Environnement S.A.; *Int'l*, pg. 8161
VEOLIA WATER ISRAEL—See Veolia Environnement S.A.; *Int'l*, pg. 8161
VEOLIA WATER JAPAN K.K.—See Veolia Environnement S.A.; *Int'l*, pg. 8161
VEOLIA WATER MALAYSIA HOLDING SDN BHD—See Veolia Environnement S.A.; *Int'l*, pg. 8161

CORPORATE AFFILIATIONS

VEOLIA WATER NORTH AMERICA OPERATING SERVICES, LLC—See Veolia Environnement S.A.; *Int'l*, pg. 8163
VEOLIA WATER SA—See Veolia Environnement S.A.; *Int'l*, pg. 8161
VEOLIA WATER SOLUTIONS & TECHNOLOGIES ARGENTINA—See Veolia Environnement S.A.; *Int'l*, pg. 8162
VEOLIA WATER SOLUTIONS & TECHNOLOGIES (BEIJING) CO., LTD.—See Veolia Environnement S.A.; *Int'l*, pg. 8162
VEOLIA WATER SOLUTIONS & TECHNOLOGIES BRAZIL LTDA.—See Veolia Environnement S.A.; *Int'l*, pg. 8162
VEOLIA WATER SOLUTIONS & TECHNOLOGIES CANADA INC.—See Veolia Environnement S.A.; *Int'l*, pg. 8163
VEOLIA WATER SOLUTIONS & TECHNOLOGIES CHILE LIMITADA—See Veolia Environnement S.A.; *Int'l*, pg. 8162
VEOLIA WATER SOLUTIONS & TECHNOLOGIES CHINA—See Veolia Environnement S.A.; *Int'l*, pg. 8162
VEOLIA WATER SOLUTIONS TECHNOLOGIES DEUTSCHLAND HOLDING GMBH—See Veolia Environnement S.A.; *Int'l*, pg. 8163
VEOLIA WATER SOLUTIONS & TECHNOLOGIES EGYPT—See Veolia Environnement S.A.; *Int'l*, pg. 8162
VEOLIA WATER SOLUTIONS & TECHNOLOGIES IBERICA—See Veolia Environnement S.A.; *Int'l*, pg. 8162
VEOLIA WATER SOLUTIONS & TECHNOLOGIES ITALIA S.R.L.—See Veolia Environnement S.A.; *Int'l*, pg. 8162
VEOLIA WATER SOLUTIONS & TECHNOLOGIES JAPAN K.K.—See Veolia Environnement S.A.; *Int'l*, pg. 8162
VEOLIA WATER SOLUTIONS & TECHNOLOGIES LEBANON—See Veolia Environnement S.A.; *Int'l*, pg. 8162
VEOLIA WATER SOLUTIONS & TECHNOLOGIES LTD—See Veolia Environnement S.A.; *Int'l*, pg. 8162
VEOLIA WATER SOLUTIONS & TECHNOLOGIES MAGYARORSZAG ZRT.—See Veolia Environnement S.A.; *Int'l*, pg. 8162
VEOLIA WATER SOLUTIONS & TECHNOLOGIES (NEW ZEALAND) LIMITED—See Veolia Environnement S.A.; *Int'l*, pg. 8162
VEOLIA WATER SOLUTIONS & TECHNOLOGIES NORDIC REGION—See Veolia Environnement S.A.; *Int'l*, pg. 8162
VEOLIA WATER SOLUTIONS & TECHNOLOGIES (PHILIPPINES), INC.—See Veolia Environnement S.A.; *Int'l*, pg. 8162
VEOLIA WATER SOLUTIONS & TECHNOLOGIES PTY LIMITED—See Veolia Environnement S.A.; *Int'l*, pg. 8162
VEOLIA WATER SOLUTIONS & TECHNOLOGIES PUERTO RICO—See Veolia Environnement S.A.; *Int'l*, pg. 8163
VEOLIA WATER SOLUTIONS & TECHNOLOGIES ROMANIA SRL—See Veolia Environnement S.A.; *Int'l*, pg. 8162
VEOLIA WATER SOLUTIONS & TECHNOLOGIES SAUDI ARABIA—See Veolia Environnement S.A.; *Int'l*, pg. 8162
VEOLIA WATER SOLUTIONS TECHNOLOGIES (SEA) PTE LTD—See Veolia Environnement S.A.; *Int'l*, pg. 8163
VEOLIA WATER SOLUTIONS & TECHNOLOGIES (SEA) PTE LTD—See Veolia Environnement S.A.; *Int'l*, pg. 8162
VEOLIA WATER SOLUTIONS & TECHNOLOGIES (SHANGHAI) CO., LTD.—See Veolia Environnement S.A.; *Int'l*, pg. 8162
VEOLIA WATER SOLUTIONS & TECHNOLOGIES—See Veolia Environnement S.A.; *Int'l*, pg. 8161
VEOLIA WATER SOLUTIONS & TECHNOLOGIES—See Veolia Environnement S.A.; *Int'l*, pg. 8163
VEOLIA WATER SOLUTIONS & TECHNOLOGIES SOUTH AFRICA (PTY) LTD.—See Veolia Environnement S.A.; *Int'l*, pg. 8162
VEOLIA WATER SOLUTIONS & TECHNOLOGIES SOUTH KOREA—See Veolia Environnement S.A.; *Int'l*, pg. 8163
VEOLIA WATER SOLUTIONS & TECHNOLOGIES TAIWAN CORPORATION—See Veolia Environnement S.A.; *Int'l*, pg. 8163
VEOLIA WATER SOLUTIONS & TECHNOLOGIES (THAILAND) LTD.—See Veolia Environnement S.A.; *Int'l*, pg. 8162
VEOLIA WATER SOLUTIONS & TECHNOLOGIES TURKEY—See Veolia Environnement S.A.; *Int'l*, pg. 8163
VEOLIA WATER SOLUTIONS & TECHNOLOGIES VENEZUELA—See Veolia Environnement S.A.; *Int'l*, pg. 8163
VEOLIA WATER STI—See Veolia Environnement S.A.; *Int'l*, pg. 8162
VEOLIA WATER SYSTEMS (GULF) FZC—See Veolia Environnement S.A.; *Int'l*, pg. 8163

VEOLIA WATER SYSTEMS LTD—See Veolia Environnement S.A.; *Int'l*, pg. 8163
VEOLIA WATER SYSTEMS—See Veolia Environnement S.A.; *Int'l*, pg. 8163
VEOLIA WATER SYSTEMS SOUTH ASIA SDN—See Veolia Environnement S.A.; *Int'l*, pg. 8163
VEOLIA WATER SYSTEMS SP. Z O.O.—See Veolia Environnement S.A.; *Int'l*, pg. 8163
VEOLIA WATER SYSTEMS SWITZERLAND—See Veolia Environnement S.A.; *Int'l*, pg. 8163
VEOLIA WATER TECHNOLOGIES BENELUX—See Veolia Environnement S.A.; *Int'l*, pg. 8163
VEOLIA WATER TECHNOLOGIES, INC.—See Veolia Environnement S.A.; *Int'l*, pg. 8163
VEOLIA WATER TECHNOLOGIES SA—See Veolia Environnement S.A.; *Int'l*, pg. 8163
VEOLIA WATER UK PLC—See Veolia Environnement S.A.; *Int'l*, pg. 8163
VEOLIA WODA SP. Z O.O.—See Veolia Environnement S.A.; *Int'l*, pg. 8163
VEONEER, INC.—See SSW Partners LP; *U.S. Private*, pg. 3770
VEON LTD.; *Int'l*, pg. 8163
VEPEMA OY—See Blackstone Inc.; *U.S. Public*, pg. 351
VERA ASSICURAZIONI S.P.A.—See Assicurazioni Generali S.p.A.; *Int'l*, pg. 648
VERABANK, INC.; *U.S. Private*, pg. 4359
VERABANK, N.A.—See VeraBank Inc.; *U.S. Private*, pg. 4359
VERA BRADLEY DESIGNS, INC.—See Vera Bradley, Inc.; *U.S. Public*, pg. 2279
VERA BRADLEY, INC.; *U.S. Public*, pg. 2279
VERA BRADLEY SALES, LLC—See Vera Bradley, Inc.; *U.S. Public*, pg. 2279
VERACEN FUNDS LP; *U.S. Private*, pg. 4359
VERACENTRA, INC.; *U.S. Private*, pg. 4359
VERA CHIMIE DEVELOPPEMENTS S.A.S.—See Floridienne SA; *Int'l*, pg. 2708
VERACITY CONSULTING GROUP, LLC—See Resources Connection, Inc.; *U.S. Public*, pg. 1792
VERACITY CONSULTING, INC.; *U.S. Private*, pg. 4359
VERACITY ENGINEERING; *U.S. Private*, pg. 4359
VERACITY MANAGEMENT GLOBAL, INC.; *U.S. Private*, pg. 4359
VERACITY NETWORK INC.; *U.S. Private*, pg. 4359
VERACITY NETWORKS; *U.S. Private*, pg. 4359
VERACITY RESEARCH CO.—See Trinity Hunt Management, L.P.; *U.S. Private*, pg. 4235
VERACITY SOLUTIONS, INC.; *U.S. Private*, pg. 4359
VERACODE, INC.—See Thoma Bravo, L.P.; *U.S. Private*, pg. 4154
VERACODE LTD—See Thoma Bravo, L.P.; *U.S. Private*, pg. 4154
VERA CRUZ SEGURADORA, S.A.—See MAPFRE S.A.; *Int'l*, pg. 4684
VERACYTE, INC.; *U.S. Public*, pg. 2279
VERADIGM INC.; *U.S. Public*, pg. 2279
VERA FE—See RHI Magnesita N.V.; *Int'l*, pg. 6326
VERA FINANCIAL DESIGNATED ACTIVITY COMPANY—See Assicurazioni Generali S.p.A.; *Int'l*, pg. 648
VERAFIN SOLUTIONS ULC—See Nasdaq, Inc.; *U.S. Public*, pg. 1492
VERA KLIPPAN AB—See Sdiptech AB; *Int'l*, pg. 6659
VERALIA S.A.—See Vocento, S.A.; *Int'l*, pg. 8284
VERALLIA ARGENTINA—See Apollo Global Management, Inc.; *U.S. Public*, pg. 167
VERALLIA CHILE—See Apollo Global Management, Inc.; *U.S. Public*, pg. 167
VERALLIA FRANCE—See Apollo Global Management, Inc.; *U.S. Public*, pg. 167
VERALLIA SA; *Int'l*, pg. 8164
VERALTO CORPORATION; *U.S. Public*, pg. 2280
VERALYTIC INC.; *U.S. Private*, pg. 4359
VERANDA BEACH PATTAYA CO., LTD.—See Veranda Resort Public Company Limited; *Int'l*, pg. 8164
VERANDA CUISINE CO., LTD.—See Veranda Resort Public Company Limited; *Int'l*, pg. 8164
VERANDA HOTEL—See Rogers & Company Limited; *Int'l*, pg. 6383
VERANDA IAS LEARNING SOLUTIONS PRIVATE LIMITED—See Veranda Learning Solutions Ltd.; *Int'l*, pg. 8164
VERANDA LEARNING SOLUTIONS LTD.; *Int'l*, pg. 8164
VERANDA LEISURE & HOSPITALITY LIMITED—See Rogers & Company Limited; *Int'l*, pg. 6383
VERANDA PALMAR BEACH HOTEL—See Rogers & Company Limited; *Int'l*, pg. 6383
VERANDA POINTE AUX BICHES HOTEL—See Rogers & Company Limited; *Int'l*, pg. 6383
VERANDA RACE LEARNING SOLUTIONS PRIVATE LIMITED—See Veranda Learning Solutions Ltd.; *Int'l*, pg. 8164
VERANDA RESORT PUBLIC COMPANY LIMITED; *Int'l*, pg. 8164
VERANDA—See The Hearst Corporation; *U.S. Private*, pg. 4047
VERANEX; *U.S. Private*, pg. 4359

VERAN MEDICAL TECHNOLOGIES, INC.—See Olympus Corporation; *Int'l*, pg. 5558
VERANO ENERGY (SWITZERLAND) AG—See Parex Resources Inc.; *Int'l*, pg. 5741
VERANO HOLDINGS CORP.; *U.S. Public*, pg. 2280
VERANSA GROUP, INC.—See RFE Investment Partners; *U.S. Private*, pg. 3419
VERANTIS CORPORATION—See Tanglewood Investments Inc.; *U.S. Private*, pg. 3931
VERA PROTEZIONE S.P.A.—See Assicurazioni Generali S.p.A.; *Int'l*, pg. 648
VERASTEM, INC.; *U.S. Public*, pg. 2280
VERA SYNTHETIC LIMITED; *Int'l*, pg. 8164
VERATEX, INC.; *U.S. Private*, pg. 4359
VERA THERAPEUTICS, INC.; *U.S. Public*, pg. 2279
VERATHON INC.—See Roper Technologies, Inc.; *U.S. Public*, pg. 1814
VERATHON MEDICAL (AUSTRAILIA) PTY LIMITED—See Roper Technologies, Inc.; *U.S. Public*, pg. 1814
VERATHON MEDICAL (CANADA) ULC—See Roper Technologies, Inc.; *U.S. Public*, pg. 1814
VERATHON MEDICAL (EUROPE) B.V.—See Roper Technologies, Inc.; *U.S. Public*, pg. 1814
VERATHON MEDICAL (FRANCE) S.A.R.L.—See Roper Technologies, Inc.; *U.S. Public*, pg. 1814
VERATTA TECHNOLOGIES INC.—See ARCpoint Inc.; *U.S. Public*, pg. 186
VERA VARLIK YONETIM A.S.—See Bogazici Varlik Yonetim A.S.; *Int'l*, pg. 1100
VERAVIS GMBH—See AGRAVIS Raiffeisen AG; *Int'l*, pg. 216
VERA VITA S.P.A.—See Assicurazioni Generali S.p.A.; *Int'l*, pg. 648
VERA WANG BRIDAL HOUSE LTD.; *U.S. Private*, pg. 4359
VERA WHOLE HEALTH, INC.—See Clayton, Dubilier & Rice, LLC; *U.S. Private*, pg. 928
VERAXX ENGINEERING CORP.—See Sagewind Capital LLC; *U.S. Private*, pg. 3527
VERBAG AG—See Arthur J. Gallagher & Co.; *U.S. Public*, pg. 206
VERBALIZEIT, INC.—See Smartling, Inc.; *U.S. Private*, pg. 3692
VERBALYS—See CNIM Constructions Industrielles de la Mediterranee SA; *Int'l*, pg. 1677
VERBAND DER VEREINE CREDITREFORM E.V.; *Int'l*, pg. 8164
VERBA S.R.L. ADVERTISING—See Omnicom Group Inc.; *U.S. Public*, pg. 1582
VERBA TECHNOLOGIES ASIA PACIFIC PTE LTD.—See Verint Systems Inc.; *U.S. Public*, pg. 2281
VERBA TECHNOLOGIES LIMITED—See Verint Systems Inc.; *U.S. Public*, pg. 2281
VERBATIM AMERICAS, LLC—See CMC Magnetics Corporation; *Int'l*, pg. 1669
VERBATIM ASSET MANAGEMENT LIMITED—See Simplybiz Group plc; *Int'l*, pg. 6934
VERBATIM AUSTRALIA PTY LTD—See CMC Magnetics Corporation; *Int'l*, pg. 1669
VERBATIM CORPORATION—See CMC Magnetics Corporation; *Int'l*, pg. 1669
VERBATIM ESPANA S.A—See CMC Magnetics Corporation; *Int'l*, pg. 1669
VERBATIM GMBH—See CMC Magnetics Corporation; *Int'l*, pg. 1669
VERBATIM (HONG KONG) LIMITED—See CMC Magnetics Corporation; *Int'l*, pg. 1669
VERBATIM ITALIA SPA A SOCIO UNICO—See CMC Magnetics Corporation; *Int'l*, pg. 1669
VERBATIM LIMITED—See CMC Magnetics Corporation; *Int'l*, pg. 1669
VERBATIM MARKETING INDIA PVT. LTD.—See CMC Magnetics Corporation; *Int'l*, pg. 1669
VERBATIM REPORTING SERVICES—See Litigation Services, LLC; *U.S. Public*, pg. 2468
VERBATIM (SHENZHEN) INT'L TRADING CORP. LTD.—See CMC Magnetics Corporation; *Int'l*, pg. 1669
VERBATIM TAIWAN INTERNATIONAL TRADING CORPORATE LTD.—See CMC Magnetics Corporation; *Int'l*, pg. 1669
VERBA VERWALTUNGSGESELLSCHAFT MBH—See UniCredit S.p.A.; *Int'l*, pg. 8041
VERBE—See Publicis Groupe S.A.; *Int'l*, pg. 6112
VERBIO AGRAR GMBH—See Verbio SE; *Int'l*, pg. 8164
VERBIO BITTERFELD GMBH—See Verbio SE; *Int'l*, pg. 8164
VERBIO BITTERFELD GMBH—See Verbio SE; *Int'l*, pg. 8164
VERBIO DIESEL SCHWEDT GMBH & CO. KG—See Verbio SE; *Int'l*, pg. 8164
VERBIO ETHANOL SCHWEDT GMBH & CO. KG—See Verbio SE; *Int'l*, pg. 8164
VERBIO ETHANOL ZORBIG GMBH & CO. KG—See Verbio SE; *Int'l*, pg. 8164
VERBIO LOGISTIK GMBH—See Verbio SE; *Int'l*, pg. 8164
VERBIO NORTH AMERICA CORPORATION—See Verbio SE; *Int'l*, pg. 8164
VERBIO PINNOW GMBH—See Verbio SE; *Int'l*, pg. 8164

VERBIO POLSKA SPOLKA Z O.O.—See Verbio SE; *Int'l*, pg. 8164
VERBIO SCHWEDT GMBH—See Verbio SE; *Int'l*, pg. 8164
VERBIO SE; *Int'l*, pg. 8164
VERBIO ZORBIG GMBH—See Verbio SE; *Int'l*, pg. 8164
VERBIT SOFTWARE LIMITED; *Int'l*, pg. 8165
VERBREC LIMITED; *Int'l*, pg. 8165
VERB TECHNOLOGY COMPANY, INC.; *U.S. Public*, pg. 2280
VERBUND AG; *Int'l*, pg. 8165
VERBUND-AUSTRIAN HYDRO POWER AG—See Verbund AG; *Int'l*, pg. 8165
VERBUND-AUSTRIAN POWER SALES GMBH—See Verbund AG; *Int'l*, pg. 8165
VERBUND-AUSTRIAN POWER TRADING SLOVAKIA, S.R.O.—See Verbund AG; *Int'l*, pg. 8165
VERBUND ENERGY4 BUSINESS GERMANY GMBH—See Verbund AG; *Int'l*, pg. 8165
VERBUND-FINANZIERUNGSSERVICE GMBH—See Verbund AG; *Int'l*, pg. 8165
VERBUND GREEN POWER DEUTSCHLAND GMBH—See Verbund AG; *Int'l*, pg. 8165
VERBUND GREEN POWER DEUTSCHLAND PHOTOVOLTAIK GMBH—See Verbund AG; *Int'l*, pg. 8165
VERBUND GREEN POWER IBERIA, S.L.U.—See Verbund AG; *Int'l*, pg. 8165
VERBUND MANAGEMENT SERVICE GMBH—See Verbund AG; *Int'l*, pg. 8165
VERBUND SALES GMBH—See Verbund AG; *Int'l*, pg. 8165
VERBUND TOURISMUS GMBH—See Verbund AG; *Int'l*, pg. 8165
VERBUND-UMWELTTECHNIK GMBH—See Verbund AG; *Int'l*, pg. 8165
VERCO ADVISORY SERVICES LTD.—See CVC Capital Partners SICAV-FIS S.A.; *Int'l*, pg. 1882
VERCOR S.A—See ASSA ABLOY AB; *Int'l*, pg. 638
VERDANE CAPITAL ADVISORS AS; *Int'l*, pg. 8165
VERDANTAS LLC—See Sterling Investment Partners, L.P.; *U.S. Private*, pg. 3806
VERDANT EARTH TECHNOLOGIES LIMITED; *Int'l*, pg. 8165
VERDANT ENVIRONMENTAL TECHNOLOGIES INC.—See Emerson Electric Co.; *U.S. Public*, pg. 752
VERDANT MINERALS LTD.—See CD Capital Asset Management Ltd.; *Int'l*, pg. 1370
VERDBREFASKRANING ISLANDS HF.—See Nasdaq, Inc.; *U.S. Public*, pg. 1492
VERDE AGRITECH PLC; *Int'l*, pg. 8165
VERDE BIO HOLDINGS, INC.—See Formation Minerals, Inc.; *U.S. Public*, pg. 868
VERDE CLEAN FUELS, INC.; *U.S. Public*, pg. 2280
VERDE ELECTRIC CORP.; *U.S. Private*, pg. 4359
VERDE ENERGY USA, INC.—See Via Renewables, Inc.; *U.S. Public*, pg. 2290
VERDE ENERGY USA TEXAS, LLC—See Via Renewables, Inc.; *U.S. Public*, pg. 2290
VERDE FERTILIZANTES LTDA—See Verde AgriTech Plc; *Int'l*, pg. 8166
VERDEMAR INVESTMENT CORPORATION SA; *Int'l*, pg. 8166
VERDE MEDIA GROUP, INC.; *U.S. Public*, pg. 2280
VERDENS GANG AS—See Schibsted ASA; *Int'l*, pg. 6618
VERDER AG—See Verder International B.V.; *Int'l*, pg. 8167
VERDERA OY—See Lallemand, Inc.; *U.S. Private*, pg. 4400
VERDER A/S—See Verder International B.V.; *Int'l*, pg. 8167
VERDER BULGARIA EOOD—See Verder International B.V.; *Int'l*, pg. 8167
VERDER B.V.—See Verder International B.V.; *Int'l*, pg. 8167
VERDE RESOURCES, INC.; *Int'l*, pg. 8166
VERDER GMBH—See Verder International B.V.; *Int'l*, pg. 8167
VERDER HUNGARY KFT—See Verder International B.V.; *Int'l*, pg. 8167
VERDER INC.—See Verder International B.V.; *Int'l*, pg. 8167
VERDER INDIA PUMPS PVT. LTD—See Verder International B.V.; *Int'l*, pg. 8167
VERDER INTERNATIONAL B.V.; *Int'l*, pg. 8166
VERDERMIX BV—See Verder International B.V.; *Int'l*, pg. 8168
VERDER N.V.—See Verder International B.V.; *Int'l*, pg. 8167
VERDER - POLSKA SP. Z O.O.—See Verder International B.V.; *Int'l*, pg. 8167
VERDER PUMPS SOUTH-AFRICA—See Verder International B.V.; *Int'l*, pg. 8168
VERDER RETSCH SHANGHAI TRADING CO., LTD.—See Verder International B.V.; *Int'l*, pg. 8168
VERDER ROMANIA S.R.L.—See Verder International B.V.; *Int'l*, pg. 8168
VERDER SARL—See Verder International B.V.; *Int'l*, pg. 8168
VERDER SCIENTIFIC CO. LTD.—See Verder International B.V.; *Int'l*, pg. 8167

VERDER INTERNATIONAL B.V.

VERDER SCIENTIFIC GMBH & CO. KG—See Verder International B.V.; *Int'l*, pg. 8167
VERDER SCIENTIFIC, INC.—See Verder International B.V.; *Int'l*, pg. 8167
VERDER SCIENTIFIC LLC—See Verder International B.V.; *Int'l*, pg. 8167
VERDER SCIENTIFIC PRIVATE LIMITED—See Verder International B.V.; *Int'l*, pg. 8168
VERDER SCIENTIFIC SRL—See Verder International B.V.; *Int'l*, pg. 8167
VERDER SHANGHAI INSTRUMENTS AND EQUIPMENT CO., LTD.—See Verder International B.V.; *Int'l*, pg. 8168
VERDER SLOVAKIA SRO—See Verder International B.V.; *Int'l*, pg. 8168
VERDER S.R.O.—See Verder International B.V.; *Int'l*, pg. 8168
VERDER UK LTD—See Verder International B.V.; *Int'l*, pg. 8168
VERDE SCIENCE, INC.; *U.S. Public*, pg. 2280
VERDES DEL ORIENTE PRESERVATION, L.P.—See Apartment Investment and Management Company; *U.S. Public*, pg. 144
VERDESIAN LIFE SCIENCES, LLC—See AEA Investors LP; *U.S. Private*, pg. 116
VERDE SPORT S.P.A.—See Edizione S.r.l.; *Int'l*, pg. 2312
VERDE VALLEY NEWSPAPERS INC.—See Western Newspapers, Inc.; *U.S. Private*, pg. 4495
VERDI CONSULTING INC; *U.S. Private*, pg. 4359
VERDICT MEDIA LIMITED—See GlobalData Plc; *Int'l*, pg. 3003
VERDIGRIS VALLEY ELECTRIC COOPERATIVE; *U.S. Private*, pg. 4359
VERDITEK PLC; *Int'l*, pg. 8168
VERDO A/S; *Int'l*, pg. 8168
VERDO ENERGY A/S—See Verdo A/S; *Int'l*, pg. 8168
VERDO HILLEROD EL-NET A/S—See Verdo A/S; *Int'l*, pg. 8168
VERDOME EXPLOITATION SA—See O-I Glass, Inc.; *U.S. Public*, pg. 1559
VERDO PRODUKTION A/S—See Verdo A/S; *Int'l*, pg. 8168
VERDO RANDERS EL-NET A/S—See Verdo A/S; *Int'l*, pg. 8168
VERDO RENEWABLES LTD.—See Verdo A/S; *Int'l*, pg. 8168
VERDO VAND A/S—See Verdo A/S; *Int'l*, pg. 8168
VERDO VARME A/S—See Verdo A/S; *Int'l*, pg. 8168
VERDURE XCHANGE TECH INC.—See SUTL Enterprise Limited; *Int'l*, pg. 7347
VEREBUS ENGINEERING B.V.—See TUV NORD AG; *Int'l*, pg. 7981
VEREDELUNGSTECHNIK KRIEGLACH GMBH—See Georgsmarienhutte Holding GmbH; *Int'l*, pg. 2941
VEREDUS CORP.—See Hays PLC; *Int'l*, pg. 3294
VEREDUS LABORATORIES PTE. LTD.—See Sekisui Chemical Co., Ltd.; *Int'l*, pg. 6696
VEREINIGTE FILZFABRIKEN AG; *Int'l*, pg. 8168
VEREINIGTE GAS- UND WASSERVERSORGUNG GMBH—See Gelsenwasser AG; *Int'l*, pg. 2914
VEREINIGTE KREIDEWERKE DAMMANN KG - LAGERDORF PLANT—See Omya (Schweiz) AG; *Int'l*, pg. 5572
VEREINIGTE KREIDEWERKE DAMMANN KG - RUGEN PLANT—See Omya (Schweiz) AG; *Int'l*, pg. 5572
VEREINIGTE KREIDEWERKE DAMMANN KG—See Omya (Schweiz) AG; *Int'l*, pg. 5572
VEREINTE SPEZIAL KRANKENVERSICHERUNG AKTIENGESELLSCHAFT—See Allianz SE; *Int'l*, pg. 356
VEREIT, INC.—See Realty Income Corporation; *U.S. Public*, pg. 1768
VEREIT OPERATING PARTNERSHIP, L.P.—See Realty Income Corporation; *U.S. Public*, pg. 1769
VERENDRYE ELECTRIC COOPERATIVE; *U.S. Private*, pg. 4359
VERENGO INC.—See Crius Energy, LLC; *U.S. Private*, pg. 1102
VEREN INC.; *Int'l*, pg. 8168
VERES LLC—See Onexim Group Limited; *Int'l*, pg. 5581
VERETECH HOLDINGS, INC.—See The Hearst Corporation; *U.S. Private*, pg. 4045
VERETEC LIMITED—See Aukett Swanke Group Plc; *Int'l*, pg. 704
VEREYA-TOUR AD; *Int'l*, pg. 8168
VERGANI & ASSOCIATES, LLC; *U.S. Private*, pg. 4359
VERGE180, LLC; *U.S. Private*, pg. 4360
VERGELEGEN WINES (PTY) LTD.—See Anglo American PLC; *Int'l*, pg. 462
VERGE PROMOTIONAL MARKETING; *U.S. Private*, pg. 4359
VERGE SOLUTIONS, LLC—See Rothschild & Co SCA; *Int'l*, pg. 6403
VERGE SOLUTIONS, LLC—See TA Associates, Inc.; *U.S. Private*, pg. 3918
VERGNET HYDRO SAS—See Vergnet S.A.; *Int'l*, pg. 8168
VERGNET S.A.; *Int'l*, pg. 8168
VERHAGEN GLENDENNING & WALKER LLP—See Brown & Brown, Inc.; *U.S. Public*, pg. 398

VERHALEN INC.; *U.S. Private*, pg. 4360
VER HOEF AUTOMOTIVE INC.; *U.S. Private*, pg. 4358
VERHOFF MACHINE & WELDING, INC.; *U.S. Private*, pg. 4360
VERIAN TECHNOLOGIES, INC.—See Accel Partners L.P.; *U.S. Private*, pg. 48
VERIAN TECHNOLOGIES, INC.—See KKR & Co. Inc.; *U.S. Public*, pg. 1238
VERIAN TECHNOLOGIES, INC.—See Long Path Partners, LP; *U.S. Private*, pg. 2491
VERIATO, INC.; *U.S. Private*, pg. 4360
VERICAST—See MacAndrews & Forbes Incorporated; *U.S. Private*, pg. 2532
VERICEL CORPORATION; *U.S. Public*, pg. 2280
VERICHEM LABORATORIES INC; *U.S. Private*, pg. 4360
VERICI DX LIMITED—See Renalytix plc; *Int'l*, pg. 6273
VERICITY, INC.—See iA Financial Corporation Inc.; *Int'l*, pg. 3568
VERICLAIM UK LIMITED—See The Carlyle Group Inc.; *U.S. Public*, pg. 2054
VERICON OUTSOURCING (PTY) LIMITED—See The Bidvest Group Limited; *Int'l*, pg. 7626
VERICOR POWER SYSTEMS LLC—See CSL Capital Management, LLC; *U.S. Private*, pg. 1117
VERICORR PACKAGING LLC; *U.S. Private*, pg. 4360
VERIDAS DIGITAL AUTHENTICATION SOLUTIONS S.L.—See Banco Bilbao Vizcaya Argentaria, S.A.; *Int'l*, pg. 818
VERIDEX, LLC—See Johnson & Johnson; *U.S. Public*, pg. 1200
VERIDIAM, INC.—See William Harris Investors, Inc.; *U.S. Private*, pg. 4523
VERIDIAN CREDIT UNION; *U.S. Private*, pg. 4360
VERIDIEN CORP.; *U.S. Private*, pg. 4360
VERIDIS ENVIRONMENT LTD; *Int'l*, pg. 8168
VERIDOS AMERICA INC.—See Giesecke & Devrient GmbH; *Int'l*, pg. 2970
VERIDOS GMBH—See Bundesdruckerei GmbH; *Int'l*, pg. 1216
VERIDOS GMBH—See Giesecke & Devrient GmbH; *Int'l*, pg. 2970
VERIDOS MATSOUKIS S.A.—See Giesecke & Devrient GmbH; *Int'l*, pg. 2970
VERIFACTS LLC—See TransUnion; *U.S. Public*, pg. 2185
VERIFACT TRAFFIC PTY LTD.—See AVADA Group Limited; *Int'l*, pg. 734
VERIFIED LAB SERVICES LIMITED—See Seeka Limited; *Int'l*, pg. 6679
VERIFIER CAPITAL LLC; *U.S. Private*, pg. 4360
VERIFI, INC.—See Visa, Inc.; *U.S. Public*, pg. 2301
VERIFONE AFRICA (PTY) LTD—See British Columbia Investment Management Corp.; *Int'l*, pg. 1170
VERIFONE AFRICA (PTY) LTD—See Francisco Partners Management, LP; *U.S. Private*, pg. 1592
VERIFONE ASIA PACIFIC—See British Columbia Investment Management Corp.; *Int'l*, pg. 1170
VERIFONE ASIA PACIFIC—See Francisco Partners Management, LP; *U.S. Private*, pg. 1592
VERIFONE AUSTRALIA (HAPL) PTY LTD—See British Columbia Investment Management Corp.; *Int'l*, pg. 1170
VERIFONE AUSTRALIA (HAPL) PTY LTD—See Francisco Partners Management, LP; *U.S. Private*, pg. 1592
VERIFONE DENMARK A/S—See British Columbia Investment Management Corp.; *Int'l*, pg. 1170
VERIFONE DENMARK A/S—See Francisco Partners Management, LP; *U.S. Private*, pg. 1592
VERIFONE DO BRASIL LTDA.—See British Columbia Investment Management Corp.; *Int'l*, pg. 1171
VERIFONE DO BRASIL LTDA.—See Francisco Partners Management, LP; *U.S. Private*, pg. 1593
VERIFONE FINLAND OY—See British Columbia Investment Management Corp.; *Int'l*, pg. 1170
VERIFONE FINLAND OY—See Francisco Partners Management, LP; *U.S. Private*, pg. 1592
VERIFONE GMBH—See British Columbia Investment Management Corp.; *Int'l*, pg. 1170
VERIFONE GMBH—See Francisco Partners Management, LP; *U.S. Private*, pg. 1592
VERIFONE, INC.—See British Columbia Investment Management Corp.; *Int'l*, pg. 1170
VERIFONE, INC.—See Francisco Partners Management, LP; *U.S. Private*, pg. 1592
VERIFONE ISRAEL LTD.—See British Columbia Investment Management Corp.; *Int'l*, pg. 1170
VERIFONE ISRAEL LTD.—See Francisco Partners Management, LP; *U.S. Private*, pg. 1592
VERIFONE ITALIA S.R.L.—See British Columbia Investment Management Corp.; *Int'l*, pg. 1170
VERIFONE ITALIA S.R.L.—See Francisco Partners Management, LP; *U.S. Private*, pg. 1592
VERIFONE LATIN AMERICA & THE CARIBBEAN—See British Columbia Investment Management Corp.; *Int'l*, pg. 1170
VERIFONE LATIN AMERICA & THE CARIBBEAN—See Francisco Partners Management, LP; *U.S. Private*, pg. 1592
VERIFONE MEDIA, LLC—See British Columbia Investment Management Corp.; *Int'l*, pg. 1170

CORPORATE AFFILIATIONS

VERIFONE MEDIA, LLC—See Francisco Partners Management, LP; *U.S. Private*, pg. 1592
VERIFONE NEW ZEALAND—See British Columbia Investment Management Corp.; *Int'l*, pg. 1170
VERIFONE NEW ZEALAND—See Francisco Partners Management, LP; *U.S. Private*, pg. 1592
VERIFONE NORWAY AS—See British Columbia Investment Management Corp.; *Int'l*, pg. 1170
VERIFONE NORWAY AS—See Francisco Partners Management, LP; *U.S. Private*, pg. 1592
VERIFONE, S.A. DE C.V.—See British Columbia Investment Management Corp.; *Int'l*, pg. 1171
VERIFONE, S.A. DE C.V.—See Francisco Partners Management, LP; *U.S. Private*, pg. 1593
VERIFONE SERVICES UK & IRELAND LTD.—See British Columbia Investment Management Corp.; *Int'l*, pg. 1170
VERIFONE SERVICES UK & IRELAND LTD.—See Francisco Partners Management, LP; *U.S. Private*, pg. 1592
VERIFONE SINGAPORE PTE. LTD.—See British Columbia Investment Management Corp.; *Int'l*, pg. 1170
VERIFONE SINGAPORE PTE. LTD.—See Francisco Partners Management, LP; *U.S. Private*, pg. 1592
VERIFONE SP. Z O.O—See British Columbia Investment Management Corp.; *Int'l*, pg. 1170
VERIFONE SP. Z O.O—See Francisco Partners Management, LP; *U.S. Private*, pg. 1592
VERIFONE SWEDEN AB—See British Columbia Investment Management Corp.; *Int'l*, pg. 1170
VERIFONE SWEDEN AB—See Francisco Partners Management, LP; *U.S. Private*, pg. 1592
VERIFONE SYSTEMS AUSTRALIA PTY. LTD.—See British Columbia Investment Management Corp.; *Int'l*, pg. 1170
VERIFONE SYSTEMS AUSTRALIA PTY. LTD.—See Francisco Partners Management, LP; *U.S. Private*, pg. 1592
VERIFONE SYSTEMS (CHINA), INC.—See British Columbia Investment Management Corp.; *Int'l*, pg. 1170
VERIFONE SYSTEMS (CHINA), INC.—See Francisco Partners Management, LP; *U.S. Private*, pg. 1592
VERIFONE SYSTEMS FRANCE SAS—See British Columbia Investment Management Corp.; *Int'l*, pg. 1170
VERIFONE SYSTEMS FRANCE SAS—See Francisco Partners Management, LP; *U.S. Private*, pg. 1592
VERIFONE SYSTEMS, INC.—See British Columbia Investment Management Corp.; *Int'l*, pg. 1170
VERIFONE SYSTEMS, INC.—See Francisco Partners Management, LP; *U.S. Private*, pg. 1592
VERIFONE SYSTEMS SPAIN SLU—See British Columbia Investment Management Corp.; *Int'l*, pg. 1170
VERIFONE SYSTEMS SPAIN SLU—See Francisco Partners Management, LP; *U.S. Private*, pg. 1593
VERIFONE (U.K.) LIMITED—See British Columbia Investment Management Corp.; *Int'l*, pg. 1170
VERIFONE (U.K.) LIMITED—See Francisco Partners Management, LP; *U.S. Private*, pg. 1592
VERIFONE URUGUAY—See British Columbia Investment Management Corp.; *Int'l*, pg. 1170
VERIFONE URUGUAY—See Francisco Partners Management, LP; *U.S. Private*, pg. 1593
VERIFORCE, LLC—See Thoma Bravo, L.P.; *U.S. Private*, pg. 4150
VERIFY HOLDINGS, LLC—See Optel Vision Inc.; *Int'l*, pg. 5601
VERIFYME, INC.; *U.S. Public*, pg. 2280
VERIFY SMART CORP.; *U.S. Public*, pg. 2280
VERIGENT, LLC; *U.S. Private*, pg. 4360
VERIGOLD JEWELLERY (UK) LTD.—See Renaissance Global Limited; *Int'l*, pg. 6272
VERILOGUE, INC.—See Publicis Groupe S.A.; *Int'l*, pg. 6106
VERILY LIFE SCIENCES LLC—See Alphabet Inc.; *U.S. Public*, pg. 84
VERIMARK HOLDINGS LIMITED; *Int'l*, pg. 8168
VERIMARK (PTY) LTD.—See VERIMARK HOLDINGS LIMITED; *Int'l*, pg. 8168
VERIMATRIX GMBH—See Verimatrix SA; *Int'l*, pg. 8169
VERIMATRIX, INC.—See Verimatrix SA; *Int'l*, pg. 8169
VERIMATRIX SA; *Int'l*, pg. 8169
VERIND S.P.A.—See Durr AG; *Int'l*, pg. 2233
VERINON TECHNOLOGY SOLUTIONS LTD; *U.S. Private*, pg. 4360
VERINT SYSTEMS (ASIA PACIFIC) LIMITED—See Verint Systems Inc.; *U.S. Public*, pg. 2281
VERINT SYSTEMS (AUSTRALIA) PTY LTD.—See Verint Systems Inc.; *U.S. Public*, pg. 2281
VERINT SYSTEMS, INC. - ALPHARETTA—See Verint Systems Inc.; *U.S. Public*, pg. 2281
VERINT SYSTEMS INC.; *U.S. Public*, pg. 2280
VERINT SYSTEMS (PHILIPPINES) CORPORATION—See Verint Systems Inc.; *U.S. Public*, pg. 2281
VERINT SYSTEMS UK LTD.—See Verint Systems Inc.; *U.S. Public*, pg. 2281
VERINT VIDEO SOLUTIONS INC.—See Verint Systems Inc.; *U.S. Public*, pg. 2281
VERINT WITNESS SYSTEMS LLC - SANTA CLARA—See Verint Systems Inc.; *U.S. Public*, pg. 2281
VERIO EUROPE GMBH—See Nippon Telegraph & Telephone Corporation; *Int'l*, pg. 5345

COMPANY NAME INDEX

VERIO INC.—See Nippon Telegraph & Telephone Corporation; *Int'l*, pg. 5345
VERIPACK EMBALAJES SL—See Groupe Guillin SA; *Int'l*, pg. 3104
VERIPOS INC.—See Hexagon AB; *Int'l*, pg. 3368
VERISAE, INC.—See Fortive Corporation; *U.S. Public*, pg. 870
VERISANTE TECHNOLOGY, INC.; *Int'l*, pg. 8169
VERIS CONSULTING, INC.—See Bow River Asset Management Corp.; *U.S. Private*, pg. 625
VERISEC APAC PTY. LTD.—See Freja eID Group AB; *Int'l*, pg. 2772
VERISEC LATAM S.A. DE C.V.—See Freja eID Group AB; *Int'l*, pg. 2772
VERISEC TECHNOLOGY D.O.O.—See Freja eID Group AB; *Int'l*, pg. 2772
VERISERVE CORPORATION—See Sumitomo Corporation; *Int'l*, pg. 7270
VERIS FARMACEUTICA LIMITADA—See FAES Farma, S.A.; *Int'l*, pg. 2601
VERIS GOLD CORP.; *Int'l*, pg. 8169
VERIS GROUP, LLC—See Apax Partners LLP; *Int'l*, pg. 503
VERISIGN COLOMBIA SAS—See VeriSign, Inc.; *U.S. Public*, pg. 2282
VERISIGN, INC.; *U.S. Public*, pg. 2282
VERISIGN, INC.—See VeriSign, Inc.; *U.S. Public*, pg. 2282
VERISIGN INFORMATION SERVICES, INC.—See VeriSign, Inc.; *U.S. Public*, pg. 2282
VERISIGN SERVICES INDIA PRIVATE LIMITED—See VeriSign, Inc.; *U.S. Public*, pg. 2282
VERISILICON EUROPE—See VeriSilicon Holdings Co., Ltd.; *Int'l*, pg. 8169
VERISILICON HOLDINGS CO., LTD.; *Int'l*, pg. 8169
VERISILICON, INC.—See VeriSilicon Holdings Co., Ltd.; *Int'l*, pg. 8169
VERISILICON K.K.—See VeriSilicon Holdings Co., Ltd.; *Int'l*, pg. 8169
VERISILICON MICROELECTRONICS (BEIJING) CO., LTD.—See VeriSilicon Holdings Co., Ltd.; *Int'l*, pg. 8169
VERISILICON MICROELECTRONICS (CHENGDU) CO., LTD.—See VeriSilicon Holdings Co., Ltd.; *Int'l*, pg. 8169
VERISILICON MICROELECTRONICS (SHANGHAI) CO., LTD.—See VeriSilicon Holdings Co., Ltd.; *Int'l*, pg. 8169
VERISILICON TAIWAN, INC.—See VeriSilicon Holdings Co., Ltd.; *Int'l*, pg. 8169
VERISIM LIMITED—See The Core Banking Group Ltd.; *Int'l*, pg. 7635
VERIS INDUSTRIES LLC—See Schneider Electric SE; *Int'l*, pg. 6636
VERISK ANALYTICS, INC.; *U.S. Public*, pg. 2282
VERIS LIMITED; *Int'l*, pg. 8169
VERISMA SYSTEMS, INC.—See NewSpring Capital LLC; *U.S. Private*, pg. 2918
VERIS RESIDENTIAL, INC.; *U.S. Public*, pg. 2281
VERISSIMO GLOBAL, INC.; *U.S. Private*, pg. 4360
VERISTA INC.—See Lightview Capital LLC; *U.S. Private*, pg. 2454
VERISTAR LLC; *U.S. Private*, pg. 4360
VERISTAT LLC—See MTS Health Partners, L.P.; *U.S. Private*, pg. 2810
VERISTOR SYSTEMS, INC.; *U.S. Private*, pg. 4360
VERISURE—See Bain Capital, LP; *U.S. Private*, pg. 444
VERISURE—See Hellman & Friedman LLC; *U.S. Private*, pg. 1910
VERISYS CORP.—See Cressey & Company, LP; *U.S. Private*, pg. 1095
VERISYS CORP.—See Spectrum Equity Investors, L.P.; *U.S. Private*, pg. 3752
VERITABLE, LP—See Affiliated Managers Group, Inc.; *U.S. Public*, pg. 56
VERITAS ADVISORY GROUP, INC.—See Cobepa S.A.; *Int'l*, pg. 1683
VERITAS ASSET MANAGEMENT LLP—See Affiliated Managers Group, Inc.; *U.S. Public*, pg. 56
VERITAS CAPITAL FUND MANAGEMENT, LLC; *U.S. Private*, pg. 4360
VERITAS COMMUNICATIONS, INC.—See Stagwell, Inc.; *U.S. Public*, pg. 1928
VERITAS CONSULTING KFT.—See 4iG Nyrt.; *Int'l*, pg. 12
VERITAS DGC (MALAYSIA) SDN. BHD.—See CGG; *Int'l*, pg. 1432
VERITAS DOCUMENT SOLUTIONS, LLC—See Chatham Asset Management, LLC; *U.S. Private*, pg. 863
VERITAS FARMS, INC.; *U.S. Public*, pg. 2283
VERITAS (INDIA) LIMITED—See Swan Energy Ltd.; *Int'l*, pg. 7360
VERITAS KAPITAL ASSURANCE PLC—See Unity Bank Plc.; *Int'l*, pg. 8076
VERITAS PENSIONSFORSAKRING; *Int'l*, pg. 8169
VERITAS PETROLEUM SERVICES—See IK Investment Partners Limited; *Int'l*, pg. 3610
VERITAS PHARMA, INC.; *Int'l*, pg. 8169
VERITAS PREP, LLC—See Varsity Tutors LLC; *U.S. Private*, pg. 4347
VERITAS RISK SERVICES, LLC—See New Mountain Capital, LLC; *U.S. Private*, pg. 2901
VERITAS STEEL LLC - EAU CLAIRE PLANT—See Atlas Holdings, LLC; *U.S. Private*, pg. 378
VERITAS STEEL LLC—See Atlas Holdings, LLC; *U.S. Private*, pg. 378
VERITAS TECHNOLOGIES LLC—See The Carlyle Group Inc.; *U.S. Public*, pg. 2056
VERITAS TITLE PARTNERS LLC—See Old Republic International Corporation; *U.S. Public*, pg. 1569
VERITAS TOTAL SOLUTIONS, LLC—See Marsh & McLennan Companies, Inc.; *U.S. Public*, pg. 1388
VERITEC, INC.; *U.S. Public*, pg. 2283
VERITE CO., LTD.; *Int'l*, pg. 8169
VERITEK AUSTRALASIA PTY LTD—See Mobeus Equity Partners LLP; *Int'l*, pg. 5008
VERITEK BENELUX BV—See Mobeus Equity Partners LLP; *Int'l*, pg. 5008
VERITEK CZECH REPUBLIC S.R.O.—See Mobeus Equity Partners LLP; *Int'l*, pg. 5008
VERITEK GLOBAL LTD—See Mobeus Equity Partners LLP; *Int'l*, pg. 5008
VERITEK GMBH—See Mobeus Equity Partners LLP; *Int'l*, pg. 5008
VERITEK IBERIA S.L.—See Mobeus Equity Partners LLP; *Int'l*, pg. 5008
VERITEK ITALY SRL—See Mobeus Equity Partners LLP; *Int'l*, pg. 5008
VERITEQ CORPORATION; *U.S. Private*, pg. 4366
VERITEST, INC.—See H.I.G. Capital, LLC; *U.S. Private*, pg. 1830
VERITEX COMMUNITY BANK—See Veritex Holdings, Inc.; *U.S. Public*, pg. 2283
VERITEX HOLDINGS, INC.; *U.S. Public*, pg. 2283
VERITEXT LEGAL SOLUTIONS - SACRAMENTO—See Pamplona Capital Management LLP; *Int'l*, pg. 5713
VERITEXT LEGAL SOLUTIONS—See Pamplona Capital Management LLP; *Int'l*, pg. 5713
VERITIV CANADA, INC.—See Bain Capital, LP; *U.S. Private*, pg. 441
VERITIV CORPORATION—See Clayton, Dubilier & Rice, LLC; *U.S. Private*, pg. 928
VERITIV - DENVER—See Clayton, Dubilier & Rice; *U.S. Private*, pg. 929
VERITIV DISTRIBUTION GROUP—See Clayton, Dubilier & Rice, LLC; *U.S. Private*, pg. 929
VERITIV EUROPE GMBH—See Clayton, Dubilier & Rice, LLC; *U.S. Private*, pg. 928
VERITIV EXPRESS—See Clayton, Dubilier & Rice, LLC; *U.S. Private*, pg. 929
VERITIV EXPRESS—See Clayton, Dubilier & Rice, LLC; *U.S. Private*, pg. 929
VERITIV EXPRESS—See Clayton, Dubilier & Rice, LLC; *U.S. Private*, pg. 929
VERITIV EXPRESS—See Clayton, Dubilier & Rice, LLC; *U.S. Private*, pg. 929
VERITIV - INDIANAPOLIS—See Clayton, Dubilier & Rice, LLC; *U.S. Private*, pg. 929
VERITIV OPERATING COMPANY - NEW BERLIN—See Clayton, Dubilier & Rice, LLC; *U.S. Private*, pg. 929
VERITIV OPERATING COMPANY—See Clayton, Dubilier & Rice, LLC; *U.S. Private*, pg. 928
VERITIV, S.A. DE C.V.—See Clayton, Dubilier & Rice, LLC; *U.S. Private*, pg. 930
VERITIV—See Clayton, Dubilier & Rice, LLC; *U.S. Private*, pg. 929
VERITIV—See Clayton, Dubilier & Rice, LLC; *U.S. Private*, pg. 929
VERITIV—See Clayton, Dubilier & Rice, LLC; *U.S. Private*, pg. 929
VERITIV—See Clayton, Dubilier & Rice, LLC; *U.S. Private*, pg. 929
VERITIV—See Clayton, Dubilier & Rice, LLC; *U.S. Private*, pg. 929
VERITIV—See Clayton, Dubilier & Rice, LLC; *U.S. Private*, pg. 929
VERITIV—See Clayton, Dubilier & Rice, LLC; *U.S. Private*, pg. 929
VERITIV—See Clayton, Dubilier & Rice, LLC; *U.S. Private*, pg. 929
VERITIV—See Clayton, Dubilier & Rice, LLC; *U.S. Private*, pg. 929
VERITIV—See Clayton, Dubilier & Rice, LLC; *U.S. Private*, pg. 929
VERITIV—See Clayton, Dubilier & Rice, LLC; *U.S. Private*, pg. 929
VERITIV—See Clayton, Dubilier & Rice, LLC; *U.S. Private*, pg. 929

VERIZON COMMUNICATIONS INC.

VERITIV—See Clayton, Dubilier & Rice, LLC; *U.S. Private*, pg. 929
VERITIV—See Clayton, Dubilier & Rice, LLC; *U.S. Private*, pg. 929
VERITIV—See Clayton, Dubilier & Rice, LLC; *U.S. Private*, pg. 929
VERITIV—See Clayton, Dubilier & Rice, LLC; *U.S. Private*, pg. 929
VERITIV—See Clayton, Dubilier & Rice, LLC; *U.S. Private*, pg. 929
VERITONE, INC.; *U.S. Public*, pg. 2283
VERITRANS INC.—See Digital Garage, Inc.; *Int'l*, pg. 2122
VERITY CORPORATION; *Int'l*, pg. 8169
VERITY CREDIT UNION; *U.S. Private*, pg. 4366
VERITY ENTERPRISES LIMITED—See Li & Fung Limited; *Int'l*, pg. 4481
VERITY SOLUTIONS GROUP, INC.—See The Cigna Group; *U.S. Public*, pg. 2061
VERITYSTREAM, INC.—See HealthStream, Inc.; *U.S. Public*, pg. 1017
VERIUM AG; *Int'l*, pg. 8169
VERIVOX GMBH—See ProSiebenSat.1 Media SE; *Int'l*, pg. 6001
VERIZON AMERICAS INC.—See Verizon Communications Inc.; *U.S. Public*, pg. 2285
VERIZON BUSINESS GLOBAL LLC—See Verizon Communications Inc.; *U.S. Public*, pg. 2285
VERIZON BUSINESS NETWORK SERVICES INC.—See Verizon Communications Inc.; *U.S. Public*, pg. 2285
VERIZON BUSINESS SECURITY SOLUTIONS—See Verizon Communications Inc.; *U.S. Public*, pg. 2285
VERIZON CENTER—See Lincoln Holdings LLC; *U.S. Private*, pg. 2457
VERIZON COMMUNICATIONS INC. - BUFFALO, WV—See Verizon Communications Inc.; *U.S. Public*, pg. 2285
VERIZON COMMUNICATIONS INC. - CLARKSBURG, WV—See Verizon Communications Inc.; *U.S. Public*, pg. 2285
VERIZON COMMUNICATIONS INC. - HAYES, VA—See Verizon Communications Inc.; *U.S. Public*, pg. 2285
VERIZON COMMUNICATIONS INC. - JOHNSTOWN, PA—See Verizon Communications Inc.; *U.S. Public*, pg. 2285
VERIZON COMMUNICATIONS INC. - LIVERPOOL, NY—See Verizon Communications Inc.; *U.S. Public*, pg. 2285
VERIZON COMMUNICATIONS INC. - MONTGOMERY-VILLE, PA—See Verizon Communications Inc.; *U.S. Public*, pg. 2285
VERIZON COMMUNICATIONS INC. - ROANOKE, VA—See Verizon Communications Inc.; *U.S. Public*, pg. 2285
VERIZON COMMUNICATIONS INC.; *U.S. Public*, pg. 2283
VERIZON COMMUNICATIONS INC. - WATERTOWN, NY—See Verizon Communications Inc.; *U.S. Public*, pg. 2285
VERIZON COMMUNICATIONS INC. - WHITE PLAINS, NY—See Verizon Communications Inc.; *U.S. Public*, pg. 2285
VERIZON CONNECT FLEET—See Verizon Communications Inc.; *U.S. Public*, pg. 2285
VERIZON CONNECT INC.—See Verizon Communications Inc.; *U.S. Public*, pg. 2286
VERIZON CREDIT INC.—See Verizon Communications Inc.; *U.S. Public*, pg. 2285
VERIZON DATA SERVICES—See Verizon Communications Inc.; *U.S. Public*, pg. 2286
VERIZON DATA SERVICES—See Verizon Communications Inc.; *U.S. Public*, pg. 2286
VERIZON DELAWARE INC.—See Verizon Communications Inc.; *U.S. Public*, pg. 2286
VERIZON DIGITAL MEDIA SERVICES INC.—See Apollo Global Management, Inc.; *U.S. Public*, pg. 167
VERIZON DIRECTORY SUPPORT CENTER—See Verizon Communications Inc.; *U.S. Public*, pg. 2286
VERIZON ENHANCED COMMUNITIES—See Verizon Communications Inc.; *U.S. Public*, pg. 2286
VERIZON ENTERPRISE SOLUTIONS GROUP—See Verizon Communications Inc.; *U.S. Public*, pg. 2286
VERIZON ENTERPRISE SOLUTIONS GROUP—See Verizon Communications Inc.; *U.S. Public*, pg. 2286
VERIZON LICENSE ADMINISTRATION GROUP—See Verizon Communications Inc.; *U.S. Public*, pg. 2286
VERIZON NETWORKFLEET, INC.—See Verizon Communications Inc.; *U.S. Public*, pg. 2286
VERIZON NETWORK INTEGRATION CORPORATION—See Verizon Communications Inc.; *U.S. Public*, pg. 2286
VERIZON NEW JERSEY INC.—See Verizon Communications Inc.; *U.S. Public*, pg. 2286
VERIZON NEW YORK INC.—See Verizon Communications Inc.; *U.S. Public*, pg. 2286
VERIZON NORTHWEST INC.—See Verizon Communications Inc.; *U.S. Public*, pg. 2286
VERIZON PENNSYLVANIA INC.—See Verizon Communications Inc.; *U.S. Public*, pg. 2286
VERIZON PRIVACY GROUP—See Verizon Communications Inc.; *U.S. Public*, pg. 2286

VERIZON COMMUNICATIONS INC.

VERIZON SELECT SERVICES INC.—See Verizon Communications Inc.; *U.S. Public*, pg. 2286
VERIZON SERVICES GROUP INC.—See Verizon Communications Inc.; *U.S. Public*, pg. 2286
VERIZON TELEPRODUCTS—See Verizon Communications Inc.; *U.S. Public*, pg. 2286
VERIZON VIRGINIA INC.—See Verizon Communications Inc.; *U.S. Public*, pg. 2286
VERIZON VIRGINIA INC.—See Verizon Communications Inc.; *U.S. Public*, pg. 2286
VERIZON WIRELESS - BARTLETT—See Verizon Communications Inc.; *U.S. Public*, pg. 2284
VERIZON WIRELESS - BEDMINSTER—See Verizon Communications Inc.; *U.S. Public*, pg. 2284
VERIZON WIRELESS - BELLEVUE—See Verizon Communications Inc.; *U.S. Public*, pg. 2285
VERIZON WIRELESS - BERGENFIELD—See Verizon Communications Inc.; *U.S. Public*, pg. 2284
VERIZON WIRELESS - BIRMINGHAM—See Verizon Communications Inc.; *U.S. Public*, pg. 2284
VERIZON WIRELESS - BOCA RATON—See Verizon Communications Inc.; *U.S. Public*, pg. 2284
VERIZON WIRELESS - BUFFALO—See Verizon Communications Inc.; *U.S. Public*, pg. 2284
VERIZON WIRELESS - CHANDLER—See Verizon Communications Inc.; *U.S. Public*, pg. 2284
VERIZON WIRELESS - CHANDLER—See Verizon Communications Inc.; *U.S. Public*, pg. 2285
VERIZON WIRELESS - CHAPMANVILLE—See Verizon Communications Inc.; *U.S. Public*, pg. 2284
VERIZON WIRELESS - CHARLOTTE—See Verizon Communications Inc.; *U.S. Public*, pg. 2284
VERIZON WIRELESS - CLEVELAND—See Verizon Communications Inc.; *U.S. Public*, pg. 2284
VERIZON WIRELESS - COLUMBIA—See Verizon Communications Inc.; *U.S. Public*, pg. 2284
VERIZON WIRELESS - DOWNINGTOWN—See Verizon Communications Inc.; *U.S. Public*, pg. 2284
VERIZON WIRELESS - DUBLIN—See Verizon Communications Inc.; *U.S. Public*, pg. 2284
VERIZON WIRELESS - EL PASO—See Verizon Communications Inc.; *U.S. Public*, pg. 2284
VERIZON WIRELESS - ENGLEWOOD—See Verizon Communications Inc.; *U.S. Public*, pg. 2285
VERIZON WIRELESS - FAIRFIELD—See Verizon Communications Inc.; *U.S. Public*, pg. 2285
VERIZON WIRELESS - FAIR LAWN—See Verizon Communications Inc.; *U.S. Public*, pg. 2284
VERIZON WIRELESS - FALLS CHURCH—See Verizon Communications Inc.; *U.S. Public*, pg. 2284
VERIZON WIRELESS - FLORENCE—See Verizon Communications Inc.; *U.S. Public*, pg. 2284
VERIZON WIRELESS FLORIDA—See Verizon Communications Inc.; *U.S. Public*, pg. 2285
VERIZON WIRELESS - FREDERICKSBURG—See Verizon Communications Inc.; *U.S. Public*, pg. 2284
VERIZON WIRELESS - FREDERICK—See Verizon Communications Inc.; *U.S. Public*, pg. 2284
VERIZON WIRELESS - GREENSBORO—See Verizon Communications Inc.; *U.S. Public*, pg. 2284
VERIZON WIRELESS - GREENVILLE—See Verizon Communications Inc.; *U.S. Public*, pg. 2284
VERIZON WIRELESS - GREENWOOD—See Verizon Communications Inc.; *U.S. Public*, pg. 2284
VERIZON WIRELESS - HENDERSONVILLE—See Verizon Communications Inc.; *U.S. Public*, pg. 2284
VERIZON WIRELESS - HOUSTON—See Verizon Communications Inc.; *U.S. Public*, pg. 2285
VERIZON WIRELESS - INDIANAPOLIS—See Verizon Communications Inc.; *U.S. Public*, pg. 2284
VERIZON WIRELESS - JERSEY CITY—See Verizon Communications Inc.; *U.S. Public*, pg. 2284
VERIZON WIRELESS - KNOXVILLE—See Verizon Communications Inc.; *U.S. Public*, pg. 2285
VERIZON WIRELESS - LANCASTER—See Verizon Communications Inc.; *U.S. Public*, pg. 2284
VERIZON WIRELESS - LANSING—See Verizon Communications Inc.; *U.S. Public*, pg. 2284
VERIZON WIRELESS MESSAGING SERVICES LTD.—See Verizon Communications Inc.; *U.S. Public*, pg. 2285
VERIZON WIRELESS - MIDWEST—See Verizon Communications Inc.; *U.S. Public*, pg. 2284
VERIZON WIRELESS - MINNEAPOLIS—See Verizon Communications Inc.; *U.S. Public*, pg. 2284
VERIZON WIRELESS - NASHVILLE—See Verizon Communications Inc.; *U.S. Public*, pg. 2285
VERIZON WIRELESS - NORTHEAST—See Verizon Communications Inc.; *U.S. Public*, pg. 2284
VERIZON WIRELESS - ORANGEBURG—See Verizon Communications Inc.; *U.S. Public*, pg. 2284
VERIZON WIRELESS - OVERLAND PARK—See Verizon Communications Inc.; *U.S. Public*, pg. 2284
VERIZON WIRELESS - OVIEDO—See Verizon Communications Inc.; *U.S. Public*, pg. 2285
VERIZON WIRELESS - SAINT LOUIS—See Verizon Communications Inc.; *U.S. Public*, pg. 2284
VERIZON WIRELESS - SANTA MONICA—See Verizon Communications Inc.; *U.S. Public*, pg. 2285
VERIZON WIRELESS - SOUTHFIELD—See Verizon Communications Inc.; *U.S. Public*, pg. 2284
VERIZON WIRELESS - SOUTH—See Verizon Communications Inc.; *U.S. Public*, pg. 2284
VERIZON WIRELESS - STROUDSBURG—See Verizon Communications Inc.; *U.S. Public*, pg. 2284
VERIZON WIRELESS - VANCOUVER—See Verizon Communications Inc.; *U.S. Public*, pg. 2285
VERIZON WIRELESS - WEST—See Verizon Communications Inc.; *U.S. Public*, pg. 2285
VERIZON WIRELESS - WILMINGTON—See Verizon Communications Inc.; *U.S. Public*, pg. 2284
VERIZON YELLOW PAGES—See Verizon Communications Inc.; *U.S. Public*, pg. 2286
VERIZON YELLOW PAGES—See Verizon Communications Inc.; *U.S. Public*, pg. 2286
VERKAUFSBURO LILLEHEDEN GMBH—See Maj Invest Holding A/S; *Int'l*, pg. 4653
VERKEHRSBETRIEBE PEINE-SALZGITTER GESELLSCHAFT MIT BESCHRANKTER HAFTUNG—See Salzgitter AG; *Int'l*, pg. 6499
VERKEHRSGESELLSCHAFT MBH UNTERMAIN -VU—See Deutsche Bahn AG; *Int'l*, pg. 2055
VERKEHRSGESELLSCHAFT START NRW MBH—See Deutsche Bahn AG; *Int'l*, pg. 2055
VERKEHRSGESELLSCHAFT START UNTERELBE MBH—See Deutsche Bahn AG; *Int'l*, pg. 2055
VERKEHRSTRIEBE BILS GMBH—See Ferrovie dello Stato Italiane S.p.A.; *Int'l*, pg. 2645
VERKEHRSVERBUND ROTTWEIL GMBH—See Deutsche Bahn AG; *Int'l*, pg. 2055
VERKERK GROEP BV—See VINCI S.A.; *Int'l*, pg. 8240
VERKHNEKAMSK POTASH COMPANY—See Public Joint Stock Company Acron; *Int'l*, pg. 6095
VERKKOKAUPPA.COM OYJ; *Int'l*, pg. 8169
VERKLER INC.; *U.S. Private*, pg. 4366
VERKOL S.A.—See Quaker Chemical Corporation; *U.S. Public*, pg. 1747
VERKOOPKANTOOR ALLBOX EN DESOUTER NV—See KBC Group NV; *Int'l*, pg. 4104
VERLAG AENNE BURDA GMBH & CO. KG—See Hubert Burda Media Holding Kommanditgesellschaft; *Int'l*, pg. 3520
VERLAG AUTOMOBIL WIRTSCHAFT (PTY) LTD.—See Bertelsmann SE & Co. KGaA; *Int'l*, pg. 996
VERLAG DAS BESTE GES.M.B.H.—See RDA Holding Co.; *U.S. Private*, pg. 3364
VERLAG DAS BESTE GMBH; *Int'l*, pg. 8169
VERLAG DER TAGESSPIEGEL GMBH—See Verlagsgruppe Georg von Holtzbrinck GmbH; *Int'l*, pg. 8171
VERLAG E. DORNER GMBH—See Verlagsgruppe Georg von Holtzbrinck GmbH; *Int'l*, pg. 8171
VERLAG FINANZ UND WIRTSCHAFT AG—See TX Group AG; *Int'l*, pg. 7992
VERLAG KIEPENHEUER & WITSCH GMBH & CO. KG—See Verlagsgruppe Georg von Holtzbrinck GmbH; *Int'l*, pg. 8171
VERLAG MORITZ DIESTERWEG GMBH & CO.—See Verlagsgruppe Georg von Holtzbrinck GmbH; *Int'l*, pg. 8171
VERLAGSGRUPPE DROEMER KNAUR GMBH—See Verlagsgruppe Georg von Holtzbrinck GmbH; *Int'l*, pg. 8171
VERLAGSGRUPPE GEORG VON HOLTZBRINCK GMBH; *Int'l*, pg. 8169
VERLAGSGRUPPE HANDELSBLATT GMBH—See Verlagsgruppe Georg von Holtzbrinck GmbH; *Int'l*, pg. 8172
VERLAGSGRUPPE HARPERCOLLINS DEUTSCHLAND GMBH—See News Corporation; *U.S. Public*, pg. 1521
VERLAGSGRUPPE WELTBILD GMBH—See Droege Group AG; *Int'l*, pg. 2205
VERLEGERDIENST MUNCHEN GMBH—See Bertelsmann SE & Co. KGaA; *Int'l*, pg. 996
VERLINDE S.A.—See Konecranes Plc; *Int'l*, pg. 4253
VERLINVEST S.A.; *Int'l*, pg. 8172
VERMED, INC.—See Nissha Co., Ltd.; *Int'l*, pg. 5371
VERMEER CORPORATION; *U.S. Private*, pg. 4366
VERMEER EEMHAVEN INTERNATIONAL BV—See Nimbus B.V.; *Int'l*, pg. 5297
VERMEER EQUIPMENT OF TEXAS INC.; *U.S. Private*, pg. 4366
VERMEER GREAT PLAINS INC.; *U.S. Private*, pg. 4366
VERMEER GREAT PLAINS INC.—See Vermeer Great Plains Inc.; *U.S. Private*, pg. 4366
VERMEER GREAT PLAINS INC.—See Vermeer Great Plains Inc.; *U.S. Private*, pg. 4366
VERMEER GREAT PLAINS INC.—See Vermeer Great Plains Inc.; *U.S. Private*, pg. 4366
VERMEER MID ATLANTIC, LLC—See All Roads Company; *U.S. Private*, pg. 172
VERMEER MIDSOUTH INC; *U.S. Private*, pg. 4366
VERMEER MIDWEST, INC.; *U.S. Private*, pg. 4366
VERMEER MV SOLUTIONS, INC—See Vermeer Corporation; *U.S. Private*, pg. 4366
VERMEER NORTHEAST—See All Roads Company; *U.S. Private*, pg. 172
VERMEER SALES & SERVICE INC.—See Vermeer Southeast Sales & Service, Inc.; *U.S. Private*, pg. 4367

CORPORATE AFFILIATIONS

VERMEER SALES & SERVICE OF COLORADO, INC.; *U.S. Private*, pg. 4366
VERMEER SALES SOUTHWEST INC.; *U.S. Private*, pg. 4366
VERMEER SOUTHEAST SALES & SERVICE, INC.; *U.S. Private*, pg. 4367
VERMEER-WISCONSIN INC.; *U.S. Private*, pg. 4367
VERMEG COMPLIANCE LIMITED—See Vermeg Group N.V; *Int'l*, pg. 8172
VERMEG GROUP N.V; *Int'l*, pg. 8172
VERMEG INTERNATIONAL (HONG KONG) LIMITED—See Vermeg Group N.V; *Int'l*, pg. 8172
VERMEG INTERNATIONAL SINGAPORE PTE. LIMITED—See Vermeg Group N.V; *Int'l*, pg. 8172
VERMEG INTERNATIONAL (USA) INC.—See Vermeg Group N.V; *Int'l*, pg. 8172
VERMEG MANAGEMENT LIMITED—See Vermeg Group N.V; *Int'l*, pg. 8172
VERMES MICRODISPENSING GMBH—See Chaozhou Three-Circle Group Co., Ltd.; *Int'l*, pg. 1447
VERMILION BANCSHARES CORPORATION; *U.S. Private*, pg. 4367
VERMILION BANK & TRUST COMPANY—See Vermilion Bancshares Corporation; *U.S. Private*, pg. 4367
VERMILION ENERGY GERMANY GMBH & CO. KG—See Vermilion Energy Inc.; *Int'l*, pg. 8173
VERMILION ENERGY HUNGARY KFT.—See Vermilion Energy Inc.; *Int'l*, pg. 8173
VERMILION ENERGY INC.; *Int'l*, pg. 8172
VERMILION ENERGY NETHERLANDS BV—See Vermilion Energy Inc.; *Int'l*, pg. 8173
VERMILION EXPLORATION & PRODUCTION IRELAND LIMITED—See Vermilion Energy Inc.; *Int'l*, pg. 8173
VERMILION HOSPITAL, LLC—See Acadia Healthcare Company, Inc.; *U.S. Public*, pg. 31
VERMILION OIL & GAS AUSTRALIA PTY LTD.—See Vermilion Energy Inc.; *Int'l*, pg. 8173
VERMILION PARTNERS LIMITED—See Groupe BPCE; *Int'l*, pg. 3099
VERMILION PARTNERS (UK) LIMITED—See Groupe BPCE; *Int'l*, pg. 3099
VERMILION REP SAS—See Vermilion Energy Inc.; *Int'l*, pg. 8173
VERMILION SOFTWARE INC.—See FactSet Research Systems Inc.; *U.S. Public*, pg. 820
VERMITECH CORPORATION—See Sojitz Corporation; *Int'l*, pg. 7066
VERMODA S.P.A.; *Int'l*, pg. 8173
VERMOGENSVERWALTUNG EMAILLIERWERK GMBH—See Helaba Landesbank Hessen-Thuringen; *Int'l*, pg. 3328
VERMOGENSVERWALTUNG ERBEN DR. KARL GOLDSCHMIDT GMBH; *Int'l*, pg. 8173
VERMOGENSVERWALTUNGSGESELLSCHAFT DAIMLER ATLANTA MBH—See Mercedes-Benz Group AG; *Int'l*, pg. 4829
VERMOGENSVERWALTUNGSGESELLSCHAFT MERKUR MBH—See KBC Group NV; *Int'l*, pg. 4107
VERMOGENSVERWALTUNGSGESELLSCHAFT TKAS MBH—See ThyssenKrupp AG; *Int'l*, pg. 7734
VERMOGENSVERWALTUNGSGESELLSCHAFT TKW MBH—See ThyssenKrupp AG; *Int'l*, pg. 7734
VERMONT ACCIDENT INSURANCE CO., INC.—See Concord General Mu; *U.S. Private*, pg. 1010
VERMONT AMERICAN—See Robert Bosch GmbH; *Int'l*, pg. 6364
VERMONT CLOCK COMPANY; *U.S. Private*, pg. 4367
THE VERMONT COMMUNITY FOUNDATION; *U.S. Private*, pg. 4130
VERMONT COUNTRY STORE, INC.; *U.S. Private*, pg. 4367
VERMONT ELECTRIC COOPERATIVE; *U.S. Private*, pg. 4367
VERMONT ELECTRIC POWER COMPANY, INC.—See Caisse de Depot et Placement du Quebec; *Int'l*, pg. 1256
VERMONT ENERGY INVESTMENT CORPORATION; *U.S. Private*, pg. 4367
VERMONT GAS SYSTEMS, INC.—See Caisse de Depot et Placement du Quebec; *Int'l*, pg. 1256
VERMONT HARD CIDER COMPANY, LLC—See Northeast Drinks Group LLC; *U.S. Private*, pg. 2950
VERMONT HISTORICAL SOCIETY; *U.S. Private*, pg. 4367
VERMONT HOUSING FINANCE AGENCY; *U.S. Private*, pg. 4367
VERMONT INFORMATION CONSORTIUM, LLC—See Tyler Technologies, Inc.; *U.S. Public*, pg. 2209
VERMONT LAND TRUST INC.; *U.S. Private*, pg. 4367
VERMONT MUTUAL INSURANCE CO., INC.; *U.S. Private*, pg. 4367
VERMONT RAILWAY INC.; *U.S. Private*, pg. 4367
VERMONT SKI AREAS ASSOCIATION, INC.; *U.S. Private*, pg. 4367
VERMONT STATE EMPLOYEES CREDIT UNION; *U.S. Private*, pg. 4367
VERMONT SYMPHONY ORCHESTRA; *U.S. Private*, pg. 4367
VERMONT SYSTEMS, INC.—See Clubessential Holdings, LLC; *U.S. Private*, pg. 949

COMPANY NAME INDEX

THE VERMONT TEDDY BEAR COMPANY—See The Mustang Group, LLC; *U.S. Private*, pg. 4081
VERMONT YANKEE NUCLEAR POWER CORPORATION—See Caisse de Depot et Placement du Quebec; *Int'l*, pg. 1256
VERMOREL SRL—See Exel Industries SA; *Int'l*, pg. 2583
VERMOT SAS—See VINCI S.A.; *Int'l*, pg. 8240
VERNACARE LIMITED—See H.I.G. Capital, LLC; *U.S. Private*, pg. 1832
VERNALIS DEVELOPMENT LIMITED—See Ligand Pharmaceuticals Incorporated; *U.S. Public*, pg. 1314
VERNALIS PLC—See Ligand Pharmaceuticals Incorporated; *U.S. Public*, pg. 1314
VERNALIS (R&D) LTD—See Ligand Pharmaceuticals Incorporated; *U.S. Public*, pg. 1314
VERNAY BRASIL LTDA—See Vernay Laboratories, Inc.; *U.S. Private*, pg. 4368
VERNAY EUROPA B.V.—See Vernay Laboratories, Inc.; *U.S. Private*, pg. 4368
VERNAY ITALIA, S.R.L.—See Vernay Laboratories, Inc.; *U.S. Private*, pg. 4368
VERNAY LABORATORIES, INC.; *U.S. Private*, pg. 4368
VERNAY LABORATORIES, INC—See Vernay Laboratories, Inc.; *U.S. Private*, pg. 4368
VERNAY MANUFACTURING, INC.—See Vernay Laboratories, Inc.; *U.S. Private*, pg. 4368
VERNAY MANUFACTURING (SUZHOU) CO., LTD.—See Vernay Laboratories, Inc.; *U.S. Private*, pg. 4368
THE VERNDALE CORPORATION; *U.S. Private*, pg. 4130
VERNDALE PRODUCTS INC.; *U.S. Private*, pg. 4368
VERN EIDE MOTORCARS, INC.; *U.S. Private*, pg. 4367
VERNET BEHRINGER SA—See Behringer GmbH; *Int'l*, pg. 942
VERNET SAS—See Stirling Square Capital Partners LLP; *Int'l*, pg. 7216
VERNEY-CARRON S.A.—See Cybergun SA; *Int'l*, pg. 1893
VERN FONK INSURANCE, INC.—See Stone Point Capital LLC; *U.S. Private*, pg. 3819
VERNON AND CO. LIMITED—See STERIS plc; *Int'l*, pg. 7211
VERNON BUILDING SOCIETY; *Int'l*, pg. 8173
THE VERNON COMPANY; *U.S. Private*, pg. 4130
THE VERNON COMPANY - VERNON DISPLAY GRAPHICS DIVISION—See The Vernon Company; *U.S. Private*, pg. 4130
VERNON D'EON LOBSTER PLUGS LTD.; *Int'l*, pg. 8173
VERNON DOWNS CASINO & HOTEL; *U.S. Private*, pg. 4368
VERNON E. FAULCONER INC.; *U.S. Private*, pg. 4368
THE VERNON GRAPHICS GROUP—See The Vernon Company; *U.S. Private*, pg. 4130
VERNON KIA; *Int'l*, pg. 8173
VERNON PROMOTIONS—See The Vernon Company; *U.S. Private*, pg. 4130
VERNON TELEPHONE CO.—See Telephone & Data Systems, Inc.; *U.S. Public*, pg. 1998
VERNON TOOL COMPANY, LTD.—See Lincoln Electric Holdings, Inc.; *U.S. Public*, pg. 1318
VERO BEACH AVIONICS, INC.—See Sun Aviation, Inc.; *U.S. Private*, pg. 3858
VERO BEACH MUSEUM OF ART, INC.; *U.S. Private*, pg. 4368
VERO CHINA—See Hexagon AB; *Int'l*, pg. 3367
VEROD CAPITAL MANAGEMENT LIMITED; *Int'l*, pg. 8173
VERODIN, LLC—See Alphabet Inc.; *U.S. Public*, pg. 84
VERO FRANCE—See Hexagon AB; *Int'l*, pg. 3367
VERO INSURANCE LIMITED—See Suncorp Group Limited; *Int'l*, pg. 7311
VERO INSURANCE NEW ZEALAND LIMITED—See Suncorp Group Limited; *Int'l*, pg. 7311
VERO ITALIA SRL—See Hexagon AB; *Int'l*, pg. 3367
VERO ITALIA SRL—See Hexagon AB; *Int'l*, pg. 3367
VERO ITALIA SRL—See Hexagon AB; *Int'l*, pg. 3367
VERO JAPAN K.K.—See Hexagon AB; *Int'l*, pg. 3367
VERO LIABILITY INSURANCE LIMITED—See Suncorp Group Limited; *Int'l*, pg. 7311
VEROLME SPECIAL EQUIPMENT B.V.—See BENCIS Capital Partners B.V.; *Int'l*, pg. 970
VERO MARINE INSURANCE LIMITED—See Suncorp Group Limited; *Int'l*, pg. 7311
VEROMATIC INTERNATIONAL BV—See Godrej & Boyce Mfg. Co. Ltd.; *Int'l*, pg. 3021
VERONA INVESTMENTS (PTY) LTD—See Oryx Properties Limited; *Int'l*, pg. 5645
VERONA OIL CO., INC.; *U.S. Private*, pg. 4368
VERONA PHARMA PLC; *Int'l*, pg. 8173
VERON GRAUER AG—See Deutsche Post AG; *Int'l*, pg. 2083
VERONI BRANDS CORP.; *U.S. Public*, pg. 2286
VERONICA FOODS COMPANY; *U.S. Private*, pg. 4368
VERONICA PRODUCTION LTD.; *Int'l*, pg. 8173
VERONICA (TELEVISIE)—See Talpa Holding B.V.; *Int'l*, pg. 7448
VERONICA UITGEVERIJ B.V.—See Sanoma Oyj; *Int'l*, pg. 6553
VERONIS SUHLER STEVENSON INTERNATIONAL LTD.—See Veronis Suhler Stevenson Partners LLC; *U.S. Private*, pg. 4368
VERONIS SUHLER STEVENSON PARTNERS LLC; *U.S. Private*, pg. 4368
VEROPAM S.A.; *Int'l*, pg. 8173
VERO SOFTWARE GMBH—See Hexagon AB; *Int'l*, pg. 3367
VERO SOFTWARE LTD.—See Hexagon AB; *Int'l*, pg. 3367
VEROTEC GMBH—See Sto SE & Co. KGaA; *Int'l*, pg. 7219
VEROTOOL TECHNIK GMBH; *Int'l*, pg. 8173
VEROTRADE SARL—See Veropam S.A.; *Int'l*, pg. 8173
VERO USA INC.—See Hexagon AB; *Int'l*, pg. 3367
VERPLAS LIMITED—See Indutrade AB; *Int'l*, pg. 3682
VERRA MOBILITY CORPORATION; *U.S. Public*, pg. 2286
VERRERIE AURYS—See Compagnie de Saint-Gobain SA; *Int'l*, pg. 1737
VERRERIE DE SAINT-JUST—See Compagnie de Saint-Gobain SA; *Int'l*, pg. 1737
VERRERIES BROSSE SAS—See Zignago Vetro S.p.A.; *Int'l*, pg. 8682
VERRERIES & DECORS D'ARMAGNAC S.A.—See Orora Limited; *Int'l*, pg. 5643
VERRERIES DE L'ORNE SAS—See Compagnie de Saint-Gobain SA; *Int'l*, pg. 1733
VERRICA PHARMACEUTICALS, INC.; *U.S. Public*, pg. 2287
VERRILL DANA LLP; *U.S. Private*, pg. 4368
VERRILLON, INC.—See Fujikura Ltd.; *Int'l*, pg. 2827
VERRUS UK LIMITED—See PayPoint plc; *Int'l*, pg. 5764
VERSABANK; *Int'l*, pg. 8173
VERSABANQ INNOVATIONS INC.—See VersaBank; *Int'l*, pg. 8173
VERSA CAPITAL MANAGEMENT, LLC—See Independence Capital Partners, LLC; *U.S. Private*, pg. 2057
VERSACE AUSTRALIA PTY LIMITED—See Capri Holdings Limited; *Int'l*, pg. 1316
VERSACE AUSTRIA GMBH—See Capri Holdings Limited; *Int'l*, pg. 1316
VERSACE BELGIQUE SA—See Capri Holdings Limited; *Int'l*, pg. 1316
VERSACE CANADA, INC.—See Capri Holdings Limited; *Int'l*, pg. 1316
VERSACE DEUTSCHLAND GMBH—See Capri Holdings Limited; *Int'l*, pg. 1316
VERSACE FRANCE S.A.—See Capri Holdings Limited; *Int'l*, pg. 1316
VERSACE MONTE-CARLO S.A.M.—See Capri Holdings Limited; *Int'l*, pg. 1316
VERSACHEM CHILE S.A.—See Illinois Tool Works Inc.; *U.S. Public*, pg. 1111
VERSACOLD INTERNATIONAL CORPORATION—See Bay Grove Capital LLC; *U.S. Private*, pg. 493
VERSACOLD LOGISTICS, LLC—See Americold Realty Trust, Inc.; *U.S. Public*, pg. 113
VERSA COMPANIES; *U.S. Private*, pg. 4368
VERSA ELECTRONICS—See Versa Companies; *U.S. Private*, pg. 4368
VERSAFLEX, INC.—See PPG Industries, Inc.; *U.S. Public*, pg. 1711
VERSAFORM CORPORATION—See SONACA S.A; *Int'l*, pg. 7088
VERSAILLES FINANCIAL CORPORATION; *U.S. Public*, pg. 2287
VERSALIFT NORTHWEST, LLC.—See The Sterling Group, L.P.; *U.S. Private*, pg. 4123
VERSALINK HOLDINGS LIMITED; *Int'l*, pg. 8173
VERSALIS PACIFIC TRADING (SHANGHAI) CO. LTD.—See Eni S.p.A.; *Int'l*, pg. 2438
VERSALIS S.P.A.—See Eni S.p.A.; *Int'l*, pg. 2438
VERSA-MATIC TOOL, INC.—See IDEX Corp; *U.S. Public*, pg. 1092
VERSANT GMBH—See HCL Technologies Ltd.; *Int'l*, pg. 3298
VERSANT HEALTH HOLDCO, INC.—See MetLife, Inc.; *U.S. Public*, pg. 1431
VERSANT, INC. - NEW YORK OFFICE—See Versant, Inc.; *U.S. Private*, pg. 4369
VERSANT, INC.; *U.S. Private*, pg. 4369
VERSAPAY CORPORATION—See Great Hill Partners, L.P; *U.S. Private*, pg. 1763
VERSA POWER SYSTEMS, INC.—See FuelCell Energy, Inc.; *U.S. Public*, pg. 891
VERSA POWER SYSTEMS, LTD.—See FuelCell Energy, Inc.; *U.S. Public*, pg. 891
VERSA PRESS, INC.; *U.S. Private*, pg. 4369
VERSA PRODUCTS COMPANY, INC.; *U.S. Private*, pg. 4369
VERSARA LENDING LLC; *U.S. Private*, pg. 4369
VERSAR-DENVER—See Kingswood Capital Management LLC; *U.S. Private*, pg. 2313
VERSAR ESM OPERATIONS—See Kingswood Capital Management LLC; *U.S. Private*, pg. 2312
VERSARE SOLUTIONS, LLC—See WILsquare Capital LLC; *U.S. Private*, pg. 4532
VERSARIEN PLC; *Int'l*, pg. 8173
VERSARIEN TECHNOLOGIES LIMITED—See Versarien plc; *Int'l*, pg. 8173

VERST GROUP LOGISTICS, INC.

VERSAR, INC.—See Kingswood Capital Management LLC; *U.S. Private*, pg. 2312
VERSAR RISK MANAGEMENT, INC.—See Kingswood Capital Management LLC; *U.S. Private*, pg. 2313
VERSATA, INC.—See ESW Capital, LLC; *U.S. Private*, pg. 1430
VERSATA SOFTWARE, INC.—See ESW Capital, LLC; *U.S. Private*, pg. 1430
VERSATECH AUTOMATION SERVICES, LLC - HARVEY—See VersaTech Automation Services, LLC; *U.S. Private*, pg. 4369
VERSATECH AUTOMATION SERVICES, LLC; *U.S. Private*, pg. 4369
VERSATECH LIMITED—See ENL Limited; *Int'l*, pg. 2441
VERSATERM INC.—See Banneker Partners, LLC; *U.S. Private*, pg. 469
VERSATEX BUILDING PRODUCTS, LLC—See The AZEK Company Inc.; *U.S. Public*, pg. 2035
VERSATILE CREATIVE BERHAD; *Int'l*, pg. 8173
VERSATILE CREATIVE PLASTIC SDN BHD—See Versatile Creative Berhad; *Int'l*, pg. 8174
VERSATILE EUROPE LTD.—See Versatile Systems Inc.; *U.S. Private*, pg. 4369
VERSATILE METALS INC.; *U.S. Private*, pg. 4369
VERSATILE MOBILE SYSTEMS (EUROPE) LTD.—See Versatile Systems Inc.; *U.S. Private*, pg. 4369
VERSATILE PACKAGERS, INC.; *U.S. Private*, pg. 4369
VERSATILE PAPER BOXES SDN. BHD.—See Versatile Creative Berhad; *Int'l*, pg. 8174
VERSATILE POWER, INC.—See Advanced Energy Industries, Inc.; *U.S. Public*, pg. 48
VERSATILE SYSTEMS INC.; *U.S. Private*, pg. 4369
VERSATURE CORP.—See IDT Corporation; *U.S. Public*, pg. 1094
VERSAX, S.A. DE C.V.—See ALFA, S.A.B. de C.V.; *Int'l*, pg. 314
VERSCEND TECHNOLOGIES, INC.—See Veritas Capital Fund Management, LLC; *U.S. Private*, pg. 4365
VERSE COMMUNICATIONS; *U.S. Private*, pg. 4369
VERSEIDAG AG—See Gilde Buy Out Partners B.V.; *Int'l*, pg. 2974
VERSEIDAG AG—See Parcom Capital Management B.V.; *Int'l*, pg. 5740
VERSEIDAG-INDUTEX GMBH—See Gilde Buy Out Partners B.V.; *Int'l*, pg. 2974
VERSEIDAG-INDUTEX GMBH—See Parcom Capital Management B.V.; *Int'l*, pg. 5740
VERSEIDAG-INDUTEX GMBH—See Serge Ferrari SAS; *Int'l*, pg. 6722
VERSE INNOVATION PRIVATE LIMITED; *U.S. Private*, pg. 4369
VERSE MUSIC GROUP LLC—See Bertelsmann SE & Co. KGaA; *Int'l*, pg. 990
VERSEON CORPORATION; *U.S. Public*, pg. 2287
VERSE PAYMENTS LITHUANIA UAB—See Block, Inc.; *U.S. Public*, pg. 362
VERSES AI INC.; *Int'l*, pg. 8174
VERSICHERUNGSAGENTUR WILHELM STEINER GMBH—See UNIQA Insurance Group AG; *Int'l*, pg. 8059
VERSICHERUNGSKONTOR SAARSTAHL GMBH—See Saarstahl AG; *Int'l*, pg. 6461
VERSICHERUNGSMARKT-SERVICEGESELLSCHAFT M.B.H.—See UNIQA Insurance Group AG; *Int'l*, pg. 8059
VERSICHERUNGSSERVICE DER FRANKFURTER SPARKASSE GMBH—See Frankfurter Sparkasse; *Int'l*, pg. 2761
VERSICO, LLC—See Carlisle Companies Incorporated; *U.S. Public*, pg. 436
VERSION 1 SOFTWARE LTD.; *Int'l*, pg. 8174
VERSIONONE, INC.—See TPG Capital, L.P.; *U.S. Public*, pg. 2173
VERSLO ZINIOS, UAB—See Bonnier AB; *Int'l*, pg. 1108
VERSO ADVERTISING, INC.; *U.S. Private*, pg. 4369
VERSOBANK AS; *Int'l*, pg. 8174
VERSO BUCKSPORT LLC—See Billerud AB; *Int'l*, pg. 1030
VERSO CORPORATION - ESCANABA MILL—See Billerud AB; *Int'l*, pg. 1030
VERSO CORPORATION - LUKE MILL—See Billerud AB; *Int'l*, pg. 1030
VERSO CORPORATION - STEVENS POINT MILL—See Goldberg Lindsay & Co., LLC; *U.S. Private*, pg. 1729
VERSO CORPORATION - WISCONSIN RAPIDS MILL—See Billerud AB; *Int'l*, pg. 1030
VERSO MAINE ENERGY LLC—See Billerud AB; *Int'l*, pg. 1030
VERSO PAPER HOLDINGS LLC—See Billerud AB; *Int'l*, pg. 1030
VERSO PAPER LLC—See Billerud AB; *Int'l*, pg. 1030
VERSO QUINNESEC LLC—See Billerud AB; *Int'l*, pg. 1030
VERSO QUINNESEC REP LLC—See Billerud AB; *Int'l*, pg. 1030
VERSORGUNGSBETRIEBE HELGOLAND GMBH—See E.ON SE; *Int'l*, pg. 2260
VERSPEETEN CARTAGE LTD.; *Int'l*, pg. 8174
VERST GROUP LOGISTICS, INC.; *U.S. Private*, pg. 4369

VERST GROUP LOGISTICS, INC.

VERSUM MATERIALS HYT INC.—See Merck KGaA; *Int'l*, pg. 4833
VERSUM MATERIALS INC.—See Merck KGaA; *Int'l*, pg. 4832
VERSUM MATERIALS KOREA INC.—See Merck KGaA; *Int'l*, pg. 4833
VERSUM MATERIALS NETHERLANDS B.V.—See Merck KGaA; *Int'l*, pg. 4833
VERSUM MATERIALS SINGAPORE PTE. LTD.—See Merck KGaA; *Int'l*, pg. 4833
VERSUM MATERIALS TAIWAN CO. LTD.—See Merck KGaA; *Int'l*, pg. 4833
VERSUS SYSTEMS INC.; *Int'l*, pg. 8174
VERSYSS COMMERCIAL SYSTEMS, INC.—See StarDyne Technologies Inc.; *Int'l*, pg. 7176
VERTAFORE, INC.—See Roper Technologies, Inc.; *U.S. Public*, pg. 1814
VERTASEFLI LIMITED—See FLI International Limited; *Int'l*, pg. 2705
VERTBAUDET UK LTD.—See Kering S.A.; *Int'l*, pg. 4136
VERTBOIS S.A R.L.—See Allianz SE; *Int'l*, pg. 356
VERT COMPANHIA SECURITIZADORA S.A.; *Int'l*, pg. 8174
VERTE AUTO SIA—See Tallinna Kaubamaja AS; *Int'l*, pg. 7448
VERTEC BIOSOLVENTS, INC.; *U.S. Private*, pg. 4369
VERTECH GROUP PTY LTD—See Global Energy (Holdings) Ltd.; *Int'l*, pg. 2995
VERTECH UK—See Global Energy (Holdings) Ltd.; *Int'l*, pg. 2995
VERTEC LTD.; *Int'l*, pg. 8174
VERTEC POLYMERS, INC.—See Edgewater Capital Partners, L.P.; *U.S. Private*, pg. 1334
VERTEC SCIENTIFIC LTD.—See discoverIE Group plc; *Int'l*, pg. 2134
VERTEC SCIENTIFIC SA (PTY) LTD.; *Int'l*, pg. 8174
VERTEC—See Compagnie de Saint-Gobain SA; *Int'l*, pg. 1737
VERTEK CORP; *U.S. Private*, pg. 4369
VERTEK SOLUTIONS INC; *U.S. Private*, pg. 4369
VERTELLUS AGRICULTURE & NUTRITION SPECIALTIES LLC—See Black Diamond Capital Holdings, LLC; *U.S. Private*, pg. 571
VERTELLUS AGRICULTURE & NUTRITION SPECIALTIES LLC—See Brightwood Capital Advisors, LLC; *U.S. Private*, pg. 653
VERTELLUS HEALTH & SPECIALTY PRODUCTS LLC - DELAWARE WATER GAP—See Black Diamond Capital Holdings, LLC; *U.S. Private*, pg. 571
VERTELLUS HEALTH & SPECIALTY PRODUCTS LLC - DELAWARE WATER GAP—See Brightwood Capital Advisors, LLC; *U.S. Private*, pg. 653
VERTELLUS HEALTH & SPECIALTY PRODUCTS LLC - ELMA—See Black Diamond Capital Holdings, LLC; *U.S. Private*, pg. 571
VERTELLUS HEALTH & SPECIALTY PRODUCTS LLC - ELMA—See Brightwood Capital Advisors, LLC; *U.S. Private*, pg. 653
VERTELLUS HEALTH & SPECIALTY PRODUCTS LLC—See Black Diamond Capital Holdings, LLC; *U.S. Private*, pg. 571
VERTELLUS HEALTH & SPECIALTY PRODUCTS LLC—See Brightwood Capital Advisors, LLC; *U.S. Private*, pg. 653
VERTELLUS HEALTH & SPECIALTY PRODUCTS LLC - ZEELAND—See Black Diamond Capital Holdings, LLC; *U.S. Private*, pg. 571
VERTELLUS HEALTH & SPECIALTY PRODUCTS LLC - ZEELAND—See Brightwood Capital Advisors, LLC; *U.S. Private*, pg. 654
VERTELLUS PERFORMANCE MATERIALS, INC.—See Black Diamond Capital Holdings, LLC; *U.S. Private*, pg. 571
VERTELLUS PERFORMANCE MATERIALS, INC.—See Brightwood Capital Advisors, LLC; *U.S. Private*, pg. 654
VERTELLUS SPECIALTIES ASIA PACIFIC—See Black Diamond Capital Holdings, LLC; *U.S. Private*, pg. 571
VERTELLUS SPECIALTIES ASIA PACIFIC—See Brightwood Capital Advisors, LLC; *U.S. Private*, pg. 654
VERTELLUS SPECIALTIES INC.—See Black Diamond Capital Holdings, LLC; *U.S. Private*, pg. 571
VERTELLUS SPECIALTIES INC.—See Brightwood Capital Advisors, LLC; *U.S. Private*, pg. 653
VERTELLUS SPECIALTIES UK LTD.—See Black Diamond Capital Holdings, LLC; *U.S. Private*, pg. 571
VERTELLUS SPECIALTIES UK LTD.—See Brightwood Capital Advisors, LLC; *U.S. Private*, pg. 654
VERTERE S.R.L.—See Star7 S.p.A.; *Int'l*, pg. 7175
VERTESI EROMU ZRT.—See MVM Magyar Villamos Muvek Zrt.; *Int'l*, pg. 5108
VERTEX AEROSPACE LLC—See V2X, Inc.; *U.S. Public*, pg. 2270
VERTEX BODY SCIENCES INC.; *U.S. Private*, pg. 4369
VERTEX BUSINESS SERVICES LLC—See Keystone Group, L.P.; *U.S. Private*, pg. 2300
VERTEX CHEMICAL CORPORATION—See Hawkins, Inc.; *U.S. Public*, pg. 989
THE VERTEX COMPANIES, INC.—See Wind Point Advisors LLC; *U.S. Private*, pg. 4536

VERTEX CUSTOMER SERVICES INDIA PRIVATE LIMITED—See Keystone Group, L.P.; *U.S. Private*, pg. 2300
VERTEX DATA SCIENCE LIMITED—See Keystone Group, L.P.; *U.S. Private*, pg. 2300
VERTEX-DENTAL B.V.—See 3D Systems Corporation; *U.S. Public*, pg. 4
VERTEX DISTRIBUTION; *U.S. Private*, pg. 4369
VERTEX ENERGY, INC.; *U.S. Public*, pg. 2287
VERTEX ENGINEERING SERVICES, INC.; *U.S. Private*, pg. 4370
VERTEX FASTENERS, INC.—See Leggett & Platt, Incorporated; *U.S. Public*, pg. 1304
VERTEX, INC.; *U.S. Public*, pg. 2287
VERTEX LOGISTICS USA INC.—See Vertex Resource Group Ltd.; *Int'l*, pg. 8174
VERTEX MINERALS LIMITED; *Int'l*, pg. 8174
VERTEX PHARMACEUTICALS (AUSTRALIA) PTY. LTD.—See Vertex Pharmaceuticals Incorporated; *U.S. Public*, pg. 2287
VERTEX PHARMACEUTICALS (CANADA) INCORPORATED—See Vertex Pharmaceuticals Incorporated; *U.S. Public*, pg. 2287
VERTEX PHARMACEUTICALS (EUROPE) LIMITED—See Vertex Pharmaceuticals Incorporated; *U.S. Public*, pg. 2287
VERTEX PHARMACEUTICALS GMBH—See Vertex Pharmaceuticals Incorporated; *U.S. Public*, pg. 2287
VERTEX PHARMACEUTICALS INCORPORATED; *U.S. Public*, pg. 2287
VERTEX PHARMACEUTICALS (ITALY) S.R.L.—See Vertex Pharmaceuticals Incorporated; *U.S. Public*, pg. 2287
VERTEX PHARMACEUTICALS (NETHERLANDS) B.V.—See Vertex Pharmaceuticals Incorporated; *U.S. Public*, pg. 2287
VERTEX PHARMACEUTICALS (SAN DIEGO) LLC—See Vertex Pharmaceuticals Incorporated; *U.S. Public*, pg. 2287
VERTEX PHARMACEUTICALS (SPAIN), S.L.—See Vertex Pharmaceuticals Incorporated; *U.S. Public*, pg. 2287
VERTEX RECOVERY L.P.—See Vertex Energy, Inc.; *U.S. Public*, pg. 2287
VERTEX RESOURCE GROUP, INC.; *U.S. Private*, pg. 4370
VERTEX RESOURCE GROUP LTD.; *Int'l*, pg. 8174
VERTEX RSI—See General Dynamics Corporation; *U.S. Public*, pg. 916
VERTEX SECURITIES LIMITED; *Int'l*, pg. 8174
VERTEX SYSTEM CORPORATION—See Marketech International Corp.; *Int'l*, pg. 4696
VERTEX VENDING SERVICES LTD.—See Nayax Ltd.; *Int'l*, pg. 5178
VERTEX WIRELESS LLC; *U.S. Private*, pg. 4370
VERTICAL APPLICATIONS, INC.—See MindPetal Software Solutions, Inc.; *U.S. Private*, pg. 2741
VERTICAL BRIDGE, LLC—See DigitalBridge Group, Inc.; *U.S. Public*, pg. 665
VERTICAL COMPUTER SYSTEMS, INC.; *U.S. Private*, pg. 4370
VERTICAL CUBED—See Fine Sounds S.p.A.; *Int'l*, pg. 2673
VERTICAL DIMENSIONS, LLC—See Golden Gate Capital Management II, LLC; *U.S. Private*, pg. 1732
VERTICAL EXPLORATION INC.; *Int'l*, pg. 8174
VERTICAL INDUSTRIES LIMITED; *Int'l*, pg. 8175
VERTICAL INTERNATIONAL HOLDINGS LIMITED - DONGGUAN FACTORY—See Vertical International Holdings Limited; *Int'l*, pg. 8175
VERTICAL INTERNATIONAL HOLDINGS LIMITED; *Int'l*, pg. 8175
VERTICAL LIMIT CONSTRUCTION, LLC—See QualTek Services Inc.; *U.S. Public*, pg. 1748
VERTICAL MANAGEMENT SYSTEMS, INC.—See NewSpring Capital LLC; *U.S. Private*, pg. 2918
VERTICAL MARKETING NETWORK LLC; *U.S. Private*, pg. 4370
VERTICAL MEASURES, LLC—See Investis Limited; *Int'l*, pg. 3780
VERTICAL MEDIA GMBH—See Axel Springer SE; *Int'l*, pg. 767
VERTICAL PEAK HOLDINGS INC; *Int'l*, pg. 8175
VERTICAL PHARMACEUTICALS, LLC—See RVL Pharmaceuticals plc; *U.S. Public*, pg. 1827
VERTICAL PLUS LIMITED—See Software Circle plc; *Int'l*, pg. 7057
VERTICALRESPONSE, INC.; *U.S. Private*, pg. 4370
VERTICAL SALES & MARKETING, INC.; *U.S. Private*, pg. 4370
VERTICALSCOPE HOLDINGS INC.; *Int'l*, pg. 8175
VERTICAL SEARCH WORKS INC.; *U.S. Private*, pg. 4370
VERTICAL SOFTWARE, INC.—See Valsef Group; *Int'l*, pg. 8123
VERTICAL S.P.A.—See Franklin Electric Co., Inc.; *U.S. Public*, pg. 879
VERTICAL STATION SAS—See Television Francaise 1 S.A.; *Int'l*, pg. 7543
VERTICAL SUPPLY GROUP—See Gridiron Capital, LLC; *U.S. Private*, pg. 1786

CORPORATE AFFILIATIONS

VERTICAL SYSTEMS, INC.—See Atlantic Street Capital Management LLC; *U.S. Private*, pg. 374
VERTICAL TRANSPORTATION EXCELLENCE—See OceanSound Partners, LP; *U.S. Private*, pg. 2991
VERTICAL VENTURES PARTNERS, INC.; *U.S. Private*, pg. 4370
VERTICAL VET LLC—See Vimian Group AB; *Int'l*, pg. 8208
VERTICAL WEB MEDIA LLC; *U.S. Private*, pg. 4370
VERTICA SYSTEMS, LLC—See Micro Focus International plc; *Int'l*, pg. 4877
VERTICE 360 S.A.—See Grupo Ezentis S.A.; *Int'l*, pg. 3129
VERTICE TRESCIENTOS SESENTA GRADOS, S.A.; *Int'l*, pg. 8175
VERTIC INTERNATIONAL, SA—See Delta Plus Group; *Int'l*, pg. 2020
VERTIC NEDERLAND BV—See Delta Plus Group; *Int'l*, pg. 2020
VERTICORE COMMUNICATIONS LTD.—See TEGNA Inc.; *U.S. Public*, pg. 1991
VERTICO XTREME LLC—See EdiliziAcrobatica S.p.A.; *Int'l*, pg. 2310
VERTIC SUISSE SARL—See Delta Plus Group; *Int'l*, pg. 2020
VERTIGIS HOLDINGS LTD.—See Battery Ventures, L.P.; *U.S. Private*, pg. 489
VERTIGLO; *U.S. Private*, pg. 4370
VERTIGO COMICS—See Warner Bros. Discovery, Inc.; *U.S. Public*, pg. 2328
VERTIGO FILMS S.L—See Wild Bunch AG; *Int'l*, pg. 8409
VERTIGO S.R.L.—See CTS Eventim AG & Co. KGaA; *Int'l*, pg. 1874
VERTIKAL HELSEASSISTANSE AS—See Sampo plc; *Int'l*, pg. 6508
VERTIKOM AUSTRIA GMBH—See ASM Group S.A.; *Int'l*, pg. 625
VERTIKOM GMBH—See ASM Group S.A.; *Int'l*, pg. 625
VERTIKOM SALES BERLIN GMBH—See ASM Group S.A.; *Int'l*, pg. 625
VERTIKOM SALES GMBH—See ASM Group S.A.; *Int'l*, pg. 625
VERTIKOM SWITZERLAND GMBH—See ASM Group S.A.; *Int'l*, pg. 625
VERTILUX LTD.; *U.S. Private*, pg. 4370
VERTIQUE, INC.—See Krones AG; *Int'l*, pg. 4306
VERTIV (AUSTRALIA) PTY. LTD.—See Vertiv Holdings Co; *U.S. Public*, pg. 2288
VERTIV CANADA ULC—See Vertiv Holdings Co; *U.S. Public*, pg. 2288
VERTIV CZECH REPUBLIC S.R.O—See Vertiv Holdings Co; *U.S. Public*, pg. 2288
VERTIV DEL PERU S.A.C.—See Vertiv Holdings Co; *U.S. Public*, pg. 2289
VERTIVE, LLC; *U.S. Private*, pg. 4370
VERTIV ENERGY PRIVATE LIMITED—See Vertiv Holdings Co; *U.S. Public*, pg. 2288
VERTI VERSICHERUNG AG—See MAPFRE S.A.; *Int'l*, pg. 4685
VERTIV FRANCE—See Vertiv Holdings Co; *U.S. Public*, pg. 2289
VERTIV GMBH—See Vertiv Holdings Co; *U.S. Public*, pg. 2288
VERTIV GROUP CORPORATION—See Vertiv Holdings Co; *U.S. Public*, pg. 2288
VERTIV HOLDINGS CO; *U.S. Public*, pg. 2287
VERTIV HOLDINGS, LLC—See Vertiv Holdings Co; *U.S. Public*, pg. 2288
VERTIV (HONG KONG) LTD.—See Vertiv Holdings Co; *U.S. Public*, pg. 2289
VERTIV INTEGRATED SYSTEMS GMBH—See Vertiv Holdings Co; *U.S. Public*, pg. 2289
VERTIV INTERNATIONAL DESIGNATED ACTIVITY COMPANY—See Vertiv Holdings Co; *U.S. Public*, pg. 2289
VERTIV MIDDLE EAST DMCC—See Vertiv Holdings Co; *U.S. Public*, pg. 2289
VERTIV S.A.—See Vertiv Holdings Co; *U.S. Public*, pg. 2289
VERTIV (SINGAPORE) PTE. LTD.—See Vertiv Holdings Co; *U.S. Public*, pg. 2288
VERTIV SWEDEN AB—See Vertiv Holdings Co; *U.S. Public*, pg. 2289
VERTIX SGPS SA—See Promotora de Informaciones S.A.; *Int'l*, pg. 5996
VERTMARKETS, INC.—See Jameson Publishing Inc.; *U.S. Private*, pg. 2185
VERTOGAS B.V.—See N.V. Nederlandse Gasunie; *Int'l*, pg. 5117
VERTOS MEDICAL INC.—See Stryker Corporation; *U.S. Public*, pg. 1958
VERTOZ ADVERTISING LIMITED; *Int'l*, pg. 8175
VERTOZ LTD.—See Vertoz Advertising Limited; *Int'l*, pg. 8175
VERTRIEB DEUTSCHLAND IMMOBILIEN GMBH—See MLP SE; *Int'l*, pg. 5004
VERTRIEBSBURO WEBASTO PRODUCT BENELUX—See Webasto SE; *Int'l*, pg. 8364

COMPANY NAME INDEX

VERTRIEBSGESELLSCHAFT MBH DER DEUTSCHEN BANK PRIVAT- UND GESCHAFTSKUNDEN—See Deutsche Bank Aktiengesellschaft; *Int'l*, pg. 2062
VERTRO, INC.—See Inuvo, Inc.; *U.S. Public*, pg. 1161
VERTRUE INC.; *U.S. Private*, pg. 4370
VERTUA LTD.; *Int'l*, pg. 8175
VERTU MOTORS (CHINGFORD) LIMITED—See General Motors Company; *U.S. Public*, pg. 928
VERTU MOTORS PLC; *Int'l*, pg. 8175
VERTU MOTORS (VMC) LIMITED—See Vertu Motors plc; *Int'l*, pg. 8175
VERTU SECURITY LIMITED—See Emerson Electric Co.; *U.S. Public*, pg. 752
VERU INC.; *U.S. Public*, pg. 2289
VERUSA HOLDING A.S.; *Int'l*, pg. 8175
VERUSATURK GIRISIM SERMAYESI YATIRIM ORTAKLIGI A.S.; *Int'l*, pg. 8175
VERUS BANK OF COMMERCE; *U.S. Private*, pg. 4370
VERUS CONSULTING GROUP LLP; *U.S. Private*, pg. 4370
VERUS INTERNATIONAL, INC.; *U.S. Public*, pg. 2290
VERUS TECHNOLOGY GROUP, INC.—See Arlington Capital Partners LLC; *U.S. Private*, pg. 327
VERUS TITLE INC.—See Fathom Holdings Inc.; *U.S. Public*, pg. 824
VERVE, A CREDIT UNION; *U.S. Private*, pg. 4370
VERVE CLOUD, INC.—See Digerati Technologies, Inc.; *U.S. Public*, pg. 661
VERVE GROUP SE; *Int'l*, pg. 8176
VERVENT INC.; *U.S. Private*, pg. 4371
VERVE THERAPEUTICS, INC.; *U.S. Public*, pg. 2290
VERWALTUNG MS PACIFIC BETEILIGUNGSGESELLSCHAFT MBH—See M.M. Warburg & Co. KGaA; *Int'l*, pg. 4616
VERWALTUNGSGESELLSCHAFT BAUSTOFFWERKE DRESDEN MBH—See Heidelberg Materials AG; *Int'l*, pg. 3320
VERWALTUNGSGESELLSCHAFT HANSEATISCHES WEIN- UND SEKT-KONTOR HAWESKO M.B.H.—See Hawesko Holding AG; *Int'l*, pg. 3288
VERWALTUNGSGESELLSCHAFT KATHARINENHOF MBH—See UniCredit S.p.A.; *Int'l*, pg. 8041
VERWALTUNGSGESELLSCHAFT MAX VERLAG MBH—See Hubert Burda Media Holding Kommanditgesellschaft; *Int'l*, pg. 3520
VERWALTUNG SVEA BUILDING CONTROL SYSTEMS GMBH—See Schneider Electric SE; *Int'l*, pg. 6635
VERY GOOD ESTATE SDN BHD—See IOI Corporation Berhad; *Int'l*, pg. 3792
THE VERY GOOD FOOD COMPANY, INC.; *Int'l*, pg. 7698
VERY GOOD TOUR CO., LTD.; *Int'l*, pg. 8176
VERY, INC.; *U.S. Private*, pg. 4371
VERY ITALIAN FOOD (V.I.F.) S.R.L.—See InfraVia Capital Partners SAS; *Int'l*, pg. 3699
VERYKOOL USA, INC.—See Simply, Inc.; *U.S. Public*, pg. 1882
VERYS, LLC—See West Monroe Partners, LLC; *U.S. Private*, pg. 4486
VERZATEC, S.A.B. DE C.V.; *Int'l*, pg. 8176
VESA HEALTH & TECHNOLOGY, INC.; *U.S. Private*, pg. 4371
VESCO FOODS PTY. LTD.; *Int'l*, pg. 8176
VESCO MATERIAL HANDLING EQUIPMENT; *U.S. Private*, pg. 4371
VESCO OIL CORPORATION; *U.S. Private*, pg. 4371
VESELIN MASLESA A.D. BANJA LUKA; *Int'l*, pg. 8176
VESEY STREET CAPITAL PARTNERS, L.L.C; *U.S. Private*, pg. 4371
VES ISRAEL—See Veolia Environnement S.A.; *Int'l*, pg. 8159
VESNA TRADING PLC—See Einhell Germany AG; *Int'l*, pg. 2334
VESON HOLDINGS LIMITED; *Int'l*, pg. 8176
VESPA CAPITAL FRANCE—See Vespa Capital LLP; *Int'l*, pg. 8176
VESPA CAPITAL LLP; *Int'l*, pg. 8176
VESPA CAPITAL SA—See Vespa Capital LLP; *Int'l*, pg. 8176
VESPA GROUP, LLC; *U.S. Private*, pg. 4371
VESPA INC.; *Int'l*, pg. 8176
VESPA LABORATORIES, INC.—See Lundbeckfonden; *Int'l*, pg. 4579
VESPER HEALTHCARE, INC.—See The Ensign Group, Inc.; *U.S. Public*, pg. 2072
VESPYR BRANDS LLC—See Aurobindo Pharma Ltd.; *Int'l*, pg. 713
VES SA—See VINCI S.A.; *Int'l*, pg. 8240
VES S.A.; *Int'l*, pg. 8176
VESSCO LLC; *U.S. Private*, pg. 4371
VESSEL CO., LTD.; *Int'l*, pg. 8176
VESTA CORP.; *U.S. Private*, pg. 4371
VEST ADVERTISING; *U.S. Private*, pg. 4371
VESTA EQUITY, LLC; *U.S. Private*, pg. 4371
VESTA GLOBAL LIMITED—See Illinois Tool Works Inc.; *U.S. Public*, pg. 1111
VESTA (GUANGZHOU) CATERING EQUIPMENT CO. LTD—See Illinois Tool Works Inc.; *U.S. Public*, pg. 1111
VESTA HOUSING SOLUTIONS LLC—See McGrath RentCorp.; *U.S. Public*, pg. 1407

VESTA INC.—See Sientra, Inc.; *U.S. Public*, pg. 1876
VESTA, INC.; *U.S. Private*, pg. 4371
VESTAL MANUFACTURING ENTERPRISES, INC.; *U.S. Private*, pg. 4371
VESTAR CAPITAL PARTNERS, LLC; *U.S. Private*, pg. 4371
VESTAR/GRAY INVESTORS LLC; *U.S. Private*, pg. 4373
VESTAS-AMERICAN WIND TECHNOLOGY, INC.—See Vestas Wind Systems A/S; *Int'l*, pg. 8177
VESTAS AMERICAS A/S—See Vestas Wind Systems A/S; *Int'l*, pg. 8177
VESTAS ARGENTINA S.A.—See Vestas Wind Systems A/S; *Int'l*, pg. 8177
VESTAS ASIA PACIFIC A/S—See Vestas Wind Systems A/S; *Int'l*, pg. 8177
VESTAS ASIA PACIFIC WIND TECHNOLOGY PTE. LTD.—See Vestas Wind Systems A/S; *Int'l*, pg. 8177
VESTAS-AUSTRALIAN WIND TECHNOLOGY PTY. LTD.—See Vestas Wind Systems A/S; *Int'l*, pg. 8177
VESTAS BENELUX B.V.—See Vestas Wind Systems A/S; *Int'l*, pg. 8177
VESTAS BLADES AMERICA, INC.—See Vestas Wind Systems A/S; *Int'l*, pg. 8177
VESTAS BLADES A/S—See Vestas Wind Systems A/S; *Int'l*, pg. 8177
VESTAS BLADES DEUTSCHLAND GMBH—See Vestas Wind Systems A/S; *Int'l*, pg. 8177
VESTAS BLADES ITALIA S.R.L.—See Vestas Wind Systems A/S; *Int'l*, pg. 8177
VESTAS BLADES SPAIN S.L.U.—See Vestas Wind Systems A/S; *Int'l*, pg. 8177
VESTAS-CANADIAN WIND TECHNOLOGY INC.—See Vestas Wind Systems A/S; *Int'l*, pg. 8177
VESTAS-CELTIC WIND TECHNOLOGY LTD.—See Vestas Wind Systems A/S; *Int'l*, pg. 8177
VESTAS CENTRAL EUROPE A/S—See Vestas Wind Systems A/S; *Int'l*, pg. 8177
VESTAS CHILE TURBINAS EOLICA LIMITADE—See Vestas Wind Systems A/S; *Int'l*, pg. 8177
VESTAS CONTROL SYSTEMS A/S—See Vestas Wind Systems A/S; *Int'l*, pg. 8177
VESTAS CONTROL SYSTEMS SPAIN S.L.U.—See Vestas Wind Systems A/S; *Int'l*, pg. 8177
VESTAS DEUTSCHLAND GMBH—See Vestas Wind Systems A/S; *Int'l*, pg. 8177
VESTAS DO BRASIL LTDA.—See Vestas Wind Systems A/S; *Int'l*, pg. 8178
VESTAS EOLICA S.A.U.—See Vestas Wind Systems A/S; *Int'l*, pg. 8177
VESTAS FRANCE SAS—See Vestas Wind Systems A/S; *Int'l*, pg. 8177
VESTAS HELLAS WIND TECHNOLOGY S.A.—See Vestas Wind Systems A/S; *Int'l*, pg. 8177
VESTASIA LIMITED; *Int'l*, pg. 8178
VESTAS ITALIA S.R.L.—See Vestas Wind Systems A/S; *Int'l*, pg. 8177
VESTAS KOREA WIND TECHNOLOGY LTD.—See Vestas Wind Systems A/S; *Int'l*, pg. 8177
VESTAS MANUFACTURING A/S—See Vestas Wind Systems A/S; *Int'l*, pg. 8177
VESTAS MED (CYPRUS) LTD.—See Vestas Wind Systems A/S; *Int'l*, pg. 8177
VESTAS MEDITERRANEAN A/S—See Vestas Wind Systems A/S; *Int'l*, pg. 8177
VESTAS NACELLES AMERICA, INC.—See Vestas Wind Systems A/S; *Int'l*, pg. 8177
VESTAS NACELLES A/S—See Vestas Wind Systems A/S; *Int'l*, pg. 8177
VESTAS NEW ZEALAND WIND TECHNOLOGY LTD.—See Vestas Wind Systems A/S; *Int'l*, pg. 8177
VESTAS NORTHERN EUROPE AB—See Vestas Wind Systems A/S; *Int'l*, pg. 8178
VESTAS NORTHERN EUROPE A/S—See Vestas Wind Systems A/S; *Int'l*, pg. 8178
VESTAS NORWAY AS—See Vestas Wind Systems A/S; *Int'l*, pg. 8178
VESTA—See Hypemarks, Inc.; *U.S. Private*, pg. 2019
VESTAS OSTERREICH GMBH—See Vestas Wind Systems A/S; *Int'l*, pg. 8177
VESTAS POLAND SP. Z O.O.—See Vestas Wind Systems A/S; *Int'l*, pg. 8178
VESTAS RUZGAR ENERJISI SISTEMLERI SANAYI VE TICARET LTD. SIRKETI—See Vestas Wind Systems A/S; *Int'l*, pg. 8177
VESTAS SERVICES GMBH—See Vestas Wind Systems A/S; *Int'l*, pg. 8177
VESTAS SPARE PARTS & REPAIR A/S—See Vestas Wind Systems A/S; *Int'l*, pg. 8178
VESTAS SPARE PARTS & REPAIR SPAIN, S.L.—See Vestas Wind Systems A/S; *Int'l*, pg. 8178
VESTAS TAIWAN LTD.—See Vestas Wind Systems A/S; *Int'l*, pg. 8177
VESTAS TECHNOLOGY R&D CHENNAI PTE. LTD.—See Vestas Wind Systems A/S; *Int'l*, pg. 8178
VESTAS TECHNOLOGY R&D SINGAPORE PTE. LTD.—See Vestas Wind Systems A/S; *Int'l*, pg. 8178
VESTAS TECHNOLOGY (UK) LIMITED—See Vestas Wind Systems A/S; *Int'l*, pg. 8178

VESTUS GROUP

VESTAS TOWERS AMERICA, INC.—See Vestas Wind Systems A/S; *Int'l*, pg. 8177
VESTAS WIND SYSTEMS A/S; *Int'l*, pg. 8176
VESTAS WIND TECHNOLOGY (BEIJING) CO., LTD.—See Vestas Wind Systems A/S; *Int'l*, pg. 8177
VESTAS WIND TECHNOLOGY JAPAN CO., LTD.—See Vestas Wind Systems A/S; *Int'l*, pg. 8177
VESTATE GROUP HOLDINGS LIMITED; *Int'l*, pg. 8178
VESTBASE AS—See Eidesvik Holding A/S; *Int'l*, pg. 2329
VESTBASE AS—See Simon Mokster Shipping A/S; *Int'l*, pg. 6932
VESTBASE AS—See Wilh. Wilhelmsen Holding ASA; *Int'l*, pg. 8410
VESTCOM INTERNATIONAL, INC.—See Charlesbank Capital Partners, LLC; *U.S. Private*, pg. 856
THE VESTCOR COMPANIES; *U.S. Private*, pg. 4130
VESTED HEALTH LLC; *U.S. Private*, pg. 4373
VESTED METALS INTERNATIONAL, LLC; *U.S. Private*, pg. 4373
VESTEH LTD.—See Leifheit AG; *Int'l*, pg. 4447
VESTEL BEYAZ ESYA SANAYI VE TICARET AS; *Int'l*, pg. 8178
VESTEL ELEKTRONIK SANAYI VE TICARET A.S.; *Int'l*, pg. 8178
VESTERALENS NATURPRODUKTER AB—See Pfizer Inc.; *U.S. Public*, pg. 1683
VESTERALENS NATURPRODUKTER AS—See Pfizer Inc.; *U.S. Public*, pg. 1683
VESTFOLD FJELLBORING AS—See Nordisk Bergteknik AB; *Int'l*, pg. 5424
VESTFROST A/S; *Int'l*, pg. 8178
VESTIGO CAPITAL ADVISORS LLP; *Int'l*, pg. 8178
VESTIGO PETROLEUM SDN BHD—See Petroliam Nasional Berhad; *Int'l*, pg. 5831
VESTIN GROUP, INC.; *U.S. Private*, pg. 4373
VESTIN MORTGAGE, LLC—See Vestin Group, Inc.; *U.S. Private*, pg. 4373
VESTIN REALTY MORTGAGE II, INC.; *U.S. Private*, pg. 4373
VESTIN REALTY MORTGAGE I, INC.—See Vestin Group, Inc.; *U.S. Private*, pg. 4373
VESTIS CORP; *U.S. Public*, pg. 2290
VESTIS RETAIL GROUP, LLC—See Independence Capital Partners, LLC; *U.S. Private*, pg. 2057
VESTIS (ROCHESTER), LLC—See Vestis Corp; *U.S. Public*, pg. 2290
VESTIS (SYRACUSE), LLC—See Vestis Corp; *U.S. Public*, pg. 2290
VESTJYSK BANK A/S—See Arbejdernes Landsbank A/S; *Int'l*, pg. 537
VESTKANTEN AS—See Olav Thon Eiendomsselskap ASA; *Int'l*, pg. 5552
VESTMARK, INC.; *U.S. Private*, pg. 4373
VESTNER AUFZUGE GMBH; *Int'l*, pg. 8178
VESTNER FUJITEC DEUTSCHLAND GMBH—See Vestner Aufzuge GmbH; *Int'l*, pg. 8178
VESTNYTT AS—See Schibsted ASA; *Int'l*, pg. 6617
VESTOLIT GMBH—See Grupo Empresarial Kaluz S.A. de C.V.; *Int'l*, pg. 3128
VESTOR CAPITAL, LLC—See Clayton, Dubilier & Rice, LLC; *U.S. Private*, pg. 924
VESTOR CAPITAL, LLC—See Stone Point Capital LLC; *U.S. Private*, pg. 3824
VESTPAK AS—See Freudenberg SE; *Int'l*, pg. 2791
VESTUM AB; *Int'l*, pg. 8178
VESTURE CORPORATION; *U.S. Private*, pg. 4373
VESTURE GROUP INC.; *U.S. Private*, pg. 4373
VESTUS GROUP; *U.S. Private*, pg. 4373
VESUVIUS ADVANCED CERAMICS (CHINA) CO., LTD.—See Vesuvius plc; *Int'l*, pg. 8179
VESUVIUS ADVANCED CERAMICS (SUZHOU) CO. LTD.—See Vesuvius plc; *Int'l*, pg. 8179
VESUVIUS AUSTRALIA PTY. LTD.—See Vesuvius plc; *Int'l*, pg. 8179
VESUVIUS BELGIUM N.V.—See Vesuvius plc; *Int'l*, pg. 8179
VESUVIUS CANADA, INC.—See Vesuvius plc; *Int'l*, pg. 8179
VESUVIUS CHINA HOLDINGS CO. LIMITED—See Vesuvius plc; *Int'l*, pg. 8179
VESUVIUS COLOMBIA SAS—See Vesuvius plc; *Int'l*, pg. 8179
VESUVIUS CORPORATION SA—See Vesuvius plc; *Int'l*, pg. 8179
VESUVIUS CSD SP Z.O.O.—See Vesuvius plc; *Int'l*, pg. 8179
VESUVIUS EMIRATES FZE—See Vesuvius plc; *Int'l*, pg. 8179
VESUVIUS FOUNDRY PRODUCTS (SUZHOU) CO., LTD.—See Vesuvius plc; *Int'l*, pg. 8179
VESUVIUS FOUNDRY TECHNOLOGIES (JIANGSU) CO., LTD.—See Vesuvius plc; *Int'l*, pg. 8179
VESUVIUS GMBH—See Vesuvius plc; *Int'l*, pg. 8179
VESUVIUS GROUP S.A./N.V.—See Vesuvius plc; *Int'l*, pg. 8179
VESUVIUS IBERICA REFRACTARIOS S.A.—See Vesuvius plc; *Int'l*, pg. 8179
VESUVIUS INDIA LIMITED - MEHSANA FACTORY—See Vesuvius India Limited; *Int'l*, pg. 8178

VESUVIUS INDIA LIMITED

VESUVIUS INDIA LIMITED; *Int'l*, pg. 8178
VESUVIUS INDIA LIMITED - VISAKHAPATNAM FACTORY 1—See Vesuvius India Limited; *Int'l*, pg. 8178
VESUVIUS INDIA LIMITED - VISAKHAPATNAM FACTORY 2—See Vesuvius India Limited; *Int'l*, pg. 8178
VESUVIUS ISTANBUL REFRAKTER SANAYI VE TICARET AS—See Vesuvius plc; *Int'l*, pg. 8179
VESUVIUS ITALIA SPA—See Vesuvius plc; *Int'l*, pg. 8179
VESUVIUS JAPAN INC.—See Vesuvius plc; *Int'l*, pg. 8179
VESUVIUS LLC—See Vesuvius plc; *Int'l*, pg. 8179
VESUVIUS MALAYSIA SDN. BHD.—See Vesuvius plc; *Int'l*, pg. 8179
VESUVIUS MEXICO S.A. DE C.V.—See Vesuvius plc; *Int'l*, pg. 8179
VESUVIUS MID-EAST LIMITED—See Vesuvius plc; *Int'l*, pg. 8179
VESUVIUS MORAVIA, S.R.L.—See Vesuvius plc; *Int'l*, pg. 8179
VESUVIUS PLC; *Int'l*, pg. 8178
VESUVIUS POLAND SPOLKA Z.O.O—See Vesuvius plc; *Int'l*, pg. 8179
VESUVIUS RAS AL KHAIMAH FZ-LLC—See Vesuvius plc; *Int'l*, pg. 8179
VESUVIUS REFRACTARIOS DE CHILE SA—See Vesuvius plc; *Int'l*, pg. 8179
VESUVIUS REFRATARIOS LTDA.—See Vesuvius plc; *Int'l*, pg. 8179
VESUVIUS SCANDINAVIA AB—See Vesuvius plc; *Int'l*, pg. 8179
VESUVIUS SOUTH AFRICA (PTY) LTD.—See Vesuvius plc; *Int'l*, pg. 8179
VESUVIUS UK LIMITED—See Vesuvius plc; *Int'l*, pg. 8179
VESUVIUS USA CORP.—See Vesuvius plc; *Int'l*, pg. 8180
VESUVIUS (V.E.A.R.) S.A.—See Vesuvius plc; *Int'l*, pg. 8179
VESUVIUS ZYAROCK CERAMICS (SUZHOU) CO., LTD.—See Vesuvius plc; *Int'l*, pg. 8180
VESZPREM-KOGENERACIO ENERGIATERMELO ZRT.—See E.ON SE; *Int'l*, pg. 2260
VESZTER KFT.—See PHOENIX Pharmahandel GmbH & Co. KG; *Int'l*, pg. 5855
VETA PHARMA AD—See Sopharma AD; *Int'l*, pg. 7108
VETCO ENTERPRISE GMBH—See NOV, Inc.; *U.S. Public*, pg. 1547
VETDEPOT.COM; *U.S. Private*, pg. 4373
VETEKS AD; *Int'l*, pg. 8180
VETEK SAU—See Arkema S.A.; *Int'l*, pg. 571
VETERA GMBH—See Nordhealth AS; *Int'l*, pg. 5419
VETERAN CONSTRUCTORS, INC.; *U.S. Private*, pg. 4373
VETERAN CORPS OF AMERICA; *U.S. Private*, pg. 4373
VETERAN INFRASTRUCTURE PRODUCTS LLC; *U.S. Private*, pg. 4373
VETERAN LOGISTICS, INC.; *U.S. Private*, pg. 4373
VETERANPOOLEN AB; *Int'l*, pg. 8180
VETERANS ENTERPRISE TECHNOLOGY SOLUTIONS, INC.; *U.S. Private*, pg. 4373
VETERANS HOME CARE LLC; *U.S. Private*, pg. 4374
VETERANS INC.; *U.S. Private*, pg. 4374
VETERANS OF FOREIGN WARS OF THE UNITED STATES; *U.S. Private*, pg. 4374
VETERANS OIL INC.; *U.S. Private*, pg. 4374
VETERANS TRADING CO., LLC.; *U.S. Private*, pg. 4374
VETERAN TICKETS FOUNDATION; *U.S. Private*, pg. 4373
VETERINARIAN'S OUTLET INCORPORATED; *U.S. Private*, pg. 4374
VETERINARSKA STANICA A.D., BANJA LUKA; *Int'l*, pg. 8180
VETERINARSKA STANICA A.D., BIJELJINA; *Int'l*, pg. 8180
VETERINARSKA STANICA A.D., DOBOJ; *Int'l*, pg. 8180
VETERINARSKA STANICA A.D., KIKINDA; *Int'l*, pg. 8180
VETERINARSKA STANICA A.D., NEVESINJE; *Int'l*, pg. 8180
VETERINARSKA STANICA A.D.; *Int'l*, pg. 8180
VETERINARSKA STANICA A.D.; *Int'l*, pg. 8180
VETERINARSKA STANICA A.D., VLASENICA; *Int'l*, pg. 8180
VETERINARSKA STANICA A.D., ZVORNIK; *Int'l*, pg. 8180
VETERINARSKA STANICA KOCELJEVA A.D.; *Int'l*, pg. 8180
VETERINARSKA STANICA KRAGUJEVAC A.D.; *Int'l*, pg. 8180
VETERINARSKA STANICA MIONICA A.D.; *Int'l*, pg. 8180
VETERINARSKA STANICA SABAC A.D.; *Int'l*, pg. 8180
VETERINARSKA STANICA TOPOLA A.D.; *Int'l*, pg. 8180
VETERINARSKA STANICA ZRENJANIN AD; *Int'l*, pg. 8180
VETERINARSKI CENTAR KRALJEVO A.D.; *Int'l*, pg. 8180
VETERINARSKI ZAVOD SUBOTICA A.D.—See Labiana Life Sciences, S.A.; *Int'l*, pg. 4389
VETERINARY MEDICINE INSTITUTE ZEMUN INC., BELGRADE; *Int'l*, pg. 8180
VETERINARY ORTHOPEDIC IMPLANTS, LLC—See Vimian Group AB; *Int'l*, pg. 8208

VETERINARY & POULTRY SUPPLY; *U.S. Private*, pg. 4374
VETERINARY SERVICE INC.; *U.S. Private*, pg. 4374
VETFAMILY APS—See Vimian Group AB; *Int'l*, pg. 8208
VETFAMILY BRAZIL LTDA.—See Vimian Group AB; *Int'l*, pg. 8208
VETFAMILY B.V.—See Vimian Group AB; *Int'l*, pg. 8208
VETFAMILY GMBH—See Vimian Group AB; *Int'l*, pg. 8208
VETFAMILY LIMITED—See Vimian Group AB; *Int'l*, pg. 8208
VETFAMILY PARTNERS S.L.U.—See Vimian Group AB; *Int'l*, pg. 8208
VET FOOD AGRO DIAGNOSTICS (M) SDN. BHD.—See Rhone Ma Holdings Berhad; *Int'l*, pg. 6327
VETH PROPULSION B.V.—See Twin Disc, Incorporated; *U.S. Public*, pg. 2207
VETH RESEARCH ASSOCIATES LLC—See AEVEX Aerospace; *U.S. Private*, pg. 121
VETIO ANIMAL HEALTH—See Swedencare AB; *Int'l*, pg. 7365
VETLAB OY—See IDEXX Laboratories, Inc.; *U.S. Public*, pg. 1093
VETNIQUE LABS LLC—See Gryphon Investors, LLC; *U.S. Private*, pg. 1800
VETNOSTRUM ANIMAL HEALTH CO., LTD.—See Yung-Shin Global Holding Corporation; *Int'l*, pg. 8614
VETO OVERSEAS PRIVATE F.Z.E.—See Veto Switchgears & Cables Limited; *Int'l*, pg. 8180
VETOPHAMA S.A.S.—See UPL Limited; *Int'l*, pg. 8090
VETOQUINOL AG—See Vetoquinol S.A.; *Int'l*, pg. 8181
VETOQUINOL AUSTRALIA PTY LTD—See Vetoquinol S.A.; *Int'l*, pg. 8181
VETOQUINOL BIOWET POLAND SP. Z.O.O.—See Vetoquinol S.A.; *Int'l*, pg. 8181
VETOQUINOL BIOWET SP.Z O.O.—See Vetoquinol S.A.; *Int'l*, pg. 8181
VETOQUINOL B.V.—See Vetoquinol S.A.; *Int'l*, pg. 8181
VETOQUINOL DE MEXICO S.A DE C.V—See Vetoquinol S.A.; *Int'l*, pg. 8181
VETOQUINOL ESPECIALIDADES VETERINARIAS S.A.—See Vetoquinol S.A.; *Int'l*, pg. 8181
VETOQUINOL E.V.S.A.—See Vetoquinol S.A.; *Int'l*, pg. 8181
VETOQUINOL GMBH—See Vetoquinol S.A.; *Int'l*, pg. 8181
VETOQUINOL INDIA ANIMAL HEALTH PRIVATE LTD.—See Vetoquinol S.A.; *Int'l*, pg. 8181
VETOQUINOL ITALIA S.R.L.—See Vetoquinol S.A.; *Int'l*, pg. 8181
VETOQUINOL NORTH AMERICA, INC.—See Vetoquinol S.A.; *Int'l*, pg. 8181
VETOQUINOL N.V.—See Vetoquinol S.A.; *Int'l*, pg. 8181
VETOQUINOL OSTERREICH GMBH—See Vetoquinol S.A.; *Int'l*, pg. 8181
VETOQUINOL S.A.; *Int'l*, pg. 8180
VETOQUINOL SAUDE ANIMAL LTDA—See Vetoquinol S.A.; *Int'l*, pg. 8181
VETOQUINOL SCANDINAVIA AB—See Vetoquinol S.A.; *Int'l*, pg. 8181
VETOQUINOL S.R.O.—See Vetoquinol S.A.; *Int'l*, pg. 8181
VETOQUINOL TRADING (SHANGHAI) CO., LTD.—See Vetoquinol S.A.; *Int'l*, pg. 8181
VETOQUINOL UK LTD.—See Vetoquinol S.A.; *Int'l*, pg. 8181
VETOQUINOL UNIPESSOAL LDA.—See Vetoquinol S.A.; *Int'l*, pg. 8181
VETOQUINOL USA, INC.—See Vetoquinol S.A.; *Int'l*, pg. 8181
VETOQUINOL-ZENOAQ K.K.—See Vetoquinol S.A.; *Int'l*, pg. 8181
VETO SWITCHGEARS & CABLES LIMITED; *Int'l*, pg. 8180
VET PHARMA FRIESOYTHE GMBH—See Merck & Co., Inc.; *U.S. Public*, pg. 1421
VET PHARM, INC.; *U.S. Private*, pg. 4373
VETRECO S.R.L.—See Zignago Vetro S.p.A.; *Int'l*, pg. 8682
VETRERIE MERIDIONALI S.P.A.—See O-I Glass, Inc.; *U.S. Public*, pg. 1560
VETRICERAMICI DE MEXICO, S. DE R.L. DE C.V.—See American Securities LLC; *U.S. Private*, pg. 252
VETRICERAMICI POLSKA SPOKA Z OGRANICZONA ODPOWIEDZIALNOSCIA—See American Securities LLC; *U.S. Private*, pg. 252
VETRICERAMICI SERAMIK MAMULLERI HIZMETLERI SANAYI VE TICARET LIMITED SIRKETI—See American Securities LLC; *U.S. Private*, pg. 252
VETRICERAMICI S.P.A.—See American Securities LLC; *U.S. Private*, pg. 252
VETRI FOUNDATION FOR CHILDREN—See Vetri Holdings LLC; *U.S. Private*, pg. 4374
VETRI HOLDINGS LLC; *U.S. Private*, pg. 4374
VETRI MANAGEMENT CORPORATION—See Vetri Holdings LLC; *U.S. Private*, pg. 4374
VETRI RESTAURANT CORP.—See Vetri Holdings LLC; *U.S. Private*, pg. 4374
VETRI SPECIALI S.P.A.—See Zignago Vetro S.p.A.; *Int'l*, pg. 8682
VETRI SPECIAL SPA—See Industrie Zignago Santa Margherita SpA; *Int'l*, pg. 3674

CORPORATE AFFILIATIONS

VETROCONSULT AG—See Vetropack Holding AG; *Int'l*, pg. 8181
VETRONIX CORPORATION—See Robert Bosch GmbH; *Int'l*, pg. 6362
VETRON TYPICAL EUROPE GMBH—See Xi'an Typical Industries Co., Ltd.; *Int'l*, pg. 8522
VETROPACK AG—See Vetropack Holding AG; *Int'l*, pg. 8181
VETROPACK AUSTRIA GMBH—See Vetropack Holding AG; *Int'l*, pg. 8181
VETROPACK HOLDING AG; *Int'l*, pg. 8181
VETROPACK ITALIA S.R.L.—See Vetropack Holding AG; *Int'l*, pg. 8181
VETROPACK MORAVIA GLASS A.S.—See Vetropack Holding AG; *Int'l*, pg. 8181
VETROPACK NEMSOVA S.R.O.—See Vetropack Holding AG; *Int'l*, pg. 8181
VETROPACK STRAZA D.D.—See Vetropack Holding AG; *Int'l*, pg. 8181
VETROREAL AG—See Vetropack Holding AG; *Int'l*, pg. 8181
VETRO-RECYCLING AG—See Vetropack Holding AG; *Int'l*, pg. 8181
VETRO REVET SRL—See Zignago Vetro S.p.A.; *Int'l*, pg. 8682
VETROTECH SAINT-GOBAIN ATLANTIQUE SARL—See Compagnie de Saint-Gobain SA; *Int'l*, pg. 1737
VETROTECH SAINT-GOBAIN BENELUX NV—See Compagnie de Saint-Gobain SA; *Int'l*, pg. 1737
VETROTECH SAINT-GOBAIN CENTRAL & EASTERN EUROPE AG—See Compagnie de Saint-Gobain SA; *Int'l*, pg. 1737
VETROTECH SAINT-GOBAIN FRANCE—See Compagnie de Saint-Gobain SA; *Int'l*, pg. 1737
VETROTECH SAINT-GOBAIN INTERNATIONAL AG—See Compagnie de Saint-Gobain SA; *Int'l*, pg. 1737
VETROTECH SAINT-GOBAIN NORTH AMERICA INC.—See Compagnie de Saint-Gobain SA; *Int'l*, pg. 1732
VETROTECH SAINT-GOBAIN POLAND SP. Z O.O.—See Compagnie de Saint-Gobain SA; *Int'l*, pg. 1737
VETROTECH SAINT-GOBAIN UK LTD—See Compagnie de Saint-Gobain SA; *Int'l*, pg. 1737
VETROTEX ITALIA S.P.A.—See Compagnie de Saint-Gobain SA; *Int'l*, pg. 1737
VETRYA S.P.A.; *Int'l*, pg. 8181
VETS4PETS UK LIMITED—See Pets at Home Group Plc; *Int'l*, pg. 5834
VETSAMERICA BUSINESS CONSULTING, INC.; *U.S. Private*, pg. 4374
VETSCH AG, INTERNATIONALE TRANSPORTE—See Deutsche Post AG; *Int'l*, pg. 2083
VET'S CHOICE JAPAN CORPORATION—See Arata Corporation; *Int'l*, pg. 536
VETS PLUS, INC.; *U.S. Private*, pg. 4374
VETSQUARE.COM PTE LTD—See Zagro Asia Ltd; *Int'l*, pg. 8620
VETTA JEWELRY INC.; *U.S. Private*, pg. 4374
VETTED LIMITED—See Brookfield Corporation; *Int'l*, pg. 1189
VETTEL OU—See PRFoods AS; *Int'l*, pg. 5968
VETTER EQUIPMENT COMPANY; *U.S. Private*, pg. 4374
VETTER STONE COMPANY; *U.S. Private*, pg. 4374
VETTER UK LIMITED—See Laing O'Rourke Plc; *Int'l*, pg. 4396
VET THERAPEUTICS, INC.—See Elanco Animal Health Incorporated; *U.S. Public*, pg. 722
VETUS N.V.—See AAC Capital Partners Holding B.V.; *Int'l*, pg. 30
VEURNE SNACK FOODS BVBA—See PepsiCo, Inc.; *U.S. Public*, pg. 1672
VEUVE AMIOT SAS—See Schloss Wachenheim AG; *Int'l*, pg. 6622
VEUVE CLICQUOT IMPORT GMBH—See LVMH Moet Hennessy Louis Vuitton SE; *Int'l*, pg. 4599
VEUVE CLICQUOT PONSARDIN S.A.—See LVMH Moet Hennessy Louis Vuitton SE; *Int'l*, pg. 4604
VEUVE CLICQUOT (SUISSE) S.A.—See LVMH Moet Hennessy Louis Vuitton SE; *Int'l*, pg. 4600
VEVA COMMUNICATIONS; *U.S. Private*, pg. 4374
VEVEO, INC.—See Xperi Inc.; *U.S. Public*, pg. 2392
VEVO LLC—See Abu Dhabi Media; *Int'l*, pg. 72
VEVO LLC—See Sony Group Corporation; *Int'l*, pg. 7105
VEVO LLC—See Universal Music Group N.V.; *Int'l*, pg. 8081
VE WONG CORPORATION; *Int'l*, pg. 8143
VEXCEL HOLDINGS, INC.; *U.S. Private*, pg. 4374
VEXILLA VIET NAM GROUP JOINT STOCK COMPANY; *Int'l*, pg. 8181
VEXIM ITALIA SRL—See Stryker Corporation; *U.S. Public*, pg. 1958
VEXIM SA—See Stryker Corporation; *U.S. Public*, pg. 1958
VEXIM SPINE SL—See Stryker Corporation; *U.S. Public*, pg. 1958
VEXTER OUTSOURCING S.A.—See Randstad N.V.; *Int'l*, pg. 6206
VEXT SCIENCE, INC.; *Int'l*, pg. 8182
VEXVE OY—See DevCo Partners Oy; *Int'l*, pg. 2086

COMPANY NAME INDEX

VEYANCE TECHNOLOGIES EUROPE, D.O.O.—See Continental Aktiengesellschaft; *Int'l*, pg. 1780
VEYANCE TECHNOLOGIES, INC.—See Continental Aktiengesellschaft; *Int'l*, pg. 1780
VEYO, LLC; *U.S. Private*, pg. 4374
VEZERS PRECISION INDUSTRIAL CO.; *U.S. Private*, pg. 4374
VEZINA ASSURANCES INC.—See Marsh & McLennan Companies, Inc.; *U.S. Public*, pg. 1388
VFA, INC.—See Fortive Corporation; *U.S. Public*, pg. 870
VF ALTERNATIVE AD; *Int'l*, pg. 8182
VF ASIA LTD.—See V. F. Corporation; *U.S. Public*, pg. 2269
VF BRANDS INDIA PRIVATE LIMITED—See V. F. Corporation; *U.S. Public*, pg. 2269
VF CAPITAL GMBH; *Int'l*, pg. 8182
VFC CAMBO LTD.—See Vietnam Fumigation Joint Stock Company; *Int'l*, pg. 8199
VF COMMERCIALIZADORA LIMITADA—See V. F. Corporation; *U.S. Public*, pg. 2269
V. F. CORPORATION; *U.S. Public*, pg. 2268
VF CZECH S.R.O.—See V. F. Corporation; *U.S. Public*, pg. 2269
VF DO BRASIL LTDA.—See V. F. Corporation; *U.S. Public*, pg. 2269
VF EGE SOKE GIYIM SANAYI VE TICARET A.S.—See V. F. Corporation; *U.S. Public*, pg. 2269
VF EUROPE B.V.B.A.—See V. F. Corporation; *U.S. Public*, pg. 2269
VF GERMANY TEXTIL-HANDELS GMBH—See V. F. Corporation; *U.S. Public*, pg. 2269
V.F. GRACE INC.; *U.S. Private*, pg. 4328
VF IMAGEWEAR CANADA CO.—See V. F. Corporation; *U.S. Public*, pg. 2269
VF IMAGEWEAR DE MEXICO, S. DE R.L. DE C.V.—See V. F. Corporation; *U.S. Public*, pg. 2269
VF IMAGEWEAR, INC.—See V. F. Corporation; *U.S. Public*, pg. 2269
VF IMAGEWEAR—See V. F. Corporation; *U.S. Public*, pg. 2269
VFINANCE, INC.—See B. Riley Financial, Inc.; *U.S. Public*, pg. 261
VFINANCE INVESTMENTS, INC.—See B. Riley Financial, Inc.; *U.S. Public*, pg. 261
VF INTERNACIONAL, S. DE R.L. DE C.V.—See V. F. Corporation; *U.S. Public*, pg. 2269
VF INTERNATIONAL S.A.G.L.—See V. F. Corporation; *U.S. Public*, pg. 2269
VF ISRAEL (APPAREL) LTD.—See V. F. Corporation; *U.S. Public*, pg. 2269
VF ITALIA, S.R.L.—See V. F. Corporation; *U.S. Public*, pg. 2269
VF ITALY SERVICES S.R.L.—See V. F. Corporation; *U.S. Public*, pg. 2269
VF JEANSWEAR DE MEXICO SA DE CV—See Kontoor Brands, Inc.; *U.S. Public*, pg. 1271
VF JEANSWEAR - EL PASO—See Kontoor Brands, Inc.; *U.S. Public*, pg. 1271
VF JEANSWEAR ESPANA S.L.—See Kontoor Brands, Inc.; *U.S. Public*, pg. 1271
VF JEANSWEAR LIMITED PARTNERSHIP—See Kontoor Brands, Inc.; *U.S. Public*, pg. 1271
VF JEANSWEAR SALES, INC.—See Kontoor Brands, Inc.; *U.S. Public*, pg. 1271
VF JEANSWEAR - SEMINOLE—See Kontoor Brands, Inc.; *U.S. Public*, pg. 1271
VF (J) FRANCE, S.A.—See Kontoor Brands, Inc.; *U.S. Public*, pg. 1271
VFLI—See SNCF; *Int'l*, pg. 7027
VF LUXEMBOURG S.A.R.L.—See V. F. Corporation; *U.S. Public*, pg. 2269
VF NORTHERN EUROPE LTD.—See V. F. Corporation; *U.S. Public*, pg. 2269
VF NORTHERN EUROPE SERVICES LTD.—See V. F. Corporation; *U.S. Public*, pg. 2269
VF OUTDOOR (CANADA), INC.—See V. F. Corporation; *U.S. Public*, pg. 2269
VF OUTDOOR, INC.—See V. F. Corporation; *U.S. Public*, pg. 2269
VF OUTLET INC.—See Kontoor Brands, Inc.; *U.S. Public*, pg. 1271
VFP FIRE SYSTEMS, INC.—See APi Group Corporation; *Int'l*, pg. 514
VFP INC.; *U.S. Private*, pg. 4374
VF POLSKA DISTRIBUTION SP.Z.O.O.—See V. F. Corporation; *U.S. Public*, pg. 2269
VFS CANADA INC—See AB Volvo; *Int'l*, pg. 44
VF SCANDINAVIA A/S—See V. F. Corporation; *U.S. Public*, pg. 2269
VFS DENMARK AS—See AB Volvo; *Int'l*, pg. 44
VFS DEUTSCHLAND GMBH—See AB Volvo; *Int'l*, pg. 44
VF SERVICES, LLC—See V. F. Corporation; *U.S. Public*, pg. 2269
VFS FINANCE FRANCE S.A.S.—See AB Volvo; *Int'l*, pg. 44
VFS FINANCIAL SERVICES (AUSTRIA) GMBH—See AB Volvo; *Int'l*, pg. 44
VFS FINANCIAL SERVICES BELGIUM NV—See AB Volvo; *Int'l*, pg. 44

VFS FINANCIAL SERVICES BV—See AB Volvo; *Int'l*, pg. 44
VFS FINANCIAL SERVICES CZECH REPUBLIC, S.R.O.—See AB Volvo; *Int'l*, pg. 44
VFS FINANCIAL SERVICES SLOVAKIA, S.R.O.—See AB Volvo; *Int'l*, pg. 44
VFS FINANCIAL SERVICES SPAIN EFC, SA—See AB Volvo; *Int'l*, pg. 44
VFS FINANCIAL SERVICES (UK) LTD—See AB Volvo; *Int'l*, pg. 44
VFS FINANSAL KIRALAMA A.S.—See AB Volvo; *Int'l*, pg. 44
VFS FINLAND AB—See AB Volvo; *Int'l*, pg. 44
VFS FRANCE—See AB Volvo; *Int'l*, pg. 44
VFS GLOBAL SERVICES PVT. LTD.—See EQT AB; *Int'l*, pg. 2478
VFS INTERNATIONAL AB—See AB Volvo; *Int'l*, pg. 44
VFS JAPAN CO., LTD.—See AB Volvo; *Int'l*, pg. 44
VFS LATVIA SIA—See AB Volvo; *Int'l*, pg. 44
VFS LOCATION FRANCE S.A.S.—See AB Volvo; *Int'l*, pg. 44
VFS LT, UAB—See AB Volvo; *Int'l*, pg. 44
VFS NORDIC AB—See AB Volvo; *Int'l*, pg. 44
VF SOURCING INDIA PRIVATE LIMITED—See V. F. Corporation; *U.S. Public*, pg. 2269
VFS PENZUGYI SZOLGALTATO KFT.—See AB Volvo; *Int'l*, pg. 44
VF SPORTSWEAR, INC.—See V. F. Corporation; *U.S. Public*, pg. 2269
VFS RENTING SOCIEDADE UNIPESSOAL LDA.—See AB Volvo; *Int'l*, pg. 42
VFS THREAD DYEING LTD.; *Int'l*, pg. 8182
VFS US LLC—See AB Volvo; *Int'l*, pg. 44
VFS USLUGI FINANSOWE POLSKA SP. Z O.O.—See AB Volvo; *Int'l*, pg. 44
VFS VOSTOK—See AB Volvo; *Int'l*, pg. 44
VFT, INC.—See Shinih Enterprise Co., Ltd.; *Int'l*, pg. 6845
VFUSA MARKETING SDN. BHD.—See Asia Brands Berhad; *Int'l*, pg. 610
VF WORLDWIDE HOLDINGS LTD.—See EQT AB; *Int'l*, pg. 2478
VG ANGOULEME S.A.S.—See Van Genechten Packaging N.V.; *Int'l*, pg. 8126
V-GAS BULGARIA PLC—See Synergon Holding PLC; *Int'l*, pg. 7384
VGCM, LLC—See Vulcan Materials Company; *U.S. Public*, pg. 2314
VG CONTOURS ZAO—See Van Genechten Packaging N.V.; *Int'l*, pg. 8126
VGD; *Int'l*, pg. 8182
VG EMBALLAGE SAS—See Compagnie de Saint-Gobain SA; *Int'l*, pg. 1733
V-GEN LTD.—See MKS Instruments, Inc.; *U.S. Public*, pg. 1453
VG ENTREPRENOR A/S—See Per Aarsleff Holding A/S; *Int'l*, pg. 5796
VG EXTRUSION GMBH & CO. KG—See Van Genechten Packaging N.V.; *Int'l*, pg. 8126
VGFS FINANCIAL SERVICES ESTONIA OU—See AB Volvo; *Int'l*, pg. 44
VGF VERKEHRS-GEMEINSCHAFT LANDKREIS FREUDENSTADT GMBH—See Deutsche Bahn AG; *Int'l*, pg. 2055
VGI GLOBAL MEDIA (MALAYSIA) SDN. BHD.—See BTS Group Holdings Public Company Limited; *Int'l*, pg. 1206
VGI PARTNERS GLOBAL INVESTMENTS LIMITED; *Int'l*, pg. 8182
VGI PUBLIC COMPANY LIMITED—See BTS Group Holdings Public Company Limited; *Int'l*, pg. 1205
VG KVADRA PAK JSC—See Van Genechten Packaging N.V.; *Int'l*, pg. 8126
VG LIFE SCIENCES INC.; *U.S. Public*, pg. 2290
VGL PUBLISHING AG—See Team Internet Group plc; *Int'l*, pg. 7500
VG MEYZIEU S.A.S.—See Van Genechten Packaging N.V.; *Int'l*, pg. 8126
VGN DEVELOPERS PVT. LTD.; *Int'l*, pg. 8182
VG NICOLAUS GMBH & CO. KG—See Van Genechten Packaging N.V.; *Int'l*, pg. 8126
VG OSTPRINT, OOO—See Van Genechten Packaging N.V.; *Int'l*, pg. 8126
VGP DENMARK APS—See VGP n.v.; *Int'l*, pg. 8182
VGP ESTONIA OU—See VGP n.v.; *Int'l*, pg. 8182
VGP HOLDINGS LLC—See Saudi Arabian Oil Company; *Int'l*, pg. 6589
VGP INDUSTRIALNI STAVBY S.R.O.—See VGP n.v.; *Int'l*, pg. 8182
VGP LATVIA S.I.A.—See VGP n.v.; *Int'l*, pg. 8182
VGP LATVIJA, SIA—See VGP n.v.; *Int'l*, pg. 8182
VGP N.V.; *Int'l*, pg. 8182
VG POLSKA SP. Z O.O.—See Van Genechten Packaging N.V.; *Int'l*, pg. 8126
VG POWER AB—See Voith GmbH & Co. KGaA; *Int'l*, pg. 8297
VGR HOLDING LLC—See Japan Tobacco Inc.; *Int'l*, pg. 3907
V GROUP INC.; *U.S. Private*, pg. 4327
V-GROWTH CO., LTD.—See T-Gaia Corp.; *Int'l*, pg. 7396
V-G SUPPLY COMPANY INC.; *U.S. Private*, pg. 4328

VHS GROUP, LLC

VGTEL, INC.; *U.S. Public*, pg. 2290
VGT VORBEREITUNGSGESELLSCHAFT TRANSPORTTECHNIK GMBH—See Alstom S.A.; *Int'l*, pg. 383
V-GUARD INDUSTRIES LTD.; *Int'l*, pg. 8105
VGWATT ENERGY CO., LTD.—See Billion Electric Co., Ltd.; *Int'l*, pg. 1031
VGX ANIMAL HEALTH, INC.—See Inovio Pharmaceuticals, Inc.; *U.S. Public*, pg. 1128
VHA CORP.; *U.S. Private*, pg. 4374
VH AMBER BALTIC SP. Z O.O.—See U City Public Company Limited; *Int'l*, pg. 7996
VH ANDEL'S LODZ SP. Z O.O.—See U City Public Company Limited; *Int'l*, pg. 7996
VHC INC.; *U.S. Private*, pg. 4374
VHCL INDUSTRIES LIMITED; *Int'l*, pg. 8182
V.H.C LTD., INC.—See Cerberus Capital Management, L.P.; *U.S. Private*, pg. 839
VHDK BETEILIGUNGSGESELLSCHAFT MBH—See Munchener Ruckversicherungs AG; *Int'l*, pg. 5092
VHE BERLIN HOTELBETRIEBS GMBH—See U City Public Company Limited; *Int'l*, pg. 7996
VHE BRATISLAVA S.R.O.—See U City Public Company Limited; *Int'l*, pg. 7996
VHE CONSTRUCTION PLC—See Renew Holdings plc; *Int'l*, pg. 6278
VHE LEIPZIG HOTELBETRIEBS GMBH—See U City Public Company Limited; *Int'l*, pg. 7996
VH FIBRE OPTICS PROPRIETARY LIMITED—See Alviva Holdings Limited; *Int'l*, pg. 402
VH GLOBAL SUSTAINABLE ENERGY OPPORTUNITIES PLC; *Int'l*, pg. 8182
V&H, INC.; *U.S. Private*, pg. 4327
VHIT S.P.A.—See Robert Bosch GmbH; *Int'l*, pg. 6368
VH KRONBERG HOTELBETRIEBS GMBH—See U City Public Company Limited; *Int'l*, pg. 7996
VHM LIMITED; *Int'l*, pg. 8182
VHMNETWORK LLLC; *U.S. Private*, pg. 4375
VHQ DIGITAL MEDIA BEIJING CO LTD.—See VHQ Media Holdings Ltd.; *Int'l*, pg. 8182
VHQ MEDIA HOLDINGS LTD.; *Int'l*, pg. 8182
VHS ACQUISITION CORPORATION—See Tenet Healthcare Corporation; *U.S. Public*, pg. 2014
VHS ACQUISITION PARTNERSHIP NUMBER 2, L.P.—See Tenet Healthcare Corporation; *U.S. Public*, pg. 2014
VHS ACQUISITION SUBSIDIARY NUMBER 1, INC.—See Tenet Healthcare Corporation; *U.S. Public*, pg. 2014
VHS ACQUISITION SUBSIDIARY NUMBER 3, INC.—See Tenet Healthcare Corporation; *U.S. Public*, pg. 2014
VHS ACQUISITION SUBSIDIARY NUMBER 4, INC.—See Tenet Healthcare Corporation; *U.S. Public*, pg. 2014
VHS ACQUISITION SUBSIDIARY NUMBER 7, INC.—See Tenet Healthcare Corporation; *U.S. Public*, pg. 2014
VHS ACQUISITION SUBSIDIARY NUMBER 9, INC.—See Tenet Healthcare Corporation; *U.S. Public*, pg. 2014
VHS ARIZONA HEART INSTITUTE, INC.—See Tenet Healthcare Corporation; *U.S. Public*, pg. 2014
VHS BROWNSVILLE HOSPITAL COMPANY, LLC—See Tenet Healthcare Corporation; *U.S. Public*, pg. 2015
VHS CHILDREN'S HOSPITAL OF MICHIGAN, INC.—See Tenet Healthcare Corporation; *U.S. Public*, pg. 2015
VHS DETROIT RECEIVING HOSPITAL, INC.—See Tenet Healthcare Corporation; *U.S. Public*, pg. 2015
VHS GROUP, LLC; *U.S. Private*, pg. 4375
VHS HARLINGEN HOSPITAL COMPANY, LLC—See Tenet Healthcare Corporation; *U.S. Public*, pg. 2015
VHS HARPER-HUTZEL HOSPITAL, INC.—See Tenet Healthcare Corporation; *U.S. Public*, pg. 2015
VHS HURON VALLEY-SINAI HOSPITAL, INC.—See Tenet Healthcare Corporation; *U.S. Public*, pg. 2015
VHS OF MICHIGAN, INC.—See Tenet Healthcare Corporation; *U.S. Public*, pg. 2015
VHS OF PHOENIX, INC.—See Tenet Healthcare Corporation; *U.S. Public*, pg. 2014
VHS OF SOUTH PHOENIX, INC.—See Tenet Healthcare Corporation; *U.S. Public*, pg. 2014
VHSOFT TECHNOLOGIES COMPANY LIMITED—See Yau Lee Holdings Limited; *Int'l*, pg. 8572
VHSOFT TECHNOLOGIES (SZ) COMPANY LIMITED—See Yau Lee Holdings Limited; *Int'l*, pg. 8572
VHS OUTPATIENT CLINICS, INC.—See Tenet Healthcare Corporation; *U.S. Public*, pg. 2014
VHS REHABILITATION INSTITUTE OF MICHIGAN, INC.—See Tenet Healthcare Corporation; *U.S. Public*, pg. 2015
VHS SAN ANTONIO IMAGING PARTNERS, L.P.—See Tenet Healthcare Corporation; *U.S. Public*, pg. 2014
VHS SINAI-GRACE HOSPITAL, INC.—See Tenet Healthcare Corporation; *U.S. Public*, pg. 2015
VHS UNIVERSITY LABORATORIES, INC.—See Tenet Healthcare Corporation; *U.S. Public*, pg. 2015
VHS VALLEY HEALTH SYSTEM, LLC—See Tenet Healthcare Corporation; *U.S. Public*, pg. 2015
VHS WESTLAKE HOSPITAL, INC.—See Tenet Healthcare Corporation; *U.S. Public*, pg. 2015
VIA4 S.A.—See Stalexport Autostrady S.A.; *Int'l*, pg. 7164
VIAADUC—See Neurones S.A.; *Int'l*, pg. 5219

VHS GROUP, LLC

CORPORATE AFFILIATIONS

Company Index

VIA AFRIKA LIMITED—See Naspers Limited; *Int'l*, pg. 5149
VIAAN INDUSTRIES LIMITED; *Int'l*, pg. 8183
VIABAL MANTENIMENT I CONSERVACIO, S.A.—See ACS, Actividades de Construccion y Servicios, S.A.; *Int'l*, pg. 114
VIACCESS-ORCA LTD—See Orange S.A.; *Int'l*, pg. 5611
VIACCESS SA—See Orange S.A.; *Int'l*, pg. 5611
VIA CHRISTI HEALTH PARTNERS, INC.; *U.S. Private*, pg. 4375
VIACOM 18 MEDIA PVT. LTD.—See National Amusements, Inc.; *U.S. Private*, pg. 2844
VIACOM 18 MEDIA PVT. LTD.—See Reliance - ADA Group Limited; *Int'l*, pg. 6263
VIACOM A.G.—See National Amusements, Inc.; *U.S. Private*, pg. 2844
VIACOM BRAND SOLUTIONS LIMITED—See National Amusements, Inc.; *U.S. Private*, pg. 2844
VIACOM CONSUMER PRODUCTS INC.—See National Amusements, Inc.; *U.S. Private*, pg. 2844
VIACOM GLOBAL HUNGARY KFT.—See National Amusements, Inc.; *U.S. Private*, pg. 2844
VIACOM GLOBAL SERVICES INC.—See National Amusements, Inc.; *U.S. Private*, pg. 2844
VIACOM INTERNATIONAL MEDIA NETWORKS—See National Amusements, Inc.; *U.S. Private*, pg. 2842
VIACOM INTERNATIONAL PTY. LIMITED—See National Amusements, Inc.; *U.S. Private*, pg. 2844
VIACOM INTERNATIONAL SERVICES INC.—See National Amusements, Inc.; *U.S. Private*, pg. 2844
VIA COMMUNICATION, INC.—See VIA Technologies, Inc.; *Int'l*, pg. 8183
VIACOM NETWORKS BRASIL PROGRAMACAO TELEVISIVA E PUBLICIDADE LTDA.—See National Amusements, Inc.; *U.S. Private*, pg. 2844
VIACORD, LLC—See Revvity, Inc.; *U.S. Public*, pg. 1795
VIACOR POLYMER GMBH—See Sto SE & Co. KGaA; *Int'l*, pg. 7219
VIA CREDIT UNION; *U.S. Private*, pg. 4375
VIA-CYRIX, INC.—See VIA Technologies, Inc.; *Int'l*, pg. 8183
VIACYTE, INC.; *U.S. Private*, pg. 4375
VIAD CORP.; *U.S. Public*, pg. 2290
VIADEO SA—See Groupe Industriel Marcel Dassault S.A.; *Int'l*, pg. 3105
VIADERMA, INC.; *U.S. Public*, pg. 2291
VIADIX SAS—See Carrefour SA; *Int'l*, pg. 1346
VIADOR GMBH—See Starwood Capital Group Global I, LLC; *U.S. Private*, pg. 3789
VIA EGENCIA AS—See Expedia Group, Inc.; *U.S. Public*, pg. 810
VIA EGENCIA DENMARK A/S—See Expedia Group, Inc.; *U.S. Public*, pg. 810
VIA FIELD; *U.S. Private*, pg. 4375
VIAFIN SERVICE OYJ; *Int'l*, pg. 8183
VIAFINTECH GMBH—See GLORY Ltd.; *Int'l*, pg. 3010
VIAFRANCE NORMANDIE SAS—See VINCI S.A.; *Int'l*, pg. 8240
VIAGEN, L.C.—See Precigen, Inc.; *U.S. Public*, pg. 1713
VIAGOGO AG; *Int'l*, pg. 8183
VIAGOLD RARE EARTH RESOURCES HOLDINGS LIMITED; *Int'l*, pg. 8183
THE VIA GROUP LLC; *U.S. Private*, pg. 4130
VIAG TELECOM BETEILIGUNGS GMBH—See E.ON SE; *Int'l*, pg. 2260
VIA HOLDINGS INC.; *Int'l*, pg. 8182
VIA IMC GMBH—See VINCI S.A.; *Int'l*, pg. 8240
VIA, INC.—See Groupe Lacasse Inc.; *Int'l*, pg. 3105
VIAJES CARREFOUR, S.L.U.—See Carrefour SA; *Int'l*, pg. 1345
VIAJES EL CORTE INGLES, S.A.—See El Corte Ingles, S.A.; *Int'l*, pg. 2340
VIAJES EROSKI SA—See Grupo Eroski; *Int'l*, pg. 3128
VIAJES INTEROPA, S.A—See Barcelo Corporacion Empresarial S.A.; *Int'l*, pg. 859
VIAJES KUONI, S.A.—See EQT AB; *Int'l*, pg. 2478
VIAJES MARSANS S.A.; *Int'l*, pg. 8183
VIAJES PARIS S.A.—See Cencosud S.A.; *Int'l*, pg. 1400
VIAJES VERGER SA—See TUI AG; *Int'l*, pg. 7969
VIA LABS, INC.—See VIA Technologies, Inc.; *Int'l*, pg. 8183
VIALAB S.R.O—See VINCI S.A.; *Int'l*, pg. 8230
VIALIFE SA; *Int'l*, pg. 8183
VIALINK SAS—See Groupe BPCE; *Int'l*, pg. 3099
VIALIVRE, S.A.—See Ferrovial S.A.; *Int'l*, pg. 2645
VIALTA, INC.; *U.S. Private*, pg. 4375
VIA LUNA GROUP (VLG); *U.S. Private*, pg. 4375
VIA MARKETING, INC.; *U.S. Private*, pg. 4375
VIAMERICAS CORPORATION; *U.S. Private*, pg. 4375
VIAMETRICS GROUP AB—See Storskogen Group AB; *Int'l*, pg. 7228
VIA METROPOLITAN TRANSIT; *U.S. Private*, pg. 4375
VIAMICHELIN NORTH AMERICA LLC—See Compagnie Generale des Etablissements Michelin SCA; *Int'l*, pg. 1745
VIAM MANUFACTURING, INC.—See Freudenberg SE; *Int'l*, pg. 2790
VIA MOTORS INC.—See Ideanomics, Inc.; *U.S. Public*, pg. 1088

VIANCE, LLC—See Dow Inc.; *U.S. Public*, pg. 686
VIANCE, LLC—See Huntsman Corporation; *U.S. Public*, pg. 1075
VIAN ENTERPRISES, INC.—See Crane Company; *U.S. Public*, pg. 589
VIANET GROUP PLC; *Int'l*, pg. 8183
VIANET LIMITED—See Vianet Group plc; *Int'l*, pg. 8183
VIA NETWORKING TECHNOLOGIES, INC.—See VIA Technologies, Inc.; *Int'l*, pg. 8183
VIA NEXT TECHNOLOGIES (SHANGHAI) CO., LTD.—See VIA Technologies, Inc.; *Int'l*, pg. 8183
VIANINI LAVORI S.P.A.—See Caltagirone Editore S.p.A.; *Int'l*, pg. 1266
VIANINI PIPE INC.—See Cementir Holding N.V.; *Int'l*, pg. 1397
VIANINI S.P.A.—See Salcef Costruzioni Edili e Ferroviarie SpA; *Int'l*, pg. 6491
VIANOR AB—See Nokian Renkaat Oyj; *Int'l*, pg. 5407
VIANOR AG—See Nokian Renkaat Oyj; *Int'l*, pg. 5407
VIANOR A/S—See Nokian Renkaat Oyj; *Int'l*, pg. 5407
VIANOR HOLDING OY—See Nokian Renkaat Oyj; *Int'l*, pg. 5407
VIANORM B.V.—See DEKRA e.V.; *Int'l*, pg. 2010
VIANOR OY—See Nokian Renkaat Oyj; *Int'l*, pg. 5407
VIANORTE, S.A.—See Industry Super Holdings Pty. Ltd.; *Int'l*, pg. 3676
VIANOVA GEOSUITE AB—See Trimble, Inc.; *U.S. Public*, pg. 2193
VIANOVA SYSTEMS SWEDEN AB—See Trimble, Inc.; *U.S. Public*, pg. 2193
VIANSA WINERY; *U.S. Private*, pg. 4375
VIANT COLLEGEVILLE, LLC—See Integer Holdings Corporation; *U.S. Public*, pg. 1135
VIANT, INC.—See MultiPlan Corp.; *U.S. Public*, pg. 1486
VIANT MEDICAL, INC.-SOUTH PLAINFIELD—See Viant Medical, LLC; *U.S. Private*, pg. 4375
VIANT MEDICAL, LLC; *U.S. Private*, pg. 4375
VIANT MEDICAL, LLC; *U.S. Private*, pg. 4375
VIA-ONLINE GMBH—See Oakley Capital Limited; *Int'l*, pg. 5504
VIA OPTICAL SOLUTION, INC.—See VIA Technologies, Inc.; *Int'l*, pg. 8183
VIA OPTRONICS GMBH—See Ayala Corporation; *Int'l*, pg. 774
VIA OPTRONICS LLC—See Ayala Corporation; *Int'l*, pg. 774
VIA OPTRONICS, LTD.—See Ayala Corporation; *Int'l*, pg. 774
VIA OPTRONICS (SUZHOU) CO., LTD—See Ayala Corporation; *Int'l*, pg. 774
VIA PHILIPPINES TRAVEL CORPORATION—See Ebix Inc.; *U.S. Public*, pg. 710
VIAPLAY GROUP AB; *Int'l*, pg. 8183
VIAPOL LTDA.—See RPM International Inc.; *U.S. Public*, pg. 1820
VIAPRINTO GMBH & CO. KG—See CEWE Stiftung & Co. KGaA; *Int'l*, pg. 1425
VIA PRODUCTION—See Groupe AB S.A.; *Int'l*, pg. 3091
VIA RAIL CANADA INC.; *Int'l*, pg. 8182
VIA RENEWABLES, INC.; *U.S. Public*, pg. 2290
VIARO ENERGY LIMITED—See Viaro Investment Ltd.; *Int'l*, pg. 8183
VIARO INVESTMENT LTD.; *Int'l*, pg. 8183
VIAROM CONSTRUCT SRL—See VINCI S.A.; *Int'l*, pg. 8220
VIASAT AS NORGE—See Modern Times Group MTG AB; *Int'l*, pg. 5014
VIASAT AUSTRALIA PTY LIMITED—See ViaSat, Inc.; *U.S. Public*, pg. 2292
VIASAT BROADCASTING AB—See Modern Times Group MTG AB; *Int'l*, pg. 5015
VIASAT BROADCASTING G LTD—See Modern Times Group MTG AB; *Int'l*, pg. 5015
VIASAT BROADCASTING U.K.—See Modern Times Group MTG AB; *Int'l*, pg. 5015
VIASAT CREDIT CORP—See ViaSat, Inc.; *U.S. Public*, pg. 2292
VIASAT DENMARK—See Modern Times Group MTG AB; *Int'l*, pg. 5014
VIASAT EUROPE LIMITED—See ViaSat, Inc.; *U.S. Public*, pg. 2292
VIASAT FILM AB—See Modern Times Group MTG AB; *Int'l*, pg. 5015
VIASAT GLOBAL LLC—See Modern Times Group MTG AB; *Int'l*, pg. 5015
VIASAT, INC.; *U.S. Public*, pg. 2291
VIASAT, INC.—See ViaSat, Inc.; *U.S. Public*, pg. 2292
VIASAT IRELAND LIMITED—See ViaSat, Inc.; *U.S. Public*, pg. 2292
VIASAT SINGAPORE HOLDINGS PTE, LTD.—See ViaSat, Inc.; *U.S. Public*, pg. 2292
VIASAT SPORT/TV3 SPORT—See Modern Times Group MTG AB; *Int'l*, pg. 5015
VIASAT SWEDEN—See Modern Times Group MTG AB; *Int'l*, pg. 5015
VIASAT UK LIMITED—See ViaSat, Inc.; *U.S. Public*, pg. 2292
VIASAT UKRAINE LLC—See Modern Times Group MTG AB; *Int'l*, pg. 5015

VIASAT - WIRELESS SERVICES DIVISION—See ViaSat, Inc.; *U.S. Public*, pg. 2292
VIASAT WORLD LTD—See Modern Times Group MTG AB; *Int'l*, pg. 5015
VIAS IMPORTS LTD.; *U.S. Private*, pg. 4375
VIA SOLUTIONS SUDWEST GMBH—See VINCI S.A.; *Int'l*, pg. 8239
VIASPACE GREEN ENERGY INC.—See VIASPACE INC.; *U.S. Public*, pg. 2292
VIASPACE INC.; *U.S. Public*, pg. 2292
VIASS Y CONSTRUCCIONES S.A.—See ACS, Actividades de Construccion y Servicios, S.A.; *Int'l*, pg. 117
VIASTAR SERVICES, LP—See Roper Technologies, Inc.; *U.S. Public*, pg. 1814
VIA STRUCTURE GMBH—See VINCI S.A.; *Int'l*, pg. 8230
VIAS Y CONSTRUCCIONES S.A.—See ACS, Actividades de Construccion y Servicios, S.A.; *Int'l*, pg. 117
VIASYSTEMS ASIA LIMITED—See TTM Technologies, Inc.; *U.S. Public*, pg. 2203
VIASYSTEMS TECHNOLOGIES CORP., L.L.C. - CANADA—See TTM Technologies, Inc.; *U.S. Public*, pg. 2203
VIASYSTEMS TECHNOLOGIES CORP., L.L.C. - FOREST GROVE—See TTM Technologies, Inc.; *U.S. Public*, pg. 2203
VIASYSTEMS TECHNOLOGIES CORP., L.L.C. - SAN JOSE—See TTM Technologies, Inc.; *U.S. Public*, pg. 2203
VIATAR CTC SOLUTIONS INC.; *U.S. Public*, pg. 2292
VIA TECHNICAL, LLC—See Stone Point Capital LLC; *U.S. Private*, pg. 3823
VIA TECHNOLOGIES (CHINA) LTD.—See VIA Technologies, Inc.; *Int'l*, pg. 8183
VIA TECHNOLOGIES GMBH—See VIA Technologies, Inc.; *Int'l*, pg. 8183
VIA TECHNOLOGIES (HK) INC. LTD.—See VIA Technologies, Inc.; *Int'l*, pg. 8183
VIA TECHNOLOGIES, INC.; *Int'l*, pg. 8182
VIA TECHNOLOGIES JAPAN K.K.—See VIA Technologies, Inc.; *Int'l*, pg. 8183
VIA TECHNOLOGIES, KOREA—See VIA Technologies, Inc.; *Int'l*, pg. 8183
VIA TECHNOLOGIES (SHANGHAI) CO., LTD.—See VIA Technologies, Inc.; *Int'l*, pg. 8183
VIA TECHNOLOGIES (SHENZHEN) CO., LTD.—See VIA Technologies, Inc.; *Int'l*, pg. 8183
VIATECH PUBLISHING SOLUTIONS LIMITED—See ViaTech Publishing Solutions; *U.S. Private*, pg. 4376
VIATECH PUBLISHING SOLUTIONS; *U.S. Private*, pg. 4376
VIA TELECOM CO., LTD.—See VIA Technologies, Inc.; *Int'l*, pg. 8183
VIA TELECOM INC.—See VIA Technologies, Inc.; *Int'l*, pg. 8183
VIATEL HOLDING (EUROPE) LIMITED—See Digiweb Ltd.; *Int'l*, pg. 2124
VIATEL INFRASTRUCTURE FRANCE SA—See Digiweb Ltd.; *Int'l*, pg. 2124
VIATEL INFRASTRUCTURE NEDERLAND B.V.—See Digiweb Ltd.; *Int'l*, pg. 2124
VIATEL INFRASTRUCTURE SWITZERLAND AG—See Digiweb Ltd.; *Int'l*, pg. 2124
VIATEL INFRASTRUCTURE (UK) LIMITED—See Digiweb Ltd.; *Int'l*, pg. 2124
VIATOR, INC.—See TripAdvisor, Inc.; *U.S. Public*, pg. 2195
VIATRACK SYSTEMS, LLC—See Thoma Bravo, L.P.; *U.S. Private*, pg. 4150
VIA TRADING CORPORATION; *U.S. Private*, pg. 4375
VIATRAN CORPORATION—See Roper Technologies, Inc.; *U.S. Public*, pg. 1814
VIATRIS INC.; *U.S. Public*, pg. 2293
VIATRON S.A.—See Herkules S.A.; *Int'l*, pg. 3362
VIATRON TECHNOLOGIES, INC.; *Int'l*, pg. 8184
VIAU FORD (1990) INC.; *Int'l*, pg. 8184
VIA VAREJO S.A.—See Companhia Brasileira de Distribuicao; *Int'l*, pg. 1746
VIAVID BROADCASTING, INC.; *Int'l*, pg. 8184
VIAVI SOLUTIONS AB—See Viavi Solutions Inc.; *U.S. Public*, pg. 2295
VIAVI SOLUTIONS DE MEXICO S.A. DE C.V.—See Viavi Solutions Inc.; *U.S. Public*, pg. 2295
VIAVI SOLUTIONS DEUTSCHLAND GMBH—See Viavi Solutions Inc.; *U.S. Public*, pg. 2295
VIAVI SOLUTIONS DO BRASIL LTDA.—See Viavi Solutions Inc.; *U.S. Public*, pg. 2295
VIAVI SOLUTIONS FRANCE SAS—See Viavi Solutions Inc.; *U.S. Public*, pg. 2295
VIAVI SOLUTIONS GMBH—See Viavi Solutions Inc.; *U.S. Public*, pg. 2295
VIAVI SOLUTIONS HABERLESME TEST VE OLCUM TEKNOLOJILERI TICARET LIMITED SIRKETI—See Viavi Solutions Inc.; *U.S. Public*, pg. 2295
VIAVI SOLUTIONS INC. - INDIANAPOLIS SALES OFFICE—See Viavi Solutions Inc.; *U.S. Public*, pg. 2295
VIAVI SOLUTIONS INC.; *U.S. Public*, pg. 2295
VIAVI SOLUTIONS ITALIA S.R.L.—See Viavi Solutions Inc.; *U.S. Public*, pg. 2295

VIAVI SOLUTIONS JAPAN K.K.—See Viavi Solutions Inc.; U.S. Public, pg. 2295
VIAVI SOLUTIONS (SHENZHEN) CO., LTD.—See Viavi Solutions Inc.; U.S. Public, pg. 2295
VIAVI SOLUTIONS SPAIN, S.A.—See Viavi Solutions Inc.; U.S. Public, pg. 2295
VIAVI SOLUTIONS (SUZHOU) CO., LTD.—See Viavi Solutions Inc.; U.S. Public, pg. 2295
VIAVI SOLUTIONS UK LIMITED—See Viavi Solutions Inc.; U.S. Public, pg. 2295
VIBBEK AG—See Aduno Holding AG; Int'l, pg. 154
VIBBEK GMBH—See Aduno Holding AG; Int'l, pg. 154
VIBCO INC.; U.S. Private, pg. 4376
VIBCO VIBRATION PRODUCTS—See Vibco Inc.; U.S. Private, pg. 4376
VIBE CREDIT UNION; U.S. Private, pg. 4376
VIBE GROWTH CORPORATION; Int'l, pg. 8184
VIBE INC.—See BANDAI NAMCO Holdings Inc.; Int'l, pg. 829
VIBER MEDIA LTD.—See Rakuten Group, Inc.; Int'l, pg. 6195
VIBES TECHNOLOGIES, INC.—See Black Box Limited; Int'l, pg. 1058
VIBETON SAFNERN AG—See Vicat S.A.; Int'l, pg. 8186
VIBEV FOOD & BEVERAGE JOINT VENTURE COMPANY LIMITED—See Vietnam Dairy Products Joint Stock Company; Int'l, pg. 8199
VIBHAVADI MEDICAL CENTER PUBLIC COMPANY LIMITED; Int'l, pg. 8184
VIBOGARD AB—See Samhallsbyggnadsbolaget I Norden AB; Int'l, pg. 6504
VIBRACHOC S.A.U.—See TotalEnergies SE; Int'l, pg. 7844
VIBRACOUSTIC AG—See Freudenberg SE; Int'l, pg. 2791
VIBRACOUSTIC CV AIR SPRINGS GMBH—See Freudenberg SE; Int'l, pg. 2791
VIBRACOUSTIC DE MEXICO S.A. DE C.V.—See Freudenberg SE; Int'l, pg. 2791
VIBRACOUSTIC DO BRASIL INDUSTRIA E COMERCIO DE ARTEFATOS DE BORRACHA LTDA.—See Freudenberg SE; Int'l, pg. 2791
VIBRACOUSTIC JAPAN KK—See Freudenberg SE; Int'l, pg. 2791
VIBRACOUSTIC NANTES SAS—See Freudenberg SE; Int'l, pg. 2791
VIBRACOUSTIC NORTH AMERICA LP—See Freudenberg SE; Int'l, pg. 2791
VIBRA ENERGIA S.A.—See Petroleo Brasileiro S.A. - PETROBRAS; Int'l, pg. 5827
VIBRA FINISH, LIMITED; Int'l, pg. 8184
VIBRA HEALTHCARE, LLC; U.S. Private, pg. 4376
VIBRA HOSPITAL OF CHARLESTON—See Vibra Healthcare, LLC; U.S. Private, pg. 4376
VIBRA HOSPITAL OF SAN DIEGO, LLC—See Select Medical Holdings Corporation; U.S. Public, pg. 1862
VIBRALIGN INC.—See ACOEM Group; Int'l, pg. 107
VIBRA-METRICS, INC.—See Mistras Group, Inc.; U.S. Public, pg. 1451
VIBRANT ENERGY MATTERS LIMITED—See The Skipton Building Society; Int'l, pg. 7687
VIBRANT GLOBAL CAPITAL LIMITED; Int'l, pg. 8184
VIBRANT GLOBAL SALT PRIVATE LIMITED—See Vibrant Global Capital Limited; Int'l, pg. 8184
VIBRANT GROUP LIMITED; Int'l, pg. 8184
VIBRANT MED-EL HEARING TECHNOLOGY—See MED-EL GmbH; Int'l, pg. 4767
VIBRANT MEDIA FRANCE—See Vibrant Media; U.S. Private, pg. 4376
VIBRANT MEDIA GMBH—See Vibrant Media; U.S. Private, pg. 4376
VIBRANT MEDIA LTD.—See Vibrant Media; U.S. Private, pg. 4376
VIBRANT MEDIA; U.S. Private, pg. 4376
VIBRANT MEDIA—See Vibrant Media; U.S. Private, pg. 4376
VIBRANT SOLAR, LLC—See National Grid plc; Int'l, pg. 5158
VIBRANTZ TECHNOLOGIES INC—See American Securities LLC; U.S. Private, pg. 250
VIBRA SCREW INC.; U.S. Private, pg. 4376
VIBRATECHNIQUES S.A.S.—See Atlas Copco AB; Int'l, pg. 684
VIBRATION CONTROL LTD.—See Embelton Limited; Int'l, pg. 2375
VIBRATION MOUNTINGS & CONTROLS, INC.; U.S. Private, pg. 4376
VIBRATION TECHNOLOGY, INC.—See Granite Construction Incorporated; U.S. Public, pg. 958
THE VIBROFLOTATION GROUP—See VINCI S.A.; Int'l, pg. 8234
VIBRO FOUNDATIONS LTD. UAE—See VINCI S.A.; Int'l, pg. 8234
VIBRO MENARD LIMITED—See VINCI S.A.; Int'l, pg. 8240
VIBROPOWER CORPORATION LIMITED; Int'l, pg. 8184
VIBROPOWER GENERATORS (INDIA) PRIVATE LIMITED—See VibroPower Corporation Limited; Int'l, pg. 8185

VIBROPOWER GENERATORS SDN. BHD.—See VibroPower Corporation Limited; Int'l, pg. 8185
VIBROPOWER PTE. LTD.—See VibroPower Corporation Limited; Int'l, pg. 8185
VIBROPOWER (UK) LIMITED—See VibroPower Corporation Limited; Int'l, pg. 8185
VIBRO SERVICES GMBH—See VINCI S.A.; Int'l, pg. 8234
VIBROS ORGANICS LIMITED; Int'l, pg. 8185
VIBROSYSTM INC.; Int'l, pg. 8185
VIB VERKEHRSINFORMATIONSAGENTUR BAYERN GMBH—See Siemens Aktiengesellschaft; Int'l, pg. 6901
VIB VERMOGEN AG; Int'l, pg. 8184
VICAMPO.DE GMBH—See Viva Wine Group AB; Int'l, pg. 8265
VICARIOUS SURGICAL INC.; U.S. Public, pg. 2295
VICARIOUS VISIONS, INC.—See Microsoft Corporation; U.S. Public, pg. 1439
VICAR OPERATING, INC.—See Mars, Incorporated; U.S. Private, pg. 2590
VICAR PROMOCOES DESPORTIVAS S.A.—See T4F Entretenimento S.A.; Int'l, pg. 7398
VICAT INTERNATIONAL TRADING—See Vicat S.A.; Int'l, pg. 8186
VICAT L'ISLE D'ABEAU—See Vicat S.A.; Int'l, pg. 8186
VICAT S.A.; Int'l, pg. 8185
VIC BAILEY HONDA INC.; U.S. Private, pg. 4376
VIC BAILEY-LINCOLN MERCURY; U.S. Private, pg. 4376
VIC BOND SALES, INC.; U.S. Private, pg. 4376
VIC CANEVER CHEVROLET CO.; U.S. Private, pg. 4376
VIC-DAWN ENTERPRISE CO., LTD.—See Nichidenbo Corporation; Int'l, pg. 5269
VICE MEDIA LLC—See Monroe Capital LLC; U.S. Private, pg. 2773
VICE MEDIA LLC—See SoftBank Group Corp.; Int'l, pg. 7054
VICE MEDIA LLC—See Soros Fund Management LLC; U.S. Public, pg. 3715
VICEM GYPSUM & CEMENT JOINT STOCK COMPANY; Int'l, pg. 8186
VICEM PACKAGING BIM SON JOINT STOCK COMPANY; Int'l, pg. 8186
VICEM PACKAGING BUT SON JOINT STOCK COMPANY; Int'l, pg. 8186
VICENTE CAPITAL PARTNERS, LLC; U.S. Private, pg. 4376
VICEROY HOMES INC.—See Viceroy Homes Limited; Int'l, pg. 8186
VICEROY HOMES LIMITED; Int'l, pg. 8186
VICEROY HOTEL MANAGEMENT, LLC; U.S. Private, pg. 4376
VICEROY HOTELS LTD; Int'l, pg. 8186
VICEROY RUBBER LIMITED—See Allied Plastic Skylight; Int'l, pg. 358
VICE SQUAD; U.S. Private, pg. 4376
VICGRAIN PTY LIMITED—See GrainCorp Limited; Int'l, pg. 3052
VICHITBHAN PALMOIL PUBLIC COMPANY LIMITED; Int'l, pg. 8187
VICINITY CENTRES PM PTY LTD—See Vicinity Limited; Int'l, pg. 8187
VICINITY CENTRES RE LTD.—See Vicinity Limited; Int'l, pg. 8187
VICINITY LIMITED; Int'l, pg. 8187
VICINITY MOTOR CORP.; Int'l, pg. 8187
VICIOUS CYCLE SOFTWARE, INC.—See Little Orbit LLC; U.S. Private, pg. 2469
VICI PROPERTIES INC.; U.S. Public, pg. 2295
VICI PROPERTIES L.P.; U.S. Public, pg. 2296
VICKERS ENGINEERING, INC.; U.S. Private, pg. 4377
VICKERS (LAKESIDE) LIMITED—See General Motors Company; U.S. Public, pg. 928
VICKERS STOCK RESEARCH CORPORATION—See The Argus Research Group, Inc.; U.S. Private, pg. 3988
VICKERS SYSTEMS LTD.—See Eaton Corporation plc; Int'l, pg. 2281
VICKERS SYSTEMS SBPD—See Eaton Corporation plc; Int'l, pg. 2281
VICKERS-WARNICK; Int'l, pg. 8187
VICKERY ENVIRONMENTAL, INC.—See Waste Management, Inc.; U.S. Public, pg. 2332
VICKIE MILAZZO INSTITUTE; U.S. Private, pg. 4377
VICKMANS LABORATORIES LIMITED—See Jacobson Pharma Corporation Limited; Int'l, pg. 3866
VICKSBURG CHRYSLER DODGE JEEP RAM; U.S. Private, pg. 4377
VICKSBURG HEALTHCARE, LLC—See Community Health Systems, Inc.; U.S. Public, pg. 557
VICKSBURG VIDEO INC.—See Wehco Media, Inc.; U.S. Private, pg. 4469
VICKS LITHOGRAPH & PRINTING; U.S. Private, pg. 4377
VIC LEAK DETECTION, AIR LEAK TESTING DIVISION—See Valero Capital Partners LLC; U.S. Private, pg. 4331
VICMARR AUDIO INC.; U.S. Private, pg. 4377
VICN AUTOMATED INSPECTION TECHNOLOGY (HUIZHOU) CO., LTD.—See Viscom AG; Int'l, pg. 8250

VICO INTERNATIONAL HOLDINGS LIMITED; Int'l, pg. 8187
VICOM 2002 S.L.—See HEXPOL AB; Int'l, pg. 3373
VICOM LTD.—See ComfortDelGro Corporation Limited; Int'l, pg. 1713
VICON BUSINESS MEDIA, INC.—See Owner Resource Group, LLC; U.S. Private, pg. 3055
VICON DEUTSCHLAND GMBH—See Vicon Industries, Inc.; U.S. Private, pg. 4377
VICON HOLDINGS LIMITED; Int'l, pg. 8187
VICON INDUSTRIES, INC.; U.S. Private, pg. 4377
VICON INDUSTRIES LIMITED—See Vicon Industries, Inc.; U.S. Private, pg. 4377
VICON MACHINERY, LLC—See Plasma Automation, Inc.; U.S. Private, pg. 3198
VICON MOTION SYSTEMS LIMITED—See Oxford Metrics plc; Int'l, pg. 5675
VICOR CORPORATION; U.S. Public, pg. 2296
VICORE PHARMA AB—See Vicore Pharma Holding AB; Int'l, pg. 8187
VICORE PHARMA HOLDING AB; Int'l, pg. 8187
VICOR GMBH—See Vicor Corporation; U.S. Public, pg. 2296
VICOR HONG KONG LTD.—See Vicor Corporation; U.S. Public, pg. 2296
VICOR ITALY SRL—See Vicor Corporation; U.S. Public, pg. 2296
VICOR JAPAN COMPANY, LTD.—See Vicor Corporation; U.S. Public, pg. 2296
VICOR TECHNOLOGIES, INC.; U.S. Private, pg. 4377
VICOR U.K. LTD.—See Vicor Corporation; U.S. Public, pg. 2296
VICOSTONE JOINT STOCK COMPANY—See Vietnam Construction Stock Corporation; Int'l, pg. 8198
VICPLAS HOLDINGS PTE LTD—See Vicplas International Ltd; Int'l, pg. 8187
VICPLAS INTERNATIONAL LTD; Int'l, pg. 8187
VICSA COMMERCE & TRADING (SHANGHAI) CO., LTD.—See Bunzl plc; Int'l, pg. 1219
VICSA SAFETY COMERCIAL LIMITADA—See Bunzl plc; Int'l, pg. 1219
VICSA SAFETY PERU S.A.C.—See Bunzl plc; Int'l, pg. 1219
VICSA STEELPRO COLOMBIA S.A.S—See Bunzl plc; Int'l, pg. 1219
VICSA STEELPRO S.A.—See Bunzl plc; Int'l, pg. 1220
VICTALL TRANSPORTATION (CANADA) CO., LTD.—See Qingdao Victall Railway Co., Ltd.; Int'l, pg. 6144
VICTAULIC ASIA-PACIFIC—See Victaulic Company; U.S. Private, pg. 4377
VICTAULIC COMPANY OF CANADA LIMITED—See Victaulic Company; U.S. Private, pg. 4377
VICTAULIC COMPANY; U.S. Private, pg. 4377
VICTAULIC COMPANY - VICTAULIC CONSTRUCTION PIPING SERVICES DIVISION—See Victaulic Company; U.S. Private, pg. 4377
VICTAULIC EUROPE—See Victaulic Company; U.S. Private, pg. 4377
VICTAULIC FIRE SAFETY COMPANY, LLC—See Victaulic Company; U.S. Private, pg. 4377
VICTAULIC INTERNATIONAL—See Victaulic Company; U.S. Private, pg. 4377
VICTAULIC MIDDLE EAST—See Victaulic Company; U.S. Private, pg. 4377
VICTAULIC TOOL COMPANY—See Victaulic Company; U.S. Private, pg. 4377
VICTEK CO., LTD.; Int'l, pg. 8187
VICTOR CHANDLER INTERNATIONAL LTD.; Int'l, pg. 8187
VICTOR COMPANY OF JAPAN, LTD.—See JVCKENWOOD Corporation; Int'l, pg. 4034
VICTOR CREATIVE MEDIA CO., LTD.—See JVCKENWOOD Corporation; Int'l, pg. 4034
VICTOR DEUTSCHLAND GMBH—See Marsh & McLennan Companies, Inc.; U.S. Public, pg. 1388
VICTOR DISTRIBUTING COMPANY; U.S. Private, pg. 4377
VICTOR EQUIPMENT COMPANY—See Enovis Corporation; U.S. Public, pg. 771
VICTOR EQUIPMENT DE MEXICO, S.A. DE C.V.—See Enovis Corporation; U.S. Public, pg. 771
VICTOR GRAPHICS INC.; U.S. Private, pg. 4377
VICTOR GROUP HOLDINGS LIMITED; Int'l, pg. 8187
VICTOR GUEDES-INDUSTRIA E COMERCIO, S.A.—See Jeronimo Martins SGPS SA; Int'l, pg. 3931
VICTOR HASSELBLAD AB; Int'l, pg. 8187
VICTORIA ADVOCATE PUBLISHING COMPANY; U.S. Private, pg. 4378
VICTORIA AIR CONDITIONING, LTD.; U.S. Private, pg. 4378
VICTORIA & ALBERT BATH, LLC—See Fortune Brands Innovations, Inc.; U.S. Public, pg. 873
VICTORIA & ALBERT BATHS LIMITED—See Fortune Brands Innovations, Inc.; U.S. Public, pg. 873
VICTORIA & ALBERT PRODUCTS PROPRIETARY LIMITED—See Fortune Brands Innovations, Inc.; U.S. Public, pg. 873
VICTORIA AMBULATORY SURGERY CENTER, L.P.—See Tenet Healthcare Corporation; U.S. Public, pg. 2014

VICTORIA CAPITAL PARTNERS LP

VICTORIA CAPITAL PARTNERS LP; *Int'l*, pg. 8188
THE VICTORIA CARPET COMPANY PTY LIMITED—See Victoria Plc; *Int'l*, pg. 8189
VICTORIA CARPETS LIMITED—See Victoria Plc; *Int'l*, pg. 8189
VICTORIA ERSTE BETEILIGUNGSGESELLSCHAFT MBH—See Munchener Ruckversicherungs AG; *Int'l*, pg. 5092
THE VICTORIA FALLS HOTEL—See African Sun Limited; *Int'l*, pg. 192
THE VICTORIA FALLS HOTEL—See Meikles Limited; *Int'l*, pg. 4802
VICTORIA GENERAL INSURANCE COMPANY S.A.—See Munchener Ruckversicherungs AG; *Int'l*, pg. 5088
VICTORIA GOLD CORP.; *Int'l*, pg. 8188
VICTORIA GOSDEN TRAVEL LIMITED—See MBH Corporation Plc; *Int'l*, pg. 4752
VICTORIA GROUP A.D.; *Int'l*, pg. 8188
VICTORIA HEALTHCARE, INC.—See Select Medical Holdings Corporation; *U.S. Public*, pg. 1862
VICTORIAHEM AB—See Vonovia SE; *Int'l*, pg. 8305
VICTORIA HOUSE PTE LTD—See OSIM International Ltd.; *Int'l*, pg. 5650
VICTORIA IMMOBILIEN-FONDS GMBH—See Munchener Ruckversicherungs AG; *Int'l*, pg. 5092
VICTORIA INTERNATIONAL CONTAINER TERMINAL LTD.—See International Container Terminal Services, Inc.; *Int'l*, pg. 3747
VICTORIA-JUNGFRAU COLLECTION AG—See AEVIS VICTORIA SA; *Int'l*, pg. 183
VICTORIA KRANKENVERSICHERUNG AG—See Munchener Ruckversicherungs AG; *Int'l*, pg. 5088
VICTORIA LANDFILL TX, LP—See Republic Services, Inc.; *U.S. Public*, pg. 1788
VICTORIA LEBENSVERSICHERUNG AG—See Munchener Ruckversicherungs AG; *Int'l*, pg. 5088
VICTORIA LOGISTIC D.O.O.—See Victoria Group a.d.; *Int'l*, pg. 8188
VICTORIA MILLS LTD.; *Int'l*, pg. 8188
VICTORIA MINING CORPORATION—See Stakeholder Gold Corp.; *Int'l*, pg. 7164
VICTORIAN CORRECTIONAL INFRASTRUCTURE PARTNERSHIP PTY. LTD.—See Bilfinger SE; *Int'l*, pg. 1029
VICTORIAN EXPRESS PTY LTD—See Japan Post Holdings Co., Ltd.; *Int'l*, pg. 3902
VICTORIAN GREETINGS—See Victorian Paper Company; *U.S. Private*, pg. 4378
VICTORIA NISSAN LTD; *Int'l*, pg. 8188
VICTORIAN NURSE SPECIALISTS PTY LTD—See PeopleIn Limited; *Int'l*, pg. 5794
VICTORIAN PAPER COMPANY; *U.S. Private*, pg. 4378
VICTORIAN PAPERS—See Victorian Paper Company; *U.S. Private*, pg. 4378
VICTORIAN PLUMBING GROUP PLC; *Int'l*, pg. 8189
VICTORIAN RADIO NETWORK PTY LTD—See Pacific Star Network Limited; *Int'l*, pg. 5692
THE VICTORIAN REHABILITATION CENTRE PTY. LTD.—See Brookfield Corporation; *Int'l*, pg. 1176
VICTORIAN SECURITIES—See Bendigo & Adelaide Bank Ltd.; *Int'l*, pg. 971
VICTORIAN TRADING CO.—See Victorian Paper Company; *U.S. Private*, pg. 4378
VICTORIA NURSING & REHABILITATION CENTER, INC.; *U.S. Private*, pg. 4378
VICTORIA OF TEXAS, L.P.—See Community Health Systems, Inc.; *U.S. Public*, pg. 557
VICTORIAOIL A.D.—See Victoria Group a.d.; *Int'l*, pg. 8188
VICTORIA OIL & GAS PLC; *Int'l*, pg. 8188
VICTORIA PACKAGE (SUZHOU) COMPANY LIMITED—See CPMC Holdings Limited; *Int'l*, pg. 1826
VICTORIA PARK BORAS AB—See Vonovia SE; *Int'l*, pg. 8305
VICTORIA PARK MALMO CENTRUM AB—See Vonovia SE; *Int'l*, pg. 8305
VICTORIA PARK MARKARYD AB—See Vonovia SE; *Int'l*, pg. 8305
VICTORIA PARK NYKOPING AB—See Vonovia SE; *Int'l*, pg. 8305
VICTORIA PARK OREBRO AB—See Vonovia SE; *Int'l*, pg. 8305
VICTORIA PARK VAXJO S AB—See Vonovia SE; *Int'l*, pg. 8305
VICTORIA PHOSPHATE D.O.O.—See Victoria Group a.d.; *Int'l*, pg. 8188
VICTORIA PLACE SHOPPING CENTRE LTD.—See Network Rail Limited; *Int'l*, pg. 5218
VICTORIA PLC; *Int'l*, pg. 8188
VICTORIA PROPERTIES A/S—See Gefion Group A/S; *Int'l*, pg. 2911
VICTORIA RACING CLUB LIMITED; *Int'l*, pg. 8189
VICTORIA-SEGUROS DE VIDA, S.A.—See Munchener Ruckversicherungs AG; *Int'l*, pg. 5088
VICTORIA SEGUROS S.A.—See Bago Group; *Int'l*, pg. 799
VICTORIAS FOODS CORPORATION—See Victorias Milling Company, Inc.; *Int'l*, pg. 8189
VICTORIA SHIPYARDS CO. LTD.—See Washington Corporations; *U.S. Private*, pg. 4447

VICTORIAS MILLING COMPANY, INC.; *Int'l*, pg. 8189
VICTORIA SQUARE VENTURES INC.—See Power Corporation of Canada; *Int'l*, pg. 5945
VICTORIA'S SECRET (CANADA) CORPORATION—See Victoria's Secret & Co.; *U.S. Public*, pg. 2296
VICTORIA'S SECRET & CO.; *U.S. Public*, pg. 2296
VICTORIA'S SECRET STORES, LLC—See Victoria's Secret & Co.; *U.S. Public*, pg. 2296
VICTORIA'S SECRET UK LIMITED—See Bath & Body Works, Inc.; *U.S. Public*, pg. 279
VICTORIA STARCH D.O.O.—See Victoria Group a.d.; *Int'l*, pg. 8188
VICTORIA STAR MOTORS INC.; *Int'l*, pg. 8189
VICTORIA STATION INC.—See A.S. Management Corporation; *U.S. Private*, pg. 28
VICTORIA STS (LABUAN) SDN. BHD.—See Straits Energy Resources Berhad; *Int'l*, pg. 7235
VICTORIA TEXAS HOME CARE SERVICES, LLC—See Community Health Systems, Inc.; *U.S. Public*, pg. 557
VICTORIA THEATRE ASSOCIATION; *U.S. Private*, pg. 4378
VICTORIA VENTURA HEALTHCARE LLC—See The Ensign Group, Inc.; *U.S. Public*, pg. 2072
VICTORIA VIERTE BETEILIGUNGSGESELLSCHAFT MBH—See Munchener Ruckversicherungs AG; *Int'l*, pg. 5092
VICTORIA VIERTER BAUABSCHNITT MANAGEMENT GMBH—See Munchener Ruckversicherungs AG; *Int'l*, pg. 5092
VICTORIA-VOLKSBANKEN BIZTOSITO ZRT.—See Munchener Ruckversicherungs AG; *Int'l*, pg. 5092
VICTORIA-VOLKSBANKEN VERSICHERUNGSAKTIENGESELLSCHAFT—See Munchener Ruckversicherungs AG; *Int'l*, pg. 5088
VICTOR INDUSTRIAL EQUIPMENT (PTY) LTD.—See Federal Signal Corporation; *U.S. Public*, pg. 826
VICTOR INNOVATEX INC.; *Int'l*, pg. 8188
VICTOR INNOVATIVE TEXTILES—See Victor Innovatex Inc.; *Int'l*, pg. 8188
VICTORINOX AG; *Int'l*, pg. 8189
VICTORINOX SWISS ARMY, INC.—See Victorinox AG; *Int'l*, pg. 8189
VICTOR INSURANCE EUROPE B.V.—See Marsh & McLennan Companies, Inc.; *U.S. Public*, pg. 1388
VICTOR INSURANCE ITALIA S.R.L.—See Marsh & McLennan Companies, Inc.; *U.S. Public*, pg. 1388
VICTOR INSURANCE MANAGERS INC.—See Marsh & McLennan Companies, Inc.; *U.S. Public*, pg. 1388
VICTOR INTERNATIONAL A/S; *Int'l*, pg. 8188
VICTOR KRAMER CO., INC.—See Compass Group PLC; *Int'l*, pg. 1752
THE VICTOR L. PHILLIPS COMPANY INC.—See VLP Holding Co. Inc.; *U.S. Private*, pg. 4408
VICTOR L. ROBILIO COMPANY, INC.—See Glazer's Family of Companies; *U.S. Private*, pg. 1707
VICTOR MEDICAL CO.; *U.S. Private*, pg. 4377
VICTOR MINING INDUSTRY GROUP, INC.; *U.S. Public*, pg. 2296
VICTOROPS, INC.—See Cisco Systems, Inc.; *U.S. Public*, pg. 500
VICTOR O. SCHINNERER & COMPANY, INC.—See Marsh & McLennan Companies, Inc.; *U.S. Public*, pg. 1383
VICTOR O. SCHINNERER & COMPANY, INC.—See Marsh & McLennan Companies, Inc.; *U.S. Public*, pg. 1383
VICTOR PRODUCTS LIMITED—See Federal Signal Corporation; *U.S. Public*, pg. 826
VICTOR PRODUCTS USA INCORPORATED—See Federal Signal Corporation; *U.S. Public*, pg. 826
VICTOR SECURITIES; *U.S. Private*, pg. 4377
VICTOR TECHNOLOGIES ASIA SDN BHD—See Enovis Corporation; *U.S. Public*, pg. 771
VICTOR TECHNOLOGIES AUSTRALIA PTY LTD—See Enovis Corporation; *U.S. Public*, pg. 774
VICTOR TECHNOLOGIES CANADA LTD.—See Enovis Corporation; *U.S. Public*, pg. 771
VICTOR TECHNOLOGIES GROUP, INC.—See Enovis Corporation; *U.S. Public*, pg. 771
VICTOR TECHNOLOGIES INTERNATIONAL, INC.—See Enovis Corporation; *U.S. Public*, pg. 774
VICTOR TECHNOLOGIES S.R.L.—See Enovis Corporation; *U.S. Public*, pg. 772
VICTOR TECHNOLOGY; *U.S. Private*, pg. 4378
VICTORY 1 PERFORMANCE, INC.—See MiddleGround Management, LP; *U.S. Private*, pg. 2712
VICTORY ASSET MANAGEMENT CO., LTD.—See Sena Development Public Company Limited; *Int'l*, pg. 6707
VICTORY AUTOMOTIVE GROUP, INC.; *U.S. Private*, pg. 4378
THE VICTORY BANCORP, INC.; *U.S. Public*, pg. 2136
THE VICTORY BANK—See The Victory Bancorp, Inc.; *U.S. Public*, pg. 2137
VICTORY BATTERY METALS CORP.; *Int'l*, pg. 8189
VICTORY CAPITAL HOLDINGS, INC.; *U.S. Public*, pg. 2296
VICTORY CAPITAL JOINT STOCK COMPANY; *Int'l*, pg. 8189

CORPORATE AFFILIATIONS

VICTORY CAPITAL MANAGEMENT, INC.—See Crestview Partners, L.P.; *U.S. Private*, pg. 1098
VICTORY CITY COMPANY LIMITED—See Victory City International Holdings Limited; *Int'l*, pg. 8189
VICTORY CITY INTERNATIONAL HOLDINGS LIMITED; *Int'l*, pg. 8189
VICTORY CLIMATE SYSTEMS—See Hickman Investments Inc.; *U.S. Private*, pg. 1933
VICTORY COMMERCIAL MANAGEMENT, INC.; *U.S. Private*, pg. 4378
VICTORY DEVELOPERS INC.; *U.S. Private*, pg. 4378
VICTORY DIALYSIS, LLC—See DaVita Inc.; *U.S. Public*, pg. 644
VICTORY ENTERPRISE SDN. BHD.—See Minho (M) Berhad; *Int'l*, pg. 4910
VICTORY FINANCIAL GROUP, INC.; *U.S. Private*, pg. 4378
VICTORY FOAM, INC.; *U.S. Private*, pg. 4378
VICTORY FOOD SERVICE DISTRIBUTORS; *U.S. Private*, pg. 4378
VICTORY GIANT TECHNOLOGY HUIZHOU CO., LTD.; *Int'l*, pg. 8189
VICTORY GROUND SUPPORT EQUIPMENT; *U.S. Private*, pg. 4378
VICTORY GROUP LIMITED; *Int'l*, pg. 8189
VICTORY HOUSING, INC.; *U.S. Private*, pg. 4378
VICTORY INDUSTRIES, INC—See PAO Severstal; *Int'l*, pg. 5732
VICTORY LAYNE CHEVROLET; *U.S. Private*, pg. 4378
VICTORY MARINE HOLDINGS CORP.; *U.S. Public*, pg. 2296
VICTORY MARITIME INC.—See Sealift Holdings Inc.; *U.S. Private*, pg. 3585
VICTORY MEDIA INC.; *U.S. Private*, pg. 4379
VICTORY METALS, INC.; *Int'l*, pg. 8189
VICTORY MINES LIMITED; *Int'l*, pg. 8189
VICTORY MOTORCYCLES AUSTRALIA PTY LTD—See Polaris, Inc.; *U.S. Public*, pg. 1701
VICTORY MOTORS OF CRAIG; *U.S. Private*, pg. 4379
VICTORY MOUNTAIN VENTURES LTD.; *Int'l*, pg. 8189
VICTORY NEW MATERIALS LIMITED COMPANY; *Int'l*, pg. 8189
VICTORY NICKEL INC.; *Int'l*, pg. 8190
VICTORY OF WEST VIRGINIA, INC.; *U.S. Private*, pg. 4379
VICTORY OILFIELD TECH, INC.; *U.S. Public*, pg. 2296
VICTORY PACKAGING DE MEXICO, S. DE R.L. DE C.V.—See WestRock Company; *U.S. Public*, pg. 2361
VICTORY PACKAGING, LP—See WestRock Company; *U.S. Public*, pg. 2362
VICTORY PACKAGING MAQUILA DORA LLC—See WestRock Company; *U.S. Public*, pg. 2361
VICTORY PACKAGING; *U.S. Private*, pg. 4379
VICTORY PARK CAPITAL ADVISORS, LLC; *U.S. Private*, pg. 4379
VICTORY PERSONNEL SERVICES, INC.; *U.S. Private*, pg. 4379
VICTORY PHYSICAL THERAPY, LIMITED PARTNERSHIP—See U.S. Physical Therapy, Inc.; *U.S. Public*, pg. 2216
VICTORY PRODUCTION & COMPANY; *Int'l*, pg. 8190
VICTORY PRODUCTIONS, INC.—See A Pass Educational Group LLC; *U.S. Private*, pg. 18
VICTORY RANCH; *U.S. Private*, pg. 4379
VICTORY REFRIGERATION COMPANY LLC—See Ali Holding S.r.l; *Int'l*, pg. 322
VICTORY RESOURCES CORPORATION U.S.A.—See Victory Battery Metals Corp.; *Int'l*, pg. 8189
VICTORY SECURITIES (HOLDINGS) COMPANY LTD.; *Int'l*, pg. 8190
VICTORY SQUARE TECHNOLOGIES, INC.; *Int'l*, pg. 8190
VICTORY STATE BANK—See Northfield Bancorp, Inc.; *U.S. Public*, pg. 1539
VICTORY STEEL PRODUCTS CORP.; *U.S. Private*, pg. 4379
VICTORY SUPERMARKET CHAIN LTD.; *Int'l*, pg. 8190
VICTORY TAILGATE, LLC—See Escalade, Incorporated; *U.S. Public*, pg. 793
VICTORY TECHNOLOGY POLSKA SP.Z O.O.—See Suzhou Victory Precision Manufacture Co., Ltd; *Int'l*, pg. 7352
VICTORY TRANSPORTATION SYSTEMS, INC.; *U.S. Private*, pg. 4379
VICTORY VAN CORP.; *U.S. Private*, pg. 4379
VICTORY WHITE METAL COMPANY, INC.; *U.S. Private*, pg. 4379
VICTORY WORLDWIDE TRANSPORATION; *U.S. Private*, pg. 4379
VICTRA; *U.S. Private*, pg. 4379
VICTREX EUROPA GMBH—See Victrex plc; *Int'l*, pg. 8190
VICTREX HIGH-PERFORMANCE MATERIALS (SHANGHAI) CO., LTD.—See Victrex plc; *Int'l*, pg. 8190
VICTREX PLC; *Int'l*, pg. 8190
VICTREX USA, INC—See Victrex plc; *Int'l*, pg. 8190
VICTURA CONSTRUCTION GROUP, INC.—See Saint James Holding & Investment Company Trust; *U.S. Private*, pg. 3529

COMPANY NAME INDEX — VIENNA INSURANCE GROUP AG WIENER VERSICHERUNG GRUPPE

VICTUS EMAK SP. Z O.O.—See Emak S.p.A.; *Int'l*, pg. 2373
VICTUS, INC.; *U.S. Private*, pg. 4380
VICUNHA TEXTIL S.A.; *Int'l*, pg. 8190
VICURON PHARMACEUTICALS, INC—See AbbVie Inc.; *U.S. Public*, pg. 23
VICUS GROUP AG; *Int'l*, pg. 8190
VICWEST INC.—See Kingspan Group PLC; *Int'l*, pg. 4179
VIDACAIXA, S.A. DE SEGUROS Y REASEGUROS—See Lone Star Funds; *U.S. Private*, pg. 2485
VIDA CAPITAL, INC.—See RedBird Capital Partners L.P.; *U.S. Private*, pg. 3377
VIDA CAPITAL, INC.—See Reverence Capital Partners LLC; *U.S. Private*, pg. 3415
VIDACARE CORP.—See Teleflex Incorporated; *U.S. Public*, pg. 1996
VIDA CELL S.A.—See Abbott Laboratories; *U.S. Public*, pg. 21
VIDAHIM AD; *Int'l*, pg. 8190
VIDA FLASH ACQUISITIONS; *U.S. Private*, pg. 4380
VIDA HERBAL SUPLEMENTOS ALIMENTICIOS, C.A. (VENEZUELA)—See Herbalife Nutrition Ltd.; *Int'l*, pg. 3360
VIDA LAVANDERIAS ESPECIALIZADA S.A.—See Servizi Italia SpA; *Int'l*, pg. 6726
VIDANT EDGECOMBE HOSPITAL—See HCA Healthcare, Inc.; *U.S. Public*, pg. 1013
VIDAROO CORPORATION; *U.S. Private*, pg. 4380
VIDAR SYSTEMS CORPORATION—See 3D Systems Corporation; *U.S. Public*, pg. 4
VIDAVO SA; *Int'l*, pg. 8190
VIDCOM NEW ZEALAND LIMITED—See Vp PLC; *Int'l*, pg. 8312
VIDCON ENTERPRISES, INC.; *U.S. Private*, pg. 4380
VIDEE S.P.A.; *Int'l*, pg. 8190
VIDEK, INC.; *U.S. Private*, pg. 4380
VIDELIO SA; *Int'l*, pg. 8190
VIDENDUM PLC; *Int'l*, pg. 8190
VIDENTE CO., LTD.; *Int'l*, pg. 8191
VIDEOAMP, INC.; *U.S. Private*, pg. 4380
VIDEO AND AUDIO CENTER; *U.S. Private*, pg. 4380
VIDEO ARTS LTD.—See Vitruvian Partners LLP; *Int'l*, pg. 8263
VIDEOCIETY GMBH—See Splendid Medien AG; *Int'l*, pg. 7141
VIDEOCINE, S.A. DE C.V.—See Grupo Televisa, S.A.B.; *Int'l*, pg. 3137
VIDEO COMMUNICATION FRANCE S.A.—See Bertelsmann SE & Co. KGaA; *Int'l*, pg. 996
VIDEOCOM TECHNOLOGY (HK) LIMITED—See Mobicon Group Limited; *Int'l*, pg. 5010
VIDEOCON INDUSTRIES LIMITED; *Int'l*, pg. 8191
VIDEO CORPORATION OF AMERICA; *U.S. Private*, pg. 4380
VIDEO DESIGN SOFTWARE (USA), INC.—See LTN Global Communications, Inc.; *U.S. Private*, pg. 2510
VIDEO DISPLAY CORPORATION; *U.S. Public*, pg. 2296
VIDEO DISPLAY NOVATRON TUBE DIVISION—See Video Display Corporation; *U.S. Public*, pg. 2297
VIDEO FUTUR ENTERTAINMENT GROUP SA—See Netgem SA; *Int'l*, pg. 5214
VIDEO GAMING TECHNOLOGIES, INC.—See Aristocrat Leisure Limited; *Int'l*, pg. 566
VIDEO GAMING TECHNOLOGIES, INC. - TULSA—See Aristocrat Leisure Limited; *Int'l*, pg. 567
VIDEO GROUP DISTRIBUTORS; *U.S. Private*, pg. 4380
VIDEO GUIDANCE, INC.; *U.S. Private*, pg. 4380
VIDEO, INC.—See Telephone Electronics Corporation; *U.S. Private*, pg. 3961
VIDEO INDUSTRIAL SERVICE INC.—See Carylon Corporation; *U.S. Private*, pg. 777
VIDEO INJECTION-INSITUFORM SAS—See New Mountain Capital, LLC; *U.S. Private*, pg. 2900
VIDEO INSIGHT, INC.—See Panasonic Holdings Corporation; *Int'l*, pg. 5721
VIDEOJET ARGENTINA S.R.L.—See Danaher Corporation; *U.S. Public*, pg. 631
VIDEOJET CHILE CODIFICADORA LIMITED—See Danaher Corporation; *U.S. Public*, pg. 631
VIDEOJET ITALIA SRL—See Danaher Corporation; *U.S. Public*, pg. 631
VIDEOJET TECHNOLOGIES B.V.—See Danaher Corporation; *U.S. Public*, pg. 632
VIDEOJET TECHNOLOGIES CANADA L.P.—See Danaher Corporation; *U.S. Public*, pg. 632
VIDEOJET TECHNOLOGIES EUROPE B.V.—See Danaher Corporation; *U.S. Public*, pg. 632
VIDEOJET TECHNOLOGIES EUROPE B.V.—See Danaher Corporation; *U.S. Public*, pg. 632
VIDEOJET TECHNOLOGIES GMBH—See Danaher Corporation; *U.S. Public*, pg. 632
VIDEOJET TECHNOLOGIES INC.—See Danaher Corporation; *U.S. Public*, pg. 632
VIDEOJET TECHNOLOGIES INC.—See Danaher Corporation; *U.S. Public*, pg. 631
VIDEOJET TECHNOLOGIES (I) PVT. LTD—See Danaher Corporation; *U.S. Public*, pg. 631
VIDEOJET TECHNOLOGIES JSC—See Danaher Corporation; *U.S. Public*, pg. 632
VIDEOJET TECHNOLOGIES LTD—See Danaher Corporation; *U.S. Public*, pg. 632
VIDEOJET TECHNOLOGIES MEXICO S. DE R.L. DE C.V.—See Danaher Corporation; *U.S. Public*, pg. 632
VIDEOJET TECHNOLOGIES S.A.S.—See Danaher Corporation; *U.S. Public*, pg. 632
VIDEOJET TECHNOLOGIES (SHANGHAI) CO., LTD.—See Danaher Corporation; *U.S. Public*, pg. 632
VIDEOJET TECHNOLOGIES (S) PTE. LTD.—See Danaher Corporation; *U.S. Public*, pg. 631
VIDEOJET X-RITE K.K.—See Danaher Corporation; *U.S. Public*, pg. 632
VIDEO KING GAMING & ENTERTAINMENT CANADA LIMITED—See Video King Gaming Systems, LLC; *U.S. Private*, pg. 4380
VIDEO KING GAMING SYSTEMS, LLC - BINGO KING DIVISION—See Video King Gaming Systems, LLC; *U.S. Private*, pg. 4380
VIDEO KING GAMING SYSTEMS, LLC - BINGO TECHNOLOGY & SUPPLY DIVISION—See Video King Gaming Systems, LLC; *U.S. Private*, pg. 4380
VIDEO KING GAMING SYSTEMS, LLC - MANUFACTURING DIVISION—See Video King Gaming Systems, LLC; *U.S. Private*, pg. 4380
VIDEO KING GAMING SYSTEMS, LLC; *U.S. Private*, pg. 4380
VIDEOLAND, INC.; *U.S. Private*, pg. 4380
VIDEOLAND, INC.—See Grand Pacific Petrochemical Corporation; *Int'l*, pg. 3055
VIDEOALARM, INC.—See Moog Inc.; *U.S. Public*, pg. 1470
VIDEOLINK LLC—See Marlin Equity Partners, LLC; *U.S. Private*, pg. 2583
VIDEOLLE PRODUCTIONS OY—See Sanoma Oyj; *Int'l*, pg. 6554
VIDEOLOCITY INTERNATIONAL, INC.; *U.S. Private*, pg. 4380
VIDEOLOGY, INC.—See Nexxen International Ltd.; *Int'l*, pg. 5251
VIDEOMED S.R.L.—See Baxter International Inc.; *U.S. Public*, pg. 283
VIDEO MONITORING SERVICES OF AMERICA, LP; *U.S. Private*, pg. 4380
VIDEON CENTRAL, INC.; *U.S. Private*, pg. 4380
VIDEO NETWORKS, INC.; *U.S. Private*, pg. 4380
VIDEO ONLY INC.; *U.S. Private*, pg. 4380
VIDEOPERSEL, LTD.—See Grupo Televisa, S.A.B.; *Int'l*, pg. 3137
VIDEO PIPE SERVICES INC.—See Carylon Corporation; *U.S. Private*, pg. 777
VIDEOPOLIS, S.A.S.—See Amadeus IT Group, S.A.; *Int'l*, pg. 407
VIDEO PROFESSOR INC.; *U.S. Private*, pg. 4380
VIDEOPROPULSION INTERACTIVE TELEVISION, INC.; *U.S. Public*, pg. 2297
VIDEO RESEARCH INTERACTIVE INC.—See Dentsu Group Inc.; *Int'l*, pg. 2039
VIDEO RESEARCH LTD.—See Dentsu Group Inc.; *Int'l*, pg. 2040
VIDEO RIVER NETWORKS, INC.; *U.S. Public*, pg. 2297
VIDEO SECURITY SPECIALISTS, INC.; *U.S. Private*, pg. 4380
VIDEOTAPE PRODUCTS INC.; *U.S. Private*, pg. 4380
VIDEO TECHNIC VIDEO SYSTEMS S.R.L.—See Shape Robotics A/S; *Int'l*, pg. 6788
VIDEOTEL MARINE ASIA LTD.—See Oakley Capital Limited; *Int'l*, pg. 5504
VIDEOTEL MARINE INTERNATIONAL LTD.—See Oakley Capital Limited; *Int'l*, pg. 5504
VIDEOTIME S.P.A.—See Mediaset S.p.A.; *Int'l*, pg. 4773
VIDEOTON AUTOELEKTRONIKA KFT—See Videoton Holding Zrt.; *Int'l*, pg. 8191
VIDEOTON ELECTRONIC ASSEMBLY SERVICES KFT.—See Videoton Holding Zrt.; *Int'l*, pg. 8191
VIDEOTON ELEKTRO-PLAST KFT.—See Videoton Holding Zrt.; *Int'l*, pg. 8191
VIDEOTON HOLDING ZRT.; *Int'l*, pg. 8191
VIDEOTON MECHLABOR FEJLESZTO ES GYARTO KFT—See Videoton Holding Zrt.; *Int'l*, pg. 8191
VIDEOTON PRECISION KFT.—See Videoton Holding Zrt.; *Int'l*, pg. 8191
VIDEOTRONIX INC.; *U.S. Private*, pg. 4381
VIDEOTRON LTD.—See Quebecor Inc.; *Int'l*, pg. 6159
VIDERA OY—See Elisa Corporation; *Int'l*, pg. 2362
VIDERITY INC.; *U.S. Private*, pg. 4381
VIDEX, INC.; *U.S. Private*, pg. 4381
VIDGRID INC.—See Paylocity Holding Corporation; *U.S. Public*, pg. 1656
VIDHI SPECIALTY FOOD INGREDIENTS LIMITED; *Int'l*, pg. 8192
VIDI EMI, INC.; *U.S. Private*, pg. 4381
VIDILLION CORP.—See Sabio Holdings Inc.; *Int'l*, pg. 6462
VIDISPINE AB—See Bertelsmann SE & Co. KGaA; *Int'l*, pg. 996
VIDISTAR, LLC—See Hitachi, Ltd.; *Int'l*, pg. 3414
VIDLER WATER RESOURCES, INC.—See D.R. Horton, Inc.; *U.S. Public*, pg. 620
VIDLI RESTAURANTS LTD.; *Int'l*, pg. 8192
VIDMAR HONDA; *U.S. Private*, pg. 4381
VID PUBLIC BANK—See Public Bank Berhad; *Int'l*, pg. 6094
VIDRALA S.A.; *Int'l*, pg. 8192
VIDRARU SA; *Int'l*, pg. 8192
VIDRIERA GUADALAJAURA S.A. DE C.V.—See Vitro, S.A.B. de C.V.; *Int'l*, pg. 8262
VIDRIERA GUATEMALTECA, S.A.—See Vitro, S.A.B. de C.V.; *Int'l*, pg. 8262
VIDRIERA MONTERREY, S.A. DE C.V.—See Vitro, S.A.B. de C.V.; *Int'l*, pg. 8262
VIDRIERIA ARGENTINA SA—See Nippon Sheet Glass Co. Ltd.; *Int'l*, pg. 5332
VIDRIERIA ROVIRA, S.A.—See O-I Glass, Inc.; *U.S. Public*, pg. 1560
VIDRIERIA Y REACTIVOS, S.A. DE C.V.—See HORIBA Ltd; *Int'l*, pg. 3478
VIDRIO LUX S.A.—See Vitro, S.A.B. de C.V.; *Int'l*, pg. 8262
VIDRIOS DELL ORTO, S.A.—See CRH plc; *Int'l*, pg. 1849
VIDULLANKA PLC; *Int'l*, pg. 8192
VIDWRX INC.; *Int'l*, pg. 8192
VIDYA BRANDS GROUP LLC; *U.S. Private*, pg. 4381
VIDYO ASIA PACIFIC—See Enghouse Systems Limited; *Int'l*, pg. 2428
VIDYO EMEA—See Enghouse Systems Limited; *Int'l*, pg. 2428
VIDYO, INC.—See Enghouse Systems Limited; *Int'l*, pg. 2428
VIDYO INDIA—See Enghouse Systems Limited; *Int'l*, pg. 2428
VIDYO ITALY—See Enghouse Systems Limited; *Int'l*, pg. 2428
VIDYO JAPAN—See Enghouse Systems Limited; *Int'l*, pg. 2428
VIDYO NETHERLANDS—See Enghouse Systems Limited; *Int'l*, pg. 2428
VIDYO NORDICS & BALTICS—See Enghouse Systems Limited; *Int'l*, pg. 2428
VIDYO UNITED KINGDOM—See Enghouse Systems Limited; *Int'l*, pg. 2428
VIEAU ASSOCIATES INC.—See GZA GeoEnvironmental Inc.; *U.S. Private*, pg. 1822
VIECELI & FURLAN ASSOCIADOS INDUSTRIA E COMERCIO LTDA.—See Aiphone Co., Ltd.; *Int'l*, pg. 235
VIECORE FEDERAL SYSTEMS DIVISION, INC.—See Microsoft Corporation; *U.S. Public*, pg. 1443
VIE DE FRANCE CO., LTD—See Yamazaki Baking Co., Ltd.; *Int'l*, pg. 8557
VIE DE FRANCE YAMAZAKI, INC.—See Yamazaki Baking Co., Ltd.; *Int'l*, pg. 8557
VIE-DEL COMPANY; *U.S. Private*, pg. 4381
VIEGA GMBH & CO. KG; *Int'l*, pg. 8192
VIEGA NORTH AMERICA—See Viega GmbH & Co. KG; *Int'l*, pg. 8192
VIEGA—See Viega GmbH & Co. KG; *Int'l*, pg. 8192
VIELA BIO, INC.—See Amgen Inc.; *U.S. Public*, pg. 123
VIEL & COMPAGNIE SA; *Int'l*, pg. 8192
VIELIFE LIMITED—See The Cigna Group; *U.S. Public*, pg. 2061
VIEL TRADITION S.A.—See Viel & Compagnie SA; *Int'l*, pg. 8193
VIEMED HEALTHCARE, INC.; *U.S. Public*, pg. 2297
VIEN DONG INVESTMENT DEVELOPMENT TRADING CORPORATION—See Mayr-Melnhof Karton AG; *Int'l*, pg. 4747
VIEN LIEN JOINT STOCK COMPANY; *Int'l*, pg. 8193
VIENNA AIRCRAFT HANDLING GESELLSCHAFT M.B.H.—See Flughafen Wien Aktiengesellschaft; *Int'l*, pg. 2713
VIENNA AIRPORT HEALTH CENTER GMBH—See Flughafen Wien Aktiengesellschaft; *Int'l*, pg. 2713
VIENNA AIRPORT TECHNIK GMBH—See Flughafen Wien Aktiengesellschaft; *Int'l*, pg. 2713
VIENNA CINE & TV SERVICES GMBH—See Bavaria Film GmbH; *Int'l*, pg. 899
VIENNA HOUSE ANDEL'S CRACOW SP. Z O.O.—See U City Public Company Limited; *Int'l*, pg. 7996
VIENNA HOUSE EASY BREMEN GMBH—See U City Public Company Limited; *Int'l*, pg. 7996
VIENNA HOUSE EASY CRACOW RE SP. Z O.O.—See U City Public Company Limited; *Int'l*, pg. 7996
VIENNA HOUSE EASY KATOWICE SP. Z O.O.—See U City Public Company Limited; *Int'l*, pg. 7996
VIENNA HOUSE EASY MUNCHEN GMBH—See U City Public Company Limited; *Int'l*, pg. 7996
VIENNA HOUSE EASY PILSEN S.R.O.—See U City Public Company Limited; *Int'l*, pg. 7997
VIENNA HOUSE EASY POTSDAM GMBH—See U City Public Company Limited; *Int'l*, pg. 7997
VIENNA HOUSE EISENACH GMBH—See U City Public Company Limited; *Int'l*, pg. 7997
VIENNA HOUSE ROSTOCK GMBH—See U City Public Company Limited; *Int'l*, pg. 7997
VIENNA HOUSE STRALSUND GMBH—See U City Public Company Limited; *Int'l*, pg. 7997
VIENNA INSURANCE GROUP AG WIENER VERSICHERUNG GRUPPE; *Int'l*, pg. 8193

VIENNA INSURANCE GROUP AG WIENER VERSICHERUNG GRUPPE

CORPORATE AFFILIATIONS

VIENNA INTERNATIONAL AIRPORT SECURITY SERVICES GES.M.B.H.—See Flughafen Wien Aktiengesellschaft; *Int'l*, pg. 2713
VIENNA INTERNATIONAL ASSET GMBH—See U City Public Company Limited; *Int'l*, pg. 7997
VIENNA INTERNATIONAL UNDERWRITERS GMBH—See Vienna Insurance Group AG Wiener Versicherung Gruppe; *Int'l*, pg. 8196
VIENNA-LIFE LEBENSVERSICHERUNG AG—See Vienna Insurance Group AG Wiener Versicherung Gruppe; *Int'l*, pg. 8196
VIENNA LIFE TOWARZYSTWO UBEZPIECZEN NA ZYCIE S.A.—See Vienna Insurance Group AG Wiener Versicherung Gruppe; *Int'l*, pg. 8196
VIENNA SAUSAGE MFG. CO.; *U.S. Private*, pg. 4381
VIENU CORPORATION; *U.S. Private*, pg. 4381
THE VIERA COMPANY—See A. Duda & Sons Inc.; *U.S. Private*, pg. 23
VIERPOOL B.V.; *Int'l*, pg. 8196
VIERTE KORSCHENBROICHER ARMATUREN VERWALTUNGS GMBH—See Pentair plc; *Int'l*, pg. 5791
VIERTEL MOTOREN GMBH; *Int'l*, pg. 8196
VIERTE REAL,- SB-WARENHAUS GMBH—See Metro AG; *Int'l*, pg. 4859
VIESGO, S.L.—See Macquarie Group Limited; *Int'l*, pg. 4626
VIE SHOW CINEMAS CO. LTD.—See Orange Sky Golden Harvest Entertainment (Holdings) Limited; *Int'l*, pg. 5611
VIESSMANN A/S—See Viessmann Werke GmbH & Co. KG; *Int'l*, pg. 8196
VIESSMANN-BELGIUM BVBA—See Viessmann Werke GmbH & Co. KG; *Int'l*, pg. 8197
VIESSMANN CHINA LTD.—See Viessmann Werke GmbH & Co. KG; *Int'l*, pg. 8196
VIESSMANN D.O.O.—See Viessmann Werke GmbH & Co. KG; *Int'l*, pg. 8197
VIESSMANN D.O.O.—See Viessmann Werke GmbH & Co. KG; *Int'l*, pg. 8197
VIESSMANN D.O.O.—See Viessmann Werke GmbH & Co. KG; *Int'l*, pg. 8197
VIESSMANN EIS-ENERGIESPEICHER GMBH—See Viessmann Werke GmbH & Co. KG; *Int'l*, pg. 8196
VIESSMANN FRANCE SAS—See Viessmann Werke GmbH & Co. KG; *Int'l*, pg. 8196
VIESSMANN FUTESTECHNIKA KFT—See Viessmann Werke GmbH & Co. KG; *Int'l*, pg. 8196
VIESSMANN GESELLSCHAFT M.B.H.—See Viessmann Werke GmbH & Co. KG; *Int'l*, pg. 8196
VIESSMANN HEATING TECHNOLOGY BEIJING CO., LTD.—See Viessmann Werke GmbH & Co. KG; *Int'l*, pg. 8196
VIESSMANN HOLZHEIZTECHNIK GMBH—See Viessmann Werke GmbH & Co. KG; *Int'l*, pg. 8196
VIESSMANN ISI TEKNIKLERI TICARET A.S.—See Viessmann Werke GmbH & Co. KG; *Int'l*, pg. 8196
VIESSMANN KRAFT-WARME-KOPPLUNG GMBH—See Viessmann Werke GmbH & Co. KG; *Int'l*, pg. 8196
VIESSMANN KUHLSYSTEME GMBH—See Viessmann Werke GmbH & Co. KG; *Int'l*, pg. 8196
VIESSMANN LIMITED—See Viessmann Werke GmbH & Co. KG; *Int'l*, pg. 8196
VIESSMANN-LUXEMBOURG—See Viessmann Werke GmbH & Co. KG; *Int'l*, pg. 8197
VIESSMANN MANUFACTURING COMPANY INC.—See Viessmann Werke GmbH & Co. KG; *Int'l*, pg. 8196
VIESSMANN MANUFACTURING COMPANY (U.S.) INC.—See Viessmann Werke GmbH & Co. KG; *Int'l*, pg. 8196
VIESSMANN MIDDLE EAST FZE—See Viessmann Werke GmbH & Co. KG; *Int'l*, pg. 8196
VIESSMANN-NEDERLAND B.V.—See Viessmann Werke GmbH & Co. KG; *Int'l*, pg. 8197
VIESSMANN (SCHWEIZ) AG—See Viessmann Werke GmbH & Co. KG; *Int'l*, pg. 8196
VIESSMANN SIA—See Viessmann Werke GmbH & Co. KG; *Int'l*, pg. 8196
VIESSMANN SIA—See Viessmann Werke GmbH & Co. KG; *Int'l*, pg. 8196
VIESSMANN S.L.—See Viessmann Werke GmbH & Co. KG; *Int'l*, pg. 8196
VIESSMANN, SPOL. S R.O.—See Viessmann Werke GmbH & Co. KG; *Int'l*, pg. 8197
VIESSMANN SP. Z O.O.—See Viessmann Werke GmbH & Co. KG; *Int'l*, pg. 8196
VIESSMANN S.R.L.—See Viessmann Werke GmbH & Co. KG; *Int'l*, pg. 8196
VIESSMANN SRL—See Viessmann Werke GmbH & Co. KG; *Int'l*, pg. 8196
VIESSMANN, S.R.O.—See Viessmann Werke GmbH & Co. KG; *Int'l*, pg. 8197
VIESSMANN UAB—See Viessmann Werke GmbH & Co. KG; *Int'l*, pg. 8197
VIESSMANN WERKE GMBH & CO. KG; *Int'l*, pg. 8196
VIET AN ENVIRONMENT TECHNOLOGY JOINT STOCK COMPANY—See Endress+Hauser (International) Holding AG; *Int'l*, pg. 2409
VIET BOKUTO CO., LTD.—See Luckland Co., Ltd.; *Int'l*, pg. 4574

VIETCOMBANK AN GIANG—See Joint Stock Commercial Bank of Vietnam; *Int'l*, pg. 3995
VIETCOMBANK ASSET MANAGEMENT COMPANY—See Joint Stock Commercial Bank of Vietnam; *Int'l*, pg. 3995
VIETCOMBANK BINH DUONG—See Joint Stock Commercial Bank of Vietnam; *Int'l*, pg. 3995
VIETCOMBANK BINH TAY—See Joint Stock Commercial Bank of Vietnam; *Int'l*, pg. 3995
VIETCOMBANK CA MAU—See Joint Stock Commercial Bank of Vietnam; *Int'l*, pg. 3995
VIETCOMBANK CAN THO—See Joint Stock Commercial Bank of Vietnam; *Int'l*, pg. 3995
VIETCOMBANK DAKLAK—See Joint Stock Commercial Bank of Vietnam; *Int'l*, pg. 3995
VIETCOMBANK DA NANG—See Joint Stock Commercial Bank of Vietnam; *Int'l*, pg. 3995
VIETCOMBANK DONG NAI—See Joint Stock Commercial Bank of Vietnam; *Int'l*, pg. 3995
VIETCOMBANK GIA LAI—See Joint Stock Commercial Bank of Vietnam; *Int'l*, pg. 3995
VIETCOMBANK HAI DUONG—See Joint Stock Commercial Bank of Vietnam; *Int'l*, pg. 3995
VIETCOMBANK HAI PHONG—See Joint Stock Commercial Bank of Vietnam; *Int'l*, pg. 3995
VIETCOMBANK HANOI—See Joint Stock Commercial Bank of Vietnam; *Int'l*, pg. 3995
VIETCOMBANK HA TINH—See Joint Stock Commercial Bank of Vietnam; *Int'l*, pg. 3995
VIETCOMBANK HO CHI MINH CITY—See Joint Stock Commercial Bank of Vietnam; *Int'l*, pg. 3995
VIETCOMBANK HUE—See Joint Stock Commercial Bank of Vietnam; *Int'l*, pg. 3995
VIETCOMBANK KIEN GIANG—See Joint Stock Commercial Bank of Vietnam; *Int'l*, pg. 3995
VIETCOMBANK LEASING CORP.—See Joint Stock Commercial Bank of Vietnam; *Int'l*, pg. 3995
VIETCOMBANK NHA TRANG—See Joint Stock Commercial Bank of Vietnam; *Int'l*, pg. 3995
VIETCOMBANK QUANG NGAI—See Joint Stock Commercial Bank of Vietnam; *Int'l*, pg. 3995
VIETCOMBANK QUANG NINH—See Joint Stock Commercial Bank of Vietnam; *Int'l*, pg. 3996
VIETCOMBANK QUY NHON—See Joint Stock Commercial Bank of Vietnam; *Int'l*, pg. 3996
VIETCOMBANK SECURITIES COMPANY—See Joint Stock Commercial Bank of Vietnam; *Int'l*, pg. 3996
VIETCOMBANK TAN THUAN—See Joint Stock Commercial Bank of Vietnam; *Int'l*, pg. 3996
VIETCOMBANK THAI BINH—See Joint Stock Commercial Bank of Vietnam; *Int'l*, pg. 3996
VIETCOMBANK VINH—See Joint Stock Commercial Bank of Vietnam; *Int'l*, pg. 3996
VIET-DUC WELDING ELECTRODE JOINT STOCK COMPANY—See Masan Consumer Corp.; *Int'l*, pg. 4719
VIE TECHNOLOGIES SDN. BHD.—See ViTrox Corporation Berhad; *Int'l*, pg. 8262
VIETFRACHT TRANSPORT AND CHARTERING CORP.; *Int'l*, pg. 8197
VIET HAN CO., LTD.—See Test-Rite International Co., Ltd.; *Int'l*, pg. 7575
VIETHOMES REAL ESTATE JOINT STOCK COMPANY—See Dat Xanh Group Joint Stock Company; *Int'l*, pg. 1975
VIET HUNG MANGEMENT CORPORATION; *Int'l*, pg. 8197
VIETINBANK DEBT MANAGEMENT & ASSET EXPLOITATION COMPANY LTD.—See Vietnam Joint Stock Commercial Bank for Industry and Trade; *Int'l*, pg. 8200
VIETINBANK FUND MANAGEMENT COMPANY LTD.—See Vietnam Joint Stock Commercial Bank for Industry and Trade; *Int'l*, pg. 8200
VIETINBANK GOLD & JEWELLERY TRADING COMPANY LTD.—See Vietnam Joint Stock Commercial Bank for Industry and Trade; *Int'l*, pg. 8200
VIETINBANK INSURANCE COMPANY LTD.—See Vietnam Joint Stock Commercial Bank for Industry and Trade; *Int'l*, pg. 8200
VIETINBANK LAO LIMITED—See Vietnam Joint Stock Commercial Bank for Industry and Trade; *Int'l*, pg. 8200
VIETINBANK LEASING COMPANY LTD.—See Vietnam Joint Stock Commercial Bank for Industry and Trade; *Int'l*, pg. 8200
VIETINBANK SECURITIES JOINT STOCK COMPANY—See Vietnam Joint Stock Commercial Bank for Industry and Trade; *Int'l*, pg. 8200
VIET ITALIA S.R.L.—See Biesse S.p.A.; *Int'l*, pg. 1020
VIETNAM AIRLINES CATERERS LTD.—See Vietnam Airlines Corporation; *Int'l*, pg. 8197
VIETNAM AIRLINES CORPORATION; *Int'l*, pg. 8197
VIET NAM AIR SERVICES COMPANY—See Vietnam Airlines Corporation; *Int'l*, pg. 8197
VIETNAM AMERICAN EXPLORATION COMPANY LLC—See Repsol, S.A.; *Int'l*, pg. 6293
VIETNAM ASSET DEVELOPMENT JOINT STOCK COMPANY—See PVI Holdings; *Int'l*, pg. 6125
VIETNAM AUTOMOBILE INDUSTRY DEVELOPMENT LTD.—See Nissan Motor Co., Ltd.; *Int'l*, pg. 5369

VIETNAM BANK FOR INDUSTRY & TRADE SECURITIES JSC; *Int'l*, pg. 8197
VIETNAM BEVERAGE COMPANY LIMITED—See Thai Beverage Public Company Limited; *Int'l*, pg. 7592
VIETNAM BIKEN COMPANY LIMITED—See Biken Techno Corporation Ltd.; *Int'l*, pg. 1023
VIETNAM CENTER POWER TECH CO., LTD.—See Shenzhen Center Power Tech. Co., Ltd.; *Int'l*, pg. 6806
VIET NAM CHEMICAL IMPORT & EXPORT CORPORATION—See Masan Consumer Corp.; *Int'l*, pg. 4719
VIETNAM CHERNG TAY TECHNOLOGY CO., LTD.—See Cherng Tay Technology Co., Ltd.; *Int'l*, pg. 1471
VIETNAM CONSTRUCTION STOCK CORPORATION; *Int'l*, pg. 8197
VIETNAM CONTAINER SHIPPING CORPORATION; *Int'l*, pg. 8198
VIETNAM CORPORATION; *Int'l*, pg. 8198
VIETNAM CREATE MEDIC CO., LTD.—See CREATE MEDIC CO. LTD.; *Int'l*, pg. 1832
VIETNAM DAEWOO BUS CO., LTD—See Young An Hat Co., Ltd.; *Int'l*, pg. 8602
VIETNAM DAI-ICHI SEIKO CO., LTD.—See I-PEX Inc.; *Int'l*, pg. 3564
VIETNAM DAI-ICHI SEIKO CO., LTD. - VIETNAM PLANT—See I-PEX Inc.; *Int'l*, pg. 3564
VIETNAM DAIRY COW ONE MEMBER LIMITED COMPANY—See Vietnam Dairy Products Joint Stock Company; *Int'l*, pg. 8199
VIETNAM DAIRY PRODUCTS JOINT STOCK COMPANY - BEVERAGE FACTORY—See Vietnam Dairy Products Joint Stock Company; *Int'l*, pg. 8199
VIETNAM DAIRY PRODUCTS JOINT STOCK COMPANY - BINH DINH MILK FACTORY—See Vietnam Dairy Products Joint Stock Company; *Int'l*, pg. 8199
VIETNAM DAIRY PRODUCTS JOINT STOCK COMPANY - CAN THO DAIRY FACTORY—See Vietnam Dairy Products Joint Stock Company; *Int'l*, pg. 8199
VIETNAM DAIRY PRODUCTS JOINT STOCK COMPANY - DA NANG DAIRY FACTORY—See Vietnam Dairy Products Joint Stock Company; *Int'l*, pg. 8199
VIETNAM DAIRY PRODUCTS JOINT STOCK COMPANY - DIELAC DAIRY FACTORY—See Vietnam Dairy Products Joint Stock Company; *Int'l*, pg. 8199
VIETNAM DAIRY PRODUCTS JOINT STOCK COMPANY - LAM SON DAIRY FACTORY—See Vietnam Dairy Products Joint Stock Company; *Int'l*, pg. 8199
VIETNAM DAIRY PRODUCTS JOINT STOCK COMPANY - NGHE AN DAIRY FACTORY—See Vietnam Dairy Products Joint Stock Company; *Int'l*, pg. 8199
VIETNAM DAIRY PRODUCTS JOINT STOCK COMPANY - SAI GON MILK FACTORY—See Vietnam Dairy Products Joint Stock Company; *Int'l*, pg. 8199
VIETNAM DAIRY PRODUCTS JOINT STOCK COMPANY; *Int'l*, pg. 8198
VIETNAM DAIRY PRODUCTS JOINT STOCK COMPANY - THONG NHAT MILK FACTORY—See Vietnam Dairy Products Joint Stock Company; *Int'l*, pg. 8199
VIETNAM DAIRY PRODUCTS JOINT STOCK COMPANY - TIEN SON DAIRY FACTORY—See Vietnam Dairy Products Joint Stock Company; *Int'l*, pg. 8199
VIETNAM DAIRY PRODUCTS JOINT STOCK COMPANY - TRUONG THO DAIRY FACTORY—See Vietnam Dairy Products Joint Stock Company; *Int'l*, pg. 8199
VIETNAM DAIRY PRODUCTS JOINT STOCK COMPANY - VIETNAM BEVERAGES FACTORY—See Vietnam Dairy Products Joint Stock Company; *Int'l*, pg. 8199
VIETNAM DAIRY PRODUCTS JOINT STOCK COMPANY - VIETNAM DAIRY FACTORY—See Vietnam Dairy Products Joint Stock Company; *Int'l*, pg. 8199
VIETNAM DAIRY PRODUCTS JOINT STOCK COMPANY - VIETNAM POWDERED MILK FACTORY—See Vietnam Dairy Products Joint Stock Company; *Int'l*, pg. 8199
VIETNAM DARCO ENVIRONMENT COMPANY LIMITED—See Darco Water Technologies Limited; *Int'l*, pg. 1972
VIETNAM DATA COMMUNICATION COMPANY—See Vietnam Posts & Telecommunications Corporation; *Int'l*, pg. 8203
VIETNAM DEVELOPMENT CONSTRUCTION CO. LTD.—See Hazama Ando Corporation; *Int'l*, pg. 3295
VIETNAM DIARY COW ONE MEMBER CO., LTD.—See Vietnam Dairy Products Joint Stock Company; *Int'l*, pg. 8199
VIETNAM ECONOMIC TIMES—See Ringier Holding AG; *Int'l*, pg. 6344
VIETNAM ELECTRICITY CONSTRUCTION 2 JSC—See Vietnam Electricity Construction Joint Stock Corporation; *Int'l*, pg. 8199
VIETNAM ELECTRICITY CONSTRUCTION JOINT STOCK CORPORATION; *Int'l*, pg. 8199
VIETNAM ENGINE AND AGRICULTURAL MACHINERY CORPORATION—See Iseki & Co., Ltd.; *Int'l*, pg. 3814
VIETNAM ENTERPRISE INVESTMENT & DEVELOPMENT JOINT STOCK COMPANY; *Int'l*, pg. 8199
VIETNAM ENTERPRISE INVESTMENTS LTD.; *Int'l*, pg. 8199

COMPANY NAME INDEX

VIETNAM EXPORT IMPORT COMMERCIAL JOINT STOCK BANK; *Int'l*, pg. 8199
VIETNAM F&B ALLIANCE INVESTMENT JOINT STOCK COMPANY—See Thai Beverage Public Company Limited; *Int'l*, pg. 7592
VIETNAM FINANCE COMPANY LTD—See Joint Stock Commercial Bank of Vietnam; *Int'l*, pg. 3996
VIETNAM FLOUR MILLS LTD.—See Kuok Brothers Sdn. Bhd.; *Int'l*, pg. 4335
VIETNAM FUMIGATION JOINT STOCK COMPANY; *Int'l*, pg. 8199
VIET NAM GAS AND CHEMICALS TRANSPORTATION CORPORATION—See Vietnam Oil and Gas Group; *Int'l*, pg. 8202
VIETNAM GEM ELECTRONIC & METAL CO., LTD.—See Gem Terminal Ind. Co., Ltd.; *Int'l*, pg. 2915
VIETNAM GERMANY STEEL PIPE JOINT STOCK COMPANY; *Int'l*, pg. 8199
VIETNAM GREAT WATER ENVIRONMENTAL PROTECTION CO., LTD.—See China TianYF Holdings Group Limited; *Int'l*, pg. 1559
VIETNAM HOLDING ASSET MANAGEMENT LTD.—See VietNam Holding Ltd; *Int'l*, pg. 8200
VIETNAM HOLDING LTD; *Int'l*, pg. 8200
VIETNAM INDUSTRIAL & COMMERCIAL SECURITIES JOINT STOCK COMPANY; *Int'l*, pg. 8200
VIETNAM INDUSTRIAL INVESTMENTS LIMITED; *Int'l*, pg. 8200
VIETNAM INFRASTRUCTURE DEVELOPMENT AND FINANCIAL INVESTMENT CORPORATION—See Vietnam Construction Stock Corporation; *Int'l*, pg. 8198
VIETNAM INTERNATIONAL ASSURANCE COMPANY—See Tokio Marine Holdings, Inc.; *Int'l*, pg. 7786
VIETNAM INTERNATIONAL LEASING COMPANY LIMITED—See Mizuho Leasing Company, Limited; *Int'l*, pg. 4999
VIETNAM INVESTMENT PRODUCTION & TRADING JSC; *Int'l*, pg. 8200
VIETNAM ITALY STEEL JSC—See Kyoei Steel Ltd.; *Int'l*, pg. 4362
VIETNAM-JAPAN ENGINEERING CONSULTANTS CO., LTD.—See SE Corporation; *Int'l*, pg. 6660
VIETNAM JAPAN GAS JOINT STOCK COMPANY—See Mitsubishi Chemical Group Corporation; *Int'l*, pg. 4937
VIETNAM JAPAN GAS JOINT STOCK COMPANY—See TOMOE SHOKAI Co., Ltd.; *Int'l*, pg. 7801
VIETNAM JOINT STOCK COMMERCIAL BANK FOR INDUSTRY AND TRADE; *Int'l*, pg. 8200
VIETNAM KANDENKO CO., LTD.—See Kandenko Co., Ltd.; *Int'l*, pg. 4065
VIET NAM KIN LONG COMPANY LIMITED—See Guangdong Kinlong Hardware Prdcts Co., Ltd.; *Int'l*, pg. 3158
VIETNAM LIVESTOCK CORPORATION—See Vietnam Dairy Products Joint Stock Company; *Int'l*, pg. 8199
VIETNAM LOGISTICS & SUPPLY CHAIN COMPANY LIMITED—See Thai Beverage Public Company Limited; *Int'l*, pg. 7592
VIETNAM LPG TRADING JOINT STOCK COMPANY; *Int'l*, pg. 8200
VIETNAM MACHINERY INSTALLATION CORPORATION JSC; *Int'l*, pg. 8200
VIETNAM MANPOWER SUPPLY AND COMMERCIAL JOINT-STOCK COMPANY—See Vietnam Construction Stock Corporation; *Int'l*, pg. 8198
VIETNAM MANUFACTURING AND EXPORT PROCESSING (HOLDINGS) LIMITED; *Int'l*, pg. 8200
VIETNAM MAYER CORP., LTD.—See Mayer Steel Pipe Corporation; *Int'l*, pg. 4744
VIETNAM MECHANIZATION ELECTRIFICATION AND CONSTRUCTION JOINT STOCK COMPANY; *Int'l*, pg. 8200
VIETNAM MOBILE TELECOM SERVICES COMPANY—See Vietnam Posts & Telecommunications Corporation; *Int'l*, pg. 8203
VIETNAM NATIONAL AVIATION INSURANCE COMPANY—See Vietnam Airlines Corporation; *Int'l*, pg. 8197
VIETNAM NATIONAL CHEMICAL GROUP—See Masan Consumer Corp.; *Int'l*, pg. 4719
THE VIETNAM NATIONAL GENERAL EXPORT IMPORT JOINT STOCK COMPANY NO.1; *Int'l*, pg. 7698
VIETNAM NATIONAL PETROLEUM CORPORATION; *Int'l*, pg. 8201
VIETNAM NATIONAL REINSURANCE CORPORATION; *Int'l*, pg. 8202
VIETNAM NATIONAL SEED CORPORATION—See The Pan Group Joint Stock Company; *Int'l*, pg. 7673
VIETNAM NATIONAL SEED GROUP JOINT STOCK COMPANY—See The Pan Group Joint Stock Company; *Int'l*, pg. 7673
VIETNAM NATURAL RESOURCES TRADING COMPANY LIMITED—See Xiamen C&D Inc.; *Int'l*, pg. 8523
VIETNAMNET INVESTMENT JOINT STOCK COMPANY; *Int'l*, pg. 8204
VIETNAM NIPPON SEIKI CO., LTD.—See Nippon Seiki Co., Ltd.; *Int'l*, pg. 5330
VIETNAM OCEAN SHIPPING JOINT STOCK COMPANY; *Int'l*, pg. 8202

VIETNAM OIL AND GAS GROUP; *Int'l*, pg. 8202
VIETNAM ONAMBA CO., LTD.—See Onamba Co., Ltd.; *Int'l*, pg. 5573
VIETNAM PAIHO LIMITED—See Taiwan Paiho Limited; *Int'l*, pg. 7423
VIETNAM PARKERIZING CO., LTD.—See Nihon Parkerizing Co., Ltd.; *Int'l*, pg. 5287
VIETNAM PARKERIZING (HANOI) CO., LTD.—See Nihon Parkerizing Co., Ltd.; *Int'l*, pg. 5287
VIETNAM PESTICIDE JOINT STOCK COMPANY—See Masan Consumer Corp.; *Int'l*, pg. 4719
VIETNAM PETROLEUM TRANSPORT JOINT STOCK COMPANY—See Vietnam National Petroleum Corporation; *Int'l*, pg. 8202
VIETNAM PONTEX POLYBLEND CO., LTD.—See Pontex Polyblend Co., Ltd.; *Int'l*, pg. 5920
VIETNAM POSTS & TELECOMMUNICATIONS CORPORATION; *Int'l*, pg. 8203
VIET NAM POWER INVESTMENT AND DEVELOPMENT JSC; *Int'l*, pg. 8197
VIETNAM PRECISION INDUSTRIAL NO.1 CO., LTD.—See Eurocharm Holdings Co., Ltd.; *Int'l*, pg. 2533
VIETNAM PROSPERITY JOINT-STOCK COMMERCIAL BANK; *Int'l*, pg. 8203
VIETNAM RAILWAY CORPORATION; *Int'l*, pg. 8203
VIET NAM RENEWABLE ENERGY GROUP JSC—See Duc Long Gia Lai Group JSC; *Int'l*, pg. 2222
VIET NAM RUBBER GROUP LTD.; *Int'l*, pg. 8197
VIETNAM SCHLEMMER AUTOMOTIVE PARTS CO. LTD.—See Ningbo Huaxiang Electronic Co., Ltd.; *Int'l*, pg. 5302
VIETNAM SEA TRANSPORT AND CHARTERING JOINT STOCK COMPANY; *Int'l*, pg. 8203
VIETNAM STANLEY ELECTRIC CO., LTD.—See Stanley Electric Co., Ltd.; *Int'l*, pg. 7171
VIETNAM STEEL CORPORATION; *Int'l*, pg. 8203
VIETNAM STEEL PIPE CORP.—See POSCO Holdings Inc.; *Int'l*, pg. 5937
VIETNAM SUGAR JOINT STOCK COMPANY—See Vietnam Dairy Products Joint Stock Company; *Int'l*, pg. 8199
VIETNAM SUN CORPORATION; *Int'l*, pg. 8203
VIETNAM SUNERGY JOINT STOCK COMPANY—See Abalance Corporation Ltd.; *Int'l*, pg. 48
VIETNAM TANKER JOINT STOCK COMPANY—See Vietnam National Petroleum Corporation; *Int'l*, pg. 8202
VIETNAM TAXI CO., LTD.—See ComfortDelGro Corporation Limited; *Int'l*, pg. 1713
VIETNAM TECHNOLOGICAL & COMMERCIAL JOINT STOCK BANK; *Int'l*, pg. 8203
VIETNAM TELECOM INTERNATIONAL—See Vietnam Posts & Telecommunications Corporation; *Int'l*, pg. 8203
VIETNAM TELECOM NATIONAL—See Vietnam Posts & Telecommunications Corporation; *Int'l*, pg. 8203
VIETNAM TELECOM SERVICES COMPANY—See Vietnam Posts & Telecommunications Corporation; *Int'l*, pg. 8203
VIETNAM TNT FIBERS CO., LTD.—See Toray Industries, Inc.; *Int'l*, pg. 7827
VIETNAM TOMITA CO., LTD.—See TOMITA CO., LTD.; *Int'l*, pg. 7800
VIETNAM URBAN DEVELOPMENT INVESTMENT CORPORATION; *Int'l*, pg. 8203
VIETNAM VETERANS OF AMERICA, INC.; *U.S. Private*, pg. 4381
VIETNAM VETERANS WORKSHOP INC.; *U.S. Private*, pg. 4381
VIETNAM WACOAL CORP.—See Wacoal Holdings Corp.; *Int'l*, pg. 8326
VIET NAM YADEA ELECTRIC MOTORCYCLE CO., LTD.—See Yadea Group Holdings Ltd; *Int'l*, pg. 8544
VIETNAM YUTO PRINTING & PACKING CO., LTD—See Shenzhen YUTO Packaging Technology Co., Ltd.; *Int'l*, pg. 6825
VIET NHAT SEAFOOD CORPORATION; *Int'l*, pg. 8197
VIETRANSTIMEX MULTIMODAL TRANSPORT HOLDING COMPANY—See Southern International Logistics Joint Stock Company; *Int'l*, pg. 7120
VIET THANG CORPORATION; *Int'l*, pg. 8197
VIET THANH GARMENT TRADING J.S.C.; *Int'l*, pg. 8197
VIET TIEN GARMENT COMPANY—See Vinatex; *Int'l*, pg. 8210
VIET TIEN SON REAL ESTATE HOLDING CO; *Int'l*, pg. 8197
VIETTI FOODS COMPANY, INC.—See Zwanenberg Food Group B.V.; *Int'l*, pg. 8700
VIET TRI CHEMICAL JOINT STOCK COMPANY—See Masan Consumer Corp.; *Int'l*, pg. 4719
VIETTRONICS TAN BINH JOINT STOCK COMPANY; *Int'l*, pg. 8204
VIEVU LLC—See Axon Enterprise, Inc.; *U.S. Public*, pg. 256
VIEWBIX INC.; *Int'l*, pg. 8204
VIEWCAST.COM, INC.; *U.S. Public*, pg. 2297
VIEW, INC.; *U.S. Public*, pg. 2297
VIEWLOCITY TECHNOLOGIES U.S. LLC—See Constellation Software Inc.; *Int'l*, pg. 1773

VIFAH MANUFACTURING COMPANY

VIEW LOGISTICS LIMITED—See Victoria Plc; *Int'l*, pg. 8189
VIEWMARKET INC.; *U.S. Private*, pg. 4381
VIEW MICRO-METROLOGY, INC.—See Quality Vision International Inc.; *U.S. Private*, pg. 3321
VIEWMONT SURGERY CENTER, L.L.C.—See Apollo Global Management, Inc.; *U.S. Public*, pg. 155
VIEWNET COMPUTER SYSTEM SDN. BHD.—See Harvest Miracle Capital Berhad; *Int'l*, pg. 3281
VIEWORKS AMERICA, LTD.—See Vieworks Co., Ltd.; *Int'l*, pg. 8204
VIEWORKS CO., LTD.; *Int'l*, pg. 8204
VIEWORKS EU GMBH—See Vieworks Co., Ltd.; *Int'l*, pg. 8204
VIEWPOINT COMPUTER ANIMATION, INCORPORATED—See Dolphin Entertainment, Inc.; *U.S. Public*, pg. 673
VIEWPOINT CONSTRUCTION SOFTWARE LIMITED—See Trimble, Inc.; *U.S. Public*, pg. 2193
VIEWPOINT CONSULTING, INC.—See Research America, Inc.; *U.S. Private*, pg. 3403
VIEWPOINTE ARCHIVE SERVICES, LLC—See Truist Financial Corporation; *U.S. Public*, pg. 2200
VIEWPOINT FIELD AND STUDIOS—See The BDRC Group; *Int'l*, pg. 7620
VIEWPOINT HEALTHCARE, INC.—See The Ensign Group, Inc.; *U.S. Public*, pg. 2072
VIEWPOINT, INC.—See Trimble, Inc.; *U.S. Public*, pg. 2193
VIEWRAY, INC.—See Mitsubishi Gas Chemical Company, Inc.; *Int'l*, pg. 4948
THE VIEW (REDDITCH) MANAGEMENT COMPANY LIMITED—See Persimmon plc; *Int'l*, pg. 5817
VIEWSONIC AUSTRALIA PTY. LTD.—See ViewSonic Corporation; *U.S. Private*, pg. 4381
VIEWSONIC CHINA LIMITED—See ViewSonic Corporation; *U.S. Private*, pg. 4381
VIEWSONIC CORPORATION; *U.S. Private*, pg. 4381
VIEWSONIC EUROPE LTD.—See ViewSonic Corporation; *U.S. Private*, pg. 4381
VIEWSONIC HONG KONG LTD—See ViewSonic Corporation; *U.S. Private*, pg. 4381
VIEWSONIC SINGAPORE PTE LTD—See ViewSonic Corporation; *U.S. Private*, pg. 4381
VIEWSONIC TECHNOLOGY GMBH—See ViewSonic Corporation; *U.S. Private*, pg. 4381
VIEWTECH CHUGOKU CO., LTD—See Nippon Telegraph & Telephone Corporation; *Int'l*, pg. 5355
VIEWTECH CO., LTD.—See Nippon Telegraph & Telephone Corporation; *Int'l*, pg. 5355
VIEWTECH KYUSHU CO., LTD.—See Nippon Telegraph & Telephone Corporation; *Int'l*, pg. 5355
VIEWTECH TOKAI CO., LTD.—See Nippon Telegraph & Telephone Corporation; *Int'l*, pg. 5355
VIEWTEL CORPORATION—See Vimicro International Corporation; *Int'l*, pg. 8208
VIEWTRADE SECURITIES INC.; *U.S. Private*, pg. 4381
VIEWTRAK TECHNOLOGIES INC.—See TrustBIX, Inc.; *Int'l*, pg. 7945
VIEWTRAN GROUP, INC.; *Int'l*, pg. 8204
VIEXAL S.A.—See Viohalco SA/NV; *Int'l*, pg. 8244
VIFAH MANUFACTURING COMPANY; *U.S. Private*, pg. 4381
VIFOR AG—See CSL Limited; *Int'l*, pg. 1866
VIFOR FRANCE SA—See CSL Limited; *Int'l*, pg. 1866
VIFOR FRESENIUS KABI (BEIJING) PHARMACEUTICAL CONSULTING CO. LTD—See CSL Limited; *Int'l*, pg. 1866
VIFOR (INTERNATIONAL) INC.—See CSL Limited; *Int'l*, pg. 1866
VIFOR PHARMA AMERICA LATINA S.A.—See CSL Limited; *Int'l*, pg. 1866
VIFOR PHARMA ASIA PACIFIC PTE. LIMITED—See CSL Limited; *Int'l*, pg. 1866
VIFOR PHARMA ASPREVA INTERNATIONAL LTD.—See CSL Limited; *Int'l*, pg. 1866
VIFOR PHARMA ASPREVA PHARMACEUTICALS INC.—See CSL Limited; *Int'l*, pg. 1866
VIFOR PHARMA ASPREVA PHARMACEUTICALS LIMITED—See CSL Limited; *Int'l*, pg. 1866
VIFOR PHARMA ASPREVA PHARMACEUTICALS SA—See CSL Limited; *Int'l*, pg. 1866
VIFOR PHARMA BELGIE NV—See CSL Limited; *Int'l*, pg. 1866
VIFOR PHARMA DEUTSCHLAND GMBH—See CSL Limited; *Int'l*, pg. 1866
VIFOR PHARMA ESPANA, S.L.—See CSL Limited; *Int'l*, pg. 1866
VIFOR PHARMA ITALIA S.R.L.—See CSL Limited; *Int'l*, pg. 1867
VIFOR PHARMA LTD.—See CSL Limited; *Int'l*, pg. 1866
VIFOR PHARMA MANAGEMENT LTD.—See CSL Limited; *Int'l*, pg. 1867
VIFOR PHARMA NEDERLAND B.V.—See CSL Limited; *Int'l*, pg. 1867
VIFOR PHARMA NORDISKA AB—See CSL Limited; *Int'l*, pg. 1867
VIFOR PHARMA OSTERREICH GMBH—See CSL Limited; *Int'l*, pg. 1867

VIFOR PHARMA PTY LTD.—See CSL Limited; *Int'l*, pg. 1867
VIFOR PHARMA ROMANIA S.R.L.—See CSL Limited; *Int'l*, pg. 1867
VIFOR PHARMA—See CSL Limited; *Int'l*, pg. 1866
VIFOR PHARMA UK LIMITED—See CSL Limited; *Int'l*, pg. 1867
VIG ASSET MANAGEMENT, A.S.—See Vienna Insurance Group AG Wiener Versicherung Gruppe; *Int'l*, pg. 8195
VIGCONIC (INTERNATIONAL) LIMITED—See LUKS GROUP (Vietnam Holdings) Company Limited; *Int'l*, pg. 4576
VIGENCELL INC.; *Int'l*, pg. 8204
VIGEN CONSTRUCTION INC.; *U.S. Private*, pg. 4381
VIGENE BIOSCIENCES, INC.—See Charles River Laboratories International, Inc.; *U.S. Public*, pg. 480
VIGEO BELGIUM NV—See Moody's Corporation; *U.S. Public*, pg. 1469
VIGEO EIRIS CHILE SPA—See Moody's Corporation; *U.S. Public*, pg. 1469
VIGEO EIRIS HONG KONG LIMITED—See Moody's Corporation; *U.S. Public*, pg. 1469
VIGEO EIRIS USA, LLC—See Moody's Corporation; *U.S. Public*, pg. 1469
VIGEO ITALIA S.R.L—See Moody's Corporation; *U.S. Public*, pg. 1469
VIGEO—See Moody's Corporation; *U.S. Public*, pg. 1469
VIGERS INVESTMENT CONSULTANTS (SHENZHEN) LTD.—See Lafe Corporation Limited; *Int'l*, pg. 4393
VIGERS MACAO COMPANY LIMITED—See Lafe Corporation Limited; *Int'l*, pg. 4393
VIGERS PROPERTY CONSULTANTS (BEIJING) LTD.—See Lafe Corporation Limited; *Int'l*, pg. 4393
VIGERS PROPERTY CONSULTANTS (SHANGHAI) LTD.—See Lafe Corporation Limited; *Int'l*, pg. 4393
VIGERS PROPERTY MANAGEMENT SERVICES (HONG KONG) LIMITED—See Lafe Corporation Limited; *Int'l*, pg. 4393
VIGET LABS LLC; *U.S. Private*, pg. 4381
VIGGO WAHL PEDERSEN AS—See NIBE Industrier AB; *Int'l*, pg. 5263
VIGIER BETON ROMANDIE SA—See Vicat S.A.; *Int'l*, pg. 8186
VIGIER CEMENT AG—See Vicat S.A.; *Int'l*, pg. 8186
VIGIER HOLDING AG—See Vicat S.A.; *Int'l*, pg. 8186
VIGIER MANAGEMENT AG—See Vicat S.A.; *Int'l*, pg. 8186
VIGIER RAIL AG—See Vicat S.A.; *Int'l*, pg. 8186
VIGILANT ASIA (M) SDN BHD—See Efficient E-Solutions Berhad; *Int'l*, pg. 2319
VIGILANT DIVERSIFIED HOLDINGS, INC.; *U.S. Private*, pg. 4382
VIGILANTE ADVERTISING—See Publicis Groupe S.A.; *Int'l*, pg. 6112
VIGILANT INSURANCE COMPANY—See Chubb Limited; *Int'l*, pg. 1591
VIGILANT SECURITY (SCOTLAND) LIMITED—See Croma Security Solutions Group Plc; *Int'l*, pg. 1853
VIGILANT SOFTWARE LTD.—See Bloom Equity Partners Management, LLC; *U.S. Private*, pg. 583
VIGILANT TECHNOLOGIES LTD—See BATM Advanced Communications Ltd.; *Int'l*, pg. 890
VIGILANT TECHNOLOGY INC.—See BATM Advanced Communications Ltd.; *Int'l*, pg. 890
VIGILANT TECHNOLOGY, LLC; *U.S. Private*, pg. 4382
VIGILANZ CORPORATION—See Inovalon Holdings, Inc.; *U.S. Public*, pg. 1128
VIGILENT CORPORATION; *U.S. Private*, pg. 4382
VIGIL HEALTH SOLUTIONS INC.—See ASSA ABLOY AB; *Int'l*, pg. 641
VIGILISTICS, INC.—See SafetyChain Software, Inc.; *U.S. Private*, pg. 3525
VIGILLO LLC—See ABRY Partners, LLC; *U.S. Private*, pg. 43
VIGIL NEUROSCIENCE, INC.; *U.S. Public*, pg. 2297
VIGIPROM SARL—See VINCI S.A.; *Int'l*, pg. 8240
VIGLACERA HA LONG J.S.C.; *Int'l*, pg. 8204
VIGLACERA TUSON JSC; *Int'l*, pg. 8204
VIGLEN LTD.; *Int'l*, pg. 8204
VIGLINK, INC.—See sovrn Holdings, Inc.; *U.S. Private*, pg. 3743
VIGMED HOLDING AB; *Int'l*, pg. 8204
VIGNADORO S.R.L.—See Assicurazioni Generali S.p.A.; *Int'l*, pg. 648
VIGNAL SYSTEMS SA—See Eurazeo SE; *Int'l*, pg. 2530
VIGNOBLES CLEMENT FAYAT ST EMILION—See FAYAT SAS; *Int'l*, pg. 2626
VIGNOBLEXPORT S.A.S.—See Deutsche Post AG; *Int'l*, pg. 2083
VIGNYAN INDUSTRIES LIMITED—See BEML Limited; *Int'l*, pg. 969
VIGO FINANCE A.S.; *Int'l*, pg. 8204
VIGO IMPORTING COMPANY INC.; *U.S. Private*, pg. 4382
VIGO INVESTMENTS A.S.—See VIGO Finance a.s.; *Int'l*, pg. 8204
VIGON INTERNATIONAL, INC.—See EQT AB; *Int'l*, pg. 2469
VIGO PHOTONICS S.A.; *Int'l*, pg. 8204

VIGOR ALASKA SHIP & DRYDOCK INC.—See Stellex Capital Management LP; *U.S. Private*, pg. 3800
VIGOR ALASKA SHIP & DRYDOCK INC.—See The Carlyle Group Inc.; *U.S. Public*, pg. 2056
VIGOR ALIMENTOS S.A.—See Grupo LALA S.A. de C.V.; *Int'l*, pg. 3131
VIGOR EHF.—See Origo hf.; *Int'l*, pg. 5631
VIGOR GROUP, LLC—See On-Point Group, LLC; *U.S. Private*, pg. 3019
VIGOR INDUSTRIAL LLC—See Stellex Capital Management LP; *U.S. Private*, pg. 3800
VIGOR INDUSTRIAL LLC—See The Carlyle Group Inc.; *U.S. Public*, pg. 2056
VIGORIS HANDELS GMBH—See Stadtwerke Hannover AG; *Int'l*, pg. 7161
VIGOR KOBO CO., LTD.; *Int'l*, pg. 8204
VIGOR MACHINE LLC—See Stellex Capital Management LP; *U.S. Private*, pg. 3800
VIGOR MACHINE LLC—See The Carlyle Group Inc.; *U.S. Public*, pg. 2056
VIGOR MARINE LLC—See Stellex Capital Management LP; *U.S. Private*, pg. 3800
VIGOR MARINE LLC—See The Carlyle Group Inc.; *U.S. Public*, pg. 2056
VIGOR SHIPYARDS—See Stellex Capital Management LP; *U.S. Private*, pg. 3801
VIGOR SHIPYARDS—See The Carlyle Group Inc.; *U.S. Public*, pg. 2056
VIGORTONE AG PRODUCTS—See Cargill, Inc.; *U.S. Private*, pg. 760
VIGOR TOURS LIMITED—See KWOON CHUNG BUS HOLDINGS LIMITED; *Int'l*, pg. 4351
VIGOR WORKS LLC—See Stellex Capital Management LP; *U.S. Private*, pg. 3801
VIGOR WORKS LLC—See The Carlyle Group Inc.; *U.S. Public*, pg. 2056
VIGOTECAKATHERM N.V.—See Aliaxis S.A./N.V.; *Int'l*, pg. 323
VI-GRADE GMBH—See Spectris Plc; *Int'l*, pg. 7132
VI-GRADE S.R.L.—See Spectris Plc; *Int'l*, pg. 7132
VI-GRADE SYSTEMS GMBH—See Spectris Plc; *Int'l*, pg. 7132
VIG RE ZAJIST'OVNA, A.S.—See Vienna Insurance Group AG Wiener Versicherung Gruppe; *Int'l*, pg. 8195
VIG SERVICES BULGARIA EOOD—See Vienna Insurance Group AG Wiener Versicherung Gruppe; *Int'l*, pg. 8195
VIGTECH LABS SDN. BHD.—See Insas Berhad; *Int'l*, pg. 3718
VIG VODOVOD I GREJANJE A.D.; *Int'l*, pg. 8204
VIIV HEALTHCARE BV—See GSK plc; *Int'l*, pg. 3149
VIIV HEALTHCARE COMPANY—See GSK plc; *Int'l*, pg. 3150
VIIV HEALTHCARE PTY LTD—See GSK plc; *Int'l*, pg. 3150
VIIV HEALTHCARE SAS—See GSK plc; *Int'l*, pg. 3150
VIIV HEALTHCARE—See GSK plc; *Int'l*, pg. 3149
VIIV HEALTHCARE—See Pfizer Inc.; *U.S. Public*, pg. 1683
VIIV HEALTHCARE S.R.L.—See GSK plc; *Int'l*, pg. 3150
VIIV HEALTHCARE ULC—See GSK plc; *Int'l*, pg. 3150
VIIVHIV HEALTHCARE UNIPESSOAL LDA—See GSK plc; *Int'l*, pg. 3150
VII VOYES SPRL—See Clariane SE; *Int'l*, pg. 1645
VIJALL, INC.—See Innospec Inc.; *U.S. Public*, pg. 1125
VIJAYA DIAGNOSTIC CENTRE PVT. LTD.; *Int'l*, pg. 8205
VIJAYA LAGHUBITTA BITTIYA SANSTHA LTD.; *Int'l*, pg. 8205
VIJAY SHANTHI BUILDERS LIMITED; *Int'l*, pg. 8205
VIJAY SOLVEX LIMITED; *Int'l*, pg. 8205
VIJAY TELEVISION PRIVATE LIMITED—See National Amusements, Inc.; *U.S. Private*, pg. 2844
VIJAY TELEVISION PRIVATE LIMITED—See Reliance - ADA Group Limited; *Int'l*, pg. 6263
VIJAY TEXTILES LTD.; *Int'l*, pg. 8205
VIJI FINANCE LIMITED; *Int'l*, pg. 8205
VI-JON, INC.—See Berkshire Partners LLC; *U.S. Private*, pg. 535
VI-JON, INC.—See Berkshire Partners LLC; *U.S. Private*, pg. 535
THE VIJOY STEEL & GENERAL MILLS CO. LTD.—See Sukhjit Starch & Chemicals Ltd.; *Int'l*, pg. 7255
VIKA B.V.—See Givaudan S.A.; *Int'l*, pg. 2982
VIK A.D.; *Int'l*, pg. 8205
VIKALP SECURITIES LIMITED; *Int'l*, pg. 8205
VIKA PROJECT FINANCE AS—See ABG Sundal Collier Holding ASA; *Int'l*, pg. 60
VIKARIEPOOLEN AB—See NGS Group AB; *Int'l*, pg. 5256
VIKAS ECOTECH LIMITED; *Int'l*, pg. 8205
VIKAS LIFECARE LTD.; *Int'l*, pg. 8205
VIKAS PROPPANT & GRANITE LIMITED; *Int'l*, pg. 8205
VIKAS PUBLISHING HOUSE PRIVATE LIMITED—See S Chand & Company Limited; *Int'l*, pg. 6442
VIKAS WSP LIMITED; *Int'l*, pg. 8205
VIKAY AMERICA INCORPORATED—See Polaris Ltd.; *Int'l*, pg. 5907
VIKCO INSURANCE SERVICES, INC.; *U.S. Private*, pg. 4382
VIKENCO AS—See Salmar ASA; *Int'l*, pg. 6494
VIKING ACQUISITIONS, S. DE RL DE CV—See Spectrum Brands Holdings, Inc.; *U.S. Public*, pg. 1917

VIKING AIR CONDITIONING—See Systemair AB; *Int'l*, pg. 7392
VIKING AIRTECH PTE. LTD.—See 9R Limited; *Int'l*, pg. 17
VIKING AIRTECH SDN. BHD.—See 9R Limited; *Int'l*, pg. 17
VIKING AIRTECH (SHANGHAI) CO., LTD.—See 9R Limited; *Int'l*, pg. 17
VIKING AIRTECH (YANTAI) CO., LTD.—See 9R Limited; *Int'l*, pg. 17
VIKING ALUMINUM PRODUCTS INC.; *U.S. Private*, pg. 4382
VIKING AQUACULTURE (PTY) LTD.—See Brimstone Investment Corporation Ltd.; *Int'l*, pg. 1164
VIKING AUTOMATIC SPRINKLER COMPANY—See APi Group Corporation; *U.S. Public*, pg. 514
VIKING BANK, N.A.—See Viking Financial Corporation; *U.S. Private*, pg. 4382
VIKING BOND SERVICE, INC.—See Arthur J. Gallagher & Co.; *U.S. Public*, pg. 207
VIKING BUICK GMC; *U.S. Private*, pg. 4382
VIKING CHEMICAL COMPANY—See Arkema S.A.; *Int'l*, pg. 569
VIKING-CIVES, LTD.—See Cives Corporation; *U.S. Private*, pg. 908
VIKING COCA COLA BOTTLING CO; *U.S. Private*, pg. 4382
VIKING CONSTRUCTION INC.; *U.S. Private*, pg. 4382
VIKING COOKING SCHOOLS, LLC—See The Middleby Corporation; *U.S. Public*, pg. 2115
VIKING DIRECT B.V.—See Aurelius Equity Opportunities SE & Co. KGaA; *Int'l*, pg. 709
VIKING DIRECT (HOLDINGS) LIMITED—See Aurelius Equity Opportunities SE & Co. KGaA; *Int'l*, pg. 709
VIKING DIRECT (IRELAND) LIMITED—See Aurelius Equity Opportunities SE & Co. KGaA; *Int'l*, pg. 709
VIKING DIREKT GESMBH—See Aurelius Equity Opportunities SE & Co. KGaA; *Int'l*, pg. 709
VIKING DRILL & TOOL INC.; *U.S. Private*, pg. 4382
VIKING ELECTRIC SUPPLY, INC.—See Sonepar S.A.; *Int'l*, pg. 7094
VIKING ELECTRONICS, INC.—See Eaton Corporation plc; *Int'l*, pg. 2282
VIKING ENERGY GROUP, INC.—See Camber Energy, Inc.; *U.S. Public*, pg. 425
VIKING ENERGY MANAGEMENT LLC—See National Utility Service, Inc.; *U.S. Private*, pg. 2864
VIKING ENGINEERING AND DEVELOPMENT INCORPORATED; *U.S. Private*, pg. 4382
VIKING ENTERPRISE SOLUTIONS—See Sanmina Corporation; *U.S. Public*, pg. 1841
VIKING EQUIPMENT CO. KNOXVILLE; *U.S. Private*, pg. 4382
VIKING FINANCIAL CORPORATION; *U.S. Private*, pg. 4382
VIKING FINANCIAL SERVICES INC.—See Viking Engineering and Development Incorporated; *U.S. Private*, pg. 4382
VIKING FOOTWEAR AB—See Bertel O. Steen AS; *Int'l*, pg. 989
VIKING FOOTWEAR A/S—See Bertel O. Steen AS; *Int'l*, pg. 989
VIKING FOREST PRODUCTS, LLC—See Forest City Trading Group, LLC; *U.S. Private*, pg. 1566
VIKING FOTTOY A/S—See Bertel O. Steen AS; *Int'l*, pg. 989
VIKING FUND MANAGERS LTD.; *Int'l*, pg. 8205
VIKING GAS TRANSMISSION COMPANY—See ONEOK, Inc.; *U.S. Public*, pg. 1603
VIKING GOLD EXPLORATION INC.; *Int'l*, pg. 8205
VIKING GROUP, INC.—See Intermediate Capital Group plc; *Int'l*, pg. 3743
VIKING GROUP, INC.—See Kirkbi A/S; *Int'l*, pg. 4191
VIKING INC.; *U.S. Private*, pg. 4382
VIKING INDUSTRIES LLC; *U.S. Private*, pg. 4382
VIKING INSURANCE COMPANY OF WISCONSIN—See Sentry Insurance Group; *U.S. Private*, pg. 3611
VIKING INVESTMENTS GROUP, LLC—See Camber Energy, Inc.; *U.S. Public*, pg. 425
VIKING JALKINEET OY—See Bertel O. Steen AS; *Int'l*, pg. 989
VIKING JOHNSON LTD.—See Crane NXT, Co.; *U.S. Public*, pg. 591
VIKING KAGIT VE SELULOZ AS; *Int'l*, pg. 8205
VIKING LINE ABP; *Int'l*, pg. 8205
VIKING LINE BUS AB—See Viking Line Abp; *Int'l*, pg. 8205
VIKING LINE FINNLANDVERKEHR GMBH—See Viking Line Abp; *Int'l*, pg. 8205
VIKING LINE SKANDINAVIEN AB—See Viking Line Abp; *Int'l*, pg. 8205
VIKING LLC—See Dema Engineering Co.; *U.S. Private*, pg. 1203
VIKING MALT A/S—See Polttimo Oy; *Int'l*, pg. 5913
VIKING MALT OY—See Polttimo Oy; *Int'l*, pg. 5913
VIKING MATERIALS, INC.—See Reliance Steel & Aluminum Co.; *U.S. Public*, pg. 1782
VIKING METAL CABINET CO.—See Krueger International, Inc.; *U.S. Private*, pg. 2353
VIKING MINES LIMITED; *Int'l*, pg. 8205

COMPANY NAME INDEX

VIKING MOTORS AS—See Tallinna Kaubamaja AS; *Int'l*, pg. 7448
VIKING NETHERLANDS B.V.—See Aurelius Equity Opportunities SE & Co. KGaA; *Int'l*, pg. 709
VIKING OFFICE PRODUCTS, INC.—See The ODP Corporation; *U.S. Public*, pg. 2118
VIKING PAPER CORP.; *U.S. Private*, pg. 4382
VIKING PLASTICS INC.—See The Hoffmann Family of Companies; *U.S. Private*, pg. 4053
VIKING POLYMERS, LLC—See Teknor Apex Company; *U.S. Private*, pg. 3959
VIKING POOLS LLC—See Pamplona Capital Management LLP; *Int'l*, pg. 5711
VIKING PROCESSING CORPORATION; *U.S. Private*, pg. 4382
VIKING PUMP (EUROPE) LTD.—See IDEX Corp; *U.S. Public*, pg. 1092
VIKING PUMP, INC.—See IDEX Corp; *U.S. Public*, pg. 1092
VIKING PUMP OF CANADA, INC.—See IDEX Corp; *U.S. Public*, pg. 1092
VIKING RADIO LTD.—See Heinrich Bauer Verlag KG; *Int'l*, pg. 3324
VIKING RANGE CORPORATION DO BRASIL IMPORTACAO E COMERCIO LTDA.—See The Middleby Corporation; *U.S. Public*, pg. 2115
VIKING RANGE LLC—See The Middleby Corporation; *U.S. Public*, pg. 2115
VIKING RANGE, LLC; *U.S. Private*, pg. 4382
VIKING READY MIXED COMPANY, INC—See Vicat S.A.; *Int'l*, pg. 8186
VIKING RECREATIONAL VEHICLES LLC—See Berkshire Hathaway Inc.; *U.S. Public*, pg. 305
VIKING REDERI AB—See Viking Line Abp; *Int'l*, pg. 8205
VIKING SEATECH LTD.—See Buckthorn Partners LLP; *Int'l*, pg. 1210
VIKING SEATECH LTD.—See OEP Capital Advisors, L.P.; *U.S. Private*, pg. 2997
VIKING SECURITY AS—See Tallinna Kaubamaja AS; *Int'l*, pg. 7448
VIKINGSUN AB—See Storskogen Group AB; *Int'l*, pg. 7228
VIKING SUPPLY SHIPS AB—See Kistefos AS; *Int'l*, pg. 4193
VIKING SUPPLY SHIPS A/S—See Kistefos AS; *Int'l*, pg. 4193
VIKING TECHNOLOGY—See Sanmina Corporation; *U.S. Public*, pg. 1841
VIKING TERMITE & PEST CONTROL, LLC—See EQT AB; *Int'l*, pg. 2468
VIKING THERAPEUTICS, INC.; *U.S. Public*, pg. 2297
VIKING TRUCK & EQUIPMENT SALES (OH), INC.—See Oshkosh Corporation; *U.S. Public*, pg. 1621
VIKING VENTURE MANAGEMENT AS; *Int'l*, pg. 8205
VIKING VILLAGE INC.; *U.S. Private*, pg. 4382
VIKING YACHT COMPANY; *U.S. Private*, pg. 4382
THE VIKING YACHTING CENTER INC—See Viking Yacht Company; *U.S. Private*, pg. 4383
THE VIKING YACHT SERVICE CENTER—See Viking Yacht Company; *U.S. Private*, pg. 4383
VIKOS S.A.; *Int'l*, pg. 8206
VIKRAM THERMO (INDIA) LTD.; *Int'l*, pg. 8206
VIKSIT ENGINEERING LTD.; *Int'l*, pg. 8206
VIKTEAM A/S—See Lundbeckfonden; *Int'l*, pg. 4581
VIKTOR BENES BAKERY, INC.; *U.S. Private*, pg. 4383
VIKTOR SERVISI D.O.O.—See Palumbo Group S.P.A; *Int'l*, pg. 5710
VIKVINS CONSULTANTS PRIVATE LIMITED—See Vinsys IT Services India Limited; *Int'l*, pg. 8241
VILA LUSITANO - UNIDADES DE SAUDE, S.A.—See Fosun International Limited; *Int'l*, pg. 2751
VILA & SON LANDSCAPING CORP.; *U.S. Private*, pg. 4383
VILBOMEX S.A. DE C.V.—See Villeroy & Boch AG; *Int'l*, pg. 8207
VILEBREQUIN INTERNATIONAL SA—See G-III Apparel Group, Ltd.; *U.S. Public*, pg. 894
VILEBREQUIN SAINT MAARTEN—See G-III Apparel Group, Ltd.; *U.S. Public*, pg. 894
VILEDA GMBH—See Freudenberg SE; *Int'l*, pg. 2791
VILENE CREATE CO., LTD.—See Freudenberg SE; *Int'l*, pg. 2791
VILEX IN TENNESSEE, INC.—See OrthoPediatrics Corp.; *U.S. Public*, pg. 1619
VILKYSKIU PIENINE AB; *Int'l*, pg. 8206
VILLA ANGELINA APARTMENT FUND, LTD—See Essex Property Trust, Inc.; *U.S. Public*, pg. 796
VILLA ASTRA BV—See Clariane SE; *Int'l*, pg. 1645
VILLA AT SAN MATEO—See LCS Holdings Inc.; *U.S. Private*, pg. 2404
VILLA AUENWALD SENIORENHEIM GMBH—See MK-Kliniken AG; *Int'l*, pg. 5002
VILLA AUREA, S.L.—See ACS, Actividades de Construccion y Servicios, S.A.; *Int'l*, pg. 117
VILLA CHICOUTIMI INC.—See Welltower Inc.; *U.S. Public*, pg. 2349
VILLA CONSTRUCTION OF CONNECTICUT, INC.; *U.S. Private*, pg. 4383

VILLA CREST HEALTHCARE CENTER, LLC—See National HealthCare Corporation; *U.S. Public*, pg. 1497
VILLADCO INC.—See Banfi Product Corp.; *U.S. Private*, pg. 465
VILLA DE HORSTING BV—See Clariane SE; *Int'l*, pg. 1645
VILLA DELLE TERME SPA—See Clariane SE; *Int'l*, pg. 1645
VILLA DUBROVNIK D.D.—See Dogus Holding AS; *Int'l*, pg. 2155
VILLA ENTERPRISES MANAGEMENT LTD., INC.; *U.S. Private*, pg. 4383
VILLA ESPERANZA SERVICES; *U.S. Private*, pg. 4383
VILLAGE AMBULANCE SERVICE, INC.—See Northern Berkshire EMS, Inc.; *U.S. Private*, pg. 2952
VILLAGE AT MAYFIELD LLC—See Varia US Properties AG; *Int'l*, pg. 8133
THE VILLAGE AT MORRISONS COVE; *U.S. Private*, pg. 4131
VILLAGE AUTOMOTIVE GROUP; *U.S. Private*, pg. 4383
VILLAGE BANCSHARES, INC.; *U.S. Private*, pg. 4383
VILLAGE BANK MORTGAGE CORPORATION—See Village Bank & Trust Financial Corp.; *U.S. Public*, pg. 2297
VILLAGE BANK—See Village Bancshares, Inc.; *U.S. Private*, pg. 4383
VILLAGE BANK—See Village Bank & Trust Financial Corp.; *U.S. Public*, pg. 2297
THE VILLAGE BANK; *U.S. Private*, pg. 4131
VILLAGE BANK & TRUST FINANCIAL CORP.; *U.S. Public*, pg. 2297
VILLAGE BANK & TRUST—See Wintrust Financial Corporation; *U.S. Public*, pg. 2375
VILLAGE BEHAVIORAL HEALTH, LLC—See Acadia Healthcare Company, Inc.; *U.S. Public*, pg. 31
VILLAGE CAR COMPANY; *U.S. Private*, pg. 4383
VILLAGECARE; *U.S. Private*, pg. 4384
VILLAGE CHARTERS, INC.; *U.S. Private*, pg. 4383
VILLAGE CHEVROLET COMPANY - WAYZATA AUTO CENTER—See North American Automotive Services, Inc.; *U.S. Private*, pg. 2940
VILLAGE CHEVROLET CO.—See North American Automotive Services, Inc.; *U.S. Private*, pg. 2940
VILLAGE CHRYSLER DODGE JEEP LTD.; *Int'l*, pg. 8206
VILLAGE FAMILY SERVICE CENTER; *U.S. Private*, pg. 4383
THE VILLAGE FAMILY SERVICES; *U.S. Private*, pg. 4131
VILLAGE FARM DAIRY; *U.S. Private*, pg. 4383
VILLAGE FARMS, INC. DISTRIBUTION CENTER—See Village Farms International Inc.; *Int'l*, pg. 8206
VILLAGE FARMS INTERNATIONAL INC.; *Int'l*, pg. 8206
VILLAGE FARMS, LP—See Village Farms International Inc.; *Int'l*, pg. 8206
VILLAGE FARMS OF MARFA—See Village Farms International Inc.; *Int'l*, pg. 8206
VILLAGE FARMS OF TEXAS—See Village Farms International Inc.; *Int'l*, pg. 8206
VILLAGE FORD INC.; *U.S. Private*, pg. 4383
VILLAGE FORD LINCOLN SALES LTD.; *Int'l*, pg. 8206
THE VILLAGE FOR FAMILIES & CHILDREN, INC.; *U.S. Private*, pg. 4131
VILLAGE GREEN COMMUNICATIONS, INC.; *U.S. Private*, pg. 4383
VILLAGE GREEN MANAGEMENT COMPANY; *U.S. Private*, pg. 4383
VILLAGE GREEN RESTAURANTS LIMITED—See Shepherd Neame Limited; *Int'l*, pg. 6826
VILLAGEHEALTH DM, LLC—See DaVita Inc.; *U.S. Public*, pg. 644
VILLAGE HEALTH WORKS; *U.S. Private*, pg. 4383
VILLAGE HEARTH & HOME DISTRIBUTION, LLC; *U.S. Private*, pg. 4383
VILLAGE HOMES OF COLORADO, INC.—See Brookfield Corporation; *Int'l*, pg. 1183
VILLAGE INN RESTAURANTS—See Fidelity National Financial, Inc.; *U.S. Public*, pg. 830
VILLAGE INSURANCE AGENCY, INC.—See Village Bank & Trust Financial Corp.; *U.S. Public*, pg. 2297
VILLAGE INVESTMENTS; *U.S. Private*, pg. 4383
VILLAGE JEWELERS GROUP INC.; *U.S. Private*, pg. 4384
VILLAGE LUXURY IMPORTS INC.—See North American Automotive Services, Inc.; *U.S. Private*, pg. 2940
VILLAGE MARINA; *U.S. Private*, pg. 4384
VILLAGE MARKET, INC.; *U.S. Private*, pg. 4384
VILLAGE MOTORS, LLC—See AutoNation, Inc.; *U.S. Public*, pg. 238
THE VILLAGE NETWORK; *U.S. Private*, pg. 4131
VILLAGE NISSAN; *Int'l*, pg. 8206
VILLAGE NURSERIES WHOLESALE LLC—See TreeSap Farms, LLC; *U.S. Private*, pg. 4217
VILLAGE PARK HOMES, LLC—See Dream Finders Homes, Inc.; *U.S. Public*, pg. 687
VILLAGE PARK PLAZA, LLC—See Washington Prime Group Inc.; *U.S. Private*, pg. 4449
VILLAGE PLASTICS CO.—See Keene Building Products Company, Inc.; *U.S. Private*, pg. 2272

VILLE-MARIE SUZUKI

VILLAGE PRACTICE MANAGEMENT COMPANY, LLC—See Four Corners Property Trust, Inc.; *U.S. Public*, pg. 875
VILLAGE RESIDENTIAL PLC—See The Cardiff Property plc; *Int'l*, pg. 7630
VILLAGE ROADSHOW ENTERTAINMENT GROUP (BVI) LTD.—See Village Roadshow Limited; *Int'l*, pg. 8206
VILLAGE ROADSHOW LIMITED; *Int'l*, pg. 8206
VILLAGE ROADSHOW THEME PARKS PTY LTD—See Village Roadshow Limited; *Int'l*, pg. 8206
THE VILLAGER—See Gannett Co., Inc.; *U.S. Public*, pg. 903
THE VILLAGES, FLORIDA INC.; *U.S. Private*, pg. 4131
VILLAGE SHALOM, INC.; *U.S. Private*, pg. 4384
THE VILLAGES INSURANCE PARTNERS, LLC—See The Baldwin Insurance Group, Inc.; *U.S. Public*, pg. 2036
VILLAGES OF JACKSON CREEK, LLC—See National HealthCare Corporation; *U.S. Public*, pg. 1497
VILLAGES OF JACKSON CREEK MEMORY CARE, LLC—See National HealthCare Corporation; *U.S. Public*, pg. 1497
VILLAGES OF ST. PETERS, LLC—See National HealthCare Corporation; *U.S. Public*, pg. 1497
VILLAGE SQUARE APARTMENT HOMES—See Kennedy-Wilson Holdings, Inc.; *U.S. Public*, pg. 1223
THE VILLAGES; *U.S. Private*, pg. 4131
VILLAGE SUBARU—See Village Car Company; *U.S. Private*, pg. 4383
VILLAGE SUPER MARKET INC.; *U.S. Public*, pg. 2297
VILLAGES URBAN INVESTMENTS, LLC—See Bank of America Corporation; *U.S. Public*, pg. 272
VILLAGE SURGICENTER, LIMITED PARTNERSHIP—See Bain Capital, LP; *U.S. Private*, pg. 447
VILLAGE TOURS, LLC—See Village Charters, Inc.; *U.S. Private*, pg. 4383
VILLAGE VANGUARD CO., LTD.; *Int'l*, pg. 8206
VILLAGE VOICE; *U.S. Private*, pg. 4384
VILLAGE VOICE MEDIA HOLDINGS, LLC; *U.S. Private*, pg. 4384
VILLA IMMOBILIARE SRL—See Steel Partners Holdings L.P.; *U.S. Public*, pg. 1943
VILLA, INC.; *U.S. Private*, pg. 4383
VILLA KUNALAI PUBLIC COMPANY LIMITED; *Int'l*, pg. 8206
VILLA LA PAGLIAIA S.R.L.—See Allianz SE; *Int'l*, pg. 356
VILLA LIGHTING SUPPLY CO. INC.; *U.S. Private*, pg. 4383
VILLA MARIA HEALTHCARE CENTER, LLC—See The Ensign Group, Inc.; *U.S. Public*, pg. 2072
VILLA MODA LIFESTYLE COMPANY K.S.C.C.—See DIFC Investments LLC; *Int'l*, pg. 2118
VILLANOVA, S.A.—See ACS, Actividades de Construccion y Servicios, S.A.; *Int'l*, pg. 117
VILLA OOSTERVELD BV—See Clariane SE; *Int'l*, pg. 1645
VILLA RADIOLOGY SYSTEMS—See Villa Sistemi Medicali S.p.A.; *Int'l*, pg. 8206
VILLA RENE LALIQUE SAS—See Lalique Group S.A.; *Int'l*, pg. 4399
VILLARES METALS INTERNATIONAL B.V.—See voestalpine AG; *Int'l*, pg. 8292
VILLARES METALS S.A.—See voestalpine AG; *Int'l*, pg. 8292
VILLAR INTERNATIONAL LTD.; *Int'l*, pg. 8206
VILLARS HOLDING SA; *Int'l*, pg. 8207
VILLA SAINT JOSEPH—See Ascension Health Alliance; *U.S. Private*, pg. 347
VILLA SAN CLEMENTE SRL—See Clariane SE; *Int'l*, pg. 1645
VILLA SAN MICHELE S.R.L.—See LVMH Moet Hennessy Louis Vuitton SE; *Int'l*, pg. 4591
VILLA SILVANA SPA—See Clariane SE; *Int'l*, pg. 1645
VILLA SISTEMI MEDICALI S.P.A.; *Int'l*, pg. 8206
VILLA SPES NOSTRA BV—See Clariane SE; *Int'l*, pg. 1645
VILLA S. STEFANO FLAG SPA—See SOPREMA SAS; *Int'l*, pg. 7111
VILLAS VALRICHE RESORTS LTD.—See ENL Limited; *Int'l*, pg. 2442
VILLAUME INDUSTRIES, INC.—See Bain Capital, LP; *U.S. Private*, pg. 451
VILLA VON SIEBENTHAL S.R.L.—See Garofalo Health Care SpA; *Int'l*, pg. 2886
VILLAWAY, INC.; *U.S. Private*, pg. 4384
VILLA WORLD DEVELOPMENTS PTY LTD—See AVID Property Group; *Int'l*, pg. 743
VILLA WORLD GROUP—See AVID Property Group; *Int'l*, pg. 743
VILLA WORLD HOMES—See AVID Property Group; *Int'l*, pg. 743
VILLA WORLD LIMITED—See AVID Property Group; *Int'l*, pg. 743
VILLA WORLD (VIC) PTY LTD—See AVID Property Group; *Int'l*, pg. 743
VILLE-MARIE SUZUKI; *Int'l*, pg. 8207
VILLENEUVE CONSTRUCTION - COCHRANE—See Villeneuve Construction Co. Ltd.; *Int'l*, pg. 8207

VILLE-MARIE SUZUKI

VILLENEUVE CONSTRUCTION CO. LTD. - READY-MIX CEMENT OPERATIONS FACILITY—See Villeneuve Construction Co. Ltd.; *Int'l*, pg. 8207
VILLENEUVE CONSTRUCTION CO. LTD.; *Int'l*, pg. 8207
VILLEROY & BOCH AG; *Int'l*, pg. 8207
VILLEROY & BOCH ASIA PACIFIC PTE. LTD.—See Villeroy & Boch AG; *Int'l*, pg. 8207
VILLEROY & BOCH AUSTRALIA PTY. LTD.—See Villeroy & Boch AG; *Int'l*, pg. 8207
VILLEROY & BOCH DANMARK A/S—See Villeroy & Boch AG; *Int'l*, pg. 8207
VILLEROY & BOCH GUSTAVSBERG AB—See Villeroy & Boch AG; *Int'l*, pg. 8207
VILLEROY & BOCH GUSTAVSBERG OY—See Villeroy & Boch AG; *Int'l*, pg. 8207
VILLEROY & BOCH MAGYARORSZAG KFT.—See Villeroy & Boch AG; *Int'l*, pg. 8207
VILLEROY & BOCH OOO—See Villeroy & Boch AG; *Int'l*, pg. 8207
VILLEROY & BOCH POLSKA SP. Z O.O.—See Villeroy & Boch AG; *Int'l*, pg. 8207
VILLEROY & BOCH (SCHWEIZ) AG—See Villeroy & Boch AG; *Int'l*, pg. 8207
VILLEROY & BOCH TABLEWARE B.V.—See Villeroy & Boch AG; *Int'l*, pg. 8207
VILLEROY & BOCH TABLEWARE LTD.—See Villeroy & Boch AG; *Int'l*, pg. 8207
VILLEROY & BOCH TABLEWARE OY—See Villeroy & Boch AG; *Int'l*, pg. 8207
VILLEROY & BOCH TRADING (SHANGHAI) CO. LTD.—See Villeroy & Boch AG; *Int'l*, pg. 8207
VILLEROY & BOCH USA, INC.—See Villeroy & Boch AG; *Int'l*, pg. 8207
VILLEROY & BOCH WELLNESS N.V.—See Villeroy & Boch AG; *Int'l*, pg. 8207
VILLING & COMPANY, INC.; *U.S. Private*, pg. 4384
VILMORIN ANADOLU TOHUMCULUK—See Groupe Limagrain Holding SA; *Int'l*, pg. 3108
VILMORIN & CIE SA—See Groupe Limagrain Holding SA; *Int'l*, pg. 3108
VILMORIN IBERICA S.A.—See Groupe Limagrain Holding SA; *Int'l*, pg. 3108
VILMORIN INC.—See Groupe Limagrain Holding SA; *Int'l*, pg. 3108
VILMORIN ITALIA S.R.L.—See Groupe Limagrain Holding SA; *Int'l*, pg. 3108
VILMORIN JARDIN SA—See Groupe Limagrain Holding SA; *Int'l*, pg. 3108
VILMORIN S.A.—See Groupe Limagrain Holding SA; *Int'l*, pg. 3108
VILNIAUS BALDAI AB; *Int'l*, pg. 8207
VILNIAUS ENERGIJA—See Veolia Environnement S.A.; *Int'l*, pg. 8158
VIL RESINS LIMITED; *Int'l*, pg. 8206
VILSMEIER AUCTION CO.—See Hunyady Auction Company; *U.S. Private*, pg. 2011
VILTECHMEDA UAB—See Moog Inc.; *U.S. Public*, pg. 1471
VILTER MANUFACTURING LLC—See Emerson Electric Co.; *U.S. Public*, pg. 744
VILTORIA INVEST SA; *Int'l*, pg. 8207
VIMAFLOUR LTD.—See Malayan Flour Mills Berhad; *Int'l*, pg. 4661
VIMAL OIL & FOODS LTD.; *Int'l*, pg. 8207
VI MANUFACTURING INC.; *U.S. Private*, pg. 4375
VIMAX (KUNSHAN) CO., LTD.—See Coretronic Corporation; *Int'l*, pg. 1800
VIMCO INC.; *U.S. Private*, pg. 4384
VIMECO JOINT-STOCK COMPANY—See Vietnam Construction Stock Corporation; *Int'l*, pg. 8198
VIMEC SRL—See Investment AB Latour; *Int'l*, pg. 3783
VIMEDIMEX MEDI - PHARMA JOINT STOCK COMPANY; *Int'l*, pg. 8207
VIMEK AB—See Investindustrial Advisors Ltd.; *Int'l*, pg. 3779
VIMEO.COM, INC.—See Vimeo, Inc.; *U.S. Public*, pg. 2298
VIMEO, INC.; *U.S. Public*, pg. 2297
VIMETCO MANAGEMENT GMBH—See Vimetco N.V.; *Int'l*, pg. 8207
VIMETCO N.V.; *Int'l*, pg. 8207
VIMETCO TRADING S.R.L.—See Vimetco N.V.; *Int'l*, pg. 8207
VIMIAN GROUP AB; *Int'l*, pg. 8208
VIMICRO ELECTRONICS INTERNATIONAL LIMITED—See Vimicro International Corporation; *Int'l*, pg. 8208
VIMICRO INTERNATIONAL CORPORATION; *Int'l*, pg. 8208
VIMI FASTENERS INC.—See Vimi Fasteners S.p.A.; *Int'l*, pg. 8208
VIMI FASTENERS S.P.A.; *Int'l*, pg. 8207
VIMIKE SA—See PLANSEE Holding AG; *Int'l*, pg. 5890
VIMN BELGIUM BVBA—See National Amusements, Inc.; *U.S. Private*, pg. 2844
VIMN GERMANY GMBH—See National Amusements, Inc.; *U.S. Private*, pg. 2844
VIMN NETHERLANDS B.V.—See National Amusements, Inc.; *U.S. Private*, pg. 2844
VIMN NORDIC AB—See National Amusements, Inc.; *U.S. Private*, pg. 2844
VIMN POLAND SP. Z O.O.—See National Amusements, Inc.; *U.S. Private*, pg. 2844
VIMN POLSKA B.V.—See National Amusements, Inc.; *U.S. Private*, pg. 2844
VIMOND MEDIA SOLUTIONS INC.—See Egmont Fonden; *Int'l*, pg. 2326
VIMOND MEDIA SOLUTIONS—See Egmont Fonden; *Int'l*, pg. 2326
VIMPEX (AUSTRIA) CO., LTD.—See VIMPEX Handelsgesellschaft mbH; *Int'l*, pg. 8209
VIMPEX BRASIL REPRESENTACOES LTDA—See VIMPEX Handelsgesellschaft mbH; *Int'l*, pg. 8209
VIMPEX GERMANY GMBH—See VIMPEX Handelsgesellschaft mbH; *Int'l*, pg. 8209
VIMPEX HANDELSGESELLSCHAFT MBH; *Int'l*, pg. 8208
VIMPEX NORTH AFRICA S.A.R.L.—See VIMPEX Handelsgesellschaft mbH; *Int'l*, pg. 8209
VIMPEX NORTH AMERICA—See VIMPEX Handelsgesellschaft mbH; *Int'l*, pg. 8209
VIMPLECOM LAO CO., LTD.—See VEON Ltd.; *Int'l*, pg. 8164
VIMTA LABS LIMITED; *Int'l*, pg. 8209
VIMTO (OUT OF HOME) LIMITED—See Nichols Plc; *Int'l*, pg. 5271
VIMUT HOSPITAL COMPANY LIMITED—See Pruksa Holding Public Company Limited; *Int'l*, pg. 6010
VIMUT HOSPITAL HOLDING CO., LTD.—See Pruksa Holding Public Company Limited; *Int'l*, pg. 6010
VIMY RESOURCES LIMITED—See Deep Yellow Limited; *Int'l*, pg. 2002
VINA2 INVESTMENT AND CONSTRUCTION JSC—See Vietnam Construction Stock Corporation; *Int'l*, pg. 8198
VINA AGE CO., LTD.—See Asia Green Energy Public Company Limited; *Int'l*, pg. 612
VINA ALMAVIVA S.A.—See Vina Concha y Toro S.A.; *Int'l*, pg. 8209
VINA ASAHI CO., LTD.—See ASAHI EITO Co., Ltd.; *Int'l*, pg. 593
VINA BIRZ CO., LTD.—See Onward Holdings Co., Ltd.; *Int'l*, pg. 5593
VINACAFE BIEN HOA JOINT STOCK COMPANY—See Masan Consumer Corp.; *Int'l*, pg. 4719
VINA CANEPA S.A.—See Vina Concha y Toro S.A.; *Int'l*, pg. 8209
VINACAPITAL VIETNAM OPPORTUNITY FUND, LTD.; *Int'l*, pg. 8209
VINA CARMEN S.A.—See Compania Electro Metalurgica S.A.; *Int'l*, pg. 1749
VINACOMIN - CAO SON COAL JOINT STOCK COMPANY; *Int'l*, pg. 8209
VINACOMIN-COAL IMPORT EXPORT JOINT STOCK COMPANY; *Int'l*, pg. 8210
VINACOMIN - COC SAU COAL JOINT STOCK COMPANY; *Int'l*, pg. 8209
VINACOMIN - DEO NAI COAL JOINT STOCK COMPANY; *Int'l*, pg. 8210
VINACOMIN - HA TU COAL JOINT STOCK COMPANY; *Int'l*, pg. 8210
VINACOMIN - MONG DUONG COAL JOINT STOCK COMPANY; *Int'l*, pg. 8210
VINACOMIN - VANG DANH COAL JOINT STOCK COMPANY; *Int'l*, pg. 8210
VINA CONCHA Y TORO S.A.; *Int'l*, pg. 8209
VINACONEX 15 JSC—See Vietnam Construction Stock Corporation; *Int'l*, pg. 8198
VINACONEX 21 JOINT STOCK COMPANY—See Vietnam Construction Stock Corporation; *Int'l*, pg. 8198
VINACONEX 25 JSC—See Vietnam Construction Stock Corporation; *Int'l*, pg. 8198
VINACONEX 39 JOINT STOCK COMPANY—See Vietnam Construction Stock Corporation; *Int'l*, pg. 8198
VINACONEX CONSTRUCTION CONSULTANT JOINT-STOCK COMPANY—See Vietnam Construction Stock Corporation; *Int'l*, pg. 8198
VINACONEX DUNG QUAT JOINT-STOCK COMPANY—See Vietnam Construction Stock Corporation; *Int'l*, pg. 8198
VINACONEX HOUSING & URBAN DEVELOPMENT INVESTMENT JOINT-STOCK COMPANY—See Vietnam Construction Stock Corporation; *Int'l*, pg. 8198
VINACONEX INFRASTRUCTURE DEVELOPMENT AND CONSTRUCTION INVESTMENT JOINT STOCK COMPANY—See Vietnam Construction Stock Corporation; *Int'l*, pg. 8198
VINACONEX INVESTMENT AND TOURISM DEVELOPMENT JOINT STOCK COMPANY—See Vietnam Construction Stock Corporation; *Int'l*, pg. 8198
VINACONEX SAI GON JOINT-STOCK COMPANY—See Vietnam Construction Stock Corporation; *Int'l*, pg. 8198
VINACONEX SERVICE AND CONSTRUCTION JOINT-STOCK COMPANY—See Vietnam Construction Stock Corporation; *Int'l*, pg. 8198
VINACONEX TRADING JOINT-STOCK COMPANY—See Vietnam Construction Stock Corporation; *Int'l*, pg. 8198
VINACONEX TRANSPORTATION JSC—See Vietnam Construction Stock Corporation; *Int'l*, pg. 8198

CORPORATE AFFILIATIONS

VINA CONO SUR S.A.—See Vina Concha y Toro S.A.; *Int'l*, pg. 8209
VINACONTROL GROUP CORPORATION; *Int'l*, pg. 8210
VINACONTROL PROPERTY VALUATION JOINT STOCK COMPANY—See Vinacontrol Group Corporation; *Int'l*, pg. 8210
VINA DAESUNG CABLE COMPANY—See Nexans S.A.; *Int'l*, pg. 5241
VINA DAEWOO INFORMATION SYSTEM COMPANY LIMITED—See Metanet, Inc.; *Int'l*, pg. 4851
VINA ECO BOARD CO., LTD.—See Sumitomo Forestry Co., Ltd.; *Int'l*, pg. 7286
VINAFCO JOINT STOCK CORPORATION; *Int'l*, pg. 8210
VINAFREIGHT JOINT STOCK COMPANY; *Int'l*, pg. 8210
VINA G7 JOINT STOCK COMPANY—See Phu Tai Joint Stock Company; *Int'l*, pg. 5857
VINA KINDEN CORPORATION—See Kinden Corporation; *Int'l*, pg. 4166
VINAKO FORWARDING CO., LTD.—See Konoike Transport Co., Ltd.; *Int'l*, pg. 4275
VINA KRAFT PAPER CO., LTD.—See The Siam Cement Public Company Limited; *Int'l*, pg. 7685
VINA KYOEI STEEL COMPANY LIMITED—See Kyoei Steel Ltd.; *Int'l*, pg. 4362
VINALCOOL SA; *Int'l*, pg. 8210
VINALINK LOGISTICS (CAMBODIA) CO., LTD.—See Cong ty Co Phan Logistics Vinalink; *Int'l*, pg. 1768
VINA MAYCAS DEL LIMARI LTDA.—See Vina Concha y Toro S.A.; *Int'l*, pg. 8209
VINAMILK EUROPESPOSTKA Z OGRANICZONA ODPOWIEDZIALNOSCIA—See Vietnam Dairy Products Joint Stock Company; *Int'l*, pg. 8199
VINAM JSC; *Int'l*, pg. 8210
VINA OFFSHORE ENGINEERING CO., LTD.—See Technics Oil & Gas Limited; *Int'l*, pg. 7506
VINA OKAMOTO CO., LTD.—See Okamoto Industries, Inc.; *Int'l*, pg. 5544
VINA OKAYA INTERNATIONAL CO., LTD—See Okaya & Co., Ltd.; *Int'l*, pg. 5548
VINA PALO ALTO LTDA.—See Vina Concha y Toro S.A.; *Int'l*, pg. 8209
VINARIA BARDAR SA—See Purcari Wineries Public Company Limited; *Int'l*, pg. 6121
VINARIA BOSTAVAN SRL—See Purcari Wineries Public Company Limited; *Int'l*, pg. 6121
VINARICE CO., LTD.—See The Pan Group Joint Stock Company; *Int'l*, pg. 7673
VINARIJA CITLUK D.D.; *Int'l*, pg. 8210
VINAR SYSTEMS PVT. LTD.; *Int'l*, pg. 8210
VINART ENTERPRISES INC.; *U.S. Private*, pg. 4384
VINA SAN PEDRO S.A.—See L'Arche Green N.V.; *Int'l*, pg. 4377
VINA SAN PEDRO S.A.—See Quinenco S.A.; *Int'l*, pg. 6164
VINA-SANWA COMPANY LIABILITY LTD.—See Sanwa Holdings Corporation; *Int'l*, pg. 6561
VINAS SAS—See Sofiprim S.A.S.; *Int'l*, pg. 7050
VI NA TA BA TRADING & INVESTMENT JOINT STOCK COMPANY; *Int'l*, pg. 8182
VINATA INTERNATIONAL CO., LTD.—See Taisei Corporation; *Int'l*, pg. 7416
VINATA INTERNATIONAL JOINT VENTURE LTD. CO.—See Taisei Corporation; *Int'l*, pg. 7416
VINA TAWANA CONTAINER CO., LTD.—See Cheng Loong Corp.; *Int'l*, pg. 1466
VINA TECH CO., LTD.; *Int'l*, pg. 8209
VINATEX; *Int'l*, pg. 8210
VINATEX TRADING JOINT-STOCK COMPANY—See Vinatex; *Int'l*, pg. 8210
VINATI ORGANICS LTD; *Int'l*, pg. 8210
VINATRANS INTERNATIONAL FREIGHT FORWARDERS; *Int'l*, pg. 8210
VINAVIL AMERICAS CORP. - ILLINOIS FACILITY—See Mapei SpA; *Int'l*, pg. 4683
VINAVIL AMERICAS CORPORATION—See Mapei SpA; *Int'l*, pg. 4683
VINAVIL AMERICAS INC.—See Mapei SpA; *Int'l*, pg. 4683
VINAVIL EGYPT FOR CHEMICALS S.A.E.—See Mapei SpA; *Int'l*, pg. 4683
VINAVIL S.P.A. - RAVENNA PLANT—See Mapei SpA; *Int'l*, pg. 4683
VINAVIL S.P.A.—See Mapei SpA; *Int'l*, pg. 4683
VINAVIL S.P.A. - VILLADOSSOLA PLANT—See Mapei SpA; *Int'l*, pg. 4683
VINAYAK POLYCON INTERNATIONAL LIMITED; *Int'l*, pg. 8210
VINAY CEMENTS LTD; *Int'l*, pg. 8210
VINBIGDATA JSC—See Vingroup Joint Stock Company; *Int'l*, pg. 8241
VINBUS ECOLOGY TRANSPORT SERVICES LLC—See Vingroup Joint Stock Company; *Int'l*, pg. 8241
VINCE HAGAN COMPANY; *U.S. Private*, pg. 4384
VINCE HOLDING CORP.—See Sun Capital Partners, Inc.; *U.S. Private*, pg. 3859
VINCE, LLC—See Sun Capital Partners, Inc.; *U.S. Private*, pg. 3860
VINCENNES NEWSPAPERS, INC.—See Paxton Media Group LLC; *U.S. Private*, pg. 3116

COMPANY NAME INDEX

VINCENT BACH CO.—See Paulson & Co. Inc.; *U.S. Private*, pg. 3114
VINCENT BACH INTERNATIONAL, LTD.—See Paulson & Co. Inc.; *U.S. Private*, pg. 3114
VINCENT CAMUTO LLC—See Schottenstein Stores Corporation; *U.S. Private*, pg. 3569
VINCENT FISTER INC.—See Fister Incorporated; *U.S. Private*, pg. 1535
VINCENT GIORDANO CORPORATION; *U.S. Private*, pg. 4385
VINCENT LIGHTING SYSTEMS CO.; *U.S. Private*, pg. 4385
VINCENT MEDICAL HOLDINGS LIMITED - DONGGUAN FACTORY—See Vincent Medical Holdings Limited; *Int'l*, pg. 8211
VINCENT MEDICAL HOLDINGS LIMITED; *Int'l*, pg. 8210
VINCENT PRINTING COMPANY INCORPORATED; *U.S. Private*, pg. 4385
VINCENTS PHARMA TRADING COMPANY LIMITED—See Jacobson Pharma Corporation Limited; *Int'l*, pg. 3866
VINCENT, URBAN, WALKER & ASSOCIATES, INC.—See Seeman Holtz Property & Casualty, LLC; *U.S. Private*, pg. 3598
VINCENT & VINCENT COMPANIES, INC.; *U.S. Private*, pg. 4385
VINCENT & VINCENT MICROSYSTEMS—See Vincent & Vincent Companies, Inc.; *U.S. Private*, pg. 4385
VINCENZO ZUCCHI S.P.A.; *Int'l*, pg. 8211
VINCERE GROUP B.V.—See Dustin Group AB; *Int'l*, pg. 2235
VINCERX PHARMA, INC.; *U.S. Public*, pg. 2298
VINCE WHIBBS PONTIAC-GMC TRUCKS; *U.S. Private*, pg. 4384
VINCE WIESE CHEVROLET, INC.—See AutoNation, Inc.; *U.S. Public*, pg. 238
VINCI AIRPORTS JAPAN KK—See VINCI S.A.; *Int'l*, pg. 8230
VINCI AIRPORTS SAS—See VINCI S.A.; *Int'l*, pg. 8230
VINCI CONCESSIONS CANADA INC.—See VINCI S.A.; *Int'l*, pg. 8230
VINCI CONCESSIONS COLOMBIA SAS—See VINCI S.A.; *Int'l*, pg. 8239
VINCI CONCESSIONS DEUTSCHLAND GMBH—See VINCI S.A.; *Int'l*, pg. 8230
VINCI CONCESSIONS INDIA PVT. LTD.—See VINCI S.A.; *Int'l*, pg. 8230
VINCI CONCESSIONS SA—See VINCI S.A.; *Int'l*, pg. 8230
VINCI CONCESSIONS SAS—See VINCI S.A.; *Int'l*, pg. 8230
VINCI CONCESSIONS UK LIMITED—See VINCI S.A.; *Int'l*, pg. 8230
VINCI CONCESSIONS USA INC.—See VINCI S.A.; *Int'l*, pg. 8239
VINCI CONSTRUCTION DOM TOM SAS—See VINCI S.A.; *Int'l*, pg. 8230
VINCI CONSTRUCTION FRANCE SAS—See VINCI S.A.; *Int'l*, pg. 8234
VINCI CONSTRUCTION GRANDS PROJETS (ABU DHABI)—See VINCI S.A.; *Int'l*, pg. 8235
VINCI CONSTRUCTION GRANDS PROJETS (ALGERIE)—See VINCI S.A.; *Int'l*, pg. 8235
VINCI CONSTRUCTION GRANDS PROJETS (BEIJING)—See VINCI S.A.; *Int'l*, pg. 8235
VINCI CONSTRUCTION GRANDS PROJETS (BRITISH ISLES)—See VINCI S.A.; *Int'l*, pg. 8235
VINCI CONSTRUCTION GRANDS PROJETS-HONG KONG—See VINCI S.A.; *Int'l*, pg. 8235
VINCI CONSTRUCTION GRANDS PROJETS-MOSCOW—See VINCI S.A.; *Int'l*, pg. 8235
VINCI CONSTRUCTION GRANDS PROJETS (PAKISTAN)—See VINCI S.A.; *Int'l*, pg. 8235
VINCI CONSTRUCTION GRANDS PROJETS-PRAGUE—See VINCI S.A.; *Int'l*, pg. 8235
VINCI CONSTRUCTION GRANDS PROJETS SDN. BHD.—See VINCI S.A.; *Int'l*, pg. 8235
VINCI CONSTRUCTION GRANDS PROJETS—See VINCI S.A.; *Int'l*, pg. 8235
VINCI CONSTRUCTION GRANDS PROJETS (VIETNAM)—See VINCI S.A.; *Int'l*, pg. 8235
VINCI CONSTRUCTION HELLAS S.A.—See VINCI S.A.; *Int'l*, pg. 8235
VINCI CONSTRUCTION MARITIME ET FLUVIAL SAS—See VINCI S.A.; *Int'l*, pg. 8235
VINCI CONSTRUCTION MONACO SARL—See VINCI S.A.; *Int'l*, pg. 8235
VINCI CONSTRUCTION SAS—See VINCI S.A.; *Int'l*, pg. 8230
VINCI CONSTRUCTION TERRASSEMENT DEUTSCHLAND GMBH—See VINCI S.A.; *Int'l*, pg. 8236
VINCI CONSTRUCTION TERRASSEMENT SAS—See VINCI S.A.; *Int'l*, pg. 8236
VINCI CONSTRUCTION UK LIMITED—See VINCI S.A.; *Int'l*, pg. 8236
VINCI DEUTSCHLAND GMBH—See VINCI S.A.; *Int'l*, pg. 8236
VINCI EDUCATION LTD.—See VINCI S.A.; *Int'l*, pg. 8236

VINCI ENERGIES BELGIUM NV—See VINCI S.A.; *Int'l*, pg. 8239
VINCI ENERGIES BENELUX SA—See VINCI S.A.; *Int'l*, pg. 8238
VINCI ENERGIES CHILE SPA—See VINCI S.A.; *Int'l*, pg. 8239
VINCI ENERGIES DEUTSCHLAND GMBH—See VINCI S.A.; *Int'l*, pg. 8238
VINCI ENERGIES DO BRAZIL LTDA.—See VINCI S.A.; *Int'l*, pg. 8239
VINCI ENERGIES ESPANA S.A.—See VINCI S.A.; *Int'l*, pg. 8239
VINCI ENERGIES INTERNATIONAL EAST GMBH—See VINCI S.A.; *Int'l*, pg. 8238
VINCI ENERGIES ITALIA SRL—See VINCI S.A.; *Int'l*, pg. 8239
VINCI ENERGIES NETHERLANDS BV—See VINCI S.A.; *Int'l*, pg. 8238
VINCI ENERGIES NEW ZEALAND LIMITED—See VINCI S.A.; *Int'l*, pg. 8239
VINCI ENERGIES NORDIC AB—See VINCI S.A.; *Int'l*, pg. 8239
VINCI ENERGIES POLAND—See VINCI S.A.; *Int'l*, pg. 8238
VINCI ENERGIES PORTUGAL LTDA.—See VINCI S.A.; *Int'l*, pg. 8239
VINCI ENERGIES ROMANIA S.A.—See VINCI S.A.; *Int'l*, pg. 8238
VINCI ENERGIES SCHWEIZ AG—See VINCI S.A.; *Int'l*, pg. 8238
VINCI ENERGIES—See VINCI S.A.; *Int'l*, pg. 8236
VINCI ENERGIES SRL—See VINCI S.A.; *Int'l*, pg. 8239
VINCI ENERGIES SRL—See VINCI S.A.; *Int'l*, pg. 8239
VINCI ENERGIES SRO—See VINCI S.A.; *Int'l*, pg. 8239
VINCI ENERGIES UNITED KINGDOM PLC—See VINCI S.A.; *Int'l*, pg. 8238
VINCI ENVIRONNEMENT CENTRAL EUROPE SP. Z.O.O.—See VINCI S.A.; *Int'l*, pg. 8239
VINCI ENVIRONNEMENT POLSKA SP. Z O O—See VINCI S.A.; *Int'l*, pg. 8236
VINCI ENVIRONNEMENT SAS—See VINCI S.A.; *Int'l*, pg. 8236
VINCI FACILITIES BELGIUM NV/SA—See VINCI S.A.; *Int'l*, pg. 8239
VINCI FACILITIES DEUTSCHLAND GMBH—See VINCI S.A.; *Int'l*, pg. 8239
VINCI FACILITIES - FRANCE NORD—See VINCI S.A.; *Int'l*, pg. 8239
VINCI FACILITIES GMBH—See VINCI S.A.; *Int'l*, pg. 8239
VINCI FACILITIES ITALIA S.R.L.—See VINCI S.A.; *Int'l*, pg. 8239
VINCI FACILITIES MANAGEMENT GMBH—See VINCI S.A.; *Int'l*, pg. 8239
VINCI FACILITIES OSTERREICH GMBH—See VINCI S.A.; *Int'l*, pg. 8239
VINCI FACILITIES POLSKA SP Z O.O.—See VINCI S.A.; *Int'l*, pg. 8239
VINCI FACILITIES SCHWEIZ AG—See VINCI S.A.; *Int'l*, pg. 8239
VINCI FACILITIES SOLUTIONS GMBH—See VINCI S.A.; *Int'l*, pg. 8239
VINCI FACILITIES—See VINCI S.A.; *Int'l*, pg. 8239
VINCI FACILITIES S.R.O.—See VINCI S.A.; *Int'l*, pg. 8239
VINCI FACILITIES UK LTD.—See VINCI S.A.; *Int'l*, pg. 8239
VINCI HIGHWAYS SAS—See VINCI S.A.; *Int'l*, pg. 8239
VINCI IMMOBILIER CONSEIL SAS—See VINCI S.A.; *Int'l*, pg. 8239
VINCI IMMOBILIER GESTION—See VINCI S.A.; *Int'l*, pg. 8239
VINCI IMMOBILIER MEDITERRANNEE SAS—See VINCI S.A.; *Int'l*, pg. 8239
VINCI IMMOBILIER MONACO SARL—See VINCI S.A.; *Int'l*, pg. 8239
VINCI IMMOBILIER NORD EST SAS—See VINCI S.A.; *Int'l*, pg. 8239
VINCI IMMOBILIER PROPERTY MANAGEMENT SAS—See VINCI S.A.; *Int'l*, pg. 8239
VINCI IMMOBILIER RESIDENCES GEREES SAS—See VINCI S.A.; *Int'l*, pg. 8239
VINCI IMMOBILIER RHONE ALPES AUVERGNE SAS—See VINCI S.A.; *Int'l*, pg. 8239
VINCI IMMOBILIER SAS—See VINCI S.A.; *Int'l*, pg. 8239
VINCI INVESTMENTS LTD—See VINCI S.A.; *Int'l*, pg. 8236
VINCI PARTNERS INVESTIMENTOS LTDA.; *Int'l*, pg. 8211
VINCI PARTNERS INVESTMENTS LTD.; *Int'l*, pg. 8211
VINCI PARTNERS USA LLC—See Vinci Partners Investments Ltd.; *Int'l*, pg. 8211
VINCI PLC—See VINCI S.A.; *Int'l*, pg. 8236
VINCI S.A.; *Int'l*, pg. 8211
VINCI SAS—See VINCI S.A.; *Int'l*, pg. 8240
VINCITAG INVESTMENT MANAGEMENT AG; *Int'l*, pg. 8240
VINCI UK DEVELOPMENTS LIMITED—See VINCI S.A.; *Int'l*, pg. 8240
VINCODO, LLC—See Brookfield Corporation; *Int'l*, pg. 1188

VINCOMPASS CORP.; *U.S. Private*, pg. 4385
VINCORION ADVANCED SYSTEMS GMBH—See Jenoptik AG; *Int'l*, pg. 3929
VINCORION POWER SYSTEMS GMBH—See Jenoptik AG; *Int'l*, pg. 3928
VINCO VENTURES, INC.; *U.S. Public*, pg. 2298
VINCULUM JAPAN CORPORATION—See FUJISOFT INCORPORATED; *Int'l*, pg. 2830
VINCULUMS SERVICES, INC.—See QualTek Services Inc.; *U.S. Public*, pg. 1748
VINDA HOUSEHOLD PAPER (HONG KONG) LIMITED—See Essity Aktiebolag; *Int'l*, pg. 2517
VINDA INTERNATIONAL HOLDINGS LIMITED—See Essity Aktiebolag; *Int'l*, pg. 2517
VINDA NORTH PAPER (BEIJING) COMPANY LIMITED—See Essity Aktiebolag; *Int'l*, pg. 2517
VINDA PAPER (BEIJING) LIMITED—See Essity Aktiebolag; *Int'l*, pg. 2517
VINDA PAPER (CHINA) COMPANY LIMITED—See Essity Aktiebolag; *Int'l*, pg. 2517
VINDA PAPER (SICHUAN) LIMITED—See Essity Aktiebolag; *Int'l*, pg. 2517
VINDA PAPER (ZHEJIANG) COMPANY LIMITED—See Essity Aktiebolag; *Int'l*, pg. 2517
VINDEA GROUP OY—See Panostaja Oyj; *Int'l*, pg. 5730
VIN DEVERS INC.; *U.S. Private*, pg. 4384
VINDHYA TELELINKS LTD; *Int'l*, pg. 8240
VINDICATOR SECURITY SOLUTIONS—See Honeywell International Inc.; *U.S. Public*, pg. 1049
VINDICATOR SILVER LEAD MINING CO.; *U.S. Public*, pg. 2298
VINDICIA, INC.—See Amdocs Limited; *Int'l*, pg. 420
VINE & BRANCH, INC.—See Apax Partners LLP; *Int'l*, pg. 506
VINE ENERGY INC.—See Expand Energy Corporation; *U.S. Public*, pg. 809
VINEET LABORATORIES LIMITED; *Int'l*, pg. 8240
VINE HILL HARDWARE INC.; *U.S. Private*, pg. 4385
VINE INTERNATIONAL; *U.S. Private*, pg. 4385
VINELAND KOSHER POULTRY INC.; *U.S. Private*, pg. 4385
VINE RESOURCES INC.; *U.S. Private*, pg. 4385
VINERGY CAPITAL INC.; *Int'l*, pg. 8240
VINES ENERGY SOLUTIONS JSC—See Vingroup Joint Stock Company; *Int'l*, pg. 8241
VINESTOR AS—See Katalysator S.A.; *Int'l*, pg. 4089
VINET HOLDINGS INC.; *U.S. Private*, pg. 4385
VINE VILLAGE, INC.; *U.S. Private*, pg. 4385
VINEXPO OVERSEAS S.A.S.—See Vinexpo S.A.S.; *Int'l*, pg. 8240
VINEXPO S.A.S.; *Int'l*, pg. 8240
VINEX SLAVIANTSI POLAND SP. Z.O.O.—See AMBRA S.A.; *Int'l*, pg. 415
VINEX VIETNAM CO., LTD.—See FUJISOFT INCORPORATED; *Int'l*, pg. 2830
VINEYARD BRANDS INC.; *U.S. Private*, pg. 4385
VINEYARD INDUSTRIES INC.; *U.S. Private*, pg. 4385
VINEYARDS DEVELOPMENT CORP.; *U.S. Private*, pg. 4385
VINEYARDS REALTY INC.; *U.S. Private*, pg. 4385
VINEYARD VINES LLC; *U.S. Private*, pg. 4385
VINFAST AUTO LTD.—See Vingroup Joint Stock Company; *Int'l*, pg. 8241
VINFEN CORPORATION; *U.S. Private*, pg. 4385
VINGAKER FACTORY OUTLET AB—See Friheden Invest A/S; *Int'l*, pg. 2793
VINGCARD ELSAFE AS—See ASSA ABLOY AB; *Int'l*, pg. 641
VINGCARD ELSAFE JAPAN CORPORATION—See ASSA ABLOY AB; *Int'l*, pg. 641
VINGCARD ELSAFE PACIFIC CORPORATION—See ASSA ABLOY AB; *Int'l*, pg. 641
VINGHOG AS—See Rheinmetall AG; *Int'l*, pg. 6324
VINGROUP JOINT STOCK COMPANY; *Int'l*, pg. 8240
VINGRUPPEN I NORDEN AB—See Arcus ASA; *Int'l*, pg. 552
VINGTECH CORP.—See Rheinmetall AG; *Int'l*, pg. 6324
VINH HOAN CORPORATION; *Int'l*, pg. 8241
VINHMS SOFTWARE PRODUCTION & TRADING JSC—See Vingroup Joint Stock Company; *Int'l*, pg. 8241
VINH PHUC INFRASTRUCTURE DEVELOPMENT JOINT STOCK COMPANY; *Int'l*, pg. 8241
VINH PLASTIC & BAGS JSC; *Int'l*, pg. 8241
VINH SON - SONG HINH HYDRO POWER JOINT STOCK COMPANY; *Int'l*, pg. 8241
VINH TECHNOLOGY PTE. LTD.—See Vinh Hoan Corporation; *Int'l*, pg. 8241
VINIDEX PTY LTD.—See Aliaxis S.A./N.V.; *Int'l*, pg. 325
VINIFERA IMPORTS LTD.; *U.S. Private*, pg. 4385
VINILIT S.A.—See Aliaxis S.A./N.V.; *Int'l*, pg. 325
VINILIT S.A.—See Etex SA/NV; *Int'l*, pg. 2523
VINING OIL & GAS LLC; *U.S. Private*, pg. 4385
VINING-SPARKS IBG LP; *U.S. Private*, pg. 4385
VINISA FUEGUINA S.R.L.—See Amcor plc; *Int'l*, pg. 418
VINITECH, INC.; *U.S. Private*, pg. 4385
VINIZIUS/Y&R—See WPP plc; *Int'l*, pg. 8493
VINK A/S—See Blackfriars Corp.; *U.S. Private*, pg. 574

VINK + CO GMBH HANDELSGESELLSCHAFT UND CO KG; *Int'l,* pg. 8241
VINK FINLAND OY—See Blackfriars Corp.; *U.S. Private,* pg. 574
VINK KUNSTSTOFFE GMBH & CO. KG—See Blackfriars Corp.; *U.S. Private,* pg. 574
VINK KUNSTSTOFFEN B.V.—See Blackfriars Corp.; *U.S. Private,* pg. 574
VINKLUBBEN I NORDEN AB—See Viva Wine Group AB; *Int'l,* pg. 8265
VINK NORWAY AS—See Blackfriars Corp.; *U.S. Private,* pg. 574
VINK N.V.—See Blackfriars Corp.; *U.S. Private,* pg. 574
VINMAR INTERNATIONAL LIMITED; *U.S. Private,* pg. 4385
VINMEC INTERNATIONAL HOSPITAL JOINT STOCK COMPANY—See Vingroup Joint Stock Company; *Int'l,* pg. 8241
VINNINGA CEMENTVARUFABRIK AB—See Volati AB; *Int'l,* pg. 8301
VINNOLIT GMBH & CO. KG—See Westlake Corporation; *U.S. Public,* pg. 2360
VINNOLIT HILLHOUSE LTD.—See Westlake Corporation; *U.S. Public,* pg. 2360
VINNOLIT LIMITED—See Westlake Corporation; *U.S. Public,* pg. 2360
VINNOLIT SCHKOPAU GMBH—See Westlake Corporation; *U.S. Public,* pg. 2360
VINNY OVERSEAS LTD.; *Int'l,* pg. 8241
VINNYS GARDEN CENTER INC.; *U.S. Private,* pg. 4385
VINO KALEM A.D.; *Int'l,* pg. 8241
VINO-KLUB.CZ, S. R. O.—See AMBRA S.A.; *Int'l,* pg. 415
VINORDIA AS—See Arcus ASA; *Int'l,* pg. 552
VINO VAULT, INC.; *U.S. Private,* pg. 4386
VINO WEINHANDELS GMBH—See Schloss Wachenheim AG; *Int'l,* pg. 6622
THE VINOY RENAISSANCE ST. PETERSBURG RESORT & GOLF CLUB—See Marriott International, Inc.; *U.S. Public,* pg. 1373
VINO ZUPA INC; *Int'l,* pg. 8241
VINPAC INTERNATIONAL PTY. LIMITED; *Int'l,* pg. 8241
VINPAI SA; *Int'l,* pg. 8241
VINPEARL LANDMARK 81 JSC—See Vingroup Joint Stock Company; *Int'l,* pg. 8241
VINSAT DIGITAL PRIVATE LIMITED—See Hinduja Global Solutions Ltd.; *Int'l,* pg. 3398
VIN SERVICE S.R.L.—See Aalberts N.V.; *Int'l,* pg. 36
VINSOLUTIONS, INC.—See Cox Enterprises, Inc.; *U.S. Private,* pg. 1076
VINSON & ELKINS LLP; *U.S. Private,* pg. 4386
VINSON GUARD SERVICE INC.—See Allied Universal Manager LLC; *U.S. Private,* pg. 191
VINSON PROCESS CONTROLS CO. LP; *U.S. Private,* pg. 4386
VINSTOCK OY—See Wulff-Group Plc; *Int'l,* pg. 8503
VINSYS CORPORATION—See Vinsys IT Services India Limited; *Int'l,* pg. 8242
VINSYS IT SERVICES INDIA LIMITED; *Int'l,* pg. 8241
VINTAGE CAPITAL GROUP LLC; *U.S. Private,* pg. 4386
VINTAGE CAPITAL MANAGEMENT LLC; *U.S. Private,* pg. 4386
VINTAGE COFFEE & BEVERAGES LTD.; *Int'l,* pg. 8242
VINTAGE COFFEE PRIVATE LIMITED—See Vintage Coffee & Beverages Ltd.; *Int'l,* pg. 8242
VINTAGE DESIGN INC.—See The Sterling Group, L.P.; *U.S. Private,* pg. 4122
VINTAGE ENERGY LIMITED; *Int'l,* pg. 8242
VINTAGE FOOD CORP.—See Peak Rock Capital LLC; *U.S. Private,* pg. 3124
VINTAGE HOUSING HOLDINGS, LLC—See Kennedy-Wilson Holdings, Inc.; *U.S. Public,* pg. 1223
VINTAGE IT SERVICES; *U.S. Private,* pg. 4386
VINTAGE NURSERIES LLC; *U.S. Private,* pg. 4386
VINTAGE NURSERIES—See Vintage Nurseries LLC; *U.S. Private,* pg. 4386
VINTAGE PAPER, S.A.—See Pabrik Kertas Tjiwi Kimia Tbk; *Int'l,* pg. 5684
VINTAGE PARK AT LENEXA, LLC—See Chicago Pacific Founders; *U.S. Private,* pg. 878
VINTAGE PARTS, INC.—See GenNx360 Capital Partners, L.P.; *U.S. Private,* pg. 1672
VINTAGE PARTS; *U.S. Private,* pg. 4386
VINTAGE PRODUCTION CALIFORNIA LLC—See Occidental Petroleum Corporation; *U.S. Public,* pg. 1562
VINTAGE SECURITIES LTD.; *Int'l,* pg. 8242
VINTAGE SECURITY LLC—See Armstrong Holdings, Inc.; *U.S. Private,* pg. 331
VINTAGE SENIOR MANAGEMENT INC.; *U.S. Private,* pg. 4386
VINTAGE STOCK, INC.—See Live Ventures Incorporated; *U.S. Public,* pg. 1332
VINTAGE WINE ESTATES, INC.; *U.S. Public,* pg. 2298
VINTAGE WINE SDN. BHD.—See Hai-O Enterprise Berhad; *Int'l,* pg. 3209
VINTAGE WINES, LLC—See The Winebow Group, LLC; *U.S. Private,* pg. 4137
VINTANA PLC; *Int'l,* pg. 8242
VINTCOM TECHNOLOGY PUBLIC COMPANY LIMITED; *Int'l,* pg. 8242

VINTERBRO SENTER DA—See Klepierre SA; *Int'l,* pg. 4200
VINTE VIVIENDAS INTEGRALES, S.A.B. DE C.V.; *Int'l,* pg. 8242
VINTNER SELECT, INC.—See Michael Skurnik Wines, Inc.; *U.S. Private,* pg. 2698
VINTNERS GLOBAL RESOURCE LLC; *U.S. Private,* pg. 4386
VINTNERS INC.—See Kamei Corporation; *Int'l,* pg. 4062
THE VINTON COUNTY NATIONAL BANK—See Community Bancshares, Inc.; *U.S. Public,* pg. 549
VINTROL, INC.—See Emerson Electric Co.; *U.S. Public,* pg. 752
VINTRON INFORMATICS LIMITED; *Int'l,* pg. 8242
VINURI SI BAUTURI SA; *Int'l,* pg. 8242
VINVEST CAPITAL HOLDINGS BERHAD; *Int'l,* pg. 8242
VINX SYSTEM SERVICE (THAILAND) CO., LTD.—See FUJISOFT INCORPORATED; *Int'l,* pg. 2830
VINX VIETNAM CO.,LTD.—See FUJISOFT INCORPORATED; *Int'l,* pg. 2830
VINYAS INNOVATIVE TECHNOLOGIES LIMITED; *Int'l,* pg. 8242
VINYFRAME INDUSTRY CO., LTD.—See NIPPON CARBIDE INDUSTRIES CO., INC.; *Int'l,* pg. 5311
VINYL AB—See Warner Bros. Discovery, Inc.; *U.S. Public,* pg. 2326
VINYL CHEMICALS (INDIA) LTD.; *Int'l,* pg. 8242
VINYL CORP.—See Worthington Industries, Inc.; *U.S. Public,* pg. 2382
VINYLEX CORPORATION; *U.S. Private,* pg. 4386
VINYLTECH CORPORATION—See Otter Tail Corporation; *U.S. Public,* pg. 1624
VINYL WINDOW DESIGNS LTD.; *Int'l,* pg. 8242
VINYOFLEX LIMITED; *Int'l,* pg. 8242
VINYTHAI HOLDING PTE. LTD.—See AGC Inc.; *Int'l,* pg. 204
VINYTHAI PUBLIC COMPANY LTD.—See AGC Inc.; *Int'l,* pg. 204
VINZAVOD AD-ASENOVGRAD; *Int'l,* pg. 8242
VINZEO TECHNOLOGIES S.A.U.—See Esprinet S.p.A.; *Int'l,* pg. 2506
VIOHALCO SA/NV; *Int'l,* pg. 8242
VIOHALCO S.A.; *Int'l,* pg. 8242
VIOLA FINANZA SRL—See BNP Paribas SA; *Int'l,* pg. 1093
VIOL CO., LTD.; *Int'l,* pg. 8244
VIOLED INTERNATIONAL PTE. LTD—See Allgreentech International PLC; *Int'l,* pg. 338
VIOLETA D.O.O.; *Int'l,* pg. 8244
VIOLIN MEMORY DATA STORAGE SYSTEM COMPANY, LTD.—See Quantum Corporation; *U.S. Public,* pg. 1754
VIOLIN MEMORY EMEA LTD.—See Quantum Corporation; *U.S. Public,* pg. 1754
VIOLIN MEMORY FEDERAL SYSTEMS, INC.—See Quantum Corporation; *U.S. Public,* pg. 1754
VIOLIN MEMORY, INC.—See Quantum Corporation; *U.S. Public,* pg. 1754
VIOLIN MEMORY K.K.—See Quantum Corporation; *U.S. Public,* pg. 1754
VIOLIN MEMORY SINGAPORE PTE. LTD.—See Quantum Corporation; *U.S. Public,* pg. 1754
VIOLIO HEALTHCARE LIMITED—See Zydus Lifesciences Limited; *Int'l,* pg. 8700
VIOMAL S.A.—See Viohalco SA/NV; *Int'l,* pg. 8242
VIOMEDEX LIMITED—See Inspiration Healthcare Group Plc; *Int'l,* pg. 3720
VIOMI TECHNOLOGY CO., LTD; *Int'l,* pg. 8244
VIONA PHARMACEUTICALS INC.—See Zydus Lifesciences Limited; *Int'l,* pg. 8700
VION BRAZIL—See VION Holding N.V.; *Int'l,* pg. 8244
VION BULGARIA LTD.—See VION Holding N.V.; *Int'l,* pg. 8244
VION B.V.—See VION Holding N.V.; *Int'l,* pg. 8244
VION DENMARK APS—See VION Holding N.V.; *Int'l,* pg. 8244
VION FOOD GROUP LIMITED—See VION Holding N.V.; *Int'l,* pg. 8244
VION FOOD HELLAS LTD.—See VION Holding N.V.; *Int'l,* pg. 8244
VION FOOD INTERNATIONAL B.V.—See VION Holding N.V.; *Int'l,* pg. 8244
VION FOOD INTERNATIONAL CHINA—See VION Holding N.V.; *Int'l,* pg. 8244
VION FOOD INTERNATIONAL PACIFIC LTD.—See VION Holding N.V.; *Int'l,* pg. 8244
VION FOOD INTERNATIONAL SINGAPORE PTE LTD.—See VION Holding N.V.; *Int'l,* pg. 8244
VION FOOD NEDERLAND B.V.—See VION Holding N.V.; *Int'l,* pg. 8244
VION FOOD PORTUGAL—See VION Holding N.V.; *Int'l,* pg. 8244
VION FRANCE—See VION Holding N.V.; *Int'l,* pg. 8244
VION GMBH—See VION Holding N.V.; *Int'l,* pg. 8244
VION HOLDING N.V.; *Int'l,* pg. 8244
VION HUNGARY KFT.—See VION Holding N.V.; *Int'l,* pg. 8244
VIONIC GROUP LLC—See Caleres, Inc.; *U.S. Public,* pg. 422

VION INTERNATIONAL LJUBLJANA D.O.O.—See VION Holding N.V.; *Int'l,* pg. 8244
VION INTERNATIONAL UKRAINE—See VION Holding N.V.; *Int'l,* pg. 8244
VION POLAND SP.Z.O.O.—See VION Holding N.V.; *Int'l,* pg. 8244
VION PRAHA S.R.O.—See VION Holding N.V.; *Int'l,* pg. 8244
VION ROMANIA SRL—See VION Holding N.V.; *Int'l,* pg. 8244
VION SA—See VION Holding N.V.; *Int'l,* pg. 8244
VION SPAIN S.L.—See VION Holding N.V.; *Int'l,* pg. 8244
VION SWEDEN AB—See VION Holding N.V.; *Int'l,* pg. 8244
VIOO COMPANY LIMITED—See Bexcellent Group Holdings Limited; *Int'l,* pg. 1005
VIOR INC.; *Int'l,* pg. 8244
VIOR VELIKA MORAVA A.D.—See Trace Group Hold PLC; *Int'l,* pg. 7886
VIOSOLAR INC.; *Int'l,* pg. 8244
VIOTIKOS ANEMOS SA—See ELLAKTOR S.A.; *Int'l,* pg. 2365
VIOX SERVICES, INC.—See EMCOR Group, Inc.; *U.S. Public,* pg. 737
V I PACKAGING PTY LTD—See Woolworths Group Limited; *Int'l,* pg. 8452
VIPA GMBH—See Yaskawa Electric Corporation; *Int'l,* pg. 8569
VIPA USA, INC.—See Yaskawa Electric Corporation; *Int'l,* pg. 8569
VIP CINEMA, LLC; *U.S. Private,* pg. 4386
VIP CLOTHING LIMITED; *Int'l,* pg. 8245
VIPCOLOR TECHNOLOGIES PTE LTD—See Venture Corporation Limited; *Int'l,* pg. 8152
VIPCOLOR TECHNOLOGIES USA, INC—See Venture Corporation Limited; *Int'l,* pg. 8152
VIP COMMUNICATIONS, INC.; *U.S. Private,* pg. 4386
V.I.P. COMPUTER CENTRE LIMITED; *Int'l,* pg. 8106
VIP COMPUTERS BV—See V.I.P. Computer Centre Limited; *Int'l,* pg. 8106
VIP COMPUTERS LLC—See V.I.P. Computer Centre Limited; *Int'l,* pg. 8106
VIPDESK, INC.; *U.S. Private,* pg. 4387
VIPER COMMUNICATION SYSTEMS—See Microwave Transmission Systems, Inc.; *U.S. Private,* pg. 2705
VIPER ENERGY, INC.—See Diamondback Energy, Inc.; *U.S. Public,* pg. 659
VIPER NETWORKS, INC.; *U.S. Public,* pg. 2298
VIP GLOVE SDN. BHD.—See VIP Gloves Limited; *Int'l,* pg. 8245
VIP GLOVES LIMITED; *Int'l,* pg. 8245
VIP HEALTH CARE SERVICES, INC.—See Addus HomeCare Corporation; *U.S. Public,* pg. 40
VIPI INDUSTRIA, COMERCIO, EXPORTACAO E IMPORTACAO DE PRODUTOS ODONTOLOGICOS LTDA.—See DENTSPLY SIRONA Inc.; *U.S. Public,* pg. 655
VIP INC.—See The Edward S. Quirk Co., Inc.; *U.S. Private,* pg. 4025
VIP INDUSTRIES LTD; *Int'l,* pg. 8245
VIPINGO DEVELOPMENT LIMITED—See Centum Investment Company Limited; *Int'l,* pg. 1416
VIP INTERNATIONAL INC.; *U.S. Private,* pg. 4386
VIP LOYALTY CORP.; *U.S. Private,* pg. 4386
VIPMEK OY—See Indutrade AB; *Int'l,* pg. 3682
VIP MOBILE D.O.O.—See America Movil, S.A.B. de C.V.; *Int'l,* pg. 421
VIP MORTGAGE, INC.; *U.S. Private,* pg. 4386
VIP MOTOR CARS LTD.; *U.S. Private,* pg. 4386
VIPNET USLUGE D.O.O.—See America Movil, S.A.B. de C.V.; *Int'l,* pg. 421
VIPO A.S.; *Int'l,* pg. 8245
VIPOM JSC; *Int'l,* pg. 8245
VIPOND FIRE PROTECTION, INC.—See APi Group Corporation; *Int'l,* pg. 514
VIPOND FIRE PROTECTION, LTD.—See APi Group Corporation; *Int'l,* pg. 514
VIPOND, INC.—See APi Group Corporation; *Int'l,* pg. 514
VIP OPERATOR DOOEL—See America Movil, S.A.B. de C.V.; *Int'l,* pg. 421
VIP OPTICAL LABORATORIES, INC.—See EssilorLuxottica SA; *Int'l,* pg. 2514
VIP PLASTIC PACKAGING PTY. LTD.—See Pact Group Holdings Ltd.; *Int'l,* pg. 5693
VIPPS AS—See DNB Bank ASA; *Int'l,* pg. 2148
VIPPY INDUSTRIES LTD; *Int'l,* pg. 8245
VIPPY SPINPRO LTD. - DEWAS WORKS—See VIPPY SPINPRO LTD.; *Int'l,* pg. 8245
VIPPY SPINPRO LTD.; *Int'l,* pg. 8245
VIP REALTY GROUP, INC.; *U.S. Private,* pg. 4386
VIPR INDUSTRIES, INC.; *U.S. Private,* pg. 4386
VIP SALES COMPANY, INC.; *U.S. Private,* pg. 4387
V.I.P SALES LTD; *Int'l,* pg. 8106
VIP SARL—See Piscines Desjoyaux SA; *Int'l,* pg. 5876
VIPSHOP HOLDINGS LIMITED; *Int'l,* pg. 8245
VIPS INC.—See General Dynamics Corporation; *U.S. Public,* pg. 914
VIP STAFFING, INC.; *U.S. Private,* pg. 4387

COMPANY NAME INDEX

VIP STEEL PACKAGING PTY. LTD.—See Pact Group Holdings Ltd.; *Int'l*, pg. 5693
VIP TRAVEL OF WOOSTER, INC.—See ABRY Partners, LLC; *U.S. Private*, pg. 41
VIPUL LIMITED; *Int'l*, pg. 8245
VIPUL ORGANICS LIMITED—See Vipul Limited; *Int'l*, pg. 8245
VIP WHOLESALE, INC.—See GrubMarket, Inc.; *U.S. Private*, pg. 1797
VIP WIRELESS, INC.; *U.S. Private*, pg. 4387
VIQ AUSTRALIA—See VIQ Solutions Inc.; *Int'l*, pg. 8245
VIQ SOLUTIONS INC.; *Int'l*, pg. 8245
VIQ SOLUTIONS, INC—See VIQ Solutions Inc.; *Int'l*, pg. 8245
VIQUA—See Danaher Corporation; *U.S. Public*, pg. 632
VIQUEL S.A.; *Int'l*, pg. 8245
VIRACON GEORGIA, INC.—See Apogee Enterprises, Inc.; *U.S. Public*, pg. 145
VIRACON, INC.—See Apogee Enterprises, Inc.; *U.S. Public*, pg. 145
VIRACOR-IBT LABORATORIES, INC.—See Eurofins Scientific S.E.; *Int'l*, pg. 2549
VIRACTA THERAPEUTICS, INC.; *U.S. Public*, pg. 2298
VIRALGEN COMMERCIAL THERAPEUTIC VECTOR CORE, S.L.—See Bayer Aktiengesellschaft; *Int'l*, pg. 910
VIRALGEN VECTOR CORE, S.L.—See Bayer Aktiengesellschaft; *Int'l*, pg. 910
VIRAL SHIELD LIFE SCIENCE SDN. BHD.—See Ideal Capital Berhad; *Int'l*, pg. 3589
VIRAL STYLE LLC; *U.S. Private*, pg. 4387
VIRALYTICS LIMITED—See Merck & Co., Inc.; *U.S. Public*, pg. 1419
VIRARDI ENTERPRISES LTD—See Nippon Sheet Glass Co. Ltd.; *Int'l*, pg. 5332
VIRAT CRANE INDUSTRIES LIMITED; *Int'l*, pg. 8245
VIRATHERAPEUTICS GMBH—See C.H. Boehringer Sohn AG & Co. KG; *Int'l*, pg. 1243
VIRAT INDUSTRIES LTD.; *Int'l*, pg. 8245
VIRAT LEASING LTD.; *Int'l*, pg. 8245
VIRAX BIOLABS GROUP LIMITED; *Int'l*, pg. 8246
VIRAX S.A.—See Dr. Helmut Rothenberger Holding GmbH; *Int'l*, pg. 2192
VIRBAC ANIMAL HEALTH INDIA PVT. LTD.—See Virbac S.A.; *Int'l*, pg. 8246
VIRBAC (AUSTRALIA) PTY LTD.—See Virbac S.A.; *Int'l*, pg. 8246
VIRBAC BELGIUM SA—See Virbac S.A.; *Int'l*, pg. 8246
VIRBAC CHILE SPA—See Virbac S.A.; *Int'l*, pg. 8246
VIRBAC COLOMBIA LTDA—See Virbac S.A.; *Int'l*, pg. 8246
VIRBAC CORPORATION—See Virbac S.A.; *Int'l*, pg. 8246
VIRBAC DANMARK A/S—See Virbac S.A.; *Int'l*, pg. 8246
VIRBAC DE PORTUGAL LABORATORIOS LDA—See Virbac S.A.; *Int'l*, pg. 8247
VIRBAC DO BRASIL INDUSTRIA E COMERCIO LTDA.—See Virbac S.A.; *Int'l*, pg. 8247
VIRBAC ESPANA SA—See Virbac S.A.; *Int'l*, pg. 8246
VIRBAC FRANCE SAS—See Virbac S.A.; *Int'l*, pg. 8246
VIRBAC HELLAS SA—See Virbac S.A.; *Int'l*, pg. 8246
VIRBAC JAPAN CO. LTD.—See Virbac S.A.; *Int'l*, pg. 8246
VIRBAC KOREA CO. LTD.—See Virbac S.A.; *Int'l*, pg. 8246
VIRBAC LTD.—See Virbac S.A.; *Int'l*, pg. 8246
VIRBAC MEXICO SA DE CV—See Virbac S.A.; *Int'l*, pg. 8246
VIRBAC NEDERLAND B.V.—See Virbac S.A.; *Int'l*, pg. 8246
VIRBAC NEW ZEALAND LTD.—See Virbac S.A.; *Int'l*, pg. 8246
VIRBAC NUTRITION SAS—See Virbac S.A.; *Int'l*, pg. 8246
VIRBAC OSTERREICH GMBH—See Virbac S.A.; *Int'l*, pg. 8246
VIRBAC PHARMA HANDELSGESELLSHAFT MBH—See Virbac S.A.; *Int'l*, pg. 8246
VIRBAC PHILIPPINES INC.—See Virbac S.A.; *Int'l*, pg. 8246
VIRBAC RSA (PTY) LTD.—See Virbac S.A.; *Int'l*, pg. 8246
VIRBAC S.A.; *Int'l*, pg. 8246
VIRBAC SP ZOO—See Virbac S.A.; *Int'l*, pg. 8246
VIRBAC SRL—See Virbac S.A.; *Int'l*, pg. 8246
VIRBAC (SWITZERLAND) AG—See Virbac S.A.; *Int'l*, pg. 8246
VIRBAC TAIWAN CO. LTD.—See Virbac S.A.; *Int'l*, pg. 8246
VIRBAC THAILAND CO. LTD.—See Virbac S.A.; *Int'l*, pg. 8246
VIRBAC TIERARZNEIMITTEL GMBH—See Virbac S.A.; *Int'l*, pg. 8246
VIRBAC URUGUAY SA—See Virbac S.A.; *Int'l*, pg. 8246
VIRBAC VIETNAM CO. LTD.—See Virbac S.A.; *Int'l*, pg. 8246
VIRBAC VIETNAM JV COMPANY—See Virbac S.A.; *Int'l*, pg. 8246
VIR BIOTECHNOLOGY, INC.; *U.S. Public*, pg. 2298
VIRCO BVBA—See Johnson & Johnson; *U.S. Public*, pg. 1200
VIRCO-CONWAY DIVISION—See Virco Mfg. Corporation; *U.S. Public*, pg. 2299
VIRCO INC.—See Virco Mfg. Corporation; *U.S. Public*, pg. 2299
VIRCO MFG. CORPORATION; *U.S. Public*, pg. 2299
VIRENT ENERGY SYSTEMS, INC; *U.S. Private*, pg. 4387
VIRENT, INC.—See Marathon Petroleum Corporation; *U.S. Public*, pg. 1363
VIREO GROWTH INC.; *U.S. Public*, pg. 2299
VIRESCENT RENEWABLE ENERGY TRUST—See KKR & Co. Inc.; *U.S. Public*, pg. 1266
VIRE TECHNOLOGIES, LLC; *U.S. Private*, pg. 4387
VIREXIT TECHNOLOGIES, INC.; *U.S. Public*, pg. 2299
VIRGIN ACTIVE AUSTRALIA PTY LIMITED—See Virgin Management Limited; *Int'l*, pg. 8247
VIRGIN ACTIVE ITALIA S.P.A.—See Virgin Management Limited; *Int'l*, pg. 8247
VIRGIN ACTIVE LIMITED—See Brait S.E.; *Int'l*, pg. 1137
VIRGIN ACTIVE SINGAPORE PTE. LTD.—See Virgin Management Limited; *Int'l*, pg. 8247
VIRGIN ACTIVE SOUTH AFRICA (PROPRIETARY) LIMITED—See Virgin Management Limited; *Int'l*, pg. 8247
VIRGIN ATLANTIC AIRWAYS LTD.—See Virgin Management Limited; *Int'l*, pg. 8247
VIRGIN ATLANTIC CARGO—See Virgin Management Limited; *Int'l*, pg. 8247
VIRGIN ATLANTIC LTD.—See Virgin Management Limited; *Int'l*, pg. 8247
VIRGIN AUSTRALIA AIRLINES PTY. LTD.—See Virgin Australia Holdings Limited; *Int'l*, pg. 8247
VIRGIN AUSTRALIA HOLDINGS LIMITED; *Int'l*, pg. 8247
VIRGIN BALLOON FLIGHTS LTD—See Virgin Management Limited; *Int'l*, pg. 8247
VIRGIN BEC-TERO RADIO (THAILAND) CO., LTD.—See BEC World Public Company Limited; *Int'l*, pg. 936
VIRGIN CARE LIMITED—See Virgin Management Limited; *Int'l*, pg. 8247
VIRGIN CONNECT, ZAO—See Virgin Management Limited; *Int'l*, pg. 8247
VIRGIN EMI RECORDS—See Universal Music Group N.V.; *Int'l*, pg. 8081
VIRGIN ENTERPRISES LTD—See Virgin Management Limited; *Int'l*, pg. 8247
VIRGIN EXPERIENCE DAYS LTD.—See Inflexion Private Equity Partners LLP; *Int'l*, pg. 3689
VIRGIN GALACTIC HOLDINGS, INC.; *U.S. Public*, pg. 2299
VIRGIN GALACTIC, LLC—See Virgin Galactic Holdings, Inc.; *U.S. Public*, pg. 2299
VIRGIN HEALTH BANK LIMITED—See Virgin Management Limited; *Int'l*, pg. 8247
VIRGIN HOLIDAYS—See Virgin Management Limited; *Int'l*, pg. 8247
VIRGINIA ABRASIVES CORPORATION—See Barton Mines Company LLC; *U.S. Private*, pg. 483
VIRGINIA AIR DISTRIBUTORS INC.; *U.S. Private*, pg. 4387
VIRGINIA AMERICAN INDUSTRIES, LLC—See CenterOak Partners LLC; *U.S. Private*, pg. 816
VIRGINIA AMERICAN WATER CO.—See American Water Works Company, Inc.; *U.S. Public*, pg. 112
VIRGINIA BANK BANKSHARES, INC.; *U.S. Private*, pg. 4387
VIRGINIA BANK & TRUST CO.—See Virginia Bank Bankshares, Inc.; *U.S. Private*, pg. 4387
VIRGINIA BUILDERS' SUPPLY, INC.—See American Securities LLC; *U.S. Private*, pg. 249
VIRGINIA BUSINESS MAGAZINE—See Lee Enterprises, Incorporated; *U.S. Public*, pg. 1299
VIRGINIA-CAROLINA BELTING, INC.—See AEA Investors LP; *U.S. Private*, pg. 115
VIRGINIA CENTER COMMONS, LLC—See Washington Prime Group Inc.; *U.S. Public*, pg. 4449
VIRGINIA COMMONWEALTH BANK—See Blue Ridge Bankshares, Inc.; *U.S. Public*, pg. 365
VIRGINIA COMMUNITY BANKSHARES, INC.—See Blue Ridge Bankshares, Inc.; *U.S. Public*, pg. 365
VIRGINIA COMMUNITY BANK—See Blue Ridge Bankshares, Inc.; *U.S. Public*, pg. 365
VIRGINIA CREDIT & FINANCE, INC.—See Encore Capital Group, Inc.; *U.S. Public*, pg. 760
VIRGINIA DARE EXTRACT CO., INC.; *U.S. Private*, pg. 4387
VIRGINIA ELECTRIC AND POWER COMPANY—See Dominion Energy, Inc.; *U.S. Public*, pg. 674
VIRGINIA ELECTRONIC COMPONENTS LLC; *U.S. Private*, pg. 4387
VIRGINIA FARM BUREAU FIRE & CASUALTY INSURANCE COMPANY—See Virginia Farm Bureau Mutual Insurance Company; *U.S. Private*, pg. 4387
VIRGINIA FARM BUREAU MUTUAL INSURANCE COMPANY; *U.S. Private*, pg. 4387
VIRGINIA GAZETTE COMPANIES, LLC—See Tribune Publishing Company; *U.S. Private*, pg. 4228
VIRGINIA GLASS PRODUCTS CORPORATION—See Virginia Mirror Company Incorporated; *U.S. Private*, pg. 4388
VIRGINIA GYNECOLOGIC ONCOLOGY, LLC—See HCA Healthcare, Inc.; *U.S. Public*, pg. 1013
VIRGINIA GYNECOLOGIC ONCOLOGY, LLC—See HCA Healthcare, Inc.; *U.S. Public*, pg. 1013
VIRGINIA HARBOUR SERVICES—See Trelleborg AB; *Int'l*, pg. 7912
VIRGINIA HARDWOOD CO.; *U.S. Private*, pg. 4387
VIRGINIA HEMATOLOGY & ONCOLOGY ASSOCIATES, INC.—See HCA Healthcare, Inc.; *U.S. Public*, pg. 1013
VIRGINIA HILLS OIL CORP.; *Int'l*, pg. 8248
THE VIRGINIA HOME; *U.S. Private*, pg. 4131
VIRGINIA HOSPITALISTS, INC.—See HCA Healthcare, Inc.; *U.S. Public*, pg. 1013
VIRGINIA INDUSTRIAL PLSTCS INC.; *U.S. Private*, pg. 4387
VIRGINIA INDUSTRIES INC.; *U.S. Private*, pg. 4387
VIRGINIA IN-HOME PARTNER-VIII, LLC—See UnitedHealth Group Incorporated; *U.S. Public*, pg. 2247
VIRGINIA IN-HOME PARTNER-V, LLC—See UnitedHealth Group Incorporated; *U.S. Public*, pg. 2247
VIRGINIA INTERNATIONAL TERMINALS, INC.; *U.S. Private*, pg. 4387
VIRGINIA INVESTMENT COUNSELORS, INC.—See Guardian Capital Group Limited; *Int'l*, pg. 3170
VIRGINIA LANDING CORPORATION—See Equity LifeStyle Properties, Inc.; *U.S. Public*, pg. 790
VIRGINIA LEAGUE FOR PLANNED PARENTHOOD INC.; *U.S. Private*, pg. 4387
VIRGINIA LOGOS, LLC—See Lamar Advertising Company; *U.S. Public*, pg. 1291
VIRGINIA MASON HEALTH SYSTEM—See Franciscan Health System; *U.S. Private*, pg. 1587
VIRGINIA MASON INSTITUTE; *U.S. Private*, pg. 4387
VIRGINIA MASSAGE THERAPY, INC.—See Catterton Management Company, LLC; *U.S. Private*, pg. 794
VIRGINIA MIRROR COMPANY INCORPORATED; *U.S. Private*, pg. 4387
VIRGINIA NATIONAL BANKSHARES CORPORATION; *U.S. Public*, pg. 2299
VIRGINIA NATIONAL BANK—See Virginia National Bankshares Corporation; *U.S. Public*, pg. 2299
VIRGINIA NATURAL GAS, INC.—See The Southern Company; *U.S. Public*, pg. 2131
THE VIRGINIAN-PILOT—See Tribune Publishing Company; *U.S. Private*, pg. 4228
VIRGINIA PAVING COMPANY—See VINCI S.A.; *Int'l*, pg. 8220
VIRGINIA PELLA INC.; *U.S. Private*, pg. 4388
VIRGINIA PIZZA CO., INC.—See Daland Corporation; *U.S. Private*, pg. 1148
VIRGINIA PORT AUTHORITY; *U.S. Private*, pg. 4388
VIRGINIA POWER ENERGY MARKETING, INC.—See Dominion Energy, Inc.; *U.S. Public*, pg. 674
VIRGINIA PROPANE, INC.—See Superior Plus Corp.; *Int'l*, pg. 7338
THE VIRGINIA PROPERTIES—See The Long & Foster Companies, Inc.; *U.S. Private*, pg. 4072
VIRGINIA PUBLISHING OOD—See Universal Music Group N.V.; *Int'l*, pg. 8081
VIRGINIA QUILTING INC.; *U.S. Private*, pg. 4388
VIRGINIA SOUTHERN RAILROAD—See Brookfield Infrastructure Partners L.P.; *Int'l*, pg. 1192
VIRGINIA SOUTHERN RAILROAD—See GIC Pte. Ltd.; *Int'l*, pg. 2966
VIRGINIA & SOUTHWESTERN RAILWAY CO.—See Norfolk Southern Corporation; *U.S. Public*, pg. 1536
VIRGINIA SRL—See UniCredit S.p.A.; *Int'l*, pg. 8041
VIRGINIA SURETY COMPANY, INC.—See Assurant, Inc.; *U.S. Public*, pg. 216
VIRGINIA SYMPHONY ORCHESTRA; *U.S. Private*, pg. 4388
VIRGINIA SYSTEMS & TECHNOLOGY, INC.—See Altamira Technologies Corporation; *U.S. Private*, pg. 204
VIRGINIA TILE COMPANY, LLC—See Transom Capital Group, LLC; *U.S. Private*, pg. 4209
VIRGINIA TILE COMPANY; *U.S. Private*, pg. 4388
VIRGINIA TRANSFORMER CORP.; *U.S. Private*, pg. 4388
VIRGINIA TREATMENT CENTER, INC.—See Acadia Healthcare Company, Inc.; *U.S. Public*, pg. 31
VIRGINIA TRUCK CENTER INC.; *U.S. Private*, pg. 4388
VIRGINIA T'S INC.; *U.S. Private*, pg. 4388
VIRGIN ISLAND WATER & POWER AUTHORITY; *U.S. Private*, pg. 4387
VIRGIN LIMITED EDITION—See Virgin Management Limited; *Int'l*, pg. 8247
VIRGIN MANAGEMENT LIMITED; *Int'l*, pg. 8247
VIRGIN MEDIA BUSINESS LTD.—See Liberty Global plc; *Int'l*, pg. 4486
VIRGIN MEDIA BUSINESS LTD.—See Telefonica, S.A.; *Int'l*, pg. 7537
VIRGIN MEDIA BUSINESS LTD.—See Liberty Global plc; *Int'l*, pg. 4486
VIRGIN MEDIA BUSINESS LTD.—See Telefonica, S.A.; *Int'l*, pg. 7537
VIRGIN MEDIA INC.—See Liberty Global plc; *Int'l*, pg. 4486
VIRGIN MEDIA INVESTMENT HOLDINGS LIMITED—See Liberty Global plc; *Int'l*, pg. 4486

VIRGIN MANAGEMENT LIMITED

VIRGIN MEDIA IRELAND LTD—See Liberty Global plc; *Int'l*, pg. 4486
VIRGIN MEDIA LTD.—See Liberty Global plc; *Int'l*, pg. 4485
VIRGIN MEDIA LTD.—See Telefonica, S.A.; *Int'l*, pg. 7536
VIRGIN MEDIA TELEVISION LIMITED—See Liberty Global plc; *Int'l*, pg. 4486
VIRGIN MOBILE (AUSTRALIA) PTY LTD—See Virgin Management Limited; *Int'l*, pg. 8247
VIRGIN MOBILE CANADA—See BCE Inc.; *Int'l*, pg. 927
VIRGIN MOBILE POLSKA SP. Z O.O—See Iliad S.A.; *Int'l*, pg. 3614
VIRGIN MOBILE SOUTH AFRICA (PTY) LTD—See Virgin Management Limited; *Int'l*, pg. 8247
VIRGIN MOBILE USA, INC.—See EchoStar Corporation; *U.S. Public*, pg. 711
VIRGIN MONEY (AUSTRALIA) PTY LIMITED—See Virgin Management Limited; *Int'l*, pg. 8247
VIRGIN MONEY GIVING LIMITED—See Virgin Management Limited; *Int'l*, pg. 8247
VIRGIN MONEY HOLDINGS (UK) LIMITED—See Virgin Money UK PLC; *Int'l*, pg. 8247
VIRGIN MONEY PLC—See Virgin Money UK PLC; *Int'l*, pg. 8248
VIRGIN MONEY UK PLC; *Int'l*, pg. 8247
VIRGIN ORBIT HOLDINGS, INC.; *U.S. Private*, pg. 4387
VIRGIN PULSE, INC.—See Marlin Equity Partners, LLC; *U.S. Private*, pg. 2585
VIRGIN RADIO RESEAU NORD—See Vivendi SE; *Int'l*, pg. 8275
VIRGIN RECORDS AMERICA, INC.—See Universal Music Group N.V.; *Int'l*, pg. 8079
VIRGIN RIVER CASINO CORPORATION—See Mesquite Gaming, LLC; *U.S. Private*, pg. 2679
VIRGIN RIVER HEALTHCARE, INC.—See The Ensign Group, Inc.; *U.S. Public*, pg. 2072
VIRGIN TRAINS USA INC.; *U.S. Private*, pg. 4387
VIRGIN TRAVEL GROUP LTD—See Virgin Management Limited; *Int'l*, pg. 8247
VIRGIN VACATIONS—See Virgin Management Limited; *Int'l*, pg. 8247
VIRGIN WIFI LIMITED—See Liberty Global plc; *Int'l*, pg. 4486
VIRGIN WINE ONLINE LIMITED—See Virgin Wines UK Plc; *Int'l*, pg. 8248
VIRGIN WINES LTD.—See Direct Wines Limited; *Int'l*, pg. 2130
VIRGIN WINES UK PLC; *Int'l*, pg. 8248
VIRGO CAPITAL; *U.S. Private*, pg. 4388
VIRGO INVESTMENT GROUP LLC; *U.S. Private*, pg. 4388
VIRGO PUBLISHING, LLC—See Arlington Capital Partners LLC; *U.S. Private*, pg. 328
VIRGO VALVES & CONTROLS PRIVATE LIMITED—See Emerson Electric Co.; *U.S. Public*, pg. 752
VIRIBRIGHT LIGHTING INC.—See Matrix Holdings Limited; *Int'l*, pg. 4729
VIRIDAX CORPORATION; *U.S. Private*, pg. 4388
VIRIDIAN ENERGY, LLC—See Vistra Corp.; *U.S. Public*, pg. 2306
VIRIDIAN GROUP LTD.—See I Squared Capital Advisors (US) LLC; *U.S. Private*, pg. 2026
VIRIDIAN PARTNERS LLC; *U.S. Private*, pg. 4388
VIRIDIAN REVERSE LOGISTICS, LLC—See V.I.P. Computer Centre Limited; *Int'l*, pg. 8106
VIRIDIAN SOLAR LIMITED—See Marshalls plc; *Int'l*, pg. 4702
VIRIDIAN—See Crescent Capital Partners Ltd.; *Int'l*, pg. 1839
VIRIDIAN THERAPEUTICS, INC.; *U.S. Public*, pg. 2299
VIRID INTERATIVIDADE DIGITAL LTDA—See Experian plc; *Int'l*, pg. 2588
VIRIDIS TECHNOLOGIES INC.; *Int'l*, pg. 8248
VIRIDITY ENERGY, INC.—See Ormat Technologies, Inc.; *U.S. Public*, pg. 1618
VIRIDIUM HOLDING AG—See Cinven Limited; *Int'l*, pg. 1616
VIRIDIUM HOLDING AG—See Talanx AG; *Int'l*, pg. 7445
VIRIDOR ENVIROSCOT LIMITED—See KKR & Co. Inc.; *U.S. Public*, pg. 1266
VIRIDOR GLASS RECYCLING LIMITED—See KKR & Co. Inc.; *U.S. Public*, pg. 1266
VIRIDOR LIMITED—See KKR & Co. Inc.; *U.S. Public*, pg. 1266
VIRIDOR LONDON RECYCLING LIMITED—See KKR & Co. Inc.; *U.S. Public*, pg. 1266
VIRIDOR (MARTOCK) LIMITED—See KKR & Co. Inc.; *U.S. Public*, pg. 1266
VIRIDOR POLYMER RECYCLING LIMITED—See KKR & Co. Inc.; *U.S. Public*, pg. 1266
VIRIDOR RESOURCE MANAGEMENT LIMITED—See KKR & Co. Inc.; *U.S. Public*, pg. 1266
VIRIDOR WASTE (BRISTOL HOLDINGS) LIMITED—See KKR & Co. Inc.; *U.S. Public*, pg. 1266
VIRIDOR WASTE (BRISTOL) LIMITED—See KKR & Co. Inc.; *U.S. Public*, pg. 1266
VIRIDOR WASTE DISPOSAL LIMITED—See KKR & Co. Inc.; *U.S. Public*, pg. 1266
VIRIDOR WASTE EXETER LIMITED—See KKR & Co. Inc.; *U.S. Public*, pg. 1266
VIRIDOR WASTE (GREATER MANCHESTER) LIMITED—See KKR & Co. Inc.; *U.S. Public*, pg. 1266
VIRIDOR WASTE KENT LIMITED—See KKR & Co. Inc.; *U.S. Public*, pg. 1266
VIRIDOR WASTE (LANDFILL RESTORATION) LIMITED—See KKR & Co. Inc.; *U.S. Public*, pg. 1266
VIRIDOR WASTE LIMITED—See KKR & Co. Inc.; *U.S. Public*, pg. 1266
VIRIDOR WASTE MANAGEMENT LTD.—See KKR & Co. Inc.; *U.S. Public*, pg. 1266
VIRIDOR WASTE (SHEFFIELD) LIMITED—See KKR & Co. Inc.; *U.S. Public*, pg. 1266
VIRIDOR WASTE (SOMERSET) LIMITED—See KKR & Co. Inc.; *U.S. Public*, pg. 1266
VIRIDOR WASTE (SUFFOLK) LIMITED—See KKR & Co. Inc.; *U.S. Public*, pg. 1266
VIRIDOR WASTE (THAMES) LIMITED—See KKR & Co. Inc.; *U.S. Public*, pg. 1266
VIRIDOR WASTE (WEST SUSSEX) LIMITED—See KKR & Co. Inc.; *U.S. Public*, pg. 1266
VIRINCHI HEALTH CARE PVT. LTD.—See Virinchi Ltd.; *Int'l*, pg. 8248
VIRINCHI LTD.; *Int'l*, pg. 8248
VIRION LABORDIAGNOSTIK GMBH—See Sonic Healthcare Limited; *Int'l*, pg. 7099
VIRIOS THERAPEUTICS, INC.; *U.S. Public*, pg. 2299
VIRMEDICA INC.—See General Atlantic Service Company, L.P.; *U.S. Private*, pg. 1662
VIRNECT CO., LTD.; *Int'l*, pg. 8248
VIRNETX HOLDING CORP.; *U.S. Public*, pg. 2299
VIRNETX, INC.—See VirnetX Holding Corp.; *U.S. Public*, pg. 2299
VIRO AG—See Vicat S.A.; *Int'l*, pg. 8186
VIROBAY, INC.; *U.S. Private*, pg. 4388
VIROCYT, INC.—See Sartorius AG; *Int'l*, pg. 6581
VIRO-IMMUN LABOR-DIAGNOSTIKA GMBH; *Int'l*, pg. 8248
VIRO-MED LABORATORIES, INC.—See Laboratory Corporation of America Holdings; *U.S. Public*, pg. 1287
VIRONEX TECHNICAL SERVICES LLC—See TruArc Partners, L.P.; *U.S. Private*, pg. 4245
VIROSTAT, INC.—See DevCo Partners Oy; *Int'l*, pg. 2086
VIROTEC GLOBAL SOLUTIONS PTY. LTD.; *Int'l*, pg. 8248
VIROTECH DIAGNOSTICS GMBH—See Eurofins Scientific S.E.; *Int'l*, pg. 2552
VIRQTEC ITALIA SRL—See Virotec Global Solutions Pty. Ltd.; *Int'l*, pg. 8248
VIRO TVORNICA SECERA D.D.; *Int'l*, pg. 8248
VIROXIS CORPORATION—See Quintis Limited; *Int'l*, pg. 6165
VIRPAX PHARMACEUTICALS, INC.; *U.S. Public*, pg. 2299
VIRPIE INC.; *U.S. Private*, pg. 4388
VIRPIE TECH—See Virpie Inc.; *U.S. Private*, pg. 4388
VIRSCEND EDUCATION CO. LTD.; *Int'l*, pg. 8248
VIRSTRA I-TECHNOLOGY SERVICES LIMITED—See Nucleus Software Exports Limited; *Int'l*, pg. 5486
VIRSTRA I-TECHNOLOGY (SINGAPORE) PTE. LTD.—See Nucleus Software Exports Limited; *Int'l*, pg. 5486
VIRTA INC.—See Fluor Corporation; *U.S. Public*, pg. 860
VIRTALIS INC.—See Alpina Capital Partners LLP; *Int'l*, pg. 371
VIRTEK VISION INTERNATIONAL, INC.—See Vector Capital Management, L.P.; *U.S. Private*, pg. 4351
VIRTELLIGENCE; *U.S. Private*, pg. 4388
VIRTEVA—See The RLJ Companies, LLC; *U.S. Private*, pg. 4111
VIRTEXCO CORPORATION; *U.S. Private*, pg. 4388
VIRTEX ENTERPRISES LP—See Insight Equity Holdings LLC; *U.S. Private*, pg. 2086
VIRTIUM TECHNOLOGY, INC.—See Court Square Capital Partners, L.P.; *U.S. Private*, pg. 1070
VIRTRA, INC.; *U.S. Public*, pg. 2299
VIRTUAL1 LTD.; *Int'l*, pg. 8248
VIRTUAL ACCESS (IRELAND) LTD.—See Ependion AB; *Int'l*, pg. 2459
VIRTUAL-AGENT SERVICES; *U.S. Private*, pg. 4389
VIRTUALARMOUR INTERNATIONAL, INC.; *U.S. Public*, pg. 2300
VIRTUALARMOUR, LLC—See VirtualArmour International, Inc.; *U.S. Public*, pg. 2300
VIRTUAL CHIP EXCHANGE, INC.—See HPI AG; *Int'l*, pg. 3500
VIRTUAL CLARITY LIMITED—See DXC Technology Company; *U.S. Public*, pg. 697
VIRTUAL DRIVER INTERACTIVE, INC.—See Cemtrex, Inc.; *U.S. Public*, pg. 466
VIRTUAL ED LINK, INC.; *U.S. Private*, pg. 4388
VIRTUALEX CONSULTING, INC.—See The Carlyle Group Inc.; *U.S. Public*, pg. 2055
VIRTUALEX HOLDINGS, INC.—See The Carlyle Group Inc.; *U.S. Public*, pg. 2055
VIRTUAL FARM CREATIVE INC.; *U.S. Private*, pg. 4389
VIRTUAL GLOBAL EDUCATION LIMITED; *Int'l*, pg. 8248

CORPORATE AFFILIATIONS

VIRTUAL GRAFFITI, INC.—See Source Capital, LLC; *U.S. Private*, pg. 3718
VIRTUAL HOLD TECHNOLOGY, LLC—See Thoma Bravo, L.P.; *U.S. Private*, pg. 4149
VIRTUAL IMAGES—See Taylor Corporation; *U.S. Private*, pg. 3939
VIRTUAL, INC; *U.S. Private*, pg. 4389
VIRTUAL INFORMATION SYSTEMS CORP.—See Print Reach, Inc.; *U.S. Private*, pg. 3265
VIRTUAL INSTRUMENTS, INC.; *U.S. Private*, pg. 4389
VIRTUAL INTERACTIVE TECHNOLOGIES CORP.; *U.S. Public*, pg. 2300
VIRTUAL LEASE SERVICES LIMITED—See NetSol Technologies, Inc.; *U.S. Public*, pg. 1509
VIRTUAL MARKETING SERVICES (UK) LIMITED—See evoke plc; *Int'l*, pg. 2572
VIRTUAL MEDIA INTEGRATION, LLC—See Varex Imaging Corporation; *U.S. Public*, pg. 2275
VIRTUAL MEDICAL INTERNATIONAL, INC.; *U.S. Public*, pg. 2300
VIRTUAL MIND HOLDING COMPANY LIMITED—See Guotai Junan Securities Co., Ltd.; *Int'l*, pg. 3187
VIRTUAL OBSERVER PTY. LTD.—See Micro-X Limited; *Int'l*, pg. 4878
VIRTUAL PLANET GROUP GMBH—See SES S.A.; *Int'l*, pg. 6728
VIRTUALPREMISE, INC.—See CoStar Group, Inc.; *U.S. Public*, pg. 586
VIRTUAL PROPERTIES REALTY, LLC—See United Real Estate Group, LLC; *U.S. Private*, pg. 4296
VIRTUAL RADIOLOGIC CORPORATION—See MEDNAX, Inc.; *U.S. Public*, pg. 1413
VIRTUAL RECALL LIMITED—See Zoetis, Inc.; *U.S. Public*, pg. 2410
VIRTUALSCOPICS, INC.—See Koninklijke Philips N.V.; *Int'l*, pg. 4267
VIRTUALSOFT SYSTEMS LTD.; *Int'l*, pg. 8248
VIRTUAL SOURCING, LLC; *U.S. Private*, pg. 4389
VIRTUAL TECH GURUS INC.; *U.S. Private*, pg. 4389
VIRTUAL TECHNOLOGIES GROUP LLC—See Jacmel Growth Partners Management LLC; *U.S. Private*, pg. 2179
VIRTUAL THERAPEUTICS CORPORATION—See UnitedHealth Group Incorporated; *U.S. Public*, pg. 2252
THE VIRTUAL TRY-OUT SPACE S.L.—See Keysight Technologies, Inc.; *U.S. Public*, pg. 1227
VIRTUAL UNIVERSE CORPORATION; *Int'l*, pg. 8248
VIRTUAL VOUCHER (PROPRIETARY) LIMITED—See Blue Label Telecoms Limited; *Int'l*, pg. 1068
VIRTUALWARE 2007, S.A.; *Int'l*, pg. 8248
VIRTU AMERICAS LLC—See Virtu Financial, Inc.; *U.S. Public*, pg. 2300
VIRTUA SURGICAL GROUP; *U.S. Private*, pg. 4388
VIRTUE CAPITAL MANAGEMENT LLC; *U.S. Private*, pg. 4389
VIRTUE GROUP; *U.S. Private*, pg. 4389
VIRTUEMED PTE. LTD.—See Livingstone Health Holdings Limited; *Int'l*, pg. 4533
VIRTUE SOLAR, LLC—See National Grid plc; *Int'l*, pg. 5158
VIRTU FINANCIAL GLOBAL MARKETS LLC—See Virtu Financial, Inc.; *U.S. Public*, pg. 2300
VIRTU FINANCIAL GLOBAL SERVICES SINGAPORE PTE LTD.—See Virtu Financial, Inc.; *U.S. Public*, pg. 2300
VIRTU FINANCIAL, INC.; *U.S. Public*, pg. 2299
VIRTU GETCO HOLDING COMPANY, LLC—See Virtu Financial, Inc.; *U.S. Public*, pg. 2300
VIRTU INVESTMENTS; *U.S. Private*, pg. 4388
VIRTU ITG HOLDINGS LLC—See Virtu Financial, Inc.; *U.S. Public*, pg. 2300
VIRTU KCG HOLDINGS LLC—See Virtu Financial, Inc.; *U.S. Public*, pg. 2300
VIRTU KNIGHT CAPITAL GROUP, LLC—See Virtu Financial, Inc.; *U.S. Public*, pg. 2300
VIRTUMUNDO, INC.; *U.S. Private*, pg. 4389
VIRTUOSO ACQUISITION CORP.—See Wejo Group Limited; *Int'l*, pg. 8371
VIRTUOSO LLC—See Enveric Biosciences, Inc.; *U.S. Public*, pg. 780
VIRTUOSO LTD.; *U.S. Private*, pg. 4389
VIRTUOSO OPTOELECTRONICS LIMITED; *Int'l*, pg. 8248
VIRTUSA AUSTRIA GMBH—See EQT AB; *Int'l*, pg. 2472
VIRTUSA CONSULTING & SERVICES LIMITED—See EQT AB; *Int'l*, pg. 2472
VIRTUSA CONSULTING SERVICES PRIVATE LIMITED—See EQT AB; *Int'l*, pg. 2472
VIRTUSA CORPORATION - CONNECTICUT—See EQT AB; *Int'l*, pg. 2472
VIRTUSA CORPORATION—See EQT AB; *Int'l*, pg. 2471
VIRTUSA HUNGARY KFT.—See EQT AB; *Int'l*, pg. 2472
VIRTUSA INTERNATIONAL, B.V.—See EQT AB; *Int'l*, pg. 2472
VIRTUSA MALAYSIA PRIVATE LIMITED—See EQT AB; *Int'l*, pg. 2472
VIRTUSA MEXICO S DE RL DE CV—See EQT AB; *Int'l*, pg. 2472
VIRTUSA MIDDLE EAST FZ LLC—See EQT AB; *Int'l*, pg. 2472

COMPANY NAME INDEX

VIRTUSA PHILIPPINES, INC—See EQT AB; *Int'l*, pg. 2472
VIRTUSA (PRIVATE) LIMITED—See EQT AB; *Int'l*, pg. 2472
VIRTUSA QFC IT CONSULTING LLC—See EQT AB; *Int'l*, pg. 2472
VIRTUSA SINGAPORE PRIVATE LIMITED—See EQT AB; *Int'l*, pg. 2472
VIRTUSA SWITZERLAND GMBH—See EQT AB; *Int'l*, pg. 2472
VIRTUSA UK LIMITED—See EQT AB; *Int'l*, pg. 2472
VIRTUS BENEFITS, LLC—See Genstar Capital, LLC; *U.S. Private*, pg. 1675
VIRTUS CONVERTIBLE & INCOME FUND II; *U.S. Public*, pg. 2300
VIRTUS DIVIDEND, INTEREST & PREMIUM STRATEGY FUND; *U.S. Public*, pg. 2300
VIRTUS EQUITY & CONVERTIBLE INCOME FUND; *U.S. Public*, pg. 2300
VIRTUS ETF SOLUTIONS LLC—See Virtus Investment Partners, Inc.; *U.S. Public*, pg. 2301
VIRTUS FERTILITY CENTRE SINGAPORE PTE LIMITED—See Virtus Health Limited; *Int'l*, pg. 8249
VIRTUS HEALTH LIMITED; *Int'l*, pg. 8248
VIRTUS HOLDING APS; *Int'l*, pg. 8249
VIRTUS INC.—See DCC plc; *Int'l*, pg. 1991
VIRTUS INVESTMENT ADVISERS, INC.—See Virtus Investment Partners, Inc.; *U.S. Public*, pg. 2301
VIRTUS INVESTMENT PARTNERS, INC.; *U.S. Public*, pg. 2300
VIRTUS LLC; *U.S. Private*, pg. 4389
VIRTUS NUTRITION, LLC—See Cargill, Inc.; *U.S. Private*, pg. 760
VIRTUS PARTNERS LLC; *U.S. Private*, pg. 4389
VIRTUS REAL ESTATE CAPITAL; *U.S. Private*, pg. 4389
VIRTUS TOTAL RETURN FUND, INC.; *U.S. Public*, pg. 2301
VIRU NET OU—See Telia Company AB; *Int'l*, pg. 7543
VIRURL, INC.—See Revenue.com Corporation; *U.S. Private*, pg. 3414
VIRU SA; *Int'l*, pg. 8249
VIRYA RESOURCES LTD.; *Int'l*, pg. 8249
VIRY S.A.S.; *Int'l*, pg. 8249
VISA AP (AUSTRALIA) PTY LIMITED—See Visa, Inc.; *U.S. Public*, pg. 2301
VISA ARGENTINA S.A.—See Banco Macro S.A.; *Int'l*, pg. 823
VISA CANADA CORPORATION—See Visa, Inc.; *U.S. Public*, pg. 2301
VISA CEMEA (UK) LIMITED—See Visa, Inc.; *U.S. Public*, pg. 2301
VISACO MINERAL AND INVESTMENT JOINT STOCK COMPANY; *Int'l*, pg. 8249
VISA EUROPE LIMITED—See Visa, Inc.; *U.S. Public*, pg. 2301
VISAGAR FINANCIAL SERVICES LIMITED; *Int'l*, pg. 8249
VISAGAR POLYTEX LTD.; *Int'l*, pg. 8249
VISAGE DERMATOLOGY & LASER CENTER, LLC; *U.S. Private*, pg. 4389
VISAGE GROUP LIMITED—See Li & Fung Limited; *Int'l*, pg. 4481
VISAGE LIMITED—See Li & Fung Limited; *Int'l*, pg. 4481
VISAGE MOBILE, INC.; *U.S. Private*, pg. 4389
VISAHQ.COM INC.; *U.S. Private*, pg. 4389
VISA, INC.; *U.S. Public*, pg. 2301
VISA INTERNATIONAL SERVICE ASSOCIATION—See Visa, Inc.; *U.S. Public*, pg. 2301
VISAKA CEMENT INDUSTRY LIMITED—See The India Cements Limited; *Int'l*, pg. 7655
VISAKA INDUSTRIES LIMITED; *Int'l*, pg. 8249
VISALIA NEWSPAPERS LLC—See Gannett Co., Inc.; *U.S. Public*, pg. 901
VISALIA TIMES-DELTA—See Gannett Co., Inc.; *U.S. Public*, pg. 901
VISA LIGHTING CORPORATION—See Oldenburg Group, Inc.; *U.S. Private*, pg. 3010
VISALIGN LLC; *U.S. Private*, pg. 4389
VISALLO, LLC—See S&P Global Inc.; *U.S. Public*, pg. 1832
VISAM S.R.L.—See WAMGROUP S.p.A.; *Int'l*, pg. 8338
VISANG EDUCATION, INC.; *Int'l*, pg. 8249
VISASQ, INC.; *Int'l*, pg. 8249
VISA STEEL LIMITED; *Int'l*, pg. 8249
VISA U.S.A., INC.—See Visa, Inc.; *U.S. Public*, pg. 2301
VISA WORLDWIDE PTE. LIMITED—See Visa, Inc.; *U.S. Public*, pg. 2302
VISCHER & BOLLI AG—See OSG Corporation; *Int'l*, pg. 5649
VISCIRA LLC—See WPP plc; *Int'l*, pg. 8492
VISCOFAN CANADA INC.—See Viscofan SA; *Int'l*, pg. 8250
VISCOFAN CENTROAMERICA COMERCIAL, S.A.—See Viscofan SA; *Int'l*, pg. 8250
VISCOFAN COLLAGEN USA INC.—See Viscofan SA; *Int'l*, pg. 8250
VISCOFAN CZ S.R.O.—See Viscofan SA; *Int'l*, pg. 8250
VISCOFAN DE MEXICO SERVICIOS S.R.L. DE C.V.—See Viscofan SA; *Int'l*, pg. 8250

VISCOFAN DE MEXICO S.R.L. DE C.V.—See Viscofan SA; *Int'l*, pg. 8250
VISCOFAN DO BRASIL SOC. COM. E IND. LTDA.—See Viscofan SA; *Int'l*, pg. 8250
VISCOFAN GLOBUS AUSTRALIA PTY LTD.—See Viscofan SA; *Int'l*, pg. 8250
VISCOFAN GLOBUS NEW ZEALAND LTD.—See Viscofan SA; *Int'l*, pg. 8250
VISCOFAN SA; *Int'l*, pg. 8250
VISCOFAN TECHNOLOGY (SUZHOU) CO. LTD.—See Viscofan SA; *Int'l*, pg. 8250
VISCOFAN U.K.—See Viscofan SA; *Int'l*, pg. 8250
VISCOFAN URUGUAY, S.A.—See Viscofan SA; *Int'l*, pg. 8250
VISCOFAN USA INC.—See Viscofan SA; *Int'l*, pg. 8250
VISCOGLIOSI BROTHERS ACQUISITION CORP.; *U.S. Public*, pg. 2302
VIS CO., LTD.—See Freudenberg SE; *Int'l*, pg. 2790
VISCOLUBE S.P.A—See Stirling Square Capital Partners LLP; *Int'l*, pg. 7216
VISCOM AG; *Int'l*, pg. 8250
VISCOM FRANCE S.A.R.L.—See Viscom AG; *Int'l*, pg. 8250
VISCOM INC.—See Viscom AG; *Int'l*, pg. 8250
VISCOM INC.—See Viscom AG; *Int'l*, pg. 8250
VISCOM MACHINE VISION (INDIA) PRIVATE LIMITED—See Viscom AG; *Int'l*, pg. 8250
VISCOM MACHINE VISION PTE. LTD.—See Viscom AG; *Int'l*, pg. 8250
VISCOM MACHINE VISION TRADING CO. LTD.—See Viscom AG; *Int'l*, pg. 8250
VISCOM TUNISIE S.A.R.L.—See Viscom AG; *Int'l*, pg. 8250
VISCOM VXS S. DE R.L. DE C.V.—See Viscom AG; *Int'l*, pg. 8250
VIS CONTAINERS MANUFACTURING CO., LTD.; *Int'l*, pg. 8249
VISCOTEC AUTOMOTIVE PRODUCTS, LLC—See Seiren Co., Ltd.; *Int'l*, pg. 6692
VISCO TECHNOLOGIES CORPORATION; *Int'l*, pg. 8249
VISCO TECHNOLOGIES (SHANGHAI) CO. LTD.—See ViSCO Technologies Corporation; *Int'l*, pg. 8250
VISCO TECHNOLOGIES (SHENZHEN) CO. LTD.—See ViSCO Technologies Corporation; *Int'l*, pg. 8250
VISCO TECHNOLOGIES (THAILAND) CO., LTD.—See ViSCO Technologies Corporation; *Int'l*, pg. 8250
VISCO TECHNOLOGIES USA, INC.—See ViSCO Technologies Corporation; *Int'l*, pg. 8250
VISCO TECHNOLOGIES VIETNAM COMPANY LIMITED—See ViSCO Technologies Corporation; *Int'l*, pg. 8250
VISCO TRADE ASSOCIATES LIMITED; *Int'l*, pg. 8250
VISCOUNT MINING CORP.; *Int'l*, pg. 8250
VISCOUNT PLASTICS (NZ) LTD.—See Pact Group Holdings Ltd.; *Int'l*, pg. 5693
VISCOUNT PLASTICS PTY. LTD.—See Pact Group Holdings Ltd.; *Int'l*, pg. 5693
VISCOUNT SYSTEMS, INC.—See Identiv, Inc.; *U.S. Public*, pg. 1089
VIS D.D.; *Int'l*, pg. 8249
VISDYNAMICS HOLDINGS BERHAD; *Int'l*, pg. 8250
VISDYNAMICS RESEARCH SDN. BHD.—See VisDynamics Holdings Berhad; *Int'l*, pg. 8251
VISEAN INFORMATION SERVICES PTY LTD—See Weatherford International plc; *U.S. Public*, pg. 2339
VISECA CARD SERVICES SA—See Aduno Holding AG; *Int'l*, pg. 154
VISENTA FORSAKRINGS AB—See Outokumpu Oyj; *Int'l*, pg. 5669
VISEO S.A.S.; *Int'l*, pg. 8251
VISEO USA INC.—See Viseo S.A.S.; *Int'l*, pg. 8251
VISERA TECHNOLOGIES COMPANY LTD.—See Taiwan Semiconductor Manufacturing Company Ltd.; *Int'l*, pg. 7424
VISGENEER, INC.; *Int'l*, pg. 8251
VIS GMBH—See ManpowerGroup Inc.; *U.S. Public*, pg. 1362
VISHAL BEARINGS LIMITED; *Int'l*, pg. 8251
VISHAL FABRICS LIMITED; *Int'l*, pg. 8251
VISHAY AMERICAS, INC.—See Vishay Intertechnology, Inc.; *U.S. Public*, pg. 2302
VISHAY BCCOMPONENTS BEYSCHLAG GMBH—See Vishay Intertechnology, Inc.; *U.S. Public*, pg. 2302
VISHAY BCCOMPONENTS HONG KONG LTD.—See Vishay Intertechnology, Inc.; *U.S. Public*, pg. 2302
VISHAY BLH CANADA—See Vishay Intertechnology, Inc.; *U.S. Public*, pg. 2303
VISHAY BLH—See Vishay Intertechnology, Inc.; *U.S. Public*, pg. 2303
VISHAY CELTRON TECHNOLOGIES, INC.—See Vishay Precision Group, Inc.; *U.S. Public*, pg. 2303
VISHAY CHINA CO. LTD.—See Vishay Intertechnology, Inc.; *U.S. Public*, pg. 2302
VISHAY COMPONENTS (HUIZHOU) CO. LTD.—See Vishay Intertechnology, Inc.; *U.S. Public*, pg. 2302
VISHAY COMPONENTS, S.A.—See Vishay Intertechnology, Inc.; *U.S. Public*, pg. 2302
VISHAY ELCTRONIC GMBH—See Vishay Intertechnology, Inc.; *U.S. Public*, pg. 2303

VISHAY ELECTRONICA PORTUGAL LDA.—See Vishay Intertechnology, Inc.; *U.S. Public*, pg. 2302
VISHAY ELECTRONIC GMBH—See Vishay Intertechnology, Inc.; *U.S. Public*, pg. 2303
VISHAY GENERAL SEMICONDUCTOR OF TAIWAN, LTD.—See Vishay Intertechnology, Inc.; *U.S. Public*, pg. 2302
VISHAY HIREL SYSTEMS ASIA LIMITED—See Vishay Intertechnology, Inc.; *U.S. Public*, pg. 2303
VISHAY HIREL SYSTEMS LLC—See Vishay Intertechnology, Inc.; *U.S. Public*, pg. 2303
VISHAY HONG KONG LTD.—See Vishay Intertechnology, Inc.; *U.S. Public*, pg. 2303
VISHAY INTERTECHNOLOGY ASIA PTE., LTD.—See Vishay Intertechnology, Inc.; *U.S. Public*, pg. 2303
VISHAY INTERTECHNOLOGY, INC.; *U.S. Public*, pg. 2302
VISHAY ISRAEL LIMITED—See Vishay Intertechnology, Inc.; *U.S. Public*, pg. 2303
VISHAY JAPAN CO., LTD.—See Vishay Intertechnology, Inc.; *U.S. Public*, pg. 2303
VISHAY KOREA CO. LTD.—See Vishay Intertechnology, Inc.; *U.S. Public*, pg. 2303
VISHAY LTD.—See Vishay Intertechnology, Inc.; *U.S. Public*, pg. 2303
VISHAY MEASUREMENTS GROUP FRANCE S.A.S.—See Vishay Precision Group, Inc.; *U.S. Public*, pg. 2303
VISHAY MEASUREMENTS GROUP (U.K.) LTD.—See Vishay Intertechnology, Inc.; *U.S. Public*, pg. 2303
VISHAY MEASUREMENTS GROUP UK LTD.—See Vishay Precision Group, Inc.; *U.S. Public*, pg. 2303
VISHAY MICRO-MEASUREMENT—See Vishay Intertechnology, Inc.; *U.S. Public*, pg. 2303
VISHAY PME FRANCE SARL—See Vishay Precision Group, Inc.; *U.S. Public*, pg. 2304
VISHAY POLYTECH CO. LTD.—See Vishay Intertechnology, Inc.; *U.S. Public*, pg. 2303
VISHAY PRECISION FOIL, INC.—See Vishay Precision Group, Inc.; *U.S. Public*, pg. 2304
VISHAY PRECISION FOIL K.K.—See Vishay Precision Group, Inc.; *U.S. Public*, pg. 2304
VISHAY PRECISION GROUP CANADA ULC—See Vishay Precision Group, Inc.; *U.S. Public*, pg. 2303
VISHAY PRECISION GROUP, INC.; *U.S. Public*, pg. 2303
VISHAY PRECISION TRANSDUCERS INDIA PRIVATE LIMITED—See Vishay Precision Group, Inc.; *U.S. Public*, pg. 2304
VISHAY RESISTORS BELGIUM BVBA—See Vishay Intertechnology, Inc.; *U.S. Public*, pg. 2303
VISHAY SANMAR LTD.—See Sanmar Holdings Ltd.; *Int'l*, pg. 6546
VISHAY SANMAR LTD.—See Vishay Intertechnology, Inc.; *U.S. Public*, pg. 2303
VISHAY S.A.—See Vishay Intertechnology, Inc.; *U.S. Public*, pg. 2303
VISHAY SEMICONDUCTOR GES.MBH—See Vishay Intertechnology, Inc.; *U.S. Public*, pg. 2303
VISHAY SEMICONDUCTOR INDIA LTD.—See Vishay Intertechnology, Inc.; *U.S. Public*, pg. 2303
VISHAY SEMICONDUCTOR ITALIANA S.P.A.—See Vishay Intertechnology, Inc.; *U.S. Public*, pg. 2303
VISHAY SPECTROL—See Vishay Intertechnology, Inc.; *U.S. Public*, pg. 2303
VISHAY TRANSDUCERS LTD.—See Vishay Intertechnology, Inc.; *U.S. Public*, pg. 2303
VISHNU CHEMICALS LTD.; *Int'l*, pg. 8251
VISHNU PRAKASH R PUNGLIA LIMITED; *Int'l*, pg. 8251
VISHNUSURYA PROJECTS & INFRA LIMITED; *Int'l*, pg. 8251
VISHVAS PROJECTS LIMITED; *Int'l*, pg. 8251
VISHVPRABHA VENTURES LIMITED; *Int'l*, pg. 8251
VISHWARAJ SUGAR INDUSTRIES LIMITED; *Int'l*, pg. 8251
VISIATIV SA; *Int'l*, pg. 8251
VISIBLE ASSETS, INC.—See NOV, Inc.; *U.S. Public*, pg. 1547
VISIBLE CHANGES; *U.S. Private*, pg. 4390
VISIBLE EQUITY, LLC—See nCino, Inc.; *U.S. Public*, pg. 1501
VISIBLEGAINS, INC.; *U.S. Private*, pg. 4390
VISIBLE GOLD MINES INC.; *Int'l*, pg. 8251
VISIBLE MEASURES CORPORATION—See AcuityAds Inc.; *Int'l*, pg. 121
VISIBLE.NET, INC.; *U.S. Private*, pg. 4390
VISIBLE PATH CORP.—See Carinae Holdings, Inc.; *U.S. Public*, pg. 430
VISIBLE PATH CORP.—See CC Capital Partners, LLC; *U.S. Private*, pg. 798
VISIBLE PATH CORP.—See Intercontinental Exchange, Inc.; *U.S. Public*, pg. 1142
VISIBLE SUPPLY CHAIN MANAGEMENT, LLC—See A.P. Moller-Maersk A/S; *Int'l*, pg. 28
VISIBLE SYSTEMS CORPORATION; *U.S. Private*, pg. 4390
VISIBLE TECHNOLOGIES—See Platinum Equity, LLC; *U.S. Private*, pg. 3202
VISIBLETHREAD, LLC; *U.S. Private*, pg. 4390

VISIBLETHREAD, LLC CORPORATE AFFILIATIONS
Company Index

VISIBLETHREAD LTD.—See VisibleThread, LLC; *U.S. Private*, pg. 4390
VISICON POWER ELECTRONICS PVT. LTD.—See Ruttonsha International Rectifier Ltd.; *Int'l*, pg. 6433
VISICONS CONSTRUCTION AND INVESTMENT JOINT STOCK COMPANY—See Vietnam Construction Stock Corporation; *Int'l*, pg. 8198
VISICU, INC.—See Koninklijke Philips N.V.; *Int'l*, pg. 4270
VISIKOL, INC.—See BICO Group AB; *Int'l*, pg. 1019
VISINOR AS—See Nordisk Bergteknik AB; *Int'l*, pg. 5424
VISINOR REHAB AS—See Nordisk Bergteknik AB; *Int'l*, pg. 5424
VIS INSURANCE LTD.—See Klakki ehf.; *Int'l*, pg. 4199
VISIOCOM INTERNATIONAL PTE LTD—See Stanley Black & Decker, Inc.; *U.S. Public*, pg. 1936
VISIODENT S.A.—See Cegedim S.A.; *Int'l*, pg. 1390
VISIOMED GROUP LTD—See Avita Medical, Inc.; *U.S. Public*, pg. 249
VISIOMED SAS - EXPORT DIVISION—See Visiomed SAS; *Int'l*, pg. 8251
VISIOMED SAS; *Int'l*, pg. 8251
VISION2COMM GMBH—See LS telcom AG; *Int'l*, pg. 4570
VISION33 INC.; *U.S. Private*, pg. 4392
VISION4CE LIMITED—See Cohort plc; *Int'l*, pg. 1696
VISION 7 INTERNATIONAL ULC—See Bluefocus Intelligent Communications Group Co., Ltd.; *Int'l*, pg. 1071
VISION ACE HARDWARE, LLC; *U.S. Private*, pg. 4390
VISIONAEL CORPORATION—See Upland Software, Inc.; *U.S. Public*, pg. 2264
VISIONAEL CORP. - TULSA—See Upland Software, Inc.; *U.S. Public*, pg. 2264
VISIONAID, INC.—See Radians, Inc.; *U.S. Private*, pg. 3343
VISION AIR AND SEA SERVICES INC.—See Transnational Diversified Group of Companies; *Int'l*, pg. 7902
VISIONAIRE PARTNERS; *U.S. Private*, pg. 4392
VISION AIRLINES INC.; *U.S. Private*, pg. 4390
VISIONARY EDUCATION TECHNOLOGY HOLDINGS GROUP INC.; *Int'l*, pg. 8253
VISIONARY GOLD CORP.; *Int'l*, pg. 8253
VISIONARY HOLDINGS CO., LTD.; *Int'l*, pg. 8253
VISIONARY INTEGRATION PROFESSIONALS; *U.S. Private*, pg. 4392
VISIONARY PRODUCTS, INC.; *U.S. Private*, pg. 4392
VISIONARY SOLUTIONS, LLC; *U.S. Private*, pg. 4392
VISION ATLANTA INC.; *U.S. Private*, pg. 4390
VISION AUTO, INC.; *U.S. Private*, pg. 4390
VISION BANCSHARES, INC.; *U.S. Private*, pg. 4390
VISION BANK, N.A.—See Vision Bancshares, Inc.; *U.S. Private*, pg. 4390
VISION BATTERY USA, INC.—See Shenzhen Center Power Tech. Co., Ltd.; *Int'l*, pg. 6806
VISION BEVERAGE CORP.; *U.S. Private*, pg. 4390
VISION CAPITAL - GENEVA—See Vision Capital LP; *U.S. Private*, pg. 4390
VISION CAPITAL, LLP; *Int'l*, pg. 8251
VISION CAPITAL LP; *U.S. Private*, pg. 4390
VISION CARE COMPANY—See Hoya Corporation; *Int'l*, pg. 3498
VISION CARE COMPANY—See Hoya Corporation; *Int'l*, pg. 3498
VISION CINEMAS LIMITED; *Int'l*, pg. 8252
VISION COMMUNICATIONS—See RTC Holdings, L.L.C.; *U.S. Private*, pg. 3498
VISION CONSTRUCTION SERVICES OF ATLANTA—See James Group, Inc.; *U.S. Private*, pg. 2184
VISION CONSULTING GROUP LLC—See HCA Healthcare, Inc.; *U.S. Public*, pg. 1013
VISION COUNCIL OF AMERICA; *U.S. Private*, pg. 4390
VISION CREATIVE GROUP, INC.; *U.S. Private*, pg. 4390
VISION CRITICAL COMMUNICATIONS PTY LIMITED—See Vision Critical Inc.; *Int'l*, pg. 8252
VISION CRITICAL COMMUNICATIONS SAS—See Vision Critical Inc.; *Int'l*, pg. 8252
VISION CRITICAL COMMUNICATIONS (US) INC.—See Vision Critical Inc.; *Int'l*, pg. 8252
VISION CRITICAL GMBH—See Vision Critical Inc.; *Int'l*, pg. 8252
VISION CRITICAL (HONG KONG) LIMITED—See Vision Critical Inc.; *Int'l*, pg. 8252
VISION CRITICAL INC.; *Int'l*, pg. 8252
VISION CRITICAL PTE. LTD.—See Vision Critical Inc.; *Int'l*, pg. 8252
VISION CRITICAL RESEARCH SOLUTIONS (UK) LTD—See Vision Critical Inc.; *Int'l*, pg. 8252
VISION DEAL HK ACQUISITION CORP.; *Int'l*, pg. 8252
VISION DYNAMICS, LLC—See New England Low Vision & Blindness; *U.S. Private*, pg. 2894
VISION EASE, LP—See Wind Point Advisors LLC; *U.S. Private*, pg. 4536
VISIONEERING CORP—See Leviton Manufacturing Company, Inc.; *U.S. Private*, pg. 2437
VISIONEERING INC.; *U.S. Private*, pg. 4392
VISIONEERING TECHNOLOGIES, INC.; *U.S. Public*, pg. 2304
VISION ENERGY CORPORATION; *U.S. Public*, pg. 2304
VISION ENGINEERING INC.; *U.S. Private*, pg. 4390
VISION ENGINEERING ITALIA—See Vision Engineering Inc.; *U.S. Private*, pg. 4390
VISION ENGINEERING LTD.—See Vision Engineering Inc.; *U.S. Private*, pg. 4390
VISION ENVELOPE, INC.—See Western States Envelope & Label; *U.S. Private*, pg. 4497
VISIO NERF SA—See Pattyn Belgium NV; *Int'l*, pg. 5760
VISION EUROPE BVBA—See Shenzhen Center Power Tech. Co., Ltd.; *Int'l*, pg. 6806
VISION EXPERTS GMBH—See Atlas Copco AB; *Int'l*, pg. 683
VISION EXTRUSIONS LTD.; *Int'l*, pg. 8252
VISION EYE INSTITUTE LIMITED—See Jangho Group Company Limited; *Int'l*, pg. 3879
VISION FINANCIAL GROUP, INC.—See Civista Bancshares, Inc.; *U.S. Public*, pg. 507
VISION FINANCIAL MARKETS LLC; *U.S. Private*, pg. 4390
VISIONFLEX GROUP LIMITED; *Int'l*, pg. 8253
VISIONFLEX PTY. LTD.—See Visionflex Group Limited; *Int'l*, pg. 8253
VISION FOUNDATION PTE. LTD.—See Green Economy Development Limited; *Int'l*, pg. 3071
VISION FS INC.; *U.S. Private*, pg. 4390
VISIONGLOBAL CORP.; *U.S. Public*, pg. 2304
VISION GRAPHICS INC.; *U.S. Private*, pg. 4390
VISION GROUP HOLDINGS LLC; *U.S. Private*, pg. 4390
VISION GROUP S.P.A.; *Int'l*, pg. 8252
VISION HEALTHCARE N.V.; *Int'l*, pg. 8252
VISION HOLLOW METAL LIMITED—See Vision Extrusions Ltd.; *Int'l*, pg. 8252
VISION HUAQING (BEIJING) DEVELOPMENT CO., LTD—See Frasers Property Limited; *Int'l*, pg. 2766
VISION, INC; *Int'l*, pg. 8253
VISION INDEPENDENT FINANCIAL PLANNING LIMITED—See Rathbones Group Plc; *Int'l*, pg. 6214
VISION INDUSTRIES CORP.; *U.S. Private*, pg. 4391
VISION INFOSOFT CORP.—See JDM Technology Group; *Int'l*, pg. 3925
VISION INTEGRATED GRAPHICS GROUP; *U.S. Private*, pg. 4391
VISION INTERNATIONAL HOLDINGS LTD.; *Int'l*, pg. 8252
VISION INTERNATIONAL PEOPLE GROUP PUBLIC LIMITED; *Int'l*, pg. 8252
VISION INTERNATIONAL ROADSHOW COMPANY LIMITED—See Vivendi SE; *Int'l*, pg. 8271
VISION INVESTMENT SERVICES CO. (S.A.O.C)—See EFG Holding; *Int'l*, pg. 2319
VISION INVESTMENTS LIMITED; *Int'l*, pg. 8252
VISION INVESTMENTS, LLC; *U.S. Private*, pg. 4391
VISIONIT; *U.S. Private*, pg. 4392
VISION LAND CONSULTANTS, INC.; *U.S. Private*, pg. 4391
VISION LINENS LIMITED—See Icahn Enterprises L.P.; *U.S. Public*, pg. 1085
VISION LINKS MYANMAR CO., LTD.—See MIT Holdings Co., Ltd.; *Int'l*, pg. 4923
VISION LITHIUM INC.; *Int'l*, pg. 8252
VISION MARINE TECHNOLOGIES INC.; *Int'l*, pg. 8252
VISION MEDIA & MARKETING LLC; *U.S. Private*, pg. 4391
VISION MOBILE KOREA INC.—See Vision, Inc; *Int'l*, pg. 8253
VISION MOBILE USA CORP.—See Vision, Inc; *Int'l*, pg. 8253
VISIONONE, INC.—See accesso Technology Group Plc; *Int'l*, pg. 89
VISION OUTDOOR PRODUCTS LIMITED—See Vision Extrusions Ltd.; *Int'l*, pg. 8252
VISIONOX TECHNOLOGY INC.; *Int'l*, pg. 8253
VISION PAYMENT SOLUTIONS, LLC—See Global Payments Inc.; *U.S. Public*, pg. 943
VISION PLASTICS, INC.; *U.S. Private*, pg. 4391
VISION PLUS OF AMERICA INC.—See Medical Benefits Mutual Life Insurance Co. Inc.; *U.S. Private*, pg. 2654
VISION PRODUCTS INC—See Sampco Inc.; *U.S. Private*, pg. 3537
VISION QUEST INDUSTRIES INCORPORATED; *U.S. Private*, pg. 4391
VISIONREFINE LIMITED—See Heidelberg Materials AG; *Int'l*, pg. 3320
VISION RESEARCH, INC.—See AMETEK, Inc.; *U.S. Public*, pg. 118
VISION RIDGE PARTNERS, LLC; *U.S. Private*, pg. 4391
VISION SECURITY LLC; *U.S. Private*, pg. 4391
VISION & SECURITY SYSTEM CO., LTD.—See Samart Corporation Public Company Limited; *Int'l*, pg. 6502
VISION SENSING ACQUISITION CORP.; *U.S. Public*, pg. 2304
VISION SERVICE PLAN; *U.S. Private*, pg. 4391
VISION SHARE; *U.S. Private*, pg. 4391
VISION SIGMA LTD.; *Int'l*, pg. 8252
VISIONSOFT INTERNATIONAL INC.; *U.S. Private*, pg. 4392
VISION SOLUTIONS, INC.—See Clearlake Capital Group, L.P.; *U.S. Private*, pg. 937
VISION SOLUTIONS, INC.—See TA Associates, Inc.; *U.S. Private*, pg. 3917
VISIONSPRING; *U.S. Private*, pg. 4392
VISIONS PRODUCTIONS, INC.—See National Amusements, Inc.; *U.S. Private*, pg. 2844
VISIONSTATE CORP.; *Int'l*, pg. 8253
VISION SUPPORT SERVICES LIMITED—See Icahn Enterprises L.P.; *U.S. Public*, pg. 1085
VISION SUPPORT SERVICES PAKISTAN LTD.—See Icahn Enterprises L.P.; *U.S. Public*, pg. 1085
VISION SUPPORT SERVICES PVT. LTD.—See Icahn Enterprises L.P.; *U.S. Public*, pg. 1085
VISION SURVEYS (QLD) PTY. LTD.—See PeopleIn Limited; *Int'l*, pg. 5794
VISIONTECH ENGINEERING PTE., LTD.—See Temasek Holdings (Private) Limited; *Int'l*, pg. 7552
VISION TECH INFORMATION TECHNOLOGY, INC.—See Acer Incorporated; *Int'l*, pg. 100
VISION TECHNOLOGIES, INC.; *U.S. Private*, pg. 4391
VISION TECHNOLOGIES SYSTEMS, INC.—See Temasek Holdings (Private) Limited; *Int'l*, pg. 7552
VISION TECHNOLOGY CORP.; *U.S. Private*, pg. 4391
VISION TECHNOLOGY JOINT STOCK COMPANY—See Shenzhen Center Power Tech. Co., Ltd.; *Int'l*, pg. 6806
VISION TECHNOLOGY SERVICES, LLC—See BGSF, Inc.; *U.S. Public*, pg. 330
VISIONTEK PRODUCTS, LLC—See Impero Electronics, Inc.; *U.S. Private*, pg. 2050
VISION TRANSPORTATION INC.; *Int'l*, pg. 8253
VISION TRAVEL SOLUTIONS; *Int'l*, pg. 8253
VISIONTREE SOFTWARE, INC.—See Intel Corporation; *U.S. Public*, pg. 1138
VISION VALUES AVIATION SERVICES LIMITED—See Vision Values Holdings Limited; *Int'l*, pg. 8253
VISION VALUES HOLDINGS LIMITED; *Int'l*, pg. 8253
VISION VIETNAM ONE MEMBER LIMITED LIABILITY COMPANY—See Vision, Inc; *Int'l*, pg. 8253
VISION WHEEL, INC.; *U.S. Private*, pg. 4391
VISIONWORKS OF AMERICA, INC.—See Vision Service Plan; *U.S. Private*, pg. 4391
VISION Y COMPROMISO; *U.S. Private*, pg. 4392
VISIORAMA AG—See APG/SGA SA; *Int'l*, pg. 513
VISIPAK—See Cameron Holdings Corporation; *U.S. Private*, pg. 729
VISIQUATE, INC.—See Accel Partners L.P.; *U.S. Private*, pg. 49
VISIQUATE, INC.—See KKR & Co. Inc.; *U.S. Public*, pg. 1239
VISISTAT, INC.; *U.S. Private*, pg. 4392
VISITALK CAPITAL CORPORATION; *U.S. Private*, pg. 4392
VISITBRITAIN; *Int'l*, pg. 8253
VISITECH, INC.; *U.S. Private*, pg. 4392
VISIT INDY, INC.; *U.S. Private*, pg. 4392
VISITING NURSE ASSOCIATION OF CENTRAL JERSEY—See Visiting Nurse Service of New York; *U.S. Private*, pg. 4393
VISITING NURSE ASSOCIATION OF SOMERSET HILLS INC.; *U.S. Private*, pg. 4393
VISITING NURSE ASSOCIATION OF SOUTH CENTRAL CONNECTICUT; *U.S. Private*, pg. 4393
VISITING NURSE ASSOCIATION OF STATEN ISLAND; *U.S. Private*, pg. 4393
VISITING NURSE CORPORATION OF COLORADO, INC.; *U.S. Private*, pg. 4393
VISITING NURSE & HOSPICE OF FAIRFIELD COUNTY; *U.S. Private*, pg. 4392
VISITING NURSE & HOSPICE OF VERMONT AND NEW HAMPSHIRE; *U.S. Private*, pg. 4392
VISITING NURSE SERVICE AT ST. FRANCIS, INC.; *U.S. Private*, pg. 4393
VISITING NURSE SERVICE & HOSPICE OF SUFFOLK, INC.; *U.S. Private*, pg. 4393
VISITING NURSE SERVICE OF NEW YORK; *U.S. Private*, pg. 4393
VISITING NURSE SERVICES IN WESTCHESTER, INC.; *U.S. Private*, pg. 4393
VISITING NURSE SERVICES OF NEWPORT AND BRISTOL COUNTIES; *U.S. Private*, pg. 4393
VISIT NAPA VALLEY; *U.S. Private*, pg. 4392
THE VISITOR ATTRACTION COMPANY LIMITED—See Paragon Entertainment Limited; *Int'l*, pg. 5736
VISIT ORLANDO; *U.S. Private*, pg. 4392
VISITURE, LLC—See ZelnickMedia Corp.; *U.S. Private*, pg. 4600
VISIT WALES; *Int'l*, pg. 8253
VISIUM RESOURCES, INC.; *U.S. Private*, pg. 4393
VISIUM TECHNOLOGIES, INC.; *U.S. Public*, pg. 2304
VISIX, INC.; *U.S. Private*, pg. 4393
VISKASE BRASIL EMBALAGENS LTDA.—See Icahn Enterprises L.P.; *U.S. Public*, pg. 1085
VISKASE COMPANIES, INC.—See Icahn Enterprises L.P.; *U.S. Public*, pg. 1085
VISKASE FILMS, INC.—See Icahn Enterprises L.P.; *U.S. Public*, pg. 1085
VISKASE GMBH—See Icahn Enterprises L.P.; *U.S. Public*, pg. 1085
VISKASE POLSKA SP Z O.O.—See Icahn Enterprises L.P.; *U.S. Public*, pg. 1085
VISKASE S.A.S.—See Icahn Enterprises L.P.; *U.S. Public*, pg. 1085
VISKASE S.P.A.—See Icahn Enterprises L.P.; *U.S. Public*, pg. 1085

COMPANY NAME INDEX

VISKO INDUSTRIES SDN. BHD.—See PT EKADHARMA INTERNATIONAL TBK; *Int'l*, pg. 6037
VISLAB S.R.L.—See Ambarella, Inc.; *U.S. Public*, pg. 92
VISLINK TECHNOLOGIES INC.; *U.S. Public*, pg. 2304
VISMA AS—See Cinven Limited; *Int'l*, pg. 1616
VISMA AS—See HgCapital Trust plc; *Int'l*, pg. 3377
VISMA AS—See KKR & Co. Inc.; *U.S. Public*, pg. 1266
VISMA MAMUT AS—See Cinven Limited; *Int'l*, pg. 1616
VISMA MAMUT AS—See HgCapital Trust plc; *Int'l*, pg. 3377
VISMA MAMUT AS—See KKR & Co. Inc.; *U.S. Public*, pg. 1266
VISNIC HOMES, INC.; *U.S. Private*, pg. 4393
VISO FARMACEUTICA S.L.U.—See Glenmark Pharmaceuticals Limited; *Int'l*, pg. 2992
VI SOLE FZC—See HORIBA Ltd; *Int'l*, pg. 3478
VISONEX, LLC—See Renesan Software; *U.S. Private*, pg. 3398
VISONIC IBERICA DE SEGURIDAD, S.L.—See Johnson Controls International plc; *Int'l*, pg. 3989
VISONIC INC.—See Johnson Controls International plc; *Int'l*, pg. 3989
VISONIC LIMITED—See Johnson Controls International plc; *Int'l*, pg. 3990
VISONIC LTD.—See Johnson Controls International plc; *Int'l*, pg. 3989
VISONIC SICHERHEITSTECHNIK GMBH—See Johnson Controls International plc; *Int'l*, pg. 3990
VISPAK D.D.; *Int'l*, pg. 8253
VISP.NET; *U.S. Private*, pg. 4393
VISPOT INC.—See Sunstar Suisse S.A.; *Int'l*, pg. 7324
VI-SPRING LTD.—See Flex Equipos de Descanso SA; *Int'l*, pg. 2701
VISSA ELECTRONIC LTD.—See STMicroelectronics N.V.; *Int'l*, pg. 7218
VISSEM ELECTRONICS CO., LTD.; *Int'l*, pg. 8253
VISSERING CONSTRUCTION CO.; *U.S. Private*, pg. 4393
VISSER & SMIT BOUW BV—See Koninklijke VolkerWessels N.V.; *Int'l*, pg. 4272
VISSER & SMIT HANAB BV—See Koninklijke VolkerWessels N.V.; *Int'l*, pg. 4272
VISTA ALEGRE ATLANTIS SGPS S.A.; *Int'l*, pg. 8254
VISTA ALEGRE ESPANA S.A.—See Vista Alegre Atlantis SGPS S.A.; *Int'l*, pg. 8254
VISTA ALEGRE USA CORP—See Vista Alegre Atlantis SGPS S.A.; *Int'l*, pg. 8254
VISTA BANK; *U.S. Private*, pg. 4393
VISTA BEHAVIORAL HEALTH, LLC—See Acadia Healthcare Company, Inc.; *U.S. Public*, pg. 31
VISTACAL LUXURY IMPORTS, INC.—See AutoNation, Inc.; *U.S. Public*, pg. 238
VISTA CAPITAL LLC; *U.S. Private*, pg. 4393
VISTA CLINICAL DIAGNOSTICS, LLC; *U.S. Private*, pg. 4393
VISTA COLOR CORPORATION; *U.S. Private*, pg. 4394
VISTACOM, INC.—See Conference Technologies, Inc.; *U.S. Private*, pg. 1013
VISTA COMPUTER SERVICES LLC—See Ingenta plc; *Int'l*, pg. 3702
VISTA CREDIT STRATEGIC LENDING CORP.; *U.S. Private*, pg. 4394
VISTA DEL MAR CHILD AND FAMILY SERVICES; *U.S. Private*, pg. 4394
VISTA DESARROLLO, S.A. SCR DE REGIMEN SIMPLIFICADO—See Banco Santander, S.A.; *Int'l*, pg. 828
VISTA DIRECT; *U.S. Private*, pg. 4394
VISTA ENERGY, S.A.B. DE C.V.; *Int'l*, pg. 8254
VISTA EQUITY PARTNERS, LLC; *U.S. Private*, pg. 4394
VISTA EQUITY PARTNERS MANAGEMENT, LLC—See Vista Equity Partners, LLC; *U.S. Private*, pg. 4402
VISTA FINANCE INC.—See Gentry Finance Corporation; *U.S. Private*, pg. 1680
VISTA FOOD EXCHANGE, INC.; *U.S. Private*, pg. 4402
VISTA FORD; *U.S. Private*, pg. 4403
VISTAGE FLORIDA—See Providence Equity Partners L.L.C.; *U.S. Private*, pg. 3294
VISTAGEN THERAPEUTICS, INC.—See VistaGen Therapeutics, Inc.; *U.S. Public*, pg. 2305
VISTAGEN THERAPEUTICS, INC.; *U.S. Public*, pg. 2305
VISTA GEOWISSENSCHAFTLICHE FERNERKUNDUNG GMBH—See BayWa AG; *Int'l*, pg. 919
VISTAGE WORLDWIDE, INC.—See Providence Equity Partners L.L.C.; *U.S. Private*, pg. 3294
VISTA GLOBAL HOLDING LTD.; *Int'l*, pg. 8254
VISTA GOLD CORP.; *U.S. Public*, pg. 2305
VISTA GOLD HOLDINGS INC.—See Hycroft Mining Holding Corporation; *U.S. Public*, pg. 1079
VISTA GRANDE VILLA; *U.S. Private*, pg. 4403
VISTA GROUP INC.; *U.S. Private*, pg. 4403
VISTA GROUP INTERNATIONAL LIMITED; *Int'l*, pg. 8254
VISTA HEALTH—See Centene Corporation; *U.S. Public*, pg. 470
VISTA HOTEL MANAGEMENT CO., LTD.—See Uni-Asia Group Limited; *Int'l*, pg. 8028
VISTA HYPOTHEKEN B.V.—See Cooperatieve Centrale Raiffeisen-Boerenleenbank B.A.; *Int'l*, pg. 1792
VISTA IMAGING SERVICES, INC.; *U.S. Private*, pg. 4403

VISTA INSURANCE PARTNERS OF ILLINOIS, INC.—See Caisse de Depot et Placement du Quebec; *Int'l*, pg. 1257
VISTA INSURANCE PARTNERS OF ILLINOIS, INC.—See KKR & Co. Inc.; *U.S. Public*, pg. 1266
VISTA INTERNATIONAL LTD—See Ingenta plc; *Int'l*, pg. 3701
VISTA INTERNATIONAL OPERATIONS, INC.—See Bristol Bay Native Corporation; *U.S. Private*, pg. 656
VISTA INTERNATIONAL PACKAGING, LLC.—See Keystone Capital, Inc.; *U.S. Private*, pg. 2295
VISTA INTERNATIONAL TECHNOLOGIES, INC.; *U.S. Private*, pg. 4403
VISTAJET HOLDING S.A.; *Int'l*, pg. 8254
VISTAJET INC.—See VistaJet Holding S.A.; *Int'l*, pg. 8254
VISTAJET US, INC.—See VistaJet Holding S.A.; *Int'l*, pg. 8254
VISTA LAGO CONDOS, LLC—See RAIT Financial Trust; *U.S. Private*, pg. 3349
VISTA LAND & LIFESCAPES, INC.; *Int'l*, pg. 8254
VISTAL GDYNIA S.A.; *Int'l*, pg. 8254
VISTAMALLS, INC.; *Int'l*, pg. 8254
VISTA METALS INC.; *U.S. Private*, pg. 4403
VISTANA DEVELOPMENT, INC.—See Marriott International, Inc.; *U.S. Public*, pg. 1372
VISTANA PORTFOLIO SERVICES, INC.—See Marriott International, Inc.; *U.S. Public*, pg. 1372
VISTANA SIGNATURE EXPERIENCES, INC.—See Marriott Vacations Worldwide Corporation; *U.S. Public*, pg. 1374
VISTANA VACATION OWNERSHIP, INC.—See Marriott International, Inc.; *U.S. Public*, pg. 1372
VISTA OUTDOOR INC.; *U.S. Public*, pg. 2304
VISTA PAINT CORPORATION; *U.S. Private*, pg. 4403
VISTAPAK INDUSTRIES INC.; *U.S. Private*, pg. 4403
VISTA PANELS LTD.—See Tessenderlo Group NV; *Int'l*, pg. 7574
VISTAPHARM, INC.—See Warburg Pincus LLC; *U.S. Private*, pg. 4440
VISTA PHYSICIAN GROUP—See Quorum Health Corporation; *U.S. Private*, pg. 3330
VISTA POINT TECHNOLOGIES, INC.—See Flex Ltd.; *Int'l*, pg. 2703
VISTA POINT TECHNOLOGIES, INC.—See Flex Ltd.; *Int'l*, pg. 2703
VISTA POINT TECHNOLOGIES, INC.—See Flex Ltd.; *Int'l*, pg. 2703
VISTA POINT TECHNOLOGIES (MALAYSIA) SDN. BHD.—See Flex Ltd.; *Int'l*, pg. 2704
VISTAPRINT AUSTRALIA PTY LTD—See Cimpress plc; *Int'l*, pg. 1609
VISTAPRINT B.V.—See Cimpress plc; *Int'l*, pg. 1609
VISTAPRINT CANADA LIMITED—See Cimpress plc; *Int'l*, pg. 1609
VISTAPRINT CORPORATE SOLUTIONS INCORPORATED—See Cimpress plc; *Int'l*, pg. 1609
VISTAPRINT ESPANA S.L.—See Cimpress plc; *Int'l*, pg. 1609
VISTAPRINT JAMAICA LIMITED—See Cimpress plc; *Int'l*, pg. 1609
VISTAPRINT NETHERLANDS B.V.—See Cimpress plc; *Int'l*, pg. 1609
VISTAPRINT NORTH AMERICAN SERVICES CORP.—See Cimpress plc; *Int'l*, pg. 1609
VISTAPRINT TUNISIE SARL—See Cimpress plc; *Int'l*, pg. 1609
VISTAPRINT USA, INCORPORATED—See Cimpress plc; *Int'l*, pg. 1609
VISTA-PRO AUTOMOTIVE, LLC—See Wynnchurch Capital, L.P.; *U.S. Private*, pg. 4578
VISTA PRODUCTS INC.; *U.S. Private*, pg. 4403
VISTA PROJECTS INC.; *U.S. Private*, pg. 4403
VISTA PROPERTIES LLC—See Edison International; *U.S. Public*, pg. 719
VISTA PROPPANTS AND LOGISTICS INC.; *U.S. Private*, pg. 4403
VISTAR AMAR LIMITED; *Int'l*, pg. 8254
VISTA REAL ESTATE INC.; *U.S. Private*, pg. 4403
VISTAREIT, INC.; *Int'l*, pg. 8254
VISTA RESIDENCES, INC.—See Vista Land & Lifescapes, Inc.; *Int'l*, pg. 8254
VISTAR HOLDINGS LIMITED; *Int'l*, pg. 8254
VISTASCAPE SECURITY SYSTEMS CORP.—See Siemens Aktiengesellschaft; *Int'l*, pg. 6891
VISTAS MEDIA ACQUISITION COMPANY INC; *U.S. Public*, pg. 2305
VISTAS OF VANCE JACKSON, LTD—See American Realty Investors, Inc.; *U.S. Public*, pg. 109
VISTASOURCE INC.—See Parallax Capital Partners, LLC; *U.S. Private*, pg. 3092
VISTA STAFFING SERVICES, INC.—See ASGN Incorporated; *U.S. Public*, pg. 211
VISTA STAFFING SOLUTIONS, INC.—See KKR & Co. Inc.; *U.S. Public*, pg. 1249
VISTA STEEL COMPANY, INC.; *U.S. Private*, pg. 4403
VISTA SURETY INSURANCE SOLUTIONS, LLC—See Stone Point Capital LLC; *U.S. Private*, pg. 3821
VISTA SYSTEM, LLC; *U.S. Private*, pg. 4403
VISTATECH ENTERPRISES LTD.; *U.S. Private*, pg. 4403

VISTA TECHNOLOGY SERVICES, INC.; *U.S. Private*, pg. 4403
VISTAUXX LTD.; *U.S. Private*, pg. 4403
VISTAVU SOLUTIONS INC.; *Int'l*, pg. 8254
VISTAVU SOLUTIONS LTD.—See VistaVu Solutions Inc.; *Int'l*, pg. 8254
VISTA WEST, INC.; *U.S. Private*, pg. 4403
VISTA WINDOW COMPANY, LLC; *U.S. Private*, pg. 4403
VISTA WOODS HEALTH ASSOCIATES LLC—See The Ensign Group, Inc.; *U.S. Public*, pg. 2072
VISTECH MANUFACTURING SOLUTIONS, LLC—See Angeles Equity Partners, LLC; *U.S. Private*, pg. 282
VISTEON AMAZONAS LTDA.—See Visteon Corporation; *U.S. Public*, pg. 2305
VISTEON ASIA PACIFIC, INC.—See Visteon Corporation; *U.S. Public*, pg. 2305
VISTEON AUTOMOTIVE ELECTRONICS (THAILAND) LIMITED—See Visteon Corporation; *U.S. Public*, pg. 2305
VISTEON AUTOMOTIVE SYSTEMS INDIA PRIVATE LTD.—See Hahn & Company; *Int'l*, pg. 3208
VISTEON-AUTOPAL S.R.O.—See Visteon Corporation; *U.S. Public*, pg. 2306
VISTEON CORPORATION; *U.S. Public*, pg. 2305
VISTEON ELECTRONICS BULGARIA EOOD—See Visteon Corporation; *U.S. Public*, pg. 2305
VISTEON ELECTRONICS KOREA LTD.—See Visteon Corporation; *U.S. Public*, pg. 2306
VISTEON ENGINEERING SERVICES LIMITED—See Visteon Corporation; *U.S. Public*, pg. 2306
VISTEON EUROPEAN HOLDINGS, INC.—See Visteon Corporation; *U.S. Public*, pg. 2306
VISTEON HOLDINGS FRANCE SAS—See Visteon Corporation; *U.S. Public*, pg. 2306
VISTEON HOLDINGS GMBH—See Visteon Corporation; *U.S. Public*, pg. 2306
VISTEON INTERIOR SYSTEMS ITALIA S.P.A.—See Cerberus Capital Management, L.P.; *U.S. Public*, pg. 839
VISTEON PORTUGUESA, LTD.—See Visteon Corporation; *U.S. Public*, pg. 2306
VISTEON S.A.—See Visteon Corporation; *U.S. Public*, pg. 2306
VISTEON SOFTWARE TECHNOLOGIES SAS—See Visteon Corporation; *U.S. Public*, pg. 2306
VISTERRA, INC.—See Otsuka Holdings Co., Ltd.; *Int'l*, pg. 5660
VISTEX, INC.; *U.S. Private*, pg. 4403
VISTIN PHARMA ASA; *Int'l*, pg. 8254
VISTIN PHARMA AS—See Vistin Pharma ASA; *Int'l*, pg. 8255
VISTRACKS, INC.—See Vista Equity Partners, LLC; *U.S. Private*, pg. 4399
VISTRA COMMUNICATIONS; *U.S. Private*, pg. 4403
VISTRA CORP.; *U.S. Public*, pg. 2306
VISTRA GROUP HOLDINGS S.A.—See EQT AB; *Int'l*, pg. 2472
VISTRA HOLDINGS (USA) LLC—See EQT AB; *Int'l*, pg. 2472
VISTRA IE UK LTD.—See EQT AB; *Int'l*, pg. 2472
VISTRA MANAGEMENT SERVICES (NETHERLANDS) B.V.—See EQT AB; *Int'l*, pg. 2472
VISTRA—See Oshidori International Holdings Limited; *Int'l*, pg. 5650
THE VISTRIA GROUP, LP; *U.S. Private*, pg. 4131
VISTRONIX, INC.; *U.S. Private*, pg. 4403
VISTRY GROUP PLC; *Int'l*, pg. 8255
VISTRY (JERSEY) LIMITED—See Vistry Group PLC; *Int'l*, pg. 8255
VISTRY PARTNERSHIPS YORKSHIRE LIMITED—See Vistry Group PLC; *Int'l*, pg. 8255
VISTRY VENTURES LIMITED—See Vistry Group PLC; *Int'l*, pg. 8255
VISU ACADEMY LIMITED—See Ed & Tech International Limited; *Int'l*, pg. 2302
VISUAL ACUMEN, INC.; *U.S. Private*, pg. 4403
VISUAL AIDS ELECTRONICS CORP.; *U.S. Private*, pg. 4404
VISUAL APEX, INC.; *U.S. Private*, pg. 4404
VISUALASE, INC.—See Medtronic plc; *Int'l*, pg. 4790
VISUAL AWARENESS TECHNOLOGIES & CONSULTING, INC.; *U.S. Private*, pg. 4404
VISUAL CHINA GROUP CO., LTD.; *Int'l*, pg. 8255
VISUAL COMMUNICATIONS COMPANY, INC.; *U.S. Private*, pg. 4404
VISUAL COMMUNICATIONS GROUP LTD; *Int'l*, pg. 8255
VISUAL COMMUNICATIONS INC.; *U.S. Private*, pg. 4404
VISUAL CONCEPTS, LLC; *U.S. Private*, pg. 4404
VISUAL CONTROLS/CHAMP INC.; *U.S. Private*, pg. 4404
VISUAL DEFENCE, INC.; *Int'l*, pg. 8255
VISUAL DOMAIN AUSTRALIA PTY LIMITED—See News Corporation; *U.S. Public*, pg. 1521
VISUAL EDGE TECHNOLOGY, INC.; *U.S. Private*, pg. 4404
VISUAL EFFECTS SOCIETY; *U.S. Private*, pg. 4404
VISUAL GRAPHICS SYSTEMS, INC.; *U.S. Private*, pg. 4404
VISUAL IMAGE ADVERTISING; *U.S. Private*, pg. 4404
VISUALIMITS, LLC—See NRT Technologies Inc.; *U.S. Private*, pg. 2970

VISUAL INNOVATIONS COMPANY INC; *U.S. Private*, pg. 4404
VISUAL INTERNATIONAL HOLDINGS LIMITED; *Int'l*, pg. 8255
VISUAL IQ, INC.—See Brookfield Corporation; *Int'l*, pg. 1180
VISUAL IQ, INC.—See Brookfield Corporation; *Int'l*, pg. 1180
VISUAL IQ, INC.—See Elliott Management Corporation; *U.S. Private*, pg. 1373
VISUAL IQ, INC.—See Elliott Management Corporation; *U.S. Private*, pg. 1373
VISUALJAPAN INC.—See Dai Nippon Printing Co., Ltd.; *Int'l*, pg. 1916
VISUAL LEASE, LLC—See CoStar Group, Inc.; *U.S. Public*, pg. 586
VISUAL LOGIC GROUP; *U.S. Private*, pg. 4404
VISUALMAX; *U.S. Private*, pg. 4404
VISUALMED CLINICAL SOLUTIONS CORP.; *Int'l*, pg. 8255
VISUAL META GMBH—See Axel Springer SE; *Int'l*, pg. 767
VISUAL PAK COMPANY; *U.S. Private*, pg. 4404
VISUAL PERCEPT SOLAR PROJECTS PRIVATE LIMITED—See Torrent Power Limited; *Int'l*, pg. 7831
VISUAL PHOTONICS EPITAXY CO., LTD.; *Int'l*, pg. 8255
VISUALSHARE, LLC—See GTCR LLC; *U.S. Private*, pg. 1807
VISUAL SOUND INC.; *U.S. Private*, pg. 4404
VISUAL TECHNOLOGIES CORP.; *U.S. Private*, pg. 4404
VISUAL TURISMO LTDA—See CVC Brasil Operadora e Agencia de Viagens S.A.; *Int'l*, pg. 1881
VISUALVEST GMBH—See DZ BANK AG Deutsche Zentral-Genossenschaftsbank; *Int'l*, pg. 2245
VISUALZ—See Vomela Specialty Company; *U.S. Private*, pg. 4412
VISUMO INC.—See Softcreate Holdings Corp.; *Int'l*, pg. 7054
VISURA S.P.A.—See Tinexta S.p.A.; *Int'l*, pg. 7753
VISUS HEALTH IT GMBH—See PAO Severstal; *Int'l*, pg. 5732
VISY BOARD-NEW ZEALAND—See Visy Industries Holdings Pty. Ltd.; *Int'l*, pg. 8256
VISY BOARD PTY. LTD.—See Visy Industries Holdings Pty. Ltd.; *Int'l*, pg. 8256
VISY BOARD PTY. LTD.—See Visy Industries Holdings Pty. Ltd.; *Int'l*, pg. 8256
VISY BOARD PTY. LTD.—See Visy Industries Holdings Pty. Ltd.; *Int'l*, pg. 8256
VISY BOARD PTY. LTD.—See Visy Industries Holdings Pty. Ltd.; *Int'l*, pg. 8256
VISY BOARD PTY. LTD.—See Visy Industries Holdings Pty. Ltd.; *Int'l*, pg. 8256
VISY BOARD PTY. LTD.—See Visy Industries Holdings Pty. Ltd.; *Int'l*, pg. 8256
VISY BOARD PTY. LTD.—See Visy Industries Holdings Pty. Ltd.; *Int'l*, pg. 8256
VISY BOARD PTY. LTD.—See Visy Industries Holdings Pty. Ltd.; *Int'l*, pg. 8256
VISY BOARD PTY. LTD.—See Visy Industries Holdings Pty. Ltd.; *Int'l*, pg. 8256
VISY BOARD PTY. LTD.—See Visy Industries Holdings Pty. Ltd.; *Int'l*, pg. 8256
VISYFLEX PREPRINT—See Visy Industries Holdings Pty. Ltd.; *Int'l*, pg. 8256
VISY INDUSTRIES HOLDINGS PTY. LTD.; *Int'l*, pg. 8255
VISY PAPER 3&6—See Visy Industries Holdings Pty. Ltd.; *Int'l*, pg. 8256
VISY PAPER 8—See Visy Industries Holdings Pty. Ltd.; *Int'l*, pg. 8256
VISY PAPER COATINGS—See Visy Industries Holdings Pty. Ltd.; *Int'l*, pg. 8256
VISY RECYCLING EUROPE LIMITED—See Visy Industries Holdings Pty. Ltd.; *Int'l*, pg. 8256
VISY RECYCLING—See Visy Industries Holdings Pty. Ltd.; *Int'l*, pg. 8256
VISY RECYCLING—See Visy Industries Holdings Pty. Ltd.; *Int'l*, pg. 8256
VISY RECYCLING—See Visy Industries Holdings Pty. Ltd.; *Int'l*, pg. 8256
VISY RECYCLING—See Visy Industries Holdings Pty. Ltd.; *Int'l*, pg. 8256
VISY SPECIALITIES—See Visy Industries Holdings Pty. Ltd.; *Int'l*, pg. 8256
VISY SPECIALITIES—See Visy Industries Holdings Pty. Ltd.; *Int'l*, pg. 8256
VISY TECHNICAL CENTRE—See Visy Industries Holdings Pty. Ltd.; *Int'l*, pg. 8256
VISY TRADING GERMANY GMBH—See Visy Industries Holdings Pty. Ltd.; *Int'l*, pg. 8256
VISY TRADING SINGAPORE PTE LTD—See Visy Industries Holdings Pty. Ltd.; *Int'l*, pg. 8256
VITA 34 AG; *Int'l*, pg. 8256
VITA 34 GESELLSCHAFT FUR ZELLTRANSPLANTATE MBH—See VITA 34 AG; *Int'l*, pg. 8257

VITA 34 SLOVAKIA S.R.O.—See VITA 34 AG; *Int'l*, pg. 8257
VITA AS—See Validus AS; *Int'l*, pg. 8116
VITABANK PJSC—See Sovcombank PJSC; *Int'l*, pg. 7121
VITA BARENTZ CO. LTD.—See Cinven Limited; *Int'l*, pg. 1611
VITA BARIATRIC CLINICS STOCKHOLM AB—See Apax Partners LLP; *Int'l*, pg. 502
VITA BIOPHARMA PVT. LIMITED—See VVF Limited; *Int'l*, pg. 8319
VITABLOM NIGERIA LIMITED—See Vitafoam Nigeria Plc.; *Int'l*, pg. 8257
VITACARE PRESCRIPTION SERVICES, INC.—See GoodRx Holdings, Inc.; *U.S. Public*, pg. 952
VITAC CORPORATION—See Verbit Software Limited; *Int'l*, pg. 8165
VITA CLINICS UK LTD—See Apax Partners LLP; *Int'l*, pg. 502
THE VITA COCO COMPANY, INC.; *U.S. Public*, pg. 2137
VITA CORPORATION PTE LIMITED—See Vita Life Sciences Limited; *Int'l*, pg. 8257
VITACOST.COM, INC.—See The Kroger Co.; *U.S. Public*, pg. 2109
VITAE INVESTMENT CO., INC.—See Neville Chemical Company; *U.S. Private*, pg. 2891
VITAE WELLNESS BEAUTY LIMITED—See Miricor Enterprises Holdings Limited; *Int'l*, pg. 4919
VITAFOAM LIMITED—See TPG Capital, L.P.; *U.S. Public*, pg. 2175
VITAFOAM NIGERIA PLC.; *Int'l*, pg. 8257
VITA FOOD PRODUCTS, INC.—See SVB Food & Beverage Co.; *U.S. Private*, pg. 3888
VITAFOSS INTERNATIONAL GROUP CO., LTD.; *Int'l*, pg. 8258
VITA GROUP LIMITED; *Int'l*, pg. 8257
VITAHEALTH ASIA PACIFIC (S) PTE LIMITED—See Vita Life Sciences Limited; *Int'l*, pg. 8257
VITA HEALTHCARE ASIA PACIFIC SDN BHD.—See Vita Life Sciences Limited; *Int'l*, pg. 8257
VITAHEALTH LABORATORIES AUSTRALIA PTY LIMITED—See Vita Life Sciences Limited; *Int'l*, pg. 8257
VITA HEALTH PRODUCTS, INC.—See KKR & Co. Inc.; *U.S. Public*, pg. 1264
VITA ITALIA SRL—See VITA Zahnfabrik H. Rauter GmbH & Co. KG; *Int'l*, pg. 8257
VITAKEM NUTRACEUTICAL, INC.; *U.S. Private*, pg. 4405
VITAL A.D.; *Int'l*, pg. 8258
VITAL AGENCY CO., LTD.—See VITAL KSK HOLDINGS, INC.; *Int'l*, pg. 8258
VITAL AGUAS S.A.—See Embotelladora Andina S.A.; *Int'l*, pg. 2375
VITALAIRE ARABIA LLC—See L'Air Liquide S.A.; *Int'l*, pg. 4376
VITALAIRE AVATTVON SINGAPORE PTE. LTD.—See L'Air Liquide S.A.; *Int'l*, pg. 4376
VITALAIRE B.V.—See L'Air Liquide S.A.; *Int'l*, pg. 4370
VITALAIRE CANADA, INC.—See L'Air Liquide S.A.; *Int'l*, pg. 4374
VITALAIRE GMBH—See L'Air Liquide S.A.; *Int'l*, pg. 4374
VITALAIRE ITALIA S.P.A.—See L'Air Liquide S.A.; *Int'l*, pg. 4374
VITALAIRE KOREA INC.—See L'Air Liquide S.A.; *Int'l*, pg. 4376
VITALAIRE S.A.—See L'Air Liquide S.A.; *Int'l*, pg. 4374
VITAL AIR JAPAN K.K.—See L'Air Liquide S.A.; *Int'l*, pg. 4376
VITALAND SERVICES LIMITED—See Vitasoy International Holdings Ltd.; *Int'l*, pg. 8259
VITALBERRY BV—See Argent Group Europe Limited; *Int'l*, pg. 560
VITAL CARE; *U.S. Private*, pg. 4405
VITAL CHOICE SEAFOOD LLC—See 1-800-FLOWERS.COM, Inc.; *U.S. Public*, pg. 1
VITAL ENERGY INC.; *Int'l*, pg. 8258
VITAL ENERGY, INC.; *U.S. Public*, pg. 2306
VITAL EXPRESS CO., LTD.—See VITAL KSK HOLDINGS, INC.; *Int'l*, pg. 8258
VITAL FARMS, INC; *U.S. Public*, pg. 2306
VITAL FARMS OF MISSOURI, LLC—See Vital Farms, Inc; *U.S. Public*, pg. 2306
VITALHARVEST FREEHOLD TRUST—See Macquarie Group Limited; *Int'l*, pg. 4625
VITAL HEALTH SCIENCES PTY LTD—See Avecho Biotechnology Ltd.; *Int'l*, pg. 737
VITALHUB CORP.; *Int'l*, pg. 8258
VITAL HUMAN CAPITAL, INC.; *U.S. Public*, pg. 2306
VITALIA AT TRADITION, LLC—See Brookfield Corporation; *Int'l*, pg. 1183
VITALI ASCENSORI S.R.L.—See KONE Oyj; *Int'l*, pg. 4251
VITALIA VIE—See Groupe BPCE; *Int'l*, pg. 3096
VITALIBIS, INC.; *U.S. Public*, pg. 2306
VITALICIO TORRE CERDA S.L.—See Assicurazioni Generali S.p.A.; *Int'l*, pg. 644
VITA LIFE SCIENCES LIMITED; *Int'l*, pg. 8257
VITAL IMAGES CHINA—See Canon Inc.; *Int'l*, pg. 1298
VITAL IMAGES EUROPE B.V.—See Canon Inc.; *Int'l*, pg. 1298

VITAL IMAGES, INC.—See Canon Inc.; *Int'l*, pg. 1298
VITALINK INDUSTRY (SHENZHEN) COMPANY LIMITED-PINGHU—See CN Innovations Holdings Limited; *Int'l*, pg. 1673
VITALINK INDUSTRY (SHENZHEN) COMPANY LIMITED—See CN Innovations Holdings Limited; *Int'l*, pg. 1673
VITALINK KOREA CO., LTD.—See CN Innovations Holdings Limited; *Int'l*, pg. 1673
VITALINK THIN FILM TECHNOLOGY (SUZHOU) CO., LTD.—See CN Innovations Holdings Limited; *Int'l*, pg. 1673
VITALINK VIETNAM CO., LTD.—See CN Innovations Holdings Limited; *Int'l*, pg. 1673
VITAL INNOVATIONS HOLDINGS LIMITED; *Int'l*, pg. 8258
VITAL I/O, INC.—See Netsurit (Pty) Ltd; *Int'l*, pg. 5215
VITALISKLINIK VERWALTUNGS-GMBH—See Asklepios Kliniken GmbH & Co. KGaA; *Int'l*, pg. 623
VITALITY BOWLS ENTERPRISES, LLC; *U.S. Private*, pg. 4405
VITALITY CORPORATE SERVICES LIMITED—See Discovery Limited; *Int'l*, pg. 2134
VITALITY FOODSERVICE HOLDING CORPORATION—See Nestle S.A.; *Int'l*, pg. 5210
THE VITALITY GROUP INC—See Discovery Limited; *Int'l*, pg. 2134
VITALITY PRODUCTS INC.; *Int'l*, pg. 8258
VITALITY SENIOR LIVING MANAGEMENT, LLC; *U.S. Private*, pg. 4405
VITAL KSK HOLDINGS, INC.; *Int'l*, pg. 8258
VITALLIFE CORPORATION LTD.—See Bumrungrad Hospital Public Company Limited; *Int'l*, pg. 1215
VITAL LIMITED; *Int'l*, pg. 8258
VITAL LINK, INC.—See Atec, Inc.; *U.S. Private*, pg. 365
VITALL S.R.L.; *Int'l*, pg. 8258
VITAL MARKETING GROUP LLC; *U.S. Private*, pg. 4405
VITALMED, INC.—See Kohlberg & Company, LLC; *U.S. Private*, pg. 2338
VITAL METALS LTD; *Int'l*, pg. 8258
VITAL-NET, INC.—See VITAL KSK HOLDINGS, INC.; *Int'l*, pg. 8258
VITALOX INDUSTRIAL S.L.U.—See Air Products & Chemicals, Inc.; *U.S. Public*, pg. 67
VITAL PATH, INC.—See Xybion Corporation; *U.S. Private*, pg. 4583
VITAL PEPPER (BEIJING) MANAGEMENT CO., LTD.—See Tang Palace (China) Holdings Ltd.; *Int'l*, pg. 7457
VITAL PHARMACEUTICALS, INC.—See Monster Beverage Corporation; *U.S. Public*, pg. 1465
VITAL PLASTICS, INC.—See Wolverine Capital Partners LLC; *U.S. Private*, pg. 4555
VITAL RECORDS INC.; *U.S. Private*, pg. 4405
VITAL SCIENCE CORP.—See Bausch Health Companies Inc.; *Int'l*, pg. 898
VITALSMARTS LLC—See Leeds Equity Partners, LLC; *U.S. Private*, pg. 2415
VITAL SOURCE TECHNOLOGIES INC.—See Ingram Industries, Inc.; *U.S. Public*, pg. 2076
VITALS; *U.S. Private*, pg. 4405
VITAL TECHNICAL SDN. BHD.—See Nippon Paint Holdings Co., Ltd.; *Int'l*, pg. 5326
VITAL VOICES GLOBAL PARTNERSHIP; *U.S. Private*, pg. 4405
VITALWARE, LLC—See Health Catalyst, Inc.; *U.S. Public*, pg. 1014
VITALWEAR, INC.; *U.S. Private*, pg. 4405
VITAMEDICA, INC.—See Upexi, Inc.; *U.S. Public*, pg. 2264
VITAMEDMD, LLC—See TherapeuticsMD, Inc.; *U.S. Public*, pg. 2145
VITAMEX AB—See Midsona AB; *Int'l*, pg. 4887
VITA MI HOLDINGS S.A.; *Int'l*, pg. 8257
VITAMIN ANGEL ALLIANCE, INC.; *U.S. Private*, pg. 4405
VITAMIN BLUE, INC.; *U.S. Public*, pg. 2306
VITAMIN CLASSICS INC.; *U.S. Private*, pg. 4405
VITAMIN DISCOUNT CENTER INC.—See Recommerce Holdings, LLC; *U.S. Private*, pg. 3371
VITAMIN EXPRESS, INC.; *U.S. Private*, pg. 4405
VITAMIN FACTORY, INC.—See Integrated Biopharma, Inc.; *U.S. Public*, pg. 1136
VITAMINHAUS PTY LTD—See The Procter & Gamble Company; *U.S. Public*, pg. 2124
VITAMINKA; *Int'l*, pg. 8258
VITAMINS DIRECT HOLDINGS, LLC—See Vitamins Direct (UK) Limited; *Int'l*, pg. 8258
VITAMINS DIRECT (UK) LIMITED; *Int'l*, pg. 8258
VITAMIN SHOPPE, INC.—See B. Riley Financial, Inc.; *U.S. Public*, pg. 261
VITAMIN SHOPPE, INC.—See Irradiant Partners, LP; *U.S. Private*, pg. 2140
VITAMIN SHOPPE INDUSTRIES, INC.—See B. Riley Financial, Inc.; *U.S. Public*, pg. 261
VITAMIN SHOPPE INDUSTRIES, INC.—See Irradiant Partners, LP; *U.S. Private*, pg. 2141
VITAMINSPICE; *U.S. Private*, pg. 4405
THE VITAMIN STORE, LLC—See Healthier Choices Management Corp.; *U.S. Public*, pg. 1016

VITAMIN WORLD, INC.—See Centre Lane Partners, LLC; U.S. Private, pg. 828
VITAMIN WORLD USA CORPORATION—See China Feihe Limited; Int'l, pg. 1502
VITA-MIX CORPORATION; U.S. Private, pg. 4405
VITA MOBILE SYSTEMS, INC.; U.S. Public, pg. 2306
VITAN AGRO INDUSTRIES LIMITED; Int'l, pg. 8258
VITANA-X, INC.; U.S. Public, pg. 2306
VITANIA LTD.; Int'l, pg. 8258
VITA NONWOVENS, LLC; U.S. Private, pg. 4404
VITA NONWOVENS—See Vita Nonwovens, LLC; U.S. Private, pg. 4404
VITA NOVA, LLC—See Acadia Healthcare Company, Inc.; U.S. Public, pg. 31
VITA-PAKT CITRUS PRODUCTS CO.; U.S. Private, pg. 4405
VITA PI S.A.—See Atlantic Super Market S.A.; Int'l, pg. 675
VITA PLUS CORPORATION; U.S. Private, pg. 4404
VITAPUR NIGERIA LIMITED—See Vitafoam Nigeria Plc.; Int'l, pg. 8257
VITA QUEST INTERNATIONAL INC.; U.S. Private, pg. 4405
VITARICH CORPORATION; Int'l, pg. 8259
VITAR INSULATION HOLDINGS LIMITED; Int'l, pg. 8259
VITARON JAYA SDN BHD.—See Vita Life Sciences Limited; Int'l, pg. 8257
VITASCANNING AG; Int'l, pg. 8259
VITASCO GMBH—See Walgreens Boots Alliance, Inc.; U.S. Public, pg. 2324
VITAS, CORP.—See Chemed Corporation; U.S. Public, pg. 484
VITAS HEALTHCARE CORPORATION OF CALIFORNIA—See Chemed Corporation; U.S. Public, pg. 484
VITAS HEALTHCARE CORPORATION OF GEORGIA—See Chemed Corporation; U.S. Public, pg. 484
VITAS HEALTHCARE CORPORATION OF OHIO—See Chemed Corporation; U.S. Public, pg. 484
VITAS HEALTHCARE CORPORATION—See Chemed Corporation; U.S. Public, pg. 484
VITAS HEALTHCARE, INC.—See Chemed Corporation; U.S. Public, pg. 484
VITAS HEALTHCARE, INC.—See Chemed Corporation; U.S. Public, pg. 484
VITAS HEALTHCARE—See Chemed Corporation; U.S. Public, pg. 484
VITAS HME SOLUTIONS, INC.—See Chemed Corporation; U.S. Public, pg. 484
VITAS HOSPICE CARE—See Chemed Corporation; U.S. Public, pg. 484
VITAS HOSPICE SERVICES, LLC—See Chemed Corporation; U.S. Public, pg. 484
VITAS, INC.—See Chemed Corporation; U.S. Public, pg. 484
VITAS, INC.—See Chemed Corporation; U.S. Public, pg. 484
VITAS INNOVATIVE HOSPICE CARE—See Chemed Corporation; U.S. Public, pg. 484
VITA SOCIETA EDITORIALE SPA; Int'l, pg. 8257
VITA SOLUTIONS, INC.—See Novartis AG; Int'l, pg. 5461
VITASOY AUSTRALIA PRODUCTS PTY. LTD.—See Bega Cheese Ltd.; Int'l, pg. 940
VITASOY AUSTRALIA PRODUCTS PTY. LTD.—See Vitasoy International Holdings Ltd.; Int'l, pg. 8259
VITASOY COMPANY LIMITED—See Vitasoy International Holdings Ltd.; Int'l, pg. 8259
VITASOY (DONGGUAN) COMPANY LIMITED—See Vitasoy International Holdings Ltd.; Int'l, pg. 8259
VITASOY (FOSHAN) COMPANY LIMITED—See Vitasoy International Holdings Ltd.; Int'l, pg. 8259
VITASOY INTERNATIONAL HOLDINGS LTD.; Int'l, pg. 8259
VITASOY INTERNATIONAL SINGAPORE PTE. LTD.—See Vitasoy International Holdings Ltd.; Int'l, pg. 8259
VITASOY (SHANGHAI) COMPANY LIMITED—See Vitasoy International Holdings Ltd.; Int'l, pg. 8259
VITASOY (WUHAN) COMPANY LIMITED—See Vitasoy International Holdings Ltd.; Int'l, pg. 8259
VITA SPECIALTY FOODS—See SVB Food & Beverage Co.; U.S. Private, pg. 3888
VITAS PORTUGAL, LDA.—See Compagnie Financiere et de Participations Roullier SA; Int'l, pg. 1740
VITASPRING BIOMEDICAL CO. LTD.; U.S. Public, pg. 2306
VITAS SOLUTIONS, INC.—See Chemed Corporation; U.S. Public, pg. 484
VITAS—See Chemed Corporation; U.S. Public, pg. 484
VITAS—See Chemed Corporation; U.S. Public, pg. 484
VITATENE S.A.U.—See Koninklijke DSM N.V.; Int'l, pg. 4265
VITATEX INC.—See Applied DNA Sciences, Inc.; U.S. Public, pg. 170
VITA THERMOPLASTIC SHEET LIMITED—See TPG Capital, L.P.; U.S. Public, pg. 2175
VITATRON BELGIUM S.A./N.V.—See Medtronic plc; Int'l, pg. 4789

VITATRON HOLDING B.V.—See Medtronic plc; Int'l, pg. 4789
VITAVIVA ITALIA SRL—See Certina Holding AG; Int'l, pg. 1423
VITA ZAHNFABRIK H. RAUTER GMBH & CO. KG; Int'l, pg. 8257
VITA ZAHNFABRIK IBERICA, S.L.—See VITA Zahnfabrik H. Rauter GmbH & Co. KG; Int'l, pg. 8257
VIT-BEST NUTRITION, INC.—See Kingdomway Nutrition, Inc.; U.S. Private, pg. 2310
VITEC ACUTE OY—See Vitec Software Group AB; Int'l, pg. 8259
VITEC AGRANDO AB—See Vitec Software Group AB; Int'l, pg. 8259
VITEC AGRANDO AS—See Vitec Software Group AB; Int'l, pg. 8259
VITEC ALOC A/S—See Vitec Software Group AB; Int'l, pg. 8259
VITEC ALOC AS—See Vitec Software Group AB; Int'l, pg. 8259
VITEC APPVA AB—See Vitec Software Group AB; Int'l, pg. 8259
VITEC AUTODATA AS—See Vitec Software Group AB; Int'l, pg. 8259
VITEC BROADCAST SERVICES INC.—See The Carlyle Group Inc.; U.S. Public, pg. 2050
VITEC CAPITEX AB—See Vitec Software Group AB; Int'l, pg. 8259
VITEC CITO A/S—See Vitec Software Group AB; Int'l, pg. 8259
VITEC ELECTRONICS (SINGAPORE) PTE. LTD.—See Restar Holdings Corporation; Int'l, pg. 6303
VITEC ELECTRONICS (TAIWAN) CO., LTD.—See Restar Holdings Corporation; Int'l, pg. 6303
VITEC ELECTRONICS TRADING (SHANGHAI) CO., LTD.—See Restar Holdings Corporation; Int'l, pg. 6303
VITEC ENERGY AB—See Vitec Software Group AB; Int'l, pg. 8259
VITEC FASTIGHETSSYSTEM AB—See Vitec Software Group AB; Int'l, pg. 8259
VITEC FIXIT SYSTEMER AS—See Vitec Software Group AB; Int'l, pg. 8259
VITEC FUTURSOFT OY—See Vitec Software Group AB; Int'l, pg. 8259
VITEC GLOBAL OPERATIONS - HONG KONG—See Restar Holdings Corporation; Int'l, pg. 6303
VITEC GMBH—See VITEC Multimedia S.A.; Int'l, pg. 8259
VITEC HK DATA AS—See Vitec Software Group AB; Int'l, pg. 8259
VITEC IMAGING DISTRIBUTION AUSTRALIA PTY LTD—See Videndum plc; Int'l, pg. 8191
VITEC IMAGING DISTRIBUTION GMBH—See Videndum plc; Int'l, pg. 8191
VITEC IMAGING DISTRIBUTION HK LIMITED—See Videndum plc; Int'l, pg. 8191
VITEC IMAGING DISTRIBUTION KK—See Videndum plc; Int'l, pg. 8191
VITEC IMAGING DISTRIBUTION SHANGHAI LIMITED—See Videndum plc; Int'l, pg. 8191
VITEC IMAGING SOLUTIONS SPA—See Videndum plc; Int'l, pg. 8191
VITEC IMAGING SOLUTIONS UK LIMITED—See Videndum plc; Int'l, pg. 8191
VITEC, INC.; U.S. Private, pg. 4405
VITEC INFOEASY AS—See Vitec Software Group AB; Int'l, pg. 8259
VITEC IT-MAKERIET AS—See Vitec Software Group AB; Int'l, pg. 8259
VITEC KATRINA OY—See Vitec Software Group AB; Int'l, pg. 8259
VITEC LJ SYSTEM AB—See Vitec Software Group AB; Int'l, pg. 8259
VITEC MAKLARSYSTEM AB—See Vitec Software Group AB; Int'l, pg. 8259
VITEC MULTIMEDIA, INC.—See VITEC Multimedia S.A.; Int'l, pg. 8259
VITEC MULTIMEDIA S.A.; Int'l, pg. 8259
VITEC MV AB—See Vitec Software Group AB; Int'l, pg. 8259
VITEC MV AS—See Vitec Software Group AB; Int'l, pg. 8259
VITECO COMMUNICATION TECHNOLOGY JOINT STOCK COMPANY; Int'l, pg. 8260
VITEC PRODUCTION SOLUTIONS GMBH—See Videndum plc; Int'l, pg. 8191
VITEC PRODUCTION SOLUTIONS KK—See Videndum plc; Int'l, pg. 8191
VITEC PRODUCTION SOLUTIONS LIMITED—See Videndum plc; Int'l, pg. 8191
VITEC PRODUCTION SOLUTIONS PTE. LIMITED—See Videndum plc; Int'l, pg. 8191
VITEC PRODUCTIONS SOLUTIONS LIMITADA—See Videndum plc; Int'l, pg. 8191
VITEC SMART VISITOR SYSTEM AB—See Vitec Software Group AB; Int'l, pg. 8259
VITEC SOFTWARE GROUP AB; Int'l, pg. 8259
VITEC VIDEOCOM LTD—See Videndum plc; Int'l, pg. 8191

VITEC VIENNA INFORMATION TECHNOLOGY CONSULTING GMBH—See adesso SE; Int'l, pg. 144
VITEC VISIOLINK APS—See Vitec Software Group AB; Int'l, pg. 8260
VITEC WIMS AS—See Vitec Software Group AB; Int'l, pg. 8260
VITERION TELEHEALTHCARE LLC—See Bayer Aktiengesellschaft; Int'l, pg. 902
VITERI/TBWA—See Omnicom Group Inc.; U.S. Public, pg. 1599
VITERRA INC.—See Glencore plc; Int'l, pg. 2990
VITERRA LTD.—See Glencore plc; Int'l, pg. 2990
VITESCO TECHNOLOGIES GROUP AG—See INA-Holding Schaeffler GmbH & Co. KG; Int'l, pg. 3641
VITESSE AGRO LIMITED; Int'l, pg. 8260
VITESSE ENERGY, INC.; U.S. Public, pg. 2307
VITESSE, LLC—See Meta Platforms, Inc.; U.S. Public, pg. 1427
VITESSE SYSTEMS—See Trive Capital Inc.; U.S. Private, pg. 4240
VITEX EXTRUSION, LLC—See OEP Capital Advisors, L.P.; U.S. Private, pg. 2999
VITEX PACKAGING GROUP—See The Pritzker Group - Chicago, LLC; U.S. Private, pg. 4099
VITHERM FRANCE S.A.S.—See McBride plc; Int'l, pg. 4756
VITHERM S.A.S.—See McBride plc; Int'l, pg. 4756
VITIELLO COMMUNICATIONS GROUP, LLC—See Clayton, Dubilier & Rice, LLC; U.S. Private, pg. 925
VITI, INC.; U.S. Private, pg. 4405
VITIL SOLUTIONS; U.S. Private, pg. 4405
VITINKA A.D. KOZLUK; Int'l, pg. 8260
VITIS D.O.O.—See BERICAP GmbH & Co. KG; Int'l, pg. 981
VITIS LIFE S.A.—See Monceau Assurances Mutuelles Associees; Int'l, pg. 5025
VITIVA PROIZVODNJA IN STORITVE D.D.—See International Flavors & Fragrances Inc.; U.S. Public, pg. 1154
VITKOVICE DOPRAVA A.S.—See Vitkovice Holding, A.S.; Int'l, pg. 8260
VITKOVICE GEAR WORKS A.S.—See Vitkovice Holding, A.S.; Int'l, pg. 8260
VITKOVICE HEAVY MACHINERY A.S.—See Vitkovice Holding, A.S.; Int'l, pg. 8260
VITKOVICE HOLDING, A.S.; Int'l, pg. 8260
VITKOVICE ITS A.S.—See Vitkovice Holding, A.S.; Int'l, pg. 8260
VITKOVICE IT SOLUTIONS A.S.—See Vitkovice Holding, A.S.; Int'l, pg. 8260
VITKOVICE MECHANIKA A.S.—See Vitkovice Holding, A.S.; Int'l, pg. 8260
VITKOVICE - POWER ENGINEERING A.S.—See Vitkovice Holding, A.S.; Int'l, pg. 8260
VITKOVICE RECYCLING A.S.—See Vitkovice Holding, A.S.; Int'l, pg. 8260
VITKOVICE SLOVAKIA A.S.—See Vitkovice Holding, A.S.; Int'l, pg. 8260
VITKOVICE TESTING CENTER S.R.O.—See Vitkovice Holding, A.S.; Int'l, pg. 8260
VITM GMBH—See Randstad N.V.; Int'l, pg. 6201
VITOGAZ—See Rubis SCA; Int'l, pg. 6423
VITOL ARGENTINA S.A.—See Vitol Holding B.V.; Int'l, pg. 8260
VITOL ASIA PTE LTD.—See Vitol Holding B.V.; Int'l, pg. 8260
VITOL AVIATION COMPANY—See Vitol Holding B.V.; Int'l, pg. 8261
VITOL AVIATION UK LTD.—See Vitol Holding B.V.; Int'l, pg. 8260
VITOL BAHRAIN E.C.—See Vitol Holding B.V.; Int'l, pg. 8260
VITOL CAPITAL MANGEMENT LTD.—See Vitol Holding B.V.; Int'l, pg. 8260
VITOL CDI LTD—See Vitol Holding B.V.; Int'l, pg. 8260
VITOL CENTRAL ASIA S.A.—See Vitol Holding B.V.; Int'l, pg. 8261
VITOL COLOMBIA S.A.—See Vitol Holding B.V.; Int'l, pg. 8260
VITOL DO BRASIL LTDA.—See Vitol Holding B.V.; Int'l, pg. 8261
VITOL DUBAI LTD.—See Vitol Holding B.V.; Int'l, pg. 8260
VITOL ENERGY MEXICO S.A. DE C.V—See Vitol Holding B.V.; Int'l, pg. 8260
VITOL HOLDING B.V.; Int'l, pg. 8260
VITOL INC. - CRUDE OIL MARKETING DIVISION—See Vitol Holding B.V.; Int'l, pg. 8261
VITOL INC.—See Vitol Holding B.V.; Int'l, pg. 8261
VITOL REFINING S.A.—See Vitol Holding B.V.; Int'l, pg. 8261
VITOL S.A.—See Vitol Holding B.V.; Int'l, pg. 8261
VITOL TANK TERMINALS INTERNATIONAL B.V.—See Industry Super Holdings Pty. Ltd.; U.S. Private, pg. 3676
VITOL TANK TERMINALS INTERNATIONAL B.V.—See Vitol Holding B.V.; Int'l, pg. 8261
VITOL TRADING MALAYSIA LABUAN LTD.—See Vitol Holding B.V.; Int'l, pg. 8261
VITOL UPSTREAM GHANA LTD.—See Vitol Holding B.V.; Int'l, pg. 8261

VITOL HOLDING B.V.   CORPORATE AFFILIATIONS

VITOPEL DO BRASIL LTDA.—See Vision Capital, LLP; *Int'l*, pg. 8252
VITOROG A.D.; *Int'l*, pg. 8261
VITO TECHNOLOGY (SUQIAN) CO., LTD.—See Catcher Technology Co., Ltd; *Int'l*, pg. 1359
VITO TEKNISK ENTREPRENOR AS—See Instalco AB; *Int'l*, pg. 3723
VITRA AG; *Int'l*, pg. 8261
VITRA BAD GMBH—See Eczacibasi Holding A.S.; *Int'l*, pg. 2301
VITRADO GMBH—See freenet AG; *Int'l*, pg. 2770
VITRAN CORPORATION INC.—See TFI International Inc.; *Int'l*, pg. 7587
VITRAN EXPRESS CANADA, INC.—See TFI International Inc.; *Int'l*, pg. 7587
VITRANS SA—See Vicat S.A.; *Int'l*, pg. 8186
VITRA (UK) LTD.—See Eczacibasi Holding A.S.; *Int'l*, pg. 2301
VITRA USA INC.—See Eczacibasi Holding A.S.; *Int'l*, pg. 2302
VITREK CORPORATION—See Branford Castle, Inc.; *U.S. Private*, pg. 639
VITREOSHEALTH, INC.—See Veritas Capital Fund Management, LLC; *U.S. Private*, pg. 4362
VITREOUS GLASS INC.; *Int'l*, pg. 8261
VITRERIE NOVY GLASS—See Koch Industries, Inc.; *U.S. Private*, pg. 2330
VITREX LIMITED—See Q.E.P. Co., Inc.; *U.S. Public*, pg. 1741
VITRIA TECHNOLOGY, INC.—See Innovation Technology Group; *U.S. Private*, pg. 2081
VITRO AUTOGLASS LLC—See Vitro, S.A.B. de C.V.; *Int'l*, pg. 8262
VITRO AUTOMOTIVE S.A. DE C.V.—See Vitro, S.A.B. de C.V.; *Int'l*, pg. 8262
VITRO BIOPHARMA, INC.; *U.S. Private*, pg. 4405
VITROCAR, S.A. DE C.V.—See Vitro, S.A.B. de C.V.; *Int'l*, pg. 8262
VITRO CHEMICALS, FIBERS & MINING LLC—See Vitro, S.A.B. de C.V.; *Int'l*, pg. 8262
VITROCISET BELGIUM SPRL—See Leonardo S.p.A.; *Int'l*, pg. 4461
VITROCISET FRANCE SARL—See Leonardo S.p.A.; *Int'l*, pg. 4461
VITROCISET SPA—See Leonardo S.p.A.; *Int'l*, pg. 4461
VITROCOM INC.—See H&Q Asia Pacific, Ltd.; *U.S. Private*, pg. 1823
VITROCRISA, S. DE R.L. DE C.V.—See Vitro, S.A.B. de C.V.; *Int'l*, pg. 8262
VITRO ENVASES, S.A. DE C.V.—See Vitro, S.A.B. de C.V.; *Int'l*, pg. 8262
VITRO FLEX, S.A. DE C.V.—See Vitro, S.A.B. de C.V.; *Int'l*, pg. 8262
VITROLIFE AB; *Int'l*, pg. 8262
VITROLIFE A/S—See Vitrolife AB; *Int'l*, pg. 8262
VITROLIFE (BEIJING) TECHNICAL SERVICE CO. LTD.—See Vitrolife AB; *Int'l*, pg. 8262
VITROLIFE BV—See Vitrolife AB; *Int'l*, pg. 8262
VITROLIFE K.K.—See Vitrolife AB; *Int'l*, pg. 8262
VITROLIFE SWEDEN AB—See Vitrolife AB; *Int'l*, pg. 8262
VITROLIFE SWEDEN INSTRUMENTS AB—See Vitrolife AB; *Int'l*, pg. 8262
VITRO MEADVILLE FLAT GLASS LLC—See Vitro, S.A.B. de C.V.; *Int'l*, pg. 8262
VITROMEX, S.A. DE C.V.—See Grupo Industrial Saltillo S.A. de C.V.; *Int'l*, pg. 3130
VITRON ELECTRONIC SERVICES, INC.—See Omega Electronics Manufacturing Services; *U.S. Private*, pg. 3015
VITRONICS SOLTEC B.V.—See Illinois Tool Works Inc.; *U.S. Public*, pg. 1111
VITRONICS SOLTEC CORPORATION—See Illinois Tool Works Inc.; *U.S. Public*, pg. 1111
VITRONICS SOLTEC TECHNOLOGIES (SUZHOU) CO., LTD.—See Illinois Tool Works Inc.; *U.S. Public*, pg. 1111
VITRO PARTNERS LLC—See Stagwell, Inc.; *U.S. Public*, pg. 1928
VITROROBERTSON LLC—See Stagwell, Inc.; *U.S. Public*, pg. 1928
VITRO, S.A.B. DE C.V.; *Int'l*, pg. 8261
VITROSCREEN S.R.L.—See SenzaGen AB; *Int'l*, pg. 6715
VITROSILICON S.A.—See Kulczyk Investments S.A.; *Int'l*, pg. 4328
VITRO, SOCIEDAD ANONIMA—See Vitro, S.A.B. de C.V.; *Int'l*, pg. 8262
VITROX CORPORATION BERHAD; *Int'l*, pg. 8262
VITROX TECHNOLOGIES SDN. BHD.—See ViTrox Corporation Berhad; *Int'l*, pg. 8263
VITROX TECHNOLOGIES (SUZHOU) CO., LTD.—See ViTrox Corporation Berhad; *Int'l*, pg. 8262
VITRULAN COMPOSITES OY—See ADCURAM Group AG; *Int'l*, pg. 128
VITRULAN HOLDING GMBH—See ADCURAM Group AG; *Int'l*, pg. 128
VITRU LIMITED; *Int'l*, pg. 8263
VITRUM GLASS LTD.—See Vitrum Industries Ltd.; *Int'l*, pg. 8263
VITRUM INDUSTRIES LTD.; *Int'l*, pg. 8263

VITRUVIAN PARTNERS LLP; *Int'l*, pg. 8263
VITRUVIO REAL ESTATE SOCIMI SA; *Int'l*, pg. 8263
VITRUVIT SA—See Viohalco SA/NV; *Int'l*, pg. 8244
VITTA SCIENTIFIC - TECHNICAL COMPANY—See HORIBA Ltd; *Int'l*, pg. 3478
VITTLES; *U.S. Private*, pg. 4405
VITTORIA ASSICURAZIONI S.P.A.; *Int'l*, pg. 8263
VITTORIA FOOD & BEVERAGE PTY. LIMITED; *Int'l*, pg. 8264
VITTORIA IMMOBILIARE S.P.A.—See Vittoria Assicurazioni S.p.A.; *Int'l*, pg. 8264
VITTORIA SRL—See Clariane SE; *Int'l*, pg. 1645
VITTRA AB—See Bure Equity AB; *Int'l*, pg. 1221
VITURA HEALTH LIMITED; *Int'l*, pg. 8264
VITURA—See Northwood Investors, LLC; *U.S. Private*, pg. 2963
VITUSA CORP.; *U.S. Private*, pg. 4406
VITUSA PRODUCTS INC.; *U.S. Private*, pg. 4406
VITUS MARINE LLC; *U.S. Private*, pg. 4406
VITVARUEXPERTEN.COM NORDIC AB—See BHG Group AB; *Int'l*, pg. 1014
VITZROCELL CO., LTD.; *Int'l*, pg. 8264
VITZROSYS CO.; *Int'l*, pg. 8264
VITZROTECH CO., LTD.; *Int'l*, pg. 8264
VIVAA TRADECOM LIMITED; *Int'l*, pg. 8265
VIVA BIOTECH HOLDINGS; *Int'l*, pg. 8265
VIVABOX SOLUTIONS, LLC—See Clayton, Dubilier & Rice, LLC; *U.S. Private*, pg. 930
VIVACITY HEALTH PTY. LTD.—See IQVIA Holdings Inc.; *U.S. Public*, pg. 1170
VIVACTIS ALINA—See Newton 21 Europe SA; *Int'l*, pg. 5239
VIVACTIS BENELUX—See Newton 21 Europe SA; *Int'l*, pg. 5239
VIVACTIS CONSEIL—See Newton 21 Europe SA; *Int'l*, pg. 5239
VIVA ENERGI A/S—See Bravida Holding AB; *Int'l*, pg. 1142
VIVA ENERGY GROUP LIMITED; *Int'l*, pg. 8264
VIVA ENTERTAINMENT GROUP INC.; *U.S. Public*, pg. 2307
VIVA ENTERTAINMENT, LLC; *U.S. Private*, pg. 4406
VIVA GOLD CORP.; *Int'l*, pg. 8264
VIVA GOODS COMPANY LIMITED; *Int'l*, pg. 8264
VIVA! GROUP; *Int'l*, pg. 8265
VIVA INTERNATIONAL MARKETING- UND HANDELS-GMBH—See OMV Aktiengesellschaft; *Int'l*, pg. 5569
VIVAIT INVESTMENT COMPANY LTD.; *Int'l*, pg. 8265
VIVAKOR, INC.; *U.S. Public*, pg. 2307
VIVALDI CAPITAL MANAGEMENT, LLC; *U.S. Private*, pg. 4406
VIVALDI MUSIC ACADEMY, LLC; *U.S. Private*, pg. 4406
VIVALDIS HEALTH & FOODS PRIVATE LIMITED—See Sun Pharmaceutical Industries Ltd.; *Int'l*, pg. 7308
VIVA LEISURE LIMITED; *Int'l*, pg. 8264
VIVA LIFE SCIENCE CORP—See Westar Nutrition Corp.; *U.S. Private*, pg. 4488
VIVA MEDIA—See Viva Partnership, Inc.; *U.S. Private*, pg. 4406
VIVAMED S.R.O.—See Centene Corporation; *U.S. Public*, pg. 471
VIVANCO GRUPPE AG; *Int'l*, pg. 8265
VIVANI MEDICAL, INC.; *U.S. Public*, pg. 2307
VIVANIUM GMBH—See Bilfinger SE; *Int'l*, pg. 1027
VIVANTA INDUSTRIES LIMITED; *Int'l*, pg. 8265
VIVANT CORPORATION; *Int'l*, pg. 8265
VIVANZA BIOSCIENCES LTD.; *Int'l*, pg. 8265
VIVA PARADISE SDN. BHD.—See Eksons Corporation Berhad; *Int'l*, pg. 2340
VIVA PARTNERSHIP, INC.; *U.S. Private*, pg. 4406
VIVA! PRAG—See Viva! Group; *Int'l*, pg. 8265
VIVA RAILINGS LLC; *U.S. Private*, pg. 4406
VIVARA PARTICIPACOES S.A.; *Int'l*, pg. 8265
VIVARIS GETRANKE GMBH & CO. KG—See Berentzen-Gruppe AG; *Int'l*, pg. 978
VIVARIS GETRANKE VERWALTUNG GMBH—See Berentzen-Gruppe AG; *Int'l*, pg. 978
VIVARTE S.A.; *Int'l*, pg. 8265
VIVARTIA HOLDINGS S.A.—See Marfin Investment Group Holdings S.A.; *Int'l*, pg. 4692
VIVASA (PVT) LTD.—See Daikin Industries, Ltd.; *Int'l*, pg. 1937
VIVAT DIRECT LIMITED; *Int'l*, pg. 8265
VIVATICKET; *Int'l*, pg. 8265
VIVATIS HOLDING AG—See Raiffeisenlandesbank Oberosterreich Aktiengesellschaft; *Int'l*, pg. 6187
VIVAT N.V.—See Apollo Global Management, Inc.; *U.S. Public*, pg. 147
VIVAWEST GMBH—See RAG-Stiftung; *Int'l*, pg. 6181
VIVA WINE GROUP AB; *Int'l*, pg. 8264
VIVA WINE & SPIRITS AB—See Viva Wine Group AB; *Int'l*, pg. 8265
VIVA WORLD TRADE, INC.; *Int'l*, pg. 8265
VIVAX CO., LTD.—See Kirin Holdings Company, Limited; *Int'l*, pg. 4189
VIVAX PRO PAINTING; *U.S. Private*, pg. 4406
VIVECHROM DR. STEFANOS D. PATERAS S.A.—See Akzo Nobel N.V.; *Int'l*, pg. 275

VIVE FINANCIAL, LLC—See Aaron's Company, Inc.; *U.S. Public*, pg. 13
VIVEICA, S.A. DE C.V.—See Empresas ICA S.A.B. de C.V.; *Int'l*, pg. 2391
VIVEIROS DO FURADOURO UNIPESSOAL, LDA.—See Altri, SGPS, S.A.; *Int'l*, pg. 398
VIVE LA PROD—See NRJ Group SA; *Int'l*, pg. 5474
VIVELYS USA—See OENEO SA; *Int'l*, pg. 5529
VIVENDI MOBILE ENTERTAINMENT S.A.—See Vivendi SE; *Int'l*, pg. 8278
VIVENDI SE; *Int'l*, pg. 8265
VIVENO GROUP GMBH—See Bertelsmann SE & Co. KGaA; *Int'l*, pg. 995
VIVENT HEALTH, INC.; *U.S. Private*, pg. 4406
VIVENTO INTERIM SERVICES GMBH—See Manpower-Group Inc.; *U.S. Public*, pg. 1362
VIVEO FRANCE SAS—See Temenos AG; *Int'l*, pg. 7555
VIVEO GROUP SA—See Temenos AG; *Int'l*, pg. 7555
VIVEON HEALTH ACQUISITION CORP.; *U.S. Public*, pg. 2307
VIVEO ROMANIA SRL—See Temenos AG; *Int'l*, pg. 7556
VIVERE HEALTH LLC—See Prelude Fertility, Inc.; *U.S. Private*, pg. 3249
VIVER INCORPORADORA E CONSTRUTORA S.A.; *Int'l*, pg. 8278
VIVESCIA; *Int'l*, pg. 8278
VIVEVE, INC.—See Viveve Medical Inc.; *U.S. Public*, pg. 2307
VIVEVE MEDICAL INC.; *U.S. Public*, pg. 2307
VIVEX BIOMEDICAL, INC.; *U.S. Private*, pg. 4406
VIVIAL, INC.; *U.S. Private*, pg. 4406
THE VIVIAN BEAUMONT THEATER, INC.; *U.S. Private*, pg. 4132
VIVICARE GMBH—See SOL S.p.A.; *Int'l*, pg. 7068
VIVIC CORP.; *U.S. Public*, pg. 2307
VIVID AUTOMOTIVE DATA (UK) LTD—See Apax Partners LLP; *Int'l*, pg. 502
VIVID AUTOMOTIVE DATA (UK) LTD—See TowerBrook Capital Partners, L.P.; *U.S. Private*, pg. 4195
VIVIDFRONT, LLC; *U.S. Private*, pg. 4406
VIVID GAMES SA; *Int'l*, pg. 8279
VIVID GLOBAL INDUSTRIES LIMITED; *Int'l*, pg. 8279
VIVID IMAGINATIONS LTD—See Phoenix Equity Partners Ltd.; *Int'l*, pg. 5850
VIVID IMPACT CORPORATION; *U.S. Private*, pg. 4406
VIVID INK INC.; *U.S. Private*, pg. 4406
VIVIDION THERAPEUTICS, INC.; *U.S. Public*, pg. 2307
VIVID ITALIA SRL—See Apax Partners LLP; *Int'l*, pg. 502
VIVID ITALIA SRL—See TowerBrook Capital Partners, L.P.; *U.S. Private*, pg. 4195
VIVID LEARNING SYSTEMS, INC.—See Waud Capital Partners LLC; *U.S. Private*, pg. 4457
VIVID MERCANTILE LIMITED; *Int'l*, pg. 8279
VIVID PRINT SOLUTIONS INC.—See Securian Financial Group, Inc.; *U.S. Private*, pg. 3594
VIVID SEATS, INC.; *U.S. Public*, pg. 2307
VIVID TECHNOLOGY LIMITED; *Int'l*, pg. 8279
VIVIDTHREE HOLDINGS LTD.; *Int'l*, pg. 8279
VIVIDWIRELESS PTY. LIMITED—See Temasek Holdings (Private) Limited; *Int'l*, pg. 7553
VIVIEN CORP.; *Int'l*, pg. 8279
VIVIENNE WESTWOOD LTD.; *Int'l*, pg. 8279
VIVIFY HEALTH, INC.—See UnitedHealth Group Incorporated; *U.S. Public*, pg. 2252
VIVIMED LABS EUROPE LTD—See Vivimed Labs Limited; *Int'l*, pg. 8280
VIVIMED LABS LIMITED; *Int'l*, pg. 8279
VIVINT, INC.—See NRG Energy, Inc.; *U.S. Public*, pg. 1551
VIVINT SMART HOME, INC.—See NRG Energy, Inc.; *U.S. Public*, pg. 1551
VIVINT SOLAR, INC.—See Sunrun Inc.; *U.S. Public*, pg. 1965
VIVINT SOLAR OPERATIONS, LLC—See Sunrun Inc.; *U.S. Public*, pg. 1966
VIVIONE BIOSCIENCES INC.; *Int'l*, pg. 8280
VIVIONE BIOSCIENCES, LLC—See Vivione Biosciences Inc.; *Int'l*, pg. 8280
VIVION INC.—See Operio Group, LLC; *U.S. Private*, pg. 3032
VIVISOL ADRIA DOO—See SOL S.p.A.; *Int'l*, pg. 7068
VIVISOL BRASIL LTDA.—See SOL S.p.A.; *Int'l*, pg. 7068
VIVISOL B S.P.R.L.—See SOL S.p.A.; *Int'l*, pg. 7068
VIVISOL CALABRIA SRL—See SOL S.p.A.; *Int'l*, pg. 7068
VIVISOL CZECHIA S.R.O.—See SOL S.p.A.; *Int'l*, pg. 7068
VIVISOL DELLO STRETTO SRL—See SOL S.p.A.; *Int'l*, pg. 7068
VIVISOL DEUTSCHLAND GMBH—See SOL S.p.A.; *Int'l*, pg. 7068
VIVISOL FRANCE SARL—See SOL S.p.A.; *Int'l*, pg. 7068
VIVISOL HEIMBEHANDLUNGSGERATE GMBH—See SOL S.p.A.; *Int'l*, pg. 7068
VIVISOL HELLAS SA—See SOL S.p.A.; *Int'l*, pg. 7068
VIVISOL INTENSIVSERVICE GMBH—See SOL S.p.A.; *Int'l*, pg. 7068
VIVISOL NAPOLI SRL—See SOL S.p.A.; *Int'l*, pg. 7068
VIVISOL SILARUS S.R.L.—See SOL S.p.A.; *Int'l*, pg. 7068
VIVISOL SRL—See SOL S.p.A.; *Int'l*, pg. 7068

COMPANY NAME INDEX

VIVISOL UMBRIA S.R.L.—See SOL S.p.A.; *Int'l*, pg. 7068
VIVITIDE, LLC—See Ampersand Management LLC; *U.S. Private*, pg. 266
VIVIUM S.A.—See P&V Assurances SCRL; *Int'l*, pg. 5681
VIVO BIOTECH LIMITED; *Int'l*, pg. 8280
VIVO CANNABIS INC.—See MediPharm Labs Corp.; *Int'l*, pg. 4779
VIVO COLLABORATION SOLUTIONS LIMITED; *Int'l*, pg. 8280
VIVO CONCERTI S.R.L.—See CTS Eventim AG & Co. KGAA; *Int'l*, pg. 1873
VIVO ENERGY AFRICA SERVICES SARL—See Vitol Holding B.V.; *Int'l*, pg. 8261
VIVO ENERGY BOTSWANA PTY LTD.—See Vitol Holding B.V.; *Int'l*, pg. 8261
VIVO ENERGY BURKINA S.A.—See Vitol Holding B.V.; *Int'l*, pg. 8261
VIVO ENERGY CABO VERDE S.A.—See Vitol Holding B.V.; *Int'l*, pg. 8261
VIVO ENERGY COTE D'IVOIRE—See Shell plc; *Int'l*, pg. 6799
VIVO ENERGY DE GUINEE S.A.—See Vitol Holding B.V.; *Int'l*, pg. 8261
VIVO ENERGY GABON S.A.—See Vitol Holding B.V.; *Int'l*, pg. 8261
VIVO ENERGY GHANA LTD.—See Vitol Holding B.V.; *Int'l*, pg. 8261
VIVO ENERGY KENYA LTD.—See Vitol Holding B.V.; *Int'l*, pg. 8261
VIVO ENERGY MALI S.A.—See Vitol Holding B.V.; *Int'l*, pg. 8261
VIVO ENERGY MAROC S.A.—See Vitol Holding B.V.; *Int'l*, pg. 8261
VIVO ENERGY MOCAMBIQUE LDA—See Vitol Holding B.V.; *Int'l*, pg. 8261
VIVO ENERGY PLC—See Vitol Holding B.V.; *Int'l*, pg. 8261
VIVO ENERGY REUNION S.A.—See Vitol Holding B.V.; *Int'l*, pg. 8261
VIVO ENERGY RWANDA LTD.—See Vitol Holding B.V.; *Int'l*, pg. 8261
VIVO ENERGY SENEGAL S.A.—See Vitol Holding B.V.; *Int'l*, pg. 8261
VIVO ENERGY TANZANIA LIMITED—See Vitol Holding B.V.; *Int'l*, pg. 8261
VIVO ENERGY UGANDA LTD.—See Vitol Holding B.V.; *Int'l*, pg. 8261
VIVO ENERGY ZAMBIA MARKETING LTD.—See Vitol Holding B.V.; *Int'l*, pg. 8261
VIVO, INC.; *U.S. Private*, pg. 4406
VIVO MITARBEITER-SERVICE GMBH—See voestalpine AG; *Int'l*, pg. 8295
VIVONIO FURNITURE GMBH; *Int'l*, pg. 8280
VIVO PARTICIPACOES S.A.—See Telefonica, S.A.; *Int'l*, pg. 7537
VIVOPHARM EUROPE, LTD.—See Vyant Bio, Inc.; *U.S. Public*, pg. 2315
VIVOPHARM PTY, LTD.—See Vyant Bio, Inc.; *U.S. Public*, pg. 2315
VIVOPOWER INTERNATIONAL PLC; *Int'l*, pg. 8280
VIVORYON THERAPEUTICS N.V.; *Int'l*, pg. 8280
VIVOS, INC.; *U.S. Public*, pg. 2307
VIVOS PROFESSIONALS SERVICES LLC—See Kellton Tech Solutions Ltd.; *Int'l*, pg. 4121
VIVOS THERAPEUTICS, INC.; *U.S. Public*, pg. 2307
VIVOTEK INC.; *Int'l*, pg. 8280
VIVOTEK USA INC—See Vivotek Inc.; *Int'l*, pg. 8280
VIVOX, INC.; *U.S. Private*, pg. 4406
VIVOZON PHARMACEUTICAL CO., LTD.—See Kumho Electric, Inc.; *Int'l*, pg. 4330
VIVRE, INC.; *U.S. Private*, pg. 4406
VIVTERA GLOBAL BUSINESS LLP—See Warburg Pincus LLC; *U.S. Private*, pg. 4440
VIVUS, INC.; *U.S. Public*, pg. 2307
VIWACO JOINT-STOCK COMPANY—See Vietnam Construction Joint Stock Corporation; *Int'l*, pg. 8198
VIWIS GMBH—See Munchener Ruckversicherungs AG; *Int'l*, pg. 5092
VIWO LLC—See Gannett Co., Inc.; *U.S. Public*, pg. 906
VIXAR INC.—See ams AG; *Int'l*, pg. 439
VIXEN COMPOSITES, LLC—See Thor Industries, Inc.; *U.S. Public*, pg. 2157
VIXEN STUDIOS, LLC—See The Walt Disney Company; *U.S. Public*, pg. 2141
VIXIMO, INC.—See Pocket Games, Inc.; *U.S. Private*, pg. 3219
VIX, INC.—See ForgeLight, LLC; *U.S. Private*, pg. 1568
VIX, INC.—See Searchlight Capital Partners, L.P.; *U.S. Private*, pg. 3591
VIXS SYSTEMS INC.—See Pixelworks, Inc.; *U.S. Public*, pg. 1696
VIYYA TECHNOLOGIES, INC.; *U.S. Private*, pg. 4406
VIZADA AS—See Airbus SE; *Int'l*, pg. 245
VIZADA B.V.—See Airbus SE; *Int'l*, pg. 245
VIZADA GMBH—See Airbus SE; *Int'l*, pg. 245
VIZADA NETWORKS LTD.—See Airbus SE; *Int'l*, pg. 245
VIZADA RO HONG KONG—See Airbus SE; *Int'l*, pg. 245
VIZADA RO SINGAPORE—See Airbus SE; *Int'l*, pg. 245
VIZADA SAS—See Airbus SE; *Int'l*, pg. 245

VIZAG GENERAL CARGO BERTH PVT. LTD.—See Vedanta Resources Ltd.; *Int'l*, pg. 8146
VIZAG PROFILES LIMITED; *Int'l*, pg. 8280
VIZAG SEAPORT PRIVATE LIMITED; *Int'l*, pg. 8280
VIZ BRANZ LIMITED—See Investcorp Holdings B.S.C.; *Int'l*, pg. 3777
VIZCAYA LAKES COMMUNITIES, LLC—See Sun Communities, Inc.; *U.S. Public*, pg. 1963
VIZCONNECT, INC.; *U.S. Private*, pg. 4406
VIZER GROUP, INC.; *U.S. Private*, pg. 4406
VIZERGY; *U.S. Private*, pg. 4406
VIZEUM CANADA INC.—See Dentsu Group Inc.; *Int'l*, pg. 2038
VIZEUM CANADA INC. - VANCOUVER—See Dentsu Group Inc.; *Int'l*, pg. 2038
VIZEUM UK LTD.—See Dentsu Group Inc.; *Int'l*, pg. 2038
VIZEUM USA—See Dentsu Group Inc.; *Int'l*, pg. 2038
VIZIENT, INC.; *U.S. Private*, pg. 4407
VIZIENT MANUFACTURING SOLUTIONS, INC.—See Lincoln Electric Holdings, Inc.; *U.S. Public*, pg. 1318
VIZIO HOLDING CORP.; *U.S. Public*, pg. 2307
VIZIO, INC.—See VIZIO Holding Corp.; *U.S. Public*, pg. 2307
VIZIONE DEVELOPMENT SDN. BHD.—See Vizione Holdings Berhad; *Int'l*, pg. 8280
VIZIONE HOLDINGS BERHAD; *Int'l*, pg. 8280
VIZION HEALTH LLC; *U.S. Private*, pg. 4407
VIZIYA CORPORATION—See Genstar Capital, LLC; *U.S. Private*, pg. 1678
VIZOLUTION LTD.—See Lightico Ltd.; *Int'l*, pg. 4496
VIZOR ENTERIJERI A.D.; *Int'l*, pg. 8280
VIZRT AG—See Nordic Capital AB; *Int'l*, pg. 5421
VIZRT AUSTRALIA PTY. LTD.—See Nordic Capital AB; *Int'l*, pg. 5421
VIZRT AUSTRIA GMBH—See Nordic Capital AB; *Int'l*, pg. 5421
VIZRT (BEIJING) TECHNOLOGY LTD.—See Nordic Capital AB; *Int'l*, pg. 5421
VIZRT GROUP AS—See Nordic Capital AB; *Int'l*, pg. 5421
VIZRT HONG KONG & MACAU—See Nordic Capital AB; *Int'l*, pg. 5421
VIZRT INDIA PRIVATE LIMITED—See Nordic Capital AB; *Int'l*, pg. 5421
VIZRT JAPAN—See Nordic Capital AB; *Int'l*, pg. 5421
VIZRT LATIN AMERICA—See Nordic Capital AB; *Int'l*, pg. 5421
VIZRT MIDDLE EAST—See Nordic Capital AB; *Int'l*, pg. 5421
VIZRT NORWAY AS—See Nordic Capital AB; *Int'l*, pg. 5421
VIZRT PHILIPPINES—See Nordic Capital AB; *Int'l*, pg. 5421
VIZRT SINGAPORE—See Nordic Capital AB; *Int'l*, pg. 5421
VIZRT SPAIN & PORTUGAL S.L.—See Nordic Capital AB; *Int'l*, pg. 5421
VIZRT SWEDEN AB—See Nordic Capital AB; *Int'l*, pg. 5421
VIZRT (THAILAND) LIMITED—See Nordic Capital AB; *Int'l*, pg. 5421
VIZRT UK LTD.—See Nordic Capital AB; *Int'l*, pg. 5421
VIZRT USA LLC—See Nordic Capital AB; *Int'l*, pg. 5421
VIZRT USA LLC - SOUTH REGIONAL OFFICE—See Nordic Capital AB; *Int'l*, pg. 5421
VIZSLA COPPER CORP.; *Int'l*, pg. 8280
VIZSLA SILVER CORP.; *Int'l*, pg. 8280
VIZ-STAL LLC—See Novolipetski Metallurgicheski Komb OAO; *Int'l*, pg. 5466
VIZSTONE PTY. LTD.—See ActivePort Group Limited; *Int'l*, pg. 120
VIZTEK, INC.; *U.S. Private*, pg. 4407
VIZTU TECHNOLOGIES, INC.—See 3D Systems Corporation; *U.S. Public*, pg. 4
VIZUAL HUMAN RESOURCES PLC—See Automatic Data Processing, Inc.; *U.S. Public*, pg. 230
VIZUAL LEARNING PLC—See Automatic Data Processing, Inc.; *U.S. Public*, pg. 230
V. J. CATALANO INC.; *U.S. Private*, pg. 4328
VJC-MANAGEMENT AG—See AEVIS VICTORIA SA; *Int'l*, pg. 183
VJETRENICA D.D.; *Int'l*, pg. 8280
VJETROELEKTRANE GLUNCA D.O.O.—See Petrol, Slovenska energetska druzba, d.d.; *Int'l*, pg. 5827
VJII PRODUCTIONS AG—See Allgeier SE; *Int'l*, pg. 338
VJK INC.—See National Amusements, Inc.; *U.S. Private*, pg. 2844
V&J NATIONAL ENTERPRISES LLC; *U.S. Private*, pg. 4327
VJP CO., LTD.—See ASIA PILE HOLDINGS CORPORATION; *Int'l*, pg. 614
VJ STANLEY, INC.—See Stritt & Priebe, Inc.; *U.S. Private*, pg. 3840
VJTF EDUSERVICES LIMITED; *Int'l*, pg. 8281
VJ USINA CONTRACTING, INC.; *U.S. Private*, pg. 4407
VKC HOLDINGS JSC; *Int'l*, pg. 8281
VK COMPANY LTD.; *Int'l*, pg. 8281
VK COMPANY; *Int'l*, pg. 8281
VK DIRECT LIMITED—See Vorwerk & Co. KG; *Int'l*, pg. 8307

VKIDZ, INC.—See Veritas Capital Fund Management, LLC; *U.S. Private*, pg. 4361
VKJ INFRADEVELOPERS LIMITED; *Int'l*, pg. 8281
V.K. KNOWLTON CONSTRUCTION & UTILITIES, INC.—See TETCO, Inc.; *U.S. Private*, pg. 3973
VK NORTH AMERICA LLC—See Kadant Inc.; *U.S. Public*, pg. 1212
V-KOOL INTERNATIONAL PTE. LTD.—See Eastman Chemical Company; *U.S. Public*, pg. 706
VKR FRANCE S.A.S.—See VKR Holding A/S; *Int'l*, pg. 8282
VKR HOLDING A/S; *Int'l*, pg. 8281
VKS VINDKRAFT SVERIGE AB—See PNE AG; *Int'l*, pg. 5901
VKT PHARMA PRIVATE LIMITED—See SMS Pharmaceuticals Ltd; *Int'l*, pg. 7017
VK UNDERWRITERS LLC—See Howden Group Holdings Limited; *Int'l*, pg. 3494
VLAAMSE AUDIOVISUELE REGIE N.V.—See Vlaamse Radio en Televisieomroep NV; *Int'l*, pg. 8283
VLAAMSE MEDIA MAATSCHAPPIJ—See Roularta Media Group NV; *Int'l*, pg. 6407
VLAAMSE PARTICIPATIEMAATSCHAPPIJ NV; *Int'l*, pg. 8283
VLAAMSE RADIO EN TELEVISIEOMROEP NV; *Int'l*, pg. 8283
VLADIMIR CHEMICAL PLANT PJSC; *Int'l*, pg. 8283
VLADIMIR JONES; *U.S. Private*, pg. 4407
VLADIMIR JONES—See Vladimir Jones; *U.S. Private*, pg. 4407
VLADI PRIVATE ISLANDS (CANADA) LIMITED—See Vladi Private Islands GmbH; *Int'l*, pg. 8283
VLADI PRIVATE ISLANDS GMBH; *Int'l*, pg. 8283
VLADI PRIVATE ISLANDS PACIFIC LIMITED—See Vladi Private Islands GmbH; *Int'l*, pg. 8283
VLADMIR, LTD.; *U.S. Private*, pg. 4407
VLASIC INVESTMENTS LLC; *U.S. Private*, pg. 4407
VLBF CORP.; *U.S. Private*, pg. 4407
VLC DISTRIBUTION COMPANY; *U.S. Private*, pg. 4408
VLC, INC.—See International Game Technology PLC; *Int'l*, pg. 3749
VLC PHOTONICS SOCIEDAD LIMITADA—See Hitachi, Ltd.; *Int'l*, pg. 3424
V.L. ENTERPRISE PUBLIC COMPANY LIMITED; *Int'l*, pg. 8106
VLESIA GMBH—See PAUL HARTMANN AG; *Int'l*, pg. 5762
VLEX NETWORKS, SL—See Oakley Capital Limited; *Int'l*, pg. 5504
VLEXX GMBH—See Ferrovie dello Stato Italiane S.p.A.; *Int'l*, pg. 2645
VLG ADVERTISING; *U.S. Private*, pg. 4408
VLG CHEM S.A.S.—See Eurazeo SE; *Int'l*, pg. 2530
VLIEGASUNIE B.V.—See RWE AG; *Int'l*, pg. 6436
VLIKO B.V.—See Renewi plc; *Int'l*, pg. 6279
VLI MULTIMODAL S.A.—See Vale S.A.; *Int'l*, pg. 8112
VLINK INCORPORATED; *U.S. Private*, pg. 4408
VLINK OPTICS CORPORATION—See Advanced Fiber Resources (Zhuhai) Ltd; *Int'l*, pg. 159
VLISCO FRANCE S.A.—See General Atlantic Service Company, L.P.; *U.S. Private*, pg. 1661
VLISCO HELMOND B.V.—See General Atlantic Service Company, L.P.; *U.S. Private*, pg. 1661
VLISCO NETHERLANDS B.V.—See General Atlantic Service Company, L.P.; *U.S. Private*, pg. 1661
VLOCITY AR SRL—See Salesforce, Inc.; *U.S. Public*, pg. 1838
VLOCITY AUSTRALIA PTY LTD—See Salesforce, Inc.; *U.S. Public*, pg. 1838
VLOCITY CLOUD APPLICATIONS INDIA PRIVATE LIMITED—See Salesforce, Inc.; *U.S. Public*, pg. 1838
VLOCITY CLOUD APPLICATIONS MEXICO S. DE R.L. DE C.V.—See Salesforce, Inc.; *U.S. Public*, pg. 1838
VLOCITY CLOUD COMPUTING ISRAEL LTD.—See Salesforce, Inc.; *U.S. Public*, pg. 1838
VLOCITY JAPAN K.K.—See Salesforce, Inc.; *U.S. Public*, pg. 1838
VLOCITY SINGAPORE PTE. LTD.—See Salesforce, Inc.; *U.S. Public*, pg. 1838
VLP HOLDING CO. INC.; *U.S. Private*, pg. 4408
V.L. RENDINA INC.; *U.S. Private*, pg. 4328
VLR GERMANY GMBH—See Valartis Group AG; *Int'l*, pg. 8111
VLS ASSET MANAGEMENT LIMITED—See VLS Finance Ltd.; *Int'l*, pg. 8283
VLS CAPITAL LTD.; *Int'l*, pg. 8283
VLS FINANCE LTD.; *Int'l*, pg. 8283
VLSI RESEARCH, INC.—See CVC Capital Partners SICAV-FIS S.A.; *Int'l*, pg. 1888
VLSI RESEARCH, INC.—See Oakley Capital Limited; *Int'l*, pg. 5504
VLSI STANDARDS, INC.—See KLA Corporation; *U.S. Public*, pg. 1269
VLS IT CONSULTING; *U.S. Private*, pg. 4408
VLS RECOVERY SERVICES, LLC—See Aurora Capital Group, LLC; *U.S. Private*, pg. 394
VLS SECURITIES LTD.—See VLS Finance Ltd.; *Int'l*, pg. 8283
V.L.S SYSTEMS, INC.; *U.S. Private*, pg. 4328

VLYBY DIGITAL GMBH—See Azerion Group N.V.; *Int'l*, pg. 778
V MANE FILS GHANA (PTY) LTD—See V. Mane Fils SA; *Int'l*, pg. 8106
V. MANE FILS JAPAN, LTD.—See V. Mane Fils SA; *Int'l*, pg. 8106
V. MANE FILS NIGERIA LTD—See V. Mane Fils SA; *Int'l*, pg. 8106
V. MANE FILS SA; *Int'l*, pg. 8106
V. MANE FILS (THAILAND) CO., LTD—See V. Mane Fils SA; *Int'l*, pg. 8106
VMA NV—See Ackermans & van Haaren NV; *Int'l*, pg. 105
V-MARC INDIA LIMITED; *Int'l*, pg. 8105
V-MART RETAIL LTD; *Int'l*, pg. 8105
V & M (BEIJING) CO. LTD.—See Vallourec SA; *Int'l*, pg. 8117
VMB VORSORGEMANAGEMENT FUR BANKEN GMBH—See DZ BANK AG Deutsche Zentral-Genossenschaftsbank; *Int'l*, pg. 2245
VMC CONSULTING CORPORATION—See Canada Pension Plan Investment Board; *Int'l*, pg. 1281
VMC CONSULTING CORPORATION—See EQT AB; *Int'l*, pg. 2483
VMC CONSULTING CORPORATION—See Temasek Holdings (Private) Limited; *Int'l*, pg. 7548
VMC CONSULTING EUROPE LIMITED—See American CyberSystems, Inc.; *U.S. Private*, pg. 230
VMC DENMARK A/S—See TKH Group N.V.; *Int'l*, pg. 7765
V & M CHANGZHOU CO. LTD—See Vallourec SA; *Int'l*, pg. 8117
VMC PECHE SA—See Rapala VMC Oyj; *Int'l*, pg. 6210
VM CREDIT PTE. LTD.—See ValueMax Group Limited; *Int'l*, pg. 8125
VMC—See Danone; *Int'l*, pg. 1968
VMC WATERQUEEN UKRAINE—See Rapala VMC Oyj; *Int'l*, pg. 6210
VMD SYSTEMS INTEGRATORS, INC.; *U.S. Private*, pg. 4408
VMED O2 UK LIMITED—See Liberty Global plc; *Int'l*, pg. 4485
VMED O2 UK LIMITED—See Telefonica, S.A.; *Int'l*, pg. 7536
VME SYSTEMS PTY LTD—See Wentronic Holding GmbH; *Int'l*, pg. 8377
V&M FLORESTAL LTDA.—See Vallourec SA; *Int'l*, pg. 8118
VMG CONSUMER ACQUISITION CORP.; *U.S. Public*, pg. 2307
VMG PARTNERS, LLC; *U.S. Private*, pg. 4408
VMI-AZ EXTRUSION GMBH—See TKH Group N.V.; *Int'l*, pg. 7765
VMI HOLLAND B.V.—See TKH Group N.V.; *Int'l*, pg. 7765
VMI, INC.; *U.S. Private*, pg. 4408
VMI LTD.—See TKH Group N.V.; *Int'l*, pg. 7765
VM IMPIANTI ELETTRICI S.R.L.—See VINCI S.A.; *Int'l*, pg. 8239
VMI SOUTH AMERICA LTDA.—See TKH Group N.V.; *Int'l*, pg. 7765
VMI (YANTAI) MACHINERY CO. LTD.—See TKH Group N.V.; *Int'l*, pg. 7765
VM KOMPENSATOR A/S—See Investment AB Latour; *Int'l*, pg. 3784
VML, INC. - KALAMAZOO—See WPP plc; *Int'l*, pg. 8491
VML, INC.—See WPP plc; *Int'l*, pg. 8490
VML-NEW YORK—See WPP plc; *Int'l*, pg. 8491
VML-WHITE SALMON—See WPP plc; *Int'l*, pg. 8491
VMLY&R DUBAI—See WPP plc; *Int'l*, pg. 8493
VMLY&R HUNGARY—See WPP plc; *Int'l*, pg. 8493
V&M MINERACAO LTDA.—See Vallourec SA; *Int'l*, pg. 8118
VM MONEY PTE. LTD.—See ValueMax Group Limited; *Int'l*, pg. 8125
VM MOTORI S.P.A.—See General Motors Company; *U.S. Public*, pg. 929
VM MOTORI S.P.A.—See Stellantis N.V.; *Int'l*, pg. 7200
V- MODAL MEXICANA, S.C.—See Grupo Traxion, S. A. B. de C. V.; *Int'l*, pg. 3138
VMORE SYSTEM PTE. LTD.—See Noble Vici Group, Inc.; *Int'l*, pg. 5398
VMOTO LIMITED; *Int'l*, pg. 8283
VMOTO MOTOR CYCLES AUSTRALIA—See Vmoto Limited; *Int'l*, pg. 8283
V MOTOR LIMITED—See Johnson Electric Holdings Limited; *Int'l*, pg. 3991
VMR SERVICE—See Handl-It Inc.; *U.S. Private*, pg. 1852
VMS AIRCRAFT COMPANY, INC.—See ADDEV Material SAS; *Int'l*, pg. 128
VMS ALARMS; *U.S. Private*, pg. 4408
VM, S.A.—See Vodafone Group Plc; *Int'l*, pg. 8285
VMS BIOMARKETING; *U.S. Private*, pg. 4408
VMS DEUTSCHLAND HOLDINGS G.M.B.H.—See Siemens Aktiengesellschaft; *Int'l*, pg. 6894
VMS INDUSTRIES LTD.; *Int'l*, pg. 8283
VMS PTY. LTD.—See Eagers Automotive Limited; *Int'l*, pg. 2264
VMS REHAB SYSTEMS INC.; *Int'l*, pg. 8283
VMT GMBH; *Int'l*, pg. 8283
VMTP PJSC—See Far Eastern Shipping Company OJSC; *Int'l*, pg. 2617

VMT (SHANGHAI) TECHNICAL MEASUREMENT CO., LTD.—See VMT GmbH; *Int'l*, pg. 8283
VMT TUNNEL GUIDANCE PTY LTD—See VMT GmbH; *Int'l*, pg. 8283
VMT (USA) TECHNICAL MEASUREMENT SOLUTIONS, INC.—See VMT GmbH; *Int'l*, pg. 8283
VMV PADUCAHBILT—See National Railway Equipment Company; *U.S. Private*, pg. 2861
VMWARE ARGENTINA S.R.L.—See Dell Technologies Inc.; *U.S. Public*, pg. 651
VMWARE AUSTRALIA PTY LTD—See Broadcom Inc.; *U.S. Public*, pg. 390
VMWARE BELGIUM—See Broadcom Inc.; *U.S. Public*, pg. 390
VMWARE BULGARIA EOOD—See Broadcom Inc.; *U.S. Public*, pg. 390
VMWARE CANADA INC.—See Broadcom Inc.; *U.S. Public*, pg. 390
VMWARE DENMARK APS.—See Broadcom Inc.; *U.S. Public*, pg. 390
VMWARE EASTERN EUROPE—See Broadcom Inc.; *U.S. Public*, pg. 390
VMWARE FRANCE SAS.—See Broadcom Inc.; *U.S. Public*, pg. 390
VMWARE GLOBAL, INC.—See Broadcom Inc.; *U.S. Public*, pg. 390
VMWARE GLOBAL, INC.—See Dell Technologies Inc.; *U.S. Public*, pg. 651
VMWARE HONG KONG LIMITED—See Broadcom Inc.; *U.S. Public*, pg. 390
VMWARE INFORMATION TECHNOLOGY(CHINA) CO. LTD—See Broadcom Inc.; *U.S. Public*, pg. 390
VMWARE INTERNATIONAL LIMITED—See Broadcom Inc.; *U.S. Public*, pg. 390
VMWARE INTERNATIONAL SPAIN, S.L.—See Dell Technologies Inc.; *U.S. Public*, pg. 651
VMWARE ISRAEL LTD.—See Broadcom Inc.; *U.S. Public*, pg. 391
VMWARE ITALY S.R.L.—See Broadcom Inc.; *U.S. Public*, pg. 391
VMWARE, K.K.—See Broadcom Inc.; *U.S. Public*, pg. 391
VMWARE KOREA CO., LTD.—See Broadcom Inc.; *U.S. Public*, pg. 391
VMWARE LLC—See Broadcom Inc.; *U.S. Public*, pg. 390
VMWARE MALAYSIA SDN. BHD.—See Dell Technologies Inc.; *U.S. Public*, pg. 651
VMWARE MARKETING AUSTRIA GMBH—See Broadcom Inc.; *U.S. Public*, pg. 391
VMWARE MEXICO S. DE R.L. DE C.V.—See Dell Technologies Inc.; *U.S. Public*, pg. 651
VMWARE NETHERLANDS B.V.—See Broadcom Inc.; *U.S. Public*, pg. 391
VMWARE POLAND SP. Z O.O.—See Dell Technologies Inc.; *U.S. Public*, pg. 651
VMWARE RUS LLC—See Dell Technologies Inc.; *U.S. Public*, pg. 651
VMWARE SINGAPORE PTE. LTD.—See Broadcom Inc.; *U.S. Public*, pg. 391
VMWARE SOFTWARE INDIA PVT. LTD—See Broadcom Inc.; *U.S. Public*, pg. 391
VMWARE SOUTH AFRICA (PTY.) LTD.—See Dell Technologies Inc.; *U.S. Public*, pg. 651
VMWARE SPAIN, S.L.—See Broadcom Inc.; *U.S. Public*, pg. 391
VMWARE SWEDEN AB—See Broadcom Inc.; *U.S. Public*, pg. 391
VMWARE SWITZERLAND S.A.R.L.—See Broadcom Inc.; *U.S. Public*, pg. 391
VMWARE UK LIMITED—See Broadcom Inc.; *U.S. Public*, pg. 391
VM WORLDWIDE SERVICES PTE. LTD.—See ValueMax Group Limited; *Int'l*, pg. 8125
VMZ BERLIN BETREIBERGESELLSCHAFT MBH—See Siemens Aktiengesellschaft; *Int'l*, pg. 6901
V&N ADVANCED AUTOMATION SYSTEMS, LLC; *U.S. Private*, pg. 4327
VNA HOLDING INC.—See AB Volvo; *Int'l*, pg. 42
VNA & HOSPICE OF THE SOUTHWEST REGION, INC.; *U.S. Private*, pg. 4408
VNA HOSPICE & PALLIATIVE CARE OF SOUTHERN CALIFORNIA; *U.S. Private*, pg. 4408
VNA OF RHODE ISLAND; *U.S. Private*, pg. 4408
VNB NEW YORK, LLC—See Valley National Bancorp; *U.S. Public*, pg. 2273
VNDIRECT SECURITIES CORPORATION—See IPA Investments Corporation; *Int'l*, pg. 3795
VND S.P.A.—See Vodafone Group Plc; *Int'l*, pg. 8285
VNECO 1 ELECTRICITY CONSTRUCTION JSC—See Vietnam Electricity Construction Joint Stock Corporation; *Int'l*, pg. 8199
VNECO 3 ELECTRICITY CONSTRUCTION JSC—See Vietnam Electricity Construction Joint Stock Corporation; *Int'l*, pg. 8199
VNECO4 ELECTRICITY CONSTRUCTION JSC—See Vietnam Electricity Construction Joint Stock Corporation; *Int'l*, pg. 8199
VNECO 9 INVESTMENT & CONSTRUCTION JSC—See Vietnam Electricity Construction Joint Stock Corporation; *Int'l*, pg. 8199

VNE S.P.A.; *Int'l*, pg. 8283
VNET GROUP, INC.—See Tsinghua Holdings Co., Ltd.; *Int'l*, pg. 7951
VNG AG—See EnBW Energie Baden-Wurttemberg AG; *Int'l*, pg. 2400
VNG AUSTRIA GMBH—See EnBW Energie Baden-Wurttemberg AG; *Int'l*, pg. 2400
VNG ENERGIE CZECH S.R.O.—See EnBW Energie Baden-Wurttemberg AG; *Int'l*, pg. 2400
VNG GASSPEICHER GMBH—See EnBW Energie Baden-Wurttemberg AG; *Int'l*, pg. 2400
VNG HANDEL & VERTRIEB GMBH—See EnBW Energie Baden-Wurttemberg AG; *Int'l*, pg. 2400
VNG INNOVATION GMBH—See EnBW Energie Baden-Wurttemberg AG; *Int'l*, pg. 2400
VNG VIERTELENERGIE GMBH—See EnBW Energie Baden-Wurttemberg AG; *Int'l*, pg. 2400
VNH FABRYKA - GRZEJNIKOW SP.Z O.O.—See Rettig Group Ltd.; *Int'l*, pg. 6311
VN LABS LIMITED—See Supreme Plc; *Int'l*, pg. 7341
VNOMICS CORP.; *U.S. Private*, pg. 4408
VNS CORPORATION; *U.S. Private*, pg. 4408
VNS HOMECARE INC.; *U.S. Private*, pg. 4408
VNSNY CHOICE—See Visiting Nurse Service of New York; *U.S. Private*, pg. 4393
VNSTEEL HOCHIMINH CITY METAL CORPORATION; *Int'l*, pg. 8283
VNU BUSINESS PUBLICATIONS B.V.—See Roularta Media Group NV; *Int'l*, pg. 6407
VNU BUSINESS PUBLICATIONS LIMITED—See Apax Partners LLP; *Int'l*, pg. 504
VNUE, INC.; *U.S. Public*, pg. 2308
VNU EXHIBITIONS EUROPE BV—See Jaarbeurs Holding B.V.; *Int'l*, pg. 3860
VNV GLOBAL LTD.; *Int'l*, pg. 8283
VOA ASSOCIATES INCORPORATED—See Stantec Inc.; *Int'l*, pg. 7172
VOA CANADA, INC.—See Autoliv, Inc.; *Int'l*, pg. 730
VOA CANADA—See Autoliv, Inc.; *Int'l*, pg. 730
VOALTE, INC.—See Baxter International Inc.; *U.S. Public*, pg. 283
VOA VERRERIE D'ALBI SA—See Compagnie de Saint-Gobain SA; *Int'l*, pg. 1733
VOBILE GROUP LIMITED; *U.S. Private*, pg. 4408
VOB-ZVD PROCESSING GMBH—See Deutsche Bank Aktiengesellschaft; *Int'l*, pg. 2062
VOCALTEC COMMUNICATIONS, LLC—See B. Riley Financial, Inc.; *U.S. Public*, pg. 262
VOCAR A.D.; *Int'l*, pg. 8283
VOCARE LIMITED—See Totally Plc; *Int'l*, pg. 7844
VOCATIONAL DEVELOPMENT CENTER; *U.S. Private*, pg. 4408
THE VOCATIONAL DEVELOPMENT FOUNDATION; *U.S. Private*, pg. 4132
VOCATIONAL GUIDANCE SERVICES; *U.S. Private*, pg. 4409
VOCATIONAL INDEPENDENCE PROGRAM INC; *U.S. Private*, pg. 4409
VOCE COMMUNICATIONS—See Omnicom Group Inc.; *U.S. Public*, pg. 1592
VOCELLI PIZZA; *U.S. Private*, pg. 4409
VOC ENERGY TRUST; *U.S. Public*, pg. 2308
VOCENTO, S.A.; *Int'l*, pg. 8283
VOCERA CANADA, LTD.—See Stryker Corporation; *U.S. Public*, pg. 1958
VOCERA COMMUNICATIONS AUSTRALIA PTY LTD.—See Stryker Corporation; *U.S. Public*, pg. 1958
VOCERA COMMUNICATIONS, INC.—See Stryker Corporation; *U.S. Public*, pg. 1958
VOCERA COMMUNICATIONS UK LTD.—See Stryker Corporation; *U.S. Public*, pg. 1958
VOCIS LIMITED—See OC Oerlikon Corporation AG; *Int'l*, pg. 5515
VOCI TECHNOLOGIES, INC.—See Thoma Bravo, L.P.; *U.S. Private*, pg. 4149
VOCODIA HOLDINGS CORP.; *U.S. Public*, pg. 2308
VOCOLLECT, INC.—See Honeywell International Inc.; *U.S. Public*, pg. 1050
VOCOLLECT INTERNATIONAL LIMITED—See Honeywell International Inc.; *U.S. Public*, pg. 1050
VOCON DESIGN, INC.; *U.S. Private*, pg. 4409
VOCUS EUROPE LIMITED—See Platinum Equity, LLC; *U.S. Private*, pg. 3202
VOCUS FIBRE PTY LIMITED—See Aware Super Pty Ltd; *Int'l*, pg. 752
VOCUS FIBRE PTY LIMITED—See Macquarie Group Limited; *Int'l*, pg. 4629
VOCUS GROUP LIMITED—See Aware Super Pty Ltd; *Int'l*, pg. 752
VOCUS GROUP LIMITED—See Macquarie Group Limited; *Int'l*, pg. 4629
VOCUS GROUP LTD.—See Aware Super Pty Ltd; *Int'l*, pg. 752
VOCUS GROUP LTD.—See Macquarie Group Limited; *Int'l*, pg. 4629
VOCUS PTY LIMITED—See Aware Super Pty Ltd; *Int'l*, pg. 752
VOCUS PTY LIMITED—See Macquarie Group Limited; *Int'l*, pg. 4629

COMPANY NAME INDEX

VOCUS UK LIMITED—See Platinum Equity, LLC; *U.S. Private*, pg. 3202
VODACOM DRCONGO S.P.R.L—See Vodafone Group Plc; *Int'l*, pg. 8285
VODACOM GROUP LIMITED—See Vodafone Group Plc; *Int'l*, pg. 8285
VODACOM INTERNATIONAL HOLDINGS (PROPRIETARY) LIMITED—See Vodafone Group Plc; *Int'l*, pg. 8285
VODACOM LESOTHO (PTY) LTD—See Vodafone Group Plc; *Int'l*, pg. 8285
VODACOM LIFE ASSURANCE COMPANY (RF) LIMITED—See Vodafone Group Plc; *Int'l*, pg. 8285
VODACOM MOZAMBIQUE—See Vodafone Group Plc; *Int'l*, pg. 8285
VODACOM PAYMENT SERVICES (PROPRIETARY) LIMITED—See Vodafone Group Plc; *Int'l*, pg. 8285
VODACOM PTY. LTD.—See Vodafone Group Plc; *Int'l*, pg. 8285
VODACOM SERVICE PROVIDER COMPANY (PROPRIETARY) LIMITED—See Vodafone Group Plc; *Int'l*, pg. 8285
VODACOM TANZANIA LIMITED—See Vodafone Group Plc; *Int'l*, pg. 8285
VODACOM TANZANIA PUBLIC LIMITED COMPANY—See Vodafone Group Plc; *Int'l*, pg. 8285
VODAFONE ALBANIA SH.A—See Vodafone Group Plc; *Int'l*, pg. 8285
VODAFONE AUTOMOTIVE UK LIMITED—See Vodafone Group Plc; *Int'l*, pg. 8285
VODAFONE CZECH REPUBLIC A.S.—See Vodafone Group Plc; *Int'l*, pg. 8285
VODAFONE EGYPT TELECOMMUNICATIONS S.A.E—See Vodafone Group Plc; *Int'l*, pg. 8285
VODAFONE ESPANA S.A.U.—See Zegona Communications PLC; *Int'l*, pg. 8629
VODAFONE FIJI LTD.—See Fiji National Provident Fund; *Int'l*, pg. 2661
VODAFONE GMBH—See Vodafone Group Plc; *Int'l*, pg. 8285
VODAFONE GROUP PLC; *Int'l*, pg. 8284
VODAFONE GROUP SERVICES LIMITED—See Vodafone Group Plc; *Int'l*, pg. 8285
VODAFONE HOLDINGS EUROPE S.L—See Zegona Communications PLC; *Int'l*, pg. 8629
VODAFONE HUNGARY MOBILE TELECOMMUNICATIONS LIMITED—See Vodafone Group Plc; *Int'l*, pg. 8286
VODAFONE IDEA LIMITED; *Int'l*, pg. 8286
VODAFONE INNOVUS S.A.—See Vodafone Group Plc; *Int'l*, pg. 8286
VODAFONE INSTITUT FUR GESELLSCHAFT UND KOMMUNIKATION GMBH—See Vodafone Group Plc; *Int'l*, pg. 8286
VODAFONE INVESTMENTS LUXEMBOURG S.A.R.L.—See Vodafone Group Plc; *Int'l*, pg. 8286
VODAFONE IRELAND LTD—See Vodafone Group Plc; *Int'l*, pg. 8286
VODAFONE ITALIA S.P.A.—See Vodafone Group Plc; *Int'l*, pg. 8286
VODAFONE LIBERTEL N.V—See Liberty Global plc; *Int'l*, pg. 4486
VODAFONE LIMITED—See Vodafone Group Plc; *Int'l*, pg. 8286
VODAFONE MAGYARORSZAG MOBILE TAVKOZLESI ZARTKORUEN MUKODO RESZVENYTARSASAG—See Vodafone Group Plc; *Int'l*, pg. 8286
VODAFONE MAGYARORSZAG TAVKOZLESI ZARTKORUEN MUKODO RESZVENYTARSASAG—See Vodafone Group Plc; *Int'l*, pg. 8286
VODAFONE MALTA LTD.—See Bahrain Telecommunications Company BSC; *Int'l*, pg. 801
VODAFONE NETHERLANDS—See Vodafone Group Plc; *Int'l*, pg. 8286
VODAFONE NEW ZEALAND LTD.—See Brookfield Corporation; *Int'l*, pg. 1189
VODAFONE NEW ZEALAND LTD.—See Infratil Limited; *Int'l*, pg. 3698
VODAFONE-PANAFON HELLENIC TELECOMMUNICATIONS COMPANY S.A—See Vodafone Group Plc; *Int'l*, pg. 8286
VODAFONE PORTUGAL COMUNICACOES PESSOAIS S.A.—See Vodafone Group Plc; *Int'l*, pg. 8286
VODAFONE QATAR Q.S.C.—See Vodafone Group Plc; *Int'l*, pg. 8286
VODAFONE ROAMING SERVICES S.A.R.L.—See Vodafone Group Plc; *Int'l*, pg. 8286
VODAFONE ROMANIA S.A.—See Vodafone Group Plc; *Int'l*, pg. 8286
VODAFONE STIFTUNG DEUTSCHLAND GEMEINNUTZIGE GMBH—See Vodafone Group Plc; *Int'l*, pg. 8286
VODAFONE TELEKOMUNIKASYON A.S.—See Vodafone Group Plc; *Int'l*, pg. 8286
VODAFONE US INC.—See Vodafone Group Plc; *Int'l*, pg. 8286
VODATEL NETWORKS (H.K.) LIMITED—See Vodatel Networks Holdings Limited; *Int'l*, pg. 8286
VODATEL NETWORKS HOLDINGS LIMITED; *Int'l*, pg. 8286
VODA VRNJCI A.D.; *Int'l*, pg. 8284
VODIEN INTERNET SOLUTIONS PTE LTD—See Dreamscape Networks Limited; *Int'l*, pg. 2203
VODKA BRANDS CORP.; *U.S. Public*, pg. 2308
VODNANSKA DRUBEZ, A.S.—See Agrofert Holding, a.s.; *Int'l*, pg. 219
VODOHOD CRUISE COMPANY—See Universal Cargo Logistics Holding B.V.; *Int'l*, pg. 8078
VODOOPSKRBA I ODVODNJA D.O.O.—See Zagrebacki holding d.o.o.; *Int'l*, pg. 8620
VODOPRIVREDA A.D.; *Int'l*, pg. 8286
VODOPRIVREDA A.D.; *Int'l*, pg. 8286
VODOPRIVREDA TREBISNJICA A.D.; *Int'l*, pg. 8286
VODOPRIVREDA ZAGREB DD; *Int'l*, pg. 8286
VODOPRIVREDNO DRUSTVO DUNAV AD; *Int'l*, pg. 8286
VODOPRIVREDNO PREDUZECE A.D.; *Int'l*, pg. 8286
VODOTECH, SPOL. S.R.O.—See Fomento de Construcciones y Contratas, S.A.; *Int'l*, pg. 2723
VODOVOD I KANALIZACIJA A.D.; *Int'l*, pg. 8286
VOD PTY LTD—See Swift Networks Group Limited; *Int'l*, pg. 7368
VOEGELE CO., INC.—See Burns & Scalo Roofing Co., Inc.; *U.S. Private*, pg. 690
VOERMOL FEEDS PROPRIETARY LIMITED—See Tongaat Hulett Limited; *Int'l*, pg. 7807
VOESTALPINE ADDITIVE MANUFACTURING CENTER GMBH—See voestalpine AG; *Int'l*, pg. 8290
VOESTALPINE ADDITIVE MANUFACTURING CENTRE LTD.—See voestalpine AG; *Int'l*, pg. 8290
VOESTALPINE AG; *Int'l*, pg. 8287
VOESTALPINE ANARBEITUNG GMBH—See voestalpine AG; *Int'l*, pg. 8295
VOESTALPINE AUSTRIA DRAHT GMBH—See voestalpine AG; *Int'l*, pg. 8295
VOESTALPINE AUTOMOTIVE COMPONENTS AGUASCALIENTES S. DE R.L. DE C.V.—See voestalpine AG; *Int'l*, pg. 8290
VOESTALPINE AUTOMOTIVE COMPONENTS BIRKENFELD GMBH & CO. KG—See voestalpine AG; *Int'l*, pg. 8290
VOESTALPINE AUTOMOTIVE COMPONENTS BOHMENKIRCH GMBH & CO. KG—See voestalpine AG; *Int'l*, pg. 8290
VOESTALPINE AUTOMOTIVE COMPONENTS BUNSCHOTEN B.V.—See voestalpine AG; *Int'l*, pg. 8290
VOESTALPINE AUTOMOTIVE COMPONENTS CARTERSVILLE LLC—See voestalpine AG; *Int'l*, pg. 8290
VOESTALPINE AUTOMOTIVE COMPONENTS DETTINGEN GMBH & CO. KG—See voestalpine AG; *Int'l*, pg. 8290
VOESTALPINE AUTOMOTIVE COMPONENTS FONTAINE SA—See voestalpine AG; *Int'l*, pg. 8290
VOESTALPINE AUTOMOTIVE COMPONENTS LINZ GMBH—See voestalpine AG; *Int'l*, pg. 8290
VOESTALPINE AUTOMOTIVE COMPONENTS NAGOLD GMBH & CO. KG—See voestalpine AG; *Int'l*, pg. 8290
VOESTALPINE AUTOMOTIVE COMPONENTS SCHMOLLN GMBH—See voestalpine AG; *Int'l*, pg. 8290
VOESTALPINE AUTOMOTIVE COMPONENTS SCHWABISCH GMUND GMBH & CO. KG—See voestalpine AG; *Int'l*, pg. 8290
VOESTALPINE AUTOMOTIVE COMPONENTS SHENYANG CO., LTD.—See voestalpine AG; *Int'l*, pg. 8290
VOESTALPINE AUTOMOTIVE COMPONENTS (TIANJIN) CO., LTD.—See voestalpine AG; *Int'l*, pg. 8290
VOESTALPINE BAHNSYSTEME GMBH AND CO KG—See voestalpine AG; *Int'l*, pg. 8289
VOESTALPINE BAHNSYSTEME GMBH—See voestalpine AG; *Int'l*, pg. 8290
VOESTALPINE BAHNSYSTEME VERMOGENSVERWALTUNGS GMBH—See voestalpine AG; *Int'l*, pg. 8290
VOESTALPINE BELGIUM NV/SA—See voestalpine AG; *Int'l*, pg. 8295
VOESTALPINE BOHLER AEROSPACE GMBH & CO. KG—See voestalpine AG; *Int'l*, pg. 8290
VOESTALPINE BOHLER BLECHE GMBH & CO. KG—See voestalpine AG; *Int'l*, pg. 8290
VOESTALPINE BOHLER EDELSTAHL GMBH & CO. KG—See voestalpine AG; *Int'l*, pg. 8290
VOESTALPINE BOHLER WELDCARE AB—See voestalpine AG; *Int'l*, pg. 8290
VOESTALPINE BOHLER WELDING AUSTRIA GMBH—See voestalpine AG; *Int'l*, pg. 8288
VOESTALPINE BOHLER WELDING (CHINA) CO., LTD.—See voestalpine AG; *Int'l*, pg. 8288
VOESTALPINE BOHLER WELDING FRANCE SAS—See voestalpine AG; *Int'l*, pg. 8290
VOESTALPINE BOHLER WELDING GERMANY GMBH—See voestalpine AG; *Int'l*, pg. 8290
VOESTALPINE BOHLER WELDING GERMANY VERTRIEBS-GMBH—See voestalpine AG; *Int'l*, pg. 8290
VOESTALPINE BOHLER WELDING GROUP GMBH—See voestalpine AG; *Int'l*, pg. 8290
VOESTALPINE BOHLER WELDING HELLAS S.A.—See voestalpine AG; *Int'l*, pg. 8290

VOESTALPINE AG

VOESTALPINE BOHLER WELDING INDIA PRIVATE LIMITED—See voestalpine AG; *Int'l*, pg. 8290
VOESTALPINE BOHLER WELDING INDIA TECHNOLOGY PRIVATE LIMITED—See voestalpine AG; *Int'l*, pg. 8290
VOESTALPINE BOHLER WELDING ITALIA S.R.L.—See voestalpine AG; *Int'l*, pg. 8290
VOESTALPINE BOHLER WELDING MIDDLE EAST FZE—See voestalpine AG; *Int'l*, pg. 8290
VOESTALPINE BOHLER WELDING NEDERLAND B.V.—See voestalpine AG; *Int'l*, pg. 8290
VOESTALPINE BOHLER WELDING ROMANIA SRL—See voestalpine AG; *Int'l*, pg. 8290
VOESTALPINE BOHLER WELDING RUSSIA LLC—See voestalpine AG; *Int'l*, pg. 8288
VOESTALPINE BOHLER WELDING SCHWEIZ AG—See voestalpine AG; *Int'l*, pg. 8290
VOESTALPINE BOHLER WELDING SELCO S.R.L.—See voestalpine AG; *Int'l*, pg. 8290
VOESTALPINE BOHLER WELDING SOLDAS DO BRASIL LTDA.—See voestalpine AG; *Int'l*, pg. 8290
VOESTALPINE BOHLER WELDING SPAIN, S.A.—See voestalpine AG; *Int'l*, pg. 8290
VOESTALPINE BOHLER WELDING TRADING (SHANGHAI) CO., LTD.—See voestalpine AG; *Int'l*, pg. 8290
VOESTALPINE BOHLER WELDING UK LIMITED—See voestalpine AG; *Int'l*, pg. 8290
VOESTALPINE BOHLER WELDING UTP MAINTENANCE GMBH—See voestalpine AG; *Int'l*, pg. 8291
VOESTALPINE BWG GMBH & CO. KG—See voestalpine AG; *Int'l*, pg. 8290
VOESTALPINE BWG LTD.—See voestalpine AG; *Int'l*, pg. 8290
VOESTALPINE CAMTEC CORP.—See voestalpine AG; *Int'l*, pg. 8291
VOESTALPINE CAMTEC GMBH—See voestalpine AG; *Int'l*, pg. 8291
VOESTALPINE CR, S.R.O.—See voestalpine AG; *Int'l*, pg. 8295
VOESTALPINE CZECH REPUBLIC S.R.O.—See voestalpine AG; *Int'l*, pg. 8291
VOESTALPINE DANMARK APS.—See voestalpine AG; *Int'l*, pg. 8295
VOESTALPINE DEUTSCHLAND GMBH—See voestalpine AG; *Int'l*, pg. 8291
VOESTALPINE DIENSTLEISTUNGS- UND FINANZIERUNGS GMBH—See voestalpine AG; *Int'l*, pg. 8292
VOESTALPINE D.O.O.—See voestalpine AG; *Int'l*, pg. 8296
VOESTALPINE D.O.O.—See voestalpine AG; *Int'l*, pg. 8297
VOESTALPINE D.O.O.—See voestalpine AG; *Int'l*, pg. 8296
VOESTALPINE EDELSTAHL DEUTSCHLAND GMBH—See voestalpine AG; *Int'l*, pg. 8291
VOESTALPINE EDELSTAHL GMBH—See voestalpine AG; *Int'l*, pg. 8291
VOESTALPINE EDELSTAHL WARMEBEHANDLUNG GMBH—See voestalpine AG; *Int'l*, pg. 8292
VOESTALPINE EIFELER COATING GMBH—See voestalpine AG; *Int'l*, pg. 8292
VOESTALPINE EIFELER COATINGS, INC.—See voestalpine AG; *Int'l*, pg. 8292
VOESTALPINE ELMSTEEL GROUP LIMITED—See voestalpine AG; *Int'l*, pg. 8289
VOESTALPINE EUROPLATINEN GMBH & CO.—See voestalpine AG; *Int'l*, pg. 8292
VOESTALPINE EUROSTAHL GMBH—See voestalpine AG; *Int'l*, pg. 8295
VOESTALPINE FINANZIERUNGS GMBH—See voestalpine AG; *Int'l*, pg. 8292
VOESTALPINE FINANZIERUNGS HOLDING GMBH—See voestalpine AG; *Int'l*, pg. 8292
VOESTALPINE FRANCE SAS—See voestalpine AG; *Int'l*, pg. 8292
VOESTALPINE GIESSEREI LINZ GMBH—See voestalpine AG; *Int'l*, pg. 8296
VOESTALPINE GIESSEREI TRAISEN GMBH—See voestalpine AG; *Int'l*, pg. 8296
VOESTALPINE GROBBLECH GMBH—See voestalpine AG; *Int'l*, pg. 8296
VOESTALPINE GROUP-IT AB—See voestalpine AG; *Int'l*, pg. 8297
VOESTALPINE GROUP-IT GMBH—See voestalpine AG; *Int'l*, pg. 8297
VOESTALPINE GROUP-IT GMBH—See voestalpine AG; *Int'l*, pg. 8297
VOESTALPINE GROUP-IT TECNOLOGIA DA INFORMACAO LTDA—See voestalpine AG; *Int'l*, pg. 8297
VOESTALPINE HIGH PERFORMANCE METAL ANONIM SIRKETI—See voestalpine AG; *Int'l*, pg. 8292
VOESTALPINE HIGH PERFORMANCE METALS AFRICA (PTY) LTD.—See voestalpine AG; *Int'l*, pg. 8292
VOESTALPINE HIGH PERFORMANCE METALS ARGENTINA S.A.—See voestalpine AG; *Int'l*, pg. 8292
VOESTALPINE HIGH PERFORMANCE METALS (AUSTRALIA) PTY. LTD.—See voestalpine AG; *Int'l*, pg. 8292

VOESTALPINE AG

VOESTALPINE HIGH PERFORMANCE METALS COLOMBIA S.A.—See voestalpine AG; *Int'l*, pg. 8292
VOESTALPINE HIGH PERFORMANCE METALS CORPORATION—See voestalpine AG; *Int'l*, pg. 8292
VOESTALPINE HIGH PERFORMANCE METALS CZ S.R.O.—See voestalpine AG; *Int'l*, pg. 8292
VOESTALPINE HIGH PERFORMANCE METALS DEL ECUADOR S.A.—See voestalpine AG; *Int'l*, pg. 8293
VOESTALPINE HIGH PERFORMANCE METALS DEL PERU S.A.—See voestalpine AG; *Int'l*, pg. 8293
VOESTALPINE HIGH PERFORMANCE METALS DEUTSCHLAND GMBH—See voestalpine AG; *Int'l*, pg. 8292
VOESTALPINE HIGH PERFORMANCE METALS FINLAND OY AB—See voestalpine AG; *Int'l*, pg. 8292
VOESTALPINE HIGH PERFORMANCE METALS FRANCE S.A.S.—See voestalpine AG; *Int'l*, pg. 8292
VOESTALPINE HIGH PERFORMANCE METALS GMBH—See voestalpine AG; *Int'l*, pg. 8292
VOESTALPINE HIGH PERFORMANCE METALS HUNGARY KFT.—See voestalpine AG; *Int'l*, pg. 8292
VOESTALPINE HIGH PERFORMANCE METALS IBERICA, S.A.U.—See voestalpine AG; *Int'l*, pg. 8292
VOESTALPINE HIGH PERFORMANCE METALS INDIA PRIVATE LIMITED—See voestalpine AG; *Int'l*, pg. 8293
VOESTALPINE HIGH PERFORMANCE METALS INTERNATIONAL GMBH—See voestalpine AG; *Int'l*, pg. 8293
VOESTALPINE HIGH PERFORMANCE METALS ITALIA S.P.A.—See voestalpine AG; *Int'l*, pg. 8293
VOESTALPINE HIGH PERFORMANCE METALS LTD.—See voestalpine AG; *Int'l*, pg. 8293
VOESTALPINE HIGH PERFORMANCE METALS NORWAY AS—See voestalpine AG; *Int'l*, pg. 8293
VOESTALPINE HIGH PERFORMANCE METALS PACIFIC PTE. LTD.—See voestalpine AG; *Int'l*, pg. 8293
VOESTALPINE HIGH PERFORMANCE METALS POLSKA SP. Z O. O.—See voestalpine AG; *Int'l*, pg. 8293
VOESTALPINE HIGH PERFORMANCE METALS ROMANIA S.R.L.—See voestalpine AG; *Int'l*, pg. 8293
VOESTALPINE HIGH PERFORMANCE METALS S.A. DE C.V.—See voestalpine AG; *Int'l*, pg. 8293
VOESTALPINE HIGH PERFORMANCE METALS SCHWEIZ AG—See voestalpine AG; *Int'l*, pg. 8293
VOESTALPINE HIGH PERFORMANCE METALS SLOVAKIA, S.R.O.—See voestalpine AG; *Int'l*, pg. 8293
VOESTALPINE HIGH PERFORMANCE METALS SWEDEN AB—See voestalpine AG; *Int'l*, pg. 8293
VOESTALPINE HIGH PERFORMANCE METALS UK LIMITED—See voestalpine AG; *Int'l*, pg. 8293
VOESTALPINE HPM DENMARK A/S—See voestalpine AG; *Int'l*, pg. 8292
VOESTALPINE HPM ZAGREB D.O.O.—See voestalpine AG; *Int'l*, pg. 8292
VOESTALPINE HUNGARIA KFT.—See voestalpine AG; *Int'l*, pg. 8296
VOESTALPINE HYTRONICS GMBH—See voestalpine AG; *Int'l*, pg. 8289
VOESTALPINE IBERIA S.L.—See voestalpine AG; *Int'l*, pg. 8293
VOESTALPINE INSURANCE SERVICES GMBH—See voestalpine AG; *Int'l*, pg. 8293
VOESTALPINE ITALIA S.R.L.—See voestalpine AG; *Int'l*, pg. 8296
VOESTALPINE KLOCKNER BAHNTECHNIK GMBH—See voestalpine AG; *Int'l*, pg. 8289
VOESTALPINE KREMS FINALTECHNIK GMBH—See voestalpine AG; *Int'l*, pg. 8293
VOESTALPINE KREMS GMBH—See voestalpine AG; *Int'l*, pg. 8293
VOEST-ALPINE KREMS U.K. PLC—See voestalpine AG; *Int'l*, pg. 8294
VOESTALPINE MEINCOL S.A.—See voestalpine AG; *Int'l*, pg. 8294
VOESTALPINE METAL FORMING GMBH—See voestalpine AG; *Int'l*, pg. 8293
VOESTALPINE METAL FORMING US HOLDING LLC—See voestalpine AG; *Int'l*, pg. 8293
VOESTALPINE METSEC PLC—See voestalpine AG; *Int'l*, pg. 8293
VOESTALPINE NEDERLAND B.V.—See voestalpine AG; *Int'l*, pg. 8293
VOESTALPINE NORTRAK INC. - BIRMINGHAM PLANT—See voestalpine AG; *Int'l*, pg. 8293
VOESTALPINE NORTRAK INC. - CHICAGO HEIGHTS PLANT—See voestalpine AG; *Int'l*, pg. 8293
VOESTALPINE NORTRAK INC. - DECATUR PLANT—See voestalpine AG; *Int'l*, pg. 8293
VOESTALPINE NORTRAK INC. - NEWTON PLANT—See voestalpine AG; *Int'l*, pg. 8293
VOESTALPINE NORTRAK INC. - PUEBLO PLANT—See voestalpine AG; *Int'l*, pg. 8293
VOESTALPINE NORTRAK INC. - SEATTLE PLANT—See voestalpine AG; *Int'l*, pg. 8293
VOESTALPINE NORTRAK INC.—See voestalpine AG; *Int'l*, pg. 8293
VOESTALPINE NORTRAK LTD.—See voestalpine AG; *Int'l*, pg. 8293

VOESTALPINE PERSONAL SERVICES GMBH—See voestalpine AG; *Int'l*, pg. 8293
VOESTALPINE POLSKA SP.Z O.O.—See voestalpine AG; *Int'l*, pg. 8296
VOESTALPINE POLYNORM BETEILIGUNGSGESELLSCHAFT M.B.H.—See voestalpine AG; *Int'l*, pg. 8294
VOESTALPINE POLYNORM BV—See voestalpine AG; *Int'l*, pg. 8293
VOESTALPINE POLYNORM GMBH & CO. KG—See voestalpine AG; *Int'l*, pg. 8294
VOESTALPINE PRAZISIONSPROFIL GMBH—See voestalpine AG; *Int'l*, pg. 8294
VOESTALPINE PRECISION STRIP AB—See voestalpine AG; *Int'l*, pg. 8294
VOESTALPINE PRECISION STRIP, S.A.U.—See voestalpine AG; *Int'l*, pg. 8294
VOESTALPINE PRECISION STRIP TRADING (SUZHOU) CO., LTD.—See voestalpine AG; *Int'l*, pg. 8294
VOESTALPINE PRECISION STRIP WI, INC.—See voestalpine AG; *Int'l*, pg. 8294
VOESTALPINE PROFILFORM BETEILIGUNG GMBH—See voestalpine AG; *Int'l*, pg. 8294
VOESTALPINE PROFILFORM (CHINA) CO., LTD.—See voestalpine AG; *Int'l*, pg. 8294
VOESTALPINE PROFILFORM GMBH—See voestalpine AG; *Int'l*, pg. 8294
VOESTALPINE PROFILFORM S.R.O.—See voestalpine AG; *Int'l*, pg. 8293
VOESTALPINE RAIL CENTER DUISBURG GMBH—See voestalpine AG; *Int'l*, pg. 8294
VOESTALPINE RAILPRO B.V.—See voestalpine AG; *Int'l*, pg. 8294
VOESTALPINE RAIL TECHNOLOGY GMBH—See voestalpine AG; *Int'l*, pg. 8294
VOESTALPINE RAILWAY SYSTEMS AUSTRALIA PTY. LTD.—See voestalpine AG; *Int'l*, pg. 8294
VOESTALPINE RAILWAY SYSTEMS BEIJING CO. LTD.—See voestalpine AG; *Int'l*, pg. 8294
VOESTALPINE RAILWAY SYSTEMS BULGARIA OOD—See voestalpine AG; *Int'l*, pg. 8294
VOESTALPINE RAILWAY SYSTEMS JEZ, S.L.—See voestalpine AG; *Int'l*, pg. 8294
VOESTALPINE RAILWAY SYSTEMS LATVIA SIA—See voestalpine AG; *Int'l*, pg. 8294
VOESTALPINE RAILWAY SYSTEMS MFA SASU—See voestalpine AG; *Int'l*, pg. 8294
VOESTALPINE RAILWAY SYSTEMS POLSKA SP. Z O.O.—See voestalpine AG; *Int'l*, pg. 8294
VOESTALPINE RAILWAY SYSTEMS ROMANIA SA—See voestalpine AG; *Int'l*, pg. 8294
VOESTALPINE RAILWAY SYSTEMS SAUDI ARABIA LIMITED—See voestalpine AG; *Int'l*, pg. 8294
VOESTALPINE ROHSTOFFBESCHAFFUNGS-GMBH—See voestalpine AG; *Int'l*, pg. 8296
VOESTALPINE ROHSTOFFHANDEL GMBH—See voestalpine AG; *Int'l*, pg. 8294
VOESTALPINE ROMANIA S.R.L.—See voestalpine AG; *Int'l*, pg. 8296
VOESTALPINE ROTEC AB—See voestalpine AG; *Int'l*, pg. 8294
VOESTALPINE ROTEC FRANCE S.A.—See voestalpine AG; *Int'l*, pg. 8295
VOESTALPINE ROTEC GMBH & CO. KG—See voestalpine AG; *Int'l*, pg. 8295
VOESTALPINE ROTEC GMBH—See voestalpine AG; *Int'l*, pg. 8289
VOESTALPINE ROTEC IBERICA S.A.—See voestalpine AG; *Int'l*, pg. 8295
VOESTALPINE ROTEC INCORPORATED—See voestalpine AG; *Int'l*, pg. 8295
VOESTALPINE ROTEC LIMITED—See voestalpine AG; *Int'l*, pg. 8295
VOESTALPINE ROTEC NORTH AMERICA CORP.—See voestalpine AG; *Int'l*, pg. 8295
VOESTALPINE ROTEC SP. Z.O.O—See voestalpine AG; *Int'l*, pg. 8295
VOESTALPINE SADEF NV—See voestalpine AG; *Int'l*, pg. 8295
VOESTALPINE S.A.P.—See voestalpine AG; *Int'l*, pg. 8295
VOESTALPINE SCANDINAVIA AB—See voestalpine AG; *Int'l*, pg. 8295
VOESTALPINE SCHIENEN GMBH & CO. KG—See voestalpine AG; *Int'l*, pg. 8295
VOESTALPINE SCHIENENTECHNIK BETEILIGUNGS GMBH—See voestalpine AG; *Int'l*, pg. 8295
VOESTALPINE SCHWEIZ GMBH—See voestalpine AG; *Int'l*, pg. 8295
VOESTALPINE SIGNALING AUSTRIA GMBH—See voestalpine AG; *Int'l*, pg. 8295
VOESTALPINE SIGNALING CHINA CO., LTD.—See voestalpine AG; *Int'l*, pg. 8295
VOESTALPINE SIGNALING POLAND SP. Z O.O.—See voestalpine AG; *Int'l*, pg. 8295
VOESTALPINE SIGNALING SAINERHOLZ GMBH—See voestalpine AG; *Int'l*, pg. 8295
VOESTALPINE SIGNALING SIERSHAHN GMBH—See voestalpine AG; *Int'l*, pg. 8295
VOESTALPINE SIGNALING UK LTD.—See voestalpine AG; *Int'l*, pg. 8295

CORPORATE AFFILIATIONS

VOESTALPINE SIGNALING USA LLC—See voestalpine AG; *Int'l*, pg. 8295
VOESTALPINE SLOVAKIA S.R.O.—See voestalpine AG; *Int'l*, pg. 8296
VOESTALPINE SPECIALTY METALS (SHANGHAI) CO. LTD.—See voestalpine AG; *Int'l*, pg. 8295
VOESTALPINE STAHL APS—See voestalpine AG; *Int'l*, pg. 8295
VOESTALPINE STAHL DONAWITZ GMBH & CO KG—See voestalpine AG; *Int'l*, pg. 8295
VOESTALPINE STAHL DONAWITZ GMBH—See voestalpine AG; *Int'l*, pg. 8295
VOESTALPINE STAHL DONAWITZ IMMOBILIEN GMBH—See voestalpine AG; *Int'l*, pg. 8290
VOESTALPINE STAHL D.O.O.—See voestalpine AG; *Int'l*, pg. 8295
VOESTALPINE STAHL D.O.O.—See voestalpine AG; *Int'l*, pg. 8296
VOESTALPINE STAHL D.O.O.—See voestalpine AG; *Int'l*, pg. 8296
VOESTALPINE STAHL GMBH—See voestalpine AG; *Int'l*, pg. 8295
VOESTALPINE STAHLHANDEL GMBH—See Zlomrex SA; *Int'l*, pg. 8687
VOESTALPINE STAHL N.V./S.A.—See voestalpine AG; *Int'l*, pg. 8296
VOESTALPINE STAHL SERVICE CENTER GMBH—See voestalpine AG; *Int'l*, pg. 8296
VOESTALPINE STAHL S.P.A.—See voestalpine AG; *Int'l*, pg. 8296
VOESTALPINE STAHL SP.Z.O.O.—See voestalpine AG; *Int'l*, pg. 8295
VOESTALPINE STAHLWELT GMBH—See voestalpine AG; *Int'l*, pg. 8296
VOESTALPINE STAMPTEC BETEILIGUNGS GMBH—See voestalpine AG; *Int'l*, pg. 8296
VOESTALPINE STAMPTEC BIRKENFELD GMBH—See voestalpine AG; *Int'l*, pg. 8289
VOESTALPINE STAMPTEC BOHMENKIRCH GMBH & CO. KG—See voestalpine AG; *Int'l*, pg. 8296
VOESTALPINE STAMPTEC FRANCE S.A.—See voestalpine AG; *Int'l*, pg. 8296
VOESTALPINE STAMPTEC GMBH—See voestalpine AG; *Int'l*, pg. 8289
VOESTALPINE STAMPTEC HOLDING GMBH—See voestalpine AG; *Int'l*, pg. 8296
VOESTALPINE STAMPTEC NAGOLD GMBH & CO. KG—See voestalpine AG; *Int'l*, pg. 8296
VOESTALPINE STAMPTEC PFAFFENHOFEN GMBH & CO. KG—See voestalpine AG; *Int'l*, pg. 8296
VOESTALPINE STAMPTEC ROMANIA S.R.L.—See voestalpine AG; *Int'l*, pg. 8289
VOESTALPINE STANDORTSERVICE GMBH—See voestalpine AG; *Int'l*, pg. 8296
VOESTALPINE STEEL MIDDLE EAST FZE—See voestalpine AG; *Int'l*, pg. 8296
VOESTALPINE STEEL & SERVICE CENTER GMBH—See voestalpine AG; *Int'l*, pg. 8296
VOESTALPINE STEEL SERVICE CENTER POLSKA SP. Z O.O.—See voestalpine AG; *Int'l*, pg. 8296
VOESTALPINE STEEL SERVICE CENTER ROMANIA SRL—See voestalpine AG; *Int'l*, pg. 8296
VOESTALPINE STEEL TRADING (SHENYANG) CO., LTD.—See voestalpine AG; *Int'l*, pg. 8296
VOESTALPINE STEEL US LLC—See voestalpine AG; *Int'l*, pg. 8296
VOESTALPINE STRASSENSICHERHEIT GMBH—See voestalpine AG; *Int'l*, pg. 8294
VOESTALPINE TENS SP. Z O.O.—See voestalpine AG; *Int'l*, pg. 8296
VOESTALPINE TEXAS HOLDING LLC—See voestalpine AG; *Int'l*, pg. 8296
VOEST ALPINE TUBULARS GMBH & CO KG—See NOV, Inc.; *U.S. Public*, pg. 1547
VOESTALPINE TUBULARS GMBH & CO. KG—See voestalpine AG; *Int'l*, pg. 8295
VOEST ALPINE TUBULARS GMBH—See NOV, Inc.; *U.S. Public*, pg. 1547
VOESTALPINE TURKEY CELIK LIMITED—See voestalpine AG; *Int'l*, pg. 8296
VOESTALPINE TURNOUT TECHNOLOGY GERMANY GMBH—See voestalpine AG; *Int'l*, pg. 8296
VOESTALPINE TURNOUT TECHNOLOGY NETHERLANDS B.V.—See voestalpine AG; *Int'l*, pg. 8296
VOESTALPINE TURNOUT TECHNOLOGY UK LIMITED—See voestalpine AG; *Int'l*, pg. 8296
VOESTALPINE U.K. LTD.—See voestalpine AG; *Int'l*, pg. 8296
VOESTALPINE U.S.A. CORP.—See voestalpine AG; *Int'l*, pg. 8296
VOESTALPINE VAE AFRICA (PTY) LTD.—See voestalpine AG; *Int'l*, pg. 8297
VOESTALPINE VAE APCAROM—See voestalpine AG; *Int'l*, pg. 8296
VOESTALPINE VAE GMBH—See voestalpine AG; *Int'l*, pg. 8289
VOESTALPINE VAE ITALIA S.R.L.—See voestalpine AG; *Int'l*, pg. 8297

COMPANY NAME INDEX

VOESTALPINE VAE LEGETECHA UAB—See voestalpine AG; *Int'l*, pg. 8297
VOESTALPINE VAE POLSKA SP. Z O.O.—See voestalpine AG; *Int'l*, pg. 8297
VOESTALPINE VAE RAILWAY SYSTEMS PTY.LTD.—See voestalpine AG; *Int'l*, pg. 8297
VOESTALPINE VAE SA (PTY) LTD.—See voestalpine AG; *Int'l*, pg. 8297
VOESTALPINE VAE UK LTD.—See voestalpine AG; *Int'l*, pg. 8297
VOESTALPINE VAE VKN INDIA PRIVATE LIMITED—See voestalpine AG; *Int'l*, pg. 8297
VOESTALPINE WBN B.V.—See voestalpine AG; *Int'l*, pg. 8297
VOESTALPINE WEICHENSYSTEME GMBH—See voestalpine AG; *Int'l*, pg. 8289
VOESTALPINE WIRE GERMANY GMBH—See voestalpine AG; *Int'l*, pg. 8297
VOESTALPINE WIRE ITALY S.R.L.—See voestalpine AG; *Int'l*, pg. 8297
VOESTALPINE WIRE ROD AUSTRIA GMBH—See voestalpine AG; *Int'l*, pg. 8297
VOF STATIONSEILAND—See ARCADIS N.V.; *Int'l*, pg. 541
VOGEL BROS BUILDING CO. INC.; *U.S. Private*, pg. 4409
VOGEL DISPOSAL SERVICE INC.; *U.S. Private*, pg. 4409
VOGEL DRUCK UND MEDIENSERVICE GMBH—See Bertelsmann SE & Co. KGaA; *Int'l*, pg. 996
VOGEL PAINT, INC.; *U.S. Private*, pg. 4409
VOGEL SEED & FERTILIZER, INC.; *U.S. Private*, pg. 4409
VOGEL VINS SA—See Hawesko Holding AG; *Int'l*, pg. 3288
VOGEL WEST INC.—See Diamond Vogel Paint, Inc.; *U.S. Private*, pg. 1224
VOGIATZOGLOU SYSTEMS S.A.; *Int'l*, pg. 8297
VOGLER MOTOR COMPANY, INC.; *U.S. Private*, pg. 4409
VOGO S.A.; *Int'l*, pg. 8297
VOGTLE SERVICE GMBH & CO. KG—See ANDRITZ AG; *Int'l*, pg. 456
VOGT POWER INTERNATIONAL INC.—See Babcock Power, Inc.; *U.S. Private*, pg. 422
VOGTRONICS GMBH—See Sumida Corporation; *Int'l*, pg. 7262
VOGUE INTERNATIONAL LLC—See Kenvue Inc.; *U.S. Public*, pg. 1224
VOGUE LAUNDRY SERVICES LIMITED—See Cathay Pacific Airways Limited; *Int'l*, pg. 1360
VOGUE MAGAZINE—See Advance Publications, Inc.; *U.S. Private*, pg. 86
VOGUE TYRE & RUBBER CO., INC.; *U.S. Private*, pg. 4409
VOHKUS LTD.; *Int'l*, pg. 8297
VOHRINGER HOME TECHNOLOGY CO., LTD.; *Int'l*, pg. 8297
VOICE 1 DIRECT LTD.; *U.S. Private*, pg. 4409
VOICE ASSIST, INC.; *U.S. Public*, pg. 2308
VOICE COMM, LLC—See Tygon Peak Capital; *U.S. Private*, pg. 4267
VOICE COMMUNICATIONS CORP.—See Alden Global Capital LLC; *U.S. Private*, pg. 159
VOICEINTEROP, INC.; *U.S. Private*, pg. 4409
VOICENATION, LLC—See ECI Partners LLP; *Int'l*, pg. 2289
VOICENET SOLUTIONS LIMITED—See 8x8, Inc.; *U.S. Public*, pg. 10
VOICE OF PROPHECY, INC.; *U.S. Private*, pg. 4409
VOICEPORT, LLC—See Enghouse Systems Limited; *Int'l*, pg. 2428
VOICE PROVIDER SWEDEN AB—See Addnode Group AB; *Int'l*, pg. 131
VOICESERVE, INC.; *Int'l*, pg. 8297
VOICES FOR INDEPENDENCE; *U.S. Private*, pg. 4409
VOICE SIGNAL IRELAND LIMITED—See Microsoft Corporation; *U.S. Public*, pg. 1443
VOICE SIGNAL K.K.—See Microsoft Corporation; *U.S. Public*, pg. 1443
VOICE-TECH, INC.; *U.S. Private*, pg. 4409
VOIDU B.V.—See Azerion Group N.V.; *Int'l*, pg. 778
VOI EUROPE, S.A.R.L.—See Vimian Group AB; *Int'l*, pg. 8208
VOIGHT ENTERPRISES, INC.; *U.S. Private*, pg. 4409
VOIGT-ABERNATHY COMPANY, INC.; *U.S. Private*, pg. 4409
VOIGT & CO. BAUGESELLSCHAFT GMBH—See Skanska AB; *Int'l*, pg. 6979
VOIGT & SCHWEITZER LLC—See Hill & Smith PLC; *Int'l*, pg. 3392
VOIGT SOFTWARE UND BERATUNG AG—See MEDIQON Group AG; *Int'l*, pg. 4780
VOIP GORILLA—See Odyssey Telecommunications, Inc.; *U.S. Private*, pg. 2996
VOIP INNOVATIONS LLC—See Sangoma Technologies Corporation; *Int'l*, pg. 6538
VOIPLINK CORPORATION; *U.S. Private*, pg. 4409
VOIP-PAL.COM INC.; *U.S. Public*, pg. 2308

VOIP SUPPLY LLC—See Sangoma Technologies Corporation; *Int'l*, pg. 6538
VOIRIES ET PAVAGES DU NORD SAS—See VINCI S.A.; *Int'l*, pg. 8240
VOISARD MANUFACTURING INC.; *U.S. Private*, pg. 4409
VOISIN CONSULTING, INC.; *U.S. Private*, pg. 4409
VOIT COMMERCIAL BROKERAGE LP—See Voit Real Estate Services, Inc.; *U.S. Private*, pg. 4410
VOITH CANADA INC.-FABRICS DIVISION—See Voith GmbH & Co. KGaA; *Int'l*, pg. 8298
VOITH FABRICS BENELUX—See Voith GmbH & Co. KGaA; *Int'l*, pg. 8298
VOITH FABRICS DE MEXICO, S.A. DE C.V.—See Voith GmbH & Co. KGaA; *Int'l*, pg. 8298
VOITH GMBH & CO. KGAA; *Int'l*, pg. 8297
VOITH HYDRO AB—See Voith GmbH & Co. KGaA; *Int'l*, pg. 8297
VOITH HYDRO AS—See Voith GmbH & Co. KGaA; *Int'l*, pg. 8297
VOITH HYDRO DA AMAZONIA LTDA.—See Voith GmbH & Co. KGaA; *Int'l*, pg. 8298
VOITH HYDRO HOLDING GMBH & CO. KG—See Voith GmbH & Co. KGaA; *Int'l*, pg. 8297
VOITH HYDRO INC.—See Voith GmbH & Co. KGaA; *Int'l*, pg. 8297
VOITH HYDRO INC.—See Voith GmbH & Co. KGaA; *Int'l*, pg. 8297
VOITH HYDRO LTDA.—See Voith GmbH & Co. KGaA; *Int'l*, pg. 8297
VOITH HYDRO LTDA.—See Voith GmbH & Co. KGaA; *Int'l*, pg. 8297
VOITH HYDRO PRIVATE LIMITED—See Voith GmbH & Co. KGaA; *Int'l*, pg. 8297
VOITH HYDRO SARPSBORG AS—See Voith GmbH & Co. KGaA; *Int'l*, pg. 8297
VOITH HYDRO SHANGHAI LTD.—See Voith GmbH & Co. KGaA; *Int'l*, pg. 8297
VOITH HYDRO S.R.L.—See Voith GmbH & Co. KGaA; *Int'l*, pg. 8297
VOITH HYDRO S.R.L.—See Voith GmbH & Co. KGaA; *Int'l*, pg. 8297
VOITH HYDRO S.R.O.—See Voith GmbH & Co. KGaA; *Int'l*, pg. 8298
VOITH IHI PAPER TECHNOLOGY CO., LTD.—See IHI Corporation; *Int'l*, pg. 3606
VOITH IT SOLUTIONS INC.—See Voith GmbH & Co. KGaA; *Int'l*, pg. 8298
VOITH MERI ENVIRONMENTAL SOLUTIONS, INC.—See Voith GmbH & Co. KGaA; *Int'l*, pg. 8298
VOITH MIDDLE EAST FZE—See Voith GmbH & Co. KGaA; *Int'l*, pg. 8298
VOITH PAPER ARGENTINA S.A.—See Voith GmbH & Co. KGaA; *Int'l*, pg. 8298
VOITH PAPER AS—See Voith GmbH & Co. KGaA; *Int'l*, pg. 8298
VOITH PAPER B.V.—See Voith GmbH & Co. KGaA; *Int'l*, pg. 8298
VOITH PAPER (CHINA) CO., LTD.—See Voith GmbH & Co. KGaA; *Int'l*, pg. 8298
VOITH PAPER FABRIC & ROLL SYSTEMS GMBH & CO. KG—See Voith GmbH & Co. KGaA; *Int'l*, pg. 8298
VOITH PAPER FABRIC & ROLL SYSTEMS, INC.—See Voith GmbH & Co. KGaA; *Int'l*, pg. 8298
VOITH PAPER FABRICS ASIA PACIFIC SDN. BHD.—See Voith GmbH & Co. KGaA; *Int'l*, pg. 8298
VOITH PAPER FABRICS B.V.—See Voith GmbH & Co. KGaA; *Int'l*, pg. 8298
VOITH PAPER FABRICS DUREN GMBH—See Voith GmbH & Co. KGaA; *Int'l*, pg. 8298
VOITH PAPER FABRICS GMBH—See Voith GmbH & Co. KGaA; *Int'l*, pg. 8298
VOITH PAPER FABRICS GUSUM AB—See Voith GmbH & Co. KGaA; *Int'l*, pg. 8298
VOITH PAPER FABRICS HOGSJO AB—See Voith GmbH & Co. KGaA; *Int'l*, pg. 8298
VOITH PAPER FABRICS INDIA LTD.—See Voith GmbH & Co. KGaA; *Int'l*, pg. 8298
VOITH PAPER FABRICS, S.A.—See Voith GmbH & Co. KGaA; *Int'l*, pg. 8298
VOITH PAPER FABRICS—See Voith GmbH & Co. KGaA; *Int'l*, pg. 8298
VOITH PAPER FABRICS STUBBINS, LTD.—See Voith GmbH & Co. KGaA; *Int'l*, pg. 8298
VOITH PAPER GMBH & CO. KG—See Voith GmbH & Co. KGaA; *Int'l*, pg. 8298
VOITH PAPER GMBH & CO. KG—See Voith GmbH & Co. KGaA; *Int'l*, pg. 8298
VOITH PAPER HOLDING GMBH & CO. KG—See Voith GmbH & Co. KGaA; *Int'l*, pg. 8298
VOITH PAPER INC.—See Voith GmbH & Co. KGaA; *Int'l*, pg. 8298
VOITH PAPER KAGIT SANAYI LIMITED SIRKETI—See Voith GmbH & Co. KGaA; *Int'l*, pg. 8298
VOITH PAPER LTD.—See Voith GmbH & Co. KGaA; *Int'l*, pg. 8298
VOITH PAPER MAQUINAS E EQUIPAMENTOS LTDA.—See Voith GmbH & Co. KGaA; *Int'l*, pg. 8298

VOITH GMBH & CO. KGAA

VOITH PAPER MEXICO S DE RL DE CV—See Voith GmbH & Co. KGaA; *Int'l*, pg. 8298
VOITH PAPER OY—See Voith GmbH & Co. KGaA; *Int'l*, pg. 8298
VOITH PAPER ROLLS GMBH & CO KG—See Voith GmbH & Co. KGaA; *Int'l*, pg. 8298
VOITH PAPER ROLLS GUANGZHOU CO., LTD.—See Voith GmbH & Co. KGaA; *Int'l*, pg. 8298
VOITH PAPER S.A.—See Voith GmbH & Co. KGaA; *Int'l*, pg. 8298
VOITH PAPER S.R.L.—See Voith GmbH & Co. KGaA; *Int'l*, pg. 8298
VOITH PAPER TECHNOLOGY (INDIA) PRIVATE LIMITED—See Voith GmbH & Co. KGaA; *Int'l*, pg. 8299
VOITH PAPER TECHNOLOGY RUSSIA GMBH—See Voith GmbH & Co. KGaA; *Int'l*, pg. 8299
VOITH PAPER (THAILAND) CO., LTD.—See Voith GmbH & Co. KGaA; *Int'l*, pg. 8298
VOITH PAPER WALZTECHNIK AG—See Voith GmbH & Co. KGaA; *Int'l*, pg. 8299
VOITH SAFESET AB—See Voith GmbH & Co. KGaA; *Int'l*, pg. 8299
VOITH SIEMENS HYDRO POWER GENERATION S.L.—See Voith GmbH & Co. KGaA; *Int'l*, pg. 8298
VOITH SIEMENS HYDRO POWER GENERATION S.P.A.—See Voith GmbH & Co. KGaA; *Int'l*, pg. 8298
VOITH TURBO AS—See Voith GmbH & Co. KGaA; *Int'l*, pg. 8299
VOITH TURBO A/S—See Voith GmbH & Co. KGaA; *Int'l*, pg. 8299
VOITH TURBO BHS GETRIEBE GMBH—See Voith GmbH & Co. KGaA; *Int'l*, pg. 8299
VOITH TURBO B.V.—See Voith GmbH & Co. KGaA; *Int'l*, pg. 8299
VOITH TURBO COLOMBIA S.A.S.—See Voith GmbH & Co. KGaA; *Int'l*, pg. 8299
VOITH TURBO D.O.O.—See Voith GmbH & Co. KGaA; *Int'l*, pg. 8299
VOITH TURBO GMBH & CO. KG—See Voith GmbH & Co. KGaA; *Int'l*, pg. 8299
VOITH TURBO GMBH & CO. KG—See Voith GmbH & Co. KGaA; *Int'l*, pg. 8299
VOITH TURBO GUC AKTARMA TEKNIGI LTD. STI.—See Voith GmbH & Co. KGaA; *Int'l*, pg. 8299
VOITH TURBO H + L HYDRAULIC GMBH & CO. KG—See Voith GmbH & Co. KGaA; *Int'l*, pg. 8299
VOITH TURBO INC.—See Voith GmbH & Co. KGaA; *Int'l*, pg. 8299
VOITH TURBO KFT.—See Voith GmbH & Co. KGaA; *Int'l*, pg. 8299
VOITH TURBO LIMITED—See Voith GmbH & Co. KGaA; *Int'l*, pg. 8299
VOITH TURBO LIMITED—See Voith GmbH & Co. KGaA; *Int'l*, pg. 8299
VOITH TURBO LOKOMOTIVTECHNIK, EINE ZWEIGNIEDERLASSUNG DER VOITH TURBO GMBH & CO. KG—See Voith GmbH & Co. KGaA; *Int'l*, pg. 8299
VOITH TURBO LTD.—See Voith GmbH & Co. KGaA; *Int'l*, pg. 8299
VOITH TURBO NZ PTY LIMITED—See Voith GmbH & Co. KGaA; *Int'l*, pg. 8299
VOITH TURBO OOO—See Voith GmbH & Co. KGaA; *Int'l*, pg. 8299
VOITH TURBO POWER TRANSMISSION (SHANGHAI) CO., LTD.—See Voith GmbH & Co. KGaA; *Int'l*, pg. 8299
VOITH TURBO PRIVATE LTD.—See Voith GmbH & Co. KGaA; *Int'l*, pg. 8299
VOITH TURBO PTE. LTD.—See Voith GmbH & Co. KGaA; *Int'l*, pg. 8299
VOITH TURBO PTY. LTD.—See Voith GmbH & Co. KGaA; *Int'l*, pg. 8299
VOITH TURBO (PTY) LTD—See Voith GmbH & Co. KGaA; *Int'l*, pg. 8299
VOITH TURBO S.A.C.—See Voith GmbH & Co. KGaA; *Int'l*, pg. 8299
VOITH TURBO SAFESET AB—See Voith GmbH & Co. KGaA; *Int'l*, pg. 8299
VOITH TURBO S.A./N.V.—See Voith GmbH & Co. KGaA; *Int'l*, pg. 8299
VOITH TURBO S.A.—See Voith GmbH & Co. KGaA; *Int'l*, pg. 8299
VOITH TURBO S.A.—See Voith GmbH & Co. KGaA; *Int'l*, pg. 8299
VOITH TURBO SAS—See Voith GmbH & Co. KGaA; *Int'l*, pg. 8299
VOITH TURBO SCHARFENBERG GMBH & CO. KG—See Voith GmbH & Co. KGaA; *Int'l*, pg. 8299
VOITH TURBO SMI TECHNOLOGIES GMBH & CO. KG—See Voith GmbH & Co. KGaA; *Int'l*, pg. 8299
VOITH TURBO SP. Z O.O.—See Voith GmbH & Co. KGaA; *Int'l*, pg. 8299
VOITH TURBO S.R.L.—See Voith GmbH & Co. KGaA; *Int'l*, pg. 8299
VOITH TURBO S.R.O.—See Voith GmbH & Co. KGaA; *Int'l*, pg. 8299

VOITH GMBH & CO. KGAA — CORPORATE AFFILIATIONS

Company Index

VOITH TURBO VERTRIEBS GMBH & CO KG—See Voith GmbH & Co. KGaA; *Int'l*, pg. 8299
VOIT REAL ESTATE SERVICES, INC.; *U.S. Private*, pg. 4410
VOJVODINA A.D.; *Int'l*, pg. 8299
VOJVODINA A.D.; *Int'l*, pg. 8299
VOJVODINA A.D.; *Int'l*, pg. 8299
VOJVODINAPUT A.D.; *Int'l*, pg. 8300
VOJVODINAPUT BACKAPUT A.D.—See Baumeister doo; *Int'l*, pg. 895
VOJVODINAPUT-PANCEVO A.D.—See STRABAG SE; *Int'l*, pg. 7233
VOJVODINASPED A.D.; *Int'l*, pg. 8300
VOJVODINA SPORT A.D.; *Int'l*, pg. 8299
VOJVODINA TEHNOPROMET A.D.; *Int'l*, pg. 8300
VOJVODJANSKA BANKA A.D.—See OTP Bank Plc; *Int'l*, pg. 5658
VOK BEVERAGES PTY. LTD.; *Int'l*, pg. 8300
VOK E MEXICO S. DE R.L. DE C.V.—See Xiamen Voke Mold & Plastic Engineering Co., Ltd.; *Int'l*, pg. 8526
VOKE TECHNOLOGY GERMANY GMBH—See Xiamen Voke Mold & Plastic Engineering Co., Ltd.; *Int'l*, pg. 8526
VOKUS PERSONAL AG—See Storskogen Group AB; *Int'l*, pg. 7228
VOLAC AGRO-BEST SPOL. S R.O.—See Volac International Limited; *Int'l*, pg. 8300
VOLAC INGREDIENTS SDN BHD—See Wilmar International Limited; *Int'l*, pg. 8421
VOLAC INTERNATIONAL LIMITED; *Int'l*, pg. 8300
VOLAC IRELAND LTD—See Volac International Limited; *Int'l*, pg. 8300
VOLAC SOCOOR S.R.L.—See Volac International Limited; *Int'l*, pg. 8300
VOLANKA EXPORTS LIMITED—See Hayleys PLC; *Int'l*, pg. 3292
VOLANKA INSURANCE SERVICES (PVT) LTD.—See Hayleys PLC; *Int'l*, pg. 3292
VOLANKA LTD—See Hayleys PLC; *Int'l*, pg. 3292
VOLANT AEROSPACE, LLC—See Temasek Holdings (Private) Limited; *Int'l*, pg. 7552
VOLANT TEXTILE MILLS LIMITED; *Int'l*, pg. 8300
VOLARIS EXEC RECRUITMENT LIMITED—See ManpowerGroup Inc.; *U.S. Public*, pg. 1362
VOLARIS GROUP INC.—See Constellation Software Inc.; *Int'l*, pg. 1775
VOLA S.R.L—See Corporacion America Airports S.A.; *Int'l*, pg. 1803
VOLATI AB; *Int'l*, pg. 8300
VOLATILE ANALYSIS CORPORATION; *U.S. Private*, pg. 4410
VOLATO GROUP, INC.; *U.S. Public*, pg. 2308
VOLATUS AEROSPACE CORP.—See Drone Delivery Canada Corp.; *Int'l*, pg. 2205
VOLATUS CAPITAL CORP.; *Int'l*, pg. 8301
VOLCAFE FRANCE—See ED&F Man Holdings Limited; *Int'l*, pg. 2303
VOLCAFE IBERIA S.A.—See ED&F Man Holdings Limited; *Int'l*, pg. 2303
VOLCAFE LIMITED—See ED&F Man Holdings Limited; *Int'l*, pg. 2303
VOLCAFE LTDA—See ED&F Man Holdings Limited; *Int'l*, pg. 2303
VOLCAFE SPECIALITY COFFEE LLC—See ED&F Man Holdings Limited; *Int'l*, pg. 2303
VOLCAFE SPECIALTY COFFEE CORP.—See ED&F Man Holdings Limited; *Int'l*, pg. 2303
VOLCAFE USA LLC—See ED&F Man Holdings Limited; *Int'l*, pg. 2303
VOLCAN HOLDINGS, INC.; *Int'l*, pg. 8301
VOLCANIC GOLD MINES INC.; *Int'l*, pg. 8301
VOLCANO COMMUNICATIONS CO.; *U.S. Private*, pg. 4410
VOLCANO CORPORATION—See Koninklijke Philips N.V.; *Int'l*, pg. 4271
VOLCANO EUROPE BVBA—See Koninklijke Philips N.V.; *Int'l*, pg. 4271
VOLCANO SPRING INTERNATIONAL HOLDINGS LIMITED; *Int'l*, pg. 8301
THE VOLCKER ALLIANCE; *U.S. Private*, pg. 4132
VOLCLAY JAPAN CO., LTD.—See Minerals Technologies, Inc.; *U.S. Public*, pg. 1449
VOLCOM, INC.—See Kering S.A.; *Int'l*, pg. 4136
VOLCON, INC.; *U.S. Public*, pg. 2308
VOLEX (ASIA) PTE LTD—See Volex plc; *Int'l*, pg. 8301
VOLEX CABLE ASSEMBLIES (PHILS) INC.—See Volex plc; *Int'l*, pg. 8301
VOLEX CABLE ASSEMBLIES SDN BHD—See Volex plc; *Int'l*, pg. 8302
VOLEX CABLE ASSEMBLY (SHENZHEN) CO. LTD.—See Volex plc; *Int'l*, pg. 8302
VOLEX CABLE ASSEMBLY (VIETNAM) PTE LTD—See Volex plc; *Int'l*, pg. 8301
VOLEX CABLE ASSEMBLIES (ZHONGSHAN) CO., LTD.—See Volex plc; *Int'l*, pg. 8302
VOLEX CABLES (HK) LTD.—See Volex plc; *Int'l*, pg. 8302
VOLEX DO BRASIL LTDA—See Volex plc; *Int'l*, pg. 8302
VOLEX EUROPE LTD—See Volex plc; *Int'l*, pg. 8302

VOLEX INTERCONNECT (INDIA) PVT LTD—See Volex plc; *Int'l*, pg. 8302
VOLEX INTERCONNECT SYSTEMS (SUZHOU) CO., LTD.—See Volex plc; *Int'l*, pg. 8302
VOLEX JAPAN CO., LTD.—See Volex plc; *Int'l*, pg. 8302
VOLEX PLC; *Int'l*, pg. 8301
VOLEX POLAND SP. Z.O.O.—See Volex plc; *Int'l*, pg. 8302
VOLEX (TAIWAN) CO. LTD.—See Volex plc; *Int'l*, pg. 8301
VOLEX (THAILAND) CO. LTD.—See Volex plc; *Int'l*, pg. 8301
VOLFAS ENGELMAN, AB—See Olvi Oyj; *Int'l*, pg. 5555
VOLGA-DNEPR AIRLINES LLC—See Volga-Dnepr Group; *Int'l*, pg. 8302
VOLGA-DNEPR CHINA—See Volga-Dnepr Group; *Int'l*, pg. 8302
VOLGA-DNEPR GROUP; *Int'l*, pg. 8302
VOLGA-DNEPR JAPAN—See Volga-Dnepr Group; *Int'l*, pg. 8302
VOLGA-DNEPR TECHNICS (FZC)—See Volga-Dnepr Group; *Int'l*, pg. 8302
VOLGA-DNEPR TECHNICS GMBH—See Volga-Dnepr Group; *Int'l*, pg. 8302
VOLGA-DNEPR TECHNICS—See Volga-Dnepr Group; *Int'l*, pg. 8302
VOLGA-DNEPR UK LTD.—See Volga-Dnepr Group; *Int'l*, pg. 8302
VOLGA-DNEPR UNIQUE AIR CARGO INC.—See Volga-Dnepr Group; *Int'l*, pg. 8302
VOLGA GAS PLC; *Int'l*, pg. 8302
VOLGA SHIPPING COMPANY—See Universal Cargo Logistics Holding B.V.; *Int'l*, pg. 8078
VOLGATELECOM - CHUVASHIAN REPUBLIC BRANCH—See PJSC Rostelecom; *Int'l*, pg. 5884
VOLGATELECOM - KIROV BRANCH—See PJSC Rostelecom; *Int'l*, pg. 5884
VOLGATELECOM - MARII-EI REPUBLIC BRANCH—See PJSC Rostelecom; *Int'l*, pg. 5884
VOLGATELECOM - ORENBURG BRANCH—See PJSC Rostelecom; *Int'l*, pg. 5884
VOLGATELECOM - SARATOV BRANCH—See PJSC Rostelecom; *Int'l*, pg. 5884
VOLGATELECOM - UDMURTIA REPUBLIC BRANCH—See PJSC Rostelecom; *Int'l*, pg. 5884
VOLGATELECOM - ULYANOVSK BRANCH—See PJSC Rostelecom; *Int'l*, pg. 5884
VOLIA; *Int'l*, pg. 8302
VOLICON INC.—See Apollo Global Management, Inc.; *U.S. Public*, pg. 167
VOLI FUAR HIZMETLERI A.S.—See Ihlas Holding A.S.; *Int'l*, pg. 3606
VOLIM VOLKSWAGEN IMMOBILIEN VERNIETGESELLSCHAFT FUR VW AUDI HANDLERBETRIEBE GMBH—See Porsche Automobil Holding SE; *Int'l*, pg. 5931
VOLITION CAPITAL LLC; *U.S. Private*, pg. 4410
VOLITIONRX LIMITED; *U.S. Public*, pg. 2308
VOLK CONSTRUCTION COMPANY—See Kennedy Associates/Architects, Inc.; *U.S. Private*, pg. 2284
VOLK CORPORATION; *U.S. Private*, pg. 4410
VOLK DO BRASIL LTDA—See Bunzl plc; *Int'l*, pg. 1220
VOLKEL & WINKLER GMBH—See Knauf Interfer SE; *Int'l*, pg. 4205
VOLK ENTERPRISES, INC.; *U.S. Private*, pg. 4410
VOLKER AUSTRALIA PTY LTD—See Paragon Care Limited; *Int'l*, pg. 5736
VOLKER GMBH—See CoBe Capital LLC; *U.S. Private*, pg. 957
VOLKERINFRA LTD.—See Koninklijke VolkerWessels N.V.; *Int'l*, pg. 4272
VOLKERLASER LTD.—See Koninklijke VolkerWessels N.V.; *Int'l*, pg. 4272
VOLKERRAIL LTD.—See Koninklijke VolkerWessels N.V.; *Int'l*, pg. 4272
VOLKER STEVIN CONTRACTING LTD—See Koninklijke VolkerWessels N.V.; *Int'l*, pg. 4272
VOLKER STEVIN MATERIEEL BV—See Koninklijke VolkerWessels N.V.; *Int'l*, pg. 4272
VOLKERT ENVIRONMENTAL, INC.—See Volkert, Inc.; *U.S. Private*, pg. 4410
VOLKERT, INC. - GEORGIA—See Volkert, Inc.; *U.S. Private*, pg. 4410
VOLKERT, INC.; *U.S. Private*, pg. 4410
VOLKERT, INC.—See Volkert, Inc.; *U.S. Private*, pg. 4410
VOLKERT, INC.—See Volkert, Inc.; *U.S. Private*, pg. 4410
VOLKERT, INC.—See Volkert, Inc.; *U.S. Private*, pg. 4410
VOLKERT, INC.—See Volkert, Inc.; *U.S. Private*, pg. 4410
VOLKERT, INC. - TAMPA—See Volkert, Inc.; *U.S. Private*, pg. 4410
VOLKERWESSELS BOUWMATERIEEL BV—See Koninklijke VolkerWessels N.V.; *Int'l*, pg. 4272
VOLKERWESSELS BOUW & VASTGOEDONTWIKKELING BV—See Koninklijke VolkerWessels N.V.; *Int'l*, pg. 4272
VOLKERWESSELS INTEGRAAL BV—See Koninklijke VolkerWessels N.V.; *Int'l*, pg. 4272
VOLKER WESSELS TELECOM BV—See Koninklijke VolkerWessels N.V.; *Int'l*, pg. 4272

VOLKERWESSELS UK LTD.—See Koninklijke VolkerWessels N.V.; *Int'l*, pg. 4272
VOLKERWESSELS VASTGOEDBEHEER—See Koninklijke VolkerWessels N.V.; *Int'l*, pg. 4272
VOLKERWESSELS VASTGOED BV—See Koninklijke VolkerWessels N.V.; *Int'l*, pg. 4272
VOLKES AIR LIMITED—See SPX Technologies, Inc.; *U.S. Public*, pg. 1921
VOLK EUROPE LTD—See Volk Enterprises, Inc.; *U.S. Private*, pg. 4410
VOLKL SPORTS GMBH & CO. KG—See Kohlberg & Company, LLC; *U.S. Private*, pg. 2338
VOLKMANN RAILROAD BUILDERS; *U.S. Private*, pg. 4410
VOLK OPTICAL INC.—See Halma plc; *Int'l*, pg. 3233
VOLKOVGEOLOGY JSC—See JSC National Atomic Company Kazatomprom; *Int'l*, pg. 4009
VOLKSBANK A.D.—See OJSC Sberbank of Russia; *Int'l*, pg. 5542
VOLKSBANK BH D.D.—See OJSC Sberbank of Russia; *Int'l*, pg. 5542
VOLKSBANK CZ, A.S.—See OJSC Sberbank of Russia; *Int'l*, pg. 5542
VOLKSBANK D.D.—See OJSC Sberbank of Russia; *Int'l*, pg. 5542
VOLKSBANK ROMANIA S.A.—See Osterreichische Volksbanken AG; *Int'l*, pg. 5654
VOLKSBANK SLOVENSKO, A.S.—See OJSC Sberbank of Russia; *Int'l*, pg. 5542
VOLKSBANK VORARLBERG E GEN; *Int'l*, pg. 8302
VOLKSBANK WIEN AG—See Osterreichische Volksbanken AG; *Int'l*, pg. 5654
VOLKSFREUND-DRUCKEREI NIKOLAUS KOCH GMBH & CO. KG—See Verlagsgruppe Georg von Holtzbrinck GmbH; *Int'l*, pg. 8172
VOLKSFURSORGE 1. IMMOBILIEN AG & CO. KG—See Cinven Limited; *Int'l*, pg. 1616
VOLKSFURSORGE 1. IMMOBILIEN AG & CO. KG—See Talanx AG; *Int'l*, pg. 7445
VOLKSFURSORGE FIXED ASSET GMBH—See Cinven Limited; *Int'l*, pg. 1616
VOLKSFURSORGE FIXED ASSET GMBH—See Talanx AG; *Int'l*, pg. 7445
VOLKSVERMOGEN NV; *Int'l*, pg. 8302
VOLKSWAGEN AG—See Porsche Automobil Holding SE; *Int'l*, pg. 5926
VOLKSWAGEN ARGENTINA S.A.—See Porsche Automobil Holding SE; *Int'l*, pg. 5931
VOLKSWAGEN AUTOVERSICHERUNG AG—See Allianz SE; *Int'l*, pg. 356
VOLKSWAGEN BANK GMBH—See Porsche Automobil Holding SE; *Int'l*, pg. 5931
VOLKSWAGEN BANK POLSKA S.A.—See Porsche Automobil Holding SE; *Int'l*, pg. 5931
VOLKSWAGEN BANK—See Porsche Automobil Holding SE; *Int'l*, pg. 5931
VOLKSWAGEN-BILDUNGSINSTITUT GMBH—See Porsche Automobil Holding SE; *Int'l*, pg. 5933
VOLKSWAGEN BRUXELLES S.A.—See Porsche Automobil Holding SE; *Int'l*, pg. 5931
VOLKSWAGEN CANADA, INC.—See Porsche Automobil Holding SE; *Int'l*, pg. 5931
VOLKSWAGEN (CHINA) INVESTMENT COMPANY LIMITED—See Porsche Automobil Holding SE; *Int'l*, pg. 5931
VOLKSWAGEN COMERCIAL S.A. DE C.V.—See Porsche Automobil Holding SE; *Int'l*, pg. 5931
VOLKSWAGEN COMERCIO E PARTICIPACOES LTDA.—See Porsche Automobil Holding SE; *Int'l*, pg. 5931
VOLKSWAGEN CREDIT AUTO RECEIVABLES CORP.—See Porsche Automobil Holding SE; *Int'l*, pg. 5931
VOLKSWAGEN DE MEXICO S.A. DE C.V.—See Porsche Automobil Holding SE; *Int'l*, pg. 5933
VOLKSWAGEN DO BRASIL LTDA.—See Porsche Automobil Holding SE; *Int'l*, pg. 5931
VOLKSWAGEN DO BRASIL—See Porsche Automobil Holding SE; *Int'l*, pg. 5931
VOLKSWAGEN DOGUS TUKETICI FINANSMANI ANONIM SIRKETI—See Porsche Automobil Holding SE; *Int'l*, pg. 5932
VOLKSWAGEN FINANCE JAPAN K.K.—See Porsche Automobil Holding SE; *Int'l*, pg. 5932
VOLKSWAGEN FINANCE LUXEMBURG S.A.—See Porsche Automobil Holding SE; *Int'l*, pg. 5931
VOLKSWAGEN FINANCE S.A.—See Porsche Automobil Holding SE; *Int'l*, pg. 5932
VOLKSWAGEN FINANCE, S.A.—See Porsche Automobil Holding SE; *Int'l*, pg. 5932
VOLKSWAGEN FINANCIAL CONSULTANT SERVICE K.K.—See Porsche Automobil Holding SE; *Int'l*, pg. 5932
VOLKSWAGEN FINANCIAL SERVICES AG—See Porsche Automobil Holding SE; *Int'l*, pg. 5931
VOLKSWAGEN FINANCIAL SERVICES COMPANIA FINANCIERA SA—See Banco Bilbao Vizcaya Argentaria, S.A.; *Int'l*, pg. 818

COMPANY NAME INDEX — VOLUNTEERS FOR ECONOMIC GROWTH ALLIANCE

VOLKSWAGEN FINANCIAL SERVICES, S.A. DE C.V.—See Porsche Automobil Holding SE; *Int'l*, pg. 5933
VOLKSWAGEN FINANCIAL SERVICES (U.K.) LTD.—See Porsche Automobil Holding SE; *Int'l*, pg. 5932
VOLKSWAGEN FINANCNE SLUZBY SLOVENSKO S.R.O.—See Porsche Automobil Holding SE; *Int'l*, pg. 5932
VOLKSWAGEN GROUP AUSTRALIA PTY. LTD.—See Porsche Automobil Holding SE; *Int'l*, pg. 5932
VOLKSWAGEN GROUP INSURANCE & RISK MANAGEMENT SERVICES (UK) LTD.—See Porsche Automobil Holding SE; *Int'l*, pg. 5932
VOLKSWAGEN GROUP JAPAN K.K.—See Porsche Automobil Holding SE; *Int'l*, pg. 5932
VOLKSWAGEN GROUP OF AMERICA, INC.—See Porsche Automobil Holding SE; *Int'l*, pg. 5932
VOLKSWAGEN GROUP SERVICES—See Porsche Automobil Holding SE; *Int'l*, pg. 5932
VOLKSWAGEN GROUP SINGAPORE PTE. LTD.—See Porsche Automobil Holding SE; *Int'l*, pg. 5932
VOLKSWAGEN GROUP UNITED KINGDOM LTD.—See Porsche Automobil Holding SE; *Int'l*, pg. 5932
VOLKSWAGEN HOLDING FINANCIERE S.A.—See Porsche Automobil Holding SE; *Int'l*, pg. 5932
VOLKSWAGEN IMMOBILIEN SERVICE GMBH—See Porsche Automobil Holding SE; *Int'l*, pg. 5932
VOLKSWAGEN INSURANCE COMPANY LTD.—See Porsche Automobil Holding SE; *Int'l*, pg. 5932
VOLKSWAGEN INSURANCE SERVICE (GREAT BRITAIN) LIMITED—See Porsche Automobil Holding SE; *Int'l*, pg. 5932
VOLKSWAGEN INVESTMENTS LTD.—See Porsche Automobil Holding SE; *Int'l*, pg. 5932
VOLKSWAGEN LEASING GMBH—See Porsche Automobil Holding SE; *Int'l*, pg. 5932
VOLKSWAGEN LEASING POLSKA SP. Z O.O.—See Porsche Automobil Holding SE; *Int'l*, pg. 5932
VOLKSWAGEN LEASING THAILAND CO., LTD.—See Porsche Automobil Holding SE; *Int'l*, pg. 5932
VOLKSWAGEN LOGISTICS GMBH & CO. OHG—See Porsche Automobil Holding SE; *Int'l*, pg. 5932
VOLKSWAGEN NAVARRA, S.A.—See Porsche Automobil Holding SE; *Int'l*, pg. 5929
VOLKSWAGEN OF ALAMO HEIGHTS; *U.S. Private*, pg. 4410
VOLKSWAGEN OF AMERICA ADMINISTRATION CENTER WEST—See Porsche Automobil Holding SE; *Int'l*, pg. 5933
VOLKSWAGEN OF OLD SAYBROOK; *U.S. Private*, pg. 4410
VOLKSWAGEN OF SOUTH AFRICA (PTY.) LTD.—See Porsche Automobil Holding SE; *Int'l*, pg. 5933
VOLKSWAGEN OTLG LTD.—See Porsche Automobil Holding SE; *Int'l*, pg. 5932
VOLKSWAGEN POZNAN SP. Z O.O.—See Porsche Automobil Holding SE; *Int'l*, pg. 5932
VOLKSWAGEN RETAIL GMBH—See Porsche Automobil Holding SE; *Int'l*, pg. 5932
VOLKSWAGEN SACHSEN IMMOBILIENVERWALTUNGS GMBH—See Porsche Automobil Holding SE; *Int'l*, pg. 5933
VOLKSWAGEN SANTA MONICA, INC.; *U.S. Private*, pg. 4410
VOLKSWAGEN SARAJEVO, D.O.O.—See Porsche Automobil Holding SE; *Int'l*, pg. 5933
VOLKSWAGEN SERVICOS S.A.—See Porsche Automobil Holding SE; *Int'l*, pg. 5931
VOLKSWAGEN SLOVAKIA A.S.—See Porsche Automobil Holding SE; *Int'l*, pg. 5933
VOLKSWAGEN TRANSPORT OF SOUTH AMERICA LTDA.—See Porsche Automobil Holding SE; *Int'l*, pg. 5932
VOLKSWAGEN UBEZPIECZENIA SP. Z O.O.—See Porsche Automobil Holding SE; *Int'l*, pg. 5933
VOLKSWAGEN-VERSICHERUNGSDIENST AG—See Porsche Automobil Holding SE; *Int'l*, pg. 5932
VOLKSWAGEN VERSICHERUNGSDIENST GMBH OSTERREICH—See Porsche Automobil Holding SE; *Int'l*, pg. 5932
VOLKSWAGEN-VERSICHERUNGSDIENST GMBH—See Porsche Automobil Holding SE; *Int'l*, pg. 5932
VOLKSWAGEN-VERZEKERINGS SERVICE N.V.—See Porsche Automobil Holding SE; *Int'l*, pg. 5933
VOLKSWAGEN VICTORIA—See German Auto Import Network - Vancouver Island; *Int'l*, pg. 2943
VOLKSWAGEN ZENTRUM AACHEN (VW) GMBH—See Penske Automotive Group, Inc.; *U.S. Public*, pg. 1666
VOLLAND ELECTRIC EQUIPMENT; *U.S. Private*, pg. 4410
VOLLERS EXCAVATING & CONSTRUCTION INC.—See Vollers, Inc.; *U.S. Private*, pg. 4411
VOLLERS, INC.; *U.S. Private*, pg. 4410
VOLLMAR GMBH—See Serafin Unternehmensgruppe GmbH; *Int'l*, pg. 6720
VOLLMER AUSTRIA GMBH—See Vollmer Werke Maschinenfabrik GmbH; *Int'l*, pg. 8302

VOLLMER DO BRASIL INDUSTRIA DE MAQUINAS LTDA.—See Vollmer Werke Maschinenfabrik GmbH; *Int'l*, pg. 8302
VOLLMER FRANCE S.A.R.L.—See Vollmer Werke Maschinenfabrik GmbH; *Int'l*, pg. 8302
VOLLMER ITALIA SRL—See Vollmer Werke Maschinenfabrik GmbH; *Int'l*, pg. 8302
VOLLMER JAPAN CORP.—See Vollmer Werke Maschinenfabrik GmbH; *Int'l*, pg. 8302
VOLLMER OF AMERICA CORP.—See Vollmer Werke Maschinenfabrik GmbH; *Int'l*, pg. 8303
VOLLMER POLSKA SP.Z O.O—See Vollmer Werke Maschinenfabrik GmbH; *Int'l*, pg. 8302
VOLLMER SCANDINAVIA AB—See Vollmer Werke Maschinenfabrik GmbH; *Int'l*, pg. 8302
VOLLMER TAICANG CO. LTD.—See Vollmer Werke Maschinenfabrik GmbH; *Int'l*, pg. 8302
VOLLMER TECHNIQUE D'AFFUTAGE S.A.R.L.—See Vollmer Werke Maschinenfabrik GmbH; *Int'l*, pg. 8302
VOLLMER TECHNOLOGIES INDIA PRIVATE LTD.—See Vollmer Werke Maschinenfabrik GmbH; *Int'l*, pg. 8302
VOLLMER UK LTD—See Vollmer Werke Maschinenfabrik GmbH; *Int'l*, pg. 8303
VOLLMER WERKE MASCHINENFABRIK GMBH; *Int'l*, pg. 8302
THE VOLLRATH COMPANY LLC; *U.S. Private*, pg. 4132
VOLLRATH DE MEXICO S. DE R.L. DE C.V.—See The Vollrath Company LLC; *U.S. Private*, pg. 4132
VOLLRATH EUROPE B.V.—See The Vollrath Company LLC; *U.S. Private*, pg. 4132
VOLLRATH SHANGHAI TRADING LIMITED—See The Vollrath Company LLC; *U.S. Private*, pg. 4132
VOLMAR CONSTRUCTION INC.; *U.S. Private*, pg. 4411
VOLM BAG COMPANY, INC.; *U.S. Private*, pg. 4411
VOLO DIALYSIS, LLC—See DaVita Inc.; *U.S. Public*, pg. 644
VOLPAK PACKAGING MACHINES—See Coesia S.p.A.; *Int'l*, pg. 1690
VOLPAK S.A—See Coesia S.p.A.; *Int'l*, pg. 1690
VOLPARA HEALTH, INC.—See Volpara Health Technologies Limited; *Int'l*, pg. 8303
VOLPARA HEALTH LIMITED—See Volpara Health Technologies Limited; *Int'l*, pg. 8303
VOLPARA HEALTH TECHNOLOGIES LIMITED; *Int'l*, pg. 8303
VOLTA ALUMINIUM CO. LTD. (VALCO); *Int'l*, pg. 8303
VOLTABOX AG; *Int'l*, pg. 8303
VOLTABOX OF TEXAS, INC.—See Paragon GmbH & Co. KGaA; *Int'l*, pg. 5736
VOLTA FINANCE LIMITED; *Int'l*, pg. 8303
VOLTAGE ENTERTAINMENT USA, INC.—See Voltage Inc.; *Int'l*, pg. 8303
VOLTAGE INC.; *Int'l*, pg. 8303
VOLTAGE METALS CORP.; *Int'l*, pg. 8303
VOLTA INC—See Shell plc; *Int'l*, pg. 6800
VOLTA INDUSTRIES, INC.—See Shell plc; *Int'l*, pg. 6800
VOLTAIR CONSULTING ENGINEERS, INC.; *U.S. Private*, pg. 4411
VOLTAIRE LEASING & FINANCE LIMITED; *Int'l*, pg. 8303
VOLTAIX LLC; *U.S. Private*, pg. 4411
VOLTALIA DISTRIBUTION S.A.S.—See Voltalia S.A.; *Int'l*, pg. 8303
VOLTALIA GREECE S.A.—See Voltalia S.A.; *Int'l*, pg. 8303
VOLTALIA JAPAN KK—See Voltalia S.A.; *Int'l*, pg. 8303
VOLTALIA S.A.; *Int'l*, pg. 8303
VOLTA LIMBURG B.V.—See RWE AG; *Int'l*, pg. 6436
VOLTA, LLC—See CSE Global Ltd.; *Int'l*, pg. 1864
VOLTA METALS LTD.; *Int'l*, pg. 8303
VOLTAMP ENERGY SAOG; *Int'l*, pg. 8303
VOLTAMP TRANSFORMERS LIMITED; *Int'l*, pg. 8303
VOLTARI CORPORATION; *U.S. Private*, pg. 4411
VOLT ASIA ENTERPRISES (TAIWAN) CO. LTD.—See American CyberSystems, Inc.; *U.S. Private*, pg. 230
VOLTAS LIMITED—See Tata Sons Limited; *Int'l*, pg. 7473
VOLTAS NETHERLANDS B.V.—See Tata Sons Limited; *Int'l*, pg. 7473
VOLTA SOLAR B.V.—See RWE AG; *Int'l*, pg. 6436
VOLTAS OMAN LLC—See Tata Sons Limited; *Int'l*, pg. 7473
VOLTA S.P.A.—See PJSC Gazprom; *Int'l*, pg. 5880
VOLT ATHLETICS, INC.; *U.S. Private*, pg. 4411
VOLT CARBON TECHNOLOGIES INC.; *Int'l*, pg. 8303
VOLTCOM SPOL. S R.O.—See EnBW Energie Baden-Wurttemberg AG; *Int'l*, pg. 2400
VOLT CONSULTING GROUP LIMITED—See American CyberSystems, Inc.; *U.S. Private*, pg. 230
VOLT CONSULTING GROUP, LTD.—See American CyberSystems, Inc.; *U.S. Private*, pg. 230
VOLT DELTA INTERNATIONAL B.V.—See ESW Capital, LLC; *U.S. Private*, pg. 1431
VOLT DELTA INTERNATIONAL GMBH—See ESW Capital, LLC; *U.S. Private*, pg. 1431
VOLT DELTA RESOURCES, INC.—See ESW Capital, LLC; *U.S. Private*, pg. 1431
VOLT DELTA RESOURCES, LLC—See ESW Capital, LLC; *U.S. Private*, pg. 1431
VOLTERRA SA—See Avax S.A.; *Int'l*, pg. 737
VOLTERRA S.A.—See Nippon Paper Industries Co., Ltd.; *Int'l*, pg. 5328

VOLT EUROPE (BELGIUM) SPRL—See American CyberSystems, Inc.; *U.S. Private*, pg. 230
VOLT EUROPE (FRANCE) SARL—See American CyberSystems, Inc.; *U.S. Private*, pg. 230
VOLT EUROPE (GERMANY) GMBH—See American CyberSystems, Inc.; *U.S. Private*, pg. 230
VOLT EUROPE HOLDINGS LIMITED—See American CyberSystems, Inc.; *U.S. Private*, pg. 230
VOLT EUROPE LIMITED—See American CyberSystems, Inc.; *U.S. Private*, pg. 230
VOLTEX NAMIBIA (PTY) LIMITED—See The Bidvest Group Limited; *Int'l*, pg. 7627
VOLTEX (PTY) LIMITED—See The Bidvest Group Limited; *Int'l*, pg. 7626
VOLTH2 OPERATING BV—See VISION ENERGY CORPORATION; *U.S. Public*, pg. 2304
VOLTIC (GH) LIMITED—See The Coca-Cola Company; *U.S. Public*, pg. 2065
VOLTIMUM BRASIL—See Prysmian S.p.A.; *Int'l*, pg. 6013
VOLTIMUM GMBH—See Prysmian S.p.A.; *Int'l*, pg. 6013
VOLTIMUM PORTUGAL—See Prysmian S.p.A.; *Int'l*, pg. 6013
VOLT INFORMATION SCIENCES, INC.—See American CyberSystems, Inc.; *U.S. Private*, pg. 229
VOLT INFORMATION SCIENCES-WEST—See American CyberSystems, Inc.; *U.S. Private*, pg. 230
VOLT MANAGEMENT CORP.—See American CyberSystems, Inc.; *U.S. Private*, pg. 230
VOLTMEN OY—See Instalco AB; *Int'l*, pg. 3723
VOLTRAN S.A. DE C.V.—See WEG S.A.; *Int'l*, pg. 8368
VOLTRANS SA; *Int'l*, pg. 8304
VOLTREK, LLC—See Orion Energy Systems, Inc.; *U.S. Public*, pg. 1618
VOLT RESOURCES LTD.; *Int'l*, pg. 8303
VOLT ROAD BORING CORP.—See American CyberSystems, Inc.; *U.S. Private*, pg. 230
VOLTRONIC POWER TECHNOLOGY CORPORATION; *Int'l*, pg. 8304
VOLT SERVICE CORPORATION PTE, LTD.—See American CyberSystems, Inc.; *U.S. Private*, pg. 230
VOLT TECHNICAL RESOURCES, LLC—See American CyberSystems, Inc.; *U.S. Private*, pg. 230
VOLT TELECOM GROUP—See American CyberSystems, Inc.; *U.S. Private*, pg. 230
VOLT TELECOMMUNICATIONS GROUP—See American CyberSystems, Inc.; *U.S. Private*, pg. 230
VOLT TELECOMMUNICATIONS GROUP, INC.—See American CyberSystems, Inc.; *U.S. Private*, pg. 230
VOLT TELECOMMUNICATIONS GROUP—See American CyberSystems, Inc.; *U.S. Private*, pg. 230
VOLT TEMPORARY SERVICES—See American CyberSystems, Inc.; *U.S. Private*, pg. 230
VOLT VIEWTECH, INC.—See American CyberSystems, Inc.; *U.S. Private*, pg. 230
VOLTWERK ELECTRONICS GMBH—See Robert Bosch GmbH; *Int'l*, pg. 6360
VOLT WORKFORCE SOLUTIONS, INC.—See American CyberSystems, Inc.; *U.S. Private*, pg. 230
VOLUE AG—See Arendals Fossekompani ASA; *Int'l*, pg. 559
VOLUE GERMANY GMBH—See Arendals Fossekompani ASA; *Int'l*, pg. 559
VOLUE GMBH—See Arendals Fossekompani ASA; *Int'l*, pg. 559
VOLUMATIC LIMITED—See NVM Private Equity Limited; *Int'l*, pg. 5498
VOLUME 9 INC; *U.S. Private*, pg. 4411
VOLUME CHEVROLET BUICK; *U.S. Private*, pg. 4411
VOLUME DISTRIBUTORS INC.; *U.S. Private*, pg. 4411
VOLUME LIMITED; *Int'l*, pg. 8304
VOLUME PUBLIC RELATIONS; *U.S. Private*, pg. 4411
VOLUMES PUBLISHING COMPANY—See Northern United Publishing & Media (Group) Company Limited; *Int'l*, pg. 5445
VOLUMETRIC BUILDING COMPANIES; *U.S. Private*, pg. 4411
VOLUND VARMETEKNIK A/S—See NIBE Industrier AB; *Int'l*, pg. 5263
VOLUNTARY PENSION FUND M.DELTA—See Assicurazioni Generali S.p.A.; *Int'l*, pg. 646
VOLUNTARY PURCHASING GROUPS, INC.; *U.S. Private*, pg. 4411
VOLUNTEER CORPORATE CREDIT UNION; *U.S. Private*, pg. 4411
VOLUNTEER ENERGY COOPERATIVE, INC.; *U.S. Private*, pg. 4411
VOLUNTEER EXPRESS, INC.—See Central Freight Lines, Inc.; *U.S. Private*, pg. 821
VOLUNTEER FEDERAL SAVINGS BANK; *U.S. Private*, pg. 4411
VOLUNTEER FIREMEN'S INSURANCE SERVICES, INC.—See American International Group, Inc.; *U.S. Public*, pg. 107
VOLUNTEER FOAM AND SUPPLY CORPORATION—See Hickory Springs Manufacturing Company; *U.S. Private*, pg. 1934
VOLUNTEERS FOR ECONOMIC GROWTH ALLIANCE; *U.S. Private*, pg. 4411

VOLUNTEERS FOR INTERAMERICAN DEVELOPMENT ASSISTANCE / CORPORATE AFFILIATIONS

VOLUNTEERS FOR INTERAMERICAN DEVELOPMENT ASSISTANCE; *U.S. Private*, pg. 4411
VOLUNTEER TREATMENT CENTER, INC.—See Acadia Healthcare Company, Inc.; *U.S. Public*, pg. 31
VOLUNTEER VOLVO AND GMC INC.—See Worldwide Equipment, Inc.; *U.S. Private*, pg. 4569
VOLUNTIS SA—See AptarGroup, Inc.; *U.S. Public*, pg. 175
VOLUSIA MALL, LLC—See CBL & Associates Properties, Inc.; *U.S. Public*, pg. 459
VOLUSIA MALL SAC, LLC—See CBL & Associates Properties, Inc.; *U.S. Public*, pg. 459
VOLUSION, INC.; *U.S. Private*, pg. 4411
VOLUTION GROUP PLC; *Int'l*, pg. 8304
VOLVALB SH.P.K—See AB Volvo; *Int'l*, pg. 42
VOLVE CAR NORWAY A.S.—See GKN plc; *Int'l*, pg. 2986
VOLVERE CENTRAL SERVICES LIMITED—See Volvere plc; *Int'l*, pg. 8304
VOLVERE PLC; *Int'l*, pg. 8304
VOLVIK, INC - EUMSEONG FACTORY—See Volvik, Inc; *Int'l*, pg. 8304
VOLVIK, INC; *Int'l*, pg. 8304
VOLVO AERO CORPORATION—See GKN plc; *Int'l*, pg. 2986
VOLVO AERO ENGINE SERVICES AB—See GKN plc; *Int'l*, pg. 2986
VOLVO AERO ENGINE SERVICES ARBOGA AB—See GKN plc; *Int'l*, pg. 2986
VOLVO AERO TURBINES (UK) LTD.—See GKN plc; *Int'l*, pg. 2986
VOLVO ARTICULATED HAULERS AB—See AB Volvo; *Int'l*, pg. 42
VOLVO AUTO BANK DEUTSCHLAND GMBH—See Ford Motor Company; *U.S. Public*, pg. 867
VOLVO AUTO DE MEXICO S.A DE C.V—See Zhejiang Geely Holding Group Co., Ltd.; *Int'l*, pg. 8653
VOLVO AUTO INDIA PVT. LTD—See Zhejiang Geely Holding Group Co., Ltd.; *Int'l*, pg. 8653
VOLVO AUTO ITALIA SPA—See Zhejiang Geely Holding Group Co., Ltd.; *Int'l*, pg. 8653
VOLVO AUTOMOBILES FRANCE SA—See Zhejiang Geely Holding Group Co., Ltd.; *Int'l*, pg. 8653
VOLVO AUTOMOTIVE FINANCE (CHINA) LTD—See AB Volvo; *Int'l*, pg. 42
VOLVO AUTO OY AB—See Zhejiang Geely Holding Group Co., Ltd.; *Int'l*, pg. 8653
VOLVO BULGARIA LTD.—See AB Volvo; *Int'l*, pg. 42
VOLVO BUS AUSTRALIA—See AB Volvo; *Int'l*, pg. 43
VOLVO BUS CORPORATION—See AB Volvo; *Int'l*, pg. 42
VOLVO BUS HONG KONG LIMITED—See AB Volvo; *Int'l*, pg. 43
VOLVO BUSINESS SERVICES AB—See AB Volvo; *Int'l*, pg. 43
VOLVO BUS NEDERLAND B.V.—See AB Volvo; *Int'l*, pg. 43
VOLVO BUS POLAND CO.—See AB Volvo; *Int'l*, pg. 43
VOLVO BUSSAR AB—See AB Volvo; *Int'l*, pg. 43
VOLVO BUSSE DEUTSCHLAND GMBH—See AB Volvo; *Int'l*, pg. 43
VOLVO BUSSER DANMARK A/S—See AB Volvo; *Int'l*, pg. 43
VOLVO CAR AB—See Zhejiang Geely Holding Group Co., Ltd.; *Int'l*, pg. 8653
VOLVO CAR AUSTRIA GMBH—See Zhejiang Geely Holding Group Co., Ltd.; *Int'l*, pg. 8653
VOLVO CAR BRASIL IMPORTACAO E COMERCIA DE VEICULOS LTDA—See Zhejiang Geely Holding Group Co., Ltd.; *Int'l*, pg. 8653
VOLVO CAR COMPONENTS CORP. - ENGINES—See Zhejiang Geely Holding Group Co., Ltd.; *Int'l*, pg. 8653
VOLVO CAR COMPONENTS CORPORATION—See Zhejiang Geely Holding Group Co., Ltd.; *Int'l*, pg. 8653
VOLVO CAR CZECH REPUBLIC S.R.O.—See Zhejiang Geely Holding Group Co., Ltd.; *Int'l*, pg. 8653
VOLVO CAR ESPANA S.A.—See Zhejiang Geely Holding Group Co., Ltd.; *Int'l*, pg. 8653
VOLVO CAR FINANCE HOLDING AB—See Zhejiang Geely Holding Group Co., Ltd.; *Int'l*, pg. 8653
VOLVO CAR FINANCIAL SERVICES US LLC—See Zhejiang Geely Holding Group Co., Ltd.; *Int'l*, pg. 8653
VOLVO CAR FRANCE SAS—See Zhejiang Geely Holding Group Co., Ltd.; *Int'l*, pg. 8653
VOLVO CAR GERMANY GMBH—See Zhejiang Geely Holding Group Co., Ltd.; *Int'l*, pg. 8653
VOLVO CAR HELLAS SA—See Zhejiang Geely Holding Group Co., Ltd.; *Int'l*, pg. 8653
VOLVO CAR IRELAND LTD—See Zhejiang Geely Holding Group Co., Ltd.; *Int'l*, pg. 8653
VOLVO CAR MALAYSIA SDN BHD—See Zhejiang Geely Holding Group Co., Ltd.; *Int'l*, pg. 8653
VOLVO CAR NEDERLAND B.V.—See Zhejiang Geely Holding Group Co., Ltd.; *Int'l*, pg. 8653
VOLVO CAR POLAND SP Z.O.O—See Zhejiang Geely Holding Group Co., Ltd.; *Int'l*, pg. 8653
VOLVO CARS AUSTRIA GMBH—See AB Volvo; *Int'l*, pg. 43
VOLVO CARS N.V.—See Zhejiang Geely Holding Group Co., Ltd.; *Int'l*, pg. 8654
VOLVO CARS OF CANADA LTD.—See Zhejiang Geely Holding Group Co., Ltd.; *Int'l*, pg. 8654
VOLVO CARS OF NORTH AMERICA LLC—See Zhejiang Geely Holding Group Co., Ltd.; *Int'l*, pg. 8654
VOLVO CAR SOUTH AFRICA PTY LTD—See Zhejiang Geely Holding Group Co., Ltd.; *Int'l*, pg. 8654
VOLVO CARS S.L—See AB Volvo; *Int'l*, pg. 42
VOLVO CARS UK LTD.—See Zhejiang Geely Holding Group Co., Ltd.; *Int'l*, pg. 8654
VOLVO CAR TURKEY OTOMOBIL LTD SIRKETI—See Zhejiang Geely Holding Group Co., Ltd.; *Int'l*, pg. 8654
VOLVO CAR UK LIMITED—See Zhejiang Geely Holding Group Co., Ltd.; *Int'l*, pg. 8654
VOLVO CE EUROPE S.A.S.—See AB Volvo; *Int'l*, pg. 44
VOLVO (CHINA) INVESTMENT CO. LTD—See AB Volvo; *Int'l*, pg. 42
VOLVO COMPACT EQUIPMENT S.A.S.—See AB Volvo; *Int'l*, pg. 44
VOLVO CONSTRUCTION EQUIPMENT AUSTRALIA PTY. LTD.—See AB Volvo; *Int'l*, pg. 43
VOLVO CONSTRUCTION EQUIPMENT CABS AB—See AB Volvo; *Int'l*, pg. 43
VOLVO CONSTRUCTION EQUIPMENT COMPONENTS AB—See AB Volvo; *Int'l*, pg. 43
VOLVO CONSTRUCTION EQUIPMENT CORPORATION—See AB Volvo; *Int'l*, pg. 43
VOLVO CONSTRUCTION EQUIPMENT CUSTOMER SUPPORT AB—See AB Volvo; *Int'l*, pg. 43
VOLVO CONSTRUCTION EQUIPMENT EAST ASIA (PTE.) LTD.—See AB Volvo; *Int'l*, pg. 43
VOLVO CONSTRUCTION EQUIPMENT EUROPE AB—See AB Volvo; *Int'l*, pg. 43
VOLVO CONSTRUCTION EQUIPMENT EUROPE GMBH—See AB Volvo; *Int'l*, pg. 43
VOLVO CONSTRUCTION EQUIPMENT EUROPE HOLDING GMBH—See AB Volvo; *Int'l*, pg. 43
VOLVO CONSTRUCTION EQUIPMENT EUROPE SAS—See AB Volvo; *Int'l*, pg. 43
VOLVO CONSTRUCTION EQUIPMENT INTERNATIONAL AB—See AB Volvo; *Int'l*, pg. 43
VOLVO CONSTRUCTION EQUIPMENT KOREA LTD.—See AB Volvo; *Int'l*, pg. 43
VOLVO CONSTRUCTION EQUIPMENT LTD.—See AB Volvo; *Int'l*, pg. 43
VOLVO CONSTRUCTION EQUIPMENT NORTH AMERICA, INC.—See AB Volvo; *Int'l*, pg. 43
VOLVO DANMARK A/S—See AB Volvo; *Int'l*, pg. 43
VOLVO DEUTSCHLAND GMBH—See AB Volvo; *Int'l*, pg. 43
VOLVO DO BRASIL VEICULOS LTDA.—See AB Volvo; *Int'l*, pg. 47
VOLVO DO BRASIL VEICULOS LTDA.—See AB Volvo; *Int'l*, pg. 47
VOLVO EAST ASIA (PTE.) LTD.—See AB Volvo; *Int'l*, pg. 43
VOLVO EQUIPAMENTOS DE CONSTRUCAO LTDA.—See AB Volvo; *Int'l*, pg. 43
VOLVO ESPANA, S.A.U.—See AB Volvo; *Int'l*, pg. 42
VOLVO EUROPA TRUCK N.V.—See AB Volvo; *Int'l*, pg. 46
VOLVO FINANCE AUSTRALIA PTY LTD.—See AB Volvo; *Int'l*, pg. 43
VOLVO FINANCE NORTH AMERICA INC.; *U.S. Private*, pg. 4411
VOLVO FINANCE PERU S.A.—See AB Volvo; *Int'l*, pg. 43
VOLVO FINANCE (SUISSE) SA VAUD—See AB Volvo; *Int'l*, pg. 44
VOLVO FINANCIAL SERVICES AB—See AB Volvo; *Int'l*, pg. 44
VOLVO FINANCIAL SERVICES GMBH—See AB Volvo; *Int'l*, pg. 44
VOLVO FINANCIAL SERVICES LLC—See AB Volvo; *Int'l*, pg. 44
VOLVOFINANS BANK AB—See Zhejiang Geely Holding Group Co., Ltd.; *Int'l*, pg. 8654
VOLVO FINANS NORGE AS—See AB Volvo; *Int'l*, pg. 44
VOLVO GROUP AUSTRALIA PTY LTD—See AB Volvo; *Int'l*, pg. 44
VOLVO GROUP AUTOMOTIVE TICARET, LTD—See AB Volvo; *Int'l*, pg. 44
VOLVO GROUP CANADA INC.—See AB Volvo; *Int'l*, pg. 44
VOLVO GROUP INSURANCE FORSAKRINGS AB—See AB Volvo; *Int'l*, pg. 44
VOLVO GROUP MEXICO—See AB Volvo; *Int'l*, pg. 44
VOLVO GROUP NORTH AMERICA, LLC—See AB Volvo; *Int'l*, pg. 44
VOLVO GROUP REAL ESTATE AB—See AB Volvo; *Int'l*, pg. 44
VOLVO GROUP REPRESENTATION—See AB Volvo; *Int'l*, pg. 44
VOLVO GROUP UK LTD—See AB Volvo; *Int'l*, pg. 46
VOLVO GROUP VENTURE CAPITAL AB—See AB Volvo; *Int'l*, pg. 44
VOLVO HOLDING DANMARK A/S—See AB Volvo; *Int'l*, pg. 44
VOLVO HOLDING FRANCE SA—See AB Volvo; *Int'l*, pg. 44
VOLVO HOLDING MEXICO, S.A. DE C.V.—See AB Volvo; *Int'l*, pg. 44
VOLVO HOLDING SVERIGE AB—See AB Volvo; *Int'l*, pg. 44
VOLVO HRVATSKA D.O.O.—See AB Volvo; *Int'l*, pg. 45
VOLVO INDIA LTD - VOLVO FINANCIAL SERVICES INDIA DIVISION—See AB Volvo; *Int'l*, pg. 46
VOLVO INDIA PRIVATE LTD.—See AB Volvo; *Int'l*, pg. 46
VOLVO INFORMATION TECHNOLOGY AB—See AB Volvo; *Int'l*, pg. 45
VOLVO INFORMATION TECHNOLOGY FRANCE—See AB Volvo; *Int'l*, pg. 45
VOLVO INFORMATION TECHNOLOGY MALAYSIA—See AB Volvo; *Int'l*, pg. 45
VOLVO INFORMATION TECHNOLOGY MEXICO—See AB Volvo; *Int'l*, pg. 45
VOLVO INFORMATION TECHNOLOGY NORTH AMERICA INC.—See AB Volvo; *Int'l*, pg. 45
VOLVO INFORMATION TECHNOLOGY POLAND—See AB Volvo; *Int'l*, pg. 45
VOLVO INFORMATION TECHNOLOGY ROCKLEIGH—See AB Volvo; *Int'l*, pg. 45
VOLVO INFORMATION TECHNOLOGY (TIANJIN) CO., LTD—See AB Volvo; *Int'l*, pg. 45
VOLVO INTERNATIONAL HOLDING BV—See AB Volvo; *Int'l*, pg. 45
VOLVO ITALIA SPA—See AB Volvo; *Int'l*, pg. 45
VOLVO IT BELGIUM—See AB Volvo; *Int'l*, pg. 45
VOLVO IT CANADA—See AB Volvo; *Int'l*, pg. 45
VOLVO IT ESKILSTUNA—See AB Volvo; *Int'l*, pg. 45
VOLVO IT KOPING—See AB Volvo; *Int'l*, pg. 45
VOLVO IT KOREA—See AB Volvo; *Int'l*, pg. 45
VOLVO IT SOUTH AFRICA—See AB Volvo; *Int'l*, pg. 45
VOLVO IT THAILAND—See AB Volvo; *Int'l*, pg. 45
VOLVO KUORMA-JA LINJA-AUTOT OY AB—See AB Volvo; *Int'l*, pg. 46
VOLVO LASTVAGNAR AB—See AB Volvo; *Int'l*, pg. 45
VOLVO LASTVAGNAR SVERIGE AB—See AB Volvo; *Int'l*, pg. 46
VOLVO LASTVOGNE DANMARK A/S—See AB Volvo; *Int'l*, pg. 46
VOLVO LOGISTICS AB—See AB Volvo; *Int'l*, pg. 45
VOLVO LOGISTICS CORPORATION—See AB Volvo; *Int'l*, pg. 45
VOLVO MAKEDONIJA LTD.—See AB Volvo; *Int'l*, pg. 45
VOLVO MALAYSIA SDN. BHD.—See Zhejiang Geely Holding Group Co., Ltd.; *Int'l*, pg. 8654
VOLVO MASKIN AS—See AB Volvo; *Int'l*, pg. 45
VOLVO NORGE A/S—See AB Volvo; *Int'l*, pg. 46
VOLVO OF EDISON; *U.S. Private*, pg. 4411
VOLVO OF FORT WASHINGTON; *U.S. Private*, pg. 4412
VOLVO OF LISLE; *U.S. Private*, pg. 4412
VOLVO OF THE TRIAD; *U.S. Private*, pg. 4412
VOLVO PARTS CORPORATION—See AB Volvo; *Int'l*, pg. 46
VOLVO PARTS GENT NV—See AB Volvo; *Int'l*, pg. 45
VOLVO PENTA BENELUX B.V.—See AB Volvo; *Int'l*, pg. 42
VOLVO PENTA CANADA LTD.—See AB Volvo; *Int'l*, pg. 42
VOLVO PENTA CENTRAL EUROPE GMBH—See AB Volvo; *Int'l*, pg. 42
VOLVO PENTA DO BRASIL LTDA.—See AB Volvo; *Int'l*, pg. 42
VOLVO PENTA FRANCE S.A.—See AB Volvo; *Int'l*, pg. 42
VOLVO PENTA NORDEN AB—See AB Volvo; *Int'l*, pg. 42
VOLVO-PENTA NORTH AMERICA, INC.—See AB Volvo; *Int'l*, pg. 42
VOLVO PENTA OF THE AMERICAS, INC.—See AB Volvo; *Int'l*, pg. 42
VOLVO PENTA SINGAPORE—See AB Volvo; *Int'l*, pg. 42
VOLVO PENTA SVERIGE—See AB Volvo; *Int'l*, pg. 42
VOLVO PENTA TURKEY—See AB Volvo; *Int'l*, pg. 42
VOLVO PENTA UK LIMITED—See AB Volvo; *Int'l*, pg. 42
VOLVO PERSONBILAR SVERIGE AB—See Zhejiang Geely Holding Group Co., Ltd.; *Int'l*, pg. 8654
VOLVO PERSONBILER NORGE A/S—See Zhejiang Geely Holding Group Co., Ltd.; *Int'l*, pg. 8654
VOLVO PERSONVAGNAR AB—See Zhejiang Geely Holding Group Co., Ltd.; *Int'l*, pg. 8654
VOLVO PERSONVAGNAR HOLDING AB—See Zhejiang Geely Holding Group Co., Ltd.; *Int'l*, pg. 8654
VOLVO PERSONVOGNE DANMARK A/S—See Zhejiang Geely Holding Group Co., Ltd.; *Int'l*, pg. 8654
VOLVO PERU S.A.—See AB Volvo; *Int'l*, pg. 42
VOLVO POLAND SP. Z.O.O.—See AB Volvo; *Int'l*, pg. 46
VOLVO POWERTRAIN AB—See AB Volvo; *Int'l*, pg. 45
VOLVO-SAFFLE AB—See AB Volvo; *Int'l*, pg. 43
VOLVO SALES & SERVICE CENTER; *U.S. Private*, pg. 4412
VOLVO (SOUTHERN AFRICA) PTY LTD—See AB Volvo; *Int'l*, pg. 42
VOLVO TECHNOLOGY TRANSFER AB—See AB Volvo; *Int'l*, pg. 45
VOLVO THAILAND LTD.—See Zhejiang Geely Holding Group Co., Ltd.; *Int'l*, pg. 8654
VOLVO TREASURY AB—See AB Volvo; *Int'l*, pg. 45
VOLVO TREASURY ASIA LTD.—See AB Volvo; *Int'l*, pg. 45
VOLVO TRUCK AUSTRALIA PTY. LTD.—See AB Volvo; *Int'l*, pg. 46

VOLVO TRUCK & BUS BOTSWANA PTY. LTD.—See AB Volvo; *Int'l*, pg. 46
VOLVO TRUCK & BUS (THAILAND) CO. LTD.—See AB Volvo; *Int'l*, pg. 46
VOLVO TRUCK CENTER SWEDEN AB—See AB Volvo; *Int'l*, pg. 46
VOLVO TRUCK CORPORATION POWERTRAIN DIVISION ENGINE—See AB Volvo; *Int'l*, pg. 46
VOLVO TRUCK CORPORATION—See AB Volvo; *Int'l*, pg. 45
VOLVO TRUCK CZECH S.R.O.—See AB Volvo; *Int'l*, pg. 46
VOLVO TRUCK EN BUS NEDERLAND B.V.—See AB Volvo; *Int'l*, pg. 46
VOLVO TRUCK LATVIA SIA—See AB Volvo; *Int'l*, pg. 46
VOLVO TRUCKS AUSTRIA GMBH—See AB Volvo; *Int'l*, pg. 47
VOLVO TRUCKS BELGIUM N.V.—See AB Volvo; *Int'l*, pg. 47
VOLVO TRUCKS BULGARIA EOOD—See AB Volvo; *Int'l*, pg. 46
VOLVO TRUCKS CANADA—See AB Volvo; *Int'l*, pg. 47
VOLVO TRUCKS DE MEXICO S.A. DE C.V.—See AB Volvo; *Int'l*, pg. 47
VOLVO TRUCKS (DEUTSCHLAND) GMBH—See AB Volvo; *Int'l*, pg. 46
VOLVO TRUCKS ESPANA, S.A.—See AB Volvo; *Int'l*, pg. 47
VOLVO TRUCKS ESTONIA—See AB Volvo; *Int'l*, pg. 46
VOLVO TRUCKS FINLAND—See AB Volvo; *Int'l*, pg. 46
VOLVO TRUCKS INDIA PVT LTD—See AB Volvo; *Int'l*, pg. 47
VOLVO TRUCKS INDONESIA—See AB Volvo; *Int'l*, pg. 47
VOLVO TRUCKS IRAN—See AB Volvo; *Int'l*, pg. 46
VOLVO TRUCKS LITHUANIA—See AB Volvo; *Int'l*, pg. 46
VOLVO TRUCK SLOVAK, S.R.O.—See AB Volvo; *Int'l*, pg. 46
VOLVO TRUCKS MACEDONIA—See AB Volvo; *Int'l*, pg. 46
VOLVO TRUCKS NETHERLANDS—See AB Volvo; *Int'l*, pg. 46
VOLVO TRUCKS NIGERIA—See AB Volvo; *Int'l*, pg. 46
VOLVO TRUCKS NORTH AMERICA, INC.—See AB Volvo; *Int'l*, pg. 47
VOLVO TRUCKS OF OMAHA INC—See North American Truck & Trailer, Inc.; *U.S. Private*, pg. 2941
VOLVO TRUCK—See AB Volvo; *Int'l*, pg. 46
VOLVO TRUCKS PHILIPPINES—See AB Volvo; *Int'l*, pg. 47
VOLVO TRUCKS POLAND—See AB Volvo; *Int'l*, pg. 46
VOLVO TRUCKS REGION CENTRAL EUROPE GMBH—See AB Volvo; *Int'l*, pg. 47
VOLVO TRUCKS RUSSIA—See AB Volvo; *Int'l*, pg. 46
VOLVO TRUCKS SAUDI ARABIA—See AB Volvo; *Int'l*, pg. 46
VOLVO TRUCKS (SCHWEIZ) AG—See AB Volvo; *Int'l*, pg. 46
VOLVO TRUCKS (SUISSE) SA—See AB Volvo; *Int'l*, pg. 47
VOLVO TRUCKS SWEDEN AB—See AB Volvo; *Int'l*, pg. 47
VOLVO TRUCKS SYRIA—See AB Volvo; *Int'l*, pg. 46
VOLVO TRUCKS THAILAND—See AB Volvo; *Int'l*, pg. 47
VOLVO WHEEL LOADERS AB—See AB Volvo; *Int'l*, pg. 43
VOLVOX GROUP (LEEDS) LTD.—See Rubicon Partners Limited; *Int'l*, pg. 6422
VOLYNGAZ, PJSC; *Int'l*, pg. 8304
VOLZHSKY ABRASIVE WORKS JSC—See The Murugappa Group, Ltd.; *Int'l*, pg. 7668
VOMAX—See Triton Systems Inc.; *U.S. Private*, pg. 4239
VOMELA SPECIALTY COMPANY; *U.S. Private*, pg. 4412
VOM, LLC—See Velocity Portfolio Group, Inc.; *U.S. Private*, pg. 4354
VONAGE AMERICA INC.—See Telefonaktiebolaget LM Ericsson; *Int'l*, pg. 7534
VONAGE BUSINESS SOLUTIONS, INC.—See Telefonaktiebolaget LM Ericsson; *Int'l*, pg. 7534
VONAGE HOLDINGS CORPORATION—See Telefonaktiebolaget LM Ericsson; *Int'l*, pg. 7534
VONAGE INTERNATIONAL INC.—See Telefonaktiebolaget LM Ericsson; *Int'l*, pg. 7534
VONAGE LIMITED—See Telefonaktiebolaget LM Ericsson; *Int'l*, pg. 7535
VONAGE MARKETING LLC—See Telefonaktiebolaget LM Ericsson; *Int'l*, pg. 7535
VONAGE NETWORK LLC—See Telefonaktiebolaget LM Ericsson; *Int'l*, pg. 7535
VONAGE WORLDWIDE INC.—See Telefonaktiebolaget LM Ericsson; *Int'l*, pg. 7535
VON ARX AG—See Emerson Electric Co.; *U.S. Public*, pg. 749
VON CAPITAL CORP.; *Int'l*, pg. 8304
VONCO PRODUCTS, LLC—See Jacsten Holdings, LLC; *U.S. Private*, pg. 2181
VON DER HEYDEN GROUP FINANCE PLC; *Int'l*, pg. 8304
VON DREHLE CORPORATION—See Atlas Holdings, LLC; *U.S. Private*, pg. 378
VON DUPRIN LLC—See Allegion Public Limited Company; *Int'l*, pg. 335
VONESEALS TECHNOLOGY (SHANGHAI) INC.; *Int'l*, pg. 8304
VON ESSEN GMBH & CO. KG BANKGESELLSCHAFT—See BNP Paribas SA; *Int'l*, pg. 1084
V-ONE TECH CO., LTD.; *Int'l*, pg. 8105
VONEX LTD.; *Int'l*, pg. 8304
VONEY AG—See ProMinent Dosiertechnik GmbH; *Int'l*, pg. 5994
VONFELDT, BAUER, & VONFELDT CHARTERED—See Adams Brown, LLC; *U.S. Private*, pg. 74
VONGROUP LTD; *Int'l*, pg. 8304
VON HEYDEN PHARMA GMBH—See Bristol-Myers Squibb Company; *U.S. Public*, pg. 387
VON HOUSEN'S MOTORS; *U.S. Private*, pg. 4412
VON HOUSEN'S SACRAMENTO, INC.—See Von Housen's Motors; *U.S. Private*, pg. 4412
VONLANE, LLC; *U.S. Private*, pg. 4412
VONLEHMAN & CO. INC.—See Dean Dorton Allen Ford, PLLC; *U.S. Private*, pg. 1183
VON MANNSTEIN WERBEAGENTUR GMBH; *Int'l*, pg. 8304
VON MAUR INC.; *U.S. Private*, pg. 4412
VON OERTZEN GMBH—See L. Possehl & Co. mbH; *Int'l*, pg. 4382
VONOVIA EIGENTUMSSERVICE GMBH—See Vonovia SE; *Int'l*, pg. 8305
VONOVIA IMMOBILIEN TREUHAND GMBH—See Vonovia SE; *Int'l*, pg. 8305
VONOVIA SE; *Int'l*, pg. 8304
VONPENDE HOLDINGS PLC; *Int'l*, pg. 8305
VON ROHR ARCA BV—See ARCA Regler GmbH; *Int'l*, pg. 540
VON ROHR ARMATUREN AG—See ARCA Regler GmbH; *Int'l*, pg. 540
VON ROLL ASIA PTE. LTD.—See SKion GmbH; *Int'l*, pg. 6987
VON ROLL AUSTRAL, INC.—See SKion GmbH; *Int'l*, pg. 6988
VON ROLL AUTOMOTIVE GMBH—See SKion GmbH; *Int'l*, pg. 6987
VON ROLL BHU UMWELTTECHNIK GMBH—See SKion GmbH; *Int'l*, pg. 6987
VON ROLL CASTING (EMMENBRUCKE) AG—See SKion GmbH; *Int'l*, pg. 6988
VON ROLL COMPOSITE S.A.S.—See SKion GmbH; *Int'l*, pg. 6987
VON ROLL DEUTSCHLAND GMBH—See SKion GmbH; *Int'l*, pg. 6987
VON ROLL DEUTSCHLAND GMBH—See SKion GmbH; *Int'l*, pg. 6987
VON ROLL DEUTSCHLAND HOLDING GMBH—See SKion GmbH; *Int'l*, pg. 6987
VON ROLL DO BRASIL LTDA. - PRODUCTION PLANT—See SKion GmbH; *Int'l*, pg. 6988
VON ROLL DO BRASIL LTDA.—See SKion GmbH; *Int'l*, pg. 6988
VON ROLL EISEN & STAHLGIESSEREI AG—See SKion GmbH; *Int'l*, pg. 6988
VON ROLL FRANCE S.A.—See SKion GmbH; *Int'l*, pg. 6987
VON ROLL HOLDING AG—See SKion GmbH; *Int'l*, pg. 6987
VONROLL HYDROSERVICES AG—See SKion GmbH; *Int'l*, pg. 6988
VON ROLL HYDRO TECH GMBH—See SKion GmbH; *Int'l*, pg. 6988
VON ROLL HYDROTEC S.A.—See SKion GmbH; *Int'l*, pg. 6988
VON ROLL (INDIA) PVT. LTD.—See SKion GmbH; *Int'l*, pg. 6987
VON ROLL INFRATEC HOLDING AG—See SKion GmbH; *Int'l*, pg. 6987
VON ROLL INSULATION & COMPOSITES HOLDING AG—See SKion GmbH; *Int'l*, pg. 6988
VON ROLL ISOLA CZECH REPUBLIC—See SKion GmbH; *Int'l*, pg. 6988
VON ROLL ISOLA, EL PASO—See SKion GmbH; *Int'l*, pg. 6988
VON ROLL ISOLA FRANCE S.A., RESINS & VARNISH DIVISION—See SKion GmbH; *Int'l*, pg. 6988
VON ROLL ISOLA FRANCE S.A., SAMICA DIVISION—See SKion GmbH; *Int'l*, pg. 6988
VON ROLL ISOLA FRANCE S.A.—See SKion GmbH; *Int'l*, pg. 6988
VON ROLL ISOLA GMBH—See SKion GmbH; *Int'l*, pg. 6988
VON ROLL ISOLA-MIDWEST—See SKion GmbH; *Int'l*, pg. 6988
VON ROLL ISOLA MTEC LTD.—See SKion GmbH; *Int'l*, pg. 6988
VON ROLL ISOLA POLAND—See SKion GmbH; *Int'l*, pg. 6988
VON ROLL ISOLA S.A.—See SKion GmbH; *Int'l*, pg. 6988
VON ROLL ISOLA, WINDING SYSTEMS GMBH—See SKion GmbH; *Int'l*, pg. 6988
VON ROLL ITALIA S.P.A.—See SKion GmbH; *Int'l*, pg. 6988
VON ROLL MANAGEMENT AG—See SKion GmbH; *Int'l*, pg. 6988
VON ROLL REACH GMBH—See SKion GmbH; *Int'l*, pg. 6988
VON ROLL SCHWEIZ AG—See SKion GmbH; *Int'l*, pg. 6988
VON ROLL SHANGHAI CO., LTD—See SKion GmbH; *Int'l*, pg. 6988
VON ROLL SOLAR AG—See SKion GmbH; *Int'l*, pg. 6988
VON ROLL SWITZERLAND AG—See SKion GmbH; *Int'l*, pg. 6988
VON ROLL TRADING (SHANGHAI) CO., LTD.—See SKion GmbH; *Int'l*, pg. 6988
VON ROLL UK LTD—See SKion GmbH; *Int'l*, pg. 6988
VON ROLL USA HOLDING, INC.—See SKion GmbH; *Int'l*, pg. 6988
VON ROLL USA, INC.—See SKion GmbH; *Int'l*, pg. 6988
VON ROLL WATER HOLDING AG—See SKion GmbH; *Int'l*, pg. 6988
VONS A SAFEWAY COMPANY—See Cerberus Capital Management, L.P.; *U.S. Private*, pg. 836
VON SCHRADER COMPANY; *U.S. Private*, pg. 4412
THE VONS COMPANIES, INC.—See Cerberus Capital Management, L.P.; *U.S. Private*, pg. 836
VONTHRON ENTREPRISES SAS—See VINCI S.A.; *Int'l*, pg. 8240
VONTIER CORPORATION; *U.S. Public*, pg. 2308
VONTOBEL ASIA PACIFIC LTD.—See Vontobel Holding AG; *Int'l*, pg. 8306
VONTOBEL ASSET MANAGEMENT AG—See Vontobel Holding AG; *Int'l*, pg. 8306
VONTOBEL ASSET MANAGEMENT ASIA PACIFIC LIMITED—See Vontobel Holding AG; *Int'l*, pg. 8306
VONTOBEL ASSET MANAGEMENT AUSTRALIA PTY. LTD.—See Vontobel Holding AG; *Int'l*, pg. 8306
VONTOBEL ASSET MANAGEMENT, INC.—See Vontobel Holding AG; *Int'l*, pg. 8306
VONTOBEL ASSET MANAGEMENT S.A.—See Vontobel Holding AG; *Int'l*, pg. 8306
VONTOBEL ASSET MANAGEMENT SGR SPA—See Vontobel Holding AG; *Int'l*, pg. 8306
VON TOBEL CORPORATION; *U.S. Private*, pg. 4412
VONTOBEL EUROPE S.A.—See Vontobel Holding AG; *Int'l*, pg. 8306
VONTOBEL FINANCIAL PRODUCTS GMBH—See Vontobel Holding AG; *Int'l*, pg. 8306
VONTOBEL FINANCIAL PRODUCTS LTD.—See Vontobel Holding AG; *Int'l*, pg. 8306
VONTOBEL FONDS SERVICES AG—See Vontobel Holding AG; *Int'l*, pg. 8306
VONTOBEL FUND ADVISORY S.A.—See Vontobel Holding AG; *Int'l*, pg. 8306
VONTOBEL HOLDING AG; *Int'l*, pg. 8305
VONTOBEL (HONG KONG) LTD.—See Vontobel Holding AG; *Int'l*, pg. 8306
VONTOBEL INVEST LTD.—See Vontobel Holding AG; *Int'l*, pg. 8306
VONTOBEL LIMITED—See Vontobel Holding AG; *Int'l*, pg. 8306
VONTOBEL MANAGEMENT S.A.—See Vontobel Holding AG; *Int'l*, pg. 8306
VONTOBEL PTE. LTD.—See Vontobel Holding AG; *Int'l*, pg. 8306
VONTOBEL SECURITIES AG—See Vontobel Holding AG; *Int'l*, pg. 8306
VONTOBEL SWISS WEALTH ADVISORS AG—See Vontobel Holding AG; *Int'l*, pg. 8306
VONTOBEL TREUHAND AG—See Vontobel Holding AG; *Int'l*, pg. 8306
VONTOBEL WEALTH MANAGEMENT (HONG KONG) LTD.—See Vontobel Holding AG; *Int'l*, pg. 8306
VONTOBEL WEALTH MANAGEMENT SOCIETA DI INTERMEDIAZIONE MOBILIARE S.P.A.—See Vontobel Holding AG; *Int'l*, pg. 8306
VONTRON TECHNOLOGY CO., LTD; *Int'l*, pg. 8306
VONTU, INC.—See Gen Digital Inc.; *U.S. Public*, pg. 911
VOODOO BBQ & GRILL; *U.S. Private*, pg. 4412
THE VOORHEES NJ ENDOSCOPY ASC, LLC—See KKR & Co. Inc.; *U.S. Public*, pg. 1248
VOORHIES SUPPLY COMPANY; LLC—See Genuine Parts Company; *U.S. Public*, pg. 933
VOORTMAN COOKIES LIMITED—See The J.M. Smucker Company; *U.S. Public*, pg. 2107
VOPAK AGENCIES AMSTERDAM B.V.—See Koninklijke Vopak N.V.; *Int'l*, pg. 4272
VOPAK AGENCIES ANTWERPEN NV—See Koninklijke Vopak N.V.; *Int'l*, pg. 4272
VOPAK AGENCIES TERNEUZEN B.V.—See Koninklijke Vopak N.V.; *Int'l*, pg. 4272
VOPAK AGENCY GERMANY GMBH—See Wilh. Wilhelmsen Holding ASA; *Int'l*, pg. 8411
VOPAK ASIA PTE. LTD.—See Koninklijke Vopak N.V.; *Int'l*, pg. 4272
VOPAK BRASIL S.A.—See Koninklijke Vopak N.V.; *Int'l*, pg. 4272
VOPAK CHEMICALS EMEA B.V.—See Koninklijke Vopak N.V.; *Int'l*, pg. 4272

VOPAK CHEMICALS LOGISTICS FINLAND OY—See Koninklijke Vopak N.V.; *Int'l*, pg. 4272
VOPAK CHEMICAL TERMINALS BELGIUM NV—See Koninklijke Vopak N.V.; *Int'l*, pg. 4272
VOPAK CHILE LIMITADA—See Koninklijke Vopak N.V.; *Int'l*, pg. 4272
VOPAK CHINA MANAGEMENT COMPANY LTD.—See Koninklijke Vopak N.V.; *Int'l*, pg. 4272
VOPAK COLOMBIA S.A.—See Koninklijke Vopak N.V.; *Int'l*, pg. 4272
VOPAK EMEA B.V.—See Koninklijke Vopak N.V.; *Int'l*, pg. 4272
VOPAK GLOBAL SHARED SERVICES B.V.—See Koninklijke Vopak N.V.; *Int'l*, pg. 4272
VOPAK LNG HOLDING B.V.—See Koninklijke Vopak N.V.; *Int'l*, pg. 4272
VOPAK LOGISTIC SERVICES OSV B.V.—See Koninklijke Vopak N.V.; *Int'l*, pg. 4272
VOPAK MEXICO-COATZACOALCOS TERMINAL—See Koninklijke Vopak N.V.; *Int'l*, pg. 4273
VOPAK MEXICO, S.A DE C.V.—See Koninklijke Vopak N.V.; *Int'l*, pg. 4273
VOPAK NEDERLAND B.V.—See Koninklijke Vopak N.V.; *Int'l*, pg. 4273
VOPAK OIL EMEA B.V.—See Koninklijke Vopak N.V.; *Int'l*, pg. 4273
VOPAK; *Int'l*, pg. 8306
VOPAK TERMINAL ALTAMIRA—See Koninklijke Vopak N.V.; *Int'l*, pg. 4273
VOPAK TERMINAL AMSTERDAM B.V.—See Koninklijke Vopak N.V.; *Int'l*, pg. 4273
VOPAK TERMINAL BOTLEK B.V.—See Koninklijke Vopak N.V.; *Int'l*, pg. 4273
VOPAK TERMINAL BOTLEK-NOORD B.V.—See Koninklijke Vopak N.V.; *Int'l*, pg. 4273
VOPAK TERMINAL CHEMIEHAVEN B.V.—See Koninklijke Vopak N.V.; *Int'l*, pg. 4273
VOPAK TERMINAL DARWIN PTY. LTD.—See Koninklijke Vopak N.V.; *Int'l*, pg. 4273
VOPAK TERMINAL DEER PARK INC.—See Koninklijke Vopak N.V.; *Int'l*, pg. 4273
VOPAK TERMINAL DURBAN (PTY) LTD.—See Koninklijke Vopak N.V.; *Int'l*, pg. 4273
VOPAK TERMINAL EUROPOORT B.V.—See Koninklijke Vopak N.V.; *Int'l*, pg. 4273
VOPAK TERMINAL EUROTANK NV—See Koninklijke Vopak N.V.; *Int'l*, pg. 4273
VOPAK TERMINAL GALENA PARK INC.—See Koninklijke Vopak N.V.; *Int'l*, pg. 4273
VOPAK TERMINAL LAURENSHAVEN B.V.—See Koninklijke Vopak N.V.; *Int'l*, pg. 4273
VOPAK TERMINAL LONDON LIMITED—See Koninklijke Vopak N.V.; *Int'l*, pg. 4273
VOPAK TERMINAL LONG BEACH INC.—See Koninklijke Vopak N.V.; *Int'l*, pg. 4273
VOPAK TERMINAL LOS ANGELES INC.—See Koninklijke Vopak N.V.; *Int'l*, pg. 4273
VOPAK TERMINAL NORTH WILMINGTON INC.—See Koninklijke Vopak N.V.; *Int'l*, pg. 4273
VOPAK TERMINAL PENJURU PTE. LTD.—See Koninklijke Vopak N.V.; *Int'l*, pg. 4273
VOPAK TERMINALS AUSTRALIA PTY. LTD.—See Koninklijke Vopak N.V.; *Int'l*, pg. 4273
VOPAK TERMINAL SAVANNAH INC.—See Koninklijke Vopak N.V.; *Int'l*, pg. 4273
VOPAK TERMINAL SHANDONG LANSHAN LIMITED—See Koninklijke Vopak N.V.; *Int'l*, pg. 4273
VOPAK TERMINALS KOREA LTD.—See Koninklijke Vopak N.V.; *Int'l*, pg. 4273
VOPAK TERMINALS NORTH AMERICA INC.—See Koninklijke Vopak N.V.; *Int'l*, pg. 4273
VOPAK TERMINALS OF CANADA INC.—See Koninklijke Vopak N.V.; *Int'l*, pg. 4273
VOPAK TERMINALS OF EASTERN CANADA INC.—See Koninklijke Vopak N.V.; *Int'l*, pg. 4273
VOPAK TERMINALS SINGAPORE PTE. LTD.—See Koninklijke Vopak N.V.; *Int'l*, pg. 4273
VOPAK TERMINALS SYDNEY PTY. LTD.—See Koninklijke Vopak N.V.; *Int'l*, pg. 4273
VOPAK TERMINAL TEESSIDE LTD.—See Koninklijke Vopak N.V.; *Int'l*, pg. 4273
VOPAK TERMINAL TTR B.V.—See Koninklijke Vopak N.V.; *Int'l*, pg. 4273
VOPAK TERMINAL VERACRUZ—See Koninklijke Vopak N.V.; *Int'l*, pg. 4273
VOPAK TERMINAL VLAARDINGEN B.V.—See Koninklijke Vopak N.V.; *Int'l*, pg. 4273
VOPAK TERMINAL VLISSINGEN B.V.—See Koninklijke Vopak N.V.; *Int'l*, pg. 4273
VOPAK TERMINAL WESTPOORT B.V.—See Koninklijke Vopak N.V.; *Int'l*, pg. 4273
VOPAK TERMINAL WINDMILL LTD.—See Koninklijke Vopak N.V.; *Int'l*, pg. 4273
VOPAK TERMINAL ZHANGJIAGANG LTD.—See Koninklijke Vopak N.V.; *Int'l*, pg. 4273
VOPAK VENEZUELA S.A.—See Koninklijke Vopak N.V.; *Int'l*, pg. 4273
VOPAK VIETNAM CO. LTD.—See Koninklijke Vopak N.V.; *Int'l*, pg. 4273

VOP BERRY PARK, LLC—See Ventas, Inc.; *U.S. Public*, pg. 2278
VOPELIUS CHEMIE AG; *Int'l*, pg. 8306
VORA TECHNOLOGY PARK LLC—See Vora Ventures LLC; *U.S. Private*, pg. 4412
VORA VENTURES LLC; *U.S. Private*, pg. 4412
VOR BIOPHARMA INC.; *U.S. Public*, pg. 2309
VORDERE PLC; *Int'l*, pg. 8306
VORDERMAN MOTOR WERKS INC.; *U.S. Private*, pg. 4413
VORK TECHNOLOGIES (MALAYSIA) SDN.BHD.—See Xiamen Voke Mold & Plastic Engineering Co., Ltd.; *Int'l*, pg. 8526
V.ORLANDI AUSTRALIA PTY LTD.—See SAF-Holland S.A.; *Int'l*, pg. 6468
V.ORLANDI S.P.A.—See SAF-Holland S.A.; *Int'l*, pg. 6468
VORMETRIC, INC.—See Thales S.A.; *Int'l*, pg. 7602
VORNADO AIR, LLC—See AEA Investors LP; *U.S. Private*, pg. 116
VORNADO OFFICE INC.—See Vornado Realty Trust; *U.S. Public*, pg. 2310
VORNADO OFFICE MANAGEMENT LLC—See Vornado Realty Trust; *U.S. Public*, pg. 2310
VORNADO REALTY L.P.—See Vornado Realty Trust; *U.S. Public*, pg. 2309
VORNADO REALTY TRUST; *U.S. Public*, pg. 2309
VORNADO SPRINGFIELD MALL MANAGER LLC—See Vornado Realty Trust; *U.S. Public*, pg. 2310
VORNDRAN MANNHEIMS CAPITAL ADVISORS GMBH; *Int'l*, pg. 8306
VORONEZHSKIE DROJJI LLC—See Compagnie des Levures Lesaffre SA; *Int'l*, pg. 1739
VORONOI, INC.; *Int'l*, pg. 8307
VORSIGHT LLC—See Acquirent, LLC; *U.S. Private*, pg. 65
VORSORGE LEBENSVERSICHERUNG AG—See Munchener Ruckversicherungs AG; *Int'l*, pg. 5088
VORSORGE LUXEMBURG LEBENSVERSICHERUNG S.A.—See Munchener Ruckversicherungs AG; *Int'l*, pg. 5088
VORSORGE SERVICE GMBH—See Munchener Ruckversicherungs AG; *Int'l*, pg. 5092
VORSPANN-TECHNIK GMBH AND CO.KG—See PORR AG; *Int'l*, pg. 5925
VORSPANN-TECHNIK GMBH—See PORR AG; *Int'l*, pg. 5925
VORST MEDIA B.V.—See ITV plc; *Int'l*, pg. 3845
VORTAL COMERCIO ELECTRONICO, CONSULTADORIAE MULTIMEDIA, S.A.—See Byggfakta Group Nordic HoldCo AB; *Int'l*, pg. 1235
VORTEK INSTRUMENTS, LLC—See Azbil Corporation; *Int'l*, pg. 777
VORTEQ ALLENTOWN, LLC—See Vorteq Coil Finishers, LLC; *U.S. Private*, pg. 4413
VORTEQ COIL FINISHERS, LLC; *U.S. Private*, pg. 4413
VORTEQ JACKSON, LLC—See Vorteq Coil Finishers, LLC; *U.S. Private*, pg. 4413
VORTEQ VALENCIA, LLC—See Vorteq Coil Finishers, LLC; *U.S. Private*, pg. 4413
VORTEQ WOODSTOCK, LLC—See Vorteq Coil Finishers, LLC; *U.S. Private*, pg. 4413
VORTEX AQUATIC STRUCTURES INTERNATIONAL INC.; *Int'l*, pg. 8307
VORTEX BRANDS CO.; *U.S. Public*, pg. 2310
VORTEX COMPANY, LLC; *U.S. Private*, pg. 4413
VORTEX ENERGY CORP.; *Int'l*, pg. 8307
VORTEX ENTERPRISES INCORPORATED; *U.S. Private*, pg. 4413
VORTEX INDUSTRIES INC.; *U.S. Private*, pg. 4413
VORTEX INSURANCE AGENCY, LLC—See MS&AD Insurance Group Holdings, Inc.; *Int'l*, pg. 5067
VORTEX MARINE CONSTRUCTION; *U.S. Private*, pg. 4413
VORTEX MEDICAL—See AngioDynamics, Inc.; *U.S. Public*, pg. 137
VORTEX PRODUCTION SERVICES LTD.; *Int'l*, pg. 8307
VORTEX RECYCLING; *U.S. Private*, pg. 4413
VORTIV LIMITED; *Int'l*, pg. 8307
VORTX INC.—See Constellation Software Inc.; *Int'l*, pg. 1773
VORWERK ASIA MITTELSTEN SCHEID & CO—See Vorwerk & Co. KG; *Int'l*, pg. 8308
VORWERK AUSTRIA GES.M.B.H.—See Vorwerk & Co. KG; *Int'l*, pg. 8308
VORWERK & CO. INTERHOLDING GMBH—See Vorwerk & Co. KG; *Int'l*, pg. 8307
VORWERK & CO. KG; *Int'l*, pg. 8307
VORWERK CONTEMPORA S.R.L.—See Vorwerk & Co. KG; *Int'l*, pg. 8307
VORWERK & CO. TEPPICHWERKE GMBH & CO. KG.—See Vorwerk & Co. KG; *Int'l*, pg. 8307
VORWERK & CO. THERMOMIX GMBH—See Vorwerk & Co. KG; *Int'l*, pg. 8307
VORWERK DEUTSCHLAND STIFTUNG & CO. KG—See Vorwerk & Co. KG; *Int'l*, pg. 8308
VORWERK ELEKTROWERKE GMBH & CO. KG—See Vorwerk & Co. KG; *Int'l*, pg. 8308
VORWERK ESPANA M.S.L.S.C.—See Vorwerk & Co. KG; *Int'l*, pg. 8308

VORWERK FOLLETTO S.A.S. DI ACHIM SCHWANITZ & CO.—See Vorwerk & Co. KG; *Int'l*, pg. 8308
VORWERK FRANCE S.C.S.—See Vorwerk & Co. KG; *Int'l*, pg. 8308
VORWERK HOUSEHOLD APPLIANCES CO., LTD.—See Vorwerk & Co. KG; *Int'l*, pg. 8308
VORWERK HOUSEHOLD APPLIANCES MANUFACTURING (SHANGHAI) CO,, LTD—See Vorwerk & Co. KG; *Int'l*, pg. 8308
VORWERK INTERNATIONAL STRECKER & CO—See Vorwerk & Co. KG; *Int'l*, pg. 8308
VORWERK LUX (FAR EAST) LTD.—See Vorwerk & Co. KG; *Int'l*, pg. 8308
VORWERK MEXICO S. DE R.L. DE C.V.—See Vorwerk & Co. KG; *Int'l*, pg. 8308
VORWERK POLSKA SP.Z.O.O.—See Vorwerk & Co. KG; *Int'l*, pg. 8308
VORWERK PORTUGAL ELECTRODOMESTICOS LDA—See Vorwerk & Co. KG; *Int'l*, pg. 8308
VORWERK SEMCO S.A.—See Vorwerk & Co. KG; *Int'l*, pg. 8308
VORWERK TEPPICHWERKE CO FRANCE—See Vorwerk & Co. KG; *Int'l*, pg. 8308
VORWERK TORNADO AG—See Vorwerk & Co. KG; *Int'l*, pg. 8308
VORYS, SATER, SEYMOUR & PEASE LLP; *U.S. Private*, pg. 4413
VOSCO AGENCY AND LOGISTICS ONE MEMBER LIMITED COMPANY—See Vietnam Ocean Shipping Joint Stock Company; *Int'l*, pg. 8202
VOSCO MARITIME SERVICES ONE MEMBER LIMITED COMPANY—See Vietnam Ocean Shipping Joint Stock Company; *Int'l*, pg. 8202
VOSCO TRADING AND SERVICE JOINT STOCK COMPANY—See Vietnam Ocean Shipping Joint Stock Company; *Int'l*, pg. 8202
VOS ELECTRIC INC.—See VHC Inc.; *U.S. Private*, pg. 4375
VOSGES HAUT-CHOCOLAT, LTD.; *U.S. Private*, pg. 4413
VOSS CHEVROLET, INC.; *U.S. Private*, pg. 4413
VOSS ELECTRIC COMPANY; *U.S. Private*, pg. 4413
VOSSEN GMBH & CO. AG—See Linz Textil Holding AG; *Int'l*, pg. 4517
VOSSEN UK LTD.—See Linz Textil Holding AG; *Int'l*, pg. 4517
VOSS EQUIPMENT INCORPORATED; *U.S. Private*, pg. 4413
VOSS GMBH & CO. KG—See BayWa AG; *Int'l*, pg. 919
VOSS INDUSTRIES, LLC—See Tinicum Enterprises, Inc.; *U.S. Private*, pg. 4174
VOSSLOH AG; *Int'l*, pg. 8308
VOSSLOH BEEKAY CASTINGS LTD.—See Vossloh AG; *Int'l*, pg. 8308
VOSSLOH COGIFER AUSTRALIA PTY. LTD.—See Vossloh AG; *Int'l*, pg. 8308
VOSSLOH COGIFER DO BRASIL METALURGICA MBM SA—See Vossloh AG; *Int'l*, pg. 8309
VOSSLOH COGIFER FINLAND OY—See Vossloh AG; *Int'l*, pg. 8309
VOSSLOH COGIFER ITALIA S.R.L.—See Vossloh AG; *Int'l*, pg. 8308
VOSSLOH COGIFER KIHN SA—See Vossloh AG; *Int'l*, pg. 8309
VOSSLOH COGIFER KLOOS BV—See Vossloh AG; *Int'l*, pg. 8308
VOSSLOH COGIFER POLSKA SP.Z O.O.—See Vossloh AG; *Int'l*, pg. 8308
VOSSLOH COGIFER SA—See Vossloh AG; *Int'l*, pg. 8308
VOSSLOH COGIFER SIGNALLING INDIA PRIVATE LIMITED—See Vossloh AG; *Int'l*, pg. 8309
VOSSLOH COGIFER SOUTHERN AFRICA PROPRIETARY LIMITED—See Vossloh AG; *Int'l*, pg. 8309
VOSSLOH COGIFER TURNOUTS INDIA PRIVATE LIMITED—See Vossloh AG; *Int'l*, pg. 8309
VOSSLOH COGIFER UK LIMITED—See Vossloh AG; *Int'l*, pg. 8309
VOSSLOH DRAZNI TECHNICA S.R.O.—See Vossloh AG; *Int'l*, pg. 8309
VOSSLOH FASTENING SYSTEMS AMERICA CORPORATION—See Vossloh AG; *Int'l*, pg. 8309
VOSSLOH FASTENING SYSTEMS CHINA CO. LTD.—See Vossloh AG; *Int'l*, pg. 8309
VOSSLOH FASTENING SYSTEMS GMBH—See Vossloh AG; *Int'l*, pg. 8309
VOSSLOH LAEIS GMBH—See Vossloh AG; *Int'l*, pg. 8309
VOSSLOH LOCOMOTIVES FRANCE SAS—See CRRC Corporation Limited; *Int'l*, pg. 1859
VOSSLOH LOCOMOTIVES GMBH—See CRRC Corporation Limited; *Int'l*, pg. 1859
VOSSLOH LOGISTICS GMBH—See Vossloh AG; *Int'l*, pg. 8309
VOSSLOH MOBILE RAIL SERVICES GMBH—See Vossloh AG; *Int'l*, pg. 8309
VOSSLOH NORDIC SWITCH SYSTEMS AB—See Vossloh AG; *Int'l*, pg. 8309
VOSSLOH RAIL CENTER GMBH—See Vossloh AG; *Int'l*, pg. 8309
VOSSLOH RAIL INSPECTION GMBH—See Vossloh AG; *Int'l*, pg. 8309

COMPANY NAME INDEX

VOSSLOH RAIL SERVICES FINLAND OY—See Vossloh AG; *Int'l*, pg. 8309
VOSSLOH RAIL SERVICES GMBH—See Vossloh AG; *Int'l*, pg. 8309
VOSSLOH RAIL SERVICES SCANDINAVIA AB—See Vossloh AG; *Int'l*, pg. 8309
VOSSLOH RAIL TECHNOLOGY LIMITET SIRKETI—See Vossloh AG; *Int'l*, pg. 8309
VOSSLOH RAY HIZMETLERI LIMITED SIRKETI—See Vossloh AG; *Int'l*, pg. 8309
VOSSLOH SERVICES FRANCE SAS—See Vossloh AG; *Int'l*, pg. 8309
VOSSLOH SIGNALING USA, INC.—See Vossloh AG; *Int'l*, pg. 8309
VOSSLOH SISTEMI S.R.L.—See Vossloh AG; *Int'l*, pg. 8309
VOSSLOH SKAMO SP.Z.O.O.—See Vossloh AG; *Int'l*, pg. 8309
VOSSLOH TEHNICA FEROVIARA SRL—See Vossloh AG; *Int'l*, pg. 8309
VOSSLOH TEHNIKA FEROVIARA S.R.L.—See Vossloh AG; *Int'l*, pg. 8309
VOSSLOH TIE TECHNOLOGIES CANADA ULC—See Vossloh AG; *Int'l*, pg. 8309
VOSSLOH TRACK MATERIAL, INC.—See Vossloh AG; *Int'l*, pg. 8309
VOSSLOH UTENZILIJA D.D.—See Vossloh AG; *Int'l*, pg. 8309
VOSSLOH WERDOHL GMBH—See Vossloh AG; *Int'l*, pg. 8309
VOSSLOH-WERKE GMBH—See Vossloh AG; *Int'l*, pg. 8309
VOSS VEKSEL-OG LANDMANDSBANK ASA; *Int'l*, pg. 8308
VOSTA LMG DESIGN GMBH—See ASL Marine Holdings Ltd; *Int'l*, pg. 625
VOSTA LMG INDIA PVT. LTD.—See ASL Marine Holdings Ltd; *Int'l*, pg. 625
VOSTA LMG IP & SOFTWARE B.V.—See ASL Marine Holdings Ltd; *Int'l*, pg. 625
VOSTA LMG (ZHUHAI) LTD.—See ASL Marine Holdings Ltd; *Int'l*, pg. 625
VOSTOCHNAYA STEVEDORING COMPANY—See Delo Group; *Int'l*, pg. 2014
VOSTOCHNAYA TECHNICA UK LTD—See Barloworld Ltd.; *Int'l*, pg. 866
VOSTOK NAFTA SVERIGE AB—See VNV Global Ltd.; *Int'l*, pg. 8283
VOSTOKNEFTEGAZ LLC—See International Petroleum Limited; *Int'l*, pg. 3751
VOSTRO INSTITUTE OF TRAINING AUSTRALIA PTY. LIMITED—See Academies Australasia Group Limited; *Int'l*, pg. 77
VOS WINDOW & DOOR INC.; *U.S. Private*, pg. 4413
VOTACALL, INC.; *U.S. Private*, pg. 4413
VOTAN LEO BURNETT—See Publicis Groupe S.A.; *Int'l*, pg. 6102
VOTAW PRECISION TECHNOLOGIES, INC.—See Doerfer Corporation; *U.S. Private*, pg. 1253
VOTAW PRECISION TECHNOLOGIES, INC.—See Stone River Capital Partners, LLC; *U.S. Private*, pg. 3826
VOTAW PRECISION TECHNOLOGIES, INC.—See Wynnchurch Capital, L.P.; *U.S. Private*, pg. 4577
VOTER CONSUMER RESEARCH, INC.—See Texas Market Research Group LLC; *U.S. Private*, pg. 3976
VOTG NORTH AMERICA INC.—See Joachim Herz Stiftung; *Int'l*, pg. 3976
VOTG NORTH AMERICA INC.—See Morgan Stanley; *U.S. Public*, pg. 1476
VOTG TANKTAINER GMBH—See Joachim Herz Stiftung; *Int'l*, pg. 3976
VOTG TANKTAINER GMBH—See Morgan Stanley; *U.S. Public*, pg. 1476
VOTI DETECTION, INC.; *Int'l*, pg. 8309
VOTIGO, INC.; *U.S. Private*, pg. 4413
VOTIGO SOFTWARE PRIVATE LIMITED—See Votigo, Inc.; *U.S. Private*, pg. 4413
VOTI SECURITY SCANNING INTERNATIONAL DWC-LLC.—See VOTI Detection, Inc.; *Int'l*, pg. 8309
VOTIVO, LLC—See Grace Management Group, LLC; *U.S. Private*, pg. 1749
VOTOCEL FILMES FLEXIVEIS LTDA.—See Votorantim S.A.; *Int'l*, pg. 8310
VOTO MANUFACTURERS SALES CO. INC.; *U.S. Private*, pg. 4413
VOTORANTIM CEMENTOS EAA INVERSIONES, S.L.—See Votorantim S.A.; *Int'l*, pg. 8310
VOTORANTIM CEMENTOS INTERNATIONAL S.A.—See Votorantim S.A.; *Int'l*, pg. 8310
VOTORANTIM CIMENTOS S.A.—See Votorantim S.A.; *Int'l*, pg. 8310
VOTORANTIM ENERGIA LTDA.—See Votorantim S.A.; *Int'l*, pg. 8310
VOTORANTIM METAIS LTDA.—See Votorantim S.A.; *Int'l*, pg. 8310
VOTORANTIM S.A.; *Int'l*, pg. 8309
VOTORANTIM SIDERURGIA S.A.—See ArcelorMittal S.A.; *Int'l*, pg. 543

VOTRAINT NO 1537 PTY LTD—See ICM Limited; *Int'l*, pg. 3582
VOTSCH INDUSTRIETECHNIK GMBH—See Schunk GmbH; *Int'l*, pg. 6643
VOTUM-REHAPLUS S.A—See Votum S.A.; *Int'l*, pg. 8310
VOTUM S.A.; *Int'l*, pg. 8310
VOUCHER TRAVEL CLUB LIMITED—See Co-operative Group Limited; *Int'l*, pg. 1679
VOUK TRANSPORTATION INC.; *U.S. Private*, pg. 4413
VOUSSE CORP S.A.; *Int'l*, pg. 8310
VOUVRAY ACQUISITION LIMITED—See Ackermans & van Haaren NV; *Int'l*, pg. 106
VOUVRAY ACQUISITION LIMITED—See STAR Capital Partners Limited; *Int'l*, pg. 7173
VOVICI CORPORATION—See Verint Systems Inc.; *U.S. Public*, pg. 2281
VOVIS AUTOMOBILE GMBH—See AGRAVIS Raiffeisen AG; *Int'l*, pg. 216
VOW ASA; *Int'l*, pg. 8310
VOW EUROPE LTD.; *Int'l*, pg. 8310
VOW FINANCIAL PTY. LTD.—See Yellow Brick Road Holdings Ltd.; *Int'l*, pg. 8576
VOXAN-SCCM S.A.—See Venturi Automobiles S.A.M.; *Int'l*, pg. 8152
VOX COMMUNICATIONS GROUP LLC; *U.S. Private*, pg. 4414
VOX COMMUNICATIONS - WESTERN MASSACHUSETTS—See Vox Communications Group LLC; *U.S. Private*, pg. 4414
VOXEL DOT NET, INC.—See Internap Holding LLC; *U.S. Private*, pg. 2114
VOXELJET AG; *Int'l*, pg. 8310
VOXELJET CHINA CO. LTD.—See voxeljet AG; *Int'l*, pg. 8310
VOXELJET INDIA PVT. LTD.—See voxeljet AG; *Int'l*, pg. 8310
VOXELJET OF AMERICA INC.—See voxeljet AG; *Int'l*, pg. 8310
VOXEL S.A.; *Int'l*, pg. 8310
VOXEO CORPORATION—See Vector Capital Management, L.P.; *U.S. Private*, pg. 4350
VOX FILM & FERNSEH GMBH & CO. KG—See Bertelsmann SE & Co. KGaA; *Int'l*, pg. 996
VOXITAS; *U.S. Private*, pg. 4414
VOXMOBILI S.A.—See Synchronoss Technologies, Inc.; *U.S. Public*, pg. 1970
VOX NETWORK SOLUTIONS, INC.; *U.S. Private*, pg. 4414
VOXPOP COMMUNITIES, INC.—See Marlin Equity Partners, LLC; *U.S. Private*, pg. 2584
VOX PUBLIC RELATIONS INDIA PRIVATE LIMITED—See Next 15 Group plc; *Int'l*, pg. 5247
VOX ROYALTY CORP.; *Int'l*, pg. 8310
VOXTEL, INC.—See Sanken Electric Co., Ltd.; *Int'l*, pg. 6540
VOXTEL RNIS TELECOMMUNICATIONS INC.—See ATW Tech Inc.; *Int'l*, pg. 697
VOX TRADING CO., LTD.—See House Foods Group Inc.; *Int'l*, pg. 3491
VOX TRADING (THAILAND) CO., LTD.—See House Foods Group Inc.; *Int'l*, pg. 3491
VOXTUR ANALYTICS CORP.; *Int'l*, pg. 8310
VOX VALOR CAPITAL LIMITED; *Int'l*, pg. 8310
VOXWARE, INC.; *U.S. Private*, pg. 4414
VOXX ACCESSORIES CORP.; *U.S. Private*, pg. 4414
VOXX AUTOMOTIVE CORPORATION—See VOXX International Corporation; *U.S. Public*, pg. 2311
VOXX ELECTRONICS CORPORATION—See VOXX International Corporation; *U.S. Public*, pg. 2311
VOXX GERMAN HOLDINGS GMBH—See VOXX International Corporation; *U.S. Public*, pg. 2311
VOXX INTERNATIONAL CORPORATION; *U.S. Public*, pg. 2310
VOYA ASIA PACIFIC HIGH DIVIDEND EQUITY INCOME FUND; *U.S. Public*, pg. 2311
VOYA EMERGING MARKETS HIGH DIVIDEND EQUITY FUND; *U.S. Public*, pg. 2311
VOYA FINANCIAL ADVISORS, INC.—See Genstar Capital, LLC; *U.S. Private*, pg. 1676
VOYA FINANCIAL, INC. - SERVICE CENTER—See Voya Financial, Inc.; *U.S. Public*, pg. 2311
VOYA FINANCIAL, INC.; *U.S. Public*, pg. 2311
VOYA FUNDS SERVICES, LLC—See Voya Financial, Inc.; *U.S. Public*, pg. 2311
VOYAGE-AIR GUITAR, INC.; *U.S. Private*, pg. 4414
VOYAGE BB INC—See CyberAgent, Inc.; *Int'l*, pg. 1892
VOYAGER CAPITAL, LLC; *U.S. Private*, pg. 4414
VOYAGER DIGITAL LTD; *U.S. Public*, pg. 2312
VOYAGER EMBLEMS, INC.—See Grant Emblems Limited; *Int'l*, pg. 3059
VOYAGER INC.; *U.S. Private*, pg. 4414
VOYAGER INTERESTS, LLC; *U.S. Private*, pg. 4414
VOYAGER LEARNING COMPANY—See Veritas Capital Fund Management, LLC; *U.S. Private*, pg. 4361
VOYAGER METALS INC.—See Cerrado Gold Inc.; *Int'l*, pg. 1422
VOYAGER MOINS CHER S.A.S.—See Rakuten Group, Inc.; *Int'l*, pg. 6195
VOYAGER SPACE HOLDINGS, INC.; *U.S. Private*, pg. 4414

VP HOLDINGS CORPORATION

VOYAGER THERAPEUTICS, INC.; *U.S. Public*, pg. 2312
VOYAGER TRAVEL PTE. LTD.—See Stamford Land Corporation Ltd.; *Int'l*, pg. 7165
VOYAGES HOTEL & RESORTS LTD.—See GPT Group; *Int'l*, pg. 3047
VOYAGES HOTELS & RESORTS PTY LIMITED—See GPT Group; *Int'l*, pg. 3047
VOYAGEUR AIRWAYS LIMITED—See Chorus Aviation Inc.; *Int'l*, pg. 1584
VOYAGEUR AVIATION CORP.—See Chorus Aviation Inc.; *Int'l*, pg. 1584
VOYAGEUR MINERAL EXPLORERS CORP.; *Int'l*, pg. 8311
VOYAGEUR PHARMACEUTICALS LTD.; *Int'l*, pg. 8311
VOYAGEURS DU MONDE SA; *Int'l*, pg. 8311
VOYAGE VENTURES INC—See Polaris Capital Group Co., Ltd.; *Int'l*, pg. 5906
VOYA GLOBAL ADVANTAGE & PREMIUM OPPORTUNITY FUND; *U.S. Public*, pg. 2312
VOYA GLOBAL EQUITY DIVIDEND & PREMIUM OPPORTUNITY FUND; *U.S. Public*, pg. 2312
VOYA INFRASTRUCTURE, INDUSTRIALS & MATERIALS FUND; *U.S. Public*, pg. 2312
VOYA INSTITUTIONAL PLAN SERVICES, LLC—See Voya Financial, Inc.; *U.S. Public*, pg. 2312
VOYA INSTITUTIONAL PLAN SERVICES, LLC—See Voya Financial, Inc.; *U.S. Public*, pg. 2312
VOYA INSURANCE & ANNUITY COMPANY—See Voya Financial, Inc.; *U.S. Public*, pg. 2311
VOYA INTERNATIONAL HIGH DIVIDEND EQUITY INCOME FUND; *U.S. Public*, pg. 2312
VOYA INVESTMENT MANAGEMENT LLC—See Voya Financial, Inc.; *U.S. Public*, pg. 2311
VOYA INVESTMENT MANAGEMENT—See Voya Financial, Inc.; *U.S. Public*, pg. 2311
VOYA INVESTMENT MANAGEMENT—See Voya Financial, Inc.; *U.S. Public*, pg. 2311
VOYA INVESTMENT MANAGEMENT—See Voya Financial, Inc.; *U.S. Public*, pg. 2311
VOYA INVESTMENTS DISTRIBUTOR, LLC—See Voya Financial, Inc.; *U.S. Public*, pg. 2311
VOYA INVESTMENTS, LLC—See Voya Financial, Inc.; *U.S. Public*, pg. 2311
VOYA NATURAL RESOURCES EQUITY INCOME FUND; *U.S. Public*, pg. 2312
VOYANT BEAUTY—See Wind Point Advisors LLC; *U.S. Private*, pg. 4536
VOYANT COMMUNICATIONS, LLC—See Sinch AB; *Int'l*, pg. 6937
VOYA PRIME RATE TRUST; *U.S. Public*, pg. 2312
VOYA REINSURANCE—See Voya Financial, Inc.; *U.S. Public*, pg. 2311
VOYA RETIREMENT INSURANCE & ANNUITY COMPANY—See Voya Financial, Inc.; *U.S. Public*, pg. 2311
VOYA SERVICES COMPANY—See Voya Financial, Inc.; *U.S. Public*, pg. 2312
VOYA SERVICES CO.—See Voya Financial, Inc.; *U.S. Public*, pg. 2312
VOYA SERVICES CO.—See Voya Financial, Inc.; *U.S. Public*, pg. 2312
VOYETRA TURTLE BEACH INC.—See Turtle Beach Corporation; *U.S. Public*, pg. 2205
VOZ MOBILE CLOUD LTD.; *Int'l*, pg. 8311
VOZROZHDENIE BANK JSC—See PJSC VTB Bank; *Int'l*, pg. 5886
VOZTELECOM OIGAA360, S.A.—See Gamma Communications PLC; *Int'l*, pg. 2878
VOZZCOM, INC.; *U.S. Private*, pg. 4414
VPAY BENEFITS CORPORATION—See UnitedHealth Group Incorporated; *U.S. Public*, pg. 2252
VPAY INC.—See UnitedHealth Group Incorporated; *U.S. Public*, pg. 2248
VP BANK AG; *Int'l*, pg. 8311
VP BANK (BVI) LTD.—See VP Bank AG; *Int'l*, pg. 8311
VP BANK FONDSLEITUNG AG—See VP Bank AG; *Int'l*, pg. 8311
VP BANK (LUXEMBOURG) S.A.—See VP Bank AG; *Int'l*, pg. 8311
VP BANK (SCHWEIZ) AG—See VP Bank AG; *Int'l*, pg. 8311
VPC SPECIALTY LENDING INVESTMENTS PLC; *Int'l*, pg. 8312
VP DISTRIBUTORS, LLC—See Virtus Investment Partners, Inc.; *U.S. Public*, pg. 2301
VPE INVESTMENT MANAGEMENT LIMITED; *Int'l*, pg. 8312
VPE WERTPAPIERHANDELSBANK AG; *Int'l*, pg. 8312
VP EXPLOITATIE N.V.; *Int'l*, pg. 8311
VP GMBH—See Vp PLC; *Int'l*, pg. 8312
VPG SYSTEMS UK, LTD.—See Vishay Precision Group, Inc.; *U.S. Public*, pg. 2303
VP HOLDINGS CORPORATION; *U.S. Private*, pg. 4414
V P HOLDINGS, INC.—See Platinum Equity, LLC; *U.S. Private*, pg. 3209
VPI ACQUISITION CORP.—See Spell Capital Partners, LLC; *U.S. Private*, pg. 3754
VPI IMMINGHAM LLP—See Vitol Holding B.V.; *Int'l*, pg. 8260

VP HOLDINGS CORPORATION / CORPORATE AFFILIATIONS

VP INC.—See KT Corporation; *Int'l*, pg. 4315
VPI PACKAGING INC.—See O. Berk Company L.L.C.; *U.S. Private*, pg. 2981
VPIPHOTONICS GMBH—See VPI Systems; *U.S. Private*, pg. 4414
VPI QUALITY WINDOWS, INC.—See ONEX Corporation; *Int'l*, pg. 5580
VPI SYSTEMS; *U.S. Private*, pg. 4414
VPI SYSTEMS—See VPI Systems; *U.S. Private*, pg. 4414
VPK DISPLAY NV—See VPK Packaging Group NV; *Int'l*, pg. 8312
VPK PACKAGING BV—See VPK Packaging Group NV; *Int'l*, pg. 8312
VPK PACKAGING GROUP NV; *Int'l*, pg. 8312
VPK PAPER NV—See VPK Packaging Group NV; *Int'l*, pg. 8313
VPL LIMITED—See AB Volvo; *Int'l*, pg. 46
VPLS INC.—See Evocative, Inc.; *U.S. Private*, pg. 1442
VP METALL AS—See Lagercrantz Group AB; *Int'l*, pg. 4395
VPN SOLUTIONS PTY LTD—See Over the Wire Holdings Limited; *Int'l*, pg. 5671
VPN TECHNOLOGIES INC.; *Int'l*, pg. 8313
V&P NURSERIES INC.; *U.S. Private*, pg. 4327
VPOWER ENGINEERING (SHENZHEN) LIMITED—See VPower Group International Holdings Limited; *Int'l*, pg. 8313
VPOWER GROUP INTERNATIONAL HOLDINGS LIMITED; *Int'l*, pg. 8313
VPP GROUP, LLC; *U.S. Private*, pg. 4414
VP PLC; *Int'l*, pg. 8312
VP RACING FUELS INC.—See Texas Allied Holdings Inc.; *U.S. Private*, pg. 3974
VPR BRANDS, L.P.; *U.S. Public*, pg. 2312
VP SALESTECH AB—See Nayax Ltd.; *Int'l*, pg. 5178
THE VPS COMPANIES INC.; *U.S. Private*, pg. 4132
VPS HOLDINGS LIMITED—See PAI Partners S.A.S.; *Int'l*, pg. 5702
VPSI INC.; *U.S. Private*, pg. 4414
VPS INFRASTRUKTUR GMBH—See Salzgitter AG; *Int'l*, pg. 6499
VP SUPPLY CORP.; *U.S. Private*, pg. 4414
VPT, INC.—See HEICO Corporation; *U.S. Public*, pg. 1021
VP TRANSPORTATION CO. INC.—See Texas Allied Holdings Inc.; *U.S. Private*, pg. 3974
V. QUATTRO SPA—See UniCredit S.p.A.; *Int'l*, pg. 8041
VRACO SA—See VINCI S.A.; *Int'l*, pg. 8233
VR AGRAR CENTER WITTELSBACHER LAND GMBH—See AGRAVIS Raiffeisen AG; *Int'l*, pg. 216
VRANCART SA—See SIF Banat-Crisana S.A.; *Int'l*, pg. 6905
VRANKEN-POMMERY MONOPOLE SA; *Int'l*, pg. 8313
VRANLACT SA; *Int'l*, pg. 8313
VRATSINAS CONSTRUCTION COMPANY, INC.; *U.S. Private*, pg. 4415
VRBAS G.P. A.D.; *Int'l*, pg. 8313
VRC COMPANIES, LLC—See Windjammer Capital Investors, LLC; *U.S. Private*, pg. 4538
VR CONSULTINGPARTNER GMBH—See DZ BANK AG Deutsche Zentral-Genossenschaftsbank; *Int'l*, pg. 2245
VRC REAL ESTATE & INVESTMENT JOINT STOCK COMPANY; *Int'l*, pg. 8313
V & R DRYWALL, INC.; *U.S. Private*, pg. 4327
VRDT CORPORATION; *U.S. Private*, pg. 4415
VREC, INC.—See Viad Corp.; *U.S. Public*, pg. 2291
VREDESTEIN CONSULTING B.V.—See Apollo Tyres Ltd.; *Int'l*, pg. 519
VREDESTEIN FRANCE S.A.—See Apollo Tyres Ltd.; *Int'l*, pg. 519
VREDESTEIN GMBH—See Apollo Tyres Ltd.; *Int'l*, pg. 519
VREDESTEIN GMBH—See Apollo Tyres Ltd.; *Int'l*, pg. 519
VREDESTEIN IBERICA S.A.—See Apollo Tyres Ltd.; *Int'l*, pg. 519
VREDESTEIN NORDIC AB—See Apollo Tyres Ltd.; *Int'l*, pg. 519
VREF SEVILLE REAL ESTATE HOLDCO SOCIMI, S.A.; *Int'l*, pg. 8313
VREMEPLOV D.O.O.—See SEMIKRON International GmbH; *Int'l*, pg. 6705
VR EQUITYPARTNER GMBH—See DZ BANK AG Deutsche Zentral-Genossenschaftsbank; *Int'l*, pg. 2245
VRESS ET ROSE CO., LTD.—See Polaris Capital Group Co., Ltd.; *Int'l*, pg. 5907
VR FACTOREM GMBH—See DZ BANK AG Deutsche Zentral-Genossenschaftsbank; *Int'l*, pg. 2245
V R FILMS & STUDIOS LIMITED; *Int'l*, pg. 8104
VRG CAPITAL CORP.; *Int'l*, pg. 8313
VR-GROUP PLC; *Int'l*, pg. 8313
VRG SA; *Int'l*, pg. 8313
VRH CONSTRUCTION CORP.; *U.S. Private*, pg. 4415
VR HOLDINGS, INC.; *U.S. Private*, pg. 4415
VR-IMMOBILIEN NORDDEUTSCHLAND; *Int'l*, pg. 8313
VRK AUTOMOTIVE SYSTEMS S.A. DE C.V.—See KIRCHHOFF Gruppe; *Int'l*, pg. 4185
VR KREDITSERVICE GMBH—See DZ BANK AG Deutsche Zentral-Genossenschaftsbank; *Int'l*, pg. 2245
VR LABORATORIES, LLC; *U.S. Private*, pg. 4415
VR-LEASING AG; *Int'l*, pg. 8313
VRL LOGISTICS LIMITED; *Int'l*, pg. 8313

VRNET (S) PTE. LTD.—See MIRAIT ONE Corporation; *Int'l*, pg. 4918
VROEGOP RUHE & CO. B.V.; *Int'l*, pg. 8313
VROMAN SYSTEMS INC.—See PSG Equity L.L.C.; *U.S. Private*, pg. 3297
VROMAN SYSTEMS INC.—See Silversmith Management, L.P.; *U.S. Private*, pg. 3663
VROOM CO., LTD.—See Sojitz Corporation; *Int'l*, pg. 7066
VROOM, INC.; *U.S. Public*, pg. 2312
VR PAYMENT GMBH—See DZ BANK AG Deutsche Zentral-Genossenschaftsbank; *Int'l*, pg. 2245
V.R. PROPERTY MANAGEMENT; *U.S. Private*, pg. 4328
VR SHIPPING (ARUBA) N.V.—See Albert Ballin KG; *Int'l*, pg. 297
VR SHIPPING NV—See Albert Ballin KG; *Int'l*, pg. 297
VRS INDUSTRIES S.A—See KSB SE & Co. KGaA; *Int'l*, pg. 4313
VRS (MALAYSIA) SDN BHD—See Berjaya Corporation Berhad; *Int'l*, pg. 984
VRS VALVE RECONDITIONING SERVICES B.V.—See KSB SE & Co. KGaA; *Int'l*, pg. 4311
VR TELECOMMUNICATIONS GMBH & CO.—See E.ON SE; *Int'l*, pg. 2260
VRTUAL, INC.—See XWELL, Inc.; *U.S. Public*, pg. 2393
VRUNDAVAN PLANTATION LIMITED; *Int'l*, pg. 8313
VRV ASIA PACIFIC PRIVATE LIMITED—See Chart Industries, Inc.; *U.S. Public*, pg. 482
VRV S.R.L.—See Chart Industries, Inc.; *U.S. Public*, pg. 482
VR WERT GESELLSCHAFT FUR IMMOBILIENBEWERTUNG MBH—See DZ BANK AG Deutsche Zentral-Genossenschaftsbank; *Int'l*, pg. 2245
V. R. WOODART LIMITED; *Int'l*, pg. 8106
VRX, LLC—See Centene Corporation; *U.S. Public*, pg. 470
VRX MEDIA GROUP LLC—See Zillow Group, Inc.; *U.S. Public*, pg. 2405
VRX PHARMACY, LLC—See Centene Corporation; *U.S. Public*, pg. 470
VRX SILICA LIMITED; *Int'l*, pg. 8313
VRX STUDIOS INC.—See Symphony Technology Group, LLC; *U.S. Private*, pg. 3902
THE VRYHEID (NATAL) RAILWAY COAL AND IRON COMPANY LIMITED—See Exxaro Resources Ltd.; *Int'l*, pg. 2592
VSA CAPITAL GROUP PLC; *Int'l*, pg. 8314
VS&A COMMUNICATIONS PARTNERS III—See Veronis Suhler Stevenson Partners LLC; *U.S. Private*, pg. 4368
VSA, INC.; *U.S. Private*, pg. 4415
V&S AMBOY GALVANIZING LLC—See Hill & Smith PLC; *Int'l*, pg. 3392
VSA PARTNERS, INC.—See Innovatus Capital Partners LLC; *U.S. Private*, pg. 2083
VSA PARTNERS, INC.—See Innovatus Capital Partners LLC; *U.S. Private*, pg. 2083
VSA PARTNERS, INC.—See Innovatus Capital Partners LLC; *U.S. Private*, pg. 2083
VSB BANCORP, INC.—See Northfield Bancorp, Inc.; *U.S. Public*, pg. 1539
VSBLTY GROUPE TECHNOLOGIES CORP.; *U.S. Public*, pg. 2312
V&S BRISTOL GALVANIZING LLC—See Hill & Smith PLC; *Int'l*, pg. 3392
VS BROSCHEK DRUCK GMBH—See Schiessl & Co. GmbH; *Int'l*, pg. 6618
VSC BUILDING PRODUCTS COMPANY LIMITED—See Hong Kong Shanghai Alliance Holdings Limited; *Int'l*, pg. 3467
VSC FIRE & SECURITY, INC.; *U.S. Private*, pg. 4415
VSC INTERNATIONAL PTE LTD—See Varun Shipping Company Limited; *Int'l*, pg. 8134
V&S COLUMBUS GALANIZING LLC—See Hill & Smith PLC; *Int'l*, pg. 3392
V&S COLUMBUS GALVANIZING LLC—See Hill & Smith PLC; *Int'l*, pg. 3392
V.SCOPE RISK MANAGEMENT LTD.—See Ackermans & van Haaren NV; *Int'l*, pg. 106
V.SCOPE RISK MANAGEMENT LTD.—See STAR Capital Partners Limited; *Int'l*, pg. 7173
VSC PLASTICS COMPANY LIMITED—See Hong Kong Shanghai Alliance Holdings Limited; *Int'l*, pg. 3467
VSC-POSCO STEEL CORP.—See POSCO Holdings Inc.; *Int'l*, pg. 5937
V&S DELAWARE GALVANIZING LLC—See Hill & Smith PLC; *Int'l*, pg. 3392
V&S DETROIT GALVANIZING LLC—See Hill & Smith PLC; *Int'l*, pg. 3392
VS DIRECT INC.—See B. Riley Financial, Inc.; *U.S. Public*, pg. 261
VS DIRECT INC.—See Irradiant Partners, LP; *U.S. Private*, pg. 2141
VSE AGENTUR GMBH—See RWE AG; *Int'l*, pg. 6436
VSE AVIATION, INC.—See VSE Corporation; *U.S. Public*, pg. 2313
VSE CORPORATION; *U.S. Public*, pg. 2312
VSEE HEALTH, INC.; *U.S. Public*, pg. 2313
VSEE LAB, INC.—See VSee Health, Inc.; *U.S. Public*, pg. 2313
VS ENERGY INTERNATIONAL UKRAINE LLC; *Int'l*, pg. 8314

VSE NET GMBH—See RWE AG; *Int'l*, pg. 6436
VSEOBECNA UVEROVA BANKA A.S.—See Intesa Sanpaolo S.p.A.; *Int'l*, pg. 3766
VSERVEPLUS COMPANY LIMITED—See Vintcom Technology Public Company Limited; *Int'l*, pg. 8242
VSE SERVICES INTERNATIONAL, INC.—See VSE Corporation; *U.S. Public*, pg. 2313
VSE VERTEILNETZ GMBH—See RWE AG; *Int'l*, pg. 6436
VSF PROJECTS LIMITED; *Int'l*, pg. 8314
VSG VANGE SOFTWARE GROUP AG; *Int'l*, pg. 8314
VS HERCULES LLC—See B. Riley Financial, Inc.; *U.S. Public*, pg. 261
VS HERCULES LLC—See Irradiant Partners, LP; *U.S. Private*, pg. 2141
VSH FABRIEKEN B.V.—See Aalberts N.V.; *Int'l*, pg. 36
VSH FITTINGS B.V.—See Aalberts N.V.; *Int'l*, pg. 36
VSHIP LIMITED—See Tradelink Electronic Commerce Limited; *Int'l*, pg. 7888
V.SHIPS GROUP LTD.—See Ackermans & van Haaren NV; *Int'l*, pg. 106
V.SHIPS GROUP LTD.—See STAR Capital Partners Limited; *Int'l*, pg. 7173
V.SHIPS LEISURE LTD.—See Ackermans & van Haaren NV; *Int'l*, pg. 106
V.SHIPS LEISURE LTD.—See STAR Capital Partners Limited; *Int'l*, pg. 7173
V.SHIPS LEISURE (USA) LLC—See Ackermans & van Haaren NV; *Int'l*, pg. 106
V.SHIPS LEISURE (USA) LLC—See STAR Capital Partners Limited; *Int'l*, pg. 7173
V.SHIPS OFFSHORE (ASIA) PTE. LTD.—See Ackermans & van Haaren NV; *Int'l*, pg. 106
V.SHIPS OFFSHORE (ASIA) PTE. LTD.—See STAR Capital Partners Limited; *Int'l*, pg. 7173
V.SHIPS UK LTD.—See Ackermans & van Haaren NV; *Int'l*, pg. 106
V.SHIPS UK LTD.—See STAR Capital Partners Limited; *Int'l*, pg. 7173
VSI GMBH—See VIB Vermogen AG; *Int'l*, pg. 8184
VSI METER SERVICES, INC.—See Asplundh Tree Expert Co.; *U.S. Private*, pg. 353
V.S. INDUSTRY BERHAD; *Int'l*, pg. 8106
VSI NEARSHORE OUTSOURCING; *U.S. Private*, pg. 4415
V.S. INTEGRATED MANAGEMENT SDN. BHD.—See V.S. Industry Berhad; *Int'l*, pg. 8106
V.S. INTERNATIONAL GROUP LIMITED—See V.S. Industry Berhad; *Int'l*, pg. 8106
VSI RESPUBLIKINIS ENERGETIKU MOKYMO CENTRAS—See UAB Ignitis grupe; *Int'l*, pg. 7999
VSK ELECTRONICS N.V.—See Blum Capital Partners, L.P.; *U.S. Private*, pg. 599
VSL DATA SYSTEMS PRIVATE LIMITED—See Vedavaag Systems Limited; *Int'l*, pg. 8146
V&S LEBANON GALVANIZING LLC—See Hill & Smith PLC; *Int'l*, pg. 3392
VS LIGNITE POWER PRIVATE LIMITED—See KSK Energy Ventures Limited; *Int'l*, pg. 4314
VSL INTERNATIONAL LTD.—See Bouygues S.A.; *Int'l*, pg. 1123
VSL—See Structural Group, Inc.; *U.S. Private*, pg. 3841
VSMA INC.—See BlueScope Steel Limited; *Int'l*, pg. 1073
VSM AUSTRIA GMBH—See Platinum Equity, LLC; *U.S. Private*, pg. 3208
VSM BELGIE BVBA—See Platinum Equity, LLC; *U.S. Private*, pg. 3208
VSM BELGIUM BVBA—See Dr. Willmar Schwabe GmbH & Co. KG; *Int'l*, pg. 2196
VSM COLOMBIA, S.A.S.—See Sacyr, S.A.; *Int'l*, pg. 6466
VS MEDIA HOLDINGS LIMITED; *Int'l*, pg. 8314
V&S MEMPHIS GALVANIZING LLC—See Hill & Smith PLC; *Int'l*, pg. 3392
VSM GENEESMIDDELEN BV—See Dr. Willmar Schwabe GmbH & Co. KG; *Int'l*, pg. 2196
VSM GERMANY GMBH—See Platinum Equity, LLC; *U.S. Private*, pg. 3208
VSM GROUP AB—See Platinum Equity, LLC; *U.S. Private*, pg. 3208
V&S MIDWEST CARRIERS CORP.; *U.S. Private*, pg. 4327
VSM NETHERLANDS BV—See Platinum Equity, LLC; *U.S. Private*, pg. 3208
VSMPO - AVISMA CORPORATION; *Int'l*, pg. 8314
VSMPO-TIRUS (BEIJING) METALLIC MATERIALS LTD.—See VSMPO - AVISMA Corporation; *Int'l*, pg. 8314
VSMPO-TIRUS GMBH—See VSMPO - AVISMA Corporation; *Int'l*, pg. 8314
VSMPO-TIRUS LIMITED—See VSMPO - AVISMA Corporation; *Int'l*, pg. 8314
VSMPO-TIRUS US INC.—See VSMPO - AVISMA Corporation; *Int'l*, pg. 8314
VSMPO TITAN UKRAINE—See VSMPO - AVISMA Corporation; *Int'l*, pg. 8314
VSM SEWING INC.—See Platinum Equity, LLC; *U.S. Private*, pg. 3208
VSM SVERIGE AB—See Platinum Equity, LLC; *U.S. Private*, pg. 3208
VSM SWITZERLAND GMBH—See Platinum Equity, LLC; *U.S. Private*, pg. 3208

COMPANY NAME INDEX

VSM (UK) LTD—See Platinum Equity, LLC; *U.S. Private*, pg. 3208
V&S NEW YORK GALVANIZING LLC—See Hill & Smith PLC; *Int'l*, pg. 3392
V-SOFT CONSULTING GROUP, INC.; *U.S. Private*, pg. 4328
VSOFT CORPORATION; *U.S. Private*, pg. 4415
VSOLAR GROUP BHD; *Int'l*, pg. 8314
VSPC LTD.—See Lithium Australia NL; *Int'l*, pg. 4527
VSPEED CAPITAL, LLC; *U.S. Private*, pg. 4415
VSPEED CAPITAL LLC—See AG Hill Partners LLC; *U.S. Private*, pg. 124
VSP TECHNOLOGIES, INC.—See Diploma PLC; *Int'l*, pg. 2129
VSR FINANCIAL SERVICES, INC.—See RCAP Holdings, LLC; *U.S. Private*, pg. 3361
VSR GROUP, INC.—See RCAP Holdings, LLC; *U.S. Private*, pg. 3361
V&S SCHULER ENGINEERING INC.—See Hill & Smith PLC; *Int'l*, pg. 3392
V&S SCHULER TUBULAR PRODUCTS LLC—See Hill & Smith PLC; *Int'l*, pg. 3392
VSSCO INCORPORATED; *U.S. Private*, pg. 4415
VSS, LLC—See Converge Technology Solutions Corp.; *Int'l*, pg. 1787
VSS MONITORING, INC.—See Danaher Corporation; *U.S. Public*, pg. 631
V-STAR CREATIONS PVT. LTD.—See V-Guard Industries Ltd.; *Int'l*, pg. 8105
VSTAR INDUSTRIES LIMITED—See Sparton Resources Inc.; *Int'l*, pg. 7127
V&S TAUNTON GALVANIZING, LLC—See Hill & Smith PLC; *Int'l*, pg. 3392
VST COMPUTERS HK LIMITED—See VSTECS Holdings Limited; *Int'l*, pg. 8315
VST CONSULTING, INC.; *U.S. Private*, pg. 4415
V.S. TECHNOLOGY SDN. BHD.—See V.S. Industry Berhad; *Int'l*, pg. 8106
VSTECS ASTAR SDN. BHD.—See VSTECS Berhad; *Int'l*, pg. 8314
VSTECS BERHAD; *Int'l*, pg. 8314
VSTECS (CAMBODIA) CO., LTD.—See VSTECS Holdings Limited; *Int'l*, pg. 8315
VSTECS HOLDINGS LIMITED; *Int'l*, pg. 8314
VSTECS (MYANMAR) CO., LTD—See VSTECS Holdings Limited; *Int'l*, pg. 8315
VSTECS (SINGAPORE) PTE. LTD.—See VSTECS Holdings Limited; *Int'l*, pg. 8315
VST ECS (THAILAND) CO., LTD.—See VSTECS Holdings Limited; *Int'l*, pg. 8315
VST HEMOVET D.O.O. - PESTICIDE FACTORY—See VST Hemovet d.o.o.; *Int'l*, pg. 8314
VST HEMOVET D.O.O.; *Int'l*, pg. 8314
VST INDUSTRIES LIMITED; *Int'l*, pg. 8314
VSTITLE, LLC—See F&M Bank Corp.; *U.S. Public*, pg. 818
V.S.T TILLERS TRACTORS LIMITED; *Int'l*, pg. 8106
V. SUAREZ & COMPANY, INC.; *U.S. Private*, pg. 4328
VSUN JAPAN CO., LTD.—See Abalance Corporation Ltd.; *Int'l*, pg. 48
VSV ADVANCED CERAMICS (ANSHAN) CO., LTD.—See Vesuvius plc; *Int'l*, pg. 8179
VS VISUAL STATEMENTS INC.—See Trimble, Inc.; *U.S. Public*, pg. 2193
VT5 ACQUISITION COMPANY AG; *Int'l*, pg. 8315
V-TAC TECHNOLOGY CO., LTD.; *Int'l*, pg. 8105
VTA MANAGEMENT SERVICES, LLC—See Apollo Global Management, Inc.; *U.S. Public*, pg. 158
VT-ARRIVA SZEMELYSZALLITO ES SZOLGALTATO KFT.—See Deutsche Bahn AG; *Int'l*, pg. 2055
VTB BANK (ARMENIA) CJSC—See PJSC VTB Bank; *Int'l*, pg. 5886
VTB BANK (AUSTRIA) AG—See PJSC VTB Bank; *Int'l*, pg. 5886
VTB BANK (BELARUS) CJSC—See PJSC VTB Bank; *Int'l*, pg. 5886
VTB BANK (DEUTSCHLAND) AG—See PJSC VTB Bank; *Int'l*, pg. 5886
VTB BANK (EUROPE) SE—See PJSC VTB Bank; *Int'l*, pg. 5886
VTB BANK (FRANCE) SA—See PJSC VTB Bank; *Int'l*, pg. 5886
VTB BANK GEORGIA JSC; *Int'l*, pg. 8316
VTB-CAPITAL CJSC—See PJSC VTB Bank; *Int'l*, pg. 5886
VTB CAPITAL PLC—See PJSC VTB Bank; *Int'l*, pg. 5886
VTB-DEVELOPMENT CJSC—See PJSC VTB Bank; *Int'l*, pg. 5886
VTB FACTORING LTD—See PJSC VTB Bank; *Int'l*, pg. 5886
VTBH-DZU BULGARIA—See Videoton Holding Zrt.; *Int'l*, pg. 8191
VTB INSURANCE, LTD.—See Sogaz JSC; *Int'l*, pg. 7058
VTB LEASING (EUROPE) LTD—See PJSC VTB Bank; *Int'l*, pg. 5886
VTB LEASING JSC—See PJSC VTB Bank; *Int'l*, pg. 5886
VTB LIFE INSURANCE JSC; *Int'l*, pg. 8316
VTB SPECIALIZED DEPOSITORY CJSC—See PJSC VTB Bank; *Int'l*, pg. 5886
VTCD KFT.—See Videoton Holding Zrt.; *Int'l*, pg. 8191

VTC ENTERPRISES; *U.S. Private*, pg. 4415
VT CO., LTD.; *Int'l*, pg. 8315
VTC PARTNERS GMBH; *Int'l*, pg. 8316
VTC TELECOMMUNICATIONS JSC; *Int'l*, pg. 8316
VTC VIDEO SERVICES—See Visual Technologies Corp.; *U.S. Private*, pg. 4404
VTD VAKUUMTECKNIK DRESDEN GMBH—See Icahn Enterprises L.P.; *U.S. Public*, pg. 1085
V-TEC CO., LTD.—See V-Technology Co., Ltd.; *Int'l*, pg. 8105
V-TECH AB—See AddLife AB; *Int'l*, pg. 130
VTECH ADVANCED AMERICAN TELEPHONES; *U.S. Private*, pg. 4415
VTECH COMMUNICATIONS, INC.—See VTech Holdings Ltd.; *Int'l*, pg. 8316
VTECH COMMUNICATIONS JAPAN LTD.—See VTech Holdings Ltd.; *Int'l*, pg. 8316
VTECH COMMUNICATIONS LTD.—See VTech Holdings Ltd.; *Int'l*, pg. 8316
VTECH COMMUNICATIONS LTD.—See VTech Holdings Ltd.; *Int'l*, pg. 8316
VTECH COMMUNICATIONS (MALAYSIA) SDN. BHD.—See VTech Holdings Ltd.; *Int'l*, pg. 8316
VTECH ELECTRONICS EUROPE B.V.—See VTech Holdings Ltd.; *Int'l*, pg. 8316
VTECH ELECTRONICS EUROPE GMBH—See VTech Holdings Ltd.; *Int'l*, pg. 8317
VTECH ELECTRONICS EUROPE PLC—See VTech Holdings Ltd.; *Int'l*, pg. 8317
VTECH ELECTRONICS EUROPE S.A.S.—See VTech Holdings Ltd.; *Int'l*, pg. 8317
VTECH ELECTRONICS EUROPE, S.L.—See VTech Holdings Ltd.; *Int'l*, pg. 8317
VTECH ELECTRONICS INDUSTRIAL (SHENZHEN) CO., LTD.—See VTech Holdings Ltd.; *Int'l*, pg. 8317
VTECH ELECTRONICS (JAPAN) INC.—See VTech Holdings Ltd.; *Int'l*, pg. 8316
VTECH ELECTRONICS LIMITED—See VTech Holdings Ltd.; *Int'l*, pg. 8317
VTECH ELECTRONICS NORTH AMERICA, LLC—See VTech Holdings Ltd.; *Int'l*, pg. 8317
VTECH HOLDINGS LTD.; *Int'l*, pg. 8316
V-TECHNOLOGY CO., LTD.; *Int'l*, pg. 8105
V TECHNOLOGY KOREA CO., LTD.—See V-Technology Co., Ltd.; *Int'l*, pg. 8105
VTECH (OEM), INC.—See VTech Holdings Ltd.; *Int'l*, pg. 8316
VTECH (QINGYUAN) PLASTIC & ELECTRONICS CO., LTD.—See VTech Holdings Ltd.; *Int'l*, pg. 8316
VTECH TECHNOLOGIES CANADA LTD.—See VTech Holdings Ltd.; *Int'l*, pg. 8317
VTECH TELECOM, L.L.C.—See VTech Holdings Ltd.; *Int'l*, pg. 8317
VTECH TELECOMMUNICATIONS (AUSTRALIA) PTY LIMITED—See VTech Holdings Ltd.; *Int'l*, pg. 8317
VTECH TELECOMMUNICATIONS LIMITED—See VTech Holdings Ltd.; *Int'l*, pg. 8317
V-TEK INCORPORATED; *U.S. Private*, pg. 4328
VTEL PRODUCTS CORPORATION; *U.S. Private*, pg. 4415
VTES KFT. - TOROKSZENTMIKLOS PLANT—See Videoton Holding Zrt.; *Int'l*, pg. 8191
VTESSE NETWORKS LIMITED; *Int'l*, pg. 8317
VTEX AMERICA INC.—See Hitachi Zosen Corporation; *Int'l*, pg. 3412
V TEX CORPORATION—See Hitachi Zosen Corporation; *Int'l*, pg. 3412
V TEX KOREA CO., LTD.—See Hitachi Zosen Corporation; *Int'l*, pg. 3412
V TEX SHANGHAI CO., LTD.—See Hitachi Zosen Corporation; *Int'l*, pg. 3412
VTEX; *Int'l*, pg. 8317
VTEX; *Int'l*, pg. 8317
VT FINANCE AG—See Vontobel Holding AG; *Int'l*, pg. 8306
VTF QUEST—See Serval SAS; *Int'l*, pg. 6724
VTG AKTIENGESELLSCHAFT—See Joachim Herz Stiftung; *Int'l*, pg. 3976
VTG AKTIENGESELLSCHAFT—See Morgan Stanley; *U.S. Public*, pg. 1476
VTG CORP.; *U.S. Private*, pg. 4415
VTG DEUTSCHLAND GMBH - BELGIUM REPRESENTATIVE OFFICE—See Joachim Herz Stiftung; *Int'l*, pg. 3976
VTG DEUTSCHLAND GMBH - BELGIUM REPRESENTATIVE OFFICE—See Morgan Stanley; *U.S. Public*, pg. 1476
VTG DEUTSCHLAND GMBH - NETHERLANDS REPRESENTATIVE OFFICE—See Joachim Herz Stiftung; *Int'l*, pg. 3976
VTG DEUTSCHLAND GMBH - NETHERLANDS REPRESENTATIVE OFFICE—See Morgan Stanley; *U.S. Public*, pg. 1476
VTG RAIL ESPANA S.L.—See Joachim Herz Stiftung; *Int'l*, pg. 3976
VTG RAIL ESPANA S.L.—See Morgan Stanley; *U.S. Public*, pg. 1476
VTG RAIL—See Joachim Herz Stiftung; *Int'l*, pg. 3976
VTG RAIL—See Morgan Stanley; *U.S. Public*, pg. 1476

VTRON GROUP CO., LTD.

VT GRIFFIN SERVICES, INC.—See Babcock International Group PLC; *Int'l*, pg. 793
VT GROUP (US) PLC—See Alvarez & Marsal, Inc.; *U.S. Private*, pg. 213
VTGTE INC.—See Kelso & Company, L.P.; *U.S. Private*, pg. 2278
VT HALTER MARINE, INC—See Bollinger Shipyards, Inc.; *U.S. Private*, pg. 611
VT HOLDINGS CO., LTD.; *Int'l*, pg. 8315
VT IDIRECT, INC.—See Temasek Holdings (Private) Limited; *Int'l*, pg. 7552
VTI INSTRUMENTS CORPORATION—See AMETEK, Inc.; *U.S. Public*, pg. 122
VTI INSTRUMENTS PRIVATE LIMITED—See AMETEK, Inc.; *U.S. Public*, pg. 122
VT INC.; *U.S. Private*, pg. 4415
VT INDUSTRIAL TECHNOLOGY CO., LTD.; *Int'l*, pg. 8315
VT INDUSTRIES, INC.; *U.S. Private*, pg. 4415
VT INFORMATIKA KFT—See Videoton Holding Zrt.; *Int'l*, pg. 8191
VTI OF GEORGIA, INC.—See VT Industries, Inc.; *U.S. Private*, pg. 4415
VTI OF IOWA, INC.—See VT Industries, Inc.; *U.S. Private*, pg. 4415
VTI OF TEXAS INC.—See VT Industries, Inc.; *U.S. Private*, pg. 4415
VTION WIRELESS TECHNOLOGY AG - CORPORATE HEADQUARTERS—See Vtion Wireless Technology AG; *Int'l*, pg. 8317
VTION WIRELESS TECHNOLOGY AG; *Int'l*, pg. 8317
VTI VENTIL TECHNIK GMBH—See Aalberts N.V.; *Int'l*, pg. 36
VT KINETICS, INC.—See Temasek Holdings (Private) Limited; *Int'l*, pg. 7552
VT LEEBOY—See Temasek Holdings (Private) Limited; *Int'l*, pg. 7552
VTL GROUP (USA) INC—See VTL (Holdings) Ltd; *Int'l*, pg. 8317
VTL HOLDING, INC.—See Littlejohn & Co., LLC; *U.S. Private*, pg. 2472
VTL (HOLDINGS) LTD; *Int'l*, pg. 8317
VTL PRECISION (BRADLEY) LIMITED—See VTL (Holdings) Ltd; *Int'l*, pg. 8317
VTL PRECISION (JAPAN)—See VTL (Holdings) Ltd; *Int'l*, pg. 8317
VTL PRECISION—See VTL (Holdings) Ltd; *Int'l*, pg. 8317
VTLS, INC.—See HGGC, LLC; *U.S. Private*, pg. 1930
VTLS, INC.—See JMI Services, Inc.; *U.S. Private*, pg. 2216
V T MANCUSI, INC.—See Southfield Capital Advisors, LLC; *U.S. Private*, pg. 3736
VT MECHATRONICS KFT.—See Videoton Holding Zrt.; *Int'l*, pg. 8191
VT METAL KFT—See Videoton Holding Zrt.; *Int'l*, pg. 8191
VTM LIMITED; *Int'l*, pg. 8317
VT PLASTIC KFT.—See Videoton Holding Zrt.; *Int'l*, pg. 8191
VTQ VIDEOTRONIK GMBH; *Int'l*, pg. 8317
VTR AMS, INC.—See Ventas, Inc.; *U.S. Public*, pg. 2278
VT RENDSZERTECHNIKA KFT—See Videoton Holding Zrt.; *Int'l*, pg. 8191
VTR LS ODU 2, LLC—See Ventas, Inc.; *U.S. Public*, pg. 2279
VTR MEDIA INVESTMENTS LTD.—See Prime Focus Limited; *Int'l*, pg. 5977
VTRON GROUP CO., LTD.; *Int'l*, pg. 8317
VTRON TECHNOLOGIES (HONG KONG) LIMITED—See Vtron Group Co., Ltd.; *Int'l*, pg. 8317
VTR SCIENCE & TECHNOLOGY, LLC—See Ventas, Inc.; *U.S. Public*, pg. 2279
VT SERVICES, INC. - ALPHARETTA DIVISION—See Alvarez & Marsal, Inc.; *U.S. Private*, pg. 213
VT SERVICES, INC. - CHARLESTON DIVISION—See Alvarez & Marsal, Inc.; *U.S. Private*, pg. 213
VT SERVICES, INC. - CHESAPEAKE DIVISION—See Alvarez & Marsal, Inc.; *U.S. Private*, pg. 213
VT SERVICES, INC. - GROTON DIVISION—See Alvarez & Marsal, Inc.; *U.S. Private*, pg. 213
VT SERVICES, INC. - HAWAII DIVISION—See Alvarez & Marsal, Inc.; *U.S. Private*, pg. 213
VT SERVICES, INC. - JACKSONVILLE DIVISION—See Alvarez & Marsal, Inc.; *U.S. Private*, pg. 213
VT SERVICES, INC. - MADISON DIVISION—See Alvarez & Marsal, Inc.; *U.S. Private*, pg. 213
VT SERVICES, INC. - PENSACOLA DIVISION—See Alvarez & Marsal, Inc.; *U.S. Private*, pg. 213
VT SERVICES, INC. - SAN DIEGO DIVISION—See Alvarez & Marsal, Inc.; *U.S. Private*, pg. 213
VT SERVICES, INC.—See Alvarez & Marsal, Inc.; *U.S. Private*, pg. 213
VT SERVICES, INC. - STERLING DIVISION—See Alvarez & Marsal, Inc.; *U.S. Private*, pg. 213
VT SERVICES, INC. - VIRGINIA BEACH DIVISION—See Alvarez & Marsal, Inc.; *U.S. Private*, pg. 213
VT SOFT KFT—See Videoton Holding Zrt.; *Int'l*, pg. 8191
VT-SOFT SOFTWARE KFT.—See UNIT4 N.V.; *Int'l*, pg. 8063
VTU-ENGINEERING GMBH—See DPE Deutsche Private Equity GmbH; *Int'l*, pg. 2188

VTRON GROUP CO., LTD.

VTV THERAPEUTICS INC.—See MacAndrews & Forbes Incorporated; *U.S. Private*, pg. 2534
VTV THERAPEUTICS LLC—See MacAndrews & Forbes Incorporated; *U.S. Private*, pg. 2534
V-T WEST INC.—See VT Industries, Inc.; *U.S. Private*, pg. 4415
VT ZERO LIMITED—See Cybernaut International Holdings Company Limited; *Int'l*, pg. 1893
VU1 CORPORATION; *U.S. Public*, pg. 2313
VUAB PHARMA A. S.—See Saficham Group AG; *Int'l*, pg. 6471
VUADENS CONTROLES SA—See Burkhalter Holding AG; *Int'l*, pg. 1226
VUB BANKA; *Int'l*, pg. 8317
VUBIQUITY GROUP LIMITED—See Amdocs Limited; *Int'l*, pg. 420
VUBIQUITY, INC.—See Amdocs Limited; *Int'l*, pg. 420
VUBIQUITY MANAGEMENT LIMITED—See Amdocs Limited; *Int'l*, pg. 420
VUCOVICH INC.; *U.S. Private*, pg. 4415
VUDU INC.—See Comcast Corporation; *U.S. Public*, pg. 540
VUELING AIRLINES S.A.—See International Consolidated Airlines Group S.A.; *Int'l*, pg. 3746
VUENOW INFRATECH LIMITED; *Int'l*, pg. 8317
VUI I CO., LTD.—See Senshu Ikeda Holdings, Inc.; *Int'l*, pg. 6713
VUKILE PROPERTY FUND LIMITED; *Int'l*, pg. 8317
VUKUZA EARTH WORKS (PTY) LIMITED—See Vuwa Investments (Pty) Ltd; *Int'l*, pg. 8318
VULCABRAS AZALEIA BA, CALCADOS E ARTIGOS ESPORTIVOS S.A.—See Vulcabras Azaleia S.A.; *Int'l*, pg. 8318
VULCABRAS AZALEIA CE, CALCADOS E ARTIGOS ESPORTIVOS S.A.—See Vulcabras Azaleia S.A.; *Int'l*, pg. 8318
VULCABRAS AZALEIA RS, CALCADOS E ARTIGOS ESPORTIVOS S.A.—See Vulcabras Azaleia S.A.; *Int'l*, pg. 8318
VULCABRAS AZALEIA S.A.; *Int'l*, pg. 8317
VULCABRAS AZALEIA SP, COMERCIO DE ARTIGOS ESPORTIVOS LTDA.—See Vulcabras Azaleia S.A.; *Int'l*, pg. 8318
VULCAN CAPITAL—See Vulcan Inc.; *U.S. Private*, pg. 4416
VULCAN CATERING EQUIPMENT (PTY) LTD.—See The Bidvest Group Limited; *Int'l*, pg. 7627
VULCAN CORPORATION—See Vulcan International Corporation; *U.S. Private*, pg. 4416
VULCAN DATA CENTRE SOLUTIONS LIMITED—See Sterlite Technologies Limited; *Int'l*, pg. 7212
VULCAN ELECTRIC COMPANY; *U.S. Private*, pg. 4415
VULCAN ENERGY RESOURCES LIMITED; *Int'l*, pg. 8318
VULCAN ENGINEERING CO.—See Wafra Investment Advisory Group, Inc.; *U.S. Private*, pg. 4425
VULCAN FLEX CIRCUIT CORPOATION—See Vulcan Electric Company; *U.S. Private*, pg. 4416
VULCANFORMS INC.; *U.S. Private*, pg. 4416
VULCAN-HART—See Illinois Tool Works Inc.; *U.S. Public*, pg. 1111
VULCAN, INC.; *U.S. Private*, pg. 4416
VULCAN INC.; *U.S. Private*, pg. 4416
VULCAN, INC. - VULCAN ALUMINUM DIVISION—See Vulcan, Inc.; *U.S. Private*, pg. 4416
VULCAN, INC. - VULCAN TECHNOLOGY CENTER DIVISION—See Vulcan, Inc.; *U.S. Private*, pg. 4416
VULCAN INDUSTRIAL & MINING CORPORATION; *Int'l*, pg. 8318
VULCAN INFORMATION PACKAGING—See NAPCO, Inc.; *U.S. Private*, pg. 2834
VULCAN INTERNATIONAL CORPORATION; *U.S. Private*, pg. 4416
VULCAN INVESTMENT PARTNERS, LLC; *U.S. Private*, pg. 4416
VULCAN MACHINE, INC.—See HC Private Investments LLC; *U.S. Private*, pg. 1888
VULCAN MATERIAL PLASTICO LTDA.—See Grupo Brasil Participacoes; *Int'l*, pg. 3123
VULCAN MATERIALS CO. - CENTRAL REGION—See Vulcan Materials Company; *U.S. Public*, pg. 2314
VULCAN MATERIALS CO. - EAST REGION—See Vulcan Materials Company; *U.S. Public*, pg. 2314
VULCAN MATERIALS CO. - FRESNO—See Vulcan Materials Company; *U.S. Public*, pg. 2314
VULCAN MATERIALS CO. - HELOTES—See Vulcan Materials Company; *U.S. Public*, pg. 2314
VULCAN MATERIALS COMPANY; *U.S. Public*, pg. 2313
VULCAN MATERIALS CO. - SOUTH REGION—See Vulcan Materials Company; *U.S. Public*, pg. 2314
VULCAN MATERIALS CO. - TAFT YARD—See Vulcan Materials Company; *U.S. Public*, pg. 2314
VULCAN MATERIALS CO. - WEST REGION—See Vulcan Materials Company; *U.S. Public*, pg. 2314
VULCAN MINERALS INC.; *Int'l*, pg. 8318
VULCAN PAINTERS INC.; *U.S. Private*, pg. 4416
VULCAN PLASTICS INC—See Consolidated Pipe & Supply Company; *U.S. Private*, pg. 1021
VULCAN PRODUCTIONS INC.—See Vulcan Inc.; *U.S. Private*, pg. 4416

VULCAN PROPERTY MANAGEMENT CO.—See Vulcan International Corporation; *U.S. Private*, pg. 4416
VULCAN REAL ESTATE—See Vulcan Inc.; *U.S. Private*, pg. 4416
VULCAN RESIDENTIAL PARK SRL—See NEPI Rockcastle N.V.; *Int'l*, pg. 5200
VULCAN S.A.; *Int'l*, pg. 8318
VULCAN SPORTS & ENTERTAINMENT LLC—See Vulcan Inc.; *U.S. Private*, pg. 4416
VULCAN SPRING & MFG. CO.; *U.S. Private*, pg. 4416
VULCAN STEEL STRUCTURES, INC.; *U.S. Private*, pg. 4416
VULCAN THREADED PRODUCTS, INC.—See Steel Dynamics, Inc.; *U.S. Public*, pg. 1942
VULCAN TIRE & AUTOMOTIVE, INC.; *U.S. Private*, pg. 4416
VULCO DEVELOPPEMENT—See The Goodyear Tire & Rubber Company; *U.S. Public*, pg. 2085
VULCO PERU SA—See The Weir Group PLC; *Int'l*, pg. 7699
VULCO SA—See The Weir Group PLC; *Int'l*, pg. 7699
VULCO TRUCK SERVICES—See The Goodyear Tire & Rubber Company; *U.S. Public*, pg. 2085
VULCRAFT-ALABAMA—See Nucor Corporation; *U.S. Public*, pg. 1555
VULCRAFT-INDIANA—See Nucor Corporation; *U.S. Public*, pg. 1555
VULCRAFT-NEBRASKA—See Nucor Corporation; *U.S. Public*, pg. 1555
VULCRAFT OF NEW YORK, INC.—See Nucor Corporation; *U.S. Public*, pg. 1555
VULCRAFT-SOUTH CAROLINA—See Nucor Corporation; *U.S. Public*, pg. 1555
VULCRAFT-TEXAS—See Nucor Corporation; *U.S. Public*, pg. 1555
VULCRAFT-UTAH—See Nucor Corporation; *U.S. Public*, pg. 1555
VULGANUS OY—See Aspo Oyj; *Int'l*, pg. 632
VULKAN BENELUX BV—See Varova BV; *Int'l*, pg. 8133
VULKAN INOX GMBH—See INDUS Holding AG; *Int'l*, pg. 3664
VULNERABILITY RESEARCH LABS, LLC—See General Dynamics Corporation; *U.S. Public*, pg. 916
VULSAY INDUSTRIES, LTD.—See Greif Inc.; *U.S. Public*, pg. 969
VULTURUL SA; *Int'l*, pg. 8318
VULTUS AB; *Int'l*, pg. 8318
VUM VERFAHREN UMWELT MANAGEMENT GMBH—See Verbund AG; *Int'l*, pg. 8165
VUNANI FUND MANAGERS (PTY) LTD—See Vunani Limited; *Int'l*, pg. 8318
VUNANI LIMITED; *Int'l*, pg. 8318
VUNAR AS; *Int'l*, pg. 8318
VUNGLE, INC.—See Blackstone Inc.; *U.S. Public*, pg. 361
VUNO INC.; *Int'l*, pg. 8318
VURAL, INC.; *Int'l*, pg. 8318
VURUP A.S.—See MOL Magyar Olaj- es Gazipari Nyrt.; *Int'l*, pg. 5021
VUSIONGROUP—See BOE Technology Group Co., Ltd.; *Int'l*, pg. 1099
VU VIET CO. LTD.—See Wurth Verwaltungsgesellschaft mbH; *Int'l*, pg. 8508
VUWA INVESTMENTS (PTY) LTD; *Int'l*, pg. 8318
VUZIX CORPORATION; *U.S. Public*, pg. 2314
V-VALLEY ADVANCED SOLUTIONS ESPANA, S.A.—See Esprinet S.p.A.; *Int'l*, pg. 2506
VV-AUTO GROUP OY—See Kesko Corporation; *Int'l*, pg. 4143
VV-AUTOTALOT OY—See Kesko Corporation; *Int'l*, pg. 4143
VVC EXPLORACION DE MEXICO, S. DE R.L. DE C.V.—See VVC Exploration Corporation; *Int'l*, pg. 8319
VVC EXPLORATION CORPORATION; *Int'l*, pg. 8318
VV-CONSULTING GESELLSCHAFT FUR RISIKOANALYSE, VORSORGEBERATUNG UND VERSICHERUNGSVERMITTLUNG GMBH—See Munchener Ruckversicherungs AG; *Int'l*, pg. 5092
VVD VOLKSWAGEN CORRETAGEM DE SEGUROS LTDA—See Porsche Automobil Holding SE; *Int'l*, pg. 5931
VVF FZE—See VVF Limited; *Int'l*, pg. 8319
VVF LIMITED; *Int'l*, pg. 8319
VVF LIMITED—See VVF Limited; *Int'l*, pg. 8319
V V FOOD & BEVERAGE CO., LTD.; *Int'l*, pg. 8104
VVF SINGAPORE PTE. LIMITED—See VVF Limited; *Int'l*, pg. 8319
VVF SPOLKA Z.O.O—See VVF Limited; *Int'l*, pg. 8319
VVL BBDO—See Omnicom Group Inc.; *U.S. Public*, pg. 1577
VV MINING MEXICO S DE R.L. DE C.V.—See Vatic Ventures Corp.; *Int'l*, pg. 8135
VVM N.V.—See CRH plc; *Int'l*, pg. 1849
VVS-KRAFT TEKNIKSERVICE I STOCKHOLM AB—See Instalco AB; *Int'l*, pg. 3723
VVS METODER I STOCKHOLM AB—See Instalco AB; *Int'l*, pg. 3722
V.V. & SONS LLC—See Bhatia Brothers Group; *Int'l*, pg. 1014
VVS TRADING A/S—See Ahlsell AB; *Int'l*, pg. 223

CORPORATE AFFILIATIONS

V&V SUPREMO FOODS, INC.; *U.S. Private*, pg. 4327
V.V.S. VERZEKERINGEN B.V.—See Porsche Automobil Holding SE; *Int'l*, pg. 5933
VV TIKVES AD SKOPJE; *Int'l*, pg. 8318
VVV CORPORATION; *U.S. Private*, pg. 4416
VVW VERKEHRSVERBUND WARNOW GMBH—See Deutsche Bahn AG; *Int'l*, pg. 2055
VW AUDI VERTRIEB GMBH—See Porsche Automobil Holding SE; *Int'l*, pg. 5931
VW AUDI VERTRIEBSZENTRUM WESTFALEN GMBH & CO. KG—See Porsche Automobil Holding SE; *Int'l*, pg. 5931
VW CREDIT, INC.—See Porsche Automobil Holding SE; *Int'l*, pg. 5932
VWD ACADEMY AG—See Infront ASA; *Int'l*, pg. 3699
VWD GROUP ITALIA S.R.L.—See Infront ASA; *Int'l*, pg. 3699
VWD INFORMATION SOLUTIONS AG—See Infront ASA; *Int'l*, pg. 3699
VWD NETSOLUTIONS GMBH—See Borsenmedien AG; *Int'l*, pg. 1115
VWD PORTFOLIONET SERVICE AG—See Infront ASA; *Int'l*, pg. 3699
VWD TRANSACTION SOLUTIONS AG—See Infront ASA; *Int'l*, pg. 3699
VWD VEREINIGTE WIRTSCHAFTSDIENSTE GMBH—See Infront ASA; *Int'l*, pg. 3699
VWH VORRICHTUNGS- UND WERKZEUGBAU HERSCHBACH GMBH—See Gesco AG; *Int'l*, pg. 2945
VW KRAFTWERK GMBH—See Porsche Automobil Holding SE; *Int'l*, pg. 5931
VW ORIGINAL TEILE LOGISTIK GMBH & CO. KG VERTRIEBSZENTRUM SUDWEST FRANKEN—See Porsche Automobil Holding SE; *Int'l*, pg. 5931
VWORKER.COM—See Freelancer Ltd.; *Int'l*, pg. 2770
VWR ADVANCED INSTRUMENTS, LLC—See Avantor, Inc.; *U.S. Public*, pg. 241
VWR CORPORATION—See Avantor, Inc.; *U.S. Public*, pg. 241
VWR FUNDING, INC.—See Avantor, Inc.; *U.S. Public*, pg. 241
VWR INTERNATIONAL AB—See Avantor, Inc.; *U.S. Public*, pg. 241
VWR INTERNATIONAL AS—See Avantor, Inc.; *U.S. Public*, pg. 242
VWR INTERNATIONAL A/S—See Avantor, Inc.; *U.S. Public*, pg. 242
VWR INTERNATIONAL BVBA—See Avantor, Inc.; *U.S. Public*, pg. 242
VWR INTERNATIONAL B.V.—See Avantor, Inc.; *U.S. Public*, pg. 241
VWR INTERNATIONAL CO.—See Avantor, Inc.; *U.S. Public*, pg. 241
VWR INTERNATIONAL EUROLAB, S.L.—See Avantor, Inc.; *U.S. Public*, pg. 242
VWR INTERNATIONAL GMBH—See Avantor, Inc.; *U.S. Public*, pg. 241
VWR INTERNATIONAL GMBH—See Avantor, Inc.; *U.S. Public*, pg. 242
VWR INTERNATIONAL KFT.—See Avantor, Inc.; *U.S. Public*, pg. 242
VWR INTERNATIONAL LIMITADA—See Avantor, Inc.; *U.S. Public*, pg. 242
VWR INTERNATIONAL, LLC—See Avantor, Inc.; *U.S. Public*, pg. 241
VWR INTERNATIONAL LTD.—See Avantor, Inc.; *U.S. Public*, pg. 242
VWR INTERNATIONAL LTD—See Avantor, Inc.; *U.S. Public*, pg. 242
VWR INTERNATIONAL - MATERIAL DE LABORATORIO, LDA.—See Avantor, Inc.; *U.S. Public*, pg. 241
VWR INTERNATIONAL OY—See Avantor, Inc.; *U.S. Public*, pg. 242
VWR INTERNATIONAL PBI S.R.L.—See Avantor, Inc.; *U.S. Public*, pg. 242
VWR INTERNATIONAL S.A.S.—See Avantor, Inc.; *U.S. Public*, pg. 242
VWR INTERNATIONAL S. DE R.L. DE C.V.—See Avantor, Inc.; *U.S. Public*, pg. 242
VWR INTERNATIONAL SP. Z O.O.—See Avantor, Inc.; *U.S. Public*, pg. 242
VWR INTERNATIONAL S.R.O.—See Avantor, Inc.; *U.S. Public*, pg. 242
VWR INTERNATIONAL S. R. O.—See Avantor, Inc.; *U.S. Public*, pg. 242
VWR LAB PRODUCTS PRIVATE LIMITED—See Avantor, Inc.; *U.S. Public*, pg. 242
VWR NA SERVICES, LTD.—See Avantor, Inc.; *U.S. Public*, pg. 242
VWR SINGAPORE PTE. LTD.—See Avantor, Inc.; *U.S. Public*, pg. 242
VWS EMIRATES LLC—See Veolia Environnement S.A.; *Int'l*, pg. 8162
VWS ENVIG BOTSWANA PTY LTD—See Veolia Environnement S.A.; *Int'l*, pg. 8163
VWS ENVIG (PTY) LTD.-MEMBRATEK DIVISION—See Veolia Environnement S.A.; *Int'l*, pg. 8163
VWS-HUNGARY INC.—See Veolia Environnement S.A.; *Int'l*, pg. 8162

COMPANY NAME INDEX

VWS INDUSTRIAL SERVICES (MALAYSIA) SDN BHD—See Veolia Environnement S.A.; *Int'l*, pg. 8162
VWS MEMSEP S.R.O.—See Veolia Environnement S.A.; *Int'l*, pg. 8156
VWS MPP SYSTEMS B.V.—See Veolia Environnement S.A.; *Int'l*, pg. 8162
VWS NETHERLANDS—See Veolia Environnement S.A.; *Int'l*, pg. 8162
VWS OIL & GAS—See Veolia Environnement S.A.; *Int'l*, pg. 8162
VWS PIPELINE CONTROL B.V.—See Koninklijke Volker-Wessels N.V.; *Int'l*, pg. 4272
VWS ROMANIA INDUSTRIAL SRL—See Veolia Environnement S.A.; *Int'l*, pg. 8162
VWS SERBIA—See Veolia Environnement S.A.; *Int'l*, pg. 8162
V&W SUPPLY COMPANY; *U.S. Private*, pg. 4327
VWS VERBUNDWERKE SUDWESTSACHSEN GMBH—See RWE AG; *Int'l*, pg. 6436
VWS WESTGARTH LTD.—See Veolia Environnement S.A.; *Int'l*, pg. 8162
VWT PARTICIPACOES LTDA.—See Porsche Automobil Holding SE; *Int'l*, pg. 5932
VW-VERSICHERUNGSVERMITTLUNGS—See Porsche Automobil Holding SE; *Int'l*, pg. 5931
VW WIN CENTURY INC.—See Ameritek Ventures; *U.S. Private*, pg. 115
VXCHNGE HOLDINGS, LLC—See The Stephens Group, LLC; *U.S. Private*, pg. 4121
VXI CORPORATION—See GN Store Nord A/S; *Int'l*, pg. 3016
VXI GLOBAL SOLUTIONS, INC.—See Bain Capital, LP; *U.S. Private*, pg. 451
VXL INSTRUMENTS, INC—See VXL Instruments Limited; *Int'l*, pg. 8319
VXL INSTRUMENTS LIMITED; *Int'l*, pg. 8319
VXL INSTRUMENTS LIMITED—See VXL Instruments Limited; *Int'l*, pg. 8319
VYAIRE MEDICAL, INC.—See Apax Partners LLP; *Int'l*, pg. 507
VYAIRE MEDICAL, INC.—See Becton, Dickinson & Company; *U.S. Public*, pg. 292
VYAIRE MEDICAL—See Apax Partners LLP; *Int'l*, pg. 507
VYAIRE MEDICAL—See Apax Partners LLP; *Int'l*, pg. 507
VYAIRE MEDICAL—See Becton, Dickinson & Company; *U.S. Public*, pg. 292
VYAIRE MEDICAL—See Becton, Dickinson & Company; *U.S. Public*, pg. 292
VYANT BIO, INC.; *U.S. Public*, pg. 2314
VYAPAR INDUSTRIES LTD.; *Int'l*, pg. 8319
VYARTSILYA METAL PRODUCTS PLANT—See Mechel PAO; *Int'l*, pg. 4766
VYBORG SHIPYARD PJSC; *Int'l*, pg. 8319
VYCHODOCESKA ENERGETIKA, A.S.—See CEZ, a.s.; *Int'l*, pg. 1429
VYCHODOCESKA OBALOVNA, S.R.O.—See VINCI S.A.; *Int'l*, pg. 8219
VYCHODOCESKA PLYNARENSKA, A.S.—See RWE AG; *Int'l*, pg. 6436
VYCHODOSLOVENSKA ENERGETIKA A.S.; *Int'l*, pg. 8319
VYCMEX MEXICO, S.A. DE C.V.—See Applied Industrial Technologies, Inc.; *U.S. Public*, pg. 170
VYCOM PLASTICS—See The AZEK Company Inc.; *U.S. Public*, pg. 2035
VYCON, INC.—See Calnetix Technologies, LLC; *U.S. Private*, pg. 723
VYCOR MEDICAL, INC.; *U.S. Public*, pg. 2315
VYKIN CORPORATION—See SOS International LLC; *U.S. Private*, pg. 3716
VYKSA STEEL WORKS JSC; *Int'l*, pg. 8319
VYNAMIC LLC—See Clayton, Dubilier & Rice, LLC; *U.S. Private*, pg. 928
VYNCKIER ENCLOSURE SYSTEMS, INC.—See nVent Electric plc; *Int'l*, pg. 5498
VYNCO INDUSTRIES (NZ) LIMITED; *Int'l*, pg. 8319
VYNCOLIT N.V.—See Sumitomo Bakelite Co., Ltd.; *Int'l*, pg. 7264
VYNE PHARMACEUTICALS LTD.—See VYNE Therapeutics Inc.; *U.S. Public*, pg. 2315
VYNE THERAPEUTICS INC.; *U.S. Public*, pg. 2315
VYNLEADS, INC., *U.S. Public*, pg. 2315
VYOPTA INCORPORATED; *U.S. Private*, pg. 4416
VYRIAN, INC.; *U.S. Private*, pg. 4417
VYSARN LIMITED; *Int'l*, pg. 8319
VYSNOVA PARTNERS, INC.—See Hale Capital Partners, L.P.; *U.S. Private*, pg. 1842
VYSTAR CREDIT UNION; *U.S. Private*, pg. 4417
VYTRUS BIOTECH SA; *Int'l*, pg. 8319
VYYO LTD.—See Gilo Ventures, LLC; *U.S. Private*, pg. 1701
VYZKUMNY A ZKUSEBNI USTAV PLZEN S.R.O.—See CEZ, a.s.; *Int'l*, pg. 1429
VZ BUTSURYU CORPORATION—See KKR & Co. Inc.; *U.S. Public*, pg. 1259
VZ DEPOSITORY BANK LTD.—See VZ Holding AG; *Int'l*, pg. 8319
VZ HOLDING AG; *Int'l*, pg. 8319

VZI INVESTMENT CORP.—See Li & Fung Limited; *Int'l*, pg. 4480
VZ LEGAL & TAX CONSULTING LTD.—See VZ Holding AG; *Int'l*, pg. 8319
VZ OPERATIONS LTD.—See VZ Holding AG; *Int'l*, pg. 8319
VZ RECHTS- UND STEUERBERATUNG LTD.—See VZ Holding AG; *Int'l*, pg. 8319
V-ZUG AG—See Metall Zug AG; *Int'l*, pg. 4847
V-ZUG AUSTRALIA PTY. LTD.—See Metall Zug AG; *Int'l*, pg. 4847
V-ZUG EUROPE BVBA—See Metall Zug AG; *Int'l*, pg. 4847
V-ZUG HOLDING AG; *Int'l*, pg. 8105
V-ZUG HONG KONG CO., LTD.—See Metall Zug AG; *Int'l*, pg. 4847
V-ZUG (SHANGHAI) DOMESTIC APPLIANCE CO., LTD.—See Metall Zug AG; *Int'l*, pg. 4847
V-ZUG SINGAPORE PTE. LTD.—See Metall Zug AG; *Int'l*, pg. 4847
VZ VERMOGENSZENTRUM BANK LTD.—See VZ Holding AG; *Int'l*, pg. 8319
VZ VERMOGENSZENTRUM GMBH—See VZ Holding AG; *Int'l*, pg. 8319
VZ VERMOGENSZENTRUM LTD.—See VZ Holding AG; *Int'l*, pg. 8319
VZ VERSICHERUNGSPOOL LTD.—See VZ Holding AG; *Int'l*, pg. 8319
VZ VERSICHERUNGSZENTRUM LTD.—See VZ Holding AG; *Int'l*, pg. 8319

W

W2BI, INC.—See Advantest Corporation; *Int'l*, pg. 165
W2O GROUP—See New Mountain Capital, LLC; *U.S. Private*, pg. 2903
W3 COMM INMOBILIARIA, S.A. DE C.V.—See Promotora de Informaciones S.A.; *Int'l*, pg. 5996
W 3 ERRICHTUNGS UND BETRIEBS-AKTIENGESELLSCHAFT—See PORR AG; *Int'l*, pg. 5925
W3I, LLC; *U.S. Private*, pg. 4423
W3LL PEOPLE LLC—See e.l.f. Beauty, Inc.; *U.S. Public*, pg. 701
W5 OMNIFINITY AB—See W5 Solutions AB; *Int'l*, pg. 8322
W5 SOLUTIONS AB; *Int'l*, pg. 8322
W82, LLC—See Camping World Holdings, Inc.; *U.S. Public*, pg. 428
WA1 RESOURCES LTD.; *Int'l*, pg. 8322
WAAGAN BIL AS—See DSV A/S; *Int'l*, pg. 2216
WAAGNER-BIRO AG; *Int'l*, pg. 8322
WAAGNER-BIRO AUSTRIA STAGE SYSTEMS AG; *Int'l*, pg. 8323
WAAGNER-BIRO BAVARIA STAGE SYSTEMS GMBH—See Waagner-Biro Austria Stage Systems AG; *Int'l*, pg. 8323
WAAGNER-BIRO BIN BUTTI ENGINEERING L.L.C.—See Waagner-Biro AG; *Int'l*, pg. 8323
WAAGNER-BIRO EMIRATES CONTRACTING L.L.C.—See Waagner-Biro AG; *Int'l*, pg. 8323
WAAGNER BIRO GULF L.L.C.—See Waagner-Biro AG; *Int'l*, pg. 8323
WAAGNER BIRO LIMITED—See Waagner-Biro AG; *Int'l*, pg. 8323
WAAGNER-BIRO LUXEMBOURG STAGE SYSTEMS S.A.—See Waagner-Biro Austria Stage Systems AG; *Int'l*, pg. 8323
WAAGNER BIRO PHILIPPINES, INC.—See Waagner-Biro AG; *Int'l*, pg. 8323
WAAGNER-BIRO SPAIN STAGE SYSTEMS S.A.—See Waagner-Biro Austria Stage Systems AG; *Int'l*, pg. 8323
WAAGNER-BIRO STAHLBAU AG—See Waagner-Biro AG; *Int'l*, pg. 8323
WAAH TAXIS PRIVATE LIMITED—See Ebix Inc.; *U.S. Public*, pg. 710
WAAREE ENERGIES LTD.; *Int'l*, pg. 8323
WAAREE RENEWABLE TECHNOLOGIES LIMITED—See Waaree Energies Ltd.; *Int'l*, pg. 8323
WAAREE TECHNOLOGIES LIMITED; *Int'l*, pg. 8323
WAA SOLAR LTD.; *Int'l*, pg. 8322
WAAT MEDIA CORP.—See Digital Turbine, Inc.; *U.S. Public*, pg. 664
WABAG MUHIBBAH JV SDN. BHD.—See VA TECH WABAG Limited; *Int'l*, pg. 8107
WABAG WASSERTECHNIK AG—See VA TECH WABAG Limited; *Int'l*, pg. 8107
WABAG WATER SERVICES (MACAO) LTD.—See VA TECH WABAG Limited; *Int'l*, pg. 8107
WABAG WATER SERVICES SRL—See Circular Waters Solutions S.R.L; *Int'l*, pg. 1618
WABASH CASTINGS INC.—See Callidus Capital Corporation; *Int'l*, pg. 8319
WABASH CENTER INC.; *U.S. Private*, pg. 4423
WABASH ELECTRIC SUPPLY INC.; *U.S. Private*, pg. 4423

W.A. BAUM COMPANY, INC.

WABASH MEMORIAL HOSPITAL ASSOCIATION; *U.S. Private*, pg. 4423
WABASH METAL PRODUCTS INC—See Harbour Group Industries, Inc.; *U.S. Private*, pg. 1860
WABASH MFG. INC.; *Int'l*, pg. 8323
WABASH NATIONAL CORPORATION; *U.S. Public*, pg. 2320
WABASH NATIONAL, L.P.—See WABASH NATIONAL CORPORATION; *U.S. Public*, pg. 2320
WABASH NATIONAL SERVICES, L.P.—See WABASH NATIONAL CORPORATION; *U.S. Public*, pg. 2320
WABASH NATIONAL TRAILER CENTERS, INC.—See WABASH NATIONAL CORPORATION; *U.S. Public*, pg. 2320
WABASH PLAIN DEALER COMPANY INC.—See Paxton Media Group LLC; *U.S. Private*, pg. 3116
WABASH PLASTICS INC.; *U.S. Private*, pg. 4423
WABASH STEEL COMPANY, LLC; *U.S. Private*, pg. 4424
WABASH TECHNOLOGIES DE MEXICO, S DE R L DE C V—See Sensata Technologies Holding plc; *U.S. Public*, pg. 1866
WABASH TECHNOLOGIES DE MEXICO TECHNOLOGIES S. DE R.L. DE C.V.—See Sensata Technologies Holding plc; *U.S. Public*, pg. 1866
WABASH TECHNOLOGIES, INC.—See Sensata Technologies Holding plc; *U.S. Public*, pg. 1866
WABASH TECHNOLOGIES, INC. - TROY PLANT—See Sensata Technologies Holding plc; *U.S. Public*, pg. 1866
WABASH TECHNOLOGIES MEXICO S. DE R.L. DE C.V.—See Sensata Technologies Holding plc; *U.S. Public*, pg. 1866
WABASH VALLEY ASPHALT CO., LLC—See Milestone Contractors, LP; *U.S. Private*, pg. 2728
WABASH VALLEY POWER ASSOCIATION INC.—See Touchstone Energy Cooperative, Inc.; *U.S. Private*, pg. 4192
WABASH VALLEY SERVICE CO.; *U.S. Private*, pg. 4424
W.A. BAUM COMPANY, INC.; *U.S. Private*, pg. 4418
WABCO ARAC KONTROL SISTEMLERI DESTEK VE PAZARLAMA LIMITED SIRKETI—See ZF Friedrichshafen AG; *Int'l*, pg. 8641
WABCO AUSTRALIA PTY LTD.—See ZF Friedrichshafen AG; *Int'l*, pg. 8641
WABCO AUSTRIA GESMBH.—See ZF Friedrichshafen AG; *Int'l*, pg. 8641
WABCO AUTOMOTIVE AB—See ZF Friedrichshafen AG; *Int'l*, pg. 8642
WABCO AUTOMOTIVE B.V.—See ZF Friedrichshafen AG; *Int'l*, pg. 8642
WABCO AUTOMOTIVE ITALIA S.R.L.—See ZF Friedrichshafen AG; *Int'l*, pg. 8642
WABCO AUTOMOTIVE SOUTH AFRICA (PTY) LTD.—See ZF Friedrichshafen AG; *Int'l*, pg. 8642
WABCO AUTOMOTIVE UK LTD.—See ZF Friedrichshafen AG; *Int'l*, pg. 8642
WABCO BELGIUM BVBA—See ZF Friedrichshafen AG; *Int'l*, pg. 8642
WABCO (CHINA) CO LTD.—See ZF Friedrichshafen AG; *Int'l*, pg. 8641
WABCO COMPRESSOR MANUFACTURING CO.—See Cummins Inc.; *U.S. Public*, pg. 609
WABCO COMPRESSOR MANUFACTURING CO.—See ZF Friedrichshafen AG; *Int'l*, pg. 8642
WABCO DO BRASIL INDUSTRIA E COMERCIO DE FREIOS LTDA—See ZF Friedrichshafen AG; *Int'l*, pg. 8642
WABCO ESPANA, S.L.U.—See ZF Friedrichshafen AG; *Int'l*, pg. 8642
WABCO EUROPE BVBA—See ZF Friedrichshafen AG; *Int'l*, pg. 8642
WABCO FAHRZEUGSYSTEME GMBH—See ZF Friedrichshafen AG; *Int'l*, pg. 8642
WABCO FRANCE SAS—See ZF Friedrichshafen AG; *Int'l*, pg. 8642
WABCO GLOBAL GMBH—See ZF Friedrichshafen AG; *Int'l*, pg. 8642
WABCO GMBH—See ZF Friedrichshafen AG; *Int'l*, pg. 8642
WABCO HOLDING GMBH—See ZF Friedrichshafen AG; *Int'l*, pg. 8642
WABCO HOLDINGS INC.—See ZF Friedrichshafen AG; *Int'l*, pg. 8642
WABCO JAPAN INC.—See ZF Friedrichshafen AG; *Int'l*, pg. 8642
WABCO LOCOMOTIVE—See Westinghouse Air Brake Technologies Corporation; *U.S. Public*, pg. 2359
WABCO LOGISTIK GMBH—See ZF Friedrichshafen AG; *Int'l*, pg. 8642
WABCO POLSKA SPOLKA Z OGRANICZONA ODPOWIEDZIALNOSCIA—See ZF Friedrichshafen AG; *Int'l*, pg. 8642
WABCO RADBREMSEN GMBH—See ZF Friedrichshafen AG; *Int'l*, pg. 8642
WABCO (SCHWEIZ) AG—See ZF Friedrichshafen AG; *Int'l*, pg. 8641
WABCO (SCHWEIZ) GMBH—See ZF Friedrichshafen AG; *Int'l*, pg. 8641

W.A. BAUM COMPANY, INC.

WABCO SOUTH AFRICA (PTY) LTD.—See ZF Friedrichshafen AG; *Int'l*, pg. 8642
WABCO-TVS (INDIA)—See ZF Friedrichshafen AG; *Int'l*, pg. 8642
WABCO VERTRIEBS GMBH & CO. KG—See ZF Friedrichshafen AG; *Int'l*, pg. 8642
WABC-TV INC.—See The Walt Disney Company; *U.S. Public*, pg. 2138
WABERER'S INTERNATIONAL NYRT; *Int'l*, pg. 8323
WABERER'S ROMANIA S.A.—See Waberer's International Nyrt; *Int'l*, pg. 8323
WABERER'S - SZEMEREY LOGISZTIKA KFT.—See Waberer's International Nyrt; *Int'l*, pg. 8323
WAB HOLDINGS, LLC—See Walgreens Boots Alliance, Inc.; *U.S. Public*, pg. 2323
WABI IRON & STEEL CORP.; *Int'l*, pg. 8323
WABI-TV—See Gray Television, Inc.; *U.S. Public*, pg. 960
WABM-TV—See Sinclair, Inc.; *U.S. Public*, pg. 1886
W A BRAGG & CO INC.—See Plumbing Distributors Inc.; *U.S. Private*, pg. 3215
WABTEC ASSEMBLY SERVICES S. DE R.L. DE C.V.—See Westinghouse Air Brake Technologies Corporation; *U.S. Public*, pg. 2359
WABTEC AUSTRALIA PTY LTD—See Westinghouse Air Brake Technologies Corporation; *U.S. Public*, pg. 2359
WABTEC (BEIJING) INVESTMENT CO. LTD.—See Westinghouse Air Brake Technologies Corporation; *U.S. Public*, pg. 2359
WABTEC BRASIL FABRICACAO E MANUTENCAO DE EQUIPAMENTOS LTDA—See Westinghouse Air Brake Technologies Corporation; *U.S. Public*, pg. 2359
WABTEC BRASIL FABRICACOA MANUTENCAO DE EQUIPAMENTOS FERROVIAROS LTDA—See Westinghouse Air Brake Technologies Corporation; *U.S. Public*, pg. 2359
WABTEC CANADA, INC.—See Westinghouse Air Brake Technologies Corporation; *U.S. Public*, pg. 2359
WABTEC CONTROL SYSTEMS PTY LTD—See Westinghouse Air Brake Technologies Corporation; *U.S. Public*, pg. 2359
WABTEC DE MEXICO, S. DE R.L. DE C.V.—See Westinghouse Air Brake Technologies Corporation; *U.S. Public*, pg. 2360
WABTEC EQUIPAMENTOS FERROVIARIOS LTDA.—See Westinghouse Air Brake Technologies Corporation; *U.S. Public*, pg. 2359
WABTEC EUROPE GMBH—See Westinghouse Air Brake Technologies Corporation; *U.S. Public*, pg. 2359
WABTEC FOUNDRY—See Westinghouse Air Brake Technologies Corporation; *U.S. Public*, pg. 2359
WABTEC GLOBAL SERVICES—See Westinghouse Air Brake Technologies Corporation; *U.S. Public*, pg. 2359
WAB TECHNIQUE S.A.R.L.—See BKW AG; *Int'l*, pg. 1056
WABTEC MZT AD SKOPJE—See Westinghouse Air Brake Technologies Corporation; *U.S. Public*, pg. 2359
WABTEC PASSENGER TRANSIT—See Westinghouse Air Brake Technologies Corporation; *U.S. Public*, pg. 2359
WABTEC RAIL LIMITED—See Westinghouse Air Brake Technologies Corporation; *U.S. Public*, pg. 2359
WABTEC RAIL SCOTLAND LIMITED—See Westinghouse Air Brake Technologies Corporation; *U.S. Public*, pg. 2359
WABTEC RAILWAY ELECTRONICS CORPORATION—See Westinghouse Air Brake Technologies Corporation; *U.S. Public*, pg. 2360
WABTEC RAILWAY ELECTRONICS CORPORATION—See Westinghouse Air Brake Technologies Corporation; *U.S. Public*, pg. 2360
WABTEC RUBBER PRODUCTS—See Westinghouse Air Brake Technologies Corporation; *U.S. Public*, pg. 2360
WABTEC SERVICIOS ADMINISTRATIVOS, S.A. DE C.V.—See Westinghouse Air Brake Technologies Corporation; *U.S. Public*, pg. 2360
WABTEC SOUTH AFRICA PROPRIETARY LIMITED—See Westinghouse Air Brake Technologies Corporation; *U.S. Public*, pg. 2360
WAC DE MEXICO SA DE CV, SOFOM, ENR—See World Acceptance Corporation; *U.S. Public*, pg. 2379
WACHENDORF GMBH—See Pema Holding AG; *Int'l*, pg. 5785
W.A. CHESTER, LLC—See Bernhard Capital Partners Management, LP; *U.S. Private*, pg. 537
WAC HOLDINGS LTD.; *Int'l*, pg. 8323
WACHS CANADA LTD.—See Illinois Tool Works Inc.; *U.S. Public*, pg. 1111
WACHTEL GMBH & CO; *Int'l*, pg. 8323
WACHTELL LIPTON ROSEN & KATZ; *U.S. Private*, pg. 4424
WACHTER MANAGEMENT COMPANY INC.; *U.S. Private*, pg. 4424
WACKENHUT CAMEROON S.A.—See Allied Universal Manager LLC; *U.S. Private*, pg. 189
WACKENHUT DE BOLIVIA S.A.—See Allied Universal Manager LLC; *U.S. Private*, pg. 189
WACKENHUT DEL ECUADOR S.A.—See Allied Universal Manager LLC; *U.S. Private*, pg. 189
WACKENHUT DOMINICANA, S.A.—See Allied Universal Manager LLC; *U.S. Private*, pg. 189
WACKENHUT EL SALVADOR S.A.—See Allied Universal Manager LLC; *U.S. Private*, pg. 189
WACKENHUT PAKISTAN (PRIVATE) LIMITED; *Int'l*, pg. 8323
WACKENHUT PARAGUAY S.A.—See Allied Universal Manager LLC; *U.S. Private*, pg. 189
WACKENHUT S.A.—See Allied Universal Manager LLC; *U.S. Private*, pg. 189
WACKENHUT VENEZOLANA C.A.—See Allied Universal Manager LLC; *U.S. Private*, pg. 189
WACKER ASAHIKASEI SILICONE CO., LTD.—See Wacker Chemie AG; *Int'l*, pg. 8323
WACKER BIOTECH GMBH—See Wacker Chemie AG; *Int'l*, pg. 8324
WACKER BIOTECH US INC.—See Wacker Chemie AG; *Int'l*, pg. 8324
WACKER-CHEMIA POLSKA SP. Z O.O.—See Wacker Chemie AG; *Int'l*, pg. 8324
WACKER CHEMICAL CORPORATION—See Wacker Chemie AG; *Int'l*, pg. 8324
WACKER CHEMICALS AUSTRALIA PTY. LTD.—See Wacker Chemie AG; *Int'l*, pg. 8324
WACKER CHEMICALS (CHINA) CO., LTD.—See Wacker Chemie AG; *Int'l*, pg. 8324
WACKER CHEMICALS EAST ASIA LTD.—See Wacker Chemie AG; *Int'l*, pg. 8324
WACKER CHEMICALS FUMED SILICA (ZHANGJIAGANG) CO. LTD.—See Wacker Chemie AG; *Int'l*, pg. 8324
WACKER CHEMICALS HONG KONG LTD.—See Wacker Chemie AG; *Int'l*, pg. 8324
WACKER CHEMICALS KOREA INC.—See Wacker Chemie AG; *Int'l*, pg. 8324
WACKER CHEMICALS LTD.—See Wacker Chemie AG; *Int'l*, pg. 8324
WACKER CHEMICALS MALAYSIA SDN. BHD.—See Wacker Chemie AG; *Int'l*, pg. 8324
WACKER CHEMICALS MIDDLE EAST—See Wacker Chemie AG; *Int'l*, pg. 8323
WACKER CHEMICALS (NANJING) CO. LTD.—See Wacker Chemie AG; *Int'l*, pg. 8324
WACKER CHEMICALS NORWAY AS—See Wacker Chemie AG; *Int'l*, pg. 8324
WACKER CHEMICALS (SOUTH ASIA) PTE. LTD.—See Wacker Chemie AG; *Int'l*, pg. 8324
WACKER CHEMICALS (SOUTH ASIA) PTE. LTD.—See Wacker Chemie AG; *Int'l*, pg. 8324
WACKER CHEMICALS (SOUTH ASIA) PTE. LTD.—See Wacker Chemie AG; *Int'l*, pg. 8324
WACKER CHEMICALS (SOUTH ASIA) PTE. LTD.—See Wacker Chemie AG; *Int'l*, pg. 8324
WACKER CHEMICALS (ZHANGJIAGANG) CO. LTD.—See Wacker Chemie AG; *Int'l*, pg. 8324
WACKER CHEMIE AG - NUNCHRITZ—See Wacker Chemie AG; *Int'l*, pg. 8324
WACKER CHEMIE AG; *Int'l*, pg. 8323
WACKER-CHEMIE BENELUX B.V.—See Wacker Chemie AG; *Int'l*, pg. 8324
WACKER-CHEMIE HUNGARY KFT.—See Wacker Chemie AG; *Int'l*, pg. 8324
WACKER CHEMIE INDIA PVT. LTD.—See Wacker Chemie AG; *Int'l*, pg. 8323
WACKER CHEMIE ITALIA S.R.L.—See Wacker Chemie AG; *Int'l*, pg. 8324
WACKER-CHEMIE, S.R.O.—See Wacker Chemie AG; *Int'l*, pg. 8324
WACKER-CHEMIE VERSICHERUNGSVERMITTLUNG GMBH—See Wacker Chemie AG; *Int'l*, pg. 8324
WACKER CHIMIE S.A.S.—See Wacker Chemie AG; *Int'l*, pg. 8324
WACKER COLOMBIA S.A.S.—See Wacker Chemie AG; *Int'l*, pg. 8324
WACKER DYMATIC SILICONES (SHUNDE) CO., LTD.—See Wacker Chemie AG; *Int'l*, pg. 8324
WACKER-KEMI AB—See Wacker Chemie AG; *Int'l*, pg. 8324
WACKER KIMYA TIC. LTD. STI.—See Wacker Chemie AG; *Int'l*, pg. 8324
WACKERLI AUTO CENTER; *U.S. Private*, pg. 4424
WACKER METROARK CHEMICALS PVT. LTD.—See Wacker Chemie AG; *Int'l*, pg. 8324
WACKER MEXICANA, S.A. DE C.V.—See Wacker Chemie AG; *Int'l*, pg. 8324
WACKER NEUSON AB—See Wacker Neuson SE; *Int'l*, pg. 8324
WACKER NEUSON AG—See Wacker Neuson SE; *Int'l*, pg. 8324
WACKER NEUSON AS—See Wacker Neuson SE; *Int'l*, pg. 8324
WACKER NEUSON BETEILIGUNGS GMBH—See Wacker Neuson SE; *Int'l*, pg. 8324
WACKER NEUSON B.V.—See Wacker Neuson SE; *Int'l*, pg. 8324
WACKER NEUSON CORPORATION—See Wacker Neuson SE; *Int'l*, pg. 8325
WACKER NEUSON EQUIPMENT PRIVATE LTD.—See Wacker Neuson SE; *Int'l*, pg. 8325

CORPORATE AFFILIATIONS

WACKER NEUSON GMBH—See Wacker Neuson SE; *Int'l*, pg. 8325
WACKER NEUSON GMBH—See Wacker Neuson SE; *Int'l*, pg. 8325
WACKER NEUSON KFT—See Wacker Neuson SE; *Int'l*, pg. 8325
WACKER NEUSON LIMITED—See Wacker Neuson SE; *Int'l*, pg. 8325
WACKER NEUSON LIMITED—See Wacker Neuson SE; *Int'l*, pg. 8325
WACKER NEUSON LINZ GMBH—See Wacker Neuson SE; *Int'l*, pg. 8325
WACKER NEUSON LTD.—See Wacker Neuson SE; *Int'l*, pg. 8325
WACKER NEUSON LTD.—See Wacker Neuson SE; *Int'l*, pg. 8325
WACKER NEUSON MACHINERY TRADING (SHENZHEN) LTD. CO.—See Wacker Neuson SE; *Int'l*, pg. 8325
WACKER NEUSON MAKINE LTD. STI.—See Wacker Neuson SE; *Int'l*, pg. 8325
WACKER NEUSON MANILA, INC.—See Wacker Neuson SE; *Int'l*, pg. 8325
WACKER NEUSON MAQUINAS LTDA.—See Wacker Neuson SE; *Int'l*, pg. 8325
WACKER NEUSON (PTY) LTD.—See Wacker Neuson SE; *Int'l*, pg. 8325
WACKER NEUSON PTY LTD—See Wacker Neuson SE; *Int'l*, pg. 8325
WACKER NEUSON S.A. DE C.V.—See Wacker Neuson SE; *Int'l*, pg. 8325
WACKER NEUSON S.A.—See Wacker Neuson SE; *Int'l*, pg. 8325
WACKER NEUSON S.A.S.—See Wacker Neuson SE; *Int'l*, pg. 8325
WACKER NEUSON SE; *Int'l*, pg. 8324
WACKER NEUSON SRL CON SOCIO UNICO—See Wacker Neuson SE; *Int'l*, pg. 8325
WACKER NEUSON S.R.O.—See Wacker Neuson SE; *Int'l*, pg. 8325
WACKER POLYMERS GMBH & CO. KG.—See Wacker Chemie AG; *Int'l*, pg. 8324
WACKER POLYSILICON NORTH AMERICA, L.L.C—See Wacker Chemie AG; *Int'l*, pg. 8324
WACKER QUIMICA DO BRASIL LTDA.—See Wacker Chemie AG; *Int'l*, pg. 8324
WACKER QUIMICA IBERICA, S.A.—See Wacker Chemie AG; *Int'l*, pg. 8324
WACKER STERBEKASSE VVAG—See Wacker Chemie AG; *Int'l*, pg. 8324
WACKY WORLD STUDIOS, LLC—See Court Square Capital Partners, L.P.; *U.S. Private*, pg. 1070
WACO AFRICA PTY. LTD.—See Waco International Ltd.; *Int'l*, pg. 8325
WACOAL AMERICA, INC.—See Wacoal Holdings Corp.; *Int'l*, pg. 8326
WACOAL ART CENTER CO., LTD.—See Wacoal Holdings Corp.; *Int'l*, pg. 8326
WACOAL CANADA INC.—See Wacoal Holdings Corp.; *Int'l*, pg. 8326
WACOAL CAREER SERVICE CORP.—See Wacoal Holdings Corp.; *Int'l*, pg. 8326
WACOAL CHINA CO., LTD.—See Wacoal Holdings Corp.; *Int'l*, pg. 8326
WACOAL CORP.—See Wacoal Holdings Corp.; *Int'l*, pg. 8326
WACOAL DISTRIBUTION CORP.—See Wacoal Holdings Corp.; *Int'l*, pg. 8326
WACOAL DOMINICANA CORP.—See Wacoal Holdings Corp.; *Int'l*, pg. 8326
WACOAL EMEA LTD.—See Wacoal Holdings Corp.; *Int'l*, pg. 8326
WACOAL EUROPE SAS—See Wacoal Holdings Corp.; *Int'l*, pg. 8326
WACOAL HOLDINGS CORP.; *Int'l*, pg. 8325
WACOAL HONG KONG CO., LTD.—See Wacoal Holdings Corp.; *Int'l*, pg. 8326
WACOAL INDIA PRIVATE LIMITED—See Wacoal Holdings Corp.; *Int'l*, pg. 8326
WACOAL I NEXT CORP.—See Wacoal Holdings Corp.; *Int'l*, pg. 8326
WACOAL INTERNATIONAL CORP.—See Wacoal Holdings Corp.; *Int'l*, pg. 8326
WACOAL INTERNATIONAL HONG KONG CO., LTD.—See Wacoal Holdings Corp.; *Int'l*, pg. 8326
WACOAL LANKA(PRIVATE) LIMITED—See Wacoal Holdings Corp.; *Int'l*, pg. 8326
WACOAL MALAYSIA SDN. BHD.—See Wacoal Holdings Corp.; *Int'l*, pg. 8326
WACOAL MANUFACTURING JAPAN CORP.—See Wacoal Holdings Corp.; *Int'l*, pg. 8326
WACOAL MINETTE CO., LTD.—See Wacoal Holdings Corp.; *Int'l*, pg. 8326
WACOAL NETHERLANDS B.V.—See Wacoal Holdings Corp.; *Int'l*, pg. 8326
WACOAL SERVICE CO., LTD.—See Wacoal Holdings Corp.; *Int'l*, pg. 8326
WACOAL (SHANGHAI) HUMAN SCIENCE R&D CO., LTD.—See Wacoal Holdings Corp.; *Int'l*, pg. 8326

COMPANY NAME INDEX

WACOAL SINGAPORE PTE. LTD.—See Wacoal Holdings Corp.; *Int'l*, pg. 8326
WACOAL SPORTS SCIENCE CORP.—See Wacoal Holdings Corp.; *Int'l*, pg. 8326
WACO ASSOCIATES INC. - SAN DIEGO OFFICE—See Waco Associates Inc.; *U.S. Private*, pg. 4424
WACO ASSOCIATES INC.; *U.S. Private*, pg. 4424
WACO BV—See Concrete Valley Group BV; *Int'l*, pg. 1766
WACO GASTROENTEROLOGY ENDOSCOPY CENTER, LLC—See KKR & Co. Inc.; *U.S. Public*, pg. 1249
WACO, INC.; *U.S. Private*, pg. 4424
WACO INTERNATIONAL LTD.; *Int'l*, pg. 8325
WACO JONSEREDS AB—See Michael Weinig AG; *Int'l*, pg. 4875
WACOM AUSTRALIA PTY. LTD.—See Wacom Co., Ltd.; *Int'l*, pg. 8327
WACOM CO., LTD.; *Int'l*, pg. 8326
WACO MEMORIAL PARK, INC.—See Service Corporation International; *U.S. Public*, pg. 1871
WACOM EUROPE GMBH—See Wacom Co., Ltd.; *Int'l*, pg. 8327
WACOM KOREA CO., LTD.—See Wacom Co., Ltd.; *Int'l*, pg. 8327
WACOM TAIWAN INFORMATION CO., LTD.—See Wacom Co., Ltd.; *Int'l*, pg. 8327
WACONIA DODGE INC.; *U.S. Private*, pg. 4424
WACONIA FARM SUPPLY; *U.S. Private*, pg. 4424
WACO N.V.—See Fagerhult Group AB; *Int'l*, pg. 2602
WACO OIL & GAS CO., INC.; *U.S. Private*, pg. 4424
WACUL, INC.; *Int'l*, pg. 8327
WADA DENKI CO., LTD.—See Ablerex Electronics Co., Ltd.; *Int'l*, pg. 63
WADAKOHSAN CORPORATION; *Int'l*, pg. 8327
WADCORPP INDIAN PRIVATE LIMITED—See Franklin Electric Co., Inc.; *U.S. Public*, pg. 879
WADDELL DISPLAY CASES—See GMi Companies, Inc.; *U.S. Private*, pg. 1722
WADDELL & REED FINANCIAL, INC.—See Macquarie Group Limited; *Int'l*, pg. 4625
WADDELL & REED FINANCIAL SERVICES, INC.—See Macquarie Group Limited; *Int'l*, pg. 4625
WADDELL & REED, INC.—See Macquarie Group Limited; *Int'l*, pg. 4626
WADDELL & REED INVESTMENT MANAGEMENT CO.—See Macquarie Group Limited; *Int'l*, pg. 4625
WADDELL & REED SERVICES CO.—See Macquarie Group Limited; *Int'l*, pg. 4625
WADDINGTON GROUP, INC.—See Apollo Global Management, Inc.; *U.S. Public*, pg. 154
WADDINGTON NORTH AMERICA, INC.—See Apollo Global Management, Inc.; *U.S. Public*, pg. 154
WADDINGTON-RICHMAN, INC.; *U.S. Private*, pg. 4424
WADDLE LOANS PTY. LTD.—See Xero Limited; *Int'l*, pg. 8521
WADE-CARY ENTERPRISES INC.; *U.S. Private*, pg. 4424
WADE COUPLINGS LTD.—See Crane NXT, Co.; *U.S. Public*, pg. 591
WADE INC.; *U.S. Private*, pg. 4424
WADE INC.—See Wade Inc.; *U.S. Private*, pg. 4424
WADE MANUFACTURING COMPANY; *U.S. Private*, pg. 4424
WADE PAPER CORPORATION; *U.S. Private*, pg. 4424
WADES FOODS, INC.; *U.S. Private*, pg. 4424
WADE-TRIM ASSOCIATES INC.—See Wade-Trim Group Inc.; *U.S. Private*, pg. 4424
WADE-TRIM GROUP INC.; *U.S. Private*, pg. 4424
WADE-TRIM INC. (MICHIGAN)—See Wade-Trim Group Inc.; *U.S. Private*, pg. 4424
WADE-TRIM INC.—See Wade-Trim Group Inc.; *U.S. Private*, pg. 4424
WADE WALKER (PROPRIETARY) LIMITED—See Murray & Roberts Holdings Ltd.; *Int'l*, pg. 5100
WADEWARE LLC—See Hands-On Learning Solutions LLC; *U.S. Private*, pg. 1853
WADEX SA; *Int'l*, pg. 8327
WADHAM ENERGY LIMITED PARTNERSHIP—See Enpower Corp.; *U.S. Public*, pg. 1401
WADHAMS ENTERPRISES INC.; *U.S. Private*, pg. 4424
WADIA DIGITAL—See Fine Sounds S.p.A.; *Int'l*, pg. 2673
THE WADIA GROUP; *Int'l*, pg. 7698
WADIA TECHNO-ENGINEERING SERVICES LIMITED—See The Wadia Group; *Int'l*, pg. 7698
WADLE BAUUNTERNEHMUNG GMBH—See Swietelsky Baugesellschaft m.b.H.; *Int'l*, pg. 7367
WADLEY-DONOVAN GROUP; *U.S. Private*, pg. 4425
WADLEY-DONOVAN GROWTHTECH LLC—See Wadley-Donovan Group; *U.S. Private*, pg. 4425
WADLEY-DONOVAN-GUTSHAW CONSULTING, LLC—See Wadley-Donovan Group; *U.S. Private*, pg. 4425
WADMAN CORPORATION; *U.S. Private*, pg. 4425
WADO-AM—See ForgeLight, LLC; *U.S. Public*, pg. 1568
WADO-AM—See Searchlight Capital Partners, L.P.; *U.S. Private*, pg. 3590
WADSWORTH ATHENEUM MUSEUM OF ART; *U.S. Private*, pg. 4425
WADSWORTH CENGAGE LEARNING—See Apax Partners LLP; *Int'l*, pg. 503
WADSWORTH CENGAGE LEARNING—See Apollo Global Management, Inc.; *U.S. Public*, pg. 168
WADSWORTH CENGAGE LEARNING—See KKR & Co. Inc.; *U.S. Public*, pg. 1256
WADSWORTH CENGAGE LEARNING—See Searchlight Capital Partners, L.P.; *U.S. Private*, pg. 3587
WADSWORTH OIL CO. OF CLANTON INC.; *U.S. Private*, pg. 4425
WAECO GERMANY WSE GMBH—See Dometic Group AB; *Int'l*, pg. 2160
WAE CO., LTD.—See TOKAI Holdings Corporation; *Int'l*, pg. 7780
WAECO SWEDEN WSE AB—See Dometic Group AB; *Int'l*, pg. 2161
WAEKON CORP.—See Crawford United Corporation; *U.S. Public*, pg. 592
WAELTI-SCHOENFELD S.A—See ED&F Man Holdings Limited; *Int'l*, pg. 2303
WAEN INTERNATIONAL LIMITED—See Hotland Co., Ltd.; *Int'l*, pg. 3489
WAFAB INTERNATIONAL—See M+W Group GmbH; *Int'l*, pg. 4613
WAFA INSURANCE, INC.; *Int'l*, pg. 8327
WAFA KUNSTSTOFFTECHNIK GMBH; *Int'l*, pg. 8327
WAFANGDIAN BEARING CO., LTD.; *Int'l*, pg. 8327
WAFD, INC.; *U.S. Public*, pg. 2321
WAFD INSURANCE GROUP, INC.—See WaFd, Inc.; *U.S. Public*, pg. 2321
WAFERGEN BIO-SYSTEMS, INC.—See Takara Holdings, Inc.; *Int'l*, pg. 7432
WAFERING TECHNOLOGY CORPORATION—See GIGASTORAGE Corp.; *Int'l*, pg. 2972
WAFER SPACE SEMICONDUCTORS TECHNOLOGIES PVT. LTD.—See Alten S.A.; *Int'l*, pg. 391
WAFER SYSTEMS (HONG KONG) LIMITED—See GET Holdings Limited; *Int'l*, pg. 2946
WAFER SYSTEMS LIMITED—See InvesTech Holdings Limited; *Int'l*, pg. 3778
WAFERTECH, LLC—See Taiwan Semiconductor Manufacturing Company Ltd.; *Int'l*, pg. 7424
WAFER TECHNOLOGY LTD.—See IQE plc; *Int'l*, pg. 3803
WAFFER TECHNOLOGY, CORP.; *Int'l*, pg. 8327
WAFFER TECHNOLOGY (MAANSHAN) LIMITED—See Waffer Technology, Corp.; *Int'l*, pg. 8327
WAFFLE HOUSE, INCORPORATED; *U.S. Private*, pg. 4425
WAFI ENERGY CO.—See Asyad Holding Group; *Int'l*, pg. 664
WAFO SCHNECKEN UND ZYLINDER GMBH—See Nordson Corporation; *U.S. Public*, pg. 1535
WAFRAH FOR INDUSTRY & DEVELOPMENT CO.; *Int'l*, pg. 8327
WAFRA, INC.; *U.S. Private*, pg. 4425
WAFRA INVESTMENT ADVISORY GROUP, INC.; *U.S. Private*, pg. 4425
WAFRA PARTNERS LLC—See Wafra Investment Advisory Group, Inc.; *U.S. Private*, pg. 4425
WAGA ENERGY SA; *Int'l*, pg. 8327
WAGE INDUSTRI AB; *Int'l*, pg. 8327
WAGENER & SIMON WASI GMBH & CO. KG—See Wurth Verwaltungsgesellschaft mbH; *Int'l*, pg. 8508
WAGERS INC.; *U.S. Private*, pg. 4425
WAGEWORKS, INC.—See HealthEquity, Inc.; *U.S. Public*, pg. 1016
THE WAGGA DAILY ADVERTISER PTY LTD—See Nine Entertainment Co. Holdings Limited; *Int'l*, pg. 5299
WAGGENER EDSTROM GMBH—See Waggener Edstrom; *U.S. Private*, pg. 4425
WAGGENER EDSTROM—See Waggener Edstrom; *U.S. Private*, pg. 4425
WAGGENER EDSTROM—See Waggener Edstrom; *U.S. Private*, pg. 4425
WAGGENER EDSTROM—See Waggener Edstrom; *U.S. Private*, pg. 4425
WAGGENER EDSTROM; *U.S. Private*, pg. 4425
WAGGENER EDSTROM—See Waggener Edstrom; *U.S. Private*, pg. 4425
WAGGENER EDSTROM—See Waggener Edstrom; *U.S. Private*, pg. 4425
WAGGENER EDSTROM—See Waggener Edstrom; *U.S. Private*, pg. 4425
WAGGENER EDSTROM—See Waggener Edstrom; *U.S. Private*, pg. 4425
WAGGENER EDSTROM—See Waggener Edstrom; *U.S. Private*, pg. 4425
WAGGL, INC.—See Perceptyx, Inc.; *U.S. Private*, pg. 3146
THE WAGGONERS TRUCKING; *U.S. Private*, pg. 4132
WAG! GROUP CO.; *U.S. Public*, pg. 2321
WAGIC INC; *U.S. Private*, pg. 4425
W & A GILBEY SA—See Diageo plc; *Int'l*, pg. 2102
WAGMAN COMPANIES, INC.; *U.S. Private*, pg. 4426
WAGMAN CONSTRUCTION, INC.—See Wagman Companies, Inc.; *U.S. Private*, pg. 4426
WAGNER AUSTRALIA PTY. LTD.—See J. Wagner AG; *Int'l*, pg. 3857
WAGNER & BROWN, LTD.; *U.S. Private*, pg. 4426
WAGNER CADILLAC CO., LP; *U.S. Private*, pg. 4426
WAGNER COLORA SRL—See J. Wagner AG; *Int'l*, pg. 3857

THE WAGNER SMITH COMPANY

THE WAGNER COMPANIES, INC.; *U.S. Private*, pg. 4132
WAGNER CONSTRUCTION COMPANY, LLC—See A.O. Construction Company, Inc.; *U.S. Private*, pg. 27
WAGNER & CO SOLAR FRANCE SARL—See Wagner & Co Solar Technology GmbH; *Int'l*, pg. 8327
WAGNER & CO SOLAR-ITALIA S.R.L.—See Wagner & Co Solar Technology GmbH; *Int'l*, pg. 8327
WAGNER & CO SOLAR TECHNOLOGY GMBH; *Int'l*, pg. 8327
WAGNER ENTERPRISES; *U.S. Private*, pg. 4426
WAGNER EQUIPMENT CO.; *U.S. Private*, pg. 4426
WAGNER-HOSOKAWA MICRON LTD—See Hosokawa Micron Corporation; *Int'l*, pg. 3486
WAGNER- HOSOKAWA MICRON LTD.—See J. Wagner AG; *Int'l*, pg. 3857
WAGNER INDUSTRIAL ELECTRIC, INC.—See MDU Resources Group, Inc.; *U.S. Public*, pg. 1411
WAGNER INDUSTRIES, INC.; *U.S. Private*, pg. 4426
WAGNER KABLO SANAYI VE TICARET A.S.; *Int'l*, pg. 8327
WAGNER MOTORS; *U.S. Private*, pg. 4426
WAGNER OIL CO. INC.; *U.S. Private*, pg. 4426
WAGNER POOLS; *U.S. Private*, pg. 4426
WAGNER REALTY; *U.S. Private*, pg. 4426
WAGNER RESOURCE GROUP, INC.—See Integrated Wealth Concepts, LLC; *U.S. Private*, pg. 2101
WAGNERS CFT LLC—See Wagners Holding Company Limited; *Int'l*, pg. 8327
WAGNERS GLOBAL SERVICES (MALAYSIA) SDN BHD—See Wagners Holding Company Limited; *Int'l*, pg. 8327
WAGNERS HOLDING COMPANY LIMITED; *Int'l*, pg. 8327
WAGNER'S LLC; *U.S. Private*, pg. 4426
WAGNER'S LLC—See Wagner's LLC; *U.S. Private*, pg. 4426
THE WAGNER SMITH COMPANY; *U.S. Private*, pg. 4132
THE WAGNER-SMITH COMPANY—See MDU Resources Group, Inc.; *U.S. Public*, pg. 1410
WAGNER-SMITH EQUIPMENT CO.—See MDU Resources Group, Inc.; *U.S. Public*, pg. 1411
WAGNER SOLAR GMBH—See Wagner & Co Solar Technology GmbH; *Int'l*, pg. 8327
WAGNER SOLAR S.L.—See Wagner & Co Solar Technology GmbH; *Int'l*, pg. 8327
WAGNEH SOLAR UK LTD—See Wagner & Co Solar Technology GmbH; *Int'l*, pg. 8327
WAGNER SPRAYTECH BENELUX B.V.—See J. Wagner AG; *Int'l*, pg. 3857
WAGNER SPRAY TECH CORPORATION—See J. Wagner AG; *Int'l*, pg. 3857
WAGNER SPRAY TECH DO BRASIL LTDA—See J. Wagner AG; *Int'l*, pg. 3857
WAGNER SPRAYTECH IBERICA, S.A.—See J. Wagner AG; *Int'l*, pg. 3857
WAGNER SPRAYTECH JAPAN LTD.—See J. Wagner AG; *Int'l*, pg. 3857
WAGNER SPRAYTECH SCANDINAVIA A/S—See J. Wagner AG; *Int'l*, pg. 3857
WAGNER SPRAYTECH (SHANGHAI) CO LTD.—See J. Wagner AG; *Int'l*, pg. 3857
WAGNER SPRAYTECH (UK) LTD.—See J. Wagner AG; *Int'l*, pg. 3857
WAGNER S.R.O.—See J. Wagner AG; *Int'l*, pg. 3857
WAGNER SUPPLY CO, INC.—See Bain Capital, LP; *U.S. Private*, pg. 441
WAGNER SVERIGE AB—See J. Wagner AG; *Int'l*, pg. 3857
WAGNER SYSTEMS, INC.—See J. Wagner AG; *Int'l*, pg. 3857
WAGO BELUX NV—See WAGO Kontakttechnik GmbH & Co. KG; *Int'l*, pg. 8327
WAGO CONTACT, LTD.—See WAGO Kontakttechnik GmbH & Co. KG; *Int'l*, pg. 8328
WAGO CONTACT SA—See WAGO Kontakttechnik GmbH & Co. KG; *Int'l*, pg. 8328
WAGO CONTACT SA—See WAGO Kontakttechnik GmbH & Co. KG; *Int'l*, pg. 8328
WAGO & CONTROLS (INDIA) LTD.—See WAGO Kontakttechnik GmbH & Co. KG; *Int'l*, pg. 8327
WAGO CO. OF JAPAN LTD.—See WAGO Kontakttechnik GmbH & Co. KG; *Int'l*, pg. 8327
WAGO CORPORATION—See WAGO Kontakttechnik GmbH & Co. KG; *Int'l*, pg. 8328
WAGO DENMARK A/S—See WAGO Kontakttechnik GmbH & Co. KG; *Int'l*, pg. 8328
WAGO ELECTRONIC PTE LTD.—See WAGO Kontakttechnik GmbH & Co. KG; *Int'l*, pg. 8328
WAGO ELECTRONIC (TIANJIN) CO. LTD—See WAGO Kontakttechnik GmbH & Co. KG; *Int'l*, pg. 8328
WAGO ELEKTRONIK SANAYI VE TICARET LTD. STI.—See WAGO Kontakttechnik GmbH & Co. KG; *Int'l*, pg. 8328
WAGO ELEKTRO SPOL. SR. O.—See WAGO Kontakttechnik GmbH & Co. KG; *Int'l*, pg. 8328
WAGO ELETROELETRONICOS LTDA—See WAGO Kontakttechnik GmbH & Co. KG; *Int'l*, pg. 8328
WAGO ELETTRONICA SRL—See WAGO Kontakttechnik GmbH & Co. KG; *Int'l*, pg. 8328

WAGO ELWAG SP. Z O. O.—See WAGO Kontakttechnik GmbH & Co. KG; *Int'l*, pg. 8328
WAGO FINLAND OY—See WAGO Kontakttechnik GmbH & Co. KG; *Int'l*, pg. 8328
WAGO HUNGARIA KFT—See WAGO Kontakttechnik GmbH & Co. KG; *Int'l*, pg. 8328
WAGO KONTAKTTECHNIK GES.M.B.H.—See WAGO Kontakttechnik GmbH & Co. KG; *Int'l*, pg. 8328
WAGO KONTAKTTECHNIK GMBH & CO. KG; *Int'l*, pg. 8327
WAGO KOREA CO., LTD.—See WAGO Kontakttechnik GmbH & Co. KG; *Int'l*, pg. 8328
WAGOKORO CO., LTD.; *Int'l*, pg. 8328
WAGO LIMITED—See WAGO Kontakttechnik GmbH & Co. KG; *Int'l*, pg. 8328
WAGO MIDDLE EAST (FZC)—See WAGO Kontakttechnik GmbH & Co. KG; *Int'l*, pg. 8328
WAGO NEDERLAND B.V.—See WAGO Kontakttechnik GmbH & Co. KG; *Int'l*, pg. 8328
WAGO NORGE AS—See WAGO Kontakttechnik GmbH & Co. KG; *Int'l*, pg. 8328
WAGON SERVICE S.R.O.—See OBB-Holding AG; *Int'l*, pg. 5510
WAGON WHEEL REALTY, LLC—See The TJX Companies, Inc.; *U.S. Public*, pg. 2134
WAGONYSWIDNICA S.A.—See The Greenbrier Companies, Inc.; *U.S. Public*, pg. 2086
WAGONYSWIDNICA SP. Z O.O.—See The Greenbrier Companies, Inc.; *U.S. Public*, pg. 2086
WAGO PTY. LTD.—See WAGO Kontakttechnik GmbH & Co. KG; *Int'l*, pg. 8328
WAGO SA DE CV—See WAGO Kontakttechnik GmbH & Co. KG; *Int'l*, pg. 8328
WAGO SVERIGE AB—See WAGO Kontakttechnik GmbH & Co. KG; *Int'l*, pg. 8328
W.A.G. PAYMENT SOLUTIONS, A.S.—See W.A.G Payment Solutions Plc; *Int'l*, pg. 8321
W.A.G. PAYMENT SOLUTIONS BG EOOD—See W.A.G Payment Solutions Plc; *Int'l*, pg. 8321
W.A.G. PAYMENT SOLUTIONS DE GMBH—See W.A.G Payment Solutions Plc; *Int'l*, pg. 8321
W.A.G. PAYMENT SOLUTIONS LT, UAB—See W.A.G Payment Solutions Plc; *Int'l*, pg. 8321
W.A.G PAYMENT SOLUTIONS PLC; *Int'l*, pg. 8321
W.A.G. PAYMENT SOLUTIONS RO, S.R.L.—See W.A.G Payment Solutions Plc; *Int'l*, pg. 8321
WAGRAM EQUITY PARTNERS BV; *Int'l*, pg. 8328
WAG SALZGITTER WOHNUNGS-GMBH—See TUI AG; *Int'l*, pg. 7969
WAGSTAFF INC.; *U.S. Private*, pg. 4426
WAGUESPACK OIL CO. INC.; *U.S. Private*, pg. 4426
WAHA CAPITAL PJSC; *Int'l*, pg. 8330
WAHA ELECTRIC SUPPLY COMPANY OF SAUDI ARABIA—See Ali Zaid Al-Quraishi & Brothers Co.; *Int'l*, pg. 323
WAHAH ELECTRIC SUPPLY COMPANY OF SAUDI ARABIA LIMITED—See Electrical Industries Company; *Int'l*, pg. 2350
WAHANA PRONATURAL TBK; *Int'l*, pg. 8330
WAH FU EDUCATION GROUP LIMITED; *Int'l*, pg. 8328
WAH HA CONSTRUCTION COMPANY LIMITED—See Wah Ha Realty Company Limited; *Int'l*, pg. 8328
WAH HA REALTY COMPANY LIMITED; *Int'l*, pg. 8328
WAH HONG INDUSTRIAL CORP.; *Int'l*, pg. 8328
WAH KWONG MARITIME TRANSPORT HOLDINGS LIMITED; *Int'l*, pg. 8329
WAHL CLIPPER CORPORATION; *U.S. Private*, pg. 4426
WAH LEE INDUSTRIAL CORP.; *Int'l*, pg. 8329
WAH LEE JAPAN CORP.—See Wah Lee Industrial Corp.; *Int'l*, pg. 8329
WAH LEE KOREA LTD.—See Wah Lee Industrial Corp.; *Int'l*, pg. 8329
WAH LEE PHILIPPINES INC.—See Wah Lee Industrial Corp.; *Int'l*, pg. 8329
WAH LEE PHILIPPINES INTERNATIONAL CORP.—See Wah Lee Industrial Corp.; *Int'l*, pg. 8329
WAH LEE TECH (SINGAPORE) A PTE. LTD.—See Wah Lee Industrial Corp.; *Int'l*, pg. 8329
WAH LEE TECH(SINGAPORE) PTE. LTD—See Wah Lee Industrial Corp.; *Int'l*, pg. 8329
WAH LEE VIETNAM CO., LTD.—See Wah Lee Industrial Corp.; *Int'l*, pg. 8329
WAH LOON ENGINEERING PTE. LTD.—See VINCI S.A.; *Int'l*, pg. 8240
WAH LOON (M) SDN. BHD.—See VINCI S.A.; *Int'l*, pg. 8240
WAHL REFRACTORY SOLUTIONS, LLC; *U.S. Private*, pg. 4426
WAHLSTROM GROUP—See The Interpublic Group of Companies, Inc.; *U.S. Public*, pg. 2096
WAHLSTROM GROUP—See The Interpublic Group of Companies, Inc.; *U.S. Public*, pg. 2096
WAHLSTROM GROUP—See The Interpublic Group of Companies, Inc.; *U.S. Public*, pg. 2096
WAH MA TECHNOLOGY SDN. BHD.—See Wah Hong Industrial Corp.; *Int'l*, pg. 8329
WAH MIE TRADING SDN. BHD.—See WMG Holdings Berhad; *Int'l*, pg. 8441

WAH NOBEL ACETATES LTD.—See WAH NOBEL CHEMICALS LIMITED; *Int'l*, pg. 8329
WAH NOBEL CHEMICALS LIMITED; *Int'l*, pg. 8329
W.A. HOLDING COMPANY—See KSL Capital Partners, LLC; *U.S. Private*, pg. 2355
WAH SENG FAR EAST LTD.—See Bridgestone Corporation; *Int'l*, pg. 1160
WAH SEONG CHINA LIMITED—See Wah Seong Corporation Berhad; *Int'l*, pg. 8330
WAH SEONG CORPORATION BERHAD; *Int'l*, pg. 8329
WAH SHING TOYS COMPANY LIMITED—See South China Holdings Company Limited; *Int'l*, pg. 7116
WAH SUN HANDBAGS INTERNATIONAL HOLDINGS LIMITED; *Int'l*, pg. 8330
WAH SUN HK FACTORY (CAMBODIA) CO., LTD.—See Wah Sun Handbags International Holdings Limited; *Int'l*, pg. 8330
WAH TECH INDUSTRIAL CO., LTD.—See Wah Lee Industrial Corp.; *Int'l*, pg. 8329
WAH WO HOLDINGS GROUP LIMITED; *Int'l*, pg. 8330
WAH YUET HONG KONG LIMITED—See dormakaba Holding AG; *Int'l*, pg. 2178
WAH YUET INDUSTRIAL COMPANY LIMITED—See dormakaba Holding AG; *Int'l*, pg. 2178
WAIANAE DISTRICT COMPREHENSIVE HEALTH & HOSPITAL BOARD, INCORPORATED; *U.S. Private*, pg. 4426
WAI CAPITAL INVESTMENTS CORP.; *Int'l*, pg. 8330
WAI CHI HOLDINGS COMPANY LIMITED; *Int'l*, pg. 8330
WAI CHI OPTO TECHNOLOGY (SHENZHEN) LIMITED—See Wai Chi Holdings Company Limited; *Int'l*, pg. 8331
WAI CHUN BIO-TECHNOLOGY LIMITED; *Int'l*, pg. 8331
WAI CHUN GROUP HOLDINGS LIMITED; *Int'l*, pg. 8331
WAIDA MFG. CO., LTD. - GIFU PLANT—See WAIDA MFG. CO., LTD.; *Int'l*, pg. 8331
WAIDA MFG. CO., LTD.; *Int'l*, pg. 8331
WAID CORP.—See Keystone Group, L.P.; *U.S. Private*, pg. 2299
WAI EUROPE B.V.—See Wetherill Associates Inc.; *U.S. Private*, pg. 4502
WAIFE & ASSOCIATES, INC.—See Leonard Green & Partners, L.P.; *U.S. Private*, pg. 2430
WAI GLOBAL—See Wetherill Associates Inc.; *U.S. Private*, pg. 4502
WAIHI MEDICAL CENTRE LIMITED—See Green Cross Health Limited; *Int'l*, pg. 3070
WAI HUNG GROUP HOLDINGS LTD; *Int'l*, pg. 8331
WAI HUNG HONG ENGINEERING COMPANY LIMITED—See Wai Hung Group Holdings Ltd; *Int'l*, pg. 8331
WAI HUNG HONG ENGINEERING (MACAU) CO., LTD.—See Wai Hung Group Holdings Ltd; *Int'l*, pg. 8331
WAIKATO MILKING SYSTEMS IRELAND LTD.—See Interpump Group S.p.A.; *Int'l*, pg. 3757
WAIKATO MILKING SYSTEMS LEASE LTD.—See Interpump Group S.p.A.; *Int'l*, pg. 3757
WAIKATO MILKING SYSTEMS LP—See Interpump Group S.p.A.; *Int'l*, pg. 3757
WAIKATO TIMES—See Nine Entertainment Co. Holdings Limited; *Int'l*, pg. 5298
WAI KEE HOLDINGS LIMITED; *Int'l*, pg. 8331
WAIKELE GOLF CLUB INC.—See Walton Street Capital, LLC; *U.S. Private*, pg. 4435
WAIKEM, GEORGE FORD, INC.; *U.S. Private*, pg. 4426
WAIKIKI RESORT HOTEL, INC.—See Korean Air Lines Co., Ltd.; *Int'l*, pg. 4288
WAILUKU AGRIBUSINESS CO., INC.—See C. Brewer & Co. Ltd.; *U.S. Private*, pg. 705
WA, INC.; *Int'l*, pg. 8322
WAINHOMES (NORTHERN) LIMITED—See Taylor Wimpey plc; *Int'l*, pg. 7478
WAINHOMES (SOUTHERN) LIMITED—See Taylor Wimpey plc; *Int'l*, pg. 7478
WAINWRIGHT INDUSTRIES, INCORPORATED—See TVS Logistics Services Ltd.; *Int'l*, pg. 7989
WAI ON SERVICE LIMITED—See Digital China Holdings Limited; *Int'l*, pg. 2121
WAIPARA HILLS WINE—See The Carlyle Group Inc.; *U.S. Public*, pg. 2044
WAITAKI INTERNATIONAL LTD—See Alliance Group Limited; *Int'l*, pg. 339
WAITE SPECIALTY MACHINE, INC.; *U.S. Private*, pg. 4426
WAITEX INTERNATIONAL CO. LTD; *U.S. Private*, pg. 4427
WAITOMO CAVES LIMITED—See Tourism Holdings Limited; *Int'l*, pg. 7848
WAITR HOLDINGS INC.; *U.S. Public*, pg. 2321
WAITROSE LIMITED—See John Lewis Partnership plc; *Int'l*, pg. 3979
WAITTCORP LLC; *U.S. Private*, pg. 4427
WAI YUEN TONG MEDICINE COMPANY LIMITED—See Wang On Group Ltd; *Int'l*, pg. 8341
WAI YUEN TONG MEDICINE HOLDINGS LIMITED—See Wang On Group Ltd; *Int'l*, pg. 8341
WAJA KONSORTIUM BERHAD; *Int'l*, pg. 8331
WAJAX CORPORATION; *Int'l*, pg. 8331

WAJAX EQUIPMENT—See Wajax Corporation; *Int'l*, pg. 8331
WAJAX INDUSTRIAL COMPONENTS—See Wajax Corporation; *Int'l*, pg. 8331
WAJAX INDUSTRIAL COMPONENTS—See Wajax Corporation; *Int'l*, pg. 8331
WAJAX INDUSTRIAL COMPONENTS—See Wajax Corporation; *Int'l*, pg. 8331
WAJAX INDUSTRIAL COMPONENTS—See Wajax Corporation; *Int'l*, pg. 8331
WAJAX INDUSTRIAL COMPONENTS—See Wajax Corporation; *Int'l*, pg. 8331
WAJAX POWER SYSTEMS—See Wajax Corporation; *Int'l*, pg. 8332
WAKACHIKU CONSTRUCTION CO., LTD.; *Int'l*, pg. 8332
WAKACJE.PL S.A.—See Wirtualna Polska Holding S.A.; *Int'l*, pg. 8434
WAKAMATSU GAS K.K.—See Idemitsu Kosan Co., Ltd.; *Int'l*, pg. 3592
WAKAMATSU KONPOU UNYU SOKO, INC.—See Daiwa House Industry Co., Ltd.; *Int'l*, pg. 1947
WAKAMOTO PHARMACEUTICAL CO., LTD.; *Int'l*, pg. 8332
WA KAOLIN LIMITED; *Int'l*, pg. 8322
WAKARUSA AG LLC—See Tym Corporation; *Int'l*, pg. 7995
WAKASU CO., LTD.—See The Sumitomo Warehouse Co. Ltd.; *Int'l*, pg. 7690
WAKAYAMA GARDEN CREATE CO. LTD.—See Takasho Co.,Ltd.; *Int'l*, pg. 7436
WAKAYAMA HINO MOTOR LTD.—See Toyota Motor Corporation; *Int'l*, pg. 7872
WAKAYAMA ICOM INC.—See ICOM INCORPORATED; *Int'l*, pg. 3583
WAKAYAMA PETROLEUM REFINING CO., LTD.—See ENEOS Holdings, Inc.; *Int'l*, pg. 2417
WAKAYAMA SANGYO CO., LTD.—See Kato Sangyo Co., Ltd.; *Int'l*, pg. 4090
WAKAYAMA STATION BUILDING CO., LTD.—See West Japan Railway Company; *Int'l*, pg. 8385
WAKAYAMA TERMINAL BUILDING CO., LTD.—See West Japan Railway Company; *Int'l*, pg. 8385
WAKAYANAGI TAMURA CORPORATION—See Tamura Corporation; *Int'l*, pg. 7452
WAKAZURU ENTERPRISES INC.; *U.S. Private*, pg. 4427
WAKE COUNTY MEDICAL SOCIETY; *U.S. Private*, pg. 4427
WAKE COUNTY SMARTSTART, INC.; *U.S. Private*, pg. 4427
WAKEFELD MUNICIPAL GAS LIGHT DEPARTMENT; *U.S. Private*, pg. 4427
WAKEFERN FOOD CORPORATION; *U.S. Private*, pg. 4427
WAKEFIELD & ASSOCIATES, LLC; *U.S. Private*, pg. 4427
WAKEFIELD CANADA INC. - EDMONTON WAREHOUSE FACILITY—See Wakefield Canada Inc.; *Int'l*, pg. 8332
WAKEFIELD CANADA INC. - LAVAL WAREHOUSE FACILITY—See Wakefield Canada Inc.; *Int'l*, pg. 8332
WAKEFIELD CANADA INC.; *Int'l*, pg. 8332
WAKEFIELD CANADA INC. - VANCOUVER WAREHOUSE FACILITY—See Wakefield Canada Inc.; *Int'l*, pg. 8332
WAKEFIELD DISTRIBUTION SYSTEMS; *U.S. Private*, pg. 4427
WAKEFIELD OBSERVER—See Gannett Co., Inc.; *U.S. Public*, pg. 903
WAKEFIELDS INC.; *U.S. Private*, pg. 4427
WAKEFIELD THERMAL SOLUTIONS—See The Heico Companies, L.L.C.; *U.S. Private*, pg. 4051
WAKEFIELD-VETTE, INC. - COOLCENTRIC DIVISION—See The Heico Companies, L.L.C.; *U.S. Private*, pg. 4051
WAKEFIELD-VETTE, INC.—See The Heico Companies, L.L.C.; *U.S. Private*, pg. 4051
WAKEFLY; *U.S. Private*, pg. 4427
WAKE FOREST BANCSHARES, INC.; *U.S. Public*, pg. 2321
WAKE FOREST FEDERAL SAVINGS AND LOAN ASSOCIATION—See Wake Forest Bancshares, Inc.; *U.S. Public*, pg. 2321
WAKELEE ASSOCIATES LLC—See Kelso & Company, L.P.; *U.S. Private*, pg. 2278
WAKEMED; *U.S. Private*, pg. 4427
WAKENBY LIMITED; *Int'l*, pg. 8332
WAKE STONE CORPORATION; *U.S. Private*, pg. 4427
WAKE SUPPLY CO. INC.; *U.S. Private*, pg. 4427
WAKE UP NOW, INC.; *U.S. Public*, pg. 2321
WAKITA & CO., LTD.; *Int'l*, pg. 8332
W.A. KLINGER, LLC.; *U.S. Private*, pg. 4418
WAKMANN WATCH (INTERNATIONAL) COMPANY LIMITED—See Asia Commercial Holdings Limited; *Int'l*, pg. 611
WAKO CO., LTD.—See Seiko Group Corporation; *Int'l*, pg. 6689
WAKODO CO., LTD.—See Asahi Group Holdings Ltd.; *Int'l*, pg. 594
WAKOL ADHESA AG—See Wakol GmbH; *Int'l*, pg. 8332
WAKOL FORECO SRL—See Wakol GmbH; *Int'l*, pg. 8332
WAKOL GMBH; *Int'l*, pg. 8332
WAKOL GMBH—See Wakol GmbH; *Int'l*, pg. 8332

COMPANY NAME INDEX

WAKONI DIALYSIS, LLC—See DaVita Inc.; *U.S. Public*, pg. 644
WAKO TOSHI KAIHATSU CO., LTD.—See Nippon Kayaku Co., Ltd.; *Int'l*, pg. 5321
WAKOU SHOKUHIN CO., LTD.; *Int'l*, pg. 8332
WAKOU USA INC.—See Wakou Shokuhin Co., Ltd.; *Int'l*, pg. 8332
WAKUNAGA AGRICULTURAL DEVELOPMENT CO., LTD.—See Wakunaga Pharmaceutical Co., Ltd.; *Int'l*, pg. 8332
WAKUNAGA OF AMERICA CO., LTD.—See Wakunaga Pharmaceutical Co., Ltd.; *Int'l*, pg. 8332
WAKUNAGA PHARMACEUTICAL CO., LTD.; *Int'l*, pg. 8332
WAKURA MURATA MANUFACTURING CO., LTD.—See Murata Manufacturing Co., Ltd.; *Int'l*, pg. 5099
WAKUWAKU JAPAN CORPORATION—See SKY Perfect JSAT Holdings Inc.; *Int'l*, pg. 6993
WALAA COOPERATIVE INSURANCE COMPANY; *Int'l*, pg. 8332
WALAA COOPERATIVE INSURANCE CO; *Int'l*, pg. 8332
WALA, INC.—See Data443 Risk Mitigation, Inc.; *U.S. Public*, pg. 635
WALA-TV—See Meredith Corporation; *U.S. Public*, pg. 1423
WALBAR INC.—See RTX Corporation; *U.S. Public*, pg. 1822
WALBERER AUTOMATEN GMBH & CO. KG—See Gauselmann AG; *Int'l*, pg. 2890
WALB, LLC—See Gray Television, Inc.; *U.S. Public*, pg. 959
WALBON AND COMPANY INC.; *U.S. Private*, pg. 4427
WAL-BON OF OHIO, INC.; *U.S. Private*, pg. 4427
WALBRIDGE ALDINGER LLC; *U.S. Private*, pg. 4427
WALBROOK MILL & LUMBER CO. INC.; *U.S. Private*, pg. 4427
WALCHANDNAGAR INDUSTRIES LTD - FOUNDRY—See Walchandnagar Industries Ltd.; *Int'l*, pg. 8332
WALCHANDNAGAR INDUSTRIES LTD - PRECISION INSTRUMENT DIVISION—See Walchandnagar Industries Ltd.; *Int'l*, pg. 8332
WALCHANDNAGAR INDUSTRIES LTD.; *Int'l*, pg. 8332
WALCHANDNAGAR INDUSTRIES LTD - TIWAC DIVISION—See Walchandnagar Industries Ltd.; *Int'l*, pg. 8332
WALCHANDNAGAR INDUSTRIES LTD - WALCHANDNAGAR INDUSTRIES LTD. OIL AND GAS DIVISION—See Walchandnagar Industries Ltd.; *Int'l*, pg. 8332
WALCHAND PEOPLEFIRST LIMITED; *Int'l*, pg. 8332
WALCHEM—See Iwaki Co., Ltd.; *Int'l*, pg. 3849
WALCHERSE BOUWUNIE B.V.—See Heijmans N.V.; *Int'l*, pg. 3322
WALCHERSE BOUWUNIE B.V.—See Heijmans N.V.; *Int'l*, pg. 3323
WALCO MACHINES COMPANY INC.—See Chargeurs SA; *Int'l*, pg. 1450
WALCOM BIO-CHEMICALS INDUSTRIAL LIMITED—See Walcom Group Limited; *Int'l*, pg. 8333
WALCOM GROUP LIMITED; *Int'l*, pg. 8333
WALCOTT DIALYSIS, LLC—See DaVita Inc.; *U.S. Public*, pg. 644
WALCOWNIA METALI LABEDY S.A.—See KGHM Polska Miedz S.A.; *Int'l*, pg. 4149
WALCOWNIA METALI NIEZELAZNYCH SP. Z O.O.—See KGHM Polska Miedz S.A.; *Int'l*, pg. 4149
WALCRO, INC.—See ShoreView Industries, LLC; *U.S. Private*, pg. 3642
WALDBAUM'S SUPERMARKETS, INC.—See The Great Atlantic & Pacific Tea Company, Inc.; *U.S. Private*, pg. 4038
WALD + CORBE CONSULTING GMBH—See BKW AG; *Int'l*, pg. 1056
WALDENBURGER VERSICHERUNG AG—See Wurth Verwaltungsgesellschaft mbH; *Int'l*, pg. 8508
WALDEN CAPITAL ADVISORS, LLC—See Beacon Pointe Holdings, LLC; *U.S. Private*, pg. 505
WALDENCAST PLC; *U.S. Public*, pg. 2321
WALDEN ENERGY, LLC.; *U.S. Private*, pg. 4427
WALDEN FARMS CANADA—See Hammond, Kennedy, Whitney & Company, Inc.; *U.S. Private*, pg. 1850
WALDEN FARMS, LLC—See Hammond, Kennedy, Whitney & Company, Inc.; *U.S. Private*, pg. 1850
WALDEN GREEN ENERGY LLC—See RWE AG; *Int'l*, pg. 6436
WALDEN GROUP; *Int'l*, pg. 8333
WALDEN MEDIA, LLC—See The Anschutz Corporation; *U.S. Private*, pg. 3987
WALDEN RENEWABLES DEVELOPMENT LLC—See RWE AG; *Int'l*, pg. 6436
WALDEN SAVINGS BANKS; *U.S. Private*, pg. 4428
WALDEN SECURITY COMPANY; *U.S. Private*, pg. 4428
WALDEN'S MACHINE LLC—See Berkshire Hathaway Inc.; *U.S. Public*, pg. 314
WALDEN VENTURE CAPITAL; *U.S. Private*, pg. 4428
THE WALDINGER CORPORATION; *U.S. Private*, pg. 4133
WALDO BROS. COMPANY—See Waldo Bros. Company; *U.S. Private*, pg. 4428

WALDO BROS. COMPANY; *U.S. Private*, pg. 4428
WALDO IMPLEMENT INC.—See Tym Corporation; *Int'l*, pg. 7995
WALDON ELECTRICAL CONTRACTORS LIMITED—See Regent Gas Holdings Limited; *Int'l*, pg. 6252
WALDON STUDIO ARCHITECTS & PLANNERS, PC—See Michael Graves & Associates, Inc.; *U.S. Private*, pg. 2698
WALDORF ASTORIA MANAGEMENT LLC—See Hilton Worldwide Holdings Inc.; *U.S. Public*, pg. 1041
THE WALDORF ENDOSCOPY ASC, LLC—See KKR & Co. Inc.; *U.S. Public*, pg. 1248
WALDORF FORD INC.; *U.S. Private*, pg. 4428
WALDRICH COBURG WERKZEUGMASCHINENFABRIK GMBH—See Beijing Jingcheng Machinery Electric Holding Co., Ltd.; *Int'l*, pg. 953
WALDRON & COMPANY; *U.S. Private*, pg. 4428
WALDROP CONSTRUCTION CO. INC.; *U.S. Private*, pg. 4428
WALDROP ENGINEERING, P.A.—See Atwell, LLC; *U.S. Private*, pg. 384
WALD & SCHLOSSHOTEL FRIEDRICHSRUHE—See Wurth Verwaltungsgesellschaft mbH; *Int'l*, pg. 8506
WALEED CATERING & SERVICES CO. LLC—See Omar Zawawi Establishment LLC; *Int'l*, pg. 5561
WALEED COMMUNICATIONS CO. (WACOM) LTD.—See Omar Zawawi Establishment LLC; *Int'l*, pg. 5561
WALEED PHARMACY & STORES LLC—See Omar Zawawi Establishment LLC; *Int'l*, pg. 5561
WALEK & ASSOCIATES—See Peppercom, Inc.; *U.S. Private*, pg. 3145
WALERY SECURITY MANAGEMENT LTD.—See Mercantile Ventures Limited; *Int'l*, pg. 4819
WALGREEN ARIZONA DRUG CO.—See Walgreens Boots Alliance, Inc.; *U.S. Public*, pg. 2323
WALGREEN CO.—See Walgreens Boots Alliance, Inc.; *U.S. Public*, pg. 2323
WALGREEN EASTERN CO., INC.—See Walgreens Boots Alliance, Inc.; *U.S. Public*, pg. 2323
WALGREEN HASTINGS CO.—See Walgreens Boots Alliance, Inc.; *U.S. Public*, pg. 2323
WALGREEN LOUISIANA CO., INC.—See Walgreens Boots Alliance, Inc.; *U.S. Public*, pg. 2323
WALGREEN MEDICAL SUPPLY, LLC—See Walgreens Boots Alliance, Inc.; *U.S. Public*, pg. 2324
WALGREEN MERCANTILE CORP.—See Walgreens Boots Alliance, Inc.; *U.S. Public*, pg. 2323
WALGREEN NATIONAL CORPORATION—See Walgreens Boots Alliance, Inc.; *U.S. Public*, pg. 2323
WALGREEN OF HAWAII, LLC—See Walgreens Boots Alliance, Inc.; *U.S. Public*, pg. 2324
WALGREEN OF MAUI, INC.—See Walgreens Boots Alliance, Inc.; *U.S. Public*, pg. 2324
WALGREEN OF PUERTO RICO, INC.—See Walgreens Boots Alliance, Inc.; *U.S. Public*, pg. 2324
WALGREEN OF SAN PATRICIO, INC.—See Walgreens Boots Alliance, Inc.; *U.S. Public*, pg. 2324
WALGREENS BOOTS ALLIANCE, INC.; *U.S. Public*, pg. 2321
WALGREENS.COM, INC.—See Walgreens Boots Alliance, Inc.; *U.S. Public*, pg. 2324
WALGREENS HEALTH SERVICES—See Walgreens Boots Alliance, Inc.; *U.S. Public*, pg. 2324
WALGREENS HEALTH & WELLNESS—See Walgreens Boots Alliance, Inc.; *U.S. Public*, pg. 2324
WALGREENS HOME CARE, INC.—See Option Care Health, Inc.; *U.S. Public*, pg. 1610
WALGREENS MAIL SERVICE, INC.—See Walgreens Boots Alliance, Inc.; *U.S. Public*, pg. 2324
WALGREENS OF NORTH CAROLINA, INC.—See Walgreens Boots Alliance, Inc.; *U.S. Public*, pg. 2324
WALGREENS SPECIALTY CARE CENTERS, LLC—See Walgreens Boots Alliance, Inc.; *U.S. Public*, pg. 2324
WALGREENS SPECIALTY PHARMACY HOLDINGS, INC.—See Walgreens Boots Alliance, Inc.; *U.S. Public*, pg. 2324
WALGREENS SPECIALTY PHARMACY, LLC—See Walgreens Boots Alliance, Inc.; *U.S. Public*, pg. 2324
WALHALLA DELIKATESSEN GMBH—See J. Bauer GmbH & Co. KG; *Int'l*, pg. 3854
WALHALLA KALK GMBH & CO. KG—See Heidelberg Materials AG; *Int'l*, pg. 3320
WALHALLA KALK VERWALTUNGSGESELLSCHAFT MBH—See Heidelberg Materials AG; *Int'l*, pg. 3320
WALIBI HOLLAND BV—See Compagnie des Alpes S.A.; *Int'l*, pg. 1738
WALISCHMILLER ENGINEERING GMBH—See Carr's Group PLC; *Int'l*, pg. 1343
WALITOYS & GARMENT LIMITED—See Kader Holdings Company Limited; *Int'l*, pg. 4047
WALKABOUT RESOURCES LTD; *Int'l*, pg. 8333
THE WALK COMPANY LIMITED—See Index Living Mall Public Company Limited; *Int'l*, pg. 3651
WALKER ADVERTISING, INC.; *U.S. Private*, pg. 4428
THE WALKER AGENCY; *U.S. Private*, pg. 7698
WALKER AGGREGATES INC.—See Walker Industries Holdings Ltd.; *Int'l*, pg. 8333
WALKER & ASSOCIATES, INC.; *U.S. Private*, pg. 4428
WALKER & ASSOCIATES, INC.; *U.S. Private*, pg. 4428

WALKER AUSTRALIA PTY. LIMITED—See Apollo Global Management, Inc.; *U.S. Public*, pg. 163
WALKER AUTO GROUP, INC.; *U.S. Private*, pg. 4428
WALKER AUTOMOTIVE; *U.S. Private*, pg. 4428
WALKER AUTOMOTIVE SUPPLY INC.; *U.S. Private*, pg. 4428
WALKER CANCER CENTER—See Community Health Systems, Inc.; *U.S. Public*, pg. 551
WALKER & COMPANY, INC.; *U.S. Private*, pg. 4428
WALKER COMPONENT GROUP INC.; *U.S. Private*, pg. 4428
WALKER CONCRETE COMPANY INC.; *U.S. Private*, pg. 4428
WALKER CONTRACTING GROUP INC.; *U.S. Private*, pg. 4429
WALKER COUNTY HOSPITAL CORPORATION; *U.S. Private*, pg. 4429
WALKER CRANE & RIGGING CORP.—See US Service Group, LLC; *U.S. Private*, pg. 4320
WALKER CRIPS GROUP PLC; *Int'l*, pg. 8333
WALKER CRIPS STOCKBROKERS LIMITED—See Walker Crips Group plc; *Int'l*, pg. 8333
WALKER CRIPS WEALTH MANAGEMENT LIMITED—See Walker Crips Group plc; *Int'l*, pg. 8333
WALKER, CRIPS, WEDDLE, BECK PLC—See Phillip Capital Pte. Ltd.; *Int'l*, pg. 5847
WALKER DANMARK APS.—See Apollo Global Management, Inc.; *U.S. Public*, pg. 163
WALKER DESIGN GROUP, INC.; *U.S. Private*, pg. 4429
WALKER DIE CASTING, INC.—See Allison Transmission Holdings, Inc.; *U.S. Public*, pg. 81
WALKER & DUNLOP CAPITAL, LLC—See Walker & Dunlop, Inc.; *U.S. Public*, pg. 2324
WALKER & DUNLOP, INC.; *U.S. Public*, pg. 2324
WALKER & DUNLOP INVESTMENT PARTNERS, INC.—See Walker & Dunlop, Inc.; *U.S. Public*, pg. 2324
WALKER & DUNLOP, LLC—See Walker & Dunlop, Inc.; *U.S. Public*, pg. 2324
WALKER EDISON FURNITURE COMPANY LLC—See Prospect Hill Growth Partners, L.P.; *U.S. Private*, pg. 3288
WALKER EMULSIONS INC.—See Walker Industries Holdings Ltd.; *Int'l*, pg. 8333
WALKER EMULSIONS LIMITED—See Walker Industries Holdings Ltd.; *Int'l*, pg. 8333
WALKER EMULSIONS (USA) INC.—See Walker Industries Holdings Ltd.; *Int'l*, pg. 8333
WALKER ENGINEERING, INC.; *U.S. Private*, pg. 4429
WALKER ENVIRONMENTAL - GREASE TRAP, UCO & ORGANIC RECYCLING—See Walker Industries Holdings Ltd.; *Int'l*, pg. 8333
WALKER ENVIRONMENTAL GROUP INC.—See Walker Industries Holdings Ltd.; *Int'l*, pg. 8333
WALKER EXHAUST (THAILAND) CO. LTD.—See Apollo Global Management, Inc.; *U.S. Public*, pg. 163
WALKER FILTRATION INC.—See Atlas Copco AB; *Int'l*, pg. 681
WALKER FILTRATION LIMITED—See Atlas Copco AB; *Int'l*, pg. 681
WALKER FORD CO., INC.; *U.S. Private*, pg. 4429
WALKER FORGE INC.; *U.S. Private*, pg. 4429
WALKER FURNITURE CO.; *U.S. Private*, pg. 4429
WALKER GOLF (SCOTLAND) LIMITED—See Springfield Properties PLC; *Int'l*, pg. 7144
WALKER INDUSTRIAL PRODUCTS, INC.—See Graybar Electric Company, Inc.; *U.S. Private*, pg. 1760
WALKER INDUSTRIES HOLDINGS LTD.; *Int'l*, pg. 8333
WALKER INFORMATION INC.; *U.S. Private*, pg. 4429
WALKER-JONES CHEVROLET-BUICK—See Jones Company, Inc.; *U.S. Private*, pg. 2232
WALKER-J-WALKER, INC.—See EMCOR Group, Inc.; *U.S. Public*, pg. 739
WALKER & LABERGE COMPANY INCORPORATED; *U.S. Private*, pg. 4428
WALKER LANE EXPLORATION, INC.; *U.S. Public*, pg. 2324
WALKER LUMBER COMPANY, INC.—See Hardwoods Distribution Inc.; *Int'l*, pg. 3273
WALKER MAGNETICS GROUP, INC.—See Alliance Holdings, Inc.; *U.S. Private*, pg. 183
WALKER MAGNETICS NATIONAL, LTD.—See Alliance Holdings, Inc.; *U.S. Private*, pg. 183
WALKER MEDIA—See M&C Saatchi plc; *Int'l*, pg. 4611
WALKER MOTOR CO.; *U.S. Private*, pg. 4429
WALKER NATIONAL, INC.—See Alliance Holdings, Inc.; *U.S. Private*, pg. 183
WALKER OLDSMOBILE COMPANY, INC.; *U.S. Private*, pg. 4429
WALKER PARKING CONSULTANTS & ENGINEERS, INC.; *U.S. Private*, pg. 4429
WALKER PRODUCTS INC.; *U.S. Private*, pg. 4429
WALKER RIVER RESOURCES CORP.; *Int'l*, pg. 8333
WALKER SAND & GRAVEL LTD. CO.—See Summit Materials, Inc.; *U.S. Public*, pg. 1960
WALKER SANDS, INC.; *U.S. Private*, pg. 4429
WALKERS CHARNWOOD BAKERY—See Samworth Brothers Ltd.; *Int'l*, pg. 6519

WALKER-SCHORK INTERNATIONAL INC.

WALKER-SCHORK INTERNATIONAL INC.; *U.S. Private,* pg. 4429
WALKERS FURNITURE INC.; *U.S. Private,* pg. 4429
WALKERS GROUP LIMITED—See PepsiCo, Inc.; *U.S. Public,* pg. 1672
WALKER SHOP FOOTWEAR LIMITED—See Vestate Group Holdings Limited; *Int'l,* pg. 8178
WALKERS MIDSHIRE FOODS LIMITED—See Samworth Brothers Ltd.; *Int'l,* pg. 6519
WALKERS SHORTBREAD, INC.—See Walkers Shortbread Ltd.; *Int'l,* pg. 8333
WALKERS SHORTBREAD LTD.; *Int'l,* pg. 8333
WALKERS SNACK FOODS LIMITED—See PepsiCo, Inc.; *U.S. Public,* pg. 1672
WALKER'S SUPPLY COMPANY INC.—See Wallace Hardware Company, Inc.; *U.S. Private,* pg. 4431
WALKERS TOURS LTD.—See John Keells Holdings PLC; *Int'l,* pg. 3979
WALKER STREET IMAGING CARE, INC.—See Tenet Healthcare Corporation; *U.S. Public,* pg. 2005
WALKERTEK INTERACTIVE MARKETING, INC.; *U.S. Private,* pg. 4429
WALKER WIRE & STEEL COMPANY—See ArcelorMittal S.A.; *Int'l,* pg. 545
WALKER & ZANGER, INC - MOUNT VERNON—See Walker & Zanger, Inc.; *U.S. Private,* pg. 4428
WALKER & ZANGER, INC.; *U.S. Private,* pg. 4428
WALKER & ZANGER STONEWORKS—See Walker & Zanger, Inc.; *U.S. Private,* pg. 4428
WALKI GMBH—See Oji Holdings Corporation; *Int'l,* pg. 5538
WALKI GROUP OY—See Oji Holdings Corporation; *Int'l,* pg. 5538
WALKI LTD.—See Oji Holdings Corporation; *Int'l,* pg. 5538
THE WALKING COMPANY HOLDINGS, INC.; *U.S. Private,* pg. 4133
THE WALKING COMPANY, INC.—See The Walking Company Holdings, Inc.; *U.S. Private,* pg. 4133
WALKI OY—See Oji Holdings Corporation; *Int'l,* pg. 5538
WALKME LTD.—See SAP SE; *Int'l,* pg. 6571
WALK-ON PRODUCTS, INC.—See Leggett & Platt, Incorporated; *U.S. Public,* pg. 1304
WALKRO BELGIE NV—See Monaghan Middlebrook Mushrooms Unlimited Company; *Int'l,* pg. 5024
WALKRO BLITTERSWIJCK BV—See Monaghan Middlebrook Mushrooms Unlimited Company; *Int'l,* pg. 5024
WALKRO DEUTSCHLAND & CO. KG—See Monaghan Middlebrook Mushrooms Unlimited Company; *Int'l,* pg. 5024
WALKRO INTERNATIONAL BV—See Monaghan Middlebrook Mushrooms Unlimited Company; *Int'l,* pg. 5024
WALK VASCULAR, LLC—See Abbott Laboratories; *U.S. Public,* pg. 21
WALLABY YOGURT COMPANY, LLC—See Danone; *Int'l,* pg. 1967
WALLACE AUTOMOTIVE MANAGEMENT CORPORATION, INC.; *U.S. Private,* pg. 4430
WALLACE BISHOP PTY LTD; *Int'l,* pg. 8333
WALLACE & CAREY INC.; *Int'l,* pg. 8333
WALLACE CASCADE TRANSPORT, INC.; *U.S. Private,* pg. 4430
WALLACE CHEVROLET, LLC—See Wallace Automotive Management Corporation, Inc.; *U.S. Private,* pg. 4430
WALLACE CHRYSLER JEEP, LLC—See Wallace Automotive Management Corporation, Inc.; *U.S. Private,* pg. 4430
WALLACE & COOK FOOD SALES, INC.; *U.S. Private,* pg. 4430
WALLACE ENGINEERING, INC.—See Comfort Systems USA, Inc.; *U.S. Public,* pg. 543
WALLACE FORD, LLC—See AutoNation, Inc.; *U.S. Public,* pg. 238
WALLACE FORD, LLC—See AutoNation, Inc.; *U.S. Public,* pg. 238
WALLACE FORGE COMPANY INC.; *U.S. Private,* pg. 4430
WALLACE HARDWARE COMPANY, INC.; *U.S. Private,* pg. 4430
WALLACE OIL COMPANY INC; *U.S. Private,* pg. 4431
WALLACE PACKAGING, LLC.; *U.S. Private,* pg. 4431
WALLACE ROBERTS & TODD LLC; *U.S. Private,* pg. 4431
WALLACE SPECIALTY INSURANCE GROUP, LLC.—See Kelso & Company, L.P.; *U.S. Private,* pg. 2280
WALLACE WELCH & WILLINGHAM, INC.—See IMA Financial Group, Inc.; *U.S. Private,* pg. 2044
WALLACH & COMPANY—See LM Funding America, Inc.; *U.S. Public,* pg. 1337
WALLACH SURGICAL DEVICES, INC.; *U.S. Private,* pg. 4431
WALLA WALLA UNION BULLETIN INC.—See Blethen Corporation; *U.S. Private,* pg. 581
WALLBOARD, INC.—See American Securities LLC; *U.S. Private,* pg. 249
WALLBOX N.V.; *Int'l,* pg. 8333
WALLBRIDGE MINING COMPANY LIMITED; *Int'l,* pg. 8334

WALL COLMONOY CORPORATION - AEROBRAZE ENGINEERED TECHNOLOGIES DIVISION—See Wall Colmonoy Corporation; *U.S. Private,* pg. 4429
WALL COLMONOY CORPORATION; *U.S. Private,* pg. 4429
WALL COLMONOY CORPORATION - WALL COLMONOY TECHNOLOGIES DIVISION—See Wall Colmonoy Corporation; *U.S. Private,* pg. 4429
WALL COLMONOY LIMITED—See Wall Colmonoy Corporation; *U.S. Private,* pg. 4429
THE WALL COMPANY; *U.S. Private,* pg. 4133
WALLCUR, LLC—See J.H. Whitney & Co., LLC; *U.S. Private,* pg. 2166
WALLDESIGN INC.; *U.S. Private,* pg. 4431
WALL DRUG STORE INC.; *U.S. Private,* pg. 4430
WALLE CORPORATION - FLEXOGRAPHIC DIVISION—See Walle Corporation; *U.S. Private,* pg. 4431
WALLE CORPORATION - LITHOGRAPHIC DIVISION—See Walle Corporation; *U.S. Private,* pg. 4431
WALLE CORPORATION; *U.S. Private,* pg. 4431
WALLENIUS WILHELMSEN ASA; *Int'l,* pg. 8334
WALLENIUS WILHELMSEN LOGISTICS AMERICAS LLC—See Wallenius Wilhelmsen ASA; *Int'l,* pg. 8334
WALLENIUS WILHELMSEN LOGISTICS AMERICAS LLC—See Wallenius Wilhelmsen ASA; *Int'l,* pg. 8334
WALLENIUS WILHELMSEN LOGISTICS ZEEBRUGGE NV—See Wallenius Wilhelmsen ASA; *Int'l,* pg. 8334
WALLENSTAM AB; *Int'l,* pg. 8334
WALLENSTEIN FEED & SUPPLY LTD.; *Int'l,* pg. 8334
WALLEO, INC.; *Int'l,* pg. 8334
WALLER LANSDEN DORTCH & DAVIS LLP—See Holland & Knight LLP; *U.S. Private,* pg. 1964
WALLEYE CAPITAL, LLC; *U.S. Private,* pg. 4431
WALL FAMILY ENTERPRISE, INC.; *U.S. Private,* pg. 4430
WALL FINANCIAL CORPORATION; *Int'l,* pg. 8333
WALLFORT FINANCIAL SERVICES LTD.; *Int'l,* pg. 8334
WALL GMBH—See JCDecaux S.A.; *Int'l,* pg. 3923
WALLICH & MATTHES BV—See RP Martin Holdings Limited; *Int'l,* pg. 6414
WALLICH & MATTHES DUBAI LIMITED—See RP Martin Holdings Limited; *Int'l,* pg. 6414
WALLICH RESIDENCE PTE. LTD.—See Hong Leong Investment Holdings Pte. Ltd.; *Int'l,* pg. 3468
WALLICK AND VOLK INC.; *U.S. Private,* pg. 4431
THE WALLING CO., INC.—See The Walling Company, Inc.; *U.S. Private,* pg. 4133
THE WALLING COMPANY, INC.; *U.S. Private,* pg. 4133
WALLINGFORD AUTO COMPANY; *U.S. Private,* pg. 4431
WALLINGFORD COFFEE MILLS INC.; *U.S. Private,* pg. 4431
WALLINGFORD DIALYSIS CARE, LLC—See Nautic Partners, LLC; *U.S. Private,* pg. 4431
WALLINGS NURSERY LTD—See Fresca Group Limited; *Int'l,* pg. 2774
WALLIS COMPANIES, INC.; *U.S. Private,* pg. 4431
WALLIS ENERGY CO. INC.—See Wallis Companies, Inc.; *U.S. Private,* pg. 4431
WALLISER KANTONALBANK; *Int'l,* pg. 8334
WALLISMOTOR LJUBLJAJNA D.O.O.—See AutoWallis Public Limited Company; *Int'l,* pg. 732
WALLIS NOMINEES (COMPUTING) PTY. LTD.—See DWS Limited; *Int'l,* pg. 2236
WALLIS OIL CO. INC.—See Wallis Companies, Inc.; *U.S. Private,* pg. 4431
WALLIS STATE BANK INC.; *U.S. Private,* pg. 4431
WALLIS ZRT.; *Int'l,* pg. 8334
WALLIX GROUP SA; *Int'l,* pg. 8334
WALLKILL VALLEY BANCORP INC.; *U.S. Private,* pg. 4431
WALLKILL VALLEY FEDERAL SAVINGS & LOAN ASSOCIATION—See Wallkill Valley Bancorp Inc.; *U.S. Private,* pg. 4431
WALL LENK CORPORATION; *U.S. Private,* pg. 4430
WALLMONKEYS, LLC—See HC Brands; *U.S. Private,* pg. 1888
WALLNER TOOLING/EXPAC INC.; *U.S. Private,* pg. 4431
WALLON IMPRIMEUR S.A.S.—See Nestle S.A.; *Int'l,* pg. 5205
WALLOVER OIL COMPANY INCORPORATED—See Quaker Chemical Corporation; *U.S. Public,* pg. 1747
WALLOWA COUNTY GRAIN GROWERS; *U.S. Private,* pg. 4431
WALLPAPERS-TO-GO, INC.; *U.S. Private,* pg. 4431
WALLS & FUTURES REIT PLC; *Int'l,* pg. 8334
WALLS INDUSTRIES LLC—See V. F. Corporation; *U.S. Public,* pg. 2269
WALL STREET ACCESS CORP.; *U.S. Private,* pg. 4430
WALL STREET ACQUISITIONS CORP.; *U.S. Private,* pg. 4430
WALL STREET COMMUNICATIONS; *U.S. Private,* pg. 4430
WALL STREET CONCEPTS—See Fidelity National Infor; *U.S. Public,* pg. 832
WALL STREET DELI, INC.—See TruFoods LLC; *U.S. Private,* pg. 4249

WALL STREET ENGLISH LIMITED LIABILITY COMPANY—See Asia Strategic Holdings Limited; *Int'l,* pg. 615
WALL STREET ENGLISH (THAILAND) CO., LTD.—See Wave Exponential Public Company Limited; *Int'l,* pg. 8359
WALL STREET EXCHANGE CENTRE L.L.C—See Emirates Post; *Int'l,* pg. 2382
WALL STREET FINANCIAL GROUP—See Reverence Capital Partners LLC; *U.S. Private,* pg. 3415
WALL STREET FOREX LONDON LTD—See Emirates Post; *Int'l,* pg. 2382
WALL STREET INSTITUTE INTERNATIONAL INC—See Pearson plc; *Int'l,* pg. 5778
WALL STREET INSURANCE INC.—See ABRY Partners, LLC; *U.S. Private,* pg. 42
THE WALL STREET JOURNAL ASIA—See News Corporation; *U.S. Public,* pg. 1518
THE WALL STREET JOURNAL EUROPE S.P.R.L.—See News Corporation; *U.S. Public,* pg. 1519
THE WALL STREET JOURNAL—See News Corporation; *U.S. Public,* pg. 1518
WALL STREET MANAGER, LLC—See Hyatt Hotels Corporation; *U.S. Public,* pg. 1078
WALL STREET NETWORK SOLUTIONS; *U.S. Private,* pg. 4430
WALLSTREET SECURITIES, INC.; *U.S. Public,* pg. 2324
WALL STREET SECURITIES JOINT STOCK COMPANY; *Int'l,* pg. 8333
WALL STREET SYSTEMS INC.—See ION Investment Group Ltd.; *Int'l,* pg. 3794
WALL STREET SYSTEMS INC.; *U.S. Private,* pg. 4430
WALL STREET TULLETT PREBON LIMITED—See TP ICAP Finance PLC; *Int'l,* pg. 7882
WALL STREET TULLETT PREBON SECURITIES LIMITED—See TP ICAP Finance PLC; *Int'l,* pg. 7882
WALL SYSTEMS, INC.; *U.S. Private,* pg. 4430
WALL-TECH, INC.; *U.S. Private,* pg. 4430
WALL TIMBER PRODUCTS INC.; *U.S. Private,* pg. 4430
WALL TO WALL MEDIA LIMITED—See Warner Bros. Discovery, Inc.; *U.S. Public,* pg. 2329
WALLWIN ELECTRIC SERVICES LTD.; *Int'l,* pg. 8334
WALLWORK CURRY MCKENNA; *U.S. Private,* pg. 4431
WALLWORK FINANCIAL CORP.—See W.W. Wallwork, Inc.; *U.S. Private,* pg. 4423
WALL WORKS USA INC.; *U.S. Private,* pg. 4430
WALLY FINDLAY GALLERIES, INC.—See Wally Findlay Galleries International Inc; *U.S. Private,* pg. 4431
WALLY FINDLAY GALLERIES, INC.—See Wally Findlay Galleries International Inc; *U.S. Private,* pg. 4431
WALLY FINDLAY GALLERIES INTERNATIONAL INC; *U.S. Private,* pg. 4431
WALLY MCCARTHY'S CADILLAC; *U.S. Private,* pg. 4431
WALLY WORLD MEDIA, INC.; *U.S. Public,* pg. 2324
THE WALMAN INSTRUMENT GROUP—See Walman Optical Company; *U.S. Private,* pg. 4432
WALMAN OPTICAL COMPANY - IMAGEWEAR DIVISION—See Walman Optical Company; *U.S. Private,* pg. 4432
WALMAN OPTICAL COMPANY; *U.S. Private,* pg. 4431
WAL-MARK CONTRACTING GROUP INC.—See National Construction Enterprises Inc.; *U.S. Private,* pg. 2851
WAL-MART CANADA CORP.—See Walmart Inc.; *U.S. Public,* pg. 2325
WALMART CHILE S.A.—See Walmart Inc.; *U.S. Public,* pg. 2325
WALMART.COM—See Walmart Inc.; *U.S. Public,* pg. 2325
WAL-MART DE MEXICO, S.A. DE C.V.—See Walmart Inc.; *U.S. Public,* pg. 2325
WAL-MART DISTRIBUTION CENTER 6012—See Walmart Inc.; *U.S. Public,* pg. 2325
WAL-MART DISTRIBUTION CENTER—See Walmart Inc.; *U.S. Public,* pg. 2325
WAL-MART DISTRIBUTION CENTER—See Walmart Inc.; *U.S. Public,* pg. 2325
WAL-MART DISTRIBUTION CENTER—See Walmart Inc.; *U.S. Public,* pg. 2325
WAL-MART DISTRIBUTION CENTER—See Walmart Inc.; *U.S. Public,* pg. 2325
WAL-MART DISTRIBUTION CENTER—See Walmart Inc.; *U.S. Public,* pg. 2325
WAL-MART DISTRIBUTION CENTER—See Walmart Inc.; *U.S. Public,* pg. 2325
WAL-MART DISTRIBUTION CENTER—See Walmart Inc.; *U.S. Public,* pg. 2325
WAL-MART DISTRIBUTION CENTER—See Walmart Inc.; *U.S. Public,* pg. 2325
WAL-MART DISTRIBUTION CENTER—See Walmart Inc.; *U.S. Public,* pg. 2325
WAL-MART DISTRIBUTION CENTER—See Walmart Inc.; *U.S. Public,* pg. 2325
WALMART INC. - INTERNATIONAL DIVISION—See Walmart Inc.; *U.S. Public,* pg. 2325
WALMART INC.; *U.S. Public,* pg. 2324
WAL-MART JAPAN HOLDINGS K.K.—See KKR & Co. Inc.; *U.S. Public,* pg. 1267
WAL-MART LABS—See Walmart Inc.; *U.S. Public,* pg. 2325
WAL-MART REAL ESTATE BUSINESS TRUST—See Walmart Inc.; *U.S. Public,* pg. 2325

COMPANY NAME INDEX

WAL-MART REALTY COMPANY—See Walmart Inc.; *U.S. Public*, pg. 2325
WAL-MART STORES EAST, LP—See Walmart Inc.; *U.S. Public*, pg. 2325
WAL-MART STORES TEXAS, LLC—See Walmart Inc.; *U.S. Public*, pg. 2325
WALMSLEY PARK (LEIGH) MANAGEMENT COMPANY LIMITED—See Persimmon plc; *Int'l*, pg. 5818
WALNUT CAPITAL LIMITED; *Int'l*, pg. 8334
WALNUT CIRCLE PRESS, INC.—See Chatham Asset Management, LLC; *U.S. Private*, pg. 866
WALNUT CREEK ASSOCIATES; *U.S. Private*, pg. 4432
THE WALNUT GROUP; *U.S. Private*, pg. 4133
WALNUT HIGHLANDER—See Alden Global Capital LLC; *U.S. Private*, pg. 158
WALNUT HILLS PRESERVATION, L.P.—See Apartment Investment and Management Company; *U.S. Public*, pg. 144
WALNUT INVESTMENT CORP.; *U.S. Private*, pg. 4432
WALNUTS AUSTRALIA PTY. LTD.—See Public Sector Pension Investment Board; *Int'l*, pg. 6097
WALNUT STREET ABSTRACT, L.P.—See Pennsylvania Real Estate Investment Trust; *U.S. Public*, pg. 1664
WALNUT STREET THEATRE CORPORATION; *U.S. Private*, pg. 4432
WALON B.V.—See DBAY Advisors Limited; *Int'l*, pg. 1986
WALON CZ S.R.O.—See DBAY Advisors Limited; *Int'l*, pg. 1986
WALOP LTD.—See Citizen Watch Co., Ltd.; *Int'l*, pg. 1625
WALPA GESELLSCHAFT FUR UBERSEE- UND SPEZIALVERPACKUNG MBH—See Deufol SE; *Int'l*, pg. 2049
WALPAR LLC—See Rock Gate Partners LLC; *U.S. Private*, pg. 3464
WALPAR NUTRITIONS LIMITED; *Int'l*, pg. 8334
WALPOLE COOPERATIVE BANK; *U.S. Private*, pg. 4432
WALPOLE INC.; *U.S. Private*, pg. 4432
WALPOLE LEASING COMPANY—See Walpole Inc.; *U.S. Private*, pg. 4432
WALPOLE WOODWORKERS, INC.; *U.S. Private*, pg. 4432
WALRUS CORPORATION—See Clyde, Inc.; *U.S. Private*, pg. 949
WALRUS; *U.S. Private*, pg. 4432
WALSDORF AGENCY, INC.—See Arthur J. Gallagher & Co.; *U.S. Public*, pg. 208
WALSER AUTOMOTIVE GROUP, LLC; *U.S. Private*, pg. 4432
WALSER BURNSVILLE M, LLC—See Walser Automotive Group, LLC; *U.S. Private*, pg. 4432
WALSER BURNSVILLE MOTORS, LLC—See Walser Automotive Group, LLC; *U.S. Private*, pg. 4432
WALSER H., LLC—See Walser Automotive Group, LLC; *U.S. Private*, pg. 4432
WALSER HY., LLC—See Walser Automotive Group, LLC; *U.S. Private*, pg. 4432
WALSER PRIVATBANK AG; *Int'l*, pg. 8334
WALSH ADVERTISING INC.; *U.S. Private*, pg. 4432
WALSH & ALBERT COMPANY, LTD.; *U.S. Private*, pg. 4432
WALSH & ASSOCIATES, INC.; *U.S. Private*, pg. 4432
WALSH - BLYTH & TURTON WHOLESALE—See Bunzl plc; *Int'l*, pg. 1217
WALSH BROTHERS INC.; *U.S. Private*, pg. 4432
WALSH COLORADO SPRINGS—See WSP Global, Inc.; *Int'l*, pg. 8496
WALSH CONSTRUCTION CO. OF ILLINOIS—See The Walsh Group; *U.S. Private*, pg. 4133
WALSH CONSTRUCTION CO.; *U.S. Private*, pg. 4432
WALSH COUNTY MUTUAL INSURANCE COMPANY; *U.S. Private*, pg. 4432
WALSH DUFFIELD COMPANIES, INC.; *U.S. Private*, pg. 4433
THE WALSHE GROUP LIMITED HONG KONG—See Southern Travel Holdings Limited; *Int'l*, pg. 7121
THE WALSHE GROUP (SINGAPORE) PTE. LTD—See Southern Travel Holdings Limited; *Int'l*, pg. 7121
WALSH ENVIRONMENTAL SCIENTISTS AND ENGINEERS, LLC—See WSP Global, Inc.; *Int'l*, pg. 8496
THE WALSH GROUP; *U.S. Private*, pg. 4133
WALSH HONDA; *U.S. Private*, pg. 4433
WALSH INVESTMENT COMPANY INC.; *U.S. Private*, pg. 4433
WALSH & KELLY, INC.—See Milestone Contractors, LP; *U.S. Private*, pg. 2728
WALSH PARTS & SERVICE; *U.S. Private*, pg. 4433
WALSH PERU, S.A.—See WSP Global, Inc.; *Int'l*, pg. 8496
WALSH PUBLIC RELATIONS; *Int'l*, pg. 8334
WALSH SHEPPARD; *U.S. Private*, pg. 4433
WALSH TIMBER COMPANY LLC; *U.S. Private*, pg. 4433
WALSH TRUCKING CO. LTD; *U.S. Private*, pg. 4433
WALSH & WATTS INC.; *U.S. Private*, pg. 4432
WALSIN CHINA INVESTMENT CO., LTD.—See Walsin Lihwa Corporation; *Int'l*, pg. 8335
WALSIN ELECTRONICS (S) PTE. LTD.—See Walsin Technology Corporation; *Int'l*, pg. 8335
WALSIN INFO-ELECTRIC CORP.—See Walsin Lihwa Corporation; *Int'l*, pg. 8335

WALSIN LIHWA CORPORATION - HSINCHUANG PLANT—See Walsin Lihwa Corporation; *Int'l*, pg. 8335
WALSIN LIHWA CORPORATION; *Int'l*, pg. 8334
WALSIN LIHWA CORPORATION - YANGMEI PLANT—See Walsin Lihwa Corporation; *Int'l*, pg. 8335
WALSIN LIHWA CORPORATION - YENSHUI PLANT—See Walsin Lihwa Corporation; *Int'l*, pg. 8335
WALSIN LIWHA CORP.—See Corner Growth Acquisition Corp.; *U.S. Public*, pg. 577
WALSIN (NANJING) DEVELOPMENT CO., LTD.—See Walsin Lihwa Corporation; *Int'l*, pg. 8335
WALSIN PRECISION TECHNOLOGY SDN. BHD.—See Walsin Lihwa Corporation; *Int'l*, pg. 8335
WALSIN TECHNOLOGY CORPORATION - DALANG PLANT—See Walsin Technology Corporation; *Int'l*, pg. 8335
WALSIN TECHNOLOGY CORPORATION - KAOHSIUNG PLANT—See Walsin Technology Corporation; *Int'l*, pg. 8335
WALSIN TECHNOLOGY CORPORATION; *Int'l*, pg. 8335
WALSIN TECHNOLOGY CORPORATION - SUZHOU PLANT—See Walsin Technology Corporation; *Int'l*, pg. 8335
WALSIN TECHNOLOGY CORPORATION - YANG-MEI PLANT—See Walsin Technology Corporation; *Int'l*, pg. 8335
WALSON, INC.—See Elm Creek Partners; *U.S. Private*, pg. 1375
WALSRODER CASINGS GMBH—See Icahn Enterprises L.P.; *U.S. Public*, pg. 1085
WALSRODER CASINGS POLSKA SP.ZO.O—See Icahn Enterprises L.P.; *U.S. Public*, pg. 1085
WALSTEAD INVESTMENTS LTD.; *Int'l*, pg. 8335
WALSWORTH PUBLISHING COMPANY, INC. - MARCELINE PRINTING AND BINDERY FACILITY—See Walsworth Publishing Company, Inc.; *U.S. Private*, pg. 4433
WALSWORTH PUBLISHING COMPANY, INC. - SAINT JOSEPH PRINTING AND BINDERY FACILITY—See Walsworth Publishing Company, Inc.; *U.S. Private*, pg. 4433
WALSWORTH PUBLISHING COMPANY, INC.; *U.S. Private*, pg. 4433
WALTCO LIFT CORP.—See Cargotec Corporation; *Int'l*, pg. 1329
WALT & COMPANY COMMUNICATIONS INC.; *U.S. Private*, pg. 4433
THE WALT DISNEY COMPANY (FRANCE) S.A.S.—See The Walt Disney Company; *U.S. Public*, pg. 2139
THE WALT DISNEY COMPANY (GERMANY) GMBH—See The Walt Disney Company; *U.S. Public*, pg. 2139
THE WALT DISNEY COMPANY IBERIA S.L.—See The Walt Disney Company; *U.S. Public*, pg. 2139
THE WALT DISNEY COMPANY ITALIA S.R.L.—See The Walt Disney Company; *U.S. Public*, pg. 2140
THE WALT DISNEY COMPANY (JAPAN) LTD.—See The Walt Disney Company; *U.S. Public*, pg. 2139
THE WALT DISNEY COMPANY LTD.—See The Walt Disney Company; *U.S. Public*, pg. 2140
THE WALT DISNEY COMPANY; *U.S. Public*, pg. 2137
THE WALT DISNEY COMPANY (SOUTHEAST ASIA) PTE LTD.—See The Walt Disney Company; *U.S. Public*, pg. 2139
WALT DISNEY ENTERPRISES OF JAPAN LTD.—See The Walt Disney Company; *U.S. Public*, pg. 2140
WALT DISNEY HOLDINGS (HONG KONG) LIMITED—See The Walt Disney Company; *U.S. Public*, pg. 2140
WALT DISNEY INTERNATIONAL LTD.—See The Walt Disney Company; *U.S. Public*, pg. 2138
WALT DISNEY PARKS & RESORTS U.S., INC.—See The Walt Disney Company; *U.S. Public*, pg. 2138
WALT DISNEY STUDIOS MOTION PICTURES, INC—See The Walt Disney Company; *U.S. Public*, pg. 2140
WALT DISNEY WORLD SWAN & DOLPHIN RESORTS—See AECOM; *U.S. Public*, pg. 52
WALTECH INC.; *U.S. Private*, pg. 4433
WALTECH PLC; *Int'l*, pg. 8336
WALTER AG SINGAPORE PTE. LTD.—See Sandvik AB; *Int'l*, pg. 6534
WALTER AG—See Sandvik AB; *Int'l*, pg. 6534
WALTER ARGENTINA S.A.—See Sandvik AB; *Int'l*, pg. 6534
WALTER AUSTRALIA PTY. LTD.—See Sandvik AB; *Int'l*, pg. 6534
WALTER AUSTRIA GMBH—See Sandvik AB; *Int'l*, pg. 6534
WALTER BENELUX N.V. / S.A.—See Sandvik AB; *Int'l*, pg. 6534
WALTERBORO COMMUNITY HOSPITAL, INC.—See HCA Healthcare, Inc.; *U.S. Public*, pg. 1013
WALTER BOSCH GMBH & CO KG—See Max Weishaupt GmbH; *Int'l*, pg. 4735
WALTER CAPITAL PARTNERS INC.; *Int'l*, pg. 8336
WALTER CUTTING TOOLS INDUSTRY AND TRADE LLC—See Sandvik AB; *Int'l*, pg. 6534
WALTER CZ S.R.O.—See Sandvik AB; *Int'l*, pg. 6534
WALTER DE GRUYTER GMBH & CO. KG; *Int'l*, pg. 8336
WALTER DE GRUYTER, INC.—See Walter de Gruyter GmbH & Co. KG; *Int'l*, pg. 8336

WALTER DEUTSCHLAND GMBH—See Sandvik AB; *Int'l*, pg. 6534
WALTER DO BRASIL LTDA.—See Sandvik AB; *Int'l*, pg. 6535
WALTER DO BRAZIL LTDA.—See Sandvik AB; *Int'l*, pg. 6535
WALTER DORWIN TEAGUE ASSOCIATES INC.; *U.S. Private*, pg. 4433
WALTER DRAKE INC.—See The Carlyle Group Inc.; *U.S. Public*, pg. 2052
WALTER E. NELSON CO.; *U.S. Private*, pg. 4433
WALTER E. SMITHE FURNITURE INC.; *U.S. Private*, pg. 4433
WALTER ESSER; *Int'l*, pg. 8336
WALTER EWAG ASIA PACIFIC PTE. LTD.—See United Grinding Group AG; *Int'l*, pg. 8067
WALTER EWAG ITALIA S.R.L.—See United Grinding Group AG; *Int'l*, pg. 8067
WALTER EWAG JAPAN K.K.—See United Grinding Group AG; *Int'l*, pg. 8068
WALTER EWAG UK LTD.—See United Grinding Group AG; *Int'l*, pg. 8068
WALTER F. CAMERON ADVERTISING INC.; *U.S. Private*, pg. 4433
WALTER FOSTER PUBLISHING INC—See The Quarto Group, Inc.; *Int'l*, pg. 7677
WALTER FRANCE S.A.S.—See Sandvik AB; *Int'l*, pg. 6534
WALTER FRANK & SONS LIMITED—See Westley Group Limited; *Int'l*, pg. 8391
WALTER G. ANDERSON INC.—See Graphic Packaging Holding Company; *U.S. Public*, pg. 959
WALTER GB LTD.—See Sandvik AB; *Int'l*, pg. 6534
WALTER G. LEGGE COMPANY, INC.; *U.S. Private*, pg. 4433
WALTER HERZOG GMBH—See Roper Technologies, Inc.; *U.S. Public*, pg. 1812
WALTER HOLLANDS—See Boparan Holdings Limited; *Int'l*, pg. 1111
WALTER HUNDHAUSEN GMBH—See CE Capital Partner GmbH; *Int'l*, pg. 1372
WALTER HUNGARIA KFT.—See Sandvik AB; *Int'l*, pg. 6535
WALTER HUNGER KG HYDRAULICS; *Int'l*, pg. 8336
WALTER ITALIA S.R.L.—See Sandvik AB; *Int'l*, pg. 6534
WALTER J. MUELLER INC.; *U.S. Private*, pg. 4433
WALTER KIDDE PORTABLE EQUIPMENT INC.—See Carrier Global Corporation; *U.S. Public*, pg. 441
WALTER KLUXEN GMBH—See Wurth Verwaltungsgesellschaft mbH; *Int'l*, pg. 8508
WALTER KOREA LTD.—See Sandvik AB; *Int'l*, pg. 6534
WALTER LAGESTEE, INC.; *U.S. Private*, pg. 4434
WALTER L. CLARK & ASSOCIATES, INC.—See Aquiline Capital Partners LLC; *U.S. Private*, pg. 305
WALTER LILLY & CO LTD; *Int'l*, pg. 8336
WALTER LYONS & ASSOCIATES; *U.S. Private*, pg. 4434
WALTER LYONS & ASSOCIATES—See Walter Lyons & Associates; *U.S. Private*, pg. 4434
WALTER MALAYSIA SDN. BHD.—See Sandvik AB; *Int'l*, pg. 6534
WALTER MARTINEZ S. A.—See Wurth Verwaltungsgesellschaft mbH; *Int'l*, pg. 8508
WALTER MASCHINENBAU GMBH—See United Grinding Group AG; *Int'l*, pg. 8067
WALTER MEIER (CLIMATE BEIJING) LTD.—See Meier Capital AG; *Int'l*, pg. 4799
WALTER MEIER (FERTIGUNGSLOSUNGEN) AG—See Meier Capital AG; *Int'l*, pg. 4799
WALTER MEIER (KLIMA OSTERREICH) GMBH—See Meier Capital AG; *Int'l*, pg. 4799
WALTER MEIER (KLIMA SCHWEIZ) AG—See Meier Capital AG; *Int'l*, pg. 4799
WALTER MEIER (SERVICES) AG—See Meier Capital AG; *Int'l*, pg. 4799
WALTER NORDEN AB—See Sandvik AB; *Int'l*, pg. 6534
WALTER PATZ GMBH—See Knauf Interfer SE; *Int'l*, pg. 4205
WALTER PAYTON POWER EQUIPMENT—See The Manitowoc Company, Inc.; *U.S. Public*, pg. 2111
WALTER P MOORE AND ASSOCIATES, INC.; *U.S. Private*, pg. 4433
WALTER P MOORE & ASSOCIATES, INC.—See Walter P Moore and Associates, Inc.; *U.S. Private*, pg. 4434
WALTER P MOORE & ASSOCIATES, INC.—See Walter P Moore and Associates, Inc.; *U.S. Private*, pg. 4434
WALTER POLSKA SP. Z O.O.—See Sandvik AB; *Int'l*, pg. 6535
WALTER POTTHOFF GMBH; *Int'l*, pg. 8336
WALTER RAU LEBENSMITTELWERKE GMBH; *Int'l*, pg. 8336
WALTER RAU NEUSSER OL UND FETT AG—See Bunge Limited; *U.S. Public*, pg. 412
WALTER (SCHWEIZ) AG—See Sandvik AB; *Int'l*, pg. 6534
WALTER SCOTT & PARTNERS LIMITED—See The Bank of New York Mellon Corporation; *U.S. Public*, pg. 2038
WALTER SERVICES GMBH—See H.I.G. Capital, LLC; *U.S. Private*, pg. 1828
WALTER SERVICES POLAND SP. Z. O. O.—See H.I.G. Capital, LLC; *U.S. Private*, pg. 1828

WALTER RAU LEBENSMITTELWERKE GMBH / CORPORATE AFFILIATIONS

WALTER SERVICES SWISS AG—See H.I.G. Capital, LLC; *U.S. Private*, pg. 1828
WALTERS GROUP; *U.S. Private*, pg. 4434
WALTERS INTERIM SA—See Robert Walters plc; *Int'l*, pg. 6369
WALTER SLOVAKIA S.R.O.—See Sandvik AB; *Int'l*, pg. 6535
WALTERS-MORGAN CONSTRUCTION; *U.S. Private*, pg. 4434
WALTERS PEOPLE BV—See Robert Walters plc; *Int'l*, pg. 6369
WALTERS PEOPLE CHILE EMPRESA DE SERVICIOS TRANSITORIOS SPA—See Robert Walters plc; *Int'l*, pg. 6369
WALTERS PEOPLE SA—See Robert Walters plc; *Int'l*, pg. 6369
WALTERS PEOPLE—See Robert Walters plc; *Int'l*, pg. 6369
WALTER S.R.O.—See United Grinding Group AG; *Int'l*, pg. 8067
WALTER STOCKLIN GES.M.B.H.—See Stocklin Logistik AG; *Int'l*, pg. 7220
WALTER'S WHOLESALE ELECTRIC COMPANY INC.; *U.S. Private*, pg. 4434
WALTERS & WOLF CONSTRUCTION SPECIALTIES, INC.—See Walters & Wolf; *U.S. Private*, pg. 4434
WALTERS & WOLF CURTAIN WALL, LLC—See Walters & Wolf; *U.S. Private*, pg. 4434
WALTERS & WOLF INTERIORS—See Walters & Wolf; *U.S. Private*, pg. 4434
WALTERS & WOLF PRECAST—See Walters & Wolf; *U.S. Private*, pg. 4434
WALTERS & WOLF; *U.S. Private*, pg. 4434
WALTER (THAILAND) CO., LTD.—See Sandvik AB; *Int'l*, pg. 6534
WALTER TOOLING JAPAN K.K.—See Sandvik AB; *Int'l*, pg. 6534
WALTER TOOLS D.O.O.—See Sandvik AB; *Int'l*, pg. 6585
WALTER TOOLS IBERICA S.A.U.—See Sandvik AB; *Int'l*, pg. 6534
WALTER TOOLS INDIA PVT. LTD.—See Sandvik AB; *Int'l*, pg. 6534
WALTER TOOLS S.A. DE C.V.—See Sandvik AB; *Int'l*, pg. 6534
WALTER TOOLS SRL—See Sandvik AB; *Int'l*, pg. 6535
WALTER TOSTO S.P.A.; *Int'l*, pg. 8336
WALTER USA, LLC—See Sandvik AB; *Int'l*, pg. 6535
WALTER WOOD SUPPLY CO.; *U.S. Private*, pg. 4434
WALTER WUXI CO. LTD.—See Sandvik AB; *Int'l*, pg. 6535
WALTHALL OIL COMPANY; *U.S. Private*, pg. 4434
WALTHAM DIALYSIS LLC—See Nautic Partners, LLC; *U.S. Private*, pg. 2871
WALTHAM NEWS TRIBUNE—See Gannett Co., Inc.; *U.S. Public*, pg. 903
WALTHAM SERVICES LLC—See Rollins, Inc.; *U.S. Public*, pg. 1810
WALTHER ELECTRIC GMBH—See Walther-Werke Ferdinand Walther GmbH; *Int'l*, pg. 8337
WALTHER-WERKE FERDINAND WALTHER GMBH; *Int'l*, pg. 8336
WALTKOCH LTD.; *U.S. Private*, pg. 4434
WALT MASSEY AUTOMOTIVE, INC.; *U.S. Private*, pg. 4433
WALTON ADVANCED ENGINEERING, INC.; *Int'l*, pg. 8337
WALTON ADVANCED ENGINEERING (SUZHOU) INC—See Walton Advanced Engineering, Inc.; *Int'l*, pg. 8337
WALTON BEVERAGE CO.; *U.S. Private*, pg. 4434
WALTON & CO. INC.; *U.S. Private*, pg. 4434
WALTON CONSTRUCTION-A CORE COMPANY, LLC—See Otto Baum Company, Inc.; *U.S. Private*, pg. 3050
WALTON DIALYSIS, LLC—See DaVita Inc.; *U.S. Public*, pg. 644
WALTON ELECTRIC MEMBERSHIP CORP.; *U.S. Private*, pg. 4434
THE WALTON FAMILY FOUNDATION, INC.; *U.S. Private*, pg. 4133
WALTON INDUSTRIES, INC.; *U.S. Private*, pg. 4434
WALTON INTERNATIONAL GROUP INC—See Giordano International Limited; *Int'l*, pg. 2978
WALTON SIGNAGE CORPORATION; *U.S. Private*, pg. 4435
WALTON'S INC.; *U.S. Private*, pg. 4435
WALTONS NAMIBIA PROPRIETARY LIMITED—See The Bidvest Group Limited; *Int'l*, pg. 7627
WALTONS STATIONERY COMPANY (NAMIBIA) (PTY) LIMITED—See The Bidvest Group Limited; *Int'l*, pg. 7627
WALTON/STOUT, INC.—See Harbour Group Industries, Inc.; *U.S. Private*, pg. 1860
WALTON STREET CAPITAL, LLC; *U.S. Private*, pg. 4435
THE WALTON SUN—See Gannett Co., Inc.; *U.S. Public*, pg. 906
WALTRUST PROPERTIES, INC.—See Walgreens Boots Alliance, Inc.; *U.S. Public*, pg. 2323
WALT'S AUTO CARE CENTERS—See Roark Capital Group Inc.; *U.S. Private*, pg. 3454

WALT SWEENEY; *U.S. Private*, pg. 4433
WALTZFANCY CO., LTD.—See Fuji Oil Holdings Inc.; *Int'l*, pg. 2816
WALTZING MATILDA HOTEL (BMG) PTY LTD—See Woolworths Group Limited; *Int'l*, pg. 8452
WALVAX BIOTECHNOLOGY CO., LTD.; *Int'l*, pg. 8337
WALVIS BAY STEVEDORING COMPANY (PTY) LIMITED—See The Bidvest Group Limited; *Int'l*, pg. 7627
WALVOIL CANADA INC.—See Interpump Group S.p.A.; *Int'l*, pg. 3757
WALVOIL FLUID POWER AUSTRALASIA PTY. LTD.—See Interpump Group S.p.A.; *Int'l*, pg. 3757
WALVOIL FLUID POWER (DONGGUAN) CO., LTD.—See Interpump Group S.p.A.; *Int'l*, pg. 3757
WALVOIL FLUID POWER FRANCE S.A.R.L.—See Interpump Group S.p.A.; *Int'l*, pg. 3757
WALVOIL FLUID POWER KOREA LLC.—See Interpump Group S.p.A.; *Int'l*, pg. 3757
WALVOIL FLUID POWER PVT. LTD.—See Interpump Group S.p.A.; *Int'l*, pg. 3757
WALVOIL S.P.A.—See Interpump Group S.p.A.; *Int'l*, pg. 3757
WALZCRAFT INDUSTRIES INC.; *U.S. Private*, pg. 4435
WALZENGIESSEREI COSWIG GMBH—See DIHAG Holding GmbH; *Int'l*, pg. 2125
WALZ HARMAN HUFFMAN COMPANIES; *U.S. Private*, pg. 4435
WALZ TETRICK ADVERTISING; *U.S. Private*, pg. 4435
WALZWERK BURG GMBH—See Georgsmarienhutte Holding GmbH; *Int'l*, pg. 2941
WAM ACTIVE LIMITED; *Int'l*, pg. 8337
WAM ADRIA D.O.O.—See WAMGROUP S.p.A.; *Int'l*, pg. 8338
WAM ALTERNATIVE ASSET LIMITED—See WAM Capital Limited; *Int'l*, pg. 8337
WAM ARGENTINA S.A.—See WAMGROUP S.p.A.; *Int'l*, pg. 8338
WAMARRAGU TRANSPORT SERVICES PTY. LTD.—See Ricardo plc; *Int'l*, pg. 6329
WAMATEC SA—See NIBE Industrier AB; *Int'l*, pg. 5262
WAM AUSTRALIA PTY LTD—See WAMGROUP S.p.A.; *Int'l*, pg. 8338
WAMBERG GENOMIC ADVISORS, INC.; *U.S. Private*, pg. 4435
WAM B.H.E.I. (THAILAND) CO. LTD.—See WAMGROUP S.p.A.; *Int'l*, pg. 8338
WAM B.H.M. (BULK HANDLING MACHINERY) N.V.—See WAMGROUP S.p.A.; *Int'l*, pg. 8338
WAMBO COAL TERMINAL PTY LTD—See Peabody Energy Corporation; *U.S. Public*, pg. 1659
WAM BULK HANDLING EQUIPMENT INDUSTRY (THAILAND) CO., LTD.—See WAMGROUP S.p.A.; *Int'l*, pg. 8338
WAM BULK HANDLING MACHINERY (SHANGHAI) CO. LTD.—See WAMGROUP S.p.A.; *Int'l*, pg. 8339
WAM BULK SOLID HANDLING (M) SDN BHD—See WAMGROUP S.p.A.; *Int'l*, pg. 8339
WAM BULK SOLID HANDLING (MT) SDN BHD—See WAMGROUP S.p.A.; *Int'l*, pg. 8339
WAM CAPITAL LIMITED; *Int'l*, pg. 8337
WAM CHILE S.A.—See WAMGROUP S.p.A.; *Int'l*, pg. 8339
WAM DO BRASIL EQUIPAMENTOS INDUSTRIAIS LTDA—See WAMGROUP S.p.A.; *Int'l*, pg. 8339
WAMEGO BANCSHARES, INC.; *U.S. Private*, pg. 4435
WAMEGO SAND COMPANY, INC.; *U.S. Private*, pg. 4435
WAM EGYPT S.A.E.—See WAMGROUP S.p.A.; *Int'l*, pg. 8339
WAMEJA LIMITED; *Int'l*, pg. 8337
WAMELING DRYWALL CORP.—See Hendricks Holding Company, Inc.; *U.S. Private*, pg. 1915
W.A.M. EQUIPMENT TRADING (PVT.) LTD.—See WAMGROUP S.p.A.; *Int'l*, pg. 8338
WAMET (DEMETRIADES) LTD.; *Int'l*, pg. 8337
WAM FINLAND OY—See WAMGROUP S.p.A.; *Int'l*, pg. 8339
WAM FRANCE S.A.—See WAMGROUP S.p.A.; *Int'l*, pg. 8339
WAM GLOBAL LIMITED; *Int'l*, pg. 8337
WAM GMBH—See WAMGROUP S.p.A.; *Int'l*, pg. 8339
WAM GROUP EGYPT—See WAMGROUP S.p.A.; *Int'l*, pg. 8339
WAMGROUP (MHE) LTD.—See WAMGROUP S.p.A.; *Int'l*, pg. 8338
WAMGROUP S.P.A.; *Int'l*, pg. 8337
WAMGROUP VIETNAM LTD—See WAMGROUP S.p.A.; *Int'l*, pg. 8339
WAM HELVETIA GMBH—See WAMGROUP S.p.A.; *Int'l*, pg. 8339
WAM HOLLAND B.H.E. (BULK HANDLING EQUIPMENT) B.V.—See WAMGROUP S.p.A.; *Int'l*, pg. 8339
WAM HOLLAND BULK HANDLING EQUIPMENT B.V.—See WAMGROUP S.p.A.; *Int'l*, pg. 8339
WAM INC.—See WAMGROUP S.p.A.; *Int'l*, pg. 8339
WAM INDIA PVT. LTD.—See WAMGROUP S.p.A.; *Int'l*, pg. 8339
WAM ITALIA S.P.A—See WAMGROUP S.p.A.; *Int'l*, pg. 8339

WAM JAPAN CO. LTD.—See WAMGROUP S.p.A.; *Int'l*, pg. 8339
WAM KOREA CO., LTD.—See WAMGROUP S.p.A.; *Int'l*, pg. 8339
WAM LEADERS LIMITED; *Int'l*, pg. 8337
WAM MAROC SARL—See WAMGROUP S.p.A.; *Int'l*, pg. 8339
WAM (M.H.E.) LTD.—See WAMGROUP S.p.A.; *Int'l*, pg. 8338
WAM MICROCAP LIMITED; *Int'l*, pg. 8337
WAM MIDDLE EAST FZ CO—See WAMGROUP S.p.A.; *Int'l*, pg. 8339
WAMINET JAPAN K.K.—See Sumitomo Corporation; *Int'l*, pg. 7276
WAMN-FM—See First Media Services, LLC; *U.S. Private*, pg. 1521
WAMO 100.1 FM—See Martz Communications Group Inc.; *U.S. Private*, pg. 2597
WAMPLER REALTY, INC.; *U.S. Private*, pg. 4435
WAMPLERS FARM SAUSAGE CO. INC.; *U.S. Private*, pg. 4435
WAM POLSKA SP. Z.O.O.—See WAMGROUP S.p.A.; *Int'l*, pg. 8339
WAM (RE) DEVELOPMENT MANAGEMENT LP—See Katz Group Inc.; *Int'l*, pg. 4092
WAM RESEARCH LTD.; *Int'l*, pg. 8337
WAM ROMANIA S.R.L.—See WAMGROUP S.p.A.; *Int'l*, pg. 8339
WAM SCANDINAVIA A/S—See WAMGROUP S.p.A.; *Int'l*, pg. 8339
WAM SINGAPORE BHM PTE. LTD.—See WAMGROUP S.p.A.; *Int'l*, pg. 8339
WAM SOUTH AFRICA (PTY) LTD.—See WAMGROUP S.p.A.; *Int'l*, pg. 8339
WAM SPAIN 2004, S.L.—See WAMGROUP S.p.A.; *Int'l*, pg. 8339
WAM STRATEGIC VALUE LIMITED; *Int'l*, pg. 8337
WAM SYSTEMS, INC.—See TA Associates, Inc.; *U.S. Private*, pg. 3919
WAM UKRAINE LTD.—See WAMGROUP S.p.A.; *Int'l*, pg. 8339
WAM U.S.A INC—See WAMGROUP S.p.A.; *Int'l*, pg. 8339
WAM U.S.A INC. - TEXAS DIVISION—See WAMGROUP S.p.A.; *Int'l*, pg. 8339
WANAKBORI CEMENT GRINDING UNIT—See The Aditya Birla Group; *Int'l*, pg. 7611
WANBANGDE PHARMACEUTICAL HOLDING GROUP CO., LTD.; *Int'l*, pg. 8340
WANBISHI ARCHIVES CO., LTD.—See Toyota Industries Corporation; *Int'l*, pg. 7869
WANBURY LIMITED; *Int'l*, pg. 8340
WAN CHENG METAL PACKAGING COMPANY LIMITED; *Int'l*, pg. 8339
WANCHESE FISH COMPANY, INC.—See Daniels Enterprises Inc.; *U.S. Private*, pg. 1156
WANCHIO ADHESIVE PRODUCT (JIANGSU) CO., LTD.—See Yem Chio Co., Ltd.; *Int'l*, pg. 8577
WAN CHUNG CONSTRUCTION (SINGAPORE) PTE. LIMITED—See Green Economy Development Limited; *Int'l*, pg. 3071
WANDA HOTEL DEVELOPMENT COMPANY LIMITED—See Dalian Wanda Group Corporation Ltd.; *Int'l*, pg. 1953
WANDA MOVIE CO., LTD.; *Int'l*, pg. 8340
WANDA SPORTS GROUP COMPANY LIMITED—See Dalian Wanda Group Corporation Ltd.; *Int'l*, pg. 1953
WAND DENTAL, INC.—See Milestone Scientific Inc.; *U.S. Public*, pg. 1446
WANDER AG—See The Garfield Weston Foundation; *Int'l*, pg. 7649
WANDERER WERKE AG; *Int'l*, pg. 8340
WANDERFLY, INC.—See TripAdvisor, Inc.; *U.S. Public*, pg. 2195
WANDERFUL MEDIA—See OwnLocal, Inc.; *U.S. Private*, pg. 3055
WANDERLUST; *U.S. Private*, pg. 4435
WANDERPORT CORPORATION; *U.S. Public*, pg. 2325
WAND, INC.; *U.S. Private*, pg. 4435
WANDISCO, INC.—See Cirata PLC; *Int'l*, pg. 1617
WANDISCO INTERNATIONAL LIMITED—See Cirata PLC; *Int'l*, pg. 1617
WANDISCO, PTY LTD—See Cirata PLC; *Int'l*, pg. 1617
WANDISCO SOFTWARE (CHENGDU) LTD.—See Cirata PLC; *Int'l*, pg. 1617
WANDO TRUCKING, LLC—See Universal Logistics Holdings, Inc.; *U.S. Public*, pg. 2261
WAND PARTNERS INC.; *U.S. Private*, pg. 4435
WANDS LIMITED—See Simonds Farsons Cisk plc; *Int'l*, pg. 6933
WAND TELEVISION, INC.—See Block Communications, Inc.; *U.S. Private*, pg. 582
WANFENG AUTO HOLDING GROUP CO., LTD.; *Int'l*, pg. 8340
WANFRIED-DRUCK KALDEN GMBH; *Int'l*, pg. 8340
WANFU PLASTIC (SHENZHEN) CO., LTD.—See Copartner Technology Corporation; *Int'l*, pg. 1793
WANGARD PARTNERS, INC.; *U.S. Private*, pg. 4435
WANG ENGINEERING, INC.—See Terracon Consultants, Inc.; *U.S. Private*, pg. 3971

COMPANY NAME INDEX

WANGFU CENTRAL REAL ESTATE DEVELOPMENT CO. LTD.—See Hong Kong Land Holdings Ltd.; *Int'l*, pg. 3467
WANGFUJING GROUP CO., LTD.; *Int'l*, pg. 8341
WANGI KMB BHD.—See Syarikat Kayu Wangi Berhad; *Int'l*, pg. 7377
WANG & LEE GROUP, INC.; *Int'l*, pg. 8340
WANGLE TECHNOLOGIES LIMITED; *Int'l*, pg. 8341
WANGLI SECURITY & SURVEILLANCE PRODUCT CO., LTD.; *Int'l*, pg. 8341
WANGNENG ENVIRONMENT CO., LTD.; *Int'l*, pg. 8341
WANG ON GROUP LTD; *Int'l*, pg. 8341
WANG ON MAJORLUCK LIMITED—See Wang On Group Ltd; *Int'l*, pg. 8341
WANG ON PROPERTIES LTD.; *Int'l*, pg. 8341
WANG ON SHOPPING CENTRE MANAGEMENT LIMITED—See Wang On Group Ltd; *Int'l*, pg. 8341
WANGSAGA INDUSTRIES SDN. BHD.—See Tek Seng Holdings Berhad; *Int'l*, pg. 7526
WANGSA TEGAP SDN BHD—See Berjaya Corporation Berhad; *Int'l*, pg. 984
WANGSU SCIENCE & TECHNOLOGY CO., LTD.; *Int'l*, pg. 8341
WANGTON CAPITAL CORP.; *Int'l*, pg. 8341
WANGUO INTERNATIONAL MINING GROUP LIMITED; *Int'l*, pg. 8341
WANG-ZHENG BERHAD—See Hengan International Group Co. Ltd.; *Int'l*, pg. 3346
WANG-ZHENG CORPORATION SDN. BHD.—See Hengan International Group Co. Ltd.; *Int'l*, pg. 3346
WANHAI LINES ECUADOR S.A.—See Wan Hai Lines Ltd.; *Int'l*, pg. 8340
WAN HAI LINES (HK) LTD.—See Wan Hai Lines Ltd.; *Int'l*, pg. 8340
WAN HAI LINES (INDIA) PVT. LTD.—See Wan Hai Lines Ltd.; *Int'l*, pg. 8339
WAN HAI LINES (KOREA) LTD.—See Wan Hai Lines Ltd.; *Int'l*, pg. 8339
WAN HAI LINES LTD.; *Int'l*, pg. 8339
WAN HAI LINES PERU S.A.C.—See Wan Hai Lines Ltd.; *Int'l*, pg. 8340
WAN HAI LINES (PHILS.), INC.—See Wan Hai Lines Ltd.; *Int'l*, pg. 8339
WAN HAI LINES (SINGAPORE) PTE LTD.—See Wan Hai Lines Ltd.; *Int'l*, pg. 8339
WAN HAI LINES (USA) LTD.—See Wan Hai Lines Ltd.; *Int'l*, pg. 8340
WAN HAI (VIETNAM) LTD.—See Wan Hai Lines Ltd.; *Int'l*, pg. 8339
WAN HE DA MANUFACTURING COMPANY LTD.—See PCCS Group Berhad; *Int'l*, pg. 5767
WANHO MANUFACTURING LLC—See Wise Equity SGR S.p.A.; *Int'l*, pg. 8435
WANHUA BORSODCHEM LATIN AMERICA COMERCIO DE PRODUTOS QUIMICOS LTDA—See Wanhua Chemical Group Co., Ltd.; *Int'l*, pg. 8341
WANHUA BORSODCHEM RUS LLC—See Wanhua Chemical Group Co., Ltd.; *Int'l*, pg. 8342
WANHUA CHEMICAL (AMERICA) CO., LTD.—See Wanhua Chemical Group Co., Ltd.; *Int'l*, pg. 8342
WANHUA CHEMICAL GROUP CO., LTD.; *Int'l*, pg. 8341
WANHUA CHEMICAL (JAPAN) CO., LTD.—See Wanhua Chemical Group Co., Ltd.; *Int'l*, pg. 8341
WANHUA CHEMICAL (SINGAPORE) PTE. LTD.—See Wanhua Chemical Group Co., Ltd.; *Int'l*, pg. 8342
WANHUA INTERNATIONAL (INDIA) PRIVATE LIMITED—See Wanhua Chemical Group Co., Ltd.; *Int'l*, pg. 8342
WANHUA (JAPAN) CO., LTD.—See Wanhua Chemical Group Co., Ltd.; *Int'l*, pg. 8341
WANHUA (NETHERLANDS) B.V.—See Wanhua Chemical Group Co., Ltd.; *Int'l*, pg. 8341
WANHWA ENTERPRISE CO., LTD.; *Int'l*, pg. 8342
WANIT FULGURIT GMBH—See Etex SA/NV; *Int'l*, pg. 2523
WANJIA GROUP HOLDINGS LIMITED; *Int'l*, pg. 8342
WANKAI NEW MATERIALS CO., LTD.; *Int'l*, pg. 8342
WANKA ONLINE, INC.; *Int'l*, pg. 8342
WANKE CASCADE DISTRIBUTION LTD.—See Buckwold Western Ltd.; *Int'l*, pg. 1210
WAN KEI GROUP HOLDINGS LIMITED; *Int'l*, pg. 8340
WAN LEADER INTERNATIONAL LTD.; *Int'l*, pg. 8340
WANLIN INTERNATIONAL(H.K.)CO., LTD.—See Jiangsu Wanlin Modern Logistics Co., Ltd.; *Int'l*, pg. 3955
WANMA TECHNOLOGY CO., LTD.; *Int'l*, pg. 8342
WANMO; *Int'l*, pg. 8342
WANMO—See Wanmo; *Int'l*, pg. 8342
WANNAPAY SDN. BHD.—See Revenue Group Bhd; *Int'l*, pg. 6313
WANNEMACHER ENTERPRISES INC.; *U.S. Private*, pg. 4435
WANNEMACHER JENSEN ARCHITECTS INC.; *U.S. Private*, pg. 4435
WANNENWETSCH GMBH HOCHDRUCKWASSERTECHNIK—See Keller Group plc; *Int'l*, pg. 4121
WANNER ENGINEERING INC.; *U.S. Private*, pg. 4436
WANNER INTERNATIONAL LTD.—See Wanner Engineering Inc.; *U.S. Private*, pg. 4436

WANNERIT AG—See swisspor Management AG; *Int'l*, pg. 7375
WANNER PUMPS LTD.—See Wanner Engineering Inc.; *U.S. Private*, pg. 4436
WANNING HNA DAKANGLE INVESTMENT AND DEVELOPMENT CO., LTD.—See Hainan Traffic Administration Holding Co., Ltd.; *Int'l*, pg. 3216
WANNITUBE; *Int'l*, pg. 8342
WANOBA GROUP INC.; *U.S. Private*, pg. 4436
WANSHIH ELECTRONIC ELEMENT COMPANY LIMITED—See Wanshih Electronics Co., Ltd.; *Int'l*, pg. 8342
WANSHIH ELECTRONIC (H.K) CO., LTD.—See Wanshih Electronics Co., Ltd.; *Int'l*, pg. 8342
WANSHIH ELECTRONICS CO., LTD.; *Int'l*, pg. 8342
WAN SHYH SHING CO., LTD.; *Int'l*, pg. 8340
WANTAGE AVENUE HOLDING COMPANY, INC.—See Selective Insurance Group, Inc.; *U.S. Public*, pg. 1863
WANTAGH AUTO SALES INC.; *U.S. Private*, pg. 4436
WANTED LAB INC.; *Int'l*, pg. 8342
WANTEDLY, INC.; *Int'l*, pg. 8343
WAN THAI FOODS INDUSTRY CO., LTD.—See Ajinomoto Company, Inc.; *Int'l*, pg. 256
WANTMAN GROUP, INC.; *U.S. Private*, pg. 4436
WANT WANT CHINA HOLDINGS LTD.; *Int'l*, pg. 8342
WANT WANT FOOD PTE LTD—See Want Want China Holdings Ltd.; *Int'l*, pg. 8342
WANT WANT HOLDINGS LTD.—See Want Want China Holdings Ltd.; *Int'l*, pg. 8342
WANXIANG AMERICA CAPITAL, LLC; *U.S. Private*, pg. 4436
WANXIANG AMERICA CORPORATION—See Wanxiang Group Corporation; *Int'l*, pg. 8343
WANXIANG AUSTRALIA PTY, LTD.—See Wanxiang Group Corporation; *Int'l*, pg. 8343
WANXIANG DONEED CO., LTD.; *Int'l*, pg. 8343
WANXIANG EUROPE GMBH—See Wanxiang Group Corporation; *Int'l*, pg. 8343
WANXIANG GROUP CORPORATION; *Int'l*, pg. 8343
WANXIANG INTERNATIONAL (EUROPE) LIMITED—See Wanxiang International Limited; *Int'l*, pg. 8343
WANXIANG INTERNATIONAL FLAVORS & FRAGRANCES PTE LTD—See Wanxiang International Limited; *Int'l*, pg. 8343
WANXIANG INTERNATIONAL LIMITED; *Int'l*, pg. 8343
WANXIANG INTERNATIONAL (USA) LTD—See Wanxiang International Limited; *Int'l*, pg. 8343
WANXIANG QIANCHAO CO., LTD.; *Int'l*, pg. 8343
WANYOU FIRE ENGINEERING GROUP COMPANY LIMITED—See CIMC-TianDa Holdings Company Limited; *Int'l*, pg. 1609
WANZEK CONSTRUCTION INC.—See MasTec, Inc.; *U.S. Public*, pg. 1393
WANZL AUSTRALIA PTY. LTD.—See Wanzl Metallwarenfabrik GmbH; *Int'l*, pg. 8343
WANZL B.V.B.A.—See Wanzl Metallwarenfabrik GmbH; *Int'l*, pg. 8343
WANZL COMMERCIAL EQUIPMENT (SHANGHAI) CO. LTD.—See Wanzl Metallwarenfabrik GmbH; *Int'l*, pg. 8343
WANZL EQUIPAMIENTO COMERCIAL, S.L.—See Wanzl Metallwarenfabrik GmbH; *Int'l*, pg. 8343
WANZL GESELLSCHAFT M.B.H.—See Wanzl Metallwarenfabrik GmbH; *Int'l*, pg. 8343
WANZL INDIA PVT LTD—See Wanzl Metallwarenfabrik GmbH; *Int'l*, pg. 8343
WANZL ITALIA S.R.L.—See Wanzl Metallwarenfabrik GmbH; *Int'l*, pg. 8343
WANZL KOREA LTD.—See Wanzl Metallwarenfabrik GmbH; *Int'l*, pg. 8343
WANZL LTD.—See Wanzl Metallwarenfabrik GmbH; *Int'l*, pg. 8343
WANZL MAGYARORSZAG KFT—See Wanzl Metallwarenfabrik GmbH; *Int'l*, pg. 8343
WANZL METALLWARENFABRIK GMBH; *Int'l*, pg. 8343
WANZL MIDDLE EAST FZE—See Wanzl Metallwarenfabrik GmbH; *Int'l*, pg. 8343
WANZL NEDERLAND B.V.—See Wanzl Metallwarenfabrik GmbH; *Int'l*, pg. 8343
WANZL SAS—See Wanzl Metallwarenfabrik GmbH; *Int'l*, pg. 8343
WANZL (SCHWEIZ) AG—See Wanzl Metallwarenfabrik GmbH; *Int'l*, pg. 8343
WANZL SK, S.R.O.—See Wanzl Metallwarenfabrik GmbH; *Int'l*, pg. 8343
WANZL SPOL. S R.O.—See Wanzl Metallwarenfabrik GmbH; *Int'l*, pg. 8343
WANZL SP. Z O.O.—See Wanzl Metallwarenfabrik GmbH; *Int'l*, pg. 8343
WAON DEVELOPMENT LIMITED—See Airmate (Cayman) International Co. Limited; *Int'l*, pg. 248
WAPA AMERICA INC.—See Hemisphere Media Group, Inc.; *U.S. Private*, pg. 1913
WAPIC INSURANCE PLC—See Access Corporation; *Int'l*, pg. 89
WAPMED TPA SERVICES COMPANY K.S.C.C.—See Warba Insurance and Reinsurance Company K.S.C.P.; *Int'l*, pg. 8344
WAPPLE.NET LTD; *Int'l*, pg. 8343

WAPRO AB—See Lagercrantz Group AB; *Int'l*, pg. 4395
WAPS CO., LTD.; *Int'l*, pg. 8343
WAPSIE VALLEY CREAMERY, INC.; *U.S. Private*, pg. 4436
WAPT HEARST-ARGYLE TELEVISION, INC.—See The Hearst Corporation; *U.S. Private*, pg. 4048
WAQOO, INC.—See Vector Inc.; *Int'l*, pg. 8144
WARABA GOLD LIMITED; *Int'l*, pg. 8343
WARABEYA NICHIYO HOLDINGS CO., LTD.; *Int'l*, pg. 8344
WARATAH COAL LIMITED—See Mineralogy Pty. Ltd.; *Int'l*, pg. 4907
WARATAH FORESTRY EQUIPMENT CANADA LIMITED—See Deere & Company; *U.S. Public*, pg. 647
WARATAH RESOURCES LIMITED; *Int'l*, pg. 8344
WARBA BANK (K.S.C.P.); *Int'l*, pg. 8344
WARBA CAPITAL HOLDING COMPANY K.S.C.P.—See Boubyan Petrochemical Co. KSC; *Int'l*, pg. 1119
WARBA CAPITAL HOLDING COMPANY; *Int'l*, pg. 8344
WARBA INSURANCE AND REINSURANCE COMPANY K.S.C.P.; *Int'l*, pg. 8344
WARBA MECHANICAL EQUIPMENTS L.L.C.—See Arabi Holding Group Company K.S.C.C.; *Int'l*, pg. 533
WARBIRD CORPORATION—See Coteminas Companhia de Tecidos Norte de Minas; *Int'l*, pg. 1817
WARBIRD CORPORATION—See Springs Global, Inc.; *U.S. Private*, pg. 3764
WARBUD BETON SP. Z O.O.—See VINCI S.A.; *Int'l*, pg. 8240
WARBUD SP. Z O.O.—See VINCI S.A.; *Int'l*, pg. 8240
WARBURG ALTERNATIVE INVESTMENTS AG—See M.M. Warburg & Co. KGaA; *Int'l*, pg. 4616
WARBURG ASSET MANAGEMENT GMBH—See M.M. Warburg & Co. KGaA; *Int'l*, pg. 4616
WARBURG - HENDERSON KAPITALANLAGEGESELLSCHAFT FUR IMMOBILIEN MBH—See M.M. Warburg & Co. KGaA; *Int'l*, pg. 4616
WARBURG - HENDERSON KAPITALANLAGEGESELLSCHAFT FUR IMMOBILIEN MBH—See Teachers Insurance Association - College Retirement Fund; *U.S. Private*, pg. 3945
WARBURG INVEST KAPITALANLAGEGESELLSCHAFT MBH—See M.M. Warburg & Co. KGaA; *Int'l*, pg. 4616
WARBURG PINCUS LLC; *U.S. Private*, pg. 4436
WARBURG RESEARCH GMBH—See M.M. Warburg & Co. KGaA; *Int'l*, pg. 4616
WARBURG VENDING MALAYSIA SDN. BHD.—See Thai Beverage Public Company Limited; *Int'l*, pg. 7590
WARBURG VENDING PTE. LTD.—See Thai Beverage Public Company Limited; *Int'l*, pg. 7590
WARBURTONS LIMITED; *Int'l*, pg. 8344
WARBY PARKER INC.; *U.S. Public*, pg. 2325
WARC AMERICAS—See Informa plc; *Int'l*, pg. 3691
WARC ASIA—See Informa plc; *Int'l*, pg. 3691
WARC LTD.—See Informa plc; *Int'l*, pg. 3691
WARCO CONSTRUCTION INC.; *U.S. Private*, pg. 4440
WARD ASSOCIATES, PC—See KB Engineering, PC; *U.S. Private*, pg. 2268
WARD CORPORATION; *U.S. Private*, pg. 4440
WARD DAVIS ASSOCIATES INC.; *U.S. Private*, pg. 4441
WARDENS OFFICE INC.; *U.S. Private*, pg. 4441
WARD FINANCIAL GROUP, INC.—See Aon plc; *Int'l*, pg. 495
THE WARD GROUP; *U.S. Private*, pg. 4133
WARDHA POWER COMPANY LIMITED—See KSK Energy Ventures Limited; *Int'l*, pg. 4314
WARD HOME, INC.—See Auberle; *U.S. Private*, pg. 385
WARD IMPLEMENT COMPANY; *U.S. Private*, pg. 4441
WARD INDUSTRIAL EQUIPMENT LTD—See Dynamic Technologies Group Inc.; *Int'l*, pg. 2241
WARD INTERNATIONAL TRUCKS INC.; *U.S. Private*, pg. 4441
WARDJET, INC.—See AXYZ Automation Group Inc.; *Int'l*, pg. 773
WARD/KRAFT, INC. - KANSAS PLANT—See Ward/Kraft, Inc.; *U.S. Private*, pg. 4441
WARD/KRAFT, INC.; *U.S. Private*, pg. 4441
WARD LEONARD CT LLC—See Arcline Investment Management LP; *U.S. Private*, pg. 313
WARD MANUFACTURING, INC.—See Tailwind Capital Group, LLC; *U.S. Private*, pg. 3923
WARD MANUFACTURING LLC - WISCONSIN NIPPLE FACILITY—See Tailwind Capital Group, LLC; *U.S. Private*, pg. 3923
WARD MECHANICAL EQUIPMENT INC.; *U.S. Private*, pg. 4441
WARD MUSCATELL AUTOMOTIVE GROUP; *U.S. Private*, pg. 4441
WARD PETROLEUM CORPORATION; *U.S. Private*, pg. 4441
WARDS COVE PACKING COMPANY; *U.S. Private*, pg. 4441
WARD TIMBER LTD; *U.S. Private*, pg. 4441
WARD TRUCKING CORP.; *U.S. Private*, pg. 4441
WARD VILLAGE PROPERTIES, LLC—See Howard Hughes Holdings Inc.; *U.S. Public*, pg. 1061
WARDWELL BRAIDING MACHINE CO.—See SKET Verseilmaschinenbau GmbH; *Int'l*, pg. 6981

WARD WILLISTON OIL COMPANY

WARD WILLISTON OIL COMPANY; *U.S. Private*, pg. 4441
WARDWIZARD HEALTHCARE LIMITED; *Int'l*, pg. 8344
WARDWIZARD INNOVATIONS & MOBILITY LIMITED; *Int'l*, pg. 8344
WARDWIZARD SOLUTIONS INDIA PRIVATE LIMITED; *Int'l*, pg. 8344
WARDY IT SOLUTIONS PTY LIMITED—See Brennan IT Pty. Limited; *Int'l*, pg. 1145
WAREHAUS GMBH—See MEDIQON Group AG; *Int'l*, pg. 4780
WAREHEIM INSURANCE CONSULTANTS, INC.; *U.S. Private*, pg. 4441
WAREHOUSE AUTOMATION IBERIA, S.L.—See Illinois Tool Works Inc.; *U.S. Public*, pg. 1111
WAREHOUSE DIRECT, INC; *U.S. Private*, pg. 4441
WAREHOUSE EQUIPMENT & SUPPLY CO.; *U.S. Private*, pg. 4441
WAREHOUSE EXPRESS LTD.—See Aurelius Equity Opportunities SE & Co. KGaA; *Int'l*, pg. 709
WAREHOUSE GOODS LLC—See Greenlane Holdings, Inc.; *U.S. Public*, pg. 965
THE WAREHOUSE GROUP LIMITED; *Int'l*, pg. 7698
WAREHOUSE HOME FURNISHINGS DISTRIBUTOR, INC.; *U.S. Private*, pg. 4441
THE WAREHOUSE LIMITED—See The Warehouse Group Limited; *Int'l*, pg. 7699
WAREHOUSE MARKET INC.; *U.S. Private*, pg. 4442
WAREHOUSE REIT PLC; *Int'l*, pg. 8344
WAREHOUSES DE PAUW COMM. VA; *Int'l*, pg. 8344
WAREHOUSE SERVICES INC.; *U.S. Private*, pg. 4442
WAREHOUSES ESTATES BELGIUM SCA; *Int'l*, pg. 8344
WAREHOUSE SOLUTIONS INC.; *U.S. Private*, pg. 4442
WAREHOUSE SPECIALISTS, INC.—See The Van Hoof Companies; *U.S. Private*, pg. 4130
THE WAREHOUSE STORE FIXTURE COMPANY; *U.S. Private*, pg. 4133
WAREHOUSING EDUCATION AND RESEARCH COUNCIL—See Material Handling Industry; *U.S. Private*, pg. 2609
WARE INDUSTRIES; *U.S. Private*, pg. 4441
WARE MALCOMB; *U.S. Private*, pg. 4441
WARE MILLING, INC.—See Kalmbach Feeds, Inc.; *U.S. Private*, pg. 2257
WARENDORFER KUCHEN GMBH—See CoBe Capital LLC; *U.S. Private*, pg. 957
WARE OIL & SUPPLY COMPANY INC.; *U.S. Private*, pg. 4441
WARFEL CONSTRUCTION CO.; *U.S. Private*, pg. 4442
WARFORD-WALKER MORTUARY, INC.—See Service Corporation International; *U.S. Public*, pg. 1871
WARGAMING AMERICA INC.—See Wargaming Public Company Limited; *Int'l*, pg. 8344
WARGAMING PUBLIC COMPANY LIMITED; *Int'l*, pg. 8344
WARGAMING SEATTLE—See Wargaming Public Company Limited; *Int'l*, pg. 8344
WARGNY BBR SA—See Rothschild & Co SCA; *Int'l*, pg. 6404
WARHAFTIG & LITTMAN ADV/SALES PROMOTION/PR; *U.S. Private*, pg. 4442
WARI INC.; *U.S. Private*, pg. 4442
WARIMPEX FINANZ- UND BETEILIGUNGS AG; *Int'l*, pg. 8344
WARIMPEX LEASING GMBH—See Warimpex Finanz- und Beteiligungs AG; *Int'l*, pg. 8345
WARIMPEX POLSKA SP.Z.O.O.—See Warimpex Finanz- und Beteiligungs AG; *Int'l*, pg. 8345
WARING OIL COMPANY, LLC; *U.S. Private*, pg. 4442
WARING PRODUCTS, INC.—See American Securities LLC; *U.S. Private*, pg. 248
WARISAN CAPTIVE INCORPORATED—See Warisan TC Holdings Berhad; *Int'l*, pg. 8345
WARISAN TC AUTOMOTIVE MANUFACTURERS (M) SDN BHD—See Warisan TC Holdings Berhad; *Int'l*, pg. 8345
WARISAN TC HOLDINGS BERHAD; *Int'l*, pg. 8345
WARKA BANK FOR INVESTMENT & FINANCE J.S.C.; *Int'l*, pg. 8345
WARKAUS WORKS OY—See ANDRITZ AG; *Int'l*, pg. 457
WARKENTINE, INC.—See BlackRock, Inc.; *U.S. Public*, pg. 347
WARKO ROOFING COMPANY INC.; *U.S. Private*, pg. 4442
WARMAFLOOR (GB) LTD.—See Bharti Enterprises Limited; *Int'l*, pg. 1012
WARMAN INTERNATIONAL (INDIA) PRIVATE LTD.—See The Weir Group PLC; *Int'l*, pg. 7699
WARMEL CORP.; *U.S. Private*, pg. 4442
WAR MEMORIAL HOSPITAL; *U.S. Private*, pg. 4436
WARMEVERSORGUNGSGESELLSCHAFT KONIGS WUSTERHAUSEN MBH—See E.ON SE; *Int'l*, pg. 2260
WARMEVERSORGUNG WOLGAST GMBH—See Stadtwerke Hannover AG; *Int'l*, pg. 7161
THE WARMINGTON GROUP - NORTHERN CALIFORNIA DIVISION OFFICE—See The Warmington Group; *U.S. Private*, pg. 4133
THE WARMINGTON GROUP; *U.S. Private*, pg. 4133

WARMINGTON PROPERTIES, INC.—See The Warmington Group; *U.S. Private*, pg. 4133
WARMINGTON RESIDENTIAL—See The Warmington Group; *U.S. Private*, pg. 4133
WARMINSTER FIBERGLASS CO.—See Warminster Fiberglass, LLC; *U.S. Private*, pg. 4442
WARMINSTER FIBERGLASS, LLC; *U.S. Private*, pg. 4442
WARMLYYOURS.COM INC.; *U.S. Private*, pg. 4442
WARM SPRINGS ECONOMIC DEVELOPMENT CORPORATION—See Confederated Tribes of; *U.S. Private*, pg. 1013
THE WARNACO GROUP, INC.—See PVH Corp.; *U.S. Public*, pg. 1739
WARN AUTOMOTIVE, LLC—See Dover Corporation; *U.S. Public*, pg. 683
WARNE MARKETING & COMMUNICATIONS; *Int'l*, pg. 8345
WARNER BROS. ANIMATION INC.—See Warner Bros. Discovery, Inc.; *U.S. Public*, pg. 2328
WARNER BROS. DIGITAL NETWORKS LABS INC.—See Warner Bros. Discovery, Inc.; *U.S. Public*, pg. 2328
WARNER BROS. DISCOVERY, INC.; *U.S. Public*, pg. 2326
WARNER BROS. DISTRIBUTING INC.—See Warner Bros. Discovery, Inc.; *U.S. Public*, pg. 2328
WARNER BROS. DOMESTIC TELEVISION DISTRIBUTION—See Warner Bros. Discovery, Inc.; *U.S. Public*, pg. 2329
WARNER BROS. ENTERTAINMENT CANADA INC.—See Warner Bros. Discovery, Inc.; *U.S. Public*, pg. 2328
WARNER BROS. ENTERTAINMENT INC.—See Warner Bros. Discovery, Inc.; *U.S. Public*, pg. 2328
WARNER BROS. ENTERTAINMENT UK LIMITED—See Warner Bros. Discovery, Inc.; *U.S. Public*, pg. 2329
WARNER BROS. HOME ENTERTAINMENT GROUP—See Warner Bros. Discovery, Inc.; *U.S. Public*, pg. 2328
WARNER BROS. INTERACTIVE ENTERTAINMENT INC.—See Warner Bros. Discovery, Inc.; *U.S. Public*, pg. 2328
WARNER BROS. INTERNATIONAL TELEVISION DISTRIBUTION INC.—See Warner Bros. Discovery, Inc.; *U.S. Public*, pg. 2329
WARNER BROS. INTERNATIONAL TELEVISION PRODUCTION HOLDING B.V.—See Warner Bros. Discovery, Inc.; *U.S. Public*, pg. 2329
WARNER BROS. INTERNATIONAL TELEVISION PRODUCTION NEW ZEALAND LIMITED—See Warner Bros. Discovery, Inc.; *U.S. Public*, pg. 2329
WARNER BROS. RECORDS, INC.—See Access Industries, Inc.; *U.S. Private*, pg. 52
WARNER BROS. SINGAPORE PTE LTD.—See Warner Bros. Discovery, Inc.; *U.S. Public*, pg. 2329
WARNER BROS. TELEVISION GROUP—See Warner Bros. Discovery, Inc.; *U.S. Public*, pg. 2329
WARNER BROS. TELEVISION PRODUCTION, INC.—See Warner Bros. Discovery, Inc.; *U.S. Public*, pg. 2329
WARNER BROS. TELEVISION PRODUCTIONS UK LTD—See Warner Bros. Discovery, Inc.; *U.S. Public*, pg. 2329
WARNER BROS. TELEVISION PRODUCTION UK—See Warner Bros. Discovery, Inc.; *U.S. Public*, pg. 2329
WARNER BROS. WORLDWIDE CONSUMER PRODUCTS—See Warner Bros. Discovery, Inc.; *U.S. Public*, pg. 2329
WARNER CANDY COMPANY; *U.S. Private*, pg. 4442
WARNER/CHAPPELL MUSIC, INC.—See Access Industries, Inc.; *U.S. Private*, pg. 52
WARNER CHILCOTT COMPANY, LLC—See AbbVie Inc.; *U.S. Public*, pg. 24
WARNER CHILCOTT CORPORATION—See AbbVie Inc.; *U.S. Public*, pg. 24
WARNER CHILCOTT DEUTSCHLAND GMBH—See AbbVie Inc.; *U.S. Public*, pg. 24
WARNER CHILCOTT (IRELAND) LIMITED—See AbbVie Inc.; *U.S. Public*, pg. 24
WARNER CHILCOTT ITALY S.R.L.—See AbbVie Inc.; *U.S. Public*, pg. 24
WARNER CHILCOTT NEDERLAND B.V.—See AbbVie Inc.; *U.S. Public*, pg. 24
WARNER CHILCOTT PHARMACEUTICALS B.V.B.A.—See AbbVie Inc.; *U.S. Public*, pg. 24
WARNER CHILCOTT PHARMACEUTICALS S.A.R.L.—See AbbVie Inc.; *U.S. Public*, pg. 24
WARNER CHILCOTT PUERTO RICO LLC—See AbbVie Inc.; *U.S. Public*, pg. 24
WARNER CHILCOTT UK LTD.—See AbbVie Inc.; *U.S. Public*, pg. 24
WARNER CHILCOTT (US), LLC—See AbbVie Inc.; *U.S. Public*, pg. 24
WARNER COMMUNICATIONS CORP.; *U.S. Private*, pg. 4442
WARNER COMMUNICATIONS—See Millwright Holdings LLC; *U.S. Private*, pg. 2738
WARNER CONNECT, INC.; *U.S. Private*, pg. 4442
WARNER DESIGN ASSOCIATES, INC.—See Banko Design LLC; *U.S. Private*, pg. 468

CORPORATE AFFILIATIONS

WARNER ELECTRIC, INC.—See Regal Rexnord Corporation; *U.S. Public*, pg. 1772
WARNER ELECTRIC (SINGAPORE) PTY. LTD.—See Regal Rexnord Corporation; *U.S. Public*, pg. 1772
WARNER ELECTRIC (TAIWAN) LTD.—See Regal Rexnord Corporation; *U.S. Public*, pg. 1772
WARNER ELECTRIC (THAILAND) LTD.—See Regal Rexnord Corporation; *U.S. Public*, pg. 1772
WARNER ENTERTAINMENT JAPAN INC.—See Warner Bros. Discovery, Inc.; *U.S. Public*, pg. 2329
WARNER FERTILIZER COMPANY; *U.S. Private*, pg. 4442
WARNER HOME VIDEO INC.—See Warner Bros. Discovery, Inc.; *U.S. Public*, pg. 2329
WARNER INSTRUMENTS LLC—See Harvard Bioscience, Inc.; *U.S. Public*, pg. 987
WARNER LAMBERT DEL URUGUAY S.A.—See Pfizer Inc.; *U.S. Public*, pg. 1683
WARNER LEISURE LTD.—See Blackstone Inc.; *U.S. Public*, pg. 352
WARNER MANUFACTURING COMPANY; *U.S. Private*, pg. 4442
WARNER MEDIA, LLC—See Warner Bros. Discovery, Inc.; *U.S. Public*, pg. 2327
WARNER MULTIMEDIA LIMITED; *Int'l*, pg. 8345
WARNER MUSIC AUSTRALIA PTY LTD—See Access Industries, Inc.; *U.S. Private*, pg. 52
WARNER MUSIC BENELUX N.V.—See Access Industries, Inc.; *U.S. Private*, pg. 52
WARNER MUSIC DENMARK—See Access Industries, Inc.; *U.S. Private*, pg. 52
WARNER MUSIC FRANCE—See Access Industries, Inc.; *U.S. Private*, pg. 52
WARNER MUSIC GROUP CORP.—See Access Industries, Inc.; *U.S. Private*, pg. 51
WARNER MUSIC NORWAY—See Access Industries, Inc.; *U.S. Private*, pg. 52
WARNER MUSIC SWEDEN—See Access Industries, Inc.; *U.S. Private*, pg. 52
WARNER PACIFIC INSURANCE SERVICES, INC.; *U.S. Private*, pg. 4442
WARNER PARK SURGERY CENTER, L.P.—See Tenet Healthcare Corporation; *U.S. Public*, pg. 2014
WARNER POWER CONVERSION, LLC—See Blackford Capital LLC; *U.S. Private*, pg. 574
WARNER POWER, LLC—See Blackford Capital LLC; *U.S. Private*, pg. 574
WARNER PRESS, INC.; *U.S. Private*, pg. 4442
WARNER ROBINS SUPPLY CO. INC.; *U.S. Private*, pg. 4442
WARNERS MOTOR EXPRESS INC.; *U.S. Private*, pg. 4443
WARNER SPECIAL PRODUCTS—See Access Industries, Inc.; *U.S. Private*, pg. 52
WARNER'S STELLIAN CO., INC.; *U.S. Private*, pg. 4442
WARNER VINEYARDS; *U.S. Private*, pg. 4442
WARNER & WEBSTER PTY LTD—See EBOS Group Limited; *Int'l*, pg. 2286
WARN INDUSTRIES, INC.—See Dover Corporation; *U.S. Public*, pg. 680
WARNING LITES INC OF COLORADO—See Kohlberg & Company, LLC; *U.S. Private*, pg. 2337
WARNING SAS; *Int'l*, pg. 8345
THE WARNOCK AGENCY, INC.—See Boston Omaha Corporation; *U.S. Public*, pg. 372
WARNOCK FOOD PRODUCTS, INC.—See Calbee, Inc.; *Int'l*, pg. 1261
WAROM TECHNOLOGY INCORPORATED COMPANY; *Int'l*, pg. 8345
W.A. ROOSEVELT COMPANY; *U.S. Private*, pg. 4418
WAROQUIER COAL INC.; *U.S. Private*, pg. 4443
WARPAINT LONDON PLC; *Int'l*, pg. 8345
WARP BROTHERS—See Flex-O-Glass, Inc.; *U.S. Private*, pg. 1543
WARPSPEED TAXI INC.; *U.S. Public*, pg. 2329
WARP TECHNOLOGIES INC.; *U.S. Private*, pg. 4443
WARQ-FM—See YMF Media LLC; *U.S. Public*, pg. 4589
WARRAN ELECTRIC MANUFACTURING LIMITED—See Allan International Holdings Limited; *Int'l*, pg. 332
WARRANTECH AUTOMOTIVE, INC.—See Stone Point Capital LLC; *U.S. Private*, pg. 3821
WARRANTECH CONSUMER PRODUCT SERVICES GROUP—See Stone Point Capital LLC; *U.S. Private*, pg. 3821
WARRANTECH CORPORATION—See Stone Point Capital LLC; *U.S. Private*, pg. 3821
WARRANTECH DIRECT, INC.—See Stone Point Capital LLC; *U.S. Private*, pg. 3821
WARRANTECH HOME SERVICE COMPANY—See Stone Point Capital LLC; *U.S. Private*, pg. 3821
WARRANT HUB S.P.A.—See Tinexta S.p.A.; *Int'l*, pg. 7753
WARRANTY CORPORATION AMERICA; *U.S. Private*, pg. 4443
WARRANTY DIRECT LTD—See BNP Paribas SA; *Int'l*, pg. 1093
THE WARRANTY GROUP AUSTRALIA PTY. LTD.—See Assurant, Inc.; *U.S. Public*, pg. 215
THE WARRANTY GROUP COLOMBIA S.A.—See Assurant, Inc.; *U.S. Public*, pg. 215

COMPANY NAME INDEX

THE WARRANTY GROUP DE MEXICO S.A. DE C.V.—See Assurant, Inc.; *U.S. Public*, pg. 216
THE WARRANTY GROUP KOREA, INC.—See Assurant, Inc.; *U.S. Public*, pg. 215
WARRANTY SOLUTIONS MANAGEMENT CORPORATION—See Stone Point Capital LLC; *U.S. Private*, pg. 3821
WARREGO ENERGY LIMITED; *Int'l*, pg. 8346
WARREGO ENERGY UK LTD.—See Warrego Energy Limited; *Int'l*, pg. 8346
THE WARRELL CORP.—See Nassau Candy Distributors Inc.; *U.S. Private*, pg. 2837
WARREN ALLOY VALVE FITTING LP; *U.S. Private*, pg. 4443
WARREN AVERETT, LLC; *U.S. Private*, pg. 4443
WARREN BROTHERS SASH & DOOR COMPANY—See Hardwoods Distribution Inc.; *Int'l*, pg. 3273
WARREN COUNTY WATER DISTRICT; *U.S. Private*, pg. 4443
WARRENDER ENTERPRISE INC.; *U.S. Private*, pg. 4444
WARREN DIALYSIS CENTER LLC—See Nautic Partners, LLC; *U.S. Private*, pg. 2871
WARREN DIAMOND POWDER COMPANY, INC.—See Compagnie de Saint-Gobain SA; *Int'l*, pg. 1732
WARREN DISTRIBUTING CO.; *U.S. Private*, pg. 4443
WARREN DISTRIBUTING INC.; *U.S. Private*, pg. 4443
WARREN DISTRIBUTION, INC.; *U.S. Private*, pg. 4443
WARREN ELECTRIC SUPPLY INC.; *U.S. Private*, pg. 4443
WARREN ENERGY SERVICES, LLC—See Warren Resources, Inc.; *U.S. Private*, pg. 4444
WARREN EQUITY PARTNERS, LLC; *U.S. Private*, pg. 4443
WARREN FABRICATING CORPORATION - HUBBARD FACILITY—See Warren Fabricating Corporation; *U.S. Private*, pg. 4444
WARREN FABRICATING CORPORATION - NILES—See Warren Fabricating Corporation; *U.S. Private*, pg. 4444
WARREN FABRICATING CORPORATION; *U.S. Private*, pg. 4444
WARREN GIBSON LIMITED; *Int'l*, pg. 8346
WARREN HENRY AUTOMOBILES INC.; *U.S. Private*, pg. 4444
WARREN INC.—See Sonepar S.A.; *Int'l*, pg. 7094
WARREN INDUSTRIES INC.; *U.S. Private*, pg. 4444
WARREN LUMBER & MILLWORK; *U.S. Private*, pg. 4444
WARREN MARKETING, INC.; *U.S. Private*, pg. 4444
WARREN MATERIALS—See Haines & Kibblehouse Inc.; *U.S. Private*, pg. 1841
WARREN MIDTOWN MOTORS INC.; *U.S. Private*, pg. 4444
WARREN MILLER ENTERTAINMENT—See Bonnier AB; *Int'l*, pg. 1108
WARREN MOTORS, INC.; *U.S. Private*, pg. 4444
WARREN OIL COMPANY INC.; *U.S. Private*, pg. 4444
WARREN PANAMA S.A—See Sonepar S.A.; *Int'l*, pg. 7094
WARREN PAVING INC.; *U.S. Private*, pg. 4444
WARREN POWER & MACHINERY, INC.; *U.S. Private*, pg. 4444
WARREN PROPERTIES, INC.; *U.S. Private*, pg. 4444
WARREN RESOURCES, INC.; *U.S. Private*, pg. 4444
WARREN RESOURCES OF CALIFORNIA, INC.—See Warren Resources, Inc.; *U.S. Private*, pg. 4444
WARREN ROOFING & INSULATING CO.—See AC Holding Co.; *U.S. Private*, pg. 45
WARREN RUPP, INC.—See IDEX Corp; *U.S. Public*, pg. 1092
WARREN RURAL ELECTRIC COOPERATIVE CORP.; *U.S. Private*, pg. 4444
WARREN'S AIR CONDITIONING & HEATING SERVICE, INC.; *U.S. Private*, pg. 4444
WARRENS MOTORS INC.—See Barbados Shipping & Trading Co. Ltd.; *Int'l*, pg. 858
WARREN STEEL PRODUCTS INC.; *U.S. Private*, pg. 4444
WARREN'S WOOD WORKS, INC.; *U.S. Private*, pg. 4444
WARREN SYSTEMS GROUP, INC.—See Fairdinkum Consulting, LLC; *U.S. Private*, pg. 1462
WARREN TEA LIMITED; *Int'l*, pg. 8346
WARREN TIRE SERVICE CENTER, INC.; *U.S. Private*, pg. 4444
WARRENTON OIL CO.; *U.S. Private*, pg. 4444
WARREN TRASK COMPANY INC.—See Gerrity Company Incorporated; *U.S. Private*, pg. 1687
WARREN TRUCKING COMPANY INC.—See Worldwide Logistics, Inc.; *U.S. Private*, pg. 4569
WARREN WOOD INC.; *U.S. Private*, pg. 4444
WARRICK PUBLISHING CO. INC.—See Brehm Communications Inc.; *U.S. Private*, pg. 644
WARRIEDAR RESOURCES LIMITED; *Int'l*, pg. 8346
WARRIOR ENERGY SERVICES CORPORATION—See Superior Energy Services, Inc.; *U.S. Private*, pg. 3877
WARRIOR GIRL CORP.; *U.S. Public*, pg. 2329
THE WARRIOR GROUP, INC.; *U.S. Private*, pg. 4133
WARRIOR & GULF NAVIGATION COMPANY—See SoftBank Group Corp.; *Int'l*, pg. 7053
WARRIOR INSURANCE NETWORK, INC; *U.S. Private*, pg. 4444
WARRIOR MET COAL, INC; *U.S. Public*, pg. 2329

WARRIOR RIG TECHNOLOGIES LIMITED—See Patterson-UTI Energy, Inc.; *U.S. Public*, pg. 1654
WARRIOR TECHNOLOGIES ACQUISITION COMPANY; *U.S. Public*, pg. 2329
WARRIOR TRACTOR & EQUIPMENT COMPANY INC.; *U.S. Private*, pg. 4445
WARRI REFINING & PETROCHEMICAL COMPANY LIMITED—See Nigerian National Petroleum Corporation; *Int'l*, pg. 5282
WARRIX SPORT PUBLIC COMPANY LIMITED; *Int'l*, pg. 8346
THE WARRNAMBOOL CHEESE AND BUTTER FACTORY COMPANY LIMITED—See Saputo Inc.; *Int'l*, pg. 6575
WARRNAMBOOL CHEESE & BUTTER FACTORY COMPANY HOLDINGS LTD.—See Saputo Inc.; *Int'l*, pg. 6575
WARRNAMBOOL MILK PRODUCTS PTY LIMITED—See Saputo Inc.; *Int'l*, pg. 6575
WARRNAMBOOL STANDARD—See Nine Entertainment Co. Holdings Limited; *Int'l*, pg. 5299
WARRNAMBOOL VETERINARY CLINIC PTY. LTD.—See Apiam Animal Health Limited; *Int'l*, pg. 515
WARSCHAWSKI; *U.S. Private*, pg. 4445
WARSCHAWSKI—See Warschawski; *U.S. Private*, pg. 4445
WARSHAUER ELECTRIC SUPPLY COMPANY; *U.S. Private*, pg. 4445
WARSHAW, INC.—See Dunes Point Capital, LLC; *U.S. Private*, pg. 1289
WARSTEINER BRAUEREI HAUS CRAMER KG; *Int'l*, pg. 8346
WARSTEINER IMPORTERS AGENCY, INC.—See Warsteiner Brauerei Haus Cramer KG; *Int'l*, pg. 8346
WARSTEINER INTERNATIONAL KG—See Warsteiner Brauerei Haus Cramer KG; *Int'l*, pg. 8346
WARSZAWSKA FABRYKA PLATEROW HEFRA S.A.—See KGHM Polska Miedz S.A.; *Int'l*, pg. 4149
WARSZAWSKA KOLEJ DOJAZDOWA SP. Z O.O.; *Int'l*, pg. 8346
WARSZAWSKI HOLDING NIERUCHOMOSCI S.A.—See Polski Holding Nieruchomosci S.A.; *Int'l*, pg. 5912
WARTECK INVEST AG; *Int'l*, pg. 8346
WARTSILA ARGENTINA S.A.—See Wartsila Corporation; *Int'l*, pg. 8347
WARTSILA AUSTRALIA PTY. LTD., BASSENDEEN—See Wartsila Corporation; *Int'l*, pg. 8347
WARTSILA AUSTRALIA PTY LTD. - HENDERSON POWER PLANT—See Wartsila Corporation; *Int'l*, pg. 8347
WARTSILA AUSTRALIA PTY. LTD.—See Wartsila Corporation; *Int'l*, pg. 8347
WARTSILA AUTOMATION SERVICES FRANCE S.A.S.—See Wartsila Corporation; *Int'l*, pg. 8348
WARTSILA AZERBAIJAN LLC—See Wartsila Corporation; *Int'l*, pg. 8347
WARTSILA BANGLADESH LTD.—See Wartsila Corporation; *Int'l*, pg. 8347
WARTSILA BLRT ESTONIA OU—See Wartsila Corporation; *Int'l*, pg. 8347
WARTSILA BRASIL LTDA. - INFOGLOBO POWER PLANT—See Wartsila Corporation; *Int'l*, pg. 8347
WARTSILA BRASIL LTDA. - PETROLINA POWER PLANT—See Wartsila Corporation; *Int'l*, pg. 8347
WARTSILA BRASIL LTDA.—See Wartsila Corporation; *Int'l*, pg. 8347
WARTSILA CANADA, INC.—See Wartsila Corporation; *Int'l*, pg. 8347
WARTSILA CANADA INC. - VANCOUVER POWER PLANT—See Wartsila Corporation; *Int'l*, pg. 8347
WARTSILA CARIBBEAN, INC.—See Wartsila Corporation; *Int'l*, pg. 8347
WARTSILA CENTRAL AFRICA LTD.—See Wartsila Corporation; *Int'l*, pg. 8347
WARTSILA CHILE LTDA.—See Wartsila Corporation; *Int'l*, pg. 8347
WARTSILA CHINA LTD. - BEIJING POWER PLANT—See Wartsila Corporation; *Int'l*, pg. 8347
WARTSILA CHINA LTD.—See Wartsila Corporation; *Int'l*, pg. 8347
WARTSILA-CME ZHENJIANG PROPELLER CO. LTD—See Wartsila Corporation; *Int'l*, pg. 8347
WARTSILA COLOMBIA S.A. - CAACOLITO POWER PLANT—See Wartsila Corporation; *Int'l*, pg. 8347
WARTSILA COLOMBIA S.A.—See Wartsila Corporation; *Int'l*, pg. 8347
WARTSILA CORPORATION; *Int'l*, pg. 8346
WARTSILA CORP. - SERVICES BUSINESS—See Wartsila Corporation; *Int'l*, pg. 8347
WARTSILA CYPRUS LTD—See Wartsila Corporation; *Int'l*, pg. 8347
WARTSILA DANMARK A/S - COPENHAGEN—See Wartsila Corporation; *Int'l*, pg. 8347
WARTSILA DANMARK A/S - HIRTSHALS POWER PLANT—See Wartsila Corporation; *Int'l*, pg. 8347
WARTSILA DANMARK A/S—See Wartsila Corporation; *Int'l*, pg. 8347
WARTSILA DEFENCE INC.—See Wartsila Corporation; *Int'l*, pg. 8348

WARTSILA CORPORATION

WARTSILA DEFENSE, INC.—See Wartsila Corporation; *Int'l*, pg. 8348
WARTSILA DE MEXICO SA—See Wartsila Corporation; *Int'l*, pg. 8350
WARTSILA DEUTSCHLAND GMBH - HAMBURG POWER PLANT—See Wartsila Corporation; *Int'l*, pg. 8347
WARTSILA DEUTSCHLAND GMBH—See Wartsila Corporation; *Int'l*, pg. 8347
WARTSILA DEVELOPMENT & FINANCIAL SERVICES INC.—See Wartsila Corporation; *Int'l*, pg. 8349
WARTSILA DEVELOPMENT & FINANCIAL SERVICES OY—See Wartsila Corporation; *Int'l*, pg. 8347
WARTSILA DEVELOPMENT & FINANCIAL SERVICES OY, VAASA—See Wartsila Corporation; *Int'l*, pg. 8347
WARTSILA DOHA WLL—See Wartsila Corporation; *Int'l*, pg. 8347
WARTSILA DYNAMIC POSITIONING INC.—See Wartsila Corporation; *Int'l*, pg. 8347
WARTSILA ECUADOR S.A. - QUITO POWER PLANT—See Wartsila Corporation; *Int'l*, pg. 8348
WARTSILA ECUADOR S.A.—See Wartsila Corporation; *Int'l*, pg. 8347
WARTSILA-ENPA A.S.—See Wartsila Corporation; *Int'l*, pg. 8350
WARTSILA ENPA DIS TICARET A.S. - ISTANBUL POWER PLANT—See Wartsila Corporation; *Int'l*, pg. 8348
WARTSILA ENPA DIS TICARET A.S.—See Wartsila Corporation; *Int'l*, pg. 8348
WARTSILA FINLAND OY—See Wartsila Corporation; *Int'l*, pg. 8348
WARTSILA FINLAND OY - TURKU—See Wartsila Corporation; *Int'l*, pg. 8348
WARTSILA FINLAND OY - VAASA, POWER PLANTS & SERVICES—See Wartsila Corporation; *Int'l*, pg. 8348
WARTSILA FINLAND OY - VAASA, SHIP POWER & SERVICES—See Wartsila Corporation; *Int'l*, pg. 8348
WARTSILA FRANCE S.A.S. - MULHOUSE POWER PLANT—See Wartsila Corporation; *Int'l*, pg. 8348
WARTSILA FRANCE S.A.S. - PARIS POWER PLANT—See Wartsila Corporation; *Int'l*, pg. 8348
WARTSILA FRANCE S.A.S.—See Wartsila Corporation; *Int'l*, pg. 8348
WARTSILA FUNA INTERNATIONAL GMBH—See Videlio SA; *Int'l*, pg. 8190
WARTSILA FUNA INTERNATIONAL INC.—See Wartsila Corporation; *Int'l*, pg. 8348
WARTSILA GREECE S.A. - PIRAEUS POWER PLANT—See Wartsila Corporation; *Int'l*, pg. 8348
WARTSILA GREECE S.A.—See Wartsila Corporation; *Int'l*, pg. 8348
WARTSILA GUATEMALA S.A.—See Wartsila Corporation; *Int'l*, pg. 8348
WARTSILA GULF FZE—See Wartsila Corporation; *Int'l*, pg. 8348
WARTSILA HAMWORTHY LIMITED—See Wartsila Corporation; *Int'l*, pg. 8349
WARTSILA HUNGARY KFT—See Wartsila Corporation; *Int'l*, pg. 8348
WARTSILA HUNGARY KFT - VARNA POWER PLANT—See Wartsila Corporation; *Int'l*, pg. 8348
WARTSILA IBERICA S.A. - BERMEO POWER PLANT—See Wartsila Corporation; *Int'l*, pg. 8348
WARTSILA IBERICA S.A.—See Wartsila Corporation; *Int'l*, pg. 8348
WARTSILA INDIA LTD. - CHENNAI POWER PLANT—See Wartsila Corporation; *Int'l*, pg. 8348
WARTSILA INDIA LTD. - NAVI MUMBAI POWER PLANT—See Wartsila Corporation; *Int'l*, pg. 8348
WARTSILA INDIA LTD. - SECUNDERABAD POWER PLANT—See Wartsila Corporation; *Int'l*, pg. 8348
WARTSILA INDIA LTD.—See Wartsila Corporation; *Int'l*, pg. 8348
WARTSILA ITALIA S.P.A. ENERGY SOLUTIONS—See Wartsila Corporation; *Int'l*, pg. 8348
WARTSILA ITALIA S.P.A.—See Wartsila Corporation; *Int'l*, pg. 8348
WARTSILA JAPAN COMPANY LTD - KOBE POWER PLANT—See Wartsila Corporation; *Int'l*, pg. 8348
WARTSILA JAPAN COMPANY LTD - TOKYO POWER PLANT—See Wartsila Corporation; *Int'l*, pg. 8348
WARTSILA JAPAN COMPANY LTD - TOYAMA FACTORY—See Wartsila Corporation; *Int'l*, pg. 8348
WARTSILA JAPAN LTD.—See Wartsila Corporation; *Int'l*, pg. 8348
WARTSILA JOVYATLAS EUROATLAS GMBH—See L3Harris Technologies, Inc.; *U.S. Public*, pg. 1284
WARTSILA KOREA LTD.—See Wartsila Corporation; *Int'l*, pg. 8348
WARTSILA LANKA (PVT) LTD.—See Wartsila Corporation; *Int'l*, pg. 8348
WARTSILA LLC—See Wartsila Corporation; *Int'l*, pg. 8348
WARTSILA (MALAYSIA) SDN BHD—See Wartsila Corporation; *Int'l*, pg. 8347
WARTSILA MARINE AND POWER SERVICES NIGERIA LTD.—See Wartsila Corporation; *Int'l*, pg. 8348
WARTSILA MARINE SYSTEMS KOREA CO. LTD.—See L3Harris Technologies, Inc.; *U.S. Public*, pg. 1284
WARTSILA MOSS AS—See Wartsila Corporation; *Int'l*, pg. 8349

WARTSILA NETHERLANDS B.V.—See Wartsila Corporation; *Int'l*, pg. 8348
WARTSILA NETHERLANDS B.V. - ZWOLLE POWER PLANT—See Wartsila Corporation; *Int'l*, pg. 8348
WARTSILA NEW ZEALAND LTD—See Wartsila Corporation; *Int'l*, pg. 8348
WARTSILA NORTH AMERICA, INC. - ANNAPOLIS POWER PLANT—See Wartsila Corporation; *Int'l*, pg. 8349
WARTSILA NORTH AMERICA, INC.—See Wartsila Corporation; *Int'l*, pg. 8348
WARTSILA NORWAY ALESUND ASA—See Wartsila Corporation; *Int'l*, pg. 8349
WARTSILA NORWAY A/S—See Wartsila Corporation; *Int'l*, pg. 8349
WARTSILA OIL & GAS SYSTEMS AS—See Wartsila Corporation; *Int'l*, pg. 8350
WARTSILA PAKISTAN (PVT.) LTD. - KARACHI POWER PLANT—See Wartsila Corporation; *Int'l*, pg. 8349
WARTSILA PAKISTAN (PVT.) LTD.—See Wartsila Corporation; *Int'l*, pg. 8349
WARTSILA PANAMA S.A.—See Wartsila Corporation; *Int'l*, pg. 8349
WARTSILA PERU S.A.C. - LIMA POWER PLANT—See Wartsila Corporation; *Int'l*, pg. 8349
WARTSILA PERU S.A.C.—See Wartsila Corporation; *Int'l*, pg. 8349
WARTSILA PHILIPPINES INC.—See Wartsila Corporation; *Int'l*, pg. 8349
WARTSILA PNG LTD—See Wartsila Corporation; *Int'l*, pg. 8349
WARTSILA POLSKA SP. Z.O.O.—See Wartsila Corporation; *Int'l*, pg. 8349
WARTSILA POLSKA SP.Z.O.O. - WARSZAWA POWER PLANT—See Wartsila Corporation; *Int'l*, pg. 8349
WARTSILA PORTUGAL LDA.—See Wartsila Corporation; *Int'l*, pg. 8349
WARTSILA POWER CONTRACTING SAUDI ARABIA LTD.—See Wartsila Corporation; *Int'l*, pg. 8349
WARTSILA PROPULSION (WUXI) CO. LTD.—See Wartsila Corporation; *Int'l*, pg. 8349
WARTSILA PUREGAS SOLUTIONS AB—See Wartsila Corporation; *Int'l*, pg. 8349
WARTSILA PUREGAS SOLUTIONS A/S—See Wartsila Corporation; *Int'l*, pg. 8349
WARTSILA PUREGAS SOLUTIONS GMBH—See Wartsila Corporation; *Int'l*, pg. 8349
WARTSILA PUREGAS SOLUTIONS LTD.—See Wartsila Corporation; *Int'l*, pg. 8349
WARTSILA SERVICES (SHANGHAI) CO., LTD.—See Wartsila Corporation; *Int'l*, pg. 8347
WARTSILA SHANGHAI SERVICES LTD.—See Wartsila Corporation; *Int'l*, pg. 8349
WARTSILA SHIP DESIGN, CONAN WU & ASSOCIATES PTE LTD—See Wartsila Corporation; *Int'l*, pg. 8349
WARTSILA SHIP DESIGN GERMANY GMBH—See Wartsila Corporation; *Int'l*, pg. 8349
WARTSILA SHIP DESIGN POLAND SP. Z.O.O.—See Wartsila Corporation; *Int'l*, pg. 8349
WARTSILA SHIP DESIGN (SHANGHAI) CO., LTD.—See Wartsila Corporation; *Int'l*, pg. 8349
WARTSILA SHIP DESIGN SINGAPORE PTE LTD—See Wartsila Corporation; *Int'l*, pg. 8349
WARTSILA SINGAPORE PTE LTD—See Wartsila Corporation; *Int'l*, pg. 8349
WARTSILA SINGAPORE PTE LTD.—See Wartsila Corporation; *Int'l*, pg. 8349
WARTSILA SOUTH AFRICA (PTY) LTD. - CAPE TOWN POWER PLANT—See Wartsila Corporation; *Int'l*, pg. 8349
WARTSILA SOUTH AFRICA (PTY) LTD—See Wartsila Corporation; *Int'l*, pg. 8349
WARTSILA SWEDEN AB - GOTHENBURG POWER PLANT—See Wartsila Corporation; *Int'l*, pg. 8349
WARTSILA SWEDEN AB—See Wartsila Corporation; *Int'l*, pg. 8349
WARTSILA SWITZERLAND LTD.—See Wartsila Corporation; *Int'l*, pg. 8349
WARTSILA TAIWAN LTD.—See Wartsila Corporation; *Int'l*, pg. 8349
WARTSILA TECHNOLOGY OY AB—See Wartsila Corporation; *Int'l*, pg. 8349
WARTSILA UK LTD - SEALS & BEARINGS FACTORY—See Wartsila Corporation; *Int'l*, pg. 8350
WARTSILA UK LTD.—See Wartsila Corporation; *Int'l*, pg. 8349
WARTSILA VALMARINE AS—See Wartsila Corporation; *Int'l*, pg. 8350
WARTSILA VALVES LTD.—See Wartsila Corporation; *Int'l*, pg. 8350
WARTSILA VENEZUELA, C.A.—See Wartsila Corporation; *Int'l*, pg. 8350
WARTSILA VENEZUELA, C.A. - VALENCIA POWER PLANT—See Wartsila Corporation; *Int'l*, pg. 8350
WARTSILA VOSTOK, LLC; *Int'l*, pg. 8350
WARTSILA VOSTOK, LLC - ST. PETERSBURG PLANT—See Wartsila Vostok, LLC; *Int'l*, pg. 8350
WARTSILA VOYAGE LIMITED—See Wartsila Corporation; *Int'l*, pg. 8350

WARTSILA VOYAGE MIDDLE EAST DMCEST—See Wartsila Corporation; *Int'l*, pg. 8350
WARTSILA VOYAGE PACIFIC PTE. LTD.—See Wartsila Corporation; *Int'l*, pg. 8350
WARTSILA VOYAGE UK LIMITED—See Wartsila Corporation; *Int'l*, pg. 8350
WARTSILA WATER SYSTEMS LTD.—See Wartsila Corporation; *Int'l*, pg. 8350
WARTSILA WEST AFRICA S.A.—See Wartsila Corporation; *Int'l*, pg. 8350
WARTSLA ARGENTINA S.A.—See Wartsila Corporation; *Int'l*, pg. 8350
WARTSLA COLOMBIA S.A.—See Wartsila Corporation; *Int'l*, pg. 8350
WARTSLA EASTERN AFRICA S.A.—See Wartsila Corporation; *Int'l*, pg. 8350
WARTSLA ECUADOR S.A.—See Wartsila Corporation; *Int'l*, pg. 8350
WARTSLA ENERGY MAURITANIE SAU—See Wartsila Corporation; *Int'l*, pg. 8350
WARTSLA GUATEMALA S.A.—See Wartsila Corporation; *Int'l*, pg. 8350
WARWICK CAPITAL PARTNERS LLP; *Int'l*, pg. 8350
WARWICK CONSTRUCTION, INC.; *U.S. Private*, pg. 4445
WARWICK HOLDING GMBH—See Morgan Stanley; *U.S. Public*, pg. 1475
WARWICK INTERNATIONAL GROUP LIMITED—See Berkshire Hathaway Inc.; *U.S. Public*, pg. 319
WARWICK PLUMBING AND HEATING CORPORATION; *U.S. Private*, pg. 4445
THE WARWICKSHIRE NUFFIELD HOSPITAL—See Nuffield Health; *Int'l*, pg. 5488
WASA ELECTRICAL SERVICES, INC.—See Kinden Corporation; *Int'l*, pg. 4166
WASATCH ADVANTAGE GROUP, LLC; *U.S. Private*, pg. 4445
WASATCH ELECTRIC—See EMCOR Group, Inc.; *U.S. Public*, pg. 737
THE WASATCH ENDOSCOPY CENTER, LTD.—See HCA Healthcare, Inc.; *U.S. Public*, pg. 1012
WASATCH ENDOSCOPY CENTER—See HCA Healthcare, Inc.; *U.S. Public*, pg. 1013
WASATCH FRONT SURGERY CENTER, LLC—See HCA Healthcare, Inc.; *U.S. Public*, pg. 1013
WASATCH ORTHOTICS & PEDORTHICS, LLC—See Patient Square Capital, L.P.; *U.S. Private*, pg. 3107
WASATCH PRODUCT DEVELOPMENT, LLC—See Nu Skin Enterprises, Inc.; *U.S. Public*, pg. 1552
WASATCH PROPERTY MANAGEMENT, INC.—See Wasatch Advantage Group, LLC; *U.S. Private*, pg. 4445
WASATCH REGIONAL LANDFILL, INC.—See Republic Services, Inc.; *U.S. Public*, pg. 1788
WASATCH SOFTWARE, INC.; *U.S. Private*, pg. 4445
WASATCH VALLEY REHABILITATION—See Apollo Global Management, Inc.; *U.S. Public*, pg. 158
WASAUKEE COMPOSITES OWOSSO, INC.—See Sintex Industries, Ltd.; *Int'l*, pg. 6958
WASAYA AIRWAYS LP; *Int'l*, pg. 8350
WASCHEREI ELLERICH GMBH—See Clariane SE; *Int'l*, pg. 1643
WASCHKE FAMILY GM CENTER; *U.S. Private*, pg. 4445
WASCO ARMS—See Apartment Investment and Management Company; *U.S. Public*, pg. 144
WASCO (AUSTRALIA) PTY. LTD.—See Wah Seong Corporation Berhad; *Int'l*, pg. 8330
WASCO COUNTY LANDFILL, INC.—See Waste Connections, Inc.; *Int'l*, pg. 8354
WASCO ENERGY LTD. - KOTA KINABALU PLANT—See Wah Seong Corporation Berhad; *Int'l*, pg. 8330
WASCO ENERGY LTD. - KUANTAN PLANT—See Wah Seong Corporation Berhad; *Int'l*, pg. 8330
WASCO ENERGY LTD. - PIPECOATING DIVISION—See Wah Seong Corporation Berhad; *Int'l*, pg. 8330
WASCO ENERGY LTD.—See Wah Seong Corporation Berhad; *Int'l*, pg. 8330
WASCO ENERGY—See Wah Seong Corporation Berhad; *Int'l*, pg. 8330
WASCO ENGINEERING GROUP LIMITED—See Wah Seong Corporation Berhad; *Int'l*, pg. 8330
WASCO ENGINEERING INTERNATIONAL LTD.—See Wah Seong Corporation Berhad; *Int'l*, pg. 8330
WASCO GROOTHANDELSGROEP CENTRAL VERWARMING BV—See Ferguson plc; *Int'l*, pg. 2638
WASCO HOLDING BV—See Gilde Equity Management (GEM) Benelux Partners B.V.; *Int'l*, pg. 2975
WASCO INC.; *U.S. Private*, pg. 4445
WASCO OILFIELD SERVICES SDN BHD—See Wah Seong Corporation Berhad; *Int'l*, pg. 8330
WASCO PRODUCTS, INC.—See VKR Holding A/S; *Int'l*, pg. 8282
WASCOSA AG; *Int'l*, pg. 8350
WASCOSA GMBH—See Wascosa AG; *Int'l*, pg. 8350
WASECO RESOURCES INC.; *Int'l*, pg. 8350
WASEDA ACADEMY CO., LTD.; *Int'l*, pg. 8350
WASEDA EDUCATION (THAILAND) CO., LTD.—See Saha Pathanapibul Public Company Limited; *Int'l*, pg. 6479
WASGAU BACKEREI GMBH—See Wasgau Produktions & Handels AG; *Int'l*, pg. 8351

WASGAU FRISCHWAREN GMBH—See Wasgau Produktions & Handels AG; *Int'l*, pg. 8351
WASGAU METZGEREI GMBH—See Wasgau Produktions & Handels AG; *Int'l*, pg. 8351
WASGAU PRODUKTIONS & HANDELS AG; *Int'l*, pg. 8350
WASHBURN CENTER FOR CHILDREN; *U.S. Private*, pg. 4445
WASHBURN GARFIELD CORPORATION—See Collins Pipe & Supply Co., Inc.; *U.S. Private*, pg. 969
WASHCO BANCSHARES, INC.; *U.S. Private*, pg. 4445
WASH DEPOT HOLDINGS, INC.; *U.S. Private*, pg. 4445
W.A. SHEETS & SONS, INC.; *U.S. Private*, pg. 4419
WASHEX, INC.—See Machinefabriek Goudkuil Apeldoorn B.V.; *Int'l*, pg. 4622
WASH HOUSE CO., LTD.; *Int'l*, pg. 8351
WASHING EQUIPMENT OF TEXAS; *U.S. Private*, pg. 4445
WASHING EQUIPMENT TECHNOLOGIES, INC.—See Simoniz USA, Inc.; *U.S. Private*, pg. 3666
WASHING SYSTEMS, LLC; *U.S. Private*, pg. 4446
WASHINGTON AIR REPS INC.; *U.S. Private*, pg. 4446
WASHINGTON ALDER, LLC; *U.S. Private*, pg. 4446
WASHINGTON ATHLETIC CLUB; *U.S. Private*, pg. 4446
WASHINGTON AUTOMATED, LLC—See EVI Industries, Inc.; *U.S. Public*, pg. 803
WASHINGTON BUILDERS SUPPLY CO.—See GMS Inc.; *U.S. Public*, pg. 948
WASHINGTON BUSINESS BANK; *U.S. Public*, pg. 2329
WASHINGTON BUSINESS INFORMATION, INC.—See Leonard Green & Partners, L.P.; *U.S. Private*, pg. 2430
WASHINGTON BUSINESS JOURNAL, INC.—See Advance Publications, Inc.; *U.S. Private*, pg. 85
WASHINGTON CAPITAL MANAGEMENT, INC.; *U.S. Private*, pg. 4446
WASHINGTON CAPITALS—See Lincoln Holdings LLC; *U.S. Private*, pg. 2457
WASHINGTON CARE CENTER; *U.S. Private*, pg. 4446
WASHINGTON CEDAR & SUPPLY CO.; *U.S. Private*, pg. 4446
THE WASHINGTON CONSULTING GROUP INC.; *U.S. Private*, pg. 4133
WASHINGTON CORPORATIONS; *U.S. Private*, pg. 4446
WASHINGTON COUNTY CHAMBER OF COMMERCE; *U.S. Private*, pg. 4447
WASHINGTON COUNTY ENTERPRISE-LEADER—See Wehco Media, Inc.; *U.S. Private*, pg. 4470
WASHINGTON CRAB PRODUCERS INC.—See Dulcich, Inc.; *U.S. Private*, pg. 1286
WASHINGTON CROSSING ADVISORS, LLC—See Stifel Financial Corp.; *U.S. Public*, pg. 1950
WASHINGTON DERMATOLOGY CENTER—See Ridgemont Partners Management LLC; *U.S. Private*, pg. 3433
WASHINGTON DESIGN CENTER L.L.C.—See Vornado Realty Trust; *U.S. Public*, pg. 2310
WASHINGTON DEVELOPMENT—See Washington Corporations; *U.S. Private*, pg. 4446
WASHINGTON EARLY LEARNING FUND; *U.S. Private*, pg. 4447
WASHINGTON EDUCATIONAL TELECOMMUNICATIONS ASSOCIATION; *U.S. Private*, pg. 4447
WASHINGTON ELECTRIC CO. INC.; *U.S. Private*, pg. 4447
WASHINGTON ELECTRIC COOPERATIVE, INC.; *U.S. Private*, pg. 4447
WASHINGTON ELECTRIC MEMBERSHIP CORPORATION; *U.S. Private*, pg. 4447
WASHINGTON ENERGY SERVICES COMPANY INC.—See Northwest Water Heater Inc.; *U.S. Private*, pg. 2962
WASHINGTON EQUITY PARTNERS L.L.C.; *U.S. Private*, pg. 4447
THE WASHINGTON EVENING JOURNAL—See Inland Industries, Inc.; *U.S. Private*, pg. 2078
WASHINGTON FEDERAL, NATIONAL ASSOCIATION—See WaFd, Inc.; *U.S. Public*, pg. 2321
WASHINGTON FINANCIAL GROUP—See Hellman & Friedman LLC; *U.S. Private*, pg. 1909
WASHINGTON FOOTBALL, INC.; *U.S. Private*, pg. 4447
WASHINGTON GAS ENERGY SERVICES, INC.—See AltaGas Ltd.; *Int'l*, pg. 384
WASHINGTON GAS ENERGY SYSTEMS, INC.—See AltaGas Ltd.; *Int'l*, pg. 384
WASHINGTON GAS LIGHT COMPANY—See AltaGas Ltd.; *Int'l*, pg. 384
WASHINGTON GAS RESOURCES CORP.—See AltaGas Ltd.; *Int'l*, pg. 384
WASHINGTON GOLD CASINOS LLC—See Maverick Gold LLC; *U.S. Private*, pg. 2616
WASHINGTON HILTON, L.L.C.—See Hilton Worldwide Holdings Inc.; *U.S. Public*, pg. 1041
WASHINGTON HOME CENTER INC.; *U.S. Private*, pg. 4447
WASHINGTON HOTEL CORPORATION; *Int'l*, pg. 8351
WASHINGTON H. SOUL PATTINSON & COMPANY LIMITED; *Int'l*, pg. 8351
WASHINGTONIAN LIMOUSINE COACH CORP.; *U.S. Private*, pg. 4449

COMPANY NAME INDEX

WASHINGTON IRON WORKS, INC.—See Professional Rebuild & Optimal Service LLC; *U.S. Private*, pg. 3276

WASHINGTON LABORATORIES, LTD.—See Mace Security International, Inc.; *U.S. Public*, pg. 1352

WASHINGTON LIFTRUCK INC.; *U.S. Private*, pg. 4447

WASHINGTON MANAGEMENT GROUP, INC.—See Aronson LLC; *U.S. Private*, pg. 334

WASHINGTON MARINE GROUP—See Washington Corporations; *U.S. Private*, pg. 4446

WASHINGTON MEDICAL BILLING—See CareCloud, Inc.; *U.S. Public*, pg. 435

WASHINGTON METROPOLITAN AREA TRANSIT AUTHORITY; *U.S. Private*, pg. 4447

WASHINGTON MILL LOFTS LLC—See Bank of America Corporation; *U.S. Public*, pg. 272

WASHINGTON MILLS CERAMICS CORPORATION—See Washington Mills Company Inc.; *U.S. Private*, pg. 4447

WASHINGTON MILLS COMPANY INC.; *U.S. Private*, pg. 4447

WASHINGTON MILLS COMPANY INC.—See Washington Mills Company Inc.; *U.S. Private*, pg. 4447

WASHINGTON MILLS ELECTRO MINERALS CORPORATION—See Washington Mills Company Inc.; *U.S. Private*, pg. 4447

WASHINGTON MILLS TONAWANDA, INC.—See Washington Mills Company Inc.; *U.S. Private*, pg. 4447

WASHINGTON MUSIC SALES CENTER; *U.S. Private*, pg. 4447

WASHINGTON MYSTICS—See Lincoln Holdings LLC; *U.S. Private*, pg. 2457

WASHINGTON NATIONAL INSURANCE COMPANY—See CNO Financial Group, Inc.; *U.S. Public*, pg. 520

WASHINGTON NATIONAL INSURANCE CO.—See CNO Financial Group, Inc.; *U.S. Public*, pg. 520

WASHINGTON NATIONALS, L.P.; *U.S. Private*, pg. 4448

THE WASHINGTON NEWSPAPER PUBLISHING COMPANY, LLC—See The Anschutz Corporation; *U.S. Private*, pg. 3987

WASHINGTON ORNAMENTAL IRON WORKS; *U.S. Private*, pg. 4448

WASHINGTON PARK MALL, LLC—See Brookfield Corporation; *Int'l*, pg. 1185

WASHINGTON PENN PLASTIC CO., INC. - FRANKFORT DIVISION—See Audia International, Inc.; *U.S. Private*, pg. 391

WASHINGTON PENN PLASTIC CO., INC.—See Audia International, Inc.; *U.S. Private*, pg. 390

THE WASHINGTON POST NEWS SERVICE & SYNDICATE—See Nash Holdings LLC; *U.S. Private*, pg. 2836

WASHINGTONPOST.NEWSWEEK INTERACTIVE COMPANY, LLC—See Nash Holdings LLC; *U.S. Private*, pg. 2836

WASHINGTON PRIME GROUP INC.; *U.S. Private*, pg. 4448

WASHINGTON PRIME GROUP, L.P.—See Washington Prime Group Inc.; *U.S. Private*, pg. 4449

WASHINGTON PRIME PROPERTIES LLC—See Washington Prime Group Inc.; *U.S. Private*, pg. 4449

WASHINGTON PRIME PROPERTY LIMITED PARTNERSHIP—See Washington Prime Group Inc.; *U.S. Private*, pg. 4449

WASHINGTON PRODUCE—See Caruso Produce, Inc.; *U.S. Private*, pg. 777

WASHINGTON PRODUCTS INC.; *U.S. Private*, pg. 4449

WASHINGTON QUALITY FOODS—See Wilkins-Rogers, Inc.; *U.S. Private*, pg. 4520

WASHINGTON REGIONAL TRANSPLANT COMMUNITY; *U.S. Private*, pg. 4449

WASHINGTON-SAINT TAMMANY ELECTRIC COOPERATIVE INC.; *U.S. Private*, pg. 4449

WASHINGTON SQUARE CENTER—See Saul Centers, Inc.; *U.S. Public*, pg. 1842

WASHINGTON STATE HOSPITAL ASSOCIATION; *U.S. Private*, pg. 4449

WASHINGTON STREET INVESTMENTS LLC—See Prudential Financial, Inc.; *U.S. Public*, pg. 1734

WASHINGTON ST. TAMMANY ELECTRIC COOPERATIVE INC.; *U.S. Private*, pg. 4449

WASHINGTON SUBURBAN SANITARY COMMISSION; *U.S. Private*, pg. 4449

WASHINGTON TERMINAL COMPANY—See National Railroad Passenger Corporation; *U.S. Private*, pg. 2861

THE WASHINGTON TIMES, LLC—See Family Federation for World Peace & Unification; *U.S. Private*, pg. 1469

WASHINGTON TRUST BANCORP, INC.; *U.S. Public*, pg. 2329

WASHINGTON TRUST BANK—See W.T.B. Financial Corporation; *U.S. Public*, pg. 2319

THE WASHINGTON TRUST COMPANY, OF WESTERLY—See Washington Trust Bancorp, Inc.; *U.S. Public*, pg. 2329

WASHINGTON WATER SERVICE COMPANY—See California Water Service Group; *U.S. Public*, pg. 424

WASHINGTON WHOLESALE LIQUOR COMPANY, LLC—See Breakthru Beverage Group, LLC; *U.S. Private*, pg. 643

WASHINGTON WIZARDS—See Lincoln Holdings LLC; *U.S. Private*, pg. 2457

WASHITA VALLEY LOGISTICS, LLC—See Arcosa, Inc.; *U.S. Public*, pg. 186

WASH ME FAST, LLC—See Red Dog Equity LLC; *U.S. Private*, pg. 3374

WASH MULTIFAMILY LAUNDRY SYSTEMS, LLC—See EQT AB; *Int'l*, pg. 2481

WASHOE BUILDING SUPPLY COMPANY, INC.—See Leonard Green & Partners, L.P.; *U.S. Private*, pg. 2429

WASHREIT ALEXANDRIA LLC—See Elme Communities; *U.S. Public*, pg. 735

WASHREIT DULLES LLC—See Elme Communities; *U.S. Public*, pg. 735

WASHREIT GERMANTOWN LLC—See Elme Communities; *U.S. Public*, pg. 735

WASHREIT LANDMARK LLC—See Elme Communities; *U.S. Public*, pg. 735

WASHREIT LEESBURG LLC—See Elme Communities; *U.S. Public*, pg. 735

WASHREIT WATKINS MILL LLC—See Elme Communities; *U.S. Public*, pg. 735

WASHROOM HYGIENE CONCEPTS PRIVATE LIMITED—See Updater Services Limited; *Int'l*, pg. 8087

WASHTEC AG; *Int'l*, pg. 8351

WASHTEC BENELUX B.V.—See WashTec AG; *Int'l*, pg. 8351

WASHTEC BILVASK AS—See WashTec AG; *Int'l*, pg. 8351

WASHTEC CAR CLEANING EQUIPMENT (SHANGHAI) CO. LTD.; *Int'l*, pg. 8352

WASHTEC CLEANING TECHNOLOGY GMBH—See WashTec AG; *Int'l*, pg. 8351

WASHTEC CLEANING TECHNOLOGY GMBH—See WashTec AG; *Int'l*, pg. 8351

WASHTEC CZ, SPOL. S.R.O.—See WashTec AG; *Int'l*, pg. 8351

WASHTEC DENMARK AS—See WashTec AG; *Int'l*, pg. 8351

WASHTEC FINANCIAL SERVICES GMBH—See WashTec AG; *Int'l*, pg. 8351

WASHTEC FRANCE SAS—See WashTec AG; *Int'l*, pg. 8351

WASHTECH—See Ali Holding S.r.l; *Int'l*, pg. 322

WASHTEC IRELAND LTD.—See WashTec AG; *Int'l*, pg. 8351

WASHTEC POLSKA SP. Z O.O.—See WashTec AG; *Int'l*, pg. 8351

WASHTEC SPAIN SA—See WashTec AG; *Int'l*, pg. 8351

WASHTEC S.R.L.—See WashTec AG; *Int'l*, pg. 8351

WASHTEC UK LTD.—See WashTec AG; *Int'l*, pg. 8351

WASHTENAW COUNTY ROAD COMMISSION; *U.S. Private*, pg. 4449

THE WASH TUB; *U.S. Private*, pg. 4133

WASHWORLD, INC.; *U.S. Private*, pg. 4450

WASI BULGARIEN E.O.O.D.—See Wurth Verwaltungsgesellschaft mbH; *Int'l*, pg. 8508

WASI D.O.O.—See Wurth Verwaltungsgesellschaft mbH; *Int'l*, pg. 8508

WASI D.O.O.—See Wurth Verwaltungsgesellschaft mbH; *Int'l*, pg. 8508

WASI, INC.—See The Atlas Group; *U.S. Private*, pg. 3990

WASI INOX DENMARK APS—See Wurth Verwaltungsgesellschaft mbH; *Int'l*, pg. 8508

WASION ENERGY TECHNOLOGY CO., LTD.—See Wasion Holdings Limited; *Int'l*, pg. 8352

WASION HOLDINGS LIMITED; *Int'l*, pg. 8352

WASI TIANJIN FASTENER CO., LTD.—See Wurth Verwaltungsgesellschaft mbH; *Int'l*, pg. 8508

WASKAHIGAN OIL & GAS CORP.; *Int'l*, pg. 8352

WASK LTD.—See Crane NXT, Co.; *U.S. Public*, pg. 591

WASKOM GAS PROCESSING CO.—See CenterPoint Energy, Inc.; *U.S. Public*, pg. 472

WASKO S.A.; *Int'l*, pg. 8352

WASMER, SCHROEDER & COMPANY, LLC—See The Charles Schwab Corporation; *U.S. Public*, pg. 2058

WASP BARCODE TECHNOLOGIES LTD.—See Datalogic S.p.A.; *Int'l*, pg. 1978

WASP INC.; *U.S. Private*, pg. 4450

WA-SPOK DH CRNA, LLC—See Community Health Systems, Inc.; *U.S. Public*, pg. 557

WA-SPOK MEDICAL CARE, LLC—See Community Health Systems, Inc.; *U.S. Public*, pg. 557

WA-SPOK PRIMARY CARE, LLC—See Community Health Systems, Inc.; *U.S. Public*, pg. 557

WA-SPOK PULMONARY & CRITICAL CARE, LLC—See Community Health Systems, Inc.; *U.S. Public*, pg. 557

WA-SPOK VH CRNA, LLC—See Community Health Systems, Inc.; *U.S. Public*, pg. 557

WASSCO; *U.S. Private*, pg. 4450

WASSENBURG MEDICAL B.V.—See Hoya Corporation; *Int'l*, pg. 3498

WASSERBURGER ARZNEIMITTELWERK GMBH—See Recipharm AB; *Int'l*, pg. 6236

WASSER FILTRATION INC.; *U.S. Private*, pg. 4450

WASSERMAN MEDIA GROUP, LLC; *U.S. Private*, pg. 4450

WASSERMAN & PARTNERS ADVERTISING INC.; *Int'l*, pg. 8352

WASSERMAN VORNADO STRATEGIC REAL ESTATE FUND LLC—See Vornado Realty Trust; *U.S. Public*, pg. 2310

WASSERSTEIN & CO., LP; *U.S. Private*, pg. 4450

WASSERSTROM COMPANY; *U.S. Private*, pg. 4450

WASTBYGG GRUPPEN AB; *Int'l*, pg. 8352

WASTE ASSOCIATES, LLC—See BlackEagle Partners, LLC; *U.S. Private*, pg. 573

WASTEBOX DEUTSCHLAND GMBH—See Veolia Environnement S.A.; *Int'l*, pg. 8163

WASTEBUILT ENVIRONMENTAL SOLUTIONS, LLC—See H.I.G. Capital, LLC; *U.S. Private*, pg. 1833

WASTECH CONTROLS & ENGINEERING, INC.—See SKion GmbH; *Int'l*, pg. 6990

WASTECH SERVICES LTD.—See Belkorp Industries, Inc.; *Int'l*, pg. 965

WASTE COLLECTION & RECYCLING CO. LTD.—See Middle East Paper Company; *Int'l*, pg. 4884

WASTE CONNECTIONS BAYOU, INC.—See Waste Connections, Inc.; *Int'l*, pg. 8354

WASTE CONNECTIONS, INC.; *Int'l*, pg. 8352

WASTE CONNECTIONS OF CANADA INC.—See Waste Connections, Inc.; *Int'l*, pg. 8355

WASTE CONNECTIONS OF COLORADO, INC.—See Waste Connections, Inc.; *Int'l*, pg. 8354

WASTE CONNECTIONS OF IOWA, INC.—See Waste Connections, Inc.; *Int'l*, pg. 8354

WASTE CONNECTIONS OF KANSAS, INC.—See Waste Connections, Inc.; *Int'l*, pg. 8354

WASTE CONNECTIONS OF KENTUCKY, INC.—See Waste Connections, Inc.; *Int'l*, pg. 8354

WASTE CONNECTIONS OF LOUISIANA, INC.—See Waste Connections, Inc.; *Int'l*, pg. 8354

WASTE CONNECTIONS OF MINNESOTA, INC.—See Waste Connections, Inc.; *Int'l*, pg. 8354

WASTE CONNECTIONS OF MISSISSIPPI, INC.—See Waste Connections, Inc.; *Int'l*, pg. 8354

WASTE CONNECTIONS OF MISSOURI, INC.—See Waste Connections, Inc.; *Int'l*, pg. 8354

WASTE CONNECTIONS OF MONTANA, INC.—See Waste Connections, Inc.; *Int'l*, pg. 8354

WASTE CONNECTIONS OF NEBRASKA, INC.—See Waste Connections, Inc.; *Int'l*, pg. 8354

WASTE CONNECTIONS OF NORTH CAROLINA, INC.—See Waste Connections, Inc.; *Int'l*, pg. 8354

WASTE CONNECTIONS OF NORTH DAKOTA, INC.—See Waste Connections, Inc.; *Int'l*, pg. 8354

WASTE CONNECTIONS OF OSCEOLA COUNTY, LLC—See Waste Connections, Inc.; *Int'l*, pg. 8354

WASTE CONNECTIONS OF PENNSYLVANIA, INC.—See Waste Connections, Inc.; *Int'l*, pg. 8354

WASTE CONNECTIONS OF SOUTH CAROLINA, INC.—See Waste Connections, Inc.; *Int'l*, pg. 8354

WASTE CONNECTIONS OF TENNESSEE, INC.—See Waste Connections, Inc.; *Int'l*, pg. 8354

WASTE CONNECTIONS OF WASHINGTON, INC.—See Waste Connections, Inc.; *Int'l*, pg. 8354

WASTE CONNECTIONS OF WYOMING, INC.—See Waste Connections, Inc.; *Int'l*, pg. 8355

WASTE CONNECTIONS US, INC.—See Waste Connections, Inc.; *Int'l*, pg. 8352

WASTE CONSOLIDATORS, INC.—See Ally Waste Services, LLC; *U.S. Private*, pg. 194

WASTE CONTROL SPECIALISTS LLC—See J.F. Lehman & Company, Inc.; *U.S. Private*, pg. 2164

WASTE CORPORATION OF KANSAS, INC.—See BC Partners LLP; *Int'l*, pg. 924

WASTE CORPORATION OF TEXAS, LP—See BC Partners LLP; *Int'l*, pg. 924

WASTECYCLE LTD.—See DCC plc; *Int'l*, pg. 1991

WASTE HARMONICS, LLC—See TPG Capital, L.P.; *U.S. Public*, pg. 2174

WASTE INDUSTRIES USA, LLC—See BC Partners LLP; *Int'l*, pg. 924

WASTE ITALIA S.P.A.—See Gruppo Waste Italia S.p.A.; *Int'l*, pg. 3141

WASTE MANAGEMENT COLLECTION AND RECYCLING, INC.—See Waste Management, Inc.; *U.S. Public*, pg. 2333

WASTE MANAGEMENT DISPOSAL SERVICES OF COLORADO, INC.—See Waste Management, Inc.; *U.S. Public*, pg. 2333

WASTE MANAGEMENT DISPOSAL SERVICES OF MAINE, INC.—See Waste Management, Inc.; *U.S. Public*, pg. 2333

WASTE MANAGEMENT DISPOSAL SERVICES OF MASSACHUSETTS - HOLYOKE LANDFILL—See Waste Management, Inc.; *U.S. Public*, pg. 2333

WASTE MANAGEMENT DISPOSAL SERVICES OF OREGON - ARLINGTON HAZARDOUS WASTE FACILITY—See Waste Management, Inc.; *U.S. Public*, pg. 2333

WASTE MANAGEMENT DISPOSAL SERVICES OF OREGON - COLUMBIA RIDGE LANDFILL—See Waste Management, Inc.; *U.S. Public*, pg. 2333

WASTE MANAGEMENT HOLDINGS, INC.—See Waste Management, Inc.; *U.S. Public*, pg. 2333

WASTE CONNECTIONS, INC. — CORPORATE AFFILIATIONS

WASTE MANAGEMENT INC. OF FLORIDA - BRADENTON—See Waste Management, Inc.; *U.S. Public*, pg. 2333

WASTE MANAGEMENT INC. OF FLORIDA - HOBE SOUND—See Waste Management, Inc.; *U.S. Public*, pg. 2333

WASTE MANAGEMENT INC. OF FLORIDA - MELBOURNE—See Waste Management, Inc.; *U.S. Public*, pg. 2333

WASTE MANAGEMENT, INC. OF TENNESSEE - NASHVILLE—See Waste Management, Inc.; *U.S. Public*, pg. 2334

WASTE MANAGEMENT, INC.; *U.S. Public*, pg. 2330

WASTE MANAGEMENT NATIONAL TRANSPORTATION SERVICES, INC.—See Waste Management, Inc.; *U.S. Public*, pg. 2333

WASTE MANAGEMENT NZ LIMITED—See Capital Environment Holdings Limited; *Int'l*, pg. 1310

WASTE MANAGEMENT OF ALAMEDA COUNTY, INC.—See Waste Management, Inc.; *U.S. Public*, pg. 2333

WASTE MANAGEMENT OF ARIZONA - PHOENIX SOUTH HAULING—See Waste Management, Inc.; *U.S. Public*, pg. 2333

WASTE MANAGEMENT OF ARKANSAS, INC.—See Waste Management, Inc.; *U.S. Public*, pg. 2333

WASTE MANAGEMENT OF CALIFORNIA - CASTROVILLE—See Waste Management, Inc.; *U.S. Public*, pg. 2333

WASTE MANAGEMENT OF CALIFORNIA - GOLD RIVER—See Waste Management, Inc.; *U.S. Public*, pg. 2333

WASTE MANAGEMENT OF CALIFORNIA - HEALTH SANITATION SERVICE—See Waste Management, Inc.; *U.S. Public*, pg. 2333

WASTE MANAGEMENT OF CALIFORNIA - SUN VALLEY HAULING—See Waste Management, Inc.; *U.S. Public*, pg. 2333

WASTE MANAGEMENT OF CANADA CORP. - BARRIE—See Waste Management, Inc.; *U.S. Public*, pg. 2333

WASTE MANAGEMENT OF CANADA CORPORATION—See Waste Management, Inc.; *U.S. Public*, pg. 2333

WASTE MANAGEMENT OF CANADA CORP. - QUEBEC DIVISIONAL OFFICE-GMA—See Waste Management, Inc.; *U.S. Public*, pg. 2333

WASTE MANAGEMENT OF CAROLINAS - GASTONIA—See Waste Management, Inc.; *U.S. Public*, pg. 2333

WASTE MANAGEMENT OF COLORADO - DENVER- 48TH AVENUE—See Waste Management, Inc.; *U.S. Public*, pg. 2333

WASTE MANAGEMENT OF CONNECTICUT, INC.—See Waste Management, Inc.; *U.S. Public*, pg. 2333

WASTE MANAGEMENT OF FLORIDA INC. - PINE RIDGE RECYCLING & DISPOSAL FACILITY—See Waste Management, Inc.; *U.S. Public*, pg. 2333

WASTE MANAGEMENT OF HAWAII, INC.—See Waste Management, Inc.; *U.S. Public*, pg. 2333

WASTE MANAGEMENT OF IDAHO, INC.—See Waste Management, Inc.; *U.S. Public*, pg. 2333

WASTE MANAGEMENT OF INDIANA, L.L.C.—See Waste Management, Inc.; *U.S. Public*, pg. 2334

WASTE MANAGEMENT OF IOWA, INC.—See Waste Management, Inc.; *U.S. Public*, pg. 2334

WASTE MANAGEMENT OF LOUISIANA, L.L.C.—See Waste Management, Inc.; *U.S. Public*, pg. 2334

WASTE MANAGEMENT OF MAINE, INC.—See Waste Management, Inc.; *U.S. Public*, pg. 2334

WASTE MANAGEMENT OF MARYLAND, INC.—See Waste Management, Inc.; *U.S. Public*, pg. 2334

WASTE MANAGEMENT OF MICHIGAN, INC.—See Waste Management, Inc.; *U.S. Public*, pg. 2334

WASTE MANAGEMENT OF MISSISSIPPI - JACKSON HAULING—See Waste Management, Inc.; *U.S. Public*, pg. 2334

WASTE MANAGEMENT OF MISSOURI, INC.—See Waste Management, Inc.; *U.S. Public*, pg. 2334

WASTE MANAGEMENT OF NEBRASKA, INC.—See Waste Management, Inc.; *U.S. Public*, pg. 2334

WASTE MANAGEMENT OF NEVADA, INC.—See Waste Management, Inc.; *U.S. Public*, pg. 2334

WASTE MANAGEMENT OF NEW JERSEY, INC.—See Waste Management, Inc.; *U.S. Public*, pg. 2334

WASTE MANAGEMENT OF NEW MEXICO, INC.—See Waste Management, Inc.; *U.S. Public*, pg. 2334

WASTE MANAGEMENT OF NEW YORK - ROCHESTER—See Waste Management, Inc.; *U.S. Public*, pg. 2334

WASTE MANAGEMENT OF NEW YORK - VARICK I TRANSFER STATION—See Waste Management, Inc.; *U.S. Public*, pg. 2334

WASTE MANAGEMENT OF NORTH DAKOTA, INC.—See Waste Management, Inc.; *U.S. Public*, pg. 2334

WASTE MANAGEMENT OF OKLAHOMA, INC.—See Waste Management, Inc.; *U.S. Public*, pg. 2334

WASTE MANAGEMENT OF OREGON, INC.—See Waste Management, Inc.; *U.S. Public*, pg. 2334

WASTE MANAGEMENT OF PENNSYLVANIA - DUNMORE—See Waste Management, Inc.; *U.S. Public*, pg. 2334

WASTE MANAGEMENT OF RHODE ISLAND, INC.—See Waste Management, Inc.; *U.S. Public*, pg. 2334

WASTE MANAGEMENT OF SOUTH CAROLINA, INC.—See Waste Management, Inc.; *U.S. Public*, pg. 2334

WASTE MANAGEMENT OF WASHINGTON - KIRKLAND COLLECTIONS—See Waste Management, Inc.; *U.S. Public*, pg. 2334

WASTE MANAGEMENT OF WEST VIRGINIA, INC.—See Waste Management, Inc.; *U.S. Public*, pg. 2334

WASTE MANAGEMENT OF WISCONSIN, INC.—See Waste Management, Inc.; *U.S. Public*, pg. 2334

WASTE MANAGEMENT PACIFIC PTY. LIMITED—See Cleanaway Waste Management Limited; *Int'l*, pg. 1655

WASTE MANAGEMENT & PROCESSORS, INC—See Reading Anthracite Company; *U.S. Private*, pg. 3366

WASTE MANAGEMENT PTE LTD—See Tan Chong International Limited; *Int'l*, pg. 7453

WASTE MANAGEMENT RECYCLING AND DISPOSAL SERVICES OF CALIFORNIA, INC.—See Waste Management, Inc.; *U.S. Public*, pg. 2333

WASTE MANAGEMENT SIAM LTD.—See Dowa Holdings Co., Ltd.; *Int'l*, pg. 2183

WASTE MANAGEMENT TECHNICAL SERVICES (NZ) LTD.—See Capital Environment Holdings Limited; *Int'l*, pg. 1310

WASTE MASTERS SOLUTIONS, LLC—See Waste Connections, Inc.; *Int'l*, pg. 8355

WASTE NEWS—See Crain Communications, Inc.; *U.S. Private*, pg. 1084

WASTE OIL RECYCLERS, INC.—See Neste Oyj; *Int'l*, pg. 5201

WASTE PLASTIC UPCYCLING A/S; *Int'l*, pg. 8355

WASTE PRO OF GEORGIA, INC.—See Waste Pro USA, Inc.; *U.S. Private*, pg. 4450

WASTE PRO USA, INC.; *U.S. Private*, pg. 4450

WASTEQUIP, LLC—See H.I.G. Capital, LLC; *U.S. Private*, pg. 1832

WASTE RECYCLING INC.; *U.S. Private*, pg. 4450

WASTE SERVICES AUSTRALIA PTY LTD—See Cleanaway Waste Management Limited; *Int'l*, pg. 1655

WASTE SOLUTIONS LIMITED—See Downer EDI Limited; *Int'l*, pg. 2186

WASTE-STREAM, INC.—See Casella Waste Systems, Inc.; *U.S. Public*, pg. 446

WASTE STREAM TECHNOLOGY, INC.—See Sevenson Environmental Services, Inc.; *U.S. Private*, pg. 3619

WASTE TEC GMBH—See Zheneng Jinjiang Environment Holding Company Limited; *Int'l*, pg. 8669

WASTETECH—See Sulzer Ltd.; *Int'l*, pg. 7259

WASTREN ADVANTAGE, INC.—See Wastren Advantage, Inc.; *U.S. Private*, pg. 4451

WASTREN ADVANTAGE, INC.; *U.S. Private*, pg. 4451

WASU MEDIA HOLDING CO., LTD.; *Int'l*, pg. 8355

WATABE EUROPE S.A.R.L.—See Kowa Co., Ltd.; *Int'l*, pg. 4294

WATABE SINGAPORE. PTE. LTD.—See Kowa Co., Ltd.; *Int'l*, pg. 4294

WATABE WEDDING CORPORATION—See Kowa Co., Ltd.; *Int'l*, pg. 4294

WATABE WEDDING (SHANGHAI) CO., LTD.—See Kowa Co., Ltd.; *Int'l*, pg. 4294

WATA CHEMICALS LTD.; *Int'l*, pg. 8355

WATACHUKIKAI CORP.—See Kanematsu Corporation; *Int'l*, pg. 4069

WATAHAN & CO., LTD.; *Int'l*, pg. 8355

WATAHAN FRESH MARKET CO., LTD.—See Watahan & Co., Ltd.; *Int'l*, pg. 8355

WATAHAN HOME-AID CO., LTD.—See Watahan & Co., Ltd.; *Int'l*, pg. 8355

WATAHAN-NOHARA SEKIZENKAI, A SOCIAL WELFARE CORPORATION—See Watahan & Co., Ltd.; *Int'l*, pg. 8355

WATAHAN SOLUTIONS CO., LTD.—See Watahan & Co., Ltd.; *Int'l*, pg. 8355

WATAIR INC.; *U.S. Private*, pg. 4451

WATAMI (CHINA) CO., LTD.—See Watami Co., Ltd.; *Int'l*, pg. 8355

WATAMI CO., LTD.; *Int'l*, pg. 8355

WATAMI FARM CO., LTD.—See Watami Co., Ltd.; *Int'l*, pg. 8355

WATANABE FLORAL, INC.; *U.S. Private*, pg. 4451

WATANABE PIPE CO., LTD.; *Int'l*, pg. 8355

WATANABE SATO CO., LTD.; *Int'l*, pg. 8355

WATANA INTER - TRADE CO., LTD.—See Kanematsu Corporation; *Int'l*, pg. 4069

WATANI FINANCIAL BROKERAGE COMPANY K.S.C.—See National Bank of Kuwait S.A.K.; *Int'l*, pg. 5154

WATANI INVESTMENT COMPANY—See National Bank of Kuwait S.A.K.; *Int'l*, pg. 5154

WATANI WEALTH MANAGEMENT COMPANY—See National Bank of Kuwait S.A.K.; *Int'l*, pg. 5154

WATANIYA INSURANCE COMPANY; *Int'l*, pg. 8355

WATAUGA DEMOCRAT NEWSPAPERS, INC.—See Adams Publishing Group, LLC; *U.S. Private*, pg. 75

WATAUGA GROUP LLC; *U.S. Private*, pg. 4451

WATAUGA MEDICAL CENTER; *U.S. Private*, pg. 4451

WATAWALA PLANTATIONS PLC; *Int'l*, pg. 8355

WATCHDATA SYSTEM CO., LTD.; *Int'l*, pg. 8355

WATCHDATA TECHNOLOGIES CO. LTD.—See Watchdata System Co., Ltd.; *Int'l*, pg. 8355

WATCHDATA TECHNOLOGIES PRIVATE LIMITED—See Watchdata System Co., Ltd.; *Int'l*, pg. 8355

WATCHDATA TECHNOLOGIES USA INC.—See Watchdata System Co., Ltd.; *Int'l*, pg. 8355

WATCHDOX, INC.—See BlackBerry Limited; *Int'l*, pg. 1060

WATCHES OF SWITZERLAND GROUP PLC; *Int'l*, pg. 8355

WATCHES OF SWITZERLAND (NEVADA) LLC—See Watches of Switzerland Group PLC; *Int'l*, pg. 8355

WATCHES OF SWITZERLAND OPERATIONS LIMITED—See Apollo Global Management, Inc.; *U.S. Public*, pg. 167

WATCHES OF SWITZERLAND PTE. LTD.—See The Hour Glass Limited; *Int'l*, pg. 7653

WATCHFINDER.CO.UK LIMITED—See Compagnie Financiere Richemont S.A.; *Int'l*, pg. 1741

WATCHFIRE SIGNS, LLC—See H.I.G. Capital, LLC; *U.S. Private*, pg. 1834

WATCHGUARD, INC.—See Motorola Solutions, Inc.; *U.S. Public*, pg. 1479

WATCHGUARD TECHNOLOGIES CANADA, INC.—See Francisco Partners Management, LP; *U.S. Private*, pg. 1593

WATCHGUARD TECHNOLOGIES, INC.—See Francisco Partners Management, LP; *U.S. Private*, pg. 1593

WATCH LA JEANS; *U.S. Private*, pg. 4451

WATCHSTONE GROUP PLC; *Int'l*, pg. 8356

WATCO COMPANIES, LLC—See Kinder Morgan, Inc.; *U.S. Public*, pg. 1233

WATCO GMBH—See RPM International Inc.; *U.S. Public*, pg. 1820

WATCO MECHANICAL SERVICES, LLC - CUDAHY—See Kinder Morgan, Inc.; *U.S. Public*, pg. 1233

WATCO MECHANICAL SERVICES, LLC - CUDAHY—See The Greenbrier Companies, Inc.; *U.S. Public*, pg. 2085

WATCO MECHANICAL SERVICES, LLC - JACKSONVILLE—See Kinder Morgan, Inc.; *U.S. Public*, pg. 1233

WATCO MECHANICAL SERVICES, LLC - JACKSONVILLE—See The Greenbrier Companies, Inc.; *U.S. Public*, pg. 2085

WAT CONSULTING CO., LTD.—See Willtec Co., Ltd.; *Int'l*, pg. 8420

WATCO RAILROAD COMPANY HOLDINGS, INC.—See Kinder Morgan, Inc.; *U.S. Public*, pg. 1233

WATCO S.AR.L.—See RPM International Inc.; *U.S. Public*, pg. 1820

WATCO SUPPLY CHAIN SERVICES, LLC—See Kinder Morgan, Inc.; *U.S. Public*, pg. 1233

WATCO UK LIMITED—See RPM International Inc.; *U.S. Public*, pg. 1820

WATEEN TELECOM LIMITED—See Abu Dhabi Group; *Int'l*, pg. 71

WATELET TP SAS—See VINCI S.A.; *Int'l*, pg. 8240

WATER ASSET MANAGEMENT, LLC; *U.S. Private*, pg. 4451

WATER BABE COMPANY LIMITED—See Water Oasis Group Limited; *Int'l*, pg. 8356

THE WATERBASE LIMITED; *Int'l*, pg. 7699

WATER BLAST MANUFACTURING B.C. LTD.—See Exchange Income Corporation; *Int'l*, pg. 2579

WATER BLAST MANUFACTURING LP—See Exchange Income Corporation; *Int'l*, pg. 2579

WATERBORNE ENVIRONMENTAL INC.; *U.S. Private*, pg. 4452

WATERBOSS EUROPE, SRL—See A. O. Smith Corporation; *U.S. Public*, pg. 12

WATERBRIDGE RESOURCES LLC—See Five Point Energy LLC; *U.S. Private*, pg. 1537

WATERBURY COMPANIES, INC.; *U.S. Private*, pg. 4452

WATERBURY FARREL TECHNOLOGIES—See Magnum Integrated Technologies, Inc.; *Int'l*, pg. 4642

WATERBURY GENERATION LLC—See Hull Street Energy, LLC; *U.S. Private*, pg. 2005

WATERBURY HOSPITAL; *U.S. Private*, pg. 4452

WATERBURY STYLE, INC.—See Custom Metal Crafters, Inc.; *U.S. Private*, pg. 1129

WATERCARE CORPORATION—See A. O. Smith Corporation; *U.S. Public*, pg. 12

WATERCELL INC.—See Mitsubishi Corporation; *Int'l*, pg. 4943

WATERCO ENGINEERING SDN BHD—See Waterco Limited; *Int'l*, pg. 8357

WATERCO (EUROPE) LTD—See Waterco Limited; *Int'l*, pg. 8357

WATERCO (GUANGZHOU) LTD.—See Waterco Limited; *Int'l*, pg. 8357

WATERCO INTERNATIONAL PTE LTD—See Waterco Limited; *Int'l*, pg. 8357

WATERCO LIMITED; *Int'l*, pg. 8356

WATERCOLOR INN & RESORT—See Noble House Hotels & Resorts, Ltd.; *U.S. Private*, pg. 2932

COMPANY NAME INDEX

WATERCOMPANY BV—See The Bidvest Group Limited; *Int'l*, pg. 7622
WATER CONSULTING SPECIALISTS, INC.—See Xylem Inc.; *U.S. Public*, pg. 2394
WATERCO (NZ) LTD—See Waterco Limited; *Int'l*, pg. 8357
WATER COOLERS (SCOTLAND) LIMITED—See Primo Water Corporation; *U.S. Public*, pg. 1718
WATER COUNTRY CORP.—See Newgate Private Equity LLP; *Int'l*, pg. 5234
WATER COUNTRY USA—See United Parks & Resorts Inc.; *U.S. Public*, pg. 2234
WATERCOURSE DISTILLERY LTD—See Pernod Ricard S.A.; *Int'l*, pg. 5811
WATERCO USA INC—See Waterco Limited; *Int'l*, pg. 8357
WATERDROP INC.; *Int'l*, pg. 8357
WATER ENGINEERING, INC.—See Nolan Capital, Inc.; *U.S. Private*, pg. 2934
WATER ENGINEERING TECHNOLOGY SDN BHD—See Loh & Loh Corporation Berhad; *Int'l*, pg. 4543
WATER ENVIRONMENT FEDERATION; *U.S. Private*, pg. 4451
WATERFALL ASSET MANAGEMENT LLC; *U.S. Private*, pg. 4452
WATERFALL QUARRIES PTY LIMITED—See Heidelberg Materials AG; *Int'l*, pg. 3320
WATERFIELD COMPANY LIMITED—See Consolidated Water Co. Ltd.; *Int'l*, pg. 1771
WATERFIELD TECHNOLOGIES, INC.; *U.S. Private*, pg. 4453
WATERFILTERS.NET LLC.; *U.S. Private*, pg. 4453
WATERFORD CASTLE GOLF & COUNTRY CLUB LIMITED—See Smurfit Kappa Group plc; *Int'l*, pg. 7024
WATERFORD FINANCE & INVESTMENT LTD.; *Int'l*, pg. 8357
WATERFORD GAMING FINANCE CORP.—See Waterford Group, LLC; *U.S. Private*, pg. 4453
WATERFORD GAMING, LLC—See Waterford Group, LLC; *U.S. Private*, pg. 4453
WATERFORD GROUP, LLC; *U.S. Private*, pg. 4453
WATERFORD HIRE SERVICES LIMITED—See Speedy Hire Plc; *Int'l*, pg. 7133
WATERFORD HOTEL GROUP, INC.—See Waterford Group, LLC; *U.S. Private*, pg. 4453
WATERFORD LAKES TOWN CENTER, LLC—See Kimco Realty Corporation; *U.S. Public*, pg. 1232
WATERFORD SPEED BOWL; *U.S. Private*, pg. 4453
WATERFORD STANLEY LTD.—See The Middleby Corporation; *U.S. Public*, pg. 2114
WATERFORD WEDGWOOD DOULTON COMMERCIAL (SHANGHAI) LTD.—See Fiskars Oyj Abp; *Int'l*, pg. 2694
WATERFRONT A, LLC—See Shidler Investment Company, LLC; *U.S. Private*, pg. 3635
WATERFRONT CEBU CITY CASINO HOTEL, INC.—See Waterfront Philippines, Incorporated; *Int'l*, pg. 8357
WATERFRONT CONFERENCE COMPANY LIMITED—See Freshwater UK PLC; *Int'l*, pg. 2782
WATERFRONT FOOD CONCEPTS, INC.—See Waterfront Philippines, Incorporated; *Int'l*, pg. 8357
WATERFRONT INSULAR HOTEL DAVAO INC—See Waterfront Philippines, Incorporated; *Int'l*, pg. 8357
WATERFRONT PHILIPPINES, INCORPORATED; *Int'l*, pg. 8357
WATERFRONT PROPERTIES PTE LTD—See Keppel Corporation Limited; *Int'l*, pg. 4132
WATERFRONT PROPERTIES (PVT.) LTD.—See John Keells Holdings PLC; *Int'l*, pg. 3979
WATERFRONT RESCUE MISSION; *U.S. Private*, pg. 4453
WATERFRONT SHIPPING COMPANY LIMITED—See Methanex Corporation; *Int'l*, pg. 4853
WATERFURNACE INTERNATIONAL INC.—See NIBE Industrier AB; *Int'l*, pg. 5263
WATERFURNACE RENEWABLE ENERGY, INC.—See NIBE Industrier AB; *Int'l*, pg. 5263
WATER GAS & LIGHT COMMISSION; *U.S. Private*, pg. 4451
WATER GREMLIN AQUILA COMPANY S.P.A.—See Okabe Co., Ltd.; *Int'l*, pg. 5544
WATER GREMLIN COMPANY; *U.S. Private*, pg. 4451
WATER HALL (ENGLAND) LIMITED—See Petards Group Plc; *Int'l*, pg. 5823
WATER HALL GROUP PLC—See Petards Group Plc; *Int'l*, pg. 5823
WATER HEATERS ONLY INCORPORATED; *U.S. Private*, pg. 4451
WATERHOUSE DONUT COMPANY, INC—See The Predictive Index LLC; *U.S. Private*, pg. 4097
WATER & INDUSTRIAL SERVICES COMPANY SPA—See Enel S.p.A.; *Int'l*, pg. 2415
WATER INTELLIGENCE PLC; *U.S. Public*, pg. 2334
WATER.IO LTD.; *Int'l*, pg. 8356
WATER-JEL TECHNOLOGIES, LLC—See Water Street Healthcare Partners, LLC; *U.S. Private*, pg. 4452
WATERJET HOLDINGS, INC.—See AIP, LLC; *U.S. Private*, pg. 137
WATERKEEPER ALLIANCE INC.; *U.S. Private*, pg. 4453
WATERKOTTE AUSTRIA GMBH—See NIBE Industrier AB; *Int'l*, pg. 5263

WATERKOTTE GMBH—See NIBE Industrier AB; *Int'l*, pg. 5263
WATERLAND CEMENT INDUSTRY N.V.—See Rudisa Holdingmaatschappij N.V.; *Int'l*, pg. 6424
WATERLAND PRIVATE EQUITY GMBH—See Waterland Private Equity Investments B.V.; *Int'l*, pg. 8357
WATERLAND PRIVATE EQUITY INVESTMENTS B.V.; *Int'l*, pg. 8357
WATERLAND PRIVATE EQUITY N.V.—See Waterland Private Equity Investments B.V.; *Int'l*, pg. 8357
WATERLAND PRIVATE EQUITY SP. Z.O.O—See Waterland Private Equity Investments B.V.; *Int'l*, pg. 8357
WATERLAND VENTURE CAPITAL CO., LTD.—See IBF Financial Holdings Co., Ltd.; *Int'l*, pg. 3574
WATERLINKS INVESTMENTS LTD.; *Int'l*, pg. 8357
WATERLOGIC AMERICAS LLC—See Castik Capital S.a.r.l.; *Int'l*, pg. 1356
WATERLOGIC AUSTRALIA PTY—See Castik Capital S.a.r.l.; *Int'l*, pg. 1356
WATERLOGIC COMMERCIAL PRODUCTS, LLC—See Castik Capital S.a.r.l.; *Int'l*, pg. 1356
WATERLOGIC DANMARK AS—See Castik Capital S.a.r.l.; *Int'l*, pg. 1356
WATERLOGIC FRANCE SA—See Castik Capital S.a.r.l.; *Int'l*, pg. 1356
WATERLOGIC GMBH—See Castik Capital S.a.r.l.; *Int'l*, pg. 1356
WATERLOGIC NORGE AS—See Castik Capital S.a.r.l.; *Int'l*, pg. 1356
WATERLOGIC PLC—See Castik Capital S.a.r.l.; *Int'l*, pg. 1356
WATERLOGIC USA (WEST)—See Castik Capital S.a.r.l.; *Int'l*, pg. 1356
WATERLOO AIR PRODUCTS LIMITED—See Investment AB Latour; *Int'l*, pg. 3784
WATERLOO BREWING LTD.—See Carlsberg A/S; *Int'l*, pg. 1341
WATERLOO DE NOGALES, S.A. DE C.V.—See Fortune Brands Innovations, Inc.; *U.S. Public*, pg. 873
WATERLOO IMPORTED CARS INC; *Int'l*, pg. 8357
WATERLOO INDUSTRIES, INC.—See Fortune Brands Innovations, Inc.; *U.S. Public*, pg. 873
WATERLOO INVESTMENTS LIMITED—See SHUAA Capital psc; *Int'l*, pg. 6868
WATERLOO MAPLE INC.—See FUJISOFT INCORPORATED; *Int'l*, pg. 2831
WATER MANAGEMENT INTERNATIONAL COLOMBIA LTDA.—See VINCI S.A.; *Int'l*, pg. 8240
WATER MANAGEMENT INTERNATIONAL—See VINCI S.A.; *Int'l*, pg. 8236
WATER MANAGEMENT SERVICES DIVISION—See Thielsch Engineering, Inc.; *U.S. Private*, pg. 4144
WATERMAN AHW PTY LIMITED—See CTI Engineering Co., Ltd.; *Int'l*, pg. 1871
WATERMAN ASPEN LIMITED—See CTI Engineering Co., Ltd.; *Int'l*, pg. 1871
WATERMAN BROADCASTING CORP.; *U.S. Private*, pg. 4454
WATERMAN BUILDING SERVICES LIMITED—See CTI Engineering Co., Ltd.; *Int'l*, pg. 1871
WATERMAN ENERGY, ENVIRONMENT & DESIGN LIMITED—See CTI Engineering Co., Ltd.; *Int'l*, pg. 1871
WATERMAN GROUP (AUS) PTY LIMITED—See CTI Engineering Co., Ltd.; *Int'l*, pg. 1871
WATERMAN GROUP PLC—See CTI Engineering Co., Ltd.; *Int'l*, pg. 1871
WATERMAN INDUSTRIES, LLC—See CVF Capital Partners, Inc.; *U.S. Private*, pg. 1132
WATERMAN INFRASTRUCTURE & ENVIRONMENT LIMITED—See CTI Engineering Co., Ltd.; *Int'l*, pg. 1871
WATERMAN INTERNATIONAL (ASIA) PTY LIMITED—See CTI Engineering Co., Ltd.; *Int'l*, pg. 1871
WATERMAN INTERNATIONAL HOLDINGS LIMITED—See CTI Engineering Co., Ltd.; *Int'l*, pg. 1871
WATERMAN INTERNATIONAL LIMITED—See CTI Engineering Co., Ltd.; *Int'l*, pg. 1871
WATERMAN LOGISTICS, INC.—See AIP, LLC; *U.S. Private*, pg. 137
WATERMAN S.A.S.—See Newell Brands Inc.; *U.S. Public*, pg. 1515
WATERMAN STEAMSHIP CORPORATION—See AIP, LLC; *U.S. Public*, pg. 136
WATERMAN STRUCTURES LIMITED—See CTI Engineering Co., Ltd.; *Int'l*, pg. 1871
WATERMARK DONUT COMPANY; *U.S. Private*, pg. 4454
WATERMARKE HOMES LLC; *U.S. Private*, pg. 4454
WATERMARK ENVIRONMENTAL, INC.; *U.S. Private*, pg. 4454
WATERMARK GROUP, INC.; *U.S. Private*, pg. 4454
WATERMARK GROUP SERVICES (UK) LIMITED—See Harwood Capital LLP; *Int'l*, pg. 3282
THE WATERMARK HOTEL NAGASAKI CO., LTD.—See H.I.S. Co., Ltd.; *Int'l*, pg. 3196
WATERMARK LEARNING, INC.—See Morgan Stanley; *U.S. Public*, pg. 1474
WATERMARK LODGING TRUST, INC.—See W.P. Carey Inc.; *U.S. Public*, pg. 2316

WATERMARK PRESS, LTD.—See Chatham Asset Management, LLC; *U.S. Private*, pg. 866
WATERMARK RESEARCH PARTNERS, INC.—See Genstar Capital, LLC; *U.S. Private*, pg. 1673
WATERMARK RESTORATION INC.—See FirstService Corporation; *Int'l*, pg. 2691
WATERMARK SEARCH INTERNATIONAL PTY LIMITED—See Ambition Group Limited; *Int'l*, pg. 415
WATERMARK TECHNOLOGIES LIMITED—See Software Circle plc; *Int'l*, pg. 7057
WATERMILL EXPRESS LLC; *U.S. Private*, pg. 4454
WATERMILL EXPRESS—See Watermill Express LLC; *U.S. Private*, pg. 4454
WATERMILL PRODUCTS LTD.—See The Poul Due Jensen Foundation; *Int'l*, pg. 7676
WATERMILL VENTURES, LTD.—See HMK Enterprises, Inc.; *U.S. Private*, pg. 1955
WATER MIST ENGINEERING AS; *Int'l*, pg. 8356
WATER MOVERS, INC.—See WillScot Mobile Mini Holdings Corp.; *U.S. Public*, pg. 2372
WATER OASIS COMPANY LIMITED—See Water Oasis Group Limited; *Int'l*, pg. 8356
WATER OASIS E.L. (HK) COMPANY LIMITED—See Water Oasis Group Limited; *Int'l*, pg. 8356
WATER OASIS GROUP LIMITED; *Int'l*, pg. 8356
WATEROUS COMPANY—See American Cast Iron Pipe Company; *U.S. Private*, pg. 226
WATEROUS ENERGY FUND; *Int'l*, pg. 8357
WATER PIK, INC.—See Church & Dwight Co., Inc.; *U.S. Public*, pg. 493
WATER & POWER COMMUNITY CREDIT UNION; *U.S. Private*, pg. 4451
WATER PRODUCTS COMPANY OF ILLINOIS, INC.; *U.S. Private*, pg. 4451
WATERPROOF DIVING INTERNATIONAL AB—See Lagercrantz Group AB; *Int'l*, pg. 4395
WATERPURE INTERNATIONAL, INC.; *U.S. Private*, pg. 4454
WATER QUALITY GMBH—See Danaher Corporation; *U.S. Public*, pg. 632
WATER REDEVELOPMENT COMPANY—See Two Rivers Water & Farming Company; *U.S. Private*, pg. 4266
WATER REMEDIATION TECHNOLOGY LLC; *U.S. Private*, pg. 4451
WATER RESOURCES INTERNATIONAL, INC.—See Barnwell Industries, Inc.; *U.S. Public*, pg. 278
WATER RESOURCES INTERNATIONAL, INC.; *U.S. Private*, pg. 4451
WATER RETICULATION SYSTEMS (VIRGINIA) PTY LIMITED—See Pentair plc; *Int'l*, pg. 5791
WATER-RIGHT, INC.—See A. O. Smith Corporation; *U.S. Public*, pg. 12
WATERS AG—See Waters Corporation; *U.S. Public*, pg. 2335
WATERS ANALYTICAL INSTRUMENTS SDN BHD—See Waters Corporation; *U.S. Public*, pg. 2335
WATERS AS—See Waters Corporation; *U.S. Public*, pg. 2335
WATERS A/S—See Waters Corporation; *U.S. Public*, pg. 2335
WATERS AUSTRALIA PTY. LTD.—See Waters Corporation; *U.S. Public*, pg. 2335
WATERSAVR GLOBAL SOLUTIONS INC.—See Flexible Solutions International, Inc.; *Int'l*, pg. 2704
WATERS CHINA LTD.—See Waters Corporation; *U.S. Public*, pg. 2335
WATERS CHROMATOGRAPHY B.V.—See Waters Corporation; *U.S. Public*, pg. 2335
WATERS CHROMATOGRAPHY EUROPE BV—See Waters Corporation; *U.S. Public*, pg. 2335
WATERS CHROMATOGRAPHY IRELAND LTD.—See Waters Corporation; *U.S. Public*, pg. 2335
WATER SCIENCE TECHNOLOGIES, LLC—See Bain Capital, LP; *U.S. Private*, pg. 441
WATERS CORPORATION; *U.S. Public*, pg. 2334
WATER SERVICES OF AMERICA, INC.; *U.S. Private*, pg. 4451
WATERS GES.M.B.H—See Waters Corporation; *U.S. Public*, pg. 2335
WATERS GMBH—See Waters Corporation; *U.S. Public*, pg. 2335
WATERSHED INVESTMENT CONSULTANTS, INC.—See J.H. Ellwood & Associates; *U.S. Private*, pg. 2165
WATERSHED SYSTEMS, INC.—See Learning Technologies Group plc; *Int'l*, pg. 4435
WATERSIDE BUILDERS INC.; *U.S. Private*, pg. 4454
WATERSIDE MEDICAL CENTER LLC—See Adeptus Health Inc.; *U.S. Private*, pg. 78
WATERSIDE TOWERS, L.L.C.—See UDR, Inc.; *U.S. Public*, pg. 2218
WATERS INC.; *U.S. Private*, pg. 4454
WATERS INDIA PVT LTD.—See Waters Corporation; *U.S. Public*, pg. 2335
WATERS KFT.—See Waters Corporation; *U.S. Public*, pg. 2335
WATERS KOREA LIMITED—See Waters Corporation; *U.S. Public*, pg. 2335
WATERS LIMITED—See Waters Corporation; *U.S. Public*, pg. 2335

WATERS INC. CORPORATE AFFILIATIONS

Company Index

WATERS LTD.—See Waters Corporation; *U.S. Public*, pg. 2335

WATERS NV—See Waters Corporation; *U.S. Public*, pg. 2335

WATER SOLUTIONS HOLDINGS LLC—See American Water Works Company, Inc.; *U.S. Public*, pg. 112

WATER SOLUTIONS UNLIMITED, INC.—See Hawkins, Inc.; *U.S. Public*, pg. 989

WATERSOUND ORIGINS TOWN CENTER, LLC—See The St. Joe Company; *U.S. Public*, pg. 2131

WATERSOURCE PTY LTD—See Hitachi Zosen Corporation; *Int'l*, pg. 3412

WATERS PACIFIC PTE LTD—See Waters Corporation; *U.S. Public*, pg. 2335

WATERS S.A. DE C.V.—See Waters Corporation; *U.S. Public*, pg. 2335

WATERS S.A.S.—See Waters Corporation; *U.S. Public*, pg. 2335

WATERS SPA—See Waters Corporation; *U.S. Public*, pg. 2336

WATERS SP Z.O.O—See Waters Corporation; *U.S. Public*, pg. 2335

WATERS SVERIGE AB—See Waters Corporation; *U.S. Public*, pg. 2335

WATER STANDARD MANAGEMENT; *U.S. Private*, pg. 4451

WATER STAR, INC.—See Tennant Company; *U.S. Public*, pg. 2016

WATERS (TC) ISRAEL LIMITED—See Waters Corporation; *U.S. Public*, pg. 2335

WATERS TECHNOLOGIES CORPORATION—See Waters Corporation; *U.S. Public*, pg. 2335

WATERS TECHNOLOGIES DO BRASIL LTDA.—See Waters Corporation; *U.S. Public*, pg. 2336

WATERSTONE BANK, SSB—See Waterstone Financial, Inc.; *U.S. Public*, pg. 2336

WATERSTONE COLLEGE (PTY) LTD.—See Curro Holdings Ltd.; *Int'l*, pg. 1879

WATERSTONE FINANCIAL, INC.; *U.S. Public*, pg. 2336

WATERSTONE MORTGAGE CORP.; *U.S. Private*, pg. 4454

WATERSTONES BOOKSELLERS LIMITED—See Elliott Management Corporation; *U.S. Private*, pg. 1365

WATER STREET BREWERY; *U.S. Private*, pg. 4451

WATERSTREET COMPANY; *U.S. Private*, pg. 4454

WATER STREET HEALTHCARE PARTNERS, LLC; *U.S. Private*, pg. 4451

WATERSTREET, LTD.; *U.S. Private*, pg. 4454

WATERS TRUCK & TRACTOR INC.; *U.S. Private*, pg. 4454

THE WATER SUPPLY & SEWERAGE CONSTRUCTION & INVESTMENT JOINT-STOCK COMPANY; *Int'l*, pg. 7699

WATERSWIDGREN/TBWA AB—See Omnicom Group Inc.; *U.S. Public*, pg. 1599

WATER SYSTEMS OPTIMIZATION, INC.—See Align Capital Partners, LLC; *U.S. Private*, pg. 167

WATER TECHNOLOGIES CORPORATION—See Waters Corporation; *U.S. Public*, pg. 2335

WATER TECHNOLOGIES INTERNATIONAL, INC.; *U.S. Public*, pg. 2334

WATERTEK INTERNATIONAL (HONG KONG) LIMITED—See Beijing Watertek Information Technology Co., Ltd.; *Int'l*, pg. 960

WATER-TITE COMPANY, LLC—See Installed Building Products, Inc.; *U.S. Public*, pg. 1134

WATERTITE GUTTERING (PTY) LIMITED; *Int'l*, pg. 8358

WATERTON ASSOCIATES LLC—See Waterford Group, LLC; *U.S. Private*, pg. 4453

WATERTON GLOBAL RESOURCE MANAGEMENT INC.; *Int'l*, pg. 8358

WATERTOWN COOPERATIVE ELEVATOR ASSOCIATION; *U.S. Private*, pg. 4454

WATERTOWN CROP NUTRIENTS LLC—See CHS INC.; *U.S. Public*, pg. 493

WATERTOWN HOPS COMPANY—See Molson Coors Beverage Company; *U.S. Public*, pg. 1459

WATERTOWN MEDICAL CENTER, LLC—See Apollo Global Management, Inc.; *U.S. Public*, pg. 159

WATERTOWN PHYSICIAN PRACTICES, LLC—See Apollo Global Management, Inc.; *U.S. Public*, pg. 159

WATERTOWN SAVINGS BANK INC.; *U.S. Private*, pg. 4454

WATERTOWN SAVINGS BANK; *U.S. Private*, pg. 4454

WATERTOWN TRUCK & TRAILER INC.—See North American Truck & Trailer, Inc.; *U.S. Private*, pg. 2941

WATER TREATMENT PRODUCTS HOLDING LTD.—See Sdiptech AB; *Int'l*, pg. 6659

WATER TREATMENT PRODUCTS LIMITED—See Sdiptech AB; *Int'l*, pg. 6659

WATER TREATMENT SOLUTION LTD.—See BRENNTAG SE; *Int'l*, pg. 1150

WATERTRONICS, LLC—See Lindsay Corporation; *U.S. Public*, pg. 1320

WATERVIEW AT HANOVER, LLC—See Lennar Corporation; *U.S. Public*, pg. 1307

WATERVILLE TG INC.—See Toyoda Gosei Co., Ltd.; *Int'l*, pg. 7863

WATERVILLE VALLEY SKI RESORT, INC.; *U.S. Private*, pg. 4454

WATERWAY HOTEL HOLDINGS, LLC—See Howard Hughes Holdings Inc.; *U.S. Public*, pg. 1061

WATERWAY PRIMARY CARE, LLC—See HCA Healthcare, Inc.; *U.S. Public*, pg. 1013

WATER WAYS TECHNOLOGIES INC.; *Int'l*, pg. 8356

WATER WORKS FABRICATION, LLC—See Wind Point Advisors LLC; *U.S. Private*, pg. 4534

WATERWORKS OPERATING COMPANY LLC—See RH; *U.S. Public*, pg. 1796

WATER WORKS & SANITARY SEWER; *U.S. Private*, pg. 4452

WATERWORKS SUPPLIES & SERVICES LIMITED—See Blackfriars Corp.; *U.S. Private*, pg. 575

WATER WORKS SUPPLY COMPANY—See Core & Main, Inc.; *U.S. Public*, pg. 576

WATES CONSTRUCTION LTD—See Wates Group Limited; *Int'l*, pg. 8358

WATES GROUP LIMITED; *Int'l*, pg. 8358

WATES HOMES (CAMBRIDGE) LIMITED—See Wates Group Limited; *Int'l*, pg. 8358

THE WATFORD ASSOCIATION FOOTBALL CLUB LIMITED—See Watford Leisure Limited; *Int'l*, pg. 8358

WATFORD HOLDINGS LTD.—See Arch Capital Group Ltd.; *Int'l*, pg. 547

WATFORD LEISURE LIMITED; *Int'l*, pg. 8358

WATFORD ROOF TRUSS LTD.; *Int'l*, pg. 8358

WATHAGAR GINNING COMPANY PTY LTD—See Louis Dreyfus Company B.V.; *Int'l*, pg. 4562

WATHNE IMPORTS LTD.; *U.S. Private*, pg. 4454

W.A. THOMAS CO.; *U.S. Private*, pg. 4419

WATKIN JONES PLC; *Int'l*, pg. 8358

WATKIN JONES & SON LIMITED; *Int'l*, pg. 8358

WATKIN MOTORS; *Int'l*, pg. 8358

WATKINS AND SHEPARD TRUCKING, INC.—See Schneider National, Inc.; *U.S. Public*, pg. 1847

WATKINS ASSOCIATED DEVELOPERS—See Watkins Associated Industries Inc.; *U.S. Private*, pg. 4455

WATKINS ASSOCIATED INDUSTRIES INC.; *U.S. Private*, pg. 4454

WATKINS AUTOMOTIVE GROUP; *U.S. Private*, pg. 4455

THE WATKINS COMPANY INC.; *U.S. Private*, pg. 4133

THE WATKINS COMPANY INC.; *U.S. Private*, pg. 4133

WATKINS CONSTRUCTION CO., INC.; *U.S. Private*, pg. 4455

WATKINS DISTRIBUTION UK LIMITED—See Masco Corporation; *U.S. Public*, pg. 1391

WATKINS GLEN INTERNATIONAL, INC.—See National Association for Stock Car Auto Racing, Inc.; *U.S. Private*, pg. 2846

WATKINS HIRE LIMITED—See Carrier Global Corporation; *U.S. Public*, pg. 444

WATKINS INCORPORATED; *U.S. Private*, pg. 4455

WATKINS INSURANCE GROUP INC.; *U.S. Private*, pg. 4455

WATKINS MANUFACTURING CORPORATION—See Masco Corporation; *U.S. Public*, pg. 1392

WATKINS SYNDICATE HONG KONG LIMITED—See Munchener Ruckversicherungs AG; *Int'l*, pg. 5092

WATKINS SYNDICATE MIDDLE EAST LIMITED—See Munchener Ruckversicherungs AG; *Int'l*, pg. 5092

WATKINS SYNDICATE SINGAPORE PTE. LIMITED—See Munchener Ruckversicherungs AG; *Int'l*, pg. 5092

W ATLANTA BUCKHEAD BEVERAGE LLC—See Marriott International, Inc.; *U.S. Public*, pg. 1373

W ATLANTA - DOWNTOWN HOTEL—See Marriott International, Inc.; *U.S. Public*, pg. 1372

W. ATLEE BURPEE & CO.; *U.S. Private*, pg. 4417

WATLOW AUSTRALIA PTY. LTD.—See Tinicum Enterprises, Inc.; *U.S. Private*, pg. 4174

WATLOW COLUMBIA, INC.—See Tinicum Enterprises, Inc.; *U.S. Private*, pg. 4174

WATLOW DE MEXICO S.A. DE C.V.—See Tinicum Enterprises, Inc.; *U.S. Private*, pg. 4175

WATLOW ELECTRIC MANUFACTURING COMPANY—See Tinicum Enterprises, Inc.; *U.S. Private*, pg. 4174

WATLOW ENGINEERING—See Tinicum Enterprises, Inc.; *U.S. Private*, pg. 4174

WATLOW FRANCE S.A.R.L.—See Tinicum Enterprises, Inc.; *U.S. Private*, pg. 4174

WATLOW GMBH—See Tinicum Enterprises, Inc.; *U.S. Private*, pg. 4174

WATLOW HANNIBAL—See Tinicum Enterprises, Inc.; *U.S. Private*, pg. 4175

WATLOW HEATER TECHNOLOGY CENTER—See Tinicum Enterprises, Inc.; *U.S. Private*, pg. 4174

WATLOW JAPAN LTD.—See Tinicum Enterprises, Inc.; *U.S. Private*, pg. 4174

WATLOW LIMITED—See Tinicum Enterprises, Inc.; *U.S. Private*, pg. 4174

WATLOW POLYMER TECHNOLOGIES, INC.—See Tinicum Enterprises, Inc.; *U.S. Private*, pg. 4174

WATLOW RICHMOND—See Tinicum Enterprises, Inc.; *U.S. Private*, pg. 4175

WATLOW SINGAPORE PTE. LTD.—See Tinicum Enterprises, Inc.; *U.S. Private*, pg. 4175

WATLOW ST. LOUIS, INC.—See Tinicum Enterprises, Inc.; *U.S. Private*, pg. 4175

WATLOW TAIWAN CORPORATION—See Tinicum Enterprises, Inc.; *U.S. Private*, pg. 4175

WATLOW WINONA, INC.—See Tinicum Enterprises, Inc.; *U.S. Private*, pg. 4175

WATL-TV—See TEGNA Inc.; *U.S. Public*, pg. 1990

WATONGA BANCSHARES, INC.—See Bank7 Corp.; *U.S. Public*, pg. 274

WATONWAN FARM SERVICE CO. INC.; *U.S. Private*, pg. 4455

WATOS COREA CO., LTD.; *Int'l*, pg. 8358

WATPAC CONSTRUCTION (NSW) PTY LTD—See Orascom Construction PLC; *Int'l*, pg. 5613

WATPAC CONSTRUCTION PTY LTD—See Orascom Construction PLC; *Int'l*, pg. 5613

WATPAC CONSTRUCTION (VIC) PTY LTD—See Orascom Construction PLC; *Int'l*, pg. 5613

WATPAC LIMITED—See Orascom Construction PLC; *Int'l*, pg. 5612

WATPAC SPECIALTY SERVICES PTY LTD—See Orascom Construction PLC; *Int'l*, pg. 5613

WATRIUM AS; *Int'l*, pg. 8358

WATRY INDUSTRIES LLC—See Ligon Industries LLC; *U.S. Private*, pg. 2455

WATSCO, INC.; *U.S. Public*, pg. 2336

WATSEKA FORD-LINCOLN MERCURY, INC.; *U.S. Private*, pg. 4455

WATSEKA INTERSTATE, LLC; *U.S. Private*, pg. 4455

WATSON BOWMAN ACME CORP.—See BASF SE; *Int'l*, pg. 876

WATSON & CHALIN HOLDING CORP.; *U.S. Private*, pg. 4455

WATSON & CHALIN MANUFACTURING, INC.—See Watson & Chalin Holding Corp.; *U.S. Private*, pg. 4455

WATSON CHEVROLET, INC.; *U.S. Private*, pg. 4455

WATSON CLINIC LLP; *U.S. Private*, pg. 4455

WATSON & COX CONSTRUCTION LTD; *Int'l*, pg. 8358

WATSON-CRICK INC.—See Dentsu Group Inc.; *Int'l*, pg. 2040

WATSON FURNITURE GROUP, INC.; *U.S. Private*, pg. 4455

WATSON GRAVEL, INC.; *U.S. Private*, pg. 4455

WATSON GROUP FINANCIAL CORPORATION; *U.S. Private*, pg. 4455

WATSON HEGNER CORPORATION; *U.S. Private*, pg. 4455

WATSON INDUSTRIES, INC.; *U.S. Private*, pg. 4455

WATSON LLC—See Glanbia Co-Operative Society Limited; *Int'l*, pg. 2988

WATSON-MARLOW ALITEA AB—See Spirax-Sarco Engineering plc; *Int'l*, pg. 7139

WATSON-MARLOW AUSTRIA GMBH—See Spirax-Sarco Engineering plc; *Int'l*, pg. 7139

WATSON-MARLOW BOMBAS CHILE LTDA.—See Spirax-Sarco Engineering plc; *Int'l*, pg. 7139

WATSON-MARLOW BREDEL HOLDINGS BV—See Spirax-Sarco Engineering plc; *Int'l*, pg. 7139

WATSON-MARLOW BREDEL IND E COM DE BOMBAS—See Spirax-Sarco Engineering plc; *Int'l*, pg. 7139

WATSON MARLOW BREDEL S.A. (PTY.) LTD.—See Spirax-Sarco Engineering plc; *Int'l*, pg. 7139

WATSON-MARLOW B.V.—See Spirax-Sarco Engineering plc; *Int'l*, pg. 7139

WATSON-MARLOW CANADA INC.—See Spirax-Sarco Engineering plc; *Int'l*, pg. 7139

WATSON-MARLOW COLOMBIA SAS—See Spirax-Sarco Engineering plc; *Int'l*, pg. 7139

WATSON-MARLOW CO. LTD.—See Spirax-Sarco Engineering plc; *Int'l*, pg. 7139

WATSON-MARLOW CO. LTD.—See Spirax-Sarco Engineering plc; *Int'l*, pg. 7139

WATSON-MARLOW FLEXICON A/S—See Spirax-Sarco Engineering plc; *Int'l*, pg. 7139

WATSON-MARLOW FLOW SMART INC.—See Spirax-Sarco Engineering plc; *Int'l*, pg. 7139

WATSON MARLOW FZCO—See Spirax-Sarco Engineering plc; *Int'l*, pg. 7139

WATSON-MARLOW GMBH—See Spirax-Sarco Engineering plc; *Int'l*, pg. 7139

WATSON-MARLOW, INC.—See Spirax-Sarco Engineering plc; *Int'l*, pg. 7139

WATSON-MARLOW INDIA PRIVATE LTD.—See Spirax-Sarco Engineering plc; *Int'l*, pg. 7139

WATSON-MARLOW LIMITED—See Spirax-Sarco Engineering plc; *Int'l*, pg. 7139

WATSON-MARLOW LLC—See Spirax-Sarco Engineering plc; *Int'l*, pg. 7139

WATSON-MARLOW LTD—See Spirax-Sarco Engineering plc; *Int'l*, pg. 7139

WATSON-MARLOW LTD—See Spirax-Sarco Engineering plc; *Int'l*, pg. 7139

WATSON-MARLOW N.V.—See Spirax-Sarco Engineering plc; *Int'l*, pg. 7139

WATSON-MARLOW PTE. LTD.—See Spirax-Sarco Engineering plc; *Int'l*, pg. 7139

WATSON-MARLOW PTY LTD—See Spirax-Sarco Engineering plc; *Int'l*, pg. 7139

COMPANY NAME INDEX

WATSON-MARLOW S.A.—See Spirax-Sarco Engineering plc; *Int'l*, pg. 7139
WATSON-MARLOW S DE R L DE C V—See Spirax-Sarco Engineering plc; *Int'l*, pg. 7139
WATSON-MARLOW SDN. BHD.—See Spirax-Sarco Engineering plc; *Int'l*, pg. 7139
WATSON-MARLOW SP ZOO—See Spirax-Sarco Engineering plc; *Int'l*, pg. 7139
WATSON-MARLOW S.R.L.—See Spirax-Sarco Engineering plc; *Int'l*, pg. 7139
WATSON MORTGAGE CORP.; *U.S. Private*, pg. 4455
WATSON REALTY CORP.; *U.S. Private*, pg. 4455
WATSONS PERSONAL CARE STORES SDN. BHD.—See CK Hutchison Holdings Limited; *Int'l*, pg. 1638
WATSON-STANDARD COMPANY—See Watson Industries, Inc.; *U.S. Private*, pg. 4455
WATSON STEEL STRUCTURES LTD.—See Severfield Plc; *Int'l*, pg. 6735
WATSON SYSCO FOOD SERVICES, INC.—See Sysco Corporation; *U.S. Public*, pg. 1977
WATSONTOWN BRICK COMPANY—See Wienerberger AG; *Int'l*, pg. 8405
WATSON TRUCK & SUPPLY, INC.; *U.S. Private*, pg. 4456
WATSONVILLE HOSPITAL CORPORATION; *U.S. Private*, pg. 4456
WATSON WOODS HEALTHCARE, INC.—See The Ensign Group, Inc.; *U.S. Public*, pg. 2072
WATTA BATTERY INDUSTRIES SDN. BHD.—See Watta Holding Berhad; *Int'l*, pg. 8358
WATTA HOLDING BERHAD; *Int'l*, pg. 8358
WATTANA KARNPAET PCL; *Int'l*, pg. 8359
WATTANAPAT HOSPITAL TRANG PCL LTD.; *Int'l*, pg. 8359
WATT COMMUNITIES—See Watt Companies, Inc.; *U.S. Private*, pg. 4456
WATT COMPANIES, INC.; *U.S. Private*, pg. 4456
WATT DEUTSCHLAND GMBH—See EnBW Energie Baden-Wurttemberg AG; *Int'l*, pg. 2400
WATT DRIVE ANTRIEBSTECHNIK GMBH—See WEG S.A.; *Int'l*, pg. 8368
WATT DRIVE GMBH—See WEG S.A.; *Int'l*, pg. 8368
WATTELIER SAS; *Int'l*, pg. 8359
WATTENBERG HOLDING, LLC—See Energy Transfer LP; *U.S. Public*, pg. 704
WATTENS VIETNAM CO. LTD.—See delfortgroup AG; *Int'l*, pg. 2013
WATTEREDGE LLC—See Southwire Company, LLC; *U.S. Private*, pg. 3742
WATT FUEL CELL CORP.; *U.S. Private*, pg. 4456
WATT INTERNATIONAL, INC.; *Int'l*, pg. 8358
WATTLE HEALTH AUSTRALIA LIMITED; *Int'l*, pg. 8359
WATTLE HILL RHC FUNDS; *Int'l*, pg. 8359
WATT LINE SERVICE CO., LTD.—See Takaoka Toko Co., Ltd.; *Int'l*, pg. 7431
WATT MANN CO., LTD.; *Int'l*, pg. 8358
WATTMASTER CONTROLS, INC.—See AAON, Inc.; *U.S. Public*, pg. 12
WATT PROPERTIES & LEASING—See Watt Companies, Inc.; *U.S. Private*, pg. 4456
WATT PUBLISHING COMPANY; *U.S. Private*, pg. 4456
WATT REALTY ADVISORS—See Watt Companies, Inc.; *U.S. Private*, pg. 4456
WATT RETAIL DEVELOPMENT—See Watt Companies, Inc.; *U.S. Private*, pg. 4456
WATTS AUTOMATIC CONTROL VALVES, INC.—See Watts Water Technologies, Inc.; *U.S. Public*, pg. 2337
WATTS BENELUX—See Watts Water Technologies, Inc.; *U.S. Public*, pg. 2337
WATTS CHESNEE—See Watts Water Technologies, Inc.; *U.S. Public*, pg. 2337
WATTS CO., LTD.; *Int'l*, pg. 8359
WATTS CONSTRUCTORS, LLC—See Orascom Construction PLC; *Int'l*, pg. 5613
WATTS COPY SYSTEMS INC.; *U.S. Private*, pg. 4456
WATTSENSE S.A.S.—See Siemens Aktiengesellschaft; *Int'l*, pg. 6901
WATTS EQUIPMENT CO., INC.; *U.S. Private*, pg. 4456
WATTS FREIGHT SYSTEMS, INC.—See Watts Trucking Service, Inc.; *U.S. Private*, pg. 4456
WATTS INDUSTRIES BELGIUM BVBA—See Watts Water Technologies, Inc.; *U.S. Public*, pg. 2337
WATTS INDUSTRIES BULGARIA EAD—See Watts Water Technologies, Inc.; *U.S. Public*, pg. 2337
WATTS INDUSTRIES DEUTCHLAND GMBH—See Watts Water Technologies, Inc.; *U.S. Public*, pg. 2337
WATTS INDUSTRIES DEUTSCHLAND GMBH—See Watts Water Technologies, Inc.; *U.S. Public*, pg. 2337
WATTS INDUSTRIES EUROPE B.V.—See Watts Water Technologies, Inc.; *U.S. Public*, pg. 2337
WATTS INDUSTRIES TUNISIA S.A.S.—See Watts Water Technologies, Inc.; *U.S. Public*, pg. 2337
WATTS INDUSTRIES U.K. LTD.—See Watts Water Technologies, Inc.; *U.S. Public*, pg. 2338
WATTS INSULATION NV—See Watts Water Technologies, Inc.; *U.S. Public*, pg. 2338
WATTS INTERNATIONAL MARITIME COMPANY LIMITED; *Int'l*, pg. 8359

WATTS (NINGBO) INTERNATIONAL TRADING CO., LTD.—See Watts Water Technologies, Inc.; *U.S. Public*, pg. 2337
WATTS PETROLEUM CORPORATION; *U.S. Private*, pg. 4456
THE WATTS PUBLISHING GROUP LTD.—See Vivendi SE; *Int'l*, pg. 8274
WATTS REGULATOR/WATTS ACV—See Watts Water Technologies, Inc.; *U.S. Public*, pg. 2338
WATT'S S.A.; *Int'l*, pg. 8358
WATT STOPPER/LEGRAND—See Legrand S.A.; *Int'l*, pg. 4446
WATTS TRUCKING SERVICE, INC.; *U.S. Private*, pg. 4456
WATTS VALVE (NINGBO) CO., LTD.—See Watts Water Technologies, Inc.; *U.S. Public*, pg. 2338
WATTS WATER TECHNOLOGIES (CANADA), INC.—See Watts Water Technologies, Inc.; *U.S. Public*, pg. 2338
WATTS WATER TECHNOLOGIES EMEA B.V.—See Watts Water Technologies, Inc.; *U.S. Public*, pg. 2338
WATTS WATER TECHNOLOGIES, INC.; *U.S. Public*, pg. 2337
WATTS WATER TECHNOLOGIES—See Watts Water Technologies, Inc.; *U.S. Public*, pg. 2338
WATT SYNERGIA GMBH—See EnBW Energie Baden-Wurttemberg AG; *Int'l*, pg. 2400
WATTYL AUSTRALIA PTY LTD—See The Sherwin-Williams Company; *U.S. Public*, pg. 2130
WATTYL AUSTRALIA PTY LTD—See The Sherwin-Williams Company; *U.S. Public*, pg. 2130
WATTYL AUSTRALIA PTY LTD—See The Sherwin-Williams Company; *U.S. Public*, pg. 2130
WATTYL LIMITED—See The Sherwin-Williams Company; *U.S. Public*, pg. 2129
WATTYL (NZ) LTD.—See The Sherwin-Williams Company; *U.S. Public*, pg. 2129
WATU CREDIT LIMITED—See Car & General (Kenya) Limited; *Int'l*, pg. 1319
WATUMULL BROTHERS LTD. INC.; *U.S. Private*, pg. 4456
WAUCONDA TOOL & ENGINEERING LLC—See NN, Inc.; *U.S. Public*, pg. 1531
WAUD CAPITAL PARTNERS LLC; *U.S. Private*, pg. 4456
WAUKEGAN HOSPICE, LLC—See Community Health Systems, Inc.; *U.S. Public*, pg. 557
WAUKEGAN ILLINOIS HOSPITAL COMPANY, LLC—See Quorum Health Corporation; *U.S. Public*, pg. 3330
WAUKESHA BEARINGS CORP.—See Dover Corporation; *U.S. Public*, pg. 679
WAUKESHA-CJD, INC.—See Lithia Motors, Inc.; *U.S. Public*, pg. 1326
WAUKESHA FOUNDRY INC.; *U.S. Private*, pg. 4457
WAUKESHA HEALTH CARE, INC.—See ProHealth Care, Inc.; *U.S. Private*, pg. 3280
WAUKESHA METAL PRODUCTS; *U.S. Private*, pg. 4457
WAUKESHA-PEARCE INDUSTRIES—See Pearce Industries Inc.; *U.S. Private*, pg. 3125
WAUKESHA STATE BANK; *U.S. Private*, pg. 4457
WAUKESHA STATE BANK - WEALTH MANAGEMENT—See Waukesha State Bank; *U.S. Private*, pg. 4457
WAUKESHA WHOLESALE FOODS, INC.—See US Foods Holding Corp.; *U.S. Public*, pg. 2266
WAUKON YAMAHA, INC.; *U.S. Private*, pg. 4457
WAUPACA ELEVATOR CO, INC.—See Gardner Standard LLC; *U.S. Private*, pg. 1644
WAUPACA FOUNDRY, INC.—See Monomoy Capital Partners LLC; *U.S. Private*, pg. 2772
WAUSAU COATED PRODUCTS INC.; *U.S. Private*, pg. 4457
WAUSAU DAILY HERALD—See Gannett Co., Inc.; *U.S. Public*, pg. 901
WAUSAU EQUIPMENT COMPANY, INC.—See Alamo Group Inc.; *U.S. Public*, pg. 71
WAUSAU FINANCIAL SYSTEMS, INC.—See Augeo Affinity Marketing, Inc.; *U.S. Private*, pg. 392
WAUSAU HOMES, INC.; *U.S. Private*, pg. 4457
WAUSAU INSURANCE CO.—See Liberty Mutual Holding Company Inc.; *U.S. Private*, pg. 2445
WAUSAUKEE COMPOSITES INC.—See Sintex Industries, Ltd.; *Int'l*, pg. 6957
WAUSAU SUPPLY COMPANY; *U.S. Private*, pg. 4457
WAUSAU TILE, INC.; *U.S. Private*, pg. 4457
WAUSAU WINDOW & WALL SYSTEMS—See Apogee Enterprises, Inc.; *U.S. Public*, pg. 145
WAUSEON DIALYSIS, LLC—See DaVita Inc.; *U.S. Public*, pg. 644
WAUSEON MACHINE AND MANUFACTURING, INC.; *U.S. Private*, pg. 4457
WAUTERS ET FILS; *Int'l*, pg. 8359
WAUWATOSA INVESTMENTS, INC.—See Waterstone Financial, Inc.; *U.S. Public*, pg. 2336
WAUWATOSA SURGERY CENTER, LIMITED PARTNERSHIP—See UnitedHealth Group Incorporated; *U.S. Public*, pg. 2252
WAVE 3 COMMUNICATIONS INC.; *U.S. Private*, pg. 4458
WAVEBAND CORPORATION—See Mercury Systems, Inc.; *U.S. Public*, pg. 1422

WAVELOCK HOLDINGS CO., LTD.

WAVECOM SOLUTIONS CORPORATION—See Macquarie Group Limited; *Int'l*, pg. 4628
WAVEDANCER, INC.; *U.S. Public*, pg. 2338
WAVE DISPERSION TECHNOLOGIES, INC.; *U.S. Private*, pg. 4458
WAVEDIVISION HOLDINGS, LLC—See Stonepeak Partners L.P.; *U.S. Private*, pg. 3829
WAVE ELECTRONICS CO., LTD. - OLED FACTORY—See Wave Electronics Co., Ltd.; *Int'l*, pg. 8359
WAVE ELECTRONICS CO., LTD.; *Int'l*, pg. 8359
WAVE ELECTRONICS JAPAN CO., LTD.—See Seoul Semiconductor Co., Ltd.; *Int'l*, pg. 6717
WAVE ELECTRONICS—See Kingswood Capital Management LLC; *U.S. Private*, pg. 2312
WAVE EXPONENTIAL PUBLIC COMPANY LIMITED; *Int'l*, pg. 8359
WAVE FORM SYSTEMS INC.; *U.S. Private*, pg. 4458
WAVEFRONT TECHNOLOGIES, INC.—See Ball Corporation; *U.S. Public*, pg. 266
WAVEFRONT TECHNOLOGY SOLUTIONS INC.; *Int'l*, pg. 8359
WAVEGARD, INC.; *U.S. Private*, pg. 4458
WAVEGUIDE, INC.; *U.S. Private*, pg. 4458
WAVE HOLDINGS, LLC—See Gray Television, Inc.; *U.S. Public*, pg. 959
WAVELAB INC.—See Comba Telecom Systems Holdings Limited; *Int'l*, pg. 1708
WAVELAND INVESTMENTS, LLC; *U.S. Private*, pg. 4458
WAVELENGTH ELECTRONICS LIMITED—See APC Technology Group plc; *Int'l*, pg. 508
WAVELENGTH ENTERPRISES, INC.—See SK Capital Partners, LP; *U.S. Private*, pg. 3680
WAVELENGTH PHARMACEUTICALS LTD.—See SK Capital Partners, LP; *U.S. Private*, pg. 3680
WAVE LIFE SCIENCES LTD.; *Int'l*, pg. 8359
WAVE LIFE SCIENCES USA, INC.—See Wave Life Sciences Ltd.; *Int'l*, pg. 8359
WAVELIGHT GMBH—See Novartis AG; *Int'l*, pg. 5461
WAVELOCK ADVANCED TECHNOLOGY CO., LTD.—See Wavelock Holdings Co., Ltd.; *Int'l*, pg. 8359
WAVELOCK ADVANCED TECHNOLOGY GMBH.—See Wavelock Holdings Co., Ltd.; *Int'l*, pg. 8359
WAVELOCK ADVANCED TECHNOLOGY INC.—See Wavelock Holdings Co., Ltd.; *Int'l*, pg. 8359
WAVELOCK HOLDINGS CO., LTD.; *Int'l*, pg. 8359
WAVELOCK INTERIOR CO., LTD.—See Wavelock Holdings Co., Ltd.; *Int'l*, pg. 8360
WAVEMAKER AG—See WPP plc; *Int'l*, pg. 8473
WAVEMAKER A/S—See WPP plc; *Int'l*, pg. 8473
WAVEMAKER AS—See WPP plc; *Int'l*, pg. 8473
WAVEMAKER - BANGALORE—See WPP plc; *Int'l*, pg. 8474
WAVEMAKER-BELGIUM—See WPP plc; *Int'l*, pg. 8473
WAVEMAKER B.V.—See WPP plc; *Int'l*, pg. 8473
WAVEMAKER CANADA—See WPP plc; *Int'l*, pg. 8474
WAVEMAKER CZECH S.R.O.—See WPP plc; *Int'l*, pg. 8473
WAVEMAKER DUBAI—See WPP plc; *Int'l*, pg. 8474
WAVEMAKER EGYPT—See WPP plc; *Int'l*, pg. 8473
WAVEMAKER GLOBAL LIMITED—See WPP plc; *Int'l*, pg. 8472
WAVEMAKER GLOBAL, LLC—See WPP plc; *Int'l*, pg. 8473
WAVEMAKER GLOBAL LLC—See WPP plc; *Int'l*, pg. 8474
WAVEMAKER GMBH—See WPP plc; *Int'l*, pg. 8473
WAVEMAKER GMBH—See WPP plc; *Int'l*, pg. 8473
WAVEMAKER - GREECE—See WPP plc; *Int'l*, pg. 8473
WAVEMAKER - GURGAON—See WPP plc; *Int'l*, pg. 8474
WAVEMAKER HUNGARY KFT.—See WPP plc; *Int'l*, pg. 8473
WAVEMAKER IRELAND—See WPP plc; *Int'l*, pg. 8473
WAVEMAKER ITALY—See WPP plc; *Int'l*, pg. 8473
WAVEMAKER LEBANON—See WPP plc; *Int'l*, pg. 8473
WAVEMAKER LIMITED—See WPP plc; *Int'l*, pg. 8473
WAVEMAKER MANCHESTER—See WPP plc; *Int'l*, pg. 8474
WAVEMAKER - MEDELLIN—See WPP plc; *Int'l*, pg. 8474
WAVEMAKER MIDDLE EAST—See WPP plc; *Int'l*, pg. 8473
WAVEMAKER - MOROCCO—See WPP plc; *Int'l*, pg. 8473
WAVEMAKER NETHERLANDS—See WPP plc; *Int'l*, pg. 8473
WAVEMAKER NEW ZEALAND LIMITED—See WPP plc; *Int'l*, pg. 8474
WAVEMAKER POLAND—See WPP plc; *Int'l*, pg. 8473
WAVEMAKER PORTUGAL—See WPP plc; *Int'l*, pg. 8473
WAVEMAKER PUBLICIDAD SPAIN SL -BARCELONA—See WPP plc; *Int'l*, pg. 8473
WAVEMAKER PUBLICIDAD SPAIN SL—See WPP plc; *Int'l*, pg. 8473
WAVEMAKER - ROMANIA—See WPP plc; *Int'l*, pg. 8473
WAVEMAKER RUSSIA—See WPP plc; *Int'l*, pg. 8473
WAVEMAKER SAN FRANCISCO—See WPP plc; *Int'l*, pg. 8474
WAVEMAKER - SLOVAKIA—See WPP plc; *Int'l*, pg. 8473
WAVEMAKER SOUTH AFRICA—See WPP plc; *Int'l*, pg. 8473
WAVEMAKER SWITZERLAND—See WPP plc; *Int'l*, pg. 8473

WAVELOCK HOLDINGS CO., LTD.   CORPORATE AFFILIATIONS

WAVEMAKER TURKEY—See WPP plc; *Int'l*, pg. 8473
WAVEMAKER - VENEZUELA—See WPP plc; *Int'l*, pg. 8474
WAVEMARK, INC.—See Cardinal Health, Inc.; *U.S. Public*, pg. 434
WAVEMASTER, INC—See Sega Sammy Holdings, Inc.; *Int'l*, pg. 6681
WAVENET LIMITED—See Macquarie Group Limited; *Int'l*, pg. 4630
WAVEPOINT 3PL EXPEDITE LLC; *U.S. Private*, pg. 4458
THE WAVERLEY BAKERY LIMITED—See Orkla ASA; *Int'l*, pg. 5638
WAVERLEY PHARMA, INC.; *Int'l*, pg. 8360
WAVERLY ADVISORS, LLC—See Affiliated Managers Group, Inc.; *U.S. Public*, pg. 56
WAVERLY ADVISORS, LLC—See HGGC, LLC; *U.S. Private*, pg. 1930
WAVERLY FABRICS—See Iconix Acquisition LLC; *U.S. Private*, pg. 2033
WAVERLY HEIGHTS LTD.; *U.S. Private*, pg. 4458
WAVERLY LUMBER & MANUFACTURING; *U.S. Private*, pg. 4458
WAVERLY PARTNERS INC.; *U.S. Private*, pg. 4458
WAVERLY REGENCY, LLC—See Regency Centers Corporation; *U.S. Public*, pg. 1774
WAVERLY SURGERY CENTER, LLC—See KKR & Co. Inc.; *U.S. Public*, pg. 1250
WAVERTON INVESTMENT MANAGEMENT LIMITED—See ICM Limited; *Int'l*, pg. 3582
WAVES CORPORATION LIMITED—See Retail Holdings N.V.; *Int'l*, pg. 6306
WAVES HOME APPLIANCES LIMITED; *Int'l*, pg. 8360
WAVE SINE TECHNOLOGY LTD.—See Hi Sharp Electronics Co., Ltd.; *Int'l*, pg. 3379
WAVE SOFTWARE, LLC; *U.S. Private*, pg. 4458
WAVESPEC LIMITED—See Braemar PLC; *Int'l*, pg. 1136
WAVESPLITTER TECHNOLOGIES, INC.; *U.S. Private*, pg. 4458
WAVESTONE ADVISORS SAS—See Wavestone SA; *Int'l*, pg. 8360
WAVESTONE HK LIMITED—See Wavestone SA; *Int'l*, pg. 8360
WAVESTONE LUXEMBOURG SA—See Wavestone SA; *Int'l*, pg. 8360
WAVESTONE SA; *Int'l*, pg. 8360
WAVESTONE US, INC.—See Wavestone SA; *Int'l*, pg. 8360
WAVESTREAM CORP.—See Gilat Satellite Networks Ltd.; *Int'l*, pg. 2973
WAVE SYNC CORP.; *U.S. Public*, pg. 2338
WAVETABLE LABS LLC; *U.S. Private*, pg. 4458
WAVETECH GLOBAL, INC.; *U.S. Private*, pg. 4458
WAVE TECHNOLOGY SOLUTIONS GROUP; *U.S. Private*, pg. 4458
WAVETEK MICROELECTRONICS CORPORATION—See United Microelectronics Corporation; *Int'l*, pg. 8071
WAVETRONIX CORP.—See Electro Technik Industries; *U.S. Private*, pg. 1354
WAVEX TECHNOLOGIES PTE. LTD.—See HKC International Holdings Limited; *Int'l*, pg. 3428
WAVICLE DATA SOLUTIONS LLC; *U.S. Private*, pg. 4458
WAVIN ASSURANTIE B.V.—See Bharti Enterprises Limited; *Int'l*, pg. 1012
WAVIN BALKAN D.O.O.—See Bharti Enterprises Limited; *Int'l*, pg. 1012
WAVIN BELGIUM N.V.—See Bharti Enterprises Limited; *Int'l*, pg. 1012
WAVIN B.V.—See Bharti Enterprises Limited; *Int'l*, pg. 1012
WAV, INC.; *U.S. Private*, pg. 4457
WAVIN DIENSTEN B.V.—See Bharti Enterprises Limited; *Int'l*, pg. 1012
WAVIN EKOPLASTIK S.R.O.—See Bharti Enterprises Limited; *Int'l*, pg. 1012
WAVIN ESTONIA OU—See Bharti Enterprises Limited; *Int'l*, pg. 1012
WAVIN FRANCE S.A.S.—See Bharti Enterprises Limited; *Int'l*, pg. 1012
WAVIN GMBH—See Bharti Enterprises Limited; *Int'l*, pg. 1012
WAVIN HUNGARY KFT.—See Grupo Empresarial Kaluz S.A. de C.V.; *Int'l*, pg. 3128
WAVIN IRELAND LTD.—See Bharti Enterprises Limited; *Int'l*, pg. 1012
WAVIN ITALIA S.P.A.—See Bharti Enterprises Limited; *Int'l*, pg. 1012
WAVIN-LABKO OY - PE FACTORY—See Bharti Enterprises Limited; *Int'l*, pg. 1013
WAVIN-LABKO OY—See Bharti Enterprises Limited; *Int'l*, pg. 1013
WAVIN LATVIA SIA—See Bharti Enterprises Limited; *Int'l*, pg. 1012
WAVIN METALPLAST-BUK SP.Z.O.O.—See Bharti Enterprises Limited; *Int'l*, pg. 1013
WAVIN NEDERLAND B.V.—See Bharti Enterprises Limited; *Int'l*, pg. 1012
WAVIN NOVOTECH S.A.S.—See Bharti Enterprises Limited; *Int'l*, pg. 1013

WAVIN N.V.—See Bharti Enterprises Limited; *Int'l*, pg. 1012
WAVIN OVERSEAS B.V.—See Bharti Enterprises Limited; *Int'l*, pg. 1012
WAVIN PLASTICS LTD.—See Bharti Enterprises Limited; *Int'l*, pg. 1013
WAVIN POLYFEMOS AS—See Bharti Enterprises Limited; *Int'l*, pg. 1013
WAVIN PORTUGAL-PLASTICOS S.A.—See Bharti Enterprises Limited; *Int'l*, pg. 1013
WAVIN ROMANIA S.R.L.—See Bharti Enterprises Limited; *Int'l*, pg. 1013
WAVIN SLOVAKIA SPOL S.R.O.—See Bharti Enterprises Limited; *Int'l*, pg. 1013
WAVIN SWISSPIPE AG—See Bharti Enterprises Limited; *Int'l*, pg. 1013
WAVIN TECHNOLOGY & INNOVATION B.V.—See Bharti Enterprises Limited; *Int'l*, pg. 1012
WAVIN UKRAIN O.O.O.T.O.V.—See Bharti Enterprises Limited; *Int'l*, pg. 1013
WAVSYS LLC; *U.S. Private*, pg. 4458
WAV WARME AUSTRIA VERTRIEBSGMBH—See BayWa AG; *Int'l*, pg. 919
WAWA, INC.; *U.S. Private*, pg. 4458
WA WALLVISION AB—See Litorina Capital Management AB; *U.S. Private*, pg. 4528
WAWANESA GENERAL INSURANCE COMPANY—See The Wawanesa Mutual Insurance Company; *Int'l*, pg. 7699
THE WAWANESA LIFE INSURANCE COMPANY—See The Wawanesa Mutual Insurance Company; *Int'l*, pg. 7699
THE WAWANESA MUTUAL INSURANCE COMPANY; *Int'l*, pg. 7699
WAWASAN QI PROPERTIES SDN BHD—See QI Ltd.; *Int'l*, pg. 6139
WAW CREATION LIMITED—See Media Chinese International Limited; *Int'l*, pg. 4770
WAWEL S.A.; *Int'l*, pg. 8360
W.A. WHITNEY CO.—See Mega Manufacturing Inc.; *U.S. Private*, pg. 2660
WAWI CHOCOLATE (AUS) PTY. LTD.—See WAWI-Schokolade AG; *Int'l*, pg. 8360
WAWI CHOCOLATE (XIAMEN) CO., LTD.—See WAWI-Schokolade AG; *Int'l*, pg. 8360
WAWI-EURO GMBH—See WAWI-Schokolade AG; *Int'l*, pg. 8360
W.A. WILSON & SONS, INC.; *U.S. Private*, pg. 4419
WAWI PRAGUE, SPOL SR.O.—See WAWI-Schokolade AG; *Int'l*, pg. 8360
WAWI-SCHOKOLADE AG; *Int'l*, pg. 8360
WAWI-SUSSWAREN SAISONSPEZIALITATEN GMBH—See WAWI-Schokolade AG; *Int'l*, pg. 8360
WAWONA FROZEN FOODS INC.; *U.S. Private*, pg. 4459
W.A.W. SPOL S.R.O.—See Compagnie de Saint-Gobain SA; *Int'l*, pg. 1737
WAWS-TV—See Providence Equity Partners L.L.C.; *U.S. Private*, pg. 3293
WAXAHACHIE NEWSPAPERS, INC.—See American Consolidated Media LP; *U.S. Private*, pg. 228
WAX LYRICAL LIMITED—See The Carlyle Group Inc.; *U.S. Public*, pg. 2052
WAX LYRICAL LTD.; *Int'l*, pg. 8360
WAXMAN CONSUMER PRODUCTS GROUP INC.—See Waxman Industries, Inc.; *U.S. Private*, pg. 4459
WAXMAN INDUSTRIES, INC.; *U.S. Private*, pg. 4459
WAX WORKS INC.; *U.S. Private*, pg. 4459
WAY 2 VAT LTD.; *Int'l*, pg. 8360
WAYBILL USA INC.; *U.S. Private*, pg. 4459
WAY CHONG FINANCE LIMITED—See HSBC Holdings plc; *Int'l*, pg. 3506
WAYCROSS COCA-COLA BOTTLING COMPANY—See Coca-Cola Bottling Co. United, Inc.; *U.S. Private*, pg. 959
WAYFAIR GMBH—See Wayfair Inc.; *U.S. Public*, pg. 2338
WAYFAIR INC.; *U.S. Public*, pg. 2338
WAYFAIR LLC—See Wayfair Inc.; *U.S. Public*, pg. 2338
WAYFAIR STORES LIMITED—See Wayfair Inc.; *U.S. Public*, pg. 2338
WAYFIELD FOODS INC.; *U.S. Private*, pg. 4459
WAYFIELD FOODS, INC.—See Wayfield Foods Inc.; *U.S. Private*, pg. 4459
WAYFIELD FOODS, INC.—See Wayfield Foods Inc.; *U.S. Private*, pg. 4459
WAYGATE TECHNOLOGIES USA, LP—See Baker Hughes Company; *U.S. Public*, pg. 265
WAY HOLDING LTD; *U.S. Private*, pg. 4459
WAYI INTERNATIONAL DIGITAL ENTERTAINMENT CO., LTD.; *Int'l*, pg. 8360
WAYIN, INC.—See Vector Capital Management, L.P.; *U.S. Private*, pg. 4350
WAYLAND, INC.—See ALP Industries, Inc.; *U.S. Private*, pg. 196
WAYLAND TOWN CRIER—See Gannett Co., Inc.; *U.S. Public*, pg. 903
WAY MEDIA INC.; *U.S. Private*, pg. 4459
WAYMO LLC—See Alphabet Inc.; *U.S. Public*, pg. 84
WAYNE ACTION GROUP FOR ECONOMIC SOLVENCY, INC.; *U.S. Private*, pg. 4459

WAYNE ASPHALT & CONSTRUCTION CO.; *U.S. Private*, pg. 4459
WAYNE AUTOMATIC FIRE SPRINKLERS, INC.; *U.S. Private*, pg. 4459
WAYNE BANK—See Norwood Financial Corp.; *U.S. Public*, pg. 1543
WAYNE COUNTY BANK; *U.S. Private*, pg. 4459
WAYNE COUNTY HOSPITAL, INC.; *U.S. Private*, pg. 4459
WAYNE CROUSE INC.; *U.S. Private*, pg. 4459
WAYNE DAIRY PRODUCTS, INC.—See Smith Dairy Products Company Inc.; *U.S. Private*, pg. 3694
WAYNE-DALTON CORP.—See Sanwa Holdings Corporation; *Int'l*, pg. 6561
WAYNE DAVIS CONCRETE CO.; *U.S. Private*, pg. 4459
WAYNE DISPOSAL, INC.—See Republic Services, Inc.; *U.S. Public*, pg. 1788
WAYNE FARMS LLC—See Continental Grain Company; *U.S. Private*, pg. 1029
WAYNE FUELING SYSTEMS LLC—See Dover Corporation; *U.S. Public*, pg. 683
WAYNE FUELING SYSTEMS SWEDEN AB—See Dover Corporation; *U.S. Public*, pg. 683
WAYNE GRETZKY ESTATES LIMITED—See Andrew Peller Limited; *Int'l*, pg. 452
WAYNE HUMMER INVESTMENTS LLC—See Wintrust Financial Corporation; *U.S. Public*, pg. 2375
WAYNE HUMMER TRUST COMPANY, N.A.—See Wintrust Financial Corporation; *U.S. Public*, pg. 2375
WAYNE INDUSTRIES INC.; *U.S. Private*, pg. 4459
WAYNE J. GRIFFIN ELECTRIC INC.; *U.S. Private*, pg. 4459
WAYNE J. GRIFFIN ELECTRIC INC.—See Wayne J. Griffin Electric Inc.; *U.S. Private*, pg. 4460
WAYNE J. GRIFFIN ELECTRIC INC.—See Wayne J. Griffin Electric Inc.; *U.S. Private*, pg. 4460
WAYNE LEES GROCERY & MARKET; *U.S. Private*, pg. 4460
WAYNE MAPLES PLUMBING & HEATING; *U.S. Private*, pg. 4460
WAYNE NURSING & REHABILITATION CENTER, INC.; *U.S. Private*, pg. 4460
WAYNE PERRY, INC.; *U.S. Private*, pg. 4460
WAYNE PIGMENT CORP.; *U.S. Private*, pg. 4460
WAYNE PITMAN FORD LINCOLN; *Int'l*, pg. 8360
WAYNE-SANDERSON FARMS; *U.S. Private*, pg. 4460
WAYNE SAVINGS BANCSHARES, INC.—See Main Street Financial Services Corp.; *U.S. Public*, pg. 1355
WAYNE SAVINGS COMMUNITY BANK—See Main Street Financial Services Corp.; *U.S. Public*, pg. 1355
WAYNESBORO CONSTRUCTION CO. INC.; *U.S. Private*, pg. 4460
WAYNESBORO NURSERIES, INC.; *U.S. Private*, pg. 4460
WAYNES MOBILE HOME SALES INC.; *U.S. Private*, pg. 4460
WAYNES TIRE INC.; *U.S. Private*, pg. 4460
WAYNE THOMAS CHEVROLET, INC; *U.S. Private*, pg. 4460
WAYNE TRAIL TECHNOLOGIES, INC.—See Lincoln Electric Holdings, Inc.; *U.S. Public*, pg. 1318
WAYNE TRANSPORTS INC.; *U.S. Private*, pg. 4460
WAYNE WATER SYSTEMS—See Berkshire Hathaway Inc.; *U.S. Public*, pg. 300
WAYNE WATSON CONSTRUCTION LTD.; *Int'l*, pg. 8360
WAYNE WILES FLOOR COVERINGS, INC.; *U.S. Private*, pg. 4460
WAYNE WIRE AIR BAG COMPONENTS, INC. - JUAREZ FACILITY—See Wayne Wire Cloth Products, Inc.; *U.S. Private*, pg. 4460
WAYNE WIRE CLOTH PRODUCTS HILLMAN DIVISION—See Wayne Wire Cloth Products, Inc.; *U.S. Private*, pg. 4460
WAYNE WIRE CLOTH PRODUCTS, INC.; *U.S. Private*, pg. 4460
WAY OF WILL INC.; *Int'l*, pg. 8360
WAYPOINT ADVISORS LLC—See Cary Street Partners Financial LLC; *U.S. Private*, pg. 777
WAYPOINT BIOMEDICAL HOLDINGS, INC.; *U.S. Public*, pg. 2338
WAYPOINT CAPITAL PARTNERS; *U.S. Private*, pg. 4460
WAYPOINT GLOBAL LLC; *U.S. Private*, pg. 4460
WAYPOINT INSURANCE GROUP, INC.—See Banco Santander, S.A.; *Int'l*, pg. 827
WAYPOINT REIT LIMITED; *Int'l*, pg. 8360
WAYPOINT SOLUTIONS GROUP, LLC.; *U.S. Private*, pg. 4460
WAYPOINT SYSTEMS, INC.—See ATS Automation Inc.; *U.S. Private*, pg. 382
WAYPORT (H.K) CO., LTD.; *Int'l*, pg. 8360
WAYPORT, INC.—See AT&T Inc.; *U.S. Public*, pg. 220
WAYS ELECTRON CO., LTD.; *Int'l*, pg. 8360
WAYSIDE CHRISTIAN MISSION; *U.S. Private*, pg. 4460
WAYSIDE FURNITURE INC.; *U.S. Private*, pg. 4460
WAYSIDE YOUTH & FAMILY SUPPORT NETWORK; *U.S. Private*, pg. 4460
WAYSIS BV; *Int'l*, pg. 8361
WAYSS & FREYTAG INGENIEURBAU AG—See Zech Group SE; *Int'l*, pg. 8628
WAYSTAR, INC.—See Canada Pension Plan Investment Board; *Int'l*, pg. 1282

COMPANY NAME INDEX WDD INC.

WAYSTAR, INC.—See EQT AB; *Int'l*, pg. 2481
WAYS TECHNICAL CORP.; *Int'l*, pg. 8360
WAY'S TRANSPORT LTD.—See Armour Transportation Systems; *Int'l*, pg. 575
WAYSTREAM AB—See Waystream Group AB; *Int'l*, pg. 8361
WAYSTREAM GROUP AB; *Int'l*, pg. 8361
THE WAY TO HAPPINESS FOUNDATION INTERNATIONAL; *U.S. Private*, pg. 4134
WAYZATA INVESTMENT PARTNERS LLC; *U.S. Private*, pg. 4461
WAYZATA MARINE, INC.; *U.S. Private*, pg. 4461
WAYZATA NISSAN; *U.S. Private*, pg. 4461
WAZANA BROTHERS INTERNATIONAL INC.; *U.S. Private*, pg. 4461
WAZE LTD.—See Alphabet Inc.; *U.S. Public*, pg. 83
WAZIR ALI INDUSTRIES LTD.; *Int'l*, pg. 8361
WAZ-LOGISTIK NRW GMBH & CO. KG—See Westdeutsche Allgemeine verlagsgesellschaft; *Int'l*, pg. 8387
WAZ NEWMEDIA GMBH & CO. KG—See Westdeutsche Allgemeine verlagsgesellschaft; *Int'l*, pg. 8387
WAZOKU LIMITED; *Int'l*, pg. 8361
WBAL-AM—See The Hearst Corporation; *U.S. Private*, pg. 4048
WBAL HEARST-ARGYLE TELEVISION, INC.—See The Hearst Corporation; *U.S. Private*, pg. 4048
W BAR E INVESTMENTS CORP.; *U.S. Private*, pg. 4417
WBBB-FM—See Curtis Media Group; *U.S. Private*, pg. 1126
WBB MANAGEMENT COMPANY, INC.—See Thompson Builders Corporation; *U.S. Private*, pg. 4159
WBB MINERALS—See SCR Sibelco SA; *Int'l*, pg. 6654
WBBM-TV—See National Amusements, Inc.; *U.S. Private*, pg. 2840
WB BURGERS ASIA, INC.; *Int'l*, pg. 8361
WBC CORP.—See Wells Concrete Products Company Inc.; *U.S. Private*, pg. 4476
WB COMMUNITY HEALTH; *U.S. Private*, pg. 4461
WBFF-TV—See Sinclair, Inc.; *U.S. Public*, pg. 1886
WBF RESORT OKINAWA CO., LTD.; *Int'l*, pg. 8361
WB GAMES INC.—See Warner Bros. Discovery, Inc.; *U.S. Public*, pg. 2328
WBG GMBH—See E.ON SE; *Int'l*, pg. 2260
WB GUIMARIN & COMPANY INC.; *U.S. Private*, pg. 4461
WBG WEICHENWERK BRANDENBURG GMBH—See voestalpine AG; *Int'l*, pg. 8290
WBH INDUSTRIES INC; *U.S. Private*, pg. 4461
WBHO CONSTRUCTION (PTY) LIMITED—See Wilson Bayly Holmes-Ovcon Limited; *Int'l*, pg. 8423
WBHO CONSTRUCTION PVT. LTD.—See Wilson Bayly Holmes-Ovcon Limited; *Int'l*, pg. 8423
WBHO INFRASTRUCTURE PTY LTD—See Wilson Bayly Holmes-Ovcon Limited; *Int'l*, pg. 8423
W.B. HOPKE CO.; *U.S. Private*, pg. 4419
W.B. HUNT CO., INC.; *U.S. Private*, pg. 4419
WBI ENERGY MIDSTREAM, LLC—See MDU Resources Group, Inc.; *U.S. Public*, pg. 1411
WBI ENERGY SERVICES, INC.—See MDU Resources Group, Inc.; *U.S. Public*, pg. 1411
WBI ENERGY TRANSMISSION, INC.—See MDU Resources Group, Inc.; *U.S. Public*, pg. 1410
WBI ENERGY WIND RIDGE PIPELINE, LLC—See MDU Resources Group, Inc.; *U.S. Public*, pg. 1411
WBI HOLDINGS, INC.—See MDU Resources Group, Inc.; *U.S. Public*, pg. 1410
WBIR, INC.—See TEGNA Inc.; *U.S. Public*, pg. 1991
WBIR-TV—See TEGNA Inc.; *U.S. Public*, pg. 1991
WBK 1, INC.; *U.S. Private*, pg. 4461
WBK NIERUCHOMOSCI S.A.—See Banco Santander, S.A.; *Int'l*, pg. 826
WBL ENGINEERING & DISTRIBUTION PTE. LTD.—See Yanlord Land Group Limited; *Int'l*, pg. 8563
WBL (USA) INC.—See Yanlord Land Group Limited; *Int'l*, pg. 8563
W.B. MASON COMPANY; *U.S. Private*, pg. 4419
W.B. MCCARTNEY OIL COMPANY; *U.S. Private*, pg. 4419
W.B. MCCLOUD & COMPANY, INC.; *U.S. Private*, pg. 4419
WBM ENTERPRISES INC.; *U.S. Private*, pg. 4461
WBM PTY. LTD.—See BMT Group Limited; *Int'l*, pg. 1078
WBM - SYDNEY—See BMT Group Limited; *Int'l*, pg. 1078
WBNS TV, INC.—See TEGNA Inc.; *U.S. Public*, pg. 1991
WBOC INC.—See Draper Holdings Business Trust; *U.S. Private*, pg. 1272
WB-PRC LASER SERVICE GMBH—See Coherent Corp.; *U.S. Public*, pg. 528
WBPR HUNGARIA KFT.—See wbpr Public Relations & Marketing mbH; *Int'l*, pg. 8361
WB PROMOTIONS, INC.; *U.S. Private*, pg. 4461
WBPR PUBLIC RELATIONS & MARKETING MBH; *Int'l*, pg. 8361
WBPR PUBLIC RELATIONS & MARKETING MBH—See wbpr Public Relations & Marketing mbH; *Int'l*, pg. 8361
WBPR PUBLIC RELATIONS & MARKETING MBH—See wbpr Public Relations & Marketing mbH; *Int'l*, pg. 8361
WBRC, LLC—See Gray Television, Inc.; *U.S. Public*, pg. 959

WBRE-TV—See Nexstar Media Group, Inc.; *U.S. Public*, pg. 1523
W. BROTHERTON SEED CO , INC.—See Suba Seeds Company Srl; *Int'l*, pg. 7246
W. BROWN & ASSOCIATES INSURANCE SERVICES, INC.—See Sompo Holdings, Inc.; *Int'l*, pg. 7087
WBS CONNECT, LLC—See GTT Communications, Inc.; *U.S. Private*, pg. 1808
WB SUPPLY LLC—See J Fitzgibbons LLC; *U.S. Private*, pg. 2153
WBS WOHNWIRTSCHAFTLICHE BAUBETREUUNGS- UND SERVICEGESELLSCHAFT MBH—See DZ BANK AG Deutsche Zentral-Genossenschaftsbank; *Int'l*, pg. 2245
WBT LLC—See nVent Electric plc; *Int'l*, pg. 5498
WBT SYSTEMS, INC.—See Avnet, Inc.; *U.S. Public*, pg. 254
WBT SYSTEMS LTD.—See TD Synnex Corp; *U.S. Public*, pg. 1985
WBTV, LLC—See Gray Television, Inc.; *U.S. Public*, pg. 959
WBTW-TV—See Nexstar Media Group, Inc.; *U.S. Public*, pg. 1523
WBV WOHNBAU BETREUUNGS & VERWALTUNGS GMBH—See Salzgitter AG; *Int'l*, pg. 6499
WB WESTFALEN BUS GMBH—See Deutsche Bahn AG; *Int'l*, pg. 2055
WBW GMBH—See Clariane SE; *Int'l*, pg. 1645
THE W.B. WOOD COMPANY; *U.S. Private*, pg. 4132
WBZ-TV—See National Amusements, Inc.; *U.S. Private*, pg. 2840
WCA HOSPITAL; *U.S. Private*, pg. 4461
WCAL, LLC—See National Storage Affiliates Trust; *U.S. Public*, pg. 1498
W.C. & A.N. MILLER COMPANIES; *U.S. Private*, pg. 4419
W. CANNING INTERNATIONAL B.V.—See Element Solutions Inc.; *U.S. Public*, pg. 728
WCA OF OKLAHOMA, LLC—See BC Partners LLP; *Int'l*, pg. 924
W CAPITAL MANAGEMENT LLC; *U.S. Private*, pg. 4417
W. CAPRA CONSULTING GROUP, INC.; *U.S. Private*, pg. 4417
WCA SERVICES CORP.—See WCA Hospital; *U.S. Private*, pg. 4461
WCA SHILOH LANDFILL, LLC—See BC Partners LLP; *Int'l*, pg. 924
WCAU-TV—See Comcast Corporation; *U.S. Public*, pg. 540
WCA WASTE CORPORATION—See BC Partners LLP; *Int'l*, pg. 924
WCBD-TV—See Nexstar Media Group, Inc.; *U.S. Public*, pg. 1523
WCB MEDICAL CENTER LLC—See Adeptus Health Inc.; *U.S. Private*, pg. 78
W.C. BRADLEY CO.; *U.S. Private*, pg. 4419
W.C. BRADLEY FARMS INC.—See W.C. Bradley Co.; *U.S. Private*, pg. 4419
WCBS-TV—See National Amusements, Inc.; *U.S. Private*, pg. 2840
WCC CABLE, INC.; *U.S. Private*, pg. 4461
WCC HOLDING B.V.—See Westmoreland Coal Company; *U.S. Private*, pg. 4500
WCCO-TV—See National Amusements, Inc.; *U.S. Private*, pg. 2841
WCCT, INC.—See Nexstar Media Group, Inc.; *U.S. Public*, pg. 1524
WCCV FLOOR COVERINGS, LLC—See The Sterling Group, L.P.; *U.S. Private*, pg. 4122
WC DESIGNS; *U.S. Private*, pg. 4461
WCE HOLDINGS BERHAD; *Int'l*, pg. 8361
W.C. ENGLISH INCORPORATED; *U.S. Private*, pg. 4419
W.C. EQUIPMENT COMPANY INC.—See William Charles, Ltd.; *U.S. Private*, pg. 4522
WCF BANCORP, INC.; *U.S. Private*, pg. 2338
WCF DISTRIBUTION—See WCF Ltd; *Int'l*, pg. 8361
WCF FINANCIAL BANK—See WCF Bancorp, Inc.; *U.S. Public*, pg. 2338
WCF FUELS NORTH WEST—See WCF Ltd; *Int'l*, pg. 8361
WCF HORTICULTURE—See WCF Ltd; *Int'l*, pg. 8361
WCF LTD; *Int'l*, pg. 8361
WCF PET & EQUESTRIAN—See WCF Ltd; *Int'l*, pg. 8361
WCG CLINICAL, INC.; *U.S. Private*, pg. 2338
WCG INTERNATIONAL CONSULTANTS LTD.—See ModivCare, Inc.; *U.S. Public*, pg. 1456
WCG—See New Mountain Capital, LLC; *U.S. Private*, pg. 2904
WCGV, INC.—See Sinclair, Inc.; *U.S. Public*, pg. 1886
W.C. HELLER & CO.; *U.S. Private*, pg. 4419
W CHICAGO - CITY CENTER HOTEL—See Marriott International, Inc.; *U.S. Public*, pg. 1372
W CHICAGO - LAKESHORE HOTEL—See Park Hotels & Resorts Inc.; *U.S. Public*, pg. 1638
WC HOLDING, INC.; *U.S. Private*, pg. 4461
WCHO RADIO—See iHeartMedia, Inc.; *U.S. Public*, pg. 1097
WCHS, INC.—See Acadia Healthcare Company, Inc.; *U.S. Public*, pg. 31
WCHS-TV—See Sinclair, Inc.; *U.S. Public*, pg. 1886

WCI COMMUNITIES, INC.—See Lennar Corporation; *U.S. Public*, pg. 1307
W&CIE—See Vivendi SE; *Int'l*, pg. 8267
WC INVESTMENT COMPANY—See William Charles, Ltd.; *U.S. Private*, pg. 4522
WCIT ARCHITECTURE, INC.; *U.S. Private*, pg. 4461
WCIV-TV—See Sinclair, Inc.; *U.S. Public*, pg. 1886
WCJB-TV—See Gray Television, Inc.; *U.S. Public*, pg. 960
WCM BETEILIGUNGS- UND GRUNDBESITZ- AKTIENGESELLSCHAFT—See Aroundtown SA; *Int'l*, pg. 578
W.C. MCQUAIDE INC.; *U.S. Private*, pg. 4419
WCM GLOBAL GROWTH LIMITED; *Int'l*, pg. 8361
WCM GLOBAL LONG SHORT LIMITED; *Int'l*, pg. 8361
WCM INDUSTRIES INC.; *U.S. Private*, pg. 4461
W.C. MOTOR COMPANY, INC.—See Southland Imports, Inc.; *U.S. Private*, pg. 3737
WCNC-TV, INC.—See TEGNA Inc.; *U.S. Public*, pg. 1990
WCON ELECTRONICS EUROPE S.R.L.—See Wcon Electronics (Guangdong) Co., Ltd.; *Int'l*, pg. 8361
WCON ELECTRONICS (GUANGDONG) CO., LTD.; *Int'l*, pg. 8361
WC PHARMACEUTICALS I LIMITED—See AbbVie Inc.; *U.S. Public*, pg. 24
W C P, INC.—See AGNORA Ltd.; *Int'l*, pg. 212
WCPO-TV—See The E.W. Scripps Company; *U.S. Public*, pg. 2069
WCPR-FM—See Alpha Media LLC; *U.S. Private*, pg. 198
WCREM CANADIAN MANAGEMENT INC.—See UniCredit S.p.A.; *Int'l*, pg. 8041
WCRS—See The Engine Group; *Int'l*, pg. 7640
WCS-333 SOUTH STREET, INC.; *U.S. Private*, pg. 4462
WC SACD ONE, INC.—See General Catalyst Partners; *U.S. Private*, pg. 1664
WC SACD ONE, INC.—See iSubscribed Inc.; *U.S. Private*, pg. 2147
WC SACD ONE, INC.—See WndrCo Holdings, LLC; *U.S. Private*, pg. 4552
WCSC, LLC—See Gray Television, Inc.; *U.S. Public*, pg. 959
WCS CONTRACTORS, LTD.; *U.S. Private*, pg. 4461
WCSH-TV—See TEGNA Inc.; *U.S. Public*, pg. 1991
WCS, INC.; *U.S. Private*, pg. 4462
WCS LENDING, LLC; *U.S. Private*, pg. 4462
WCT CONSTRUCTION SDN. BHD.—See WCT Holdings Berhad; *Int'l*, pg. 8362
WCT ENGINEERING VIETNAM COMPANY LIMITED—See WCT Holdings Berhad; *Int'l*, pg. 8362
WCT HOLDINGS BERHAD; *Int'l*, pg. 8361
WC TINGLE COMPANY; *U.S. Private*, pg. 4461
WCT LAND SDN. BHD.—See WCT Holdings Berhad; *Int'l*, pg. 8362
WCT MACHINERY SDN. BHD.—See WCT Holdings Berhad; *Int'l*, pg. 8362
WCT OUG DEVELOPMENT SDN. BHD.—See WCT Holdings Berhad; *Int'l*, pg. 8362
WCTV-TV—See Gray Television, Inc.; *U.S. Public*, pg. 960
WCVB HEARST-ARGYLE TELEVISION, INC.—See The Hearst Corporation; *U.S. Private*, pg. 4048
WCWJ-TV—See Graham Holdings Company; *U.S. Public*, pg. 955
WCWN LLC—See Sinclair, Inc.; *U.S. Public*, pg. 1886
W.C. WOOD COMPANY LIMITED; *Int'l*, pg. 8322
WD-40 COMPANY (AUSTRALIA) PTY. LTD.—See WD-40 Company; *U.S. Public*, pg. 2338
WD-40 COMPANY (CANADA) LTD.—See WD-40 Company; *U.S. Public*, pg. 2339
WD-40 COMPANY LTD.—See WD-40 Company; *U.S. Public*, pg. 2339
WD-40 COMPANY; *U.S. Public*, pg. 2338
WD-40 MANUFACTURING CO.—See WD-40 Company; *U.S. Public*, pg. 2339
WD-40 PRODUCTS (CANADA) LTD.—See WD-40 Company; *U.S. Public*, pg. 2339
WDAF TELEVISION, INC.—See Nexstar Media Group, Inc.; *U.S. Public*, pg. 1525
WDB COCO CO., LTD.; *Int'l*, pg. 8362
WDB HOLDINGS CO., LTD.; *Int'l*, pg. 8362
WDB MEDICAL DATA, INC.—See WDB Holdings Co., Ltd.; *Int'l*, pg. 8362
WDC ACQUISITION LLC—See TRM Equity LLC; *U.S. Private*, pg. 4241
WDC MIAMI INC.—See Sonepar S.A.; *Int'l*, pg. 7094
WDC PUERTO RICO INC.—See Sonepar S.A.; *Int'l*, pg. 7094
WDCW , LLC—See Nexstar Media Group, Inc.; *U.S. Public*, pg. 1524
WDD INC.; *U.S. Private*, pg. 4462
WDEF AM/FM—See Bahakel Communications, Ltd.; *U.S. Private*, pg. 425
WDEF-TV—See Morris Multimedia, Inc.; *U.S. Private*, pg. 2788
WD EUROPE SAS—See V. F. Corporation; *U.S. Public*, pg. 2270
WDEV SOLUCOES EM TECNOLOGIA S.A.—See Ebix Inc.; *U.S. Public*, pg. 710
W DEXTER BENDER & ASSOCIATES, LLC—See Atwell, LLC; *U.S. Private*, pg. 384

WDF/FIVE STAR HOLDING CORPORATION — CORPORATE AFFILIATIONS

WDF/FIVE STAR HOLDING CORPORATION; *U.S. Private*, pg. 4462
WDFG UK LIMITED—See Avolta AG; *Int'l*, pg. 749
WDF INC.—See WDF/Five Star Holding Corporation; *U.S. Private*, pg. 4462
WDF/NAGELBUSH HOLDING CORP—See Tutor Perini Corporation; *U.S. Public*, pg. 2206
WDG RESOURCES SDN. BHD.—See Wah Seong Corporation Berhad; *Int'l*, pg. 8330
WD HALL EXPLORATION COMPANY; *U.S. Private*, pg. 4462
W.D. HOARD & SONS COMPANY INC.; *U.S. Private*, pg. 4419
WDHT—See Alpha Media LLC; *U.S. Private*, pg. 198
W-DIAMOND GROUP CORPORATION; *U.S. Private*, pg. 4417
WDI CORPORATION; *Int'l*, pg. 8362
WDI INTERNATIONAL, INC.—See WDI Corporation; *Int'l*, pg. 8362
WDIO-TV, LLC—See Hubbard Broadcasting, Inc.; *U.S. Private*, pg. 2000
WDIT, INCORPORATED; *U.S. Private*, pg. 4462
WDKY, INC.—See Sinclair, Inc.; *U.S. Public*, pg. 1886
WDLA-FM—See iHeartMedia, Inc.; *U.S. Public*, pg. 1097
W.D. LARAMORE MANUFACTURING INC.—See Hillenbrand, Inc.; *U.S. Public*, pg. 1037
W.D. MATHEWS INC.; *U.S. Private*, pg. 4419
W.D. MATTHEWS MACHINERY CO.; *U.S. Private*, pg. 4419
WDM AUTORYZOWANY DORADCA SP. Z.O.O—See Graviton Capital S.A.; *Int'l*, pg. 3062
WD MEDIA (SINGAPORE) PTE. LTD.—See Western Digital Corporation; *U.S. Public*, pg. 2355
WDMP LIMITED—See Samsung BioLogics Co., Ltd.; *Int'l*, pg. 6511
WDM PUMPS, INC.—See Corporacion EG S.A.; *Int'l*, pg. 1803
WDP NEDERLAND N.V.—See Warehouses De Pauw Comm. VA; *Int'l*, pg. 8344
WDR MEDIAGROUP GMBH—See Westdeutscher Rundfunk WDR; *Int'l*, pg. 8388
WDS COMPONENT PARTS LTD.; *Int'l*, pg. 8362
WDTR, INC.—See Republic Services, Inc.; *U.S. Public*, pg. 1788
WDTV-TV—See Gray Television, Inc.; *U.S. Public*, pg. 960
WDX S.A.; *Int'l*, pg. 8362
WE22 GMBH—See IONOS Group SE; *Int'l*, pg. 3795
WE22 SOLUTIONS GMBH—See IONOS Group SE; *Int'l*, pg. 3795
WE3 TECHNOLOGY COMPANY LIMITED—See Solomon Systech (International) Limited; *Int'l*, pg. 7075
WEABER, INC.—See Resilience Capital Partners, LLC; *U.S. Private*, pg. 3405
WEAKLEY COUNTY MUNICIPAL ELECTRIC SYSTEM; *U.S. Private*, pg. 4462
WEALINS S.A.—See Foyer S.A.; *Int'l*, pg. 2756
WEALTHBAR FINANCIAL SERVICES INC.—See CI Financial Corporation; *Int'l*, pg. 1601
WEALTHCAP FLUGZEUG PORTFOLIO 25 GMBH & CO. KG—See UniCredit S.p.A.; *Int'l*, pg. 8041
WEALTHCAP FONDS GMBH—See UniCredit S.p.A.; *Int'l*, pg. 8041
WEALTHCAP IMMOBILIENFONDS DEUTSCHLAND 34 GMBH & CO. KG—See UniCredit S.p.A.; *Int'l*, pg. 8041
WEALTHCAP IMMOBILIENFONDS DEUTSCHLAND 35 GMBH & CO. KG—See UniCredit S.p.A.; *Int'l*, pg. 8041
WEALTHCAP IMMOBILIENFONDS EUROPA 11 GMBH & CO. KG—See UniCredit S.p.A.; *Int'l*, pg. 8041
WEALTHCAP INVESTORENBETREUUNG GMBH—See UniCredit S.p.A.; *Int'l*, pg. 8041
WEALTH CAPITAL INVESTMENT INC.—See UniCredit S.p.A.; *Int'l*, pg. 8041
WEALTH CAPITAL MANAGEMENT INC.—See UniCredit S.p.A.; *Int'l*, pg. 8041
WEALTHCAP KAPITALVERWALTUNGSGESELLSCHAFT MBH—See UniCredit S.p.A.; *Int'l*, pg. 8042
WEALTHCAP LEBENSWERT 3 GMBH & CO. KG—See UniCredit S.p.A.; *Int'l*, pg. 8041
WEALTHCAP PEIA MANAGEMENT GMBH—See UniCredit S.p.A.; *Int'l*, pg. 8041
WEALTHCAP PEIA SEKUNDAR GMBH—See UniCredit S.p.A.; *Int'l*, pg. 8041
WEALTHCAP PHOTOVOLTAIK 2 GMBH & CO. KG—See UniCredit S.p.A.; *Int'l*, pg. 8041
WEALTHCAP PHOTOVOLTAIK 3 GMBH & CO. KG—See UniCredit S.p.A.; *Int'l*, pg. 8041
WEALTHCAP PRIVATE EQUITY GMBH—See UniCredit S.p.A.; *Int'l*, pg. 8041
WEALTHCAP REAL ESTATE KOMPLEMENTAR GMBH—See UniCredit S.p.A.; *Int'l*, pg. 8041
WEALTHCAP REAL ESTATE SEKUNDAR GMBH—See UniCredit S.p.A.; *Int'l*, pg. 8041
WEALTHCLASSES, LLC; *U.S. Private*, pg. 4462
WEALTHCRAFT CAPITAL, INC.; *U.S. Public*, pg. 2339
WEALTH DEFENDER EQUITIES LIMITED; *Int'l*, pg. 8362
WEALTH DESIGN, LLC—See Beacon Pointe Holdings, LLC; *U.S. Private*, pg. 505
WEALTH DRAGONS GROUP PLC; *Int'l*, pg. 8363
WEALTHENGINE.COM; *U.S. Private*, pg. 4462

WEALTH ENHANCEMENT BROKERAGE SERVICES, LLC—See TA Associates, Inc.; *U.S. Private*, pg. 3919
WEALTH ENHANCEMENT GROUP, LLC—See TA Associates, Inc.; *U.S. Private*, pg. 3919
WEALTH FIRST PORTFOLIO MANAGERS LIMITED; *Int'l*, pg. 8363
WEALTHFRONT CORPORATION; *U.S. Private*, pg. 4462
WEALTH GLORY HOLDINGS LIMITED; *Int'l*, pg. 8363
WEALTHINK AI-INNOVATION CAPITAL LIMITED; *Int'l*, pg. 8363
WEALTH MANAGEMENT CAPITAL HOLDING GMBH—See UniCredit S.p.A.; *Int'l*, pg. 8041
WEALTH MANAGEMENT INC.; *Int'l*, pg. 8363
WEALTHMED AUSTRALIA PTY. LTD.—See Azimut Holding SpA; *Int'l*, pg. 779
WEALTH MINERALS LTD.; *Int'l*, pg. 8363
WEALTHNAVI, INC.; *Int'l*, pg. 8363
WEALTH PARTNERS CAPITAL GROUP, LLC—See Affiliated Managers Group, Inc.; *U.S. Public*, pg. 56
WEALTHPARTNERS, LLP—See Warburg Pincus LLC; *U.S. Private*, pg. 4439
WEALTHPIRE INC; *U.S. Private*, pg. 4462
WEALTHPLUS PTE LTD—See Koh Brothers Group Limited; *Int'l*, pg. 4228
WEALTHSIMPLE FINANCIAL CORP.—See Power Corporation of Canada; *Int'l*, pg. 5944
WEALTHSOURCE PARTNERS, LLC—See New Mountain Capital, LLC; *U.S. Private*, pg. 2901
WEALTHSPIRE ADVISORS, L.P.—See Aon plc; *Int'l*, pg. 498
WEALTH STRATEGIES GROUP INC.—See MAS Advisors, LLC; *U.S. Private*, pg. 2600
WEALTH TODAY PTY. LTD.—See WT Financial Group Limited; *Int'l*, pg. 8498
WEALTHWISE PTY. LTD.—See Azimut Holding SpA; *Int'l*, pg. 780
WEALTHY DEVELOPMENT (HK) LIMITED—See Simplicity Holding Ltd.; *Int'l*, pg. 6934
WEALTHY GROWTH SDN BHD—See IOI Corporation Berhad; *Int'l*, pg. 3792
WEALTHY RISE INTERNATIONAL LIMITED—See Solargiga Energy Holdings Limited; *Int'l*, pg. 7070
WEALTHY WAY (CHINA) FINANCE LEASE LIMITED—See Wealthy Way Group Limited; *Int'l*, pg. 8363
WEALTHY WAY GROUP LIMITED; *Int'l*, pg. 8363
WEA MIDSTATE; *U.S. Private*, pg. 4462
W.E. ANDERSON DIV.—See Arcline Investment Management LP; *U.S. Private*, pg. 313
W.E. ANDREWS—See Chatham Asset Management, LLC; *U.S. Private*, pg. 866
WEAPON 7—See Omnicom Group Inc.; *U.S. Public*, pg. 1599
WEARABLE DEVICES LTD.; *Int'l*, pg. 8363
WEARABLE HEALTH SOLUTIONS, INC.; *U.S. Public*, pg. 2339
WEARBEST SIL-TEX MILLS LTD.; *U.S. Private*, pg. 4462
WEARCHECK AFRICA (PTY) LTD.—See Set Point Group Limited; *Int'l*, pg. 6730
WE ARE CLOUD SAS—See Hellman & Friedman LLC; *U.S. Private*, pg. 1911
WE ARE CLOUD SAS—See Permira Advisers LLP; *Int'l*, pg. 5809
WE ARE ERA GMBH—See Bertelsmann SE & Co. KGaA; *Int'l*, pg. 996
WE ARE SOCIAL LTD.—See Bluefocus Intelligent Communications Group Co., Ltd.; *Int'l*, pg. 1071
WEAR FIRST SPORTSWEAR INC.; *U.S. Private*, pg. 4462
WEAR LICENSEE, LLC—See Sinclair, Inc.; *U.S. Public*, pg. 1886
WEAR ME APPAREL LLC—See Li & Fung Limited; *Int'l*, pg. 4480
WEARNES AUTOMOTIVE CHANGCHUN CO. LTD.—See Wearnes Automotive Pte. Ltd.; *Int'l*, pg. 8363
WEARNES AUTOMOTIVE PTE. LTD.; *Int'l*, pg. 8363
WEARNES AUTOMOTIVE SDN BHD—See Wearnes Automotive Pte. Ltd.; *Int'l*, pg. 8363
WEARNES AUTOMOTIVE SERVICES PTE. LTD.—See Wearnes Automotive Pte. Ltd.; *Int'l*, pg. 8363
WEARNES MOTORS (HK) LTD—See Wearnes Automotive Pte. Ltd.; *Int'l*, pg. 8363
WEARTECH INTERNATIONAL, INC.—See Lincoln Electric Holdings, Inc.; *U.S. Public*, pg. 1318
WEARTECH INTERNATIONAL LIMITED—See Lincoln Electric Holdings, Inc.; *U.S. Public*, pg. 1318
WEAR-TV—See Sinclair, Inc.; *U.S. Public*, pg. 1886
WEAR WELL FOOTWEAR LIMITED—See Hevea B.V.; *Int'l*, pg. 3367
WEARY DUNLOP RETIREMENT VILLAGE PTY. LTD.—See Ryman Healthcare Ltd.; *Int'l*, pg. 6440
WEASLER ENGINEERING B.V.—See Enerpac Tool Corp.; *U.S. Public*, pg. 766
WEASLER ENGINEERING INC.—See Enerpac Tool Corp.; *U.S. Public*, pg. 766
WEASLER ENGINEERING, KFT—See Enerpac Tool Group Corp.; *U.S. Public*, pg. 766
WEATHERBANK, INC.—See AccuWeather, Inc.; *U.S. Private*, pg. 56

WEATHERBY CONSTRUCTION CORP.; *U.S. Private*, pg. 4462
WEATHERBY HEALTHCARE—See Ares Management Corporation; *U.S. Public*, pg. 188
WEATHERBY HEALTHCARE—See Leonard Green & Partners, L.P.; *U.S. Private*, pg. 2425
WEATHERBY, INC.; *U.S. Private*, pg. 4462
THE WEATHER CHANNEL, LLC—See Entertainment Studios, Inc.; *U.S. Private*, pg. 1405
WEATHERCHEM CORP; *U.S. Private*, pg. 4462
THE WEATHER COMPANY—See TBG Treuhand Partner AG; *Int'l*, pg. 7480
WEATHER DECISION TECHNOLOGIES, INC.—See TBG Treuhand Partner AG; *Int'l*, pg. 7480
WEATHERFORD AARBAKKE AS—See Weatherford International plc; *U.S. Public*, pg. 2339
WEATHERFORD AEROSPACE, INC.—See KKR & Co. Inc.; *U.S. Public*, pg. 1262
WEATHERFORD ARTIFICIAL LIFT SYSTEMS CANADA LTD.—See Weatherford International plc; *U.S. Public*, pg. 2340
WEATHERFORD ARTIFICIAL LIFT SYSTEMS—See Weatherford International plc; *U.S. Public*, pg. 2339
WEATHERFORD ASIA PACIFIC PTE. LTD.—See Weatherford International plc; *U.S. Public*, pg. 2340
WEATHERFORD AUSTRALIA PTY. LTD.—See Weatherford International plc; *U.S. Public*, pg. 2340
WEATHERFORD (B) SDN. BHD.—See Weatherford International plc; *U.S. Public*, pg. 2339
WEATHERFORD CANADA LIMITED—See Weatherford International plc; *U.S. Public*, pg. 2340
WEATHERFORD CANADA PARTNERSHIP (ADMINISTRATION CENTER)—See Weatherford International plc; *U.S. Public*, pg. 2340
WEATHERFORD CANADA PARTNERSHIP—See Weatherford International plc; *U.S. Public*, pg. 2340
WEATHERFORD CAPITAL MANAGEMENT SERVICES LIMITED LIABILITY—See Weatherford International plc; *U.S. Public*, pg. 2340
WEATHERFORD CSG DRILLING PTY LTD—See Weatherford International plc; *U.S. Public*, pg. 2340
WEATHERFORD DANMARK AS—See Weatherford International plc; *U.S. Public*, pg. 2340
WEATHERFORD DIS MANUFACTURING (UK) LIMITED—See Weatherford International plc; *U.S. Public*, pg. 2340
WEATHERFORD EAST EUROPE SERVICE GMBH—See Weatherford International plc; *U.S. Public*, pg. 2340
WEATHERFORD ENERGY SERVICES GMBH—See Weatherford International plc; *U.S. Public*, pg. 2340
WEATHERFORD ENGINEERED CHEMISTRY CANADA LTD.—See Weatherford International plc; *U.S. Public*, pg. 2340
WEATHERFORD FRANCE, S.A.—See Weatherford International plc; *U.S. Public*, pg. 2340
WEATHERFORD HOME CARE SERVICES, LLC—See Community Health Systems, Inc.; *U.S. Public*, pg. 557
WEATHERFORD, INC.—See Weatherford International plc; *U.S. Public*, pg. 2341
WEATHERFORD INDUSTRIA E COMERCIO LTDA.—See Weatherford International plc; *U.S. Public*, pg. 2340
WEATHERFORD INTERNATIONAL DE ARGENTINA S.A.—See Weatherford International plc; *U.S. Public*, pg. 2340
WEATHERFORD INTERNATIONAL EASTERN EUROPE SRL—See Weatherford International plc; *U.S. Public*, pg. 2340
WEATHERFORD INTERNATIONAL, LLC—See Weatherford International plc; *U.S. Public*, pg. 2340
WEATHERFORD INTERNATIONAL PLC; *U.S. Public*, pg. 2339
WEATHERFORD KOPP GMBH—See Weatherford International plc; *U.S. Public*, pg. 2340
WEATHERFORD KSP CO., LTD.—See Weatherford International plc; *U.S. Public*, pg. 2340
WEATHERFORD LABORATORIES (CANADA) LTD.—See Weatherford International plc; *U.S. Public*, pg. 2340
WEATHERFORD LABORATORIES, INC.—See Weatherford International plc; *U.S. Public*, pg. 2340
WEATHERFORD LABORATORIES (MUSCAT) L.L.C.—See Weatherford International plc; *U.S. Public*, pg. 2340
WEATHERFORD LABORATORIES (UK) LIMITED—See Weatherford International plc; *U.S. Public*, pg. 2340
WEATHERFORD LATIN AMERICA, S.C.A—See Weatherford International plc; *U.S. Public*, pg. 2340
WEATHERFORD LINERS SYSTEMS LTD.—See Weatherford International plc; *U.S. Public*, pg. 2340
WEATHERFORD (MALAYSIA) SDN. BHD.—See Weatherford International plc; *U.S. Public*, pg. 2339
WEATHERFORD MOTORS, INC.—See Sojitz Corporation; *Int'l*, pg. 7064
WEATHERFORD NEW ZEALAND LTD.—See Weatherford International plc; *U.S. Public*, pg. 2340
WEATHERFORD NORGE, A/S—See Weatherford International plc; *U.S. Public*, pg. 2340
WEATHERFORD NORGE A/S—See Weatherford International plc; *U.S. Public*, pg. 2340

COMPANY NAME INDEX

WEATHERFORD OIL TOOL GMBH—See Weatherford International plc; *U.S. Public*, pg. 2340
WEATHERFORD OIL TOOL MIDDLE EAST LTD.—See Weatherford International plc; *U.S. Public*, pg. 2340
WEATHERFORD OIL TOOL MIDDLE EAST LTD.—See Weatherford International plc; *U.S. Public*, pg. 2340
WEATHERFORD OIL TOOL NEDERLAND B.V.—See Weatherford International plc; *U.S. Public*, pg. 2340
WEATHERFORD PETROLEUM CONSULTANTS AS—See Weatherford International plc; *U.S. Public*, pg. 2340
WEATHERFORD POLAND SP.Z.O.O—See Weatherford International plc; *U.S. Public*, pg. 2340
WEATHERFORD PRODUCTION OPTIMIZATION—See Weatherford International plc; *U.S. Public*, pg. 2341
WEATHERFORD PRODUCTS, INC.—See Weatherford International plc; *U.S. Public*, pg. 2340
WEATHERFORD SAUDI ARABIA LTD.—See Weatherford International plc; *U.S. Public*, pg. 2340
WEATHERFORD SERVICES S.A.—See Weatherford International plc; *U.S. Public*, pg. 2341
WEATHERFORD TEXAS HOSPITAL COMPANY, LLC—See HCA Healthcare, Inc.; *U.S. Public*, pg. 1013
WEATHERFORD TRINIDAD LIMITED—See Weatherford International plc; *U.S. Public*, pg. 2340
WEATHERFORD (U.K.) LIMITED—See Weatherford International plc; *U.S. Public*, pg. 2339
WEATHERFORD UK LTD.—See Weatherford International plc; *U.S. Public*, pg. 2341
WEATHERFORD U.K. LTD.—See Weatherford International plc; *U.S. Public*, pg. 2341
WEATHERFORD U.S., INC.—See Weatherford International plc; *U.S. Public*, pg. 2341
WEATHERGUARD TECTA AMERICA, LLC—See Altas Partners LP; *Int'l*, pg. 387
WEATHERHAVEN AUSTRALIA PTY LTD—See Weatherhaven; *Int'l*, pg. 8363
WEATHERHAVEN DO BRASIL LTDA.—See Weatherhaven; *Int'l*, pg. 8363
WEATHERHAVEN GLOBAL SOLUTIONS LIMITED—See Weatherhaven; *Int'l*, pg. 8363
WEATHERHAVEN INTERNATIONAL LTD.—See Weatherhaven; *Int'l*, pg. 8363
WEATHERHAVEN PERU S.A.—See Weatherhaven; *Int'l*, pg. 8363
WEATHERHAVEN RESOURCES INC.—See Weatherhaven; *Int'l*, pg. 8363
WEATHERHAVEN; *Int'l*, pg. 8363
WEATHERLY INTERNATIONAL PLC; *Int'l*, pg. 8363
WEATHERLY MINING NAMIBIA LIMITED—See Weatherly International plc; *Int'l*, pg. 8363
WEATHERMAKER LIMITED—See Tata Sons Limited; *Int'l*, pg. 7473
WEATHER MAP CO., LTD.—See Imagica Group Inc.; *Int'l*, pg. 3619
WEATHERNEWS AMERICA INC.—See Weathernews Inc.; *Int'l*, pg. 8364
WEATHERNEWS BENELUX B.V.—See Weathernews Inc.; *Int'l*, pg. 8364
WEATHERNEWS FRANCE SAS—See Weathernews Inc.; *Int'l*, pg. 8364
WEATHERNEWS HONG KONG LTD.—See Weathernews Inc.; *Int'l*, pg. 8364
WEATHERNEWS INC.; *Int'l*, pg. 8363
WEATHERNEWS KOREA INC.—See Weathernews Inc.; *Int'l*, pg. 8364
WEATHERNEWS NEPAL PVT. LTD.—See Weathernews Inc.; *Int'l*, pg. 8364
WEATHERNEWS SHANGHAI LTD.—See Weathernews Inc.; *Int'l*, pg. 8364
WEATHERNEWS SINGAPORE PTE. LTD.—See Weathernews Inc.; *Int'l*, pg. 8364
WEATHERNEWS TAIWAN LTD.—See Weathernews Inc.; *Int'l*, pg. 8364
WEATHERNEWS U.K. LTD.—See Weathernews Inc.; *Int'l*, pg. 8364
WEATHERPANEL, INC.—See Leonard Green & Partners, L.P.; *U.S. Private*, pg. 2429
WEATHERPROOFING TECHNOLOGIES, INC.—See RPM International Inc.; *U.S. Public*, pg. 1818
WEATHERSEAL COMPANY, LLC—See Installed Building Products, Inc.; *U.S. Public*, pg. 1134
WEATHERSEAL INSULATION CO., LLC—See Installed Building Products, Inc.; *U.S. Public*, pg. 1134
WEATHER SHIELD MANUFACTURING, INC.—See Weathershield Mfg. Inc.; *U.S. Private*, pg. 4463
WEATHERSHIELD MFG. INC.; *U.S. Private*, pg. 4462
WEATHERTEC CORPORATION; *U.S. Private*, pg. 4463
WEATHERTECH DISTRIBUTING CO. INC; *U.S. Private*, pg. 4463
WEATHER TELEMATICS INC.—See Predictiv AI, Inc.; *Int'l*, pg. 5958
WEATHERVANE SEAFOOD COMPANY; *U.S. Private*, pg. 4463
W.E. AUBUCHON CO., INC.; *U.S. Private*, pg. 4420
WEAVE COMMUNICATIONS, INC.; *U.S. Public*, pg. 2341
WEAVE CORPORATION; *U.S. Private*, pg. 4463
WEAVER AUTOMOTIVE, INC.—See Incline MGMT Corp.; *U.S. Private*, pg. 2054
WEAVER BROS. INSURANCE ASSOCIATES, INC.—See Kelso & Company, L.P.; *U.S. Private*, pg. 2280
WEAVER COOKE CONSTRUCTION, LLC; *U.S. Private*, pg. 4463
WEAVER ENTERPRISES LTD.; *U.S. Private*, pg. 4463
WEAVER FLUID POWER, INC.—See RG Industries, Inc.; *U.S. Private*, pg. 3420
WEAVER & HOLIHAN, INC.; *U.S. Private*, pg. 4463
WEAVER LEATHER, LLC—See Blue Point Capital Partners, LLC; *U.S. Private*, pg. 591
WEAVER MARKETS INC.; *U.S. Private*, pg. 4463
WEAVER NUT COMPANY INC.; *U.S. Private*, pg. 4463
WEAVER POPCORN COMPANY, INC.; *U.S. Private*, pg. 4463
WEAVER PRECAST INC.; *U.S. Private*, pg. 4463
WEAVER PUBLICATIONS INC.; *U.S. Private*, pg. 4463
WEAVER SALES OF SAUK CITY INC.; *U.S. Private*, pg. 4463
WEAVERS PLACE (SKELMANTHORPE) MANAGEMENT COMPANY LIMITED—See Persimmon plc; *Int'l*, pg. 5818
WEAVER & TIDWELL, L.L.P.; *U.S. Private*, pg. 4463
WEAVERTOWN TRANSPORT LEASING, INC.; *U.S. Private*, pg. 4463
WEAVEXX CORPORATION—See ANDRITZ AG; *Int'l*, pg. 457
WEAVEXX, LLC—See ANDRITZ AG; *Int'l*, pg. 457
WEB2CARZ.COM LTD; *U.S. Private*, pg. 4464
WEB4, INC.—See International Business Machines Corporation; *U.S. Public*, pg. 1149
WEBAC HOLDING AG; *Int'l*, pg. 8364
WEB ADVANCED; *U.S. Private*, pg. 4463
WEBAFFAIRS INC—See EQ Inc.; *U.S. Private*, pg. 2466
THE W.E. BASSETT COMPANY—See Levine Leichtman Capital Partners, LLC; *U.S. Private*, pg. 2436
WEBASTO AG - GLOBAL COMFORT SOLUTIONS—See Webasto SE; *Int'l*, pg. 8364
WEBASTO (CHANGCHUN) LTD.—See Webasto SE; *Int'l*, pg. 8364
WEBASTO (CHONGQING) LTD.—See Webasto SE; *Int'l*, pg. 8364
WEBASTO DONGHEE AUTO PARTS (BEIJING) CO., LTD—See Webasto SE; *Int'l*, pg. 8364
WEBASTO DONGHEE CO., LTD.—See DH Holdings Co., Ltd.; *Int'l*, pg. 2097
WEBASTO DONGHEE CO., LTD.—See Webasto SE; *Int'l*, pg. 8364
WEBASTO DONGHEE HOLDINGS CO., LTD.—See Webasto SE; *Int'l*, pg. 8364
WEBASTO DONGHEE SLOVAKIA S.R.O—See Webasto SE; *Int'l*, pg. 8364
WEBASTO-EDSCHA CABRIO GMBH—See Webasto SE; *Int'l*, pg. 8365
WEBASTO-EDSCHA CABRIO MEXICO, S.A. DE C.V.—See Webasto SE; *Int'l*, pg. 8365
WEBASTO-EDSCHA CABRIO SLOVAKIA S.R.O.—See Webasto SE; *Int'l*, pg. 8365
WEBASTO-EDSCHA CABRIO USA INC.—See Webasto SE; *Int'l*, pg. 8365
WEBASTO FAHRZEUGTECHNIK GMBH—See Webasto SE; *Int'l*, pg. 8364
WEBASTO GUANGZHOU CO., LTD.—See Webasto SE; *Int'l*, pg. 8364
WEBASTO JAPAN CO. LTD.—See Webasto SE; *Int'l*, pg. 8364
WEBASTO KOREA INC.—See Webasto SE; *Int'l*, pg. 8364
WEBASTO NEUBRANDENBURG GMBH—See Webasto SE; *Int'l*, pg. 8364
WEBASTO PETEMAR SP. Z.O.O.—See Webasto SE; *Int'l*, pg. 8364
WEBASTO PRODUCT AUSTRALIA PTY. LTD.—See Webasto SE; *Int'l*, pg. 8364
WEBASTO PRODUCT NORTH AMERICA, INC.—See Webasto SE; *Int'l*, pg. 8364
WEBASTO ROMANIA SRL—See Webasto SE; *Int'l*, pg. 8364
WEBASTO ROMANIA TRADING SRL—See Webasto SE; *Int'l*, pg. 8364
WEBASTO ROOF & COMPONENTS CZECH REPUBLIC S.R.O.—See Webasto SE; *Int'l*, pg. 8364
WEBASTO ROOF SYSTEMS BRASIL LTDA.—See Webasto SE; *Int'l*, pg. 8364
WEBASTO ROOF SYSTEMS, INC.—See Webasto SE; *Int'l*, pg. 8364
WEBASTO ROOFSYSTEMS INDIA LTD.—See Webasto SE; *Int'l*, pg. 8364
WEBASTO ROOF SYSTEMS LTD.—See Webasto SE; *Int'l*, pg. 8364
WEBASTO RUS OOO—See Webasto SE; *Int'l*, pg. 8364
WEBASTO SCHIERLING GMBH—See Webasto SE; *Int'l*, pg. 8365
WEBASTO SE; *Int'l*, pg. 8364
WEBASTO (SHANGHAI) LTD.—See Webasto SE; *Int'l*, pg. 8364
WEBASTO SOUTH AFRICA (PTY) LTD.—See Webasto SE; *Int'l*, pg. 8365
WEBASTO S.P.A.—See Webasto SE; *Int'l*, pg. 8365
WEBASTO SYSTEMES CARROSSERIE S.A.S.—See Webasto SE; *Int'l*, pg. 8365
WEBASTO TERMO & CONFORTO BRASIL LTDA—See Webasto SE; *Int'l*, pg. 8365
WEBASTO THERMO & COMFORT AUSTRALIA PTY. LTD.—See Webasto SE; *Int'l*, pg. 8365
WEBASTO THERMO & COMFORT, AVTOMOBILSKA TEHNIKA D.O.O.—See Webasto SE; *Int'l*, pg. 8365
WEBASTO THERMO & COMFORT (BEIJING) CO. LTD.—See Webasto SE; *Int'l*, pg. 8365
WEBASTO THERMO & COMFORT CZECH REPUBLIC S.R.O.—See Webasto SE; *Int'l*, pg. 8365
WEBASTO THERMO & COMFORT DENMARK A/S—See Webasto SE; *Int'l*, pg. 8365
WEBASTO THERMO & COMFORT FRANCE S.A.S.—See Webasto SE; *Int'l*, pg. 8365
WEBASTO THERMO & COMFORT HUNGARIA S.R.L.—See Webasto SE; *Int'l*, pg. 8365
WEBASTO THERMO & COMFORT IBERICA SLU—See Webasto SE; *Int'l*, pg. 8365
WEBASTO THERMO COMFORT IKLIMLENDIRME SISTEMLERI TIC. LTD. STI.—See Webasto SE; *Int'l*, pg. 8365
WEBASTO THERMO & COMFORT ITALY S.R.L.—See Webasto SE; *Int'l*, pg. 8365
WEBASTO THERMO & COMFORT JAPAN CO., LTD.—See Webasto SE; *Int'l*, pg. 8365
WEBASTO THERMO & COMFORT SCHWEIZ AG—See Webasto SE; *Int'l*, pg. 8365
WEBASTO THERMO & COMFORT SLOVAKIA S.R.O.—See Webasto SE; *Int'l*, pg. 8365
WEBASTO THERMO & COMFORT UK LTD.—See Webasto SE; *Int'l*, pg. 8365
WEBASTO THERMO & COMFORT UKRAINA TZOW—See Webasto SE; *Int'l*, pg. 8365
WEBASTO UTTING GMBH—See Webasto SE; *Int'l*, pg. 8365
WEBASTO XIANGYANG CO., LTD—See Webasto SE; *Int'l*, pg. 8365
W.E. BAXTER LIMITED—See B.L.L. Holdings Ltd; *Int'l*, pg. 790
WEBAXXS.COM—See OLM, LLC; *U.S. Private*, pg. 3011
WEBB AND PARTNERS, INC.; *U.S. Private*, pg. 4464
WEBBANK—See Steel Partners Holdings L.P.; *U.S. Public*, pg. 1943
WEBB AUTOMOTIVE GROUP, INC.—See AutoNation, Inc.; *U.S. Public*, pg. 238
WEBB CHEVROLET, INC.; *U.S. Private*, pg. 4464
WEBB CONCRETE COMPANY INC.; *U.S. Private*, pg. 4464
WEB BENEFITS DESIGN CORPORATION—See CNO Financial Group, Inc.; *U.S. Public*, pg. 520
WEBBER GAUGE DIVISION—See MiddleGround Management, LP; *U.S. Private*, pg. 2713
WEBBER LLC—See Ferrovial S.A.; *Int'l*, pg. 2644
WEBBERMCJ—See McGarrah Jessee; *U.S. Private*, pg. 2634
WEBBER METAL PRODUCTS INC.; *U.S. Private*, pg. 4464
WEBBER OIL COMPANY; *U.S. Private*, pg. 4464
WEBB FORD, INC.; *U.S. Private*, pg. 4464
WEBB FURNITURE ENTERPRISES INC.; *U.S. Private*, pg. 4464
WEBB-MASON INC.; *U.S. Private*, pg. 4464
WEBBMASON, INC.; *U.S. Private*, pg. 4464
WEBB, MURRAY & ASSOCIATES, INC.—See Littlejohn & Co.; *U.S. Private*, pg. 2472
WEBB PR; *U.S. Private*, pg. 4464
WEBB PUMP—See F.W. Webb Company; *U.S. Private*, pg. 1457
WEBB ROBOTICA S.R.L.—See EFORT Intelligent Equipment Co., Ltd.; *Int'l*, pg. 2321
WEBBROKER S.A.—See Apollo Global Management, Inc.; *U.S. Public*, pg. 147
WEBB'S FORD LTD; *Int'l*, pg. 8365
WEBBSHADE, INC.—See InPro Corporation; *U.S. Private*, pg. 2085
WEBB & SONS CONSTRUCTION CO. INC; *U.S. Private*, pg. 4464
WEBB-STILES COMPANY; *U.S. Private*, pg. 4464
WEBB WHEEL PRODUCTS INC.; *U.S. Private*, pg. 4464
WEBCALL COMMUNICATIONS AG—See Swisscom AG; *Int'l*, pg. 7374
WEBCASH CORP.; *Int'l*, pg. 8365
WEBCENTRAL GROUP PTY LTD—See 5G Networks Limited; *Int'l*, pg. 13
WEBCO GENERAL PARTNERSHIP; *U.S. Private*, pg. 4464
WEBCO INDUSTRIES INC.; *U.S. Public*, pg. 2341
WEBCO INTERNATIONAL LLC—See Balli Group plc; *Int'l*, pg. 809
WEBCOLLAGE, INC.—See Apax Partners LLP; *Int'l*, pg. 501
WEB.COM CANADA, INC.—See Siris Capital Group, LLC; *U.S. Private*, pg. 3675
WEB.COM GROUP, INC.—See Siris Capital Group, LLC; *U.S. Private*, pg. 3675
WEB.COM HOLDING COMPANY, INC.—See Siris Capital Group, LLC; *U.S. Private*, pg. 3675
WEB.COM, INC.—See Siris Capital Group, LLC; *U.S. Private*, pg. 3675
WEB CONSTRUCTION CO.; *U.S. Private*, pg. 4463

WEBCONVERT LTD.—See Windmoeller & Hoelscher KG; *Int'l*, pg. 8426
WEBCOR, LP—See Obayashi Corporation; *Int'l*, pg. 5509
WEBCOR PACKAGING CORPORATION; *U.S. Private*, pg. 4464
WEBCRAFTERS INC, *U.S. Private*, pg. 4464
WEBCREW INC.; *Int'l*, pg. 8365
WEB-DON INC.; *U.S. Private*, pg. 4464
WEBDYN—See BNP Paribas SA; *Int'l*, pg. 1089
W.E. BEDDING CORPORATION; *U.S. Private*, pg. 4420
WE BED SAS—See Weber Industries SAS; *Int'l*, pg. 8365
WEB ELEMENT SOLUTIONS LIMITED; *Int'l*, pg. 8364
WEBER AG—See BKW AG; *Int'l*, pg. 1056
WEBER AUTOMOTIVE GMBH—See Ardian SAS; *Int'l*, pg. 556
WEBERBANK AG—See Mittelbrandenburgische Sparkasse in Potsdam; *Int'l*, pg. 4994
WEBER BASIN WATER CONSERVANCY DISTRICT; *U.S. Private*, pg. 4465
WEBER CARPET INC.; *U.S. Private*, pg. 4465
WEBER DISTRIBUTION, LLC; *U.S. Private*, pg. 4465
WEBER DISTRIBUTION WAREHOUSES, LLC; *U.S. Private*, pg. 4465
WEBER ENTERPRISES INC.; *U.S. Private*, pg. 4465
WEBER ENVIRONMENTAL SERVICE, INC.; *U.S. Private*, pg. 4465
WEBER ESCAL D.O.O.—See Osterreichische Post AG; *Int'l*, pg. 5654
WEBER ETIKETTEN BV—See Weber Packaging Solutions, Inc.; *U.S. Private*, pg. 4465
WEBER ETIKET VE ETIKETLEME SISTEMLERI SAN VE TIC LTD. STI.—See Weber Packaging Solutions, Inc.; *U.S. Private*, pg. 4465
WEBER GERATE GMBH—See Tym Corporation; *Int'l*, pg. 7995
WEBER GRANITE CITY CHEVROLET COMPANY; *U.S. Private*, pg. 4465
WEBER-HYDRAULIKA SP. Z O.O.—See Weber-Hydraulik GmbH; *Int'l*, pg. 8366
WEBER-HYDRAULIK GMBH; *Int'l*, pg. 8365
WEBER-HYDRAULIK GMBH—See Weber-Hydraulik GmbH; *Int'l*, pg. 8366
WEBER-HYDRAULIK VALVETECH GMBH—See Weber-Hydraulik GmbH; *Int'l*, pg. 8366
WEBER-HYDRAULIK V.S.E—See Weber-Hydraulik GmbH; *Int'l*, pg. 8366
WEBER INC.—See BDT Capital Partners, LLC; *U.S. Private*, pg. 503
WEBER INDUSTRIES SAS; *Int'l*, pg. 8365
WEBER-INGENIEURE GMBH; *Int'l*, pg. 8366
WEBER INVESTISSEMENTS SAS; *Int'l*, pg. 8365
WEBER & JUDD PHARMACY; *U.S. Private*, pg. 4465
WEBER-KNAPP COMPANY; *U.S. Private*, pg. 4465
WEBER LABELLING & CODING LTD.—See Weber Packaging Solutions, Inc.; *U.S. Private*, pg. 4465
WEBER MANUFACTURING & SUPPLIES, INC.; *U.S. Private*, pg. 4465
WEBER MARINE INCORPORATED; *U.S. Private*, pg. 4465
WEBER MARKING SYSTEMS CANADA LTD.—See Weber Packaging Solutions, Inc.; *U.S. Private*, pg. 4465
WEBER MARKING SYSTEMS GMBH—See Weber Packaging Solutions, Inc.; *U.S. Private*, pg. 4465
WEBER MARKING SYSTEMS LTD.—See Weber Packaging Solutions, Inc.; *U.S. Private*, pg. 4465
WEBER MARKING SYSTEMS NV/SA—See Weber Packaging Solutions, Inc.; *U.S. Private*, pg. 4465
WEBER MARKING SYSTEMS (THAILAND) LTD.—See Weber Packaging Solutions, Inc.; *U.S. Private*, pg. 4465
WEBER MOTORS LTD.; *Int'l*, pg. 8365
WEBER PACKAGING SOLUTIONS, INC.; *U.S. Private*, pg. 4465
WEBER PAPER CO.; *U.S. Private*, pg. 4465
WEBER ROMANIA S.R.L—See Weber-Ingenieure GmbH; *Int'l*, pg. 8366
WEBER & ROSE, PSC—See Seiller Waterman LLC; *U.S. Private*, pg. 3599
WEBER SCREWDRIVING SYSTEMS INC.; *U.S. Private*, pg. 4465
WEBER SHANDWICK-ATLANTA—See The Interpublic Group of Companies, Inc.; *U.S. Public*, pg. 2106
WEBER SHANDWICK-AUSTIN—See The Interpublic Group of Companies, Inc.; *U.S. Public*, pg. 2106
WEBER SHANDWICK-BALTIMORE—See The Interpublic Group of Companies, Inc.; *U.S. Public*, pg. 2106
WEBER SHANDWICK-BOSTON—See The Interpublic Group of Companies, Inc.; *U.S. Public*, pg. 2106
WEBER SHANDWICK-CHICAGO—See The Interpublic Group of Companies, Inc.; *U.S. Public*, pg. 2106
WEBER SHANDWICK-DALLAS—See The Interpublic Group of Companies, Inc.; *U.S. Public*, pg. 2106
WEBER SHANDWICK-DENVER—See The Interpublic Group of Companies, Inc.; *U.S. Public*, pg. 2106
WEBER SHANDWICK-DETROIT—See The Interpublic Group of Companies, Inc.; *U.S. Public*, pg. 2106
WEBER SHANDWICK-FCC; *Int'l*, pg. 8365
WEBER SHANDWICK-LOS ANGELES—See The Interpublic Group of Companies, Inc.; *U.S. Public*, pg. 2106

WEBER SHANDWICK-MINNEAPOLIS—See The Interpublic Group of Companies, Inc.; *U.S. Public*, pg. 2106
WEBER SHANDWICK - MUMBAI—See The Interpublic Group of Companies, Inc.; *U.S. Public*, pg. 2106
WEBER SHANDWICK-SAINT LOUIS—See The Interpublic Group of Companies, Inc.; *U.S. Public*, pg. 2106
WEBER SHANDWICK-SAN FRANCISCO—See The Interpublic Group of Companies, Inc.; *U.S. Public*, pg. 2106
WEBER SHANDWICK-SEATTLE—See The Interpublic Group of Companies, Inc.; *U.S. Public*, pg. 2106
WEBER SHANDWICK—See The Interpublic Group of Companies, Inc.; *U.S. Public*, pg. 2104
WEBER SHANDWICK—See The Interpublic Group of Companies, Inc.; *U.S. Public*, pg. 2105
WEBER SHANDWICK—See The Interpublic Group of Companies, Inc.; *U.S. Public*, pg. 2105
WEBER SHANDWICK—See The Interpublic Group of Companies, Inc.; *U.S. Public*, pg. 2105
WEBER SHANDWICK—See The Interpublic Group of Companies, Inc.; *U.S. Public*, pg. 2105
WEBER SHANDWICK—See The Interpublic Group of Companies, Inc.; *U.S. Public*, pg. 2105
WEBER SHANDWICK—See The Interpublic Group of Companies, Inc.; *U.S. Public*, pg. 2105
WEBER SHANDWICK—See The Interpublic Group of Companies, Inc.; *U.S. Public*, pg. 2105
WEBER SHANDWICK—See The Interpublic Group of Companies, Inc.; *U.S. Public*, pg. 2105
WEBER SHANDWICK—See The Interpublic Group of Companies, Inc.; *U.S. Public*, pg. 2105
WEBER SHANDWICK—See The Interpublic Group of Companies, Inc.; *U.S. Public*, pg. 2105
WEBER SHANDWICK—See The Interpublic Group of Companies, Inc.; *U.S. Public*, pg. 2105
WEBER SHANDWICK—See The Interpublic Group of Companies, Inc.; *U.S. Public*, pg. 2105
WEBER SHANDWICK—See The Interpublic Group of Companies, Inc.; *U.S. Public*, pg. 2105
WEBER SHANDWICK—See The Interpublic Group of Companies, Inc.; *U.S. Public*, pg. 2105
WEBER SHANDWICK—See The Interpublic Group of Companies, Inc.; *U.S. Public*, pg. 2105
WEBER SHANDWICK—See The Interpublic Group of Companies, Inc.; *U.S. Public*, pg. 2105
WEBER SHANDWICK—See The Interpublic Group of Companies, Inc.; *U.S. Public*, pg. 2106
WEBER SHANDWICK—See The Interpublic Group of Companies, Inc.; *U.S. Public*, pg. 2106
WEBER SHANDWICK—See The Interpublic Group of Companies, Inc.; *U.S. Public*, pg. 2106
WEBER SHANDWICK—See The Interpublic Group of Companies, Inc.; *U.S. Public*, pg. 2106
WEBER SHANDWICK—See The Interpublic Group of Companies, Inc.; *U.S. Public*, pg. 2106
WEBER SHANDWICK—See The Interpublic Group of Companies, Inc.; *U.S. Public*, pg. 2106
WEBER SHANDWICK—See The Interpublic Group of Companies, Inc.; *U.S. Public*, pg. 2106
WEBER SHANDWICK—See The Interpublic Group of Companies, Inc.; *U.S. Public*, pg. 2106
WEBER SHANDWICK—See The Interpublic Group of Companies, Inc.; *U.S. Public*, pg. 2106
WEBER SHANDWICK—See The Interpublic Group of Companies, Inc.; *U.S. Public*, pg. 2106
WEBER SHANDWICK-SUNNYVALE—See The Interpublic Group of Companies, Inc.; *U.S. Public*, pg. 2106
WEBER SHANDWICK UK—See The Interpublic Group of Companies, Inc.; *U.S. Public*, pg. 2106
WEBER SHANDWICK WORLDWIDE—See The Interpublic Group of Companies, Inc.; *U.S. Public*, pg. 2106
WEBER'S INSURANCE SERVICES, INC.—See Aon plc; *Int'l*, pg. 498
WEBER-STEPHEN NORDIC APS—See BDT Capital Partners, LLC; *U.S. Private*, pg. 503
WEBER-STEPHEN OSTERREICH GMBH—See BDT Capital Partners, LLC; *U.S. Private*, pg. 503
WEBER-STEPHEN PRODUCTS BELGIUM BVBA—See BDT Capital Partners, LLC; *U.S. Private*, pg. 503
WEBER-STEPHEN PRODUCTS LLC—See BDT Capital Partners, LLC; *U.S. Private*, pg. 503
WEBEX COMMUNICATIONS DEUTSCHLAND GMBH—See Cisco Systems, Inc.; *U.S. Public*, pg. 501
WEBEX COMMUNICATIONS FRANCE SARL—See Cisco Systems, Inc.; *U.S. Public*, pg. 501
WEBEX COMMUNICATIONS, INC.—See Cisco Systems, Inc.; *U.S. Public*, pg. 501
WEBEX COMMUNICATIONS JAPAN, K.K.—See Cisco Systems, Inc.; *U.S. Public*, pg. 500
WEBEX COMMUNICATIONS UK, LTD.—See Cisco Systems, Inc.; *U.S. Public*, pg. 501

WEBEX, INC.—See Bertram Capital Management, LLC; *U.S. Private*, pg. 540
WEBEXONE—See Cisco Systems, Inc.; *U.S. Public*, pg. 501
WEBEYE BULGARIA LTD.—See W.A.G Payment Solutions Plc; *Int'l*, pg. 8322
WEBEYECARE; *U.S. Private*, pg. 4465
WEBEYE CZ S.R.O.—See W.A.G Payment Solutions Plc; *Int'l*, pg. 8321
WEBEYE DEUTSCHLAND GMBH—See W.A.G Payment Solutions Plc; *Int'l*, pg. 8321
WEBEYE HRVATSKA D.O.O.—See W.A.G Payment Solutions Plc; *Int'l*, pg. 8322
WEBEYE INTERNATIONAL D.O.O.—See W.A.G Payment Solutions Plc; *Int'l*, pg. 8322
WEBEYE INTERNATIONAL S.R.L.—See W.A.G Payment Solutions Plc; *Int'l*, pg. 8321
WEBEYE MAGYARORSZAG KERESKEDELMI ES SZOLGALTATO, KFT.—See W.A.G Payment Solutions Plc; *Int'l*, pg. 8322
WEBEYE POLSKA SP. Z.O.O.—See W.A.G Payment Solutions Plc; *Int'l*, pg. 8322
WEBEYE SLOVAKIA S.R.O—See W.A.G Payment Solutions Plc; *Int'l*, pg. 8322
WEBFIRM PTY LTD—See Adslot Ltd.; *Int'l*, pg. 154
WEBFIRM SEARCH PTY LTD—See Adslot Ltd.; *Int'l*, pg. 154
WEBFORGE AUSTRALIA PTY LTD.—See Valmont Industries, Inc.; *U.S. Public*, pg. 2274
WEB FX INC.; *U.S. Private*, pg. 4463
WEBGAINS GMBH—See ad pepper media International NV; *Int'l*, pg. 122
WEBGAINS LTD.—See ad pepper media International NV; *Int'l*, pg. 122
WEBGAINS S.L.—See ad pepper media International NV; *Int'l*, pg. 122
WEBGILITY INC.; *U.S. Private*, pg. 4465
WEBGISTIX CORPORATION—See Rakuten Group, Inc.; *Int'l*, pg. 6195
WEB GLOBAL RENTING SPA—See Omnia Network SpA; *Int'l*, pg. 5564
WEB GRAPHICS, INC.—See Taylor Corporation; *U.S. Private*, pg. 3939
WEBHALLEN SVERIGE AB—See Komplett ASA; *Int'l*, pg. 4244
WEB-HED TECHNOLOGIES, INC.; *U.S. Private*, pg. 4464
WEBHOUSE, INC.; *U.S. Private*, pg. 4466
WEBIMAX; *U.S. Private*, pg. 4466
WEBIMAX—See WebiMax; *U.S. Private*, pg. 4466
WEBIMAX—See WebiMax; *U.S. Private*, pg. 4466
WEBIMAX—See WebiMax; *U.S. Private*, pg. 4466
WEBIMAX—See WebiMax; *U.S. Private*, pg. 4466
WEBIM SERVICES CO., LTD.—See CHIEN KUO CONSTRUCTION CO., LTD.; *Int'l*, pg. 1477
WEB INDUSTRIES INC.; *U.S. Private*, pg. 4463
WEB INDUSTRIES INC.—See Web Industries Inc.; *U.S. Private*, pg. 4464
WEB INDUSTRIES, INC.—See Web Industries Inc.; *U.S. Private*, pg. 4464
WEB INDUSTRIES—See Web Industries Inc.; *U.S. Private*, pg. 4464
WEBINSTORE AG; *Int'l*, pg. 8366
WEBIS HOLDINGS PLC; *Int'l*, pg. 8366
WEBISTIX, INC.; *U.S. Private*, pg. 4466
WEBIT SERVICES, INC.; *U.S. Private*, pg. 4466
WEBJET LIMITED; *Int'l*, pg. 8366
WEBJET MARKETING NORTH AMERICA LLC; *U.S. Private*, pg. 4466
WEBJET MARKETING PTY LTD—See Webjet Limited; *Int'l*, pg. 8366
WEBJET OPERATIONS PTY LTD—See Webjet Limited; *Int'l*, pg. 8366
W. E. BLAIN & SONS, INC.; *U.S. Private*, pg. 4418
WEBLINC LLC—See VTEX; *Int'l*, pg. 8317
WEBLINK INTERNATIONAL, INC.—See Pamlico Capital Management, L.P.; *U.S. Private*, pg. 3083
WEBLINK INTERNATIONAL, INC.—See Acer Incorporated; *Int'l*, pg. 100
WEBLOYALTY.COM—See Tenerity, Inc.; *U.S. Private*, pg. 3966
WEBMARKETING123; *U.S. Private*, pg. 4466
WEBMD GLOBAL LLC—See KKR & Co. Inc.; *U.S. Public*, pg. 1254
WEBMD HEALTH CORP.—See KKR & Co. Inc.; *U.S. Public*, pg. 1253
WEBMD HEALTH SERVICES GROUP, INC.—See KKR & Co. Inc.; *U.S. Public*, pg. 1254
WEBMD, LLC—See KKR & Co. Inc.; *U.S. Public*, pg. 1254
WEB MEDIA GROUP AD; *Int'l*, pg. 8364
WEBMEDX INC.—See Microsoft Corporation; *U.S. Public*, pg. 1443
WEBMEDX INC.—See Microsoft Corporation; *U.S. Public*, pg. 1443
WEBMETHODS AUSTRALIA PTY LTD.—See Silver Lake Group, LLC; *U.S. Private*, pg. 3660
WEBO GMBH & CO. KG—See Melitta Unternehmensgruppe Bentz KG; *Int'l*, pg. 4811
WEBOLUTIONS, INC.; *U.S. Private*, pg. 4466

COMPANY NAME INDEX

WEBORAMA IBERICA SL—See Weborama SA; *Int'l*, pg. 8366
WEBORAMA ITALIA SRL—See Weborama SA; *Int'l*, pg. 8366
WEBORAMA NEDERLAND B.V.—See Weborama SA; *Int'l*, pg. 8366
WEBORAMA PORTUGAL—See Weborama SA; *Int'l*, pg. 8366
WEBORAMA RUSSIA—See Weborama SA; *Int'l*, pg. 8366
WEBORAMA SA; *Int'l*, pg. 8366
WEBORAMA UK LTD.—See Weborama SA; *Int'l*, pg. 8366
WEBPAGEFX INC.; *U.S. Private*, pg. 4466
WEBPASS, INC.—See Alphabet Inc.; *U.S. Public*, pg. 84
WEB PRINTING CONTROLS COMPANY INCORPORATED; *U.S. Private*, pg. 4464
WEB PRODUCTS INC.—See The Lackey Group; *U.S. Private*, pg. 4067
WEBPT, INC.—See Warburg Pincus LLC; *U.S. Private*, pg. 4440
WEB RESERVATIONS INTERNATIONAL, LTD.—See Hellman & Friedman LLC; *U.S. Private*, pg. 1911
WEB RIVER GROUP, INC.; *U.S. Private*, pg. 4464
WEBROOT BV—See Open Text Corporation; *Int'l*, pg. 5596
WEBROOT GMBH—See Open Text Corporation; *Int'l*, pg. 5596
WEBROOT INC.—See Open Text Corporation; *Int'l*, pg. 5598
WEBROOT ITALIA—See Open Text Corporation; *Int'l*, pg. 5596
WEBROOT LIMITED—See Open Text Corporation; *Int'l*, pg. 5596
WEBROOT PTY. LTD.—See Open Text Corporation; *Int'l*, pg. 5598
WEBROOT SARL—See Open Text Corporation; *Int'l*, pg. 5596
WEBROOT SOFTWARE, INC.—See Open Text Corporation; *Int'l*, pg. 5596
WEBRUNNERS, INC.; *U.S. Private*, pg. 4466
WEBSCAN, INC.—See Cognex Corporation; *U.S. Public*, pg. 523
WEBSCOPE; *U.S. Private*, pg. 4466
WEB SHAW LIMITED—See Brown & Brown, Inc.; *U.S. Public*, pg. 402
WEB SHOP MANAGER; *U.S. Private*, pg. 4464
WEBS, INC.—See Cimpress plc; *Int'l*, pg. 1609
WEBSITEBIZ, INC.; *U.S. Private*, pg. 4466
WEBSITE MAGAZINE INCORPORATED; *U.S. Private*, pg. 4466
WEBSITE PIPELINE, INC.; *U.S. Private*, pg. 4466
WEBSOL ENERGY SYSTEM LIMITED; *Int'l*, pg. 8366
WEBSOLUS CO., LTD.; *Int'l*, pg. 8366
WEBSOLUTE SPA; *Int'l*, pg. 8366
WEB & SONS INC.; *U.S. Private*, pg. 4463
WEBSPY US INC.—See Fastvue Inc.; *U.S. Private*, pg. 1483
WEB-STAR JAPAN CO., LTD.—See Transcosmos Inc.; *Int'l*, pg. 7899
WEBSTAR TECHNOLOGY GROUP, INC.; *U.S. Public*, pg. 2341
WEBSTARTS; *U.S. Private*, pg. 4466
WEBSTEP ASA—See Reiten & Co AS; *Int'l*, pg. 6259
WEBSTER AND HORSFALL LTD.—See NV Bekaert SA; *Int'l*, pg. 5497
WEBSTER AT RYE; *U.S. Private*, pg. 4466
WEBSTER BANK, N.A.—See Webster Financial Corporation; *U.S. Public*, pg. 2341
WEBSTER BUSINESS CREDIT CORPORATION—See Webster Financial Corporation; *U.S. Public*, pg. 2341
WEBSTER CAPITAL FINANCE, INC.—See Webster Financial Corporation; *U.S. Public*, pg. 2341
WEBSTER CHRYSLER JEEP, INC.; *U.S. Private*, pg. 4466
WEBSTER COUNTY COAL, LLC—See Alliance Holdings GP, L.P.; *U.S. Private*, pg. 183
WEBSTER ELECTRIC COMPANY, LLC—See Pentair plc; *Int'l*, pg. 5791
WEBSTER ENGINEERING & MANUFACTURING CO., L.L.C.—See Lionheart Ventures; *U.S. Private*, pg. 2464
WEBSTER EQUITY PARTNERS, LLC; *U.S. Private*, pg. 4466
WEBSTER FINANCIAL CORPORATION; *U.S. Public*, pg. 2341
WEBSTER FIVE CENTS SAVINGS BANK; *U.S. Private*, pg. 4467
WEBSTER HOUSE; *U.S. Private*, pg. 4467
WEBSTER INDUSTRIES INC.—See MPE Partners, LLC; *U.S. Private*, pg. 2803
WEBSTER LIMITED—See Public Sector Pension Investment Board; *Int'l*, pg. 6097
WEBSTER MANUFACTURING CO.—See MPE Partners, LLC; *U.S. Private*, pg. 2804
WEBSTER MORTGAGE COMPANY—See Webster Financial Corporation; *U.S. Public*, pg. 2341
WEBSTER MORTGAGE INVESTMENT CORPORATION—See Webster Financial Corporation; *U.S. Public*, pg. 2341
WEBSTER PACKAGING CORP.; *U.S. Private*, pg. 4467

WEBSTER-PORTALLOY CHAINS, INC.—See MPE Partners, LLC; *U.S. Private*, pg. 2804
WEBSTER PREFERRED CAPITAL CORPORATION—See Webster Financial Corporation; *U.S. Public*, pg. 2341
WEBSTER TRUCKING CORPORATION; *U.S. Private*, pg. 4467
WEBSTER WEALTH ADVISORS, INC.—See Webster Financial Corporation; *U.S. Public*, pg. 2341
WEBSTER WELLNESS PROFESSIONALS, LLC—See Acadia Healthcare Company, Inc.; *U.S. Public*, pg. 31
WEBTASY D.O.O.—See DHH SpA; *Int'l*, pg. 2099
WEBTEGRITY, LLC—See AiAdvertising, Inc.; *U.S. Public*, pg. 63
WEB TEKS, INC.—See DroneUp LLC; *U.S. Private*, pg. 1279
WEBTEX TRADING SDN. BHD.—See PRG Holdings Berhad; *Int'l*, pg. 5969
WEBTIVITY DESIGN SOLUTIONS; *U.S. Private*, pg. 4467
WEB TO DOOR, INC.; *U.S. Public*, pg. 2341
WEBTPA, INC.—See AmWINS Group, Inc.; *U.S. Private*, pg. 270
WEBTRAFFIC NORGE AS—See Schibsted ASA; *Int'l*, pg. 6618
WEBTRENDS AUSTRALASIA—See Webtrends Inc.; *U.S. Private*, pg. 4467
WEBTRENDS EMEA—See Webtrends Inc.; *U.S. Private*, pg. 4467
WEBTRENDS INC.; *U.S. Private*, pg. 4467
WEBTRENDS NORDIC—See Webtrends Inc.; *U.S. Private*, pg. 4467
WEBUILD S.P.A—See Salini Costruttori S.p.A.; *Int'l*, pg. 6492
WE BUY ANY CAR LIMITED; *Int'l*, pg. 8362
WEBUY GLOBAL LTD.; *Int'l*, pg. 8366
WEBWORKS ALLIANCE; *U.S. Private*, pg. 4467
WEB X.0 MEDIA—See Cyger Media; *U.S. Private*, pg. 1134
WEBYES LLC; *U.S. Private*, pg. 4468
WEBZEN, INC.; *Int'l*, pg. 8366
WEBZEN TAIWAN INC.—See Webzen, Inc.; *Int'l*, pg. 8366
WECARE DENALI, LLC—See Denali Water Solutions LLC; *U.S. Private*, pg. 1204
WE CARE FOOD STORES INC.; *U.S. Private*, pg. 4462
WECARE MEDICAL, LLC—See AdaptHealth Corp.; *U.S. Public*, pg. 39
WEC BUSINESS SERVICES LLC—See WEC Energy Group, Inc.; *U.S. Public*, pg. 2342
WEC CAROLINA ENERGY SOLUTIONS—See Brookfield Corporation; *Int'l*, pg. 1186
WECC, INC.—See Werner Enterprises, Inc.; *U.S. Public*, pg. 2349
WECCR GENERAL PARTNERSHIP—See Howard Hughes Holdings Inc.; *U.S. Public*, pg. 1060
WEC ENERGY GROUP, INC.; *U.S. Public*, pg. 2342
WECHCO, INC.; *U.S. Private*, pg. 4468
WECHTER FELDMAN WEALTH MANAGEMENT, INC.; *U.S. Private*, pg. 4468
WEC INVESTMENTS, LLC—See WEC Energy Group, Inc.; *U.S. Public*, pg. 2342
THE WECK CORPORATION; *U.S. Private*, pg. 4134
WECKWORTH ELECTRIC COMPANY, INC.; *U.S. Private*, pg. 4468
WECLAPP SE—See 3U Holding AG; *Int'l*, pg. 10
WEC MARKETING SDN. BHD.—See Wong Engineering Corporation Berhad; *Int'l*, pg. 8447
WECO INKASSO AG—See Swisscom AG; *Int'l*, pg. 7374
WECO MANUFACTURING GROUP—See Fairchild Capital Partners, LLC; *U.S. Private*, pg. 1462
WECOM ENGINEERING PTE LTD—See Technics Oil & Gas Limited; *Int'l*, pg. 7506
WECOMMERCE HOLDINGS LTD; *Int'l*, pg. 8366
WE COMPONENTS CO., LTD.—See WE Components Pte. Ltd.; *Int'l*, pg. 8362
WE COMPONENTS (HONG KONG) LIMITED—See WE Components Pte. Ltd.; *Int'l*, pg. 8362
WE COMPONENTS INDIA PVT LTD—See WE Components Pte. Ltd.; *Int'l*, pg. 8362
WE COMPONENTS (PENANG) SDN. BHD.—See WE Components Pte. Ltd.; *Int'l*, pg. 8362
WE COMPONENTS PTE. LTD.; *Int'l*, pg. 8362
WE COMPONENTS (SHANGHAI) CO., LTD.—See WE Components Pte. Ltd.; *Int'l*, pg. 8362
WE COMPONENTS (SHANGHAI) CO. LTD.—See WE Components Pte. Ltd.; *Int'l*, pg. 8362
WE COMPONENTS (SHENZHEN) CO. LTD.—See WE Components Pte. Ltd.; *Int'l*, pg. 8362
WECON HOLDINGS LTD.; *Int'l*, pg. 8366
WECON LIMITED—See Wecon Holdings Ltd.; *Int'l*, pg. 8366
WECONNECT SA; *Int'l*, pg. 8367
WECO TRADING INC.; *U.S. Private*, pg. 4468
WEC WELDING & MACHINING LLC—See Brookfield Corporation; *Int'l*, pg. 1186
WEDBUSH BANK—See Wedbush Capital Partners; *U.S. Private*, pg. 4468
WEDBUSH CAPITAL PARTNERS, L.P.—See Wedbush Capital Partners; *U.S. Private*, pg. 4468
WEDBUSH CAPITAL PARTNERS; *U.S. Private*, pg. 4468

WEDBUSH LEASING, INC.—See Wedbush Capital Partners; *U.S. Private*, pg. 4468
WEDBUSH SECURITIES, INC.—See Wedbush Capital Partners; *U.S. Private*, pg. 4468
WEDCO INC.; *U.S. Private*, pg. 4468
WEDCOR HOLDINGS, INC.—See Escalade, Incorporated; *U.S. Public*, pg. 793
WEDCO—See LyondellBasell Industries N.V.; *Int'l*, pg. 4607
WEDDINGBELLS—See St. Joseph Communications Inc.; *Int'l*, pg. 7159
WEDDINGPAGES, LLC—See Permira Advisers LLP; *Int'l*, pg. 5808
WEDDLE BROS. CONSTRUCTION CO., INC.; *U.S. Private*, pg. 4468
WEDEKIND MOTORS, INC.; *U.S. Private*, pg. 4468
WEDGCOR INC.; *U.S. Private*, pg. 4468
WEDGE COMMUNITY CO-OP INC.; *U.S. Private*, pg. 4468
WEDGE GROUP INC.; *U.S. Private*, pg. 4468
WEDGE HOLDINGS CO., LTD.—See Showa Holdings Co., Ltd.; *Int'l*, pg. 6861
WEDGE INDUSTRIAL CO., LTD.; *Int'l*, pg. 8367
WEDGE PRODUCTS, INC.—See AJD Holding Co.; *U.S. Private*, pg. 144
WEDGE ROAD DEVELOPMENT PTY. LTD.—See Nippon Telegraph & Telephone Corporation; *Int'l*, pg. 5355
WEDGEWOOD VILLAGE PHARMACY LLC—See Partners Group Holding AG; *Int'l*, pg. 5751
WEDIA S.A.; *Int'l*, pg. 8367
WEDLAKE FABRICATING, INC.—See IES Holdings, Inc.; *U.S. Public*, pg. 1094
WEDNESDAY LONDON LTD—See Saturday Group Ltd; *Int'l*, pg. 6588
W.E. DONOGHUE & CO., INC.—See Minella Capital Management LLC; *U.S. Private*, pg. 2741
WEDOTALK INC.; *U.S. Public*, pg. 2342
WEDRIVEU, INC.—See Mobico Group PLC; *Int'l*, pg. 5009
WEDRON SILICA COMPANY—See Covia Holdings Corporation; *U.S. Private*, pg. 1072
WEDS CO., LTD.; *Int'l*, pg. 8367
WEEBIT NANO LIMITED; *Int'l*, pg. 8367
WEEBIT NANO LTD.—See Weebit Nano Limited; *Int'l*, pg. 8367
WEEBIT NANO SARL—See Weebit Nano Limited; *Int'l*, pg. 8367
WEEBLY, INC.—See Block, Inc.; *U.S. Public*, pg. 362
WEE BURN COUNTRY CLUB; *U.S. Private*, pg. 4468
WEE-CIG INTERNATIONAL CORP; *U.S. Public*, pg. 2342
WEEDEN & CO., LP—See Piper Sandler Companies; *U.S. Public*, pg. 1694
WEEDEN PRIME SERVICES, LLC—See Siebert Financial Corp.; *U.S. Public*, pg. 1876
WEED GROWTH FUND, INC.; *U.S. Public*, pg. 2342
WEEDHIRE INTERNATIONAL, INC.; *U.S. Private*, pg. 4469
WEED, INC.; *U.S. Public*, pg. 2342
WEED INVESTMENT GROUP, INC.; *U.S. Private*, pg. 4468
WE-EF HELVETICA SA—See Fagerhult Group AB; *Int'l*, pg. 2602
WE-EF LEUCHTEN GMBH—See Fagerhult Group AB; *Int'l*, pg. 2602
WE-EF LIGHTING CO. LTD.—See Fagerhult Group AB; *Int'l*, pg. 2602
WE-EF LIGHTING LTD.—See Fagerhult Group AB; *Int'l*, pg. 2602
WE-EF LIGHTING PTY. LTD.—See Fagerhult Group AB; *Int'l*, pg. 2602
WE-EF LIGHTING USA LLC—See Fagerhult Group AB; *Int'l*, pg. 2602
WEE FOLK ROCKFORD CHILD CENTER, INC.—See Byrne Electrical Specialists, Inc.; *U.S. Private*, pg. 701
WEE HUR HOLDINGS LTD.; *Int'l*, pg. 8367
WEE HUR (WOODLANDS 12) PTE. LTD.—See Wee Hur Holdings Ltd.; *Int'l*, pg. 8367
WEEKDAY BRANDS AB—See H&M Hennes & Mauritz AB; *Int'l*, pg. 3192
WEEKDAY, INC.—See Nippon Television Holdings Inc.; *Int'l*, pg. 5356
WEEKENDS ONLY; *U.S. Private*, pg. 4469
WEEKEND UNLIMITED; *Int'l*, pg. 8367
WEEKES & CALLAWAY, INC.—See CBIZ, Inc.; *U.S. Public*, pg. 457
WEEKES & CALLOWAY—See CBIZ, Inc.; *U.S. Public*, pg. 457
WEEKES FOREST PRODUCTS INC.; *U.S. Private*, pg. 4469
WEEKI WACHEE SPRINGS STATE PARK; *U.S. Private*, pg. 4469
THE WEEK LTD.—See Future plc; *Int'l*, pg. 2857
WEEKLY READER CORPORATION—See RDA Holding Co.; *U.S. Private*, pg. 3364
THE WEEKLY VISTA—See Wehco Media, Inc.; *U.S. Private*, pg. 4470
WEEKS ISLAND LANDOWNER LLC—See K+S Aktiengesellschaft; *Int'l*, pg. 4041

THE WEEKS-LERMAN GROUP LLC   CORPORATE AFFILIATIONS

THE WEEKS-LERMAN GROUP LLC; *U.S. Private*, pg. 4134
WEEKS MARINE, INC.—See Kiewit Corp.; *U.S. Private*, pg. 2304
WEEKS MEDICAL CENTER; *U.S. Private*, pg. 4469
WEEKS ROBINSON PROPERTIES; *U.S. Private*, pg. 4469
WEEKS SUPPLY—See Horton Industries, Inc.; *U.S. Private*, pg. 1984
WEEK-TV—See Silver Point Capital, L.P.; *U.S. Private*, pg. 3662
WEELGO SRL—See Sesa S.p.A.; *Int'l*, pg. 6729
WEERTS FUNERAL HOME, INC.—See Service Corporation International; *U.S. Public*, pg. 1871
WEETABIX COMPANY, LLC—See Post Holdings, Inc.; *U.S. Public*, pg. 1704
WEETABIX EAST AFRICA LIMITED—See Post Holdings, Inc.; *U.S. Public*, pg. 1704
WEETABIX FOODS LIMITED—See Post Holdings, Inc.; *U.S. Public*, pg. 1704
WEETABIX LIMITED—See Post Holdings, Inc.; *U.S. Public*, pg. 1704
WEETABIX OF CANADA LIMITED—See Post Holdings, Inc.; *U.S. Public*, pg. 1704
WEETING TYRES LIMITED—See The Goodyear Tire & Rubber Company; *U.S. Public*, pg. 2085
WEEZ SRL—See DBA Group SRL; *Int'l*, pg. 1986
W.E. FAMILY OFFICES, LLC—See Truist Financial Corporation; *U.S. Public*, pg. 2199
WEFATHERM GMBH—See Aliaxis S.A./N.V.; *Int'l*, pg. 325
WE FEST HOLDINGS, LLC—See Live Nation Entertainment, Inc.; *U.S. Public*, pg. 1331
WEFIMA N.V—See Ackermans & van Haaren NV; *Int'l*, pg. 106
WEFORMA DAMPFUNGSTECHNIK GMBH; *Int'l*, pg. 8367
WEFORMA DAMPFUNGSTECHNIK GMBH—See Weforma Dampfungstechnik GmbH; *Int'l*, pg. 8367
WEFORMA DAMPFUNGSTECHNIK S.A.R.L.—See Weforma Dampfungstechnik GmbH; *Int'l*, pg. 8367
WEFORMA DAMPFUNGSTECHNIK S.R.L.—See Weforma Dampfungstechnik GmbH; *Int'l*, pg. 8367
WEFOR S.R.L.—See IVS Group S.A.; *Int'l*, pg. 3848
WEGAMES CORPORATION; *Int'l*, pg. 8368
WEGA MINING MALI S.A.—See Avocet Mining PLC; *Int'l*, pg. 749
WEG AUSTRALIA PTY LTD—See WEG S.A.; *Int'l*, pg. 8368
WEGA-VERLAG GMBH—See Schott Music GmbH & Co. KG; *Int'l*, pg. 6639
WEG BENELUX S.A.—See WEG S.A.; *Int'l*, pg. 8368
WEG CENTRAL ASIA LLP—See WEG S.A.; *Int'l*, pg. 8368
WEG-CESTARI REDUTORES E MOTORREDUTORES S.A.—See WEG S.A.; *Int'l*, pg. 8368
WEG CHILE S.A—See WEG S.A.; *Int'l*, pg. 8368
WEG COLOMBIA SAS—See WEG S.A.; *Int'l*, pg. 8368
W.EG EESTI OU—See Wurth Verwaltungsgesellschaft mbH; *Int'l*, pg. 8508
WEG ELECTRIC CIS OOO—See WEG S.A.; *Int'l*, pg. 8368
WEG ELECTRIC CORP.—See WEG S.A.; *Int'l*, pg. 8368
WEG ELECTRIC (INDIA) PRIVATE LIMITED—See WEG S.A.; *Int'l*, pg. 8368
WEG ELECTRIC MOTORS JAPAN CO., LTD.—See WEG S.A.; *Int'l*, pg. 8368
WEG ELECTRIC MOTORS (UK) LTD—See WEG S.A.; *Int'l*, pg. 8368
WEG ELEKTRIK SANAYI ANONIM SIRKETI—See WEG S.A.; *Int'l*, pg. 8368
WEGENBOUWMAATSCHAPPIJ J. HEIJMANS B.V.—See Heijmans N.V.; *Int'l*, pg. 3323
WEGENER BEDRIJFSVASTGOED BV—See DPG Media Group NV; *Int'l*, pg. 2189
WEGENER GRAFISCHE GROEP BV—See DPG Media Group NV; *Int'l*, pg. 2189
WEGENER HUIS-AAN-HUISKRANTEN BV—See DPG Media Group NV; *Int'l*, pg. 2189
WEGENER ICT MEDIA BV—See DPG Media Group NV; *Int'l*, pg. 2189
WEGENER KONINKLIJKE B.V.—See DPG Media Group NV; *Int'l*, pg. 2189
WEGENER NEDERLAND BV—See DPG Media Group NV; *Int'l*, pg. 2189
WEGENER NIEUWSDRUK—See DPG Media Group NV; *Int'l*, pg. 2189
WEGENER POST BV—See DPG Media Group NV; *Int'l*, pg. 2189
WEGENER REGIO PARTNERS BV—See DPG Media Group NV; *Int'l*, pg. 2189
WEGENER TRANSPORT BV—See DPG Media Group NV; *Int'l*, pg. 2189
WEG ENGINEERING—See Weavertown Transport Leasing, Inc; *U.S. Private*, pg. 4463
WEG EQUIPAMENTOS ELETRICOS S.A.—See WEG S.A.; *Int'l*, pg. 8368
WEG EQUIPAMIENTOS ELECTRICOS S.A.—See WEG S.A.; *Int'l*, pg. 8368
WEG EURO INDUSTRIA ELECTRICA S.A.—See WEG S.A.; *Int'l*, pg. 8368
WEG FRANCE SAS—See WEG S.A.; *Int'l*, pg. 8368

WEG GERMANY GMBH—See WEG S.A.; *Int'l*, pg. 8368
WEG HOLDING GMBH—See WEG S.A.; *Int'l*, pg. 8368
WEG IBERIA INDUSTRIAL S.L.—See WEG S.A.; *Int'l*, pg. 8368
WEG IBERIA S.A.—See WEG S.A.; *Int'l*, pg. 8368
WEG INDUSTRIAS VENEZUELA C.A.—See WEG S.A.; *Int'l*, pg. 8368
WEG INDUSTRIES (INDIA) PRIVATE LTD.—See WEG S.A.; *Int'l*, pg. 8368
WEG INTERNATIONAL TRADE GMBH—See WEG S.A.; *Int'l*, pg. 8368
WEG ITALIA S.R.L—See WEG S.A.; *Int'l*, pg. 8368
W.EG ITALIA S.R.L.—See Wurth Verwaltungsgesellschaft mbH; *Int'l*, pg. 8508
WEGL OFFSHORE INVESTMENTS PTE. LTD.—See Wah Seong Corporation Berhad; *Int'l*, pg. 8330
WEGLOKOKS S.A.; *Int'l*, pg. 8368
WEGMANN USA, INC.—See Krauss-Maffei Wegmann GmbH & Co. KG; *Int'l*, pg. 4300
WEGMANS FOOD MARKETS, INC.; *U.S. Private*, pg. 4469
WEGMANS FURNITURE INDUSTRIES SDN BHD—See Wegmans Holdings Berhad; *Int'l*, pg. 8369
WEGMANS HOLDINGS BERHAD; *Int'l*, pg. 8368
WEG MEXICO, S.A. DE C.V.—See WEG S.A.; *Int'l*, pg. 8368
WEG MIDDLE EAST FZE—See WEG S.A.; *Int'l*, pg. 8368
WEG (NANTONG) ELECTRIC MOTOR CO., LTD.—See WEG S.A.; *Int'l*, pg. 8368
WEG NANTONG ELECTRIC MOTOR MANUFACTURING CO LTD—See WEG S.A.; *Int'l*, pg. 8368
WEGO CHEMICAL & MINERAL CORPORATION; *U.S. Private*, pg. 4469
WEGO FLOORTEC GMBH—See SIG plc; *Int'l*, pg. 6907
WEGOLOOK, LLC—See Crawford & Company; *U.S. Public*, pg. 592
WEGO SYSTEMBAUSTOFFE GMBH—See SIG plc; *Int'l*, pg. 6907
WEGO TERUMO (WEIHAI) MEDICAL PRODUCTS CO., LTD.—See Terumo Corporation; *Int'l*, pg. 7571
WEGOWISE, INC.—See Measurabl, Inc.; *U.S. Private*, pg. 2648
WEG PERU S.A.—See WEG S.A.; *Int'l*, pg. 8368
W.EG POLSKA SP. Z. O.O.—See Wurth Verwaltungsgesellschaft mbH; *Int'l*, pg. 8508
W.E. GRAHAM, INC.—See EVO Transportation & Energy Services, Inc.; *U.S. Public*, pg. 804
WEG RUS LLC—See WEG S.A.; *Int'l*, pg. 8368
WEG S.A.; *Int'l*, pg. 8367
WEG SCANDINAVIA AB—See WEG S.A.; *Int'l*, pg. 8368
WEG SINGAPORE PTE. LTD.—See WEG S.A.; *Int'l*, pg. 8368
WEG TINTAS LTDA—See WEG S.A.; *Int'l*, pg. 8368
WEG (UK) LTD.—See WEG S.A.; *Int'l*, pg. 8368
WEHCO MEDIA, INC.; *U.S. Private*, pg. 4469
WEHCO NEWSPAPERS, INC.—See Wehco Media, Inc.; *U.S. Private*, pg. 4470
WEHCO VIDEO INC.—See Wehco Media, Inc.; *U.S. Private*, pg. 4469
WEH GMBH—See Fukuda Corporation; *Int'l*, pg. 2839
WEHR CONSTRUCTORS, INC.; *U.S. Private*, pg. 4470
WEHR FORD OF MOUNTAIN GROVE INC.; *U.S. Private*, pg. 4470
WEHRING & WOLFES GMBH—See UNIQA Insurance Group AG; *Int'l*, pg. 8059
WEHRUNG'S LUMBER & HOME CENTER—See Modern Precast Concrete; *U.S. Private*, pg. 2762
WEIBEL, INC.; *U.S. Private*, pg. 4470
WEIBO CORPORATION—See SINA Corporation; *Int'l*, pg. 6936
WEICHAI GROUP HOLDINGS LIMITED—See Shandong Heavy Industry Group Co., Ltd.; *Int'l*, pg. 6753
WEICHAI HEAVY MACHINERY CO., LTD.; *Int'l*, pg. 8369
WEICHAI POWER CO., LTD.—See Shandong Heavy Industry Group Co., Ltd.; *Int'l*, pg. 6753
WEICHAI POWER (WEIFANG) CASTING AND FORGING CO., LTD.—See Shandong Heavy Industry Group Co., Ltd.; *Int'l*, pg. 6754
WEICHERT CO.; *U.S. Private*, pg. 4470
WEICHERT REAL ESTATE AFFILIATES, INC.—See Weichert Co.; *U.S. Private*, pg. 4470
WEICHERT WORKFORCE MOBILITY INC. - BOSTON—See Weichert Co.; *U.S. Private*, pg. 4470
WEICHERT WORKFORCE MOBILITY INC.—See Weichert Co.; *U.S. Private*, pg. 4470
WEI CHIH STEEL INDUSTRIAL CO., LTD.; *Int'l*, pg. 8369
WEI-CHUAN FOOD CORPORATION; *Int'l*, pg. 8369
WEI-CHUAN USA—See Wei-Chuan Food Corporation; *Int'l*, pg. 8369
WEICOM S.R.L.—See Hillenbrand, Inc.; *U.S. Public*, pg. 1036
WEIDAI LTD.; *Int'l*, pg. 8369
WEIDA INTEGRATED INDUSTRIES SDN. BHD.—See Weida (M) Bhd.; *Int'l*, pg. 8369
WEIDA INTEGRATED INDUSTRIES SDN BHD—See Weida (M) Bhd.; *Int'l*, pg. 8369
WEIDALINE SDN. BHD.—See Weida (M) Bhd.; *Int'l*, pg. 8369

WEIDA MARKETING SDN. BHD.—See Weida (M) Bhd.; *Int'l*, pg. 8369
WEIDA (M) BHD. - NEGERI SEMBILAN MANUFACTURING PLANT—See Weida (M) Bhd.; *Int'l*, pg. 8369
WEIDA (M) BHD. - PHILIPPINES MANUFACTURING PLANT—See Weida (M) Bhd.; *Int'l*, pg. 8369
WEIDA (M) BHD. - SARAWAK MANUFACTURING PLANT—See Weida (M) Bhd.; *Int'l*, pg. 8369
WEIDA (M), BHD.; *Int'l*, pg. 8369
WEIDA PHILIPPINES INC.—See Weida (M) Bhd.; *Int'l*, pg. 8369
WEIDA WATER SDN. BHD.—See Weida (M) Bhd.; *Int'l*, pg. 8369
WEIDEMANN GMBH—See Wacker Neuson SE; *Int'l*, pg. 8325
WEIDEMANN MASCHINENFABRIK GOTHA GMBH—See Wacker Neuson SE; *Int'l*, pg. 8325
WEIDENHAMMER CHILE LTDA.—See Sonoco Products Company; *U.S. Public*, pg. 1909
WEIDENHAMMER HELLAS S.A.—See Sonoco Products Company; *U.S. Public*, pg. 1909
WEIDENHAMMER SYSTEMS CORPORATION; *U.S. Private*, pg. 4470
WEIDER PUBLICATIONS, LLC—See Chatham Asset Management, LLC; *U.S. Private*, pg. 860
WEIDLINGER ASSOCIATES INC.—See Thornton-Tomasetti, Inc.; *U.S. Private*, pg. 4163
WEIDMULLER INC.—See Weidmuller Interface GmbH & Co. KG; *Int'l*, pg. 8369
WEIDMULLER INTERFACE GMBH & CO. KG; *Int'l*, pg. 8369
WEIDMULLER LTD.—See Weidmuller Interface GmbH & Co. KG; *Int'l*, pg. 8369
WEIDMULLER MONITORING SYSTEMS GMBH—See Weidmuller Interface GmbH & Co. KG; *Int'l*, pg. 8369
WEIDMULLER SA DE C.V.—See Weidmuller Interface GmbH & Co. KG; *Int'l*, pg. 8369
WEIDNER INVESTMENT SERVICES; *U.S. Private*, pg. 4470
THE WEIDT GROUP, INC.—See Willdan Group, Inc.; *U.S. Public*, pg. 2371
WEIFANG GOERTEK ELECTRONICS CO., LTD.—See GoerTek Inc.; *Int'l*, pg. 3021
WEIFANG LAKELAND SAFETY PRODUCTS CO., LTD.—See Lakeland Industries, Inc.; *U.S. Public*, pg. 1289
WEIFANG MEIYANG PROTECTIVE PRODUCTS CO., LTD.—See Lakeland Industries, Inc.; *U.S. Public*, pg. 1289
WEIFANG NANYUAN AIRPORT CO., LTD.—See Hainan Traffic Administration Holding Co., Ltd.; *Int'l*, pg. 3216
WEIFANG PARASIA CHEM CO., LTD.—See Tiande Chemical Holdings Limited; *Int'l*, pg. 7738
WEIFANG SIME DARBY PORT CO. LTD.—See Sime Darby Berhad; *Int'l*, pg. 6931
WEIFANG TRICOL TRADING CO. LTD.; *Int'l*, pg. 8369
WEIFANG YAXING CHEMICAL CO., LTD.; *Int'l*, pg. 8370
WEIFIELD GROUP CONTRACTING, LLC; *U.S. Private*, pg. 4470
WEIGAND BAU GMBH—See INDUS Holding AG; *Int'l*, pg. 3664
WEIGANG ENVIRONMENTAL TECHNOLOGY HOLDING GROUP LIMITED; *Int'l*, pg. 8370
WEIGAO NIKKISO (WEIHAI) DIALYSIS EQUIPMENT CO., LTD.—See Shandong Weigao Group Medical Polymer Company Limited; *Int'l*, pg. 6759
WEIGEL BROADCASTING CO.; *U.S. Private*, pg. 4471
WEIGEL'S STORES INC.; *U.S. Private*, pg. 4471
WEIGHING & CONTROL, INC.—See Tannehill International Industries; *U.S. Private*, pg. 3931
WEIGHTMANS LLP; *Int'l*, pg. 8370
WEIGH-TRONIX CANADA, ULC—See Illinois Tool Works Inc.; *U.S. Public*, pg. 1111
WEIGHTSTONE VINEYARD ESTATE & WINERY CO., LTD.—See Sinon Corporation; *Int'l*, pg. 6953
WEIGHTWATCHERS.COM, INC.—See WW International, Inc.; *U.S. Public*, pg. 2384
WEIGHT WATCHERS DENMARK APS—See WW International, Inc.; *U.S. Public*, pg. 2384
WEIGHT WATCHERS (DEUTSCHLAND) GMBH—See WW International, Inc.; *U.S. Public*, pg. 2384
WEIGHT WATCHERS EUROPEAN HOLDING AB—See WW International, Inc.; *U.S. Public*, pg. 2384
WEIGHTWATCHERS.FR S.A.R.L.—See WW International, Inc.; *U.S. Public*, pg. 2384
WEIGHT WATCHERS INTERNATIONAL PTY. LTD.—See WW International, Inc.; *U.S. Public*, pg. 2384
WEIGHTWATCHERS.NL B.V.—See WW International, Inc.; *U.S. Public*, pg. 2384
WEIGHT WATCHERS OPERATIONS SPAIN S.L.—See WW International, Inc.; *U.S. Public*, pg. 2384
WEIGHT WATCHERS POLSKA SPZ.O.O.—See WW International, Inc.; *U.S. Public*, pg. 2384
WEIGHT WATCHERS SERVICES PTY LTD—See WW International, Inc.; *U.S. Public*, pg. 2384
WEIGHT WATCHERS SWEDEN VIKTVAKTARNA AKIEBOLAG—See WW International, Inc.; *U.S. Public*, pg. 2384

COMPANY NAME INDEX

WEIGHT WATCHERS (U.K.) LIMITED—See WW International, Inc.; *U.S. Public*, pg. 2384
WEIHAI CHINA GLASS SOLAR COMPANY LIMITED—See China Glass Holdings Limited; *Int'l*, pg. 1504
WEIHAI CITY COMMERCIAL BANK CO., LTD.; *Int'l*, pg. 8370
WEIHAI CNG COATED GLASS COMPANY LIMITED—See China Glass Holdings Limited; *Int'l*, pg. 1504
WEI HAI FU KANG ELECTRIC CO., LTD.—See Cheng Eui Precision Industry Co., Ltd.; *Int'l*, pg. 1465
WEIHAI GUANGTAI AIRPORT EQUIPMENT CO., LTD.; *Int'l*, pg. 8370
WEIHAI GUANGWEI COMPOSITES CO., LTD.; *Int'l*, pg. 8370
WEIHAI HONGLIN ELECTRONIC CO., LTD.—See InvesTech Holdings Limited; *Int'l*, pg. 3778
WEIHAI HUADONG AUTOMATION CO., LTD.; *Int'l*, pg. 8370
WEIHAI HUALING OPTO ELECTRONICS CO., LTD.—See Shandong New Beiyang Information Technology Co., Ltd.; *Int'l*, pg. 6757
WEIHAI KET ELECTRONICS CO., LTD.—See Korea Electric Terminal Co., Ltd.; *Int'l*, pg. 4284
WEIHAI LUZE AUTOMOBILE SALES SERVICES CO., LTD.—See China ZhengTong Auto Services Holdings Limited; *Int'l*, pg. 1567
WEIHAI NIPPON SHOKUHIN CO., LTD.—See NH Foods Ltd.; *Int'l*, pg. 5257
WEIHAI SAMHWA PAINTS CO., LTD.—See Samhwa Paints Industrial Co., Ltd.; *Int'l*, pg. 6505
WEIHAI SEKONIX OPTICAL ELECTRONICS CO., LTD.—See Sekonix Co., Ltd.; *Int'l*, pg. 6699
WEIHAI WANFENG AOWEI AUTO WHEEL CO., LTD.—See Wanfeng Auto Holding Group Co., Ltd.; *Int'l*, pg. 8340
WEIHAI WANFENG MAGNESIUM SCIENCE AND TECHNOLOGY DEVELOPMENT CO., LTD—See Wanfeng Auto Holding Group Co., Ltd.; *Int'l*, pg. 8340
WEIHAI WEIDA PRECISION CASTING CO., LTD—See Shandong Weida Machinery Co., Ltd.; *Int'l*, pg. 6758
WEIHAI YURA CORPORATION—See YURATECH Co., Ltd.; *Int'l*, pg. 8617
WEIHUA (RUDONG) TRADE CO., LTD.—See China Petrochemical Development Corp.; *Int'l*, pg. 1540
WEIKECORP SEMICONDUCTOR CO., LTD.—See Laser Tek Taiwan Co., Ltd.; *Int'l*, pg. 4420
WEIKENG INDUSTRIAL CO., LTD.; *Int'l*, pg. 8370
WEIKENG INTERNATIONAL CO., LTD.—See Weikeng Industrial Co., Ltd.; *Int'l*, pg. 8370
WEIKENG INTERNATIONAL (SHANGHAI) CO., LTD—See Weikeng Industrial Co., Ltd.; *Int'l*, pg. 8370
WEIKENG TECHNOLOGY PTE LTD—See Weikeng Industrial Co., Ltd.; *Int'l*, pg. 8370
WEI KUANG AUTOMATIC EQUIPMENT (XIAMEN) CO., LTD.—See Chroma ATE Inc.; *Int'l*, pg. 1588
WEIKUANG MECH. ENG. (NANJING) CO., LTD.—See Chroma ATE Inc.; *Int'l*, pg. 1588
WEILAND SLIDING DOORS & WINDOWS, INC.—See Andersen Corporation; *U.S. Private*, pg. 275
WEIL CADILLAC; *U.S. Private*, pg. 4471
WEIL CERAMICS & GLASS INC.; *U.S. Private*, pg. 4471
WEILER & COMPANY, INC.—See Henry Crown & Company; *U.S. Private*, pg. 1917
WEILER CORPORATION; *U.S. Private*, pg. 4471
WEILER LABELING SYSTEMS, LLC—See Leonard Green & Partners, L.P.; *U.S. Private*, pg. 2428
WEILER WELDING COMPANY INC.; *U.S. Private*, pg. 4471
WEIL, GOTSHAL & MANGES LLP; *U.S. Private*, pg. 4471
WEILI HOLDINGS LTD.; *Int'l*, pg. 8370
WEILL CORNELL MEDICINE; *U.S. Private*, pg. 4471
WEIL-MCLAIN—See SPX Technologies, Inc.; *U.S. Public*, pg. 1922
WEILONG DELICIOUS GLOBAL HOLDINGS LTD.; *Int'l*, pg. 8370
WEI LONG GRAPE WINE CO., LTD.; *Int'l*, pg. 8369
WEIL PUMP CO. INC.—See Wilo USA LLC; *U.S. Private*, pg. 4529
WEILWOOD INDUSTRIES, INC.—See Santee Print Works, Inc.; *U.S. Private*, pg. 3548
WEIMAN—See Interlude Home, Inc.; *U.S. Private*, pg. 2112
WEIMAR CONSTRUCTION COMPANY, INC.; *U.S. Private*, pg. 4471
WEIMAR WATER CO.—See Placer County Water Agency; *U.S. Private*, pg. 3194
WEIMER BEARING & TRANSMISSION; *U.S. Private*, pg. 4471
W.E. IMHOFF & CO. INC.; *U.S. Private*, pg. 4420
WEIMOB, INC.; *Int'l*, pg. 8370
WEINAN ZONGSHEN BAOTAI AUTOMOBILE SALES & SERVICE CO., LTD.—See Sunfonda Group Holdings Limited; *Int'l*, pg. 7313
WEINART HANDELSGESELLSCHAFT MBH—See Hawesko Holding AG; *Int'l*, pg. 3289
WEINBERG CAPITAL GROUP, INC.; *U.S. Private*, pg. 4471
WEINBERG CAPITAL PARTNERS SAS; *Int'l*, pg. 8370

WEINBERGMAIER GMBH—See Raiffeisenlandesbank Oberosterreich Aktiengesellschaft; *Int'l*, pg. 6188
WEINBRENNER SHOE COMPANY, INC.; *U.S. Private*, pg. 4471
WEIN & CO. HANDELSGESELLSCHAFT M.B.H—See Hawesko Holding AG; *Int'l*, pg. 3289
WEINERT INDUSTRIES AG; *Int'l*, pg. 8370
WEINGARTEN REALTY INVESTORS—See Kimco Realty Corporation; *U.S. Public*, pg. 1232
WEINGARTEN REALTY MANAGEMENT COMPANY—See Kimco Realty Corporation; *U.S. Public*, pg. 1232
WEINGARTZ SUPPLY CO. INC.; *U.S. Private*, pg. 4472
WEINGEROFF ENTERPRISES, INC.; *U.S. Private*, pg. 4472
WEINGUT ROBERT WEIL—See Suntory Holdings Limited; *Int'l*, pg. 7327
WEINIG DIMTER GMBH & CO. KG—See Michael Weinig AG; *Int'l*, pg. 4875
WEINIG FRANCE SARL—See Michael Weinig AG; *Int'l*, pg. 4875
WEINIG GRECON GMBH & CO. KG—See Michael Weinig AG; *Int'l*, pg. 4875
WEINIG HOLZ-HER CANADA INC.—See Michael Weinig AG; *Int'l*, pg. 4875
WEINIG HOLZ-HER ESPANA S.L.—See Michael Weinig AG; *Int'l*, pg. 4875
WEINIG HOLZ-HER FRANCE S.A.R.L.—See Michael Weinig AG; *Int'l*, pg. 4875
WEINIG HOLZ-HER ITALIA S.R.L.—See Michael Weinig AG; *Int'l*, pg. 4875
WEINIG HOLZ-HER SCHWEIZ AG—See Michael Weinig AG; *Int'l*, pg. 4875
WEINIG ITALIA S.R.L.—See Michael Weinig AG; *Int'l*, pg. 4875
WEINIG RUS OOO—See Michael Weinig AG; *Int'l*, pg. 4875
WEINIG VERTRIEB UND SERVICE GMBH & CO. KG—See Michael Weinig AG; *Int'l*, pg. 4875
WEINISCH GMBH & CO. KG—See INDUS Holding AG; *Int'l*, pg. 3664
WEINLAND ARIANE ABAYAN GMBH & CO. KG—See Hawesko Holding AG; *Int'l*, pg. 3289
WEINMANN GERATE FUR MEDIZIN GMBH & CO. KG; *Int'l*, pg. 8370
WEINMANN HOLZBAUSYSTEMTECHNIK GMBH—See Durr AG; *Int'l*, pg. 2233
WEINRICH ADVERTISING & COMMUNICATIONS, INC.; *U.S. Private*, pg. 4472
WEINSTEIN BEVERAGE CO. INC.; *U.S. Private*, pg. 4472
WEINSTEIN MINKOFF INVESTMENTS; *U.S. Private*, pg. 4472
THE WEINSTEIN ORGANIZATION, INC.; *U.S. Private*, pg. 4134
WEINSTEIN OTTERMAN & ASSOCIATES; *U.S. Private*, pg. 4472
WEINSTEIN SUPPLY CORPORATION; *U.S. Private*, pg. 4472
WEINSTOCK BROTHERS CORP.; *U.S. Private*, pg. 4472
WEINTRAUB ADVERTISING; *U.S. Private*, pg. 4472
WEINTRAUB CONSTRUCTION CO. INC.; *U.S. Private*, pg. 4472
WEINTRAUB TOBIN CHEDIAK COLEMAN GRODIN LAW CORPORATION; *U.S. Private*, pg. 4472
WEIN & VINOS GMBH—See Hawesko Holding AG; *Int'l*, pg. 3288
WEIN WOLF HOLDING GMBH & CO. KG—See Hawesko Holding AG; *Int'l*, pg. 3288
WEIN WOLF IMPORT GMBH & CO. VERTRIEBS KG—See Hawesko Holding AG; *Int'l*, pg. 3289
WEIN WOLF IMPORT GMBH & CO. VERTRIEBS KG—See Hawesko Holding AG; *Int'l*, pg. 3289
WEIQIANG INTERNATIONAL TRADE (SHANGHAI) CO., LTD.—See China Petrochemical Development Corp.; *Int'l*, pg. 1540
WEIQIAO TEXTILE COMPANY LIMITED—See Shandong Weiqiao Group Co., Ltd.; *Int'l*, pg. 6759
WEIR ARABIAN METALS COMPANY—See The Olayan Group; *Int'l*, pg. 7672
WEIR BROS. INC.; *U.S. Private*, pg. 4472
WEIR CANADA INC.—See The Weir Group PLC; *Int'l*, pg. 7699
WEIR CANADA INC.—See Axel Johnson Gruppen AB; *Int'l*, pg. 765
WEIR CANADA, INC.—See Axel Johnson Gruppen AB; *Int'l*, pg. 765
WEIR CHEVROLET, INC.; *U.S. Private*, pg. 4472
WEIR COATINGS DIVISION—See The Weir Group PLC; *Int'l*, pg. 7700
WEIR ENGINEERING PRODUCTS (SHANGHAI) CO., LTD.—See The Weir Group PLC; *Int'l*, pg. 7699
WEIR ENGINEERING SERVICES (INDIA) LTD—See The Weir Group PLC; *Int'l*, pg. 7700
WEIR ENGINEERING SERVICES—See The Weir Group PLC; *Int'l*, pg. 7699
WEIR ENGINEERING SERVICES—See The Weir Group PLC; *Int'l*, pg. 7700
WEIR ENGINEERING SERVICES—See The Weir Group PLC; *Int'l*, pg. 7700

WEISER SECURITY SERVICES INC.

WEIR ENGINEERING SERVICES—See The Weir Group PLC; *Int'l*, pg. 7700
WEIR ENGINEERING SERVICES—See The Weir Group PLC; *Int'l*, pg. 7700
WEIR ENVIRONMENTAL LLC—See NV5 Global, Inc.; *U.S. Public*, pg. 1558
WEIR-ENVIROTECH (PTY.) LTD.—See The Weir Group PLC; *Int'l*, pg. 7700
WEIR FLOWAY, INC.—See The Weir Group PLC; *Int'l*, pg. 7700
WEIR GABBIONETA SRL—See The Weir Group PLC; *Int'l*, pg. 7700
THE WEIR GROUP PLC; *Int'l*, pg. 7699
WEIR HAZLETON INC.—See The Weir Group PLC; *Int'l*, pg. 7700
WEIR MATERIALS AND FOUNDRIES LTD.—See The Weir Group PLC; *Int'l*, pg. 7700
WEIR MINERALS AUSTRALIA LTD—See The Weir Group PLC; *Int'l*, pg. 7700
WEIR MINERALS AUSTRALIA LTD.—See The Weir Group PLC; *Int'l*, pg. 7700
WEIR MINERALS CHILE—See The Weir Group PLC; *Int'l*, pg. 7700
WEIR MINERALS EUROPE LIMITED—See The Weir Group PLC; *Int'l*, pg. 7700
WEIR MINERALS FRANCE SAS—See The Weir Group PLC; *Int'l*, pg. 7700
WEIR MINERALS INDIA PRIVATE LIMITED.—See The Weir Group PLC; *Int'l*, pg. 7700
WEIR MINERALS LTD AUSTRALIA—See The Weir Group PLC; *Int'l*, pg. 7700
WEIR MINERALS MONGOLIA LLC—See The Weir Group PLC; *Int'l*, pg. 7700
WEIR MINERALS NETHERLANDS BV—See The Weir Group PLC; *Int'l*, pg. 7700
WEIR MINERALS RFW LLC (OOO)—See The Weir Group PLC; *Int'l*, pg. 7700
WEIR MINERALS SWEDEN AB—See The Weir Group PLC; *Int'l*, pg. 7700
WEIR NETHERLANDS BV—See The Weir Group PLC; *Int'l*, pg. 7700
WEIR POWER & INDUSTRIAL FRANCE SAS—See The Weir Group PLC; *Int'l*, pg. 7700
WEIR'S FURNITURE VILLAGE; *U.S. Private*, pg. 4472
WEIR SLURRY GROUP, INC.—See The Weir Group PLC; *Int'l*, pg. 7700
WEIR SOLUTIONS FZE—See The Weir Group PLC; *Int'l*, pg. 7700
WEIR SPECIALTY PUMPS—See The Weir Group PLC; *Int'l*, pg. 7700
WEIR SPECIALTY PUMPS—See The Weir Group PLC; *Int'l*, pg. 7700
WEIR SPM; *U.S. Private*, pg. 4472
WEIRTON MEDICAL CENTER; *U.S. Private*, pg. 4472
WEIR TURBOMACHINERY—See The Weir Group PLC; *Int'l*, pg. 7700
WEIR VALVES & CONTROLS SEBIM SAS—See The Weir Group PLC; *Int'l*, pg. 7700
WEIR VALVES & CONTROLS UK LTD.—See The Weir Group PLC; *Int'l*, pg. 7700
WEIR VALVES & CONTROLS USA INC.—See The Weir Group PLC; *Int'l*, pg. 7700
WEIR VULCO PERU—See The Weir Group PLC; *Int'l*, pg. 7700
WEIS BUILDERS INC.; *U.S. Private*, pg. 4472
WEISER LOCK CORPORATION—See Spectrum Brands Holdings, Inc.; *U.S. Public*, pg. 1917
WEISER REALITY ADVISORS LLC; *U.S. Private*, pg. 4472
WEISER SECURITY SERVICES INC.; *U.S. Private*, pg. 4472
WEISER TRACTOR & FEED, LLC—See Tym Corporation; *Int'l*, pg. 7995
WEISHAUPT AG—See Max Weishaupt GmbH; *Int'l*, pg. 4735
WEISHAUPT AMERICA INC.—See Max Weishaupt GmbH; *Int'l*, pg. 4735
WEISHAUPT CORPORATION—See Max Weishaupt GmbH; *Int'l*, pg. 4735
WEISHAUPT DE MEXICO S. DE R.L. DE C.V.—See Max Weishaupt GmbH; *Int'l*, pg. 4736
WEISHAUPT DO BRASIL INDUSTRIA E COMERCIO LTDA.—See Max Weishaupt GmbH; *Int'l*, pg. 4736
WEISHAUPT D.O.O.—See Max Weishaupt GmbH; *Int'l*, pg. 4736
WEISHAUPT D.O.O.—See Max Weishaupt GmbH; *Int'l*, pg. 4736
WEISHAUPT DOO—See Max Weishaupt GmbH; *Int'l*, pg. 4736
WEISHAUPT HOTECHNIKAI KFT.—See Max Weishaupt GmbH; *Int'l*, pg. 4736
WEISHAUPT ITALIA S.P.A.—See Max Weishaupt GmbH; *Int'l*, pg. 4736
WEISHAUPT LUXEMBURG S.A.R.L.—See Max Weishaupt GmbH; *Int'l*, pg. 4736
WEISHAUPT NORGE AS—See Max Weishaupt GmbH; *Int'l*, pg. 4736
WEISHAUPT PARTNER MICAL SARL—See Max Weishaupt GmbH; *Int'l*, pg. 4736

WEISER SECURITY SERVICES INC. CORPORATE AFFILIATIONS

WEISHAUPT PARTNER MIZAMI LTD.—See Max Weishaupt GmbH; *Int'l*, pg. 4736
WEISHAUPT PARTNER SARL MICAL—See Max Weishaupt GmbH; *Int'l*, pg. 4736
WEISHAUPT POLSKA SP. Z O.O.—See Max Weishaupt GmbH; *Int'l*, pg. 4736
WEISHAUPT POLSKA SP. Z.O.O.—See Max Weishaupt GmbH; *Int'l*, pg. 4736
WEISHAUPT ROMANIA S.R.L.—See Max Weishaupt GmbH; *Int'l*, pg. 4736
WEISHAUPT S.A.—See Max Weishaupt GmbH; *Int'l*, pg. 4736
WEISHAUPT SAS—See Max Weishaupt GmbH; *Int'l*, pg. 4736
WEISHAUPT (SOUTH AFRICA) PTY. LTD.—See Max Weishaupt GmbH; *Int'l*, pg. 4735
WEISHAUPT SPOL. S R.O—See Max Weishaupt GmbH; *Int'l*, pg. 4736
WEISHAUPT SPOL. S R.O—See Max Weishaupt GmbH; *Int'l*, pg. 4736
WEISHAUPT S.R.O.—See Max Weishaupt GmbH; *Int'l*, pg. 4736
WEISHAUPT SVENSKA AB—See Max Weishaupt GmbH; *Int'l*, pg. 4736
WEISHAUPT (UK) LTD—See Max Weishaupt GmbH; *Int'l*, pg. 4735
WEISHAUPT-ZAGREB D.O.O—See Max Weishaupt GmbH; *Int'l*, pg. 4736
WEISLER & ASSOCIATES INC.; *U.S. Private*, pg. 4472
WEISMAN HOME OUTLETS; *U.S. Private*, pg. 4472
WEIS MARKETS, INC.; *U.S. Public*, pg. 2342
WEISNER STEEL PRODUCTS INC.; *U.S. Private*, pg. 4472
WEISSBIOTECH GMBH—See BRAIN Biotech AG; *Int'l*, pg. 1137
WEISS CONSTRUCTION COMPANY LLC; *U.S. Private*, pg. 4472
WEISS CONSTRUCTION; *U.S. Private*, pg. 4472
WEISSE FLOTTE GMBH—See FRS GmbH & Co. KG; *Int'l*, pg. 2797
WEISS ENVIRONMENTAL TECHNOLOGY INC.—See Schunk GmbH; *Int'l*, pg. 6643
WEISS ENVIROTRONICS INC.—See Schunk GmbH; *Int'l*, pg. 6643
WEISS FRANCE SAS—See Compagnie Financiere et de Participations Roullier SA; *Int'l*, pg. 1740
WEISS GROUP, LLC; *U.S. Private*, pg. 4473
WEISS GWE GMBH—See Schunk GmbH; *Int'l*, pg. 6643
WEISS INSTRUMENTS, INC.—See Arcline Investment Management LP; *U.S. Private*, pg. 313
WEISS KLIMATECHNIK GMBH—See Schunk GmbH; *Int'l*, pg. 6643
WEISS KOREA OPPORTUNITY FUND; *Int'l*, pg. 8370
WEISSMAINKRAFTWERK ROHRENHOF AKTIENGESELLSCHAFT—See E.ON SE; *Int'l*, pg. 2260
WEISS MCNAIR, LCC—See Japan Pulp and Paper Company Limited; *Int'l*, pg. 3905
WEISS MEDIEN AG—See BT Holding AG; *Int'l*, pg. 1204
WEISS PHARMATECHNIK GMBH—See Schunk GmbH; *Int'l*, pg. 6643
WEISS REALTY LTD.; *Int'l*, pg. 8370
WEISS RESEARCH, INC.—See Weiss Group, LLC; *U.S. Private*, pg. 4473
WEISS SHEET METAL COMPANY; *U.S. Private*, pg. 4473
WEISS SPINDELTECHNOLOGIE GMBH—See Siemens Aktiengesellschaft; *Int'l*, pg. 6901
WEISS TECHNIK AG—See Schunk GmbH; *Int'l*, pg. 6643
WEISS TECHNIK BELGIUM B.V.B.A.—See Schunk GmbH; *Int'l*, pg. 6643
WEISS TECHNIK FRANCE E.U.R.L.—See Schunk GmbH; *Int'l*, pg. 6643
WEISS TECHNIK INDIA PRIVATE LIMITED—See Schunk GmbH; *Int'l*, pg. 6643
WEISS TECHNIK ITALIA S.R.L.—See Schunk GmbH; *Int'l*, pg. 6643
WEISS TECHNIK MALAYSIA SDN. BHD.—See Schunk GmbH; *Int'l*, pg. 6643
WEISS TECHNIK NEDERLAND B.V.—See Schunk GmbH; *Int'l*, pg. 6643
WEISS TECHNIK NORTH AMERICA, INC.—See Schunk GmbH; *Int'l*, pg. 6643
WEISS TECHNIK SINGAPORE PTE. LTD.—See Schunk GmbH; *Int'l*, pg. 6643
WEISS TECHNIK UK LIMITED—See Schunk GmbH; *Int'l*, pg. 6643
WEISS UMWELTTECHNIK GES. M.B.H.—See Schunk GmbH; *Int'l*, pg. 6643
WEISS UMWELTTECHNIK GMBH—See Schunk GmbH; *Int'l*, pg. 6643
WEISS-VOETSCH ENVIRONMENTAL TESTING INSTRUMENTS (TAICANG) CO. LTD.—See Schunk GmbH; *Int'l*, pg. 6644
WEITA AG—See Bunzl plc; *Int'l*, pg. 1220
WEITMANN & KONRAD GMBH & CO KG; *Int'l*, pg. 8370
WEIT MEDIA—See LOV Group Invest SAS; *Int'l*, pg. 4565
THE WEITZ COMPANY LLC - CEDAR RAPIDS—See Orascom Construction PLC; *Int'l*, pg. 5613

THE WEITZ COMPANY LLC - DENVER—See Orascom Construction PLC; *Int'l*, pg. 5613
THE WEITZ COMPANY, LLC—See Orascom Construction PLC; *Int'l*, pg. 5613
THE WEITZ COMPANY LLC - WEST PALM BEACH—See Orascom Construction PLC; *Int'l*, pg. 5613
THE WEITZ GROUP LLC—See Orascom Construction PLC; *Int'l*, pg. 5613
WEITZ SUPPLY CHAIN, LLC—See Orascom Construction PLC; *Int'l*, pg. 5613
WEIWU TECHNOLOGY (FOSHAN CITY) CO., LTD.—See Airmate (Cayman) International Co. Limited; *Int'l*, pg. 248
WEIYE CONSTRUCTION GROUP CO LTD; *Int'l*, pg. 8371
WEIYE HOLDINGS LIMITED; *Int'l*, pg. 8371
WEI YUAN HOLDINGS LIMITED; *Int'l*, pg. 8369
WEIZMANN FOREX LIMITED—See Ebix Inc.; *U.S. Public*, pg. 710
WEIZMANN LIMITED; *Int'l*, pg. 8371
WEJ-IT FASTENING SYSTEMS; *U.S. Private*, pg. 4473
WEJO GROUP LIMITED; *Int'l*, pg. 8371
W.E JOHNSON EQUIPMENT COMPANY; *U.S. Private*, pg. 4420
WEKA AG—See ARCA Regler GmbH; *Int'l*, pg. 540
WEKA HOLDING GMBH & CO.KG; *Int'l*, pg. 8371
WEKO AMERICA LATINA EQUIPAMENTOS INDUSTRIAIS LTDA—See Weitmann & Konrad GmbH & Co KG; *Int'l*, pg. 8370
WEKO ITALIA SRL—See Weitmann & Konrad GmbH & Co KG; *Int'l*, pg. 8370
WEKO NORTH AMERICA, INC.—See Weitmann & Konrad GmbH & Co KG; *Int'l*, pg. 8370
WEKO UK LTD—See Weitmann & Konrad GmbH & Co KG; *Int'l*, pg. 8371
WELBECSON GROUP LIMITED—See Heidelberg Materials AG; *Int'l*, pg. 3320
WELBE, INC.; *Int'l*, pg. 8371
WELBERT PINKUS, *U.S. Private*, pg. 4473
WELBILT ASIA PACIFIC PRIVATE LIMITED—See Ali Holding S.r.l; *Int'l*, pg. 323
WELBILT DEUTSCHLAND GMBH—See Ali Holding S.r.l; *Int'l*, pg. 323
WELBILT (HALESOWEN) LIMITED—See Ali Holding S.r.l; *Int'l*, pg. 323
WELBILT, INC.—See Ali Holding S.r.l; *Int'l*, pg. 322
WELBILT INTERNATIONAL LTD.—See Ali Holding S.r.l; *Int'l*, pg. 323
WELBILT M.E. - FZE—See Ali Holding S.r.l; *Int'l*, pg. 323
WELBILT (SHANGHAI) FOODSERVICE CO., LTD.—See Ali Holding S.r.l; *Int'l*, pg. 323
WELBILT UK LIMITED—See Ali Holding S.r.l; *Int'l*, pg. 323
WELBRO BUILDING CORPORATION; *U.S. Private*, pg. 4473
WELBY GARDENS, CO.; *U.S. Private*, pg. 4473
WELBY, INC.; *Int'l*, pg. 8371
WELCAST STEELS LTD.—See AIA Engineering Ltd.; *Int'l*, pg. 227
WELCH ALLYN AUSTRALIA (PTY) LIMITED—See Baxter International Inc.; *U.S. Public*, pg. 284
WELCH ALLYN BEAVERTON DEVELOPMENT AND TECHNOLOGY CENTER—See Baxter International Inc.; *U.S. Public*, pg. 284
WELCH ALLYN B.V.—See Baxter International Inc.; *U.S. Public*, pg. 284
WELCH ALLYN CANADA LTD.—See Baxter International Inc.; *U.S. Public*, pg. 284
WELCH ALLYN DE MEXICO S. DE R.L. DE C.V.—See Baxter International Inc.; *U.S. Public*, pg. 284
WELCH ALLYN DO BRASIL COMERCIA DE EQUIPMENTOS MEDICOS, LTDA—See Baxter International Inc.; *U.S. Public*, pg. 284
WELCH ALLYN, INC.—See Baxter International Inc.; *U.S. Public*, pg. 284
WELCH ALLYN JAPAN K.K.—See Baxter International Inc.; *U.S. Public*, pg. 284
WELCH ALLYN LTD.—See Baxter International Inc.; *U.S. Public*, pg. 284
WELCH ALLYN MALAYSIA SDN, BHD—See Baxter International Inc.; *U.S. Public*, pg. 284
WELCH ALLYN PRODUCTOS MEDICOS S. DE R.L. DE C.V.—See Baxter International Inc.; *U.S. Public*, pg. 284
WELCH ALLYN SERVICE GMBH—See Baxter International Inc.; *U.S. Public*, pg. 284
WELCH ALLYN SINGAPORE PTE. LTD.—See Baxter International Inc.; *U.S. Public*, pg. 284
WELCH ALLYN SOUTH AFRICA PTY, LTD.—See Baxter International Inc.; *U.S. Public*, pg. 284
WELCH ALLYN SVERIGE—See Baxter International Inc.; *U.S. Public*, pg. 284
WELCH ALLYN (U.K.) LTD.—See Baxter International Inc.; *U.S. Public*, pg. 284
WELCH CONSULTING—See CRA International, Inc.; *U.S. Public*, pg. 588
WELCH EQUIPMENT COMPANY INC.; *U.S. Private*, pg. 4473
WELCH FOODS INC.—See National Grape Co-Op Association, Inc.; *U.S. Private*, pg. 2855

WELCH & FORBES LLC—See Affiliated Managers Group, Inc.; *U.S. Public*, pg. 56
WELCH-ILMVAC—See Ingersoll Rand Inc.; *U.S. Public*, pg. 1119
WELCH INSURANCE LLC—See Knowles Associates, LLC; *U.S. Private*, pg. 2324
WELCH PACKAGING GROUP, INC.; *U.S. Private*, pg. 4473
WELCH PACKAGING—See Welch Packaging Group, Inc.; *U.S. Private*, pg. 4473
WELCH'S INTERNATIONAL—See National Grape Co-Op Association, Inc.; *U.S. Private*, pg. 2855
WELCIA HOLDINGS CO., LTD.—See AEON Co., Ltd.; *Int'l*, pg. 178
WELCO ACETYLENE CORP.—See Linde plc; *Int'l*, pg. 4510
WELCO LUMBER CORP.; *Int'l*, pg. 8371
WELCOME DAIRY INC.; *U.S. Private*, pg. 4473
WELCOME FINANCIAL SERVICES LIMITED—See Cattles Limited; *Int'l*, pg. 1361
WELCOME FOOD INGREDIENTS LTD—See Bakkavor Group plc; *Int'l*, pg. 806
WELCOME FUNDS, INC.; *U.S. Private*, pg. 4473
WELCOME HOTELS GMBH—See Terra Firma Capital Partners Ltd.; *Int'l*, pg. 7566
WELCOME MARKET, INC.; *U.S. Private*, pg. 4473
WELCOME S.R.L.—See General Motors Company; *U.S. Public*, pg. 928
WELCOME TRAVELERS FURNITURE CO.; *U.S. Private*, pg. 4473
WELCOME TRAVEL GROUP S.P.A.—See Carnival Corporation; *U.S. Public*, pg. 438
WELCOME WAGON INTERNATIONAL, INC.—See South Florida Media Group, LLC; *U.S. Private*, pg. 3722
WELCOMHOTELS LANKA (PRIVATE) LIMITED—See ITC Limited; *Int'l*, pg. 3832
WELCOMM, INC.; *U.S. Private*, pg. 4473
WEL COMPANIES INC.; *U.S. Private*, pg. 4473
WELCO-SKOOKUM LUMBER USA—See Merrill & Ring; *U.S. Private*, pg. 2676
WELCO TECHNOLOGY (SUZHOU) LIMITED—See Wongs International (Holdings) Ltd; *Int'l*, pg. 8447
WELCRON CO., LTD. - EUMSEONG FACTORY—See Welcron Co., Ltd.; *Int'l*, pg. 8371
WELCRON CO., LTD.; *Int'l*, pg. 8371
WELCRON GLOBAL VINA CO. LTD.—See Welcron Co., Ltd.; *Int'l*, pg. 8371
WELCRON HANTEC CO., LTD.; *Int'l*, pg. 8371
WELCRON HEALTHCARE CO., LTD. - BUPYEONG FACTORY—See Welcron Co., Ltd.; *Int'l*, pg. 8371
WELCRON HEALTHCARE CORPORATION—See Welcron Co., Ltd.; *Int'l*, pg. 8371
WELCURE DRUGS & PHARMACEUTICALS LIMITED; *Int'l*, pg. 8371
WELDABILITY SIF LIMITED—See Indutrade AB; *Int'l*, pg. 3682
WELD-AID PRODUCTS, INC.—See Berwind Corporation; *U.S. Private*, pg. 541
WELDANPOWER ENTERPRISES & ENGINEERING SERVICES PTE LTD—See Sim Lian Group Limited; *Int'l*, pg. 6927
WELD COUNTY GARAGE INC.; *U.S. Private*, pg. 4473
WELDE BULGARIA AD—See WELDE Ges.m.b.H.; *Int'l*, pg. 8371
WELDED CONSTRUCTION LP; *U.S. Private*, pg. 4474
WELDED RING PRODUCTS CO., INC.; *U.S. Private*, pg. 4474
WELDED TUBES INC.; *U.S. Private*, pg. 4474
WELDE GES.M.B.H.; *Int'l*, pg. 8371
WELDERS SUPPLIES LIMITED; *Int'l*, pg. 8371
WELDERS SUPPLY & EQUIPMENT CO., INC.—See Linde plc; *Int'l*, pg. 4508
WELDIN CONSTRUCTION LLC—See Cook Inlet Region, Inc.; *U.S. Private*, pg. 1038
WELDING ENGINEERING SUPPLY CO.; *U.S. Private*, pg. 4474
WELDING GMBH & CO—See Suheung Co., Ltd.; *Int'l*, pg. 7255
WELDING INDUSTRIES PTY LIMITED—See Illinois Tool Works Inc.; *U.S. Public*, pg. 1111
WELDING METALLURGY, INC.—See CPI Aerostructures, Inc.; *U.S. Public*, pg. 588
WELDING OUTLETS, INC.; *U.S. Private*, pg. 4474
WELDING TECHNOLOGIES, INC.—See Babcock Power, Inc.; *U.S. Public*, pg. 422
WELDING TECHNOLOGY CORPORATION—See Welding Technology Corporation; *U.S. Private*, pg. 4474
WELDING TECHNOLOGY CORPORATION; *U.S. Private*, pg. 4474
WELDMAC MANUFACTURING COMPANY—See TriMas Corporation; *U.S. Public*, pg. 2189
WELDMENTS, INC.—See Precision Metal Fabrication, Inc.; *U.S. Private*, pg. 3245
WELD NORTH LLC—See Silver Lake Group, LLC; *U.S. Private*, pg. 3661
WELDOM FRANCE S.A.—See Groupe Adeo S.A.; *Int'l*, pg. 3091
WELDON ASPHALT CORP.; *U.S. Private*, pg. 4474

WELDON DIALYSIS, LLC—See DaVita Inc.; *U.S. Public*, pg. 644
WELDON MECHANICAL CORPORATION; *U.S. Private*, pg. 4474
WELDON OWEN, INC.—See Insight Editions, LP; *U.S. Private*, pg. 2085
WELDON OWEN PUBLISHING, INC.—See Bonnier AB; *Int'l*, pg. 1109
WELDON PARTS INC.; *U.S. Private*, pg. 4474
WELDON SOLUTIONS; *U.S. Private*, pg. 4474
WELDON TECHNOLOGIES INC.—See IDEX Corp; *U.S. Public*, pg. 1089
WELDON, WILLIAMS & LICK, INC.; *U.S. Private*, pg. 4474
WELDOTRON 2000, INC.; *U.S. Private*, pg. 4474
WELD POWER SERVICE COMPANY, INC.; *U.S. Private*, pg. 4473
WELDSHIP CORPORATION—See Markel Group Inc.; *U.S. Public*, pg. 1369
WELDSHIP INDUSTRIES, INC.—See Markel Group Inc.; *U.S. Public*, pg. 1369
WELD SPEC, INC.—See Tailwind Capital Group, LLC; *U.S. Private*, pg. 3924
WELDSTAR COMPANY; *U.S. Private*, pg. 4474
WELDY-LAMONT ASSOCIATES INC.; *U.S. Private*, pg. 4474
WELESKI TRANSFER INC.; *U.S. Private*, pg. 4474
WELFARE COMPANY SRL—See Quil Group S.p.A.; *Int'l*, pg. 6161
THE WELFARE DWELLINGS TRUST LIMITED—See Grainger plc; *Int'l*, pg. 3052
WELFL CONSTRUCTION CORPORATION; *U.S. Private*, pg. 4474
THE WELFONT COMPANIES INC.; *U.S. Private*, pg. 4134
WELGENE BIOTECH CO., LTD.; *Int'l*, pg. 8371
WELICHEM BIOTECH INC.; *Int'l*, pg. 8372
WELIFE TECHNOLOGY LIMITED; *Int'l*, pg. 8372
WELIKESMALL INC.—See Thinkingbox Media & Design, Inc.; *Int'l*, pg. 7710
WELINVEST AG; *Int'l*, pg. 8372
WELINVEST IMMOBILIEN AG—See Welinvest AG; *Int'l*, pg. 8372
WELIVIT NEW ENERGY GMBH—See Munchener Ruckversicherungs AG; *Int'l*, pg. 5093
WELKER SPINTECH GMBH; *Int'l*, pg. 8372
THE WELK GROUP INC.; *U.S. Private*, pg. 4134
WELKIN ASSOCIATES, LTD—See The Carlyle Group Inc.; *U.S. Public*, pg. 2049
WELK MUSIC GROUP INC.; *U.S. Private*, pg. 4474
WELK RESORTS SAN DIEGO—See The Welk Group Inc.; *U.S. Private*, pg. 4134
WELLAHEAD ENGINEERING LIMITED—See Serba Dinamik Holdings Berhad; *Int'l*, pg. 6721
WELLAND FORGE; *Int'l*, pg. 8373
WELLARD LIMITED; *Int'l*, pg. 8373
WELLBEATS—See LifeSpeak, Inc.; *U.S. Public*, pg. 4494
WELLBE, INC.—See Orbita, Inc.; *U.S. Private*, pg. 3038
WELLBEING SOFTWARE LTD.—See Pacific Equity Partners Pty. Limited; *Int'l*, pg. 5689
WELL BIOTEC CO., LTD.; *Int'l*, pg. 8372
WELLBORE CAPITAL, LLC—See Morgan Stanley; *U.S. Public*, pg. 1476
WELLBORN CABINET, INC.—See HCI Equity Management, L.P.; *U.S. Private*, pg. 1889
WELLBORN CABINET, INC.; *U.S. Private*, pg. 4474
WELLBORN FOREST PRODUCTS, INC.—See HCI Equity Management, L.P.; *U.S. Private*, pg. 1889
WELLBORN HOLDINGS INC.—See Wellborn Cabinet, Inc.; *U.S. Private*, pg. 4475
WELL BORN REAL ESTATE MANAGEMENT LIMITED—See Henderson Land Development Co. Ltd.; *Int'l*, pg. 3345
WELLBRIDGE CLUB MANAGEMENT INC.—See Starmark Management Holdings LLC; *U.S. Private*, pg. 3787
WELL.CA LLC—See McKesson Corporation; *U.S. Public*, pg. 1409
WELLCALL HOLDINGS BERHAD; *Int'l*, pg. 8373
WELLCALL HOSE (M) SDN. BHD.—See Wellcall Holdings Berhad; *Int'l*, pg. 8373
WELLCARE HEALTH PLANS INC.—See Centene Corporation; *U.S. Public*, pg. 471
WELLCARE HEALTH PLANS OF KENTUCKY, INC.—See Centene Corporation; *U.S. Public*, pg. 471
WELLCARE, INC.—See Encompass Health Corporation; *U.S. Public*, pg. 759
WELLCARE OF GEORGIA, INC.—See Centene Corporation; *U.S. Public*, pg. 471
WELLCARE SPECIALTY PHARMACY, INC.—See Centene Corporation; *U.S. Public*, pg. 471
WELLCO HOLDINGS CORPORATION; *Int'l*, pg. 8373
WELLCOME COMPANY LIMITED—See Jardine Matheson Holdings Limited; *Int'l*, pg. 3910
WELLCOME TAIWAN COMPANY LTD.—See Jardine Matheson Holdings Limited; *Int'l*, pg. 3910
THE WELLCOME TRUST LTD.; *Int'l*, pg. 7700
WELLCOM GROUP LIMITED—See Innocean Worldwide Inc.; *Int'l*, pg. 3709

WE'LL CORPORATION CO., LTD - DIRECT MARKETING PLANT—See Wellco Holdings Corporation; *Int'l*, pg. 8373
WE'LL CORPORATION CO., LTD - KANTO NO.1 PLANT—See Wellco Holdings Corporation; *Int'l*, pg. 8373
WE'LL CORPORATION CO., LTD - KANTO NO.2 PLANT—See Wellco Holdings Corporation; *Int'l*, pg. 8373
WE'LL CORPORATION CO., LTD - KYOTO PLANT—See Wellco Holdings Corporation; *Int'l*, pg. 8373
WELLCRAFT, LLC—See Beneteau S.A.; *Int'l*, pg. 973
WELLDONE CO., LTD.; *Int'l*, pg. 8373
WELLDONE EDS GMBH—See Noble Corporation plc; *Int'l*, pg. 5397
WELLDONE LR OY—See Live Nation Entertainment, Inc.; *U.S. Public*, pg. 1330
WELLDYNERX, LLC—See The Carlyle Group Inc.; *U.S. Public*, pg. 2057
WELLE ENVIRONMENTAL GROUP CO., LTD.; *Int'l*, pg. 8373
WELLELL INC.; *Int'l*, pg. 8374
WELLEN CAPITAL, LLC; *U.S. Private*, pg. 4475
WELL ENHANCEMENT SERVICES LLC—See AusTex Oil Limited; *Int'l*, pg. 718
WELLENS & CO., INC.; *U.S. Private*, pg. 4475
WELLER AUTO PARTS INC.; *U.S. Private*, pg. 4475
WELLER TOOLS GMBH—See Bain Capital, LP; *U.S. Private*, pg. 430
WELLESLEY COUNTRY CLUB; *U.S. Private*, pg. 4475
WELLESLEY DIALYSIS LLC—See Nautic Partners, LLC; *U.S. Private*, pg. 2871
WELLESLEY INFORMATION SERVICES, LLC—See United Communications Group; *U.S. Private*, pg. 4289
WELLESLEY INVESTMENT PARTNERS, LLC—See Cambridge Bancorp; *U.S. Public*, pg. 426
WELLE (SUZHOU) ENERGY TECHNOLOGY CO., LTD.—See WELLE Environmental Group Co., Ltd.; *Int'l*, pg. 8374
WELLEX CORPORATION; *U.S. Private*, pg. 4475
WELLEX INDUSTRIES INC.; *Int'l*, pg. 8374
WELLEZ INFORMATION MANAGEMENT, LLC—See Thoma Bravo, L.P.; *U.S. Private*, pg. 4152
WELLFAM FOODS CORPORATION—See Marubeni Corporation; *Int'l*, pg. 4710
WELLFIELD TECHNOLOGIES INC.; *Int'l*, pg. 8374
WELLFLEET FLEA MARKET; *U.S. Private*, pg. 4475
WELLFOUNT CORP; *U.S. Private*, pg. 4475
WELLFRIEND (BEIJING) TRADING CO., LTD.—See Korea Electric Terminal Co., Ltd.; *Int'l*, pg. 4284
WELLFULLY LIMITED; *Int'l*, pg. 8374
WELL GRADED ENGINEERING PUBLIC COMPANY LIMITED; *Int'l*, pg. 8372
WELL HARBOUR DEVELOPMENT LIMITED—See China Automobile New Retail (Holdings) Limited; *Int'l*, pg. 1484
WELL HEALTH BRICKYARD INC.—See WELL Health Technologies Corp.; *Int'l*, pg. 8372
WELL HEALTH CITY VIEW INC.—See WELL Health Technologies Corp.; *Int'l*, pg. 8372
WELL HEALTH CLAYTON HEIGHTS INC.—See WELL Health Technologies Corp.; *Int'l*, pg. 8372
WELL HEALTH CLOVER CARE INC.—See WELL Health Technologies Corp.; *Int'l*, pg. 8372
WELL HEALTH COLEBROOK INC.—See WELL Health Technologies Corp.; *Int'l*, pg. 8372
WELL HEALTH COQUITLAM INC.—See WELL Health Technologies Corp.; *Int'l*, pg. 8372
WELL HEALTH FLEETWOOD INC.—See WELL Health Technologies Corp.; *Int'l*, pg. 8372
WELL HEALTH HASTING SUNRISE INC.—See WELL Health Technologies Corp.; *Int'l*, pg. 8372
WELL HEALTH KERRISDALE INC.—See WELL Health Technologies Corp.; *Int'l*, pg. 8372
WELL HEALTH LONSDALE INC.—See WELL Health Technologies Corp.; *Int'l*, pg. 8372
WELL HEALTH OVAL INC.—See WELL Health Technologies Corp.; *Int'l*, pg. 8372
WELL HEALTH PANORAMA VILLAGE INC.—See WELL Health Technologies Corp.; *Int'l*, pg. 8372
WELL HEALTH PEMBERTON MARINE INC.—See WELL Health Technologies Corp.; *Int'l*, pg. 8372
WELL HEALTH POINT GREY INC.—See WELL Health Technologies Corp.; *Int'l*, pg. 8372
WELL HEALTH RICHMOND CENTRAL INC.—See WELL Health Technologies Corp.; *Int'l*, pg. 8372
WELL HEALTH SCOTT ROAD INC.—See WELL Health Technologies Corp.; *Int'l*, pg. 8372
WELL HEALTH TECHNOLOGIES CORP.; *Int'l*, pg. 8372
WELL HEALTH TRITON INC.—See WELL Health Technologies Corp.; *Int'l*, pg. 8373
WELLHOPE FOODS INC.; *Int'l*, pg. 8374
WELLIGHT TECHNOLOGY CORP.—See Taiwan Surface Mounting Technology Corp.; *Int'l*, pg. 7424
WELLINGBOROUGH TYRES LIMITED—See Sumitomo Rubber Industries, Ltd.; *Int'l*, pg. 7300
WELLING HOLDING LIMITED—See Midea Group Co., Ltd.; *Int'l*, pg. 4886

WELLING INTERNATIONAL HONG KONG LTD.—See Midea Group Co., Ltd.; *Int'l*, pg. 4886
WELLINGTON CITY TRANSPORT LIMITED—See Infratil Limited; *Int'l*, pg. 3698
WELLINGTON DIAGNOSTIC SERVICES LLP—See HCA Healthcare, Inc.; *U.S. Public*, pg. 1013
WELLINGTON DIAGNOSTIC SERVICES; *U.S. Private*, pg. 4475
WELLINGTON DRIVE TECHNOLOGIES PTE LTD—See AoFrio Limited; *Int'l*, pg. 487
WELLINGTON DRIVE TECHNOLOGIES US, INC.—See AoFrio Limited; *Int'l*, pg. 487
WELLINGTON ENDO, LLC—See Tenet Healthcare Corporation; *U.S. Public*, pg. 2015
WELLINGTON EQUESTRIAN PARTNERS, LLC; *U.S. Private*, pg. 4475
WELLINGTON EQUESTRIAN REALTY, LLC; *U.S. Private*, pg. 4475
WELLINGTON GLOBAL INVESTMENT MANAGEMENT LTD—See Wellington Management Company, LLP; *U.S. Private*, pg. 4475
WELLINGTON HAMRICK, INC. - SHELBY—See Wellington Hamrick, Inc.; *U.S. Private*, pg. 4475
WELLINGTON HAMRICK, INC.; *U.S. Private*, pg. 4475
WELLINGTON HEALTHCARE, INC.—See The Ensign Group, Inc.; *U.S. Public*, pg. 2072
THE WELLINGTON HOSPITAL—See HCA Healthcare, Inc.; *U.S. Public*, pg. 1012
WELLINGTON INSURANCE GROUP, INC.—See Clayton, Dubilier & Rice, LLC; *U.S. Public*, pg. 927
WELLINGTON INSURANCE GROUP, INC.—See Mubadala Investment Company PJSC; *Int'l*, pg. 5076
WELLINGTON INSURANCE GROUP, INC.—See Stone Point Capital LLC; *U.S. Private*, pg. 3826
WELLINGTON INTERNATIONAL AIRPORT LIMITED—See Infratil Limited; *Int'l*, pg. 3698
WELLINGTON INTERNATIONAL MANAGEMENT COMPANY PTE LTD—See Wellington Management Company, LLP; *U.S. Private*, pg. 4475
WELLINGTON LATIN AMERICA SERVICES SA DE CV—See AoFrio Limited; *Int'l*, pg. 487
WELLINGTON MANAGEMENT COMPANY, LLP; *U.S. Private*, pg. 4475
WELLINGTON MANAGEMENT INTERNATIONAL LTD—See Wellington Management Company, LLP; *U.S. Private*, pg. 4475
WELLINGTON MOTOR TECNOLOJILERI SAN TIC LTD STI—See AoFrio Limited; *Int'l*, pg. 487
WELLINGTON PUB COMPANY—See Reuben Brothers SA; *Int'l*, pg. 6311
WELLINGTON REGIONAL MEDICAL CENTER—See Universal Health Services, Inc.; *U.S. Public*, pg. 2260
WELLINGTON SHIELDS & CO., LLC; *U.S. Private*, pg. 4475
WELLINGTON STATE BANK; *U.S. Private*, pg. 4475
WELLINGTON TECHNOLOGIES, INC.; *U.S. Private*, pg. 4475
WELLINGTON TRUST CO.—See Wellington Management Company, LLP; *U.S. Private*, pg. 4475
WELL IN TECHNOLOGY DEVELOPMENT LIMITED—See Finsoft Financial Investment Holdings Limited; *Int'l*, pg. 2677
WELLIVER MCGUIRE INC.; *U.S. Private*, pg. 4475
WELLKEEPER INC; *U.S. Private*, pg. 4475
WELL LEAD MEDICAL CO., LTD.; *Int'l*, pg. 8373
WELL LEAD TRADING CO., LTD.—See Well Lead Medical Co., Ltd.; *Int'l*, pg. 8373
WELL LINK GROUP HOLDINGS LTD.; *Int'l*, pg. 8373
WELLMAN BOOTH LTD—See Langley Holdings Plc; *Int'l*, pg. 4410
WELLMAN FRANCE RECYCLAGE S.A.S.—See Indorama Ventures Public Company Limited; *Int'l*, pg. 3659
WELLMAN INTERNATIONAL LIMITED—See Indorama Ventures Public Company Limited; *Int'l*, pg. 3659
WELLMAN NEUFCHATEAU RECYCLAGE S.A.—See Indorama Ventures Public Company Limited; *Int'l*, pg. 3659
WELLMAN PLASTICS RECYCLING LLC—See Shanghai PRET Composites Co., Ltd.; *Int'l*, pg. 6777
WELLMAN PRODUCTS GROUP—See Lone Star Funds; *U.S. Private*, pg. 2485
WELLMARK BLUE CROSS & BLUE SHIELD; *U.S. Private*, pg. 4475
WELLMARK INTERNATIONAL—See Central Garden & Pet Company; *U.S. Public*, pg. 473
WELLMASTER PIPE & SUPPLY INC.; *Int'l*, pg. 8374
WELL-MED GLOBAL LLC—See Vivakor, Inc.; *U.S. Public*, pg. 2307
WELLMED MEDICAL MANAGEMENT INC—See UnitedHealth Group Incorporated; *U.S. Public*, pg. 2240
WELLMED MEDICAL MANAGEMENT OF FLORIDA, INC.—See UnitedHealth Group Incorporated; *U.S. Public*, pg. 2252
WELLMETRIX, LLC—See Zivo Bioscience, Inc.; *U.S. Public*, pg. 2409
WELLMONT HEALTH SYSTEM—See Mountain States Health Alliance; *U.S. Private*, pg. 2800
WELLNEO SUGAR CO., LTD.; *Int'l*, pg. 8374

WELLNEO SUGAR CO., LTD.

WELLNEO SUGAR CO., LTD.—See WELLNEO SUGAR Co., Ltd.; *Int'l*, pg. 8374
WELLNESS AND BEAUTY SOLUTIONS LIMITED; *Int'l*, pg. 8374
WELLNESS ARENA CORPORATION—See Hulic Co., Ltd.; *Int'l*, pg. 3528
WELLNESS ASSESSMENT CENTRE PTE LTD—See AsiaMedic Ltd.; *Int'l*, pg. 617
WELLNESS BY CHOICE, LLC—See Centene Corporation; *U.S. Public*, pg. 471
WELLNESS CENTER USA, INC.; *U.S. Public*, pg. 2342
WELLNESS COMMUNICATIONS CORPORATION—See ITOCHU Corporation; *Int'l*, pg. 3841
WELLNESS CORPORATE SOLUTIONS, LLC; *U.S. Private*, pg. 4476
WELLNESS FOODS INC.—See The Simply Good Foods Company; *U.S. Public*, pg. 2130
WELLNESSFX, INC.—See Catterton Management Company, LLC; *U.S. Private*, pg. 794
WELLNESS & GYNAECOLOGY CENTRE PTE. LTD.—See Singapore Medical Group Limited; *Int'l*, pg. 6941
WELLNESS HANSHIN INC.—See Hankyu Hanshin Holdings Inc.; *Int'l*, pg. 3256
WELLNESS MARKETING CORPORATION—See Masco Corporation; *U.S. Public*, pg. 1392
WELLNESS MATRIX GROUP, INC.; *U.S. Private*, pg. 4476
WELLNESS NETWORKS INC; *U.S. Private*, pg. 4476
WELLNESS NONI LIMITED; *Int'l*, pg. 8374
WELLNESS PARTNERS LTD.—See Technogym SpA; *Int'l*, pg. 7510
WELLNESS PARTNERS USA INC.—See Technogym SpA; *Int'l*, pg. 7510
WELLNESS POINTE; *U.S. Private*, pg. 4476
WELLNET CORPORATION; *Int'l*, pg. 8374
WELLNZ LIMITED—See Marsh & McLennan Companies, Inc.; *U.S. Public*, pg. 1388
WELLONS INC.; *U.S. Private*, pg. 4476
WELLPARTNER, INC.; *U.S. Private*, pg. 4476
WELLPET LLC—See Clearlake Capital Group, L.P.; *U.S. Private*, pg. 937
WELL-PICT INC.; *U.S. Private*, pg. 4474
WELLPLACE, INC.—See Acadia Healthcare Company, Inc.; *U.S. Public*, pg. 31
WELLPOINT BEHAVIORAL HEALTH—See Elevance Health, Inc.; *U.S. Public*, pg. 730
WELLPOINT FEDERAL CORPORATION—See Elevance Health, Inc.; *U.S. Public*, pg. 730
WELLPOINT IOWA, INC.—See Elevance Health, Inc.; *U.S. Public*, pg. 730
WELLPOINT PHARMACY MANAGEMENT—See Elevance Health, Inc.; *U.S. Public*, pg. 730
WELLPOINT TENNESSEE, INC.—See Elevance Health, Inc.; *U.S. Public*, pg. 730
WELLPOWER COMMERCE HOLDING CO., LIMITED—See WW Holding Inc; *Int'l*, pg. 8517
WELLPOWER SPORTING GOODS CO., LTD.—See WW Holding Inc; *Int'l*, pg. 8517
WELLPOWER SPORTING GOODS (HK) CO., LIMITED—See WW Holding Inc; *Int'l*, pg. 8517
WELL PROSPERING LTD.—See Zhejiang Longsheng Group Co., Ltd.; *Int'l*, pg. 8659
WELLQUEST MEDICAL & WELLNESS CORPORATION; *U.S. Public*, pg. 2343
WELL SA; *Int'l*, pg. 8373
WELLS BLOOMFIELD LLC—See The Middleby Corporation; *U.S. Public*, pg. 2115
WELLSBORO & CORNING RAILROAD, LLC—See Brookfield Infrastructure Partners L.P.; *Int'l*, pg. 1193
WELLSBORO & CORNING RAILROAD, LLC—See GIC Pte. Ltd.; *Int'l*, pg. 2967
WELLS CAPITAL MANAGEMENT INCORPORATED—See Wells Fargo & Company; *U.S. Public*, pg. 2345
WELLS CAPITAL MANAGEMENT INCORPORATED—See Wells Fargo & Company; *U.S. Public*, pg. 2346
WELLS CARGO TRAILER SALES, LLC—See Corporate Partners LLC; *U.S. Private*, pg. 1055
WELLS COMMUNICATIONS, INC.; *U.S. Private*, pg. 4476
WELLS CONCRETE PRODUCTS COMPANY INC.; *U.S. Private*, pg. 4476
WELLS-CTI, INC.—See Investcorp Holdings B.S.C.; *Int'l*, pg. 3776
WELLS ENGINEERING, PSC—See Davis H. Elliot Company Inc.; *U.S. Private*, pg. 1173
WELLS ENTERPRISES, INC.; *U.S. Private*, pg. 4476
WELLSERVE CO., LTD.—See Senshukai Co., Ltd.; *Int'l*, pg. 6713
WELL SERVICES GROUP; *Int'l*, pg. 8373
WELLS FARGO ADVANTAGE FUNDS—See Wells Fargo & Company; *U.S. Public*, pg. 2345
WELLS FARGO ADVISORS FINANCIAL NETWORK, LLC—See Wells Fargo & Company; *U.S. Public*, pg. 2345
WELLS FARGO ADVISORS, LLC—See Wells Fargo & Company; *U.S. Public*, pg. 2345
WELLS FARGO AUDIT SERVICES—See Wells Fargo & Company; *U.S. Public*, pg. 2346
WELLS FARGO AUTO FINANCE—See Wells Fargo & Company; *U.S. Public*, pg. 2346
WELLS FARGO AUTO RECEIVABLES, LLC—See Wells Fargo & Company; *U.S. Public*, pg. 2345
WELLS FARGO BANK INTERNATIONAL—See Wells Fargo & Company; *U.S. Public*, pg. 2345
WELLS FARGO BANK, N.A. - HONG KONG BRANCH—See Wells Fargo & Company; *U.S. Public*, pg. 2346
WELLS FARGO BANK, N.A.—See Wells Fargo & Company; *U.S. Public*, pg. 2346
WELLS FARGO BANK NORTHWEST, NATIONAL ASSOCIATION—See Wells Fargo & Company; *U.S. Public*, pg. 2345
WELLS FARGO BANK; *U.S. Private*, pg. 4476
WELLS FARGO BUSINESS CREDIT—See Wells Fargo & Company; *U.S. Public*, pg. 2346
WELLS FARGO CAPITAL FINANCE CORPORATION CANADA—See Wells Fargo & Company; *U.S. Public*, pg. 2346
WELLS FARGO CAPITAL FINANCE, INC.—See Wells Fargo & Company; *U.S. Public*, pg. 2346
WELLS FARGO CAPITAL FINANCE, LLC—See Wells Fargo & Company; *U.S. Public*, pg. 2346
WELLS FARGO CAPITAL FINANCE (UK) LIMITED—See Wells Fargo & Company; *U.S. Public*, pg. 2346
WELLS FARGO COMMERCIAL DISTRIBUTION FINANCE, LLC—See Wells Fargo & Company; *U.S. Public*, pg. 2346
WELLS FARGO & COMPANY; *U.S. Public*, pg. 2343
WELLS FARGO DEALER SERVICES, INC.—See Wells Fargo & Company; *U.S. Public*, pg. 2346
WELLS FARGO ENERGY CAPITAL, INC.—See Wells Fargo & Company; *U.S. Public*, pg. 2346
WELLS FARGO ENERGY GROUP—See Wells Fargo & Company; *U.S. Public*, pg. 2346
WELLS FARGO EQUIPMENT FINANCE COMPANY—See Wells Fargo & Company; *U.S. Public*, pg. 2346
WELLS FARGO EQUIPMENT FINANCE, INC.—See Wells Fargo & Company; *U.S. Public*, pg. 2346
WELLS FARGO EQUIPMENT FINANCE—See Wells Fargo & Company; *U.S. Public*, pg. 2346
WELLS FARGO FINANCIAL ARIZONA, INC.—See Wells Fargo & Company; *U.S. Public*, pg. 2346
WELLS FARGO FINANCIAL CARDS—See Wells Fargo & Company; *U.S. Public*, pg. 2346
WELLS FARGO FINANCIAL CORPORATION CANADA—See Wells Fargo & Company; *U.S. Public*, pg. 2346
WELLS FARGO FINANCIAL FLORIDA, INC.—See Wells Fargo & Company; *U.S. Public*, pg. 2346
WELLS FARGO FINANCIAL, INC.—See Wells Fargo & Company; *U.S. Public*, pg. 2346
WELLS FARGO FINANCIAL LEASING, INC.—See Wells Fargo & Company; *U.S. Public*, pg. 2346
WELLS FARGO FINANCIAL OREGON, INC.—See Wells Fargo & Company; *U.S. Public*, pg. 2346
WELLS FARGO FINANCIAL—See Wells Fargo & Company; *U.S. Public*, pg. 2346
WELLS FARGO FINANCIAL WASHINGTON, INC.—See Wells Fargo & Company; *U.S. Public*, pg. 2346
WELLS FARGO FUNDS DISTRIBUTOR, LLC—See Wells Fargo & Company; *U.S. Public*, pg. 2345
WELLS FARGO FUNDS MANAGEMENT, LLC—See Wells Fargo & Company; *U.S. Public*, pg. 2345
WELLS FARGO GLOBAL FUND SERVICES (ASIA) PTE LTD.—See Wells Fargo & Company; *U.S. Public*, pg. 2346
WELLS FARGO GLOBAL FUND SERVICES (UK) LIMITED—See Wells Fargo & Company; *U.S. Public*, pg. 2346
WELLS FARGO INSURANCE, INC.—See Wells Fargo & Company; *U.S. Public*, pg. 2346
WELLS FARGO INSURANCE SERVICES, INC.—See Wells Fargo & Company; *U.S. Public*, pg. 2346
WELLS FARGO MORTGAGE LOAN TRUST II, LLC—See Wells Fargo & Company; *U.S. Public*, pg. 2346
WELLS FARGO MULTIFAMILY CAPITAL—See Wells Fargo & Company; *U.S. Public*, pg. 2346
WELLS FARGO MULTI-SECTOR INCOME FUND; *U.S. Public*, pg. 2347
WELLS FARGO PREFERRED CAPITAL, INC.—See Wells Fargo & Company; *U.S. Public*, pg. 2347
WELLS FARGO PRIME SERVICES, LLC - NEW YORK—See Wells Fargo & Company; *U.S. Public*, pg. 2347
WELLS FARGO PRIME SERVICES, LLC—See Wells Fargo & Company; *U.S. Public*, pg. 2347
WELLS FARGO PROPERTIES, INC.—See Wells Fargo & Company; *U.S. Public*, pg. 2347
WELLS FARGO RAIL CORPORATION—See Wells Fargo & Company; *U.S. Public*, pg. 2347
WELLS FARGO REAL ESTATE GROUP—See Wells Fargo & Company; *U.S. Public*, pg. 2347
WELLS FARGO REAL ESTATE INVESTMENT CORPORATION—See Wells Fargo & Company; *U.S. Public*, pg. 2346

CORPORATE AFFILIATIONS

WELLS FARGO REAL ESTATE TAX SERVICES, LLC—See Wells Fargo & Company; *U.S. Public*, pg. 2347
WELLS FARGO SECURITIES INTERNATIONAL LIMITED—See Wells Fargo & Company; *U.S. Public*, pg. 2347
WELLS FARGO SECURITIES (JAPAN) CO., LTD.—See Wells Fargo & Company; *U.S. Public*, pg. 2347
WELLS FARGO SECURITIES, LLC—See Wells Fargo & Company; *U.S. Public*, pg. 2347
WELLS FARGO SOPORTE GLOBAL LIMITADA—See Wells Fargo & Company; *U.S. Public*, pg. 2347
WELLS FARGO SPECIAL RISKS, INC.—See Wells Fargo & Company; *U.S. Public*, pg. 2347
WELLS FARGO VENDOR FINANCIAL SERVICES, LLC—See Wells Fargo & Company; *U.S. Public*, pg. 2347
WELLS FARGO WEALTH BROKERAGE INSURANCE AGENCY, LLC—See Wells Fargo & Company; *U.S. Public*, pg. 2347
WELLS GROUP LLC; *U.S. Private*, pg. 4476
WELL SHIN ELECTRONIC (KUN SHAN) CO., LTD.—See Well Shin Technology Co., Ltd.; *Int'l*, pg. 8373
WELL SHIN TECHNOLOGY CO., LTD. - KUN SHAN PLANT—See Well Shin Technology Co., Ltd.; *Int'l*, pg. 8373
WELL SHIN TECHNOLOGY CO., LTD.; *Int'l*, pg. 8373
WELL SHIN TECHNOLOGY CO., LTD. - TAIWAN PLANT—See Well Shin Technology Co., Ltd.; *Int'l*, pg. 8373
WELL SHIPMANAGEMENT AND MARITIME CONSULTANT CO., LTD.—See Wisdom Marine Lines Co., Ltd.; *Int'l*, pg. 8435
WELLSHIRE FARMS, INC.—See Land O'Frost, Inc.; *U.S. Private*, pg. 2383
WELLS HOLDINGS, INC.—See Corporate Partners LLC; *U.S. Private*, pg. 1055
WELLS INDUSTRIES—See Corporate Partners LLC; *U.S. Private*, pg. 1055
WELLS INSURANCE AGENCY, INC.—See Citizens Community Bancorp, Inc.; *U.S. Public*, pg. 505
WELLS-KEOWN & ASSOCIATES INC.; *U.S. Private*, pg. 4476
WELLSKY CORPORATION—See Leonard Green & Partners, L.P.; *U.S. Private*, pg. 2430
WELLSKY CORPORATION—See TPG Capital, L.P.; *U.S. Public*, pg. 2177
WELLS LAMONT INDUSTRY GROUP LLC—See Berkshire Hathaway Inc.; *U.S. Public*, pg. 312
WELLS LAMONT LLC—See Berkshire Hathaway Inc.; *U.S. Public*, pg. 311
WELLS LAMONT RETAIL GROUP—See Berkshire Hathaway Inc.; *U.S. Public*, pg. 312
WELLS LAND DEVELOPMENT, INC.; *U.S. Private*, pg. 4476
WELLS MANUFACTURING DE MEXICO S.A. DE C.V.—See Niterra Co., Ltd.; *Int'l*, pg. 5381
WELLS MANUFACTURING LLC; *U.S. Private*, pg. 4476
WELLS NELSON & ASSOCIATES, LLC—See D.A. Davidson Companies; *U.S. Private*, pg. 1140
WELLSOFT CORP.—See Medsphere Systems Corp.; *U.S. Private*, pg. 2658
WELLSPAN HEALTH; *U.S. Private*, pg. 4476
WELLSPECT B.V.—See DENTSPLY SIRONA Inc.; *U.S. Public*, pg. 655
WELLSPECT HEALTHCARE AB—See DENTSPLY SIRONA Inc.; *U.S. Public*, pg. 655
WELLSPECT HEALTHCARE GMBH—See DENTSPLY SIRONA Inc.; *U.S. Public*, pg. 656
WELLSPECT HEALTHCARE NORWAY—See DENTSPLY SIRONA Inc.; *U.S. Public*, pg. 656
WELLSPECT HEALTHCARE - UROLOGY DIVISION—See DENTSPLY SIRONA Inc.; *U.S. Public*, pg. 655
WELLSPECT HEALTHCARE - UROLOGY DIVISION—See DENTSPLY SIRONA Inc.; *U.S. Public*, pg. 656
WELLSPECT LTD.—See DENTSPLY SIRONA Inc.; *U.S. Public*, pg. 656
WELLSPIRE HOLDINGS BERHAD; *Int'l*, pg. 8374
WELLSPRING BY SILKS CO., LTD.—See Formosa International Hotels Corp.; *Int'l*, pg. 2735
WELLSPRING CANCER CENTER PLC; *U.S. Private*, pg. 4477
WELLSPRING CAPITAL MANAGEMENT LLC; *U.S. Private*, pg. 4477
THE WELLSPRING GROUP; *U.S. Private*, pg. 4134
WELLSPRING PHARMACEUTICAL CORPORATION—See Avista Capital Partners, L.P.; *U.S. Private*, pg. 409
WELL SPRING RETIREMENT COMMUNITY; *U.S. Private*, pg. 4474
WELLSPRING WORLDWIDE, LLC; *U.S. Private*, pg. 4478
WELLS REAL ESTATE FUNDS, INC.; *U.S. Private*, pg. 4476
WELLS RURAL ELECTRIC COMPANY; *U.S. Private*, pg. 4476
WELLSTAR ATLANTA MEDICAL CENTER, INC.—See WellStar Health System, Inc.; *U.S. Private*, pg. 4478
WELLSTAR ATLANTA MEDICAL CENTER SOUTH—See WellStar Health System, Inc.; *U.S. Private*, pg. 4478

COMPANY NAME INDEX

WELLSTAR ENTERPRISES (HONG KONG) COMPANY LIMITED—See BRENNTAG SE; *Int'l*, pg. 1150
WELLSTAR HEALTH SYSTEM, INC.; *U.S. Private*, pg. 4478
WELLSTAR MEDICAL GROUP CARDIOVASCULAR MEDICINE—See WellStar Health System, Inc.; *U.S. Private*, pg. 4478
WELLSTAR MEDICAL GROUP FAMILY MEDICINE—See WellStar Health System, Inc.; *U.S. Private*, pg. 4478
WELLSTAR MEDICAL GROUP INTERVENTIONAL NEUROLOGY—See WellStar Health System, Inc.; *U.S. Private*, pg. 4478
WELLSTAR MEDICAL GROUP NEUROSURGERY—See WellStar Health System, Inc.; *U.S. Private*, pg. 4478
WELLSTAR MEDICAL GROUP NORTHSIDE ENT—See WellStar Health System, Inc.; *U.S. Private*, pg. 4478
WELLSTAR MEDICAL GROUP RHEUMATOLOGY—See WellStar Health System, Inc.; *U.S. Private*, pg. 4478
WELLSTAR NORTH FULTON HOSPITAL, INC.—See WellStar Health System, Inc.; *U.S. Private*, pg. 4478
WELLSTAR NORTH FULTON HOSPITAL—See WellStar Health System, Inc.; *U.S. Private*, pg. 4478
WELLSTAR SPALDING REGIONAL HOSPITAL, INC.—See WellStar Health System, Inc.; *U.S. Private*, pg. 4478
WELLSTAR SYLVAN GROVE HOSPITAL, INC.—See WellStar Health System, Inc.; *U.S. Private*, pg. 4478
WELLS & TATE ELECTRIC COMPANY INC.; *U.S. Private*, pg. 4476
THE WELLSTEAD OF ROGERS DIAMONDCREST SENIOR LIVING—See AlerisLife Inc.; *U.S. Private*, pg. 162
WELLSTON ASSOCIATES LAND SURVEYORS, LLC—See Peak Rock Capital LLC; *U.S. Private*, pg. 3124
WELLSTREAM AUSTRALIA PTY LIMITED—See General Electric Company; *U.S. Public*, pg. 920
WELLSTREAM DO BRAZIL INDUSTRIA E SERVICOS LTDA—See General Electric Company; *U.S. Public*, pg. 920
WELLSTREAM HOLDINGS LIMITED—See General Electric Company; *U.S. Public*, pg. 920
WELLSTREAM, INC.—See General Electric Company; *U.S. Public*, pg. 920
WELLS VEHICLE ELECTRONICS, L.P.—See Niterra Co., Ltd.; *Int'l*, pg. 5381
WELLSVILLE DAILY REPORTER—See Gannett Co., Inc.; *U.S. Public*, pg. 905
WELLTEC CORPORATION—See JUTEC Holdings Corporation; *Int'l*, pg. 4032
WELLTECH CONSTRUCTION PTE. LTD.—See CNQC International Holdings Ltd.; *Int'l*, pg. 1678
WELLTEC KANSAI CORPORATION—See JUTEC Holdings Corporation; *Int'l*, pg. 4032
WELLTEC MACHINERY LIMITED—See Cosmos Machinery Enterprises Limited; *Int'l*, pg. 1813
WELLTEK CORPORATION; *U.S. Private*, pg. 4478
WELLTEK INCORPORATED; *U.S. Private*, pg. 4478
WELLTEND TECHNOLOGY CORPORATION; *Int'l*, pg. 8374
WELLTHERM DRILLING LTD.—See Eneraqua Technologies Plc; *Int'l*, pg. 2418
WELLTHIE, INC.—See Aflac Incorporated; *U.S. Public*, pg. 57
WELLTODESK INC.—See COSYN Limited; *Int'l*, pg. 1815
WELLTOK, INC.; *U.S. Private*, pg. 4478
WELLTONIC ASIA PTE LIMITED—See Hunting Plc; *Int'l*, pg. 3537
WELLTOWER CCRC OPCO LLC—See Welltower Inc.; *U.S. Public*, pg. 2349
WELLTOWER INC.; *U.S. Public*, pg. 2347
WELL TRANSPORTATION MYANMAR CO., LTD.—See China Merchants Group Limited; *Int'l*, pg. 1522
WELL VENTURES, LLC—See Walgreens Boots Alliance, Inc.; *U.S. Public*, pg. 2324
WELMA CO., LTD.—See K&O Energy Group Inc.; *Int'l*, pg. 4038
WELOCALIZE GMBH—See Welocalize, Inc.; *U.S. Private*, pg. 4479
WELOCALIZE, INC.; *U.S. Private*, pg. 4479
WELOCALIZE IRELAND—See Welocalize, Inc.; *U.S. Private*, pg. 4479
W.E. LOVE & ASSOCIATES INC.—See XPT Group LLC; *U.S. Private*, pg. 4582
WE LOVE RUGBY PTY LIMITED—See TUI AG; *Int'l*, pg. 7969
WELPARK CO., LTD.—See AEON Co., Ltd.; *Int'l*, pg. 178
WELSBACH ELECTRIC CORP. OF LONG ISLAND—See EMCOR Group, Inc.; *U.S. Public*, pg. 737
WELSBACH ELECTRIC CORP.—See EMCOR Group, Inc.; *U.S. Public*, pg. 737
WELSBACH TECHNOLOGY METALS ACQUISITION CORP.; *U.S. Public*, pg. 2349
WELSCH HEATING & COOLING CO.; *U.S. Private*, pg. 4479
WELSCO INC.; *U.S. Private*, pg. 4479
WELSH, CARSON, ANDERSON & STOWE; *U.S. Private*, pg. 4479

WELSH COMMISSIONING GROUP, INC.—See Performance Validation, Inc.; *U.S. Private*, pg. 3150
WELSH COMPANIES LLC; *U.S. Private*, pg. 4479
WELSH CONSTRUCTION LLC—See Welsh Companies LLC; *U.S. Private*, pg. 4479
WELSH FEED PRODUCERS LIMITED—See Wynnstay Group Plc; *Int'l*, pg. 8517
WELSH PROPERTY TRUST, INC.; *U.S. Private*, pg. 4479
WELSH SLATE—See Lagan Holdings Ltd.; *Int'l*, pg. 4393
WELSPUN CORP LIMITED - PLANT II—See Welspun Group; *Int'l*, pg. 8375
WELSPUN CORP LIMITED - PLANT I—See Welspun Group; *Int'l*, pg. 8375
WELSPUN CORP. LIMITED—See Welspun Group; *Int'l*, pg. 8375
WELSPUN ENTERPRISES LIMITED—See Welspun Group; *Int'l*, pg. 8375
WELSPUN GROUP; *Int'l*, pg. 8374
WELSPUN INDIA LIMITED—See Welspun Group; *Int'l*, pg. 8375
WELSPUN INVESTMENTS & COMMERCIALS LIMITED; *Int'l*, pg. 8375
WELSPUN MIDDLE EAST PIPES COATING COMPANY LLC—See Welspun Group; *Int'l*, pg. 8375
WELSPUN RETAIL LIMITED—See Welspun Group; *Int'l*, pg. 8375
WELSPUN SPECIALITY SOLUTIONS LTD.—See Welspun Group; *Int'l*, pg. 8375
WELSPUN STEEL LIMITED - KUTCH PLANT—See Welspun Group; *Int'l*, pg. 8375
WELSPUN TUBULAR LLC—See Welspun Group; *Int'l*, pg. 8375
WELSPUN UK LIMITED—See Welspun Group; *Int'l*, pg. 8375
WELSPUN U.S.A. INC.—See Welspun Group; *Int'l*, pg. 8375
WELTBILD RETAIL GMBH & CO. KG.—See Droege Group AG; *Int'l*, pg. 2205
WELTERMAN INTERNATIONAL LIMITED; *Int'l*, pg. 8375
WELTREND SEMICONDUCTOR, INC.; *Int'l*, pg. 8375
WELTRONICS COMPONENT LIMITED—See SEMIKRON International GmbH; *Int'l*, pg. 6705
WELTRONICS CORP.; *U.S. Private*, pg. 4480
WELTY BUILDING COMPANY, LTD.; *U.S. Private*, pg. 4480
WELTY CAPITAL MANAGEMENT, LLC—See Warburg Pincus LLC; *U.S. Private*, pg. 4439
WELVIC AUSTRALIA PTY. LTD.; *Int'l*, pg. 8375
WELWYN COMPONENTS LIMITED—See TT Electronics plc; *Int'l*, pg. 7959
WEMA AMERICAS LLC—See TE Connectivity Ltd.; *Int'l*, pg. 7499
WEMA AUTOMOTIVE SYSTEM PRIVATE LIMITED—See TE Connectivity Ltd.; *Int'l*, pg. 7499
WEMA BANK PLC.; *Int'l*, pg. 8375
WEMADE CO., LTD.; *Int'l*, pg. 8375
WEMADE MAX CO., LTD; *Int'l*, pg. 8375
WEMADE PLAY CO., LTD.; *Int'l*, pg. 8375
WEMA ENVIRONMENTAL TECHNOLOGIES LTD.—See TE Connectivity Ltd.; *Int'l*, pg. 7499
WEMA ENVIRONMENTAL TECHNOLOGIES (SHANGHAI) CO., LTD.—See TE Connectivity Ltd.; *Int'l*, pg. 7499
W.E. MANIN LIMITED—See Regent Gas Holdings Limited; *Int'l*, pg. 6252
WEMAS ABSPERRTECHNIK GMBH—See Sekisui Jushi Corporation; *Int'l*, pg. 6698
WEMASS MEDIA AUDIENCE SAFE SOLUTIONS, S.L.—See Promotora de Informaciones S.A.; *Int'l*, pg. 5996
WEMA SYSTEM AG—See TE Connectivity Ltd.; *Int'l*, pg. 7499
WEMA SYSTEM AS—See TE Connectivity Ltd.; *Int'l*, pg. 7499
WEMBLEY SOCIEDADE ANONIMA; *Int'l*, pg. 8375
WEMBLY ENTERPRISES LLC; *U.S. Private*, pg. 4480
WEMCO, INC.—See Randa Corp.; *U.S. Private*, pg. 3353
WEMETRIX S.A.—See Intracom Holdings S.A.; *Int'l*, pg. 3768
WEM GMBH—See Reclay Holding GmbH; *Int'l*, pg. 6238
WEMLO, LLC—See RE/MAX Holdings, Inc.; *U.S. Public*, pg. 1768
WEMMERS CONSULTING GROUP INC.; *U.S. Private*, pg. 4480
WEMO AUTOMATION AB—See YUSHIN PRECISION EQUIPMENT CO. LTD.; *Int'l*, pg. 8617
W.E. MONKS & CO.—See TEC, Inc.; *U.S. Private*, pg. 3951
WEMS INC.; *U.S. Private*, pg. 4480
WENA FLOOR SYSTEM SP. Z O.O.—See Impel S.A.; *Int'l*, pg. 3632
WEN-ALABAMA INC; *U.S. Private*, pg. 4480
WENATCHEE PETROLEUM CO; *U.S. Private*, pg. 4480
WENCAN GROUP CO., LTD.; *Int'l*, pg. 8376
WENCO GROUP INCORPORATED—See SunSouth LLC; *U.S. Private*, pg. 3873
WENCO, INC.; *U.S. Private*, pg. 4480
WENCO INTERNATIONAL MINING SYSTEMS LTD.—See Hitachi, Ltd.; *Int'l*, pg. 3424

WENCOR GROUP, LLC—See HEICO Corporation; *U.S. Public*, pg. 1021
WENCOR, LLC—See HEICO Corporation; *U.S. Public*, pg. 1021
WENDCO CORP.; *U.S. Private*, pg. 4480
WENDCO OF PUERTO RICO INC.; *U.S. Private*, pg. 4480
WENDEL JAPAN KK—See Wendel S.A.; *Int'l*, pg. 8376
WENDELL FOSTER'S CAMPUS FOR DEVELOPMENTAL DISABILITIES; *U.S. Private*, pg. 4480
WENDELL INDUSTRIAL CO., LTD.; *Int'l*, pg. 8376
WENDELL MOTOR SALES LTD.; *Int'l*, pg. 8376
WENDEL, ROSEN, BLACK & DEAN LLP—See Fennemore Craig, P.C.; *U.S. Private*, pg. 1495
WENDEL S.A.; *Int'l*, pg. 8376
WENDELSTEINBAHN VERTEILNETZ GMBH—See RWE AG; *Int'l*, pg. 6436
WENDENG DONGYANG PISTON CO., LTD.—See Dongyang Piston Co., Ltd.; *Int'l*, pg. 2172
WENDLAND MANUFACTURING CORPORATION—See Burnham Holdings, Inc.; *U.S. Public*, pg. 412
WENDLE MOTORS INC.; *U.S. Private*, pg. 4480
WENDLER AB—See Addtech AB; *Int'l*, pg. 136
WENDLER ENGINEERING SERVICE INC.—See Willett Hofmann & Assoc Inc.; *U.S. Private*, pg. 4522
WENDOVER FINANCIAL SERVICES CORPORATION—See Veritas Capital Fund Management, LLC; *U.S. Private*, pg. 4364
WENDT GRINDING TECHNOLOGIES LIMITED—See Wendt (India) Limited; *Int'l*, pg. 8376
WENDT, INC.; *U.S. Private*, pg. 4481
WENDT (INDIA) LIMITED; *Int'l*, pg. 8376
WENDT MIDDLE EAST FZE—See Wendt (India) Limited; *Int'l*, pg. 8376
WENDT PRODUCTIONS, INC.; *U.S. Private*, pg. 4481
WENDT-SIT GMBH—See PINOVA Capital GmbH; *Int'l*, pg. 5870
WENDY'S BOWLING GREEN INC.; *U.S. Private*, pg. 4481
THE WENDY'S COMPANY; *U.S. Public*, pg. 2141
WENDY'S INTERNATIONAL, INC.—See The Wendy's Company; *U.S. Public*, pg. 2141
WENDY'S OF COLORADO SPRINGS, INC.—See WCS, Inc.; *U.S. Private*, pg. 4462
WENDY'S OF DENVER, INC.—See The Wendy's Company; *U.S. Public*, pg. 2141
WENDY'S OF LAS VEGAS, INC.—See Cedar Enterprises Inc.; *U.S. Private*, pg. 804
WENDY'S OF MISSOURI INC.; *U.S. Private*, pg. 4481
WENDY'S OF MONTANA INC.; *U.S. Private*, pg. 4481
WENDY'S OF N.E. FLORIDA, INC.—See The Wendy's Company; *U.S. Public*, pg. 2141
WENDY'S OF SAN ANTONIO, INC.—See Cedar Enterprises Inc.; *U.S. Private*, pg. 804
WENDY'S OLD FASHIONED HAMBURGERS OF NEW YORK, INC.—See The Wendy's Company; *U.S. Public*, pg. 2141
WENDY'S RESTAURANTS OF CANADA, INC.—See The Wendy's Company; *U.S. Public*, pg. 2141
WENDY'S RESTAURANTS OF ROCHESTER, INC.; *U.S. Private*, pg. 4481
WENDY'S RESTAURANTS—See The Wendy's Company; *U.S. Public*, pg. 2141
WENDY WEIHE STORLIE, INC.; *U.S. Private*, pg. 4481
WENFENG GREAT WORLD CHAIN DEVELOPMENT CORPORATION; *Int'l*, pg. 8376
WENGER CORPORATION; *U.S. Private*, pg. 4481
WENGER MANUFACTURING INC.—See Marel hf; *Int'l*, pg. 4691
WENGER OIL INC.; *U.S. Private*, pg. 4481
WENGERS FARM MACHINERY INC.; *U.S. Private*, pg. 4481
WENGER'S FEED MILL INC.; *U.S. Private*, pg. 4481
WENG FINE ART AG; *Int'l*, pg. 8377
WENG LI SDN. BHD.—See Eu Yan Sang International Ltd.; *Int'l*, pg. 2525
WENGLON SP. Z O.O.—See Ensinger GmbH; *Int'l*, pg. 2448
WENGO SAS—See Vivendi SE; *Int'l*, pg. 8278
WENLING ZHEJIANG MEASURING & CUTTING TOOLS TRADING CENTRE COMPANY LIMITED; *Int'l*, pg. 8377
WENNER BREAD PRODUCTS, INC.—See Europastry, S.A.; *Int'l*, pg. 2555
WENNER MEDIA LLC—See Penske Media Corporation; *U.S. Private*, pg. 3139
WENNERSTROM LJUSKONTROLL AB—See Indutrade AB; *Int'l*, pg. 3682
WENNSOFT INC.—See Constellation Software Inc.; *Int'l*, pg. 1776
WENSCO MICHIGAN CORPORATION; *U.S. Private*, pg. 4481
WENS FOODSTUFF GROUP CO., LTD.; *Int'l*, pg. 8377
WENSHAN TOP NATION ELECTRONIC LIMITED—See Yao Sheng Electronics Co., Ltd.; *Int'l*, pg. 8566
WENSLEY ROOFING LIMITED—See Northern Bear Plc; *Int'l*, pg. 5443
WENSTROM COMMUNICATIONS, INC.; *U.S. Private*, pg. 4481
WENTE VINEYARDS; *U.S. Private*, pg. 4481
WENTO SP. Z O.O.—See Equinor ASA; *Int'l*, pg. 2485

WEN TRADING CO., LTD.—See Chugoku Marine Paints, Ltd.; *Int'l*, pg. 1595
WENTRONIC ASIA PACIFIC LTD.—See Wentronic Holding GmbH; *Int'l*, pg. 8377
WENTRONIC GMBH—See Wentronic Holding GmbH; *Int'l*, pg. 8377
WENTRONIC HOLDING GMBH; *Int'l*, pg. 8377
WENTRONIC ITALIA S.R.L.—See Wentronic Holding GmbH; *Int'l*, pg. 8377
WENTRONIC UK LTD.—See Wentronic Holding GmbH; *Int'l*, pg. 8377
WENTWORTH CORPORATION—See Chatham Asset Management, LLC; *U.S. Private*, pg. 863
WENTWORTH FINANCIAL PARTNERS, LLC; *U.S. Private*, pg. 4481
WENTWORTH GALLERY HOLDINGS INC.; *U.S. Private*, pg. 4481
WENTWORTH HOLDINGS; *U.S. Private*, pg. 4481
WENTWORTH INSURANCE COMPANY LTD.—See Fairfax Financial Holdings Limited; *Int'l*, pg. 2608
WENTWORTH MANAGEMENT SERVICES LLC; *U.S. Private*, pg. 4481
WENTWORTH MOLD INC.—See Wentworth Technologies Co. Ltd.; *Int'l*, pg. 8377
WENTWORTH MOLD LIMITED—See Wentworth Technologies Co. Ltd.; *Int'l*, pg. 8377
WENTWORTH PRINTING CORPORATION—See Chatham Asset Management, LLC; *U.S. Private*, pg. 863
WENTWORTH RESEARCH LIMITED—See Gartner, Inc.; *U.S. Public*, pg. 907
WENTWORTH RESOURCES LIMITED; *Int'l*, pg. 8377
WENTWORTH RESOURCES LIMITED—See Wentworth Resources Limited; *Int'l*, pg. 8377
WENTWORTH RESOURCES PLC—See PT Pertamina (Persero); *Int'l*, pg. 6063
WENTWORTH TECH CENTRAL SP. Z O.O.—See Wentworth Technologies Co. Ltd.; *Int'l*, pg. 8377
WENTWORTH TECHNOLOGIES CO. LTD.; *Int'l*, pg. 8377
WENTWORTH TECH SP. Z O.O.—See Wentworth Technologies Co. Ltd.; *Int'l*, pg. 8377
WENTWORTH TIRE SERVICE INC.; *U.S. Private*, pg. 4481
WENTZ GROUP INC.; *U.S. Private*, pg. 4481
WENWORTH HOTEL (K.L.) SDN. BHD.—See Selangor Properties Berhad; *Int'l*, pg. 6699
WENYE GROUP HOLDINGS LIMITED; *Int'l*, pg. 8377
WENZEL ASSOCIATES, INC.—See Arcline Investment Management LP; *U.S. Private*, pg. 313
WENZEL DOWNHOLE TOOLS EUROPE GMBH—See J Fitzgibbons LLC; *U.S. Private*, pg. 2153
WENZEL DOWNHOLE TOOLS LTD.—See J Fitzgibbons LLC; *U.S. Private*, pg. 2153
WENZEL DOWNHOLE TOOLS, U.S., INC.—See J Fitzgibbons LLC; *U.S. Private*, pg. 2153
WENZEL INTERNATIONAL INC.—See Arcline Investment Management LP; *U.S. Private*, pg. 313
WENZEL METAL SPINNING INC.; *U.S. Private*, pg. 4481
WENZHOU BAOZEN AUTOMOBILE SALES AND SERVICES CO., LTD.—See China Yongda Automobiles Services Holdings Limited; *Int'l*, pg. 1565
WENZHOU FOCUSEE VISION CARE TECHNOLOGIES CO., LTD.—See Menicon Co., Ltd.; *Int'l*, pg. 4816
WENZHOU HONGFENG ALLOY CO. LTD.—See Wenzhou Hongfeng Electrical Alloy Co., Ltd.; *Int'l*, pg. 8377
WENZHOU HONGFENG ELECTRICAL ALLOY CO., LTD.; *Int'l*, pg. 8377
WENZHOU HONGFENG METAL-MATRIX ENGINEERED COMPOSITE MATERIAL CO., LTD.—See Wenzhou Hongfeng Electrical Alloy Co., Ltd.; *Int'l*, pg. 8377
WENZHOU HONGFENG SPECIAL MATERIAL CO., LTD.—See Wenzhou Hongfeng Electrical Alloy Co., Ltd.; *Int'l*, pg. 8377
WENZHOU KANGNING HOSPITAL CO., LTD.; *Int'l*, pg. 8377
WENZHOU KEBODA AUTO PARTS CO., LTD.—See Keboda Technology Co., Ltd.; *Int'l*, pg. 4113
WENZHOU KINDLY MEDICAL DEVICES CO., LTD—See Shanghai Kindly Enterprise Development Group Co., Ltd; *Int'l*, pg. 6774
WENZHOU POLY GRAND THEATRE MANAGEMENT CORPORATION LIMITED—See Poly Culture Group Corporation Limited; *Int'l*, pg. 5914
WENZHOU YIHUA CONNECTOR CO., LTD.; *Int'l*, pg. 8378
WENZHOU YINING GERIATRIC HOSPITAL CO., LTD.—See Wenzhou Kangning Hospital Co., Ltd.; *Int'l*, pg. 8378
WENZHOU YONGDA LUJIE AUTOMOBILE SALES AND SERVICES CO., LTD.—See China Yongda Automobiles Services Holdings Limited; *Int'l*, pg. 1565
WENZHOU YUANFEI PET TOYS PRODUCTS CO., LTD.; *Int'l*, pg. 8378
W.E. O'NEIL CONSTRUCTION COMPANY OF ARIZONA—See O'Neil Industries Inc.; *U.S. Private*, pg. 2980
W.E. O'NEIL CONSTRUCTION COMPANY—See O'Neil Industries Inc.; *U.S. Private*, pg. 2980

W.E. O'NEIL CONSTRUCTION CO. OF CALIFORNIA—See O'Neil Industries Inc.; *U.S. Private*, pg. 2979
W.E. O'NEIL CONSTRUCTION CO. OF COLORADO—See O'Neil Industries Inc.; *U.S. Private*, pg. 2979
W.E. O'NEIL CONSTRUCTION—See O'Neil Industries Inc.; *U.S. Private*, pg. 2979
WEPA HYGIENEPRODUKTE GMBH & CO. KG; *Int'l*, pg. 8378
WEPA ITALIA S.R.L.—See WEPA Hygieneprodukte GmbH & Co. KG; *Int'l*, pg. 8378
WEPA LEUNA GMBH—See WEPA Hygieneprodukte GmbH & Co. KG; *Int'l*, pg. 8378
WEPA PAPIERFABRIK SACHSEN GMBH—See WEPA Hygieneprodukte GmbH & Co. KG; *Int'l*, pg. 8378
WEPA TROYES SAS—See WEPA Hygieneprodukte GmbH & Co. KG; *Int'l*, pg. 8378
WEPAY, INC.—See JPMorgan Chase & Co.; *U.S. Public*, pg. 1206
WEP DIGITAL SERVICES LIMITED—See WEP Solutions Ltd.; *Int'l*, pg. 8378
WEPN-FM—See Emmis Communications Corporation; *U.S. Public*, pg. 753
WEPOST S.R.L.—See Iervolino & Lady Bacardi Entertainment S.p.A.; *Int'l*, pg. 3597
WEPROMOTE ENTERTAINMENT GROUP SWITZERLAND AG—See CTS Eventim AG & Co. KGAA; *Int'l*, pg. 1874
WEP SOLUTIONS LTD.; *Int'l*, pg. 8378
WEQAYA TAKAFUL INSURANCE & REINSURANCE COMPANY; *Int'l*, pg. 8378
WEQ DEERFOOT RENTALS LP—See WesternOne Inc.; *Int'l*, pg. 8390
WEQ HEAT & PROPANE LP.—See WesternOne Inc.; *Int'l*, pg. 8390
WEQ PRODUCTION EQUIPMENT LP—See WesternOne Inc.; *Int'l*, pg. 8390
THE WERCS, LTD.—See Underwriters Laboratories Inc.; *U.S. Private*, pg. 4280
WERELDHAVE BELGIUM S.C.A.—See Wereldhave N.V.; *Int'l*, pg. 8378
WERELDHAVE DEVELOPMENT B.V.—See Wereldhave N.V.; *Int'l*, pg. 8378
WERELDHAVE FINLAND OY—See Wereldhave N.V.; *Int'l*, pg. 8378
WERELDHAVE MANAGEMENT HOLDING B.V.—See Wereldhave N.V.; *Int'l*, pg. 8378
WERELDHAVE MANAGEMENT SPAIN S.L.—See Wereldhave N.V.; *Int'l*, pg. 8378
WERELDHAVE MANAGEMENT USA, INC.—See Wereldhave N.V.; *Int'l*, pg. 8378
WERELDHAVE NEDERLAND B.V.—See Wereldhave N.V.; *Int'l*, pg. 8378
WERELDHAVE N.V.; *Int'l*, pg. 8378
WERELDHAVE PROPERTY MANAGEMENT CO. LTD.—See Wereldhave N.V.; *Int'l*, pg. 8378
WERELDHAVE U.K. HOLDINGS LTD.—See Wereldhave N.V.; *Int'l*, pg. 8378
WE RETAIL PUBLIC COMPANY LIMITED—See Property Perfect Public Company Limited; *Int'l*, pg. 5998
WEREWOLF THERAPEUTICS, INC.; *U.S. Public*, pg. 2349
WERFEN AUSTRALIA PTY LIMITED—See Werfen Life Group, S.A.U.; *Int'l*, pg. 8379
WERFEN CZECH S.R.O—See Werfen Life Group, S.A.U.; *Int'l*, pg. 8379
WERFEN HONG KONG LIMITED—See Werfen Life Group, S.A.U.; *Int'l*, pg. 8379
WERFEN HUNGARY KFT.—See Werfen Life Group, S.A.U.; *Int'l*, pg. 8379
WERFEN/ INSTRUMENTATION LABORATORY PVT LTD.—See Werfen Life Group, S.A.U.; *Int'l*, pg. 8379
WERFEN LIFE GROUP, S.A.U.; *Int'l*, pg. 8378
WERFEN LIMITED—See Werfen Life Group, S.A.U.; *Int'l*, pg. 8379
WERFEN MEDICALDEVICE TRADING (BEIJING) CO., LTD—See Werfen Life Group, S.A.U.; *Int'l*, pg. 8379
WERFEN MEDICAL IL, LTD.—See Werfen Life Group, S.A.U.; *Int'l*, pg. 8379
WERFEN MEDICAL INTERNATIONAL TRADING (SHANGHAI) CO., LTD—See Werfen Life Group, S.A.U.; *Int'l*, pg. 8379
WERGA-TOOLS GMBH—See Fiskars Oyj Abp; *Int'l*, pg. 2694
WERHAHN MUHLEN GMBH & CO. KG—See Wilh. Werhahn KG; *Int'l*, pg. 8410
WERHANE ENTERPRISES LTD.; *U.S. Private*, pg. 4481
WERK EN VAKMANSCHAP; *Int'l*, pg. 8379
WERKLUND CAPITAL CORPORATION; *Int'l*, pg. 8379
WERKLUND FOUNDATION—See Werklund Capital Corporation; *Int'l*, pg. 8379
WERKSGARTNEREI GESELLSCHAFT M.B.H.—See voestalpine AG; *Int'l*, pg. 8295
WERKSPOT BV—See IAC Inc.; *U.S. Public*, pg. 1082
WERKSTOFFPRUFUNG PETERS GMBH—See DEKRA e.V.; *Int'l*, pg. 2010
WERKZEUGBAU LAICHINGEN GMBH—See Gesco AG; *Int'l*, pg. 2946

WERKZEUGBAU LEIPZIG GMBH—See Gesco AG; *Int'l*, pg. 2946
WERKZEUGBAU WALLDURN GMBH—See Rheinmetall AG; *Int'l*, pg. 6324
WERKZEUGTECHNIK NIEDERSTETTEN GMBH & CO. KG—See Wurth Verwaltungsgesellschaft mbH; *Int'l*, pg. 8509
WER LIEFERT WAS GMBH—See Capvis AG; *Int'l*, pg. 1318
WERMERS CORPORATION; *U.S. Private*, pg. 4481
WERNER AERO SERVICES, LLC.—See Sumitomo Corporation; *Int'l*, pg. 7274
WERNER CONSTRUCTION INC.; *U.S. Private*, pg. 4481
WERNER CO.—See Triton Advisers Limited; *Int'l*, pg. 7935
WERNER CYCLE WORKS, INC.—See Werner Enterprises, Inc.; *U.S. Public*, pg. 2349
WERNER ELECTRIC SUPPLY COMPANY; *U.S. Private*, pg. 4482
WERNER ELECTRIC SUPPLY COMPANY—See Van Meter Inc.; *U.S. Private*, pg. 4340
WERNER ELECTRIC SUPPLY COMPANY—See Werner Electric Supply Company; *U.S. Private*, pg. 4482
WERNER ELECTRO AG—See BKW AG; *Int'l*, pg. 1056
WERNER ENTERPRISES CANADA CORPORATION—See Werner Enterprises, Inc.; *U.S. Public*, pg. 2349
WERNER ENTERPRISES, INC.; *U.S. Public*, pg. 2349
WERNER GLOBAL LOGISTICS AUSTRALIA PTY. LTD—See Werner Enterprises, Inc.; *U.S. Public*, pg. 2349
WERNER GLOBAL LOGISTICS (SHANGHAI) CO., LTD.—See Werner Enterprises, Inc.; *U.S. Public*, pg. 2349
WERNER KUSTER AG—See Beijer Ref AB; *Int'l*, pg. 945
WERNER SCHMITT PKD-WERKZEUG GMBH—See Sandvik AB; *Int'l*, pg. 6535
WERNERS GOURMETSERVICE AB—See Orkla ASA; *Int'l*, pg. 5639
WERNER SODERSTROM OSAKEYHTION—See Bonnier AB; *Int'l*, pg. 1108
WERNERSSON OST AB—See TINE SA; *Int'l*, pg. 7753
WERNERSSON OST DANMARK AS—See TINE SA; *Int'l*, pg. 7753
WERNER WEITNER GMBH; *Int'l*, pg. 8379
WERNER WILHELM GMBH; *Int'l*, pg. 8379
WERRES CORPORATION; *U.S. Private*, pg. 4482
WERRIBEE PLAZA TAVERN PTY. LTD.—See Woolworths Group Limited; *Int'l*, pg. 8452
WERRIBEE ZOOLOGICAL PARK—See Zoological Parks and Gardens Board; *Int'l*, pg. 8689
WERRIS CREEK COAL PTY LTD.—See Whitehaven Coal Limited; *Int'l*, pg. 8400
WERTBAU GMBH—See Arbonia AG; *Int'l*, pg. 538
WERTHAN; *U.S. Private*, pg. 4482
WERTHENSTEIN BIOPHARMA GMBH—See Merck & Co., Inc.; *U.S. Public*, pg. 1416
WERTS WELDING & TANK SERVICE; *U.S. Private*, pg. 4482
WERTZ YORK CAPITAL MANAGEMENT GROUP LLC; *U.S. Private*, pg. 4482
WERU GMBH—See VKR Holding A/S; *Int'l*, pg. 8282
W.E. SALMON INC.; *U.S. Private*, pg. 4420
WESATECH—See BluMetric Environmental Inc.; *Int'l*, pg. 1075
WESBANCO BANK, INC.—See WesBanco, Inc.; *U.S. Public*, pg. 2349
WESBANCO BANK, INC. - WESTERN PENNSYLVANIA REGIONAL OFFICE—See WesBanco, Inc.; *U.S. Public*, pg. 2350
WESBANCO, INC.; *U.S. Public*, pg. 2349
WESBANCO INSURANCE SERVICES, INC.—See WesBanco, Inc.; *U.S. Public*, pg. 2350
WESBANCO SECURITIES, INC.—See WesBanco, Inc.; *U.S. Public*, pg. 2350
WESBANCO TITLE AGENCY, LLC—See WesBanco, Inc.; *U.S. Public*, pg. 2350
WESBANK—See FirstRand Limited; *Int'l*, pg. 2690
WESBRIDGE CONSTRUCTION LIMITED; *Int'l*, pg. 8379
WESCAM INC.—See L3Harris Technologies, Inc.; *U.S. Public*, pg. 1284
WESCAN ENERGY CORP.; *Int'l*, pg. 8379
WESCAN GOLDFIELDS INC.; *Int'l*, pg. 8380
WESCAST HUNGARY AUTOIPARI ZRT.—See Wescast Industries Inc.; *Int'l*, pg. 8380
WESCAST INDUSTRIES (CHINA) CO., LTD.—See Wescast Industries Inc.; *Int'l*, pg. 8380
WESCAST INDUSTRIES GMBH—See Wescast Industries Inc.; *Int'l*, pg. 8380
WESCAST INDUSTRIES INC. - BRANTFORD MACHINING—See Wescast Industries Inc.; *Int'l*, pg. 8380
WESCAST INDUSTRIES INC.; *Int'l*, pg. 8380
WESCAST INDUSTRIES INC. - STRATFORD MAGALLOY—See Wescast Industries Inc.; *Int'l*, pg. 8380
WESCAST INDUSTRIES INC. - STRATHROY MACHINING—See Wescast Industries Inc.; *Int'l*, pg. 8380

COMPANY NAME INDEX

WESCAST INDUSTRIES INC. - WINGHAM CASTING—See Wescast Industries Inc.; *Int'l*, pg. 8380
WESCAST JAPAN, K.K—See Wescast Industries Inc.; *Int'l*, pg. 8380
WESCO ABU DHABI—See The Weir Group PLC; *Int'l*, pg. 7699
WESCO AIRCRAFT CANADA INC.—See Platinum Equity, LLC; *U.S. Private*, pg. 3210
WESCO AIRCRAFT EUROPE, LTD—See Platinum Equity, LLC; *U.S. Private*, pg. 3210
WESCO AIRCRAFT FRANCE SAS—See Platinum Equity, LLC; *U.S. Private*, pg. 3210
WESCO AIRCRAFT GERMANY GMBH—See Platinum Equity, LLC; *U.S. Private*, pg. 3210
WESCO AIRCRAFT HARDWARE CORP. - ELECTRICAL PRODUCTS GROUP—See Platinum Equity, LLC; *U.S. Private*, pg. 3210
WESCO AIRCRAFT HARDWARE CORP.—See Platinum Equity, LLC; *U.S. Private*, pg. 3210
WESCO AIRCRAFT HOLDINGS, INC.—See Platinum Equity, LLC; *U.S. Private*, pg. 3209
WESCO AIRCRAFT ITALY SRL—See Platinum Equity, LLC; *U.S. Private*, pg. 3210
WESCOAL MINING (PTY) LTD—See Salungano Group; *Int'l*, pg. 6495
WESCO - ANIXTER ISRAEL LTD.—See WESCO International, Inc.; *U.S. Public*, pg. 2351
WESCO ANIXTER USVI, LLC—See WESCO International, Inc.; *U.S. Public*, pg. 2352
WESCO DISTRIBUTION CANADA LP—See WESCO International, Inc.; *U.S. Public*, pg. 2351
WESCO DISTRIBUTION INC. - MIDLOTHIAN—See WESCO International, Inc.; *U.S. Public*, pg. 2352
WESCO DISTRIBUTION, INC.—See WESCO International, Inc.; *U.S. Public*, pg. 2352
WESCO DISTRIBUTION, INC.—See WESCO International, Inc.; *U.S. Public*, pg. 2351
WESCO DUBAI—See The Weir Group PLC; *Int'l*, pg. 7700
WESCO EQUITY CORPORATION—See WESCO International, Inc.; *U.S. Public*, pg. 2352
WESCO FOUNTAINS, INC.; *U.S. Private*, pg. 4482
WESCO GAS & WELDING SUPPLY INC.; *U.S. Private*, pg. 4482
WESCO GROUP, INC.; *U.S. Private*, pg. 4482
WESCO HOLDINGS INC.; *Int'l*, pg. 8380
WESCO INTEGRATED SUPPLY, INC.—See Nautic Partners, LLC; *U.S. Private*, pg. 2872
WESCO INTERNATIONAL, INC.; *U.S. Public*, pg. 2350
WESCO MANUFACTURED STRUCTURES-MERIDIAN—See WESCO International, Inc.; *U.S. Public*, pg. 2352
WESCOM CREDIT UNION; *U.S. Private*, pg. 4482
WESCON CONTROLS, LLC—See Suprajit Engineering Limited; *Int'l*, pg. 7340
WESCON CORP OF CONN.—See J.H. Lynch & Sons Inc.; *U.S. Private*, pg. 2166
WESCO NEVADA, LTD.—See WESCO International, Inc.; *U.S. Public*, pg. 2352
WESCO SERVICES, LLC—See WESCO International, Inc.; *U.S. Public*, pg. 2352
WESCOSVILLE AUTO SALES, INC.; *U.S. Private*, pg. 4482
WESCOT CREDIT SERVICES LIMITED—See Encore Capital Group, Inc.; *U.S. Public*, pg. 760
WESCOTT FINANCIAL ADVISORY GROUP LLC; *U.S. Private*, pg. 4482
WESCOT TOPCO LIMITED—See Encore Capital Group, Inc.; *U.S. Public*, pg. 760
WESDOME GOLD MINES LTD.; *Int'l*, pg. 8380
WESDYNE INTERNATIONAL, INC.—See Brookfield Corporation; *Int'l*, pg. 1186
WE SELL CELLULAR, INC., *U.S. Private*, pg. 4462
WESER-METALL-UMFORMTECHNIK BAVARIA GMBH—See Sungwoo Hitech Co., Ltd.; *Int'l*, pg. 7315
WESER-METALL-UMFORMTECHNIK GMBH—See Sungwoo Hitech Co., Ltd.; *Int'l*, pg. 7315
WESERNETZ BREMEN GMBH—See EWE Aktiengesellschaft; *Int'l*, pg. 2576
WESERNETZ BREMERHAVEN GMBH—See EWE Aktiengesellschaft; *Int'l*, pg. 2576
WESERWIND GMBH OFFSHORE CONSTRUCTION GEORGSMARIENHUTTE—See Georgsmarienhutte Holding GmbH; *Int'l*, pg. 2940
WESERWIND UK LTD.—See Georgsmarienhutte Holding GmbH; *Int'l*, pg. 2940
WESFAL PTY LIMITED—See Nutrien Ltd.; *Int'l*, pg. 5493
WESFAM RESTAURANTS INC.; *U.S. Private*, pg. 4482
WESFARMERS BUNNINGS LIMITED—See Wesfarmers Limited; *Int'l*, pg. 8382
WESFARMERS CHEMICALS, ENERGY & FERTILISERS—See Wesfarmers Limited; *Int'l*, pg. 8382
WESFARMERS COAL RESOURCES PTY LTD—See Wesfarmers Limited; *Int'l*, pg. 8382
WESFARMERS CURRAGH PTY LTD—See Wesfarmers Limited; *Int'l*, pg. 8382
WESFARMERS ENERGY (GAS SALES) LIMITED—See Wesfarmers Limited; *Int'l*, pg. 8382
WESFARMERS INDUSTRIAL AND SAFETY PTY LTD—See Wesfarmers Limited; *Int'l*, pg. 8382
WESFARMERS INDUSTRIAL & SAFETY HOLDINGS NZ LIMITED—See Wesfarmers Limited; *Int'l*, pg. 8382
WESFARMERS INDUSTRIAL & SAFETY NZ LIMITED—See Wesfarmers Limited; *Int'l*, pg. 8382
WESFARMERS INSURANCE INVESTMENTS PTY. LTD.—See Wesfarmers Limited; *Int'l*, pg. 8382
WESFARMERS KLEENHEAT GAS PTY. LTD.—See Wesfarmers Limited; *Int'l*, pg. 8382
WESFARMERS LIMITED; *Int'l*, pg. 8380
WESFARMERS LNG PTY LTD—See Wesfarmers Limited; *Int'l*, pg. 8382
WESFARMERS LPG PTY. LTD.—See Wesfarmers Limited; *Int'l*, pg. 8382
WESFARMERS RESOURCES LIMITED—See Wesfarmers Limited; *Int'l*, pg. 8382
WESFARMERS RETAIL PTY LTD—See Wesfarmers Limited; *Int'l*, pg. 8382
WESFARMERS SECURITIES MANAGEMENT PTY LTD—See Wesfarmers Limited; *Int'l*, pg. 8382
WESFIL AUSTRALIA PTY. LTD.—See Amotiv Limited; *Int'l*, pg. 431
WES FINCH AUTO PLAZA INC.; *U.S. Private*, pg. 4482
WES-GARDE COMPONENTS GROUP INC.; *U.S. Private*, pg. 4482
WESGAR INC.; *Int'l*, pg. 8382
WESGO CERAMICS DIV—See Morgan Advanced Materials plc; *Int'l*, pg. 5043
WESGO CERAMICS GMBH—See Morgan Advanced Materials plc; *Int'l*, pg. 5043
WESIZWE PLATINUM LIMITED; *Int'l*, pg. 8382
WESKO INDUSTRIES, INC.—See Kinplex Corp.; *U.S. Private*, pg. 2313
WESLACO REGIONAL REHABILITATION HOSPITAL, LLC—See Ernest Health, Inc.; *U.S. Private*, pg. 1421
WES LASHER INC.—See Wesley B. Lasher Investment Corp.; *U.S. Private*, pg. 4482
WESLEY ALLEN INC.; *U.S. Private*, pg. 4482
WESLEY B. LASHER INVESTMENT CORP.; *U.S. Private*, pg. 4482
WESLEY CHAPEL ANUSA, LLC—See AutoNation, Inc.; *U.S. Public*, pg. 238
WESLEY CHAPEL-C, LLC—See Lithia Motors, Inc.; *U.S. Public*, pg. 1326
WESLEY CHAPEL DIALYSIS, LLC—See DaVita Inc.; *U.S. Public*, pg. 644
WESLEY CHAPEL-HY, LLC—See Lithia Motors, Inc.; *U.S. Public*, pg. 1326
WESLEY CHAPEL-M, LLC—See Lithia Motors, Inc.; *U.S. Public*, pg. 1326
WESLEY CHAPEL-MOTO, LLC—See Lithia Motors, Inc.; *U.S. Public*, pg. 1326
WESLEY COLLEGE, INC.—See Delaware State University; *U.S. Private*, pg. 1195
WESLEY COMMUNITY SERVICES; *U.S. Private*, pg. 4482
WESLEY DAY & COMPANY, INC.; *U.S. Private*, pg. 4482
WESLEY GARDENS; *U.S. Private*, pg. 4483
WESLEY HEALTH SYSTEM, LLC—See Community Health Systems, Inc.; *U.S. Public*, pg. 557
WESLEY MEDICAL CENTER, LLC—See HCA Healthcare, Inc.; *U.S. Public*, pg. 1013
WESLEY SPECTRUM SERVICES; *U.S. Private*, pg. 4483
WESMAN SIMPSON TECHNOLOGIES PVT. LTD.—See Altor Equity Partners AB; *Int'l*, pg. 395
WESMOR CRYOGENIC LLC—See Trinity Industries, Inc.; *U.S. Public*, pg. 2194
WES OMEGA SINTO FOUNDRY MACHINERY PTY. LTD.—See Sintokogio Ltd.; *Int'l*, pg. 6959
W&E SOURCE CORP.; *U.S. Public*, pg. 2315
WESSCO INTERNATIONAL LTD.; *U.S. Private*, pg. 4483
WESSCO, LLC—See Nucor Corporation; *U.S. Public*, pg. 1554
WESSELN CONSTRUCTION CO., INC.; *U.S. Private*, pg. 4483
WESSELS COMPANY; *U.S. Private*, pg. 4483
WESSELS OIL CO., INC.; *U.S. Private*, pg. 4483
WESSEX ADVANCED SWITCHING PRODUCTS LIMITED—See RTX Corporation; *U.S. Public*, pg. 1822
WESSEX GARAGES HOLDINGS LIMITED—See VT Holdings Co., Ltd.; *Int'l*, pg. 8315
WESSEX GARRAGES HOLDING LIMITED—See VT Holdings Co., Ltd.; *Int'l*, pg. 8315
THE WESSEX NUFFIELD HOSPITAL—See Nuffield Health; *Int'l*, pg. 5488
WESSEX SERVICE CO., INC.—See Kidder Matthew, LLC; *U.S. Private*, pg. 2303
WESSIN TRANSPORT INC.; *U.S. Private*, pg. 4483
WESSON, INC.; *U.S. Private*, pg. 4483
WEST ACRES DEVELOPMENT, LLP—See The Macerich Company; *U.S. Public*, pg. 2111
WESTAD INDUSTRI A/S—See Valco Group AS; *Int'l*, pg. 8111
WEST ADVERTISING/PUBLIC RELATIONS, INC.—See KOA Holdings Inc.; *U.S. Private*, pg. 2325
WEST ADVERTISING; *U.S. Private*, pg. 4483
WESTAFF (AUSTRALIA) PTY. LTD.—See Bluestone Global Limited; *Int'l*, pg. 1075
WESTAFF NZ LIMITED—See Bluestone Global Limited; *Int'l*, pg. 1075
WESTAFLEX BATIMENT S.A.S.—See Poujoulat SA; *Int'l*, pg. 5942
WEST AFRICA CONTAINER TERMINAL NIGERIA LTD.—See A.P. Moller-Maersk A/S; *Int'l*, pg. 28
WEST AFRICAN RESOURCES LIMITED; *Int'l*, pg. 8383
WEST AFRICAN SEASONING CO., LTD.—See Ajinomoto Company, Inc.; *Int'l*, pg. 257
WESTAG AG; *Int'l*, pg. 8386
THE WESTAIM CORPORATION; *Int'l*, pg. 7701
WEST AIR CO., LTD.—See Hainan Traffic Administration Holding Co., Ltd.; *Int'l*, pg. 3216
WESTAIR CRYOGENICS COMPANY—See Linde plc; *Int'l*, pg. 4510
WESTAIR GAS & EQUIPMENT LP; *U.S. Private*, pg. 4488
WESTAK, INC.; *U.S. Private*, pg. 4488
WESTAK INTERNATIONAL SALES INC.—See Westak, Inc.; *U.S. Private*, pg. 4488
WESTAK OF OREGON INC.—See Westak, Inc.; *U.S. Private*, pg. 4488
WEST ALABAMA BANK & TRUST; *U.S. Private*, pg. 4483
WEST ALABAMA COCA-COLA BOTTLING COMPANY—See Coca-Cola Bottling Co. United, Inc.; *U.S. Private*, pg. 959
WEST ALLIS-T, INC.—See Lithia Motors, Inc.; *U.S. Public*, pg. 1326
WESTAMERICA BANCORPORATION; *U.S. Public*, pg. 2354
WESTAMERICA BANK—See Westamerica Bancorporation; *U.S. Public*, pg. 2354
WEST AMERICAN RUBBER CO., LLC; *U.S. Private*, pg. 4483
WEST AMERICAN RUBBER CO., LLC; *U.S. Private*, pg. 4483
WEST ANALYTICAL SERVICES, LLC—See West Pharmaceutical Services, Inc.; *U.S. Public*, pg. 2353
WESTAR AEROSPACE & DEFENSE GROUP, INC.—See QinetiQ Group plc; *Int'l*, pg. 6142
WESTAR CONTRACT KITCHEN & BATH CORP.; *U.S. Private*, pg. 4488
WESTAR DISPLAY TECHNOLOGIES, INC.—See QinetiQ Group plc; *Int'l*, pg. 6142
WESTAR DISTRIBUTION, LLC.; *U.S. Private*, pg. 4488
WESTAR INDUSTRIES, INC.—See Evergy, Inc.; *U.S. Public*, pg. 801
WEST ARK OIL COMPANY—See Chapman Inc.; *U.S. Private*, pg. 849
WESTAR NUTRITION CORP.; *U.S. Private*, pg. 4488
WESTAR OILFIELD RENTALS, INC.—See Enterprise Group, Inc.; *Int'l*, pg. 2451
WESTAR RESOURCES LIMITED; *Int'l*, pg. 8386
WESTAR ROOFING CORPORATION; *U.S. Private*, pg. 4488
WEST ASIA FOR LIGHTINGS NVC LLC—See NVC International Holdings Limited; *Int'l*, pg. 5498
WEST ASSET MANAGEMENT; *U.S. Private*, pg. 4483
WEST-ATANTIC PARTNERS LLC; *U.S. Private*, pg. 4488
WEST BANCORPORATION INC.; *U.S. Public*, pg. 2352
WESTBANK CORPORATION INC.—See Daybrook Holdings Inc.; *U.S. Private*, pg. 1177
WEST BANK—See West Bancorporation Inc.; *U.S. Public*, pg. 2352
WEST BANK SURGERY CENTER, LLC—See KKR & Co. Inc.; *U.S. Public*, pg. 1249
WESTBAY AUTO PARTS INC.; *U.S. Private*, pg. 4488
WEST BAY FOREST PRODUCTS LTD.; *Int'l*, pg. 8383
WEST BAY LANDSCAPE, INC.—See BrightView Holdings, Inc.; *U.S. Public*, pg. 384
WEST BAY OF TAMPA—See Formation Capital, LLC; *U.S. Private*, pg. 1571
WEST BAY RESIDENTIAL SERVICES, INC.; *U.S. Private*, pg. 4483
WEST BEND BROADCASTING CO., INC.—See Adams Publishing Group, LLC; *U.S. Private*, pg. 74
WEST BEND MUTUAL INSURANCE COMPANY INC.; *U.S. Private*, pg. 4483
WEST BENGAL STATE ELECTRICITY TRANSMISSION COMPANY LIMITED; *Int'l*, pg. 8383
WESTBIT AB—See BP plc; *Int'l*, pg. 1128
WEST BLOOMFIELD DIALYSIS, LLC—See DaVita Inc.; *U.S. Public*, pg. 644
WEST BOCA MEDICAL CENTER, INC.—See Tenet Healthcare Corporation; *U.S. Public*, pg. 2004
WESTBODEN-BAU- UND VERWALTUNGSGESELLSCHAFT MBH—See Commerzbank AG; *Int'l*, pg. 1719
WESTBOND ENTERPRISES CORPORATION; *Int'l*, pg. 8387
WEST BOND INC.; *U.S. Private*, pg. 4483
WESTBOND INDUSTRIES INC.—See WestBond Enterprises Corporation; *Int'l*, pg. 8387
WESTBORN CHRYSLER JEEP, INC.; *U.S. Private*, pg. 4488
WESTBORN SERVICE CENTER, INC.—See Cooper-Standard Holdings Inc.; *U.S. Public*, pg. 574
WESTBORO AUTO IMPORTS LTD; *Int'l*, pg. 8387
WESTBORO FLOORING AND DECOR; *Int'l*, pg. 8387

WESTBORO FLOORING AND DECOR

CORPORATE AFFILIATIONS

WESTBOROUGH NEWS—See Gannett Co., Inc.; *U.S. Public*, pg. 903
WESTBOUND COMMUNICATIONS, INC.; *U.S. Private*, pg. 4488
WEST BOYNTON BEACH OPEN IMAGING CENTER, LLC—See HCA Healthcare, Inc.; *U.S. Public*, pg. 1013
WESTBRAE NATURAL FOODS, INC.—See The Hain Celestial Group, Inc.; *U.S. Public*, pg. 2087
WESTBRAE NATURAL, INC.—See The Hain Celestial Group, Inc.; *U.S. Public*, pg. 2087
WESTBRIDGE CAPITAL LTD.; *Int'l*, pg. 8387
WESTBRIDGE FOODS (THAILAND) LTD.—See Charoen Pokphand Foods Public Company Limited; *Int'l*, pg. 1453
WESTBRIDGE RENEWABLE ENERGY CORP.; *Int'l*, pg. 8387
WESTBRIDGE RESEARCH GROUP; *U.S. Private*, pg. 4488
WEST BRIDGEWATER MA ENDOSCOPY ASC, LLC—See KKR & Co. Inc.; *U.S. Public*, pg. 1249
WEST BROMWICH BUILDING SOCIETY; *Int'l*, pg. 8383
WEST BROMWICH COMMERCIAL LIMITED—See West Bromwich Building Society; *Int'l*, pg. 8383
WEST BROMWICH HOMES LIMITED—See West Bromwich Building Society; *Int'l*, pg. 8383
WESTBROOK ENERGY CENTER, LLC—See Energy Capital Partners Management, LP; *U.S. Private*, pg. 1394
WESTBROOK MANUFACTURING INC.; *U.S. Private*, pg. 4488
WESTBROOK REAL ESTATE PARTNERS, LLC; *U.S. Private*, pg. 4488
WESTBROOK SALES & DISTRIBUTING CORP—See L.E. Simmons & Associates, Inc.; *U.S. Private*, pg. 2365
WESTBROOK TECHNOLOGIES, INC.; *U.S. Private*, pg. 4488
WEST BROTHERS TRANSFER & STORAGE; *U.S. Private*, pg. 4483
WEST BULL SECURITIES LIMITED—See Furniweb Holdings Limited; *Int'l*, pg. 2846
WESTBURNE SUPPLY, INC.; *U.S. Private*, pg. 4489
WESTBURY BANCORP, INC.; *U.S. Public*, pg. 2354
WESTBURY BANK—See Westbury Bancorp, Inc.; *U.S. Public*, pg. 2354
WESTBURY JEEP CHRYSLER DODGE, INC.; *U.S. Private*, pg. 4489
WESTBURY NATIONAL SHOW SYSTEMS LTD.; *Int'l*, pg. 8387
WESTBURY STREET HOLDINGS LIMITED; *Int'l*, pg. 8387
WESTBUS COACH SERVICES LIMITED—See ComfortDelGro Corporation Limited; *Int'l*, pg. 1712
WESTBY CO-OP CREDIT UNION; *U.S. Private*, pg. 4489
WEST CAPE SAFETY GLASS (PTY) LIMITED—See AG Industries Limited; *Int'l*, pg. 198
WEST CAPITAL MANAGEMENT—See WSFS Financial Corporation; *U.S. Public*, pg. 2384
WESTCAP MGT. LTD.; *Int'l*, pg. 8387
WEST CAROLINA FREIGHTLINER; *U.S. Private*, pg. 4483
WEST CARROLLTON PARCHMENT & CONVERTING, INC.; *U.S. Private*, pg. 4483
WEST CASTLE PROPERTIES LTD.—See Caledonian Trust PLC; *Int'l*, pg. 1263
WEST CENTRAL AGRICULTURAL SERVICE INC.; *U.S. Private*, pg. 4483
WEST CENTRAL DISTRIBUTION, LLC—See CHS INC.; *U.S. Public*, pg. 493
WEST CENTRAL ELECTRIC COOPERATIVE; *U.S. Private*, pg. 4483
WEST CENTRAL FS, INC.; *U.S. Private*, pg. 4483
WEST CENTRAL KANSAS ASSOCIATION, INC.; *U.S. Private*, pg. 4484
WEST CENTRAL MISSOURI COMMUNITY ACTION AGENCY; *U.S. Private*, pg. 4484
WEST CENTRAL OHIO GROUP, LTD.—See Catholic Healthcare Partners; *U.S. Private*, pg. 792
WESTCHASE SURGERY CENTER, LTD.—See Bain Capital, LP; *U.S. Private*, pg. 447
WESTCHESTER ACADEMIC LIBRARY DIRECTORS ORGANIZATION; *U.S. Private*, pg. 4489
WESTCHESTER BMW INC.—See Bayerische Motoren Werke Aktiengesellschaft; *Int'l*, pg. 912
WESTCHESTER COUNTRY CLUB INC.; *U.S. Private*, pg. 4489
WESTCHESTER COUNTY ASSOCIATION, INC.—See Hudson Valley Economic Development Corporation; *U.S. Private*, pg. 2002
WESTCHESTER FIRE INSURANCE COMPANY—See Chubb Limited; *Int'l*, pg. 1592
WESTCHESTER GAS COMPANY; *U.S. Private*, pg. 4489
WESTCHESTER GENERAL HOSPITAL, INC.—See Keralty Business Group; *Int'l*, pg. 4133
WEST CHESTER HOLDINGS, INC.; *U.S. Private*, pg. 4484
WESTCHESTER INSTITUTE FOR HUMAN DEVELOPMENT; *U.S. Private*, pg. 4489
WESTCHESTER KNICKS, LLC—See Madison Square Garden Sports Corp.; *U.S. Public*, pg. 1354

WESTCHESTER PLASTICS—See AMETEK, Inc.; *U.S. Public*, pg. 119
WESTCHESTER PUBLISHING SERVICES, LLC; *U.S. Private*, pg. 4489
WEST CHESTER SURGICAL SUITES, LLC—See Tenet Healthcare Corporation; *U.S. Public*, pg. 2015
WESTCHESTER SURPLUS LINES INSURANCE COMPANY—See Chubb Limited; *Int'l*, pg. 1593
WEST CHINA CEMENT LIMITED; *Int'l*, pg. 8383
WEST CHURCH PARTNERSHIP—See Universal Health Services, Inc.; *U.S. Public*, pg. 2261
WESTCLIFF UNIVERSITY; *U.S. Private*, pg. 4489
WEST COACH STATION JSC; *Int'l*, pg. 8383
WEST COAST CAPITAL LIMITED; *Int'l*, pg. 8383
WEST COAST CAPITAL LLC; *U.S. Private*, pg. 4484
WEST COAST COFFEE COMPANY INC.—See Farmer Brothers Co.; *U.S. Public*, pg. 821
WEST COAST COMMUNITY BANCORP; *U.S. Public*, pg. 2352
WEST COAST COMPUTER EXCHANGE; *U.S. Private*, pg. 4484
WEST COAST CUSTOMS, INC.; *U.S. Private*, pg. 4484
WEST COAST DISTRIBUTING, INC.—See Leonard's Express Inc.; *U.S. Private*, pg. 2430
WEST COAST ENDOSCOPY HOLDINGS, LLC—See UnitedHealth Group Incorporated; *U.S. Public*, pg. 2253
WESTCOAST ENERGY, INC.—See Enbridge Inc.; *Int'l*, pg. 2397
WEST COAST ENERGY SYSTEMS LLC—See Generac Holdings Inc.; *U.S. Public*, pg. 913
WEST COAST ENGINEERING COMPANY LIMITED—See Sahaviriya Steel Industries Public Company Limited; *Int'l*, pg. 6481
WEST COAST ENGINEERING, INC—See Valmont Industries, Inc.; *U.S. Public*, pg. 2274
WEST COAST ENGINEERING SERVICE—See Zaharoni Industries, Inc.; *U.S. Private*, pg. 4597
WEST COAST ESCROW COMPANY—See Anywhere Real Estate Inc.; *U.S. Public*, pg. 142
WEST COAST FLOORING CENTER; *U.S. Private*, pg. 4484
WEST COAST FOUNDRY, INC.; *U.S. Private*, pg. 4484
WESTCOAST GATE & ENTRY SYSTEMS, INC.—See Aurora Capital Group, LLC; *U.S. Private*, pg. 394
WEST COAST INSURANCE SERVICES, INC.—See Stone Point Capital LLC; *U.S. Private*, pg. 3819
WEST COAST LAMINATING LLC—See The E.B. Bradley Co., Inc.; *U.S. Private*, pg. 4024
WESTCOAST LANDSCAPE & LAWNS, INC.; *U.S. Private*, pg. 4489
WEST COAST LEATHER; *U.S. Private*, pg. 4484
WEST COAST LEISURE (PTY) LTD.—See Hosken Consolidated Investments Limited; *Int'l*, pg. 3485
WEST COAST LIFE INSURANCE COMPANY—See Daiichi Life Holdings, Inc.; *Int'l*, pg. 1918
WEST COAST LIQUIDATORS, INC.—See Big Lots, Inc.; *U.S. Public*, pg. 331
WEST COAST LODGING, L.P.—See Stonebridge Realty Advisors, Inc.; *U.S. Private*, pg. 3827
WEST COAST LUMBER, INC.—See Building Industry Partners LLC; *U.S. Private*, pg. 683
WEST COAST MATERIALS, INC.; *U.S. Private*, pg. 4484
WEST COAST MILLS INC.; *U.S. Private*, pg. 4484
WESTCOAST MOULDING & MILLWORK LIMITED—See E.R. Probyn Ltd.; *Int'l*, pg. 2260
WEST COAST OPTICABLE LIMITED—See West Coast Paper Mills Ltd.; *Int'l*, pg. 8383
WEST COAST PAPER COMPANY; *U.S. Private*, pg. 4484
WEST COAST PAPER MILLS LTD.; *Int'l*, pg. 8383
WEST COAST PAPER TRADERS (PTY) LTD.—See Mpact Limited; *Int'l*, pg. 5060
WEST COAST PIPE INSPECTION & MAINTENANCE INC.—See J.D. Rush Company Inc.; *U.S. Private*, pg. 2161
WEST COAST PRIME MEATS LLC; *U.S. Private*, pg. 4484
WEST COAST QUARTZ CORPORATION—See Worldex Industry & Trading Co., Ltd.; *Int'l*, pg. 8458
WEST COAST REALTY TRUST, INC.; *U.S. Private*, pg. 4484
WEST COAST RECYCLING AND TRANSFER, INC.—See Waste Connections, Inc.; *Int'l*, pg. 8354
WEST COAST SALES & ASSOCIATES LLC; *U.S. Private*, pg. 4484
WEST COAST SHOT INC.—See Metalico Inc.; *U.S. Private*, pg. 2681
WEST COAST SHUTTERS & SUNBURST, INC.; *U.S. Private*, pg. 4484
WESTCOAST STRUCTURAL CONCRETE & MASONRY, INC.; *U.S. Private*, pg. 4489
WEST COAST TOMATO LLC—See McClure Properties Ltd.; *U.S. Private*, pg. 2629
WEST COAST VENTURES GROUP CORP.; *U.S. Public*, pg. 2352
WEST COAST VINYL, INC.; *U.S. Private*, pg. 4484
WEST COAST WINSUPPLY CO.—See Winsupply Inc.; *U.S. Private*, pg. 4544
WEST COAST WIRE ROPE & RIGGING, INC.; *U.S. Private*, pg. 4484

WEST COBAR METALS LIMITED; *Int'l*, pg. 8383
WESTCO CHINNEY LIMITED—See Chinney Alliance Group Limited; *Int'l*, pg. 1570
WESTCO CLAIMS MANAGEMENT SERVICES, INC.—See American International Group, Inc.; *U.S. Public*, pg. 107
WESTCO CLOSET CORPORATION; *U.S. Private*, pg. 4489
WESTCODE INC. - BINGHAMTON PLANT—See Westcode Inc.; *U.S. Private*, pg. 4489
WESTCODE INC.; *U.S. Private*, pg. 4489
WESTCODE (UK) LTD.—See Knorr-Bremse AG; *Int'l*, pg. 4210
WESTCO FLOW CONTROL LIMITED.—See Aalberts N.V.; *Int'l*, pg. 36
WESTCO INC.; *U.S. Private*, pg. 4489
WESTCO IRON WORKS, INC.; *U.S. Private*, pg. 4489
WEST COLORADO MOTORS, LLC—See AutoNation, Inc.; *U.S. Public*, pg. 238
THE WEST COMPANY ITALIA S.R.L.—See West Pharmaceutical Services, Inc.; *U.S. Public*, pg. 2352
WESTCO MULTITEMP DISTRIBUTION CENTRES INC.—See Congebec Capital Ltee.; *Int'l*, pg. 1768
WESTCON AFRICA ANGOLA LIMITED—See Datatec Limited; *Int'l*, pg. 1981
WESTCON AFRICA DISTRIBUTION (NIGERIA) LIMITED—See Datatec Limited; *Int'l*, pg. 1981
WESTCON AFRICA (KENYA) LIMITED—See Datatec Limited; *Int'l*, pg. 1981
WESTCON AFRICA (MAURITIUS) LIMITED—See Datatec Limited; *Int'l*, pg. 1981
WESTCON AFRICA (MOROCCO) SARL—See Datatec Limited; *Int'l*, pg. 1981
WESTCON BRASIL, LTDA.—See TD Synnex Corp; *U.S. Public*, pg. 1987
WESTCON CALA, INC.—See TD Synnex Corp; *U.S. Public*, pg. 1987
WESTCON CANADA SYSTEMS (WCSI) INC.—See TD Synnex Corp; *U.S. Public*, pg. 1987
WESTCON CONVERGENCE UK—See TD Synnex Corp; *U.S. Public*, pg. 1987
WESTCON DENMARK APS—See Datatec Limited; *Int'l*, pg. 1981
WESTCON DESIGN POLAND SP. Z O.O.—See Westcon Group AS; *Int'l*, pg. 8387
WESTCON GEO AS—See Westcon Group AS; *Int'l*, pg. 8387
WESTCON GROUP AFRICA OPERATIONS LIMITED—See TD Synnex Corp; *U.S. Public*, pg. 1987
WESTCON GROUP AS; *Int'l*, pg. 8387
WESTCON GROUP AUSTRIA GMBH—See Datatec Limited; *Int'l*, pg. 1981
WESTCON GROUP EUROPEAN OPERATIONS LIMITED—See TD Synnex Corp; *U.S. Public*, pg. 1987
WESTCON GROUP GERMANY GMBH—See Datatec Limited; *Int'l*, pg. 1981
WESTCON GROUP, INC.—See TD Synnex Corp; *U.S. Public*, pg. 1987
WESTCON GROUP ITALIA S.R.L.—See Datatec Limited; *Int'l*, pg. 1981
WESTCON GROUP LIMITED—See TD Synnex Corp; *U.S. Public*, pg. 1987
WESTCON GROUP NETHERLANDS B.V.—See Datatec Limited; *Int'l*, pg. 1981
WESTCON GROUP NORTH AMERICA, INC.—See TD Synnex Corp; *U.S. Public*, pg. 1987
WESTCON GROUP POLAND SP. Z O.O.—See Datatec Limited; *Int'l*, pg. 1981
WESTCON GROUP PORTUGAL, SOCIEDADE UNIPESSOAL, LIMITADA—See Datatec Limited; *Int'l*, pg. 1981
WESTCON GROUP PTE. LIMITED—See Datatec Limited; *Int'l*, pg. 1981
WESTCON GROUP PTY LIMITED—See TD Synnex Corp; *U.S. Public*, pg. 1987
WESTCON GROUP (THAILAND) CO. LIMITED—See Datatec Limited; *Int'l*, pg. 1981
WESTCON GROUP (VIETNAM) CO. LIMITED—See Datatec Limited; *Int'l*, pg. 1981
WESTCON HELGELAND AS—See Westcon Group AS; *Int'l*, pg. 8387
WESTCON, INC.—See Bilfinger SE; *Int'l*, pg. 1026
WESTCON INSTRUMENTACAO INDUSTRIAL LTDA—See CHINO Corporation; *Int'l*, pg. 1571
WESTCON INTERNATIONAL, LIMITED—See Datatec Limited; *Int'l*, pg. 1981
WESTCON LLC—See Datatec Limited; *Int'l*, pg. 1981
WESTCON LOFTETEKNIKK AS—See Westcon Group AS; *Int'l*, pg. 8387
WESTCON MEXICO S.A. DE C.V.—See TD Synnex Corp; *U.S. Public*, pg. 1987
WESTCON MIDDLE EAST BAHRAIN WLL—See Datatec Limited; *Int'l*, pg. 1981
WESTCON OLVONDO AS—See Westcon Group AS; *Int'l*, pg. 8387
WESTCON POWER & AUTOMATION AS—See Westcon Group AS; *Int'l*, pg. 8387
WESTCON SA (PTY) LIMITED—See TD Synnex Corp; *U.S. Public*, pg. 1987

COMPANY NAME INDEX

WESTERN COOPERATIVE ELECTRIC ASSOCIATION, INC.

WESTCON SAUDI COMPANY LLC—See Datatec Limited; *Int'l*, pg. 1981
WESTCONSIN CREDIT UNION; *U.S. Private*, pg. 4489
WESTCON SOLUTIONS (HK) LIMITED—See Datatec Limited; *Int'l*, pg. 1981
WESTCON SOLUTIONS (M) SDN. BHD.—See Datatec Limited; *Int'l*, pg. 1981
WESTCON SOLUTIONS PHILIPPINES, INC.—See Datatec Limited; *Int'l*, pg. 1981
WESTCON—See Desco Corporation; *U.S. Private*, pg. 1211
WEST CONSTRUCTION COMPANY; *U.S. Private*, pg. 4484
WEST CONTRA COSTA SANITARY LANDFILL, INC.—See Republic Services, Inc.; *U.S. Public*, pg. 1788
WESTCON YARDS AS—See Westcon Group AS; *Int'l*, pg. 8387
WESTCON YARDS FLORO AS—See Westcon Group AS; *Int'l*, pg. 8387
WESTCOR CONSTRUCTION; *U.S. Private*, pg. 4489
WESTCORE ENERGY LTD.; *Int'l*, pg. 8387
WESTCORE LAND TITLE INSURANCE COMPANY—See The Orogen Group; *U.S. Private*, pg. 4089
WESTCORP PROPERTIES INC.; *Int'l*, pg. 8387
WESTCO TRUCK SALES PTY LTD—See Great Western Corporation Pty. Ltd.; *Int'l*, pg. 3066
WEST COUNTRY MOTORHOMES LTD; *Int'l*, pg. 8383
WEST COUNTY HEALTH CENTERS, INC.; *U.S. Private*, pg. 4484
WEST COUNTY TIMES—See Alden Global Capital LLC; *U.S. Private*, pg. 155
WEST COVINA HIGHLANDER—See Alden Global Capital LLC; *U.S. Private*, pg. 158
WEST CREEK FINANCIAL, INC.; *U.S. Private*, pg. 4484
WEST CUMBERLAND ENGINEERING LTD.—See Renew Holdings plc; *Int'l*, pg. 6278
WESTDALE ASSET MANAGEMENT INC.—See JGB Ventures Inc.; *U.S. Private*, pg. 2207
WESTDALE PROPERTIES; *Int'l*, pg. 8387
WEST DERMATOLOGY MED MANAGEMENT, INC.; *U.S. Private*, pg. 4485
WESTDEUTSCHE ALLGEMEINE VERLAGSGESELLSCHAFT; *Int'l*, pg. 8387
WESTDEUTSCHE GRUNDSTUCKSAUKTIONEN AG—See Deutsche Grundstuecksauktionen AG; *Int'l*, pg. 2065
WESTDEUTSCHE IMMOBILIEN SERVICING AG—See Advent International Corporation; *U.S. Private*, pg. 97
WESTDEUTSCHE IMMOBILIEN SERVICING AG—See Centerbridge Partners, L.P.; *U.S. Private*, pg. 813
WESTDEUTSCHE IMMOBILIEN SERVICING AG—See Advent International Corporation; *U.S. Private*, pg. 97
WESTDEUTSCHE IMMOBILIEN SERVICING AG—See Centerbridge Partners, L.P.; *U.S. Private*, pg. 813
WESTDEUTSCHER RUNDFUNK WDR; *Int'l*, pg. 8388
WESTEC AUTOMATION LTD.—See Convum Ltd.; *Int'l*, pg. 1788
WES-TECH AUTOMATION SOLUTIONS; *U.S. Private*, pg. 4482
WESTECH BUILDING PRODUCTS, INC.—See Westlake Corporation; *U.S. Public*, pg. 2360
WESTECH BUILDING PRODUCTS ULC—See Westlake Corporation; *U.S. Public*, pg. 2360
WESTECH CAPITAL CORP.; *U.S. Private*, pg. 4489
WESTECH CHEMICALS SDN BHD—See Jiankun International Berhad; *Int'l*, pg. 3961
WESTECH ENGINEERING, INC.—See John Swire & Sons Limited; *Int'l*, pg. 3981
WESTECH FRAMING LLC.; *U.S. Private*, pg. 4489
WESTECH INTERNATIONAL, INC.; *U.S. Private*, pg. 4489
WESTECK WINDOWS; *Int'l*, pg. 8388
WEST EDGE PARTNERS, LLC; *U.S. Private*, pg. 4485
WESTED; *U.S. Private*, pg. 4489
WESTEEL—See Ag Growth International Inc.; *Int'l*, pg. 198
WESTEK ARCHITECTURAL WOODWORKING INC.; *U.S. Private*, pg. 4490
WESTEK ELECTRONICS INC.; *U.S. Private*, pg. 4490
WESTEK LIGHTING—See Amertac Holdings Inc.; *U.S. Private*, pg. 261
WESTEL, INC.; *U.S. Private*, pg. 4490
WEST ELK GROVE DIALYSIS, LLC—See DaVita Inc.; *U.S. Public*, pg. 644
WESTELL, INC.—See Westell Technologies, Inc.; *U.S. Public*, pg. 2354
WESTELL TECHNOLOGIES, INC.; *U.S. Public*, pg. 2354
WEST END ADVERTISING; *U.S. Private*, pg. 4485
WEST END BANK, S.B.—See 3Rivers Federal Credit Union; *U.S. Private*, pg. 14
WEST END CLAYBRICK (PROPRIETARY) LIMITED—See Consolidated Infrastructure Group Limited; *Int'l*, pg. 1771
WEST END DIVING & SALVAGE, INC.; *U.S. Private*, pg. 4485
WEST END FINANCIAL CORP.; *U.S. Private*, pg. 4485
WEST END HOLDINGS LLC; *U.S. Private*, pg. 4485
THE WEST END LUMBER COMPANY; *U.S. Private*, pg. 4134
WEST END ROOFING, SIDING & WINDOWS—See Beacon Roofing Supply, Inc.; *U.S. Public*, pg. 287

WEST END THEATRE BOOKINGS LIMITED—See Great Hill Partners, L.P.; *U.S. Private*, pg. 1763
WEST ENERGY SOLUTION INC.—See West Holdings Corporation; *Int'l*, pg. 8385
WEST ENGINE FUNDING LLC—See Willis Lease Finance Corporation; *U.S. Public*, pg. 2371
WESTERBEKE CORPORATION; *U.S. Private*, pg. 4490
WESTERCHIL CONSTRUCTION CO.; *U.S. Private*, pg. 4490
WESTERKIRK CAPITAL INC.; *Int'l*, pg. 8388
WESTERMAN ACQUISITION CO., LLC—See Worthington Industries, Inc.; *U.S. Public*, pg. 2383
WESTERMAN, INC.—See Ten Oaks Group; *U.S. Private*, pg. 3964
WESTERMEYER INDUSTRIES, INC.; *U.S. Private*, pg. 4490
WESTERMO NERATEC AG—See Ependion AB; *Int'l*, pg. 2459
WESTERMO NETWORK TECHNOLOGIES AB—See Ependion AB; *Int'l*, pg. 2459
WESTERN ACQUISITION VENTURES CORP.; *U.S. Public*, pg. 2354
WESTERN AGCREDIT; *U.S. Private*, pg. 4490
WESTERN AGGREGATES LLC—See Teichert, Inc.; *U.S. Private*, pg. 3958
WESTERN AIRCRAFT, INC.—See Greenwich AeroGroup, Inc.; *U.S. Private*, pg. 1781
WESTERN ALLIANCE BANCORPORATION; *U.S. Public*, pg. 2354
WESTERN ALLIANCE BANK—See Western Alliance Bancorporation; *U.S. Public*, pg. 2354
WESTERN ALLIANCE EQUIPMENT FINANCE, INC.—See Western Alliance Bancorporation; *U.S. Public*, pg. 2354
WESTERN AMERICAN LIFE INSURANCE CO.—See Maximum Corporation; *U.S. Private*, pg. 2618
WESTERN AREA COUNCIL—See Dairy Farmers of America, Inc.; *U.S. Private*, pg. 1146
WESTERN AREAS LIMITED—See IGO Limited; *Int'l*, pg. 3603
WESTERN ASSET CORPORATE LOAN FUND, INC.—See Franklin Resources, Inc.; *U.S. Public*, pg. 882
WESTERN ASSET GLOBAL CORPORATE DEFINED OPPORTUNITY FUND, INC.—See Franklin Resources, Inc., *U.S. Public*, pg. 882
WESTERN ASSET GLOBAL HIGH INCOME FUND, INC.—See Franklin Resources, Inc.; *U.S. Public*, pg. 882
WESTERN ASSET HIGH INCOME FUND II, INC.—See Franklin Resources, Inc.; *U.S. Public*, pg. 882
WESTERN ASSET HIGH INCOME OPPORTUNITY FUND, INC.—See Franklin Resources, Inc.; *U.S. Public*, pg. 882
WESTERN ASSET HIGH YIELD DEFINED OPPORTUNITY FUND INC.—See Franklin Resources, Inc.; *U.S. Public*, pg. 882
WESTERN ASSET INFLATION-LINKED INCOME FUND; *U.S. Public*, pg. 2354
WESTERN ASSET INFLATION-LINKED OPPORTUNITIES & INCOME FUND; *U.S. Public*, pg. 2354
WESTERN ASSET INTERMEDIATE MUNI FUND, INC.—See Franklin Resources, Inc.; *U.S. Public*, pg. 882
WESTERN ASSET INVESTMENT GRADE DEFINED OPPORTUNITY TRUST, INC.—See Franklin Resources, Inc.; *U.S. Public*, pg. 882
WESTERN ASSET INVESTMENT GRADE INCOME FUND, INC.—See Franklin Resources, Inc.; *U.S. Public*, pg. 882
WESTERN ASSET MANAGED MUNICIPALS FUND, INC.—See Franklin Resources, Inc.; *U.S. Public*, pg. 882
WESTERN ASSET MANAGEMENT COMPANY DISTRIBUIDORA DE TITULOS E VALORES MOBILIARIOS LIMITADA—See Franklin Resources, Inc.; *U.S. Public*, pg. 883
WESTERN ASSET MANAGEMENT COMPANY LIMITED—See Franklin Resources, Inc.; *U.S. Public*, pg. 882
WESTERN ASSET MANAGEMENT COMPANY LTD—See Franklin Resources, Inc.; *U.S. Public*, pg. 882
WESTERN ASSET MANAGEMENT COMPANY PTE LTD.—See Franklin Resources, Inc.; *U.S. Public*, pg. 882
WESTERN ASSET MANAGEMENT COMPANY PTY LTD—See Franklin Resources, Inc.; *U.S. Public*, pg. 882
WESTERN ASSET MANAGEMENT COMPANY—See Franklin Resources, Inc.; *U.S. Public*, pg. 882
WESTERN ASSET MIDDLE MARKET INCOME FUND INC.—See Franklin Resources, Inc.; *U.S. Public*, pg. 883
WESTERN ASSET MORTGAGE CAPITAL CORPORATION—See TPG Capital, L.P.; *U.S. Public*, pg. 2166
WESTERN ASSET MUNICIPAL DEFINED OPPORTUNITY TRUST, INC.—See Franklin Resources, Inc.; *U.S. Public*, pg. 883

WESTERN ASSET MUNICIPAL HIGH INCOME FUND, INC.—See Franklin Resources, Inc.; *U.S. Public*, pg. 883
WESTERN ASSET PREMIER BOND FUND—See Franklin Resources, Inc.; *U.S. Public*, pg. 883
WESTERN ASSET VARIABLE RATE STRATEGIC FUND, INC.—See Franklin Resources, Inc.; *U.S. Public*, pg. 883
WESTERN ASSURANCE COMPANY—See Intact Financial Corporation; *Int'l*, pg. 3727
WESTERN ASSURANCE COMPANY—See Tryg A/S; *Int'l*, pg. 7947
WESTERN AUSTRALIA ENERGY RESOURCES LIMITED; *Int'l*, pg. 8388
WESTERN AUSTRALIAN SPECIALTY ALLOYS, PTY. LTD.—See Berkshire Hathaway Inc.; *U.S. Public*, pg. 315
WESTERN AUTOMATION RESEARCH & DEVELOPMENT LIMITED—See Littelfuse, Inc.; *U.S. Public*, pg. 1327
WESTERN AUTO OF ST. THOMAS, INC.—See Advance Auto Parts, Inc.; *U.S. Public*, pg. 46
WESTERN AVIATION PRODUCTS LLC—See World Kinect Corporation; *U.S. Public*, pg. 2381
WESTERN BAGEL BAKING CORP.; *U.S. Private*, pg. 4490
WESTERN BANCORPORATION, INC.; *U.S. Private*, pg. 4490
WESTERN BANCSHARES OF CLOVIS, INC.; *U.S. Private*, pg. 4491
WESTERN BANK OF CLOVIS—See Western Bancshares of Clovis, Inc.; *U.S. Private*, pg. 4491
WESTERN BEEF, INC.; *U.S. Private*, pg. 4491
WESTERN BEVERAGE COMPANY; *U.S. Private*, pg. 4491
WESTERN BEVERAGE INC; *U.S. Private*, pg. 4491
WESTERN BEVERAGES INC.; *U.S. Private*, pg. 4491
WESTERN BIOMASS OPERATING COMPANY LTD—See Mitsui E&S Holdings Co., Ltd.; *Int'l*, pg. 4986
WESTERN BIOMEDICAL PTY. LTD.—See Paragon Care Limited; *Int'l*, pg. 5736
WESTERN BLUE PRINT COMPANY LLC; *U.S. Private*, pg. 4491
WESTERN BRANCH DIESEL INCORPORATED; *U.S. Private*, pg. 4491
WESTERN BROADBAND, LLC—See Evergreen Pacific Partners Management Co., Inc.; *U.S. Private*, pg. 1440
WESTERN BUILDERS INC—See The O'Connell Companies, Incorporated; *U.S. Private*, pg. 4087
WESTERN BUILDING CENTER OF KALISPELL; *U.S. Private*, pg. 4491
WESTERN BUILDING MAINTENANCE—See WBM Enterprises Inc.; *U.S. Private*, pg. 4461
WESTERN BUS SALES INC.; *U.S. Private*, pg. 4491
WESTERN CAPITAL CORPORATION; *U.S. Private*, pg. 4491
WESTERN CAPITAL RESOURCES, INC.—See Blackstreet Capital Management, LLC; *U.S. Private*, pg. 577
WESTERN CAROLINA COMMUNITY ACTION, INC.; *U.S. Private*, pg. 4491
WESTERN CAROLINA FORKLIFT INC.; *U.S. Private*, pg. 4491
WESTERN CARPET & LINOLEUM CO.; *U.S. Private*, pg. 4491
WESTERN CARRIERS INC.; *U.S. Private*, pg. 4491
WESTERN CATHOLIC UNION; *U.S. Private*, pg. 4491
WESTERN CHEMICAL COMPANY S.A.—See Obegi Chemicals Group; *Int'l*, pg. 5510
WESTERN CHEMICAL (R)—See Obegi Chemicals Group; *Int'l*, pg. 5510
WESTERN COALFIELDS LIMITED—See Coal India Limited; *Int'l*, pg. 1680
WESTERN COLORADO COMMUNITY FOUNDATION; *U.S. Private*, pg. 4491
WESTERN COMMERCE BANK; *U.S. Private*, pg. 4491
WESTERN COMMUNICATIONS INC.; *U.S. Private*, pg. 4491
WESTERN COMMUNITY DIALYSIS CENTER, LLC—See Nautic Partners, LLC; *U.S. Private*, pg. 2871
WESTERN COMPUTER, LLC—See Alpine Investors; *U.S. Private*, pg. 201
WESTERN CONNECTICUT ORTHOPEDIC SURGICAL CENTER, LLC—See UnitedHealth Group Incorporated; *U.S. Public*, pg. 2253
WESTERN CONSOLIDATED COOPERATIVES INC.; *U.S. Private*, pg. 4492
WESTERN CONSTRUCTION GROUP; *U.S. Private*, pg. 4492
WESTERN CONSTRUCTION SERVICES, INC.; *U.S. Private*, pg. 4492
WESTERN CONTAINER CORPORATION—See The Coca-Cola Company; *U.S. Public*, pg. 2065
WESTERN CONTRACT FURNISHERS OF SACRAMENTO INC.; *U.S. Private*, pg. 4492
WESTERN COOPERATIVE COMPANY; *U.S. Private*, pg. 4492
WESTERN COOPERATIVE CREDIT UNION; *U.S. Private*, pg. 4492
WESTERN COOPERATIVE ELECTRIC ASSOCIATION, INC.; *U.S. Private*, pg. 4492

WESTERN COPPER AND GOLD CORPORATION

CORPORATE AFFILIATIONS

WESTERN COPPER AND GOLD CORPORATION; *Int'l*, pg. 8388
WESTERN CREATIVE, INC.; *U.S. Private*, pg. 4492
WESTERN-CULLEN-HAYES INC,; *U.S. Private*, pg. 4498
WESTERN DAKOTA INSURERS INC.; *U.S. Private*, pg. 4492
WESTERN DENTAL SERVICES INC.—See New Mountain Capital, LLC; *U.S. Private*, pg. 2904
WESTERN DEVELOPMENT BANK LIMITED; *Int'l*, pg. 8388
WESTERN DIESEL SERVICES, INC.; *U.S. Private*, pg. 4492
WESTERN DIGITAL CANADA—See Western Digital Corporation; *U.S. Public*, pg. 2355
WESTERN DIGITAL CORPORATION; *U.S. Public*, pg. 2355
WESTERN DIGITAL DEUTSCHLAND GMBH—See Western Digital Corporation; *U.S. Public*, pg. 2355
WESTERN DIGITAL DRIVE ENGINEERING INC.—See Western Digital Corporation; *U.S. Public*, pg. 2355
WESTERN DIGITAL HONG KONG LIMITED—See Western Digital Corporation; *U.S. Public*, pg. 2355
WESTERN DIGITAL IRELAND, LTD.—See Western Digital Corporation; *U.S. Public*, pg. 2355
WESTERN DIGITAL JAPAN, LTD.—See Western Digital Corporation; *U.S. Public*, pg. 2355
WESTERN DIGITAL KOREA INC.—See Western Digital Corporation; *U.S. Public*, pg. 2355
WESTERN DIGITAL (MALAYSIA) SDN. BHD.—See Western Digital Corporation; *U.S. Public*, pg. 2355
WESTERN DIGITAL NETHERLANDS B.V.—See Western Digital Corporation; *U.S. Public*, pg. 2355
WESTERN DIGITAL SE ASIA PTE. LTD.—See Western Digital Corporation; *U.S. Public*, pg. 2355
WESTERN DIGITAL TAIWAN CO., LTD.—See Western Digital Corporation; *U.S. Public*, pg. 2355
WESTERN DIGITAL TECHNOLOGIES, INC.—See Western Digital Corporation; *U.S. Public*, pg. 2355
WESTERN DIGITAL (UK) LTD.—See Western Digital Corporation; *U.S. Public*, pg. 2355
WESTERN DISTRICT AGRICENTRE PTY. LTD.—See AGCO Corporation; *U.S. Public*, pg. 60
WESTERN DODGE CHRYSLER JEEP; *Int'l*, pg. 8388
WESTERN DOVETAIL, INC.; *U.S. Private*, pg. 4492
WESTERN DRAIN SUPPLY, INC.—See Chemed Corporation; *U.S. Public*, pg. 484
WESTERN ELECTRICAL SALES INC.; *U.S. Private*, pg. 4492
WESTERN ELECTRICITY COORDINATING COUNCIL; *U.S. Private*, pg. 4492
WESTERN ELECTROCHEMICAL COMPANY—See H.I.G. Capital, LLC; *U.S. Private*, pg. 1829
WESTERN ELECTRONICS LLC—See DBSI, Inc.; *U.S. Private*, pg. 1179
WESTERN ELITE INCORPORATED SERVICES; *U.S. Private*, pg. 4492
WESTERN EMULSIONS, INC.—See Idaho Asphalt Supply Inc.; *U.S. Private*, pg. 2034
WESTERN ENERGY COMPANY—See Westmoreland Coal Company; *U.S. Private*, pg. 4500
WESTERN ENERGY PTY. LTD.—See AGL Energy Limited; *Int'l*, pg. 211
WESTERN ENERGY SERVICES CORP.; *Int'l*, pg. 8388
WESTERN ENGINEERING CO. INC.; *U.S. Private*, pg. 4493
WESTERN ENTERPRISES DIVISION—See Berkshire Hathaway Inc.; *U.S. Public*, pg. 300
WESTERN ENVIRONMENTAL CORP.—See Controlled Environment Systems, LLC; *U.S. Private*, pg. 1034
WESTERN ENVIRONMENTAL PROTECTION CO., LTD.—See Hongda Xingye Co., Ltd.; *Int'l*, pg. 3470
WESTERN EQUIPMENT DISTRIBUTORS, INC.; *U.S. Private*, pg. 4493
WESTERN EQUIPMENT LLC; *U.S. Private*, pg. 4493
WESTERN EXPLORATION INC.; *U.S. Public*, pg. 2356
WESTERN EXPLORATION, LLC—See Western Exploration Inc.; *U.S. Public*, pg. 2356
WESTERN EXPLOSIVES SYSTEMS COMPANY—See Incitec Pivot Limited; *Int'l*, pg. 3648
WESTERN EXPRESS HOLDINGS, INC.; *U.S. Private*, pg. 4493
WESTERN EXPRESS, INC.—See Western Express Holdings, Inc.; *U.S. Private*, pg. 4493
WESTERN EXTERMINATOR COMPANY—See Rentokil Initial plc; *Int'l*, pg. 6289
WESTERN EXTRALITE COMPANY—See Border States Industries, Inc.; *U.S. Private*, pg. 618
WESTERN EXTRUSIONS; *U.S. Private*, pg. 4493
WESTERN FAMILY FOODS INC.—See Western Family Holding Co., Inc.; *U.S. Private*, pg. 4493
WESTERN FAMILY HOLDING CO., INC.; *U.S. Private*, pg. 4493
WESTERN FARM BUREAU SERVICE CO., INC.—See Mountain West Farm Bureau Mutual Insurance Company, Inc.; *U.S. Private*, pg. 2800
WESTERN FARMERS ELECTRIC COOPERATIVE, INC.; *U.S. Private*, pg. 4493
WESTERN FILTER CORPORATION—See Donaldson Company, Inc.; *U.S. Public*, pg. 676

WESTERN FINANCE & LEASE, INC.1990—See Western State Agency, Inc.; *U.S. Private*, pg. 4496
WESTERN FINANCIAL CAPITAL CORPORATION—See Creative Media & Community Trust Corporation; *U.S. Public*, pg. 593
WESTERN FINANCIAL GROUP INC.—See The Wawanesa Mutual Insurance Company; *Int'l*, pg. 7699
WESTERN FINANCIAL, INC.—See Western State Agency, Inc.; *U.S. Private*, pg. 4497
WESTERN FLEET SERVICES, INC.—See Mansfield Energy Corp.; *U.S. Private*, pg. 2566
WESTERN FLUID COMPONENTS, INC.—See Littlejohn & Co., LLC; *U.S. Private*, pg. 2471
WESTERN FOODS LLC—See Western Milling, LLC; *U.S. Private*, pg. 4494
WESTERN FOREST PRODUCTS INC.; *Int'l*, pg. 8388
WESTERN FOREST PRODUCTS INC.; *U.S. Private*, pg. 4493
WESTERN FORGE CORPORATION—See MW Universal Inc.; *U.S. Private*, pg. 2822
WESTERN FORGE & FLANGE CO.—See Wynnchurch Capital, L.P.; *U.S. Private*, pg. 4578
WESTERN FORMS INC.; *U.S. Private*, pg. 4493
WESTERN FRATERNAL LIFE ASSOCIATION; *U.S. Private*, pg. 4493
WESTERN FUNDING INC.; *U.S. Private*, pg. 4493
WESTERN GAS HOLDINGS, LLC—See Western Midstream Partners, LP; *U.S. Public*, pg. 2356
WESTERNGECO A/S—See Schlumberger Limited; *U.S. Public*, pg. 1846
WESTERNGECO LIMITED—See Schlumberger Limited; *U.S. Public*, pg. 1846
WESTERNGECO LLC—See Schlumberger Limited; *U.S. Public*, pg. 1846
WESTERN GENERAL INSURANCE CO., INC.; *U.S. Private*, pg. 4493
WESTERNGHATS AGRO GROWERS COMPANY LIMITED—See 63 moons technologies limited; *Int'l*, pg. 14
WESTERN GMC BUICK, LTD.; *Int'l*, pg. 8388
WESTERN GOLD EXPLORATION LTD.; *Int'l*, pg. 8388
WESTERN GRADE, LLC; *U.S. Private*, pg. 4493
WESTERN GRAPHICS & DATA—See Taylor Corporation; *U.S. Private*, pg. 3939
THE WESTERN GROUP; *U.S. Private*, pg. 4134
WESTERN HARVESTERS LTD.—See Claas KGaA mbH; *Int'l*, pg. 1641
WESTERN HEATING AND AIR CONDITIONING INC.—See The SEER Group LLC; *U.S. Private*, pg. 4115
WESTERN HERITAGE BANK—See Nusenda Credit Union; *U.S. Private*, pg. 2973
WESTERN HOME COMMUNITIES INC.; *U.S. Private*, pg. 4493
WESTERN HYDRO LLC—See Franklin Electric Co., Inc.; *U.S. Public*, pg. 879
WESTERN ILLINOIS BANCSHARES, INC.; *U.S. Private*, pg. 4493
THE WESTERN INDIA PLYWOODS LIMITED; *Int'l*, pg. 7701
WESTERN INDUSTRIAL CERAMICS; *U.S. Private*, pg. 4493
WESTERN INDUSTRIAL CONTRACTORS; *Int'l*, pg. 8388
WESTERN INDUSTRIES CORPORATION, CORRUGATED DIVISION—See Western Industries Corporation; *U.S. Private*, pg. 4494
WESTERN INDUSTRIES CORPORATION; *U.S. Private*, pg. 4493
WESTERN INDUSTRIES CORP.—See Western Industries Corporation; *U.S. Private*, pg. 4493
WESTERN INDUSTRIES, INC. - PLASTIC PRODUCTS GROUP—See Western Industries, Inc.; *U.S. Private*, pg. 4494
WESTERN INDUSTRIES, INC.—See Western Industries, Inc.; *U.S. Private*, pg. 4494
WESTERN INDUSTRIES, INC.; *U.S. Private*, pg. 4494
WESTERN INSTITUTIONAL REVIEW BOARD, INC.—See Arsenal Capital Management LP; *U.S. Private*, pg. 339
WESTERN INSURANCE—See Western State Agency, Inc.; *U.S. Private*, pg. 4497
WESTERN INTEGRATED TECHNOLOGIES, INC.; *U.S. Private*, pg. 4494
WESTERN INTERNATIONAL FOREST PRODUCTS, LLC—See Forest City Trading Group, LLC; *U.S. Private*, pg. 1566
WESTERN INTERNATIONAL GAS & CYLINDERS, INC.—See Mitsubishi Chemical Group Corporation; *Int'l*, pg. 4937
WESTERN INTERNATIONAL SECURITIES, INC.—See Lee Equity Partners LLC; *U.S. Private*, pg. 2412
WESTERN INTERNATIONAL UNIVERSITY, INC.—See Apollo Global Management, Inc.; *U.S. Public*, pg. 146
WESTERN INTERNATIONAL UNIVERSITY, INC.—See The Vistria Group, LP; *U.S. Private*, pg. 4131
THE WESTERN INVESTMENT COMPANY OF CANADA LTD.—See The Wawanesa Mutual Insurance Company; *Int'l*, pg. 7699
WESTERN IOWA COOPERATIVE; *U.S. Private*, pg. 4494

WESTERN KENTUCKY COCA-COLA BOTTLING CO., INC.—See C.C. Clark, Inc.; *U.S. Private*, pg. 706
WESTERN LABRADOR RAIL SERVICES INC.—See Brookfield Infrastructure Partners L.P.; *Int'l*, pg. 1191
WESTERN LABRADOR RAIL SERVICES INC.—See GIC Pte. Ltd.; *Int'l*, pg. 2966
WESTERN LAND PROPERTIES—See Lewis Operating Corp.; *U.S. Private*, pg. 2439
WESTERN LITIGATION, INC.—See Arthur J. Gallagher & Co.; *U.S. Public*, pg. 208
WESTERN LOGISTICS; *Int'l*, pg. 8388
WESTERN LUMBER CO.; *U.S. Private*, pg. 4494
WESTERN MAGAZINE PTY LTD—See Nine Entertainment Co. Holdings Limited; *Int'l*, pg. 5299
WESTERN MAGNESIUM CORPORATION; *Int'l*, pg. 8388
WESTERN MARKETING INC.—See AIP, LLC; *U.S. Private*, pg. 136
WESTERN MASSACHUSETTS PET/CT IMAGING CENTER LLC—See Akumin, Inc.; *U.S. Public*, pg. 70
WESTERN MATERIALS INC.; *U.S. Private*, pg. 4494
WESTERN MEDICAL PRODUCTS PTY LIMITED—See Petsec Energy Ltd.; *Int'l*, pg. 5834
WESTERN MESQUITE MINES, INC.—See Equinox Gold Corp.; *Int'l*, pg. 2485
WESTERN METAL MATERIALS CO., LTD.; *Int'l*, pg. 8388
WESTERN METALS CORP.; *U.S. Public*, pg. 2356
WESTERN MIDSTREAM OPERATING, LP—See Western Midstream Partners, LP; *U.S. Public*, pg. 2356
WESTERN MIDSTREAM PARTNERS, LP; *U.S. Public*, pg. 2356
WESTERN MILLING, LLC; *U.S. Private*, pg. 4494
WESTERN MINES GROUP LTD.; *Int'l*, pg. 8389
WESTERN MINING CO., LTD.; *Int'l*, pg. 8389
WESTERN MINISTIL LIMITED; *Int'l*, pg. 8389
WESTERN MIXERS INC.; *U.S. Private*, pg. 4494
WESTERN MORTGAGE & REALTY CO.; *U.S. Private*, pg. 4494
WESTERN MORTGAGE SERVICES LIMITED—See Capita plc; *Int'l*, pg. 1308
WESTERN MOTOR COMPANY INC.; *U.S. Private*, pg. 4494
WESTERN MOTORS LLC—See Al Fahim Group; *Int'l*, pg. 277
WESTERN MUTUAL INSURANCE GROUP; *U.S. Private*, pg. 4494
WESTERN NATIONAL BANK—See Western Bancorporation, Inc.; *U.S. Private*, pg. 4491
WESTERN NATIONAL BANK—See Western Bancorporation, Inc.; *U.S. Private*, pg. 4491
WESTERN NATIONAL GROUP; *U.S. Private*, pg. 4494
WESTERN NATIONAL MUTUAL INSURANCE CO.; *U.S. Private*, pg. 4494
WESTERN NEVADA SUPPLY CO.; *U.S. Private*, pg. 4494
WESTERN NEW ENGLAND BANCORP, INC.; *U.S. Public*, pg. 2356
WESTERN NEWSPAPERS, INC.; *U.S. Private*, pg. 4495
WESTERN NEW YORK CLINICAL INFORMATION EXCHANGE, INC.; *U.S. Private*, pg. 4494
WESTERN NEW YORK PUBLIC BROADCASTING ASSOCIATION; *U.S. Private*, pg. 4494
WESTERN NORTH CAROLINA COMMUNITY HEALTH SERVICES, INC.; *U.S. Private*, pg. 4495
WESTERN NY BICS LLP—See Tomra Systems ASA; *Int'l*, pg. 7803
WESTERN OFFICE INTERIORS INC.; *U.S. Private*, pg. 4495
WESTERN OILFIELDS SUPPLY CO.; *U.S. Private*, pg. 4495
WESTERN OIL INC.; *U.S. Private*, pg. 4495
WESTERNONE INC.; *Int'l*, pg. 8390
WESTERNONE RENTALS & SALES—See United Rentals, Inc.; *U.S. Public*, pg. 2235
WESTERN ORGANICS INC.—See GRO-WELL Brands Inc.; *U.S. Private*, pg. 1791
WESTERN & ORIENTAL TRAVEL LIMITED; *Int'l*, pg. 8388
WESTERN OUTDOORS PUBLICATIONS; *U.S. Private*, pg. 4495
WESTERN OVERSEAS CORPORATION; *U.S. Private*, pg. 4495
WESTERN PACIFIC BUILDING MATERIALS; *U.S. Private*, pg. 4495
WESTERN PACIFIC CRANE & EQUIPMENT LLC—See Lanco International Inc.; *U.S. Private*, pg. 2382
WESTERN PACIFIC DISTRIBUTORS; *U.S. Private*, pg. 4495
WESTERN PACIFIC ENTERPRISES LTD.—See MYR Group Inc.; *U.S. Public*, pg. 1489
WESTERN PACIFIC FINANCIAL GROUP PTY. LTD.—See Insignia Financial Ltd.; *Int'l*, pg. 3719
WESTERN PACIFIC PACLEASE—See Greenbriar Equity Group, L.P.; *U.S. Private*, pg. 1776
WESTERN PACIFIC ROOFING CORPORATION; *U.S. Private*, pg. 4495
WESTERN PACIFIC SIGNAL, LLC—See Econolite Group, Inc.; *U.S. Private*, pg. 1330
WESTERN PACIFIC STORAGE SYSTEMS INC.; *U.S. Private*, pg. 4495
WESTERN PACIFIC TRUST COMPANY; *Int'l*, pg. 8389

COMPANY NAME INDEX

WESTERN PAPERBAG CO., LTD.—See Siko Corporation; *Int'l*, pg. 6918
WESTERN PAPER DISTRIBUTORS, INC.—See Bain Capital, LP; *U.S. Private*, pg. 441
WESTERN PAPERS—See International Paper Company; *U.S. Public*, pg. 1158
WESTERN PARTITIONS, INC.; *U.S. Private*, pg. 4495
THE WESTERN PENNSYLVANIA CONSERVANCY; *U.S. Private*, pg. 4134
WESTERN PEST SERVICES—See Rollins, Inc.; *U.S. Public*, pg. 1810
WESTERN PETERBILT, INC.—See Greenbriar Equity Group, L.P.; *U.S. Private*, pg. 1776
WESTERN PETROLEUM CO., INC.; *U.S. Private*, pg. 4495
WESTERN PETROLEUM COMPANY—See World Kinect Corporation; *U.S. Public*, pg. 2381
WESTERN PETROLEUM LLC—See Berkshire Hathaway Inc.; *U.S. Public*, pg. 313
WESTERN PHARMACEUTICALS S.A.—See Abbott Laboratories; *U.S. Public*, pg. 21
WESTERN PHOTOMETRIC LABORATORIES—See Dupree, Inc.; *U.S. Private*, pg. 1291
WESTERN PIEDMONT COUNCIL OF GOVERNMENTS; *U.S. Private*, pg. 4495
WESTERN PIEDMONT SYMPHONY; *U.S. Private*, pg. 4495
WESTERN PIONEER INC.; *U.S. Private*, pg. 4495
WESTERN PLAINS CAPITAL, INC.—See HCA Healthcare, Inc.; *U.S. Public*, pg. 1014
WESTERN PLAINS ENERGY, LLC.; *U.S. Private*, pg. 4495
WESTERN PLAINS MEDICAL COMPLEX—See Apollo Global Management, Inc.; *U.S. Public*, pg. 159
WESTERN PLASTICS, CALIFORNIA—See Western Plastics; *Int'l*, pg. 8389
WESTERN PLASTICS, CANADA—See Western Plastics; *Int'l*, pg. 8389
WESTERN PLASTICS, DUBLIN—See Western Plastics; *Int'l*, pg. 8389
WESTERN PLASTICS, GEORGIA—See Western Plastics; *Int'l*, pg. 8389
WESTERN PLASTICS—See Berkshire Hathaway Inc.; *U.S. Public*, pg. 300
WESTERN PLASTICS, *Int'l*, pg. 8389
WESTERN PLATINUM LTD.—See Sibanye-Stillwater Limited; *Int'l*, pg. 6876
WESTERN PNEUMATICS, INC.—See Insight Equity Holdings LLC; *U.S. Private*, pg. 2086
WESTERN PNEUMATIC TUBE COMPANY, LLC—See Leggett & Platt, Incorporated; *U.S. Public*, pg. 1304
WESTERN POLYMER CORPORATION—See Ingredion Incorporated; *U.S. Public*, pg. 1124
WESTERN PORTS TRANSPORTATION, INC.; *U.S. Private*, pg. 4496
WESTERN POTASH CORP.; *Int'l*, pg. 8389
WESTERN POWER DISTRIBUTION—See PPL Corporation; *U.S. Public*, pg. 1712
WESTERN POWER SPORTS INCORPORATED; *U.S. Private*, pg. 4496
WESTERN PRECISION AERO LLC—See RBC Bearings Incorporated; *U.S. Public*, pg. 1766
WESTERN PRINTING MACHINERY CO.; *U.S. Private*, pg. 4496
WESTERN PRODUCER PUBLICATIONS PARTNERSHIP—See GVIC Communications Corp.; *Int'l*, pg. 3189
WESTERN PRODUCTS, *U.S. Private*, pg. 4496
WESTERN PROPERTIES, INC.—See Biglari Holdings Inc.; *U.S. Public*, pg. 331
WESTERN PROTECTORS INSURANCE COMPANY—See Oregon Mutual Insurance Company, Inc.; *U.S. Private*, pg. 3040
WESTERN PULP PRODUCTS CO.; *U.S. Private*, pg. 4496
WESTERN QUARTZ PRODUCTS, INC.—See Forsyth Capital Investors LLC; *U.S. Private*, pg. 1573
WESTERN REFINING CO. - GALLUP REFINERY—See Marathon Petroleum Corporation; *U.S. Public*, pg. 1364
WESTERN REFINING COMPANY, L.P.—See Marathon Petroleum Corporation; *U.S. Public*, pg. 1364
WESTERN REFINING, INC.—See Marathon Petroleum Corporation; *U.S. Public*, pg. 1363
WESTERN REFINING LOGISTICS, LP—See Marathon Petroleum Corporation; *U.S. Public*, pg. 1364
WESTERN REFINING SOUTHWEST, INC.—See Marathon Petroleum Corporation; *U.S. Public*, pg. 1363
WESTERN REFRIGERATION PVT. LTD.—See Hoshizaki Corporation; *Int'l*, pg. 3484
WESTERN REGIONAL OFF-TRACK BETTING CORPORATION; *U.S. Private*, pg. 4496
WESTERN REGION GOLD CO., LTD.; *Int'l*, pg. 8389
WESTERN REGIONS TOURISM DEVELOPMENT CO., LTD.; *Int'l*, pg. 8389
WESTERN REGION TRANSMISSION (MAHARASHTRA) PRIVATE LIMITED—See Reliance - ADA Group Limited; *Int'l*, pg. 6263
WESTERN REMAC, INC.—See Investcorp Holdings B.S.C.; *Int'l*, pg. 3777

WESTERN REMAC, INC.—See Trilantic Capital Management L.P.; *U.S. Private*, pg. 4231
WESTERN RE/MANAGERS INSURANCE SERVICES, INC.—See Align Financial Group, LLC; *U.S. Private*, pg. 168
WESTERN RENTALS INCORPORATED—See Scott Equipment Incorporated; *U.S. Private*, pg. 3576
WESTERN REPACKING, LLLP—See Lipman & Lipman, Inc.; *U.S. Private*, pg. 2465
WESTERN RESERVE AREA AGENCY ON AGING; *U.S. Private*, pg. 4496
WESTERN RESERVE FARM COOPERATIVE; *U.S. Private*, pg. 4496
WESTERN RESERVE HEALTH EDUCATION, INC.—See Community Health Systems, Inc.; *U.S. Public*, pg. 557
WESTERN RESERVE LAND CONSERVANCY; *U.S. Private*, pg. 4496
WESTERN RESERVE MUTUAL CASUALTY CO., INC.; *U.S. Private*, pg. 4496
WESTERN RESERVE RESTAURANT MANAGEMENT; *U.S. Private*, pg. 4496
WESTERN RESOURCES CORPORATION; *Int'l*, pg. 8389
WESTERN RESOURCES TITLE CO—See First Team Real Estate-Orange County Inc.; *U.S. Private*, pg. 1529
WESTERN RESTAURANTS INC.; *U.S. Private*, pg. 4496
WESTERN RESTORATION & WATERPROOFING CO.—See Western Construction Group; *U.S. Private*, pg. 4492
WESTERN RIM PROPERTY SERVICES; *U.S. Private*, pg. 4496
WESTERN ROOFING & INSULATION CO.—See Western Construction Group; *U.S. Private*, pg. 4492
WESTERN ROOFING SERVICE, INC.—See Altas Partners LP; *Int'l*, pg. 387
WESTERN ROOFING SERVICE, INC.—See Altas Partners LP; *Int'l*, pg. 387
WESTERN ROTO ENGRAVERS INC.; *U.S. Private*, pg. 4496
WESTERN RV COUNTRY LTD; *Int'l*, pg. 8389
WESTERN SADDLERY & SPORTING GOODS; *U.S. Private*, pg. 4496
WESTERN SAFETY PRODUCTS, INC.—See Bunzl plc; *Int'l*, pg. 1218
WESTERN SALES (1986) LTD.—See Deere & Company; *U.S. Public*, pg. 647
WESTERN SCHOOLS, INC.—See CITIC Group Corporation; *Int'l*, pg. 1619
WESTERN SCHOOLS, INC.—See Founders Equity, Inc.; *U.S. Private*, pg. 1581
WESTERN SCREEN & SIGN LTD—See The Quarto Group, Inc.; *Int'l*, pg. 7677
WESTERN SECURITIES CO., LTD.; *Int'l*, pg. 8389
WESTERN SECURITY BANK—See Glacier Bancorp, Inc.; *U.S. Public*, pg. 939
WESTERN SECURITY SURPLUS INSURANCE BROKERS, INC.; *U.S. Private*, pg. 4496
WESTERN SECURITY SYSTEMS, INC.—See Mountain Acquisition Company, LLC; *U.S. Private*, pg. 2798
WESTERN SEEDS—See Evans Grain & Elevator Co. Inc.; *U.S. Private*, pg. 1435
WESTERN SERVICE CONTRACT CORP.—See The McGraw Group; *U.S. Private*, pg. 4076
WESTERN SHAMROCK CORPORATION; *U.S. Private*, pg. 4496
WESTERN SHIELD ACQUISITIONS LLC—See Heartwood Partners, LLC; *U.S. Private*, pg. 1901
WESTERN SIERRA ENERGY, LLC—See NRG Energy, Inc.; *U.S. Public*, pg. 1551
WESTERN SIERRA RESOURCE CORP.; *U.S. Public*, pg. 2356
WESTERN SIZZLIN CORPORATION—See Biglari Holdings Inc.; *U.S. Public*, pg. 331
WESTERN SKY COMMUNITY CARE, INC.—See Centene Corporation; *U.S. Public*, pg. 471
WESTERN SKY INDUSTRIES LLC—See TransDigm Group Incorporated; *U.S. Public*, pg. 2183
WESTERN SLING COMPANY—See Altamont Capital Partners; *U.S. Private*, pg. 205
WESTERN & SOUTHERN FINANCIAL GROUP, INC.; *U.S. Private*, pg. 4490
THE WESTERN & SOUTHERN LIFE INSURANCE COMPANY—See Western & Southern Financial Group, Inc.; *U.S. Private*, pg. 4490
WESTERN SPECIALTY CONTRACTORS; *U.S. Private*, pg. 4496
WESTERN STANDARD METALS USA, INC.—See Sailfish Royalty Corp.; *Int'l*, pg. 6483
WESTERN STAR RESOURCES INC.; *Int'l*, pg. 8389
WESTERN STAR SALES THUNDER BAY LTD.—See Mercedes-Benz Group AG; *Int'l*, pg. 4824
WESTERN STAR TRANSPORTATION; *U.S. Private*, pg. 4496
WESTERN STAR TRUCK CENTRE PTY LTD.—See Penske Automotive Group, Inc.; *U.S. Public*, pg. 1666
WESTERN STAR TRUCKS AUSTRALIA PTY. LTD.—See Penske Automotive Group, Inc.; *U.S. Public*, pg. 1666
WESTERN STAR TRUCKS INC.—See Mercedes-Benz Group AG; *Int'l*, pg. 4824
WESTERN STAR TRUCKS NORTH LTD; *Int'l*, pg. 8389

THE WESTERN UNION COMPANY

WESTERN STAR TRUCKS SALES, INC.—See Mercedes-Benz Group AG; *Int'l*, pg. 4829
WESTERN STATE AGENCY, INC.; *U.S. Private*, pg. 4496
THE WESTERN STATE BANK; *U.S. Private*, pg. 4134
WESTERN STATE BANK—See Western State Agency, Inc.; *U.S. Private*, pg. 4497
WESTERN STATE DESIGN INC.—See EVI Industries, Inc.; *U.S. Public*, pg. 803
WESTERN STATES BANCORPORATION; *U.S. Private*, pg. 4497
WESTERN STATES BANK—See Western States BanCorporation; *U.S. Private*, pg. 4497
WESTERN STATES ENVELOPE & LABEL - KENTUCKY DIVISION—See Western States Envelope & Label; *U.S. Private*, pg. 4497
WESTERN STATES ENVELOPE & LABEL - LABEL DIVISION—See Western States Envelope & Label; *U.S. Private*, pg. 4497
WESTERN STATES ENVELOPE & LABEL - MINNESOTA DIVISION—See Western States Envelope & Label; *U.S. Private*, pg. 4497
WESTERN STATES ENVELOPE & LABEL - OHIO DIVISION—See Western States Envelope & Label; *U.S. Private*, pg. 4497
WESTERN STATES ENVELOPE & LABEL; *U.S. Private*, pg. 4497
WESTERN STATES FIRE PROTECTION—See APi Group Corporation; *Int'l*, pg. 514
WESTERN STATES MACHINERY CORPORATION; *U.S. Private*, pg. 4497
WESTERN STATES PETROLEUM INC.; *U.S. Private*, pg. 4497
WESTERN STATES WHOLESALE INC.; *U.S. Private*, pg. 4497
WESTERN STATE UNIVERSITY COLLEGE OF LAW—See Dream Center Foundation, a California Nonprofit Corp.; *U.S. Private*, pg. 1275
WESTERN STEEL & PLUMBING INC.—See Dakota Supply Group Inc.; *U.S. Private*, pg. 1147
WESTERN STERLING TRUCKS LTD.; *Int'l*, pg. 8389
WESTERN SUMMIT CONSTRUCTORS, INC.—See Peter Kiewit Sons', Inc.; *U.S. Private*, pg. 3158
WESTERN SUPERCONDUCTING TECHNOLOGIES CO., LTD.; *Int'l*, pg. 8389
WESTERN SUPER MARKETS INC.; *U.S. Private*, pg. 4497
WESTERN SUPREME INC.; *U.S. Private*, pg. 4497
WESTERN SURETY COMPANY—See Loews Corporation; *U.S. Public*, pg. 1340
WESTERN SWITCHES & CONTROLS; *U.S. Private*, pg. 4497
WESTERN SYDNEY REPAIR CENTRE PTY LTD—See ComfortDelGro Corporation Limited; *Int'l*, pg. 1713
WESTERN TECHNOLOGY SERVICES INC.—See Austin Engineering Ltd.; *Int'l*, pg. 718
WESTERN TECHNOLOGY SERVICES INTERNATIONAL, INC.; *U.S. Private*, pg. 4497
WESTERNTECHSYSTEMS INC.; *U.S. Private*, pg. 4498
WESTERN TEL-COM INC.; *U.S. Private*, pg. 4497
WESTERN TILE & MARBLE CONTRACTORS, INC.; *U.S. Private*, pg. 4497
WESTERN TIMBER PRODUCTS INC.; *U.S. Private*, pg. 4497
WESTERN TIRE CENTERS INC.; *U.S. Private*, pg. 4497
WESTERN TITANIUM TECHNOLOGIES CO., LTD.—See Western Metal Materials Co., Ltd.; *Int'l*, pg. 8389
WESTERN TOOL SUPPLY CORPORATION; *U.S. Private*, pg. 4497
WESTERN TRAILER CO.; *U.S. Private*, pg. 4497
WESTERN TRANSPORTATION, INC.—See Energy Transfer LP; *U.S. Public*, pg. 765
WESTERN TRUCK EXCHANGE; *U.S. Private*, pg. 4497
WESTERN TRUCK PARTS & EQUIPMENT COMPANY LLC—See Greenbriar Equity Group, L.P.; *U.S. Private*, pg. 1776
WESTERN TUBE & CONDUIT CORPORATION—See Zekelman Industries Inc.; *U.S. Private*, pg. 4600
WESTERN UNION BUSINESS SOLUTIONS (AUSTRALIA) PTY LIMITED—See The Western Union Company; *U.S. Public*, pg. 2141
WESTERN UNION BUSINESS SOLUTIONS JAPAN KK—See The Western Union Company; *U.S. Public*, pg. 2142
WESTERN UNION BUSINESS SOLUTIONS (MALTA) LIMITED—See The Western Union Company; *U.S. Public*, pg. 2141
WESTERN UNION BUSINESS SOLUTIONS (NEW ZEALAND)—See The Western Union Company; *U.S. Public*, pg. 2141
WESTERN UNION BUSINESS SOLUTIONS (SINGAPORE) PTE LIMITED—See The Western Union Company; *U.S. Public*, pg. 2141
WESTERN UNION BUSINESS SOLUTIONS (UK) LIMITED—See The Western Union Company; *U.S. Public*, pg. 2142
WESTERN UNION BUSINESS SOLUTIONS (USA), LLC—See The Western Union Company; *U.S. Public*, pg. 2142
THE WESTERN UNION COMPANY; *U.S. Public*, pg. 2141

WESTERN UNION CONSULTING SERVICES (BEIJING), CO., LTD.—See The Western Union Company; *U.S. Public*, pg. 2142
WESTERN UNION FINANCIAL SERVICES (AUSTRALIA) PTY LTD.—See The Western Union Company; *U.S. Public*, pg. 2142
WESTERN UNION FINANCIAL SERVICES, INC.—See The Western Union Company; *U.S. Public*, pg. 2142
WESTERN UNION GLOBAL NETWORK PTE. LTD.—See The Western Union Company; *U.S. Public*, pg. 2142
WESTERN UNION INTERNATIONAL BANK GMBH—See The Western Union Company; *U.S. Public*, pg. 2142
WESTERN UNION INTERNATIONAL BANK GMBH—See The Western Union Company; *U.S. Public*, pg. 2142
WESTERN UNION MT EAST LTD.—See The Western Union Company; *U.S. Public*, pg. 2142
WESTERN UNION PROCESSING LITHUANIA, UAB—See The Western Union Company; *U.S. Public*, pg. 2142
WESTERN UNION RETAIL SERVICES BELGIUM—See The Western Union Company; *U.S. Public*, pg. 2142
WESTERN UNION RETAIL SERVICES NORWAY AS—See The Western Union Company; *U.S. Public*, pg. 2142
WESTERN UNION SERVICES INDIA PRIVATE LIMITED—See The Western Union Company; *U.S. Public*, pg. 2142
WESTERN UNION—See The Western Union Company; *U.S. Public*, pg. 2141
WESTERN UNITED LIFE ASSURANCE COMPANY; *U.S. Private*, pg. 4497
WESTERN UNITED STATES AGRICULTURAL TRADE ASSOCIATION; *U.S. Private*, pg. 4498
WESTERN URANIUM & VANADIUM CORP.; *Int'l*, pg. 8389
WESTERN UTILITY CONTRACTORS, INC.—See Hylan Datacom & Electrical, LLC; *U.S. Private*, pg. 2018
WESTERN UTILITY LLC—See Hylan Datacom & Electrical, LLC; *U.S. Private*, pg. 2018
WESTERN WAFFLES CORP.—See Conagra Brands, Inc.; *U.S. Public*, pg. 564
WESTERN WASTE INDUSTRIES—See Waste Management, Inc.; *U.S. Public*, pg. 2334
WESTERN WASTE OF TEXAS, L.L.C.—See Waste Management, Inc.; *U.S. Public*, pg. 2334
WESTERN WATERPROOFING COMPANY INC.—See Western Construction Group; *U.S. Private*, pg. 4492
WESTERN WELL PRODUCTION SERVICES LTD.; *U.S. Private*, pg. 4498
WESTERN WELL TOOL INC.; *U.S. Private*, pg. 4498
WESTERN WHOLESALE LIQUOR CO.—See Johnson Brothers Liquor Company; *U.S. Private*, pg. 2227
WESTERN WORLD INSURANCE COMPANY—See American International Group, Inc.; *U.S. Public*, pg. 107
WESTERN WORLD INSURANCE GROUP, INC.—See American International Group, Inc.; *U.S. Public*, pg. 107
WESTERN WYOMING BEVERAGES INC.; *U.S. Private*, pg. 4498
WESTERN WYOMING DERMATOLOGY & SURGERY—See Harvest Partners L.P.; *U.S. Private*, pg. 1876
WESTERN YANKEE, INC.—See AFE Industries, Inc.; *U.S. Private*, pg. 121
THE WESTERVELT COMPANY; *U.S. Private*, pg. 4134
WESTERVELT REALTY—See The Westervelt Company; *U.S. Private*, pg. 4134
WESTERWALD-NETZ GMBH—See RWE AG; *Int'l*, pg. 6436
WESTERWOOD (WG) GLOBAL LTD.; *Int'l*, pg. 8390
WESTEST, LLC—See GI Manager L.P.; *U.S. Private*, pg. 1691
WESTEX INC.—See Milliken & Company; *U.S. Private*, pg. 2737
WEST-FAIR ELECTRIC CONTRACTORS INC.; *U.S. Private*, pg. 4488
WESTFALIA BRASIL COMPONENTES METALICOS LTDA.—See Heitkamp & Thumann KG; *Int'l*, pg. 3326
WESTFALIA, INC.—See Heitkamp & Thumann KG; *Int'l*, pg. 3327
WESTFALIA METAL COMPONENTS INDIA PVT. LTD.—See Heitkamp & Thumann KG; *Int'l*, pg. 3326
WESTFALIA METAL COMPONENTS SHANGHAI CO. LTD.—See Heitkamp & Thumann KG; *Int'l*, pg. 3326
WESTFALIA METALLSCHLAUCHTECHNIK GMBH & CO. KG—See Heitkamp & Thumann KG; *Int'l*, pg. 3327
WESTFALIA METAL S.R.O.—See Heitkamp & Thumann KG; *Int'l*, pg. 3326
WESTFALIA MOBIL GMBH—See Rapido SAS; *Int'l*, pg. 6210
WESTFALIA PRESSTECHNIK GMBH & CO. KG—See Heitkamp & Thumann KG; *Int'l*, pg. 3327
WESTFALIA SHANGHAI TRADING CO. LTD.—See Heitkamp & Thumann KG; *Int'l*, pg. 3327
WESTFALIASURGE GMBH—See GEA Group Aktiengesellschaft; *Int'l*, pg. 2903
WESTFALIA TECHNOLOGIES, INC.; *U.S. Private*, pg. 4498
WESTFALICA—See Gelsenwasser AG; *Int'l*, pg. 2914

WESTFALISCHE LEBENSMITTEL WERKE LINDEMANN GMBH & CO. KG—See Bunge Limited; *U.S. Public*, pg. 412
WESTFALISCHE WASSER UND UMWELTANALYTIK GMBH—See Gelsenwasser AG; *Int'l*, pg. 2913
WESTFALL GMC TRUCK INC.—See Nextran Corporation; *U.S. Private*, pg. 2921
WESTFALL-O'DELL GMC INC.; *U.S. Private*, pg. 4498
WESTFALL ROOFING; *U.S. Private*, pg. 4498
WESTFALL TECHNIK, INC.—See BlackBern Partners LLC; *U.S. Private*, pg. 573
WESTFALL TECHNIK, INC.—See Lee Equity Partners LLC; *U.S. Private*, pg. 2412
WESTPERRY INVESTMENTS LIMITED—See Barclays PLC; *Int'l*, pg. 863
WESTFIELD BANCORP, INC.—See Ohio Farmers Insurance Company; *U.S. Private*, pg. 3004
WESTFIELD BANK, FSB—See Ohio Farmers Insurance Company; *U.S. Private*, pg. 3004
WESTFIELD BANK—See Western New England Bancorp, Inc.; *U.S. Public*, pg. 2356
WESTFIELD COATINGS CORP.—See RPM International Inc.; *U.S. Public*, pg. 1819
WESTFIELD ELECTROPLATING COMPANY; *U.S. Private*, pg. 4498
WESTFIELD EUROPE LIMITED—See Unibail-Rodamco-Westfield SE; *Int'l*, pg. 8030
WESTFIELD HOMES USA, INC.—See Lennar Corporation; *U.S. Public*, pg. 1306
WESTFIELD INDUSTRIES—See Ag Growth International Inc.; *Int'l*, pg. 198
WESTFIELD INSURANCE COMPANY—See Ohio Farmers Insurance Company; *U.S. Private*, pg. 3004
WESTFIELD MEDICAL LIMITED—See Pollen Street Limited; *Int'l*, pg. 5910
WESTFIELD STEEL INC.; *U.S. Private*, pg. 4498
WEST FINANCIAL SERVICES, INC.—See Sandy Spring Bancorp, Inc.; *U.S. Public*, pg. 1840
WESTFIRE SUDAMERICA SPA—See Johnson Controls International plc; *Int'l*, pg. 3990
WESTFIRE SUDAMERICA S.R.L.—See Johnson Controls International plc; *Int'l*, pg. 3990
WEST FIRE SYSTEMS, INC.—See The Carlyle Group Inc.; *U.S. Public*, pg. 2053
WEST FLORIDA BANK CORPORATION; *U.S. Private*, pg. 4485
WEST FLORIDA BEHAVIORAL HEALTH, INC.—See HCA Healthcare, Inc.; *U.S. Public*, pg. 1013
WEST FLORIDA CARDIOLOGY NETWORK, LLC—See HCA Healthcare, Inc.; *U.S. Public*, pg. 1013
WEST FLORIDA DIVISION, INC.—See HCA Healthcare, Inc.; *U.S. Public*, pg. 1013
WEST FLORIDA ELECTRICAL COOPERATIVE ASSOCIATION; *U.S. Private*, pg. 4485
WEST FLORIDA INTERNAL MEDICINE, LLC—See HCA Healthcare, Inc.; *U.S. Public*, pg. 1013
WEST FLORIDA PHYSICIAN NETWORK, LLC—See HCA Healthcare, Inc.; *U.S. Public*, pg. 1013
WEST FLORIDA REGIONAL MEDICAL CENTER—See HCA Healthcare, Inc.; *U.S. Public*, pg. 1013
WEST FLORIDA SUPPLY, CO.—See City Maintenance Supply; *U.S. Private*, pg. 906
WESTFOOD COMPANY—See Techno-Agricultural Supplying Joint Stock Company; *Int'l*, pg. 7509
WESTFORCE CONSTRUCTION (PTY.) LTD.—See Raubex Group Limited; *Int'l*, pg. 6221
WESTFORD EAGLE—See Gannett Co., Inc.; *U.S. Public*, pg. 903
WEST FRASER - ARMOUR DIVISION—See West Fraser Timber Co., Ltd.; *Int'l*, pg. 8384
WEST FRASER - HENDERSON DIVISION—See West Fraser Timber Co., Ltd.; *Int'l*, pg. 8384
WEST FRASER, INC. - MANSFIELD LUMBER MILL—See West Fraser Timber Co., Ltd.; *Int'l*, pg. 8384
WEST FRASER, INC.—See West Fraser Timber Co., Ltd.; *Int'l*, pg. 8384
WEST FRASER - LEOLA DIVISION—See West Fraser Timber Co., Ltd.; *Int'l*, pg. 8384
WEST FRASER - MAPLESVILLE DIVISION—See West Fraser Timber Co., Ltd.; *Int'l*, pg. 8384
WEST FRASER - MCDAVID DIVISION—See West Fraser Timber Co., Ltd.; *Int'l*, pg. 8384
WEST FRASER MILLS - AUGUSTA DIVISION—See West Fraser Timber Co., Ltd.; *Int'l*, pg. 8384
WEST FRASER MILLS LTD. - HUTTIG SAWMILL DIVISION—See West Fraser Timber Co., Ltd.; *Int'l*, pg. 8384
WEST FRASER MILLS LTD. - JOYCE SAWMILL DIVISION—See West Fraser Timber Co., Ltd.; *Int'l*, pg. 8384
WEST FRASER MILLS LTD.—See West Fraser Timber Co., Ltd.; *Int'l*, pg. 8384
WEST FRASER - NEWBERRY DIVISION—See West Fraser Timber Co., Ltd.; *Int'l*, pg. 8384
WEST FRASER - NEW BOSTON DIVISION—See West Fraser Timber Co., Ltd.; *Int'l*, pg. 8384
WEST FRASER NEWSPRINT LTD.—See West Fraser Timber Co., Ltd.; *Int'l*, pg. 8384

WEST FRASER - OPELIKA DIVISION—See West Fraser Timber Co., Ltd.; *Int'l*, pg. 8384
WEST FRASER - SEABOARD DIVISION—See West Fraser Timber Co., Ltd.; *Int'l*, pg. 8384
WEST FRASER TIMBER CO., LTD. - 100 MILE LUMBER DIVISION—See West Fraser Timber Co., Ltd.; *Int'l*, pg. 8384
WEST FRASER TIMBER CO., LTD. - ALBERTA PLYWOOD DIVISION—See West Fraser Timber Co., Ltd.; *Int'l*, pg. 8384
WEST FRASER TIMBER CO., LTD. - ALBERTA PLYWOOD MILL—See West Fraser Timber Co., Ltd.; *Int'l*, pg. 8384
WEST FRASER TIMBER CO., LTD. - CHASM SAWMILLS DIVISION—See West Fraser Timber Co., Ltd.; *Int'l*, pg. 8384
WEST FRASER TIMBER CO., LTD. - CHETWYND FOREST INDUSTRIES DIVISION—See West Fraser Timber Co., Ltd.; *Int'l*, pg. 8384
WEST FRASER TIMBER CO., LTD. - FRASER LAKE SAWMILLS DIVISION—See West Fraser Timber Co., Ltd.; *Int'l*, pg. 8384
WEST FRASER TIMBER CO., LTD. - HINTON PULP—See West Fraser Timber Co., Ltd.; *Int'l*, pg. 8384
WEST FRASER TIMBER CO., LTD. - HINTON WOOD PRODUCTS—See West Fraser Timber Co., Ltd.; *Int'l*, pg. 8384
WEST FRASER TIMBER CO., LTD. - PACIFIC INLAND RESOURCES DIVISION—See West Fraser Timber Co., Ltd.; *Int'l*, pg. 8384
WEST FRASER TIMBER CO., LTD. - QUESNEL PLYWOOD—See West Fraser Timber Co., Ltd.; *Int'l*, pg. 8384
WEST FRASER TIMBER CO., LTD. - QUESNEL RIVER PULP DIVISION—See Atlas Holdings, LLC; *U.S. Private*, pg. 377
WEST FRASER TIMBER CO., LTD. - QUESNEL SAWMILLS—See West Fraser Timber Co., Ltd.; *Int'l*, pg. 8384
WEST FRASER TIMBER CO., LTD. - RANGER BOARD DIVISION—See West Fraser Timber Co., Ltd.; *Int'l*, pg. 8384
WEST FRASER TIMBER CO., LTD. - SLAVE LAKE PULP DIVISION—See Atlas Holdings, LLC; *U.S. Private*, pg. 377
WEST FRASER TIMBER CO., LTD.; *Int'l*, pg. 8383
WEST FRASER TIMBER CO., LTD. - SUNDRE FOREST PRODUCTS DIVISION—See West Fraser Timber Co., Ltd.; *Int'l*, pg. 8384
WEST FRASER TIMBER CO., LTD. - WEST FRASER LVL DIVISION—See West Fraser Timber Co., Ltd.; *Int'l*, pg. 8384
WEST FRASER TIMBER CO., LTD. - WESTPINE MDF DIVISION—See West Fraser Timber Co., Ltd.; *Int'l*, pg. 8384
WEST FRASER TIMBER CO., LTD. - WILLIAMS LAKE PLYWOOD—See West Fraser Timber Co., Ltd.; *Int'l*, pg. 8384
WEST FRASER TIMBER CO., LTD. - WILLIAMS LAKE TIMBER—See West Fraser Timber Co., Ltd.; *Int'l*, pg. 8384
WEST FRASER - WHITEHOUSE DIVISION—See West Fraser Timber Co., Ltd.; *Int'l*, pg. 8384
WESTFREIGHT HOLDINGS (U.S.A.) INC—See TFI International Inc.; *Int'l*, pg. 7587
WESTFREIGHT SYSTEMS INC.—See TFI International Inc.; *Int'l*, pg. 7587
WEST GABLES REHABILITATION HOSPITAL, LLC—See Select Medical Holdings Corporation; *U.S. Public*, pg. 1862
WESTGATE CHEVROLET, LTD.—See AutoNation, Inc.; *U.S. Public*, pg. 238
WESTGATE ENERGY INC; *Int'l*, pg. 8390
WEST GATE HOME SALES INC; *U.S. Private*, pg. 4485
THE WESTGATE HOTEL—See HF Sinclair Corporation; *U.S. Public*, pg. 1034
WESTGATE, INC.; *U.S. Private*, pg. 4498
WESTGATE MANAGEMENT CO. INC.; *U.S. Private*, pg. 4498
WESTGATE SURGERY CENTER, LLC—See Tenet Healthcare Corporation; *U.S. Public*, pg. 2015
WEST GERMAN MOTOR IMPORTS, INCORPORATED; *U.S. Private*, pg. 4485
WESTGKA MANAGEMENT GESELLSCHAFT FUR KOMMUNALE ANLAGEN MBH—See Erste Abwicklungsanstalt AoR; *Int'l*, pg. 2497
WEST GLACIER MERCANTILE, INC.—See Viad Corp.; *U.S. Public*, pg. 2291
THE WESTGLEN ENDOSCOPY CENTER, LLC—See KKR & Co. Inc.; *U.S. Public*, pg. 1249
WESTGOLD RESOURCES LIMITED; *Int'l*, pg. 8390
WEST GROUP MANAGEMENT LLC; *U.S. Private*, pg. 4485
WEST GROVE HOSPITAL COMPANY, LLC—See Tower Health; *U.S. Private*, pg. 4193
WESTGRUND AG—See ADLER Group SA; *Int'l*, pg. 150

COMPANY NAME INDEX

WEST GUJARAT EXPRESSWAY LIMITED—See Infrastructure Leasing & Financial Services Limited; *Int'l*, pg. 3698
WESTHAB; *U.S. Private*, pg. 4498
WESTHAMPTON REGIONAL DIALYSIS, LLC—See Nautic Partners, LLC; *U.S. Private*, pg. 2871
WESTHAM TRADE COMPANY LIMITED; *U.S. Private*, pg. 4498
WESTHAVEN GOLD CORP.; *Int'l*, pg. 8390
WESTHEALTH SURGERY CENTER, LLC—See UnitedHealth Group Incorporated; *U.S. Public*, pg. 2253
WEST HERR AUTOMOTIVE GROUP, INC.; *U.S. Private*, pg. 4485
WEST HERR CHEVROLET OF HAMBURG; *U.S. Private*, pg. 4485
WEST HERR TOYOTA OF ROCHESTER—See West Herr Automotive Group, Inc.; *U.S. Private*, pg. 4485
WEST HIGHLAND SUPPORT SERVICES, LLC—See Koch Industries, Inc.; *U.S. Private*, pg. 2333
WEST HIGH YIELD (W.H.Y.) RESOURCES LTD.; *Int'l*, pg. 8384
WEST HILLS HOSPITAL & MEDICAL CENTER—See HCA Healthcare, Inc.; *U.S. Public*, pg. 1013
WEST HILLS SURGICAL CENTER, LTD.—See HCA Healthcare, Inc.; *U.S. Public*, pg. 1013
WEST HILLS SURGICAL CENTER, LTD.—See HCA Healthcare, Inc.; *U.S. Public*, pg. 1013
WEST HOLDINGS CORPORATION; *Int'l*, pg. 8384
WEST HOME HEALTH CARE, INC.—See Quipt Home Medical Corp.; *U.S. Public*, pg. 1757
WESTHOUSE HOLDINGS PLC—See ICM Limited; *Int'l*, pg. 3582
WESTHOUSE MEDICAL SERVICES PLC; *Int'l*, pg. 8390
WESTHOUSE SECURITIES LIMITED—See ICM Limited; *Int'l*, pg. 3582
WEST HOUSTON LUXURY IMPORTS, INC.—See AutoNation, Inc.; *U.S. Public*, pg. 238
WEST HOUSTON SURGICARE, INC.—See HCA Healthcare, Inc.; *U.S. Public*, pg. 1013
WEST HOUSTON SURGICARE, INC.—See HCA Healthcare, Inc.; *U.S. Public*, pg. 1013
WEST-HUB BUILDING CORP.—See Crown Packaging International Inc.; *U.S. Private*, pg. 1111
WESTIN AUTOMOTIVE PRODUCTS, INC.; *U.S. Private*, pg. 4498
WESTIN CONSTRUCTION COMPANY INC.; *U.S. Private*, pg. 4498
WESTIN CROWN CENTER HOTEL—See Hallmark Cards, Inc.; *U.S. Private*, pg. 1845
THE WESTIN DENVER DOWNTOWN—See Marriott International, Inc.; *U.S. Public*, pg. 1372
WESTINDIA AB; *Int'l*, pg. 8390
WEST INDIAN ENERGY GROUP LTD.—See Challenger Energy Group PLC; *Int'l*, pg. 1438
WEST INDIAN TOBACCO LIMITED—See British American Tobacco plc; *Int'l*, pg. 1166
WEST INDIES ALLIANCE INSURANCE LIMITED—See Guardian Holdings Limited; *Int'l*, pg. 3171
WEST INDIES ALUMINA COMPANY—See United Company RUSAL Plc; *Int'l*, pg. 8066
THE WEST INDIES RUM DISTILLERY LIMITED—See Cognac Ferrand SASU; *Int'l*, pg. 1695
WEST INDIES STOCKBROKERS LIMITED—See Royal Bank of Canada; *Int'l*, pg. 6411
WEST INDIES TRUST CO. LIMITED—See Portland Investment Counsel Inc.; *Int'l*, pg. 5934
WESTIN FOODS, INC.; *U.S. Private*, pg. 4498
THE WESTIN FORT LAUDERDALE—See Marriott International, Inc.; *U.S. Public*, pg. 1372
THE WESTIN GALLERIA HOUSTON—See Marriott International, Inc.; *U.S. Public*, pg. 1372
WESTING GREEN (TIANJIN) PLASTIC CO., LTD—See Jabil Inc.; *U.S. Public*, pg. 1182
WESTINGHOUSE AIR BRAKE TECHNOLOGIES CORPORATION; *U.S. Public*, pg. 2356
WESTINGHOUSE ELECTRIC COMPANY LLC—See Brookfield Corporation; *Int'l*, pg. 1186
WESTINGHOUSE ELECTRIC GERMANY GMBH—See Brookfield Corporation; *Int'l*, pg. 1187
WESTINGHOUSE ENERGY SYSTEMS EUROPE S.A.—See Brookfield Corporation; *Int'l*, pg. 1187
WESTINGHOUSE LIGHTING CORPORATION; *U.S. Private*, pg. 4498
WESTIN HOTEL MANAGEMENT, LP—See Marriott International, Inc.; *U.S. Public*, pg. 1372
THE WESTIN INDIANAPOLIS—See Marriott International, Inc.; *U.S. Public*, pg. 1372
WESTIN INTERNATIONAL (MALTA) LTD.—See Marriott International, Inc.; *U.S. Public*, pg. 1373
THE WESTIN LONG BEACH—See Marriott International, Inc.; *U.S. Public*, pg. 1373
THE WESTIN LOS ANGELES AIRPORT—See Marriott International, Inc.; *U.S. Public*, pg. 1373
THE WESTIN NEW YORK AT TIMES SQUARE—See Marriott International, Inc.; *U.S. Public*, pg. 1373
THE WESTIN PHILADELPHIA—See Marriott International, Inc.; *U.S. Public*, pg. 1373

THE WESTIN PRINCETON AT FORRESTAL VILLAGE HOTEL—See Marriott International, Inc.; *U.S. Public*, pg. 1373
WESTIN SAN ANTONIO RESORT COMPANY—See Marriott International, Inc.; *U.S. Public*, pg. 1373
THE WESTIN SAN FRANCISCO AIRPORT—See Marriott International, Inc.; *U.S. Public*, pg. 1373
WESTIN SAVANNAH HOLDINGS, LLC—See Marriott International, Inc.; *U.S. Public*, pg. 1373
THE WESTIN SEATTLE—See Marriott International, Inc.; *U.S. Public*, pg. 1373
THE WESTIN SOUTH COAST PLAZA, COSTA MESA—See Marriott International, Inc.; *U.S. Public*, pg. 1373
THE WESTIN SOUTHFIELD DETROIT—See Marriott International, Inc.; *U.S. Public*, pg. 1373
THE WESTIN ST. FRANCIS SAN FRANCISCO ON UNION SQUARE—See Marriott International, Inc.; *U.S. Public*, pg. 1373
THE WESTIN ST. JOHN RESORT VILLAS—See Marriott International, Inc.; *U.S. Public*, pg. 1373
WESTINVEST GESELLSCHAFT FUR INVESTMENTFONDS MBH—See DekaBank; *Int'l*, pg. 2005
THE WESTIN WALTHAM BOSTON—See Marriott International, Inc.; *U.S. Public*, pg. 1373
WEST ISLE ENERGY INC.; *Int'l*, pg. 8385
WEST JAPAN ELECTRIC SYSTEM CO., LTD.—See West Japan Railway Company; *Int'l*, pg. 8385
WEST JAPAN ENGINEERING CONSULTANTS, INC.—See Kyushu Electric Power Co., Inc.; *Int'l*, pg. 4368
WEST JAPAN RAILWAY COMPANY; *Int'l*, pg. 8385
WEST JAPAN RAILWAY DAILY SERVICE NET COMPANY—See West Japan Railway Company; *Int'l*, pg. 8385
WEST JAPAN RAILWAY FASHION GOODS CO., LTD.—See West Japan Railway Company; *Int'l*, pg. 8385
WEST JAPAN RAILWAY FOOD SERVICE NET COMPANY—See West Japan Railway Company; *Int'l*, pg. 8385
WEST JAPAN RAILWAY FUKUCHIYAMA MAINTEC CO., LTD.—See West Japan Railway Company; *Int'l*, pg. 8385
WEST JAPAN RAILWAY FUKUOKA MAINTEC CO., LTD.—See West Japan Railway Company; *Int'l*, pg. 8386
WEST JAPAN RAILWAY HIROSHIMA MAINTEC CO., LTD.B—See West Japan Railway Company; *Int'l*, pg. 8386
WEST JAPAN RAILWAY HOTEL DEVELOPMENT LIMITED—See West Japan Railway Company; *Int'l*, pg. 8386
WEST JAPAN RAILWAY ISETAN LIMITED—See West Japan Railway Company; *Int'l*, pg. 8386
WEST JAPAN RAILWAY KANAZAWA MAINTEC CO., LTD.—See West Japan Railway Company; *Int'l*, pg. 8386
WEST JAPAN RAILWAY MAINTEC CO., LTD.—See West Japan Railway Company; *Int'l*, pg. 8386
WEST JAPAN RAILWAY TECHNOS CORPORATION—See West Japan Railway Company; *Int'l*, pg. 8386
WEST JAPAN RAILWAY TECHSIA CO.,LTD—See West Japan Railway Company; *Int'l*, pg. 8386
WEST JAPAN RAILWAY YONAGO MAINTEC CO., LTD.—See West Japan Railway Company; *Int'l*, pg. 8386
WEST JAPAN SERVICE COMPANY LIMITED—See Coca-Cola Bottlers Japan Holdings Inc.; *Int'l*, pg. 1684
WESTJET AIRLINES LTD.—See ONEX Corporation; *Int'l*, pg. 5580
WESTJET VACATIONS INC.—See ONEX Corporation; *Int'l*, pg. 5580
WESTKAM GOLD CORP.; *Int'l*, pg. 8390
WEST KENDALL BAPTIST HOSPITAL—See Baptist Health South Florida, Inc.; *U.S. Private*, pg. 471
WEST KENTUCKY RURAL ELECTRIC COOPERATIVE CORP., INC.; *U.S. Private*, pg. 4485
WESTKEY GRAPHICS; *Int'l*, pg. 8390
WEST KNOX UTILITY DISTRICT; *U.S. Private*, pg. 4486
WESTLAKE ASSOCIATES INC.; *U.S. Private*, pg. 4498
WESTLAKE AUDIO INC.; *U.S. Private*, pg. 4498
WESTLAKE BUILDING PRODUCTS ULC—See Westlake Corporation; *U.S. Public*, pg. 2360
WESTLAKE CANADA INC.—See Westlake Corporation; *U.S. Public*, pg. 2360
WESTLAKE CHEMICAL PARTNERS LP—See Westlake Corporation; *U.S. Public*, pg. 2360
WEST LAKE CO., LTD.—See Univance Corporation; *Int'l*, pg. 8076
WESTLAKE CORPORATION; *U.S. Public*, pg. 2360
WESTLAKE DAVINCI ROOFSCAPES, LLC—See Westlake Corporation; *U.S. Public*, pg. 2360
WESTLAKE DEVELOPMENT CO., INC.; *U.S. Private*, pg. 4499
WEST LAKE ENERGY CORP.; *Int'l*, pg. 8386
WESTLAKE EPOXY GMBH—See Westlake Corporation; *U.S. Public*, pg. 2360

WESTLIFE DEVELOPMENT LIMITED

WESTLAKE FINANCIAL SERVICES, LLC—See Hankey Group; *U.S. Private*, pg. 1853
WEST LAKE FOOD CORPORATION; *U.S. Private*, pg. 4486
WESTLAKE HARDWARE, INC.—See Ace Hardware Corporation; *U.S. Private*, pg. 57
WESTLAKE LONGVIEW CORPORATION—See Westlake Corporation; *U.S. Public*, pg. 2360
WESTLAKE NATRIUM LLC—See Westlake Corporation; *U.S. Public*, pg. 2360
WESTLAKE OLEFINS CORPORATION—See Westlake Corporation; *U.S. Public*, pg. 2360
WESTLAKE PETROCHEMICALS LLC—See Westlake Corporation; *U.S. Public*, pg. 2360
WESTLAKE PIPE & FITTINGS CORPORATION—See Westlake Corporation; *U.S. Public*, pg. 2360
WESTLAKE PLASTICS COMPANY; *U.S. Private*, pg. 4499
WESTLAKE POLYMERS LLC—See Westlake Corporation; *U.S. Public*, pg. 2360
WESTLAKES CINEMA PTY LTD—See Reading International, Inc.; *U.S. Public*, pg. 1768
WESTLAKE STYRENE LLC—See Westlake Corporation; *U.S. Public*, pg. 2360
WESTLAKE VINNOLIT BENELUX-FRANCE B.V.—See Westlake Corporation; *U.S. Public*, pg. 2361
WESTLAKE VINNOLIT GMBH & CO. KG—See Westlake Corporation; *U.S. Public*, pg. 2361
WESTLAKE VINNOLIT ITALIA S.R.L.—See Westlake Corporation; *U.S. Public*, pg. 2361
WESTLAKE VINNOLIT LIMITED—See Westlake Corporation; *U.S. Public*, pg. 2361
WESTLAKE VINYLS COMPANY LP—See Westlake Corporation; *U.S. Public*, pg. 2361
WESTLAKE VINYLS, INC.—See Westlake Corporation; *U.S. Public*, pg. 2361
WESTLAND DISTILLERY—See Remy Cointreau S.A.; *Int'l*, pg. 6272
WESTLAND GUMMIWERKE GMBH & CO. KG; *Int'l*, pg. 8390
WESTLAND HORTICULTURE LTD.; *Int'l*, pg. 8390
WESTLAND INSURANCE GROUP LTD.; *Int'l*, pg. 8390
WESTLAND MILK PRODUCTS INVESTMENTS LIMITED—See Inner Mongolia Yili Industrial Group Co., Ltd.; *Int'l*, pg. 3708
WESTLAND PRINTERS, INC.—See Chatham Asset Management, LLC; *U.S. Private*, pg. 866
WESTLAND PRINTERS—See Chatham Asset Management, LLC; *U.S. Private*, pg. 866
WESTLAND RESOURCES, INC.—See Keystone Group, L.P.; *U.S. Private*, pg. 2299
WESTLANDS WATER DISTRICT INC.; *U.S. Private*, pg. 4499
WESTLAND TECHNOLOGIES INC.—See ESCO Technologies, Inc.; *U.S. Public*, pg. 794
WESTLAND TRANSMISSIONS LIMITED—See Leonardo S.p.A.; *Int'l*, pg. 4458
WESTLANDUTRECHT BANK N.V.—See ING Groep N.V.; *Int'l*, pg. 3700
WEST LEISURE RESORTS LIMITED; *Int'l*, pg. 8386
WESTLEX INC.; *U.S. Private*, pg. 4499
WESTLEY GROUP LIMITED; *Int'l*, pg. 8390
WESTLEY OF CARDIFF LIMITED—See Westley Group Limited; *Int'l*, pg. 8391
WESTLEYS LIMITED—See Westley Group Limited; *Int'l*, pg. 8391
WEST LIBERTY FOODS - BOLINGBROOK—See Iowa Turkey Growers Cooperative; *U.S. Private*, pg. 2136
WEST LIBERTY FOODS, LLC—See Iowa Turkey Growers Cooperative; *U.S. Private*, pg. 2136
WESTLIE MOTOR COMPANY; *U.S. Private*, pg. 4499
WESTLIFE DEVELOPMENT LIMITED; *Int'l*, pg. 8391
WEST LINN PAPER COMPANY—See Stern Partners Inc.; *Int'l*, pg. 7212
WESTLITE DORMITORY (BUKIT MINYAK) SDN. BHD.—See Centurion Corporation Limited; *Int'l*, pg. 1417
WESTLITE DORMITORY (JB TECHPARK) SDN. BHD.—See Centurion Corporation Limited; *Int'l*, pg. 1417
WESTLITE DORMITORY MANAGEMENT PTE. LTD.—See Centurion Corporation Limited; *Int'l*, pg. 1417
WESTLITE DORMITORY MANAGEMENT SDN. BHD.—See Centurion Corporation Limited; *Int'l*, pg. 1417
WESTLITE DORMITORY (PASIR GUDANG) SDN. BHD.—See Centurion Corporation Limited; *Int'l*, pg. 1417
WESTLITE DORMITORY (SENAI) SDN. BHD.—See Centurion Corporation Limited; *Int'l*, pg. 1417
WESTLITE DORMITORY (SN II) SDN. BHD.—See Centurion Corporation Limited; *Int'l*, pg. 1417
WESTLITE DORMITORY (TAMPOI) SDN. BHD.—See Centurion Corporation Limited; *Int'l*, pg. 1417
WESTLITE DORMITORY (TEBRAU) SDN. BHD.—See Centurion Corporation Limited; *Int'l*, pg. 1417
WESTLITE DORMITORY (TOH GUAN) PTE. LTD.—See Centurion Corporation Limited; *Int'l*, pg. 1417

WESTLIFE DEVELOPMENT LIMITED / CORPORATE AFFILIATIONS

Company Index

WESTLITE DORMITORY (WOODLANDS) PTE. LTD.—See Centurion Corporation Limited; *Int'l*, pg. 1417
WESTLITE JUNIPER (MANDAI) PTE. LTD.—See Centurion Corporation Limited; *Int'l*, pg. 1417
WEST-LITE SUPPLY CO., INC.—See Facility Solutions Group, Inc.; *U.S. Private*, pg. 1460
WESTLOCK CONTROLS CORPORATION—See Crane NXT, Co.; *U.S. Public*, pg. 592
WESTLOCK CONTROLS HOLDINGS, INC.—See Crane NXT, Co.; *U.S. Public*, pg. 589
WESTLOCK CONTROLS LIMITED—See Crane NXT, Co.; *U.S. Public*, pg. 589
WEST LOUISIANA HEALTH SERVICES INC; *U.S. Private*, pg. 4486
WEST LPN FORT WORTH ONCOLOGY, PLLC—See HCA Healthcare, Inc.; *U.S. Public*, pg. 1013
WESTLUND—See Blackfriars Corp.; *U.S. Private*, pg. 575
WESTLUND WARREN BUICK-GMC TRUCK; *U.S. Private*, pg. 4499
WESTMAN STEEL INDUSTRIES—See WGI Westman Group, Inc.; *Int'l*, pg. 8394
WEST MARINE, INC.—See Monomoy Capital Partners LLC; *U.S. Private*, pg. 2772
WESTMARK HOTELS, ALASKA—See Carnival Corporation; *U.S. Public*, pg. 438
WESTMARK HOTELS OF CANADA, LTD.—See Carnival Corporation; *U.S. Public*, pg. 438
WESTMARK INDUSTRIES INC.; *U.S. Private*, pg. 4499
WESTMARK PRODUCTS, INC.; *U.S. Private*, pg. 4499
WESTMATIC CORPORATION—See Lagercrantz Group AB; *Int'l*, pg. 4395
WESTMATIC I ARVIKA AB—See Lagercrantz Group AB; *Int'l*, pg. 4395
WESTMATIC, INC.—See Lagercrantz Group AB; *Int'l*, pg. 4395
WEST MAUI CONSTRUCTION, INC.; *U.S. Private*, pg. 4486
WESTMEAD BUILDING COMPANY LIMITED—See Panther Securities PLC; *Int'l*, pg. 5731
WESTMEAD PRIVATE HOSPITAL PTY LIMITED—See Ramsay Health Care Limited; *Int'l*, pg. 6199
WESTMEAD REHABILITATION HOSPITAL PTY. LTD.—See Luye Medical Group; *Int'l*, pg. 4590
WESTMED AMBULANCE SERVICE, INC.—See KKR & Co. Inc.; *U.S. Public*, pg. 1250
WEST MEDIA GROUP, INC.; *U.S. Private*, pg. 4486
WESTMED, INC.—See HCA Healthcare, Inc.; *U.S. Public*, pg. 1011
WESTMED MEDICAL GROUP, P.C.—See Apposite Capital LLP; *Int'l*, pg. 522
WESTMED PRACTICE PARTNERS LLC—See UnitedHealth Group Incorporated; *U.S. Public*, pg. 2252
WEST MICHIGAN OFFICE INTERIORS INC.; *U.S. Private*, pg. 4486
WEST MICHIGAN UNIFORM—See Wildman Business Group Inc.; *U.S. Private*, pg. 4519
WEST MIDLANDS TRAVEL LIMITED—See Mobico Group PLC; *Int'l*, pg. 5009
WEST MILL CLOTHES, TUXEDO ACCESSORIES DIVISION (DBA LORD WEST)—See Lord West Formal Wear; *U.S. Private*, pg. 2495
WEST MILTON STATE BANK; *U.S. Private*, pg. 4486
WEST MINING CORP.; *Int'l*, pg. 8386
WESTMINSTER AMERICAN INSURANCE COMPANY—See NI Holdings, Inc.; *U.S. Public*, pg. 1527
WESTMINSTER CAPITAL INC.; *U.S. Private*, pg. 4499
WESTMINSTER CRACKER COMPANY, INC.—See LSCG Management, Inc.; *U.S. Private*, pg. 2509
WESTMINSTER FOODS, LLC—See LSCG Management, Inc.; *U.S. Private*, pg. 2509
WESTMINSTER GARDENS, INC.—See Service Corporation International; *U.S. Public*, pg. 1871
WESTMINSTER GRAVELS LTD.—See HAL Trust N.V.; *Int'l*, pg. 3225
WESTMINSTER GROUP PLC; *Int'l*, pg. 8391
WESTMINSTER HOLDING; *U.S. Private*, pg. 4499
WESTMINSTER HOOTERS, INC.—See Restaurants of America, Inc.; *U.S. Public*, pg. 3408
WESTMINSTER INSURANCE AGENCY, INC.—See Toll Brothers, Inc.; *U.S. Public*, pg. 2162
WESTMINSTER INTERNATIONAL LIMITED—See Westminster Group Plc; *Int'l*, pg. 8391
WESTMINSTER LIVESTOCK AUCTION LLC; *U.S. Private*, pg. 4499
WESTMINSTER MALL, LLC—See Washington Prime Group Inc.; *U.S. Private*, pg. 4449
WESTMINSTER MANAGEMENT—See Kushner Companies; *U.S. Private*, pg. 2358
WESTMINSTER PRESBYTERIAN RETIREMENT COMMUNITY, INC.; *U.S. Private*, pg. 4499
WESTMINSTER RESEARCH ASSOCIATES LLC—See The Toronto-Dominion Bank; *Int'l*, pg. 7695
WESTMINSTER SURGERY CENTER, LLC—See Tenet Healthcare Corporation; *U.S. Public*, pg. 2015
WESTMINSTER TITLE COMPANY, INC.—See Toll Brothers, Inc.; *U.S. Public*, pg. 2162
WESTMINSTER TRAVEL CONSULTANCY (GUANGZHOU) LIMITED—See Corporate Travel Management Limited; *Int'l*, pg. 1806
WESTMINSTER TRAVEL LIMITED—See Corporate Travel Management Limited; *Int'l*, pg. 1806
WESTMINSTER TRAVEL LIMITED—See Corporate Travel Management Limited; *Int'l*, pg. 1806
WESTMINSTER TRAVEL LIMITED—See Corporate Travel Management Limited; *Int'l*, pg. 1806
WESTMINSTER TRAVEL LIMITED—See Corporate Travel Management Limited; *Int'l*, pg. 1806
WESTMINSTER VILLAGE, INC.; *U.S. Private*, pg. 4499
WESTMINSTER VILLAGE NORTH; *U.S. Private*, pg. 4499
WEST MONROE PARTNERS, LLC; *U.S. Private*, pg. 4486
WESTMONT A. IMPORTS, INC.—See AutoNation, Inc.; *U.S. Public*, pg. 238
WESTMONT A. IMPORTS, INC.—See AutoNation, Inc.; *U.S. Public*, pg. 238
WESTMONT B. IMPORTS, INC.—See AutoNation, Inc.; *U.S. Public*, pg. 238
WESTMONT COLLISION, INC.—See AutoNation, Inc.; *U.S. Public*, pg. 238
WESTMONT DEVELOPMENT INC.—See Westmont Hospitality Group; *Int'l*, pg. 8391
WEST MONTGOMERY HOTEL HOLDINGS INC.—See Sunburst Hospitality Corporation; *U.S. Private*, pg. 3865
WESTMONT HOSPITALITY GROUP; *Int'l*, pg. 8391
WESTMONT INTERIOR SUPPLY HOUSE—See GMS Inc.; *U.S. Public*, pg. 947
WESTMONT M. IMPORTS, INC.—See AutoNation, Inc.; *U.S. Public*, pg. 238
WESTMONT SERVICES B.V.—See Westmont Hospitality Group; *Int'l*, pg. 8391
WESTMORELAND CANADA HOLDINGS INC.—See Westmoreland Coal Company; *U.S. Private*, pg. 4500
WESTMORELAND CASEMANAGEMENT AND SUPPORTS, INC.; *U.S. Private*, pg. 4499
WESTMORELAND COAL COMPANY; *U.S. Private*, pg. 4499
WESTMORELAND COUNTY HOUSING AUTHORITY; *U.S. Private*, pg. 4500
WESTMORELAND ENERGY LLC—See Westmoreland Coal Company; *U.S. Private*, pg. 4500
WESTMORELANDFLINT—See Flint Communications, Inc. & Adfarm; *U.S. Private*, pg. 1545
WESTMORELAND KEMMERER, INC.—See Westmoreland Coal Company; *U.S. Private*, pg. 4500
WESTMORELAND PARTNERS—See Westmoreland Coal Company; *U.S. Private*, pg. 4500
WESTMORELAND RESOURCES GP, LLC—See Westmoreland Coal Company; *U.S. Private*, pg. 4500
WESTMORELAND RESOURCES, INC.—See Westmoreland Coal Company; *U.S. Private*, pg. 4500
WESTMORELAND SAVAGE CORPORATION—See Westmoreland Coal Company; *U.S. Private*, pg. 4500
WEST MOTOR COMPANY INC.; *U.S. Private*, pg. 4486
WEST MOUNTAIN ENVIRONMENTAL CORP.; *Int'l*, pg. 8386
WESTMOUNT ENERGY LIMITED; *Int'l*, pg. 8391
WESTMOUNT MINERALS CORP.; *Int'l*, pg. 8391
WESTMOUNT STOREFRONT SYSTEMS LTD.; *Int'l*, pg. 8391
WEST MUSIC CO.; *U.S. Private*, pg. 4486
WESTNET LTD—See CK Hutchison Holdings Limited; *Int'l*, pg. 1638
WESTNET LTD—See Vodafone Group Plc; *Int'l*, pg. 8285
WESTNOFA INDUSTRIER AS—See Recticel S.A.; *Int'l*, pg. 6242
WEST NOTIFICATION, INC.—See Apollo Global Management; *U.S. Public*, pg. 152
WESTNY BUILDING PRODUCTS CO.; *U.S. Private*, pg. 4500
WEST OAHU AGGREGATE CO., INC.; *U.S. Private*, pg. 4486
WEST OIL COMPANY INCORPORATED; *U.S. Private*, pg. 4486
WEST OIL COMPANY INC.—See First Reserve Management, L.P.; *U.S. Private*, pg. 1527
WEST OIL & GAS PRODUCTION COMPANY—See National Iranian Oil Company; *Int'l*, pg. 5160
WEST OK TRUCKING, INC.—See Energy Spectrum Securities Corporation; *U.S. Private*, pg. 1396
WESTON AEROSPACE LTD.—See TransDigm Group Incorporated; *U.S. Public*, pg. 2180
WESTON AMERICAN, INC.—See Kohlberg & Company, LLC; *U.S. Private*, pg. 2337
WESTON AMERICAN, INC.—See Partners Group Holding AG; *Int'l*, pg. 5749
WESTON BAKERIES LIMITED—See George Weston Limited; *Int'l*, pg. 2939
WESTON BEAMOR HOLDINGS LIMITED—See L. Possehl & Co. mbH; *Int'l*, pg. 4385
WESTON BRANDS, LLC—See Hamilton Beach Brands Holding Company; *U.S. Public*, pg. 981
WESTON COMPANIES—See Vantage Companies; *U.S. Private*, pg. 4344
WESTON DIALYSIS CENTER, LLC—See DaVita Inc.; *U.S. Public*, pg. 644
WESTONE LABORATORIES, INC.—See HealthEdge Investment Partners, LLC; *U.S. Private*, pg. 1896
WESTONE WHOLESALE LIMITED—See Kitwave Group Plc; *Int'l*, pg. 4196
WESTON FOODS (CANADA) INC.—See George Weston Limited; *Int'l*, pg. 2939
WESTON IMPORTERS LTD—See Marfrig Global Foods S.A.; *Int'l*, pg. 4692
WESTON OUTPATIENT SURGICAL CENTER, LTD.—See KKR & Co. Inc.; *U.S. Public*, pg. 1249
WESTON PONTIAC BUICK GMC INC.; *U.S. Private*, pg. 4500
WESTON PREMIUM WOODS INC.—See Richelieu Hardware Ltd.; *Int'l*, pg. 6331
WESTON PRESIDIO CAPITAL; *U.S. Private*, pg. 4500
WESTON & SAMPSON, INC.; *U.S. Private*, pg. 4500
THE WEST ORANGE NJ ENDOSCOPY ASC, LLC—See KKR & Co. Inc.; *U.S. Public*, pg. 1248
WEST OREGON ELECTRIC COOPERATIVE, INC.; *U.S. Private*, pg. 4486
WESTOURS MOTOR COACHES, LLC—See Carnival Corporation; *U.S. Public*, pg. 438
WESTOVER CORPORATION; *U.S. Private*, pg. 4500
WESTOVER COMMUNICATIONS, LLC—See MasTec, Inc.; *U.S. Public*, pg. 1393
WESTOZ FUNDS MANAGEMENT PTY. LTD.—See Euroz Hartleys Group Limited; *Int'l*, pg. 2559
WESTOZ INVESTMENT COMPANY LIMITED—See WAM Capital Limited; *Int'l*, pg. 8337
WESTPAC AMERICAS INC—See Westpac Banking Corporation; *Int'l*, pg. 8392
WESTPAC-AUSTRALIAN CAPITAL TERRITORY—See Westpac Banking Corporation; *Int'l*, pg. 8392
WESTPAC BANKING CORPORATION - HONG KONG OFFICE—See Westpac Banking Corporation; *Int'l*, pg. 8392
WESTPAC BANKING CORPORATION (JERSEY) LTD.—See Westpac Banking Corporation; *Int'l*, pg. 8392
WESTPAC BANKING CORPORATION - LONDON OFFICE—See Westpac Banking Corporation; *Int'l*, pg. 8392
WESTPAC BANKING CORPORATION - NEW ZEALAND OFFICE—See Westpac Banking Corporation; *Int'l*, pg. 8392
WESTPAC BANKING CORPORATION; *Int'l*, pg. 8391
WESTPAC BANK-PNG-LIMITED—See Westpac Banking Corporation; *Int'l*, pg. 8392
WESTPAC EQUITY HOLDINGS PTY LIMITED—See Westpac Banking Corporation; *Int'l*, pg. 8392
WESTPAC ESSENTIAL SERVICES TRUST—See Westpac Banking Corporation; *Int'l*, pg. 8392
WESTPAC FINANCIAL SERVICES GROUP LIMITED—See Westpac Banking Corporation; *Int'l*, pg. 8392
WESTPAC FUNDS MANAGEMENT LIMITED—See Westpac Banking Corporation; *Int'l*, pg. 8392
WEST PACIFIC ENTERPRISES CORPORATION—See Tungtex (Holdings) Co. Ltd.; *Int'l*, pg. 7972
WESTPAC INVESTMENT VEHICLE PTY LIMITED—See Westpac Banking Corporation; *Int'l*, pg. 8392
WESTPAC LABS, INC.—See Sonic Healthcare Limited; *Int'l*, pg. 7099
WESTPAC MATCHING GIFTS LIMITED—See Westpac Banking Corporation; *Int'l*, pg. 8392
WESTPAC-NEW SOUTH WALES—See Westpac Banking Corporation; *Int'l*, pg. 8392
WESTPAC-NORTHERN TERRITORY—See Westpac Banking Corporation; *Int'l*, pg. 8392
WESTPAC-QUEENSLAND—See Westpac Banking Corporation; *Int'l*, pg. 8392
WESTPAC SECURITISATION MANAGEMENT PTY LIMITED—See Westpac Banking Corporation; *Int'l*, pg. 8392
WESTPAC SINGAPORE LIMITED—See Westpac Banking Corporation; *Int'l*, pg. 8392
WESTPAC-SOUTH AUSTRALIA—See Westpac Banking Corporation; *Int'l*, pg. 8392
WESTPACTRUST FINANCIAL SERVICES—See Westpac Banking Corporation; *Int'l*, pg. 8392
WESTPAC-VICTORIA—See Westpac Banking Corporation; *Int'l*, pg. 8392
WESTPAC-WESTERN AUSTRALIA—See Westpac Banking Corporation; *Int'l*, pg. 8392
WEST PAK AVOCADO, INC.; *U.S. Private*, pg. 4486
WEST PALM BEACH AUTO AUCTION—See Cox Enterprises, Inc.; *U.S. Private*, pg. 1077
WEST PALM OUTPATIENT SURGERY & LASER CENTER, LTD—See KKR & Co. Inc.; *U.S. Public*, pg. 1249
WEST PARK BOWLING LANES INC.—See Drury Inn Inc.; *U.S. Public*, pg. 1280
WEST PARK CROSSING RETIREMENT COMMUNITY INC.—See Extendicare Inc.; *Int'l*, pg. 2591
WEST PARK PAINTING INC.—See Don C. Musick Construction Co., Inc.; *U.S. Private*, pg. 1257
WEST PARTNERS LLC; *U.S. Private*, pg. 4486
WESTPAY AB; *Int'l*, pg. 8392
WEST PENETONE, INC.—See Wechco, Inc.; *U.S. Private*, pg. 4468
WEST PENN WIRE—See Belden, Inc.; *U.S. Public*, pg. 294

COMPANY NAME INDEX

WEST PHARMACEUTICAL PACKAGING (CHINA) COMPANY LTD.—See West Pharmaceutical Services, Inc.; *U.S. Public*, pg. 2353

WEST PHARMACEUTICAL PACKAGING INDIA PRIVATE LIMITED—See West Pharmaceutical Services, Inc.; *U.S. Public*, pg. 2353

WEST PHARMACEUTICAL SERVICES ARGENTINA S.A.—See West Pharmaceutical Services, Inc.; *U.S. Public*, pg. 2353

WEST PHARMACEUTICAL SERVICES BRASIL LTDA.—See West Pharmaceutical Services, Inc.; *U.S. Public*, pg. 2353

WEST PHARMACEUTICAL SERVICES COLOMBIA S.A.—See West Pharmaceutical Services, Inc.; *U.S. Public*, pg. 2353

WEST PHARMACEUTICAL SERVICES CORNWALL LIMITED—See West Pharmaceutical Services, Inc.; *U.S. Public*, pg. 2353

WEST PHARMACEUTICAL SERVICES CORNWALL LTD.—See West Pharmaceutical Services, Inc.; *U.S. Public*, pg. 2353

WEST PHARMACEUTICAL SERVICES DANMARK A/S—See West Pharmaceutical Services, Inc.; *U.S. Public*, pg. 2353

WEST PHARMACEUTICAL SERVICES DE COLOMBIA, S.A.—See West Pharmaceutical Services, Inc.; *U.S. Public*, pg. 2353

WEST PHARMACEUTICAL SERVICES DEUTSCHLAND GMBH & CO. KG—See West Pharmaceutical Services, Inc.; *U.S. Public*, pg. 2353

WEST PHARMACEUTICAL SERVICES ESPANA, S.A.—See West Pharmaceutical Services, Inc.; *U.S. Public*, pg. 2353

WEST PHARMACEUTICAL SERVICES FINANCE DANMARK APS—See West Pharmaceutical Services, Inc.; *U.S. Public*, pg. 2353

WEST PHARMACEUTICAL SERVICES FRANCE S.A.—See West Pharmaceutical Services, Inc.; *U.S. Public*, pg. 2353

WEST PHARMACEUTICAL SERVICES HISPANIA S.A.—See West Pharmaceutical Services, Inc.; *U.S. Public*, pg. 2353

WEST PHARMACEUTICAL SERVICES HOLDING DANMARK APS—See West Pharmaceutical Services, Inc.; *U.S. Public*, pg. 2353

WEST PHARMACEUTICAL SERVICES HOLDING FRANCE SAS—See West Pharmaceutical Services, Inc.; *U.S. Public*, pg. 2353

WEST PHARMACEUTICAL SERVICES HOLDING GMBH—See West Pharmaceutical Services, Inc.; *U.S. Public*, pg. 2353

WEST PHARMACEUTICAL SERVICES, INC. - CLEARWATER—See West Pharmaceutical Services, Inc.; *U.S. Public*, pg. 2353

WEST PHARMACEUTICAL SERVICES, INC.—See West Pharmaceutical Services, Inc.; *U.S. Public*, pg. 2353

WEST PHARMACEUTICAL SERVICES, INC.—See West Pharmaceutical Services, Inc.; *U.S. Public*, pg. 2353

WEST PHARMACEUTICAL SERVICES, INC.—See West Pharmaceutical Services, Inc.; *U.S. Public*, pg. 2353

WEST PHARMACEUTICAL SERVICES, INC.—See West Pharmaceutical Services, Inc.; *U.S. Public*, pg. 2353

WEST PHARMACEUTICAL SERVICES, INC.—See West Pharmaceutical Services, Inc.; *U.S. Public*, pg. 2353

WEST PHARMACEUTICAL SERVICES, INC.—See West Pharmaceutical Services, Inc.; *U.S. Public*, pg. 2353

WEST PHARMACEUTICAL SERVICES, INC.; *U.S. Public*, pg. 2352

WEST PHARMACEUTICAL SERVICES LAKEWOOD, INC.—See West Pharmaceutical Services, Inc.; *U.S. Public*, pg. 2353

WEST PHARMACEUTICAL SERVICES LIMITED DANMARK A/S—See West Pharmaceutical Services, Inc.; *U.S. Public*, pg. 2353

WEST PHARMACEUTICAL SERVICES NORMANDIE SAS—See West Pharmaceutical Services, Inc.; *U.S. Public*, pg. 2353

WEST PHARMACEUTICAL SERVICES OF DELAWARE, INC.—See West Pharmaceutical Services, Inc.; *U.S. Public*, pg. 2353

WEST PHARMACEUTICAL SERVICES OF FLORIDA, INC.—See West Pharmaceutical Services, Inc.; *U.S. Public*, pg. 2353

WEST PHARMACEUTICAL SERVICES SINGAPORE (HOLDING) PTE. LIMITED—See West Pharmaceutical Services, Inc.; *U.S. Public*, pg. 2353

WEST PHARMACEUTICAL SERVICES SINGAPORE PTE. LTD.—See West Pharmaceutical Services, Inc.; *U.S. Public*, pg. 2353

WEST PHARMACEUTICAL SERVICES VENEZUELA C.A.—See West Pharmaceutical Services, Inc.; *U.S. Public*, pg. 2353

WEST PHARMACEUTICAL SERVICES VERWALTUNGS GMBH—See West Pharmaceutical Services, Inc.; *U.S. Public*, pg. 2353

WEST PHILADELPHIA COMMUNITY MENTAL HEALTH CONSORTIUM, INC.; *U.S. Private*, pg. 4486

WEST PHYSICS CONSULTING LLC; *U.S. Private*, pg. 4486

WEST PIONEER PROPERTIES LIMITED; *Int'l*, pg. 8386

WEST PLAINS IMPLEMENT CO., INC.; *U.S. Private*, pg. 4486

WEST PLAINS LLC; *U.S. Private*, pg. 4486

WESTPOINT AUTOS (QLD) PTY. LTD.; *Int'l*, pg. 8392

WEST POINT BANK—See First Breckenridge Bancshares; *U.S. Private*, pg. 1514

WEST POINT CHEVROLET, INC.—See North American Truck & Trailer, Inc.; *U.S. Private*, pg. 2941

WEST POINT DAIRY PRODUCTS, LLC—See Grassland Dairy Products, Inc.; *U.S. Private*, pg. 1758

WESTPOINT HOME (BAHRAIN) W.L.L.—See Icahn Enterprises L.P.; *U.S. Public*, pg. 1085

WESTPOINT HOME LLC—See Icahn Enterprises L.P.; *U.S. Public*, pg. 1085

WEST POINT HOSPITAL PTE LTD—See China Healthcare Limited; *Int'l*, pg. 1507

WESTPOINT INTERNATIONAL, INC.—See Icahn Enterprises L.P.; *U.S. Public*, pg. 1085

WEST POINT MARKET INC.; *U.S. Private*, pg. 4487

WEST POINT PRODUCTS LLC.; *U.S. Private*, pg. 4487

WESTPOINT VETERINARY GROUP—See August Equity LLP; *Int'l*, pg. 703

WESTPOOL INVESTMENT TRUST PLC—See LMS Capital plc; *Int'l*, pg. 4538

WESTPORT AB—See Westport Fuel Systems Inc.; *Int'l*, pg. 8393

WESTPORT CHRYSLER DODGE LIMITED; *Int'l*, pg. 8392

WESTPORT CORPORATION; *U.S. Private*, pg. 4500

WESTPORT CORPORATION; *U.S. Private*, pg. 4500

WESTPORT DISTRIPARK (M) SDN. BHD.—See DRB-HICOM Berhad; *Int'l*, pg. 2202

WESTPORT FUEL SYSTEMS INC.; *Int'l*, pg. 8392

WESTPORT FUEL SYSTEMS INC.—See Westport Fuel Systems Inc.; *Int'l*, pg. 8392

WESTPORT HOMES, INC.—See D.R. Horton, Inc.; *U.S. Public*, pg. 620

WESTPORT INNOVATIONS (AUSTRALIA) PTY LTD—See Westport Fuel Systems Inc.; *Int'l*, pg. 8392

WESTPORT LIGHT DUTY INC.—See Westport Fuel Systems Inc.; *Int'l*, pg. 8393

WESTPORT POWER INC.—See Westport Fuel Systems Inc.; *Int'l*, pg. 8393

WESTPORTS HOLDINGS BERHAD; *Int'l*, pg. 8393

WESTPORT TECHNOLOGY CENTER INTERNATIONAL—See Intertek Group plc; *Int'l*, pg. 3764

WESTPRO INFRASTRUCTURE LTD.—See The Ingenium Group Inc.; *Int'l*, pg. 7655

WEST PUBLISHING CORPORATION—See Thomson Reuters Corporation; *Int'l*, pg. 7715

WEST QUALITY FOOD SERVICE INC.; *U.S. Private*, pg. 4487

WEST QUAY SHOPPING CENTRE LTD—See Hammerson plc; *Int'l*, pg. 3238

WESTRAC (CHINA) MACHINERY EQUIPMENT LIMITED—See Seven Group Holdings Limited; *Int'l*, pg. 6733

WESTRAC HOLDINGS PTY. LIMITED—See Seven Group Holdings Limited; *Int'l*, pg. 6733

WESTRAC PTY. LIMITED—See Seven Group Holdings Limited; *Int'l*, pg. 6733

WESTREC EQUITIES, INC.—See Centerbridge Partners, L.P.; *U.S. Private*, pg. 816

WESTREC MARINA MANAGEMENT, INC.—See Centerbridge Partners, L.P.; *U.S. Private*, pg. 816

WESTREC MARINAS MANAGEMENT, INC.—See Centerbridge Partners, L.P.; *U.S. Private*, pg. 815

WESTREC PROPERTIES, INC.—See Centerbridge Partners, L.P.; *U.S. Private*, pg. 816

WESTREC PROPERTIES, INC.—See Centerbridge Partners, L.P.; *U.S. Private*, pg. 816

WEST RED LAKE GOLD MINES LTD.; *Int'l*, pg. 8386

WEST RED LAKE GOLD MINES (ONTARIO) LTD—See West Red Lake Gold Mines Ltd.; *Int'l*, pg. 8386

WEST-REEVES INC.; *U.S. Private*, pg. 4488

WESTRIAN GROUP, INC.; *U.S. Private*, pg. 4500

WESTRIDGE CONSTRUCTION LTD.; *Int'l*, pg. 8393

WEST RIDGE MALL, LLC—See Washington Prime Group Inc.; *U.S. Private*, pg. 4449

WESTRISE CO LTD; *Int'l*, pg. 8393

WEST RIVER ELECTRIC ASSOCIATION; *U.S. Private*, pg. 4487

WEST RIVER TELECOM COOP; *U.S. Private*, pg. 4487

WESTROC, INC.—See Summit Materials, Inc.; *U.S. Public*, pg. 1960

WESTROCK ASIA, K.K.—See WestRock Company; *U.S. Public*, pg. 2362

WESTROCK CO. - CHICAGO—See WestRock Company; *U.S. Public*, pg. 2362

WESTROCK CO. - COVINGTON—See WestRock Company; *U.S. Public*, pg. 2362

WESTROCK CO. - EVADALE MILL—See WestRock Company; *U.S. Public*, pg. 2362

WESTROCK COFFEE COMPANY; *U.S. Public*, pg. 2361

WESTROCK CO. - LANETT—See WestRock Company; *U.S. Public*, pg. 2362

WESTROCK CO. - MAHRT MILL - COTTONTON—See WestRock Company; *U.S. Public*, pg. 2362

WESTROCK CO. - MEBANE—See WestRock Company; *U.S. Public*, pg. 2362

WESTROCK COMPANY - CHINO DISTRIBUTION CENTER—See WestRock Company; *U.S. Public*, pg. 2362

WESTROCK COMPANY, INC.; *U.S. Private*, pg. 4500

WESTROCK COMPANY; *U.S. Public*, pg. 2361

WESTROCK CONSUMER PACKAGING GROUP, LLC—See WestRock Company; *U.S. Public*, pg. 2362

WESTROCK CONSUMER PAPERBOARD EMEA B.V.—See WestRock Company; *U.S. Public*, pg. 2362

WESTROCK CONVERTING COMPANY—See WestRock Company; *U.S. Public*, pg. 2363

WESTROCK CP, LLC—See WestRock Company; *U.S. Public*, pg. 2362

WESTROCK FINANCIAL, INC.—See WestRock Company; *U.S. Public*, pg. 2363

WESTROCK GMBH—See WestRock Company; *U.S. Public*, pg. 2362

WESTROCK KK—See WestRock Company; *U.S. Public*, pg. 2362

WESTROCK MANUFACTURING-BILBAO S.L.—See WestRock Company; *U.S. Public*, pg. 2362

WESTROCK MILL COMPANY, LLC—See WestRock Company; *U.S. Public*, pg. 2363

WESTROCK MINNESOTA CORPORATION—See WestRock Company; *U.S. Public*, pg. 2363

WESTROCK MWV HONG KONG LIMITED—See WestRock Company; *U.S. Public*, pg. 2362

WESTROCK MWV, LLC—See WestRock Company; *U.S. Public*, pg. 2362

WESTROCK PACKAGING SOLUTIONS KOREA, INC.—See WestRock Company; *U.S. Public*, pg. 2362

WESTROCK PACKAGING SYSTEMS FRANCE SARL—See WestRock Company; *U.S. Public*, pg. 2362

WESTROCK PACKAGING SYSTEMS, LLC—See WestRock Company; *U.S. Public*, pg. 2362

WESTROCK PACKAGING SYSTEMS NETHERLANDS B.V.—See WestRock Company; *U.S. Public*, pg. 2362

WESTROCK PACKAGING SYSTEMS UK LTD.—See WestRock Company; *U.S. Public*, pg. 2362

WESTROCK-PUERTO RICO, INC.—See WestRock Company; *U.S. Public*, pg. 2363

WESTROCK RKT CO. - DAYTON CONTAINER PLANT—See WestRock Company; *U.S. Public*, pg. 2362

WESTROCK RKT CO. - JACKSONVILLE RECYCLING CENTER—See WestRock Company; *U.S. Public*, pg. 2363

WESTROCK RKT CO. - KNOX FOOD SERVICE PACKAGING PLANT—See WestRock Company; *U.S. Public*, pg. 2363

WESTROCK RKT CO. - LIBERTY CONTAINER PLANT—See WestRock Company; *U.S. Public*, pg. 2363

WESTROCK RKT COMPANY—See WestRock Company; *U.S. Public*, pg. 2362

WESTROCK RKT CO. - NORTH TONAWANDA CONTAINER PLANT—See WestRock Company; *U.S. Public*, pg. 2363

WESTROCK RKT CO. - PLYMOUTH FOOD SERVICE PACKAGING PLANT—See WestRock Company; *U.S. Public*, pg. 2363

WESTROCK RKT CO. - PLYMOUTH LAMINATING FOOD SERVICE PLANT—See WestRock Company; *U.S. Public*, pg. 2363

WESTROCK RKT CO. - SAINT LOUIS FOOD SERVICE PACKAGING PLANT—See WestRock Company; *U.S. Public*, pg. 2363

WESTROCK RKT CO. - SAN JUAN CONTAINER PLANT—See WestRock Company; *U.S. Public*, pg. 2363

WESTROCK RKT CO. - SPRINGFIELD (MA) SHEET PLANT—See WestRock Company; *U.S. Public*, pg. 2363

WESTROCK RKT CO. - TACOMA MILL—See WestRock Company; *U.S. Public*, pg. 2363

WESTROCK RKT CO. - TUPELO CONTAINER PLANT—See WestRock Company; *U.S. Public*, pg. 2363

WESTROCK RKT CO. - WINSTON-SALEM MERCHANDISING DISPLAYS—See WestRock Company; *U.S. Public*, pg. 2363

WESTROCK SERVICES, INC.—See WestRock Company; *U.S. Public*, pg. 2363

WESTROCK SERVICES POLAND SP.Z O.O.—See WestRock Company; *U.S. Public*, pg. 2363

WESTROCK - SOUTHERN CONTAINER, LLC—See WestRock Company; *U.S. Public*, pg. 2362

WEST ROOFING SYSTEMS, INC.; *U.S. Private*, pg. 4487

WEST ROXBURY MEDICAL GROUP INC.—See Partners HealthCare System, Inc.; *U.S. Private*, pg. 3102

WEST ROXBURY TRANSCRIPT—See Gannett Co., Inc.; *U.S. Public*, pg. 903

WESTRUX INTERNATIONAL; *U.S. Private*, pg. 4500

WEST SACRAMENTO DIALYSIS, LLC—See DaVita Inc.; *U.S. Public*, pg. 644

WESTRUX INTERNATIONAL

WEST SAFETY SERVICES, INC.—See Apollo Global Management, Inc.; *U.S. Public*, pg. 152
WEST SALEM MACHINERY CO—See JCE Group AB; *Int'l*, pg. 3923
WEST SHANGHAI AUTOMOBILE SERVICE CO., LTD.; *Int'l*, pg. 8386
WEST SHELL COMMERCIAL, INC.—See Colliers International Group Inc.; *Int'l*, pg. 1701
WEST SHORE BANK CORPORATION; *U.S. Public*, pg. 2353
WEST SHORE BANK—See West Shore Bank Corporation; *U.S. Public*, pg. 2353
WESTSHORE CAPITAL PARTNERS LLC; *U.S. Private*, pg. 4500
WEST SHORE PIPE LINE COMPANY—See Energy Transfer LP; *U.S. Public*, pg. 764
WESTSHORE TERMINALS INVESTMENT CORPORATION; *Int'l*, pg. 8393
WESTSHORE TERMINALS LTD. PARTNERSHIP—See The Jim Pattison Group; *Int'l*, pg. 7660
WEST SHORE WINDOW & DOOR, INC.; *U.S. Private*, pg. 4487
WEST SIBERIAN COMMERCIAL BANK PJSC; *Int'l*, pg. 8386
WESTSIDE ANIMAL HOSPITAL, INC.—See JAB Holding Company S.a.r.l.; *Int'l*, pg. 3862
WESTSIDE BANK—See Piedmont Bancorp, Inc.; *U.S. Private*, pg. 3177
WESTSIDE BUILDING MATERIAL CORP.—See GMS Inc.; *U.S. Public*, pg. 949
WESTSIDE COMMUNITY MENTAL HEALTH CENTER; *U.S. Private*, pg. 4500
WEST SIDE CONVERTIBLE INC.—See Morris Home Holdings Limited; *Int'l*, pg. 5049
WESTSIDE CORPORATION LIMITED; *Int'l*, pg. 8393
WESTSIDE EAGLE OBSERVER—See Wehco Media, Inc.; *U.S. Private*, pg. 4470
WESTSIDE EQUIPMENT CO.; *U.S. Private*, pg. 4500
WESTSIDE FAMILY HEALTHCARE; *U.S. Private*, pg. 4500
WEST SIDE FOODS INC; *U.S. Private*, pg. 4487
WESTSIDE GALVANIZING SERVICES, INC.—See AZZ, Inc.; *U.S. Public*, pg. 259
WEST SIDE GARAGE INC.; *U.S. Private*, pg. 4487
WEST SIDE GRAIN SALES CORP.—See West Side Unlimited Corporation; *U.S. Private*, pg. 4487
WESTSIDE HABILITATION CENTER, INC.; *U.S. Private*, pg. 4501
WEST SIDE HAMMER ELECTRIC; *U.S. Private*, pg. 4487
WEST SIDE MOTORS, INC.—See AutoNation, Inc.; *U.S. Public*, pg. 238
WEST SIDE ONESTOP—See J&H Oil Company Inc.; *U.S. Private*, pg. 2154
WESTSIDE RENTALS, LLC—See CoStar Group, Inc.; *U.S. Public*, pg. 586
WEST SIDE SALVAGE, INC.—See West Side Unlimited Corporation; *U.S. Private*, pg. 4487
WESTSIDE SURGERY CENTER, LTD.—See HCA Healthcare, Inc.; *U.S. Public*, pg. 1014
WEST SIDE TRACTOR SALES CO.; *U.S. Private*, pg. 4487
WEST SIDE TRANSPORT, INC.—See West Side Unlimited Corporation; *U.S. Private*, pg. 4487
WEST SIDE UNLIMITED CORPORATION; *U.S. Private*, pg. 4487
WEST SPRINGFIELD PROPERTIES—See Healthtrax Inc.; *U.S. Private*, pg. 1898
WESTSTAR AUTOPLEX, LLC—See Leif Johnson Ford Inc.; *U.S. Private*, pg. 2419
WESTSTAR AUTO SDN BHD—See Weststar Group; *Int'l*, pg. 8393
WEST STAR AVIATION LLC—See The Sterling Group, L.P.; *U.S. Private*, pg. 4123
WESTSTAR AVIATION SERVICES SDN. BHD.—See Weststar Group; *Int'l*, pg. 8393
WESTSTAR BANK HOLDING COMPANY, INC.; *U.S. Private*, pg. 4501
WESTSTAR BANK—See Weststar Bank Holding Company, Inc.; *U.S. Private*, pg. 4501
WESTSTAR CONSTRUCTION & PROPERTY—See Weststar Group; *Int'l*, pg. 8393
WESTSTAR DISTRIBUTING LTD.; *U.S. Private*, pg. 4501
WESTSTAR GROUP; *Int'l*, pg. 8393
WESTSTAR INSURANCE LIMITED—See Weststar Group; *Int'l*, pg. 8393
WEST-STAR MANAGEMENT B.V.—See Thornico A/S; *Int'l*, pg. 7720
WESTSTAR MAXUS DISTRIBUTORS SDN. BHD.—See Weststar Group; *Int'l*, pg. 8393
WESTSTAR MAXUS SDN. BHD.—See Weststar Group; *Int'l*, pg. 8393
WESTSTAR TRUCKING INC.—See J.D. Rush Company Inc.; *U.S. Private*, pg. 2161
WEST SUBURBAN BANCORP, INC.—See Old Second Bancorp, Inc.; *U.S. Public*, pg. 1569
WEST SUBURBAN BANK—See Old Second Bancorp, Inc.; *U.S. Public*, pg. 1569
WEST SUBURBAN CURRENCY EXCHANGES; *U.S. Private*, pg. 4487

WEST SURFING PRODUCTS—See Vmoto Limited; *Int'l*, pg. 8283
WEST SYNERGY SDN BHD—See Malayan United Industries Berhad; *Int'l*, pg. 4661
WEST SYSTEM NORGE AS—See XXL ASA; *Int'l*, pg. 8541
WEST TENNESSEE ORNAMENTAL DOOR CO., INC.; *U.S. Private*, pg. 4487
WEST TENNESSEE REHABILITATION HOSPITAL, LLC—See Encompass Health Corporation; *U.S. Public*, pg. 759
WEST TENNESSEE TELEPHONE CO., INC.—See Telephone Electronics Corporation; *U.S. Private*, pg. 3961
WEST TEXAS GAS, INC.—See J.L. Davis Companies; *U.S. Private*, pg. 2167
WEST TEXAS INSURANCE EXCHANGE, INC.; *U.S. Private*, pg. 4487
WEST TEXAS ISF—See Management & Training Corporation; *U.S. Private*, pg. 2560
WEST TEXAS LPG PIPELINE LIMITED PARTNERSHIP—See ONEOK, Inc.; *U.S. Public*, pg. 1603
WEST TEXAS PHYSICAL THERAPY, LIMITED PARTNERSHIP—See U.S. Physical Therapy, Inc.; *U.S. Public*, pg. 2216
WEST TEXAS RESOURCES, INC.; *U.S. Public*, pg. 2353
WESTTOWER COMMUNICATIONS LTD.—See Exchange Income Corporation; *Int'l*, pg. 2579
WEST TOWN BANK & TRUST—See Capital Bancorp, Inc.; *U.S. Public*, pg. 431
WEST TOWN CORNERS, LLC—See Washington Prime Group Inc.; *U.S. Private*, pg. 4449
WEST UC AUSTRALIA PTY LTD.—See Apollo Global Management, Inc.; *U.S. Public*, pg. 152
WEST UC GERMANY GMBH—See Apollo Global Management, Inc.; *U.S. Public*, pg. 152
WEST UC SWEDEN AB—See Apollo Global Management, Inc.; *U.S. Public*, pg. 152
WEST UNIFIED COMMUNICATIONS SERVICES CANADA, INC.—See Apollo Global Management, Inc.; *U.S. Public*, pg. 152
WEST UNIFIED COMMUNICATIONS SERVICES, INC.—See Apollo Global Management, Inc.; *U.S. Public*, pg. 152
WEST VALLEY COLLECTION & RECYCLING, LLC—See Waste Connections, Inc.; *Int'l*, pg. 8354
WEST VALLEY CONSTRUCTION COMPANY INC.; *U.S. Private*, pg. 4487
WEST VALLEY IMAGING, LLC—See HCA Healthcare, Inc.; *U.S. Public*, pg. 1013
WEST VALLEY MEDICAL CENTER—See HCA Healthcare, Inc.; *U.S. Public*, pg. 1013
WEST VALLEY MEDICAL GROUP, LLC—See HCA Healthcare, Inc.; *U.S. Public*, pg. 1014
WEST VALLEY NURSING HOMES, INC.; *U.S. Private*, pg. 4487
WEST VALLEY RECYCLING & TRANSFER LLC—See Burrtec Waste Industries, Inc.; *U.S. Private*, pg. 692
WEST VAULT MINING INC.; *Int'l*, pg. 8386
WESTVET WHOLESALE PTY. LTD.—See Apiam Animal Health Limited; *Int'l*, pg. 515
WESTVIEW CAPITAL PARTNERS, L.P.; *U.S. Private*, pg. 4501
WESTVIEW FORD SALES LTD.; *Int'l*, pg. 8393
WESTVIEW PRESS—See Vivendi SE; *Int'l*, pg. 8273
WESTVIEW PRODUCTS, INC.—See Sierra Pacific Industries; *U.S. Private*, pg. 3647
WEST VIEW SAVINGS BANK—See WVS Financial Corp.; *U.S. Public*, pg. 2384
WEST VIRGINIA AMERICAN WATER COMPANY; *U.S. Public*, pg. 2354
WEST VIRGINIA BLACK BEARS BASEBALL, INC.—See Rich Holdings, Inc.; *U.S. Private*, pg. 3426
WEST VIRGINIA ELECTRIC CORP.—See Victory of West Virginia, Inc.; *U.S. Private*, pg. 4379
WEST VIRGINIA ELECTRIC SUPPLY CO; *U.S. Private*, pg. 4487
WEST VIRGINIA INTERACTIVE, LLC—See Tyler Technologies, Inc.; *U.S. Public*, pg. 2209
WEST VIRGINIA NATIONAL AUTO INSURANCE CO, INC.—See Warrior Insurance Network, Inc; *U.S. Private*, pg. 4445
WEST VIRGINIA NEWSPAPER PUBLISHING COMPANY—See Greer Industries Inc.; *U.S. Private*, pg. 1782
WEST VIRGINIA-OHIO MOTOR SALES; *U.S. Private*, pg. 4488
WEST VIRGINIA PAINT LLC; *U.S. Private*, pg. 4487
WEST VIRGINIA PAVING INC; *U.S. Private*, pg. 4487
WEST VIRGINIA PAVING, INC.—See CRH plc; *Int'l*, pg. 1848
WEST VIRGINIA PIPELINE, INC.—See Energy Services of America Corporation; *U.S. Public*, pg. 762
WEST VIRGINIA RADIO CORPORATION; *U.S. Private*, pg. 4487
WEST VIRGINIA STEEL CORPORATION—See Raleigh Mine & Industrial Supply, Inc.; *U.S. Private*, pg. 3350
WESTWARD360, INC.; *U.S. Private*, pg. 4501
WESTWARD ADVISORS LLC; *Int'l*, pg. 8393

CORPORATE AFFILIATIONS

WESTWARD ADVISORS LTD.—See Westward Advisors Ltd.; *Int'l*, pg. 8393
WESTWARD FORD SALES LTD.; *Int'l*, pg. 8393
WESTWARD GOLD INC.; *Int'l*, pg. 8393
WESTWARD LABORATORIES—See Samworth Brothers Ltd.; *Int'l*, pg. 6519
WEST-WARD PHARMACEUTICALS CORP.—See Hikma Pharmaceuticals PLC; *Int'l*, pg. 3390
WESTWARD SEAFOODS, INC.—See Maruha Nichiro Corporation; *Int'l*, pg. 4712
WESTWATER CONSTRUCTION, INC.; *U.S. Private*, pg. 4501
WESTWATER RESOURCES, INC.; *U.S. Public*, pg. 2363
WESTWAY COACH INC.—See Cook-Illinois Corp.; *U.S. Private*, pg. 1039
WESTWAY FEED PRODUCTS LLC—See ED&F Man Holdings Limited; *Int'l*, pg. 2303
WESTWAY FEED PRODUCTS LLC - WESTERN REGIONAL OFFICE—See ED&F Man Holdings Limited; *Int'l*, pg. 2303
WESTWAYS STAFFING SERVICES INC.; *U.S. Private*, pg. 4501
WESTWAY TERMINAL COMPANY LLC—See EQT AB; *Int'l*, pg. 2473
WESTWICKE PARTNERS, LLC—See ICR, LLC; *U.S. Private*, pg. 2033
WESTWIND INC.; *U.S. Private*, pg. 4501
WESTWIND MANOR RESORT ASSOCIATION, INC.—See Crown Resorts, Ltd.; *U.S. Private*, pg. 1112
WESTWING B.V.—See Westwing Group SE; *Int'l*, pg. 8393
WESTWING GROUP SE; *Int'l*, pg. 8393
WEST WITS MINING LIMITED; *Int'l*, pg. 8386
WESTWOOD CONTRACTORS INC.; *U.S. Private*, pg. 4501
THE WESTWOOD FUNDS—See Westwood Holdings Group, Inc.; *U.S. Public*, pg. 2363
WESTWOOD GLOBAL ENERGY GROUP; *Int'l*, pg. 8393
THE WESTWOOD GROUP, INC.; *U.S. Private*, pg. 4134
WESTWOOD HOLDINGS GROUP, INC.; *U.S. Public*, pg. 2363
WESTWOOD INSURANCE AGENCY, INC.—See The Baldwin Insurance Group, Inc.; *U.S. Public*, pg. 2036
WESTWOOD-INTRAFIN, S.A.—See Bristol-Myers Squibb Company; *U.S. Public*, pg. 387
WESTWOOD MALL, LLC—See Brookfield Corporation; *Int'l*, pg. 1185
WESTWOOD MANAGEMENT CORPORATION—See Westwood Holdings Group, Inc.; *U.S. Public*, pg. 2363
WESTWOOD ONE, INC.—See Cumulus Media Inc.; *U.S. Public*, pg. 610
WESTWOOD PRESS—See Gannett Co., Inc.; *U.S. Public*, pg. 903
WESTWOOD PROFESSIONAL SERVICES, INC.; *U.S. Private*, pg. 4501
WESTWOOD SHIPPING LINES JAPAN, INC.—See The Sumitomo Warehouse Co. Ltd.; *Int'l*, pg. 7690
WESTWOOD SHIPPING LINES—See John Swire & Sons Limited; *Int'l*, pg. 3981
WESTWOOD TRUST - HOUSTON—See Westwood Holdings Group, Inc.; *U.S. Public*, pg. 2363
WESTWOOD TRUST—See Westwood Holdings Group, Inc.; *U.S. Public*, pg. 2363
WESTWOOD UNITED SUPER INC.; *U.S. Private*, pg. 4502
WEST WORLD MEDIA LLC—See Fimalac S.A.; *Int'l*, pg. 2664
WEST YORK LEASING; *Int'l*, pg. 8386
THE WEST YORKSHIRE COMMUNITY REHABILITATION COMPANY LTD.—See Interserve Plc; *Int'l*, pg. 3760
WEST YOST ASSOCIATES, INC.-PLEASANTON—See West Yost Associates, Inc.; *U.S. Private*, pg. 4488
WEST YOST ASSOCIATES, INC.-ROSEVILLE—See West Yost Associates, Inc.; *U.S. Private*, pg. 4488
WEST YOST ASSOCIATES, INC.; *U.S. Private*, pg. 4488
WESUPPLY LIMITED—See Accellos, Inc.; *U.S. Private*, pg. 50
WESURE GLOBAL TECH LTD.; *Int'l*, pg. 8393
W.E.T. AUTOMOTIVE SYSTEMS (CHINA) LIMITED—See Gentherm Incorporated; *U.S. Public*, pg. 931
W.E.T. AUTOMOTIVE SYSTEMS (MALTA) LIMITED—See Gentherm Incorporated; *U.S. Public*, pg. 931
WETHAQ TAKAFUL INSURANCE COMPANY K.C.S.C.; *Int'l*, pg. 8394
WETHERILL ASSOCIATES INC. - MONTREAL DIVISION—See Wetherill Associates Inc.; *U.S. Private*, pg. 4502
WETHERILL ASSOCIATES INC.; *U.S. Private*, pg. 4502
WETHERILL ASSOCIATES INC. - TORONTO DIVISION—See Wetherill Associates Inc.; *U.S. Private*, pg. 4502
WETHERILL ASSOCIATES INC. - WAIGLOBAL SHANGHAI DIVISION—See Wetherill Associates Inc.; *U.S. Private*, pg. 4502
WETHERINGTON TRACTOR SERVICE, INC.; *U.S. Private*, pg. 4502
WETM-TV—See Nexstar Media Group, Inc.; *U.S. Public*, pg. 1523
WET 'N WILD ORLANDO—See Comcast Corporation; *U.S. Public*, pg. 541

COMPANY NAME INDEX

WETOUCH TECHNOLOGY INC.; *Int'l*, pg. 8394
WET PLANET BEVERAGE CO.; *U.S. Private*, pg. 4502
WE TRANSPORT, INC.; *U.S. Private*, pg. 4462
THE WET SEAL, LLC—See Independence Capital Partners, LLC; *U.S. Private*, pg. 2057
W.E.T. SISTEMAS AUTOMOTRICES, S.A. DE C.V.—See Gentherm Incorporated; *U.S. Public*, pg. 931
WETT CAFE BETRIEBS GMBH—See Novomatic AG; *Int'l*, pg. 5467
WETTER.COM AG—See ProSiebenSat.1 Media SE; *Int'l*, pg. 6001
WETTER.COM GMBH—See ProSiebenSat.1 Media SE; *Int'l*, pg. 6001
WETTERMAN INC.; *U.S. Private*, pg. 4502
WETTON CLEANING SERVICES LIMITED; *Int'l*, pg. 8394
WETTSTEIN INVESTMENTS INC.; *U.S. Private*, pg. 4502
WETTSTEIN & SONS, INC.—See Wettstein Investments Inc.; *U.S. Private*, pg. 4502
WETZEL ACADEMY GMBH—See Matthews International Corporation; *U.S. Public*, pg. 1401
WETZEL BROTHERS, LLC—See Chatham Asset Management, LLC; *U.S. Private*, pg. 863
WETZEL CHRONICLE—See The Nutting Company, Inc.; *U.S. Private*, pg. 4087
WETZEL COUNTY HOMECARE, LLC—See UnitedHealth Group Incorporated; *U.S. Public*, pg. 2247
WETZEL GMBH—See Matthews International Corporation; *U.S. Public*, pg. 1401
WETZEL HOLDING AG—See Matthews International Corporation; *U.S. Public*, pg. 1401
WETZEL & LANZI INC.—See Maury, Donnelly & Parr, Inc.; *U.S. Private*, pg. 2615
WETZEL S.A.; *Int'l*, pg. 8394
WETZEL SERVICE AG—See Matthews International Corporation; *U.S. Public*, pg. 1401
WETZEL'S PRETZELS LLC—See MTY Food Group Inc.; *Int'l*, pg. 5073
WETZEL SP. Z.O.O.—See Matthews International Corporation; *U.S. Public*, pg. 1401
WEVADA NV—See Iep Invest SA; *Int'l*, pg. 3597
WEVER PETROLEUM INC.; *U.S. Private*, pg. 4502
WEVG SALZGITTER GMBH & CO. KG—See E.ON SE; *Int'l*, pg. 2260
WEVG VERWALTUNGS GMBH—See E.ON SE; *Int'l*, pg. 2260
WEVIDEO, INC.—See Thompson Street Capital Manager LLC; *U.S. Private*, pg. 4162
WEVIN PRIVATE LIMITED—See Vinar Systems Pvt. Ltd.; *Int'l*, pg. 8210
WEWARDS, INC.; *U.S. Public*, pg. 2363
WEWELER-COLAERT NV—See VDL Groep B.V.; *Int'l*, pg. 8142
WE & WIN DEVELOPMENT CO., LTD.; *Int'l*, pg. 8362
WE&WIN DIVERSIFICATION CO., LTD.; *Int'l*, pg. 8362
WE WIN LIMITED; *Int'l*, pg. 8362
WEWORK COMPANIES INC.—See WeWork Inc.; *U.S. Public*, pg. 2364
WEWORK INC.; *U.S. Public*, pg. 2364
WEWS-TV—See The E.W. Scripps Company; *U.S. Public*, pg. 2069
WEX ASIA PTE—See WEX, Inc.; *U.S. Public*, pg. 2364
WEX AUSTRALIA PTY LTD—See WEX, Inc.; *U.S. Public*, pg. 2364
WEX BANK—See WEX, Inc.; *U.S. Public*, pg. 2365
WEXCO INCORPORATED FSC—See Wexco Incorporated; *U.S. Private*, pg. 4502
WEXCO INCORPORATED; *U.S. Private*, pg. 4502
WEX CO., LTD.—See Coca-Cola Bottlers Japan Holdings Inc.; *Int'l*, pg. 1684
WEX EUROPE LIMITED—See WEX, Inc.; *U.S. Public*, pg. 2365
WEX EUROPE SERVICES BVBA—See WEX, Inc.; *U.S. Public*, pg. 2365
WEX EUROPE SERVICES SRL—See WEX, Inc.; *U.S. Public*, pg. 2365
WEXFORD CAPITAL LIMITED PARTNERSHIP; *U.S. Private*, pg. 4502
WEXFORD CREAMERY LIMITED; *Int'l*, pg. 8394
THE WEXFORD GROUP INTERNATIONAL—See CACI International Inc.; *U.S. Public*, pg. 418
WEXFORD HEALTH SOURCES INC.; *U.S. Private*, pg. 4502
WEXFORD HOMES INC.—See The Longford Group, Inc.; *U.S. Private*, pg. 4072
WEX, INC.; *U.S. Public*, pg. 2364
WEXIODISK AB—See Ali Holding S.r.l.; *Int'l*, pg. 322
WEXLER & WALKER PUBLIC POLICY ASSOCIATES—See WPP plc; *Int'l*, pg. 8491
WEXNER COMPANIES INC.; *U.S. Private*, pg. 4502
WEXNER HERITAGE VILLAGE; *U.S. Private*, pg. 4502
WEX NEW ZEALAND—See WEX, Inc.; *U.S. Public*, pg. 2365
WEXO PRAZISIONSWERKZEUGE GMBH—See OSG Corporation; *Int'l*, pg. 5649
WEX PHARMACEUTICALS INC.—See CK Hutchison Holdings Limited; *Int'l*, pg. 1638
WEXPORT LTD.—See LEO Pharma A/S; *Int'l*, pg. 4457
WEXPRO COMPANY—See Enbridge Inc.; *U.S. Public*, pg. 2397

WEXXAR PACKAGING INC.—See Leonard Green & Partners, L.P.; *U.S. Private*, pg. 2428
WEYAND FOOD DISTRIBUTORS, INC.; *U.S. Private*, pg. 4503
WEYAND & SON INC.; *U.S. Private*, pg. 4502
WEYA SA; *Int'l*, pg. 8394
WEYAUWEGA STAR DAIRY INC.; *U.S. Private*, pg. 4503
WEYBRIDGE, LLC; *U.S. Private*, pg. 4503
WEYCO GROUP, INC.; *U.S. Public*, pg. 2365
WEY EDUCATION PLC—See Inspired Education Holdings Limited; *Int'l*, pg. 3720
WEYERHAEUSER (ASIA) LIMITED—See Weyerhaeuser Company; *U.S. Public*, pg. 2365
WEYERHAEUSER COLUMBIA TIMBERLANDS LLC—See Weyerhaeuser Company; *U.S. Public*, pg. 2365
WEYERHAEUSER COMPANY LIMITED—See Weyerhaeuser Company; *U.S. Public*, pg. 2365
WEYERHAEUSER COMPANY; *U.S. Public*, pg. 2365
WEYERHAEUSER INTERNATIONAL, INC.—See Weyerhaeuser Company; *U.S. Public*, pg. 2365
WEYERHAEUSER JAPAN LTD.—See Weyerhaeuser Company; *U.S. Public*, pg. 2365
WEYERHAEUSER KOREA LTD.—See Weyerhaeuser Company; *U.S. Public*, pg. 2365
WEYERHAEUSER NR COMPANY—See Weyerhaeuser Company; *U.S. Public*, pg. 2365
WEYERHAEUSER POLAND SP. Z O.O.—See Weyerhaeuser Company; *U.S. Public*, pg. 2365
WEYERHAEUSER PRODUCTOS, S.A.—See Weyerhaeuser Company; *U.S. Public*, pg. 2365
WEYERHAEUSER REALTY INVESTORS, INC.—See Weyerhaeuser Company; *U.S. Public*, pg. 2365
WEYERMANN MALZFABRIK; *Int'l*, pg. 8394
WEYLCHEM FRANKFURT GMBH—See International Chemical Investors S.E.; *Int'l*, pg. 3745
WEYLCHEM LAMOTTE S.A.S.—See International Chemical Investors S.E.; *Int'l*, pg. 3745
WEYLCHEM SWITZERLAND LTD.—See International Chemical Investors S.E.; *Int'l*, pg. 3745
WEYLCHEM US INC.—See International Chemical Investors S.E.; *Int'l*, pg. 3745
WEYLCHEM WIESBADEN GMBH—See International Chemical Investors S.E.; *Int'l*, pg. 3745
WEYMOUTH AUTO MALL; *U.S. Private*, pg. 4503
WEYMOUTH CONCRETE INC.—See Boston Sand & Gravel Company; *U.S. Private*, pg. 373
WEYMOUTH NEWS—See Gannett Co., Inc.; *U.S. Public*, pg. 903
WFAA-TV, INC.—See TEGNA Inc.; *U.S. Public*, pg. 1991
WF AUTOMOTIVE OF COLUMBUS, LLC; *U.S. Private*, pg. 4503
WFB ECONOMIC DEVELOPMENT GMBH; *Int'l*, pg. 8394
W.F.C. COMPANY, INC.—See Warminster Fiberglass, LLC; *U.S. Private*, pg. 4442
W.F.C. HOLDING S.P.A.—See EFORT Intelligent Equipment Co., Ltd.; *Int'l*, pg. 2321
W.F.C. PROPERTIES INC.—See Wall Financial Corporation; *Int'l*, pg. 8333
WFD CONSULTING, INC.; *U.S. Private*, pg. 4503
WFD SECURITIES, INC.—See Western New England Bancorp, Inc.; *U.S. Public*, pg. 2356
WFEC RAILROAD CO., INC.—See Western Farmers Electric Cooperative, Inc.; *U.S. Private*, pg. 4493
WF ELECTRICAL LIMITED—See Rexel, S.A.; *Int'l*, pg. 6317
WFEL LTD.—See Krauss-Maffei Wegmann GmbH & Co. KG; *Int'l*, pg. 4300
WFG-CRISTO REY FUNERAL HOME, INC.—See Service Corporation International; *U.S. Public*, pg. 1871
WFG-FULLER FUNERALS, INC.—See Service Corporation International; *U.S. Public*, pg. 1871
WFG-LOCKWOOD FUNERAL HOME, INC.—See Service Corporation International; *U.S. Public*, pg. 1871
WFG NATIONAL TITLE INSURANCE COMPANY—See Williston Financial Group, LLC; *U.S. Private*, pg. 4528
WFH, INC—See Birch Hill Equity Partners Management Inc.; *Int'l*, pg. 1046
WFH, INC—See Homesteaders Life Co. Inc.; *U.S. Private*, pg. 1974
WF HOLDINGS INC.; *U.S. Private*, pg. 4503
WFIE, LLC—See Gray Television, Inc.; *U.S. Public*, pg. 960
WFI INSURANCE LIMITED—See Insurance Australia Group Limited; *Int'l*, pg. 3725
WFI INTERNATIONAL, INC.—See Bonney Forge Corporation; *U.S. Public*, pg. 615
W FINANCE GROUPE PRIMONIAL—See Groupe Primonial SAS; *Int'l*, pg. 3110
WFI NMC CORP.—See Kratos Defense & Security Solutions, Inc.; *U.S. Public*, pg. 1277
WFKR INC.; *U.S. Private*, pg. 4503
WFLA-TV—See Nexstar Media Group, Inc.; *U.S. Public*, pg. 1523
WFLD-TV—See Fox Corporation; *U.S. Public*, pg. 876
WFL (UK) LIMITED—See World Kinect Corporation; *U.S. Public*, pg. 2381
W FLYING PLASTICS, INC.; *U.S. Private*, pg. 4417
WFM BEVERAGE CORP.—See Amazon.com, Inc.; *U.S. Public*, pg. 91

WG TECH (JIANGXI) CO., LTD.

WFM HAWAII, LLC—See Amazon.com, Inc.; *U.S. Public*, pg. 91
WFM MEDICAL & WELLNESS CENTERS, INC.—See Amazon.com, Inc.; *U.S. Public*, pg. 91
WFM MOTORS PTY LTD.; *Int'l*, pg. 8394
WFM PRIVATE LABEL, L.P.—See Amazon.com, Inc.; *U.S. Public*, pg. 91
WFM SOFTWARE AB—See InVision AG; *Int'l*, pg. 3789
WFMY TELEVISION, LLC—See TEGNA Inc.; *U.S. Public*, pg. 1991
WFN CREDIT COMPANY, LLC—See Bread Financial Holdings, Inc.; *U.S. Public*, pg. 381
WFN STRATEGIES; *U.S. Private*, pg. 4503
WFOR-TV—See National Amusements, Inc.; *U.S. Private*, pg. 2841
WFP FOREST PRODUCTS LTD.—See Western Forest Products Inc.; *Int'l*, pg. 8388
WFRIC SHENZHEN CO., LTD.—See Wong Fong Industries Limited; *Int'l*, pg. 8447
WFRV-TV—See Nexstar Media Group, Inc.; *U.S. Public*, pg. 1523
WFS ASIA PACIFIC, AFRICA & MIDDLE EAST—See Cerberus Capital Management, L.P.; *U.S. Private*, pg. 840
WFSB-TV—See Meredith Corporation; *U.S. Public*, pg. 1423
WFS EUROPE—See Cerberus Capital Management, L.P.; *U.S. Private*, pg. 840
WFS GLOBAL SAS—See Cerberus Capital Management, L.P.; *U.S. Private*, pg. 840
WFS LTD.—See W.W. Grainger, Inc.; *U.S. Public*, pg. 2320
WFS (USA) LTD.—See W.W. Grainger, Inc.; *U.S. Public*, pg. 2320
WF TAYLOR CO., INC.—See Arsenal Capital Management LP; *U.S. Private*, pg. 339
WFTS-TV—See The E.W. Scripps Company; *U.S. Public*, pg. 2069
WFTV, INC.—See Apollo Global Management, Inc.; *U.S. Public*, pg. 164
WFV WERKZEUG- FORMEN- UND VORRICHTUNGSBAU GMBH & CO. KG.; *Int'l*, pg. 8394
WFXG, LLC—See Lockwood Broadcasting Inc.; *U.S. Private*, pg. 2478
WFXT-TV FOX25—See Apollo Global Management, Inc.; *U.S. Public*, pg. 164
WGAL HEARST-ARGYLE TELEVISION, INC.—See The Hearst Corporation; *U.S. Private*, pg. 4049
W. GAMBY & CO.; *U.S. Private*, pg. 4418
WGAU RADIO—See Apollo Global Management, Inc.; *U.S. Public*, pg. 164
WGBH EDUCATIONAL FOUNDATION; *U.S. Private*, pg. 4503
WG BLOCK CO.; *U.S. Private*, pg. 4503
WGBR-AM—See Curtis Media Group; *U.S. Private*, pg. 1126
WGCHAM 1490—See iHeartMedia, Inc.; *U.S. Public*, pg. 1097
WGEM-TV—See Gray Television, Inc.; *U.S. Public*, pg. 961
W GENEST PARTNER INGENIEURGESSELLSCHAFT MBH—See VINCI S.A.; *Int'l*, pg. 8240
WGEO SWITZERLAND GMBH—See Datatec Limited; *Int'l*, pg. 1981
WGE SAS—See Concentrix Corporation; *U.S. Public*, pg. 565
W. GEUKEN B.V.—See A.A.G. STUCCHI s.r.l.; *Int'l*, pg. 23
WG HEALTHCARE UK LIMITED—See Wright Medical Group N.V.; *Int'l*, pg. 8495
WGHP, LLC—See Nexstar Media Group, Inc.; *U.S. Public*, pg. 1525
WGI HEAVY MINERALS, LLC—See SunOpta Inc.; *Int'l*, pg. 7320
WGI HOLDINGS, INC.; *U.S. Public*, pg. 2365
WGI WESTMAN GROUP, INC.; *Int'l*, pg. 8394
WGK WINDENERGIE GROSSKORBETHA GMBH & CO.KG—See RWE AG; *Int'l*, pg. 6436
WGL ENERGY SERVICES, INC.—See AltaGas Ltd.; *Int'l*, pg. 384
WGL HOLDINGS, INC.—See AltaGas Ltd.; *Int'l*, pg. 384
W. G. McKAY LIMITED; *Int'l*, pg. 8321
WGME, INC.—See Sinclair, Inc.; *U.S. Public*, pg. 1886
WGN AMERICA—See Nexstar Media Group, Inc.; *U.S. Public*, pg. 1525
WGN CONTINENTAL BROADCASTING COMPANY—See Nexstar Media Group, Inc.; *U.S. Public*, pg. 1524
WGNO-TV—See Nexstar Media Group, Inc.; *U.S. Public*, pg. 1524
WGN RADIO—See Nexstar Media Group, Inc.; *U.S. Public*, pg. 1525
W. GOHMAN CONSTRUCTION CO.; *U.S. Private*, pg. 4418
WG PARK, LP—See Pennsylvania Real Estate Investment Trust; *U.S. Public*, pg. 1664
WGR ASSET HOLDING COMPANY LLC—See Occidental Petroleum Corporation; *U.S. Public*, pg. 1561
WG&R FURNITURE CO., INC.; *U.S. Private*, pg. 4503
WGRZ-TV—See TEGNA Inc.; *U.S. Public*, pg. 1991
WGS AG—See Bunzl plc; *Int'l*, pg. 1220
WG SERVICES, INC.—See Datatec Limited; *Int'l*, pg. 1981
WG STROHWIG TOOL & DIE INC.; *U.S. Private*, pg. 4503
WG TECH (JIANGXI) CO., LTD.; *Int'l*, pg. 8394

W.G. TOMKO, INC.
CORPORATE AFFILIATIONS

W.G. TOMKO, INC.; *U.S. Private*, pg. 4420
WG VALENZUELA DRYWALL INC.; *U.S. Private*, pg. 4503
WG WEARNE LIMITED; *Int'l*, pg. 8394
WG WHITE & COMPANY; *U.S. Private*, pg. 4503
WG YATES & SONS CONSTRUCTION COMPANY, BILOXI—See W.G. Yates & Sons Construction Company; *U.S. Private*, pg. 4420
WG YATES & SONS CONSTRUCTION COMPANY, DESTIN—See W.G. Yates & Sons Construction Company; *U.S. Private*, pg. 4420
WG YATES & SONS CONSTRUCTION COMPANY - HEAVY DIVISION—See W.G. Yates & Sons Construction Company; *U.S. Private*, pg. 4420
WG YATES & SONS CONSTRUCTION COMPANY, JACKSON—See W.G. Yates & Sons Construction Company; *U.S. Private*, pg. 4420
WG YATES & SONS CONSTRUCTION COMPANY, MEMPHIS—See W.G. Yates & Sons Construction Company; *U.S. Private*, pg. 4420
WG YATES & SONS CONSTRUCTION COMPANY, MOBILE—See W.G. Yates & Sons Construction Company; *U.S. Private*, pg. 4420
W.G. YATES & SONS CONSTRUCTION COMPANY; *U.S. Private*, pg. 4420
WHA CORPORATION PUBLIC COMPANY LIMITED; *Int'l*, pg. 8396
WHA DUN BUILDING MANAGEMENT SERVICE CO., LTD.—See Chung-Hsin Electric & Machinery Manufacturing Corp.; *Int'l*, pg. 1597
WHAG-TV—See Nexstar Media Group, Inc.; *U.S. Public*, pg. 1523
WHA INDUSTRIAL DEVELOPMENT PUBLIC COMPANY LIMITED—See WHA Corporation Public Company Limited; *Int'l*, pg. 8396
WHAJ-FM—See First Media Services, LLC; *U.S. Private*, pg. 1521
WHAKATU WOOL SCOUR LIMITED—See Lempriere Pty. Ltd.; *Int'l*, pg. 4450
W. HAKING ENTERPRISES LTD.; *Int'l*, pg. 8321
W. HALDENWANGER TECHNISCHE KERAMIK GMBH & CO. KG.—See Morgan Advanced Materials plc; *Int'l*, pg. 5044
WHALEN FURNITURE MANUFACTURING; *U.S. Private*, pg. 4503
WHALER INDUSTRIAL CONTRACTING INC.—See Trotter & Morton Ltd.; *Int'l*, pg. 7939
WHALEY FOODSERVICE, LLC—See Berkshire Partners LLC; *U.S. Private*, pg. 535
WHALLEY COMPUTER ASSOCIATES INC.; *U.S. Private*, pg. 4503
WHALLEY GLASS CO., INC.; *U.S. Private*, pg. 4503
WHAM! ADVERTISING; *U.S. Private*, pg. 4503
WHAM-O, INC.; *U.S. Private*, pg. 4503
WHAMPOA GARMENT MANUFACTURING (GUANGZHOU) CO., LTD.—See Yangtzekiang Garment Limited; *Int'l*, pg. 8561
WHAM-TV—See Sinclair, Inc.; *U.S. Public*, pg. 1886
WHANAU INTERESTS LLC; *U.S. Private*, pg. 4503
WHANIN PHARAM CO LTD; *Int'l*, pg. 8396
WHA PREMIUM GROWTH FREEHOLD & LEASEHOLD REAL ESTATE INVESTMENT TRUST; *Int'l*, pg. 8396
WHARF CHINA LIMITED—See Wheelock & Company Limited; *Int'l*, pg. 8397
WHARF COL (SHANGHAI) LIMITED—See Wheelock & Company Limited; *Int'l*, pg. 8397
WHARF COMMUNICATIONS LIMITED—See Wheelock & Company Limited; *Int'l*, pg. 8397
WHARF ESTATES DEVELOPMENT LIMITED—See Wheelock & Company Limited; *Int'l*, pg. 8397
WHARF ESTATES LIMITED—See Wheelock & Company Limited; *Int'l*, pg. 8397
THE WHARF (HOLDINGS) LIMITED—See Wheelock & Company Limited; *Int'l*, pg. 8397
WHARF REAL ESTATE INVESTMENT COMPANY LIMITED.—See Wheelock & Company Limited; *Int'l*, pg. 8397
WHARF RESOURCES (USA) INC.—See Coeur Mining, Inc.; *U.S. Public*, pg. 522
WHARTON COUNTY ELECTRIC COOPERATIVE, INC.; *U.S. Private*, pg. 4504
WHARTON COUNTY FOODS, LLC—See Cal-Maine Foods, Inc.; *U.S. Public*, pg. 421
WHARTON DIALYSIS CARE, L.L.P.—See Nautic Partners, LLC; *U.S. Private*, pg. 2871
WHARTON HARDWARE & SUPPLY; *U.S. Private*, pg. 4504
WHARTON LYON & LYON—See GCP Capital Partners Holdings LLC; *U.S. Private*, pg. 1654
WHARTON-SMITH, INC.; *U.S. Private*, pg. 4504
W-HA S.A—See Orange S.A.; *Int'l*, pg. 5611
WHATABURGER, INC.; *U.S. Private*, pg. 4504
WHATABURGER OF MESQUITE INC.; *U.S. Private*, pg. 4504
WHATCOM COUNSELING & PSYCHIATRIC CLINIC—See Compass Health; *U.S. Private*, pg. 999
WHATCOM EDUCATIONAL CREDIT UNION; *U.S. Private*, pg. 4504
WHATCOUNTS, INC.—See Aquiline Capital Partners LLC; *U.S. Private*, pg. 305
WHATLEY OIL & AUTO PARTS COMPANY INC.; *U.S. Private*, pg. 4504
WHATMAN INTERNATIONAL LTD.—See GE HealthCare Technologies Inc.; *U.S. Public*, pg. 909
WHATMAN LIMITED—See General Electric Company; *U.S. Public*, pg. 920
WHAT ON EARTH; *U.S. Private*, pg. 4504
WHATSAPP INC.—See Meta Platforms, Inc.; *U.S. Public*, pg. 1427
WHAT'S COOKING GROUP NV; *Int'l*, pg. 8396
WHAT'S NEXT PARTNERS; *Int'l*, pg. 8397
WHAT'S ON INDIA MEDIA PRIVATE LIMITED—See Nexstar Media Group, Inc.; *U.S. Public*, pg. 1525
WHA UTILITIES & POWER PCL; *Int'l*, pg. 8396
WH AUTO PARTS INDUSTRIES INC.—See H-One Co., Ltd.; *Int'l*, pg. 3194
WHAWON PHARM CO., LTD.—See IMCD N.V.; *Int'l*, pg. 3623
WHAYNE SUPPLY COMPANY; *U.S. Private*, pg. 4504
WHA YU INDUSTRIAL CO., LTD.; *Int'l*, pg. 8396
W.H.B. DO BRASIL LTDA.—See Brady Corporation; *U.S. Public*, pg. 379
WHBF-TV—See Nexstar Media Group, Inc.; *U.S. Public*, pg. 1523
W.H.B. IDENTIFICATION SOLUTIONS, INC.—See Brady Corporation; *U.S. Public*, pg. 379
W. H. BRADY & CO. LTD.; *Int'l*, pg. 8321
W.H. BRADY, NV—See Brady Corporation; *U.S. Public*, pg. 379
W.H. BRADY S. DE R.L. DE C.V.—See Brady Corporation; *U.S. Public*, pg. 379
W.H. BRESHEARS, INC.; *U.S. Private*, pg. 4420
WHC, INC.; *U.S. Private*, pg. 4504
W. H. CRESS COMPANY, INC.; *U.S. Private*, pg. 4418
WHDH TV INC.—See Sunbeam Television Corporation; *U.S. Private*, pg. 3864
WHD IMMOBILIEN GMBH—See VIB Vermogen AG; *Int'l*, pg. 8184
WHEATCROFT GARDEN CENTRE LIMITED—See Notcutts Ltd.; *Int'l*, pg. 5449
WHEATCROFT (WORKSOP) LIMITED—See General Motors Company; *U.S. Public*, pg. 928
WHEATEN FINANCIAL INC.—See SoftBank Group Corp.; *Int'l*, pg. 7053
WHEAT GROUP INC.—See United Legwear & Apparel Co.; *U.S. Private*, pg. 4293
WHEATLAND ADVISORS, INC—See Orrstown Financial Services, Inc.; *U.S. Public*, pg. 1619
WHEATLAND BANK—See Glacier Bancorp, Inc.; *U.S. Public*, pg. 938
WHEATLAND ELECTRIC COOPERATIVE; *U.S. Private*, pg. 4504
WHEATLANDS CARE HOME BONNYBRIDGE—See Balhousie Holdings Limited; *Int'l*, pg. 808
WHEATLAND SEED INC.; *U.S. Private*, pg. 4504
WHEATLAND TUBE COMPANY - MILL STREET PLANT—See Zekelman Industries Inc.; *U.S. Private*, pg. 4600
WHEATLAND TUBE COMPANY—See Zekelman Industries Inc.; *U.S. Private*, pg. 4600
WHEATLEY & TIMMONS; *U.S. Private*, pg. 4504
WHEATMAN INSURANCE SERVICES, LLC—See Arthur J. Gallagher & Co.; *U.S. Public*, pg. 208
WHEATOLEO—See Vivescia; *Int'l*, pg. 8279
WHEATON BANK & TRUST, N.A.—See Wintrust Financial Corporation; *U.S. Public*, pg. 2375
WHEATON CHEVROLET; *Int'l*, pg. 8397
WHEATON-DUMONT COOP ELEVATOR INC.; *U.S. Private*, pg. 4505
WHEATON FRANCISCAN HEALTHCARE; *U.S. Private*, pg. 4504
WHEATON FRANCISCAN SERVICES INC.; *U.S. Private*, pg. 4504
WHEATON GMC BUICK CADILLAC LTD; *Int'l*, pg. 8397
WHEATON INDUSTRIES, INC.—See OEP Capital Advisors, L.P.; *U.S. Private*, pg. 2999
WHEATON-OAKS SPORT CENTER, INC.; *U.S. Private*, pg. 4505
WHEATON PARK DISTRICT; *U.S. Private*, pg. 4505
WHEATON PRECIOUS METALS CORP.; *Int'l*, pg. 8397
WHEATON VAN LINES, INC.; *U.S. Private*, pg. 4505
WHEATSHEAF GROUP LIMITED; *Int'l*, pg. 8397
WHEATSTONE RESTAURANT GROUP LLC—See Northcott Hospitality International, LLC; *U.S. Private*, pg. 2949
WHEB CAPITAL PARTNERS LLP; *Int'l*, pg. 8397
WHECO CORP.; *U.S. Private*, pg. 4505
WHEC-TV LLC—See Hubbard Broadcasting, Inc.; *U.S. Private*, pg. 2000
WHEELABRATOR AIR POLLUTION CONTROL INC.—See Siemens Aktiengesellschaft; *Int'l*, pg. 6891
WHEELABRATOR BALTIMORE, L.P.—See Macquarie Group Limited; *Int'l*, pg. 4628
WHEELABRATOR CONCORD COMPANY, L.P.—See Macquarie Group Limited; *Int'l*, pg. 4628
WHEELABRATOR CONNECTICUT INC.—See Macquarie Group Limited; *Int'l*, pg. 4628
WHEELABRATOR FALLS INC.—See Macquarie Group Limited; *Int'l*, pg. 4628
WHEELABRATOR FRACKVILLE ENERGY COMPANY INC.—See Macquarie Group Limited; *Int'l*, pg. 4628
WHEELABRATOR GLOUCESTER COMPANY, L.P.—See Macquarie Group Limited; *Int'l*, pg. 4628
WHEELABRATOR GROUP LTD.—See Altor Equity Partners AB; *Int'l*, pg. 395
WHEELABRATOR LISBON, INC.—See Macquarie Group Limited; *Int'l*, pg. 4628
WHEELABRATOR MCKAY BAY INC.—See Macquarie Group Limited; *Int'l*, pg. 4628
WHEELABRATOR MILLBURY INC.—See Macquarie Group Limited; *Int'l*, pg. 4628
WHEELABRATOR NORTH ANDOVER INC.—See Macquarie Group Limited; *Int'l*, pg. 4628
WHEELABRATOR NORWALK ENERGY COMPANY INC.—See Macquarie Group Limited; *Int'l*, pg. 4628
WHEELABRATOR PORTSMOUTH INC.—See Macquarie Group Limited; *Int'l*, pg. 4628
WHEELABRATOR PUTNAM INC.—See Macquarie Group Limited; *Int'l*, pg. 4628
WHEELABRATOR RIDGE ENERGY INC.—See Macquarie Group Limited; *Int'l*, pg. 4628
WHEELABRATOR SAUGUS INC.—See Macquarie Group Limited; *Int'l*, pg. 4628
WHEELABRATOR SHASTA ENERGY COMPANY INC.—See Macquarie Group Limited; *Int'l*, pg. 4629
WHEELABRATOR SOUTH BROWARD INC.—See Macquarie Group Limited; *Int'l*, pg. 4629
WHEELABRATOR TECHNOLOGIES INC.—See Macquarie Group Limited; *Int'l*, pg. 4628
WHEELCHAIR ADL SOLUTIONS CORPORATION; *U.S. Private*, pg. 4505
WHEEL CHAIR HOME, INC.; *U.S. Private*, pg. 4505
WHEELER BROS. GRAIN CO.—See Wheeler Brothers Grain Co.; *U.S. Private*, pg. 4505
WHEELER BROS., INC.—See VSE Corporation; *U.S. Public*, pg. 2313
WHEELER BROTHERS GRAIN CO.; *U.S. Private*, pg. 4505
WHEELER CLINIC, INC.; *U.S. Private*, pg. 4505
WHEELER INDUSTRIES, INC.—See Jenkins Electric Co.; *U.S. Private*, pg. 2199
WHEELER MACHINERY CO.; *U.S. Private*, pg. 4505
WHEELER MATERIAL HANDLING; *U.S. Private*, pg. 4505
WHEELER REAL ESTATE INVESTMENT TRUST, INC.; *U.S. Public*, pg. 2365
WHEELER REAL ESTATE LLC—See Wheeler Real Estate Investment Trust, Inc.; *U.S. Public*, pg. 2366
WHEELER REIT, L.P.—See Wheeler Real Estate Investment Trust, Inc.; *U.S. Public*, pg. 2366
WHEELER RV LAS VEGAS, LLC—See Camping World Holdings, Inc.; *U.S. Public*, pg. 428
WHEELERSBURG TERMINAL LLC—See Norfolk Southern Corporation; *U.S. Public*, pg. 1536
WHEELER'S CORPORATION; *U.S. Private*, pg. 4505
WHEELERS HILL HOTEL (BMG) PTY LTD—See Woolworths Group Limited; *Int'l*, pg. 8452
WHEELER'S MEDICAL SUPPLY LLC—See AEA Investors LP; *U.S. Private*, pg. 116
WHEELER'S-NEWNAN—See Wheeler's Corporation; *U.S. Private*, pg. 4506
WHEELER'S-ROME—See Wheeler's Corporation; *U.S. Private*, pg. 4506
WHEELFIRE INC; *U.S. Private*, pg. 4506
WHEELHOUSE ANALYTICS—See Bain Capital, LP; *U.S. Private*, pg. 439
THE WHEELHOUSE GROUP, INC.—See CI Capital Partners LLC; *U.S. Private*, pg. 896
WHEEL, INC.—See Digital Garage, Inc.; *Int'l*, pg. 2122
THE WHEELING CORPORATION INC.; *U.S. Private*, pg. 4134
WHEELING HOSPITAL, INC.; *U.S. Private*, pg. 4506
WHEELING & LAKE ERIE RAILWAY CO., INC.—See The Wheeling Corporation Inc.; *U.S. Private*, pg. 4134
WHEELING NEWSPAPERS, INC.—See The Nutting Company, Inc.; *U.S. Private*, pg. 4087
WHEELING-NIPPON STEEL, INC.—See Nippon Steel Corporation; *Int'l*, pg. 5336
WHEELING TREATMENT CENTER, LLC—See Acadia Healthcare Company, Inc.; *U.S. Public*, pg. 31
WHEELOCK & COMPANY LIMITED; *Int'l*, pg. 8397
WHEELOCK PROPERTIES (CHINA) LIMITED—See Wheelock & Company Limited; *Int'l*, pg. 8397
WHEELOCK PROPERTIES (HONG KONG) LIMITED—See Wheelock & Company Limited; *Int'l*, pg. 8397
WHEELOCK PROPERTIES LIMITED—See Wheelock & Company Limited; *Int'l*, pg. 8397
WHEELOCK PROPERTIES (SINGAPORE) LIMITED—See Wheelock & Company Limited; *Int'l*, pg. 8398
WHEELOCK STREET CAPITAL L.L.C.; *U.S. Private*, pg. 4506
WHEELOCK TRAVEL LIMITED—See Wheelock & Company Limited; *Int'l*, pg. 8398
WHEEL PROS, LLC—See Clearlake Capital Group, L.P.; *U.S. Private*, pg. 937

COMPANY NAME INDEX

WHEELS CLIPPER INC.—See Radiant Logistics, Inc.; *U.S. Public*, pg. 1759
WHEELS GROUP INC.—See Radiant Logistics, Inc.; *U.S. Public*, pg. 1759
WHEELS INC.—See Frank Consolidated Enterprises; *U.S. Private*, pg. 1594
WHEELS INDIA LIMITED—See Titan International, Inc.; *U.S. Public*, pg. 2160
WHEELS LOGISTICS INC.—See Radiant Logistics, Inc.; *U.S. Public*, pg. 1760
WHEELS MSM CANADA INC.—See Radiant Logistics, Inc.; *U.S. Public*, pg. 1760
WHEELS OF ARABIA MOTORCYCLES TRADING LLC—See Shoei Co., Ltd.; *Int'l*, pg. 6858
WHEEL SPORT MANAGEMENT SDN. BHD.—See Ancom Nylex Berhad; *Int'l*, pg. 449
WHEELS UP EXPERIENCE INC.; *U.S. Public*, pg. 2366
WHEELS UP PARTNERS LLC—See Wheels Up Experience Inc.; *U.S. Public*, pg. 2366
WHEELTRONIC LTD.—See Snap-on Incorporated; *U.S. Public*, pg. 1899
WHEELTUG PLC—See Borealis Exploration Limited; *Int'l*, pg. 1114
WHEELWRIGHT LUMBER CO.; *U.S. Private*, pg. 4506
WHELAN & ASSOCIATES INC.; *U.S. Private*, pg. 4506
WHELAN MACHINE & TOOL, LLC—See Gremada Industries Inc.; *U.S. Private*, pg. 1783
WHELAN SECURITY CO., INC.; *U.S. Private*, pg. 4506
WHELANS (WA) PTY LTD.—See Veris Limited; *Int'l*, pg. 8169
WHELEN AEROSPACE TECHNOLOGIES LLC—See Whelen Engineering Company, Inc.; *U.S. Private*, pg. 4506
WHELEN ENGINEERING COMPANY, INC.; *U.S. Private*, pg. 4506
WHEMCO, INC.—See Park Corp.; *U.S. Private*, pg. 3096
W.H. EMMART & SON INC.; *U.S. Private*, pg. 4420
WHERE FOOD COMES FROM, INC.; *U.S. Public*, pg. 2366
WHERE INTERNATIONAL LP—See Miller Publishing Group, LLC; *U.S. Private*, pg. 2735
WHEREOWARE LLC; *U.S. Private*, pg. 4506
WHERRELZ IT SOLUTIONS LTD.; *Int'l*, pg. 8398
WHER-RENA BOAT SALES INC.; *U.S. Private*, pg. 4506
WHETSTONE CHOCOLATES, INC.; *U.S. Private*, pg. 4506
WHETSTONE COMPANY; *U.S. Private*, pg. 4506
WHEYCO GMBH—See DMK Deutsches Milchkontor GmbH; *Int'l*, pg. 2146
WHEYFEED LTD.—See ForFarmers Group B.V.; *Int'l*, pg. 2733
W.H. FREEMAN & CO.—See Verlagsgruppe Georg von Holtzbrinck GmbH; *Int'l*, pg. 8170
WH GROUP LIMITED; *Int'l*, pg. 8394
WHH TRICE & CO., INC.—See The Bush Company; *U.S. Private*, pg. 4003
WHIBCO, INC. - PORT ELIZABETH PLANT—See Whibco, Inc.; *U.S. Private*, pg. 4506
WHIBCO, INC.; *U.S. Private*, pg. 4506
WHICH WICH, INC.; *U.S. Private*, pg. 4506
WHIDBEY ISLAND BANK—See Heritage Financial Corporation; *U.S. Public*, pg. 1028
WHIDBEY TELECOM; *U.S. Private*, pg. 4506
WHI GLOBAL, LLC—See Rift Valley Equity Partners, LLC; *U.S. Private*, pg. 3435
WHINK PRODUCTS COMPANY—See RPM International Inc.; *U.S. Public*, pg. 1817
WHIP INDUSTRIES INC.; *U.S. Private*, pg. 4506
WHIPLASH MERCHANDISING INC.—See Port Logistics Group, Inc.; *U.S. Private*, pg. 3230
WHIP-MIX CORPORATION; *U.S. Private*, pg. 4506
WHIPPANY ACTUATION SYSTEMS, LLC—See TransDigm Group Incorporated; *U.S. Public*, pg. 2183
WHIPP & BOURNE INC.—See Melrose Industries PLC; *Int'l*, pg. 4813
WHIPPLEHILL COMMUNICATIONS, INC.—See Blackbaud, Inc.; *U.S. Public*, pg. 341
WHIPPOORWILL ASSOCIATES, INC.; *U.S. Private*, pg. 4506
WHIPSNADE WILD ANIMAL PARK LIMITED—See The Zoological Society of London; *Int'l*, pg. 7705
WH IRELAND GROUP PLC; *Int'l*, pg. 8396
WH IRELAND LIMITED—See WH Ireland Group PLC; *Int'l*, pg. 8396
WH IRELAND TRUSTEE LIMITED—See WH Ireland Group PLC; *Int'l*, pg. 8396
WHIRLAWAY CORPORATION—See NN, Inc.; *U.S. Public*, pg. 1531
WHIRLEY INDUSTRIES, INC.; *U.S. Private*, pg. 4507
WHIRLPOOL ASIA INC.—See Whirlpool Corporation; *U.S. Public*, pg. 2367
WHIRLPOOL AUSTRIA GMBH—See Whirlpool Corporation; *U.S. Public*, pg. 2367
WHIRLPOOL BALTIC UAB—See Whirlpool Corporation; *U.S. Public*, pg. 2367
WHIRLPOOL BELUX N.V./S.A.—See Whirlpool Corporation; *U.S. Public*, pg. 2367
WHIRLPOOL BULGARIA LTD.—See Whirlpool Corporation; *U.S. Public*, pg. 2367

WHIRLPOOL CANADA CO.—See Whirlpool Corporation; *U.S. Public*, pg. 2367
WHIRLPOOL CANADA LP—See Whirlpool Corporation; *U.S. Public*, pg. 2367
WHIRLPOOL CANADA LP—See Whirlpool Corporation; *U.S. Public*, pg. 2367
WHIRLPOOL COLOMBIA S.A.—See Whirlpool Corporation; *U.S. Public*, pg. 2367
WHIRLPOOL CORP. - CLYDE—See Whirlpool Corporation; *U.S. Public*, pg. 2367
WHIRLPOOL CORP. - EVANSVILLE—See Whirlpool Corporation; *U.S. Public*, pg. 2367
WHIRLPOOL CORP. - FINDLAY—See Whirlpool Corporation; *U.S. Public*, pg. 2367
WHIRLPOOL CORP. - FORT SMITH—See Whirlpool Corporation; *U.S. Public*, pg. 2367
WHIRLPOOL CORP. - LA VERGNE—See Whirlpool Corporation; *U.S. Public*, pg. 2367
WHIRLPOOL CORP. - MARION—See Whirlpool Corporation; *U.S. Public*, pg. 2367
WHIRLPOOL CORPORATION; *U.S. Public*, pg. 2366
WHIRLPOOL CROATIA LTD.—See Whirlpool Corporation; *U.S. Public*, pg. 2367
WHIRLPOOL DO BRASIL LTDA.—See Whirlpool Corporation; *U.S. Public*, pg. 2368
WHIRLPOOL EESTI OU—See Whirlpool Corporation; *U.S. Public*, pg. 2367
WHIRLPOOL EUROPE B.V.—See Whirlpool Corporation; *U.S. Public*, pg. 2367
WHIRLPOOL EUROPE COORDINATION CENTER—See Whirlpool Corporation; *U.S. Public*, pg. 2367
WHIRLPOOL EUROPE OPERATIONS CENTER—See Whirlpool Corporation; *U.S. Public*, pg. 2367
WHIRLPOOL FRANCE SAS—See Whirlpool Corporation; *U.S. Public*, pg. 2367
WHIRLPOOL GERMANY GMBH—See Whirlpool Corporation; *U.S. Public*, pg. 2367
WHIRLPOOL HELLAS SA—See Whirlpool Corporation; *U.S. Public*, pg. 2367
WHIRLPOOL HOME APPLIANCE (SHANGHAI) CO., LTD.—See Whirlpool Corporation; *U.S. Public*, pg. 2367
WHIRLPOOL (HONG KONG) LTD.—See Whirlpool Corporation; *U.S. Public*, pg. 2367
WHIRLPOOL INTERNACIONAL S. DE R.L. DE C.V.—See Whirlpool Corporation; *U.S. Public*, pg. 2368
WHIRLPOOL IRELAND LIMITED—See Whirlpool Corporation; *U.S. Public*, pg. 2368
WHIRLPOOL IRELAND—See Whirlpool Corporation; *U.S. Public*, pg. 2368
WHIRLPOOL ITALIA S.R.L.—See Whirlpool Corporation; *U.S. Public*, pg. 2368
WHIRLPOOL LATVIA S.I.A.—See Whirlpool Corporation; *U.S. Public*, pg. 2368
WHIRLPOOL LATVIA S.I.A.—See Whirlpool Corporation; *U.S. Public*, pg. 2368
WHIRLPOOL MANAGEMENT SERVICES SAGL—See Whirlpool Corporation; *U.S. Public*, pg. 2368
WHIRLPOOL MAROC SARL—See Whirlpool Corporation; *U.S. Public*, pg. 2368
WHIRLPOOL MAROC S. AR.L.—See Whirlpool Corporation; *U.S. Public*, pg. 2368
WHIRLPOOL MEXICO, S.A. DE C.V.—See Whirlpool Corporation; *U.S. Public*, pg. 2368
WHIRLPOOL MICROWAVE PRODUCTS DEVELOPMENT LIMITED—See Whirlpool Corporation; *U.S. Public*, pg. 2368
WHIRLPOOL NEDERLAND B.V.—See Whirlpool Corporation; *U.S. Public*, pg. 2368
WHIRLPOOL NORDIC AB—See Whirlpool Corporation; *U.S. Public*, pg. 2368
WHIRLPOOL NORDIC AB—See Whirlpool Corporation; *U.S. Public*, pg. 2368
WHIRLPOOL NORDIC A/S—See Whirlpool Corporation; *U.S. Public*, pg. 2368
WHIRLPOOL NORDIC OY—See Whirlpool Corporation; *U.S. Public*, pg. 2368
WHIRLPOOL OF INDIA LIMITED—See Whirlpool Corporation; *U.S. Public*, pg. 2368
WHIRLPOOL OSTERREICH GMBH—See Whirlpool Corporation; *U.S. Public*, pg. 2368
WHIRLPOOL OVERSEAS HOLDINGS, LLC—See Whirlpool Corporation; *U.S. Public*, pg. 2368
WHIRLPOOL OVERSEAS HONG KONG LIMITED—See Whirlpool Corporation; *U.S. Public*, pg. 2368
WHIRLPOOL POLSKA APPLIANCES SP. Z O.O.—See Whirlpool Corporation; *U.S. Public*, pg. 2368
WHIRLPOOL PORTUGAL ELECTRODOMESTICOS, LDA.—See Whirlpool Corporation; *U.S. Public*, pg. 2368
WHIRLPOOL R&D S.R.L.—See Whirlpool Corporation; *U.S. Public*, pg. 2368
WHIRLPOOL REALTY CORPORATION—See Whirlpool Corporation; *U.S. Public*, pg. 2368
WHIRLPOOL RUS LLC—See Whirlpool Corporation; *U.S. Public*, pg. 2368
WHIRLPOOL S.A.—See Whirlpool Corporation; *U.S. Public*, pg. 2368

WHITE BEAR LAKE SUPERSTORE

WHIRLPOOL SLOVAKIA HOME APPLIANCES SPOL. S.R.O.—See Whirlpool Corporation; *U.S. Public*, pg. 2368
WHIRLPOOL SLOVAKIA SPOL. S.R.O.—See Whirlpool Corporation; *U.S. Public*, pg. 2368
WHIRLPOOL SOUTH AFRICA PROPRIETARY LIMITED—See Whirlpool Corporation; *U.S. Public*, pg. 2368
WHIRLPOOL SOUTHEAST ASIA PTE. LTD.—See Whirlpool Corporation; *U.S. Public*, pg. 2368
WHIRLPOOL SOUTHEAST ASIA PTE—See Whirlpool Corporation; *U.S. Public*, pg. 2368
WHIRLPOOL UK APPLIANCES LIMITED—See Whirlpool Corporation; *U.S. Public*, pg. 2368
WHIRLWIND BUILDING SYSTEM; *U.S. Private*, pg. 4507
WHIRLWIND STEEL; *U.S. Private*, pg. 4507
WHISHWORKS IT CONSULTING PRIVATE LIMITED—See Coforge Ltd.; *Int'l*, pg. 1693
WHISKEY ACQUISITION, INC.; *U.S. Private*, pg. 4507
WHI SOLUTIONS, INC.—See eBay Inc.; *U.S. Public*, pg. 709
WHISPERING PINES HOME CARE, LLC—See UnitedHealth Group Incorporated; *U.S. Public*, pg. 2247
WHISPERING WOODS LLC—See Deutsche Bank Aktiengesellschaft; *Int'l*, pg. 2062
WHISPER TECH LIMITED—See Meridian Energy Limited; *Int'l*, pg. 4835
WHISSELL CONTRACTING LTD.; *Int'l*, pg. 8398
WHISTLER BLACKCOMB CORPORATION—See Vail Resorts, Inc.; *U.S. Public*, pg. 2272
WHISTLER BLACKCOMB HOLDINGS INC.—See Vail Resorts, Inc.; *U.S. Public*, pg. 2272
WHISTLER MEDICAL MARIJUANA CORPORATION—See Aurora Cannabis Inc.; *Int'l*, pg. 713
WHISTLES LIMITED—See The Foschini Group Limited; *Int'l*, pg. 7644
WHISTLE SPORTS INC.; *U.S. Private*, pg. 4507
WHISTLING WOODS INTERNATIONAL LIMITED—See Mukta Arts Ltd; *Int'l*, pg. 5079
WHITACRE ENGINEERING CO. INC.; *U.S. Private*, pg. 4507
WHITACRE GREER COMPANY; *U.S. Private*, pg. 4507
WHITACRE LOGISTICS, LLC.; *U.S. Private*, pg. 4507
WHITAKER BANK CORPORATION OF KENTUCKY; *U.S. Private*, pg. 4507
WHITAKER BANK, INC.—See Whitaker Bank Corporation of Kentucky; *U.S. Private*, pg. 4507
WHITAKER BUICK JEEP EAGLE CO.; *U.S. Private*, pg. 4507
THE WHITAKER COMPANIES, INC.; *U.S. Private*, pg. 4134
WHITAKER CONSTRUCTION COMPANY; *U.S. Private*, pg. 4507
THE WHITAKER CORPORATION—See TE Connectivity Ltd.; *Int'l*, pg. 7497
THE WHITAKER LLC—See TE Connectivity Ltd.; *Int'l*, pg. 7497
WHITAKER OIL COMPANY; *U.S. Private*, pg. 4507
WHITAKER TAYLOR, INC.—See HR Path SAS; *Int'l*, pg. 3501
WHITAKER TECHNICAL—See The Whitaker Companies, Inc.; *U.S. Private*, pg. 4134
WHITBOY, INC.—See Stone Point Capital LLC; *U.S. Private*, pg. 3819
WHITBREAD GROUP PLC—See Whitbread PLC; *Int'l*, pg. 8398
WHITBREAD HOTEL COMPANY LTD—See Whitbread PLC; *Int'l*, pg. 8398
WHITBREAD PLC; *Int'l*, pg. 8398
WHITBREAD PROPERTIES LTD.—See Whitbread PLC; *Int'l*, pg. 8398
WHITBREAD RESTAURANTS HOLDING GMBH—See Whitbread PLC; *Int'l*, pg. 8398
WHITBY COGENERATION LIMITED PARTNERSHIP—See Energy Capital Partners Management, LP; *U.S. Private*, pg. 1394
WHITCOM PARTNERS, INC.; *U.S. Private*, pg. 4507
WHITCORP FINANCIAL COMPANY; *U.S. Private*, pg. 4507
WHITCO SUPPLY, LLC—See DNOW Inc.; *U.S. Public*, pg. 671
WHITCOULLS LTD—See Pacific Equity Partners Pty. Limited; *Int'l*, pg. 5689
WHITCRAFT LLC—See Greenbriar Equity Group, L.P.; *U.S. Private*, pg. 1776
WHITE ALUMINUM EXTRUSION LLC—See Dubai Investments PJSC; *Int'l*, pg. 2219
WHITE ARROW SERVICE STATIONS; *U.S. Private*, pg. 4508
WHITEAWAY LAIDLAW BANK LIMITED—See NatWest Group plc; *Int'l*, pg. 5172
WHITEBARK ENERGY LIMITED; *Int'l*, pg. 8399
THE WHITE BARN CANDLE CO.—See Bath & Body Works, Inc.; *U.S. Public*, pg. 279
WHITE BAUMASCHINENREIFEN GMBH—See The Yokohama Rubber Co., Ltd.; *Int'l*, pg. 7703
WHITE BEAR LAKE SUPERSTORE; *U.S. Private*, pg. 4508

WHITEBIRCH ENTERPRISES, INC.

WHITEBIRCH ENTERPRISES, INC.; *U.S. Private,* pg. 4511
WHITEBIRCH, INC.—See Whitebirch Enterprises, Inc.; *U.S. Private,* pg. 4511
WHITEBOARD LABS LLC; *U.S. Private,* pg. 4511
WHITEBOX ADVISORS, LLC; *U.S. Private,* pg. 4511
WHITE BOX CO., LTD.—See Tohokushinsha Film Corporation; *Int'l,* pg. 7777
WHITEBRIDGE PET BRANDS, LLC—See Frontenac Company LLC; *U.S. Private,* pg. 1614
WHITE BROTHERS AUTO SUPPLY, INC.—See TPH Acquisition, LLLP; *U.S. Private,* pg. 4200
THE WHITE BUFFALO SALOON, LLC; *U.S. Private,* pg. 4134
WHITECANYON SOFTWARE, INC.—See Francisco Partners Management, LP; *U.S. Private,* pg. 1589
WHITE CAP CONSTRUCTION SUPPLY, INC.—See Clayton, Dubilier & Rice, LLC; *U.S. Private,* pg. 930
WHITE CAP, INC.—See Industrias Alen S.A. de C.V.; *Int'l,* pg. 3673
WHITE CAP, L.P.—See Clayton, Dubilier & Rice, LLC; *U.S. Private,* pg. 930
WHITECAP MOTORS; *Int'l,* pg. 8399
WHITECAP RESOURCES INC.; *Int'l,* pg. 8399
WHITE CAP SUPPLY HOLDINGS LLC—See Clayton, Dubilier & Rice, LLC; *U.S. Private,* pg. 930
WHITE & CASE LLP; *U.S. Private,* pg. 4507
WHITE CASTLE DISTRIBUTING, INC.—See White Castle System, Inc.; *U.S. Private,* pg. 4508
WHITE CASTLE SYSTEM, INC.-EVENDEL—See White Castle System, Inc.; *U.S. Private,* pg. 4508
WHITE CASTLE SYSTEM, INC.; *U.S. Private,* pg. 4508
WHITECLIFF CAPITAL PARTNERS, INC.; *U.S. Private,* pg. 4511
WHITE CLIFF MINERALS LIMITED; *Int'l,* pg. 8398
WHITE CLOUD GRAIN COMPANY INC.; *U.S. Private,* pg. 4508
WHITECO INDUSTRIES INC.; *U.S. Private,* pg. 4511
THE WHITE COLLECTION PTE. LTD.—See TT International Limited; *Int'l,* pg. 7960
WHITE CONSTRUCTION COMPANY INC.; *U.S. Private,* pg. 4508
WHITE CONSTRUCTION COMPANY—See Crestview Partners, L.P.; *U.S. Private,* pg. 1098
WHITE CONSTRUCTION INC.—See MasTec, Inc.; *U.S. Public,* pg. 1393
WHITE CONTRUCTION, INC.; *U.S. Private,* pg. 4508
WHITE COUNTY COAL, LLC—See Alliance Holdings GP, L.P.; *U.S. Private,* pg. 183
WHITE COUNTY FORD-CHRYSLER; *U.S. Private,* pg. 4508
WHITE COUNTY VIDEO INC.—See Wehco Media, Inc.; *U.S. Private,* pg. 4469
WHITE COUNTY VIDEO INC.—See Wehco Media, Inc.; *U.S. Private,* pg. 4469
WHITECOURT POWER LIMITED PARTNERSHIP—See iCON Infrastructure LLP; *Int'l,* pg. 3583
WHITE CRANE CO, INC.—See Barnhart Crane & Rigging Co.; *U.S. Private,* pg. 478
WHITE CREEK WIND PROJECT; *U.S. Private,* pg. 4508
WHITECROFT ESSENTIALS LTD.; *Int'l,* pg. 8399
WHITECROFT LIGHTING LTD—See Fagerhult Group AB; *Int'l,* pg. 2602
WHITE CROSS SLEEP PRODUCTS—See Eastern Sleep Products Company Inc.; *U.S. Private,* pg. 1321
WHITE CUP SE, INC.—See Eden Capital Management LLC; *U.S. Private,* pg. 1333
WHITE DEER MANAGEMENT LLC; *U.S. Private,* pg. 4508
WHITE DEER RUN, INC.—See Acadia Healthcare Company, Inc.; *U.S. Public,* pg. 31
WHITE DEVELOPMENT CORP.—See R.H. White Companies Inc.; *U.S. Private,* pg. 3336
WHITED FORD TRUCK CENTER; *U.S. Private,* pg. 4511
WHITE DIGITAL MEDIA; *U.S. Private,* pg. 4509
WHITE EAGLE ASSURANCE COMPANY—See Helmerich & Payne, Inc.; *U.S. Public,* pg. 1024
WHITE ELECTRICAL CONSTRUCTION CO.; *U.S. Private,* pg. 4509
WHITE ENERGY COMPANY LIMITED; *Int'l,* pg. 8398
WHITE ENVIRONMENTAL CONSULTANTS, INC.—See Bernhard Capital Partners Management, LP; *U.S. Private,* pg. 536
WHITEFAB INC.; *U.S. Private,* pg. 4511
THE WHITE FAMILY COMPANIES, INC.; *U.S. Private,* pg. 4135
WHITEFEATHER FOODS INC.—See Rudolph Foods Company; *U.S. Private,* pg. 3502
WHITEFENCE, INC.—See Allconnect, Inc.; *U.S. Private,* pg. 175
WHITE FENCE SURGICAL SUITES, LLC—See Tenet Healthcare Corporation; *U.S. Public,* pg. 2015
WHITEFIELD LIMITED; *Int'l,* pg. 8399
WHITEFIELD PLASTICS CORPORATION—See Mearthane Products Corporation; *U.S. Private,* pg. 2648
WHITEFISH CREDIT UNION; *U.S. Private,* pg. 4511
WHITEFISH MOUNTAIN RESORT—See Winter Sports, Inc.; *U.S. Private,* pg. 4545
WHITE FLOWER FARM, INC.; *U.S. Private,* pg. 4509

WHITE FLYER TARGETS, LLC—See Wynnchurch Capital, L.P.; *U.S. Private,* pg. 4578
WHITE FOX VENTURES, INC.; *Int'l,* pg. 8398
WHITEGLOVE HOUSE CALL HEALTH, INC.; *U.S. Private,* pg. 4511
WHITE GLOVE PLACEMENT INC.; *U.S. Private,* pg. 4509
WHITE GOLD CORPORATION—See Tesoro Minerals Corp.; *Int'l,* pg. 7573
WHITE GOLD CORP.; *Int'l,* pg. 8398
WHITE GOLD COTTON MARKETING, LLC; *U.S. Private,* pg. 4509
WHITE GOOD & CO. ADVERTISING; *U.S. Private,* pg. 4509
WHITE GROUP PUBLIC COMPANY LIMITED—See Berli Jucker Public Co. Ltd.; *Int'l,* pg. 985
WHITEHALL ADVERTISING INC.—See Chatam International Incorporated; *U.S. Private,* pg. 860
WHITEHALL MANUFACTURING, INC.—See Acorn Engineering Company, Inc.; *U.S. Private,* pg. 63
WHITEHALL PRODUCTS, INC.; *U.S. Private,* pg. 4511
WHITEHALL SPECIALTIES INC.—See Ornua Co-operative Limited; *Int'l,* pg. 5642
WHITEHALL STREET REAL ESTATE L.P.—See The Goldman Sachs Group, Inc.; *U.S. Public,* pg. 2082
WHITEHAT INC.; *Int'l,* pg. 8399
WHITEHAT LTD.—See EPAM Systems, Inc.; *U.S. Public,* pg. 783
WHITEHAVEN COAL LIMITED; *Int'l,* pg. 8399
WHITEHAWK LIMITED; *Int'l,* pg. 8400
WHITEHEAD ALENIA SISTEMI SUBACQUEI SPA—See Leonardo S.p.A.; *Int'l,* pg. 4461
WHITEHEAD OIL CO., INC.—See Whitehead Oil Co., Inc.; *U.S. Private,* pg. 4511
WHITEHEAD OIL CO., INC.; *U.S. Private,* pg. 4511
WHITEHELM CAPITAL PTY LTD; *Int'l,* pg. 8400
WHITE HORSE BERHAD - PLANT 3—See White Horse Berhad; *Int'l,* pg. 8399
WHITE HORSE BERHAD; *Int'l,* pg. 8398
WHITE HORSE CERAMIC INDUSTRIES SDN. BHD.—See White Horse Berhad; *Int'l,* pg. 8399
WHITE HORSE CERAMIC INDUSTRIES (VIETNAM) CO., LTD.—See White Horse Berhad; *Int'l,* pg. 8399
WHITE HORSE CERAMIC (PHIL) INC.—See White Horse Berhad; *Int'l,* pg. 8399
WHITE HORSE CERAMIC (S) PTE. LTD.—See White Horse Berhad; *Int'l,* pg. 8399
WHITE HORSE CERAMIC (THAILAND) LTD.—See White Horse Berhad; *Int'l,* pg. 8399
WHITEHORSE FINANCE, INC.; *U.S. Public,* pg. 2369
WHITEHORSE FINANCE WAREHOUSE, LLC—See WhiteHorse Finance, Inc.; *U.S. Public,* pg. 2369
WHITEHORSE GOLD CORP—See New Pacific Metals Corp.; *Int'l,* pg. 5226
WHITE HORSE MARKETING SDN. BHD.—See White Horse Berhad; *Int'l,* pg. 8399
WHITEHORSE MOTORS; *Int'l,* pg. 8400
WHITEHORSE TRUCKS PTY LTD—See Eagers Automotive Limited; *Int'l,* pg. 2263
WHITE HORSE VILLAGE; *U.S. Private,* pg. 4509
WHITE HOUSE BLACK MARKET, INC.—See Sycamore Partners Management, LP; *U.S. Private,* pg. 3895
WHITE HOUSE CUSTOM COLOUR, INC.; *U.S. Private,* pg. 4509
WHITE HOUSE HISTORICAL ASSOCIATION; *U.S. Private,* pg. 4509
WHITE INDUSTRIES, INC.—See Bas Part Sales LLC; *U.S. Private,* pg. 484
WHITE IRON DIGITAL—See White Iron, Inc.; *Int'l,* pg. 8399
WHITE IRON, INC.; *Int'l,* pg. 8399
WHITE IRON PICTURES, INC.—See White Iron, Inc.; *Int'l,* pg. 8399
WHITE IRON PRODUCTIONS, INC.—See White Iron, Inc.; *Int'l,* pg. 8399
WHITE IRON VOICELINK, INC.—See White Iron, Inc.; *Int'l,* pg. 8399
WHITE KITE (DERBY) LIMITED—See The Property Franchise Group PLC; *Int'l,* pg. 7676
WHITE KITE (LEICESTER) LIMITED—See The Property Franchise Group PLC; *Int'l,* pg. 7676
WHITE KNIGHT BROADCASTING, INC.; *U.S. Private,* pg. 4509
WHITE KNIGHT FLUID HANDLING, INC.—See Graco, Inc.; *U.S. Public,* pg. 954
WHITE KNIGHT HOLDINGS PUBLIC COMPANY LTD—See SFS Group Public Company Limited; *Int'l,* pg. 6740
WHITE KNIGHT LIMOUSINE INC.; *U.S. Private,* pg. 4509
WHITE KNIGHT RESOURCES LTD.—See McEwen Mining Inc.; *Int'l,* pg. 4758
WHITE LABEL LENDING LIMITED—See West Bromwich Building Society; *Int'l,* pg. 8383
WHITE LABEL LIQUID, INC.; *U.S. Public,* pg. 2368
WHITE LAKE DOCK & DREDGE, INC.—See J.F. Lehman & Company, Inc.; *U.S. Private,* pg. 2163
WHITELAW TWINING LAW CORP.—See Inflexion Private Equity Partners LLP; *Int'l,* pg. 3689
WHITELIGHT GROUP, LLC—See CVC Capital Partners SICAV-FIS S.A.; *Int'l,* pg. 1883

CORPORATE AFFILIATIONS

WHITELINE EXPRESS LTD.—See Plastipak Holdings, Inc.; *U.S. Private,* pg. 3200
WHITE LODGE BANGSAR SOUTH CHILDCARE CENTRE SDN. BHD.—See Chip Eng Seng Corporation Ltd.; *Int'l,* pg. 1572
WHITE LODGE, BUKIT TIMAH PTE. LTD.—See Chip Eng Seng Corporation Ltd.; *Int'l,* pg. 1572
WHITE LODGE EDUCATION GROUP SERVICES PTE. LTD.—See Chip Eng Seng Corporation Ltd.; *Int'l,* pg. 1572
WHITE LODGE KINDERGARTEN, EAST COAST PTE. LTD.—See Chip Eng Seng Corporation Ltd.; *Int'l,* pg. 1572
WHITE LODGE KINDERGARTEN, PHOENIX PARK PTE. LTD.—See Chip Eng Seng Corporation Ltd.; *Int'l,* pg. 1572
WHITE LODGE MONT KIARA CHILDCARE CENTRE SDN. BHD.—See Chip Eng Seng Corporation Ltd.; *Int'l,* pg. 1572
WHITE LODGE PRESCHOOL RIVER VALLEY PTE. LTD.—See Chip Eng Seng Corporation Ltd.; *Int'l,* pg. 1572
WHITE LODGE SCHOOL OF ARTS, LOEWEN GARDENS PTE. LTD.—See Chip Eng Seng Corporation Ltd.; *Int'l,* pg. 1572
WHITE LODGE, UPPER BUKIT TIMAH PTE. LTD.—See Chip Eng Seng Corporation Ltd.; *Int'l,* pg. 1572
WHITE LODGE, UPPER EAST COAST PTE. LTD.—See Chip Eng Seng Corporation Ltd.; *Int'l,* pg. 1572
WHITE LODGE, WEST COAST PTE. LTD.—See Chip Eng Seng Corporation Ltd.; *Int'l,* pg. 1572
WHITE LOTUS HOME; *U.S. Private,* pg. 4509
WHITEMAN CHEVROLET, INC.; *U.S. Private,* pg. 4511
WHITE MARSH PLAZA, LLC—See Federal Realty Investment Trust; *U.S. Public,* pg. 826
WHITE MARTINS GASES INDUSTRIAIS LTDA—See Linde plc; *Int'l,* pg. 4510
WHITE MARTINS STEEL GASES INDUSTRIAIS LTDA.—See Linde plc; *Int'l,* pg. 4510
WHITE METALS GROUP—See Plymouth Tube Company; *U.S. Private,* pg. 3216
WHITE MOUNTAIN CABLE CONSTRUCTION, LLC—See Dycom Industries, Inc.; *U.S. Public,* pg. 699
WHITE MOUNTAIN IMAGING INC.; *U.S. Private,* pg. 4509
WHITE MOUNTAIN MALL, LLC—See Brookfield Corporation; *Int'l,* pg. 1185
WHITE MOUNTAINS ADVISORS LLC—See White Mountains Insurance Group, Ltd.; *U.S. Public,* pg. 2369
WHITE MOUNTAINS INSURANCE GROUP, LTD.; *U.S. Public,* pg. 2368
WHITE MOUNTAINS RE BERMUDA LTD.—See White Mountains Insurance Group, Ltd.; *U.S. Public,* pg. 2369
WHITE MOUNTAINS SOLUTIONS, INC.—See White Mountains Insurance Group, Ltd.; *U.S. Public,* pg. 2369
WHITE MOUNTAIN TITANIUM CORPORATION; *Int'l,* pg. 8399
WHITEMUD RESOURCES INC.; *Int'l,* pg. 8400
WHITEMYER ADVERTISING, INC.; *U.S. Private,* pg. 4511
WHITENI RCAJAL SOCIMI SA; *Int'l,* pg. 8400
WHITE NI RCAJAL SOCIMI SA; *Int'l,* pg. 8400
WHITE OAK CORPORATION; *U.S. Private,* pg. 4509
WHITE OAK EQUIPMENT INC.—See McClung-Logan Equipment Company, Inc.; *U.S. Private,* pg. 2629
WHITEOAK FORD LINCOLN SALES; *Int'l,* pg. 8400
WHITE OAK GLOBAL ADVISORS, LLC; *U.S. Private,* pg. 4509
THE WHITE OAK GROUP, INC.; *U.S. Private,* pg. 4135
WHITEOAK GROUP; *U.S. Private,* pg. 4511
WHITE OAK MILLS INC.; *U.S. Private,* pg. 4509
WHITE OAK RESOURCES LLC—See Alliance Holdings GP, L.P.; *U.S. Private,* pg. 183
WHITE OAKS PLAZA, LLC—See Washington Prime Group Inc.; *U.S. Private,* pg. 4449
WHITE OAKS STATION LLC—See Phillips Edison & Company LLC; *U.S. Private,* pg. 3171
WHITE OAK TRANSPORT LIMITED; *Int'l,* pg. 8399
WHITE ORGANIC AGRO LIMITED; *Int'l,* pg. 8399
WHITE ORGANIC RETAIL LIMITED; *Int'l,* pg. 8399
WHITEPAGES.COM INC.; *U.S. Private,* pg. 4511
WHITE & PARTNERS; *U.S. Private,* pg. 4508
WHITE PASS & YUKON ROUTE—See Carnival Corporation; *U.S. Public,* pg. 438
WHITEPATH FAB TECH INC.—See Cerberus Capital Management, L.P.; *U.S. Private,* pg. 838
WHITE PIGEON PAPER COMPANY—See Graphic Packaging Holding Company; *U.S. Public,* pg. 958
WHITE PINE INSURANCE COMPANY—See Conifer Holdings, Inc.; *U.S. Public,* pg. 567
WHITE PINES CORPORATION—See J. P. Mascaro & Sons; *U.S. Private,* pg. 2156
WHITE PLAINS HONDA; *U.S. Private,* pg. 4509
THE WHITE QUILL PRESS—See Chevrillon Philippe Industrie; *Int'l,* pg. 1474
WHITERIDGE PLASTICS, LLC—See Myers Industries, Inc.; *U.S. Public,* pg. 1488
WHITE RIVER AREA AGENCY ON AGING INC; *U.S. Private,* pg. 4509
WHITE RIVER BANCSHARES COMPANY; *U.S. Public,* pg. 2369

COMPANY NAME INDEX

WHITE RIVER CAPITAL, INC.—See PCP Enterprise, L.P.; *U.S. Private*, pg. 3121
WHITERIVER CONSTRUCTION, INC.; *U.S. Private*, pg. 4511
WHITE RIVER COOPERATIVE INC.—See Premier Cos.; *U.S. Private*, pg. 3250
WHITE RIVER ENERGY CORP.; *U.S. Public*, pg. 2369
WHITE RIVER ENGINEERING INC.—See Allgeier, Martin & Associates, Inc.; *U.S. Private*, pg. 181
WHITE RIVER HARDWOODS-WOODWORKS, INC.; *U.S. Private*, pg. 4509
WHITERIVER LAUNDRY LTD—See Afonwen Laundry Limited; *Int'l*, pg. 189
WHITE RIVER VALLEY ELECTRIC COOP; *U.S. Private*, pg. 4509
WHITE ROCK BANK—See 215 Holding Co.; *U.S. Private*, pg. 5
WHITE ROCK CHRYSLER LTD; *Int'l*, pg. 8399
WHITEROCK INCORPORATION PRIVATE LIMITED—See Boustead Singapore Limited; *Int'l*, pg. 1121
WHITE ROCK INSURANCE (EUROPE) PCC LIMITED—See Aon plc; *Int'l*, pg. 495
WHITE ROCK MINERALS LIMITED; *Int'l*, pg. 8399
WHITE ROCK MINERALS (MTC) PTY. LTD.—See White Rock Minerals Limited; *Int'l*, pg. 8399
WHITE ROCK OUTBOARD, INC.—See Portland Yacht Services, Inc.; *U.S. Private*, pg. 3233
WHITE ROCK PRODUCTS CORP.; *U.S. Private*, pg. 4509
WHITE-RODGERS—See Emerson Electric Co.; *U.S. Public*, pg. 744
WHITE ROSE BUS COMPANY LIMITED—See Deutsche Bahn AG; *Int'l*, pg. 2055
WHITE ROSE FOODS—See Rose Partners LP; *U.S. Private*, pg. 3481
WHITE ROSE NOMINEE LIMITED—See KBL European Private Bankers S.A.; *Int'l*, pg. 4107
WHITE ROSE PARK (NORWICH) RESIDENTS MANAGEMENT COMPANY LIMITED—See Persimmon plc; *Int'l*, pg. 5818
WHITE RUNWAY PTY. LTD.—See Queens Lane Capital Pty Ltd; *Int'l*, pg. 6159
WHITESBURG ARH HOSPITAL; *U.S. Private*, pg. 4512
WHITE'S ELECTRONICS; *U.S. Private*, pg. 4510
WHITE'S ELECTRONICS (UK) LTD—See White's Electronics; *U.S. Private*, pg. 4510
WHITESELL CONSTRUCTION INC.; *U.S. Private*, pg. 4512
WHITESELL CORPORATION; *U.S. Private*, pg. 4512
WHITESELL INTERNATIONAL CORPORATION—See Whitesell Corporation; *U.S. Private*, pg. 4512
WHITESELL WIRE FORM UNIT—See Whitesell Corporation; *U.S. Private*, pg. 4512
WHITES FARM SUPPLY INC.; *U.S. Private*, pg. 4511
WHITE SHIELD, INC.; *U.S. Private*, pg. 4510
WHITE SHIELD INSURANCE COMPANY LTD.—See InterContinental Hotels Group PLC; *Int'l*, pg. 3739
WHITE'S INTERNATIONAL TRUCKS—See White's International Trucks; *U.S. Private*, pg. 4510
WHITE'S INTERNATIONAL TRUCKS; *U.S. Private*, pg. 4510
WHITES KINGCO INC.; *U.S. Private*, pg. 4511
WHITES LOCATION EQUIPMENT SUPPLY INC.—See Ashtead Group Plc; *Int'l*, pg. 609
WHITES LUMBER INC.; *U.S. Private*, pg. 4511
WHITESMOKE, INC.; *Int'l*, pg. 8400
WHITE SMILE GLOBAL, INC.; *U.S. Private*, pg. 4510
WHITE'S MOUNTAIN MOTORS; *U.S. Private*, pg. 4510
WHITE'S OF LONG ISLAND, INC.—See White's Electronics; *U.S. Private*, pg. 4510
WHITESPACE CREATIVE; *U.S. Private*, pg. 4512
WHITESPACE DESIGN GROUP, INC.; *U.S. Private*, pg. 4512
WHITESPACE (SCOTLAND) LIMITED—See Dentsu Group Inc.; *Int'l*, pg. 2038
WHITESPEED; *U.S. Private*, pg. 4512
WHITE SPRINGS AGRICULTURAL CHEMICALS, INC.—See Nutrien Ltd.; *Int'l*, pg. 5494
WHITE'S RESIDENTIAL & FAMILY SERVICES, INC.; *U.S. Private*, pg. 4510
WHITE'S RESIDENTIAL & FAMILY SERVICES OF NORTHWEST INDIANA—See White's Residential & Family Services, Inc.; *U.S. Private*, pg. 4510
WHITE'S SITE DEVELOPMENT, INC.; *U.S. Private*, pg. 4510
WHITE STAR MACHINERY & SUPPLY CO.—See Berry Companies, Inc.; *U.S. Private*, pg. 538
WHITE STAR STEEL—See Nashville Steel Corp.; *U.S. Private*, pg. 2836
WHITES TIRE SERVICE OF WILSON; *U.S. Private*, pg. 4511
WHITESTONE ACQUISITION CORP.—See PAUL HARTMANN AG; *Int'l*, pg. 5762
WHITESTONE COMMUNICATIONS, INC.; *U.S. Private*, pg. 4512
THE WHITE STONE GROUP INC.—See Accel Partners L.P.; *U.S. Private*, pg. 48
THE WHITE STONE GROUP INC.—See KKR & Co. Inc.; *U.S. Public*, pg. 1238
THE WHITESTONE GROUP, INC.; *U.S. Private*, pg. 4135

WHITESTONE PINNACLE OF SCOTTSDALE, LLC—See Whitestone REIT; *U.S. Public*, pg. 2369
WHITESTONE REIT; *U.S. Public*, pg. 2369
WHITESWAN/META—See Encompass Group LLC; *U.S. Private*, pg. 1390
WHITETAIL ROCK CAPITAL MANAGEMENT, LLC—See Nelnet, Inc.; *U.S. Public*, pg. 1504
WHITETAIL ROCK QUANTITATIVE STRATEGIES I, LP—See Nelnet, Inc.; *U.S. Public*, pg. 1504
WHITE TECH S.P.Z.O.O.—See Moncler S.p.A.; *Int'l*, pg. 5025
WHITE/THOMPSON, LLC; *U.S. Private*, pg. 4510
WHITE TIRE—See Cox Enterprises, Inc.; *U.S. Private*, pg. 1076
WHITE-TUCKER COMPANY; *U.S. Private*, pg. 4510
WHITE + WARREN; *U.S. Private*, pg. 4508
WHITEWATER EXPRESS, INC.; *U.S. Private*, pg. 4512
WHITEWATER HOLDING COMPANY, LLC; *U.S. Private*, pg. 4512
WHITEWATER, INC.—See R.H. White Companies Inc.; *U.S. Private*, pg. 3336
WHITEWATER OUTDOORS INCORPORATED; *U.S. Private*, pg. 4512
WHITEWATER WEST INDUSTRIES LTD.; *Int'l*, pg. 8400
WHITEWATER WHIRLPOOL BATHS SYSTEMS; *U.S. Private*, pg. 4512
WHITE WESTINGHOUSE PUERTO RICO—See AB Electrolux; *Int'l*, pg. 40
WHITE & WILLIAMS LLP; *U.S. Private*, pg. 4508
WHITE WOLF CAPITAL LLC; *U.S. Private*, pg. 4510
WHITE WOLF PUBLISHING AB—See Paradox Interactive AB; *Int'l*, pg. 5735
WHITEWOOD INDUSTRIES, INC.; *U.S. Private*, pg. 4512
WHITFIELD FOODS, INC.; *U.S. Private*, pg. 4512
WHITFIELD TIMBER, INC.; *U.S. Private*, pg. 4512
WHITFORD CORPORATION—See PPG Industries, Inc.; *U.S. Public*, pg. 1711
WHITFORD DO BRASIL LTDA.—See PPG Industries, Inc.; *U.S. Public*, pg. 1711
WHITFORD ESPANA S.L.—See PPG Industries, Inc.; *U.S. Public*, pg. 1711
WHITFORD GMBH—See PPG Industries, Inc.; *U.S. Public*, pg. 1711
WHITFORD INDIA PRIVATE LIMITED—See PPG Industries, Inc.; *U.S. Public*, pg. 1711
WHITFORD JIANGMEN LTD.—See PPG Industries, Inc.; *U.S. Public*, pg. 1711
WHITFORD LTD.—See PPG Industries, Inc.; *U.S. Public*, pg. 1711
WHITFORD LTD.—See PPG Industries, Inc.; *U.S. Public*, pg. 1711
WHITFORD PTE LTD—See PPG Industries, Inc.; *U.S. Public*, pg. 1711
WHITFORD SARL—See PPG Industries, Inc.; *U.S. Public*, pg. 1711
WHITFORD S.R.L.—See PPG Industries, Inc.; *U.S. Public*, pg. 1711
WHITFORD WORLDWIDE COMPANY—See PPG Industries, Inc.; *U.S. Public*, pg. 1711
WHITING CANADIAN HOLDING COMPANY ULC—See Chord Energy Corporation; *U.S. Public*, pg. 490
WHITING CLINIC LASIK + EYE CARE—See Vision Group Holdings LLC; *U.S. Private*, pg. 4390
WHITING CORPORATION—See GK Enterprises, Inc.; *U.S. Private*, pg. 1703
WHITING DOOR MANUFACTURING CORP.; *U.S. Private*, pg. 4512
WHITING EQUIPMENT CANADA, INC.—See GK Enterprises, Inc.; *U.S. Private*, pg. 1703
WHITING EQUIPMENT SERVICES CO. LTD.—See GK Enterprises, Inc.; *U.S. Private*, pg. 1703
WHITING HOLDINGS LLC—See Chord Energy Corporation; *U.S. Public*, pg. 490
WHITING MANUFACTURING CO., INC.; *U.S. Private*, pg. 4512
WHITING PETROLEUM CORPORATION—See Chord Energy Corporation; *U.S. Public*, pg. 490
WHITING SERVICES INC.—See GK Enterprises, Inc.; *U.S. Private*, pg. 1703
THE WHITING-TURNER CONTRACTING COMPANY; *U.S. Private*, pg. 4135
WHITING USA TRUST II; *U.S. Public*, pg. 2369
WHITLAM GROUP; *U.S. Private*, pg. 4512
WHITLEY BROOK CREMATORIUM FOR PETS LIMITED—See CVS Group Plc; *Int'l*, pg. 1890
WHITLEY MANUFACTURING COMPANY, INC.; *U.S. Private*, pg. 4512
WHITLEY PENN LLP; *U.S. Private*, pg. 4512
WHITLOCK HOLDING COMPANY; *U.S. Private*, pg. 4513
WHITMAN CASTINGS, INC.; *U.S. Private*, pg. 4513
WHITMAN PACKAGING CORP.—See The Estee Lauder Companies Inc.; *U.S. Public*, pg. 2073
WHITMAN-WALKER CLINIC, INC.; *U.S. Private*, pg. 4513
WHIT-MART INC.; *U.S. Private*, pg. 4507
WHITMORE EUROPE LIMITED—See CSW Industrials, Inc.; *U.S. Public*, pg. 602
THE WHITMORE MANUFACTURING COMPANY—See CSW Industrials, Inc.; *U.S. Public*, pg. 602

WHOLE EARTH PROVISION COMPANY

WHITMORE'S OF EDENBRIDGE LIMITED—See General Motors Company; *U.S. Public*, pg. 928
WHITMOR, INC.; *U.S. Private*, pg. 4513
WHITMOR/WIRENETICS; *U.S. Private*, pg. 4513
WHITNELL & CO.—See Rockefeller Capital Management; *U.S. Private*, pg. 3466
WHITNEY AUTOMOTIVE GROUP, INC.—See CarParts.com, Inc.; *U.S. Public*, pg. 439
WHITNEY BLAKE CO., INC.; *U.S. Private*, pg. 4513
WHITNEY, BRADLEY & BROWN, INC.—See Serco Group plc; *Int'l*, pg. 6721
WHITNEY & CO., LLC; *U.S. Private*, pg. 4513
WHITNEY INSURANCE AGENCY, INC.; *U.S. Private*, pg. 4513
WHITNEY M. YOUNG, JR. HEALTH CENTER; *U.S. Private*, pg. 4513
WHITNEY PARTNERS INC.; *U.S. Private*, pg. 4513
WHITNEY/PIRANHA/BERTSCH—See Mega Manufacturing Inc.; *U.S. Private*, pg. 2660
WHITNEY'S VALUE FORD; *U.S. Private*, pg. 4513
WHITNEY & WHITNEY, INC.—See Itronics Inc.; *U.S. Public*, pg. 1176
WHITSON - MORGAN MOTOR COMPANY; *U.S. Private*, pg. 4513
WHITSONS FOOD SERVICE CORP.; *U.S. Private*, pg. 4513
WHITSUNDAY RADIOLOGY PTY. LTD.—See Healius Limited; *Int'l*, pg. 3303
WHITTALL BOUSTEAD LTD.—See John Keells Holdings PLC; *Int'l*, pg. 3979
WHITTALL BOUSTEAD (PVT) LTD - CARGO DIVISION—See John Keells Holdings PLC; *Int'l*, pg. 3979
WHITTALL BOUSTEAD (TRAVEL) LTD.—See John Keells Holdings PLC; *Int'l*, pg. 3979
WHITTALLS WINE MERCHANTS 1 LTD.; *Int'l*, pg. 8400
WHITTAN STORAGE SYSTEMS LTD.; *Int'l*, pg. 8400
WHITTARD OF CHELSEA PLC; *Int'l*, pg. 8400
WHITTENBERG CONSTRUCTION CO.; *U.S. Private*, pg. 4513
WHITTENLASEREYE, LLC—See Centre Partners Management LLC; *U.S. Private*, pg. 828
WHITTIER DAILY NEWS—See Alden Global Capital LLC; *U.S. Private*, pg. 158
WHITTIER FILTRATION, INC.—See Veolia Environnement S.A.; *Int'l*, pg. 8163
THE WHITTIER TRUST COMPANY OF NEVADA, INC.—See Whittier Trust Company; *U.S. Private*, pg. 4514
WHITTIER TRUST COMPANY; *U.S. Private*, pg. 4513
WHITTIER WOOD PRODUCTS CO.; *U.S. Private*, pg. 4514
WHITTLE & MUTCH, INC.—See Riverside Partners, LLC; *U.S. Private*, pg. 3446
WHITTLE PAINTING GROUP LTD.—See Roy Hankinson (Holdings) Limited; *Int'l*, pg. 6409
WHITTLE PAINTING NOTTINGHAM LTD.—See Roy Hankinson (Holdings) Limited; *Int'l*, pg. 6409
WHITTLE PROGRAMMED MAINTENANCE LIMITED—See Roy Hankinson (Holdings) Limited; *Int'l*, pg. 6409
WHITTLESEY & HADLEY, P.C. - HAMDEN OFFICE—See Whittlesey & Hadley, P.C.; *U.S. Private*, pg. 4514
WHITTLESEY & HADLEY, P.C. - HOLYOKE OFFICE—See Whittlesey & Hadley, P.C.; *U.S. Private*, pg. 4514
WHITTLESEY & HADLEY, P.C.; *U.S. Private*, pg. 4514
WHITTLESEY LANDSCAPE SUPPLIES & RECYCLING, INC.—See SiteOne Landscape Supply, Inc.; *U.S. Public*, pg. 1889
WHITWORTH BROS LTD.; *Int'l*, pg. 8400
WHITWORTH DALE MANAGEMENT COMPANY LIMITED—See Persimmon plc; *Int'l*, pg. 5818
WHIZ AUTOMOTIVE CHEMICALS DIV—See Malco Products, Inc.; *U.S. Private*, pg. 2556
W.H. KOCH CO., INC.; *U.S. Private*, pg. 4420
WHKX-FM—See First Media Services, LLC; *U.S. Private*, pg. 1521
WHL ARCHITECTS & PLANNERS, INC.—See Architects Orange LLP; *U.S. Private*, pg. 311
WHLT-TV—See Nexstar Media Group, Inc.; *U.S. Public*, pg. 1523
W.H. MAZE COMPANY; *U.S. Private*, pg. 4420
W.H. MCADAMS COMPANY; *U.S. Private*, pg. 4420
WHM LLC—See Blackstone Inc.; *U.S. Public*, pg. 351
WHNT, LLC—See Nexstar Media Group, Inc.; *U.S. Public*, pg. 1525
WHO ARE YOU LTD.—See Intelli Centrics Inc.; *U.S. Private*, pg. 2105
WHOIS PRIVACY SERVICES PTY LIMITED—See Enero Group Limited; *Int'l*, pg. 2424
WHOLE BRIGHT INDUSTRIES (HK) LIMITED—See Dejin Resources Group Company Limited; *Int'l*, pg. 2005
WHOLE EARTH BRANDS, INC.; *U.S. Public*, pg. 2369
WHOLE EARTH PROVISION COMPANY; *U.S. Private*, pg. 4514
WHOLE EARTH SWEETENER COMPANY, LLC—See MacAndrews & Forbes Incorporated; *U.S. Private*, pg. 2532

WHOLE EASY INTERNET TECHNOLOGY CO., LTD.; *Int'l,* pg. 8401
WHOLE FOODS MARKET CALIFORNIA, INC.—See Amazon.com, Inc.; *U.S. Public,* pg. 91
WHOLE FOODS MARKET CANADA, INC.—See Amazon.com, Inc.; *U.S. Public,* pg. 91
WHOLE FOODS MARKET - FLORIDA REGION—See Amazon.com, Inc.; *U.S. Public,* pg. 91
WHOLE FOODS MARKET, INC.—See Amazon.com, Inc.; *U.S. Public,* pg. 91
WHOLE FOODS MARKET - MID-ATLANTIC REGION—See Amazon.com, Inc.; *U.S. Public,* pg. 91
WHOLE FOODS MARKET - MIDWEST REGION—See Amazon.com, Inc.; *U.S. Public,* pg. 91
WHOLE FOODS MARKET NEBRASKA, LLC—See Amazon.com, Inc.; *U.S. Public,* pg. 91
WHOLE FOODS MARKET - NORTH ATLANTIC REGION—See Amazon.com, Inc.; *U.S. Public,* pg. 91
WHOLE FOODS MARKET - NORTHEAST REGION—See Amazon.com, Inc.; *U.S. Public,* pg. 91
WHOLE FOODS MARKET - NORTHERN CALIFORNIA REGION—See Amazon.com, Inc.; *U.S. Public,* pg. 91
WHOLE FOODS MARKET PACIFIC NORTHWEST, INC.—See Amazon.com, Inc.; *U.S. Public,* pg. 91
WHOLE FOODS MARKET - ROCKY MOUNTAIN REGION—See Amazon.com, Inc.; *U.S. Public,* pg. 91
WHOLE FOODS MARKET ROCKY MOUNTAIN/SOUTHWEST, L.P.—See Amazon.com, Inc.; *U.S. Public,* pg. 91
WHOLE FOODS MARKET SERVICES, INC.—See Amazon.com, Inc.; *U.S. Public,* pg. 91
WHOLE FOODS MARKET - SOUTHERN PACIFIC REGION—See Amazon.com, Inc.; *U.S. Public,* pg. 91
WHOLE FOODS MARKET - SOUTHWEST REGION—See Amazon.com, Inc.; *U.S. Public,* pg. 91
WHOLE HARVEST FOODS, LLC—See Bunge Limited; *U.S. Public,* pg. 412
WHOLE LIFE, INC; *U.S. Private,* pg. 4514
THE WHOLE PERSON, INC.; *U.S. Private,* pg. 4135
WHOLESALE BUILDERS SUPPLY INC.; *U.S. Private,* pg. 4514
WHOLESALE CARRIER SERVICES, INC.; *U.S. Private,* pg. 4514
WHOLESALE COMMERCIAL LAUNDRY EQUIPMENT SE, LLC—See EVI Industries, Inc.; *U.S. Public,* pg. 803
WHOLESALE ELECTRIC SUPPLY CO. INC.; *U.S. Private,* pg. 4514
WHOLESALE ELECTRIC SUPPLY HOUSTON LP; *U.S. Private,* pg. 4514
WHOLESALE ELECTRONIC SUPPLY, INC.; *U.S. Private,* pg. 4514
WHOLESALE EQUIPMENT BROKERS; *U.S. Private,* pg. 4514
WHOLESALE EQUIPMENT OF FRESNO; *U.S. Private,* pg. 4514
WHOLESALE EXPRESS, LLC—See RumbleON, Inc.; *U.S. Public,* pg. 1826
WHOLESALE FLOORS, INC.—See ACON Investments, LLC; *U.S. Private,* pg. 62
WHOLESALE HEATING & COOLING SUPPLY COMPANY; *U.S. Private,* pg. 4514
THE WHOLESALE HOUSE INC.; *U.S. Private,* pg. 4135
WHOLESALE, INC—See RumbleON, Inc.; *U.S. Public,* pg. 1826
WHOLESALE INDUSTRIAL ELECTRONICS, INC.; *U.S. Private,* pg. 4514
WHOLESALE LENS CORPORATION LIMITED—See EssilorLuxottica SA; *Int'l,* pg. 2516
WHOLESALE OUTLET INC.; *U.S. Private,* pg. 4514
WHOLESALE PETROLEUM INC.; *U.S. Private,* pg. 4514
WHOLESALE PLUMBING SUPPLY CO.; *U.S. Private,* pg. 4514
WHOLESALE PRODUCE SUPPLY, LLC—See Cross Rapids Capital LP; *U.S. Private,* pg. 1105
WHOLESALE PUMP & SUPPLY INC.; *U.S. Private,* pg. 4514
WHOLESALE & RETAIL TRADE VENTURE JSC; *Int'l,* pg. 8401
WHOLESALE SHEET METAL INC.—See Ridgemont Partners Management LLC; *U.S. Private,* pg. 3433
WHOLESALE SUPPLIES PLUS, LLC—See Incline MGMT Corp.; *U.S. Private,* pg. 2054
WHOLESALE SUPPLY GROUP INC.; *U.S. Private,* pg. 4514
WHOLESALE SUPPLY INC.—See Freeman Spogli & Co. Incorporated; *U.S. Private,* pg. 1606
WHOLESALE TIRE INC.; *U.S. Private,* pg. 4515
WHOLESALE TOOL CO., INC.; *U.S. Private,* pg. 4515
WHOLESALE TRADING INSURANCE SERVICES, LLC—See The Carlyle Group Inc.; *U.S. Public,* pg. 2048
WHOLESALE WOOD PRODUCTS—See Lumber Group Inc.; *U.S. Private,* pg. 2513
WHOLE SECURITY S.A.C.—See Bain Capital, LP; *U.S. Private,* pg. 435
WHOLE SHINE MEDICAL TECHNOLOGY CO., LTD.; *Int'l,* pg. 8401
WHOLESOME HARVEST BAKING LLC—See Grupo Bimbo, S.A.B. de C.V.; *Int'l,* pg. 3123

WHOLESOME & HEARTY FOODS COMPANY—See Annex Capital Management LLC; *U.S. Private,* pg. 285
WHOLESOME HOLDINGS GROUP, LLC; *U.S. Private,* pg. 4515
WHOLETECH SYSTEM HITECH LTD.; *Int'l,* pg. 8401
WHOLE WHEAT CREATIVE; *U.S. Private,* pg. 4514
WHOODLE, LLC—See Red Violet, Inc.; *U.S. Public,* pg. 1770
WHOSAY, INC.—See National Amusements, Inc.; *U.S. Private,* pg. 2844
WHO'S CALLING, INC.—See Vista Equity Partners, LLC; *U.S. Private,* pg. 4402
WHO TELEVISION, LLC—See Nexstar Media Group, Inc.; *U.S. Public,* pg. 1525
W HOTELS REAL ESTATE, LLC—See Marriott International, Inc.; *U.S. Public,* pg. 1372
WHO-TV—See Nexstar Media Group, Inc.; *U.S. Public,* pg. 1525
WHOW GAMES GMBH—See Azerion Group N.V.; *Int'l,* pg. 778
W&H PACIFIC INC.; *U.S. Private,* pg. 4417
WHP GLOBAL; *U.S. Private,* pg. 4515
W.H.P.M., INC.; *U.S. Private,* pg. 4420
WH PROPERTIES, INC.—See Hovnanian Enterprises, Inc.; *U.S. Public,* pg. 1060
WHP-TV—See Sinclair, Inc.; *U.S. Public,* pg. 1886
WHR ARCHITECTS, INC.—See EYP, Inc.; *U.S. Private,* pg. 1454
WH SMITH AUSTRALIA PTY LIMITED—See W.H. Smith PLC; *Int'l,* pg. 8322
W.H. SMITH LTD.—See W.H. Smith PLC; *Int'l,* pg. 8322
W.H. SMITH PLC; *Int'l,* pg. 8322
W. HUNGER HYDRAULICS INDIA PVT. LTD—See Walter Hunger KG Hydraulics; *Int'l,* pg. 8336
WHYALLA BEEF PTY. LTD.—See NH Foods Ltd.; *Int'l,* pg. 5256
WHYALLA NEWS PROPERTIES PTY LTD—See Nine Entertainment Co. Holdings Limited; *Int'l,* pg. 5299
WHYBIN TBWA—See Omnicom Group Inc.; *U.S. Public,* pg. 1596
THE WHY HOW DO COMPANY, INC; *Int'l,* pg. 7701
WHYTE & MACKAY GROUP LIMITED—See Alliance Global Group, Inc.; *Int'l,* pg. 339
WHYTE & MACKAY LIMITED—See Alliance Global Group, Inc.; *Int'l,* pg. 339
WHYY INC.; *U.S. Private,* pg. 4515
WI2WI CORPORATION; *U.S. Public,* pg. 2369
WIABLE CORP.; *Int'l,* pg. 8401
WIA GOLD LIMITED; *Int'l,* pg. 8401
WIALAN TECHNOLOGIES, INC.; *U.S. Public,* pg. 2369
WIAM GMBH—See I Squared Capital Advisors (US) LLC; *U.S. Private,* pg. 2024
WIAM GMBH—See TDR Capital LLP; *Int'l,* pg. 7493
THE WIARTON ECHO—See Chatham Asset Management, LLC; *U.S. Private,* pg. 861
WIATROPOL SMOLECIN SP. Z O.O.—See Athena Investments A/S; *Int'l,* pg. 669
WIATROPOL USTKA SP. Z O.O.—See Athena Investments A/S; *Int'l,* pg. 669
WIBC-FM—See Emmis Communications Corporation; *U.S. Public,* pg. 753
WIBEBA HOCHBAU GMBH AND CO. NFG. KG—See PORR AG; *Int'l,* pg. 5925
WIBERG CANADA INC.—See International Flavors & Fragrances Inc.; *U.S. Public,* pg. 1154
WIBERG CORPORATION OF CALIFORNIA—See International Flavors & Fragrances Inc.; *U.S. Public,* pg. 1154
WIBE STEGAR AB—See Investment AB Latour; *Int'l,* pg. 3782
WIB S.A.—See RotoPrecision Inc.; *Int'l,* pg. 6405
WIBW-AM—See Shivers Trading & Operating Company; *U.S. Private,* pg. 3638
WIBW-FM—See Shivers Trading & Operating Company; *U.S. Private,* pg. 3638
WICAKSANA OVERSEAS INTERNATIONAL TBK; *Int'l,* pg. 8401
WICD LICENSEE, LLC—See Sinclair, Inc.; *U.S. Public,* pg. 1887
WICD-TV—See Sinclair, Inc.; *U.S. Public,* pg. 1887
WICE LOGISTICS PUBLIC COMPANY LIMITED; *Int'l,* pg. 8401
WICE LOGISTICS (SINGAPORE) PTE. LTD.—See WICE Logistics Public Company Limited; *Int'l,* pg. 8401
WICHITA BUSINESS JOURNAL, INC.—See Advance Publications, Inc.; *U.S. Private,* pg. 85
THE WICHITA EAGLE—See Chatham Asset Management, LLC; *U.S. Private,* pg. 867
WICHITA FALLS TIMES RECORD NEWS, LLC—See Gannett Co., Inc.; *U.S. Public,* pg. 898
WICHITA KENWORTH INC.; *U.S. Private,* pg. 4515
THE WICHITA ORTHOPAEDIC ASC, LLC—See KKR & Co. Inc.; *U.S. Public,* pg. 1249
WICHITA RESTAURANT SUPPLY CO, INC.—See Ace Mart Restaurant Supply Company Inc.; *U.S. Private,* pg. 57
WICHITA SHEET METAL SUPPLY CO., INC.—See WSM Industries Inc.; *U.S. Private,* pg. 4574
WICHITA TREATMENT CENTER INC.—See Acadia Healthcare Company, Inc.; *U.S. Public,* pg. 31

WICHMAN CONSTRUCTION; *U.S. Private,* pg. 4515
WICKAISSLA; *Int'l,* pg. 8401
WICK BUILDINGS, LLC; *U.S. Private,* pg. 4515
WICK COMMUNICATIONS CO., INC.—See Wick News Corporation; *U.S. Private,* pg. 4515
WICKEDER WESTFALENSTAHL GMBH; *Int'l,* pg. 8401
WICKED GOOD CUPCAKES LLC—See Sun Capital Partners, Inc.; *U.S. Private,* pg. 3859
WICKED WEED BREWING LLC—See Anheuser-Busch InBev SA/NV; *Int'l,* pg. 465
WICKENBURG COMMUNITY HOSPITAL; *U.S. Private,* pg. 4515
WICKERS SPORTSWEAR INC.; *U.S. Private,* pg. 4515
WICKES BUILDING SUPPLIES LIMITED—See Travis Perkins plc; *Int'l,* pg. 7908
WICKES GROUP PLC; *Int'l,* pg. 8401
WICKES LAND DEVELOPMENT N.V.—See Retail Estates N.V.; *Int'l,* pg. 6305
WICKLAND OIL CO., INC.—See Wickland Oil Corporation; *U.S. Private,* pg. 4515
WICKLAND OIL CORPORATION; *U.S. Private,* pg. 4515
WICKLAND PROPERTIES—See Wickland Oil Corporation; *U.S. Private,* pg. 4516
WICKLIFFE LTD.; *Int'l,* pg. 8401
WICK NEWS CORPORATION; *U.S. Private,* pg. 4515
WICK PHARMA—See The Procter & Gamble Company; *U.S. Public,* pg. 2122
THE WICKS GROUP OF COMPANIES, LLC; *U.S. Private,* pg. 4135
WICKSTROM CHEVROLET; *U.S. Private,* pg. 4516
WICKSTROM FORD LINCOLN MERCURY; *U.S. Private,* pg. 4516
WICKS UNLIMITED, INC.—See Edwin B. Stimpson Company, Inc.; *U.S. Private,* pg. 1342
W.I. CLARK COMPANY; *U.S. Private,* pg. 4420
WICO METAL PRODUCTS CO., INC.; *U.S. Private,* pg. 4516
WICONA BENELUX N.V.—See Norsk Hydro ASA; *Int'l,* pg. 5437
WICOTEC KIRKEBJERG A/S—See Per Aarsleff Holding A/S; *Int'l,* pg. 5796
WICPACK MALAYSIA SDN BHD—See Western Industries Corporation; *U.S. Private,* pg. 4494
WICPACK SINGAPORE PTE LTD—See Western Industries Corporation; *U.S. Private,* pg. 4494
WICS-TV—See Sinclair, Inc.; *U.S. Public,* pg. 1887
WIDAD BUSINESS GROUP SDN. BHD.; *Int'l,* pg. 8401
WIDAD GROUP BERHAD—See Widad Business Group Sdn. Bhd.; *Int'l,* pg. 8401
WIDAM FOOD COMPANY Q.S.C.; *Int'l,* pg. 8402
WIDEBAND INTERACTIVE NETWORKS VIA SATELLITES LTD.—See SpeedCast International Limited; *Int'l,* pg. 7133
WIDEBAND SYSTEMS, INC.—See Delta Information Systems Inc.; *U.S. Private,* pg. 1201
WIDE BAY AUSTRALIA—See Auswide Bank Ltd.; *Int'l,* pg. 724
WIDECH S.P.A.; *Int'l,* pg. 8402
WIDE CORPORATION—See AIFUL Corporation; *Int'l,* pg. 232
WIDECO SWEDEN AB—See Wienerberger AG; *Int'l,* pg. 8406
WIDECO US INC—See Grupo BAL; *Int'l,* pg. 3121
WIDEFORM PTY. LTD.; *Int'l,* pg. 8402
WIDE LEISURE CO., LTD.; *Int'l,* pg. 8402
WIDELLS BILPLAT EFTR AB—See LKQ Corporation; *U.S. Public,* pg. 1337
WIDEN ENTERPRISES INC.—See Vista Equity Partners, LLC; *U.S. Private,* pg. 4394
WIDENET CONSULTING GROUP; *U.S. Private,* pg. 4516
WIDE OPEN AGRICULTURE LIMITED; *Int'l,* pg. 8402
WIDEOPEN PLATFORM (PTY) LIMITED—See Primedia Limited; *Int'l,* pg. 5979
WIDEOPENWEST FINANCE, LLC—See WideOpenWest, Inc.; *U.S. Public,* pg. 2369
WIDEOPENWEST, INC.; *U.S. Public,* pg. 2369
WIDEOPENWEST NETWORKS, LLC—See WideOpenWest, Inc.; *U.S. Public,* pg. 2369
WIDEORBIT INC.—See Constellation Software Inc.; *Int'l,* pg. 1773
WIDEPOINT CORPORATION; *U.S. Public,* pg. 2370
WIDEPOINT INTEGRATED SOLUTIONS CORP.—See WidePoint Corporation; *U.S. Public,* pg. 2370
WIDEPOINT SOLUTIONS CORP.—See WidePoint Corporation; *U.S. Public,* pg. 2370
WIDER PLANET INC.; *Int'l,* pg. 8402
WIDE SCOPE HOLDINGS LIMITED—See Life Concepts Holdings Limited; *Int'l,* pg. 4492
WIDE SHINE DEVELOPMENT LIMITED—See China Merchants Group Limited; *Int'l,* pg. 1523
WIDEVINE TECHNOLOGIES, INC.—See Alphabet Inc.; *U.S. Public,* pg. 84
WIDEX AKUSTIK OY—See EQT AB; *Int'l,* pg. 2480
WIDEX ALGERIE EURL—See EQT AB; *Int'l,* pg. 2480
WIDEX ARGENTINA SA—See EQT AB; *Int'l,* pg. 2480
WIDEX A/S—See EQT AB; *Int'l,* pg. 2480
WIDEX AS—See EQT AB; *Int'l,* pg. 2480
WIDEX AUDIFONOS S.A.—See EQT AB; *Int'l,* pg. 2480

COMPANY NAME INDEX

WIDEX AUSTRALIA PTY LTD—See EQT AB; *Int'l*, pg. 2480
WIDEX CANADA LTD.—See EQT AB; *Int'l*, pg. 2480
WIDEX CHILE SPA.—See EQT AB; *Int'l*, pg. 2480
WIDEX COLOMBIA LTDA.—See EQT AB; *Int'l*, pg. 2480
WIDEX CO., LTD.—See EQT AB; *Int'l*, pg. 2480
WIDEX DOMINICANA, SRL—See EQT AB; *Int'l*, pg. 2480
WIDEX D.O.O.—See EQT AB; *Int'l*, pg. 2481
WIDEX-EGYPT—See EQT AB; *Int'l*, pg. 2481
WIDEX EMIRATES HEARING CARE—See EQT AB; *Int'l*, pg. 2480
WIDEX FRANCE SAS—See EQT AB; *Int'l*, pg. 2480
WIDEX HEARING AID CO., INC.—See EQT AB; *Int'l*, pg. 2480
WIDEX HEARING AID (SHANGHAI) CO. LTD.—See EQT AB; *Int'l*, pg. 2480
WIDEX-H KFT.—See EQT AB; *Int'l*, pg. 2481
WIDEX HONG KONG HEARING & SPEECH CENTRE LTD.—See EQT AB; *Int'l*, pg. 2481
WIDEX HORGERATE AG—See EQT AB; *Int'l*, pg. 2481
WIDEX HORGERATE GMBH—See EQT AB; *Int'l*, pg. 2481
WIDEX INDIA PRIVATE LIMITED—See EQT AB; *Int'l*, pg. 2481
WIDEX IRELAND LTD.—See EQT AB; *Int'l*, pg. 2481
WIDEX ITALIA S.P.A—See EQT AB; *Int'l*, pg. 2481
WIDEX KOREA LTD.—See EQT AB; *Int'l*, pg. 2481
WIDEX LIBYA—See EQT AB; *Int'l*, pg. 2481
WIDEX LINE S.R.O.—See EQT AB; *Int'l*, pg. 2481
WIDEX MACAU HEARING & SPEECH CENTRE LIMITED—See EQT AB; *Int'l*, pg. 2481
WIDEX MAROC—See EQT AB; *Int'l*, pg. 2481
WIDEX MEDICAL EQUIPMENT—See EQT AB; *Int'l*, pg. 2481
WIDEX NEW ZEALAND LTD.—See EQT AB; *Int'l*, pg. 2481
WIDEX PANAMA—See EQT AB; *Int'l*, pg. 2481
WIDEX POLSKA SP. Z.O.O.—See EQT AB; *Int'l*, pg. 2481
WIDEX - REABILITACAO AUDITIVA, LDA.—See EQT AB; *Int'l*, pg. 2480
WIDEX SINGAPORE PTE LTD—See EQT AB; *Int'l*, pg. 2481
WIDEX SLUSNI APARATI D.O.O—See EQT AB; *Int'l*, pg. 2481
WIDEX SOUTH AFRICA (PTY) LTD.—See EQT AB; *Int'l*, pg. 2481
WIDGIE NICKEL LIMITED; *Int'l*, pg. 8402
WIDGIX, LLC; *U.S. Private*, pg. 4516
WIDMER INTERIORS INC.; *U.S. Private*, pg. 4516
WIDMEYER COMMUNICATIONS, INC.—See Ruder Finn Group, Inc.; *U.S. Private*, pg. 3501
WIDMEYER COMMUNICATIONS—See Ruder Finn Group, Inc.; *U.S. Private*, pg. 3502
WIDNES REGENERATION LIMITED—See Blackstone Inc.; *U.S. Public*, pg. 358
WIDNI OY—See Axel Johnson Gruppen AB; *Int'l*, pg. 762
WIDOS AUS NZ PTY. LTD.—See Widos Wilhelm Dommer Sohne GmbH; *Int'l*, pg. 8402
WIDOS BENELUX B.V.—See Widos Wilhelm Dommer Sohne GmbH; *Int'l*, pg. 8402
WIDOS LLC—See Widos Wilhelm Dommer Sohne GmbH; *Int'l*, pg. 8402
WIDOS TECHNOLOGY (ASIA PACIFIC) PTE. LTD.—See Widos Wilhelm Dommer Sohne GmbH; *Int'l*, pg. 8402
WIDOS WILHELM DOMMER SOHNE GMBH; *Int'l*, pg. 8402
WIDYAN TRADING COMPANY LTD.—See Hayel Saeed Anam Group of Companies; *Int'l*, pg. 3291
WIEDENBACH APPARATEBAU GMBH—See Brother Industries, Ltd.; *Int'l*, pg. 1198
WIEDENBACH APPARATEBAU GMBH—See Brother Industries, Ltd.; *Int'l*, pg. 1198
WIEDENBACH-BROWN CO. INC.—See Blackfriars Corp.; *U.S. Private*, pg. 575
WIEDEN + KENNEDY - AMSTERDAM—See Wieden + Kennedy, Inc.; *U.S. Private*, pg. 4516
WIEDEN + KENNEDY, INC.; *U.S. Private*, pg. 4516
WIEDEN + KENNEDY INDIA—See Wieden + Kennedy, Inc.; *U.S. Private*, pg. 4516
WIEDEN + KENNEDY JAPAN—See Wieden + Kennedy, Inc.; *U.S. Private*, pg. 4516
WIEDEN + KENNEDY-NEW YORK—See Wieden + Kennedy, Inc.; *U.S. Private*, pg. 4516
WIEDEN + KENNEDY—See Wieden + Kennedy, Inc.; *U.S. Private*, pg. 4516
WIEDEN + KENNEDY UK LIMITED—See Wieden + Kennedy, Inc.; *U.S. Private*, pg. 4516
WIEDERHOLT GMBH—See Black Diamond Capital Holdings, LLC; *U.S. Private*, pg. 571
WIEGAND CUSTOM WATCH, LLC; *U.S. Private*, pg. 4516
WIEGAND-GLAS GMBH; *Int'l*, pg. 8402
WIEGAND S.A. DE C.V.—See Emerson Electric Co.; *U.S. Public*, pg. 752
WIEGERS CAPITAL PARTNERS; *U.S. Private*, pg. 4516
WIEGMANN ASSOCIATES INC.; *U.S. Private*, pg. 4516
THE WIEGMANN COMPANY—See Hubbell Incorporated; *U.S. Public*, pg. 1067
WIELAND ANLAGENTECHNIK GMBH—See Wieland-Werke AG; *Int'l*, pg. 8403

WIELAND AUSTRIA GES.M.B.H.—See Wieland-Werke AG; *Int'l*, pg. 8403
WIELAND BENELUX S.A.-N.V.—See Wieland-Werke AG; *Int'l*, pg. 8403
WIELAND-BUNTMETALL S.R.O.—See Wieland-Werke AG; *Int'l*, pg. 8403
WIELAND CARO GMBH—See Wieland-Werke AG; *Int'l*, pg. 8403
WIELAND CIMSA, S.A.—See Wieland-Werke AG; *Int'l*, pg. 8403
WIELAND COPPER PRODUCTS LLC—See Wieland-Werke AG; *Int'l*, pg. 8404
WIELAND DELARI CARO SRL—See Wieland-Werke AG; *Int'l*, pg. 8403
WIELAND DESIGNS INC.; *U.S. Private*, pg. 4516
WIELAND DIVERSIFIED, LLC—See Wieland-Werke AG; *Int'l*, pg. 8403
WIELAND DO BRASIL LTDA.—See Wieland-Werke AG; *Int'l*, pg. 8404
WIELAND DURO GMBH—See Wieland-Werke AG; *Int'l*, pg. 8403
WIELAND ELECTRIC AG—See Wieland Holding GmbH; *Int'l*, pg. 8402
WIELAND ELECTRIC A/S—See Wieland Holding GmbH; *Int'l*, pg. 8402
WIELAND ELECTRIC CO., LTD.—See Wieland Holding GmbH; *Int'l*, pg. 8402
WIELAND ELECTRIC GMBH—See Wieland Holding GmbH; *Int'l*, pg. 8402
WIELAND ELECTRIC SARL—See Wieland Holding GmbH; *Int'l*, pg. 8402
WIELAND ELECTRIC S.L.—See Wieland Holding GmbH; *Int'l*, pg. 8402
WIELAND ELECTRIC SP. Z.O.O.—See Wieland Holding GmbH; *Int'l*, pg. 8402
WIELAND ELECTRIC S.R.L.—See Wieland Holding GmbH; *Int'l*, pg. 8402
WIELAND ESPANA, S.A.—See Wieland-Werke AG; *Int'l*, pg. 8403
WIELAND EUCARO GMBH—See Wieland-Werke AG; *Int'l*, pg. 8403
WIELAND FUDICKAR GMBH—See Wieland-Werke AG; *Int'l*, pg. 8403
WIELAND HOLDING GMBH; *Int'l*, pg. 8402
WIELAND HUNGARIA KFT.—See Wieland-Werke AG; *Int'l*, pg. 8403
WIELAND ITALIA S.R.L.—See Wieland-Werke AG; *Int'l*, pg. 8403
WIELAND JAPAN CO., LTD.—See Wieland-Werke AG; *Int'l*, pg. 8403
WIELAND-KESSLER, LLC—See Wieland-Werke AG; *Int'l*, pg. 8404
WIELAND METAL SERVICES LLC—See Wieland-Werke AG; *Int'l*, pg. 8403
WIELAND METAL SERVICES LLC—See Wieland-Werke AG; *Int'l*, pg. 8403
WIELAND METAL SERVICES LLC—See Wieland-Werke AG; *Int'l*, pg. 8403
WIELAND METAL SERVICES LLC—See Wieland-Werke AG; *Int'l*, pg. 8403
WIELAND METAL SERVICES LLC—See Wieland-Werke AG; *Int'l*, pg. 8403
WIELAND METALS, INC.—See Wieland-Werke AG; *Int'l*, pg. 8404
WIELAND METALS INDIA PVT. LTD.—See Wieland-Werke AG; *Int'l*, pg. 8403
WIELAND METALS RUS OOO—See Wieland-Werke AG; *Int'l*, pg. 8403
WIELAND METALS SHANGHAI LTD.—See Wieland-Werke AG; *Int'l*, pg. 8403
WIELAND METALS SHENZHEN LIMITED—See Wieland-Werke AG; *Int'l*, pg. 8403
WIELAND METALS SINGAPORE (PTE.) LTD.—See Wieland-Werke AG; *Int'l*, pg. 8404
WIELAND MEXICO SA—See Wieland-Werke AG; *Int'l*, pg. 8404
WIELAND NEMCO LTD.—See Wieland-Werke AG; *Int'l*, pg. 8404
WIELAND POLSKA SP. Z O. O.—See Wieland-Werke AG; *Int'l*, pg. 8404
WIELAND PORTUGAL, LDA.—See Wieland-Werke AG; *Int'l*, pg. 8404
WIELAND PROMETA GMBH—See Wieland-Werke AG; *Int'l*, pg. 8404
WIELAND RECYCLING GMBH—See Wieland-Werke AG; *Int'l*, pg. 8404
WIELAND ROESSLER GMBH—See Wieland-Werke AG; *Int'l*, pg. 8404
WIELAND ROLLED PRODUCTS NORTH AMERICA LLC—See Wieland-Werke AG; *Int'l*, pg. 8404
WIELAND SALES INC.; *U.S. Private*, pg. 4516
WIELAND SAS—See Wieland-Werke AG; *Int'l*, pg. 8404
WIELAND SCANDINAVIA AB—See Wieland-Werke AG; *Int'l*, pg. 8404
WIELAND SCANDINAVIA A/S—See Wieland-Werke AG; *Int'l*, pg. 8404
WIELAND SCANDINAVIA METALL AB—See Wieland-Werke AG; *Int'l*, pg. 8404

WIELAND SCANDINAVIA OY—See Wieland-Werke AG; *Int'l*, pg. 8404
WIELAND (SCHWEIZ) AG—See Wieland-Werke AG; *Int'l*, pg. 8403
WIELAND SLASKIE METALE SP. Z O.O.—See Wieland-Werke AG; *Int'l*, pg. 8404
WIELAND SMH GMBH—See Wieland-Werke AG; *Int'l*, pg. 8404
WIELAND (SOUTH AFRICA) (PTY.) LTD.—See Wieland-Werke AG; *Int'l*, pg. 8403
WIELAND THERMAL SOLUTIONS LDA.—See Wieland-Werke AG; *Int'l*, pg. 8404
WIELAND THERMAL SOLUTIONS (SHANGHAI) CO., LTD.—See Wieland-Werke AG; *Int'l*, pg. 8404
WIELAND VENTURES GMBH—See Wieland-Werke AG; *Int'l*, pg. 8403
WIELAND-WERKE AG; *Int'l*, pg. 8402
WIELAND-WERKE (UK) LTD.—See Wieland-Werke AG; *Int'l*, pg. 8404
WIELAND WICOATEC GMBH—See Wieland-Werke AG; *Int'l*, pg. 8404
WIELKOPOLSKA SPOLKA GAZOWNICTWA SP. Z O.O.—See Polskie Gornictwo Naftowe i Gazownictwo S.A.; *Int'l*, pg. 5912
WIELTON S.A.; *Int'l*, pg. 8404
WIEN CO., LTD.—See Saha Pathanapibul Public Company Limited; *Int'l*, pg. 6479
WIENERBERGER AB—See Wienerberger AG; *Int'l*, pg. 8406
WIENERBERGER AG; *Int'l*, pg. 8404
WIENERBERGER ANTEILSVERWALTUNG GMBH—See Wienerberger AG; *Int'l*, pg. 8406
WIENERBERGER AS—See Wienerberger AG; *Int'l*, pg. 8406
WIENERBERGER AS—See Wienerberger AG; *Int'l*, pg. 8406
WIENERBERGER A.S.—See Wienerberger AG; *Int'l*, pg. 8406
WIENERBERGER BACKA D.O.O.—See Wienerberger AG; *Int'l*, pg. 8406
WIENERBERGER BAUSYSTEME GMBH—See Wienerberger AG; *Int'l*, pg. 8406
WIENERBERGER BRICK INDUSTRY PRIVATE LIMITED—See Wienerberger AG; *Int'l*, pg. 8406
WIENERBERGER D.V.—See Wienerberger AG; *Int'l*, pg. 8406
WIENERBERGER CERAMIKA BUDOWLANA SP. Z O.O.—See Wienerberger AG; *Int'l*, pg. 8406
WIENERBERGER DOOEL VINICA—See Wienerberger AG; *Int'l*, pg. 8406
WIENERBERGER D.O.O.—See Wienerberger AG; *Int'l*, pg. 8407
WIENERBERGER EOOD—See Wienerberger AG; *Int'l*, pg. 8406
WIENERBERGER EUROFORM, SPOL. S R.O.—See Wienerberger AG; *Int'l*, pg. 8407
WIENERBERGER EUROSTROJ, SPOL. S R. O.—See Wienerberger AG; *Int'l*, pg. 8406
WIENERBERGER FINANCE SERVICE B.V.—See Wienerberger AG; *Int'l*, pg. 8407
WIENERBERGER FINANZ SERVICE GMBH—See Wienerberger AG; *Int'l*, pg. 8407
WIENERBERGER GMBH—See Wienerberger AG; *Int'l*, pg. 8407
WIENERBERGER ILOVAC D.O.O.—See Wienerberger AG; *Int'l*, pg. 8407
WIENERBERGER INDUSTRIEBETEILIGUNGSVERWALTUNG GMBH—See Wienerberger AG; *Int'l*, pg. 8407
WIENERBERGER INDUSTRIJA OPEKE D.J.L.—See Wienerberger AG; *Int'l*, pg. 8406
WIENERBERGER LTD.—See Wienerberger AG; *Int'l*, pg. 8407
WIENERBERGER NV—See Wienerberger AG; *Int'l*, pg. 8407
WIENERBERGER OPEKARNA ORMOZ D.D.—See Wienerberger AG; *Int'l*, pg. 8407
WIENERBERGER OSTERREICH GMBH—See Wienerberger AG; *Int'l*, pg. 8407
WIENERBERGER OY AB—See Wienerberger AG; *Int'l*, pg. 8407
WIENERBERGER PARTICIPATIONS SAS—See Wienerberger AG; *Int'l*, pg. 8406
WIENERBERGER SAS—See Wienerberger AG; *Int'l*, pg. 8406
WIENERBERGER SISTEME DE CARAMIZI S.R.L.—See Wienerberger AG; *Int'l*, pg. 8407
WIENERBERGER SLOVENSKE TEHELNE, SPOL. S R. O.—See Wienerberger AG; *Int'l*, pg. 8407
WIENERBERGER S.P.A.—See Wienerberger AG; *Int'l*, pg. 8407
WIENERBERGER S.R.L.—See Wienerberger AG; *Int'l*, pg. 8406
WIENERBERGER S.R.O.—See Wienerberger AG; *Int'l*, pg. 8407
WIENERBERGER TEGLAIPARI ZRT.—See Wienerberger AG; *Int'l*, pg. 8407
WIENERBERGER TOV—See Wienerberger AG; *Int'l*, pg. 8407

WIENERBERGER AG

WIENERBERGER WEST EUROPEAN HOLDING GMBH—See Wienerberger AG; *Int'l*, pg. 8407
WIENERBERGER ZRT.—See Wienerberger AG; *Int'l*, pg. 8407
WIENERBERGER ZZ HOLDING GMBH—See Wienerberger AG; *Int'l*, pg. 8407
WIENER BETRIEBS- UND BAUGESELLSCHAFT M.B.H.—See PORR AG; *Int'l*, pg. 5925
WIENER BOERSE AG—See CEESEG AG; *Int'l*, pg. 1389
WIENER CROWLEY & ST JOHN; *U.S. Private*, pg. 4516
WIENER FINANCIAL MANAGEMENT—See Keystone Group, L.P.; *U.S. Private*, pg. 2298
WIENER-KUHLHAUS FRIGOSCANDIA GMBH—See UniCredit S.p.A.; *Int'l*, pg. 8042
WIENER OSIGURANJE VIENNA INSURANCE GROUP D.D.—See Vienna Insurance Group AG Wiener Versicherung Gruppe; *Int'l*, pg. 8196
W-IE-NE-R PLEIN & BAUS GMBH—See Phoenix Mecano AG; *Int'l*, pg. 5853
WIENER POWER ELECTRONICS GMBH—See Phoenix Mecano AG; *Int'l*, pg. 5853
WIENER PRIVATBANK IMMOBILIENMAKLER GMBH—See Arca Capital Slovakia, A.S.; *Int'l*, pg. 540
WIENER PRIVATBANK SE; *Int'l*, pg. 8404
WIENER STADTISCHE DONAU LEASING GMBH—See Vienna Insurance Group AG Wiener Versicherung Gruppe; *Int'l*, pg. 8196
WIENER STADTISCHE OSIGURANJE A.D.O.—See Vienna Insurance Group AG Wiener Versicherung Gruppe; *Int'l*, pg. 8196
WIENER STADTISCHE VERSICHERUNG AG—See Vienna Insurance Group AG Wiener Versicherung Gruppe; *Int'l*, pg. 8196
WIENER STADTWERKE HOLDING AG—See PORR AG; *Int'l*, pg. 5925
WIENER TOWARZYSTWO UBEZPIECZEN SPOLKA AKCYJNA—See Vienna Insurance Group AG Wiener Versicherung Gruppe; *Int'l*, pg. 8196
WIENER VEREIN BESTATTUNGS- UND VERSICHERUNGSSERVICEGESELLSCHAFT M.B.H.—See Vienna Insurance Group AG Wiener Versicherung Gruppe; *Int'l*, pg. 8196
WIEN & WIEN, INC.—See Service Corporation International; *U.S. Public*, pg. 1871
WIER & ASSOCIATES, INC.; *U.S. Private*, pg. 4516
WIERTMAR SP. Z.O.O.—See PBG S.A.; *Int'l*, pg. 5765
WIESAUPLAST DE MEXICO S. DE R.L. DE C.V—See INDUS Holding AG; *Int'l*, pg. 3664
WIESAUPLAST DEUTSCHLAND GMBH & CO. KG—See INDUS Holding AG; *Int'l*, pg. 3664
WIESAUPLAST KUNSTSTOFF UND FORMENBAU GMBH & CO. KG—See INDUS Holding AG; *Int'l*, pg. 3664
WIESAUPLAST USA LLC—See INDUS Holding AG; *Int'l*, pg. 3664
WIESE INDUSTRIES; *U.S. Private*, pg. 4516
WIESER CONCRETE PRODUCTS INC.; *U.S. Private*, pg. 4517
WIESE TOYOTA; *U.S. Private*, pg. 4516
WIESE USA, INC.; *U.S. Private*, pg. 4517
WIESNER, INC.; *U.S. Private*, pg. 4517
WIESNER PUBLISHING, LLC; *U.S. Private*, pg. 4517
WIESON TECHNOLOGIES CO., LTD.; *Int'l*, pg. 8407
WIEST S.A.; *Int'l*, pg. 8407
WIETERSDORFER-INDUSTRIE—See Knoch, Kern & Co. KG; *Int'l*, pg. 4209
WIETZES TOYOTA; *Int'l*, pg. 8407
WIFAG MASCHINENFABRIK AG; *Int'l*, pg. 8407
WIFR-TV—See Gray Television, Inc.; *U.S. Public*, pg. 960
WIGAND DISPOSAL COMPANY—See Peoria Disposal Company/Area Disposal Service, Inc.; *U.S. Private*, pg. 3143
WIGDAHL ELECTRIC CO.; *U.S. Private*, pg. 4517
WIGEN COMPANIES, INC.—See METAWATER Co., Ltd.; *Int'l*, pg. 4851
WIGGINS AIRWAYS INC.; *U.S. Private*, pg. 4517
WIGGLE LTD.—See SIGNA Sports United N.V.; *Int'l*, pg. 6910
WIGGY WASH, LLC—See Red Dog Equity LLC; *U.S. Private*, pg. 3374
WIGHTLINK LIMITED—See Colliers International Group Inc.; *Int'l*, pg. 1700
WIGINTON CORP.; *U.S. Private*, pg. 4517
WIGMORE INSURANCE AGENCY, INC.—See Arthur J. Gallagher & Co.; *U.S. Public*, pg. 208
WIGMORE STREET KITCHENS LTD.—See Nobia AB; *Int'l*, pg. 5396
WIGO CHEMIE GMBH—See Berner SE; *Int'l*, pg. 988
WIGO—See Grupo Romero; *Int'l*, pg. 3135
WIGWAM MILLS, INC.; *U.S. Private*, pg. 4517
WIGWAM RESORT—See Kabuto Decom, Inc.; *Int'l*, pg. 4046
WI HARPER GROUP; *U.S. Private*, pg. 4515
WIHLBORGS A/S—See Wihlborgs Fastigheter AB; *Int'l*, pg. 8407
WIHLBORGS BOPLATSGATAN 5 AB—See Wihlborgs Fastigheter AB; *Int'l*, pg. 8407
WIHLBORGS BORGEBY AB—See Wihlborgs Fastigheter AB; *Int'l*, pg. 8407
WIHLBORGS FASTIGHETER AB; *Int'l*, pg. 8407

WIHLBORGS FISKEN 18 AB—See Wihlborgs Fastigheter AB; *Int'l*, pg. 8407
WIHLBORGS FLINTAN 3 AB—See Wihlborgs Fastigheter AB; *Int'l*, pg. 8407
WIHLBORGS HAVSKRYSSAREN AB—See Wihlborgs Fastigheter AB; *Int'l*, pg. 8407
WIHLBORGS KIRSEBERG AB—See Wihlborgs Fastigheter AB; *Int'l*, pg. 8407
WIHLBORGS KRANEN AB—See Wihlborgs Fastigheter AB; *Int'l*, pg. 8407
WIHLBORGS MOTORSEGLAREN AB—See Wihlborgs Fastigheter AB; *Int'l*, pg. 8407
WIHLBORGS POLISETT AB—See Wihlborgs Fastigheter AB; *Int'l*, pg. 8408
WIHLBORGS RITAREN 1 AB—See Wihlborgs Fastigheter AB; *Int'l*, pg. 8408
WIHLBORGS SODERARM 11 AB—See Wihlborgs Fastigheter AB; *Int'l*, pg. 8408
WIHLBORGS SQVALPAN AB—See Wihlborgs Fastigheter AB; *Int'l*, pg. 8408
WIHLBORGS VIKINGEN 10 AB—See Wihlborgs Fastigheter AB; *Int'l*, pg. 8408
WIIK PUBLIC COMPANY LIMITED—See Georg Fischer AG; *Int'l*, pg. 2938
WII NO MA CO.,LTD.—See Nintendo Co., Ltd.; *Int'l*, pg. 5308
WII REALTY MANAGEMENT—See Williams Industries, Inc.; *U.S. Private*, pg. 4526
WIIT SPA; *Int'l*, pg. 8408
WIJGULA B.V—See Dubai World Corporation; *Int'l*, pg. 2221
WIJKERTUNNEL BEHEER III B.V.—See Commerzbank AG; *Int'l*, pg. 1719
WIJKOPENAUTOS B.V.—See AUTO1 Group SE; *Int'l*, pg. 725
WIJNHANDEL LEON COLARIS B.V.—See Union InVivo - Union de Cooperatives Agricoles; *Int'l*, pg. 8053
WIJNNE & BARENDS' CARGADOORS-EN AGENTUUR-KANTOREN BV—See Spliethoff's Bevrachtingskantoor B.V.; *Int'l*, pg. 7141
WIKA ALEXANDER-WIEGAND GMBH & CO. KG; *Int'l*, pg. 8408
WIKA ARGENTINA S.A.—See WIKA Alexander-Wiegand GmbH & Co. KG; *Int'l*, pg. 8408
WIKA AUSTRALIA PTY. LTD.—See WIKA Alexander-Wiegand GmbH & Co. KG; *Int'l*, pg. 8408
WIKA AZERBAIJAN LLC—See WIKA Alexander-Wiegand GmbH & Co. KG; *Int'l*, pg. 8408
WIKA BELRUS—See WIKA Alexander-Wiegand GmbH & Co. KG; *Int'l*, pg. 8408
WIKA BENELUX—See WIKA Alexander-Wiegand GmbH & Co. KG; *Int'l*, pg. 8408
WIKA BULGARIA EOOD—See WIKA Alexander-Wiegand GmbH & Co. KG; *Int'l*, pg. 8408
WIKA CHILE S.P.A.—See WIKA Alexander-Wiegand GmbH & Co. KG; *Int'l*, pg. 8408
WIKA CROATIA D.O.O.—See WIKA Alexander-Wiegand GmbH & Co. KG; *Int'l*, pg. 8408
WIKA DO BRASIL INDUSTRIA E COMERCIO LTDA.—See WIKA Alexander-Wiegand GmbH & Co. KG; *Int'l*, pg. 8408
WIKA FINLAND OY—See WIKA Alexander-Wiegand GmbH & Co. KG; *Int'l*, pg. 8408
WIKA INSTRUMENTATION CORPORATION (THAILAND) CO., LTD.—See WIKA Alexander-Wiegand GmbH & Co. KG; *Int'l*, pg. 8408
WIKA INSTRUMENTATION (M) SDN BHD—See WIKA Alexander-Wiegand GmbH & Co. KG; *Int'l*, pg. 8408
WIKA INSTRUMENTATION PARS KISH (KFZ) LTD.—See WIKA Alexander-Wiegand GmbH & Co. KG; *Int'l*, pg. 8408
WIKA INSTRUMENTATION PTE. LTD.—See WIKA Alexander-Wiegand GmbH & Co. KG; *Int'l*, pg. 8408
WIKA INSTRUMENTATION (SUZHOU) CO., LTD.—See WIKA Alexander-Wiegand GmbH & Co. KG; *Int'l*, pg. 8408
WIKA INSTRUMENTATION TAIWAN LTD—See WIKA Alexander-Wiegand GmbH & Co. KG; *Int'l*, pg. 8408
WIKA INSTRUMENT CORPORATION—See WIKA Alexander-Wiegand GmbH & Co. KG; *Int'l*, pg. 8408
WIKA INSTRUMENTS CANADA LTD.—See WIKA Alexander-Wiegand GmbH & Co. KG; *Int'l*, pg. 8408
WIKA INSTRUMENTS INDIA PVT. LTD.—See WIKA Alexander-Wiegand GmbH & Co. KG; *Int'l*, pg. 8408
WIKA INSTRUMENTS ISTANBUL LTD.—See WIKA Alexander-Wiegand GmbH & Co. KG; *Int'l*, pg. 8408
WIKA INSTRUMENTS LIMITED—See WIKA Alexander-Wiegand GmbH & Co. KG; *Int'l*, pg. 8408
WIKA INSTRUMENTS NAMIBIA (PTY) LTD.—See WIKA Alexander-Wiegand GmbH & Co. KG; *Int'l*, pg. 8408
WIKA INSTRUMENTS PHILIPPINES INC.—See WIKA Alexander-Wiegand GmbH & Co. KG; *Int'l*, pg. 8408
WIKA INSTRUMENTS (PTY.) LTD.—See WIKA Alexander-Wiegand GmbH & Co. KG; *Int'l*, pg. 8408
WIKA INSTRUMENTS ROMANIA S.R.L.—See WIKA Alexander-Wiegand GmbH & Co. KG; *Int'l*, pg. 8409
WIKA INTERNATIONAL TRADING (SHANGHAI) CO., LTD.—See WIKA Alexander-Wiegand GmbH & Co. KG; *Int'l*, pg. 8409

CORPORATE AFFILIATIONS

WIKA ITALIA SRL & C. SAS—See WIKA Alexander-Wiegand GmbH & Co. KG; *Int'l*, pg. 8409
WIKA JAPAN K.K.—See WIKA Alexander-Wiegand GmbH & Co. KG; *Int'l*, pg. 8409
WIKA KAZAKHSTAN LLP—See WIKA Alexander-Wiegand GmbH & Co. KG; *Int'l*, pg. 8409
WIKA KERESKEDELMI KEPVISELETE—See WIKA Alexander-Wiegand GmbH & Co. KG; *Int'l*, pg. 8409
WIKA KOREA LTD.—See WIKA Alexander-Wiegand GmbH & Co. KG; *Int'l*, pg. 8409
WIKA MERNA TEHNIKA D.O.O.—See WIKA Alexander-Wiegand GmbH & Co. KG; *Int'l*, pg. 8409
WIKA MESSGERATEVERTRIEB GMBH & CO KG—See WIKA Alexander-Wiegand GmbH & Co. KG; *Int'l*, pg. 8409
WIKA MIDDLE EAST FZE—See WIKA Alexander-Wiegand GmbH & Co. KG; *Int'l*, pg. 8409
WIKANA S.A.; *Int'l*, pg. 8409
WIKA NEAR EAST LTD.—See WIKA Alexander-Wiegand GmbH & Co. KG; *Int'l*, pg. 8409
WIKA POLSKA—See WIKA Alexander-Wiegand GmbH & Co. KG; *Int'l*, pg. 8409
WIKA PROCESS SOLUTIONS LP—See WIKA Alexander-Wiegand GmbH & Co. KG; *Int'l*, pg. 8409
WIKA STADE GMBH U. CO. KG—See Heidelberg Materials AG; *Int'l*, pg. 3320
WIKERS AB—See Saab AB; *Int'l*, pg. 6460
WIKILEAF TECHNOLOGIES, INC.; *U.S. Public*, pg. 2370
WIKIMEDIA FOUNDATION INC.; *U.S. Private*, pg. 4517
WIKI PRATAMA SDN. BHD.—See Engtex Group Berhad; *Int'l*, pg. 2436
WIKOFF COLOR CORPORATION; *U.S. Private*, pg. 4517
WIKORA GMBH; *Int'l*, pg. 8409
WIKO-USA INC.—See Berry Global Group, Inc; *U.S. Public*, pg. 324
WIKREATE; *U.S. Private*, pg. 4517
WIKTOR/LEO BURNETT, S.R.O.—See Publicis Groupe S.A.; *Int'l*, pg. 6102
WILANS GMBH—See Mitsubishi Heavy Industries, Ltd.; *Int'l*, pg. 4962
WI-LAN V-CHIP CORP.—See Quarterhill Inc.; *Int'l*, pg. 6155
WILBANKS, SMITH & THOMAS ASSET MANAGEMENT, LLC.—See Edwards Capital, LLC; *U.S. Private*, pg. 1341
WILBER DUCK CHEVROLET BUICK, INC.; *U.S. Private*, pg. 4517
WILBERG AS—See Oy Karl Fazer Ab; *Int'l*, pg. 5677
WILBER-PRICE INSURANCE GROUP LTD.—See PCF Insurance Services of The West, LLC; *U.S. Private*, pg. 3120
WILBERT FUNERAL SERVICES, INC.—See Berkshire Hathaway Inc.; *U.S. Public*, pg. 298
WILBERT INC. - BELLEVUE FACILITY—See Berkshire Hathaway Inc.; *U.S. Public*, pg. 298
WILBERT INC. - BELMONT FACILITY—See Berkshire Hathaway Inc.; *U.S. Public*, pg. 298
WILBERT INC. - EASLEY FACILITY—See Berkshire Hathaway Inc.; *U.S. Public*, pg. 298
WILBERT INC. - FOREST CITY FACILITY—See Berkshire Hathaway Inc.; *U.S. Public*, pg. 298
WILBERT INC. - HARRISBURG FACILITY—See Berkshire Hathaway Inc.; *U.S. Public*, pg. 298
WILBERT INC. - LEBANON FACILITY—See Berkshire Hathaway Inc.; *U.S. Public*, pg. 298
WILBERT INC.—See Berkshire Hathaway Inc.; *U.S. Public*, pg. 298
WILBERT INC.- WHITE BEAR LAKE FACILITY—See Berkshire Hathaway Inc.; *U.S. Public*, pg. 298
WILBERT PLASTIC SERVICES, INC.—See Berkshire Hathaway Inc.; *U.S. Public*, pg. 298
WILBRAHAM IMPORT CARS, INC.—See Lia Auto Group; *U.S. Private*, pg. 2442
WILBRECHT LEDCO, INC.; *U.S. Private*, pg. 4517
WILBUR CHOCOLATE CO., INC.—See Cargill, Inc.; *U.S. Private*, pg. 756
WILBUR CURTIS CO., INC.—See SEB S.A.; *Int'l*, pg. 6668
WILBUR-DUCK CHEVROLET & BUICK; *U.S. Private*, pg. 4517
WILBUR-ELLIS COMPANY; *U.S. Private*, pg. 4517
WILBUR-ELLIS COMPANY—See Wilbur-Ellis Company; *U.S. Private*, pg. 4517
WILBUR-ELLIS COMPANY - WILBUR-ELLIS AGRIBUSINESS DIVISION—See Wilbur-Ellis Company; *U.S. Private*, pg. 4517
WILBUR-ELLIS NUTRITION, LLC—See Wilbur-Ellis Company; *U.S. Private*, pg. 4517
WILBURN OIL CO., INC.; *U.S. Private*, pg. 4518
WILBY ESTATE INTERNATIONAL PTE. LTD.—See Tan Chong International Limited; *Int'l*, pg. 7453
WILCAS CORP.; *U.S. Private*, pg. 4518
WILCHEM B.V.—See Koninklijke VolkerWessels N.V.; *Int'l*, pg. 4271
WILCO ENTERPRISES INC.; *U.S. Private*, pg. 4518
WILCO FARMERS INC.; *U.S. Private*, pg. 4518
WILCO MACHINE & FAB, INC.; *U.S. Private*, pg. 4518
WILCOM, INC.; *U.S. Private*, pg. 4518

COMPANY NAME INDEX

WILHELM SCHIMMEL PIANOFORTEFABRIK GMBH

WILCOMP SOFTWARE, LLC—See Nelnet, Inc.; *U.S. Public*, pg. 1504
WILCOMPUTE SYSTEMS GROUP, INC.; *Int'l*, pg. 8409
WILCON DEPOT, INC.; *Int'l*, pg. 8409
WILCO—See A.T. Williams Oil Company; *U.S. Private*, pg. 28
WILCO TRANSPORTATION LLC—See Marathon Petroleum Corporation; *U.S. Public*, pg. 1364
WILCOX ABSTRACT & TITLE GUARANTY AGENCY—See First American Financial Corporation; *U.S. Public*, pg. 837
WILCOX AUTOMOTIVE; *U.S. Private*, pg. 4518
WILCOX BANCSHARES, INC.; *U.S. Public*, pg. 4518
WILCOX FARMS INC.; *U.S. Private*, pg. 4518
WILCOX & FETZER LTD.—See NextGen Reporting LLC; *U.S. Private*, pg. 2921
WILCOX MEDICAL, INC.—See Option Care Health, Inc.; *U.S. Public*, pg. 1610
WILCOXON CONSTRUCTION, LLC—See Colliers International Group Inc.; *Int'l*, pg. 1701
WILCOX PAPER LLC—See Central National Gottesman Inc.; *U.S. Private*, pg. 823
WILCOXSON BUICK CADILLAC GMC TRUCK INC.; *U.S. Private*, pg. 4518
WILCOX STEEL, LLC—See Ryerson Holding Corporation; *U.S. Public*, pg. 1829
WILD ADVENTURES, INC.; *U.S. Private*, pg. 4518
WILD AMAZON FLAVORS CONCENTRADOS E CORANTES PARA BEBIDAS LTDA.—See Rudolf Wild GmbH & Co. KG; *Int'l*, pg. 6425
WILD AMAZON FLAVORS LTDA.—See Archer-Daniels-Midland Company; *U.S. Public*, pg. 185
WILD ANIMAL, INC.—See Parks! America, Inc.; *U.S. Public*, pg. 1650
WILD ANIMAL SAFARI, INC.—See Parks! America, Inc.; *U.S. Public*, pg. 1650
WILD ASEPTICS, LLC—See Rudolf Wild GmbH & Co. KG; *Int'l*, pg. 6425
WILDAUER SCHMIEDEWERKE GMBH & CO. KG—See Georgsmarienhutte Holding GmbH; *Int'l*, pg. 2941
WILD BRAIN ENTERTAINMENT, INC.—See WildBrain Ltd.; *Int'l*, pg. 8409
WILDBRAIN LTD.; *Int'l*, pg. 8409
WILD BRUSH ENERGY, INC.; *U.S. Public*, pg. 2370
WILD BUILDING CONTRACTORS INC.; *U.S. Private*, pg. 4518
WILD BUNCH AG; *Int'l*, pg. 8409
WILD BUNCH GERMANY GMBH—See Wild Bunch AG; *Int'l*, pg. 8409
WILDCAT DISCOVERY TECHNOLOGIES INC.; *U.S. Private*, pg. 4519
WILDCAT EXPLORATION LTD.; *Int'l*, pg. 8409
WILDCAT MATERIALS, INC.—See GMS Inc.; *U.S. Public*, pg. 948
WILDCAT MINERALS LLC—See Eagle Materials Inc.; *U.S. Public*, pg. 702
WILDCAT PETROLEUM PLC; *Int'l*, pg. 8409
WILDCAT RESOURCES LTD.; *Int'l*, pg. 8409
WILD CRAZE INC.; *U.S. Private*, pg. 4518
WILD CREATIONS; *U.S. Private*, pg. 4518
WILDCREEK HEALTHCARE, INC.—See The Ensign Group, Inc.; *U.S. Public*, pg. 2072
WILD DAIRY INGREDIENTS GMBH—See Rudolf Wild GmbH & Co. KG; *Int'l*, pg. 6425
WILD DAIRY INGREDIENTS NAUEN GMBH—See Rudolf Wild GmbH & Co. KG; *Int'l*, pg. 6425
WILDECK, INC.—See Holden Industries, Inc.; *U.S. Private*, pg. 1962
WILDER ARCHITECTURE, INC.; *U.S. Private*, pg. 4519
THE WILDER COMPANIES; *U.S. Private*, pg. 4136
WILDER CORPORATION; *U.S. Private*, pg. 4519
WILDER DEEM, INC.; *U.S. Private*, pg. 4519
WILDERNESS HOLDINGS LIMITED; *Int'l*, pg. 8409
WILDERNESS LAKES—See Equity LifeStyle Properties, Inc.; *U.S. Public*, pg. 790
WILDERNESS LOG HOMES INC.; *U.S. Private*, pg. 4519
WILDERNESS RIVER ADVENTURES, LLC—See Aramark; *U.S. Public*, pg. 178
WILDERNESS SAFARIS ZIMBABWE (PVT) LIMITED—See Wilderness Holdings Limited; *Int'l*, pg. 8409
WILDERNESS SOCIETY; *U.S. Private*, pg. 4519
WILDERNEST LOGISTICS SOLUTIONS INCORPORATED; *U.S. Private*, pg. 4519
WILDFIRE INTERACTIVE, INC.—See Alphabet Inc.; *U.S. Public*, pg. 84
WILDFIRE LLC; *U.S. Private*, pg. 4519
WILDFIRE SALES INC.—See CI Capital Partners LLC; *U.S. Private*, pg. 895
WILD FLAVORS AND SPECIALTY INGREDIENTS INC. - A.M. TODD DIVISION—See Archer-Daniels-Midland Company; *U.S. Public*, pg. 184
WILD FLAVORS (BEIJING) LTD.—See Archer-Daniels-Midland Company; *U.S. Public*, pg. 185
WILD FLAVORS (CANADA) INC.—See Archer-Daniels-Midland Company; *U.S. Public*, pg. 184
WILD FLAVORS GMBH—See Archer-Daniels-Midland Company; *U.S. Public*, pg. 184

WILD FLAVORS, INC.—See Archer-Daniels-Midland Company; *U.S. Public*, pg. 184
WILD FLAVORS, INC. - TARAPUR FACILITY—See Archer-Daniels-Midland Company; *U.S. Public*, pg. 184
WILD FLAVORS MIDDLE EAST FZE—See Rudolf Wild GmbH & Co. KG; *Int'l*, pg. 6425
WILD FLAVORS (SCHWEIZ) AG—See Rudolf Wild GmbH & Co. KG; *Int'l*, pg. 6425
WILDFLOWER BRANDS INC.; *Int'l*, pg. 8410
WILDFLOWER INTERNATIONAL, LTD.; *U.S. Private*, pg. 4519
WILDFLOWER VILLAS, LTD—See American Realty Investors, Inc.; *U.S. Public*, pg. 109
WILD FRANCE S.A.S—See Rudolf Wild GmbH & Co. KG; *Int'l*, pg. 6425
WILD GOOSE CANNING TECHNOLOGIES INC.; *U.S. Private*, pg. 4518
WILD GOOSE STORAGE, LLC—See Brookfield Infrastructure Partners L.P.; *Int'l*, pg. 1190
WILD HARVEST LIMITED—See Sysco Corporation; *U.S. Public*, pg. 1973
WILDISH BUILDING CO.—See Wildish Land Company; *U.S. Private*, pg. 4519
WILDISH BUILDING MATERIAL CO., INC.—See Wildish Land Company; *U.S. Private*, pg. 4519
WILDISH CONSTRUCTION CO., INC.—See Wildish Land Company; *U.S. Private*, pg. 4519
WILDISH EQUIPMENT CO.—See Wildish Land Company; *U.S. Private*, pg. 4519
WILDISH LAND COMPANY; *U.S. Private*, pg. 4519
WILDISH PAVING CO., INC.—See Wildish Land Company; *U.S. Private*, pg. 4519
WILDISH SAND & GRAVEL CO.—See Wildish Land Company; *U.S. Private*, pg. 4519
WILDISH STANDARD PAVING CO., INC.—See Wildish Land Company; *U.S. Private*, pg. 4519
WILDISH STANDARD PAVING—See Wildish Land Company; *U.S. Private*, pg. 4519
WILD JUICE B.V.—See Archer-Daniels-Midland Company; *U.S. Public*, pg. 185
WILD JUICE SERVICES B.V.—See Archer-Daniels-Midland Company; *U.S. Public*, pg. 184
WILD KK—See Rudolf Wild GmbH & Co. KG; *Int'l*, pg. 6425
THE WILDLIFE CENTER OF VIRGINIA; *U.S. Private*, pg. 4136
WILDLIFE PHARMACEUTICALS, INC.—See Partners Group Holding AG; *Int'l*, pg. 5751
WILD LIVES (THAILAND) CO., LTD.—See Saha Pathanapibul Public Company Limited; *Int'l*, pg. 6479
WILDMAN BUSINESS GROUP INC.; *U.S. Private*, pg. 4519
WILDMARE WIND ENERGY CORP.—See Solar Alliance Energy Inc.; *Int'l*, pg. 7068
WILDMARE WIND ENERGY LIMITED—See Solar Alliance Energy Inc.; *Int'l*, pg. 7068
WILDPACK BEVERAGE INC.; *Int'l*, pg. 8410
WILD PLANET FOODS, INC.; *U.S. Private*, pg. 4518
WILD POLSKA SP. Z O.O. - MRAGOWO PLANT—See Rudolf Wild GmbH & Co. KG; *Int'l*, pg. 6425
WILD POLSKA SP. Z O.O.—See Rudolf Wild GmbH & Co. KG; *Int'l*, pg. 6425
WILD RICE ELECTRIC COOPERATIVE INC.; *U.S. Private*, pg. 4518
WILD ROSE CASINO & RESORT; *U.S. Private*, pg. 4518
WILDROSE MINING, INC.; *U.S. Private*, pg. 4519
WILD SALES, LLC; *U.S. Private*, pg. 4518
WILDSIDE S.R.L.—See Bertelsmann SE & Co. KGaA; *Int'l*, pg. 996
WILDSKY RESOURCES INC.; *Int'l*, pg. 8410
WILDSTORM PRODUCTIONS—See Warner Bros. Discovery, Inc.; *U.S. Public*, pg. 2328
WILD SZYMBARK SP. Z O.O—See Rudolf Wild GmbH & Co. KG; *Int'l*, pg. 6425
WILDTANGENT, INC.—See Verve Group SE; *Int'l*, pg. 8176
WILD THINGS, LLC—See Blue Point Capital Partners, LLC; *U.S. Private*, pg. 590
WILD THINGS SNACKS, LLC; *U.S. Private*, pg. 4519
WILD TURKEY DISTILLERY—See Alicros S.p.A.; *Int'l*, pg. 327
WILD VALENCIA S.A.—See Archer-Daniels-Midland Company; *U.S. Public*, pg. 184
WILD WELL CONTROL, INC.—See Superior Energy Services, Inc.; *U.S. Public*, pg. 3877
WILD WEST DOMAINS, INC.—See KKR & Co. Inc.; *U.S. Public*, pg. 1252
WILD WEST DOMAINS, INC.—See Silver Lake Group, LLC; *U.S. Private*, pg. 3657
WILD WEST DOMAINS, INC.—See TCMI, Inc.; *U.S. Private*, pg. 3943
WILD WINGS INC.; *U.S. Private*, pg. 4519
WILDWOOD L.P.—See Sun Communities, Inc.; *U.S. Public*, pg. 1963
WILEC—See ACTOM (Pty) Ltd.; *Int'l*, pg. 121
WILEE VEGETABLE OILS SDN. BHD.; *Int'l*, pg. 8410
WILEN MEDIA; *U.S. Private*, pg. 4519
WILEN NEW YORK; *U.S. Private*, pg. 4519

WILEN PRESS—See Wilen New York; *U.S. Private*, pg. 4519
WILEY BLACKWELL PUBLISHING LTD.—See John Wiley & Sons, Inc.; *U.S. Public*, pg. 1193
WILEY BLACKWELL PUBLISHING—See John Wiley & Sons, Inc.; *U.S. Public*, pg. 1193
WILEY EUROPE LIMITED—See John Wiley & Sons, Inc.; *U.S. Public*, pg. 1193
WILEY GLOBAL TECHNOLOGY (PRIVATE) LIMITED—See John Wiley & Sons, Inc.; *U.S. Public*, pg. 1193
WILEY HIGHER EDUCATION PUBLISHING—See John Wiley & Sons, Inc.; *U.S. Public*, pg. 1193
WILEY INDIA PRIVATE LTD.—See John Wiley & Sons, Inc.; *U.S. Public*, pg. 1193
WILEY JAPAN KK—See John Wiley & Sons, Inc.; *U.S. Public*, pg. 1193
WILEY METAL FABRICATING, INC.; *U.S. Private*, pg. 4519
WILEY PROFESSIONAL/TRADE PUBLISHING—See John Wiley & Sons, Inc.; *U.S. Public*, pg. 1193
WILEY PUBLISHING AUSTRALIA PTY LTD.—See John Wiley & Sons, Inc.; *U.S. Public*, pg. 1193
WILEY PUBLISHING, INC.—See John Wiley & Sons, Inc.; *U.S. Public*, pg. 1193
WILEY PUBLISHING JAPAN KK—See John Wiley & Sons, Inc.; *U.S. Public*, pg. 1193
WILEY PUBLISHING SERVICES, INC.—See John Wiley & Sons, Inc.; *U.S. Public*, pg. 1193
WILEY REIN LLP; *U.S. Private*, pg. 4520
WILEY SANDERS TRUCK LINES INC.; *U.S. Private*, pg. 4520
WILEY SCIENTIFIC, TECHNICAL & MEDICAL PUBLISHING—See John Wiley & Sons, Inc.; *U.S. Public*, pg. 1193
WILEY-VCH GMBH—See John Wiley & Sons, Inc.; *U.S. Public*, pg. 1193
WILEY-VCH VERLAG GMBH & CO. KGAA—See John Wiley & Sons, Inc.; *U.S. Public*, pg. 1193
WILEY-VHCA AG—See John Wiley & Sons, Inc.; *U.S. Public*, pg. 1193
WILFERT CHEMICAL DENMARK A/S—See Aspo Oyj; *Int'l*, pg. 631
WILFERT CHEMICAL NORDIC A/S—See Aspo Oyj; *Int'l*, pg. 631
WILFERT CHEMICAL SWEDEN AB—See Aspo Oyj; *Int'l*, pg. 631
WILFRED EDMUNDS LTD—See JPIMedia Holdings Limited; *Int'l*, pg. 4007
WILFRED MACDONALD INC.; *U.S. Private*, pg. 4520
WILFRIED HEINZEL AG—See Heinzel Holding GmbH; *Int'l*, pg. 3325
WILH. BECKER HOLDING GMBH—See Lindengruppen AB; *Int'l*, pg. 4511
WILHEIT PACKAGING LLC; *U.S. Private*, pg. 4520
WILHELM BILSTEIN GMBH&CO.KG; *Int'l*, pg. 8411
WILHELM ERNST & SOHN GMBH & CO. KG—See John Wiley & Sons, Inc.; *U.S. Public*, pg. 1193
WILHELM FENNERS; *Int'l*, pg. 8411
WILHELM GEIGER GMBH & CO. KG; *Int'l*, pg. 8411
WILHELM GOLDMANN VERLAG GMBH—See Bertelsmann SE & Co. KGaA; *Int'l*, pg. 996
WILHELMINA INTERNATIONAL, INC.; *U.S. Public*, pg. 2370
WILHELMINA INTERNATIONAL, LTD.—See Wilhelmina International, Inc.; *U.S. Public*, pg. 2370
WILHELMINA LONDON LIMITED—See Wilhelmina International, Inc.; *U.S. Public*, pg. 2370
WILHELMINA-MIAMI, INC.—See Wilhelmina International, Inc.; *U.S. Public*, pg. 2370
WILHELMINA NEW YORK—See Wilhelmina International, Inc.; *U.S. Public*, pg. 2370
WILHELMINA WEST, INC.—See Wilhelmina International, Inc.; *U.S. Public*, pg. 2370
WILHELM MAASS GMBH; *Int'l*, pg. 8411
WILHELM ROSENSTEIN LTD.—See BASF SE; *Int'l*, pg. 885
WILHELM SANDER FERTIGUNG GMBH—See Indutrade AB; *Int'l*, pg. 3680
WILHELM SCHEIDT BAUUNTERNEHMUNG GMBH; *Int'l*, pg. 8411
WILHELM SCHIMMEL PIANOFORTEFABRIK GMBH; *Int'l*, pg. 8411
WILHELMSEN AHRENKIEL SHIP MANAGEMENT GMBH & CO. KG—See MPC Munchmeyer Petersen & Co. GmbH; *Int'l*, pg. 5061
WILHELMSEN MARITIME SERVICES AS—See Wilh. Wilhelmsen Holding ASA; *Int'l*, pg. 8410
WILHELMSEN PORT SERVICE CANARIAS S.A.—See Wilh. Wilhelmsen Holding ASA; *Int'l*, pg. 8411
WILHELMSEN PORT SERVICE (GIBRALTAR) LIMITED—See Wilh. Wilhelmsen Holding ASA; *Int'l*, pg. 8411
WILHELMSEN PORT SERVICES AMSTERDAM B.V.—See Wilh. Wilhelmsen Holding ASA; *Int'l*, pg. 8411
WILHELMSEN PORT SERVICES ANTWERP N.V.—See Wilh. Wilhelmsen Holding ASA; *Int'l*, pg. 8411
WILHELMSEN PORT SERVICES BULGARIA LTD.—See Wilh. Wilhelmsen Holding ASA; *Int'l*, pg. 8411

WILHELM SCHIMMEL PIANOFORTEFABRIK GMBH   CORPORATE AFFILIATIONS

WILHELMSEN PORT SERVICES GERMANY GMBH—See Wilh. Wilhelmsen Holding ASA; *Int'l*, pg. 8411
WILHELMSEN PORT SERVICES INDIA PRIVATE LIMITED—See Wilh. Wilhelmsen Holding ASA; *Int'l*, pg. 8411
WILHELMSEN PORT SERVICES JAPAN CO., LTD.—See Wilh. Wilhelmsen Holding ASA; *Int'l*, pg. 8411
WILHELMSEN PORT SERVICES (JAPAN) PTE. LTD.—See Wilh. Wilhelmsen Holding ASA; *Int'l*, pg. 8411
WILHELMSEN PORT SERVICES PORTUGAL S.A.—See Wilh. Wilhelmsen Holding ASA; *Int'l*, pg. 8411
WILHELMSEN PORT SERVICES ROMANIA S.R.L.—See Wilh. Wilhelmsen Holding ASA; *Int'l*, pg. 8411
WILHELMSEN PORT SERVICES ROTTERDAM B.V.—See Wilh. Wilhelmsen Holding ASA; *Int'l*, pg. 8411
WILHELMSEN PORT SERVICES, S.A.—See Wilh. Wilhelmsen Holding ASA; *Int'l*, pg. 8411
WILHELMSEN PORT SERVICES SOUTH AFRICA (PTY.) LTD.—See Wilh. Wilhelmsen Holding ASA; *Int'l*, pg. 8411
WILHELMSEN PORT SERVICES TERNEUZEN B.V.—See Wilh. Wilhelmsen Holding ASA; *Int'l*, pg. 8411
WILHELMSEN SHIP MANAGEMENT SINGAPORE PTE. LTD.—See MPC Munchmeyer Petersen & Co. GmbH; *Int'l*, pg. 5061
WILHELMSEN SHIPS SERVICE AS—See Wilh. Wilhelmsen Holding ASA; *Int'l*, pg. 8410
WILHELMSEN SHIPS SERVICE BULGARIA LTD.—See Wilh. Wilhelmsen Holding ASA; *Int'l*, pg. 8411
WILHELMSEN TECHNICAL SOLUTIONS AB—See Wilh. Wilhelmsen Holding ASA; *Int'l*, pg. 8410
WILHELMSEN TECHNICAL SOLUTIONS A/S—See Wilh. Wilhelmsen Holding ASA; *Int'l*, pg. 8410
WILHELMSEN TECHNICAL SOLUTIONS AS—See Wilh. Wilhelmsen Holding ASA; *Int'l*, pg. 8410
WILHELMSEN TECHNICAL SOLUTIONS, INC.—See Wilh. Wilhelmsen Holding ASA; *Int'l*, pg. 8411
WILHELMSEN TECHNICAL SOLUTIONS PTE. LTD.—See Wilh. Wilhelmsen Holding ASA; *Int'l*, pg. 8411
WILHELMSEN TECHNICAL SOLUTIONS SWEDEN AB—See Wilh. Wilhelmsen Holding ASA; *Int'l*, pg. 8410
WILHELMSHAVENER RAFFINERIEGESELLSCHAFT MBH—See Riverstone Holdings LLC; *U.S. Private*, pg. 3447
WILHELM STAHLECKER GMBH—See Rieter Holding Ltd.; *Int'l*, pg. 6339
WILHITE CRANE SERVICE, INC.; *U.S. Private*, pg. 4520
WILH. WERHAHN KG; *Int'l*, pg. 8410
WILH. WERHAHN KG ZN HAUS & GRUND—See Wilh. Werhahn KG; *Int'l*, pg. 8410
WILH. WILHELMSEN HOLDING ASA; *Int'l*, pg. 8410
WILIAN HOLDING CO., INC.; *U.S. Private*, pg. 4520
WILILAMSON-DICKIE MANUFACTURING COMPANY—See V. F. Corporation; *U.S. Public*, pg. 2269
WILILOY LIMITED—See Hang Lung Group Limited; *Int'l*, pg. 3245
WILKENING + HAHNE GMBH + CO. KG; *Int'l*, pg. 8411
WILKENS MANUFACTURING INC; *U.S. Private*, pg. 4520
WILKENS WEATHER TECHNOLOGIES, L.P.—See TBG Treuhand Partner AG; *Int'l*, pg. 7480
WILKERSON FUEL CO., INC.; *U.S. Private*, pg. 4520
WILKES-BARRE ACADEMIC MEDICINE, LLC—See Community Health Systems, Inc.; *U.S. Public*, pg. 557
WILKES-BARRE HOME CARE SERVICES, LLC—See Community Health Systems, Inc.; *U.S. Public*, pg. 557
WILKES-BARRE HOSPITAL COMPANY, LLC—See Community Health Systems, Inc.; *U.S. Public*, pg. 557
WILKES-BARRE PUBLISHING COMPANY, INC.—See Independence Capital Partners, LLC; *U.S. Private*, pg. 2057
WILKES-BARRE SKILLED NURSING SERVICES, LLC—See Community Health Systems, Inc.; *U.S. Public*, pg. 557
WILKES-BARRE TIMES LEADER—See Independence Capital Partners, LLC; *U.S. Private*, pg. 2057
WILKES BASHFORD COMPANY; *U.S. Private*, pg. 4520
WILKES COMMUNICATIONS; *U.S. Private*, pg. 4520
WILKES TOWERS LIMITED PARTNERSHIP—See Apartment Investment and Management Company; *U.S. Public*, pg. 144
WILKHAHN AG—See Wilkening + Hahne GmbH + Co. KG; *Int'l*, pg. 8411
WILKHAHN ASIA PACIFIC—See Wilkening + Hahne GmbH + Co. KG; *Int'l*, pg. 8411
WILKHAHN HANDELSGES.M.B.H.—See Wilkening + Hahne GmbH + Co. KG; *Int'l*, pg. 8411
WILKHAHN, INC.—See Wilkening + Hahne GmbH + Co. KG; *Int'l*, pg. 8411
WILKHAHN JAPAN CO., LTD.—See Wilkening + Hahne GmbH + Co. KG; *Int'l*, pg. 8411
WILKHAHN LTD.—See Wilkening + Hahne GmbH + Co. KG; *Int'l*, pg. 8411
WILKHAHN S.A.—See Wilkening + Hahne GmbH + Co. KG; *Int'l*, pg. 8411
WILKINSBERG-PENN JOINT WATER AUTHORITY; *U.S. Private*, pg. 4520

WILKINS BUICK, INC. & WILKINS SUBARU, LLC.; *U.S. Private*, pg. 4520
WILKINS MEDIA COMPANY—See Wilkins Media Company; *U.S. Private*, pg. 4520
WILKINS MEDIA COMPANY—See Wilkins Media Company; *U.S. Private*, pg. 4520
WILKINS MEDIA COMPANY; *U.S. Private*, pg. 4520
WILKINSON & ASSOCIATES REAL ESTATE; *U.S. Private*, pg. 4520
WILKINSON CONSTRUCTION INC—See Wilkinson Real Estate Advisors Inc; *U.S. Private*, pg. 4521
WILKINSON COUNTY INDUSTRIAL DEVELOPMENT AUTHORITY; *U.S. Private*, pg. 4521
WILKINSON O'GRADY & CO., INC.—See Fiera Capital Corporation; *Int'l*, pg. 2660
WILKINSON REAL ESTATE ADVISORS INC; *U.S. Private*, pg. 4521
WILKINSON STEEL & METALS, INC.—See Samuel, Son & Co., Limited; *Int'l*, pg. 6516
WILKINSON SUPPLY COMPANY; *U.S. Private*, pg. 4521
WILKINSON SWORD GMBH—See Edgewell Personal Care Company; *U.S. Public*, pg. 718
WILKINSON SWORD LIMITED—See Edgewell Personal Care Company; *U.S. Public*, pg. 718
WILKINS-ROGERS, INC.; *U.S. Private*, pg. 4520
WILKINS WATER CONTROL PRODUCTS—See Zurn Elkay Water Solutions Corporation; *U.S. Public*, pg. 2414
WILKO RETAIL LTD.; *Int'l*, pg. 8411
WILKS BROADCAST GROUP, LLC—See The Wicks Group of Companies, LLC; *U.S. Private*, pg. 4136
WILKS BROTHERS LLC; *U.S. Private*, pg. 4521
WILKS ENTERPRISE INC.—See AMETEK, Inc.; *U.S. Public*, pg. 122
WILK SHIRT CORP.; *U.S. Private*, pg. 4520
WILKS MASONRY CORPORATION; *U.S. Private*, pg. 4521
WILLAKENZIE VINEYARDS, INC.—See Jackson Family Wines, Inc.; *U.S. Private*, pg. 2176
WILLAMETTE BEVERAGE COMPANY; *U.S. Private*, pg. 4521
WILLAMETTE COMMUNITY BANK—See Peoples Bank of Commerce; *U.S. Private*, pg. 3141
WILLAMETTE CRUSHING CO., INC.—See Wildish Land Company; *U.S. Private*, pg. 4519
WILLAMETTE EGG FARMS LLC—See Post Holdings, Inc.; *U.S. Public*, pg. 1703
WILLAMETTE MANAGEMENT ASSOCIATES; *U.S. Private*, pg. 4521
WILLAMETTE NEIGHBORHOOD HOUSING SERVICES—See Corvallis Neighborhood Housing Services, Inc.; *U.S. Private*, pg. 1061
WILLAMETTE RESOURCES, INC.—See Republic Services, Inc.; *U.S. Public*, pg. 1789
WILLAMETTE VALLEY BANK—See Oregon Bancorp, Inc.; *U.S. Public*, pg. 1615
THE WILLAMETTE VALLEY COMPANY - IDAHO MILLING AND GRAIN DIVISION—See The Willamette Valley Company; *U.S. Private*, pg. 4136
THE WILLAMETTE VALLEY COMPANY - MIDWEST DIVISION—See The Willamette Valley Company; *U.S. Private*, pg. 4136
THE WILLAMETTE VALLEY COMPANY - PRE-TEC DIVISION—See The Willamette Valley Company; *U.S. Private*, pg. 4136
THE WILLAMETTE VALLEY COMPANY; *U.S. Private*, pg. 4136
THE WILLAMETTE VALLEY COMPANY - SOUTHERN DIVISION LOUISIANA—See The Willamette Valley Company; *U.S. Private*, pg. 4136
THE WILLAMETTE VALLEY COMPANY - WESTERN DIVISION—See The Willamette Valley Company; *U.S. Private*, pg. 4136
THE WILLAMETTE VALLEY COMPANY - WVCO WOOD PRODUCTS DIVISION—See The Willamette Valley Company; *U.S. Private*, pg. 4136
WILLAMETTE VALLEY FRUIT COMPANY—See Oregon Potato Company; *U.S. Private*, pg. 3040
WILLAMETTE VALLEY VINEYARDS, INC.; *U.S. Public*, pg. 2370
WILLAMETTE VIEW, INC.; *U.S. Private*, pg. 4521
WILLAMINA LUMBER CO., INC.—See Hampton Affiliates; *U.S. Private*, pg. 1851
WILLAMSEN-GODWIN TRUCK BODY COMPANY—See The Godwin Group; *U.S. Private*, pg. 4033
WILLANDRA VILLAGE MANAGEMENT PTY LTD—See Australian Unity Limited; *Int'l*, pg. 723
WILLARD ASPHALT PAVING, INC.; *U.S. Private*, pg. 4521
THE WILLARD GROUP ADVERTISING—See WPP plc; *Int'l*, pg. 8468
THE WILLARD GROUP—See WPP plc; *Int'l*, pg. 8468
WILLARD MARINE, INC.—See Future Mobility Solutions Ltd.; *Int'l*, pg. 2857
WILLARD MEATS INTERNATIONAL LTD.; *Int'l*, pg. 8412
WILLARD OIL COMPANY INC.; *U.S. Private*, pg. 4521
WILLAS-ARRAY ELECTRONICS (HOLDINGS) LTD.; *Int'l*, pg. 8412

WILLAS-ARRAY ELECTRONICS (HONG KONG) LIMITED—See Willas-Array Electronics (Holdings) Ltd.; *Int'l*, pg. 8412
WILLAS-ARRAY ELECTRONICS (SHANGHAI) LIMITED—See Willas-Array Electronics (Holdings) Ltd.; *Int'l*, pg. 8412
WILLAS-ARRAY ELECTRONICS (SHENZHEN) LIMITED—See Willas-Array Electronics (Holdings) Ltd.; *Int'l*, pg. 8412
WILLAS-ARRAY ELECTRONICS (TAIWAN) INC.—See Willas-Array Electronics (Holdings) Ltd.; *Int'l*, pg. 8412
WILL & BAUMER; *U.S. Private*, pg. 4521
THE WILLBES (CAMBODIA) & CO., LTD.—See The Willbes Co Ltd; *Int'l*, pg. 7701
THE WILLBES CO LTD; *Int'l*, pg. 7701
WILLBROOK SOLUTIONS, INC.—See Godspeed Capital Management LP; *U.S. Private*, pg. 1725
WILLBROS CONSTRUCTION SERVICES (CANADA) L.P.—See Primoris Services Corporation; *U.S. Public*, pg. 1719
WILLBROS GROUP, INC.—See Primoris Services Corporation; *U.S. Public*, pg. 1719
WILLBROS T&D SERVICES, LLC—See Primoris Services Corporation; *U.S. Public*, pg. 1719
WILL-BURT ADVANCED COMPOSITES, INC.—See The Will-Burt Co., Inc.; *U.S. Private*, pg. 4136
THE WILL-BURT CO., INC.; *U.S. Private*, pg. 4136
WILLCAN INC.—See Sequatchie Concrete Service Inc.; *U.S. Private*, pg. 3612
WILLCARE, INC. - NEWBURGH—See UnitedHealth Group Incorporated; *U.S. Public*, pg. 2244
WILLCARE, INC. - OLEAN—See UnitedHealth Group Incorporated; *U.S. Public*, pg. 2244
WILLCARE, INC.—See UnitedHealth Group Incorporated; *U.S. Public*, pg. 2244
WILLCARE, INC. - TRUMBULL—See UnitedHealth Group Incorporated; *U.S. Public*, pg. 2244
WILL, CO., LTD.; *Int'l*, pg. 8412
WILLCO TECHNOLOGIES, INC.—See Metisentry LLC; *U.S. Private*, pg. 2684
WILLCREST PARTNERS; *U.S. Private*, pg. 4521
WILLDALE LIMITED—See Mashonaland Holdings Limited; *Int'l*, pg. 4721
WILLDAN ENERGY SOLUTIONS—See Willdan Group, Inc.; *U.S. Public*, pg. 2371
WILLDAN ENGINEERING—See Willdan Group, Inc.; *U.S. Public*, pg. 2371
WILLDAN FINANCIAL SERVICES—See Willdan Group, Inc.; *U.S. Public*, pg. 2371
WILLDAN GROUP, INC.; *U.S. Public*, pg. 2370
WILLDAN HOMELAND SOLUTIONS—See Willdan Group, Inc.; *U.S. Public*, pg. 2371
WILLE BROS CO.; *U.S. Private*, pg. 4521
WILLE ELECTRIC SUPPLY CO.; *U.S. Private*, pg. 4521
WILLEMOT BIJZONDER VERZEKERINGSBESTUUR NV—See OVB Holding AG; *Int'l*, pg. 5671
WILLEMSBRUG B.V.—See Allianz SE; *Int'l*, pg. 356
WILLEMS STAHL GMBH—See Knauf Interfer SE; *Int'l*, pg. 4205
WILLERBY LANDSCAPES LTD.; *Int'l*, pg. 8412
WILLERT HOME PRODUCTS, INC.; *U.S. Private*, pg. 4521
WILLERT HOME PRODUCTS (SHANGHAI) CO., LTD.—See Willert Home Products, Inc.; *U.S. Private*, pg. 4522
WILLET HAUSER ARCHITECTURAL GLASS, INC.—See Associated Crafts, Inc.; *U.S. Private*, pg. 355
WILLETT HOFMANN & ASSOC INC.; *U.S. Private*, pg. 4522
WILLEY MOTORS INC.; *U.S. Private*, pg. 4522
WILLFAR INFORMATION TECHNOLOGY CO., LTD.—See Wasion Holdings Limited; *Int'l*, pg. 8352
WILLGAIN ENTERPRISES, INC.—See Tomar Industries, Inc.; *U.S. Private*, pg. 4183
WILLGATE, INC.—See Vector Inc.; *Int'l*, pg. 8144
THE WILL GROUP, INC.; *U.S. Private*, pg. 4136
WILL GROUP, INC.; *Int'l*, pg. 8412
WILLHEARTS CO., LTD.—See Willtec Co., Ltd.; *Int'l*, pg. 8420
WILLIAAM COX LTD.—See CRH plc; *Int'l*, pg. 1849
WILLIAAM COX LTD.—See Sicon Ltd.; *Int'l*, pg. 6882
WILLIAM A. COOK AUSTRALIA PTY. LTD.—See Cook Group Incorporated; *U.S. Private*, pg. 1037
WILLIAM A. HARRISON INC.; *U.S. Private*, pg. 4522
WILLIAM A. HAZEL INC.; *U.S. Private*, pg. 4522
WILLIAM A. RANDOLPH, INC.; *U.S. Private*, pg. 4522
WILLIAM ASHLEY CHINA CORPORATION—See Fairfax Financial Holdings Limited; *Int'l*, pg. 2609
WILLIAM A. STRAUB INC.; *U.S. Private*, pg. 4522
WILLIAM B. COLEMAN CO., INC.; *U.S. Private*, pg. 4522
WILLIAM B. COLLINS CO., INC.—See The Nutting Company, Inc.; *U.S. Private*, pg. 4087
WILLIAM BEAUMONT HOSPITAL—See Beaumont Health; *U.S. Private*, pg. 508
WILLIAM BLAIR & COMPANY LLC; *U.S. Private*, pg. 4522
WILLIAM BLAIR INVESTMENT MANAGEMENT LLC; *U.S. Private*, pg. 4522

COMPANY NAME INDEX WILLIAMS INTERNATIONAL

Company Index

WILLIAM BLAKE LIMITED—See Kerry Group plc; *Int'l*, pg. 4139
WILLIAM BLYTHE LTD.—See Synthomer plc; *Int'l*, pg. 7387
WILLIAM B. MEYER INC.; *U.S. Private*, pg. 4522
WILLIAM B. MORSE LUMBER CO.; *U.S. Private*, pg. 4522
WILLIAM BROJACK LUMBER COMPANY; *U.S. Private*, pg. 4522
WILLIAM BRONNER & SON CONTRACTORS INC.; *U.S. Private*, pg. 4522
WILLIAM CHARLES CONSTRUCTION COMPANY, LLC—See MasTec, Inc.; *U.S. Public*, pg. 1393
WILLIAM CHARLES CONSTRUCTION - MATERIALS DIVISION—See MasTec, Inc.; *U.S. Public*, pg. 1393
WILLIAM CHARLES LTD—See William Charles, Ltd.; *U.S. Private*, pg. 4522
WILLIAM CHARLES, LTD.; *U.S. Private*, pg. 4522
WILLIAM CHARLES REAL ESTATE CO—See William Charles, Ltd.; *U.S. Private*, pg. 4523
WILLIAM CHARLES WEST INC—See William Charles, Ltd.; *U.S. Private*, pg. 4523
WILLIAM C. HUFF COMPANIES; *U.S. Private*, pg. 4522
WILLIAM COOK CAST PRODUCTS LTD LEEDS PLANT—See William Cook Holdings Limited; *Int'l*, pg. 8413
WILLIAM COOK CAST PRODUCTS LTD PRECISION PLANT—See William Cook Holdings Limited; *Int'l*, pg. 8413
WILLIAM COOK EUROPE APS—See Cook Group Incorporated; *U.S. Private*, pg. 1037
WILLIAM COOK HOLDINGS LIMITED; *Int'l*, pg. 8412
WILLIAM C. SMITH & COMPANY; *U.S. Private*, pg. 4522
WILLIAM E. BURROWES INC.; *Int'l*, pg. 8413
WILLIAM E. COUTTS CO., LTD.—See Hallmark Cards, Inc.; *U.S. Private*, pg. 1845
WILLIAM E. DAILEY INC.—See Peckham Industries, Inc.; *U.S. Private*, pg. 3127
THE WILLIAMETTE VALLEY COMPANY - SOUTHERN DIVISION GEORGIA—See The Willamette Valley Company; *U.S. Private*, pg. 4136
WILLIAM E. WALTER INC.; *U.S. Private*, pg. 4523
WILLIAM FENTON INC.; *U.S. Private*, pg. 4523
WILLIAM F. HURST CO., INC.; *U.S. Private*, pg. 4523
WILLIAM F. MEYER COMPANY; *U.S. Private*, pg. 4523
WILLIAM FOOD COMPANY LIMITED—See Hong Kong Food Investment Holdings Limited; *Int'l*, pg. 3466
WILLIAM F. WHITE INTERNATIONAL INC.—See Ashtead Group Plc; *Int'l*, pg. 609
WILLIAM GEORGE PRODUCE CO., INC.; *U.S. Private*, pg. 4523
WILLIAM GRANT & SONS, INC.—See William Grant & Sons Ltd.; *Int'l*, pg. 8413
WILLIAM GRANT & SONS LTD.; *Int'l*, pg. 8413
WILLIAM HARRIS INVESTORS, INC.; *U.S. Private*, pg. 4523
WILLIAM HILL CREDIT LIMITED—See William Hill Plc; *Int'l*, pg. 8413
WILLIAM HILL LATVIA SIA—See evoke plc; *Int'l*, pg. 2572
WILLIAM HILL ORGANIZATION LIMITED—See William Hill Plc; *Int'l*, pg. 8413
WILLIAM HILL PLC; *Int'l*, pg. 8413
WILLIAM H. LEAHY ASSOCIATES INC.; *U.S. Private*, pg. 4523
WILLIAM HOUDE LTD.—See Compagnie Financiere et de Participations Roullier SA; *Int'l*, pg. 1740
WILLIAM H. SADLIER, INC.; *U.S. Public*, pg. 2371
WILLIAM JACKS & COMPANY (MALAYSIA) SENDIRIAN BERHAD—See Johan Holdings Berhad; *Int'l*, pg. 3977
WILLIAM JACKS & CO. (SINGAPORE) PTE. LTD.—See Johan Holdings Berhad; *Int'l*, pg. 3977
WILLIAM J. SCHULTZ INC.; *U.S. Private*, pg. 4523
WILLIAM KAVANAGH FURNITURE CO.; *U.S. Private*, pg. 4523
THE WILLIAM L. BONNELL CO., INC.—See Tredegar Corporation; *U.S. Public*, pg. 2187
WILLIAM LEE LIMITED—See Castings PLC; *Int'l*, pg. 1357
WILLIAM LEHMAN & ASSOCIATES—See Lithia Motors, Inc.; *U.S. Public*, pg. 1323
WILLIAM LEHMAN BUICK INC.—See Lithia Motors, Inc.; *U.S. Public*, pg. 1323
WILLIAM LEHMAN LEASING CORP.—See Lithia Motors, Inc.; *U.S. Public*, pg. 1323
WILLIAM L. LYON & ASSOCIATES, INC.—See Windermere Real Estate Services Company; *U.S. Private*, pg. 4537
WILLIAM L. MARTIN JR.; *U.S. Private*, pg. 4523
WILLIAM LYON HOMES, INC.—See Brookfield Corporation; *Int'l*, pg. 1183
WILLIAM LYON HOMES, INC.—See Brookfield Corporation; *Int'l*, pg. 1183
WILLIAM MACKLOWE COMPANY LLC; *U.S. Private*, pg. 4523
WILLIAM MASTERS INC.; *U.S. Private*, pg. 4523
WILLIAM M. BIRD & COMPANY, INC.; *U.S. Private*, pg. 4523
WILLIAM M. BLOOMFIELD INC.; *U.S. Private*, pg. 4523
WILLIAM MORRIS AGENCY, LLC - NEW YORK OFFICE—See William Morris Endeavor Entertainment, LLC; *U.S. Private*, pg. 4524
WILLIAM MORRIS AGENCY, LLC—See William Morris Endeavor Entertainment, LLC; *U.S. Private*, pg. 4524
WILLIAM MORRIS ENDEAVOR ENTERTAINMENT, LLC; *U.S. Private*, pg. 4523
WILLIAM MORRIS ENDEAVOR ENTERTAINMENT (U.K.) LIMITED—See Silver Lake Group, LLC; *U.S. Private*, pg. 3654
WILLIAM MORRIS HOME FASHIONS; *U.S. Private*, pg. 4524
WILLIAM MUELLER & SONS INC.; *U.S. Private*, pg. 4524
WILLIAM NEWTON HOSPITAL; *U.S. Private*, pg. 4524
WILLIAM NOBBE & CO., INC.; *U.S. Private*, pg. 4524
WILLIAM O'NEIL & CO., INC.; *U.S. Private*, pg. 4524
THE WILLIAM PEARS GROUP OF COMPANIES LIMITED; *Int'l*, pg. 7701
WILLIAM PENN ASSOCIATION; *U.S. Private*, pg. 4524
WILLIAM PENN BANCORPORATION; *U.S. Public*, pg. 2371
WILLIAM PENN BANK—See William Penn Bancorporation; *U.S. Public*, pg. 2371
WILLIAM PENN LIFE INSURANCE COMPANY OF NEW YORK—See Legal & General Group Plc; *Int'l*, pg. 4443
WILLIAM P. HEARNE INC.; *U.S. Private*, pg. 4524
WILLIAM PITTERS INTERNATIONAL S.A.S—See Marie Brizard Wine & Spirits S.A.; *Int'l*, pg. 4694
WILLIAM PITT SOTHEBY'S INTERNATIONAL REALTY; *U.S. Private*, pg. 4524
WILLIAM PRYM DE MEXICO S.A.—See William Prym GmbH & Co. KG; *Int'l*, pg. 8414
WILLIAM PRYM GMBH & CO. KG; *Int'l*, pg. 8413
WILLIAM R. BEACH GENERAL CONTRACTOR, INC.; *U.S. Private*, pg. 4524
WILLIAM R. NASH INC.; *U.S. Private*, pg. 4524
WILLIAM ROWLAND LTD—See Amalgamated Metal Corporation Plc; *Int'l*, pg. 409
WILLIAM RYAN HOMES, INC.; *U.S. Private*, pg. 4525
WILLIAMS ADVANCED MATERIALS INC.—See Materion Corporation; *U.S. Public*, pg. 1396
WILLIAM SANDERS RETIREMENT VILLAGE LIMITED—See Ryman Healthcare Ltd.; *Int'l*, pg. 6440
WILLIAMS AUTO GROUP INC.; *U.S. Private*, pg. 4525
WILLIAMS BRIDGE CO.—See Williams Industries, Inc.; *U.S. Private*, pg. 4526
WILLIAMS BROTHERS CONSTRUCTION INC.; *U.S. Private*, pg. 4525
WILLIAMS BROTHERS TRUCKING; *U.S. Private*, pg. 4525
WILLIAMSBURG ENTERPRISES LTD.; *U.S. Private*, pg. 4527
WILLIAMSBURG FURNITURE INC.—See Patrick Industries, Inc.; *U.S. Public*, pg. 1653
WILLIAMSBURG LANDING, INC.; *U.S. Private*, pg. 4527
WILLIAMSBURG MOTORS, INC.—See Onity Group Inc.; *U.S. Public*, pg. 1605
WILLIAMSBURG POTTERY FACTORY; *U.S. Private*, pg. 4527
THE WILLIAMS CAPITAL GROUP, L.P.; *U.S. Private*, pg. 4136
THE WILLIAMS COMPANIES, INC. - HOUSTON—See The Williams Companies, Inc.; *U.S. Public*, pg. 2142
THE WILLIAMS COMPANIES, INC. - NESHANIC STATION—See The Williams Companies, Inc.; *U.S. Public*, pg. 2142
THE WILLIAMS COMPANIES, INC. - OKLAHOMA CITY—See The Williams Companies, Inc.; *U.S. Public*, pg. 2142
THE WILLIAMS COMPANIES, INC.; *U.S. Public*, pg. 2142
THE WILLIAMS COMPANIES, INC. - WASHINGTON—See The Williams Companies, Inc.; *U.S. Public*, pg. 2142
WILLIAMS COMPANY INC.; *U.S. Private*, pg. 4525
WILLIAMS & CONNOLLY, LLP; *U.S. Private*, pg. 4525
WILLIAMS CONTROLS EUROPE GMBH—See Curtiss-Wright Corporation; *U.S. Public*, pg. 612
WILLIAMS CONTROLS, INC.—See Curtiss-Wright Corporation; *U.S. Public*, pg. 612
WILLIAMS CONTROLS INDIA PRIVATE LIMITED—See Curtiss-Wright Corporation; *U.S. Public*, pg. 612
WILLIAMS CONTROLS INDUSTRIES, INC.—See Curtiss-Wright Corporation; *U.S. Public*, pg. 612
WILLIAMS/CRAWFORD & ASSOCIATES; *U.S. Private*, pg. 4527
WILLIAMS DISTRIBUTING INC.; *U.S. Private*, pg. 4525
WILLIAMS DISTRIBUTING - MOTORS & DRIVES—See Williams Distributing Inc.; *U.S. Private*, pg. 4525
WILLIAMS ELECTRIC CO. INC.—See Parsons Corporation; *U.S. Public*, pg. 1651
WILLIAMS ENERGY CANADA ULC—See The Williams Companies, Inc.; *U.S. Public*, pg. 2142
WILLIAMS ENERGY CO.—See The Williams Companies, Inc.; *U.S. Public*, pg. 2142
WILLIAMS ENERGY SERVICES—See The Williams Companies, Inc.; *U.S. Public*, pg. 2142
WILLIAMS ENERGY SERVICES—See The Williams Companies, Inc.; *U.S. Public*, pg. 2142
WILLIAMS ENERGY SERVICES—See The Williams Companies, Inc.; *U.S. Public*, pg. 2142
WILLIAMS ENTERPRISES OF GEORGIA, INC.; *U.S. Private*, pg. 4525
WILLIAMS EQUIPMENT CORPORATION—See Williams Industries, Inc.; *U.S. Private*, pg. 4526
WILLIAMS EQUIPMENT & SUPPLY COMPANY—See The Sterling Group, L.P.; *U.S. Private*, pg. 4122
WILLIAMS ERECTION COMPANY INC.—See Williams Enterprises of Georgia, Inc.; *U.S. Private*, pg. 4525
WILLIAMS FIELD SERVICES COMPANY—See The Williams Companies, Inc.; *U.S. Public*, pg. 2142
WILLIAMS FIELD SERVICES GROUP, LLC—See The Williams Companies, Inc.; *U.S. Public*, pg. 2143
WILLIAMS FIELD SERVICES—See The Williams Companies, Inc.; *U.S. Public*, pg. 2142
WILLIAMS FINANCIAL GROUP, INC.; *U.S. Private*, pg. 4525
WILLIAMS FOODS INC.; *U.S. Private*, pg. 4525
WILLIAMS FOODS LLC—See The Pritzker Group - Chicago, LLC; *U.S. Private*, pg. 4098
WILLIAMS FOOD WORKS AND DISTRIBUTION, LLC—See Tyson Foods, Inc.; *U.S. Public*, pg. 2210
WILLIAMS FORM ENGINEERING CORP.; *U.S. Private*, pg. 4525
WILLIAMS FOUR CORNERS LLC—See The Williams Companies, Inc.; *U.S. Public*, pg. 2142
WILLIAMS FURNACE CO.—See Bee Street Holdings LLC; *U.S. Private*, pg. 513
WILLIAMS GAS PIPELINE COMPANY LLC—See The Williams Companies, Inc.; *U.S. Public*, pg. 2143
WILLIAMS GAS PIPELINE CORP.—See The Williams Companies, Inc.; *U.S. Public*, pg. 2144
WILLIAMS GAS PIPELINE CORP.—See The Williams Companies, Inc.; *U.S. Public*, pg. 2144
WILLIAMS GAS PIPELINE PLYMOUTH DISTRICT—See The Williams Companies, Inc.; *U.S. Public*, pg. 2144
WILLIAMS GAS PIPELINES CENTRAL—See The Williams Companies, Inc.; *U.S. Public*, pg. 2144
WILLIAMS GAS PIPELINE—See The Williams Companies, Inc.; *U.S. Public*, pg. 2143
WILLIAMS GAS PIPELINE—See The Williams Companies, Inc.; *U.S. Public*, pg. 2143
WILLIAMS GAS PIPELINE—See The Williams Companies, Inc.; *U.S. Public*, pg. 2143
WILLIAMS GAS PIPELINE—See The Williams Companies, Inc.; *U.S. Public*, pg. 2144
WILLIAMS GAS PIPELINE—See The Williams Companies, Inc.; *U.S. Public*, pg. 2143
WILLIAMS GAS PIPELINE—See The Williams Companies, Inc.; *U.S. Public*, pg. 2143
WILLIAMS GAS PIPELINE—See The Williams Companies, Inc.; *U.S. Public*, pg. 2143
WILLIAMS GAS PIPELINE—See The Williams Companies, Inc.; *U.S. Public*, pg. 2143
WILLIAMS GAS PIPELINE—See The Williams Companies, Inc.; *U.S. Public*, pg. 2144
WILLIAMS GAS PIPELINE—See The Williams Companies, Inc.; *U.S. Public*, pg. 2143
WILLIAMS GAS PIPELINE TRANSCO—See The Williams Companies, Inc.; *U.S. Public*, pg. 2144
WILLIAMS GAS PIPELINE TRANSCO—See The Williams Companies, Inc.; *U.S. Public*, pg. 2144
WILLIAMS GAS PIPELINE WEST—See The Williams Companies, Inc.; *U.S. Public*, pg. 2144
WILLIAMS GC NEWSPAPERS INC.—See Western Newspapers, Inc.; *U.S. Private*, pg. 4495
WILLIAMS/GERARD PRODUCTIONS INC.; *U.S. Private*, pg. 4527
WILLIAMS & GLYN LIMITED—See NatWest Group plc; *Int'l*, pg. 5172
WILLIAMS & GOSLING LTD.; *Int'l*, pg. 8414
WILLIAMS GRAND PRIX ENGINEERING LIMITED—See Dorilton Capital Advisors LLC; *U.S. Private*, pg. 1263
WILLIAMS GROUP INTERNATIONAL, INC.; *U.S. Private*, pg. 4526
WILLIAMS GROUP LLC; *U.S. Private*, pg. 4526
WILLIAMS GUN SIGHT COMPANY, INC.; *U.S. Private*, pg. 4526
WILLIAM S. HEIN & CO., INC.; *U.S. Private*, pg. 4525
WILLIAMS, INC.; *U.S. Private*, pg. 4527
WILLIAMS INDUSTRIAL SERVICES GROUP INC.—See The Toronto-Dominion Bank; *Int'l*, pg. 7696
WILLIAMS INDUSTRIAL SERVICES GROUP, L.L.C.—See The Toronto-Dominion Bank; *Int'l*, pg. 7696
WILLIAMS INDUSTRIES, INC.; *U.S. Private*, pg. 4526
WILLIAMS INLAND DISTRIBUTORS LLC; *U.S. Private*, pg. 4526
WILLIAMS INSTRUMENT COMPANY—See BC Partners LLP; *Int'l*, pg. 922
WILLIAMS INSTRUMENT COMPANY—See The Carlyle Group Inc.; *U.S. Public*, pg. 2044
WILLIAMS INSURANCE SERVICES, INC.—See Inszone Insurance Services, LLC; *U.S. Private*, pg. 2097
WILLIAMS INTERACTIVE LLC—See Light & Wonder, Inc.; *U.S. Public*, pg. 1315
WILLIAMS INTERNATIONAL COMPANY LLC—See The Williams Companies, Inc.; *U.S. Public*, pg. 2142
WILLIAMS INTERNATIONAL COMPANY—See The Williams Companies, Inc.; *U.S. Public*, pg. 2142
WILLIAMS INTERNATIONAL; *U.S. Private*, pg. 4526

Company Index

WILLIAMS INTERNATIONAL — CORPORATE AFFILIATIONS

WILLIAMS INTERNATIONAL VENTURES COMPANY—See The Williams Companies, Inc.; *U.S. Public*, pg. 2142

WILLIAMS INVESTMENT COMPANY; *U.S. Private*, pg. 4526

WILLIAMS LABORATORIES SERVICES—See The Williams Companies, Inc.; *U.S. Public*, pg. 2144

WILLIAMS LEA (BEIJING) LIMITED—See Advent International Corporation; *U.S. Private*, pg. 107

WILLIAMS LEA (BRAZIL) ASSESSORIA EM SOLUCOES EMPRESARIAIS LTDA.—See Advent International Corporation; *U.S. Private*, pg. 107

WILLIAMS LEA FRANCE SAS—See Advent International Corporation; *U.S. Private*, pg. 107

WILLIAMS LEA GMBH—See Advent International Corporation; *U.S. Private*, pg. 107

WILLIAMS LEA HOLDINGS PLC—See Advent International Corporation; *U.S. Private*, pg. 107

WILLIAMS LEA INC.—See Advent International Corporation; *U.S. Private*, pg. 107

WILLIAMS LEA INDIA PRIVATE LIMITED—See Advent International Corporation; *U.S. Private*, pg. 107

WILLIAMS LEA IRELAND LIMITED—See Advent International Corporation; *U.S. Private*, pg. 107

WILLIAMS LEA JAPAN LIMITED—See Advent International Corporation; *U.S. Private*, pg. 108

WILLIAMS LEA LIMITED—See Advent International Corporation; *U.S. Private*, pg. 107

WILLIAMS LEA LIMITED—See Advent International Corporation; *U.S. Private*, pg. 108

WILLIAMS LEA PRIVATE LIMITED—See Advent International Corporation; *U.S. Private*, pg. 108

WILLIAMS LEA PTY LIMITED—See Advent International Corporation; *U.S. Private*, pg. 108

WILLIAMS LEA (US ACQUISITIONS) LIMITED—See Advent International Corporation; *U.S. Private*, pg. 107

WILLIAMS LUBRICANTS INC.—See Williams Oil Company Inc.; *U.S. Private*, pg. 4526

WILLIAMS LUMBER INC.; *U.S. Private*, pg. 4526

WILLIAMSMARSTON LLC—See Kelso & Company, L.P.; *U.S. Private*, pg. 2281

WILLIAMS MECHANICAL CORPORATION; *U.S. Private*, pg. 4526

WILLIAMS MEDICAL SUPPLIES LIMITED—See DCC plc; *Int'l*, pg. 1991

WILLIAMS MERCHANT SERVICES CO.—See The Williams Companies, Inc.; *U.S. Public*, pg. 2143

WILLIAMS METALS AND WELDING ALLOYS, INC.; *U.S. Private*, pg. 4526

WILLIAMS MIDSTREAM—See The Williams Companies, Inc.; *U.S. Public*, pg. 2143

WILLIAMS MOBILE BAY PRODUCER SERVICES, L.L.C.—See The Williams Companies, Inc.; *U.S. Public*, pg. 2143

WILLIAMS MULLEN; *U.S. Private*, pg. 4526

WILLIAMS MURRAY HAMM LIMITED—See Writtle Holdings Limited; *Int'l*, pg. 8495

WILLIAMS NORTHWEST PIPELINE—See The Williams Companies, Inc.; *U.S. Public*, pg. 2144

WILLIAMS OF SWANSEA LIMITED—See Cathay Investments Limited; *Int'l*, pg. 1360

WILLIAMS OHIO VALLEY MIDSTREAM LLC—See The Williams Companies, Inc.; *U.S. Public*, pg. 2144

WILLIAMS OIL COMPANY INC.; *U.S. Private*, pg. 4526

WILLIAMSON COUNTY EQUIPMENT CO., INC.; *U.S. Private*, pg. 4527

WILLIAMSON DACAR ASSOCIATES INC.; *U.S. Private*, pg. 4527

WILLIAMSON DAILY NEWS—See HD Media Company, LLC; *U.S. Private*, pg. 1890

WILLIAMSON-DICKIE APPAREL TRADING (SHANGHAI) CO. LTD—See V. F. Corporation; *U.S. Public*, pg. 2269

WILLIAMSON-DICKIE CANADA COMPANY—See V. F. Corporation; *U.S. Public*, pg. 2269

WILLIAMSON-DICKIE EUROPE HOLDINGS LIMITED—See V. F. Corporation; *U.S. Public*, pg. 2270

WILLIAMSON-DICKIE EUROPE LIMITED—See V. F. Corporation; *U.S. Public*, pg. 2269

WILLIAMSON-DICKIE MANUFACTURING COMPANY—See V. F. Corporation; *U.S. Public*, pg. 2269

WILLIAMSON-DICKIE NEDERLAND B.V.—See V. F. Corporation; *U.S. Public*, pg. 2270

WILLIAMSON ENERGY, LLC—See Foresight Energy LP; *U.S. Public*, pg. 867

WILLIAMSON FINANCIAL SERVICES LIMITED—See Williamson Magor & Co. Limited; *Int'l*, pg. 8414

THE WILLIAMSON GROUP, INC.—See Givaudan S.A.; *Int'l*, pg. 2982

WILLIAMSON INTERNATIONAL CORP.—See T.D. Williamson, Inc.; *U.S. Private*, pg. 3912

WILLIAMSON MAGOR & CO. LIMITED; *Int'l*, pg. 8414

WILLIAMSON MOTOR CO., INC; *U.S. Private*, pg. 4527

WILLIAMSON TEA KENYA PLC; *Int'l*, pg. 8414

WILLIAMSON-THERMOFLO—See SPX Technologies, Inc.; *U.S. Public*, pg. 1922

WILLIAMSON TREATMENT CENTER, LLC—See Acadia Healthcare Company, Inc.; *U.S. Public*, pg. 31

WILLIAMS PARTNERS L.P.—See The Williams Companies, Inc.; *U.S. Public*, pg. 2143

WILLIAMS PATENT CRUSHER & PULVERIZER CO., INC.; *U.S. Private*, pg. 4526

WILLIAMS PIPELINE PARTNERS, L.P.—See The Williams Companies, Inc.; *U.S. Public*, pg. 2144

WILLIAMS PIPELINE SERVICES—See The Williams Companies, Inc.; *U.S. Public*, pg. 2144

WILLIAMS PLANT SERVICES, LLC—See The Toronto-Dominion Bank; *Int'l*, pg. 7696

WILLIAMSPORT AUTOMOTIVE, INC.—See Genuine Parts Company; *U.S. Public*, pg. 933

WILLIAMSPORT BARBER AND BEAUTY CORP.—See The Stephan Company; *U.S. Public*, pg. 2132

WILLIAMS PRODUCTION APPALACHIA LLC—See The Williams Companies, Inc.; *U.S. Public*, pg. 2144

WILLIAMS PRODUCTION COMPANY, LLC—See The Williams Companies, Inc.; *U.S. Public*, pg. 2144

WILLIAMS PURITY PIPELINES, LLC—See The Williams Companies, Inc.; *U.S. Public*, pg. 2144

WILLIAMS REFRIGERATION AUSTRALIA PTY. LTD.—See Ali Holding S.r.l; *Int'l*, pg. 322

WILLIAMS REFRIGERATION LTD.—See Ali Holding S.r.l; *Int'l*, pg. 322

WILLIAMS & ROWE CO., INC.; *U.S. Private*, pg. 4525

WILLIAMS ROWLAND ACQUISITION CORP.; *U.S. Public*, pg. 2371

WILLIAMS SAUSAGE COMPANY, INC.—See Tyson Foods, Inc.; *U.S. Public*, pg. 2210

WILLIAMS SCOTSMAN, INC.—See WillScot Mobile Mini Holdings Corp.; *U.S. Public*, pg. 2372

WILLIAMS SCOTSMAN INTERNATIONAL, INC.—See WillScot Mobile Mini Holdings Corp.; *U.S. Public*, pg. 2372

WILLIAMS SCOTSMAN MEXICO S. DE R. L. DE C.V.—See WillScot Mobile Mini Holdings Corp.; *U.S. Public*, pg. 2372

WILLIAMS-SONOMA CANADA, INC.—See Williams-Sonoma, Inc.; *U.S. Public*, pg. 2371

WILLIAMS-SONOMA DELAWARE, LLC—See Williams-Sonoma, Inc.; *U.S. Public*, pg. 2371

WILLIAMS-SONOMA, INC.; *U.S. Public*, pg. 2371

WILLIAMS-SONOMA SINGAPORE PTE. LTD.—See Williams-Sonoma, Inc.; *U.S. Public*, pg. 2371

WILLIAMS-SONOMA VIETNAM LLC—See Williams-Sonoma, Inc.; *U.S. Public*, pg. 2371

WILLIAMS SPECIALTY SERVICES, LLC—See The Toronto-Dominion Bank; *Int'l*, pg. 7696

WILLIAMS STEEL COMPANY INC.; *U.S. Private*, pg. 4526

WILLIAMS STEEL ERECTION CO., INC.—See Williams Industries, Inc.; *U.S. Private*, pg. 4526

WILLIAMS SUPPLY INC.; *U.S. Private*, pg. 4526

WILLIAMS TANK LINES; *U.S. Private*, pg. 4526

WILLIAM STEINEN MANUFACTURING CO.; *U.S. Private*, pg. 4525

WILLIAMSTON HBP SERVICES, LLC—See Quorum Health Corporation; *U.S. Private*, pg. 3331

WILLIAMSTOWN VETERINARY HOSPITAL PTY LTD.—See TPG Capital, L.P.; *U.S. Public*, pg. 2176

WILLIAMS TRACTOR INC.; *U.S. Private*, pg. 4527

WILLIAMS TREW REAL ESTATE SERVICES, LLC—See Berkshire Hathaway Inc.; *U.S. Public*, pg. 306

WILLIAMSVILLE SUBURBAN, LLC—See Safire Rehabilitation of Amherst, LLC; *U.S. Private*, pg. 3525

WILLIAMS VOLKSWAGEN INC.; *U.S. Private*, pg. 4527

WILLIAMS WEALTH MANAGEMENT GROUP, INC.; *U.S. Private*, pg. 4527

WILLIAMS WHITE & COMPANY—See Doerfer Corporation; *U.S. Private*, pg. 1253

WILLIAMS WHITTLE ASSOCIATES, INC.; *U.S. Private*, pg. 4527

WILLIAMS & WILLIAMS, INC.—See GTCR LLC; *U.S. Private*, pg. 1804

WILLIAMS WPC INTERNATIONAL COMPANY—See The Williams Companies, Inc.; *U.S. Public*, pg. 2144

WILLIAM TRACEY LIMITED—See DCC plc; *Int'l*, pg. 1991

WILLIAM T. SPAEDER CO., INC.; *U.S. Private*, pg. 4525

WILLIAM WILSON LTD.—See Ferguson plc; *Int'l*, pg. 2638

WILLIAM W. MEYER & SONS INC.; *U.S. Private*, pg. 4525

WILLICH BETEILIGUNGEN GMBH—See Bilfinger SE; *Int'l*, pg. 1029

WILLIE WASHER MANUFACTURING CO.; *U.S. Private*, pg. 4527

WILLIFE K.K.—See Rengo Co., Ltd.; *Int'l*, pg. 6282

WILLI-FOOD INVESTMENTS LTD.; *Int'l*, pg. 8412

WILLI HAUSTECHNIK AG—See Poenina Holding AG; *Int'l*, pg. 5903

WILLIMANTIC WASTE PAPER CO., INC.—See Casella Waste Systems, Inc.; *U.S. Public*, pg. 446

WILLIMENT TRAVEL GROUP LIMITED—See Helloworld Travel Limited; *Int'l*, pg. 3337

WILLINGHAM WELDING SOLUTIONS, INC.—See Gas Innovations Inc.; *U.S. Private*, pg. 1647

WILLING NEW ENERGY CO., LTD.; *Int'l*, pg. 8414

WILLINGS CO., LTD.; *Int'l*, pg. 8414

WILLIS AB (GOTHENBURG)—See Willis Towers Watson Public Limited Company; *Int'l*, pg. 8417

WILLIS AB—See Willis Towers Watson Public Limited Company; *Int'l*, pg. 8417

WILLIS ADMINISTRATIVE SERVICES CORPORATION—See Willis Towers Watson Public Limited Company; *Int'l*, pg. 8417

WILLIS AERONAUTICAL SERVICES, INC.—See Willis Lease Finance Corporation; *U.S. Public*, pg. 2371

WILLIS AFFINITY SL—See Willis Towers Watson Public Limited Company; *Int'l*, pg. 8415

WILLIS AG—See Willis Towers Watson Public Limited Company; *Int'l*, pg. 8417

WILLIS ALLEN REAL ESTATE COMPANY; *U.S. Private*, pg. 4527

WILLIS A. SMITH CONSTRUCTION, INC.; *U.S. Private*, pg. 4527

WILLIS ASSET MANAGEMENT LIMITED—See Willis Lease Finance Corporation; *U.S. Public*, pg. 2372

WILLIS AUSTRALIA GROUP SERVICES PTY LIMITED—See Willis Towers Watson Public Limited Company; *Int'l*, pg. 8417

WILLIS AUSTRALIA HOLDINGS LIMITED—See Willis Towers Watson Public Limited Company; *Int'l*, pg. 8417

WILLIS AUSTRALIA LIMITED—See Willis Towers Watson Public Limited Company; *Int'l*, pg. 8417

WILLIS (BERMUDA) 2 LIMITED—See Willis Towers Watson Public Limited Company; *Int'l*, pg. 8416

WILLIS (BERMUDA) LIMITED—See Willis Towers Watson Public Limited Company; *Int'l*, pg. 8417

WILLIS B.V.—See Willis Towers Watson Public Limited Company; *Int'l*, pg. 8417

WILLIS CASE HARWOOD MARKETING COMMUNICATIONS INC.; *U.S. Private*, pg. 4527

WILLIS CHILE LIMITADA—See Willis Towers Watson Public Limited Company; *Int'l*, pg. 8415

WILLIS CIS INSURANCE BROKER LLC—See Willis Towers Watson Public Limited Company; *Int'l*, pg. 8417

WILLIS CONSTRUCTION DIVISION—See Willis Towers Watson Public Limited Company; *Int'l*, pg. 8417

WILLIS CORREDORES DE REASEGURO LIMITADA—See Willis Towers Watson Public Limited Company; *Int'l*, pg. 8417

WILLIS CORREDORES DE REASEGUROS S.A.—See Willis Towers Watson Public Limited Company; *Int'l*, pg. 8417

WILLIS CORREDORES DE SEGUROS SA—See Willis Towers Watson Public Limited Company; *Int'l*, pg. 8417

WILLIS CORRETAJE DE REASEGUROS S.A—See Willis Towers Watson Public Limited Company; *Int'l*, pg. 8417

WILLIS CORRETORES DE SEGUROS LTDA—See Willis Towers Watson Public Limited Company; *Int'l*, pg. 8417

WILLIS CORRETORES DE SEGUROS S.A—See Willis Towers Watson Public Limited Company; *Int'l*, pg. 8417

WILLIS FABER DUMAS & ROLAND RISK SERVICES (PVT) LTD.—See Willis Towers Watson Public Limited Company; *Int'l*, pg. 8415

WILLIS GALICIA CORREDURIA DE SEGUROS S.A.—See Willis Towers Watson Public Limited Company; *Int'l*, pg. 8415

WILLIS GLOBAL MARKETS B.V.—See Willis Towers Watson Public Limited Company; *Int'l*, pg. 8417

WILLIS GMBH—See Willis Towers Watson Public Limited Company; *Int'l*, pg. 8417

WILLIS GROUP LIMITED—See Willis Towers Watson Public Limited Company; *Int'l*, pg. 8415

WILLIS GROUP LLC; *U.S. Private*, pg. 4527

WILLIS HOLDING AB—See Willis Towers Watson Public Limited Company; *Int'l*, pg. 8417

WILLIS HONG KONG LIMITED—See Willis Towers Watson Public Limited Company; *Int'l*, pg. 8417

WILLIS INSURANCE AGENCY I/S—See Willis Towers Watson Public Limited Company; *Int'l*, pg. 8419

WILLIS INSURANCE BROKERS (B) SDN BHD—See Willis Towers Watson Public Limited Company; *Int'l*, pg. 8417

WILLIS INSURANCE BROKERS LLC—See Willis Towers Watson Public Limited Company; *Int'l*, pg. 8417

WILLIS INSURANCE SERVICES OF CALIFORNIA, INC.—See Willis Towers Watson Public Limited Company; *Int'l*, pg. 8417

WILLIS INSURANCE SERVICES OF GEORGIA, INC.—See Willis Towers Watson Public Limited Company; *Int'l*, pg. 8417

WILLIS ITALIA S.P.A.—See Willis Towers Watson Public Limited Company; *Int'l*, pg. 8417

WILLIS JAPAN HOLDINGS KK—See Willis Towers Watson Public Limited Company; *Int'l*, pg. 8417

WILLIS JAPAN LIMITED—See Willis Towers Watson Public Limited Company; *Int'l*, pg. 8417

WILLIS JAPAN SERVICES KK—See Willis Towers Watson Public Limited Company; *Int'l*, pg. 8417

WILLIS LEASE FINANCE CORPORATION; *U.S. Public*, pg. 2371

WILLIS LEASE SINGAPORE PTE. LTD.—See Willis Lease Finance Corporation; *U.S. Public*, pg. 2372

WILLIS LIMITED—See Willis Towers Watson Public Limited Company; *Int'l*, pg. 8417

WILLIS MAGYARORSZAG BIZTOSITASI ALKUSZ ES TANACSADO KFT—See Willis Towers Watson Public Limited Company; *Int'l*, pg. 8419

COMPANY NAME INDEX WILLOWDALE NISSAN LTD.

Company Index

WILLIS MANAGEMENT (LABUAN) LIMITED—See Willis Towers Watson Public Limited Company; *Int'l*, pg. 8417
WILLIS MANAGEMENT (STOCKHOLM) AB—See Willis Towers Watson Public Limited Company; *Int'l*, pg. 8417
WILLIS NEDERLAND B.V.—See Willis Towers Watson Public Limited Company; *Int'l*, pg. 8417
WILLIS NETHERLANDS HOLDINGS BV—See Willis Towers Watson Public Limited Company; *Int'l*, pg. 8417
WILLIS NEW ZEALAND LIMITED—See Willis Towers Watson Public Limited Company; *Int'l*, pg. 8417
WILLIS NORTH AMERICA, INC.—See Willis Towers Watson Public Limited Company; *Int'l*, pg. 8417
WILLIS OF ALABAMA, INC.—See Willis Towers Watson Public Limited Company; *Int'l*, pg. 8417
WILLIS OF ARIZONA, INC.—See Willis Towers Watson Public Limited Company; *Int'l*, pg. 8418
WILLIS OF COLORADO, INC.—See Willis Towers Watson Public Limited Company; *Int'l*, pg. 8418
WILLIS OF CONNECTICUT, LLC—See Willis Towers Watson Public Limited Company; *Int'l*, pg. 8418
WILLIS OF FLORIDA, INC.—See Willis Towers Watson Public Limited Company; *Int'l*, pg. 8418
WILLIS OF GREATER KANSAS, INC.—See Willis Towers Watson Public Limited Company; *Int'l*, pg. 8419
WILLIS OF ILLINOIS, INC.—See Willis Towers Watson Public Limited Company; *Int'l*, pg. 8418
WILLIS OF LOUISIANA, INC.—See Willis Towers Watson Public Limited Company; *Int'l*, pg. 8418
WILLIS OF MARYLAND, INC.—See Willis Towers Watson Public Limited Company; *Int'l*, pg. 8418
WILLIS OF MASSACHUSETTS, INC.—See Willis Towers Watson Public Limited Company; *Int'l*, pg. 8418
WILLIS OF MICHIGAN, INC.—See Willis Towers Watson Public Limited Company; *Int'l*, pg. 8418
WILLIS OF MINNESOTA, INC.—See Willis Towers Watson Public Limited Company; *Int'l*, pg. 8418
WILLIS OF NEW HAMPSHIRE, INC.—See Willis Towers Watson Public Limited Company; *Int'l*, pg. 8418
WILLIS OF NEW JERSEY, INC.—See Willis Towers Watson Public Limited Company; *Int'l*, pg. 8418
WILLIS OF NEW YORK, INC.—See Willis Towers Watson Public Limited Company; *Int'l*, pg. 8418
WILLIS OF NORTH CAROLINA, INC.—See Willis Towers Watson Public Limited Company; *Int'l*, pg. 8418
WILLIS OF OHIO, INC.—See Willis Towers Watson Public Limited Company; *Int'l*, pg. 8418
WILLIS OF OKLAHOMA, INC.—See Willis Towers Watson Public Limited Company; *Int'l*, pg. 8418
WILLIS OF OREGON, INC.—See Willis Towers Watson Public Limited Company; *Int'l*, pg. 8418
WILLIS OF PENNSYLVANIA, INC.—See Willis Towers Watson Public Limited Company; *Int'l*, pg. 8418
WILLIS OF SEATTLE, INC.—See Willis Towers Watson Public Limited Company; *Int'l*, pg. 8418
WILLIS OF TENNESSEE, INC.—See Willis Towers Watson Public Limited Company; *Int'l*, pg. 8418
WILLIS OF TEXAS, INC.—See Willis Towers Watson Public Limited Company; *Int'l*, pg. 8418
WILLIS OF VIRGINIA, INC.—See Willis Towers Watson Public Limited Company; *Int'l*, pg. 8418
WILLIS OF WISCONSIN, INC.—See Willis Towers Watson Public Limited Company; *Int'l*, pg. 8418
WILLIS OF WYOMING, INC.—See Willis Towers Watson Public Limited Company; *Int'l*, pg. 8418
WILLIS OIL CO. INC.; *U.S. Private*, pg. 4528
WILLIS OY AB—See Willis Towers Watson Public Limited Company; *Int'l*, pg. 8418
WILLIS PERMIAN MOVERS, INC.; *U.S. Private*, pg. 4528
WILLIS PERSONAL LINES, LLC—See Willis Towers Watson Public Limited Company; *Int'l*, pg. 8417
WILLIS PROCESSING SERVICES (INDIA) PRIVATE LIMITED—See Willis Towers Watson Public Limited Company; *Int'l*, pg. 8418
WILLIS PROGRAMS OF CONNECTICUT, INC.—See Willis Towers Watson Public Limited Company; *Int'l*, pg. 8417
WILLIS RE BERMUDA LIMITED—See Willis Towers Watson Public Limited Company; *Int'l*, pg. 8418
WILLIS RE CANADA INC.—See Willis Towers Watson Public Limited Company; *Int'l*, pg. 8418
WILLIS RE GMBH—See Willis Towers Watson Public Limited Company; *Int'l*, pg. 8418
WILLIS RE GMBH—See Willis Towers Watson Public Limited Company; *Int'l*, pg. 8418
WILLIS RE, INC.—See Arthur J. Gallagher & Co.; *U.S. Public*, pg. 208
WILLIS REINSURANCE AUSTRALIA LIMITED—See Willis Towers Watson Public Limited Company; *Int'l*, pg. 8417
WILLIS RE JAPAN K.K.—See Willis Towers Watson Public Limited Company; *Int'l*, pg. 8418
WILLIS RE LABUAN LIMITED—See Willis Towers Watson Public Limited Company; *Int'l*, pg. 8418
WILLIS RE NORDIC REINSURANCE BROKING (NORWAY) AS—See Willis Towers Watson Public Limited Company; *Int'l*, pg. 8418
WILLIS RE (PTY) LIMITED—See Willis Towers Watson Public Limited Company; *Int'l*, pg. 8418
WILLIS RE S.A.—See Willis Towers Watson Public Limited Company; *Int'l*, pg. 8419
WILLIS RISK SERVICES HOLDINGS (IRELAND) LIMITED—See Willis Towers Watson Public Limited Company; *Int'l*, pg. 8418
WILLIS RISK SERVICES (IRELAND) LIMITED—See Willis Towers Watson Public Limited Company; *Int'l*, pg. 8418
WILLIS SAUDI ARABIA COMPANY LIMITED—See Willis Towers Watson Public Limited Company; *Int'l*, pg. 8418
WILLIS S & C C CORREDURIA DE SEGUROS Y REASEGUROS SA—See Willis Towers Watson Public Limited Company; *Int'l*, pg. 8418
WILLIS SECURITIES, INC.—See Willis Towers Watson Public Limited Company; *Int'l*, pg. 8417
WILLIS SLOVAKIA O.Z.—See Willis Towers Watson Public Limited Company; *Int'l*, pg. 8418
WILLIS & SMITH CAPITAL, LLC; *U.S. Private*, pg. 4527
WILLIS SOUTH AFRICA (PTY) LIMITED—See Willis Towers Watson Public Limited Company; *Int'l*, pg. 8418
WILLIS S.R.O.—See Willis Towers Watson Public Limited Company; *Int'l*, pg. 8419
WILLIS STEIN & PARTNERS, LLC; *U.S. Private*, pg. 4528
WILLIS SUPPLY CO LIMITED; *Int'l*, pg. 8414
WILLIS (TAIWAN) LIMITED—See Willis Towers Watson Public Limited Company; *Int'l*, pg. 8417
WILLISTON FINANCIAL GROUP, LLC; *U.S. Private*, pg. 4528
WILLISTON HOLDING CO., INC.; *U.S. Public*, pg. 2372
WILLIS TOWERS WATSON AGENCIA DE SUSCRIPCION, S.L.—See Willis Towers Watson Public Limited Company; *Int'l*, pg. 8419
WILLIS TOWERS WATSON ARGENTINA S.A.—See Willis Towers Watson Public Limited Company; *Int'l*, pg. 8418
WILLIS TOWERS WATSON A/S (AALBORG)—See Willis Towers Watson Public Limited Company; *Int'l*, pg. 8418
WILLIS TOWERS WATSON A/S (AARHUS)—See Willis Towers Watson Public Limited Company; *Int'l*, pg. 8418
WILLIS TOWERS WATSON ASSEKURANZDIENSTE GMBH—See Willis Towers Watson Public Limited Company; *Int'l*, pg. 8419
WILLIS TOWERS WATSON A/S—See Willis Towers Watson Public Limited Company; *Int'l*, pg. 8418
WILLIS TOWERS WATSON A/S—See Willis Towers Watson Public Limited Company; *Int'l*, pg. 8418
WILLIS TOWERS WATSON A/S—See Willis Towers Watson Public Limited Company; *Int'l*, pg. 8419
WILLIS TOWERS WATSON A/S—See Willis Towers Watson Public Limited Company; *Int'l*, pg. 8419
WILLIS TOWERS WATSON A/S—See Willis Towers Watson Public Limited Company; *Int'l*, pg. 8419
WILLIS TOWERS WATSON COLOMBIA CORREDORES DE SEGUROS S.A.—See Willis Towers Watson Public Limited Company; *Int'l*, pg. 8418
WILLIS TOWERS WATSON CONSULTING (SINGAPORE) PTE. LTD.—See Willis Towers Watson Public Limited Company; *Int'l*, pg. 8419
WILLIS TOWERS WATSON CONSULTORES S.A.—See Willis Towers Watson Public Limited Company; *Int'l*, pg. 8419
WILLIS TOWERS WATSON CONSULTORES S.A.—See Willis Towers Watson Public Limited Company; *Int'l*, pg. 8419
WILLIS TOWERS WATSON CONSULTORES S.A.—See Willis Towers Watson Public Limited Company; *Int'l*, pg. 8419
WILLIS TOWERS WATSON CONSULTORES S.A.—See Willis Towers Watson Public Limited Company; *Int'l*, pg. 8419
WILLIS TOWERS WATSON DANYPMANLYK LIMITED PIRKETI—See Willis Towers Watson Public Limited Company; *Int'l*, pg. 8419
WILLIS TOWERS WATSON D.D—See Willis Towers Watson Public Limited Company; *Int'l*, pg. 8419
WILLIS TOWERS WATSON FORSIKRINGSSERVICE I/S—See Willis Towers Watson Public Limited Company; *Int'l*, pg. 8419
WILLIS TOWERS WATSON GLOBAL BUSINESS SERVICES, INC.—See Willis Towers Watson Public Limited Company; *Int'l*, pg. 8419
WILLIS TOWERS WATSON GMBH—See Willis Towers Watson Public Limited Company; *Int'l*, pg. 8419
WILLIS TOWERS WATSON GREECE INSURANCE BROKERS S.A.—See Willis Towers Watson Public Limited Company; *Int'l*, pg. 8419
WILLIS TOWERS WATSON I/S—See Willis Towers Watson Public Limited Company; *Int'l*, pg. 8419
WILLIS TOWERS WATSON LEBANON SAL—See Willis Towers Watson Public Limited Company; *Int'l*, pg. 8419
WILLIS TOWERS WATSON MANAGEMENT (BERMUDA) LIMITED—See Willis Towers Watson Public Limited Company; *Int'l*, pg. 8419
WILLIS TOWERS WATSON MANAGEMENT (CAYMAN) LIMITED—See Willis Towers Watson Public Limited Company; *Int'l*, pg. 8419
WILLIS TOWERS WATSON MANAGEMENT (DUBLIN) LIMITED—See Willis Towers Watson Public Limited Company; *Int'l*, pg. 8419
WILLIS TOWERS WATSON MANAGEMENT (GIBRALTAR) LIMITED—See Willis Towers Watson Public Limited Company; *Int'l*, pg. 8419
WILLIS TOWERS WATSON MANAGEMENT (GUERNSEY) LIMITED—See Willis Towers Watson Public Limited Company; *Int'l*, pg. 8419
WILLIS TOWERS WATSON MANAGEMENT (ISLE OF MAN) LIMITED—See Willis Towers Watson Public Limited Company; *Int'l*, pg. 8419
WILLIS TOWERS WATSON MANAGEMENT (LUXEMBOURG) SA—See Willis Towers Watson Public Limited Company; *Int'l*, pg. 8419
WILLIS TOWERS WATSON MANAGEMENT (MALTA) LIMITED—See Willis Towers Watson Public Limited Company; *Int'l*, pg. 8419
WILLIS TOWERS WATSON MANAGEMENT (SINGAPORE) PTE. LIMITED—See Willis Towers Watson Public Limited Company; *Int'l*, pg. 8419
WILLIS TOWERS WATSON MANAGEMENT (VERMONT), LIMITED—See Willis Towers Watson Public Limited Company; *Int'l*, pg. 8417
WILLIS TOWERS WATSON NIGERIA LIMITED—See Willis Towers Watson Public Limited Company; *Int'l*, pg. 8419
WILLIS TOWERS WATSON NORTHEAST, INC.—See Willis Towers Watson Public Limited Company; *Int'l*, pg. 8419
WILLIS TOWERS WATSON PENSIONSFONDS AG—See Willis Towers Watson Public Limited Company; *Int'l*, pg. 8419
WILLIS TOWERS WATSON PHILIPPINES, INC.—See Willis Towers Watson Public Limited Company; *Int'l*, pg. 8419
WILLIS TOWERS WATSON POLSKA SPOLKA Z OGRANICZONA ODPOWIEDZIALNOSCIA—See Willis Towers Watson Public Limited Company; *Int'l*, pg. 8419
WILLIS TOWERS WATSON PUBLIC LIMITED COMPANY; *Int'l*, pg. 8414
WILLIS TOWERS WATSON ROMANIA-BROKER DE ASIGURARE REASIGURARE SRL—See Willis Towers Watson Public Limited Company; *Int'l*, pg. 8419
WILLIS TOWERS WATSON SARL—See Willis Towers Watson Public Limited Company; *Int'l*, pg. 8419
WILLIS TOWERS WATSON SECURITIES EUROPE LIMITED—See Willis Towers Watson Public Limited Company; *Int'l*, pg. 8417
WILLIS TOWERS WATSON (SL) LIMITED—See Willis Towers Watson Public Limited Company; *Int'l*, pg. 8410
WILLIS TOWERS WATSON VERSICHERUNGSMAKLER GMBH—See Willis Towers Watson Public Limited Company; *Int'l*, pg. 8419
WILLIS TOWERS WATSON VERSICHERUNGSMAKLER GMBH—See Willis Towers Watson Public Limited Company; *Int'l*, pg. 8419
WILLIS TRUSTSURE LIMITED—See Willis Towers Watson Public Limited Company; *Int'l*, pg. 8418
THE WILLITS NEWS—See Alden Global Capital LLC; *U.S. Private*, pg. 159
WILLKIE FARR & GALLAGHER LLP; *U.S. Private*, pg. 4528
WILLMAR POULTRY COMPANY INC.; *U.S. Private*, pg. 4528
WILLMOTT DIXON CONSTRUCTION LIMITED—See Willmott Dixon Limited; *Int'l*, pg. 8419
WILLMOTT DIXON HOUSING LIMITED—See Willmott Dixon Limited; *Int'l*, pg. 8419
WILLMOTT DIXON INTERIORS LIMITED—See Willmott Dixon Limited; *Int'l*, pg. 8419
WILLMOTT DIXON LIMITED; *Int'l*, pg. 8419
WILLMOTT DIXON PARTNERSHIPS LIMITED—See Willmott Dixon Limited; *Int'l*, pg. 8420
WILLMOTT DIXON REGEN LIMITED—See Willmott Dixon Limited; *Int'l*, pg. 8420
WILLMUT GAS & OIL COMPANY—See Sempra; *U.S. Public*, pg. 1864
WILLOF CHALLENGE, INC.—See Will Group, Inc.; *Int'l*, pg. 8412
WILLOF CONSTRUCTION, INC.—See Will Group, Inc.; *Int'l*, pg. 8412
WILLOF WORK, INC.—See Will Group, Inc.; *Int'l*, pg. 8412
WILLO PRODUCTS COMPANY INC.; *U.S. Private*, pg. 4528
THE WILLOUGHBY ASC, LLC—See KKR & Co. Inc.; *U.S. Public*, pg. 1249
WILLOUGHBY INC.; *U.S. Private*, pg. 4528
WILLOUGHBY'S INC.; *U.S. Private*, pg. 4528
WILLOWBANK CARE HOME CARNOUSTIE—See Balhousie Holdings Limited; *Int'l*, pg. 808
WILLOW BEND MORTGAGE COMPANY; *U.S. Private*, pg. 4528
WILLOW BEND SHOPPING CENTER LIMITED PARTNERSHIP—See Simon Property Group, Inc.; *U.S. Public*, pg. 1882
WILLOW BIOSCIENCES, INC.; *Int'l*, pg. 8420
WILLOWBROOK DIALYSIS CENTER, L.P.—See DaVita Inc.; *U.S. Public*, pg. 644
WILLOW CREEK APARTMENTS INVESTOR, LLC—See RAIT Financial Trust; *U.S. Private*, pg. 3349
WILLOW CREEK SENIOR LIVING, INC.—See The Ensign Group, Inc.; *U.S. Public*, pg. 2070
WILLOWDALE NISSAN LTD.; *Int'l*, pg. 8420

WILLOWDALE NISSAN LTD.

WILLOW GLEN INSURANCE AGENCY, INC.—See Inszone Insurance Services, LLC; *U.S. Private*, pg. 2097
WILLOWGLEN (MALAYSIA) SDN. BHD.—See Willowglen MSC Berhad; *Int'l*, pg. 8420
WILLOWGLEN MSC BERHAD; *Int'l*, pg. 8420
WILLOWGLEN SERVICES PTE. LTD.—See Willowglen MSC Berhad; *Int'l*, pg. 8420
WILLOWGLEN SYSTEMS INC.—See Willowglen MSC Berhad; *Int'l*, pg. 8420
WILLOWGLEN VIETNAM CO., LTD.—See Willowglen MSC Berhad; *Int'l*, pg. 8420
THE WILLOW GROUP, INC.—See Trinity Hunt Management, L.P.; *U.S. Private*, pg. 4235
WILLOW MANOR NURSING HOME, INC.—See Welltower Inc.; *U.S. Public*, pg. 2349
WILLOW MARKETING; *U.S. Private*, pg. 4528
WILLOW PUMPS LIMITED—See Franchise Brands plc; *Int'l*, pg. 2760
WILLOW RIDGE CENTER—See Formation Capital, LLC; *U.S. Private*, pg. 1571
WILLOWS CENTER CONCORD, INC.—See Regency Centers Corporation; *U.S. Public*, pg. 1774
WILLOWTREE, LLC—See TELUS CORPORATION; *Int'l*, pg. 7546
WILLOW VALLEY ASSOCIATES INC.; *U.S. Private*, pg. 4528
WILLOW VALLEY COMMUNITIES; *U.S. Private*, pg. 4529
WILLOWWOOD GLOBAL LLC—See DW Management Services, LLC; *Int'l*, pg. 2236
WILLPLUS HOLDINGS CORPORATION; *Int'l*, pg. 8420
WILLSCOT MOBILE MINI HOLDINGS CORP.; *U.S. Public*, pg. 2372
WILL SEMICONDUCTOR CO., LTD.; *Int'l*, pg. 8412
THE WILLS GROUP, INC.; *U.S. Private*, pg. 4136
WILLS, INC.; *Int'l*, pg. 8420
WILLSKY DEVELOPMENT LTD.—See Thrive Precision Health Inc.; *Int'l*, pg. 7721
WILLSON INTERNATIONAL INC.—See Willson International; *Int'l*, pg. 8420
WILLSON INTERNATIONAL; *Int'l*, pg. 8420
WILLSTAN RACING (IRELAND) LIMITED—See William Hill Plc; *Int'l*, pg. 8413
WILLS TRANSFER LIMITED; *Int'l*, pg. 8420
WILLS TRUCKING INC.—See Total Recovery Group, LLC; *U.S. Private*, pg. 4191
WILLTEC CO., LTD.; *Int'l*, pg. 8420
WILLTECH (PRC) LTD.—See Rapala VMC Oyj; *Int'l*, pg. 6210
WILLTEC MYANMAR CO., LTD.—See Willtec Co., Ltd.; *Int'l*, pg. 8420
WILLTEC VIETNAM CO., LTD.—See Willtec Co., Ltd.; *Int'l*, pg. 8420
WILLY INSTRUMENTOS DE MEDICAO E CONTROLE LTDA—See Nagano Keiki Co., Ltd.; *Int'l*, pg. 5125
WILLYS AB—See Axel Johnson Gruppen AB; *Int'l*, pg. 764
WILLYS HEMMA AB—See Axel Johnson Gruppen AB; *Int'l*, pg. 764
WILMAC BUSINESS EQUIPMENT CO, INC; *U.S. Private*, pg. 4529
WILMAR EDIBLE OILS GMBH—See Wilmar International Limited; *Int'l*, pg. 8421
WILMAR EUROPE HOLDINGS B.V.—See Wilmar International Limited; *Int'l*, pg. 8421
WILMAR INTERNATIONAL LIMITED; *Int'l*, pg. 8420
WILMAR MARKETING SDN BHD—See Wilmar International Limited; *Int'l*, pg. 8421
WILMAR OLEOCHEMICALS (SHANGHAI) CO., LTD—See Wilmar International Limited; *Int'l*, pg. 8421
WILMAR SURFACTANTS—See Wilmar International Limited; *Int'l*, pg. 8421
WILMAR TANK TERMINALS SDN. BHD.—See Wilmar International Limited; *Int'l*, pg. 8421
WILMCOTE HOLDINGS PLC; *Int'l*, pg. 8421
WILMER CUTLER PICKERING HALE & DORR LLP; *U.S. Private*, pg. 4529
WILMES CHEVROLET BUICK, INC.; *U.S. Private*, pg. 4529
WILMES FORD-LINCOLN, INC.; *U.S. Private*, pg. 4529
WILMES SUPERSTORE, INC.; *U.S. Private*, pg. 4529
WILMINGTON ADVOCATE—See Gannett Co., Inc.; *U.S. Public*, pg. 903
WILMINGTON ASC, LLC—See UnitedHealth Group Incorporated; *U.S. Public*, pg. 2253
WILMINGTON BUILDERS SUPPLY COMPANY INC.—See Arlington Coal & Lumber Co. Inc.; *U.S. Private*, pg. 329
WILMINGTON CAPITAL MANAGEMENT INC.; *Int'l*, pg. 8421
WILMINGTON COMPLIANCE WEEK INC.—See Wilmington plc; *Int'l*, pg. 8422
WILMINGTON COUNTRY CLUB; *U.S. Private*, pg. 4529
WILMINGTON FRA INC.—See Wilmington plc; *Int'l*, pg. 8422
WILMINGTON HEALTH ASSOCIATES, PA.; *U.S. Private*, pg. 4529
WILMINGTON HEALTHCARE LIMITED—See Wilmington plc; *Int'l*, pg. 8422
WILMINGTON HEALTHCARE LIMITED—See Wilmington plc; *Int'l*, pg. 8422

WILMINGTON INESE SL—See Wilmington plc; *Int'l*, pg. 8422
WILMINGTON INVESTMENTS INC.—See The Hillman Company; *U.S. Private*, pg. 4053
WILMINGTON MEDICAL SUPPLY, INC.—See ConvaTec Group PLC; *Int'l*, pg. 1786
WILMINGTON PLC; *Int'l*, pg. 8421
WILMINGTON PRODUCTS-USA INC.; *U.S. Private*, pg. 4529
WILMINGTON PUBLISHING & INFORMATION LIMITED—See Wilmington plc; *Int'l*, pg. 8422
WILMINGTON SAVINGS FUND SOCIETY, FEDERAL SAVINGS BANK—See WSFS Financial Corporation; *U.S. Public*, pg. 2384
WILMINGTON SECURITIES INC.—See The Hillman Company; *U.S. Private*, pg. 4053
WILMINGTON STAR-NEWS, INC.—See Gannett Co., Inc.; *U.S. Public*, pg. 906
WILMINGTON SURGERY CENTER, L.P.—See Bain Capital, LP; *U.S. Private*, pg. 447
WILMINGTON TERMINAL RAILROAD, LIMITED PARTNERSHIP—See Brookfield Infrastructure Partners L.P.; *Int'l*, pg. 1193
WILMINGTON TERMINAL RAILROAD, LIMITED PARTNERSHIP—See GIC Pte. Ltd.; *Int'l*, pg. 2967
WILMINGTON TRUST COMPANY—See M&T Bank Corporation; *U.S. Public*, pg. 1351
WILMINGTON TRUST CORPORATION—See M&T Bank Corporation; *U.S. Public*, pg. 1351
WILMORE COAL COMPANY—See Berwind Corporation; *U.S. Private*, pg. 540
WILMORE ELECTRONICS COMPANY; *U.S. Private*, pg. 4529
WILMORITE INC.; *U.S. Private*, pg. 4529
WILMOT-BREEDEN HOLDINGS LIMITED—See Cummins Inc.; *U.S. Public*, pg. 2272
WILMOT MOUNTAIN, INC.—See Vail Resorts, Inc.; *U.S. Public*, pg. 2272
WILMS GMBH; *Int'l*, pg. 8422
THE WILMSLOW HOSPITAL—See HCA Healthcare, Inc.; *U.S. Public*, pg. 990
WILM-TV—See Capitol Broadcasting Company, Inc.; *U.S. Private*, pg. 743
WILO USA LLC; *U.S. Private*, pg. 4529
WILRON PRODUCTS SDN BHD—See Jiankun International Berhad; *Int'l*, pg. 3961
WILSEY BENNETT COMPANY; *U.S. Private*, pg. 4529
WILSEY BENNETT REAL ESTATE DIVISION—See Wilsey Bennett Company; *U.S. Private*, pg. 4529
WILSEY TOOL CO., INC.—See The Jordan Company, L.P.; *U.S. Private*, pg. 4060
WILSHIRE ASSOCIATES EUROPE B.V.—See Wilshire Associates, Inc.; *U.S. Private*, pg. 4529
WILSHIRE ASSOCIATES, INC.; *U.S. Private*, pg. 4529
WILSHIRE AUSTRALIA PTY LIMITED—See Wilshire Associates, Inc.; *U.S. Private*, pg. 4529
WILSHIRE CONNECTION, LLC; *U.S. Private*, pg. 4529
WILSHIRE ENTERPRISES, INC.; *U.S. Private*, pg. 4529
WILSHIRE HOLDINGS I, INC.—See NEWTEKONE, INC.; *U.S. Public*, pg. 1521
WILSHIRE INSURANCE CO. INC.—See MCM Corporation; *U.S. Private*, pg. 2642
WILSON 5 SERVICE CO. INC.; *U.S. Private*, pg. 4530
WILSON AGENCY B.V.—See Caiano AS; *Int'l*, pg. 1252
WILSON AGENCY NORGE AS—See Caiano AS; *Int'l*, pg. 1252
WILSONART ASIA LIMITED—See AICA Kogyo Company, Limited; *Int'l*, pg. 229
WILSONART AUSTRALIA PTY LTD—See AICA Kogyo Company, Limited; *Int'l*, pg. 229
WILSONART ENGINEERED SURFACES—See Clayton, Dubilier & Rice, LLC; *U.S. Private*, pg. 930
WILSONART INTERNATIONAL HOLDINGS LLC—See Clayton, Dubilier & Rice, LLC; *U.S. Private*, pg. 930
WILSONART INTERNATIONAL, INC.—See Clayton, Dubilier & Rice, LLC; *U.S. Private*, pg. 930
WILSONART LLC - BOSTON—See Clayton, Dubilier & Rice, LLC; *U.S. Private*, pg. 930
WILSONART LLC—See Clayton, Dubilier & Rice, LLC; *U.S. Private*, pg. 930
WILSONART LLC - TAMPA—See Clayton, Dubilier & Rice, LLC; *U.S. Private*, pg. 930
WILSONART (SHANGHAI) CO., LTD.—See AICA Kogyo Company, Limited; *Int'l*, pg. 229
WILSONART (THAILAND) COMPANY LIMITED—See AICA Kogyo Company, Limited; *Int'l*, pg. 229
WILSON ASA—See Caiano AS; *Int'l*, pg. 1252
WILSON ASSET MANAGEMENT (INTERNATIONAL) PTY LIMITED—See WAM Capital Limited; *Int'l*, pg. 8337
WILSON ASSOCIATES; *U.S. Private*, pg. 4530
WILSON AUTO GROUP, INC.; *U.S. Private*, pg. 4530
WILSON AUTO GROUP; *U.S. Private*, pg. 4530
WILSON BAKER INC.; *U.S. Private*, pg. 4530
WILSON BANK HOLDING COMPANY; *U.S. Public*, pg. 2372
WILSON BANK & TRUST—See Wilson Bank Holding Company; *U.S. Public*, pg. 2372
WILSON BATES APPLIANCE STORES; *U.S. Private*, pg. 4530

CORPORATE AFFILIATIONS

WILSON BAYLY HOLMES-OVCON LIMITED; *Int'l*, pg. 8422
WILSON BOWDEN DEVELOPMENTS LTD.—See Barratt Developments PLC; *Int'l*, pg. 868
WILSON BRAZIL—See ANTA Sports Products Limited; *Int'l*, pg. 481
WILSON & CO. (MOTOR SALES) LIMITED—See General Motors Company; *U.S. Public*, pg. 928
WILSON & COMPANY, INC.; *U.S. Private*, pg. 4529
WILSON & COMPANY, INC.; *U.S. Private*, pg. 4529
THE WILSON COMPANY S. DE R.L. DE C.V.—See Wilson Tool International Inc.; *U.S. Private*, pg. 4531
THE WILSON COMPANY; *U.S. Private*, pg. 4136
WILSON COMPANY; *U.S. Private*, pg. 4530
WILSON CONSTRUCTION CO., INC.; *U.S. Private*, pg. 4530
WILSON CONSTRUCTION COMPANY INC.; *U.S. Private*, pg. 4530
WILSON CONSTRUCTION COMPANY—See The Wilson Holding Company; *U.S. Private*, pg. 4137
WILSON COUNTY AUTOMOTIVE DEALER GROUP; *U.S. Private*, pg. 4530
WILSON CREEK ENERGY, LLC—See Quintana Capital Group, L.P.; *U.S. Private*, pg. 3328
WILSON CREWING AGENCY LTD.—See Caiano AS; *Int'l*, pg. 1252
WILSON CREWING AGENCY ODESSA LTD.—See Caiano AS; *Int'l*, pg. 1252
WILSON DANIELS WHOLESALE LLC; *U.S. Private*, pg. 4530
WILSON-DAVIS & COMPANY; *U.S. Private*, pg. 4531
WILSON ELECTRIC SERVICES CORP.; *U.S. Private*, pg. 4530
WILSON ELSER MOSKOWITZ EDELMAN & DICKER; *U.S. Private*, pg. 4530
WILSON EQUIPMENT COMPANY INC.; *U.S. Private*, pg. 4530
WILSON EQUIPMENT LIMITED; *Int'l*, pg. 8423
WILSON EUROCARRIERS AS—See Caiano AS; *Int'l*, pg. 1252
WILSON FERTILIZER & GRAIN INC.; *U.S. Private*, pg. 4530
WILSON FINANCIAL GROUP, INC.—See Service Corporation International; *U.S. Public*, pg. 1871
WILSON-FINLEY COMPANY; *U.S. Private*, pg. 4531
WILSON FRANCE S.A.R.L.—See ANTA Sports Products Limited; *Int'l*, pg. 481
WILSON FUNERAL HOME, INC.—See Service Corporation International; *U.S. Public*, pg. 1871
WILSON GREGORY AGENCY INC.—See Arch Capital Group Ltd.; *Int'l*, pg. 547
WILSON GROUP HOLDINGS LIMITED.—See WW Holding Inc; *Int'l*, pg. 8517
WILSON GROUP HOLDINGS (SAMOA) LIMITED—See WW Holding Inc; *Int'l*, pg. 8517
THE WILSON GROUP KW23, LLC; *U.S. Public*, pg. 4136
WILSON GROUP LTD.; *U.S. Private*, pg. 4530
WILSON HARTNELL PUBLIC RELATIONS—See WPP plc; *Int'l*, pg. 8490
WILSON H. FLOCK INSURANCE, INC.—See GTCR LLC; *U.S. Private*, pg. 1804
THE WILSON HOLDING COMPANY; *U.S. Private*, pg. 4136
WILSON HOLDINGS, INC.—See Service Corporation International; *U.S. Public*, pg. 1871
WILSON HOTEL MANAGEMENT COMPANY, INC.—See Kemmons Wilson, Inc.; *U.S. Private*, pg. 2281
WILSON HTM CORPORATE FINANCE LIMITED—See Pinnacle Investment Management Group Limited; *Int'l*, pg. 5870
WILSON HTM LTD—See Pinnacle Investment Management Group Limited; *Int'l*, pg. 5870
WILSON HTM SERVICES PTY LTD.—See Pinnacle Investment Management Group Limited; *Int'l*, pg. 5870
WILSON HUMAN CAPITAL GROUP, LLC; *U.S. Private*, pg. 4530
WILSON-HURD MANUFACTURING CO., INC.—See Nelson-Miller, Inc.; *U.S. Private*, pg. 2884
WILSON INDUSTRIAL SALES CO.; *U.S. Private*, pg. 4531
WILSON INSULATION COMPANY, LLC—See Installed Building Products, Inc.; *U.S. Public*, pg. 1134
WILSON INTERNATIONAL IND. CO., LTD.—See WW Holding Inc; *Int'l*, pg. 8517
WILSON IRON WORKS INC.; *U.S. Private*, pg. 4531
WILSON IRON WORKS INC.—See Wilson Iron Works Inc.; *U.S. Private*, pg. 4531
WILSON IRRIGATION & ORCHARD SUPPLY, INC.—See Clearview Capital, LLC; *U.S. Private*, pg. 939
WILSON, KEMP & ASSOCIATES, INC.—See Comerica Incorporated; *U.S. Public*, pg. 542
WILSON & KRATZER MORTUARIES INC.—See Carriage Services, Inc.; *U.S. Public*, pg. 440
WILSON LEARNING ANDINA Y RIO DE LA PLATA S.A.—See WILSON LEARNING WORLDWIDE INC.; *Int'l*, pg. 8423
WILSON LEARNING AUSTRALIA PTY LTD—See WILSON LEARNING WORLDWIDE INC.; *Int'l*, pg. 8423

COMPANY NAME INDEX

W INC.

WILSON LEARNING CHINA LIMITED—See WILSON LEARNING WORLDWIDE INC.; *Int'l*, pg. 8423
WILSON LEARNING CORPORATION—See WILSON LEARNING WORLDWIDE INC.; *Int'l*, pg. 8423
WILSON LEARNING EUROPA LIMITED.—See WILSON LEARNING WORLDWIDE INC.; *Int'l*, pg. 8423
WILSON LEARNING FRANCE SAS—See WILSON LEARNING WORLDWIDE INC.; *Int'l*, pg. 8423
WILSON LEARNING FZ LLC—See WILSON LEARNING WORLDWIDE INC.; *Int'l*, pg. 8423
WILSON LEARNING INDIA PVT LTD.—See WILSON LEARNING WORLDWIDE INC.; *Int'l*, pg. 8423
WILSON LEARNING SA (PTY) LTD—See WILSON LEARNING WORLDWIDE INC.; *Int'l*, pg. 8423
WILSON LEARNING SEM LTD.—See WILSON LEARNING WORLDWIDE INC.; *Int'l*, pg. 8423
WILSON LEARNING SINGAPORE PTE LTD—See WILSON LEARNING WORLDWIDE INC.; *Int'l*, pg. 8423
WILSON LEARNING WORLDWIDE INC.; *Int'l*, pg. 8423
WILSON LOGISTICS, INC.; *U.S. Private*, pg. 4531
WILSON LUMBER COMPANY INC.; *U.S. Private*, pg. 4531
WILSON MACHINE KNIFE CO., INC.—See Hyde Manufacturing Company; *U.S. Private*, pg. 2016
WILSON MANAGEMENT AS—See Caiano AS; *Int'l*, pg. 1252
WILSON MANAGEMENT COMPANY—See The Wilson Holding Company; *U.S. Private*, pg. 4137
WILSON MARINE CORPORATION; *U.S. Private*, pg. 4531
WILSON M. BECK INSURANCE SERVICE INC.; *Int'l*, pg. 8423
WILSON M. BECK INSURANCE SERVICES (ALBERTA) INC—See Wilson M. Beck Insurance Service Inc.; *Int'l*, pg. 8423
WILSON-MCSHANE CORP.; *U.S. Private*, pg. 4531
WILSONMILLER, INC.—See Stantec Inc.; *Int'l*, pg. 7172
WILSON MINING SERVICES PTY LIMITED—See Metarock Group Limited; *Int'l*, pg. 4851
WILSON MOTOR COMPANY; *U.S. Private*, pg. 4531
WILSON & MUIR BANCORP INC - MORTGAGE DIVISION—See Wilson & Muir Bancorp Inc; *U.S. Private*, pg. 4530
WILSON & MUIR BANCORP INC; *U.S. Private*, pg. 4530
WILSON & MUIR BANK & TRUST COMPANY—See Wilson & Muir Bancorp Inc; *U.S. Private*, pg. 4530
WILSON & MUIR BANK & TRUST CO—See Wilson & Muir Bancorp Inc; *U.S. Private*, pg. 4530
WILSON MURMANSK LTD.—See Caiano AS; *Int'l*, pg. 1252
WILSON NIBLETT; *Int'l*, pg. 8423
WILSON NRL TRANSPORT GMBH—See Caiano AS; *Int'l*, pg. 1252
WILSON OFFICE INTERIORS LLC—See HNI Corporation; *U.S. Public*, pg. 1043
WILSON OIL, INC.; *U.S. Private*, pg. 4531
WILSON PERKINS ALLEN OPINION RESEARCH (WPA); *U.S. Private*, pg. 4531
WILSON PLYWOOD & DOOR, INC.; *U.S. Private*, pg. 4531
WILSON RESORT MANAGEMENT CORP.—See Kemmons Wilson, Inc.; *U.S. Private*, pg. 2281
WILSONS FUEL COMPANY LIMITED; *Int'l*, pg. 8423
WILSON SHIP MANAGEMENT AS—See Caiano AS; *Int'l*, pg. 1252
WILSON SONS AGENCIA MARITIMA LTD.—See Ocean Wilsons Holdings Limited; *Int'l*, pg. 5517
WILSON SONSINI GOODRICH & ROSATI; *U.S. Private*, pg. 4531
WILSON SONS LTD.; *Int'l*, pg. 8423
WILSON SONS S.A., COMERCIO, INDUSTRIA, E AGENCIA DE NAVEGACAO LTDA.—See Ocean Wilsons Holdings Limited; *Int'l*, pg. 5517
WILSON'S PIPE FABRICATION PTY. LTD.—See Duratec Limited; *Int'l*, pg. 2228
WILSON SPORTING GOODS CO. DE MEXICO—See ANTA Sports Products Limited; *Int'l*, pg. 481
WILSON SPORTING GOODS COMPANY KAOHSIUNG BRANCH—See ANTA Sports Products Limited; *Int'l*, pg. 481
WILSON SPORTING GOODS CO.—See ANTA Sports Products Limited; *Int'l*, pg. 481
WILSON SPORTING GOODS CO.—See ANTA Sports Products Limited; *Int'l*, pg. 481
WILSON SPORTS EQUIPMENT CANADA SHIELDS—See ANTA Sports Products Limited; *Int'l*, pg. 481
WILSONS TM LIMITED—See AVADA Group Limited; *Int'l*, pg. 734
WILSON STRATEGIC COMMUNICATIONS, INC.—See Health Management Associates, Inc.; *U.S. Private*, pg. 1894
WILSON STRUCTURAL CONSULTANTS, INC.; *U.S. Private*, pg. 4531
WILSON TEXTILE LIMITED—See Li & Fung Limited; *Int'l*, pg. 4481
WILSON TOOL ARGENTINA, S.R.L.—See Wilson Tool International Inc.; *U.S. Private*, pg. 4531
WILSON TOOL CANADA INC.—See Wilson Tool International Inc.; *U.S. Private*, pg. 4531
WILSON TOOL INTERNATIONAL A/S—See Wilson Tool International Inc.; *U.S. Private*, pg. 4531
WILSON TOOL INTERNATIONAL INC.; *U.S. Private*, pg. 4531
WILSON TRAILER COMPANY INC.; *U.S. Private*, pg. 4531
WILSON TRUCKING CORPORATION; *U.S. Private*, pg. 4531
WILSON TUPHOLME LTD.—See S&U PLC; *Int'l*, pg. 6446
WILSON UTILITY EQUIPMENT CO.—See Wilson Construction Co., Inc.; *U.S. Private*, pg. 4530
WILSON VALE CATERING MANAGEMENT LIMITED—See Aramark; *U.S. Public*, pg. 178
WILSONVILLE JUST STORE IT, LLC—See National Storage Affiliates Trust; *U.S. Public*, pg. 1498
WILSONVILLE THRIFTWAY; *U.S. Private*, pg. 4532
WILSON, WASHBURN & FORSTER, INC.—See Genstar Capital, LLC; *U.S. Private*, pg. 1675
WILSON WAY TIRE COMPANY INC.; *U.S. Private*, pg. 4531
WILSON WOLF CORPORATION—See Level Biotechnology, Inc.; *Int'l*, pg. 4470
WILSQUARE CAPITAL LLC; *U.S. Private*, pg. 4532
WILTEC INDUSTRIES LIMITED—See CCT Fortis Holdings Limited; *Int'l*, pg. 1370
WILTIC CHEMICAL MANUFACTURING—See Genova Products, Inc.; *U.S. Private*, pg. 1673
WILTON ARMETALE INC.—See Lifetime Brands, Inc.; *U.S. Public*, pg. 1313
WILTON INDUSTRIES, INC.—See GTCR LLC; *U.S. Private*, pg. 1806
WILTON MALL, LLC—See The Macerich Company; *U.S. Public*, pg. 2111
WILTON RE HOLDINGS LTD.—See Vestar Capital Partners, LLC; *U.S. Private*, pg. 4372
WILTON RESOURCES CORPORATION LIMITED; *Int'l*, pg. 8423
WILTON RESOURCES INC.; *Int'l*, pg. 8423
WILTON SURGERY CENTER, LLC—See KKR & Co. Inc.; *U.S. Public*, pg. 1249
WILTROM CO., LTD.; *Int'l*, pg. 8423
WILTS AND DORSET BUS COMPANY LTD.—See GLOBALVIA Inversiones, S.A.U.; *Int'l*, pg. 3005
WILTS AND DORSET BUS COMPANY LTD.—See Kinetic Group Services Pty Ltd.; *Int'l*, pg. 4107
WILTSHIRE & GRANNIS LLP; *U.S. Private*, pg. 4532
WILUNA MINING CORPORATION LIMITED; *Int'l*, pg. 8423
WIMAN CORPORATION—See RTP Company; *U.S. Private*, pg. 3498
WIMAX ONLINE S.L.—See Orange S.A.; *Int'l*, pg. 5609
WIMBERLY ALLISON TONG & GOO INC.; *U.S. Private*, pg. 4532
WIMBERLY CLAIM SERVICES—See RYZE Claim Solutions LLC; *U.S. Private*, pg. 3511
WIMBLE MANUFACTURING BELGIUM BVBA—See Kellanova; *U.S. Public*, pg. 1218
THE WIMBLEY GROUP, INC.; *U.S. Private*, pg. 4137
WIMCO CORP.; *U.S. Private*, pg. 4532
WIMCO LIMITED—See ITC Limited; *Int'l*, pg. 3832
WIMEX AGRARPRODUKTE IMPORT UND EXPORT GMBH; *Int'l*, pg. 8424
WIMI HOLOGRAM CLOUD INC.; *Int'l*, pg. 8424
WIMM-BILL-DANN JSC—See PepsiCo, Inc.; *U.S. Public*, pg. 1672
WIMMERA MAIL TIMES PTY LTD—See Rural Press Pty Limited; *Int'l*, pg. 6429
WIMMER BROTHERS REALTY INC.; *U.S. Private*, pg. 4532
WIMMERS MEAT PRODUCTS INC.—See Land O'Frost, Inc.; *U.S. Private*, pg. 2383
WIMMER SOLUTIONS; *U.S. Private*, pg. 4532
WIMMER TRANSPORTDIENST GMBH—See Hoyer GmbH; *Int'l*, pg. 3499
WIMPEY OVERSEAS HOLDINGS LIMITED—See Taylor Wimpey plc; *Int'l*, pg. 7478
WIM PLAST LTD.; *Int'l*, pg. 8423
WIMSATT BUILDING MATERIALS CORPORATION; *U.S. Private*, pg. 4532
WINAB VIKVAGGAR AB—See Indutrade AB; *Int'l*, pg. 3682
WIN AEROSOL GMBH & CO. KG—See DALLI-WERKE GmbH & Co. KG; *Int'l*, pg. 1954
WINALL HI-TECH SEED CO., LTD.; *Int'l*, pg. 8424
THE WINATIC CORP.—See Electro Technik Industries; *U.S. Private*, pg. 1354
WINBCO TANK COMPANY; *U.S. Private*, pg. 4533
WINBEL CO., LTD.—See Harmonic Drive Systems Inc.; *Int'l*, pg. 3277
WINBO-DONGJIAN AUTOMOTIVE TECHNOLOGY CO., LTD.; *Int'l*, pg. 8424
WINBOND ELECTRONICS CORPORATION AMERICA—See Winbond Electronics Corporation; *Int'l*, pg. 8424
WINBOND ELECTRONICS CORPORATION JAPAN—See Winbond Electronics Corporation; *Int'l*, pg. 8424
WINBOND ELECTRONICS CORPORATION; *Int'l*, pg. 8424
WINBOND ELECTRONICS (H.K.) LTD.—See Winbond Electronics Corporation; *Int'l*, pg. 8424
WINBON SCHOELLER NEW MATERIALS CO., LTD.—See Felix Schoeller Holding GmbH & Co. KG; *Int'l*, pg. 2633
WINBRO GROUP LTD.; *U.S. Private*, pg. 4533
WINBROOK INC.; *U.S. Private*, pg. 4533
WINCAL BIOPHARM, INC.—See PharmAbcine Inc.; *Int'l*, pg. 5840
WINCAN DEUTSCHLAND GMBH—See IDEX Corp; *U.S. Public*, pg. 1092
WINCANTON GROUP LIMITED—See GXO Logistics, Inc.; *U.S. Public*, pg. 976
WINCANTON HOLDINGS LIMITED—See GXO Logistics, Inc.; *U.S. Public*, pg. 976
WINCANTON INTERNATIONAL LIMITED—See GXO Logistics, Inc.; *U.S. Public*, pg. 976
WINCANTON PLC—See GXO Logistics, Inc.; *U.S. Public*, pg. 976
WINCANTON UK LIMITED—See GXO Logistics, Inc.; *U.S. Public*, pg. 976
WINCARE VERSICHERUNGEN—See Sanitas Krankenversicherung; *Int'l*, pg. 6540
WINCASA AG—See Implenia AG; *Int'l*, pg. 3636
WINCA TRADING LIMITED—See Texwinca Holdings Limited; *Int'l*, pg. 7584
WINC AUSTRALIA PTY. LIMITED—See Platinum Equity, LLC; *U.S. Private*, pg. 3210
WINCERE, INC.—See Indegene Lifesystems Pvt. Ltd.; *Int'l*, pg. 3649
WIN CHANCE FOODS CO., LTD.; *Int'l*, pg. 8424
WINCHELL'S DONUT HOUSES OPERATING CO., LP—See Yum Yum Donut Shops, Inc.; *U.S. Private*, pg. 4595
WIN CHEOUNG INTERNATIONAL INDUSTRIES LIMITED—See Xiwang Special Steel Company Limited; *Int'l*, pg. 8535
WINCHESTER AUSTRALIA LIMITED—See Olin Corporation; *U.S. Public*, pg. 1570
WINCHESTER CAPITAL INVESTMENT MANAGEMENT CORPORATION; *U.S. Private*, pg. 4533
WINCHESTER CAPITAL PARTNERS, LLC—See Winchester Capital Investment Management Corporation; *U.S. Private*, pg. 4533
WINCHESTER CARPET & RUG, LLC—See L2 Capital Partners; *U.S. Private*, pg. 2367
WINCHESTER ENDOSCOPY, LLC—See UnitedHealth Group Incorporated; *U.S. Public*, pg. 2253
WINCHESTER ENERGY LIMITED; *Int'l*, pg. 8424
WINCHESTER ENERGY USA HOLDING INC.—See Winchester Energy Limited; *Int'l*, pg. 8424
WINCHESTER EQUIPMENT CO.; *U.S. Private*, pg. 4533
WINCHESTER HOMES, INC.—See Tri Pointe Homes, Inc.; *U.S. Public*, pg. 2188
WINCHESTER INTERCONNECT CORPORATION—See Aptiv PLC; *Int'l*, pg. 526
WINCHESTER INTERCONNECT RF CORPORATION—See Aptiv PLC; *Int'l*, pg. 526
WINCHESTER OPTICAL COMPANY; *U.S. Private*, pg. 4533
WINCHESTER SAVINGS BANK; *U.S. Private*, pg. 4533
WINCHESTER STAR—See Gannett Co., Inc.; *U.S. Public*, pg. 903
WINCHESTER & WESTERN RAILROAD COMPANY—See The Broe Companies, Inc.; *U.S. Private*, pg. 4001
WINCHESTER WOODWORKING CORP.; *U.S. Private*, pg. 4533
WINCHESTO FINANCE COMPANY LIMITED—See CK Hutchison Holdings Limited; *Int'l*, pg. 1638
WIN CHEVROLET, INC.; *U.S. Private*, pg. 4532
WINC, INC.; *U.S. Public*, pg. 2372
WINCO FOODS, INC.; *U.S. Private*, pg. 4533
WINCO FOODS—See WinCo Foods, Inc.; *U.S. Private*, pg. 4533
WINCO GENERATORS; *U.S. Private*, pg. 4533
WINCO, INC.—See Quanta Services, Inc.; *U.S. Public*, pg. 1753
WINCO, INC.; *U.S. Private*, pg. 4533
WINCO INC—See Winco Generators; *U.S. Private*, pg. 4533
WINCONCEPT AG—See CSL Limited; *Int'l*, pg. 1867
WIN-CON ENTERPRISES INC.; *U.S. Private*, pg. 4532
WINCO PRECISION ENGINEERING (MELAKA) SDN. BHD.—See Luster Industries Bhd.; *Int'l*, pg. 4587
WINCOR NIXDORF INTERNATIONAL GMBH—See Diebold Nixdorf, Inc.; *U.S. Public*, pg. 661
WINCOR NIXDORF LTD.—See Diebold Nixdorf, Inc.; *U.S. Public*, pg. 660
WINCOR NIXDORF N.V.—See Diebold Nixdorf, Inc.; *U.S. Public*, pg. 660
WINCORP INTERNATIONAL INC.—See Jamaica Broilers Group Limited; *Int'l*, pg. 3874
WIN COSMETIC GMBH & CO. KG—See DALLI-WERKE GmbH & Co. KG; *Int'l*, pg. 1954
WINCOVE PRIVATE HOLDINGS, LP; *U.S. Private*, pg. 4533
WINCRAFT INCORPORATED—See Kynetic LLC; *U.S. Private*, pg. 2360
W INC.; *U.S. Private*, pg. 4417

W INC.

CORPORATE AFFILIATIONS

WINCUT MACHINING SOLUTIONS INDIA PVT. LTD.—See PLANSEE Holding AG; *Int'l*, pg. 5890
WINDA OPTO-ELECTRONIC CO., LTD.—See Yem Chio Co., Ltd.; *Int'l*, pg. 8577
WINDAR PHOTONICS PLC; *Int'l*, pg. 8425
WINDBER HOSPITAL INC; *U.S. Private*, pg. 4537
WIND CAPITAL GROUP, LLC—See NTR Plc; *Int'l*, pg. 5484
WINDCAT WORKBOATS B.V.—See AIP, LLC; *U.S. Private*, pg. 137
WINDCAT WORKBOATS INTERNATIONAL LIMITED—See AIP, LLC; *U.S. Private*, pg. 137
WINDCHILL HOLDINGS LTD; *Int'l*, pg. 8425
WIND COMPOSITE SERVICE GROUP, LLC; *U.S. Private*, pg. 4533
WINDELN.DE SE; *Int'l*, pg. 8425
WINDEMERE AT SYCAMORE HIGHLANDS, LLC—See UDR, Inc.; *U.S. Public*, pg. 2218
WINDEMULLER ELECTRIC INC.; *U.S. Private*, pg. 4537
WINDEMULLER TECHNICAL SERVICES, INC.; *U.S. Private*, pg. 4537
WIND ENERGY TRADING WET AG—See BKW AG; *Int'l*, pg. 1056
WINDEQ TECHNICAL CENTRE LLC—See Komax Holding AG; *Int'l*, pg. 4241
WINDER HMA, LLC—See Northeast Georgia Health System Inc.; *U.S. Private*, pg. 2950
WINDERMERE REAL ESTATE SERVICES COMPANY; *U.S. Private*, pg. 4537
WINDERMERE UTILITY COMPANY—See JPMorgan Chase & Co.; *U.S. Public*, pg. 1207
WINDERMERE UTILITY COMPANY—See Water Asset Management, LLC; *U.S. Private*, pg. 4451
WINDES, INC.; *U.S. Private*, pg. 4537
WINDFALL GEOTEK INC.; *Int'l*, pg. 8425
WINDFALL INVESTORS, LLC—See Limoneira Company; *U.S. Public*, pg. 1316
WINDFARM SEEHAUSEN GMBH—See Infigen Energy Limited; *Int'l*, pg. 3685
WINDFIRE CAPITAL CORP.; *Int'l*, pg. 8425
WINDGATE ACQUISITION LTD.; *U.S. Private*, pg. 4537
WINDGEN ENERGY, INC.; *U.S. Public*, pg. 2372
WINDHAGER HANDELSGESMBH—See Gale Pacific Limited; *Int'l*, pg. 2872
WINDHAM INJURY MANAGEMENT GROUP, INC.; *U.S. Private*, pg. 4537
WINDHAM & MCDONALD CONSTRUCTION., INC.; *U.S. Private*, pg. 4537
WIND HELLAS TELECOMMUNICATIONS S.A.—See VEON Ltd.; *Int'l*, pg. 8164
WINDHOFF BAHN- UND ANLAGENTECHNIK GMBH—See Georgsmarienhutte Holding GmbH; *Int'l*, pg. 2941
WINDHURST SAS; *Int'l*, pg. 8425
WINDISH RV CENTER INC.; *U.S. Private*, pg. 4537
WINDJAMMER CAPITAL INVESTORS, LLC; *U.S. Private*, pg. 4537
WINDJAMMER LANDING VILLA BEACH RESORT & SPA—See EllisDon Corporation; *Int'l*, pg. 2367
WINDKRAFT HOCHHEIM GMBH & CO. KG—See RWE AG; *Int'l*, pg. 6436
WINDLAB LIMITED—See Tattarang Pty. Ltd.; *Int'l*, pg. 7474
WINDLAS BIOTECH LIMITED; *Int'l*, pg. 8425
WIND LION PLAZA CORPORATION—See Taiwan Land Development Corporation; *Int'l*, pg. 7421
WINDMILL ENGINEERING COMPANY LIMITED—See WINDMILL Group Limited; *Int'l*, pg. 8425
WINDMILL FARMS—See AGF Management Limited; *Int'l*, pg. 207
WINDMILL FARMS—See Instar Group Inc.; *Int'l*, pg. 3723
WINDMILL GROUP LIMITED; *Int'l*, pg. 8425
WINDMILL INTERNATIONAL, INC.; *U.S. Private*, pg. 4538
WIND MILL WOODWORKING, INC.—See Amerhart Limited; *U.S. Private*, pg. 219
WINDMOELLER & HOELSCHER AG—See Windmoeller & Hoelscher KG; *Int'l*, pg. 8426
WINDMOELLER & HOELSCHER ASIA CO. (TAIWAN)—See Windmoeller & Hoelscher KG; *Int'l*, pg. 8426
WINDMOELLER & HOELSCHER ASIA PACIFIC CO., LTD.—See Windmoeller & Hoelscher KG; *Int'l*, pg. 8426
WINDMOELLER & HOELSCHER ASIA—See Windmoeller & Hoelscher KG; *Int'l*, pg. 8426
WINDMOELLER & HOELSCHER ASIA—See Windmoeller & Hoelscher KG; *Int'l*, pg. 8426
WINDMOELLER & HOELSCHER AUSTRALASIA PTY. LTD.—See Windmoeller & Hoelscher KG; *Int'l*, pg. 8426
WINDMOELLER & HOELSCHER BENELUX B.V.—See Windmoeller & Hoelscher KG; *Int'l*, pg. 8426
WINDMOELLER & HOELSCHER CORP.—See Windmoeller & Hoelscher KG; *Int'l*, pg. 8426
WINDMOELLER & HOELSCHER DIS TICARET A.S.—See Windmoeller & Hoelscher KG; *Int'l*, pg. 8426
WINDMOELLER & HOELSCHER DO BRASIL LTDA.—See Windmoeller & Hoelscher KG; *Int'l*, pg. 8426
WINDMOELLER & HOELSCHER INDIA PVT. LTD.—See Windmoeller & Hoelscher KG; *Int'l*, pg. 8426
WINDMOELLER & HOELSCHER ITALIANA S.R.L.—See Windmoeller & Hoelscher KG; *Int'l*, pg. 8426
WINDMOELLER & HOELSCHER KG; *Int'l*, pg. 8425
WINDMOELLER & HOELSCHER MACHINERY (TAICANG) CO., LTD.—See Windmoeller & Hoelscher KG; *Int'l*, pg. 8426
WINDMOELLER & HOELSCHER VIETNAM COMPANY LIMITED—See Windmoeller & Hoelscher KG; *Int'l*, pg. 8426
WINDMOLLER & HOLSCHER AMERICA LATINA—See Windmoeller & Hoelscher KG; *Int'l*, pg. 8426
WINDMOLLER & HOLSCHER AUSTRIA CEE GMBH & CO. KG—See Windmoeller & Hoelscher KG; *Int'l*, pg. 8426
WINDMOLLER & HOLSCHER DIS. TICARET A.S.—See Windmoeller & Hoelscher KG; *Int'l*, pg. 8426
WINDMOLLER & HOLSCHER GMBH—See Windmoeller & Hoelscher KG; *Int'l*, pg. 8426
WINDMOLLER & HOLSCHER INDIA PVT. LTD.—See Windmoeller & Hoelscher KG; *Int'l*, pg. 8426
WINDMOLLER & HOLSCHER KG (POLEN)—See Windmoeller & Hoelscher KG; *Int'l*, pg. 8426
WINDMOLLER & HOLSCHER KG—See Windmoeller & Hoelscher KG; *Int'l*, pg. 8426
WINDMOLLER & HOLSCHER MACHINERY GMBH—See Windmoeller & Hoelscher KG; *Int'l*, pg. 8426
WINDMOLLER & HOLSCHER MACHINERY K.S.—See Windmoeller & Hoelscher KG; *Int'l*, pg. 8426
WINDMOLLER & HOLSCHER POLSKA SP.Z O.O—See Windmoeller & Hoelscher KG; *Int'l*, pg. 8426
WINDON ENERGY GROUP AB; *Int'l*, pg. 8426
WINDOOR DANMARK A/S—See Nordstjernan AB; *Int'l*, pg. 5426
WINDOOR, INC.—See Koch Industries, Inc.; *U.S. Private*, pg. 2333
WINDOOR NORGE AS—See Nordstjernan AB; *Int'l*, pg. 5426
WINDOOR SVERIGE AB—See Nordstjernan AB; *Int'l*, pg. 5426
WINDOOR UK LTD—See Nordstjernan AB; *Int'l*, pg. 5426
WINDOW AND DOOR FACTORY INC.; *U.S. Private*, pg. 4538
WINDOW AUTOMATION INDUSTRY SRL—See Somfy SA; *Int'l*, pg. 7086
WINDOW BOOK, INC.—See Platinum Equity, LLC; *U.S. Private*, pg. 3202
WINDOW DOCTORS, INC.—See ACON Investments, LLC; *U.S. Private*, pg. 62
WINDOW & DOOR MANUFACTURERS ASSOCIATION—See Northeast Window & Door Association; *U.S. Private*, pg. 2951
WINDOWIZARDS INC.; *U.S. Private*, pg. 4539
WINDOW MART, INC.; *U.S. Private*, pg. 4538
WINDOWMASTER A/S—See VKR Holding A/S; *Int'l*, pg. 8282
WINDOWMASTER CONTROL SYSTEMS LIMITED—See VKR Holding A/S; *Int'l*, pg. 8282
WINDOWMASTER GMBH—See VKR Holding A/S; *Int'l*, pg. 8282
WINDOW NATION, LLC—See AEA Investors LP; *U.S. Private*, pg. 116
WINDOW PRODUCTS, INC.—See Clayton, Dubilier & Rice, LLC; *U.S. Private*, pg. 921
WINDOW PROS; *U.S. Private*, pg. 4538
WINDOWRAMA ENTERPRISES INC.; *U.S. Private*, pg. 4539
WINDOWS AND WALLS UNLIMITED, INC.; *U.S. Private*, pg. 4539
WINDOW SOLUTIONS, INC.—See Solar Art Window Film, Inc.; *U.S. Private*, pg. 3707
WINDOW TECHNOLOGY, INC.; *U.S. Private*, pg. 4538
WINDOW TO THE WORLD COMMUNICATIONS, INC.; *U.S. Private*, pg. 4538
WINDOW WIDGETS LLP—See Owens Corning; *U.S. Public*, pg. 1627
WINDOW WORLD INC.; *U.S. Private*, pg. 4538
WINDOW WORLD OF BATON ROUGE, LLC; *U.S. Private*, pg. 4538
WINDOW WORLD OF UPSTATE—See Window World Inc.; *U.S. Private*, pg. 4538
WINDPARK BERSCHWEILER GMBH & CO. KG—See BayWa AG; *Int'l*, pg. 919
WINDPARK EIFEL GMBH & CO. KG—See Infigen Energy Limited; *Int'l*, pg. 3685
WINDPARK EMMENDORF GMBH & CO.KG—See Allianz SE; *Int'l*, pg. 356
WINDPARK GROSSBERENDTEN 2 GMBH & CO KG—See Munchener Ruckversicherungs AG; *Int'l*, pg. 5092
WINDPARK HILMERSDORF GMBH & CO KG—See Munchener Ruckversicherungs AG; *Int'l*, pg. 5092
WINDPARK KESFELD HECKHUSCHEID GMBH & CO. KG—See Allianz SE; *Int'l*, pg. 356
WINDPARK KIRCHGEM GMBH & CO. KG—See MVV Energie AG; *Int'l*, pg. 5109
WINDPARK KIRF GMBH & CO. KG—See Allianz SE; *Int'l*, pg. 356
WINDPARK KREEKRAKSLUIS B.V.—See Delta N.V.; *Int'l*, pg. 2019
WINDPARK KRUGE GMBH & CO. KG—See Munchener Ruckversicherungs AG; *Int'l*, pg. 5092
WINDPARK LANGENDORF GMBH & CO. KG—See 3U Holding AG; *Int'l*, pg. 10
WINDPARK MARWITZ GMBH & CO KG—See Munchener Ruckversicherungs AG; *Int'l*, pg. 5092
WINDPARK MITTELHAUSEN GMBH & CO KG—See Munchener Ruckversicherungs AG; *Int'l*, pg. 5092
WINDPARK MUTZSCHEN OHG—See E.ON SE; *Int'l*, pg. 2260
WINDPARK NAUNDORF OHG—See E.ON SE; *Int'l*, pg. 2260
WINDPARK QUITZOW GMBH & CO. KG—See Allianz SE; *Int'l*, pg. 356
WINDPARK REDEKIN GMBH & CO KG—See Allianz SE; *Int'l*, pg. 356
WINDPARK SASSENBERG GMBH & CO KG—See Munchener Ruckversicherungs AG; *Int'l*, pg. 5092
WINDPARK WERDER ZINNDORF GMBH & CO. KG—See Allianz SE; *Int'l*, pg. 356
WIND POINT ADVISORS LLC; *U.S. Private*, pg. 4533
WIND PROSPECT AFRICA (PTY) LTD—See Wind Prospect Group Ltd; *Int'l*, pg. 8424
WIND PROSPECT ASIA PACIFIC—See Wind Prospect Group Ltd; *Int'l*, pg. 8424
WIND PROSPECT ENTERPRISES LTD—See Wind Prospect Group Ltd; *Int'l*, pg. 8424
WIND PROSPECT GMBH—See Wind Prospect Group Ltd; *Int'l*, pg. 8425
WIND PROSPECT GROUP LTD; *Int'l*, pg. 8424
WIND PROSPECT (HK) LTD—See Wind Prospect Group Ltd; *Int'l*, pg. 8424
WIND PROSPECT INC.—See Wind Prospect Group Ltd; *Int'l*, pg. 8424
WIND PROSPECT INC.—See Wind Prospect Group Ltd; *Int'l*, pg. 8425
WIND PROSPECT IRELAND LTD; *Int'l*, pg. 8425
WIND PROSPECT LTD—See Wind Prospect Group Ltd; *Int'l*, pg. 8425
WIND PROSPECT LTD—See Wind Prospect Group Ltd; *Int'l*, pg. 8425
WIND PROSPECT LTD—See Wind Prospect Group Ltd; *Int'l*, pg. 8425
WIND PROSPECT LTD—See Wind Prospect Group Ltd; *Int'l*, pg. 8425
WIND PROSPECT LTD—See Wind Prospect Group Ltd; *Int'l*, pg. 8425
WIND PROSPECT LTD—See Wind Prospect Group Ltd; *Int'l*, pg. 8425
WIND PROSPECT LTD—See Wind Prospect Group Ltd; *Int'l*, pg. 8425
WIND PROSPECT OPERATIONS LTD—See Wind Prospect Group Ltd; *Int'l*, pg. 8425
WIND PROSPECT POLSKA SP. Z O.O—See Wind Prospect Group Ltd; *Int'l*, pg. 8425
WIND PROSPECT PTY LTD - NEWCASTLE—See Wind Prospect Group Ltd; *Int'l*, pg. 8425
WIND PROSPECT PTY LTD—See Wind Prospect Group Ltd; *Int'l*, pg. 8425
WIND PROSPECT PTY LTD—See Wind Prospect Group Ltd; *Int'l*, pg. 8425
WIND PROSPECT SAS—See Wind Prospect Group Ltd; *Int'l*, pg. 8425
WIND PROSPTECT - CHINA—See Wind Prospect Group Ltd; *Int'l*, pg. 8424
WINDRIDGE IMPLEMENTS LLC; *U.S. Private*, pg. 4539
WINDRIDGE PROPERTIES LTD; *Int'l*, pg. 8426
WIND RIVER AB—See TPG Capital, L.P.; *U.S. Public*, pg. 2177
WIND RIVER ENERGY CORP.; *Int'l*, pg. 8425
WIND RIVER ENVIRONMENTAL LLC—See Gryphon Investors, LLC; *U.S. Private*, pg. 1800
WIND RIVER GMBH—See TPG Capital, L.P.; *U.S. Public*, pg. 2177
WIND RIVER HEALTH CARE & REHABILITATION CENTER—See Apollo Global Management, Inc.; *U.S. Public*, pg. 158
WIND RIVER HOLDINGS, L.P.; *U.S. Private*, pg. 4536
WIND RIVER HYDROCARBONS, INC.—See Wind River Energy Corp.; *Int'l*, pg. 8425
WIND RIVER K.K.—See TPG Capital, L.P.; *U.S. Public*, pg. 2177
WIND RIVER MATERIALS, LLC—See Summit Materials, Inc.; *U.S. Public*, pg. 1960
WIND RIVER PETROLEUM; *U.S. Private*, pg. 4536
WIND RIVER REINSURANCE COMPANY LTD—See Paine Schwartz Partners, LLC; *U.S. Private*, pg. 3076
WIND RIVER SALES CO., INC.—See TPG Capital, L.P.; *U.S. Public*, pg. 2177
WIND RIVER SYSTEMS, INC.—See TPG Capital, L.P.; *U.S. Public*, pg. 2177
WIND RIVER SYSTEMS INC.—See TPG Capital, L.P.; *U.S. Public*, pg. 2177
WIND RIVER SYSTEMS INTERNATIONAL, INC.—See TPG Capital, L.P.; *U.S. Public*, pg. 2177
WIND RIVER UK LTD.—See TPG Capital, L.P.; *U.S. Public*, pg. 2177
WINDROCK, INC.—See ChampionX Corporation; *U.S. Public*, pg. 478

COMPANY NAME INDEX

WINDROCK LAND COMPANY; *U.S. Public*, pg. 2372
WINDROCK PARK, LLC—See Windrock Land Company; *U.S. Public*, pg. 2372
WINDROSE GOLF CLUB—See OnCourse Strategies; *U.S. Private*, pg. 3020
WINDROSE HEALTH INVESTORS, LLC—See MTS Health Partners, L.P.; *U.S. Private*, pg. 2809
WINDROSE SIERRA PROPERTIES, LTD.—See Welltower Inc.; *U.S. Public*, pg. 2349
WINDSAIL CAPITAL GROUP, LLC; *U.S. Private*, pg. 4539
WINDS DIALYSIS, LLC—See DaVita Inc.; *U.S. Public*, pg. 644
WIND & SEA RESTAURANTS INC.; *U.S. Private*, pg. 4533
WINDSOR AIRMOTIVE ASIA PTE. LTD.—See Barnes Group Inc.; *U.S. Public*, pg. 276
WINDSOR AND DISTRICT HOUSING ASSOCIATION LIMITED—See Radian Group Limited; *Int'l*, pg. 6174
WINDSOR AUTOMOTIVE INC.; *U.S. Private*, pg. 4539
WINDSOR CASINO LIMITED—See Caesars Entertainment, Inc.; *U.S. Public*, pg. 420
WINDSOR CIRCLE INC.—See Aquiline Capital Partners LLC; *U.S. Private*, pg. 305
WINDSOR COURT HOTEL INC.—See LVMH Moet Hennessy Louis Vuitton SE; *Int'l*, pg. 4591
WINDSOR ENERGY RESOURCES, INC.; *U.S. Private*, pg. 4539
WINDSOR ENTERTAINMENT CO., LTD.—See Pou Chen Corporation; *Int'l*, pg. 5941
WINDSOR FACTORY SUPPLY INC.—See W.W. Grainger, Inc.; *U.S. Public*, pg. 2320
WINDSOR FASHIONS, INC.; *U.S. Private*, pg. 4539
WINDSOR FROZEN FOODS CO.; *U.S. Private*, pg. 4539
WINDSOR GMBH; *Int'l*, pg. 8426
WINDSOR HEALTH AND REHAB CENTER; *U.S. Private*, pg. 4539
WINDSOR HEALTH GROUP, INC.—See Centene Corporation; *U.S. Public*, pg. 471
WINDSOR HEALTH PLAN, INC.—See Munchener Ruckversicherungs AG; *Int'l*, pg. 5092
WINDSOR HOMECARE NETWORK, LLC—See Munchener Ruckversicherungs AG; *Int'l*, pg. 5092
THE WINDSOR HOTELS INTERNATIONAL CO., LTD.—See Meiji Shipping Co., Ltd.; *Int'l*, pg. 4802
WINDSOR INDUSTRIES, INC.—See Alfred Karcher GmbH & Co. KG; *Int'l*, pg. 316
WINDSOR LIFE ASSURANCE LTD.—See New York Life Insurance Company; *U.S. Private*, pg. 2911
WINDSOR LOCKS NONWOVENS, INC.—See Suominen Oyj; *Int'l*, pg. 7334
WINDSOR MACHINES LTD; *Int'l*, pg. 8426
WINDSOR MARINE PTE. LTD.—See Financiere SYZ & CO SA; *Int'l*, pg. 2669
WINDSOR MILL COMPANY; *U.S. Private*, pg. 4539
WINDSOR MILL SURGERY CENTER, LLC—See Tenet Healthcare Corporation; *U.S. Public*, pg. 2015
WINDSOR-MOUNT JOY MUTUAL INSURANCE CO.; *U.S. Private*, pg. 4539
WINDSOR OFFICE PRODUCTS INC.; *U.S. Private*, pg. 4539
WINDSOR PLC—See Ostrakon Capital Ltd.; *Int'l*, pg. 5655
WINDSOR PROPERTIES INC.; *U.S. Private*, pg. 4539
WINDSOR PROPERTY MANAGEMENT COMPANY—See GID Investment Advisor LLC; *U.S. Private*, pg. 1697
THE WINDSOR RACECOURSE COMPANY LIMITED—See Reuben Brothers SA; *Int'l*, pg. 6311
WINDSOR REALTY CORP.—See Citizens Financial Group, Inc.; *U.S. Public*, pg. 506
WINDSOR ROCK PRODUCTS, INC.—See GMS Inc.; *U.S. Public*, pg. 948
WINDSOR SERVICE, INC.—See Haines & Kibblehouse Inc.; *U.S. Private*, pg. 1841
WINDSOR SHADE TOBACCO COMPANY, INC.; *U.S. Private*, pg. 4539
THE WINDSOR STAR—See Chatham Asset Management, LLC; *U.S. Private*, pg. 861
WINDSOR WINDOWS & DOORS CO—See Woodgrain, Inc.; *U.S. Private*, pg. 4558
WINDSTAR CRUISES, LLC—See The Anschutz Corporation; *U.S. Private*, pg. 3987
WINDSTAR MEDICAL GMBH—See Oakley Capital Limited; *Int'l*, pg. 5504
WINDSTONE FARMS, LLC—See Algood Food Company; *U.S. Private*, pg. 166
WINDSTREAM ALABAMA—See Windstream Holdings, Inc.; *U.S. Public*, pg. 2373
WINDSTREAM COMMUNICATIONS—See Windstream Holdings, Inc.; *U.S. Public*, pg. 2373
WINDSTREAM CORPORATION—See Windstream Holdings, Inc.; *U.S. Public*, pg. 2373
WINDSTREAM D&E, INC.—See Windstream Holdings, Inc.; *U.S. Public*, pg. 2373
WINDSTREAM FLORIDA, INC.—See Windstream Holdings, Inc.; *U.S. Public*, pg. 2373
WINDSTREAM HOLDINGS, INC.; *U.S. Public*, pg. 2373
WINDSTREAM IOWA-COM, INC.—See Windstream Holdings, Inc.; *U.S. Public*, pg. 2373
WINDSTREAM KDL, INC.—See Windstream Holdings, Inc.; *U.S. Public*, pg. 2373
WINDSTREAM LEXCOM COMMUNICATIONS, INC.—See Windstream Holdings, Inc.; *U.S. Public*, pg. 2373
WINDSTREAM MISSOURI, INC.—See Windstream Holdings, Inc.; *U.S. Public*, pg. 2373
WINDSTREAM NEBRASKA, INC.—See Windstream Holdings, Inc.; *U.S. Public*, pg. 2373
WINDSTREAM NEW YORK, INC.—See Windstream Holdings, Inc.; *U.S. Public*, pg. 2373
WINDSTREAM SUGAR LAND, INC.—See Windstream Holdings, Inc.; *U.S. Public*, pg. 2373
WINDSTREAM TECHNOLOGIES, INC.; *U.S. Private*, pg. 4539
WINDSUN SCIENCE & TECHNOLOGY CO., LTD.; *Int'l*, pg. 8426
WIND TELECOM SP. O.O.; *Int'l*, pg. 8425
WIND TELECOMUNICAZIONI S.P.A.—See VEON Ltd.; *Int'l*, pg. 8164
WINDTEST IBERICA S.L.—See DNV GL Group AS; *Int'l*, pg. 2150
WINDTREE THERAPEUTICS, INC.; *U.S. Public*, pg. 2373
WIND-UP ENTERTAINMENT, INC.; *U.S. Private*, pg. 4537
WIND-UP RECORDS—See Wind-up Entertainment, Inc.; *U.S. Private*, pg. 4537
W-INDUSTRIES, INC.—See CSE Global Ltd.; *Int'l*, pg. 1864
W-INDUSTRIES - LOUISIANA LLC—See CSE Global Ltd.; *Int'l*, pg. 1864
WINDWARD BUILDERS INC.; *U.S. Private*, pg. 4539
WINDWARD CAPITAL PARTNERS LP; *U.S. Private*, pg. 4539
THE WINDWARD DESIGN GROUP, INC.; *U.S. Private*, pg. 4137
WINDWARD ISLAND BANK LTD.; *Int'l*, pg. 8426
WINDWARD LTD.; *Int'l*, pg. 8426
WINDWARD PETROLEUM—See Booth Waltz Enterprises, Inc.; *U.S. Private*, pg. 617
WINDWARD ROOFING & CONSTRUCTION, INC.; *U.S. Private*, pg. 4539
WINDWARD STUDIOS, INC.—See Thoma Bravo, L.P.; *U.S. Private*, pg. 4146
WINDWARTS ENERGIE GMBH—See MVV Energie AG; *Int'l*, pg. 5109
WINDWAY CAPITAL CORP.; *U.S. Private*, pg. 4539
WIND WORKS POWER CORP.; *Int'l*, pg. 8425
WINDY CITY DISTRIBUTION; *U.S. Private*, pg. 4540
WINDY CITY ELECTRIC COMPANY; *U.S. Private*, pg. 4540
WINDY CITY EQUIPMENT SERVICE, INC.; *U.S. Private*, pg. 4540
WINDY CITY FIELDHOUSE; *U.S. Private*, pg. 4540
WINDY CITY LIMOUSINE; *U.S. Private*, pg. 4540
WINDY CITY NOVELTIES, INC.; *U.S. Private*, pg. 4540
WINDY CITY PROMOTIONS, LLC; *U.S. Private*, pg. 4540
WINDY CITY WIRE CABLE & TECHNOLOGY PRODUCTS LLC—See Diploma PLC; *Int'l*, pg. 2129
THE WINE ADVOCATE, INC.—See Compagnie Generale des Etablissements Michelin SCA; *Int'l*, pg. 1745
WINE AG VALENTIN & VON SALIS—See Coop-Gruppe Genossenschaft; *Int'l*, pg. 1790
WINE ARK PTY. LTD.—See National Storage REIT; *Int'l*, pg. 5164
WINEBID.COM, INC.—See Third Leaf Partners; *U.S. Private*, pg. 4145
THE WINEBOW GROUP, LLC; *U.S. Private*, pg. 4137
WINEBOW, INC.—See The Winebow Group, LLC; *U.S. Private*, pg. 4137
THE WINE CLUB INC.; *U.S. Private*, pg. 4137
WINE.COM, INC.—See Baker Capital Partners, LLC; *U.S. Private*, pg. 455
WINECOMMUNE LLC; *U.S. Private*, pg. 4540
THE WINE COMPANY HAWESKO GMBH—See Hawesko Holding AG; *Int'l*, pg. 3288
WINECO PRODUCTIONS, INC.; *U.S. Public*, pg. 2374
WINE COUNTRY PUBLICATIONS, INC.—See Brehm Communications Inc.; *U.S. Private*, pg. 644
WINEDIRECT, INC.; *U.S. Private*, pg. 4540
WINE DOCK GMBH—See Hawesko Holding AG; *Int'l*, pg. 3289
WINE EXCEL BV—See Union InVivo - Union de Cooperatives Agricoles; *Int'l*, pg. 8053
WINEGARD COMPANY; *U.S. Private*, pg. 4540
WINEGARDNER & HAMMONS, INC.; *U.S. Private*, pg. 4540
WINEGAR'S SUPERMARKETS INC.; *U.S. Private*, pg. 4540
THE WINE GROUP, INC.; *U.S. Private*, pg. 4137
WINE IN BLACK GMBH—See Viva Wine Group AB; *Int'l*, pg. 8265
THE WINE LOCKER, INC.—See Vino Vault, Inc.; *U.S. Private*, pg. 4386
WINEMAKER CHOICE PTY LTD.—See Treasury Wine Estates Limited; *Int'l*, pg. 7909
WINEMAN TECHNOLOGY, INC.—See CertTech, L.L.C.; *U.S. Private*, pg. 842
WINEMARKET PTY LTD—See Woolworths Group Limited; *Int'l*, pg. 8452
WIN ENERGY REMC; *U.S. Private*, pg. 4532
WINE RACK—See Ontario Teachers' Pension Plan; *Int'l*, pg. 5587

WINERGY AG—See Siemens Aktiengesellschaft; *Int'l*, pg. 6901
WINERGY DRIVE SYSTEMS CORP.—See Siemens Aktiengesellschaft; *Int'l*, pg. 6891
WINERGY DRIVE SYSTEMS (TIANJIN) CO. LTD.—See Siemens Aktiengesellschaft; *Int'l*, pg. 6901
WINERITE LTD.—See Palmer & Harvey McLane (Holdings) Limited; *Int'l*, pg. 5709
WINERY EXCHANGE INC.; *U.S. Private*, pg. 4540
WINE'S LINK INTERNATIONAL HOLDINGS LIMITED; *Int'l*, pg. 8426
WINE & SPIRITS WHOLESALERS OF AMERICA, INC.; *U.S. Private*, pg. 4540
THE WINETASTING NETWORK—See 1-800-FLOWERS.COM, Inc.; *U.S. Public*, pg. 1
THE WINE TEAM GLOBAL AB—See Viva Wine Group AB; *Int'l*, pg. 8264
WINE WAREHOUSE, LLC—See Breakthru Beverage Group, LLC; *U.S. Private*, pg. 643
WINE&WINE CULTURE CO., LTD.—See Credit Saison Co., Ltd.; *Int'l*, pg. 1836
WINEYASAN, INC.—See GMO Internet Group, Inc.; *Int'l*, pg. 3014
WINEZJA SP. Z O.O.—See Schloss Wachenheim AG; *Int'l*, pg. 6622
WINFAIR INVESTMENT COMPANY LIMITED; *Int'l*, pg. 8427
WINFARM SA; *Int'l*, pg. 8427
WINFAST TECHNOLOGY LTD.—See Achilles Corporation; *Int'l*, pg. 103
WINFIELD ASSOCIATES, INC.—See Keystone Group, L.P.; *U.S. Private*, pg. 2298
WINFIELD DAILY COURIER—See Winfield Publishing Co.; *U.S. Private*, pg. 4541
WINFIELD MOTOR CO., INC.; *U.S. Private*, pg. 4540
WINFIELD NURSERY, INC.—See The Robert Baker Companies; *U.S. Private*, pg. 4111
WINFIELD PUBLISHING CO.; *U.S. Private*, pg. 4540
WINFIELD UNITED, LLC; *U.S. Private*, pg. 4541
WINFRESH LIMITED; *Int'l*, pg. 8427
WINFULL GROUP HOLDINGS LIMITED; *Int'l*, pg. 8427
WING ACE CORPORATION—See Kamei Corporation; *Int'l*, pg. 4062
WINGARA AG LIMITED; *Int'l*, pg. 8428
WINGARC1ST INC.—See The Carlyle Group Inc.; *U.S. Public*, pg. 2057
WINGARC DALIAN INC.—See The Carlyle Group Inc.; *U.S. Public*, pg. 2057
WINGARC SHANGHAI INC.—See The Carlyle Group Inc.; *U.S. Public*, pg. 2057
WINGARC SINGAPORE PTE. LTD.—See The Carlyle Group Inc.; *U.S. Public*, pg. 2057
WINGAS BELGIUM S.P.R.L./B.V.B.A.—See BASF SE; *Int'l*, pg. 885
WINGAS BELGIUM S.P.R.L./B.V.B.A.—See PJSC Gazprom; *Int'l*, pg. 5880
WINGAS GMBH—See BASF SE; *Int'l*, pg. 885
WINGAS GMBH—See PJSC Gazprom; *Int'l*, pg. 5880
WINGAS HOLDING GMBH—See BASF SE; *Int'l*, pg. 885
WINGAS HOLDING GMBH—See PJSC Gazprom; *Int'l*, pg. 5880
WINGAS TRANSPORT GMBH & CO. KG—See BASF SE; *Int'l*, pg. 885
WINGAS TRANSPORT GMBH & CO. KG—See PJSC Gazprom; *Int'l*, pg. 5880
WINGAS UK LTD.—See BASF SE; *Int'l*, pg. 885
WINGAS UK LTD.—See PJSC Gazprom; *Int'l*, pg. 5880
WINGAS VERWALTUNGS-GMBH—See BASF SE; *Int'l*, pg. 885
WINGAS VERWALTUNGS-GMBH—See PJSC Gazprom; *Int'l*, pg. 5880
WINGATE & ASSOCIATES REALTY, INC.; *U.S. Private*, pg. 4541
WINGATE INNS INTERNATIONAL, INC.—See Travel & Leisure Co.; *U.S. Public*, pg. 2185
WINGATE OVERSEAS HOLDINGS LTD.—See Want Want China Holdings Ltd.; *Int'l*, pg. 8342
WINGATE PARTNERS, LLP; *U.S. Private*, pg. 4541
WING AVIATION, LLC; *U.S. Private*, pg. 4541
WING CHI HOLDINGS LIMITED; *Int'l*, pg. 8427
WING CO., LTD.—See Hanwa Co., Ltd.; *Int'l*, pg. 3263
WINGDALE MATERIALS LLC—See Peckham Industries, Inc.; *U.S. Private*, pg. 3127
WINGED KEEL GROUP, LLC; *U.S. Private*, pg. 4541
WINGED MEDIA LLC; *U.S. Private*, pg. 4541
WINGENBACK INC.; *Int'l*, pg. 8428
WINGENFELD ENERGIE GMBH—See BayWa AG; *Int'l*, pg. 919
WING ENTERPRISES, INCORPORATED—See Industrial Opportunity Partners, LLC; *U.S. Private*, pg. 2067
WINGER CONTRACTING CO.; *U.S. Private*, pg. 4541
THE WING FAT PRINTING CO., LTD.—See Shanghai Industrial Holdings Limited; *Int'l*, pg. 6771
WINGFOOT AUSTRALIA PARTNER PTY LTD—See The Goodyear Tire & Rubber Company; *U.S. Public*, pg. 2085
WINGFOOT COMMERCIAL TIRE SYSTEMS, LLC—See The Goodyear Tire & Rubber Company; *U.S. Public*, pg. 2085

WINGER CONTRACTING CO. CORPORATE AFFILIATIONS

WINGFOOT CORPORATION—See The Goodyear Tire & Rubber Company; *U.S. Public*, pg. 2085
WINGFOOT ENTERPRISES INC.; *U.S. Private*, pg. 4541
WING FUNG GROUP ASIA LTD.; *Int'l*, pg. 8427
WINGHAM BEEF EXPORT PTY LTD—See NH Foods Ltd.; *Int'l*, pg. 5257
WING HANG BANK (CHINA) LTD.—See Oversea-Chinese Banking Corporation Limited; *Int'l*, pg. 5672
WING INFLATABLES, INC.; *U.S. Private*, pg. 4541
WING KWONG ELECTRICAL CO., LTD—See Sonepar S.A.; *Int'l*, pg. 7091
WINGLAND FOODS—See Bakkavor Group plc; *Int'l*, pg. 806
WING LEE PROPERTY INVESTMENTS LIMITED; *Int'l*, pg. 8427
WING LUNG BANK LIMITED—See China Merchants Group Limited; *Int'l*, pg. 1520
WING LUNG BANK (TRUSTEE) LTD.—See China Merchants Group Limited; *Int'l*, pg. 1520
WING LUNG FINANCE LTD.—See China Merchants Group Limited; *Int'l*, pg. 1520
WING LUNG FUTURES LIMITED—See China Merchants Group Limited; *Int'l*, pg. 1520
WING LUNG INSURANCE CO. LTD.—See China Merchants Group Limited; *Int'l*, pg. 1520
WING LUNG PROPERTY MANAGEMENT LIMITED—See China Merchants Group Limited; *Int'l*, pg. 1520
WING LUNG SECURITIES LTD.—See China Merchants Group Limited; *Int'l*, pg. 1520
WINGMAN MEDIA; *U.S. Private*, pg. 4541
WING MARITIME SERVICE CORPORATION—See Nippon Yusen Kabushiki Kaisha; *Int'l*, pg. 5360
WING-MIAMI—See WPP plc; *Int'l*, pg. 8472
WING NED BV—See Leonardo S.p.A.; *Int'l*, pg. 4458
WING ON COMPANY INTERNATIONAL LIMITED; *Int'l*, pg. 8427
WING ON FOODS CO., LTD.—See Nissin Foods Holdings Co., Ltd.; *Int'l*, pg. 5377
WINGRA STONE COMPANY; *U.S. Private*, pg. 4541
WING REAL ESTATE DEVELOPER AND INVESTOR PRIVATE LIMITED COMPANY; *Int'l*, pg. 8427
WINGROUP AG—See Nordstjernan AB; *Int'l*, pg. 5426
WINGROUP S.COOP—See Mondragon Corporation; *Int'l*, pg. 5031
WINGSCAPES, INC.—See EBSCO Industries, Inc.; *U.S. Private*, pg. 1325
WINGS FINANCIAL ADVISORS, LLC; *U.S. Private*, pg. 4541
WING'S FOOT INC.; *Int'l*, pg. 8428
WING SHING CHEMICAL COMPANY LIMITED—See Long Well International Holdings Limited; *Int'l*, pg. 4549
WING—See WPP plc; *Int'l*, pg. 8472
WINGSPAN TECHNOLOGY, INC.; *U.S. Private*, pg. 4541
WINGS & THINGS, INC.; *U.S. Public*, pg. 2374
WINGSTOP INC.—See Roark Capital Group Inc.; *U.S. Private*, pg. 3456
WINGSTOP RESTAURANTS, INC.—See Roark Capital Group Inc.; *U.S. Private*, pg. 3456
WINGSTREET, LLC—See Yum! Brands, Inc.; *U.S. Public*, pg. 2400
WINGSWEPT; *U.S. Private*, pg. 4541
WING TAI CLOTHING PTE LTD—See Wing Tai Holdings Limited; *Int'l*, pg. 8427
WING TAI CLOTHING SDN. BHD.—See Wing Tai Holdings Limited; *Int'l*, pg. 8427
WING TAI HOLDINGS LIMITED; *Int'l*, pg. 8427
WING TAI INVESTMENT & DEVELOPMENT PTE LTD—See Wing Tai Holdings Limited; *Int'l*, pg. 8427
WING TAI INVESTMENT MANAGEMENT PTE LTD—See Wing Tai Holdings Limited; *Int'l*, pg. 8427
WING TAI INVESTMENT PTE LTD—See Wing Tai Holdings Limited; *Int'l*, pg. 8427
WING TAI LAND PTE LTD—See Wing Tai Holdings Limited; *Int'l*, pg. 8427
WING TAI MALAYSIA SDN. BHD.—See Wing Tai Holdings Limited; *Int'l*, pg. 8427
WING TAI PROPERTIES LIMITED; *Int'l*, pg. 8428
WING TAI PROPERTY MANAGEMENT PTE LTD—See Wing Tai Holdings Limited; *Int'l*, pg. 8427
WING TAI RETAIL MANAGEMENT PTE. LTD—See Wing Tai Holdings Limited; *Int'l*, pg. 8427
WING TAI RETAIL PTE. LTD.—See Wing Tai Holdings Limited; *Int'l*, pg. 8427
WING TAT STEREO COMPONENT LTD.—See Lasonic Electronics Corporation; *U.S. Private*, pg. 2395
WINGTECH TECHNOLOGY CO LTD; *Int'l*, pg. 8428
WING YIP FOOD (CHINA) HOLDINGS GROUP LTD.; *Int'l*, pg. 8428
WIN HANVERKY HOLDINGS LIMITED; *Int'l*, pg. 8424
WINIHITECH CO., LTD.; *Int'l*, pg. 8428
WINHOLD LIMITED; *Int'l*, pg. 8428
WINHOLD MANAGEMENT COMPANY (PTY) LIMITED—See Winhold Limited; *Int'l*, pg. 8428
WIN-HOLT EQUIPMENT GROUP; *U.S. Private*, pg. 4532
WIN HOUSE INDUSTRIES LIMITED—See Kerry Group Limited; *Int'l*, pg. 4137
WINIA CO., LTD; *Int'l*, pg. 8428
WINIARY S.A.—See Nestle S.A.; *Int'l*, pg. 5207
WINICK & GALLAHER, PC; *U.S. Private*, pg. 4541

THE WINIFRED MASTERSON BURKE REHABILITATION HOSPITAL, INC.; *U.S. Private*, pg. 4137
WIN INTERNATIONAL CO., LTD.—See WIN-Partners Co., Ltd.; *Int'l*, pg. 8424
WINIX CO., LTD.—See Wonik Corporation; *Int'l*, pg. 8448
WINIX INC.—See Wonik Corporation; *Int'l*, pg. 8448
WINKEL DISTRIBUTING COMPANY; *U.S. Private*, pg. 4542
WINKEL GMBH; *Int'l*, pg. 8428
WINKELMANN ELEKTRO AG—See BKW AG; *Int'l*, pg. 1056
WINKEL SRL—See WINKEL GmbH; *Int'l*, pg. 8428
WINK, INCORPORATED; *U.S. Private*, pg. 4542
WINKING LIZARD INC.; *U.S. Private*, pg. 4542
WINKING TECHNOLOGY CO., LTD.—See Advanced Analog Technology, Inc.; *Int'l*, pg. 157
WINKLE INDUSTRIES, INC.—See Groupe R.Y. Beaudoin, Inc.; *Int'l*, pg. 3110
WINKLER+DUNNEBIER GMBH—See Barry-Wehmiller Companies, Inc.; *U.S. Private*, pg. 482
WINKLER INCORPORATED; *U.S. Private*, pg. 4542
WINKLER TREGER & ASSOCIATES LLC; *U.S. Private*, pg. 4542
WINKLEVOSS BITCOIN TRUST; *U.S. Private*, pg. 4542
WINKOWSKI DEUTSCHLAND GMBH—See Quad/Graphics, Inc.; *U.S. Public*, pg. 1745
WINKWORTH CLIENT SERVICES LIMITED—See M Winkworth Plc; *Int'l*, pg. 4610
WINKWORTH MACHINERY LIMITED; *Int'l*, pg. 8428
WINLAND ELECTRONICS, INC.; *U.S. Private*, pg. 4542
WINLAND OCEAN SHIPPING CORP.; *Int'l*, pg. 8428
WIN, LLC; *U.S. Private*, pg. 4532
WINMARK CAPITAL CORPORATION—See Winmark Corporation; *U.S. Public*, pg. 2374
WINMARK CORPORATION; *U.S. Public*, pg. 2374
WINMARK HOMES INC.—See D.G. Jenkins Development Corp.; *U.S. Private*, pg. 1142
WINMARK INVESTMENT HOLDINGS LIMITED; *Int'l*, pg. 8428
WINMARKT MANAGEMENT S.R.L.—See IGD SIIQ S.p.A; *Int'l*, pg. 3602
WINMAR RESOURCES LIMITED; *Int'l*, pg. 8428
WINMATE COMMUNICATION INC.; *Int'l*, pg. 8428
WINMAX HI-TECH (SHENZHEN) CO., LTD.—See Lumax International Corp., Ltd.; *Int'l*, pg. 4577
WINMAX TECHNOLOGY CORP.—See Acter Co., Ltd.; *Int'l*, pg. 117
WINMEDIA GROUP; *Int'l*, pg. 8429
WINMEGA TECHNOLOGY CORP.—See Acter Co., Ltd.; *Int'l*, pg. 117
WINMILL & CO., INCORPORATED; *U.S. Public*, pg. 2374
WINMILL SOFTWARE COMPANY; *U.S. Private*, pg. 4542
WINMO, LLC—See Northlane Capital Partners, LLC; *U.S. Private*, pg. 2956
WINNAN CORP.; *U.S. Private*, pg. 4542
WINN BURNER ASIA SDN BHD—See Max Weishaupt GmbH; *Int'l*, pg. 4735
WINNCOM TECHNOLOGIES CORP.—See Winncom Technologies Holding Limited; *Int'l*, pg. 8429
WINNCOM TECHNOLOGIES HOLDING LIMITED; *Int'l*, pg. 8429
WINN DESIGN, LLC; *U.S. Private*, pg. 4542
WINN DEVON ART GROUP—See Encore Art Group; *Int'l*, pg. 2402
WINN-DIXIE LOGISTICS, INC.—See Aldi Einkauf SE & Co. oHG; *Int'l*, pg. 304
WINN-DIXIE STORES, INC. - JACKSONVILLE DIVISION—See Aldi Einkauf SE & Co. oHG; *Int'l*, pg. 304
WINN-DIXIE STORES, INC. - ORLANDO DIVISION—See Aldi Einkauf SE & Co. oHG; *Int'l*, pg. 304
WINN-DIXIE STORES, INC.—See Aldi Einkauf SE & Co. oHG; *Int'l*, pg. 304
WINNEBAGO FLEET SERVICE, INC.—See William Charles, Ltd.; *U.S. Private*, pg. 4523
WINNEBAGO INDUSTRIES, INC.; *U.S. Public*, pg. 2374
WINNEBAGO LANDFILL COMPANY, LLC—See Waste Connections, Inc.; *Int'l*, pg. 8355
WINNEBAGO OF INDIANA, LLC—See Winnebago Industries, Inc.; *U.S. Public*, pg. 2374
WINNEBAGO RECLAMATION SERVICE INC.—See William Charles, Ltd.; *U.S. Private*, pg. 4523
WINNEMUCCA FARMS INC.; *U.S. Private*, pg. 4542
WINNER & ASSOCIATES—See Publicis Groupe S.A.; *Int'l*, pg. 6112
WINNER AUTOMOTIVE GROUP, INC.; *U.S. Private*, pg. 4542
WINNER AUTOWORLD; *U.S. Private*, pg. 4542
WINNER CHEVROLET INC.; *U.S. Private*, pg. 4542
WINNERCOMM, INC.—See Kroenke Sports & Entertainment, LLC; *U.S. Private*, pg. 2352
WINNER COMMUNICATIONS, INC.; *U.S. Private*, pg. 4542
WINNER DOVER AUTOCENTER; *U.S. Private*, pg. 4542
WINNER ENGINEERING PTE. LTD.—See EXEO Group Inc.; *Int'l*, pg. 2584
WINNER FOOD MANUFACTURERS LTD.—See Nissin Foods Holdings Co., Ltd.; *Int'l*, pg. 5377

WINNER FOOD PRODUCTS LTD.—See Nissin Foods Holdings Co., Ltd.; *Int'l*, pg. 5377
WINNER GROUP ENTERPRISE PUBLIC COMPANY LIMITED; *Int'l*, pg. 8429
WINNER GROUP INCORPORATED; *U.S. Private*, pg. 4542
WINNER HOLDING LIMITED; *Int'l*, pg. 8429
WINNER INDUSTRIES (SHENZHEN) CO., LTD—See Winner Holding Limited; *Int'l*, pg. 8429
WINNER INTERNATIONAL, LLC; *U.S. Private*, pg. 4542
WINNER MEDICAL CO.LTD—See Winner Holding Limited; *Int'l*, pg. 8429
WINNER MEDICAL GROUP INC.—See Winner Holding Limited; *Int'l*, pg. 8429
WINNER MEDICAL (HONG KONG) LIMITED—See Winner Holding Limited; *Int'l*, pg. 8429
WINNERS MERCHANTS INTERNATIONAL LP—See The TJX Companies, Inc.; *U.S. Public*, pg. 2134
WINNERSOFT CO., LTD.—See NSD CO., LTD.; *Int'l*, pg. 5477
WINNERTEX FASHIONS LIMITED—See Tungtex (Holdings) Co. Ltd.; *Int'l*, pg. 7972
WINNESHIEK COOPERATIVE ASSOCIATION; *U.S. Private*, pg. 4542
WINNING APPLIANCES PTY. LTD.; *Int'l*, pg. 8429
WINNING BRANDS CORPORATION; *U.S. Private*, pg. 4542
WINNING CHANCE INVESTMENTS PTE LTD—See Second Chance Properties Ltd.; *Int'l*, pg. 6672
WINNING HEALTH TECHNOLOGY GROUP CO., LTD.; *Int'l*, pg. 8429
WINNING MOVES GAMES, INC.; *U.S. Private*, pg. 4542
WINNING SECURITY, S.L.—See Centene Corporation; *U.S. Public*, pg. 471
WINNING STRATEGIES PUBLIC RELATIONS; *U.S. Private*, pg. 4543
WINNING STRATEGIES WASHINGTON—See Winning Strategies Public Relations; *U.S. Private*, pg. 4543
WINNING TOWER GROUP HOLDINGS LIMITED; *Int'l*, pg. 8429
THE WINNIPEG JETS HOCKEY CLUB LP—See True North Sports & Entertainment Limited; *Int'l*, pg. 7941
WINNITEX LIMITED—See Texhong Textile Group Limited; *Int'l*, pg. 7584
WINN MANAGEMENT CORPORATION; *U.S. Private*, pg. 4542
WINN MATERIALS, LLC—See Natural Resource Partners L.P.; *U.S. Public*, pg. 1499
WINN MATERIALS OF KENTUCKY, LLC—See Natural Resource Partners L.P.; *U.S. Public*, pg. 1499
WINNOCK ZORG B.V.—See Achmea B.V.; *Int'l*, pg. 104
WINNORTH INVESTMENT PTE LTD—See Wing Tai Holdings Limited; *Int'l*, pg. 8427
WINNOVA CO., LTD; *Int'l*, pg. 8429
WINN PARISH MEDICAL CENTER—See Progressive Acute Care LLC; *U.S. Private*, pg. 3278
WINNRESIDENTIAL LIMITED PARTNERSHIP; *U.S. Private*, pg. 4543
WINNSBORO FIBERS LLC—See Indorama Ventures Public Company Limited; *Int'l*, pg. 3659
WINNSBORO PETROLEUM CO. INC.; *U.S. Private*, pg. 4543
WINN TECHNOLOGY GROUP, INC.; *U.S. Private*, pg. 4542
WIN-OMT SOFTWARE INC—See WinMedia Group; *Int'l*, pg. 8429
WINONA CAPITAL MANAGEMENT, LLC—See Laird Norton Company, LLC; *U.S. Private*, pg. 2374
WINONA DAILY NEWS—See Lee Enterprises, Incorporated; *U.S. Public*, pg. 1300
WINONA HEATING & VENT CO.; *U.S. Private*, pg. 4543
WINORA STAIGER GMBH—See Accell Group N.V.; *Int'l*, pg. 80
WINOX HOLDINGS LIMITED - DALANG FACTORY—See Winox Holdings Limited; *Int'l*, pg. 8429
WINOX HOLDINGS LIMITED - HUIZHOU FACTORY—See Winox Holdings Limited; *Int'l*, pg. 8429
WINOX HOLDINGS LIMITED; *Int'l*, pg. 8429
WINPAC INC.; *Int'l*, pg. 8429
WINPAC NETHERLANDS B.V.—See Metsaliitto Osuuskunta; *Int'l*, pg. 4865
WINPAK CONTROL GROUP, INC.—See Winpak Ltd.; *Int'l*, pg. 8429
WINPAK FILMS INC.—See Winpak Ltd.; *Int'l*, pg. 8429
WINPAK HEAT SEAL CORPORATION—See Winpak Ltd.; *Int'l*, pg. 8429
WINPAK HEAT SEAL PACKAGING INC.—See Winpak Ltd.; *Int'l*, pg. 8429
WINPAK INC.—See Winpak Ltd.; *Int'l*, pg. 8430
WINPAK LANE INC.—See Winpak Ltd.; *Int'l*, pg. 8430
WINPAK LTD.; *Int'l*, pg. 8429
WINPAK PORTION PACKAGING INC—See Winpak Ltd.; *Int'l*, pg. 8430
WINPAK PORTION PACKAGING LTD.—See Winpak Ltd.; *Int'l*, pg. 8430
WINPAR HOLDINGS LIMITED; *Int'l*, pg. 8430
WIN-PARTNERS CO., LTD.; *Int'l*, pg. 8424
WIN PLASTIC EXTRUSIONS, LLC—See ShoreView Industries, LLC; *U.S. Private*, pg. 3642

COMPANY NAME INDEX

WINPOWER INC.—See Winco Generators; *U.S. Private*, pg. 4533
WINPRO INDUSTRIES LTD.; *Int'l*, pg. 8430
WINRIDGE APARTMENTS—See Deutsche Bank Aktiengesellschaft; *Int'l*, pg. 2058
WINROCK ENTERPRISES, INC.; *U.S. Private*, pg. 4543
WINRO COMMERCIAL (INDIA) LIMITED; *Int'l*, pg. 8430
WINROC—See Superior Plus Corp.; *Int'l*, pg. 7338
WINROSE INVESTMENT PTE LTD—See Wing Tai Holdings Limited; *Int'l*, pg. 8428
WINSAN CHENGDU MEDICAL SCIENCE AND TECHNOLOGY CO LTD.; *Int'l*, pg. 8430
WIN SCHULER FOODS; *U.S. Private*, pg. 4532
WINS CO., LTD.; *Int'l*, pg. 8430
WINSCRIBE EUROPE LTD.—See Microsoft Corporation; *U.S. Public*, pg. 1443
WINSCRIBE GMBH—See Microsoft Corporation; *U.S. Public*, pg. 1443
WINSCRIBE INC LTD.—See Microsoft Corporation; *U.S. Public*, pg. 1443
WIN SEMICONDUCTORS CORP.; *Int'l*, pg. 8424
WINSERT, INC.—See Altus Capital Partners, Inc.; *U.S. Private*, pg. 211
WINS FINANCE GROUP LTD.—See Arta TechFin Corporation Limited; *Int'l*, pg. 581
WINS FINANCE HOLDINGS INC.—See Arta TechFin Corporation Limited; *Int'l*, pg. 581
THE WINSFORD CORPORATION—See Winsford II Corporation; *U.S. Private*, pg. 4543
WINSFORD II CORPORATION; *U.S. Private*, pg. 4543
WINSHARE EDUCATION CO., LTD.—See Xinhua Winshare Publishing and Media Co., Ltd.; *Int'l*, pg. 8530
WINSHARE INTERNATIOINAL CULTURAL MEDIA CO., LTD.—See Xinhua Winshare Publishing and Media Co., Ltd.; *Int'l*, pg. 8530
WINSHARE INVESTMENT CO., LTD.—See Xinhua Winshare Publishing and Media Co., Ltd.; *Int'l*, pg. 8530
WINSHARE MUSICAND CULTURE MEDIA CO., LTD.—See Xinhua Winshare Publishing and Media Co., Ltd.; *Int'l*, pg. 8530
WINSHARE MUSIC & CULTURE MEDIA CO., LTD.—See Xinhua Winshare Publishing and Media Co., Ltd.; *Int'l*, pg. 8530
WINSHEAR GOLD CORP.; *Int'l*, pg. 8430
WINSHENG PLASTIC INDUSTRY SDN. BHD.—See ATA IMS Berhad; *Int'l*, pg. 665
WINSHINE INDUSTRIES SDN. BHD.—See Jaycorp Berhad; *Int'l*, pg. 3915
WINSHINE INVESTMENT PTE LTD—See Wing Tai Holdings Limited; *Int'l*, pg. 8428
WINSHINE SCIENCE COMPANY LIMITED; *Int'l*, pg. 8430
WINSHUTTLE LLC—See Symphony Technology Group, LLC; *U.S. Private*, pg. 3902
WINSIGHT LLC—See Informa plc; *Int'l*, pg. 3694
WINSKY INDUSTRY HONG KONG LIMITED—See CN Innovations Holdings Limited; *Int'l*, pg. 1673
WINSLAND INVESTMENT PTE LTD—See Wing Tai Holdings Limited; *Int'l*, pg. 8428
WINSLOW BMW; *U.S. Private*, pg. 4543
WINSLOW CAPITAL MANAGEMENT, LLC—See Teachers Insurance Association - College Retirement Fund; *U.S. Private*, pg. 3948
WINSLOW CONSTRUCTORS PTY LTD; *Int'l*, pg. 8430
WINSLOW INFRASTRUCTURE PTY LTD—See Winslow Constructors Pty Ltd; *Int'l*, pg. 8430
WINSLOW MARINE PRODUCTS CORPORATION—See RTX Corporation; *U.S. Public*, pg. 1822
WINSLOWS INC.; *U.S. Private*, pg. 4543
WINSLOW TECHNOLOGY GROUP, LLC; *U.S. Private*, pg. 4543
WINSOME BREWERIES LTD.; *Int'l*, pg. 8430
WINSOME DIAMONDS & JEWELLERY LTD.; *Int'l*, pg. 8430
WINSOME RESOURCES LIMITED; *Int'l*, pg. 8430
WINSOME TEXTILE INDUSTRIES LTD.; *Int'l*, pg. 8430
WINSOME TRADING INC.; *U.S. Private*, pg. 4543
WINSOME YARNS LIMITED; *Int'l*, pg. 8430
WINSON HOLDINGS HONG KONG LIMITED; *Int'l*, pg. 8431
WINSON MACHINERY CO., LTD.; *Int'l*, pg. 8431
WIN SOON AUTO SUPPLIERS (JB) SDN. BHD.—See Solid Automotive Berhad; *Int'l*, pg. 7071
WINSOR LEARNING INC.—See Silver Lake Group, LLC; *U.S. Private*, pg. 3661
WINSOUTH CREDIT UNION; *U.S. Private*, pg. 4543
WINSPER INC.; *U.S. Private*, pg. 4543
WIN SPORTS S.A.S.—See AT&T Inc.; *U.S. Public*, pg. 220
WINSTANLEY PARTNERS; *U.S. Private*, pg. 4543
WINSTEAD PC; *U.S. Private*, pg. 4543
WINSTECH PRECISION HOLDING CO., LTD.; *Int'l*, pg. 8431
WINSTED PRECISION BALL CO.—See INA-Holding Schaeffler GmbH & Co. KG; *Int'l*, pg. 3641
WINSTEK SEMICONDUCTOR CO., LTD.—See Sigurd Microelectronics Corp.; *Int'l*, pg. 6913
WINSTON ADVERTISING; *U.S. Private*, pg. 4544
THE WINSTON CO.; *U.S. Private*, pg. 4137
WINSTON COUNTY MEDICAL FOUNDATION; *U.S. Private*, pg. 4544

WINSTON ELECTRIC; *U.S. Private*, pg. 4544
WINSTONE WALLBOARDS LIMITED—See Fletcher Building Limited; *Int'l*, pg. 2701
WINSTON GOLD CORP.; *Int'l*, pg. 8431
WINSTON HARTON HOLDINGS, LLC; *U.S. Private*, pg. 4544
WINSTON INDUSTRIES, LLC; *U.S. Private*, pg. 4544
WINSTON-JAMES DEVELOPMENT, INC.; *U.S. Private*, pg. 4544
WINSTON PHARMACEUTICALS, INC.; *U.S. Public*, pg. 2374
WINSTON PRINTING COMPANY; *U.S. Private*, pg. 4544
WINSTON RESOURCES, LLC; *U.S. Private*, pg. 4544
THE WINSTON-SALEM FOUNDATION; *U.S. Private*, pg. 4137
WINSTON-SALEM INDUSTRIES FOR THE BLIND, INC.; *U.S. Private*, pg. 4544
WINSTON-SALEM JOURNAL—See Lee Enterprises, Incorporated; *U.S. Public*, pg. 1299
WINSTON & STRAWN LLP; *U.S. Private*, pg. 4543
WINSTON TRACTOR COMPANY—See BobCo Inc.; *U.S. Private*, pg. 607
WIN-SUM SKI CORPORATION; *U.S. Private*, pg. 4533
WINSUN AG—See EnBW Energie Baden-Wuerttemberg AG; *Int'l*, pg. 2400
WINSUN (CAMBODIA) CO., LTD.—See Taisun Int'l (Holding) Corp; *Int'l*, pg. 7418
WINSUPPLY, INC.; *U.S. Private*, pg. 4544
WINSUPPLY INC.; *U.S. Private*, pg. 4544
WIN SYSTEM CO., LTD.—See Koyo Electronics Industries Co., Ltd.; *Int'l*, pg. 4295
WINTAL MACHINES S.R.L.—See Windsor Machines Ltd; *Int'l*, pg. 8426
WINTAO COMMUNICATIONS CO., LTD.; *Int'l*, pg. 8431
WINTAX CAPS (SHENZHEN) CO., LTD.—See Mainland Headwear Holdings Ltd.; *Int'l*, pg. 4651
WINTECH CO., LTD.—See EO Technics Co., Ltd.; *Int'l*, pg. 2457
WINTECH POLYMER LTD.—See Daicel Corporation; *Int'l*, pg. 1920
WINTECH POLYMER LTD.—See Teijin Limited; *Int'l*, pg. 7524
WINTEC INDUSTRIES INC.; *U.S. Private*, pg. 4545
WINTEK CENTRAL EUROPE GMBH—See Wintek Corporation; *Int'l*, pg. 8431
WINTEK CORPORATION; *Int'l*, pg. 8431
WINTEK ELECTRO-OPTICS CORPORATION—See Wintek Corporation; *Int'l*, pg. 8431
WINTELLECT LLC—See Atmosera, Inc.; *U.S. Private*, pg. 381
W INTERACTIVE MEDIA; *Int'l*, pg. 8319
WINTERBERRY GROUP, LLC; *U.S. Private*, pg. 4545
WINTER CHEVROLET HONDA; *U.S. Private*, pg. 4545
WINTER CONSTRUCTION COMPANY; *U.S. Private*, pg. 4545
WINTERFLOOD SECURITIES LIMITED—See Close Brothers Group plc; *Int'l*, pg. 1661
WINTER GARDEN PRESERVATION, L.P.—See Apartment Investment and Management Company; *U.S. Public*, pg. 144
WINTER GARDENS QUALITY FOODS, INC.—See Sandridge Food Corporation; *U.S. Private*, pg. 3544
WINTER GROUP, INC.—See Kelso & Company, L.P.; *U.S. Private*, pg. 2280
WINTERHALTER & FENNER AG—See Sonepar S.A.; *Int'l*, pg. 7093
WINTER HAVEN AMBULATORY SURGICAL CENTER, L.L.C.—See Tenet Healthcare Corporation; *U.S. Public*, pg. 2005
WINTER HAVEN DODGE-CHRYSLER-JEEP INC.; *U.S. Private*, pg. 4545
THE WINTER HAVEN/SEBRING FL OPHTHALMOLOGY ASC, LLC—See KKR & Co. Inc.; *U.S. Public*, pg. 1249
WINTERHAWK CONSULTING LLC—See PentaFour Solutions, LLC; *U.S. Private*, pg. 3139
WINTERHILL ASSET LIMITED; *Int'l*, pg. 8431
WINTER HILL BANK; *U.S. Private*, pg. 4545
WINTER, KLOMAN, MOTER & REPP, S.C.; *U.S. Private*, pg. 4545
WINTER LIVESTOCK INC.; *U.S. Private*, pg. 4545
WINTER PROPERTIES INC.; *U.S. Private*, pg. 4545
WINTERS BROADBAND LLC—See Cal.net, Inc.; *U.S. Private*, pg. 715
WINTERS BROS WASTE SYSTEMS OF LONG ISLAND LLC; *U.S. Private*, pg. 4545
WINTERS BROTHERS, INC.—See Casella Waste Systems, Inc.; *U.S. Public*, pg. 446
WINTERSHALL AG DOHA—See BASF SE; *Int'l*, pg. 885
WINTERSHALL AG—See BASF SE; *Int'l*, pg. 885
WINTERSHALL AG VERTRETUNG MOSKAU—See BASF SE; *Int'l*, pg. 885
WINTERSHALL CHILE LDA.—See BASF SE; *Int'l*, pg. 885
WINTERSHALL DEA AG—See BASF SE; *Int'l*, pg. 885
WINTERSHALL ENERGIA S.A.—See BASF SE; *Int'l*, pg. 885
WINTERSHALL ERDGAS BETEILIGUNGS GMBH—See BASF SE; *Int'l*, pg. 885
WINTERSHALL ERDGAS HANDELSHAUS GMBH AG—See BASF SE; *Int'l*, pg. 885

WINTRONICS INC.

WINTERSHALL ERDGAS HANDELSHAUS ZUG AG—See BASF SE; *Int'l*, pg. 885
WINTERSHALL EXPLORATION AND PRODUCTION INTERNATIONAL C.V.—See BASF SE; *Int'l*, pg. 885
WINTERSHALL HOLDING GMBH—See BASF SE; *Int'l*, pg. 886
WINTERSHALL LIBYA—See BASF SE; *Int'l*, pg. 885
WINTERSHALL LIBYEN OIL & GAS GMBH—See BASF SE; *Int'l*, pg. 886
WINTERSHALL MIDDLE EAST GMBH-ABU DHABI—See BASF SE; *Int'l*, pg. 885
WINTERSHALL NEDERLAND B.V.—See BASF SE; *Int'l*, pg. 885
WINTERSHALL NEDERLAND TRANSPORT AND TRADING B.V.—See BASF SE; *Int'l*, pg. 885
WINTERSHALL NOORDZEE B.V.—See BASF SE; *Int'l*, pg. 885
WINTERSHALL NORGE AS—See BASF SE; *Int'l*, pg. 886
WINTERSHALL NORWEGEN EXPLORATIONS- UND PRODUKTIONS- GMBH—See BASF SE; *Int'l*, pg. 886
WINTERSHALL OIL AG—See BASF SE; *Int'l*, pg. 886
WINTERSHALL PETROLEUM (E&P) B.V.—See BASF SE; *Int'l*, pg. 885
WINTERSHALL PETROLEUM IBERIA S.A.—See BASF SE; *Int'l*, pg. 886
WINTERSHALL RUSSIA HOLDING GMBH—See BASF SE; *Int'l*, pg. 886
WINTERSHALL SERVICES B.V.—See BASF SE; *Int'l*, pg. 886
WINTERSHALL (UK NORTH SEA) LTD.—See BASF SE; *Int'l*, pg. 885
WINTERSHALL VERMOGENSVERWALTUNGSGESELLSCHAFT MBH—See BASF SE; *Int'l*, pg. 886
WINTERSHALL WOLGA PETROLEUM GMBH—See BASF SE; *Int'l*, pg. 886
WINTER SPORTS, INC.; *U.S. Private*, pg. 4545
WINTER & TAYLOR PTY LTD—See AMA Group Limited; *Int'l*, pg. 403
WINTERTHUR INSURANCE CO—See AXA S.A.; *Int'l*, pg. 758
WINTERTHUR LIFE & PENSIONS AG—See AXA S.A.; *Int'l*, pg. 758
WINTERTHUR SCHLEIFTECHNIK AG—See 3M Company; *U.S. Public*, pg. 8
WINTERTHUR TECHNOLOGIE AG—See 3M Company; *U.S. Public*, pg. 8
WINTERTHUR TECHNOLOGY (FRANCE) S.A.R.L.—See 3M Company; *U.S. Public*, pg. 9
WINTERTHUR TECHNOLOGY KOREA LTD.—See 3M Company; *U.S. Public*, pg. 9
WINTERTHUR TECHNOLOGY TAICANG CO. LTD.—See 3M Company; *U.S. Public*, pg. 9
WINTERTHUR TECHNOLOGY UK LTD.—See 3M Company; *U.S. Public*, pg. 9
WINTER VALLEY TOURISM INVESTMENT COMPANY PLC; *Int'l*, pg. 8431
WINTER, WYMAN & COMPANY, INC.—See Odyssey Investment Partners, LLC; *U.S. Private*, pg. 2996
WINTEST CORP.; *Int'l*, pg. 8431
WINTEX-DEPARTMENT VLISCO—See General Atlantic Service Company, L.P.; *U.S. Private*, pg. 1661
WINTHER WIRELESS AB—See DistIT AB; *Int'l*, pg. 2136
WINTHROP ARZNEIMITTEL GMBH—See Sanofi; *Int'l*, pg. 6549
THE WINTHROP CORPORATION; *U.S. Private*, pg. 4137
WINTHROP FINANCIAL ASSOCIATES LP; *U.S. Private*, pg. 4545
WINTHROP MEDICAMENTS S.A.—See Sanofi; *Int'l*, pg. 6550
WINTHROP PHARMACEUTICALS (MALAYSIA) SDN. BHD.—See Sanofi; *Int'l*, pg. 6550
WINTHROP PHARMACEUTICALS (PROPRIETARY) LIMITED—See Sanofi; *Int'l*, pg. 6550
WINTHROP PHARMA SAIDAL S.P.A.—See Sanofi; *Int'l*, pg. 6550
WINTHROP REALTY LIQUIDATING TRUST; *U.S. Public*, pg. 2374
WINTHROP RESOURCES CORPORATION—See Huntington Bancshares Incorporated; *U.S. Public*, pg. 1071
WINTIME ENERGY CO., LTD.; *Int'l*, pg. 8431
WINTLE HEATING & PLUMBING LTD; *Int'l*, pg. 8431
WINTO GROUP (HOLDINGS) LIMITED; *Int'l*, pg. 8431
WINTON CAPITAL ASIA LIMITED—See Affiliated Managers Group, Inc.; *U.S. Public*, pg. 56
WINTON CAPITAL US LLC—See Affiliated Managers Group, Inc.; *U.S. Public*, pg. 56
WINTON GROUP LIMITED—See Affiliated Managers Group, Inc.; *U.S. Public*, pg. 56
WINTON HOLDINGS (BERMUDA) LIMITED—See Public Bank Berhad; *Int'l*, pg. 6094
WINTONI GROUP BHD; *Int'l*, pg. 8431
WINTON LAND LIMITED; *Int'l*, pg. 8431
WIN TOP SHIPPING COMPANY LIMITED—See Dafeng Port Heshun Technology Company Limited; *Int'l*, pg. 1911
WINTRON ELECTRONICS CO., LTD.—See Taitien Electronics Co., Ltd.; *Int'l*, pg. 7418
WINTRONICS INC.; *U.S. Private*, pg. 4545

WINTRONICS INC.

WINTRUST BANK, N.A.—See Wintrust Financial Corporation; *U.S. Public*, pg. 2376
WINTRUST FINANCIAL CORPORATION; *U.S. Public*, pg. 2374
WINTRUST INVESTMENT PTE LTD—See Wing Tai Holdings Limited; *Int'l*, pg. 8428
WINTRUST MORTGAGE CORP.—See Wintrust Financial Corporation; *U.S. Public*, pg. 2374
WINVEST ACQUISITION CORP.; *U.S. Public*, pg. 2376
WINVEST GROUP LTD.; *U.S. Public*, pg. 2376
WIN WARTH GMBH—See DALLI-WERKE GmbH & Co. KG; *Int'l*, pg. 1954
WINWIND OY—See Siva Ventures Limited; *Int'l*, pg. 6966
WIN WIN, INC.; *U.S. Private*, pg. 4532
WINY COMMERCIAL & FISCAL SERVICES LIMITED; *Int'l*, pg. 8431
WINZA PTE. LTD.—See Salzgitter AG; *Int'l*, pg. 6499
WINZELER GEAR; *U.S. Private*, pg. 4546
WINZELER STAMPING CO.; *U.S. Private*, pg. 4546
WINZER CORPORATION—See ShoreView Industries, LLC; *U.S. Private*, pg. 3642
WINZIP COMPUTING LLC—See KKR & Co. Inc.; *U.S. Public*, pg. 1243
WIPAC LIMITED—See Carclo plc; *Int'l*, pg. 1321
WIPAIRE INC.; *U.S. Private*, pg. 4546
WIPAK B.V.—See Winpak Ltd.; *Int'l*, pg. 8430
WIPAK GRYSPEERT S.A.S.—See Winpak Ltd.; *Int'l*, pg. 8430
WIPAK IBERICA S.L.—See Winpak Ltd.; *Int'l*, pg. 8430
WIPAK PACKAGING (CHANGSHU) CO. LTD.—See Winpak Ltd.; *Int'l*, pg. 8430
WIPAK UK LTD.—See Winpak Ltd.; *Int'l*, pg. 8430
WIPAK WALSRODE GMBH & CO. KG—See Winpak Ltd.; *Int'l*, pg. 8430
WIPAM, INC.; *Int'l*, pg. 8431
WIPER BLADES LIMITED—See Vertu Motors plc; *Int'l*, pg. 8175
WIPLIANCE, LLC; *U.S. Private*, pg. 4546
WIPRO 4C CONSULTING FRANCE SAS—See Wipro Limited; *Int'l*, pg. 8433
WIPRO 4C DANMARK APS—See Wipro Limited; *Int'l*, pg. 8433
WIPRO ARABIA LIMITED-RIYADH—See Wipro Limited; *Int'l*, pg. 8433
WIPRO ARABIA LIMITED—See Wipro Limited; *Int'l*, pg. 8433
WIPRO CHENGDU LIMITED—See Wipro Limited; *Int'l*, pg. 8433
WIPRO CONSUMER CARE LIMITED—See Wipro Limited; *Int'l*, pg. 8433
WIPRO CYPRUS PRIVATE LIMITED—See Wipro Limited; *Int'l*, pg. 8433
WIPRO (DALIAN) LIMITED—See Wipro Limited; *Int'l*, pg. 8432
WIPRO DO BRASIL TECNOLOGIA LTDA—See Wipro Limited; *Int'l*, pg. 8433
WIPRO DOHA LLC—See Wipro Limited; *Int'l*, pg. 8433
WIPRO ENTERPRISES (P) LIMITED—See Wipro Limited; *Int'l*, pg. 8433
WIPRO FLUID POWER LTD.—See Wipro Limited; *Int'l*, pg. 8433
WIPRO FRANCE SAS—See Wipro Limited; *Int'l*, pg. 8433
WIPRO GALLAGHER SOLUTIONS—See Wipro Limited; *Int'l*, pg. 8433
WIPRO GE HEALTHCARE PRIVATE LIMITED—See General Electric Company; *U.S. Public*, pg. 920
WIPRO GULF LLC—See Wipro Limited; *Int'l*, pg. 8433
WIPRO HOLDING AUSTRIA GMBH—See Wipro Limited; *Int'l*, pg. 8433
WIPRO INFORMATION TECHNOLOGY (EGYPT) SAE—See Wipro Limited; *Int'l*, pg. 8433
WIPRO INFORMATION TECHNOLOGY NETHERLANDS BV—See Wipro Limited; *Int'l*, pg. 8433
WIPRO INFRASTRUCTURE ENGINEERING AB—See Wipro Limited; *Int'l*, pg. 8433
WIPRO INFRASTRUCTURE ENGINEERING OY—See Wipro Limited; *Int'l*, pg. 8433
WIPRO IT SERVICES AUSTRIA GMBH—See Wipro Limited; *Int'l*, pg. 8433
WIPRO IT SERVICES UK SOCIETAS—See Wipro Limited; *Int'l*, pg. 8433
WIPRO JAPAN KK—See Wipro Limited; *Int'l*, pg. 8433
WIPRO KAWASAKI PRECISION MACHINERY PRIVATE LIMITED—See Kawasaki Heavy Industries, Ltd.; *Int'l*, pg. 4098
WIPRO LIMITED; *Int'l*, pg. 8431
WIPRO NETWORKS PTE LIMITED—See Wipro Limited; *Int'l*, pg. 8433
WIPRO NEWLOGIC—See Wipro Limited; *Int'l*, pg. 8433
WIPRO OUTSOURCING SERVICES (IRELAND) LIMITED—See Wipro Limited; *Int'l*, pg. 8433
WIPRO PORTUGAL S.A.—See Wipro Limited; *Int'l*, pg. 8433
WIPRO RETAIL—See Wipro Limited; *Int'l*, pg. 8433
WIPRO (SHANGHAI) LIMITED—See Wipro Limited; *Int'l*, pg. 8433
WIPRO SOLUTIONS CANADA LIMITED—See Wipro Limited; *Int'l*, pg. 8433

WIPRO TECHNOLOGIES ARGENTINA SA—See Wipro Limited; *Int'l*, pg. 8433
WIPRO TECHNOLOGIES AUSTRALIA PTY LTD—See Wipro Limited; *Int'l*, pg. 8433
WIPRO TECHNOLOGIES BPO—See Wipro Limited; *Int'l*, pg. 8433
WIPRO TECHNOLOGIES NIGERIA LIMITED—See Wipro Limited; *Int'l*, pg. 8433
WIPRO TECHNOLOGIES S.A. DE C.V.—See Wipro Limited; *Int'l*, pg. 8433
WIPRO TECHNOLOGIES SDN. BHD.—See Wipro Limited; *Int'l*, pg. 8433
WIPRO TECHNOLOGIES SOUTH AFRICA (PROPRIETARY) LIMITED—See Wipro Limited; *Int'l*, pg. 8433
WIPRO TECHNOLOGIES S.R.L.—See Wipro Limited; *Int'l*, pg. 8433
WIPRO TECHNOLOGIES/WIPRO BPO—See Wipro Limited; *Int'l*, pg. 8433
WIPRO TECHNOLOGIES/WIPRO BPO—See Wipro Limited; *Int'l*, pg. 8433
WIPRO (THAILAND) CO. LIMITED—See Wipro Limited; *Int'l*, pg. 8433
WIPRO UK LIMITED—See Wipro Limited; *Int'l*, pg. 8433
WIPRO UNZA SINGAPORE PTE LTD—See Wipro Limited; *Int'l*, pg. 8432
WIPRO WEARE4C UK LIMITED—See Wipro Limited; *Int'l*, pg. 8433
WIPSNADE WILD ANIMAL PARK—See The Zoological Society of London; *Int'l*, pg. 7705
WIP WEITERBILDUNG IN DER PFLEGE GMBH—See SOL S.p.A.; *Int'l*, pg. 7068
WIRA FAHRZEUG- UND MASCHINENTEILE GMBH; *Int'l*, pg. 8434
WIRA SYUKUR (M) SDN. BHD.—See Vizione Holdings Berhad; *Int'l*, pg. 8280
WIRB-COPERNICUS GROUP, INC.—See Leonard Green & Partners, L.P.; *U.S. Private*, pg. 2429
WIRE AND WIRELESS TISAI SATELLITE LIMITED—See Essel Corporate Resources Pvt. Ltd.; *Int'l*, pg. 2510
WIRECARD AFRICA HOLDING PROPRIETARY LTD.—See Wirecard AG; *Int'l*, pg. 8434
WIRECARD AG; *Int'l*, pg. 8434
WIRECARD ASIA HOLDING PTE. LTD.—See Wirecard AG; *Int'l*, pg. 8434
WIRECARD AUSTRALIA A&I PTE. LTD.—See Wirecard AG; *Int'l*, pg. 8434
WIRECARD AUSTRALIA PTY. LTD.—See Wirecard AG; *Int'l*, pg. 8434
WIRECARD BANK AG—See Wirecard AG; *Int'l*, pg. 8434
WIRECARD BRAZIL S.A.—See Wirecard AG; *Int'l*, pg. 8434
WIRECARD CARD SOLUTIONS LTD.—See Railsbank Technology Limited; *Int'l*, pg. 6188
WIRECARD CENTRAL EASTERN EUROPE GMBH—See Aurin Investment Group GmbH; *Int'l*, pg. 711
WIRECARD COMMUNICATION SERVICES GMBH—See Wirecard AG; *Int'l*, pg. 8434
WIRECARD E-MONEY PHILIPPINES INC.—See Wirecard AG; *Int'l*, pg. 8434
WIRECARD FOREX INDIA PTE. LTD.—See Wirecard AG; *Int'l*, pg. 8434
WIRECARD (GIBRALTAR) LTD.—See Wirecard AG; *Int'l*, pg. 8434
WIRECARD HONG KONG LTD.—See Wirecard AG; *Int'l*, pg. 8434
WIRECARD MALAYSIA SDN. BHD.—See Wirecard AG; *Int'l*, pg. 8434
WIRECARD MYANMAR LTD.—See Wirecard AG; *Int'l*, pg. 8434
WIRECARD ODEME VE ELEKTRONIK PARA HIZMETLERI A.S.—See Wirecard AG; *Int'l*, pg. 8434
WIRECARD PAYMENT SOLUTIONS MALAYSIA SDN. BHD.—See Finch Capital Partners B.V.; *Int'l*, pg. 2672
WIRECARD UK & IRELAND LTD.—See Wirecard AG; *Int'l*, pg. 8434
WIRECARD (VIETNAM) LTD.—See KT Corporation; *Int'l*, pg. 4314
WIRE CLOTH MANUFACTURERS, INC.—See Graycliff Partners LP; *U.S. Private*, pg. 1761
WIRECOMM SYSTEMS, INC.—See Littlejohn & Co., LLC; *U.S. Private*, pg. 2472
WIRECOMM SYSTEMS, INC.—See New Mountain Capital, LLC; *U.S. Private*, pg. 2903
WIRECO WORLDGROUP, INC.—See ONEX Corporation; *Int'l*, pg. 5580
WIRECO WORLDGROUP—See ONEX Corporation; *Int'l*, pg. 5580
WIRECO WORLDGROUP—See ONEX Corporation; *Int'l*, pg. 5580
WIRECO WORLDGROUP—See ONEX Corporation; *Int'l*, pg. 5580
WIREDCOMMUTE, LLC.—See Edenred S.A.; *Int'l*, pg. 2308
WIRED REAL ESTATE GROUP INC.; *U.S. Private*, pg. 4546
WIREDRIVE; *U.S. Private*, pg. 4546
WIRED—See Advance Publications, Inc.; *U.S. Private*, pg. 86
WIREDTREE; *U.S. Private*, pg. 4546

CORPORATE AFFILIATIONS

WIREGRASS CENTRAL RAILWAY, L.L.C.—See Brookfield Infrastructure Partners L.P.; *Int'l*, pg. 1193
WIREGRASS CENTRAL RAILWAY, L.L.C.—See GIC Pte. Ltd.; *Int'l*, pg. 2967
WIREGRASS CONSTRUCTION COMPANY; *U.S. Private*, pg. 4546
WIREGRASS ELECTRIC COOPERATIVE, INC.; *U.S. Private*, pg. 4546
WIREGRASS ELECTRIC COOPERATIVE; *U.S. Private*, pg. 4546
WIRELESS ANALYTICS, LLC—See Thoma Bravo, L.P.; *U.S. Private*, pg. 4150
WIRELESS COMMUNICATIONS INC.; *U.S. Private*, pg. 4546
WIRELESS COMMUNICATIONS INC.; *U.S. Private*, pg. 4546
WIRELESS DEVICE SUPPLY CO., LTD.—See Advanced Info Service Plc; *Int'l*, pg. 160
WIRELESS ELECTRONICS, INC.; *U.S. Private*, pg. 4547
WIRELESS EMPORIUM, INC.; *U.S. Private*, pg. 4547
WIRELESS ENERGY MANAGEMENT SYSTEMS INTERNATIONAL LIMITED—See WHEB Capital Partners LLP; *Int'l*, pg. 8397
WIRELESS ENVIRONMENT, LLC; *U.S. Private*, pg. 4547
THE WIRELESS EXPERIENCE GROUP—See Centre Partners Management LLC; *U.S. Private*, pg. 829
WIRELESSGATE, INC.; *Int'l*, pg. 8434
WIRELESS GROUP LIMITED—See News Corporation; *U.S. Public*, pg. 1520
WIRELESS INNOVATION LTD.—See Horizon Capital LLP; *Int'l*, pg. 3479
WIRELESS LOGIC GROUP LIMITED—See Montagu Private Equity LLP; *Int'l*, pg. 5036
WIRELESS LOGIC LTD.—See Montagu Private Equity LLP; *Int'l*, pg. 5036
WIRELESS MAINGATE AB—See Sierra Wireless, Inc.; *Int'l*, pg. 6904
WIRELESS PLUS, INC.—See Sentinel Capital Partners, L.L.C.; *U.S. Private*, pg. 3609
WIRELESS RONIN TECHNOLOGIES, (CANADA), INC.—See Creative Realities, Inc.; *U.S. Public*, pg. 593
WIRELESS SOLUTION SWEDEN AB—See LumenRadio AB; *Int'l*, pg. 4577
WIRELESS TECHNOLOGIES, INC.—See Cresco, Ltd.; *Int'l*, pg. 1840
WIRELESS TECHNOLOGY EQUIPMENT COMPANY, INC.—See Motorola Solutions, Inc.; *U.S. Public*, pg. 1479
WIRELESS TELECOM GROUP, INC.—See Artemis Capital Partners Management Co., LLC; *U.S. Private*, pg. 340
WIRELESS TOYZ LLC; *U.S. Private*, pg. 4547
WIRELESSTUDIOS INC.—See Cameron Thomson Group Ltd.; *Int'l*, pg. 1272
WIRELESSUSA, INC.; *U.S. Private*, pg. 4547
WIRELESS VENTURES LLC; *U.S. Private*, pg. 4547
WIRELESS WORLD; *U.S. Private*, pg. 4547
WIRELESS XCESSORIES GROUP, INC.; *U.S. Public*, pg. 2376
WIRELESS ZONE LLC—See Round Room LLC; *U.S. Private*, pg. 3488
WIRE MASTER SPRING SDN. BHD.—See MyTech Group Bhd; *Int'l*, pg. 5114
THE WIREMOLD COMPANY—See Legrand S.A.; *Int'l*, pg. 4446
WIREMOLD INTERNATIONAL SALES CORPORATION—See Legrand S.A.; *Int'l*, pg. 4446
THE WIRENUT; *U.S. Private*, pg. 4138
WIRE PRODUCTS COMPANY INC.; *U.S. Private*, pg. 4546
WIRE PRODUCTS LTD—See Aga Khan Development Network; *Int'l*, pg. 199
WIRE ROPE CORPORATION OF THE PHILIPPINES—See DMCI Holdings, Inc.; *Int'l*, pg. 2143
WIRE SANDVIKEN AB—See Sandvik AB; *Int'l*, pg. 6535
WIRES & FABRIKS (S.A.) LIMITED; *Int'l*, pg. 8434
WIRE SHOP INC.; *U.S. Private*, pg. 4546
WIRE STONE, LLC; *U.S. Private*, pg. 4546
WIRESTONE, LLC—See Wire Stone, LLC; *U.S. Private*, pg. 4546
WIRESTONE—See Wire Stone, LLC; *U.S. Private*, pg. 4546
WIRESTONE—See Wire Stone, LLC; *U.S. Private*, pg. 4546
WIRESTONE—See Wire Stone, LLC; *U.S. Private*, pg. 4546
WIRESTONE—See Wire Stone, LLC; *U.S. Private*, pg. 4546
WIRESTONE—See Wire Stone, LLC; *U.S. Private*, pg. 4546
WIRE TECHNO, LTD.—See Godo Steel, Ltd.; *Int'l*, pg. 3020
WIREVIBE; *U.S. Private*, pg. 4547
WIREWAY/HUSKY CORPORATION; *U.S. Private*, pg. 4547
WIRE WELD USA INC.; *U.S. Private*, pg. 4546
WIRE & WIRELESS CO., LTD.—See KDDI Corporation; *Int'l*, pg. 4112
WIREX LIMITED; *Int'l*, pg. 8434

COMPANY NAME INDEX

WIRICHS IMMOBILIEN GMBH—See Metro AG; *Int'l*, pg. 4859
WIRING DEVICE-KELLEMS—See Hubbell Incorporated; *U.S. Public*, pg. 1067
WIRMACHENDRUCK GMBH—See Cimpress plc; *Int'l*, pg. 1609
WIROM GAS S.A.—See BASF SE; *Int'l*, pg. 885
WIROP INDUSTRIAL CO., LTD.—See SE Corporation; *Int'l*, pg. 6660
WIRTEK A/S; *Int'l*, pg. 8434
WIRTGEN AMERICA INC.—See Deere & Company; *U.S. Public*, pg. 648
WIRTGEN ANKARA MAKINA SANAYI VE TICARET LTD. STI.—See Deere & Company; *U.S. Public*, pg. 648
WIRTGEN AUSTRALIA PTY LTD—See Deere & Company; *U.S. Public*, pg. 648
WIRTGEN BELGIUM B.V.B.A.—See Deere & Company; *U.S. Public*, pg. 648
WIRTGEN (CHINA) MACHINERY CO., LTD.—See Deere & Company; *U.S. Public*, pg. 647
WIRTGEN EESTI OU—See Deere & Company; *U.S. Public*, pg. 648
WIRTGEN FRANCE SAS—See Deere & Company; *U.S. Public*, pg. 648
WIRTGEN GMBH—See Deere & Company; *U.S. Public*, pg. 647
WIRTGEN GROUP HOLDING GMBH—See Deere & Company; *U.S. Public*, pg. 647
WIRTGEN INDIA PVT. LTD.—See Deere & Company; *U.S. Public*, pg. 648
WIRTGEN MACCHINE SRL.—See Deere & Company; *U.S. Public*, pg. 648
WIRTGEN NORWAY AS—See Deere & Company; *U.S. Public*, pg. 648
WIRTGEN OSTERREICH GMBH—See Deere & Company; *U.S. Public*, pg. 648
WIRTGEN SINGAPORE PTE. LTD.—See Deere & Company; *U.S. Public*, pg. 648
WIRTGEN SOUTH AFRICA (PTY) LTD.—See Deere & Company; *U.S. Public*, pg. 648
WIRTGEN-SRBIJA D.O.O.—See Deere & Company; *U.S. Public*, pg. 648
WIRTGEN (THAILAND) CO. LTD.—See Deere & Company; *U.S. Public*, pg. 648
WIRTGEN ZWICKAU VERTRIEBS- UND SERVICE GMBH—See Deere & Company; *U.S. Public*, pg. 648
WIRTH BUSINESS CREDIT, INC.—See Winmark Corporation; *U.S. Public*, pg. 2374
WIRTHS LUMBER CO., INC.; *U.S. Private*, pg. 4547
WIRTH STEEL, A GENERAL PARTNERSHIP—See Russel Metals Inc.; *Int'l*, pg. 6430
WIRTUALNA POLSKA HOLDING S.A.; *Int'l*, pg. 8434
WIRTZ CORPORATION; *U.S. Private*, pg. 4547
WIRTZ INSURANCE AGENCY, INC.—See Wirtz Corporation; *U.S. Private*, pg. 4547
WIRTZ MANUFACTURING COMPANY INC.; *U.S. Private*, pg. 4547
WIRTZ REALTY CORPORATION—See Wirtz Corporation; *U.S. Private*, pg. 4547
WIRUTEC RUSCH MEDICAL VERTRIEBS GMBH—See Teleflex Incorporated; *U.S. Public*, pg. 1996
WIRWINZER GMBH—See Hawesko Holding AG; *Int'l*, pg. 3289
WIRYE ENERGY SERVICE CO., LTD.—See SK Innovation Co., Ltd.; *Int'l*, pg. 6973
WIRZ COMMUNICATIONS AG—See Anton Borer Immobilien AG; *Int'l*, pg. 484
WIRZ & HAFNER WERBEBERATUNG GMBH—See Anton Borer Immobilien AG; *Int'l*, pg. 484
WIRZ WERBEAGENTUR GMBH—See Anton Borer Immobilien AG; *Int'l*, pg. 484
WISAP GESELLSCHAFT FUR WISSENSCHAFTLICHEN APPARATEBAU MBH; *Int'l*, pg. 8434
WISAPOWER OY—See Pohjolan Voima Oy; *Int'l*, pg. 5904
WISAP WIEN HANDELSGESELLSCHAFT MBH—See WISAP Gesellschaft fur Wissenschaftlichen Apparatebau mbH; *Int'l*, pg. 8435
WISA TECHNOLOGIES, INC.; *U.S. Public*, pg. 2376
WISBET INTERNATIONAL CO., LTD.; *Int'l*, pg. 8435
WISBY ASSISTANS AB—See Humana AB; *Int'l*, pg. 3530
WISCNET; *U.S. Private*, pg. 4547
WISCO ECHENG IRON & STEEL CO., LTD.—See China Baowu Steel Group Corp., Ltd.; *Int'l*, pg. 1485
WISCO ENVELOPE—See Ennis, Inc.; *U.S. Public*, pg. 769
WISCO, INC.—See Gibson Energy Inc.; *Int'l*, pg. 2963
WISCO INDUSTRIES INC.; *U.S. Private*, pg. 4547
WISCO LASERTECHNIK GMBH—See ThyssenKrupp AG; *Int'l*, pg. 7730
WISCOM CO., LTD - ANSAN 2 FACTORY—See WISCOM Co., Ltd; *Int'l*, pg. 8435
WISCOM CO., LTD - ANSUNG FACTORY—See WISCOM Co., Ltd; *Int'l*, pg. 8435
WISCOM CO., LTD - SIHWA FACTORY—See WISCOM Co., Ltd; *Int'l*, pg. 8435
WISCOM CO., LTD; *Int'l*, pg. 8435
WISCOM CO., LTD - YEOSU FACTORY—See WISCOM Co., Ltd; *Int'l*, pg. 8435
WISCOM ENGINEERING PLASTICS (WUXI) CO., LTD.—See WISCOM Co., Ltd; *Int'l*, pg. 8435

WISCOM SYSTEM CO., LTD.; *Int'l*, pg. 8435
WISCONSIN ALUMINUM FOUNDRY COMPANY, INC.; *U.S. Private*, pg. 4547
WISCONSIN ALUMNI RESEARCH FOUNDATION; *U.S. Private*, pg. 4547
WISCONSIN AVENUE PSYCHIATRIC CENTER, INC.,—See Universal Health Services, Inc.; *U.S. Public*, pg. 2261
WISCONSIN AVIATION INC.; *U.S. Private*, pg. 4548
WISCONSIN BANK & TRUST—See Heartland Financial USA, Inc.; *U.S. Public*, pg. 1018
WISCONSIN BIOPRODUCTS—See Molecular Biology Resources; *U.S. Private*, pg. 2767
WISCONSIN BOX COMPANY; *U.S. Private*, pg. 4548
WISCONSIN BREWING COMPANY LLC; *U.S. Private*, pg. 4548
WISCONSIN BUILT INC.; *U.S. Private*, pg. 4548
WISCONSIN CENTRIFUGAL, INC.—See MetalTek International; *U.S. Private*, pg. 2682
WISCONSIN CHEESE GROUP INC.; *U.S. Private*, pg. 4548
WISCONSIN CHEESE INC.; *U.S. Private*, pg. 4548
WISCONSIN DISTRIBUTORS L.P.; *U.S. Private*, pg. 4548
WISCONSIN EARLY CHILDHOOD ASSOCIATION; *U.S. Private*, pg. 4548
WISCONSIN EDUCATIONAL COMMUNICATIONS BOARD; *U.S. Private*, pg. 4548
WISCONSIN ELECTRIC POWER COMPANY—See WEC Energy Group, Inc.; *U.S. Public*, pg. 2342
WISCONSIN ELEVATOR COMPANY, LLC—See Gardner Standard LLC; *U.S. Private*, pg. 1644
WISCONSIN FILM & BAG, INC.—See Apollo Global Management, Inc.; *U.S. Public*, pg. 154
WISCONSIN GAS LLC—See WEC Energy Group, Inc.; *U.S. Public*, pg. 2342
WISCONSIN HEALTH FUND; *U.S. Private*, pg. 4548
WISCONSIN HOMES INC.; *U.S. Private*, pg. 4548
WISCONSIN HUMANE SOCIETY; *U.S. Private*, pg. 4548
WISCONSIN INDUSTRIAL SAND COMPANY, LLC—See Covia Holdings Corporation; *U.S. Private*, pg. 1072
WISCONSIN INVESTCAST INC.—See MetalTek International; *U.S. Private*, pg. 2682
WISCONSIN LIFT TRUCK CORP.; *U.S. Private*, pg. 4548
WISCONSIN MANAGEMENT COMPANY; *U.S. Private*, pg. 4548
WISCONSIN METAL PRODUCTS CO.; *U.S. Private*, pg. 4548
WISCONSIN MUTUAL INSURANCE CO.; *U.S. Private*, pg. 4548
WISCONSIN OVEN CORPORATION—See PLC Holding Co.; *Int'l*, pg. 5895
WISCONSIN PACKING CO. INC. DELAWARE; *U.S. Private*, pg. 4548
WISCONSIN PHARMACAL COMPANY, LLC; *U.S. Private*, pg. 4548
WISCONSIN PHYSICIANS SERVICE INSURANCE CORPORATION; *U.S. Private*, pg. 4548
WISCONSIN PIPE TRADES HEALTH FUND; *U.S. Private*, pg. 4549
WISCONSIN POWER AND LIGHT COMPANY—See Alliant Energy Corporation; *U.S. Public*, pg. 79
WISCONSIN PUBLIC SERVICE CORPORATION—See WEC Energy Group, Inc.; *U.S. Public*, pg. 2342
WISCONSIN RAPIDS SENIOR LIVING, INC.—See The Ensign Group, Inc.; *U.S. Public*, pg. 2070
WISCONSIN REINSURANCE CORP.; *U.S. Private*, pg. 4549
WISCONSIN RIVER CO-OP; *U.S. Private*, pg. 4549
WISCONSIN RIVER POWER COMPANY—See Alliant Energy Corporation; *U.S. Public*, pg. 79
WISCONSIN RIVER POWER COMPANY—See WEC Energy Group, Inc.; *U.S. Public*, pg. 2342
WISCONSIN & SOUTHERN RAILROAD COMPANY—See Kinder Morgan, Inc.; *U.S. Public*, pg. 1233
WISCONSIN & SOUTHERN RAILROAD COMPANY—See Kinder Morgan, Inc.; *U.S. Public*, pg. 1233
WISCONSIN & SOUTHERN RAILROAD COMPANY—See Kinder Morgan, Inc.; *U.S. Public*, pg. 1233
WISCONSIN & SOUTHERN RAILROAD COMPANY—See Kinder Morgan, Inc.; *U.S. Public*, pg. 1233
WISCONSIN SPECIALTY SURGERY CENTER, LLC—See Tenet Healthcare Corporation; *U.S. Public*, pg. 2015
WISCONSIN STATE JOURNAL—See Lee Enterprises, Incorporated; *U.S. Public*, pg. 1299
WISCONSIN STATE JOURNAL—See The Capital Times Company; *U.S. Private*, pg. 4004
WISCONSIN STEEL & TUBE CORPORATION; *U.S. Private*, pg. 4549
WISCONSIN STRUCTURAL STEEL COMPANY—See APi Group Corporation; *Int'l*, pg. 514
WISCONSIN TECHNICOLOR LLC; *U.S. Private*, pg. 4549
WISCONSIN THERMOSET MOLDING, INC.; *U.S. Private*, pg. 4549
WISCONSIN TITLE SERVICE COMPANY, INC.—See First American Financial Corporation; *U.S. Public*, pg. 838
WISCONSIN VALLEY IMPROVEMENT COMPANY—See WEC Energy Group, Inc.; *U.S. Public*, pg. 2342
WISCONSIN VENEER & PLYWOOD, INC.—See The Hoffmann Family of Companies; *U.S. Private*, pg. 4053

WISCONSIN VISION ASSOCIATES INC.; *U.S. Private*, pg. 4549
WISCO PRODUCTS, INC.; *U.S. Private*, pg. 4547
WISCO TAILORED BLANKS GMBH—See China Baowu Steel Group Corp., Ltd.; *Int'l*, pg. 1485
WISDEK CORP.; *Int'l*, pg. 8435
WISDOMCOME GROUP HOLDINGS LIMITED; *Int'l*, pg. 8435
WISDOM DISTRIBUTION SERVICE CORP.—See Uni-President Enterprises Corporation; *Int'l*, pg. 8029
WISDOM EDUCATION INTERNATIONAL HOLDINGS COMPANY LIMITED; *Int'l*, pg. 8435
WISDOMFORCE TECHNOLOGIES, INC.—See Canada Pension Plan Investment Board; *Int'l*, pg. 1280
WISDOMFORCE TECHNOLOGIES, INC.—See Permira Advisers LLP; *Int'l*, pg. 5806
WISDOM HOMES OF AMERICA, INC.; *U.S. Private*, pg. 4549
WISDOM INFOTECH; *U.S. Private*, pg. 4549
WISDOM MARINE INTERNATIONAL INC.—See Wisdom Marine Lines Co., Ltd.; *Int'l*, pg. 8435
WISDOM MARINE LINES CO., LTD.; *Int'l*, pg. 8435
WISDOM SPORTS GROUP; *Int'l*, pg. 8435
WISDOM TMIC B.V.—See Sopra Steria Group S.A.; *Int'l*, pg. 7110
WISDOMTOOLS, LLC; *U.S. Private*, pg. 4549
WISDOM TOOTHBRUSHES LTD.; *Int'l*, pg. 8435
WISDOMTREE ASSET MANAGEMENT CANADA, INC.—See CI Financial Corporation; *Int'l*, pg. 1601
WISDOMTREE EUROPE LTD.—See WisdomTree, Inc.; *U.S. Public*, pg. 2376
WISDOMTREE, INC.; *U.S. Public*, pg. 2376
WISDOMTREE INTERNATIONAL REAL ESTATE FUND—See WisdomTree, Inc.; *U.S. Public*, pg. 2376
WISDOM WEALTH RESOURCES INVESTMENT HOLDING GROUP LIMITED; *Int'l*, pg. 8435
WISE ALLOYS LLC; *U.S. Private*, pg. 4549
WISE ALLY INTERNATIONAL HOLDINGS LIMITED; *Int'l*, pg. 8435
WISE.ART AG—See WISeKey International Holding Ltd; *Int'l*, pg. 8436
WISE AUTOMOTIVE, INC.; *U.S. Private*, pg. 4549
WISE BRASIL CORRETORA DE CAMBIO LTDA.—See Wise Plc; *Int'l*, pg. 8436
WISE BUSINESS FORMS INCORPORATED - COMMERCIAL PRINTING PLANT—See Wise Business Forms Incorporated; *U.S. Private*, pg. 4549
WISE BUSINESS FORMS INCORPORATED - INDIANA PLANT—See Wise Business Forms Incorporated; *U.S. Private*, pg. 4549
WISE BUSINESS FORMS INCORPORATED - PENNSYLVANIA PLANT—See Wise Business Forms Incorporated; *U.S. Private*, pg. 4549
WISE BUSINESS FORMS INCORPORATED; *U.S. Private*, pg. 4549
WISE BUSINESS FORMS INCORPORATED - SOUTH CAROLINA PLANT—See Wise Business Forms Incorporated; *U.S. Private*, pg. 4549
WISE BUSINESS—See Wise Business Forms Incorporated; *U.S. Private*, pg. 4549
WISEC GLOBAL LIMITED; *Int'l*, pg. 8436
WISECHIP SEMICONDUCTOR INC.; *Int'l*, pg. 8436
WISE COACHES, INC.—See Mobico Group PLC; *Int'l*, pg. 5009
WISECOIN AG—See WISeKey International Holding Ltd; *Int'l*, pg. 8436
THE WISE CO. INC.; *U.S. Private*, pg. 4138
WISE COMPONENTS INC.; *U.S. Private*, pg. 4549
WISE CONNECT, INC.—See Hastings Equity Partners, LLC; *U.S. Private*, pg. 1879
WISE CONSULTING ASSOCIATES, LLC—See RSM US LLP; *U.S. Private*, pg. 3497
WISE ELECTRIC COOPERATIVE, INC.; *U.S. Private*, pg. 4550
WISE EL SANTO COMPANY INC.; *U.S. Private*, pg. 4549
WISE EQUITY SGR S.P.A.; *Int'l*, pg. 8435
WISE FOODS, INC.—See Arca Continental, S.A.B. de C.V.; *Int'l*, pg. 540
WISE FORKLIFT INC.; *U.S. Private*, pg. 4550
WISE GAS, INC.; *U.S. Private*, pg. 4550
WISE GROUP AB; *Int'l*, pg. 8436
WISE INTEGRATION CO., LTD.—See Sunny Side Up Group Inc.; *Int'l*, pg. 7319
WISE ITECH CO., LTD.; *Int'l*, pg. 8436
WISEKEY INDIA PRIVATE LTD.—See WISeKey International Holding Ltd; *Int'l*, pg. 8436
WISEKEY INTERNATIONAL HOLDING LTD; *Int'l*, pg. 8436
WISEKEY LOT JAPAN KK—See WISeKey International Holding Ltd; *Int'l*, pg. 8436
WISEKEY SEMICONDUCTORS SAS—See WISeKey International Holding Ltd; *Int'l*, pg. 8436
WISE LAUSNIR EHF—See Centara ehf; *Int'l*, pg. 1402
WISELINK CO., LTD.; *Int'l*, pg. 8436
WISE LUCK INTERNATIONAL (HK) LIMITED—See Come Sure Group (Holdings) Limited; *Int'l*, pg. 1710
WISEMAN GLOBAL LIMITED; *Int'l*, pg. 8436
WISEMAN GROUP INTERIOR DESIGN INC.; *U.S. Private*, pg. 4550

WISENBAKER BUILDER SERVICES LTD. | CORPORATE AFFILIATIONS

WISENBAKER BUILDER SERVICES LTD.; *U.S. Private,* pg. 4550
WISENLARGE, INC.—See KeyHolder, Inc.; *Int'l,* pg. 4146
WISE OIL & FUEL INCORPORATED; *U.S. Private,* pg. 4550
WISEOPS CO., LIMITED—See Kaga Electronics Co., Ltd.; *Int'l,* pg. 4048
THE WISE OPTICAL VISION GROUP; *U.S. Private,* pg. 4138
WISE PLC; *Int'l,* pg. 8436
WISEPOWER CO., LTD.; *Int'l,* pg. 8436
WISE PROPERTY CARE LIMITED—See Rentokil Initial plc; *Int'l,* pg. 6289
WISER CAPITAL LLC; *U.S. Private,* pg. 4550
WISE RECYCLING LLC; *U.S. Private,* pg. 4550
WISEROCK AG—See BKW AG; *Int'l,* pg. 1056
WISERTOGETHER, INC.—See Evive Health, LLC; *U.S. Private,* pg. 1442
WISESCAN ENGINEERING SERVICES PTE. LTD.—See CSC Holdings Limited; *Int'l,* pg. 1862
WISE SIGMA INTERNATIONAL HOLDING COMPANY LIMITED—See Cal-Comp Electronics (Thailand) pcl; *Int'l,* pg. 1261
WISESOFT CO., LTD.; *Int'l,* pg. 8436
WISETECH ACADEMY PTY LTD—See WiseTech Global Limited; *Int'l,* pg. 8437
WISETECH GLOBAL (AUSTRALIA) PTY. LTD.—See WiseTech Global Limited; *Int'l,* pg. 8437
WISETECH GLOBAL FZ-LLC—See WiseTech Global Limited; *Int'l,* pg. 8437
WISETECH GLOBAL (HK) LTD.—See WiseTech Global Limited; *Int'l,* pg. 8437
WISETECH GLOBAL (JAPAN) K.K.—See WiseTech Global Limited; *Int'l,* pg. 8437
WISETECH GLOBAL LIMITED; *Int'l,* pg. 8436
WISETECH GLOBAL (NZ) LTD.—See WiseTech Global Limited; *Int'l,* pg. 8437
WISETECH GLOBAL (PTY) LTD.—See WiseTech Global Limited; *Int'l,* pg. 8437
WISETECH GLOBAL (SG) PTE LTD—See WiseTech Global Limited; *Int'l,* pg. 8437
WISETECH GLOBAL (TAIWAN) LTD.—See WiseTech Global Limited; *Int'l,* pg. 8437
WISETECH GLOBAL (US) INC.—See WiseTech Global Limited; *Int'l,* pg. 8437
WISETIME GMBH—See IPH Limited; *Int'l,* pg. 3797
WISETIME LLC—See IPH Limited; *Int'l,* pg. 3797
WISETIME OY—See Samvardhana Motherson International Limited; *Int'l,* pg. 6518
WISE-TV, INC.—See Silver Point Capital, L.P.; *U.S. Private,* pg. 3662
WISEWAY LOGISTICS PTY. LTD.; *Int'l,* pg. 8437
WISEWAY MOTOR FREIGHT INC.; *U.S. Private,* pg. 4550
WISEWAY SUPPLY INC.; *U.S. Private,* pg. 4550
WISHBONE GOLD PLC; *Int'l,* pg. 8437
WISHER INDUSTRIAL CO., LTD.; *Int'l,* pg. 4138
WISHNATZKI, INC.; *U.S. Private,* pg. 4550
WISHON & CARTER BUILDERS; *U.S. Private,* pg. 4550
WISHPOND TECHNOLOGIES LTD.; *Int'l,* pg. 8437
WIS INTERNATIONAL—See Ares Management Corporation; *U.S. Public,* pg. 191
WIS KUNSTSTOFFE GMBH; *Int'l,* pg. 8434
WI-SKY INFLIGHT, INC.; *U.S. Private,* pg. 4515
WISLER ELEKTRO AG—See Burkhalter Holding AG; *Int'l,* pg. 1226
WIS, LLC—See Gray Television, Inc.; *U.S. Public,* pg. 960
WISMA ATRIA HOLDING GMBH & CO. SINGAPUR KG—See Munchener Ruckversicherungs AG; *Int'l,* pg. 5092
WISMA DEVELOPMENT SDN. BHD.—See Gromutual Berhad; *Int'l,* pg. 3088
WISMETAC ASIAN FOODS, INC.—See Nishimoto Co., Ltd.; *Int'l,* pg. 5365
WISMETAC FOODS, INC.—See Nishimoto Co., Ltd.; *Int'l,* pg. 5365
WISN HEARST-ARGYLE TELEVISION, INC.—See The Hearst Corporation; *U.S. Private,* pg. 4049
WISOL CO., LTD; *Int'l,* pg. 8437
WISON ENGINEERING LIMITED—See Wison Engineering Services Co., Ltd.; *Int'l,* pg. 8437
WISON ENGINEERING SERVICES CO., LTD.; *Int'l,* pg. 8437
WISON PETROCHEMICALS (NA), LLC—See Wison Engineering Services Co., Ltd.; *Int'l,* pg. 8437
WISON (YANGZHOU) CHEMICAL MACHINERY CO., LTD.—See Wison Engineering Services Co., Ltd.; *Int'l,* pg. 8437
WIS-PAK, INC.; *U.S. Private,* pg. 4547
WISPARK LLC—See WEC Energy Group, Inc.; *U.S. Public,* pg. 2342
WISPECO HOLDINGS LIMITED—See Remgro Limited; *Int'l,* pg. 6271
WISPRY, INC.—See AAC Technologies Holdings Inc.; *Int'l,* pg. 31
WISR FINANCE PTY LTD; *Int'l,* pg. 8437
WISSENSCHAFTICH TECHNISCHE WERKSTAETTEN GMBH—See Xylem Inc.; *U.S. Public,* pg. 2395
WISS, JANNEY, ELSTNER ASSOCIATES, INC.; *U.S. Private,* pg. 4550

WISSLER MOTORS, INC.; *U.S. Private,* pg. 4550
WISTA STAHLHANDEL WITTEN GMBH—See Georgsmarienhutte Holding GmbH; *Int'l,* pg. 2941
WIST CO., LTD.—See Mutual Corporation; *Int'l,* pg. 5106
WIST ENTERPRISES, INC.—See The Jordan Company, L.P.; *U.S. Private,* pg. 4063
WISTIL S.A.; *Int'l,* pg. 8438
WISTRA CERINNOV GMBH—See Cerinnov Group SA; *Int'l,* pg. 1422
WISTRON CORPORATION; *Int'l,* pg. 8438
WISTRON EUROPE HOLDING COOPERATIE U.A.—See Wistron Corporation; *Int'l,* pg. 8438
WISTRON INFOCOMM (PHILIPPINES) CORP.—See Wistron Corporation; *Int'l,* pg. 8438
WISTRON INFOCOMM (SHANGHAI) CORPORATION—See Wistron Corporation; *Int'l,* pg. 8438
WISTRON INFOCOMM TECHNOLOGY (AMERICA) CORPORATION—See Wistron Corporation; *Int'l,* pg. 8438
WISTRON INFOCOMM (ZHONGSHAN) CO., LTD—See Wistron Corporation; *Int'l,* pg. 8438
WISTRON INFORMATION TECHNOLOGY & SERVICES CORPORATION—See Wistron Corporation; *Int'l,* pg. 8438
WISTRON K.K.—See Wistron Corporation; *Int'l,* pg. 8438
WISTRON MEXICO S.A. DE C.V.—See Wistron Corporation; *Int'l,* pg. 8438
WISTRON NEWEB CORPORATION—See Wistron Corporation; *Int'l,* pg. 8438
WISTRON NEXUS INC.—See Acer Incorporated; *Int'l,* pg. 100
WISURA GMBH—See FUCHS SE; *Int'l,* pg. 2804
WISVEST LLC—See WEC Energy Group, Inc.; *U.S. Public,* pg. 2342
WISYNCO GROUP LTD.; *Int'l,* pg. 8438
W.I. SYSTEM INC.—See Menicon Co., Ltd.; *Int'l,* pg. 4816
WITAN INVESTMENT TRUST PLC; *Int'l,* pg. 8438
WITBE SA; *Int'l,* pg. 8438
WITCH EQUIPMENT COMPANY, INC.; *U.S. Private,* pg. 4550
WITCO SPECIALTIES (THAILAND) LTD.—See LANXESS AG; *Int'l,* pg. 4415
WITCO SYSTEMS INC.—See Wisconsin Lift Truck Corp.; *U.S. Private,* pg. 4548
WIT DEEP SAND AND STONE (PTY) LIMITED—See Vuwa Investments (Pty) Ltd; *Int'l,* pg. 8318
WITEG LABORTECHNIK GMBH; *Int'l,* pg. 8438
WITEKIO GMBH—See Avnet, Inc.; *U.S. Public,* pg. 254
WITELLAS INC.—See Relia, Inc.; *Int'l,* pg. 6260
WIT GROUP INC.; *U.S. Private,* pg. 4550
WITHAM AUTO CENTERS, INC.; *U.S. Private,* pg. 4550
WITH CLARITY INC.; *U.S. Private,* pg. 4550
WITHERS BROADCASTING COMPANY OF ILLINOIS, LLC—See Withers Broadcasting Company of West Virginia; *U.S. Private,* pg. 4550
WITHERS BROADCASTING COMPANY OF WEST VIRGINIA; *U.S. Private,* pg. 4550
WITHERS L.P.—See Mullen Group Ltd.; *Int'l,* pg. 5080
WITHERS/SUDDATH VAN LINES, INC.—See The Suddath Companies; *U.S. Private,* pg. 4125
WITHERS WORLDWIDE; *U.S. Private,* pg. 4550
WITHIN TECHNOLOGIES LIMITED—See Autodesk, Inc.; *U.S. Public,* pg. 229
WITHINTEC INC.—See TIS Inc.; *Int'l,* pg. 7758
WITH KURITA LTD.—See Kurita Water Industries Ltd.; *Int'l,* pg. 4341
WITHLACOOCHEE RIVER ELECTRIC COOPERATIVE, INC.; *U.S. Private,* pg. 4550
WITHLINK CO.,LTD.—See Yoshinoya Holdings Co., Ltd.; *Int'l,* pg. 8600
WITHNELL MOTOR COMPANY; *U.S. Private,* pg. 4550
WITHPHOTO INC.—See Canon Inc.; *Int'l,* pg. 1296
WITHSECURE CORPORATION; *Int'l,* pg. 8438
WITHTECH INC.; *Int'l,* pg. 8439
WITHUMSMITH+BROWN PC; *U.S. Private,* pg. 4550
WITH US CO., LTD.—See El.En. S.p.A.; *Int'l,* pg. 2342
WITHUS CORP.; *Int'l,* pg. 8439
WITHUS PHARMACEUTICAL CO., LTD.; *Int'l,* pg. 8439
WITHUS TECHNOLOGY CORP.; *Int'l,* pg. 8439
WITH YOU—See Places for People Group Limited; *Int'l,* pg. 5888
WITI TELEVISION, LLC—See Nexstar Media Group, Inc.; *U.S. Public,* pg. 1525
WITI-TV—See Nexstar Media Group, Inc.; *U.S. Public,* pg. 1525
WITKEMPER INSURANCE GROUP—See GTCR LLC; *U.S. Private,* pg. 1804
WITLAB (PROPRIETARY) LTD—See ALS Limited; *Int'l,* pg. 378
WITMER PUBLIC SAFETY GROUP, INC.; *U.S. Private,* pg. 4551
WITN-TV—See Gray Television, Inc.; *U.S. Public,* pg. 960
WITRE AB—See Manutan International SA; *Int'l,* pg. 4680
WITRE A/S—See Manutan International SA; *Int'l,* pg. 4680
WITRE DANMARK A/S—See Manutan International SA; *Int'l,* pg. 4680
WITRE OY—See Manutan International SA; *Int'l,* pg. 4680
WI-TRON, INC.; *U.S. Public,* pg. 2369

WITS BASIN PRECIOUS MINERALS, INC.; *U.S. Private,* pg. 4551
WITS CO., LTD.—See Chemtronics Co., Ltd.; *Int'l,* pg. 1464
WITSVINA COMPANY LIMITED—See Chemtronics Co., Ltd.; *Int'l,* pg. 1464
WITT BUILDING MATERIAL COMPANY; *U.S. Private,* pg. 4551
WITTCHEN SA; *Int'l,* pg. 8439
WITTE BROTHERS EXCHANGE INC.; *U.S. Private,* pg. 4551
WITTEMAN & CO. B.V.—See Kebol B.V.; *Int'l,* pg. 4113
WITTENBACH BUSINESS SYSTEMS, INC.—See Argosy Capital Group, LLC; *U.S. Private,* pg. 321
WITTENBERG WEINER CONSULTING, LLC; *U.S. Private,* pg. 4551
THE WITTERN GROUP; *U.S. Private,* pg. 4138
THE WITTERS CONSTRUCTION COMPANY; *U.S. Private,* pg. 4138
WITT GALVANIZING - CINCINNATI, LLC—See AZZ, Inc.; *U.S. Public,* pg. 260
WITT GALVANIZING - MUNCIE, LLC—See AZZ, Inc.; *U.S. Public,* pg. 260
WITT GALVANIZING - PLYMOUTH, LLC—See AZZ, Inc.; *U.S. Public,* pg. 260
WITTICHEN SUPPLY COMPANY—See Gryphon Investors, LLC; *U.S. Private,* pg. 1800
WITTIGS OFFICE INTERIORS LTD.; *U.S. Private,* pg. 4551
WITT INDUSTRIES, INC.—See The Armor Group, Inc.; *U.S. Private,* pg. 3988
WITTINGTON INVESTMENTS LIMITED—See The Garfield Weston Foundation; *Int'l,* pg. 7647
WITT, KIEFFER, HADELMAN, LLOYD & FORD CO. INC.; *U.S. Private,* pg. 4551
WITT LINCOLN; *U.S. Private,* pg. 4551
WITTMANN BATTENFELD AUSTRALIA PTY LTD—See Wittmann Kunststoffgerate GmbH; *Int'l,* pg. 8439
WITTMANN BATTENFELD BENELUX NV—See Wittmann Kunststoffgerate GmbH; *Int'l,* pg. 8439
WITTMANN BATTENFELD BULGARIEN EOOD—See Wittmann Kunststoffgerate GmbH; *Int'l,* pg. 8439
WITTMANN BATTENFELD CZ SPOL. S.R.O.—See Wittmann Kunststoffgerate GmbH; *Int'l,* pg. 8439
WITTMANN BATTENFELD DO BRASIL LTDA.—See Wittmann Kunststoffgerate GmbH; *Int'l,* pg. 8440
WITTMANN BATTENFELD FRANCE SAS—See Wittmann Kunststoffgerate GmbH; *Int'l,* pg. 8439
WITTMANN BATTENFELD GMBH & CO. KG—See Wittmann Kunststoffgerate GmbH; *Int'l,* pg. 8440
WITTMANN BATTENFELD GMBH—See Wittmann Kunststoffgerate GmbH; *Int'l,* pg. 8440
WITTMANN BATTENFELD INDIA PVT LTD.—See Wittmann Kunststoffgerate GmbH; *Int'l,* pg. 8439
WITTMANN BATTENFELD ITALIA SRL—See Wittmann Kunststoffgerate GmbH; *Int'l,* pg. 8439
WITTMANN BATTENFELD (MALAYSIA) SDN BHD—See Wittmann Kunststoffgerate GmbH; *Int'l,* pg. 8439
WITTMANN BATTENFELD MAQUILAS, INC.—See Wittmann Kunststoffgerate GmbH; *Int'l,* pg. 8439
WITTMANN BATTENFELD MEXICO S.A. DE C.V.—See Wittmann Kunststoffgerate GmbH; *Int'l,* pg. 8439
WITTMANN BATTENFELD PLASTIK MAKINELERI LTD. STI.—See Wittmann Kunststoffgerate GmbH; *Int'l,* pg. 8439
WITTMANN BATTENFELD (SHANGHAI) CO., LTD.—See Wittmann Kunststoffgerate GmbH; *Int'l,* pg. 8439
WITTMANN BATTENFELD (SINGAPORE) PTE. LTD.—See Wittmann Kunststoffgerate GmbH; *Int'l,* pg. 8439
WITTMANN BATTENFELD SPAIN S.L.—See Wittmann Kunststoffgerate GmbH; *Int'l,* pg. 8439
WITTMANN BATTENFELD S.R.L.—See Wittmann Kunststoffgerate GmbH; *Int'l,* pg. 8439
WITTMANN BATTENFELD (TAIWAN) CO. LTD.—See Wittmann Kunststoffgerate GmbH; *Int'l,* pg. 8439
WITTMANN BATTENFELD (THAILAND) CO. LTD.—See Wittmann Kunststoffgerate GmbH; *Int'l,* pg. 8439
WITTMANN BATTENFELD UK LTD—See Wittmann Kunststoffgerate GmbH; *Int'l,* pg. 8440
WITTMANN CANADA INC.—See Wittmann Kunststoffgerate GmbH; *Int'l,* pg. 8440
WITTMANN INC.—See Wittmann Kunststoffgerate GmbH; *Int'l,* pg. 8440
WITTMANN KUNSTSTOFFGERATE GMBH; *Int'l,* pg. 8439
WITTMANN KUNSTSTOFFTECHNIK AG—See Wittmann Kunststoffgerate GmbH; *Int'l,* pg. 8440
WITTMANN ROBOT (KUNSHAN) CO., LTD.—See Wittmann Kunststoffgerate GmbH; *Int'l,* pg. 8440
WITTMANN ROBOT SYSTEME GMBH—See Wittmann Kunststoffgerate GmbH; *Int'l,* pg. 8440
WITTMANN ROBOTTECHNIKAI KFT.—See Wittmann Kunststoffgerate GmbH; *Int'l,* pg. 8440
WITT O'BRIEN'S, LLC—See Ambipar Participacoes e Empreendimentos SA; *Int'l,* pg. 414
WITT O'BRIEN'S LTD—See AIP, LLC; *U.S. Private,* pg. 137

WITT PRINTING COMPANY—See Ennis, Inc.; *U.S. Public*, pg. 769
WITTS FOODS INC.; *U.S. Private*, pg. 4551
WITTUR HOLDING GMBH—See Bain Capital, LP; *U.S. Private*, pg. 452
WITZ CORPORATION; *Int'l*, pg. 8440
WIWORLD CO., LTD.; *Int'l*, pg. 8440
WIWYNN CORP.; *Int'l*, pg. 8440
WIX.COM LTD.; *Int'l*, pg. 8440
WIXON INDUSTRIES INC.; *U.S. Private*, pg. 4551
WIYY-FM—See The Hearst Corporation; *U.S. Private*, pg. 4048
WIZARD PROMOTIONS KONZERTAGENTUR GMBH—See DEAG Deutsche Entertainment AG; *Int'l*, pg. 1998
WIZARDS OF THE COAST, LLC—See Hasbro, Inc.; *U.S. Public*, pg. 988
WIZARD SOFTWARE SOLUTIONS INCORPORATED; *U.S. Private*, pg. 4551
WIZ CO., LTD.—See BANDAI NAMCO Holdings Inc.; *Int'l*, pg. 829
WIZ CORP, INC.; *Int'l*, pg. 8440
WIZCORP INC.—See Canada Pension Plan Investment Board; *Int'l*, pg. 1281
WIZCORP INC.—See EQT AB; *Int'l*, pg. 2483
WIZCORP INC.—See Temasek Holdings (Private) Limited; *Int'l*, pg. 7548
WIZEHIVE, INC.; *U.S. Private*, pg. 4551
WIZE SOLUTIONS INC.—See Argosy Capital Group, LLC; *U.S. Private*, pg. 322
WIZIBOAT SA; *Int'l*, pg. 8440
WIZIT CO., LTD.; *Int'l*, pg. 8440
WIZLEARN TECHNOLOGIES PTE LTD.—See Educomp Solutions, Ltd.; *Int'l*, pg. 2315
WIZLEARN TECHNOLOGIES—See Educomp Solutions, Ltd.; *Int'l*, pg. 2315
WIZ SOLUCOES E CORRETAGEM DE SEGUROS S.A.; *Int'l*, pg. 8440
WIZTEC CO., LTD.—See MIMAKI ENGINEERING CO., LTD.; *Int'l*, pg. 4898
WIZZ AIR HOLDINGS PLC; *Int'l*, pg. 8440
WIZZ AIR UK LIMITED—See Wizz Air Holdings Plc; *Int'l*, pg. 8440
WJAC-TV—See Sinclair, Inc.; *U.S. Public*, pg. 1887
WJAR-TV—See Sinclair, Inc.; *U.S. Public*, pg. 1887
WJBF-TV—See Nexstar Media Group, Inc.; *U.S. Public*, pg. 1523
W.J. BRADLEY MORTGAGE CAPITAL, LLC; *U.S. Private*, pg. 4420
W.J. BYRNES & CO. - ARIZONA-PHOENIX—See Janel Corporation; *U.S. Public*, pg. 1187
W.J. BYRNES & CO. - OREGON—See Janel Corporation; *U.S. Public*, pg. 1187
W.J. BYRNES & CO.—See Janel Corporation; *U.S. Public*, pg. 1187
W.J. BYRNES & CO. - WISCONSIN—See Janel Corporation; *U.S. Public*, pg. 1187
WJCL-TV—See The Hearst Corporation; *U.S. Private*, pg. 4049
W.J. DEUTSCH & SONS LTD.; *U.S. Private*, pg. 4421
W.J. HAGERTY & SONS CANADA LTD.—See W.J. Hagerty & Sons, Ltd., Inc.; *U.S. Private*, pg. 4421
W.J. HAGERTY & SONS, LTD., INC.; *U.S. Private*, pg. 4421
WJHG-TV—See Gray Television, Inc.; *U.S. Public*, pg. 960
WJHL-TV—See Nexstar Media Group, Inc.; *U.S. Public*, pg. 1523
WJ HOLDING COMPANY—See Hy-Vee, Inc.; *U.S. Private*, pg. 2016
W. J. MOUNTFORD CO.; *U.S. Private*, pg. 4418
W. JOE SHAW INCORPORATED; *U.S. Private*, pg. 4418
W. J. O'NEIL COMPANY; *U.S. Private*, pg. 4418
W. JOSEPH MCPHILLIPS, INC.—See Arrow Financial Corporation; *U.S. Public*, pg. 200
WJ PARTNERS, LLC; *U.S. Private*, pg. 4551
WJRT, INC.—See Entertainment Studios, Inc.; *U.S. Private*, pg. 1405
W.J. TOWELL & CO. LLC; *Int'l*, pg. 8322
WJTV-TV—See Nexstar Media Group, Inc.; *U.S. Public*, pg. 1523
WJW ASSOCIATES, LTD.; *U.S. Private*, pg. 4551
WJW ENTERPRISES SAN DIEGO INC.; *U.S. Private*, pg. 4551
WJW TELEVISION, LLC—See Nexstar Media Group, Inc.; *U.S. Public*, pg. 1525
WJW-TV—See Nexstar Media Group, Inc.; *U.S. Public*, pg. 1525
WJYY; *U.S. Private*, pg. 4551
WJZ-TV—See National Amusements, Inc.; *U.S. Private*, pg. 2841
WJZY-TV—See Capitol Broadcasting Company, Inc.; *U.S. Private*, pg. 743
WKA B.V.—See AUTO1 Group SE; *Int'l*, pg. 725
WKDA OSTERREICH GMBH—See AUTO1 Group SE; *Int'l*, pg. 725
WK ENDUSTRI SANAYI VE TICARET LIMITED SIRKETI—See W&K Gesellschaft fur Industrietechnik mbH; *Int'l*, pg. 8320

W&K GESELLSCHAFT FUR INDUSTRIETECHNIK MBH; *Int'l*, pg. 8320
W&K HISPANA TECNICA INDUSTRIAL S.L.—See W&K Gesellschaft fur Industrietechnik mbH; *Int'l*, pg. 8320
WK INDUSTRIAL SERVICES CORP.—See W&K Gesellschaft fur Industrietechnik mbH; *Int'l*, pg. 8320
WK INDUSTRIAL TECHNOLOGY CONSULTING (SHANGHAI) CO., LTD.—See W&K Gesellschaft fur Industrietechnik mbH; *Int'l*, pg. 8320
W&K INDUSTRIETECHNIK SP. Z O.O.—See W&K Gesellschaft fur Industrietechnik mbH; *Int'l*, pg. 8320
W&K INDUSTRIETECHNIK S.R.O.—See W&K Gesellschaft fur Industrietechnik mbH; *Int'l*, pg. 8320
WKK AMERICA (HOLDINGS) INC.—See Wong's Kong King International (Holdings) Limited; *Int'l*, pg. 8447
WKK DISTRIBUTION LIMITED—See Wong's Kong King International (Holdings) Limited; *Int'l*, pg. 8447
WKK DISTRIBUTION (MALAYSIA) SDN. BHD.—See Wong's Kong King International (Holdings) Limited; *Int'l*, pg. 8447
WKK DISTRIBUTION (SINGAPORE) PTE LTD—See Wong's Kong King International (Holdings) Limited; *Int'l*, pg. 8447
WKK ELECTRONIC EQUIPMENT (XI'AN) LTD.—See Wong's Kong King International (Holdings) Limited; *Int'l*, pg. 8447
WK KELLOGG CO; *U.S. Public*, pg. 2376
WKK EMS EQUIPMENT (BEIJING) LTD.—See Wong's Kong King International (Holdings) Limited; *Int'l*, pg. 8447
WKK EMS EQUIPMENT (CHENGDU) LTD.—See Wong's Kong King International (Holdings) Limited; *Int'l*, pg. 8447
WKK EMS EQUIPMENT (CHONGQING) LTD.—See Wong's Kong King International (Holdings) Limited; *Int'l*, pg. 8447
WKK EMS EQUIPMENT (SHENZHEN) LTD.—See INTEKPLUS Co., Ltd.; *Int'l*, pg. 3733
WKK ENGINEERING SERVICE LTD.—See Wong's Kong King International (Holdings) Limited; *Int'l*, pg. 8447
WKK JAPAN LTD.—See Wong's Kong King International (Holdings) Limited; *Int'l*, pg. 8447
WKK TECHNOLOGY LIMITED—See Wong's Kong King International (Holdings) Limited; *Int'l*, pg. 8447
WKK (THAILAND) LTD.—See Wong's Kong King International (Holdings) Limited; *Int'l*, pg. 8447
WKK TRADING (SHANGHAI) CO., LTD.—See Wong's Kong King International (Holdings) Limited; *Int'l*, pg. 8447
WKK TRAVEL LIMITED—See Wong's Kong King International (Holdings) Limited; *Int'l*, pg. 8447
WK MINING (USA) LTD.—See West Vault Mining Inc.; *Int'l*, pg. 8386
WKN FRANCE S.A.S.U.—See PNE AG; *Int'l*, pg. 5901
WKN GMBH—See PNE AG; *Int'l*, pg. 5901
WKN ITALIA S.R.L.—See PNE AG; *Int'l*, pg. 5901
WKN WERTEWIND GMBH—See PNE AG; *Int'l*, pg. 5901
WKN WINDCURRENT SA (PTY) LTD.—See PNE AG; *Int'l*, pg. 5901
WKO INVESTMENTS INC.; *U.S. Private*, pg. 4551
WKOW-TV—See Gray Television, Inc.; *U.S. Public*, pg. 961
WKQR-FM—See First Media Services, LLC; *U.S. Private*, pg. 1521
WKQX-FM—See Emmis Communications Corporation; *U.S. Public*, pg. 753
WKRC-TV—See Sinclair, Inc.; *U.S. Public*, pg. 1887
WKRG-TV—See Nexstar Media Group, Inc.; *U.S. Public*, pg. 1523
WK SECURITIES LIMITED—See Wai Kee Holdings Limited; *Int'l*, pg. 8331
WKT-LETSCH PRODUKTIONS- UND HANDELS GMBH; *Int'l*, pg. 8440
WKTV, LLC—See Heartland Media, LLC; *U.S. Private*, pg. 1900
WKYC-TV—See TEGNA Inc.; *U.S. Public*, pg. 1991
WKYT-TV—See Gray Television, Inc.; *U.S. Public*, pg. 960
WKZO AM 590—See Midwest Communications, Inc.; *U.S. Private*, pg. 2720
WLAJ-TV—See Sinclair, Inc.; *U.S. Public*, pg. 1887
WLBT, LLC—See Gray Television, Inc.; *U.S. Public*, pg. 960
W.L. BUTLER CONSTRUCTION INC.; *U.S. Private*, pg. 4421
WLBZ-TV—See TEGNA Inc.; *U.S. Public*, pg. 1991
W-L CONSTRUCTION & PAVING, INC.—See CRH plc; *Int'l*, pg. 1848
WLC WURTH-LOGISTIK GMBH & CO. KG—See Wurth Verwaltungsgesellschaft mbH; *Int'l*, pg. 8508
WLDE OLDIES 101 7 FM—See iHeartMedia, Inc.; *U.S. Public*, pg. 1097
W. LEE FLOWERS & COMPANY INC.; *U.S. Private*, pg. 4418
W LEICESTER SQUARE LTD.—See Marriott International, Inc.; *U.S. Public*, pg. 1373
WLEX COMMUNICATIONS, LLC—See Evening Post Publishing Co.; *U.S. Private*, pg. 1436
WLFL, INC.—See Sinclair, Inc.; *U.S. Public*, pg. 1887

W. L. GORE & ASSOCIATES (AUSTRALIA) PTY, LTD.—See W.L. Gore & Associates, Inc.; *U.S. Private*, pg. 4421
W. L. GORE & ASSOCIATES CANADA, INC.—See W.L. Gore & Associates, Inc.; *U.S. Private*, pg. 4421
W. L. GORE & ASSOCIATES, CO., LTD.—See W.L. Gore & Associates, Inc.; *U.S. Private*, pg. 4421
W. L. GORE & ASSOCIATES DE MEXICO, S. DE R.L. DE C.V.—See W.L. Gore & Associates, Inc.; *U.S. Private*, pg. 4421
W. L. GORE & ASSOCIATES DO BRASIL LTDA.—See W.L. Gore & Associates, Inc.; *U.S. Private*, pg. 4421
W. L. GORE & ASSOCIATES HONG KONG, LTD.—See W.L. Gore & Associates, Inc.; *U.S. Private*, pg. 4421
W.L. GORE & ASSOCIATES, INC.; *U.S. Private*, pg. 4421
W. L. GORE & ASSOCIATES (KOREA), LTD.—See W.L. Gore & Associates, Inc.; *U.S. Private*, pg. 4421
W. L. GORE & ASSOCIATES (PACIFIC) PTE.LTD. - INDIA BRANCH—See W.L. Gore & Associates, Inc.; *U.S. Private*, pg. 4421
W. L. GORE & ASSOCIATES (PACIFIC) PTE LTD.—See W.L. Gore & Associates, Inc.; *U.S. Private*, pg. 4421
W. L. GORE & ASSOCIATES, POLSKA SP.Z.O.O.—See W.L. Gore & Associates, Inc.; *U.S. Private*, pg. 4421
W. L. GORE & ASSOCIATES SCANDINAVIA AB—See W.L. Gore & Associates, Inc.; *U.S. Private*, pg. 4421
W. L. GORE & ASSOCIATES (SOUTH AFRICA) (PROPRIETARY) LTD.—See W.L. Gore & Associates, Inc.; *U.S. Private*, pg. 4421
W. L. GORE & ASSOCIATES TECHNOLOGIES (SHENZHEN) CO., LTD—See W.L. Gore & Associates, Inc.; *U.S. Private*, pg. 4421
W. L. GORE & ASSOCIATES (UK) LTD.—See W.L. Gore & Associates, Inc.; *U.S. Private*, pg. 4421
W. L. GORE & ASSOCIATI S.R.L.—See W.L. Gore & Associates, Inc.; *U.S. Private*, pg. 4421
W. L. GORE & ASSOCIES S.A.R.L.—See W.L. Gore & Associates, Inc.; *U.S. Private*, pg. 4421
W. L. GORE Y ASOCIADOS, S.L.—See W.L. Gore & Associates, Inc.; *U.S. Private*, pg. 4421
W.L. HAILEY & COMPANY, INC.—See Reynolds Construction, LLC; *U.S. Private*, pg. 3418
W.L. HALSEY GROCERY COMPANY, INC.; *U.S. Private*, pg. 4421
WLHK FM—See Emmis Communications Corporation; *U.S. Public*, pg. 753
WLH STILLWATER, LLC—See Brookfield Corporation; *Int'l*, pg. 1183
WLH STONEWALL, LLC—See Brookfield Corporation; *Int'l*, pg. 1183
WLH TRAILS AT LEANDER, LLC—See Brookfield Corporation; *Int'l*, pg. 1183
WLIF-FM—See AUDACY, INC.; *U.S. Public*, pg. 226
WLI TRADING LTD.—See Castik Capital S.a.r.l.; *Int'l*, pg. 1356
WLI (UK) LIMITED—See Castik Capital S.a.r.l.; *Int'l*, pg. 1356
WLKY HEARST-ARGYLE TELEVISION, INC.—See The Hearst Corporation; *U.S. Private*, pg. 4049
THE W.L. MAY COMPANY; *U.S. Private*, pg. 4132
W.L. MCCORMACK & CO. INC.; *U.S. Private*, pg. 4421
WLMD; *U.S. Private*, pg. 4551
WL-MEDICAL OY—See Interogo Holding AG; *Int'l*, pg. 3754
W.L. MILLER CO. INC.; *U.S. Private*, pg. 4421
W-L MOLDING COMPANY; *U.S. Private*, pg. 4417
WLM PARTICIPACOES E COMERCIO DE MAQUINAS E VEICULOS S.A.; *Int'l*, pg. 8440
WLNE-TV—See Standard General LP; *U.S. Private*, pg. 3778
WLOFM, CORP.; *U.S. Private*, pg. 4551
WLOS-TV—See Sinclair, Inc.; *U.S. Public*, pg. 1887
WLOX, LLC—See Gray Television, Inc.; *U.S. Public*, pg. 960
WLP ENERGY SERVICES, LLC; *U.S. Private*, pg. 4551
W.L. PETREY WHOLESALE COMPANY, INC.; *U.S. Private*, pg. 4421
W.L. ROSS & CO., LLC—See Invesco Ltd.; *U.S. Public*, pg. 1163
W&L SALES CO., INC.; *U.S. Private*, pg. 4417
W&L SALES—See W&L Sales Co., Inc.; *U.S. Private*, pg. 4417
WLS HOLDINGS LIMITED; *Int'l*, pg. 8440
WLS STAMPING & FABRICATING CO.; *U.S. Private*, pg. 4551
WLS TELEVISION, INC.—See The Walt Disney Company; *U.S. Public*, pg. 2138
WLT DISTRIBUTORS INC.; *Int'l*, pg. 8440
W.L. TOURISME—See Accor S.A.; *Int'l*, pg. 92
WLTX-TV—See TEGNA Inc.; *U.S. Public*, pg. 1991
W. LUCY & CO. LTD.; *Int'l*, pg. 8321
WLUK-TV—See Sinclair, Inc.; *U.S. Public*, pg. 1887
WLVI-TV—See Sunbeam Television Corporation; *U.S. Private*, pg. 3864
WLWC-TV—See Nexstar Media Group, Inc.; *U.S. Public*, pg. 1523
W.L. (WEI LEE) PTE. LTD.—See Wah Lee Industrial Corp.; *Int'l*, pg. 8329

W. LUCY & CO. LTD.

WLWT-TV—See The Hearst Corporation; *U.S. Private*, pg. 4049
WLX, LLC; *U.S. Private*, pg. 4552
WMAQ-TV—See Comcast Corporation; *U.S. Public*, pg. 540
WM ARGENTINA SA—See HORIBA Ltd; *Int'l*, pg. 3478
W MARKETING INC.—See ProBility Media Corporation; *U.S. Public*, pg. 1723
WMAR-TV—See The E.W. Scripps Company; *U.S. Public*, pg. 2069
W.M. AUTOMOTIVE WAREHOUSE INC.; *U.S. Private*, pg. 4421
WMAZ-TV—See TEGNA Inc.; *U.S. Public*, pg. 1991
W.M. BARR & COMPANY, INC.; *U.S. Private*, pg. 4421
WMBB-TV—See Nexstar Media Group, Inc.; *U.S. Public*, pg. 1523
WMB DROGBUD SP. Z O.O.—See STRABAG SE; *Int'l*, pg. 7233
WMBD-TV—See Nexstar Media Group, Inc.; *U.S. Public*, pg. 1523
W.M. BERG INC.—See Zurn Elkay Water Solutions Corporation; *U.S. Public*, pg. 2413
WM. BLANCHARD CO.; *U.S. Private*, pg. 4552
WM. BOLTHOUSE FARMS, INC.—See Butterfly Equity LP; *U.S. Private*, pg. 698
WM BROKERS LIMITED—See Brown & Brown, Inc.; *U.S. Public*, pg. 402
WM CAPITAL S.P.A.; *Int'l*, pg. 8440
WM CCP SOLUTIONS, LLC—See Waste Management, Inc.; *U.S. Public*, pg. 2332
WMC/GREY—See WPP plc; *Int'l*, pg. 8472
WMCH GLOBAL INVESTMENT LIMITED; *Int'l*, pg. 8441
WMCK-VENTURE CORP.—See Century Casinos, Inc.; *U.S. Public*, pg. 474
WM COFFMAN RESOURCES LLC—See Prophet Equity L.P.; *U.S. Private*, pg. 3286
W.M. CRAMER LUMBER CO. INC.; *U.S. Private*, pg. 4421
WMCR CO. LLC; *U.S. Private*, pg. 4552
WMDT-TV—See Marquee Broadcasting, Inc.; *U.S. Private*, pg. 2586
WME IMG, LLC—See William Morris Endeavor Entertainment, LLC; *U.S. Private*, pg. 4524
WMET 1160—See IDT Corporation; *U.S. Public*, pg. 1094
WMF AMERICAS, INC.—See SEB S.A.; *Int'l*, pg. 6668
WMF GROUP GMBH—See SEB S.A.; *Int'l*, pg. 6668
WMF JAPAN CONSUMER GOODS CO., LTD.—See SANYEI CORPORATION; *Int'l*, pg. 6563
WM. F. MCDONOUGH PLUMBING, INC.; *U.S. Private*, pg. 4552
WMG AS; *Int'l*, pg. 8441
WMGD PTY. LIMITED—See Koninklijke Philips N.V.; *Int'l*, pg. 4271
WMG HOLDINGS BERHAD; *Int'l*, pg. 8441
W.M. GRACE DEVELOPMENT COMPANY; *U.S. Private*, pg. 4421
WM GREEN SQUAD, LLC—See Waste Management, Inc.; *U.S. Public*, pg. 2333
WM GROUP PTY LIMITED—See National Australia Bank Limited; *Int'l*, pg. 5151
WM GTL, INC.—See Waste Management, Inc.; *U.S. Public*, pg. 2333
WM. HILGERS GMBH & CO. KG—See Dortmunder Gussasphalt GmbH & Co. KG; *Int'l*, pg. 2180
WMHW HOLDINGS LIMITED; *Int'l*, pg. 8441
WMI KONECRANES INDIA LTD.—See Konecranes Plc; *Int'l*, pg. 4253
WMI LIQUIDATING TRUST; *U.S. Private*, pg. 4552
W.M. JORDAN COMPANY INC.; *U.S. Private*, pg. 4422
W.M. JORDAN COMPANY—See W.M. Jordan Company Inc.; *U.S. Private*, pg. 4422
WMK, LLC—See Edwards Capital, LLC; *U.S. Public*, pg. 1342
WM K LYONS AGENCY, INC.—See Stone Point Capital LLC; *U.S. Private*, pg. 3819
WM KS ENERGY RESOURCES, LLC—See Waste Management, Inc.; *U.S. Public*, pg. 2333
WM. K. WALTHERS, INC.; *U.S. Private*, pg. 4552
WM LAMPTRACKER, INC.—See Waste Management, Inc.; *U.S. Public*, pg. 2333
WM LAWRENCE LIMITED; *Int'l*, pg. 8440
WM LIFE AUSTRALIA LIMITED—See National Australia Bank Limited; *Int'l*, pg. 5151
WM LOGISTICS INDIA PRIVATE LIMITED—See Waste Management, Inc.; *U.S. Public*, pg. 2333
WM LOGISTICS, LLC—See Waste Management, Inc.; *U.S. Public*, pg. 2333
W.M. LYLES CO. INC.—See Lyles Diversified Inc.; *U.S. Private*, pg. 2520
WMMB AM 1240—See iHeartMedia, Inc.; *U.S. Public*, pg. 1097
WM MORRISON (HK) LIMITED—See Morrison (Wm) Supermarkets PLC; *Int'l*, pg. 5049
WM MORRISON PRODUCE LIMITED—See Clayton, Dubilier & Rice, LLC; *U.S. Private*, pg. 930
WM MORRISON SUPERMARKETS PLC—See Clayton, Dubilier & Rice, LLC; *U.S. Private*, pg. 930
WMMP-TV—See Sinclair, Inc.; *U.S. Public*, pg. 1887
WM NETHERLANDS C.V.—See Stryker Corporation; *U.S. Public*, pg. 1958

WMODE INC.—See AppDirect Inc.; *U.S. Private*, pg. 296
WM OF TEXAS, L.L.C.—See Waste Management, Inc.; *U.S. Public*, pg. 2333
WM OHS INC.; *U.S. Private*, pg. 4552
WM PARTNERS CO., LTD.; *Int'l*, pg. 8440
WM PARTNERS LP; *U.S. Private*, pg. 4552
WMPARTNERS WEALTH MANAGEMENT LTD.—See Julius Baer Group Ltd.; *Int'l*, pg. 4025
WMPH VACATIONS, LLC—See 3i Group plc; *Int'l*, pg. 8
WMPI PTY., LLC—See Reading Anthracite Company; *U.S. Private*, pg. 3366
THE WM. POWELL COMPANY; *U.S. Private*, pg. 4138
WM RECYCLE AMERICA, LLC - PICO RIVERA—See Waste Management, Inc.; *U.S. Public*, pg. 2333
WM RECYCLE AMERICA, LLC—See Waste Management, Inc.; *U.S. Public*, pg. 2333
WM RECYCLE AMERICA, LLC - (SPRINGFIELD) ECYCLING SERVICES—See Waste Management, Inc.; *U.S. Public*, pg. 2333
WM RECYCLE AMERICA, LLC - SPRINGFIELD—See Waste Management, Inc.; *U.S. Public*, pg. 2333
WM REPLY GMBH—See Reply S.p.A.; *Int'l*, pg. 6291
WM REPLY INC.—See Reply S.p.A.; *Int'l*, pg. 6291
WM REPLY LLC—See Reply S.p.A.; *Int'l*, pg. 6291
WM REPLY LTD.—See Reply S.p.A.; *Int'l*, pg. 6291
WM REPLY S.R.L.—See Reply S.p.A.; *Int'l*, pg. 6291
W.M. SCHLOSSER CO. INC.; *U.S. Private*, pg. 4422
WM. SCHMIDT MECHANICAL CONTRACTORS, LTD.; *Int'l*, pg. 8441
WM SE; *Int'l*, pg. 8441
WMS GAMING AFRICA (PTY) LTD.—See Light & Wonder, Inc.; *U.S. Public*, pg. 1315
WMS GAMING AUSTRALIA PTY LTD.—See Light & Wonder, Inc.; *U.S. Public*, pg. 1315
WMS GAMING INC.—See Light & Wonder, Inc.; *U.S. Public*, pg. 1315
WMS GAMING INTERNATIONAL, S.L.—See Light & Wonder, Inc.; *U.S. Public*, pg. 1315
WMS GAMING MEXICO, S. DE R.L. DE C.V.—See Light & Wonder, Inc.; *U.S. Public*, pg. 1315
WMS GAMING SERVICES EUROPE, S.L.—See Light & Wonder, Inc.; *U.S. Public*, pg. 1315
W.M. SHIPPING LIMITED—See Santova Ltd.; *Int'l*, pg. 6560
WMS INDUSTRIES INC.—See Light & Wonder, Inc.; *U.S. Public*, pg. 1315
WMS INTERNATIONAL (MACAU) LIMITED—See Light & Wonder, Inc.; *U.S. Public*, pg. 1315
WMSN LICENSEE, LLC—See Sinclair, Inc.; *U.S. Public*, pg. 1887
WMSN-TV—See Sinclair, Inc.; *U.S. Public*, pg. 1887
W & M SPRINKLER COMPANY, INC.—See APi Group Corporation; *Int'l*, pg. 513
W & M SPRINKLER NYC LLC—See APi Group Corporation; *Int'l*, pg. 513
W.M. SPRINKMAN CORP.; *U.S. Private*, pg. 4422
WMS SALES INC.; *U.S. Private*, pg. 4552
WM T. BURNETT & CO. - FOAM DIVISION—See Wm. T. Burnett & Co.; *U.S. Private*, pg. 4552
WM T. BURNETT & CO. - NONWOVENS DIVISION—See Wm T. Burnett & Co.; *U.S. Private*, pg. 4552
WM T. BURNETT & CO.; *U.S. Private*, pg. 4552
WM TECHNOLOGY, INC.; *U.S. Public*, pg. 2376
W.M. TINDER INCORPORATED; *U.S. Private*, pg. 4422
WM TRANSLOGISTICS (PTY) LTD—See Grindrod Limited; *Int'l*, pg. 3086
WMTW-TV—See The Hearst Corporation; *U.S. Private*, pg. 4049
WM UNIVERSAL SOLUTIONS PRIVATE LIMITED—See Waste Management, Inc.; *U.S. Public*, pg. 2333
WMUR-TV—See The Hearst Corporation; *U.S. Private*, pg. 4049
WMW MACHINERY COMPANY, INC.—See SKF AB; *Int'l*, pg. 6985
WM. WRIGLEY JR. COMPANY—See Mars, Incorporated; *U.S. Private*, pg. 2590
WMYD-TV—See The E.W. Scripps Company; *U.S. Public*, pg. 2069
WMYV-TV—See Sinclair, Inc.; *U.S. Public*, pg. 1886
WNBA ENTERPRISES, LLC—See National Basketball Association; *U.S. Private*, pg. 2848
WNBC-TV—See Comcast Corporation; *U.S. Public*, pg. 540
W.N. BEST—See PUMC Holding Corporation; *U.S. Private*, pg. 3303
WNC CLOUD MERGER SUB, INC.—See WABASH NATIONAL CORPORATION; *U.S. Public*, pg. 2320
WNC CORPORATION; *U.S. Private*, pg. 4552
WNC PALLET & FOREST PRODUCTS CO.; *U.S. Private*, pg. 4552
WNC REAL ESTATE; *U.S. Private*, pg. 4552
WNCT-TV—See Nexstar Media Group, Inc.; *U.S. Public*, pg. 1523
WNDRCO HOLDINGS, LLC; *U.S. Private*, pg. 4552
WNEM-TV—See Meredith Corporation; *U.S. Public*, pg. 1423
WNEP, LLC—See Nexstar Media Group, Inc.; *U.S. Public*, pg. 1525

CORPORATE AFFILIATIONS

WNE SOLARFONDS SUDDEUTSCHLAND 2 GMBH & CO. KG—See Munchener Ruckversicherungs AG; *Int'l*, pg. 5092
WNET; *U.S. Private*, pg. 4552
W. NEWELL & CO., LLC—See United Natural Foods, Inc.; *U.S. Public*, pg. 2232
W NEW ORLEANS - FRENCH QUARTER HOTEL—See Marriott International, Inc.; *U.S. Public*, pg. 1372
WNM COMMUNICATIONS—See LICT Corporation; *U.S. Public*, pg. 1312
WNNE-TV—See The Hearst Corporation; *U.S. Private*, pg. 4049
WNOL-TV—See Nexstar Media Group, Inc.; *U.S. Public*, pg. 1524
WNOU-FM—See Urban One, Inc.; *U.S. Public*, pg. 2265
WNR INC.; *U.S. Private*, pg. 4553
WNR INC.—See Partners HealthCare System, Inc.; *U.S. Private*, pg. 3102
WNS BUSINESS CONSULTING SERVICES PRIVATE LIMITED—See WNS (Holdings) Limited; *Int'l*, pg. 8441
WNS GLOBAL SERVICES PRIVATE LIMITED—See WNS (Holdings) Limited; *Int'l*, pg. 8441
WNS GLOBAL SERVICES (ROMANIA) S.R.L.—See WNS (Holdings) Limited; *Int'l*, pg. 8441
WNS GLOBAL SERVICES (UK) LTD.—See WNS (Holdings) Limited; *Int'l*, pg. 8441
WNS (HOLDINGS) LIMITED; *Int'l*, pg. 8441
WNS NORTH AMERICA, INC.—See WNS (Holdings) Limited; *Int'l*, pg. 8441
WNS WORKFLOW TECHNOLOGIES LIMITED—See WNS (Holdings) Limited; *Int'l*, pg. 8441
WNT CESKA REPUBLIKA S.R.O.—See PLANSEE Holding AG; *Int'l*, pg. 5890
WNT FRANCE S.A.S.—See PLANSEE Holding AG; *Int'l*, pg. 5890
WNT IBERICA S.L.—See PLANSEE Holding AG; *Int'l*, pg. 5890
WNT ITALIA S.P.A.—See PLANSEE Holding AG; *Int'l*, pg. 5890
WNT ONASYA KESICI TAKIMLAR SAN.VE TIC. LTD. STI.—See PLANSEE Holding AG; *Int'l*, pg. 5890
WNT POLSKA SP. Z O.O.—See PLANSEE Holding AG; *Int'l*, pg. 5890
WNT SCANDINAVIA AB—See PLANSEE Holding AG; *Int'l*, pg. 5890
W.N. VAN ALSTINE & SONS INC.; *U.S. Private*, pg. 4422
WNYQ, INC.—See Sinclair, Inc.; *U.S. Public*, pg. 1887
WNYT-TV—See Hubbard Broadcasting, Inc.; *U.S. Private*, pg. 2000
WNYW-TV—See Fox Corporation; *U.S. Public*, pg. 876
WOAI-TV—See Sinclair, Inc.; *U.S. Public*, pg. 1887
WOANS SARL; *Int'l*, pg. 8441
WOB AG; *Int'l*, pg. 8441
W.O. BLACKSTONE & COMPANY, INC.; *U.S. Private*, pg. 4422
WOBURN ADVOCATE—See Gannett Co., Inc.; *U.S. Public*, pg. 903
WOBURN ENERGY PLC; *Int'l*, pg. 8441
WOBURN FOREIGN MOTORS INC.; *U.S. Private*, pg. 4553
WOCKHARDT BIO AG—See Wockhardt Limited; *Int'l*, pg. 8441
WOCKHARDT LIMITED; *Int'l*, pg. 8441
WOCKHARDT UK LIMITED—See Wockhardt Limited; *Int'l*, pg. 8441
WOCO EISENACHER KUNSTSTOFFTECHNIK GMBH—See Woco Industrietechnik GmbH; *Int'l*, pg. 8442
WOCO INDUSTRIETECHNIK GMBH; *Int'l*, pg. 8441
WOCO INVESTMENT CORPORATION—See WING ON COMPANY INTERNATIONAL LIMITED; *Int'l*, pg. 8427
WOCO IPARTECHNIKA MAGYARORSZAG KFT.—See Woco Industrietechnik GmbH; *Int'l*, pg. 8442
WOCO KRONACHER KUNSTSTOFFWERK GMBH—See Woco Industrietechnik GmbH; *Int'l*, pg. 8442
WOCO MOTOR ACOUSTIC SYSTEMS, INC.—See Woco Industrietechnik GmbH; *Int'l*, pg. 8442
W & O CONSTRUCTION CO., INC.; *U.S. Private*, pg. 4417
WOCO STV, S.R.O.—See Woco Industrietechnik GmbH; *Int'l*, pg. 8442
WOCO TECH ELASTOMERE NOIDA LTD.—See Woco Industrietechnik GmbH; *Int'l*, pg. 8442
WOCO TECH KANDLA LTD.—See Woco Industrietechnik GmbH; *Int'l*, pg. 8442
WOCO TECH LTD.—See Woco Industrietechnik GmbH; *Int'l*, pg. 8442
WOCO TECH USA INC.—See Woco Industrietechnik GmbH; *Int'l*, pg. 8442
WOCO TECNICA, S. A.—See Woco Industrietechnik GmbH; *Int'l*, pg. 8442
WODA CORP.; *U.S. Public*, pg. 2376
WODA GROUP INC.; *U.S. Private*, pg. 4553
WODA MANAGEMENT & REAL ESTATE, LLC.; *U.S. Private*, pg. 4553
WODEN VENTURE CAPITAL CORPORATION; *Int'l*, pg. 8442
WODPOL SP. Z O.O.—See Apator S.A.; *Int'l*, pg. 501
WOD RETAIL SOLUTIONS, INC.; *U.S. Public*, pg. 2376

COMPANY NAME INDEX

WOEBER MUSTARD MANUFACTURING COMPANY; *U.S. Private*, pg. 4553
WOERNER HOLDINGS INC.; *U.S. Private*, pg. 4553
WOERNER SOUTH INC.—See Woerner Holdings Inc.; *U.S. Private*, pg. 4553
WOERNER TURF GROUP INC.—See Woerner Holdings Inc.; *U.S. Private*, pg. 4553
WOFE KORN/FERRY INTERNATIONAL HUMAN CAPITAL CONSULTING (BEIJING) LIMITED—See Korn Ferry; *U.S. Public*, pg. 1275
WOFL-TV—See Fox Corporation; *U.S. Public*, pg. 876
WOGEN GROUP; *Int'l*, pg. 8442
WOGEN METAL COMMERCIAL (SHANGHAI) LTD—See Wogen Group; *Int'l*, pg. 8442
WOGEN METALS LLC—See Wogen Group; *Int'l*, pg. 8442
WOGEN PACIFIC LTD—See Wogen Group; *Int'l*, pg. 8442
WOGEN RESOURCES SOUTH AFRICA (PTY) LTD—See Wogen Group; *Int'l*, pg. 8442
W.O. GRUBB STEEL ERECTION INC.; *U.S. Private*, pg. 4422
W.O.G. WORLD OF GOLF PTE LTD—See Ossia International Limited; *Int'l*, pg. 5652
WOGX-TV—See Fox Corporation; *U.S. Public*, pg. 876
WOHLERS ASSOCIATES INC.—See American Society for Testing & Materials; *U.S. Private*, pg. 254
WOHLER TECHNIK GMBH; *Int'l*, pg. 8442
WOHLSEN CONSTRUCTION COMPANY; *U.S. Private*, pg. 4553
WOHLT CHEESE CORPORATION; *U.S. Private*, pg. 4553
WOHNBAU NORDWEST GMBH—See Vonovia SE; *Int'l*, pg. 8305
WOHNEN AM LERCHENBERG GMBH & CO. KG—See BayWa AG; *Int'l*, pg. 919
WOHNEN AM LERCHENBERG VERWALTUNGS GMBH—See BayWa AG; *Int'l*, pg. 919
WOHNIMMOBILIEN GMBH & CO. KG—See Wuestenrot & Wuerttembergische AG; *Int'l*, pg. 8499
WOHNPARK LAAER BERG VERWERTUNGS- UND BETEILIGUNGS-GMBH & CO. BAUPLATZ 3 TURKIS PROJEKT-OG—See PORR AG; *Int'l*, pg. 5925
WOHNPARK LAAER BERG VERWERTUNGS- UND BETEILIGUNGS-GMBH & CO. BAUPLATZ 4 BLAU PROJEKT-OG—See PORR AG; *Int'l*, pg. 5925
WOHN- UND PFLEGEWELT LAHNBLICK GMBH—See Deutsche Wohnen SE; *Int'l*, pg. 2085
WOHN- UND PFLEGEZENTRUM SALMENPARK AG—See Swiss Prime Site AG; *Int'l*, pg. 7371
WOHNUNGSBAUGESELLSCHAFT MIT BESCHRANKTER HAFTUNG—See Salzgitter AG; *Int'l*, pg. 6499
WOHNUNGSGESELLSCHAFT BRELA MBH—See Munchener Ruckversicherungs AG; *Int'l*, pg. 5092
WOHNUNGSGESELLSCHAFT OLYMPIA MBH—See PATRIZIA SE; *Int'l*, pg. 5759
WOI-DT—See TEGNA Inc.; *U.S. Public*, pg. 1991
WOJAN WINDOW & DOOR CORPORATION; *U.S. Private*, pg. 4553
WOJAS S.A.; *Int'l*, pg. 8442
WOJCIK BUILDERS, INC.; *U.S. Private*, pg. 4553
WOJTA-HANSEN INSURANCE AGENCY—See Ansay & Associates, LLC; *U.S. Private*, pg. 285
WOKEN TECHNOLOGY INC.—See GigaLane Co., Ltd.; *Int'l*, pg. 2971
WOKER FREIGHT SERVICES PROPRIETARY LIMITED—See The Bidvest Group Limited; *Int'l*, pg. 7627
THE WOKING NUFFIELD HOSPITAL—See Nuffield Health; *Int'l*, pg. 5488
WOKSAL A.D.; *Int'l*, pg. 8442
WOK TO WALK FRANCHISE B.V.—See TORIDOLL Holdings Corporation; *Int'l*, pg. 7828
WOLBERG ELECTRICAL SUPPLY CO. INC; *U.S. Private*, pg. 4553
WOLCOTT ARCHITECTURE INTERIORS; *U.S. Private*, pg. 4553
WOLCOTT BANCORP; *U.S. Private*, pg. 4553
WOLD ARCHITECTS, INC.; *U.S. Private*, pg. 4553
WOLDCAM AS—See Schibsted ASA; *Int'l*, pg. 6617
WOLDE FLOORING, LLC; *U.S. Private*, pg. 4553
WOL DIRECT; *U.S. Private*, pg. 4553
WOLFANGEL GMBH—See G. Siempelkamp GmbH & Co. KG; *Int'l*, pg. 2865
WOLF APPLIANCE CO., LLC—See Sub-Zero Freezer Co., Inc.; *U.S. Private*, pg. 3847
WOLF BLASS WINES PTY. LTD—See Treasury Wine Estates Limited; *Int'l*, pg. 7909
WOLFBONE MARKETING; *U.S. Private*, pg. 4554
THE WOLF BOOKINGS B.V.—See Live Nation Entertainment, Inc.; *U.S. Public*, pg. 1331
WOLF & COMPANY, P.C.—See BKD, LLP; *U.S. Private*, pg. 568
WOLF CREEK COMPANY INC—See Leonard Green & Partners, L.P.; *U.S. Private*, pg. 2429
WOLF CREEK NUCLEAR OPERATING CORPORATION—See Evergy, Inc.; *U.S. Public*, pg. 801
WOLFDEN RESOURCES CORPORATION; *Int'l*, pg. 8442
WOLFEBORO BAY CENTER—See Formation Capital, LLC; *U.S. Private*, pg. 1571
WOLFE/DOYLE ADVERTISING; *U.S. Private*, pg. 4554

WOLFE DYE & BLEACH WORKS INC.; *U.S. Private*, pg. 4554
WOLFE ENGINEERING INC.; *U.S. Private*, pg. 4554
WOLFE INDUSTRIES, INC.; *U.S. Private*, pg. 4554
WOLF ENERGIESPARSYSTEME OOO—See CENTROTEC SE; *Int'l*, pg. 1415
WOLF ENERGIESYSTEMEN B.V.—See CENTROTEC SE; *Int'l*, pg. 1415
WOLF ENERGY SERVICES INC.; *U.S. Public*, pg. 2376
WOLFENSON ELECTRIC, INC.; *U.S. Private*, pg. 4554
WOLFER & GOEBEL BAU GMBH—See STRABAG SE; *Int'l*, pg. 7233
WOLFE ROOFING, A TECTA AMERICA COMPANY, LLC—See Altas Partners LP; *Int'l*, pg. 387
WOLFE'S EVANSVILLE AUTO AUCTION INC.—See Great Lakes Auto Auction, Inc.; *U.S. Private*, pg. 1764
WOLFE-TORY MEDICAL, INC.—See Teleflex Incorporated; *U.S. Public*, pg. 1996
WOLFE & TRAVIS ELECTRIC COMPANY, INC.; *U.S. Private*, pg. 4554
WOLFF BROTHERS SUPPLY, INC.; *U.S. Private*, pg. 4554
WOLFFERTS HAUS- UND WARMETECHNIK GMBH—See Bilfinger SE; *Int'l*, pg. 1028
WOLFF GMBH & CO. KG—See Uzin Utz AG; *Int'l*, pg. 8104
WOLFFKRAN GMBH; *Int'l*, pg. 8442
WOLFF OLINS-NEW YORK—See Omnicom Group Inc.; *U.S. Public*, pg. 1599
WOLFF OLINS—See Omnicom Group Inc.; *U.S. Public*, pg. 1599
WOLF FRANCE S.A.S.—See CENTROTEC SE; *Int'l*, pg. 1415
WOLFF SHOE COMPANY INC.; *U.S. Private*, pg. 4554
WOLFF URBAN DEVELOPMENT, LLC—See Wolff Urban Management, Inc.; *U.S. Private*, pg. 4554
WOLFF URBAN MANAGEMENT, INC.; *U.S. Private*, pg. 4554
WOLFGANG KRUEGER VERLAG GMBH—See Verlagsgruppe Georg von Holtzbrinck GmbH; *Int'l*, pg. 8171
WOLFGANG STEUBING AG; *Int'l*, pg. 8442
WOLF GMBH—See CENTROTEC SE; *Int'l*, pg. 1415
WOLF-GORDON INC.—See Charger Investment Partners LP; *U.S. Private*, pg. 850
WOLF HOLLOW I, LP—See Constellation Energy Corporation; *U.S. Public*, pg. 572
WOLF HVAC SYSTEMS CO., LTD.—See CENTROTEC SE; *Int'l*, pg. 1415
WOLFINGTON BODY COMPANY, INC.; *U.S. Private*, pg. 4554
WOLF ITALIA S.R.L.—See CENTROTEC SE; *Int'l*, pg. 1415
WOLFKILL FEED & FERTILIZER CORPORATION; *U.S. Private*, pg. 4554
THE WOLF MACHINE CO.; *U.S. Private*, pg. 4138
WOLF MANUFACTURING COMPANY; *U.S. Private*, pg. 4554
WOLF MINERALS LIMITED; *Int'l*, pg. 8442
WOLF MOTOR COMPANY INC.; *U.S. Private*, pg. 4553
WOLFNET TECHNOLOGIES, LLC—See The Northwestern Mutual Life Insurance Company; *U.S. Private*, pg. 4085
WOLFORD AG—See Fosun International Limited; *Int'l*, pg. 2752
WOLFORD AMERICA, INC.—See Fosun International Limited; *Int'l*, pg. 2752
WOLFORD BELGIUM N.V.—See Fosun International Limited; *Int'l*, pg. 2752
WOLFORD CANADA INC.—See Fosun International Limited; *Int'l*, pg. 2752
WOLFORD DEUTSCHLAND GMBH—See Fosun International Limited; *Int'l*, pg. 2752
WOLFORD ESPANA, S.L.—See Fosun International Limited; *Int'l*, pg. 2752
WOLFORD ITALIA S.R.L.—See Fosun International Limited; *Int'l*, pg. 2752
WOLFORD LONDON LTD.—See Fosun International Limited; *Int'l*, pg. 2752
WOLFORD NEDERLAND B.V.—See Fosun International Limited; *Int'l*, pg. 2752
WOLFORD PARIS S.A.R.L.—See Fosun International Limited; *Int'l*, pg. 2752
WOLFORD SCANDINAVIA APS—See Fosun International Limited; *Int'l*, pg. 2752
WOLFORD (SCHWEIZ) AG—See Fosun International Limited; *Int'l*, pg. 2752
THE WOLF ORGANIZATION, LLC; *U.S. Private*, pg. 4138
WOLF PAVING CO. INC.—See Lowell Wolf Industries Inc.; *U.S. Private*, pg. 2505
WOLF PAVING & EXCAVATING OF MADISON—See Lowell Wolf Industries Inc.; *U.S. Private*, pg. 2505
WOLF POWER SYSTEMS GMBH—See CENTROTEC SE; *Int'l*, pg. 1415
WOLF PRESS & PUBLIC RELATIONS—See Daniel J. Edelman, Inc.; *U.S. Private*, pg. 1155
WOLF PVG GMBH & CO. KG—See Melitta Unternehmensgruppe Bentz KG; *Int'l*, pg. 4811
WOLFRAM ALPHA LLC—See Wolfram Research Inc.; *U.S. Private*, pg. 4554

WOLTER GROUP LLC

WOLFRAM BERGBAU UND HUTTEN AG—See Sandvik AB; *Int'l*, pg. 6535
WOLFRAM RESEARCH INC.; *U.S. Private*, pg. 4554
WOLF RIVER BANCORP, INC.; *U.S. Private*, pg. 4553
WOLF RIVER COMMUNITY BANK—See Wolf River Bancorp, Inc.; *U.S. Private*, pg. 4553
WOLF ROBOTICS, LLC—See Lincoln Electric Holdings, Inc.; *U.S. Public*, pg. 1318
WOLFSBURG AG—See Porsche Automobil Holding SE; *Int'l*, pg. 5933
WOLFSON CASING CORP.; *U.S. Private*, pg. 4554
WOLFSON ENTERTAINMENT, INC.—See Live Nation Entertainment, Inc.; *U.S. Public*, pg. 1331
WOLFSPEED, INC.; *U.S. Public*, pg. 2376
WOLFSPEED—See Wolfspeed, Inc.; *U.S. Public*, pg. 2377
WOLFSTRIKE DISTRIBUTORS LTD.—See FE Investments Limited; *Int'l*, pg. 2629
WOLFSTRIKE DISTRIBUTORS PTY LIMITED—See FE Investments Limited; *Int'l*, pg. 2629
WOLFTANK-ADISA HOLDING AG; *Int'l*, pg. 8442
WOLFTRAP FOUNDATION FOR THE PERFORMING ARTS; *U.S. Private*, pg. 4554
WOLF TREE, INC.—See The Davey Tree Expert Company; *U.S. Private*, pg. 4018
WOLFVISION CANADA, INC.—See WolfVision Holding AG; *Int'l*, pg. 8442
WOLFVISION CO. LTD.—See WolfVision Holding AG; *Int'l*, pg. 8442
WOLFVISION GMBH—See WolfVision Holding AG; *Int'l*, pg. 8442
WOLFVISION HOLDING AG; *Int'l*, pg. 8442
WOLFVISION INC.—See WolfVision Holding AG; *Int'l*, pg. 8443
WOLFVISION INC.—See WolfVision Holding AG; *Int'l*, pg. 8443
WOLFVISION MIDDLE EAST UAE—See WolfVision Holding AG; *Int'l*, pg. 8443
WOLFVISION PTE LTD—See WolfVision Holding AG; *Int'l*, pg. 8443
WOLFVISION UK LTD.—See WolfVision Holding AG; *Int'l*, pg. 8443
WOLGAST CORPORATION; *U.S. Private*, pg. 4554
W. OLIVER TRIPP COMPANY, INC.; *U.S. Private*, pg. 4418
WOLKE INKS & PRINTERS GMBH—See Danaher Corporation; *U.S. Public*, pg. 632
WOLKOFF ET ARNODIN; *Int'l*, pg. 8443
WOLLAR SOLAR HOLDING PTY LTD—See Beijing Energy International Holding Co., Ltd.; *Int'l*, pg. 949
WOLLONGONG COAL LIMITED—See Jindal Holdings Limited; *Int'l*, pg. 3966
WOLMAN CONSTRUCTION—See Waterford Group, LLC; *U.S. Private*, pg. 4453
WOLO MANUFACTURING CORP.—See 1847 Holdings LLC; *U.S. Public*, pg. 2
WOLONG AMERICAS LLC—See Wolong Electric Group Co., Ltd.; *Int'l*, pg. 8443
WOLONG ELECTRIC GROUP CO., LTD.; *Int'l*, pg. 8443
WOLONG ELECTRIC PRIVATE LIMITED—See Wolong Electric Group Co., Ltd.; *Int'l*, pg. 8443
WOLONG EMEA (GERMANY) GMBH—See Wolong Electric Group Co., Ltd.; *Int'l*, pg. 8443
WOLONG HOLDING GROUP CO., LTD.; *Int'l*, pg. 8443
WOLONG INTERNATIONAL BUSINESS CO., LTD.—See Wolong Electric Group Co., Ltd.; *Int'l*, pg. 8443
WOLONG INTERNATIONAL KOREA CO.,LTD.—See Wolong Electric Group Co., Ltd.; *Int'l*, pg. 8443
WOLONG INTERNATIONAL (MALAYSIA) SDN BHD—See Wolong Electric Group Co., Ltd.; *Int'l*, pg. 8443
WOLONG RESOURCES GROUP CO., LTD.—See Wolong Holding Group Co., Ltd.; *Int'l*, pg. 8443
WOLSDORFF TOBACCO GMBH—See Oettinger IMEX AG; *Int'l*, pg. 5530
WOLSELEY AUSTRIA AG—See Ferguson plc; *Int'l*, pg. 2638
WOLSELEY CANADA INC.—See Ferguson plc; *Int'l*, pg. 2638
WOLSELEY CENTRAL AND EASTERN EUROPE AG—See Ferguson plc; *Int'l*, pg. 2638
WOLSELEY FRANCE SAS—See Ferguson plc; *Int'l*, pg. 2638
WOLSELEY HOLDINGS CANADA INC.—See Ferguson plc; *Int'l*, pg. 2638
WOLSELEY HOLDINGS DENMARK A/S—See Ferguson plc; *Int'l*, pg. 2638
WOLSELEY HVAC R GROUP—See Ferguson plc; *Int'l*, pg. 2638
WOLSELEY INDUSTRIAL PRODUCTS GROUP INC—See Ferguson plc; *Int'l*, pg. 2638
WOLSELEY OVERSEAS LTD.—See Ferguson plc; *Int'l*, pg. 2638
WOLSELEY (SCHWEIZ) AG—See Ferguson plc; *Int'l*, pg. 2638
WOLSELEY UK LTD.—See Ferguson plc; *Int'l*, pg. 2638
WOLSEY LTD—See Matalan Retail Ltd.; *Int'l*, pg. 4726
WOLTCOM, INC. - EASTERN DIVISION—See Woltcom, Inc.; *U.S. Private*, pg. 4554
WOLTCOM, INC.; *U.S. Private*, pg. 4554
WOLTER GROUP LLC; *U.S. Private*, pg. 4554

WOLTER GROUP LLC

WOLTERS KLUWER CORPORATE LEGAL SERVICES—See Wolters Kluwer n.v.; *Int'l*, pg. 8445
WOLTERS KLUWER DEUTSCHLAND GMBH—See Wolters Kluwer n.v.; *Int'l*, pg. 8444
WOLTERS KLUWER DEUTSCHLAND INFORMATION SERVICES GMBH—See Wolters Kluwer n.v.; *Int'l*, pg. 8444
WOLTERS KLUWER ELM SOLUTIONS, INC.—See Wolters Kluwer n.v.; *Int'l*, pg. 8444
WOLTERS KLUWER FINANCIAL SERVICES/CCH—See Wolters Kluwer n.v.; *Int'l*, pg. 8444
WOLTERS KLUWER FINANCIAL SERVICES, INC.—See Wolters Kluwer n.v.; *Int'l*, pg. 8444
WOLTERS KLUWER FINANCIAL SERVICES—See Wolters Kluwer n.v.; *Int'l*, pg. 8444
WOLTERS KLUWER FINANCIAL SERVICES UK LTD.—See Wolters Kluwer n.v.; *Int'l*, pg. 8445
WOLTERS KLUWER FRANCE SA—See Wolters Kluwer n.v.; *Int'l*, pg. 8444
WOLTERS KLUWER HEALTH MEXICO, S.A. DE C.V—See Wolters Kluwer n.v.; *Int'l*, pg. 8444
WOLTERS KLUWER HEALTH—See Wolters Kluwer n.v.; *Int'l*, pg. 8444
WOLTERS KLUWER HOLDINGS (UK) PLC—See Wolters Kluwer n.v.; *Int'l*, pg. 8444
WOLTERS KLUWER INDIA—See Wolters Kluwer n.v.; *Int'l*, pg. 8445
WOLTERS KLUWER ITALIA S.R.L.—See Wolters Kluwer n.v.; *Int'l*, pg. 8445
WOLTERS KLUWER LEGAL & REGULATORY EUROPE—See Wolters Kluwer n.v.; *Int'l*, pg. 8445
WOLTERS KLUWER LIMITED—See Wolters Kluwer n.v.; *Int'l*, pg. 8445
WOLTERS KLUWER N.V.; *Int'l*, pg. 8443
WOLTERS KLUWER POLSKA - SOPOT—See Wolters Kluwer n.v.; *Int'l*, pg. 8445
WOLTERS KLUWER POLSKA SP. Z.O.O.—See Wolters Kluwer n.v.; *Int'l*, pg. 8445
WOLTERS KLUWER SRL—See Wolters Kluwer n.v.; *Int'l*, pg. 8445
WOLTERS KLUWER TAX & ACCOUNTING—See Wolters Kluwer n.v.; *Int'l*, pg. 8445
WOLTERS KLUWER (UK) LTD.—See Wolters Kluwer n.v.; *Int'l*, pg. 8444
WOLTERS-NOORDHOFF GRONINGEN—See SHV Holdings N.V.; *Int'l*, pg. 6872
WOLTERS REISEN GMBH—See TUI AG; *Int'l*, pg. 7969
WOLUWE SHOPPING CENTER; *Int'l*, pg. 8446
THE WOLVERHAMPTON NUFFIELD HOSPITAL—See Nuffield Health; *Int'l*, pg. 5488
WOLVERHAMPTON RACECOURSE LIMITED—See Reuben Brothers SA; *Int'l*, pg. 6311
WOLVERHAMPTON WANDERERS FOOTBALL CLUB (1986) LIMITED—See Fosun International Limited; *Int'l*, pg. 2752
WOLVERINE ADVANCED MATERIALS GMBH—See ITT Inc.; *U.S. Public*, pg. 1179
WOLVERINE ADVANCED MATERIALS GMBH—See GTCR LLC; *U.S. Private*, pg. 1805
WOLVERINE ADVANCED MATERIALS, LLC—See ITT Inc.; *U.S. Public*, pg. 1179
WOLVERINE ADVANCED MATERIALS LLC—See Center Rock Capital Partners, LP; *U.S. Private*, pg. 811
WOLVERINE ADVANCE MATERIALS GMBH—See ITT Inc.; *U.S. Public*, pg. 1179
WOLVERINE BRASS, INC.—See Dunes Point Capital, LLC; *U.S. Private*, pg. 1289
WOLVERINE BUILDING GROUP; *U.S. Private*, pg. 4554
WOLVERINE CAPITAL PARTNERS LLC; *U.S. Private*, pg. 4555
WOLVERINE COIL SPRING CO.; *U.S. Private*, pg. 4555
WOLVERINE ENERGY & INFRASTRUCTURE, INC.; *Int'l*, pg. 8446
WOLVERINE EUROPE LIMITED—See Wolverine World Wide, Inc.; *U.S. Public*, pg. 2377
WOLVERINE EUROPE RETAIL LIMITED—See Wolverine World Wide, Inc.; *U.S. Public*, pg. 2377
WOLVERINE FIRE PROTECTION CO.; *U.S. Private*, pg. 4555
WOLVERINE HARDWOODS INC.; *U.S. Private*, pg. 4555
WOLVERINE INTERNATIONAL, S.L.—See Wolverine World Wide, Inc.; *U.S. Public*, pg. 2377
WOLVERINE MUTUAL INSURANCE COMPANY; *U.S. Private*, pg. 4555
WOLVERINE OUTDOORS, INC.—See Wolverine World Wide, Inc.; *U.S. Public*, pg. 2377
WOLVERINE PACKING CO.; *U.S. Private*, pg. 4555
WOLVERINE PIPE LINE COMPANY; *U.S. Private*, pg. 4555
WOLVERINE POWER SUPPLY COOPERATIVE INC.; *U.S. Private*, pg. 4555
WOLVERINE PRESS (CHANGSHU) CO. LTD.—See ITT Inc.; *U.S. Public*, pg. 1179
WOLVERINE RESOURCES CORP.; *Int'l*, pg. 8446
WOLVERINE SPORTS—See School-Tech, Inc.; *U.S. Private*, pg. 3568
WOLVERINE SUPPLY INC.; *U.S. Private*, pg. 4555
WOLVERINE TRUCK SALES INC.; *U.S. Private*, pg. 4555

WOLVERINE TUBE INC.—See Wieland-Werke AG; *Int'l*, pg. 8404
WOLVERINE WAREHOUSING & DISTRIBUTION LIMITED—See 591182 ONTARIO LIMITED; *Int'l*, pg. 13
WOLVERINE WORLD WIDE - BATES FOOTWEAR—See Wolverine World Wide, Inc.; *U.S. Public*, pg. 2377
WOLVERINE WORLD WIDE, INC.; *U.S. Public*, pg. 2377
WOLVERTON & ASSOCIATES, INC.—See H.I.G. Capital, LLC; *U.S. Private*, pg. 1827
WOMACK ELECTRIC SUPPLY CO., INC.—See Crescent Electric Supply Company; *U.S. Private*, pg. 1093
WOMACK ELECTRIC & SUPPLY CO.; *U.S. Private*, pg. 4555
WOMACK MACHINE SUPPLY CO.—See Platte River Ventures, LLC; *U.S. Private*, pg. 3211
WOMACK PUBLISHING COMPANY, INC.; *U.S. Private*, pg. 4555
WOMANCART LIMITED; *Int'l*, pg. 8446
WOMAN'S CHRISTIAN ASSOCIATION—See WCA Hospital; *U.S. Private*, pg. 4461
WOMANS DAY—See The Hearst Corporation; *U.S. Private*, pg. 4047
WOMAN'S HEALTH GROUP, PLLC—See HCA Healthcare, Inc.; *U.S. Public*, pg. 1014
THE WOMAN'S HOSPITAL OF TEXAS—See HCA Healthcare, Inc.; *U.S. Public*, pg. 1012
WOMAN'S LIFE INSURANCE SOCIETY; *U.S. Private*, pg. 4555
WOMANSTAFF CO., LTD.—See Nakabayashi Co., Ltd.; *Int'l*, pg. 5131
WOMANWISE LLC; *U.S. Private*, pg. 4555
WOMBAT FINANCIAL SOFTWARE, INC.—See Insight Venture Management, LLC; *U.S. Private*, pg. 2091
WOMBAT SECURITY TECHNOLOGIES, INC.—See Thoma Bravo, L.P.; *U.S. Private*, pg. 4151
WOMBLE CARLYLE SANDRIDGE & RICE, LLP; *U.S. Private*, pg. 4555
WOMBLE COMPANY INC.; *U.S. Private*, pg. 4556
WOMEN FOR WOMEN INTERNATIONAL; *U.S. Private*, pg. 4556
WOMEN HELPING WOMEN; *U.S. Private*, pg. 4556
WOMEN IN BUSINESS/FABRIQUE; *U.S. Private*, pg. 4556
WOMEN'S AND CHILDREN'S PROFESSIONAL MANAGEMENT, L.L.C.—See HCA Healthcare, Inc.; *U.S. Public*, pg. 1014
WOMEN'S AND CHILDREN'S SPECIALISTS, LLC—See HCA Healthcare, Inc.; *U.S. Public*, pg. 1014
WOMEN'S APPAREL GROUP, LLC—See Monomoy Capital Partners LLC; *U.S. Private*, pg. 2772
WOMEN'S BUSINESS PARK TECHNOLOGIES LIMITED—See Wipro Limited; *Int'l*, pg. 8433
WOMENS CAMPAIGN INTERNATIONAL; *U.S. Private*, pg. 4556
THE WOMEN'S CANCER CENTRE LIMITED—See Advanced Oncotherapy plc; *Int'l*, pg. 161
WOMEN'S CENTER AT BROOKSIDE, LLC—See HCA Healthcare, Inc.; *U.S. Public*, pg. 1014
WOMEN'S COLLEGE PARTNERSHIP—See Bilfinger SE; *Int'l*, pg. 1029
WOMENSFORUM.COM, INC.—See ForgeLight, LLC; *U.S. Private*, pg. 1568
WOMENSFORUM.COM, INC.—See Searchlight Capital Partners, L.P.; *U.S. Private*, pg. 3591
WOMENSFORUM MEDIA GROUP—See H.I.G. Capital, LLC; *U.S. Private*, pg. 1829
WOMEN'S HEALTH AND WELLNESS OF JUPITER MEDICAL SPECIALISTS, LLC—See KKR & Co. Inc.; *U.S. Public*, pg. 1249
WOMEN'S HEALTH CONNECTICUT, INC.; *U.S. Private*, pg. 4556
WOMEN'S HEALTH PARTNERS, LLC—See Community Health Systems, Inc.; *U.S. Public*, pg. 557
WOMENS HEALTH PARTNERS, LLC—See Community Health Systems, Inc.; *U.S. Public*, pg. 557
WOMENS HEALTH SPECIALISTS OF BIRMINGHAM, INC.—See Community Health Systems, Inc.; *U.S. Public*, pg. 557
WOMENS HEALTH SPECIALISTS OF CARLISLE, LLC—See Community Health Systems, Inc.; *U.S. Public*, pg. 557
WOMEN'S HOUSING & ECONOMIC DEVELOPMENT CORPORATION; *U.S. Private*, pg. 4556
WOMEN'S INTERNATIONAL PHARMACY; *U.S. Private*, pg. 4556
WOMENSLINK CENTER OF WYLIE - A MEDICAL CENTER OF PLANO FACILITY, LLC—See HCA Healthcare, Inc.; *U.S. Public*, pg. 1014
WOMEN'S MARKETING, INC. - NEW YORK OFFICE—See SF Holding Corp.; *U.S. Private*, pg. 3621
WOMEN'S MARKETING, INC.—See SF Holding Corp.; *U.S. Private*, pg. 3621
WOMENS NETWORK—See Corus Entertainment Inc.; *Int'l*, pg. 1809
WOMEN'S NEXT LOUNGERIES LTD; *Int'l*, pg. 8446
WOMEN SPECIALISTS OF CLEAR LAKE, PLLC—See HCA Healthcare, Inc.; *U.S. Public*, pg. 1014

CORPORATE AFFILIATIONS

WOMEN SPECIALISTS OF MAINLAND, PLLC—See HCA Healthcare, Inc.; *U.S. Public*, pg. 1014
WOMEN'S WEAR DAILY—See Penske Media Corporation; *U.S. Private*, pg. 3139
WOMPI S.A.S.—See Bancolombia S.A.; *Int'l*, pg. 828
W.O.M. WORLD OF MEDICINE ASIA LTD.—See Novanta Inc.; *U.S. Public*, pg. 1548
W.O.M. WORLD OF MEDICINE GMBH—See Novanta Inc.; *U.S. Public*, pg. 1548
W.O.M. WORLD OF MEDICINE PRODUKTIONS-GMBH—See Novanta Inc.; *U.S. Public*, pg. 1548
W.O.M. WORLD OF MEDICINE USA, INC.—See Novanta Inc.; *U.S. Public*, pg. 1548
WOM WRECKONLINEMARKET GMBH—See Copart, Inc.; *U.S. Public*, pg. 575
WONBIOGEN CO., LTD.; *Int'l*, pg. 8446
WONCHANG SEMICONDUCTOR CO., LTD.—See WT Microelectronics Co., Ltd.; *Int'l*, pg. 8499
WONDER AUTO TECHNOLOGY, INC.; *Int'l*, pg. 8446
WONDER BANCORP, INC.; *U.S. Private*, pg. 4556
WONDER CORPORATION CO., LTD.—See RIZAP GROUP, Inc.; *Int'l*, pg. 6354
WONDERCRUISES AB—See TUI AG; *Int'l*, pg. 7969
WONDER ELECTRICALS LIMITED; *Int'l*, pg. 8446
THE WONDERFILM MEDIA CORP.; *Int'l*, pg. 7701
WONDERFI TECHNOLOGIES INC.; *Int'l*, pg. 8446
WONDERFUEL, LLC—See Duraflame, Inc.; *U.S. Private*, pg. 1292
WONDERFUL CABLING SYSTEMS CORP.—See Wonderful Hi-Tech Co., Ltd.; *Int'l*, pg. 8446
WONDERFUL CITRUS LLC—See The Wonderful Company LLC; *U.S. Private*, pg. 4138
WONDERFUL CITRUS PACKING LLC—See The Wonderful Company LLC; *U.S. Private*, pg. 4138
THE WONDERFUL COMPANY LLC; *U.S. Private*, pg. 4138
WONDERFUL HI-TECH CO., LTD.; *Int'l*, pg. 8446
WONDERFUL PHOTOELECTRICITY (DONG GUAN) CO., LTD.—See Wonderful Hi-Tech Co., Ltd.; *Int'l*, pg. 8446
WONDERFUL PISTACHIOS & ALMONDS LLC—See The Wonderful Company LLC; *U.S. Private*, pg. 4139
WONDERFUL SAIGON GARMENT CO., LTD.—See Marubeni Corporation; *Int'l*, pg. 4710
WONDERFUL SKY FINANCIAL GROUP HOLDINGS LIMITED; *Int'l*, pg. 8446
WONDERFUL SKY FINANCIAL GROUP—See Wonderful Sky Financial Group Holdings Limited; *Int'l*, pg. 8446
WONDERFUL TIMES GROUP AB; *Int'l*, pg. 8446
WONDERFUL (VIETNAM) WIRE & CABLE CO., LTD.—See Wonderful Hi-Tech Co., Ltd.; *Int'l*, pg. 8446
WONDER GROUP, INC.; *U.S. Private*, pg. 4556
WONDER HOUSEHOLD LIMITED—See King's Flair International (Holdings) Ltd.; *Int'l*, pg. 4170
WONDER ICE CREAM CO.; *U.S. Private*, pg. 4556
WONDER INTERNATIONAL EDUCATION & INVESTMENT GROUP CORPORATION; *U.S. Private*, pg. 4556
WONDERKEEP TAKAHAGI CO., LTD.—See Powdertech Co., Ltd.; *Int'l*, pg. 5942
WONDERLA HOLIDAYS LTD.; *Int'l*, pg. 8446
WONDERLA HOLIDAYS LTD—See Wonderla Holidays Ltd.; *Int'l*, pg. 8446
WONDERMEDIA TECHNOLOGIES, INC.—See VIA Technologies, Inc.; *Int'l*, pg. 8183
WONDER PRECISION PRIVATE LIMITED—See Kranti Industries Ltd.; *Int'l*, pg. 4300
WONDERSHARE TECHNOLOGY CO., LTD.; *Int'l*, pg. 8446
WONDERS INFORMATION CO., LTD.; *Int'l*, pg. 8446
WONDER STATE BOX CO.—See Southern Missouri Container Packaging Group; *U.S. Private*, pg. 3733
WONDERSTONE LIMITED—See Assore Limited; *Int'l*, pg. 649
WONDERWARE, INC.; *U.S. Private*, pg. 4556
WONDFO USA CO., LTD.—See Guangzhou Wondfo Biotech Co., Ltd.; *Int'l*, pg. 3168
WONDO MOBILITY, S.L.U.—See Ferrovial S.A.; *Int'l*, pg. 2645
WON-DOOR CORPORATION; *U.S. Private*, pg. 4556
WONGA.COM LTD.; *Int'l*, pg. 8447
WONG CHIO LAND DEVELOPMENT CO., LTD.—See Yem Chio Co., Ltd.; *Int'l*, pg. 8577
WONGDOODY - CULVER—See Infosys Limited; *Int'l*, pg. 3696
WONGDOODY HOLDING COMPANY, INC.—See Infosys Limited; *Int'l*, pg. 3696
WONG ENGINEERING CORPORATION BERHAD; *Int'l*, pg. 8447
WONG ENGINEERING ELECTRONICS SDN. BHD.—See Wong Engineering Corporation Berhad; *Int'l*, pg. 8447
WONG ENGINEERING INDUSTRIES SDN. BHD.—See Wong Engineering Corporation Berhad; *Int'l*, pg. 8447
WONG FONG INDUSTRIES LIMITED; *Int'l*, pg. 8447
WONG FONG MYANMAR COMPANY LIMITED—See Wong Fong Industries Limited; *Int'l*, pg. 8447
WONG'S ELECTRONICS CO., LIMITED—See Wongs International (Holdings) Ltd; *Int'l*, pg. 8448
WONG'S INTERNATIONAL (EUROPE) LIMITED—See Wongs International (Holdings) Ltd; *Int'l*, pg. 8448

COMPANY NAME INDEX

WONGS INTERNATIONAL (HOLDINGS) LTD; *Int'l*, pg. 8447
WONG'S INTERNATIONAL (JAPAN), INC.—See Wongs International (Holdings) Ltd; *Int'l*, pg. 8448
WONG'S INTERNATIONAL USA CORPORATION—See Wongs International (Holdings) Ltd; *Int'l*, pg. 8448
WONG'S KONG KING INTERNATIONAL (HOLDINGS) LIMITED; *Int'l*, pg. 8447
WONG'S TECHNOLOGY (SHANGHAI) LIMITED—See Wongs International (Holdings) Ltd; *Int'l*, pg. 8448
WONHE HIGH-TECH INTERNATIONAL, INC.; *Int'l*, pg. 8448
WONIK CO., LTD.—See Wonik Corporation; *Int'l*, pg. 8448
WONIK CORPORATION; *Int'l*, pg. 8448
WONIK CORPORATION USA, LTD.—See Wonik Corporation; *Int'l*, pg. 8448
WONIK CUBE CORP.—See Wonik Corporation; *Int'l*, pg. 8448
WONIK HOLDINGS CO., LTD.—See Wonik Corporation; *Int'l*, pg. 8448
WONIK INVESTMENT PARTNERS CO., LTD.—See Wonik Corporation; *Int'l*, pg. 8448
WONIK IPS CO., LTD.—See Wonik Corporation; *Int'l*, pg. 8448
WONIK IPS (XIAN) SEMICONDUCTOR EQUIPMENT CO., LTD.—See Wonik Corporation; *Int'l*, pg. 8448
WONIK L&D CO., LTD.—See Wonik Corporation; *Int'l*, pg. 8449
WONIK MATERIALS CO., LTD.—See Wonik Corporation; *Int'l*, pg. 8449
WONIK MATERIALS NORTH AMERICA LLC—See Wonik Corporation; *Int'l*, pg. 8448
WONIK PNE CO., LTD.—See Wonik Corporation; *Int'l*, pg. 8448
WONIK QNC CORPORATION - CERAMICS & CLEANING DIVISION—See Wonik Corporation; *Int'l*, pg. 8448
WONIK QNC CORPORATION—See Wonik Corporation; *Int'l*, pg. 8448
WONIK QNC EUROPE—See Wonik Corporation; *Int'l*, pg. 8448
WONIK QNC INTERNATIONAL—See Wonik Corporation; *Int'l*, pg. 8448
WONIK QUARTZ EUROPE GMBH—See Wonik Corporation; *Int'l*, pg. 8448
WONIK ROBOTICS CO., LTD.—See Wonik Corporation; *Int'l*, pg. 8449
WONIK TAIWAN QNC CO., LTD—See Wonik Corporation; *Int'l*, pg. 8448
WONIL SPECIAL STEEL; *Int'l*, pg. 8449
WONJIN PRECISION CO., LTD.—See Futaba Corporation; *Int'l*, pg. 2851
WONLIM CORPORATION; *Int'l*, pg. 8449
WONPOONG CHINA (ZHEJIANG) SPECIALTY TEXTILES CO., LTD—See Wonpoong Corporation; *Int'l*, pg. 8449
WONPOONG CORPORATION - CHEONG-JU FACTORY—See Wonpoong Corporation; *Int'l*, pg. 8449
WONPOONG CORPORATION (M) SDN.BHD.—See Wonpoong Corporation; *Int'l*, pg. 8449
WONPOONG CORPORATION; *Int'l*, pg. 8449
WONPUNG MULSAN CO., LTD.—See Wonpoong Corporation; *Int'l*, pg. 8449
WON TECH CO., LTD.; *Int'l*, pg. 8446
WONTON FOOD INC.; *U.S. Private*, pg. 4556
WOOCHANG PRECISION CO., LTD.—See Mobase Co., Ltd.; *Int'l*, pg. 5007
WOO COMMUNICATIONS LIMITED—See The Engine Group; *Int'l*, pg. 7640
THE WOOD AGENCY; *U.S. Private*, pg. 4139
WOODALL CONSTRUCTION CO. INC.; *U.S. Private*, pg. 4557
WOODALL CONSTRUCTION CO. LIMITED; *Int'l*, pg. 8449
WOOD AND COMPANY LIMITED—See John Wood Group PLC; *Int'l*, pg. 3983
WOOD AND HUSTON BANCORPORATION; *U.S. Private*, pg. 4556
WOOD AND HUSTON BANK—See Wood and Huston Bancorporation; *U.S. Private*, pg. 4556
WOOD AND LOGISTICS AS—See Norske Skog ASA; *Int'l*, pg. 5438
WOODARD CREEK HEALTHCARE, INC.—See The Ensign Group, Inc.; *U.S. Public*, pg. 2072
WOODARD & CURRAN INC.; *U.S. Private*, pg. 4557
WOODARD, LLC—See Craftmade International, Inc.; *U.S. Private*, pg. 1082
WOODARD TECHNOLOGY & INVESTMENTS LLC; *U.S. Private*, pg. 4557
WOODBINE PROPERTIES—See Equity Residential; *U.S. Public*, pg. 792
WOODBOIS GABON LTD.—See WoodBois Ltd.; *Int'l*, pg. 8449
WOODBOIS LTD.; *Int'l*, pg. 8449
WOODBOLT DISTRIBUTION, LLC; *U.S. Private*, pg. 4557
WOODBRIDGE BUICK GMC, INC.—See General Motors Company; *U.S. Public*, pg. 929
THE WOODBRIDGE COMPANY LIMITED; *Int'l*, pg. 7701
WOODBRIDGE FOAM CORPORATION; *Int'l*, pg. 8449
WOODBRIDGE INTERNATIONAL LLC—See Mariner Wealth Advisors, LLC; *U.S. Private*, pg. 2576
WOODBRIDGE VENTURES, INC.; *Int'l*, pg. 8449

WOODBURY AUTO WHOLESALER ENTERPRISE LLC; *U.S. Private*, pg. 4557
WOODBURY FINANCIAL SERVICES, INC.—See Reverence Capital Partners LLC; *U.S. Private*, pg. 3415
WOODBURY PRODUCTS, INC.—See MTS Health Partners, L.P.; *U.S. Private*, pg. 2810
WOODCOCK & ASSOCIATES, PC—See Yount, Hyde & Barbour PC; *U.S. Private*, pg. 4594
WOODCOTE RETIREMENT VILLAGE—See Ryman Healthcare Ltd.; *Int'l*, pg. 6440
WOOD COUNTY HOSPITAL; *U.S. Private*, pg. 4556
WOODCRAFTERS HOME PRODUCTS, LLC—See MasterBrand, Inc.; *U.S. Public*, pg. 1394
WOODCRAFT INDUSTRIES INC. - MOUNDS VIEW PLANT—See Quanex Building Products Corp.; *U.S. Public*, pg. 1750
WOODCRAFT INDUSTRIES, INC.—See Quanex Building Products Corp.; *U.S. Public*, pg. 1750
WOODCRAFT SUPPLY, LLC; *U.S. Private*, pg. 4557
WOOD CREEK CAPITAL MANAGEMENT, LLC—See Massachusetts Mutual Life Insurance Company; *U.S. Private*, pg. 2605
WOOD CULTURE PTE. LTD.—See Hap Seng Consolidated Berhad; *Int'l*, pg. 3268
WOOD DIALYSIS, LLC—See DaVita Inc.; *U.S. Public*, pg. 644
WOOD E&IS GMBH—See John Wood Group PLC; *Int'l*, pg. 3984
WOODEN CAMERA, INC.—See Videndum plc; *Int'l*, pg. 8191
WOODEN MCLAUGHLIN LLP—See Dinsmore & Shohl LLP; *U.S. Private*, pg. 1234
WOODEN SHIPS OF HOBOKEN; *U.S. Private*, pg. 4557
WOODEN SOLDIER LTD.; *U.S. Private*, pg. 4557
WOOD ENVIRONMENT AND INFRASTRUCTURE SOLUTIONS—See John Wood Group PLC; *Int'l*, pg. 3982
WOOD ENVIRONMENT & INFRASTRUCTURE SOLUTIONS UK LIMITED—See John Wood Group PLC; *Int'l*, pg. 3983
WOODFIELD GROUP INC.; *U.S. Private*, pg. 4558
WOODFIELD INC.; *U.S. Private*, pg. 4558
WOODFIELD SYSTEMS INTERNATIONAL PVT LTD.; *Int'l*, pg. 8449
WOODFIELD SYSTEMS LIMITED—See Woodfield Systems International Pvt Ltd.; *Int'l*, pg. 8449
WOODFIN HEATING INC.; *U.S. Private*, pg. 4558
WOODFIN SUITE HOTELS—See Hardage Investments, Inc.; *U.S. Private*, pg. 1862
WOODFORD INVESTMENT MANAGEMENT LLP; *Int'l*, pg. 8449
WOODFORD PLYWOOD INC.; *U.S. Private*, pg. 4558
THE WOODFORD RESERVE DISTILLERY—See Brown-Forman Corporation; *U.S. Public*, pg. 403
WOODFOREST FINANCIAL GROUP, INC.; *U.S. Private*, pg. 4558
WOODFOREST NATIONAL BANK—See Woodforest Financial Group, Inc.; *U.S. Private*, pg. 4558
WOOD FRIENDS CO., LTD.; *Int'l*, pg. 8449
WOOD&FRUITS D.O.O—See Nisauto holding a.d.; *Int'l*, pg. 5363
WOODGRAIN DISTRIBUTION, INC.—See Woodgrain, Inc.; *U.S. Private*, pg. 4558
WOODGRAIN DOORS—See Woodgrain, Inc.; *U.S. Private*, pg. 4558
WOODGRAIN, INC.; *U.S. Private*, pg. 4558
WOODGRAIN MILLWORK, INC. - NATURE'S DIVISION—See Woodgrain, Inc.; *U.S. Private*, pg. 4558
WOODGREEN (BLYTH) RESIDENTS MANAGEMENT COMPANY LIMITED—See Bellway plc; *Int'l*, pg. 968
WOODGROUP APS—See WoodBois Ltd.; *Int'l*, pg. 8449
WOOD GROUP COLOMBIA S.A.—See John Wood Group PLC; *Int'l*, pg. 3984
WOOD GROUP ENGINEERING (NORTH SEA) LIMITED—See John Wood Group PLC; *Int'l*, pg. 3984
WOOD GROUP FRANCE SAS—See John Wood Group PLC; *Int'l*, pg. 3984
WOOD GROUP INTEGRITY MANAGEMENT PTY. LTD.—See John Wood Group PLC; *Int'l*, pg. 3983
WOOD GROUP KAZAKHSTAN LLP—See John Wood Group PLC; *Int'l*, pg. 3984
WOOD GROUP KENNY INDIA PRIVATE LIMITED—See John Wood Group PLC; *Int'l*, pg. 3984
WOOD GROUP KENNY IRELAND LIMITED—See John Wood Group PLC; *Int'l*, pg. 3984
WOOD GROUP KENNY—See John Wood Group PLC; *Int'l*, pg. 3983
WOOD GROUP MUSTANG, INC.—See John Wood Group PLC; *Int'l*, pg. 3984
WOOD GROUP NORWAY AS—See John Wood Group PLC; *Int'l*, pg. 3984
WOOD GROUP PRATT & WHITNEY INDUSTRIAL TURBINE SERVICES, LLC—See John Wood Group PLC; *Int'l*, pg. 3984
WOOD GROUP PRATT & WHITNEY INDUSTRIAL TURBINE SERVICES, LLC—See Mitsubishi Heavy Industries, Ltd.; *Int'l*, pg. 4956

WOOD GROUP PRODUCTION SERVICES, INC. - HOUMA—See John Wood Group PLC; *Int'l*, pg. 3983
WOOD GROUP PRODUCTION SERVICES, INC.—See John Wood Group PLC; *Int'l*, pg. 3983
WOOD GROUP PSN UGANDA LIMITED—See John Wood Group PLC; *Int'l*, pg. 3984
WOOD GROUP SOMIAS SPA—See John Wood Group PLC; *Int'l*, pg. 3984
WOOD GROUP TRINIDAD & TOBAGO LIMITED—See John Wood Group PLC; *Int'l*, pg. 3984
WOOD GROUP USA, INC.—See John Wood Group PLC; *Int'l*, pg. 3984
WOOD GUTMANN & BOGART INSURANCE BROKERS; *U.S. Private*, pg. 4556
WOODHARBOR MOLDING & MILLWORKS, INC.—See HCI Equity Management, L.P.; *U.S. Private*, pg. 1889
WOODHAVEN DIALYSIS CENTER, LLC—See Nautic Partners, LLC; *U.S. Private*, pg. 2871
WOODHAVEN FURNITURE INDUSTRIES—See Aaron's Company, Inc.; *U.S. Public*, pg. 13
WOODHAVEN LEARNING CENTER; *U.S. Private*, pg. 4558
WOODHAVEN LUMBER & MILLWORK; *U.S. Private*, pg. 4558
WOODHEAD ASIA PTE. LTD.—See Koch Industries, Inc.; *U.S. Private*, pg. 2335
WOODHEAD CONNECTIVITY S.A.S.U.—See Koch Industries, Inc.; *U.S. Private*, pg. 2335
WOODHEAD DE MEXICO S.A. DE C.V.—See Koch Industries, Inc.; *U.S. Private*, pg. 2335
WOODHEAD INDUSTRIES, INC.—See Koch Industries, Inc.; *U.S. Private*, pg. 2335
WOODHEAD SOFTWARE & ELECTRONICS S.A.S.U.—See Koch Industries, Inc.; *U.S. Private*, pg. 2335
WOODHEADS SEEDS LIMITED—See Wynnstay Group Plc; *Int'l*, pg. 8517
WOODHILL COLLEGE PROPERTY HOLDINGS (PTY) LTD.—See Curro Holdings Ltd.; *Int'l*, pg. 1879
WOODHILL SUPPLY INC.—See The Macomb Group, Inc.; *U.S. Private*, pg. 4073
WOODHORN MEADOWS (ASHINGTON) RESIDENTS MANAGEMENT COMPANY LIMITED—See Persimmon plc; *Int'l*, pg. 5818
WOODHOUSE CHRYSLER DODGE JEEP RAM; *U.S. Private*, pg. 4558
WOODHOUSE GROUP LIMITED—See Marshalls plc; *Int'l*, pg. 4702
WOODIE'S DIY LIMITED—See Grafton Group plc; *Int'l*, pg. 3051
WOODIE'S DIY—See Grafton Group plc; *Int'l*, pg. 3051
WOODINGS INDUSTRIAL CORPORATION; *U.S. Private*, pg. 4558
WOODINVILLE LUMBER, INC.; *U.S. Private*, pg. 4558
THE WOODITCH COMPANY INSURANCE SERVICES, INC.—See Hellman & Friedman LLC; *U.S. Private*, pg. 1909
WOODLAKE REALTY, LLC—See Ventas, Inc.; *U.S. Public*, pg. 2279
WOOD-LAM STRUCTURES INC.—See Tumac Lumber Co. Inc.; *U.S. Private*, pg. 4258
WOODLAND AVIATION INC.; *U.S. Private*, pg. 4559
WOODLAND BURIAL PARKS GROUP LTD.—See Bibby Line Group Limited; *Int'l*, pg. 1018
WOODLAND DIAGNOSTIC IMAGING, LLC—See Akumin, Inc.; *U.S. Public*, pg. 70
WOODLAND FOODS INC.; *U.S. Private*, pg. 4559
WOODLAND FOREST PRODUCTS INC.; *U.S. Private*, pg. 4559
WOODLAND HEALTHCARE—See Catholic Health Initiatives; *U.S. Private*, pg. 790
WOODLAND HEIGHTS MEDICAL CENTER, LLC—See Community Health Systems, Inc.; *U.S. Public*, pg. 552
WOODLAND MOTORS CORP.; *U.S. Private*, pg. 4559
WOODLANDOR BUILDMAT SDN. BHD.—See Woodlandor Holdings Berhad; *Int'l*, pg. 8450
WOODLANDOR HOLDINGS BERHAD; *Int'l*, pg. 8449
WOODLANDOR ROOF SYSTEMS SDN. BHD.—See Woodlandor Holdings Berhad; *Int'l*, pg. 8450
WOODLANDOR WOOD PRODUCTS SDN. BHD.—See Woodlandor Holdings Berhad; *Int'l*, pg. 8450
WOODLAND PARK DIALYSIS CENTER, LLC—See Nautic Partners, LLC; *U.S. Private*, pg. 2871
WOODLAND PARK ZOOLOGICAL SOCIETY; *U.S. Private*, pg. 4559
WOODLAND PARTNERS LLC; *U.S. Private*, pg. 4559
WOODLAND PULP, LLC—See Charmwell Holdings Ltd.; *Int'l*, pg. 1451
WOODLAND RESORT CONFERENCE CENTRE—See Woodlands Operating Company LP; *U.S. Private*, pg. 4559
WOODLANDS BANK—See Woodlands Financial Services Company; *U.S. Public*, pg. 2377
THE WOODLANDS BEVERAGE, INC.—See Howard Hughes Holdings Inc.; *U.S. Public*, pg. 1060
THE WOODLANDS FINANCIAL GROUP—See Texans Credit Union; *U.S. Private*, pg. 3974
WOODLANDS FINANCIAL SERVICES COMPANY; *U.S. Public*, pg. 2377

WOODLANDS FINANCIAL SERVICES COMPANY / CORPORATE AFFILIATIONS

WOODLANDS NATIONAL BANK—See Mille Lacs Bancorporation, Inc.; *U.S. Private*, pg. 2731
THE WOODLANDS OF VAN BUREN, INC.—See Waste Management, Inc.; *U.S. Public*, pg. 2332
WOODLANDS OPERATING COMPANY LP; *U.S. Private*, pg. 4559
WOODLANDS RELIGIOUS COMMUNITY INC.; *U.S. Private*, pg. 4559
WOODLANDS SUNNY FOODS PTE. LTD.—See Fuji Oil Holdings Inc.; *Int'l*, pg. 2816
WOOD LANE RESIDENTIAL SERVICES, INC.; *U.S. Private*, pg. 4557
WOODLAWN CEMETERY OF CHICAGO, INC.—See Service Corporation International; *U.S. Public*, pg. 1871
WOODLAWN CONSTRUCTION COMPANY; *U.S. Private*, pg. 4559
WOODLAWN MANUFACTURING, LTD.—See National Presto Industries, Inc; *U.S. Public*, pg. 1497
WOODLAWN PARTNERS, INC.; *U.S. Private*, pg. 4559
WOODLEIGH GARDENS PTE LTD—See Savills plc; *Int'l*, pg. 6598
WOODLEY SDN. BHD.—See Ta Ann Holdings Berhad; *Int'l*, pg. 7399
WOODLEYS FINE FURNITURE INC.; *U.S. Private*, pg. 4559
WOODLOCH PINES INC.; *U.S. Private*, pg. 4559
WOODLORE INTERNATIONAL INC.; *Int'l*, pg. 8450
WOODLORE—See Caleres, Inc.; *U.S. Public*, pg. 422
WOOD MACKENZIE LTD.—See Veritas Capital Fund Management, LLC; *U.S. Private*, pg. 4366
WOODMAN CONSTRUCTION INC.; *U.S. Private*, pg. 4559
WOODMAN'S FOOD MARKET INC.; *U.S. Private*, pg. 4559
WOODMEN OF THE WORLD LIFE INSURANCE SOCIETY, INC.; *U.S. Private*, pg. 4559
WOODMERE MANAGEMENT INC.—See Delta Holdings, Inc.; *U.S. Private*, pg. 1200
WOOD-MIZER PRODUCTS INC.; *U.S. Private*, pg. 4557
WOOD-MODE INCORPORATED; *U.S. Private*, pg. 4557
WOODMONT COUNTRY CLUB; *U.S. Private*, pg. 4559
WOODMONT REAL ESTATE SERVICES LTD. - COMMERCIAL DIVISION—See Woodmont Real Estate Services Ltd.; *U.S. Private*, pg. 4559
WOODMONT REAL ESTATE SERVICES LTD.; *U.S. Private*, pg. 4559
WOODMONT REALTY ADVISORS INC.—See Woodmont Real Estate Services Ltd.; *U.S. Private*, pg. 4559
WOOD MOTOR COMPANY INC.; *U.S. Private*, pg. 4557
WOOD'N PALLETS, INC.; *U.S. Private*, pg. 4557
WOOD OF SALISBURY LIMITED—See Marshall of Cambridge (Holdings) Limited; *Int'l*, pg. 4702
WOOD ONE CO., LTD.; *Int'l*, pg. 8449
WOOD PARTNERS, L.L.C. - ORLANDO—See Wood Partners, L.L.C.; *U.S. Private*, pg. 4557
WOOD PARTNERS, L.L.C.; *U.S. Private*, pg. 4557
WOODPECKER.CO SA; *Int'l*, pg. 8450
WOODPECKER TRUCK & EQUIPMENT INCORPORATED; *U.S. Private*, pg. 4559
WOOD PETROLEUM CO., INC.; *U.S. Private*, pg. 4557
WOODPITA CO., LTD.—See Yahagi Construction Co., Ltd.; *Int'l*, pg. 8546
WOOD PRESERVERS, INC.—See Stella-Jones, Inc.; *Int'l*, pg. 7196
WOOD PRO INC.; *U.S. Private*, pg. 4557
WOOD PROTECTION LP—See Koppers Holdings Inc.; *U.S. Public*, pg. 1272
WOODRIDGE ADVISORS LLC—See Frontenac Company LLC; *U.S. Private*, pg. 1614
WOODRIDGE BEHAVIORAL CARE—See Ridgemont Partners Management LLC; *U.S. Private*, pg. 3433
WOODROW W. CROSS AGENCY—See Cross Financial Corporation; *U.S. Private*, pg. 1104
WOODROW WILSON CONSTRUCTION COMPANY, INC.; *U.S. Private*, pg. 4559
WOODRUFF CONSTRUCTION LLC; *U.S. Private*, pg. 4560
WOODRUFF CORPORATION—See ICC Industries, Inc.; *U.S. Private*, pg. 2030
WOODRUFF ELECTRIC COOPERATIVE CORPORATION; *U.S. Private*, pg. 4560
WOODRUFF ENERGY; *U.S. Private*, pg. 4560
WOODRUFF-SAWYER & CO.; *U.S. Private*, pg. 4560
WOODRUFF & SONS INC.; *U.S. Private*, pg. 4560
WOODRUFF SWEITZER CANADA INC.—See Woodruff Sweitzer; *U.S. Private*, pg. 4560
WOODRUFF SWEITZER; *U.S. Private*, pg. 4560
WOODSAGE HOLDINGS, LLC; *U.S. Private*, pg. 4560
WOODSAGE INDUSTRIES—See Woodsage Holdings, LLC; *U.S. Private*, pg. 4560
WOOD SARDEGNA S.R.L.—See John Wood Group PLC; *Int'l*, pg. 3984
WOODS BAGOT PTY. LTD.; *Int'l*, pg. 8450
WOOD'S BOOTS—See Boot Barn Holdings, Inc.; *U.S. Public*, pg. 368
WOODSBORO BANK; *U.S. Private*, pg. 4560
WOODS BROS REALTY, INC.—See Berkshire Hathaway Inc.; *U.S. Public*, pg. 307

WOODS COACHES LIMITED—See Mobico Group PLC; *Int'l*, pg. 5009
WOODS CROSS REFINING COMPANY, LLC—See HF Sinclair Corporation; *U.S. Public*, pg. 1034
WOODS EQUIPMENT COMPANY—See American Securities LLC; *U.S. Private*, pg. 247
WOODS EQUIPMENT COMPANY—See P2 Capital Partners, LLC; *U.S. Private*, pg. 3062
WOODSIDE CAPITAL PARTNERS; *U.S. Private*, pg. 4560
WOODSIDE ELECTRONICS CORPORATION—See Warburg Pincus LLC; *U.S. Private*, pg. 4438
WOODSIDE ENERGY GROUP LTD; *Int'l*, pg. 8450
WOODSIDE ENERGY LTD.—See Woodside Energy Group Ltd; *Int'l*, pg. 8450
WOODSIDE ENERGY (UK) LIMITED—See Woodside Energy Group Ltd; *Int'l*, pg. 8450
WOODSIDE ENERGY (USA), INC.—See Woodside Energy Group Ltd; *Int'l*, pg. 8450
WOODSIDE HOMES, INC.—See Sekisui House, Ltd.; *Int'l*, pg. 6698
WOODSIDE HOTELS & RESORTS; *U.S. Private*, pg. 4560
WOODSIDE MAURITANIA PTY. LTD.—See Woodside Energy Group Ltd; *Int'l*, pg. 8450
WOODSMAN KITCHENS & FLOORS; *U.S. Private*, pg. 4560
WOODSON ENGINEERING & SURVEYING, INC.—See Littlejohn & Co., LLC; *U.S. Private*, pg. 2470
WOODSON EQUITY LLC; *U.S. Private*, pg. 4560
WOODSONS CASH STORE INC.; *U.S. Private*, pg. 4560
WOOD SOURCE, INC.—See Patrick Lumber Company, Inc.; *U.S. Private*, pg. 3110
WOODS ROGERS PLC; *U.S. Private*, pg. 4560
WOODS SUPER MARKET INC.; *U.S. Private*, pg. 4560
WOODSTOCK FARM & FLEET INC.—See Blain Supply, Inc.; *U.S. Private*, pg. 577
WOODSTOCK HOLDINGS, INC.; *U.S. Private*, pg. 2377
WOODSTOCK WIRE WORKS INC.; *U.S. Private*, pg. 4561
THE WOODSTREAM CORPORATION—See Vestar Capital Partners, LLC; *U.S. Private*, pg. 4372
WOODSTREAM EUROPE LTD.—See Vestar Capital Partners, LLC; *U.S. Private*, pg. 4372
WOOD STRUCTURES, INC.—See Roark Capital Group Inc.; *U.S. Private*, pg. 3456
WOODSVILLA LIMITED; *Int'l*, pg. 8450
WOODSVILLE GUARANTY SAVINGS BANK; *U.S. Private*, pg. 4561
WOODS WITT DEALY & SONS, INC.; *U.S. Private*, pg. 4560
WOODTEX INTERNATIONAL CO., LTD.—See Vanachai Group Public Company Limited; *Int'l*, pg. 8128
WOOD TRADE INTERNATIONAL LLC; *U.S. Private*, pg. 4557
WOODTRUST BANK, N.A.—See WoodTrust Financial Corporation; *U.S. Private*, pg. 4561
WOODTRUST FINANCIAL CORPORATION; *U.S. Private*, pg. 4561
WOOD TUBE SWEDEN AB—See Norvik hf; *Int'l*, pg. 5448
WOODVINE GROUP, LLC; *U.S. Private*, pg. 4561
WOODWARD AKEN GMBH—See Woodward, Inc.; *U.S. Public*, pg. 2378
WOODWARD ASSET CAPITAL LLC; *U.S. Private*, pg. 4561
WOODWARD BULGARIA EOOD—See Woodward, Inc.; *U.S. Public*, pg. 2377
WOODWARD CIS LIMITED LIABILITY COMPANY—See Woodward, Inc.; *U.S. Public*, pg. 2378
WOODWARD COMERCIO DE SISTEMAS DE CONTROLE E PROTECAO ELECTRICA LTDA.—See Woodward, Inc.; *U.S. Public*, pg. 2378
WOODWARD COMMUNICATIONS, INC.; *U.S. Private*, pg. 4561
WOODWARD COMPRESSOR SALES INC—See Atlas Copco AB; *Int'l*, pg. 680
WOODWARD CONTROLS, INC.—See Woodward, Inc.; *U.S. Public*, pg. 2378
WOODWARD CONTROLS (SUZHOU) CO., LTD.—See Woodward, Inc.; *U.S. Public*, pg. 2378
WOODWARD DESIGN+BUILD; *U.S. Private*, pg. 4561
WOODWARD FST, INC.—See Woodward, Inc.; *U.S. Public*, pg. 2378
WOODWARD GMBH—See Woodward, Inc.; *U.S. Public*, pg. 2378
WOODWARD HEALTH SYSTEM, LLC—See Community Health Systems, Inc.; *U.S. Public*, pg. 557
WOODWARD HOME CARE SERVICES, LLC—See Community Health Systems, Inc.; *U.S. Public*, pg. 557
WOODWARD HRT, INC.—See Woodward, Inc.; *U.S. Public*, pg. 2378
WOODWARD IDS BULGARIA EOOD—See Woodward, Inc.; *U.S. Public*, pg. 2378
WOODWARD IDS SWITZERLAND AG—See Woodward, Inc.; *U.S. Public*, pg. 2378
WOODWARD IDS SWITZERLAND GMBH—See Woodward, Inc.; *U.S. Public*, pg. 2378
WOODWARD, INC. - DUARTE—See Woodward, Inc.; *U.S. Public*, pg. 2378

WOODWARD, INC. - LOVELAND—See Woodward, Inc.; *U.S. Public*, pg. 2378
WOODWARD, INC. - LOVES PARK—See Woodward, Inc.; *U.S. Public*, pg. 2378
WOODWARD, INC.; *U.S. Public*, pg. 2377
WOODWARD INC.—See Woodward, Inc.; *U.S. Public*, pg. 2378
WOODWARD INDIA PRIVATE LIMITED—See Woodward, Inc.; *U.S. Public*, pg. 2378
WOODWARD INDUSTRIES, INC.; *U.S. Private*, pg. 4561
WOODWARD INTERNATIONAL, INC. - GLOUCESTER PLANT—See Woodward, Inc.; *U.S. Public*, pg. 2378
WOODWARD INTERNATIONAL, INC. - PRESTWICK PLANT—See Woodward, Inc.; *U.S. Public*, pg. 2378
WOODWARD IODINE CORPORATION (USA)—See ISE CHEMICALS CORPORATION; *Int'l*, pg. 3813
WOODWARD (JAPAN) LTD.—See Woodward, Inc.; *U.S. Public*, pg. 2377
WOODWARD KEMPEN GMBH—See Woodward, Inc.; *U.S. Public*, pg. 2378
WOODWARD LANDSCAPE SUPPLY, INC.; *U.S. Private*, pg. 4561
WOODWARD L'ORANGE GMBH—See Woodward, Inc.; *U.S. Public*, pg. 2378
WOODWARD MPC—See Woodward, Inc.; *U.S. Public*, pg. 2378
WOODWARD NEDERLAND B.V.—See Woodward, Inc.; *U.S. Public*, pg. 2378
WOODWARD POLAND SP. Z O.O.—See Woodward, Inc.; *U.S. Public*, pg. 2378
WOODWARD POWER SOLUTIONS GMBH—See Woodward, Inc.; *U.S. Public*, pg. 2378
WOODWARD (TIANJIN) CONTROLS COMPANY LIMITED—See Woodward, Inc.; *U.S. Public*, pg. 2377
WOODWARD YOUTH CORPORATION; *U.S. Private*, pg. 4561
WOODWAY COUNTRY CLUB, INC.; *U.S. Private*, pg. 4561
WOOD WHEATON CHEVROLET CADILLAC LTD; *Int'l*, pg. 8449
WOODWING USA, INC.; *U.S. Private*, pg. 4561
WOODWORKS BY BERGS AB—See Norvik hf; *Int'l*, pg. 5448
WOODWORKS UNLIMITED; *U.S. Private*, pg. 4561
WOODWORTH CHEVROLET-CADILLAC-BUICK; *U.S. Private*, pg. 4561
WOOD WYANT, INC.—See Sani-Marc inc.; *Int'l*, pg. 6539
WOODYARD & ASSOCIATES, LLC; *U.S. Private*, pg. 4561
WOODY SANDER FORD INC.; *U.S. Private*, pg. 4561
WOODY'S ENTERPRISES LTD.; *U.S. Private*, pg. 4561
WOOFOUND, INC.; *U.S. Private*, pg. 4561
WOOGA GMBH—See Playtika Holding Corp.; *Int'l*, pg. 5895
WOOGENE B&G CO., LTD. - HWASEONG FACTORY—See Woogene B&G Co., Ltd.; *Int'l*, pg. 8450
WOOGENE B&G CO., LTD.; *Int'l*, pg. 8450
WOOJEON CO., LTD.; *Int'l*, pg. 8450
WOOJEON CORPORATION—See Woojeon Co., Ltd.; *Int'l*, pg. 8450
WOOJEON JAPAN CO., LTD.—See Woojeon Co., Ltd.; *Int'l*, pg. 8450
WOOJIN ELECTRO-NITE INC.—See Heraeus Holding GmbH; *Int'l*, pg. 3358
WOOJIN INC.; *Int'l*, pg. 8450
WOOJIN INDUSTRY COMPANY LTD.; *Int'l*, pg. 8450
WOOJIN I&S CO., LTD.; *Int'l*, pg. 8450
WOOJIN PLAIMM CO., LTD.; *Int'l*, pg. 8450
WOOJIN SELEX (AMERICA), INC.—See Woojin Plaimm Co., Ltd.; *Int'l*, pg. 8450
WOOJUNG BIO, INC.; *Int'l*, pg. 8450
WOOL AND TUSK LTD.; *U.S. Private*, pg. 4561
WOOLCAN, INC.—See Woolrich, Inc.; *U.S. Private*, pg. 4562
WOOLDRIDGE CONSTRUCTION CO., INC.; *U.S. Private*, pg. 4561
WOOLDRIDGE CONSTRUCTION CO., INC.—See Wooldridge Construction Co., Inc.; *U.S. Private*, pg. 4562
WOOLDRIDGE CONSTRUCTION OF PENNSYLVANIA INC.—See Wooldridge Construction Co., Inc.; *U.S. Private*, pg. 4562
WOOLEE AIRTECH KOREA CO., LTD.—See AIRTECH JAPAN, LTD.; *Int'l*, pg. 249
WOOLF DISTRIBUTING COMPANY INC.; *U.S. Private*, pg. 4562
WOOLIES LIQUOR STORES PTY. LTD.—See Woolworths Group Limited; *Int'l*, pg. 8452
WOOL INDUSTRY TRIA ALFA S.A.; *Int'l*, pg. 8451
WOOLPERT INC.; *U.S. Private*, pg. 4562
WOOLPERT LLP; *U.S. Private*, pg. 4562
WOOLRICH, INC.; *U.S. Private*, pg. 4562
WOOLRICH, INC. - STORE DIVISION—See Woolrich, Inc.; *U.S. Private*, pg. 4562
WOOLRICH JAPAN INC.—See Goldwin, Inc.; *Int'l*, pg. 3035
WOOLTEX UK LTD.; *Int'l*, pg. 8451
WOOL WHOLESALE PLUMBING SUPPLY, INC.; *U.S. Private*, pg. 4561

COMPANY NAME INDEX

WOOLWICH HOMES LIMITED—See Barclays PLC; *Int'l*, pg. 863
WOOLWICH SURVEYING SERVICES LIMITED—See Barclays PLC; *Int'l*, pg. 863
WOOLWINE FORD LINCOLN, INC.; *U.S. Private*, pg. 4562
WOOLWORTH PROPERTIES PLC; *Int'l*, pg. 8451
WOOLWORTHS GROUP LIMITED; *Int'l*, pg. 8451
WOOLWORTHS (HK) PROCUREMENT LIMITED—See Woolworths Group Limited; *Int'l*, pg. 8452
WOOLWORTHS (HK) SALES LIMITED—See Woolworths Group Limited; *Int'l*, pg. 8452
WOOLWORTHS HOLDINGS LIMITED; *Int'l*, pg. 8452
WOOLWORTHS (INTERNATIONAL) PTY LIMITED—See Woolworths Group Limited; *Int'l*, pg. 8452
WOOLWORTHS MANAGEMENT PTY. LTD.—See Woolworths Group Limited; *Int'l*, pg. 8452
WOOLWORTHS NEW ZEALAND GROUP LIMITED—See Woolworths Group Limited; *Int'l*, pg. 8452
WOOLWORTHS NEW ZEALAND LIMITED—See Woolworths Group Limited; *Int'l*, pg. 8452
WOOLWORTHS (NEW ZEALAND) LTD.—See Woolworths Group Limited; *Int'l*, pg. 8452
WOOLWORTHS (PROJECT FINANCE) PTY. LIMITED—See Woolworths Group Limited; *Int'l*, pg. 8452
WOOLWORTHS PROPERTIES PTY. LTD.—See Woolworths Group Limited; *Int'l*, pg. 8452
WOOLWORTHS (PROPRIETARY) LIMITED—See Woolworths Holdings Limited; *Int'l*, pg. 8453
WOOLWORTHS (VICTORIA) PTY LIMITED—See Woolworths Group Limited; *Int'l*, pg. 8452
WOOMERA MINING LIMITED; *Int'l*, pg. 8453
WOONGJIN CO., LTD.; *Int'l*, pg. 8453
WOONGJIN ENERGY CO., LTD.—See SunPower Corporation; *U.S. Public*, pg. 1965
WOONGJIN ENERGY CO., LTD.—See Woongjin Co., Ltd.; *Int'l*, pg. 8453
WOONGJIN THINKBIG CO., LTD.; *Int'l*, pg. 8453
WOOPRA INC.—See Appier Group, Inc.; *Int'l*, pg. 520
WOOREE BIO CO., LTD.—See Wooree E&L Co., Ltd.; *Int'l*, pg. 8453
WOOREE E&L CO., LTD.; *Int'l*, pg. 8453
WOOREE ENTERPRISE CO., LTD.—See Wooree E&L Co., Ltd.; *Int'l*, pg. 0463
WOOREE LITECH INC.—See Wooree E&L Co., Ltd.; *Int'l*, pg. 8453
WOOREE VINA CO., LTD.—See Wooree E&L Co., Ltd.; *Int'l*, pg. 8453
WOORI AMERICA BANK—See Woori Financial Group Inc.; *Int'l*, pg. 8453
WOORI ASSET MANAGEMENT CORP.—See Woori Financial Group Inc.; *Int'l*, pg. 8453
WOORI ASSET TRUST CO., LTD.—See Woori Financial Group Inc.; *Int'l*, pg. 8453
WOORI BANK—See Woori Financial Group Inc.; *Int'l*, pg. 8453
WOORI BANK VIETNAM LIMITED—See Woori Financial Group Inc.; *Int'l*, pg. 8453
WOORI BIOME, INC.—See Woori Technology Inc.; *Int'l*, pg. 8454
WOORI CARD CO., LTD.—See Woori Financial Group Inc.; *Int'l*, pg. 8453
WOORIDUL HUEBRAIN LTD.; *Int'l*, pg. 8454
WOORIDUL PHARMACEUTICAL LTD. - HYANGNAM PLANT—See PharmGen Science Inc.; *Int'l*, pg. 5842
WOORIEN CO., LTD.—See Vatech Co., Ltd.; *Int'l*, pg. 8135
WOORI FINANCE MYANMAR CO., LTD.—See Woori Financial Group Inc.; *Int'l*, pg. 8453
WOORI FINANCE RESEARCH INSTITUTE CO., LTD.—See Woori Financial Group Inc.; *Int'l*, pg. 8453
WOORI FINANCIAL CAPITAL CO., LTD.—See Woori Financial Group Inc.; *Int'l*, pg. 8453
WOORI FINANCIAL F&I CO., LTD.—See Woori Financial Group Inc.; *Int'l*, pg. 8453
WOORI FINANCIAL GROUP INC.; *Int'l*, pg. 8453
WOORI FINE CHEM CO., LTD.—See SK Inc.; *Int'l*, pg. 6973
WOORI FUND SERVICE CO., LTD.—See Woori Financial Group Inc.; *Int'l*, pg. 8453
WOORI GLOBAL ASSET MANAGEMENT CO., LTD.—See Woori Financial Group Inc.; *Int'l*, pg. 8453
WOORI GLOBAL MARKETS ASIA LIMITED—See Woori Financial Group Inc.; *Int'l*, pg. 8453
WOORI INVESTMENT BANK CO., LTD.—See Woori Financial Group Inc.; *Int'l*, pg. 8453
WOORI & LEO PMC LTD. CO., LTD.—See Leopalace21 Corporation; *Int'l*, pg. 4465
WOORIM MACHINERY CO., LTD. - FACTORY 1—See Woorim Power Train Solution Co., Ltd.; *Int'l*, pg. 8454
WOORIM POWER TRAIN SOLUTION CO., LTD.; *Int'l*, pg. 8454
WOORINET, INC.; *Int'l*, pg. 8454
WOORI PRIVATE EQUITY ASSET MANAGEMENT CO., LTD.—See Woori Financial Group Inc.; *Int'l*, pg. 8453
WOORIRO CO., LTD.; *Int'l*, pg. 8454
WOORISON F&G CO., LTD.; *Int'l*, pg. 8454
WOORI SPECIAL PURPOSE ACQUISITION 3 CO., LTD.; *Int'l*, pg. 8454
WOORI TECHNOLOGY INC.; *Int'l*, pg. 8454
WOORI TECHNOLOGY INVESTMENT CO., LTD.; *Int'l*, pg. 8454
WOORY AUTOMOTIVE INDIA PVT LTD—See Woory Industrial Holdings Co., Ltd.; *Int'l*, pg. 8454
WOORY INDUSTRIAL CO., LTD.; *Int'l*, pg. 8454
WOORY INDUSTRIAL HOLDINGS CO., LTD.; *Int'l*, pg. 8454
WOORY INDUSTRIAL (THAILAND) CO., LTD.—See Woory Industrial Holdings Co., Ltd.; *Int'l*, pg. 8454
WOORY PLATECH CO., LTD.—See Woory Industrial Holdings Co., Ltd.; *Int'l*, pg. 8454
WOORY SLOVAKIA S.R.O.—See Woory Industrial Holdings Co., Ltd.; *Int'l*, pg. 8454
WOOSHIN ENGINEERING PVT. LTD.—See Wooshin Systems Co., Ltd.; *Int'l*, pg. 8454
WOOSHIN SYSTEMS CO., LTD. - DANGJIN PLANT—See Wooshin Systems Co., Ltd.; *Int'l*, pg. 8454
WOOSHIN SYSTEMS CO., LTD. - HWASEONG PLANT—See Wooshin Systems Co., Ltd.; *Int'l*, pg. 8454
WOOSHIN SYSTEMS CO., LTD. - SIHWA 2ND PLANT—See Wooshin Systems Co., Ltd.; *Int'l*, pg. 8454
WOOSHIN SYSTEMS CO., LTD.; *Int'l*, pg. 8454
WOOSHIN VENTURE INVESTMENT CO., LTD.—See Asia Holdings Co., Ltd.; *Int'l*, pg. 613
THE WOOSTER BRUSH COMPANY - RENO—See The Wooster Brush Company; *U.S. Private*, pg. 4139
THE WOOSTER BRUSH COMPANY; *U.S. Private*, pg. 4139
WOOSTER DAILY RECORD, INC., LLC—See Gannett Co., Inc.; *U.S. Public*, pg. 905
WOOSTER PRODUCTS, INC.; *U.S. Private*, pg. 4562
WOOSU AMS CO., LTD.; *Int'l*, pg. 8455
WOOSU AMS CO., LTD. - ULSAN PLANT—See WOOSU AMS Co., Ltd.; *Int'l*, pg. 8455
WOOSU INDIA PVT. LTD.—See WOOSU AMS Co., Ltd.; *Int'l*, pg. 8455
WOOSUNG CO., LTD.; *Int'l*, pg. 8455
WOOSUNG TRANSPORTATION CO., LTD—See Woosung Co., Ltd.; *Int'l*, pg. 8455
WOOSUNG VIETNAM CO., LTD—See Woosung Co., Ltd.; *Int'l*, pg. 8455
WOOSUNG YANGHANG—See Woosung Co., Ltd.; *Int'l*, pg. 8455
WOOSU PRECISION CO., LTD.—See WOOSU AMS Co., Ltd.; *Int'l*, pg. 8455
WOOTTON TRANSPORTATION SERVICES; *U.S. Private*, pg. 4562
WOOWA BROTHERS CORP.—See Delivery Hero SE; *Int'l*, pg. 2013
WOOWON DEVELOPMENT CO., LTD.; *Int'l*, pg. 8455
WOOYANG CO., LTD.; *Int'l*, pg. 8455
WOOYUN CO., LTD.—See Shimano, Inc.; *Int'l*, pg. 6834
WOOZWORLD INC.—See Azerion Group N.V.; *Int'l*, pg. 778
WOPF BEFESTIGUNGSELEMENTE GMBH—See Johnson Controls International plc; *Int'l*, pg. 3990
WOQOD VEHICLE INSPECTION CO. (FAHES) W.L.L.—See Qatar Fuel Company Q.S.C.; *Int'l*, pg. 6133
WOQU.COM; *Int'l*, pg. 8455
WORCESTER CENTER FOR PERFORMING ARTS; *U.S. Private*, pg. 4562
WORCESTER CENTER, L.P.—See Tenet Healthcare Corporation; *U.S. Public*, pg. 2005
WORCESTER COMMUNITY ACTION COUNCIL, INC.; *U.S. Private*, pg. 4562
WORCESTER CONTROLS UK—See Flowserve Corporation; *U.S. Public*, pg. 857
WORCESTER COUNTY FOOD BANK; *U.S. Private*, pg. 4562
WORCESTER ENVELOPE COMPANY—See Moore DM Group, LLC; *U.S. Private*, pg. 2780
WORCESTER GROUP PLC—See Robert Bosch GmbH; *Int'l*, pg. 6368
WORCESTER RACECOURSE LIMITED—See Reuben Brothers SA; *Int'l*, pg. 6311
WORCESTER REGIONAL TRANSIT AUTHORITY; *U.S. Private*, pg. 4562
WORCESTER TELEGRAM & GAZETTE CORPORATION—See Gannett Co., Inc.; *U.S. Public*, pg. 906
WORD & BROWN, INSURANCE ADMINISTRATORS, INC.; *U.S. Private*, pg. 4562
WORDEN BROTHERS, INC.; *U.S. Private*, pg. 4563
WORDEN COMPANY; *U.S. Private*, pg. 4563
WORDEN MARTIN INC.; *U.S. Private*, pg. 4563
WORD ENTERTAINMENT LLC—See Curb Records, Inc.; *U.S. Private*, pg. 1124
WORD OF GOD FELLOWSHIP INC.; *U.S. Private*, pg. 4562
WORD OF MOUTH FINE CATERING; *U.S. Private*, pg. 4562
WORD ON THE STREET (UK EVENTS) LIMITED—See Aramark; *U.S. Public*, pg. 178
WORDS+, INC.—See Prentke Romich Company; *U.S. Private*, pg. 3252
WORDSMITH DESIGN & ADVERTISING—See 2Gen Net; *Int'l*, pg. 5
WORDSMITH MEDIA, INC.; *U.S. Public*, pg. 2378
WORDS OF WISDOM, LLC—See Perdoceo Education Corporation; *U.S. Public*, pg. 1673
WORDSTREAM, INC.—See Gannett Co., Inc.; *U.S. Public*, pg. 901
WORD SYSTEMS, INC.; *U.S. Private*, pg. 4562
WORDZXPRESSED, INC.—See VIQ Solutions Inc.; *Int'l*, pg. 8245
WORK ABLE CENTRES INC.—See CareRx Corporation; *Int'l*, pg. 1325
WORK ABLE CENTRES NORTH YORK INC.—See CareRx Corporation; *Int'l*, pg. 1325
WORKBASE ENGINEERING LIMITED—See Basetrophy Group Holdings Limited; *Int'l*, pg. 871
WORKBIT CORPORATION—See Kaga Electronics Co., Ltd.; *Int'l*, pg. 4049
WORKBOAT INTERNATIONAL DMCCO—See Alam Maritim Resources Berhad; *Int'l*, pg. 290
WORKBOOK SOFTWARE A/S—See Roper Technologies, Inc.; *U.S. Public*, pg. 1814
WORKCARE, INC.; *U.S. Private*, pg. 4563
THE WORK CENTER, INC.—See Athletico Ltd.; *U.S. Private*, pg. 368
WORKCOMPEDI, INC.; *U.S. Private*, pg. 4563
WORK & CO—See Accenture plc; *Int'l*, pg. 88
WORKDAY ASIA PACIFIC LIMITED—See Workday, Inc.; *U.S. Public*, pg. 2379
WORKDAY AUSTRALIA PTY. LTD.—See Workday, Inc.; *U.S. Public*, pg. 2379
WORKDAY AUSTRIA GMBH—See Workday, Inc.; *U.S. Public*, pg. 2379
WORKDAY B.V.—See Workday, Inc.; *U.S. Public*, pg. 2379
WORKDAY DENMARK APS—See Workday, Inc.; *U.S. Public*, pg. 2379
WORKDAY FINLAND OY—See Workday, Inc.; *U.S. Public*, pg. 2379
WORKDAY FRANCE—See Workday, Inc.; *U.S. Public*, pg. 2379
WORKDAY GMBH—See Workday, Inc.; *U.S. Public*, pg. 2379
WORKDAY, INC.; *U.S. Public*, pg. 2378
WORKDAY INTERNATIONAL LIMITED—See Workday, Inc.; *U.S. Public*, pg. 2379
WORKDAY ITALY S.R.L.—See Workday, Inc.; *U.S. Public*, pg. 2379
WORKDAY K.K.—See Workday, Inc.; *U.S. Public*, pg. 2379
WORKDAY LIMITED—See Workday, Inc.; *U.S. Public*, pg. 2379
WORKDAY MALAYSIA SDN. BHD.—See Workday, Inc.; *U.S. Public*, pg. 2379
WORKDAY MEXICO, S. DE R.L. DE C.V.—See Workday, Inc.; *U.S. Public*, pg. 2379
WORKDAY NORWAY AS—See Workday, Inc.; *U.S. Public*, pg. 2379
WORKDAY SINGAPORE PTE. LTD.—See Workday, Inc.; *U.S. Public*, pg. 2379
WORKDAY SOUTH AFRICA (PTY.) LTD.—See Workday, Inc.; *U.S. Public*, pg. 2379
WORKDAY SWEDEN AKTIEBOLAG—See Workday, Inc.; *U.S. Public*, pg. 2379
WORKDAY SWITZERLAND GMBH—See Workday, Inc.; *U.S. Public*, pg. 2379
WORKDAY (UK) LIMITED—See Workday, Inc.; *U.S. Public*, pg. 2379
WORKDRY INTERNATIONAL LIMITED—See Arcus Infrastructure Partners LLP; *Int'l*, pg. 553
WORKER BEES, INC.; *U.S. Private*, pg. 4563
WORKERS' COMPENSATION RATING & INSPECTION BUREAU OF MASSACHUSETTS; *U.S. Private*, pg. 4563
WORKERS' CREDIT UNION; *U.S. Private*, pg. 4563
WORKERS UNITED; *U.S. Private*, pg. 4563
WORKFORCE DELTA PTY. LTD.—See Cyient Limited; *Int'l*, pg. 1896
THE WORKFORCE GROUP MAURITIUS LIMITED—See Workforce Holdings Ltd.; *Int'l*, pg. 8456
THE WORKFORCE GROUP (PROPRIETARY) LIMITED—See Workforce Holdings Ltd.; *Int'l*, pg. 8456
WORKFORCE HEALTHCARE (PROPRIETARY) LIMITED—See Workforce Holdings Ltd.; *Int'l*, pg. 8456
WORKFORCE HOLDINGS LTD.; *Int'l*, pg. 8455
WORKFORCE INSIGHT LLC—See Accenture plc; *Int'l*, pg. 88
WORKFORCE INVESTMENT BOARD OF HERKIMER, MADISON & ONEIDA COUNTIES; *U.S. Private*, pg. 4563
WORKFORCE INVESTMENT BOARD OF THE SOUTHWEST REGION, INC.; *U.S. Private*, pg. 4563
WORKFORCE MANAGEMENT—See Crain Communications, Inc.; *U.S. Public*, pg. 1084
WORKFORCE OUTSOURCE SERVICES, INC.; *U.S. Private*, pg. 4563
WORKFORCE SOFTWARE, INC.—See Insight Venture Management, LLC; *U.S. Private*, pg. 2091

WORKFORCE OUTSOURCE SERVICES, INC.   CORPORATE AFFILIATIONS

WORKFORCE SOFTWARE LTD—See Insight Venture Management, LLC; *U.S. Private*, pg. 2091
WORKFORCE SOFTWARE (PROPRIETARY) LIMITED—See Workforce Holdings Ltd.; *Int'l*, pg. 8456
WORKFORCE SOLUTIONS CAMERON; *U.S. Private*, pg. 4563
WORKFORCE SOLUTIONS CAPITAL AREA WORKFORCE BOARD; *U.S. Private*, pg. 4563
WORKFORCE SOLUTIONS FOR SOUTH TEXAS; *U.S. Private*, pg. 4563
WORKFORCE SOLUTIONS GROUP, INCORPORATED—See Cross Country Healthcare, Inc.; *U.S. Public*, pg. 595
WORKFORCETACTIX, INC.—See GTCR LLC; *U.S. Private*, pg. 1804
WORKFORCE WORLDWIDE STAFFING (PROPRIETARY) LIMITED—See Workforce Holdings Ltd.; *Int'l*, pg. 8456
WORKFRONT, INC.—See Adobe Inc.; *U.S. Public*, pg. 43
WORKGROUP IT (PTY) LIMITED—See Alviva Holdings Limited; *Int'l*, pg. 402
WORKGROUP TECHNOLOGY PARTNERS; *U.S. Private*, pg. 4563
WORKHORSE GROUP INC.; *U.S. Public*, pg. 2379
WORKHORSE RAIL, LLC—See Westinghouse Air Brake Technologies Corporation; *U.S. Public*, pg. 2360
WORKHOUSE PUBLICITY; *U.S. Private*, pg. 4563
WORK, INC.; *U.S. Private*, pg. 4563
WORKING BUILDINGS, LLC—See Keystone Group, L.P.; *U.S. Private*, pg. 2299
WORKING CLASS, INC.; *U.S. Private*, pg. 4564
WORKING MEDIA GROUP; *U.S. Private*, pg. 4564
WORKING MOTHER MEDIA, INC.—See Bonnier AB; *Int'l*, pg. 1109
WORKING SYSTEMS SOLUTIONS PTY. LTD.—See Global Health Limited; *Int'l*, pg. 2997
WORKING TITLE FILMS LIMITED—See Comcast Corporation; *U.S. Public*, pg. 542
WORKING WORD PUBLIC RELATIONS LTD.; *Int'l*, pg. 8456
WORKIVA FRANCE SAS—See Workiva Inc.; *U.S. Public*, pg. 2379
WORKIVA GERMANY GMBH—See Workiva Inc.; *U.S. Public*, pg. 2379
WORKIVA INC.; *U.S. Public*, pg. 2379
WORKJOY ARGENTINA S.A.—See AT&T Inc.; *U.S. Public*, pg. 220
WORKLETE, INC.—See The Stage Fund, LLC; *U.S. Private*, pg. 4120
WORKLINK AG—See Swisscom AG; *Int'l*, pg. 7374
WORKLINK SERVICES, INC.—See Chelsea Logistics and Infrastructure Holdings Corp.; *Int'l*, pg. 1460
WORK-LOSS DATA INSTITUTE, LLC—See The Hearst Corporation; *U.S. Private*, pg. 4045
WORKLYN PARTNERS; *U.S. Private*, pg. 4564
WORKMAN CO., LTD.; *Int'l*, pg. 8456
WORKMAN COMMERCIAL CONSTRUCTION SERVICES, LTD.; *U.S. Private*, pg. 4564
WORKMAN PUBLISHING COMPANY—See Vivendi SE; *Int'l*, pg. 8273
WORK MARKET INC.—See Automatic Data Processing, Inc.; *U.S. Public*, pg. 230
WORKMEN'S AUTO INSURANCE COMPANY—See Mercury General Corporation; *U.S. Public*, pg. 1422
WORKMENS CIRCLE INC.; *U.S. Private*, pg. 4564
WORKNET PINELLAS INC.; *U.S. Private*, pg. 4564
WORK OPTIONS GROUP, INC.—See Bain Capital, LP; *U.S. Private*, pg. 437
WORKOTEL LIMITED—See TEE International Limited; *Int'l*, pg. 7520
WORKPLACE HEALTH SOLUTIONS INC.—See Community Bank System, Inc.; *U.S. Public*, pg. 550
WORKPLACE IMPACT; *U.S. Private*, pg. 4564
THE WORKPLACE, INC.; *U.S. Private*, pg. 4139
WORKPLACE INSTALL NETWORK, INC.; *U.S. Private*, pg. 4564
WORKPLACE INTEGRA INC.—See Demant A/S; *Int'l*, pg. 2025
WORKPLACE OPTIONS, LLC—See Accor S.A.; *Int'l*, pg. 91
WORKPLACE SOLUTIONS INC.; *U.S. Private*, pg. 4564
WORKPLACE SOLUTIONS, LLC; *U.S. Private*, pg. 4564
WORKPLACE SYSTEMS INTERNATIONAL LIMITED—See Insight Venture Management, LLC; *U.S. Private*, pg. 2091
WORKPLACE TECHNOLOGY CENTER, INC.—See Direct Companies, LLC; *U.S. Private*, pg. 1234
WORKPOINT ENTERTAINMENT PUBLIC COMPANY LIMITED; *Int'l*, pg. 8456
WORKS24 CORPORATION; *U.S. Private*, pg. 4564
WORKSCAPE INC.—See Automatic Data Processing, Inc.; *U.S. Public*, pg. 230
WORKSCAPES INC.—See Workscapes Inc.; *U.S. Private*, pg. 4564
WORKSCAPES INC.; *U.S. Private*, pg. 4564
THE WORKS COMMUNITY MANAGEMENT CO., LTD.—See Ananda Development Public Company Limited; *Int'l*, pg. 447
WORKS COMPUTING LLC—See Converge Technology Solutions Corp.; *Int'l*, pg. 1787

WORK SERVICE CZECH S.R.O.—See Work Service S.A.; *Int'l*, pg. 8455
WORK SERVICE INTERNATIONAL SP. Z O.O.—See Work Service S.A.; *Int'l*, pg. 8455
WORK SERVICE S.A.; *Int'l*, pg. 8455
WORK SERVICES CORPORATION; *U.S. Private*, pg. 4563
WORKS FINANCE (NZ) LIMITED—See Downer EDI Limited; *Int'l*, pg. 2186
WORKSHOP BEMANNING OG KOMPETANSE AS—See ManpowerGroup Inc.; *U.S. Public*, pg. 1362
WORKSHOP HOLDING AS—See ManpowerGroup Inc.; *U.S. Public*, pg. 1362
WORKSIGHTED; *U.S. Private*, pg. 4564
WORKSITE COMMUNICATIONS—See Arthur J. Gallagher & Co.; *U.S. Public*, pg. 205
WORKSMART; *U.S. Private*, pg. 4564
WORKSOFT, INC.—See Marlin Equity Partners, LLC; *U.S. Private*, pg. 2585
WORKSPACE 15 LTD.—See Workspace Group Plc; *Int'l*, pg. 8456
WORKSPACE DEVELOPMENT LLC; *U.S. Private*, pg. 4564
WORKSPACE DYNAMICS, INC.—See Goodmans, Inc.; *U.S. Private*, pg. 1740
WORKSPACE GROUP PLC; *Int'l*, pg. 8456
WORKSPACE HOLDINGS, LTD.—See Workspace Group Plc; *Int'l*, pg. 8456
WORKSPACE MANAGEMENT, LTD.—See Workspace Group Plc; *Int'l*, pg. 8456
WORKSPACE TECHNOLOGY LTD.; *Int'l*, pg. 8456
WORKSPORT, LTD.; *Int'l*, pg. 8456
WORKSQUARED INC.; *U.S. Private*, pg. 4564
THE WORKS STORES LTD.—See Endless LLP; *Int'l*, pg. 2403
WORKSTREAM INC.—See H.S. Morgan Limited Partnership; *U.S. Private*, pg. 1836
WORKSTRINGS INTERNATIONAL LIMITED—See Superior Energy Services, Inc.; *U.S. Private*, pg. 3877
WORKSTRINGS INTERNATIONAL, L.L.C.—See Superior Energy Services, Inc.; *U.S. Private*, pg. 3877
WORKSTRINGS, LLC—See Superior Energy Services, Inc.; *U.S. Private*, pg. 3877
WORKS ZEBRA CO., LTD.—See Amana Inc.; *Int'l*, pg. 409
WORKTECH INC.—See StarDyne Technologies Inc.; *Int'l*, pg. 7176
WORK TECHNOLOGY CORPORATION—See Genstar Capital, LLC; *U.S. Private*, pg. 1678
WORKTHING.COM—See The Scott Trust Limited; *Int'l*, pg. 7681
WORK TRAINING CENTER, INC; *U.S. Private*, pg. 4563
WORK UNIFORMS DIRECT LIMITED—See MWUK Holding Company Limited; *Int'l*, pg. 5110
WORKWAVE LLC—See EQT AB; *Int'l*, pg. 2478
WORKWAY, INC.; *U.S. Private*, pg. 4564
THE WORKWEAR GROUP HOLDING PTY LTD—See Wesfarmers Limited; *Int'l*, pg. 8382
WORKWELL SYSTEMS, INC.—See Chrysalis Ventures; *U.S. Private*, pg. 893
WORKWELL TECHNOLOGIES, INC.; *U.S. Private*, pg. 4564
WORKWISE, LLC; *U.S. Private*, pg. 4564
WORK WORLD AMERICA INC.—See The Gart Companies, Inc.; *U.S. Private*, pg. 4032
WORLCO MANAGEMENT SERVICES, INC.—See Centene Corporation; *U.S. Public*, pg. 471
WORLD4YOU INTERNET SERVICES GMBH—See United Internet AG; *Int'l*, pg. 8069
WORLD ACADEMY LLC—See Vingroup Joint Stock Company; *Int'l*, pg. 8241
WORLD ACCEPTANCE CORPORATION OF ALABAMA—See World Acceptance Corporation; *U.S. Public*, pg. 2379
WORLD ACCEPTANCE CORPORATION OF MISSOURI—See World Acceptance Corporation; *U.S. Public*, pg. 2379
WORLD ACCEPTANCE CORPORATION OF OKLAHOMA, INC.—See World Acceptance Corporation; *U.S. Public*, pg. 2379
WORLD ACCEPTANCE CORPORATION; *U.S. Public*, pg. 2379
WORLD ACCESS SERVICE CORP.—See Allianz SE; *Int'l*, pg. 342
WORLD AEROSPACE CORPORATION; *U.S. Private*, pg. 4564
WORLD AFFAIRS COUNCIL OF PHILADELPHIA; *U.S. Private*, pg. 4564
WORLD AGRICULTURE, INC.—See Lipman & Lipman, Inc.; *U.S. Private*, pg. 2465
WORLD ALMANAC EDUCATION GROUP, INC.—See Centre Lane Partners, LLC; *U.S. Private*, pg. 827
WORLD AM, INC.; *U.S. Public*, pg. 2379
WORLDAPP, INC.—See Diversis Capital, LLC; *U.S. Private*, pg. 1244
WORLDATA INFOCENTER, INC.; *U.S. Private*, pg. 4568
WORLD AXIS TRADING COMPANY—See OFFTEC Holding Group, Plc.; *Int'l*, pg. 5530
THE WORLD BANK GROUP; *U.S. Private*, pg. 4139

WORLD BOOK/SCOTT FETZER COMPANY, INC.—See Berkshire Hathaway Inc.; *U.S. Public*, pg. 300
WORLDBRANDS EUROPE B.V.—See B&S Group S.A.; *Int'l*, pg. 784
WORLD BRANDS INC.—See Topco Holdings Inc.; *U.S. Private*, pg. 4187
WORLD BRANDS SERVICES LTD.—See GraceKennedy Limited; *Int'l*, pg. 3049
WORLDBRIDGE LOGISTICS INC.—See V. Alexander & Co. Inc.; *U.S. Public*, pg. 4328
WORLDBRIDGE SECURE LOGISTICS CO., LTD.—See The Brink's Company; *U.S. Public*, pg. 2043
WORLDCALL TELECOM LIMITED; *Int'l*, pg. 8458
WORLD CAREERS NETWORK PLC - NEW YORK BRANCH—See Oleeo, plc; *U.S. Private*, pg. 5553
WORLD CAT LTD—See Kering S.A.; *Int'l*, pg. 4136
WORLDCELL, INC.; *U.S. Private*, pg. 4568
WORLDCENTRIC.ORG; *U.S. Private*, pg. 4568
WORLD CHALLENGE (DUBAI) LIMITED—See TUI AG; *Int'l*, pg. 7969
WORLD CHALLENGE EXPEDITIONS, INC.—See TUI AG; *Int'l*, pg. 7969
WORLD CHALLENGE EXPEDITIONS LIMITED—See TUI AG; *Int'l*, pg. 7968
WORLD CHALLENGE EXPEDITIONS PTY LTD—See TUI AG; *Int'l*, pg. 7969
WORLD CHALLENGE (HONG KONG) LIMITED—See TUI AG; *Int'l*, pg. 7969
WORLD CHAMPIONSHIP SPORTS NETWORK, INC.—See Comcast Corporation; *U.S. Public*, pg. 539
WORLD CHAMPIONSHIP SPORTS NETWORK, INC.—See InterMedia Advisors, LLC; *U.S. Private*, pg. 2112
WORLD CHOICE LIMITED—See Co-operative Group Limited; *Int'l*, pg. 1679
WORLD CLASS DRIVING; *U.S. Private*, pg. 4565
WORLD CLASS FLOWERS; *U.S. Private*, pg. 4565
WORLD CLASS GLOBAL LIMITED—See Aspial Corporation Limited; *Int'l*, pg. 630
WORLD CLASSICS—See Topco Holdings Inc.; *U.S. Private*, pg. 4187
WORLD CLASS INDUSTRIES INC.; *U.S. Private*, pg. 4565
WORLDCLASS PROCESSING CORP.—See Samuel, Son & Co., Limited; *Int'l*, pg. 6516
WORLD CLEAN FACILITY SERVICES PTE. LTD.—See Advancer Global Limited; *Int'l*, pg. 163
WORLD COLLEGE—See Cleveland Institute of Electronics; *U.S. Private*, pg. 941
WORLD CO., LTD.; *Int'l*, pg. 8456
WORLDCOM EXCHANGE, INC.; *U.S. Private*, pg. 4568
THE WORLD COMPANY; *U.S. Private*, pg. 4139
WORLD COOPERAGE COMPANY INC.—See Isco Holding Company Inc.; *U.S. Private*, pg. 2143
WORLD COPPER LTD.; *Int'l*, pg. 8457
WORLD CORPORATION PUBLIC COMPANY LIMITED; *Int'l*, pg. 8457
WORLD COUNCIL OF CREDIT UNIONS, INC.; *U.S. Private*, pg. 4565
WORLD COURIER INC.—See Cencora, Inc.; *U.S. Public*, pg. 467
WORLD COURIER MANAGEMENT INC.—See Cencora, Inc.; *U.S. Public*, pg. 467
WORLD-DIRECT EBUSINESS SOLUTIONS GMBH—See America Movil, S.A.B. de C.V.; *Int'l*, pg. 421
WORLDDOC, INC.; *U.S. Private*, pg. 4568
WORLD DRYER CORPORATION—See Zurn Elkay Water Solutions Corporation; *U.S. Public*, pg. 2413
WORLD DUTY FREE GROUP ESPANA S.A.—See Avolta AG; *Int'l*, pg. 749
WORLD DUTY FREE GROUP GERMANY GMBH—See Avolta AG; *Int'l*, pg. 749
WORLD DUTY FREE GROUP S.A.U.—See Avolta AG; *Int'l*, pg. 749
WORLD DUTY FREE S.P.A.—See Avolta AG; *Int'l*, pg. 749
WORLD ELECTRIC SUPPLY—See Sonepar S.A.; *Int'l*, pg. 7094
WORLD ELECTRONICS SALES & SERVICE; *U.S. Private*, pg. 4565
WORLD EMBLEM INTERNATIONAL, INC.; *U.S. Private*, pg. 4565
WORLD EMERGENCY RELIEF; *U.S. Private*, pg. 4565
WORLD ENERGY ALTERNATIVES, LLC; *U.S. Private*, pg. 4565
WORLD ENERGY BUSINESS S.A.—See Grupo EMES S.A.; *Int'l*, pg. 3126
WORLD ENTERPRISES; *U.S. Private*, pg. 4565
WORLD ENTERTAINMENT SERVICES, LLC—See Bonnier AB; *Int'l*, pg. 1109
WORLD EQUITY GROUP, INC.—See Wentworth Management Services LLC; *U.S. Private*, pg. 4481
WORLD EVENTS PRODUCTIONS, LTD.—See Koplar Communications International, Inc.; *U.S. Private*, pg. 2343
WORLD EXCELLENT PRODUCT SA; *Int'l*, pg. 8457
WORLDEX INDUSTRY & TRADING CO., LTD.; *Int'l*, pg. 8458
WORLD EXPRESS LOGISTICS LTD.—See Attard & Co. Ltd.; *Int'l*, pg. 696

COMPANY NAME INDEX

WORLD FINANCE COMPANY OF KENTUCKY, LLC—See World Acceptance Corporation; *U.S. Public*, pg. 2379
WORLD FINANCE CORP.—See World Acceptance Corporation; *U.S. Public*, pg. 2379
WORLD FINANCE INC.—See World Acceptance Corporation; *U.S. Public*, pg. 2379
WORLD FINANCE INC.—See World Acceptance Corporation; *U.S. Public*, pg. 2379
WORLD FINANCE INC.—See World Acceptance Corporation; *U.S. Public*, pg. 2379
WORLD FINANCIAL CAPITAL BANK—See Bread Financial Holdings Inc.; *U.S. Public*, pg. 381
THE WORLD FINANCIAL HOLDING GROUP CO., LIMITED; *Int'l*, pg. 7701
WORLD FINANCIAL NETWORK CREDIT CARD MASTER TRUST; *U.S. Private*, pg. 4565
WORLD FINANCIAL SPLIT CORP.; *Int'l*, pg. 8457
WORLD FINER FOODS, INC.; *U.S. Private*, pg. 4565
WORLDFLIX, INC.; *U.S. Public*, pg. 2382
WORLD FORD PENSACOLA; *U.S. Private*, pg. 4565
WORLD FORD - STONE MOUNTAIN—See Group 1 Automotive, Inc.; *U.S. Public*, pg. 972
WORLD FRANCHISE SYSTEMS CO., LTD.—See World Co., Ltd.; *Int'l*, pg. 8457
WORLD FUEL INTERNATIONAL S.R.L.—See World Kinect Corporation; *U.S. Public*, pg. 2381
WORLD FUEL SERVICES AVIATION LIMITED—See World Kinect Corporation; *U.S. Public*, pg. 2381
WORLD FUEL SERVICES COMPANY, INC.—See World Kinect Corporation; *U.S. Public*, pg. 2381
WORLD FUEL SERVICES (DENMARK) APS—See World Kinect Corporation; *U.S. Public*, pg. 2381
WORLD FUEL SERVICES EUROPE, LTD.—See World Kinect Corporation; *U.S. Public*, pg. 2381
WORLD FUEL SERVICES, INC.—See World Kinect Corporation; *U.S. Public*, pg. 2381
WORLD FUEL SERVICES LTD.—See World Kinect Corporation; *U.S. Public*, pg. 2381
WORLD FUEL SERVICES MEXICO, S.A. DE C.V.—See World Kinect Corporation; *U.S. Public*, pg. 2381
WORLD FUEL SERVICES (SINGAPORE) PTE LTD.—See World Kinect Corporation; *U.S. Public*, pg. 2381
WORLD FUEL SERVICES (SOUTH AFRICA) (PTY) LTD—See World Kinect Corporation; *U.S. Public*, pg. 2381
WORLD FUEL SERVICES TRADING DMCC—See World Kinect Corporation; *U.S. Public*, pg. 2381
WORLD GAS (THAILAND) CO., LTD.; *Int'l*, pg. 8457
WORLDGATE COMMUNICATIONS, INC.; *U.S. Private*, pg. 4568
WORLDGATE GLOBAL LOGISTICS LTD; *Int'l*, pg. 8458
WORLD GOLD TRUST; *U.S. Public*, pg. 2379
WORLD GOLF FOUNDATION; *U.S. Private*, pg. 4565
WORLD GOLF TOUR—See Topgolf Callaway Brands Corp.; *U.S. Public*, pg. 2164
WORLD GRAND HOLDINGS LIMITED—See AMVIG Holdings Limited; *Int'l*, pg. 442
WORLD HEALTH ENERGY HOLDINGS, INC.; *U.S. Public*, pg. 2380
WORLD HI-VISION CHANNEL, INC.—See Mitsui & Co., Ltd.; *Int'l*, pg. 4980
WORLD HOLDINGS CO., LTD.; *Int'l*, pg. 8457
WORLD HOLDINGS INC.; *U.S. Private*, pg. 4565
WORLD HOME LINEN MANUFACTURING COMPANY LIMITED—See World Houseware (Holdings) Limited; *Int'l*, pg. 8457
WORLD HOPE INTERNATIONAL; *U.S. Private*, pg. 4565
WORLD HOUSEWARE (HOLDINGS) LIMITED; *Int'l*, pg. 8457
WORLD HOUSEWARE PRODUCING COMPANY LIMITED—See World Houseware (Holdings) Limited; *Int'l*, pg. 8457
WORLDIA EUROPE GMBH—See Beijing Worldia Diamond Tools Co., Ltd.; *Int'l*, pg. 960
WORLDIA NICE NOVA DIAMOND TECHNOLOGY (JIAXING) CO., LTD.—See Beijing Worldia Diamond Tools Co., Ltd.; *Int'l*, pg. 961
WORLD IMAGE (CHINA) COMPANY LTD.—See Pico Far East Holdings Limited; *Int'l*, pg. 5861
WORLD IMAGE INTERNATIONAL LTD.—See Pico Far East Holdings Limited; *Int'l*, pg. 5861
WORLD IMAGE (MIDDLE EAST) L.L.C.—See Pico Far East Holdings Limited; *Int'l*, pg. 5861
WORLD IMAGE PLUS PTE LTD.—See Pico Far East Holdings Limited; *Int'l*, pg. 5862
WORLD IMAGE (SHANGHAI) DESIGN & ENGINEERING CO., LTD.—See Pico Far East Holdings Limited; *Int'l*, pg. 5861
WORLD IMAGE SIGNS (BEIJING) COMPANY LTD.—See Pico Far East Holdings Limited; *Int'l*, pg. 5861
WORLD INSPECTION NETWORK INTERNATIONAL, INC.—See Agamya Capital LLC; *U.S. Private*, pg. 126
WORLD INSURANCE ASSOCIATES LLC; *U.S. Private*, pg. 4565
WORLD JOINT CORP.; *U.S. Private*, pg. 4566
WORLD KINECT CORPORATION; *U.S. Public*, pg. 2380
WORLD LEISURE HOLIDAYS (PTY) LTD—See Sun Limited; *Int'l*, pg. 7306
WORLDLINE B.V.—See Worldline SA; *Int'l*, pg. 8458

WORLDLINE SA; *Int'l*, pg. 8458
WORLDLINK CORPORATION—See Stonepeak Partners L.P.; *U.S. Private*, pg. 3829
WORLDLINK GROUP PLC; *Int'l*, pg. 8458
WORLDLINK, INC.; *U.S. Private*, pg. 4568
WORLD-LINK LOGISTICS (ASIA) HOLDING LIMITED; *Int'l*, pg. 8458
WORLD LOCK CO. LTD.—See The Eastern Company; *U.S. Public*, pg. 2069
WORLD LOGISTICS SERVICE (U.S.A.), INC.—See Mitsui O.S.K. Lines, Ltd.; *Int'l*, pg. 4991
WORLD LUNG FOUNDATION; *U.S. Private*, pg. 4566
WORLD MARKET INTELLIGENCE LIMITED—See GlobalData Plc; *Int'l*, pg. 3003
WORLDMARK INTERNATIONAL LTD.; *Int'l*, pg. 8458
WORLDMARK SERVICES LTD.—See Brookfield Corporation; *Int'l*, pg. 1181
WORLDMARK (SHENZHEN) CO., LTD.—See Worldmark International Ltd.; *Int'l*, pg. 8459
WORLDMARK (SUZHOU) CO., LTD.—See Worldmark International Ltd.; *Int'l*, pg. 8459
WORLDMARK (TIANJIN) CO. LTD.—See Worldmark International Ltd.; *Int'l*, pg. 8459
WORLDMEDIA INTERACTIVE; *U.S. Private*, pg. 4568
WORLD MEDICAL RELIEF, INC.; *U.S. Private*, pg. 4566
WORLD MEDICAL S.A.S.—See Biotronik GmbH & Co.; *Int'l*, pg. 1044
WORLD MICRO, INC.; *U.S. Private*, pg. 4566
WORLD MINERALS FRANCE—See Groupe Bruxelles Lambert SA; *Int'l*, pg. 3100
WORLD MINERALS, INC.—See Groupe Bruxelles Lambert SA; *Int'l*, pg. 3100
WORLD MINERALS INTERNATIONAL SALES SA—See Groupe Bruxelles Lambert SA; *Int'l*, pg. 3100
WORLD MINERALS ITALIA SRL—See Groupe Bruxelles Lambert SA; *Int'l*, pg. 3100
WORLD MOBILE CORPORATION—See GEO Holdings Corporation; *Int'l*, pg. 2932
WORLD MOBILE HOLDINGS INC.; *U.S. Public*, pg. 2381
WORLD MONUMENTS FUND, INC.; *U.S. Private*, pg. 4566
WORLD MOTO, INC.; *Int'l*, pg. 8457
WORLD NEIGHBORS, INC.—See Feed The Children, Inc.; *U.S. Private*, pg. 1492
WORLDNET, INC. OF NEVADA; *U.S. Private*, pg. 4569
WORLD.NET SERVICES LIMITED; *Int'l*, pg. 8458
WORLD NET SERVICES SDN. BHD.—See World.Net Services Limited; *Int'l*, pg. 8458
THE WORLD NEWSPAPER—See Lee Enterprises, Incorporated; *U.S. Public*, pg. 1300
WORLD OF BEER FRANCHISING, INC.; *U.S. Private*, pg. 4566
WORLD OF BOOKS LIMITED—See Livingbridge EP LLP; *Int'l*, pg. 4532
WORLD OF FLOORS, INC.—See Thomas H. Lee Partners, L.P.; *U.S. Private*, pg. 4156
WORLD OF FORD SALES INC.; *U.S. Private*, pg. 4566
WORLD OF GOOD TASTES, INC.; *U.S. Private*, pg. 4566
WORLD OF LEASING GMBH—See Johnson Health Tech. Co., Ltd.; *Int'l*, pg. 3991
THE WORLD OF MINIATURE BEARS, INC.; *U.S. Private*, pg. 4139
WORLD OF WEED, INC.; *U.S. Public*, pg. 2381
WORLD OIL CORP.; *U.S. Private*, pg. 4566
WORLD OIL GROUP, INC.; *U.S. Public*, pg. 2381
WORLD OMNI FINANCIAL CORP.—See JM Family Enterprises Inc.; *U.S. Private*, pg. 2214
WORLDONE, INC.; *U.S. Private*, pg. 4569
WORLD ONLINE INTERNATIONAL NV—See Tiscali S.p.A.; *Int'l*, pg. 7758
WORLD OUTFITTERS CORPORATION SAFARI NORDIK; *Int'l*, pg. 8457
WORLDPAC, CANADA, INC.—See Advance Auto Parts, Inc.; *U.S. Public*, pg. 46
WORLDPAC, INC.—See The Carlyle Group Inc.; *U.S. Public*, pg. 2057
WORLDPACK TRADING B.V.—See Bunzl plc; *Int'l*, pg. 1220
WORLD PAC PAPER, LLC; *U.S. Private*, pg. 4566
WORLDPAY COMPANY, LLC—See GTCR LLC; *U.S. Private*, pg. 1806
WORLDPAY, INC.—See GTCR LLC; *U.S. Private*, pg. 1806
WORLDPAY LTD.—See Advent International Corporation; *U.S. Private*, pg. 108
WORLDPAY LTD.—See Bain Capital, LP; *U.S. Private*, pg. 452
WORLDPAY US, INC.—See Advent International Corporation; *U.S. Private*, pg. 108
WORLDPAY US, INC.—See Bain Capital, LP; *U.S. Private*, pg. 452
WORLD PEACE INDUSTRIAL CO., LTD.—See WPG Holdings Limited; *Int'l*, pg. 8461
WORLD PEACE INTERNATIONAL (INDIA) PVT., LTD.—See WPG Holdings Limited; *Int'l*, pg. 8461
WORLD PEACE INTERNATIONAL PTE. LTD.—See WPG Holdings Limited; *Int'l*, pg. 8461
WORLD PEACE INTERNATIONAL (SOUTH ASIA) PTE. LTD.—See WPG Holdings Limited; *Int'l*, pg. 8461

WORLD PET CARE—See Sunshine Mills Inc.; *U.S. Private*, pg. 3872
WORLD PET FOODS INC.—See Sunshine Mills Inc.; *U.S. Private*, pg. 3872
WORLD POINT TERMINALS, INC.; *U.S. Private*, pg. 4566
WORLD POINT TERMINALS, LP—See World Point Terminals, Inc.; *U.S. Private*, pg. 4566
WORLD POKER STORE, INC.; *U.S. Public*, pg. 2381
WORLDPORT LLC—See Decurion Corp.; *U.S. Private*, pg. 1188
WORLD PRECISION MACHINERY LIMITED; *Int'l*, pg. 8457
WORLD PRODUCTIONS LIMITED—See ITV plc; *Int'l*, pg. 3845
WORLD PRODUCTS INC.; *U.S. Private*, pg. 4566
WORLD PUBLICATIONS INC.; *U.S. Private*, pg. 4567
WORLDQUANT, LLC; *U.S. Private*, pg. 4569
WORLD QUANTUM GROWTH ACQUISITION CORP.; *Int'l*, pg. 8457
WORLD REACH HEALTH, LLC—See Healthtech Solutions, Inc.; *U.S. Public*, pg. 1017
WORLD REAL ESTATE S.R.L.—See Atlas Estates Limited; *Int'l*, pg. 685
WORLD REALTY & DEVELOPMENT, LTD.; *U.S. Private*, pg. 4567
WORLDREMIT CORPORATION—See WorldRemit Ltd.; *Int'l*, pg. 8459
WORLDREMIT INC.—See WorldRemit Ltd.; *Int'l*, pg. 8459
WORLDREMIT LTD.; *Int'l*, pg. 8459
WORLDREMIT PTY, LTD.—See WorldRemit Ltd.; *Int'l*, pg. 8459
WORLD RESORT OPERATION, INC.—See Relo Group, Inc.; *Int'l*, pg. 6265
WORLD RESOURCE PARTNERS—See G&T Industries Inc.; *U.S. Private*, pg. 1629
WORLD RESOURCES COMPANY; *U.S. Private*, pg. 4567
WORLD RETECH CO., LTD.—See World Holdings Co., Ltd.; *Int'l*, pg. 8457
WORLD SAHA FASHION CO., LTD.—See World Co., Ltd.; *Int'l*, pg. 8457
WORLD SCAN PROJECT, INC.; *Int'l*, pg. 8458
WORLDSEC LIMITED; *Int'l*, pg. 8459
WORLD SECURITY FZE—See Dubai World Corporation; *Int'l*, pg. 2222
WORLDSENSING SL; *Int'l*, pg. 8459
WORLD SERVICES ITALIANA S.R.L.—See John Wood Group PLC; *Int'l*, pg. 3983
WORLD'S FINEST CHOCOLATE CANADA COMPANY—See World's Finest Chocolate, Inc.; *U.S. Private*, pg. 4568
WORLD'S FINEST CHOCOLATE, INC.; *U.S. Private*, pg. 4568
WORLD SHIPPING, INC.; *U.S. Private*, pg. 4567
WORLD SHIP SUPPLY TEXAS INCORPORATED; *U.S. Private*, pg. 4567
WORLDS INC.; *U.S. Public*, pg. 2382
WORLDS OF FUN—See Six Flags Entertainment Corporation; *U.S. Public*, pg. 1890
WORLDS OF WOW, LLC—See Court Square Capital Partners, L.P.; *U.S. Private*, pg. 1070
WORLDSOURCE FINANCIAL MANAGEMENT INC.—See Guardian Capital Group Limited; *Int'l*, pg. 3170
WORLDSOURCE HOLDING CORP—See Guardian Capital Group Limited; *Int'l*, pg. 3170
WORLDSOURCE INSURANCE NETWORK INC.—See Guardian Capital Group Limited; *Int'l*, pg. 3170
WORLDSOURCE SECURITIES INC.—See Guardian Capital Group Limited; *Int'l*, pg. 3170
WORLDSOURCE WEALTH MANAGEMENT INC.—See Guardian Capital Group Limited; *Int'l*, pg. 3170
WORLD SPACE SOLUTIONS CO., LTD.—See World Co., Ltd.; *Int'l*, pg. 8457
WORLDSPAN SERVICES LTD.—See Elliott Management Corporation; *U.S. Private*, pg. 1373
WORLDSPAN SERVICES LTD.—See Siris Capital Group, LLC; *U.S. Private*, pg. 3674
WORLD SPORT GROUP BEIJING LTD—See Vivendi SE; *Int'l*, pg. 8277
WORLD SPORT GROUP INDIA LTD—See Vivendi SE; *Int'l*, pg. 8277
WORLD SPORT GROUP LTD—See Vivendi SE; *Int'l*, pg. 8277
WORLD SPORT GROUP PTE LTD—See Vivendi SE; *Int'l*, pg. 8277
WORLD SPORT GROUP PTY LTD—See Vivendi SE; *Int'l*, pg. 8277
WORLD SPORTS, INC.—See Globeride, Inc.; *Int'l*, pg. 3007
WORLD STAFFING CO., LTD.—See World Holdings Co., Ltd.; *Int'l*, pg. 8457
WORLDSTAGE, INC.; *U.S. Private*, pg. 4569
WORLD STORE PARTNERS CO., LTD.—See World Co., Ltd.; *Int'l*, pg. 8457
WORLDSTRIDES PTY. LTD.—See Eurazeo SE; *Int'l*, pg. 2530
WORLD SUPER HOLDINGS LIMITED; *Int'l*, pg. 8458
WORLD SUPER LIMITED—See World Super Holdings Limited; *Int'l*, pg. 8458

WORLD SURVEILLANCE GROUP INC.   CORPORATE AFFILIATIONS

WORLD SURVEILLANCE GROUP INC.; *U.S. Private*, pg. 4567
WORLD'S WING SA—See Leonardo S.p.A.; *Int'l*, pg. 4458
WORLD TABLEWARE INC.—See Libbey, Inc.; *U.S. Private*, pg. 2442
WORLD TAIWAN FASHION CO., LTD.—See World Co., Ltd.; *Int'l*, pg. 8457
WORLD TARIFF, LIMITED—See FedEx Corporation; *U.S. Public*, pg. 828
WORLDTECH COMPUTERS INC.; *U.S. Private*, pg. 4569
WORLDTEK EVENTS, LLC—See InteleTravel.com; *U.S. Private*, pg. 2104
WORLD TELECOM GROUP—See AppDirect Inc.; *U.S. Private*, pg. 296
WORLD TELEVISION GROUP PLC; *Int'l*, pg. 8458
WORLD TESTING INC.; *U.S. Private*, pg. 4567
WORLD TOURIST REJSEBUREAU A/S—See Accor S.A.; *Int'l*, pg. 92
WORLD TOYOTA—See Group 1 Automotive, Inc.; *U.S. Public*, pg. 972
WORLD TRADE CAPITAL GROUP LIMITED—See First Shanghai Investments Limited; *Int'l*, pg. 2687
WORLD TRADE CENTER STOCKHOLM AB—See Alecta pensionsforsakring, omsesidigt; *Int'l*, pg. 305
WORLD TRADE & MARKETING, LTD.—See Tootsie Roll Industries, Inc.; *U.S. Public*, pg. 2163
WORLD TRADE ORGANIZATION; *Int'l*, pg. 8458
WORLD TRADE SYSTEMS PLC; *Int'l*, pg. 8458
WORLD TRADING (DELAWARE) INC.—See Deutsche Bank Aktiengesellschaft; *Int'l*, pg. 2062
WORLD TRANSPORT SERVICES, LLC—See Roadrunner Transportation Systems, Inc.; *U.S. Public*, pg. 1802
WORLD TRAVEL HOLDINGS, INC.; *U.S. Private*, pg. 4567
WORLD TRAVEL HOLDINGS—See World Travel Holdings, Inc.; *U.S. Private*, pg. 4567
WORLD TRAVEL MEDIA LTD.; *Int'l*, pg. 8458
WORLD TRAVEL PARTNERS ORLANDO; *U.S. Private*, pg. 4567
WORLD TRAVEL SYSTEM INC.—See Rakuten Group, Inc.; *Int'l*, pg. 6196
WORLD TRIATHLON CORPORATION—See Dalian Wanda Group Corporation Ltd.; *Int'l*, pg. 1953
WORLDUNION GROUP INCORPORATED; *Int'l*, pg. 8459
WORLD VALVE B.V.—See AVK Holding A/S; *Int'l*, pg. 748
WORLD VARIETY PRODUCE, INC.; *U.S. Private*, pg. 4567
WORLDVEST EQUITY, INC.; *U.S. Public*, pg. 2382
WORLD VISION INC.; *U.S. Private*, pg. 4567
WORLD WAREHOUSE & DISTRIBUTION INC.—See NFI Industries, Inc.; *U.S. Private*, pg. 2923
WORLD WATER WORKS, INC.; *U.S. Private*, pg. 4567
WORLDWAYS, INC.; *U.S. Private*, pg. 4569
WORLD WEB PARTNERS, INC.; *U.S. Private*, pg. 4567
WORLD WEB PUBLISHING.COM CORP.; *Int'l*, pg. 8458
WORLDWEST LIMITED LIABILITY COMPANY—See The World Company; *U.S. Private*, pg. 4139
WORLDWIDE AIR LOGISTICS GROUP, INC.—See Apollo Global Management, Inc.; *U.S. Public*, pg. 148
WORLDWIDE AIR LOGISTICS GROUP, INC.—See J.F. Lehman & Company, Inc.; *U.S. Private*, pg. 2163
WORLDWIDE ALUMINIUM LTD.; *Int'l*, pg. 8459
WORLDWIDE APARTMENT SERVICES PTE LTD—See Allgreen Properties Ltd.; *Int'l*, pg. 338
WORLDWIDE AUTO PARTS, INC.—See Advance Auto Parts, Inc.; *U.S. Public*, pg. 46
WORLDWIDE CASUALTY INSURANCE COMPANY—See American Financial Group, Inc.; *U.S. Public*, pg. 103
WORLDWIDE CLINICAL TRIALS EARLY PHASE SERVICES & BIOANALYTICAL SCIENCES—See The Jordan Company, L.P.; *U.S. Private*, pg. 4063
WORLDWIDE CLINICAL TRIALS, INC.—See The Jordan Company, L.P.; *U.S. Private*, pg. 4063
WORLDWIDE CONSTRUCTION EQUIPMENT INC.; *U.S. Private*, pg. 4569
WORLDWIDE DIAMOND CO.; *U.S. Private*, pg. 4569
WORLDWIDE DISTRIBUTORS; *U.S. Private*, pg. 4569
WORLDWIDE ELECTRIC CORP.—See AEA Investors LP; *U.S. Public*, pg. 116
WORLD WIDE ENTERTAINMENT PRODUCTION & SALES PTY. LTD.—See Ausmani Limited; *Int'l*, pg. 716
WORLDWIDE EQUIPMENT, INC. - LEXINGTON DIVISION—See Worldwide Equipment, Inc.; *U.S. Private*, pg. 4569
WORLDWIDE EQUIPMENT, INC.; *U.S. Private*, pg. 4569
WORLDWIDE ERC; *U.S. Private*, pg. 4569
WORLDWIDE EXCHANGE PTY. LTD.—See I-Remit, Inc.; *Int'l*, pg. 3564
WORLDWIDE EXPRESS OPERATIONS, LLC—See Ridgemont Partners Management LLC; *U.S. Private*, pg. 3433
WORLDWIDE FACILITIES, LLC—See AmWINS Group, Inc.; *U.S. Private*, pg. 270
WORLD WIDE FITTINGS, INC.; *U.S. Private*, pg. 4567
WORLDWIDE FLIGHT SERVICES BANGKOK AIR GROUND HANDLING CO., LTD.—See Bangkok Airways Public Company Limited; *Int'l*, pg. 882
WORLDWIDE FLIGHT SERVICES, INC.—See Temasek Holdings (Private) Limited; *Int'l*, pg. 7550

WORLDWIDE FOOD PRODUCTS INC.; *U.S. Private*, pg. 4569
WORLDWIDE GOLF ENTERPRISES, INC.; *U.S. Private*, pg. 4569
WORLDWIDE GROUND TRANSPORTATION SOLUTIONS INC.; *U.S. Private*, pg. 4569
WORLDWIDE HEALTHCARE TRUST PLC; *Int'l*, pg. 8459
WORLD-WIDE HOLDINGS CORP.; *U.S. Private*, pg. 4569
WORLDWIDE HOLDINGS CORP.; *U.S. Public*, pg. 2382
WORLDWIDE INSURANCE SERVICES LLC—See GuideWell Mutual Holding Corporation; *U.S. Private*, pg. 1814
WORLDWIDE INSURANCE SERVICES, LTD.—See Korean Reinsurance Company; *Int'l*, pg. 4288
WORLDWIDE INVENTORY NETWORK; *U.S. Private*, pg. 4569
WORLDWIDE JET CHARTER, INC.; *U.S. Private*, pg. 4569
WORLDWIDE KNOWLEDGE (BEIJING) BUSINESS CONSULTING COMPANY LTD.—See British Broadcasting Corporation; *Int'l*, pg. 1169
WORLDWIDE LAUNDRY, INC.—See EVI Industries, Inc.; *U.S. Public*, pg. 803
WORLDWIDE LICENSING & MERCHANDISING, INC.—See Premier Exhibitions, Inc.; *U.S. Public*, pg. 1715
WORLD WIDE LINE, INC.—See Gold Bond Inc.; *U.S. Private*, pg. 1727
WORLDWIDE LOGISTICS, INC.; *U.S. Private*, pg. 4569
WORLDWIDE LOGISTICS LIMITED; *U.S. Private*, pg. 4569
WORLDWIDE MACHINERY INC.; *U.S. Private*, pg. 4570
WORLDWIDE MARIJUANA INC.; *Int'l*, pg. 8459
WORLD WIDE MINERALS LTD.—See Dundee Corporation; *Int'l*, pg. 2226
WORLDWIDE NATURAL RESOURCES PLC; *Int'l*, pg. 8459
WORLDWIDE NFT INC.; *Int'l*, pg. 8459
WORLDWIDE OILFIELD MACHINE, INC.; *U.S. Private*, pg. 4570
WORLD WIDE PACKAGING, LLC—See Bain Capital, LP; *U.S. Private*, pg. 452
WORLD WIDE PARTS & ACCESSORIES CORPORATION; *U.S. Private*, pg. 4567
WORLDWIDE PERISHABLES ENTERPRISE INC.—See American Holdco Inc.; *U.S. Private*, pg. 236
WORLDWIDE POWER PRODUCTS, LLC; *U.S. Private*, pg. 4570
WORLDWIDE PRODUCE, INC.—See La Preferida, Inc.; *U.S. Private*, pg. 2369
WORLDWIDE REBATES INC.—See Global Industrial Company; *U.S. Public*, pg. 942
WORLDWIDE RECRUITING AND STAFFING SERVICES LLC—See Cerberus Capital Management, L.P.; *U.S. Private*, pg. 838
WORLDWIDE REINSURANCE LTD.; *Int'l*, pg. 8459
WORLDWIDE RESOURCES CORP.; *Int'l*, pg. 8459
WORLD WIDE SECURITY GROUP; *U.S. Private*, pg. 4567
WORLD WIDE SIRES, LTD.; *U.S. Private*, pg. 4567
WORLDWIDE STRATEGIES, INC.; *U.S. Public*, pg. 2382
WORLDWIDE SUPPLY; *U.S. Private*, pg. 4570
WORLD WIDE TECHNOLOGY ASYNCHRONY LABS, LLC—See World Wide Technology Holding Co., LLC; *U.S. Private*, pg. 4568
WORLD WIDE TECHNOLOGY HOLDING CO., LLC; *U.S. Private*, pg. 4567
WORLD WIDE TECHNOLOGY - HONG KONG SALES OFFICE—See World Wide Technology Holding Co., LLC; *U.S. Private*, pg. 4568
WORLD WIDE TECHNOLOGY, LLC—See World Wide Technology Holding Co., LLC; *U.S. Private*, pg. 4568
WORLDWIDE TECHSERVICES, INC; *U.S. Private*, pg. 4570
WORLDWIDE TERMINALS FERNANDINA, LLC; *U.S. Private*, pg. 4570
WORLDWIDE TRADE PARTNERS, LLC—See Ryan, LLC; *U.S. Private*, pg. 3511
WORLDWIDE TRAVEL STAFFING, LIMITED; *U.S. Private*, pg. 4570
WORLD WIDE WEB FOUNDATION; *U.S. Private*, pg. 4568
WORLDWIDE WHOLESALE FLOOR COVERINGS; *U.S. Private*, pg. 4570
WORLDWIDE WOOL PTY. LTD.—See Lempriere Pty. Ltd.; *Int'l*, pg. 4450
WORLD WILDLIFE FUND CANADA—See WWF International; *Int'l*, pg. 8517
WORLD WILDLIFE FUND, INC.—See WWF International; *Int'l*, pg. 8517
WORLD WINDOWS CO., LTD.—See Zero Co., Ltd.; *Int'l*, pg. 8638
WORLD WIRELESS COMMUNICATIONS INC; *U.S. Private*, pg. 4568
WORLD WIRE PROCESSING CO., LTD.—See Millcon Steel Public Company Limited; *Int'l*, pg. 4895
WORLDWISE, INC.—See Alvarez & Marsal, Inc.; *U.S. Private*, pg. 213

WORLD WOOD CO., INC.—See Baillie Lumber Co., Inc.; *U.S. Private*, pg. 426
WORLD WOODS CORPORATION; *U.S. Private*, pg. 4568
WORLD WRESTLING ENTERTAINMENT (INTERNATIONAL) LIMITED—See Silver Lake Group, LLC; *U.S. Private*, pg. 3654
WORLD WRESTLING ENTERTAINMENT, LLC—See Silver Lake Group, LLC; *U.S. Private*, pg. 3654
WORLD WRITERS LIMITED—See Dentsu Group Inc.; *Int'l*, pg. 2039
WORLEY CLAIMS SERVICES, LLC—See Aquiline Capital Partners LLC; *U.S. Private*, pg. 305
WORLEY EQUIPMENT INCORPORATED—See Worley Limited; *Int'l*, pg. 8459
WORLEY LIMITED; *Int'l*, pg. 8459
WORLEYPARSONS CORPORATION—See Worley Limited; *Int'l*, pg. 8459
WORLEYPARSONS RSA (PTY) LTD.—See Worley Limited; *Int'l*, pg. 8459
WORLEYPARSONSTWP—See Worley Limited; *Int'l*, pg. 8459
WORLY PLUMBING SUPPLY INC.; *U.S. Private*, pg. 4570
WORMALD AUSTRALIA PTY. LTD.—See Johnson Controls International plc; *Int'l*, pg. 3988
WORMALD AUSTRALIA PTY. LTD.—See Evergreen Capital L.P.; *U.S. Private*, pg. 1438
WORMALD ENGINEERING SERVICES LTD.—See Johnson Controls International plc; *Int'l*, pg. 3989
WORMALD HOLDINGS (U.K.) LTD.—See Johnson Controls International plc; *Int'l*, pg. 3990
WORMALD ITALIANA S.P.A.—See Johnson Controls International plc; *Int'l*, pg. 3989
THE WORNICK COMPANY—See Veritas Capital Fund Management, LLC; *U.S. Private*, pg. 4365
THE WORNICK COMPANY—See Veritas Capital Fund Management, LLC; *U.S. Private*, pg. 4365
WORRY FREE COMFORT SYSTEMS, INC—See Brookfield Corporation; *Int'l*, pg. 1188
WORRY FREE TEA HOUSE HOLDINGS CO; *U.S. Public*, pg. 2382
WORSLEY INVESTORS LIMITED; *Int'l*, pg. 8459
WORSWICK INDUSTRIES, INC.—See RF Industries, Ltd.; *U.S. Public*, pg. 1796
WORTH & CO., INC.; *U.S. Private*, pg. 4570
WORTH COLLECTION LTD.—See New Water Capital, L.P.; *U.S. Private*, pg. 2908
THE WORTH COMPANY; *U.S. Private*, pg. 4139
WORTH GROUP, LLC—See Curtco Media Labs LLC; *U.S. Private*, pg. 1126
WORTHGROUP MASTERBUILDERS, INC.; *U.S. Private*, pg. 4570
WORTH HIGGINS & ASSOCIATES INC.; *U.S. Private*, pg. 4570
WORTH INC.—See Major League Baseball; *U.S. Private*, pg. 2555
WORTH INC.—See The Seidler Company, LLC; *U.S. Private*, pg. 4116
WORTHING COACHES LIMITED—See Mobico Group PLC; *Int'l*, pg. 5009
WORTHINGTON ARMSTRONG VENTURE—See Armstrong World Industries, Inc.; *U.S. Public*, pg. 194
WORTHINGTON ARMSTRONG VENTURE—See Worthington Industries, Inc.; *U.S. Public*, pg. 2383
WORTHINGTON AVIATION PARTS, INC.—See Churchill Equity, Inc.; *U.S. Private*, pg. 895
WORTHINGTON CONSTRUCTION GROUP, INC.—See Worthington Industries, Inc.; *U.S. Public*, pg. 2382
WORTHINGTON CYLINDER CORPORATION—See Worthington Industries, Inc.; *U.S. Public*, pg. 2383
WORTHINGTON CYLINDERS-EMBALAGENS INDUSTRIAIS DE GAS, S.A.—See Worthington Industries, Inc.; *U.S. Public*, pg. 2383
WORTHINGTON CYLINDERS GMBH—See Worthington Industries, Inc.; *U.S. Public*, pg. 2383
WORTHINGTON DEALERSHIP GROUP; *U.S. Private*, pg. 4570
WORTHINGTON ENERGY, INC.; *U.S. Private*, pg. 4570
WORTHINGTON INDUSTRIES CONSUMER PRODUCTS, LLC—See Worthington Industries, Inc.; *U.S. Public*, pg. 2383
WORTHINGTON INDUSTRIES ENGINEERED CABS, INC.—See Angeles Equity Partners, LLC; *U.S. Private*, pg. 282
WORTHINGTON INDUSTRIES ENGINEERED CABS, LLC—See Angeles Equity Partners, LLC; *U.S. Private*, pg. 282
WORTHINGTON INDUSTRIES, INC.; *U.S. Public*, pg. 2382
WORTHINGTON INDUSTRIES MEDICAL CENTER, INC.—See Worthington Industries, Inc.; *U.S. Public*, pg. 2383
WORTHINGTON INDUSTRIES POLAND SP. Z O.O.—See Worthington Industries, Inc.; *U.S. Public*, pg. 2383
WORTHINGTON JEWELERS; *U.S. Private*, pg. 4570
WORTHINGTON MID-RISE CONSTRUCTION, INC.—See Worthington Industries, Inc.; *U.S. Public*, pg. 2382
WORTHINGTON NATIONAL BANK—See BancFirst Corporation; *U.S. Public*, pg. 269

COMPANY NAME INDEX — WRAGG & CASAS PUBLIC RELATIONS, INC.

WORTHINGTON SAMUEL COIL PROCESSING, LLC—See United States Steel Corporation; *U.S. Public*, pg. 2237
WORTHINGTON SAMUEL COIL PROCESSING, LLC—See Worthington Industries, Inc.; *U.S. Public*, pg. 2383
WORTHINGTON S.P.A.—See Flowserve Corporation; *U.S. Public*, pg. 857
WORTHINGTON S.R.L.—See Flowserve Corporation; *U.S. Public*, pg. 857
THE WORTHINGTON STEEL COMPANY—See Worthington Industries, Inc.; *U.S. Public*, pg. 2383
WORTHINGTON STEEL OF MICHIGAN, INC.—See Worthington Industries, Inc.; *U.S. Public*, pg. 2383
WORTHINGTON STEELPAC SYSTEMS, LLC—See Worthington Industries, Inc.; *U.S. Public*, pg. 2383
WORTH INVESTMENT GROUP, LLC; *U.S. Private*, pg. 4570
WORTH INVESTMENT & TRADING COMPANY LIMITED; *Int'l*, pg. 8459
WORTH PERIPHERALS LIMITED; *Int'l*, pg. 8459
WORTHPOINT CORPORATION; *U.S. Private*, pg. 4570
WORWAG COATINGS (LANGFANG) CO., LTD.—See PPG Industries, Inc.; *U.S. Public*, pg. 1711
WORXTIME LLC—See Equifax Inc.; *U.S. Public*, pg. 787
WORZALLA, INC.—See CJK Group, Inc.; *U.S. Private*, pg. 909
W.O. STINSON & SON LTD.; *Int'l*, pg. 8322
W. & O. SUPPLY, INC.—See MiddleGround Management, LP; *U.S. Private*, pg. 2712
WOTAI PAPER (SHENZHEN) CO., LTD.—See Japan Pulp and Paper Company Limited; *Int'l*, pg. 3905
WOTCO, INC.—See Western Technology Services International, Inc.; *U.S. Private*, pg. 4497
WOT CO., LTD.; *Int'l*, pg. 8460
WOTIF.COM HOLDINGS PTY. LTD.—See Expedia Group, Inc.; *U.S. Public*, pg. 810
WOTIF.COM (NZ) LTD.—See Expedia Group, Inc.; *U.S. Public*, pg. 810
WOTIF.COM PTY. LTD.—See Expedia Group, Inc.; *U.S. Public*, pg. 810
WOT.IO, INC.—See InterDigital, Inc.; *U.S. Public*, pg. 1144
WOTSO AT RFW MANLY PTY. LTD.—See Wotso Property; *Int'l*, pg. 8460
WOTSO CHERMSIDE PTY. LTD.—See Wotso Property; *Int'l*, pg. 8460
WOTSO PROPERTY; *Int'l*, pg. 8460
WOTTON HOUSE HOTEL OPCO LIMITED—See InterContinental Hotels Group PLC; *Int'l*, pg. 3739
WOTTON TRAVEL LIMITED—See Renishaw plc; *Int'l*, pg. 6283
WOUND CARE ADVANTAGE; *U.S. Private*, pg. 4570
WOUTER WITZEL EUROVALVE B.V.—See AVK Holding A/S; *Int'l*, pg. 747
WOVEN DIGITAL, INC.; *U.S. Private*, pg. 4571
WOVEN ELECTRONICS LLC—See RTX Corporation; *U.S. Public*, pg. 1822
WOVEN LEGENDS INC.; *U.S. Private*, pg. 4571
WOVENWARE INC.—See Advent International Corporation; *U.S. Private*, pg. 104
THE WOW FACTOR, INC.; *U.S. Private*, pg. 4139
WOWIO, INC.; *U.S. Public*, pg. 2383
WOWJOINT HOLDINGS LIMITED; *Int'l*, pg. 8460
WOWK-TV, LLC—See Nexstar Media Group, Inc.; *U.S. Public*, pg. 1523
WOW LOGISTICS COMPANY; *U.S. Private*, pg. 4571
WOW MEDIA PRODUCTS, INC.; *U.S. Private*, pg. 4571
WOWOW COMMUNICATIONS INC—See WOWOW, Inc.; *Int'l*, pg. 8460
WOWOW, INC.; *Int'l*, pg. 8460
WOWPRIME CORP.; *Int'l*, pg. 8460
WOWT-TV—See Gray Television, Inc.; *U.S. Public*, pg. 960
WOW UNLIMITED MEDIA INC.—See Kartoon Studios, Inc.; *U.S. Public*, pg. 1214
WOW VISION PTE LTD—See Centurion Corporation Limited; *Int'l*, pg. 1417
WOWWEE HOLDINGS INC.; *Int'l*, pg. 8460
WOW WORLD GROUP INC.; *Int'l*, pg. 8460
WOW WORLD INC; *Int'l*, pg. 8460
WOW! WURTH ONLINE WORLD GMBH—See Wurth Verwaltungsgesellschaft mbH; *Int'l*, pg. 8508
WOZNIAK INDUSTRIES, INC.; *U.S. Private*, pg. 4571
WP ACQUISITION SUB, LLC—See Acadia Healthcare Company, Inc.; *U.S. Public*, pg. 31
WPB COLLISION, INC.—See AutoNation, Inc.; *U.S. Public*, pg. 238
WP BEVERAGES, LLC; *U.S. Private*, pg. 4571
WP BULGARIA 12 EOOD—See Enel S.p.A.; *Int'l*, pg. 2415
W. P. CAREY & CO. B.V.—See W.P. Carey Inc.; *U.S. Public*, pg. 2316
W. P. CAREY EQUITY INVESTMENT MANAGEMENT (SHANGHAI) CO., LTD.—See W.P. Carey Inc.; *U.S. Public*, pg. 2316
W.P. CAREY INC.; *U.S. Public*, pg. 2315
WPC III, INC.; *U.S. Private*, pg. 4571
WPC, INC.—See Terracon Consultants, Inc.; *U.S. Public*, pg. 3971
WPCM-AM—See Curtis Media Group; *U.S. Private*, pg. 1126
WPC MAN-STRASSE 1 GMBH—See W.P. Carey Inc.; *U.S. Public*, pg. 2316
WP COMPANY LLC—See Nash Holdings LLC; *U.S. Private*, pg. 2835
WP COOLING SYSTEMS (DALIAN) CO., LTD.—See Pierer Konzerngesellschaft mbH; *Int'l*, pg. 5863
WPC POLA SP. Z O.O.—See W.P. Carey Inc.; *U.S. Public*, pg. 2316
WPCS INCORPORATED—See AYRO, Inc.; *U.S. Public*, pg. 256
WPCS INTERNATIONAL - SUISUN CITY, INC.; *U.S. Private*, pg. 4571
WPC SP. Z O.O.—See Pilot Corporation; *Int'l*, pg. 5867
WPDE-TV—See Sinclair, Inc.; *U.S. Public*, pg. 1887
WPD PHARMACEUTICALS INC.; *Int'l*, pg. 8460
WPD WINDPARK WERGZAHNA GMBH & CO KG—See Munchener Ruckversicherungs AG; *Int'l*, pg. 5093
WPEC-TV—See Sinclair, Inc.; *U.S. Public*, pg. 1887
WP ENERGY PCL; *Int'l*, pg. 8460
WPENGINE, INC.; *U.S. Private*, pg. 4571
WPF HOLDINGS, INC.; *U.S. Public*, pg. 2383
WPG AMERICAS INC.—See WPG Holdings Limited; *Int'l*, pg. 8461
WPG C&C COMPUTERS AND PERIPHERAL (INDIA) PRIVATE LIMITED—See WPG Holdings Limited; *Int'l*, pg. 8461
WPG C&C (MALAYSIA) SDN BHD.—See WPG Holdings Limited; *Int'l*, pg. 8461
WPG C&C (THAILAND) CO., LTD.—See WPG Holdings Limited; *Int'l*, pg. 8461
WPG CHINA INC.—See WPG Holdings Limited; *Int'l*, pg. 8461
WPG CHINA (SZ) INC.—See WPG Holdings Limited; *Int'l*, pg. 8461
WPG CLOUD SERVICE LIMITED—See WPG Holdings Limited; *Int'l*, pg. 8461
WPG ELECTRONICS (HONG KONG) LIMITED—See WPG Holdings Limited; *Int'l*, pg. 8461
WPG ELECTRONICS LIMITED—See WPG Holdings Limited; *Int'l*, pg. 8461
WPG ELECTRONICS (PHILIPPINES) INC.—See WPG Holdings Limited; *Int'l*, pg. 8461
WPG EMEA B.V.—See WPG Holdings Limited; *Int'l*, pg. 8461
WP GERMANY GMBH—See Pierer Konzerngesellschaft mbH; *Int'l*, pg. 5863
WPG HOLDINGS LIMITED; *Int'l*, pg. 8460
WPG INDIA ELECTRONICS PVT LTD.—See WPG Holdings Limited; *Int'l*, pg. 8461
WPG KOREA CO., LTD.—See WPG Holdings Limited; *Int'l*, pg. 8461
WPG MALAYSIA SDN. BHD—See WPG Holdings Limited; *Int'l*, pg. 8461
WPG ORE MARKETING PTY LTD—See WPG Resources Ltd; *Int'l*, pg. 8461
WPG RESOURCES LTD; *Int'l*, pg. 8461
WP GROSS WARNOW GMBH & CO. KG—See Electricite de France S.A.; *Int'l*, pg. 2350
WP GROUP, LLC—See Affiliated Managers Group, Inc.; *U.S. Public*, pg. 56
WPG SCM LIMITED—See WPG Holdings Limited; *Int'l*, pg. 8461
WPG SHANGHAI SMART WATER PCL; *Int'l*, pg. 8462
WPG (THAILAND) CO., LTD.—See WPG Holdings Limited; *Int'l*, pg. 8461
WPG VIETNAM CO., LTD.—See WPG Holdings Limited; *Int'l*, pg. 8461
WPG WESTSHORE, LLC—See Washington Prime Group Inc.; *U.S. Private*, pg. 4449
WPG WOLF RANCH, LLC—See Washington Prime Group Inc.; *U.S. Private*, pg. 4449
WPGX, LLC—See Lockwood Broadcasting, Inc.; *U.S. Private*, pg. 2478
WPH AIRPORT ASSOCIATES; *U.S. Private*, pg. 4571
WP HECKELBERG-BREYDIN GMBH & CO. KG—See Electricite de France S.A.; *Int'l*, pg. 2350
WPHL, LLC—See Nexstar Media Group, Inc.; *U.S. Public*, pg. 1525
WP HOLDING CORP.—See Verlagsgruppe Georg von Holtzbrinck GmbH; *Int'l*, pg. 8170
WPI-BOSTON DIVISION, INC.—See Eaton Corporation plc; *Int'l*, pg. 2282
WPI INTERNATIONAL (HONG KONG) LIMITED—See WPG Holdings Limited; *Int'l*, pg. 8461
WPIL LIMITED; *Int'l*, pg. 8462
WPIX, LLC—See Nexstar Media Group, Inc.; *U.S. Public*, pg. 1525
W.P. LAW, INC.; *U.S. Private*, pg. 4422
WPLG, INC.—See Berkshire Hathaway Inc.; *U.S. Public*, pg. 319
WP MANNHEIM GMBH—See International Chemical Investors S.E.; *Int'l*, pg. 3745
WPMI, LLC—See Elevance Health, Inc.; *U.S. Public*, pg. 730
WPM INC.; *U.S. Private*, pg. 4571
WPMI-TV, Inc.—See Sinclair, Inc.; *U.S. Public*, pg. 1887
WPM PROJEKTMANAGEMENT GMBH—See Airbus SE; *Int'l*, pg. 242
WPMT, LLC—See Nexstar Media Group, Inc.; *U.S. Public*, pg. 1525
WPNH—See Northeast Communications Inc.; *U.S. Private*, pg. 2949
WPO ALBA S.A.—See Alba SE; *Int'l*, pg. 293
WPP AUNZ ANALYTICS PTY. LTD.—See WPP plc; *Int'l*, pg. 8462
WPP AUNZ LTD.—See WPP plc; *Int'l*, pg. 8462
WP PERFORMANCE SYSTEMS GMBH—See Pierer Konzerngesellschaft mbH; *Int'l*, pg. 5863
WPP GROUP USA INC.—See WPP plc; *Int'l*, pg. 8467
WPP PLC; *Int'l*, pg. 8462
WPP SCANGROUP LIMITED—See WPP plc; *Int'l*, pg. 8494
WP RADIATOR ITALIA S.R.L.—See Pierer Konzerngesellschaft mbH; *Int'l*, pg. 5863
WPRA, INC.—See Empresas Bechara, Inc.; *U.S. Private*, pg. 1388
WPROMOTE, INC. - DALLAS—See ZelnickMedia Corp.; *U.S. Private*, pg. 4601
WPROMOTE, LLC—See ZelnickMedia Corp.; *U.S. Private*, pg. 4600
W.P. & R.S. MARS COMPANY; *U.S. Private*, pg. 4422
WPS ADVISORS, INC.—See Equitable Holdings, Inc.; *U.S. Public*, pg. 789
WPS COMMUNITY BANK—See Wisconsin Physicians Service Insurance Corporation; *U.S. Private*, pg. 4549
WPSG-TV—See Nexstar Media Group, Inc.; *U.S. Public*, pg. 1524
WPS, INC.; *U.S. Private*, pg. 4571
WPS INDUSTRIES INC.; *U.S. Private*, pg. 4571
WPS PARKING SYSTEMS BV—See Electricite de France S.A.; *Int'l*, pg. 2352
W.P. STEWART ASSET MANAGEMENT (CURACAO) N.V.—See Equitable Holdings, Inc.; *U.S. Public*, pg. 789
W.P. STEWART ASSET MANAGEMENT LTD.—See Equitable Holdings, Inc.; *U.S. Public*, pg. 789
W.P. STEWART ASSET MANAGEMENT (NA), INC.—See Equitable Holdings, Inc.; *U.S. Public*, pg. 789
W.P. STEWART & CO., LTD.—See Equitable Holdings, Inc.; *U.S. Public*, pg. 789
WP SUSPENSION NORTH AMERICA, INC.—See Pierer Konzerngesellschaft mbH; *Int'l*, pg. 5863
WPTA-TV—See Gray Television, Inc.; *U.S. Public*, pg. 961
WPT ENTERPRISE INC.—See Allied Gaming & Entertainment, Inc.; *U.S. Public*, pg. 80
WPTF-AM—See Curtis Media Group; *U.S. Private*, pg. 1126
WPT INDUSTRIAL REAL ESTATE INVESTMENT TRUST—See Blackstone Inc.; *U.S. Public*, pg. 352
WPT LLC—See Westlake Corporation; *U.S. Public*, pg. 2360
WPTV—See The E.W. Scripps Company; *U.S. Public*, pg. 2069
WPTZ-TV—See The Hearst Corporation; *U.S. Private*, pg. 4049
WPVIP INC.—See Automattic Inc.; *U.S. Private*, pg. 400
WPVI-TV INC.—See The Walt Disney Company; *U.S. Public*, pg. 2138
WPX ENERGY APPALACHIA, LLC—See Devon Energy Corporation; *U.S. Public*, pg. 657
WPX ENERGY, INC.—See Devon Energy Corporation; *U.S. Public*, pg. 657
WPX ENERGY WILLISTON, LLC—See Devon Energy Corporation; *U.S. Public*, pg. 657
WPXI, INC.—See Apollo Global Management, Inc.; *U.S. Public*, pg. 164
WQAD, LLC—See Nexstar Media Group, Inc.; *U.S. Public*, pg. 1525
WQDR-FM—See Curtis Media Group; *U.S. Private*, pg. 1126
WQHH 96 5 FM—See The Macdonald Broadcasting Company; *U.S. Private*, pg. 4073
WQHT-FM—See Emmis Communications Corporation; *U.S. Public*, pg. 753
WQRF-TV—See Nexstar Media Group, Inc.; *U.S. Public*, pg. 1523
WQSR-FM—See AUDACY, INC.; *U.S. Public*, pg. 226
WQXR FM—See New York Public Radio; *U.S. Private*, pg. 2911
WRAFTON LABORATORIES LIMITED—See Perrigo Company plc; *Int'l*, pg. 5813
WRAGG & CASAS PUBLIC RELATIONS, INC.; *U.S. Private*, pg. 4571
WRAGG & CASAS PUBLIC RELATIONS, INC.—See Wragg & Casas Public Relations, Inc.; *U.S. Private*, pg. 4572
WRAGG & CASAS PUBLIC RELATIONS, INC.—See Wragg & Casas Public Relations, Inc.; *U.S. Private*, pg. 4572
WRAL-FM, INC.—See Capitol Broadcasting Company, Inc.; *U.S. Private*, pg. 743
WRAL SPORTS FAN—See Capitol Broadcasting Company, Inc.; *U.S. Private*, pg. 743
WRAL-TV—See Capitol Broadcasting Company, Inc.; *U.S. Private*, pg. 743
WR AMERICA, INC.—See Woory Industrial Holdings Co., Ltd.; *Int'l*, pg. 8454

WRAGG & CASAS PUBLIC RELATIONS, INC.

CORPORATE AFFILIATIONS

WRANGYER BEVERAGE (2008) CO., LTD.—See Thai Beverage Public Company Limited; *Int'l*, pg. 7592
WRAPID SPECIALTY, INC.—See Aon plc; *Int'l*, pg. 495
WRAP MEDIA, LLC—See DXC Technology Company; *U.S. Public*, pg. 697
WRAP & SEND SERVICES, LLC; *U.S. Private*, pg. 4572
WRAP TECHNOLOGIES, INC.; *U.S. Public*, pg. 2383
WRA; *U.S. Private*, pg. 4571
WRAY FORD INC.; *U.S. Private*, pg. 4572
WRAY MAZDA VOLKSWAGEN; *U.S. Private*, pg. 4572
WRAY'S INC.; *U.S. Private*, pg. 4572
WRAY WARD MARKETING COMMUNICATIONS; *U.S. Private*, pg. 4572
WRAZ-TV—See Capitol Broadcasting Company, Inc.; *U.S. Private*, pg. 743
W&R BARNETT LTD.; *Int'l*, pg. 8320
WRBC SUPPORT SERVICES, LLC—See W.R. Berkley Corporation; *U.S. Public*, pg. 2318
WRB ENTERPRISES, INC.; *U.S. Private*, pg. 4572
W.R. BERKLEY CORPORATION; *U.S. Public*, pg. 2316
W. R. BERKLEY EUROPE AG—See W.R. Berkley Corporation; *U.S. Public*, pg. 2318
W. R. BERKLEY SPAIN, S. L. U.—See W.R. Berkley Corporation; *U.S. Public*, pg. 2318
W. R. BERKLEY SYNDICATE LIMITED—See W.R. Berkley Corporation; *U.S. Public*, pg. 2318
WRBL-TV—See Nexstar Media Group, Inc.; *U.S. Public*, pg. 1523
W.R. CASE & SONS CUTLERY COMPANY—See Zippo Manufacturing Company, Inc.; *U.S. Private*, pg. 4606
WRCC HOLDINGS, LLC—See Howard Hughes Holdings Inc.; *U.S. Public*, pg. 1060
WRC LIMITED—See MBf Holdings Berhad; *Int'l*, pg. 4752
W.R. COBB COMPANY; *U.S. Private*, pg. 4422
WRC-TV—See Comcast Corporation; *U.S. Public*, pg. 540
WRDW-TV—See Gray Television, Inc.; *U.S. Public*, pg. 960
WREDE & NIEDECKEN GMBH—See VINCI S.A.; *Int'l*, pg. 8240
WREG, LLC—See Nexstar Media Group, Inc.; *U.S. Public*, pg. 1525
WRENA LLC—See Angstrom Usa, Llc.; *U.S. Private*, pg. 283
WRENCH GROUP LLC—See Leonard Green & Partners, L.P.; *U.S. Private*, pg. 2430
WREN CORPORATION; *U.S. Private*, pg. 4572
WREN EXTRA CARE GROUP PLC; *Int'l*, pg. 8494
WREN HOUSE INFRASTRUCTURE MANAGEMENT LIMITED—See Kuwait Investment Authority; *Int'l*, pg. 4345
WRENN CONSTRUCTION; *U.S. Private*, pg. 4572
WRENN FINANCIAL STRATEGIES, INC.—See Genstar Capital, LLC; *U.S. Private*, pg. 1677
WRENN FINANCIAL STRATEGIES, INC.—See Keystone Group, L.P.; *U.S. Private*, pg. 2298
W RESOURCES PLC; *Int'l*, pg. 8320
WRGB-TV—See Sinclair, Inc.; *U.S. Public*, pg. 1887
WRG CREATIVE COMMUNICATION LTD.; *Int'l*, pg. 8494
W. R. GRACE ARGENTINA S.A.—See Standard Industries Holdings Inc.; *U.S. Private*, pg. 3780
W. R. GRACE BRASIL INDUSTRIA E COMERCIO DE PRODUTOS QUIMICOS LTDA.—See Standard Industries Holdings Inc.; *U.S. Private*, pg. 3780
W. R. GRACE CANADA CORP.—See Standard Industries Holdings Inc.; *U.S. Private*, pg. 3780
W. R. GRACE CAPITAL CORPORATION—See Standard Industries Holdings Inc.; *U.S. Private*, pg. 3780
W. R. GRACE & CO.-CONN—See Standard Industries Holdings Inc.; *U.S. Private*, pg. 3779
W. R. GRACE HOLDINGS, S.A. DE C.V.—See Standard Industries Holdings Inc.; *U.S. Private*, pg. 3780
W. R. GRACE (HONG KONG) LTD.—See Standard Industries Holdings Inc.; *U.S. Private*, pg. 3780
W. R. GRACE ITALIANA S.P.A.—See Standard Industries Holdings Inc.; *U.S. Private*, pg. 3780
W. R. GRACE KOREA INC.—See Standard Industries Holdings Inc.; *U.S. Private*, pg. 3780
W. R. GRACE LIMITED—See Standard Industries Holdings Inc.; *U.S. Private*, pg. 3780
W. R. GRACE (MALAYSIA) SDN. BHD.—See Standard Industries Holdings Inc.; *U.S. Private*, pg. 3780
W. R. GRACE (PANAMA) S.A.—See Standard Industries Holdings Inc.; *U.S. Private*, pg. 3780
W. R. GRACE (PHILIPPINES), INC.—See Standard Industries Holdings Inc.; *U.S. Private*, pg. 3780
W. R. GRACE S.A.—See Standard Industries Holdings Inc.; *U.S. Private*, pg. 3780
W. R. GRACE (THAILAND) LTD.—See Standard Industries Holdings Inc.; *U.S. Private*, pg. 3780
W. R. GRACE VIETNAM COMPANY LIMITED—See Standard Industries Holdings Inc.; *U.S. Private*, pg. 3780
WRG SERVICES, INC.; *U.S. Private*, pg. 4572
WR HAMBRECHT & CO. LLC; *U.S. Private*, pg. 4571
W.R. HESS COMPANY; *U.S. Private*, pg. 4422
WRH REALTY SERVICES, INC.; *U.S. Private*, pg. 4572
W.R. HUFF ASSET MANAGEMENT CO., INC.; *U.S. Private*, pg. 4422
WRH WALTER REIST HOLDING AG; *Int'l*, pg. 8494

WRICO STAMPING OF ARIZONA—See Griffiths Corporation; *U.S. Private*, pg. 1789
WRICO STAMPING OF FLORIDA—See Griffiths Corporation; *U.S. Private*, pg. 1789
WRICO STAMPING OF MINNESOTA—See Griffiths Corporation; *U.S. Private*, pg. 1789
WRICO STAMPING OF NORTH CAROLINA—See Griffiths Corporation; *U.S. Private*, pg. 1789
WRICO STAMPING OF TEXAS—See Griffiths Corporation; *U.S. Private*, pg. 1789
WRICO STAMPING OF WISCONSIN—See Griffiths Corporation; *U.S. Private*, pg. 1789
WRIC-TV—See Nexstar Media Group, Inc.; *U.S. Public*, pg. 1523
WRIDGWAYS AUSTRALIA LIMITED—See EAC Invest AS; *Int'l*, pg. 2262
WRIDGWAYS AUSTRALIA LIMITED - WRIDGWAYS MOVE SOLUTIONS—See EAC Invest AS; *Int'l*, pg. 2262
WRI FLAMINGO PINES, LLC—See Kimco Realty Corporation; *U.S. Public*, pg. 1232
WRIGHT ASPHALT PRODUCTS COMPANY LLC—See Delek Group Ltd.; *Int'l*, pg. 2011
WRIGHT AUTOMOTIVE GROUP; *U.S. Private*, pg. 4572
WRIGHT BROTHERS BUILDING CO.; *U.S. Private*, pg. 4572
WRIGHT BUSINESS FORMS, INC. - CHINO FACILITY—See Wright Business Forms, Inc.; *U.S. Private*, pg. 4572
WRIGHT BUSINESS FORMS, INC. - KENT FACILITY—See Wright Business Forms, Inc.; *U.S. Private*, pg. 4572
WRIGHT BUSINESS FORMS, INC.; *U.S. Private*, pg. 4572
WRIGHT CONSTRUCTION GROUP, INC.; *U.S. Private*, pg. 4573
WRIGHT DISTRIBUTING CO., INC.; *U.S. Private*, pg. 4573
WRIGHT DO IT CENTER; *U.S. Private*, pg. 4573
WRIGHT ENERGY PARTNERS, LLC; *U.S. Private*, pg. 4573
WRIGHT ENGINEERED PLASTICS, INC.; *U.S. Private*, pg. 4573
WRIGHT EXPRESS AUSTRALIA HOLDINGS PTY LTD—See WEX, Inc.; *U.S. Public*, pg. 2365
WRIGHT EXPRESS PREPAID CARDS AUSTRALIA PTY LTD—See WEX, Inc.; *U.S. Public*, pg. 2365
WRIGHT & FILIPPIS INC.; *U.S. Private*, pg. 4572
WRIGHT FLOW TECHHNOLOGIES, INC.—See IDEX Corp; *U.S. Public*, pg. 1092
WRIGHT FLOW TECHNOLOGIES LIMITED—See IDEX Corp; *U.S. Public*, pg. 1092
WRIGHT FLOW TECHNOLOGIES LTD.—See IDEX Corp; *U.S. Public*, pg. 1092
WRIGHT FLOW TECHNOLOGIES—See IDEX Corp; *U.S. Public*, pg. 1092
WRIGHT GRAPHICS INC.; *U.S. Private*, pg. 4573
THE WRIGHT GROUP; *U.S. Private*, pg. 4139
WRIGHT-HENNEPIN COOPERATIVE ELECTRIC ASSOCIATION; *U.S. Private*, pg. 4573
WRIGHT IMAGING SOLUTIONS—See Wright Business Forms, Inc.; *U.S. Private*, pg. 4572
WRIGHTIMC, LLC.; *U.S. Private*, pg. 4573
WRIGHT INDUSTRIES, INC.—See Doerfer Corporation; *U.S. Private*, pg. 1253
WRIGHT INDUSTRIES LTD.; *Int'l*, pg. 8494
THE WRIGHT INSURANCE GROUP LLC—See Brown & Brown, Inc.; *U.S. Public*, pg. 402
WRIGHT INVESTORS' SERVICE HOLDINGS, INC.; *U.S. Public*, pg. 2383
WRIGHT-K TECHNOLOGY, INC.; *U.S. Private*, pg. 4573
WRIGHT LINE LLC—See Eaton Corporation plc; *Int'l*, pg. 2282
WRIGHT MANAGEMENT COMPANY, LLC; *U.S. Private*, pg. 4573
WRIGHTMAN, INC.—See Arthur J. Gallagher & Co.; *U.S. Public*, pg. 208
WRIGHT & MCGILL CO.; *U.S. Private*, pg. 4572
WRIGHT MEDICAL AUSTRALIA PTY LTD.—See Wright Medical Group N.V.; *Int'l*, pg. 8495
WRIGHT MEDICAL BRASIL LTDA—See Wright Medical Group N.V.; *Int'l*, pg. 8495
WRIGHT MEDICAL DEVICE (SHANGHAI) CO., LTD—See Wright Medical Group N.V.; *Int'l*, pg. 8495
WRIGHT MEDICAL GROUP, INC.—See Wright Medical Group N.V.; *Int'l*, pg. 8495
WRIGHT MEDICAL GROUP N.V.; *Int'l*, pg. 8494
WRIGHT MEDICAL ITALY SRL—See Wright Medical Group N.V.; *Int'l*, pg. 8495
WRIGHT MEDICAL JAPAN, K.K.—See Wright Medical Group N.V.; *Int'l*, pg. 8495
WRIGHT MEDICAL NETHERLANDS, B.V.—See Wright Medical Group N.V.; *Int'l*, pg. 8495
WRIGHT MEDICAL TECHNOLOGY CANADA LTD.—See Wright Medical Group N.V.; *Int'l*, pg. 8495
WRIGHT MEDICAL TECHNOLOGY, INC.—See Wright Medical Group N.V.; *Int'l*, pg. 8495
WRIGHT MEDICAL UK LIMITED—See Wright Medical Group N.V.; *Int'l*, pg. 8495

WRIGHT METAL PRODUCTS, INC.—See Trans Machine Technologies; *U.S. Private*, pg. 4205
WRIGHT & MORRISSEY, INC.; *U.S. Private*, pg. 4572
WRIGHT NATIONAL FLOOD INSURANCE COMPANY—See Brown & Brown, Inc.; *U.S. Public*, pg. 402
WRIGHT PAVING CONTRACTORS INC—See Armada Materials, LLC; *U.S. Private*, pg. 329
WRIGHT & PERCY INSURANCE AGENCY INC.; *U.S. Private*, pg. 4572
WRIGHT PLASTIC PRODUCTS CO., LLC; *U.S. Private*, pg. 4573
WRIGHT PROGRAM MANAGEMENT, LLC—See Brown & Brown, Inc.; *U.S. Public*, pg. 402
WRIGHT RISK CONSULTING, LLC—See Brown & Brown, Inc.; *U.S. Public*, pg. 402
WRIGHT RISK MANAGEMENT COMPANY, LLC—See Brown & Brown, Inc.; *U.S. Public*, pg. 402
WRIGHT RUNSTAD & COMPANY; *U.S. Private*, pg. 4573
WRIGHT-RYAN CONSTRUCTION INC.; *U.S. Private*, pg. 4573
WRIGHT'S FOODLANE INC.; *U.S. Private*, pg. 4573
WRIGHT'S FOODLINER INC.; *U.S. Private*, pg. 4573
WRIGHT'S MEDIA, LLC; *U.S. Private*, pg. 4573
WRIGHTSON ICAP LLC—See CME Group, Inc.; *U.S. Public*, pg. 517
WRIGHTSON PAS S.A. LIMITED—See Agria Corporation; *Int'l*, pg. 216
WRIGHT SPECIALTY INSURANCE AGENCY, LLC—See Brown & Brown, Inc.; *U.S. Public*, pg. 402
WRIGHTSPEED, INC.—See Firsthand Capital Management, Inc.; *U.S. Public*, pg. 1532
WRIGHT THERAPY PRODUCTS, INC.—See Svenska Cellulosa Aktiebolaget SCA; *Int'l*, pg. 7356
WRIGHT TOOL COMPANY, INC.; *U.S. Private*, pg. 4573
WRIGHT TOTAL INDOOR COMFORT, INC.; *U.S. Private*, pg. 4573
WRIGHT TRAVEL AGENCY INC.; *U.S. Private*, pg. 4573
WRIGHT TRAVEL CORPORATION—See EchoStar Corporation; *U.S. Public*, pg. 711
WRIGHT TREE SERVICE INC.; *U.S. Private*, pg. 4573
WRIGHT VALLEY OIL INC.; *U.S. Private*, pg. 4573
WRIGHTWAY CREATIVE GROUP; *U.S. Private*, pg. 4573
WRIGHT WISNER DISTRIBUTING CORP.; *U.S. Private*, pg. 4573
WRIG, INC.—See Midwest Communications, Inc.; *U.S. Private*, pg. 2720
WRIGLEY AUSTRIA GES.M.B.H.—See Mars, Incorporated; *U.S. Private*, pg. 2591
WRIGLEY BULGARIA EOOD—See Mars, Incorporated; *U.S. Private*, pg. 2591
WRIGLEY CHEWING GUM COMPANY LTD.—See Mars, Incorporated; *U.S. Private*, pg. 2591
THE WRIGLEY COMPANY (E.A.) LTD.—See Mars, Incorporated; *U.S. Private*, pg. 2590
THE WRIGLEY COMPANY (H.K.) LIMITED—See Mars, Incorporated; *U.S. Private*, pg. 2590
WRIGLEY & COMPANY LTD., JAPAN—See Mars, Incorporated; *U.S. Private*, pg. 2591
THE WRIGLEY COMPANY LTD.—See Mars, Incorporated; *U.S. Private*, pg. 2590
THE WRIGLEY COMPANY (MALAYSIA) SDN. BHD.—See Mars, Incorporated; *U.S. Private*, pg. 2590
THE WRIGLEY COMPANY (N.Z.) LIMITED—See Mars, Incorporated; *U.S. Private*, pg. 2590
THE WRIGLEY COMPANY PTY. LTD.—See Mars, Incorporated; *U.S. Private*, pg. 2591
WRIGLEY CONFECTIONS CR, KOM. SPOL.—See Mars, Incorporated; *U.S. Private*, pg. 2591
WRIGLEY CO., S.A.U.—See Mars, Incorporated; *U.S. Private*, pg. 2591
WRIGLEY D.O.O.—See Mars, Incorporated; *U.S. Private*, pg. 2591
WRIGLEY FRANCE SNC—See Mars, Incorporated; *U.S. Private*, pg. 2591
WRIGLEY GMBH—See Mars, Incorporated; *U.S. Private*, pg. 2591
WRIGLEY HUNGARIA, KFT.—See Mars, Incorporated; *U.S. Private*, pg. 2591
WRIGLEY INDIA PRIVATE LIMITED—See Mars, Incorporated; *U.S. Private*, pg. 2591
WRIGLEY PHILIPPINES, INC.—See Mars, Incorporated; *U.S. Private*, pg. 2591
WRIGLEY POLAND SP. ZO,O.—See Mars, Incorporated; *U.S. Private*, pg. 2591
WRIGLEY ROMANIA SRL—See Mars, Incorporated; *U.S. Private*, pg. 2591
WRIGLEY SCANDINAVIA AB—See Mars, Incorporated; *U.S. Private*, pg. 2591
WRIGLEY SCANDINAVIA AS—See Mars, Incorporated; *U.S. Private*, pg. 2591
WRIGLEY S.R.O.—See Mars, Incorporated; *U.S. Private*, pg. 2591
WRIGLEY TAIWAN LTD.—See Mars, Incorporated; *U.S. Private*, pg. 2591
WRI GOLDEN STATE, LLC—See Kimco Realty Corporation; *U.S. Public*, pg. 1232
WRI INSURANCE BROKERS PTY LTD—See AUB Group Limited; *Int'l*, pg. 698

COMPANY NAME INDEX

WRIKE, INC.—See Elliott Management Corporation; *U.S. Private*, pg. 1367
WRIKE, INC.—See Vista Equity Partners, LLC; *U.S. Private*, pg. 4396
WRISCO INDUSTRIES INC. - ATLANTA DIVISION—See Wrisco Industries Inc.; *U.S. Private*, pg. 4574
WRISCO INDUSTRIES INC. - CHICAGO DIVISION—See Wrisco Industries Inc.; *U.S. Private*, pg. 4574
WRISCO INDUSTRIES INC. - DALLAS DIVISION—See Wrisco Industries Inc.; *U.S. Private*, pg. 4574
WRISCO INDUSTRIES INC. - EDISON DIVISION—See Wrisco Industries Inc.; *U.S. Private*, pg. 4574
WRISCO INDUSTRIES INC.; *U.S. Private*, pg. 4574
WRIT BRADDOCK OFFICE LLC—See Elme Communities; *U.S. Public*, pg. 735
WRITERACCESS—See Blackstone Inc.; *U.S. Public*, pg. 353
WRITERACCESS—See Vista Equity Partners, LLC; *U.S. Private*, pg. 4396
WRITEUP CO., LTD.; *Int'l*, pg. 8495
WRITING ASSISTANCE, INC.—See Orbis Technologies, Inc.; *U.S. Private*, pg. 3038
WRIT MEDIA GROUP, INC.; *U.S. Public*, pg. 2383
WRITTLE HOLDINGS LIMITED; *Int'l*, pg. 8495
WRKCO INC.—See WestRock Company; *U.S. Public*, pg. 2362
WRKR LTD; *Int'l*, pg. 8495
WRL ADVERTISING, INC.; *U.S. Private*, pg. 4574
WRLH-TV—See Sinclair, Inc.; *U.S. Public*, pg. 1886
W. R. MEADOWS, INC.; *U.S. Private*, pg. 4418
WRM GROUP, LLC—See Galiot Insurance Services, Inc.; *U.S. Private*, pg. 1638
WROCLAWSKIE CENTRUM PRASOWE SP. Z O.O.—See Polski Holding Nieruchomosci S.A.; *Int'l*, pg. 5912
WROC-TV—See Nexstar Media Group, Inc.; *U.S. Public*, pg. 1523
W. ROGERS COMPANY; *U.S. Private*, pg. 4418
WRO-LOT USLUGI LOTNISKOWE SP. Z O.O.—See LOT Polish Airlines S.A.; *Int'l*, pg. 4558
WROUGHT WASHER MFG., INC.; *U.S. Private*, pg. 4574
WRR ENVIRONMENTAL SERVICES CO., INC.—See Caribou Corporation; *U.S. Private*, pg. 761
WR RESTAURANTS MANAGEMENT LLC; *U.S. Private*, pg. 4571
WRS GROUP LTD.; *U.S. Private*, pg. 4574
WR SIMS AGENCY INCORPORATED—See Bain Capital, LP; *U.S. Private*, pg. 441
WR SIMS AGENCY INCORPORATED—See Keystone Insurers Group, Inc.; *U.S. Private*, pg. 2300
W.R. STARKEY MORTGAGE LLP; *U.S. Private*, pg. 4422
WRTV—See The E.W. Scripps Company; *U.S. Public*, pg. 2069
WRT WORLD ENTERPRISES INC.; *U.S. Private*, pg. 4574
WR VERMILLION CO., INC.; *U.S. Private*, pg. 4571
W.R. VERNON PRODUCE CO., INC.; *U.S. Private*, pg. 4422
WRWD COUNTRY 1073—See iHeartMedia, Inc.; *U.S. Public*, pg. 1097
WR WEBEREI RUSSIKON AG—See Getzner Textil AG; *Int'l*, pg. 2954
WRZ BANKSHARES, INC.; *U.S. Private*, pg. 4574
WS ACQUISITION, LLC—See Guardian Capital Partners, LLC; *U.S. Private*, pg. 1810
W.S. ADAMSON & ASSOCIATES, INC.; *U.S. Private*, pg. 4422
W SAN FRANCISCO HOTEL—See Keck Seng Investments (Hong Kong) Limited; *Int'l*, pg. 4114
W SAN FRANCISCO—See Keck Seng Investments (Hong Kong) Limited; *Int'l*, pg. 4114
WSA SYSTEMS-BOCA INC.—See Huron Capital Partners LLC; *U.S. Private*, pg. 2012
WS ATKINS IRELAND LIMITED—See AtkinsRealis Group Inc.; *Int'l*, pg. 673
WS ATKINS LIMITED—See AtkinsRealis Group Inc.; *Int'l*, pg. 673
WS ATKINS & PARTNERS OVERSEAS ENGINEERING CONSULTANTS—See AtkinsRealis Group Inc.; *Int'l*, pg. 673
WS ATKINS & PARTNERS OVERSEAS—See AtkinsRealis Group Inc.; *Int'l*, pg. 673
WSAV-TV—See Nexstar Media Group, Inc.; *U.S. Public*, pg. 1523
WSAZ-TV—See Gray Television, Inc.; *U.S. Public*, pg. 960
W.S. BADCOCK LLC—See Conn's, Inc.; *U.S. Public*, pg. 567
W.S. BADGER COMPANY, INC; *U.S. Private*, pg. 4422
WSB & ASSOCIATES, INC.—See GHK Capital Partners LP; *U.S. Private*, pg. 1690
W.S. BELLOWS CONSTRUCTION CORPORATION; *U.S. Private*, pg. 4422
WSB TITAN INC.—See GMS Inc.; *U.S. Public*, pg. 948
W. SCHILDMEYER GMBH & CO. KG; *Int'l*, pg. 8321
W. SCHILLER & CO., INC.; *U.S. Private*, pg. 4418
W. SCHRAML SOFTWAREHAUS GMBH; *Int'l*, pg. 8321
WS CONSTRUCTION INC—See Gray Inc.; *U.S. Private*, pg. 1759
W-SCOPE CHUNGJU PLANT CO., LTD.—See W-SCOPE Corporation; *Int'l*, pg. 8321

W-SCOPE CORPORATION; *Int'l*, pg. 8321
W-SCOPE KOREA CO., LTD.—See W-SCOPE Corporation; *Int'l*, pg. 8321
W-SCOPE NEW ENERGY (SHENZHEN) CO., LIMITED—See W-SCOPE Corporation; *Int'l*, pg. 8321
WSCR CORP.—See Dover Corporation; *U.S. Public*, pg. 683
W.S. CUMBY, INC.; *U.S. Private*, pg. 4422
W.S. DARLEY & CO., INC.; *U.S. Private*, pg. 4422
W SEATTLE HOTEL—See Marriott International, Inc.; *U.S. Public*, pg. 1372
W.S. EMERSON CO., INC.; *U.S. Private*, pg. 4422
WS ENGINEERING TECHNOLOGIES PTE. LTD.—See Wah Seong Corporation Berhad; *Int'l*, pg. 8330
W SERVICE SPA.—See Toy Marine S.p.A; *Int'l*, pg. 7851
WSET, INCORPORATED—See Sinclair, Inc.; *U.S. Public*, pg. 1886
WSFA, LLC—See Gray Television, Inc.; *U.S. Public*, pg. 960
WSF INDUSTRIES, INC.; *U.S. Private*, pg. 4574
WSFL, LLC—See Nexstar Media Group, Inc.; *U.S. Public*, pg. 1525
WSFS CAPITAL MANAGEMENT, LLC—See WSFS Financial Corporation; *U.S. Public*, pg. 2383
WSFS FINANCIAL CORPORATION; *U.S. Public*, pg. 2383
WSFS INVESTMENT GROUP, INC.—See WSFS Financial Corporation; *U.S. Public*, pg. 2384
WSFX GLOBAL PAY LIMITED—See DiGiSPICE Technologies Ltd.; *Int'l*, pg. 2120
WSG PARTNERS, LLC; *U.S. Private*, pg. 4574
WSI CORPORATION—See International Business Machines Corporation; *U.S. Public*, pg. 1151
WSI EDUCATION BRAZIL LICENCIA—See Pearson plc; *Int'l*, pg. 5778
WSI EDUCATION GMBH—See Pearson plc; *Int'l*, pg. 5778
WSIG 96.9FM—See Vox Communications Group LLC; *U.S. Private*, pg. 4414
WSI INDUSTRIES, INC.—See Polaris, Inc.; *U.S. Public*, pg. 1701
WSI INTERNATIONAL, LLC; *U.S. Private*, pg. 4574
W. SILVER RECYCLING, INC. - DONNA FACILITY—See W. Silver Recycling, Inc.; *U.S. Private*, pg. 4418
W. SILVER RECYCLING, INC.; *U.S. Private*, pg. 4418
W. SILVER RECYCLING OF NEW MEXICO, INC.—See W. Silver Recycling, Inc.; *U.S. Private*, pg. 4418
W.S. INDUSTRIES (INDIA) LIMITED; *Int'l*, pg. 8322
W.S. INDUSTRIES (INDIA) LIMITED - VIZAG PLANT—See W.S. Industries (India) Limited; *Int'l*, pg. 8322
WSIP-FM—See Forcht Group of Kentucky, Inc.; *U.S. Private*, pg. 1564
WSJV-TV—See Gray Television, Inc.; *U.S. Public*, pg. 961
W. S. KEEL LUMBER CO., INC.; *U.S. Private*, pg. 4418
WSLS-TV—See Graham Holdings Company; *U.S. Public*, pg. 955
WSM-AM—See Ryman Hospitality Properties, Inc.; *U.S. Public*, pg. 1829
WSMC INC.; *U.S. Private*, pg. 4574
WSMH, INC.—See Sinclair, Inc.; *U.S. Public*, pg. 1887
WSM INDUSTRIES INC.; *U.S. Private*, pg. 4574
WSM VENTURES CORP.; *Int'l*, pg. 8495
WSMV-TV—See Meredith Corporation; *U.S. Public*, pg. 1424
W.S. NEWELL, INC.; *U.S. Private*, pg. 4423
W.S. NICHOLLS CONSTRUCTION INC.—See Southwest Gas Holdings, Inc.; *U.S. Public*, pg. 1913
W.S. NICHOLLS INDUSTRIES INC.—See Southwest Gas Holdings, Inc.; *U.S. Public*, pg. 1914
W.S. NIELSEN CO., INC.; *U.S. Private*, pg. 4423
WSOC TELEVISION, INC.—See Apollo Global Management, Inc.; *U.S. Public*, pg. 164
W.SOHNGEN GMBH; *Int'l*, pg. 8322
WSOS COMMUNITY ACTION COMMISSION, INC.; *U.S. Private*, pg. 4574
W. SOULE & COMPANY; *U.S. Private*, pg. 4418
WS PACKAGING GROUP INC. - FRANKLIN—See Platinum Equity, LLC; *U.S. Private*, pg. 3206
WS PACKAGING GROUP INC. - MASON—See Platinum Equity, LLC; *U.S. Private*, pg. 3206
WS PACKAGING GROUP INC.—See Platinum Equity, LLC; *U.S. Private*, pg. 3206
WSP ASIA LIMITED—See WSP Global, Inc.; *Int'l*, pg. 8497
WSP ASIA PACIFIC PTY. LTD.—See WSP Global, Inc.; *Int'l*, pg. 8497
WSPA-TV—See Nexstar Media Group, Inc.; *U.S. Public*, pg. 1523
WSP AUSTRALIA PTY LTD—See WSP Global, Inc.; *Int'l*, pg. 8497
WSP BUILDINGS PTY. LTD.—See WSP Global, Inc.; *Int'l*, pg. 8497
WSP CONSULTANTS INDIA LIMITED—See WSP Global, Inc.; *Int'l*, pg. 8497
WSP DEUTSCHLAND AG—See WSP Global, Inc.; *Int'l*, pg. 8497
WSP ENVIRONMENTAL LIMITED—See WSP Global, Inc.; *Int'l*, pg. 8497
WSP ENVIRONMENT & ENERGY LLC—See WSP Global, Inc.; *Int'l*, pg. 8498
WSP FINLAND OY—See WSP Global, Inc.; *Int'l*, pg. 8497

WSP FRANCE SAS—See WSP Global, Inc.; *Int'l*, pg. 8497
WSP GLOBAL, INC.; *Int'l*, pg. 8495
WSP GROUP AFRICA PTY. LTD.—See WSP Global, Inc.; *Int'l*, pg. 8497
WSP HOLDINGS LIMITED; *Int'l*, pg. 8498
WSP HONG KONG LIMITED—See WSP Global, Inc.; *Int'l*, pg. 8497
W. SPITZNER ARZNEIMITTELFABRIK GMBH—See Dr. Willmar Schwabe GmbH & Co. KG; *Int'l*, pg. 2196
WSP MANAGEMENT SERVICES LIMITED—See WSP Global, Inc.; *Int'l*, pg. 8497
WSP MIDDLE EAST LIMITED—See WSP Global, Inc.; *Int'l*, pg. 8497
WSP NEW ZEALAND LIMITED—See WSP Global, Inc.; *Int'l*, pg. 8497
WSP PARSONS BRINCKERHOFF (ASIA) LIMITED—See WSP Global, Inc.; *Int'l*, pg. 8497
WSP PARSONS BRINCKERHOFF—See WSP Global, Inc.; *Int'l*, pg. 8497
WSP PIPE COMPANY LIMITED—See WSP Holdings Limited; *Int'l*, pg. 8498
WSP POLSKA SP. Z O.O.—See WSP Global, Inc.; *Int'l*, pg. 8497
WSP REMEDIATION LIMITED—See WSP Global, Inc.; *Int'l*, pg. 8497
WSP SVERIGE AB—See WSP Global, Inc.; *Int'l*, pg. 8497
WSP UK LIMITED—See WSP Global, Inc.; *Int'l*, pg. 8497
WSP USA CORP.—See WSP Global, Inc.; *Int'l*, pg. 8498
W SQUARED DYNAMICS, INC.—See Comprehensive Health Services, Inc.; *U.S. Private*, pg. 1003
W.S. REICHENBACH & SON INC.; *U.S. Private*, pg. 4423
WSRP, LLC; *U.S. Private*, pg. 4574
WSRW 101.5—See iHeartMedia, Inc.; *U.S. Public*, pg. 1097
WSS ALARBAB SHIPPING CO.—See Albert Ballin KG; *Int'l*, pg. 297
WSS IT SAGL—See Sesa S.p.A.; *Int'l*, pg. 6729
WS SYSTEMS MEXICO S.A DE C.V.—See Wooshin Systems Co., Ltd.; *Int'l*, pg. 8454
W.S. THOMAS TRANSFER, INC.—See Online Transport System, Inc.; *U.S. Private*, pg. 3027
W.S. TOWNSEND COMPANY; *U.S. Private*, pg. 4423
WST QUARZ GMBH—See L. Possehl & Co. mbH; *Int'l*, pg. 4385
W.S. TRIMBLE CO., INC.; *U.S. Private*, pg. 4423
WSVN-TV—See Sunbeam Television Corporation; *U.S. Private*, pg. 3864
W.S. VOGEL AGENCY, INC.; *U.S. Private*, pg. 4423
WSYM-TV FOX 47—See The E.W. Scripps Company; *U.S. Public*, pg. 2069
WSYR-TV—See Nexstar Media Group, Inc.; *U.S. Public*, pg. 1523
WSYT-TV—See Sinclair, Inc.; *U.S. Public*, pg. 1887
WSYX LICENSEE, INC.—See Sinclair, Inc.; *U.S. Public*, pg. 1887
WSYX-TV—See Sinclair, Inc.; *U.S. Public*, pg. 1887
WTAE HEARST-ARGYLE TELEVISION, INC.—See The Hearst Corporation; *U.S. Private*, pg. 4049
WTA TOUR, INC.; *U.S. Private*, pg. 4574
WTA - WASSERTECHNISCHER ANLAGENBAU PLAUEN GMBH—See BWT Aktiengesellschaft; *Int'l*, pg. 1233
W.T.B. FINANCIAL CORPORATION; *U.S. Public*, pg. 2318
WTC AUTOMOTIF (M) SDN BHD.—See Warisan TC Holdings Berhad; *Int'l*, pg. 8345
WTC (CLUB) LIMITED—See Sun Hung Kai Properties Limited; *Int'l*, pg. 7304
W.T. CHEN & CO., INC.; *U.S. Private*, pg. 4423
WTC INSURANCE CORP, LTD.—See International Business Machines Corporation; *U.S. Public*, pg. 1151
WTC INSURANCE CORPORATION, LTD.—See International Business Machines Corporation; *U.S. Public*, pg. 1151
WTCN-CA—See Sinclair, Inc.; *U.S. Public*, pg. 1887
W.T. COX SUBSCRIPTIONS, INC.; *U.S. Private*, pg. 4423
WTC—See Welding Technology Corporation; *U.S. Private*, pg. 4474
WTC WOHNEN & TELECOMMUNICATION GMBH & CO. KG—See Morgan Stanley; *U.S. Public*, pg. 1473
WTE BETRIEBSGESELLSCHAFT MBH—See EVN AG; *Int'l*, pg. 2571
W TECHNOLOGIES CORP; *U.S. Public*, pg. 2315
WTECH; *U.S. Private*, pg. 4574
WTEN-TV—See Nexstar Media Group, Inc.; *U.S. Public*, pg. 1523
WTE PROJEKTGESELLSCHAFT SUD-WEST WASSER MBH—See EVN AG; *Int'l*, pg. 2571
WTE PROJEKTNA DRUZBA BLED D.O.O.—See EVN AG; *Int'l*, pg. 2571
WTE PROJEKTNA DRUZBA KRANJSKA GORA D.O.O.—See EVN AG; *Int'l*, pg. 2571
WTE WASSERTECHNIK GMBH—See EVN AG; *Int'l*, pg. 2571
WTE WASSERTECHNIK (POLSKA) SP. Z O.O.—See EVN AG; *Int'l*, pg. 2571
WT FINANCIAL GROUP LIMITED; *Int'l*, pg. 8498
WTG EXPLORATION, INC.—See J.L. Davis Companies; *U.S. Private*, pg. 2167
WT GROUP HOLDINGS LIMITED; *Int'l*, pg. 8498

WT GROUP HOLDINGS LIMITED

W.T. HARVEY LUMBER CO., INC.—See Tyndale Advisors, LLC; *U.S. Private*, pg. 4268
W.T. HENLEY LIMITED—See TT Electronics plc; *Int'l*, pg. 7959
WTHI-FM—See Midwest Communications, Inc.; *U.S. Private*, pg. 2720
WT HOWARD FUNERAL SERVICES PTY LTD—See Propel Funeral Partners Limited; *Int'l*, pg. 5997
WTHR-TV—See TEGNA Inc.; *U.S. Public*, pg. 1991
WTI ADVANCED TECHNOLOGY LIMITED—See Tata Sons Limited; *Int'l*, pg. 7470
WTIC-TV—See Nexstar Media Group, Inc.; *U.S. Public*, pg. 1524
WTI TRANSPORT, INC.—See Daseke, Inc.; *U.S. Private*, pg. 1162
WTK-ELEKTRONIK GMBH—See Trimble, Inc.; *U.S. Public*, pg. 2190
W T K HOLDINGS BERHAD; *Int'l*, pg. 8320
WTKR-TV—See Nexstar Media Group, Inc.; *U.S. Public*, pg. 1525
WTKS REAL RADIO 104 1 FM—See iHeartMedia, Inc.; *U.S. Public*, pg. 1097
WT MICROELECTRONICS CO., LTD.; *Int'l*, pg. 8498
WT MICROELECTRONICS (HK) LTD.—See WT Microelectronics Co., Ltd.; *Int'l*, pg. 8498
WT MICROELECTRONICS INDIA PRIVATE LIMITED—See WT Microelectronics Co., Ltd.; *Int'l*, pg. 8498
WT MICROELECTRONICS KOREA CO., LTD.—See WT Microelectronics Co., Ltd.; *Int'l*, pg. 8498
WT MICROELECTRONICS (SHANGHAI) CO., LTD.—See WT Microelectronics Co., Ltd.; *Int'l*, pg. 8498
WT MICROELECTRONICS (SHENZHEN) CO., LTD.—See WT Microelectronics Co., Ltd.; *Int'l*, pg. 8498
WT MICROELECTRONICS SINGAPORE PTE. LTD.—See WT Microelectronics Co., Ltd.; *Int'l*, pg. 8498
WT MICROELECTRONICS (THAILAND) CO., LTD.—See WT Microelectronics Co., Ltd.; *Int'l*, pg. 8498
WT MICROELETRCONICS (MALAYSIA) SDN., BHD.—See WT Microelectronics Co., Ltd.; *Int'l*, pg. 8498
WTN SERVICES LLC—See 1-800-FLOWERS.COM, Inc.; *U.S. Public*, pg. 1
WTOC, LLC—See Gray Television, Inc.; *U.S. Public*, pg. 960
W&T OFFSHORE INC.; *U.S. Public*, pg. 2315
W TOKYO INC.—See Vector Inc.; *Int'l*, pg. 8144
WTOL, LLC—See TEGNA Inc.; *U.S. Public*, pg. 1991
WTOV, INC.—See Sinclair, Inc.; *U.S. Public*, pg. 1887
WTP PLETTENBERG GMBH & CO. KG; *Int'l*, pg. 8499
WTRF-TV, LLC—See Nexstar Media Group, Inc.; *U.S. Public*, pg. 1523
WT SA; *Int'l*, pg. 8499
WTS INTERNATIONAL, INC.—See CI Capital Partners LLC; *U.S. Private*, pg. 896
WTS PARADIGM LLC—See Builders FirstSource, Inc.; *U.S. Public*, pg. 410
WTSP-TV—See TEGNA Inc.; *U.S. Public*, pg. 1991
WTTA-TV—See Nexstar Media Group, Inc.; *U.S. Public*, pg. 1523
WTT CAMPUSONE GMBH—See EnBW Energie Baden-Wurttemberg AG; *Int'l*, pg. 2400
WTTG-TV—See Fox Corporation; *U.S. Public*, pg. 876
WTT HK LIMITED—See MBK Partners Ltd.; *Int'l*, pg. 4754
WTT HK LIMITED—See TPG Capital, L.P.; *U.S. Public*, pg. 2177
WTTO, INC.—See Sinclair, Inc.; *U.S. Public*, pg. 1887
WTTO LICENSEE, LLC—See Sinclair, Inc.; *U.S. Public*, pg. 1887
WTTV-TV—See Nexstar Media Group, Inc.; *U.S. Public*, pg. 1525
WTU RETAIL ENERGY LP—See NRG Energy, Inc.; *U.S. Public*, pg. 1550
WTVC-TV—See Sinclair, Inc.; *U.S. Public*, pg. 1887
WTVD-TV INC.—See The Walt Disney Company; *U.S. Public*, pg. 2138
WTVG, INC.—See SJL Broadcast Management Corp.; *U.S. Private*, pg. 3678
WTVH, LLC—See Silver Point Capital, L.P.; *U.S. Private*, pg. 3662
WTVJ-TV—See Comcast Corporation; *U.S. Public*, pg. 540
WTVO-TV—See Mission Broadcasting, Inc.; *U.S. Private*, pg. 2747
WTVQ-TV—See Morris Multimedia, Inc.; *U.S. Private*, pg. 2788
WTVR, LLC—See Nexstar Media Group, Inc.; *U.S. Public*, pg. 1525
WTVT-TV—See Fox Corporation; *U.S. Public*, pg. 876
WTVX-TV—See Sinclair, Inc.; *U.S. Public*, pg. 1887
WTVZ, INC.—See Sinclair, Inc.; *U.S. Public*, pg. 1887
WTW ARCHITECT, INC.—See AE Works Ltd.; *U.S. Private*, pg. 112
WTW-BETEILIGUNGSGESELLSCHAFT MBH; *Int'l*, pg. 8499
WTWC-TV—See Sinclair, Inc.; *U.S. Public*, pg. 1887
WTWH MEDIA, LLC; *U.S. Private*, pg. 4574
WTW SERVICES SPOLKA Z OGRANICZONA ODPOWIEDZIALNOSCIA—See Willis Towers Watson Public Limited Company; *Int'l*, pg. 8415

WTXF-TV—See Fox Corporation; *U.S. Public*, pg. 876
WU BA SUPERIOR PRODUCTS HOLDING GROUP, INC.; *U.S. Private*, pg. 4574
WUBBEN HANDELSMIJ B.V.—See Avista Oil AG; *Int'l*, pg. 745
WUBS PAYMENTS LTD.—See The Western Union Company; *U.S. Public*, pg. 2141
WUCATO MARKETPLACE GMBH—See Wurth Verwaltungsgesellschaft mbH; *Int'l*, pg. 8508
WUCHANG SHIPBUILDING INDUSTRY CO., LTD.—See China Shipbuilding Industry Company Limited; *Int'l*, pg. 1551
WUCHAN ZHONGDA GERON CO., LTD.; *Int'l*, pg. 8499
WUCHAN ZHONGDA GROUP CO., LTD.; *Int'l*, pg. 8499
WUCW-TV—See Sinclair, Inc.; *U.S. Public*, pg. 1887
WUDA GEOINFORMATICS CO., LTD.—See Taoping Inc.; *Int'l*, pg. 7461
WUENSCHE HANDELSGESELLSCHAFT INTERNATIONAL MBH & CO. KG; *Int'l*, pg. 8499
WUERTH ELECTRONIC TIANJIN CO., LTD.—See Wurth Verwaltungsgesellschaft mbH; *Int'l*, pg. 8510
WUERTH ELEKTRONIK INDIA PVT. LTD.—See Wurth Verwaltungsgesellschaft mbH; *Int'l*, pg. 8509
WUERTH INDIA PVT. LTD.—See Wurth Verwaltungsgesellschaft mbH; *Int'l*, pg. 8509
WUERTH KAZAKHSTAN LTD.—See Wurth Verwaltungsgesellschaft mbH; *Int'l*, pg. 8509
WUERTH KENYA LTD.—See Wurth Verwaltungsgesellschaft mbH; *Int'l*, pg. 8509
WUERTH (MALAYSIA) SDN. BHD.—See Wurth Verwaltungsgesellschaft mbH; *Int'l*, pg. 8509
WUERTH PHILIPPINES, INC.—See Wurth Verwaltungsgesellschaft mbH; *Int'l*, pg. 8509
WUERTTEMBERGISCHE LEBENSVERSICHERUNG AG—See Wuestenrot & Wuerttembergische AG; *Int'l*, pg. 8499
WUESTENROT BANK AG PFANDBRIEFBANK—See Wuestenrot & Wuerttembergische AG; *Int'l*, pg. 8499
WUESTENROT BAUSPARKASSE AG—See Wuestenrot & Wuerttembergische AG; *Int'l*, pg. 8499
WUESTENROT GRUNDSTUECKSVERWERTUNGS-GMBH—See Wuestenrot & Wuerttembergische AG; *Int'l*, pg. 8499
WUESTENROT INTERNATIONAL MANAGEMENT-GESELLSCHAFT AG—See Wuestenrot & Wuerttembergische AG; *Int'l*, pg. 8499
WUESTENROT STAEDTEBAU UND ENTWICKLUNGSGESELLSCHAFT MBH—See Wuestenrot & Wuerttembergische AG; *Int'l*, pg. 8499
WUESTENROT STAVEBNI SPORITELNA A.S.—See MONETA Money Bank a.s.; *Int'l*, pg. 5032
WUESTENROT & WUERTTEMBERGISCHE AG; *Int'l*, pg. 8499
WUEST'S INC.; *U.S. Private*, pg. 4574
WUEST'S OF SAN MARCOS—See Wuest's Inc.; *U.S. Private*, pg. 4575
WUHAI CNG SPECIAL GLASS COMPANY LIMITED—See China Glass Holdings Limited; *Int'l*, pg. 1504
WUHAI GUANGYU CHEMICAL METALLURGY CO., LTD.—See Hongda Xingye Co., Ltd.; *Int'l*, pg. 3470
WUHAN ACCELINK POLYTRON TECHNOLOGIES INC—See Accelink Technologies Co., Ltd.; *Int'l*, pg. 80
WUHAN AUTO PARTS ALLIANCE (CHINA) CO., LTD.—See G-TEKT Corporation; *Int'l*, pg. 2864
WUHAN BAOSTEEL METAL DECORATING CO., LTD.—See Shanghai Baosteel Packaging Co., Ltd.; *Int'l*, pg. 6762
WUHAN BAOZE AUTOMOBILE SALES SERVICES CO., LTD.—See China ZhengTong Auto Services Holdings Limited; *Int'l*, pg. 1567
WUHAN BIOCAUSE PHARMACEUTICAL DEVELOPMENT CO., LTD.—See Hubei Biocause Pharmaceutical Co., Ltd.; *Int'l*, pg. 3517
WUHAN BOILER COMPANY LIMITED—See General Electric Company; *U.S. Public*, pg. 918
WUHAN CHANGYUAN LANGHONG TECHNOLOGY CO., LTD.—See Xiangyang Changyuan Donggu Industrial Co., Ltd.; *Int'l*, pg. 8527
WUHAN CHIA TAI CO., LTD.—See Charoen Pokphand Foods Public Company Limited; *Int'l*, pg. 1453
WUHAN CITY CIRCLE (XIANTAO) URBAN MINERAL RESOURCES MARKET CO., LTD.—See GEM Co., Ltd.; *Int'l*, pg. 2914
WUHAN CLARION KOTEI SOFTWARE TECHNOLOGY CO., LTD.—See Wuhan Kotei Informatics Co., Ltd.; *Int'l*, pg. 8501
WUHAN CML GRANDLINK LOGISTICS CO., LTD.—See China Master Logistics Co., Ltd.; *Int'l*, pg. 1518
WUHAN C&Y E-COMMERCE CO., LTD.—See Shanxi C&Y Pharmaceutical Group Co., Ltd.; *Int'l*, pg. 6786
WUHAN DDMC CULTURE & SPORTS CO., LTD.; *Int'l*, pg. 8500
WUHAN DEPARTMENT STORE GROUP CO., LTD.; *Int'l*, pg. 8500
WUHAN DR LASER TECHNOLOGY CO., LTD.; *Int'l*, pg. 8500
WUHAN EAST LAKE HIGH TECHNOLOGY GROUP CO., LTD.; *Int'l*, pg. 8500

CORPORATE AFFILIATIONS

WUHAN EASYDIAGNOSIS BIOMEDICINE CO., LTD.; *Int'l*, pg. 8500
WUHAN FAR EASTERN NEW MATERIAL LTD.—See The Far Eastern Group; *Int'l*, pg. 7642
WUHAN FINGU ELECTRONIC TECHNOLOGY CO., LTD.; *Int'l*, pg. 8500
WUHAN FUBOHE AUTO PARTS CO., LTD.—See Hanwa Co., Ltd.; *Int'l*, pg. 3263
WUHAN FURUKAWA AUTOMOTIVE SYSTEMS CO., LTD.—See The Furukawa Electric Co., Ltd.; *Int'l*, pg. 7647
WUHAN FUTURE CITY HOTEL MANAGEMENT COMPANY LIMITED—See China City Infrastructure Group Limited; *Int'l*, pg. 1489
WUHAN FUTURE CITY PROPERTY MANAGEMENT COMPANY LIMITED—See China City Infrastructure Group Limited; *Int'l*, pg. 1489
WUHAN GEM RESOURCES RECYCLING CO., LTD—See GEM Co., Ltd.; *Int'l*, pg. 2914
WUHAN GENERAL GROUP (CHINA), INC.; *Int'l*, pg. 8500
WUHAN GLOBAL SENSOR TECHNOLOGY CO., LTD.—See Wuhan Guide Infrared Co., Ltd.; *Int'l*, pg. 8500
WUHAN GOLDEN LASER CO., LTD.; *Int'l*, pg. 8500
WUHAN GOME ELECTRICAL APPLIANCE COMPANY LIMITED—See Gome Retail Holdings Limited; *Int'l*, pg. 3037
WUHAN GRAND HOYO COMPANY LIMITED—See Grand Pharmaceutical Group Limited; *Int'l*, pg. 3056
WUHAN GUIDE INFRARED CO., LTD.; *Int'l*, pg. 8500
WUHAN GUIDE SENSMART TECH CO., LTD.—See Wuhan Guide Infrared Co., Ltd.; *Int'l*, pg. 8500
WUHAN HANFU SUPERMARKET CO. LTD—See Carrefour SA; *Int'l*, pg. 1344
WUHAN HANNENGTONG NEW ENERGY VEHICLE SERVICE CO., LTD.—See GEM Co., Ltd.; *Int'l*, pg. 2914
WUHAN HANREN ELECTRONIC CO., LTD.—See Shenzhen Deren Electronic Co., Ltd.; *Int'l*, pg. 6808
WUHAN HIROYOSHI AUTOMOTIVE TRIM CO., LTD.—See Hiroca Holdings Ltd.; *Int'l*, pg. 3404
WUHAN HITECK BIOLOGICAL PHARMA CO., LTD.; *Int'l*, pg. 8500
WUHAN HONGLIN ELECTRONIC CO., LTD.—See InvesTech Holdings Limited; *Int'l*, pg. 3778
WUHAN HONGXIN COMMUNICATION TECHNOLOGIES CO., LTD.—See FiberHome Technologies Group; *Int'l*, pg. 2652
WUHAN HUAKANG CENTURY MEDICAL CO., LTD.; *Int'l*, pg. 8500
WUHAN HUALONG HIGHWAY RESOURCES COMPANY LIMITED—See Shanghai Dasheng Agriculture Finance Technology Co., Ltd.; *Int'l*, pg. 6764
WUHAN HUAZHONG NUMERICAL CONTROL CO., LTD.; *Int'l*, pg. 8500
WUHAN HVSEN BIOTECHNOLOGY CO., LTD.; *Int'l*, pg. 8500
WUHAN INFOCHAMP I.T. CO., LTD.—See China Steel Corporation; *Int'l*, pg. 1556
WUHAN INTERNATIONAL CONTAINER COMPANY LIMITED—See China Infrastructure & Logistics Group Ltd.; *Int'l*, pg. 1510
WUHAN IRON & STEEL CO., LTD.—See China Baowu Steel Group Corp., Ltd.; *Int'l*, pg. 1485
WUHAN JINGCE ELECTRONIC GROUP CO., LTD.; *Int'l*, pg. 8500
WUHAN JIN JIANG INTERNATIONAL HOTEL COMPANY LIMITED—See Shanghai Jin Jiang Capital Company Limited; *Int'l*, pg. 6772
WUHAN JINRONG ELECTROMECHANICAL CO., LTD.—See Tianjin Jinrong Tianyu Precision Machinery, Inc.; *Int'l*, pg. 7739
WUHAN KAIDI WATER MANAGEMENT & OPERATION CO., LTD.—See SIIC Environment Holdings Ltd.; *Int'l*, pg. 6913
WUHAN KAIDI WATER PROJECT & ENGINEERING CO., LTD.—See SIIC Environment Holdings Ltd.; *Int'l*, pg. 6913
WUHAN KAIDI WATER SERVICES CO., LTD.—See Darco Water Technologies Limited; *Int'l*, pg. 1972
WUHAN KAWASAKI MARINE MACHINERY CO., LTD.—See Kawasaki Heavy Industries, Ltd.; *Int'l*, pg. 4098
WUHAN KEQIAN BIOLOGY CO., LTD.; *Int'l*, pg. 8500
WUHAN KERNEL BIO-TECHNOLOGY CO., LTD.—See Grand Pharmaceutical Group Limited; *Int'l*, pg. 3056
WUHAN KINGFA SCI & TECH CO., LTD.—See Kingfa Sci &Tech Co., Ltd.; *Int'l*, pg. 4172
WUHAN KINGOLD JEWELRY COMPANY LIMITED—See Kingold Jewelry, Inc.; *Int'l*, pg. 4174
WUHAN KOTEI INFORMATICS CO., LTD.; *Int'l*, pg. 8500
WUHAN KUANGDA AUTOMOBILE FABRIC CO., LTD.—See Kuangda Technology Group Co., Ltd.; *Int'l*, pg. 4319
WUHAN LANGDE ELECTRICS CO., LTD.—See Sun.King Technology Group Limited; *Int'l*, pg. 7309
WUHAN LASERWARE LASER TECHNOLOGY CO., LTD.—See Key Ware Electronics Co., Ltd.; *Int'l*, pg. 4145
WUHAN LIGONG GUANGKE CO.,LTD.; *Int'l*, pg. 8501

WUHAN LINCONTROL AUTOMOTIVE ELECTRONICS CO., LTD.; *Int'l*, pg. 8501
WUHAN LONGKING EP TECHNOLOGIES CO., LTD—See Fujian Longking Co., Ltd.; *Int'l*, pg. 2818
WUHAN LUZE AUTOMOBILE SALES SERVICES CO., LTD.—See China ZhengTong Auto Services Holdings Limited; *Int'l*, pg. 1567
WUHAN MARUJUN CO., LTD.—See J-MAX Co., Ltd.; *Int'l*, pg. 3854
WUHAN MECAPLAST CO LTD—See Equistone Partners Europe Limited; *Int'l*, pg. 2487
WUHAN MINGJIE MOULD & PLASTIC CO., LTD.—See Jiangnan Mould & Plastic Technology Co., Ltd.; *Int'l*, pg. 3943
WUHAN MINHUI AUTO PARTS CO., LTD.—See Minth Group Limited; *Int'l*, pg. 4914
WUHAN MORIROKU TECHNOLOGY CO., LTD.—See Moriroku Holdings Company, Ltd.; *Int'l*, pg. 5047
WUHAN NANTIAN COMPUTER SYSTEM CO., LTD.—See Yunnan Nantian Electronics Information Co., Ltd.; *Int'l*, pg. 8616
WUHAN NATURAL GAS COMPANY LIMITED—See Henderson Land Development Co. Ltd.; *Int'l*, pg. 3344
WUHAN NATURE'S FAVOUR BIOENGINEEING COMPANY LIMITED—See Wai Kee Holdings Limited; *Int'l*, pg. 8331
WUHAN NISSEI DISPLAY SYSTEM CO., LTD.—See Nippon Seiki Co., Ltd.; *Int'l*, pg. 5330
WUHAN NUSUN LANDSCAPE CO., LTD.; *Int'l*, pg. 8501
WUHAN OWENS GLASS CONTAINER COMPANY LIMITED—See O-I Glass, Inc.; *U.S. Public*, pg. 1559
WUHAN PARKERIZING CHEMICAL CO., LTD.—See Nihon Parkerizing Co., Ltd.; *Int'l*, pg. 5287
WUHAN PIOLAX CO., LTD.—See Piolax Inc.; *Int'l*, pg. 5871
WUHAN PROLTO SUPPLY CHAIN MANAGEMENT CO., LTD.—See Shenzhen Prolto Supply Chain Management Co., Ltd.; *Int'l*, pg. 6819
WUHAN P&S INFORMATION TECHNOLOGY CO., LTD.; *Int'l*, pg. 8501
WUHAN QINTAI GRAND THEATRE MANAGEMENT CORPORATION LIMITED—See Poly Culture Group Corporation Limited; *Int'l*, pg. 5914
WUHAN RAYCUS FIBER LASER TECHNOLOGIES CO., LTD.; *Int'l*, pg. 8501
WUHAN RISONG HOKUTO AUTOMOTIVE EQUIPMENT CO., LTD.—See Guangzhou Risong Intelligent Technology Holding Co., Ltd.; *Int'l*, pg. 3167
WUHAN SAILI SI MEDICAL TECHNOLOGY CO., LTD; *Int'l*, pg. 8501
WUHAN SANKO GOSEI CO., LTD.—See Sanko Gosei Ltd.; *Int'l*, pg. 6542
WUHAN SANTE CABLEWAYS GROUP CO., LTD.; *Int'l*, pg. 8501
WUHAN SANYONG GEM AUTO PARTS REMANUFACTURING CO., LTD.—See GEM Co., Ltd.; *Int'l*, pg. 2914
WUHAN SANZHEN INDUSTRY HOLDING CO., LTD.; *Int'l*, pg. 8501
WUHAN SCHLEMMER AUTOMOTIVE PARTS CO., LTD.—See Ningbo Huaxiang Electronic Co., Ltd.; *Int'l*, pg. 5302
WUHAN SHIJIA PHOTOELECTRIC TECHNOLOGY CO., LTD.—See Henan Shijia Photons Technology Co., Ltd.; *Int'l*, pg. 3343
WUHAN SHUI ON TIANDI PROPERTY DEVELOPMENT CO., LTD.—See Shui On Company Limited; *Int'l*, pg. 6869
WUHAN SOWA AUTO PARTS CO., LTD.—See TS Tech Co Ltd; *Int'l*, pg. 7948
WUHAN STANLEY ELECTRIC CO., LTD.—See Stanley Electric Co., Ltd.; *Int'l*, pg. 7171
WUHAN SUMIDEN WIRING SYSTEMS CO., LTD.—See Sumitomo Electric Industries, Ltd.; *Int'l*, pg. 7285
WUHAN SUNWILL ELECTRIC CO., LTD.—See Guangdong Sunwill Precising Plastic Co., Ltd.; *Int'l*, pg. 3160
WUHAN SUPOR CO. LTD.—See SEB S.A.; *Int'l*, pg. 6668
WUHAN SYP KANGQIAO AUTOGLASS CO., LTD.—See Shanghai Yaohua Pilkington Glass Group Co., Ltd.; *Int'l*, pg. 6782
WUHAN TECOM CO., LTD.—See Teco Electric & Machinery Co., Ltd.; *Int'l*, pg. 7518
WUHAN TENGLONG UNITED AUTO ACCESSORIES MANUFACTURING CO., LTD.—See Changzhou Tenglong Auto Parts Co., Ltd.; *Int'l*, pg. 1445
WUHAN TIANHE TECHNOLOGY CO., LTD.—See Guodian Nanjing Automation Co., Ltd.; *Int'l*, pg. 3186
WUHAN TIANYUAN ENVIRONMENTAL PROTECTION CO., LTD.; *Int'l*, pg. 8501
WUHAN TIANYU INFORMATION INDUSTRY CO., LTD.; *Int'l*, pg. 8501
WUHAN TINGYI FOOD CO., LTD.—See Tingyi (Cayman Islands) Holding Corp.; *Int'l*, pg. 7754
WUHAN TOPWIN OPTOELECTRONICS TECHNOLOGY CO.—See MKS Instruments, Inc.; *U.S. Public*, pg. 1452
WUHAN TS-GSK AUTO PARTS CO., LTD.—See TS Tech Co Ltd; *Int'l*, pg. 7948
WUHAN VANKE REAL ESTATE COMPANY LIMITED—See China Vanke Co., Ltd.; *Int'l*, pg. 1562

WUHAN WEIFU LIDA CATALYTIC CONVERTER CO., LTD.—See Wuxi Weifu High-technology Co., Ltd.; *Int'l*, pg. 8516
WUHAN WOOSHIN MACHINERY CO., LTD.—See Wooshin Systems Co., Ltd.; *Int'l*, pg. 8455
WUHAN WUYAO PHARMACEUTICAL CO., LTD.—See Grand Pharmaceutical Group Limited; *Int'l*, pg. 3056
WUHAN XIANGDA CAMEL FEED CO., LTD.—See Tangrenshen Group Co., Ltd.; *Int'l*, pg. 7458
WUHAN XIANGLONG POWER INDUSTRY CO., LTD.; *Int'l*, pg. 8501
WUHAN XINGTU XINKE ELECTRONICS CO., LTD.; *Int'l*, pg. 8501
WUHAN XINYUAN SEMICONDUCTOR CO., LTD.—See Wuhan P&S Information Technology Co., Ltd.; *Int'l*, pg. 8501
WUHAN YANGTZE COMMUNICATIONS INDUSTRY GROUP CO.; *Int'l*, pg. 8501
WUHAN YANGTZE LED LIGHTING TECHNOLOGY CO., LTD.—See Wuhan Yangtze Communications Industry Group Co.; *Int'l*, pg. 8502
WUHAN YOROZU BAO MIT AUTOMOTIVE CO., LTD.—See Yorozu Corporation; *Int'l*, pg. 8599
WUHAN YUNJINGFEI OPTICAL FIBER MATERIALS CO., LTD.—See Yunnan Lincang Xinyuan Germanium Industrial Co., Ltd.; *Int'l*, pg. 8615
WUHAN YUTO PRINTING & PACKAGING CO., LTD.—See Shenzhen YUTO Packaging Technology Co., Ltd.; *Int'l*, pg. 6825
WUHAN ZHENGTONG YUECHI AUTOMOBILE SALES SERVICES CO., LTD.—See China ZhengTong Auto Services Holdings Limited; *Int'l*, pg. 1567
WUHAN ZHONGSHENG JUXING AUTOMOBILE SALES & SERVICE CO., LTD.—See Zhongsheng Group Holdings Limited; *Int'l*, pg. 8674
WUHAN ZHONGYUAN HUADIAN; *Int'l*, pg. 8502
WUHE ZHONGYU GAS CO.—See Zhongyu Energy Holdings Limited; *Int'l*, pg. 8676
WUHF-TV—See Sinclair, Inc.; *U.S. Public*, pg. 1887
WU HOLDCO, INC.—See TA Associates, Inc.; *U.S. Private*, pg. 3919
WU HOLDCO, INC.—See The Carlyle Group Inc.; *U.S. Public*, pg. 2057
WUHU 37 INTERACTIVE ENTERTAINMENT NETWORK TECHNOLOGY GROUP CO., LTD.; *Int'l*, pg. 8502
WUHUAN ENGINEERING CO., LTD.—See China National Chemical Engineering Co., Ltd.; *Int'l*, pg. 1531
WUHU ANRUI OPTOELECTRONICS CO., LTD.—See San'an Optoelectronics Co., Ltd.; *Int'l*, pg. 6522
WUHU BENTELER-POSCO AUTOMOTIVE CO., LTD.—See Benteler International AG; *Int'l*, pg. 977
WUHU CHANGCHUN AUTOMOTIVE INTERIORS CO., LTD.—See Jiangsu Changshu Automotive Trim Group Co., Ltd.; *Int'l*, pg. 3945
WUHU CIMC RUIJIANG AUTOMOBILE CO LTD—See China International Marine Containers (Group) Co., Ltd.; *Int'l*, pg. 1512
WUHU CJ ELECTRICAL SYSTEM CO., LTD.—See Pan-International Industrial Corporation; *Int'l*, pg. 5716
WUHU EFTEC CHEMICAL PRODUCTS LTD.—See EMS-Chemie Holding AG; *Int'l*, pg. 2394
WUHU FEISHANG MINING DEVELOPMENT CO., LTD.—See China Natural Resources, Inc.; *Int'l*, pg. 1534
WUHU FUCHUN DYE & WEAVE CO., LTD.; *Int'l*, pg. 8502
WUHU NEW UNIVERSAL ENVIRONMENTAL SCIENCE & TECHNOLOGY CO., LTD.—See Beijing New Universal Science and Technology Co., Ltd.; *Int'l*, pg. 954
WUHU STERLING STEERING SYSTEM CO., LTD.—See Zhejiang Shibao Company Limited; *Int'l*, pg. 8663
WUHU TENGLONG AUTO PARTS CO., LTD.—See Changzhou Tenglong Auto Parts Co., Ltd.; *Int'l*, pg. 1445
WUHU TOKEN SCIENCES CO., LTD.; *Int'l*, pg. 8502
WUHU VALEO AUTOMOTIVE LIGHTING SYSTEMS CO. LTD.—See Valeo S.A.; *Int'l*, pg. 8115
WUHU VANKE REAL ESTATE COMPANY LIMITED—See China Vanke Co., Ltd.; *Int'l*, pg. 1562
WUJIANG DAFA REAL ESTATE DEVELOPMENT CO., LTD.—See Thakral Corp. Ltd.; *Int'l*, pg. 7598
WUJIANG MITSUMI ELECTRONICS CO., LTD.—See Minebea Mitsumi Inc.; *Int'l*, pg. 4904
WUJIANG SIGMATRON ELECTRONICS CO., LTD.—See SigmaTron International, Inc.; *U.S. Public*, pg. 1878
WUJIANG TRANSFORMER CO., LTD.—See Shanghai Electric Group Company Limited; *Int'l*, pg. 6766
WUJIANG WANFENG PLASTIC CEMENT CO., LTD.—See Copartner Technology Corporation; *Int'l*, pg. 1793
WULCO INC.; *U.S. Private*, pg. 4575
WULFF BELTTON AB—See Wulff-Group Plc; *Int'l*, pg. 8503
WULFF BELTTON—See Wulff-Group Plc; *Int'l*, pg. 8503
WULFF CARE—See Wulff-Group Plc; *Int'l*, pg. 8503
WULFF DIRECT AS—See Wulff-Group Plc; *Int'l*, pg. 8503
WULFF ENTRE OY—See Wulff-Group Plc; *Int'l*, pg. 8503
WULFF-GROUP PLC; *Int'l*, pg. 8502
WULFF OY AB—See Wulff-Group Plc; *Int'l*, pg. 8503

WULFF SUPPLIES A/S—See Wulff-Group Plc; *Int'l*, pg. 8503
WULFF VISUAL GLOBE OY—See Wulff-Group Plc; *Int'l*, pg. 8503
WULFF YHTIOT OYJ; *Int'l*, pg. 8502
WULF GAERTNER AUTOPARTS AG; *Int'l*, pg. 8502
WULF GAERTNER AUTOPARTS (M) SDN BHD—See Wulf Gaertner Autoparts AG; *Int'l*, pg. 8502
WULF GAERTNER AUTOPARTS (S) PTE LTD—See Wulf Gaertner Autoparts AG; *Int'l*, pg. 8502
WULF GAERTNER AUTOPARTS (THAILAND) LTD—See Wulf Gaertner Autoparts AG; *Int'l*, pg. 8502
WULIANGYE YIBIN CO., LTD.; *Int'l*, pg. 8503
WULING ELECTRIC CO., LTD.—See Shihlin Electric & Engineering Corp.; *Int'l*, pg. 6829
WULING MOTORS HOLDINGS LIMITED; *Int'l*, pg. 8503
WU LING POWER CORPORATION—See China Power International Development Limited; *Int'l*, pg. 1542
WULSER LOSTORF AG—See Burkhalter Holding AG; *Int'l*, pg. 1226
WULSER ZOFINGEN AG—See Burkhalter Holding AG; *Int'l*, pg. 1226
WUMART STORES, INC.—See Beijing Jingxi Culture & Tourism Co., Ltd.; *Int'l*, pg. 953
WUNDER-BAR DISPENSING UK LTD.—See The Middleby Corporation; *U.S. Public*, pg. 2115
WUNDER-BAR INTERNATIONAL, INC.—See The Middleby Corporation; *U.S. Public*, pg. 2115
WUNDERKIND, LLC; *U.S. Private*, pg. 4575
WUNDERKNABEN KOMMUNIKATION GMBH—See ASM Group S.A.; *Int'l*, pg. 625
WUNDERLICH-MALEC ENGINEERING, INC.; *U.S. Private*, pg. 4575
WUNDERMAN BEIJING—See WPP plc; *Int'l*, pg. 8482
WUNDERMAN DENTSU INC.—See Dentsu Group Inc.; *Int'l*, pg. 2040
WUNDERMAN DIRECT—See WPP plc; *Int'l*, pg. 8482
WUNDERMAN INTERACTIVE—See WPP plc; *Int'l*, pg. 8482
WUNDERMAN KOREA—See WPP plc; *Int'l*, pg. 8482
WUNDERMAN LIMITED—See WPP plc; *Int'l*, pg. 8483
WUNDERMAN SEATTLE—See WPP plc; *Int'l*, pg. 8483
WUNDERMAN—See WPP plc; *Int'l*, pg. 8482
WUNDERMAN—See WPP plc; *Int'l*, pg. 8482
WUNDERMAN—See WPP plc; *Int'l*, pg. 8482
WUNDERMAN—See WPP plc; *Int'l*, pg. 8482
WUNDERMAN—See WPP plc; *Int'l*, pg. 8482
WUNDERMAN—See WPP plc; *Int'l*, pg. 8482
WUNDERMAN—See WPP plc; *Int'l*, pg. 8482
WUNDERMAN—See WPP plc; *Int'l*, pg. 8482
WUNDERMAN—See WPP plc; *Int'l*, pg. 8482
WUNDERMAN—See WPP plc; *Int'l*, pg. 8482
WUNDERMAN—See WPP plc; *Int'l*, pg. 8482
WUNDERMAN—See WPP plc; *Int'l*, pg. 8482
WUNDERMAN—See WPP plc; *Int'l*, pg. 8482
WUNDERMAN—See WPP plc; *Int'l*, pg. 8482
WUNDERMAN—See WPP plc; *Int'l*, pg. 8482
WUNDERMAN—See WPP plc; *Int'l*, pg. 8482
WUNDERMAN—See WPP plc; *Int'l*, pg. 8482
WUNDERMAN—See WPP plc; *Int'l*, pg. 8482
WUNDERMAN—See WPP plc; *Int'l*, pg. 8482
WUNDERMAN—See WPP plc; *Int'l*, pg. 8482
WUNDERMAN—See WPP plc; *Int'l*, pg. 8482
WUNDERMAN—See WPP plc; *Int'l*, pg. 8482
WUNDERMAN—See WPP plc; *Int'l*, pg. 8482
WUNDERMAN—See WPP plc; *Int'l*, pg. 8482
WUNDERMAN—See WPP plc; *Int'l*, pg. 8482
WUNDERMAN—See WPP plc; *Int'l*, pg. 8482
WUNDERMAN—See WPP plc; *Int'l*, pg. 8482
WUNDERMAN—See WPP plc; *Int'l*, pg. 8482
WUNDERMAN—See WPP plc; *Int'l*, pg. 8482
WUNDERMAN—See WPP plc; *Int'l*, pg. 8482
WUNDERMAN—See WPP plc; *Int'l*, pg. 8482
WUNDERMAN TEAM DETROIT—See WPP plc; *Int'l*, pg. 8483
WUNDERMAN THOMPSON - GUANGZHOU—See WPP plc; *Int'l*, pg. 8483
WUNDERMAN THOMPSON—See WPP plc; *Int'l*, pg. 8483
WUNONG ASIA PACIFIC COMPANY LIMITED; *Int'l*, pg. 8503
WUNSCHENDORFER DOLOMITWERK GMBH; *Int'l*, pg. 8503
WUPPERMANN AG; *Int'l*, pg. 8503
WUPPERMANN AUSTRIA GMBH—See Wuppermann AG; *Int'l*, pg. 8503
WUPPERMANN BANDSTAHL GMBH—See Wuppermann AG; *Int'l*, pg. 8503
WUPPERMANN BUSINESS SERVICES GMBH—See Wuppermann AG; *Int'l*, pg. 8503
WUPPERMANN FRANCE S.A.S.—See Wuppermann AG; *Int'l*, pg. 8503
WUPPERMANN KLB AG—See Wuppermann AG; *Int'l*, pg. 8503

WUPPERMANN AG

WUPPERMANN KOVOTECHNIKA S.R.O.—See Wuppermann AG; *Int'l*, pg. 8503
WUPPERMANN OTEL ROMANIA S.R.L.—See Wuppermann AG; *Int'l*, pg. 8503
WUPPERMANN POLSKA SP. Z O.O.—See Wuppermann AG; *Int'l*, pg. 8503
WUPPERMANN ROHRTECHNIK GMBH—See Wuppermann AG; *Int'l*, pg. 8503
WUPPERMANN TECHNOLOGIES C.V.—See Wuppermann AG; *Int'l*, pg. 8503
WUPPERMANN TUBE & STEEL AB—See Wuppermann AG; *Int'l*, pg. 8503
WUQIAO ZHONGYU GAS CO., LTD.—See Zhongyu Energy Holdings Limited; *Int'l*, pg. 8676
WURFBAIN B.V. - ZAANDAM—See Tong Teik Pte Ltd; *Int'l*, pg. 7806
WURL, INC.—See AppLovin Corp.; *U.S. Public*, pg. 173
WURMSER OGILVY & MATHER—See WPP plc; *Int'l*, pg. 8488
WURO PAPIERVERWERTUNG GMBH & CO KG—See Mayr-Melnhof Karton AG; *Int'l*, pg. 4747
WURTH ADAMS NUT & BOLT COMPANY—See Wurth Verwaltungsgesellschaft mbH; *Int'l*, pg. 8511
WURTH ADAMS NUT & BOLT CO.—See Wurth Verwaltungsgesellschaft mbH; *Int'l*, pg. 8511
WURTH AG—See Wurth Verwaltungsgesellschaft mbH; *Int'l*, pg. 8509
WURTH A ISLANDI EHF.—See Wurth Verwaltungsgesellschaft mbH; *Int'l*, pg. 8513
WURTH ALBANIA LTD.—See Wurth Verwaltungsgesellschaft mbH; *Int'l*, pg. 8509
WURTH ARGENTINA S.A.—See Wurth Verwaltungsgesellschaft mbH; *Int'l*, pg. 8509
WURTH AS—See Wurth Verwaltungsgesellschaft mbH; *Int'l*, pg. 8509
WURTH AUSTRALIA PTY. LTD.—See Wurth Verwaltungsgesellschaft mbH; *Int'l*, pg. 8509
WURTH AVIATION GMBH—See Wurth Verwaltungsgesellschaft mbH; *Int'l*, pg. 8509
WURTH AZERBAIJAN LLC—See Wurth Verwaltungsgesellschaft mbH; *Int'l*, pg. 8509
WURTH BAER SUPPLY CO.—See Wurth Verwaltungsgesellschaft mbH; *Int'l*, pg. 8511
WURTH BAIER & MICHELS ESPANA, S.A.—See Wurth Verwaltungsgesellschaft mbH; *Int'l*, pg. 8509
WURTH BAIER & MICHELS MEXICO SA.DE C.V.—See Wurth Verwaltungsgesellschaft mbH; *Int'l*, pg. 8509
WURTH BAIER MICHELS OTOMOTIV LTD. STI.—See Wurth Verwaltungsgesellschaft mbH; *Int'l*, pg. 8509
WURTH BAIER & MICHELS (SHANGHAI) AUTOMOTIVE FASTENER CO., LTD.—See Wurth Verwaltungsgesellschaft mbH; *Int'l*, pg. 8509
WURTH BELGIE N.V.—See Wurth Verwaltungsgesellschaft mbH; *Int'l*, pg. 8509
WURTH BH D.O.O.—See Wurth Verwaltungsgesellschaft mbH; *Int'l*, pg. 8509
WURTH BULGARIEN E.O.O.D.—See Wurth Verwaltungsgesellschaft mbH; *Int'l*, pg. 8509
WURTH CAMBODIA LTD.—See Wurth Verwaltungsgesellschaft mbH; *Int'l*, pg. 8509
WURTH CANADA LTD., LTEE—See Wurth Verwaltungsgesellschaft mbH; *Int'l*, pg. 8511
WURTH CANARIAS, S.L.—See Wurth Verwaltungsgesellschaft mbH; *Int'l*, pg. 8509
WURTH CARAIBES SARL—See Wurth Verwaltungsgesellschaft mbH; *Int'l*, pg. 8510
WURTH CENTROAMERICA S.A.—See Wurth Verwaltungsgesellschaft mbH; *Int'l*, pg. 8510
WURTH CHILE LTDA.—See Wurth Verwaltungsgesellschaft mbH; *Int'l*, pg. 8509
WURTH (CHINA) CO., LTD.—See Wurth Verwaltungsgesellschaft mbH; *Int'l*, pg. 8509
WURTH (CHINA) HOLDING CO., LTD.—See Wurth Verwaltungsgesellschaft mbH; *Int'l*, pg. 8509
WURTH (CHONGQING) HARDWARE & TOOLS CO., LTD.—See Wurth Verwaltungsgesellschaft mbH; *Int'l*, pg. 8509
WURTH COLOMBIA S.A.—See Wurth Verwaltungsgesellschaft mbH; *Int'l*, pg. 8510
WURTH CO. LTD.—See Wurth Verwaltungsgesellschaft mbH; *Int'l*, pg. 8510
WURTH CONSTRUCTION TOOLS COMMERCIAL (BEIJING) CO., LTD.—See Wurth Verwaltungsgesellschaft mbH; *Int'l*, pg. 8510
WURTH COSTA RICA, S.A.—See Wurth Verwaltungsgesellschaft mbH; *Int'l*, pg. 8510
WURTH DANMARK A/S—See Wurth Verwaltungsgesellschaft mbH; *Int'l*, pg. 8511
WURTH DEL URUGUAY S.A.—See Wurth Verwaltungsgesellschaft mbH; *Int'l*, pg. 8513
WURTH DES MOINES BOLT INC.—See Wurth Verwaltungsgesellschaft mbH; *Int'l*, pg. 8511
WURTH DO BRASIL PECAS DE FIXACAO LTDA.—See Wurth Verwaltungsgesellschaft mbH; *Int'l*, pg. 8513
WURTH DOMINICANA S.A.—See Wurth Verwaltungsgesellschaft mbH; *Int'l*, pg. 8510
WURTH D.O.O.—See Wurth Verwaltungsgesellschaft mbH; *Int'l*, pg. 8513
WURTH D.O.O.—See Wurth Verwaltungsgesellschaft mbH; *Int'l*, pg. 8513
WURTH D.O.O.—See Wurth Verwaltungsgesellschaft mbH; *Int'l*, pg. 8513
WURTH ELECTRONICS AUSTRALIA PTY. LTD.—See Wurth Verwaltungsgesellschaft mbH; *Int'l*, pg. 8510
WURTH ELECTRONICS CO., LTD.—See Wurth Verwaltungsgesellschaft mbH; *Int'l*, pg. 8510
WURTH ELECTRONICS (HK) LIMITED—See Wurth Verwaltungsgesellschaft mbH; *Int'l*, pg. 8510
WURTH ELECTRONICS ICS, INC.—See Wurth Verwaltungsgesellschaft mbH; *Int'l*, pg. 8511
WURTH ELECTRONICS JAPAN CO., LTD.—See Wurth Verwaltungsgesellschaft mbH; *Int'l*, pg. 8510
WURTH ELECTRONICS MIDCOM INC.—See Wurth Verwaltungsgesellschaft mbH; *Int'l*, pg. 8510
WURTH ELECTRONICS SERVICES INDIA PRIVATE LIMITED—See Wurth Verwaltungsgesellschaft mbH; *Int'l*, pg. 8510
WURTH ELECTRONICS (SHENYANG) CO., LTD.—See Wurth Verwaltungsgesellschaft mbH; *Int'l*, pg. 8510
WURTH ELECTRONICS SINGAPORE PTE. LTD.—See Wurth Verwaltungsgesellschaft mbH; *Int'l*, pg. 8510
WURTH ELECTRONICS UK LIMITED—See Wurth Verwaltungsgesellschaft mbH; *Int'l*, pg. 8510
WURTH ELEKTRONIK BELGIE—See Wurth Verwaltungsgesellschaft mbH; *Int'l*, pg. 8510
WURTH ELEKTRONIK CBT INDIA PRIVATE LIMITED—See Wurth Verwaltungsgesellschaft mbH; *Int'l*, pg. 8510
WURTH ELEKTRONIK EISOS CZECH S.R.O.—See Wurth Verwaltungsgesellschaft mbH; *Int'l*, pg. 8511
WURTH ELEKTRONIK EISOS GMBH & CO. KG—See Wurth Verwaltungsgesellschaft mbH; *Int'l*, pg. 8510
WURTH ELEKTRONIK EISOS, IZDELAVA IN PRODAJA ELEK- TRONSKIH TER ELEKTROMEHANSKIH KOMPONENT D.O.O.—See Wurth Verwaltungsgesellschaft mbH; *Int'l*, pg. 8511
WURTH ELEKTRONIK ESPAFIA, S.L.—See Wurth Verwaltungsgesellschaft mbH; *Int'l*, pg. 8510
WURTH ELEKTRONIK FRANCE SARL—See Wurth Verwaltungsgesellschaft mbH; *Int'l*, pg. 8510
WURTH ELEKTRONIK GMBH & CO. KG - CIRCUIT BOARD TECHNOLOGY—See Wurth Verwaltungsgesellschaft mbH; *Int'l*, pg. 8510
WURTH ELEKTRONIK GMBH & CO. KG—See Wurth Verwaltungsgesellschaft mbH; *Int'l*, pg. 8510
WURTH ELEKTRONIK HUNGARY KFT.—See Wurth Verwaltungsgesellschaft mbH; *Int'l*, pg. 8510
WURTH ELEKTRONIK IBE BG EOOD—See Wurth Verwaltungsgesellschaft mbH; *Int'l*, pg. 8511
WURTH ELEKTRONIK IBE GMBH—See Wurth Verwaltungsgesellschaft mbH; *Int'l*, pg. 8511
WURTH ELEKTRONIK ICS GMBH & CO. KG—See Wurth Verwaltungsgesellschaft mbH; *Int'l*, pg. 8510
WURTH ELEKTRONIK ISRAEL LTD.—See Wurth Verwaltungsgesellschaft mbH; *Int'l*, pg. 8510
WURTH ELEKTRONIK ITALIA S.R.L.—See Wurth Verwaltungsgesellschaft mbH; *Int'l*, pg. 8510
WURTH ELEKTRONIK ITHALAT IHRACAT VE TICARET LTD. STI.—See Wurth Verwaltungsgesellschaft mbH; *Int'l*, pg. 8510
WURTH ELEKTRONIK MEXICO S.A. DE C.V.—See Wurth Verwaltungsgesellschaft mbH; *Int'l*, pg. 8510
WURTH ELEKTRONIK NEDERLAND B.V.—See Wurth Verwaltungsgesellschaft mbH; *Int'l*, pg. 8510
WURTH ELEKTRONIK OSTERREICH GMBH—See Wurth Verwaltungsgesellschaft mbH; *Int'l*, pg. 8510
WURTH ELEKTRONIK OY—See Wurth Verwaltungsgesellschaft mbH; *Int'l*, pg. 8510
WURTH ELEKTRONIK POLSKA SP. Z O.O.—See Wurth Verwaltungsgesellschaft mbH; *Int'l*, pg. 8510
WURTH ELEKTRONIK ROT AM SEE GMBH & CO. KG—See Wurth Verwaltungsgesellschaft mbH; *Int'l*, pg. 8510
WURTH ELEKTRONIK RUS OOO—See Wurth Verwaltungsgesellschaft mbH; *Int'l*, pg. 8510
WURTH ELEKTRONIK SCHOPFHEIM GMBH & CO. KG—See Wurth Verwaltungsgesellschaft mbH; *Int'l*, pg. 8510
WURTH ELEKTRONIK (SCHWEIZ) AG—See Wurth Verwaltungsgesellschaft mbH; *Int'l*, pg. 8510
WURTH ELEKTRONIK STELVIO KONTEK S.P.A.—See Wurth Verwaltungsgesellschaft mbH; *Int'l*, pg. 8510
WURTH ELEKTRONIK SWEDEN AB—See Wurth Verwaltungsgesellschaft mbH; *Int'l*, pg. 8510
WURTH ESPANA, S.A.—See Wurth Verwaltungsgesellschaft mbH; *Int'l*, pg. 8511
WURTH FINANCE INTERNATIONAL B.V.—See Wurth Verwaltungsgesellschaft mbH; *Int'l*, pg. 8511
WURTH FINANCIAL SERVICES AG—See Wurth Verwaltungsgesellschaft mbH; *Int'l*, pg. 8511
WURTH FOREIGN SWISS COMPANY LTD.—See Wurth Verwaltungsgesellschaft mbH; *Int'l*, pg. 8511
WURTH FRANCE S.A.—See Wurth Verwaltungsgesellschaft mbH; *Int'l*, pg. 8511
WURTH GEORGIA LTD.—See Wurth Verwaltungsgesellschaft mbH; *Int'l*, pg. 8511
WURTH GROUP OF NORTH AMERICA, INC.—See Wurth Verwaltungsgesellschaft mbH; *Int'l*, pg. 8511
WURTH (GUANGZHOU) INTERNATIONAL TRADING CO., LTD.—See Wurth Verwaltungsgesellschaft mbH; *Int'l*, pg. 8509
WURTH GULF FZE—See Wurth Verwaltungsgesellschaft mbH; *Int'l*, pg. 8511
WURTH HANDELSGESELLSCHAFT M.B.H.—See Wurth Verwaltungsgesellschaft mbH; *Int'l*, pg. 8511
WURTH HELLAS S.A.—See Wurth Verwaltungsgesellschaft mbH; *Int'l*, pg. 8511
WURTH HONG KONG CO., LTD.—See Wurth Verwaltungsgesellschaft mbH; *Int'l*, pg. 8512
WURTH INDONESIA P.T.—See Wurth Verwaltungsgesellschaft mbH; *Int'l*, pg. 8512
WURTH INDUSTRIA ESPANA, S.A.—See Wurth Verwaltungsgesellschaft mbH; *Int'l*, pg. 8512
WURTH INDUSTRIAL SERVICES INDIA PVT. LTD.—See Wurth Verwaltungsgesellschaft mbH; *Int'l*, pg. 8512
WURTH INDUSTRIAL SERVICES MALAYSIA SDN. BHD.—See Wurth Verwaltungsgesellschaft mbH; *Int'l*, pg. 8512
WURTH INDUSTRI DANMARK A/S—See Wurth Verwaltungsgesellschaft mbH; *Int'l*, pg. 8512
WURTH INDUSTRIE FRANCE S.A.S.—See Wurth Verwaltungsgesellschaft mbH; *Int'l*, pg. 8512
WURTH INDUSTRIE SERVICE ENDUSTRIYEL HIZMETLER PAZARLAMA LIMITED SIRKETI—See Wurth Verwaltungsgesellschaft mbH; *Int'l*, pg. 8512
WURTH INDUSTRIE SERVICE GMBH & CO. KG—See Wurth Verwaltungsgesellschaft mbH; *Int'l*, pg. 8512
WURTH INDUSTRI NORGE AS—See Wurth Verwaltungsgesellschaft mbH; *Int'l*, pg. 8512
WURTH INDUSTRY BELGIUM N.V.—See Wurth Verwaltungsgesellschaft mbH; *Int'l*, pg. 8512
WURTH INDUSTRY BELUX S.A.—See Wurth Verwaltungsgesellschaft mbH; *Int'l*, pg. 8512
WURTH INDUSTRY DE MEXICO S DE RL DE CV—See Wurth Verwaltungsgesellschaft mbH; *Int'l*, pg. 8512
WURTH INDUSTRY NORTH AMERICA LLC—See Wurth Verwaltungsgesellschaft mbH; *Int'l*, pg. 8511
WURTH INDUSTRY OF CANADA LTD.—See Wurth Verwaltungsgesellschaft mbH; *Int'l*, pg. 8512
WURTH INFORMATION TECHNOLOGY INDIA PRIVATE LIMITED—See Wurth Verwaltungsgesellschaft mbH; *Int'l*, pg. 8512
WURTH INFORMATION TECHNOLOGY (SHANGHAI) CO., LTD.—See Wurth Verwaltungsgesellschaft mbH; *Int'l*, pg. 8512
WURTH INTERNATIONAL AG—See Wurth Verwaltungsgesellschaft mbH; *Int'l*, pg. 8512
WURTH INTERNATIONAL TRADING AMERICA, INC.—See Wurth Verwaltungsgesellschaft mbH; *Int'l*, pg. 8511
WURTH INTERNATIONAL TRADING (SHANGHAI) CO., LTD.—See Wurth Verwaltungsgesellschaft mbH; *Int'l*, pg. 8512
WURTH INTERNATIONAL TRADING (SINGAPORE) PTE. LTD.—See Wurth Verwaltungsgesellschaft mbH; *Int'l*, pg. 8512
WURTH INTERNATIONAL TRADING S.R.O.—See Wurth Verwaltungsgesellschaft mbH; *Int'l*, pg. 8512
WURTH IRELAND LTD.—See Wurth Verwaltungsgesellschaft mbH; *Int'l*, pg. 8512
WURTH ISRAEL LTD.—See Wurth Verwaltungsgesellschaft mbH; *Int'l*, pg. 8512
WURTH ITENSIS AG—See Wurth Verwaltungsgesellschaft mbH; *Int'l*, pg. 8512
WURTH IT GMBH—See Wurth Verwaltungsgesellschaft mbH; *Int'l*, pg. 8512
WURTH JAPAN CO., LTD.—See Wurth Verwaltungsgesellschaft mbH; *Int'l*, pg. 8512
WURTH - JORDAN CO., LTD.—See Wurth Verwaltungsgesellschaft mbH; *Int'l*, pg. 8509
WURTH KOREA CO., LTD.—See Wurth Verwaltungsgesellschaft mbH; *Int'l*, pg. 8512
WURTH-KOSOVA SH.P.K.—See Wurth Verwaltungsgesellschaft mbH; *Int'l*, pg. 8514
WURTH LANKA (PRIVATE) LIMITED—See Wurth Verwaltungsgesellschaft mbH; *Int'l*, pg. 8512
WURTH LEASING AG—See Wurth Verwaltungsgesellschaft mbH; *Int'l*, pg. 8512
WURTH LEASING DANMARK A/S—See Wurth Verwaltungsgesellschaft mbH; *Int'l*, pg. 8512
WURTH LEASING GMBH & CO. KG—See Wurth Verwaltungsgesellschaft mbH; *Int'l*, pg. 8512
WURTH LEASING GMBH—See Wurth Verwaltungsgesellschaft mbH; *Int'l*, pg. 8512
WURTH LEBANON SAL—See Wurth Verwaltungsgesellschaft mbH; *Int'l*, pg. 8512
WURTH LIETUVA UAB—See Wurth Verwaltungsgesellschaft mbH; *Int'l*, pg. 8512
WURTH LIMITED—See Wurth Verwaltungsgesellschaft mbH; *Int'l*, pg. 8512
WURTH LOGISTICS AG—See Wurth Verwaltungsgesellschaft mbH; *Int'l*, pg. 8512
WURTH LOGISTICS ASIA-PACIFIC SDN. BHD.—See Wurth Verwaltungsgesellschaft mbH; *Int'l*, pg. 8512

COMPANY NAME INDEX

WURTH LOGISTICS DEUTSCHLAND GMBH—See Wurth Verwaltungsgesellschaft mbH; *Int'l*, pg. 8512
WURTH LOGISTICS USA INC.—See Wurth Verwaltungsgesellschaft mbH; *Int'l*, pg. 8511
WURTH LOUIS & COMPANY—See Wurth Verwaltungsgesellschaft mbH; *Int'l*, pg. 8511
WURTH MAKEDONIJA DOOEL—See Wurth Verwaltungsgesellschaft mbH; *Int'l*, pg. 8512
WURTH MANAGEMENT AG—See Wurth Verwaltungsgesellschaft mbH; *Int'l*, pg. 8503
WURTH MCALLEN BOLT & SCREW CO.—See Wurth Verwaltungsgesellschaft mbH; *Int'l*, pg. 8511
WURTH MEXICO S.A. DE C.V.—See Wurth Verwaltungsgesellschaft mbH; *Int'l*, pg. 8512
WURTH MODYF AS—See Wurth Verwaltungsgesellschaft mbH; *Int'l*, pg. 8512
WURTH MODYF DANMARK A/S—See Wurth Verwaltungsgesellschaft mbH; *Int'l*, pg. 8513
WURTH MODYF FRANCE S.A.R.L.—See Wurth Verwaltungsgesellschaft mbH; *Int'l*, pg. 8513
WURTH MODYF GMBH & CO. KG—See Wurth Verwaltungsgesellschaft mbH; *Int'l*, pg. 8512
WURTH MODYF LDA.—See Wurth Verwaltungsgesellschaft mbH; *Int'l*, pg. 8513
WURTH-MODYF N.V.—See Wurth Verwaltungsgesellschaft mbH; *Int'l*, pg. 8513
WURTH MODYF S.A.—See Wurth Verwaltungsgesellschaft mbH; *Int'l*, pg. 8513
WURTH MONGOLIA LLC—See Wurth Verwaltungsgesellschaft mbH; *Int'l*, pg. 8513
WURTH NAMIBIA (PTY) LTD.—See Wurth Verwaltungsgesellschaft mbH; *Int'l*, pg. 8513
WURTH NEDERLAND B.V.—See Wurth Verwaltungsgesellschaft mbH; *Int'l*, pg. 8513
WURTH NEW ZEALAND LTD.—See Wurth Verwaltungsgesellschaft mbH; *Int'l*, pg. 8513
WURTH NORGE AS—See Wurth Verwaltungsgesellschaft mbH; *Int'l*, pg. 8513
WURTH NORTH PTY. LTD.—See Wurth Verwaltungsgesellschaft mbH; *Int'l*, pg. 8509
WURTH NORTH-WEST JSC—See Wurth Verwaltungsgesellschaft mbH; *Int'l*, pg. 8513
WURTH OY—See Wurth Verwaltungsgesellschaft mbH; *Int'l*, pg. 8513
WURTH PERU S.A.C.—See Wurth Verwaltungsgesellschaft mbH; *Int'l*, pg. 8513
WURTH PHOENIX GMBH—See Wurth Verwaltungsgesellschaft mbH; *Int'l*, pg. 8513
WURTH PHOENIX KFT.—See Wurth Verwaltungsgesellschaft mbH; *Int'l*, pg. 8513
WURTH PHOENIX S.R.L.—See Wurth Verwaltungsgesellschaft mbH; *Int'l*, pg. 8513
WURTH POLSKA SP. Z O.O.—See Wurth Verwaltungsgesellschaft mbH; *Int'l*, pg. 8513
WURTH (PORTUGAL) TECNICA DE MONTAGEM LDA.—See Wurth Verwaltungsgesellschaft mbH; *Int'l*, pg. 8509
WURTH REINSURANCE COMPANY, S.A.—See Wurth Verwaltungsgesellschaft mbH; *Int'l*, pg. 8513
WURTH REVCAR FASTENERS, INC.—See Wurth Verwaltungsgesellschaft mbH; *Int'l*, pg. 8511
WURTH ROMANIA S.R.L.—See Wurth Verwaltungsgesellschaft mbH; *Int'l*, pg. 8513
WURTH SANAYI URUNLERI TIC. LTD. STI.—See Wurth Verwaltungsgesellschaft mbH; *Int'l*, pg. 8513
WURTH SAUDI ARABIA LLC—See Wurth Verwaltungsgesellschaft mbH; *Int'l*, pg. 8513
WURTH SERVICE SUPPLY INC.—See Wurth Verwaltungsgesellschaft mbH; *Int'l*, pg. 8511
WURTH (SHANGHAI) HARDWARE & TOOLS CO., LTD.—See Wurth Verwaltungsgesellschaft mbH; *Int'l*, pg. 8509
WURTH (SHENYANG) HARDWARE & TOOL CO., LTD.—See Wurth Verwaltungsgesellschaft mbH; *Int'l*, pg. 8509
WURTH SNIDER BOLT & SCREW, INC.—See Wurth Verwaltungsgesellschaft mbH; *Int'l*, pg. 8511
WURTH SOUTH AFRICA (PTY.) LTD.—See Wurth Verwaltungsgesellschaft mbH; *Int'l*, pg. 8513
WURTH SOUTH PTY. LTD.—See Wurth Verwaltungsgesellschaft mbH; *Int'l*, pg. 8509
WURTH SPOL. S R.O.—See Wurth Verwaltungsgesellschaft mbH; *Int'l*, pg. 8513
WURTH, SPOL. S R.O.—See Wurth Verwaltungsgesellschaft mbH; *Int'l*, pg. 8514
WURTH S.R.L.—See Wurth Verwaltungsgesellschaft mbH; *Int'l*, pg. 8513
WURTH S.R.L.—See Wurth Verwaltungsgesellschaft mbH; *Int'l*, pg. 8513
WURTH SVENSKA AB—See Wurth Verwaltungsgesellschaft mbH; *Int'l*, pg. 8513
WURTH SW INDUSTRY PECAS DE FIXACAO LTDA.—See Wurth Verwaltungsgesellschaft mbH; *Int'l*, pg. 8513
WURTH SZERELESTECHNIKA KFT—See Wurth Verwaltungsgesellschaft mbH; *Int'l*, pg. 8513
WURTH TAIWAN CO., LTD.—See Wurth Verwaltungsgesellschaft mbH; *Int'l*, pg. 8513

WURTH TELESERVICES GMBH & CO. KG—See Wurth Verwaltungsgesellschaft mbH; *Int'l*, pg. 8513
WURTH (THAILAND) COMPANY, LIMITED—See Wurth Verwaltungsgesellschaft mbH; *Int'l*, pg. 8509
WURTH (TIANJIN) INTERNATIONAL TRADE CO., LTD.—See Wurth Verwaltungsgesellschaft mbH; *Int'l*, pg. 8509
WURTH (TIANJIN) INTERNATIONAL TRADING CO., LTD.—See Wurth Verwaltungsgesellschaft mbH; *Int'l*, pg. 8509
WURTH TRUCK LEASE GMBH—See Wurth Verwaltungsgesellschaft mbH; *Int'l*, pg. 8513
WURTH U.K. LTD.—See Wurth Verwaltungsgesellschaft mbH; *Int'l*, pg. 8513
WURTH UKRAINE LTD.—See Wurth Verwaltungsgesellschaft mbH; *Int'l*, pg. 8513
WURTH USA INC.—See Wurth Verwaltungsgesellschaft mbH; *Int'l*, pg. 8511
WURTH VERSICHERUNGSDIENST GMBH—See Wurth Verwaltungsgesellschaft mbH; *Int'l*, pg. 8513
WURTH VERWALTUNGSGESELLSCHAFT MBH; *Int'l*, pg. 8503
WURTH VIETNAM COMPANY LIMITED—See Wurth Verwaltungsgesellschaft mbH; *Int'l*, pg. 8513
WURTH WEST PTY. LTD.—See Wurth Verwaltungsgesellschaft mbH; *Int'l*, pg. 8509
WURTH WOOD GROUP INC.—See Wurth Verwaltungsgesellschaft mbH; *Int'l*, pg. 8511
WURTTEMBERGISCHE ELEKTROMOTOREN GMBH—See WEG S.A.; *Int'l*, pg. 8368
WURTTEMBERGISCHE FILZTUCHFABRIK D. GESCHMAY GMBH—See Albany International Corp.; *U.S. Public*, pg. 72
WURTTEMBERGISCHE RECHTSSCHUTZ SCHADEN-SERVICE- GMBH—See Wuestenrot & Wuerttembergische AG; *Int'l*, pg. 8499
WURTTEMBERGISCHE VERSICHERUNG AG—See Wuestenrot & Wuerttembergische AG; *Int'l*, pg. 8499
WURTTEMBERGISCHE VERTRIEBSPARTNER GMBH—See Wuestenrot & Wuerttembergische AG; *Int'l*, pg. 8499
WURZEL BUILDERS, LTD.; *U.S. Private*, pg. 4575
WUSA-TV—See TEGNA Inc.; *U.S. Public*, pg. 1991
WUS PRINTED CIRCUIT CO., LTD.; *Int'l*, pg. 8514
WUS PRINTED CIRCUIT (KUNSHAN) CO., LTD.; *Int'l*, pg. 8514
WUSTEC GMBH & CO. KG—See Komax Holding AG; *Int'l*, pg. 4241
WUSTENROT HAUS- UND STADTEBAU GMBH—See Wuestenrot & Wuerttembergische AG; *Int'l*, pg. 8499
WUSTENROT IMMOBILIEN GMBH—See Wuestenrot & Wuerttembergische AG; *Int'l*, pg. 8500
WUTONG HOLDING GROUP CO., LTD.; *Int'l*, pg. 8514
WUTV-TV—See Sinclair, Inc.; *U.S. Public*, pg. 1886
WUXI ACRYL TECHNOLOGY CO., LTD.; *Int'l*, pg. 8514
WUXI ADVANCED KAYAKU CHEMICAL CO., LTD—See Nippon Kayaku Co., Ltd.; *Int'l*, pg. 5321
WUXI ALPS ELECTRONICS CO., LTD.—See Alps Alpine Co., Ltd.; *Int'l*, pg. 377
WUXI APPTEC, INC.—See WuXi PharmaTech (Cayman) Inc.; *Int'l*, pg. 8515
WUXI APPTEC (SUZHOU) TESTING TECHNOLOGY CO., LTD.—See WuXi Biologics (Cayman) Inc.; *Int'l*, pg. 8514
WUXI AUTOWELL TECHNOLOGY CO., LTD.; *Int'l*, pg. 8514
WUXI BAOZEN AUTOMOBILE SALES AND SERVICES CO., LTD.—See China Yongda Automobiles Services Holdings Limited; *Int'l*, pg. 1565
WUXI BEST PRECISION MACHINERY CO., LTD.; *Int'l*, pg. 8514
WUXI BIOLOGICS (CAYMAN) INC.; *Int'l*, pg. 8514
WUXI BOTON TECHNOLOGY LTD.; *Int'l*, pg. 8514
WUXI CAS PHOTONICS CO., LTD.—See Focused Photonics (Hangzhou), Inc.; *Int'l*, pg. 2720
WUXI CHEMICAL EQUIPMENT CO., LTD.; *Int'l*, pg. 8514
WUXI CHENGCHANG SEATS MANUFACTURING CO LTD—See Tan Chong International Limited; *Int'l*, pg. 7453
WUXI CHENGHONG ELECTRONIC CHEMICALS CO., LTD.—See Nagase & Co., Ltd.; *Int'l*, pg. 5128
WUXI CHINA RESOURCES HUAJING MICROELECTRONICS CO., LTD.—See China Resources (Holdings) Co., Ltd.; *Int'l*, pg. 1548
WUXI CHINA RESOURCES SEMICO CO., LTD.—See China Resources (Holdings) Co., Ltd.; *Int'l*, pg. 1548
WUXI CHIPOWN MICROELECTRONICS LTD.; *Int'l*, pg. 8514
WUXI CITY HENG HUI CABLE CO.—See Jiangsu Zhongchao Holding Co., Ltd.; *Int'l*, pg. 3957
WUXI COMMERCIAL MANSION GRAND ORIENT CO., LTD.; *Int'l*, pg. 8514
WUXI COMPRESSOR CO.—See Kobe Steel, Ltd.; *Int'l*, pg. 4221
WUXI CREATIVE SENSOR TECHNOLOGY CO., LTD—See Creative Sensor Inc.; *Int'l*, pg. 1833
WUXI CRITICAL MECHANICAL COMPONENTS—See TechPrecision Corporation; *U.S. Public*, pg. 1988

WUXI LONGSHENG TECHNOLOGY CO., LTD.

WUXI CUMMINS TURBO TECHNOLOGIES CO., LTD.—See Cummins Inc.; *U.S. Public*, pg. 607
WUXI DAIDONG ELECTRONICS CO., LTD.—See Daidong Electronics Co., Ltd.; *Int'l*, pg. 1924
WUXI DELINHAI ENVIRONMENTAL TECHNOLOGY CO., LTD.; *Int'l*, pg. 8514
WUXI DOUBLE ELEPHANT MICRO FIBRE MATERIAL CO., LTD.; *Int'l*, pg. 8514
WUXI EASYWAY MODEL DESIGN & MANUFACTURE CO, LTD.—See 3D Systems Corporation; *U.S. Public*, pg. 4
WUXI ELBE POLYMER TECHNOLOGY CO., LTD.—See Woco Industrietechnik GmbH; *Int'l*, pg. 8442
WUXI FEDS CO., LTD.—See The Far Eastern Group; *Int'l*, pg. 7641
WUXI FLANGE FORGING CO., LTD.—See Jiangsu Shentong Valve Co., Ltd.; *Int'l*, pg. 3954
WUXI FUJI ELECTRIC FA CO., LTD.—See Fuji Electric Co., Ltd.; *Int'l*, pg. 2813
WUXI GENEZYS TECHNOLOGY LTD.—See Unizyx Holding Corporation; *Int'l*, pg. 8084
WUXI GUANYUN HEAT EXCHANGER CO., LTD.—See Hongsheng Heat Exchanger Manufacturing Co.,ltd; *Int'l*, pg. 3471
WUXI HATAL ALUMINIUM CO., LTD.—See Jiangsu Asia-Pacific Light Alloy Technology Co., Ltd.; *Int'l*, pg. 3943
WUXI HODGEN TECHNOLOGY CO., LTD.; *Int'l*, pg. 8514
WUXI HONGHUI NEW MATERIALS TECHNOLOGY CO., LTD.; *Int'l*, pg. 8515
WUXI HOTA PRECISION GEAR CO., LTD.—See Hota Industrial Mfg. Co., Ltd.; *Int'l*, pg. 3487
WUXI HUADONG HEAVY MACHINERY CO., LTD.; *Int'l*, pg. 8515
WUXI HUAGUANG ENVIRONMENT & ENERGY GROUP CO., LTD.; *Int'l*, pg. 8515
WUXI HU AN WIRE AND CABLE CO., LTD.—See Hu An Cable Holdings Ltd.; *Int'l*, pg. 3509
WUXI HUAPENG CLOSURES COMPANY LIMITED—See CPMC Holdings Limited; *Int'l*, pg. 1826
WUXI HUAYANG ELECTRICAL POWER EQUIPMENT CO., LTD—See Sharing Economy International Inc; *Int'l*, pg. 6789
WUXI HYATECH CO., LTD.; *Int'l*, pg. 8515
WUXI IHI TURBO CO., LTD.—See IHI Corporation; *Int'l*, pg. 3606
WUXI INOUE HUAGUANG AUTOMOBILE PARTS CO., LTD.—See INOAC Corporation; *Int'l*, pg. 3715
WUXI INTERPUMP WEIFU HYDRAULICS COMPANY LTD.—See Interpump Group S.p.A.; *Int'l*, pg. 3756
WUXI JAKE PLASTIC INDUSTRY CO., LTD.—See Henan Shijia Photons Technology Co., Ltd.; *Int'l*, pg. 3343
WUXI JAPANA SPORTS GOODS CO., LTD.—See Alpen Co., Ltd.; *Int'l*, pg. 366
WUXI JENTECH PRECISION INDUSTRIAL CO., LTD.—See Jentech Precision Industrial Co., Ltd.; *Int'l*, pg. 3929
WUXI JIACHENG SOLAR ENERGY TECHNOLOGY CO., LTD.—See EMEREN GROUP LTD; *U.S. Public*, pg. 739
WUXI JIANGNAN CABLE CO., LTD.—See Jiangnan Group Limited; *Int'l*, pg. 3942
WUXI JINGXIN PRECISION MACHINING CO. LTD.—See Patec Precision Industry Co., Ltd.; *Int'l*, pg. 5755
WUXI JINXIN GROUP COMPANY LIMITED—See Westinghouse Air Brake Technologies Corporation; *U.S. Public*, pg. 2360
WUXI JINXIN SURFACE DECORATION CO., LTD.—See Xin Point Holdings Limited; *Int'l*, pg. 8529
WUXI KEDI AUTOMATION EQUIPMENT CO., LTD.—See Endress+Hauser (International) Holding AG; *Int'l*, pg. 2409
WUXI KEEN POINT ELECTRONICS CO., LTD.—See Xin Point Holdings Limited; *Int'l*, pg. 8529
WUXI KFC CO., LTD.—See Yum China Holdings, Inc.; *U.S. Public*, pg. 2399
WUXI K LASER TECHNOLOGIES CO., LTD.—See K Laser Technology Inc.; *Int'l*, pg. 4037
WUXI KOA ELECTROCERAMICS CO.,LTD.—See Koa Corporation; *Int'l*, pg. 4215
WUXI KOYO BEARING CO., LTD.—See JTEKT Corporation; *Int'l*, pg. 4019
WUXI KROSAKI SUJIA REFRACTORIES CO., LTD.—See Krosaki Harima Corporation; *Int'l*, pg. 4307
WUXI KYB TOP ABSORBER CO., LTD.—See KYB Corporation; *Int'l*, pg. 4354
WUXI LEAD INTELLIGENT EQUIPMENT CO.,LTD.; *Int'l*, pg. 8515
WUXI LEGGETT & PLATT-HUAGUANG AUTOMOBILE PARTS CO. LTD.—See Leggett & Platt, Incorporated; *U.S. Public*, pg. 1304
WUXI LEILI CONTROLS TECHNOLOGY CO., LTD.—See Jiangsu Leili Motor Corporation Limited; *Int'l*, pg. 3950
WUXI LIHU CORPORATION LIMITED; *Int'l*, pg. 8515
WUXI LITTLE SWAN COMPANY LIMITED—See Midea Group Co., Ltd.; *Int'l*, pg. 4886
WUXI LONGSHENG TECHNOLOGY CO., LTD.; *Int'l*, pg. 8515

WUXI LONGSHENG TECHNOLOGY CO., LTD.
CORPORATE AFFILIATIONS

WUXI MAN YUE ELECTRONICS COMPANY LIMITED—See Man Yue Technology Holdings Limited; *Int'l*, pg. 4665
WUXI MATEX PRECISION CO., LTD.—See Nippon Sheet Glass Co. Ltd.; *Int'l*, pg. 5331
WUXI MCD GASKET CO., LTD.—See Alfa Laval AB; *Int'l*, pg. 312
WUXI MINGCI CARDIOVASCULAR HOSPITAL CO., LTD.—See Jiangnan Mould & Plastic Technology Co., Ltd.; *Int'l*, pg. 3943
WUXI MIYOSHI PRECISION CO., LTD.—See Miyoshi Limited; *Int'l*, pg. 4996
WUXI MOBIS AUTOMOTIVE PARTS CO., LTD.—See Hyundai MOBIS Co., Ltd.; *Int'l*, pg. 3558
WUXI MORESCO TRADING CO., LTD.—See MORESCO Corporation; *Int'l*, pg. 5040
WUXI MORE TEX TECHNOLOGY CO., LTD.—See Tex Year Industries Inc.; *Int'l*, pg. 7582
WUXI MRC ORIGIN WATER MEMBRANE TECH. CO., LTD.—See Mitsubishi Chemical Group Corporation; *Int'l*, pg. 4933
WUXI-MSA SAFETY EQUIPMENT CO. LTD.—See MSA Safety Incorporated; *U.S. Public*, pg. 1482
WUXI MURATA ELECTRONICS CO., LTD.—See Murata Manufacturing Co., Ltd.; *Int'l*, pg. 5099
WUXI NCE POWER CO., LTD.; *Int'l*, pg. 8515
WUXI NEW HONGTAI ELECTRICAL TECH CO LTD; *Int'l*, pg. 8515
WUXI NICHICON ELECTRONICS R&D CENTER CO., LTD.—See NICHICON CORPORATION; *Int'l*, pg. 5268
WUXI NOK-FREUDENBERG OILSEAL CO., LTD.—See Freudenberg SE; *Int'l*, pg. 2791
WUXI NSC HONGYUAN—See NSC Groupe SA; *Int'l*, pg. 5476
WUXIN TECHNOLOGY HOLDINGS, INC.; *Int'l*, pg. 8516
WUXI NTT DATA CO., LTD.—See Nippon Telegraph & Telephone Corporation; *Int'l*, pg. 5346
WUXI OKURA PACKING MATERIAL CO., LTD.—See Okura Industrial Co., Ltd.; *Int'l*, pg. 5551
WUXI ONLINE OFFLINE COMMUNICATION INFORMATION TECHNOLOGY CO., LTD.; *Int'l*, pg. 8515
WUXI PAIHONG REAL ESTATE CO., LTD.—See Taiwan Paiho Limited; *Int'l*, pg. 7423
WUXI PAIHO TEXTILES CO., LTD.—See Taiwan Paiho Limited; *Int'l*, pg. 7423
WUXI PAIKE NEW MATERIALS TECHNOLOGY CO., LTD.; *Int'l*, pg. 8515
WUXI PAISEN CHEMICAL FIBRE CO., LTD.—See Taiwan Paiho Limited; *Int'l*, pg. 7423
WUXI PAISEN COMMERCE CO., LTD.—See Taiwan Paiho Limited; *Int'l*, pg. 7423
WUXI PAIWEI BIOTECHNOLOGY CO., LTD.—See Taiwan Paiho Limited; *Int'l*, pg. 7423
WUXI PHARMATECH (CAYMAN) INC.; *Int'l*, pg. 8515
WUXI PNEUMATECH AIR/GAS PURITY EQUIPMENT CO LTD—See Atlas Copco AB; *Int'l*, pg. 684
WUXI PROFACE ELECTRONIC CO. LTD—See Schneider Electric SE; *Int'l*, pg. 6635
WUXI PUBLIC UTILITIES INDUSTRIAL GROUP CO., LTD.; *Int'l*, pg. 8515
WUXI QIANHUI SEWAGE TREATMENT CO., LTD.—See Build King Holdings Limited; *Int'l*, pg. 1212
WUXI RAYON MEMBRANE TECHNOLOGY CO., LTD.—See Beijing Origin Water Technology Co., Ltd.; *Int'l*, pg. 955
WUXI RENGO PACKAGING CO., LTD.—See Rengo Co., Ltd.; *Int'l*, pg. 6282
WUXI RISECOMM COMMUNICATION TECHNOLOGY COMPANY LIMITED—See Risecomm Group Holdings Limited; *Int'l*, pg. 6349
WUXI RISHO TECHNOLOGY CO., LTD.—See Tokai Rika Co., Ltd.; *Int'l*, pg. 7781
WUXI RONGZHI ELECTRONICS CO., LTD.—See Di-Nikko Engineering Co., Ltd.; *Int'l*, pg. 2101
WUXI RURAL COMMERCIAL BANK CO., LTD; *Int'l*, pg. 8515
WUXI SANWA PLASTICS CO., LTD.; *Int'l*, pg. 8515
WUXI SHAGANG MATERIALS TRADE CO., LTD.—See Jiangsu Shagang Group Ltd.; *Int'l*, pg. 3954
WUXI SHENDGA MACHINERY CO. LTD.—See Komatsu Ltd.; *Int'l*, pg. 4236
WUXI SHIHLIN ELECTRIC & ELECTRIC & ENGINEERING CO., LTD.—See Shihlin Electric & Engineering Corp.; *Int'l*, pg. 6829
WUXI SHINKO PLANTECH CO., LTD.—See RAIZNEXT Corporation; *Int'l*, pg. 6192
WUXI SINGUAN METAL SCIENCE & TECHNOLOGY CO., LTD.—See Eson Precision Ind. Co., Ltd.; *Int'l*, pg. 2504
WUXI SMART AUTO-CONTROL ENGINEERING CO., LTD.; *Int'l*, pg. 8515
WUXI SONGXING ELECTRONIC COMPONENTS CO., LTD.—See SATO Holdings Corporation; *Int'l*, pg. 6586
WUXI SSS-DIAMOND PLASTICS CO., LTD.—See Sekisui Chemical Co., Ltd.; *Int'l*, pg. 6696
WUXI SUNDIRO ELECTRIC MOBILES CO., LTD.—See Sundiro Holding Co., Ltd.; *Int'l*, pg. 7313
WUXI SUNKING POWER CAPACITOR CO., LTD.—See Sun.King Technology Group Limited; *Int'l*, pg. 7309

WUXI SUNLIT SCIENCE AND TECHNOLOGY COMPANY LIMITED; *Int'l*, pg. 8516
WUXI TAIJI INDUSTRY CO., LTD.; *Int'l*, pg. 8516
WUXI TAI SINTONG MACHINERY CO., LTD.—See Sintokogio Ltd.; *Int'l*, pg. 6959
WUXI TAKACHIHO-SUN INDUSTRY CO., LTD.—See Toyota Tsusho Corporation; *Int'l*, pg. 7877
WUXI TDK-LAMBDA ELECTRONICS CO., LTD.—See TDK Corporation; *Int'l*, pg. 7488
WUXI TECO ELECTRIC & MACHINERY CO., LTD.—See Teco Electric & Machinery Co., Ltd.; *Int'l*, pg. 7518
WUXI TECO PRECISION INDUSTRY CO., LTD.—See Teco Electric & Machinery Co., Ltd.; *Int'l*, pg. 7518
WUXI TEXTRON SPECIALIZED VEHICLES CO., LTD.—See Textron Inc.; *U.S. Public*, pg. 2029
WUXI TEX YEAR INTERNATIONAL TRADING CO., LTD.—See Tex Year Industries Inc.; *Int'l*, pg. 7582
WUXI TONYI DAIWA INDUSTRIAL CO., LTD.—See Uni-President Enterprises Corporation; *Int'l*, pg. 8028
WUXI TRELLEBORG VIBRATION ISOLATORS CO., LTD.—See Trelleborg AB; *Int'l*, pg. 7914
WUXI TSANG YOW AUTO PARTS CO., LTD.—See Tsang Yow Industrial Co., Ltd.; *Int'l*, pg. 7949
WUXI TURBINE BLADE COMPANY LIMITED—See Shanghai Electric Group Company Limited; *Int'l*, pg. 6766
WUXI UNI-KING LAB CO., LTD.—See Shanxi C&Y Pharmaceutical Group Co., Ltd.; *Int'l*, pg. 6786
WUXI VALEO AUTOMOTIVE COMPONENTS & SYSTEM CO. LTD.—See Valeo S.A.; *Int'l*, pg. 8115
WUXI WEIFU CHANGAN CO., LTD.—See Wuxi Weifu High-technology Co., Ltd.; *Int'l*, pg. 8516
WUXI WEIFU ELECTRIC DRIVE TECHNOLOGY CO., LTD.—See Wuxi Weifu High-technology Co., Ltd.; *Int'l*, pg. 8516
WUXI WEIFU HIGH-TECHNOLOGY CO., LTD.; *Int'l*, pg. 8516
WUXI WEIFU LIDA CATALYTIC CONVERTER CO., LTD.—See Wuxi Weifu High-technology Co., Ltd.; *Int'l*, pg. 8516
WUXI WEIFU MASHAN FUEL INJECTION EQUIPMENT CO., LTD.—See Wuxi Weifu High-technology Co., Ltd.; *Int'l*, pg. 8516
WUXI WEIFU SCHMIDT POWER SYSTEM CO., LTD.—See Wuxi Weifu High-technology Co., Ltd.; *Int'l*, pg. 8516
WUXI WEIR MINERALS EQUIPMENTS CO., LTD.—See The Weir Group PLC; *Int'l*, pg. 7700
WUXI WISSEN INTELLIGENT SENSING TECHNOLOGY CO., LTD.—See Sunny Optical Technology (Group) Company Limited; *Int'l*, pg. 7319
WUXI WOCO MOTOR ACOUSTIC SYSTEM CO., LTD.—See Woco Industrietechnik GmbH; *Int'l*, pg. 8442
WUXI WONIK IPS SEMICONDUCTOR EQUIPMENT TECHNOLOGY CO., LTD.—See Wonik Corporation; *Int'l*, pg. 8448
WUXI WORLDBEST KAMA POWER CO., LTD.—See China Hi-Tech Group Corporation; *Int'l*, pg. 1508
WUXI XINJE ELECTRIC CO., LTD; *Int'l*, pg. 8516
WUXI XIZHOU MAGNET WIRES CO., LTD.—See Jiangsu Zhongchao Holding Co., Ltd.; *Int'l*, pg. 3957
WUXI XUELANG ENVIRONMENTAL TECHNOLOGY CO., LTD.; *Int'l*, pg. 8516
WUXI YAKULT CO., LTD.—See Yakult Honsha Co., Ltd.; *Int'l*, pg. 8546
WUXI YICHENG AUTOMOBILE SALES & SERVICES CO., LTD.—See China Yongda Automobiles Services Holdings Limited; *Int'l*, pg. 1565
WUXI YONGDA ORIENTAL AUTOMOBILE SALES AND SERVICES CO., LTD.—See China Yongda Automobiles Services Holdings Limited; *Int'l*, pg. 1565
WUXI YUSHOU MEDICAL APPLIANCES CO., LTD.—See Canmax Technologies Co., Ltd.; *Int'l*, pg. 1291
WUXI ZHENHUA AUTO PARTS CO., LTD.; *Int'l*, pg. 8516
WUXI ZHONGDING INTEGRATION TECHNOLOGY CO., LTD.—See Noblelift Intelligent Equipment Co.,Ltd; *Int'l*, pg. 5398
WUXI ZHONGSHENG XINGHUI AUTOMOBILE SALES & SERVICE CO., LTD.—See Zhongsheng Group Holdings Limited; *Int'l*, pg. 8674
WUYANG PARKING; *Int'l*, pg. 8516
WUYISHAN CHINA INTERNATIONAL TRAVEL SERVICE CO., LTD.—See China Tourism Group Duty Free Corporation Limited; *Int'l*, pg. 1560
WUYI STAR TEA INDUSTRIAL CO., LTD.—See Tongguan Gold Group Ltd.; *Int'l*, pg. 7807
WUZHI ZHONGYU GAS CO., LTD.—See Zhongyu Energy Holdings Limited; *Int'l*, pg. 8676
WUZHONG INSTRUMENT COMPANY LIMITED—See China Automation Group Limited; *Int'l*, pg. 1484
WUZHOU ARAKAWA CHEMICAL INDUSTRIES, LTD.—See Arakawa Chemical Industries, Ltd.; *Int'l*, pg. 535
WUZHOU INTERNATIONAL HOLDINGS LIMITED; *Int'l*, pg. 8516
WUZHOU SE BORDNETZE COMPANY LTD.—See Sumitomo Electric Industries, Ltd.; *Int'l*, pg. 7285

WUZHOU SPECIAL PAPER GROUP CO., LTD.; *Int'l*, pg. 8516
WUZHOU TAIKISHA ENGINEERING CO., LTD.—See Taikisha Ltd.; *Int'l*, pg. 7414
WVEC-TELEVISION, INC.—See TEGNA Inc.; *U.S. Public*, pg. 1990
WVEE-FM—See AUDACY, INC.; *U.S. Public*, pg. 226
W VERWALTUNGS AG—See Pierer Konzerngesellschaft mbH; *Int'l*, pg. 5863
WVF-PARAMOUNT 745 INVESTOR, L.P.—See Paramount Group Inc.; *U.S. Public*, pg. 1637
WVG MEDIEN GMBH—See Splendid Medien AG; *Int'l*, pg. 7141
WVI FILMS B.V.—See National Amusements, Inc.; *U.S. Private*, pg. 2844
WVI GMBH; *Int'l*, pg. 8516
WVIT-TV—See Comcast Corporation; *U.S. Public*, pg. 540
WVLT-TV, INC.—See Gray Television, Inc.; *U.S. Public*, pg. 960
WVNS-TV, LLC—See Nexstar Media Group, Inc.; *U.S. Public*, pg. 1524
WVS FINANCIAL CORP.; *U.S. Public*, pg. 2384
WVTM-TV—See The Hearst Corporation; *U.S. Private*, pg. 4049
WVTV-TV—See Sinclair, Inc.; *U.S. Public*, pg. 1887
WVVA-TV—See Gray Television, Inc.; *U.S. Public*, pg. 961
WVZ-WARMEVERSORGUNG ZINNOWITZ GMBH—See Stadtwerke Hannover AG; *Int'l*, pg. 7161
W.W. ADCOCK INC.; *U.S. Private*, pg. 4423
WWAV RAPP COLLINS WEST—See Omnicom Group Inc.; *U.S. Public*, pg. 1592
WWAV—See Omnicom Group Inc.; *U.S. Public*, pg. 1593
WW BELGIUM NV—See WW International, Inc.; *U.S. Public*, pg. 2384
W&W BRANDPOOL GMBH—See Wuestenrot & Wuerttembergische AG; *Int'l*, pg. 8499
WWBT, LLC—See Gray Television, Inc.; *U.S. Public*, pg. 960
W W CAPITAL CORPORATION; *U.S. Private*, pg. 4417
WWCI INC.—See Window to the World Communications, Inc.; *U.S. Private*, pg. 4538
W.W. CLYDE AND COMPANY—See Clyde Companies Inc.; *U.S. Private*, pg. 949
WW.COM, LLC—See WW International, Inc.; *U.S. Public*, pg. 2384
WWDM-FM—See YMF Media LLC; *U.S. Private*, pg. 4589
WWE CANADA, INC.—See Silver Lake Group, LLC; *U.S. Private*, pg. 3654
WWE GERMANY GMBH—See Silver Lake Group, LLC; *U.S. Private*, pg. 3654
WWE MIDDLE EAST FZ-LLC—See Silver Lake Group, LLC; *U.S. Private*, pg. 3654
WW ENERGY, INC.; *U.S. Private*, pg. 4575
W&W ENERGY SERVICES INC.—See Petrofac Limited; *Int'l*, pg. 5826
WW E-SERVICES IBERIA S.L.—See Westwing Group SE; *Int'l*, pg. 8393
WWE STUDIOS, INC.—See Silver Lake Group, LLC; *U.S. Private*, pg. 3654
WWF INTERNATIONAL; *Int'l*, pg. 8517
WWF OPERATING COMPANY LLC—See Danone; *Int'l*, pg. 1967
WW.FR SARL—See WW International, Inc.; *U.S. Public*, pg. 2384
W. W. GAY FIRE & INTEGRATED SYSTEMS, INC.—See Huron Capital Partners LLC; *U.S. Private*, pg. 2012
W.W. GAY MECHANICAL CONTRACTOR, INC.; *U.S. Private*, pg. 4423
W.W. GRAINGER, INC.; *U.S. Public*, pg. 2319
W.W. GRAINGER - JANESVILLE—See W.W. Grainger, Inc.; *U.S. Public*, pg. 2320
WW GROUP INC.; *U.S. Private*, pg. 4575
WWHB-CA—See Sinclair, Inc.; *U.S. Public*, pg. 1887
W. WHITE (WHOLESALE) LTD.—See Shoei Co., Ltd.; *Int'l*, pg. 6858
WWH, LLC—See The Southern Company; *U.S. Public*, pg. 2131
WW HOLDING INC; *Int'l*, pg. 8516
WWHO-TV—See Sinclair, Inc.; *U.S. Public*, pg. 1887
W&W INFORMATIK GMBH—See Wuestenrot & Wuerttembergische AG; *Int'l*, pg. 8499
WW INTERNATIONAL, INC.; *U.S. Public*, pg. 2384
W&W INVESTMENT MANAGERS DAC—See Wuestenrot & Wuerttembergische AG; *Int'l*, pg. 8499
WW JOHNSON MEAT COMPANY; *U.S. Private*, pg. 4575
W.W. LEISURE, INC.; *U.S. Private*, pg. 4423
W.W. LODGING, INC.—See W.W. Leisure, Inc.; *U.S. Private*, pg. 4423
WWL-TV, INC.—See TEGNA Inc.; *U.S. Public*, pg. 1990
WW MANUFACTURING CO. INC.—See W W Capital Corporation; *U.S. Private*, pg. 4417
WWMT-TV—See Sinclair, Inc.; *U.S. Public*, pg. 1887
WWNC AM—See iHeartMedia, Inc.; *U.S. Public*, pg. 1097
W.W. NORTON & COMPANY, INC. - COUNTRYMAN PRESS DIVISION—See W.W. Norton & Company, Inc.; *U.S. Private*, pg. 4423
W.W. NORTON & COMPANY, INC.; *U.S. Private*, pg. 4423
W. W. NORTON & COMPANY LTD.—See W.W. Norton & Company, Inc.; *U.S. Private*, pg. 4423

COMPANY NAME INDEX

WWOR-TV—See Fox Corporation; *U.S. Public*, pg. 876
WWPKG HOLDINGS COMPANY LIMITED; *Int'l*, pg. 8517
WWPS, LLC.—See Alberici Corporation; *U.S. Private*, pg. 152
WWRD AUSTRALIA PTY LIMITED—See Fiskars Oyj Abp; *Int'l*, pg. 2694
WWRD IRELAND LIMITED—See Fiskars Oyj Abp; *Int'l*, pg. 2694
WWRD UNITED KINGDOM LIMITED—See Fiskars Oyj Abp; *Int'l*, pg. 2694
WWRD US, LLC—See Fiskars Oyj Abp; *Int'l*, pg. 2694
WWS ACQUISITION LLC—See Koch Industries, Inc.; *U.S. Private*, pg. 2333
W&W SERVICE GMBH—See Wuestenrot & Wuerttembergische AG; *Int'l*, pg. 8499
W&W STEEL COMPANY INC.; *U.S. Private*, pg. 4417
WW (SWITZERLAND) SA—See WW International, Inc.; *U.S. Public*, pg. 2384
WWT APJ-SINGAPORE PTE. LTD.—See World Wide Technology Holding Co., LLC; *U.S. Private*, pg. 4568
WWT BRASIL COMERCIO E SERVICOS LTDA.—See World Wide Technology Holding Co., LLC; *U.S. Private*, pg. 4568
WWT EMEA UK LTD.—See World Wide Technology Holding Co., LLC; *U.S. Private*, pg. 4568
WWT GEORGIA RC GROUP LLC—See Water Ways Technologies Inc.; *Int'l*, pg. 8356
W W T, INC.; *U.S. Private*, pg. 4417
W.W. TIRE SERVICE, INC.; *U.S. Private*, pg. 4423
W.W. TRANSPORT, INC.; *U.S. Private*, pg. 4423
WWUS 104.1FM—See Vox Communications Group LLC; *U.S. Private*, pg. 4414
WW VENTURE CORP.—See World-Wide Holdings Corp.; *U.S. Private*, pg. 4568
W.W. WALLWORK, INC.; *U.S. Private*, pg. 4423
WWWB-TV—See Capitol Broadcasting Company, Inc.; *U.S. Private*, pg. 743
W&W WHOLESALE INCORPORATED; *U.S. Private*, pg. 4417
WWWINS ISOBAR—See Dentsu Group Inc.; *Int'l*, pg. 2037
WXBB FM 105 3, INC.—See Brookfield Corporation; *Int'l*, pg. 1184
WXDJ LICENSING, INC.—See Spanish Broadcasting System Inc.; *U.S. Public*, pg. 1914
WXIA-TV—See TEGNA Inc.; *U.S. Public*, pg. 1991
WXII HEARST-ARGYLE TELEVISION, INC.—See The Hearst Corporation; *U.S. Private*, pg. 4049
WXIN-TV—See Nexstar Media Group, Inc.; *U.S. Public*, pg. 1525
WXLV-TV—See Sinclair, Inc.; *U.S. Public*, pg. 1886
WXMI, LLC—See Nexstar Media Group, Inc.; *U.S. Public*, pg. 1525
WXXA-TV; *U.S. Private*, pg. 4575
WXXI PUBLIC BROADCASTING COUNCIL; *U.S. Private*, pg. 4575
WXYT-FM—See AUDACY, INC.; *U.S. Public*, pg. 226
WXYZ-TV—See The E.W. Scripps Company; *U.S. Public*, pg. 2069
WYANDOT INC.; *U.S. Private*, pg. 4575
WYANDOTTE CENTRAL DIALYSIS, LLC—See DaVita Inc.; *U.S. Public*, pg. 644
WYANDOTTE NETTEL—See Wyandotte Tribal Corporation; *U.S. Private*, pg. 4575
WYANDOTTE TRIBAL CORPORATION; *U.S. Private*, pg. 4575
WYANDOTTE TRIBAL PETROLEUM, INC.—See Wyandotte Tribal Corporation; *U.S. Private*, pg. 4575
WYATT FIELD SERVICE CO.—See CIC Group, Inc.; *U.S. Private*, pg. 896
WYATT INCORPORATED; *U.S. Private*, pg. 4575
WYATT INSURANCE SERVICES, INC.—See Hellman & Friedman LLC; *U.S. Private*, pg. 1910
WYATT IRRIGATION CO.—See Winsupply Inc.; *U.S. Private*, pg. 4544
WYATT-JOHNSON BUICK, PONTIAC, GMC TRUCK, INC.; *U.S. Private*, pg. 4575
WYATT MANAGEMENT, INC.; *U.S. Private*, pg. 4575
WYATT SEAL INC.; *U.S. Private*, pg. 4575
WYATT TECHNOLOGY CORPORATION—See Waters Corporation; *U.S. Public*, pg. 2336
WYBLE ADVERTISING; *U.S. Private*, pg. 4575
WYBOROWA SA—See Pernod Ricard S.A.; *Int'l*, pg. 5811
W.Y. CAMPBELL & COMPANY—See Comerica Incorporated; *U.S. Public*, pg. 542
WYCHEM LTD.—See Aurelius Equity Opportunities SE & Co. KGaA; *Int'l*, pg. 710
WYCKOFF FARMS, INCORPORATED; *U.S. Private*, pg. 4575
WYCKOFF HEIGHTS MEDICAL CENTER; *U.S. Private*, pg. 4575
THE WYCO TOOL COMPANY—See Badger Meter, Inc.; *U.S. Public*, pg. 263
WYCW-TV—See Nexstar Media Group, Inc.; *U.S. Public*, pg. 1523
WYDAWNICTWA SZKOLNE I PEDAGOGICZNE SA—See Central Group; *Int'l*, pg. 1407
WYDAWNICTWO LEKTORKLETT SP. Z O.O.—See Ernst Klett AG; *Int'l*, pg. 2495

WYDE CORPORATION—See Blackstone Inc.; *U.S. Public*, pg. 356
WYDE INTERIOR COMPANY LIMITED—See Origin Property Public Company Limited; *Int'l*, pg. 5630
WYELANDS BANK PLC; *Int'l*, pg. 8517
WYETH LEDERLE S.R.L.—See Pfizer Inc.; *U.S. Public*, pg. 1683
WYETH (MALAYSIA) SDN. BHD.—See Pfizer Inc.; *U.S. Public*, pg. 1683
WYETH NUTRITIONAL (CHINA) CO., LTD.—See Pfizer Inc.; *U.S. Public*, pg. 1683
WYETH PAKISTAN LIMITED—See Pfizer Inc.; *U.S. Public*, pg. 1683
WYETH PHARMACEUTICAL CO., LTD.—See Pfizer Inc.; *U.S. Public*, pg. 1683
WYEVALE GARDEN CENTRES LIMITED—See Terra Firma Capital Partners Ltd.; *Int'l*, pg. 7567
THE WYE VALLEY NUFFIELD HOSPITAL—See Nuffield Health; *Int'l*, pg. 5488
WYFFEL'S HYBRIDS, INC.; *U.S. Private*, pg. 4576
WYFF HEARST-ARGYLE TELEVISION, INC.—See The Hearst Corporation; *U.S. Private*, pg. 4049
WYG CONSULTING LIMITED—See Tetra Tech, Inc.; *U.S. Public*, pg. 2024
WYG ENVIRONMENTAL (IRELAND) LIMITED—See Tetra Tech, Inc.; *U.S. Public*, pg. 2024
WYG ENVIRONMENTAL LIMITED—See Tetra Tech, Inc.; *U.S. Public*, pg. 2024
WYG ENVIRONMENT PLANNING TRANSPORT LIMITED—See Tetra Tech, Inc.; *U.S. Public*, pg. 2024
WYG INTERNATIONAL LIMITED—See Tetra Tech, Inc.; *U.S. Public*, pg. 2024
WYG IRELAND LIMITED—See Tetra Tech, Inc.; *U.S. Public*, pg. 2024
WYG MANAGEMENT SERVICES LIMITED—See Tetra Tech, Inc.; *U.S. Public*, pg. 2024
WYG NOLAN RYAN TWEEDS LIMITED—See Tetra Tech, Inc.; *U.S. Public*, pg. 2024
WYG PLC—See Tetra Tech, Inc.; *U.S. Public*, pg. 2024
WYKO TIRE TECHNOLOGY INC—See Mesnac Co., Ltd.; *Int'l*, pg. 4840
WYKO TIRE TECHNOLOGY LTD.—See Mesnac Co., Ltd.; *Int'l*, pg. 4840
WYK SORBENTS, LLC; *U.S. Private*, pg. 4576
WYKSTRA OIL CO., INC.; *U.S. Private*, pg. 4576
WYLACO SUPPLY COMPANY, INC.; *U.S. Private*, pg. 4576
WYLAND ENTERPRISES HAWAII LLC—See Wyland Worldwide LLC; *U.S. Private*, pg. 4576
WYLAND STUDIOS INC.—See Wyland Worldwide LLC; *U.S. Private*, pg. 4576
WYLAND WORLDWIDE LLC; *U.S. Private*, pg. 4576
WYLAX INTERNATIONAL B.V.—See Camellia Plc; *Int'l*, pg. 1271
WYLE LABORATORIES, INC.—See KBR, Inc.; *U.S. Public*, pg. 1216
WYLIE IMPLEMENT & SPRAY CENTER-AMARILLO—See Wylie Manufacturing Company; *U.S. Private*, pg. 4576
WYLIE MANUFACTURING COMPANY; *U.S. Private*, pg. 4576
WYLIE MUSSER CHEVROLET CADILLAC; *U.S. Private*, pg. 4576
WYLIE STEEL INC.—See Eagle National Steel Ltd; *U.S. Private*, pg. 1310
WYLLIE GROUP PTY LTD; *Int'l*, pg. 8517
WYLOO METALS PTY. LTD.—See Tattarang Pty. Ltd.; *Int'l*, pg. 7475
WYMAN-GORDON CO. - BRIGHTON—See Berkshire Hathaway Inc.; *U.S. Public*, pg. 315
WYMAN-GORDON COMPANY—See Berkshire Hathaway Inc.; *U.S. Public*, pg. 315
WYMAN-GORDON DE MONTERREY S. DE R.L. DE C.V.—See Berkshire Hathaway Inc.; *U.S. Public*, pg. 315
WYMAN GORDON FORGINGS (CLEVELAND), INC.—See Berkshire Hathaway Inc.; *U.S. Public*, pg. 315
WYMAN-GORDON FORGINGS, INC.—See Berkshire Hathaway Inc.; *U.S. Public*, pg. 315
WYMAN-GORDON LIMITED—See Berkshire Hathaway Inc.; *U.S. Public*, pg. 315
WYMAN-GORDON (LINCOLN) LIMITED—See Berkshire Hathaway Inc.; *U.S. Public*, pg. 315
WYMAN, GREEN & BLALOCK REAL ESTATE, INC.; *U.S. Private*, pg. 4576
WYMT-TV—See Gray Television, Inc.; *U.S. Public*, pg. 960
WYNCOAST INDUSTRIAL PARK PUBLIC COMPANY LIMITED; *Int'l*, pg. 8517
WYNCREST GROUP, INC.; *U.S. Public*, pg. 2384
WYNDALL'S ENTERPRISES INC.; *U.S. Private*, pg. 4576
WYND COMMUNICATIONS CORPORATION—See Kinderhook Industries, LLC; *U.S. Private*, pg. 2306
WYNDEHAM GAIT LIMITED—See Walstead Investments Ltd.; *Int'l*, pg. 8336
WYNDEHAM GRANGE LIMITED—See Walstead Investments Ltd.; *Int'l*, pg. 8336
WYNDEHAM HERON LIMITED—See Walstead Investments Ltd.; *Int'l*, pg. 8336
WYNDEHAM IMPACT LIMITED—See Walstead Investments Ltd.; *Int'l*, pg. 8336

WYNN STARR FLAVORS INC.

WYNDEHAM PETERBOROUGH LIMITED—See Walstead Investments Ltd.; *Int'l*, pg. 8336
WYNDEHAM PRESS GROUP LIMITED—See Walstead Investments Ltd.; *Int'l*, pg. 8336
WYNDEHAM PRINT DIRECT LIMITED—See Walstead Investments Ltd.; *Int'l*, pg. 8336
WYNDEHAM ROCHE LIMITED—See Walstead Investments Ltd.; *Int'l*, pg. 8336
WYNDHAM BRANSON AT THE MEADOWS—See Travel & Leisure Co.; *U.S. Public*, pg. 2185
WYNDHAM CAPITAL MORTGAGE, INC.—See SoFi Technologies, Inc.; *U.S. Public*, pg. 1899
WYNDHAM CONSUMER FINANCE, INC.—See Travel & Leisure Co.; *U.S. Public*, pg. 2185
WYNDHAM EXCHANGE AND RENTALS, INC.—See Travel & Leisure Co.; *U.S. Public*, pg. 2185
WYNDHAM GOVERNOR'S GREEN—See Travel & Leisure Co.; *U.S. Public*, pg. 2185
WYNDHAM GROUP INC.; *U.S. Private*, pg. 4576
WYNDHAM HOTELS & RESORTS, INC.; *U.S. Public*, pg. 2384
WYNDHAM HOTELS & RESORTS, LLC—See Travel & Leisure Co.; *U.S. Public*, pg. 2185
WYNDHAM JADE LLC; *U.S. Private*, pg. 4576
WYNDHAM KINGSGATE—See Travel & Leisure Co.; *U.S. Public*, pg. 2185
WYNDHAM OCEAN RIDGE—See Travel & Leisure Co.; *U.S. Public*, pg. 2186
WYNDHAM PAGOSA—See Travel & Leisure Co.; *U.S. Public*, pg. 2186
WYNDHAM RESORT AT FAIRFIELD BAY—See Travel & Leisure Co.; *U.S. Public*, pg. 2186
WYNDHAM RESORT AT FAIRFIELD MOUNTAINS—See Travel & Leisure Co.; *U.S. Public*, pg. 2186
WYNDHAM RESORT AT FAIRFIELD PLANTATION—See Travel & Leisure Co.; *U.S. Public*, pg. 2186
WYNDHAM ROYAL VISTA—See Travel & Leisure Co.; *U.S. Public*, pg. 2186
WYNDHAM SANTA BARBARA RESORT & YACHT CLUB—See Travel & Leisure Co.; *U.S. Public*, pg. 2186
WYNDHAM SEAWATCH PLANTATION—See Travel & Leisure Co.; *U.S. Public*, pg. 2186
WYNDHAM SUPPLIES PTE LTD—See Allgreen Properties Ltd.; *Int'l*, pg. 338
WYNDHAM VACATION OWNERSHIP AT PATRIOTS PLACE—See Travel & Leisure Co.; *U.S. Public*, pg. 2185
WYNDHAM VACATION OWNERSHIP, INC.—See Travel & Leisure Co.; *U.S. Public*, pg. 2185
WYNDHAM VACATION RESORTS, INC.—See Travel & Leisure Co.; *U.S. Public*, pg. 2185
WYNDHAM VACATION RESORTS—See Travel & Leisure Co.; *U.S. Public*, pg. 2186
WYNDHAM WESTWINDS—See Travel & Leisure Co.; *U.S. Public*, pg. 2186
WYNGATE INTERNATIONAL, INC.; *U.S. Private*, pg. 4576
WYNIT DISTRIBUTION, LLC—See WYNIT, Inc; *U.S. Private*, pg. 4576
WYNIT, INC.; *U.S. Private*, pg. 4576
WYNNCHURCH CAPITAL, L.P.; *U.S. Private*, pg. 4576
WYNNCOM, INC.—See Fortran Corporation; *U.S. Public*, pg. 872
WYNNDEL BOX AND LUMBER CO. LTD.—See Canfor Corporation; *Int'l*, pg. 1291
WYNN DESIGN & DEVELOPMENT, LLC—See Wynn Resorts Limited; *U.S. Public*, pg. 2384
WYNNE BUILDING CORPORATION; *U.S. Private*, pg. 4578
WYNNE RESIDENTIAL CORPORATE HOUSING; *U.S. Private*, pg. 4578
WYNNE SYSTEMS, INC.—See Constellation Software Inc.; *Int'l*, pg. 1776
WYNNE TRANSPORT SERVICE INC.; *U.S. Private*, pg. 4578
WYNN LAS VEGAS, LLC—See Wynn Resorts Limited; *U.S. Public*, pg. 2384
WYNN MACAU, LIMITED—See Wynn Resorts Limited; *U.S. Public*, pg. 2385
WYNN OIL COMPANY—See Illinois Tool Works Inc.; *U.S. Public*, pg. 1111
WYNN OIL (SOUTH AFRICA) (PTY) LTD.—See Illinois Tool Works Inc.; *U.S. Public*, pg. 1111
WYNN O. JONES & ASSOCIATES; *U.S. Private*, pg. 4576
WYNN PROPERTIES, INC.; *U.S. Private*, pg. 4576
WYNN RESORTS LIMITED; *U.S. Public*, pg. 2384
WYNN'S AUTOMOTIVE FRANCE SAS—See Illinois Tool Works Inc.; *U.S. Public*, pg. 1111
WYNNS COONAWARRA ESTATE PTY. LTD—See Treasury Wine Estates Limited; *Int'l*, pg. 7909
WYNNS SALES & SERVICE INC.; *U.S. Private*, pg. 4578
WYNN STARR FLAVORS INC.; *U.S. Private*, pg. 4576
WYNNSTAY (AGRICULTURAL SUPPLIES) LIMITED—See Wynnstay Group Plc; *Int'l*, pg. 8517
WYNNSTAY ARABLE—See Wynnstay Group Plc; *Int'l*, pg. 8517
WYNNSTAY & CLWYD FARMERS LIMITED—See Wynnstay Group Plc; *Int'l*, pg. 8517

WYNNSTAY GROUP PLC; *Int'l*, pg. 8517
WYNNSTAY PROPERTIES PLC; *Int'l*, pg. 8517
WYNNSTAY—See Wynnstay Group Plc; *Int'l*, pg. 8517
WYNRIGHT CORPORATION—See Daifuku Co., Ltd.; *Int'l*, pg. 1926
WYNSTON HILL CAPITAL LLC—See ALT5 Sigma Corporation; *U.S. Public*, pg. 85
WYNWOOD BREWING COMPANY, LLC—See Anheuser-Busch InBev SA/NV; *Int'l*, pg. 465
WYNYARD PROPERTIES HOLDINGS LIMITED—See Brookfield Corporation; *Int'l*, pg. 1189
WYNYARD PROPERTIES PTY LIMITED—See Brookfield Corporation; *Int'l*, pg. 1189
WYODAK RESOURCES DEVELOPMENT CORP.—See Black Hills Corporation; *U.S. Public*, pg. 341
WYOMING BANK & TRUST; *U.S. Private*, pg. 4578
WYOMING BUSINESS COUNCIL - AGRIBUSINESS DIVISION—See Wyoming Business Council; *U.S. Private*, pg. 4578
WYOMING BUSINESS COUNCIL; *U.S. Private*, pg. 4578
WYOMING BUSINESS REPORT—See Adams Publishing Group, LLC; *U.S. Private*, pg. 75
WYOMING COMMUNITY FOUNDATION; *U.S. Private*, pg. 4578
WYOMING FINANCIAL INSURANCE COMPANY—See Hellman & Friedman LLC; *U.S. Private*, pg. 1910
WYOMING INTERSTATE COMPANY, L.L.C.—See Kinder Morgan, Inc.; *U.S. Public*, pg. 1232
WYOMING MACHINERY COMPANY; *U.S. Private*, pg. 4579
WYOMING MEDICAL CENTER; *U.S. Private*, pg. 4579
WYOMING MILLWORK CO.—See Builders FirstSource, Inc.; *U.S. Public*, pg. 410
WYOMING NEWSPAPERS INC.—See News Media Corporation; *U.S. Private*, pg. 2917
WYOMING NEWSPAPERS INC.—See News Media Corporation; *U.S. Private*, pg. 2917
WYOMING TITLE & ESCROW COMPANY, INC.—See First American Financial Corporation; *U.S. Public*, pg. 838
WYOMING URANIUM LLC—See Strathmore Plus Uranium Corp; *Int'l*, pg. 7237
WYOMING VALLEY MOTORS; *U.S. Private*, pg. 4579
WYOMING WHISKEY, INC—See The Edrington Group; *Int'l*, pg. 7638
WYOU-TV—See Mission Broadcasting, Inc.; *U.S. Private*, pg. 2747
WYSADA; *Int'l*, pg. 8517
WYSE ADVERTISING, INC.—See Falls Communications, Inc; *U.S. Private*, pg. 1468
WYSEPOWER LIMITED—See Dubai World Corporation; *Int'l*, pg. 2220
WYSE; *U.S. Private*, pg. 4579
WYSE TECHNOLOGY AUSTRALIA PTY LIMITED—See Dell Technologies Inc.; *U.S. Public*, pg. 650
WYSE TECHNOLOGY INC.—See Dell Technologies Inc.; *U.S. Public*, pg. 650
WYSE TECHNOLOGY (UK) LIMITED—See Dell Technologies Inc.; *U.S. Public*, pg. 650
WYSIWYG STUDIOS CO., LTD.; *Int'l*, pg. 8517
WYSOKA WIND FARM SP. Z.O.O.—See Falck S.p.A.; *Int'l*, pg. 2610
WYSS KIESWERK AG—See Vicat S.A.; *Int'l*, pg. 8186
WYSTRACH GMBH—See Hexagon Composites ASA; *Int'l*, pg. 3370
WYTECH INDUSTRIES, INC.—See Vance Street Capital LLC; *U.S. Private*, pg. 4342
WYTEC INTERNATIONAL, INC.; *U.S. Private*, pg. 4579
WYTHE COUNTY COMMUNITY HOSPITAL, LLC—See Apollo Global Management, Inc.; *U.S. Public*, pg. 159
WYTWORNIA PODKLADOW STRUNOBETONOWYCH S.A.—See Bain Capital, LP; *U.S. Private*, pg. 438
WYTWORNIA SPRZETU KOMUNIKACYJNEGO S.A.—See Leonardo S.p.A.; *Int'l*, pg. 4461
WYVERN RESTAURANTS INC.; *U.S. Private*, pg. 4579
WYZZ, INC.—See Sinclair, Inc.; *U.S. Public*, pg. 1887
WZ FRANCHISE CORP.; *U.S. Private*, pg. 4579
WZLX-FM—See AUDACY, INC.; *U.S. Public*, pg. 226
WZS BINARAYA SDN BHD—See Citaglobal Berhad; *Int'l*, pg. 1619
WZS MISI SETIA SDN BHD—See Citaglobal Berhad; *Int'l*, pg. 1619
WZTV-TV—See Sinclair, Inc.; *U.S. Public*, pg. 1888
WZVN TV ABC 7—See Waterman Broadcasting Corp.; *U.S. Private*, pg. 4454
WZZM-TV—See TEGNA Inc.; *U.S. Public*, pg. 1991

X

X1 ESPORTS & ENTERTAINMENT LTD.; *Int'l*, pg. 8518
X20 JOINT STOCK COMPANY; *Int'l*, pg. 8518
X2 DEVELOPMENT CORPORATION—See Follett Corporation; *U.S. Private*, pg. 1559
X2M CONNECT LIMITED; *Int'l*, pg. 8518
X2NSAT, INC.; *U.S. Private*, pg. 4579
X3 HOLDINGS CO., LTD.; *Int'l*, pg. 8518
X3 TELECOMUNICACOES E EQUIPAMENTOS LTDA.; *Int'l*, pg. 8518

X4 PHARMACEUTICALS (AUSTRIA) GMBH—See X4 Pharmaceuticals, Inc.; *U.S. Public*, pg. 2385
X4 PHARMACEUTICALS, INC.; *U.S. Public*, pg. 2385
X5 RETAIL GROUP N.V.; *Int'l*, pg. 8518
X5 SOLUTIONS—See NewSpring Capital LLC; *U.S. Private*, pg. 2918
X8E, INC; *U.S. Private*, pg. 4579
X8NET SDN. BHD.—See N2N Connect Berhad; *Int'l*, pg. 5117
XAAR AMERICAS INC.—See Xaar PLC; *Int'l*, pg. 8518
XAAR ASIA-PACIFIC—See Xaar PLC; *Int'l*, pg. 8518
XAARJET LIMITED—See Xaar PLC; *Int'l*, pg. 8519
XAARJET (OVERSEAS) LIMITED—See Xaar PLC; *Int'l*, pg. 8518
XAAR KOREA—See Xaar PLC; *Int'l*, pg. 8518
XAAR PLC; *Int'l*, pg. 8518
XAAR TECHNOLOGY LIMITED—See Xaar PLC; *Int'l*, pg. 8518
XAC AUTOMATION CORP.; *Int'l*, pg. 8519
XACCT ACCOUNTING AS—See TowerBrook Capital Partners, L.P.; *U.S. Private*, pg. 4195
XACT ERP SOLUTIONS (PTY) LTD—See ARB HOLDINGS LIMITED; *Int'l*, pg. 537
XACT FONDER AB—See Svenska Handelsbanken AB; *Int'l*, pg. 7358
XACTI CORPORATION—See Advantage Partners LLP; *Int'l*, pg. 164
XACTLY CORPORATION—See Vista Equity Partners, LLC; *U.S. Private*, pg. 4402
XACTWARE INC.; *U.S. Private*, pg. 4579
XACTWARE SOLUTIONS, INC.—See Verisk Analytics, Inc.; *U.S. Public*, pg. 2283
XADCERA BIOPHARMACEUTICAL (SUZHOU) CO., LTD.—See Biocytogen Pharmaceuticals (Beijing) Co., Ltd.; *Int'l*, pg. 1037
XAEL CHARTERS INC.; *U.S. Private*, pg. 4579
XAFINITY CONSULTING LIMITED—See XPS Pensions Group; *Int'l*, pg. 8538
XAIT AS; *Int'l*, pg. 8519
XALI GOLD CORP.; *Int'l*, pg. 8519
XALLES HOLDINGS INC.; *U.S. Public*, pg. 2385
XALOY EXTRUSION LLC—See Nordson Corporation; *U.S. Public*, pg. 1534
XALT ENERGY, LLC—See Freudenberg SE; *Int'l*, pg. 2788
XAMARIN INC.—See Microsoft Corporation; *U.S. Public*, pg. 1440
XAMAX INDUSTRIES, INC.; *U.S. Private*, pg. 4580
XAMBLE GROUP LIMITED; *Int'l*, pg. 8519
XANADU MINES LIMITED; *Int'l*, pg. 8519
XANADU MINES MONGOLIA LLC—See Xanadu Mines Limited; *Int'l*, pg. 8519
XANADU PUBLISHING (AUSTRALIA) LTD.—See Jiangsu Phoenix Publishing & Media Corporation Ltd.; *Int'l*, pg. 3952
XANADU PUBLISHING LTD.—See Jiangsu Phoenix Publishing & Media Corporation Ltd.; *Int'l*, pg. 3952
XANDER INTERNATIONAL CORP.—See VIA Technologies, Inc.; *Int'l*, pg. 8183
XANDER RESOURCES INC.; *Int'l*, pg. 8519
XANDR INC.—See AT&T Inc.; *U.S. Public*, pg. 220
XANDRION BELGIE BVBA—See Compass Group PLC; *Int'l*, pg. 1752
XANDRION B.V.—See Compass Group PLC; *Int'l*, pg. 1752
XANDROS INC.; *U.S. Private*, pg. 4580
XANEDU PUBLISHING, INC.—See Frontenac Company LLC; *U.S. Private*, pg. 1614
XANGATI, INC.—See Virtual Instruments, Inc.; *U.S. Private*, pg. 4389
XANGE PRIVATE EQUITY, S.A.—See Groupe Siparex; *Int'l*, pg. 3111
XANGO GOODNESS—See XanGo, LLC; *U.S. Private*, pg. 4580
XANGO, LLC; *U.S. Private*, pg. 4580
XANITOS, INC.—See Angeles Equity Partners, LLC; *U.S. Private*, pg. 282
XANO INDUSTRI AB; *Int'l*, pg. 8519
XANTERRA LEISURE HOLDING, LLC—See The Anschutz Corporation; *U.S. Private*, pg. 3987
XANTERRA PARKS & RESORTS, INC.—See The Anschutz Corporation; *U.S. Private*, pg. 3987
XANTERRA SOUTH RIM, LLC—See The Anschutz Corporation; *U.S. Private*, pg. 3987
XANTREX TECHNOLOGY, INC.—See Windjammer Capital Investors, LLC; *U.S. Private*, pg. 4538
XANTRION, INC.; *U.S. Private*, pg. 4580
XAP CORPORATION; *U.S. Private*, pg. 4580
XARA GROUP LTD.—See MAGIX AG; *Int'l*, pg. 4638
XARXA OBERTA DE COMUNICACIO I TECNOLOGIA DE CATALUNYA S.A.—See Orient Securities Company Limited; *Int'l*, pg. 5622
XA, THE EXPERIENTIAL AGENCY, INC.; *U.S. Private*, pg. 4579
XATOR CORPORATION—See Parsons Corporation; *U.S. Public*, pg. 1651
XAU RESOURCES, INC.; *Int'l*, pg. 8519
XAUTOMATA TECHNOLOGY GMBH—See Sesa S.p.A.; *Int'l*, pg. 6729

XAVER BACHNER GMBH—See STRABAG SE; *Int'l*, pg. 7233
XAVER FASSIN GMBH; *Int'l*, pg. 8519
XAVIENT INFORMATION SYSTEMS, INC.—See TELUS CORPORATION; *Int'l*, pg. 7546
XAVIER CREATIVE HOUSE LLC; *U.S. Private*, pg. 4580
XAVIS CO., LTD.; *Int'l*, pg. 8520
XAXIS, LLC—See WPP plc; *Int'l*, pg. 8491
XBIOTECH INC.; *U.S. Public*, pg. 2385
XBOX GAME STUDIOS—See Microsoft Corporation; *U.S. Public*, pg. 1440
XBOX—See Microsoft Corporation; *U.S. Public*, pg. 1440
XBRANE BIOPHARMA AB; *Int'l*, pg. 8520
XBRIDGE LIMITED—See The Travelers Companies, Inc.; *U.S. Public*, pg. 2136
XBYTE TECHNOLOGIES, INC.; *U.S. Private*, pg. 4580
XCALIBRE RISK SERVICES, INC.—See Atlantic American Corporation; *U.S. Public*, pg. 222
XCANA PETROLEUM CORP.; *U.S. Public*, pg. 2385
XCCENT INC.; *U.S. Private*, pg. 4580
XCD ENERGY PTY LTD—See 88 Energy Limited; *Int'l*, pg. 15
XCEDE TECHNOLOGIES, INC.—See Dynasil Corporation of America; *U.S. Public*, pg. 1300
XCEED CUSTOMER CARE MAROC—See Telecom Egypt; *Int'l*, pg. 7530
XCEED GROUP LIMITED—See Wavestone SA; *Int'l*, pg. 8360
XCEED MORTGAGE CORPORATION—See MCAN Mortgage Corporation; *Int'l*, pg. 4755
XCEED PASIFIKA LIMITED—See Fiji National Provident Fund; *Int'l*, pg. 2661
XCEIVE CORPORATION—See Sofinnova Ventures, Inc.; *U.S. Private*, pg. 3704
XCELAERO CORP.—See Bascom Hunter Technologies Inc.; *U.S. Private*, pg. 484
XCEL BRANDS, INC.; *U.S. Public*, pg. 2385
X-CEL CONTACTS—See Walman Optical Company; *U.S. Private*, pg. 4432
XCEL ENERGY INC.; *U.S. Public*, pg. 2385
XCEL ENERGY SERVICES INCORPORATED—See Xcel Energy Inc.; *U.S. Public*, pg. 2385
XCELERA INC.; *Int'l*, pg. 8520
XCELERATE MEDIA; *U.S. Private*, pg. 4580
XCEL ERECTORS, INC.—See SPX Technologies, Inc.; *U.S. Public*, pg. 1921
XCELERON, INC.—See Pharmaron Beijing Co., Ltd.; *Int'l*, pg. 5841
XCEL FINANCIAL LLC; *U.S. Private*, pg. 4580
XCELIENCE, LLC—See Lonza Group AG; *Int'l*, pg. 4553
XCELIGENT, INC.; *U.S. Private*, pg. 4580
XCELIRON CORP.—See PLANSEE Holding AG; *Int'l*, pg. 5890
XCELLENCE, INC.—See JLL Partners, LLC; *U.S. Private*, pg. 2213
XCELLENT AUTOMATISERING B.V.—See Dustin Group AB; *Int'l*, pg. 2235
X-CELL TOOL & MOLD, INC.—See Crestview Partners, L.P.; *U.S. Private*, pg. 1099
XCEL MANAGEMENT, INC.; *U.S. Private*, pg. 4580
XCEL MECHANICAL SYSTEMS, INC.; *U.S. Private*, pg. 4580
XCELMOBILITY INC.; *U.S. Public*, pg. 2385
XCELOM LIMITED—See Berry Genomics Co., Ltd.; *Int'l*, pg. 989
X-CEL OPTICAL CO.; *U.S. Private*, pg. 4579
XCELPLUS INTERNATIONAL, INC.; *U.S. Public*, pg. 2385
XCEL POWER SYSTEMS LTD.—See TransDigm Group Incorporated; *U.S. Public*, pg. 2182
XCEL SOLUTIONS, CORP.; *U.S. Public*, pg. 2385
X-CEL STEEL FABRICATING, INC.—See Hess Industries, Inc.; *U.S. Private*, pg. 1927
XCENDA, LLC—See Cencora, Inc.; *U.S. Public*, pg. 467
XCEND GROUP, INC.; *U.S. Private*, pg. 4580
XCENTRIC MOLD & ENGINEERING, LLC—See Trilantic Capital Management L.P.; *U.S. Private*, pg. 4231
XCEO, INC.; *U.S. Private*, pg. 4580
XCERRA CORPORATION - MILPITAS—See Cohu, Inc.; *U.S. Public*, pg. 530
XCERRA CORPORATION—See Cohu, Inc.; *U.S. Public*, pg. 530
XCHANGE BENEFITS, LLC—See Ambac Financial Group, Inc.; *U.S. Public*, pg. 92
XCHANGE GROUP LLC; *U.S. Private*, pg. 4580
XCHANGE SOFTWARE; *U.S. Private*, pg. 4580
XCHANGE TELECOM CORP.—See Nova Infrastructure Management, LLC; *U.S. Private*, pg. 2965
XCHANGING GLOBAL INSURANCE SOLUTIONS LIMITED—See DXC Technology Company; *U.S. Public*, pg. 697
XCHANGING, INC.—See DXC Technology Company; *U.S. Public*, pg. 697
XCHANGING ITALY S.P.A.—See DXC Technology Company; *U.S. Public*, pg. 697
XCHANGING LIMITED—See DXC Technology Company; *U.S. Public*, pg. 695
XCHANGING SOLUTIONS LIMITED—See DXC Technology Company; *U.S. Public*, pg. 695

COMPANY NAME INDEX

XCHEM INTERNATIONAL LLC—See H.B. Fuller Company; *U.S. Public*, pg. 978
XCINA CONSULTING LIMITED—See Shearwater Group plc; *Int'l*, pg. 6792
XCIRA, LLC—See RB Global, Inc.; *Int'l*, pg. 6227
XCLINICAL GMBH; *Int'l*, pg. 8520
XCLUTCHUSA, INC.—See Amotiv Limited; *Int'l*, pg. 431
XCMG CONSTRUCTION MACHINERY CO., LTD.—See Xuzhou Construction Machinery Group Co., Ltd.; *Int'l*, pg. 8540
XCMG XUZHOU TRUCK-MOUNTED CRANE CO., LTD.—See Xuzhou Construction Machinery Group Co., Ltd.; *Int'l*, pg. 8541
XCOM MEDIA PTY LTD—See OtherLevels Holdings Limited; *Int'l*, pg. 5657
X.COMMERCE, INC.—See Adobe Inc.; *U.S. Public*, pg. 43
XCONNECT AMERICAS, INC.—See Somos, Inc.; *U.S. Private*, pg. 3712
XCONNECT GLOBAL NETWORKS (ISRAEL) LTD—See Somos, Inc.; *U.S. Private*, pg. 3712
XCONNECT GLOBAL NETWORKS LTD—See Somos, Inc.; *U.S. Private*, pg. 3712
XCONOMY, INC.; *U.S. Private*, pg. 4580
XCOR AEROSPACE, INC.; *U.S. Private*, pg. 4580
X CORP.; *U.S. Private*, pg. 4579
XC TRADING HONG KONG LIMITED—See Xerox Holdings Corporation; *U.S. Public*, pg. 2388
XC TRADING SINGAPORE PTE LTD—See Xerox Holdings Corporation; *U.S. Public*, pg. 2388
XC TRAINS LIMITED—See Deutsche Bahn AG; *Int'l*, pg. 2055
XCURE CORP, LTD.; *Int'l*, pg. 8520
XDATA SOLUTIONS INC.—See Constellation Software Inc.; *Int'l*, pg. 1773
XDC INDUSTRIES (SHENZHEN) LTD.; *Int'l*, pg. 8520
XDC S.A.—See EVS Broadcast Equipment S.A.; *Int'l*, pg. 2574
XD INC.; *Int'l*, pg. 8520
X-DIN INC.—See Alten S.A.; *Int'l*, pg. 391
XDSL NETWORKING SOLUTIONS (PTY) LTD—See Stellar Capital Partners Limited; *Int'l*, pg. 7204
XDUCE CORP.; *U.S. Private*, pg. 4581
XEBEC ADSORPTION ASIA PTE LTD.—See Xebec Adsorption Inc.; *Int'l*, pg. 8520
XEBEC ADSORPTION EUROPE SRL.—See Xebec Adsorption Inc.; *Int'l*, pg. 8520
XEBEC ADSORPTION INC.; *Int'l*, pg. 8520
XEBEC ADSORPTION (SHANGHAI) CO. LTD.—See Xebec Adsorption Inc.; *Int'l*, pg. 8520
XEBEC ADSORPTION USA, INC.—See Xebec Adsorption Inc.; *Int'l*, pg. 8520
XEBEC CORPORATION; *U.S. Private*, pg. 4581
XEBEC CORPORATION—See TOA Corporation; *Int'l*, pg. 7769
XEBEX, INC.—See Ushio, Inc.; *Int'l*, pg. 8098
XEBIO HOLDINGS CO., LTD.; *Int'l*, pg. 8520
XEBRA BRANDS LTD.; *Int'l*, pg. 8521
XE.COM INC.—See Daseke, Inc.; *U.S. Private*, pg. 1162
XEGO-IT GMBH—See Nippon Telegraph & Telephone Corporation; *Int'l*, pg. 5355
XEIKON AMERICA, INC.—See Koch Industries, Inc.; *U.S. Private*, pg. 2327
XEIKON AMERICA, INC.—See The Goldman Sachs Group, Inc.; *U.S. Public*, pg. 2077
XEIKON JAPAN CO., LTD.—See Koch Industries, Inc.; *U.S. Private*, pg. 2327
XEIKON JAPAN CO., LTD.—See The Goldman Sachs Group, Inc.; *U.S. Public*, pg. 2077
XEIKON MANUFACTURING AND R&D CENTER—See Koch Industries, Inc.; *U.S. Private*, pg. 2327
XEIKON MANUFACTURING AND R&D CENTER—See The Goldman Sachs Group, Inc.; *U.S. Public*, pg. 2077
XEIKON NV—See Koch Industries, Inc.; *U.S. Private*, pg. 2327
XEIKON NV—See The Goldman Sachs Group, Inc.; *U.S. Public*, pg. 2077
XEI SCIENTIFIC, INC.; *U.S. Private*, pg. 4581
XELEB TECHNOLOGIES, INC.—See Xurpas Inc.; *Int'l*, pg. 8540
XELERATED AB—See Marvell Technology Group Ltd.; *Int'l*, pg. 4717
XELLA INTERNATIONAL GMBH—See Lone Star Global Acquisitions, LLC; *U.S. Private*, pg. 2489
XELLA KALKZANDSTEENFABRIEK HOOGDONK B.V.—See Lone Star Global Acquisitions, LLC; *U.S. Private*, pg. 2489
XELLA NEDERLAND B.V.—See Lone Star Global Acquisitions, LLC; *U.S. Private*, pg. 2489
XELLERATION, LLC—See Speridian Technologies, LLC; *U.S. Private*, pg. 3756
XELLIA PHARMACEUTICALS APS—See Novo Nordisk Fonden; *Int'l*, pg. 5465
XELLIA PHARMACEUTICALS AS—See Novo Nordisk Fonden; *Int'l*, pg. 5465
XELLIA PHARMACEUTICALS LTD.—See Novo Nordisk Fonden; *Int'l*, pg. 5465
XELLIA (TAIZHOU) PHARMACEUTICALS CO., LTD.—See Novo Nordisk Fonden; *Int'l*, pg. 5465
XELPMOC DESIGN & TECH LTD.; *Int'l*, pg. 8521

XEMEX GROUP, INC.; *U.S. Public*, pg. 2385
XEMPLAR ENERGY CORP.; *Int'l*, pg. 8521
XENCOR, INC.; *U.S. Public*, pg. 2385
XENEL INDUSTRIES LTD.; *Int'l*, pg. 8521
XENEMETRIX LTD.; *Int'l*, pg. 8521
XENER SYSTEMS INC.; *Int'l*, pg. 8521
XENESYS INC. - IMARI PLANT—See POSCO Holdings Inc.; *Int'l*, pg. 5938
XENESYS INC.—See POSCO Holdings Inc.; *Int'l*, pg. 5938
XENETIC BIOSCIENCES, INC.; *U.S. Public*, pg. 2386
XENETIC BIOSCIENCES PLC—See Xenetic Biosciences, Inc.; *U.S. Public*, pg. 2386
XENETIC OY—See Elisa Corporation; *Int'l*, pg. 2362
XENIA BROKING GROUP LIMITED—See Brown & Brown, Inc.; *U.S. Public*, pg. 402
XENIA BROKING LIMITED—See Brown & Brown, Inc.; *U.S. Public*, pg. 402
XENIA HOTELLERIE SOLUTION S.P.A.; *Int'l*, pg. 8521
XENIA HOTELS & RESORTS, INC.; *U.S. Public*, pg. 2386
XENIA INSURANCE CO. LTD.—See Societe BIC S.A.; *Int'l*, pg. 7037
XENIA MANUFACTURING INC.; *U.S. Private*, pg. 4581
XENIA PHARMA PVT. LTD.—See Pila Pharma AB; *Int'l*, pg. 5866
XENIA REPLY S.R.L.—See Reply S.p.A.; *Int'l*, pg. 6291
XENIA VENTURE CAPITAL LTD.; *Int'l*, pg. 8521
XENICS N.V.; *Int'l*, pg. 8521
XENITH IP GROUP PTY. LIMITED—See IPH Limited; *Int'l*, pg. 3797
XENOBIOTIC LABORATORIES, INC.—See WuXi PharmaTech (Cayman) Inc.; *Int'l*, pg. 8515
XENOMAX-JAPAN CO., LTD.—See Nagase & Co., Ltd.; *Int'l*, pg. 5128
XENON PHARMACEUTICALS INC.; *Int'l*, pg. 8521
XENOPHON STRATEGIES; *U.S. Private*, pg. 4581
XENOSOFT TECHNOLOGIES; *U.S. Private*, pg. 4581
XENOTECH, LLC—See BioIVT, LLC; *U.S. Private*, pg. 562
XENOUS HOLDINGS, INC.; *Int'l*, pg. 8521
XENSPIRE, INC.; *U.S. Private*, pg. 4581
XENTEL INC.—See iMarketing Solutions Group Inc.; *Int'l*, pg. 3620
XENTIQ (PTE.) LTD.—See Vicplas International Ltd; *Int'l*, pg. 8187
XENTURY CITY DEVELOPMENT COMPANY, L.C.; *U.S. Private*, pg. 4581
XEOHEALTH CORPORATION—See Lesaka Technologies, Inc.; *Int'l*, pg. 4469
XEONICS CO., LTD.—See Aroot Co., Ltd.; *Int'l*, pg. 577
XEOS SP. Z O.O.—See Deutsche Lufthansa AG; *Int'l*, pg. 2071
XEPA-SOUL PATTINSON (MALAYSIA) SDN. BHD.—See Apex Healthcare Berhad; *Int'l*, pg. 511
XEPA-SOUL PATTINSON (S) PTE. LTD.—See Apex Healthcare Berhad; *Int'l*, pg. 511
XERAYA CAPITAL SDN BHD—See Khazanah Nasional Berhad; *Int'l*, pg. 4154
XERIANT, INC.; *U.S. Public*, pg. 2386
XERIA S.A.—See VINCI S.A.; *Int'l*, pg. 8240
XERIDIEM MEDICAL DEVICES, INC.—See Kohlberg & Company, LLC; *U.S. Private*, pg. 2338
XERIS BIOPHARMA HOLDINGS, INC.; *U.S. Public*, pg. 2386
XERIS PHARMACEUTICALS, INC.—See Xeris Biopharma Holdings, Inc.; *U.S. Public*, pg. 2386
XERIUM CANADA INC.—See ANDRITZ AG; *Int'l*, pg. 457
XERIUM CHINA CO., LTD.—See ANDRITZ AG; *Int'l*, pg. 457
XERIUM GERMANY HOLDING GMBH—See ANDRITZ AG; *Int'l*, pg. 457
XERIUM TECHNOLOGIES BRASIL INDUSTRIA E COMERCIO S.A.—See ANDRITZ AG; *Int'l*, pg. 457
XERIUM TECHNOLOGIES, INC.—See ANDRITZ AG; *Int'l*, pg. 457
XERIUM TECHNOLOGIES LIMITED—See ANDRITZ AG; *Int'l*, pg. 457
XERO LIMITED; *Int'l*, pg. 8521
XERON, INC.—See Chesapeake Utilities Corporation; *U.S. Public*, pg. 486
XERO PTY LIMITED—See Xero Limited; *Int'l*, pg. 8521
XEROS TECHNOLOGY GROUP PLC; *Int'l*, pg. 8521
XEROX AB—See Xerox Holdings Corporation; *U.S. Public*, pg. 2388
XEROX AG—See Xerox Holdings Corporation; *U.S. Public*, pg. 2389
XEROX ARGENTINA, I.C.S.A.—See Xerox Holdings Corporation; *U.S. Public*, pg. 2389
XEROX AS—See Xerox Holdings Corporation; *U.S. Public*, pg. 2389
XEROX A/S—See Xerox Holdings Corporation; *U.S. Public*, pg. 2388
XEROX AUSTRIA GMBH—See Xerox Holdings Corporation; *U.S. Public*, pg. 2389
XEROX AUSTRIA GMBH—See Xerox Holdings Corporation; *U.S. Public*, pg. 2389
XEROX BURO ARACLARI TICARET VE SERVIS A.S.—See Xerox Holdings Corporation; *U.S. Public*, pg. 2389
XEROX BUSINESS EQUIPMENT LIMITED—See Xerox Holdings Corporation; *U.S. Public*, pg. 2389

XEROX HOLDINGS CORPORATION

XEROX BUSINESS SERVICES—See Xerox Holdings Corporation; *U.S. Public*, pg. 2390
XEROX BUSINESS SOLUTIONS, INC.—See Xerox Holdings Corporation; *U.S. Public*, pg. 2389
XEROX BUSINESS SOLUTIONS NORTHEAST, INC.—See Xerox Holdings Corporation; *U.S. Public*, pg. 2387
XEROX BUSINESS SOLUTIONS SOUTHEAST, LLC—See Xerox Holdings Corporation; *U.S. Public*, pg. 2387
XEROX CANADA FINANCE INC.—See Xerox Holdings Corporation; *U.S. Public*, pg. 2390
XEROX CANADA I LIMITED PARTNERSHIP—See Xerox Holdings Corporation; *U.S. Public*, pg. 2387
XEROX CANADA INC.—See Xerox Holdings Corporation; *U.S. Public*, pg. 2390
XEROX CANADA LTD.—See Xerox Holdings Corporation; *U.S. Public*, pg. 2390
XEROX CANADA N.S. ULC—See Xerox Holdings Corporation; *U.S. Public*, pg. 2390
XEROX CARE & QUALITY SOLUTIONS, INC.—See Xerox Holdings Corporation; *U.S. Public*, pg. 2390
XEROX COMERCIO E INDUSTRIA LTDA—See Xerox Holdings Corporation; *U.S. Public*, pg. 2391
XEROX CORPORATION—See Xerox Holdings Corporation; *U.S. Public*, pg. 2387
XEROX CORP.—See Xerox Holdings Corporation; *U.S. Public*, pg. 2390
XEROX CORP.—See Xerox Holdings Corporation; *U.S. Public*, pg. 2390
XEROX CORP.—See Xerox Holdings Corporation; *U.S. Public*, pg. 2390
XEROX CORP.—See Xerox Holdings Corporation; *U.S. Public*, pg. 2390
XEROX CORP.—See Xerox Holdings Corporation; *U.S. Public*, pg. 2390
XEROX CORP.—See Xerox Holdings Corporation; *U.S. Public*, pg. 2390
XEROX CORP.—See Xerox Holdings Corporation; *U.S. Public*, pg. 2390
XEROX CZECH REPUBLIC S R.O.—See Xerox Holdings Corporation; *U.S. Public*, pg. 2388
XEROX DE CHILE S.A.—See Xerox Holdings Corporation; *U.S. Public*, pg. 2390
XEROX DE COLOMBIA S.A.—See Xerox Holdings Corporation; *U.S. Public*, pg. 2390
XEROX DEL ECUADOR, S.A.—See Xerox Holdings Corporation; *U.S. Public*, pg. 2391
XEROX DEL PERU, S.A.—See Xerox Holdings Corporation; *U.S. Public*, pg. 2391
XEROX DE PANAMA SA—See Xerox Holdings Corporation; *U.S. Public*, pg. 2390
XEROX DE VENEZUELA, C.A.—See Xerox Holdings Corporation; *U.S. Public*, pg. 2390
XEROX DO BRASIL S.A.—See Xerox Holdings Corporation; *U.S. Public*, pg. 2391
XEROX EGYPT S.A.E.—See Xerox Holdings Corporation; *U.S. Public*, pg. 2390
XEROX ESPANA, S.A.U.—See Xerox Holdings Corporation; *U.S. Public*, pg. 2390
XEROX ESPANA, THE DOCUMENT COMPANY SAU—See Xerox Holdings Corporation; *U.S. Public*, pg. 2387
XEROX (EUROPE) LIMITED—See Xerox Holdings Corporation; *U.S. Public*, pg. 2387
XEROX (EUROPE) LTD.—See Xerox Holdings Corporation; *U.S. Public*, pg. 2388
XEROX FINANCE AG—See Xerox Holdings Corporation; *U.S. Public*, pg. 2389
XEROX FINANCE LIMITED—See Xerox Holdings Corporation; *U.S. Public*, pg. 2390
XEROX FINANCIAL SERVICES BELUX NV—See Xerox Holdings Corporation; *U.S. Public*, pg. 2390
XEROX FINANCIAL SERVICES B.V.—See Xerox Holdings Corporation; *U.S. Public*, pg. 2390
XEROX FINANCIAL SERVICES INTERNATIONAL LIMITED—See Xerox Holdings Corporation; *U.S. Public*, pg. 2391
XEROX FINANCIAL SERVICES NORWAY AS—See Xerox Holdings Corporation; *U.S. Public*, pg. 2390
XEROX FINANCIAL SERVICES SVERIGE AB—See Xerox Holdings Corporation; *U.S. Public*, pg. 2390
THE XEROX FOUNDATION INC.—See Xerox Holdings Corporation; *U.S. Public*, pg. 2388
XEROX GLOBAL SERVICES GMBH—See Xerox Holdings Corporation; *U.S. Public*, pg. 2390
XEROX GLOBAL SERVICES LTD.—See Xerox Holdings Corporation; *U.S. Public*, pg. 2389
XEROX GMBH—See Xerox Holdings Corporation; *U.S. Public*, pg. 2389
XEROX HELLAS AEE—See Xerox Holdings Corporation; *U.S. Public*, pg. 2390
XEROX HOLDING DEUTSCHLAND GMBH—See Xerox Holdings Corporation; *U.S. Public*, pg. 2390
XEROX HOLDINGS CORPORATION; *U.S. Public*, pg. 2386
XEROX INTERNATIONAL PARTNERS—See FUJIFILM Holdings Corporation; *Int'l*, pg. 2825
XEROX (IRELAND) LIMITED—See Xerox Holdings Corporation; *U.S. Public*, pg. 2388
XEROX ISRAEL LTD—See Xerox Holdings Corporation; *U.S. Public*, pg. 2390

XEROX HOLDINGS CORPORATION   CORPORATE AFFILIATIONS

XEROX ITALIA RENTAL SERVICES SRL—See Xerox Holdings Corporation; *U.S. Public*, pg. 2390
XEROX IT SERVICES LIMITED—See Xerox Holdings Corporation; *U.S. Public*, pg. 2390
XEROX LEASING DEUTSCHLAND GMBH—See Xerox Holdings Corporation; *U.S. Public*, pg. 2389
XEROX LIMITED AG—See Xerox Holdings Corporation; *U.S. Public*, pg. 2389
XEROX LIMITED—See Xerox Holdings Corporation; *U.S. Public*, pg. 2389
XEROX LUXEMBOURG SA—See Xerox Holdings Corporation; *U.S. Public*, pg. 2390
XEROX MANUFACTURING NEDERLAND B.V.—See Xerox Holdings Corporation; *U.S. Public*, pg. 2389
XEROX MAROC S.A.—See Xerox Holdings Corporation; *U.S. Public*, pg. 2390
XEROX MEXICANA, S.A. DE C.V.—See Xerox Holdings Corporation; *U.S. Public*, pg. 2390
XEROX (NEDERLAND) BV—See Xerox Holdings Corporation; *U.S. Public*, pg. 2389
XEROX (NETHERLAND) B.V.—See Xerox Holdings Corporation; *U.S. Public*, pg. 2389
XEROX OY—See Xerox Holdings Corporation; *U.S. Public*, pg. 2389
XEROX PENSIONS LTD—See Xerox Holdings Corporation; *U.S. Public*, pg. 2389
XEROX POLSKA SP ZOO—See Xerox Holdings Corporation; *U.S. Public*, pg. 2389
XEROX PORTUGAL—See Xerox Holdings Corporation; *U.S. Public*, pg. 2389
XEROX PROPERTY SERVICES LIMITED—See Xerox Holdings Corporation; *U.S. Public*, pg. 2390
XEROX REAL ESTATE & GENERAL SERVICES—See Xerox Holdings Corporation; *U.S. Public*, pg. 2390
XEROX REALTY CORPORATION—See Xerox Holdings Corporation; *U.S. Public*, pg. 2390
XEROX RENTING S.A.U.—See Xerox Holdings Corporation; *U.S. Public*, pg. 2390
XEROX REPROGRAPHISCHE SERVICES GMBH—See Xerox Holdings Corporation; *U.S. Public*, pg. 2390
XEROX RESEARCH CENTER OF WEBSTER (XRCW)—See Xerox Holdings Corporation; *U.S. Public*, pg. 2390
XEROX SA—See Xerox Holdings Corporation; *U.S. Public*, pg. 2389
XEROX SLOVENIA D.O.O—See Xerox Holdings Corporation; *U.S. Public*, pg. 2390
XEROX SOUTH AFRICA (PROPRIETARY) LIMITED—See Xerox Holdings Corporation; *U.S. Public*, pg. 2390
XEROX S.P.A.—See Xerox Holdings Corporation; *U.S. Public*, pg. 2389
XEROX UKRAINE—See Xerox Holdings Corporation; *U.S. Public*, pg. 2390
XERVICES GMBH—See flatexDEGIRO AG; *Int'l*, pg. 2698
XERVON GMBH—See RETHMANN AG & Co. KG; *Int'l*, pg. 6307
XERXES COMPUTER COMPANY, LLC—See PosNavitas Retail Services, Inc.; *U.S. Private*, pg. 3234
XERXES CORPORATION—See ShawCor Ltd.; *Int'l*, pg. 6791
XETEX INC.; *U.S. Private*, pg. 4581
XETICS GMBH—See TRUMPF SE + Co. KG; *Int'l*, pg. 7943
XEVO INC.—See Lear Corporation; *U.S. Public*, pg. 1298
XEXEC INC.—See ABRY Partners, LLC; *U.S. Private*, pg. 43
XEXEC INC.—See Castik Capital S.a.r.l.; *Int'l*, pg. 1356
XEXEC LIMITED—See ABRY Partners, LLC; *U.S. Private*, pg. 43
XEXEC LIMITED—See Castik Capital S.a.r.l.; *Int'l*, pg. 1356
XEY CORP. EMPRESARIAL, S.L.—See Masco Corporation; *U.S. Public*, pg. 1391
X-FAB DRESDEN GMBH & CO. KG—See X-FAB Silicon Foundries GmbH; *Int'l*, pg. 8518
X-FAB FRANCE SAS—See X-FAB Silicon Foundries GmbH; *Int'l*, pg. 8518
X-FAB MEMS FOUNDRY ITZEHOE GMBH—See X-FAB Silicon Foundries GmbH; *Int'l*, pg. 8518
X-FAB SARAWAK SDN. BHD.—See X-FAB Silicon Foundries GmbH; *Int'l*, pg. 8518
X-FAB SEMICONDUCTOR FOUNDRIES GMBH—See X-FAB Silicon Foundries GmbH; *Int'l*, pg. 8518
X-FAB SILICON FOUNDRIES GMBH; *Int'l*, pg. 8518
X-FAB TEXAS, INC.—See X-FAB Silicon Foundries GmbH; *Int'l*, pg. 8518
XFACT, INC.; *U.S. Private*, pg. 4581
X-FACTOR COMMUNICATIONS HOLDINGS, INC.; *U.S. Public*, pg. 2385
XF ENTERPRISES INC.; *U.S. Private*, pg. 4581
XFERA MOVILES S.A.—See Orange S.A.; *Int'l*, pg. 5609
X FINANCIAL; *Int'l*, pg. 8517
XFIT BRANDS, INC.; *U.S. Public*, pg. 2391
XFL, LLC—See RedBird Capital Partners L.P.; *U.S. Private*, pg. 3377
X-FLOW B.V.—See Pentair plc; *U.S. Public*, pg. 5791
XFL PROPERTIES LLC—See RedBird Capital Partners L.P.; *U.S. Private*, pg. 3377
XFONE 018 LTD.; *Int'l*, pg. 8521

XFONE USA, INC.—See Keystone Group, L.P.; *U.S. Private*, pg. 2297
XFONE USA, INC.—See Pamlico Capital Management, L.P.; *U.S. Private*, pg. 3083
XFS GLOBAL LLC; *U.S. Private*, pg. 4581
XGAINS4KEEPS INC.; *Int'l*, pg. 8522
XGD INC.; *Int'l*, pg. 8522
XGIGA COMMUNICATION TECHNOLOGY CO., LTD.—See Amphenol Corporation; *U.S. Public*, pg. 132
XGILITY, LLC.—See Applied Information Sciences, Inc.; *U.S. Private*, pg. 299
XG SCIENCES, INC.; *U.S. Private*, pg. 4581
XHALE, INC.; *U.S. Private*, pg. 4581
XIABUXIABU CATERING MANAGEMENT (CHINA) HOLDINGS CO., LTD.; *Int'l*, pg. 8522
XIAMEN AIRLINES CO., LTD.—See China Southern Airlines Co., Ltd.; *Int'l*, pg. 1553
XIAMEN AJINOMOTO LIFE IDEAL FOODS CO., LTD.—See Ajinomoto Company, Inc.; *Int'l*, pg. 257
XIAMEN AMBER DAILY CHEMICAL TECHNOLOGY CO., LTD.—See Huabao International Holdings Limited; *Int'l*, pg. 3510
XIAMEN AMOYTOP BIOTECH CO., LTD.; *Int'l*, pg. 8523
XIAMEN ANNE CORPORATION LIMITED; *Int'l*, pg. 8523
XIAMEN BOE ELECTRONICS CO., LTD.—See BOE Technology Group Co., Ltd.; *Int'l*, pg. 1099
XIAMEN BONDED AREA AIRPORT LOGISTICS PARK CONSTRUCTION CO., LTD.—See BES Engineering Corporation; *Int'l*, pg. 998
XIAMEN BRV ENVIRONMENTAL TECHNOLOGY CO., LTD.—See Xiamen Zhongchuang Environmental Technology Co., Ltd.; *Int'l*, pg. 8526
XIAMEN CCRE GROUP CO., LTD.—See Xiamen ITG Group Corp., Ltd.; *Int'l*, pg. 8524
XIAMEN C&D AUTOMOBILE CO., LTD.—See Xiamen C&D Inc.; *Int'l*, pg. 8523
XIAMEN C&D HITEK CO.,LTD.—See Xiamen C&D Inc.; *Int'l*, pg. 8523
XIAMEN C&D INC.; *Int'l*, pg. 8523
XIAMEN C&D SHIP TRADING CO., LTD.—See Xiamen C&D Inc.; *Int'l*, pg. 8523
XIAMEN CHANGELIGHT CO., LTD.; *Int'l*, pg. 8523
XIAMEN CHANGELIGHT LIGHTING CO., LTD.—See Xiamen Changelight Co., Ltd.; *Int'l*, pg. 8523
XIAMEN CHANGSU INDUSTRIAL CORPORATION LIMITED—See Green Seal Holding Limited; *Int'l*, pg. 3072
XIAMEN CHANGTIAN ENTERPRISE CO., LTD.—See Changtian Plastic & Chemical Limited; *Int'l*, pg. 1444
XIAMEN CHENG SHIN ENTERPRISE CO., LTD.—See Cheng Shin Rubber (Xiamen) Ind., Ltd; *Int'l*, pg. 1466
XIAMEN CLARION ELECTRICAL ENTERPRISE CO., LTD.—See FORVIA SE; *Int'l*, pg. 2745
XIAMEN COMFORT SCIENCE & TECHNOLOGY GROUP CO. LTD.; *Int'l*, pg. 8523
XIAMEN CONFERENCE & EXHIBITION GROUP INC.—See Xiamen C&D Inc.; *Int'l*, pg. 8523
XIAMEN DA JUN ACCURATE INDUSTRIAL CO., LTD.—See Changzhou Tenglong Auto Parts Co., Ltd.; *Int'l*, pg. 1445
XIAMEN DALING SEAFOOD CO., LTD.—See Mitsubishi Corporation; *Int'l*, pg. 4943
XIAMEN DARONG IMPORT & EXPORT TRADE CO., LTD.—See Vedan International (Holdings) Ltd.; *Int'l*, pg. 8145
XIAMEN DBTS AUTOMOBILE TRADING CO., LTD.—See Xiamen ITG Group Corp., Ltd.; *Int'l*, pg. 8524
XIAMEN DOINGCOM CHEMICAL CO., LTD.—See EcoGreen International Group Limited; *Int'l*, pg. 2295
XIAMEN DOINGCOM FOOD CO., LTD.—See EcoGreen International Group Limited; *Int'l*, pg. 2295
XIAMEN EAGLE DON PHARMACEUTICALS CO., LTD.—See Eagle Health Holdings Limited; *Int'l*, pg. 2264
XIAMEN EAST ASIA MACHINERY INDUSTRIAL CO., LTD.; *Int'l*, pg. 8523
XIAMEN ETIMBRE HEARING TECHNOLOGY CO. LTD.—See Merry Electronics Co., Ltd.; *Int'l*, pg. 4838
XIAMEN FARATRONIC CO., LTD.; *Int'l*, pg. 8523
XIAMEN FDK CORPORATION—See Fujitsu Limited; *Int'l*, pg. 2833
XIAMEN GOLDEN EGRET SPECIAL ALLOY CO., LTD.—See Xiamen Tungsten Co., Ltd.; *Int'l*, pg. 8526
XIAMEN GRUENLUFT MOLDING ENGINEERING CO., LTD.—See Xiamen Voke Mold & Plastic Engineering Co., Ltd.; *Int'l*, pg. 8526
XIAMEN GRUNLIFT TECHNOLOGY CO., LTD.—See Xiamen Voke Mold & Plastic Engineering Co., Ltd.; *Int'l*, pg. 8526
XIAMEN GUANG HONG ELECTRONICS CO., LTD.—See Wah Hong Industrial Corp.; *Int'l*, pg. 8329
XIAMEN GUANGPU ELECTRONICS CO., LTD.; *Int'l*, pg. 8524
XIAMEN HEXING PACKAGING PRINTING CO., LTD.; *Int'l*, pg. 8524
XIAMEN HONGFA ELECTROACOUSTIC CO., LTD.—See Hongfa Technology Co Ltd; *Int'l*, pg. 8524

XIAMEN HONGFA ELECTROACOUSTIC SCIENCE & TECHNOLOGY CO., LTD.—See Hongfa Technology Co Ltd; *Int'l*, pg. 3470
XIAMEN HONGLU TUNGSTEN & MOLYBDENUM INDUSTRY CO., LTD.—See Xiamen Tungsten Co., Ltd.; *Int'l*, pg. 8526
XIAMEN HONGXIN ELECTRON-TECH CO., LTD.; *Int'l*, pg. 8524
XIAMEN HUALIAN ELECTRONICS CO., LTD.—See Jiangxi Lianchuang Optoelectronic Science & Technology Co., Ltd; *Int'l*, pg. 3960
XIAMEN HUA RI FOODS INDUSTRIAL CO., LTD.—See Takasago International Corporation; *Int'l*, pg. 7434
XIAMEN HUA RUI SHENG INTELLIGENT TECHNOLOGY CO., LTD.—See Kehua Data Co., Ltd.; *Int'l*, pg. 4116
XIAMEN INNOVAX BIOTECH CO., LTD.—See Beijing Wantai Biological Pharmacy Enterprise Co., Ltd.; *Int'l*, pg. 960
XIAMEN INTERNATIONAL AIRPORT CO., LTD.; *Int'l*, pg. 8524
XIAMEN INTERNATIONAL BANK CO., LTD.; *Int'l*, pg. 8524
XIAMEN INTERNATIONAL PORT CO., LTD.; *Int'l*, pg. 8524
XIAMEN INTRETECH INC.; *Int'l*, pg. 8524
XIAMEN ISO STANDARD SAND CO., LTD.—See China National Materials; *Int'l*, pg. 1532
XIAMEN ITG ASSETS OPERATION GROUP CO., LTD.—See Xiamen ITG Holding Group Co., Ltd.; *Int'l*, pg. 8525
XIAMEN ITG CHEMICAL FIBRE CO., LTD.—See Xiamen ITG Group Corp., Ltd.; *Int'l*, pg. 8524
XIAMEN ITG DONGFENG HONDA SALES & SERVICE CO., LTD.—See Xiamen ITG Group Corp., Ltd.; *Int'l*, pg. 8524
XIAMEN ITG FINANCIAL GROUP CO., LTD.—See Xiamen ITG Group Corp., Ltd.; *Int'l*, pg. 8524
XIAMEN ITG GROUP CORP., LTD.; *Int'l*, pg. 8524
XIAMEN ITG HOLDING GROUP CO., LTD.; *Int'l*, pg. 8525
XIAMEN ITG KEERUN MOTOR SALES & SERVICE CO., LTD.—See Xiamen ITG Group Corp., Ltd.; *Int'l*, pg. 8524
XIAMEN ITG MICE GROUP CO., LTD.—See Xiamen ITG Holding Group Co., Ltd.; *Int'l*, pg. 8525
XIAMEN ITG REAL ESTATE GROUP CO., LTD.—See Xiamen ITG Group Corp., Ltd.; *Int'l*, pg. 8524
XIAMEN ITG SHIPBUILDING IMP. & EXP. CO., LTD.—See Xiamen ITG Group Corp., Ltd.; *Int'l*, pg. 8524
XIAMEN ITG TERMINALS LTD.—See Xiamen ITG Group Corp., Ltd.; *Int'l*, pg. 8524
XIAMEN JAMES FINLAY TRADING CO. LTD.—See John Swire & Sons Limited; *Int'l*, pg. 3981
XIAMEN JARLLY ELECTRONICS CO., LTD.—See Jarllytec Co., Ltd.; *Int'l*, pg. 3911
XIAMEN JIARONG TECHNOLOGY CO., LTD.; *Int'l*, pg. 8525
XIAMEN JIAWEI SOLAR ENERGY TECHNOLOGY CO., LTD.—See Jiawei Renewable Energy Co., Ltd.; *Int'l*, pg. 3961
XIAMEN JIHONG PACKAGE & TECHNOLOGY CO., LTD - LANGFANG FACTORY—See Xiamen Jihong Technology Co., Ltd.; *Int'l*, pg. 8525
XIAMEN JIHONG TECHNOLOGY CO., LTD.; *Int'l*, pg. 8525
XIAMEN KEERUN DONGHENG MOTOR SALES & SERVICE CO., LTD.—See Xiamen ITG Group Corp., Ltd.; *Int'l*, pg. 8524
XIAMEN KEERUN INFINITI MOTOR SALES & SERVICE CO., LTD.—See Xiamen ITG Group Corp., Ltd.; *Int'l*, pg. 8525
XIAMEN KFC CO., LTD.—See Yum China Holdings, Inc.; *U.S. Public*, pg. 2399
XIAMEN KINGDEE SOFTWARE CO., LTD.—See Kingdee International Software Group Company Ltd.; *Int'l*, pg. 4172
XIAMEN KINGDOMWAY GROUP COMPANY; *Int'l*, pg. 8525
XIAMEN KING LONG MOTOR GROUP CO., LTD.; *Int'l*, pg. 8525
XIAMEN KOGE MICRO TECH CO., LTD.—See Koge Micro Tech Co., Ltd.; *Int'l*, pg. 4228
XIAMEN KYOSEI SPORTING GOODS CO. LTD—See SSK Corporation; *Int'l*, pg. 7156
XIAMEN LEADING OPTICS CO., LTD.; *Int'l*, pg. 8525
XIAMEN LUTONG INTERNATIONAL TRAVEL AGENCY CO. LTD.; *Int'l*, pg. 8525
XIAMEN MEIDONG AUTO SALES & SERVICES CO., LTD.—See China MeiDong Auto Holdings Limited; *Int'l*, pg. 1519
XIAMEN MEIYA PICO INFORMATION CO.,LTD.; *Int'l*, pg. 8525
XIAMEN MINGFA HOTEL CO., LTD.—See Mingfa Group (International) Company Limited; *Int'l*, pg. 4909
XIAMEN MODERN TERMINAL CO., LTD.—See Xiamen Xiangyu Co., Ltd.; *Int'l*, pg. 8526
XIAMEN NAGASE TRADING CO., LTD.—See Nagase & Co., Ltd.; *Int'l*, pg. 5128
XIAMEN ORIENTAL MOTOR CO., LTD.—See Oriental Motor Co., Ltd.; *Int'l*, pg. 5626

COMPANY NAME INDEX

XIAMEN OVERSEAS CHINESE ELECTRONIC CO., LTD.; *Int'l*, pg. 8525
XIAMEN PACIFIC CONTAINER MANUFACTURING CO., LTD.—See Singamas Container Holdings Limited; *Int'l*, pg. 6939
XIAMEN PORT DEVELOPMENT CO., LTD.; *Int'l*, pg. 8525
XIAMEN POWERLONG INDUSTRY CO., LTD.—See Powerlong Real Estate Holdings Limited; *Int'l*, pg. 5947
XIAMEN RONGJI PRECISION TECHNOLOGY CO., LTD.—See Shenzhen Megmeet Electrical Co.,Ltd; *Int'l*, pg. 6818
XIAMEN SAN'AN INTEGRATED CIRCUIT CO., LTD.—See San'an Optoelectronics Co., Ltd.; *Int'l*, pg. 6522
XIAMEN SAN'AN OPTOELECTRONICS CO., LTD.—See San'an Optoelectronics Co., Ltd.; *Int'l*, pg. 6522
XIAMEN SHIHLIN ELECTRIC & ENGINEERING CO., LTD.—See Shihlin Electric & Engineering Corp.; *Int'l*, pg. 6829
XIAMEN SHIN-PO PROPERTY SERVICE CO., LTD.—See Taiwan Shin Kong Security Co., Ltd.; *Int'l*, pg. 7424
XIAMEN SHIN-PO SECURITY EQUIPMENT LTD.—See Taiwan Shin Kong Security Co., Ltd.; *Int'l*, pg. 7424
XIAMEN SHI ZHONGMIN BAIHUI COMMERCIAL CO., LTD.—See Zhongmin Baihui Retail Group Ltd.; *Int'l*, pg. 8674
XIAMEN SILAN ADVANCED COMPOUND SEMICONDUCTOR CO., LTD.—See Hangzhou Silan Microelectronics Co., Ltd.; *Int'l*, pg. 3250
XIAMEN SILAN MICROCHIP MANUFACTURING CO., LTD.—See Hangzhou Silan Microelectronics Co., Ltd.; *Int'l*, pg. 3250
XIAMEN SILICON TOUCH TECHNOLOGY INC.—See Silicon Touch Technology, Inc.; *Int'l*, pg. 6920
XIAMEN SMART CONCEPT PNEUMATICS CO.—See SMC Corporation; *Int'l*, pg. 7005
XIAMEN SOLEX HIGH-TECH INDUSTRIES CO., LTD.; *Int'l*, pg. 8525
XIAMEN SONGZ AUTOMOBILE AIR CONDITIONING CO., LTD.—See Songzhi Kallang Automotive Air Conditioning Co., Ltd.; *Int'l*, pg. 7096
XIAMEN SUNRISE GROUP CO. LTD.; *Int'l*, pg. 8525
XIAMEN TIGER MEDICALS CO., LTD.—See Haw Par Corporation Limited; *Int'l*, pg. 3287
XIAMEN TUNGSTEN CO., LTD.; *Int'l*, pg. 8525
XIAMEN UNITECH COMPUTER CO., LTD.—See Unitech Computer Co., Ltd.; *Int'l*, pg. 8064
XIAMEN VOKE MOLD & PLASTIC ENGINEERING CO., LTD.; *Int'l*, pg. 8526
XIAMEN VORK HEALTH INDUSTRY CO., LTD.—See Xiamen Voke Mold & Plastic Engineering Co., Ltd.; *Int'l*, pg. 8526
XIAMEN WANLI STONE STOCK CO., LTD.; *Int'l*, pg. 8526
XIAMEN XGMA MACHINERY CO., LTD.; *Int'l*, pg. 8526
XIAMEN XIAHUI RUBBER METAL INDUSTRIAL CO., LTD.—See Lu Hai Holding Corp.; *Int'l*, pg. 4571
XIAMEN XIANGYU CO., LTD.; *Int'l*, pg. 8526
XIAMEN XIANGYU SINGAMAS CONTAINER CO., LTD.—See Xiamen Xiangyu Co., Ltd.; *Int'l*, pg. 8526
XIAMEN XINDE CO., LTD.; *Int'l*, pg. 8526
XIAMEN XINRELI SCIENTIFIC AND TECHNOLOGY CO., LTD.—See KongZhong Corporation; *Int'l*, pg. 4257
XIAMEN YANJAN NEW MATERIAL CO., LTD.; *Int'l*, pg. 8526
XIAMEN YINLU FOOD GROUP CO., LTD.—See Nestle S.A.; *Int'l*, pg. 5211
XIAMEN YONG YU MACHINERY CO., LTD.—See Yusin Holding Corp; *Int'l*, pg. 8618
XIAMEN ZETTLER ELECTRONICS CO., LTD.—See Zettler Components, Inc.; *U.S. Private*, pg. 4603
XIAMEN ZHONGCHUANG ENVIRONMENTAL TECHNOLOGY CO., LTD.; *Int'l*, pg. 8526
XIAMEN ZHONGSHENG TOYOTA SALES & SERVICE CO., LTD.—See Xiamen ITG Group Corp., Ltd.; *Int'l*, pg. 8525
XIAMEN ZHUOYUE BIOMASS ENERGY CO., LTD.—See Longyan Zhuoyue New Energy Co., Ltd.; *Int'l*, pg. 4551
XIAMEN ZIJIN ENGINEERING DESIGN COMPANY LIMITED.—See Zijin Mining Group Company Limited; *Int'l*, pg. 8683
XIAM TECHNOLOGIES LIMITED—See QUALCOMM Incorporated; *U.S. Public*, pg. 1748
XI'AN AEROSPACE FIRE ENGINEERING CO., LTD.—See Shaanxi Aerospace Power High-tech Co., Ltd.; *Int'l*, pg. 6746
XIANA MINING INC.; *Int'l*, pg. 8527
XIAN BEILIN PHARMACEUTICAL COMPANY LIMITED—See Grand Pharmaceutical Group Limited; *Int'l*, pg. 3056
XIAN BRIGHT LASER TECHNOLOGIES CO., LTD.; *Int'l*, pg. 8526
XIAN BROTHER INDUSTRIES CO., LTD.—See Brother Industries, Ltd.; *Int'l*, pg. 1198
XI'AN CATERING CO., LTD.; *Int'l*, pg. 8522
XI'AN CEA SAFRAN LANDING SYSTEMS CO., LTD.—See Safran SA; *Int'l*, pg. 6476
XI'AN CHANG'AN PARKSON STORE CO., LTD.—See Parkson Holdings Berhad; *Int'l*, pg. 5744
XIAN CHENXI AVIATION TECHNOLOGY CORP LTD; *Int'l*, pg. 8526

XIAN CHINA INTERNATIONAL TRAVEL SERVICE CO., LTD.—See China Tourism Group Duty Free Corporation Limited; *Int'l*, pg. 1560
XIANDAI INVESTMENT CO., LTD.; *Int'l*, pg. 8527
XI'AN DAIKIN QING'AN COMPRESSOR CO., LTD.—See Daikin Industries, Ltd.; *Int'l*, pg. 1937
XIAN DALING SEAFOOD CO., LTD.—See Mitsubishi Corporation; *Int'l*, pg. 4943
XI AN ENGINEERING DESIGN CO., LTD.—See China Coal Energy Company Limited; *Int'l*, pg. 1490
XI'AN FILTER METAL MATERIALS CO., LTD.—See Western Metal Materials Co., Ltd.; *Int'l*, pg. 8389
XIANGCAI CO., LTD.; *Int'l*, pg. 8527
XI'AN GLOBAL PRINTING CO.,LTD.; *Int'l*, pg. 8522
XIANGPIAOPIAO FOOD CO., LTD.; *Int'l*, pg. 8527
XI'AN GRID ELECTRIC POWER CO., LTD.—See Troy Information Technology Co., Ltd.; *Int'l*, pg. 7940
XIANGTAN BAOZE AUTOMOBILE SALES SERVICES CO., LTD.—See China ZhengTong Auto Services Holdings Limited; *Int'l*, pg. 1567
XIANGTAN ELECTRIC MANUFACTURING GROUP CO., LTD.; *Int'l*, pg. 8527
XIANGTAN ELECTROCHEMICAL SCIENTIFIC CO., LTD.; *Int'l*, pg. 8527
XIANGTAN IM DIGITAL ELECTRONICS CO. LTD—See IM Co., Ltd.; *Int'l*, pg. 3617
XIANG TONG (SHANGHAI) INTERNATIONAL TRADING PTE CO., LTD—See SHS Holdings Ltd.; *Int'l*, pg. 6867
XIANGXING INTERNATIONAL HOLDING LIMITED; *Int'l*, pg. 8527
XIANGXUE PHARMACEUTICAL CO., LTD.; *Int'l*, pg. 8527
XIANGYANG AUTOMOBILE BEARING CO., LTD.; *Int'l*, pg. 8527
XIANGYANG BAOZE AUTOMOBILE SALES SERVICES CO., LTD.—See China ZhengTong Auto Services Holdings Limited; *Int'l*, pg. 1567
XIANGYANG BOYA PRECISION INDUSTRIAL EQUIPMENTS CO., LTD.,; *Int'l*, pg. 8527
XIANGYANG CHANGYUAN DONGGU INDUSTRIAL CO., LTD.,; *Int'l*, pg. 8527
XIANGYANG CHANGYUAN EAST GRAIN STREAM CO., LTD.—See Xiangyang Changyuan Donggu Industrial Co., Ltd.,; *Int'l*, pg. 8527
XIANGYANG CHANGYUAN LANGHONG TECHNOLOGY CO., LTD.—See Xiangyang Changyuan Donggu Industrial Co., Ltd.,; *Int'l*, pg. 8527
XIANGYANG NTN-YULON DRIVETRAIN CO., LTD.—See NTN Corporation; *Int'l*, pg. 5484
XIANGYANG SANGO AUTOMOTIVE PARTS CO., LTD.—See Sango Co., Ltd.; *Int'l*, pg. 6538
XIANGYU MEDICAL CO., LTD.; *Int'l*, pg. 8527
XI'AN HAITIAN ANTENNA TECHNOLOGIES CO., LTD.; *Int'l*, pg. 8522
XI'AN HAIXIN PHARMACEUTICAL CO., LTD.—See Shanghai Haixin Group Co., Ltd.; *Int'l*, pg. 6769
XI'AN HAOTIAN BIO-ENGINEERING TECHNOLOGY CO. LIMITED—See Cathay International Holdings Limited; *Int'l*, pg. 1360
XIANHE CO., LTD.; *Int'l*, pg. 8527
XI'AN HEKEDA WATER TREATMENT TECHNOLOGY LIMITED—See Shenzhen Hekeda Precision Cleaning Equipment Co., Ltd.; *Int'l*, pg. 6811
XI'AN HOPERUN SOFTWARE INFORMATION TECHNOLOGY CO., LTD—See Jiangsu Hoperun Software Co., Ltd.; *Int'l*, pg. 3948
XI'AN HUATIAN TELECOM INC.—See KMW Inc.; *Int'l*, pg. 4205
XI'AN HUIDA CHEMICAL INDUSTRIES CO., LTD.—See Daicel Corporation; *Int'l*, pg. 1920
XI'AN INTERNATIONAL MEDICAL INVESTMENT COMPANY LIMITED; *Int'l*, pg. 8522
XIAN-JANSSEN PHARMACEUTICAL LTD.—See Johnson & Johnson; *U.S. Public*, pg. 1197
XI'AN KINGTONE INFORMATION TECHNOLOGY CO.LTD—See Luokung Technology Corp.; *Int'l*, pg. 4584
XIAN LENG AQUATIC MERCHANT SDN. BHD.—See XL Holdings Berhad; *Int'l*, pg. 8536
XIAN LIJUN PHARMACEUTICAL CO., LTD.; *Int'l*, pg. 8527
XI'AN MANARECO NEW MATERIALS CO., LTD.; *Int'l*, pg. 8522
XI'AN NANTIAN COMPUTER SYSTEM CO., LTD.—See Yunnan Nantian Electronics Information Co., Ltd.; *Int'l*, pg. 8616
XI'AN NEWTOUCH INFORMATION TECHNOLOGY CO., LTD.—See Shanghai Newtouch Software Co., Ltd.; *Int'l*, pg. 6776
XI'AN PENGYUAN METALLURGICAL EQUIPMENT CO., LTD.—See Lygend Resources & Technology Co., Ltd.; *Int'l*, pg. 4605
XI'AN PERI POWER SEMICONDUCTOR CONVERTING TECHNOLOGY CO., LTD.; *Int'l*, pg. 8522
XI'AN QUJIANG CULTURAL TOURISM CO., LTD.; *Int'l*, pg. 8522
XI'AN REFRA TUNGSTEN & MOLYBDENUM CO., LTD.—See Western Metal Materials Co., Ltd.; *Int'l*, pg. 8389

XI'AN RIVER ELECTRONICS CORPORATION—See River Eletec Corporation; *Int'l*, pg. 6352
XI'AN SHAANGU POWER CO., LTD.; *Int'l*, pg. 8522
XIAN SHIMADZU VACUUM EQUIPMENT CO., LTD.—See Shimadzu Corporation; *Int'l*, pg. 6833
XI'AN SILVER BUS CORPORATION—See AB Volvo; *Int'l*, pg. 47
XI'AN SINOFUSE ELECTRIC CO., LTD.; *Int'l*, pg. 8522
XI'AN SITAN INSTRUMENT CO., LTD.—See Haimo Technologies Group Corp.; *Int'l*, pg. 3211
XI'AN SYSTEM SENSOR ELECTRONICS LTD.—See Honeywell International Inc.; *U.S. Public*, pg. 1049
XI'AN TECH FULL SIMO MOTOR CO., LTD.; *Int'l*, pg. 8522
XI'AN THIEBAUT PHARMACEUTICAL PACKAGING CO., LTD.—See Xi'An Global Printing Co.,LTD.; *Int'l*, pg. 8522
XI'AN TIANHE DEFENSE TECHNOLOGY CO., LTD.; *Int'l*, pg. 8522
XI'AN TIANLI CLAD METAL MATERIALS CO., LTD.—See Western Metal Materials Co., Ltd.; *Int'l*, pg. 8389
XI'AN TONGYUAN INTELLIGENT ELECTRIC CO., LTD.—See Troy Information Technology Co., Ltd.; *Int'l*, pg. 7940
XI'AN TOURISM CO., LTD.; *Int'l*, pg. 8522
XI'AN TRIANGLE DEFENSE CO., LTD.; *Int'l*, pg. 8522
XI'AN TYPICAL INDUSTRIES CO., LTD.; *Int'l*, pg. 8522
XI'AN UNITED PRESSURE VESSEL CO., LTD.—See Western Metal Materials Co., Ltd.; *Int'l*, pg. 8389
XIAN WALSIN METAL PRODUCT CO., LTD. - BAOJI PLANT—See Walsin Lihwa Corporation; *Int'l*, pg. 8335
XIAN WALSIN UNITED TECHNOLOGY CO., LTD.—See Walsin Lihwa Corporation; *Int'l*, pg. 8335
XI'AN XIGU MICROELECTRONICS CO., LTD.—See Beijing Watertek Information Technology Co., Ltd.; *Int'l*, pg. 960
XI'AN XINHAI MICROELECTRONICS TECHNOLOGY CO., LTD.—See Chipsea Technologies (Shenzhen) Corp.; *Int'l*, pg. 1573
XIAOGAN CHUHATSU LIOHO AUTOMOTIVE COMPONENTS CO., LTD.—See Chuo Spring Co., Ltd.; *Int'l*, pg. 1599
XIAOGAN ZHONGXING AUTOMOTIVE COMPONENTS CO., LTD.—See Chuo Spring Co., Ltd.; *Int'l*, pg. 1600
XIAO-I CORPORATION; *Int'l*, pg. 8527
XIAOMEIJI TECHNOLOGY CO., LTD.—See MYS Group Co., Ltd.; *Int'l*, pg. 5114
XIAOMI CORPORATION; *Int'l*, pg. 8527
XIAOMI INC.—See Xiaomi Corporation; *Int'l*, pg. 8528
XIAOSHAN YAMAHA MUSICAL INSTRUMENT CO., LTD.—See Yamaha Corporation; *Int'l*, pg. 8549
XIAOTAI INTERNATIONAL INVESTMENT INC.; *Int'l*, pg. 8528
XICE TESTING TECHNOLOGY CO., LTD.; *Int'l*, pg. 8528
@XI COMPUTER CORPORATION; *U.S. Private*, pg. 17
XICOM TECHNOLOGY EUROPE LTD.—See Comtech Telecommunications Corp.; *U.S. Public*, pg. 563
XICON INTERNATIONAL LIMITED—See Kaiser Corporation Limited; *Int'l*, pg. 4053
XIDAX, LLC; *U.S. Private*, pg. 4581
XIDELANG (FUJIAN) SPORTS CO., LTD.; *Int'l*, pg. 8528
XIDELANG HOLDINGS LTD; *Int'l*, pg. 8528
XIDERA S.R.L.—See GPI S.p.A.; *Int'l*, pg. 3046
XIE YI TECH MACHINERY (CHINA) CO., LTD.—See Shieh Yih Machinery Industry Co., Ltd.; *Int'l*, pg. 6828
XIEZHONG INTERNATIONAL HOLDINGS LIMITED; *Int'l*, pg. 8528
XIFIN, INC.—See GTCR LLC; *U.S. Private*, pg. 1807
XIGEM TECHNOLOGIES CORPORATION; *Int'l*, pg. 8528
XIGNITE, INC.—See NewSpring Capital LLC; *U.S. Private*, pg. 2917
XIGO, LLC—See Asignet USA, Inc.; *U.S. Private*, pg. 351
XILAM ANIMATION S.A.; *Int'l*, pg. 8528
XILINMEN FURNITURE CO., LTD.; *Int'l*, pg. 8528
XILINX AB—See Advanced Micro Devices, Inc.; *U.S. Public*, pg. 49
XILINX ASIA PACIFIC PTE. LTD.—See Advanced Micro Devices, Inc.; *U.S. Public*, pg. 49
XILINX BENELUX B.V.B.A.—See Advanced Micro Devices, Inc.; *U.S. Public*, pg. 49
XILINX DEVELOPMENT CORPORATION—See Advanced Micro Devices, Inc.; *U.S. Public*, pg. 49
XILINX ESTONIA O.U.—See Advanced Micro Devices, Inc.; *U.S. Public*, pg. 49
XILINX GMBH—See Advanced Micro Devices, Inc.; *U.S. Public*, pg. 49
XILINX HONG KONG LIMITED—See Advanced Micro Devices, Inc.; *U.S. Public*, pg. 49
XILINX, INC.- ALBUQUERQUE—See Advanced Micro Devices, Inc.; *U.S. Public*, pg. 49
XILINX, INC.- LONGMONT—See Advanced Micro Devices, Inc.; *U.S. Public*, pg. 49
XILINX, INC.—See Advanced Micro Devices, Inc.; *U.S. Public*, pg. 49
XILINX INDIA TECHNOLOGY SERVICES PVT. LTD.—See Advanced Micro Devices, Inc.; *U.S. Public*, pg. 49
XILINX INTERNATIONAL, INC.—See Advanced Micro Devices, Inc.; *U.S. Public*, pg. 49

XILINX IRELAND—See Advanced Micro Devices, Inc.; *U.S. Public*, pg. 49
XILINX IRELAND UNLIMITED COMPANY—See Advanced Micro Devices, Inc.; *U.S. Public*, pg. 49
XILINX ISRAEL LIMITED—See Advanced Micro Devices, Inc.; *U.S. Public*, pg. 49
XILINX K.K.—See Advanced Micro Devices, Inc.; *U.S. Public*, pg. 49
XILINX LTD.—See Advanced Micro Devices, Inc.; *U.S. Public*, pg. 49
XILINX SARL—See Advanced Micro Devices, Inc.; *U.S. Public*, pg. 49
XILIO THERAPEUTICS, INC.; *U.S. Public*, pg. 2391
XILONG SCIENTIFIC CO., LTD.; *Int'l*, pg. 8528
XIMALAYA INC.; *Int'l*, pg. 8528
XIMANTIX SOFTWARE GMBH—See Cegedim S.A.; *Int'l*, pg. 1390
XIMEDICA LLC—See SV Health Investors, LLP; *U.S. Private*, pg. 3888
XIMEI RESOURCES HOLDING LIMITED; *Int'l*, pg. 8528
XIMEN MINING CORP.; *Int'l*, pg. 8528
XIN AN TOWN LUOXIN NEW MATERIAL INDUSTRIAL PARK DEVELOPMENT CO., LTD.—See Zhengzhou Sino-Crystal Diamond Co., Ltd.; *Int'l*, pg. 8670
XINCHANG PHARMACEUTICAL FACTORY—See Zhejiang Medicine Co. Ltd.; *Int'l*, pg. 8660
XINCHEN CHINA POWER HOLDINGS LIMITED; *Int'l*, pg. 8529
XINCHEN ENGINE (SHENYANG) CO., LIMITED—See Xinchen China Power Holdings Limited; *Int'l*, pg. 8529
XINCHENG CONSTRUCTION SUPERVISION & CONSULTING CO., LTD.—See China Nonferrous Metal Mining (Group) Co., Ltd.; *Int'l*, pg. 1535
XINCHENG ELECTRONIC TECHNOLOGY CO., LTD.—See P-Duke Technology Co., Ltd.; *Int'l*, pg. 5682
XINDA INVESTMENT HOLDINGS LIMITED; *Int'l*, pg. 8529
XINDI ENERGY ENGINEERING TECHNOLOGY CO., LTD.—See ENN Natural Gas Co., Ltd.; *Int'l*, pg. 2443
XINET, INC.—See North Plains Systems Inc.; *Int'l*, pg. 5441
XINFA AIRPORT EQUIPMENT LTD.—See China International Marine Containers (Group) Co., Ltd.; *Int'l*, pg. 1512
XINFENG INVESTMENT MANAGEMENT CO., LTD.—See China Cinda Asset Management Co., Ltd.; *Int'l*, pg. 1488
XINFENGMING GROUP CO., LTD.; *Int'l*, pg. 8529
X-INFOTECH AFRICA LIMITED—See Silverlake Axis Ltd.; *Int'l*, pg. 6926
XIN FURUKAWA METAL (WUXI) CO., LTD.—See The Furukawa Electric Co., Ltd.; *Int'l*, pg. 7647
XINGDA INTERNATIONAL HOLDINGS LTD; *Int'l*, pg. 8529
XINGFA ALUMINIUM (CHENGDU) CO., LTD—See Xingfa Aluminum Holdings Limited; *Int'l*, pg. 8529
XINGFA ALUMINIUM (HONG KONG) LIMITED—See Xingfa Aluminum Holdings Limited; *Int'l*, pg. 8529
XINGFA ALUMINUM HOLDINGS LIMITED; *Int'l*, pg. 8529
XINGHUA PORT HOLDINGS LTD.; *Int'l*, pg. 8529
XING INC.—See Brother Industries, Ltd.; *Int'l*, pg. 1198
XING INTERNATIONAL HOLDING GMBH—See Hubert Burda Media Holding Kommanditgesellschaft; *Int'l*, pg. 3520
XINGMIN INTELLIGENT TRANSPORTATION SYSTEMS (GROUP) CO., LTD.; *Int'l*, pg. 8529
XING MUSIC ENTERTAINMENT, INC.—See Brother Industries, Ltd.; *Int'l*, pg. 1198
XING NETWORKING SPAIN, S.L.—See Hubert Burda Media Holding Kommanditgesellschaft; *Int'l*, pg. 3520
XINGQUAN INTERNATIONAL SPORTS HOLDINGS LIMITED; *Int'l*, pg. 8529
XINGTAI HENGYUAN CHEMICAL GROUP CO., LTD.—See China National Chemical Corporation; *Int'l*, pg. 1530
XINGTANG ZHONGYU GAS CO., LTD.—See Zhongyu Energy Holdings Limited; *Int'l*, pg. 8676
XINGYE ALLOY MATERIALS GROUP LTD.; *Int'l*, pg. 8530
XINGYE LEATHER TECHNOLOGY CO., LTD.; *Int'l*, pg. 8530
XINGYE WULIAN SERVICE GROUP CO., LTD.; *Int'l*, pg. 8530
XINGYUAN ENVIRONMENT TECHNOLOGY CO., LTD.; *Int'l*, pg. 8530
XING YUAN (SINGAPORE) PTE. LTD.—See China COSCO Shipping Corporation Limited; *Int'l*, pg. 1492
XINHE COUNTY ZHONGYU GAS CO., LTD.—See Zhongyu Energy Holdings Limited; *Int'l*, pg. 8676
XIN HEE CO., LTD.; *Int'l*, pg. 8528
XINHUANET CO., LTD.; *Int'l*, pg. 8530
XINHUA NEWS MEDIA HOLDINGS LIMITED; *Int'l*, pg. 8530
XINHUA PHARMACEUTICAL (GAOMI) CO., LTD.—See Shandong Xinhua Pharmaceutical Company Limited; *Int'l*, pg. 6759
XINHUA PHARMACEUTICAL (SHOUGUANG) CO., LTD.—See Shandong Xinhua Pharmaceutical Company Limited; *Int'l*, pg. 6759

XINHUA SPORTS & ENTERTAINMENT LTD.; *Int'l*, pg. 8530
XINHUA WINSHARE PUBLISHING AND MEDIA CO., LTD.; *Int'l*, pg. 8530
XINHUI CIMC CONTAINER CO., LTD.—See China International Marine Containers (Group) Co., Ltd.; *Int'l*, pg. 1512
XINHUI CIMC SPECIAL TRANSPORTATION EQUIPMENT CO., LTD.—See China International Marine Containers (Group) Co., Ltd.; *Int'l*, pg. 1512
XINHUI CIMC WOOD CO., LTD.—See China International Marine Containers (Group) Co., Ltd.; *Int'l*, pg. 1512
XIN HWA HOLDINGS BERHAD; *Int'l*, pg. 8528
XINING SPECIAL STEEL CO.; *Int'l*, pg. 8530
XINJIANG ALAR XINNONG LICORICE INDUSTRY LIMITED LIABILITY COMPANY—See Xinjiang Talimu Agriculture Development Co., Ltd.; *Int'l*, pg. 8532
XINJIANG ASHELE COPPER COMPANY LIMITED—See Zijin Mining Group Company Limited; *Int'l*, pg. 8683
XINJIANG BAIHUACUN CO., LTD.; *Int'l*, pg. 8530
XINJIANG BA YI IRON & STEEL CO., LTD.—See China Baowu Steel Group Corp., Ltd.; *Int'l*, pg. 1486
XINJIANG BEIKEN ENERGY ENGINEERING LIMITED; *Int'l*, pg. 8530
XINJIANG BEIXIN ROAD & BRIDGE GROUP CO., LTD.; *Int'l*, pg. 8530
XINJIANG CHANGMEI MINING MACHINERY CO., LTD.—See Shandong Mining Machinery Group Co., Ltd.; *Int'l*, pg. 6756
XINJIANG COMMUNICATIONS CONSTRUCTION GROUP CO., LTD.; *Int'l*, pg. 8531
XINJIANG DAQO NEW ENERGY CO., LTD.—See Daqo New Energy Corp.; *Int'l*, pg. 1971
XINJIANG EASTERN HOSHINE SILICON INDUSTRY CO., LTD.—See Hoshine Silicon Industry Co., Ltd.; *Int'l*, pg. 3483
XINJIANG EAST UNIVERSE (GROUP) GAS CO., LTD.; *Int'l*, pg. 8531
XINJIANG ELECTRIC POWER COMPANY—See State Grid Corporation of China; *Int'l*, pg. 7183
XINJIANG FUFENG BIOTECHNOLOGIES CO., LTD.—See Fufeng Group Limited; *Int'l*, pg. 2805
XINJIANG GOLDWIND SCIENCE & TECHNOLOGY CO., LTD.; *Int'l*, pg. 8531
XINJIANG GUANGHUI INDUSTRY INVESTMENT GROUP CO., LTD.; *Int'l*, pg. 8531
XINJIANG GUANNONG FRUIT AND VELVET CO., LTD.; *Int'l*, pg. 8531
XINJIANG GUOTONG PIPELINE CO., LTD.; *Int'l*, pg. 8531
XINJIANG HAOYUAN GAS CO., LTD.; *Int'l*, pg. 8531
XINJIANG HONGTONG NATURAL GAS CO., LTD.; *Int'l*, pg. 8531
XINJIANG INTERNATIONAL INDUSTRY CO., LTD.; *Int'l*, pg. 8531
XINJIANG JICHUANG ASSET MANAGEMENT CO., LTD.—See GI Technology Group Co., Ltd.; *Int'l*, pg. 2960
XINJIANG JINSONG SILICON INDUSTRY CO., LTD.—See Hoshine Silicon Industry Co., Ltd.; *Int'l*, pg. 3483
XINJIANG JOINWORLD CO., LTD.; *Int'l*, pg. 8531
XINJIANG JUNPENG CAPS MAKING CO., LTD.—See Shandong Chiway Industry Development Co., Ltd.; *Int'l*, pg. 6752
XINJIANG KORLA PEAR CO., LTD.; *Int'l*, pg. 8531
XINJIANG LIXIN ENERGY CO., LTD.; *Int'l*, pg. 8531
XINJIANG MACHINERY RESEARCH INSTITUTE CO., LTD.; *Int'l*, pg. 8531
XINJIANG MIDDLE HOSHINE SILICON INDUSTRY CO., LTD.—See Hoshine Silicon Industry Co., Ltd.; *Int'l*, pg. 3483
XINJIANG QINGSONG CHEMICALS (GROUP) CO., LTD.; *Int'l*, pg. 8531
XIN JIANG READY HEALTH INDUSTRY CO., LTD.; *Int'l*, pg. 8528
XINJIANG RIETER TEXTILE INSTRUMENTS CO., LTD.—See Rieter Holding Ltd.; *Int'l*, pg. 6339
XINJIANG SAILING INFORMATION TECHNOLOGY CO., LTD.; *Int'l*, pg. 8532
XINJIANG SAYRAM MODERN AGRICULTURE CO., LTD.; *Int'l*, pg. 8532
XINJIANG TALIMU AGRICULTURE DEVELOPMENT CO., LTD.; *Int'l*, pg. 8532
XINJIANG TIANFENG POWER GENERATION CO., LTD.—See China Guodian Corporation; *Int'l*, pg. 1506
XINJIANG TIANFU ENERGY CO., LTD.; *Int'l*, pg. 8532
XINJIANG TIANRUN DAIRY CO., LTD.; *Int'l*, pg. 8532
XINJIANG TIANSHAN ANIMAL HUSBANDRY BIO-ENGINEERING CO., LTD.; *Int'l*, pg. 8532
XINJIANG TIANSHAN PHARMACEUTICALS INDUSTRY CO., LTD.—See China Meheco Group Co., Ltd.; *Int'l*, pg. 1519
XINJIANG TIANSHUN SUPPLY CHAIN CO LTD; *Int'l*, pg. 8532
XINJIANG TIANYE CO., LTD.; *Int'l*, pg. 8532
XINJIANG TIANYE WATER SAVING IRRIGATION SYSTEM COMPANY LIMITED—See Xinjiang Tianye Co., Ltd.; *Int'l*, pg. 8532

XINJIANG TOPFOND HENGDE PHARMACEUTICAL CO., LTD.—See China Meheco Group Co., Ltd.; *Int'l*, pg. 1519
XINJIANG TORCH GAS CO., LTD.; *Int'l*, pg. 8532
XINJIANG WESTERN ANIMAL HUSBANDRY CO., LTD.; *Int'l*, pg. 8532
XINJIANG WESTERN HOSHINE SILICON INDUSTRY CO., LTD.—See Hoshine Silicon Industry Co., Ltd.; *Int'l*, pg. 3483
XINJIANG WINKA TIMES DEPARTMENT STORE CO; *Int'l*, pg. 8532
XINJIANG XINLIANXIN ENERGY CHEMICAL CO., LTD.—See China XLX Fertiliser Ltd; *Int'l*, pg. 1564
XINJIANG XINTAI NATURAL GAS CO., LTD.; *Int'l*, pg. 8532
XINJIANG XINXIN MINING INDUSTRY CO., LTD.; *Int'l*, pg. 8532
XINJIANG XUEFENG SCI-TECH GROUP CO., LTD.; *Int'l*, pg. 8532
XINJIANG YILITE INDUSTRY CO., LTD.; *Int'l*, pg. 8532
XINJIANG YILU WANYUAN INDUSTRIAL INVESTMENT HOLDING CO., LTD.; *Int'l*, pg. 8533
XINJIANG YOUHAO (GROUP) CO., LTD.; *Int'l*, pg. 8533
XINJIANG ZHONGTAI CHEMICAL CO., LTD.; *Int'l*, pg. 8533
XINJIANG ZHUNDONG PETROLEUM TECHNOLOGY CO., LTD.; *Int'l*, pg. 8533
XINJI SHAXI GROUP CO., LTD.; *Int'l*, pg. 8530
XINLAB, INC.—See Pacific Century Group Holdings Limited; *Int'l*, pg. 5687
XINLEI COMPRESSOR CO., LTD.; *Int'l*, pg. 8533
XINLING ELECTRICAL CO., LTD.; *Int'l*, pg. 8533
XINLIWANG INTERNATIONAL HOLDINGS COMPANY LTD.; *Int'l*, pg. 8533
XINLONG HOLDING (GROUP) COMPANY LTD.; *Int'l*, pg. 8533
XINLUN NEW MATERIALS CO., LTD.; *Int'l*, pg. 8533
XINMING CHINA HOLDINGS LTD.; *Int'l*, pg. 8533
XINMING GROUP HOLDING LIMITED—See Xinming China Holdings Ltd.; *Int'l*, pg. 8533
XIN MING HUA PTE LTD—See XMH Holdings Ltd.; *Int'l*, pg. 8536
XINMI ZHONGYU GAS CO., LTD.—See Zhongyu Energy Holdings Limited; *Int'l*, pg. 8676
XINNOVATION, INC.—See Bigtincan Holdings Limited; *U.S. Public*, pg. 331
XINOVA, LLC—See North Peak Resources Ltd.; *Int'l*, pg. 5441
XIN POINT HOLDINGS LIMITED; *Int'l*, pg. 8528
XIN POINT NORTH AMERICA INC.—See Xin Point Holdings Limited; *Int'l*, pg. 8529
XINREN ALUMINUM HOLDINGS LIMITED; *Int'l*, pg. 8533
XINTE ENERGY CO., LTD.—See TBEA Co., Ltd.; *Int'l*, pg. 7479
XINTELA AB; *Int'l*, pg. 8533
XINXIANG CHEMICAL FIBER CO., LTD.; *Int'l*, pg. 8533
XINXIANG HAIBIN PHARMACEUTICAL CO., LTD—See Joincare Pharmaceutical Industry Group Co., Ltd; *Int'l*, pg. 3995
XINXIANG RICHFUL LUBE ADDITIVE CO., LTD.; *Int'l*, pg. 8533
XINXIANG RUICHENG TECHNOLOGY CO., LTD.—See China XLX Fertiliser Ltd; *Int'l*, pg. 1564
XINXIANG TIANLI ENERGY CO., LTD.; *Int'l*, pg. 8533
XINXING CATHAY INTERNATIONAL GROUP CO., LTD.; *Int'l*, pg. 8533
XINXING DUCTILE IRON PIPES CO., LTD.; *Int'l*, pg. 8534
XINYA ELECTRONIC CO., LTD.; *Int'l*, pg. 8534
XINYANG BURGESS-NORTON YINGUANG PISTON PIN CO., LTD.—See AMSTED Industries Incorporated; *U.S. Private*, pg. 268
XINYANGFENG AGRICULTURAL TECHNOLOGY CO., LTD.; *Int'l*, pg. 8534
XINYANG IRON & STEEL CO., LTD.—See Anyang Iron & Steel Group Co., Ltd.; *Int'l*, pg. 487
XINYAQIANG SILICON CHEMISTRY CO., LTD.; *Int'l*, pg. 8534
XINYI AUTO GLASS (NORTH AMERICA) CORPORATION—See Xinyi Glass Holdings Limited; *Int'l*, pg. 8534
XINYI AUTOMOBILE GLASS (SHENZHEN) COMPANY LIMITED—See Xinyi Glass Holdings Limited; *Int'l*, pg. 8534
XINYI AUTOMOBILE PARTS (WUHU) COMPANY LIMITED—See Xinyi Glass Holdings Limited; *Int'l*, pg. 8534
XINYI ELECTRIC STORAGE HOLDINGS LIMITED; *Int'l*, pg. 8534
XINYI ELECTRONIC GLASS (WUHU) COMPANY LIMITED—See Xinyi Glass Holdings Limited; *Int'l*, pg. 8534
XINYI ENERGY HOLDINGS LIMITED—See Xinyi Solar Holdings Limited; *Int'l*, pg. 8534
XINYI ENERGY-SAVING GLASS (SICHUAN) CO., LTD.—See Xinyi Glass Holdings Limited; *Int'l*, pg. 8534
XINYI ENERGY SMART (WUHU) COMPANY LIMITED—See Xinyi Glass Holdings Limited; *Int'l*, pg. 8534

COMPANY NAME INDEX

XINYI ENERGY STORAGE MICRO-GRID RESEARCH INSTITUTE (DONGGUAN) COMPANY LIMITED—See Xinyi Electric Storage Holdings Limited; *Int'l*, pg. 8534
XINYI ENVIRONMENT-FRIENDLY SPECIAL GLASS (JIANGMEN) CO., LTD.—See Xinyi Glass Holdings Limited; *Int'l*, pg. 8534
XINYI GLAS DEUTSCHLAND GMBH—See Xinyi Glass Holdings Limited; *Int'l*, pg. 8534
XINYI GLASS ENGINEERING (DONGGUAN) COMPANY LIMITED—See Xinyi Glass Holdings Limited; *Int'l*, pg. 8534
XINYI GLASS HOLDINGS LIMITED; *Int'l*, pg. 8534
XINYI GLASS (HONG KONG) CO., LTD—See Xinyi Glass Holdings Limited; *Int'l*, pg. 8534
XINYI GLASS (INDIA) CO., LTD.—See Xinyi Glass Holdings Limited; *Int'l*, pg. 8534
XINYI GLASS JAPAN COMPANY LIMITED—See Xinyi Glass Holdings Limited; *Int'l*, pg. 8534
XINYI GLASS (PHILIPPINES) CO., LTD.—See Xinyi Glass Holdings Limited; *Int'l*, pg. 8534
XINYI GLASS (POLAND) CO., LTD.—See Xinyi Glass Holdings Limited; *Int'l*, pg. 8534
XINYI GLASS (TAIWAN) CO., LTD.—See Xinyi Glass Holdings Limited; *Int'l*, pg. 8534
XINYI GLASS (TIANJIN) COMPANY LIMITED—See Xinyi Glass Holdings Limited; *Int'l*, pg. 8534
XINYI GLASS (YINGKOU) COMPANY LIMITED—See Xinyi Glass Holdings Limited; *Int'l*, pg. 8534
XINYI GROUP (GLASS) COMPANY LIMITED—See Xinyi Glass Holdings Limited; *Int'l*, pg. 8534
XINYI RIHONG PLASTIC CHEMICAL CO., LTD.—See Harima Chemicals Group, Inc.; *Int'l*, pg. 3276
XINYI SOLAR HOLDINGS LIMITED; *Int'l*, pg. 8534
XINYI SOLAR (MALAYSIA) SDN BHD—See Xinyi Solar Holdings Limited; *Int'l*, pg. 8534
XINYI ULTRA-THIN GLASS (DONGGUAN) COMPANY LIMITED—See Xinyi Glass Holdings Limited; *Int'l*, pg. 8534
XINYI ZHONGLIN ROSIN CO., LTD.—See Harima Chemicals Group, Inc.; *Int'l*, pg. 3276
XINYUAN CHINA REAL ESTATE LTD.—See Xinyuan Real Estate Co., Ltd.; *Int'l*, pg. 8535
XIN YUAN ENTERPRISES GROUP LIMITED; *Int'l*, pg. 8529
XINYUAN REAL ESTATE CO., LTD.; *Int'l*, pg. 8535
XINYU DONGBU TOYOTA AUTO SALES & SERVICES CO., LTD.—See China MeiDong Auto Holdings Limited; *Int'l*, pg. 1519
XIN YUE LOGISTICS LIMITED—See Jolimark Holdings Limited; *Int'l*, pg. 3996
XINYU IRON & STEEL CO., LTD.; *Int'l*, pg. 8534
XINZHI GROUP CO., LTD.; *Int'l*, pg. 8535
XIOM CORP.—See Environmental Infrastructure Holdings Corp.; *U.S. Private*, pg. 1408
XIONG'AN NEW POWER TECHNOLOGY CO., LTD.; *Int'l*, pg. 8535
XIOR STUDENT HOUSING NV; *Int'l*, pg. 8535
XIO STRATEGIES, INC.—See Elliott Management Corporation; *U.S. Private*, pg. 1368
XIO STRATEGIES, INC.—See Veritas Capital Fund Management, LLC; *U.S. Private*, pg. 4362
XIOTECH CORPORATION—See Oak Investment Partners; *U.S. Private*, pg. 2983
XIO (UK) LLP; *Int'l*, pg. 8535
XIPHIAS ENTERPRISES INC.; *U.S. Private*, pg. 4581
XIQING CDB VILLAGE BANK CO., LTD.—See China Development Bank Corporation; *Int'l*, pg. 1497
XIRGO TECHNOLOGIES, INC.—See Sensata Technologies Holding plc; *U.S. Public*, pg. 1866
XIRRUS, LLC—See Cambium Networks Corporation; *U.S. Public*, pg. 425
XI S&D, INC.—See GS Holdings Corp.; *Int'l*, pg. 3142
XISHAN COAL ELECTRICITY GROUP CO., LTD.—See Shanxi Coking Coal Energy Group Co., Ltd.; *Int'l*, pg. 6786
XISHUI STRONG YEAR CO., LTD.; *Int'l*, pg. 8535
XISTER REPLY S.R.L.—See Reply S.p.A.; *Int'l*, pg. 6291
XIT2 LIMITED—See Rainbow HoldCo Limited; *Int'l*, pg. 6190
XITRON, LLC—See Hybrid Software Group PLC; *Int'l*, pg. 3544
XITRON TECHNOLOGIES, INC.—See ImpediMed Limited; *Int'l*, pg. 3631
XIUM CORPORATION; *U.S. Private*, pg. 4581
XIUS-BCGI—See Megasoft Ltd.; *Int'l*, pg. 4794
XIUS CORP.—See Megasoft Ltd.; *Int'l*, pg. 4794
XIUS S DE RL DE CV—See Megasoft Ltd.; *Int'l*, pg. 4794
XIUWU ZHONGYU GAS DEVELOPMENT CO., LTD.—See Zhongyu Energy Holdings Limited; *Int'l*, pg. 8676
XIWANG FOODSTUFFS CO., LTD.; *Int'l*, pg. 8535
XIWANG PROPERTY HOLDINGS CO. LTD.; *Int'l*, pg. 8535
XIWANG SPECIAL STEEL COMPANY LIMITED; *Int'l*, pg. 8535
XIZANG C&Y PHARMACEUTICAL CO., LTD.—See Shanxi C&Y Pharmaceutical Group Co., Ltd.; *Int'l*, pg. 6786
XIZANG RUNHE PHARMACEUTICAL CO., LTD.—See Chengdu Easton Biopharmaceuticals Co., Ltd.; *Int'l*, pg. 1467

XIZI CLEAN ENERGY EQUIPMENT MANUFACTURING CO., LTD.; *Int'l*, pg. 8535
XJ ELECTRIC CO., LTD.; *Int'l*, pg. 8535
XLA, INC.; *U.S. Private*, pg. 4581
XL BERMUDA LTD.—See AXA S.A.; *Int'l*, pg. 760
XL-BYGG BERGSLAGEN AB—See Kesko Corporation; *Int'l*, pg. 4143
X-L CABLE CORPORATION; *U.S. Private*, pg. 4579
XL CATLIN JAPAN KK—See AXA S.A.; *Int'l*, pg. 760
XL CATLIN MIDDLE EAST—See AXA S.A.; *Int'l*, pg. 760
XLDENT—See Valsef Group; *Int'l*, pg. 8123
XL DESIGN PROFESSIONAL—See AXA S.A.; *Int'l*, pg. 761
XL DIGITAL SERVICES INC.—See Creative Vistas Inc.; *Int'l*, pg. 1834
X-LEGEND ENTERTAINMENT CO., LTD.; *Int'l*, pg. 8518
XL ENERGY LTD.; *Int'l*, pg. 8535
XLENT AB; *Int'l*, pg. 8536
XLERATE DRIVELINE INDIA LIMITED—See Raunaq EPC International Limited; *Int'l*, pg. 6221
XL FINANCIAL SERVICES (IRELAND) LTD—See AXA S.A.; *Int'l*, pg. 760
XL FIRE PROTECTION CO.; *U.S. Private*, pg. 4581
XL FOODS INC.—See Nilsson Bros., Inc.; *Int'l*, pg. 5295
XL GROUP - INSURANCE - ENVIRONMENTAL INTERNATIONAL DIVISION—See AXA S.A.; *Int'l*, pg. 760
XL GROUP - INSURANCE - NEW YORK ENVIRONMENTAL DIVISION—See AXA S.A.; *Int'l*, pg. 760
XL GROUP - INSURANCE—See AXA S.A.; *Int'l*, pg. 760
XL GROUP LTD.—See AXA S.A.; *Int'l*, pg. 760
XL HOLDINGS BERHAD; *Int'l*, pg. 8535
XL HYBRIDS, INC.—See The Shyft Group, Inc.; *U.S. Public*, pg. 2130
XL-ID SOLUTIONS INC.; *Int'l*, pg. 8536
XLIFE SCIENCES AG; *Int'l*, pg. 8536
XL, INC.; *U.S. Private*, pg. 4581
XL INDIA BUSINESS SERVICES PRIVATE LIMITED—See AXA S.A.; *Int'l*, pg. 760
XL INDIA BUSINESS SERVICES PVT LTD—See AXA S.A.; *Int'l*, pg. 760
X-LINE HYPERMEDIA LTD.—See Dentsu Group Inc.; *Int'l*, pg. 2038
XL INNOVATE, LLC—See AXA S.A.; *Int'l*, pg. 760
XL INSURANCE AMERICA INC.—See AXA S.A.; *Int'l*, pg. 761
XL INSURANCE ARGENTINA S.A.—See AXA S.A.; *Int'l*, pg. 760
XL INSURANCE (CHINA) COMPANY LIMITED—See AXA S.A.; *Int'l*, pg. 760
XL INSURANCE COMPANY LIMITED—See AXA S.A.; *Int'l*, pg. 760
XL INSURANCE COMPANY OF NEW YORK, INC—See AXA S.A.; *Int'l*, pg. 761
XL INSURANCE COMPANY SE—See AXA S.A.; *Int'l*, pg. 760
XL INSURANCE COMPANY SE—See AXA S.A.; *Int'l*, pg. 761
XL INSURANCE COMPANY SE—See AXA S.A.; *Int'l*, pg. 761
XL INSURANCE COMPANY—See AXA S.A.; *Int'l*, pg. 760
XL INSURANCE—See AXA S.A.; *Int'l*, pg. 760
XL INSURANCE SWITZERLAND LTD—See AXA S.A.; *Int'l*, pg. 761
XL INSURANCE SWITZERLAND—See AXA S.A.; *Int'l*, pg. 761
XL INSURANCE (UK) HOLDINGS LIMITED—See AXA S.A.; *Int'l*, pg. 760
XL INVESTMENT MANAGEMENT LTD—See AXA S.A.; *Int'l*, pg. 761
X-LISTING CO., LTD.—See Nippon Telegraph & Telephone Corporation; *Int'l*, pg. 5345
XL LAKESIDE PACKERS, INC.—See Nilsson Bros., Inc.; *Int'l*, pg. 5295
XL LITERIE S.A.S.—See Recticel S.A.; *Int'l*, pg. 6242
XL LONDON MARKET GROUP LTD—See AXA S.A.; *Int'l*, pg. 761
XL LONDON MARKET LTD.—See AXA S.A.; *Int'l*, pg. 761
XLMEDIA PLC; *Int'l*, pg. 8536
XLN TELECOM LTD.; *Int'l*, pg. 8536
XLO INDIA LIMITED—See Hindustan Hardy Limited; *Int'l*, pg. 3400
XL PARTS LLC—See Marubeni Corporation; *Int'l*, pg. 4707
X-L PLASTICS INC.; *U.S. Private*, pg. 4579
XL PRECISION TECHNOLOGIES, LTD.—See QHP Capital, L.P.; *U.S. Private*, pg. 3313
XL RE EUROPE SE—See AXA S.A.; *Int'l*, pg. 761
XL REINSURANCE AMERICA INC.—See AXA S.A.; *Int'l*, pg. 761
XL REINSURANCE AMERICAN—See AXA S.A.; *Int'l*, pg. 761
XL REINSURANCE AMERICA—See AXA S.A.; *Int'l*, pg. 761
XL REINSURANCE AMERICA—See AXA S.A.; *Int'l*, pg. 761
XL REINSURANCE CORPORATION—See AXA S.A.; *Int'l*, pg. 761
XL REINSURANCE INC.—See AXA S.A.; *Int'l*, pg. 761
XL REINSURANCE LIMITED—See AXA S.A.; *Int'l*, pg. 761

XONEX INC.

XL RE LATIN AMERICA (ARGENTINA SA)—See AXA S.A.; *Int'l*, pg. 760
XL RE LTD—See AXA S.A.; *Int'l*, pg. 761
XL SEGUROS BRASIL S.A.—See AXA S.A.; *Int'l*, pg. 761
XL SEGUROS MEXICO S.A. DE C.V.—See AXA S.A.; *Int'l*, pg. 761
XL SERVICES UK LTD.—See AXA S.A.; *Int'l*, pg. 761
XL SPECIALIZED TRAILERS, INC.—See Caparo Group Ltd.; *Int'l*, pg. 1302
XL SYSTEMS EUROPE B.V.—See NOV, Inc.; *U.S. Public*, pg. 1547
XL SYSTEMS, L.P.—See NOV, Inc.; *U.S. Public*, pg. 1547
XM 1500 ECKINGTON LLC—See Liberty Media Corporation; *U.S. Public*, pg. 1311
XMATTERS, INC.—See Thoma Bravo, L.P.; *U.S. Private*, pg. 4148
XM COMPANIA DE EXPERTOS EN MERCADOS SA ESP—See Ecopetrol S.A.; *Int'l*, pg. 2299
XMH HOLDINGS LTD.; *Int'l*, pg. 8536
XM INTERNATIONAL INC.; *U.S. Private*, pg. 4581
XML FINANCIAL GROUP; *U.S. Private*, pg. 4581
XMOS, INC.—See XMOS Ltd.; *Int'l*, pg. 8536
XMOS LTD.; *Int'l*, pg. 8536
XMPIE, INC.—See Xerox Holdings Corporation; *U.S. Public*, pg. 2388
XMPIE, LTD.—See Xerox Holdings Corporation; *U.S. Public*, pg. 2388
XMREALITY AB; *Int'l*, pg. 8536
XNET CORPORATION—See Nippon Telegraph & Telephone Corporation; *Int'l*, pg. 5348
XO CARE THE NETHERLANDS BV—See Fagron NV; *Int'l*, pg. 2604
XO COLORADO, LLC—See XO Holdings, Inc.; *U.S. Private*, pg. 4582
XO COMMUNICATIONS, LLC—See XO Holdings, Inc.; *U.S. Private*, pg. 4582
XODUS GROUP LTD.—See Subsea 7 S.A.; *Int'l*, pg. 7249
XOFT, INC.—See iCad, Inc.; *U.S. Public*, pg. 1083
XOGRAPH HEALTHCARE LTD.; *Int'l*, pg. 8536
XOGRAPH HEALTHCARE LTD.; *Int'l*, pg. 8536
XO GROUP INC.—See Permira Advisers LLP; *Int'l*, pg. 5808
XO HOLDINGS, INC.; *U.S. Private*, pg. 4582
XOJET, INC.; *U.S. Private*, pg. 4582
XQL TECHNOLOGIES PRIVATE LIMITED—See TE Connectivity Ltd.; *Int'l*, pg. 7499
XOMA CORPORATION; *U.S. Public*, pg. 2391
XOMA (US) LLC—See XOMA Corporation; *U.S. Public*, pg. 2391
XOMETRY EUROPE GMBH—See Xometry, Inc.; *U.S. Public*, pg. 2391
XOMETRY, INC.; *U.S. Public*, pg. 2391
XOMETRY UK LTD.—See Xometry, Inc.; *U.S. Public*, pg. 2391
XOM MATERIALS GMBH—See Klockner & Co. SE; *Int'l*, pg. 4203
XOMOX CANADA LTD.—See Crane NXT, Co.; *U.S. Public*, pg. 590
XOMOX CHIHUAHUA S.A. DE C.V.—See Crane NXT, Co.; *U.S. Public*, pg. 591
XOMOX CORPORATION—See Crane NXT, Co.; *U.S. Public*, pg. 590
XOMOX FRANCE S.A.—See Crane NXT, Co.; *U.S. Public*, pg. 590
XOMOX FRANCE S.A.S.—See Crane NXT, Co.; *U.S. Public*, pg. 591
XOMOX HUNGARY KFT.—See Crane NXT, Co.; *U.S. Public*, pg. 590
XOMOX INTERNATIONAL GMBH & CO.—See Crane NXT, Co.; *U.S. Public*, pg. 590
XOMOX JAPAN LTD.—See Crane NXT, Co.; *U.S. Public*, pg. 590
XOMOX KOREA LTD.—See Crane NXT, Co.; *U.S. Public*, pg. 590
XOMOX SANMAR LTD.—See Crane NXT, Co.; *U.S. Public*, pg. 590
XOMOX SANMAR LTD.—See Sanmar Holdings Ltd.; *Int'l*, pg. 6546
X-ONE CO., LTD.—See Stream Co., Ltd.; *Int'l*, pg. 7239
XONEX INC.; *U.S. Private*, pg. 4582
XOOM CORPORATION—See PayPal Holdings, Inc.; *U.S. Public*, pg. 1657
XOOM ENERGY CANADA, ULC—See NRG Energy, Inc.; *U.S. Public*, pg. 1551
XOOM ENERGY GEORGIA, LLC—See NRG Energy, Inc.; *U.S. Public*, pg. 1551
XOOM ENERGY, LLC—See NRG Energy, Inc.; *U.S. Public*, pg. 1551
XOOM ENERGY, LLC—See NRG Energy, Inc.; *U.S. Public*, pg. 1551
XOOM ENERGY MICHIGAN, LLC—See NRG Energy, Inc.; *U.S. Public*, pg. 1551
XOOM ENERGY NEW JERSEY, LLC—See NRG Energy, Inc.; *U.S. Public*, pg. 1551
XOOM ENERGY ONT, ULC—See NRG Energy, Inc.; *U.S. Public*, pg. 1551
XOOM ENERGY TEXAS, LLC—See NRG Energy, Inc.; *U.S. Public*, pg. 1551

XONEX INC.
CORPORATE AFFILIATIONS

XORAIL, INC. - SHAWNEE MISSION—See Westinghouse Air Brake Technologies Corporation; *U.S. Public*, pg. 2360
XORAIL, INC.—See Westinghouse Air Brake Technologies Corporation; *U.S. Public*, pg. 2360
XORIANT CANADA—See ChrysCapital Management Co.; *Int'l*, pg. 1589
XORIANT CORPORATION—See ChrysCapital Management Co.; *Int'l*, pg. 1588
XORIANT INDIA—See ChrysCapital Management Co.; *Int'l*, pg. 1589
XOR SECURITY LLC—See Enlightenment Capital LLC; *U.S. Private*, pg. 1400
XORTX THERAPEUTICS, INC.; *Int'l*, pg. 8536
XOS DIGITAL INC.—See Catapult Group International Ltd.; *Int'l*, pg. 1358
XOS, INC.; *U.S. Public*, pg. 2391
XO UTAH INC.—See XO Holdings, Inc.; *U.S. Private*, pg. 4582
XO WINDOWS, LLC—See Younger Brothers Group Inc.; *U.S. Private*, pg. 4593
XOX BHD; *Int'l*, pg. 8536
XOX COM SDN. BHD.—See XOX Bhd; *Int'l*, pg. 8536
XOXIDE, INC.; *U.S. Private*, pg. 4582
XOX MOBILE SDN BHD—See XOX Bhd; *Int'l*, pg. 8536
XOX NETWORKS BERHAD; *Int'l*, pg. 8536
XOXO—See Sun Capital Partners, Inc.; *U.S. Private*, pg. 3860
XOX TECHNOLOGY BHD; *Int'l*, pg. 8536
XPANDA SECURITY PROPRIETARY LIMITED—See ARGENT INDUSTRIAL LIMITED; *Int'l*, pg. 561
XPAND GROUP PTY LIMITED—See Rubicor Group Limited; *Int'l*, pg. 6423
XPANSIV DATA SYSTEMS INC.; *U.S. Private*, pg. 4582
XPANXION, LLC—See UST Global Inc.; *U.S. Private*, pg. 4324
XPART LIMITED—See Caterpillar, Inc.; *U.S. Public*, pg. 454
XP CHEMISTRIES AB; *Int'l*, pg. 8537
XPD INC.—See AOI TYO Holdings Inc.; *Int'l*, pg. 488
XPD SOCCER GEAR GROUP LIMITED; *Int'l*, pg. 8537
XPEDX, S.A. DE C.V.—See Clayton, Dubilier & Rice, LLC; *U.S. Private*, pg. 930
XPEL B.V.—See XPEL, Inc.; *U.S. Public*, pg. 2391
XPEL CANADA CORP.—See XPEL, Inc.; *U.S. Public*, pg. 2391
XPEL DE MEXICO S. DE R.L. DE C.V.—See XPEL, Inc.; *U.S. Public*, pg. 2391
XPEL, INC.; *U.S. Public*, pg. 2391
XPEL LTD.—See XPEL, Inc.; *U.S. Public*, pg. 2391
XPENG INC.; *Int'l*, pg. 8537
XPERA, INC.—See Wind Point Advisors LLC; *U.S. Private*, pg. 4536
XPERIA SOLUTIONS APPAREL SOFTWARE; *U.S. Private*, pg. 4582
XPERI CORPORATION—See Adeia Inc.; *U.S. Public*, pg. 40
XPERIENCE XRG RESTAURANT GROUP—See Z Capital Group, LLC; *U.S. Private*, pg. 4596
XPERI INC.; *U.S. Public*, pg. 2391
X PERION CONSULTING AG—See Atos SE; *Int'l*, pg. 692
XPERTLINK GMBH—See Softline AG; *Int'l*, pg. 7055
XPERTTECH INC.; *U.S. Private*, pg. 4582
XP FACTORY PLC; *Int'l*, pg. 8537
XP INC.; *Int'l*, pg. 8537
XP INVESTMENTS US, LLC—See XP Inc.; *Int'l*, pg. 8537
XPIQ-SSI—See XP Power Limited; *Int'l*, pg. 8537
XPLACE GMBH—See Ceconomy AG; *Int'l*, pg. 1388
XPLANE CORP.; *U.S. Private*, pg. 4582
XPLORA MOBILE AB—See Xplora Technologies AS; *Int'l*, pg. 8538
XPLORA MOBILE AS—See Xplora Technologies AS; *Int'l*, pg. 8538
XPLORA MOBILE DENMARK APS—See Xplora Technologies AS; *Int'l*, pg. 8538
XPLORA MOBILE OY—See Xplora Technologies AS; *Int'l*, pg. 8538
XPLORA TECHNOLOGIES AS; *Int'l*, pg. 8537
XPLORE RESOURCES HOLDINGS CORP.—See VON Capital Corp.; *Int'l*, pg. 8304
XPLORE TECHNOLOGIES CORPORATION OF AMERICA—See Zebra Technologies Corporation; *U.S. Public*, pg. 2402
XPLORE TECHNOLOGIES CORP.—See Zebra Technologies Corporation; *U.S. Public*, pg. 2402
XPLORE TRAVEL GROUP—See Symphony Technology Group, LLC; *U.S. Private*, pg. 3902
XPLORE WEALTH LIMITED; *Int'l*, pg. 8538
XPLORNET COMMUNICATIONS INC.—See Stonepeak Partners L.P.; *U.S. Private*, pg. 3829
XPLOSION INCORPORATED; *U.S. Private*, pg. 4582
XPLUS, INC.; *Int'l*, pg. 8538
XPO AIR CHARTER, LLC—See XPO, Inc.; *U.S. Public*, pg. 2392
XPO BULK UK LTD.—See XPO, Inc.; *U.S. Public*, pg. 2392
XPO EXPRESS, INC.—See XPO, Inc.; *U.S. Public*, pg. 2392

XPO GLOBAL FORWARDING, INC.—See XPO, Inc.; *U.S. Public*, pg. 2392
XPO GLOBAL LOGISTICS INC.—See XPO, Inc.; *U.S. Public*, pg. 2392
XPO HOLDINGS UK & IRELAND LIMITED—See XPO, Inc.; *U.S. Public*, pg. 2392
XPO HOLDING TRANSPORT SOLUTIONS EUROPE—See XPO, Inc.; *U.S. Public*, pg. 2392
XPO, INC.; *U.S. Public*, pg. 2392
XPO INTERMODAL, INC.—See XPO, Inc.; *U.S. Public*, pg. 2392
XPO LAST MILE CANADA INC.—See XPO, Inc.; *U.S. Public*, pg. 2392
XPO LAST MILE, INC.—See XPO, Inc.; *U.S. Public*, pg. 2392
XPO LOGISTICS CANADA INC.—See XPO, Inc.; *U.S. Public*, pg. 2392
XPO LOGISTICS EUROPE S.A.—See XPO, Inc.; *U.S. Public*, pg. 2392
XPO LOGISTICS EXPRESS, LLC—See XPO, Inc.; *U.S. Public*, pg. 2392
XPO LOGISTICS, LLC—See XPO, Inc.; *U.S. Public*, pg. 2392
XPO LOGISTICS SUPPLY CHAIN, INC.—See XPO, Inc.; *U.S. Public*, pg. 2392
XPONENTIAL FITNESS, INC.; *U.S. Public*, pg. 2392
XPONENTIAL, INC.; *U.S. Private*, pg. 4582
XPO NLM, INC.—See XPO, Inc.; *U.S. Public*, pg. 2392
XPON TECHNOLOGIES GROUP LIMITED; *Int'l*, pg. 8538
XPO SUPPLY CHAIN ITALY S.P.A.—See XPO, Inc.; *U.S. Public*, pg. 2392
XPO TRANSPORT SOLUTIONS ITALY S.R.L.—See XPO, Inc.; *U.S. Public*, pg. 2392
XPO TRANSPORT SOLUTIONS PORTUGAL, LDA.—See XPO, Inc.; *U.S. Public*, pg. 2392
XP PLC—See XP Power Limited; *Int'l*, pg. 8537
XP POWER AG—See XP Power Limited; *Int'l*, pg. 8537
XP POWER APS—See XP Power Limited; *Int'l*, pg. 8537
XP POWER GMBH—See XP Power Limited; *Int'l*, pg. 8537
XP POWER LIMITED; *Int'l*, pg. 8537
XP POWER LLC—See XP Power Limited; *Int'l*, pg. 8537
XP POWER NORWAY AS—See XP Power Limited; *Int'l*, pg. 8537
XP POWER SA—See XP Power Limited; *Int'l*, pg. 8537
XP POWER (SHANGHAI) CO., LIMITED—See XP Power Limited; *Int'l*, pg. 8537
XP POWER SINGAPORE HOLDINGS PTE LIMITED—See XP Power Limited; *Int'l*, pg. 8537
XP POWER—See XP Power Limited; *Int'l*, pg. 8537
XP POWER (S) PTE LIMITED—See XP Power Limited; *Int'l*, pg. 8537
XP POWER SRL—See XP Power Limited; *Int'l*, pg. 8537
XP POWER SWEDEN AB—See XP Power Limited; *Int'l*, pg. 8537
XPRESSBET, INC.—See The Stronach Group Inc.; *Int'l*, pg. 7689
XPRESSDOCS PARTNERS, LTD.—See The Reynolds & Reynolds Company; *U.S. Private*, pg. 4106
XPRESS FINANCE LIMITED—See Zensun Enterprises Limited; *Int'l*, pg. 8635
XPRESS GLOBAL SYSTEMS, LLC—See Aterian Investment Management, L.P.; *U.S. Private*, pg. 367
XPRESS MEDIA PHILIPPINES INC.—See A-Smart Holdings Ltd.; *Int'l*, pg. 20
XPRESS MEDIA PTE LTD—See A-Smart Holdings Ltd.; *Int'l*, pg. 20
XPRESSPA AMSTERDAM AIRPORT B.V.—See XWELL, Inc.; *U.S. Public*, pg. 2393
XPRESS PRINT (AUSTRALIA) PTY LTD—See A-Smart Holdings Ltd.; *Int'l*, pg. 20
XPRESS PRINT (PTE) LTD.—See A-Smart Holdings Ltd.; *Int'l*, pg. 20
XPRESS PRINT (SHANGHAI) CO., LTD.—See A-Smart Holdings Ltd.; *Int'l*, pg. 20
XPRESS PRINT (SHENYANG) CO., LTD.—See A-Smart Holdings Ltd.; *Int'l*, pg. 20
XPRESS SOURCE—See Echo, LLC; *U.S. Private*, pg. 1327
XPRICE INC.—See DCM Holdings Co., Ltd.; *Int'l*, pg. 1992
XPR LLC; *U.S. Private*, pg. 4582
XPROCURE LTD.—See Primedia Limited; *Int'l*, pg. 5979
XPRO GLOBAL LIMITED—See Xpro India Limited; *Int'l*, pg. 8538
XPRO INDIA LIMITED - BARJORA UNIT—See Xpro India Limited; *Int'l*, pg. 8538
XPRO INDIA LIMITED - RANJANGAON UNIT—See Xpro India Limited; *Int'l*, pg. 8538
XPRO INDIA LIMITED; *Int'l*, pg. 8538
X! PROMOS; *U.S. Private*, pg. 4579
XPROTS SPORTS CO., LTD.—See TOPCO Scientific Co., Ltd.; *Int'l*, pg. 7814
XP SOFTWARE PTY. LTD.—See Cardno Limited; *Int'l*, pg. 1323
XP SOLUTIONS INC.—See EQT AB; *Int'l*, pg. 2481
XPS PENSIONS GROUP; *Int'l*, pg. 8538
XP SYSTEMS CORPORATION—See Fiserv, Inc.; *U.S. Public*, pg. 851
XPT GROUP LLC; *U.S. Private*, pg. 4582
XPURE GMBH—See Adecco Group AG; *Int'l*, pg. 140

XPV WATER PARTNERS; *Int'l*, pg. 8538
XRAPPLIED TECHNOLOGIES INC.; *Int'l*, pg. 8538
X-RAY INC. OF RHODE ISLAND; *U.S. Private*, pg. 4579
X-RAY INDUSTRIES INC.; *U.S. Private*, pg. 4579
XRAY ONE S.R.L.—See Garofalo Health Care SpA; *Int'l*, pg. 2886
X-RAY OPTICAL SYSTEMS, INC.—See Danaher Corporation; *U.S. Public*, pg. 632
X-RAY VISIONS, INC.—See Atlantic Street Capital Management LLC; *U.S. Private*, pg. 374
XREALITY GROUP LTD; *Int'l*, pg. 8538
XREF LIMITED; *Int'l*, pg. 8538
XRF CHEMICALS PTY LTD—See XRF Scientific Limited; *Int'l*, pg. 8538
XRF LABWARE—See XRF Scientific Limited; *Int'l*, pg. 8538
XRF SCIENTIFIC AMERICAS INC.—See XRF Scientific Limited; *Int'l*, pg. 8538
XRF SCIENTIFIC EUROPE GMBH—See XRF Scientific Limited; *Int'l*, pg. 8538
XRF SCIENTIFIC EUROPE SPRL—See XRF Scientific Limited; *Int'l*, pg. 8538
XRF SCIENTIFIC LIMITED; *Int'l*, pg. 8538
XRF TECHNOLOGY (VIC) PTY LTD—See XRF Scientific Limited; *Int'l*, pg. 8538
XRF TECHNOLOGY (WA) PTY LTD—See XRF Scientific Limited; *Int'l*, pg. 8538
X-RITE ASIA PACIFIC LIMITED—See Danaher Corporation; *U.S. Public*, pg. 632
X-RITE EUROPE AG—See Danaher Corporation; *U.S. Public*, pg. 632
X-RITE EUROPE GMBH—See Danaher Corporation; *U.S. Public*, pg. 632
X-RITE GMBH—See Danaher Corporation; *U.S. Public*, pg. 632
X-RITE, INCORPORATED—See Danaher Corporation; *U.S. Public*, pg. 632
X-RITE LIMITED—See Danaher Corporation; *U.S. Public*, pg. 632
X-R-I TESTING—See X-Ray Industries Inc.; *U.S. Private*, pg. 4579
XRONOS, INC.—See PCA Corporation; *Int'l*, pg. 5766
XROSS SPORTS MARKETING CO., LTD.—See XEBIO Holdings Co., Ltd.; *Int'l*, pg. 8521
XRX INTERNATIONAL ENTERTAINMENT HOLDING GROUP, INC.; *U.S. Public*, pg. 2393
XS4ALL INTERNET B.V.—See Koninklijke KPN N.V.; *Int'l*, pg. 4267
XS CARGO—See KarpReilly, LLC; *U.S. Private*, pg. 2263
X-SECURE CO., LTD.—See The Practical Solution Public Company Limited; *Int'l*, pg. 7676
XSEED JKS, INC.—See Marvelous Inc.; *Int'l*, pg. 4717
XSEEDWEALTH PTY LTD—See Centrepoint Alliance Limited; *Int'l*, pg. 1412
XSE GROUP INC.; *U.S. Private*, pg. 4582
XSELL RESOURCES, INC.; *U.S. Private*, pg. 4582
XSEMI CORPORATION—See Hon Hai Precision Industry Co., Ltd.; *Int'l*, pg. 3459
XSFERA S.R.L.—See Nippon Telegraph & Telephone Corporation; *Int'l*, pg. 5355
XS FINANCIAL INC.; *Int'l*, pg. 8539
XS FINANCIAL, INC.—See Axar Capital Management L.P.; *U.S. Private*, pg. 412
XS FINANCIAL, INC.—See Mavik Capital Management, LP; *U.S. Private*, pg. 2616
XS INTERNATIONAL, INC.; *U.S. Private*, pg. 4582
XSOLIS, INC.; *U.S. Private*, pg. 4582
XSOMO INTERNATIONAL LIMITED; *Int'l*, pg. 8539
XSOVT BRANDS, INC.; *U.S. Public*, pg. 2393
X-SPINE SYSTEMS, INC.—See Xtant Medical Holdings, Inc.; *U.S. Public*, pg. 2393
XSPRAY PHARMA AB; *Int'l*, pg. 8539
XSPRING CAPITAL PUBLIC COMPANY LIMITED; *Int'l*, pg. 8539
XSTATE RESOURCES LIMITED; *Int'l*, pg. 8539
XSTATIC PUBLIC RELATIONS; *U.S. Private*, pg. 4582
XSTELOS HOLDINGS, INC.; *U.S. Private*, pg. 4582
XSTRATA COPPER CHILE S.A.—See Glencore plc; *Int'l*, pg. 2991
XSTRATA LAS BAMBAS S.A.—See China Rare Earth Resources And Technology Co., Ltd.; *Int'l*, pg. 1545
XSTREAM NORTH AMERICA, INC.—See SeaChange International, Inc.; *U.S. Public*, pg. 1851
XSTREAM SP. Z O.O.—See SeaChange International, Inc.; *U.S. Public*, pg. 1851
XSTREAM SYSTEMS, INC.—See Veracity Network Inc.; *U.S. Private*, pg. 4359
X STUDIOS INC.; *U.S. Private*, pg. 4579
XTANT MEDICAL HOLDINGS, INC.; *U.S. Public*, pg. 2393
XTAVA LLC—See Aterian; *U.S. Public*, pg. 221
XTB SA; *Int'l*, pg. 8539
XTC CABARET (DALLAS), INC.—See RCI Hospitality Holdings, Inc.; *U.S. Public*, pg. 1767
XTC CABARET, INC.—See RCI Hospitality Holdings, Inc.; *U.S. Public*, pg. 1767
XTC LITHIUM LIMITED; *Int'l*, pg. 8539
XTC PRODUCTS, INC.; *U.S. Private*, pg. 4583
XTECH CO., LTD.; *Int'l*, pg. 8539
XTECH HP CO., LTD—See XTech Co., Ltd.; *Int'l*, pg. 8539

COMPANY NAME INDEX

XYLEM INC.

X TECHNOLOGIES INC.—See Abbott Laboratories; *U.S. Public*, pg. 21
XTEK EUROPE S.R.O.—See Xtek, Inc.; *U.S. Private*, pg. 4583
XTEK, INC.; *U.S. Private*, pg. 4583
XTEK LIMITED; *Int'l*, pg. 8539
X-TEK SYSTEMS LTD—See Nikon Corporation; *Int'l*, pg. 5293
XTELESIS CORP.—See Protel Communications, Inc.; *U.S. Private*, pg. 3290
X-TEND B.V.—See New Wave Group AB; *Int'l*, pg. 5231
XTEND HEALTHCARE LLC—See CorroHealth, Inc.; *U.S. Private*, pg. 1059
XTEND INDUSTRIAL DESIGNERS & ENGINEERS PRIVATE LIMITED—See Indoco Remedies Ltd; *Int'l*, pg. 3657
XT ENERGY GROUP, INC.; *Int'l*, pg. 8539
XTENSIBLE SOLUTIONS, INC.—See ESCO Technologies, Inc.; *U.S. Public*, pg. 794
X-TENTION INFORMATIONSTECHNOLOGIE GMBH; *Int'l*, pg. 8518
XTEP (CHINA) CO., LTD.—See Xtep International Holdings Limited; *Int'l*, pg. 8539
XTEP INTERNATIONAL HOLDINGS LIMITED; *Int'l*, pg. 8539
XTERA COMMUNICATIONS, INC.—See H.I.G. Capital, LLC; *U.S. Private*, pg. 1833
XTERPRISE, INC.—See SML Group Ltd.; *Int'l*, pg. 7014
X-TERRA RESOURCES INC.; *Int'l*, pg. 8518
XTGLOBAL INFOTECH LTD.; *Int'l*, pg. 8539
XTI AEROSPACE, INC., *U.S. Public*, pg. 2393
XTIERRA INC.; *Int'l*, pg. 8539
XTIME, INC.—See Cox Automotive LLC; *U.S. Private*, pg. 1074
XTIVA FINANCIAL SYSTEMS, INC.; *U.S. Private*, pg. 4583
XTIVIA, INC.—See Asseco Poland S.A.; *Int'l*, pg. 642
XTL BIOPHARMACEUTICALS LTD.; *Int'l*, pg. 8539
XTM, INC.; *Int'l*, pg. 8539
XTO ENERGY CANADA ULC—See Whitecap Resources Inc.; *Int'l*, pg. 8399
XTO ENERGY INC.—See Exxon Mobil Corporation; *U.S. Public*, pg. 817
XTPL SA; *Int'l*, pg. 8539
XTRAC GROUP LIMITED—See MiddleGround Management, LP; *U.S. Private*, pg. 2713
XTRAC, INC.—See MiddleGround Management, LP; *U.S. Private*, pg. 2713
XTRAC LIMITED—See MiddleGround Management, LP; *U.S. Private*, pg. 2713
XTRACON A/S—See TowerBrook Capital Partners, L.P.; *U.S. Private*, pg. 4195
XTRA CORPORATION—See Berkshire Hathaway Inc.; *U.S. Public*, pg. 319
XTRACT ONE TECHNOLOGIES INC.; *Int'l*, pg. 8540
XTRACT RESOURCES PLC; *Int'l*, pg. 8540
XTRA-GOLD RESOURCES CORP.; *Int'l*, pg. 8540
XTRA GRASS—See ABN AMRO Group N.V.; *Int'l*, pg. 65
XTRA GRASS—See Gilde Buy Out Partners B.V.; *Int'l*, pg. 2975
XTRA GRASS—See Parcom Capital Management B.V.; *Int'l*, pg. 5740
XTRA LEASE LLC—See Berkshire Hathaway Inc.; *U.S. Public*, pg. 319
XTRALIS, INC.—See Blum Capital Partners, L.P.; *U.S. Private*, pg. 599
XTRALIS PTY. LTD.—See Blum Capital Partners, L.P.; *U.S. Private*, pg. 599
XTRALIS UK LTD—See Blum Capital Partners, L.P.; *U.S. Private*, pg. 599
XTRA LLC—See Berkshire Hathaway Inc.; *U.S. Public*, pg. 319
XTRAMIX CONCRETE SOLUTION MIX LLC—See Al Jaber Group; *Int'l*, pg. 280
XTRAPACK LIMITED—See Mondelez International, Inc.; *U.S. Public*, pg. 1464
XTRA TEXTIL, S.A. DE C.V.—See Grupo Xtra S.A. de C.V.; *Int'l*, pg. 3139
XTRATHERM LIMITED—See Mohawk Industries, Inc.; *U.S. Public*, pg. 1458
XTRATHERM UK LIMITED—See Mohawk Industries, Inc.; *U.S. Public*, pg. 1458
XTRA-VISION LIMITED—See Hilco Trading, LLC; *U.S. Private*, pg. 1944
XTREME COMMUNICATIONS, INC.; *U.S. Private*, pg. 4583
XTREME CONSULTING GROUP, INC.; *U.S. Private*, pg. 4583
XTREME FIGHTING CHAMPIONSHIPS, INC.; *U.S. Public*, pg. 2393
XTREME GREEN ELECTRIC VEHICLES INC.; *U.S. Private*, pg. 4583
XTREME HEALTHCARE CORPORATION; *U.S. Private*, pg. 4583
X-TREME INVESTMENTS, INC., *U.S. Private*, pg. 4579
XTREME LASHES, LLC; *U.S. Private*, pg. 4583
XTREME MANUFACTURING, LLC; *U.S. Private*, pg. 4583
XTREME RFID—See Cascade Engineering, Inc.; *U.S. Private*, pg. 779

XTREME TECHNOLOGIES GMBH—See Ushio, Inc.; *Int'l*, pg. 8098
XTRIBE P.L.C.; *Int'l*, pg. 8540
XTRO IT SOLUTIONS GMBH—See Kontron AG; *Int'l*, pg. 4278
XTRONIC GMBH—See INA-Holding Schaeffler GmbH & Co. KG; *Int'l*, pg. 3642
XTTRIUM LABORATORIES INC.; *U.S. Private*, pg. 4583
XTV NETWORKS LTD.; *Int'l*, pg. 8540
XTWO GMBH—See Schneider Electric SE; *Int'l*, pg. 6625
XUANCHENG VALIN PRECISION TECHNOLOGY CO., LTD.; *Int'l*, pg. 8540
XUAN MAI INVESTMENT AND CONSTRUCTION CORPORATION—See Vietnam Construction Stock Corporation; *Int'l*, pg. 8198
XUANRUN (SHANGHAI) CHEMICAL TECHNOLOGY CO., LTD.—See Xinxiang Richful Lube Additive Co., Ltd.; *Int'l*, pg. 8533
XUAN WU CLOUD TECHNOLOGY HOLDINGS LIMITED; *Int'l*, pg. 8540
XUANYUAN IDRIVE TECHNOLOGY (SHENZHEN) CO., LTD.—See Wuhan Guide Infrared Co., Ltd.; *Int'l*, pg. 8500
XUANYUAN INTERNATIONAL HOTEL OF HUANGSHAN TOURISM DEVELOPMENT CO., LTD.—See Huangshan Tourism Development Co., Ltd.; *Int'l*, pg. 3513
XUCHANG KETOP TESTING RESEARCH INSTITUTE CO., LTD.; *Int'l*, pg. 8540
XUCHANG YUANDONG DRIVE SHAFT CO., LTD.; *Int'l*, pg. 8540
XUCHANG ZHONGXING FORGING CO., LTD.—See Xuchang Yuandong Drive Shaft Co., Ltd.; *Int'l*, pg. 8540
XUEDA EDUCATION GROUP—See Xueda (Xiamen) Education Technology Group Co., Ltd.; *Int'l*, pg. 8540
XUEDA (XIAMEN) EDUCATION TECHNOLOGY GROUP CO., LTD.; *Int'l*, pg. 8540
XUELONG GROUP CO., LTD.; *Int'l*, pg. 8540
XUNLEI LIMITED; *Int'l*, pg. 8540
XURONG ELECTRONIC (SHENZHEN) CO., LTD.—See Silitech Technology Corporation; *Int'l*, pg. 6921
XURPAS ENTERPRISE INC.—See Xurpas Inc.; *Int'l*, pg. 8540
XURPAS INC.; *Int'l*, pg. 8540
XU YUAN PACKAGING TECHNOLOGY CO., LTD.; *Int'l*, pg. 8540
XUZHOU CONSTRUCTION MACHINERY GROUP CO., LTD.; *Int'l*, pg. 8540
XUZHOU HANDLER SPECIAL VEHICLE CO., LTD.; *Int'l*, pg. 8541
XUZHOU HEAVY MACHINERY CO., LTD.—See Xuzhou Construction Machinery Group Co., Ltd.; *Int'l*, pg. 8541
XUZHOU HIRSCHMANN ELECTRONICS CO., LTD.—See Belden, Inc.; *U.S. Public*, pg. 294
XUZHOU HIRSCHMANN ELECTRONICS CO., LTD.—See Xuzhou Construction Machinery Group Co., Ltd.; *Int'l*, pg. 8541
XUZHOU KERONG ENVIRONMENTAL RESOURCES CO., LTD.; *Int'l*, pg. 8541
XUZHOU LIEBHERR CONCRETE MACHINERY CO. LTD.—See Liebherr-International AG; *Int'l*, pg. 4491
XUZHOU METALFORMING MACHINE GROUP CO., LTD; *Int'l*, pg. 8541
XUZHOU PAT CONTROL TECHNOLOGY CO.—See Quarterhill Inc.; *Int'l*, pg. 6155
XUZHOU PAT CONTROL TECHNOLOGY CO.—See Xuzhou Construction Machinery Group Co., Ltd.; *Int'l*, pg. 8541
XUZHOU ROTHE ERDE RING MILL CO., LTD.—See ThyssenKrupp AG; *Int'l*, pg. 7734
XUZHOU SINOTRANS MARUZEN TRANSPORTATION CO., LTD.—See Maruzen Showa Unyu Co., Ltd.; *Int'l*, pg. 4716
XUZHOU TEXHONG YINFENG TEXTILE CO., LTD.—See Texhong Textile Group Limited; *Int'l*, pg. 7584
XUZHOU XIANGDA CAMEL FEED CO., LTD—See Tangrenshen Group Co., Ltd.; *Int'l*, pg. 7458
XUZHOU YIJIA MEDICAL APPLIANCE CO., LTD.—See PW Medtech Group Limited; *Int'l*, pg. 6126
XUZHOU YUEJIA COMMERCIAL CO., LTD.—See Carrefour SA; *Int'l*, pg. 1344
XVIVO PERFUSION AB; *Int'l*, pg. 8541
XVIVO PERFUSION LUND AB—See XVIVO Perfusion AB; *Int'l*, pg. 8541
X WARE AKTIEBOLAG—See WiseTech Global Limited; *Int'l*, pg. 8437
XWAVE—See BCE Inc.; *Int'l*, pg. 926
XWELL, INC.; *U.S. Public*, pg. 2393
XWINSYS TECHNOLOGY DEVELOPMENT LTD.; *Int'l*, pg. 8541
XXENTRIA INTERNATIONAL (USA) CORP.—See Xxentria Technology Materials Co., Ltd.; *Int'l*, pg. 8541
XXENTRIA TECHNOLOGY MATERIALS CO., LTD.; *Int'l*, pg. 8541
XXI CENTURY INVESTMENTS PUBLIC LIMITED; *Int'l*, pg. 8541
XXL ADVENTURE AS—See XXL ASA; *Int'l*, pg. 8541
XXL ASA; *Int'l*, pg. 8541
XXL ENERGY CORP.; *Int'l*, pg. 8541

XXL SPORT OG VILDMARK AB—See XXL ASA; *Int'l*, pg. 8541
XXL SPORTS & OUTDOOR GMBH—See XXL ASA; *Int'l*, pg. 8541
XXL SPORTS & OUTDOOR OY—See XXL ASA; *Int'l*, pg. 8541
XXL SPORT & VILLMARK AS—See XXL ASA; *Int'l*, pg. 8541
XXXLUTZ KG; *Int'l*, pg. 8541
XYBERNAUT CORPORATION; *U.S. Private*, pg. 4583
XYBERNET, INC.—See Blue Hill Data Services, Inc.; *U.S. Private*, pg. 589
XYBION CORPORATION; *U.S. Private*, pg. 4583
XYCARB CERAMICS B.V.—See Schunk GmbH; *Int'l*, pg. 6644
XYCARB CERAMICS INC.—See Schunk GmbH; *Int'l*, pg. 6643
XYCARB CERAMICS SINGAPORE PTE LTD—See Schunk GmbH; *Int'l*, pg. 6644
XYCARB CERAMICS TAIWAN LTD.—See Schunk GmbH; *Int'l*, pg. 6644
XYCOM AUTOMATION, INC.—See Schneider Electric SE; *Int'l*, pg. 6632
XYLAZEL S.A.—See Akzo Nobel N.V.; *Int'l*, pg. 275
XYLEM ANALYTICS AUSTRALIA PTY LIMITED—See Xylem Inc.; *U.S. Public*, pg. 2395
XYLEM ANALYTICS AUSTRALIA PTY LIMITED—See Xylem Inc.; *U.S. Public*, pg. 2395
XYLEM ANALYTICS FRANCE S.A.S.—See Xylem Inc.; *U.S. Public*, pg. 2395
XYLEM ANALYTICS GERMANY GMBH—See Xylem Inc.; *U.S. Public*, pg. 2396
XYLEM ANALYTICS UK LTD—See Xylem Inc.; *U.S. Public*, pg. 2395
XYLEM APPLIED WATER SYSTEMS - GUELPH—See Xylem Inc.; *U.S. Public*, pg. 2396
XYLEM APPLIED WATER SYSTEMS - OTTAWA—See Xylem Inc.; *U.S. Public*, pg. 2396
XYLEM APPLIED WATER SYSTEMS - SAINT-LAURENT—See Xylem Inc.; *U.S. Public*, pg. 2396
XYLEM AUSTRALIA HOLDINGS PTY LTD—See Xylem Inc.; *U.S. Public*, pg. 2396
XYLEM DEWATERING SOLUTIONS, INC.—See Xylem Inc.; *U.S. Public*, pg. 2396
XYLEME, INC.—See Battery Ventures, L.P.; *U.S. Private*, pg. 489
XYLEM EUROPE GMBH—See Xylem Inc.; *U.S. Public*, pg. 2395
XYLEM FLOW CONTROL LIMITED—See Xylem Inc.; *U.S. Public*, pg. 2395
XYLEM INC. - ANALYTICS—See Xylem Inc.; *U.S. Public*, pg. 2395
XYLEM INC. - APPLIED WATER SYSTEMS—See Xylem Inc.; *U.S. Public*, pg. 2396
XYLEM INC. - BELL & GOSSETT DIVISION—See Xylem Inc.; *U.S. Public*, pg. 2396
XYLEM INC.; *U.S. Public*, pg. 2393
XYLEM INC. - WATER SOLUTIONS—See Xylem Inc.; *U.S. Public*, pg. 2396
XYLEM MANUFACTURING AUSTRIA GMBH—See Xylem Inc.; *U.S. Public*, pg. 2397
XYLEM (NANJING) CO. LTD—See Xylem Inc.; *U.S. Public*, pg. 2396
XYLEM PCI MEMBRANES POLSKA S.P. Z.O.O.—See Xylem Inc.; *U.S. Public*, pg. 2397
XYLEMPORIKI PATRON S.A.—See Shelman Swiss-Hellenic Wood Product Manufacturers SA; *Int'l*, pg. 6800
XYLEM (SHANGHAI) TRADING CO., LTD.—See Xylem Inc.; *U.S. Public*, pg. 2396
XYLEM SHARED SERVICES SP. Z.O.O.—See Xylem Inc.; *U.S. Public*, pg. 2397
XYLEM WATER SOLUTIONS AB—See Xylem Inc.; *U.S. Public*, pg. 2396
XYLEM WATER SOLUTIONS ARGENTINA S.A.—See Xylem Inc.; *U.S. Public*, pg. 2396
XYLEM WATER SOLUTIONS AUSTRALIA LIMITED—See Xylem Inc.; *U.S. Public*, pg. 2396
XYLEM WATER SOLUTIONS AUSTRIA GMBH—See Xylem Inc.; *U.S. Public*, pg. 2396
XYLEM WATER SOLUTIONS AUSTRIA GMBH—See Xylem Inc.; *U.S. Public*, pg. 2396
XYLEM WATER SOLUTIONS BELGIUM BVBA—See Xylem Inc.; *U.S. Public*, pg. 2396
XYLEM WATER SOLUTIONS CANADA—See Xylem Inc.; *U.S. Public*, pg. 2397
XYLEM WATER SOLUTIONS CANADA—See Xylem Inc.; *U.S. Public*, pg. 2397
XYLEM WATER SOLUTIONS COLOMBIA LTDA—See Xylem Inc.; *U.S. Public*, pg. 2397
XYLEM WATER SOLUTIONS DENMARK APS—See Xylem Inc.; *U.S. Public*, pg. 2397
XYLEM WATER SOLUTIONS DEUTSCHLAND GMBH—See Xylem Inc.; *U.S. Public*, pg. 2397
XYLEM WATER SOLUTIONS ESPANA S.A.—See Xylem Inc.; *U.S. Public*, pg. 2397
XYLEM WATER SOLUTIONS FLORIDA LLC—See Xylem Inc.; *U.S. Public*, pg. 2397

XYLEM INC.

XYLEM WATER SOLUTIONS FRANCE SAS—See Xylem Inc.; *U.S. Public*, pg. 2397
XYLEM WATER SOLUTIONS GLOBAL SERVICES AB—See Xylem Inc.; *U.S. Public*, pg. 2397
XYLEM WATER SOLUTIONS HERFORD GMBH—See Xylem Inc.; *U.S. Public*, pg. 2397
XYLEM WATER SOLUTIONS (HONG KONG) LIMITED—See Xylem Inc.; *U.S. Public*, pg. 2396
XYLEM WATER SOLUTIONS INDIA PRIVATE LIMITED—See Xylem Inc.; *U.S. Public*, pg. 2397
XYLEM WATER SOLUTIONS INDIA PVT. LTD.—See Xylem Inc.; *U.S. Public*, pg. 2397
XYLEM WATER SOLUTIONS IRELAND LTD.—See Xylem Inc.; *U.S. Public*, pg. 2397
XYLEM WATER SOLUTIONS IRELAND LTD.—See Xylem Inc.; *U.S. Public*, pg. 2397
XYLEM WATER SOLUTIONS ITALIA S.R.L.—See Xylem Inc.; *U.S. Public*, pg. 2397
XYLEM WATER SOLUTIONS LIETUVA, UAB—See Xylem Inc.; *U.S. Public*, pg. 2397
XYLEM WATER SOLUTIONS MAGYARORSZAG KFT.—See Xylem Inc.; *U.S. Public*, pg. 2397
XYLEM WATER SOLUTIONS MALAYSIA SDN. BHD.—See Xylem Inc.; *U.S. Public*, pg. 2397
XYLEM WATER SOLUTIONS METZ SAS—See Xylem Inc.; *U.S. Public*, pg. 2397
XYLEM WATER SOLUTIONS MIDDLE EAST REGION FZCO—See Xylem Inc.; *U.S. Public*, pg. 2397
XYLEM WATER SOLUTIONS NEDERLAND B.V.—See Xylem Inc.; *U.S. Public*, pg. 2397
XYLEM WATER SOLUTIONS NEW ZEALAND LIMITED—See Xylem Inc.; *U.S. Public*, pg. 2397
XYLEM WATER SOLUTIONS PERU S.A.—See Xylem Inc.; *U.S. Public*, pg. 2397
XYLEM WATER SOLUTIONS POLSKA SP. Z. O. O.—See Xylem Inc.; *U.S. Public*, pg. 2397
XYLEM WATER SOLUTIONS PORTUGAL, UNIPESSOA LDA—See Xylem Inc.; *U.S. Public*, pg. 2397
XYLEM WATER SOLUTIONS (SHENYANG) CO. LTD.—See Xylem Inc.; *U.S. Public*, pg. 2396
XYLEM WATER SOLUTIONS SINGAPORE PTE. LTD.—See Xylem Inc.; *U.S. Public*, pg. 2397
XYLEM WATER SOLUTIONS SOUTH AFRICA (PTY) LTD.—See Xylem Inc.; *U.S. Public*, pg. 2397
XYLEM WATER SOLUTIONS SUOMI OY—See Xylem Inc.; *U.S. Public*, pg. 2397
XYLEM WATER SOLUTIONS UK HOLDINGS LIMITED—See Xylem Inc.; *U.S. Public*, pg. 2397
XYLEM WATER SOLUTIONS UK LTD.—See Xylem Inc.; *U.S. Public*, pg. 2397
XYLEM WATER SOLUTIONS U.S.A., INC. - INDIANAPOLIS—See Xylem Inc.; *U.S. Public*, pg. 2397
XYLEM WATER SOLUTIONS U.S.A., INC.—See Xylem Inc.; *U.S. Public*, pg. 2397
XYLEM WATER SOLUTIONS USA, INC.—See Xylem Inc.; *U.S. Public*, pg. 2397
XYLEM WATER SYSTEMS HUNGARY KFT—See Xylem Inc.; *U.S. Public*, pg. 2397
XYLEM WATER SYSTEMS MEXICO S. DE R.L. DE C.V.—See Xylem Inc.; *U.S. Public*, pg. 2397
XYLO TECHNOLOGIES, INC.; *U.S. Private*, pg. 4583
XYLO TECHNOLOGIES LTD.; *Int'l*, pg. 8542
XYLOTEK SOLUTIONS INC.; *Int'l*, pg. 8542
XYMAX ALPHA CORPORATION—See XYMAX Corporation; *Int'l*, pg. 8542
XYMAX ASSET CONSULTING CORPORATION—See XYMAX Corporation; *Int'l*, pg. 8542
XYMAX BOSAI TECHNICA CORPORTATION—See XYMAX Corporation; *Int'l*, pg. 8542
XYMAX CORPORATION; *Int'l*, pg. 8542
XYMAX GEPPETTO CORPORATION—See XYMAX Corporation; *Int'l*, pg. 8542
XYMAX INFONISTA CORPORATION—See XYMAX Corporation; *Int'l*, pg. 8542
XYMAX KANSAI CORPORATION—See XYMAX Corporation; *Int'l*, pg. 8542
XYMAX KYUSHU CORPORATION—See XYMAX Corporation; *Int'l*, pg. 8542
XYMAX REAL ESTATE INSTITUTE CORPORATION—See XYMAX Corporation; *Int'l*, pg. 8542
XYMAX REAL ESTATE INVESTMENT ADVISORS CORPORATION—See XYMAX Corporation; *Int'l*, pg. 8542
XYMAX REIT INVESTMENT CORPORATION; *Int'l*, pg. 8542
XYMAX SALA CORPORATION—See XYMAX Corporation; *Int'l*, pg. 8542
XYMAX TRAVEL DESIGN CORPORATION—See XYMAX Corporation; *Int'l*, pg. 8542
XYMAX WITH CORPORATION—See XYMAX Corporation; *Int'l*, pg. 8542
XYMID LLC; *U.S. Private*, pg. 4584
XYMOX TECHNOLOGIES INC.—See Brookfield Corporation; *Int'l*, pg. 1182
XYNMANAGAMENT, INC.—See CareDx, Inc.; *U.S. Public*, pg. 435
XYNOMIC PHARMACEUTICALS HOLDINGS, INC.; *Int'l*, pg. 8542
XYNYTH MANUFACTURING CORP.; *Int'l*, pg. 8542

XYONICZ CORPORATION; *U.S. Private*, pg. 4584
XYPRO TECHNOLOGY CORPORATION; *U.S. Private*, pg. 4584
XYRON INC.—See ACCO Brands Corporation; *U.S. Public*, pg. 33
XY - THE PERSISTENT COMPANY; *U.S. Private*, pg. 4583
XYTRONICS, LTD.—See Season Group International Co., Ltd.; *Int'l*, pg. 6666
XYZ MACHINE TOOLS LIMITED; *Int'l*, pg. 8542
XYZPRINTING, INC.—See New Kinpo Group; *Int'l*, pg. 5226
XZERES CORP.; *U.S. Private*, pg. 4584

Y

Y28.COM LIMITED—See Champion Technology Holdings Ltd; *Int'l*, pg. 1440
Y2 SOLUTION CO., LTD.; *Int'l*, pg. 8544
Y95 RADIO STATION INC.—See Wehco Media, Inc.; *U.S. Private*, pg. 4470
YA'ACOBI BROTHERS GROUP (YSB) LTD.; *Int'l*, pg. 8544
YAAKOV SERLE ADVERTISING; *U.S. Private*, pg. 4584
YAARI DIGITAL INTEGRATED SERVICES LIMITED; *Int'l*, pg. 8544
YABAO PHARMACEUTICAL GROUP CO., LTD.; *Int'l*, pg. 8544
YABEZ (HONG KONG) COMPANY LIMITED—See Greenpro Capital Corp.; *Int'l*, pg. 3076
YABOO, INC.; *U.S. Private*, pg. 4584
YABROFARMA LDA—See Astellas Pharma Inc.; *Int'l*, pg. 652
YABU APPAREL LTD.—See Gunze Limited; *Int'l*, pg. 3186
Y.A.C. CO. LTD. - FEL DIVISION—See Y.A.C. HOLDINGS CO., LTD.; *Int'l*, pg. 8543
Y.A.C. CO. LTD. - MEMORY DISK DIVISION—See Y.A.C. HOLDINGS CO., LTD.; *Int'l*, pg. 8543
Y.A.C. CO. LTD. - PLASMA ECHING & ASHING MANUFACTURING UNIT—See Y.A.C. HOLDINGS CO., LTD.; *Int'l*, pg. 8543
Y.A.C. CO. LTD. - SEMICONDUCTOR DIVISION—See Y.A.C. HOLDINGS CO., LTD.; *Int'l*, pg. 8543
THE YACHIYO BANK, LIMITED—See Tokyo Kiraboshi Financial Group , Inc.; *Int'l*, pg. 7793
YACHIYO DO BRASIL INDUSTRIA E COMERCIO DE PECAS LTDA.—See Honda Motor Co., Ltd.; *Int'l*, pg. 3464
YACHIYO GERMANY GMBH—See Honda Motor Co., Ltd.; *Int'l*, pg. 3464
YACHIYO INDIA MANUFACTURING PRIVATE LTD.—See Honda Motor Co., Ltd.; *Int'l*, pg. 3464
YACHIYO INDUSTRY CO., LTD. - KASHIWABARA PLANT—See Honda Motor Co., Ltd.; *Int'l*, pg. 3464
YACHIYO INDUSTRY CO., LTD.—See Honda Motor Co., Ltd.; *Int'l*, pg. 3464
YACHIYO INDUSTRY CO., LTD. - SUZUKA PLANT—See Honda Motor Co., Ltd.; *Int'l*, pg. 3464
YACHIYO INDUSTRY CO., LTD. - YOKKAICHI FACTORY—See Honda Motor Co., Ltd.; *Int'l*, pg. 3464
YACHIYO MANUFACTURING OF AMERICA, LLC—See Honda Motor Co., Ltd.; *Int'l*, pg. 3464
YACHIYO MEXICO MANUFACTURING S.A. DE C.V.—See Honda Motor Co., Ltd.; *Int'l*, pg. 3464
YACHIYO OF AMERICA INC.—See Honda Motor Co., Ltd.; *Int'l*, pg. 3464
YACHIYO URBAN CO., LTD.—See Toda Corporation; *Int'l*, pg. 7773
YACHIYO WUHAN MANUFACTURING CO., LTD.—See Honda Motor Co., Ltd.; *Int'l*, pg. 3464
YACHIYO ZHONGSHAN MANUFACTURING CO., LTD.—See Honda Motor Co., Ltd.; *Int'l*, pg. 3464
Y.A.C. HOLDINGS CO., LTD.; *Int'l*, pg. 8543
YACHT FRANCE—See Randstad N.V.; *Int'l*, pg. 6206
YACHT FUEL SERVICES LIMITED—See World Kinect Corporation; *U.S. Public*, pg. 2381
YACHT GROUP NEDERLAND B.V.—See Randstad N.V.; *Int'l*, pg. 6206
YACHT GROUP—See Randstad N.V.; *Int'l*, pg. 6206
YACHTING PROMOTIONS, INC.—See Informa plc; *Int'l*, pg. 3694
YACHT SYSTEMS S.R.L—See Boero Bartolomeo S.p.A.; *Int'l*, pg. 1100
YACHT TECCON—See Randstad N.V.; *Int'l*, pg. 6206
YACKTMAN ASSET MANAGEMENT LP—See Affiliated Managers Group, Inc.; *U.S. Public*, pg. 56
YAC NIIGATA SEIKI CO., LTD.—See Y.A.C. HOLDINGS CO., LTD.; *Int'l*, pg. 8543
YAC SYSTEMS SINGAPORE PTE LTD.—See Y.A.C. HOLDINGS CO., LTD.; *Int'l*, pg. 8543
YADAV ENTERPRISES, INC.; *U.S. Private*, pg. 4584
YADEA GROUP HOLDINGS LTD; *Int'l*, pg. 8544
YADKIN RAILROAD CO.—See Norfolk Southern Corporation; *U.S. Public*, pg. 1536
YADONG GROUP HOLDINGS LIMITED; *Int'l*, pg. 8544
YADRAN-OIL GROUP; *Int'l*, pg. 8544
YAESU BOOK CENTER CO., LTD.—See Kajima Corporation; *Int'l*, pg. 4056
YAEYAMA FARM CO., LTD.—See Rohto Pharmaceutical Co. Ltd.; *Int'l*, pg. 6387

YAEYAMA SHOKUSAN CO., LTD.—See euglena Co., Ltd.; *Int'l*, pg. 2526
YAFFE/DEUTSER—See Yaffe Group; *U.S. Private*, pg. 4584
YAFFE DIRECT—See Yaffe Group; *U.S. Private*, pg. 4584
YAFFE GROUP; *U.S. Private*, pg. 4584
YAFFE IRON & METAL COMPANY INC.; *U.S. Private*, pg. 4584
YAGAMI, INC.; *Int'l*, pg. 8545
YAGEO CORPORATION; *Int'l*, pg. 8545
YAGEO EUROPE B.V.—See Yageo Corporation; *Int'l*, pg. 8545
YAGEO HONG KONG LIMITED—See Yageo Corporation; *Int'l*, pg. 8545
YAGEO HUNGARY KFT.—See Yageo Corporation; *Int'l*, pg. 8545
YAGEO ITALY S.R.L.—See Yageo Corporation; *Int'l*, pg. 8545
YAGEO SUZHOU CO., LTD.—See Yageo Corporation; *Int'l*, pg. 8545
YAGER MATERIALS LLC—See Carmeuse Holding SA; *Int'l*, pg. 1341
YAGI ANTENNA INC—See KKR & Co. Inc.; *U.S. Public*, pg. 1258
YAGI & CO., LTD.; *Int'l*, pg. 8545
YAGI TSUSHO—See Yagi & Co., Ltd.; *Int'l*, pg. 8545
YAGUANG TECHNOLOGY GROUP COMPANY LIMITED; *Int'l*, pg. 8545
YAGUKI AGGREGATE CO., LTD.—See Nittetsu Mining Co., Ltd.; *Int'l*, pg. 5384
YAHAGI AOI BUILDING CO.,LTD.—See Yahagi Construction Co., Ltd.; *Int'l*, pg. 8546
YAHAGI CONSTRUCTION CO., LTD.; *Int'l*, pg. 8546
YAHAGI GREEN CO.,LTD.—See Yahagi Construction Co., Ltd.; *Int'l*, pg. 8546
YAHAGI JISHO CO., LTD.—See Yahagi Construction Co., Ltd.; *Int'l*, pg. 8546
YAHAGI ROAD CO.,LTD.—See Yahagi Construction Co., Ltd.; *Int'l*, pg. 8546
YAHATA READY MIXED CONCRETE CO., LTD.—See Sojitz Corporation; *Int'l*, pg. 7066
YAHOO! 350 SAS—See Apollo Global Management, Inc.; *U.S. Public*, pg. 167
YAHOO! CANADA CO.—See Apollo Global Management, Inc.; *U.S. Public*, pg. 167
YAHOO! (CHINA) LIMITED—See Alibaba Group Holding Limited; *Int'l*, pg. 326
YAHOO! COMMUNICATIONS & COMMUNITIES—See Apollo Global Management, Inc.; *U.S. Public*, pg. 167
YAHOO! CONNECTED LIFE—See Apollo Global Management, Inc.; *U.S. Public*, pg. 167
YAHOO! DE MEXICO, S.A. DE C.V.—See Apollo Global Management, Inc.; *U.S. Public*, pg. 168
YAHOO! DO BRASIL INTERNET LTDA.—See Apollo Global Management, Inc.; *U.S. Public*, pg. 168
YAHOO! ENTERTAINMENT—See Apollo Global Management, Inc.; *U.S. Public*, pg. 167
YAHOO! FINANCE—See Apollo Global Management, Inc.; *U.S. Public*, pg. 167
YAHOO! FRANCE S.A.S.—See Apollo Global Management, Inc.; *U.S. Public*, pg. 167
YAHOO! GLOBAL PARTNER SOLUTIONS—See Apollo Global Management, Inc.; *U.S. Public*, pg. 167
YAHOO! GROUPS—See Apollo Global Management, Inc.; *U.S. Public*, pg. 167
YAHOO HOLDINGS, INC.—See Apollo Global Management, Inc.; *U.S. Public*, pg. 167
YAHOO! HUNGARY LABS KFT—See Apollo Global Management, Inc.; *U.S. Public*, pg. 167
YAHOO, INC.—See Apollo Global Management, Inc.; *U.S. Public*, pg. 167
YAHOO! JAPAN CORPORATION—See SoftBank Group Corp.; *Int'l*, pg. 7052
YAHOO! LOCAL—See Apollo Global Management, Inc.; *U.S. Public*, pg. 168
YAHOO! MAIL—See Apollo Global Management, Inc.; *U.S. Public*, pg. 167
YAHOO! MEDIA—See Apollo Global Management, Inc.; *U.S. Public*, pg. 167
YAHOO! NETWORK—See Apollo Global Management, Inc.; *U.S. Public*, pg. 167
YAHOO! NEWS—See Apollo Global Management, Inc.; *U.S. Public*, pg. 167
YAHOO! RESEARCH—See Apollo Global Management, Inc.; *U.S. Public*, pg. 168
YAHOO! RESEARCH & STRATEGIC DATA SOLUTIONS—See Apollo Global Management, Inc.; *U.S. Public*, pg. 168
YAHOO! SEARCH—See Apollo Global Management, Inc.; *U.S. Public*, pg. 168
YAHOO SOFTWARE DEVELOPMENT INDIA PRIVATE LIMITED—See Apollo Global Management, Inc.; *U.S. Public*, pg. 167
YAHOO! SPORTS—See Apollo Global Management, Inc.; *U.S. Public*, pg. 168
YAHOO! TECHNOLOGIES NORWAY AS—See Apollo Global Management, Inc.; *U.S. Public*, pg. 168
YA HORNG (DONGGUAN) ELECTRONIC CO., LTD.—See Ya Horng Electronic Co., Ltd.; *Int'l*, pg. 8544

COMPANY NAME INDEX

YA HORNG ELECTRONIC CO., LTD.; *Int'l*, pg. 8544
YA HORNG (HK) ELECTRONIC CO., LTD.—See Ya Horng Electronic Co., Ltd.; *Int'l*, pg. 8544
YAHSGS LLC; *U.S. Private*, pg. 4584
YAHYA COSTAIN LLC—See Costain Group PLC; *Int'l*, pg. 1815
YAIZU SHINTO CO., LTD.—See Toyo Suisan Kaisha, Ltd.; *Int'l*, pg. 7858
YAIZU SUISANKAGAKU INDUSTRY CO., LTD.; *Int'l*, pg. 8546
YAKGEAR, INC.—See T-H Marine Supplies Inc.; *U.S. Private*, pg. 3910
YAKIMA BAIT CO.; *U.S. Private*, pg. 4584
YAKIMA COOPERATIVE ASSOCIATION; *U.S. Private*, pg. 4584
YAKIMA FEDERAL SAVINGS & LOAN ASSOCIATION; *U.S. Private*, pg. 4584
YAKIMA PRODUCTS INC.—See Kemflo International Co. Ltd; *Int'l*, pg. 4122
YAKIMA VALLEY MEMORIAL HOSPITAL; *U.S. Private*, pg. 4584
YAKIMBI ICT SDN BHD—See Omesti Berhad; *Int'l*, pg. 5562
YAKINIKU SAKAI HOLDINGS, INC.; *Int'l*, pg. 8546
YAKIN OHEYAMA CO., LTD.—See Nippon Yakin Kogyo Co., Ltd.; *Int'l*, pg. 5357
YAKKYO S.P.A.; *Int'l*, pg. 8546
YAKOVLEV CORPORATION; *Int'l*, pg. 8546
YAKUHAN PHARMACEUTICAL CO., LTD.—See Nakakita Yakuhin Co., Ltd.; *Int'l*, pg. 5131
YAKULT AUSTRALIA PTY. LTD.—See Yakult Honsha Co., Ltd.; *Int'l*, pg. 8546
YAKULT (CHINA) CO., LTD.—See Yakult Honsha Co., Ltd.; *Int'l*, pg. 8546
YAKULT DANONE INDIA PRIVATE LIMITED—See Yakult Honsha Co., Ltd.; *Int'l*, pg. 8546
YAKULT DEUTSCHLAND GMBH—See Yakult Honsha Co., Ltd.; *Int'l*, pg. 8546
YAKULT EUROPE B.V.—See Yakult Honsha Co., Ltd.; *Int'l*, pg. 8546
YAKULT FUKUOKA PLANT CO., LTD.—See Yakult Honsha Co., Ltd.; *Int'l*, pg. 8546
YAKULT HONSHA CO., LTD.; *Int'l*, pg. 8546
YAKULT (MALAYSIA) SDN. BHD.—See Yakult Honsha Co., Ltd.; *Int'l*, pg. 8546
YAKULT MIDDLE EAST FZCO—See Yakult Honsha Co., Ltd.; *Int'l*, pg. 8546
YAKULT MYANMAR CO., LTD.—See Yakult Honsha Co., Ltd.; *Int'l*, pg. 8546
YAKULT OESTERREICH GMBH—See Yakult Honsha Co., Ltd.; *Int'l*, pg. 8546
YAKULT PHARMACEUTICAL INDUSTRY CO., LTD.—See Yakult Honsha Co., Ltd.; *Int'l*, pg. 8546
YAKULT (SINGAPORE) PTE. LTD.—See Yakult Honsha Co., Ltd.; *Int'l*, pg. 8546
YAKULT SWALLOWS BASEBALL CLUB—See Yakult Honsha Co., Ltd.; *Int'l*, pg. 8546
YAKULT UK LTD.—See Yakult Honsha Co., Ltd.; *Int'l*, pg. 8546
YAKULT VIETNAM CO., LTD.—See Yakult Honsha Co., Ltd.; *Int'l*, pg. 8546
YAKUODO CO., LTD.; *Int'l*, pg. 8546
YAKUODO HOLDING CO., LTD.; *Int'l*, pg. 8546
YAKUTSKENERGO PJSC; *Int'l*, pg. 8547
YAKUTSK FUEL AND ENERGY COMPANY JSC; *Int'l*, pg. 8547
YAKUTUGOL AO—See Mechel PAO; *Int'l*, pg. 4766
YAKUTUGOL HOLDING COMPANY OAO—See Mechel PAO; *Int'l*, pg. 4766
YAK & YETI HOTEL LTD.; *Int'l*, pg. 8546
YALA VILLAGE (PVT) LTD.—See John Keells Holdings PLC; *Int'l*, pg. 3979
YALCO - SOCRATES D. CONSTANTINOU & SON S.A.; *Int'l*, pg. 8547
YALE APPLIANCE GROUP PTY., LTD.—See Nu-World Holdings Ltd.; *Int'l*, pg. 5485
THE YALE CLUB OF NEW YORK CITY; *U.S. Private*, pg. 4139
YALE-CORBIN CANADA LIMITED—See ASSA ABLOY AB; *Int'l*, pg. 637
YALE ELECTRIC SUPPLY CO.; *U.S. Private*, pg. 4585
YALE ENFORCEMENT SERVICES, INC.—See Allied Universal Manager LLC; *U.S. Private*, pg. 191
YALE ENGINEERING PRODUCTS (PTY.) LTD.—See Columbus McKinnon Corporation; *U.S. Public*, pg. 536
YALE EQUIPMENT & SERVICES INC.; *U.S. Private*, pg. 4585
YALE FORDERTECHNIK HANDELSGESELLSCHAFT MBH—See Hyster-Yale Materials Handling, Inc.; *U.S. Public*, pg. 1080
YALE INDUSTRIAL PRODUCTS ASIA CO. LTD.—See Columbus McKinnon Corporation; *U.S. Public*, pg. 536
YALE KENTUCKIANA INC.; *U.S. Private*, pg. 4585
YALE LA FONTE SISTEMAS DE SEGURANCA LTDA—See ASSA ABLOY AB; *Int'l*, pg. 641
YALE LIFTING & MINING PRODUCTS (PTY.) LTD.—See Columbus McKinnon Corporation; *U.S. Public*, pg. 536
YALE LIFTING SOLUTIONS (PTY.) LTD.—See Columbus McKinnon Corporation; *U.S. Public*, pg. 536
YALELOCK SPAIN—See ASSA ABLOY AB; *Int'l*, pg. 641
YALE PRIMA PROPRIETARY LIMITED—See Nu-World Holdings Ltd.; *Int'l*, pg. 5485
YALE RESIDENTIAL SECURITY PRODUCTS, INC.—See ASSA ABLOY AB; *Int'l*, pg. 641
YALE SECURITY PRODUCTS (HONG KONG) LIMITED—See ASSA ABLOY AB; *Int'l*, pg. 636
YALE SECURITY PRODUCTS S.P.A. (ITALY)—See ASSA ABLOY AB; *Int'l*, pg. 636
YALE SECURITY (SA) (PTY) LTD—See ASSA ABLOY AB; *Int'l*, pg. 641
YALE TRANSACTION FINDERS, INC.; *U.S. Public*, pg. 2398
YALE UK LTD.—See ASSA ABLOY AB; *Int'l*, pg. 636
YALE UNIVERSITY PRESS; *U.S. Private*, pg. 4585
YALIAN STEEL CORPORATION; *Int'l*, pg. 8547
YA LI PRECAST & PRESTRESSED CONCRETE INDUSTRIES CORP.—See Asia Cement Corporation; *Int'l*, pg. 611
YALITECH SPA—See HORIBA Ltd; *Int'l*, pg. 3478
YALLA GROUP LIMITED; *Int'l*, pg. 8547
YALLA MEDITERRANEAN FRANCHISING COMPANY, LLC—See Fog Cutter Capital Group Inc.; *U.S. Private*, pg. 1557
YALOVA AMBALAJ SANAYI VE TICARET A.S.—See Cukurova Holding A.S.; *Int'l*, pg. 1876
YAMABIKO CHUBU CO., LTD.—See Yamabiko Corporation; *Int'l*, pg. 8547
YAMABIKO CORPORATION - HIROSHIMA PLANT—See Yamabiko Corporation; *Int'l*, pg. 8547
YAMABIKO CORPORATION - MORIOKA PLANT—See Yamabiko Corporation; *Int'l*, pg. 8547
YAMABIKO CORPORATION; *Int'l*, pg. 8547
YAMABIKO CORPORATION - YOKOSUKA PLANT—See Yamabiko Corporation; *Int'l*, pg. 8547
YAMABIKO ENGINEERING CO., LTD.—See Yamabiko Corporation; *Int'l*, pg. 8547
YAMABIKO HOKKAIDO CO., LTD.—See Yamabiko Corporation; *Int'l*, pg. 8547
YAMABIKO LOGISTICS CO., LTD.—See Yamabiko Corporation; *Int'l*, pg. 8547
YAMABIKO SEIBU CO., LTD.—See Yamabiko Corporation; *Int'l*, pg. 8547
YAMABIKO SERVICES CO., LTD.—See The Hachijuni Dank Ltd.; *Int'l*, pg. 7051
YAMABIKO TOHOKU CO., LTD.—See Yamabiko Corporation; *Int'l*, pg. 8547
YAMABOSHIYA CO., LTD—See Marubeni Corporation; *Int'l*, pg. 4710
YAMABUN ELECTRONICS CO., LTD.—See Kurabo Industries Ltd.; *Int'l*, pg. 4336
YAMADA AMERICA, INC.—See Yamada Corporation; *Int'l*, pg. 8548
YAMADA AUTO JAPAN CO., LTD.—See Yamada Holdings Co., Ltd.; *Int'l*, pg. 8548
YAMADA BEE COMPANY, INC.; *Int'l*, pg. 8547
YAMADA CONSULTING GROUP CO., LTD.; *Int'l*, pg. 8547
YAMADA CONSULTING GROUP (SHANGHAI) CO., LTD.—See YAMADA Consulting Group Co., Ltd.; *Int'l*, pg. 8547
YAMADA CONSULTING & SPIRE (THAILAND) CO., LTD.—See YAMADA Consulting Group Co., Ltd.; *Int'l*, pg. 8547
YAMADA CONSULTING & SPIRE VIETNAM CO., LTD.—See YAMADA Consulting Group Co., Ltd.; *Int'l*, pg. 8547
YAMADA CORPORATION; *Int'l*, pg. 8547
YAMADA DANBORU CO., LTD.—See Oji Holdings Corporation; *Int'l*, pg. 5537
YAMADA ECO SOLUTION CO LTD—See Yamada Holdings Co., Ltd.; *Int'l*, pg. 8548
YAMADA FINANCIAL CO., LTD.—See Yamada Holdings Co., Ltd.; *Int'l*, pg. 8548
YAMADA GOMU KOUGYOU CO., LTD.—See Tigers Polymer Corporation; *Int'l*, pg. 7747
YAMADA GREEN RESOURCES LIMITED; *Int'l*, pg. 8548
YAMADA GROUP USA LTD.; *U.S. Private*, pg. 4585
YAMADA HOLDINGS CO., LTD.; *Int'l*, pg. 8548
YAMADA HOMES CO., LTD.—See Yamada Holdings Co., Ltd.; *Int'l*, pg. 8548
YAMADAI CORPORATION; *Int'l*, pg. 8548
YAMADA INDUSTRIES CO., LTD.—See Sanoyas Holdings Corporation; *Int'l*, pg. 6554
YAMADA KASEI COMPANY., LTD.—See Mitsubishi Gas Chemical Company, Inc.; *Int'l*, pg. 4950
YAMADA KIKAI KOGYO CO., LTD.—See Rengo Co., Ltd.; *Int'l*, pg. 6282
YAMADA KIKAI KOGYO CO., LTD. - STAR MAINTENANCE DIVISION—See Rengo Co., Ltd.; *Int'l*, pg. 6282
YAMADA PHARMACEUTICAL CO., LTD.—See Nicca Chemical Co., Ltd.; *Int'l*, pg. 5264
YAMADA PHARMACEUTICAL COMPANY - KASUMIGAURA FACTORY—See Nicca Chemical Co., Ltd.; *Int'l*, pg. 5264
YAMADA SEISAKUSHO CO., LTD.—See Honda Motor Co., Ltd.; *Int'l*, pg. 3465

YAMAHA CORPORATION

YAMADA SERVICER SYNTHETIC OFFICE CO., LTD.; *Int'l*, pg. 8548
YAMADA SHADOWLESS LAMP CO., LTD.—See Ship Healthcare Holdings, Inc.; *Int'l*, pg. 6852
YAMADA SHANGHAI CO., LTD.—See Yamada Corporation; *Int'l*, pg. 8548
YAMADA SHOMEI LIGHTING CO., LTD.—See ODELIC Company Limited; *Int'l*, pg. 5525
YAMADA THAILAND CO., LTD.—See Yamada Corporation; *Int'l*, pg. 8548
YAMAE HISANO CO., LTD.; *Int'l*, pg. 8548
YAMAGATA AD BUREAU CORP.—See Dentsu Group Inc.; *Int'l*, pg. 2040
THE YAMAGATA BANK, LTD.; *Int'l*, pg. 7701
YAMAGATA CASIO CO., LTD.—See Casio Computer Co., Ltd.; *Int'l*, pg. 1353
YAMAGATA CLUTCH CO., LTD.—See AISIN Corporation; *Int'l*, pg. 254
YAMAGATA CREATIVE CO., LTD.—See JEOL Ltd.; *Int'l*, pg. 3930
YAMAGATA ECO-CREATION CO., LTD.—See Mitsubishi Heavy Industries, Ltd.; *Int'l*, pg. 4962
YAMAGATA-IHARA CORPORATION—See IHARA SCIENCE CORPORATION; *Int'l*, pg. 3603
YAMAGATA KYOWA DENGYO CO., LTD.—See Kyowa Electronic Instruments Co., Ltd.; *Int'l*, pg. 4366
YAMAGATA MEIKO ELECTRONICS CO., LTD.—See Meiko Electronics Co., Ltd.; *Int'l*, pg. 4803
YAMAGATA MITSUBISHI PENCIL PRECISION CO., LTD.—See Mitsubishi Pencil Co., Ltd.; *Int'l*, pg. 4967
YAMAGATA NEWCITY DEVELOPMENT CO., LTD—See Sojitz Corporation; *Int'l*, pg. 7066
YAMAGATA NISSHIN ELECTRONICS CO., LTD.—See Nippon Signal Co., Ltd.; *Int'l*, pg. 5334
YAMAGATA SANKEN CO., LTD.—See Sanken Electric Co., Ltd.; *Int'l*, pg. 6541
YAMAGATA SHIKI CO., LTD.—See Oji Holdings Corporation; *Int'l*, pg. 5537
YAMAGATA SHIN-ETSU QUARTZ PRODUCTS CO., LTD.—See Shin-Etsu Chemical Co. Ltd.; *Int'l*, pg. 6841
YAMAGATA TOYOPET CO., LTD.—See Kamei Corporation; *Int'l*, pg. 4062
YAMAGIN CARD CO., LTD.—See Yamaguchi Financial Group Inc.; *Int'l*, pg. 8548
YAMAGIN CREDIT GUARANTEE CO., LTD.—See Yamaguchi Financial Group Inc.; *Int'l*, pg. 8549
YAMAGUCHI BANK, LTD.—See Yamaguchi Financial Group Inc.; *Int'l*, pg. 8549
YAMAGUCHI ECO-TECH CORPORATION—See UBE Corporation; *Int'l*, pg. 8002
YAMAGUCHI FINANCIAL GROUP INC.; *Int'l*, pg. 8548
YAMAGUCHI KOUN CORPORATION—See Tosoh Corporation; *Int'l*, pg. 7834
YAMAGUCHI SEIKEN KOGYO CO., LTD.—See Arakawa Chemical Industries, Ltd.; *Int'l*, pg. 535
YAMAGUCHI TOHO K.K.—See Toho Holdings Co., Ltd.; *Int'l*, pg. 7776
YAMAHA AI WORKS CO., LTD.—See Yamaha Corporation; *Int'l*, pg. 8549
YAMAHA A&R, INC.—See Yamaha Corporation; *Int'l*, pg. 8549
YAMAHA ARTIST SERVICES INCORPORATED—See Yamaha Corporation; *Int'l*, pg. 8549
YAMAHA ATELIER FUR BLASINSTRUMENTE—See Yamaha Corporation; *Int'l*, pg. 8549
YAMAHA BUSINESS SUPPORT CORPORATION—See Yamaha Corporation; *Int'l*, pg. 8549
YAMAHA CANADA MUSIC LTD.—See Yamaha Corporation; *Int'l*, pg. 8549
YAMAHA COMMERCIAL AUDIO SYSTEMS, INC.—See Yamaha Corporation; *Int'l*, pg. 8549
YAMAHA CORPORATION OF AMERICA—See Yamaha Corporation; *Int'l*, pg. 8549
YAMAHA CORPORATION; *Int'l*, pg. 8549
YAMAHA CORPORATION—See Yamaha Corporation; *Int'l*, pg. 8549
YAMAHA CREDIT CORPORATION—See Yamaha Corporation; *Int'l*, pg. 8550
YAMAHA DE MEXICO, S.A. DE C.V.—See Yamaha Corporation; *Int'l*, pg. 8552
YAMAHA ELECTRONICS (CHINA) LTD.—See Yamaha Corporation; *Int'l*, pg. 8550
YAMAHA ELECTRONICS CORPORATION USA—See Yamaha Corporation; *Int'l*, pg. 8549
YAMAHA ELECTRONICS MANUFACTURING (M) SDN. BHD.—See Yamaha Corporation; *Int'l*, pg. 8550
YAMAHA ELECTRONICS MARKETING CORPORATION—See Hojgaard Holding A/S; *Int'l*, pg. 3442
YAMAHA ELECTRONICS (SUZHOU) CO., LTD.—See Yamaha Corporation; *Int'l*, pg. 8550
YAMAHA ELECTRONICS (U.K.) LTD.—See Yamaha Corporation; *Int'l*, pg. 8550
YAMAHA EXPORTING, INC.—See Yamaha Corporation; *Int'l*, pg. 8549
YAMAHA FINE TECHNOLOGIES CO., LTD. - AUTOMOTIVE COMPONENT DIVISION—See Yamaha Corporation; *Int'l*, pg. 8550

YAMAHA CORPORATION / CORPORATE AFFILIATIONS

YAMAHA FINE TECHNOLOGIES CO., LTD. - FACTORY AUTOMATION DIVISION—See Yamaha Corporation; *Int'l*, pg. 8550
YAMAHA FINE TECHNOLOGIES CO., LTD.—See Yamaha Corporation; *Int'l*, pg. 8550
YAMAHA-HAZEN ELECTRONICA MUSICAL S.A.—See Yamaha Corporation; *Int'l*, pg. 8552
YAMAHA HI-TECH DESIGN CORPORATION—See Yamaha Corporation; *Int'l*, pg. 8550
YAMAHA KHS MUSIC CO. LTD.—See Yamaha Corporation; *Int'l*, pg. 8550
YAMAHA MOTOR CANADA LTD.—See Yamaha Corporation; *Int'l*, pg. 8550
YAMAHA MOTOR CO., LTD.—See Yamaha Corporation; *Int'l*, pg. 8550
YAMAHA MOTOR CORPORATION USA—See Yamaha Corporation; *Int'l*, pg. 8550
YAMAHA MOTOR DO BRASIL LTDA.—See Yamaha Corporation; *Int'l*, pg. 8551
YAMAHA MOTOR EUROPE N.V.—See Yamaha Corporation; *Int'l*, pg. 8549
YAMAHA MOTOR MANUFACTURING CORPORATION—See Yamaha Corporation; *Int'l*, pg. 8550
YAMAHA MOTOR ROBOTICS HOLDINGS, CO., LTD.—See Yamaha Corporation; *Int'l*, pg. 8550
YAMAHA MUSICA ITALIA S.P.A.—See Yamaha Corporation; *Int'l*, pg. 8552
YAMAHA MUSICAL DO BRASIL LTDA.—See Yamaha Corporation; *Int'l*, pg. 8552
YAMAHA MUSICAL PRODUCTS, INC.—See Yamaha Corporation; *Int'l*, pg. 8549
YAMAHA MUSIC AND VISUALS, INC.—See Yamaha Corporation; *Int'l*, pg. 8552
YAMAHA MUSIC ARTIST, INC.—See Yamaha Corporation; *Int'l*, pg. 8551
YAMAHA MUSIC (ASIA) PTE., LTD.—See Yamaha Corporation; *Int'l*, pg. 8551
YAMAHA MUSIC AUSTRALIA PTY., LTD.—See Yamaha Corporation; *Int'l*, pg. 8551
YAMAHA MUSIC CENTRAL EUROPE GMBH—See Yamaha Corporation; *Int'l*, pg. 8551
YAMAHA MUSIC COMMUNICATIONS CO., LTD.—See Yamaha Corporation; *Int'l*, pg. 8551
YAMAHA MUSIC CRAFT CORPORATION—See Yamaha Corporation; *Int'l*, pg. 8551
YAMAHA MUSIC & ELECTRONICS (CHINA) CO., LTD.—See Yamaha Corporation; *Int'l*, pg. 8551
YAMAHA MUSIC ENTERTAINMENT HOLDINGS, INC.—See Yamaha Corporation; *Int'l*, pg. 8551
YAMAHA MUSIC EUROPE GMBH—See Yamaha Corporation; *Int'l*, pg. 8551
YAMAHA MUSIC EUROPE GMBH (UK)—See Yamaha Corporation; *Int'l*, pg. 8551
YAMAHA MUSIC EUROPE SP. Z O.O.—See Yamaha Corporation; *Int'l*, pg. 8551
YAMAHA MUSIC GULF FZE—See Yamaha Corporation; *Int'l*, pg. 8551
YAMAHA MUSIC HOKKAIDO CO., LTD—See Yamaha Corporation; *Int'l*, pg. 8551
YAMAHA MUSIC INDIA PVT. LTD.—See Yamaha Corporation; *Int'l*, pg. 8551
YAMAHA MUSIC INTERACTIVE, INC.—See Yamaha Corporation; *Int'l*, pg. 8549
YAMAHA MUSIC JAPAN CO., LTD.—See Yamaha Corporation; *Int'l*, pg. 8551
YAMAHA MUSIC KANTO CO., LTD.—See Yamaha Corporation; *Int'l*, pg. 8551
YAMAHA MUSIC KOREA LTD.—See Yamaha Corporation; *Int'l*, pg. 8551
YAMAHA MUSIC KYUSHU CO., LTD.—See Yamaha Corporation; *Int'l*, pg. 8551
YAMAHA MUSIC LATIN AMERICA, S.A.—See Yamaha Corporation; *Int'l*, pg. 8551
YAMAHA MUSIC LATIN AMERICA S.A. SUCURSAL ARGENTINA—See Yamaha Corporation; *Int'l*, pg. 8551
YAMAHA MUSIC LEASE CORPORATION—See Yamaha Corporation; *Int'l*, pg. 8551
YAMAHA MUSIC LLC—See Yamaha Corporation; *Int'l*, pg. 8551
YAMAHA MUSIC (MALAYSIA) SDN. BHD.—See Yamaha Corporation; *Int'l*, pg. 8551
YAMAHA MUSIC MEDIA CORPORATION—See Yamaha Corporation; *Int'l*, pg. 8551
YAMAHA MUSIC OSAKA CO., LTD.—See Yamaha Corporation; *Int'l*, pg. 8551
YAMAHA MUSIC PUBLISHING, INC.—See Yamaha Corporation; *Int'l*, pg. 8551
YAMAHA MUSIC (RUSSIA) LLC—See Yamaha Corporation; *Int'l*, pg. 8551
YAMAHA MUSIC TECHNICAL (SHANGHAI) CO., LTD.—See Yamaha Corporation; *Int'l*, pg. 8551
YAMAHA MUSIC TOKAI CO., LTD.—See Yamaha Corporation; *Int'l*, pg. 8551
YAMAHA MUSIC TOKYO CO., LTD.—See Yamaha Corporation; *Int'l*, pg. 8551
YAMAHA MUSIC TRADING CORPORATION - LM DIVISION—See Yamaha Corporation; *Int'l*, pg. 8551
YAMAHA MUSIC TRADING CORPORATION - MUSICIAN SUPPORT GOODS DIVISION—See Yamaha Corporation; *Int'l*, pg. 8551
YAMAHA MUSIC TRADING CORPORATION - PERCUSSION DIVISION—See Yamaha Corporation; *Int'l*, pg. 8551
YAMAHA MUSIC TRADING CORPORATION—See Yamaha Corporation; *Int'l*, pg. 8551
YAMAHA MUSIC TRADING CORPORATION - VISCOUNT & WENGER DIVISION—See Yamaha Corporation; *Int'l*, pg. 8551
YAMAHA MUSIC TRADING CORPORATION - WIND & EDUCATIONAL INSTRUMENTS DIVISION—See Yamaha Corporation; *Int'l*, pg. 8552
YAMAHA MUSIC WINDS CORPORATION—See Yamaha Corporation; *Int'l*, pg. 8552
YAMAHA OFFICE LINK CO.—See Yamaha Corporation; *Int'l*, pg. 8552
YAMAHA PIANO ARTISTES SERVICES EUROPE—See Yamaha Corporation; *Int'l*, pg. 8552
YAMAHA PIANO SERVICE CO., LTD.—See Yamaha Corporation; *Int'l*, pg. 8552
YAMAHA R&D CENTRE LONDON—See Yamaha Corporation; *Int'l*, pg. 8552
YAMAHA RESORT INC.—See Yamaha Corporation; *Int'l*, pg. 8552
YAMAHA SOUND SYSTEMS INC.—See Yamaha Corporation; *Int'l*, pg. 8552
YAMAHA SUZUKI OF TEXAS; *U.S. Private*, pg. 4585
YAMAHA TRADING (SHANGHAI) CO., LTD.—See Yamaha Corporation; *Int'l*, pg. 8552
YAMAHA TRAVEL SERVICE CO., LTD.—See Yamaha Corporation; *Int'l*, pg. 8552
YAMAHATSU NIHON CO., LTD.—See Cheng Loong Corp.; *Int'l*, pg. 1466
YAMAHATSU (THAILAND) CO., LTD.—See Henkel AG & Co. KGaA; *Int'l*, pg. 3349
YAMAHA UNIFIED COMMUNICATIONS, INC.—See Yamaha Corporation; *Int'l*, pg. 8550
YAMAICHI ELECTRONICS CO., LTD. - SAKURA FACTORY—See YAMAICHI ELECTRONICS Co Ltd; *Int'l*, pg. 8552
YAMAICHI ELECTRONICS CO LTD; *Int'l*, pg. 8552
YAMAICHI ELECTRONICS DEUTSCHLAND GMBH—See YAMAICHI ELECTRONICS Co Ltd; *Int'l*, pg. 8552
YAMAICHI ELECTRONICS DEUTSCHLAND MANUFACTURING GMBH—See YAMAICHI ELECTRONICS Co Ltd; *Int'l*, pg. 8552
YAMAICHI ELECTRONICS GREAT BRITAIN LTD.—See YAMAICHI ELECTRONICS Co Ltd; *Int'l*, pg. 8552
YAMAICHI ELECTRONICS HONG KONG LTD.—See YAMAICHI ELECTRONICS Co Ltd; *Int'l*, pg. 8552
YAMAICHI ELECTRONICS ITALIA S.R.L.—See YAMAICHI ELECTRONICS Co Ltd; *Int'l*, pg. 8552
YAMAICHI ELECTRONICS SHENZHEN LTD.—See YAMAICHI ELECTRONICS Co Ltd; *Int'l*, pg. 8552
YAMAICHI ELECTRONICS SINGAPORE PTE. LTD.—See YAMAICHI ELECTRONICS Co Ltd; *Int'l*, pg. 8552
YAMAICHI ELECTRONICS TAIWAN CO., LTD.—See YAMAICHI ELECTRONICS Co Ltd; *Int'l*, pg. 8552
YAMAICHI ELECTRONICS U.S.A. INC. - ARIZONA UNIT—See YAMAICHI ELECTRONICS Co Ltd; *Int'l*, pg. 8552
YAMAICHI ELECTRONICS U.S.A. INC.—See YAMAICHI ELECTRONICS Co Ltd; *Int'l*, pg. 8552
YAMAIMPORT S.A.—See Shoei Co., Ltd.; *Int'l*, pg. 6858
YAMAISHI METAL CO., LTD.—See UBE Corporation; *Int'l*, pg. 8002
YAMAKAWA TRANSPORTATIONS CO., LTD.—See Unipres Corporation; *Int'l*, pg. 8057
YAMAKICHI CO., LTD.—See Toyota Tsusho Corporation; *Int'l*, pg. 7880
YAMAKI CO., LTD.—See Komeri Co., Ltd.; *Int'l*, pg. 4242
YAMAKIN (JAPAN) CO., LTD.—See The Furukawa Electric Co., Ltd.; *Int'l*, pg. 7647
YAMAKO ELECTRIC MANUFACTURE CO., LTD.—See Oki Electric Industry Co., Ltd.; *Int'l*, pg. 5549
YAMAMA SAUDI CEMENT COMPANY; *Int'l*, pg. 8552
YAMAMI COMPANY; *Int'l*, pg. 8552
YAMAMOTO CHEMICALS, INC.—See Mitsui Chemicals, Inc.; *Int'l*, pg. 4984
YAMAMOTO MOSS AND MACKENZIE MARKETING; *U.S. Private*, pg. 4585
YAMAMOTO MOSS MACKENZIE—See Stagwell, Inc.; *U.S. Public*, pg. 1928
YAMAMURA GLASS WORKS CO.,LTD.—See Nihon Yamamura Glass Co., Ltd.; *Int'l*, pg. 5288
YAMAMURA INTERNATIONAL (SHANGHAI) CO., LTD.—See Nihon Yamamura Glass Co., Ltd.; *Int'l*, pg. 5288
YAMAMURA KOSAN CO., LTD.—See Nihon Yamamura Glass Co., Ltd.; *Int'l*, pg. 5288
YAMAMURA PHOTONICS CO., LTD.—See Nihon Yamamura Glass Co., Ltd.; *Int'l*, pg. 5288
YAMAMURA WAREHOUSE CO., LTD.—See Nihon Yamamura Glass Co., Ltd.; *Int'l*, pg. 5288
YAMANA DESENVOLVIMENTO MINERAL S.A.—See Pan American Silver Corp.; *Int'l*, pg. 5713
YAMANA GOLD INC.—See Pan American Silver Corp.; *Int'l*, pg. 5713
YAMANAKA DAIICHI TRAFFIC CO., LTD.—See Daiichi Koutsu Sangyo Co., Ltd.; *Int'l*, pg. 1929
YAMANASHI ASAHI DIAMOND INDUSTRIAL CO., LTD.—See Asahi Diamond Industrial Co. Ltd.; *Int'l*, pg. 593
YAMANASHI CHUGIN DC CARD CO., LTD.—See The Yamanashi Chuo Bank, Ltd.; *Int'l*, pg. 7701
THE YAMANASHI CHUO BANK, LTD.; *Int'l*, pg. 7701
YAMANASHI DAIICHI TRAFFIC CO., LTD.—See Daiichi Koutsu Sangyo Co., Ltd.; *Int'l*, pg. 1929
YAMANASHI ELECTRONICS CO., LTD.—See Ricoh Company, Ltd.; *Int'l*, pg. 6336
YAMANASHI KOGEI CO., LTD.—See Yamaha Corporation; *Int'l*, pg. 8552
YAMANASHI K-TECHNO CO., LTD.—See Kandenko Co., Ltd.; *Int'l*, pg. 4065
YAMANASHI MORI SHIGYO CO., LTD.—See Oji Holdings Corporation; *Int'l*, pg. 5537
YAMANASHI OHKA CO., LTD.—See Tokyo Ohka Kogyo Co., Ltd.; *Int'l*, pg. 7794
YAMANASHI RPB SUPPLY CO.—See Eastman Kodak Company; *U.S. Public*, pg. 707
YAMANASHI SANKO CO., LTD.—See CMK Corporation; *Int'l*, pg. 1671
YAMANDO GMBH—See Euronet Worldwide, Inc.; *U.S. Public*, pg. 798
YAMANE TULLETT PREBON (JAPAN) LIMITED—See TP ICAP Finance PLC; *Int'l*, pg. 7882
YA-MAN, LTD.; *Int'l*, pg. 8544
YAMANO HOLDINGS CORPORATION - JEWELRY BUSINESS DIVISION—See Yamano Holdings Corporation; *Int'l*, pg. 8553
YAMANO HOLDINGS CORPORATION; *Int'l*, pg. 8553
YAMANOUCHI (THAILAND) CO., LTD.—See Astellas Pharma Inc.; *Int'l*, pg. 653
YAMAROKU KASEI INDUSTRY CO., LTD.—See Sumitomo Bakelite Co., Ltd.; *Int'l*, pg. 7264
YAMASA CORPORATION - BIOCHEMICALS DIVISION—See YAMASA CORPORATION; *Int'l*, pg. 8553
YAMASA CORPORATION - DIAGNOSTICS DIVISION—See YAMASA CORPORATION; *Int'l*, pg. 8553
YAMASA CORPORATION—See YAMASA CORPORATION; *Int'l*, pg. 8553
YAMASA CORPORATION; *Int'l*, pg. 8553
YAMASA SOHGYOU CO., LTD.—See Toho Gas Co., Ltd.; *Int'l*, pg. 7776
YAMASA (THAILAND) CO., LTD.—See YAMASA CORPORATION; *Int'l*, pg. 8553
YAMASATO, FUJIWARA, HIGA & ASSOCIATES, INC.—See Fortive Corporation; *U.S. Public*, pg. 871
YAMA SEIKI USA INC.—See GOODWAY MACHINE CORP.; *Int'l*, pg. 3041
YAMASHINA CORPORATION; *Int'l*, pg. 8553
YAMASHIN AMERICA INC.—See Yamashin-Filter Corp.; *Int'l*, pg. 8553
YAMASHIN CEBU FILTER MANUFACTURING CORP.—See Yamashin-Filter Corp.; *Int'l*, pg. 8553
YAMASHIN CEBU FILTER MFG. CORP.—See Yamashin-Filter Corp.; *Int'l*, pg. 8553
YAMASHIN EUROPE BRUSSELS BVBA—See Yamashin-Filter Corp.; *Int'l*, pg. 8553
YAMASHIN-FILTER CORP.; *Int'l*, pg. 8553
YAMASHIN FILTER (SIP) TECHNOLOGY INC.—See Yamashin-Filter Corp.; *Int'l*, pg. 8553
YAMASHIN THAI LIMITED—See Yamashin-Filter Corp.; *Int'l*, pg. 8553
YAMASHIN VIETNAM CO., LTD.—See Yamashin-Filter Corp.; *Int'l*, pg. 8553
YAMASHIRO DAIICHI TRAFFIC CO., LTD.—See Daiichi Koutsu Sangyo Co., Ltd.; *Int'l*, pg. 1929
YAMASHITA CORPORATION; *Int'l*, pg. 8553
YAMASHITA HEALTH CARE HOLDINGS, INC.; *Int'l*, pg. 8553
YAMASHITA MEDICAL INSTRUMENTS CO., LTD.; *Int'l*, pg. 8553
YAMASHO INC.—See Takara Holdings, Inc.; *Int'l*, pg. 7433
YAMATAKE AUTOMATION PRODUCTS (SHANGHAI) CO., LTD.—See Azbil Corporation; *Int'l*, pg. 777
YAMATAKE ENGINEERING (M) SDN. BHD.—See Azbil Corporation; *Int'l*, pg. 777
YAMATAKE ENVIRONMENTAL CONTROL TECHNOLOGY (BEIJING) CO., LTD.—See Azbil Corporation; *Int'l*, pg. 777
YAMATANE CORPORATION; *Int'l*, pg. 8553
YAMATO 365 EXPRESS COMPANY LIMITED—See Yamato Holdings Co., Ltd.; *Int'l*, pg. 8554
YAMATO ASIA PTE. LTD.—See Yamato Holdings Co., Ltd.; *Int'l*, pg. 8554
YAMATO AUTOWORKS CO., LTD.—See Yamato Holdings Co., Ltd.; *Int'l*, pg. 8554
YAMATO AUTOWORKS HOKUSHINETSU CO., LTD.—See Yamato Holdings Co., Ltd.; *Int'l*, pg. 8554
YAMATO AUTOWORKS IWATE CO., LTD.—See Yamato Holdings Co., Ltd.; *Int'l*, pg. 8554

YAMATO AUTOWORKS OKINAWA CO., LTD.—See Yamato Holdings Co., Ltd.; *Int'l*, pg. 8554
YAMATO AUTOWORKS SHIKOKU CO., LTD.—See Yamato Holdings Co., Ltd.; *Int'l*, pg. 8554
YAMATO BOX CHARTER CO., LTD.—See Yamato Holdings Co., Ltd.; *Int'l*, pg. 8554
YAMATO CAREER SERVICE CO., LTD.—See Yamato Holdings Co., Ltd.; *Int'l*, pg. 8554
YAMATO (CHINA) TRANSPORT CO., LTD.—See Yamato Holdings Co., Ltd.; *Int'l*, pg. 8554
YAMATO CONTACT SERVICE CO., LTD.—See Yamato Holdings Co., Ltd.; *Int'l*, pg. 8554
YAMATO DIALOG & MEDIA CO., LTD.—See Yamato Holdings Co., Ltd.; *Int'l*, pg. 8554
YAMATO FINANCIAL CO., LTD.—See Yamato Holdings Co., Ltd.; *Int'l*, pg. 8554
YAMATO FOODS CO., LTD.—See CSS Holdings, Ltd.; *Int'l*, pg. 1867
YAMATOGAWA CO., LTD.—See Kurimoto Ltd; *Int'l*, pg. 4340
YAMATO GLOBAL EXPRESS CO., LTD.—See Yamato Holdings Co., Ltd.; *Int'l*, pg. 8554
YAMATO GLOBAL LOGISTICS JAPAN CO., LTD.—See Yamato Holdings Co., Ltd.; *Int'l*, pg. 8554
YAMATO GLOBAL LOGISTICS MYANMAR CO., LTD.—See Yamato Holdings Co., Ltd.; *Int'l*, pg. 8554
YAMATO HOLDINGS CO., LTD.; *Int'l*, pg. 8553
YAMATO HOME CONVENIENCE CO., LTD.—See Yamato Holdings Co., Ltd.; *Int'l*, pg. 8554
YAMATO, INC.; *Int'l*, pg. 8555
YAMATO INC.—See Japan Pulp and Paper Company Limited; *Int'l*, pg. 3905
YAMATO INDUSTRY CO., LTD.; *Int'l*, pg. 8555
YAMATO INTERNATIONAL INC.; *Int'l*, pg. 8555
YAMATO INTERNATIONAL LOGISTICS CO., LTD.—See Yamato Holdings Co., Ltd.; *Int'l*, pg. 8554
YAMATO INTERNATIONAL LOGISTICS (HK) LTD.—See Yamato Holdings Co., Ltd.; *Int'l*, pg. 8554
YAMATO INVESTMENT (HONG KONG) LIMIED—See Yamato Holdings Co., Ltd.; *Int'l*, pg. 8554
YAMATO KOGYO CO. LTD.; *Int'l*, pg. 8555
YAMATO LEASE CO., LTD.—See Yamato Holdings Co., Ltd.; *Int'l*, pg. 8554
YAMATO LOGISTICS CO., LTD.—See Yamato Holdings Co., Ltd.; *Int'l*, pg. 8554
YAMATO LOGISTICS (HONG KONG) LIMITED—See Yamato Holdings Co., Ltd.; *Int'l*, pg. 8554
YAMATO LOGISTICS INDIA PVT. LTD.—See Yamato Holdings Co., Ltd.; *Int'l*, pg. 8554
YAMATO LOGISTICS VIETNAM COMPANY LIMITED—See Yamato Holdings Co., Ltd.; *Int'l*, pg. 8554
YAMATO MANAGEMENT SERVICE CO., LTD.—See Yamato Holdings Co., Ltd.; *Int'l*, pg. 8554
YAMATO MANUFACTURING COMPANY, LTD.; *Int'l*, pg. 8555
YAMATO MULTI CHARTER CO., LTD.—See Yamato Holdings Co., Ltd.; *Int'l*, pg. 8555
YAMATO MULTI-MAINTENANCE SOLUTIONS CO., LTD.—See Yamato Holdings Co., Ltd.; *Int'l*, pg. 8555
YAMATO PACKING SERVICE CO., LTD.—See Yamato Holdings Co., Ltd.; *Int'l*, pg. 8555
YAMATO PACKING TECHNOLOGY INSTITUTE CO., LTD.—See Yamato Holdings Co., Ltd.; *Int'l*, pg. 8555
YAMATO REBUILT CO., LTD.—See The Japan Steel Works, Ltd.; *Int'l*, pg. 7659
YAMATO SEIKO CO., LTD.—See JTEKT Corporation; *Int'l*, pg. 4019
YAMATO SHIKI CO., LTD.—See Rengo Co., Ltd.; *Int'l*, pg. 6282
YAMATO SHIKI (THAILAND) CO., LTD.—See Rengo Co., Ltd.; *Int'l*, pg. 6282
YAMATO SHIKO CO., LTD.—See Dynic Corporation; *Int'l*, pg. 2243
YAMATO STAFF SUPPLY CO., LTD.—See Yamato Holdings Co., Ltd.; *Int'l*, pg. 8555
YAMATO STEEL COMPANY LIMITED—See Yamato Kogyo Co. Ltd.; *Int'l*, pg. 8555
YAMATO SYSTEM DEVELOPMENT CO., LTD.—See Yamato Holdings Co., Ltd.; *Int'l*, pg. 8555
YAMATO TRACKWORK SYSTEM CO., LTD—See Yamato Kogyo Co. Ltd.; *Int'l*, pg. 8555
YAMATO TRANSPORT CO., LTD.—See Yamato Holdings Co., Ltd.; *Int'l*, pg. 8555
YAMATO TRANSPORT EUROPE B.V.—See Yamato Holdings Co., Ltd.; *Int'l*, pg. 8555
YAMATO TRANSPORT MEXICO S.A.DE C.V.—See Yamato Holdings Co., Ltd.; *Int'l*, pg. 8555
YAMATO TRANSPORT (M) SDN. BHD.—See Yamato Holdings Co., Ltd.; *Int'l*, pg. 8555
YAMATO TRANSPORT (S) PTE LTD.-SEAFREIGHT—See Yamato Holdings Co., Ltd.; *Int'l*, pg. 8555
YAMATO TRANSPORT U.S.A., INC.—See Yamato Holdings Co., Ltd.; *Int'l*, pg. 8555
YAMATO UNYU (THAILAND) CO., LTD.—See Yamato Holdings Co., Ltd.; *Int'l*, pg. 8555
YAMATO WEB SOLUTIONS CO., LTD.—See Yamato Holdings Co., Ltd.; *Int'l*, pg. 8555

YAMATOYA CO., LTD.—See Rengo Co., Ltd.; *Int'l*, pg. 6282
YAMATSU SUISAN CO., LTD—See Nissui Corporation; *Int'l*, pg. 5379
YAMAUCHI CORP., LTD. - KANUMA FACTORY—See Yamauchi Corp., Ltd.; *Int'l*, pg. 8556
YAMAUCHI CORP., LTD. - KYOTO OSADANO FACTORY—See Yamauchi Corp., Ltd.; *Int'l*, pg. 8556
YAMAUCHI CORP., LTD.; *Int'l*, pg. 8556
YAMAUCHI CORP. N.V.—See Yamauchi Corp., Ltd.; *Int'l*, pg. 8556
YAMAUCHI HONG KONG LTD.—See Yamauchi Corp., Ltd.; *Int'l*, pg. 8556
YAMAUCHI MALAYSIA SDN. BHD.—See Yamauchi Corp., Ltd.; *Int'l*, pg. 8556
YAMAUCHI PRECISION SHANGHAI CO., LTD.—See Yamauchi Corp., Ltd.; *Int'l*, pg. 8556
YAMAUCHI PRECISION SHENZHEN LTD.—See Yamauchi Corp., Ltd.; *Int'l*, pg. 8556
YAMAUCHI (SEOUL OFFICE) CORPORATION—See Yamauchi Corp., Ltd.; *Int'l*, pg. 8556
YAMAUCHI SINGAPORE PTE. LTD.—See Yamauchi Corp., Ltd.; *Int'l*, pg. 8556
YAMAUCHI (U.S.A.) CORPORATION—See Yamauchi Corp., Ltd.; *Int'l*, pg. 8556
YAMAU CO., LTD. - FUKUOKA FACTORY—See Yamau Holdings Co., Ltd.; *Int'l*, pg. 8555
YAMAU CO., LTD. - KAGOSHIMA FACTORY—See Yamau Holdings Co., Ltd.; *Int'l*, pg. 8555
YAMAU CO., LTD. - KAWAMINAMI FACTORY—See Yamau Holdings Co., Ltd.; *Int'l*, pg. 8555
YAMAU CO., LTD. - KITAKYUSHU FACTORY—See Yamau Holdings Co., Ltd.; *Int'l*, pg. 8555
YAMAU CO., LTD. - OITA FACTORY—See Yamau Holdings Co., Ltd.; *Int'l*, pg. 8555
YAMAU CO., LTD. - REC FACTORY—See Yamau Holdings Co., Ltd.; *Int'l*, pg. 8555
YAMAU CO., LTD. - SAGA FACTORY—See Yamau Holdings Co., Ltd.; *Int'l*, pg. 8555
YAMAU CO., LTD. - TAKASAKI FACTORY—See Yamau Holdings Co., Ltd.; *Int'l*, pg. 8556
YAMAU HOLDINGS CO., LTD.; *Int'l*, pg. 8555
YAMAURA CORPORATION; *Int'l*, pg. 8556
YAMAX CORP.; *Int'l*, pg. 8556
YAMAYA CORPORATION; *Int'l*, pg. 8556
YAMAYO TRADING CO., LTD.—See UBE Corporation; *Int'l*, pg. 8002
YAMAZAKI BAKING CO., LTD.; *Int'l*, pg. 8556
YAMAZAKI BISCUITS CO., LTD.—See Yamazaki Baking Co., Ltd.; *Int'l*, pg. 8557
YAMAZAKI CALIFORNIA INC.—See Yamazaki Baking Co., Ltd.; *Int'l*, pg. 8557
YAMAZAKI CLEAN SERVICE CO., LTD.—See Yamazaki Baking Co., Ltd.; *Int'l*, pg. 8557
YAMAZAKI CO., LTD.; *Int'l*, pg. 8557
YAMAZAKI DELICA CO., LTD—See Yamazaki Baking Co., Ltd.; *Int'l*, pg. 8557
YAMAZAKI DENKI CO., LTD.—See Denkiro Service Co., Ltd.; *Int'l*, pg. 2027
YAMAZAKI ENGINEERING CO., LTD.—See Yamazaki Baking Co., Ltd.; *Int'l*, pg. 8557
YAMAZAKI FRANCE S.A.—See Yamazaki Baking Co., Ltd.; *Int'l*, pg. 8557
YAMAZAKI LOGISTICS CO., LTD—See Yamazaki Baking Co., Ltd.; *Int'l*, pg. 8557
YAMAZAKI MACHINERY CO., LTD.—See Nishio Holdings Co., Ltd.; *Int'l*, pg. 5366
YAMAZAKI MAZAK CENTRAL EUROPE SP. Z O.O.—See Yamazaki Mazak Corporation; *Int'l*, pg. 8557
YAMAZAKI MAZAK CENTRAL EUROPE S.R.O. MAGYARORSZAGI FIOKTELEPE—See Yamazaki Mazak Corporation; *Int'l*, pg. 8557
YAMAZAKI MAZAK CENTRAL EUROPE S.R.O.—See Yamazaki Mazak Corporation; *Int'l*, pg. 8557
YAMAZAKI MAZAK CORPORATION; *Int'l*, pg. 8557
YAMAZAKI MAZAK DANMARK A/S—See Yamazaki Mazak Corporation; *Int'l*, pg. 8557
YAMAZAKI MAZAK DEUTSCHLAND GMBH—See Yamazaki Mazak Corporation; *Int'l*, pg. 8557
YAMAZAKI MAZAK EUROPE N.V.—See Yamazaki Mazak Corporation; *Int'l*, pg. 8557
YAMAZAKI MAZAK FRANCE S.A.S.—See Yamazaki Mazak Corporation; *Int'l*, pg. 8557
YAMAZAKI MAZAK INDIA PVT. LTD.—See Yamazaki Mazak Corporation; *Int'l*, pg. 8557
YAMAZAKI MAZAK INDONESIA, PT—See Yamazaki Mazak Corporation; *Int'l*, pg. 8557
YAMAZAKI MAZAK ITALIA S.R.L.—See Yamazaki Mazak Corporation; *Int'l*, pg. 8557
YAMAZAKI MAZAK KOREA CO., LTD.—See Yamazaki Mazak Corporation; *Int'l*, pg. 8557
YAMAZAKI MAZAK LLC—See Yamazaki Mazak Corporation; *Int'l*, pg. 8557
YAMAZAKI MAZAK MACHINE TOOL (DALIAN) CO., LTD.—See Yamazaki Mazak Corporation; *Int'l*, pg. 8557
YAMAZAKI MAZAK MACHINE TOOL (GUANGZHOU) CO., LTD.—See Yamazaki Mazak Corporation; *Int'l*, pg. 8557

YAMAZAKI MAZAK MACHINE TOOL (LIAONING) CO, LTD.—See Yamazaki Mazak Corporation; *Int'l*, pg. 8557
YAMAZAKI MAZAK MACHINE TOOL (SHANGHAI) CO., LTD.—See Yamazaki Mazak Corporation; *Int'l*, pg. 8557
YAMAZAKI MAZAK MINOKAMO CORPORATION - MINOKAMO PLANT 2—See Yamazaki Mazak Corporation; *Int'l*, pg. 8557
YAMAZAKI MAZAK MINOKAMO CORPORATION—See Yamazaki Mazak Corporation; *Int'l*, pg. 8557
YAMAZAKI MAZAK NEDERLAND B.V.—See Yamazaki Mazak Corporation; *Int'l*, pg. 8557
YAMAZAKI MAZAK SEIKO CORPORATION—See Yamazaki Mazak Corporation; *Int'l*, pg. 8558
YAMAZAKI MAZAK SINGAPORE PTE LTD.—See Yamazaki Mazak Corporation; *Int'l*, pg. 8558
YAMAZAKI MAZAK TAIWAN CORP.—See Yamazaki Mazak Corporation; *Int'l*, pg. 8558
YAMAZAKI MAZAK TECHNOLOGY (SHANGHAI) CO., LTD.—See Yamazaki Mazak Corporation; *Int'l*, pg. 8558
YAMAZAKI MAZAK TURKEY MAKINA LTD. STI.—See Yamazaki Mazak Corporation; *Int'l*, pg. 8558
YAMAZAKI MAZAK UK LTD—See Yamazaki Mazak Corporation; *Int'l*, pg. 8558
YAMAZAKI MAZAK VIETNAM COMPANY LIMITED—See Yamazaki Mazak Corporation; *Int'l*, pg. 8558
YAMAZAKI NABISCO CO., LTD—See Yamazaki Baking Co., Ltd.; *Int'l*, pg. 8557
YAMAZAWA CO., LTD.; *Int'l*, pg. 8558
YAMAZEN CO., LTD.—See Yamazen Corporation; *Int'l*, pg. 8558
YAMAZEN CORPORATION; *Int'l*, pg. 8558
YAMAZEN CREATE CO., LTD.—See Yamazen Corporation; *Int'l*, pg. 8558
YAMAZEN EUROPE GMBH—See Yamazen Corporation; *Int'l*, pg. 8558
YAMAZEN HOMES CO., LTD.; *Int'l*, pg. 8558
YAMAZEN HONG KONG LTD.—See Yamazen Corporation; *Int'l*, pg. 8558
YAMAZEN INC.—See Yamazen Corporation; *Int'l*, pg. 8558
YAMAZEN KOREA LTD.—See Yamazen Corporation; *Int'l*, pg. 8558
YAMAZEN LOGISTICS CO., LTD.—See Yamazen Corporation; *Int'l*, pg. 8558
YAMAZEN MACHINERY & TOOLS INDIA PRIVATE LTD.—See Yamazen Corporation; *Int'l*, pg. 8558
YAMAZEN MACHINERY & TOOLS PHILIPPINES INC.—See Yamazen Corporation; *Int'l*, pg. 8558
YAMAZEN (MALAYSIA) SDN. BHD.—See Yamazen Corporation; *Int'l*, pg. 8558
YAMAZEN MEXICANA, S.A. DE C.V.—See Yamazen Corporation; *Int'l*, pg. 8558
YAMAZEN (SHANGHAI) TRADING CO., LTD.—See Yamazen Corporation; *Int'l*, pg. 8558
YAMAZEN (SHENZHEN) TRADING CO., LTD.—See Yamazen Corporation; *Int'l*, pg. 8558
YAMAZEN (SINGAPORE) PTE. LTD.—See Yamazen Corporation; *Int'l*, pg. 8558
YAMAZEN THAI ENGINEERING CO., LTD.—See Yamazen Corporation; *Int'l*, pg. 8558
YAMAZEN (THAILAND) CO., LTD.—See Yamazen Corporation; *Int'l*, pg. 8558
YAMAZEN VIET NAM CO., LTD.—See Yamazen Corporation; *Int'l*, pg. 8558
YAMBOLEN AD; *Int'l*, pg. 8558
YAMBOL-TABAC A.D.—See Bulgarian Investment Holding; *Int'l*, pg. 1213
YAMEN MEDICAL CO., LTD; *Int'l*, pg. 8558
YAMERYU INC.—See KAYAC Inc.; *Int'l*, pg. 4102
YAMHILL COMMUNITY CARE ORGANIZATION; *U.S. Private*, pg. 4585
YAMHILL COUNTY MUSHROOMS, INC.; *U.S. Private*, pg. 4585
YAMINI INVESTMENTS COMPANY LIMITED; *Int'l*, pg. 8559
YAMMER, INC.—See Microsoft Corporation; *U.S. Public*, pg. 1441
YAMPA VALLEY ELECTRIC ASSOCIATION; *U.S. Private*, pg. 4585
YAMPA VALLEY MEDICAL CENTER; *U.S. Private*, pg. 4585
YAMRON JEWELERS; *U.S. Private*, pg. 4585
THE YAMUNA SYNDICATE LIMITED; *Int'l*, pg. 7701
YANAGAWA SEIKI CO., LTD.—See Honda Motor Co., Ltd.; *Int'l*, pg. 3465
YANAGIHARA SEIFUNKI CO., LTD.—See Meiji Machine Co., Ltd.; *Int'l*, pg. 4801
YANAGI KANZAI INC.—See Okaya & Co., Ltd.; *Int'l*, pg. 5548
YANAGISAWA MANUFACTURING CO., LTD.—See Rinnai Corporation; *Int'l*, pg. 6345
YANAGISAWA MATAI CO., LTD.—See Rengo Co., Ltd.; *Int'l*, pg. 6282
YANAI CHEMICAL INDUSTRY CO., LTD.—See Fujibo Holdings, Inc.; *Int'l*, pg. 2820
YANAN BICON PHARMACEUTICAL LISTED COMPANY; *Int'l*, pg. 8559

YANAN BICON PHARMACEUTICAL LISTED COMPANY — CORPORATE AFFILIATIONS

Company Index

YANASE & CO., LTD.—See ITOCHU Corporation; *Int'l*, pg. 3841
YANBIAN COSLIGHT STORAGE BATTERY LTD.—See Coslight Technology International Group Limited; *Int'l*, pg. 1810
YANBIAN NONGSHIM MINERAL WATER BEVERAGE CO., LTD.—See Nongshim Co., Ltd.; *Int'l*, pg. 5414
YANBU CEMENT COMPANY; *Int'l*, pg. 8559
YANBU CEMENT COMPANY - YANBU PLANT—See Yanbu Cement Company; *Int'l*, pg. 8559
YANBU NATIONAL PETROCHEMICAL COMPANY; *Int'l*, pg. 8559
YANBU SAUDI KUWAITI FOR PAPER PRODUCTS COMPANY—See Yanbu Cement Company; *Int'l*, pg. 8559
YANCEY BROS. CO.; *U.S. Private*, pg. 4585
YANCEY BUS SALES & SERVICE, LLC—See Yancey Bros. Co.; *U.S. Private*, pg. 4585
YANCEY ENGINEERED SOLUTIONS—See Yancey Bros. Co.; *U.S. Private*, pg. 4585
YANCEY POWER SYSTEMS, INC.—See Yancey Bros. Co.; *U.S. Private*, pg. 4585
YANCHANG PETROLEUM INTERNATIONAL LIMITED; *Int'l*, pg. 8559
YANCHENG BAOZEN AUTOMOBILE SALES AND SERVICES CO., LTD.—See China Yongda Automobiles Services Holdings Limited; *Int'l*, pg. 1565
YANCHENG CITY CHUNZHU AROMA CO., LTD.—See Huabao International Holdings Limited; *Int'l*, pg. 3511
YANCHENG FUHUI TEXTILES LIMITED—See Fountain Set (Holdings) Limited; *Int'l*, pg. 2754
YANCHENG GAOCE NEW ENERGY TECHNOLOGY CO., LTD.—See Qingdao GaoCe Technology Co., Ltd.; *Int'l*, pg. 6143
YANCHENG NETUREN CO., LTD.—See Neturen Co., Ltd.; *Int'l*, pg. 5217
YANCHENG NEW UNIVERSE SOLID WASTE DISPOSAL COMPANY LIMITED—See New Universe Environmental Group Limited; *Int'l*, pg. 5229
YANCHENG NUHF ENVIRONMENTAL TECHNOLOGY LIMITED—See New Universe Environmental Group Limited; *Int'l*, pg. 5229
YANCHENG SEJONG AUTO PARTS CO., LTD.—See SJG Sejong Co., Ltd.; *Int'l*, pg. 6969
YANCOAL AUSTRALIA LIMITED—See Yankuang Group Co., Limited; *Int'l*, pg. 8562
YANCOAL SCN LIMITED; *Int'l*, pg. 8559
YANDAL RESOURCES LIMITED; *Int'l*, pg. 8559
YANDEX DC LLC—See Yandex N.V.; *Int'l*, pg. 8559
YANDEX EUROPE AG—See Yandex N.V.; *Int'l*, pg. 8559
YANDEX INC.—See Yandex N.V.; *Int'l*, pg. 8559
YANDEX LLC—See Yandex N.V.; *Int'l*, pg. 8559
YANDEX N.V.; *Int'l*, pg. 8559
YANDEX.PROBKI LLC—See Yandex N.V.; *Int'l*, pg. 8559
YANDEX.UKRAINE LLC—See Yandex N.V.; *Int'l*, pg. 8559
YANDEX ZURICH AG—See Yandex N.V.; *Int'l*, pg. 8559
YANFU COPARTNER TECHNOLOGY (SHENZHEN) CO., LTD—See Copartner Technology Corporation; *Int'l*, pg. 1793
YANGAROO INC.; *Int'l*, pg. 8560
YANGARRA HOLDING CORP.—See Yangarra Resources Ltd.; *Int'l*, pg. 8560
YANGARRA PRODUCTION PARTNERSHIP—See Yangarra Resources Ltd.; *Int'l*, pg. 8560
YANGARRA RESOURCES LTD.; *Int'l*, pg. 8560
YANG ENTERPRISES, INC.; *U.S. Private*, pg. 4585
YANG GUANG CO., LTD.; *Int'l*, pg. 8559
YANGJIANG MEIBAOHANG AUTO SALES & SERVICES CO., LTD.—See China MeiDong Auto Holdings Limited; *Int'l*, pg. 1519
YANGJISA CO., LTD.; *Int'l*, pg. 8560
YANG KEE LOGISTICS PTE LTD.; *Int'l*, pg. 8559
YANGLING DAILYHEALTH BIO-ENGINEERING TECHNOLOGY CO. LIMITED—See Cathay International Holdings Limited; *Int'l*, pg. 1360
YANGLING METRON NEW MATERIAL CO., LTD.; *Int'l*, pg. 8561
YANGLIN SOYBEAN, INC.; *Int'l*, pg. 8560
YANGMEI CHEMICAL CO., LTD.; *Int'l*, pg. 8561
YANG MING (AMERICA) CORP.—See Yang Ming Marine Transport Corporation; *Int'l*, pg. 8560
YANG MING (AMERICA) CO.—See Yang Ming Marine Transport Corporation; *Int'l*, pg. 8560
YANG MING (BELGIUM) N.V.—See Yang Ming Marine Transport Corporation; *Int'l*, pg. 8560
YANG MING (FRANCE) S.A.S.—See Yang Ming Marine Transport Corporation; *Int'l*, pg. 8560
YANGMING INDUSTRY (ZHEJIANG) LTD.—See Pihsiang Machinery MFG. Co., Ltd.; *Int'l*, pg. 5865
YANGMING (JAPAN) CO., LTD.—See Yang Ming Marine Transport Corporation; *Int'l*, pg. 8560
YANG MING (KOREA) CO., LTD.—See Yang Ming Marine Transport Corporation; *Int'l*, pg. 8560
YANG MING (LATIN AMERICA) CORP.—See Yang Ming Marine Transport Corporation; *Int'l*, pg. 8560
YANG MING LINE HOLDING CO.—See Yang Ming Marine Transport Corporation; *Int'l*, pg. 8560
YANG MING LINE (HONG KONG) CO., LTD.—See Yang Ming Marine Transport Corporation; *Int'l*, pg. 8560
YANG MING LINE (HONG KONG) LTD.—See Yang Ming Marine Transport Corporation; *Int'l*, pg. 8560
YANG MING LINE (INDIA) PVT LTD.—See Yang Ming Marine Transport Corporation; *Int'l*, pg. 8560
YANG MING LINE (M) SDN BHD—See Yang Ming Marine Transport Corporation; *Int'l*, pg. 8560
YANG MING MARINE TRANSPORT CORPORATION; *Int'l*, pg. 8559
YANG MING MARINE TRANSPORT CORPORATION; *U.S. Private*, pg. 4585
YANG MING (MEDITERRANEAN) MARINE SERVICES SINGLE-MEMBER LIMITED LIABLITY COMPANY—See Yang Ming Marine Transport Corporation; *Int'l*, pg. 8560
YANG MING (NETHERLANDS) B.V.—See Yang Ming Marine Transport Corporation; *Int'l*, pg. 8560
YANG MING (RUSSIA) LLC.—See Yang Ming Marine Transport Corporation; *Int'l*, pg. 8560
YANG MING SHIPPING (CANADA) LTD.—See Yang Ming Marine Transport Corporation; *Int'l*, pg. 8560
YANG MING SHIPPING EUROPE GMBH—See Yang Ming Marine Transport Corporation; *Int'l*, pg. 8560
YANG MING SHIPPING PHILIPPINES, INC.—See Yang Ming Marine Transport Corporation; *Int'l*, pg. 8560
YANGMING SHIPPING (SINGAPORE) PTE LTD.—See Yang Ming Marine Transport Corporation; *Int'l*, pg. 8560
YANG MING SHIPPING (VIETNAM) CO., LTD.—See Yang Ming Marine Transport Corporation; *Int'l*, pg. 8560
YANG MING (SINGAPORE) PTE. LTD.—See Yang Ming Marine Transport Corporation; *Int'l*, pg. 8560
YANG MING (SPAIN), S.L.—See Yang Ming Marine Transport Corporation; *Int'l*, pg. 8560
YANGMING (UK) LTD.—See Yang Ming Marine Transport Corporation; *Int'l*, pg. 8560
YANG MING (VIETNAM) CORPORATION—See Yang Ming Marine Transport Corporation; *Int'l*, pg. 8560
YANGO FINANCIAL HOLDING INVESTMENT GROUP CO., LTD.; *Int'l*, pg. 8561
YANGO GROUP CO., LTD.; *Int'l*, pg. 8561
YANGON AMATA SMART & ECO CITY LIMITED—See Amata Corporation Public Company Limited; *Int'l*, pg. 413
YANGON CAN MANUFACTURING CO., LTD.—See Toyo Seikan Group Holdings, Ltd.; *Int'l*, pg. 7858
YANGON CONVENTION CENTRE LTD.—See Pico Far East Holdings Limited; *Int'l*, pg. 5862
YANGON PAN-PACIFIC INTERNATIONAL CO., LTD.—See Pan-Pacific Co., Ltd.; *Int'l*, pg. 5716
YANG TING TECH CO., LTD.—See ASE Technology Holding Co., Ltd.; *Int'l*, pg. 605
YANGTZEKIANG GARMENT LIMITED; *Int'l*, pg. 8561
YANGTZEKIANG INDUSTRIES SDN. BHD.; *Int'l*, pg. 8561
YANGTZE OPTICAL FIBRE & CABLE JOINT STOCK LIMITED COMPANY—See China Telecommunications Corporation; *Int'l*, pg. 1558
YANGTZE OPTICAL FIBRE & CABLE JOINT STOCK LIMITED COMPANY—See Prysmian S.p.A.; *Int'l*, pg. 6013
YANGTZE OPTICAL FIBRE & CABLE JOINT STOCK LIMITED COMPANY—See Wuhan Yangtze Communications Industry Group Co.; *Int'l*, pg. 8502
YANGTZE RIVER ACETYLS CO. LTD.—See BP plc; *Int'l*, pg. 1128
YANGTZE RIVER PORT & LOGISTICS LIMITED; *U.S. Public*, pg. 2398
YANGUFANG INTERNATIONAL GROUP CO., LTD.; *Int'l*, pg. 8561
YANGWOO ENGINEERING & CONSTRUCTION CO., LTD.; *Int'l*, pg. 8561
YANGZHOU AIDEA PHARMACEUTICAL CO., LTD.—See Jiangsu Aidea Pharmaceutical Co., Ltd.; *Int'l*, pg. 3943
YANGZHOU ASIASTAR BUS CO., LTD.; *Int'l*, pg. 8561
YANGZHOU AUCHAN HYPERMARKETS CO., LTD.—See Alibaba Group Holding Limited; *Int'l*, pg. 326
YANGZHOU CHANGELIGHT CO., LTD.—See Xiamen Changelight Co., Ltd.; *Int'l*, pg. 8523
YANGZHOU CHENHUA NEW MATERIAL CO.,LTD.; *Int'l*, pg. 8561
YANGZHOU CHUNG-MEI AUTO PARTS CO., LTD.—See Enterex International Limited; *Int'l*, pg. 2451
YANGZHOU CIMC TONG HUA SPECIAL VEHICLES CO., LTD.—See China International Marine Containers (Group) Co., Ltd.; *Int'l*, pg. 1512
YANGZHOU CIMC TONGHUA TANK EQUIPMENT CO., LTD.—See CIMC Vehicle (Group) Co., Ltd.; *Int'l*, pg. 1608
YANGZHOU EDISON OPTO CORPORATION—See Edison Opto Corp.; *Int'l*, pg. 2311
YANGZHOU ENTEREX INDUSTRIAL CO., LTD.—See Enterex International Limited; *Int'l*, pg. 2451
YANGZHOU GUANGLING DISTRICT TAIHE RURAL MICRO-FINANCE COMPANY LIMITED; *Int'l*, pg. 8561
YANGZHOU NINGDA PRECIOUS METAL CO., LTD.—See GEM Co., Ltd.; *Int'l*, pg. 2914
YANGZHOU RUNYANG LOGISTICS EQUIPMENTS CO., LTD.—See China International Marine Containers (Group) Co., Ltd.; *Int'l*, pg. 1512
YANGZHOU SAC SWITCHGEAR CO., LTD.—See ABB Ltd.; *Int'l*, pg. 49
YANGZHOU SEASHINE NEW MATERIALS CO., LTD.; *Int'l*, pg. 8561
YANGZHOU TONGLEE REEFER CONTAINER CO. LTD.—See China International Marine Containers (Group) Co., Ltd.; *Int'l*, pg. 1512
YANGZHOU TONGLEE REEFER EQUIPMENT CO.,LTD—See China International Marine Containers (Group) Co., Ltd.; *Int'l*, pg. 1512
YANGZHOU YANGJIE ELECTRONIC TECHNOLOGY CO., LTD.; *Int'l*, pg. 8561
YANGZHOU YOUNGTEK ELECTRONICS LTD.—See Harvatek Corporation; *Int'l*, pg. 3280
YANGZIJIANG FINANCIAL HOLDING LTD.; *Int'l*, pg. 8561
YANGZIJIANG SHIPBUILDING (HOLDINGS) LTD; *Int'l*, pg. 8561
YANKEE ALLIANCE; *U.S. Private*, pg. 4585
YANKEE CANDLE COMPANY (EUROPE) LIMITED—See Newell Brands Inc.; *U.S. Public*, pg. 1515
THE YANKEE CANDLE COMPANY, INC.—See Newell Brands Inc.; *U.S. Public*, pg. 1515
YANKEE ENERGY FINANCIAL SERVICES COMPANY—See Eversource Energy; *U.S. Public*, pg. 802
YANKEE ENERGY SERVICES COMPANY—See Eversource Energy; *U.S. Public*, pg. 802
YANKEE ENVIRONMENTAL SERVICES, LLC; *U.S. Private*, pg. 4585
YANKEE EQUIPMENT SYSTEMS, INC.—See EVI Industries, Inc.; *U.S. Public*, pg. 803
YANKEE GAS SERVICES COMPANY—See Eversource Energy; *U.S. Public*, pg. 802
YANKEE GREYHOUND RACING INC.; *U.S. Private*, pg. 4585
YANKEE HILL BRICK & TILE - OMAHA BRICK YARD—See Murdock Holdings, LLC; *U.S. Private*, pg. 2815
YANKEE HILL BRICK & TILE—See Murdock Holdings, LLC; *U.S. Private*, pg. 2814
YANKEE PUBLISHING INC.; *U.S. Private*, pg. 4585
YANKEE RETAIL COMPANY LLC; *U.S. Private*, pg. 4586
YANKEES ENTERTAINMENT & SPORTS NETWORK, LLC—See New York Yankees Partnership; *U.S. Private*, pg. 2912
YANKEE SPIRITS INC.; *U.S. Private*, pg. 4586
YANKEE TELECOM INC.; *U.S. Private*, pg. 4586
YANKERSHOP FOOD CO LTD; *Int'l*, pg. 8561
YANKTON DAILY PRESS & DAKOTAN—See Yankton Media, Inc.; *U.S. Private*, pg. 4586
YANKTON MEDIA, INC.; *U.S. Private*, pg. 4586
YANKTON TITLE COMPANY, INC.—See Stewart Information Services Corporation; *U.S. Public*, pg. 1948
YANKUANG ENERGY GROUP COMPANY LIMITED—See Yankuang Group Co., Limited; *Int'l*, pg. 8562
YANKUANG GROUP CO., LIMITED; *Int'l*, pg. 8562
YANLORD (CHINA) INVESTMENT GROUP CO., LTD.—See Yanlord Land Group Limited; *Int'l*, pg. 8563
YANLORD ISETAN COMMERCIAL CO., LTD.—See Isetan Mitsukoshi Holdings Ltd.; *Int'l*, pg. 3815
YANLORD LAND GROUP LIMITED; *Int'l*, pg. 8562
YANMAR AGRICULTURAL EQUIPMENT (CHINA) CO., LTD.—See Yanmar Co., Ltd.; *Int'l*, pg. 8563
YANMAR AGRICULTURAL MACHINERY (KOREA) CO., LTD.—See Yanmar Co., Ltd.; *Int'l*, pg. 8563
YANMAR AGRICULTURAL MACHINERY MANUFACTURING CO., LTD. - KOUCHI PLANT—See Yanmar Co., Ltd.; *Int'l*, pg. 8564
YANMAR AGRICULTURAL MACHINERY MANUFACTURING CO., LTD.—See Yanmar Co., Ltd.; *Int'l*, pg. 8564
YANMAR AGRI JAPAN CO., LTD.—See Yanmar Co., Ltd.; *Int'l*, pg. 8564
YANMAR AMERICA CORPORATION—See Yanmar Co., Ltd.; *Int'l*, pg. 8564
YANMAR ASIA (SINGAPORE) CORPORATION PTE. LTD.—See Yanmar Co., Ltd.; *Int'l*, pg. 8563
YANMAR BENELUX B.V.—See Yanmar Co., Ltd.; *Int'l*, pg. 8564
YANMAR CAPITAL (THAILAND) CO., LTD.—See Yanmar Co., Ltd.; *Int'l*, pg. 8563
YANMAR CASTING TECHNOLOGY CO., LTD.—See Yanmar Co., Ltd.; *Int'l*, pg. 8564
YANMAR CO., LTD. - AMAGASAKI PLANT—See Yanmar Co., Ltd.; *Int'l*, pg. 8564
YANMAR CO., LTD. - BIWA PLANT—See Yanmar Co., Ltd.; *Int'l*, pg. 8564
YANMAR CO., LTD. - KINOMOTO PLANT—See Yanmar Co., Ltd.; *Int'l*, pg. 8564
YANMAR CO., LTD. - NAGAHARA PLANT—See Yanmar Co., Ltd.; *Int'l*, pg. 8564
YANMAR CO., LTD. - OMORI PLANT—See Yanmar Co., Ltd.; *Int'l*, pg. 8564
YANMAR CO., LTD.; *Int'l*, pg. 8563
YANMAR CO., LTD. - YAMAMOTO PLANT—See Yanmar Co., Ltd.; *Int'l*, pg. 8564
YANMAR CONSTRUCTION EQUIPMENT CO., LTD.—See Yanmar Co., Ltd.; *Int'l*, pg. 8563
YANMAR CONSTRUCTION EQUIPMENT EUROPE S.A.S.—See Yanmar Co., Ltd.; *Int'l*, pg. 8563
YANMAR ENERGY SYSTEM CO., LTD.—See Yanmar Co., Ltd.; *Int'l*, pg. 8563

COMPANY NAME INDEX

YANMAR ENERGY SYSTEM MFG.CO., LTD.—See Yanmar Co., Ltd.; *Int'l*, pg. 8563
YANMAR ENGINEERING CO., LTD.—See Yanmar Co., Ltd.; *Int'l*, pg. 8563
YANMAR ENGINEERING (HK) CO., LTD.—See Yanmar Co., Ltd.; *Int'l*, pg. 8563
YANMAR ENGINE (SHANDONG) CO., LTD.—See Yanmar Co., Ltd.; *Int'l*, pg. 8563
YANMAR ENGINE (SHANGHAI) CO., LTD.—See Yanmar Co., Ltd.; *Int'l*, pg. 8563
YANMAR EQUIPMENT IBERICA SL—See Yanmar Co., Ltd.; *Int'l*, pg. 8564
YANMAR INDIA PRIVATE LIMITED—See Yanmar Co., Ltd.; *Int'l*, pg. 8563
YANMAR INFORMATION SYSTEM SERVICE CO., LTD—See Yanmar Co., Ltd.; *Int'l*, pg. 8564
YANMAR INTERNATIONAL SINGAPORE PTE. LTD.—See Yanmar Co., Ltd.; *Int'l*, pg. 8563
YANMAR ITALY S.P.A.—See Yanmar Co., Ltd.; *Int'l*, pg. 8563
YANMAR KOTA KINABALU R&D CENTER SDN. BHD.—See Yanmar Co., Ltd.; *Int'l*, pg. 8563
YANMAR MARINE SYSTEM CO., LTD.—See Yanmar Co., Ltd.; *Int'l*, pg. 8564
YANMAR NORGE A.S.—See Yanmar Co., Ltd.; *Int'l*, pg. 8564
YANMAR OKINAWA CO., LTD.—See Yanmar Co., Ltd.; *Int'l*, pg. 8564
YANMAR R&D EUROPE S.R.L.—See Yanmar Co., Ltd.; *Int'l*, pg. 8564
YANMAR RUS LLC—See Yanmar Co., Ltd.; *Int'l*, pg. 8564
YANMAR SHIPBUILDING & ENGINEERING CO., LTD.—See Yanmar Co., Ltd.; *Int'l*, pg. 8564
YANMAR SOUTH AMERICA INDUSTRIA DE MAQUINAS LTDA.—See Yanmar Co., Ltd.; *Int'l*, pg. 8564
YANMAR S.P. CO., LTD.—See Yanmar Co., Ltd.; *Int'l*, pg. 8564
YANMAR SVERIGE A.B.—See Yanmar Co., Ltd.; *Int'l*, pg. 8564
YANMAR TECHNICAL SERVICE CO., LTD.—See Yanmar Co., Ltd.; *Int'l*, pg. 8564
YANPAI FILTRATION TECHNOLOGY CO., LTD.; *Int'l*, pg. 8564
YANSHI ZHONGYU GAS CO., LTD.—See Zhongyu Energy Holdings Limited; *Int'l*, pg. 8676
YANTAI AEROSPACE YIHUA SCIENCE AND TECHNOLOGY CO., LTD.—See Shaanxi Aerospace Power Hightech Co., Ltd.; *Int'l*, pg. 6746
YANTAI AQLI FOODSTUFFS CO., LTD.—See Maruha Nichiro Corporation; *Int'l*, pg. 4712
YANTAI BEER ASAHI CO., LTD.—See Asahi Group Holdings Ltd.; *Int'l*, pg. 594
YANTAI CHANGYU PIONEER WINE COMPANY LTD.; *Int'l*, pg. 8564
YANTAI CHINA PET FOODS CO., LTD.; *Int'l*, pg. 8564
YANTAI CIMC RAFFLES SHIP CO., LTD.—See China International Marine Containers (Group) Co., Ltd.; *Int'l*, pg. 1513
YANTAI CSG ZHENGXIN ELECTRIC TECHNOLOGY CO., LTD.—See CSG Smart Science & Technology Co., Ltd.; *Int'l*, pg. 1865
YANTAI DAYANG PHARMACEUTICAL CO., LTD—See Yantai Dongcheng Pharmaceutical Group Co., Ltd.; *Int'l*, pg. 8564
YANTAI DONGCHENG PHARMACEUTICAL GROUP CO., LTD.; *Int'l*, pg. 8564
YANTAI DUAL CAR INTERIOR CO., LTD.—See DUAL Co. Ltd; *Int'l*, pg. 2217
YANTAI EBARA AIR CONDITIONING EQUIPMENT CO., LTD.—See Ebara Corporation; *Int'l*, pg. 2284
YANTAI EDDIE HYDRAULIC TECHNOLOGY CO., LTD—See Yantai Eddie Precision Machinery Co., Ltd.; *Int'l*, pg. 8564
YANTAI EDDIE PRECISION MACHINERY CO., LTD.; *Int'l*, pg. 8564
YANTAI FRONTIER SPIRITS SHINWA MAINTENANCE TECHNOLOGY CO., LTD.—See Shinwa Co., Ltd.; *Int'l*, pg. 6850
YANTAI FUYAN MOULD CO., LTD.—See F-Tech Inc.; *Int'l*, pg. 2595
YANTAI GEM CHEMICALS CO., LTD.—See Valiant Co., Ltd.; *Int'l*, pg. 8115
YANTAI HAICHUAN CHEMICALS CO., LTD.—See Valiant Co., Ltd.; *Int'l*, pg. 8115
YANTAI HONGHUI FOOD CO., LTD.—See Great-Sun Foods Co.,LTD.; *Int'l*, pg. 3066
YANTAI HUF AUTOMOTIVE LOCK CO., LTD.—See Huf Hulsbeck & Furst GmbH & Co. KG; *Int'l*, pg. 3523
YANTAI HUF TOOLS CO. LTD.—See Huf Hulsbeck & Furst GmbH & Co. KG; *Int'l*, pg. 3523
YANTAI HYUNDAI HEAVY INDUSTRIES CO., LTD.—See Moon Environment Technology Co., Ltd.; *Int'l*, pg. 5038
YANTAI INTERNATIONAL CONTAINER TERMINALS LIMITED—See International Container Terminal Services, Inc.; *Int'l*, pg. 3747
YANTAI ISHIKAWA SEALING TECHNOLOGY CO., LTD.; *Int'l*, pg. 8564

YANTAI JEREH COMPRESSION EQUIPMENT CO., LTD.—See Yantai Jereh Oilfield Services Group Co., Ltd.; *Int'l*, pg. 8565
YANTAI JEREH FUNAIKE HEAT EXCHANGER EQUIPMENT CO., LTD.—See Yantai Jereh Oilfield Services Group Co., Ltd.; *Int'l*, pg. 8565
YANTAI JEREH MACHINERY EQUIPMENT CO., LTD.—See Yantai Jereh Oilfield Services Group Co., Ltd.; *Int'l*, pg. 8565
YANTAI JEREH OILFIELD SERVICES CO., LTD—See Yantai Jereh Oilfield Services Group Co., Ltd.; *Int'l*, pg. 8565
YANTAI JEREH OILFIELD SERVICES GROUP CO., LTD.; *Int'l*, pg. 8565
YANTAI JEREH PETROLEUM EQUIPMENT & TECHNOLOGIES CO., LTD.—See Yantai Jereh Oilfield Services Group Co., Ltd.; *Int'l*, pg. 8565
YANTAI JEREH POWER-TECH CO., LTD.—See Yantai Jereh Oilfield Services Group Co., Ltd.; *Int'l*, pg. 8565
YANTAI JIRAY ELECTRONIC TECHNOLOGY CO., LTD.—See Eson Precision Ind. Co., Ltd.; *Int'l*, pg. 2504
YANTAI J-WITEX METAL PRODUCTS CORPORATION—See Nichia Steel Works Co., Ltd.; *Int'l*, pg. 5267
YANTAI J-WITEX WIRE PRODUCT CO., LTD.—See Nichia Steel Works Co., Ltd.; *Int'l*, pg. 5267
YANTAI KEDA REAL ESTATE CO., LTD.—See Zhewen Interactive Group Co Ltd; *Int'l*, pg. 8671
YANTAI KEDA ZHENGXIN ELECTRIC CO., LTD.—See CSG Smart Science & Technology Co., Ltd.; *Int'l*, pg. 1865
YANTAI LONGKOU ANDRE JUICE CO., LTD.—See Yantai North Andre Juice Co., Ltd.; *Int'l*, pg. 8565
YANTAI LONGYUAN POWER TECHNOLOGY CO., LTD.; *Int'l*, pg. 8565
YANTAI LUBAO STEEL PIPE CO., LTD.—See China Baowu Steel Group Corp., Ltd.; *Int'l*, pg. 1486
YANTAI LUDOWICI MINERAL PROCESSING EQUIPMENT LIMITED—See FLSmidth & Co. A/S; *Int'l*, pg. 2712
YANTAI MARSOL CO., LTD.—See Rengo Co., Ltd.; *Int'l*, pg. 6282
YANTAI MECAPLAST CAR COMPONENTS CO., LTD.—See Equistone Partners Europe Limited; *Int'l*, pg. 2487
YANTAI MINGYUE MOULD & PLASTIC CO., LTD.—See Jiangnan Mould & Plastic Technology Co., Ltd.; *Int'l*, pg. 3943
YANTAI MOON HEAT EXCHANGE TECHNOLOGY CO., LTD.—See Moon Environment Technology Co., Ltd.; *Int'l*, pg. 5038
YANTAI MOON HEAVY CASTING MACHINERY CO., LTD.—See Moon Environment Technology Co., Ltd.; *Int'l*, pg. 5038
YANTAI NORTH ANDRE JUICE CO., LTD.; *Int'l*, pg. 8565
YANTAI ORIENTAL PRECISION & ENGINEERING CO., LTD.—See oriental precision & engineering co., ltd.; *Int'l*, pg. 5626
YANTAI ORIENTAL PROTEIN TECH CO., LTD.; *Int'l*, pg. 8565
YANTAI PARTRON ELECTRONICS CO., LTD.—See Partron Co., Ltd.; *Int'l*, pg. 5751
YANTAI POLY GRAND THEATRE MANAGEMENT CORPORATION LIMITED—See Poly Culture Group Corporation Limited; *Int'l*, pg. 5914
YANTAI RAYTRON TECHNOLOGY CO., LTD.; *Int'l*, pg. 8565
YANTAI RILUDA FOODSTUFFS CO., LTD.—See Maruha Nichiro Corporation; *Int'l*, pg. 4712
YANTAI SANDIE PLASTIC PRODUCTS CO., LTD.—See Sojitz Corporation; *Int'l*, pg. 7066
YANTAI SCHLEMMER AUTOMOTIVE PARTS CO., LTD.—See Ningbo Huaxiang Electronic Co., Ltd.; *Int'l*, pg. 5302
YANTAI SEAYU NEW MATERIALS CO., LTD.—See Tianyang New Materials (Shanghai) Technology Co., Ltd.; *Int'l*, pg. 7742
YANTAI SHANSHUI CEMENT CO.,LTD—See China Shanshui Cement Group Ltd.; *Int'l*, pg. 1550
YANTAI SHINWA JOINT TECHNOLOGY CO., LTD.—See Shinwa Co., Ltd.; *Int'l*, pg. 6850
YANTAI SHUANGTA FOOD CO., LTD.; *Int'l*, pg. 8565
YANTAI SJM CO., LTD.—See SJM CO., LTD.; *Int'l*, pg. 6969
YANTAI TAEYANG METAL CO.—See Taeyang Metal Industrial Co., Ltd; *Int'l*, pg. 7406
YANTAI TAYHO ADVANCED MATERIALS CO., LTD.; *Int'l*, pg. 8565
YANTAI T. FULL BIOTECH CO., LTD.; *Int'l*, pg. 8565
YANTAI TIEZHONGBAO STEEL PROCESSING CO., LTD.—See China International Marine Containers (Group) Co., Ltd.; *Int'l*, pg. 1513
YANTAI TONGTAI RENEWABLE RESOURCES CO. LTD.—See Shanghai Yongmaotai Automotive Technology Co., Ltd.; *Int'l*, pg. 6782
YANTAI TSK CABLE SYSTEM CO., LTD.—See Hi-Lex Corporation; *Int'l*, pg. 3381
YANTAI WALSIN STAINLESS STEEL CO., LTD.—See Walsin Lihwa Corporation; *Int'l*, pg. 8335

YAQARA GROUP LIMITED

YANTAI WOOSHIN SCIENCE AND TECHNOLOGY CO., LTD.—See Wooshin Systems Co., Ltd.; *Int'l*, pg. 8455
YANTAI YAZAKI AUTOMOTIVE PARTS CO., LTD.—See Yazaki Corporation; *Int'l*, pg. 8573
YANTAI YUANCHENG GOLD CO., LTD.; *Int'l*, pg. 8565
YAN TAI YURA CORPORATION—See YURATECH Co., Ltd.; *Int'l*, pg. 8617
YANTAI YUXIANG FINE CHEMICALS CO., LTD—See Yantai Tayho Advanced Materials Co., Ltd.; *Int'l*, pg. 8565
YANTAI ZHENGHAI BIO-TECH CO., LTD.; *Int'l*, pg. 8565
YANTAI ZHENGHAI MAGNETIC MATERIAL CO., LTD.; *Int'l*, pg. 8565
YANTAI ZHENGYI PRECISION ELECTRONIC CO., LTD.—See Eson Precision Ind. Co., Ltd.; *Int'l*, pg. 2504
YANTARENERGO OPEN JOINT-STOCK COMPANY—See JSC ROSSETI; *Int'l*, pg. 4011
YAN TAT GROUP HOLDINGS LIMITED; *Int'l*, pg. 8559
YAN TAT (HK) INDUSTRIAL LIMITED—See Yan Tat Group Holdings Limited; *Int'l*, pg. 8559
YANTIAN INTERNATIONAL CONTAINER TERMINALS LIMITED—See Hutchison Port Holdings Trust; *Int'l*, pg. 3540
YANTIS COMPANY; *U.S. Private*, pg. 4586
YANTRA NATURAL RESOURCES LIMITED; *Int'l*, pg. 8566
YAN YING HAO TRADING (SHENZHEN) CO., LTD.—See Qisda Corporation; *Int'l*, pg. 6146
YAO I FABRIC CO., LTD.; *Int'l*, pg. 8566
YAOKO CO., LTD.; *Int'l*, pg. 8566
YAO OFFICE & PLANT—See GMB Corp.; *Int'l*, pg. 3012
YAOPHARMA CO., LTD.—See Shanghai Fosun Pharmaceutical (Group) Co., Ltd.; *Int'l*, pg. 6767
YAO SHENG ELECTRONICS CO., LTD.; *Int'l*, pg. 8566
YA OTTA PINATA—See Thomas H. Lee Partners, L.P.; *U.S. Private*, pg. 4156
YAO YANG ENTERPRISE LLC; *U.S. Private*, pg. 4586
YAP AH SHAK HOUSE SDN. BHD.—See Advance Synergy Berhad; *Int'l*, pg. 157
YAPI KREDI BANKASI NEDERLAND N.V.—See Koc Holding A.S.; *Int'l*, pg. 4224
YAPI KREDI BANK AZERBAIJAN JSC—See Koc Holding A.S.; *Int'l*, pg. 4224
YAPI KREDI BANK NEDERLAND N.V.—See Koc Holding A.S.; *Int'l*, pg. 4224
YAPI KREDI BANK NEDERLAND N.V.—See UniCredit S.p.A.; *Int'l*, pg. 8042
YAPI KREDI FAKTORING A.S.; *Int'l*, pg. 8566
YAPI KREDI KORAY GAYRIMENKUL YATIRIM ORTAKLIGI A.S.; *Int'l*, pg. 8566
YAPI KREDI KULTUR VE SANAT YAYINCILIK TIC.VE SAN.A.S.—See Koc Holding A.S.; *Int'l*, pg. 4224
YAPI KREDI YATIRIM MENKUL DEGERLER A.S.—See Koc Holding A.S.; *Int'l*, pg. 4224
YAPI MERKEZI CONSTRUCTION & INDUSTRY INC.—See Yapi Merkezi Holding A.S.; *Int'l*, pg. 8566
YAPI MERKEZI HOLDING A.S.; *Int'l*, pg. 8566
YAPI MERKEZI PREFABRIKASYON A.S. - LULEBURGAZ PLANT—See Yapi Merkezi Holding A.S.; *Int'l*, pg. 8566
YAPI MERKEZI PREFABRIKASYON A.S.—See Yapi Merkezi Holding A.S.; *Int'l*, pg. 8566
YAPIRAY INSAAT SISTEMLERI SANAYI VE TICARET A.S. - AFYON RAYTON FACTORY—See Yapi Merkezi Holding A.S.; *Int'l*, pg. 8566
YAPIRAY INSAAT SISTEMLERI SANAYI VE TICARET A.S. - KARABUK RAYTON FACTORY—See Yapi Merkezi Holding A.S.; *Int'l*, pg. 8566
YAPIRAY INSAAT SISTEMLERI SANAYI VE TICARET A.S.—See Yapi Merkezi Holding A.S.; *Int'l*, pg. 8566
YAPISAN ELEKTRIK URETIM AS—See Bilgin Enerji Yatirim Holding A.S.; *Int'l*, pg. 1029
YAPITAL FINANCIAL AG—See Otto GmbH & Co. KG; *Int'l*, pg. 5663
YAPI VE KREDI BANKASI A.S.—See Koc Holding A.S.; *Int'l*, pg. 4224
YAPP AUTOMOTIVE SYSTEMS CO., LTD.; *Int'l*, pg. 8566
YAPPA WORLD INCORPORATED; *U.S. Private*, pg. 4586
YAPPLI, INC.; *Int'l*, pg. 8566
YAPPN CORP.; *U.S. Public*, pg. 2398
YAPRAK SUT VE BESI CIFTLIKLERI SANAYI VE TICARET A.S.; *Int'l*, pg. 8566
Y&A PROFESSIONAL SERVICES LIMITED—See Computer & Technologies Holdings Limited; *Int'l*, pg. 1758
YAPSTONE INC.—See Liturgical Publications, Inc.; *U.S. Private*, pg. 2472
YAQARA GROUP LIMITED; *Int'l*, pg. 8566
YARA AB—See Yara International ASA; *Int'l*, pg. 8567
YARA AGRI CZECH REPUBLIC S.R.O.—See Yara International ASA; *Int'l*, pg. 8567
YARA ARGENTINA S.A.—See Yara International ASA; *Int'l*, pg. 8567
YARA ASIA PTE. LTD.—See Yara International ASA; *Int'l*, pg. 8567
YARA AUSTRALIA PTY. LTD.—See Yara International ASA; *Int'l*, pg. 8567
YARA BELGIUM S.A.—See Yara International ASA; *Int'l*, pg. 8567
YARA BELLE PLAINE INC.—See Yara International ASA; *Int'l*, pg. 8567

YAQARA GROUP LIMITED

YARA BENELUX B.V.—See Yara International ASA; *Int'l*, pg. 8567
YARA BRASIL FERTILIZANTES S.A—See Yara International ASA; *Int'l*, pg. 8567
YARA CANADA INC.—See Yara International ASA; *Int'l*, pg. 8567
YARA CHILE FERTILIZANTES LTDA.—See Yara International ASA; *Int'l*, pg. 8567
YARA CHINA LIMITED—See Yara International ASA; *Int'l*, pg. 8567
YARA COLOMBIA LTDA.—See Yara International ASA; *Int'l*, pg. 8567
YARA COMMODITIES LTD.—See Ecom Agroindustrial Corporation Ltd.; *Int'l*, pg. 2296
YARA DANMARK A/S—See Yara International ASA; *Int'l*, pg. 8567
YARA DANMARK GODNING A/S—See Yara International ASA; *Int'l*, pg. 8568
YARA EAST AFRICA LTD.—See Yara International ASA; *Int'l*, pg. 8567
YARA FERTILISERS INDIA PVT. LTD. - BABRALA PLANT—See Yara International ASA; *Int'l*, pg. 8567
YARA FERTILISERS INDIA PVT. LTD.—See Yara International ASA; *Int'l*, pg. 8567
YARA FERTILIZERS PHILIPPINES, INC.—See Yara International ASA; *Int'l*, pg. 8567
YARA FRANCE S.A.—See Yara International ASA; *Int'l*, pg. 8567
YARA GHANA LTD.—See Yara International ASA; *Int'l*, pg. 8567
YARA GMBH & CO. KG—See Yara International ASA; *Int'l*, pg. 8567
YARA GUATEMALA S.A.—See Yara International ASA; *Int'l*, pg. 8567
YARA HELLAS S.A.—See Yara International ASA; *Int'l*, pg. 8567
YARA HUNGARIA KFT.—See Yara International ASA; *Int'l*, pg. 8567
YARA IBERIAN S.A.—See Yara International ASA; *Int'l*, pg. 8567
YARA INDUSTRIAL B.V.—See Yara International ASA; *Int'l*, pg. 8567
YARA INDUSTRIAL GMBH—See Yara International ASA; *Int'l*, pg. 8567
YARA INTERNATIONAL ASA; *Int'l*, pg. 8566
YARA INTERNATIONAL (M) SDN BHD—See Yara International ASA; *Int'l*, pg. 8567
YARA ITALIA SPA—See Yara International ASA; *Int'l*, pg. 8567
YARA KOREA LIMITED—See Yara International ASA; *Int'l*, pg. 8567
YARA LATIN AMERICA—See Yara International ASA; *Int'l*, pg. 8567
YARA LIETUVA, UAB—See Yara International ASA; *Int'l*, pg. 8567
YARA MARINE TECHNOLOGIES AS—See Yara International ASA; *Int'l*, pg. 8567
YARA MEXICO S.A. DE C.V.—See Yara International ASA; *Int'l*, pg. 8567
YARA NORGE AS—See Yara International ASA; *Int'l*, pg. 8567
YARA NORTH AMERICA, INC.—See Yara International ASA; *Int'l*, pg. 8567
YARA NORTH AMERICA, INC.—See Yara International ASA; *Int'l*, pg. 8567
YARA PERU S.R.L.—See Yara International ASA; *Int'l*, pg. 8567
YARA PILBARA HOLDINGS LTD.—See Yara International ASA; *Int'l*, pg. 8567
YARA POLAND SP.Z.O.O.—See Yara International ASA; *Int'l*, pg. 8567
YARA S.A—See Yara International ASA; *Int'l*, pg. 8567
YARA SERVICIOS LOGISTICOS, S.A.—See Yara International ASA; *Int'l*, pg. 8567
YARA SLUISKIL B.V.—See Yara International ASA; *Int'l*, pg. 8567
YARA SUOMI OY MECHELININKATU—See Yara International ASA; *Int'l*, pg. 8567
YARA SUOMI OY—See Yara International ASA; *Int'l*, pg. 8568
YARA SWITZERLAND—See Yara International ASA; *Int'l*, pg. 8568
YARA TANZANIA LTD.—See Yara International ASA; *Int'l*, pg. 8568
YARA (THAILAND) LTD.—See Yara International ASA; *Int'l*, pg. 8567
YARA TRINIDAD LTD.—See Yara International ASA; *Int'l*, pg. 8568
YARA UK LTD.—See Yara International ASA; *Int'l*, pg. 8568
YARA UK LTD.—See Yara International ASA; *Int'l*, pg. 8568
YARA UKRAINE—See Yara International ASA; *Int'l*, pg. 8568
YARA VIETNAM LTD.—See Yara International ASA; *Int'l*, pg. 8568
YARA VLAARDINGEN B.V.—See Yara International ASA; *Int'l*, pg. 8568

YARCDATA LLC—See Hewlett Packard Enterprise Company; *U.S. Public*, pg. 1031
YARDE METALS INC.; *U.S. Private*, pg. 4586
YARD & HOME, LLC—See UFP Industries, Inc.; *U.S. Public*, pg. 2221
YARD HOUSE IRVINE SPECTRUM, LLC—See Darden Restaurants, Inc.; *U.S. Public*, pg. 633
THE YARD HOUSE, L.P.—See Darden Restaurants, Inc.; *U.S. Public*, pg. 633
YARD HOUSE RANCHO MIRAGE, LLC—See Darden Restaurants, Inc.; *U.S. Public*, pg. 633
YARD HOUSE RESTAURANTS, LLC—See Darden Restaurants, Inc.; *U.S. Public*, pg. 633
YARD HOUSE SAN DIEGO, LLC—See Darden Restaurants, Inc.; *U.S. Public*, pg. 633
YARD HOUSE TRIANGLE SQUARE, LLC—See Darden Restaurants, Inc.; *U.S. Public*, pg. 633
YARD HOUSE USA, INC.—See Darden Restaurants, Inc.; *U.S. Public*, pg. 633
YARDI CANADA LTD.—See Yardi Systems, Inc.; *U.S. Private*, pg. 4586
YARDI SINGAPORE PTE LTD—See Yardi Systems, Inc.; *U.S. Private*, pg. 4586
YARDI SOFTWARE INDIA PVT LTD—See Yardi Systems, Inc.; *U.S. Private*, pg. 4586
YARDI SYDNEY LTD—See Yardi Systems, Inc.; *U.S. Private*, pg. 4586
YARDI SYSTEMS BV—See Yardi Systems, Inc.; *U.S. Private*, pg. 4586
YARDI SYSTEMS GMBH—See Yardi Systems, Inc.; *U.S. Private*, pg. 4586
YARDI SYSTEMS (HK) LTD.—See Yardi Systems, Inc.; *U.S. Private*, pg. 4586
YARDI SYSTEMS, INC.; *U.S. Private*, pg. 4586
YARDI SYSTEMS LTD—See Yardi Systems, Inc.; *U.S. Private*, pg. 4586
YARDLEY PRODUCTS CORPORATION—See Dixon Valve & Coupling Company; *U.S. Private*, pg. 1246
YARDS BREWING COMPANY; *U.S. Private*, pg. 4586
YARD WORKS, LLC—See SiteOne Landscape Supply, Inc.; *U.S. Public*, pg. 1889
YARECUADOR CIA LTDA.—See Yara International ASA; *Int'l*, pg. 8568
YAREMA DIE & ENGINEERING CO.; *U.S. Private*, pg. 4586
YARGOL DIALYSIS, LLC—See DaVita Inc.; *U.S. Public*, pg. 644
YARGUS MANUFACTURING—See Ag Growth International Inc.; *Int'l*, pg. 198
YARI MINERALS LIMITED; *Int'l*, pg. 8568
YARIX SRL—See Sesa S.p.A.; *Int'l*, pg. 6729
YARNALL WAREHOUSE, INC.; *U.S. Private*, pg. 4586
YARNAPUND PUBLIC COMPANY LIMITED; *Int'l*, pg. 8568
YARN SYNDICATE LTD.; *Int'l*, pg. 8568
YARRA TRAIL PTY. LTD.—See Queens Lane Capital Pty Ltd; *Int'l*, pg. 6159
YARRA VALLEY CHOCOLATERIE & ICE CREAMERY—See PMC Capital Partners, LLC; *U.S. Private*, pg. 3218
YARROW LODGE, LLC—See Universal Health Services, Inc.; *U.S. Public*, pg. 2261
YARRUM MARKETING, INC.; *U.S. Private*, pg. 4586
YARUKI SWITCH CAREER CO., LTD.—See TBS Holdings, Inc.; *Int'l*, pg. 7481
YARWIL AS—See Wilh. Wilhelmsen Holding ASA; *Int'l*, pg. 8411
YARWIL AS—See Yara International ASA; *Int'l*, pg. 8568
YASAKA GAC CO., LTD.—See Denso Corporation; *Int'l*, pg. 2033
YASAM BANKASI SAGLIK HIZMETLERI IC VE DIS TICARET ANONIM SIRKETI—See VITA 34 AG; *Int'l*, pg. 8257
YASASHIITE RAITO CO., LTD.—See RAITO KOGYO Co., Ltd.; *Int'l*, pg. 6191
YASCO CO., LTD.—See Yaskawa Electric Corporation; *Int'l*, pg. 8570
YASCO CO., LTD. - TAKARAYAMA PLANT—See Yaskawa Electric Corporation; *Int'l*, pg. 8570
YAS CO., LTD.; *Int'l*, pg. 8568
THE YASH BIRLA GROUP; *Int'l*, pg. 7701
YASH CHEMEX LIMITED; *Int'l*, pg. 8568
YASHENG GROUP; *U.S. Public*, pg. 2398
YASHICA HONG KONG CO., LTD.—See KYOCERA Corporation; *Int'l*, pg. 4356
YASHI, INC.—See Nexstar Media Group, Inc.; *U.S. Public*, pg. 1525
YASHILI INTERNATIONAL HOLDINGS LTD.—See China Mengniu Dairy Company Limited; *Int'l*, pg. 1520
YASHILI NEW ZEALAND DAIRY CO., LTD.—See China Mengniu Dairy Company Limited; *Int'l*, pg. 1520
YASHIMA CHEMICAL ENGINEERING CO., LTD.—See Kurimoto Ltd; *Int'l*, pg. 4340
YASHIMA CO., LTD.—See CK SAN-ETSU Co., Ltd.; *Int'l*, pg. 1639
YASHIMA CONTROL SYSTEMS CO., LTD. - ANJO PLANT—See Yashima Denki Co., Ltd.; *Int'l*, pg. 8569
YASHIMA CONTROL SYSTEMS CO., LTD. - OGAWARA PLANT—See Yashima Denki Co., Ltd.; *Int'l*, pg. 8569

CORPORATE AFFILIATIONS

YASHIMA CONTROL SYSTEMS CO., LTD.—See Yashima Denki Co., Ltd.; *Int'l*, pg. 8568
YASHIMA DENKI CO., LTD.; *Int'l*, pg. 8568
YASHIMA ECO SYSTEMS CO., LTD.—See Yashima Denki Co., Ltd.; *Int'l*, pg. 8569
YASHIMA ELECTRONIC SOLUTIONS CO., LTD.—See Yashima Denki Co., Ltd.; *Int'l*, pg. 8569
YASHIMA INDUSTRIAL EQUIPMENT SYSTEM, LTD.—See Yashima Denki Co., Ltd.; *Int'l*, pg. 8569
YASHIMANADA CORPORATION—See JFE Holdings, Inc.; *Int'l*, pg. 3937
YASHIMA SANGYO CO., LTD.—See Sumitomo Chemical Company, Limited; *Int'l*, pg. 7267
YASH INNOVENTURE LTD.; *Int'l*, pg. 8568
YASH MANAGEMENT & SATELLITE LTD.; *Int'l*, pg. 8568
YASHO INDUSTRIES LTD.; *Int'l*, pg. 8569
YASH PAKKA LIMITED; *Int'l*, pg. 8568
YASHRAJ CONTAINEURS LTD.; *Int'l*, pg. 8569
YASH TECHNOLOGIES, INC.; *U.S. Private*, pg. 4586
YASH TRADING & FINANCE LTD.; *Int'l*, pg. 8568
YASHYL DUNYA LLC—See Endress+Hauser (International) Holding AG; *Int'l*, pg. 2409
YASKAWA AMERICA, INC. - CYPRESS DIVISION—See Yaskawa Electric Corporation; *Int'l*, pg. 8570
YASKAWA AMERICA, INC. - ENGINEERED SYSTEMS GROUP—See Yaskawa Electric Corporation; *Int'l*, pg. 8570
YASKAWA AMERICA, INC. - MOTOMAN ROBOTICS DIVISION - IRVINE—See Yaskawa Electric Corporation; *Int'l*, pg. 8570
YASKAWA AMERICA, INC. - MOTOMAN ROBOTICS DIVISION—See Yaskawa Electric Corporation; *Int'l*, pg. 8570
YASKAWA AMERICA, INC.—See Yaskawa Electric Corporation; *Int'l*, pg. 8569
YASKAWA AUTOMATION & DRIVES CORP.—See Yaskawa Electric Corporation; *Int'l*, pg. 8570
YASKAWA BENELUX B.V.—See Yaskawa Electric Corporation; *Int'l*, pg. 8569
YASKAWA BROOKS AUTOMATION, INC.—See Azenta, Inc.; *U.S. Public*, pg. 258
YASKAWA BUSINESS STAFF CO., LTD.—See Pasona Group Inc.; *Int'l*, pg. 5754
YASKAWA CONTROLS CO., LTD.—See Yaskawa Electric Corporation; *Int'l*, pg. 8570
YASKAWA CZECH S.R.O.—See Yaskawa Electric Corporation; *Int'l*, pg. 8570
YASKAWA ELECTRIC CORPORATION - NAKAMA PLANT—See Yaskawa Electric Corporation; *Int'l*, pg. 8570
YASKAWA ELECTRIC CORPORATION; *Int'l*, pg. 8569
YASKAWA ELECTRIC CORPORATION - TOKYO PLANT—See Yaskawa Electric Corporation; *Int'l*, pg. 8570
YASKAWA ELECTRIC CORPORATION - YAHATA-HIGASHI PLANT—See Yaskawa Electric Corporation; *Int'l*, pg. 8570
YASKAWA ELECTRIC CORPORATION - YAHATA-NISHI PLANT—See Yaskawa Electric Corporation; *Int'l*, pg. 8570
YASKAWA ELECTRIC CORPORATION - YUKUHASHI PLANT—See Yaskawa Electric Corporation; *Int'l*, pg. 8570
YASKAWA ELECTRIC ENGINEERING CORPORATION—See Yaskawa Electric Corporation; *Int'l*, pg. 8570
YASKAWA ELECTRIC KOREA CORPORATION—See Yaskawa Electric Corporation; *Int'l*, pg. 8570
YASKAWA ELECTRIC (SHENYANG) CO., LTD.—See Yaskawa Electric Corporation; *Int'l*, pg. 8570
YASKAWA ELECTRIC (SINGAPORE) PTE LTD—See Yaskawa Electric Corporation; *Int'l*, pg. 8570
YASKAWA ELECTRIC TAIWAN CORPORATION—See Yaskawa Electric Corporation; *Int'l*, pg. 8570
YASKAWA ELECTRIC (THAILAND) CO., LTD.—See Yaskawa Electric Corporation; *Int'l*, pg. 8570
YASKAWA ELECTRIC UK LTD.—See Yaskawa Electric Corporation; *Int'l*, pg. 8569
YASKAWA ELECTRIC VIETNAM CO., LTD.—See Yaskawa Electric Corporation; *Int'l*, pg. 8570
YASKAWA ELETRICO DO BRASIL LTDA.—See Yaskawa Electric Corporation; *Int'l*, pg. 8570
YASKAWA ESHED TECHNOLOGY LTD.—See RoboGroup T.E.K. Ltd.; *Int'l*, pg. 6371
YASKAWA ESHED TECHNOLOGY LTD.—See Yaskawa Electric Corporation; *Int'l*, pg. 8570
YASKAWA EUROPE GMBH—See Yaskawa Electric Corporation; *Int'l*, pg. 8569
YASKAWA EUROPE TECHNOLOGY LTD.—See Yaskawa Electric Corporation; *Int'l*, pg. 8569
YASKAWA FINLAND OY—See Yaskawa Electric Corporation; *Int'l*, pg. 8570
YASKAWA FRANCE S.A.—See Yaskawa Electric Corporation; *Int'l*, pg. 8570
YASKAWA IBERICA S.L.—See Yaskawa Electric Corporation; *Int'l*, pg. 8569
YASKAWA INDIA PRIVATE LIMITED—See Yaskawa Electric Corporation; *Int'l*, pg. 8570

COMPANY NAME INDEX

YASKAWA ITALIA S.R.L.—See Yaskawa Electric Corporation; *Int'l*, pg. 8569
YASKAWA LOGISTEC CORPORATION—See Yaskawa Electric Corporation; *Int'l*, pg. 8570
YASKAWA MANUFACTURING CORPORATION—See Yaskawa Electric Corporation; *Int'l*, pg. 8570
YASKAWA MECHATREC CORPORATION—See Yaskawa Electric Corporation; *Int'l*, pg. 8570
YASKAWA MOTOMAN CANADA LTD.—See Yaskawa Electric Corporation; *Int'l*, pg. 8570
YASKAWA MOTOMAN MEXICO, S.A. DE C.V.—See Yaskawa Electric Corporation; *Int'l*, pg. 8570
YASKAWA MOTOR CORPORATION—See Yaskawa Electric Corporation; *Int'l*, pg. 8570
YASKAWA NORDIC AB—See Yaskawa Electric Corporation; *Int'l*, pg. 8569
YASKAWA OBVIOUS COMMUNICATIONS INC.—See Yaskawa Electric Corporation; *Int'l*, pg. 8570
YASKAWA POLSKA SP. Z O.O.—See Yaskawa Electric Corporation; *Int'l*, pg. 8570
YASKAWA RISTRO D.O.O.—See Yaskawa Electric Corporation; *Int'l*, pg. 8570
YASKAWA SHOUGANG ROBOT CO., LTD.—See Yaskawa Electric Corporation; *Int'l*, pg. 8570
YASKAWA SLOVENIJA D.O.O.—See Yaskawa Electric Corporation; *Int'l*, pg. 8570
YASKAWA SOUTHERN AFRICA (PTY) LTD.—See Yaskawa Electric Corporation; *Int'l*, pg. 8570
YASKAWA TECHNO PLATE CORPORATION—See Yaskawa Electric Corporation; *Int'l*, pg. 8570
YASKAWA TURKEY ELEKTRIK TICARET LTD. STI.—See Yaskawa Electric Corporation; *Int'l*, pg. 8570
YASKAWA UK LTD.—See Yaskawa Electric Corporation; *Int'l*, pg. 8570
YASONS CHEMEX CARE LIMITED—See Yash Chemex Limited; *Int'l*, pg. 8568
THE YASUDA BUILDING CO., LTD.—See Yasuda Logistics Corporation; *Int'l*, pg. 8571
YASUDA LOGISTICS CORPORATION; *Int'l*, pg. 8570
YASUDA LOGISTICS (SHANGHAI) LTD.—See Yasuda Logistics Corporation; *Int'l*, pg. 8571
YASUDA LOGISTICS (VIETNAM) CO., LTD.—See Yasuda Logistics Corporation; *Int'l*, pg. 8571
YASUDA MEDICAL LOGISTICS CO., LTD.—See Yasuda Logistics Corporation; *Int'l*, pg. 8571
YASUDA SEGUROS, S.A.—See Sompo Holdings, Inc.; *Int'l*, pg. 7086
YASUDA TRANSPORTATION CO., LTD.—See Yasuda Logistics Corporation; *Int'l*, pg. 8571
YASUDA WORKS CO., LTD.—See Yasuda Logistics Corporation; *Int'l*, pg. 8571
YASUE CORPORATION—See Sala Corporation; *Int'l*, pg. 6490
YASUHARA CHEMICAL CO., LTD.; *Int'l*, pg. 8571
YASUMA CO., LTD.—See Sapporo Holdings Limited; *Int'l*, pg. 6574
YASUNAGA AIR PUMP INC.—See YASUNAGA CORPORATION; *Int'l*, pg. 8571
YASUNAGA CORPORATION - CASTING PLANT—See YASUNAGA CORPORATION; *Int'l*, pg. 8571
YASUNAGA CORPORATION - NABARI PLANT—See YASUNAGA CORPORATION; *Int'l*, pg. 8571
YASUNAGA CORPORATION - SAIMYOJI PLANT—See YASUNAGA CORPORATION; *Int'l*, pg. 8571
YASUNAGA CORPORATION; *Int'l*, pg. 8571
YASUNAGA CORPORATION - YUMEPORISU PLANT—See YASUNAGA CORPORATION; *Int'l*, pg. 8571
YASUNAGA TRANSPORT CO., LTD.—See YASUNAGA CORPORATION; *Int'l*, pg. 8571
YASUTOMO & CO.; *U.S. Private*, pg. 4586
YATAI INDUSTRIAL DEVELOPMENT CO., LTD.; *Int'l*, pg. 8571
YATAS YATAK VE YORGAN SANAYI TICARET A.S.; *Int'l*, pg. 8571
YATEC ENGINEERING CORPORATION—See Teco Electric & Machinery Co., Ltd.; *Int'l*, pg. 7518
YATEC ENGINEERING (VN) COMPANY LIMITED—See Teco Electric & Machinery Co., Ltd.; *Int'l*, pg. 7518
YATEEM OXYGEN W.L.L.—See Linde plc; *Int'l*, pg. 4510
YATES-AMERICAN MACHINE COMPANY; *U.S. Private*, pg. 4587
YATES BUICK GMC; *U.S. Private*, pg. 4587
YATES BUICK PONTIAC GMC, INC.; *U.S. Private*, pg. 4587
YAT FUNG MOTORS LTD.—See Inchcape plc; *Int'l*, pg. 3647
YATIRIM FINANSMAN MENKUL DEGERLER A.S.; *Int'l*, pg. 8571
YATIRIM VARLIK KIRALAMA A.S.; *Int'l*, pg. 8571
YATO TOOLS (JIAXING) CO. LTD.—See Toya S.A.; *Int'l*, pg. 7851
YATO TOOLS (SHANGHAI) CO. LTD.—See Toya S.A.; *Int'l*, pg. 7851
YATRA ONLINE, INC.; *Int'l*, pg. 8571
YATRA ONLINE LIMITED; *Int'l*, pg. 8571
YATSEN HOLDING LIMITED; *Int'l*, pg. 8571
YATSUGATAKE KOGEN LODGE CO., LTD.—See Seven & i Holdings Co., Ltd.; *Int'l*, pg. 6731

YATSUGATAKE MILK CO., LTD.—See MEGMILK SNOW BRAND Co., Ltd.; *Int'l*, pg. 4796
YA TUNG READY-MIXED CONCRETE CORP.—See Asia Cement Corporation; *Int'l*, pg. 611
YAT YUE INDUSTRIAL CO. (HK) LTD.—See Igarashi Motors India Limited; *Int'l*, pg. 3601
YAT YUEN HONG CO., LTD.—See Hong Fok Corporation Limited; *Int'l*, pg. 3465
YAU LEE BUILDING CONSTRUCTION AND DECORATION COMPANY LIMITED—See Yau Lee Holdings Limited; *Int'l*, pg. 8572
YAU LEE BUILDING MATERIALS TRADING COMPANY LIMITED—See Yau Lee Holdings Limited; *Int'l*, pg. 8572
YAU LEE CONSTRUCTION COMPANY LIMITED—See Yau Lee Holdings Limited; *Int'l*, pg. 8572
YAU LEE CONSTRUCTION MATERIALS & TECHNOLOGY (B.V.I.) LTD.—See Yau Lee Holdings Limited; *Int'l*, pg. 8572
YAU LEE CONSTRUCTION MATERIALS & TECHNOLOGY LIMITED—See Yau Lee Holdings Limited; *Int'l*, pg. 8572
YAU LEE CONSTRUCTION (SINGAPORE) PTE. LTD.—See Yau Lee Holdings Limited; *Int'l*, pg. 8572
YAU LEE CONSTRUCTION (UAE) COMPANY LIMITED—See Yau Lee Holdings Limited; *Int'l*, pg. 8572
YAU LEE CURTAIN WALL AND STEEL WORKS LIMITED—See Yau Lee Holdings Limited; *Int'l*, pg. 8572
YAU LEE DEVELOPMENT (SINGAPORE) PTE. LTD.—See Yau Lee Holdings Limited; *Int'l*, pg. 8572
YAU LEE HOLDINGS LIMITED; *Int'l*, pg. 8571
YAU LEE WAH CONCRETE PRECAST PRODUCTS COMPANY LIMITED—See Yau Lee Holdings Limited; *Int'l*, pg. 8572
YAU LEE WAH CONCRETE PRECAST PRODUCTS (SHENZHEN) COMPANY LIMITED—See Yau Lee Holdings Limited; *Int'l*, pg. 8572
YAVAPAI COMMUNITY HOSPITAL ASSOCIATION; *U.S. Private*, pg. 4587
YAVOR PLC; *Int'l*, pg. 8572
YAWAL S.A.; *Int'l*, pg. 8572
YAWATA ELECTRODE (THAILAND) CO., LTD.—See Nippon Steel Corporation; *Int'l*, pg. 5339
YAXING MOTOR PERU S.A.C.; *Int'l*, pg. 8572
YAYASAN BURSA MALAYSIA—See Bursa Malaysia Berhad; *Int'l*, pg. 1227
YAYLA ENERJI URETIM TURIZM VE INSAAT TICARET A.S.; *Int'l*, pg. 8572
YAYOI CO., LTD.—See KKR & Co. Inc.; *U.S. Public*, pg. 1267
YAYOI SUNFOODS CO., LTD. - NAGAOKA FACTORY—See Maruha Nichiro Corporation; *Int'l*, pg. 4712
YAYOI SUNFOODS CO., LTD.—See Maruha Nichiro Corporation; *Int'l*, pg. 4712
YAZAKI ARGENTINA S.R.L.—See Yazaki Corporation; *Int'l*, pg. 8573
YAZAKI A.S.—See Yazaki Corporation; *Int'l*, pg. 8573
YAZAKI AUTOMOTIVE PRODUCTS DO BRASIL SISTEMAS ELETRICOS LTDA—See Yazaki Corporation; *Int'l*, pg. 8573
YAZAKI AUTOMOTIVE PRODUCTS POLAND SP. Z O.O.—See Yazaki Corporation; *Int'l*, pg. 8573
YAZAKI AUTOMOTIVE PRODUCTS TUNISIA S.A.R.L—See Yazaki Corporation; *Int'l*, pg. 8573
YAZAKI BULGARIA EOOD—See Yazaki Corporation; *Int'l*, pg. 8573
YAZAKI CIEMEL FTZ LTDA—See Yazaki Corporation; *Int'l*, pg. 8573
YAZAKI CIEMEL S.A.—See Yazaki Corporation; *Int'l*, pg. 8573
YAZAKI COMPONENT TECHNOLOGY S.R.L.—See Yazaki Corporation; *Int'l*, pg. 8573
YAZAKI CORPORATION; *Int'l*, pg. 8572
YAZAKI DO BRAZIL LTDA.—See Yazaki Corporation; *Int'l*, pg. 8573
YAZAKI EDS VIETNAM, LTD.—See Yazaki Corporation; *Int'l*, pg. 8573
YAZAKI ENERGY SYSTEMS, INC. (YESI)—See Yazaki Corporation; *Int'l*, pg. 8573
YAZAKI EUROPE LIMITED ITALIA S.R.L—See Yazaki Corporation; *Int'l*, pg. 8573
YAZAKI EUROPE LTD.—See Yazaki Corporation; *Int'l*, pg. 8573
YAZAKI INDIA LIMITED—See Yazaki Corporation; *Int'l*, pg. 8573
YAZAKI MOROCCO S.A.—See Yazaki Corporation; *Int'l*, pg. 8573
YAZAKI NORTH AMERICA, INC.—See Yazaki Corporation; *Int'l*, pg. 8573
YAZAKI OTOMOTIV YAN SANAYI VE TICARET A.S—See Yazaki Corporation; *Int'l*, pg. 8573
YAZAKI PARTS CO., LTD.—See Yazaki Corporation; *Int'l*, pg. 8573
YAZAKI ROMANIA S.R.L.—See Yazaki Corporation; *Int'l*, pg. 8573

YDA INSAAT SANAYI VE TICARET A.S.

YAZAKI SABANCI OTOMOTIV KABLO DONANIMI SAN. VE TIC. A.S.—See Haci Omer Sabanci Holding A.S.; *Int'l*, pg. 3204
YAZAKI SABANCI OTOMOTIV KABLO DONANIMI SAN. VE TIC. A.S.—See Yazaki Corporation; *Int'l*, pg. 8573
YAZAKI SALTANO DE OVAR PRODUCTOS ELECTRICOS, LDA.—See Yazaki Corporation; *Int'l*, pg. 8573
YAZAKI SERVICE S. DE R.L. DE C.V.—See Yazaki Corporation; *Int'l*, pg. 8573
YAZAKI SLOVAKIA SPOL. S.R.O.—See Yazaki Corporation; *Int'l*, pg. 8573
YAZAKI-TORRES MANUFACTURING INCORPORATED—See Yazaki Corporation; *Int'l*, pg. 8573
YAZAKI TUNISIA SARL—See Yazaki Corporation; *Int'l*, pg. 8573
YAZAKI UKRAINE LLC—See Yazaki Corporation; *Int'l*, pg. 8573
YAZAKI WIRING TECHNOLOGIES CZECH S.R.O.—See Yazaki Corporation; *Int'l*, pg. 8573
YAZAKI WIRING TECHNOLOGIES INDIA PRIVATE LIMITED—See Yazaki Corporation; *Int'l*, pg. 8573
YAZAKI WIRING TECHNOLOGIES TURKIYE ELEKTRIK SISTEMLERI SANAYI VE TIC. LTD. STI.—See Yazaki Corporation; *Int'l*, pg. 8572
YAZDBAF FACTORY; *Int'l*, pg. 8573
YAZHOU ZHOUKAN LIMITED—See Media Chinese International Limited; *Int'l*, pg. 4770
YA ZHU SILK, INC.; *Int'l*, pg. 8544
YAZOO VALLEY ELECTRIC POWER ASSOCIATION; *U.S. Private*, pg. 4587
YBBSTALER FRUIT AUSTRIA GMBH—See AGRANA Beteiligungs-AG; *Int'l*, pg. 214
YBBSTALER FRUIT AUSTRIA GMBH—See BayWa AG; *Int'l*, pg. 919
YBBSTALER FRUIT POLSKA SP. Z O.O—See AGRANA Beteiligungs-AG; *Int'l*, pg. 214
YBBSTALER FRUIT POLSKA SP. Z O.O—See BayWa AG; *Int'l*, pg. 919
YB COMMUNICATIONS LIMITED; *Int'l*, pg. 8573
YBM NET, INC.; *Int'l*, pg. 8573
YBOR CITY DIALYSIS, LLC—See DaVita Inc.; *U.S. Public*, pg. 644
YBOX REAL ESTATE LTD.; *Int'l*, pg. 8573
Y.B. PAKISTAN LIMITED—See Lucky Cement Limited; *Int'l*, pg. 4574
YBS INTERNATIONAL BERHAD; *Int'l*, pg. 8574
YB VEHICLE SERVICES—See Younger Brothers Group Inc.; *U.S. Private*, pg. 4593
YB VENTURES BERHAD; *Int'l*, pg. 8573
Y.C.C. PARTS MFG. CO., LTD.; *Int'l*, pg. 8543
YCE CORP.—See Yokogawa Bridge Holdings Corp.; *Int'l*, pg. 8591
YCH DISTRICENTRE PTE LTD—See YCH Group Pte. Ltd.; *Int'l*, pg. 8574
YCH DISTRIPARK PTE LTD—See YCH Group Pte. Ltd.; *Int'l*, pg. 8574
YCH GLOBAL LOGISTICS PTE LTD—See YCH Group Pte. Ltd.; *Int'l*, pg. 8574
YCH GROUP PTE. LTD.; *Int'l*, pg. 8574
YCH LOGISTICS AUSTRALIA PTY LTD—See YCH Group Pte. Ltd.; *Int'l*, pg. 8574
YCIH GREEN HIGH-PERFORMANCE CONCRETE COMPANY LIMITED; *Int'l*, pg. 8574
YC INOX CO., LTD.; *Int'l*, pg. 8574
YC INOX TR CELIK SANAYI VE TICARET A.S.—See YC Inox Co., Ltd.; *Int'l*, pg. 8574
YC INOX TR COMPANY—See YC Inox Co., Ltd.; *Int'l*, pg. 8574
YCK (THAILAND) CO., LTD.—See AISIN Corporation; *Int'l*, pg. 254
YCO GROUP PLC; *Int'l*, pg. 8574
YCO GROUP PLC - YCO CREW—See YCO Group plc; *Int'l*, pg. 8574
YCO LTD.—See YCO Group plc; *Int'l*, pg. 8574
YCO S.A.M.—See YCO Group plc; *Int'l*, pg. 8574
YCO YACHT LIMITED—See YCO Group plc; *Int'l*, pg. 8574
YCP HOLDINGS (GLOBAL) LIMITED; *Int'l*, pg. 8574
YCQH AGRICULTURAL TECHNOLOGY CO., LTD.; *Int'l*, pg. 8574
YCS CO., LTD.—See Nippon Yusen Kabushiki Kaisha; *Int'l*, pg. 5360
YCY INTERNATIONAL LIMITED—See China-Hong Kong Photo Products Holdings Limited; *Int'l*, pg. 1568
YDA INSAAT SANAYI VE TICARET A.S.; *Int'l*, pg. 8574
YDC CORPORATION—See Future Corporation; *Int'l*, pg. 2853
YDILO ADVANCED VOICE SOLUTIONS S.A.—See Espiga Capital Gestion S.G.E.C.R, S.A.; *Int'l*, pg. 2506
YD MECHATRO SOLUTIONS INC. - NIIGATA PLANT—See Yaskawa Electric Corporation; *Int'l*, pg. 8569
YD MECHATRO SOLUTIONS INC.—See Yaskawa Electric Corporation; *Int'l*, pg. 8569
YD PLASTICS CO., LTD.—See DIC Corporation; *Int'l*, pg. 2111
YDT TECHNOLOGY CO. LTD.—See Korea Electric Terminal Co., Ltd.; *Int'l*, pg. 4284

YDUQS PARTICIPACOES SA · CORPORATE AFFILIATIONS

YDUQS PARTICIPACOES SA; *Int'l*, pg. 8575
YDX INNOVATION CORP.; *Int'l*, pg. 8575
YD YNVISIBLE, S.A.; *Int'l*, pg. 8574
YEAGER ENTERPRISES CORP.; *U.S. Private*, pg. 4587
YEAGER SUPPLY, INC.; *U.S. Private*, pg. 4587
YEAHKA LIMITED; *Int'l*, pg. 8575
YEAH YEAH GROUP HOLDINGS LIMITED; *Int'l*, pg. 8575
YEAL ELECTRIC CO., LTD.; *Int'l*, pg. 8575
YEALINK NETWORK TECHNOLOGY CO.,LTD.; *Int'l*, pg. 8575
YEARGIN POTTER SHACKELFORD CONSTRUCTION, INC.; *U.S. Private*, pg. 4587
YEARIMDANG PUBLISHING CO., LTD.; *Int'l*, pg. 8575
YEAR ONE INC.; *U.S. Private*, pg. 4587
YEA SHIN INTERNATIONAL DEVELOPMENT CO., LTD.; *Int'l*, pg. 8575
YEA SHIN TECHNOLOGY CO., LTD.—See Diodes Incorporated; *U.S. Public*, pg. 667
YEBISU GARDEN PLACE CO., LTD.—See Sapporo Holdings Limited; *Int'l*, pg. 6574
YEBISU WINEMART CO., LTD.—See Sapporo Holdings Limited; *Int'l*, pg. 6574
YEBOYETHU LTD.; *Int'l*, pg. 8575
YEC ELECTRONICS LIMITED—See AAC Technologies Holdings Inc.; *Int'l*, pg. 31
YECHIU METAL RECYCLING CHINA LTD.; *Int'l*, pg. 8575
YECHIU METAL SMELTING SDN. BHD.—See Yechiu Metal Recycling China Ltd.; *Int'l*, pg. 8575
YECHIU NON-FERROUS METAL (M) SDN. BHD.—See Yechiu Metal Recycling China Ltd.; *Int'l*, pg. 8575
Y-E DATA INC.—See Yaskawa Electric Corporation; *Int'l*, pg. 8569
YEDIDIM PENSION ARRANGEMENTS INSURANCE AGENCY LTD.—See Harel Insurance Investments & Financial Services Ltd.; *Int'l*, pg. 3274
YE DIGITAL CORPORATION—See Yaskawa Electric Corporation; *Int'l*, pg. 8569
YEDITEPE FAKTORING A.S.; *Int'l*, pg. 8575
YEEBO (INTERNATIONAL HOLDINGS) LIMITED; *Int'l*, pg. 8575
YEEDEX ELECTRONIC CORPORATION; *Int'l*, pg. 8576
YEE HOP ENGINEERING COMPANY LIMITED—See Yee Hop Holdings Ltd.; *Int'l*, pg. 8575
YEE HOP HOLDINGS LTD.; *Int'l*, pg. 8575
YEE LEE CORPORATION BHD.; *Int'l*, pg. 8575
YEE LEE PALM OIL INDUSTRIES SDN BHD—See Yee Lee Corporation Bhd.; *Int'l*, pg. 8575
YEE LEE TRADING CO SDN BHD—See Yee Lee Corporation Bhd.; *Int'l*, pg. 8575
YEELIM INSURANCE AGENCY LTD.—See Harel Insurance Investments & Financial Services Ltd.; *Int'l*, pg. 3274
YEH-CHIANG TECHNOLOGY CORP.; *Int'l*, pg. 8576
YEHOSHUA TBWA—See Omnicom Group Inc.; *U.S. Public*, pg. 1599
YELED V'YALDA EARLY CHILDHOOD CENTER INC.; *U.S. Private*, pg. 4587
YEL ELECTRONICS HONG KONG LIMITED—See Avnet, Inc.; *U.S. Public*, pg. 254
YEL ELECTRONICS PTE LTD—See Avnet, Inc.; *U.S. Public*, pg. 254
YE LIANG HOW CATERING SERVICE PTE. LTD.—See Neo Group Limited; *Int'l*, pg. 5196
YELLIN/MCCARRON, INC.; *U.S. Private*, pg. 4587
YELLO STROM GMBH—See EnBW Energie Baden-Wurttemberg AG; *Int'l*, pg. 2400
YELLO STROM VERWALTUNGSGESELLSCHAFT MBH—See EnBW Energie Baden-Wurttemberg AG; *Int'l*, pg. 2400
YELLOW BALLOON TOUR CO., LTD.; *Int'l*, pg. 8576
YELLOW BIRD—See De Agostini S.p.A.; *Int'l*, pg. 1995
YELLOW BRICK ROAD HOLDINGS LTD.; *Int'l*, pg. 8576
YELLOW CAB COMPANY OF TAMPA, INC.; *U.S. Private*, pg. 4587
YELLOW CABS OF SYDNEY PTY. LTD.—See ComfortDelGro Corporation Limited; *Int'l*, pg. 1712
YELLOW CAKE PLC; *Int'l*, pg. 8576
YELLOW CHIPS BV—See Campbell Soup Company; *U.S. Public*, pg. 427
YELLOW CORPORATION; *U.S. Public*, pg. 2398
YELLOWFIN ASSET MANAGEMENT GMBH—See Commerzbank AG; *Int'l*, pg. 1719
YELLOWHAMMER, LLC; *U.S. Private*, pg. 4587
YELLOW HAT LTD.; *Int'l*, pg. 8576
YELLOWHEAD INVESTMENTS CORPORATION; *Int'l*, pg. 8576
YELLOWHEAD MINING INC.—See Taseko Mines Limited; *Int'l*, pg. 7465
YELLOWHEAD PETROLEUM PRODUCTS LTD; *Int'l*, pg. 8576
YELLOWHOUSE MACHINERY CO.; *U.S. Private*, pg. 4587
YELLOWKNIFE INN—See Clarke Inc.; *Int'l*, pg. 1650
YELLOWKNIFE MOTORS LTD; *Int'l*, pg. 8576
YELLOWKNIFE SUPER 8—See Pacrim International Capital Inc.; *Int'l*, pg. 5693
YELLOW MAPLE II B.V.—See Moody's Corporation; *U.S. Public*, pg. 1469

YELLOW PAGES COMMERCE COMPANY LIMITED—See Advanced Info Service Plc; *Int'l*, pg. 160
YELLOW PAGES DIGITAL & MEDIA SOLUTIONS LIMITED—See Yellow Pages Limited; *Int'l*, pg. 8576
YELLOW PAGES GROUP CO.—See Yellow Pages Limited; *Int'l*, pg. 8576
YELLOW PAGES GROUP, LLC—See Yellow Pages Limited; *Int'l*, pg. 8576
YELLOW PAGES LIMITED; *Int'l*, pg. 8576
YELLOW POINT EQUITY PARTNERS; *Int'l*, pg. 8576
YELLOW PRODUCTIONS USA, INC.—See ITV plc; *Int'l*, pg. 3845
YELLOW RIVER, INC.—See Tungtex (Holdings) Co. Ltd.; *Int'l*, pg. 7972
YELLOWSTONE COMMUNICATIONS; *U.S. Private*, pg. 4587
YELLOWSTONE ENERGY LP; *U.S. Private*, pg. 4588
YELLOWSTONE LANDSCAPE GROUP, INC.—See Harvest Partners L.P.; *U.S. Private*, pg. 1877
YELLOWSTONE NEWSPAPERS—See Yellowstone Communications; *U.S. Private*, pg. 4587
YELLOWSTONE PLASTICS, INC.; *U.S. Private*, pg. 4588
YELLOWSTONE TREE SURGEONS, INC.—See Apax Partners LLP; *Int'l*, pg. 506
YELLOW THUNDER CORPORATION; *U.S. Private*, pg. 4587
YELLOWWOOD ACRES INC; *U.S. Private*, pg. 4588
YELLOW WOOD PARTNERS LLC; *U.S. Private*, pg. 4587
YELO BANK OJSC; *Int'l*, pg. 8576
YELP INC.; *U.S. Public*, pg. 2398
YELSTER DIGITAL GMBH—See Solocal Group; *Int'l*, pg. 7074
YEM CHIO CO., LTD.; *Int'l*, pg. 8576
YEM CHIO DISTRIBUTION CO., LTD—See Yem Chio Co., Ltd.; *Int'l*, pg. 8577
YEMEN COMPANY FOR FLOUR MILLS & SILOS-HODEIDAH—See Hayel Saeed Anam Group of Companies; *Int'l*, pg. 3291
YEMEN COMPANY FOR GHEE AND SOAP INDUSTRY LTD.—See Hayel Saeed Anam Group of Companies; *Int'l*, pg. 3291
YEMEN COMPANY FOR INDUSTRY AND COMMERCIAL LTD.—See Hayel Saeed Anam Group of Companies; *Int'l*, pg. 3291
YEMEN COMPANY FOR PACKAGING MATERIAL INDUSTRY—See Hayel Saeed Anam Group of Companies; *Int'l*, pg. 3291
YEMEN GULF BANK; *Int'l*, pg. 8577
YEMEN HUNT OIL COMPANY, INC.—See Hunt Consolidated, Inc.; *U.S. Private*, pg. 2009
YEMEN LUBRICANTS MANUFACTURING COMPANY LTD.—See Hayel Saeed Anam Group of Companies; *Int'l*, pg. 3291
YEMEN TRAVEL AGENCIES—See Hayel Saeed Anam Group of Companies; *Int'l*, pg. 3291
YENBAI CEMENT & MINERALS JSC; *Int'l*, pg. 8577
YEN BAI JOINT STOCK FOREST AGRICULTURAL PRODUCTS & FOODSTUFF COMPANY; *Int'l*, pg. 8577
YENI GIMAT GAYRIMENKUL YATIRIM ORTAKLIGI A.S.; *Int'l*, pg. 8577
YENI RECORDATILAC VE HAMMADDELERI SANAYI VE TICARET A.S.—See Recordati S.p.A.; *Int'l*, pg. 6240
YENKIN-MAJESTIC PAINT CORPORATION; *U.S. Private*, pg. 4588
YENNI CAPITAL, INC.; *U.S. Private*, pg. 4588
YEN SUN TECHNOLOGY CORP.; *Int'l*, pg. 8577
Y-ENTEC CO., LTD.; *Int'l*, pg. 8543
YENTER COMPANIES INC.; *U.S. Private*, pg. 4588
YENYO TECHNOLOGY CO., LTD.—See Thinking Electronic Industrial Co., Ltd.; *Int'l*, pg. 7709
YEO AIK HEVEA (M) SDN. BHD.—See Jaycorp Berhad; *Int'l*, pg. 3915
YEO AIK WOOD SDN. BHD.—See Jaycorp Berhad; *Int'l*, pg. 3915
YEOCHUN NCC CO., LTD.—See Daelim Industrial Co., Ltd.; *Int'l*, pg. 1908
YEOCHUN NCC CO., LTD.—See Hanwha Group; *Int'l*, pg. 3266
YEO HIAP SENG (GUANGZHOU) FOOD & BEVERAGES LTD—See Far East Organization Pte. Ltd.; *Int'l*, pg. 2617
YEO HIAP SENG LIMITED—See Far East Organization Pte. Ltd.; *Int'l*, pg. 2617
YEO HIAP SENG (MALAYSIA) BERHAD—See Far East Organization Pte. Ltd.; *Int'l*, pg. 2617
YEO HIAP SENG (SARAWAK) SDN BHD—See Far East Organization Pte. Ltd.; *Int'l*, pg. 2617
YEOJU ENERGY SERVICE CO., LTD.—See SK Inc.; *Int'l*, pg. 6973
YE OLDE OAK FOODS LTD—See Struik Holding N.V.; *Int'l*, pg. 7243
YEOMAN POLAND SP. Z O.O.—See Holcim Ltd.; *Int'l*, pg. 3446
YEOMANS CHICAGO CORPORATION—See The Poul Due Jensen Foundation; *Int'l*, pg. 7676
YEOMANS DISTRIBUTING COMPANY; *U.S. Private*, pg. 4588

YEONG CHEN ASIA PACIFIC CO., LTD.—See Yeong Guan Energy Technology Group Co., Ltd.; *Int'l*, pg. 8577
YEONGCHENG ASIA-PACIFIC LIMITED—See Yeong Guan Energy Technology Group Co., Ltd.; *Int'l*, pg. 8577
YEONG GUAN ENERGY TECHNOLOGY GROUP CO., LTD.; *Int'l*, pg. 8577
YEONG HWA METAL CO., LTD. - PLANT 2—See Yeong Hwa Metal Co., Ltd.; *Int'l*, pg. 8577
YEONG HWA METAL CO., LTD.; *Int'l*, pg. 8577
YEONGNAM ENERGY SERVICE CO., LTD.—See SK Innovation Co., Ltd.; *Int'l*, pg. 6973
YEOU YIH STEEL CO., LTD.; *Int'l*, pg. 8578
YEO & YEO COMPUTER CONSULTING, LLC—See Yeo & Yeo, P.C.; *U.S. Private*, pg. 4588
YEO & YEO, P.C.; *U.S. Private*, pg. 4588
YEPREMYAN LAW FIRM INC.; *U.S. Private*, pg. 4588
YEPSTR AB—See Schibsted ASA; *Int'l*, pg. 6618
YERBA BUENA ENGINEERING & CONSTRUCTION; *U.S. Private*, pg. 4588
YERBAE BRANDS CORP.; *U.S. Public*, pg. 2398
YEREVAN BRANDY COMPANY—See Pernod Ricard S.A.; *Int'l*, pg. 5811
YEREVAN FACTORY OF CHAMPAGNE WINES OJSC; *Int'l*, pg. 8578
YEREVAN JEWELLERY FACTORY - 1 GNOMON OJSC; *Int'l*, pg. 8578
YES24 CO., LTD.; *Int'l*, pg. 8578
YESASIA HOLDINGS LTD.; *Int'l*, pg. 8578
YES ASSET MANAGEMENT (INDIA) LIMITED—See Yes Bank Ltd.; *Int'l*, pg. 8578
YES BANK LTD.; *Int'l*, pg. 8578
YESCO ELECTRICAL SUPPLY, INC.; *U.S. Private*, pg. 4588
YESCO HOLDINGS CO., LTD; *Int'l*, pg. 8578
YES& HOLDINGS, LLC; *U.S. Private*, pg. 4588
YESIL GAYRIMENKUL YATIRIM ORTAKLIGI AS; *Int'l*, pg. 8578
YESIL YAPI ENDUSTRISI AS; *Int'l*, pg. 8578
YESIL YATIRIM HOLDING AS; *Int'l*, pg. 8578
YES INC.; *U.S. Private*, pg. 4588
YES LOGISTICS BENELUX B.V.—See Yang Ming Marine Transport Corporation; *Int'l*, pg. 8560
YES LOGISTICS COMPANY, LTD.—See Yang Ming Marine Transport Corporation; *Int'l*, pg. 8560
YES LOGISTICS CORP.—See Yang Ming Marine Transport Corporation; *Int'l*, pg. 8560
YES LOGISTICS EUROPE GMBH—See Yang Ming Marine Transport Corporation; *Int'l*, pg. 8560
YES LOGISTICS (SHANGHAI) CORP.—See Yang Ming Marine Transport Corporation; *Int'l*, pg. 8560
YESMAIL, INC.—See CCMP Capital Advisors, LP; *U.S. Private*, pg. 800
YESMARITIME AS—See Egersund Group AS; *Int'l*, pg. 2324
YES MLC GMBH—See Yang Ming Marine Transport Corporation; *Int'l*, pg. 8560
YES OPTOELECTRONICS CO., LTD.; *Int'l*, pg. 8578
YES SECURITIES (INDIA) LIMITED—See Yes Bank Ltd.; *Int'l*, pg. 8578
YESSTYLE.COM LIMITED—See YesAsia Holdings Ltd.; *Int'l*, pg. 8578
YESTAR BIOTECH (JIANGSU) CO., LTD.—See Yestar Healthcare Holdings Company Limited; *Int'l*, pg. 8578
YESTAR HEALTHCARE HOLDINGS COMPANY LIMITED; *Int'l*, pg. 8578
YEST CO., LTD.; *Int'l*, pg. 8578
YESTECH, INC.—See Nordson Corporation; *U.S. Public*, pg. 1535
YES TRANS, INC.—See Roadrunner Transportation Systems, Inc.; *U.S. Public*, pg. 1802
YESWAY, INC.; *U.S. Private*, pg. 4588
YES YES YES QY—See NoHo Partners Plc; *Int'l*, pg. 5400
YET2.COM, INC.; *U.S. Private*, pg. 4588
YETI COOLERS LLC; *U.S. Private*, pg. 4588
YETI HOLDINGS, INC.; *U.S. Public*, pg. 1535
YETTEL BULGARIA EAD—See PPF Group N.V.; *Int'l*, pg. 5951
YETTEL D.O.O.—See PPF Group N.V.; *Int'l*, pg. 5951
YETTEL MAGYARORSZAG ZRT—See PPF Group N.V.; *Int'l*, pg. 5951
YETTER MANUFACTURING CO., INC.; *U.S. Private*, pg. 4588
YEUN CHYANG INDUSTRIAL CO., LTD - DOULIU MILL—See YC Inox Co., Ltd.; *Int'l*, pg. 8574
YEUN CHYANG INDUSTRIAL CO., LTD. - PUOSHING MILL—See YC Inox Co., Ltd.; *Int'l*, pg. 8574
YEW BIO-PHARM GROUP, INC.; *U.S. Private*, pg. 4589
YEWGLADE PTE LTD—See Tuan Sing Holdings Limited; *Int'l*, pg. 7962
YEW GROVE REIT PLC—See Slate Office REIT; *Int'l*, pg. 6996
YEW HOCK MARINE ENGINEERING PTE. LTD.—See Charisma Energy Services Limited; *Int'l*, pg. 1450
YEW LEAN FOUNDRY & CO. SDN. BHD.—See YLI Holdings Berhad; *Int'l*, pg. 8590
YEW LEE HOLDINGS SDN BERHAD—See MHC Plantations Bhd; *Int'l*, pg. 4872

COMPANY NAME INDEX

YEW LEE SENG METAL PTE LTD—See Union Steel Holdings Limited; *Int'l*, pg. 8054
YEW LI FOUNDRY & CO. SDN. BHD.—See YLI Holdings Berhad; *Int'l*, pg. 8590
YEW SANG HONG LIMITED; *Int'l*, pg. 8578
YEW SANG HONG TRADING (CHINA) LIMITED—See Yew Sang Hong Limited; *Int'l*, pg. 8578
YEW SANG HONG TRADING LIMITED—See Yew Sang Hong Limited; *Int'l*, pg. 8578
YE XING GROUP HOLDINGS LIMITED; *Int'l*, pg. 8575
YEXT GMBH—See Yext, Inc.; *U.S. Public*, pg. 2399
YEXT, INC.; *U.S. Public*, pg. 2398
YFACTOR INC.—See StarDyne Technologies Inc.; *Int'l*, pg. 7176
YFC-BONEAGLE ELECTRIC CO., LTD.; *Int'l*, pg. 8578
YFG BERHAD; *Int'l*, pg. 8579
YF INTERNATIONAL; *U.S. Private*, pg. 4589
YF LEASING CO., LTD.—See Fuyo General Lease Co., Ltd.; *Int'l*, pg. 2859
YFM EQUITY PARTNERS LLP; *Int'l*, pg. 8579
YFM PRIVATE EQUITY LIMITED—See YFM Equity Partners LLP; *Int'l*, pg. 8579
YFY, INC.; *Int'l*, pg. 8579
YG-1 AUSTRALIA PTY. LTD—See YG-1 Co., Ltd; *Int'l*, pg. 8579
YG-1 CANADA INC.—See YG-1 Co., Ltd; *Int'l*, pg. 8579
YG-1 CO., LTD - ANSAN PLANT—See YG-1 Co., Ltd; *Int'l*, pg. 8579
YG-1 CO., LTD. - CHEONGCHEON 2 PLANT—See YG-1 Co., Ltd; *Int'l*, pg. 8579
YG-1 CO., LTD. - CHUNGJU PLANT—See YG-1 Co., Ltd; *Int'l*, pg. 8579
YG-1 CO., LTD - GWANGJU PLANT—See YG-1 Co., Ltd; *Int'l*, pg. 8579
YG-1 CO., LTD - INCHEON PLANT—See YG-1 Co., Ltd; *Int'l*, pg. 8579
YG-1 CO., LTD; *Int'l*, pg. 8579
YG-1 CORPORATION TRADING SRL—See YG-1 Co., Ltd; *Int'l*, pg. 8579
YG-1 DEUTSCHLAND GMBH—See YG-1 Co., Ltd; *Int'l*, pg. 8579
YG-1 EUROPE SAS—See YG-1 Co., Ltd; *Int'l*, pg. 8579
YG-1 (HONG KONG) LIMITED—See YG-1 Co., Ltd; *Int'l*, pg. 8579
YG-1 INDUSTRIES INDIA PVT. LTD—See YG-1 Co., Ltd; *Int'l*, pg. 8579
YG-1 JAPAN—See YG-1 Co., Ltd; *Int'l*, pg. 8580
YG-1 POLAND SP. Z.O.O—See YG-1 Co., Ltd; *Int'l*, pg. 8580
YG-1 RUS LLC—See YG-1 Co., Ltd; *Int'l*, pg. 8580
YG-1 (THAILAND) CO—See YG-1 Co., Ltd; *Int'l*, pg. 8579
YG-1 TOOLS ASIA PTE. LTD—See YG-1 Co., Ltd; *Int'l*, pg. 8580
Y&G CORPORATION BERHAD; *Int'l*, pg. 8543
YG CUTTING TOOL CORP.—See YG-1 Co., Ltd; *Int'l*, pg. 8579
YG ENTERTAINMENT INC.; *Int'l*, pg. 8579
YGGDRAZIL GROUP PUBLIC COMPANY LIMITED; *Int'l*, pg. 8580
YGI, INC.—See 451 Group, LLC; *U.S. Private*, pg. 15
YG INVESTMENT INC.—See YG Plus Inc.; *Int'l*, pg. 8579
YGL CONVERGENCE BERHAD; *Int'l*, pg. 8580
YGM ADVERTISING—See YGM Trading Ltd; *Int'l*, pg. 8580
YG MARKETING PTE. LTD.—See Travelite Holdings Ltd.; *Int'l*, pg. 7907
YGM CLOTHING LIMITED—See YGM Trading Ltd; *Int'l*, pg. 8580
YGM FASHION LIMITED—See YGM Trading Ltd; *Int'l*, pg. 8580
YGM MARKETING LIMITED—See YGM Trading Ltd; *Int'l*, pg. 8580
YGM TRADING LTD; *Int'l*, pg. 8580
YGNIS INDUSTRIE—See Atlantic Societe Francaise Develop Thermique S.A.; *Int'l*, pg. 675
YGOMI LLC; *U.S. Private*, pg. 4589
YG PLUS INC.; *Int'l*, pg. 8579
YGP REAL ESTATE CO., LTD.—See Sapporo Holdings Limited; *Int'l*, pg. 6574
YGSOFT INC.; *Int'l*, pg. 8580
YG TECH CO., LTD.—See Honda Motor Co., Ltd.; *Int'l*, pg. 3464
YH AMERICA, INC—See The Yokohama Rubber Co., Ltd.; *Int'l*, pg. 7703
Y. HATA & CO. LTD.; *U.S. Private*, pg. 4584
Y.H.DIMRI BUILDING & DEVELOPMENT LTD.; *Int'l*, pg. 8543
YH ENTERTAINMENT GROUP; *Int'l*, pg. 8580
YH GROUP LIMITED—See L & A International Holdings Limited; *Int'l*, pg. 4369
YHI ADVANTI MANUFACTURING (SUZHOU) CO., LTD.—See YHI International Limited; *Int'l*, pg. 8581
YHI AUNG (MYANMAR) COMPANY LIMITED—See YHI International Limited; *Int'l*, pg. 8580
YHI CORPORATION (BEIJING) CO., LTD.—See YHI International Limited; *Int'l*, pg. 8580
YHI CORPORATION (B) SDN BHD—See YHI International Limited; *Int'l*, pg. 8580
YHI CORPORATION (GUANGZHOU) CO., LTD.—See YHI International Limited; *Int'l*, pg. 8580
YHI CORPORATION JAPAN CO., LTD.—See YHI International Limited; *Int'l*, pg. 8581
YHI CORPORATION (SHANGHAI) CO., LTD.—See YHI International Limited; *Int'l*, pg. 8580
YHI CORPORATION (SINGAPORE) PTE LTD—See YHI International Limited; *Int'l*, pg. 8580
YHI CORPORATION (THAILAND) CO., LTD.—See YHI International Limited; *Int'l*, pg. 8580
YHI DISTRIBUTION (TAIWAN) CO., LTD.—See YHI International Limited; *Int'l*, pg. 8580
YHI (EAST MALAYSIA) SDN. BHD.—See YHI International Limited; *Int'l*, pg. 8580
YHI (HONG KONG) CO., LIMITED—See YHI International Limited; *Int'l*, pg. 8580
YHI INTERNATIONAL LIMITED; *Int'l*, pg. 8580
YHI INTERNATIONAL (TAIWAN) CO., LTD.—See YHI International Limited; *Int'l*, pg. 8580
YHI (MALAYSIA) SDN. BHD.—See YHI International Limited; *Int'l*, pg. 8580
YHI MANUFACTURING (MALAYSIA) SDN. BHD.—See YHI International Limited; *Int'l*, pg. 8580
YHI MANUFACTURING (SHANGHAI) CO., LTD.—See YHI International Limited; *Int'l*, pg. 8581
YHI MANUFACTURING (SINGAPORE) PTE LTD—See YHI International Limited; *Int'l*, pg. 8581
YHI (PHILIPPINES) INC.—See YHI International Limited; *Int'l*, pg. 8580
YHI POWER (MALAYSIA) SDN. BHD.—See YHI International Limited; *Int'l*, pg. 8581
YHI POWER PTY LIMITED—See YHI International Limited; *Int'l*, pg. 8581
YHI (VIETNAM) CO., LTD.—See YHI International Limited; *Int'l*, pg. 8580
Y.H.O CO., LTD.; *Int'l*, pg. 8543
YHS HONG KONG (2000) PTE LIMITED—See Far East Organization Pte. Ltd.; *Int'l*, pg. 2617
YHS TRADING (USA) INC.—See Far East Organization Pte. Ltd.; *Int'l*, pg. 2617
YHT & COMPANY LIMITED—See PT Asuransi Tugu Pratama Indonesia Tbk; *Int'l*, pg. 6024
YIACO MEDICAL COMPANY K.S.C.C.; *Int'l*, pg. 8581
YIBIN GAOCE NEW ENERGY TECHNOLOGY CO., LTD.—See Qingdao GaoCe Technology Co., Ltd.; *Int'l*, pg. 6143
YIBIN PAPER INDUSTRY CO., LTD.; *Int'l*, pg. 8581
YIBIN TIANYUAN GROUP CO., LTD.; *Int'l*, pg. 8581
YIBITAS YOZGAT ISCI BIRLIGI INSAAT MALZEMELERI TICARET VE SANAYI A.S.; *Int'l*, pg. 8581
YIC ASIA PACIFIC CORPORATION LIMITED—See Yazaki Corporation; *Int'l*, pg. 8572
YICHANG BAOZE AUTOMOBILE SALES SERVICES CO., LTD.—See China ZhengTong Auto Services Holdings Limited; *Int'l*, pg. 1567
YICHANG CHIA TAI CO., LTD.—See Charoen Pokphand Foods Public Company Limited; *Int'l*, pg. 1453
YICHANG HEC CHANGJIANG PHARMACEUTICAL CO., LTD—See Guangdong Hec Technology Holding Co., Ltd.; *Int'l*, pg. 3155
YICHANG SANXIA AIRPORT CO., LTD.—See Hainan Traffic Administration Holding Co., Ltd.; *Int'l*, pg. 3216
YICHANG TINCI MATERIALS TECHNOLOGY CO., LTD.—See Guangzhou Tinci Materials Technology Company Limited; *Int'l*, pg. 3168
YICHENG CDB VILLAGE BANK CO., LTD.—See China Development Bank Corporation; *Int'l*, pg. 1497
YI-CHI CONSTRUCTION CORPORATION—See Formosa Petrochemical Corporation; *Int'l*, pg. 2735
YICHUN BAOZE AUTOMOBILE SALES SERVICES CO., LTD.—See China ZhengTong Auto Services Holdings Limited; *Int'l*, pg. 1567
YICHUN XINGANLING WIND POWER CO., LTD.—See China Guodian Corporation; *Int'l*, pg. 1506
YICK FUNG FUR LTD.; *U.S. Private*, pg. 4589
YICK KWAN TAT ENTERPRISES COMPANY LIMITED—See China Kunda Technology Holdings Limited; *Int'l*, pg. 1514
YIDA CHINA HOLDINGS LIMITED—See China Minsheng Investment Group Corp., Ltd.; *Int'l*, pg. 1524
YIDA NIPPEI MACHINE TOOL CORPORATION—See Komatsu Ltd.; *Int'l*, pg. 4239
YIDU TECH INC.; *Int'l*, pg. 8581
YIEH HSING ENTERPRISE CO., LTD.; *Int'l*, pg. 8581
YIEH PHUI ENTERPRISE CO., LTD. - PINGTUNG WORKS—See Yieh Phui Enterprise Co., Ltd.; *Int'l*, pg. 8581
YIEH PHUI ENTERPRISE CO., LTD.; *Int'l*, pg. 8581
YIEH PHUI ENTERPRISE CO., LTD. - YANCHAO PLANT—See Yieh Phui Enterprise Co., Ltd.; *Int'l*, pg. 8581
YIEH PHUI ENTERPRISE CO., LTD. - YIEH PHUI (CHINA) CHANGSHU WORKS—See Yieh Phui Enterprise Co., Ltd.; *Int'l*, pg. 8581
YIEH UNITED STEEL CORP.; *Int'l*, pg. 8581
YIELD10 BIOSCIENCE, INC.; *U.S. Public*, pg. 2399
YIELD ADVANTAGE INCOME TRUST—See CI Financial Corporation; *Int'l*, pg. 1601

YING HAI GROUP HOLDINGS COMPANY LIMITED

THE YIELD BOOK INC.—See London Stock Exchange Group plc; *Int'l*, pg. 4548
YIELD GO HOLDINGS LTD.; *Int'l*, pg. 8581
YIELDLOVE GMBH—See Stroer SE & Co. KGaA; *Int'l*, pg. 7242
YIELD MICROELECTRONICS CORP.; *Int'l*, pg. 8581
YIELDREPORT PTY LTD—See Finexia Financial Group Ltd.; *Int'l*, pg. 2674
YIELDSTREET, INC.; *U.S. Private*, pg. 4589
YIFAN PHARMACEUTICAL CO., LTD.; *Int'l*, pg. 8582
YIFENG PHARMACY CHAIN CO., LTD.; *Int'l*, pg. 8582
YIHAI INTERNATIONAL HOLDINGS LIMITED; *Int'l*, pg. 8582
YIHAI KERRY ARAWANA HOLDINGS CO., LTD.; *Int'l*, pg. 8582
YIHAI KERRY—See Wilmar International Limited; *Int'l*, pg. 8421
YIHAI (LIANYUNGANG) OLEOCHEMICAL INDUSTRIES CO., LTD—See Wilmar International Limited; *Int'l*, pg. 8421
YIHUA HEALTHCARE CO., LTD.; *Int'l*, pg. 8582
YI HUA HOLDINGS LIMITED; *Int'l*, pg. 8581
YIHUA LIFESTYLE TECHNOLOGY CO., LTD.; *Int'l*, pg. 8582
YIHUA TORAY POLYESTER FILM CO., LTD.—See Toray Industries, Inc.; *Int'l*, pg. 7827
YIJIA GROUP CORP.; *Int'l*, pg. 8583
YIJIAHE TECHNOLOGY CO., LTD.; *Int'l*, pg. 8583
YI JINN INDUSTRIAL CO., LTD.; *Int'l*, pg. 8581
YIK CORPORATION; *Int'l*, pg. 8583
YIKED-DXN STARGATE SDN. BHD.—See DXN Holdings Bhd.; *Int'l*, pg. 2237
YIK WO INTERNATIONAL HOLDINGS LIMITED; *Int'l*, pg. 8583
YI-LAI INDUSTRY BERHAD—See YB Ventures Berhad; *Int'l*, pg. 8573
YI-LAI MARKETING SDN. BHD.—See YB Ventures Berhad; *Int'l*, pg. 8573
YI-LAI TRADING PTE. LTD.—See YB Ventures Berhad; *Int'l*, pg. 8573
YILDIRIM HOLDING INC.; *Int'l*, pg. 8583
YILDIZ GRANINI MEYVE SUYU SANAYI VE TICARET A.S.—See Eckes AG; *Int'l*, pg. 2291
YILDIZ HOLDING AS; *Int'l*, pg. 8583
YI-LIANG INTERNATIONAL TRADE (SHANGHAI) LTD.—See Everlight Electronics Co., Ltd.; *Int'l*, pg. 2567
YILIANG KIBING SILICON INDUSTRY CO., LTD.—See Zhuzhou Kibing Group Co., Ltd.; *Int'l*, pg. 8680
YILI CHUANNIG BIOTECHNOLOGY CO., LTD.; *Int'l*, pg. 8583
YILIDA INDUSTRIES SDN. BHD.—See Zhejiang Yilida Ventilator Co., Ltd.; *Int'l*, pg. 8667
YILI INNOVATION CENTRE EUROPE B.V.—See Inner Mongolia Yili Industrial Group Co., Ltd.; *Int'l*, pg. 3708
YILING PHARMACEUTICAL LTD.—See Shijiazhuang Yiling Pharmaceutical Co., Ltd.; *Int'l*, pg. 6829
YILIN KIBUN CORPORATION.—See Kibun Foods Inc.; *Int'l*, pg. 4157
YILIN PRESS LTD.—See Jiangsu Phoenix Publishing & Media Corporation Ltd.; *Int'l*, pg. 3952
YILU TRAVEL SERVICES GMBH—See Deutsche Lufthansa AG; *Int'l*, pg. 2071
YIMIKANG TECHNOLOGY GROUP CO., LTD.; *Int'l*, pg. 8583
YINBANG CLAD MATERIAL CO., LTD.; *Int'l*, pg. 8583
YINCHENG INTERNATIONAL HOLDING CO., LTD.; *Int'l*, pg. 8583
YINCHENG LIFE SERVICE CO., LTD.; *Int'l*, pg. 8583
YINCHENG REAL ESTATE GROUP CO., LTD.—See Yincheng Life Service Co., Ltd.; *Int'l*, pg. 8584
YINCHUAN BUILDING MATERIALS COMPANY—See Dalian Shide Group Co., Ltd.; *Int'l*, pg. 1952
YINCHUAN XINHUA COMMERCIAL GROUP CO., LTD.; *Int'l*, pg. 8584
YINDA COMMUNICATIONS (PHILIPPINES) INC.—See Shanghai Yinda Technology Industrial Co. Ltd.; *Int'l*, pg. 6782
YINDA TECHNOLOGY MALAYSIA SDN. BHD.—See Shanghai Yinda Technology Industrial Co. Ltd.; *Int'l*, pg. 6782
YINDA TECHNOLOGY (THAILAND) COMPANY LTD.—See Shanghai Yinda Technology Industrial Co. Ltd.; *Int'l*, pg. 6782
YINDU KITCHEN EQUIPMENT CO., LTD.; *Int'l*, pg. 8584
YINFU GOLD CORPORATION; *Int'l*, pg. 8584
YINGCHENG SHINDOO IMPORT & EXPORT TRADING CO., LTD.—See Chengdu Wintrue Holding Co., Ltd.; *Int'l*, pg. 1469
YING CHUANG (WINSUN) BUILDING TECH (SHANGHAI) CO., LTD.—See Zhejiang Yasha Decoration Co., Ltd.; *Int'l*, pg. 8666
YINGDA SECURITY CORPORATION LTD.—See State Grid Corporation of China; *Int'l*, pg. 7183
YINGDE GASES GROUP COMPANY LIMITED—See PAG Capital; *Int'l*, pg. 5697
YINGGAO HOLDINGS PLC; *Int'l*, pg. 8584
YING HAI GROUP HOLDINGS COMPANY LIMITED; *Int'l*, pg. 8584

3045

YING HAN TECHNOLOGY CO., LTD.; *Int'l*, pg. 8584
YING INTERACTIVE MARKETING SERVICES LTD.—See Grand Vision Media Holdings PLC; *Int'l*, pg. 3057
YING KEE TEA HOUSE GROUP LTD.; *Int'l*, pg. 8584
YING KOU ABE HARNESS CO., LTD.—See Air Water Inc.; *Int'l*, pg. 241
YINGKOU AIRPORT CO., LTD.—See Hainan Traffic Administration Holding Co., Ltd.; *Int'l*, pg. 3216
YINGKOU ASTRON MINERAL RESOURCES CO., LTD.—See Astron Corporation Limited; *Int'l*, pg. 662
YINGKOU BAYUQUAN REFRACTORIES CO., LTD.—See Vesuvius plc; *Int'l*, pg. 8180
YINGKOU CHENGUANG FOODS CO LTD—See Chenguang Biotech Group Co., Ltd.; *Int'l*, pg. 1470
YINGKOU EBARA CO., LTD.—See Ebara Corporation; *Int'l*, pg. 2284
YINGKOU FENGGUANG ADVANCED MATERIAL CO., LTD.; *Int'l*, pg. 8584
YINGKOU JINCHEN MACHINERY CO., LTD.; *Int'l*, pg. 8584
YINGKOU KROSAKIHARIMA REFRACTORIES CO., LTD.—See Krosaki Harima Corporation; *Int'l*, pg. 4307
YINGKOU NEW YOTAI REFRACTORIES CO., LTD.—See Yotai Refractories Co., Ltd.; *Int'l*, pg. 8601
YINGKOU PORT LIABILITY CO., LTD.; *Int'l*, pg. 8584
YING LI INTERNATIONAL REAL ESTATE LIMITED; *Int'l*, pg. 8584
YINGLING AIRCRAFT, LLC—See AE Industrial Partners, LP; *U.S. Private*, pg. 112
YINGST HOMES INC.; *U.S. Private*, pg. 4589
YINGTONG TELECOMMUNICATION CO., LTD.; *Int'l*, pg. 8584
YINHANG INTERNET TECHNOLOGIES DEVELOPMENT, INC.; *Int'l*, pg. 8584
YINHUAN TRAFFIC INSTRUMENT CO., LTD.—See Keli Sensing Technology Ningbo Co., Ltd.; *Int'l*, pg. 4119
YINJI ENTERTAINMENT AND MEDIA CO., LTD.; *Int'l*, pg. 8584
YINLIPS TECHNOLOGY, INC.; *Int'l*, pg. 8584
YINSHENG DIGIFAVOR COMPANY LIMITED; *Int'l*, pg. 8584
YIN SHENG HOLDINGS LIMITED; *Int'l*, pg. 8583
YINSON CORPORATION SDN. BHD.—See Liannex Corporation (S) Pte. Ltd.; *Int'l*, pg. 4482
YINSON HAULAGE SDN. BHD.—See Yinson Holdings Berhad; *Int'l*, pg. 8585
YINSON HOLDINGS BERHAD; *Int'l*, pg. 8584
YINSON MARINE SERVICES SDN. BHD.—See Yinson Holdings Berhad; *Int'l*, pg. 8585
YINSON POWER MARINE SDN. BHD.—See Hwa Tai Industries Berhad; *Int'l*, pg. 3541
YINSON PRODUCTION AS—See Yinson Holdings Berhad; *Int'l*, pg. 8585
YINSON PRODUCTION (THE NETHERLANDS) B.V.—See Yinson Holdings Berhad; *Int'l*, pg. 8585
YINTAI GOLD CO., LTD.; *Int'l*, pg. 8585
YINTECH INVESTMENT HOLDINGS LIMITED; *Int'l*, pg. 8585
Y INTERNATIONAL CO., LTD.—See The Riverside Company; *U.S. Private*, pg. 4110
YIN YANG SPA PRODUCTS PTE LTD—See Eu Yan Sang International Ltd.; *Int'l*, pg. 2525
YINYI CO., LTD.; *Int'l*, pg. 8585
YINZCAM, INC.—See National Basketball Association; *U.S. Private*, pg. 2848
YIOULA GLASSWORKS S.A.; *Int'l*, pg. 8585
YIPINHONG PHARMACEUTICAL CO., LTD.; *Int'l*, pg. 8585
YIP IN TSOI & CO., LTD.; *Int'l*, pg. 8585
YIPINTSOI CONSULTING LIMITED—See Yip In Tsoi & Co., Ltd.; *Int'l*, pg. 8585
YIP IN TSOI & JACKS LTD.—See Yip In Tsoi & Co., Ltd.; *Int'l*, pg. 8585
YI PO INTERNATIONAL HOLDINGS LIMITED; *Int'l*, pg. 8581
YIPPY, INC.; *U.S. Public*, pg. 2399
YIP'S CAMEL (HONG KONG) LIMITED—See Yips Chemical Holdings Limited; *Int'l*, pg. 8585
YIPS CHEMICAL HOLDINGS LIMITED; *Int'l*, pg. 8585
YIP'S H.C. (HOLDING) LIMITED—See Yips Chemical Holdings Limited; *Int'l*, pg. 8585
YIP'S INK AND CHEMICALS COMPANY LIMITED—See Yips Chemical Holdings Limited; *Int'l*, pg. 8585
YIP'S LUBRICANT LIMITED—See Yips Chemical Holdings Limited; *Int'l*, pg. 8586
YIRED (PROPRIETARY) LIMITED—See Hosken Consolidated Investments Limited; *Int'l*, pg. 3485
YIREN DIGITAL LTD.; *Int'l*, pg. 8586
YIRONGZHAN FINTECH (SHENZHEN) LIMITED—See Allied Group Limited; *Int'l*, pg. 357
YIT AUSTRIA GMBH—See YIT Corporation; *Int'l*, pg. 8587
YIT CORPORATION; *Int'l*, pg. 8586
YIT EESTI AS—See YIT Corporation; *Int'l*, pg. 8587
YITENG ELECTRONIC SCIENCE & TECHNOLOGY (KUNSHAN) CO., LTD.—See Zhejiang Yonggui Electric Equipment Co., Ltd.; *Int'l*, pg. 8667
YIT INVEST EXPORT OY—See YIT Corporation; *Int'l*, pg. 8587
YIT KALUSTO OY—See YIT Corporation; *Int'l*, pg. 8587

YIT LATVIJA SIA—See YIT Corporation; *Int'l*, pg. 8587
YITOA MICRO TECHNOLOGY CORP; *Int'l*, pg. 8587
YIT POLAND SP. Z O. O.—See YIT Corporation; *Int'l*, pg. 8587
YIT ROMANIA S.R.L.—See YIT Corporation; *Int'l*, pg. 8587
YIT STAVO S.R.O.—See YIT Corporation; *Int'l*, pg. 8587
YIWU HUADING NYLON CO., LTD.; *Int'l*, pg. 8587
YIXIN (DALIAN) LOGISTICS CO., LTD.—See ITOCHU Corporation; *Int'l*, pg. 3837
YI XIN FASHION GROUP CO., LTD.; *Int'l*, pg. 8581
YIXING HALDENWANGER FINE CERAMIC CO. LTD.—See Morgan Advanced Materials plc; *Int'l*, pg. 5044
YIXING MORGAN THERMAL CERAMICS CO. LTD.—See Morgan Advanced Materials plc; *Int'l*, pg. 5044
YIXIN GROUP LTD.; *Int'l*, pg. 8587
YIXING TAIXING ENVIRONTAEC CO. LTD.—See Amiad Water Systems Ltd.; *Int'l*, pg. 427
YIXING XINWEI LEESHING RARE EARTH COMPANY LIMITED—See China Rare Earth Holdings Limited; *Int'l*, pg. 1544
YIXINTANG PHARMACEUTICAL GROUP CO., LTD.; *Int'l*, pg. 8587
YI XI XIN, INC.; *Int'l*, pg. 8581
YIYANG CORUN BATTERY CO., LTD—See Hunan Corun New Energy Co., Ltd.; *Int'l*, pg. 3532
YIYANG DONGXIN AUTO SALES & SERVICES CO., LTD.—See China MeiDong Auto Holdings Limited; *Int'l*, pg. 1519
YIYANG RUBBER & PLASTICS MACHINERY GROUP CO, LTD—See China National Chemical Corporation; *Int'l*, pg. 1530
YIYANG YISHEN RUBBER MACHINERY CO., LTD.—See Kobe Steel, Ltd.; *Int'l*, pg. 4221
YIYANG ZHONGHAI SHIPYARD CO, LTD—See China National Chemical Corporation; *Int'l*, pg. 1530
YIYI MOTORS INC.; *U.S. Private*, pg. 4589
YIZHENG SYP AUTOGLASS CO., LTD.—See Shanghai Yaohua Pilkington Glass Group Co., Ltd.; *Int'l*, pg. 6782
YIZUMI GERMANY COMPANY—See Yizumi Holdings Co., Ltd.; *Int'l*, pg. 8587
YIZUMI HOLDINGS CO., LTD.; *Int'l*, pg. 8587
YIZUMI INDIAN COMPANY—See Yizumi Holdings Co., Ltd.; *Int'l*, pg. 8587
YJK SOLUTIONS CO., LTD.—See Nippon Yusen Kabushiki Kaisha; *Int'l*, pg. 5360
YJL INFRASTRUCTURE LTD.—See Renew Holdings plc; *Int'l*, pg. 6278
YJL LTD.—See Walter Lilly & Co Ltd.; *Int'l*, pg. 8336
Y-JUST CO., LTD.—See Yamada Holdings Co., Ltd.; *Int'l*, pg. 8548
Y.K. ALMOAYYED & SONS B.S.C.—See Nissan Motor Co., Ltd.; *Int'l*, pg. 5369
YK BAKING COMPANY CO., LTD.—See Yamazaki Baking Co., Ltd.; *Int'l*, pg. 8557
YK FOOD SERVICE CO., LTD.—See Dong Won Fisheries Co., Ltd.; *Int'l*, pg. 2164
YKGI HOLDINGS BERHAD - KLANG—See YKGI Holdings Berhad; *Int'l*, pg. 8587
YKGI HOLDINGS BERHAD; *Int'l*, pg. 8587
YKGI LIMITED; *Int'l*, pg. 8587
YKK AP, AMERICA INC.—See YKK Corporation; *Int'l*, pg. 8588
YKK AP FACADE PTE. LTD.—See YKK Corporation; *Int'l*, pg. 8588
YKK AP, INC.—See YKK Corporation; *Int'l*, pg. 8588
YKK ARGENTINA S.A.—See YKK Corporation; *Int'l*, pg. 8588
YKK AUSTRIA GMBH—See YKK Corporation; *Int'l*, pg. 8588
YKK BANGLADESH PTE. LTD.—See YKK Corporation; *Int'l*, pg. 8588
YKK BUSINESS SUPPORT INC.—See YKK Corporation; *Int'l*, pg. 8588
YKK CANADA, INC.—See YKK Corporation; *Int'l*, pg. 8588
YKK CORPORATION OF AMERICA - RUTHERFORD—See YKK Corporation; *Int'l*, pg. 8588
YKK CORPORATION OF AMERICA—See YKK Corporation; *Int'l*, pg. 8588
YKK CORPORATION; *Int'l*, pg. 8587
YKK COSTA RICA LTDA.—See YKK Corporation; *Int'l*, pg. 8588
YKK CZECH SPOL S.R.O.—See YKK Corporation; *Int'l*, pg. 8588
YKK DANMARK A/S—See YKK Corporation; *Int'l*, pg. 8588
YKK DEUTSCHLAND GMBH—See YKK Corporation; *Int'l*, pg. 8588
YKK DO BRAZIL LTDA.—See YKK Corporation; *Int'l*, pg. 8589
YKK EGYPT S.A.E.—See YKK Corporation; *Int'l*, pg. 8588
YKK ESPANA SA—See YKK Corporation; *Int'l*, pg. 8588
YKK EUROPE LIMITED—See YKK Corporation; *Int'l*, pg. 8588
YKK FASTENING PRODUCTS SALES INC.—See YKK Corporation; *Int'l*, pg. 8588
YKK FRANCE SARL—See YKK Corporation; *Int'l*, pg. 8588
YKK FUDOSAN CO., LTD.—See YKK Corporation; *Int'l*, pg. 8588

YKK HELLAS A.E.B.E—See YKK Corporation; *Int'l*, pg. 8589
YKK HOLDING ASIA PTE. LTD.—See YKK Corporation; *Int'l*, pg. 8589
YKK HONDURAS S.A.—See YKK Corporation; *Int'l*, pg. 8588
YKK HONG KONG LTD.—See YKK Corporation; *Int'l*, pg. 8589
YKK HONG KONG LTD. - TUEN MUN FACTORY—See YKK Corporation; *Int'l*, pg. 8589
YKK INDIA PVT. LTD.—See YKK Corporation; *Int'l*, pg. 8589
YKK ITALIA SPA - CARPI PLANT—See YKK Corporation; *Int'l*, pg. 8589
YKK ITALIA SPA—See YKK Corporation; *Int'l*, pg. 8589
YKK ITALIA SPA - VERCELLI PLANT—See YKK Corporation; *Int'l*, pg. 8589
YKK KENYA EPZ LTD.—See YKK Corporation; *Int'l*, pg. 8589
YKK (KOREA) CO., LTD. - PYONGTAEK FACTORY—See YKK Corporation; *Int'l*, pg. 8588
YKK (KOREA) CO., LTD.—See YKK Corporation; *Int'l*, pg. 8588
YKK LANKA (PRIVATE) LTD.—See YKK Corporation; *Int'l*, pg. 8589
YKK MACAU LTD.—See YKK Corporation; *Int'l*, pg. 8589
YKK (MALAYSIA) SDN BHD—See YKK Corporation; *Int'l*, pg. 8588
YKK MAROC S.A.R.L.—See YKK Corporation; *Int'l*, pg. 8589
YKK MEDITERRANEO SPA—See YKK Corporation; *Int'l*, pg. 8589
YKK METAL VE PLASTIK URUNLERI SANAYI VE TICARET A.S.—See YKK Corporation; *Int'l*, pg. 8589
YKK MEXICANA S.A. DE C.V.—See YKK Corporation; *Int'l*, pg. 8589
YKK MIDDLE EAST SAL—See YKK Corporation; *Int'l*, pg. 8589
YKK NEDERLAND BV—See YKK Corporation; *Int'l*, pg. 8589
YKK NORGE FILIAL AV (UK) LTD—See YKK Corporation; *Int'l*, pg. 8589
YKK OCEANIA LTD—See YKK Corporation; *Int'l*, pg. 8589
YKK PHILIPPINES, INC. - BATANGAS PLANT—See YKK Corporation; *Int'l*, pg. 8589
YKK PHILIPPINES INC.—See YKK Corporation; *Int'l*, pg. 8589
YKK POLAND SP. Z.O.O.—See YKK Corporation; *Int'l*, pg. 8589
YKK PORTUGAL LDA.—See YKK Corporation; *Int'l*, pg. 8589
YKK ROKKO CORP.—See YKK Corporation; *Int'l*, pg. 8589
YKK ROMANIA SRL—See YKK Corporation; *Int'l*, pg. 8589
YKK SNAP FASTENERS AMERICA INC.—See YKK Corporation; *Int'l*, pg. 8588
YKK SNAP FASTENERS MEXICO S.A. DE C.V.—See YKK Corporation; *Int'l*, pg. 8588
YKK SNAP FASTERNERS ASIA LTD.—See YKK Corporation; *Int'l*, pg. 8589
YKK SOUTHERN AFRICA (PTY) LTD.—See YKK Corporation; *Int'l*, pg. 8589
YKK STOCKO FASTENERS GMBH—See YKK Corporation; *Int'l*, pg. 8589
YKK TAIWAN CO., LTD. - ARCHITECTURAL PRODUCTS DIVISION—See YKK Corporation; *Int'l*, pg. 8589
YKK TAIWAN CO., LTD.—See YKK Corporation; *Int'l*, pg. 8589
YKK THAILAND CO., LTD.—See YKK Corporation; *Int'l*, pg. 8589
YKK TOURIST CO., LTD.—See YKK Corporation; *Int'l*, pg. 8589
YKK TRADING TUNISIA S.A.—See YKK Corporation; *Int'l*, pg. 8589
YKK (U.K.) LTD.—See YKK Corporation; *Int'l*, pg. 8588
YKK (U.S.A.) INC.—See YKK Corporation; *Int'l*, pg. 8588
YKK VIETNAM CO., LTD.—See YKK Corporation; *Int'l*, pg. 8589
YKK (XIAMEN) TRADING CO. LTD.—See YKK Corporation; *Int'l*, pg. 8589
YKK ZIPPER (SHENZHEN) CO., LTD. - FU YONG FACTORY—See YKK Corporation; *Int'l*, pg. 8589
YKK ZIPPER (SHENZHEN) CO., LTD. - GONG MING FACTORY—See YKK Corporation; *Int'l*, pg. 8589
YKK ZIPPER (SHENZHEN) CO., LTD.—See YKK Corporation; *Int'l*, pg. 8589
YK STEEL CORP.—See Daehan Steel Co., Ltd.; *Int'l*, pg. 1907
YKT CORPORATION; *Int'l*, pg. 8589
YKT EUROPE GMBH—See YKT CORPORATION; *Int'l*, pg. 8590
YKT (SHANGHAI) INTERNATIONAL TRADING CO., LTD.—See YKT CORPORATION; *Int'l*, pg. 8589
YKT (TAIWAN) CORPORATION—See YKT CORPORATION; *Int'l*, pg. 8589
YKT (THAILAND) CO., LTD.—See YKT CORPORATION; *Int'l*, pg. 8590
YKV CORPORATION—See KITZ CORPORATION; *Int'l*, pg. 4197

YLI HOLDINGS BERHAD; *Int'l*, pg. 8590
YLLER BIOMATERIAIS S.A.—See Straumann Holding AG; *Int'l*, pg. 7238
YLS STEEL PTE LTD—See Union Steel Holdings Limited; *Int'l*, pg. 8054
YLZ INFORMATION TECHNOLOGY CO., LTD; *Int'l*, pg. 8590
Y-MABS THERAPEUTICS A/S—See Y-mAbs Therapeutics, Inc.; *U.S. Public*, pg. 2398
Y-MABS THERAPEUTICS, INC.; *U.S. Public*, pg. 2398
YMAGIS DEUTSCHLAND GMBH—See Ymagis S.A.S.; *Int'l*, pg. 8590
YMAGIS ENGINEERING SERVICES SAS—See Ymagis S.A.S.; *Int'l*, pg. 8590
YMAGIS S.A.S.; *Int'l*, pg. 8590
YMAGIS SPAIN SLU—See Ymagis S.A.S.; *Int'l*, pg. 8590
YMARKETING, LLC—See Keystone Capital, Inc.; *U.S. Private*, pg. 2295
YMC AVIATION INC.; *U.S. Private*, pg. 4589
YMC CO., LTD.—See Dream T Entertainment Co., Ltd.; *Int'l*, pg. 2203
YM CO., LTD.; *Int'l*, pg. 8590
YMF ARQUITETURA FINANCEIRA DE NEGOCIOS S.A.—See TOTVS S.A.; *Int'l*, pg. 7846
YMFG ZONE PLANNING CO., LTD.—See Yamaguchi Financial Group Inc.; *Int'l*, pg. 8548
YMF MEDIA LLC; *U.S. Private*, pg. 4589
YMF MEDIA MISSISSIPPI LLC—See YMF Media LLC; *U.S. Private*, pg. 4589
YMF MEDIA NEW YORK LLC—See YMF Media LLC; *U.S. Private*, pg. 4589
YMF MEDIA SOUTH CAROLINA LLC—See YMF Media LLC; *U.S. Private*, pg. 4589
YMH TORRANCE INC.; *U.S. Private*, pg. 4589
YM INTERNATIONAL INC.; *U.S. Private*, pg. 4589
YMIRLINK INC—See Cybozu Inc.; *Int'l*, pg. 1894
YM LEASE CO., LTD.—See Yamaguchi Financial Group Inc.; *Int'l*, pg. 8548
YMOBILE CORP.; *Int'l*, pg. 8590
Y.M.P.-INTERNATIONAL CORPORATION—See Fair Friend Group; *Int'l*, pg. 2605
Y.M.P. (THAILAND) CO., LTD.—See Fair Friend Group; *Int'l*, pg. 2605
YM SECURITIES CO., LTD.—See Yamaguchi Financial Group Inc.; *Int'l*, pg. 8548
YMT CO., LTD., *Int'l*, pg. 8590
YM TECH CO., LTD.; *Int'l*, pg. 8590
YMT INTERNATIONAL MEXICANA S.A. DE C.V.—See Yamato Industry Co., LTD.; *Int'l*, pg. 8555
YMT VACATIONS; *U.S. Private*, pg. 4589
YNB REAL ESTATE LLC—See HomeStreet, Inc.; *U.S. Public*, pg. 1046
YNB—See International Bancshares of Oklahoma, Inc.; *U.S. Private*, pg. 2114
YNCORIS GMBH & CO. KG—See LyondellBasell Industries N.V.; *Int'l*, pg. 4608
YNE PROJECT ENGINEERING PTE. LTD.—See Yongnam Holdings Limited; *Int'l*, pg. 8597
YNFINITI GLOBAL ENERGY SERVICES, S.L.U.; *Int'l*, pg. 8590
YNH CONSTRUCTION SDN BHD—See YNH Property Bhd; *Int'l*, pg. 8590
YNH ENGINEERING SDN. BHD.—See YNH Property Bhd; *Int'l*, pg. 8590
YNH PROPERTY BHD; *Int'l*, pg. 8590
YNVISIBLE INTERACTIVE INC.; *Int'l*, pg. 8590
YNVISIBLE, S.A—See Ynvisible Interactive Inc.; *Int'l*, pg. 8590
YOANTION INDUSTRIAL INC., LTD.; *Int'l*, pg. 8590
YOCABITO CO., LTD.—See Future Corporation; *Int'l*, pg. 2853
YOC AG; *Int'l*, pg. 8591
YOC CENTRAL EASTERN EUROPE GMBH—See Yoc AG; *Int'l*, pg. 8591
YOC GERMANY GMBH—See Yoc AG; *Int'l*, pg. 8591
THE YOC GROUP; *Int'l*, pg. 7702
YOC LTD—See Yoc AG; *Int'l*, pg. 8591
YOCO STAYS PVT. LTD.—See Global Education Limited; *Int'l*, pg. 2995
YOCREAM INTERNATIONAL INC.—See Danone; *Int'l*, pg. 1968
YOC SPAIN, S.L.—See Yoc AG; *Int'l*, pg. 8591
YOC SWITZERLAND AG—See Yoc AG; *Int'l*, pg. 8591
YOCTOIT S.R.L.—See Sesa S.p.A.; *Int'l*, pg. 6729
YODER - FORMTEK METAL FORMING, INC.—See Mestek, Inc.; *U.S. Public*, pg. 1426
YODER & FREY AUCTIONEERS LLC—See Gardrum Holdings Limited; *Int'l*, pg. 2884
YODER INDUSTRIES INC.; *U.S. Private*, pg. 4589
YODER OIL COMPANY INC.; *U.S. Private*, pg. 4589
YODER & SONS INC.; *U.S. Private*, pg. 4589
YODLEE CANADA, INC.—See Bain Capital, LP; *U.S. Private*, pg. 439
YODLEE GROUP AUSTRALIA PTY LTD—See Bain Capital, LP; *U.S. Private*, pg. 439
YODLEE, INC.—See Bain Capital, LP; *U.S. Private*, pg. 439
YODLEE INFOTECH PRIVATE LIMITED—See Bain Capital, LP; *U.S. Private*, pg. 439

YODLE WEB.COM, INC.—See Siris Capital Group, LLC; *U.S. Private*, pg. 3675
YODOGAWA STEEL WORKS, LTD.; *Int'l*, pg. 8591
YODOGAWA TRANSFORMER CO., LTD.—See ORIX Corporation; *Int'l*, pg. 5636
YODOSHI CORPORATION—See Kyoei Steel Ltd.; *Int'l*, pg. 4362
YO ELEVEN GAMING, INC.; *Int'l*, pg. 8590
THE YOFARM COMPANY, INC.—See Danone; *Int'l*, pg. 1968
YOGA JOURNAL—See Active Interest Media, Inc.; *U.S. Private*, pg. 69
YOGA WORKS, INC.; *U.S. Private*, pg. 4589
YOGEN FRUZ CANADA, INC.—See ABR Holdings, Ltd.; *Int'l*, pg. 8591
YOGEN FRUZ; *Int'l*, pg. 8591
YOGEN FRUZ USA INC.—See Yogen Fruz; *Int'l*, pg. 8591
YOGI INFRA PROJECTS LIMITED; *Int'l*, pg. 8591
YOGI LTD.; *Int'l*, pg. 8591
Y-OGURA AUTOMOTIVE (THAILAND) CO., LTD.—See Yorozu Corporation; *Int'l*, pg. 8599
YOGURTLAND FRANCHISING, INC.; *U.S. Private*, pg. 4589
YOHAY BAKING COMPANY, INC.; *U.S. Private*, pg. 4589
YOHJI YAMAMOTO INC.; *Int'l*, pg. 8591
YOHKOH BUSSAN CO., LTD.—See Nippon Steel Corporation; *Int'l*, pg. 5340
YOHO GROUP HOLDINGS LIMITED; *Int'l*, pg. 8591
YOHO RESOURCES INC.—See One Stone Energy Partners, L.P.; *U.S. Private*, pg. 3023
YOH SERVICES, LLC—See The Day & Zimmermann Group, Inc.; *U.S. Private*, pg. 4019
YOJEE LIMITED; *Int'l*, pg. 8591
YOJEE PTE LTD—See Yojee Limited; *Int'l*, pg. 8591
YOKE FOOD INDUSTRIES SDN. BHD.—See Thai Beverage Public Company Limited; *Int'l*, pg. 7590
YOKE'S WASHINGTON FOODS INC.; *U.S. Private*, pg. 4589
YOKKAICHI CHEMICAL CO., LTD. - ROKUROMI FACILITY.—See DKS Co. Ltd.; *Int'l*, pg. 2140
YOKKAICHI CHEMICAL CO., LTD.—See DKS Co. Ltd.; *Int'l*, pg. 2140
YOKKAICHI KASUMI POWER CO., LTD.—See Cosmo Energy Holdings Co., Ltd.; *Int'l*, pg. 1812
YOKOBI CO., LTD.—See ITOCHU Corporation; *Int'l*, pg. 3836
YOKO CORPORATION—See Uchida Yoko Co., Ltd.; *Int'l*, pg. 8013
YOKOGAWA AFRICA HOLDING B.V.—See Yokogawa Electric Corporation; *Int'l*, pg. 8592
YOKOGAWA AFRICAN ANGLOPHONE REGION (PTY) LTD.—See Yokogawa Electric Corporation; *Int'l*, pg. 8592
YOKOGAWA AMERICA DO SUL LTDA.—See Yokogawa Electric Corporation; *Int'l*, pg. 8592
YOKOGAWA ANALYTICAL SOLUTIONS SDN. BHD.—See Yokogawa Electric Corporation; *Int'l*, pg. 8592
YOKOGAWA ANALYTICAL SYSTEMS, INC.—See Agilent Technologies, Inc.; *U.S. Public*, pg. 62
YOKOGAWA ARGENTINA—See Yokogawa Electric Corporation; *Int'l*, pg. 8593
YOKOGAWA AUSTRALIA PTY. LTD.—See Yokogawa Electric Corporation; *Int'l*, pg. 8593
YOKOGAWA BELGIUM N.V./S.A.—See Yokogawa Electric Corporation; *Int'l*, pg. 8593
YOKOGAWA BIO FRONTIER INC.—See Yokogawa Electric Corporation; *Int'l*, pg. 8593
YOKOGAWA BRIDGE CORP.—See Yokogawa Bridge Holdings Corp.; *Int'l*, pg. 8591
YOKOGAWA BRIDGE HOLDINGS CORP.; *Int'l*, pg. 8591
YOKOGAWA CANADA, INC.—See Yokogawa Electric Corporation; *Int'l*, pg. 8593
YOKOGAWA CHILE—See Yokogawa Electric Corporation; *Int'l*, pg. 8593
YOKOGAWA CHINA CO., LTD.—See Yokogawa Electric Corporation; *Int'l*, pg. 8593
YOKOGAWA COLOMBIA—See Yokogawa Electric Corporation; *Int'l*, pg. 8593
YOKOGAWA & CO., LTD.—See Yokogawa Electric Corporation; *Int'l*, pg. 8592
YOKOGAWA CORPORATION OF AMERICA—See Yokogawa Electric Corporation; *Int'l*, pg. 8593
YOKOGAWA CORPORATION OF AMERICA—See Yokogawa Electric Corporation; *Int'l*, pg. 8593
YOKOGAWA DE MEXICO, S.A. DE C.V.—See Yokogawa Electric Corporation; *Int'l*, pg. 8595
YOKOGAWA DENSHIKIKI CO., LTD.—See Yokogawa Electric Corporation; *Int'l*, pg. 8593
YOKOGAWA DEUTSCHLAND GMBH—See Yokogawa Electric Corporation; *Int'l*, pg. 8593
YOKOGAWA DIGITAL COMPUTER CORPORATION—See DTS Corporation; *Int'l*, pg. 2217
YOKOGAWA ELECTRIC ASIA PTE. LTD.—See Yokogawa Electric Corporation; *Int'l*, pg. 8593
YOKOGAWA ELECTRIC CHINA CO., LTD.—See Yokogawa Electric Corporation; *Int'l*, pg. 8593
YOKOGAWA ELECTRIC CIS LTD.—See Yokogawa Electric Corporation; *Int'l*, pg. 8593
YOKOGAWA ELECTRIC CORPORATION; *Int'l*, pg. 8592

YOKOGAWA ELECTRIC INTERNATIONAL PTE. LTD.—See Yokogawa Electric Corporation; *Int'l*, pg. 8593
YOKOGAWA ELECTRIC KAZAKHSTAN LTD.—See Yokogawa Electric Corporation; *Int'l*, pg. 8593
YOKOGAWA ELECTRIC KOREA CO., LTD.—See Yokogawa Electric Corporation; *Int'l*, pg. 8593
YOKOGAWA ELECTRIC (MALAYSIA) SDN. BHD.—See Yokogawa Electric Corporation; *Int'l*, pg. 8593
YOKOGAWA ELECTRIC SAKHALIN LTD.—See Yokogawa Electric Corporation; *Int'l*, pg. 8593
YOKOGAWA ELECTRIC UKRAINE LTD.—See Yokogawa Electric Corporation; *Int'l*, pg. 8593
YOKOGAWA ELECTRONICS MANUFACTURING KOREA CO., LTD.—See Yokogawa Electric Corporation; *Int'l*, pg. 8593
YOKOGAWA ENGINEERING ASIA PTE. LTD.—See Yokogawa Electric Corporation; *Int'l*, pg. 8593
YOKOGAWA ENGINEERING BAHRAIN W.L.L—See Yokogawa Electric Corporation; *Int'l*, pg. 8593
YOKOGAWA ENGINEERING MIDDLE EAST & AFRICA FZE—See Yokogawa Electric Corporation; *Int'l*, pg. 8593
YOKOGAWA ENGINEERING MIDDLE EAST FZE—See Yokogawa Electric Corporation; *Int'l*, pg. 8593
YOKOGAWA EUROPE BRANCHES B.V.—See Yokogawa Electric Corporation; *Int'l*, pg. 8593
YOKOGAWA EUROPE B.V.—See Yokogawa Electric Corporation; *Int'l*, pg. 8593
YOKOGAWA EUROPE SOLUTIONS B.V.—See Yokogawa Electric Corporation; *Int'l*, pg. 8593
YOKOGAWA FIELD ENGINEERING SERVICE CORPORATION—See Yokogawa Electric Corporation; *Int'l*, pg. 8593
YOKOGAWA FLUENCE ANALYTICS, INC.—See Yokogawa Electric Corporation; *Int'l*, pg. 8593
YOKOGAWA FLUID IMAGING TECHNOLOGIES INC.—See Yokogawa Electric Corporation; *Int'l*, pg. 8593
YOKOGAWA FOUNDRY CORPORATION—See Yokogawa Electric Corporation; *Int'l*, pg. 8593
YOKOGAWA FRANCE S.A.S.—See Yokogawa Electric Corporation; *Int'l*, pg. 8593
YOKOGAWA GESMBH—See Yokogawa Electric Corporation; *Int'l*, pg. 8593
YOKOGAWA HUNGARIA KFT.—See Yokogawa Electric Corporation; *Int'l*, pg. 8593
YOKOGAWA IA TECHNOLOGIES INDIA PRIVATE LIMITED—See Yokogawa Electric Corporation; *Int'l*, pg. 8593
YOKOGAWA IBERIA S.A.—See Yokogawa Electric Corporation; *Int'l*, pg. 8593
YOKOGAWA INDIA LTD.—See Yokogawa Electric Corporation; *Int'l*, pg. 8594
YOKOGAWA INDUSTRIAL SAFETY SYSTEMS SDN. BHD.—See Yokogawa Electric Corporation; *Int'l*, pg. 8594
YOKOGAWA INFORMATION SYSTEMS (DALIAN) CORPORATION—See Yokogawa Electric Corporation; *Int'l*, pg. 8594
YOKOGAWA INNOVATION SWITZERLAND GMBH—See Yokogawa Electric Corporation; *Int'l*, pg. 8594
YOKOGAWA IRELAND—See Yokogawa Electric Corporation; *Int'l*, pg. 8594
YOKOGAWA ITALIA S.R.L.—See Yokogawa Electric Corporation; *Int'l*, pg. 8594
YOKOGAWA KONTROL (MALAYSIA) SDN. BHD.—See Yokogawa Electric Corporation; *Int'l*, pg. 8594
YOKOGAWA MANUFACTURING CORPORATION—See Yokogawa Electric Corporation; *Int'l*, pg. 8594
YOKOGAWA MAREX LIMITED—See Yokogawa Electric Corporation; *Int'l*, pg. 8594
YOKOGAWA MEASUREMENT TECHNOLOGIES AB—See Yokogawa Electric Corporation; *Int'l*, pg. 8594
YOKOGAWA MEASUREMENT TECHNOLOGIES LTD.—See Yokogawa Electric Corporation; *Int'l*, pg. 8594
YOKOGAWA MEASURING INSTRUMENTS KOREA CORP.—See Yokogawa Electric Corporation; *Int'l*, pg. 8594
YOKOGAWA MEDICAL SOLUTIONS CORPORATION—See FUJIFILM Holdings Corporation; *Int'l*, pg. 2823
YOKOGAWA METERS & INSTRUMENTS CORPORATION—See Yokogawa Electric Corporation; *Int'l*, pg. 8594
YOKOGAWA MIDDLE EAST B.S.C.(C)—See Yokogawa Electric Corporation; *Int'l*, pg. 8594
YOKOGAWA NEW LIFE CORP.—See Yokogawa Bridge Holdings Corp.; *Int'l*, pg. 8591
YOKOGAWA NEW ZEALAND LTD.—See Yokogawa Electric Corporation; *Int'l*, pg. 8594
YOKOGAWA NORGE AS—See Yokogawa Electric Corporation; *Int'l*, pg. 8594
YOKOGAWA NORWAY—See Yokogawa Electric Corporation; *Int'l*, pg. 8594
YOKOGAWA NS ENGINEERING CORP.—See Yokogawa Bridge Holdings Corp.; *Int'l*, pg. 8591

YOKOGAWA ELECTRIC CORPORATION   CORPORATE AFFILIATIONS

YOKOGAWA NUCLEAR SOLUTIONS, LLC—See Yokogawa Electric Corporation; *Int'l*, pg. 8594
YOKOGAWA ODDZIA W POLSCE—See Yokogawa Electric Corporation; *Int'l*, pg. 8594
YOKOGAWA OMAN LIMITED L.L.C.—See Yokogawa Electric Corporation; *Int'l*, pg. 8594
YOKOGAWA PERU—See Yokogawa Electric Corporation; *Int'l*, pg. 8594
YOKOGAWA PHILIPPINES INC.—See Yokogawa Electric Corporation; *Int'l*, pg. 8594
YOKOGAWA PIONICS CO., LTD.—See Yokogawa Electric Corporation; *Int'l*, pg. 8594
YOKOGAWA POLSKA SP. Z O.O.—See Yokogawa Electric Corporation; *Int'l*, pg. 8594
YOKOGAWA PROCESS ANALYZERS EUROPE B.V.—See Yokogawa Electric Corporation; *Int'l*, pg. 8594
YOKOGAWA PROCESS CONTROL (SHANGHAI) CO., LTD.—See Yokogawa Electric Corporation; *Int'l*, pg. 8594
YOKOGAWA QATAR QFZ LLC—See Yokogawa Electric Corporation; *Int'l*, pg. 8594
YOKOGAWA RAP LIMITED—See Yokogawa Electric Corporation; *Int'l*, pg. 8594
YOKOGAWA RENTAL & LEASE CORPORATION—See Yokogawa Electric Corporation; *Int'l*, pg. 8594
YOKOGAWA SAUDI ARABIA COMPANY LLC—See Yokogawa Electric Corporation; *Int'l*, pg. 8594
YOKOGAWA SAUDI ARABIA LTD.—See Yokogawa Electric Corporation; *Int'l*, pg. 8594
YOKOGAWA SERVICE LTDA.—See Yokogawa Electric Corporation; *Int'l*, pg. 8594
YOKOGAWA SERVICES SAUDI ARABIA LTD.—See Yokogawa Electric Corporation; *Int'l*, pg. 8594
YOKOGAWA SHANGHAI INSTRUMENTATION CO., LTD.—See Yokogawa Electric Corporation; *Int'l*, pg. 8594
YOKOGAWA SHANGHAI TRADING CO., LTD.—See Yokogawa Electric Corporation; *Int'l*, pg. 8594
YOKOGAWA SICHUAN INSTRUMENT CO., LTD.—See Yokogawa Electric Corporation; *Int'l*, pg. 8594
YOKOGAWA SLOVAKIA S.R.O.—See Yokogawa Electric Corporation; *Int'l*, pg. 8594
YOKOGAWA SOFTWARE ENGINEERING (WUXI) CO., LTD.—See Yokogawa Electric Corporation; *Int'l*, pg. 8594
YOKOGAWA SOLUTIONS CORPORATION—See Yokogawa Electric Corporation; *Int'l*, pg. 8594
YOKOGAWA SOLUTION SERVICE CORPORATION—See Yokogawa Electric Corporation; *Int'l*, pg. 8594
YOKOGAWA SOUTH AFRICA (PTY) LTD.—See Yokogawa Electric Corporation; *Int'l*, pg. 8595
YOKOGAWA SUMIKIN BRIDGE CORP.—See Yokogawa Bridge Holdings Corp.; *Int'l*, pg. 8591
YOKOGAWA SWITZERLAND S.A.—See Yokogawa Electric Corporation; *Int'l*, pg. 8595
YOKOGAWA SYSTEM BUILDINGS CORP.—See Yokogawa Bridge Holdings Corp.; *Int'l*, pg. 8591
YOKOGAWA SYSTEM INTEGRATION & PROCUREMENT (WUXI) CO., LTD.—See Yokogawa Electric Corporation; *Int'l*, pg. 8595
YOKOGAWA TAIWAN CORPORATION—See Yokogawa Electric Corporation; *Int'l*, pg. 8595
YOKOGAWA TECHINVENT AS—See Yokogawa Electric Corporation; *Int'l*, pg. 8595
YOKOGAWA TECHNO-INFORMATION SERVICE INC.—See Yokogawa Bridge Holdings Corp.; *Int'l*, pg. 8592
YOKOGAWA TECHNOLOGIES SOLUTIONS INDIA PRIVATE LIMITED—See Yokogawa Electric Corporation; *Int'l*, pg. 8595
YOKOGAWA TECHNO PHILIPPINES INC.—See Yokogawa Bridge Holdings Corp.; *Int'l*, pg. 8592
YOKOGAWA TEST & MEASUREMENT CORPORATION—See Yokogawa Electric Corporation; *Int'l*, pg. 8595
YOKOGAWA TEST & MEASUREMENT (SHANGHAI) CO., LTD.—See Yokogawa Electric Corporation; *Int'l*, pg. 8595
YOKOGAWA TEST SOLUTIONS CORPORATION—See Yokogawa Electric Corporation; *Int'l*, pg. 8595
YOKOGAWA (THAILAND) LTD—See Yokogawa Electric Corporation; *Int'l*, pg. 8592
YOKOGAWA TURKEY INDUSTRIAL AUTOMATION SOLUTIONS A.S.—See Yokogawa Electric Corporation; *Int'l*, pg. 8595
YOKOGAWA UAE INDUSTRY-S.P. LLC—See Yokogawa Electric Corporation; *Int'l*, pg. 8595
YOKOGAWA UNITED KINGDOM LTD.—See Yokogawa Electric Corporation; *Int'l*, pg. 8595
YOKOGAWA USA, INC.—See Yokogawa Electric Corporation; *Int'l*, pg. 8595
YOKOGAWA VIETNAM COMPANY LTD.—See Yokogawa Electric Corporation; *Int'l*, pg. 8595
YOKOHAMA AEROSPACE AMERICA, INC.—See The Yokohama Rubber Co., Ltd.; *Int'l*, pg. 7703
YOKOHAMA AKARENGA INC.—See Mitsubishi Corporation; *Int'l*, pg. 4943
YOKOHAMA ARENA CO., LTD.—See Seibu Holdings Inc.; *Int'l*, pg. 6685

YOKOHAMA ASIA CO., LTD.—See The Yokohama Rubber Co., Ltd.; *Int'l*, pg. 7703
YOKOHAMA AUSTRIA GMBH—See The Yokohama Rubber Co., Ltd.; *Int'l*, pg. 7703
THE YOKOHAMA BAYSTARS BASEBALL CLUB, INC.—See DeNa Co., Ltd.; *Int'l*, pg. 2026
YOKOHAMA CAPITAL CO., LTD.—See Concordia Financial Group, Ltd.; *Int'l*, pg. 1765
YOKOHAMA CEE SPOLKA Z.O.O.—See The Yokohama Rubber Co., Ltd.; *Int'l*, pg. 7703
THE YOKOHAMA CHAMBER OF COMMERCE & INDUSTRY—See Azuma Shipping Co., Ltd.; *Int'l*, pg. 782
YOKOHAMA CORPORATION OF AMERICA—See The Yokohama Rubber Co., Ltd.; *Int'l*, pg. 7703
YOKOHAMA CORPORATION OF NORTH AMERICA—See The Yokohama Rubber Co., Ltd.; *Int'l*, pg. 7703
YOKOHAMA CREATIVE CENTER—See BANDAI NAMCO Holdings Inc.; *Int'l*, pg. 829
YOKOHAMA DANMARK A/S—See The Yokohama Rubber Co., Ltd.; *Int'l*, pg. 7703
YOKOHAMA DIA BUILDING MANAGEMENT CORPORATION—See Mitsubishi Logistics Corporation; *Int'l*, pg. 4963
YOKOHAMA DISTRICT HEATING & COOLING CO., LTD.—See Sotetsu Holdings, Inc.; *Int'l*, pg. 7113
YOKOHAMA DRUM MANUFACTURING CO., LTD.—See The Furukawa Electric Co., Ltd.; *Int'l*, pg. 7647
YOKOHAMA EUROPE GMBH—See The Yokohama Rubber Co., Ltd.; *Int'l*, pg. 7703
YOKOHAMAGOMU FINANCE CO., LTD.—See The Yokohama Rubber Co., Ltd.; *Int'l*, pg. 7704
YOKOHAMA GRAND INTERCONTINENTAL HOTEL CO. LTD.—See InterContinental Hotels Group PLC; *Int'l*, pg. 3739
YOKOHAMA GYORUI CO., LTD.; *Int'l*, pg. 8595
YOKOHAMA HAKKEIJIMA INC.—See Seibu Holdings Inc.; *Int'l*, pg. 6685
YOKOHAMA HAMATITE (HANGZHOU) CO., LTD—See The Yokohama Rubber Co., Ltd.; *Int'l*, pg. 7704
YOKOHAMA HINO MOTOR LTD.—See Toyota Motor Corporation; *Int'l*, pg. 7872
YOKOHAMA HOSES & COUPLING (HANGZHOU) CO., LTD.—See The Yokohama Rubber Co., Ltd.; *Int'l*, pg. 7704
YOKOHAMA HPT LTD.—See The Yokohama Rubber Co., Ltd.; *Int'l*, pg. 7703
YOKOHAMA IBERIA, S.A.—See The Yokohama Rubber Co., Ltd.; *Int'l*, pg. 7704
YOKOHAMA INDIA PVT. LTD.—See The Yokohama Rubber Co., Ltd.; *Int'l*, pg. 7704
YOKOHAMA INDUSTRIAL PRODUCTS ASIA-PACIFIC PTE. LTD.—See The Yokohama Rubber Co., Ltd.; *Int'l*, pg. 7704
YOKOHAMA INDUSTRIAL PRODUCTS EUROPE GMBH—See The Yokohama Rubber Co., Ltd.; *Int'l*, pg. 7703
YOKOHAMA INDUSTRIAL PRODUCTS-HANGZHOU CO., LTD.—See The Yokohama Rubber Co., Ltd.; *Int'l*, pg. 7704
YOKOHAMA INDUSTRIAL PRODUCTS ITALY S.R.L.—See The Yokohama Rubber Co., Ltd.; *Int'l*, pg. 7704
YOKOHAMA INDUSTRIAL PRODUCTS SALES - SHANGHAI CO., LTD.—See The Yokohama Rubber Co., Ltd.; *Int'l*, pg. 7704
YOKOHAMA INDUSTRIES AMERICAS INC.—See The Yokohama Rubber Co., Ltd.; *Int'l*, pg. 7703
YOKOHAMA INDUSTRIES AMERICAS OHIO INC.—See The Yokohama Rubber Co., Ltd.; *Int'l*, pg. 7704
YOKOHAMA INDUSTRIES BERHAD; *Int'l*, pg. 8595
YOKOHAMA ITALIA S.P.A.—See The Yokohama Rubber Co., Ltd.; *Int'l*, pg. 7704
YOKOHAMA KAIRYODO CENTER CO., LTD.—See Taiheiyo Cement Corporation; *Int'l*, pg. 7412
YOKOHAMA KEIKYU BUS CO., LTD.—See Keikyu Corporation; *Int'l*, pg. 4117
YOKOHAMA KEIWA BUILDING CO., LTD.—See Sapporo Holdings Limited; *Int'l*, pg. 6574
YOKOHAMA KIKO CO., LTD.—See NHK Spring Co., Ltd.; *Int'l*, pg. 5258
YOKOHAMA KYORITSU WAREHOUSE CO., LTD.—See Nippon Yusen Kabushiki Kaisha; *Int'l*, pg. 5360
YOKOHAMA LIQUIFIED GAS TERMINAL CO., LTD.—See Azuma Shipping Co., Ltd.; *Int'l*, pg. 782
YOKOHAMA MARINOS LTD.—See Nissan Motor Co., Ltd.; *Int'l*, pg. 5369
YOKOHAMA MARUUO CO., LTD.; *Int'l*, pg. 8595
YOKOHAMA MIRAI-KENKYUSHO—See BANDAI NAMCO Holdings Inc.; *Int'l*, pg. 829
YOKOHAMA MOLD CO., LTD.—See The Yokohama Rubber Co., Ltd.; *Int'l*, pg. 7704
YOKOHAMA OFF-HIGHWAY TIRES AMERICA, INC.—See The Yokohama Rubber Co., Ltd.; *Int'l*, pg. 7703
YOKOHAMA REIFEN GMBH—See The Yokohama Rubber Co., Ltd.; *Int'l*, pg. 7703
YOKOHAMA ROYAL PARK HOTEL CO., LTD.—See Mitsubishi Estate Co., Ltd.; *Int'l*, pg. 4947

YOKOHAMA RUBBER (CHINA) CO., LTD.—See The Yokohama Rubber Co., Ltd.; *Int'l*, pg. 7704
THE YOKOHAMA RUBBER CO., LTD. - HAMATITE PLANT—See The Yokohama Rubber Co., Ltd.; *Int'l*, pg. 7702
THE YOKOHAMA RUBBER CO., LTD. - HIRATSUKA-EAST PLANT—See The Yokohama Rubber Co., Ltd.; *Int'l*, pg. 7702
THE YOKOHAMA RUBBER CO., LTD. - IBARAKI PLANT—See The Yokohama Rubber Co., Ltd.; *Int'l*, pg. 7702
THE YOKOHAMA RUBBER CO., LTD. - MIE PLANT—See The Yokohama Rubber Co., Ltd.; *Int'l*, pg. 7702
THE YOKOHAMA RUBBER CO., LTD. - MISHIMA PLANT—See The Yokohama Rubber Co., Ltd.; *Int'l*, pg. 7702
THE YOKOHAMA RUBBER CO., LTD. - NAGANO PLANT—See The Yokohama Rubber Co., Ltd.; *Int'l*, pg. 7702
THE YOKOHAMA RUBBER CO., LTD. - ONOMICHI PLANT—See The Yokohama Rubber Co., Ltd.; *Int'l*, pg. 7702
THE YOKOHAMA RUBBER CO., LTD. - PANAMA—See The Yokohama Rubber Co., Ltd.; *Int'l*, pg. 7703
THE YOKOHAMA RUBBER CO., LTD. - SHINSHIRO-MINAMI PLANT—See The Yokohama Rubber Co., Ltd.; *Int'l*, pg. 7702
THE YOKOHAMA RUBBER CO., LTD. - SHINSHIRO PLANT—See The Yokohama Rubber Co., Ltd.; *Int'l*, pg. 7702
THE YOKOHAMA RUBBER CO., LTD.; *Int'l*, pg. 7702
YOKOHAMA RUBBER LATIN AMERICA INDUSTRIA E COMERCIO LTDA.—See The Yokohama Rubber Co., Ltd.; *Int'l*, pg. 7704
YOKOHAMA RUBBER (THAILAND) CO., LTD.—See The Yokohama Rubber Co., Ltd.; *Int'l*, pg. 7704
YOKOHAMA RUSSIA L.L.C.—See The Yokohama Rubber Co., Ltd.; *Int'l*, pg. 7704
YOKOHAMA SCANDINAVIA AB—See The Yokohama Rubber Co., Ltd.; *Int'l*, pg. 7704
YOKOHAMA SKY BUILDING CO., LTD.—See Mitsubishi Estate Co., Ltd.; *Int'l*, pg. 4947
YOKOHAMA (SUISSE) S.A.—See The Yokohama Rubber Co., Ltd.; *Int'l*, pg. 7703
YOKOHAMA SUPER FACTORY CO., LTD.—See Dentsu Group Inc.; *Int'l*, pg. 2040
YOKOHAMA TEXTILE CLUB CO., LTD.—See Sankyo Seiko Co., Ltd.; *Int'l*, pg. 6543
YOKOHAMA TIRE (CANADA), INC.—See The Yokohama Rubber Co., Ltd.; *Int'l*, pg. 7703
YOKOHAMA TIRE CORPORATION—See The Yokohama Rubber Co., Ltd.; *Int'l*, pg. 7703
YOKOHAMA TIRE JAPAN CO., LTD.—See The Yokohama Rubber Co., Ltd.; *Int'l*, pg. 7704
YOKOHAMA TIRE KOREA CO., LTD.—See The Yokohama Rubber Co., Ltd.; *Int'l*, pg. 7704
YOKOHAMA TIRE MANUFACTURING MISSISSIPPI, LLC—See The Yokohama Rubber Co., Ltd.; *Int'l*, pg. 7703
YOKOHAMA TIRE MANUFACTURING (THAILAND) CO., LTD.—See The Yokohama Rubber Co., Ltd.; *Int'l*, pg. 7704
YOKOHAMA TIRE MANUFACTURING VIRGINIA, LLC—See The Yokohama Rubber Co., Ltd.; *Int'l*, pg. 7703
YOKOHAMA TIRE PHILIPPINES, INC.—See The Yokohama Rubber Co., Ltd.; *Int'l*, pg. 7704
YOKOHAMA TIRE SALES PHILIPPINES, INC.—See The Yokohama Rubber Co., Ltd.; *Int'l*, pg. 7704
YOKOHAMA TIRE SALES (SHANGHAI) CO., LTD.—See The Yokohama Rubber Co., Ltd.; *Int'l*, pg. 7704
YOKOHAMA TIRE SALES (THAILAND) CO., LTD.—See The Yokohama Rubber Co., Ltd.; *Int'l*, pg. 7704
YOKOHAMA TIRE TAIWAN CO., LTD.—See The Yokohama Rubber Co., Ltd.; *Int'l*, pg. 7704
YOKOHAMA TRADING CORP. LTD.—See Nissui Corporation; *Int'l*, pg. 5379
YOKOHAMA TWS AUSTRALIA PTY. LTD.—See The Yokohama Rubber Co., Ltd.; *Int'l*, pg. 7704
YOKOHAMA TWS AUSTRIA GMBH—See The Yokohama Rubber Co., Ltd.; *Int'l*, pg. 7704
YOKOHAMA TWS BELGIUM N.V.—See The Yokohama Rubber Co., Ltd.; *Int'l*, pg. 7704
YOKOHAMA TWS BRAZIL LTDA.—See The Yokohama Rubber Co., Ltd.; *Int'l*, pg. 7704
YOKOHAMA TWS CZECH REPUBLIC A.S.—See The Yokohama Rubber Co., Ltd.; *Int'l*, pg. 7704
YOKOHAMA TWS GERMANY GMBH—See The Yokohama Rubber Co., Ltd.; *Int'l*, pg. 7704
YOKOHAMA TWS LATVIA LSEZ SIA—See The Yokohama Rubber Co., Ltd.; *Int'l*, pg. 7704
YOKOHAMA TWS (MALAYSIA) SDN. BHD.—See The Yokohama Rubber Co., Ltd.; *Int'l*, pg. 7704
YOKOHAMA TWS MEXICO S.A. DE C.V.—See The Yokohama Rubber Co., Ltd.; *Int'l*, pg. 7704
YOKOHAMA TWS NORTH AMERICA, INC.—See The Yokohama Rubber Co., Ltd.; *Int'l*, pg. 7704
YOKOHAMA TWS POLAND SP. Z O.O.—See The Yokohama Rubber Co., Ltd.; *Int'l*, pg. 7704

COMPANY NAME INDEX

YOKOHAMA TWS RUS OOO—See The Yokohama Rubber Co., Ltd.; *Int'l*, pg. 7704
YOKOHAMA TWS SERBIA D.O.O.—See The Yokohama Rubber Co., Ltd.; *Int'l*, pg. 7704
YOKOHAMA TWS SINGAPORE PTE. LTD.—See The Yokohama Rubber Co., Ltd.; *Int'l*, pg. 7704
YOKOHAMA TWS SLOVENIA, D.O.O.—See The Yokohama Rubber Co., Ltd.; *Int'l*, pg. 7704
YOKOHAMA TWS S.P.A.—See The Yokohama Rubber Co., Ltd.; *Int'l*, pg. 7704
YOKOHAMA TWS SWEDEN AB—See The Yokohama Rubber Co., Ltd.; *Int'l*, pg. 7704
YOKOHAMA TWS SWITZERLAND GMBH—See The Yokohama Rubber Co., Ltd.; *Int'l*, pg. 7704
YOKOHAMA TWS (XINGTAI) CO. LTD.—See The Yokohama Rubber Co., Ltd.; *Int'l*, pg. 7704
YOKOHAMA TYRE AUSTRALIA PTY., LTD.—See The Yokohama Rubber Co., Ltd.; *Int'l*, pg. 7704
YOKOHAMA TYRE VIETNAM INC.—See The Yokohama Rubber Co., Ltd.; *Int'l*, pg. 7704
YOKOHAMA UOICHIBA UNSOU CO., LTD.—See Yokohama Maruuo Co., Ltd.; *Int'l*, pg. 8595
YOKO INDUSTRY CO., LTD.—See Nippon Steel Corporation; *Int'l*, pg. 5339
YOKOREI CO.,LTD.; *Int'l*, pg. 8595
YOKOSHIN SOFTWARE ENGINEERING (WUXI) CO., LTD.—See Yokogawa Electric Corporation; *Int'l*, pg. 8595
YOKOTA APPAREL CO., LTD.—See Gunze Limited; *Int'l*, pg. 3186
YOKOTA MANUFACTURING CO., LTD.; *Int'l*, pg. 8595
YOKOWO AMERICA CORPORATION—See YOKOWO Co., Ltd.; *Int'l*, pg. 8596
YOKOWO CO., LTD.; *Int'l*, pg. 8595
YOKOWO CO., LTD. - TOMIOKA PLANT—See YOKOWO Co., Ltd.; *Int'l*, pg. 8595
YOKOWO COMMUNICATION COMPONENTS & SYSTEMS CO., LTD.—See YOKOWO Co., Ltd.; *Int'l*, pg. 8596
YOKOWO COMMUNICATION EQUIPMENT CO., LTD.—See YOKOWO Co., Ltd.; *Int'l*, pg. 8595
YOKOWO CORP. (H.K.) LTD.—See YOKOWO Co., Ltd.; *Int'l*, pg. 8596
YOKOWO DELIVERY CENTER CO., LTD.—See YOKOWO Co., Ltd.; *Int'l*, pg. 8596
YOKOWO ELECTRONICS (M) SDN. BHD.—See YOKOWO Co., Ltd.; *Int'l*, pg. 8596
YOKOWO EUROPE GMBH—See YOKOWO Co., Ltd.; *Int'l*, pg. 8596
YOKOWO FINE MECHANICS CO., LTD.—See YOKOWO Co., Ltd.; *Int'l*, pg. 8596
YOKOWO (HONG KONG) LTD.—See YOKOWO Co., Ltd.; *Int'l*, pg. 8595
YOKOWO KOREA CO., LTD.—See YOKOWO Co., Ltd.; *Int'l*, pg. 8596
YOKOWO MANUFACTURING OF AMERICA LLC—See YOKOWO Co., Ltd.; *Int'l*, pg. 8596
YOKOWO MICRO TECH CO., LTD.—See YOKOWO Co., Ltd.; *Int'l*, pg. 8596
YOKOWO PRECISION CO.—See YOKOWO Co., Ltd.; *Int'l*, pg. 8596
YOKOWO (SINGAPORE) PTE. LTD.—See YOKOWO Co., Ltd.; *Int'l*, pg. 8596
YOKOWO (THAILAND) CO., LTD.—See YOKOWO Co., Ltd.; *Int'l*, pg. 8596
YOKOWO VIETNAM CO., LTD.—See YOKOWO Co., Ltd.; *Int'l*, pg. 8596
YOLA INC.; *U.S. Private*, pg. 4589
YOLANI MINERALS (PROPRIETARY) LTD.—See Frontier Rare Earths Limited; *Int'l*, pg. 2753
YOLOBUS PRIVATE LIMITED—See Easy Trip Planners Limited; *Int'l*, pg. 2276
YOLO GROUP S.P.A.; *Int'l*, pg. 8596
YOMA FLEET LIMITED—See YOMA Strategic Holdings Ltd.; *Int'l*, pg. 8596
YOMA STRATEGIC HOLDINGS LTD.; *Int'l*, pg. 8596
YOMEISHU SEIZO CO., LTD.; *Int'l*, pg. 8596
YOMIKO ADVERTISING INC.—See Hakuhodo DY Holdings Incorporated; *Int'l*, pg. 3222
YOMIKO ADVERTISING—See Hakuhodo DY Holdings Incorporated; *Int'l*, pg. 3222
YOMIKO ADVERTISING—See Hakuhodo DY Holdings Incorporated; *Int'l*, pg. 3222
YOMIKO ADVERTISING—See Hakuhodo DY Holdings Incorporated; *Int'l*, pg. 3222
YOMIKO ADVERTISING—See Hakuhodo DY Holdings Incorporated; *Int'l*, pg. 3222
YOMIKO ADVERTISING—See Hakuhodo DY Holdings Incorporated; *Int'l*, pg. 3222
THE YOMIURI SHIMBUN; *Int'l*, pg. 7704
YONAGO BIOMASS POWER GENERATION LLC—See Chubu Electric Power Co., Inc.; *Int'l*, pg. 1593
YONCELLO SANGYO CO., LTD.—See Mitsui Chemicals, Inc.; *Int'l*, pg. 4984
YONDASHI HOLDINGS INC.; *Int'l*, pg. 8596

YONDEN BUSINESS COMPANY, INCORPORATED—See Shikoku Electric Power Co., Incorporated; *Int'l*, pg. 6830
YONDEN CONSULTANTS COMPANY, INCORPORATED—See Shikoku Electric Power Co., Incorporated; *Int'l*, pg. 6830
YONDEN ENERGY SERVICE COMPANY, INCORPORATED—See Shikoku Electric Power Co., Incorporated; *Int'l*, pg. 6830
YONDEN ENGINEERING COMPANY, INCORPORATED—See Shikoku Electric Power Co., Incorporated; *Int'l*, pg. 6830
YONDENKO CORPORATION—See Shikoku Electric Power Co., Incorporated; *Int'l*, pg. 6830
YONDEN LIFE CARE CO., INC.—See Shikoku Electric Power Co., Incorporated; *Int'l*, pg. 6830
THE YONDER DIGITAL GROUP LIMITED; *Int'l*, pg. 7705
YONE AUTOMOBILE CO., LTD.—See Valuence Holdings Inc.; *Int'l*, pg. 8125
YONEKAWA SUISAN CORPORATION—See Daisyo Corporation; *Int'l*, pg. 1943
YONEKYU CORPORATION - FUJI PLANT—See Itoham Yonekyu Holdings Inc.; *Int'l*, pg. 3843
YONEKYU CORPORATION - FUJIYAMA PLANT—See Itoham Yonekyu Holdings Inc.; *Int'l*, pg. 3843
YONEKYU CORPORATION—See Itoham Yonekyu Holdings Inc.; *Int'l*, pg. 3843
YONEKYU DELICA FOODS CORP. - MAEBASHI PLANT—See Itoham Yonekyu Holdings Inc.; *Int'l*, pg. 3843
YONEKYU DELICA FOODS CORP. - SHIZUOKA PLANT—See Itoham Yonekyu Holdings Inc.; *Int'l*, pg. 3843
YONEKYU DELICA FOODS CORP.—See Itoham Yonekyu Holdings Inc.; *Int'l*, pg. 3843
YONEKYU KAGAYAKI CORP. - HANA PLANT—See Itoham Yonekyu Holdings Inc.; *Int'l*, pg. 3843
YONEKYU KAGAYAKI CORP.—See Itoham Yonekyu Holdings Inc.; *Int'l*, pg. 3843
YONEKYU OISHII TORI CORP. - SHIZUOKA PLANT—See Itoham Yonekyu Holdings Inc.; *Int'l*, pg. 3843
YONEKYU OISHII TORI CORP.—See Itoham Yonekyu Holdings Inc.; *Int'l*, pg. 3843
YONEKYU U.S.A., INC.—See Itoham Yonekyu Holdings Inc.; *Int'l*, pg. 3843
YONEX CANADA LTD.—See Yonex Co., Ltd.; *Int'l*, pg. 8596
YONEX CO., LTD.; *Int'l*, pg. 8596
YONEX CORPORATION—See Yonex Co., Ltd.; *Int'l*, pg. 8596
YONEX GMBH—See Yonex Co., Ltd.; *Int'l*, pg. 8596
YONEX SPORTS (CHINA) CO., LTD.—See Yonex Co., Ltd.; *Int'l*, pg. 8596
YONEX TAIWAN CO.,LTD.—See Yonex Co., Ltd.; *Int'l*, pg. 8596
YONEX UK LTD.—See Yonex Co., Ltd.; *Int'l*, pg. 8596
YONEZAWA DIA ELECTRONICS CO., LTD.—See Mitsubishi Gas Chemical Company, Inc.; *Int'l*, pg. 4950
YONEZAWA ELECTRIC WIRE CO., LTD.—See Fujikura Ltd.; *Int'l*, pg. 2829
YONGA MOBILYA SANAYI VE TICARET A.S.; *Int'l*, pg. 8597
YONG'AN DEPARTMENT STORE—See Bailian Group Co., Ltd.; *Int'l*, pg. 802
YONGCHANG SEKISUI COMPOSITES CO., LTD.—See Sekisui Chemical Co., Ltd.; *Int'l*, pg. 6697
YONGCHENG ZHONGYU GAS CO., LTD.—See Zhongyu Energy Holdings Limited; *Int'l*, pg. 8676
YONGHE MEDICAL GROUP CO., LTD.; *Int'l*, pg. 8597
YONGHUI SUPERSTORES CO., LTD.; *Int'l*, pg. 8597
YONGJIA BAOZEN AUTOMOBILE SALES AND SERVICES CO., LTD.—See China Yongda Automobiles Services Holdings Limited; *Int'l*, pg. 1565
YONGJI PRINTING CO LTD; *Int'l*, pg. 8597
YONG KANG LAVORWASH EQUIPMENT CO., LTD.—See Emak S.p.A.; *Int'l*, pg. 2373
YONGLE TAPE CO., LTD.—See Avery Dennison Corporation; *U.S. Public*, pg. 245
YONGLI EUROPE B.V.—See Shanghai Yongli Belting Co., Ltd.; *Int'l*, pg. 6782
YONGMA LOGIS CO., LTD.—See Dong-A Socio Holdings Co., Ltd.; *Int'l*, pg. 2165
YONGMAO HOLDINGS LIMITED; *Int'l*, pg. 8597
YONGNAM ENGINEERING & CONSTRUCTION (PRIVATE) LIMITED—See Yongnam Holdings Limited; *Int'l*, pg. 8597
YONGNAM ENGINEERING (HK) LIMITED—See Yongnam Holdings Limited; *Int'l*, pg. 8597
YONGNAM ENGINEERING SDN. BHD.—See Yongnam Holdings Limited; *Int'l*, pg. 8597
YONGNAM HOLDINGS LIMITED; *Int'l*, pg. 8597
YONGO CO., LTD.—See Adeka Corporation; *Int'l*, pg. 142
YONG PYONG RESORT CORP; *Int'l*, pg. 8596
YONGSAN CHEMICALS, INC.; *Int'l*, pg. 8597
YONGSAN CHEMICALS, INC. - ULSAN PLANT—See Yongsan Chemicals, Inc.; *Int'l*, pg. 8597
YONGSAN MITSUI CHEMICALS, INC.—See Mitsui Chemicals, Inc.; *Int'l*, pg. 4984

YONGSAN MITSUI CHEMICALS, INC.—See Yongsan Chemicals, Inc.; *Int'l*, pg. 8597
YONGSHENG ADVANCED MATERIALS COMPANY LIMITED; *Int'l*, pg. 8597
YONGSHENG CAPITAL INC.; *Int'l*, pg. 8597
YONG SHUN CHEMICAL CO., LTD.; *Int'l*, pg. 8596
YONG SHUN LTD.—See United Renewable Energy Co., Ltd.; *Int'l*, pg. 8073
YONG TAI BERHAD; *Int'l*, pg. 8596
YONGTAIYUN CHEMICAL LOGISTICS CO., LTD.; *Int'l*, pg. 8597
YONGTAIYUN CHEMICAL LOGISTICS (TAICANG) CO., LTD.—See Yongtaiyun Chemical Logistics Co., Ltd.; *Int'l*, pg. 8598
YONGTAIYUN CHEMICAL LOGISTICS (YIWU) CO., LTD.—See Yongtaiyun Chemical Logistics Co., Ltd.; *Int'l*, pg. 8598
YONGTAIYUN (NINGBO) CROSS-BORDER E-COMMERCE LOGISTICS CO., LTD.—See Yongtaiyun Chemical Logistics Co., Ltd.; *Int'l*, pg. 8598
YONGTAIYUN (ZHEJIANG) SUPPLY CHAIN CO., LTD.—See Yongtaiyun Chemical Logistics Co., Ltd.; *Int'l*, pg. 8598
YONG THAI PUBLIC COMPANY LIMITED; *Int'l*, pg. 8597
YONGXING SPECIAL MATERIALS TECHNOLOGY CO., LTD.; *Int'l*, pg. 8598
YONGYUE SCIENCE & TECHNOLOGY CO., LTD.; *Int'l*, pg. 8598
YONGZHOU SHANXIANG FLAVOUR CO., LTD.—See Huabao International Holdings Limited; *Int'l*, pg. 3511
YONGZHOU XIANGDA CAMEL FEED CO., LTD—See Tangrenshen Group Co., Ltd.; *Int'l*, pg. 7458
YONI ADVERTISING PRODUCTIONS (Y.A.) LTD.—See Messe Munchen GmbH; *Int'l*, pg. 4842
YONKER ENVIRONMENTAL PROTECTION CO., LTD.—See Hunan Yonker Investment Group Co., Ltd.; *Int'l*, pg. 3534
YONKERS CONTRACTING COMPANY INC.; *U.S. Private*, pg. 4590
YONKERS MOTORS CORP.; *U.S. Private*, pg. 4590
YONKERS RACING CORPORATION—See MGM Resorts International; *U.S. Public*, pg. 1435
THE YONKYU CO., LTD.; *Int'l*, pg. 7705
YONWOO CO., LTD—See Korea Kolmar Holdings Co., Ltd; *Int'l*, pg. 1286
YONYAKU CO., LTD.—See Medipal Holdings Corporation; *Int'l*, pg. 4779
YONYOU (HONG KONG) CO., LTD.—See Yonyou Network Technology Co., Ltd.; *Int'l*, pg. 8598
YONYOU (MACAU) CO., LTD.—See Yonyou Network Technology Co., Ltd.; *Int'l*, pg. 8598
YONYOU (MALAYSIA) SDN BHD.—See Yonyou Network Technology Co., Ltd.; *Int'l*, pg. 8598
YONYOU NETWORK TECHNOLOGY CO., LTD.; *Int'l*, pg. 8598
YONYOU (SINGAPORE) PTE LTD.—See Yonyou Network Technology Co., Ltd.; *Int'l*, pg. 8598
YONYU APPLIED TECHNOLOGY MATERIAL CO., LTD.—See Yonyu Plastics Co., Ltd.; *Int'l*, pg. 8598
YONYU PLASTICS CO., LTD.; *Int'l*, pg. 8598
YOOMEDIA ENHANCED SOLUTIONS—See Mirada Plc; *Int'l*, pg. 4916
YOOMEDIA GAMBLING & GAMES—See Mirada Plc; *Int'l*, pg. 4916
YOONG ONN CORPORATION BERHAD; *Int'l*, pg. 8598
YOOSHIN ENGINEERING CORPORATION; *Int'l*, pg. 8598
YOOSUNG ENTERPRISE CO., LTD.; *Int'l*, pg. 8598
YOOSUNG T&S CO., LTD.; *Int'l*, pg. 8598
YOOX ASIA LIMITED—See Compagnie Financiere Richemont S.A.; *Int'l*, pg. 1741
YOOX NET-A-PORTER GROUP S.P.A.—See Compagnie Financiere Richemont S.A.; *Int'l*, pg. 1741
YOPLAIT CANADA CO.—See General Mills, Inc.; *U.S. Public*, pg. 923
YOPLAIT CANADA CO.—See SODIAAL International SAS; *Int'l*, pg. 7047
YOPLAIT FRANCE SAS—See General Mills, Inc.; *U.S. Public*, pg. 923
YOPLAIT FRANCE SAS—See SODIAAL International SAS; *Int'l*, pg. 7047
YOPLAIT IRELAND LIMITED—See General Mills, Inc.; *U.S. Public*, pg. 923
YOPLAIT IRELAND LIMITED—See SODIAAL International SAS; *Int'l*, pg. 7048
YOPLAIT S.A.S.—See General Mills, Inc.; *U.S. Public*, pg. 923
YOPLAIT S.A.S.—See SODIAAL International SAS; *Int'l*, pg. 7047
YOPLAIT SVERIGE AB—See General Mills, Inc.; *U.S. Public*, pg. 923
YOPLAIT SVERIGE AB—See SODIAAL International SAS; *Int'l*, pg. 7048
YOPLAIT UK LTD.—See General Mills, Inc.; *U.S. Public*, pg. 923
YOPLAIT UK LTD.—See SODIAAL International SAS; *Int'l*, pg. 7048
YOPLAIT USA, INC.—See General Mills, Inc.; *U.S. Public*, pg. 923

YOOSUNG T&S CO., LTD.   CORPORATE AFFILIATIONS

YOPLAIT USA, INC.—See SODIAAL International SAS; *Int'l*, pg. 8598
Y-OPTICS MANUFACTURE CO., LTD.; *Int'l*, pg. 8543
Y.O. RANCH RESORT HOTEL & CONFERENCE CENTER—See Gal-Tex Hotel Corporation; *U.S. Private*, pg. 1635
YORBEAU RESOURCES INC.; *Int'l*, pg. 8598
YOR HEALTH; *U.S. Private*, pg. 4590
YORHE FLUID INTELLIGENT CONTROL CO., LTD.; *Int'l*, pg. 8598
YORK AGENCY, INC.—See Matthews International Corporation; *U.S. Public*, pg. 1401
YORK AIR CONDITIONING & REFRIGERATION (THAILAND) CO., LTD.—See Johnson Controls International plc; *Int'l*, pg. 3986
YORK ANALYTICAL LABORATORIES, INC—See ALS Limited; *Int'l*, pg. 379
YORK ANESTHESIOLOGY PHYSICIAN SERVICES, LLC—See Community Health Systems, Inc.; *U.S. Public*, pg. 557
YORK AUTO GROUP; *U.S. Private*, pg. 4590
YORK BARBELL COMPANY, INC.; *U.S. Private*, pg. 4590
YORK-BENIMARU CO., LTD.—See Seven & i Holdings Co., Ltd.; *Int'l*, pg. 6731
YORK BRIDGE CONCEPTS; *U.S. Private*, pg. 4590
YORK BRUKAN B.I. ASSESSORIA ADMINISTRACAO E CORRETAGEM DE SEGUROS LTDA.—See Alper Consultoria e Corretora de Seguros S.A.; *Int'l*, pg. 366
YORK BUILDING PRODUCTS CO., INC.; *U.S. Private*, pg. 4590
YORK CAPITAL MANAGEMENT GLOBAL ADVISORS, LLC; *U.S. Private*, pg. 4590
YORK CASKET DEVELOPMENT COMPANY, INC.—See Matthews International Corporation; *U.S. Public*, pg. 1401
YORK CHRYSLER DODGE JEEP INC.; *U.S. Private*, pg. 4590
YORK CLINIC COMPANY, LLC—See Community Health Systems, Inc.; *U.S. Public*, pg. 557
YORK CO., LTD.—See Seven & i Holdings Co., Ltd.; *Int'l*, pg. 6731
YORK CORRUGATING CO.; *U.S. Private*, pg. 4590
YORK COUNTY COMMUNITY ACTION CORPORATION; *U.S. Private*, pg. 4590
YORK DAILY RECORD-YORK SUNDAY NEWS LLC—See Gannett Co., Inc.; *U.S. Public*, pg. 900
YORK DISPATCH LLC—See Gannett Co., Inc.; *U.S. Public*, pg. 901
THE YORKE AGENCY INC.—See ABRY Partners, LLC; *U.S. Private*, pg. 42
YORK ELECTRIC COOPERATIVE INC.; *U.S. Private*, pg. 4590
YORK EXPORTS LTD.; *Int'l*, pg. 8598
YORKEY OPTICAL INTERNATIONAL (CAYMAN) LTD; *Int'l*, pg. 8599
YORKEY OPTICAL TECHNOLOGY LIMITED—See YORKEY OPTICAL INTERNATIONAL (CAYMAN) LTD; *Int'l*, pg. 8599
YORK FORD INC.—See Mcgovern Auto Group Corp Services, Inc.; *U.S. Private*, pg. 2635
YORK GRAPHIC SERVICES CO.; *U.S. Private*, pg. 4590
THE YORK GROUP, INC.—See Matthews International Corporation; *U.S. Public*, pg. 1401
YORK GUANGZHOU AIR CONDITIONING & REFRIGERATION CO., LTD.—See Johnson Controls International plc; *Int'l*, pg. 3986
YORK HARBOUR METALS INC.; *Int'l*, pg. 8598
YORK HOLDINGS, INC.; *U.S. Private*, pg. 4590
YORK HOME CARE SERVICES, LLC—See Community Health Systems, Inc.; *U.S. Public*, pg. 557
YORK HOSPITAL; *U.S. Private*, pg. 4590
YORK INDUSTRIAL (THAILAND) CO., LTD.—See Johnson Controls International plc; *Int'l*, pg. 3986
YORK INTERNATIONAL CORPORATION—See Johnson Controls International plc; *Int'l*, pg. 3985
YORK INTERNATIONAL GESMBH—See Johnson Controls International plc; *Int'l*, pg. 3986
YORK INTERNATIONAL LTD.—See Johnson Controls International plc; *Int'l*, pg. 3986
YORK INTERNATIONAL, S.A. DE C.V.—See Johnson Controls International plc; *Int'l*, pg. 3986
YORK MAILING LIMITED; *Int'l*, pg. 8599
YORK MANAGEMENT SERVICES, INC.; *U.S. Private*, pg. 4590
YORK NEWSPAPER COMPANY—See Gannett Co., Inc.; *U.S. Public*, pg. 901
THE YORK NEWS-TIMES—See Lee Enterprises, Incorporated; *U.S. Public*, pg. 1298
YORK POTASH LIMITED—See Anglo American PLC; *Int'l*, pg. 461
YORK PROPERTIES, INC. OF RALEIGH; *U.S. Private*, pg. 4591
YORK RAIL LOGISTICS, INC.—See Brookfield Infrastructure Partners L.P.; *Int'l*, pg. 1193
YORK RAIL LOGISTICS, INC.—See GIC Pte. Ltd.; *Int'l*, pg. 2967
YORK RAILWAY COMPANY—See Brookfield Infrastructure Partners L.P.; *Int'l*, pg. 1193

YORK RAILWAY COMPANY—See GIC Pte. Ltd.; *Int'l*, pg. 2967
YORK REFRIGERATION PHILIPPINES, INC.—See Johnson Controls International plc; *Int'l*, pg. 3986
YORK RISK SERVICES GROUP, INC.—See The Carlyle Group Inc.; *U.S. Public*, pg. 2054
YORK RIVER ELECTRIC, INC.; *U.S. Private*, pg. 4591
YORK SALES (THAILAND) CO. LTD.—See SAF-Holland S.A.; *Int'l*, pg. 6468
YORK S.A—See Hypera Pharma S.A.; *Int'l*, pg. 3553
YORKSBON DEVELOPMENT LIMITED—See Cheuk Nang (Holdings) Limited; *Int'l*, pg. 1473
YORKSHINE HOLDINGS LIMITED; *Int'l*, pg. 8599
YORK SHIPLEY GLOBAL—See AESYS Technologies, LLC; *U.S. Private*, pg. 120
YORKSHIRE BANK HOME LOANS LIMITED—See Virgin Money UK PLC; *Int'l*, pg. 8247
YORKSHIRE BANK PLC—See Virgin Money UK PLC; *Int'l*, pg. 8247
YORKSHIRE BUILDING SOCIETY; *Int'l*, pg. 8599
YORKSHIRE COPPER TUBE—See Mueller Industries, Inc.; *U.S. Public*, pg. 1485
YORKSHIRE FITTINGS GYARTO KFT—See Aalberts N.V.; *Int'l*, pg. 36
YORKSHIRE FOOD SALES CORP.; *U.S. Private*, pg. 4591
YORKSHIRE POST NEWSPAPERS LTD.—See JPIMedia Holdings Limited; *Int'l*, pg. 4007
YORKSHIRE PURCHASING ORGANISATION; *Int'l*, pg. 8599
YORKS OF HOULTON, INC.; *U.S. Private*, pg. 4591
YORK SOLUTIONS, LLC.; *U.S. Private*, pg. 4591
YORKSON LEGAL INC.—See Apax Partners LLP; *Int'l*, pg. 503
YORK STATE BANK—See York Holdings, Inc.; *U.S. Private*, pg. 4590
YORK STEEL INC.—See OSCO Construction Group; *Int'l*, pg. 5648
YORKSTON OIL CO.—See Christensen Inc.; *U.S. Private*, pg. 890
YORK STREET CAPITAL PARTNERS; *U.S. Private*, pg. 4591
YORKTEL FRANCE SAS—See Yorktel, Inc.; *U.S. Private*, pg. 4591
YORKTEL, INC.—See Yorktel, Inc.; *U.S. Private*, pg. 4591
YORKTEL, INC.; *U.S. Private*, pg. 4591
YORKTEL, INC.—See Yorktel, Inc.; *U.S. Private*, pg. 4591
YORKTEL, INC.—See Yorktel, Inc.; *U.S. Private*, pg. 4591
YORKTEL, INC.—See Yorktel, Inc.; *U.S. Private*, pg. 4591
YORKTEL—See Yorktel, Inc.; *U.S. Private*, pg. 4591
YORK TIMBER HOLDINGS LIMITED; *Int'l*, pg. 8599
YORKTON CROSSING RETIREMENT COMMUNITY INC.—See Extendicare Inc.; *Int'l*, pg. 2591
YORKTON VENTURES INC.; *Int'l*, pg. 8599
YORKTOWN BANK—See Yorktown Financial Holdings, Inc.; *U.S. Private*, pg. 4591
YORKTOWNE, INC.—See Zurn Elkay Water Solutions Corporation; *U.S. Public*, pg. 2412
YORKTOWN FINANCIAL HOLDINGS, INC.; *U.S. Private*, pg. 4591
YORKTOWN SYSTEMS GROUP, INC.; *U.S. Private*, pg. 4591
YORK TRADITIONS BANK; *U.S. Public*, pg. 2399
YORK TRANSPORT EQUIPMENT (ASIA) PTE. LTD.—See SAF-Holland S.A.; *Int'l*, pg. 6468
YORK TRANSPORT EQUIPMENT (INDIA) PVT. LTD.—See SAF-Holland S.A.; *Int'l*, pg. 6468
YORK TRANSPORT EQUIPMENT (MALAYASIA) SDN BHD—See TRF Ltd; *Int'l*, pg. 7918
YORK TRANSPORT EQUIPMENT (SHANGHAI) CO. LTD.—See SAF-Holland S.A.; *Int'l*, pg. 6468
YORKVILLE ADVISORS, LLC; *U.S. Private*, pg. 4591
YORK WALLCOVERINGS, INC.—See High Road Capital Partners, LLC; *U.S. Private*, pg. 1936
THE YORK WATER COMPANY; *U.S. Public*, pg. 2144
YORKWEST PLUMBING SUPPLY INC.; *Int'l*, pg. 8599
YOROI S.R.L.—See Tinexta S.p.A.; *Int'l*, pg. 7753
YORO NO TAKI CO. LTD.; *Int'l*, pg. 8599
YOROZU AICHI CORPORATION—See Yorozu Corporation; *Int'l*, pg. 8599
YOROZU AMERICA CORPORATION—See Yorozu Corporation; *Int'l*, pg. 8599
YOROZU AUTOMOTIVE ALABAMA, INC.—See Yorozu Corporation; *Int'l*, pg. 8599
YOROZU AUTOMOTIVE GUANAJUATO DE MEXICO, S.A. DE C.V.—See Yorozu Corporation; *Int'l*, pg. 8599
YOROZU AUTOMOTIVE NORTH AMERICA, INC.—See Yorozu Corporation; *Int'l*, pg. 8599
YOROZU AUTOMOTIVE TENNESSEE, INC.—See Yorozu Corporation; *Int'l*, pg. 8599
YOROZU BAO MIT AUTOMOTIVE CO., LTD.—See Yorozu Corporation; *Int'l*, pg. 8599
YOROZU CORPORATION; *Int'l*, pg. 8599
YOROZU ENGINEERING CORPORATION—See Yorozu Corporation; *Int'l*, pg. 8600
YOROZU ENGINEERING SYSTEMS (THAILAND) CO., LTD.—See Yorozu Corporation; *Int'l*, pg. 8600
YOROZU JBM AUTOMOTIVE TAMIL NADU PVT. LTD.—See Yorozu Corporation; *Int'l*, pg. 8600

YOROZU MEXICANA S.A. DE C.V.—See Yorozu Corporation; *Int'l*, pg. 8600
YOROZU OITA CORPORATION—See Yorozu Corporation; *Int'l*, pg. 8600
YOROZU SERVICE CORPORATION—See Yorozu Corporation; *Int'l*, pg. 8600
YOROZU (THAILAND) CO., LTD.—See Yorozu Corporation; *Int'l*, pg. 8599
YOROZU TOCHIGI CORPORATION—See Yorozu Corporation; *Int'l*, pg. 8600
YORTER INTERNATIONAL LIMITED—See Franklin Electronic Publishers, Inc.; *U.S. Public*, pg. 1597
YOSEMITE CONCESSION SERVICES MAIL ORDER DEPT—See Delaware North Companies, Inc.; *U.S. Private*, pg. 1194
YOSEMITE EXPRESS CO.—See Kingswood Capital Management LLC; *U.S. Private*, pg. 2312
YOSEMITE FOUNDATION; *U.S. Private*, pg. 4591
YOSEMITE MANAGEMENT GROUP LLC; *U.S. Private*, pg. 4591
YOSHICON CO., LTD.; *Int'l*, pg. 8600
YOSHIDA FUDOSAN CO., LTD.—See Relo Group, Inc.; *Int'l*, pg. 6265
YOSHIDA GAS CO., LTD.—See Shizuokagas Co., Ltd.; *Int'l*, pg. 6856
YOSHIDA SEISAKUSHO CO., LTD.—See Sanwa Holdings Corporation; *Int'l*, pg. 6561
YOSHIHARU GLOBAL CO.; *U.S. Public*, pg. 2399
YOSHIKAWA INC.; *Int'l*, pg. 8600
YOSHIKAWA LABEL (KUNSHAN) CO., LTD—See Yoshikawa Inc.; *Int'l*, pg. 8600
YOSHIKAWA TRADING INC VIET NAM CONPANY LIMITED—See Yoshikawa Inc.; *Int'l*, pg. 8600
YOSHIMOTO YOSHITEN CO., LTD.—See Japan Pulp and Paper Company Limited; *Int'l*, pg. 3905
YOSHIMURA FOOD HOLDINGS K.K.; *Int'l*, pg. 8600
YOSHIN CONSTRUCTION CO., LTD.—See Penta-Ocean Construction Co., Ltd.; *Int'l*, pg. 5788
YOSHINOYA AMERICA, INC—See Yoshinoya Holdings Co., Ltd.; *Int'l*, pg. 8600
YOSHINOYA CHINA HOLDINGS CO., LTD.—See Yoshinoya Holdings Co., Ltd.; *Int'l*, pg. 8600
YOSHINOYA CO., LTD.—See Yoshinoya Holdings Co., Ltd.; *Int'l*, pg. 8600
YOSHINOYA HOLDINGS CO., LTD.; *Int'l*, pg. 8600
YOSHINOYA NEW YORK, INC—See Yoshinoya Holdings Co., Ltd.; *Int'l*, pg. 8600
YOSHINOYA (S) PTE LTD—See Wing Tai Holdings Limited; *Int'l*, pg. 8428
YOSHIOKA SHANGHAI CO., LTD—See Yoshikawa Inc.; *Int'l*, pg. 8600
YOSHITAKE-ARMSTRONG, LTD.—See Yoshitake Inc.; *Int'l*, pg. 8601
YOSHITAKE INC.; *Int'l*, pg. 8601
YOSHITAKE WORKS (THAILAND) LTD.—See Yoshitake Inc.; *Int'l*, pg. 8601
YOSHITOMI ENGINEERING, LTD.—See Mitsubishi Chemical Group Corporation; *Int'l*, pg. 4935
YOSHITOMI-MAHSHIN, CO., LTD.—See Nagano Keiki Co., Ltd.; *Int'l*, pg. 5125
YOSHITOMIYAKUHIN CORPORATION—See Mitsubishi Chemical Group Corporation; *Int'l*, pg. 4935
YOSHITSU CO., LTD.; *Int'l*, pg. 8601
YOSHIZAWA IRONWORKS CO., LTD.—See Toyota Motor Corporation; *Int'l*, pg. 7872
YOSPACE TECHNOLOGIES LIMITED—See Bertelsmann SE & Co. KGaA; *Int'l*, pg. 996
YOSSIX HOLDINGS CO., LTD.; *Int'l*, pg. 8601
YOSTO VENTURE (INDIA) PRIVATE LIMITED—See Tilak Ventures Limited; *Int'l*, pg. 7748
YOST VISES, LLC—See Kian Capital Partners, LLC; *U.S. Private*, pg. 2302
YOSUN HONG KONG CORP. LTD.—See WPG Holdings Limited; *Int'l*, pg. 8461
YOSUN INDUSTRIAL CORPORATION—See WPG Holdings Limited; *Int'l*, pg. 8461
YOSUN JAPAN CORP.—See WPG Holdings Limited; *Int'l*, pg. 8461
YOSUN SHANGHAI CORP. LTD.—See WPG Holdings Limited; *Int'l*, pg. 8461
YOSUN SINGAPORE PTE. LTD.—See WPG Holdings Limited; *Int'l*, pg. 8461
YOSUN SOUTH CHINA CORP. LTD.—See WPG Holdings Limited; *Int'l*, pg. 8461
YO! SUSHI WORLDS—See Mayfair Equity Partners LLP; *Int'l*, pg. 4745
YOTAI REFRACTORIES CO., LTD.; *Int'l*, pg. 8601
YOTRIO GROUP CO., LTD.; *Int'l*, pg. 8601
YOTTA280, INC.—See Ziff Davis, Inc.; *U.S. Public*, pg. 2404
YOTTA ACQUISITION CORPORATION; *U.S. Public*, pg. 2399
YOTTA GLOBAL, INC.; *U.S. Public*, pg. 2399
YOTTA LIMITED—See Causeway Technologies Limited; *Int'l*, pg. 1361
YOU ARE SPECIAL EVENTS AG—See CTS Eventim AG & Co. KGAA; *Int'l*, pg. 1874
YOU BANK CO., LTD.—See Postal Savings Bank of China Co., Ltd.; *Int'l*, pg. 5939

COMPANY NAME INDEX

YOUBET.COM, LLC—See Churchill Downs, Inc.; *U.S. Public*, pg. 494
YOUBIKE CO., LTD.—See Giant Manufacturing Co., Ltd.; *Int'l*, pg. 2961
YOUBISHENG GREEN PAPER AG; *Int'l*, pg. 8601
YOU BROADBAND INDIA LIMITED—See Vodafone Idea Limited; *Int'l*, pg. 8286
YOU CAN GROUP S.R.L.—See Quantum Blockchain Technologies Plc; *Int'l*, pg. 6154
YOUCARE PHARMACEUTICAL GROUP CO., LTD.; *Int'l*, pg. 8601
YOUCEL INC; *Int'l*, pg. 8601
YOUDAO, INC.; *Int'l*, pg. 8601
YOU FIT, INC.; *U.S. Private*, pg. 4592
YOUGOV DEUTSCHLAND AG—See YouGov plc; *Int'l*, pg. 8601
YOUGOV FINANCE LIMITED—See YouGov plc; *Int'l*, pg. 8601
YOUGOVM.E. FZ LLC.—See YouGov plc; *Int'l*, pg. 8601
YOUGOV NORDIC & BALTIC A/S.—See YouGov plc; *Int'l*, pg. 8601
YOUGOV NORWAY AS.—See YouGov plc; *Int'l*, pg. 8601
YOUGOV PLC; *Int'l*, pg. 8601
YOUGOV SWEDEN AB.—See YouGov plc; *Int'l*, pg. 8601
YOUHUI OPTOELECTRONICS CO., LTD.—See Shin Kong Group; *Int'l*, pg. 6837
YOUI HOLDINGS PROPRIETARY LIMITED—See OUTsurance Group Limited; *Int'l*, pg. 5669
YOUIL ENERGY TECH CO., LTD.; *Int'l*, pg. 8601
YOUJI CORPORATION; *Int'l*, pg. 8601
YOUKESHU TECHNOLOGY CO., LTD.; *Int'l*, pg. 8601
YOUKOSHA CO., LTD.; *Int'l*, pg. 8602
YOUKU TUDOU INC.—See Alibaba Group Holding Limited; *Int'l*, pg. 326
YOULCHON CHEMICAL LTD. - 1ST FILM FACTORY—See YoulChon Chemical Ltd.; *Int'l*, pg. 8602
YOULCHON CHEMICAL LTD. - 1ST FLEXIBLE PACKAGING FACTORY—See YoulChon Chemical Ltd.; *Int'l*, pg. 8602
YOULCHON CHEMICAL LTD. - 2ND FLEXIBLE PACKAGING FACTORY—See YoulChon Chemical Ltd.; *Int'l*, pg. 8602
YOULCHON CHEMICAL LTD.; *Int'l*, pg. 8602
YOUME CARD CO., LTD.—See RASA Corporation; *Int'l*, pg. 6212
YOUMEMIRU INC.—See EDION Corporation; *Int'l*, pg. 2310
YOU & MR JONES INC.; *U.S. Private*, pg. 4591
YOUNAN PROPERTIES, INC.; *U.S. Private*, pg. 4592
YOUNEEQAI TECHNICAL SERVICES, INC.; *U.S. Public*, pg. 2399
YOUNG ADULT INSTITUTE, INC.; *U.S. Private*, pg. 4592
YOUNG AMERICA'S FOUNDATION; *U.S. Private*, pg. 4592
YOUNG AN HAT (BD) S.A - FACTORY NO. 1—See Young An Hat Co., Ltd.; *Int'l*, pg. 8602
YOUNG AN HAT CO., LTD.; *Int'l*, pg. 8602
YOUNG AN HAT, S.A.—See Young An Hat Co., Ltd.; *Int'l*, pg. 8602
YOUNG AN LANKA (PVT) LTD.—See Young An Hat Co., Ltd.; *Int'l*, pg. 8602
YOUNG & ASSOCIATES INC.; *U.S. Private*, pg. 4592
YOUNG & ASSOCIATES; *U.S. Private*, pg. 4592
YOUNG & ASSOCIATES; *U.S. Private*, pg. 4592
YOUNG AUSTRALIAN MINES LTD.; *Int'l*, pg. 8602
YOUNG AUTOMOTIVE GROUP, INC.; *U.S. Private*, pg. 4592
YOUNG AUTOMOTIVE GROUP; *U.S. Private*, pg. 4592
YOUNG & BEASLEY INCORPORATED; *U.S. Private*, pg. 4592
YOUNGBERG INDUSTRIES, INC.; *U.S. Private*, pg. 4593
YOUNG BLACK IS LTD.—See Indutrade AB; *Int'l*, pg. 3682
YOUNGBLOOD OIL CO. INC.; *U.S. Private*, pg. 4593
YOUNGBLOOD SKIN CARE PRODUCTS, LLC—See Luxury Brands, LLC; *U.S. Private*, pg. 2518
YOUNGBO CHEMICAL CO., LTD.—See Sekisui Chemical Co., Ltd.; *Int'l*, pg. 6697
YOUNGBO HPP (LANGFANG) CO., LTD.—See Sekisui Chemical Co., Ltd.; *Int'l*, pg. 6697
YOUNG BRAND APPAREL PRIVATE LIMITED—See S. P. Apparels Limited; *Int'l*, pg. 6447
YOUNG BROADCASTING OF DAVENPORT, INC.—See Gray Television, Inc.; *U.S. Public*, pg. 960
YOUNG BROADCASTING OF GREEN BAY, INC.—See Gray Television, Inc.; *U.S. Public*, pg. 961
YOUNG BROTHERS, LIMITED—See Saltchuk Resources Inc.; *U.S. Private*, pg. 3534
YOUNG & CHAMPAGNE COMPANY—See Young & Champagne Electrical Sales Inc.; *U.S. Private*, pg. 4592
YOUNG & CHAMPAGNE ELECTRICAL SALES INC.; *U.S. Private*, pg. 4592
YOUNG CHANG AKKI CO. LTD.; *Int'l*, pg. 8602
YOUNG CHANG AKKI CO. LTD. - YOUNG CHANG CANADA DIVISION—See Young Chang Akki Co. Ltd.; *Int'l*, pg. 8602
YOUNG CHANG NORTH AMERICA, INC.—See Young Chang Akki Co. Ltd.; *Int'l*, pg. 8602

YOUNG CHEVROLET COMPANY; *U.S. Private*, pg. 4592
YOUNG COMPANY CREATIVE MARKETING COMMUNICATIONS, INC.; *U.S. Private*, pg. 4592
YOUNG CORPORATION; *U.S. Private*, pg. 4592
YOUNG & CO.'S BREWERY PLC; *Int'l*, pg. 8602
YOUNG DAN TIPTON LLC; *U.S. Private*, pg. 4592
YOUNG DENTAL MANUFACTURING I, LLC—See The Jordan Company, L.P.; *U.S. Private*, pg. 4063
YOUNG DESIGNERS EMPORIUM (PTY) LIMITED—See Truworths International Limited; *Int'l*, pg. 7946
YOUNG DIGITAL PLANET S.A.—See Sanoma Oyj; *Int'l*, pg. 6553
YOUNG ELECTRIC SIGN CO. - BOISE—See Young Electric Sign Company; *U.S. Private*, pg. 4593
YOUNG ELECTRIC SIGN CO. - DENVER—See Young Electric Sign Company; *U.S. Private*, pg. 4593
YOUNG ELECTRIC SIGN CO. - LAS VEGAS—See Young Electric Sign Company; *U.S. Private*, pg. 4593
YOUNG ELECTRIC SIGN COMPANY; *U.S. Private*, pg. 4593
YOUNG ELECTRIC SIGN CO. - PHOENIX—See Young Electric Sign Company; *U.S. Private*, pg. 4593
YOUNG ELECTRIC SIGN CO. - RENO—See Young Electric Sign Company; *U.S. Private*, pg. 4593
YOUNG ELECTRIC SIGN CO. - SALT LAKE CITY—See Young Electric Sign Company; *U.S. Private*, pg. 4593
THE YOUNG ENGINEERS, INC.—See KKR & Co. Inc.; *U.S. Public*, pg. 1262
THE YOUNG ENTREPRENEURS ACADEMY INC.; *U.S. Private*, pg. 4139
YOUNG ENVIRONMENTAL CLEAN UP—See R.S. Young Excavating, Inc.; *U.S. Private*, pg. 3339
YOUNGER BROTHERS BUILDERS EXPRESS LIBERTY LLC—See Younger Brothers Group Inc.; *U.S. Private*, pg. 4594
YOUNGER BROTHERS COMPONENTS INC.—See Younger Brothers Group Inc.; *U.S. Private*, pg. 4594
YOUNGER BROTHERS CONSTRUCTION COMPANY—See Younger Brothers Group Inc.; *U.S. Private*, pg. 4594
YOUNGER BROTHERS DOOR & TRIM, LLC—See Younger Brothers Group Inc.; *U.S. Private*, pg. 4594
YOUNGER BROTHERS EXTERMINATING—See Younger Brothers Group Inc.; *U.S. Private*, pg. 4594
YOUNGER BROTHERS GROUP INC.; *U.S. Private*, pg. 4603
YOUNGER MFG. CO.; *U.S. Private*, pg. 4594
YOUNGER MOTOR CARS INC.; *U.S. Private*, pg. 4594
YOUNGER OPTICS EUROPE S.R.O.—See Younger Mfg. Co.; *U.S. Private*, pg. 4594
YOUNGEVITY INTERNATIONAL CORP.; *U.S. Public*, pg. 2399
YOUNGEVITY NZ, LTD.—See Youngevity International Corp.; *U.S. Public*, pg. 2399
YOUNGEVITY RUSSIA, LLC—See Youngevity International Corp.; *U.S. Public*, pg. 2399
YOUNG FAST OPTOELECTRONICS CO., LTD.; *Int'l*, pg. 8603
YOUNG FORD, INC.—See Tym Corporation; *Int'l*, pg. 7995
YOUNG & FRANKLIN, INC.—See TransDigm Group Incorporated; *U.S. Public*, pg. 2183
YOUNG GAS STORAGE COMPANY—See Colorado Springs Utilities, Inc.; *U.S. Private*, pg. 974
YOUNG GAS STORAGE COMPANY—See Kinder Morgan, Inc.; *U.S. Public*, pg. 1232
YOUNG GAS STORAGE COMPANY—See Xcel Energy Inc.; *U.S. Public*, pg. 2385
YOUNG GREEN ENERGY CO., LTD.—See Coretronic Corporation; *Int'l*, pg. 1800
YOUNGHEUNG TAICANG KANGSASUNG—See YoungWire Co. Ltd.; *Int'l*, pg. 8604
YOUNG HWA TECH CO., LTD.; *Int'l*, pg. 8603
YOUNGHYUN TRADING CO.,LTD; *Int'l*, pg. 8603
YOUNG HYUN VINA COMPANY LIMITED—See Younghyun Trading co.,Ltd; *Int'l*, pg. 8603
YOUNG INNOVATIONS, INC.—See The Jordan Company, L.P.; *U.S. Private*, pg. 4063
YOUNG-IN SCIENTIFIC CO., LTD.—See Agilent Technologies, Inc.; *U.S. Public*, pg. 62
YOUNGJETS, LLC—See Fly Victor Ltd.; *Int'l*, pg. 2716
YOUNG JIN CHEMICAL INDUSTRIES CO., LTD.; *Int'l*, pg. 8603
YOUNG & LARAMORE; *U.S. Private*, pg. 4592
YOUNG LIGHTING (SUZHOU) CORPORATION—See Coretronic Corporation; *Int'l*, pg. 1800
YOUNG LIGHTING TECHNOLOGY INC.—See Coretronic Corporation; *Int'l*, pg. 1800
YOUNGLIMWON SOFTLAB CO., LTD.; *Int'l*, pg. 8603
YOUNG LIVING ESSENTIAL OILS, LC; *U.S. Private*, pg. 4593
YOUNG MARINES OF THE MARINE CORPS LEAGUE; *U.S. Private*, pg. 4593
YOUNG & MCQUEEN GRADING COMPANY, INC.; *U.S. Private*, pg. 4593
YOUNG MICROBRUSH INTERNATIONAL, LLC—See The Jordan Company, L.P.; *U.S. Private*, pg. 4063
YOUNG MICROBRUSH IRELAND, LTD.—See The Jordan Company, L.P.; *U.S. Private*, pg. 4063

YOUNG'S HOLDINGS, INC.

YOUNG OFFICE SOLUTIONS LLC—See HNI Corporation; *U.S. Public*, pg. 1043
YOUNGONE CORPORATION—See Youngone Holdings Co., Ltd.; *Int'l*, pg. 8603
YOUNGONE HOLDINGS CO., LTD.; *Int'l*, pg. 8603
YOUNGONE OUTDOOR CORPORATION—See Goldwin, Inc.; *Int'l*, pg. 3035
YOUNG OPTICS (BD) LTD.—See Young Optics Inc.; *Int'l*, pg. 8603
YOUNG OPTICS INC.; *Int'l*, pg. 8603
YOUNGOPTICS INC.—See Coretronic Corporation; *Int'l*, pg. 1800
YOUNG OPTICS (KUNSHAN) CO., LTD.—See Young Optics Inc.; *Int'l*, pg. 8603
YOUNG OPTICS (SUZHOU) CO., LTD.—See Young Optics Inc.; *Int'l*, pg. 8603
YOUNGOR FASHION CO., LTD.—See Youngor Group Co. Ltd.; *Int'l*, pg. 8604
YOUNGOR GROUP CO. LTD.; *Int'l*, pg. 8603
YOUNGOR SHIRTS CO., LTD.—See Youngor Group Co. Ltd.; *Int'l*, pg. 8604
YOUNG PECAN, INC.—See King Ranch, Inc.; *U.S. Private*, pg. 2310
YOUNG PECAN - LAS CRUCES PROCESSING PLANT—See King Ranch, Inc.; *U.S. Private*, pg. 2310
YOUNG POONG BOOK STORE CO., LTD.—See Young Poong Precision Corporation; *Int'l*, pg. 8603
YOUNG POONG, CORP.; *Int'l*, pg. 8603
YOUNG POONG ELECTRONICS CO., LTD.—See Young Poong Precision Corporation; *Int'l*, pg. 8603
YOUNG POONG PAPER MFG CO., LTD.; *Int'l*, pg. 8603
YOUNG POONG PRECISION CORPORATION - FRP PLANT—See Young Poong Precision Corporation; *Int'l*, pg. 8603
YOUNG POONG PRECISION CORPORATION; *Int'l*, pg. 8603
YOUNG POONG PRECISION CORPORATION - VALVE PLANT—See Young Poong Precision Corporation; *Int'l*, pg. 8603
YOUNG RANCH INC.—See Rod Fraser Enterprises Inc.; *U.S. Private*, pg. 3469
YOUNG & RUBICAM AUSTRALIA/NEW ZEALAND—See WPP plc; *Int'l*, pg. 8493
YOUNG & RUBICAM BOGOTA—See WPP plc; *Int'l*, pg. 8494
YOUNG & RUBICAM BRANDS AFRICA—See WPP plc; *Int'l*, pg. 8494
YOUNG & RUBICAM BRANDS, SAN FRANCISCO—See WPP plc; *Int'l*, pg. 8494
YOUNG & RUBICAM BRANDS, SOUTHERN CALIFORNIA—See WPP plc; *Int'l*, pg. 8494
YOUNG & RUBICAM CHICAGO—See WPP plc; *Int'l*, pg. 8494
YOUNG & RUBICAM GUANGZHOU—See WPP plc; *Int'l*, pg. 8494
YOUNG & RUBICAM INC.—See WPP plc; *Int'l*, pg. 8491
YOUNG & RUBICAM KOREA CO., LTD.—See WPP plc; *Int'l*, pg. 8494
YOUNG & RUBICAM LTD.—See WPP plc; *Int'l*, pg. 8494
YOUNG & RUBICAM LTD.—See WPP plc; *Int'l*, pg. 8494
YOUNG & RUBICAM NZ LTD.—See WPP plc; *Int'l*, pg. 8494
YOUNG & RUBICAM S.A. CALI—See WPP plc; *Int'l*, pg. 8494
YOUNG & RUBICAM S. DE. R.L. DE C.V.—See WPP plc; *Int'l*, pg. 8494
YOUNG & RUBICAM SDN. BHD.—See WPP plc; *Int'l*, pg. 8494
YOUNG & RUBICAM SHANGHAI—See WPP plc; *Int'l*, pg. 8494
YOUNG & RUBICAM TAIWAN LTD.—See WPP plc; *Int'l*, pg. 8494
YOUNG & RUBICAM VIETNAM—See WPP plc; *Int'l*, pg. 8494
YOUNG & RUBICAM WELLINGTON—See WPP plc; *Int'l*, pg. 8494
YOUNGS ANIMAL FEEDS LIMITED—See Wynnstay Group Plc; *Int'l*, pg. 8517
YOUNG'S COMMUNICATIONS CO, INC.—See Cotton Creek Capital Management LLC; *U.S. Private*, pg. 1064
YOUNG'S CORPORATION—See BERICAP GmbH & Co. KG; *Int'l*, pg. 981
YOUNG'S ENGINEERING COMPANY LIMITED—See FSE Services Group Limited; *Int'l*, pg. 2798
YOUNG'S EQUIPMENT INC.; *Int'l*, pg. 8603
YOUNG'S FURNITURE COMPANY; *U.S. Private*, pg. 4593
YOUNG SHIN QUARTZ CO., LTD.—See Shin-Etsu Chemical Co. Ltd.; *Int'l*, pg. 6841
YOUNG'S HOLDINGS, INC.; *U.S. Private*, pg. 4593
YOUNGSIN METAL (THAILAND) CO., LTD.—See YM CO., LTD.; *Int'l*, pg. 8590
YOUNG'S L&S DENTAL SUPPLIES LTD.—See Danaher Corporation; *U.S. Public*, pg. 632
YOUNG'S MARKET COMPANY, LLC—See Young's Holdings, Inc.; *U.S. Private*, pg. 4593
YOUNG'S MARKET COMPANY OF ARIZONA, LLC—See Young's Holdings, Inc.; *U.S. Private*, pg. 4593
YOUNG'S MARKET COMPANY OF OREGON, LLC—See Young's Holdings, Inc.; *U.S. Private*, pg. 4593

YOUNG'S HOLDINGS, INC.

CORPORATE AFFILIATIONS

YOUNG'S MARKET COMPANY OF WASHINGTON, LLC—See Young's Holdings, Inc.; *U.S. Private*, pg. 4593

YOUNG'S MARKET - HAWAII—See Young's Holdings, Inc.; *U.S. Private*, pg. 4593

YOUNG'S NURSERIES INC.; *U.S. Private*, pg. 4593

YOUNG'S PROPANE—See UGI Corporation; *U.S. Public*, pg. 2222

YOUNG'S RV CENTERS, INC.; *U.S. Private*, pg. 4593

YOUNG'S SEAFOOD LIMITED—See CapVest Limited; *Int'l*, pg. 1318

YOUNGSTEDT INC.; *U.S. Private*, pg. 4594

YOUNGSTOWN & AUSTINTOWN RAILROAD, INC.—See Brookfield Infrastructure Partners L.P.; *Int'l*, pg. 1193

YOUNGSTOWN & AUSTINTOWN RAILROAD, INC.—See GIC Pte. Ltd.; *Int'l*, pg. 2967

YOUNGSTOWN OHIO PHYSICIAN SERVICES COMPANY, LLC—See Steward Health Care System LLC; *U.S. Private*, pg. 3811

YOUNGSTOWN-WARREN HOME DIALYSIS, LLC—See Nautic Partners, LLC; *U.S. Private*, pg. 2871

YOUNG'S TRUCK CENTER INC.; *U.S. Private*, pg. 4593

YOUNG SUPPLY CO.; *U.S. Private*, pg. 4593

YOUNGTECH PHARMACEUTICAL INC.—See Zhejiang Yongtai Technology Co., Ltd.; *Int'l*, pg. 8667

YOUNGTEK ELECTRONICS CORP.; *Int'l*, pg. 8604

YOUNGTEK MICRO ELECTRONICS (SHENZHEN) LTD.—See Youngtek Electronics Corp.; *Int'l*, pg. 8604

YOUNGTIMERS AG; *Int'l*, pg. 8604

YOUNG TOUCHSTONE COMPANY—See Westinghouse Air Brake Technologies Corporation; *U.S. Public*, pg. 2360

YOUNGTOWN HEALTH, INC.—See The Ensign Group, Inc.; *U.S. Public*, pg. 2073

YOUNG TRUCK SALES INC.; *U.S. Private*, pg. 4593

YOUNGWIRE CO. LTD.; *Int'l*, pg. 8604

YOUNG WIRE VINA CO., LTD.—See YoungWire Co. Ltd.; *Int'l*, pg. 8604

YOUNGWOO DSP CO., LTD.; *Int'l*, pg. 8604

YOUNGWOO FROZEN FOODS CO., LTD.—See CJ Corporation; *Int'l*, pg. 1632

YOUNGWORLD INC.—See Youngworld Stores Group Inc.; *U.S. Private*, pg. 4594

YOUNGWORLD STORES GROUP INC.; *U.S. Private*, pg. 4594

YOUNGY CO., LTD.; *Int'l*, pg. 8604

YOUNGY HEALTH CO., LTD.; *Int'l*, pg. 8604

YOUNICOS GMBH—See I Squared Capital Advisors (US) LLC; *U.S. Private*, pg. 2021

YOUNICOS GMBH—See TDR Capital LLP; *Int'l*, pg. 7490

YOUNIFI LIMITED—See HFBG Holding B.V.; *Int'l*, pg. 3375

YOUNT, HYDE & BARBOUR PC; *U.S. Private*, pg. 4594

YOUNYI ELECTRONICS (SUZHOU) CO., LTD.—See IME Younyi Co., Ltd.; *Int'l*, pg. 3623

YOUNYI ELECTRONICS (TIANJIN) CO., LTD.—See IME Younyi Co., Ltd.; *Int'l*, pg. 3623

YOUNYI INFORMATION & COMMUNICATION CO., LTD. - THE SECOND FACTORY—See IME Younyi Co., Ltd.; *Int'l*, pg. 3623

YOUON TECHNOLOGY CO., LTD.; *Int'l*, pg. 8604

YOUPERIENCE LIMITED—See Persistent Systems Ltd.; *Int'l*, pg. 5818

YOURA SILICASTONE CO., LTD.—See Nittetsu Mining Co., Ltd.; *Int'l*, pg. 5384

YOUR AUCTION, INC.—See Huron Capital Partners LLC; *U.S. Private*, pg. 2012

YOUR BIG BACKYARD—See National Wildlife Federation; *U.S. Private*, pg. 2865

YOUR BUILDING CENTERS, INC.; *U.S. Private*, pg. 4594

YOURCAREERGROUP AUSTRIA GMBH—See Axel Springer SE; *Int'l*, pg. 767

YOURCAREERGROUP GMBH—See Axel Springer SE; *Int'l*, pg. 767

YOURCASH LIMITED—See Euronet Worldwide, Inc.; *U.S. Public*, pg. 798

YOURCAUSE, LLC—See Blackbaud, Inc.; *U.S. Public*, pg. 341

YOUR CONSULTING CO., LTD.—See YOKOWO Co., Ltd.; *Int'l*, pg. 8596

YOUR CREDIT INC.—See Gentry Finance Corporation; *U.S. Private*, pg. 1680

YOUR DOLLAR STORE WITH MORE INC.; *Int'l*, pg. 8604

YOURENCORE, INC.—See Genstar Capital, LLC; *U.S. Private*, pg. 1673

YOUR FAMILY ENTERTAINMENT AG; *Int'l*, pg. 8604

YOUR HEARING NETWORK LLC—See Demant A/S; *Int'l*, pg. 2025

YOUR HOME FINANCIAL LLC—See Rithm Capital Corp.; *U.S. Public*, pg. 1800

YOUR HOME IMPROVEMENT, CO.—See Great Day Improvements LLC; *U.S. Private*, pg. 1762

YOUR HOME MAGAZINE—See Your Home Publishing, Inc.; *U.S. Private*, pg. 4594

YOUR HOME PUBLISHING, INC.; *U.S. Private*, pg. 4594

YOUR HOME SOLD GUARANTEED REALTY, INC.; *U.S. Private*, pg. 4594

YOUR INSPIRATION AT HOME PTY. LTD.—See JRjr33, Inc.; *U.S. Private*, pg. 2240

YOUR LOCATION LUBRICATION, LLC—See Get Spiffy, Inc.; *U.S. Private*, pg. 1688

YOURMEMBERSHIP.COM INC.—See Insight Venture Management, LLC; *U.S. Private*, pg. 2088

YOUR OTHER WAREHOUSE—See The Home Depot, Inc.; *U.S. Public*, pg. 2089

YOURPEOPLE, INC.—See General Atlantic Service Company, L.P.; *U.S. Private*, pg. 1663

YOUR SPEAKEASY LLC—See DallasNews Corporation; *U.S. Public*, pg. 621

YOUR SUPERFOODS GMBH—See The Healing Company Inc.; *U.S. Public*, pg. 2088

YOUR TECHNICA CO., LTD.—See Yuasa Trading Co., Ltd.; *Int'l*, pg. 8609

YOUR TICKET PROVIDER B.V.—See CM.com N.V.; *Int'l*, pg. 1666

YOUR TRAVEL CENTER, INC.; *U.S. Private*, pg. 4594

YOURTROVE, INC.—See Live Nation Entertainment, Inc.; *U.S. Public*, pg. 1331

YOURWAY CANNABIS BRANDS INC.; *U.S. Private*, pg. 4604

YOUSEE A/S—See Arbejdsmarkedets Tillaegspension; *Int'l*, pg. 537

YOUSEE A/S—See Macquarie Group Limited; *Int'l*, pg. 4626

YOUSEE A/S—See PFA Holding A/S; *Int'l*, pg. 5835

YOUSEE A/S—See PKA A/S; *Int'l*, pg. 5887

YOUSENDIT, INC.; *U.S. Private*, pg. 4594

YOUSUF WEAVING MILLS LTD.; *Int'l*, pg. 8604

YOUTECH & ASSOCIATES, INC.; *U.S. Private*, pg. 4594

YOUTH CARE OF UTAH, INC.—See Acadia Healthcare Company, Inc.; *U.S. Public*, pg. 31

YOUTH CHEMICAL CO. LTD.—See Jiangsu Yangnong Chemical Co., Ltd.; *Int'l*, pg. 3956

YOUTH CO-OP, INC.; *U.S. Private*, pg. 4594

YOUTH DEVELOPMENT, INC.; *U.S. Private*, pg. 4594

YOUTH & FAMILY CENTERED SERVICES OF NEW MEXICO, INC.—See Acadia Healthcare Company, Inc.; *U.S. Public*, pg. 31

YOUTH FOR UNDERSTANDING INC.; *U.S. Private*, pg. 4594

YOUTHFUL AGING HOME HEALTH, INC.; *U.S. Private*, pg. 4594

YOUTH IN NEED, INC.; *U.S. Private*, pg. 4594

YOUTH OPPORTUNITIES UPHELD, INC.—See Seven Hills Foundation; *U.S. Private*, pg. 3618

YOUTRANSACTOR SAS—See Jabil Inc.; *U.S. Public*, pg. 1182

YOUTUBE, LLC—See Alphabet Inc.; *U.S. Public*, pg. 84

YOUVIA B.V.—See European Directories S.A.; *Int'l*, pg. 2556

YOU WANG CO., LTD.—See Dong Won Fisheries Co., Ltd.; *Int'l*, pg. 2164

YOUYING (SHANGHAI) INFORMATION TECH. CO., LTD.—See Apex International Financial Engineering Research & Technology Co., Limited; *Int'l*, pg. 511

YOUYOU FOODS CHONGQING MANUFACTURING CO., LTD.—See YouYou Foods Co., Ltd.; *Int'l*, pg. 8604

YOUYOU FOODS CO., LTD.; *Int'l*, pg. 8604

YOUYU SMART TECHNOLOGIES LIMITED—See Yunfeng Financial Group Limited; *Int'l*, pg. 8614

YOUZOOM INSURANCE SERVICES, INC.—See Brown & Brown, Inc.; *U.S. Public*, pg. 402

YOUZU INTERACTIVE CO., LTD.; *Int'l*, pg. 8604

YOWA ENGINEERING CO., LTD.—See Dowa Holdings Co., Ltd.; *Int'l*, pg. 2184

YOWA KOUEI CO., LTD.—See Dowa Holdings Co., Ltd.; *Int'l*, pg. 2184

YOW BELL CASTING (TAI CANG) CO., LTD.—See Chia Yi Steel Co.; *Int'l*, pg. 1475

YOWIE GROUP LTD.; *Int'l*, pg. 8605

YOWN'S BOILER & FURNACE SERVICE, INC.—See Audax Group, Limited Partnership; *U.S. Private*, pg. 390

YPB GROUP LTD.; *Int'l*, pg. 8605

YPB PRINT SOLUTIONS INC.—See YPB Group Ltd.; *Int'l*, pg. 8605

YP ELECTRONICS LTD.—See Palmer & Harvey McLane (Holdings) Limited; *Int'l*, pg. 5709

YPF BRASIL COMERCIO DERIVADO DE PETROLEO LTDA.—See YPF S.A.; *Int'l*, pg. 8605

YPF ENERGIA ELECTRICA S.A.—See YPF S.A.; *Int'l*, pg. 8605

YPF GAS, S.A.; *Int'l*, pg. 8605

YPF GUYANA, LTD.—See Repsol, S.A.; *Int'l*, pg. 6294

YPF HOLDINGS INC.—See YPF S.A.; *Int'l*, pg. 8605

YPF INVERSORA ENERGETICA, S.A.—See YPF S.A.; *Int'l*, pg. 8605

YPF S.A.; *Int'l*, pg. 8605

Y-PHARMA S.A.—See DIAGNOSTIC AND THERAPEUTIC CENTER OF ATHENS-HYGEIA S.A.; *Int'l*, pg. 2103

YPI CREW SARL—See YCO Group plc; *Int'l*, pg. 8574

YPK MACHINE TRADING (SHENZHEN) CO., LTD.—See The Japan Steel Works, Ltd.; *Int'l*, pg. 7659

YPK TRADING (HONG KONG) CO., LTD.—See The Japan Steel Works, Ltd.; *Int'l*, pg. 7659

YP LLC—See Thryv Holdings, Inc.; *U.S. Public*, pg. 2157

YPO CAMP MURET CAMPINGS-CARS; *Int'l*, pg. 8605

YPSI-ARBOR LANES—See Great Lakes Realty Corp.; *U.S. Private*, pg. 1765

YPSOMED AB—See Ypsomed Holding AG; *Int'l*, pg. 8605

YPSOMED AB—See Ypsomed Holding AG; *Int'l*, pg. 8605

YPSOMED APS—See Ypsomed Holding AG; *Int'l*, pg. 8605

YPSOMED AS—See Ypsomed Holding AG; *Int'l*, pg. 8605

YPSOMED AUSTRALIA PTY. LTD.—See Ypsomed Holding AG; *Int'l*, pg. 8605

YPSOMED BV—See Ypsomed Holding AG; *Int'l*, pg. 8605

YPSOMED DIABETES, S.L.—See Ypsomed Holding AG; *Int'l*, pg. 8605

YPSOMED GMBH—See Ypsomed Holding AG; *Int'l*, pg. 8605

YPSOMED GMBH—See Ypsomed Holding AG; *Int'l*, pg. 8605

YPSOMED HOLDING AG; *Int'l*, pg. 8605

YPSOMED INDIA PRIVATE LTD.—See Ypsomed Holding AG; *Int'l*, pg. 8605

YPSOMED ITALIA S.R.L.—See Ypsomed Holding AG; *Int'l*, pg. 8605

YPSOMED LTD.—See Ypsomed Holding AG; *Int'l*, pg. 8605

YPSOMED MEDICAL DEVICES CO., LTD.—See Ypsomed Holding AG; *Int'l*, pg. 8605

YPSOMED S.A.S.—See Ypsomed Holding AG; *Int'l*, pg. 8605

YPSOMED S.R.L.—See Ypsomed Holding AG; *Int'l*, pg. 8605

YPSOTEC AG—See Ypsomed Holding AG; *Int'l*, pg. 8605

YPSOTEC S.R.O.—See Ypsomed Holding AG; *Int'l*, pg. 8605

YPSWITCH CO., LTD.—See TBS Holdings, Inc.; *Int'l*, pg. 7481

YPV DISTRIBUTION, INC.—See Kelso & Company, L.P.; *U.S. Private*, pg. 2279

YPV DISTRIBUTION, INC.—See Warburg Pincus LLC; *U.S. Private*, pg. 4437

Y&R ABU DHABI—See WPP plc; *Int'l*, pg. 8493

Y&R ANZ—See WPP plc; *Int'l*, pg. 8462

Y&R ANZ - SYDNEY—See WPP plc; *Int'l*, pg. 8462

Y&R ARGENTINA S.A.—See WPP plc; *Int'l*, pg. 8493

Y&R-ATLANTIC—See WPP plc; *Int'l*, pg. 8493

Y&R AUSTIN—See WPP plc; *Int'l*, pg. 8493

Y&R BELGIUM S.A.—See WPP plc; *Int'l*, pg. 8493

Y&R BUDAPEST—See WPP plc; *Int'l*, pg. 8493

Y&R CAPE TOWN—See WPP plc; *Int'l*, pg. 8493

YRC, INC.—See Yellow Corporation; *U.S. Public*, pg. 2398

YRC NORTH AMERICAN TRANSPORTATION, INC.—See Yellow Corporation; *U.S. Public*, pg. 2398

YRC REGIONAL TRANSPORTATION, INC.—See Yellow Corporation; *U.S. Public*, pg. 2398

YRGLM INC.; *Int'l*, pg. 8605

Y&R GMBH—See WPP plc; *Int'l*, pg. 8493

Y&R HONG KONG—See WPP plc; *Int'l*, pg. 8493

Y-RISK, LLC—See The Hartford Financial Services Group, Inc.; *U.S. Public*, pg. 2088

Y&R ITALIA, SRL—See WPP plc; *Int'l*, pg. 8493

YRITYSTELE OY—See Ratos AB; *Int'l*, pg. 6220

Y&R JOHANNESBURG—See WPP plc; *Int'l*, pg. 8493

Y&R LATIN AMERICAN HEADQUARTERS—See WPP plc; *Int'l*, pg. 8493

Y&R LTD.—See WPP plc; *Int'l*, pg. 8493

Y&R MEDIA—See WPP plc; *Int'l*, pg. 8474

Y&R MEDIA—See WPP plc; *Int'l*, pg. 8474

Y&R MEDIA—See WPP plc; *Int'l*, pg. 8474

Y&R MEDIA—See WPP plc; *Int'l*, pg. 8474

Y&R MIAMI—See WPP plc; *Int'l*, pg. 8493

Y&R PARIS S.A.—See WPP plc; *Int'l*, pg. 8493

Y&R PARIS—See WPP plc; *Int'l*, pg. 8493

Y&R PERU—See WPP plc; *Int'l*, pg. 8493

Y&R PORTUGAL—See WPP plc; *Int'l*, pg. 8493

Y&R PRAHA, S.R.O.—See WPP plc; *Int'l*, pg. 8493

Y&R PUERTO RICO, INC.—See WPP plc; *Int'l*, pg. 8493

Y&R SAO PAULO—See WPP plc; *Int'l*, pg. 8493

Y&R SINGAPORE—See WPP plc; *Int'l*, pg. 8493

Y&R—See WPP plc; *Int'l*, pg. 8493

Y&R—See WPP plc; *Int'l*, pg. 8493

Y&R—See WPP plc; *Int'l*, pg. 8493

Y&R TURKEY—See WPP plc; *Int'l*, pg. 8493

Y&R URUGUAY—See WPP plc; *Int'l*, pg. 8493

Y&R WEST—See WPP plc; *Int'l*, pg. 8493

Y.S. ASHKENAZI AGENCIES LTD.—See BRENNTAG SE; *Int'l*, pg. 1150

Y & S CANDIES—See The Hershey Co.; *U.S. Public*, pg. 2089

YSD DOORS, S.A. DE C.V—See The Greenbrier Companies, Inc.; *U.S. Public*, pg. 2086

Y.S. ENGINEERING LTD.—See Yuasa Trading Co., Ltd.; *Int'l*, pg. 8609

Y.S. FOOD CO., LTD.; *Int'l*, pg. 8543

Y'S GB LTD—See Yohji Yamamoto Inc.; *Int'l*, pg. 8591

YSG DOOR SECURITY CONSULTANTS—See ASSA ABLOY AB; *Int'l*, pg. 637

Y&S HANDBAG CO. INC.; *U.S. Private*, pg. 4584

YSI (HONG KONG) LTD.—See Xylem Inc.; *U.S. Public*, pg. 2395

YSI INCORPORATED—See Xylem Inc.; *U.S. Public*, pg. 2395

YSI INTEGRATED SYSTEMS & SERVICES—See Xylem Inc.; *U.S. Public*, pg. 2395
YSI NANOTECH—See Xylem Inc.; *U.S. Public*, pg. 2395
YSI (UK) LTD.—See Xylem Inc.; *U.S. Public*, pg. 2395
YS LOGISTICS PTE. LTD.—See Yamatane Corporation; *Int'l*, pg. 8553
Y.S. LOGISTICS SERVICE CO., LTD.—See Daicel Corporation; *Int'l*, pg. 1920
Y.S.P. (CAMBODIA) PTE. LTD.—See Y.S.P. Southeast Asia Holding Berhad; *Int'l*, pg. 8544
Y.S.P. INDUSTRIES (M) SDN. BHD. - CGMP FACTORY—See Y.S.P. Southeast Asia Holding Berhad; *Int'l*, pg. 8544
Y.S.P. INDUSTRIES (M) SDN. BHD.—See Y.S.P. Southeast Asia Holding Berhad; *Int'l*, pg. 8544
Y.S.P. INDUSTRIES VIETNAM CO., LTD.—See Y.S.P. Southeast Asia Holding Berhad; *Int'l*, pg. 8544
Y.S.P. SOUTHEAST ASIA HOLDING BERHAD; *Int'l*, pg. 8543
YSS CORP.; *Int'l*, pg. 8606
Y'S TABLE CORPORATION; *Int'l*, pg. 8543
YS TECH (THAILAND) CO., LTD.—See Honda Motor Co., Ltd.; *Int'l*, pg. 3465
Y.S. TECH USA INC.—See Yen Sun Technology Corp.; *Int'l*, pg. 8577
YSTRATEGIES CORP.; *U.S. Public*, pg. 2399
Y SUITES AUSTRALIA PTY. LTD.—See Wee Hur Holdings Ltd.; *Int'l*, pg. 8367
YT AUTOMATION SINGAPORE PTE. LTD.—See M2I Corporation; *Int'l*, pg. 4617
YTB INTERNATIONAL, INC.; *U.S. Private*, pg. 4595
YTC AMERICA INC.—See Yazaki Corporation; *Int'l*, pg. 8573
Y-TEKS CO., LTD.—See Kasai Kogyo Co., Ltd.; *Int'l*, pg. 4087
YTE TRANSPORT EQUIPMENT (SA) (PTY) LTD—See SAF-Holland S.A.; *Int'l*, pg. 6468
YTL CEMENT BERHAD—See YTL Corporation Berhad; *Int'l*, pg. 8606
YTL CORPORATION BERHAD; *Int'l*, pg. 8606
YTL HOSPITALITY REIT; *Int'l*, pg. 8606
YTL LAND & DEVELOPMENT BERHAD—See YTL Corporation Berhad; *Int'l*, pg. 8606
YTL POWER INTERNATIONAL BERHAD—See YTL Corporation Berhad; *Int'l*, pg. 8606
YTLS—See LS Corp.; *Int'l*, pg. 4560
YTL TECHNOLOGIES SDN BHD—See YTL Corporation Berhad; *Int'l*, pg. 8606
YTM-INDUSTRIAL OY—See Atlas Copco AB; *Int'l*, pg. 684
YTM-INDUSTRIAL OY—See Indutrade AB; *Int'l*, pg. 3682
YTN CO., LTD.; *Int'l*, pg. 8606
YTO EXPRESS GROUP CO., LTD.; *Int'l*, pg. 8606
YTO INTERNATIONAL EXPRESS AND SUPPLY CHAIN TECHNOLOGY LIMITED—See YTO Express Group Co., Ltd.; *Int'l*, pg. 8606
YT PARKSONG AUSTRALIA HOLDING PTY LIMITED—See Greentech Technology International Limited; *Int'l*, pg. 3076
Y&T POWER TECH., INC.—See TPR Co., Ltd.; *Int'l*, pg. 7884
Y. T. REALTY GROUP LIMITED; *Int'l*, pg. 8543
YUAN CHENG CABLE CO., LTD.; *Int'l*, pg. 8607
YUANCHENG ENVIRONMENT CO., LTD.; *Int'l*, pg. 8607
YUANDA ALUMINIUM INDUSTRY ENGINEERING (GERMANY) GMBH—See Yuanda China Holdings Limited; *Int'l*, pg. 8607
YUANDA ALUMINIUM INDUSTRY ENGINEERING (SINGAPORE) PTE LTD.—See Yuanda China Holdings Limited; *Int'l*, pg. 8607
YUANDA AUSTRALIA PTY LTD—See Yuanda China Holdings Limited; *Int'l*, pg. 8607
YUANDA CHINA HOLDINGS LIMITED; *Int'l*, pg. 8607
YUANDA CURTAIN WALL (SINGAPORE) PTE. LTD.—See Yuanda China Holdings Limited; *Int'l*, pg. 8607
YUANDA EUROPE LTD.—See Yuanda China Holdings Limited; *Int'l*, pg. 8607
YUANDA INTERNATIONAL ALUMINIUM ENGINEERING INDIA PRIVATE LIMITED—See Yuanda China Holdings Limited; *Int'l*, pg. 8607
YUANDA ITALY S.R.L.—See Yuanda China Holdings Limited; *Int'l*, pg. 8607
YUANDA (UK) CO., LTD.—See Yuanda China Holdings Limited; *Int'l*, pg. 8607
YUANDA WA PTY LTD.—See Yuanda China Holdings Limited; *Int'l*, pg. 8607
YUANFENG TRADING CO., LTD.—See Pabrik Kertas Tjiwi Kimia Tbk; *Int'l*, pg. 5684
YUAN HENG GAS HOLDINGS LIMITED; *Int'l*, pg. 8607
YUAN HIGH-TECH DEVELOPMENT CO., LTD.; *Int'l*, pg. 8607
YUAN HUA TECHNICAL & SUPPLY CORPORATION—See China COSCO Shipping Corporation Limited; *Int'l*, pg. 1492
YUAN JEN ENTERPRISES CO., LTD.; *Int'l*, pg. 8607
YUANLI CHEMICAL GROUP CO., LTD.; *Int'l*, pg. 8608
YUAN LONG PING HIGH-TECH AGRICULTURE CO., LTD.; *Int'l*, pg. 8607
YUAN LONG STAINLESS STEEL CORP.—See Asia Cement Corporation; *Int'l*, pg. 611

YUAN MEI XIN TECHNOLOGY (SHENZHEN) COMPANY LIMITED—See Perfect Optronics Ltd; *Int'l*, pg. 5799
YUAN RONG INDUSTRIAL GASES COMPANY LIMITED—See Linde plc; *Int'l*, pg. 4508
YUANSHENGTAI DAIRY FARM LIMITED; *Int'l*, pg. 8608
YUANTA COMMERCIAL BANK COMPANY LIMITED—See Yuanta Financial Holding Co., Ltd.; *Int'l*, pg. 8608
YUANTA FINANCIAL HOLDING CO., LTD.; *Int'l*, pg. 8608
YUANTA FUTURES (HONG KONG) LIMITED—See Yuanta Financial Holding Co., Ltd.; *Int'l*, pg. 8608
YUANTA INVESTMENT CONSULTING (BEIJING) CO., LTD.—See Yuanta Financial Holding Co., Ltd.; *Int'l*, pg. 8608
YUANTA LEASING CO., LTD.—See Yuanta Financial Holding Co., Ltd.; *Int'l*, pg. 8608
YUANTAL FUTURES CO., LTD.—See Yuanta Financial Holding Co., Ltd.; *Int'l*, pg. 8608
YUANTA LIFE INSURANCE CO., LTD.—See Yuanta Financial Holding Co., Ltd.; *Int'l*, pg. 8608
YUANTA SAVINGS BANK (KOREA) INC.—See Yuanta Financial Holding Co., Ltd.; *Int'l*, pg. 8608
YUANTA SAVINGS BANK (PHILIPPINES) INC.—See Yuanta Financial Holding Co., Ltd.; *Int'l*, pg. 8608
YUANTA SECURITIES (CAMBODIA) PLC—See Yuanta Financial Holding Co., Ltd.; *Int'l*, pg. 8608
YUANTA SECURITIES CO., LTD.—See Yuanta Financial Holding Co., Ltd.; *Int'l*, pg. 8608
YUANTA SECURITIES FINANCE CO., LTD.—See Yuanta Financial Holding Co., Ltd.; *Int'l*, pg. 8608
YUANTA SECURITIES (HONG KONG) COMPANY LIMITED—See Yuanta Financial Holding Co., Ltd.; *Int'l*, pg. 8608
YUANTA SECURITIES INVESTMENT CONSULTING CO., LTD.—See Yuanta Financial Holding Co., Ltd.; *Int'l*, pg. 8608
YUANTA SECURITIES INVESTMENT TRUST CO., LTD.—See Yuanta Financial Holding Co., Ltd.; *Int'l*, pg. 8608
YUANTA SECURITIES KOREA CO., LTD.—See TONGYANG Group; *Int'l*, pg. 7809
YUANTA SECURITIES THAILAND CO., LTD.—See Yuanta Financial Holding Co., Ltd.; *Int'l*, pg. 8608
YUANTA SECURITIES VIETNAM JOINT STOCK CO., LTD.—See Yuanta Financial Holding Co., Ltd.; *Int'l*, pg. 8608
YUANTA SECURITIES VIETNAM LIMITED COMPANY—See Yuanta Financial Holding Co., Ltd.; *Int'l*, pg. 8608
YUANTA VENTURE CAPITAL CORP.—See Yuanta Financial Holding Co., Ltd.; *Int'l*, pg. 8608
YUANTONG MARINE SERVICE CO. LIMITED—See China COSCO Shipping Corporation Limited; *Int'l*, pg. 1492
YUANTONG MARINE TRADE (SHANGHAI) CO. LIMITED—See China COSCO Shipping Corporation Limited; *Int'l*, pg. 1492
YUASA BATTERY (EAST AFRICA) LTD.—See GS Yuasa Corporation; *Int'l*, pg. 3143
YUASA BATTERY EUROPE LTD.—See GS Yuasa Corporation; *Int'l*, pg. 3143
YUASA BATTERY INC.; *U.S. Public*, pg. 4595
YUASA BATTERY (MALAYSIA) SDN. BHD. - MANUFACTURING PLANT—See GS Yuasa Corporation; *Int'l*, pg. 3143
YUASA BATTERY (MALAYSIA) SDN. BHD.—See GS Yuasa Corporation; *Int'l*, pg. 3143
YUASA BATTERY (SHUNDE) CO., LTD.—See GS Yuasa Corporation; *Int'l*, pg. 3143
YUASA BATTERY (THAILAND) PUBLIC COMPANY LIMITED; *Int'l*, pg. 8608
YUASA BUSINESS SUPPORT CO., LTD.—See Yuasa Trading Co., Ltd.; *Int'l*, pg. 8609
YUASA CONSTRUCTION EQUIPMENT SDN. BHD.—See Yuasa Trading Co., Ltd.; *Int'l*, pg. 8609
YUASA ENGINEERING SOLUTION (THAILAND) CO., LTD.—See Yuasa Trading Co., Ltd.; *Int'l*, pg. 8609
YUASA FUNASHOKU CO., LTD.; *Int'l*, pg. 8608
YUASA LUMBER CO., LTD.—See Yuasa Trading Co., Ltd.; *Int'l*, pg. 8609
YUASA MACROS CO., LTD.—See Yuasa Trading Co., Ltd.; *Int'l*, pg. 8609
YUASA MECHATRONICS (M) SDN. BHD.—See Yuasa Trading Co., Ltd.; *Int'l*, pg. 8609
YUASA MEMBRANE SYSTEMS CO., LTD.—See GS Yuasa Corporation; *Int'l*, pg. 3143
YUASA NENRYO CO., LTD.—See Yuasa Trading Co., Ltd.; *Int'l*, pg. 8609
YUASA POWER SYSTEMS (M) SDN BHD—See GS Yuasa Corporation; *Int'l*, pg. 3143
YUASA PRIMUS CO., LTD.—See Yuasa Trading Co., Ltd.; *Int'l*, pg. 8609
YUASA QUOBIS CO., LTD.—See Yuasa Trading Co., Ltd.; *Int'l*, pg. 8609
YUASA SALES & DISTRIBUTION CO., LTD.—See Yuasa Battery (Thailand) Public Company Limited; *Int'l*, pg. 8608
YUASA SATO (THAILAND) CO., LTD.—See Sato shoji Corporation; *Int'l*, pg. 6586

YUASA SHOJI MEXICO S.A. DE C.V.—See Yuasa Trading Co., Ltd.; *Int'l*, pg. 8609
YUASA SYSTEM SOLUTIONS CO., LTD.—See Yuasa Trading Co., Ltd.; *Int'l*, pg. 8609
YUASA TECHNICAL ENGINEERING CO., LTD.—See Yuasa Trading Co., Ltd.; *Int'l*, pg. 8609
YUASA (TIANJIN) TECHNOLOGY LTD.—See GS Yuasa Corporation; *Int'l*, pg. 3143
YUASA TRADING CO., LTD.; *Int'l*, pg. 8608
YUASA TRADING DEUTSCHLAND GMBH—See Yuasa Trading Co., Ltd.; *Int'l*, pg. 8609
YUASA TRADING INDIA PRIVATE LIMITED—See Yuasa Trading Co., Ltd.; *Int'l*, pg. 8609
YUASA TRADING (PHILIPPINES) INC.—See Yuasa Trading Co., Ltd.; *Int'l*, pg. 8609
YUASA TRADING (SHANGHAI) CO.—See Yuasa Trading Co., Ltd.; *Int'l*, pg. 8609
YUASA TRADING (TAIWAN) CO., LTD.—See Yuasa Trading Co., Ltd.; *Int'l*, pg. 8609
YUASA TRADING (THAILAND) CO., LTD.—See Yuasa Trading Co., Ltd.; *Int'l*, pg. 8609
YUASA TRADING VIETNAM CO., LTD.—See Yuasa Trading Co., Ltd.; *Int'l*, pg. 8609
YUASA-YI, INC.—See Yuasa Trading Co., Ltd.; *Int'l*, pg. 8609
YUBA CITY-CJD, INC.—See Lithia Motors, Inc.; *U.S. Public*, pg. 1326
YUBA COUNTY WATER AGENCY; *U.S. Private*, pg. 4595
YUBA RIVER MOULDING MILL WORK; *U.S. Private*, pg. 4595
YUBICO AB; *Int'l*, pg. 8609
YUBO INTERNATIONAL BIOTECH LTD.; *U.S. Public*, pg. 2399
YU BROTHERS, INC.; *U.S. Private*, pg. 4595
YUCAIPA ACQUISITION CORPORATION—See SIGNA Sports United N.V.; *Int'l*, pg. 6910
THE YUCAIPA COMPANIES LLC; *U.S. Private*, pg. 4139
YUCAIPA DIALYSIS, LLC—See DaVita Inc.; *U.S. Public*, pg. 644
YUCATAN FOODS, LLC—See Flagship Food Group, LLC; *U.S. Private*, pg. 1539
YUCCA VALLEY CHRYSLER CENTER; *U.S. Private*, pg. 4595
YUCCA VALLEY FORD CENTER, INC.; *U.S. Private*, pg. 4595
YUCHENGCO GROUP OF COMPANIES; *Int'l*, pg. 8609
YU CHENG MATERIALS CO., LTD.—See Headway Advanced Materials Inc.; *Int'l*, pg. 3302
YUCHENG TECHNOLOGIES LIMITED; *Int'l*, pg. 8609
YUDEN BUILDING KANRI CO., LTD.—See Mitsubishi Estate Co., Ltd.; *Int'l*, pg. 4947
YU DING PRECISION ELECTRONICS (HUAIAN) CO., LTD.—See Zhen Ding Technology Holding Limited; *Int'l*, pg. 8669
YUDIZ SOLUTIONS LIMITED; *Int'l*, pg. 8610
Y.U.D YANGTZE RIVER INVESTMENT INDUSTRY CO., LTD.; *Int'l*, pg. 8544
YUE DA INTERNATIONAL HOLDINGS LIMITED; *Int'l*, pg. 8610
YUEH CHYANG CANNED FOOD CO., LTD.—See Thai Union Group Public Company Limited; *Int'l*, pg. 7597
YUE KAN HOLDINGS LIMITED; *Int'l*, pg. 8610
YUEN CHANG STAINLESS STEEL CO., LTD.; *Int'l*, pg. 8610
YUENGLING BEER COMPANY OF TAMPA, INC.—See D.G. Yuengling & Son Incorporated; *U.S. Private*, pg. 1142
YUENGLING'S ICE CREAM CORPORATION; *U.S. Public*, pg. 2399
YUEN SANG WATCH INDUSTRIES LIMITED—See Chuang's Consortium International Limited; *Int'l*, pg. 1590
YUEQING ZHONGSHENG XINGHUI AUTOMOBILE SALES & SERVICE CO.—See Zhongsheng Group Holdings Limited; *Int'l*, pg. 8674
YUEQING ZHONGYU GAS CO.—See Zhongyu Energy Holdings Limited; *Int'l*, pg. 8676
YUE SHENG INDUSTRIAL CO., LTD.—See Central Glass Co., Ltd.; *Int'l*, pg. 1407
YUE-SHEN (TAICANG) FOOTWEAR CO. LTD.—See Pou Sheng International (Holdings) Limited; *Int'l*, pg. 5942
YUES INTERNATIONAL HOLDINGS GROUP LIMITED; *Int'l*, pg. 8610
YUE XIU APT PARKING LIMITED—See Yuexiu Property Company Limited; *Int'l*, pg. 8611
YUE XIU ENTERPRISES (HOLDINGS) LIMITED; *Int'l*, pg. 8610
YUEXIU FINANCIAL HOLDINGS LIMITED—See Yue Xiu Enterprises (Holdings) Limited; *Int'l*, pg. 8610
YUEXIU PROPERTY COMPANY LIMITED; *Int'l*, pg. 8611
YUEXIU REAL ESTATE INVESTMENT TRUST; *Int'l*, pg. 8611
YUE XIU SECURITIES COMPANY LIMITED—See Yue Xiu Enterprises (Holdings) Limited; *Int'l*, pg. 8610
YUEXIU SERVICES GROUP LIMITED; *Int'l*, pg. 8611
YUEXIU TRANSPORT INFRASTRUCTURE LIMITED; *Int'l*, pg. 8611
YUEYANG CAMEL FEED CO., LTD—See Tangrenshen Group Co., Ltd.; *Int'l*, pg. 7458
YUEYANG FOREST & PAPER CO., LTD.; *Int'l*, pg. 8611

YUEYANG MEIBAOHANG AUTO SALES & SERVICES CO., LTD.—See China MeiDong Auto Holdings Limited; *Int'l*, pg. 1519
YUEYANG XINGCHANG PETRO-CHEMICAL CO., LTD.; *Int'l*, pg. 8611
YUE YUEN INDUSTRIAL HOLDINGS LIMITED; *Int'l*, pg. 8610
YUE YUEN INDUSTRIAL LIMITED—See Yue Yuen Industrial Holdings Limited; *Int'l*, pg. 8610
YUFLOW ENGINEERING PVT LTD—See Yuken India Ltd.; *Int'l*, pg. 8612
YUFO ELECTRONICS CO., LTD.; *Int'l*, pg. 8611
YUG DECOR LIMITED; *Int'l*, pg. 8611
YUGOSLAVIA COMMERCE A.D.; *Int'l*, pg. 8611
YU GROUP PLC; *Int'l*, pg. 8607
YUHAN ANZ PTY LTD.—See Yuhan Corporation; *Int'l*, pg. 8611
YUHAN CHEMICAL, INC.—See Yuhan Corporation; *Int'l*, pg. 8611
YUHAN CORPORATION; *Int'l*, pg. 8611
YUHAN CORPORATION - SYNTHETIC PLANT—See Yuhan Corporation; *Int'l*, pg. 8611
YUHAN-KIMBERLY, LIMITED—See Kimberly-Clark Corporation; *U.S. Public*, pg. 1230
YUHAN MEDICA CORPORATION—See Yuhan Corporation; *Int'l*, pg. 8611
YUHAN USA CORPORATION—See Yuhan Corporation; *Int'l*, pg. 8611
YUHE INTERNATIONAL, INC.; *Int'l*, pg. 8611
YUHO CO., LTD.—See Toyobo Co., Ltd.; *Int'l*, pg. 7861
YUHO NIITAKA CO., LTD.—See Niitaka Co., Ltd.; *Int'l*, pg. 5289
YUHOR A.D.—See Delta Holding; *Int'l*, pg. 2018
YUHSHIN INDUSTRIAL CO., LTD.—See Minebea Mitsumi Inc.; *Int'l*, pg. 4905
YUHSHIN U.S.A. LIMITED—See Minebea Mitsumi Inc.; *Int'l*, pg. 4905
YU HUA LOONG TRADING SDN. BHD.—See Sinochem Corporation; *Int'l*, pg. 6951
YUHUAN CNC MACHINE TOOL CO., LTD.; *Int'l*, pg. 8611
YUHWA SECURITIES CO., LTD.; *Int'l*, pg. 8611
YUIL ROBOTICS CO., LTD.; *Int'l*, pg. 8611
YUJIN CO., LTD.; *Int'l*, pg. 8611
YUJIN ROBOT CO., LTD.; *Int'l*, pg. 8611
YUJIN SMRC AUTOMOTIVE TECHNO CORP.—See Samvardhana Motherson International Limited; *Int'l*, pg. 6518
YUJI SUGAI—See Hitachi, Ltd.; *Int'l*, pg. 3419
YUKA DENSHI COMPANY LIMITED - IBARAKI PLANT—See Mitsubishi Chemical Group Corporation; *Int'l*, pg. 4935
YUKA DENSHI COMPANY LIMITED—See Mitsubishi Chemical Group Corporation; *Int'l*, pg. 4934
YUKA DENSHI COMPANY LIMITED - SUZUKA PLANT—See Mitsubishi Chemical Group Corporation; *Int'l*, pg. 4935
YUKA DENSHI COMPANY LIMITED - YOKKAICHI PLANT—See Mitsubishi Chemical Group Corporation; *Int'l*, pg. 4935
YUKA PRECISION (WUJIANG) CO., LTD.—See Audix Corporation; *Int'l*, pg. 702
YUKA SANGYO CO., LTD.—See NOF Corporation; *Int'l*, pg. 5400
YUKA SANSHO KENZAI CO., LTD.—See Mitsubishi Gas Chemical Company, Inc.; *Int'l*, pg. 4948
YUK CUISINE LIMITED—See Echo International Holdings Group Limited; *Int'l*, pg. 2289
YUKEN CR S.R.O.—See Yuken Kogyo Co., Ltd.; *Int'l*, pg. 8612
YUKEN EUROPE LTD.—See Yuken Kogyo Co., Ltd.; *Int'l*, pg. 8612
YUKEN HYDRAULICS (T.W.) CO., LTD.—See Yuken Kogyo Co., Ltd.; *Int'l*, pg. 8612
YUKEN HYDRAULICS (ZHANGJIAGANG) CO., LTD.—See Yuken Kogyo Co., Ltd.; *Int'l*, pg. 8612
YUKEN INDIA LTD.; *Int'l*, pg. 8612
YUKEN KOGYO CO., LTD. - FUKURODA FACTORY—See Yuken Kogyo Co., Ltd.; *Int'l*, pg. 8612
YUKEN KOGYO CO., LTD.; *Int'l*, pg. 8612
YUKEN KOGYO (FOSHAN) CO., LTD.—See Yuken Kogyo Co., Ltd.; *Int'l*, pg. 8612
YUKEN KOGYO (H.K.) CO., LTD.—See Yuken Kogyo Co., Ltd.; *Int'l*, pg. 8612
YUKEN KOGYO (NINGBO) HYDRAULIC TECHNOLOGY CO., LTD.—See Yuken Kogyo Co., Ltd.; *Int'l*, pg. 8612
YUKEN KOGYO (SHANGHAI) CO., LTD.—See Yuken Kogyo Co., Ltd.; *Int'l*, pg. 8612
YUKEN KOREA CO., LTD.—See Yuken Kogyo Co., Ltd.; *Int'l*, pg. 8612
YUKEN SEA CO., LTD.—See Yuken Kogyo Co., Ltd.; *Int'l*, pg. 8612
YUKES CO., LTD.; *Int'l*, pg. 8612
YUKI GOSEI KOGYO CO.LTD. - JOBAN FACTORY—See Yuki Gosei Kogyo Co., Ltd.; *Int'l*, pg. 8612
YUKI GOSEI KOGYO CO., LTD.; *Int'l*, pg. 8612
YUKIGUNI MAITAKE CO., LTD.; *Int'l*, pg. 8612
YUKI SANGYO CO., LTD.—See ES-CON JAPAN Ltd.; *Int'l*, pg. 2500

YUKON DELTA FISHERIES DEVELOPMENT ASSOCIATION; *U.S. Private*, pg. 4595
THE YUKON ELECTRICAL CO. LTD.—See ATCO Ltd.; *Int'l*, pg. 667
YUKON MINT CORPORATION.—See Victoria Gold Corp.; *Int'l*, pg. 8188
YUKON PARTNERS MANAGEMENT LLC; *U.S. Private*, pg. 4595
YUKON TITLE COMPANY, INC.—See Stewart Information Services Corporation; *U.S. Public*, pg. 1948
YUKON ZINC CORPORATION—See Jinduicheng Molybdenum Group Co., Ltd.; *Int'l*, pg. 3967
YUKOTERRE RESOURCES, INC.; *Int'l*, pg. 8612
YUKOU CO., LTD.—See Moriroku Holdings Company, Ltd.; *Int'l*, pg. 5047
YUKSELEN CELIK A.S.; *Int'l*, pg. 8612
YUKSEL INSAAT A.S.—See Torunlar Gayrimenkul Yatirim Ortakligi AS; *Int'l*, pg. 7831
YUK WING DEVELOPMENT LTD.—See Tah Hsin Industrial Corporation; *Int'l*, pg. 7407
YUK WING GROUP HOLDINGS LIMITED; *Int'l*, pg. 8612
YULE CATTO HOLDINGS GMBH—See Synthomer plc; *Int'l*, pg. 7387
YULHO CO., LTD.; *Int'l*, pg. 8612
YULI ELECTRONIC CO., LTD.—See FSP Technology Inc.; *Int'l*, pg. 2800
YULIN TIANNING MINING SERVICE CO., LTD.—See Shandong Mining Machinery Group Co., Ltd.; *Int'l*, pg. 6756
YULISTA HOLDING, LLC—See Chiulista Services, Inc.; *U.S. Private*, pg. 887
YULISTA MANAGEMENT SERVICES, INC.—See Chiulista Services, Inc.; *U.S. Private*, pg. 887
YULON FINANCE CORPORATION; *Int'l*, pg. 8612
YULON FINANCE PHILIPPINES CORPORATION—See Yulon Finance Corporation; *Int'l*, pg. 8613
YULONG ECO-MATERIALS LIMITED; *Int'l*, pg. 8613
YULON MOTOR CO., LTD.—See Nissan Motor Co., Ltd.; *Int'l*, pg. 5369
YULON NISSAN MOTOR CO., LTD.; *Int'l*, pg. 8613
YUMA ADVANCED SURGICAL SUITES, LLC—See Tenet Healthcare Corporation; *U.S. Public*, pg. 2015
THE YUMA AZ ENDOSCOPY ASC, LLC—See KKR & Co. Inc.; *U.S. Public*, pg. 1249
THE YUMA COMPANIES; *U.S. Private*, pg. 4140
YUMA HOSPITALITY PROPERTIES, LTD.—See InnSuites Hospitality Trust; *U.S. Public*, pg. 1128
YUMA REHABILITATION HOSPITAL, LLC—See Encompass Health Corporation; *U.S. Public*, pg. 759
YUMA RESOURCES, INC.; *Int'l*, pg. 8613
YUMA SUN—See Horizon Publications Inc.; *U.S. Private*, pg. 1982
YUMBA RECORDS STORAGE, INC.; *Int'l*, pg. 8613
YUM! BRANDS, INC.; *U.S. Public*, pg. 2400
YUM CHINA HOLDINGS, INC.; *U.S. Public*, pg. 2399
YUMCO A.D.; *Int'l*, pg. 8613
YUME CORPORATION CO., LTD.—See Dynam Japan Holdings, Co., Ltd.; *Int'l*, pg. 2239
YUME HOUSE CO., LTD.—See Watahan & Co., Ltd.; *Int'l*, pg. 8355
YUMEI BIOTEC CORPORATION—See Sinon Corporation; *Int'l*, pg. 6953
YUMEI TECHNOLOGIES SDN. BHD.—See Advanced Systems Automation Limited; *Int'l*, pg. 162
YUMEMITSUKETAI CO., LTD.; *Int'l*, pg. 8613
YUME PROENG CO., LTD.—See Yumeshin Holdings Co., Ltd.; *Int'l*, pg. 8613
YUMESHIN CO., LTD.—See Yumeshin Holdings Co., Ltd.; *Int'l*, pg. 8613
YUMESHIN EXPERT CO., LTD.—See Open Up Group Inc; *Int'l*, pg. 5599
YUMESHIN HOLDINGS CO., LTD.; *Int'l*, pg. 8613
YUMESHO LTD.—See Autobacs Seven Co., Ltd.; *Int'l*, pg. 726
YUME TECHNOLOGY CO., LTD.—See Yumeshin Holdings Co., Ltd.; *Int'l*, pg. 8613
YUMIGAHAMA SUISAN CO., LTD.—See Nissui Corporation; *Int'l*, pg. 5379
YUMI YUMI CATERERS LIMITED—See Cafe de Coral Holdings Limited; *Int'l*, pg. 1250
YUMMIES, INC.; *Int'l*, pg. 8613
YUMMLY, INC.—See Whirlpool Corporation; *U.S. Public*, pg. 2368
YUMMY MARKET INC.; *Int'l*, pg. 8613
YUMMY (S) PTE. LTD.—See Natural Cool Holdings Limited; *Int'l*, pg. 5168
YUM! RESTAURANTS AUSTRALIA PTY. LIMITED—See Yum! Brands, Inc.; *U.S. Public*, pg. 2400
YUM! RESTAURANTS CHINA HOLDINGS LIMITED—See Yum China Holdings, Inc.; *U.S. Public*, pg. 2399
YUM! RESTAURANTS CONSULTING (SHANGHAI) CO., LTD.—See Yum China Holdings, Inc.; *U.S. Public*, pg. 2400
YUM! RESTAURANTS EUROPE LIMITED—See Yum! Brands, Inc.; *U.S. Public*, pg. 2400
YUM! RESTAURANTS INTERNATIONAL—See Yum! Brands, Inc.; *U.S. Public*, pg. 2400
YUM! RESTAURANTS (SHENZHEN) CO., LTD.—See Yum China Holdings, Inc.; *U.S. Public*, pg. 2400

YUM! RESTAURANTS (XIAN) CO., LTD.—See Yum China Holdings, Inc.; *U.S. Public*, pg. 2400
YUM YUM DONUT SHOPS, INC.; *U.S. Private*, pg. 4595
YUNARI CO., LTD.—See create restaurants holdings inc.; *Int'l*, pg. 1832
YUNCHENG BAOZEN AUTOMOBILE SALES AND SERVICES CO., LTD.—See China Yongda Automobiles Services Holdings Limited; *Int'l*, pg. 1565
YUNDA HOLDING CO., LTD.; *Int'l*, pg. 8613
YUNDING TECHNOLOGY CO., LTD.; *Int'l*, pg. 8613
YUNFENG CAPITAL; *Int'l*, pg. 8613
YUNFENG FINANCIAL GROUP LIMITED; *Int'l*, pg. 8613
YUNG CHI PAINT & VARNISH MFG CO., LTD.; *Int'l*, pg. 8614
YUNG CHI PAINT & VARNISH MFG., (KUNSHAN) CO., LTD.—See Yung Chi Paint & Varnish Mfg Co., Ltd.; *Int'l*, pg. 8614
YUNG CHI PAINT & VARNISH MFG., (MALAYSIA) CO., LTD.—See Yung Chi Paint & Varnish Mfg Co., Ltd.; *Int'l*, pg. 8614
YUNG CHI PAINT & VARNISH MFG., (VIETNAM) CO., LTD.—See Yung Chi Paint & Varnish Mfg Co., Ltd.; *Int'l*, pg. 8614
YUNG-FU CO., LTD.—See Taiwan Styrene Monomer Corporation; *Int'l*, pg. 7424
YUNG FU ELECTRICAL APPLIANCES CORP.—See Lasonic Electronics Corporation; *U.S. Private*, pg. 2395
YUNG HSIN CONTAIN INDUSTRY CO. LTD.—See Time Technoplast Limited; *Int'l*, pg. 7751
YUNGJIN PHARMACEUTICAL COMPANY LTD.—See KT&G Corporation; *Int'l*, pg. 4316
YUNGSHIN CO (HONG KONG) LTD.—See YungShin Global Holding Corporation; *Int'l*, pg. 8614
YUNG SHIN COMPANY LIMITED—See YungShin Global Holding Corporation; *Int'l*, pg. 8614
YUNGSHIN CONSTRUCTION & DEVELOPMENT CO., LTD.; *Int'l*, pg. 8614
YUNGSHIN GLOBAL HOLDING CORPORATION; *Int'l*, pg. 8614
YUNG SHIN PHARMACEUTICAL IND. (KUNSHAN) CO., LTD.—See YungShin Global Holding Corporation; *Int'l*, pg. 8614
YUNG SHIN PHARMACEUTICAL INDUSTRIAL CO.—See YungShin Global Holding Corporation; *Int'l*, pg. 8614
YUNG SHIN PHARMACEUTICAL (SINGAPORE) PTE. LTD.—See Y.S.P. Southeast Asia Holding Berhad; *Int'l*, pg. 8544
YUNGSHIN PHARM. IND. (KS) CO., LTD.—See YungShin Global Holding Corporation; *Int'l*, pg. 8614
YUNG SHIN PHARM IND (KUNGSHAN) CO., LTD.—See Y.S.P. Southeast Asia Holding Berhad; *Int'l*, pg. 8544
YUNGSHIN. PHARM. INDONESIA, PT—See YungShin Global Holding Corporation; *Int'l*, pg. 8614
YUNG SHIN (PHILIPPINES), INC.—See Y.S.P. Southeast Asia Holding Berhad; *Int'l*, pg. 8544
YUNGTAY ENGINEERING CO., LTD.—See Hitachi, Ltd.; *Int'l*, pg. 3424
YUNGTAY ENGINEERING CO., LTD. - TAOYUAN FACTORY—See Hitachi, Ltd.; *Int'l*, pg. 3425
YUNGTAY-HITACHI CONSTRUCTION MACHINERY CO., LTD.—See Hitachi, Ltd.; *Int'l*, pg. 3416
YUNG ZIP CHEMICAL CO., LTD.—See YungShin Global Holding Corporation; *Int'l*, pg. 8614
YUNG ZIP CHEMICAL IND. CO., LTD.—See Y.S.P. Southeast Asia Holding Berhad; *Int'l*, pg. 8544
YUNHONG GREEN CTI LTD.; *U.S. Public*, pg. 2400
YUNHONG GUIXIN GROUP HOLDINGS LIMITED; *Int'l*, pg. 8614
YUNHONG INTERNATIONAL; *Int'l*, pg. 8614
YUNJI INC.; *Int'l*, pg. 8614
YUNKANG GROUP LIMITED; *Int'l*, pg. 8614
YUNKE CHINA INFORMATION TECHNOLOGY LIMITED—See Digital China Holdings Limited; *Int'l*, pg. 2121
YUN LEE MARINE GROUP HOLDINGS LTD.; *Int'l*, pg. 8613
YUNNAN ALUMINIUM CO., LTD.; *Int'l*, pg. 8614
YUNNAN BAIYAO GROUP CO., LTD.; *Int'l*, pg. 8614
YUNNAN BOTANEE BIO-TECHNOLOGY GROUP CO., LTD.; *Int'l*, pg. 8614
YUNNAN BOWIN TECHNOLOGY & INDUSTRY CO., LTD.; *Int'l*, pg. 8615
YUNNAN BOW YUE VEHICLE TRADING CO. LTD.—See Sime Darby Berhad; *Int'l*, pg. 6931
YUNNAN CHIHONG ZINC & GERMANIUM CO., LTD.; *Int'l*, pg. 8615
YUNNAN CHUN WU ZHI FLORAL CO.,LTD.; *Int'l*, pg. 8615
YUNNAN COAL & ENERGY CO., LTD.; *Int'l*, pg. 8615
YUNNAN COPPER CO., LTD.; *Int'l*, pg. 8615
YUNNAN COPPER FURUKAWA ELECTRIC CO.,LTD.—See The Furukawa Electric Co., Ltd.; *Int'l*, pg. 7647
YUNNAN DALI CQRC VILLAGE & TOWNSHIP BANK CO., LTD.—See Chongqing Rural Commercial Bank Co., Ltd.; *Int'l*, pg. 1581
YUNNAN DALI FOODS CO., LTD.—See Dali Foods Group Co. Ltd.; *Int'l*, pg. 1951

COMPANY NAME INDEX — YU TAK INTERNATIONAL HOLDINGS LIMITED

YUNNAN ENERGY INTERNATIONAL CO. LTD.; *Int'l*, pg. 8615
YUNNAN ENERGY INVESTMENT CO., LTD.; *Int'l*, pg. 8615
YUNNAN ENERGY NEW MATERIAL CO., LTD.; *Int'l*, pg. 8615
YUNNAN HEQING CQRC VILLAGE & TOWNSHIP BANK CO., LTD.—See Chongqing Rural Commercial Bank Co., Ltd.; *Int'l*, pg. 1581
YUNNAN HUAFANG INDUSTRIAL HEMP CO., LTD.—See Stemcell United Limited; *Int'l*, pg. 7205
YUNNAN JIANZHIJIA HEALTH-CHAIN CO., LTD.; *Int'l*, pg. 8615
YUNNAN JINGGU FORESTRY CO., LTD.; *Int'l*, pg. 8615
YUNNAN KUNLENE FILM INDUSTRIES CO., LTD.—See PT Indopoly Swakarsa Industry Tbk; *Int'l*, pg. 6046
YUNNAN LINCANG XINYUAN GERMANIUM INDUSTRIAL CO., LTD.; *Int'l*, pg. 8615
YUNNAN LONGRUN TEA GROUP COMPANY LIMITED; *Int'l*, pg. 8615
YUNNAN LUOPING ZINC & ELECTRICITY CO., LTD.; *Int'l*, pg. 8615
YUNNAN MACCURA SCIENCE & TECHNOLOGY CO., LTD.—See Maccura Biotechnology Co., Ltd.; *Int'l*, pg. 4620
YUNNAN METROPOLITAN REAL ESTATE DEVELOPMENT CO., LTD.; *Int'l*, pg. 8616
YUNNAN MILE PHOSPHORUS ELECTRICITY CO., LTD.—See Jiangsu Chengxing Phosph-Chemicals Co., Ltd.; *Int'l*, pg. 3945
YUNNAN NANTIAN ELECTRONICS INFORMATION CO., LTD.; *Int'l*, pg. 8616
YUNNAN NANTIAN INFORMATION EQUIPMENT CO., LTD.—See Yunnan Nantian Electronics Information Co., Ltd.; *Int'l*, pg. 8616
YUNNAN QIAOTONG PACKAGE PRINTING CO., LTD.—See Tesson Holdings Limited; *Int'l*, pg. 7575
YUNNAN SHANGRI-LA CQRC VILLAGE & TOWNSHIP BANK CO., LTD.—See Chongqing Rural Commercial Bank Co., Ltd.; *Int'l*, pg. 1581
YUNNAN SHENNONG AGRICULTURAL INDUSTRY GROUP CO., LTD.; *Int'l*, pg. 8616
YUNNAN SHENYU NEW ENERGY COMPANY LIMITED—See China Sandi Holdings Limited; *Int'l*, pg. 1549
YUNNAN TAIKOO FLOWERS LIMITED—See John Swire & Sons Limited; *Int'l*, pg. 3981
YUNNAN TELINDUS TECHNOLOGY CO. LTD.—See Proximus PLC; *Int'l*, pg. 6008
YUNNAN TIN CO., LTD.; *Int'l*, pg. 8616
YUNNAN TOURISM CO., LTD.; *Int'l*, pg. 8616
YUNNAN VOLCAFE COMPANY LIMITED—See ED&F Man Holdings Limited; *Int'l*, pg. 2303
YUNNAN WATER INVESTMENT CO., LIMITED; *Int'l*, pg. 8616
YUNNAN WENSHAN ELECTRIC POWER CO., LTD.; *Int'l*, pg. 8616
YUNNAN XIANGYUN CQRC VILLAGE AND TOWNSHIP BANK CO., LTD.—See Shenguan Holdings (Group) Limited; *Int'l*, pg. 6802
YUNNAN XISHAN CQRC VILLAGE & TOWNSHIP BANK CO., LTD.—See Chongqing Rural Commercial Bank Co., Ltd.; *Int'l*, pg. 1581
YUNNAN XIYI INDUSTRY CO., LTD.; *Int'l*, pg. 8616
YUNNAN XUANWEI PHOSPHORUS ELECTRICITY CO., LTD.—See Jiangsu Chengxing Phosph-Chemicals Co., Ltd.; *Int'l*, pg. 3945
YUNNAN YULINQUAN LIQUOR CO., LTD.—See Thai Beverage Public Company Limited; *Int'l*, pg. 7592
YUNNAN YUNTIANHUA CO., LTD.; *Int'l*, pg. 8616
YUNNAN YUNTOU ECOLOGY & ENVIRONMENT TECHNOLOGY CO., LTD.; *Int'l*, pg. 8616
YUNNAN YUNWEI CO., LTD.; *Int'l*, pg. 8616
YUNNAN ZHONGSHENG STAR AUTOMOBILE SALES & SERVICE CO., LTD.—See Zhongsheng Group Holdings Limited; *Int'l*, pg. 8674
YUNNAN ZHONGSHENG YUANAN KUNXING AUTOMOBILE SALES & SERVICE CO., LTD.—See Zhongsheng Group Holdings Limited; *Int'l*, pg. 8675
YUNNUN XIANGYUN CQRC VILLAGE & TOWNSHIP BANK CO., LTD.—See Chongqing Rural Commercial Bank Co., Ltd.; *Int'l*, pg. 1581
YUNONA OAO—See Silvano Fashion Group AS; *Int'l*, pg. 6922
YUNSA YUNLU SANAYI VE TICARET A.S.—See Haci Omer Sabanci Holding A.S.; *Int'l*, pg. 3204
YUNSHENG USA INC.—See Ningbo Yunsheng Co., Ltd.; *Int'l*, pg. 5307
YUNTINIC (HONG KONG) RESOURCES CO., LTD.—See Yunnan Tin Co., Ltd.; *Int'l*, pg. 8616
YUNTINIC RESOURCES, GMBH—See Yunnan Tin Co., Ltd.; *Int'l*, pg. 8616
YUNTINIC RESOURCES, INC.—See Yunnan Tin Co., Ltd.; *Int'l*, pg. 8616
YUNUS TEXTILE MILLS LIMITED—See Lucky Cement Limited; *Int'l*, pg. 4574
YUPINGLOU HOTEL OF HUANGSHAN TOURISM DEVELOPMENT CO., LTD.—See Huangshan Tourism Development Co., Ltd.; *Int'l*, pg. 3513

YURA CHILE SA—See Consorcio Cementero del Sur SA; *Int'l*, pg. 1772
YURA CORPORATION D.O.O—See YURATECH Co., Ltd.; *Int'l*, pg. 8617
YURA CORPORATION RUS—See YURATECH Co., Ltd.; *Int'l*, pg. 8617
YURA CORPORATION SLOVAKIA, S.R.O—See YURATECH Co., Ltd.; *Int'l*, pg. 8617
YURA CORPORATION—See YURATECH Co., Ltd.; *Int'l*, pg. 8617
YURA CORPORATION TUNISIA SARL—See YURATECH Co., Ltd.; *Int'l*, pg. 8617
YURA HARNESS CO., LTD.—See YURATECH Co., Ltd.; *Int'l*, pg. 8617
YURATECH CO., LTD. - GYOENGJU PLANT—See YURATECH Co., Ltd.; *Int'l*, pg. 8617
YURATECH CO., LTD. - PYEONGTAEK PLANT—See YURATECH Co., Ltd.; *Int'l*, pg. 8617
YURATECH CO., LTD.; *Int'l*, pg. 8617
YURI GAGARIN PLC; *Int'l*, pg. 8617
YURMAN DESIGN, INC.; *U.S. Private*, pg. 4595
YURTEC CORPORATION; *Int'l*, pg. 8617
YURTEC VIETNAM CO., LTD.—See Yurtec Corporation; *Int'l*, pg. 8617
YUSEI HOLDINGS LTD.; *Int'l*, pg. 8617
YUSEI NISHI-KYUSHU SEIKA CO.,LTD.—See Crest Investments Co., Ltd.; *Int'l*, pg. 1840
YUSEN INCI LOJISTIK VE TICARET A.S.—See Nippon Yusen Kabushiki Kaisha; *Int'l*, pg. 5360
YUSEN KOUN CO., LTD.—See Nippon Yusen Kabushiki Kaisha; *Int'l*, pg. 5360
YUSEN LOGISTICS (AMERICAS) INC.—See Nippon Yusen Kabushiki Kaisha; *Int'l*, pg. 5360
YUSEN LOGISTICS (AMERICAS) INC.—See Nippon Yusen Kabushiki Kaisha; *Int'l*, pg. 5360
YUSEN LOGISTICS (ARGENTINA) S.A.—See Nippon Yusen Kabushiki Kaisha; *Int'l*, pg. 5360
YUSEN LOGISTICS (AUSTRALIA) PTY. LTD.—See Nippon Yusen Kabushiki Kaisha; *Int'l*, pg. 5361
YUSEN LOGISTICS (BANGLADESH) LTD.—See Nippon Yusen Kabushiki Kaisha; *Int'l*, pg. 5360
YUSEN LOGISTICS (BENELUX) B.V.—See Nippon Yusen Kabushiki Kaisha; *Int'l*, pg. 5360
YUSEN LOGISTICS (CAMBODIA) CO., LTD.—See Nippon Yusen Kabushiki Kaisha; *Int'l*, pg. 5360
YUSEN LOGISTICS (CANADA) INC.—See Nippon Yusen Kabushiki Kaisha; *Int'l*, pg. 5360
YUSEN LOGISTICS CENTER, INC.—See Nippon Yusen Kabushiki Kaisha; *Int'l*, pg. 5360
YUSEN LOGISTICS (CHINA) CO., LTD.—See Nippon Yusen Kabushiki Kaisha; *Int'l*, pg. 5360
YUSEN LOGISTICS CO., LTD.—See Nippon Yusen Kabushiki Kaisha; *Int'l*, pg. 5360
YUSEN LOGISTICS (CZECH) S.R.O.—See Nippon Yusen Kabushiki Kaisha; *Int'l*, pg. 5360
YUSEN LOGISTICS (DEUTSCHLAND) GMBH—See Nippon Yusen Kabushiki Kaisha; *Int'l*, pg. 5360
YUSEN LOGISTICS DO BRASIL LTDA.—See Nippon Yusen Kabushiki Kaisha; *Int'l*, pg. 5361
YUSEN LOGISTICS (EDAM) B.V.—See Nippon Yusen Kabushiki Kaisha; *Int'l*, pg. 5360
YUSEN LOGISTICS (EUROPE) B.V.—See Nippon Yusen Kabushiki Kaisha; *Int'l*, pg. 5360
YUSEN LOGISTICS (FRANCE) S.A.S.—See Nippon Yusen Kabushiki Kaisha; *Int'l*, pg. 5361
YUSEN LOGISTICS (HONG KONG) LTD.—See Nippon Yusen Kabushiki Kaisha; *Int'l*, pg. 5360
YUSEN LOGISTICS (HUNGARY) KFT.—See Nippon Yusen Kabushiki Kaisha; *Int'l*, pg. 5360
YUSEN LOGISTICS (IBERICA) S.A.—See Nippon Yusen Kabushiki Kaisha; *Int'l*, pg. 5360
YUSEN LOGISTICS (INDIA) PTE. LTD.—See Nippon Yusen Kabushiki Kaisha; *Int'l*, pg. 5360
YUSEN LOGISTICS (ITALY) S.P.A.—See Nippon Yusen Kabushiki Kaisha; *Int'l*, pg. 5360
YUSEN LOGISTICS (KOREA) CO., LTD.—See Nippon Yusen Kabushiki Kaisha; *Int'l*, pg. 5360
YUSEN LOGISTICS & KUSUHARA LANKA PVT LTD—See Nippon Yusen Kabushiki Kaisha; *Int'l*, pg. 5360
YUSEN LOGISTICS (LAO) CO., LTD.—See Nippon Yusen Kabushiki Kaisha; *Int'l*, pg. 5360
YUSEN LOGISTICS (MEXICO), S.A. DE C.V.—See Nippon Yusen Kabushiki Kaisha; *Int'l*, pg. 5360
YUSEN LOGISTICS (MIDDLE EAST) L.L.C.—See Nippon Yusen Kabushiki Kaisha; *Int'l*, pg. 5360
YUSEN LOGISTICS (MYANMAR) CO., LTD.—See Nippon Yusen Kabushiki Kaisha; *Int'l*, pg. 5360
YUSEN LOGISTICS PAKISTAN (PTE.) LTD.—See Nippon Yusen Kabushiki Kaisha; *Int'l*, pg. 5361
YUSEN LOGISTICS (PHILIPPINES) INC.—See Nippon Yusen Kabushiki Kaisha; *Int'l*, pg. 5360
YUSEN LOGISTICS (POLSKA) SP.ZO.O.—See Nippon Yusen Kabushiki Kaisha; *Int'l*, pg. 5360
YUSEN LOGISTICS (ROMANIA) SRL—See Nippon Yusen Kabushiki Kaisha; *Int'l*, pg. 5360
YUSEN LOGISTICS RUS LLC—See Nippon Yusen Kabushiki Kaisha; *Int'l*, pg. 5361

YUSEN LOGISTICS (SHENZHEN) CO., LTD.—See Nippon Yusen Kabushiki Kaisha; *Int'l*, pg. 5360
YUSEN LOGISTICS (SINGAPORE) PTE. LTD.—See Nippon Yusen Kabushiki Kaisha; *Int'l*, pg. 5360
YUSEN LOGISTICS—See TPG Capital, L.P.; *U.S. Public*, pg. 2177
YUSEN LOGISTICS (TAIWAN) LTD.—See Nippon Yusen Kabushiki Kaisha; *Int'l*, pg. 5360
YUSEN LOGISTICS (THAILAND) CO., LTD.—See Nippon Yusen Kabushiki Kaisha; *Int'l*, pg. 5360
YUSEN LOGISTICS UK LTD—See Nippon Yusen Kabushiki Kaisha; *Int'l*, pg. 5361
YUSEN LOGISTICS (VIETNAM) CO., LTD.—See Nippon Yusen Kabushiki Kaisha; *Int'l*, pg. 5360
YUSEN REAL ESTATE CORPORATION—See Nippon Yusen Kabushiki Kaisha; *Int'l*, pg. 5361
YUSEN TERMINAL LOGOPARK LLC—See Nippon Yusen Kabushiki Kaisha; *Int'l*, pg. 5361
YUSEN TERMINALS, LLC—See Kawasaki Kisen Kaisha, Ltd.; *Int'l*, pg. 4101
YUSEN TERMINALS, LLC—See Mitsui O.S.K. Lines, Ltd.; *Int'l*, pg. 4991
YUSEN TERMINALS, LLC—See Nippon Yusen Kabushiki Kaisha; *Int'l*, pg. 5359
YUSEN TRAVEL CO., LTD.—See Nippon Yusen Kabushiki Kaisha; *Int'l*, pg. 5361
YUSEN TRAVEL (HONG KONG) LTD.—See Nippon Yusen Kabushiki Kaisha; *Int'l*, pg. 5361
YUSEN TRAVEL (SINGAPORE) PTE., LTD.—See Nippon Yusen Kabushiki Kaisha; *Int'l*, pg. 5361
YUSEN TRAVEL (U.S.A.) INC.—See Nippon Yusen Kabushiki Kaisha; *Int'l*, pg. 5361
YUSEN ZHONGYUN LOGISTICS (DALIAN) CO., LTD.—See Nippon Yusen Kabushiki Kaisha; *Int'l*, pg. 5361
YUSHIN AMERICA INC.—See YUSHIN PRECISION EQUIPMENT CO. LTD.; *Int'l*, pg. 8617
YUSHIN AUTOMATION LTD.—See YUSHIN PRECISION EQUIPMENT CO. LTD.; *Int'l*, pg. 8617
YUSHIN KOREA CO., LTD.—See YUSHIN PRECISION EQUIPMENT CO. LTD.; *Int'l*, pg. 8617
YUSHIN PRECISION EQUIPMENT CO. LTD.; *Int'l*, pg. 8617
YUSHIN PRECISION EQUIPMENT (INDIA) PVT. LTD.—See YUSHIN PRECISION EQUIPMENT CO. LTD.; *Int'l*, pg. 8617
YUSHIN PRECISION EQUIPMENT SDN. BHD.—See YUSHIN PRECISION EQUIPMENT CO. LTD.; *Int'l*, pg. 8617
YUSHIN PRECISION EQUIPMENT (TAIWAN) CO., LTD.—See YUSHIN PRECISION EQUIPMENT CO. LTD.; *Int'l*, pg. 8617
YUSHIN PRECISION EQUIPMENT TECHNICAL CENTER—See YUSHIN PRECISION EQUIPMENT CO. LTD.; *Int'l*, pg. 8617
YUSHIN PRECISION EQUIPMENT (THAILAND) CO., LTD.—See YUSHIN PRECISION EQUIPMENT CO. LTD.; *Int'l*, pg. 8617
YUSHIRO CHEMICAL INDUSTRY CO. LTD.; *Int'l*, pg. 8617
YUSHIRO MANUFACTURING AMERICA INC.—See Yushiro Chemical Industry Co. Ltd.; *Int'l*, pg. 8618
YUSHODO (KYOTO) CO., LTD.—See Dai Nippon Printing Co., Ltd.; *Int'l*, pg. 1916
YUSHSHIN INDUSTRIAL CO., LTD.—See Minebea Mitsumi Inc.; *Int'l*, pg. 4905
YUSIN HOLDING CORP; *Int'l*, pg. 8618
YUS INTERNATIONAL GROUP LIMITED; *Int'l*, pg. 8617
YU-SMART LIMITED—See Yu Group PLC; *Int'l*, pg. 8607
YUSOKI KOGYO K.K.—See Subaru Corporation; *Int'l*, pg. 7248
YUSUF BIN AHMED KANOO & CO.—See The Kanoo Group, LLC; *Int'l*, pg. 7661
YUSUF BIN AHMED KANOO & CO—See The Kanoo Group, LLC; *Int'l*, pg. 7661
YUSUF BIN AHMED KANOO—See The Kanoo Group, LLC; *Int'l*, pg. 7661
YUSUF BIN AHMED KANOO—See The Kanoo Group, LLC; *Int'l*, pg. 7661
YUSYS TECHNOLOGIES CO., LTD.; *Int'l*, pg. 8618
YUTAKA CHEMICALS CORPORATION—See Mitsubishi Gas Chemical Company, Inc.; *Int'l*, pg. 4950
YUTAKA ELECTRIC MANUFACTURING COMPANY LTD.—See Glass One Technology Corporation; *Int'l*, pg. 2989
YUTAKA ELECTRIC MFG. CO., LTD.—See NICHICON CORPORATION; *Int'l*, pg. 5268
YUTAKA FOODS CORPORATION; *Int'l*, pg. 8618
YUTAKA GIKEN CO., LTD.—See Honda Motor Co., Ltd.; *Int'l*, pg. 3465
YUTAKA HIGH-TECH, LTD.—See JTEKT Corporation; *Int'l*, pg. 4019
YUTAKA SEIMITSU KOGYO, LTD.—See JTEKT Corporation; *Int'l*, pg. 4019
YUTAKA TRUSTY SECURITIES CO., LTD.; *Int'l*, pg. 8618
YU TAK INTERNATIONAL HOLDINGS LIMITED; *Int'l*, pg. 8607
YUTIAN COUNTY ZHONGYU GAS CO., LTD.—See Zhongyu Energy Holdings Limited; *Int'l*, pg. 8676

YUTONG BUS CO., LTD.   CORPORATE AFFILIATIONS

YUTONG BUS CO., LTD.; *Int'l*, pg. 8618
YUTORI FORM CO., LTD.—See Bunka Shutter Co., Ltd.; *Int'l*, pg. 1216
YUUZOO CORPORATION LIMITED; *Int'l*, pg. 8618
YUVALIM GROUP INVESTMENTS LTD.; *Int'l*, pg. 8618
YUVRAAJ HYGIENE PRODUCTS LIMITED; *Int'l*, pg. 8618
YUWAKOGYO CORPORATION—See MIRAIT ONE Corporation; *Int'l*, pg. 4918
YUWANG GROUP; *Int'l*, pg. 8618
YUWANG PLANTATION SDN BHD—See Yuwang Group; *Int'l*, pg. 8618
YUWELL GERMANY GMBH—See Jiangsu Yuyue Medical Equipment & Supply Co., Ltd.; *Int'l*, pg. 3957
YUXIAN ZHONGYU GAS CO., LTD.—See Zhongyu Energy Holdings Limited; *Int'l*, pg. 8676
YUXING INFOTECH INVESTMENT HOLDINGS LIMITED; *Int'l*, pg. 8618
YUYAO PACIFIC WEIGHING ENGINEERING CO., LTD.—See Keli Sensing Technology Ningbo Co., Ltd.; *Int'l*, pg. 4119
YUYAO XINGYOU METAL MATERIALS CO., LTD.—See GEM Co., Ltd.; *Int'l*, pg. 2914
YUYUAN CULTURE PROMOTING & PUBLICIZING CO., LTD.—See Shanghai Yuyuan Tourist Mart (Group) Co., Ltd.; *Int'l*, pg. 6783
YUYU PHARMA INC.; *Int'l*, pg. 8618
YUYU TEIJIN MEDICARE INC—See Teijin Limited; *Int'l*, pg. 7524
YUZAWA GEOTHERMAL POWER COPRATION—See Mitsubishi Gas Chemical Company, Inc.; *Int'l*, pg. 4950
YUZHOU GROUP HOLDINGS COMPANY LIMITED; *Int'l*, pg. 8618
YUZURU INC.—See create restaurants holdings inc.; *Int'l*, pg. 1832
YUZZU SA—See AXA S.A.; *Int'l*, pg. 761
YVAN PAQUE S.A.—See Eiffage S.A.; *Int'l*, pg. 2330
YVAN PAQUE S.A. - VILLEROUX PLANT—See Eiffage S.A.; *Int'l*, pg. 2330
YVC HOLDINGS, INC; *U.S. Public*, pg. 2400
Y VENTURES GROUP LTD.; *Int'l*, pg. 8543
YVES SAINT LAURENT BEAUTE S.A.—See Kering S.A.; *Int'l*, pg. 4135
YVES SAINT LAURENT SAS—See Kering S.A.; *Int'l*, pg. 4136
YVES SAINT LAURENT SPAIN SA—See Kering S.A.; *Int'l*, pg. 4135
YVES SAINT LAURENT UK LTD—See Kering S.A.; *Int'l*, pg. 4135
YVETTE WILLIAMS RETIREMENT VILLAGE LIMITED—See Ryman Healthcare Ltd.; *Int'l*, pg. 6440
YVONNE MOBILIEN-LEASING GMBH—See Asklepios Kliniken GmbH & Co. KGaA; *Int'l*, pg. 623
YW CO., LTD.; *Int'l*, pg. 8618
Y-W ELECTRIC ASSOCIATION INC; *U.S. Private*, pg. 4584
YX ASSET RECOVERY LIMITED; *Int'l*, pg. 8618
YX ENERGI NORGE AS—See Reitangruppen AS; *Int'l*, pg. 6258
YXLON (BEIJING) X-RAY EQUIPMENT TRADING CO. LTD.—See Comet Holding AG; *Int'l*, pg. 1711
YXLON INTERNATIONAL A/S—See Comet Holding AG; *Int'l*, pg. 1711
YXLON INTERNATIONAL CT DEVELOPMENT GMBH—See Comet Holding AG; *Int'l*, pg. 1711
YXLON INTERNATIONAL FEINFOCUS GMBH—See Comet Holding AG; *Int'l*, pg. 1711
YXLON INTERNATIONAL GMBH—See Comet Holding AG; *Int'l*, pg. 1711
YXLON INTERNATIONAL INC.—See Comet Holding AG; *Int'l*, pg. 1711
YXLON INTERNATIONAL K.K.—See Comet Holding AG; *Int'l*, pg. 1711
YX PRECIOUS METALS BERHAD; *Int'l*, pg. 8618
YY CABLE ACCESSORIES CO., LTD.—See Yonyu Plastics Co., Ltd.; *Int'l*, pg. 8598
YY GROUP HOLDING LIMITED; *Int'l*, pg. 8618
YZ QUEENCO LTD.; *Int'l*, pg. 8619
Y-Z SYSTEMS INC.—See BC Partners LLP; *Int'l*, pg. 922
Y-Z SYSTEMS INC.—See The Carlyle Group Inc.; *U.S. Public*, pg. 2044

Z

ZAAD HOLDINGS PROPRIETARY LIMITED—See Zeder Investments Limited; *Int'l*, pg. 8629
ZABALA ERICKSON, LLC.; *U.S. Private*, pg. 4596
ZABALGARBI, S.A.—See Ente Vasco de la Energia; *Int'l*, pg. 2450
THE ZABEL COMPANIES, LLC; *U.S. Private*, pg. 4140
ZAB INDUSTRIETECHNIK & SERVICE GMBH—See KHD Humboldt Wedag International AG; *Int'l*, pg. 4154
ZABIN INDUSTRIES INC.; *U.S. Private*, pg. 4596
ZABKA POLSKA SP. Z. O. O.—See CVC Capital Partners SICAV-FIS S.A.; *Int'l*, pg. 1889
ZAB ZEMENTANLAGENBAU GMBH—See KHD Humboldt Wedag International AG; *Int'l*, pg. 4154
ZACAPA RESOURCES LTD.—See Outcrop Silver & Gold Corporation; *Int'l*, pg. 5667
ZACATECAS SILVER CORP.; *Int'l*, pg. 8619

ZACD GROUP LTD.; *Int'l*, pg. 8619
ZACHARY CONFECTIONS INC.; *U.S. Private*, pg. 4596
ZACH COMPANY CORPORATION—See Zambon Company S.p.A.; *Int'l*, pg. 8622
ZACHEM UCR SP. Z.O.O.—See Kulczyk Investments S.A.; *Int'l*, pg. 4328
ZACHERL MOTOR TRUCK SALES; *U.S. Private*, pg. 4596
ZACHERT PRIVATE EQUITY GMBH; *Int'l*, pg. 8619
ZACHRY CONSTRUCTION CORPORATION—See Zachry Holdings, Inc.; *U.S. Private*, pg. 4596
ZACHRY CORPORATION—See Zachry Holdings, Inc.; *U.S. Private*, pg. 4596
ZACHRY ENGINEERING CORP. - AMARILLO—See Zachry Holdings, Inc.; *U.S. Private*, pg. 4596
ZACHRY ENGINEERING CORPORATION—See Zachry Holdings, Inc.; *U.S. Private*, pg. 4596
ZACHRY HOLDINGS, INC.; *U.S. Private*, pg. 4596
ZACHRY NUCLEAR ENGINEERING, INC.—See Zachry Holdings, Inc.; *U.S. Private*, pg. 4596
ZACH SYSTEM S.P.A.—See Zambon Company S.p.A.; *Int'l*, pg. 8622
ZACK BURKETT CO.; *U.S. Private*, pg. 4596
ZACK DARLING CREATIVE ASSOCIATES, LLC—See Greenlane Holdings, Inc.; *U.S. Public*, pg. 965
ZACK ELECTRONICS, INC.; *U.S. Private*, pg. 4597
ZACKS INVESTMENT RESEARCH INC.; *U.S. Private*, pg. 4597
ZACKY FARMS, INC.; *U.S. Private*, pg. 4597
ZA CLOTHING IRELAND LTD.—See Industria de Diseno Textil, S.A.; *Int'l*, pg. 3668
ZACROS AMERICA, INC.—See ZACROS Corporation; *Int'l*, pg. 8619
ZACROS CORPORATION; *Int'l*, pg. 8619
ZACROS MALAYSIA SDN. BHD.—See ZACROS Corporation; *Int'l*, pg. 8619
ZACROS TAIWAN CO., LTD.—See ZACROS Corporation; *Int'l*, pg. 8619
ZADAR INTERNATIONAL PORT OPERATIONS D.O.O.—See Global Yatirim Holding A.S.; *Int'l*, pg. 3003
ZAD HOLDING COMPANY S.A.Q.; *Int'l*, pg. 8619
ZAD VICTORIA AD—See Assicurazioni Generali S.p.A.; *Int'l*, pg. 648
ZAFE CARE SYSTEMS AB—See AddLife AB; *Int'l*, pg. 130
ZAFIN LABS; *Int'l*, pg. 8619
ZAFIN LABS UK LIMITED—See Zafin Labs; *Int'l*, pg. 8619
ZAGAT SURVEY, LLC; *U.S. Private*, pg. 4597
ZAGG INCORPORATED—See Evercel, Inc.; *U.S. Private*, pg. 1437
ZAGGLE PREPAID OCEAN SERVICES LIMITED; *Int'l*, pg. 8619
ZA GIYIM ITHALAT IHRACAT VE TICARET LTD.—See Industria de Diseno Textil, S.A.; *Int'l*, pg. 3668
ZAGORSKI METALAC D.O.O.—See Petrol, Slovenska energetska druzba, d.d.; *Int'l*, pg. 5827
ZAGREBACKA BANKA DD—See UniCredit S.p.A.; *Int'l*, pg. 8040
ZAGREBACKA BURZA D.D.; *Int'l*, pg. 8619
ZAGREBACKA PIVOVARA D.D.—See Molson Coors Beverage Company; *U.S. Public*, pg. 1459
ZAGREBACKA STANOGRADNJA D.O.O.—See Zagrebacki holding d.o.o.; *Int'l*, pg. 8620
ZAGREBACKE PEKARNE KLARA D.D.; *Int'l*, pg. 8619
ZAGREBACKI HOLDING D.O.O.; *Int'l*, pg. 8620
ZAGREB NEKRETNINE DOO—See UniCredit S.p.A.; *Int'l*, pg. 8040
ZAGREB PLAKAT D.O.O.—See Zagrebacki holding d.o.o.; *Int'l*, pg. 8620
ZAGRO ANIMAL HEALTH PTE LTD—See Zagro Asia Ltd; *Int'l*, pg. 8620
ZAGRO ASIA LTD; *Int'l*, pg. 8620
ZAGRO CHEMICALS SDN BHD—See Zagro Asia Ltd; *Int'l*, pg. 8620
ZAGRO CORPORATION—See Zagro Asia Ltd; *Int'l*, pg. 8620
ZAGRO EUROPE GMBH—See Zagro Asia Ltd; *Int'l*, pg. 8620
ZAGRO SINGAPORE PTE LTD—See Zagro Asia Ltd; *Int'l*, pg. 8620
ZAGRO SINGAPORE PTE LTD—See Zagro Asia Ltd; *Int'l*, pg. 8620
ZAGROS PETROHEMICAL CO.—See Parsian Oil & Gas Development Co.; *Int'l*, pg. 5747
ZAGRO TAIWAN INTERNATIONAL LTD—See Zagro Asia Ltd; *Int'l*, pg. 8620
ZAGRO (THAILAND) LTD.—See Zagro Asia Ltd; *Int'l*, pg. 8620
ZA GROUP, INC.; *U.S. Public*, pg. 2400
ZAGRO VIETNAM COMPANY LTD—See Zagro Asia Ltd; *Int'l*, pg. 8620
ZAG USA, INC.—See Stanley Black & Decker, Inc.; *U.S. Public*, pg. 1936
ZAHA HADID HOLDINGS LTD.; *Int'l*, pg. 8620
ZAHARONI INDUSTRIES, INC.; *U.S. Private*, pg. 4597
ZAHEEN SPINNING LTD.; *Int'l*, pg. 8620
ZAHIDJEE TEXTILES MILLS LTD; *Int'l*, pg. 8620
ZAHINTEX INDUSTRIES LTD; *Int'l*, pg. 8620
ZAHM & MATSON INC.; *U.S. Private*, pg. 4597

ZAHRA SECURITY SYSTEMS & ELECTRICALS LLC—See Aiphone Co., Ltd.; *Int'l*, pg. 235
ZAHRAT AL WAHA FOR TRADING CO; *Int'l*, pg. 8620
ZAHRAVI PHARMACEUTICAL COMPANY; *Int'l*, pg. 8620
ZAHROOF VALVES, INC.—See Atlas Copco AB; *Int'l*, pg. 684
ZAHUR COTTON MILLS LIMITED; *Int'l*, pg. 8620
ZAIGLE CO. LTD.; *Int'l*, pg. 8620
ZAI LAB LIMITED; *Int'l*, pg. 8620
ZAIM CREDIT SYSTEMS PLC; *Int'l*, pg. 8620
ZAIN BAHRAIN B.S.C (CLOSED)—See Mobile Telecommunications Company K.S.C; *Int'l*, pg. 5010
ZAIN PARTICIPACOES SA; *Int'l*, pg. 8621
ZAIS GROUP HOLDINGS, INC.; *U.S. Private*, pg. 4597
ZAIS GROUP, LLC—See ZAIS Group Holdings, Inc.; *U.S. Private*, pg. 4597
ZAIS GROUP (UK) LIMITED—See ZAIS Group Holdings, Inc.; *U.S. Private*, pg. 4597
ZAKANG, INC.—See Cal-Comp Electronics (Thailand) pcl; *Int'l*, pg. 1261
ZAK DESIGNS INC.; *U.S. Private*, pg. 4597
ZAKKAYA BULLDOG CO., LTD.—See AXAS Holdings Co., Ltd.; *Int'l*, pg. 761
ZAKLAD BUDOWY MASZYN ZREMB CHOJNICE S.A.; *Int'l*, pg. 8621
ZAKLAD GOSPODARKI MIESZKANIOWEJ SP. Z O.O.—See Polskie Gornictwo Naftowe i Gazownictwo S.A.; *Int'l*, pg. 5912
ZAKLAD OBROBKI PLASTYCZNEJ SP. Z.O.O.—See Leonardo S.p.A.; *Int'l*, pg. 4461
ZAKLAD PRODUKCYJNO - REMONTOWY "REM-SUW" SP. Z. O.O.—See Pojazdy Szynowe Pesa Bydgoszcz S.A. Holding; *Int'l*, pg. 5905
ZAKLAD REMONTOWY SP. Z.O.O.—See Leonardo S.p.A.; *Int'l*, pg. 4461
ZAKLAD REMONTOWY URZADZEN GAZOWNICZYCH SP. Z.O.O.—See Polskie Gornictwo Naftowe i Gazownictwo S.A.; *Int'l*, pg. 5913
ZAKLAD URZADZEN NAFTOWYCH NAFTOMET SP. Z.O.O.—See Polskie Gornictwo Naftowe i Gazownictwo S.A.; *Int'l*, pg. 5913
ZAKLAD USLUG TELEINFORMATYCZNYCH ZZE S.A. ITSERWIS SP. Z O.O.—See ENEA S.A.; *Int'l*, pg. 2410
ZAKLAD UTRZYMANIA RUCHU SP. Z O.O.—See Leonardo S.p.A.; *Int'l*, pg. 4461
ZAKLADY AUTOMATYKI POLNA S.A.; *Int'l*, pg. 8621
ZAKLADY AZOTOWE PULAWY S.A.—See Grupa Azoty S.A.; *Int'l*, pg. 3116
ZAKLADY CHEMICZNE POLICE S.A.; *Int'l*, pg. 8621
ZAKLADY CHEMICZNE ZACHEM S.A.—See Kulczyk Investments S.A.; *Int'l*, pg. 4328
ZAKLADY MAGNEZYTOWE ROPCZYCE S.A.; *Int'l*, pg. 8621
ZAKLADY MIESNE AGRYF S.A.—See WH Group Limited; *Int'l*, pg. 8395
ZAKLADY MIESNE HENRYK KANIA S.A.; *Int'l*, pg. 8621
ZAKLADY MIESNE MAZURY W ELKU SP. Z O.O.—See WH Group Limited; *Int'l*, pg. 8395
ZAKLADY PLYT WIOROWYCH PROSPAN S.A.—See Pfleiderer GmbH; *Int'l*, pg. 5836
ZAKLADY PRZEMYSLU CUKIERNICZEGO MIESZKO S.A.; *Int'l*, pg. 8621
ZAKLADY TLUSZCZOWE KRUSZWICA S.A. - BRZEG PLANT—See Zaklady Tluszczowe Kruszwica S.A.; *Int'l*, pg. 8621
ZAKLADY TLUSZCZOWE KRUSZWICA S.A.; *Int'l*, pg. 8621
ZAKLADY TLUSZOZOWE W BODACZOWIE SP.Z.O.O.—See Glencore plc; *Int'l*, pg. 2991
ZAKLADY URZADZEN KOMPUTEROWYCH ELZAB S.A.; *Int'l*, pg. 8621
ZAKLADY URZADZEN KOTLOWYCH STAPORKOW S.A.; *Int'l*, pg. 8621
ZAKLADY WAPIENNICZE LHOIST S.A.—See Lhoist S.A.; *Int'l*, pg. 4478
ZAK PRODUCTS INC.; *U.S. Private*, pg. 4597
ZAKSA S.A.—See Grupa Azoty S.A.; *Int'l*, pg. 3116
ZAKUM DEVELOPMENT COMPANY—See Abu Dhabi National Oil Company; *Int'l*, pg. 73
ZAKURA INC.—See Future Corporation; *Int'l*, pg. 2853
ZALAKERAMIA RT.—See Lasselsberger GmbH; *Int'l*, pg. 4421
ZALANDO SE; *Int'l*, pg. 8621
ZALANTA RESORT AT THE VILLAGE, LLC—See Waterfall Asset Management LLC; *U.S. Private*, pg. 4453
ZALARIS ASA; *Int'l*, pg. 8621
ZALARIS CONSULTING LTD.—See Zalaris ASA; *Int'l*, pg. 8621
ZALARIS CONSULTING POLAND SP. Z. O. O.—See Zalaris ASA; *Int'l*, pg. 8621
ZALARIS DEUTSCHLAND GMBH—See Zalaris ASA; *Int'l*, pg. 8621
ZALARIS HR SERVICES DENMARK A/S—See Zalaris ASA; *Int'l*, pg. 8621
ZALARIS HR SERVICES FINLAND OY—See Zalaris ASA; *Int'l*, pg. 8621
ZALARIS HR SERVICES INDIA PVT. LTD.—See Zalaris ASA; *Int'l*, pg. 8621

COMPANY NAME INDEX

ZALARIS HR SERVICES LATVIA SIA—See Zalaris ASA; *Int'l*, pg. 8621
ZALARIS HR SERVICES POLAND SP Z O.O.—See Zalaris ASA; *Int'l*, pg. 8621
ZALARIS HR SERVICES SVERIGE AB—See Zalaris ASA; *Int'l*, pg. 8621
ZALAR PATIKA KFT.—See PHOENIX Pharmahandel GmbH & Co. KG; *Int'l*, pg. 5855
ZALATORIS ACQUISITION CORP.; *U.S. Public*, pg. 2401
ZALATORIS II ACQUISITION CORP.; *U.S. Public*, pg. 2401
ZALE CORPORATION—See Signet Jewelers Limited; *Int'l*, pg. 6911
ZALE DELAWARE, INC.—See Signet Jewelers Limited; *Int'l*, pg. 6911
ZALE EMPLOYEES CHILD CARE ASSOCIATION, INC.—See Signet Jewelers Limited; *Int'l*, pg. 6911
ZALE INDEMNITY COMPANY—See Signet Jewelers Limited; *Int'l*, pg. 6911
ZALEKTA PUBLIC COMPANY LIMITED; *Int'l*, pg. 8621
ZALE LIFE INSURANCE COMPANY—See Signet Jewelers Limited; *Int'l*, pg. 6911
ZALEMARK HOLDING COMPANY, INC.; *Int'l*, pg. 8622
ZALE OFFSHORE RESPONSE PTE. LTD.—See Kim Heng Limited; *Int'l*, pg. 4162
ZALE PUERTO RICO INC.—See Signet Jewelers Limited; *Int'l*, pg. 6911
ZALEV BROTHERS COMPANY—See Soave Enterprises, LLC; *U.S. Private*, pg. 3702
ZA LIFE LIMITED—See ZhongAn Online P & C Insurance Co., Ltd.; *Int'l*, pg. 8672
ZALK JOSEPHS FABRICATORS, LLC—See The Heico Companies, L.L.C.; *U.S. Private*, pg. 4051
ZALK STEEL & SUPPLY CO.—See AZZ, Inc.; *U.S. Public*, pg. 260
ZALL DEVELOPMENT (HK) HOLDING COMPANY LIMITED—See Zall Smart Commerce Group Ltd.; *Int'l*, pg. 8622
ZALL SMART COMMERCE GROUP LTD.; *Int'l*, pg. 8622
ZALMAN TECH CO., LTD.; *Int'l*, pg. 8622
ZALMAN USA, INC—See Zalman Tech Co., Ltd.; *Int'l*, pg. 8622
ZALOZBA ROKUS KLETT, D.O.O.—See Ernst Klett AG; *Int'l*, pg. 2495
ZAMACOM S.A.—See Ecom Agroindustrial Corporation Ltd.; *Int'l*, pg. 2296
ZAMANCO MINERALS LIMITED; *Int'l*, pg. 8622
ZAMANO PLC; *Int'l*, pg. 8622
ZAMANO SOLUTIONS LIMITED—See Zamano plc; *Int'l*, pg. 8622
ZAMAZ PLC; *Int'l*, pg. 8622
ZAMBAL SPAIN SOCIMI SA; *Int'l*, pg. 8622
ZAMBEEF PRODUCTS PLC; *Int'l*, pg. 8622
ZAMBEZI; *U.S. Private*, pg. 4597
ZAMBIA LEAF TOBACCO CO., LTD.—See Universal Corporation; *U.S. Public*, pg. 2254
ZAMBIA NATIONAL COMMERCIAL BANK PLC.; *Int'l*, pg. 8622
ZAMBIA NONFERROUS METALS EXPLORATION & CONSTRUCTION COMPANY LIMITED—See Sinomine Resource Group Co., Ltd.; *Int'l*, pg. 6953
ZAMBIA SUGAR PLC—See The Garfield Weston Foundation; *Int'l*, pg. 7648
ZAMBIA TELECOMMUNICATIONS COMPANY LIMITED; *Int'l*, pg. 8622
ZAMBON ADVANCE LUXEMBOURG S.A.—See Zambon Company S.p.A.; *Int'l*, pg. 8622
ZAMBON COLOMBIA S.A.—See Zambon Company S.p.A.; *Int'l*, pg. 8622
ZAMBON COMPANY S.P.A.; *Int'l*, pg. 8622
ZAMBON CORPORATION—See Zambon Company S.p.A.; *Int'l*, pg. 8623
ZAMBON FRANCE S.A.—See Zambon Company S.p.A.; *Int'l*, pg. 8623
ZAMBON G.M.B.H.—See Zambon Company S.p.A.; *Int'l*, pg. 8623
ZAMBON (INDIA) PVT. LTD.—See Zambon Company S.p.A.; *Int'l*, pg. 8622
ZAMBON LABORATORIOS FARMACEUTICOS LTDA.—See Zambon Company S.p.A.; *Int'l*, pg. 8623
ZAMBON NEDERLAND B.V.—See Zambon Company S.p.A.; *Int'l*, pg. 8623
ZAMBON PHARMA LTD.—See Zambon Company S.p.A.; *Int'l*, pg. 8623
ZAMBON PRODUTOS FARMACEUTICOS LDA.—See Zambon Company S.p.A.; *Int'l*, pg. 8623
ZAMBON RUSSIA—See Zambon Company S.p.A.; *Int'l*, pg. 8623
ZAMBON S.A./N.V.—See Zambon Company S.p.A.; *Int'l*, pg. 8623
ZAMBON S.A.—See Zambon Company S.p.A.; *Int'l*, pg. 8623
ZAMBON S.P.A.—See Zambon Company S.p.A.; *Int'l*, pg. 8623
ZAMBON SVIZZERA SA—See Zambon Company S.p.A.; *Int'l*, pg. 8623
ZAMBON SWITZERLAND LTD.—See Zambon Company S.p.A.; *Int'l*, pg. 8623

ZAMBRA LEGAL PTY LIMITED—See Parker Hannifin Corporation; *U.S. Public*, pg. 1643
ZAM CO., LTD.; *Int'l*, pg. 8622
ZAMEE CORP.; *Int'l*, pg. 8623
ZAMET BUDOWA MASZYN S.A.—See Zamet Industry S.A.; *Int'l*, pg. 8623
ZAMET INDUSTRY S.A.; *Int'l*, pg. 8623
ZAMFARMA - PRODUTOS PHARMACEUTICALS LDA.—See Zambon Company S.p.A.; *Int'l*, pg. 8623
ZAMIA METALS LIMITED; *Int'l*, pg. 8623
ZAMIAS SERVICES INC.; *U.S. Private*, pg. 4597
ZAMIL AIR CONDITIONERS HOLDING COMPANY LIMITED—See Zamil Industrial Investment Company; *Int'l*, pg. 8623
ZAMIL AIR CONDITIONERS INDIA PRIVATE LIMITED—See Zamil Industrial Investment Company; *Int'l*, pg. 8623
ZAMIL ALPLA PLASTIC - MIDDLE EAST, LIMITED—See Alpla-Werke Alwin Lehner GmbH & Co. KG; *Int'l*, pg. 374
ZAMIL ARCHITECTURAL CO. LTD—See Zamil Group Holding Company; *Int'l*, pg. 8623
ZAMIL FOOD INDUSTRIES LTD.—See Zamil Group Holding Company; *Int'l*, pg. 8623
ZAMIL GROUP COMMERCIAL DIVISION—See Zamil Group Holding Company; *Int'l*, pg. 8623
ZAMIL GROUP HOLDING COMPANY; *Int'l*, pg. 8623
ZAMIL INDUSTRIAL COATING—See Zamil Group Holding Company; *Int'l*, pg. 8623
ZAMIL INDUSTRIAL INVESTMENT COMPANY; *Int'l*, pg. 8623
ZAMIL INFORMATION TECHNOLOGY GLOBAL PRIVATE LIMITED—See Zamil Industrial Investment Company; *Int'l*, pg. 8623
ZAMIL INSPECTION & MAINTENANCE OF INDUSTRIAL PROJECTS COMPANY LIMITED—See Zamil Industrial Investment Company; *Int'l*, pg. 8624
ZAMIL LADDER FACTORY—See Zamil Group Holding Company; *Int'l*, pg. 8623
ZAMIL OPERATIONS & MAINTENANCE CO. LTD—See Zamil Group Holding Company; *Int'l*, pg. 8623
ZAMIL PARTITION INDUSTRIES COMPANY—See Zamil Group Holding Company; *Int'l*, pg. 8623
ZAMIL PLASTIC INDUSTRIES—See Zamil Group Holding Company; *Int'l*, pg. 8623
ZAMIL PROCESS EQUIPMENT COMPANY LIMITED—See Zamil Industrial Investment Company; *Int'l*, pg. 8624
ZAMIL STEEL BUILDINGS CO., EGYPT (S.A.E.)—See Zamil Industrial Investment Company; *Int'l*, pg. 8624
ZAMIL STEEL BUILDINGS INDIA (P) LTD.—See Zamil Industrial Investment Company; *Int'l*, pg. 8624
ZAMIL STEEL BUILDINGS VIETNAM CO., LTD.—See Zamil Industrial Investment Company; *Int'l*, pg. 8624
ZAMIL STEEL CONSTRUCTION COMPANY LIMITED—See Zamil Industrial Investment Company; *Int'l*, pg. 8624
ZAMIL STEEL ENGINEERING INDIA PRIVATE LIMITED—See Zamil Industrial Investment Company; *Int'l*, pg. 8624
ZAMIL STEEL HOLDING COMPANY LIMITED—See Zamil Industrial Investment Company; *Int'l*, pg. 8624
ZAMIL STEEL INDUSTRIES L.L.C—See Zamil Industrial Investment Company; *Int'l*, pg. 8624
ZAMIL STEEL POLSKA SP. Z O.O.—See Zamil Industrial Investment Company; *Int'l*, pg. 8624
ZAMIL STEEL PRE-ENGINEERED BUILDINGS COMPANY LIMITED—See Zamil Industrial Investment Company; *Int'l*, pg. 8624
ZAMIL STRUCTURAL STEEL COMPANY LIMITED—See Zamil Industrial Investment Company; *Int'l*, pg. 8624
ZAMIL TOWERS & GALVANIZING COMPANY—See Zamil Industrial Investment Company; *Int'l*, pg. 8624
ZAMIL TRAVEL—See Zamil Group Holding Company; *Int'l*, pg. 8623
ZAMINE SERVICE PERU S.A.C.—See Marubeni Corporation; *Int'l*, pg. 4710
ZAMIRA FASHION LTD.—See Pearl Global Industries Limited; *Int'l*, pg. 5774
ZAMIR TELECOM LTD.; *Int'l*, pg. 8624
ZAMLEATHER LTD—See Zambeef Products Plc; *Int'l*, pg. 8622
ZAMORA S.R.O.—See Schlott Gruppe AG; *Int'l*, pg. 6622
ZAMPELL REFRACTORIES INC.; *U.S. Private*, pg. 4597
ZAMPHR, INC.; *U.S. Private*, pg. 4597
ZAMP SA; *Int'l*, pg. 8624
ZAMURAI CORPORATION—See Elliott Management Corporation; *U.S. Private*, pg. 1369
ZAMURAI CORPORATION—See Francisco Partners Management, LP; *U.S. Private*, pg. 1590
ZAMZOWS INC.; *U.S. Private*, pg. 4597
ZANAGA IRON ORE COMPANY LIMITED; *Int'l*, pg. 8624
ZANA TOOLS SHPK—See Einhell Germany AG; *Int'l*, pg. 2334
ZANDER & INGESTROM AB—See Christian Berner Tech Trade AB; *Int'l*, pg. 1586
ZANDER THERAPEUTICS, INC.; *U.S. Private*, pg. 4597
ZANDHANDEL J. VAN VLIET B.V.—See HAL Trust N.V.; *Int'l*, pg. 3227

ZAO BESTROM

ZANDICA, INC.—See Publishers Clearing House, Inc.; *U.S. Private*, pg. 3301
ZANDU REALTY LIMITED—See Emami Group; *Int'l*, pg. 2374
ZANE BH DOO—See UniCredit S.p.A.; *Int'l*, pg. 8040
ZANE HOLDINGS LTD; *Int'l*, pg. 8624
ZANELLA LTD. INC.; *U.S. Private*, pg. 4597
ZANER-BLOSER, INC.—See Highlights for Children, Inc.; *U.S. Private*, pg. 1940
ZANE SOLAR SYSTEMS AUSTRALIA PTY LTD—See Waterco Limited; *Int'l*, pg. 8357
ZANGAN ELECTRICAL EQUIPMENT COMPANY; *Int'l*, pg. 8624
ZANGAN PARS CO.—See Pars Switch Company; *Int'l*, pg. 5746
ZANGAN ZINC INDUSTRY LLP—See National Iranian Lead & Zinc Company; *Int'l*, pg. 5160
ZANGEZUR COPPER & MOLYBDENUM COMBINE CJSC—See CRONIMET Holding GmbH; *Int'l*, pg. 1855
ZANGGE MINING COMPANY LIMITED; *Int'l*, pg. 8624
ZANIBONI LIGHTING, LLC; *U.S. Private*, pg. 4597
ZANINI AUTO GRUP, S.A.; *Int'l*, pg. 8624
ZANINI CZ, S.R.O—See Zanini Auto Grup, S.A.; *Int'l*, pg. 8624
ZANINI DO BRASIL, LTDA.—See Zanini Auto Grup, S.A.; *Int'l*, pg. 8624
ZANINI EPILA, S.L.—See Zanini Auto Grup, S.A.; *Int'l*, pg. 8624
ZANINI FRANCE S.L.—See Zanini Auto Grup, S.A.; *Int'l*, pg. 8624
ZANINI MEXICO. S.A. DE C.V—See Zanini Auto Grup, S.A.; *Int'l*, pg. 8624
ZANINI PARETS S.L.—See Zanini Auto Grup, S.A.; *Int'l*, pg. 8624
ZANINI TENNESSEE, INC.—See Zanini Auto Grup, S.A.; *Int'l*, pg. 8624
ZANINI USA, INC.—See Zanini Auto Grup, S.A.; *Int'l*, pg. 8624
ZANINONI SLOVAKIA, S.R.O.—See Zeleziarne Podbrezova a.s.; *Int'l*, pg. 8631
ZANJAN ACID MAKERS COMPANY—See National Iranian Lead & Zinc Company; *Int'l*, pg. 5160
ZANLAKOL LTD.; *Int'l*, pg. 8624
ZANONTIAN & SONS INC.; *U.S. Private*, pg. 4598
ZANOTTI S.P.A.—See Daikin Industries, Ltd.; *Int'l*, pg. 1937
ZANOTTO MARKET INC.; *U.S. Private*, pg. 4598
ZANSA LIMITED—See Sopra Steria Group S.A.; *Int'l*, pg. 7111
ZANTECH IT SERVICES, INC.; *U.S. Private*, pg. 4598
ZANUS A.D.; *Int'l*, pg. 8624
ZANYU TECHNOLOGY GROUP CO., LTD.; *Int'l*, pg. 8624
ZANZIBAR GOLD, INC.; *Int'l*, pg. 8625
ZANZICO; *U.S. Private*, pg. 4598
ZAO AD PLASTIK KALUGA—See AD Plastik d.d.; *Int'l*, pg. 122
ZAO AEROMAR—See Deutsche Lufthansa AG; *Int'l*, pg. 2068
ZAO AEROMAR—See PJSC Aeroflot Russian Airlines; *Int'l*, pg. 5878
ZAO AHLSELL SPB—See Ahlsell AB; *Int'l*, pg. 223
ZAO AJINOMOTO-GENETIKA RESEARCH INSTITUTE—See Ajinomoto Company, Inc.; *Int'l*, pg. 257
ZAO AKZO NOBEL DEKOR—See Akzo Nobel N.V.; *Int'l*, pg. 275
ZAO ALGOL CHEMICALS—See Algol Oy; *Int'l*, pg. 318
ZAO AL-KO ST. PETERSBURG GMBH—See PRIMEPULSE SE; *Int'l*, pg. 5979
ZAO ALPOS—See ALPOS, d.d.; *Int'l*, pg. 375
ZAO AMER SPORTS—See ANTA Sports Products Limited; *Int'l*, pg. 480
ZAO ARCTICNEFT—See Urals Energy Public Company Limited; *Int'l*, pg. 8094
ZAO ASHLAND MSP—See Ashland Inc.; *U.S. Public*, pg. 213
ZAO ASTELLAS PHARMA—See Astellas Pharma Inc.; *Int'l*, pg. 653
ZAO ATLAS COPCO—See Atlas Copco AB; *Int'l*, pg. 684
ZAO AVENA ST.PETERSBURG—See Apetit Plc; *Int'l*, pg. 509
ZAO AVENTIS PHARMA—See Sanofi; *Int'l*, pg. 6551
ZAO BALKANSKAYA ZVEZDA—See Imperial Brands PLC; *Int'l*, pg. 3634
ZAO BALTIC TOOL—See Fiskars Oyj Abp; *Int'l*, pg. 2695
ZAO BASF—See BASF SE; *Int'l*, pg. 886
ZAO BAYER—See Bayer Aktiengesellschaft; *Int'l*, pg. 910
ZAO BECEMA; *Int'l*, pg. 8625
ZAO BESTROM; *Int'l*, pg. 8625
ZAO BTI RUSSIA—See Global Business Travel Group, Inc.; *U.S. Public*, pg. 941
ZAO CEGELEC—See VINCI S.A.; *Int'l*, pg. 8214
ZAO CITIBANK—See Citigroup Inc.; *U.S. Public*, pg. 504
ZAO CITY SERVICE—See City Service SE; *Int'l*, pg. 1628
ZAO CONVATEC—See ConvaTec Group PLC; *Int'l*, pg. 1786
ZAO DANFOSS—See Danfoss A/S; *Int'l*, pg. 1962
ZAO DANSKE BANK—See Danske Bank A/S; *Int'l*, pg. 1969

ZAO DEFI RUSSIE—See DEFI Group SAS; *Int'l*, pg. 2004
ZAO DEUTSCHE SECURITIES—See Deutsche Bank Aktiengesellschaft; *Int'l*, pg. 2062
ZAO DHL INTERNATIONAL RUSSIA—See Deutsche Post AG; *Int'l*, pg. 2078
ZAO EGMONT RUSSIA LTD.—See Egmont Fonden; *Int'l*, pg. 2326
ZAO ELOPAK—See Ferd AS; *Int'l*, pg. 2636
ZAO EXACT SYSTEMS—See CVI Dom Maklerski sp. z o.o.; *Int'l*, pg. 1889
ZAO FISKARS BRANDS RUS—See Fiskars Oyj Abp; *Int'l*, pg. 2694
ZAO FRESENIUS SP—See Fresenius Medical Care AG; *Int'l*, pg. 2777
ZAO FUJIFILM-RU—See FUJIFILM Holdings Corporation; *Int'l*, pg. 2823
ZAO GAZPROM INVEST YUG—See PJSC Gazprom; *Int'l*, pg. 5880
ZAO GAZPROMNEFT SEVERO ZAPAD—See PJSC Gazprom; *Int'l*, pg. 5880
ZAO GREEN TERMINAL—See Caiano AS; *Int'l*, pg. 1252
ZAO HALDOR TOPSOE—See Topsoe A/S; *Int'l*, pg. 7821
ZAOH COMPANY, LTD.; *Int'l*, pg. 8625
ZAO HEWLETT-PACKARD AO—See HP Inc.; *U.S. Public*, pg. 1065
ZAO HIKVISION—See Hangzhou Hikvision Digital Technology Co., Ltd.; *Int'l*, pg. 3248
ZAO HUNTSMAN-NMG—See Huntsman Corporation; *U.S. Public*, pg. 1075
ZAO IFD KAPITAL; *Int'l*, pg. 8625
ZAO INDUSTRIAL AND COMMERCIAL BANK OF CHINA (MOSCOW)—See Industrial & Commercial Bank of China Limited; *Int'l*, pg. 3670
ZAO INDUTEK STP—See Indutrade AB; *Int'l*, pg. 3682
ZAO INTERNATIONAL PAPER—See International Paper Company; *U.S. Public*, pg. 1158
ZAO IRKUT AVIASTEP—See Yakovlev Corporation; *Int'l*, pg. 8546
ZAO KARAT POLEVSKOY—See Omya (Schweiz) AG; *Int'l*, pg. 5572
ZAO KEMIRA HIM—See Kemira Oyj; *Int'l*, pg. 4124
ZAO KINNARPS—See Kinnarps AB; *Int'l*, pg. 4181
ZAO KONDI—See Barilla Holding S.p.A.; *Int'l*, pg. 865
ZAO KONECRANES—See Konecranes Plc; *Int'l*, pg. 4253
ZAO KONE LIFTS MOSCOW—See KONE Oyj; *Int'l*, pg. 4251
ZAO KONE LIFTS ST. PETERSBURG—See KONE Oyj; *Int'l*, pg. 4251
Z.A.O. LECO CENTER MOSCOW—See LECO Corporation; *U.S. Private*, pg. 2410
ZAO LEMMINKAINEN DORSTROI—See YIT Corporation; *Int'l*, pg. 8587
ZAO LEMMINKAINEN RUS—See YIT Corporation; *Int'l*, pg. 8587
ZAO L'OREAL—See L'Oreal S.A.; *Int'l*, pg. 4381
ZAO MAKIZ-PHARMA; *Int'l*, pg. 8625
ZAO MAPEI—See Mapei SpA; *Int'l*, pg. 4683
ZAO MAREM—See En+ Group Ltd.; *Int'l*, pg. 2395
ZAO MARY KAY—See Mary Kay Holding Corporation; *U.S. Private*, pg. 2599
ZAO METSO MINERALS (CIS)—See Metso Oyj; *Int'l*, pg. 4867
ZAO MILFORD MOSCOW—See Laurens Spethmann Holding Aktiengesellschaft & Co. KG; *Int'l*, pg. 4424
ZAO MIZUHO CORPORATE BANK (MOSCOW)—See Mizuho Financial Group, Inc.; *Int'l*, pg. 4998
ZAO MOBILEYES—See HiQ International AB; *Int'l*, pg. 3402
ZAO MOSCOW-EFES BREWERY—See Anadolu Efes Biracilik ve Malt Sanayii A.S.; *Int'l*, pg. 445
ZAO NEC NEVA COMMUNICATIONS SYSTEMS—See NEC Corporation; *Int'l*, pg. 5187
ZAO NOKIA—See Nokia Corporation; *Int'l*, pg. 5406
ZAO NORMA-OSVAR—See Autoliv, Inc.; *Int'l*, pg. 730
ZAO NORMARK—See Rapala VMC Oyj; *Int'l*, pg. 6210
ZAO NORTGAZ—See PJSC Gazprom; *Int'l*, pg. 5880
ZAO NOVOBALT TERMINAL—See PCC SE; *Int'l*, pg. 5767
ZAO OUTOKUMPU MOSKVA—See Outokumpu Oyj; *Int'l*, pg. 5669
ZAO OUTOKUMPU ST. PETERSBURG—See Outokumpu Oyj; *Int'l*, pg. 5669
ZAO OUTOTEC—See Metso Oyj; *Int'l*, pg. 4868
ZAO PHILIP MORRIS IZHORA—See Philip Morris International Inc.; *U.S. Public*, pg. 1688
ZAO PRICEWATERHOUSECOOPERS AUDIT—See PricewaterhouseCoopers Russia B.V.; *Int'l*, pg. 5972
ZAO "ALPINE-GAZ"—See ALPINE Bau GmbH; *Int'l*, pg. 371
ZAO "SAINT-GOBAIN KAVMINSTEKLO"—See Compagnie de Saint-Gobain SA; *Int'l*, pg. 1737
ZAO "SPECTRUM BRANDS" RUSSIA—See Spectrum Brands Holdings, Inc.; *U.S. Public*, pg. 1917
ZAO RAMBOLL RUSSIA—See Ramboll Gruppen A/S; *Int'l*, pg. 6197
ZAO RAMIRENT—See Loxam SAS; *Int'l*, pg. 4566
ZAO RANNILA MINSK—See SSAB AB; *Int'l*, pg. 7154
ZAO RETTIG VARME RUS—See Rettig Group Ltd.; *Int'l*, pg. 6311

ZAO RIDAN—See Danfoss A/S; *Int'l*, pg. 1962
ZAO ROSNEFTEFLOT—See OJSC Rosneftegaz; *Int'l*, pg. 5541
ZAO SANDOZ—See Sandoz Group AG; *Int'l*, pg. 6527
ZAO SARTOGOSM—See Sartorius AG; *Int'l*, pg. 6581
ZAO SCHENKER—See Deutsche Bahn AG; *Int'l*, pg. 2054
ZAO SCHINDLER—See Schindler Holding AG; *Int'l*, pg. 6621
ZAO SCHNEIDER ELECTRIC—See Schneider Electric SE; *Int'l*, pg. 6635
ZAO SEVERSTALBEL—See PAO Severstal; *Int'l*, pg. 5732
ZAO SEVERSTAL SMZ-KOLPINO—See PAO Severstal; *Int'l*, pg. 5732
ZAO SEVERSTAL TPZ-SHEKSNA—See PAO Severstal; *Int'l*, pg. 5732
ZAO SHERWIN-WILLIAMS—See The Sherwin-Williams Company; *U.S. Public*, pg. 2130
ZAO SHOKUHIN KAISHA, LTD.—See Meiji Holdings Co., Ltd.; *Int'l*, pg. 4801
ZAO SK TRANSNEFT—See OAO AK Transneft; *Int'l*, pg. 5506
ZAO SLALOM—See Lone Star Funds; *U.S. Private*, pg. 2487
ZAO SOLNTSE MEXICO—See Gruma, S.A.B. de C.V.; *Int'l*, pg. 3114
ZAO SONOCO ALCORE—See Sonoco Products Company; *U.S. Public*, pg. 1906
ZAO SOTEX PHARM FIRM—See Protek OAO; *Int'l*, pg. 6004
ZAO STOCKMANN—See Stockmann plc; *Int'l*, pg. 7220
ZAO STORA ENSO—See Stora Enso Oyj; *Int'l*, pg. 7225
ZAO STROYMASTER—See Kesko Corporation; *Int'l*, pg. 4143
ZAO SULZER PUMPS—See Sulzer Ltd.; *Int'l*, pg. 7259
ZAO SUMITOMO MITSUI RUS BANK—See Sumitomo Mitsui Financial Group, Inc.; *Int'l*, pg. 7295
ZAO TAF ORIFLAME COSMETICS LTD—See Oriflame Cosmetics S.A.; *Int'l*, pg. 5628
ZAO TELIASONERA INTERNATIONAL CARRIER RUSSIA—See Telia Company AB; *Int'l*, pg. 7545
ZAO UFG INVEST—See Deutsche Bank Aktiengesellschaft; *Int'l*, pg. 2062
ZAO UNICREDIT BANK—See UniCredit S.p.A.; *Int'l*, pg. 8040
ZAO UPONOR RUS—See Georg Fischer AG; *Int'l*, pg. 2938
ZAO URALS TURBINE PLANT—See Renova Group; *Int'l*, pg. 6285
ZAO VOESTALPINE ARKADA PROFIL—See voestalpine AG; *Int'l*, pg. 8294
ZAO VOLVO VOSTOK—See AB Volvo; *Int'l*, pg. 47
ZAO VTORCHERMET—See PAO Severstal; *Int'l*, pg. 5732
ZAO YEINTERNATIONAL RUSSIA—See Preato Capital AB; *Int'l*, pg. 5955
ZAO YIT CITYSTROI—See YIT Corporation; *Int'l*, pg. 8587
ZAO YIT MOSKOVIA—See YIT Corporation; *Int'l*, pg. 8587
ZAO YIT-PETER—See YIT Corporation; *Int'l*, pg. 8587
ZAO YIT URALSTROI—See YIT Corporation; *Int'l*, pg. 8587
ZAO ZAVOD MINPLITA—See Compagnie de Saint-Gobain SA; *Int'l*, pg. 1737
ZAPA BETON A.S.—See Buzzi SpA; *Int'l*, pg. 1230
ZAPA BETON SK S.R.O.—See Buzzi SpA; *Int'l*, pg. 1230
ZAPADOCESKA ENERGETIKA, A.S.—See CEZ, a.s.; *Int'l*, pg. 1429
ZAPADOSLOVENSKA ENERGETIKA, A.S.—See E.ON SE; *Int'l*, pg. 2254
ZAPADOSLOVENSKA ENERGETIKA, A.S.—See National Property Fund of the Slovak Republic; *Int'l*, pg. 5162
ZAPAROH S.P. Z O.O.—See Frasers Group plc; *Int'l*, pg. 2765
ZAPATA COMPUTING HOLDINGS INC.; *U.S. Public*, pg. 2401
ZAPATA ENGINEERING - BLACKHAWK DIVISION—See Zapata Engineering; *U.S. Private*, pg. 4598
ZAPATA ENGINEERING; *U.S. Private*, pg. 4598
ZAPATO FAR EAST TRADING LTD.—See Isa-Traesko GmbH; *Int'l*, pg. 3812
ZAP ENGINEERING & CONSTRUCTION SERVICES, INC.; *U.S. Private*, pg. 4598
ZAPF CREATION LOGISTICS GMBH & CO. KG—See MGA Entertainment, Inc.; *U.S. Private*, pg. 2694
ZAPF CREATION (POLSKA) SP. Z O.O.—See MGA Entertainment, Inc.; *U.S. Private*, pg. 2694
ZAPF CREATION (U.K.) LTD.—See MGA Entertainment, Inc.; *U.S. Private*, pg. 2694
ZAPI, INC.—See ZAPI S.p.A; *Int'l*, pg. 8625
ZAPI S.p.A; *Int'l*, pg. 8625
ZAPLABS LLC—See Anywhere Real Estate Inc.; *U.S. Public*, pg. 142
ZAPORIZHSTAL JSC; *Int'l*, pg. 8625
ZAPOROZHTRANSFORMATOR PJSC; *Int'l*, pg. 8625
ZAPPALLAS, INC.; *Int'l*, pg. 8625
ZAPP ELECTRIC VEHICLES GROUP LIMITED; *Int'l*, pg. 8625
ZAPPOS.COM, INC.—See Amazon.com, Inc.; *U.S. Public*, pg. 91
ZAPPROVED LLC—See Leeds Equity Partners, LLC; *U.S. Private*, pg. 2414

ZAPP'S POTATO CHIPS, INC.; *U.S. Private*, pg. 4598
ZAPSIBNEFTEKHIM LLC—See OAO SIBUR Holding; *Int'l*, pg. 5507
ZAP; *U.S. Public*, pg. 2401
ZAPTEC ASA; *Int'l*, pg. 8625
ZAPTEL CORPORATION; *U.S. Private*, pg. 4598
ZAPWATER COMMUNICATIONS, INC.; *U.S. Private*, pg. 4598
ZARA ARGENTINA S.A.—See Industria de Diseno Textil, S.A.; *Int'l*, pg. 3668
ZARA ASIA, LTD.—See Industria de Diseno Textil, S.A.; *Int'l*, pg. 3668
ZARA BELGIQUE S.A.—See Industria de Diseno Textil, S.A.; *Int'l*, pg. 3668
ZARA BRASIL, LTDA.—See Industria de Diseno Textil, S.A.; *Int'l*, pg. 3668
ZARA BUCURESTI, SRL—See Industria de Diseno Textil, S.A.; *Int'l*, pg. 3668
ZARA CANADA INC.—See Industria de Diseno Textil, S.A.; *Int'l*, pg. 3668
ZARA CESKA REPUBLIKA S.R.O.—See Industria de Diseno Textil, S.A.; *Int'l*, pg. 3668
ZARA CHILE S.A.—See Industria de Diseno Textil, S.A.; *Int'l*, pg. 3668
ZARA COMMERCIAL (SHANGHAI), CO LTD.—See Industria de Diseno Textil, S.A.; *Int'l*, pg. 3668
ZARA DENMARK A/S—See Industria de Diseno Textil, S.A.; *Int'l*, pg. 3668
ZARA DEUTSCHLAND GMBH—See Industria de Diseno Textil, S.A.; *Int'l*, pg. 3668
ZARA DISENO, S.L.—See Industria de Diseno Textil, S.A.; *Int'l*, pg. 3668
ZARA ESPANA S.A.—See Industria de Diseno Textil, S.A.; *Int'l*, pg. 3668
ZARA FASHION (SHANGHAI) CO., LTD.—See Industria de Diseno Textil, S.A.; *Int'l*, pg. 3669
ZARA FRANCE, S.A.R.L.—See Industria de Diseno Textil, S.A.; *Int'l*, pg. 3669
ZARA HELLAS, S.A.—See Industria de Diseno Textil, S.A.; *Int'l*, pg. 3668
ZARA HOLDING B.V.—See Industria de Diseno Textil, S.A.; *Int'l*, pg. 3668
ZARA HOME AUSTRALIA PTY. LTD.—See Industria de Diseno Textil, S.A.; *Int'l*, pg. 3669
ZARA HOME BELGIQUE S.A.—See Industria de Diseno Textil, S.A.; *Int'l*, pg. 3669
ZARA HOME BRASIL PRODUTOS PARA O LAR, LTDA.—See Industria de Diseno Textil, S.A.; *Int'l*, pg. 3669
ZARA HOME CANADA, INC.—See Industria de Diseno Textil, S.A.; *Int'l*, pg. 3669
ZARA HOME CESKA REPUBLICA, SRO—See Industria de Diseno Textil, S.A.; *Int'l*, pg. 3669
ZARA HOME CHILE SPA—See Industria de Diseno Textil, S.A.; *Int'l*, pg. 3669
ZARA HOME CIS LTD.—See Industria de Diseno Textil, S.A.; *Int'l*, pg. 3669
ZARA HOME DISENO, S.L.—See Industria de Diseno Textil, S.A.; *Int'l*, pg. 3669
ZARA HOME ESPANA S.A.—See Industria de Diseno Textil, S.A.; *Int'l*, pg. 3669
ZARA HOME FRANCIA, S.A.R.L.—See Industria de Diseno Textil, S.A.; *Int'l*, pg. 3669
ZARA HOME GIYIM ITHALAT IHRACAT VE TICARET LTD.—See Industria de Diseno Textil, S.A.; *Int'l*, pg. 3669
ZARA HOME HELLAS, S.A.—See Industria de Diseno Textil, S.A.; *Int'l*, pg. 3669
ZARA HOME HONG KONG LTD.—See Industria de Diseno Textil, S.A.; *Int'l*, pg. 3669
ZARA HOME IRELAND LIMITED—See Industria de Diseno Textil, S.A.; *Int'l*, pg. 3669
ZARA HOME ITALIA S.R.L.—See Industria de Diseno Textil, S.A.; *Int'l*, pg. 3669
ZARA HOME KOREA LIMITED—See Industria de Diseno Textil, S.A.; *Int'l*, pg. 3669
ZARA HOME LOGISTICA, S.A.—See Industria de Diseno Textil, S.A.; *Int'l*, pg. 3669
ZARA HOME MAGYARORSZAG KFT—See Industria de Diseno Textil, S.A.; *Int'l*, pg. 3669
ZARA HOME MEXICO, S.A. DE C.V.—See Industria de Diseno Textil, S.A.; *Int'l*, pg. 3669
ZARA HOME NEDERLAND B.V.—See Industria de Diseno Textil, S.A.; *Int'l*, pg. 3669
ZARA HOME OSTERREICH CLOTHING GMBH—See Industria de Diseno Textil, S.A.; *Int'l*, pg. 3669
ZARA HOME POLSKA, SP ZO.O.—See Industria de Diseno Textil, S.A.; *Int'l*, pg. 3669
ZARA HOME SRB D.O.O.—See Industria de Diseno Textil, S.A.; *Int'l*, pg. 3669
ZARA HOME U.K., LTD.—See Industria de Diseno Textil, S.A.; *Int'l*, pg. 3669
ZARA HOME UKRAINE, LLC—See Industria de Diseno Textil, S.A.; *Int'l*, pg. 3669
ZARA IMMOBILIARE ITALIA SRL—See Industria de Diseno Textil, S.A.; *Int'l*, pg. 3669
ZARA INVESTMENT HOLDING CO. LTD.; *Int'l*, pg. 8625
ZARA INVESTMENT HOLDING COMPANY LTD.; *Int'l*, pg. 8625

COMPANY NAME INDEX

ZARA@ISOTEAM PTE. LTD.—See ISOTeam Ltd.; *Int'l*, pg. 3821
ZARA ITALIA, S.R.L.—See Industria de Diseno Textil, S.A.; *Int'l*, pg. 3668
ZARA JAPAN CORP.—See Industria de Diseno Textil, S.A.; *Int'l*, pg. 3668
ZARA LOGISTICA S.A.—See Industria de Diseno Textil, S.A.; *Int'l*, pg. 3668
ZARA LUXEMBOURG S.A.—See Industria de Diseno Textil, S.A.; *Int'l*, pg. 3668
ZARA MAGYARORSZAG, KFT.—See Industria de Diseno Textil, S.A.; *Int'l*, pg. 3668
ZARA MEXICO, S.A. DE C.V.—See Industria de Diseno Textil, S.A.; *Int'l*, pg. 3669
ZARA MONACO SAM—See Industria de Diseno Textil, S.A.; *Int'l*, pg. 3668
ZARAM TECHNOLOGY, INC.; *Int'l*, pg. 8625
ZARA NEDERLAND B.V.—See Industria de Diseno Textil, S.A.; *Int'l*, pg. 3668
ZARA NORGE, AS—See Industria de Diseno Textil, S.A.; *Int'l*, pg. 3668
ZARA OSTERREICH CLOTHING GMBH—See Industria de Diseno Textil, S.A.; *Int'l*, pg. 3668
ZARA POLSKA, SP. Z.O.O.—See Industria de Diseno Textil, S.A.; *Int'l*, pg. 3668
ZARA PORTUGAL CONFECCOES LDA.—See Industria de Diseno Textil, S.A.; *Int'l*, pg. 3668
ZARA RETAIL KOREA LTD.—See Industria de Diseno Textil, S.A.; *Int'l*, pg. 3668
ZARA, S.A.—See Industria de Diseno Textil, S.A.; *Int'l*, pg. 3669
ZARA SUISSE S.A.R.L.—See Industria de Diseno Textil, S.A.; *Int'l*, pg. 3668
ZARA SVERIGE AB—See Industria de Diseno Textil, S.A.; *Int'l*, pg. 3668
ZARA TAIWAN, B.V.—See Industria de Diseno Textil, S.A.; *Int'l*, pg. 3668
ZARAT BETEILIGUNGSGESELLSCHAFT MBH & CO. OBJEKT LEBEN II KG—See Deutsche Bank Aktiengesellschaft; *Int'l*, pg. 2062
ZARA UK LTD.—See Industria de Diseno Textil, S.A.; *Int'l*, pg. 3668
ZARA UKRAINE LLC—See Industria de Diseno Textil, S.A.; *Int'l*, pg. 3668
ZARA USA, INC.—See Industria de Diseno Textil, S.A.; *Int'l*, pg. 3668
ZARBEE'S, INC.—See Kenvue Inc.; *U.S. Public*, pg. 1224
ZARCLEAR HOLDINGS LIMITED; *Int'l*, pg. 8625
ZARDOYA OTIS, S.A.—See Otis Worldwide Corporation; *U.S. Public*, pg. 1623
ZAREA S.A.—See AMBRA S.A.; *Int'l*, pg. 415
ZAREMBA CONTRACTORS, LLC—See Zaremba Group, LLC; *U.S. Private*, pg. 4598
ZAREMBA GROUP, LLC; *U.S. Private*, pg. 4598
ZARGES GMBH—See Triton Advisers Limited; *Int'l*, pg. 7935
ZARGES INC.—See Triton Advisers Limited; *Int'l*, pg. 7935
ZARGON OIL & GAS LTD.; *Int'l*, pg. 8625
ZARIN FABRICS; *U.S. Private*, pg. 4598
ZARI ZARDOZI—See NMC Health PLC; *Int'l*, pg. 5392
ZARNENI HRANI BULGARIA AD; *Int'l*, pg. 8625
ZARSKY LUMBER CO., INC.—See Kodiak Building Partners LLC; *U.S. Private*, pg. 2336
ZARS PHARMA, INC.—See Searchlight Pharma, Inc.; *Int'l*, pg. 6666
ZARTMAN CONSTRUCTION INC.; *U.S. Private*, pg. 4598
ZARZAD MORSKIEGO PORTU POLICE SP. Z O.O.—See Zaklady Chemiczne POLICE S.A.; *Int'l*, pg. 8621
ZARZIS BETON—See SODIM, SGPS, SA; *Int'l*, pg. 7049
ZASER & LONGSTON INC.; *U.S. Private*, pg. 4598
ZASOBOVANI TEPLEM VSETIN A.S.—See Groupe BPCE; *Int'l*, pg. 3094
ZASTAVA AUTO PROMET A.D.; *Int'l*, pg. 8625
ZASTAVA ISTRABENZ LIZING, D.O.O.—See Istrabenz, holdinska druzba, d.d.; *Int'l*, pg. 3824
ZASTAVA KOVACNICA A.D.; *Int'l*, pg. 8626
ZASTAVA PROMET A.D.; *Int'l*, pg. 8626
ZASTAVA TAPACIRNICA A.D.; *Int'l*, pg. 8626
ZATARAIN'S BRANDS, INC.—See McCormick & Company, Incorporated; *U.S. Public*, pg. 1404
ZA TECH GLOBAL LIMITED—See ZhongAn Online P & C Insurance Co., Ltd.; *Int'l*, pg. 8672
ZATEC HOP COMPANY—See S.S. Steiner Inc.; *U.S. Private*, pg. 3518
ZATKOFF SEALS & PACKINGS; *U.S. Private*, pg. 4598
ZAT RUUKKI UKRAINA—See SSAB AB; *Int'l*, pg. 7154
ZAVANTE THERAPEUTICS, INC.—See Nabriva Therapeutics PLC; *Int'l*, pg. 5119
ZAVARCO PLC; *Int'l*, pg. 8626
ZAVARIVAC A.D.; *Int'l*, pg. 8626
ZAVAROVALNICA SAVA ZAVAROVALNA DRUZBA, D.D.—See Pozavarovalnica Sava, d.d.; *Int'l*, pg. 5949
ZAVAROVALNICA TILIA, D. D.—See Pozavarovalnica Sava, d.d.; *Int'l*, pg. 5949
ZAVAROVALNICA TRIGLAV, D.D.; *Int'l*, pg. 8626
ZAVATION MEDICAL PRODUCTS, LLC—See Gemspring Capital Management, LLC; *U.S. Private*, pg. 1659
ZAVDA TECHNOLOGIES, LLC—See CACI International Inc.; *U.S. Public*, pg. 417

ZAVOD BBDO—See Omnicom Group Inc.; *U.S. Public*, pg. 1577
ZAVOD ZA EKONOMIKU I RAZVOJ A.D.; *Int'l*, pg. 8627
ZAVOD ZA GEOTEHNIKU A.D.; *Int'l*, pg. 8627
ZAVOD ZA SHLIFOVACHNI MASHINI AD; *Int'l*, pg. 8627
ZAVOD ZA SUDSKA VESTACENJA A.D.; *Int'l*, pg. 8627
ZAVOD ZA VODOPRIVREDU D.D.; *Int'l*, pg. 8627
ZAVOLI, S.R.L.—See Westport Fuel Systems Inc.; *Int'l*, pg. 8392
ZAWAWI BUSINESS MACHINES LLC—See Omar Zawawi Establishment LLC; *Int'l*, pg. 5561
ZAWAWI TRADING COMPANY LLC—See Omar Zawawi Establishment LLC; *Int'l*, pg. 5561
ZAXBY'S FRANCHISING, INC.; *U.S. Private*, pg. 4598
Z-AXIS, INC.—See Video Display Corporation; *U.S. Public*, pg. 2297
ZAYANI LEASING W.L.L.—See Al Zayani Investments WLL; *Int'l*, pg. 283
ZAYANI MOTORS WLL—See Al Zayani Investments WLL; *Int'l*, pg. 283
ZAYANI PROPERTIES WLL—See Al Zayani Investments WLL; *Int'l*, pg. 283
ZAYO FRANCE SAS—See DigitalBridge Group, Inc.; *U.S. Public*, pg. 665
ZAYO FRANCE SAS—See EQT AB; *Int'l*, pg. 2482
ZAYO GROUP HOLDINGS, INC.—See DigitalBridge Group, Inc.; *U.S. Public*, pg. 665
ZAYO GROUP HOLDINGS, INC.—See EQT AB; *Int'l*, pg. 2481
ZAYO GROUP, LLC-LOUISVILLE—See DigitalBridge Group, Inc.; *U.S. Public*, pg. 665
ZAYO GROUP, LLC-LOUISVILLE—See EQT AB; *Int'l*, pg. 2482
ZAYO GROUP, LLC—See DigitalBridge Group, Inc.; *U.S. Public*, pg. 665
ZAYO GROUP, LLC—See EQT AB; *Int'l*, pg. 2482
ZAYO GROUP UK LIMITED—See DigitalBridge Group, Inc.; *U.S. Public*, pg. 665
ZAYO GROUP UK LIMITED—See EQT AB; *Int'l*, pg. 2482
ZAZA ENERGY CORPORATION; *U.S. Public*, pg. 2401
ZAZITKOVA AKADEMIE S.R.O.—See Erlebnis Akademie AG; *Int'l*, pg. 2494
ZAZOO LIMITED—See Lesaka Technologies, Inc.; *Int'l*, pg. 4469
ZAZZLE, INC.; *U.S. Private*, pg. 4598
Z BAU GMBH—See STRABAG SE; *Int'l*, pg. 7200
Z. BAVELLONI SOUTH AMERICA LTDA—See Glaston Oyj Abp; *Int'l*, pg. 2989
ZB BANK LIMITED - CONSUMER BANKING UNIT—See ZB FINANCIAL HOLDINGS LIMITED; *Int'l*, pg. 8627
ZB BANK LIMITED - GROUP CREDIT SERVICES BULAWAYO UNIT—See ZB FINANCIAL HOLDINGS LIMITED; *Int'l*, pg. 8627
ZB BANK LIMITED - GROUP TREASURY UNIT—See ZB FINANCIAL HOLDINGS LIMITED; *Int'l*, pg. 8627
ZB BANK LIMITED - INVESTMENT BANKING UNIT—See ZB FINANCIAL HOLDINGS LIMITED; *Int'l*, pg. 8627
ZBB ENERGY PTY. LTD.—See EnSync, Inc.; *U.S. Public*, pg. 776
Z-BEST PRODUCTS; *U.S. Private*, pg. 4596
ZB FINANCIAL HOLDINGS LIMITED; *Int'l*, pg. 8627
ZB IMPORTING, INC.—See Peak Rock Capital LLC; *U.S. Private*, pg. 3124
ZB INVEST DOO—See UniCredit S.p.A.; *Int'l*, pg. 8041
ZBI ZENTRAL BODEN IMMOBILIEN AG; *Int'l*, pg. 8627
ZBOM HOME COLLECTION CO., LTD.; *Int'l*, pg. 8622
ZB REINSURANCE LIMITED—See ZB FINANCIAL HOLDINGS LIMITED; *Int'l*, pg. 8627
Z CAPITAL GROUP, LLC; *U.S. Private*, pg. 4595
Z CAPITAL PARTNERS, LLC—See Z Capital Group, LLC; *U.S. Private*, pg. 4595
Z. CAVARICCI INC.—See Z. Cavaricci Inc.; *U.S. Private*, pg. 4596
Z. CAVARICCI INC.—See Z. Cavaricci Inc.; *U.S. Private*, pg. 4596
Z. CAVARICCI INC.; *U.S. Private*, pg. 4596
ZCC EUROPE GMBH—See Hunan Nonferrous Metals Corporation Ltd.; *Int'l*, pg. 3533
ZCCM INVESTMENTS HOLDINGS PLC.; *Int'l*, pg. 8627
ZCH ALWERNIA S.A.—See Kulczyk Investments S.A.; *Int'l*, pg. 4328
ZCHOCOLAT—See zChocolat; *Int'l*, pg. 8627
ZCHOCOLAT; *Int'l*, pg. 8627
ZCH ORGANIKA SARZYNA S.A.—See Kulczyk Investments S.A.; *Int'l*, pg. 4328
ZCL COMPOSITES INC.—See ShawCor Ltd.; *Int'l*, pg. 6791
ZCL COMPOSITES INC. - ZCL EVERLAST—See ShawCor Ltd.; *Int'l*, pg. 6791
Z-COM, INC.; *Int'l*, pg. 8619
ZCORUM INC.; *U.S. Private*, pg. 4598
ZC&R COATINGS FOR OPTICS, INC.—See The Graham Group, Inc.; *U.S. Private*, pg. 4036
Z-CUBE S.R.L.—See Zambon Company S.p.A.; *Int'l*, pg. 8622
ZDAS, A.S.—See CEFC China Energy Company Limited; *Int'l*, pg. 1389
ZDI IMAGES & MOTION INC.—See Stirista, LLC; *U.S. Private*, pg. 3813

ZDRAVLJE AD—See Frontier Pharma Limited; *Int'l*, pg. 2795
ZDS JESENICE DOO—See SOL S.p.A.; *Int'l*, pg. 7068
ZDZHB VOLGA FORM ZAO—See OAO Group of Companies PIK; *Int'l*, pg. 5506
ZEA BBDO—See Omnicom Group Inc.; *U.S. Public*, pg. 1577
ZEABORN CHARTERING GMBH & CO. KG—See ZEABORN Ship Management GmbH & Cie. KG; *Int'l*, pg. 8627
ZEABORN SHIP MANAGEMENT GMBH & CIE. KG; *Int'l*, pg. 8627
ZEAG ENERGIE AG—See EnBW Energie Baden-Wurttemberg AG; *Int'l*, pg. 2400
ZEAG ENERGIE AG—See EnBW Energie Baden-Wurttemberg AG; *Int'l*, pg. 2401
ZEAG ENGINEERING GMBH—See EnBW Energie Baden-Wurttemberg AG; *Int'l*, pg. 2401
ZEALAND PHARMA A/S; *Int'l*, pg. 8628
ZEAL AQUA LIMITED; *Int'l*, pg. 8628
ZEAL CREDIT UNION; *U.S. Private*, pg. 4598
ZEAL INTERNATIONAL CO., LTD.—See Eson Precision Ind. Co., Ltd.; *Int'l*, pg. 2504
ZEALNET INC.—See GENDAI AGENCY INC.; *Int'l*, pg. 2917
ZEAL NETWORK SE; *Int'l*, pg. 8628
ZEALOT NETWORKS, INC.; *U.S. Private*, pg. 4598
ZEBAN NOMINEES LIMITED—See Barclays PLC; *Int'l*, pg. 863
ZEBCO—See W.C. Bradley Co.; *U.S. Private*, pg. 4419
ZEB NICKEL COMPANY (PTY.) LTD.—See URU Metals Limited; *Int'l*, pg. 8096
ZEB NICKEL CORP.; *Int'l*, pg. 8628
ZEBRA CABS PROPRIETARY LIMITED—See Transaction Capital Limited; *Int'l*, pg. 7895
ZEBRA ENTERPRISE SOLUTIONS B.V.B.A.—See Zebra Technologies Corporation; *U.S. Public*, pg. 2402
ZEBRA ENVIRONMENTAL AND INDUSTRIAL SERVICES, INC.; *U.S. Private*, pg. 4599
ZEBRA IMAGING, INC.; *U.S. Private*, pg. 4599
ZEBRA RAPP MADRID—See Omnicom Group Inc.; *U.S. Public*, pg. 1593
ZEBRA TECHNOLOGIES AB—See Zebra Technologies Corporation; *U.S. Public*, pg. 2402
ZEBRA TECHNOLOGIES ARGENTINA S.A.—See Zebra Technologies Corporation; *U.S. Public*, pg. 2402
ZEBRA TECHNOLOGIES ASIA PACIFIC, LLC—See Zebra Technologies Corporation; *U.S. Public*, pg. 2402
ZEBRA TECHNOLOGIES AUSTRIA GMBH—See Zebra Technologies Corporation; *U.S. Public*, pg. 2402
ZEBRA TECHNOLOGIES B.V.—See Zebra Technologies Corporation; *U.S. Public*, pg. 2402
ZEBRA TECHNOLOGIES COLOMBIA S.A.S.—See Zebra Technologies Corporation; *U.S. Public*, pg. 2402
ZEBRA TECHNOLOGIES CORPORATION; *U.S. Public*, pg. 2401
ZEBRA TECHNOLOGIES CORP.—See Zebra Technologies Corporation; *U.S. Public*, pg. 2402
ZEBRA TECHNOLOGIES EUROPE LIMITED—See Zebra Technologies Corporation; *U.S. Public*, pg. 2402
ZEBRA TECHNOLOGIES EUROPE SALES COMPANY, LLC—See Zebra Technologies Corporation; *U.S. Public*, pg. 2402
ZEBRA TECHNOLOGIES GERMANY GMBH—See Zebra Technologies Corporation; *U.S. Public*, pg. 2402
ZEBRA TECHNOLOGIES (HONG KONG) LIMITED—See Zebra Technologies Corporation; *U.S. Public*, pg. 2402
ZEBRA TECHNOLOGIES INTERNATIONAL, LLC—See Zebra Technologies Corporation; *U.S. Public*, pg. 2402
ZEBRA TECHNOLOGIES ITALY S.R.L.—See Zebra Technologies Corporation; *U.S. Public*, pg. 2402
ZEBRA TECHNOLOGIES JAPAN CO. LTD.—See Zebra Technologies Corporation; *U.S. Public*, pg. 2402
ZEBRA TECHNOLOGIES KOREA YCH—See Zebra Technologies Corporation; *U.S. Public*, pg. 2402
ZEBRA TECHNOLOGIES LANKA (PRIVATE) LIMITED—See Zebra Technologies Corporation; *U.S. Public*, pg. 2402
ZEBRA TECHNOLOGIES LATIN AMERICA, LLC—See Zebra Technologies Corporation; *U.S. Public*, pg. 2402
ZEBRA TECHNOLOGIES MAGYARORSZAG KFT.—See Zebra Technologies Corporation; *U.S. Public*, pg. 2402
ZEBRA TECHNOLOGIES NETHERLANDS B.V.—See Zebra Technologies Corporation; *U.S. Public*, pg. 2402
ZEBRA TECHNOLOGIES (NEW ZEALAND) LIMITED—See Zebra Technologies Corporation; *U.S. Public*, pg. 2402
ZEBRA TECHNOLOGIES SPAIN, S.L.—See Zebra Technologies Corporation; *U.S. Public*, pg. 2402
ZEBRA TEKNOLOJILERI SISTEM COZUMLERI ANONIM SIRKETA—See Zebra Technologies Corporation; *U.S. Public*, pg. 2402
ZEBULON SOLUTIONS LLC; *U.S. Private*, pg. 4599
ZECHBAU GMBH—See Zech Group SE; *Int'l*, pg. 8629
ZECH BAU HOLDING GMBH—See Zech Group SE; *Int'l*, pg. 8628
ZECH BUILDING SE—See Zech Group SE; *Int'l*, pg. 8628
ZECH GROUP SE; *Int'l*, pg. 8628
ZECH HOCHBAU AG—See Zech Group SE; *Int'l*, pg. 8628

ZECH GROUP SE — CORPORATE AFFILIATIONS

ZECH HOTEL HOLDING GMBH—See Zech Group SE; *Int'l*, pg. 8629
ZECH HOTELS GMBH—See Zech Group SE; *Int'l*, pg. 8629
ZECH SICHERHEITSTECHNIK GMBH—See Zech Group SE; *Int'l*, pg. 8628
ZECH TECHNIK AUSTRIA GMBH—See Zech Group SE; *Int'l*, pg. 8628
ZECH UMWELT GMBH—See Zech Group SE; *Int'l*, pg. 8629
ZECK FORD; *U.S. Private*, pg. 4599
ZECOL INC.—See Twinco Automotive Warehouse, Inc.; *U.S. Private*, pg. 4266
ZECON BERHAD; *Int'l*, pg. 8629
ZECO SYSTEMS PTE. LTD.—See Shell plc; *Int'l*, pg. 6800
ZECOTEK PHOTONICS INC.; *Int'l*, pg. 8629
ZECOTEK PHOTONICS SINGAPORE PTE. LTD.—See Zecotek Photonics Inc.; *Int'l*, pg. 8629
ZEDA CAR LEASING (PTY) LIMITED—See Barloworld Ltd.; *Int'l*, pg. 866
ZEDA GESELLSCHAFT FUR DATENVERARBEITUNG UND EDV-BERATUNG MBH & CO.—See Vorwerk & Co. KG; *Int'l*, pg. 8308
ZEDCOR HOLDINGS (USA), INC.—See Zedcor Inc.; *Int'l*, pg. 8629
ZEDCOR INC.; *Int'l*, pg. 8629
ZEDCOR SECURITY SOLUTIONS CORP.—See Zedcor Inc.; *Int'l*, pg. 8629
ZEDER INVESTMENTS LIMITED; *Int'l*, pg. 8629
ZE DESIGN INC.—See TRADERS HOLDINGS CO., LTD.; *Int'l*, pg. 7888
ZEDGE, INC.; *U.S. Public*, pg. 2402
ZEDI INC.—See IGP Industries, LLC; *U.S. Private*, pg. 2040
ZEDRA TRUST CO. LTD; *Int'l*, pg. 8629
ZEDX, INC.—See BASF SE; *Int'l*, pg. 876
ZEE AUTOMOTIVE; *U.S. Private*, pg. 4599
ZEECOL INTERNATIONAL, INC.; *Int'l*, pg. 8629
ZEE ENTERTAINMENT ENTERPRISES LTD.—See Essel Corporate Resources Pvt. Ltd.; *Int'l*, pg. 2510
ZEEKLITE CO., LTD.—See ORIX Corporation; *Int'l*, pg. 5637
ZEELAND ALUMINUM COMPANY NV—See Klesch & Company SA; *Int'l*, pg. 4201
ZEELAND FARM SERVICES INC.; *U.S. Private*, pg. 4599
ZEELAND LUMBER & SUPPLY CO.; *U.S. Private*, pg. 4599
ZEELANDNET B.V.—See EQT AB; *Int'l*, pg. 2482
ZEELAND REFINERY NV—See TotalEnergies SE; *Int'l*, pg. 7844
ZEE LEARN LIMITED; *Int'l*, pg. 8629
ZEE MEDIA CORPORATION LTD.—See Essel Corporate Resources Pvt. Ltd.; *Int'l*, pg. 2510
ZEE MULTIMEDIA (MAURICE) LIMITED—See Essel Corporate Resources Pvt. Ltd.; *Int'l*, pg. 2510
ZEE MULTIMEDIA WORLDWIDE (MAURITIUS) LIMITED—See Essel Corporate Resources Pvt. Ltd.; *Int'l*, pg. 2510
ZEENAT BOOK SUPPLY LTD—See Thames & Hudson Ltd; *Int'l*, pg. 7607
ZE ENERGY INC.—See TRADERS HOLDINGS CO., LTD.; *Int'l*, pg. 7888
ZEESHAN ENERGY LIMITED—See National Group of Companies LLC; *Int'l*, pg. 5158
ZEE TELEFILMS MIDDLE EAST FZ-LLC—See Essel Corporate Resources Pvt. Ltd.; *Int'l*, pg. 2510
ZEE TURNER LIMITED—See Essel Corporate Resources Pvt. Ltd.; *Int'l*, pg. 2510
ZEE TURNER LIMITED—See Warner Bros. Discovery, Inc.; *U.S. Public*, pg. 2328
ZEE TV SOUTH AFRICA PTY. LTD.—See Essel Corporate Resources Pvt. Ltd.; *Int'l*, pg. 2510
ZEFIRO METHANE CORP; *Int'l*, pg. 8629
ZEGERS, INC.—See Vorteq Coil Finishers, LLC; *U.S. Private*, pg. 4413
ZEGLUGA BYDGOSKA SP. Z O.O.—See OT Logistics S.A.; *Int'l*, pg. 5656
ZEGLUGA POLSKA S.A.—See Polska Zegluga Morska; *Int'l*, pg. 5912
ZEGONA COMMUNICATIONS PLC; *Int'l*, pg. 8629
ZEGRAHM EXPEDITIONS, INC.—See TUI AG; *Int'l*, pg. 7969
ZEHDENICK INNOVATIVE METALL- UND KUNSTSTOFFTECHNIK GMBH—See Diehl Stiftung & Co. KG; *Int'l*, pg. 2115
ZEHNDER AMERICA, INC.—See Zehnder Group AG; *Int'l*, pg. 8630
ZEHNDER BALTICS OU—See Zehnder Group AG; *Int'l*, pg. 8630
ZEHNDER CALADAIR INTERNATIONAL S.A.S.—See Zehnder Group AG; *Int'l*, pg. 8630
ZEHNDER (CHINA) INDOOR CLIMATE CO., LTD.—See Zehnder Group AG; *Int'l*, pg. 8630
ZEHNDER COMFOSYSTEMS CESOVENT AG—See Zehnder Group AG; *Int'l*, pg. 8630
ZEHNDER COMMUNICATIONS, INC.; *U.S. Private*, pg. 4599
ZEHNDER COMMUNICATIONS—See Zehnder Communications, Inc.; *U.S. Private*, pg. 4599
ZEHNDER GMBH—See Zehnder Group AG; *Int'l*, pg. 8630
ZEHNDER GROUP AG; *Int'l*, pg. 8629
ZEHNDER GROUP BELGIUM N.V.—See Zehnder Group AG; *Int'l*, pg. 8630
ZEHNDER GROUP BOLESLAWIEC SP. Z O.O.—See Zehnder Group AG; *Int'l*, pg. 8630
ZEHNDER GROUP CZECH REPUBLIC S.R.O.—See Zehnder Group AG; *Int'l*, pg. 8630
ZEHNDER GROUP DEUTSCHLAND GMBH—See Zehnder Group AG; *Int'l*, pg. 8630
ZEHNDER GROUP FINANCE LTD.—See Zehnder Group AG; *Int'l*, pg. 8630
ZEHNDER GROUP FRANCE SAS—See Zehnder Group AG; *Int'l*, pg. 8630
ZEHNDER GROUP IBERICA INDOOR CLIMATE, S.A.—See Zehnder Group AG; *Int'l*, pg. 8630
ZEHNDER GROUP IC MEKAN IKLIMLENDIRME SANAYI VE TICARET LIMITET SIRKETI—See Zehnder Group AG; *Int'l*, pg. 8630
ZEHNDER GROUP ITALIA S.R.L.—See Zehnder Group AG; *Int'l*, pg. 8630
ZEHNDER GROUP NORDIC AB—See Zehnder Group AG; *Int'l*, pg. 8630
ZEHNDER GROUP PRODUKTION GRANICHEN AG—See Zehnder Group AG; *Int'l*, pg. 8630
ZEHNDER GROUP SCHWEIZ AG—See Zehnder Group AG; *Int'l*, pg. 8630
ZEHNDER GROUP UK LIMITED—See Zehnder Group AG; *Int'l*, pg. 8630
ZEHNDER GROUP UK LTD - BISQUE DIVISION—See Zehnder Group AG; *Int'l*, pg. 8630
ZEHNDER GROUP VAUX ANDIGNY SAS—See Zehnder Group AG; *Int'l*, pg. 8630
ZEHNDER NEDERLAND B.V.—See Zehnder Group AG; *Int'l*, pg. 8630
ZEHNDER POLSKA SP. Z O.O.—See Zehnder Group AG; *Int'l*, pg. 8630
ZEHNDERS OF FRANKENMUTH INC.; *U.S. Private*, pg. 4599
ZEHNDER TECNOSYSTEMS S.R.L.—See Zehnder Group AG; *Int'l*, pg. 8630
ZEHRMART INC.—See George Weston Limited; *Int'l*, pg. 2939
ZEIDLER; *Int'l*, pg. 8630
ZEIDLER & WIMMEL-BURO STUTTGART—See Zeidler & Wimmel Verwaltungs-GmbH; *Int'l*, pg. 8631
ZEIDLER & WIMMEL NATURSTEININDUSTRIE GMBH & CO. KG—See H. Geiger GmbH; *Int'l*, pg. 3194
ZEIDLER & WIMMEL-NIEDERLASSUNG BERLIN—See Zeidler & Wimmel Verwaltungs-GmbH; *Int'l*, pg. 8631
ZEIDLER & WIMMEL-NIEDERLASSUNG DRESDEN—See Zeidler & Wimmel Verwaltungs-GmbH; *Int'l*, pg. 8631
ZEIDLER & WIMMEL-NIEDERLASSUNG DUSSELDORF—See Zeidler & Wimmel Verwaltungs-GmbH; *Int'l*, pg. 8631
ZEIDLER & WIMMEL-NIEDERLASSUNG FRANKFURT—See Zeidler & Wimmel Verwaltungs-GmbH; *Int'l*, pg. 8631
ZEIDLER & WIMMEL-NIEDERLASSUNG HANNOVER—See Zeidler & Wimmel Verwaltungs-GmbH; *Int'l*, pg. 8631
ZEIDLER & WIMMEL-NIEDERLASSUNG MUNICH—See Zeidler & Wimmel Verwaltungs-GmbH; *Int'l*, pg. 8631
ZEIDLER & WIMMEL VERWALTUNGS-GMBH; *Int'l*, pg. 8631
ZEIDLER & WIMMEL-ZWEIGSTELLE HAMBURG—See Zeidler & Wimmel Verwaltungs-GmbH; *Int'l*, pg. 8631
ZEIGLER BROS INC; *U.S. Private*, pg. 4599
ZEIGLER CHRYSLER DODGE JEEP OF SCHAUMBURG; *U.S. Private*, pg. 4599
ZEILER INSURANCE INC.; *U.S. Private*, pg. 4599
ZEIRISHI-HOJIN PRICEWATERHOUSECOOPERS—See PricewaterhouseCoopers Co., Ltd.; *Int'l*, pg. 5970
ZEISER INC.—See Orell Fussli Holding AG; *Int'l*, pg. 5616
ZEISER MOTORS, INC.; *U.S. Private*, pg. 4599
ZEISS-BELOMO OOO—See Carl-Zeiss-Stiftung; *Int'l*, pg. 1337
ZEIT O&M CO., LTD.—See GS Holdings Corp.; *Int'l*, pg. 3142
ZEITVERLAG GERD BUCERIUS GMBH—See Verlagsgruppe Georg von Holtzbrinck GmbH; *Int'l*, pg. 8172
ZEKELMAN INDUSTRIES INC.; *U.S. Private*, pg. 4599
ZEKIAH TECHNOLOGIES, INC.; *U.S. Private*, pg. 4600
ZEKS COMPRESSED AIR SOLUTIONS LLC—See Ingersoll Rand Inc.; *U.S. Public*, pg. 1122
ZEKU CORPORATION—See en-japan Inc.; *Int'l*, pg. 2395
ZELAN BERHAD; *Int'l*, pg. 8631
ZELAN DEVELOPMENT SDN. BHD.—See Zelan Berhad; *Int'l*, pg. 8631
ZELEZARNA RAVNE MONTER DRAVOGRAD D.D.; *Int'l*, pg. 8631
ZELEZIARNE PODBREZOVA A.S.; *Int'l*, pg. 8631
ZELEZOKRIVNICA SCT - MERKUR, D.O.O.—See Merkur, d.d.; *Int'l*, pg. 4837
ZELIGSTUDIO—See WPP plc; *Int'l*, pg. 8477
ZELIRA THERAPEUTICS LIMITED; *Int'l*, pg. 8631
ZELIS CLAIMS INTEGRITY, INC.—See PCP Enterprise, L.P.; *U.S. Private*, pg. 3121
ZELIS HEALTHCARE CORPORATION—See PCP Enterprise, L.P.; *U.S. Private*, pg. 3121
ZELIS NETWORK SOLUTIONS, LLC—See PCP Enterprise, L.P.; *U.S. Private*, pg. 3121
ZELIS PAYMENTS, INC.—See PCP Enterprise, L.P.; *U.S. Private*, pg. 3121
ZELJEZARA ILIJAS D.D.; *Int'l*, pg. 8631
ZELJEZNIACAR KONFEKCIJA A.D.; *Int'l*, pg. 8631
ZELJEZNICE RS A.D.; *Int'l*, pg. 8631
ZELLER ENGINEERING GMBH—See Berry Global Group, Inc; *U.S. Public*, pg. 326
ZELLER MOTOR COMPANY; *U.S. Private*, pg. 4600
ZELLER PLASTIK SHANGHAI LIMITED—See Berry Global Group, Inc; *U.S. Public*, pg. 326
ZELLIS UK LIMITED—See Bain Capital, LP; *U.S. Private*, pg. 452
ZELLNER CONSTRUCTION COMPANY, INC.; *U.S. Private*, pg. 4600
ZELLSTOFF CELGAR LIMITED PARTNERSHIP—See Mercer International Inc.; *Int'l*, pg. 4829
ZELLSTOFF CELGAR LIMITED—See Mercer International Inc.; *Int'l*, pg. 4829
ZELLSTOFF CELGAR LP—See Mercer International Inc.; *Int'l*, pg. 4829
ZELLSTOFF POLS AG—See Heinzel Holding GmbH; *Int'l*, pg. 3326
ZELLSTOFF STENDAL GMBH—See Mercer International Inc.; *Int'l*, pg. 4830
ZELLWOOD INT'L CORP.—See BizLink Holding Inc.; *Int'l*, pg. 1053
ZELNICKMEDIA CORP; *U.S. Private*, pg. 4600
ZELNOVA S.A.—See Zeltia, S.A.; *Int'l*, pg. 8632
ZELOR TECHNOLOGY PTE LTD—See Frencken Group Limited; *Int'l*, pg. 2773
ZEL TECHNOLOGIES, LLC; *U.S. Private*, pg. 4600
ZELTECH TRAINING SOLUTIONS, LLC—See Zel Technologies, LLC; *U.S. Private*, pg. 4600
ZELTIA, S.A.; *Int'l*, pg. 8631
ZELTIQ AESTHETICS, INC.—See AbbVie Inc.; *U.S. Public*, pg. 24
ZELTIQ LIMITED—See AbbVie Inc.; *U.S. Public*, pg. 24
ZELUCK INC.; *U.S. Private*, pg. 4601
ZEMACH HAMMERMAN LTD.; *Int'l*, pg. 8632
ZEMAITIJOS PIENAS AB; *Int'l*, pg. 8632
ZEMAX EUROPE LIMITED—See ANSYS, Inc.; *U.S. Public*, pg. 139
ZEMAX JAPAN K.K.—See ANSYS, Inc.; *U.S. Public*, pg. 139
ZEMAX, LLC—See EQT AB; *Int'l*, pg. 2482
ZEMAX OPTICAL TECHNOLOGY CONSULTING (SHANGHAI) CO., LTD.—See ANSYS, Inc.; *U.S. Public*, pg. 139
ZEMBA BROS INC; *U.S. Private*, pg. 4601
ZEMCO INDUSTRIES, INC.—See Tyson Foods, Inc.; *U.S. Public*, pg. 2210
ZEMENICK & WALKER, INC.; *U.S. Private*, pg. 4601
ZEMENTIS, INC.—See Silver Lake Group, LLC; *U.S. Private*, pg. 3660
ZEMENTWERK LEUBE GMBH; *Int'l*, pg. 8632
ZEMIC EUROPE B.V.—See Zhonghang Electronic Measuring Instruments Co., Ltd.; *Int'l*, pg. 8673
ZEMIC(USA) INC—See Zhonghang Electronic Measuring Instruments Co., Ltd.; *Int'l*, pg. 8673
ZEMOGA, INC.—See S4 Capital plc; *Int'l*, pg. 6458
ZEMPER FRANCE S.A.R.L—See F.W. Thorpe plc; *Int'l*, pg. 2597
ZEMPLEO, INC.; *U.S. Private*, pg. 4601
ZEMSPOL, S.R.O.—See CPI Property Group, S.A.; *Int'l*, pg. 1825
ZENABIS GLOBAL INC.—See SNDL Inc.; *Int'l*, pg. 7027
ZENAD GROUP CO. FOR TRADING & CONTRACTING. & PHARMASOM LTD.—See Dar Al Dawa Development & Investment Co.; *Int'l*, pg. 1971
ZENA MINING CORP.; *Int'l*, pg. 8632
ZENARA PHARMA PRIVATE LIMITED—See Permira Advisers LLP; *Int'l*, pg. 5803
ZENAR CORPORATION; *U.S. Private*, pg. 4601
ZENARO LIGHTING GMBH—See Everlight Electronics Co., Ltd.; *Int'l*, pg. 2568
ZENCARD SP. Z O.O.—See PKO Bank Polski SA; *Int'l*, pg. 5887
ZEN CARGO MOVERS PVT. LTD.—See Gati Ltd.; *Int'l*, pg. 2889
ZENCODER INC.—See Brightcove, Inc.; *U.S. Public*, pg. 383
ZEN CONTINENTAL CO., INC.; *U.S. Private*, pg. 4601
ZEN CORP GROUP PCL; *Int'l*, pg. 8632
ZENCOS CONSULTING LLC—See Executive Information Systems, LLC; *U.S. Private*, pg. 1447
ZENDER FORD; *Int'l*, pg. 8632
ZENDESK APAC—See Hellman & Friedman LLC; *U.S. Private*, pg. 1911
ZENDESK APAC—See Permira Advisers LLP; *Int'l*, pg. 5809
ZENDESK EMEA—See Hellman & Friedman LLC; *U.S. Private*, pg. 1911
ZENDESK EMEA—See Permira Advisers LLP; *Int'l*, pg. 5809

COMPANY NAME INDEX

ZENDESK, INC.—See Hellman & Friedman LLC; *U.S. Private*, pg. 1911
ZENDESK, INC.—See Permira Advisers LLP; *Int'l*, pg. 5809
ZENDESK KOREA LLC—See Hellman & Friedman LLC; *U.S. Private*, pg. 1911
ZENDESK KOREA LLC—See Permira Advisers LLP; *Int'l*, pg. 5809
ZENDESK SINGAPORE PTE. LTD—See Hellman & Friedman LLC; *U.S. Private*, pg. 1911
ZENDESK SINGAPORE PTE. LTD—See Permira Advisers LLP; *Int'l*, pg. 5809
ZENDEX HOLDINGS, INC.; *U.S. Private*, pg. 4601
ZENDIS SL—See Vivendi SE; *Int'l*, pg. 8276
ZEND TECHNOLOGIES, INC.—See Clearlake Capital Group, L.P.; *U.S. Private*, pg. 936
ZEND TECHNOLOGIES, INC.—See Francisco Partners Management, LP; *U.S. Private*, pg. 1591
ZENECA INTERNATIONAL LTD.—See AstraZeneca PLC; *Int'l*, pg. 661
ZENERGY AB; *Int'l*, pg. 8632
Z ENERGY LIMITED—See Ampol Limited; *Int'l*, pg. 437
ZENER STEWARD ELECTROMECHANICAL—See Stefanutti Stocks Holdings Limited; *Int'l*, pg. 7193
ZENER STEWARD LLC—See Stefanutti Stocks Holdings Limited; *Int'l*, pg. 7192
ZENETEX LLC—See V2X, Inc.; *U.S. Public*, pg. 2270
ZENFOLIO, INC.—See Centre Lane Partners, LLC; *U.S. Private*, pg. 828
ZENGAME TECHNOLOGY HOLDING LIMITED; *Int'l*, pg. 8632
ZENIC INC.—See Optex Group Co., Ltd.; *Int'l*, pg. 5602
ZENICOM CORPORATION—See Zenitron Corporation; *Int'l*, pg. 8633
ZENICOR MEDICAL SYSTEMS AB; *Int'l*, pg. 8632
ZENIMAX MEDIA, INC.—See Microsoft Corporation; *U.S. Public*, pg. 1443
THE ZENITAKA CORPORATION; *Int'l*, pg. 7705
ZENITAS CARING CHOICE PTY LTD—See Adamantem Capital Management Pty Limited; *Int'l*, pg. 124
ZENITAS CARING CHOICE PTY LTD—See Liverpool Partners Pty Ltd; *Int'l*, pg. 4530
ZENITAS HEALTHCARE LIMITED—See Adamantem Capital Management Pty Limited; *Int'l*, pg. 124
ZENITAS HEALTHCARE LIMITED—See Liverpool Partners Pty Ltd; *Int'l*, pg. 4530
ZENITAS ONTRAC PTY LTD—See Adamantem Capital Management Pty Limited; *Int'l*, pg. 124
ZENITAS ONTRAC PTY LTD—See Liverpool Partners Pty Ltd; *Int'l*, pg. 4530
ZENIT BAUPLANUNGS- UND ERRICHTUNGSGESELLSCHAFT M.B.H.—See PORR AG; *Int'l*, pg. 5925
ZENITEL CSS FRANCE S.A.—See Zenitel N.V.; *Int'l*, pg. 8632
ZENITEL DENMARK A/S—See Zenitel N.V.; *Int'l*, pg. 8632
ZENITEL ITALIA SRL—See Zenitel N.V.; *Int'l*, pg. 8632
ZENITEL MARINE ASIA PTE. LTD.—See Zenitel N.V.; *Int'l*, pg. 8632
ZENITEL MARINE BRAZIL—See Zenitel N.V.; *Int'l*, pg. 8633
ZENITEL MARINE GERMANY—See Zenitel N.V.; *Int'l*, pg. 8633
ZENITEL MARINE MED.—See Zenitel N.V.; *Int'l*, pg. 8633
ZENITEL NORWAY AS—See Zenitel N.V.; *Int'l*, pg. 8633
ZENITEL N.V.; *Int'l*, pg. 8632
ZENITEL USA INC—See Zenitel N.V.; *Int'l*, pg. 8633
ZENITH ADMINISTRATORS, INC.—See Ullico Inc.; *U.S. Private*, pg. 4276
ZENITH AMERICAN SOLUTIONS INC.—See Advanced Solutions International Inc.; *U.S. Private*, pg. 92
ZENITH BIRLA INDIA LTD; *Int'l*, pg. 8633
ZENITH BR MEDIA—See Publicis Groupe S.A.; *Int'l*, pg. 6113
ZENITH CAPITAL CORPORATION; *U.S. Public*, pg. 2402
ZENITH CAPITALS LIMITED; *Int'l*, pg. 8633
ZENITH COMPUTERS LIMITED; *Int'l*, pg. 8633
ZENITH CORPORATION—See KKR & Co. Inc.; *U.S. Public*, pg. 1242
ZENITH CUTTER CO.; *U.S. Private*, pg. 4601
ZENITH ELECTRONICS CORP.—See LG Corp.; *Int'l*, pg. 4476
ZENITH ENERGY LOGISTICS PARTNERS LP—See Warburg Pincus LLC; *U.S. Private*, pg. 4440
ZENITH ENERGY, L.P.—See Warburg Pincus LLC; *U.S. Private*, pg. 4440
ZENITH ENERGY LTD.; *Int'l*, pg. 8633
ZENITH EXPORTS LIMITED; *Int'l*, pg. 8633
ZENITH FIBRES LTD.; *Int'l*, pg. 8633
ZENITH FREIGHT LINES INC.—See Bassett Furniture Industries, Incorporated; *U.S. Public*, pg. 279
ZENITH FUEL SYSTEMS LLC—See Aeries Enterprises, LLC; *U.S. Private*, pg. 117
ZENITH GESTION DE MEDIOS—See Publicis Groupe S.A.; *Int'l*, pg. 6113
ZENITH GLOBAL, INC.—See PMC Capital Partners, LLC; *U.S. Private*, pg. 3218
ZENITH HEALTHCARE LIMITED; *Int'l*, pg. 8633
ZENITH INSURANCE COMPANY—See Fairfax Financial Holdings Limited; *Int'l*, pg. 2609
ZENITH INSURANCE PLC—See Guardian Holdings Limited; *Int'l*, pg. 3171
ZENITH INTERNATIONAL S.A.—See LVMH Moet Hennessy Louis Vuitton SE; *Int'l*, pg. 4603
ZENITH LIFE S.A.; *Int'l*, pg. 8633
ZENITH LOGISTICS INC.—See Deutsche Post AG; *Int'l*, pg. 2083
ZENITHMEDIA DUSSELDORF GMBH—See Publicis Groupe S.A.; *Int'l*, pg. 6114
ZENITH MEDIA SERVICES, INC.—See Publicis Groupe S.A.; *Int'l*, pg. 6114
ZENITH MEDIA SERVICES—See Publicis Groupe S.A.; *Int'l*, pg. 6114
ZENITH MEDIA SERVICES—See Publicis Groupe S.A.; *Int'l*, pg. 6114
ZENITH MEDIA—See Publicis Groupe S.A.; *Int'l*, pg. 6113
ZENITH MEDIA—See Publicis Groupe S.A.; *Int'l*, pg. 6113
ZENITH MEDIA—See Publicis Groupe S.A.; *Int'l*, pg. 6113
ZENITH MEDIA—See Publicis Groupe S.A.; *Int'l*, pg. 6113
ZENITH MEDIA—See Publicis Groupe S.A.; *Int'l*, pg. 6113
ZENITH MEDIA—See Publicis Groupe S.A.; *Int'l*, pg. 6114
ZENITH MEDIA—See Publicis Groupe S.A.; *Int'l*, pg. 6114
ZENITH MEDIA—See Publicis Groupe S.A.; *Int'l*, pg. 6114
ZENITH MEDIA—See Publicis Groupe S.A.; *Int'l*, pg. 6114
ZENITH MEDIA—See Publicis Groupe S.A.; *Int'l*, pg. 6114
ZENITH MINERALS LIMITED; *Int'l*, pg. 8633
ZENITH NATIONAL INSURANCE CORP.—See Fairfax Financial Holdings Limited; *Int'l*, pg. 2609
ZENITHOPTIMEDIA AG—See Publicis Groupe S.A.; *Int'l*, pg. 6114
ZENITHOPTIMEDIA CANADA INC.—See Publicis Groupe S.A.; *Int'l*, pg. 6114
ZENITHOPTIMEDIA CANADA INC.—See Publicis Groupe S.A.; *Int'l*, pg. 6114
ZENITHOPTIMEDIA INDIA—See Publicis Groupe S.A.; *Int'l*, pg. 6114
ZENITHOPTIMEDIA INTERACTIVE DIRECT—See Publicis Groupe S.A.; *Int'l*, pg. 6114
ZENITH OPTIMEDIA INTERNATIONAL LIMITED—See Publicis Groupe S.A.; *Int'l*, pg. 6113
ZENITHOPTIMEDIA LTD.—See Publicis Groupe S.A.; *Int'l*, pg. 6112
ZENITHOPTIMEDIA; *Int'l*, pg. 8633
ZENITHOPTIMEDIA—See Publicis Groupe S.A.; *Int'l*, pg. 6113
ZENITHOPTIMEDIA—See Publicis Groupe S.A.; *Int'l*, pg. 6113
ZENITHOPTIMEDIA—See Publicis Groupe S.A.; *Int'l*, pg. 6113
ZENITHOPTIMEDIA—See Publicis Groupe S.A.; *Int'l*, pg. 6113
ZENITHOPTIMEDIA—See Publicis Groupe S.A.; *Int'l*, pg. 6113
ZENITHOPTIMEDIA—See Publicis Groupe S.A.; *Int'l*, pg. 6113
ZENITHOPTIMEDIA—See Publicis Groupe S.A.; *Int'l*, pg. 6113
ZENITHOPTIMEDIA—See Publicis Groupe S.A.; *Int'l*, pg. 6113
ZENITHOPTIMEDIA—See Publicis Groupe S.A.; *Int'l*, pg. 6113
ZENITHOPTIMEDIA—See Publicis Groupe S.A.; *Int'l*, pg. 6113
ZENITHOPTIMEDIA—See Publicis Groupe S.A.; *Int'l*, pg. 6114
ZENITHOPTIMEDIA—See Publicis Groupe S.A.; *Int'l*, pg. 6114
ZENITHOPTIMEDIA—See Publicis Groupe S.A.; *Int'l*, pg. 6114
ZENITHOPTIMEDIA—See Publicis Groupe S.A.; *Int'l*, pg. 6114
ZENITHOPTIMEDIA—See Publicis Groupe S.A.; *Int'l*, pg. 6114
ZENITHOPTIMEDIA—See Publicis Groupe S.A.; *Int'l*, pg. 6114
ZENITHOPTIMEDIA—See Publicis Groupe S.A.; *Int'l*, pg. 6114
ZENITHOPTIMEDIA—See Publicis Groupe S.A.; *Int'l*, pg. 6114
ZENITHOPTIMEDIA—See Publicis Groupe S.A.; *Int'l*, pg. 6114

ZENITH PRODUCTS CORPORATION—See ONEX Corporation; *Int'l*, pg. 5578
ZENITH PROPERTIES LIMITED—See LSL Property Services plc; *Int'l*, pg. 4571
ZENITH PROPERTIES REIT; *Int'l*, pg. 8633
ZENITH R.S.—See Cefla S.C.; *Int'l*, pg. 1390
ZENITH SERVICE S.P.A.—See Arrow Global Group PLC; *Int'l*, pg. 579
ZENITH SPECIALTY BAG CO. INC.—See Apollo Global Management, Inc.; *U.S. Public*, pg. 154
ZENITH TECH INC.; *U.S. Private*, pg. 4601
ZENITH TECHNOLOGIES BVBA—See Cognizant Technology Solutions Corporation; *U.S. Public*, pg. 525
ZENITH TECHNOLOGIES LIMITED—See Cognizant Technology Solutions Corporation; *U.S. Public*, pg. 525
ZENITH TIME FRANCE S.A.—See LVMH Moet Hennessy Louis Vuitton SE; *Int'l*, pg. 4603
ZENIT INVESTMENT HOLDING AD; *Int'l*, pg. 8632
ZENIT NEPREMICNINE, INZENIRING IN TRZENJE D.D.—See Zavarovalnica Triglav, d.d.; *Int'l*, pg. 8627
ZENITRON CORPORATION; *Int'l*, pg. 8633
ZENIT SERVICIOS INTEGRALES, S.A.—See ACS, Actividades de Construccion y Servicios, S.A.; *Int'l*, pg. 117
ZENKAIDO YAKKYOKU CO., LTD.—See Toho Holdings Co., Ltd.; *Int'l*, pg. 7776
ZENKEN CARE CO.—See Zenken Corporation; *Int'l*, pg. 8633
ZENKEN CORPORATION; *Int'l*, pg. 8633
ZENKOKU BUSINESS CENTER CO., LTD—See T&D Holdings, Inc.; *Int'l*, pg. 7395
ZENKOKU BUSINESS CENTRE CO., LTD.—See T&D Holdings, Inc.; *Int'l*, pg. 7395
ZENKOKU HOSHO CO., LTD.; *Int'l*, pg. 8633
ZENKYOKEN CO., LTD.—See Gakken Holdings Co., Ltd.; *Int'l*, pg. 2870
ZENLABS ETHICA LTD.; *Int'l*, pg. 8633
ZEN MEDICAL TECHNOLOGIES PRIVATE LIMITED—See Zen Technologies Ltd; *Int'l*, pg. 8632
ZENMONICS INC.—See Fidelity National Infor; *U.S. Public*, pg. 833
ZENNE INFINITY SDN BHD—See Kein Hing International Berhad; *Int'l*, pg. 4117
ZENNER METERING TECHNOLOGY (SHANGHAI) LTD.; *Int'l*, pg. 8633
ZENN MOTOR COMPANY LIMITED—See FuelPositive Corporation; *Int'l*, pg. 2804
ZENNOH CHICKEN FOODS CORP.; *Int'l*, pg. 8633
ZEN-NOH GRAIN CORPORATION—See National Federation of Agricultural Co-Operative Associations; *Int'l*, pg. 5156
ZEN-NOH KEWPIE EGG-STATION CO., LTD.—See Kewpie Corporation; *Int'l*, pg. 4144
ZEN NORITAKE CO., LTD.—See Noritake Co., Limited; *Int'l*, pg. 5429
ZENO DIGITAL SOLUTIONS, LLC—See Visual Edge Technology, Inc.; *U.S. Private*, pg. 4404
ZENO GROUP; *U.S. Private*, pg. 4601
ZENO GROUP—See ZENO Group; *U.S. Private*, pg. 4601
ZENO GROUP—See ZENO Group; *U.S. Private*, pg. 4601
ZENO GROUP—See ZENO Group; *U.S. Private*, pg. 4601
ZENON DIGITAL RADIO, S.L.—See Cellnex Telecom, S.A.; *Int'l*, pg. 1394
ZENON NATIONAL DISTRIBUTION CENTRE LTD.—See Cyprus Airways Public Limited; *Int'l*, pg. 1897
ZENO OFFICE SOLUTIONS, INC.; *U.S. Private*, pg. 4601
ZENOSENSE, INC.; *Int'l*, pg. 8634
ZENOSIS LIMITED—See Digital Learning Marketplace plc; *Int'l*, pg. 2122
ZENOSS, INC.; *U.S. Private*, pg. 4601
ZENOSYS LLC; *U.S. Private*, pg. 4601
ZENOTECH LABORATORIES LIMITED—See Sun Pharmaceutical Industries Ltd.; *Int'l*, pg. 7308
ZENOVA GROUP PLC; *Int'l*, pg. 8634
ZENOVIA DIGITAL EXCHANGE CORPORATION; *U.S. Public*, pg. 2402
ZENO ZANINI GMBH—See A.A.G. STUCCHI s.r.l.; *Int'l*, pg. 23
ZENPAYROLL, INC.; *U.S. Private*, pg. 4601
ZENPRINT, LLC; *U.S. Private*, pg. 4601
ZENRIN BIZNEXUS CO., LTD.—See Zenrin Co., Ltd.; *Int'l*, pg. 8634
ZENRIN CO., LTD.; *Int'l*, pg. 8634
ZENRIN DATACOM CO., LTD.—See Zenrin Co., Ltd.; *Int'l*, pg. 8634
ZENRIN EUROPE GMBH—See Zenrin Co., Ltd.; *Int'l*, pg. 8634
ZENRIN PRINTEX CO., LTD.—See Zenrin Co., Ltd.; *Int'l*, pg. 8634
ZENRIN PROMO CO., LTD.—See Zenrin Co., Ltd.; *Int'l*, pg. 8634
ZENRIN USA, INC.—See Zenrin Co., Ltd.; *Int'l*, pg. 8634
ZENSAR OBT TECHNOLOGIES LIMITED—See RPG Group; *Int'l*, pg. 6415
ZENSAR TECHNOLOGIES, INC. - NEW JERSEY—See RPG Group; *Int'l*, pg. 6415
ZENSAR TECHNOLOGIES INC—See RPG Group; *Int'l*, pg. 6415
ZENSAR TECHNOLOGIES LTD—See RPG Group; *Int'l*, pg. 6415

ZENSHIN CAPITAL PARTNERS LLC   CORPORATE AFFILIATIONS

ZENSHIN CAPITAL PARTNERS LLC; *U.S. Private*, pg. 4601
ZENSHO COOCA CO., LTD.—See Zensho Holdings Co., Ltd.; *Int'l*, pg. 8635
ZENSHO FOODS MALAYSIA SDN. BHD.—See Zensho Holdings Co., Ltd.; *Int'l*, pg. 8635
ZENSHO HOLDINGS CO., LTD.; *Int'l*, pg. 8634
ZENSHO TRADINGS CO., LTD.—See Zensho Holdings Co., Ltd.; *Int'l*, pg. 8635
ZENSUN ENTERPRISES LIMITED; *Int'l*, pg. 8635
ZENSURANCE BROKERS INC.—See The Travelers Companies, Inc.; *U.S. Public*, pg. 2136
ZENSURANCE INC.—See The Travelers Companies, Inc.; *U.S. Public*, pg. 2136
ZENTALIS PHARMACEUTICALS, INC.; *U.S. Public*, pg. 2402
ZENTARIS IVF GMBH—See COSCIENS Biopharma Inc.; *U.S. Public*, pg. 585
ZENTECH DALLAS, LLC—See BlackBern Partners LLC; *U.S. Private*, pg. 573
ZENTECH FREDERICKSBURG LLC—See BlackBern Partners LLC; *U.S. Private*, pg. 573
ZEN TECH INTERNATIONAL BERHAD; *Int'l*, pg. 8632
ZENTECH MANUFACTURING, INC.—See BlackBern Partners LLC; *U.S. Private*, pg. 573
ZEN TECHNOLOGIES LTD; *Int'l*, pg. 8632
ZEN TECHNOLOGIES USA INC.—See Zen Technologies Ltd; *Int'l*, pg. 8632
ZENTEK LTD.; *Int'l*, pg. 8635
ZENT-FRENGER GMBH—See Investment AB Latour; *Int'l*, pg. 3784
ZENTIS GMBH & CO. KG - (AACHEN-EILENDORF) PLANT II—See Zentis GmbH & Co. KG; *Int'l*, pg. 8635
ZENTIS GMBH & CO. KG; *Int'l*, pg. 8635
ZENTIS HUNGARIA BT.—See Zentis GmbH & Co. KG; *Int'l*, pg. 8635
ZENTIS NORTH AMERICA, LLC—See Zentis GmbH & Co. KG; *Int'l*, pg. 8635
ZENTIS NORTH AMERICA OPERATING, LLC—See Zentis GmbH & Co. KG; *Int'l*, pg. 8635
ZENTIS POLSKA SP. Z O.O.—See Zentis GmbH & Co. KG; *Int'l*, pg. 8635
ZENTITH INFORMATION SYSTEMS, INC.—See Axos Financial, Inc.; *U.S. Public*, pg. 256
ZENTIVA GROUP, A.S.—See Advent International Corporation; *U.S. Private*, pg. 108
ZENTIVA INHALATIONSPRODUKTE GMBH—See Advent International Corporation; *U.S. Private*, pg. 108
ZENTIVA INTERNATIONAL A.S.—See Advent International Corporation; *U.S. Private*, pg. 108
ZENTIVA N.V.—See Advent International Corporation; *U.S. Private*, pg. 108
ZENTIVA SAGLIK URUNLERI SAN.VE TIC.A.S.—See Advent International Corporation; *U.S. Private*, pg. 108
ZENTIVA S.A.—See Advent International Corporation; *U.S. Private*, pg. 108
ZENTRALDEPONIE HUBBELRATH GMBH—See EnBW Energie Baden-Wurttemberg AG; *Int'l*, pg. 2146
ZENTRALKASEREI MV GMBH—See DMK Deutsches Milchkontor GmbH; *Int'l*, pg. 2146
ZENTRALKLINIK BAD BERKA GMBH—See Asklepios Kliniken GmbH & Co. KGaA; *Int'l*, pg. 624
ZENTRALKOKEREI SAAR GMBH—See Saarstahl AG; *Int'l*, pg. 6461
ZENTRALLAGER WEINFELDEN DER STADLER BUSSNANG AG—See Stadler Rail AG; *Int'l*, pg. 7161
ZENTRA LLC; *U.S. Private*, pg. 4601
ZENTRAL-OMNIBUSBAHNHOF BERLIN GMBH—See Deutsche Bahn AG; *Int'l*, pg. 2055
ZENTRA-WARTUNG ENGINEERING COMPANY LIMITED—See Millcon Steel Public Company Limited; *Int'l*, pg. 4895
ZENTRIC, INC.; *U.S. Private*, pg. 4601
ZENTRI, INC.—See Silicon Laboratories Inc.; *U.S. Public*, pg. 1880
ZENTRUM FUR INTEGRIERTE VERKEHRSSYSTEME GMBH—See Fraport AG; *Int'l*, pg. 2764
ZENTRUM FUR NIEREN- UND HOCH-DRUCKKRANKHEITEN BENSHEIM GMBH—See Fresenius Medical Care AG; *Int'l*, pg. 2777
ZENTRUM HOLDINGS, INC.; *Int'l*, pg. 8635
ZENTRUM MIKROELEKTRONIK DRESDEN AG—See Renesas Electronics Corporation; *Int'l*, pg. 6276
ZENTRUM RENNWEG S-BAHN IMMOBILIENENTWICKLUNG GMBH—See STRABAG SE; *Int'l*, pg. 7233
ZENVERGE, INC.—See NXP Semiconductors N.V.; *Int'l*, pg. 5499
ZENVIA INC.; *Int'l*, pg. 8635
ZEN VOCE CORPORATION; *Int'l*, pg. 8632
ZEN VOCE (PG) SDN BHD—See Zen Voce Corporation; *Int'l*, pg. 8632
ZEN VOCE (SUZHOU) CORPORATION—See Zen Voce Corporation; *Int'l*, pg. 8632
ZENVOCE TECHNOLOGY PTE LTD—See Okins Electronics Co., Ltd.; *Int'l*, pg. 5550
ZENWORLD HOLDINGS BHD—See UOB-Kay Hian Holdings Limited; *Int'l*, pg. 8086
ZENZI COMMUNICATIONS; *U.S. Private*, pg. 4602

ZEOCHEM AG—See CPH Chemie + Papier Holding AG; *Int'l*, pg. 1824
ZEOCHEM D.O.O.—See CPH Chemie + Papier Holding AG; *Int'l*, pg. 1825
ZEOCHEM L.L.C—See CPH Chemie + Papier Holding AG; *Int'l*, pg. 1824
ZEOCHEM PTE. LTD.—See CPH Chemie + Papier Holding AG; *Int'l*, pg. 1824
ZEO CORPORATION—See AOI TYO Holdings Inc.; *Int'l*, pg. 488
ZEO ENERGY CORP.; *U.S. Public*, pg. 2402
ZEOLYST INTERNATIONAL—See Shell plc; *Int'l*, pg. 6797
ZEOLYST INTERNATIONAL—See The Carlyle Group Inc.; *U.S. Public*, pg. 2052
ZEON ADVANCED POLYMIX CO., LTD.—See Zeon Corporation; *Int'l*, pg. 8636
ZEON ASIA MALAYSIA SDN. BHD.—See Zeon Corporation; *Int'l*, pg. 8636
ZEON ASIA PTE. LTD.—See Zeon Corporation; *Int'l*, pg. 8636
ZEON CHEMICALS ASIA CO., LTD.—See Zeon Corporation; *Int'l*, pg. 8636
ZEON CHEMICALS L.P.—See Zeon Corporation; *Int'l*, pg. 8636
ZEON CHEMICALS SINGAPORE PTE. LTD.—See Zeon Corporation; *Int'l*, pg. 8636
ZEON CHEMICALS (THAILAND) CO., LTD.—See Zeon Corporation; *Int'l*, pg. 8636
ZEON CHEMICALS YONEZAWA CO., LTD.—See Zeon Corporation; *Int'l*, pg. 8636
ZEON CORPORATION; *Int'l*, pg. 8635
ZEON CSC CORPORATION—See Zeon Corporation; *Int'l*, pg. 8636
ZEON DO BRASIL LTDA—See Zeon Corporation; *Int'l*, pg. 8636
ZEON EUROPE GMBH—See Zeon Corporation; *Int'l*, pg. 8636
ZEON FAR EAST LIMITED—See Herald Holdings Limited; *Int'l*, pg. 3358
ZEON F&B CO., LTD.—See Zeon Corporation; *Int'l*, pg. 8636
ZEON INDIA PRIVATE LIMITED—See Zeon Corporation; *Int'l*, pg. 8636
ZEON KASEI (CHANGSHU) CO., LTD.—See Zeon Corporation; *Int'l*, pg. 8636
ZEON KASEI CO., LTD.—See Zeon Corporation; *Int'l*, pg. 8636
ZEON KASEI MEXICO S.A. DE C.V.—See Zeon Corporation; *Int'l*, pg. 8636
ZEON KOREA CO., LTD.—See Zeon Corporation; *Int'l*, pg. 8636
ZEON LIMITED—See Herald Holdings Limited; *Int'l*, pg. 3358
ZEON MANUFACTURING VIETNAM CO., LTD.—See Zeon Corporation; *Int'l*, pg. 8636
ZEON MEDICAL (GUANGZHOU) INC.—See Zeon Corporation; *Int'l*, pg. 8636
ZEON MEDICAL INC.—See Zeon Corporation; *Int'l*, pg. 8636
ZEON NANO TECHNOLOGY CO., LTD.—See Zeon Corporation; *Int'l*, pg. 8636
ZEON NORTH CO., LTD.—See Zeon Corporation; *Int'l*, pg. 8636
ZEON OPTO BIO LAB CO., LTD.—See Zeon Corporation; *Int'l*, pg. 8636
ZEON POLYMIX (GUANGZHOU) CO., LTD.—See Zeon Corporation; *Int'l*, pg. 8636
ZEON POLYMIX INC.—See Zeon Corporation; *Int'l*, pg. 8636
ZEON RESEARCH VIETNAM CO., LTD.—See Zeon Corporation; *Int'l*, pg. 8636
ZEONS CORP.; *U.S. Public*, pg. 2402
ZEON (SHANGHAI) CO., LTD.—See Zeon Corporation; *Int'l*, pg. 8636
ZEON SHINHWA (ZESHIN) INC.—See Zeon Corporation; *Int'l*, pg. 8636
ZEON SPECIALTY MATERIALS LNC.—See Zeon Corporation; *Int'l*, pg. 8636
ZEON TAIWAN CO., LTD.—See Zeon Corporation; *Int'l*, pg. 8636
ZEON TRADING (SHANGHAI) CO., LTD.—See Zeon Corporation; *Int'l*, pg. 8636
ZEON YAMAGUCHI CO., LTD.—See Zeon Corporation; *Int'l*, pg. 8636
ZEOTECH LIMITED; *Int'l*, pg. 8636
ZEP EUROPE B.V.—See New Mountain Capital, LLC; *U.S. Private*, pg. 2904
ZEPF TECHNOLOGIES—See Barry-Wehmiller Companies, Inc.; *U.S. Private*, pg. 482
ZEPF TECHNOLOGIES UK LIMITED—See Diageo plc; *Int'l*, pg. 2103
ZEPHYR ACQUISITION COMPANY—See Heritage Insurance Holdings, Inc.; *U.S. Public*, pg. 1028
ZEPHYR ALUMINUM INC.; *U.S. Private*, pg. 4602
ZEPHYR COVE RESORT—See Aramark; *U.S. Public*, pg. 176
ZEPHYR ENERGY PLC; *Int'l*, pg. 8636
ZEPHYR ENVIRONMENTAL CORPORATION—See WSP Global, Inc.; *Int'l*, pg. 8497

ZEPHYR GRAF-X INC.; *U.S. Private*, pg. 4602
ZEPHYRHILLS DIALYSIS CENTER, LLC—See DaVita Inc.; *U.S. Public*, pg. 644
ZEPHYRHILLS SPRING WATER COMPANY—See Metropoulos & Co.; *U.S. Private*, pg. 2691
ZEPHYRHILLS SPRING WATER COMPANY—See One Rock Capital Partners, LLC; *U.S. Private*, pg. 3021
ZEPHYR INSURANCE COMPANY, INC.—See Heritage Insurance Holdings, Inc.; *U.S. Public*, pg. 1028
ZEPHYR MANAGEMENT, L.P.; *U.S. Private*, pg. 4602
ZEPHYR MANUFACTURING CO., INC.—See SHG Holdings Corp.; *U.S. Private*, pg. 3635
ZEPHYR MEDIA GROUP—See Zephyr Media Group; *U.S. Private*, pg. 4602
ZEPHYR MEDIA GROUP—See Zephyr Media Group; *U.S. Private*, pg. 4602
ZEPHYR MEDIA GROUP; *U.S. Private*, pg. 4602
ZEPHYR MINERALS LTD.; *Int'l*, pg. 8636
ZEPHYR REAL ESTATE; *U.S. Private*, pg. 4602
ZEPHYR TECHNOLOGY LLC—See Medtronic plc; *Int'l*, pg. 4790
ZEPHYRTEL, INC.—See ESW Capital, LLC; *U.S. Private*, pg. 1430
ZEPHYR TEXTILES LIMITED; *Int'l*, pg. 8637
ZEPHYR VENTILATION, LLC—See Melrose Industries PLC; *Int'l*, pg. 4813
ZEP INC. - ENFORCER PRODUCTS—See New Mountain Capital, LLC; *U.S. Private*, pg. 2904
ZEP INC. - NIAGARA NATIONAL DIVISION—See New Mountain Capital, LLC; *U.S. Private*, pg. 2904
ZEP INC.—See New Mountain Capital, LLC; *U.S. Private*, pg. 2904
ZEP INDUSTRIES B.V.—See New Mountain Capital, LLC; *U.S. Private*, pg. 2904
ZEP INDUSTRIES N.V.—See New Mountain Capital, LLC; *U.S. Private*, pg. 2904
ZEP ITALIA S.R.L.—See New Mountain Capital, LLC; *U.S. Private*, pg. 2904
ZEPNICK SOLUTIONS, INC.—See Salas O'Brien Engineers, Inc.; *U.S. Private*, pg. 3531
ZEPPELIN ARMENIEN LLC—See Zeppelin GmbH; *Int'l*, pg. 8637
ZEPPELIN BAUMASCHINEN GMBH—See Zeppelin GmbH; *Int'l*, pg. 8637
ZEPPELIN CENTRAL ASIA MACH. LLC—See Zeppelin GmbH; *Int'l*, pg. 8637
ZEPPELIN CZ S.R.O.—See Zeppelin GmbH; *Int'l*, pg. 8637
ZEPPELIN DANMARK A/S—See Zeppelin GmbH; *Int'l*, pg. 8637
ZEPPELIN GMBH; *Int'l*, pg. 8637
ZEPPELIN INTERNATIONAL AG—See Zeppelin GmbH; *Int'l*, pg. 8637
ZEPPELIN-KOROS SPEDIT KFT.—See Zeppelin GmbH; *Int'l*, pg. 8637
ZEPPELIN MOBILE SYSTEMS INDIA LIMITED—See Sintex Industries, Ltd.; *Int'l*, pg. 6958
ZEPPELIN OESTERREICH GMBH—See Zeppelin GmbH; *Int'l*, pg. 8637
ZEPPELIN POLSKA SP. Z O.O.—See Zeppelin GmbH; *Int'l*, pg. 8637
ZEPPELIN POWER SYSTEMS GMBH & CO. KG—See Zeppelin GmbH; *Int'l*, pg. 8637
ZEPPELIN POWER SYSTEMS RUSSIA LLC—See Zeppelin GmbH; *Int'l*, pg. 8637
ZEPPELIN RENTAL GMBH & CO. KG—See Zeppelin GmbH; *Int'l*, pg. 8637
ZEPPELIN RENTAL OSTERREICH GMBH & CO. KG—See Zeppelin GmbH; *Int'l*, pg. 8637
ZEPPELIN RENTAL RUSSLAND OOO—See Zeppelin GmbH; *Int'l*, pg. 8637
ZEPPELIN RUSSLAND OOO—See Zeppelin GmbH; *Int'l*, pg. 8637
ZEPPELIN SK S.R.O.—See Zeppelin GmbH; *Int'l*, pg. 8637
ZEPPELIN STREIF BAULOGISTIK OSTERREICH. GMBH—See Zeppelin GmbH; *Int'l*, pg. 8637
ZEPPELIN SYSTEMS BENELUX N. V.—See Zeppelin GmbH; *Int'l*, pg. 8637
ZEPPELIN SYSTEMS CHINA (BEJING) CO. LTD.—See Zeppelin GmbH; *Int'l*, pg. 8637
ZEPPELIN SYSTEMS CHINA (SHANGHAI) CO. LTD.—See Zeppelin GmbH; *Int'l*, pg. 8637
ZEPPELIN SYSTEMS FRANCE SARL—See Zeppelin GmbH; *Int'l*, pg. 8637
ZEPPELIN SYSTEMS GMBH—See Zeppelin GmbH; *Int'l*, pg. 8637
ZEPPELIN SYSTEMS GULF CO. LTD.—See Zeppelin GmbH; *Int'l*, pg. 8637
ZEPPELIN SYSTEMS INDIA PVT. LTD.—See Zeppelin GmbH; *Int'l*, pg. 8637
ZEPPELIN SYSTEMS ITALY SRL—See Zeppelin GmbH; *Int'l*, pg. 8638
ZEPPELIN SYSTEMS KOREA CORP.—See Zeppelin GmbH; *Int'l*, pg. 8637
ZEPPELIN SYSTEMS LATIN AMERICA EQUIPAMENTOS INDUSTRIAIS LTDA.—See Zeppelin GmbH; *Int'l*, pg. 8638

COMPANY NAME INDEX

ZEPPELIN SYSTEMS LTD.—See Zeppelin GmbH; *Int'l*, pg. 8638
ZEPPELIN SYSTEMS SINGAPORE PTE LTD.—See Zeppelin GmbH; *Int'l*, pg. 8638
ZEPPELIN SYSTEMS UK LIMITED—See Zeppelin GmbH; *Int'l*, pg. 8638
ZEPPELIN SYSTEMS USA INC.—See Zeppelin GmbH; *Int'l*, pg. 8638
ZEPPELIN SYSTEMS USA, INC.—See Zeppelin GmbH; *Int'l*, pg. 8638
ZEPPELIN TADSCHIKISTAN OOO—See Zeppelin GmbH; *Int'l*, pg. 8637
ZEPPELIN TELEVISION, S.A.—See LOV Group Invest SAS; *Int'l*, pg. 4565
ZEPPELIN TURKMENISTAN LLC—See Zeppelin GmbH; *Int'l*, pg. 8637
ZEPPELIN UKRAINE LLC—See Zeppelin GmbH; *Int'l*, pg. 8637
ZEPPELIN WEISSRUSSLAND OOO—See Zeppelin GmbH; *Int'l*, pg. 8637
ZEPP HEALTH CORPORATION; *Int'l*, pg. 8637
ZEPPOS & ASSOCIATES, INC.; *U.S. Private*, pg. 4602
ZEPPOTRON LTD—See LOV Group Invest SAS; *Int'l*, pg. 4565
ZEPRO DANMARK A/S—See Cargotec Corporation; *Int'l*, pg. 1329
ZEPTOMETRIX CORPORATION—See GTCR LLC; *U.S. Private*, pg. 1804
ZEP UK LIMITED—See New Mountain Capital, LLC; *U.S. Private*, pg. 2904
ZERA GMBH; *Int'l*, pg. 8638
ZERA INDIA PVT LTD—See ZERA GmbH; *Int'l*, pg. 8638
ZERBEE, LLC—See The ODP Corporation; *U.S. Public*, pg. 2118
ZERIA ECOTECH CO., LTD.—See Zeria Pharmaceutical Co., Ltd.; *Int'l*, pg. 8638
ZERIA HEALTHWAY CO., LTD.—See Zeria Pharmaceutical Co., Ltd.; *Int'l*, pg. 8638
ZERIAP CO., LTD.—See Zeria Pharmaceutical Co., Ltd.; *Int'l*, pg. 8638
ZERIA PHARMACEUTICAL CO., LTD. - SAITAMA PLANT—See Zeria Pharmaceutical Co., Ltd.; *Int'l*, pg. 8638
ZERIA PHARMACEUTICAL CO., LTD.; *Int'l*, pg. 8638
ZERIA PHARMACEUTICAL CO., LTD. - TSUKUBA PLANT—See Zeria Pharmaceutical Co., Ltd.; *Int'l*, pg. 8638
ZERIA SHOJI CO., LTD.—See Zeria Pharmaceutical Co., Ltd.; *Int'l*, pg. 8638
ZERIA USA, INC.—See Zeria Pharmaceutical Co., Ltd.; *Int'l*, pg. 8638
ZERIFY, INC.; *U.S. Public*, pg. 2402
ZERIGO, INC.—See 8x8, Inc.; *U.S. Public*, pg. 10
ZER MERKEZI HIZMETLER VE TICARET A.S.—See Koc Holding A.S.; *Int'l*, pg. 4224
ZERNA INGENIEURE GMBH; *Int'l*, pg. 8638
ZERNIKE GROUP HOLDING B.V.; *Int'l*, pg. 8638
ZERNIKE META - VENTURES S.P.A.—See META Group S.r.l.; *Int'l*, pg. 4843
ZERO12 SRL—See Sesa S.p.A.; *Int'l*, pg. 6729
ZERO2IPO HOLDINGS, INC.; *Int'l*, pg. 8639
ZEROCHAOS, LLC—See TruArc Partners, L.P.; *U.S. Private*, pg. 4246
ZERO CO., LTD.; *Int'l*, pg. 8638
ZERO COMMISSION NZ LTD.; *Int'l*, pg. 8638
ZERODIO TECHNOLOGY SOLUTIONS, INC.—See Warren Equity Partners, LLC; *U.S. Private*, pg. 4443
ZERODESKTOP, INC.; *U.S. Private*, pg. 4602
ZERODIX SARL—See CPI Property Group, S.A.; *Int'l*, pg. 1825
ZERO FIRST CO., LTD.—See Marui Group Co., Ltd.; *Int'l*, pg. 4713
ZEROFOX HOLDINGS, INC.—See Whanau Interests LLC; *U.S. Private*, pg. 4503
ZEROFOX, INC.—See Whanau Interests LLC; *U.S. Private*, pg. 4504
ZEROG GMBH—See Deutsche Lufthansa AG; *Int'l*, pg. 2071
ZERO GRAVITY SOLUTIONS, INC.; *U.S. Public*, pg. 2403
ZERO HALLIBURTON, INC.; *U.S. Private*, pg. 4602
ZERO INTERNATIONAL, INC.—See Allegion Public Limited Company; *Int'l*, pg. 335
Z.E.R.O. - JAPAN CO., LTD.—See Matsuda Sangyo Co., Ltd.; *Int'l*, pg. 4729
ZERO-MAX, INC.—See Miki Pulley Co., Ltd.; *Int'l*, pg. 4891
ZERO MOUNTAIN, INC.—See Americold Realty Trust, Inc.; *U.S. Public*, pg. 113
ZERO NOMINEES PTY. LTD.—See Euroz Hartleys Group Limited; *Int'l*, pg. 2559
ZERO ONE TECHNOLOGY CO., LTD.; *Int'l*, pg. 8638
ZERO POINT; *U.S. Private*, pg. 4602
ZEROREZ MINNESOTA; *U.S. Private*, pg. 4602
ZERO SCM LOGISTICS (BEIJING) CO., LTD.—See Zero Co., Ltd.; *Int'l*, pg. 8638
ZERO SEAL SYSTEMS LIMITED—See Allegion Public Limited Company; *Int'l*, pg. 336
ZERO TO SEVEN INC.; *Int'l*, pg. 8638
ZERO TO THREE: NATIONAL CENTER FOR INFANTS, TODDLERS AND FAMILIES; *U.S. Private*, pg. 4602
ZEROVA TECHNOLOGIES (DONGGUAN) CO., LTD.—See Phihong Technology Co., Ltd.; *Int'l*, pg. 5844
ZEROVA TECHNOLOGIES EUROPE B.V.—See Phihong Technology Co., Ltd.; *Int'l*, pg. 5844
ZEROVA TECHNOLOGIES JAPAN CO., LTD.—See Phihong Technology Co., Ltd.; *Int'l*, pg. 5844
ZEROVA TECHNOLOGIES TAIWAN LIMITED—See Phihong Technology Co., Ltd.; *Int'l*, pg. 5844
ZEROVA TECHNOLOGIES USA LLC—See Phihong Technology Co., Ltd.; *Int'l*, pg. 5844
ZERO ZONE, INC. - REFRIGERATION SYSTEMS DIVISION—See Zero Zone, Inc.; *U.S. Private*, pg. 4602
ZERO ZONE, INC.; *U.S. Private*, pg. 4602
ZERT AB—See AFRY AB; *Int'l*, pg. 196
ZERTO, INC.—See Hewlett Packard Enterprise Company; *U.S. Public*, pg. 1032
ZERTO LTD.—See Hewlett Packard Enterprise Company; *U.S. Public*, pg. 1032
ZERTUS GMBH; *Int'l*, pg. 8639
ZERUST AB—See Northern Technologies International Corporation; *U.S. Public*, pg. 1538
ZERUST-EXCOR MEXICO, S. DE R.L. DE C.V—See Northern Technologies International Corporation; *U.S. Public*, pg. 1538
ZERUST-NIC (TAIWAN) CORP.—See Northern Technologies International Corporation; *U.S. Public*, pg. 1538
ZERUST OY—See Northern Technologies International Corporation; *U.S. Public*, pg. 1538
ZERUST PREVENCAO DE CORROSAO S.A.—See Northern Technologies International Corporation; *U.S. Public*, pg. 1538
ZERUST PREVENCOA DE CORROSAO S.A.—See Northern Technologies International Corporation; *U.S. Public*, pg. 1538
ZERUST SINGAPORE PTE. LTD.—See Northern Technologies International Corporation; *U.S. Public*, pg. 1538
ZERUST SPECIALTY TECH CO., LTD.—See Northern Technologies International Corporation; *U.S. Public*, pg. 1538
ZERUST (U.K.) LIMITED—See Northern Technologies International Corporation; *U.S. Public*, pg. 1538
ZESKIND'S HARDWARE, INC.; *U.S. Private*, pg. 4602
ZESPOL ELEKTROCIEPLOWNI WROCLAWSKICH KOGENERACJA S.A.; *Int'l*, pg. 8639
ZESPOL ELEKTROWNI PATNOW-ADAMOW-KONIN S.A. - ADAMOW POWER PLANT—See Zespol Elektrowni Patnow-Adamow-Konin S.A.; *Int'l*, pg. 8639
ZESPOL ELEKTROWNI PATNOW-ADAMOW-KONIN S.A.; *Int'l*, pg. 8639
ZEST ANCHORS LLC—See BC Partners LLP; *Int'l*, pg. 925
ZEST CORPORATION—See Patdiam Jewellery Ltd.; *Int'l*, pg. 5755
ZEST LABS, INC—See RiskOn International, Inc.; *U.S. Public*, pg. 1799
ZEST S.P.A.; *Int'l*, pg. 8639
ZEST ST; *Int'l*, pg. 8639
ZEST TECHNOLOGY LIMITED—See Simplybiz Group plc; *Int'l*, pg. 6934
ZEST WEG ELECTRIC (PTY) LTD.—See WEG S.A.; *Int'l*, pg. 8368
ZETA ASSOCIATES, INC.—See Lockheed Martin Corporation; *U.S. Public*, pg. 1339
ZETA AUTOMOTIVE LIMITED—See Deutsche Bahn AG; *Int'l*, pg. 2055
ZETA BRIDGE CORPORATION; *Int'l*, pg. 8639
ZETA COMMUNITIES; *U.S. Private*, pg. 4602
ZETADISPLAY AB; *Int'l*, pg. 8639
ZETADISPLAY BV—See ZetaDisplay AB; *Int'l*, pg. 8639
ZETA EMAIL SOLUTIONS; *U.S. Private*, pg. 4602
ZETA EMAIL SOLUTIONS—See Zeta Email Solutions; *U.S. Private*, pg. 4602
ZETA GLOBAL HOLDINGS CORP.; *U.S. Public*, pg. 2403
ZETA GLOBAL LTD.—See Zeta Interactive Corporation; *U.S. Private*, pg. 4603
ZETA INSTRUMENTS, INC.—See KLA Corporation; *U.S. Public*, pg. 1269
ZETA INSTRUMENTS (SHANGHAI) CO., LTD.—See KLA Corporation; *U.S. Public*, pg. 1269
ZETA INTERACTIVE CORPORATION; *U.S. Private*, pg. 4602
ZETA PETROLEUM PLC; *Int'l*, pg. 8639
ZETA PETROLEUM (ROMANIA) SRL—See Zeta Petroleum plc; *Int'l*, pg. 8639
ZETA RESOURCES LIMITED—See ICM Limited; *Int'l*, pg. 3582
ZETAS ZEMIN TECHNOLOGY AS—See VINCI S.A.; *Int'l*, pg. 8240
ZETEC FRANCE—See Roper Technologies, Inc.; *U.S. Public*, pg. 1814
ZETEC, INC.—See Roper Technologies, Inc.; *U.S. Public*, pg. 1814
ZETEC (SHANGHAI) CO., LTD.—See Roper Technologies, Inc.; *U.S. Public*, pg. 1814

ZETTLER COMPONENTS, INC.

ZETES AUTO ID SYSTEMS LTD—See Panasonic Holdings Corporation; *Int'l*, pg. 5725
ZETES BV—See Panasonic Holdings Corporation; *Int'l*, pg. 5725
ZETES FASTRACE SA—See Panasonic Holdings Corporation; *Int'l*, pg. 5725
ZETES HOLDING GMBH—See Panasonic Holdings Corporation; *Int'l*, pg. 5725
ZETES INDUSTRIES (ISRAEL) LTD—See Panasonic Holdings Corporation; *Int'l*, pg. 5725
ZETES INDUSTRIES SA—See Panasonic Holdings Corporation; *Int'l*, pg. 5725
ZETES IRELAND LTD—See Panasonic Holdings Corporation; *Int'l*, pg. 5725
ZETES LTD—See Panasonic Holdings Corporation; *Int'l*, pg. 5725
ZETES MULTICOM SA—See Panasonic Holdings Corporation; *Int'l*, pg. 5725
ZETES PASS BV—See Panasonic Holdings Corporation; *Int'l*, pg. 5725
ZETES SA—See Panasonic Holdings Corporation; *Int'l*, pg. 5725
ZETES TECHNOLOGIES BV—See Panasonic Holdings Corporation; *Int'l*, pg. 5725
ZETEX INC.—See Diodes Incorporated; *U.S. Public*, pg. 667
ZET FARMA LOJISTIK HIZMETLERI SANAYI VE TICARET A.S.—See Kuehne + Nagel International AG; *Int'l*, pg. 4325
ZETHCON CORP.—See Stichting INGKA Foundation; *Int'l*, pg. 7215
ZETIQ DEVELOPMENT AB—See Prevas AB; *Int'l*, pg. 5967
ZETKAMA R&D SP. Z O.O.—See Mangata Holding S.A.; *Int'l*, pg. 4670
ZETLAND CAPITAL PARTNERS LLP; *Int'l*, pg. 8639
ZETLAND COPORATE SERVICES JAPAN LIMITED—See Zetland Financial Group Limited; *Int'l*, pg. 8639
ZETLAND CORPORATE SERVICES BELIZE LIMITED—See Zetland Financial Group Limited; *Int'l*, pg. 8640
ZETLAND CORPORATE SERVICES LIMITED—See Zetland Financial Group Limited; *Int'l*, pg. 8640
ZETLAND CORPORATE SERVICES PTE LIMITED—See Zetland Financial Group Limited; *Int'l*, pg. 8640
ZETLAND FIDUCIARIES (NEW ZEALAND) LIMITED—See Zetland Financial Group Limited; *Int'l*, pg. 8640
ZETLAND FINANCIAL GROUP LIMITED; *Int'l*, pg. 8639
ZETLAND SERVICES (UK) LIMITED—See Zetland Financial Group Limited; *Int'l*, pg. 8640
ZETOR DEUTSCHLAND, GMBH—See HTC holding a.s.; *Int'l*, pg. 3508
ZETOR FRANCE SARL—See HTC holding a.s.; *Int'l*, pg. 3508
ZETOR NORTH AMERICA, INC.—See HTC holding a.s.; *Int'l*, pg. 3508
ZETOR POLSKA, SP.Z O.O.—See HTC holding a.s.; *Int'l*, pg. 3508
ZETOR TRACTORS A.S.—See HTC holding a.s.; *Int'l*, pg. 3508
ZETOR UK, LTD.—See HTC holding a.s.; *Int'l*, pg. 3508
ZETRO AEROSPACE CORPORATION SDN. BHD.; *Int'l*, pg. 8640
ZETRON AUSTRALASIA PTY LTD.—See Codan Limited; *Int'l*, pg. 1688
ZETRON, INC.—See Codan Limited; *Int'l*, pg. 1688
ZETRON, INC.—See Codan Limited; *Int'l*, pg. 1688
ZETTA, INC.—See Marlin Equity Partners, LLC; *U.S. Private*, pg. 2583
ZETTASCALE TECHNOLOGY B.V.—See ADLINK Technology, Inc.; *Int'l*, pg. 151
ZETTASPHERE LIMITED; *Int'l*, pg. 8640
ZETT CORPORATION; *Int'l*, pg. 8640
ZETTICS, INC.—See DRW Holdings, LLC; *U.S. Private*, pg. 1280
ZETTICS, INC.—See Emergence Capital Partners; *U.S. Private*, pg. 1380
ZETTICS, INC.—See North Bridge Venture Management Company, Inc.; *U.S. Private*, pg. 2942
ZETTICS, INC.—See Voyager Capital, LLC; *U.S. Private*, pg. 4414
ZETTLER COMPONENTS, INC.; *U.S. Private*, pg. 4603
ZETTLER CONTROLS, INC.—See Zettler Components, Inc.; *U.S. Private*, pg. 4603
ZETTLER ELECTRONICS BELGIUM B.V.B.A. - S.P.R.L.—See Zettler Components, Inc.; *U.S. Private*, pg. 4603
ZETTLER ELECTRONICS GMBH—See Zettler Components, Inc.; *U.S. Private*, pg. 4603
ZETTLER ELECTRONICS (HK) LTD.—See Zettler Components, Inc.; *U.S. Private*, pg. 4603
ZETTLER ELECTRONICS NEDERLAND B.V.—See Zettler Components, Inc.; *U.S. Private*, pg. 4603
ZETTLER ELECTRONICS POLAND SP.Z.O.O.—See Zettler Components, Inc.; *U.S. Private*, pg. 4603
ZETTLER MAGNETICS, INC.—See Zettler Components, Inc.; *U.S. Private*, pg. 4603
ZETTLEX (UK) LIMITED—See Novanta Inc.; *U.S. Public*, pg. 1548

ZETTLER COMPONENTS, INC.

CORPORATE AFFILIATIONS

ZETTON, INC.—See Adastria Co., Ltd.; *Int'l*, pg. 126
ZEUS CHINA CO., LTD.—See ZEUS CO., Ltd; *Int'l*, pg. 8640
ZEUS CO., LTD - ANSAN PLANT 1—See ZEUS CO., Ltd; *Int'l*, pg. 8640
ZEUS CO., LTD; *Int'l*, pg. 8640
ZEUS CO., LTD - YONGIN PLANT—See ZEUS CO., Ltd; *Int'l*, pg. 8640
ZEUS GROUP LIMITED; *Int'l*, pg. 8640
ZEUS HOLDINGS INC.; *Int'l*, pg. 8640
ZEUS INDUSTRIAL PRODUCTS INC.; *U.S. Private*, pg. 4603
ZEUS PACKAGING GROUP LTD.; *Int'l*, pg. 8640
ZEUS QUIMICA S.A.U.—See Diethelm Keller Holding Limited; *Int'l*, pg. 2117
ZEUS RESOURCES LIMITED; *Int'l*, pg. 8640
ZEUS SCIENTIFIC, INC.—See Caisse de Depot et Placement du Quebec; *Int'l*, pg. 1255
ZEUS SCIENTIFIC, INC.—See CVC Capital Partners SICAV-FIS S.A.; *Int'l*, pg. 1884
ZEUS SCIENTIFIC, INC.—See Tethys Invest SAS; *Int'l*, pg. 7576
ZEU TECHNOLOGIES, INC.; *Int'l*, pg. 8640
ZEUUS, INC.; *U.S. Public*, pg. 2403
ZEVA INC.; *U.S. Private*, pg. 4603
ZEVERSOLAR GMBH—See SMA Solar Technology AG; *Int'l*, pg. 6999
ZEVIA PBC; *U.S. Public*, pg. 2403
ZEVICE CO., LTD.—See Zeria Pharmaceutical Co., Ltd.; *Int'l*, pg. 8638
ZEVOLI 151 (PTY) LIMITED—See Reunert Limited; *Int'l*, pg. 6312
ZEVOTEK, INC.; *U.S. Private*, pg. 4603
ZEVRA THERAPEUTICS, INC.; *U.S. Public*, pg. 2403
ZEW IMMOBILIEN AG—See Zug Estates Holding AG; *Int'l*, pg. 8693
ZF ACTIVE SAFETY AND ELECTRONICS US LLC—See ZF Friedrichshafen AG; *Int'l*, pg. 8646
ZF ACTIVE SAFETY FRANCE SAS—See ZF Friedrichshafen AG; *Int'l*, pg. 8642
ZF ACTIVE SAFETY GMBH—See ZF Friedrichshafen AG; *Int'l*, pg. 8642
ZF AFTERMARKET JAPAN CO., LTD.—See ZF Friedrichshafen AG; *Int'l*, pg. 8642
ZF AFTERMARKET MALAYSIA SDN. BHD.—See ZF Friedrichshafen AG; *Int'l*, pg. 8642
ZF ALGERIE S.A.R.L.—See ZF Friedrichshafen AG; *Int'l*, pg. 8642
ZF ANSA LEMFORDER S. L. U.—See ZF Friedrichshafen AG; *Int'l*, pg. 8645
ZF ARGENTINA S.A.—See ZF Friedrichshafen AG; *Int'l*, pg. 8642
Z-FASHION FINLAND OY—See Industria de Diseno Textil, S.A.; *Int'l*, pg. 3668
ZF ASIA PACIFIC GROUP CO., LTD.—See ZF Friedrichshafen AG; *Int'l*, pg. 8642
ZF ASIA PACIFIC PTE. LTD.—See ZF Friedrichshafen AG; *Int'l*, pg. 8642
ZF AUTOMOTIVE CANADA LIMITED—See ZF Friedrichshafen AG; *Int'l*, pg. 8643
ZF AUTOMOTIVE CZECH S.R.O.—See ZF Friedrichshafen AG; *Int'l*, pg. 8643
ZF AUTOMOTIVE ITALIA S.R.L.—See ZF Friedrichshafen AG; *Int'l*, pg. 8643
ZF AUTOMOTIVE JAPAN CO. LTD.—See ZF Friedrichshafen AG; *Int'l*, pg. 8643
ZF AUTOMOTIVE LTDA.—See ZF Friedrichshafen AG; *Int'l*, pg. 8643
ZF AUTOMOTIVE MALAYSIA SDN BHD.—See ZF Friedrichshafen AG; *Int'l*, pg. 8643
ZF AUTOMOTIVE TECHNOLOGIES (SHANGHAI) CO., LTD.—See ZF Friedrichshafen AG; *Int'l*, pg. 8643
ZF AUTOMOTIVE TECHNOLOGIES (ZHANGJIAGANG) CO., LTD.—See ZF Friedrichshafen AG; *Int'l*, pg. 8643
ZF AXLE DRIVES MARYSVILLE LLC—See ZF Friedrichshafen AG; *Int'l*, pg. 8643
ZF BAIC (BEIJING) CHASSIS SYSTEMS CO., LTD.—See ZF Friedrichshafen AG; *Int'l*, pg. 8643
ZF BEIBEN DRIVETECH (CHONGQING) CO., LTD.—See ZF Friedrichshafen AG; *Int'l*, pg. 8642
ZF BOGE ELASTMETALL GMBH—See ZF Friedrichshafen AG; *Int'l*, pg. 8643
ZF BOGE ELASTMETALL GMBH—See ZF Friedrichshafen AG; *Int'l*, pg. 8643
ZF BOUTHEON S.A.—See ZF Friedrichshafen AG; *Int'l*, pg. 8643
ZF BRAKING SYSTEMS POLAND SP. Z O.O.—See ZF Friedrichshafen AG; *Int'l*, pg. 8643
ZF CAR EWALLET GMBH—See ZF Friedrichshafen AG; *Int'l*, pg. 8643
ZF CHASSIS COMPONENTS LLC—See ZF Friedrichshafen AG; *Int'l*, pg. 8643
ZF CHASSIS COMPONENTS TOLUCA S.A. DE C.V.—See ZF Friedrichshafen AG; *Int'l*, pg. 8643
ZF CHASSIS SYSTEMS CHICAGO LLC—See ZF Friedrichshafen AG; *Int'l*, pg. 8643
ZF CHASSIS SYSTEMS DUNCAN LLC—See ZF Friedrichshafen AG; *Int'l*, pg. 8643

ZF CHASSIS SYSTEMS LLC—See ZF Friedrichshafen AG; *Int'l*, pg. 8646
ZF CHASSIS SYSTEMS SDN. BHD.—See ZF Friedrichshafen AG; *Int'l*, pg. 8643
ZF CHASSIS SYSTEMS TUSCALOOSA LLC—See ZF Friedrichshafen AG; *Int'l*, pg. 8643
ZF CHASSIS SYSTEMS ZATEC S.R.O.—See ZF Friedrichshafen AG; *Int'l*, pg. 8643
ZF CHASSISTECH COMMERCIAL VEHICLES (SHANGHAI) CO., LTD.—See ZF Friedrichshafen AG; *Int'l*, pg. 8642
ZF CHASSIS TECHNOLOGY S.A. DE C.V.—See ZF Friedrichshafen AG; *Int'l*, pg. 8643
ZF (CHINA) INVESTMENT CO., LTD.—See ZF Friedrichshafen AG; *Int'l*, pg. 8642
ZF COMMERCIAL VEHICLE CONTROL SYSTEMS INDIA LIMITED—See ZF Friedrichshafen AG; *Int'l*, pg. 8642
ZF DO BRASIL LTDA.—See ZF Friedrichshafen AG; *Int'l*, pg. 8647
ZF DONGFENG SHOCK ABSORBER SHIYAN CO., LTD.—See ZF Friedrichshafen AG; *Int'l*, pg. 8642
ZF DRIVETECH (HANGZHOU) CO., LTD.—See ZF Friedrichshafen AG; *Int'l*, pg. 8642
ZF DRIVETECH (SUZHOU) CO., LTD.—See ZF Friedrichshafen AG; *Int'l*, pg. 8642
ZF ELECTRONICS ASIA LIMITED—See ZF Friedrichshafen AG; *Int'l*, pg. 8643
ZF ELECTRONICS FRANCE S.A.R.L.—See ZF Friedrichshafen AG; *Int'l*, pg. 8643
ZF ELECTRONICS GMBH—See ZF Friedrichshafen AG; *Int'l*, pg. 8643
ZF ELECTRONICS KLASTEREC S.R.O.—See ZF Friedrichshafen AG; *Int'l*, pg. 8643
ZF ELECTRONICS UK, LTD—See ZF Friedrichshafen AG; *Int'l*, pg. 8643
ZF ELECTRONIC SYSTEMS JUAREZ S.A. DE. C.V.—See ZF Friedrichshafen AG; *Int'l*, pg. 8643
ZF ELECTRONIC SYSTEMS PLEASANT PRAIRIE, LLC—See ZF Friedrichshafen AG; *Int'l*, pg. 8643
ZF ELECTRONICS (ZHUHAI) CO., LTD.—See ZF Friedrichshafen AG; *Int'l*, pg. 8642
ZF ENGINEERING PLZEN S.R.O.—See ZF Friedrichshafen AG; *Int'l*, pg. 8643
ZFERRAL, INC.; *U.S. Private*, pg. 4603
ZF FASTER PROPULSION SYSTEMS CO., LTD.—See ZF Friedrichshafen AG; *Int'l*, pg. 8643
ZF FAWER CHASSIS TECHNOLOGY (CHANGCHUN) CO., LTD.—See ZF Friedrichshafen AG; *Int'l*, pg. 8642
ZF FONDERIE LORRAINE S.A.S.—See ZF Friedrichshafen AG; *Int'l*, pg. 8644
ZF FRIEDRICHSHAFEN AG; *Int'l*, pg. 8640
ZF GAINESVILLE LLC—See ZF Friedrichshafen AG; *Int'l*, pg. 8644
ZF GROUP NORTH AMERICAN OPERATIONS INC.—See ZF Friedrichshafen AG; *Int'l*, pg. 8644
ZF GUSSTECHNOLOGIE GMBH—See ZF Friedrichshafen AG; *Int'l*, pg. 8644
ZF HERO CHASSIS SYSTEMS PRIVATE LTD.—See ZF Friedrichshafen AG; *Int'l*, pg. 8644
ZF HOLDINGS AUSTRALIA PTY. LTD.—See ZF Friedrichshafen AG; *Int'l*, pg. 8644
ZF HUNGARIA IPARI ES KERESKEDELMI KORLATOLT FELELOSSEGU TARSASAG—See ZF Friedrichshafen AG; *Int'l*, pg. 8644
ZF HUNGARIA KFT.—See ZF Friedrichshafen AG; *Int'l*, pg. 8644
ZF INDIA PRIVATE LIMITED—See ZF Friedrichshafen AG; *Int'l*, pg. 8644
ZF INDUSTRIEANTRIEBE WITTEN GMBH—See ZF Friedrichshafen AG; *Int'l*, pg. 8644
ZF ITALIA S.R.L.—See ZF Friedrichshafen AG; *Int'l*, pg. 8644
ZF JAPAN CO., LTD.—See ZF Friedrichshafen AG; *Int'l*, pg. 8643
ZF LEMFORDER ACHSSYSTEME GES.M.B.H—See ZF Friedrichshafen AG; *Int'l*, pg. 8644
ZF LEMFORDER AKS MODULLERI SANAYI VE TICARET A.S.—See ZF Friedrichshafen AG; *Int'l*, pg. 8644
ZF LEMFORDER AUTOMOTIVE SYSTEMS (SHENYANG) CO., LTD.—See ZF Friedrichshafen AG; *Int'l*, pg. 8642
ZF LEMFORDER CHASSIS TECHNOLOGY KOREA CO., LTD.—See ZF Friedrichshafen AG; *Int'l*, pg. 8644
ZF LEMFORDER METAL FRANCE S.A.—See ZF Friedrichshafen AG; *Int'l*, pg. 8644
ZF LEMFORDER SA (PTY.) LTD.—See ZF Friedrichshafen AG; *Int'l*, pg. 8644
ZF LEMFORDER (THAILAND) CO., LTD.—See ZF Friedrichshafen AG; *Int'l*, pg. 8643
ZF LEMFORDER TVA S.A.—See ZF Friedrichshafen AG; *Int'l*, pg. 8644
ZF LEMFORDER UK LTD.—See ZF Friedrichshafen AG; *Int'l*, pg. 8641
ZF LENKSYSTEME NACAM GMBH—See Robert Bosch GmbH; *Int'l*, pg. 6362
ZF LUFTFAHRTTECHNIK GMBH—See ZF Friedrichshafen AG; *Int'l*, pg. 8644
ZF MARINE KRIMPEN B.V.—See ZF Friedrichshafen AG; *Int'l*, pg. 8644

ZF MARINE MIDDLE EAST LLC—See ZF Friedrichshafen AG; *Int'l*, pg. 8644
ZF MARINE PROPULSION SYSTEMS MIRAMAR LLC—See ZF Friedrichshafen AG; *Int'l*, pg. 8644
ZF MIDDLE EAST FZE—See ZF Friedrichshafen AG; *Int'l*, pg. 8644
ZF OSTERREICH GES.M.B.H.—See ZF Friedrichshafen AG; *Int'l*, pg. 8644
ZF OVERSEAS INC.—See ZF Friedrichshafen AG; *Int'l*, pg. 8644
ZF PADOVA S.R.L.—See ZF Friedrichshafen AG; *Int'l*, pg. 8644
ZF PASSIVE SAFETY CZECH S.R.O.—See ZF Friedrichshafen AG; *Int'l*, pg. 8644
ZF PASSIVE SAFETY SYSTEMS US INC.—See ZF Friedrichshafen AG; *Int'l*, pg. 8644
ZF PEGASUS GMBH—See ZF Friedrichshafen AG; *Int'l*, pg. 8644
ZF PHILIPPINES INC.—See ZF Friedrichshafen AG; *Int'l*, pg. 8643
ZF POWERTRAIN MODULES SHANGHAI CO., LTD.—See ZF Friedrichshafen AG; *Int'l*, pg. 8644
ZF POWERTRAIN SYSTEMS (BEIJING) CO., LTD.—See ZF Friedrichshafen AG; *Int'l*, pg. 8644
ZF RACE ENGINEERING GMBH—See ZF Friedrichshafen AG; *Int'l*, pg. 8644
ZF RANE AUTOMOTIVE INDIA PRIVATE LIMITED—See Rane Holdings Limited; *Int'l*, pg. 6206
ZF RANE AUTOMOTIVE INDIA PRIVATE LIMITED—See ZF Friedrichshafen AG; *Int'l*, pg. 8646
ZF SACHS AG—See ZF Friedrichshafen AG; *Int'l*, pg. 8644
ZF SACHS AG—See ZF Friedrichshafen AG; *Int'l*, pg. 8644
ZF SACHS AUTOMOTIVE MEXICO SA DE CV—See ZF Friedrichshafen AG; *Int'l*, pg. 8644
ZF SACHS BRASIL LTDA—See ZF Friedrichshafen AG; *Int'l*, pg. 8644
ZF SACHS ESPANA S.A—See ZF Friedrichshafen AG; *Int'l*, pg. 8644
ZF SACHS KOREA CO., LTD.—See ZF Friedrichshafen AG; *Int'l*, pg. 8644
ZF SACHS MICRO MOBILITY GMBH—See ZF Friedrichshafen AG; *Int'l*, pg. 8644
ZF SACHS SLOVAKIA A.S.—See ZF Friedrichshafen AG; *Int'l*, pg. 8644
ZF SACHS SOUTH AFRICA (PTY.) LTD.—See ZF Friedrichshafen AG; *Int'l*, pg. 8644
ZF SACHS SUSPANSIYON SISTEMLERI SANAYI VE TICARET A.S.—See ZF Friedrichshafen AG; *Int'l*, pg. 8644
ZF SALES & SERVICE (MALAYSIA) SDN. BHD.—See ZF Friedrichshafen AG; *Int'l*, pg. 8643
ZF SERBIA D.O.O.—See ZF Friedrichshafen AG; *Int'l*, pg. 8644
ZF SERVICES AUSTRALIA PTY. LTD.—See ZF Friedrichshafen AG; *Int'l*, pg. 8643
ZF SERVICES BELGIUM N.V. - S.A.—See ZF Friedrichshafen AG; *Int'l*, pg. 8644
ZF SERVICES BOGOTA SAS—See ZF Friedrichshafen AG; *Int'l*, pg. 8644
ZF SERVICES (CHINA) CO., LTD.—See ZF Friedrichshafen AG; *Int'l*, pg. 8642
ZF SERVICES ESPANA S.A.U.—See ZF Friedrichshafen AG; *Int'l*, pg. 8644
ZF SERVICES FRANCE S.A.S.—See ZF Friedrichshafen AG; *Int'l*, pg. 8645
ZF SERVICES HONG KONG LTD.—See ZF Friedrichshafen AG; *Int'l*, pg. 8643
ZF SERVICES KOREA CO., LTD.—See ZF Friedrichshafen AG; *Int'l*, pg. 8645
ZF SERVICES LLC—See ZF Friedrichshafen AG; *Int'l*, pg. 8645
ZF SERVICES MIDDLE EAST LLC—See ZF Friedrichshafen AG; *Int'l*, pg. 8645
ZF SERVICES NEDERLAND B.V.—See ZF Friedrichshafen AG; *Int'l*, pg. 8645
ZF SERVICES PORTUGAL, UNIPESSOAL, LDA—See ZF Friedrichshafen AG; *Int'l*, pg. 8645
ZF SERVICES S.A. DE C.V.—See ZF Friedrichshafen AG; *Int'l*, pg. 8645
ZF SERVICES SCHWEIZ AG—See ZF Friedrichshafen AG; *Int'l*, pg. 8645
ZF SERVICES (SHANGHAI) CO., LTD.—See ZF Friedrichshafen AG; *Int'l*, pg. 8644
ZF SERVICES SOUTH AFRICA (PTY.) LTD.—See ZF Friedrichshafen AG; *Int'l*, pg. 8645
ZF SERVICES TURK SANAYI VE TICARET A.S.—See ZF Friedrichshafen AG; *Int'l*, pg. 8645
ZF SERVICES UK LTD.—See ZF Friedrichshafen AG; *Int'l*, pg. 8645
ZF SLOVAKIA A.S.—See ZF Friedrichshafen AG; *Int'l*, pg. 8645
ZF STANKOV S.R.O.—See ZF Friedrichshafen AG; *Int'l*, pg. 8645
ZF STEERING GEAR (INDIA) LIMITED—See Robert Bosch GmbH; *Int'l*, pg. 6363
ZF STEERING SYSTEMS POLAND SP. Z O.O.—See ZF Friedrichshafen AG; *Int'l*, pg. 8645

COMPANY NAME INDEX

ZF SUSPENSION TECHNOLOGY GUADALAJARA S.A. DE C.V.—See ZF Friedrichshafen AG; *Int'l*, pg. 8645
ZF TAIWAN LIMITED—See ZF Friedrichshafen AG; *Int'l*, pg. 8646
ZF THAILAND LTD.—See ZF Friedrichshafen AG; *Int'l*, pg. 8643
ZF TRADING ASIA PACIFIC PTE. LTD.—See ZF Friedrichshafen AG; *Int'l*, pg. 8646
ZF TRADING GMBH—See ZF Friedrichshafen AG; *Int'l*, pg. 8646
ZF TRADING UK LTD—See ZF Friedrichshafen AG; *Int'l*, pg. 8647
ZF TRANSMISSIONS GRAY COURT LLC—See ZF Friedrichshafen AG; *Int'l*, pg. 8647
ZF TRANSMISSIONS SHANGHAI CO., LTD.—See ZF Friedrichshafen AG; *Int'l*, pg. 8642
ZF TRW AUTOMOTIVE HOLDINGS CORP.—See ZF Friedrichshafen AG; *Int'l*, pg. 8645
ZF WIND POWER ANTWERPEN NV—See ZF Friedrichshafen AG; *Int'l*, pg. 8647
ZF WIND POWER COIMBATORE LTD.—See ZF Friedrichshafen AG; *Int'l*, pg. 8647
ZF WIND POWER GAINESVILLE LLC—See ZF Friedrichshafen AG; *Int'l*, pg. 8647
ZF WIND POWER (TIANJIN) CO., LTD.—See ZF Friedrichshafen AG; *Int'l*, pg. 8647
ZFX GMBH—See Zimmer Biomet Holdings, Inc.; *U.S. Public*, pg. 2406
ZFX INNOVATION GMBH—See Zimmer Biomet Holdings, Inc.; *U.S. Public*, pg. 2406
ZF YTO (LUOYANG) AXLE CO., LTD.—See ZF Friedrichshafen AG; *Int'l*, pg. 8642
ZGA AIRCRAFT PARTS, INC.—See Zotti Group Aviation, Inc.; *U.S. Private*, pg. 4609
Z GALLERIE, LLC; *U.S. Private*, pg. 4596
ZGH BOLESLAW S.A.—See Stalprodukt S.A.; *Int'l*, pg. 7164
ZG LIGHTING AUSTRALIA PTY LTD—See Zumtobel Group AG; *Int'l*, pg. 8696
ZG LIGHTING AUSTRIA GMBH—See Zumtobel Group AG; *Int'l*, pg. 8696
ZG LIGHTING BENELUX SA—See Zumtobel Group AG; *Int'l*, pg. 8696
ZG LIGHTING CZECH REPUBLIC, S R.O.—See Zumtobel Group AG; *Int'l*, pg. 8090
ZG LIGHTING DENMARK A/S—See Zumtobel Group AG; *Int'l*, pg. 8696
ZG LIGHTING D.O.O.—See Zumtobel Group AG; *Int'l*, pg. 8696
ZG LIGHTING D.O.O.—See Zumtobel Group AG; *Int'l*, pg. 8696
ZG LIGHTING FRANCE SAS—See Zumtobel Group AG; *Int'l*, pg. 8696
ZG LIGHTING HUNGARY KFT.—See Zumtobel Group AG; *Int'l*, pg. 8696
ZG LIGHTING IBERIA S.L.—See Zumtobel Group AG; *Int'l*, pg. 8696
ZG LIGHTING NETHERLANDS B.V.—See Zumtobel Group AG; *Int'l*, pg. 8696
ZG LIGHTING NORDIC AB—See Zumtobel Group AG; *Int'l*, pg. 8696
ZG LIGHTING NORWAY AS—See Zumtobel Group AG; *Int'l*, pg. 8696
ZG LIGHTING (N.Z.) LIMITED—See Zumtobel Group AG; *Int'l*, pg. 8696
ZG LIGHTING POLSKA SP. Z O.O.—See Zumtobel Group AG; *Int'l*, pg. 8696
ZG LIGHTING SINGAPORE PTE LIMITED—See Zumtobel Group AG; *Int'l*, pg. 8696
ZG LIGHTING SLOVAKIA S.R.O.—See Zumtobel Group AG; *Int'l*, pg. 8696
ZG LIGHTING (UK) LIMITED—See Zumtobel Group AG; *Int'l*, pg. 8696
ZGONEC D.O.O.—See Inles d.d.; *Int'l*, pg. 3705
ZGOP A.D.—See Integra Construction KZ LLP; *Int'l*, pg. 3729
ZGP DOBOJ A.D.; *Int'l*, pg. 8647
ZGP GP BEOGRAD A.D.; *Int'l*, pg. 8647
ZGURA'S CONCRETE SERVICES INC.; *U.S. Private*, pg. 4603
ZHAFIR PLASTICS MACHINERY GMBH—See Haitian International Holdings Ltd.; *Int'l*, pg. 3217
ZHAIKMUNAI LLP—See Nostrum Oil & Gas PLC; *Int'l*, pg. 5449
ZHANCHENG (SUZHOU) PLASTIC CO., LTD.—See Nihon Yamamura Glass Co., Ltd.; *Int'l*, pg. 5288
ZHANEL LTD—See Lotte Co., Ltd.; *Int'l*, pg. 4560
ZHANGBEI WINEY CO., LTD.—See Zhejiang Windey Co., Ltd.; *Int'l*, pg. 8666
ZHANGJIAGANG CIMC SANCTUM CRYOGENIC EQUIPMENT MACHINERY CO., LTD.—See China International Marine Containers (Group) Co., Ltd.; *Int'l*, pg. 1513
ZHANGJIAGANG CO., LTD.—See Haesung Industrial Co., Ltd.; *Int'l*, pg. 3205
ZHANGJIAGANG DONGBU HIGH TECHNOLOGY METAL PRODUCTS CO., LTD.—See SK Networks Co., Ltd.; *Int'l*, pg. 6975
ZHANGJIAGANG ELEGANT PLASTICS CO., LTD.; *Int'l*, pg. 8647
ZHANGJIAGANG FREETRADE SCIENCE & TECHNOLOGY CO., LTD.; *Int'l*, pg. 8647
ZHANG JIA GANG FREE TRADE ZONE MITSUI LINK-UPON ADVANCED MATERIALS, INC.—See Mitsui Chemicals, Inc.; *Int'l*, pg. 4984
ZHANGJIAGANG FURUI HEAVY EQUIPMENT CO., LTD.—See Zhangjiagang Furui Special Equipment Co., Ltd.; *Int'l*, pg. 8647
ZHANGJIAGANG FURUI SPECIAL EQUIPMENT CO., LTD.; *Int'l*, pg. 8647
ZHANGJIAGANG GUANGDA SPECIAL MATERIAL CO., LTD.; *Int'l*, pg. 8647
ZHANGJIAGANG GUOTAI HUARONG NEW CHEMICAL MATERIALS CO., LTD.—See Jiangsu Ruitai New Energy Materials Co., Ltd.; *Int'l*, pg. 3953
ZHANGJIAGANG HAIGUO NEW ENERGY EQUIPMENT MANUFACTURING CO., LTD.; *Int'l*, pg. 8647
ZHANG JIA GANG MANITOWOC CRANE TRADING CO. LTD.—See The Manitowoc Company, Inc.; *U.S. Public*, pg. 2111
ZHANGJIAGANG NAN-LING-CHENG STEEL STRUCTURE CO., LTD.—See Mitsubishi Heavy Industries, Ltd.; *Int'l*, pg. 4962
ZHANGJIAGANG NSK PRECISION MACHINERY CO., LTD.—See NSK Ltd.; *Int'l*, pg. 5480
ZHANGJIAGANG OTSUKA CHEMICAL CO., LTD.—See Otsuka Holdings Co., Ltd.; *Int'l*, pg. 5661
ZHANGJIAGANG POHANG STAINLESS STEEL CO., LTD.—See POSCO Holdings Inc.; *Int'l*, pg. 5938
ZHANGJIAGANG POSCO STEEL CO., LTD.—See POSCO Holdings Inc.; *Int'l*, pg. 5938
ZHANGJIAGANG PRESIDENT NISSHIN FOOD CORP.—See The Nisshin OilliO Group, Ltd.; *Int'l*, pg. 7671
ZHANGJIAGANG SHAGONG MEDICAL DEVICE CO., LTD.—See Well Lead Medical Co., Ltd.; *Int'l*, pg. 8373
ZHANGJIAGANG SHAGONG MEDICAL TECHNOLOGY CO., LTD.—See Well Lead Medical Co., Ltd.; *Int'l*, pg. 8373
ZHANGJIAGANG SHA STEEL & KINGLAND PIPLINE CO., LTD.—See Zhejiang Kingland Pipeline & Technologies Co., Ltd.; *Int'l*, pg. 8659
ZHANGJIAGANG XIAO-SHA COIL SERVICE CO., LTD.—See Hyosung Corporation; *Int'l*, pg. 3552
ZHANGJIAGANG ZHONGHUAN HAILU HIGH-END EQUIPMENT CO., LTD.; *Int'l*, pg. 8647
ZHANGJIAJIE CHINA INTERNATIONAL TRAVEL SERVICE CO., LTD.—See China Tourism Group Duty Free Corporation Limited; *Int'l*, pg. 1560
ZHANG JIA JIE TOURISM GROUP CO., LTD.; *Int'l*, pg. 8647
ZHANGJIAKOU XIAHUAYUAN ZHONGYU GAS CO., LTD.—See Zhongyu Energy Holdings Limited; *Int'l*, pg. 8676
ZHANGMEN EDUCATION INC.; *Int'l*, pg. 8647
ZHANG XIAOQUAN INC.; *Int'l*, pg. 8647
ZHANGZHOU CHENG LOONG PAPER CO., LTD.—See Cheng Loong Corp.; *Int'l*, pg. 1466
ZHANGZHOU CHIMEI CHEMICAL CO., LTD.—See Chi Mei Group; *Int'l*, pg. 1475
ZHANGZHOU CIMC CONTAINER CO., LTD.—See China International Marine Containers (Group) Co., Ltd.; *Int'l*, pg. 1513
ZHANGZHOU JINCHI AUTOMOBILE PARTS CO., LTD.—See Fujian Longxi Bearing (Group) Corporation Limited; *Int'l*, pg. 2818
ZHANGZHOU KEHUA TECHNOLOGY CO., LTD.—See Kehua Data Co., Ltd.; *Int'l*, pg. 4116
ZHANGZHOU KIBING GLASS CO., LTD.—See Zhuzhou Kibing Group Co., Ltd.; *Int'l*, pg. 8680
ZHANGZHOU KIBING PHOTOVOLTAIC NEW ENERGY TECHNOLOGY CO., LTD.—See Zhuzhou Kibing Group Co., Ltd.; *Int'l*, pg. 8680
ZHANGZHOU NEW ENERGY TECHNOLOGY CO., LTD.—See Kehua Data Co., Ltd.; *Int'l*, pg. 4116
ZHANGZHOU O.R.G PACKAGING CO., LTD.—See ORG Technology Co., Ltd.; *Int'l*, pg. 5617
ZHANGZHOU PIENTZEHUANG PHARMACEUTICAL CO., LTD.; *Int'l*, pg. 8647
ZHANGZHOU TON YI INDUSTRIAL CO., LTD.—See Uni-President Enterprises Corporation; *Int'l*, pg. 8029
ZHANGZHOU YAZAKI AUTO PARTS CO., LTD.—See Yazaki Corporation; *Int'l*, pg. 8573
ZHANGZIDAO GROUP (RONGCHENG) FOOD CO.—See Zoneco Group Co., Ltd.; *Int'l*, pg. 8688
ZHANJIANG COSCO LOGISTICS CO., LTD.—See China COSCO Shipping Corporation Limited; *Int'l*, pg. 1493
ZHANJIANG DENI CARBURETOR CO.—See Hitachi Astemo, Ltd.; *Int'l*, pg. 3409
ZHANJIANG GUOLIAN AQUATIC PRODUCTS CO., LTD.; *Int'l*, pg. 8647
ZHANJIANG PORT (GROUP) CO., LTD.—See China Merchants Group Limited; *Int'l*, pg. 1523
ZHANJIANGTON YI INDUSTRIAL CO., LTD.—See Uni-President Enterprises Corporation; *Int'l*, pg. 8029
ZHANJIANG ZHENGTONG KAIDI AUTOMOBILE SALES SERVICES CO., LTD.—See China ZhengTong Auto Services Holdings Limited; *Int'l*, pg. 1567
ZHANJIANG ZHONGFU CONTAINER CO., LTD.—See Zhuhai Zhongfu Enterprise Co., Ltd.; *Int'l*, pg. 8679
ZHANLING INTERNATIONAL LIMITED; *Int'l*, pg. 8648
ZHANYANG AUTOMATION (DONGGUAN) CO., LTD.—See Zhen Ding Technology Holding Limited; *Int'l*, pg. 8669
ZHAOBANGJI LIFESTYLE HOLDINGS LIMITED; *Int'l*, pg. 8648
ZHAOJIN MINING INDUSTRY CO., LTD.; *Int'l*, pg. 8648
ZHAOKE PHARMACEUTICAL (HEFEI) CO. LIMITED—See Lee's Pharmaceutical Holdings Limited; *Int'l*, pg. 4441
ZHAOPIN LIMITED—See SEEK Limited; *Int'l*, pg. 6679
ZHAOQING LEOCH BATTERY TECHNOLOGY CO., LTD.—See Leoch International Technology Limited; *Int'l*, pg. 4457
ZHAOQING PERFUMERY CO., LTD.—See Huabao International Holdings Limited; *Int'l*, pg. 3511
ZHAOQING SAN HUAN JINGYUE MAGNETIC MATERIALS INC. LTD.—See Beijing Zhong Ke San Huan High-tech Co., Ltd.; *Int'l*, pg. 961
ZHAOSU JINDI FLAX CO., LTD.—See Kingdom Holdings Limited; *Int'l*, pg. 4172
ZHAOTONG ANTONG PACKAGE MATERIAL CO., LTD.—See Litu Holdings Limited; *Int'l*, pg. 4528
ZHAOTONG KIBING PHOTOVOLTAIC TECHNOLOGY CO., LTD.—See Zhuzhou Kibing Group Co., Ltd.; *Int'l*, pg. 8680
ZHAYREMSKY GORNO-OBOGATITELNY KOMBINAT JSC; *Int'l*, pg. 8648
ZHEFU HOLDING GROUP CO., LTD.; *Int'l*, pg. 8648
ZHEJIANG HOLIP ELECTRONIC TECHNOLOGY CO. LTD.—See Danfoss A/S; *Int'l*, pg. 1962
ZHEJIANG AICHI INDUSTRIAL MACHINERY CO., LTD.—See Aichi Corporation; *Int'l*, pg. 229
ZHEJIANG AICHI MECHANICAL & ELECTRICAL CO., LTD.—See Aichi Steel Corporation; *Int'l*, pg. 230
ZHEJIANG AKCOME NEW ENERGY TECHNOLOGY CO.,LTD.; *Int'l*, pg. 8648
ZHEJIANG ALLEAD PRECISION TECHNOLOGY CO., LTD.—See Shenzhen Megmeet Electrical Co.,Ltd.; *Int'l*, pg. 6818
ZHEJIANG AMINO-CHEM LTD.—See Zhejiang Longsheng Group Co., Ltd.; *Int'l*, pg. 8659
ZHEJIANG ANGLIKANG CAPSULE CO., LTD.—See Zhejiang Anglikang Pharmaceutical Co., Ltd.; *Int'l*, pg. 8648
ZHEJIANG ANGLIKANG PHARMACEUTICAL CO., LTD.; *Int'l*, pg. 8648
ZHEJIANG ANT SMALL & MICRO FINANCIAL SERVICES GROUP CO., LTD.; *Int'l*, pg. 8648
ZHEJIANG ANXIAN YUAN COMPANY LIMITED—See Anxian Yuan China Holdings Limited; *Int'l*, pg. 486
ZHEJIANG AOKANG SHOES CO., LTD.; *Int'l*, pg. 8648
ZHEJIANG ASAHI BEARING CO., LTD.—See Sojitz Corporation; *Int'l*, pg. 7066
ZHEJIANG ASD HOUSEHOLD EQUIPMENT CO., LTD.—See Aishida Co., Ltd.; *Int'l*, pg. 251
ZHEJIANG ASIA-PACIFIC MECHANICAL AND ELECTRONIC CO., LTD.; *Int'l*, pg. 8648
ZHEJIANG AUSUN PHARMACEUTICAL CO., LTD.; *Int'l*, pg. 8648
ZHEJIANG BAIDA PRECISION MANUFACTURING CORP.; *Int'l*, pg. 8649
ZHEJIANG BANGJIE HOLDING GROUP CO., LTD.; *Int'l*, pg. 8649
ZHEJIANG BENLI TECHNOLOGY CO., LTD.; *Int'l*, pg. 8649
ZHEJIANG BIOMET MEDICAL PRODUCTS CO. LTD.—See Zimmer Biomet Holdings, Inc.; *U.S. Public*, pg. 2406
ZHEJIANG BOE DISPLAY TECHNOLOGY CO., LTD.—See BOE Technology Group Co., Ltd.; *Int'l*, pg. 1099
ZHEJIANG BOFAY ELECTRIC CO., LTD.; *Int'l*, pg. 8649
ZHEJIANG BUSEN GARMENTS CO., LTD.; *Int'l*, pg. 8649
ZHEJIANG CANAAN KAIXINLONG TECHNOLOGY CO., LTD.—See Zhejiang Canaan Technology Co., Ltd.; *Int'l*, pg. 8649
ZHEJIANG CANAAN TECHNOLOGY CO., LTD.; *Int'l*, pg. 8649
ZHEJIANG CANGNAN INSTRUMENT GROUP CO., LTD.; *Int'l*, pg. 8649
ZHEJIANG CAYI VACUUM CONTAINER CO., LTD.; *Int'l*, pg. 8649
ZHEJIANG CENTURY HUATONG GROUP CO., LTD.; *Int'l*, pg. 8649
ZHEJIANG CFMOTO POWER CO., LTD.; *Int'l*, pg. 8649
ZHEJIANG CHANGAN RENHENG TECHNOLOGY CO., LTD.; *Int'l*, pg. 8649
ZHEJIANG CHANGHAI BIOLOGICAL CO. LTD.—See Zhejiang Medicine Co. Ltd.; *Int'l*, pg. 8660
ZHEJIANG CHANGHUA AUTO PARTS CO., LTD.; *Int'l*, pg. 8649
ZHEJIANG CHANGSHENG SLIDING BEARINGS CO., LTD.; *Int'l*, pg. 8649

ZHEJIANG CHAOWEI CHUANGYUAN INDUSTRIAL CO., LTD.—See Chaowei Power Holdings Limited; Int'l, pg. 1447
ZHEJIANG CHENFENG SCIENCE & TECHNOLOGY CO., LTD.; Int'l, pg. 8649
ZHEJIANG CHENGCHANG TECHNOLOGY CO., LTD.; Int'l, pg. 8650
ZHEJIANG CHENGYI PHARMACEUTICAL CO., LTD; Int'l, pg. 8650
ZHEJIANG CHINA COMMODITIES CITY GROUP CO., LTD.; Int'l, pg. 8650
ZHEJIANG CHINA INTERNATIONAL TRAVEL SERVICE CO., LTD.—See China Tourism Group Duty Free Corporation Limited; Int'l, pg. 1560
ZHEJIANG CHINA LIGHT & TEXTILE INDUSTRIAL CITY GROUP CO., LTD.; Int'l, pg. 8650
ZHEJIANG CHINASTARS NEW MATERIALS GROUP CO., LTD.; Int'l, pg. 8650
ZHEJIANG CHINT ELECTRICS CO., LTD.—See Chint Group Corporation; Int'l, pg. 1571
ZHEJIANG CHUNHUI INTELLIGENT CONTROL CO., LTD.; Int'l, pg. 8650
ZHEJIANG COMMUNICATIONS INVESTMENT GROUP CO., LTD.; Int'l, pg. 8650
ZHEJIANG CONBA PHARMACEUTICAL CO., LTD.; Int'l, pg. 8650
ZHEJIANG CONSTRUCTION INVESTMENT GROUP CO., LTD.; Int'l, pg. 8650
ZHEJIANG CRYSTAL DISPLAY TECHNOLOGY CO, LTD.—See Zhejiang Crystal-optech Co., Ltd.; Int'l, pg. 8650
ZHEJIANG CRYSTAL-OPTECH CO., LTD.; Int'l, pg. 8650
ZHEJIANG DADI STEEL STRUCTURE CO., LTD.—See Long Yuan Construction Group Co., Ltd; Int'l, pg. 4549
ZHEJIANG DAFENG INDUSTRIAL CO., LTD.; Int'l, pg. 8650
ZHEJIANG DAHAO TECHNOLOGY CO., LTD.—See Beijing Dahao Technology Corporation Limited; Int'l, pg. 948
ZHEJIANG DAHUA TECHNOLOGY CO., LTD.; Int'l, pg. 8650
ZHEJIANG DAILY DIGITAL CULTURE GROUP CO., LTD.; Int'l, pg. 8651
ZHEJIANG DALI TECHNOLOGY CO., LTD.; Int'l, pg. 8651
ZHEJIANG DAXING TECHNOLOGY CO., LTD.—See Xinzhi Group Co., Ltd.; Int'l, pg. 8535
ZHEJIANG DAYANG BIOTECH GROUP CO., LTD.; Int'l, pg. 8651
ZHEJIANG DAYUAN PUMPS INDUSTRY CO., LTD.; Int'l, pg. 8651
ZHEJIANG DEHONG AUTOMOTIVE ELECTRONIC & ELECTRICAL CO.,LTD.; Int'l, pg. 8651
ZHEJIANG DEWEI CEMENTED CARBIDE MANUFACTURING CO., LTD.—See GEM Co., Ltd.; Int'l, pg. 2914
ZHEJIANG DIBAY ELECTRIC CO., LTD.; Int'l, pg. 8651
ZHEJIANG DINGLI MACHINERY CO., LTD.; Int'l, pg. 8651
ZHEJIANG DONGMU KEDA MAGNETOELECTRIC CO., LTD.—See NBTM New Materials Group Co., Ltd.; Int'l, pg. 5180
ZHEJIANG DONGRI COMPANY LIMITED; Int'l, pg. 8651
ZHEJIANG DONGWANG TIMES TECHNOLOGY CO., LTD.; Int'l, pg. 8651
ZHEJIANG DOUBLE ARROW RUBBER CO., LTD.; Int'l, pg. 8651
ZHEJIANG DUN'AN ARTIFICIAL ENVIRONMENT CO., LTD.; Int'l, pg. 8651
ZHEJIANG DUN'AN ELECTRO-MECHANICAL TECHNOLOGY CO., LTD.—See Zhejiang Dun'An Artificial Environment Co., Ltd.; Int'l, pg. 8651
ZHEJIANG DUNAN INTERNATIONAL TRADING CO., LTD.—See Zhejiang Dun'An Artificial Environment Co., Ltd.; Int'l, pg. 8651
ZHEJIANG EAST ASIA PHARMACEUTICAL CO., LTD.; Int'l, pg. 8651
ZHEJIANG EAST CRYSTAL ELECTRONIC CO., LTD.; Int'l, pg. 8652
ZHEJIANG ECO BIOK ANIMAL HEALTH PRODUCTS LIMITED—See ECO Animal Health Group plc; Int'l, pg. 2292
ZHEJIANG ELECTRIC POWER COMPANY—See State Grid Corporation of China; Int'l, pg. 7183
ZHEJIANG ENTIVE SMART KITCHEN APPLIANCE CO., LTD.; Int'l, pg. 8652
ZHEJIANG EXPRESSWAY CO., LTD.; Int'l, pg. 8652
ZHEJIANG EXPRESSWAY CO., LTD.; Int'l, pg. 8652
ZHEJIANG FACEA VEHICLE LOCKS CO LTD.—See ASSA ABLOY AB; Int'l, pg. 641
ZHEJIANG FANGYUAN YESHILI REFLECTIVE MATERIAL CO., LTD.—See Zhejiang Crystal-optech Co., Ltd.; Int'l, pg. 8650
ZHEJIANG FEIDA ENVIRONMENTAL SCIENCE & TECHNOLOGY CO., LTD.; Int'l, pg. 8652
ZHEJIANG FEIDA MHPS HIGH EFFICIENCY FLUE GAS CLEANING SYSTEMS ENGINEERING CO., LTD.—See Mitsubishi Heavy Industries, Ltd.; Int'l, pg. 4962

ZHEJIANG FENGLONG ELECTRIC CO., LTD.; Int'l, pg. 8652
ZHEJIANG FLAT GLASS CO., LTD.—See Flat Glass Group Co., Ltd.; Int'l, pg. 2698
ZHEJIANG FORE INTELLIGENT TECHNOLOGY CO., LTD.; Int'l, pg. 8652
ZHEJIANG FOUNDER MOTOR CO., LTD.; Int'l, pg. 8652
ZHEJIANG FUCHUNJIANG ENVIRONMENTAL THERMOELECTRIC CO., LTD.; Int'l, pg. 8652
ZHEJIANG FUDAR ALLOY MATERIALS TECHNOLOGY CO., LTD.—See Fuda Alloy Materials Co., Ltd.; Int'l, pg. 2804
ZHEJIANG FULAI NEW MATERIAL CO., LTD.; Int'l, pg. 8652
ZHEJIANG FURUN DIGITAL TECHNOLOGY CO., LTD.; Int'l, pg. 8652
ZHEJIANG GAOTE METAL DECORATING CO., LTD.—See Crown Holdings, Inc.; U.S. Public, pg. 599
ZHEJIANG GARDEN BIOPHARMACEUTICAL CO., LTD.; Int'l, pg. 8652
ZHEJIANG GEELY HOLDING GROUP CO., LTD.; Int'l, pg. 8652
ZHEJIANG GIUSEPPE GARMENT CO., LTD.; Int'l, pg. 8654
ZHEJIANG GLASS COMPANY LIMITED; Int'l, pg. 8654
ZHEJIANG GOLDEN EAGLE CO., LTD.; Int'l, pg. 8654
ZHEJIANG GOLDENSEA HI-TECH CO., LTD.; Int'l, pg. 8654
ZHEJIANG GONGDONG MEDICAL TECHNOLOGY CO., LTD.; Int'l, pg. 8654
ZHEJIANG GRANDWALL ELECTRIC SCIENCE & TECHNOLOGY CO., LTD.; Int'l, pg. 8654
ZHEJIANG GREAT SHENGDA PACKAGING CO., LTD.—See China Shengda Packaging Group Inc.; Int'l, pg. 1551
ZHEJIANG GREAT SOUTHEAST COMPANY LIMITED; Int'l, pg. 8654
ZHEJIANG GUANGHUA TECHNOLOGY CO., LTD.; Int'l, pg. 8654
ZHEJIANG GUYUELONGSHAN SHAOXING WINE CO., LTD.; Int'l, pg. 8654
ZHEJIANG HAERS VACUUM CONTAINERS CO., LTD.; Int'l, pg. 8654
ZHEJIANG HAILIANG CO., LTD.; Int'l, pg. 8655
ZHEJIANG HAILIANG INTERNATIONAL TRADE CO., LTD.—See Zhejiang Hailiang Co., Ltd.; Int'l, pg. 8655
ZHEJIANG HAILIDE NEW MATERIAL CO., LTD.; Int'l, pg. 8655
ZHEJIANG HAIYAN POWER SYSTEM RESOURCES ENVIRONMENTAL TECHNOLOGY CO., LTD.; Int'l, pg. 8655
ZHEJIANG HANGKE TECHNOLOGY INCORPORATED COMPANY; Int'l, pg. 8655
ZHEJIANG HANGMIN CO., LTD.; Int'l, pg. 8655
ZHEJIANG HANSON PRECISE MACHINERY CO., LTD.—See Shanghai Hanbell Precise Machinery Co., Ltd.; Int'l, pg. 6769
ZHEJIANG HAOTAI CHEMICAL CO., LTD.; Int'l, pg. 8655
ZHEJIANG HEADERBOARD BUILDING MATERIALS CO., LTD.—See Hangxiao Steel Structure Co., Ltd.; Int'l, pg. 3246
ZHE JIANG HEADMAN MACHINERY CO., LTD.; Int'l, pg. 8648
ZHEJIANG HEALTH CREATION BIO-TECHNOLOGY CO. LTD.—See Zhejiang Medicine Co. Ltd.; Int'l, pg. 8660
ZHEJIANG HEALTH CREATION PHARMACEUTICAL CO., LTD.—See Zhejiang Medicine Co. Ltd.; Int'l, pg. 8660
ZHEJIANG HELIHUA TECHNOLOGY CO., LTD.—See Endress+Hauser (International) Holding AG; Int'l, pg. 2409
ZHEJIANG HENGDIAN TOSPO IMP.&EXP. CO. LTD.—See Hengdian Group TOSPO Lighting Co Ltd; Int'l, pg. 3346
ZHEJIANG HENGLONG & VIE PUMP MANUFACTURING CO., LTD.—See Zhejiang VIE Science & Technology Co., Ltd.; Int'l, pg. 8665
ZHEJIANG HENGWEI BATTERY CO., LTD.; Int'l, pg. 8655
ZHEJIANG HISOAR PHARMACEUTICAL CO., LTD.; Int'l, pg. 8655
ZHEJIANG HISUN PHARMACEUTICAL CO., LTD.; Int'l, pg. 8655
ZHEJIANG HI-TECH ELECTRIC ASSEMBLING CO., LTD.—See Shanghai Hi-Tech Control System CO., LTD.; Int'l, pg. 6770
ZHEJIANG HONGCHANG ELECTRICAL TECHNOLOGY CO., LTD.; Int'l, pg. 8655
ZHEJIANG HONGSHENG CHEMICAL CO., LTD.—See Zhejiang Longsheng Group Co., Ltd.; Int'l, pg. 8659
ZHEJIANG HUACE FILM AND TV CO., LTD.; Int'l, pg. 8655
ZHEJIANG HUADA NEW MATERIALS CO., LTD.; Int'l, pg. 8655
ZHEJIANG HUAHAI CULTURAL DEVELOPMENT CO., LTD.—See Zhejiang Huahai Pharmaceutical Co., Ltd.; Int'l, pg. 8656
ZHEJIANG HUAHAI PHARMACEUTICAL CO., LTD.; Int'l, pg. 8655

ZHEJIANG HUAHE WANRUN INFORMATION TECHNOLOGY CO., LTD.—See China Security Co., Ltd.; Int'l, pg. 1550
ZHEJIANG HUAKANG PHARMACEUTICAL CO., LTD.; Int'l, pg. 8656
ZHEJIANG HUAMEI HOLDING CO., LTD.; Int'l, pg. 8656
ZHEJIANG HUANGMA TECHNOLOGY CO., LTD.; Int'l, pg. 8656
ZHEJIANG HUASHENG TECHNOLOGY CO., LTD.; Int'l, pg. 8656
ZHEJIANG HUATIE EMERGENCY EQUIPMENT SCIENCE & TECHNOLOGY CO., LTD.; Int'l, pg. 8656
ZHEJIANG HUATONG MEAT PRODUCTS CO LTD; Int'l, pg. 8656
ZHEJIANG HUAYOU COBALT CO., LTD.—See Huayou Cobalt Co., Ltd.; Int'l, pg. 3516
ZHEJIANG HUAYU ELECTRIC CO., LTD.—See Zhejiang Jinggong Science & Technology Co., Ltd.; Int'l, pg. 8657
ZHEJIANG HUAZHANG AUTOMATION EQUIPMENT CO., LTD.—See Rexel, S.A.; Int'l, pg. 6317
ZHEJIANG HUGE LEAF CO., LTD.—See Shenghua Group Holdings Co., Ltd.; Int'l, pg. 6801
ZHEJIANG HUILONG NEW MATERIALS CO., LTD.; Int'l, pg. 8656
ZHEJIANG IDC FLUID CONTROL CO., LTD.; Int'l, pg. 8656
ZHEJIANG IKAHE SANITARY WARE CO., LTD.—See Shenzhen Megmeet Electrical Co.,Ltd; Int'l, pg. 6818
ZHEJIANG INDUSTRIAL GROUP CO., LTD.—See Maruha Nichiro Corporation; Int'l, pg. 4712
ZHEJIANG INFROTRONIC INTELLIGENT MACHINERY TECHNOLOGY CO.,LTD.—See Zhejiang Jingxing Paper Joint Stock Co., Ltd.; Int'l, pg. 8658
ZHEJIANG INT'L GROUP CO., LTD.; Int'l, pg. 8656
ZHEJIANG IPS PHARMACEUTICAL TECHNOLOGY COMPANY LIMITED—See Sino Harbour Holdings Group Limited; Int'l, pg. 6947
ZHEJIANG IRON FORCE METAL PRODUCTS CO., LTD.—See Iron Force Industrial Co., Ltd.; Int'l, pg. 3810
ZHEJIANG JASAN HOLDING GROUP CO., LTD.; Int'l, pg. 8656
ZHEJIANG JFE SHOJI STEEL PRODUCTS CO., LTD.—See JFE Holdings, Inc.; Int'l, pg. 3937
ZHEJIANG JIAAO ENPROTECH STOCK CO., LTD.; Int'l, pg. 8656
ZHEJIANG JIAFU GLASS CO., LTD.—See Flat Glass Group Co., Ltd.; Int'l, pg. 2698
ZHEJIANG JIAHENG PACKAGING TECHNOLOGY CO., LTD.—See Jahen Household Products Co., Ltd.; Int'l, pg. 3871
ZHEJIANG JIAHUA ENERGY CHEMICAL INDUSTRY CO., LTD.; Int'l, pg. 8656
ZHEJIANG JIAHUAN ELECTRONIC CO., LTD.; Int'l, pg. 8656
ZHEJIANG JIANFENG GROUP CO., LTD.; Int'l, pg. 8656
ZHEJIANG JIANFENG HEALTH TECH. CO., LTD.—See Zhejiang Jianfeng Group Co., Ltd.; Int'l, pg. 8656
ZHEJIANG JIANGSHAN SUNNY ELECTRON CO., LTD—See NVC International Holdings Limited; Int'l, pg. 5498
ZHEJIANG JIANYE CHEMICAL CO., LTD.; Int'l, pg. 8656
ZHEJIANG JIASHAN KENENG POWER EQUIPMENT CO., LTD.—See Sun.King Technology Group Limited; Int'l, pg. 7309
ZHEJIANG JIAXING JINRONG AUTO PARTS CO., LTD.—See Tianjin Jinrong Tianyu Precision Machinery, Inc.; Int'l, pg. 7739
ZHE JIANG JIAXING LECIEN CO., LTD.—See Wacoal Holdings Corp.; Int'l, pg. 8326
ZHEJIANG JIAXIN SILK CORP., LTD.; Int'l, pg. 8656
ZHEJIANG JIECANG LINEAR MOTION TECHNOLOGY CO., LTD.; Int'l, pg. 8657
ZHEJIANG JIEMEI ELECTRONIC & TECHNOLOGY CO., LTD.; Int'l, pg. 8657
ZHEJIANG JIHUA GROUP CO., LTD.; Int'l, pg. 8657
ZHEJIANG JINDAO TECHNOLOGY CO., LTD.; Int'l, pg. 8657
ZHEJIANG JINDUN FANS CO., LTD.; Int'l, pg. 8657
ZHEJIANG JINFEI KAIDA WHEEL CO., LTD.; Int'l, pg. 8657
ZHEJIANG JINGGONG NEW MATERIALS TECHNOLOGY CO., LTD.—See Zhejiang Jinggong Science & Technology Co., Ltd.; Int'l, pg. 8657
ZHEJIANG JINGGONG PRECISION MANUFACTURING CO., LTD.—See Zhejiang Jinggong Science & Technology Co., Ltd.; Int'l, pg. 8657
ZHEJIANG JINGGONG ROBOT INTELLIGENT EQUIPMENT CO., LTD.—See Zhejiang Jinggong Science & Technology Co., Ltd.; Int'l, pg. 8657
ZHEJIANG JINGGONG SCIENCE & TECHNOLOGY CO., LTD.; Int'l, pg. 8657
ZHEJIANG JINGHENG DATA MANAGEMENT CO., LTD.—See Zhejiang Jinggong Science & Technology Co., Ltd.; Int'l, pg. 8657
ZHEJIANG JINGHUA LASER TECHNOLOGY CO., LTD.; Int'l, pg. 8657

COMPANY NAME INDEX

ZHEJIANG JINGSHENG MECHANICAL & ELECTRICAL CO., LTD.; *Int'l*, pg. 8657
ZHEJIANG JINGU CO., LTD.; *Int'l*, pg. 8657
ZHEJIANG JINGXING PAPER JOINT STOCK CO., LTD.; *Int'l*, pg. 8658
ZHEJIANG JINGXIN PHARMACEUTICAL CO., LTD.; *Int'l*, pg. 8657
ZHEJIANG JINHUA CONBA BIO-PHARM. CO., LTD.—See Zhejiang CONBA Pharmaceutical Co., Ltd.; *Int'l*, pg. 8650
ZHEJIANG JINKE CULTURE INDUSTRY CO., LTD.; *Int'l*, pg. 8658
ZHEJIANG JINKE TOM CULTURE INDUSTRY CO.,LTD.; *Int'l*, pg. 8658
ZHEJIANG JINKO SOLAR CO., LTD.—See JinkoSolar Holding Co., Ltd.; *Int'l*, pg. 3968
ZHEJIANG JINRAY ELECTRONIC MATERIAL CO., LTD.—See Zhejiang Jingsheng Mechanical & Electrical Co., Ltd.; *Int'l*, pg. 8657
ZHEJIANG JINSHENG NEW MATERIALS CO., LTD.; *Int'l*, pg. 8658
ZHEJIANG JINSHUANG BEARING CO., LTD.—See Sojitz Corporation; *Int'l*, pg. 7066
ZHEJIANG JISHAN HOLDINGS LTD.—See China Jishan Holdings Limited; *Int'l*, pg. 1513
ZHEJIANG JISHAN PRINTING & DYEING CO., LTD.—See China Jishan Holdings Limited; *Int'l*, pg. 1513
ZHEJIANG JISHENG CHEMICAL CONSTRUCTION MATERIAL CO., LTD.—See Zhejiang Longsheng Group Co., Ltd.; *Int'l*, pg. 8659
ZHEJIANG JIULI HI-TECH METALS CO., LTD.; *Int'l*, pg. 8658
ZHEJIANG JIUSHENG CROSS-LINKED CABLE CO., LTD.—See Jiusheng Electric Co., Ltd.; *Int'l*, pg. 3971
ZHEJIANG JIUZHOU PHARMACEUTICAL CO., LTD.; *Int'l*, pg. 8658
ZHEJIANG JOLLY PHARMACEUTICAL CO., LTD.; *Int'l*, pg. 8658
ZHEJIANG JONGGONG POWER TECHNOLOGY CO., LTD.—See Zhejiang Jinggong Science & Technology Co., Ltd.; *Int'l*, pg. 8657
ZHEJIANG JUHUA CO., LTD.; *Int'l*, pg. 8658
ZHEJIANG JULI CULTURE DEVELOPMENT CO., LTD.; *Int'l*, pg. 8658
ZHEJIANG JW PRECISION MACHINERY CO., LTD.; *Int'l*, pg. 8658
ZHEJIANG KAIER INDUSTRY CO., LTD—See Zhejiang Kaier New Materials Co., Ltd.; *Int'l*, pg. 8658
ZHEJIANG KAIER NEW MATERIALS CO., LTD.; *Int'l*, pg. 8658
ZHEJIANG KAISHENG FLUOROCHEMICALS CO., LTD.—See Zhejiang Juhua Co., Ltd.; *Int'l*, pg. 8658
ZHEJIANG KANDI VEHICLES CO., LTD.—See KANDI TECHNOLOGIES GROUP, INC.; *Int'l*, pg. 4066
ZHEJIANG KANGBAO HOUSEHOLD TEXTILES CO., LTD.—See Kingform Health Hometextile Group Limited; *Int'l*, pg. 4173
ZHEJIANG KANGLONGDA SPECIAL PROTECTION TECHNOLOGY CO., LTD.; *Int'l*, pg. 8659
ZHEJIANG KANGSHENG CO., LTD.; *Int'l*, pg. 8659
ZHEJIANG KAN SPECIALITIES MATERIAL CO., LTD.; *Int'l*, pg. 8658
ZHEJIANG KAWAMOTO HEALTH CARE PRODUCTS CO., LTD.—See Air Water Inc.; *Int'l*, pg. 241
ZHEJIANG KEATON TECHNOLOGY CO., LTD.—See Shanghai Putailai New Energy Technology Co., Ltd.; *Int'l*, pg. 6777
ZHEJIANG KEERUN CATERING ADMINISTRATION CORP., LTD.—See Xiamen ITG Group Corp., Ltd.; *Int'l*, pg. 8525
ZHEJIANG KESAI ADVANCED MATERIALS TECHNOLOGY CO., LTD.—See Shenzhen Wote Advanced Materials Co., Ltd.; *Int'l*, pg. 6824
ZHEJIANG KINDLY MEDICAL DEVICES CO., LTD—See Shanghai Kindly Enterprise Development Group Co., Ltd; *Int'l*, pg. 6774
ZHEJIANG KINGDOM FLAX CO., LTD.—See Kingdom Holdings Limited; *Int'l*, pg. 4172
ZHEJIANG KINGLAND PIPELINE & TECHNOLOGIES CO., LTD.; *Int'l*, pg. 8659
ZHEJIANG LANGDI GROUP CO.,LTD; *Int'l*, pg. 8659
ZHEJIANG LANTE OPTICS CO., LTD.; *Int'l*, pg. 8659
ZHEJIANG LEAPMOTOR TECHNOLOGY CO., LTD.; *Int'l*, pg. 8659
ZHEJIANG LESU METAL MATERIAL CO. LTD.—See SEB S.A.; *Int'l*, pg. 6668
ZHEJIANG LIAOYUAN PHARMACEUTICAL CO., LTD.—See Ningbo Menovo Pharmaceutical Co., Ltd.; *Int'l*, pg. 5304
ZHEJIANG LIEBHERR ZHONGCHE TRANSPORTATION SYSTEMS CO. LTD.—See Liebherr-International AG; *Int'l*, pg. 4491
ZHEJIANG LINHAI ZHEFU ELECTRIC MACHINERY CO., LTD.—See Zhefu Holding Group Co., Ltd.; *Int'l*, pg. 8648
ZHEJIANG LINUO FLOW CONTROL TECHNOLOGY CO., LTD.; *Int'l*, pg. 8659
ZHE JIANG LI ZI YUAN FOOD CO., LTD.; *Int'l*, pg. 8648

ZHEJIANG LONGHUA HOLDING GROUP CO., LTD.—See Zhejiang Longsheng Group Co., Ltd.; *Int'l*, pg. 8659
ZHEJIANG LONGOOD INTELLIGENT ELECTRIC CO., LTD—See Shenzhen Longood Intelligent Electric Co., Ltd.; *Int'l*, pg. 6817
ZHEJIANG LONGSHENG DYESTUFF CHEMICALS CO., LTD.—See Zhejiang Longsheng Group Co., Ltd.; *Int'l*, pg. 8659
ZHEJIANG LONGSHENG GROUP CO., LTD.; *Int'l*, pg. 8659
ZHEJIANG LUDAO TECHNOLOGY CO., LTD.—See China Ludao Technology Company Limited; *Int'l*, pg. 1515
ZHEJIANG MATERIALS INDUSTRY CHEMICAL GROUP CO., LTD.—See Zhejiang Materials Industry Group Corporation; *Int'l*, pg. 8659
ZHEJIANG MATERIALS INDUSTRY CIVIL EXPLOSIVES MONOPOLY CO., LTD.—See Zhejiang Materials Industry Group Corporation; *Int'l*, pg. 8659
ZHEJIANG MATERIALS INDUSTRY GROUP CORPORATION; *Int'l*, pg. 8659
ZHEJIANG MATERIALS INDUSTRY SENHUA GROUP CO., LTD.—See Zhejiang Materials Industry Group Corporation; *Int'l*, pg. 8659
ZHEJIANG MEDICINE CO. LTD.; *Int'l*, pg. 8659
ZHEJIANG MEDICINE CO. LTD. - ZMC VITAMIN FACTORY—See Zhejiang Medicine Co. Ltd.; *Int'l*, pg. 8660
ZHEJIANG MEIDA INDUSTRIAL CO., LTD.; *Int'l*, pg. 8660
ZHEJIANG MEILI HIGH TECHNOLOGY CO,.LTD.; *Int'l*, pg. 8660
ZHEJIANG MEILUN ELEVATOR CO., LTD.; *Int'l*, pg. 8660
ZHEJIANG MENOVO PHARMACEUTICAL CO., LTD.—See Ningbo Menovo Pharmaceutical Co., Ltd.; *Int'l*, pg. 5304
ZHEJIANG MEORIENT COMMERCE & EXHIBITION, INC.; *Int'l*, pg. 8660
ZHEJIANG METECNO NEW BUILDING PANELS, CO. LTD.—See Metecno S.p.A.; *Int'l*, pg. 4853
ZHEJIANG MING JEWELRY CO., LTD.; *Int'l*, pg. 8660
ZHEJIANG MTCN TECHNOLOGY CO., LTD.; *Int'l*, pg. 8660
ZHEJIANG MUSTANG BATTERY CO., LTD.; *Int'l*, pg. 8660
ZHEJIANG NARADA POWER SOURCE CO., LTD.; *Int'l*, pg. 8660
ZHEJIANG NATURAL OUTDOOR GOODS, INC.; *Int'l*, pg. 8660
ZHEJIANG NBTM KEDA MAGNETOELECTRICITY CO., LTD.—See NBTM New Materials Group Co., Ltd.; *Int'l*, pg. 5180
ZHEJIANG NETSUN CO., LTD.; *Int'l*, pg. 8660
ZHEJIANG NEW CENTURY HOTEL MANAGEMENT CO., LTD.; *Int'l*, pg. 8660
ZHEJIANG NEW CHUWA WOOL CO., LTD.—See Zhejiang Xinao Textiles Inc.; *Int'l*, pg. 8666
ZHEJIANG NEW YUHONG INTELLIGENT EQUIPMENT CO., LTD.—See CSG Smart Science & Technology Co., Ltd.; *Int'l*, pg. 1865
ZHEJIANG NHU COMPANY LTD.; *Int'l*, pg. 8660
ZHEJIANG NICCA CHEMICAL CO., LTD.—See Nicca Chemical Co., Ltd.; *Int'l*, pg. 5264
ZHEJIANG NIPPON TECHNO-CARBON CO., LTD.—See Nippon Carbon Co., Ltd.; *Int'l*, pg. 5312
ZHEJIANG NISSEI DISPLAY SYSTEM CO., LTD.—See Nippon Seiki Co., Ltd.; *Int'l*, pg. 5330
ZHEJIANG NORTH SUPREME SEAFOOD CO., LTD.—See Mitsubishi Corporation; *Int'l*, pg. 4943
ZHEJIANG NVC LAMPS CO., LTD.—See NVC International Holdings Limited; *Int'l*, pg. 5498
ZHEJIANG OMEX ENVIRONMENTAL ENGINEERING CO., LTD.—See DuPont de Nemours, Inc.; *U.S. Public*, pg. 694
ZHEJIANG O.R.G PACKAGING CO., LTD.—See ORG Technology Co., Ltd.; *Int'l*, pg. 5617
ZHEJIANG ORIENT C&E CO., LTD.—See Zhejiang Orient Financial Holdings Group Co., Ltd.; *Int'l*, pg. 8661
ZHEJIANG ORIENT CREATION I/E CO., LTD.—See Zhejiang Orient Financial Holdings Group Co., Ltd.; *Int'l*, pg. 8661
ZHEJIANG ORIENT FINANCIAL HOLDINGS GROUP CO., LTD.; *Int'l*, pg. 8661
ZHEJIANG ORIENT GARMTEX I/E CO., LTD—See Zhejiang Orient Financial Holdings Group Co., Ltd.; *Int'l*, pg. 8661
ZHEJIANG ORIENT GENE BIOTECH CO., LTD.; *Int'l*, pg. 8661
ZHEJIANG ORIENT HOLLY TRADING CO., LTD—See Zhejiang Orient Financial Holdings Group Co., Ltd.; *Int'l*, pg. 8661
ZHEJIANG ORIENT HOME TEXTILES I/E CO., LTD.—See Zhejiang Orient Financial Holdings Group Co., Ltd.; *Int'l*, pg. 8661
ZHEJIANG ORIENT HUAYE I/E CO., LTD.—See Zhejiang Orient Financial Holdings Group Co., Ltd.; *Int'l*, pg. 8661
ZHEJIANG ORIENT INTERNATIONAL TRANSPORT CO., LTD—See Zhejiang Orient Financial Holdings Group Co., Ltd.; *Int'l*, pg. 8661

ZHEJIANG SHIBAO COMPANY LIMITED

ZHEJIANG ORIENT JUNYE I/E CO., LTD.—See Zhejiang Orient Financial Holdings Group Co., Ltd.; *Int'l*, pg. 8661
ZHEJIANG ORIENT KNITEX I/E CO., LTD.—See Zhejiang Orient Financial Holdings Group Co., Ltd.; *Int'l*, pg. 8661
ZHEJIANG ORIENT KNITWEAR I/E CO., LTD.—See Zhejiang Orient Financial Holdings Group Co., Ltd.; *Int'l*, pg. 8661
ZHEJIANG ORIENT MULTITEX I/E CO., LTD.—See Zhejiang Orient Financial Holdings Group Co., Ltd.; *Int'l*, pg. 8661
ZHEJIANG ORIENT NEW HORIZON GARMENTS & ACCESSORIES I/E CO., LTD—See Zhejiang Orient Financial Holdings Group Co., Ltd.; *Int'l*, pg. 8661
ZHEJIANG ORIENT PENGLAI REAL ESTATE CO., LTD.—See Zhejiang Orient Financial Holdings Group Co., Ltd.; *Int'l*, pg. 8661
ZHEJIANG OTSUKA PHARMACEUTICAL CO., LTD.—See Otsuka Holdings Co., Ltd.; *Int'l*, pg. 5661
ZHEJIANG OZ OPTICS TECHNOLOGIES CO., LTD.—See OZ Optics Limted; *Int'l*, pg. 5679
ZHEJIANG PACIFIC MILLENNIUM PACKAGING & PAPER INDUSTRIES CO., LTD.—See Pacific Millennium Packaging Group Corporation; *Int'l*, pg. 5691
ZHEJIANG PEOPLE PUBLIC CULTURE CO., LTD.; *Int'l*, pg. 8661
ZHEJIANG PINGHU ICBC RURAL BANK CO., LTD.—See Industrial & Commercial Bank of China Limited; *Int'l*, pg. 3670
ZHEJIANG POLY. CO., LTD.—See Hainan Poly Pharm.Co.,Ltd.; *Int'l*, pg. 3212
ZHEJIANG PROVINCIAL NEW ENERGY INVESTMENT GROUP CO., LTD.; *Int'l*, pg. 8661
ZHEJIANG PU WEI LUN CHEMICALS CO., LTD.—See Proviron Holding N.V.; *Int'l*, pg. 6007
ZHEJIANG QIANJIANG BIOCHEMICAL CO., LTD.; *Int'l*, pg. 8661
ZHEJIANG QIANJIQNG MOTORCYCLE CO., LTD.; *Int'l*, pg. 8661
ZHEJIANG QUZHOU JUHUA SHOWA ELECTRONIC CHEMICAL MATERIALS CO., LTD.—See Resonac Holdings Corporation; *Int'l*, pg. 6301
ZHEJIANG RAYBOW PHARMACEUTICAL CO., LTD.—See Zhejiang Jiuzhou Pharmaceutical Co., Ltd.; *Int'l*, pg. 8658
ZHEJIANG REALSUN CHEMICAL CO., LTD.; *Int'l*, pg. 8661
ZHEJIANG RECLAIM CONSTRUCTION GROUP CO., LTD.; *Int'l*, pg. 8662
ZHEJIANG RED DRAGONFLY FOOTWEAR CO., LTD.; *Int'l*, pg. 8662
ZHEJIANG REFOND OPTOELECTRONICS CO., LTD.—See Shenzhen Refond Optoelectronics Co. Ltd.; *Int'l*, pg. 6820
ZHEJIANG RENZHI CO., LTD.; *Int'l*, pg. 8662
ZHEJIANG RICHLEO ENVIRONMETTAL TECHNOLOGY CO., LTD.—See Changzhou Tenglong Auto Parts Co., Ltd.; *Int'l*, pg. 1445
ZHEJIANG RIFA DIGITAL PRECISION MACHINERY CO., LTD.; *Int'l*, pg. 8662
ZHEJIANG RISUN INTELLIGENT TECHNOLOGY CO., LTD.; *Int'l*, pg. 8662
ZHEJIANG RONGSHENG PAPER INDUSTRY HOLDING CO., LTD.; *Int'l*, pg. 8662
ZHEJIANG RONGXIANG CHEMICAL FIBRE CO., LTD.—See Rongsheng Petro Chemical Co., Ltd.; *Int'l*, pg. 6397
ZHEJIANG RUIYUAN INTELLIGENT CONTROL TECHNOLOGY COMPANY LIMITED; *Int'l*, pg. 8662
ZHEJIANG RUNTU CO., LTD.; *Int'l*, pg. 8662
ZHEJIANG RUNYANG NEW MATERIAL TECHNOLOGY CO., LTD.; *Int'l*, pg. 8662
ZHEJIANG SANFER ELECTRIC CO., LTD.; *Int'l*, pg. 8662
ZHEJIANG SANHUA INTELLIGENT CONTROLS CO., LTD.; *Int'l*, pg. 8662
ZHEJIANG SANMEI CHEMICAL INDUSTRY CO., LTD.; *Int'l*, pg. 8662
ZHEJIANG SANXING NEW MATERIALS CO., LTD; *Int'l*, pg. 8662
ZHEJIANG SECOM SECURITY CO., LTD.—See SECOM Co., Ltd.; *Int'l*, pg. 6672
ZHEJIANG SEMIR GARMENT CO., LTD.; *Int'l*, pg. 8662
ZHEJIANG SHAGANG MATERIALS TRADE CO., LTD.—See Jiangsu Shagang Group Ltd.; *Int'l*, pg. 3954
ZHEJIANG SHAPUAISI PHARMACEUTICAL COMPANY LIMITED; *Int'l*, pg. 8662
ZHEJIANG SHENGDA BIOLOGICAL PHARMACEUTICAL CO., LTD.; *Int'l*, pg. 8663
ZHEJIANG SHENGHUA HOLDINGS CO., LTD.; *Int'l*, pg. 8663
ZHEJIANG SHENGLONG DECORATION MATERIAL CO., LTD.—See Shenglong Splendecor International Limited; *Int'l*, pg. 6802
ZHEJIANG SHENGYANG SCIENCE & TECHNOLOGY CO., LTD.; *Int'l*, pg. 8663
ZHEJIANG SHIBAO COMPANY LIMITED; *Int'l*, pg. 8663
ZHEJIANG SHIN-ETSU HIGH-TECH CHEMICAL CO., LTD.—See Shin-Etsu Chemical Co. Ltd.; *Int'l*, pg. 6841

ZHEJIANG SHOUXIANGU PHARMACEUTICAL CO., LTD.; *Int'l*, pg. 8663
ZHEJIANG SHUANGHUAN DRIVELINE CO., LTD.; *Int'l*, pg. 8663
ZHEJIANG SILICON PARADISE ASSET MANAGEMENT GROUP CO., LTD.—See Heaven-Sent Capital Management Group Co. Ltd.; *Int'l*, pg. 3305
ZHEJIANG SINTO ABRASIVE CO., LTD.—See Sintokogio Ltd.; *Int'l*, pg. 6959
ZHEJIANG SMITH SPECIAL PAPER CO., LTD.—See Shanghai Smith Adhesive New Material Co., Ltd.; *Int'l*, pg. 6779
ZHEJIANG SONGYUAN AUTOMOTIVE SAFETY SYSTEMS CO., LTD.; *Int'l*, pg. 8663
ZHEJIANG SOUTHEAST SPACE FRAME CO., LTD.; *Int'l*, pg. 8663
ZHEJIANG STARRY PHARMACEUTICAL CO., LTD.; *Int'l*, pg. 8663
ZHEJIANG SUNFLOWER GREAT HEALTH LIMITED LIABILITY COMPANY; *Int'l*, pg. 8663
ZHEJIANG SUNNY OPTICAL INTELLIGENCE TECHNOLOGY CO., LTD.—See Sunny Optical Technology (Group) Company Limited; *Int'l*, pg. 7319
ZHEJIANG SUNOREN SOLAR TECHNOLOGY CO., LTD.; *Int'l*, pg. 8663
ZHEJIANG SUPCON TECHNOLOGY CO., LTD.; *Int'l*, pg. 8663
ZHEJIANG SUPOR CO., LTD.; *Int'l*, pg. 8663
ZHEJIANG SUPOR ELECTRICAL APPLIANCES MANUFACTURING CO. LTD.—See SEB S.A.; *Int'l*, pg. 6668
ZHEJIANG TAIFU PUMP CO., LTD.; *Int'l*, pg. 8663
ZHE JIANG TAIHUA NEW MATERIAL CO., LTD.; *Int'l*, pg. 8648
ZHEJIANG TAILIN BIOENGINEERING CO., LTD.; *Int'l*, pg. 8663
ZHEJIANG TAITAN CO., LTD.; *Int'l*, pg. 8663
ZHEJIANG TALENT TELEVISION & FILM COMPANY LIMITED; *Int'l*, pg. 8664
ZHEJIANG TANCY ULTRASONIC TECHNOLOGY CO., LTD.—See Goldcard Smart Group Co., Ltd.; *Int'l*, pg. 3027
ZHEJIANG T.BEST ELECTRONIC INFORMATION TECHNOLOGY CO., LTD—See Zhejiang Crystal-optech Co., Ltd.; *Int'l*, pg. 8650
ZHEJIANG TENGEN ELECTRICS CO., LTD.; *Int'l*, pg. 8664
ZHEJIANG TENGY ENVIRONMENTAL TECHNOLOGY CO., LTD; *Int'l*, pg. 8664
ZHEJIANG TEXHONG TEXTILE CO., LTD.—See Texhong Textile Group Limited; *Int'l*, pg. 7584
ZHEJIANG TIANCHENG CONTROLS CO., LTD.; *Int'l*, pg. 8664
ZHEJIANG TIANNENG BATTERY CO., LTD.—See Tianneng Power International Limited; *Int'l*, pg. 7741
ZHEJIANG TIANTAI XIANGHE INDUSTRIAL CO., LTD.; *Int'l*, pg. 8664
ZHEJIANG TIANTIE INDUSTRY CO LTD; *Int'l*, pg. 8664
ZHEJIANG TIANYUAN BIO-PHARMACEUTICAL CO., LTD—See Novartis AG; *Int'l*, pg. 5461
ZHEJIANG TIANYU PHARMACEUTICAL CO., LTD.; *Int'l*, pg. 8664
ZHEJIANG TIANZHEN TECHNOLOGY CO., LTD.; *Int'l*, pg. 8664
ZHEJIANG TIELIU CLUTCH CO., LTD.; *Int'l*, pg. 8664
ZHEJIANG TONGLI TRANSMISSION TECHNOLOGY CO., LTD.; *Int'l*, pg. 8664
ZHEJIANG TONY ELECTRONIC CO., LTD.; *Int'l*, pg. 8664
ZHEJIANG TRUELOVE VOGUE CO., LTD.; *Int'l*, pg. 8664
ZHEJIANG TUNA ENVIRONMENTAL SCIENCE & TECHNOLOGY CO., LTD.; *Int'l*, pg. 8664
ZHEJIANG TUOSHAN MACHINERY CO., LTD.—See Anhui Tuoshan Heavy Industries Co., Ltd.; *Int'l*, pg. 470
ZHEJIANG TWINSEL ELECTRONIC TECHNOLOGY CO., LTD.—See Risen Energy Co., Ltd.; *Int'l*, pg. 6349
ZHEJIANG UNIFAN HI-TECHINDUSTRY CO., LTD.—See Zhejiang Unifull Industrial Fiber Co., Ltd.; *Int'l*, pg. 8664
ZHEJIANG UNIFULL INDUSTRIAL FIBER CO., LTD.; *Int'l*, pg. 8664
ZHEJIANG UNITED INVESTMENT HOLDINGS GROUP LIMITED; *Int'l*, pg. 8664
ZHEJIANG VIE SCIENCE & TECHNOLOGY CO., LTD.; *Int'l*, pg. 8665
ZHEJIANG VIEWSHINE INTELLGNT MTR CO LTD; *Int'l*, pg. 8665
ZHEJIANG WALRUS NEW MATERIAL CO., LTD.; *Int'l*, pg. 8665
ZHEJIANG WANDEKAI FLUID EQUIPMENT TECHNOLOGY CO., LTD.; *Int'l*, pg. 8665
ZHEJIANG WANFENG AUTO WHEEL CO., LTD.—See Wanfeng Auto Holding Group Co., Ltd.; *Int'l*, pg. 8340
ZHEJIANG WANLIYANG GROUP CO., LTD.; *Int'l*, pg. 8665
ZHEJIANG WANMA CABLE CO., LTD.; *Int'l*, pg. 8665
ZHEJIANG WANSHENG CO., LTD.—See 3SBio Inc.; *Int'l*, pg. 9
ZHEJIANG WANSHENG PHARMACEUTICAL CO., LTD.—See 3SBio Inc.; *Int'l*, pg. 9
ZHEJIANG WAZAM NEW MATERIALS GROUP CO., LTD.; *Int'l*, pg. 8665
ZHEJIANG WECOME PHARMACEUTICAL COMPANY LIMITED; *Int'l*, pg. 8665
ZHEJIANG WEIGANG TECHNOLOGY CO., LTD.; *Int'l*, pg. 8665
ZHEJIANG WEIMING ENVIRONMENT PROTECTION CO., LTD.; *Int'l*, pg. 8665
ZHEJIANG WEIXING INDUSTRIAL DEVELOPMENT CO., LTD.; *Int'l*, pg. 8665
ZHEJIANG WEIXING NEW BUILDING MATERIALS CO., LTD.; *Int'l*, pg. 8665
ZHEJIANG WEIYANG TECHNOLOGY CO., LTD.—See NetEase, Inc.; *Int'l*, pg. 5214
ZHEJIANG WELLSUN INTELLIGENT TECHNOLOGY CO., LTD.; *Int'l*, pg. 8665
ZHEJIANG WHYIS TECHNOLOGY CO., LTD.; pg. 8665
ZHEJIANG WINDEY CO., LTD.; *Int'l*, pg. 8665
ZHEJIANG WOLONG NEW ENERGY CO., LTD.—See Wolong Electric Group Co., Ltd.; *Int'l*, pg. 8443
ZHEJIANG WOLWO BIO-PHARMACEUTICAL COMPANY LIMITED; *Int'l*, pg. 8666
ZHEJIANG XCC GROUP CO.,LTD; *Int'l*, pg. 8666
ZHEJIANG XIANJU PHARMACEUTICAL CO., LTD.; *Int'l*, pg. 8666
ZHEJIANG XIANJU XIANLE PHARMACEUTICAL COMPANY LIMITED—See Grand Pharmaceutical Group Limited; *Int'l*, pg. 3056
ZHEJIANG XIANTONG RUBBER&PLASTIC CO LTD; *Int'l*, pg. 8666
ZHEJIANG XIDAMEN NEW MATERIAL CO., LTD.; *Int'l*, pg. 8666
ZHEJIANG XINAN CHEMICAL INDUSTRIAL GROUP CO., LTD.; *Int'l*, pg. 8666
ZHEJIANG XINAO TEXTILES INC.; *Int'l*, pg. 8666
ZHEJIANG XINCHAI CO.; *Int'l*, pg. 8666
ZHEJIANG XINDI REAL ESTATE CO., LTD.—See Zhejiang Orient Financial Holdings Group Co., Ltd.; *Int'l*, pg. 8661
ZHEJIANG XIN FENG MING CHEMICAL FIBER CO., LTD.—See Xinfengming Group Co., Ltd.; *Int'l*, pg. 8529
ZHEJIANG XIN FENG MING IMPORT & EXPORT CO., LTD.—See Xinfengming Group Co., Ltd.; *Int'l*, pg. 8529
ZHEJIANG XINGUANG PHARMACEUTICAL CO., LTD.; *Int'l*, pg. 8666
ZHEJIANG XINHUA CHEMICAL CO., LTD.; *Int'l*, pg. 8666
ZHEJIANG XINNONG CHEMICAL CO., LTD.; *Int'l*, pg. 8666
ZHEJIANG XIZI UNITED ENGINEERING CO., LTD.—See Xizi Clean Energy Equipment Manufacturing Co., Ltd.; *Int'l*, pg. 8535
ZHEJIANG YANGFAN NEW MATERIALS CO., LTD.; *Int'l*, pg. 8666
ZHEJIANG YANKON GROUP CO., LTD.; *Int'l*, pg. 8666
ZHEJIANG YANLI NEW MATERIALS CO., LTD.—See Yanpai Filtration Technology Co., Ltd.; *Int'l*, pg. 8564
ZHEJIANG YASHA DECORATION CO., LTD.; *Int'l*, pg. 8666
ZHEJIANG YATAI PHARMACEUTICAL CO., LTD.; *Int'l*, pg. 8666
ZHEJIANG YAYI METAL TECHNOLOGY CO., LTD.; *Int'l*, pg. 8667
ZHEJIANG YILIDA VENTILATOR CO., LTD.; *Int'l*, pg. 8667
ZHEJIANG YIMING FOOD CO., LTD.; *Int'l*, pg. 8667
ZHEJIANG YINGFENG TECHNOLOGY CO., LTD.; *Int'l*, pg. 8667
ZHEJIANG YINLUN MACHINERY CO., LTD.; *Int'l*, pg. 8667
ZHEJIANG YISHENG PETROCHEMICAL CO.,LTD.—See Rongsheng Petro Chemical Co., Ltd.; *Int'l*, pg. 6397
ZHEJIANG YONGAN RONGTONG HOLDING SHARES CO., LTD.; *Int'l*, pg. 8667
ZHEJIANG YONGGUI ELECTRIC EQUIPMENT CO., LTD.; *Int'l*, pg. 8667
ZHEJIANG YONGJIN METAL TECHNOLOGY CO., LTD.; *Int'l*, pg. 8667
ZHEJIANG YONGTAI TECHNOLOGY CO., LTD.; *Int'l*, pg. 8667
ZHEJIANG YOUNGMAN LOTUS AUTOMOBILE CO., LTD.—See China Youngman Automobile Group Co., Ltd.; *Int'l*, pg. 1565
ZHEJIANG YOUPON INTEGRATED CEILING COMPANY LIMITED; *Int'l*, pg. 8667
ZHEJIANG YUEJIAN INTELLIGENT EQUIPMENT CO., LTD.; *Int'l*, pg. 8667
ZHEJIANG YUELING COMPANY LIMITED; *Int'l*, pg. 8667
ZHEJIANG YUHUI SOLAR ENERGY SOURCE CO., LTD.—See EMEREN GROUP LTD; *U.S. Public*, pg. 739
ZHEJIANG YUSEI PLASTICS & MOULD CO.—See Yusei Holdings Ltd.; *Int'l*, pg. 8617
ZHEJIANG ZHAOFENG MECHANICAL & ELECTRONIC CO., LTD.; *Int'l*, pg. 8667
ZHEJIANG ZHAOLONG INTERCONNECT TECHNOLOGY CO., LTD.; *Int'l*, pg. 8668
ZHEJIANG ZHEDA INSIGMA GROUP CO., LTD.; *Int'l*, pg. 8668
ZHEJIANG ZHE KUANG HEAVY INDUSTRIES CO., LTD.; *Int'l*, pg. 8668
ZHEJIANG ZHENENG ELECTRIC POWER CO., LTD.; *Int'l*, pg. 8668
ZHEJIANG ZHENGGUANG INDUSTRIAL CO., LTD.; *Int'l*, pg. 8668
ZHEJIANG ZHENGTE CO., LTD.; *Int'l*, pg. 8668
ZHEJIANG ZHENGYUAN ZHIHUI TECHNOLOGY CO., LTD.; *Int'l*, pg. 8668
ZHEJIANG ZHENYUAN SHARE CO., LTD.; *Int'l*, pg. 8668
ZHEJIANG ZHONGCHENG PACKING MATERIAL CO., LTD.; *Int'l*, pg. 8668
ZHEJIANG ZHONGJIAN TECHNOLOGY CO., LTD.; *Int'l*, pg. 8668
ZHEJIANG ZHONGSHENG CHEMICAL CO., LTD.—See Zhejiang Longsheng Group Co., Ltd.; *Int'l*, pg. 8659
ZHEJIANG ZHONG SHUN PAPER INDUSTRY CO., LTD.—See C&S Paper Co., Ltd.; *Int'l*, pg. 1239
ZHEJIANG ZHONGXIN FLUORIDE MATERIALS CO., LTD.; *Int'l*, pg. 8668
ZHEJIANG ZHONGYU GAS CO., LTD.—See Zhongyu Energy Holdings Limited; *Int'l*, pg. 8676
ZHEJIANG ZOENN DESIGN CO., LTD.; *Int'l*, pg. 8668
ZHEJIANG ZOMAX TRANSMISSION CO., LTD.; *Int'l*, pg. 8668
ZHEJIANG ZUCH TECHNOLOGY CO., LTD.; *Int'l*, pg. 8668
ZHENA'S GYPSY TEA; *U.S. Private*, pg. 4603
ZHENDE MEDICAL CO., LTD.; *Int'l*, pg. 8669
ZHEN DING DEVELOPER INDIA PRIVATE LIMITED—See Zhen Ding Technology Holding Limited; *Int'l*, pg. 8669
ZHEN DING RESOURCES INC.; *Int'l*, pg. 8669
ZHEN DING TECHNOLOGY CO., LTD.—See Zhen Ding Technology Holding Limited; *Int'l*, pg. 8669
ZHEN DING TECHNOLOGY HOLDING LIMITED; *Int'l*, pg. 8669
ZHEN DING TECHNOLOGY INDIA PRIVATE LIMITED—See Zhen Ding Technology Holding Limited; *Int'l*, pg. 8669
ZHENENG JINJIANG ENVIRONMENT HOLDING COMPANY LIMITED; *Int'l*, pg. 8669
ZHENGHAI MAGNETICS EUROPE GMBH—See Yantai Zhenghai Magnetic Material Co., Ltd.; *Int'l*, pg. 8566
ZHENGHAI MAGNETICS KOREA CO., LTD.—See Yantai Zhenghai Magnetic Material Co., Ltd.; *Int'l*, pg. 8566
ZHENGHAI MAGNETICS NORTH AMERICA LLC—See Yantai Zhenghai Magnetic Material Co., Ltd.; *Int'l*, pg. 8566
ZHENGHE REAL ESTATE, INC.; *Int'l*, pg. 8669
ZHENG HSING INDUSTRIAL CO., LTD.; *Int'l*, pg. 8669
ZHENGJIANG WANSHENG PHARMACEUTICAL CO., LTD. - QINGSHAN PLANT—See 3SBio Inc.; *Int'l*, pg. 10
ZHENGJIANG WANSHENG PHARMACEUTICAL CO., LTD.—See 3SBio Inc.; *Int'l*, pg. 10
ZHENGPING ROAD & BRIDGE CONSTRUCTION CO., LTD; *Int'l*, pg. 8669
ZHENGWEI GROUP HOLDINGS COMPANY LIMITED; *Int'l*, pg. 8669
ZHENGXING WHEEL GROUP CO., LTD.—See Newrace Ltd.; *Int'l*, pg. 5236
ZHENGYE INTERNATIONAL HOLDINGS COMPANY LIMITED; *Int'l*, pg. 8669
ZHENGZHOU APPLE FOODS TECH CO., LTD.—See Apple Flavor & Fragrance Group Co., Ltd.; *Int'l*, pg. 520
ZHENGZHOU CHENG LOONG PACKING PRODUCTS CO., LTD.—See Cheng Loong Corp.; *Int'l*, pg. 1466
ZHENGZHOU CHINA RESOURCES GAS CO., LTD.—See China Resources (Holdings) Co., Ltd.; *Int'l*, pg. 1548
ZHENGZHOU COAL INDUSTRY & ELECTRIC POWER CO., LTD.; *Int'l*, pg. 8669
ZHENGZHOU COAL MINING MACHINERY GROUP CO., LTD.; *Int'l*, pg. 8670
ZHENGZHOU CTS INTERNATIONAL LOGISTICS CORPORATION LIMITED—See CTS International Logistics Corporation Limited; *Int'l*, pg. 1874
ZHENGZHOU DEHENG HONGSHENG TECHNOLOGY CO., LTD.; *Int'l*, pg. 8670
ZHENGZHOU DINGWO AUTOMOBILE SALES SERVICES CO., LTD.—See China ZhengTong Auto Services Holdings Limited; *Int'l*, pg. 1567
ZHENGZHOU GRID ELECTRIC INTELLIGENT TECHNOLOGY COMPANY—See Troy Information Technology Co., Ltd.; *Int'l*, pg. 7940
ZHENGZHOU HUASHENG PETROLEUM PRODUCTS CO. LTD.—See Shanghai Dasheng Agriculture Finance Technology Co., Ltd.; *Int'l*, pg. 6764
ZHENGZHOU HUITE REFRACTORIES CO., LTD.—See Puyang Refractories Group Co., Ltd.; *Int'l*, pg. 6124
ZHENGZHOU J & T HI-TECH CO., LTD.; *Int'l*, pg. 8670
ZHENGZHOU NISSAN AUTOMOBILE CO., LTD.—See Nissan Motor Co., Ltd.; *Int'l*, pg. 5370
ZHENGZHOU POLY INTERNATIONAL CINEMA—See China Poly Group Corporation; *Int'l*, pg. 1541
ZHENGZHOU SENYUAN NEW ENERGY TECHNOLOGY CO., LTD.—See HENAN SENYUAN ELECTRIC CO., LTD.; *Int'l*, pg. 3343
ZHENGZHOU SINO-CRYSTAL DIAMOND CO., LTD.; *Int'l*, pg. 8670
ZHENGZHOU TIAMAES TECHNOLOGY CO., LTD.; *Int'l*, pg. 8670

COMPANY NAME INDEX — ZHONGXING TIANHENG ENERGY TECHNOLOGY (BEIJING) CO., LTD.

ZHENGZHOU XINGANG CONTAINER CO., LTD—See Zhuhai Zhongfu Enterprise Co., Ltd.; *Int'l*, pg. 8679
ZHENGZHOU YONGDA HEXIE AUTOMOBILE SALES AND SERVICES CO., LTD.—See China Yongda Automobiles Services Holdings Limited; *Int'l*, pg. 1565
ZHENHAI PETROCHEMICAL ENGINEERING CO., LTD.—See China Petrochemical Corporation; *Int'l*, pg. 1540
ZHENHUA LOGISTICS GROUP CO., LTD.—See China Communications Construction Company Limited; *Int'l*, pg. 1491
ZHENJIANG AUCHAN HYPERMARKETS CO., LTD.—See Alibaba Group Holding Limited; *Int'l*, pg. 326
ZHENJIANG BELL TEXTRON AVIATION SERVICES LIMITED—See Textron Inc.; *U.S. Public*, pg. 2029
ZHENJIANG CHIMEI CHEMICAL CO., LTD.—See Chi Mei Group; *Int'l*, pg. 1475
ZHENJIANG DAQO EATON ELECTRICAL SYSTEMS COMPANY LIMITED—See Eaton Corporation plc; *Int'l*, pg. 2281
ZHENJIANG DONGFANG ELECTRIC HEATING TECHNOLOGY CO., LTD.; *Int'l*, pg. 8670
ZHENJIANG EMTRON SURFACE TREATMENT LIMITED COMPANY—See LemTech Holdings Co., Ltd.; *Int'l*, pg. 4451
ZHENJIANG LCY WAREHOUSING & STORAGE CO., LTD.—See KKR & Co. Inc.; *U.S. Public*, pg. 1258
ZHENJIANG LEE CHANG YUNG GENERAL CHEMICAL CO., LTD.—See KKR & Co. Inc.; *U.S. Public*, pg. 1258
ZHENJIANG NANTEX CHEMICAL INDUSTRY CO., LTD.—See NANTEX Industry Co., Ltd.; *Int'l*, pg. 5145
ZHENJIANG NEW UNIVERSE SOLID WASTE DISPOSAL COMPANY LIMITED—See New Universe Environmental Group Limited; *Int'l*, pg. 5229
ZHENJIANG REN DE NEW ENERGY TECHNOLOGY CO., LTD.—See Suntech Power Holdings Co., Ltd.; *Int'l*, pg. 7325
ZHENJIANG RIETECH NEW ENERGY SCIENCE TECHNOLOGY CO., LTD.—See Suntech Power Holdings Co., Ltd.; *Int'l*, pg. 7325
ZHENJIANG SHAGANG MATERIALS TRADE CO., LTD.—See Jiangsu Shagang Group Co.; *Int'l*, pg. 3954
ZHENJIANG SINOTECH ECO-ELECTROPLATING DEVELOPMENT LIMITED—See New Universe Environmental Group Limited; *Int'l*, pg. 5229
ZHENJIANG TONGZHOU PROPELLER CO., LTD.—See Fullshare Holdings Limited; *Int'l*, pg. 2843
ZHENJIANG ZHONG CHUAN HITACHI ZOSEN MACHINERY CO., LTD—See Hitachi Zosen Corporation; *Int'l*, pg. 3412
ZHENLAI CDB VILLAGE BANK CO., LTD.—See China Development Bank Corporation; *Int'l*, pg. 1497
ZHENRO PROPERTIES GROUP LIMITED; *Int'l*, pg. 8670
ZHENRO SERVICES GROUP LIMITED; *Int'l*, pg. 8670
ZHENSHI HOLDING GROUP CO., LTD.; *Int'l*, pg. 8670
ZHENZHOU SENYUAN NEW ENERGY TECHNOLOGY CO., LTD.—See HENAN SENYUAN ELECTRIC CO., LTD.; *Int'l*, pg. 3343
ZHERDEVSKY SUGAR—See Gruppa Kompaniy Rusagro OOO; *Int'l*, pg. 3140
ZHERMACK GMBH—See DENTSPLY SIRONA Inc.; *U.S. Public*, pg. 656
ZHERMACK S.P.A.—See DENTSPLY SIRONA Inc.; *U.S. Public*, pg. 654
ZHERMAPOL SP ZOO—See DENTSPLY SIRONA Inc.; *U.S. Public*, pg. 654
ZHESHANG ASSET MANAGEMENT CO., LTD.—See Zheshang Securities Co., Ltd.; *Int'l*, pg. 8670
ZHESHANG DEVELOPMENT GROUP CO., LTD.; *Int'l*, pg. 8670
ZHESHANG SECURITIES CO., LTD.; *Int'l*, pg. 8670
ZHEWEN INTERACTIVE GROUP CO LTD; *Int'l*, pg. 8670
ZHEWEN PICTURES GROUP CO., LTD.; *Int'l*, pg. 8671
ZHF (USA), INC.; *U.S. Private*, pg. 4603
ZHIDAO INTERNATIONAL (HOLDINGS) LIMITED; *Int'l*, pg. 8671
ZHIHU INC.; *Int'l*, pg. 8671
ZHIMING SOFTWARE DALIAN, LTD.—See Nomura Research Institute, Ltd.; *Int'l*, pg. 5413
ZHIMING SOFTWARE JAPAN, LTD.—See Nomura Research Institute, Ltd.; *Int'l*, pg. 5413
ZHIMING SOFTWARE JILIN, LTD.—See Nomura Research Institute, Ltd.; *Int'l*, pg. 5413
ZHI SHENG GROUP HOLDINGS LIMITED; *Int'l*, pg. 8671
ZHIXIN GROUP HOLDING LIMITED; *Int'l*, pg. 8671
ZHIYANG INNOVATION TECHNOLOGY CO., LTD.; *Int'l*, pg. 8671
ZHONE TECHNOLOGIES S. DE R.L. DE C.V.—See DZS Inc.; *U.S. Public*, pg. 701
ZHONG AN GROUP LIMITED; *Int'l*, pg. 8671
ZHONGAN ONLINE P & C INSURANCE CO., LTD.; *Int'l*, pg. 8672
ZHONG'AN XIAOXULONG ELECTRONIC TECHNOLOGY CO., LTD.—See China Security Co., Ltd.; *Int'l*, pg. 1550
ZHONG AO HOME GROUP LIMITED; *Int'l*, pg. 8671
ZHONGBAI HOLDINGS GROUP CO., LTD.; *Int'l*, pg. 8672
ZHONGBAN TRADE SHANGHAI CO., LTD.—See Cominix Co., Ltd.; *Int'l*, pg. 1714

ZHONGBAN TRADING (SHANGHAI) CO., LTD.—See Cominix Co., Ltd.; *Int'l*, pg. 1714
ZHONGBAO INTERNATIONAL, INC.; *Int'l*, pg. 8672
ZHONGCHANG BIG DATA CO., LTD.; *Int'l*, pg. 8672
ZHONGCHANG INTERNATIONAL HOLDINGS GROUP LIMITED; *Int'l*, pg. 8672
ZHONGCHAO INC.; *Int'l*, pg. 8672
ZHONGCHUANG ENVIRONMENTAL PROTECTION (XINJIANG) TECHNOLOGY CO., LTD.—See Xiamen Zhongchuang Environmental Technology Co., Ltd.; *Int'l*, pg. 8526
ZHONGCHUANG SHIPS MANAGEMENT CO., LTD.—See China Master Logistics Co., Ltd.; *Int'l*, pg. 1518
ZHONG DA ENTERPRISE CORP.—See Taisei Corporation; *Int'l*, pg. 7416
ZHONGDA GREEN VALLEY INDUSTRY CO., LTD.—See MYS Group Co., Ltd.; *Int'l*, pg. 5114
ZHONGDA INTERNATIONAL HOLDINGS LIMITED; *Int'l*, pg. 8672
ZHONGDE WASTE TECHNOLOGY AG; *Int'l*, pg. 8672
ZHONGDING SEALING PARTS (USA), INC.—See Anhui Zhongding Holding (Group) Co., Ltd.; *Int'l*, pg. 470
ZHONGDING U.S.A., INC.—See Anhui Zhongding Holding (Group) Co., Ltd.; *Int'l*, pg. 470
ZHONGFU INFORMATION, INC.; *Int'l*, pg. 8672
ZHONGFU STRAITS (PINGTAN) DEVELOPMENT CO., LTD.; *Int'l*, pg. 8673
ZHONG FU TONG GROUP CO., LTD; *Int'l*, pg. 8672
ZHONGGUANCUN SCIENCE-TECH LEASING CO., LTD.; *Int'l*, pg. 8673
ZHONGGUO PENGJIE FABRICS LIMITED; *Int'l*, pg. 8673
ZHONGHANG ELECTRONIC MEASURING INSTRUMENTS CO., LTD.; *Int'l*, pg. 8673
ZHONGHAO ALKALI INDUSTRY CO., LTD.—See China National Chemical Corporation; *Int'l*, pg. 1527
ZHONGHE CO., LTD.; *Int'l*, pg. 8673
ZHONGHONG HOLDING CO., LTD.; *Int'l*, pg. 8673
ZHONGHONG PULIN GROUP CO., LTD.—See Xiamen ITG Holding Group Co., Ltd.; *Int'l*, pg. 8525
ZHONGHONG PULIN MEDICAL PRODUCTS CO., LTD.; *Int'l*, pg. 8673
ZHONGHUA GAS HOLDINGS LIMITED; *Int'l*, pg. 8673
ZHONG HUA INTERNATIONAL HOLDINGS LIMITED; *Int'l*, pg. 8672
ZHONGJIE (JIANGSU) TECHNOLOGY CO., LTD.; *Int'l*, pg. 8673
ZHONGJI INNOLIGHT CO., LTD.; *Int'l*, pg. 8673
ZHONG JI LONGEVITY SCIENCE GROUP LTD.; *Int'l*, pg. 8672
ZHONGJING FOOD CO., LTD.; *Int'l*, pg. 8673
ZHONGJIN GOLD CORPORATION LIMITED; *Int'l*, pg. 8673
ZHONGJIN IRRADIATION INCORPORATED COMPANY; *Int'l*, pg. 8673
ZHONG KE SAN HUAN YU XIAN JINGXIU MAGNETIC MATERIALS INC., LTD—See Beijing Zhong Ke San Huan High-tech Co., Ltd.; *Int'l*, pg. 961
ZHONGKUANG ZAMBIA SERVICES COMPANY LIMITED—See Sinomine Resource Group Co., Ltd.; *Int'l*, pg. 6953
ZHONGLAN WOCO (MA ANSHAN) RUBBER & PLASTIC PRODUCTS CO., LTD.—See Woco Industrietechnik GmbH; *Int'l*, pg. 8442
ZHONGLIANG HOLDINGS GROUP COMPANY LIMITED; *Int'l*, pg. 8673
ZHONGLU (GROUP) CO., LTD.; *Int'l*, pg. 8673
ZHONGMAN PETROLEUM & NATURAL GAS GROUP CORP., LTD.; *Int'l*, pg. 8673
ZHONGMIN BAIHUI RETAIL GROUP LTD.; *Int'l*, pg. 8674
ZHONGMIN ENERGY CO., LTD.; *Int'l*, pg. 8674
ZHONGNAN RED CULTURAL GROUP CO., LTD.; *Int'l*, pg. 8674
ZHONGNONGFA SEED INDUSTRY GROUP CO., LTD.; *Int'l*, pg. 8674
ZHONGPIN INC.; *Int'l*, pg. 8674
ZHONGRUN ECONOMIC DEVELOPMENT CO., LTD.—See China Cinda Asset Management Co., Ltd.; *Int'l*, pg. 1488
ZHONGRUN RESOURCES INVESTMENT CORPORATION; *Int'l*, pg. 8674
ZHONGSHAN BIO-TECH CO., LTD.—See Da An Gene Co., Ltd.; *Int'l*, pg. 1901
ZHONGSHAN BROAD-OCEAN MOTOR CO., LTD.; *Int'l*, pg. 8674
ZHONG SHAN CHANGHONG ELECTRIC CO., LTD—See Sichuan Changhong Electric Co., Ltd.; *Int'l*, pg. 6877
ZHONGSHAN CHANGJIANG ZHAOYE REAL ESTATE DEVELOPMENT LTD.—See Kowloon Development Company Limited; *Int'l*, pg. 4295
ZHONGSHAN CITY RIDA FINE CHEMICAL CO., LTD.—See Mandom Corporation; *Int'l*, pg. 4668
ZHONGSHAN COILS METALWORK CO., LTD.—See CEC International Holdings Ltd.; *Int'l*, pg. 1372
ZHONGSHAN COLIBRI AUTOMATION CO., LTD.—See Shenzhen Colibri Technologies Co., Ltd.; *Int'l*, pg. 6807
ZHONGSHAN DIC COLOUR CO., LTD.—See DIC Corporation; *Int'l*, pg. 2111
ZHONG SHAN ENOMOTO CO. LTD.—See Enomoto Co., Ltd.; *Int'l*, pg. 2444

ZHONGSHAN FOCI FIBER OPTIC COMMUNICATIONS, INC.—See Foci Fiber Optic Communications, Inc.; *Int'l*, pg. 2718
ZHONGSHAN FULFIL TECH CO., LTD.—See Syncmold Enterprise Corp.; *Int'l*, pg. 7382
ZHONGSHAN HUALI PACKAGING CO., LTD.—See Overseas Chinese Town (Asia) Holdings Limited; *Int'l*, pg. 5672
ZHONGSHAN HUNG HING PRINTING & PACKAGING COMPANY LIMITED—See Hung Hing Printing Group Limited; *Int'l*, pg. 3535
ZHONG SHAN KUNITAKARA ELECTRIC LTD.—See Ya Horng Electronic Co., Ltd.; *Int'l*, pg. 8544
ZHONGSHAN LONGSHENG COLVA AUTO CO., LTD.—See Zhejiang Longsheng Group Co., Ltd.; *Int'l*, pg. 8659
ZHONGSHAN LONWALK MOULD PLASTIC CO., LTD.—See Yi Hua Holdings Limited; *Int'l*, pg. 8581
ZHONGSHAN MYRRA ELECTRONIC CO., LTD.—See discoverIE Group plc; *Int'l*, pg. 2134
ZHONGSHAN MYS ENVIRONMENTAL PROTECTION & TECHNOLOGY COMPANY LTD.—See MYS Group Co., Ltd.; *Int'l*, pg. 5114
ZHONGSHAN NAM HING INSULATING MATERIAL LIMITED—See China Environmental Energy Investment Limited; *Int'l*, pg. 1500
ZHONGSHAN NEW ASIA ADHESIVE PRODUCTS CO., LTD—See Luxking Group Holdings Limited; *Int'l*, pg. 4589
ZHONGSHAN NISSIN INDUSTRY CO., LTD.—See Honda Motor Co., Ltd.; *Int'l*, pg. 3463
ZHONGSHAN PRESIDENT ENTERPRISES CO., LTD.—See Uni-President Enterprises Corporation; *Int'l*, pg. 8029
ZHONGSHAN PUBLIC UTILITIES GROUP CO., LTD.; *Int'l*, pg. 8674
ZHONGSHAN RUIKE NEW ENERGY CO., LTD.—See China Ming Yang Wind Power Group Limited; *Int'l*, pg. 1524
ZHONGSHAN SAITECH ENGINEERING PLASTICS CO., LTD.—See Guangdong Sunwill Precising Plastic Co., Ltd.; *Int'l*, pg. 3161
ZHONGSHAN SCHLEMMER AUTOMOTIVE PARTS CO., LTD.—See Ningbo Huaxiang Electronic Co., Ltd.; *Int'l*, pg. 5302
ZHONGSHAN SUMIDEN HYBRID PRODUCTS CO. LTD.—See Sumitomo Electric Industries, Ltd.; *Int'l*, pg. 7285
ZHONGSHAN SUMIRUBBER PRECISION RUBBER LTD.—See Sumitomo Rubber Industries, Ltd.; *Int'l*, pg. 7300
ZHONGSHAN TAT CHUN PRINTED CIRCUIT BOARD COMPANY LIMITED—See China Silver Technology; *Int'l*, pg. 1552
ZHONGSHAN UNIROSS INDUSTRY CO. LIMITED—See Eveready Industries India Ltd; *Int'l*, pg. 2563
ZHONGSHAN UNIVERSAL ENTERPRISES LTD—See Aliaxis S.A./N.V.; *Int'l*, pg. 325
ZHONGSHAN VOLTRONIC POWER ELECTRONIC LIMITED—See Voltronic Power Technology Corporation; *Int'l*, pg. 8304
ZHONGSHAN ZHIHE ELECTRICAL EQUIPMENT CO., LTD.—See Sunningdale Tech Ltd; *Int'l*, pg. 7318
ZHONGSHAN ZHONGYUE TINPLATE INDUSTRIAL CO. LTD—See GDH Limited; *Int'l*, pg. 2896
ZHONGSHE M&E IMPORT & EXPORT CO., LTD.—See China Machinery Engineering Corporation; *Int'l*, pg. 1516
ZHONGSHENG GROUP HOLDINGS LIMITED; *Int'l*, pg. 8674
ZHONGSHI MINAN HOLDINGS LIMITED; *Int'l*, pg. 8675
ZHONG TAI ELECTRONICS (HUBEI) CO., LTD.—See Song Shang Electronics Co., Ltd.; *Int'l*, pg. 7095
ZHONGTAI FINANCIAL INTERNATIONAL LIMITED—See Zhongtai Securities Co., Ltd.; *Int'l*, pg. 8675
ZHONGTAI FUTURES COMPANY LIMITED; *Int'l*, pg. 8675
ZHONGTAI SECURITIES CO., LTD.; *Int'l*, pg. 8675
ZHONGTIAN CONSTRUCTION (HUNAN) GROUP LIMITED; *Int'l*, pg. 8675
ZHONGTIAN FINANCIAL GROUP COMPANY LIMITED; *Int'l*, pg. 8675
ZHONGTIAN SERVICE CO., LTD.; *Int'l*, pg. 8675
ZHONGTONG BUS & HOLDING CO., LTD.; *Int'l*, pg. 8675
ZHONGTONGGUOMAI COMMUNICATION CO LTD; *Int'l*, pg. 8675
ZHONGWANG FABRIC CO., LTD.; *Int'l*, pg. 8675
ZHONGXIANG PANLONG MEAT PROCESSING CO., LTD.—See China Yurun Food Group Limited; *Int'l*, pg. 1566
ZHONGXIN CHUANGZHI (BEIJING) TECHNOLOGY LTD., CO.—See Addvalue Technologies Ltd.; *Int'l*, pg. 136
ZHONGXIN FRUIT & JUICE LIMITED—See SDIC Zhonglu Fruit Juice Co., Ltd.; *Int'l*, pg. 6658
ZHONGXING SHENYANG COMMERCIAL BUILDING GROUP CO., LTD.; *Int'l*, pg. 8675
ZHONGXING TIANHENG ENERGY TECHNOLOGY (BEIJING) CO., LTD.; *Int'l*, pg. 8675

ZHONG XU ARCHITECTURE DESIGN CO., LTD.—See China Architecture Design & Research Group; *Int'l*, pg. 1483
ZHONG YA INTERNATIONAL LTD; *U.S. Public*, pg. 2403
ZHONG YANG TECHNOLOGY CO., LTD.; *Int'l*, pg. 8672
ZHONGYAN TECHNOLOGY CO., LTD.; *Int'l*, pg. 8675
ZHONGYE CHANGTIAN INTERNATIONAL ENGINEERING CO., LTD.—See China Rare Earth Resources And Technology Co., Ltd.; *Int'l*, pg. 1545
ZHONGYEDA ELECTRIC COMPANY LIMITED; *Int'l*, pg. 8675
ZHONGYIN BABI FOOD CO., LTD.; *Int'l*, pg. 8675
ZHONGYING DENTSU TEC ADVERTISING CO., LTD.—See Dentsu Group Inc.; *Int'l*, pg. 2038
ZHONGYUAN BANK CO., LTD.; *Int'l*, pg. 8676
ZHONG YUAN BIO-TECHNOLOGY HOLDINGS LIMITED; *Int'l*, pg. 8672
ZHONGYUAN UNION CELL & GENE ENGINEERING CORP.; *Int'l*, pg. 8676
ZHONGYUAN XIANGDA CAMEL FEED CO., LTD.—See Tangrenshen Group Co., Ltd.; *Int'l*, pg. 7458
ZHONGYU CITY ENERGY INVESTMENT HOLDINGS (SHENZHEN) CO., LTD.—See Zhongyu Energy Holdings Limited; *Int'l*, pg. 8676
ZHONGYU ENERGY HOLDINGS LIMITED; *Int'l*, pg. 8675
ZHONGYUE POSCO (QINHUANGDAO) TINPLATE INDUSTRIAL CO., LIMITED—See GDH Limited; *Int'l*, pg. 2896
ZHONGYU (HENAN) ENERGY TRADING CO., LTD.—See Zhongyu Energy Holdings Limited; *Int'l*, pg. 8676
ZHONG YUNG (INTERNATIONAL) CHEMICAL CO., LIMITED—See BRENNTAG SE; *Int'l*, pg. 1150
ZHONGZAI RESOURCES AND ENVIRONMENT CO., LTD.; *Int'l*, pg. 8676
ZHONGZHENG INTERNATIONAL COMPANY LIMITED; *Int'l*, pg. 8676
ZHONGZHI NEW ENERGY VEHICLE COMPANY LIMITED—See ZHEJIANG KANGSHENG CO., LTD.; *Int'l*, pg. 8659
ZHONGZHI PHARMACEUTICAL HOLDINGS LTD.; *Int'l*, pg. 8677
ZHONG ZHU HEALTHCARE HOLDING CO., LTD.; *Int'l*, pg. 8672
ZHOU HEI YA INTERNATIONAL HOLDINGS COMPANY LIMITED; *Int'l*, pg. 8677
ZHOUKOU XIANGDA CAMEL FEED CO., LTD.—See Tangrenshen Group Co., Ltd.; *Int'l*, pg. 7458
ZHOUSHAN DALING SEAFOOD CO., LTD.—See Mitsubishi Corporation; *Int'l*, pg. 4943
ZHOUSHAN NIPPON PUSNES SHIP MACHINERY CO., LTD.—See Hitachi Zosen Corporation; *Int'l*, pg. 3412
ZHRH CORPORATION; *U.S. Public*, pg. 2403
ZHUANGHE CITY AOXIN DAWEI DENTAL CO., LTD.—See Aoxin Q & M Dental Group Limited; *Int'l*, pg. 498
ZHUBO DESIGN CO., LTD.; *Int'l*, pg. 8677
ZHUCHENG ETERNAL KNITTING CO., LIMITED—See Greatime International Holdings Limited; *Int'l*, pg. 3067
ZHUDING INTERNATIONAL LTD.; *Int'l*, pg. 8677
ZHUGUANG HOLDINGS GROUP COMPANY LIMITED; *Int'l*, pg. 8677
ZHUHAI AEROSPACE MICROCHIPS SCIENCE AND TECHNOLOGY CO., LTD.; *Int'l*, pg. 8677
ZHUHAI AIRLINES COMPANY LIMITED—See China Southern Airlines Co., Ltd.; *Int'l*, pg. 1553
ZHUHAI ALLFAVOR ELECTRONIC CO., LTD.—See Jiangsu Allfavor Intelligent Circuits Technology Co., Ltd.; *Int'l*, pg. 3943
ZHUHAI BAOZE AUTOMOBILE SALES SERVICES CO., LTD.—See China ZhengTong Auto Services Holdings Limited; *Int'l*, pg. 1567
ZHUHAI BOJAY ELECTRONICS CO., LTD.; *Int'l*, pg. 8677
ZHUHAI BROTHER INDUSTRIES, LTD.—See Brother Industries, Ltd.; *Int'l*, pg. 1198
ZHUHAI CHERRY ELECTRONICS CO., LTD.—See Cherry SE; *Int'l*, pg. 1472
ZHUHAI CHINA INTERNATIONAL TRAVEL SERVICE CO., LTD.—See China Tourism Group Duty Free Corporation Limited; *Int'l*, pg. 1560
ZHUHAI COSLIGHT BATTERY CO., LTD.—See Coslight Technology International Group Limited; *Int'l*, pg. 1810
ZHUHAI COSLIGHT ELECTRIC TECHNOLOGY CO., LTD.—See Coslight Technology International Group Limited; *Int'l*, pg. 1810
ZHUHAI CRESTEC HUAGUANG ELECTRONICS TECHNOLOGY CO., LTD.—See Crestec Inc.; *Int'l*, pg. 1841
ZHUHAI DAVID ELECTRONICS CO., LTD.—See Chant Sincere Co., Ltd.; *Int'l*, pg. 1446
ZHUHAI ENPOWER ELECTRIC CO., LTD.; *Int'l*, pg. 8677
ZHUHAI GAOPING ELECTRONIC TECHNOLOGY DEVELOPMENT CO., LTD.—See Shenzhen Keanda Electronic Technology Corp., Ltd.; *Int'l*, pg. 6815
ZHUHAI GOLDPAC SECURCARD CO. LTD—See Thales S.A.; *Int'l*, pg. 7600
ZHUHAI GREE DAIKIN DEVICE CO., LTD.—See Daikin Industries, Ltd.; *Int'l*, pg. 1937
ZHUHAI HERALD DATANETICS LIMITED—See Herald Holdings Limited; *Int'l*, pg. 3358

ZHUHAI HOKAI MEDICAL INSTRUMENTS CO., LTD.; *Int'l*, pg. 8677
ZHUHAI HOLDINGS INVESTMENT GROUP LIMITED; *Int'l*, pg. 8677
ZHUHAI HOLIDAY RESORT HOTEL CO., LTD.—See Zhuhai Holdings Investment Group Limited; *Int'l*, pg. 8677
ZHUHAI HOT-FILL CONTAINER CO., LTD—See Zhuhai Zhongfu Enterprise Co., Ltd.; *Int'l*, pg. 8679
ZHUHAI HUAFA GROUP CO., LTD; *Int'l*, pg. 8677
ZHUHAI INTERNATIONAL CIRCUIT LIMITED—See LBS Bina Group Berhad; *Int'l*, pg. 4430
ZHUHAI JIAHENG DAILY CHEMICAL CO., LTD.—See Jahen Household Products Co., Ltd.; *Int'l*, pg. 3871
ZHUHAI JUTAL OFFSHORE OIL SERVICES COMPANY LIMITED—See Jutal Offshore Oil Services Limited; *Int'l*, pg. 4031
ZHUHAI KAIBANG MOTOR MANUFACTURE CO., LTD.—See Gree Electric Appliances, Inc. of Zhuhai; *Int'l*, pg. 3069
ZHUHAI KEANDA TECHOLOGY DEVELOPMENT CO., LTD.—See Shenzhen Keanda Electronic Technology Corp., Ltd.; *Int'l*, pg. 6815
ZHUHAI KELI ELECTRONIC CO., LTD.—See China Keli Electric Company Ltd.; *Int'l*, pg. 1514
ZHUHAI KINDLY MEDICAL DEVICES CO., LTD—See Shanghai Kindly Enterprise Development Group Co., Ltd; *Int'l*, pg. 6774
ZHUHAI LETONG NEW MATERIALS & TECHNOLOGY CO., LTD.—See Letong Chemical Co., Ltd.; *Int'l*, pg. 4470
ZHUHAI LIVZON DIAGNOSTICS INC.; *Int'l*, pg. 8677
ZHUHAI LUCKYSTAR ELECTRONICS CO., LTD.—See China Security Co., Ltd.; *Int'l*, pg. 1550
ZHUHAI MAOYE DEPARTMENT STORE CO., LTD.—See Maoye International Holding Limited; *Int'l*, pg. 4681
ZHUHAI MEIDONG LEXUS AUTO SALES & SERVICES CO., LTD.—See China MeiDong Auto Holdings Limited; *Int'l*, pg. 1519
ZHUHAI MITSUMI ELECTRIC CO., LTD.—See Minebea Mitsumi Inc.; *Int'l*, pg. 4904
ZHUHAI MPM FILTER LTD.—See Mitsubishi Paper Mills Limited; *Int'l*, pg. 4967
ZHU HAI OPLINK COMMUNICATIONS, INC—See Koch Industries, Inc.; *U.S. Private*, pg. 2335
ZHUHAI PORT CO., LTD.; *Int'l*, pg. 8677
ZHUHAI RAYSHARP TECHNOLOGY CO., LTD.; *Int'l*, pg. 8677
ZHUHAI RONGTAI PRECISION DIE CASTING CO., LTD.—See Jiangsu Rongtai Industry Co., Ltd.; *Int'l*, pg. 3953
ZHUHAI ROSSINI GLASSES INDUSTRY LIMITED—See Citychamp Watch & Jewellery Group Limited; *Int'l*, pg. 1629
ZHUHAI ROSSINI WATCH INDUSTRY LIMITED—See Citychamp Watch & Jewellery Group Limited; *Int'l*, pg. 1629
ZHUHAI RUNDU PHARMACEUTICAL CO., LTD.; *Int'l*, pg. 8677
ZHUHAI SAILONG PHARMACEUTICAL CO., LTD.; *Int'l*, pg. 8678
ZHUHAI SCAS AUTOMOBILE SALES SERVICES CO., LTD.—See China ZhengTong Auto Services Holdings Limited; *Int'l*, pg. 1567
ZHUHAI SCHWARZ PHARMA COMPANY LTD—See UCB S.A.; *Int'l*, pg. 8012
ZHUHAI SEINE TECHNOLOGY CO., LTD.; *Int'l*, pg. 8678
ZHUHAI S.E.Z. VIDEOJET ELECTRONICS LTD.—See Danaher Corporation; *U.S. Public*, pg. 632
ZHUHAI SHENGLONG BAR CODE TECHNOLOGY CO., LTD.—See Guangdong Guanhao High-Tech Co., Ltd.; *Int'l*, pg. 3155
ZHUHAI SINDOPOWER ELECTRONICS COMPANY LIMITED—See SEMIKRON International GmbH; *Int'l*, pg. 6705
ZHUHAI SINGYES CURTAIN WALL ENGINEERING CO., LTD.—See China Shuifa Singyes Energy Holdings Limited; *Int'l*, pg. 1551
ZHUHAI SINGYES NEW MATERIALS TECHNOLOGY CO. LTD.—See China Singyes New Materials Holdings Limited; *Int'l*, pg. 1552
ZHUHAI SINGYES RENEWABLE ENERGY TECHNOLOGY CO., LTD.—See China Shuifa Singyes Energy Holdings Limited; *Int'l*, pg. 1551
ZHUHAI SOLVAY SPECIALTY CHEMICALS CO., LTD.—See Solvay S.A.; *Int'l*, pg. 7082
ZHUHAI SUMIKA POLYMER COMPOUNDS CO., LTD.—See Sumitomo Chemical Company, Limited; *Int'l*, pg. 7267
ZHUHAI TOMITA ELECTRONICS LTD.—See Tomita Electric Co., Ltd.; *Int'l*, pg. 7800
ZHUHAI TOYO COLOR CO., LTD.—See Toyo Ink SC Holdings Co., Ltd.; *Int'l*, pg. 7855
ZHUHAI TOYO INK CO., LTD.—See Toyo Ink SC Holdings Co., Ltd.; *Int'l*, pg. 7855
ZHUHAI UNITED LABORATORIES CO., LTD.—See The United Laboratories International Holdings Ltd.; *Int'l*, pg. 7697

ZHUHAI UNITED LABORATORIES HOLDING LTD—See The United Laboratories International Holdings Ltd.; *Int'l*, pg. 7697
ZHUHAI UNITED LABORATORIES TRADING COMPANY LIMITED—See The United Laboratories International Holdings Ltd.; *Int'l*, pg. 7698
ZHUHAI UNITED LABORATORIES (ZHONGSHAN) CO., LTD.—See The United Laboratories International Holdings Ltd.; *Int'l*, pg. 7697
ZHUHAI WANLIDA ELECTRICAL AUTOMATION CO., LTD.—See Zhuhai Seine Technology Co., Ltd.; *Int'l*, pg. 8678
ZHUHAI WINBASE INTERNATIONAL CHEMICAL TANK TERMINAL CO., LTD.; *Int'l*, pg. 8678
ZHUHAI XIANG YI AVIATION TECHNOLOGY COMPANY LIMITED—See China Southern Airlines Co., Ltd.; *Int'l*, pg. 1553
ZHUHAI XUJIZHI POWER SYSTEM AUTOMATION CO. LTD.—See Japan Industrial Partners, Inc.; *Int'l*, pg. 3898
ZHUHAI ZHONGFU ENTERPRISE CO., LTD. - MEITU LABEL FACTORY—See Zhuhai Zhongfu Enterprise Co., Ltd.; *Int'l*, pg. 8679
ZHUHAI ZHONGFU ENTERPRISE CO., LTD.; *Int'l*, pg. 8678
ZHUHAI ZHONGFU HOT-FILL BOTTLES CO. LTD—See Zhuhai Zhongfu Enterprise Co., Ltd.; *Int'l*, pg. 8679
ZHUJI FURUN MECHANICAL SPRING CO., LTD.—See Zhejiang Furun Digital Technology Co., Ltd.; *Int'l*, pg. 8652
ZHUJI ROSHOW ELECTROMAGNETIC WIRE CO., LTD.—See Roshow Technology Co., Ltd.; *Int'l*, pg. 6401
ZHUJI YAOJIANG NEW CENTURY HOTEL CO., LTD.—See Zhejiang New Century Hotel Management Co., Ltd.; *Int'l*, pg. 8660
ZHULIAN CORPORATION BERHAD; *Int'l*, pg. 8679
ZHULIAN INDUSTRIES SDN. BHD.—See Zhulian Corporation Berhad; *Int'l*, pg. 8679
ZHULIAN (THAILAND) LTD.—See Zhulian Corporation Berhad; *Int'l*, pg. 8679
ZHUMADIAN CIMC HUAJUN VEHICLE CO.,LTD—See China International Marine Containers (Group) Co., Ltd.; *Int'l*, pg. 1513
ZHUMADIAN CIMC HUAJUN VEHICLE TRADING CO., LTD—See China International Marine Containers (Group) Co., Ltd.; *Int'l*, pg. 1513
ZHUOXIN INTERNATIONAL HOLDINGS LIMITED; *Int'l*, pg. 8679
ZHUZHOU CEMENTED CARBIDE CUTTING TOOLS CO., LTD.—See Hunan Nonferrous Metals Corporation Ltd.; *Int'l*, pg. 3533
ZHUZHOU CEMENTED CARBIDE GROUP HONGKONG CO. LTD.—See Hunan Nonferrous Metals Corporation Ltd.; *Int'l*, pg. 3533
ZHUZHOU CEMENTED CARBIDE WORKS IMPORT & EXPORT COMPANY—See Hunan Nonferrous Metals Corporation Ltd.; *Int'l*, pg. 3533
ZHUZHOU CEMENTED CARBIDE WORKS USA INC.—See Hunan Nonferrous Metals Corporation Ltd.; *Int'l*, pg. 3533
ZHUZHOU CRRC TIMES ELECTRIC CO. LTD.; *Int'l*, pg. 8679
ZHUZHOU EUREKA NONFERROUS EQUIPMENT CO., LTD.—See Zhuzhou Tianqiao Crane Co., Ltd.; *Int'l*, pg. 8680
ZHUZHOU FEILU HIGH-TECH MATERIALS CO., LTD.; *Int'l*, pg. 8679
ZHUZHOU HONGDA ELECTRONICS CORP., LTD.; *Int'l*, pg. 8679
ZHUZHOU HUARUI PRECISION CUTTING TOOLS CO., LTD.; *Int'l*, pg. 8679
ZHUZHOU HUASHENG TECHNOLOGY CO., LTD.—See Endress+Hauser (International) Holding AG; *Int'l*, pg. 2409
ZHUZHOU INNOPOWER TECHNOLOGY CO., LTD.—See Shenzhen Megmeet Electrical Co.,Ltd; *Int'l*, pg. 6818
ZHUZHOU KIBING GROUP CO., LTD.; *Int'l*, pg. 8679
ZHUZHOU MEGMEET ELECTRIC CO., LTD—See Shenzhen Megmeet Electrical Co.,Ltd; *Int'l*, pg. 6818
ZHUZHOU MEIBAOHANG AUTO SALES & SERVICES CO., LTD.—See China MeiDong Auto Holdings Limited; *Int'l*, pg. 1519
ZHUZHOU SMELTER GROUP CO., LTD.; *Int'l*, pg. 8680
ZHUZHOU STATE-OWNED ASSET INVESTMENT HOLDING GROUP CO., LTD.; *Int'l*, pg. 8680
ZHUZHOU TIANQIAO CRANE CO., LTD.; *Int'l*, pg. 8680
ZHUZHOU TIANQIAO CRANE FITTINGS MANUFACTURING CO.—See Zhuzhou Tianqiao Crane Co., Ltd.; *Int'l*, pg. 8680
ZHUZHOU TIANQIAO OLYMPJOY ICE TECHNOLOGY CO., LTD.—See Zhuzhou Tianqiao Crane Co., Ltd.; *Int'l*, pg. 8680
ZHUZHOU TIANQIAO SHUNCHEN COAL PREPARATION MACHINERY CO.—See Zhuzhou Tianqiao Crane Co., Ltd.; *Int'l*, pg. 8680
ZHUZHOU TIMES NEW MATERIAL TECHNOLOGY CO., LTD.; *Int'l*, pg. 8680

COMPANY NAME INDEX

ZHUZHOU TORCH SPARKPLUGS CO., LTD.—See Shandong Heavy Industry Group Co., Ltd.; *Int'l*, pg. 6754
ZHUZHOU WAVELANE TECHNOLOGY CO., LTD.—See Shenzhen Megmeet Electrical Co.,Ltd; *Int'l*, pg. 6818
ZHYTOMYRSKY BUTTER PLANT, PJSC; *Int'l*, pg. 8680
ZIA BROADCASTING COMPANY—See Allsup Enterprises Inc.; *U.S. Private*, pg. 194
ZIA ENGINEERING & ENVIRONMENTAL CONSULTANTS, LLC; *U.S. Private*, pg. 4603
ZIAG IMMOBILIEN AG—See Zublin Immobilien Holding AG; *Int'l*, pg. 8692
ZIAG PLANT ENGINEERING GMBH—See GEA Group Aktiengesellschaft; *Int'l*, pg. 2898
ZI-ARGUS AUSTRALIA PTY LTD—See The Zuellig Group Inc.; *Int'l*, pg. 7705
ZI-ARGUS LTD.—See ATS Corporation; *Int'l*, pg. 695
ZIAROMAT A.S.—See Zeleziarne Podbrezova a.s.; *Int'l*, pg. 8631
ZIATH B.V.—See Azenta, Inc.; *U.S. Public*, pg. 258
ZIATH LTD.—See Azenta, Inc.; *U.S. Public*, pg. 258
ZIBAO METALS RECYCLING HOLDINGS PLC; *Int'l*, pg. 8680
ZIBO AGC ALUMINA MATERIALS CO., LTD.—See AGC Inc.; *Int'l*, pg. 204
ZIBO ASAHI GLASS ALUMINA MATERIALS CO., LTD.—See AGC Inc.; *Int'l*, pg. 204
ZIBO FERRO PERFORMANCE MATERIALS COMPANY, LIMITED—See American Securities LLC; *U.S. Private*, pg. 253
ZIBO JINJING NEW ENERGY CO., LTD.—See Shandong Jinjing Science & Technology Co., Ltd.; *Int'l*, pg. 6755
ZIBO LIANCHENG TEXTILES & GARMENTS CO., LTD.—See Medtecs International Corporation Limited; *Int'l*, pg. 4786
ZIBO LIANHENG TEXTILES CO., LTD.—See Medtecs International Corporation Limited; *Int'l*, pg. 4786
ZIBO QIXIANG TENGDA CHEMICAL CO., LTD.; *Int'l*, pg. 8680
ZIBO SHUANGFENG SHANSHUI CEMENT CO., LTD.—See China Shanshui Cement Group Ltd.; *Int'l*, pg. 1550
ZIBRANT LIMITED—See BCD Holdings N.V.; *Int'l*, pg. 926
ZIBUYU GROUP LIMITED; *Int'l*, pg. 8680
ZICAM LLC—See Gryphon Investors, LLC; *U.S. Private*, pg. 1799
ZICCUM AB, *Int'l*, pg. 8080
ZICIX CORP.; *U.S. Public*, pg. 2403
ZICO AA SDN. BHD.—See Zico Holdings Inc.; *Int'l*, pg. 8681
ZICO CAPITAL PTE. LTD.—See Zico Holdings Inc.; *Int'l*, pg. 8681
ZICO CORPORATE SERVICES PTE. LTD.—See Zico Holdings Inc.; *Int'l*, pg. 8681
ZICO CORPORATE SERVICES SDN. BHD.—See Zico Holdings Inc.; *Int'l*, pg. 8681
ZICO HOLDINGS INC.; *Int'l*, pg. 8680
ZICOINSOURCE SDN. BHD.—See Zico Holdings Inc.; *Int'l*, pg. 8681
ZICOLAW (LAOS) SOLE CO., LTD.—See Zico Holdings Inc.; *Int'l*, pg. 8681
ZICOLAW MYANMAR LIMITED—See Zico Holdings Inc.; *Int'l*, pg. 8681
ZICOM CESCO ENGINEERING COMPANY LIMITED—See Zicom Group Limited; *Int'l*, pg. 8681
ZICOM ELECTRONIC SECURITY SYSTEMS LTD; *Int'l*, pg. 8681
ZICOM GROUP LIMITED; *Int'l*, pg. 8681
ZICOM PRIVATE LTD.—See Daikin Industries, Ltd.; *Int'l*, pg. 1937
ZICOM RETAIL PRODUCTS PRIVATE LIMITED—See Zicom Electronic Security Systems Ltd; *Int'l*, pg. 8681
ZICO SHARIAH ADVISORY SERVICES SDN. BHD.—See Zico Holdings Inc.; *Int'l*, pg. 8681
ZICO TRUST LIMITED—See Zico Holdings Inc.; *Int'l*, pg. 8681
ZICO TRUST (S) LTD.—See Zico Holdings Inc.; *Int'l*, pg. 8681
ZICUIMEX FRANCE, S.A.R.L—See Iberpapel Gestion SA; *Int'l*, pg. 3574
ZICUPAP, S.A.—See Iberpapel Gestion SA; *Int'l*, pg. 3574
ZICURO TECHNOLOGIES PRIVATE LIMITED—See ABans Enterprises Limited; *Int'l*, pg. 48
ZIDANE CAPITAL CORP.; *Int'l*, pg. 8681
ZIEBART INTERNATIONAL CORPORATION; *U.S. Private*, pg. 4603
ZIEBART JAPAN LIMITED—See Ziebart International Corporation; *U.S. Private*, pg. 4603
ZIEBART OKINAWA CO. LTD—See Ziebart International Corporation; *U.S. Private*, pg. 4603
ZIEGELMUNDSTUCKBAU BRAUN GMBH; *Int'l*, pg. 8681
ZIEGER & SONS INC.; *U.S. Private*, pg. 4603
ZIEGLER BOLT & PARTS CO.; *U.S. Private*, pg. 4603
ZIEGLER CAPITAL MANAGEMENT, LLC—See Stifel Financial Corp.; *U.S. Public*, pg. 1950
ZIEGLER CAPITAL MARKETS GROUP—See The Ziegler Companies, Inc.; *U.S. Private*, pg. 4140
ZIEGLER CHEMICAL & MINERAL CORPORATION; *U.S. Private*, pg. 4604
THE ZIEGLER COMPANIES, INC.; *U.S. Private*, pg. 4140

ZIEGLER & CO.—See The Ziegler Companies, Inc.; *U.S. Private*, pg. 4140
ZIEGLER INC. - ALTOONA—See Ziegler Inc.; *U.S. Private*, pg. 4604
ZIEGLER INC.; *U.S. Private*, pg. 4604
ZIEGLER LUMBER COMPANY; *U.S. Private*, pg. 4604
ZIEGLER TIRE & SUPPLY COMPANY, INC.; *U.S. Private*, pg. 4604
ZIEGLER TOOLS INC.—See MSCO Inc.; *U.S. Private*, pg. 2806
ZIEHM IMAGING AUSTRIA GMBH—See ATON GmbH; *Int'l*, pg. 689
ZIEHM IMAGING FINNLAND (OY)—See ATON GmbH; *Int'l*, pg. 689
ZIEHM IMAGING GMBH—See ATON GmbH; *Int'l*, pg. 689
ZIEHM IMAGING INC.—See ATON GmbH; *Int'l*, pg. 689
ZIEHM IMAGING SARL—See ATON GmbH; *Int'l*, pg. 689
ZIEHM IMAGING SA—See ATON GmbH; *Int'l*, pg. 689
ZIEHM IMAGING SINGAPORE PTE. LTD.—See ATON GmbH; *Int'l*, pg. 689
ZIEHM IMAGING SPAIN S.L.U.—See ATON GmbH; *Int'l*, pg. 689
ZIEHM IMAGING SRL—See ATON GmbH; *Int'l*, pg. 689
ZIEHM MEDICAL DO BRASIL—See ATON GmbH; *Int'l*, pg. 689
ZIEHM MEDICAL LLC—See ATON GmbH; *Int'l*, pg. 689
ZIEHM MEDICAL (SHANGHAI) CO. LTD.—See ATON GmbH; *Int'l*, pg. 689
ZIEMAN MANUFACTURING COMPANY—See LCI Industries; *U.S. Public*, pg. 1295
ZIEMANN HOLVRIEKA A/S—See China International Marine Containers (Group) Co., Ltd.; *Int'l*, pg. 1511
ZIEMANN HOLVRIEKA B.V.—See China International Marine Containers (Group) Co., Ltd.; *Int'l*, pg. 1511
ZIEMANN HOLVRIEKA GMBH—See China International Marine Containers (Group) Co., Ltd.; *Int'l*, pg. 1511
ZIEMANN HOLVRIEKA INTERNATIONAL B.V.—See China International Marine Containers (Group) Co., Ltd.; *Int'l*, pg. 1511
ZIEMANN HOLVRIEKA N.V.—See China International Marine Containers (Group) Co., Ltd.; *Int'l*, pg. 1511
ZIEMS FORD CORNERS, INC.; *U.S. Private*, pg. 4604
ZIENGS SCHOENEN BV; *Int'l*, pg. 8681
ZIETA TECHNOLOGIES LLC; *U.S. Private*, pg. 4604
ZIFF DAVIS B2B FOCUS, INC.—See Ziff Davis, Inc.; *U.S. Public*, pg. 2404
ZIFF DAVIS ENTERPRISE, INC.; *U.S. Private*, pg. 4604
ZIFF DAVIS, INC.; *U.S. Public*, pg. 2403
ZIFF DAVIS, LLP—See Ziff Davis, Inc.; *U.S. Public*, pg. 2404
ZIF FIMA SEE ACTIVIST A.D.; *Int'l*, pg. 8681
ZIFTY COM, INC.; *U.S. Private*, pg. 4604
ZIGA INNOVATION PCL; *Int'l*, pg. 8681
ZIGEXN CO., LTD.; *Int'l*, pg. 8682
ZIGEXN VENTURA CO., LTD.—See ZIGExN Co., Ltd.; *Int'l*, pg. 8682
ZIGGO B.V.—See Liberty Global plc; *Int'l*, pg. 4486
ZIGGO GROUP HOLDING BV—See Liberty Global plc; *Int'l*, pg. 4486
ZIGGO SERVICES EMPLOYMENT B.V.—See Liberty Global plc; *Int'l*, pg. 4486
ZIGMAN JOSEPH PR; *U.S. Private*, pg. 4604
ZIG.MARKETING; *U.S. Private*, pg. 4604
ZIGNAGO GLASS USA INC.—See Zignago Vetro S.p.A.; *Int'l*, pg. 8682
ZIGNAGO VETRO BROSSE SAS—See Zignago Vetro S.p.A.; *Int'l*, pg. 8682
ZIGNAGO VETRO POLSKA SA—See Zignago Vetro S.p.A.; *Int'l*, pg. 8682
ZIGNAGO VETRO S.p.A.; *Int'l*, pg. 8682
ZIGNEGO COMPANY, INCORPORATED; *U.S. Private*, pg. 4604
ZIGNEGO READY MIX INC.; *U.S. Private*, pg. 4604
ZIGNSEC AB; *Int'l*, pg. 8682
ZIGONG SEDIVER TOUGHENED GLASS INSULATOR CO., LTD.—See Seves S.p.A.; *Int'l*, pg. 6736
ZIG SHENG INDUSTRIAL CO., LTD.; *Int'l*, pg. 8681
ZIGUP PLC; *Int'l*, pg. 8682
ZIJA INTERNATIONAL, INC.—See Isagenix International, LLC; *U.S. Private*, pg. 2143
ZIJING INTERNATIONAL FINANCIAL HOLDINGS LIMITED; *Int'l*, pg. 8683
ZIJIN MINING GROUP COMPANY LIMITED; *Int'l*, pg. 8683
ZIJIN XIANGYU (LONGYAN) LOGISTICS CO., LTD.—See Zijin Mining Group Company Limited; *Int'l*, pg. 8683
ZIJTVELD GRIJPERS B.V.—See Indutrade AB; *Int'l*, pg. 3682
ZI KALTUMFORMUNG GMBH—See Heckler AG; *Int'l*, pg. 3307
ZIK ENERGY POINTS INC.—See COFRA Holding AG; *Int'l*, pg. 1694
ZILBER LTD.; *U.S. Private*, pg. 4604
ZILBERT REALTY GROUP—See Brown Harris Stevens, LLC; *U.S. Private*, pg. 667
ZILIS, LLC; *U.S. Private*, pg. 4604
ZILKER TECHNOLOGY LLC; *U.S. Private*, pg. 4604
ZILLER ELECTRIC INC.; *U.S. Private*, pg. 4604
ZILLIANT, INC.; *U.S. Private*, pg. 4604

ZIMMER BIOMET HOLDINGS, INC.

ZIL LIMITED; *Int'l*, pg. 8683
ZILLION TECHNOLOGIES; *U.S. Private*, pg. 4605
ZILLIOUS SOLUTIONS PRIVATE LIMITED—See Ebix Inc.; *U.S. Public*, pg. 710
ZILLOW GROUP, INC.; *U.S. Public*, pg. 2404
ZILLOW GROUP MARKETPLACE, INC.—See Zillow Group, Inc.; *U.S. Public*, pg. 2405
ZILLOW GROUP MORTGAGES, INC.—See Zillow Group, Inc.; *U.S. Public*, pg. 2405
ZILLOW, INC.—See Zillow Group, Inc.; *U.S. Public*, pg. 2405
ZILLTEK TECHNOLOGY CORP.; *Int'l*, pg. 8683
ZILOG INC.—See Littelfuse, Inc.; *U.S. Public*, pg. 1327
ZILOR ENERGIA E ALIMENTOS LTDA. - QUATA PRODUCTION UNIT—See Zilor Energia e Alimentos Ltda.; *Int'l*, pg. 8683
ZILOR ENERGIA E ALIMENTOS LTDA.; *Int'l*, pg. 8683
ZIM AMERICAN INTEGRATED SHIPPING CO INC—See Israel Corporation Ltd.; *Int'l*, pg. 3823
ZIM-AMERICAN ISRAELI SHIPPING CO.—See Israel Corporation Ltd.; *Int'l*, pg. 3823
ZIMAT CONSULTORES—See The Interpublic Group of Companies, Inc.; *U.S. Public*, pg. 2094
ZIMAT-WEBER SHANDWICK—See The Interpublic Group of Companies, Inc.; *U.S. Public*, pg. 2106
ZIM AUSTRIA GMBH—See Israel Corporation Ltd.; *Int'l*, pg. 3823
ZIMBABWE ELECTRICITY SUPPLY AUTHORITY; *Int'l*, pg. 8684
ZIMBABWE FERTILIZER COMPANY LIMITED (ZFC)—See Masawara PLC; *Int'l*, pg. 4720
ZIMBABWE LEAF TOBACCO COMPANY (PRIVATE) LIMITED—See Universal Corporation; *U.S. Public*, pg. 2254
ZIMBABWE NEWSPAPERS (1980) LIMITED; *Int'l*, pg. 8684
ZIMBABWE PLATINUM MINES (PVT) LIMITED—See Impala Platinum Holdings Limited; *Int'l*, pg. 3631
ZIMBABWE STOCK EXCHANGE; *Int'l*, pg. 8684
ZIM BELGIUM NV—See Israel Corporation Ltd.; *Int'l*, pg. 3823
ZIMBO CZECHIA S.R.O.—See Coop-Gruppe Genossenschaft; *Int'l*, pg. 1790
ZIMBO FLEISCH- UND WURSTWAREN GMBH & CO. KG—See Coop-Gruppe Genossenschaft; *Int'l*, pg. 1790
ZIMBO HUSIPARI TERMELO KFT.—See Coop-Gruppe Genossenschaft; *Int'l*, pg. 1790
ZIMBRA EUROPE LIMITED—See Centre Lane Partners, LLC; *U.S. Private*, pg. 827
ZIMBRA SOFTWARE, LLC—See Centre Lane Partners, LLC; *U.S. Private*, pg. 827
ZIMBRICK INC.; *U.S. Private*, pg. 4605
ZIM CORPORATION; *Int'l*, pg. 8683
ZIMDAR ENTERPRISES; *U.S. Private*, pg. 4605
ZIM D.D. ZENICA; *Int'l*, pg. 8683
ZIM FLUGSITZE GMBH—See Aurelius Equity Opportunities SE & Co. KGaA; *Int'l*, pg. 710
ZIM FRANCE S.A.—See Israel Corporation Ltd.; *Int'l*, pg. 3823
ZIM GERMANY GMBH—See Israel Corporation Ltd.; *Int'l*, pg. 3823
ZIMI; *Int'l*, pg. 8684
ZIM INDUSTRIES INC.; *U.S. Private*, pg. 4605
ZIM INTEGRATED SHIPPING SERVICES HELLAS S.A.—See Israel Corporation Ltd.; *Int'l*, pg. 3823
ZIM INTEGRATED SHIPPING SERVICES, LTD.—See Israel Corporation Ltd.; *Int'l*, pg. 3823
ZIM INTEGRATED SHIPPING SERVICE (TAIWAN) CO., LTD.—See Israel Corporation Ltd.; *Int'l*, pg. 3823
ZIM LABORATORIES LIMITED; *Int'l*, pg. 8683
ZIMMER AUSTRALIA HOLDING PTY. LTD.—See Zimmer Biomet Holdings, Inc.; *U.S. Public*, pg. 2406
ZIMMER AUSTRIA GMBH—See Zimmer Biomet Holdings, Inc.; *U.S. Public*, pg. 2406
ZIMMER BIOMET AUSTRIA GMBH—See Zimmer Biomet Holdings, Inc.; *U.S. Public*, pg. 2406
ZIMMER BIOMET BVBA—See Zimmer Biomet Holdings, Inc.; *U.S. Public*, pg. 2406
ZIMMER BIOMET BVBA—See Zimmer Biomet Holdings, Inc.; *U.S. Public*, pg. 2407
ZIMMER BIOMET CANADA, INC.—See Zimmer Biomet Holdings, Inc.; *U.S. Public*, pg. 2407
ZIMMER BIOMET CMF & THORACIC, LLC—See Zimmer Biomet Holdings, Inc.; *U.S. Public*, pg. 2407
ZIMMER BIOMET DENMARK APS—See Zimmer Biomet Holdings, Inc.; *U.S. Public*, pg. 2407
ZIMMER BIOMET DENTAL CANADA INC.—See Zimmer Biomet Holdings, Inc.; *U.S. Public*, pg. 2407
ZIMMER BIOMET DENTAL K.K.—See Zimmer Biomet Holdings, Inc.; *U.S. Public*, pg. 2407
ZIMMER BIOMET DEUTSCHLAND GMBH—See Zimmer Biomet Holdings, Inc.; *U.S. Public*, pg. 2407
ZIMMER BIOMET FINLAND OY—See Zimmer Biomet Holdings, Inc.; *U.S. Public*, pg. 2407
ZIMMER BIOMET FRANCE SAS—See Zimmer Biomet Holdings, Inc.; *U.S. Public*, pg. 2407
ZIMMER BIOMET GK—See Zimmer Biomet Holdings, Inc.; *U.S. Public*, pg. 2407
ZIMMER BIOMET HOLDINGS, INC.; *U.S. Public*, pg. 2405

ZIMMER BIOMET HOLDINGS, INC.

CORPORATE AFFILIATIONS

ZIMMER BIOMET ITALIA SRL—See Zimmer Biomet Holdings, Inc.; *U.S. Public*, pg. 2407
ZIMMER BIOMET KOREA CO., LTD.—See Zimmer Biomet Holdings, Inc.; *U.S. Public*, pg. 2407
ZIMMER BIOMET NEDERLAND B.V.—See Zimmer Biomet Holdings, Inc.; *U.S. Public*, pg. 2407
ZIMMER BIOMET NEW ZEALAND COMPANY—See Zimmer Biomet Holdings, Inc.; *U.S. Public*, pg. 2407
ZIMMER BIOMET NORWAY AS—See Zimmer Biomet Holdings, Inc.; *U.S. Public*, pg. 2407
ZIMMER BIOMET POLSKA SP. Z.O.O.—See Zimmer Biomet Holdings, Inc.; *U.S. Public*, pg. 2407
ZIMMER BIOMET PORTUGAL UNIPESSOAL, LDA.—See Zimmer Biomet Holdings, Inc.; *U.S. Public*, pg. 2407
ZIMMER BIOMET PTY. LTD.—See Zimmer Biomet Holdings, Inc.; *U.S. Public*, pg. 2407
ZIMMER BIOMET SOUTH AFRICA (PTY) LTD.—See Zimmer Biomet Holdings, Inc.; *U.S. Public*, pg. 2407
ZIMMER BIOMET SPAIN S.L.—See Zimmer Biomet Holdings, Inc.; *U.S. Public*, pg. 2407
ZIMMER BIOMET SPINE, LLC—See H.I.G. Capital, LLC; *U.S. Private*, pg. 1834
ZIMMER BIOMET SPINE—See H.I.G. Capital, LLC; *U.S. Private*, pg. 1834
ZIMMER BIOMET SWEDEN AB—See Zimmer Biomet Holdings, Inc.; *U.S. Public*, pg. 2407
ZIMMER BIOMET UK LTD.—See Zimmer Biomet Holdings, Inc.; *U.S. Public*, pg. 2407
ZIMMER CEP USA, INC.—See Zimmer Biomet Holdings, Inc.; *U.S. Public*, pg. 2407
ZIMMER CIS LTD.—See Zimmer Biomet Holdings, Inc.; *U.S. Public*, pg. 2407
ZIMMER CZECH SRO—See Zimmer Biomet Holdings, Inc.; *U.S. Public*, pg. 2407
ZIMMER DENTAL CHILE SPA—See Zimmer Biomet Holdings, Inc.; *U.S. Public*, pg. 2407
ZIMMER DENTAL DO BRASIL PARTICIPACOES LTDA.—See Zimmer Biomet Holdings, Inc.; *U.S. Public*, pg. 2407
ZIMMER DENTAL ITALY SRL—See Zimmer Biomet Holdings, Inc.; *U.S. Public*, pg. 2407
ZIMMER DENTAL LTD.—See Zimmer Biomet Holdings, Inc.; *U.S. Public*, pg. 2407
ZIMMER DENTAL SAS—See Zimmer Biomet Holdings, Inc.; *U.S. Public*, pg. 2407
ZIMMER DENTAL SWEDEN AB—See Zimmer Biomet Holdings, Inc.; *U.S. Public*, pg. 2407
ZIMMER DO BRASIL COMERCIO LTDA.—See Zimmer Biomet Holdings, Inc.; *U.S. Public*, pg. 2408
ZIMMER ENERGY TRANSITION ACQUISITION CORP.; *U.S. Public*, pg. 2408
ZIMMER GERMANY HOLDINGS GMBH—See Zimmer Biomet Holdings, Inc.; *U.S. Public*, pg. 2407
ZIMMER GMBH—See Zimmer Biomet Holdings, Inc.; *U.S. Public*, pg. 2407
ZIMMER GUNSUL FRASCA PARTNERSHIP; *U.S. Private*, pg. 4605
ZIMMER, INC.—See Zimmer Biomet Holdings, Inc.; *U.S. Public*, pg. 2408
ZIMMER INDIA PRIVATE LTD.—See Zimmer Biomet Holdings, Inc.; *U.S. Public*, pg. 2407
ZIMMER INVESTMENTS, LLC—See Zimmer Biomet Holdings, Inc.; *U.S. Public*, pg. 2407
ZIMMER KNEE CREATIONS, INC.—See Zimmer Biomet Holdings, Inc.; *U.S. Public*, pg. 2407
ZIMMERLI MESSTECHNIK AG—See Yokogawa Electric Corporation; *Int'l*, pg. 8595
ZIMMER LUCAS CAPITAL LLC; *U.S. Private*, pg. 4605
ZIMMERLUND & CO.—See Amcor plc; *Int'l*, pg. 418
ZIMMERMAN ADVERTISING LLC - CHICAGO—See Omnicom Group Inc.; *U.S. Public*, pg. 1600
ZIMMERMAN ADVERTISING LLC - LOS ANGELES—See Omnicom Group Inc.; *U.S. Public*, pg. 1600
ZIMMERMAN ADVERTISING LLC - NEW YORK—See Omnicom Group Inc.; *U.S. Public*, pg. 1600
ZIMMERMAN ADVERTISING LLC—See Omnicom Group Inc.; *U.S. Public*, pg. 1600
THE ZIMMERMAN AGENCY LLC; *U.S. Private*, pg. 4140
ZIMMERMAN ARCHITECTURAL STUDIOS, INC.; *U.S. Private*, pg. 4605
ZIMMERMAN ASSOCIATES INC.; *U.S. Private*, pg. 4605
ZIMMERMAN- AUER FUNERAL HOME, INC.—See Service Corporation International; *U.S. Public*, pg. 1872
ZIMMERMAN FORD, INC.; *U.S. Private*, pg. 4605
THE ZIMMERMAN GROUP; *U.S. Private*, pg. 4140
ZIMMERMAN HOLDING COMPANY; *U.S. Private*, pg. 4605
ZIMMERMAN-MCDONALD MACHINERY, INC.; *U.S. Private*, pg. 4605
ZIMMERMAN & JANSEN GMBH—See RHI Magnesita N.V.; *Int'l*, pg. 6326
ZIMMERMANN & JANSEN, INC.—See IMI plc; *Int'l*, pg. 3627
ZIMMERMANN & JANSEN, S.A. (PTY.) LTD.—See IMI plc; *Int'l*, pg. 3627
ZIMMER MANUFACTURING B.V.—See Zimmer Biomet Holdings, Inc.; *U.S. Public*, pg. 2407
ZIMMER MEDICAL MALAYSIA SDN BHD—See Zimmer Biomet Holdings, Inc.; *U.S. Public*, pg. 2407

ZIMMER MEDICAL (THAILAND) CO., LTD.—See Zimmer Biomet Holdings, Inc.; *U.S. Public*, pg. 2407
ZIMMER MEDIZINSYSTEME GMBH; *Int'l*, pg. 8684
ZIMMER MOTORS, INC.; *U.S. Private*, pg. 4605
ZIMMER PTE. LTD.—See Zimmer Biomet Holdings, Inc.; *U.S. Public*, pg. 2407
ZIMMER (SHANGHAI) MEDICAL INTERNATIONAL TRADING CO., LTD.—See Zimmer Biomet Holdings, Inc.; *U.S. Public*, pg. 2406
ZIMMER STAAL BVBA—See Pisec Group GmbH; *Int'l*, pg. 5876
ZIMMER SURGICAL, INC.—See Zimmer Biomet Holdings, Inc.; *U.S. Public*, pg. 2407
ZIMMER SURGICAL—See Zimmer Biomet Holdings, Inc.; *U.S. Public*, pg. 2407
ZIMMER TRABECULAR METAL TECHNOLOGY, INC.—See Zimmer Biomet Holdings, Inc.; *U.S. Public*, pg. 2407
ZIMMER US, INC.—See Zimmer Biomet Holdings, Inc.; *U.S. Public*, pg. 2407
ZIMMER WHEATON PONTAIC-BUICK-GMC LTD.; *Int'l*, pg. 8684
ZIMMITE TAIWAN LTD.; *Int'l*, pg. 8684
ZIMNAT LIFE ASSURANCE COMPANY LTD.—See Masawara PLC; *Int'l*, pg. 4720
ZIMNAT LION INSURANCE COMPANY LTD.—See SanJam Limited; *Int'l*, pg. 6545
ZIM NETHERLANDS B.V.—See Israel Corporation Ltd.; *Int'l*, pg. 3823
ZIMPA A.D.; *Int'l*, pg. 8684
ZIMPLATS HOLDINGS LIMITED—See Impala Platinum Holdings Limited; *Int'l*, pg. 3631
ZIMPLOW - C.T. BOLTS DIVISION—See Zimplow Holdings Limited; *Int'l*, pg. 8684
ZIMPLOW HOLDINGS LIMITED; *Int'l*, pg. 8684
ZIMPLOW - TASSBURG DIVISION—See Zimplow Holdings Limited; *Int'l*, pg. 8684
ZIM POLAND S.P Z O.O—See Israel Corporation Ltd.; *Int'l*, pg. 3823
ZIMRE HOLDINGS LIMITED; *Int'l*, pg. 8684
ZIMRE PROPERTY INVESTMENTS LTD.—See Zimre Holdings Limited; *Int'l*, pg. 8684
ZIMTU CAPITAL CORP.; *Int'l*, pg. 8684
ZIMVIE INC.; *U.S. Public*, pg. 2408
ZINC EXCEL CO., LTD.—See Dowa Holdings Co., Ltd.; *Int'l*, pg. 2184
ZINC INDUSTRY DEVELOPMENT COMMERCIAL COMPANY—See National Iranian Lead & Zinc Company; *Int'l*, pg. 5160
ZINC MEDIA GROUP PLC; *Int'l*, pg. 8684
ZINC OF IRELAND NL; *Int'l*, pg. 8684
ZINC ONE RESOURCES INC.; *Int'l*, pg. 8685
ZINCORE METALS INC.; *Int'l*, pg. 8685
Z INC.; *U.S. Private*, pg. 4596
ZINCX RESOURCES CORP.; *Int'l*, pg. 8685
ZINDART MANUFACTURING LIMITED; *Int'l*, pg. 8685
ZINEMA MEDIA & ENTERTAINMENT LTD.; *Int'l*, pg. 8685
ZINGLE BY ENFO AB—See Enfo Oyj; *Int'l*, pg. 2425
ZINGLE, INC.—See Thoma Bravo, L.P.; *U.S. Private*, pg. 4149
ZING SEMICONDUCTOR CORPORATION—See National Silicon Industry Group Co., Ltd.; *Int'l*, pg. 5163
ZING SP. Z.O.O—See KPP Group Holdings Co., Ltd.; *Int'l*, pg. 4298
ZINIO, LLC—See Vista Equity Partners, LLC; *U.S. Private*, pg. 4399
ZINITIX CO., LTD.; *Int'l*, pg. 8685
ZINKAN ENTERPRISES INCORPORATED; *U.S. Private*, pg. 4605
ZINKCON INTERNATIONAL B.V.—See HAL Trust N.V.; *Int'l*, pg. 3227
ZINKCON MARINE SINGAPORE PTE. LTD.—See HAL Trust N.V.; *Int'l*, pg. 3225
ZINK DISTRIBUTING INC; *U.S. Private*, pg. 4605
ZINKGRUVAN MINING AB—See Lundin Mining Corporation; *Int'l*, pg. 4584
ZINKIA ENTERTAINMENT SA; *Int'l*, pg. 8685
ZINNOV LLC; *U.S. Private*, pg. 4605
ZINNWALD LITHIUM PLC; *Int'l*, pg. 8685
ZINOPY LIMITED—See BC Partners LLP; *Int'l*, pg. 925
ZINPRO CORPORATION; *U.S. Private*, pg. 4605
ZINSER TEXTILE SYSTEMS PVT. LTD.—See OC Oerlikon Corporation AG; *Int'l*, pg. 5515
ZINSSER ANALYTIC GMBH—See Ingersoll Rand Inc.; *U.S. Public*, pg. 1120
ZINSSER ANALYTIC GMBH—See Ingersoll Rand Inc.; *U.S. Public*, pg. 1120
ZINSSER BRANDS COMPANY—See RPM International Inc.; *U.S. Public*, pg. 1817
ZINSSER CO., INC.—See RPM International Inc.; *U.S. Public*, pg. 1817
ZINSSER HOLDINGS, LLC—See RPM International Inc.; *U.S. Public*, pg. 1817
ZINSSER NA, INC.—See Ingersoll Rand Inc.; *U.S. Public*, pg. 1120
ZIN TECHNOLOGIES INC.—See Voyager Space Holdings, Inc.; *U.S. Public*, pg. 4414
ZINTEL COMMUNICATIONS LTD.—See Ziff Davis, Inc.; *U.S. Public*, pg. 2404

ZINTEL COMMUNICATIONS PTY. LIMITED—See Ziff Davis, Inc.; *U.S. Public*, pg. 2404
ZINTURA S.A.—See Industria de Diseno Textil, S.A.; *Int'l*, pg. 3669
ZINWELL CORPORATION - CHIA-YI PLANT—See ZINWELL Corporation; *Int'l*, pg. 8685
ZINWELL CORPORATION - HSINCHU PLANT—See ZINWELL Corporation; *Int'l*, pg. 8685
ZINWELL CORPORATION - SHENZHEN PLANT—See ZINWELL Corporation; *Int'l*, pg. 8685
ZINWELL CORPORATION; *Int'l*, pg. 8685
ZINZINO AB; *Int'l*, pg. 8685
ZINZINO B.V.—See Zinzino AB; *Int'l*, pg. 8685
ZINZINO OY—See Zinzino AB; *Int'l*, pg. 8685
ZIOLKOWSKI CONSTRUCTION INC.; *U.S. Private*, pg. 4605
ZIONCOM HOLDINGS LIMITED - SHENZHEN FACTORY—See Metaverse Yunji Technology Group Company Limited; *Int'l*, pg. 4851
ZIONCOM (HONG KONG) TECHNOLOGY LIMITED—See Metaverse Yunji Technology Group Company Limited; *Int'l*, pg. 4851
ZION ENERGY LLC—See Energy Capital Partners Management, LP; *U.S. Private*, pg. 1394
ZION OIL & GAS, INC.; *U.S. Public*, pg. 2408
ZION OIL & GAS - ISRAEL—See Zion Oil & Gas, Inc.; *U.S. Public*, pg. 2408
ZIONS BANCORPORATION, NATIONAL ASSOCIATION; *U.S. Public*, pg. 2408
ZIONS BANK—See Zions Bancorporation, National Association; *U.S. Public*, pg. 2408
ZIONS CREDIT CORPORATION—See Zions Bancorporation, National Association; *U.S. Public*, pg. 2408
ZIONS DIRECT, INC.—See Zions Bancorporation, National Association; *U.S. Public*, pg. 2408
ZIONS PUBLIC FINANCE, INC.—See Zions Bancorporation, National Association; *U.S. Public*, pg. 2408
ZIONSVILLE WATER CORPORATION—See Veolia Water Indianapolis, LLC; *U.S. Private*, pg. 4358
ZION & ZION; *U.S. Private*, pg. 4605
ZIPAC DEVELOPMENT SDN BHD—See Tambun Indah Land Berhad; *Int'l*, pg. 7450
ZIP BUSINESS AUSTRALIA PTY. LTD.—See Zip Co Limited; *Int'l*, pg. 8685
ZIP BUSINESS NEW ZEALAND PTY. LTD.—See Zip Co Limited; *Int'l*, pg. 8685
ZIPCAR FRANCE S.A.S.—See Avis Budget Group, Inc.; *U.S. Public*, pg. 249
ZIPCAR, INC. - SEATTLE—See Avis Budget Group, Inc.; *U.S. Public*, pg. 249
ZIPCAR, INC.—See Avis Budget Group, Inc.; *U.S. Public*, pg. 249
ZIPCAR ON CAMPUS, INC.—See Avis Budget Group, Inc.; *U.S. Public*, pg. 249
ZIP CO LIMITED; *Int'l*, pg. 8685
ZIP CO NZ LIMITED—See Zip Co Limited; *Int'l*, pg. 8685
ZIP CO PAYMENTS UK LIMITED—See Zip Co Limited; *Int'l*, pg. 8685
ZIP DRUG INC.—See Elevance Health, Inc.; *U.S. Public*, pg. 730
ZIPFIZZ CORPORATION—See Xiamen Kingdomway Group Company; *Int'l*, pg. 8525
ZIP FULFILLMENT LLC—See Pyxus International, Inc.; *U.S. Public*, pg. 1741
ZIP INC.—See EQT AB; *Int'l*, pg. 2467
ZIPLINE COMMUNICATIONS, INC.; *U.S. Private*, pg. 4606
ZIPLINE LOGISTICS LLC; *U.S. Private*, pg. 4606
ZIPLINK, INC.; *U.S. Public*, pg. 2408
ZIP MOVING & STORAGE INC.; *U.S. Private*, pg. 4606
ZIP-PAK INTERNATIONAL B.V.—See Illinois Tool Works Inc.; *U.S. Public*, pg. 1111
ZIP-PAK—See Illinois Tool Works Inc.; *U.S. Public*, pg. 1109
ZIP-PAK—See Illinois Tool Works Inc.; *U.S. Public*, pg. 1109
ZIPP BRATISLAVA SPOL. SR.O.—See STRABAG SE; *Int'l*, pg. 7233
ZIPPE GLASS INDUSTRIES INDIA PVT. LTD.—See ZIPPE Industrieanlagen GmbH; *Int'l*, pg. 8685
ZIPPE INDUSTRIEANLAGEN GMBH; *Int'l*, pg. 8685
ZIPPE ITALIA S.R.L.—See ZIPPE Industrieanlagen GmbH; *Int'l*, pg. 8685
ZIPPE POLSKA SP. Z O.O.—See ZIPPE Industrieanlagen GmbH; *Int'l*, pg. 8685
ZIPPER AIR CONDITIONING & HEATING COMPANY—See Defender Security Company; *U.S. Private*, pg. 1190
ZIPPER BY ENFO AB—See Enfo Oyj; *Int'l*, pg. 2425
ZIPPER SERVICES SRL—See ANY Security Printing Company PLC; *Int'l*, pg. 486
ZIPPER TECHNIK GMBH—See The Zippertubing Company; *U.S. Private*, pg. 4140
THE ZIPPERTUBING COMPANY; *U.S. Private*, pg. 4140
THE ZIPPERTUBING COMPANY - ZIPTAPE LABEL ID SYSTEMS DIVISION—See The Zippertubing Company; *U.S. Private*, pg. 4140

COMPANY NAME INDEX

THE ZIPPERTUBING COMPANY - ZT AUTOMOTIVE DIVISION—See The Zippertubing Company; *U.S. Private*, pg. 4140
ZIPPERTUBING (JAPAN), LTD.—See The Zippertubing Company; *U.S. Private*, pg. 4140
ZIPPO CANADA SALES, LLC—See Hyde's Distribution; *Int'l*, pg. 3546
ZIPPO GMBH—See Zippo Manufacturing Company, Inc.; *U.S. Private*, pg. 4606
ZIPPO ITALIA S.R.L.—See Zippo Manufacturing Company, Inc.; *U.S. Private*, pg. 4606
ZIPPO MANUFACTURING COMPANY, INC.; *U.S. Private*, pg. 4606
ZIPPO S.A.—See Zippo Manufacturing Company, Inc.; *U.S. Private*, pg. 4606
ZIPPO U.K. LTD.—See Zippo Manufacturing Company, Inc.; *U.S. Private*, pg. 4606
ZIPP PRAHA, S.R.O—See STRABAG SE; *Int'l*, pg. 7233
ZIPP SKUTERY SP .Z.O.O.—See KBC Group NV; *Int'l*, pg. 4107
ZIPPY (DONGGUAN) ELECTRONICS CO., LTD.—See Zippy Technology Corp.; *Int'l*, pg. 8686
ZIPPY'S, INC.; *U.S. Private*, pg. 4606
ZIPPY(SUZHOU) ELECTRONICS CO., LTD.—See Zippy Technology Corp.; *Int'l*, pg. 8686
ZIPPY TECHNOLOGY CORP.; *Int'l*, pg. 8685
ZIPPY TECHNOLOGY EUROPE GMBH—See Zippy Technology Corp.; *Int'l*, pg. 8686
ZIPPY USA INC.—See Zippy Technology Corp.; *Int'l*, pg. 8686
ZIPRECRUITER, INC.; *U.S. Public*, pg. 2409
ZIP-RIB, INC.—See Merchant & Evans, Inc.; *U.S. Private*, pg. 2669
ZIPTEL LIMITED; *Int'l*, pg. 8686
ZIPTRONIX, INC.—See Adeia Inc.; *U.S. Public*, pg. 41
ZIPWHIP, INC.—See Twilio Inc.; *U.S. Public*, pg. 2206
ZIPZAP PROCESSING INCORPORATED—See BGH Capital Pty Ltd; *Int'l*, pg. 1008
ZIPZAP PROCESSING INCORPORATED—See Sixth Street Partners LLC; *U.S. Private*, pg. 3678
ZIRAAT BANK AZERBAYCAN ASC—See T.C. Ziraat Bankasi A.S.; *Int'l*, pg. 7397
ZIRAAT BANK BH D.D.—See T.C. Ziraat Bankasi A.S.; *Int'l*, pg. 7397
ZIRAAT BANK INTERNATIONAL A.G.—See Turkiye Cumhuriyeti Ziraat Bankasi A.S.; *Int'l*, pg. 7975
ZIRAAT BANK (MOSCOW) CJSC—See Turkiye Cumhuriyeti Ziraat Bankasi A.S.; *Int'l*, pg. 7975
ZIRAAT BANK UZBEKISTAN JSC—See T.C. Ziraat Bankasi A.S.; *Int'l*, pg. 7397
ZIRAAT FINANSAL KIRALAMA A.S.—See Turkiye Cumhuriyeti Ziraat Bankasi A.S.; *Int'l*, pg. 7975
ZIRAAT GAYRIMENKUL YATIRIM ORTAKLIGI A.S.—See T.C. Ziraat Bankasi A.S.; *Int'l*, pg. 7397
ZIRAAT GIRISIM SERMAYESI YATIRIM ORTAKLIGI A.S.—See T.C. Ziraat Bankasi A.S.; *Int'l*, pg. 7397
ZIRAAT HAYAT VE EMEKLILIK A.S.—See Turkiye Varlik Fonu Yonetimi AS; *Int'l*, pg. 7978
ZIRAAT KATILIM VARLIK KIRALAMA A.S.; *Int'l*, pg. 8686
ZIRAAT PORTFOY YONETIMI A.S.—See Turkiye Cumhuriyeti Ziraat Bankasi A.S.; *Int'l*, pg. 7975
ZIRAAT TEKNOLOJI A.S.—See T.C. Ziraat Bankasi A.S.; *Int'l*, pg. 7397
ZIRAAT YATIRIM MENKUL DEGERLER A.S.—See Turkiye Cumhuriyeti Ziraat Bankasi A.S.; *Int'l*, pg. 7975
ZIRAX LIMITED; *Int'l*, pg. 8686
ZIRAX LLC—See Zirax Limited; *Int'l*, pg. 8686
ZIRAX (UK) LIMITED—See Zirax Limited; *Int'l*, pg. 8686
ZIRCOA—See RHI Magnesita N.V.; *Int'l*, pg. 6326
ZIRCON CORPORATION; *U.S. Private*, pg. 4606
ZIRCON ENGINEERING PTE LTD—See Daeyang Electric Co., Ltd.; *Int'l*, pg. 1911
ZIRCON PRECISION PRODUCTS, INC.; *U.S. Private*, pg. 4606
ZIRCOSIL (USA) INC.—See American Securities LLC; *U.S. Private*, pg. 251
ZIRDAC SARL—See Virbac S.A.; *Int'l*, pg. 8247
ZIRH HOLDINGS LLC—See The Procter & Gamble Company; *U.S. Public*, pg. 2124
ZIRKELBACH CONSTRUCTION, INC.; *U.S. Private*, pg. 4606
ZIRMED, INC.—See Canada Pension Plan Investment Board; *Int'l*, pg. 1282
ZIRMED, INC.—See EQT AB; *Int'l*, pg. 2481
THE ZISES GROUP; *U.S. Private*, pg. 4140
ZIS INFORMATION TECHNOLOGY CO., LTD.—See Zeon Corporation; *Int'l*, pg. 8636
ZISSOR AS—See INVL Technology AB; *Int'l*, pg. 3790
ZISUNG ECS CO LTD; *Int'l*, pg. 8686
ZITA WEST PRODUCTS LIMITED—See Samarkand Group Plc; *Int'l*, pg. 6501
ZI-TECHASIA SOLUTIONS LTD.—See The Zuellig Group Inc.; *Int'l*, pg. 7705
ZITERY S.A.—See Genus Plc; *Int'l*, pg. 2931
ZITIZ AB—See Duroc AB; *Int'l*, pg. 2229
ZITKO A.D.; *Int'l*, pg. 8686
ZITOBANAT A.D.; *Int'l*, pg. 8686
ZITO D.O.O.—See Podravka d.d.; *Int'l*, pg. 5903

ZITO INSURANCE AGENCY, INC.—See Kelso & Company, L.P.; *U.S. Private*, pg. 2280
ZITO LUKS A.D.—See Elbisco Holding S.A.; *Int'l*, pg. 2344
ZITO MALOPRODAJA D.O.O.—See Podravka d.d.; *Int'l*, pg. 5903
ZITOPEK A.D.; *Int'l*, pg. 8686
ZITO POLOG AD; *Int'l*, pg. 8686
ZITO PRILEP AD; *Int'l*, pg. 8686
ZITOPROMET A.D.; *Int'l*, pg. 8686
ZITOPROMET A.D.; *Int'l*, pg. 8686
ZITOPROMET-MLIN AD; *Int'l*, pg. 8686
ZITO SKOPJE AD; *Int'l*, pg. 8686
ZITOSREM A.D.; *Int'l*, pg. 8686
ZITO STRUMICA AD; *Int'l*, pg. 8686
ZIT ZENTRALINSTITUT FUR TRANSFUSIONSMEDIZIN GMBH—See Asklepios Kliniken GmbH & Co. KGaA; *Int'l*, pg. 624
ZIVARO, INC.—See AG Acquisition Group, Inc.; *U.S. Private*, pg. 124
ZIVO BIOSCIENCE, INC.; *U.S. Public*, pg. 2409
ZIX CORPORATION—See Open Text Corporation; *Int'l*, pg. 5598
ZIXING KIBING SILICON INDUSTRY CO., LTD.—See Zhuzhou Kibing Group Co., Ltd.; *Int'l*, pg. 8680
ZIXIN GROUP HOLDINGS LIMITED; *Int'l*, pg. 8686
ZIYONG HARDWARE PRODUCTS (TAICANG) CO., LTD.—See Taiwan Fu Hsing Industrial Co., Ltd.; *Int'l*, pg. 7420
ZIYUANYUAN HOLDINGS GROUP LTD.; *Int'l*, pg. 8686
ZIZZO GROUP, INC.; *U.S. Private*, pg. 4606
ZJAMP GROUP CO., LTD.; *Int'l*, pg. 8686
ZJBC INFORMATION TECHNOLOGY CO., LTD.; *Int'l*, pg. 8686
Z & J HIGH TEMPERATURE EQUIPMENT (SHANGHAI) CO., LTD.—See IMI plc; *Int'l*, pg. 3627
ZJLD GROUP INC.; *Int'l*, pg. 8686
Z&J TECHNOLOGIES GMBH—See IMI plc; *Int'l*, pg. 3627
ZK ADVERTISING—See The Interpublic Group of Companies, Inc.; *U.S. Public*, pg. 2103
ZKH GROUP LIMITED; *Int'l*, pg. 8687
ZK INTELLIGENT SOLUTIONS (PTY) LTD.—See Zkteco Co., Ltd.; *Int'l*, pg. 8687
ZK INTERNATIONAL GROUP CO., LTD.; *Int'l*, pg. 8686
ZK PELAGONIJA JSC; *Int'l*, pg. 8686
ZKTECH CHILE SPA—See Zkteco Co., Ltd.; *Int'l*, pg. 8687
ZK TECHNOLOGY LLC—See Zkteco Co., Ltd.; *Int'l*, pg. 8687
ZKTECO ARGENTINA S.A—See Zkteco Co., Ltd.; *Int'l*, pg. 8687
ZKTECO BIOMETRIC LIMITED—See Zkteco Co., Ltd.; *Int'l*, pg. 8687
ZKTECO COLOMBIA SAS—See Zkteco Co., Ltd.; *Int'l*, pg. 8687
ZKTECO CO., LTD.; *Int'l*, pg. 8687
ZKTECO DEUTSCHLAND GMBH—See Zkteco Co., Ltd.; *Int'l*, pg. 8687
ZKTECO DO BRASIL S.A.—See Zkteco Co., Ltd.; *Int'l*, pg. 8687
ZKTECO EUROPE SL—See Zkteco Co., Ltd.; *Int'l*, pg. 8687
ZKTECO IRELAND LTD.—See Zkteco Co., Ltd.; *Int'l*, pg. 8687
ZKTECO ITALIA SRL—See Zkteco Co., Ltd.; *Int'l*, pg. 8687
ZKTECO JAPAN CO., LTD.—See Zkteco Co., Ltd.; *Int'l*, pg. 8687
ZKTECO PANAMA S.A.—See Zkteco Co., Ltd.; *Int'l*, pg. 8687
ZKTECO PERU S.A.C.—See Zkteco Co., Ltd.; *Int'l*, pg. 8687
ZKTECO PHILIPPINES INC.—See Zkteco Co., Ltd.; *Int'l*, pg. 8687
ZKTECO SECURITY LLC—See Zkteco Co., Ltd.; *Int'l*, pg. 8687
ZKTECO THAI CO., LTD.—See Zkteco Co., Ltd.; *Int'l*, pg. 8687
ZKTECO TURKEY ELEKTRONIK SANAYI VE TICARET LIMITED SIRKETI—See Zkteco Co., Ltd.; *Int'l*, pg. 8687
ZKTECO UK LTD.—See Zkteco Co., Ltd.; *Int'l*, pg. 8687
ZKTECO USA LLC—See Zkteco Co., Ltd.; *Int'l*, pg. 8687
ZKTECO VIETNAM TECHNOLOGY COMPANY LIMITED—See Zkteco Co., Ltd.; *Int'l*, pg. 8687
ZLATA MONETA II DD; *Int'l*, pg. 8687
ZLATAR A.D.; *Int'l*, pg. 8687
ZLATARPLAST A.D.; *Int'l*, pg. 8687
ZLATEN LEV HOLDING AD; *Int'l*, pg. 8687
ZLATIBOR GRADNJA A.D.; *Int'l*, pg. 8687
ZLATIBOR MERMER A.D.; *Int'l*, pg. 8687
ZLATIBOR STANDARD A.D.; *Int'l*, pg. 8687
ZLATICA A.D.; *Int'l*, pg. 8687
ZLATNA PANEGA BETON EOOD—See Titan Cement Company S.A.; *Int'l*, pg. 7760
ZLATNA PANEGA CEMENT AD—See Titan Cement Company S.A.; *Int'l*, pg. 7760
ZLATNI PYASATZI AD; *Int'l*, pg. 8687
ZLB BIOPLASMA INC.—See CSL Limited; *Int'l*, pg. 1865
Z LEASING ALFA IMMOBILIEN LEASING GESELLSCHAFT M.B.H.—See UniCredit S.p.A.; *Int'l*, pg. 8038

ZODIAC ENERGY LIMITED

Z LEASING ARKTUR IMMOBILIEN LEASING GESELLSCHAFT M.B.H.—See UniCredit S.p.A.; *Int'l*, pg. 8038
Z LEASING AURIGA IMMOBILIEN LEASING GESELLSCHAFT M.B.H.—See UniCredit S.p.A.; *Int'l*, pg. 8037
Z LEASING CORVUS IMMOBILIEN LEASING GESELLSCHAFT M.B.H.—See UniCredit S.p.A.; *Int'l*, pg. 8036
Z LEASING GAMA IMMOBILIEN LEASING GESELLSCHAFT M.B.H.—See UniCredit S.p.A.; *Int'l*, pg. 8038
Z LEASING GEMINI IMMOBILIEN LEASING GESELLSCHAFT M.B.H.—See UniCredit S.p.A.; *Int'l*, pg. 8037
Z LEASING HERCULES IMMOBILIEN LEASING GESELLSCHAFT M.B.H.—See UniCredit S.p.A.; *Int'l*, pg. 8037
Z LEASING ITA IMMOBILIEN LEASING GESELLSCHAFT M.B.H.—See UniCredit S.p.A.; *Int'l*, pg. 8042
Z LEASING KALLISTO IMMOBILIEN LEASING GESELLSCHAFT M.B.H.—See UniCredit S.p.A.; *Int'l*, pg. 8038
Z LEASING KAPA IMMOBILIEN LEASING GESELLSCHAFT M.B.H.—See UniCredit S.p.A.; *Int'l*, pg. 8042
Z LEASING NEREIDE IMMOBILIEN LEASING GESELLSCHAFT M.B.H.—See UniCredit S.p.A.; *Int'l*, pg. 8038
Z LEASING OMEGA IMMOBILIEN LEASING GESELLSCHAFT M.B.H.—See UniCredit S.p.A.; *Int'l*, pg. 8042
Z LEASING PERSEUS IMMOBILIEN LEASING GESELLSCHAFT M.B.H.—See UniCredit S.p.A.; *Int'l*, pg. 8035
Z LEASING TAURUS IMMOBILIEN LEASING GESELLSCHAFT M.B.H.—See UniCredit S.p.A.; *Int'l*, pg. 8036
Z LEASING VENUS IMMOBILIEN LEASING GESELLSCHAFT M.B.H.—See UniCredit S.p.A.; *Int'l*, pg. 8038
Z LEASING VOLANS IMMOBILIEN LEASING GESELLSCHAFT M.B.H.—See UniCredit S.p.A.; *Int'l*, pg. 8038
ZLOKOWER COMPANY LLC—See CHR Group LLC; *U.S. Private*, pg. 889
ZLOMREX SA; *Int'l*, pg. 8687
THE ZLOTNICK GROUP; *U.S. Private*, pg. 4140
ZLR IGNITION; *U.S. Private*, pg. 4606
ZL STAR INC.; *U.S. Private*, pg. 4606
Z-LYFTEN PRODUKTION AB—See Cargotec Corporation; *Int'l*, pg. 1329
ZMAGS CORP.—See The Gores Group, LLC; *U.S. Private*, pg. 4035
ZMAJ A.D.; *Int'l*, pg. 8687
ZMAJ A.D.; *Int'l*, pg. 8687
Z MAKINA AS—See VINCI S.A.; *Int'l*, pg. 8240
Z-MAR TECHNOLOGY INC.; *U.S. Private*, pg. 4596
ZMC AMERICA, INC.—See FuelPositive Corporation; *Int'l*, pg. 2804
ZMC HOTELS; *U.S. Private*, pg. 4606
Z-MEDICA, LLC—See Teleflex Incorporated; *U.S. Public*, pg. 1996
ZM FINANCIAL SYSTEMS, LLC—See Moody's Corporation; *U.S. Public*, pg. 1469
ZMFY AUTOMOBILE GLASS SERVICES LIMITED; *Int'l*, pg. 8686
ZMG CONSTRUCTION, INC.; *U.S. Private*, pg. 4606
Z MICROSYSTEMS INC.; *U.S. Private*, pg. 4596
ZMM BULGARIA AD—See Industrial Holding Bulgaria AD; *Int'l*, pg. 3672
ZMM NOVA ZAGORA AD—See Industrial Holding Bulgaria AD; *Int'l*, pg. 3672
ZMM SLIVEN AD—See Industrial Holding Bulgaria AD; *Int'l*, pg. 3672
ZNAMENSKY SUGAR—See Gruppa Kompaniy Rusagro OOO; *Int'l*, pg. 3140
ZN DER SANDVIK MATERIALS TECHNOLOGY DEUTSCHLAND GMBH—See Sandvik AB; *Int'l*, pg. 6528
ZNERGY, INC.; *U.S. Private*, pg. 4607
ZNET GROUP GMBH—See WiseTech Global Limited; *Int'l*, pg. 8437
ZNEXT MINING CORP.; *Int'l*, pg. 8688
ZNLABS, LLC—See Zoetis, Inc.; *U.S. Public*, pg. 2410
ZNS ENGINEERING, L.C.; *U.S. Private*, pg. 4607
ZNYX NETWORKS, INC.; *U.S. Private*, pg. 4607
ZOA CORPORATION—See Daiwabo Holdings Co., Ltd.; *Int'l*, pg. 1949
ZOAR INTERACTIVE—See Whitemyer Advertising, Inc.; *U.S. Private*, pg. 4511
ZOB AN DER HACKERBRUCKE GMBH & CO. KG—See ACS, Actividades de Construccion y Servicios, S.A.; *Int'l*, pg. 114
ZOBITO AB; *Int'l*, pg. 8688
ZOBMONDO!! ENTERTAINMENT LLC; *U.S. Private*, pg. 4607
ZOBNATICA A.D.; *Int'l*, pg. 8688
ZOCALO GROUP—See Omnicom Group Inc.; *U.S. Public*, pg. 1587
ZOCALO L.C.—See Rreal Tacos Sandy Springs LLC; *U.S. Private*, pg. 3496
ZOCDOC, INC.; *U.S. Private*, pg. 4607
ZODIAC AEROSPACE S.A.—See Safran SA; *Int'l*, pg. 6477
ZODIAC AUTOMOTIVE TUNISIE SRL—See Safran SA; *Int'l*, pg. 6477
ZODIAC CABIN CONTROLS GMBH—See Safran SA; *Int'l*, pg. 6477
ZODIAC CAPITAL LIMITED; *Int'l*, pg. 8688
ZODIAC CLOTHING COMPANY LIMITED; *Int'l*, pg. 8688
ZODIAC ENERGY LIMITED; *Int'l*, pg. 8688

ZODIAC ENERGY LIMITED — CORPORATE AFFILIATIONS

ZODIAC ENTERPRISES, LLC—See BASF SE; *Int'l*, pg. 886
ZODIAC ESPANOLA S.A.—See The Carlyle Group Inc.; *U.S. Public*, pg. 2057
ZODIAC EUROPEAN POOLS—See The Carlyle Group Inc.; *U.S. Public*, pg. 2057
ZODIAC GROUP AUSTRALIA PTY. LTD.—See The Carlyle Group Inc.; *U.S. Public*, pg. 2057
ZODIAC HURRICANE TECHNOLOGIES INC.—See The Carlyle Group Inc.; *U.S. Public*, pg. 2057
ZODIAC INTERNATIONAL—See The Carlyle Group Inc.; *U.S. Public*, pg. 2057
ZODIAC ITALIA SRL—See The Carlyle Group Inc.; *U.S. Public*, pg. 2057
ZODIAC-JRD-MKJ LIMITED; *Int'l*, pg. 8688
ZODIAC MARINE & POOL—See The Carlyle Group Inc.; *U.S. Public*, pg. 2057
ZODIAC OF NORTH AMERICA, INC. - RECREATIONAL MARINE DIVISION—See The Carlyle Group Inc.; *U.S. Public*, pg. 2057
ZODIAC OF NORTH AMERICA, INC.—See The Carlyle Group Inc.; *U.S. Public*, pg. 2057
ZODIAC POOL CARE SOUTH AFRICA PTY. LTD.—See The Carlyle Group Inc.; *U.S. Public*, pg. 2057
ZODIAC POOL DEUTSCHLAND GMBH - MOMBRIS—See The Carlyle Group Inc.; *U.S. Public*, pg. 2057
ZODIAC POOL DEUTSCHLAND GMBH—See The Carlyle Group Inc.; *U.S. Public*, pg. 2057
ZODIAC POOL IBERICA S.L.U.—See The Carlyle Group Inc.; *U.S. Public*, pg. 2057
ZODIAC POOL SYSTEMS CANADA, INC.—See The Carlyle Group Inc.; *U.S. Public*, pg. 2057
ZODIAC POOL SYSTEMS, INC. - POLARIS PRODUCTS—See The Carlyle Group Inc.; *U.S. Public*, pg. 2057
ZODIAC POOL SYSTEMS, INC.—See The Carlyle Group Inc.; *U.S. Public*, pg. 2057
ZODIAC US CORPORATION—See Safran SA; *Int'l*, pg. 6477
ZODIAK ACTIVE S.P.A.—See De Agostini S.p.A.; *Int'l*, pg. 1994
ZODIAK AMERICAS—See De Agostini S.p.A.; *Int'l*, pg. 1994
ZODIAK BELGIUM—See De Agostini S.p.A.; *Int'l*, pg. 1994
ZODIAK FINLAND OY—See De Agostini S.p.A.; *Int'l*, pg. 1995
ZODIAK KIDS—See De Agostini S.p.A.; *Int'l*, pg. 1994
ZODIAK MEDIA GROUP - LONDON—See De Agostini S.p.A.; *Int'l*, pg. 1994
ZODIAK NEDERLAND—See De Agostini S.p.A.; *Int'l*, pg. 1994
ZODIAK NEW YORK—See De Agostini S.p.A.; *Int'l*, pg. 1994
ZODIO FRANCE—See Groupe Adeo S.A.; *Int'l*, pg. 3091
ZOEGAS KAFFE AB—See Nestle S.A.; *Int'l*, pg. 5208
ZOELLER CO.; *U.S. Private*, pg. 4607
ZOE'S KITCHEN, INC.—See Cava Group, Inc.; *U.S. Public*, pg. 454
ZOETIS ARGENTINA S.R.L.—See Zoetis, Inc.; *U.S. Public*, pg. 2410
ZOETIS BELGIUM S.A.—See Zoetis, Inc.; *U.S. Public*, pg. 2410
ZOETIS B.V.—See Zoetis, Inc.; *U.S. Public*, pg. 2410
ZOETIS CANADA INC.—See Zoetis, Inc.; *U.S. Public*, pg. 2410
ZOETIS, C.A.—See Zoetis, Inc.; *U.S. Public*, pg. 2410
ZOETIS COSTA RICA, S.R.L.—See Zoetis, Inc.; *U.S. Public*, pg. 2410
ZOETIS DE CHILE S.A.—See Zoetis, Inc.; *U.S. Public*, pg. 2410
ZOETIS DEUTSCHLAND GMBH—See Zoetis, Inc.; *U.S. Public*, pg. 2410
ZOETIS EGYPT LLC—See Zoetis, Inc.; *U.S. Public*, pg. 2410
ZOETIS FINLAND OY—See Zoetis, Inc.; *U.S. Public*, pg. 2410
ZOETIS GLOBAL POULTRY—See Zoetis, Inc.; *U.S. Public*, pg. 2410
ZOETIS HELLAS S.A.—See Zoetis, Inc.; *U.S. Public*, pg. 2410
ZOETIS HUNGARY KFT.—See Zoetis, Inc.; *U.S. Public*, pg. 2410
ZOETIS, INC. - LINCOLN—See Zoetis, Inc.; *U.S. Public*, pg. 2410
ZOETIS, INC.; *U.S. Public*, pg. 2409
ZOETIS, INC. - WHITE HALL—See Zoetis, Inc.; *U.S. Public*, pg. 2410
ZOETIS INDIA LIMITED—See Zoetis, Inc.; *U.S. Public*, pg. 2410
ZOETIS INDUSTRIA DE PRODUTOS VETERINARIOS LTDA.—See Zoetis, Inc.; *U.S. Public*, pg. 2410
ZOETIS IRELAND LIMITED—See Zoetis, Inc.; *U.S. Public*, pg. 2410
ZOETIS JAPAN K.K.—See Zoetis, Inc.; *U.S. Public*, pg. 2410
ZOETIS KOREA LTD.—See Zoetis, Inc.; *U.S. Public*, pg. 2410
ZOETIS MALAYSIA SDN. BHD.—See Zoetis, Inc.; *U.S. Public*, pg. 2410

ZOETIS MEXICO, S. DE R.L. DE C.V.—See Zoetis, Inc.; *U.S. Public*, pg. 2410
ZOETIS QOO—See Zoetis, Inc.; *U.S. Public*, pg. 2410
ZOETIS PHILIPPINES INC.—See Zoetis, Inc.; *U.S. Public*, pg. 2410
ZOETIS POLSKA SP. Z O.O—See Zoetis, Inc.; *U.S. Public*, pg. 2410
ZOETIS PORTUGAL, LDA.—See Zoetis, Inc.; *U.S. Public*, pg. 2410
ZOETIS ROMANIA S.R.L.—See Zoetis, Inc.; *U.S. Public*, pg. 2410
ZOETIS SALUD ANIMAL, C.A.—See Zoetis, Inc.; *U.S. Public*, pg. 2410
ZOETIS SCHWEIZ GMBH—See Zoetis, Inc.; *U.S. Public*, pg. 2410
ZOETIS SOUTH AFRICA (PTY) LTD.—See Zoetis, Inc.; *U.S. Public*, pg. 2410
ZOETIS SPAIN, S.L.—See Zoetis, Inc.; *U.S. Public*, pg. 2410
ZOETIS S.R.L.—See Zoetis, Inc.; *U.S. Public*, pg. 2410
ZOETIS TAIWAN LIMITED—See Zoetis, Inc.; *U.S. Public*, pg. 2410
ZOETIS UK LIMITED—See Zoetis, Inc.; *U.S. Public*, pg. 2410
ZOETIS UKRAINE LLC—See Zoetis, Inc.; *U.S. Public*, pg. 2410
ZOETIS VIETNAM LIMITED LIABILITY COMPANY—See Zoetis, Inc.; *U.S. Public*, pg. 2410
ZOG DIGITAL—See Investis Limited; *Int'l*, pg. 3780
ZOGENIX, INC.—See UCB S.A.; *Int'l*, pg. 8012
ZOGENIX INTERNATIONAL LIMITED—See UCB S.A.; *Int'l*, pg. 8012
ZOGICS, LLC; *U.S. Private*, pg. 4607
ZOGI SRL—See The Procter & Gamble Company; *U.S. Public*, pg. 2124
ZOGSPORTS LLC; *U.S. Private*, pg. 4607
ZOHAR DALIA—See Ecolab Inc.; *U.S. Public*, pg. 717
ZOHARI CREDIT LIMITED—See Centum Investment Company Limited; *Int'l*, pg. 1416
ZOHARI LEASING LIMITED—See Centum Investment Company Limited; *Int'l*, pg. 1416
ZOHO (BEIJING) TECHNOLOGY CO., LTD.—See Zoho Corporation; *U.S. Private*, pg. 4607
ZOHO CORPORATION PRIVATE LIMITED—See Zoho Corporation; *U.S. Private*, pg. 4607
ZOHO CORPORATION; *U.S. Private*, pg. 4607
ZOHO JAPAN CORPORATION—See Zoho Corporation; *U.S. Private*, pg. 4607
ZOJE RESOURCES INVESTMENT CO., LTD.; *Int'l*, pg. 8688
ZOJIRUSHI AMERICA CORPORATION—See Zojirushi Corporation; *Int'l*, pg. 8688
ZOJIRUSHI CORPORATION; *Int'l*, pg. 8688
ZOJIRUSHI SE ASIA CORPORATION LTD.—See Zojirushi Corporation; *Int'l*, pg. 8688
ZOJIRUSHI SHANGHAI CORPORATION—See Zojirushi Corporation; *Int'l*, pg. 8688
ZOJIRUSHI SIMATELEX CO., LTD.—See Zojirushi Corporation; *Int'l*, pg. 8688
ZOJIRUSHI TAIWAN CORPORATION—See Zojirushi Corporation; *Int'l*, pg. 8688
ZOLADZ CONSTRUCTION CO., INC.; *U.S. Private*, pg. 4607
ZOLA—See KarpReilly; *U.S. Private*, pg. 2263
ZOLFO COOPER BRITISH VIRGIN ISLANDS—See Zolfo Cooper, LLC; *U.S. Private*, pg. 4607
ZOLFO COOPER CAYMAN ISLANDS—See Zolfo Cooper, LLC; *U.S. Private*, pg. 4607
ZOLFO COOPER, LLC; *U.S. Private*, pg. 4607
ZOLL DATA SYSTEMS—See Asahi Kasei Corporation; *Int'l*, pg. 597
ZOLL INTERNATIONAL HOLDING BV—See Asahi Kasei Corporation; *Int'l*, pg. 597
ZOLL MEDICAL AUSTRALIA PTY. LTD.—See Asahi Kasei Corporation; *Int'l*, pg. 597
ZOLL MEDICAL CANADA, INC.—See Asahi Kasei Corporation; *Int'l*, pg. 597
ZOLL MEDICAL CORPORATION—See Asahi Kasei Corporation; *Int'l*, pg. 597
ZOLL MEDICAL DEUTSCHLAND (GMBH)—See Asahi Kasei Corporation; *Int'l*, pg. 598
ZOLL MEDICAL FRANCE S.A.—See Asahi Kasei Corporation; *Int'l*, pg. 598
ZOLL MEDICAL ITALIA SRL—See Asahi Kasei Corporation; *Int'l*, pg. 598
ZOLL MEDICAL NEW ZEALAND PTY. LTD.—See Asahi Kasei Corporation; *Int'l*, pg. 598
ZOLL MEDICAL U.K. LTD.—See Asahi Kasei Corporation; *Int'l*, pg. 598
ZOLON TECH SOLUTIONS INC.; *U.S. Private*, pg. 4607
ZOLO TECHNOLOGIES—See Pinnacle West Capital Corporation; *U.S. Public*, pg. 1692
ZOLOTO KAMCHATKI, JSC—See Renova Group; *Int'l*, pg. 6285
ZOLOTO RESOURCES LTD.; *U.S. Private*, pg. 4607
ZOLTAV RESOURCES INC.; *Int'l*, pg. 8688
ZOLTEK COMPANIES, INC.—See Toray Industries, Inc.; *Int'l*, pg. 7825

ZOLTEK CORPORATION—See Toray Industries, Inc.; *Int'l*, pg. 7827
ZOLTEK DE MEXICO SA DE C.V.—See Toray Industries, Inc.; *Int'l*, pg. 7827
ZOLTEK ZRT.—See Toray Industries, Inc.; *Int'l*, pg. 7825
ZOLTRIX MATERIAL (GUANGZHOU) LIMITED—See CN Innovations Holdings Limited; *Int'l*, pg. 1673
ZOMATO MEDIA PVT LTD.; *Int'l*, pg. 8688
ZOMAX CANADA COMPANY—See Comvest Group Holdings LLC; *U.S. Private*, pg. 1007
ZOMAX, INCORPORATED—See Comvest Group Holdings LLC; *U.S. Private*, pg. 1007
ZOMAX LIMITED—See Comvest Group Holdings LLC; *U.S. Private*, pg. 1008
ZOMBIE, INC.; *U.S. Private*, pg. 4607
ZOMEDICA CORP.; *U.S. Public*, pg. 2410
ZOM FLORIDA, INC.—See ZOM Holding, Inc.; *U.S. Private*, pg. 4607
ZOM HOLDING, INC.; *U.S. Private*, pg. 4607
ZONA FRANCA ALARI SEPAUTO S.A.—See CNH Industrial N.V.; *Int'l*, pg. 1676
ZONA FRANCA DE IQUIQUE SA; *Int'l*, pg. 8688
ZONAL HOSPITALITY SYSTEMS INC.; *U.S. Private*, pg. 4607
ZONARE MEDICAL SYSTEMS, INC.—See Mindray Medical International Ltd.; *Int'l*, pg. 4902
ZONAR SYSTEMS, LLC—See Continental Aktiengesellschaft; *Int'l*, pg. 1783
ZONAS S.A.—See Premia Real Estate Investment Company SA; *Int'l*, pg. 5959
ZONA VALUE GLOBAL, S.L.—See Substrate Artificial Inteligence SA; *Int'l*, pg. 7249
THE ZONDERVAN CORPORATION—See Charlesbank Capital Partners, LLC; *U.S. Private*, pg. 854
ZONE3, INC.; *Int'l*, pg. 8688
ZONE 5; *U.S. Private*, pg. 4608
ZONECO GROUP CO., LTD.; *Int'l*, pg. 8688
ZONE DEFENSE, LLC—See JMC Capital Partners LLC; *U.S. Private*, pg. 2215
ZONED PROPERTIES, INC.; *U.S. Public*, pg. 2411
ZONE LABS LLC—See Check Point Software Technologies Ltd.; *Int'l*, pg. 1459
ZONE LIMITED—See Great Wall Terroir Holdings Limited; *Int'l*, pg. 3066
ZONE MECHANICAL, INC.—See Wind Point Advisors LLC; *U.S. Private*, pg. 4536
ZONEPERFECT NUTRITION COMPANY; *U.S. Private*, pg. 4608
ZONE RESOURCES INC.; *Int'l*, pg. 8688
ZONES CANADA, INC.—See Zones, Inc.; *U.S. Private*, pg. 4608
ZONES EUROPE, INC.—See Zones, Inc.; *U.S. Private*, pg. 4608
ZONES, INC.; *U.S. Private*, pg. 4608
ZONETAIL, INC.; *Int'l*, pg. 8688
ZONE TELECOM PTE LTD—See Great Wall Terroir Holdings Limited; *Int'l*, pg. 3066
ZONEX INC.—See Trolex Corp.; *U.S. Private*, pg. 4241
ZONE X LEISURE PTE LTD—See Aspial Corporation Limited; *Int'l*, pg. 630
ZONE X LEISURE PTE LTD—See Fragrance Group Limited; *Int'l*, pg. 2758
ZONGSHEN INDUSTRIAL GROUP CO., LTD.; *Int'l*, pg. 8688
ZONGSHEN PEM POWER SYSTEMS INC.—See Zongshen Industrial Group Co., Ltd.; *Int'l*, pg. 8689
ZONGSHEN POWER MACHINERY CO., LTD.—See Zongshen Industrial Group Co., Ltd.; *Int'l*, pg. 8689
ZONGTAI REAL ESTATE DEVELOPMENT CO., LTD.; *Int'l*, pg. 8689
ZONGYI SOLAR (AMERICA) LIMITED—See Jiangsu Zongyi Co., Ltd.; *Int'l*, pg. 3958
ZONIAC INC.—See CEIPAL Corp.; *U.S. Private*, pg. 806
ZONK GROUP INCORPORATED; *U.S. Private*, pg. 4608
ZONKO BUILDERS INC.; *U.S. Private*, pg. 4608
ZONNEBODO PHARMACEUTICAL CO., LTD.—See Nissha Co., Ltd.; *Int'l*, pg. 5372
ZONQING ENVIRONMENTAL LIMITED; *Int'l*, pg. 8689
ZON RE-USA, LLC—See B.P. Marsh & Partners PLC; *Int'l*, pg. 790
ZON TELEVISAO POR CABO, S.G.P.S., S.A.—See NOS SGPS, S.A.; *Int'l*, pg. 5448
ZONTE METALS INC.; *Int'l*, pg. 8689
ZON TV CABO ACOREANA S.A.—See NOS SGPS, S.A.; *Int'l*, pg. 5448
ZON TV CABO PORTUGAL S.A.—See NOS SGPS, S.A.; *Int'l*, pg. 5448
ZONZIA MEDIA, INC.; *U.S. Private*, pg. 4608
ZOOGASA REALTY INC.—See eXp World Holdings, Inc.; *U.S. Public*, pg. 808
ZOO DIGITAL GROUP PLC; *Int'l*, pg. 8689
ZOO DIGITAL INC.—See ZOO Digital Group plc; *Int'l*, pg. 8689
ZOO DIGITAL LIMITED—See ZOO Digital Group plc; *Int'l*, pg. 8689
ZOO DIGITAL PRODUCTION LLC—See ZOO Digital Group plc; *Int'l*, pg. 8689
ZOO EMPLOYEE SHARE TRUST LIMITED—See ZOO Digital Group plc; *Int'l*, pg. 8689

COMPANY NAME INDEX

ZOOLOGICAL PARKS AND GARDENS BOARD; *Int'l*, pg. 8689
ZOOLOGICAL SOCIETY OF BUFFALO; *U.S. Private*, pg. 4608
ZOOLOGICAL SOCIETY OF CINCINNATI; *U.S. Private*, pg. 4608
THE ZOOLOGICAL SOCIETY OF LONDON; *Int'l*, pg. 7705
ZOOLOGICAL SOCIETY OF PHILADELPHIA; *U.S. Private*, pg. 4608
ZOOLOGICAL SOCIETY OF PITTSBURGH; *U.S. Private*, pg. 4608
ZOOLOGICAL SOCIETY OF SAN DIEGO; *U.S. Private*, pg. 4608
ZOOLOGISCHER GARTEN BERLIN AG; *Int'l*, pg. 8689
ZOOM2U TECHNOLOGIES LIMITED; *Int'l*, pg. 8689
ZOOM ADVERTISING; *U.S. Private*, pg. 4608
ZOOM ADVERTISING—See WPP plc; *Int'l*, pg. 8488
ZOOMAWAY TRAVEL, INC.; *U.S. Public*, pg. 2411
ZOOM CARE P.C.—See PeaceHealth; *U.S. Private*, pg. 3123
ZOOMCAR HOLDINGS, INC.; *Int'l*, pg. 8689
ZOOM COMPANIES, INC.; *U.S. Private*, pg. 4608
ZOOM CORPORATION; *Int'l*, pg. 8689
ZOOMDATA, INC.—See TA Associates, Inc.; *U.S. Private*, pg. 3915
ZOOMD TECHNOLOGIES LTD.; *Int'l*, pg. 8689
ZOOMEDIA, INC.—See Harris D. McKinney, Inc.; *U.S. Private*, pg. 1869
ZOOMERMEDIA LIMITED; *Int'l*, pg. 8689
ZOOM FOODS (H.K.) CO., LTD.—See Tehmag Foods Corp.; *Int'l*, pg. 7521
ZOOM IMAGING SOLUTIONS, INC.; *U.S. Private*, pg. 4608
ZOOM INFORMATION INC.—See TA Associates, Inc.; *U.S. Private*, pg. 3915
ZOOMINFO TECHNOLOGIES INC.; *U.S. Public*, pg. 2411
ZOOMLION GULF FZE—See Zoomlion Heavy Industry Science & Technology Co., Ltd.; *Int'l*, pg. 8690
ZOOMLION HEAVY INDUSTRY SCIENCE & TECHNOLOGY CO., LTD.; *Int'l*, pg. 8690
ZOOMLION HEAVY INDUSTRY (THAILAND) CO., LTD.—See Zoomlion Heavy Industry Science & Technology Co., Ltd.; *Int'l*, pg. 8690
ZOOMLION HEAVY MACHINERY CO., LTD.—See Zoomlion Heavy Industry Science & Technology Co., Ltd.; *Int'l*, pg. 8690
ZOOMLION PAKISTAN (PVT.) LTD.—See Zoomlion Heavy Industry Science & Technology Co., Ltd.; *Int'l*, pg. 8690
ZOOMLION VIETNAM COMPANY LIMITED—See Zoomlion Heavy Industry Science & Technology Co., Ltd.; *Int'l*, pg. 8690
ZOOM MEDIA CORP.—See Zoom Media Group Inc.; *Int'l*, pg. 8689
ZOOM MEDIA GROUP INC.; *Int'l*, pg. 8689
ZOOMMED INC.; *Int'l*, pg. 8690
ZOOMMED INC.—See ZoomMed Inc.; *Int'l*, pg. 8690
ZOOM NORTH AMERICA LLC—See ZOOM Corporation; *Int'l*, pg. 8689
ZOOMPASS HOLDINGS, INC.; *Int'l*, pg. 8689
ZOOM UK DISTRIBUTION LTD.—See ZOOM Corporation; *Int'l*, pg. 8689
ZOOM VIDEO COMMUNICATIONS, INC.; *U.S. Public*, pg. 2411
ZOONO GROUP LIMITED; *Int'l*, pg. 8690
ZOONO GROUP LIMITED—See Zoono Group Limited; *Int'l*, pg. 8690
ZOOOM PRINTING; *U.S. Private*, pg. 4608
ZOOPLA PROPERTY GROUP LTD.—See Daily Mail & General Trust plc; *Int'l*, pg. 1938
ZOOPLUS AG; *Int'l*, pg. 8690
ZOOSK, INC.—See Spark Networks SE; *Int'l*, pg. 7126
ZOOTS CORPORATION; *U.S. Private*, pg. 4608
ZOPITAR LIMITED—See Donegal Investment Group Plc; *Int'l*, pg. 2163
ZORANET CONNECTIVITY SERVICES BV—See Liberty Global plc; *Int'l*, pg. 4486
ZORCH INTERNATIONAL, INC.—See Satori Capital, LLC; *U.S. Private*, pg. 3553
ZORIA FARMS INC.; *U.S. Private*, pg. 4608
ZORLU ENERJI ELEKTRIK URETIM AS—See Zorlu Holding AS; *Int'l*, pg. 8690
ZORLU FAKTORING A.S.; *Int'l*, pg. 8690
ZORLU HOLDING AS; *Int'l*, pg. 8690
ZORN COMPRESSOR & EQUIPMENT CO.; *U.S. Private*, pg. 4609
ZORO TOOLS, INC.—See W.W. Grainger, Inc.; *U.S. Public*, pg. 2320
ZORREL INTERNATIONAL, INC.; *U.S. Private*, pg. 4609
ZORSE CO., LTD.—See Vision, Inc; *Int'l*, pg. 8253
ZOSANO PHARMA CORPORATION; *U.S. Public*, pg. 2411
ZOS. B.V.—See HZPC Holland B.V.; *Int'l*, pg. 3561
ZOTAC USA INC.—See PC Partner Group Limited; *Int'l*, pg. 5766
ZOTA HEALTH CARE LTD.; *Int'l*, pg. 8690
ZOTEFOAMS FAR EAST—See Zotefoams plc; *Int'l*, pg. 8690
ZOTEFOAMS INC.—See Zotefoams plc; *Int'l*, pg. 8690

ZOTEFOAMS INTERNATIONAL LIMITED—See Zotefoams plc; *Int'l*, pg. 8690
ZOTEFOAMS PLC; *Int'l*, pg. 8690
ZOTEFOAMS T-FIT MATERIAL TECHNOLOGY (KUNSHAN) LIMITED—See Zotefoams plc; *Int'l*, pg. 8690
ZOT, INC.—See T-Rex Solutions, LLC; *U.S. Private*, pg. 3911
ZOTOS INTERNATIONAL, INC.—See Henkel AG & Co. KGaA; *Int'l*, pg. 3354
ZOTTI GROUP AVIATION, INC.; *U.S. Private*, pg. 4609
ZOTYE AUTOMOBILE CO., LTD; *Int'l*, pg. 8690
ZOUM ARMADA; *U.S. Private*, pg. 8691
ZOUPING PEAK CHP CO., LTD.—See Banpu Public Company Limited; *Int'l*, pg. 852
ZOUPING PEAK PTE. LTD.—See Banpu Public Company Limited; *Int'l*, pg. 852
ZOUP!; *U.S. Private*, pg. 4609
ZOUP! SPECIALTY PRODUCTS, LLC; *U.S. Private*, pg. 4609
ZOVIO INC.; *U.S. Public*, pg. 2411
ZOY HOME FURNISHING CO., LTD.; *Int'l*, pg. 8691
ZOZO, INC.—See SoftBank Group Corp.; *Int'l*, pg. 7052
ZOZZARO BROTHERS INC.; *U.S. Private*, pg. 4609
ZP BYTOS, S.R.O.—See Zeleziarne Podbrezova a.s.; *Int'l*, pg. 8631
ZPC OTMUCHOW S.A.; *Int'l*, pg. 8691
ZPD A/S—See Zeria Pharmaceutical Co., Ltd.; *Int'l*, pg. 8638
ZPF FOUNDRY4 GMBH—See DZ BANK AG Deutsche Zentral-Genossenschaftsbank; *Int'l*, pg. 2245
ZP - GASTROSERVIS, S.R.O.—See Zeleziarne Podbrezova a.s.; *Int'l*, pg. 8631
ZPG LIMITED—See Silver Lake Group, LLC; *U.S. Private*, pg. 3661
ZP-INVEST S.R.O.—See Zeleziarne Podbrezova a.s.; *Int'l*, pg. 8631
ZPN BESEL-FORMIT LTD.—See Cantoni Motor S.A.; *Int'l*, pg. 1299
Z-POWER AUTOMATION PTE. LTD.—See XMH Holdings Ltd.; *Int'l*, pg. 8536
ZPREPAY INC.—See Zulie Venture Inc.; *U.S. Private*, pg. 4610
ZP SPORT, A.S.—See Zeleziarne Podbrezova a.s.; *Int'l*, pg. 8631
ZPSV A.S. CANA—See Leonhard Moll Betonwerke GmbH & Co KG; *Int'l*, pg. 4462
ZPSV SERVIS, S.R.O.—See Leonhard Moll Betonwerke GmbH & Co KG; *Int'l*, pg. 4462
ZPSV S.R.O.—See Leonhard Moll Betonwerke GmbH & Co KG; *Int'l*, pg. 4462
ZP TAZIRNY TRUB SVINOV, SPOL. S R O.—See Zeleziarne Podbrezova a.s.; *Int'l*, pg. 8631
ZPUE S.A.; *Int'l*, pg. 8691
ZPW TRZUSKAWICA S.A.—See CRH plc; *Int'l*, pg. 1849
ZPZ LUBLIN SP. Z O.O.—See Przedsiebiorstwo Przemyslu Spozywczego PEPEES S.A.; *Int'l*, pg. 6014
ZQ CAPITAL MANAGEMENT LIMITED; *Int'l*, pg. 8691
ZQUARED LLC; *U.S. Private*, pg. 4609
ZRAK D.D. SARAJEVO; *Int'l*, pg. 8691
ZRAK-OPTOELEKTRONIKA A.D.; *Int'l*, pg. 8691
Z.R.C. JAPAN CO., LTD.—See Kyokuto Boeki Kaisha, Ltd.; *Int'l*, pg. 4362
ZREM-BUD SP. Z O.O.—See Jastrzebska Spolka Weglowa S.A.; *Int'l*, pg. 3913
ZRG KROSNO SP. Z O.O.—See Polskie Gornictwo Naftowe i Gazownictwo S.A.; *Int'l*, pg. 5912
ZRG PARTNERS, LLC—See RFE Investment Partners; *U.S. Private*, pg. 3419
ZRII, LLC—See Zilis, LLC; *U.S. Private*, pg. 4604
THE ZRIKE COMPANY INC.; *U.S. Private*, pg. 4140
ZROKA ENGINEERING, P.C.—See Milhouse Engineering & Construction, Inc.; *U.S. Private*, pg. 2729
ZRP PRINTING GROUP CO., LTD.; *Int'l*, pg. 8691
ZRP PRINTING (KUNSHAN) COMPANY LIMITED—See ZRP Printing Group Co., Ltd.; *Int'l*, pg. 8691
ZRP PRINTING (SHENYANG) COMPANY LIMITED—See ZRP Printing Group Co., Ltd.; *Int'l*, pg. 8691
ZRP PRINTING (VIETNAM) CO., LTD.—See ZRP Printing Group Co., Ltd.; *Int'l*, pg. 8691
ZR SYSTEMS GROUP LLC—See Evocative, Inc.; *U.S. Private*, pg. 1442
ZRUG SP. Z O.O.—See Polskie Gornictwo Naftowe i Gazownictwo S.A.; *Int'l*, pg. 5912
ZSA LEGAL RECRUITMENT LTD.; *Int'l*, pg. 8691
ZS ASSOCIATES, INC.; *U.S. Private*, pg. 4609
ZSAS (ZUKEN SUPPORT AND SERVICE) INC.—See Zuken, Inc.; *Int'l*, pg. 8694
ZSCALER, INC.; *U.S. Public*, pg. 2411
ZSCALER SOFTECH INDIA PRIVATE LIMITED—See Zscaler, Inc.; *U.S. Public*, pg. 2411
ZS ELASTOMERS CO., LTD.—See Sumitomo Chemical Company, Limited; *Int'l*, pg. 7267
ZS ELASTOMERS CO., LTD.—See Zeon Corporation; *Int'l*, pg. 8636
ZS FUND L.P.; *U.S. Private*, pg. 4609
ZSH GMBH—See MLP SE; *Int'l*, pg. 5004
ZSI-FOSTER, INC.—See TruArc Partners, L.P.; *U.S. Private*, pg. 4245
ZSK-LOZOVO AD; *Int'l*, pg. 8691

ZUBLIN IMMOBILIEN HOLDING AG

ZSL LONDON ZOO—See The Zoological Society of London; *Int'l*, pg. 7705
ZSL WHIPSNADE ZOO—See The Zoological Society of London; *Int'l*, pg. 7705
ZSNP, A.S.—See Penta Investments Limited; *Int'l*, pg. 5788
ZSO GMBH—See senata GmbH; *Int'l*, pg. 6707
ZS PHARMA, INC.—See AstraZeneca PLC; *Int'l*, pg. 661
Z SQUARED MEDIA, LLC; *U.S. Private*, pg. 4596
ZSR CORPORATION LTD.—See Tate & Lyle PLC; *Int'l*, pg. 7474
ZS SVETOVANJE, STORITVE ZAVAROVALNEGA ZASTOPANJA, D.O.O.—See Pozavarovalnica Sava, d.d.; *Int'l*, pg. 5949
ZST DIGITAL NETWORKS, INC.; *Int'l*, pg. 8691
ZT AUTOMATION LIMITED—See Cognizant Technology Solutions Corporation; *U.S. Public*, pg. 525
ZTC BANJA VRUCICA A.D. TESLIC; *Int'l*, pg. 8691
ZT CORPORATE; *U.S. Private*, pg. 4609
ZTE (AUSTRALIA) PTY LTD—See ZTE Corporation; *Int'l*, pg. 8691
ZTE CANADA INC—See ZTE Corporation; *Int'l*, pg. 8691
Z-TECH LLC—See Compagnie de Saint-Gobain SA; *Int'l*, pg. 1732
ZTEC INSTRUMENTS, INC.—See Teradyne, Inc.; *U.S. Public*, pg. 2018
ZTE CORPORATION ARMENIA—See ZTE Corporation; *Int'l*, pg. 8692
ZTE CORPORATION ISTANBUL TELEKOMINIKASYON. SAN. VE TIC. LTD. STI.—See ZTE Corporation; *Int'l*, pg. 8692
ZTE CORPORATION—See ZTE Corporation; *Int'l*, pg. 8692
ZTE CORPORATION—See ZTE Corporation; *Int'l*, pg. 8692
ZTE CORPORATION; *Int'l*, pg. 8691
ZTE DEUTSCHLAND GMBH—See ZTE Corporation; *Int'l*, pg. 8692
ZTE (H.K) LIMITED—See ZTE Corporation; *Int'l*, pg. 8691
Z-TEJAS INC.; *U.S. Private*, pg. 4596
ZTE KOREA LIMITED—See ZTE Corporation; *Int'l*, pg. 8692
ZTE (MALAYSIA) CORPORATION—See ZTE Corporation; *Int'l*, pg. 8691
ZTEST ELECTRONICS INC.; *Int'l*, pg. 8692
ZTE (THAILAND) CO., LTD.—See ZTE Corporation; *Int'l*, pg. 8691
ZT GROUP INT'L INC.; *U.S. Private*, pg. 4609
Z.T. KRUSZWICA S.A.—See Bunge Limited; *U.S. Public*, pg. 412
ZT MOTORS HOLDING, L.P.—See ZT Corporate; *U.S. Private*, pg. 4609
ZTO EXPRESS (CAYMAN) INC.—See ZTO Express (Cayman) Inc.; *Int'l*, pg. 8692
ZTORE HK LIMITED—See Television Broadcasts Limited; *Int'l*, pg. 7542
ZTR ACQUISITION CORP.; *Int'l*, pg. 8692
Z TRANSPORTATION INC.; *U.S. Private*, pg. 4596
ZTS INMART AS; *Int'l*, pg. 8692
ZTS SABINOV AS; *Int'l*, pg. 8692
ZTS VYSKUMNO-VYVOJOVY USTAV KOSICE AS; *Int'l*, pg. 8692
ZTT INDIA PRIVATE LIMITED—See Jiangsu Zhongtian Technology Co., Ltd.; *Int'l*, pg. 3958
ZUARI AGRI SCIENCES LIMITED—See Adventz Group; *Int'l*, pg. 167
ZUARI AGRO CHEMICALS LIMITED—See Adventz Group; *Int'l*, pg. 167
ZUARI CEMENT—See Heidelberg Materials AG; *Int'l*, pg. 3317
ZUARI FERTILISERS & CHEMICALS LIMITED—See Adventz Group; *Int'l*, pg. 167
ZUARI GLOBAL LTD.—See Adventz Group; *Int'l*, pg. 167
ZUARI MAROC PHOSPHATES LIMITED—See Adventz Group; *Int'l*, pg. 167
ZUARI MAROC PHOSPHATES LIMITED—See OCP SA; *Int'l*, pg. 5520
ZUBATKIN OWNER REPRESENTATION, LLC—See Cumming Construction Management, Inc.; *U.S. Private*, pg. 1123
ZUBERANCE, INC.—See IZEA Worldwide, Inc.; *U.S. Public*, pg. 1179
ZUBI ADVERTISING SERVICES, INC.—See WPP plc; *Int'l*, pg. 8469
ZUBLER GERATEBAU GMBH; *Int'l*, pg. 8692
ZUBLIN A/S—See STRABAG SE; *Int'l*, pg. 7233
ZUBLIN BAUGESELLSCHAFT M.B.H.—See STRABAG SE; *Int'l*, pg. 7233
ZUBLIN CHIMNEY & REFRACTORY GMBH—See STRABAG SE; *Int'l*, pg. 7234
ZUBLIN CONSTRUCT S.R.L.—See STRABAG SE; *Int'l*, pg. 7234
ZUBLIN GROUND AND CIVIL ENGINEERING LLC—See STRABAG SE; *Int'l*, pg. 7234
ZUBLIN IMMOBILIEN HOLDING AG; *Int'l*, pg. 8692
ZUBLIN IMMOBILIEN MANAGEMENT AG—See Zublin Immobilien Holding AG; *Int'l*, pg. 8692
ZUBLIN INC.—See STRABAG SE; *Int'l*, pg. 7234
ZUBLIN INTERNATIONAL CHILE LTDA.—See STRABAG SE; *Int'l*, pg. 7234

ZUBLIN IMMOBILIEN HOLDING AG

ZUBLIN INTERNATIONAL GMBH—See STRABAG SE; *Int'l*, pg. 7234
ZUBLIN K.F.T—See STRABAG SE; *Int'l*, pg. 7234
ZUBLIN NEDERLAND B.V.—See STRABAG SE; *Int'l*, pg. 7234
ZUBLIN ROMANIA S.R.L.—See STRABAG SE; *Int'l*, pg. 7234
ZUBLIN SCANDINAVIA AB—See STRABAG SE; *Int'l*, pg. 7234
ZUBLIN SPEZIALTIEFBAU GES.M.B.H.—See STRABAG SE; *Int'l*, pg. 7234
ZUBLIN SPEZIALTIEFBAU GMBH—See STRABAG SE; *Int'l*, pg. 7234
ZUBLIN SP.Z O.O—See STRABAG SE; *Int'l*, pg. 7234
ZUBLIN STAHLBAU GMBH—See STRABAG SE; *Int'l*, pg. 7234
ZUBLIN STAVEBNI SPOL S.R.O.—See STRABAG SE; *Int'l*, pg. 7234
ZUBLIN TIMBER GAILDORF GMBH—See STRABAG SE; *Int'l*, pg. 7233
ZUBLIN TIMBER GMBH—See STRABAG SE; *Int'l*, pg. 7233
ZUBLIN UMWELTTECHNIK GMBH—See STRABAG SE; *Int'l*, pg. 7234
ZUBOR BUICK GMC, INC.; *U.S. Private*, pg. 4609
ZUBRA, INC.; *U.S. Private*, pg. 4609
ZUCCHETTI AXESS S.P.A.—See Zucchetti Group S.p.A.; *Int'l*, pg. 8692
ZUCCHETTI BRASIL SOLUCOES DE INFORMATICA LTDA—See Zucchetti Group S.p.A.; *Int'l*, pg. 8692
ZUCCHETTI CENTRO SISTEMI S.P.A.—See Zucchetti Group S.p.A.; *Int'l*, pg. 8692
ZUCCHETTI GMBH—See Zucchetti Group S.p.A.; *Int'l*, pg. 8692
ZUCCHETTI GROUP S.P.A.; *Int'l*, pg. 8692
ZUCCHETTI ROMANIA SRL—See Zucchetti Group S.p.A.; *Int'l*, pg. 8692
ZUCCHETTI S.P.A.—See Zucchetti Group S.p.A.; *Int'l*, pg. 8692
ZUCCHETTI USA LLC—See Zucchetti Group S.p.A.; *Int'l*, pg. 8692
ZUCHELLI & JOHNSON HEALTHCARE COMMUNICATIONS; *U.S. Private*, pg. 4609
ZUCKERMAN-HONICKMAN INC.; *U.S. Private*, pg. 4609
ZUCKS INC—See CyberAgent, Inc.; *Int'l*, pg. 1892
ZUCOTEC-SOCIEDADE DE CONSTRUCOES LDA—See STRABAG SE; *Int'l*, pg. 7234
THE ZUELLIG GROUP INC.; *Int'l*, pg. 7705
ZUELLIG GROUP NA, INC.—See The Zuellig Group Inc.; *Int'l*, pg. 7705
ZUELLIG PHARMA ASIA PACIFIC LTD.—See The Zuellig Group Inc.; *Int'l*, pg. 7705
ZUELLIG PHARMA BANGLADESH LTD.—See The Zuellig Group Inc.; *Int'l*, pg. 7705
ZUELLIG PHARMA CORPORATION—See The Zuellig Group Inc.; *Int'l*, pg. 7705
ZUELLIG PHARMA, INC.—See The Zuellig Group Inc.; *Int'l*, pg. 7705
ZUELLIG PHARMA KOREA LTD.—See The Zuellig Group Inc.; *Int'l*, pg. 7705
ZUELLIG PHARMA LTD.—See The Zuellig Group Inc.; *Int'l*, pg. 7705
ZUELLIG PHARMA LTD.—See The Zuellig Group Inc.; *Int'l*, pg. 7705
ZUELLIG PHARMA LTD.—See The Zuellig Group Inc.; *Int'l*, pg. 7705
ZUELLIG PHARMA PTE. LTD.—See The Zuellig Group Inc.; *Int'l*, pg. 7705
ZUELLIG PHARMA SDN. BHD.—See The Zuellig Group Inc.; *Int'l*, pg. 7705
ZUELLIG PHARMA VIETNAM LTD.—See The Zuellig Group Inc.; *Int'l*, pg. 7705
ZUERICH INSURANCE AG—See Zurich Insurance Group Limited; *Int'l*, pg. 8697
ZUERICH VERSICHERUNGS-AKTIENGESELLSCHAFT—See Zurich Insurance Group Limited; *Int'l*, pg. 8697
ZUERN BUILDING PRODUCTS INC.; *U.S. Private*, pg. 4610
ZUE S.A.; *Int'l*, pg. 8692
ZUF ACQUISITIONS I LLC—See EVI Industries, Inc.; *U.S. Public*, pg. 803
ZUFALL HEALTH; *U.S. Private*, pg. 4610
ZUFFA, LLC—See Silver Lake Group, LLC; *U.S. Private*, pg. 3654
ZUGARA INC.; *U.S. Private*, pg. 4610
ZUGER KANTONALBANK AG; *Int'l*, pg. 8693
ZUG ESTATES AG—See Zug Estates Holding AG; *Int'l*, pg. 8693
ZUG ESTATES HOLDING AG; *Int'l*, pg. 8692
ZUHNE LLC; *U.S. Private*, pg. 4610
ZUIDWENDING V.O.F—See N.V. Nederlandse Gasunie; *Int'l*, pg. 5117
ZUIKO CO., LTD.; *Int'l*, pg. 8693
ZUIKO CO., LTD. - TORIKAI-KAMI FACTORY—See Zuiko Co., Ltd.; *Int'l*, pg. 8693
ZUIKO CO., LTD. - TORIKAI-NAKA FACTORY—See Zuiko Co., Ltd.; *Int'l*, pg. 8693

ZUIKO (SHANGHAI) CORPORATION—See Zuiko Co., Ltd.; *Int'l*, pg. 8693
ZUI NOVUM SP. Z.O.O.—See Asseco Poland S.A.; *Int'l*, pg. 642
ZUI OTAGO SP. Z.O.O.—See Asseco Poland S.A.; *Int'l*, pg. 642
ZUITE AB—See Knightec AB; *Int'l*, pg. 4207
ZUIVELCOOPERATIE FRIESLANDCAMPINA U.A.; *Int'l*, pg. 8693
ZU JEDDELOH PFLANZENHANDELS GMBH; *Int'l*, pg. 8692
ZUJI LIMITED—See ZUJI Pte. Limited; *Int'l*, pg. 8694
ZUJI PTE. LIMITED; *Int'l*, pg. 8694
ZUJI TRAVEL PTE. LTD.—See ZUJI Pte. Limited; *Int'l*, pg. 8694
ZUKEN ALFATECH INC.—See Zuken, Inc.; *Int'l*, pg. 8694
ZUKEN B.V.—See Zuken, Inc.; *Int'l*, pg. 8694
ZUKEN E3 GMBH—See Zuken, Inc.; *Int'l*, pg. 8694
ZUKEN E3 GMBH SP. Z O.O—See Zuken, Inc.; *Int'l*, pg. 8694
ZUKEN ELMIC, INC.—See Zuken, Inc.; *Int'l*, pg. 8694
ZUKEN, GMBH—See Zuken, Inc.; *Int'l*, pg. 8695
ZUKEN GROUP LTD.—See Zuken, Inc.; *Int'l*, pg. 8694
ZUKEN, INC.; *Int'l*, pg. 8694
ZUKEN KOREA, INC.—See Zuken, Inc.; *Int'l*, pg. 8694
ZUKEN LTD.—See Zuken, Inc.; *Int'l*, pg. 8694
ZUKEN MODELINX INC.—See Zuken, Inc.; *Int'l*, pg. 8694
ZUKEN NETWAVE INC.—See Zuken, Inc.; *Int'l*, pg. 8694
ZUKEN PRESIGHT INC.—See Zuken, Inc.; *Int'l*, pg. 8694
ZUKEN S.A.—See Zuken, Inc.; *Int'l*, pg. 8694
ZUKEN (SHANGHAI) TECHNICAL CENTER CO., LTD.—See Zuken, Inc.; *Int'l*, pg. 8694
ZUKEN SINGAPORE PTE., LTD.—See Zuken, Inc.; *Int'l*, pg. 8694
ZUKEN S.R.L.—See Zuken, Inc.; *Int'l*, pg. 8694
ZUKEN UK LTD.—See Zuken, Inc.; *Int'l*, pg. 8694
ZUKEN USA INC.—See Zuken, Inc.; *Int'l*, pg. 8694
ZUKEN VITECH INC.—See Zuken, Inc.; *Int'l*, pg. 8694
ZUKE'S LANDSCAPE, INC.—See Landscape Developmental Inc.; *U.S. Private*, pg. 2387
ZUKUNFT VENTURES GMBH—See ZF Friedrichshafen AG; *Int'l*, pg. 8647
ZULEIKA GOLD LIMITED; *Int'l*, pg. 8695
ZULIE VENTURE INC.; *U.S. Private*, pg. 4610
ZULILY, LLC—See Regent, L.P.; *U.S. Private*, pg. 3388
ZULTRANS PROPRIETARY LIMITED—See Super Group Limited; *Int'l*, pg. 7335
ZULULAND OBSERVER (PTY) LTD.—See Caxton and CTP Publishers and Printers Ltd.; *Int'l*, pg. 1363
ZULULAND OBSERVER (PTY) LTD.—See Caxton and CTP Publishers and Printers Ltd.; *Int'l*, pg. 1363
ZULULAND OBSERVER (PTY) LTD.—See Caxton and CTP Publishers and Printers Ltd.; *Int'l*, pg. 1363
ZULULAND OBSERVER (PTY) LTD.—See Caxton and CTP Publishers and Printers Ltd.; *Int'l*, pg. 1363
ZULU MARKETING, LLC; *U.S. Private*, pg. 4610
ZUMA BANGKOK LIMITED—See Minor International PCL; *Int'l*, pg. 4913
ZUMA PRESS, INC.; *U.S. Private*, pg. 4610
ZUMASYS, INC; *U.S. Private*, pg. 4610
ZUMBACH BUREAU FRANCE—See Zumbach Electronic AG; *Int'l*, pg. 8695
ZUMBACH DO BRASIL LTDA—See Zumbach Electronic AG; *Int'l*, pg. 8695
ZUMBACH ELECTRONICA ARGENTINA S.R.L.—See Zumbach Electronic AG; *Int'l*, pg. 8695
ZUMBACH ELECTRONIC AG; *Int'l*, pg. 8695
ZUMBACH ELECTRONICA S.L.—See Zumbach Electronic AG; *Int'l*, pg. 8695
ZUMBACH ELECTRONIC GMBH—See Zumbach Electronic AG; *Int'l*, pg. 8695
ZUMBACH ELECTRONIC INDIA PVT. LTD.—See Zumbach Electronic AG; *Int'l*, pg. 8695
ZUMBACH ELECTRONIC P.R. CHINA—See Zumbach Electronic AG; *Int'l*, pg. 8695
ZUMBACH ELECTRONIC S.A.—See Zumbach Electronic AG; *Int'l*, pg. 8695
ZUMBACH ELECTRONICS CORP.—See Zumbach Electronic AG; *Int'l*, pg. 8695
ZUMBACH ELECTRONICS FAR EAST—See Zumbach Electronic AG; *Int'l*, pg. 8695
ZUMBACH ELECTRONICS LTD.—See Zumbach Electronic AG; *Int'l*, pg. 8695
ZUMBACH ELECTRONIC SRL—See Zumbach Electronic AG; *Int'l*, pg. 8695
ZUMBIEL PACKAGING CO.-BEVERAGE DIVISION—See Zumbiel Packaging Co.; *U.S. Private*, pg. 4610
ZUMBIEL PACKAGING CO.; *U.S. Private*, pg. 4610
ZUMDIECK ASIA LTD.—See ZUMDIECK GmbH; *Int'l*, pg. 8695
ZUMDIECK GMBH; *Int'l*, pg. 8695
ZUMELEC S.A.R.L.—See Zumbach Electronic AG; *Int'l*, pg. 8695
ZUMEX FRANCE SARL—See Zumex Group, S.A.; *Int'l*, pg. 8695
ZUMEX GROUP, S.A.; *Int'l*, pg. 8695
ZUMEX MEXICO S.A. DE CV—See Zumex Group, S.A.; *Int'l*, pg. 8695
ZUMEX UK LTD.—See Zumex Group, S.A.; *Int'l*, pg. 8695

CORPORATE AFFILIATIONS

ZUMIEZ INCORPORATED; *U.S. Public*, pg. 2411
ZUMIEZ SERVICES INC.—See Zumiez Incorporated; *U.S. Public*, pg. 2411
ZUMING BEAN PRODUCTS CO., LTD.; *Int'l*, pg. 8695
ZUMINTERNET CORP.; *Int'l*, pg. 8695
ZUMOT REAL ESTATE MANAGEMENT, INC.; *U.S. Private*, pg. 4610
ZUMPANO ENTERPRISES INC.; *U.S. Private*, pg. 4610
ZUMTOBEL GROUP AG; *Int'l*, pg. 8695
ZUMTOBEL GROUP DEUTSCHLAND GMBH—See Zumtobel Group AG; *Int'l*, pg. 8696
ZUMTOBEL HOLDING GMBH—See Zumtobel Group AG; *Int'l*, pg. 8696
ZUMTOBEL LIGHTING GMBH—See Zumtobel Group AG; *Int'l*, pg. 8696
ZUMTOBEL LIGHTING INC.—See Zumtobel Group AG; *Int'l*, pg. 8696
ZUMTOBEL LIGHTING ROMANIA SRL—See Zumtobel Group AG; *Int'l*, pg. 8696
ZUNG FU COMPANY LTD.—See Jardine Matheson Holdings Limited; *Int'l*, pg. 3908
ZUNGWON ENGINEERING & SYSTEM INC.; *Int'l*, pg. 8696
ZUNGWON EN-SYS, INC.; *Int'l*, pg. 8696
ZUNO BANK AG—See Raiffeisen Bank International AG; *Int'l*, pg. 6184
ZUNYI HEXIN PACKAGING CO., LTD.—See Xiamen Hexing Packaging Printing Co., Ltd.; *Int'l*, pg. 8524
ZUOAN FASHION LIMITED; *Int'l*, pg. 8696
ZUOLI KECHUANG MICRO-FINANCE COMPANY LIMITED; *Int'l*, pg. 8696
ZUORA AUSTRALIA PTY. LTD.—See Zuora, Inc.; *U.S. Public*, pg. 2412
ZUORA GERMANY GMBH—See Zuora, Inc.; *U.S. Public*, pg. 2412
ZUORA, INC.; *U.S. Public*, pg. 2411
ZUORA INDIA PRIVATE LIMITED—See Zuora, Inc.; *U.S. Public*, pg. 2412
ZUORA JAPAN KK—See Zuora, Inc.; *U.S. Public*, pg. 2412
ZUORA UK LIMITED—See Zuora, Inc.; *U.S. Public*, pg. 2412
ZUPANCICH BROS INC.; *U.S. Private*, pg. 4610
ZUPAN ENTERPRISES INC.; *U.S. Private*, pg. 4610
ZUPLJANKA A.D.; *Int'l*, pg. 8696
ZUPPS ASPLEY PTY LTD—See Eagers Automotive Limited; *Int'l*, pg. 2264
ZUPPS MT GRAVATT PTY LTD—See Eagers Automotive Limited; *Int'l*, pg. 2264
ZURA BIO LIMITED; *U.S. Public*, pg. 2412
ZURBUCHEN OIL, INC.—See Edward H. Wolf & Sons Inc.; *U.S. Private*, pg. 1341
ZURCHER KANTONALBANK; *Int'l*, pg. 8697
ZURCHER UNTERLAND MEDIEN AG—See TX Group AG; *Int'l*, pg. 7992
ZUREX CORPORATION SDN. BHD.—See Graphene Nanochem plc; *Int'l*, pg. 3060
ZURFLUH FELLER S.A.S.—See Somfy SA; *Int'l*, pg. 7086
ZURICH AG—See Zurich Insurance Group Limited; *Int'l*, pg. 8697
ZURICH AMERICAN INSURANCE COMPANY OF ILLINOIS—See Zurich Insurance Group Limited; *Int'l*, pg. 8699
ZURICH AMERICAN INSURANCE CO.—See Zurich Insurance Group Limited; *Int'l*, pg. 8699
ZURICH AMERICAN LIFE INSURANCE COMPANY—See Zurich Insurance Group Limited; *Int'l*, pg. 8698
ZURICH ASSURANCE LTD.—See Zurich Insurance Group Limited; *Int'l*, pg. 8698
ZURICH AUSTRALIA LIMITED—See Zurich Insurance Group Limited; *Int'l*, pg. 8698
ZURICH AUSTRALIAN INSURANCE LTD.—See Zurich Insurance Group Limited; *Int'l*, pg. 8698
ZURICH BETEILIGUNGS-AKTIENGESELLSCHAFT—See Zurich Insurance Group Limited; *Int'l*, pg. 8698
ZURICH BRASIL SEGUROS S.A.—See Zurich Insurance Group Limited; *Int'l*, pg. 8698
ZURICH CAPITAL MARKETS—See Zurich Insurance Group Limited; *Int'l*, pg. 8699
ZURICH COMPAGNIE MAROCAINE DASSURANCES—See Zurich Insurance Group Limited; *Int'l*, pg. 8698
ZURICH COMPANHIA DE SEGUROS S.A.—See Zurich Insurance Group Limited; *Int'l*, pg. 8698
ZURICH COMPANIA DE SEGUROS S.A.—See Zurich Insurance Group Limited; *Int'l*, pg. 8698
ZURICH DEUTSCHER HEROLD LEBENVERSICHERUNG AG—See Zurich Insurance Group Limited; *Int'l*, pg. 8697
ZURICH FINANCE COMPANY AG—See Zurich Insurance Group Limited; *Int'l*, pg. 8698
ZURICH FINANCIAL SERVICES AUSTRALIA LTD.—See Zurich Insurance Group Limited; *Int'l*, pg. 8698
ZURICH FINANCIAL SERVICES TAIWAN LTD.—See Zurich Insurance Group Limited; *Int'l*, pg. 8698
ZURICH GLOBAL CORPORATE UK LTD.—See Zurich Insurance Group Limited; *Int'l*, pg. 8698
ZURICH GROUP FRANKFURT—See Zurich Insurance Group Limited; *Int'l*, pg. 8698

COMPANY NAME INDEX

ZURICH GROUP HOLDING AG—See Zurich Insurance Group Limited; *Int'l*, pg. 8698
ZURICH GSG LTD.—See Zurich Insurance Group Limited; *Int'l*, pg. 8698
ZURICH HOLDING COMPANY OF AMERICA, INC.—See Zurich Insurance Group Limited; *Int'l*, pg. 8698
ZURICH IGUAZU COMPANIA DE SEGUROS (VIDAL)—See Zurich Insurance Group Limited; *Int'l*, pg. 8699
ZURICH INSURANCE AG—See Zurich Insurance Group Limited; *Int'l*, pg. 8697
ZURICH INSURANCE AG—See Zurich Insurance Group Limited; *Int'l*, pg. 8698
ZURICH INSURANCE COMPANY LTD.—See Zurich Insurance Group Limited; *Int'l*, pg. 8699
ZURICH INSURANCE COMPANY (POLAND) SA—See Zurich Insurance Group Limited; *Int'l*, pg. 8699
ZURICH INSURANCE COMPANY (RUSSIA) LTD.—See Zurich Insurance Group Limited; *Int'l*, pg. 8699
ZURICH INSURANCE GROUP (HONG KONG)—See Zurich Insurance Group Limited; *Int'l*, pg. 8699
ZURICH INSURANCE GROUP LIMITED; *Int'l*, pg. 8697
ZURICH INSURANCE PLC—See Zurich Insurance Group Limited; *Int'l*, pg. 8699
ZURICH INSURANCE (TAIWAN) LTD.—See Hotai Motor Co., Ltd.; *Int'l*, pg. 3487
ZURICH INTERNATIONAL (BELGIQUE) S.A.—See Zurich Insurance Group Limited; *Int'l*, pg. 8699
ZURICH INTERNATIONAL (BERMUDA) LTD.—See Zurich Insurance Group Limited; *Int'l*, pg. 8699
ZURICH INTERNATIONAL (DEUTSCHLAND) VERSICHERUNGS AG—See Zurich Insurance Group Limited; *Int'l*, pg. 8698
ZURICH INTERNATIONAL DE VENEZUELA C.A. DE CORRETAJE DE REASEGUROS—See Zurich Insurance Group Limited; *Int'l*, pg. 8699
ZURICH INTERNATIONAL (ITALIA) S.P.A.—See Zurich Insurance Group Limited; *Int'l*, pg. 8699
ZURICH INTERNATIONAL (NEDERLAND) N.V.—See Zurich Insurance Group Limited; *Int'l*, pg. 8699
ZURICH INTERNATIONAL SERVICES (LUXEMBOURG) S.A.—See Zurich Insurance Group Limited; *Int'l*, pg. 8699
ZURICH INTERNATIONAL (UK) LIMITED—See Zurich Insurance Group Limited; *Int'l*, pg. 8699
ZURICH INVESTMENT MANAGEMENT LTD.—See Zurich Insurance Group Limited; *Int'l*, pg. 8699
ZURICH INVESTMENT SERVICES LTD.—See Zurich Insurance Group Limited; *Int'l*, pg. 8699
ZURICH INVESTMENTS LIFE—See Zurich Insurance Group Limited; *Int'l*, pg. 8699
ZURICH INVESTMENTS SGR—See Zurich Insurance Group Limited; *Int'l*, pg. 8699
ZURICH ITALY BANK S.P.A.—See Zurich Insurance Group Limited; *Int'l*, pg. 8699
ZURICH LIFE ASSURANCE PLC—See Zurich Insurance Group Limited; *Int'l*, pg. 8699
ZURICH LIFE INSURANCE MALAYSIA BERHAD—See Zurich Insurance Group Limited; *Int'l*, pg. 8699
ZURICH PACIFIC INSURANCE PTY. LTD.—See Zurich Insurance Group Limited; *Int'l*, pg. 8699
ZURICH SANTANDER SEGUROS MEXICO, S.A.—See Zurich Insurance Group Limited; *Int'l*, pg. 8699
ZURICH SEGUROS S.A.—See Zurich Insurance Group Limited; *Int'l*, pg. 8699
ZURICH VERSICHERUNGS-AKTIENGESELLSCHAFT—See Zurich Insurance Group Limited; *Int'l*, pg. 8699
ZURICH VIDA COMPANIA DE SEGUROS S.A.—See Zurich Insurance Group Limited; *Int'l*, pg. 8699
ZURITIPP AG—See TX Group AG; *Int'l*, pg. 7992
ZURN ELKAY WATER SOLUTIONS CORPORATION; *U.S. Public*, pg. 2412
ZURN INDUSTRIES CAST METALS OPERATIONS—See Zurn Elkay Water Solutions Corporation; *U.S. Public*, pg. 2413
ZURN INDUSTRIES LIMITED—See Zurn Elkay Water Solutions Corporation; *U.S. Public*, pg. 2414
ZURN INDUSTRIES, LLC—See Zurn Elkay Water Solutions Corporation; *U.S. Public*, pg. 2413
ZURN INDUSTRIES—See Zurn Elkay Water Solutions Corporation; *U.S. Public*, pg. 2414
ZURN PEX, INC.—See Zurn Elkay Water Solutions Corporation; *U.S. Public*, pg. 2414
ZURN PLUMBING PRODUCTS GROUP—See Zurn Elkay Water Solutions Corporation; *U.S. Public*, pg. 2413
ZURN WATER, LLC—See Zurn Elkay Water Solutions Corporation; *U.S. Public*, pg. 2414
ZURPLE, INC.; *U.S. Private*, pg. 4610
ZUR ROSE GROUP AG; *Int'l*, pg. 8696
ZUR ROSE PHARMA GMBH—See Zur Rose Group AG; *Int'l*, pg. 8697
ZUR SHAMIR HOLDINGS LTD.; *Int'l*, pg. 8697
ZURVITA HOLDINGS, INC.; *U.S. Public*, pg. 2414
ZUTANO GLOBAL INC.; *U.S. Private*, pg. 4610
ZUTHER & HAUTMANN GMBH & CO. KG—See L'Air Liquide S.A.; *Int'l*, pg. 4374
ZUU CO., LTD.; *Int'l*, pg. 8699

ZUVAY TECHNOLOGIES PVT. LTD.—See S.C New Energy Technology Corporation; *Int'l*, pg. 6449
ZVC AUSTRALIA PTY. LTD.—See Zoom Video Communications, Inc.; *U.S. Public*, pg. 2411
ZVC FRANCE SAS—See Zoom Video Communications, Inc.; *U.S. Public*, pg. 2411
ZVC JAPAN KK—See Zoom Video Communications, Inc.; *U.S. Public*, pg. 2411
ZVC UK LTD.—See Zoom Video Communications, Inc.; *U.S. Public*, pg. 2411
ZVECEVO-LASTA D.D.; *Int'l*, pg. 8700
ZVECEVO PREHRAMBENA INDUSTRIJA D.D; *Int'l*, pg. 8699
ZVELO, INC.; *U.S. Private*, pg. 4610
ZVENTS, INC.—See eBay Inc.; *U.S. Public*, pg. 709
ZVEZDARA AVALA A.D.; *Int'l*, pg. 8700
ZVIJEZDA D.D.; *Int'l*, pg. 8700
ZVI SARFATI & SONS INVESTMENTS & CONSTRUCTIONS LTD.; *Int'l*, pg. 8700
ZVON DVA HOLDING D.D.; *Int'l*, pg. 8700
ZVON ENA HOLDING D.D.; *Int'l*, pg. 8700
ZVORNIKPUTEVI A.D.; *Int'l*, pg. 8700
ZV PATE INC; *U.S. Private*, pg. 4610
ZVS ENCO A.S.—See Enco spol. s r.o.; *Int'l*, pg. 2401
ZVU STROJIRNY, A.S.—See Safichem Group AG; *Int'l*, pg. 6471
ZWACK UNICUM RT.; *Int'l*, pg. 8700
ZWAHLEN & MAYR SA; *Int'l*, pg. 8700
ZWANENBERG FOOD GROUP B.V.; *Int'l*, pg. 8700
ZWANENBERG FOOD GROUP (USA) INC.—See Zwanenberg Food Group B.V.; *Int'l*, pg. 8700
ZWANENBERG FOOD OSS B.V.—See Zwanenberg Food Group B.V.; *Int'l*, pg. 8700
Z-WAVE ALLIANCE, LLC—See Silicon Laboratories Inc.; *U.S. Public*, pg. 1880
ZW DATA ACTION TECHNOLOGIES INC.; *Int'l*, pg. 8700
ZWEI CO., LTD.—See IBJ Inc.; *Int'l*, pg. 3576
ZWEIG ADVISERS LLC—See Virtus Investment Partners, Inc.; *U.S. Public*, pg. 2301
ZWEIGWHITE LLC; *U.S. Private*, pg. 4610
ZWEITE BASF IMMOBILIEN-GESELLSCHAFT MBH—See BASF SE; *Int'l*, pg. 886
ZWEITE ENVITEC BETEILIGUNGS GMBH & CO. KG—See EnviTec Biogas AG; *Int'l*, pg. 2456
ZWEITE K-W-A BETEILIGUNGSGESELLSCHAFT MBH—See Bayer Aktiengesellschaft; *Int'l*, pg. 910
ZWEITE REAL,- SB-WARENHAUS GMBH—See Metro AG; *Int'l*, pg. 4859
ZWICKER ELECTRIC CO., INC.; *U.S. Private*, pg. 4610
ZWICK GMBH & CO. KG; *Int'l*, pg. 8700
ZWICK USA L.P.—See Zwick GmbH & Co. KG; *Int'l*, pg. 8700
ZWICKY ELECTRONIC AG—See NEXUS AG; *Int'l*, pg. 5250
ZWILLING J.A. HENCKELS AG—See Wilh. Werhahn KG; *Int'l*, pg. 8410
ZWIPE AS; *Int'l*, pg. 8700
Z-WORK ACQUISITION CORP.; *U.S. Public*, pg. 2400
ZWP - ZERSTORUNGSFREIE WERKSTOFFPRUFUNG GMBH—See TUV SUD AG; *Int'l*, pg. 7986
ZWSOFT GUANGZHOU CO., LTD.; *Int'l*, pg. 8700
ZXY MEQQE CORPORATION—See Cresco, Ltd.; *Int'l*, pg. 1840
ZYCI LLC; *U.S. Private*, pg. 4611
ZYCRON INC.—See BGSF, Inc.; *U.S. Public*, pg. 330
ZYDUS ANIMAL HEALTH LIMITED—See Zydus Lifesciences Limited; *Int'l*, pg. 8700
ZYDUS FRANCE SAS.—See Zydus Lifesciences Limited; *Int'l*, pg. 8700
ZYDUS HEALTHCARE BRASIL LTDA.—See Zydus Lifesciences Limited; *Int'l*, pg. 8701
ZYDUS HEALTHCARE LIMITED—See Zydus Lifesciences Limited; *Int'l*, pg. 8701
ZYDUS HEALTHCARE PHILIPPINES INC.—See Zydus Lifesciences Limited; *Int'l*, pg. 8701
ZYDUS HEALTHCARE (USA) LLC—See Zydus Lifesciences Limited; *Int'l*, pg. 8701
ZYDUS HOSPIRA ONCOLOGY PRIVATE LIMITED—See Pfizer Inc.; *U.S. Public*, pg. 1683
ZYDUS LIFESCIENCES LIMITED; *Int'l*, pg. 8700
ZYDUS NIKKHO FARMACEUTICA LTDA.—See Zydus Lifesciences Limited; *Int'l*, pg. 8701
ZYDUS NYCOMED HEALTHCARE PRIVATE LTD.—See Takeda Pharmaceutical Company Limited; *Int'l*, pg. 7440
ZYDUS NYCOMED HEALTHCARE PRIVATE LTD.—See Zydus Lifesciences Limited; *Int'l*, pg. 8701
ZYDUS PHARMACEUTICALS USA INC.—See Zydus Lifesciences Limited; *Int'l*, pg. 8701
ZYDUS WELLNESS LIMITED—See Zydus Lifesciences Limited; *Int'l*, pg. 8701
ZYDUS WELLNESS PRODUCTS LIMITED—See Zydus Lifesciences Limited; *Int'l*, pg. 8701
ZYF LOPSKING ALUMINUM CO., LTD.; *Int'l*, pg. 8701
ZYF LOPSKING MATERIAL TECHNOLOGY CO LTD; *Int'l*, pg. 8701
ZYGA TECHNOLOGY, INC.—See Montagu Private Equity LLP; *Int'l*, pg. 5036

ZYVERSA THERAPEUTICS, INC.

ZYGO CORPORATION—See AMETEK, Inc.; *U.S. Public*, pg. 119
ZYGO CORPORATION - WESTERN REGIONAL OFFICE—See AMETEK, Inc.; *U.S. Public*, pg. 119
ZYGO ELECTRO-OPTICS GROUP MANUFACTURING CENTER—See AMETEK, Inc.; *U.S. Public*, pg. 119
ZYGO K.K.—See AMETEK, Inc.; *U.S. Public*, pg. 119
ZYGOLAMDA METROLOGY INSTRUMENT (SHANGHAI) CO., LTD.—See AMETEK, Inc.; *U.S. Public*, pg. 119
ZYGOLOT GMBH—See AMETEK, Inc.; *U.S. Public*, pg. 119
ZYGO PTE. LTD.—See AMETEK, Inc.; *U.S. Public*, pg. 119
ZYGO RICHMOND, INC.—See AMETEK, Inc.; *U.S. Public*, pg. 119
ZYGO TAIWAN CO., LTD.—See AMETEK, Inc.; *U.S. Public*, pg. 119
ZYKLUS HEAT TRANSFER—See LU-VE SpA; *Int'l*, pg. 4572
ZYLA LIFE SCIENCES—See Assertio Holdings, Inc.; *U.S. Public*, pg. 214
ZYLOX-TONBRIDGE MEDICAL TECHNOLOGY CO., LTD.; *Int'l*, pg. 8701
ZYMERGEN INC.—See Ginkgo Bioworks Holdings, Inc.; *U.S. Public*, pg. 938
ZYMES LESAFFRE S.A.—See Compagnie des Levures Lesaffre SA; *Int'l*, pg. 1739
ZYMETECH EHF—See Enzymatica AB; *Int'l*, pg. 2457
ZYMEWORKS BC INC.—See Zymeworks Inc.; *U.S. Public*, pg. 2414
ZYMEWORKS INC.; *U.S. Public*, pg. 2414
ZYMPHONY TECHNOLOGY SOLUTIONS; *U.S. Private*, pg. 4611
ZYNERBA PHARMACEUTICALS, INC.—See Harmony Biosciences Holdings, Inc.; *U.S. Public*, pg. 986
ZYNEX, INC.; *U.S. Public*, pg. 2414
ZYNEX NEURODIAGNOSTICS, INC.—See ZYNEX, INC.; *U.S. Public*, pg. 2414
ZYNGA GAME NETWORK INDIA PRIVATE LIMITED—See Zynga Inc.; *U.S. Private*, pg. 4611
ZYNGA INC.; *U.S. Private*, pg. 4611
ZYNGA ISRAEL LTD.—See Take-Two Interactive Software, Inc.; *U.S. Public*, pg. 1979
ZYNII CHINA CO., LTD.—See AB Dynamics plc; *Int'l*, pg. 39
ZYNP CORPORATION; *Int'l*, pg. 8701
ZYNP EUROPE GMBH—See ZYNP Corporation; *Int'l*, pg. 8701
ZYNP INTERNATIONAL CORP.—See ZYNP Corporation; *Int'l*, pg. 8701
ZYNX HEALTH INCORPORATED—See The Hearst Corporation; *U.S. Private*, pg. 4045
ZYRION, INC.—See Insight Venture Management, LLC; *U.S. Private*, pg. 2091
ZYROBOTICS LLC; *U.S. Private*, pg. 4611
ZYROFISHER; *Int'l*, pg. 8701
ZYSCOVICH INC.; *U.S. Private*, pg. 4611
ZY-TECH DE VENEZUELA S.A.—See Forum Energy Technologies, Inc.; *U.S. Public*, pg. 874
ZYTER, INC.; *U.S. Private*, pg. 4611
ZYTO TECHNOLOGIES, INC.; *U.S. Private*, pg. 4611
ZYTRONIC DISPLAYS LIMITED—See Zytronic Plc; *Int'l*, pg. 8701
ZYTRONIC PLC; *Int'l*, pg. 8701
ZYVA STUDIO CO., LTD.—See PATH Corporation; *Int'l*, pg. 5756
ZYVERSA THERAPEUTICS, INC.; *U.S. Public*, pg. 2414
ZYWAVE, INC.—See Clearlake Capital Group, L.P.; *U.S. Private*, pg. 938
ZYXEL COMMUNICATIONS A/S—See Unizyx Holding Corporation; *Int'l*, pg. 8084
ZYXEL COMMUNICATIONS B.V.—See Unizyx Holding Corporation; *Int'l*, pg. 8084
ZYXEL COMMUNICATIONS CORPORATION—See Unizyx Holding Corporation; *Int'l*, pg. 8084
ZYXEL COMMUNICATIONS DO BRASIL LTDA.—See Unizyx Holding Corporation; *Int'l*, pg. 8084
ZYXEL COMMUNICATION (SHANGHAI) CO., LTD.—See Unizyx Holding Corporation; *Int'l*, pg. 8084
ZYXEL COMMUNICATIONS, INC.—See Unizyx Holding Corporation; *Int'l*, pg. 8084
ZYXEL COMMUNICATIONS ITALY S.R.L.—See Unizyx Holding Corporation; *Int'l*, pg. 8084
ZYXEL COMMUNICATIONS RU LLC—See Unizyx Holding Corporation; *Int'l*, pg. 8084
ZYXEL COMMUNICATIONS UK LTD.—See Unizyx Holding Corporation; *Int'l*, pg. 8084
ZYXEL DEUTSCHLAND GMBH—See Unizyx Holding Corporation; *Int'l*, pg. 8084
ZYXEL FRANCE SASU—See Unizyx Holding Corporation; *Int'l*, pg. 8084
ZYXEL ILETISIM TEKNOLOJILERI A.S.—See Unizyx Holding Corporation; *Int'l*, pg. 8084
ZYXEL KOREA CO., LTD.—See Unizyx Holding Corporation; *Int'l*, pg. 8084
ZYXEL NETWORKS CORPORATION—See Unizyx Holding Corporation; *Int'l*, pg. 8084
ZYXEL TECHNOLOGY INDIA PVT LTD.—See Unizyx Holding Corporation; *Int'l*, pg. 8084

ZYVERSA THERAPEUTICS, INC.

CORPORATE AFFILIATIONS

ZYXEL (THAILAND) COMPANY LTD.—See Unizyx Holding Corporation; *Int'l*, pg. 8084

ZYX METROLOGY, S.L.U.—See I Squared Capital Advisors (US) LLC; *U.S. Private*, pg. 2024

ZYX METROLOGY, S.L.U.—See TDR Capital LLP; *Int'l*, pg. 7493

ZZLL INFORMATION TECHNOLOGY, INC.; *Int'l*, pg. 8701

ZZN PELHRIMOV A. S.—See Agrofert Holding, a.s.; *Int'l*, pg. 219

ZZN POLABI, A.S.—See Agrofert Holding, a.s.; *Int'l*, pg. 219

ZZ PERFORMANCE, LLC; *U.S. Private*, pg. 4611

ZZ-WANCOR AG—See Wienerberger AG; *Int'l*, pg. 8407

COMPANY NAME INDEX

ZURICH GROUP HOLDING AG—See Zurich Insurance Group Limited; *Int'l*, pg. 8698
ZURICH GSG LTD.—See Zurich Insurance Group Limited; *Int'l*, pg. 8698
ZURICH HOLDING COMPANY OF AMERICA, INC.—See Zurich Insurance Group Limited; *Int'l*, pg. 8698
ZURICH IGUAZU COMPANIA DE SEGUROS (VIDAL)—See Zurich Insurance Group Limited; *Int'l*, pg. 8699
ZURICH INSURANCE AG—See Zurich Insurance Group Limited; *Int'l*, pg. 8697
ZURICH INSURANCE AG—See Zurich Insurance Group Limited; *Int'l*, pg. 8698
ZURICH INSURANCE COMPANY LTD.—See Zurich Insurance Group Limited; *Int'l*, pg. 8699
ZURICH INSURANCE COMPANY (POLAND) SA—See Zurich Insurance Group Limited; *Int'l*, pg. 8699
ZURICH INSURANCE COMPANY (RUSSIA) LTD.—See Zurich Insurance Group Limited; *Int'l*, pg. 8699
ZURICH INSURANCE GROUP (HONG KONG)—See Zurich Insurance Group Limited; *Int'l*, pg. 8699
ZURICH INSURANCE GROUP LIMITED; *Int'l*, pg. 8697
ZURICH INSURANCE PLC—See Zurich Insurance Group Limited; *Int'l*, pg. 8699
ZURICH INSURANCE (TAIWAN) LTD.—See Hotai Motor Co., Ltd.; *Int'l*, pg. 3487
ZURICH INTERNATIONAL (BELGIQUE) S.A.—See Zurich Insurance Group Limited; *Int'l*, pg. 8699
ZURICH INTERNATIONAL (BERMUDA) LTD.—See Zurich Insurance Group Limited; *Int'l*, pg. 8699
ZURICH INTERNATIONAL (DEUTSCHLAND) VERSICHERUNGS AG—See Zurich Insurance Group Limited; *Int'l*, pg. 8698
ZURICH INTERNATIONAL DE VENEZUELA C.A. DE CORRETAJE DE REASEGUROS—See Zurich Insurance Group Limited; *Int'l*, pg. 8699
ZURICH INTERNATIONAL (ITALIA) S.P.A.—See Zurich Insurance Group Limited; *Int'l*, pg. 8699
ZURICH INTERNATIONAL (NEDERLAND) N.V.—See Zurich Insurance Group Limited; *Int'l*, pg. 8699
ZURICH INTERNATIONAL SERVICES (LUXEMBOURG) S.A.—See Zurich Insurance Group Limited; *Int'l*, pg. 8699
ZURICH INTERNATIONAL (UK) LIMITED—See Zurich Insurance Group Limited; *Int'l*, pg. 8699
ZURICH INVESTMENT MANAGEMENT LTD.—See Zurich Insurance Group Limited; *Int'l*, pg. 8699
ZURICH INVESTMENT SERVICES LTD.—See Zurich Insurance Group Limited; *Int'l*, pg. 8699
ZURICH INVESTMENTS LIFE—See Zurich Insurance Group Limited; *Int'l*, pg. 8699
ZURICH INVESTMENTS SGR—See Zurich Insurance Group Limited; *Int'l*, pg. 8699
ZURICH ITALY BANK S.P.A.—See Zurich Insurance Group Limited; *Int'l*, pg. 8699
ZURICH LIFE ASSURANCE PLC—See Zurich Insurance Group Limited; *Int'l*, pg. 8699
ZURICH LIFE INSURANCE MALAYSIA BERHAD—See Zurich Insurance Group Limited; *Int'l*, pg. 8699
ZURICH PACIFIC INSURANCE PTY. LTD.—See Zurich Insurance Group Limited; *Int'l*, pg. 8699
ZURICH SANTANDER SEGUROS MEXICO, S.A.—See Zurich Insurance Group Limited; *Int'l*, pg. 8699
ZURICH SEGUROS S.A.—See Zurich Insurance Group Limited; *Int'l*, pg. 8699
ZURICH VERSICHERUNGS-AKTIENGESELLSCHAFT—See Zurich Insurance Group Limited; *Int'l*, pg. 8699
ZURICH VIDA COMPANIA DE SEGUROS S.A.—See Zurich Insurance Group Limited; *Int'l*, pg. 8699
ZURITIPP AG—See TX Group AG; *Int'l*, pg. 7992
ZURN ELKAY WATER SOLUTIONS CORPORATION; *U.S. Public*, pg. 2412
ZURN INDUSTRIES CAST METALS OPERATIONS—See Zurn Elkay Water Solutions Corporation; *U.S. Public*, pg. 2413
ZURN INDUSTRIES LIMITED—See Zurn Elkay Water Solutions Corporation; *U.S. Public*, pg. 2414
ZURN INDUSTRIES, LLC—See Zurn Elkay Water Solutions Corporation; *U.S. Public*, pg. 2413
ZURN INDUSTRIES—See Zurn Elkay Water Solutions Corporation; *U.S. Public*, pg. 2414
ZURN PEX, INC.—See Zurn Elkay Water Solutions Corporation; *U.S. Public*, pg. 2414
ZURN PLUMBING PRODUCTS GROUP—See Zurn Elkay Water Solutions Corporation; *U.S. Public*, pg. 2413
ZURN WATER, LLC—See Zurn Elkay Water Solutions Corporation; *U.S. Public*, pg. 2414
ZURPLE, INC.; *U.S. Private*, pg. 4610
ZUR ROSE GROUP AG; *Int'l*, pg. 8696
ZUR ROSE PHARMA GMBH—See Zur Rose Group AG; *Int'l*, pg. 8697
ZUR SHAMIR HOLDINGS LTD.; *Int'l*, pg. 8697
ZURVITA HOLDINGS, INC.; *U.S. Public*, pg. 2414
ZUTANO GLOBAL INC.; *U.S. Private*, pg. 4610
ZUTHER & HAUTMANN GMBH & CO. KG—See L'Air Liquide S. A.; *Int'l*, pg. 4374
ZUU CO., LTD.; *Int'l*, pg. 8699

ZUVAY TECHNOLOGIES PVT. LTD.—See S.C New Energy Technology Corporation; *Int'l*, pg. 6449
ZVC AUSTRALIA PTY. LTD.—See Zoom Video Communications, Inc.; *U.S. Public*, pg. 2411
ZVC FRANCE SAS—See Zoom Video Communications, Inc.; *U.S. Public*, pg. 2411
ZVC JAPAN KK—See Zoom Video Communications, Inc.; *U.S. Public*, pg. 2411
ZVC UK LTD.—See Zoom Video Communications, Inc.; *U.S. Public*, pg. 2411
ZVECEVO-LASTA D.D.; *Int'l*, pg. 8700
ZVECEVO PREHRAMBENA INDUSTRIJA D.D; *Int'l*, pg. 8699
ZVELO, INC.; *U.S. Private*, pg. 4610
ZVENTS, INC.—See eBay Inc.; *U.S. Public*, pg. 709
ZVEZDARA AVALA A.D.; *Int'l*, pg. 8700
ZVIJEZDA D.D.; *Int'l*, pg. 8700
ZVI SARFATI & SONS INVESTMENTS & CONSTRUCTIONS LTD.; *Int'l*, pg. 8700
ZVON DVA HOLDING D.D.; *Int'l*, pg. 8700
ZVON ENA HOLDING D.D.; *Int'l*, pg. 8700
ZVORNIKPUTEVI A.D.; *Int'l*, pg. 8700
ZV PATE INC.; *U.S. Private*, pg. 4610
ZVS ENCO A.S.—See Enco spol. s r.o.; *Int'l*, pg. 2401
ZVU STROJIRNY, A.S.—See Safichem Group AG; *Int'l*, pg. 6471
ZWACK UNICUM RT.; *Int'l*, pg. 8700
ZWAHLEN & MAYR SA; *Int'l*, pg. 8700
ZWANENBERG FOOD GROUP B.V.; *Int'l*, pg. 8700
ZWANENBERG FOOD GROUP (USA) INC.—See Zwanenberg Food Group B.V.; *Int'l*, pg. 8700
ZWANENBERG FOOD OSS B.V.—See Zwanenberg Food Group B.V.; *Int'l*, pg. 8700
Z-WAVE ALLIANCE, LLC—See Silicon Laboratories Inc.; *U.S. Public*, pg. 1880
ZW DATA ACTION TECHNOLOGIES INC.; *Int'l*, pg. 8700
ZWEI CO., LTD.—See IBJ Inc.; *Int'l*, pg. 3576
ZWEIG ADVISERS LLC—See Virtus Investment Partners, Inc.; *U.S. Public*, pg. 2301
ZWEIGWHITE LLC; *U.S. Private*, pg. 4610
ZWEITE BASF IMMOBILIEN-GESELLSCHAFT MBH—See BASF SE; *Int'l*, pg. 886
ZWEITE ENVITEC BETEILIGUNGS GMBH & CO. KG—See EnviTec Biogas AG; *Int'l*, pg. 2456
ZWEITE K-W-A BETEILIGUNGSGESELLSCHAFT MBH—See Bayer Aktiengesellschaft; *Int'l*, pg. 910
ZWEITE REAL,- SB-WARENHAUS GMBH—See Metro AG; *Int'l*, pg. 4859
ZWICKER ELECTRIC CO., INC.; *U.S. Private*, pg. 4610
ZWICK GMBH & CO. KG; *Int'l*, pg. 8700
ZWICK USA L.P.—See Zwick GmbH & Co. KG; *Int'l*, pg. 8700
ZWICKY ELECTRONIC AG—See NEXUS AG; *Int'l*, pg. 5250
ZWILLING J.A. HENCKELS AG—See Wilh. Werhahn KG; *Int'l*, pg. 8410
ZWIPE AS; *Int'l*, pg. 8700
Z-WORK ACQUISITION CORP.; *U.S. Public*, pg. 2400
ZWP - ZERSTORUNGSFREIE WERKSTOFFPRUFUNG GMBH—See TUV SUD AG; *Int'l*, pg. 7986
ZWSOFT GUANGZHOU CO., LTD.; *Int'l*, pg. 8700
ZXY MEQQE CORPORATION—See Cresco, Ltd.; *Int'l*, pg. 1840
ZYCI LLC; *U.S. Private*, pg. 4611
ZYCRON INC.—See BGSF, Inc.; *U.S. Public*, pg. 330
ZYDUS ANIMAL HEALTH LIMITED—See Zydus Lifesciences Limited; *Int'l*, pg. 8700
ZYDUS FRANCE SAS.—See Zydus Lifesciences Limited; *Int'l*, pg. 8700
ZYDUS HEALTHCARE BRASIL LTDA.—See Zydus Lifesciences Limited; *Int'l*, pg. 8701
ZYDUS HEALTHCARE LIMITED—See Zydus Lifesciences Limited; *Int'l*, pg. 8701
ZYDUS HEALTHCARE PHILIPPINES INC.—See Zydus Lifesciences Limited; *Int'l*, pg. 8701
ZYDUS HEALTHCARE (USA) LLC.—See Zydus Lifesciences Limited; *Int'l*, pg. 8701
ZYDUS HOSPIRA ONCOLOGY PRIVATE LIMITED—See Pfizer Inc.; *U.S. Public*, pg. 1683
ZYDUS LIFESCIENCES LIMITED; *Int'l*, pg. 8700
ZYDUS NIKKHO FARMACEUTICA LTDA.—See Zydus Lifesciences Limited; *Int'l*, pg. 8701
ZYDUS NYCOMED HEALTHCARE PRIVATE LTD.—See Takeda Pharmaceutical Company Limited; *Int'l*, pg. 7440
ZYDUS NYCOMED HEALTHCARE PRIVATE LTD.—See Zydus Lifesciences Limited; *Int'l*, pg. 8701
ZYDUS PHARMACEUTICALS USA INC.—See Zydus Lifesciences Limited; *Int'l*, pg. 8701
ZYDUS WELLNESS LIMITED—See Zydus Lifesciences Limited; *Int'l*, pg. 8701
ZYDUS WELLNESS PRODUCTS LIMITED—See Zydus Lifesciences Limited; *Int'l*, pg. 8701
ZYF LOPSKING ALUMINUM CO., LTD.; *Int'l*, pg. 8701
ZYF LOPSKING MATERIAL TECHNOLOGY CO LTD; *Int'l*, pg. 8701
ZYGA TECHNOLOGY, INC.—See Montagu Private Equity LLP; *Int'l*, pg. 5036

ZYVERSA THERAPEUTICS, INC.

ZYGO CORPORATION—See AMETEK, Inc.; *U.S. Public*, pg. 119
ZYGO CORPORATION - WESTERN REGIONAL OFFICE—See AMETEK, Inc.; *U.S. Public*, pg. 119
ZYGO ELECTRO-OPTICS GROUP MANUFACTURING CENTER—See AMETEK, Inc.; *U.S. Public*, pg. 119
ZYGO K.K.—See AMETEK, Inc.; *U.S. Public*, pg. 119
ZYGOLAMDA METROLOGY INSTRUMENT (SHANGHAI) CO., LTD.—See AMETEK, Inc.; *U.S. Public*, pg. 119
ZYGOLOT GMBH—See AMETEK, Inc.; *U.S. Public*, pg. 119
ZYGO PTE. LTD.—See AMETEK, Inc.; *U.S. Public*, pg. 119
ZYGO RICHMOND, INC.—See AMETEK, Inc.; *U.S. Public*, pg. 119
ZYGO TAIWAN CO., LTD.—See AMETEK, Inc.; *U.S. Public*, pg. 119
ZYKLUS HEAT TRANSFER—See LU-VE SpA; *Int'l*, pg. 4572
ZYLA LIFE SCIENCES—See Assertio Holdings, Inc.; *U.S. Public*, pg. 214
ZYLOX-TONBRIDGE MEDICAL TECHNOLOGY CO., LTD.; *Int'l*, pg. 8701
ZYMERGEN INC.—See Ginkgo Bioworks Holdings, Inc.; *U.S. Public*, pg. 938
ZYMES LESAFFRE S.A.—See Compagnie des Levures Lesaffre SA; *Int'l*, pg. 1739
ZYMETECH EHF—See Enzymatica AB; *Int'l*, pg. 2457
ZYMEWORKS BC INC.—See Zymeworks Inc.; *U.S. Public*, pg. 2414
ZYMEWORKS INC.; *U.S. Public*, pg. 2414
ZYMPHONY TECHNOLOGY SOLUTIONS; *U.S. Private*, pg. 4611
ZYNERBA PHARMACEUTICALS, INC.—See Harmony Biosciences Holdings, Inc.; *U.S. Public*, pg. 986
ZYNEX, INC.; *U.S. Public*, pg. 2414
ZYNEX NEURODIAGNOSTICS, INC.—See ZYNEX, INC.; *U.S. Public*, pg. 2414
ZYNGA GAME NETWORK INDIA PRIVATE LIMITED—See Zynga Inc.; *U.S. Private*, pg. 4611
ZYNGA INC.; *U.S. Private*, pg. 4611
ZYNGA ISRAEL LTD.—See Take-Two Interactive Software, Inc.; *U.S. Public*, pg. 1979
ZYNIT CHINA CO., LTD.—See AB Dynamics plc; *Int'l*, pg. 39
ZYNP CORPORATION; *Int'l*, pg. 8701
ZYNP EUROPE GMBH—See ZYNP Corporation; *Int'l*, pg. 8701
ZYNP INTERNATIONAL CORP.—See ZYNP Corporation; *Int'l*, pg. 8701
ZYNX HEALTH INCORPORATED—See The Hearst Corporation; *U.S. Private*, pg. 4045
ZYRION, INC.—See Insight Venture Management, LLC; *U.S. Private*, pg. 2091
ZYROBOTICS LLC; *U.S. Private*, pg. 4611
ZYROFISHER; *Int'l*, pg. 8701
ZYSCOVICH INC.; *U.S. Private*, pg. 4611
ZY-TECH DE VENEZUELA S.A.—See Forum Energy Technologies, Inc.; *U.S. Public*, pg. 874
ZYTER; *U.S. Private*, pg. 4611
ZYTO TECHNOLOGIES, INC.; *U.S. Private*, pg. 4611
ZYTRONIC DISPLAYS LIMITED—See Zytronic Plc; *Int'l*, pg. 8701
ZYTRONIC PLC; *Int'l*, pg. 8701
ZYVA STUDIO CO., LTD.—See PATH Corporation; *Int'l*, pg. 5756
ZYVERSA THERAPEUTICS, INC.; *U.S. Public*, pg. 2414
ZYWAVE, INC.—See Clearlake Capital Group, L.P.; *U.S. Private*, pg. 938
ZYXEL COMMUNICATIONS A/S—See Unizyx Holding Corporation; *Int'l*, pg. 8084
ZYXEL COMMUNICATIONS B.V.—See Unizyx Holding Corporation; *Int'l*, pg. 8084
ZYXEL COMMUNICATIONS CORPORATION—See Unizyx Holding Corporation; *Int'l*, pg. 8084
ZYXEL COMMUNICATIONS DO BRASIL LTDA.—See Unizyx Holding Corporation; *Int'l*, pg. 8084
ZYXEL COMMUNICATION (SHANGHAI) CO., LTD.—See Unizyx Holding Corporation; *Int'l*, pg. 8084
ZYXEL COMMUNICATIONS, INC.—See Unizyx Holding Corporation; *Int'l*, pg. 8084
ZYXEL COMMUNICATIONS ITALY S.R.L.—See Unizyx Holding Corporation; *Int'l*, pg. 8084
ZYXEL COMMUNICATIONS RU LLC—See Unizyx Holding Corporation; *Int'l*, pg. 8084
ZYXEL COMMUNICATIONS UK LTD.—See Unizyx Holding Corporation; *Int'l*, pg. 8084
ZYXEL DEUTSCHLAND GMBH—See Unizyx Holding Corporation; *Int'l*, pg. 8084
ZYXEL FRANCE SASU—See Unizyx Holding Corporation; *Int'l*, pg. 8084
ZYXEL ILETISIM TEKNOLOJILERI A.S.—See Unizyx Holding Corporation; *Int'l*, pg. 8084
ZYXEL KOREA CO., LTD.—See Unizyx Holding Corporation; *Int'l*, pg. 8084
ZYXEL NETWORKS CORPORATION—See Unizyx Holding Corporation; *Int'l*, pg. 8084
ZYXEL TECHNOLOGY INDIA PVT LTD.—See Unizyx Holding Corporation; *Int'l*, pg. 8084

ZYVERSA THERAPEUTICS, INC.

CORPORATE AFFILIATIONS

ZYXEL (THAILAND) COMPANY LTD.—See Unizyx Holding Corporation; *Int'l*, pg. 8084
ZYX METROLOGY S.L.U.—See I Squared Capital Advisors (US) LLC; *U.S. Private*, pg. 2024
ZYX METROLOGY S.L.U.—See TDR Capital LLP; *Int'l*, pg. 7493
ZZLL INFORMATION TECHNOLOGY, INC.; *Int'l*, pg. 8701
ZZN PELHRIMOV A. S.—See Agrofert Holding, a.s.; *Int'l*, pg. 219
ZZN POLABI, A.S.—See Agrofert Holding, a.s.; *Int'l*, pg. 219
ZZ PERFORMANCE, LLC; *U.S. Private*, pg. 4611
ZZ WANCOR AG—See Wienerberger AG; *Int'l*, pg. 8407